Important Information About This Directory

How This Directory Was Compiled

Great care has been taken in compiling the information in this directory. Facts were obtained from the D&B database, telephone interviews, and annual reports. Upon request, the page proofs of proposed listings have been submitted to officials of companies for approval or correction.

We have made every effort to ensure that the information is complete, correct, and current. However, because of the human factors and possibilities for error that are inherent in compiling a directory of this size, D&B does not assume liability for the correctness of these listings or for the information upon which they have been based. Errors, after they have been detected, will be corrected in the next edition.

A listing in this directory neither constitutes nor implies in any manner whatsoever, an appraisal by D&B of the products, facilities, financial condition, credit worthiness, or any other factor bearing on the service, performance, or operations of the company listed.

No charge of any kind is made for inclusion in this publication.

Subscription Agreements

To ensure that the information you use is the most current and accurate available, most D&B publications are provided on a lease basis. Most of our subscribers renew their subscriptions each year. During the period of your annual lease, you will automatically receive the next edition of this directory when it is released. This protects you and your research by making sure the publication you use is the most current available. The information compiled in D&B publications is proprietary. Having compiled the information through various D&B resources, D&B legally owns the information. This is why publications remain the property of D&B at all times.

Our leasing policy is intended to provide you with the most up-to-date information we have available. If you have any questions about this leasing procedure, please call us, at 1.800.526.0651.

Notice Concerning Use For Compilation For Dissemination To Third Parties

Subscribers to D&B publications have, on occasion, used those publications to compile mailing lists, marketing aids, and other types of information compilations, then sell or otherwise provide those materials to third parties. D&B considers such use to be wrongful and illegal. The information contained in these publications is the legal property of The Dun & Bradstreet Corporation. Selling or otherwise providing this information to third parties violates the contractual agreement under which the directory is provided to the subscriber. This is also a violation of the federal copyright laws. D&B does not permit or acquiesce in such uses of its publications. Any subscriber or other person engaging in or facilitating such impermissible use should expect to experience legal and financial consequences.

No waiver or amendment of the agreement is binding unless it is in writing and signed by an authorized official of D&B and the subscriber. Should any subscriber or other person not understand any aspect of this policy, please contact the Legal Department of Dun & Bradstreet, at 103 JFK Parkway, Short Hills, N.J. 07078.

dun & bradstreet

Million Dollar Directory

Series

America's Leading Public & Private Companies

2017

ISSN 0742-9649
ISBN 978-1-68200-429-6

2017 Million Dollar Directory

Management

Jonathan Worrall	Publisher
John Pedernales	Executive Managing Director
Fred Jenkins	Vice President Sales
Thomas Wecera	Executive Managing Director Print Products

Editorial Department

Charlot Volny
Wayne Arnold
Davie Christna

Customer Service & Billing

Melanie Horvat
580 Kingsley Park Drive
Fort Mill, SC 29715
(704)559-7601
(800)342-5647

To Contact Mergent:

Call us at 800.342.5647
Or visit us at: www.mergentbusinesspress.com

Contents

Overview

Introduction

Thank you for using the *Million Dollar Directory*. As one of the business world's most widely recognized and frequently used reference publications, it has provided information to executives, librarians, students, researchers, sales and marketing managers, and others for more than 40 years. The *Million Dollar Directory* is a primary source of business information and is a valuable source of information on privately held companies.

You will find the *Million Dollar Directory* provides many advantages to its users. It offers extensive coverage of public and private companies, easy cross-referencing, primary and secondary lines of business (up to six for each company), and the names and titles of key decision makers.

In publishing this directory, we seek to provide several specific benefits to you:

- Quality. To provide the highest quality information available, The Dun & Bradstreet Corporation maintains unparalleled information gathering resources. First-hand information is obtained through in-person and telephone interviews by business analysts across the United States.
- Reliability. Appropriate listing criteria ensure that the top 150,000 U.S. companies are profiled using the most current, accurate and comprehensive information available today.
- Coverage. A broad range of industries is presented.
- Ease of use. The information has been designed to be thorough, yet simple to use. Complete company listings are arranged alphabetically by company name. Cross-references enable users to access information geographically and by line of business.

The sections that follow have been provided to help you obtain information from this directory more easily. A quick glance at the various headings should help you find the answers to your questions.
If you have any further questions about either the *Million Dollar Directory* or our other business reference publications, or if you would like to obtain a directory, please call us at 1.800.342.5647.

Criteria For Inclusion

For a company to be selected for the *Million Dollar Directory*, it must meet one of the two inclusion requirements:

1. More than 300 employees total if the company is a headquarters or single location; 900 or more employees at that location if the company is a branch.
2. More than $20,000,000 in sales volume.

You will find subsidiaries and branches in the *Million Dollar Directory* if they meet the listing criteria. However, divisions are not included (for precise definitions of terms such as subsidiary, branch, and division, please see the glossary on page IX).

More than 136,000 of these listings are privately owned businesses — information that can be difficult to obtain from other sources.

If you have any questions about the criteria for the *Million Dollar Directory*, please call 1.800.342.5647.

Directory Contents

To make the *Million Dollar Directory* easier for you to use, it has been published in five volumes. The first three volumes list businesses alphabetically; the fourth and fifth volumes cross-reference businesses geographically and by Standard Industrial Classification (SIC) code. Additional information on all of the sections is presented on pages VI and VII.

Description of Business Listings

Each business description includes many facts about the company. They include:

- Headquarters address and telephone number
- Trade style
- Annual sales volume (where available)
- Total employment size (where available)
- Up to six industry classifications (Standard Industrial Classification [SIC] codes), with the primary industry shown first
- Company officers and directories by name and title (for officers)
- D&B D-U-N-S® Number
- Members of the board of directors
- Founded/ownership date

Plus (where available):

- Banking and accounting relationships
- Indications of import/export business
- Indication of public ownership
- Indication of public family membership
- State of incorporation
- Indication of a parent company listing in the current *Million Dollar Directory*

Types of Businesses

Many different types of businesses are included. They generally include:

- Agriculture, Forestry, and Fishing
- Mining
- Construction
- Manufacturing
- Transportation, Communication & Public Utilities
- Wholesale Trade
- Retail Trade
- Finance, Insurance & Real Estate
- Business Services

A company may be referenced under as many as six SIC codes: the primary industry from which it derives its main source of revenue, and up to five secondary business activities.

Subsidiaries, Branches and Divisions

For your convenience, a brief glossary of reporting relationships, as defined by D&B, has been provided on page VIII. You will find subsidiaries and branches listed in the *Million Dollar Directory* if they meet the listing criteria. Divisions, however, are not included.

Public and Private Companies

In response to customer requests, D&B has begun the process of indicating public ownership of companies listed in the *Million Dollar Directory.* A triangle ▲ before a business name indicates that it is a publicly held company.

A square ■ before a business name denotes that the company is a member of a publicly traded company, but is not the trading location. If a subsidiary trades under its own ticker symbol separately from its parent, a triangle will appear before the name of the subsidiary in the listing.

To help you identify public companies more easily, the triangle and square indicators have been included in both the alphabetical and cross-reference volumes.

How to Use This Directory

To help you use the *Million Dollar Directory* more easily, it is divided into five volumes. The divisions are as follows:

Businesses Alphabetically

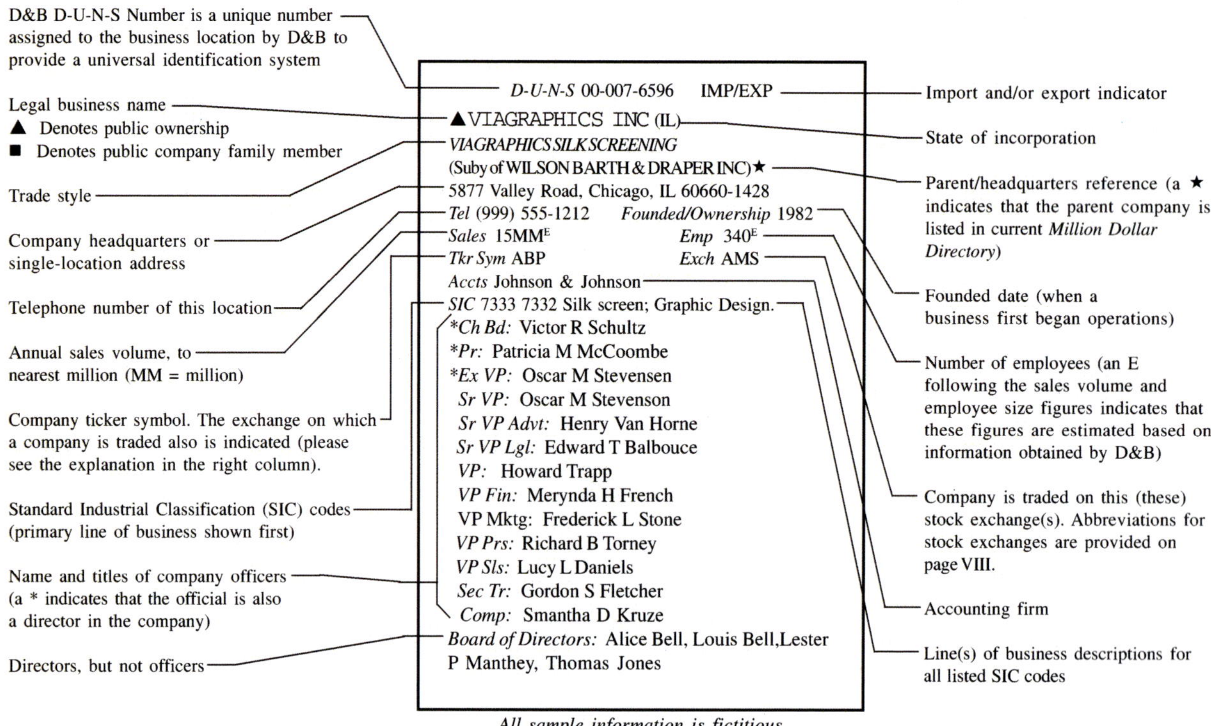

All sample information is fictitious

The first three volumes of the *Million Dollar Directory* list companies in alphabetical sequence by business name. Full details on each company are provided in this section. The listing for each company includes the following:

- Address and telephone number (headquarters and single locations only)
- Indication of public ownership, where available
- Indication of public company family membership
- SIC code (up to six; the primary SIC is listed first) and description of the line(s) of business
- Annual sales volume, where available
- Total number of employees, where available
- Names, titles and functions of officers
- Names of directors
- D&B D-U-N-S® Number
- Founded/ownership date

Also, where available

- Import/export indication
- Accounting firm
- State of incorporation
- Company ticker symbol on stock exchange, and/or stock exchange abbreviations
- Indication of parent company in current *Million Dollar Directory*

Public companies are denoted by the stock ticker symbol and/or stock exchange location and by a triangle or a square before the company name. The alphabetic volumes are particularly useful when only the name of a company is known. It enables you to:

- Identify key decision makers
- Assess the buying potential of a company by sales volume and employee size
- Determine whether a company is publicly owned
- Identify primary or secondary markets by SIC code

The fourth and fifth volumes of the *Million Dollar Directory* enable you to cross-reference businesses by geographical area or line of business.

Businesses Geographically

This volume presents a geographic cross-reference. Business names are listed in alphabetical order within states and cities. The company name, address, telephone number, and SIC codes are provided. An indication of companies noted in our file of public ownership is also included, as is a page reference for a company's listing in the alphabetical section.

You can use the information in this volume to:

- Target your sales efforts more effectively
- Identify companies by region, state or city
- Select prime sales areas
- Assess market concentrations and analyze or compare markets by area
- Align sales territories and assign quotas based on the number of prospects in each geographic area
- Compile targeted mailing and telemarketing lists by location and size
- Identify local businesses
- Create telemarketing and prospect lists
- Conduct telemarketing campaigns
- Assess new market potential
- Identify prospective employers by city and within state

ILLINOIS

CHICAGO, IL

p VIAGRAPHICS INC *p* 5307
5877 Valley Road 60660
Tel (999) 555-1212 *SIC* 7333 7332
VILLAGE NURSING HOME
p 5312
2182 South St 60661
Tel (999) 555-1212 *SIC* 2051
VITA-LINK *p* 5319
4932 Lenox Ave 60231
Tel (999) 555-1212 *SIC* 3446

All sample information is fictitious

Businesses By Industry Classification

All businesses listed in the *Million Dollar Directory* are segmented by industry. Business names are listed in geographical order by state, city and then listed alphabetically within each city. Based on the SIC code system (see explanation on page X), this volume lists company information organized by line of business. Primary and secondary SIC codes are covered; therefore, a single company may be listed under as many as six different industry classifications. Individual business descriptions in this section include the company name and address, telephone number, primary SIC code, a page reference for its appearance in the alphabetic section, and an indication of public ownership.

The industry cross-reference can help you develop more effective strategies to:

- Identify prime prospects by line of business
- Precisely define specific industries
- Assess your competition
- Evaluate market potential for new or specific products
- Identify hidden markets by secondary lines of business
- Select suppliers from industry leaders
- Identify companies active in more than one industry
- Compile targeted mailing lists by industry
- Identify new companies in existing markets
- Determine the best geographic area for an industry
- Conduct industry-concentrated telemarketing campaigns

7333 COMM PHOTOGRAPHY, ART & GRAPHIC

p VIAGRAPHICS INC *p* 5307
5877 Valley Road, Chicago, IL 60660
Tel (999) 555-1212 *SIC* 7333 7332
QUIK GRAPH *p* 4211
594 Willow Ave, Chester, NJ 07930
Tel (999) 555-1212 *SIC* 7333 7332
WINSTON OUTDOOR ADVERTISING *p* 4802
3943 McConnell Rd, Williamsport, PA 17770
Tel (999) 555-1212 *SIC* 7333 7312

All sample information is fictitious

Abbreviations and Symbols

Abbreviations

Acctg	Accounting
Admn	Administration
Advt	Advertising
AMS	American Stock Exchange
BSE	Boston Stock Exchange
CEO	Chief Executive Officer
CFO	Chief Financial Officer
Ch Bd	Chairman of the Board
Ch Em	Chairman Emeritus
CHI	Chicago Board of Trade
CIN	Cincinnati Stock Exchange
Clk	Clerk
Co	Company
Coml	Commercial
Commctns	Communications
Comp	Comptroller
Cont	Controller
COO	Chief Operating Officer
Corp	Corporation
Cshr	Cashier
Dev	Development
Dir	Director
Distrn	Distribution
Div	Division
Dt Pr	Data Processing
ECM	Emerging Company Market Place
Engg	Engineering
Ex	Executive
Ex VP	Executive Vice President
Exp	Export
FSB	Federal Savings Bank
Fin	Finance
Fndr	Founder
GC	General Counsel
Genl	General
GM	General Manager
Govt	Government
Imp	Import
Inc	Incorporated
Indus	Industrial
Intl	International
Jr	Junior
Lgl	Legal
LON	London Stock Exchange
Ltd	Limited
M	Thousand
Merchds	Merchandise
Merchdsng	Merchandising
Mfg	Manufacturing
Mgr	Manager
Mgt	Management
Mktg	Marketing
M M	Million
M M M	Billion
M M M M	Trillion
MSE	Midwest Stock Exchange
NA	Not Available or National Association
NAS	NASDAQ Stock Exchange
NMS	NASDAQ National Market System
NYS	New York Stock Exchange Inc
Opers	Operations
Optg	Operating
OTC	Over the Counter
Ownr	Owner
PBS	Philadelphia Stock Exchange
PCS	Pacific Coast Stock Exchange
Pb Rlns	Public Relations
Pers	Personal
Pr	President
Prd	Production
Prin	Principal
Prs	Personnel
Pt	Partner
Pur	Purchasing
Ret	Retail or Retailer
Rlns	Relations
Rsch	Research
Sec	Secretary
SIC	Standard Industrial Classification
Sls	Sales
Sr	Senior
Sr VP	Senior Vice President
Suby	Subsidiary
Tr	Treasurer
Trst	Trustee
Trst Ofcr	Trust Officer
TSE	Toronto Stock Exchange
V Ch Bd	Vice Chairman of the Board
VAN	Vancouver Stock Exchange
VP	Vice President
Whl	Wholesale or Wholesaler

Symbols

▲ Denotes public ownership

■ Denotes member of public family

★ Denotes parent company is in current *Million Dollar Directory*

* Denotes that the officer is also a corporate director

Glossary

Affiliate Company—A company in which another firm holds an interest of less than 50%.

Asset—Property or resources such as money, buildings and equipment.

Associate Company—A company in which another company holds an interest of less than 50% (British equivalent of affiliate company).

Branch—A secondary location of a business which reports to a headquarters. A branch never reports to another branch and always carries the parent name. *Example:* A sales office is a branch location.

Business Organization—Various types of business organizations exist including corporations, partnerships and proprietorships. A corporation may be a public or a private company. Each type may have subsidiaries, divisions, branch locations, headquarters locations, and more.

Corporation—A legal form of business organization consisting of an association of owners called stockholders.

Corporate Structure—The hierarchy of a business establishment (*i.e.,* a parent company may have a division reporting to it, with branch locations reporting to the divisions).

Division—A separate operating unit of a corporation. A division may have its own officers, but it is not incorporated nor does it issue stock. All divisions are also classified as branches. Divisions will often have an additional commonly known business name called a trade style (see Trade Style).

D&B D-U-N-S® Number—A nonindicative number assigned to business establishments by D&B and used as a numeric identifier for business locations (Dun's Universal Numbering System).

Establishment—A term used by the U.S. Bureau of Census for any business location that has one or more employees.

Founded Date—The date when a business first began operations.

Headquarters—A business establishment where the executive offices of the corporation are located. Branch locations report to headquarters. *Example:* Ford Motor Company's headquarters location is in Dearborn, Michigan.

Immediate or Direct Parent—The company to which a subsidiary directly reports.

Liability—All debts and obligations of a business.

Net Worth—A company's total assets minus its total liabilities.

Ownership Date—The ownership date represents the "control date" of the business which is the date that current management assumed ownership, or majority stock ownership, of a business. In many cases, especially smaller businesses, current ownership date and year started are synonymous. However, with the current trend of mergers and acquisitions among larger corporations, the current ownership date represents the year present management assumed control, not necessarily the founding date of the business.

Parent Company—A business that owns more than 50% of another company's stock.

Partnership—A form of business organization in which two or more persons or entities carry on a business as co-owners for profit.

Privately Held Company—A business in which most or all of the company's stock is owned by a few persons and is not available for sale to the general public.

Proprietorship—A form of business organization in which an individual owns the entire enterprise.

Publicly Held Company—A business whose stock is available for sale to the general public at one or more of the stock exchanges.

Public Family Member—Subsidiaries of publicly held companies.

Single Location—A business establishment with no branches reporting to it. A single location may still be a parent and/or a subsidiary.

Standard Industrial Classification (SIC) Code—A hierarchical system of numerically categorizing the type of business activity which is conducted at a business establishment.

State of Incorporation—The state laws under which a company was incorporated. This can have implications in legal, organizational, and tax matters.

Subsidiary—A corporation that is controlled by another corporation through ownership of greater than 50% of its voting stock. The subsidiary may have a different name than the controlling corporation.

Ticker Symbol—The code representing the corporation in the stock exchange on which the corporation is traded.

Trade Style—An additional name used by a business for advertising and/or buying purposes.

Ultimate Parent—The topmost U.S. company within the hierarchy of the entire organization.

Year Founded—The original date a business was started.

Understanding Standard Industrial Classification (SIC) Codes

The Standard Industrial Classification (SIC) code is a simple and effective coding system that is used to gather and classify information on U.S. businesses.

The SIC system divides virtually all economic activity into ten major categories:

Agriculture, Forestry, and Fishing 01-09

Mining 10-14

Construction 15-17

Manufacturing 20-39

Transport, Communications, Utilities 40-49

Wholesale Trade 50-51

Retail Trade 52-59

Finance, Insurance, Real Estate 60-67

Services 70-89

Public Administration 91-97

The SIC system places each line of business within one of these ten divisions and assigns a four-digit code. The first two digits describe the general nature of the activity:

22 Manufacturing–Textile mill products

The third and fourth digits of the SIC code describe the specific activity:

2273 Manufacturing–Tufted carpets, rugs

Under the SIC system, many companies can be categorized under several "lines of business" and therefore are assigned several SIC codes. The line of business which represents the largest percentage of sales is known as the primary SIC, others are referred to as secondary SICs.

Example: An automotive parts wholesaler (SIC 5013) also distributes automobile and truck tires (SIC 5014) and has a small retail trade in auto placement glass (SIC 5331). In this directory, the SIC codes for this firm would be displayed as follows:

SIC 5013, 5014, 5531

Each SIC code is presented according to the percentage of its sales volume. The primary SIC is listed first (largest percentage of sales) and secondary SICs are listed in descending order of their respective sales percentages.

In this example, we know at a glance that this company's main business activity is wholesale auto parts, but it also has other sales in wholesale tires and some volume in retail automotive glass.

A typical display of SIC codes in this directory not only classifies the nature of the enterprise, but shows the relative size and importance of its various business activities as well.

A complete listing of SIC codes and their descriptions is included in this directory. If you wish to know more about SIC codes, please consult the *Standard Industrial Classification Manual SIC 2+2,* published by D&B.

Who Uses SIC Codes?

Sales professionals looking for new sales prospects may use SIC codes in searching among business names and addresses.

Job hunters often use SICs as a fast way to identify appropriate or interesting prospective employers. Advertisers rely upon SIC codes to pinpoint the kind of businesses they want to reach.

Economists studying changes and trends in business and the economy, use SICs to identify and compare industries.

Marketing researchers employ SIC codes in gathering information about potential markets for new products.

Computer-assisted searches in business and research use SIC codes for fast and reliable selections, sorting, and sampling.

Standard Industrial Classification (SIC) Codes – Numerical

01 Agricultural Production — Crops
0111 Wheat
0112 Rice
0115 Corn
0116 Soybeans
0119 Cash Grains
0131 Cotton
0132 Tobacco
0133 Sugarcane & Sugar Beets
0134 Irish Potatoes
0139 Field Crops, Except Cash Grain
0161 Vegetables & Melons
0171 Berry Crops
0172 Grapes
0173 Tree Nuts
0174 Citrus Fruits
0175 Deciduous Tree Fruits
0179 Fruits & Tree Nuts
0181 Ornamental Nursery Products
0182 Food Crops Grown Under Cover
0191 General Farms, Primarily Crop

02 Agricultural Production — Livestock & Animal Specialities
0211 Beef Cattle Feedlots
0212 Beef Cattle Except Feedlots
0213 Hogs
0214 Sheep & Goats
0219 General Livestock
0241 Dairy Farms
0251 Broiler, Fryer & Roaster Chickens
0252 Chicken Eggs
0253 Turkeys & Turkey Eggs
0254 Poultry Hatcheries
0259 Poultry & Eggs
0271 Fur-bearing Animals & Rabbits
0272 Horses & Other Equines
0273 Animal Aquaculture
0279 Animal Specialties
0291 General Farms, Primarily Animals

07 Agricultural Services
0711 Soil Preparation Services
0721 Crop Planting & Protection
0722 Crop Harvesting
0723 Crop Preparation Services For Market
0724 Cotton Ginning
0741 Veterinary Services For Livestock
0742 Veterinary Services, Specialties
0751 Livestock Services, Except Veterinary
0752 Animal Specialty Services
0761 Farm Labor Contractors
0762 Farm Management Services
0781 Landscape Counseling & Planning
0782 Lawn & Garden Services
0783 Ornamental Shrub & Tree Services

08 Forestry
0811 Timber Tracts
0831 Forest Products
0851 Forestry Services

09 Fishing, Hunting & Trapping
0912 Finfish
0913 Shellfish
0919 Miscellaneous Marine Products
0921 Fish Hatcheries & Preserves
0971 Hunting, Trapping,Game Propagation

10 Metal Mining
1011 Iron Ores
1021 Copper Ores
1031 Lead & Zinc Ores
1041 Gold Ores
1044 Silver Ores
1061 Ferroalloy Ores, Except Vanadium
1081 Metal Mining Services
1094 Uranium-Radium-Vanadium Ores
1099 Metal Ores

12 Coal Mining
1221 Bituminous Coal & Lignite-Surface
1222 Bituminous Coal-Underground
1231 Anthracite Mining
1241 Coal Mining Services

13 Oil & Gas Extraction
1311 Crude Petroleum & Natural Gas
1321 Natural Gas Liquids
1381 Drilling Oil & Gas Wells
1382 Oil & Gas Exploration Services
1389 Oil & Gas Field Services

14 Mining & Quarrying of Nonmetallic Minerals, Except Fuels
1411 Dimension Stone
1422 Crushed & Broken Limestone
1423 Crushed & Broken Granite
1429 Crushed & Broken Stone
1442 Construction Sand & Gravel
1446 Industrial Sand
1455 Kaolin & Ball Clay
1459 Clay & Related Minerals
1474 Potash, Soda & Borate Minerals
1475 Phosphate Rock
1479 Chemical & Fertilizer Mining
1481 Nonmetallic Mineral Services
1499 Miscellaneous Nonmetallic Minerals

15 Building Construction — General Contractors & Operative Builders
1521 Single-family Housing Construction
1522 Residential Construction
1531 Operative Builders
1541 Industrial Buildings & Warehouses
1542 Nonresidential Construction

16 Heavy Construction Other Than Building Construction — Contractors
1611 Highway & Street Construction
1622 Bridge, Tunnel & Elevated Highway
1623 Water, Sewer & Utility Lines
1629 Heavy Construction

17 Construction — Special Trade Contractors
1711 Plumbing, Heating, Air-conditioning Contractors
1721 Painting & Paper Hanging
1731 Electrical Work
1741 Masonry & Other Stonework
1742 Plastering, Drywall & Insulation
1743 Terrazzo, Tile, Marble, Mosaic Work
1751 Carpentry Work
1752 Floor Laying & Floor Work
1761 Roofing, Siding & Sheet Metal Work
1771 Concrete Work
1781 Water Well Drilling
1791 Structural Steel Erection
1793 Glass & Glazing Work
1794 Excavation Work
1795 Wrecking & Demolition Work
1796 Installing Building Equipment
1799 Special Trade Contractors

20 Food & Kindred Products
2011 Meat Packing Plants
2013 Sausages & Other Prepared Meats
2015 Poultry Slaughtering & Processing
2021 Creamery Butter
2022 Cheese, Natural & Processed
2023 Dry, Condensed, Evaporated Dairy Products
2024 Ice Cream & Frozen Desserts
2026 Fluid Milk
2032 Canned Specialties
2033 Canned Fruits & Specialties
2034 Dehydrated Fruits, Vegetables, Soups
2035 Pickles, Sauces & Salad Dressings
2037 Frozen Fruits & Vegetables
2038 Frozen Specialties
2041 Flour & Other Grain Mill Products
2043 Cereal Breakfast Foods
2044 Rice Milling
2045 Prepared Flour Mixes & Doughs
2046 Wet Corn Milling
2047 Dog & Cat Food
2048 Prepared Feeds
2051 Bread, Cake & Related Products
2052 Cookies & Crackers
2053 Frozen Bakery Products, Except Bread
2061 Raw Cane Sugar
2062 Cane Sugar Refining
2063 Beet Sugar
2064 Candy & Other Confectionery Products
2066 Chocolate & Cocoa Products
2067 Chewing Gum
2068 Salted & Roasted Nuts & Seeds
2074 Cottonseed Oil Mills
2075 Soybean Oil Mills
2076 Vegetable Oil Mills
2077 Animal & Marine Fats & Oils
2079 Edible Fats & Oils
2082 Malt Beverages
2083 Malt
2084 Wines, Brandy & Brandy Spirits
2085 Distilled & Blended Liquors
2086 Bottled & Canned Soft Drinks
2087 Flavoring Extracts & Syrups
2091 Canned & Cured Fish & Seafoods
2092 Fresh or Frozen Packaged Fish
2095 Roasted Coffee
2096 Potato Chips & Similar Snacks
2097 Manufactured Ice
2098 Macaroni & Spaghetti
2099 Food Preparations

21 Tobacco Products
2111 Cigarettes
2121 Cigars
2131 Chewing & Smoking Tobacco
2141 Tobacco Stemming & Redrying

22 Textile Mill Products
2211 Broadwoven Fabric Mills, Cotton
2221 Broadwoven Fabric Mills, Manmade
2231 Broadwoven Fabric Mills, Wool
2241 Narrow Fabric Mills
2251 Women's Hosiery, Except Socks
2252 Hosiery
2253 Knit Outerwear Mills
2254 Knit Underwear Mills
2257 Weft Knit Fabric Mills
2258 Lace & Warp Knit Fabric Mills
2259 Knitting Mills
2261 Finishing Plants, Cotton
2262 Finishing Plants, Manmade Fiber & Silk Fabrics
2269 Finishing Plants
2273 Carpets & Rugs
2281 Yarn Spinning Mills
2282 Throwing & Winding Mills
2284 Thread Mills
2295 Coated Fabrics, Not Rubberized
2296 Tire Cord & Fabrics
2297 Nonwoven Fabrics
2298 Cordage & Twine
2299 Textile Goods

23 Apparel & Other Finished Products Made from Fabrics & Similar Materials
2311 Men's & Boys' Suits & Coats
2321 Men's & Boys' Furnishings
2322 Men's & Boys' Underwear & Nightwear
2323 Men's & Boys' Neckwear
2325 Men's & Boys' Trousers & Slacks
2326 Men's & Boys' Work Clothing
2329 Men's & Boys' Clothing
2331 Women's & Misses' Blouses & Shirts
2335 Women's, Juniors' & Misses' Dresses
2337 Women's & Misses' Suits & Coats
2339 Women's & Misses' Outerwear
2341 Women's & Children's Underwear
2342 Bras, Girdles & Allied Garments
2353 Hats, Caps & Millinery
2361 Girls' & Children's Dresses, Blouses & Shirts
2369 Girls' & Children's Outerwear
2371 Fur Goods
2381 Fabric Dress & Work Gloves
2384 Robes & Dressing Gowns
2385 Waterproof Outerwear
2386 Leather & Sheep-lined Clothing
2387 Apparel Belts
2389 Apparel & Accessories
2391 Curtains & Draperies
2392 Household Furnishings
2393 Textile Bags
2394 Canvas & Related Products
2395 Pleating & Stitching
2396 Automotive & Apparel Trimmings
2397 Schiffli Machine Embroideries
2399 Fabricated Textile Products

24 Lumber & Wood Products, Except Furniture
2411 Logging
2421 Sawmills & Planing Mills, General
2426 Hardwood Dimension & Flooring Mills
2429 Special Product Sawmills
2431 Millwork
2434 Wood Kitchen Cabinets
2435 Hardwood Veneer & Plywood
2436 Softwood Veneer & Plywood
2439 Structural Wood Members
2441 Nailed Wood Boxes & Shook
2448 Wood Pallets & Skids
2449 Wood Containers
2451 Mobile Homes
2452 Prefabricated Wood Buildings
2491 Wood Preserving
2493 Reconstituted Wood Products
2499 Wood Products

25 Furniture & Fixtures
2511 Wood Household Furniture
2512 Upholstered Household Furniture

2514 Metal Household Furniture
2515 Mattresses & Bedsprings
2517 Wood Television & Radio Cabinets
2519 Household Furniture
2521 Wood Office Furniture
2522 Office Furniture, Except Wood
2531 Public Building & Related Furniture
2541 Wood Partitions & Fixtures
2542 Partitions & Fixtures, Except Wood
2591 Drapery Hardware & Blinds & Shades
2599 Furniture & Fixtures

26 Paper & Allied Products

2611 Pulp Mills
2621 Paper Mills
2631 Paperboard Mills
2652 Setup Paperboard Boxes
2653 Corrugated & Solid Fiber Boxes
2655 Fiber Cans, Drums & Similar Products
2656 Sanitary Food Containers
2657 Folding Paperboard Boxes
2671 Packaging Paper & Plastics Film, Coated & Laminated
2672 Coated & Laminated Paper
2673 Bags: Plastic, Laminated & Coated
2674 Bags: Uncoated Paper & Multiwall
2675 Die-cut Paper & Board
2676 Sanitary Paper Products
2677 Envelopes
2678 Stationery Products
2679 Converted Paper Products

27 Printing, Publishing & Allied Industries

2711 Newspapers
2721 Periodicals
2731 Book Publishing
2732 Book Printing
2741 Miscellaneous Publishing
2752 Commercial Printing, Lithographic
2754 Commercial Printing, Gravure
2759 Commercial Printing
2761 Manifold Business Forms
2771 Greeting Cards
2782 Blankbooks & Looseleaf Binders
2789 Bookbinding & Related Work
2791 Typesetting
2796 Platemaking Services

28 Chemicals & Allied Products

2812 Alkalies & Chlorine
2813 Industrial Gases
2816 Inorganic Pigments
2819 Industrial Inorganic Chemicals
2821 Plastics Materials & Resins
2822 Synthetic Rubber
2823 Cellulosic Manmade Fibers
2824 Organic Fibers, Noncellulosic
2833 Medicinals & Botanicals
2834 Pharmaceutical Preparations
2835 In Vitro & In Vivo Diagnostic Substances
2836 Biological Products, Except Diagnostic
2841 Soap & Other Detergents
2842 Specialty Cleaning, Polishes & Sanitation Goods
2843 Surface Active Agents
2844 Toilet Preparations
2851 Paints & Allied Products
2861 Gum & Wood Chemicals
2865 Cyclic Crudes & Intermediates
2869 Industrial Organic Chemicals
2873 Nitrogenous Fertilizers
2874 Phosphatic Fertilizers
2875 Fertilizers, Mixing Only
2879 Agricultural Chemicals
2891 Adhesives & Sealants
2892 Explosives
2893 Printing Ink
2895 Carbon Black
2899 Chemical Preparations

29 Petroleum Refining & Related Industries

2911 Petroleum Refining
2951 Asphalt Paving Mixtures & Blocks
2952 Asphalt Felts & Coatings
2992 Lubricating Oils & Greases
2999 Petroleum & Coal Products

30 Rubber & Miscellaneous Plastic Products

3011 Tires & Inner Tubes
3021 Rubber & Plastic Footwear
3052 Rubber & Plastics Hose & Beltings
3053 Gaskets, Packing & Sealing Devices
3061 Mechanical Rubber Goods
3069 Fabricated Rubber Products
3081 Unsupported Plastics Film & Sheet
3082 Unsupported Plastics Profile Shapes
3083 Laminated Plastics Plate & Sheet
3084 Plastics Pipe
3085 Plastics Bottles
3086 Plastics Foam Products
3087 Custom Compound Purchased Resins
3088 Plastics Plumbing Fixtures
3089 Plastics Products

31 Leather & Leather Products

3111 Leather Tanning & Finishing
3131 Footwear Cut Stock
3142 House Slippers
3143 Men's Footwear, Except Athletic
3144 Women's Footwear, Except Athletic
3149 Footwear, Except Rubber
3151 Leather Gloves & Mittens
3161 Luggage
3171 Women's Handbags & Purses
3172 Personal Leather Goods
3199 Leather Goods

32 Stone, Clay, Glass & Concrete Products

3211 Flat Glass
3221 Glass Containers
3229 Pressed & Blown Glass
3231 Products of Purchased Glass
3241 Cement, Hydraulic
3251 Brick & Structural Clay Tile
3253 Ceramic Wall & Floor Tile
3255 Clay Refractories
3259 Structural Clay Products
3261 Vitreous Plumbing Fixtures
3262 Vitreous China Table & Kitchenware
3263 Semivitreous Table & Kitchenware
3264 Porcelain Electrical Supplies
3269 Pottery Products
3271 Concrete Block & Brick
3272 Concrete Products
3273 Ready-mixed Concrete
3274 Lime
3275 Gypsum Products
3281 Cut Stone & Stone Products
3291 Abrasive Products
3292 Asbestos Products
3295 Minerals, Ground or Treated
3296 Mineral Wool
3297 Nonclay Refractories
3299 Nonmetallic Mineral Products

33 Primary Metal Industries

3312 Blast Furnaces & Steel Mills
3313 Electrometallurgical Products
3315 Steel Wire & Related Products
3316 Cold Finishing of Steel Shapes
3317 Steel Pipe & Tubes
3321 Gray & Ductile Iron Foundries
3322 Malleable Iron Foundries
3324 Steel Investment Foundries
3325 Steel Foundries
3331 Primary Copper
3334 Primary Aluminum
3339 Primary Nonferrous Metals
3341 Secondary Nonferrous Metals
3351 Copper Rolling & Drawing
3353 Aluminum Sheet, Plate & Foil
3354 Aluminum Extruded Products
3355 Aluminum Rolling & Drawing
3356 Nonferrous Rolling & Drawing
3357 Nonferrous Wiredrawing & Insulating
3363 Aluminum Die-castings
3364 Nonferrous Die-castings Except Aluminum
3365 Aluminum Foundries
3366 Copper Foundries
3369 Nonferrous Foundries
3398 Metal Heat Treating
3399 Primary Metal Products

34 Fabricated Metal Products, Except Machinery & Transportation Equipment

3411 Metal Cans
3412 Metal Barrels, Drums & Pails
3421 Cutlery
3423 Hand & Edge Tools
3425 Saw Blades & Handsaws
3429 Manufactured Hardware (General)
3431 Metal Sanitary Ware
3432 Plumbing Fixture Fittings & Trim
3433 Heating Equipment, Except Electric
3441 Fabricated Structural Metal
3442 Metal Doors, Sash & Trim
3443 Fabricated Plate Work (Boiler Shop)
3444 Sheet Metalwork
3446 Architectural Metalwork
3448 Prefabricated Metal Buildings
3449 Miscellaneous Metalwork
3451 Screw Machine Products
3452 Bolts, Nuts, Rivets & Washers
3462 Iron & Steel Forgings
3463 Nonferrous Forgings
3465 Automotive Stampings
3466 Crowns & Closures
3469 Metal Stampings
3471 Plating & Polishing
3479 Metal Coating & Allied Service
3482 Small Arms Ammunition
3483 Ammunition, Except For Small Arms
3484 Small Arms
3489 Ordnance & Accessories
3491 Industrial Valves
3492 Fluid Power Valves & Hose Fittings
3493 Steel Springs, Except Wire
3494 Valves & Pipe Fittings
3495 Wire Springs
3496 Miscellaneous Fabricated Wire Products
3497 Metal Foil & Leaf
3498 Fabricated Pipe & Fittings
3499 Fabricated Metal Products

35 Industrial & Commercial Machinery & Computer Equipment

3511 Turbines & Turbine Generator Sets
3519 Internal Combustion Engines
3523 Farm Machinery & Equipment
3524 Lawn & Garden Equipment
3531 Construction Machinery
3532 Mining Machinery
3533 Oil & Gas Field Machinery
3534 Elevators & Moving Stairways
3535 Conveyors & Conveying Equipment
3536 Hoists, Cranes & Monorails
3537 Industrial Trucks & Tractors
3541 Machine Tools, Metal Cutting Type
3542 Machine Tools, Metal Forming Type
3543 Industrial Patterns
3544 Special Dies, Tools, Jigs & Fixtures
3545 Machine Tool Accessories
3546 Power-driven Handtools
3547 Rolling Mill Machinery
3548 Welding Apparatus
3549 Metalworking Machinery
3552 Textile Machinery
3553 Woodworking Machinery
3554 Paper Industries Machinery
3555 Printing Trade Machinery
3556 Food Products Machinery
3559 Special Industry Machinery
3561 Pumps & Pumping Equipment
3562 Ball & Roller Bearings
3563 Air & Gas Compressors
3564 Blowers & Fans
3565 Packaging Machinery
3566 Speed Changers, Drives & Gears
3567 Industrial Furnaces & Ovens
3568 Power Transmission Equipment
3569 General Industrial Machinery
3571 Electronic Computers
3572 Computer Storage Devices
3575 Computer Terminals
3577 Computer Peripheral Equipment
3578 Calculating & Accounting Equipment
3579 Office Machines
3581 Automatic Vending Machines
3582 Commercial Laundry Equipment
3585 Refrigeration & Heating Equipment
3586 Measuring & Dispensing Pumps
3589 Service Industry Machinery
3592 Carburetors, Pistons, Rings, Valves
3593 Fluid Power Cylinders & Actuators
3594 Fluid Power Pumps & Motors
3596 Scales & Balances, Except Laboratory
3599 Industrial Machinery

36 Electronic & Other Electrical Equipment & Components Except Computer Equipment

3612 Transformers, Except Electric
3613 Switchgear & Switchboard Apparatus
3621 Motors & Generators
3624 Carbon & Graphite Products
3625 Relays & Industrial Controls
3629 Electrical Industrial Apparatus
3631 Household Cooking Equipment
3632 Household Refrigerators & Freezers
3633 Household Laundry Equipment
3634 Electric Housewares & Fans
3635 Household Vacuum Cleaners
3639 Household Appliances
3641 Electric Lamps
3643 Current-carrying Wiring Devices
3644 Noncurrent-carrying Wiring Devices
3645 Residential Lighting Fixtures
3646 Commercial Indusl & Institutional Electric Lighting Fixtures
3647 Vehicular Lighting Equipment
3648 Lighting Equipment
3651 Household Audio & Video Equipment
3652 Pre-recorded Records & Tapes
3661 Telephone & Telegraph Apparatus
3663 Radio & TV Communications Equipment
3669 Communications Equipment
3671 Electron Tubes
3672 Printed Circuit Boards
3674 Semiconductors & Related Devices
3675 Electronic Capacitors
3676 Electronic Resistors
3677 Electronic Coils, Transformers & Other Inductors
3678 Electronic Connectors
3679 Electronic Components
3691 Storage Batteries
3692 Primary Batteries, Dry & Wet
3694 Engine Electrical Equipment
3695 Magnetic & Optical Recording Media
3699 Electrical Equipment & Supplies

37 Transportation Equipment

3711 Motor Vehicles & Car Bodies
3713 Truck & Bus Bodies
3714 Motor Vehicle Parts & Accessories
3715 Truck Trailers
3716 Motor Homes
3721 Aircraft
3724 Aircraft Engines & Engine Parts
3728 Aircraft Parts & Equipment
3731 Shipbuilding & Repairing
3732 Boat Building & Repairing
3743 Railroad Equipment
3751 Motorcycles, Bicycles & Parts
3761 Guided Missiles & Space Vehicles
3764 Guided Missile & Space Vehicle Propulsion Unit Parts
3769 Guided Missile & Space Vehicle Parts & Auxiliary Equipment
3792 Travel Trailers & Campers
3795 Tanks & Tank Components
3799 Transportation Equipment

38 Measuring, Analyzing & Controlling Instruments; Photographic, Medical & Optical Goods; Watches & Clocks

3812 Search & Navigation Equipment
3821 Laboratory Apparatus & Furniture
3822 Auto Controls Regulating Residential & Commercial Environment & Appliances
3823 Industrial Instruments Measurement Display/ Control Process Variable
3824 Fluid Meters & Counting Devices
3825 Instruments To Measure Electricity
3826 Analytical Instruments
3827 Optical Instruments & Lenses
3829 Measuring & Controlling Devices
3841 Surgical & Medical Instruments
3842 Surgical Appliances & Supplies
3843 Dental Equipment & Supplies
3844 X-ray Apparatus & Tubes
3845 Electromedical Equipment
3851 Ophthalmic Goods
3861 Photographic Equipment & Supplies
3873 Watches, Clocks, Watchcases & Parts

39 Miscellaneous Manufacturing Industries

3911 Jewelry, Precious Metal
3914 Silverware & Plated Ware
3915 Jewelers' Materials & Lapidary Work
3931 Musical Instruments
3942 Dolls & Stuffed Toys
3944 Games, Toys & Children's Vehicles
3949 Sporting & Athletic Goods
3951 Pens & Mechanical Pencils
3952 Lead Pencils & Art Goods
3953 Marking Devices
3955 Carbon Paper & Inked Ribbons
3961 Costume Jewelry
3965 Fasteners, Buttons, Needles & Pins
3991 Brooms & Brushes
3993 Signs & Advertising Specialties
3995 Burial Caskets
3996 Hard Surface Floor Coverings
3999 Manufacturing Industries

40 Railroad Transportation

4011 Railroads, Line-haul Operating
4013 Switching & Terminal Services

41 Local & Suburban Transit & Interurban Highway Passenger Transportation

4111 Local & Suburban Transit
4119 Local Passenger Transportation
4121 Taxicabs
4131 Intercity & Rural Bus Transportation
4141 Local Bus Charter Service
4142 Bus Charter Service, Except Local
4151 School Buses
4173 Bus Terminal & Service Facilities

42 Motor Freight Transportation & Warehousing

4212 Local Trucking, Without Storage
4213 Trucking, Except Local
4214 Local Trucking With Storage
4215 Courier Services, Except By Air
4221 Farm Product Warehousing & Storage
4222 Refrigerated Warehousing & Storage
4225 General Warehousing & Storage
4226 Special Warehousing & Storage
4231 Trucking Terminal Facilities

43 United States Postal Service

4311 U.S. Postal Service

44 Water Transportation

4412 Deep Sea Foreign Transportation of Freight
4424 Deep Sea Domestic Transportation of Freight
4432 Freight Transportation on The Great Lakes
4449 Water Transportation of Freight
4481 Deep Sea Passenger Transportation, Except Ferry
4482 Ferries
4489 Water Passenger Transportation
4491 Marine Cargo Handling
4492 Towing & Tugboat Service
4493 Marinas
4499 Water Transportation Services

45 Transportation by Air

4512 Air Transportation, Scheduled
4513 Air Courier Services
4522 Air Transportation, Nonscheduled
4581 Airports, Flying Fields & Services

46 Pipelines, Except Natural Gas

4612 Crude Petroleum Pipelines
4613 Refined Petroleum Pipelines
4619 Pipelines

47 Transportation Services

4724 Travel Agencies
4725 Tour Operators
4729 Passenger Transportation Arrangement
4731 Freight Transportation Arrangement
4741 Rental of Railroad Cars
4783 Packing & Crating
4785 Inspection & Fixed Facilities
4789 Transportation Services

48 Communications

4812 Radio Telephone Communication
4813 Telephone Communication, Except Radio
4822 Telegraph & Other Communications
4832 Radio Broadcasting Stations
4833 Television Broadcasting Stations
4841 Cable & Other Pay Television Services
4899 Communication Services

49 Electric, Gas & Sanitary Services

4911 Electric Services
4922 Natural Gas Transmission
4923 Gas Transmission & Distribution
4924 Natural Gas Distribution
4925 Gas Production and/or Distribution
4931 Electric & Other Services Combined
4932 Gas & Other Services Combined
4939 Combination Utilities
4941 Water Supply
4952 Sewerage Systems
4953 Refuse Systems
4959 Sanitary Services
4961 Steam & Air-conditioning Supply
4971 Irrigation Systems

50 Wholesale Trade — Durable Goods

5012 Automobiles & Other Motor Vehicles
5013 Motor Vehicle Supplies & New Parts
5014 Tires & Tubes
5015 Motor Vehicle Parts, Used
5021 Furniture
5023 Home Furnishings
5031 Lumber, Plywood & Millwork
5032 Brick, Stone & Related Material
5033 Roofing, Siding & Insulation
5039 Construction Materials
5043 Photographic Equipment & Supplies
5044 Office Equipment
5045 Computers, Peripherals & Software
5046 Commercial Equipment
5047 Medical & Hospital Equipment
5048 Ophthalmic Goods
5049 Professional Equipment
5051 Metals Service Centers & Offices
5052 Coal & Other Minerals & Ores
5063 Electrical Apparatus & Equipment
5064 Electrical Appliances, Television & Radio
5065 Electronic Parts & Equipment
5072 Hardware
5074 Plumbing & Hydronic Heating Supplies
5075 Warm Air Heating & Air Conditioning
5078 Refrigeration Equipment & Supplies
5082 Construction & Mining Machinery
5083 Farm & Garden Machinery
5084 Industrial Machinery & Equipment
5085 Industrial Supplies
5087 Service Establishment Equipment
5088 Transportation Equipment & Supplies
5091 Sporting & Recreation Goods
5092 Toys & Hobby Goods & Supplies
5093 Scrap & Waste Materials
5094 Jewelry & Precious Stones
5099 Durable Goods

51 Wholesale Trade — Nondurable Goods

5111 Printing & Writing Paper
5112 Stationery & Office Supplies
5113 Industrial & Personal Service Paper
5122 Drugs, Proprietaries & Sundries
5131 Piece Goods & Notions
5136 Men's & Boys' Clothing
5137 Women's & Children's Clothing
5139 Footwear
5141 Groceries, General Line
5142 Packaged Frozen Goods
5143 Dairy Products, Except Dried or Canned
5144 Poultry & Poultry Products
5145 Confectionery
5146 Fish & Seafoods
5147 Meats & Meat Products
5148 Fresh Fruits & Vegetables
5149 Groceries & Related Products
5153 Grain & Field Beans

5154 Livestock
5159 Farm-Product Raw Materials
5162 Plastics Materials & Basic Shapes
5169 Chemicals & Allied Products
5171 Petroleum Bulk Stations & Terminals
5172 Petroleum Products
5181 Beer & Ale
5182 Wine & Distilled Beverages
5191 Farm Supplies
5192 Books, Periodicals & Newspapers
5193 Flowers & Florist Supplies
5194 Tobacco & Tobacco Products
5198 Paints, Varnishes & Supplies
5199 Nondurable Goods

52 Building Materials, Hardware, Garden Supply & Mobile Home Dealers

5211 Lumber & Other Building Materials
5231 Paint, Glass & Wallpaper
5251 Hardware
5261 Nurseries & Garden Centers
5271 Mobile Homes

53 General Merchandise Stores

5311 Department Stores
5331 Variety Stores
5399 Miscellaneous General Merchandise

54 Food Stores

5411 Grocery Stores
5421 Meat & Fish Markets
5431 Fruit & Vegetable Markets
5441 Candy, Nut & Confectionery Stores
5451 Dairy Products Stores
5461 Bakeries
5499 Miscellaneous Food Stores

55 Automotive Dealers & Gasoline Service Stations

5511 New & Used Car Dealers
5521 Used Car Dealers
5531 Automotive & Home Supply Stores
5541 Gasoline Service Stations
5551 Boat Dealers
5561 Recreational Vehicle Dealers
5571 Motorcycle Dealers
5599 Automotive Dealers

56 Apparel & Accessory Stores

5611 Men's & Boys' Clothing Stores
5621 Women's Clothing Stores
5632 Women's Accessory & Specialty Stores
5641 Children's & Infants' Wear Stores
5651 Family Clothing Stores
5661 Shoe Stores
5699 Miscellaneous Apparel & Accessories

57 Home Furniture, Furnishings & Equipment Stores

5712 Furniture Stores
5713 Floor Covering Stores
5714 Drapery & Upholstery Stores
5719 Miscellaneous Home Furnishings
5722 Household Appliance Stores
5731 Radio, Television & Electronic Stores
5734 Computer & Software Stores
5735 Record & Prerecorded Tape Stores
5736 Musical Instrument Stores

58 Eating & Drinking Places

5812 Eating Places
5813 Drinking Places

59 Miscellaneous Retail

5912 Drug Stores & Proprietary Stores
5921 Liquor Stores
5932 Used Merchandise Stores
5941 Sporting Goods & Bicycle Shops
5942 Book Stores
5943 Stationery Stores
5944 Jewelry Stores
5945 Hobby, Toy & Game Shops
5946 Camera & Photographic Supply Stores
5947 Gift, Novelty & Souvenir Shops
5948 Luggage & Leather Goods Stores
5949 Sewing, Needlework & Piece Goods
5961 Catalog & Mail-Order Houses
5962 Merchandising Machine Operators
5963 Direct Selling Establishments
5983 Fuel Oil Dealers
5984 Liquefied Petroleum Gas Dealers
5989 Fuel Dealers
5992 Florists
5993 Tobacco Stores & Stands
5994 News Dealers & Newsstands
5995 Optical Goods Stores
5999 Miscellaneous Retail Stores

60 Depository Institutions

6011 Federal Reserve Banks
6019 Central Reserve Depository
6021 National Commercial Banks
6022 State Commercial Banks
6029 Commercial Banks
6035 Savings Institutions, Federally Chartered
6036 Savings Institutions, Not Federally Chartered
6061 Federal Credit Unions
6062 State Credit Unions
6081 Branches & Agencies Of Foreign Banks
6082 Foreign Trade & International Banking Institutions
6091 Nondeposit Trust Facilities
6099 Functions Related To Deposit Banking

61 Nondepository Credit Institutions

6111 Federal & Federally Sponsored Credit Agencies
6141 Personal Credit Institutions
6153 Short-Term Business Credit
6159 Miscellaneous Business Credit
6162 Mortgage Bankers & Correspondents
6163 Loan Brokers

62 Security & Commodity Brokers, Dealers, Exchanges & Services

6211 Security Brokers & Dealers
6221 Commodity Contracts Brokers, Dealers
6231 Security & Commodity Exchanges
6282 Investment Advice
6289 Security & Commodity Service

63 Insurance Carriers

6311 Life Insurance
6321 Accident & Health Insurance
6324 Hospital & Medical Service Plans
6331 Fire, Marine & Casualty Insurance
6351 Surety Insurance
6361 Title Insurance
6371 Pension, Health & Welfare Funds
6399 Insurance Carriers

64 Insurance Agents, Brokers & Service

6411 Insurance Agents, Brokers & Service

65 Real Estate

6512 Nonresidential Building Operators
6513 Apartment Building Operators
6514 Dwelling Operators, Except Apartments
6515 Mobile Home Site Operators
6517 Railroad Property Lessors
6519 Real Property Lessors
6531 Real Estate Agents & Managers
6541 Title Abstract Offices
6552 Subdividers & Developers
6553 Cemetery Subdividers & Developers

67 Holding & Other Investment Offices

6712 Bank Holding Companies
6719 Holding Companies
6722 Management Investment, Open-end
6726 Investment Offices
6732 Trusts: Educational, Religious, Etc.
6733 Trusts
6792 Oil Royalty Traders
6794 Patent Owners & Lessors
6798 Real Estate Investment Trusts
6799 Investors

70 Hotels, Rooming Houses, Camps & Other Lodging Places

7011 Hotels & Motels
7021 Rooming & Boarding Houses
7032 Sporting & Recreational Camps
7033 Trailer Parks & Campsites
7041 Membership-basis Organization Hotels

72 Personal Services

7211 Power Laundries, Family & Commercial
7212 Garment Pressing & Cleaners' Agents
7213 Linen Supply
7215 Coin-operated Laundries & Cleaning
7216 Drycleaning Plants, Except Rugs
7217 Carpet & Upholstery Cleaning
7218 Industrial Launderers
7219 Laundry & Garment Services
7221 Photographic Studios, Portrait
7231 Beauty Shops
7241 Barber Shops
7251 Shoe Repair & Shoeshine Parlors
7261 Funeral Service & Crematories
7291 Tax Return Preparation Services
7299 Miscellaneous Personal Service

73 Business Services

7311 Advertising Agencies
7312 Outdoor Advertising Services
7313 Radio, Television, Publisher Representatives
7319 Advertising
7322 Adjustment & Collection Services
7323 Credit Reporting Services
7331 Direct Mail Advertising Services
7334 Photocopying & Duplicating Services
7335 Commercial Photography
7336 Commercial Art & Graphic Design
7338 Secretarial & Court Reporting
7342 Disinfecting & Pest Control Services
7349 Building Maintenance Services
7352 Medical Equipment Rental
7353 Heavy Construction Equipment Rental
7359 Equipment Rental & Leasing
7361 Employment Agencies
7363 Help Supply Services
7371 Custom Computer Programming Services
7372 Prepackaged Software
7373 Computer Integrated Systems Design
7374 Data Processing & Preparation
7375 Information Retrieval Services
7376 Computer Facilities Management
7377 Computer Rental & Leasing
7378 Computer Maintenance & Repair
7379 Computer Related Services
7381 Detective & Armored Car Services
7382 Security Systems Services
7383 News Syndicates
7384 Photofinish Laboratories
7389 Business Services

75 Automotive Repair, Services & Parking

7513 Truck Rental & Leasing, No Drivers
7514 Passenger Car Rental
7515 Passenger Car Leasing
7519 Utility Trailer Rental
7521 Automobile Parking
7532 Top & Body Repair & Paint Shops
7533 Auto Exhaust System Repair Shops
7534 Tire Retreading & Repair Shops
7536 Automotive Glass Replacement Shops
7537 Automotive Transmission Repair Shops
7538 General Automotive Repair Shops
7539 Automotive Repair Shops
7542 Carwashes
7549 Automotive Services

76 Miscellaneous Repair Services

7622 Radio & Television Repair
7623 Refrigeration Service & Repair
7629 Electrical Repair Shops
7631 Watch, Clock & Jewelry Repair
7641 Reupholstery & Furniture Repair
7692 Welding Repair
7694 Armature Rewinding Shops
7699 Repair Services

78 Motion Pictures

7812 Motion Picture & Video Production
7819 Services Allied To Motion Pictures
7822 Motion Picture & Tape Distribution
7829 Motion Picture Distribution Services
7832 Motion Picture Theaters, Except Drive-In
7833 Drive-In Motion Picture Theaters
7841 Video Tape Rental

79 Amusement & Recreation Services

7911 Dance Studios, Schools & Halls
7922 Theatrical Producers & Services
7929 Entertainers & Entertainment Groups
7933 Bowling Centers
7941 Sports Clubs, Managers & Promoters
7948 Racing, Including Track Operation
7991 Physical Fitness Facilities
7992 Public Golf Courses
7993 Coin-operated Amusement Devices
7996 Amusement Parks
7997 Membership Sports & Recreation Clubs
7999 Amusement & Recreation

80 Health Services

8011 Offices & Clinics of Medical Doctors
8021 Offices & Clinics of Dentists
8031 Offices & Clinics of Osteopathic Physicians
8041 Offices & Clinics of Chiropractors
8042 Offices & Clinics of Optometrists
8043 Offices & Clinics of Podiatrists
8049 Offices of Health Practitioners
8051 Skilled Nursing Care Facilities
8052 Intermediate Care Facilities
8059 Nursing & Personal Care
8062 General Medical & Surgical Hospitals
8063 Psychiatric Hospitals
8069 Specialty Hospitals, Except Psychiatric
8071 Medical Laboratories
8072 Dental Laboratories
8082 Home Health Care Services
8092 Kidney Dialysis Centers
8093 Specialty Outpatient Clinics
8099 Health & Allied Services

81 Legal Services

8111 Legal Services

82 Educational Services

8211 Elementary & Secondary Schools
8221 Colleges Universities & Professional Schools
8222 Junior Colleges & Technical Institutes
8231 Libraries
8243 Data Processing Schools
8244 Business & Secretarial Schools
8249 Vocational Schools
8299 Schools & Educational Services

83 Social Services

8322 Individual & Family Services
8331 Job Training & Vocational Rehabilitation Services
8351 Child Day Care Services
8361 Residential Care
8399 Social Services

84 Museums, Art Galleries & Botanical & Zoological Gardens

8412 Museums & Art Galleries
8422 Arboreta & Botanical r Zoological Gardens

86 Membership Organizations

8611 Business Associations
8621 Professional Membership Organizations
8631 Labor Unions & Similar Labor Organizations
8641 Civic Social & Fraternal Associations
8651 Political Organizations
8661 Religious Organizations
8699 Membership Organizations

87 Engineering, Accounting, Research, Management & Related Services

8711 Engineering Services
8712 Architectural Services
8713 Surveying Services
8721 Accounting, Auditing & Bookkeeping
8731 Commercial Physical Research
8732 Commercial Nonphysical Research
8733 Noncommercial Research Organizations
8734 Testing Laboratories
8741 Management Services
8742 Management Consulting Services
8743 Public Relations Services
8744 Facilities Support Services
8748 Business Consulting

88 Private Households

8811 Private Households

89 Services, Not Elsewhere Classified

8999 Services

91 Executive, Legislative & General Government, Except Finance

9111 Executive Offices
9121 Legislative Bodies
9131 Executive & Legislative Combined
9199 General Government

92 Justice, Public Order & Safety

9211 Courts
9221 Police Protection
9222 Legal Counsel & Prosecution
9223 Correctional Institutions
9224 Fire Protection
9229 Public Order & Safety

93 Public Finance, Taxation & Monetary Policy

9311 Finance, Taxation & Monetary Policy

94 Administration of Human Resource Programs

9411 Administration of Educational Programs
9431 Administration of Public Health Programs
9441 Administration of Social & Manpower Programs
9451 Administration of Veterans' Affairs

95 Administration of Environmental Quality & Housing Programs

9511 Air, Water & Solid Waste Management
9512 Land, Mineral & Wildlife Conservation
9531 Housing Programs
9532 Urban & Community Development

96 Administration of Economic Programs

9611 Administration of General Economic Programs
9621 Regulation, Administration of Transportation
9631 Regulation, Administration of Utilities
9641 Regulation of Agricultural Marketing
9651 Regulation, Miscellaneous Commercial Sectors
9661 Space Research & Technology

97 National Security & International Affairs

9711 National Security
9721 International Affairs

99 Nonclassifiable Establishments

9999 Nonclassifiable Establishments

A

3291 Abrasive Products
6321 Accident & Health Insurance
8721 Accounting, Auditing & Bookkeeping
2891 Adhesives & Sealants
7322 Adjustment & Collection Services
9411 Administration Of Educational Programs
9611 Administration Of General Economic Programs
9431 Administration Of Public Health Programs
9441 Administration Of Social & Manpower Programs
9451 Administration Of Veterans' Affairs
7319 Advertising
7311 Advertising Agencies
2879 Agricultural Chemicals
3563 Air & Gas Compressors
4513 Air Courier Services
4522 Air Transportation, Nonscheduled
4512 Air Transportation, Scheduled
9511 Air, Water & Solid Waste Management
3721 Aircraft
3724 Aircraft Engines & Engine Parts
3728 Aircraft Parts & Equipment
4581 Airports, Flying Fields & Services
2812 Alkalies & Chlorine
3363 Aluminum Die-castings
3354 Aluminum Extruded Products
3365 Aluminum Foundries
3355 Aluminum Rolling & Drawing
3353 Aluminum Sheet, Plate & Foil
3483 Ammunition, Except For Small Arms
7999 Amusement & Recreation
7996 Amusement Parks
3826 Analytical Instruments
2077 Animal & Marine Fats & Oils
0273 Animal Aquaculture
0279 Animal Specialties
0752 Animal Specialty Services
1231 Anthracite Mining
6513 Apartment Building Operators
2389 Apparel & Accessories
2387 Apparel Belts
8422 Arboreta & Botanical Or Zoological Gardens
3446 Architectural Metalwork
8712 Architectural Services
7694 Armature Rewinding Shops
3292 Asbestos Products
2952 Asphalt Felts & Coatings
2951 Asphalt Paving Mixtures & Blocks
3822 Auto Controls Regulating Residntl & Coml Environmt & Applncs
7533 Auto Exhaust System Repair Shops
3581 Automatic Vending Machines
7521 Automobile Parking
5012 Automobiles & Other Motor Vehicles
2396 Automotive & Apparel Trimmings
5531 Automotive & Home Supply Stores
5599 Automotive Dealers
7536 Automotive Glass Replacement Shops
7539 Automotive Repair Shops
7549 Automotive Services
3465 Automotive Stampings
7537 Automotive Transmission Repair Shops

B

2673 Bags: Plastic, Laminated & Coated
2674 Bags: Uncoated Paper & Multiwall
5461 Bakeries
3562 Ball & Roller Bearings
6712 Bank Holding Companies
7241 Barber Shops
7231 Beauty Shops
0212 Beef Cattle Except Feedlots
0211 Beef Cattle Feedlots
5181 Beer & Ale
2063 Beet Sugar
0171 Berry Crops
2836 Biological Products, Except Diagnostic
1221 Bituminous Coal & Lignite-surface
1222 Bituminous Coal-underground
2782 Blankbooks & Looseleaf Binders
3312 Blast Furnaces & Steel Mills
3564 Blowers & Fans
3732 Boat Building & Repairing
5551 Boat Dealers
3452 Bolts, Nuts, Rivets & Washers
2732 Book Printing
2731 Book Publishing
5942 Book Stores
2789 Bookbinding & Related Work
5192 Books, Periodicals & Newspapers
2086 Bottled & Canned Soft Drinks
7933 Bowling Centers
6081 Branches & Agencies Of Foreign Banks
2342 Bras, Girdles & Allied Garments
2051 Bread, Cake & Related Products
3251 Brick & Structural Clay Tile
5032 Brick, Stone & Related Material
1622 Bridge, Tunnel & Elevated Highway
2211 Broadwoven Fabric Mills, Cotton
2221 Broadwoven Fabric Mills, Manmade
2231 Broadwoven Fabric Mills, Wool
0251 Broiler, Fryer & Roaster Chickens
3991 Brooms & Brushes
7349 Building Maintenance Services
3995 Burial Caskets
4142 Bus Charter Service, Except Local
4173 Bus Terminal & Service Facilities
8244 Business & Secretarial Schools
8611 Business Associations
8748 Business Consulting
7389 Business Services

C

4841 Cable & Other Pay Television Services
3578 Calculating & Accounting Equipment
5946 Camera & Photographic Supply Stores
2064 Candy & Other Confectionery Products
5441 Candy, Nut & Confectionery Stores
2062 Cane Sugar Refining
2091 Canned & Cured Fish & Seafoods
2033 Canned Fruits & Specialties
2032 Canned Specialties
2394 Canvas & Related Products
3624 Carbon & Graphite Products
2895 Carbon Black
3955 Carbon Paper & Inked Ribbons
3592 Carburetors, Pistons, Rings, Valves
1751 Carpentry Work
7217 Carpet & Upholstery Cleaning
2273 Carpets & Rugs
7542 Carwashes
0119 Cash Grains
5961 Catalog & Mail-order Houses
2823 Cellulosic Manmade Fibers
3241 Cement, Hydraulic
6553 Cemetery Subdividers & Developers
6019 Central Reserve Depository
3253 Ceramic Wall & Floor Tile
2043 Cereal Breakfast Foods
2022 Cheese, Natural & Processed
1479 Chemical & Fertilizer Mining
2899 Chemical Preparations
5169 Chemicals & Allied Products
2131 Chewing & Smoking Tobacco
2067 Chewing Gum
0252 Chicken Eggs
8351 Child Day Care Services
5641 Children's & Infants' Wear Stores
2066 Chocolate & Cocoa Products
2111 Cigarettes
2121 Cigars
0174 Citrus Fruits
8641 Civic Social & Fraternal Associations
1459 Clay & Related Minerals
3255 Clay Refractories
5052 Coal & Other Minerals & Ores
1241 Coal Mining Services
2672 Coated & Laminated Paper
2295 Coated Fabrics, Not Rubberized
7993 Coin-operated Amusement Devices
7215 Coin-operated Laundries & Cleaning
3316 Cold Finishing Of Steel Shapes
8221 Colleges Universities & Professional Schools
4939 Combination Utilities
7336 Commercial Art & Graphic Design
6029 Commercial Banks
5046 Commercial Equipment
3646 Commercial Indusl & Institutional Electric Lighting Fixtures
3582 Commercial Laundry Equipment
8732 Commercial Nonphysical Research
7335 Commercial Photography
8731 Commercial Physical Research
2759 Commercial Printing
2754 Commercial Printing, Gravure
2752 Commercial Printing, Lithographic
6221 Commodity Contracts Brokers, Dealers
4899 Communication Services
3669 Communications Equipment
5734 Computer & Software Stores
7376 Computer Facilities Management
7373 Computer Integrated Systems Design
7378 Computer Maintenance & Repair
3577 Computer Peripheral Equipment
7379 Computer Related Services
7377 Computer Rental & Leasing
3572 Computer Storage Devices
3575 Computer Terminals
5045 Computers, Peripherals & Software
3271 Concrete Block & Brick
3272 Concrete Products
1771 Concrete Work
5145 Confectionery
5082 Construction & Mining Machinery
3531 Construction Machinery
5039 Construction Materials
1442 Construction Sand & Gravel
2679 Converted Paper Products
3535 Conveyors & Conveying Equipment
2052 Cookies & Crackers
3366 Copper Foundries
1021 Copper Ores
3351 Copper Rolling & Drawing
2298 Cordage & Twine
0115 Corn
9223 Correctional Institutions
2653 Corrugated & Solid Fiber Boxes
3961 Costume Jewelry
0131 Cotton
0724 Cotton Ginning
2074 Cottonseed Oil Mills
4215 Courier Services, Except By Air
9211 Courts
2021 Creamery Butter
7323 Credit Reporting Services
0722 Crop Harvesting
0721 Crop Planting & Protection
0723 Crop Preparation Services For Market
3466 Crowns & Closures
1311 Crude Petroleum & Natural Gas
4612 Crude Petroleum Pipelines
1423 Crushed & Broken Granite
1422 Crushed & Broken Limestone
1429 Crushed & Broken Stone
3643 Current-carrying Wiring Devices
2391 Curtains & Draperies
3087 Custom Compound Purchased Resins
7371 Custom Computer Programming Services
3281 Cut Stone & Stone Products
3421 Cutlery
2865 Cyclic Crudes & Intermediates

D

0241 Dairy Farms
5451 Dairy Products Stores
5143 Dairy Products, Except Dried Or Canned
7911 Dance Studios, Schools & Halls
7374 Data Processing & Preparation
8243 Data Processing Schools
0175 Deciduous Tree Fruits
4424 Deep Sea Domestic Transportation Of Freight
4412 Deep Sea Foreign Transportation Of Freight
4481 Deep Sea Passenger Transportation, Except Ferry
2034 Dehydrated Fruits, Vegetables, Soups
3843 Dental Equipment & Supplies
8072 Dental Laboratories
5311 Department Stores
7381 Detective & Armored Car Services
2675 Die-cut Paper & Board
1411 Dimension Stone
7331 Direct Mail Advertising Services
5963 Direct Selling Establishments
7342 Disinfecting & Pest Control Services
2085 Distilled & Blended Liquors
2047 Dog & Cat Food
3942 Dolls & Stuffed Toys
5714 Drapery & Upholstery Stores
2591 Drapery Hardware & Blinds & Shades
1381 Drilling Oil & Gas Wells
5813 Drinking Places
7833 Drive-in Motion Picture Theaters
5912 Drug Stores & Proprietary Stores
5122 Drugs, Proprietaries & Sundries
2023 Dry, Condensed, Evaporated Dairy Products
7216 Drycleaning Plants, Except Rugs
5099 Durable Goods

6514 Dwelling Operators, Except Apartments

E

5812 Eating Places
2079 Edible Fats & Oils
4931 Electric & Other Services Combined
3634 Electric Housewares & Fans
3641 Electric Lamps
4911 Electric Services
5063 Electrical Apparatus & Equipment
5064 Electrical Appliances, Television & Radio
3699 Electrical Equipment & Supplies
3629 Electrical Industrial Apparatus
7629 Electrical Repair Shops
1731 Electrical Work
3845 Electromedical Equipment
3313 Electrometallurgical Products
3671 Electron Tubes
3675 Electronic Capacitors
3677 Electronic Coils, Transformers & Other Inductors
3676 Electronic Resistors
8211 Elementary & Secondary Schools
3534 Elevators & Moving Stairways
7361 Employment Agencies
3694 Engine Electrical Equipment
8711 Engineering Services
7929 Entertainers & Entertainment Groups
2677 Envelopes
7359 Equipment Rental & Leasing
1794 Excavation Work
9131 Executive & Legislative Combined
9111 Executive Offices
2892 Explosives
3679 Electronic Components
3571 Electronic Computers
3678 Electronic Connectors
5065 Electronic Parts & Equipment

F

2381 Fabric Dress & Work Gloves
3499 Fabricated Metal Products
3498 Fabricated Pipe & Fittings
3443 Fabricated Plate Work (Boiler Shop)
3069 Fabricated Rubber Products
3441 Fabricated Structural Metal
2399 Fabricated Textile Products
8744 Facilities Support Services
5651 Family Clothing Stores
5083 Farm & Garden Machinery
0761 Farm Labor Contractors
3523 Farm Machinery & Equipment
0762 Farm Management Services
4221 Farm Product Warehousing & Storage
5191 Farm Supplies
5159 Farm-product Raw Materials
3965 Fasteners, Buttons, Needles & Pins
6111 Federal & Federally Sponsored Credit Agencies
6061 Federal Credit Unions
6011 Federal Reserve Banks
4482 Ferries
1061 Ferroalloy Ores, Except Vanadium
2875 Fertilizers, Mixing Only
2655 Fiber Cans, Drums & Similar Products
0139 Field Crops, Except Cash Grain
9311 Finance, Taxation & Monetary Policy
0912 Finfish
2269 Finishing Plants
2261 Finishing Plants, Cotton
2262 Finishing Plants, Manmade Fiber & Silk Fabrics
9224 Fire Protection
6331 Fire, Marine & Casualty Insurance
5146 Fish & Seafoods
0921 Fish Hatcheries & Preserves
3211 Flat Glass
2087 Flavoring Extracts & Syrups
5713 Floor Covering Stores
1752 Floor Laying & Floor Work
5992 Florists
2041 Flour & Other Grain Mill Products
5193 Flowers & Florists' Supplies
3824 Fluid Meters & Counting Devices
2026 Fluid Milk
3593 Fluid Power Cylinders & Actuators
3594 Fluid Power Pumps & Motors
3492 Fluid Power Valves & Hose Fittings
2657 Folding Paperboard Boxes
0182 Food Crops Grown UnderCover
2099 Food Preparations
3556 Food Products Machinery
5139 Footwear
3131 Footwear Cut Stock
3149 Footwear, Except Rubber
6082 Foreign Trade & International Banking Institutions
0831 Forest Products
0851 Forestry Services
4731 Freight Transportation Arrangement
4432 Freight Transportation On The Great Lakes
5148 Fresh Fruits & Vegetables
2092 Fresh Or Frozen Packaged Fish
2053 Frozen Bakery Products, Except Bread
2037 Frozen Fruits & Vegetables
2038 Frozen Specialties
5431 Fruit & Vegetable Markets
0179 Fruits & Tree Nuts
5989 Fuel Dealers
5983 Fuel Oil Dealers
6099 Functions Related To Deposit Banking
7261 Funeral Service & Crematories
2371 Fur Goods
0271 Fur-bearing Animals & Rabbits
5021 Furniture
2599 Furniture & Fixtures
5712 Furniture Stores

G

3944 Games, Toys & Children's Vehicles
7212 Garment Pressing & Cleaners' Agents
4932 Gas & Other Services Combined
4925 Gas Production And/or Distribution
4923 Gas Transmission & Distribution
3053 Gaskets, Packing & Sealing Devices
5541 Gasoline Service Stations
7538 General Automotive Repair Shops
0291 General Farms, Primarily Animals
0191 General Farms, Primarily Crop
9199 General Government
3569 General Industrial Machinery
0219 General Livestock
8062 General Medical & Surgical Hospitals
4225 General Warehousing & Storage
5947 Gift, Novelty & Souvenir Shop
2361 Girls' & Children's Dresses, Blouses & Shirts
2369 Girls' & Children's Outerwear
1793 Glass & Glazing Work
3221 Glass Containers
1041 Gold Ores
5153 Grain & Field Beans
0172 Grapes
3321 Gray & Ductile Iron Foundries
2771 Greeting Cards
5149 Groceries & Related Products
5141 Groceries, General Line
5411 Grocery Stores
3769 Guided Missile & Space Vehicle Parts & Auxiliary Equipment
3764 Guided Missile & Space Vehicle Propulsion Unit Parts
3761 Guided Missiles & Space Vehicles
2861 Gum & Wood Chemicals
3275 Gypsum Products

H

3423 Hand & Edge Tools
3996 Hard Surface Floor Coverings
5072 Hardware
5251 Hardware
2426 Hardwood Dimension & Flooring Mills
2435 Hardwood Veneer & Plywood
2353 Hats, Caps & Millinery
8099 Health & Allied Services
3433 Heating Equipment, Except Electric
1629 Heavy Construction
7353 Heavy Construction Equipment Rental
7363 Help Supply Services
1611 Highway & Street Construction
5945 Hobby, Toy & Game Shops
0213 Hogs
3536 Hoists, Cranes & Monorails
6719 Holding Companies
5023 Home Furnishings
8082 Home Health Care Services
0272 Horses & Other Equines
2252 Hosiery
6324 Hospital & Medical Service Plans
7011 Hotels & Motels
3142 House Slippers
5722 Household Appliance Stores
3639 Household Appliances
3651 Household Audio & Video Equipment
3631 Household Cooking Equipment
2392 Household Furnishings
2519 Household Furniture
3633 Household Laundry Equipment
3632 Household Refrigerators & Freezers
3635 Household Vacuum Cleaners
9531 Housing Programs
0971 Hunting, Trapping, Game Propagation

I

2024 Ice Cream & Frozen Desserts
2835 In Vitro & In Vivo Diagnostic Substances
8322 Individual & Family Services
5113 Industrial & Personal Service Paper
1541 Industrial Buildings & Warehouses
3567 Industrial Furnaces & Ovens
2813 Industrial Gases
2819 Industrial Inorganic Chemicals
3823 Industrial Instrmnts Msrmnt Display/control Process Variable
7218 Industrial Launderers
3599 Industrial Machinery
5084 Industrial Machinery & Equipment
2869 Industrial Organic Chemicals
3543 Industrial Patterns
1446 Industrial Sand
5085 Industrial Supplies
3537 Industrial Trucks & Tractors
3491 Industrial Valves
7375 Information Retrieval Services
2816 Inorganic Pigments
4785 Inspection & Fixed Facilities
1796 Installing Building Equipment
3825 Instruments To Measure Electricity
6411 Insurance Agents, Brokers Service
6399 Insurance Carriers
4131 Intercity & Rural Bus Transportation
8052 Intermediate Care Facilities
3519 Internal Combustion Engines
9721 International Affairs
6282 Investment Advice
6726 Investment Offices
6799 Investors
0134 Irish Potatoes
3462 Iron & Steel Forgings
1011 Iron Ores
4971 Irrigation Systems

J

3915 Jewelers' Materials & Lapidary Work
5094 Jewelry & Precious Stones
5944 Jewelry Stores
3911 Jewelry, Precious Metal
8331 Job Training & Vocational Rehabilitation Services
8222 Junior Colleges & Technical Institutes

K

1455 Kaolin & Ball Clay
8092 Kidney Dialysis Centers
2253 Knit Outerwear Mills
2254 Knit Underwear Mills
2259 Knitting Mills

L

8631 Labor Unions & Similar Labor Organizations
3821 Laboratory Apparatus & Furniture
2258 Lace & Warp Knit Fabric Mills
3083 Laminated Plastics Plate & Sheet
9512 Land, Mineral & Wildlife Conservation
0781 Landscape Counseling & Planning
7219 Laundry & Garment Services
3524 Lawn & Garden Equipment
0782 Lawn & Garden Services
1031 Lead & Zinc Ores
3952 Lead Pencils & Art Goods
2386 Leather & Sheep-lined Clothing
3151 Leather Gloves & Mittens
3199 Leather Goods
3111 Leather Tanning & Finishing
9222 Legal Counsel & Prosecution
8111 Legal Services
9121 Legislative Bodies
8231 Libraries
6311 Life Insurance
3648 Lighting Equipment
3274 Lime
7213 Linen Supply
5984 Liquefied Petroleum Gas Dealers
5921 Liquor Stores
5154 Livestock
0751 Livestock Services, Except Veterinary
6163 Loan Brokers
4111 Local & Suburban Transit
4141 Local Bus Charter Service
4119 Local Passenger Transportation
4214 Local Trucking With Storage
4212 Local Trucking, Without Storage
2411 Logging

Standard Industrial Classification (SIC) Codes – Alphabetical

2992 Lubricating Oils & Greases
3161 Luggage
5948 Luggage & Leather Goods Stores
5211 Lumber & Other Building Materials
5031 Lumber, Plywood & Millwork

M

2098 Macaroni & Spaghetti
3545 Machine Tool Accessories
3541 Machine Tools, Metal Cutting Type
3542 Machine Tools, Metal Forming Type
3695 Magnetic & Optical Recording Media
3322 Malleable Iron Foundries
2083 Malt
2082 Malt Beverages
8742 Management Consulting Services
6722 Management Investment, Open-end
8741 Management Services
2761 Manifold Business Forms
3429 Manufactured Hardware (General)
2097 Manufactured Ice
3999 Manufacturing Industries
4493 Marinas
4491 Marine Cargo Handling
3953 Marking Devices
1741 Masonry & Other Stonework
2515 Mattresses & Bedsprings
3829 Measuring & Controlling Devices
3586 Measuring & Dispensing Pumps
5421 Meat & Fish Markets
2011 Meat Packing Plants
5147 Meats & Meat Products
3061 Mechanical Rubber Goods
5047 Medical & Hospital Equipment
7352 Medical Equipment Rental
8071 Medical Laboratories
2833 Medicinals & Botanicals
8699 Membership Organizations
7997 Membership Sports & Recreation Clubs
7041 Membership-basis Organization Hotels
2329 Men's & Boys' Clothing
5136 Men's & Boys' Clothing
5611 Men's & Boys' Clothing Stores
2321 Men's & Boys' Furnishings
2323 Men's & Boys' Neckwear
2311 Men's & Boys' Suits & Coats
2325 Men's & Boys' Trousers & Slacks
2322 Men's & Boys' Underwear Nightwear
2326 Men's & Boys' Work Clothing
3143 Men's Footwear, Except Athletic
5962 Merchandising Machine Operators
3412 Metal Barrels, Drums & Pails
3411 Metal Cans
3479 Metal Coating & Allied Service
3442 Metal Doors, Sash & Trim
3497 Metal Foil & Leaf
3398 Metal Heat Treating
2514 Metal Household Furniture
1081 Metal Mining Services
1099 Metal Ores
3431 Metal Sanitary Ware
3469 Metal Stampings
5051 Metals Service Centers & Offices
3549 Metalworking Machinery
2431 Millwork
3296 Mineral Wool
3295 Minerals, Ground Or Treated
3532 Mining Machinery
5699 Miscellaneous Apparel & Accessories
6159 Miscellaneous Business Credit
3496 Miscellaneous Fabricated Wire Products
5499 Miscellaneous Food Stores
5399 Miscellaneous General Merchandise
5719 Miscellaneous Home Furnishings
0919 Miscellaneous Marine Products
3449 Miscellaneous Metalwork
1499 Miscellaneous Nonmetallic Minerals
7299 Miscellaneous Personal Service
2741 Miscellaneous Publishing
5999 Miscellaneous Retail Stores
6515 Mobile Home Site Operators
2451 Mobile Homes
5271 Mobile Homes
6162 Mortgage Bankers & Correspondents
7822 Motion Picture & Tape Distribution
7812 Motion Picture & Video Production
7829 Motion Picture Distribution Services
7832 Motion Picture Theaters, Except Drive-in
3716 Motor Homes
3714 Motor Vehicle Parts & Accessories
5015 Motor Vehicle Parts, Used
5013 Motor Vehicle Supplies & New Parts
3711 Motor Vehicles & Car Bodies
5571 Motorcycle Dealers
3751 Motorcycles, Bicycles & Parts
3621 Motors & Generators
8412 Museums & Art Galleries
5736 Musical Instrument Stores
3931 Musical Instruments

N

2441 Nailed Wood Boxes & Shook
2241 Narrow Fabric Mills
6021 National Commercial Banks
9711 National Security
4924 Natural Gas Distribution
1321 Natural Gas Liquids
4922 Natural Gas Transmission
5511 New & Used Car Dealers
5994 News Dealers & Newsstands
7383 News Syndicates
2711 Newspapers
2873 Nitrogenous Fertilizers
9999 Nonclassifiable Establishments
3297 Nonclay Refractories
8733 Noncommercial Research Organizations
3644 Noncurrent-carrying Wiring Devices
6091 Nondeposit Trust Facilities
5199 Nondurable Goods
3364 Nonferrous Die-castings Except Aluminum
3463 Nonferrous Forgings
3369 Nonferrous Foundries Drawing
3357 Nonferrous Wiredrawing & Insulating
3299 Nonmetallic Mineral Products
1481 Nonmetallic Mineral Services
6512 Nonresidential Building Operators
1542 Nonresidential Construction
2297 Nonwoven Fabrics
5261 Nurseries & Garden Centers
8059 Nursing & Personal Care

O

5044 Office Equipment
2522 Office Furniture, Except Wood
3579 Office Machines
8041 Offices & Clinics Of Chiropractors
8021 Offices & Clinics Of Dentists
8011 Offices & Clinics Of Medical Doctors
8042 Offices & Clinics Of Optometrists
8031 Offices & Clinics Of Osteopathic Physicians
8043 Offices & Clinics Of Podiatrists
8049 Offices Of Health Practitioners
1382 Oil & Gas Exploration Services
3533 Oil & Gas Field Machinery
1389 Oil & Gas Field Services
6792 Oil Royalty Traders
1531 Operative Builders
3851 Ophthalmic Goods
5048 Ophthalmic Goods
5995 Optical Goods Stores
3827 Optical Instruments & Lenses
3489 Ordnance & Accessories
2824 Organic Fibers, Noncellulosic
0181 Ornamental Nursery Products
0783 Ornamental Shrub & Tree Services
7312 Outdoor Advertising Services

P

5142 Packaged Frozen Goods
3565 Packaging Machinery
2671 Packaging Paper & Plastics Film, Coated & Laminated
4783 Packing & Crating
5231 Paint, Glass & Wallpaper
1721 Painting & Paper Hanging
2851 Paints & Allied Products
5198 Paints, Varnishes & Supplies
3554 Paper Industries Machinery
2621 Paper Mills
2631 Paperboard Mills
2542 Partitions & Fixtures, Except Wood
7515 Passenger Car Leasing
7514 Passenger Car Rental
4729 Passenger Transportation Arrangement
6794 Patent Owners & Lessors
3951 Pens & Mechanical Pencils
6371 Pension, Health & Welfare Funds
2721 Periodicals
6141 Personal Credit Institutions
3172 Personal Leather Goods
2999 Petroleum & Coal Products
5171 Petroleum Bulk Stations & Terminals
5172 Petroleum Products
2911 Petroleum Refining
2834 Pharmaceutical Preparations
1475 Phosphate Rock
2874 Phosphatic Fertilizers
7334 Photocopying & Duplicating Services
7384 Photofinish Laboratories
3861 Photographic Equipment & Supplies
5043 Photographic Equipment & Supplies
7221 Photographic Studios, Portrait
7991 Physical Fitness Facilities
2035 Pickles, Sauces & Salad Dressings
5131 Piece Goods & Notions
4619 Pipelines
1742 Plastering, Drywall & Insulation
3085 Plastics Bottles
3086 Plastics Foam Products
5162 Plastics Materials & Basic Shapes
2821 Plastics Materials & Resins
3084 Plastics Pipe
3088 Plastics Plumbing Fixtures
3089 Plastics Products
2796 Platemaking Services
3471 Plating & Polishing
2395 Pleating & Stitching
5074 Plumbing & Hydronic Heating Supplies
3432 Plumbing Fixture Fittings & Trim
1711 Plumbing, Heating, Air-conditioning Contractors
9221 Police Protection
8651 Political Organizations
3264 Porcelain Electrical Supplies
1474 Potash, Soda & Borate Minerals
2096 Potato Chips & Similar Snacks
3269 Pottery Products
0259 Poultry & Eggs
5144 Poultry & Poultry Products
0254 Poultry Hatcheries
2015 Poultry Slaughtering & Processing
7211 Power Laundries, Family & Commercial
3568 Power Transmission Equipment
3546 Power-driven Handtools
3652 Pre-recorded Records & Tapes
3448 Prefabricated Metal Buildings
2452 Prefabricated Wood Buildings
7372 Prepackaged Software
2048 Prepared Feeds
2045 Prepared Flour Mixes & Doughs
3229 Pressed & Blown Glass
3334 Primary Aluminum
3692 Primary Batteries, Dry & Wet
3331 Primary Copper
3399 Primary Metal Products
3339 Primary Nonferrous Metals
3672 Printed Circuit Boards
5111 Printing & Writing Paper
2893 Printing Ink
3555 Printing Trades Machinery
8811 Private Households
3231 Products Of Purchased Glass
5049 Professional Equipment
8621 Professional Membership Organizations
8063 Psychiatric Hospitals
2531 Public Building & Related Furniture
7992 Public Golf Courses
9229 Public Order & Safety
8743 Public Relations Services
2611 Pulp Mills
3561 Pumps & Pumping Equipment

R

7948 Racing, Including Track Operation
3663 Radio & TV Communications Equipment
7622 Radio & Television Repair
4832 Radio Broadcasting Stations
4812 Radio Telephone Communication
5731 Radio, Television & Electronic Stores
7313 Radio, Television, Publisher Representatives
3743 Railroad Equipment
6517 Railroad Property Lessors
4011 Railroads, Line-haul Operating
2061 Raw Cane Sugar

3273 Ready-mixed Concrete
6531 Real Estate Agents & Managers
6798 Real Estate Investment Trusts
6519 Real Property Lessors
2493 Reconstituted Wood Products
5735 Record & Prerecorded Tape Stores
5561 Recreational Vehicle Dealers
4613 Refined Petroleum Pipelines
4222 Refrigerated Warehousing & Storage
3585 Refrigeration & Heating Equipment
5078 Refrigeration Equipment & Supplies
7623 Refrigeration Service & Repair
4953 Refuse Systems
9641 Regulation Of Agricultural Marketing
9621 Regulation, Administration Of Transportation
9631 Regulation, Administration Of Utilities
9651 Regulation, Miscellaneous Commercial Sectors
3625 Relays & Industrial Controls
8661 Religious Organizations
4741 Rental Of Railroad Cars
7699 Repair Services
8361 Residential Care
1522 Residential Construction
3645 Residential Lighting Fixtures
7641 Reupholstery & Furniture Repair
0112 Rice
2044 Rice Milling
2095 Roasted Coffee
2384 Robes & Dressing Gowns
3547 Rolling Mill Machinery
5033 Roofing, Siding & Insulation
1761 Roofing, Siding & Sheet Metal Work
7021 Rooming & Boarding Houses
3021 Rubber & Plastics Footwear
3052 Rubber & Plastics Hose & Beltings

S

2068 Salted & Roasted Nuts & Seeds
2656 Sanitary Food Containers
2676 Sanitary Paper Products
4959 Sanitary Services
2013 Sausages & Other Prepared Meats
6035 Savings Institutions, Federally Chartered
6036 Savings Institutions, Not Federally Chartered
3425 Saw Blades & Handsaws
2421 Sawmills & Planing Mills, General
3596 Scales & Balances, Except Laboratory
2397 Schiffli Machine Embroideries
4151 School Buses
8299 Schools & Educational Service
5093 Scrap & Waste Materials
3451 Screw Machine Products
3812 Search & Navigation Equipment
3341 Secondary Nonferrous Metals
7338 Secretarial & Court Reporting
6231 Security & Commodity Exchanges
6289 Security & Commodity Service
6211 Security Brokers & Dealers
7382 Security Systems Services
3674 Semiconductors & Related Devices
3263 Semivitreous Table & Kitchenware
5087 Service Establishment Equipment
3589 Service Industry Machinery
8999 Services
7819 Services Allied To Motion Pictures
2652 Setup Paperboard Boxes
4952 Sewerage Systems
5949 Sewing, Needlework & Piece Goods
0214 Sheep & Goats
3444 Sheet Metalwork
0913 Shellfish
3731 Shipbuilding & Repairing
7251 Shoe Repair & Shoeshine Parlors
5661 Shoe Stores
6153 Short-term Business Credit
3993 Signs & Advertising Specialties
1044 Silver Ores
3914 Silverware & Plated Ware
1521 Single-family Housing Construction
8051 Skilled Nursing Care Facilities
3484 Small Arms
3482 Small Arms Ammunition
2841 Soap & Other Detergents
8399 Social Services
2436 Softwood Veneer & Plywood
0711 Soil Preparation Services
2075 Soybean Oil Mills
0116 Soybeans
9661 Space Research & Technology
3259 Structural Clay Products
1791 Structural Steel Erection
2439 Structural Wood Members
6552 Subdividers & Developers
0133 Sugarcane & Sugar Beets
6351 Surety Insurance
2843 Surface Active Agents
3841 Surgical & Medical Instruments
3842 Surgical Appliances & Supplies
8713 Surveying Services
3613 Switchgear & Switchboard Apparatus
4013 Switching & Terminal Services
2822 Synthetic Rubber
5941 Sporting Goods & Bicycle Shops
7941 Sports Clubs, Managers & Promoters
6022 State Commercial Banks
6062 State Credit Unions
5112 Stationery & Office Supplies
2678 Stationery Products
5943 Stationery Stores
4961 Steam & Air-conditioning Supply
3325 Steel Foundries
3324 Steel Investment Foundries
3317 Steel Pipe & Tubes
3493 Steel Springs, Except Wire
3315 Steel Wire & Related Products
3691 Storage Batteries
3544 Special Dies, Tools, Jigs & Fixtures
3559 Special Industry Machinery
2429 Special Product Sawmills
1799 Special Trade Contractors
4226 Special Warehousing & Storage
2842 Specialty Cleaning, Polishes & Sanitation Goods
8069 Specialty Hospitals, Except Psychiatric
8093 Specialty Outpatient Clinics
3566 Speed Changers, Drives & Gears
3949 Sporting & Athletic Goods
5091 Sporting & Recreation Goods
7032 Sporting & Recreational Camps

T

3795 Tanks & Tank Components
7291 Tax Return Preparation Services
4121 Taxicabs
4822 Telegraph & Other Communications
3661 Telephone & Telegraph Apparatus
4813 Telephone Communication, Except Radio
4833 Television Broadcasting Stations
1743 Terrazzo, Tile, Marble, Mosaic Work
8734 Testing Laboratories
2393 Textile Bags
2299 Textile Goods
3552 Textile Machinery
7922 Theatrical Producers & Services
2284 Thread Mills
2282 Throwing & Winding Mills
0811 Timber Tracts
2296 Tire Cord & Fabrics
7534 Tire Retreading & Repair Shops
3011 Tires & Inner Tubes
5014 Tires & Tubes
6541 Title Abstract Offices
6361 Title Insurance
0132 Tobacco
5194 Tobacco & Tobacco Products
2141 Tobacco Stemming & Redrying
5993 Tobacco Stores & Stands
2844 Toilet Preparations
7532 Top & Body Repair & Paint Shops
4725 Tour Operators
4492 Towing & Tugboat Service
5092 Toys & Hobby Goods & Supplies
7033 Trailer Parks & Campsites
3612 Transformers, Except Electric
3799 Transportation Equipment
5088 Transportation Equipment & Supplies
4789 Transportation Services
4724 Travel Agencies
3792 Travel Trailers & Campers
0173 Tree Nuts
3713 Truck & Bus Bodies
7513 Truck Rental & Leasing, No Drivers
3715 Truck Trailers
4231 Trucking Terminal Facilities
4213 Trucking, Except Local
6733 Trusts
6732 Trusts: Educational, Religious, Etc.
3511 Turbines & Turbine Generator Sets
0253 Turkeys & Turkey Eggs
2791 Typesetting

U

4311 U.S. Postal Service
3081 Unsupported Plastics Film & Sheet
3082 Unsupported Plastics Profile Shapes
2512 Upholstered Household Furniture
1094 Uranium-radium-vanadium Ores
9532 Urban & Community Development
5521 Used Car Dealers
5932 Used Merchandise Stores
7519 Utility Trailer Rental

V

3494 Valves & Pipe Fittings
5331 Variety Stores
2076 Vegetable Oil Mills
0161 Vegetables & Melons
3647 Vehicular Lighting Equipment
0741 Veterinary Services For Livestock
0742 Veterinary Services, Specialties
7841 Video Tape Rental
3262 Vitreous China Table & Kitchenware
3261 Vitreous Plumbing Fixtures
8249 Vocational Schools

W

5075 Warm Air Heating & Air Conditioning
7631 Watch, Clock & Jewelry Repair
3873 Watches, Clocks, Watchcases & Parts
4489 Water Passenger Transportation
4941 Water Supply
4449 Water Transportation Of Freight
4499 Water Transportation Services
1781 Water Well Drilling
1623 Water, Sewer & Utility Lines
2385 Waterproof Outerwear
2257 Weft Knit Fabric Mills
3548 Welding Apparatus
7692 Welding Repair
2046 Wet Corn Milling
0111 Wheat
5182 Wine & Distilled Beverages
2084 Wines, Brandy & Brandy Spirits
3495 Wire Springs
5137 Women's & Children's Clothing
2341 Women's & Children's Underwear
2331 Women's & Misses' Blouses & Shirts
2339 Women's & Misses' Outerwear
2337 Women's & Misses' Suits & Coats
5632 Women's Accessory & Specialty Stores
5621 Women's Clothing Stores
3144 Women's Footwear, Except Athletic
3171 Women's Handbags & Purses
2251 Women's Hosiery, Except Socks
2335 Women's, Juniors' & Misses' Dresses
2449 Wood Containers
2511 Wood Household Furniture
2434 Wood Kitchen Cabinets
2521 Wood Office Furniture
2448 Wood Pallets & Skids
2541 Wood Partitions & Fixtures
2491 Wood Preserving
2499 Wood Products
2517 Wood Television & Radio Cabinets
3553 Woodworking Machinery
1795 Wrecking & Demolition Work

X

3844 X-ray Apparatus & Tubes

Y

2281 Yarn Spinning Mills

Section I

Businesses Alphabetically

0

EPI
See ESKATON PROPERTIES INC

RACLE PACKAGING COMPANY
See PINNACLE PACKAGING CO INC

1

COCHRAN AUTOMOTIVE
See COCHRAN OLDSMOBILE INC

D-U-N-S 02-849-8622
STOP ELECTRONICS CENTER INC
100 Coney Island Ave, Brooklyn, NY 11230-2344
Tel (718) 249-1211 Founded/Ownrshp 2000
Sales 162.0MM^E EMP 80
SIC 5722 5021 Household appliance stores; Furniture
Ch Bd: Albert Fourerti
*CFO: Eli Fourerti

D-U-N-S 19-056-2087
1&1 INTERNET INC
(Suby of UNITED INTERNET AG)
701 Lee Rd Ste 300, Chesterbrook, PA 19087-5612
Tel (877) 461-2631 Founded/Ownrshp 2003
Sales 356.7MM^E EMP 5,001^E
SIC 7374 4813 4822 Data processing & preparation; Computer graphics service; ; Electronic mail
Pr: Robert Hoffmann
*COO: Uwe Lamnek
*CFO: Markus Huhn
Chf Mktg O: Michael Terhardt
*VP: Sebastian Gonzalez
VP: Frederick Iwans
*VP: Louis Lombardo
CTO: Oliver Mauss
Sales Asso: John Raezer
Sales Asso: Marcel Steichen

D-U-N-S 92-697-3645
1-800 CONTACTS INC
261 W Data Dr, Draper, UT 84020-2372
Tel (801) 316-5000 Founded/Ownrshp 2014
Sales 287.5MM^E EMP 1,135
SIC 5961 3851 Catalog & mail-order houses; Contact lenses
Pr: Brian W Bethers
*CFO: Robert G Hunter
CFO: Robert Hunter
*Treas: Robert David Kretschmer
*Chf Mktg O: Allen Hwang
VP: Christine Daleo
VP: Jay J Magure
VP: Justin Olson
VP: Dave Walker
Assoc Dir: Haylen Latorre
*CIO: John R Murray

D-U-N-S 80-899-8355 IMP/EXP
▲ 1-800-FLOWERS.COM INC
1 Old Country Rd Ste 500, Carle Place, NY 11514-1847
Tel (516) 237-6000 Founded/Ownrshp 1976
Sales 1.1MMM EMP 4,524
Tkr Sym FLWS Exch NGS
SIC 5992 5961 5947 Florists; Flowers, plants & bulbs: mail order; Gift items, mail order; Gift, novelty & souvenir shop
Ch Bd: James F McCann
Pr: Thomas Hartnett
*Pr: Christopher G McCann
Pr: Mark L Nance
Pr: David Taiclet
COO: Thomes Hertnett
CFO: William E Shea
Sr VP: Gerard M Gallagher
Sr VP: Thomas G Hartnett
Sr VP: Arnie Leap
VP: Clint Conatser
VP: Ann Frisbie
VP: Mark Lefkin
VP: Brian McGee
Creative D: Hannah Farnham
Dir Bus: Lynn Wylie
Board of Directors: Geralyn R Breig, Celia R Brown, Lawrence Calcano, James A Cannavino, Eugene F Demark, Leonard J Elmore, Sean Hegarty, Larry Zarin

1-800-HANSONS
See HANSONS WINDOWS AND SIDING OF LANSING LLC

D-U-N-S 60-855-2456
1-800-PACK-RAT LLC
11640 Northpark Dr 200, Wake Forest, NC 27587-4532
Tel (202) 362-0101 Founded/Ownrshp 2006
Sales 167.0MM^E EMP 450
SIC 5932 Used merchandise stores
Pr: Bob Poirier
COO: Hal Justice
Sr VP: Kevin Barbour
VP: Andrew Friedman
VP: Joe Kozubowski
VP: Rhett Trees
Exec: Bruce Eads
Software D: Mohamed Askar
Opers Mgr: Jamie Bally
Opers Mgr: Andy Barillas
Opers Mgr: Dave Caruso

1-800-PETMEDS
See PETMED EXPRESS INC

101 CORPORATE-SACRAMENTO
See CRESTWOOD BEHAVIORAL HEALTH INC

D-U-N-S 62-458-7387
11 PENN TV LLC
(Suby of CABLEVISION) ★
11 Penn Plz Fl 2, New York, NY 10001-2028
Tel (212) 324-8506 Founded/Ownrshp 2006
Sales 65.2MM^E EMP 2,184^E
SIC 4841

1105 GOVERNMENT INFO GROUP
See 1105 MEDIA INC

D-U-N-S 61-203-1414
1105 MEDIA INC
1105 GOVERNMENT INFO GROUP
9201 Oakdale Ave Ste 101, Chatsworth, CA 91311-6546
Tel (818) 814-5200 Founded/Ownrshp 2006
Sales 147.9MM^E EMP 1,011
SIC 7313 7389 2721 2741 8748 Printed media advertising representatives; Convention & show services; Magazines: publishing only, not printed on site; Trade journals: publishing only, not printed on site; Miscellaneous publishing; Business consulting
VP: Becky Nagel
*CFO: Richard Vitale
Ex VP: Michael Valenti
*Ex VP: Mike Valenti
VP: Meighan Berberich
VP: Julius Feinstein
VP: Erik Lindgren
VP: David Myers
VP: Dan Smith
Exec: Dave Nagel
Natl Sales: Al Tiano

D-U-N-S 96-850-8023
11111 NORTH 7TH STREET PROPERTY LLC
POINTE HLTON TPTIO CLFFS RSORT
11111 N 7th St, Phoenix, AZ 85020-1176
Tel (602) 866-7500 Founded/Ownrshp 1984
Sales 32.9MM^E EMP 1,000
SIC 7011 Resort hotel
Prin: Gary Santa Cruz
Genl Mgr: Ron Simon
Mktg Mgr: Amy Satterfield

D-U-N-S 02-189-3245
1132 TRUST LLC (MD)
1 E Chase St Ste 1132a, Baltimore, MD 21202-2565
Tel (410) 601-3042 Founded/Ownrshp 2012
Sales 178.6MM EMP 75
Accts Connolly Pamela W Baltimore
SIC 8741

D-U-N-S 07-979-3534
1155 DISTRIBUTOR PARTNERS LLC
LONESTAR ELECTRIC SUPPLY
4200 N Sam Houston Pkwy W, Houston, TX 77086-1468
Tel (832) 855-3400 Founded/Ownrshp 2015
Sales 1.0MMM EMP 80
SIC 5063 Lighting fittings & accessories
CEO: Jeff Metzler
*Pr: Jason Vaughn

D-U-N-S 15-134-8281
1199 SEIU NATIONAL BENEFIT FUND
330 W 42nd St Fl 8, New York, NY 10036-6902
Tel (646) 473-6300 Founded/Ownrshp 1947
Sales NA EMP 1,400^E
SIC 6371

D-U-N-S 96-752-1290
1199 SEIU NATIONAL BENEFIT FUND FOR HEALTH AND HUMAN SERVICE EMPLOYEES
P.O. Box 842 (10108-0842)
Tel (646) 473-6020 Founded/Ownrshp 2011
Sales 135.3MM EMP 2^E
Accts Kpmg Llp New York Ny
SIC 6733 Trusts

D-U-N-S 07-526-1222
1199SEIU UNITED HEALTH CARE WORKERS EAST
310 W 43rd St, New York, NY 10036-3981
Tel (212) 582-1890 Founded/Ownrshp 1932
Sales 159.4MM^E EMP 800
Accts N Cheng & Co Pc New York Ny
SIC 8631 Labor unions & similar labor organizations
Pr: George Gresham
CFO: Louise Bayer
*CFO: Michael Cooperman
*Sec: Maria Caspaneda
VP: Elizabeth Lujan
VP: Winslow Luna
VP: Delima Macdonald
IT Man: James Obrien
Software D: Bjorn Symister

11R SALES
See EVANS FRUIT CO INC

D-U-N-S 96-109-6948
12TH MAN STUDENT FOUNDATION INC
12th Man Fndtion The Zone, College Station, TX 77844
Tel (979) 846-8892 Founded/Ownrshp 1950
Sales 262.4MM EMP 34
Accts Ingram Wallis & Company Pc Br
SIC 7389 Fund raising organizations
Ex Dir: Miles Marks

D-U-N-S 05-835-9667 IMP
1550 BAYSHORE CORP
1550 5th Ave, Bay Shore, NY 11706-3427
Tel (631) 206-7100 Founded/Ownrshp 1978
Sales 89.7MM^E EMP 801^E
SIC 5149 Groceries & related products
Pr: Manuel Pena
*VP: Jacinto Pena

1859 HISTORIC HOTELS
See GAL-TEX HOTEL CORP

D-U-N-S 13-185-9139
1859-HISTORIC HOTELS LTD
OVERTON HOTEL & CONFERENCE CTR
(Suby of 1859 HISTORIC HOTELS) ★
2302 Post Office St # 500, Galveston, TX 77550-1936
Tel (409) 763-8536 Founded/Ownrshp 2001
Sales 42.9MM^E EMP 1,200
SIC 7011 Hotels & motels
Pt: Eugene Lucas
Genl Mgr: Bill Brendel

D-U-N-S 08-295-2417 IMP
1888 MILLS LLC
1520 Kensington Rd # 115, Oak Brook, IL 60523-2140
Tel (630) 620-5222 Founded/Ownrshp 1974
Sales 230.8MM^E EMP 444
SIC 5023 5131 Linens & towels; Towels; Piece goods & notions
CEO: Jonathon R Simon
*COO: Abdul Yaqub
Ofcr: Aijaz Usman
*VP: Dan Kelly

D-U-N-S 07-923-9275
192D COMMUNICATIONS FLIGHT
165 Sweeney Blvd Ste 214, Langley Afb, VA 23665-2207
Tel (757) 764-1607 Founded/Ownrshp 1947
Sales NA EMP 1,000
SIC 9711 National Guard

D-U-N-S 03-583-4233
1ST FINANCIAL BANK USA (SD)
331 Dakota Dunes Blvd, North Sioux City, SD 57049-5176
Tel (605) 232-9310 Founded/Ownrshp 1910, 1990
Sales NA EMP 425
SIC 6022 State commercial banks
Ch Bd: Al Hegyi
Pr: Irma Barrington
Ofcr: Wendy Buss
Sr VP: Craig Dabroski
Sr VP: Tarun Kapoor
VP: Wanda Awai
VP: Gwen Farassat
VP: Arnold Hueher
*VP: Wayne Nesje
VP: Don Schulze
VP: Gregg Silver
Exec: Joyeeta Banerjee
Exec: Don Schultz

D-U-N-S 04-583-5923
1ST FRANKLIN FINANCIAL CORP
135 E Tugalo St, Toccoa, GA 30577-2357
Tel (706) 886-7571 Founded/Ownrshp 1941
Sales NA EMP 1,217^E
SIC 6141 Consumer finance companies
Pr: Virginia C Herring
*Ch Bd: Ben F Cheek IV
COO: J Michael Culpepper
*CFO: A Roger Guimond
Ex VP: Charles E Vercelli Jr
VP: Ronald Byerly
VP: Lynn E Cox
VP: Michael Whitaker
Brnch Mgr: Laura Fuqua
Brnch Mgr: Ashley Shealy
Board of Directors: James H Harris III, John G Sample Jr, C Dean Scarborough, Keith D Watson

D-U-N-S 06-157-4109
■ 1ST SOURCE BANK
(Suby of 1ST SOURCE CORP) ★
100 N Michigan St Ste 800, South Bend, IN 46601-1630
Tel (574) 235-2000 Founded/Ownrshp 1922
Sales NA EMP 1,100
SIC 6022 State trust companies accepting deposits, commercial
Pr: James R Seitz
*CFO: Larry E Lentych
Sr Cor Off: Duke Jones
Ex VP: Russell Allen
*Ex VP: Jeff Buhr
*Sr VP: Ron Zeltwanger
VP: Frank Antonovitz
VP: Lori Jean
*VP: Christopher Poulsen
VP: Gina Wolff
IT Man: Brian Hellman

D-U-N-S 06-470-4562
▲ 1ST SOURCE CORP
100 N Michigan St, South Bend, IN 46601-1630
Tel (574) 235-2000 Founded/Ownrshp 1971
Sales NA EMP 1,150^E
Tkr Sym SRCE Exch NGS
SIC 6022 State commercial banks; State trust companies accepting deposits, commercial
*Ch Bd: Christopher J Murphy III
Pr: James R Seitz
CFO: Andrea G Short
Ofcr: Joella Depra
Ofcr: John B Griffith
Ofcr: Luke Squires
Trst Ofcr: Pam Stearns
VP: Dave Martin
VP: Michele Miller
Exec: Gloria Vaughan-Mckown
CTO: Cecil Murray
Board of Directors: Allison N Egidi, Daniel B Fitzpatrick, Craig A Kapson, Vinod M Khilnani, Rex Martin, Christopher J Murphy IV, Timothy K Ozark, John T Phair, Mark D Schwabero

2

D-U-N-S 08-950-5895
2 M CO INC
5249 Holiday Ave, Billings, MT 59101-6398
Tel (406) 245-1490 Founded/Ownrshp 1978
Sales 150.9MM^E EMP 90
SIC 5084 5083 5074 5051 Pumps & pumping equipment; Irrigation equipment; Livestock equipment; Pipes & fittings, plastic; Pipe & tubing, steel
Pr: Hollis A Mills
CFO: Kevin Augustine
Exec: Susan Whittmeyer
Rgnl Mgr: Brandon Bailey
Brnch Mgr: Scott Bishop
Brnch Mgr: Chad Draper
Brnch Mgr: Brian Irwin
Sls Mgr: Steve Martinez

2-10 HOME BUYERS WARRANTY
See HOME BUYERS WARRANTY CORP

D-U-N-S 07-957-7459
20/20 COMMUNICATIONS INC
20/20 COMPANIES
3575 Lone Star Cir # 200, Fort Worth, TX 76177-8904
Tel (817) 490-0100 Founded/Ownrshp 2008
Sales 162.9MM^E EMP 1,500^E
SIC 5963 Direct sales, telemarketing
CEO: Christopher Munday
Pr: Rick Albuck
Pr: John O'Neill
Pr: Steven Peters
Pr: Ross Wissner
Treas: Steven L Zink
Genl Mgr: Dallas Goldsmith
Manager: John Fontana

20/20 COMPANIES
See 20/20 COMMUNICATIONS INC

D-U-N-S 07-857-4473
2100 FREEDOM INC
(Suby of 2100 TRUST LLC) ★
625 N Grand Ave, Santa Ana, CA 92701-4347
Tel (714) 796-7000 Founded/Ownrshp 2012
Sales 397.1MM^E EMP 7,650
SIC 2711 2721 7313 2741 5963 4813 Newspapers, publishing & printing; Periodicals; Newspaper advertising representative; Miscellaneous publishing; Newspapers, home delivery, not by printers or publishers;
CEO: Richard E Mirman
*CEO: Aaron Kushner

D-U-N-S 02-326-9909
2100 TRUST LLC
625 N Grand Ave, Santa Ana, CA 92701-4347
Tel (877) 469-7344 Founded/Ownrshp 2010
Sales 2.8MMM^E EMP 80,000
SIC 6733 Trusts
Prin: Erek J Delorenzi

D-U-N-S 07-998-1211
21C OKC LLC (OK)
21C OKC MUSEUM HOTEL LLC
900 W Main St, Oklahoma City, OK 73106-7823
Tel (502) 882-6243 Founded/Ownrshp 2012
Sales 10.8MM^E EMP 1,000^E
SIC 7011 Hotels & motels

21C OKC MUSEUM HOTEL LLC
See 21C OKC LLC

21ST CENTURY
See FANCY FOODS INC

D-U-N-S 06-821-1093
■ 21ST CENTURY FOX AMERICA INC
(Suby of TWENTY-FIRST CENTURY FOX INC) ★
1211 Ave Of The Americas, New York, NY 10036-8701
Tel (212) 852-7000 Founded/Ownrshp 2013
Sales 1.8MMM^E EMP 6,024
SIC 2752 2721 4833 7812 Promotional printing, lithographic; Magazines: publishing only, not printed on site; Television broadcasting stations; Motion picture production & distribution
CEO: James Murdoch
*CFO: John Nallen
Ex VP: Michael Regan
Sr VP: Ted Exarhakos
Sr VP: Rick Lane
Sr VP: Gerson Zweifach
VP: Marc Cacciola
VP: Jennifer Chauvin
VP: Brian Egenton
VP: Jon Furr
VP: Annie Hekker
VP: Jeff Ocampo-Tan
VP: Dominic Pagone
VP: Rodney Parnther
VP: Anthony Santabarbara
VP: Ron Stitt
VP: Chris Wilson
Assoc Dir: Hector Chacon
Assoc Dir: Bob Esparza
Creative D: Stacey Batzer

D-U-N-S 07-226-8980
21ST CENTURY INSURANCE CO
(Suby of 21ST CENTURY NORTH AMERICA INSURANCE CO) ★
6301 Owensmouth Ave, Woodland Hills, CA 91367-2216
Tel (877) 310-5687 Founded/Ownrshp 1958
Sales NA EMP 2,000
Accts Pricewaterhousecoopers Llp Lo
SIC 6411 Insurance agents, brokers & service; Fire insurance underwriters' laboratories
CEO: Glenn A Pfeil
V Ch: Bruce W Marlo
COO: William Loucks
CFO: Douglas K Howell
Ex VP: Ed Combs
*Sr VP: Richard R Andre
*Sr VP: Michael J Cassanego
*Sr VP: Dean E Stark
VP: Michael A Goggio
VP: Allen Lew
*Prin: Barbary Baer

D-U-N-S 60-645-5145
21ST CENTURY LIFE AND HEALTH CO INC
LIFECARE ASSURANCE COMPANY
21600 Oxnard St Ste 1500, Woodland Hills, CA 91367-4972
Tel (818) 887-4436 Founded/Ownrshp 1980
Sales NA EMP 246^E
SIC 6321 Accident & health insurance
Pr: James M Glickman
*CEO: Alan S Hughes
*CFO: Daniel J Di Sipio
*CFO: Julianne M Sorice
*Sr VP: Pete Diffley
Sr VP: Peter Diffley
Sr VP: Gwen Franklin
VP: Gwen D Franklin
VP: Anthony Gallotto
VP: Marc Glickman
*VP: Jay R Peters

VP: Kirk Shearburn
VP: Melissa Svoboda

D-U-N-S 00-280-2721
21ST CENTURY NEWSPAPERS INC
MACOMB DAILY
(*Suby of* JOURNAL REGISTER CO) ★
19176 Hall Rd Ste 200, Clinton Township, MI 48038-6914
Tel (586) 469-4510 *Founded/Ownrshp* 1995, 1997
Sales 110.5MM^E *EMP* 1,500
SIC 2711 Newspapers
**CEO:* Bob Jelenic
CFO: Richard Decook
CFO: Mike White
Bd of Dir: Karen Gelardi
**Sr VP:* Scott Wright
Ansthlgy: Macomb Daly

D-U-N-S 06-668-6395
21ST CENTURY NORTH AMERICA INSURANCE CO
(*Suby of* FARMERS INSURANCE) ★
3 Beaver Valley Rd, Wilmington, DE 19803-1124
Tel (877) 310-5687 *Founded/Ownrshp* 2009
Sales NA *EMP* 2,900
SIC 6411 Insurance agents, brokers & service; Fire insurance underwriters' laboratories; Patrol services, insurance
Pr: Bruce W Marlow
**Sr VP:* Richard A Andre
**Sr VP:* Michael J Cassanego
Sr VP: Laura Rock
VP: Michael T Farrell
VP: John Ingersoll
**VP:* John M Lorentz
VP: Eric Saudi
VP: Jes S C Zaragoza
Mktg Mgr: Karen Shallcross

D-U-N-S 82-506-5845
21ST CENTURY ONCOLOGY HOLDINGS INC
(*Suby of* 21ST CENTURY ONCOLOGY INVESTMENTS LLC) ★
2270 Colonial Blvd, Fort Myers, FL 33907-1412
Tel (239) 931-7254 *Founded/Ownrshp* 1983
Sales 1.0MMM^E *EMP* 3,930^E
Accts Deloitte & Touche Llp Miami
SIC 8011 Offices & clinics of medical doctors; Oncologist; Gynecologist; Thoracic physician
CEO: William R Spalding
**Ch Bd:* Robert L Rosner
CFO: Leanne M Stewart
Chf Mktg O: Constantine A Mantz
Sr VP: Joseph Biscardi
Sr VP: Gary Delanois
Board of Directors: Daniel Dosoretz, James L Elrod Jr, Christian Hensley, Robert W Miller, Erin L Russell, Howard M Sherida

D-U-N-S 01-895-2213
21ST CENTURY ONCOLOGY INC
F/K/A RADIATION THERAPY SVCS
(*Suby of* 21ST CENTURY ONCOLOGY HOLDINGS INC) ★
2270 Colonial Blvd, Fort Myers, FL 33907-1412
Tel (239) 931-7333 *Founded/Ownrshp* 2008
Sales 243.1MM^E *EMP* 1,250
Accts Ernst & Young Llp Tampa Flor
SIC 8011 7363 Oncologist; Medical help service
VP: Madlyn Dornaus
CFO: Denyse Austra
CFO: David N Watson
Treas: Jeffrey A Pkrosnis
Ex VP: Matthew Anderson
**Ex VP:* Norton L Travis
**Sr VP:* Eduardo Fernandez
**Sr VP:* H Hugo Myslicki
VP: Alice A Smith
CIO: Tim Staley
Web Dev: Sharon Salenius

D-U-N-S 96-370-9998
21ST CENTURY ONCOLOGY INVESTMENTS LLC
245 Park Ave Fl 41, New York, NY 10167-0002
Tel (239) 931-7275 *Founded/Ownrshp* 2010
Sales 1.0MMM^E *EMP* 4,630^E
SIC 6282 Investment advice

D-U-N-S 82-508-4080 IMP
2328 ON TWELFTH LLC
2328 12th Ave, New York, NY 10027-7907
Tel (212) 234-3883 *Founded/Ownrshp* 1995
Sales 73.4MM^E *EMP* 1,000
SIC 5411 Supermarkets, independent

D-U-N-S 11-509-0839 IMP
24 HOUR FITNESS USA INC
(*Suby of* 24 HOUR FITNESS WORLDWIDE INC) ★
12647 Alcosta Blvd # 500, San Ramon, CA 94583-4436
Tel (925) 543-3100 *Founded/Ownrshp* 1994
Sales 485.8MM^E *EMP* 7,148
SIC 7991 Health club
CEO: Mark Smith
**Pr:* Frank Napolitano
**CFO:* Patrick Flanagan
Bd of Dir: James Wilson
Sr VP: John Tovar
VP: Kimberly Griffin
VP Opers: Charles Huff
Opers Mgr: Samantha Nikodem
Mktg Mgr: Jennifer Galantini

D-U-N-S 02-611-2198
24 HOUR FITNESS WORLDWIDE INC
12647 Alcosta Blvd # 500, San Ramon, CA 94583-4436
Tel (925) 543-3100 *Founded/Ownrshp* 2001
Sales 485.8MM^E *EMP* 7,148
SIC 7991 Health club
**VP:* David Galvan

D-U-N-S 61-598-3488
24 HR SAFETY LLC
4912 Railroad St, Deer Park, TX 77536-2411
Tel (337) 316-0541 *Founded/Ownrshp* 2005
Sales 95.2MM^E *EMP* 115
SIC 5084 Safety equipment
Dist Mgr: Justin Lytle
Opers Mgr: Shon Williams

D-U-N-S 03-332-7866
24/7 BAIL AGENCY INC (MI)
24/7 BAIL BONDS
Elizabeth Rd, Mount Clemens, MI 48043
Tel (866) 322-2245 *Founded/Ownrshp* 2007
Sales 3.9MM *EMP* 1,300^E
SIC 7389 Bail bonding
CEO: Christopher Roberts
**CFO:* Michelle Roberts

24/7 BAIL BONDS
See 24/7 BAIL AGENCY INC

D-U-N-S 79-959-4739
24/7 CUSTOMER INC
910 E Hamilton Ave # 240, Campbell, CA 95008-0625
Tel (650) 385-2247 *Founded/Ownrshp* 2000
Sales 623.7MM^E *EMP* 9,000^E
SIC 7379
Ch Bd: Pallipuram V Kannan
**COO:* Bill Robbins
**CFO:* Tim Pebworth
CFO: Madhu Ranganathan
Ex VP: Martin Puttock
VP: Kevin Allen
VP: Andrew Johnson
IT Man: Scott Vicino
Sls&Mrk Ex: Gautam Singh
Mktg Mgr: Christina Wilson
Genl Couns: Clayton Parker

D-U-N-S 96-820-0548
■ **25 RIDGEWOOD ROAD OPERATIONS LLC**
RIDGEWOOD CENTER
(*Suby of* GENESIS HEALTHCARE LLC) ★
25 Ridgewood Rd, Bedford, NH 03110-6510
Tel (603) 623-8805
Sales 9.7MM^E *EMP* 1,034^E
SIC 8051 Skilled nursing care facilities

2800 GIFT SHOP, THE
See LITTLE CO OF MARY HOSPITAL AND HEALTH CARE CENTERS

D-U-N-S 00-755-9532
2CHECKOUT.COM INC
2CO
855 Grandview Ave Ste 110, Columbus, OH 43215-1102
Tel (614) 921-2449 *Founded/Ownrshp* 2003
Sales 269.7MM *EMP* 114
Accts Gbq Partners Llc Columbus Oh
SIC 5961 Catalog & mail-order houses
CEO: Shawn Budde
**Pr:* Mike Sayre
**CFO:* Kristin Dach
**Chf Mktg O:* Christopher Daly
**Sr VP:* Mark Bishopp
**CTO:* Thomas Blackburn II
Board of Directors: Tom E Dailey

2CO
See 2CHECKOUT.COM INC

D-U-N-S 00-793-1439 IMP/EXP
2ML REAL ESTATE INTERESTS INC (TX)
(*Suby of* C&S WHOLESALE PRODUCE) ★
952 Echo Ln Ste 314, Houston, TX 77024-2780
Tel (713) 747-5000 *Founded/Ownrshp* 1923
Sales 1.6MMM^E *EMP* 170^E
SIC 5141 5142 5122

D-U-N-S 01-891-6463
▲ **2U INC**
8201 Corporate Dr Ste 900, Landover, MD 20785-2262
Tel (301) 892-4350 *Founded/Ownrshp* 2008
Sales 150.1MM *EMP* 1,004
Tkr Sym TWOU *Exch* NGS
SIC 7372 8748 8299 Prepackaged software; Educational consultant; Educational services
CEO: Christopher J Paucek
**Ch Bd:* Paul A Maeder
COO: Susan E Cates
CFO: Catherine A Graham
Chf Mktg O: Harsha Mokkarala
Chf Mktg O: Jeff Rinehart
VP: Sheryl Friedman
Comm Man: Jemila Woodson
Off Mgr: Ken D Espinosa
CTO: James Kenigsberg
IT Man: Andrew Trivas
Board of Directors: Mark J Chernis, Timothy H Haley, Sallie L Krawcheck, John M Larson, Earl Lewis, Edward S Macias, Robert M Stavis

D-U-N-S 01-772-5727 IMP
2WIRE INC
(*Suby of* ARRIS GROUP INC) ★
1764 Automation Pkwy, San Jose, CA 95131-1873
Tel (678) 473-2907 *Founded/Ownrshp* 2010
Sales 119.8MM^E *EMP* 298
SIC 4813
CEO: Tim O'Loughlin
**Pr:* Pasquale Romano
CIO: Ravi Kohli
CTO: Chris Bajorek
Dir IT: David Whitman

3

D-U-N-S 07-852-5760 IMP
3 DAY BLINDS LLC
167 Technology Dr, Irvine, CA 92618-2402
Tel (855) 569-0087 *Founded/Ownrshp* 2009
Sales 111.0MM *EMP* 150^E
SIC 5719 Vertical blinds
CEO: Dave Hall
CFO: Julie Petritsch
**Ex VP:* Pikie Holewski
Sr VP: Frank Gutierrez
Exec: Cristin Harrigan
Netwrk Eng: Brian Holt
Site Mgr: Karin Miller
Mktg Dir: Lisa Squires
Sls Mgr: Roger Miranda
Sales Asso: Sara Young

D-U-N-S 03-307-8564 IMP
■ **3 WIRE GROUP INC** (MN)
(*Suby of* CORNELIUS INC) ★
101 Broadway St W Ste 300, Osseo, MN 55369-1546
Tel (763) 488-3000 *Founded/Ownrshp* 2001
Sales 85.1MM^E *EMP* 182
SIC 5078 Refrigerated beverage dispensers
Pr: Robert Guerra
Sftwr Eng: Mischelle Fix
Opers Mgr: Cathy Ellison
Opers Mgr: Jackie Gustafson
Opers Mgr: Reginald Heron
VP Mktg: Jennie Stenback
Snr Mgr: Ashley Briggs
Snr Mgr: Melissa Lafountain
Snr Mgr: Cory Lee
Snr Mgr: Janet Meyer
Snr Mgr: Lori Nobles

D-U-N-S 10-469-2202
3-D CONCRETE CORRECTION INC
3D STRUCTURAL SOLUTIONS
20115 Jackson Rd, South Bend, IN 46614-5207
Tel (574) 291-0771 *Founded/Ownrshp* 1998
Sales 128.0MM *EMP* 40
SIC 1771 Concrete repair
Pr: David Scarberry
**VP:* Daniel Scarberry
Ql Cn Mgr: James Quinn

D-U-N-S 07-822-6115
31-W INSULATION CO INC (GA)
7434 Cycle Ln, Goodlettsville, TN 37072-9359
Tel (615) 643-3900 *Founded/Ownrshp* 1972, 1974
Sales 223.5MM^E *EMP* 600
SIC 1742 Insulation, buildings
Pr: Wayne Day
**Sec:* Jean Day
Dir IT: Doug Gregory
Manager: Jon Graff

D-U-N-S 07-957-3745
313 ACQUISITION LLC
3301 N Thanksgiving Way, Lehi, UT 84043-4128
Tel (877) 404-4129 *Founded/Ownrshp* 2012
Sales 227.7MM^E *EMP* 9,000^E
SIC 5074 Heating equipment & panels, solar

D-U-N-S 96-820-4318
■ **331 HOLT LANE OPERATIONS LLC**
SEASONS, THE
(*Suby of* GENESIS HEALTHCARE LLC) ★
331 Holt Ln, Lewisburg, WV 24901-1774
Tel (304) 645-4453
Sales 13.5MM^E *EMP* 1,124^E
SIC 8051 Skilled nursing care facilities

D-U-N-S 05-128-6691
3801 FLAGLE SUPERMARKET LLC
SEDANOS SUPERMARKET 42
(*Suby of* SEDANOS SUPERMARKETS) ★
3801 W Flagler St, Coral Gables, FL 33134-1603
Tel (305) 846-9796 *Founded/Ownrshp* 2013
Sales 56.5MM^E *EMP* 1,401^E
SIC 5411 5912 Supermarkets, chain; Drug stores
Pr: Agustin Herran

D-U-N-S 15-205-7683 IMP
3A COMPOSITES USA INC
(*Suby of* SCHWEITER TECHNOLOGIES AG)
3480 Taylorsville Hwy, Statesville, NC 28625-2587
Tel (704) 872-8974 *Founded/Ownrshp* 2004
Sales 331.2MM^E *EMP* 1,341
SIC 3334 2679 3081 3449 Primary aluminum; Paper products, converted; Unsupported plastics film & sheet; Curtain wall, metal
Pr: Brendan Cooper
CIO: Kirk Jones
IT Man: Richard Hiebert
Opers Mgr: Rob Anderson
Plnt Mgr: Niall Coulter
Sales Exec: Diane Owens
Mktg Mgr: Brandon Wyatt

D-U-N-S 13-889-0400 IMP
3D CORPORATE SOLUTIONS LLC
601 13th St, Monett, MO 65708-1850
Tel (417) 236-9602 *Founded/Ownrshp* 2003
Sales 153.5MM^E *EMP* 72
SIC 5199 5149 2048 Advertising specialties; Pet foods; Canned pet food (except dog & cat); Dry pet food (except dog & cat); Frozen pet food (except dog & cat)
CEO: Scott Walker
CFO: Duane Williams
**VP:* Scott Clawson
Sales Asso: Karissa Bartosh

3D STRUCTURAL SOLUTIONS
See 3-D CONCRETE CORRECTION INC

D-U-N-S 86-014-9681
▲ **3D SYSTEMS CORP**
333 Three D Systems Cir, Rock Hill, SC 29730-7811
Tel (803) 326-3900 *Founded/Ownrshp* 1986
Sales 666.1MM *EMP* 2,492
Tkr Sym DDD *Exch* NYS
SIC 3577 7372 Printers, computer; Optical scanning devices; Prepackaged software
Pr: Vyomesh Joshi
Ch Bd: G Walter Loewenbaum II
Pr: Deborah Matthews
COO: Kevin P McAlea
COO: Mark W Wright
COO: Mark Wright
CFO: John N McMullen
CFO: David R Styka
Ex VP: Charles W Hull
Ex VP: Cathy L Lewis
Ex VP: Ray Saundes
VP: Ziad Abou
VP: Barry Ader
VP: Brian K Alexander
VP: Buddy Byrum
VP: Andy Christensen
VP: Mark Cook
VP: Dennis Fogle
VP: Thomas Jack
VP: Andrew Lamont
VP: Kevin P Mac-A-Lay
Board of Directors: William E Curran, Thomas W Erickson, William D Humes, Jim D Kever, Kevin S Moore, Daniel S Van Riper, Karen E Welke

D-U-N-S 17-357-4161 IMP/EXP
■ **3D SYSTEMS INC**
(*Suby of* 3D SYSTEMS CORP) ★
333 Three D Systems Cir, Rock Hill, SC 29730-7811
Tel (803) 326-3900 *Founded/Ownrshp* 1993
Sales 143.6MM^E *EMP* 331
SIC 3571 Electronic computers
CEO: Andrew Johnson
COO: Richard N Lundberg
VP: Robert M Grace
Board of Directors: Thomas W Erickson

D-U-N-S 07-940-7188
3DS ACQUISITION CORP
(*Suby of* DASSAULT SYSTEMES AMERICAS CORP) ★
175 Wyman St, Waltham, MA 02451-1223
Tel (781) 810-5011 *Founded/Ownrshp* 2014
Sales 122.1MM^E *EMP* 1,000^E
SIC 7371 Computer software systems analysis & design, custom
Ch Bd: Charles Edelstenne

3E
See ELECTRICAL ENGINEERING AND EQUIPMENT CO

3I IMPLANT INNOVATIONS
See BIOMET 3I LLC

D-U-N-S 00-617-3082 IMP/EXP
▲ **3M CO**
3m Center Bldg 22011w02, Saint Paul, MN 55144-1000
Tel (651) 733-1110 *Founded/Ownrshp* 1902
Sales 30.2MMM *EMP* 89,446
Accts Pricewaterhousecoopers Llp Mi
Tkr Sym MMM *Exch* NYS
SIC 3841 3842 3291 2842 2672 2891 Surgical instruments & apparatus; Bandages & dressings; Bandages: plastic, muslin, plaster of paris, etc.; Dressings, surgical; Gauze, surgical; Abrasive products; Coated abrasive products; Pads, scouring: soap impregnated; Specialty cleaning, polishes & sanitation goods; Tape, pressure sensitive: made from purchased materials; Gummed paper: made from purchased materials; Adhesives & sealants; Adhesives
Ch Bd: Inge G Thulin
CFO: Nicholas C Gangestad
Sr VP: Ivan K Fong
Sr VP: Ashish K Khandpur
Sr VP: Marlene M McGrath
VP: Eric D Hammes
Board of Directors: Gregory R Page, Linda G Alvarado, Robert J Ulrich, Sondra L Barbour, Thomas K Brown, Vance D Coffman, David B Dillon, Michael L Eskew, Herbert L Henkel, Muhtar Kent, Edward M Liddy

D-U-N-S 96-459-8192
3M EMPLOYEES WELFARE BENEFITS ASSOCIATION TRUST II
3m Center Bldg 224, Saint Paul, MN 55144-1001
Tel (651) 737-3201 *Founded/Ownrshp* 2010
Sales 383.7MM *EMP* 2
Accts Larsonallen Llp Minneapolis
SIC 6733 Trusts
Pr: L Joe Thompson

D-U-N-S 13-414-3291
■ **3M INNOVATIVE PROPERTIES CO**
(*Suby of* 3M CO) ★
3m Center Bldg 2253s06, Saint Paul, MN 55144-1001
Tel (651) 733-8904 *Founded/Ownrshp* 1998
Sales 87.8MM^E *EMP* 300^E
SIC 8111 Legal services
CEO: Inge G Thulin
Pr: Bill Myers
**Pr:* Kevin H Rhodes
**Ex VP:* Julie L Bushman
**Ex VP:* Joaquin Delgado
**Ex VP:* Michael A Kelly
**Ex VP:* Frederick J Palensky
Exec: Jim Hunt
Genl Mgr: Jon Ross
Tech Mgr: Jaime Penrod
Opers Mgr: Brian Barkdoll

D-U-N-S 02-049-8671 IMP/EXP
■ **3M INTERAMERICA INC**
(*Suby of* 3M CO) ★
2501 Old Hudson Rd, Maplewood, MN 55144-0001
Tel (651) 733-1110 *Founded/Ownrshp* 1970
Sales 952.3MM^E *EMP* 600
SIC 5113 5085 5065 5084 5122 8741 Pressure sensitive tape; Adhesives, tape & plasters; Connectors, electronic; Printing trades machinery, equipment & supplies; Drugs, proprietaries & sundries; Management services
CEO: Inge G Thulin
Pr: Jack Driessen
CFO: Patrick Campbell
CFO: Nicholas C Gangestad
Treas: William J Schmoll
Bd of Dir: Aimee Falk
Ex VP: Joaquin Delgado
Sr VP: Julie L Bushman
Sr VP: Ivan K Fong
Dir Rx: Ron Scherwin
Comm Man: Connie Thompson

A B C D
See ACTION FOR BOSTON COMMUNITY DEVELOPMENT INC

A B C FINE WINE & SPIRITS
See ABC LIQUORS INC

A B C STRUTURAL CONCRETE
See ASSOCIATED BRIGHAM CONTRACTORS INC

D-U-N-S 07-881-5479
A B C UNIFIED SCHOOL DISTRICT
16700 Norwalk Blvd, Cerritos, CA 90703-1838
Tel (562) 926-5567 Founded/Ownrshp 1965
Sales 130.6MME EMP 2,260
SIC 8211 Public elementary school; Public junior high school; Public senior high school
*Pr: Celia Spitzer
CFO: Toan Nguyen
Ofcr: Joshie Cox
*VP: Mr Armind Reyes
Exec: Kay Jones
CTO: Gerry Ellis
Dir IT: Jan Hite
Doctor: Mary Sieu

A B H S
See ALEXIAN BROTHERS MEDICAL CENTER INC

A B I
See APPLIED BIOSCIENCE INTERNATIONAL LLC

A B M
See ABM FACILITY SERVICES LLC

A B M
See ABM SECURITY SERVICES INC

A B M
See AMERICAN BUILDING MAINTENANCE CO OF ILLINOIS INC

A B M
See ABM ONSITE SERVICES INC

D-U-N-S 78-431-5814 IMP
A B M INC
180 N Lasalle St Ste 1700, Chicago, IL 60601
Tel (312) 469-1643 Founded/Ownrshp 1909
Sales 119.4MME EMP 5,500
SIC 7349 Janitorial service, contract basis
Ch Bd: Michael Sweig
*Pr: Nicholas Baker
*Sr VP: James Mc Coy
*Sr VP: Calvin Meyer
*VP: Gary Kligman

A BETTER MOBILE STORAGE
See MOBILE STORAGE GROUP INC

A C E
See ACE USA INC

D-U-N-S 09-845-2618 IMP/EXP
A C FURNITURE CO INC
ACF
3872 Martin Dr, Axton, VA 24054-4093
Tel (276) 650-3356 Founded/Ownrshp 1979
Sales 100.9MME EMP 475
Accts Goodman & Company Llp Danvil
SIC 2521 Chairs, office: padded, upholstered or plain: wood
Pr: J Wilson
*CFO: David O Campbell
*Sec: Annie Agee

A C H RETAIL PRODUCTS
See ACH FOOD COMPANIES INC

A C I
See CANTON WIND-DOWN CO

A C L
See ATLANTIC CONTAINER LINE AB

A C L D
See ADULTS AND CHILDREN WITH LEARNING AND DEVELOPMENTAL DISABILITIES INC

A C N
See AMERICA CHUNG NAM LLC

A C P
See ARLINGTON COMPUTER PRODUCTS INC

A C S
See ACS COMMERCIAL SOLUTIONS INC

D-U-N-S 94-597-5712
■ A C S HUMAN RESOURCES SOLUTIONS INC
(Suby of A C S) ★
112 W 34th St Ste 605, New York, NY 10120-0701
Tel (212) 685-7981 Founded/Ownrshp 2005
Sales 192.2MME EMP 3,100
Accts Grant Thornton Llp
SIC 8742 6282 Compensation & benefits planning consultant; Investment advice
Pr: Karl Lohwater
*Ch: Gary Stephen
*Treas: John Kennedy
*VP: Betty Ralston
*VP: Louis Rosamilia

D-U-N-S 02-026-0806
A CARING DOCTOR (TEXAS) PC (TX)
BANFIELD PET HOSPITAL
(Suby of BANFIELD PET HOSPITAL) ★
8000 Ne Tillamook St, Portland, OR 97213-6655
Tel (503) 922-5000 Founded/Ownrshp 2012
Sales 23.5MME EMP 1,669E
SIC 0742 5047 Animal hospital services, pets & other animal specialties; Veterinarians' equipment & supplies
Prin: Alison Marsh

D-U-N-S 06-856-3571
A CARING DOCTOR MINNESOTA PA
BANFIELD PET HOSPITAL
(Suby of BANFIELD PET HOSPITAL) ★
8000 Ne Tillamook St, Portland, OR 97213-6655
Tel (503) 922-5000 Founded/Ownrshp 2001
Sales 37.8MME EMP 3,058E
SIC 0742 5047 Animal hospital services, pets & other animal specialties; Veterinarians' equipment & supplies
Prin: Warren Wegert

A CATHOLIC HEALTHCARE TRUST
See RETA TRUST

D-U-N-S 80-830-1787
A CLARK/MCCARTHY JOINT VENTURE
18201 Von Karman Ave # 800, Irvine, CA 92612-1000
Tel (714) 429-9779 Founded/Ownrshp 2007
Sales 35.6MME EMP 1,250
SIC 1521 Single-family housing construction
Prin: W Carter Chappell
Pt: Richard Heim
Prin: Margie Rosario

A CONTINUUM OF WELLNESS, THE
See COLONIAL WILLIAMSBURG CO

A D C
See ANDALUSIA DISTRIBUTING CO INC

A D C
See APPLIANCE DEALERS COOPERATIVE INC

A D P
See NATIONAL DIVERSIFIED SALES INC

D-U-N-S 06-440-0633
■ A D P FOUNDATION
ADP
(Suby of ADP) ★
1 Adp Blvd Ste 1, Roseland, NJ 07068-1786
Tel (973) 994-5000 Founded/Ownrshp 1978
Sales 4.7MM EMP 2,000
SIC 8641 Civic social & fraternal associations
Ch Bd: Josh S Weston

A D S
See ASHLEY DISTRIBUTION SERVICES LTD

A D TRANSPORT
See AD TRANSPORT EXPRESS INC

A DIVISION OF TRANSDIGM GROUP
See AVTECHTYEE INC

D-U-N-S 00-692-3262 IMP/EXP
A DUDA & SONS INC (FL)
1200 Duda Trl, Oviedo, FL 32765-4505
Tel (407) 365-2111 Founded/Ownrshp 1925
Sales 484.3MM EMP 400
Accts Rsm Us Llp
SIC 0161 5148 2033 0133 6552 0174 Vegetables & melons; Celery farm; Rooted vegetable farms; Carrot farm; Fruits, fresh; Vegetables, fresh; Fruit juices: concentrated, hot pack; Sugarcane farm; Land subdividers & developers, commercial; Land subdividers & developers, residential; Citrus fruits
CEO: David J Duda
*CFO: Palmer B Weeks
*Ex VP: Tracy Duda Chapman
*Ex VP: Walter A Duda Jr
*Ex VP: Richard L Hanas
*VP: Steven P Bocchino
*VP: Lauri Duda Buckley
*VP: Edward D Duda Jr
VP: Lauri Duda
*VP: Thomas D Duda
*VP: Mark E Engwall
*VP: Edward L Hamilton
*VP: Stephen L Johnson
VP: William Mathews
Comm Dir: Susan Howard

A DUIE PYLE DIST & WHSNG
See A DUIE PYLE INC

D-U-N-S 09-372-3518
A DUIE PYLE INC
A DUIE PYLE DIST & WHSNG
650 Westtown Rd, West Chester, PA 19382-4900
Tel (610) 696-5800 Founded/Ownrshp 1986
Sales 324.7MME EMP 1,400
SIC 4214 4225 7519 Local trucking with storage; General warehousing; Utility trailer rental
Pr: Peter Latta
*Pr: Steven D Gast
COO: Keary Mueller
CFO: Curt Kristensen
VP: Michael Crowley
VP: Kevin Gearin
*VP: James Latta III
VP: Charity Svendgard
VP: Randy Swart
Mng Dir: Kim Roberts
Area Mgr: Brian Downing
Board of Directors: A Duie Latta

A E D
See ACADEMY FOR EDUCATIONAL DEVELOPMENT INC

A E I
See AMERICAN ENTERPRISE INSTITUTE FOR PUBLIC POLICY RESEARCH

D-U-N-S 06-421-3085 IMP
■ A E PETSCHE CO INC
(Suby of ARROW ELECTRONICS INC) ★
1501 Nolan Ryan Expy, Arlington, TX 76011-4951
Tel (817) 461-9473 Founded/Ownrshp 2009
Sales 170.0MME EMP 250
SIC 5063 Wire & cable
Pr: Joe Azevedo
*Ch Bd: Arnold E Petsche
*Pr: Glenn K Davidson
*Pr: Kent Horst
*CFO: Stuart McCallum
Ofcr: Mark Goodman
*VP: Michael Casale
*VP: Ian Locke
*VP: Mary Kathy Petsche
IT Man: Michael Howell
Opers Mgr: Kerdell Baker

D-U-N-S 06-926-5106
■ A E PROPERTIES INC
(Suby of STANDARD FIRE INSURANCE CO) ★
1 Tower Sq, Hartford, CT 06183-0001
Tel (860) 277-1295 Founded/Ownrshp 1972, 1996
Sales 10.5MME EMP 1,000
SIC 6512 Commercial & industrial building operation
Ch Bd: Jay Steven Fishman

A E R
See AER MANUFACTURING LP

D-U-N-S 07-701-8034
A EPSTEIN AND SONS INTERNATIONAL INC
600 W Fulton St Ste 800, Chicago, IL 60661-1254
Tel (312) 454-9100 Founded/Ownrshp 1921
Sales 91.4MME EMP 260E
SIC 8711 8712 7389 1542 1541 8742 Consulting engineer; Architectural engineering; Interior designer; Commercial & office building, new construction; Institutional building construction; Industrial buildings, new construction; Management consulting services
*Ch Bd: Sidney Epstein
*Pr: John Patelski
*CEO: Melvin Kupperman
*CFO: James Jirsa
*Ex VP: John Talbot
*VP: Alan Berk
Opers Mgr: Greg Osborne
Mktg Dir: Noel Abbott
Snr PM: Lawrence Dalziel

A F
See AFFILIATED FOODS INC

A F PLUMBING SUPPLY
See A F SUPPLY CORP

D-U-N-S 01-247-4128 IMP/EXP
A F SUPPLY CORP (NY)
A F PLUMBING SUPPLY
942 Lafayette Ave, Brooklyn, NY 11221-1999
Tel (212) 243-5400 Founded/Ownrshp 1934
Sales 103.6MME EMP 100
SIC 5074 Plumbing fittings & supplies; Heating equipment (hydronic)
Ch Bd: Howard Friedman
*VP: Bennett Friedman

D-U-N-S 00-512-9697 IMP/EXP
A FINKL & SONS CO
FINKL STEEL - CHICAGO
(Suby of SCHMOLZ+BICKENBACH AG)
1355 E 93rd St, Chicago, IL 60619-8004
Tel (773) 975-2510 Founded/Ownrshp 1974
Sales 202.5MME EMP 383
Accts Ernst & Young
SIC 3312 Ingots, steel; Forgings, iron & steel
CEO: Bruce C Liimatainen
*Pr: Joseph E Curci
CFO: Michael Lutter
*VP: David Laurenson
VP: Tim Neatt
CTO: Sargon Guliana
Sls Mgr: Jeff Chism
Sls Mgr: Don Fl
Sls Mgr: Danielle Smith

D-U-N-S 09-664-4372 IMP/EXP
A G EQUIPMENT CO (OK)
3401 W Albany St, Broken Arrow, OK 74012-1174
Tel (918) 250-7386 Founded/Ownrshp 1979
Sales 486.2MM EMP 420
Accts Cck Strategies Pllc Tulsa O
SIC 3563 5084 Air & gas compressors; Industrial machine parts
CEO: Henry Ash
*Pr: Grady Ash
*Pr: Kent Bright
*CFO: Douglas Bassett
*VP: Keith Miller

D-U-N-S 80-901-4207
A G HOME HEALTH LLC
700 White Plains Rd # 275, Scarsdale, NY 10583-5013
Tel (914) 722-9000 Founded/Ownrshp 2007
Sales 122.1MME EMP 3,700E
SIC 6282 Investment advisory service

D-U-N-S 83-138-8975 IMP
A G M DECO INC
STEINER DOORS
741 Myrtle Ave, Brooklyn, NY 11205-3924
Tel (718) 624-6200 Founded/Ownrshp 2004
Sales 120.0MM EMP 92
SIC 3442 Sash, door or window: metal
Pr: Gabrielle Steiner
Genl Mgr: Joie Steiner

A GY
See AGY HOLDING CORP

D-U-N-S 17-411-3787
A GLEN BARRILLEAUX LLC
1412 W Broad St, Oakwood, TX 75855-4563
Tel (903) 545-1231 Founded/Ownrshp 1985
Sales 112.6MME EMP 400E
SIC 1623 1629 Oil & gas line & compressor station construction; Oil refinery construction
Off Mgr: Jennifer Huffman

D-U-N-S 01-881-8369
A GRADE MARKET INC
360 Connecticut Ave, Norwalk, CT 06854-1824
Tel (203) 838-0504 Founded/Ownrshp 1936
Sales 115.8MME EMP 1,000
SIC 5411 Supermarkets, independent
Pr: Rocco Cingari
*Treas: Salvatore J Cingari
*VP: Salvatore Cingari Jr

D-U-N-S 04-207-5913
A GREAT AMERICAN BRAND LLC
A&W RESTAURANT
1648 Mcgrathiana Pkwy, Lexington, KY 40511-1338
Tel (859) 219-0019 Founded/Ownrshp 2011
Sales 123.8MME EMP 1,513E
SIC 5812 6794 Drive-in restaurant; Franchises, selling or licensing
Pr: Kevin M Bazner

A H A
See AISIN HOLDINGS OF AMERICA INC

D-U-N-S 80-978-9691
▲ A H BELO CORP
508 Young St, Dallas, TX 75202-4808
Tel (214) 977-8222 Founded/Ownrshp 1842
Sales 272.1MM EMP 1,160E
Tkr Sym AHC Exch NYS
SIC 2711 7313 Newspapers, publishing & printing; Electronic media advertising representatives
Ch Bd: James M Moroney III
CFO: Mary Kathryn Murray
*V Ch Bd: Robert W Decherd
Sr VP: Michael J O'Hara
VP: Teri Andrews
VP: Christine E Larkin
Board of Directors: John A Beckert, Louis E Caldera, Ronald D McCray, Tyree B Miller, John P Puerner, Nicole G Small

A H C
See AMERICAN HEALTH COMPANIES INC

D-U-N-S 01-872-8618 IMP
A H HARRIS & SONS INC (CT)
433 S Main St Ste 202, West Hartford, CT 06110-2812
Tel (860) 216-9600 Founded/Ownrshp 1916, 1993
Sales 155.8MME EMP 450
SIC 5032

D-U-N-S 02-492-1884
A H MANAGEMENT GROUP INC
A.H. VENDING & FOOD SERVICE
1151 Rohlwing Rd, Rolling Meadows, IL 60008-1030
Tel (847) 342-8065 Founded/Ownrshp 2012
Sales 83.9MME EMP 350
SIC 5962 7993 5963 7389 5046 Cigarettes vending machines; Candy & snack food vending machines; Food vending machines; Beverage vending machines; Coin-operated amusement devices; Food services, direct sales; Coffee service; Commercial equipment
Pr: Donald Hesch
VP Opers: Ken Ligon
Manager: Tim Cordt
Sls Mgr: Tim Sherwood

A H O CONSTRUCTION
See AHO CONSTRUCTION I INC

A I DUPONT HOSP FOR CHILDREN
See ALFRED IDUPONT HOSPITAL FOR CHILDREN

D-U-N-S 00-355-3562
A I FLINT LLC
(Suby of ANDROID INDUSTRIES LLC) ★
4444 W Maple Ave, Flint, MI 48507-3128
Tel (810) 732-8760 Founded/Ownrshp 2000
Sales 104.5MME EMP 1,100
SIC 3714 Motor vehicle parts & accessories
Plnt Mgr: Larry Kipp

A I FRIEDMAN
See AI FRIEDMAN LP

A I M
See ACTIVE INTEREST MEDIA INC

A I M S
See ACCLAMATION INSURANCE MANAGEMENT SERVICES

A I R
See AMERICAN INSTITUTES FOR RESEARCH IN BEHAVIORAL SCIENCES

A J C
See AJC INTERNATIONAL INC

D-U-N-S 05-715-7810
A J CATAGNUS INC
1299 W James St, Norristown, PA 19401-3607
Tel (610) 275-5328 Founded/Ownrshp 1979
Sales 116.9MME EMP 297
SIC 4953 Recycling, waste materials
Pr: Anthony Catagnus Jr
*Sec: Vincent Catagnus

A J M
See AJM PACKAGING CORP

A J MERRICK MANOR
See FREMONT HEALTH

D-U-N-S 00-178-5278 IMP
■ A J OSTER LLC
(Suby of GLOBAL BRASS AND COPPER INC) ★
457 Warwick Industrial Dr, Warwick, RI 02886-2460
Tel (401) 736-2600 Founded/Ownrshp 1933, 2007
Sales 139.7MME EMP 440
SIC 5051 Copper
CIO: Thomas Tranghese
Plnt Mgr: Greg Hefflefinger
Ql Cn Mgr: Philip Tischler
Mktg Mgr: Frank Kandrach

D-U-N-S 09-331-0324 IMP/EXP
A J RICHARD & SONS INC
150 Price Pkwy, Farmingdale, NY 11735-1315
Tel (631) 843-4300 Founded/Ownrshp 1977
Sales 490.3MME EMP 2,850
SIC 5722 5731 Household appliance stores; Radio, television & electronic stores
Ch Bd: Gregg H Richard
*CFO: Thomas Pohmer
*Treas: Kevin Hughey
*Ex VP: Peter Richard

D-U-N-S 00-415-4415 IMP
A J ROSE MFGCO (OH)
38000 Chester Rd, Avon, OH 44011-4022
Tel (216) 631-4645 Founded/Ownrshp 1922
Sales 94.9MME EMP 383
SIC 3465 3568 3469 Automotive stampings; Pulleys, power transmission; Metal stampings
Pr: Daniel T Pritchard

CFO: Douglas Kizywicki
**Treas:* Terry J Sweeney
**VP:* Douglas E Krzywicki
VP: Dana A Lambillotte
VP: Bob Nemeth
VP: Christopher Rose
Exec: Michael Cox
QA Dir: Ian Hudgins
Dir IT: Jim Hopsecger
Sys Mgr: Terry Mackin

D-U-N-S 83-320-6563
A JBEK JOINT VENTURE CO
242 Chapman Rd, Newark, DE 19702-5405
Tel (302) 452-9000 *Founded/Ownrshp* 2010
Sales 101.0MM *EMP* 2
SIC 8711 8741 Engineering services; Construction management
Prin: Keith Reece

A L C
See AUTOMATED LOGIC CORP

D-U-N-S 00-796-6682 IMP/EXP
A L GILBERT CO (CA)
BERRY SEED & FEED
304 N Yosemite Ave, Oakdale, CA 95361-3140
Tel (209) 847-1721 *Founded/Ownrshp* 1892
Sales 136.5MM^E *EMP* 225
SIC 5191

A L S
See HOUSTON TRIBOLOGY SALES & MARKETING OFFICE

A M A
See AMERICAN MEDICAL ASSOCIATION INC

D-U-N-S 00-693-4004
▲ A M CASTLE & CO
1420 Kensington Rd # 220, Oak Brook, IL 60523-2165
Tel (847) 455-7111 *Founded/Ownrshp* 1890
Sales 770.7MM *EMP* 1,515
Accts Deloitte & Touche Llp Chicag
Tkr Sym CAS *Exch* NYS
SIC 5051 5162 Metals service centers & offices; Plates, metal; Tubing, metal; Sheets, metal; Plastics materials & basic shapes
Pr: Steven W Scheinkman
**Ch Bd:* Brian P Anderson
COO: Ronald E Knopp
CFO: Patrick R Anderson
Ofcr: Marec E Edgar
Board of Directors: Reuben S Donnelley, Pamela Forbes Lieberman, Gary A Masse, Jonathan B Mellin, Kenneth H Traub, Allan J Young

A M H
See AMERICAN MARITIME HOLDINGS INC

A M I
See AMERICAN MEGATRENDS INC

A M I
See ASMO MAUNFACTURING INC

A M I ENCN-TRZANA RGNAL MED CE
See AMI-HTITARZANA ENCINO JOINT VENTURE

A M O
See ABBOTT MEDICAL OPTICS INC

A M P I
See ASSOCIATED MILK PRODUCERS INC

D-U-N-S 55-662-0979
A MICHAEL OWENS INC
OWENS TRANSPORT SERVICE
814 W Chestnut St, Bloomington, IL 61701-2816
Tel (309) 828-7750 *Founded/Ownrshp* 1986
Sales 115.6MM *EMP* 23
Accts Thoma & Associates Bloomingto
SIC 5541 4213 Filling stations, gasoline; Liquid petroleum transport, non-local
Pr: A Michael Owens

D-U-N-S 00-243-0668
A N DERINGER INC (VT)
64 N Main St, Saint Albans, VT 05478-1666
Tel (802) 524-8110 *Founded/Ownrshp* 1919
Sales 184.0MM^E *EMP* 500
Accts Kpmg Llp
SIC 4731 Customhouse brokers; Freight forwarding
Pr: Jacob E Holzscheiter
CFO: Bob Lawrence
**Treas:* Robert P Lawrence
**VP:* Melisande A C Mayotte
Brnch Mgr: Ron Hall
Brnch Mgr: Nancy Labrozzi
Dist Mgr: Erica Rawson
Off Mgr: Lisa Herr
Mktg Mgr: Pamela Baker

A N F
See AMERICAN NICARAGUAN FOUNDATION INC

A NT
See ATLANTA NETWORK TECHNOLOGIES INC

A NORDIC GROUP COMPANY
See SEATS INC

D-U-N-S 12-218-5853
A O G CORP
115 N 12th St, Fort Smith, AR 72901-2741
Tel (479) 783-3181 *Founded/Ownrshp* 1979
Sales 133.3MM^E *EMP* 260
SIC 4923 4924 Gas transmission & distribution; Natural gas distribution
Pr: W R Stephens Jr
**Treas:* Eloise D Guess
**VP:* Robert J Mulson

A O N
See AON RISK SERVICES NORTHEAST INC

D-U-N-S 02-913-2628
A O REED & CO
4777 Ruffner St, San Diego, CA 92111-1578
Tel (858) 565-4131 *Founded/Ownrshp* 1983
Sales 154.7MM^E *EMP* 400
SIC 1711 Plumbing, heating, air-conditioning contractors
Pr: Steve Andrade
Pr: John Norling
**CFO:* Clyde Blyleven
**CFO:* Craig Koehler
Sr VP: Alan Rings
**VP:* David Clarkin
**VP:* Jaimi Lomas
VP: Martin Naranjo
VP: John Skoog
Dept Mgr: Colin Berman
IT Man: Salomon Saenz

A O S
See ALEXANDER OPEN SYSTEMS INC

D-U-N-S 00-608-5815 IMP/EXP
▲ A O SMITH CORP
11270 W Park Pl Ste 1200, Milwaukee, WI 53224-3643
Tel (414) 359-4000 *Founded/Ownrshp* 1874
Sales 2.5MMM *EMP* 13,400^E
Tkr Sym AOS *Exch* NYS
SIC 3639 3433 Hot water heaters, household; Boilers, low-pressure heating: steam or hot water
Ch Bd: Ajita G Rajendra
**CFO:* John J Kita
**Ex VP:* James F Stern
Sr VP: Wilfridus M Brouwer
Sr VP: Paul R Dana
Sr VP: WEI Ding
**Sr VP:* Robert J Heideman
Sr VP: Charles T Lauber
Sr VP: Peter R Martineau
**Sr VP:* William L Vallett Jr
Sr VP: Kevin J Wheeler
VP: Randall Bednar
VP: Bob Richardson
VP: Myra Story
Board of Directors: Ronald D Brown, Gloster B Current Jr, William P Greubel, Paul W Jones, Mathias F Sandoval, Bruce M Smith, Mark D Smith, Idelle K Wolf, Gene C Wulf

A P A
See AMERICAN PSYCHOLOGICAL ASSOCIATION INC

A P C M G E
See SCHNEIDER ELECTRIC IT CORP

A P C O ASSOCIATES
See APCO WORLDWIDE INC

A P D
See AMERICAN PRODUCT DISTRIBUTORS INC

A P F
See AMERICAN PLANT FOOD CORP

A P F C
See ALASKA PERMANENT FUND CORP

A P I
See AMERICAN PHOENIX INC

D-U-N-S 00-679-1099 IMP/EXP
A P I INC (MN)
(*Suby of* API GROUP INC) ★
1100 Old Highway 8 Nw, Saint Paul, MN 55112-6447
Tel (651) 636-4320 *Founded/Ownrshp* 1929, 1997
Sales 122.9MM^E *EMP* 250
SIC 1742 5033

A P L
See APL LOGISTICS AMERICAS LTD

D-U-N-S 61-004-9231
A P R CONSULTING INC
1370 Valley Vista Dr # 280, Diamond Bar, CA 91765-3923
Tel (909) 396-5375 *Founded/Ownrshp* 1980
Sales 93.0MM^E *EMP* 2,400
SIC 7361 7379

A P S
See AMERICAS POWERSPORTS INC

D-U-N-S 12-975-2564
■ A PLAINSCAPITAL PRIMELENDING CO
(*Suby of* PLAINSCAPITAL BANK) ★
18111 Preston Rd Ste 900, Dallas, TX 75252-6601
Tel (800) 317-7463 *Founded/Ownrshp* 2013
Sales NA *EMP* 1,300
Accts Ernst & Young Llp Dallas Tx
SIC 6163 6021 Mortgage brokers arranging for loans, using money of others; National commercial banks
**CFO:* Eric Pretzlaff
Chf Inves: Richard Wyatt
**Ex VP:* Kristi Harris
**Sr VP:* Cindy Buhr
**Sr VP:* Susie Garza
Sr VP: Kathleen Heck
Sr VP: Kelly Lee
VP: Patti Conley
VP: Chris Cordry
**VP:* Scott Eggen
VP: David White
Board of Directors: Roseanna McGill

D-U-N-S 04-017-6497
A POLYCLINIC PROFESSIONAL CORP
904 7th Ave, Seattle, WA 98104-1132
Tel (206) 292-2249 *Founded/Ownrshp* 1960
Sales 128.7MM^E *EMP* 1,200
Accts Moss Adams Llp Everett Washi
SIC 8011 Primary care medical clinic
CEO: Lloyd David
**Pr:* Rex Ochi
COO: Anita Geving
**CFO:* Dennis Price
Treas: Ryan Oftebro
VP: Daron Vchulek
Ex Dir: Nicoleta Geageac
Prac Mgr: Christina Ramirez
Genl Mgr: Mairah Ocallaghan
MIS Dir: Nancy King-Larson
Opers Supe: Angela Smith

A R B
See AIR RESOURCES BOARD

A R C
See LEO BURNETT CO INC

A R C
See AMERICAN REPROGRAPHICS CO LLC

A R C
See ALTERNATIVE RESOURCES CORP

A R C O
See ATLANTIC RICHFIELD CO INC

A R C O
See VINTNERS DISTRIBUTORS INC

A R R LEARNING CENTERS
See ARR INVESTMENTS INC

D-U-N-S 01-532-4328
A RAYMOND CORPORATE NORTH AMERICA INC
(*Suby of* A RAYMOND ET COMPAGNIE)
2350 Austin Ave Ste 200, Rochester Hills, MI 48309-3679
Tel (248) 853-2500 *Founded/Ownrshp* 2009
Sales 221.7MM^E *EMP* 798
SIC 5085 3469 6719 Fasteners & fastening equipment; Metal stampings; Investment holding companies, except banks
CEO: Earl Brown
**Treas:* Tim Oneil

D-U-N-S 19-860-5354 IMP/EXP
A RAYMOND TINNERMAN AUTOMOTIVE INC
(*Suby of* A RAYMOND CORPORATE NORTH AMERICA INC) ★
3091 Research Dr, Rochester Hills, MI 48309-3581
Tel (248) 260-2121 *Founded/Ownrshp* 1986
Sales 221.7MM^E *EMP* 775^E
SIC 5085 3469

D-U-N-S 96-656-1979
■ A S A HOLDINGS INC
(*Suby of* DELTA AIRLINES) ★
100 Hartsfield Ctr Pkwy, Atlanta, GA 30354-1341
Tel (404) 766-1400 *Founded/Ownrshp* 1996
Sales 84.8MM^E *EMP* 2,504
SIC 4512 Air passenger carrier, scheduled; Air cargo carrier, scheduled
CEO: W E Barnette
Pr: Skip Barnett
VP: John A Bedson
VP: Bryan Labrecque
VP: Samuel J Watts
CIO: Jim Jansen

A S B
See AGRI SERVICES OF BRUNSWICK LLC

A S C
See AIR SYSTEM COMPONENTS INC

A S I
See ADVERTISING SPECIALTY INSTITUTE INC

A S I
See AMERICAN STRATEGIC INSURANCE CORP

A S I
See ASI COMPUTER TECHNOLOGIES INC

A S I
See ADVANCED SCIENTIFICS INC

A S I
See ARVIN SANGO INC

A S I
See ASI CONSTRUCTORS INC

A S I G
See AIRCRAFT SERVICE INTERNATIONAL INC

A S P C A
See AMERICAN SOCIETY FOR PREVENTION OF CRUELTY TO ANIMALS (INC)

A S U
See ALABAMA STATE UNIVERSITY (INC)

A S W
See AMERICAN SPRING WIRE CORP

A. SCHULMAN
See MATRIXX GROUP INC

D-U-N-S 00-699-8413
▲ A SCHULMAN INC
3637 Ridgewood Rd, Fairlawn, OH 44333-2699
Tel (330) 666-3751 *Founded/Ownrshp* 1928
Sales 2.5MMM *EMP* 4,800
Tkr Sym SHLM *Exch* NGS
SIC 2821 Plastics materials & resins; Molding compounds, plastics
Ch Bd: Joseph M Gingo
COO: Gary A Miller
CFO: Gary Phillips
CFO: John W Richardson
Ofcr: Andreas K Gunther
Ex VP: Rainer R Schewe
VP: Kristopher R Westbrooks
Board of Directors: Eugene R Allspach, Gregory T Barmore, David G Birney, Lee D Meyer, James A Mitarotonda, Ernest J Novak Jr, Kathleen M Oswald

A T A
See AEROSPACE TESTING ALLIANCE

A T C ASSOCIATES
See ATC GROUP HOLDINGS LLC

A T F
See BUREAU OF ALCOHOL TOBACCO FIREARMS & EXPLOSIVES

A T G
See AMERICAN TRANSPORT GROUP LLC

D-U-N-S 18-205-2316
A T I C MANAGEMENT CORP DE CORP
AMERICAN TRANSIT INSURANCE CO
275 7th Ave Fl 3, New York, NY 10001-6884
Tel (212) 857-8200 *Founded/Ownrshp* 1987
Sales NA *EMP* 325^E
SIC 6411 Insurance agents, brokers & service
Pr: Edward T McGettigan Jr
**VP:* Ralph Bisceglia

D-U-N-S 04-469-4797
■ A T I FUNDING CORP
ATI FUNDING
(*Suby of* ATI) ★
801 N West St Fl 2, Wilmington, DE 19801-1525
Tel (302) 656-8937 *Founded/Ownrshp* 1988
Sales 3.6MMM^E *EMP* 1,500
SIC 3462 Iron & steel forgings
Treas: Kenneth J Kubacki
**Pr:* Mary W Snyder
**VP:* Peter C Fulweilber
**Prin:* Dale Reid

D-U-N-S 00-175-0645
A T KEARNEY INC
(*Suby of* A.T. KEARNEY HOLDINGS LIMITED)
227 W Monroe St, Chicago, IL 60606-5055
Tel (312) 648-0111 *Founded/Ownrshp* 1926
Sales 635.0MM^E *EMP* 4,000
SIC 8742 Management consulting services
Ch Bd: Johan Aurik
Pt: Christine Ahn
Pt: Michael Jenkins
COO: Andrew Duncan
CFO: David Asper
CFO: Dan A Decnniere
**CFO:* Christine Laurens
Bd of Dir: Judith Craven
Bd of Dir: Hans-Joachim Koerber
Ex VP: Mike Sheldon
Ex VP: Dan Starta
Sr VP: Doug Hoover
Sr VP: James Hope
Sr VP: Robert Nason
VP: John Paterson
VP: James Rushing
Board of Directors: Laura Gurski, John Kurtz, Daniel Mahler, Phil Morgan, Gary Singer, Randi Zeller

A T P C O
See AIRLINE TARIFF PUBLISHING CO

A T S
See APPLIED TECHNICAL SERVICES CORP

A T S
See TOYOTA BOSHOKU ILLINOIS LLC

D-U-N-S 00-632-3315 IMP
A T STILL UNIVERSITY OF HEALTH SCIENCES (MO)
800 W Jefferson St, Kirksville, MO 63501-1443
Tel (660) 626-2121 *Founded/Ownrshp* 1926
Sales 133.0MM *EMP* 450
Accts Bkd Llp Kansas City Missour
SIC 8221 Professional schools
CEO: Craig M Phelps
**Pr:* Jack Magruder
Pr: Heinz Woehlk
**CFO:* Monnie Harrison
Treas: Leomar Bautista
Bd of Dir: Allison Bright
Assoc VP: Randy Rogers
VP: Robert Basham
VP: Lori Haxton
VP: Greg Rubenstein
VP: Shaun Sommerer
Assoc Dir: Deanna Hughes
Assoc Dir: Joyce Obradovich

D-U-N-S 02-489-8652
A T WILLIAMS OIL CO
WILCO HESS
5446 University Pkwy, Winston Salem, NC 27105-1366
Tel (336) 767-9883 *Founded/Ownrshp* 1963
Sales NA *EMP* 2,200
SIC 6719 Investment holding companies, except banks
CEO: Arthur T Williams Jr
**Pr:* Steve Williams
**Sec:* Roger Fulp
**VP:* Sherry Polonsky

D-U-N-S 80-197-1107 EXP
A TEICHERT & SON INC
TEICHERT CONSTRUCTION
(*Suby of* TEICHERT INC) ★
3500 American River Dr, Sacramento, CA 95864-5893
Tel (916) 484-3011 *Founded/Ownrshp* 1887
Sales 786.6MM^E *EMP* 1,800^E
SIC 5032 3273 1611 1442 1521 Brick, stone & related material; Ready-mixed concrete; Highway & street construction; Construction sand & gravel; Single-family housing construction
Pr: Judson T Riggs
**Pr:* Dana M Davis
**Pr:* Kenneth A Kayser
**CFO:* Narendra M Pathipati
Ex VP: Bert Sandman
**VP:* Terri A Bakken
Dist Mgr: Rachel Bettencourt
Software D: Randy Flemming

A UTC AEROSPACE SYSTEMS CO
See ROSEMOUNT AEROSPACE INC

D-U-N-S 14-728-8216
A V AMELIA ISLAND PLANTATION
39 Beach Lagoon Rd, Fernandina Beach, FL 32034-5477
Tel (904) 261-6161 *Founded/Ownrshp* 2004
Sales 1.2MM^E *EMP* 1,500
SIC 7011 Resort hotel
Pr: Donald Stemetz
Mktg Dir: Richard Goldman
Manager: Thomas Heeter

A V I
See AUDIO VISUAL INNOVATIONS INC

A W C
See AUTO WAREHOUSING CO INC

A W C
See ALLIED WIRE & CABLE INC

D-U-N-S 00-101-4562 IMP/EXP
A W CHESTERTON CO (MA)
860 Salem St, Groveland, MA 01834-1563
Tel (781) 438-7000 *Founded/Ownrshp* 1884
Sales 315.7MM[E] *EMP* 1,100
SIC 3053 2851 2992 2891 5169 Gaskets & sealing devices; Epoxy coatings; Lubricating oils; Sealing compounds for pipe threads or joints; Specialty cleaning & sanitation preparations
Pr: Brian O'Donnell
**Owner:* Andrew Chesterton
**CEO:* Richard Hoyle
CFO: Janet Baird
**CFO:* Ron Maxwel
**Treas:* Mary Janet Baird
Ofcr: Joe Binks
VP: Thomas Meier
Rgnl Mgr: Reed Varney
Rgnl Mgr: Ben Wittreich
Dir IT: Christine Mirabito

D-U-N-S 06-171-7294
A W S INC
1275 Lakeside Ave E, Cleveland, OH 44114-1129
Tel (216) 861-0250 *Founded/Ownrshp* 1969
Sales 9.6MM *EMP* 2,400
SIC 8331 7374 7334 7331 Vocational rehabilitation agency; Data processing & preparation; Photocopying & duplicating services; Direct mail advertising services
Genl Mgr: Teresa Lowery

A. W. WALKER LAWN & GRDN CTRS
See CN BROWN CO

A WIRELESS
See ABC PHONES OF NORTH CAROLINA INC

A X A
See AXA ADVISORS LLC

D-U-N-S 00-510-3882 IMP/EXP
A Y MCDONALD INDUSTRIES INC (IA)
AY MCDONALD MFG CO
4800 Chavenelle Rd, Dubuque, IA 52002-2630
Tel (800) 292-2737 *Founded/Ownrshp* 1856
Sales 201.5MM[E] *EMP* 700
SIC 3432 3561 3494 5074 5075 5031 Plumbers' brass goods: drain cocks, faucets, spigots, etc.; Pumps, domestic: water or sump; Valves & pipe fittings; Plumbing fittings & supplies; Heating equipment (hydronic); Boilers, hot water heating; Pipes & fittings, plastic; Air conditioning & ventilation equipment & supplies; Warm air heating equipment & supplies; Furnaces, warm air; Kitchen cabinets; Millwork
Pr: Chad A Huntington
**Treas:* Andy J Wilberding
**Ex VP:* Michael B McDonald
**Sr VP:* L J Sherman
VP: Robert D McDonald II
VP: J Sherman
**Prin:* Leroy J Sherman
Board of Directors: W Louis Beecher, Thomas M Higley

D-U-N-S 00-718-3080 IMP/EXP
A ZAHNER CO (MO)
1400 E 9th St, Kansas City, MO 64106-1719
Tel (816) 474-8882 *Founded/Ownrshp* 1897
Sales 400.0MM *EMP* 126
SIC 1799 1761

D-U-N-S 13-192-3328
A&E TELEVISION NETWORKS LLC
AETN INTERNATIONAL
235 E 45th St Frnt C, New York, NY 10017-3342
Tel (212) 210-1400 *Founded/Ownrshp* 1984
Sales 693.8MM[E] *EMP* 1,047
SIC 4841 Cable television services
Ex VP: Melvin Berning
Pt: Elana Sofko
**CFO:* Gerard Gruosso
Ex VP: Sean Cohan
Ex VP: Robert Debitetto
Ex VP: Michael Feeney
Ex VP: Dirk Hoogstra
Ex VP: Douglas P Jacobs
Ex VP: David McKillop
Ex VP: Bridget Morrison
Ex VP: Robert Sharenow
Ex VP: Marion Slaton
Sr VP: Rick Basso
Sr VP: Robert Dibitetto
Sr VP: Doug Jacobs
Sr VP: Arlene Manos
VP: Darci Bailey
VP: Bob Calvano
VP: Michael Carpio
VP: William Corbin
VP: Jonathan Davis

D-U-N-S 82-884-8569
■ **A&F TRADEMARK INC**
(*Suby of* ABERCROMBIE & FITCH MANAGEMENT CO) ★
6301 Fitch Path, New Albany, OH 43054-9269
Tel (614) 283-6500 *Founded/Ownrshp* 2002
Sales 474.8MM[E] *EMP* 375
SIC 5611 Men's & boys' clothing stores
CEO: Michael S Jeffries

D-U-N-S 07-965-9453
A&M CAPITAL-GP LP
289 Greenwich Ave Ste 2, Greenwich, CT 06830-6562
Tel (212) 759-4433 *Founded/Ownrshp* 2009
Sales 765.6MM[E] *EMP* 7,012[E]
SIC 8742 Financial consultant
Pr: Bryan Marsal

D-U-N-S 05-093-1617
A&R LOGISTICS INC
A&R TRANSPORT
(*Suby of* MASON WELLS INC) ★
600 N Hurstbourne Pkwy # 110, Louisville, KY 40222-5386
Tel (815) 941-5200 *Founded/Ownrshp* 2012
Sales 205.9MM[E] *EMP* 900
SIC 8742 4731 Business consultant; Freight transportation arrangement

CEO: Mark R Holden
**Pr:* Richard A Mitchell Jr
**CFO:* Anthony W Lenhart
**Sr VP:* Michael E Fulmer
**Sr VP:* Daniel D Jaworski
VP: Rick Blanchard
VP: Kenneth Pate
Prin: Lisa Akers
Prin: Cara Baldauf
Prin: Kristi Exstrom
Prin: Patricia Parker Lundberg

A&R TRANSPORT
See A&R LOGISTICS INC

D-U-N-S 08-001-4759
A&S ASSET RECOVERY INC
608 Sw D Ave Ste 6, Lawton, OK 73501-4560
Tel (855) 692-2786 *Founded/Ownrshp* 2013
Sales 83.0MM *EMP* 4
SIC 7389 Automobile recovery service
Pr: Albert Ortega
**VP:* Paul Pope

D-U-N-S 83-189-3651
■ **A&S SERVICES GROUP LLC**
ASKINARD
(*Suby of* CELADON GROUP INC) ★
310 N Zarfoss Dr, York, PA 17404-5832
Tel (717) 235-2456 *Founded/Ownrshp* 2009
Sales 129.9MM[E] *EMP* 490[E]
SIC 4214 4225 Local trucking with storage; General warehousing & storage
Exec: Andy Seidel

A&W CONTRACTORS
See WATKINS MANUFACTURING CORP

A&W RESTAURANT
See A GREAT AMERICAN BRAND LLC

A&W RESTAURANT
See A & W RESTAURANTS INC

D-U-N-S 13-182-6211
A-DEC DENTAL UK LTD
(*Suby of* A-DEC INC) ★
2601 Crestview Dr, Newberg, OR 97132-9528
Tel (503) 538-9471 *Founded/Ownrshp* 1985
Sales 150.7MM[E] *EMP* 950[E]
SIC 5047 Dental equipment & supplies
CEO: George K Austin J
**Pr:* Scott Harris

D-U-N-S 00-961-7473 IMP/EXP
A-DEC INC
2601 Crestview Dr, Newberg, OR 97132-9528
Tel (503) 538-9471 *Founded/Ownrshp* 1964
Sales 320.8MM[E] *EMP* 1,900
SIC 3843 Dental equipment & supplies; Cabinets, dental; Dental chairs
Pr: Scott Parrish
**Treas:* Joan Austin
IT Man: Crystal Kelley
Sftwr Eng: Andrew Northy

D-U-N-S 10-674-8192
A-T SOLUTIONS INC
PAE
(*Suby of* PAE) ★
10304 Spotsylvania Ave A, Fredericksburg, VA 22408-8602
Tel (540) 604-5492 *Founded/Ownrshp* 2015
Sales 158.1MM[E] *EMP* 800
SIC 1731 Safety & security specialization
Pr: Dennis Kelly
COO: Jeff Simons
CFO: Debbie Ricci
CFO: Michale S Wise
Ex VP: Lanny Bernier
Ex VP: John G Castles II
Ex VP: John Coster
Ex VP: Kevin Lutz
Ex VP: David Pekoske
Ex VP: Mike Wise
Sr VP: Don Ross
Sr VP: Patricia Scott
VP: James Benton
VP: Joe Cucchiari

D-U-N-S 07-538-8025
A-Z OFFICE RESOURCE INC
809 S Garden St, Columbia, TN 38401-3225
Tel (931) 388-1536 *Founded/Ownrshp* 1985
Sales 118.3MM[E] *EMP* 99
SIC 5112 5021 5044 5045 5087 Stationery & office supplies; Writing instruments & supplies; Office & public building furniture; Office furniture; Calculators, electronic; Printers, computer; Janitors' supplies
Pr: Malcolm G West Jr
**CEO:* Julia West
CTO: Ken Crouch

D-U-N-S 05-253-9152
A/Z CORP
46 Norwich Westerly Rd, North Stonington, CT 06359-1712
Tel (800) 400-2420 *Founded/Ownrshp* 1966
Sales 156.6MM *EMP* 430
Accts Blum Shapiro & Co Pc West H
SIC 1541 1542 Industrial buildings & warehouses; Nonresidential construction
CEO: Perry Lorenz
**COO:* Greg Cox
**CFO:* Paul C Maxfield
VP: William ABT
VP: Kevin Chronley
VP: Don Swanson
Ex Dir: Michael Dibacco
Genl Mgr: Liz Freeman
Dir IT: David Rowbotham
Sfty Dirs: Seth Bottone
Sfty Dirs: Jim Healey
Board of Directors: Perry Lorenz

D-U-N-S 62-509-0944
▲ **A10 NETWORKS INC**
3 W Plumeria Dr, San Jose, CA 95134-2111
Tel (408) 325-8668 *Founded/Ownrshp* 2004
Sales 198.9MM *EMP* 802[E]
Tkr Sym ATEN *Exch* NYS
SIC 7373 Computer integrated systems design; Systems software development services; Computer systems selling services
Ch Bd: Lee Chen
CFO: Greg Straughn
VP: Neil Wu Becker
VP: James Cai
VP: Robert Cochran
VP: Howard Lee
VP: Brian McDonald
VP: Michael Raymond
VP: Gunter Reiss
VP: Ray Smets
VP: Andre Stewart
VP Bus Dev: Joyce Taylor
Dir Bus: David Bell
Board of Directors: Peter Y Chung, Alan S Henricks, Phillip J Salsbury

D-U-N-S 07-874-9696 EXP
A123 SYSTEMS LLC
AUTOMOTIVE SOLUTIONS GROUP
(*Suby of* WANXIANG GROUP CORPORATION)
39000 7 Mile Rd, Livonia, MI 48152-1006
Tel (734) 772-0300 *Founded/Ownrshp* 2001, 2013
Sales 844.2MM[E] *EMP* 1,700
SIC 5063 3691 Batteries; Storage batteries
CEO: Jason Forcier
Pr: Peter Cirino
**COO:* Chris Eisenhart
**Ofcr:* Scott Pepin
VP: Sam Trinch
**CTO:* Patrick Hurley
Snr Mgr: Jonathan Ross

D-U-N-S 01-914-6567 IMP
A2 HOLDINGS LTD (TX)
XL PARTS
15701 Nw Fwy, Jersey Village, TX 77040-3047
Tel (713) 983-1100 *Founded/Ownrshp* 2003
Sales 108.1MM[E] *EMP* 210
SIC 5013 Automotive supplies & parts
Pr: Ali Attayi
COO: Frank Garcia
Treas: Sean Salahshour
VP: Mike Bryk
Genl Mgr: Jamie Harding

D-U-N-S 87-925-0306
AA MANAGEMENT GROUP INC
411 E Wisconsin Ave # 1900, Milwaukee, WI 53202-4461
Tel (414) 271-7240 *Founded/Ownrshp* 1994
Sales 32.8MM[E] *EMP* 1,050
SIC 6531 7389 Appraiser, real estate; Appraisers, except real estate; Inventory computing service
Pr: Ronald M Goergen
**Pr:* Joseph P Zvesper
**Ex VP:* Lee P Hackett
VP: Gary Frantzen
VP: Thomas Maio
Snr Mgr: Attila Juhasz

D-U-N-S 15-749-9968 IMP
AA METALS INC
11616 Landstar Blvd, Orlando, FL 32824-9025
Tel (407) 377-0246 *Founded/Ownrshp* 2004
Sales 142.6MM[E] *EMP* 45
SIC 5051 Aluminum bars, rods, ingots, sheets, pipes, plates, etc.
CEO: Jack Cheng
**CFO:* Kit Tam
**VP:* Bruce Ferguson
**VP:* Bob Frascella

D-U-N-S 96-182-4377
AA TRADING LLC
1702 S State Highway 336 B, Edinburg, TX 78539-9745
Tel (956) 618-3006 *Founded/Ownrshp* 2007
Sales 84.7MM *EMP* 25
Accts Long Chilton Llp Mcallen Tex
SIC 5147 Meats & meat products

AAA
See AMERICAN AUTOMOBILE ASSOCIATION INC

D-U-N-S 05-910-9736
AAA ALLIED GROUP INC
WORLD WIDE TRAVEL SERVICE
15 W Central Pkwy, Cincinnati, OH 45202-1005
Tel (513) 762-3100 *Founded/Ownrshp* 1901
Sales 149.1MM[E] *EMP* 1,000
SIC 4724 8699 Travel agencies; Automobile owners' association
Pr: James L Pease III
Ex VP: Johnathan Morley
Genl Mgr: Jane Jones
Off Mgr: Nadine Romay
Sales Exec: Ron Pio

D-U-N-S 06-967-8860
AAA AUTO CLUB SOUTH INC
A A A TRAVEL AGENCY
(*Suby of* AAA MICHIGAN) ★
1515 N West Shore Blvd, Tampa, FL 33607-4599
Tel (813) 289-5000 *Founded/Ownrshp* 2011
Sales 253.1MM[E] *EMP* 3,300
SIC 4724 6331 8699 6311 Travel agencies; Fire, marine & casualty insurance & carriers; Automobile owners' association; Life insurance
CEO: Charles H Podowski
**Pr:* Larry Patrick
CFO: Susan Barlis
**Sr VP:* Kevin W Bakewell
**Sr VP:* Ed Fandel
**Sr VP:* Bill Latta
**Sr VP:* Michael J Petrilli
VP: Scott Denman
**VP:* Sean H Maloney
VP: Wanda Moorhead
**VP:* Nancy Cole Odom
**VP:* James Santo

AAA CAROLINAS
See CAROLINA MOTOR CLUB INC

D-U-N-S 04-452-0435
AAA CLUB ALLIANCE INC
AAA KEYSTONE
1 River Pl, Wilmington, DE 19801-5125
Tel (302) 299-4700 *Founded/Ownrshp* 2007
Sales 454.1MM[E] *EMP* 3,500
SIC 8699 6331 6351 6512 4724 Automobile owners' association; Property damage insurance; Fire, marine & casualty insurance & carriers; Liability insurance; Commercial & industrial building operation; Tourist agency arranging transport, lodging & car rental
CEO: Bernhard Koch
Ch Bd: Allen J Dewalle
CEO: Donald Gagnon
VP: William Koch
VP: Diane Remy
VP: Eric Shephard
Ex Dir: Norman E Grimm Jr
Mng Dir: John McBride
QA Dir: Nicki D Dehn
Netwrk Eng: Brian Natter
Opers Mgr: Kharma F Wallace

D-U-N-S 06-711-2425 IMP/EXP
AAA COOPER TRANSPORTATION (AL)
ACT
1751 Kinsey Rd, Dothan, AL 36303-5877
Tel (334) 793-2284 *Founded/Ownrshp* 1956, 2008
Sales 595.3MM *EMP* 4,933
SIC 4213 Trucking, except local
Pr: Reid B Dove
**COO:* Charlie Prickett
**CFO:* J Steven Roy
VP: Steve Aronhalt
VP: Mark Griffis
**VP:* Lee McMillan
**VP:* Brad Morris
VP: Clay Scofield
Exec: Scott Bowers
VP Admn: Steve Roy
Genl Mgr: Dave Johnson

D-U-N-S 55-652-9592
AAA INSURANCE OF MICHIGAN
AAA INSURANCE OF MICHIGAN CLAR
6751 Dixie Hwy Ste 103, Clarkston, MI 48346-2080
Tel (248) 620-9120 *Founded/Ownrshp* 1996
Sales NA *EMP* 5
SIC 6411 Insurance agents, brokers & service
Pt: Denzil Arney
Pt: John Meader
Ch Bd: Stephen E Ewing
VP: Lee Haller

AAA INSURANCE OF MICHIGAN CLAR
See AAA INSURANCE OF MICHIGAN

AAA KEYSTONE
See AAA CLUB ALLIANCE INC

D-U-N-S 00-225-2422
AAA LIFE INSURANCE CO
ACLI AQUISITIONS COMPANY
17900 N Laurel Park Dr, Livonia, MI 48152-3992
Tel (734) 779-2600 *Founded/Ownrshp* 1969
Sales NA *EMP* 350[E]
SIC 6311 Life insurance
Pr: Harold Huffstetler
CFO: John W Dubose III
Sr VP: Betty Schick
Snr Sftwr: Roger Skulsky
Snr Ntwrk: James Mills
Dir IT: Pam Hensley
IT Man: Jeremy Hanson
Software D: Valenta Bedford
Snr Mgr: Heather McCormick

AAA MICHIGAN
See AUTO CLUB GROUP

D-U-N-S 06-985-6540
AAA NORTHEAST
AAA TRAVEL AGENCY
110 Royal Little Dr, Providence, RI 02904-1863
Tel (401) 868-2000 *Founded/Ownrshp* 1925
Sales 193.9MM[E] *EMP* 1,400
SIC 8699 6411 4724 Automobile owners' association; Insurance agents; Travel agencies
Pr: Mark Shaw
V Ch: Jack Laurendeau
**COO:* Sherri Ryan
**CFO:* R Stephen Manty
CFO: James McGill
CFO: Mary Nielsen
Treas: Mark Springsteel
**Sr VP:* Lloyd P Albert
VP: Gerry Gutowski
VP: Dean Patterson
VP: Mike Shaughnessy
VP: Eric Stetenfield
**VP:* Jackie Young
Exec: David Himsey

D-U-N-S 03-591-4054
AAA NORTHERN CALIFORNIA NEVADA AND UTAH
1900 Powell St Ste 1200, Emeryville, CA 94608-1814
Tel (510) 596-3669 *Founded/Ownrshp* 2012
Sales NA *EMP* 400
SIC 6331 8699 Automobile insurance; Automobile owners' association
Pr: Paul Gaffney
**CFO:* Siobhan McFeeney

AAA OF MISSOURI
See AUTOMOBILE CLUB OF MISSOURI

D-U-N-S 07-176-0206
AAA TEXAS LLC
(*Suby of* A A A AUTOMOBILE CLUB SO CAL) ★
1225 Freeport Pkwy, Coppell, TX 75019-4413
Tel (469) 221-8285 *Founded/Ownrshp* 2001
Sales NA *EMP* 400
SIC 6411 Insurance agents, brokers & service
Pr: Robert T Bouttier
**CEO:* Raju T Varma
**VP:* John F Boyle
**VP:* Avery R Brown
**VP:* Victor A Ganino

**VP:* David M Mattingly
Off Mgr: Karen Smith

AAA TRAVEL AGENCY
See AAA NORTHEAST

D-U-N-S 05-835-0190
AAA WASHINGTON
3605 132nd Ave Se, Bellevue, WA 98006-1333
Tel (425) 646-2015 *Founded/Ownrshp* 1917
Sales 88.7MM^E *EMP* 622
SIC 8699 Automobile owners' association
Pr: Kirk R Nelson
**Treas:* Robert Flowers
**VP:* Kay Riley
Mng Dir: Jon Erickson
Store Mgr: Lisa Olson
Store Mgr: Erin Rogers
MIS Dir: David Fly
Trfc Dir: Karen Gilbertson
Ql Cn Mgr: Irfan Rizvi
Advt Dir: John Hartsock
Manager: John Thompson

AAAS
See AMERICAN ASSOCIATION FOR ADVANCEMENT OF SCIENCE

AAC
See AMERICAN ACHIEVEMENT CORP

D-U-N-S 79-120-2653
AAC GROUP HOLDING CORP
(*Suby of* AMERICAN ACHIEVEMENT GROUP HOLDING CORP) ★
7211 Circle S Rd, Austin, TX 78745-6603
Tel (512) 444-0571 *Founded/Ownrshp* 2004
Sales 530.1MM^E *EMP* 1,600^E
SIC 3911 Jewelry, precious metal
CFO: Kris G Radhakrishnan
Ex VP: Sherice P Bench
VP: Jerry Ellis
Genl Mgr: Matt Isabell
Info Man: Rebecca Clark
Sfty Mgr: Collin Bond

D-U-N-S 07-957-4353
▲ AAC HOLDINGS INC
200 Powell Pl, Brentwood, TN 37027-7514
Tel (615) 732-1231 *Founded/Ownrshp* 2004
Sales 212.2MM *EMP* 1,600
Tkr Sym AAC *Exch* NYS
SIC 8093 Substance abuse clinics (outpatient)
Ch Bd: Michael T Cartwright
COO: Candance A Henderson-Grice
CFO: Kirk R Manz
VP: Russell Palk
Board of Directors: Jerry D Bostelman, Lucius E Burch III, Darrell S Freeman Sr, David C Kloeppel, Richard E Ragsdale

AACC
See ANNE ARUNDEL COMMUNITY COLLEGE

AACC
See ASSET ACCEPTANCE CAPITAL CORP

D-U-N-S 02-935-8202
AACOA EXTRUSIONS INC
(*Suby of* AACOA INC) ★
2005 Mayflower Rd, Niles, MI 49120-8625
Tel (269) 697-6063 *Founded/Ownrshp* 1998
Sales 123.8MM^E *EMP* 220
SIC 3354 Aluminum extruded products
Pr: Dan Formsma
CFO: Dave Sheaks
Exec: Lesa Moore
**VP Sls:* Jeff Teeple

D-U-N-S 05-895-9404
AACOA INC
(*Suby of* WILLIAM L BONNELL CO INC) ★
2551 County Road 10 W, Elkhart, IN 46514-8786
Tel (574) 262-4685 *Founded/Ownrshp* 2012
Sales 111.4MM^E *EMP* 220
SIC 3471 Anodizing (plating) of metals or formed products; Electroplating & plating
Pr: Daniel Gformsma
Treas: Mark J North
VP: John Jteeple
Plnt Mgr: Dave Sheaks
Plnt Mgr: David Whedon
Ql Cn Mgr: David Compton
Sales Exec: Mike Geiger
Manager: Kelly Custer

AACPS
See ANNE ARUNDEL COUNTY PUBLIC SCHOOLS

AACRES
See EMBASSY MANAGEMENT LLC

D-U-N-S 04-349-0150
AADG INC
CURRIES COMPANY INC.
(*Suby of* ASSA ABLOY USA) ★
1502 12th St Nw, Mason City, IA 50401-1814
Tel (641) 423-1334 *Founded/Ownrshp* 1997
Sales 133.7MM^E *EMP* 1,200
SIC 3442 Metal doors; Sash, door or window: metal
Ch Bd: Clas Thelin
**Pr:* Jerry N Currie
**Treas:* David W Underwood
**Ex VP:* Robert A Hubbard
VP: Krister Eriksson
Board of Directors: Jerry Currie

AAF INTERNATIONAL
See AMERICAN AIR FILTER CO INC

D-U-N-S 88-336-6668 IMP/EXP
AAF-MCQUAY GROUP INC
AMERICAN AIR FILTER
(*Suby of* DAIKIN INDUSTRIES, LTD.)
9920 Corporate Campus Dr # 2200, Louisville, KY 40223-6170
Tel (502) 637-0111 *Founded/Ownrshp* 1994
Sales 1.5MMM^E *EMP* 4,500^E
SIC 5075 3585 3564 7623 Warm air heating & air conditioning; Refrigeration & heating equipment; Blowers & fans; Refrigeration service & repair
CEO: Kevin Lynch
**Pr:* Ho Nyuk Choy
**Treas:* Ronald J Pederson
VP: Steve Richardson
Manager: Rami Muqattash
Manager: Prasad Natraj

AAFES
See ARMY & AIR FORCE EXCHANGE SERVICE

AAFMAA
See AMERICAN ARMED FORCES MUTUAL AID ASSOCIATION

AAFP
See AMERICAN ACADEMY OF FAMILY PHYSICIANS

D-U-N-S 79-374-9839
■ AAH HUDSON LP
HUDSON GARDENS
(*Suby of* AIMCO) ★
1255 N Hudson Ave, Pasadena, CA 91104-2868
Tel (626) 794-9179 *Founded/Ownrshp* 1983
Sales 200.0M *EMP* 3,400
SIC 6513 Apartment building operators
Comm Man: Victoria Miranda
**Ex VP:* Ellen Guccione

D-U-N-S 02-951-3562
AAH MEDICAL LLC
2051 W 25th St, Yuma, AZ 85364-6912
Tel (928) 344-1411 *Founded/Ownrshp* 2010
Sales 358.6MM *EMP* 3
SIC 8099 Health & allied services
Prin: Abdulkadir Hourani

D-U-N-S 00-309-0198 IMP/EXP
■ AAI CORP (MD)
TEXTRON SYSTEMS
(*Suby of* TEXTRON INC) ★
124 Industry Ln, Hunt Valley, MD 21030-3347
Tel (410) 666-1400 *Founded/Ownrshp* 1950, 2007
Sales 599.5MM^E *EMP* 1,625
SIC 3728 3769 7699 8711 Aircraft training equipment; Guided missile & space vehicle parts & auxiliary equipment; Fire control (military) equipment repair; Aviation &/or aeronautical engineering
CEO: Ellen M Lord
**CFO:* Kim Herrington
Ex VP: Michael A Boden
Ex VP: Raleigh Huntsman
Sr VP: Jim Dolan
Sr VP: John C Hayward
Sr VP: Bill Irby
Sr VP: Michael Kraft
Sr VP: Steve Mensh
Sr VP: Steve Overly
Sr VP: Thomas J Walmsley
Sr VP: Ian Walsh
VP: Jackson R Bell
VP: Steven M Lewis
**VP:* Bhaskar Ramachandran
VP: Donnie Rogers
VP: Joseph Thomas
VP Bus Dev: Jonathan Dalrymple
VP Bus Dev: Stephen Greene
Dir Bus: Leslie Orlidge
Board of Directors: Kim Herrington, Danny Lee, Ellen Lord

AAMC
See ASSOCIATION OF AMERICAN MEDICAL COLLEGES

AAMCO TRANSMISSIONS
See AMERICAN AXLE & MANUFACTURING INC

D-U-N-S 78-489-7514
■ AAON COIL PRODUCTS INC
(*Suby of* AAON INC) ★
203 Gum Springs Rd, Longview, TX 75602-1721
Tel (903) 236-4403 *Founded/Ownrshp* 1991
Sales 151.9MM^E *EMP* 965
SIC 3585 Refrigeration & heating equipment
Pr: Norman H Asbjornson
**Treas:* Kathy I Sheffield
**VP:* Scott Asbjornson
**VP:* Robert G Fergus
IT Man: David Campbell
IT Man: Sam Hymood

D-U-N-S 19-411-8642 IMP/EXP
▲ AAON INC
2425 S Yukon Ave, Tulsa, OK 74107-2728
Tel (918) 583-2266 *Founded/Ownrshp* 1987
Sales 358.6MM *EMP* 1,676^E
Tkr Sym AAON *Exch* NGS
SIC 3585 Refrigeration & heating equipment; Air conditioning units, complete: domestic or industrial; Heating equipment, complete; Air conditioning condensers & condensing units
Pr: Norman H Asbjornson
Pr: Gary D Fields
COO: Arthur Candler
CFO: Scott M Asbjornson
Treas: Kathy I Sheffield
VP: Sam J Neale
Exec: Thomas Bird
Snr Sftwr: Brett Riegel
VP Mfg: Robert G Fergus
Mtls Mgr: Cory Simmons
Plnt Mgr: Ed Johnson
Board of Directors: Angela E Kouplen, Paul K Lackey Jr, Jerry R Levine, Ah McElroy II, Jack E Short

AAP
See AMERICAN ASSOCIATED PHARMACIES INC

D-U-N-S 18-538-5374 IMP
AAP ST MARYS CORP
(*Suby of* HITACHI METALS AMERICA LTD) ★
1100 Mckinley Rd, Saint Marys, OH 45885-1815
Tel (419) 394-7840 *Founded/Ownrshp* 2016
Sales 158.5MM^E *EMP* 524
SIC 3714 Wheels, motor vehicle
Pr: Mark Masuda
**Pr:* Randy Wendel
**CEO:* Bruce Sakamoto
**Treas:* Douglas Kramer

D-U-N-S 00-542-5814
▲ AAR CORP
1100 N Wood Dale Rd, Wood Dale, IL 60191-1094
Tel (630) 227-2000 *Founded/Ownrshp* 1951
Sales 1.6MMM *EMP* 4,700
Accts Kpmg Llp Chicago Illinois
Tkr Sym AIR *Exch* NYS
SIC 3724 4581 3537 5599 7359 Aircraft engines & engine parts; Aircraft maintenance & repair services; Aircraft servicing & repairing; Containers (metal), air cargo; Aircraft, self-propelled; Aircraft rental
Ch Bd: David P Storch
**V Ch:* Timothy J Romenesko
VP: Chris Cook
VP: Peter Loeb
VP: Eric S Pachapa
VP: Robert J Regan
VP: Johnny Williams
VP Bus Dev: Robert Laird
Dir IT: Craig Shaffer
Mktg Dir: Jack Brewer
Sls Mgr: Alex Lara
Board of Directors: Ronald B Woodard, Anthony K Anderson, Norman R Bobins, Michael R Boyce, Ronald R Fogleman, James E Goodwin, Patrick J Kelly, Peter Pace, Jennifer L Vogel, Marc J Walfish

AAR DEFENSE SYSTEMS LOGISTICS
See AAR SUPPLY CHAIN INC

D-U-N-S 05-990-1053
■ AAR INTERNATIONAL INC
(*Suby of* AAR CORP) ★
1100 N Wood Dale Rd, Wood Dale, IL 60191-1060
Tel (630) 227-2000 *Founded/Ownrshp* 1999
Sales 135.2MM^E *EMP* 500^E
SIC 5088 Aircraft engines & engine parts
Pr: Timothy Romenesko
**Pr:* David P Storch
VP: Peter K Chapman
VP: Randy J Martinez
VP: David E Prusiecki
VP: Michael J Sharp
VP: Timothy O Skelly

D-U-N-S 01-462-4832 IMP
■ AAR MANUFACTURING INC
AAR MOBILITY SYSTEMS
(*Suby of* AAR CORP) ★
1100 N Wood Dale Rd, Wood Dale, IL 60191-1060
Tel (630) 227-2000 *Founded/Ownrshp* 1982
Sales 86.9MM^E *EMP* 650
SIC 7629 Electronic equipment repair
CEO: David P Storch
Ex VP: Robert Sopp
VP: Randy Martinez
VP: Dean Terry
VP Opers: Ken Hein
Opers Mgr: John Rio
Opers Mgr: Chris Wilko
Secur Mgr: Jessica Hall

AAR MOBILITY SYSTEMS
See AAR MANUFACTURING INC

D-U-N-S 10-401-2638 IMP
■ AAR SUPPLY CHAIN INC
AAR DEFENSE SYSTEMS LOGISTICS
(*Suby of* AAR CORP) ★
1100 N Wood Dale Rd, Wood Dale, IL 60191-1060
Tel (630) 227-2000 *Founded/Ownrshp* 1982
Sales 159.9MM^E *EMP* 200
SIC 5088 3728 Aircraft & parts; Aircraft parts & equipment
Pr: David Storch
**Pr:* Timothy J Romenesko
VP: Scot Cerka
VP: Peter Chapman
**VP:* John Holmes
Genl Mgr: Christopher Gross
Dir IT: Michael Cannon
Dir IT: Jim Gross
Dir IT: Craig Shaffer
IT Man: Richard Andersen
VP Opers: Bryan Rudd

D-U-N-S 60-197-2656 IMP/EXP
AARHUSKARLSHAMN USA INC
A A K
(*Suby of* AARHUS 3 A/S)
499 Thornall St Ste 5, Edison, NJ 08837-2267
Tel (973) 344-1300 *Founded/Ownrshp* 1988
Sales 90.8MM^E *EMP* 255
SIC 2079 Edible oil products, except corn oil
Pr: Mark Becker
CFO: Peter Korsholm
Ofcr: Karsten Nielsen
**VP:* Peter B Maulbeck
VP: Peter B Mauleck
**VP:* Dennis Tagarelli
**VP:* Thomas Winter
Exec: Ben Dechavez
Mng Dir: Edmond Borit
Off Mgr: Terie Simon
Tech Mgr: Sara Lampard

AARON & COMPANY PLUMBING SUPS
See AARON AND CO INC

D-U-N-S 01-154-1174
AARON AND CO INC
AARON & COMPANY PLUMBING SUPS
30 Turner Pl, Piscataway, NJ 08854-3839
Tel (732) 752-8200 *Founded/Ownrshp* 1977
Sales 83.3MM *EMP* 188^E
Accts Drucker Math & Whitman Pc
SIC 5074 5075 Plumbing & hydronic heating supplies; Heating equipment (hydronic); Warm air heating & air conditioning
Pr: Barry Portnoy
CFO: Tony Conte
**CFO:* Victor De Rosa
**VP:* Frank Laudino Jr
**VP:* Richard Laudino
Dir Bus: Kevin Manning
Brnch Mgr: Tony Mixell
Div Mgr: John Provenzano
Sales Asso: John Schlinger

AARON BROTHERS ARTS & FRAMING
See AARON BROTHERS INC

D-U-N-S 01-124-2773 IMP/EXP
■ AARON BROTHERS INC
AARON BROTHERS ARTS & FRAMING
(*Suby of* MICHAELS STORES INC) ★
8001 Ridgepoint Dr, Irving, TX 75063-3117
Tel (214) 492-6200 *Founded/Ownrshp* 1995
Sales 138.9MM^E *EMP* 1,700
SIC 7699 5945 Picture framing, custom; Arts & crafts supplies
Pr: Jim King
**CFO:* Todd Lindsey
**Treas:* Tom Molito
VP: Sue Barnhill
Brnch Mgr: Philip Mottier
Dist Mgr: Cindy McGarry
Genl Mgr: Chad Nichols
CTO: Christine Robinson
Mktg Dir: David Esmond

AARON GROUP OF COMPANIES, THE
See E AARON ENTERPRISES INC

D-U-N-S 03-350-1545
▲ AARONS INC
400 Galleria Pkwy Se # 300, Atlanta, GA 30339-5980
Tel (404) 231-0011 *Founded/Ownrshp* 1955
Sales 3.1MMM *EMP* 12,700
Tkr Sym AAN *Exch* NYS
SIC 7359 5712 5731 5722 5932 6794 Home appliance, furniture & entertainment rental services; Furniture rental; Television rental; Video cassette recorder & accessory rental; Furniture stores; Office furniture; Bedding & bedsprings; Radio, television & electronic stores; Television sets; Video recorders, players, disc players & accessories; Household appliance stores; Furniture, secondhand; Office furniture, secondhand; Household appliances, used; Franchises, selling or licensing
CEO: John W Robinson III
**Ch Bd:* Ray M Robinson
Pr: Steven A Michaels
Ofcr: Robert W Kamerschen
Ex VP: Gilbert L Danielson
Sr VP: James L Cates
Sr VP: Michael P Ryan
Sr VP: D Chad Strickland
Sr VP: John T Trainor
VP: David Bier
VP: Jeannie M Cave
VP: Joseph N Fedorchak
VP: Justin Hafer
VP: Henri G Rogers
VP: Joseph Saez Jr

D-U-N-S 06-677-8077
AARP
601 E St Nw, Washington, DC 20049-0003
Tel (202) 434-2277 *Founded/Ownrshp* 1958
Sales 1.4MMM *EMP* 1,800
Accts Grant Thornton Llp Washington
SIC 5192 8399 Magazines; Health systems agency
CEO: Jo Ann Jenkins
Pr: Neal E Lane
**COO:* Scott Frisch
**COO:* Tom Nelson
CFO: Robert R H Jr
CFO: Robert R Hagans
CFO: Linda McCutcheon
Bd of Dir: Fernando T Gils
Ex VP: Hollis Bradwell III
Ex VP: Nancy A L
**Ex VP:* Emilio Pardo
Ex VP: Debra Whitman
Sr VP: Myrna Blyth
Sr VP: Ronald Noe
Sr VP: Susan Reinhard
VP: Rawle Andrews Jr
VP: Ramesh Bulusu
VP: Robin Engel
VP: Najeeb Uddin
Dir Surg: Reija Risseeuw
Comm Dir: Lisa R Davis

D-U-N-S 95-788-5916
AARP FOUNDATION
601 E St Nw, Washington, DC 20049-0003
Tel (202) 434-2020 *Founded/Ownrshp* 1958
Sales 146.6MM *EMP* 232
SIC 8331 8399 Job training & vocational rehabilitation services; Health systems agency
Pr: Tom Malloy
Pr: Tracey Merchant
**Pr:* Lisa Marsh Ryerson
Pr: Eileen Scott
Treas: Jim Reavley
Sr Cor Off: Lisa Jern
Sr Cor Off: Robert Tunstall
Ex VP: Keith Campbell
Ex VP: Linda McNally
Ex VP: John Sivori
Sr VP: Frank Lopiccolo
VP: Gustovo Ayala
VP: Leon Clark
Exec: William Rumsey
Exec: George Santoro
Exec: Dawn Sweeney
Assoc Dir: Carol Page
Comm Man: Luci De Haan
Board of Directors: David Adame, Ronald E Daly Sr, Ann G Daw, Tim Kelly, Neal Lane, Diane D Miller

D-U-N-S 79-041-4460
AAS HOLDING CO
2401 Ne Argyle St, Portland, OR 97211-1938
Tel (503) 284-3314 *Founded/Ownrshp* 1991
Sales 155.0MM *EMP* 132
SIC 5147 5142 5141 Meats, fresh; Meat, frozen: packaged; Food brokers
Pr: Curtis Pohl
**Ch Bd:* David Allen Sr
**Pr:* David H Allen Jr

D-U-N-S 83-649-8902
AASKI TECHNOLOGY INC
1 Radar Way, Tinton Falls, NJ 07724-1290
Tel (732) 493-1700 *Founded/Ownrshp* 1997
Sales 84.2MM^E *EMP* 462

SIC 8711 Consulting engineer
Pr: Rina Parikh
*Pr: Bharat Parikh
*Sr VP: Gerard Rippon
*VP: Maria Jennings
Prgrm Mgr: Jean-Pierre Lutz
Dir IT: John Divuolo
Opers Mgr: Carly Garrett
Pgrm Dir: Tom Miller

AATECH
See ADVANCED ATOMIZATION TECHNOLOGIES LLC

D-U-N-S 96-154-6277
AAVID CORP
1 Aavid Cir, Laconia, NH 03246
Tel (603) 528-3400 Founded/Ownrshp 1964
Sales 479.6MM^E EMP 3,000
SIC 3679 Electronic circuits
Pr: Alan W Wong
*Pr: Christopher G Boehm
*Treas: Bryan A Byrne
*VP: John W Mitchell

D-U-N-S 00-257-6817 IMP/EXP
AAVID THERMALLOY LLC
(Suby of AAVID CORP) ★
1 Aavid Cir, Laconia, NH 03246
Tel (603) 528-3400 Founded/Ownrshp 2000
Sales 479.6MM^E EMP 3,000
SIC 3679 Electronic circuits
Pr: Alan W Wong
CFO: Paul Landers
*CFO: David Wall
*VP: Dean Gilliam
VP: Gilles Gusmini
VP: David Huang
VP: Norm Soucy
VP: Marc Tessier
VP: Yenho K Tree
CIO: Chip Kimball
*CTO: Sukhvinder Kang

AB
See ALLIANCEBERNSTEIN CORP

AB
See ALEXANDER & BALDWIN INC

AB
See AMERICAN BRIDGE HOLDING CO

D-U-N-S 07-880-1608
AB ACQUISITION LLC
(Suby of ALBERTSONS COMPANIES INC) ★
250 E Parkcenter Blvd, Boise, ID 83706-3940
Tel (208) 395-6200 Founded/Ownrshp 2005
Sales 58.7MMM EMP 138,000^E
Accts Deloitte & Touche Llp Boise
SIC 5411 Supermarkets, chain
CEO: Robert G Miller
*Pr: Daniel Salemi
*CFO: Richard J Navarro
Sr VP: Mark Panzer
*Sr VP: Paul G Rowan
*VP: Lisa Gray
*Prin: Justin C Dye

D-U-N-S 11-502-4598
■ **AB CELLULAR HOLDING LLC**
AT & T WIRELESS SERVICE
(Suby of AT&T MOBILITY LLC) ★
1452 Edinger Ave, Tustin, CA 92780-6246
Tel (562) 468-6846 Founded/Ownrshp 1984
Sales 263.9MM^E EMP 2,100
SIC 4813 Local & long distance telephone communications; Local telephone communications; Long distance telephone communications
Mktg Dir: Andy Lee

AB ELECTROLUX
See ELECTROLUX HOME CARE PRODUCTS INC

D-U-N-S 61-716-5738 EXP
AB FOODS LLC
(Suby of AGRI BEEF CO) ★
201 Elmwood Rd, Toppenish, WA 98948-9779
Tel (509) 865-2121 Founded/Ownrshp 2006
Sales 317.1MM^E EMP 670
SIC 5147 Meats & meat products

AB LEACH EYE HOSPITAL
See UNIVERSITY OF MIAMI MILLER SCHOOL OF MEDICINE

D-U-N-S 16-085-7553 IMP
AB MAURI FOOD INC
AB MAURI NORTH AMERICA
(Suby of AB MAURI (UK) LIMITED)
4240 Duncan Ave Ste 150, Saint Louis, MO 63110-1123
Tel (314) 392-0800 Founded/Ownrshp 2004
Sales 110.7MM^E EMP 300
SIC 2052 Bakery products, dry
CFO: Daniel Kucera
VP: Bill McKeown
VP: William McKeown
VP: Jeff Rootring
Genl Mgr: Haresh Kachalia

AB MAURI NORTH AMERICA
See AB MAURI FOOD INC

D-U-N-S 00-172-4145
AB STABLE LLC
WALDORF ASTORIA NEW YORK
(Suby of ANBANG INSURANCE GROUP CO., LTD.)
301 Park Ave, New York, NY 10022-6844
Tel (212) 355-3000 Founded/Ownrshp 1953, 2015
Sales 159.9MM^E EMP 14,000
SIC 7011 Hotels
Mng Dir: Michael Hoffman
MIS Dir: Jose Medina

AB TEXTILES
See APPAREL BRANDS INC

D-U-N-S 06-228-4666
■ **AB-TEX BEVERAGE LTD**
(Suby of PEPSICO) ★
650 Colonial Dr, Abilene, TX 79603-3199
Tel (325) 673-7171 Founded/Ownrshp 2010
Sales 86.5MM^E EMP 450
SIC 2086 Soft drinks: packaged in cans, bottles, etc.; Water, pasteurized: packaged in cans, bottles, etc.
CEO: Cleber Massey
Pr: Kirk Massey
VP: David Lawrence
Genl Mgr: Russell Smith
Opers Mgr: Randall Mostert

D-U-N-S 14-458-5619
ABACO SYSTEMS INC
12090 S Memorial Pkwy, Huntsville, AL 35803-3308
Tel (256) 382-8200 Founded/Ownrshp 2015
Sales 284.3MM^E EMP 814
SIC 3571 3672 3577 Electronic computers; Printed circuit boards; Computer peripheral equipment
CEO: Bernie Anger
CFO: George Hearn
VP: Kevin Campbell
VP: Christopher Lever

D-U-N-S 02-239-3755
ABACUS CORP
610 Gusryan St, Baltimore, MD 21224-2933
Tel (410) 633-1900 Founded/Ownrshp 1963
Sales 199.0MM^E EMP 5,000
SIC 7381 7363 7349 Protective services, guard; Employee leasing service; Janitorial service, contract basis
Ch Bd: Richard McGee Sr
*Pr: Richard McGee Jr
*COO: Michael Brady
COO: Cecilia Dubon
*CFO: David M Hausner
*Ex VP: Devin McGee
VP: Joan Beller
VP: Bill Lund
Brnch Mgr: Dede Carlisle
IT Man: Bill Francis
VP Sls: Michele Massaro

D-U-N-S 12-650-5833
ABACUS TECHNOLOGY CORP
5404 Wscnsin Ave Ste 1100, Chevy Chase, MD 20815
Tel (301) 907-8500 Founded/Ownrshp 1984
Sales 108.6MM^E EMP 435
SIC 8742 Management consulting services
Pr: Dennis Yee
*CFO: Sharon Church
*Sr VP: William R Magro
VP: William Magro
VP: Pamela Moraga
*VP: Archie Riviera
*VP: Alice C Solomon
VP: Alice Solomon
*VP: Patty Stratton
*VP: Raymond E Zdancewicz
VP Bus Dev: Shawn A Bethea
Board of Directors: Dorothy M Kong

D-U-N-S 00-193-6590
ABARTA INC
200 Alpha Dr, Pittsburgh, PA 15238-2906
Tel (412) 963-6226 Founded/Ownrshp 1972
Sales 298.7MM^E EMP 1,510
SIC 2086 2711 2721 5149 1382 5812

D-U-N-S 10-259-5931 IMP/EXP
ABATIX CORP
2400 Skyline Dr Ste 400, Mesquite, TX 75149-1990
Tel (214) 381-1146 Founded/Ownrshp 1988
Sales 99.0MM EMP 130
SIC 5084 5085 Safety equipment; Tools
CEO: Terry W Shaver
CFO: Frank J Cinatl IV
VP: Brian Lyons
Rgnl Mgr: Samantha Hauser
Rgnl Mgr: Matt White
Brnch Mgr: Todd Beaman
Genl Mgr: Paul Machart
Dir IT: Brian Adamson
Opers Mgr: Rich Godoy
Mktg Mgr: Rich Booth
Mktg Mgr: Brian Mednelsohn

D-U-N-S 55-550-3770 IMP/EXP
▲ **ABAXIS INC**
3240 Whipple Rd, Union City, CA 94587-1217
Tel (510) 675-6500 Founded/Ownrshp 1989
Sales 218.9MM EMP 549
Accts Burr Pilger Mayer Inc San Jo
Tkr Sym ABAX Exch NGS
SIC 3829 2835 Medical diagnostic systems, nuclear; In vitro & in vivo diagnostic substances; Veterinary diagnostic substances
Ch Bd: Clinton H Severson
Pr: Donald P Wood
CFO: Alberto S Ines
CFO: Ross Taylor
VP: Christopher C Bernard
VP: Coleen Bradley
VP: John Leonard
VP: Vladimir E Ostoich
VP: Craig M Tockman
Exec: Ray Duenas
Exec: Michael Solomon
Board of Directors: Vernon E Altman, Richard J Bastiani, Michael D Casey, Henk J Evenhuis

D-U-N-S 00-833-4117
ABB ENTERPRISE SOFTWARE INC
(Suby of ABB INC) ★
400 Perimeter Ctr Ter 5, Atlanta, GA 30346-1227
Tel (678) 830-1000 Founded/Ownrshp 2010
Sales 142.4MM^E EMP 835
SIC 7372 Business oriented computer software
CEO: Jeff Ray
*CFO: Jim Fitzgibbons
CFO: Thomas W Williams
VP: Linda Brown
VP: Rick Nicholson
VP: Tom Shields
VP: John Smith
VP: Andrew Soignier

VP: Sherri Taylor
VP: Kenneth J Zagzebski
Dir Surg: Bobby Slaton

D-U-N-S 13-978-1561 IMP
ABB FLEXIBLE AUTOMATION INC
(Suby of ABB INC) ★
1250 Brown Rd, Auburn Hills, MI 48326-1507
Tel (248) 391-9000 Founded/Ownrshp 2005
Sales 137.1MM^E EMP 550
SIC 5084 Industrial machinery & equipment
Ex VP: Robert Yehl
*VP: Joe Carney
Sls Mgr: Doug Niebruegge

D-U-N-S 00-822-0134 IMP
ABB HOLDINGS INC
(Suby of ABB ASEA BROWN BOVERI LTD)
12040 Regency Pkwy # 200, Cary, NC 27518-7707
Tel (919) 856-2360 Founded/Ownrshp 1998
Sales 32.9MMM^E EMP 18,000
SIC 3612 Transformers, except electric
Pr: Enrique Santacana
CFO: Ismo Haka
Treas: Daniel Hagmann
Sr VP: Michael Gray
Sr VP: David Onuscheck
VP: John Brett
Rgnl Mgr: Michael Nettemeyer
IT Man: Paul Loyson
Board of Directors: Daniel Hagmann, Enrique Santacana

D-U-N-S 80-822-9041 IMP/EXP
ABB INC
(Suby of ABB HOLDINGS INC) ★
12040 Regency Pkwy # 200, Cary, NC 27518-7707
Tel (919) 856-2360 Founded/Ownrshp 1999
Sales 32.4MMM^E EMP 18,000
SIC 8711 3612 3511 5063 3613 3625 Engineering services; Chemical engineering; Petroleum engineering; Transformers, except electric; Steam turbine generator set units, complete; Gas turbines, mechanical drive; Electrical apparatus & equipment; Power transmission equipment, electric; Switchgear; Switchgear & switchboard apparatus; Relays & industrial controls
CEO: Ulrich Spiesshofer
Pr: Samir Abou-Jaoude
Pr: Greg Scheu
CFO: Jan Allde
CFO: Hans-Anders Nilsson
Treas: Barry Wentworth
Chf Mktg O: Sven Klaka
Ofcr: Wes Patterson
Ofcr: Jerry Stroud
Sr VP: Roger Bailey
Sr VP: Martinus Brandal
Sr VP: John Brett
Sr VP: Jack Dwyer
Sr VP: Bo Elisson
Sr VP: Julietta Guarino
Sr VP: Jeff Halsey
Sr VP: Paul Kefalas
Sr VP: Herbert Parker
Sr VP: Garold Schepers
Sr VP: John Sullivan
Sr VP: Gordon Woolbert

ABB OPTICAL GROUP
See ABB/CON-CISE OPTICAL GROUP LLC

D-U-N-S 60-977-4435 EXP
ABB POWER T & D CO INC
(Suby of ABB INC) ★
940 Main Campus Dr # 400, Raleigh, NC 27606-5211
Tel (919) 856-3806 Founded/Ownrshp 2005
Sales 228.8MM^E EMP 1,300
SIC 3612 Distribution transformers, electric
Pr: Enrique Santacana
Treas: Barry Wentworth

D-U-N-S 82-771-8581
ABB/CON-CISE OPTICAL GROUP LLC
ABB OPTICAL GROUP
(Suby of ALVACO TRADING CO) ★
12301 Nw 39th St, Coral Springs, FL 33065-2403
Tel (800) 852-8089 Founded/Ownrshp 2007
Sales 1.1MMM^E EMP 951
SIC 5048 3851 8741 Ophthalmic goods; Ophthalmic goods; Management services
CEO: Angel Alvarez
*Pr: Brad Weinbrum
*CFO: Paul Sherman
Treas: Jim Teufel
VP: Rob Alessandrine
VP: Jeannette Delgado
VP: Ignacio Portuondo
VP: Aaron See
VP: Bart Tessel
Area Mgr: Lindsey Burchak
CTO: Emily Ashworth

D-U-N-S 95-625-1560
ABBEY LAFAYETTE
2 Avenue De Lafayette, Boston, MA 02111-1750
Tel (617) 542-7373 Founded/Ownrshp 2008
Sales 696.4MM EMP 2
SIC 6553 Real property subdividers & developers, cemetery lots only
Prin: Abbey Lafayette

ABBOTT ASSOCIATES
See GYPSUM SUPPLY CO

D-U-N-S 96-639-0890 IMP
■ **ABBOTT DIABETES CARE INC**
MEDISENSE
(Suby of CURATE SNACKS) ★
1360 S Loop Rd, Alameda, CA 94502-7000
Tel (510) 749-5400 Founded/Ownrshp 2004
Sales 132.6MM^E EMP 600
Accts Pricewaterhousecoopers Llp Sa
SIC 2835 3845 3823 In vitro diagnostics; Electromedical equipment; Industrial instrmnts msrmnt display/control process variable
VP: Lawrence W Huffman
VP: Tae Andrews
VP: Arthur Autorino

VP: Frank Dzvonik
VP: Robert Hance
VP: Jeff F Richardson
VP: Mark C Tatro
Assoc Dir: Rachel WEI
Prin: Robert D Brownell
Prin: Adam Heller
Prin: Charles T Liamos
Board of Directors: Brad A Bowlus, Rod F Dammeyer, Ross A Jaffe, Jonathan T Lord, Robert R Momsen, Richard P Thompson

D-U-N-S 00-130-7602 IMP/EXP
▲ **ABBOTT LABORATORIES** (IL)
CURATE SNACKS
100 Abbott Park Rd, Abbott Park, IL 60064-3500
Tel (224) 667-6100 Founded/Ownrshp 1900
Sales 20.4MMM EMP 74,000
Tkr Sym ABT Exch NYS
SIC 2834 2835 3841 3826 Pharmaceutical preparations; Druggists' preparations (pharmaceuticals); Vitamin, nutrient & hematinic preparations for human use; Vitamin preparations; In vitro & in vivo diagnostic substances; Blood derivative diagnostic agents; Hemotology diagnostic agents; Microbiology & virology diagnostic products; Diagnostic apparatus, medical; Medical instruments & equipment, blood & bone work; IV transfusion apparatus; Blood testing apparatus
Ch Bd: Miles D White
Pr: Deborah Billig
Pr: Rich Schaefer
CFO: Brian B Yoor
Treas: Quintin Noble
Bd of Dir: Kaycee Buckley
Sr Ex VP: Gwen Geraci
Ex VP: Hubert L Allen
Ex VP: Brian J Blaser
Ex VP: Thomas C Freyman
Ex VP: Stephen R Fussell
Ex VP: Heather L Mason
Sr VP: Roger M Bird
Sr VP: Thomas G Frinzi
Sr VP: Deepak Nath
Sr VP: Daniel Salvadori
Sr VP: Jared L Watkin
VP: Andy Brookes
VP: Jaime Contreras
VP: Martin Eaves
VP: Brian Ford
Board of Directors: Glenn F Tilton, Robert J Alpern, Roxanne S Austin, Sally E Blount, W James Farrell, Edward M Liddy, Nancy McKinstry, Phebe N Novakovic, William A Osborn, Samuel C Scott III

D-U-N-S 96-747-4896 IMP/EXP
■ **ABBOTT LABORATORIES INC**
(Suby of CURATE SNACKS) ★
200 Abbott Park Rd, Abbott Park, IL 60064-3537
Tel (224) 668-2076 Founded/Ownrshp 1997
Sales 228.8MM^E EMP 709^E
SIC 2834 3841 Pharmaceutical preparations; Diagnostic apparatus, medical
CEO: Miles D White
VP: Steven Lewis
Exec: Wanda Henson
Assoc Dir: Mary Gross
Prgrm Mgr: Linda Boynton
Prgrm Mgr: Jeff Jacek
Prgrm Mgr: Joan Landry
IT Man: Michael Craig
Mktg Dir: Christopher Jowett
Mktg Dir: Matt Mittino
Sls Mgr: Joseph Calabrese

D-U-N-S 10-302-1940 IMP
■ **ABBOTT MEDICAL OPTICS INC**
A M O
(Suby of CURATE SNACKS) ★
1700 E Saint Andrew Pl, Santa Ana, CA 92705-4933
Tel (714) 247-8200 Founded/Ownrshp 2009
Sales 1.2MMM^E EMP 4,100
SIC 3841 3845 Ophthalmic instruments & apparatus; Laser systems & equipment, medical
Sr VP: Thomas Frinzi
COO: M Grader
CFO: Timothy Maier
*Treas: Vincent Scullin
VP: Kevin Harley
VP: Catherine Mazzacco
VP: Cameron Rouns
VP: Sandra Selvaggi
VP: Mark Steen
Natl Sales: Mike Bolhuis
Mktg Dir: John Weberg
Board of Directors: Christopher G Chavez, Elizabeth H Davila, Daniel J Heinrich, William J Link Phd, G Mason Morfit, Michael A Mussallem, Deborah J Neff, Robert J Palmisano, James O Rollans

D-U-N-S 04-384-9918
ABBOTT NORTHWESTERN HOSPITAL
ALLINA HOSPITALS & CLINICS
(Suby of ALLINA HOSPITALS & CLINICS) ★
800 E 28th St, Minneapolis, MN 55407-3799
Tel (612) 863-4000 Founded/Ownrshp 1993
Sales 1.0MMM EMP 5,167^E
SIC 8062 General medical & surgical hospitals
CEO: Gordon M Sprenger
*Pr: Jeffrey D Peterson
*Pr: Robert K Spinner
CFO: Duncan P Gallagher
*Treas: Michael J Siegmund
Ofcr: Nancy Ebert
VP: Ben Bache-Wiig
Dir Rad: Mary J Hestne
Dir Rad: Frederick R Olson
Dir Rad: Lisa Schneider
Dir Rad: Beverly A Trombley
Dir Rad: Douglas H Yock

D-U-N-S 11-627-9183
■ **ABBOTT POINT OF CARE INC**
(Suby of CURATE SNACKS) ★
400 College Rd E, Princeton, NJ 08540-6607
Tel (609) 454-9000 Founded/Ownrshp 1983
Sales 122.7MM^E EMP 1,200
SIC 3841 Diagnostic apparatus, medical
Pr: William P Moffitt

*Pr: Sharon Bracken
Rgnl Mgr: Robert Fowler
IT Man: Chad Montgomery
Mtls Mgr: Patrick Livesey
Opers Mgr: David Jamieson
Prd Mgr: Ed Cherubini
Mktg Dir: Glen Tinevez
Manager: James Meadows

D-U-N-S 09-597-9332 IMP
■ ABBOTT VASCULAR INC
(Suby of CURATE SNACKS) ★
3200 Lakeside Dr, Santa Clara, CA 95054-2807
Tel (650) 474-3000 Founded/Ownrshp 1995
Sales 645.5MM[E] EMP 4,200[E]
SIC 3845 Ultrasonic scanning devices, medical
Pr: John M Capek
Pr: Ken Carlisle
*CEO: Charles D Foltz
*CFO: Mark Murray
VP: John Hernandez
Exec: Gary Abram
Exec: Edward Clark
Exec: Roxanne Destefano
Exec: Michael Meadors
Exec: Steve Sorenson
Prgrm Mgr: Michael WEI

D-U-N-S 79-974-5617 IMP/EXP
ABBOUD TRADING CORP
A.T.C
10910 Nw 92nd Ter, Medley, FL 33178-2515
Tel (786) 235-7007 Founded/Ownrshp 1996
Sales 411.6MM EMP 33
Accts Shomar & Company Llp Miami L
SIC 5065 Electronic parts & equipment
Pr: Roger Abboud
*VP: Ghassan Abboud
Board of Directors: Imad Abboud

D-U-N-S 07-852-1681
■ ABBVIE BIOTECHNOLOGY LTD
(Suby of ABBVIE INC) ★
Road No 2 Km 59 2, Barceloneta, PR 00617
Tel (787) 846-3500 Founded/Ownrshp 2013
Sales 228.8MM[E] EMP 2,500
SIC 2834 2844 2835 3841 3826 Pharmaceutical preparations; Toilet preparations; In vitro & in vivo diagnostic substances; Diagnostic apparatus, medical; Blood testing apparatus
Pr: Neil Edward
Genl Mgr: Jose Y Rodriguez

D-U-N-S 07-845-8370 IMP/EXP
▲ ABBVIE INC
1 N Waukegan Rd, North Chicago, IL 60064-1802
Tel (847) 932-7900 Founded/Ownrshp 2012
Sales 22.8MMM EMP 28,000[E]
Tkr Sym ABBV Exch NYS
SIC 2834 2836 Pharmaceutical preparations; Druggists' preparations (pharmaceuticals); Biological products, except diagnostic
Ch Bd: Richard A Gonzalez
CFO: William J Chase
Treas: Esperanza Arana
Treas: Brian Turner
Ex VP: Carlos Alban
Ex VP: Henry O Gosebruch
Ex VP: Laura J Schumacher
Ex VP: Michael E Severino
Sr VP: Timothy J Richmond
VP: Pearson Bownas
VP: Scott Brun
VP: Alberto Colzi
VP: Nadia Dac
VP: Mike Douma
VP: Steven Elmore
VP: Jeffrey Haas
VP: Tracie Haas
VP: Thomas A Hurwich
VP: Joe Karich
VP: David Kinrade
VP: Angela Lane
Board of Directors: Robert J Alpern, Roxanne S Austin, William H L Burnside, Edward M Liddy, Glenn F Tilton, Frederick H Waddell

D-U-N-S 04-200-9316 IMP
ABBYLAND FOODS INC (WI)
502 E Linden St, Abbotsford, WI 54405-9699
Tel (715) 223-6386 Founded/Ownrshp 1962, 1977
Sales 164.0MM[E] EMP 500
Accts Wipfli Llp Wausau Wisconsin
SIC 2013 2011 Boneless meat, from purchased meat; Beef products from beef slaughtered on site
Pr: Harland Schraufnagel
*VP: Kathleen Schraufnagel
Plnt Mgr: Steve Albers
Plnt Mgr: Paul Kern
Sls Mgr: Jane Langman

ABC
See READING TRUCK BODY LLC

ABC
See AMERICAN BROADCASTING COMPANIES INC

ABC
See AMERICAN BEVERAGE CORP

ABC
See AUCTION BROADCASTING CO LLC

ABC
See VIRGINIA DEPARTMENT OF ALCOHOLIC BEVERAGE CONTROL

ABC ACTION NEWS
See WFTS

D-U-N-S 01-677-7617 IMP
ABC APPLIANCE INC
ABC WAREHOUSE
1 W Silverdome Indus Park, Pontiac, MI 48342-2994
Tel (248) 335-4222 Founded/Ownrshp 1963
Sales 364.0MM[E] EMP 1,750
SIC 5722 5731 5999 5065 5064 5063 Household appliance stores; Electric household appliances; Gas household appliances; Electric household appliances, major; Radio, television & electronic stores; Television sets; High fidelity stereo equipment; Video recorders, players, disc players & accessories; Telephone equipment & systems; Alarm signal systems; Mobile telephone equipment; Security control equipment & systems; Radios, motor vehicle; Electrical apparatus & equipment
Pr: Gordon H Hartunian
Treas: Martin G Hartunian
VP: Paul Black
VP: Frieda M Hartunian
VP: Frieda Hartunian
VP: John Hartunian
VP: Ronald Johnson
Store Mgr: Tylar Robison
Site Mgr: Norman Kuriakuz
Site Mgr: Jim Suida

D-U-N-S 04-463-0002
ABC AUTO PARTS LTD
920 W Marshall Ave, Longview, TX 75604-5125
Tel (903) 232-3010 Founded/Ownrshp 1968
Sales 126.0MM[E] EMP 350
Accts Curtis Blakely & Co Pc Long
SIC 5013 5531 Automotive supplies & parts; Automotive parts
Pr: Larry Pyle
Pt: Karen Maddox
COO: Tim Shelton
Ex VP: David Wilkins
VP: Karen Cloud
VP: Bubba Keel
VP: Greg Smith
Genl Mgr: Carrol Williams
Site Mgr: Ron Cheatham
Site Mgr: Robert Frost
Opers Mgr: Mike Kouma

D-U-N-S 15-757-9707 IMP/EXP
ABC BUS COMPANIES INC
ABC COMPANIES
1506 30th St Nw, Faribault, MN 55021-1800
Tel (507) 334-1871 Founded/Ownrshp 1986
Sales 194.7MM[E] EMP 700
SIC 5012 4173 5599 Automobiles & other motor vehicles; Bus terminal & service facilities; Aircraft dealers
CEO: Dane Cornell
*Pr: Timothy Wayland
*CFO: Dan Axelson
*VP: Roman Cornell
Dir IT: Louis Hotard

D-U-N-S 06-244-0870 IMP
ABC BUS INC
(Suby of ABC COMPANIES) ★
1506 30th St Nw, Faribault, MN 55021-1800
Tel (507) 334-1871 Founded/Ownrshp 1979
Sales 140.9MM[E] EMP 600
SIC 5012 4173 Automobiles & other motor vehicles; Bus terminal & service facilities
CEO: Dane Cornell
*Pr: Timothy Wayland
*CFO: Dan Axelson
*Ex VP: Roman Cornell

D-U-N-S 10-307-1247 IMP
■ ABC CABLE NETWORKS GROUP
(Suby of DISNEY ENTERPRISES INC) ★
500 S Buena Vista St, Burbank, CA 91521-0007
Tel (818) 460-7477 Founded/Ownrshp 1969
Sales 271.2MM[E] EMP 857
SIC 4832 4833 Radio broadcasting stations; Television broadcasting stations
Pr: John F Cooke
Pr: Anne M Sweeney
Sr VP: Patrick Lopker
Sr VP: Julie Piepenkotter
VP: Adam Bonnett
VP: Jamie Chasalow
VP: Vicki Dummer
VP: Donna Ebbs
VP: Michael Healy
VP: Terry Holmstrom
VP: Nancy Kanter
VP: John Rouse
VP: John Willey
VP: Bob Witkowski

A.B.C. CARPET & HOME
See ABC HOME FURNISHINGS INC

ABC COMPANIES
See ABC BUS COMPANIES INC

D-U-N-S 03-407-3719
ABC EMPLOYMENT HOLDINGS LLC
MS COMPANIES
6610 N Shadeland Ave, Indianapolis, IN 46220-4392
Tel (866) 674-7678 Founded/Ownrshp 2001
Sales 87.7MM EMP 1,750
Accts Crowe Horwath Llp Indianapoli
SIC 7361 Employment agencies
CEO: Pete Butler
*COO: Scott Haller
*CFO: Nick Vandergrift

D-U-N-S 17-666-5180
■ ABC FAMILY WORLDWIDE INC
(Suby of WALT DISNEY CO) ★
500 S Buena Vista St, Burbank, CA 91521-0001
Tel (818) 560-1000 Founded/Ownrshp 2001
Sales 34.8MM[E] EMP 1,378
SIC 7812 4841 Cartoon production, television; Cable & other pay television services
Pr: Robert A Iger
Sr VP: Nne Ebong
Sr VP: Gary French
VP: Steven Milovich
VP: Jodie Platt
VP: Lee Rierson
VP: Jody Sweet
VP: Heidi Title
Sls Dir: Joseph Lannig

D-U-N-S 04-089-4243 IMP/EXP
■ ABC GROUP HOLDINGS INC
ABC GROUP SALE & MARKETING
(Suby of ABC GROUP LIMITED)
24133 Northwestern Hwy, Southfield, MI 48075-2568
Tel (248) 352-3706 Founded/Ownrshp 2001
Sales 118.2MM[E] EMP 630
SIC 3089 Blow molded finished plastic products; Injection molded finished plastic products
Pr: Mike Schmidt
*Treas: James Augustine

ABC GROUP SALE & MARKETING
See ABC GROUP HOLDINGS INC

D-U-N-S 61-705-0570
■ ABC HOLDING CO INC
(Suby of ABC INC) ★
77 W 66th St Rm 100, New York, NY 10023-6298
Tel (212) 456-7777 Founded/Ownrshp 1985
Sales 2.0MMM[E] EMP 8,000
SIC 4833 Television broadcasting stations
Pr: Robert Iger

D-U-N-S 13-169-9647 IMP
ABC HOME FURNISHINGS INC
A.B.C. CARPET & HOME
888 Brdwy Fl 4, New York, NY 10003
Tel (212) 473-3000 Founded/Ownrshp 1992
Sales 133.3MM[E] EMP 600
SIC 5712 5719 5023 Furniture stores; Beddings & linens; Home furnishings
CEO: Paulette Cole
COO: David E Lauber
CFO: Karen Coneys
VP: Su Greenberg
VP: Rick Jacobs
VP: Peter Kwan
Genl Mgr: Ryan Armstrong
Genl Mgr: Dina Shackelford
CIO: Dean Marano
IT Man: Shane Alexander
Info Man: Chris Dojnik

D-U-N-S 01-098-0667
ABC IMAGING OF WASHINGTON INC
5290 Shawnee Rd Ste 300, Alexandria, VA 22312-2377
Tel (202) 429-8870 Founded/Ownrshp 1993
Sales 226.9MM[E] EMP 512
SIC 2759 Advertising literature: printing
Pr: Medi Falsafi
*CFO: Khaled Jarrar
*VP: Reza Arvin
VP: Michael Canino
Exec: Goodwin John

D-U-N-S 00-787-5560 IMP
■ ABC INC (NY)
(Suby of WALT DISNEY CO) ★
77 W 66th St Rm 100, New York, NY 10023-6298
Tel (212) 456-7777 Founded/Ownrshp 1946
Sales 3.1MMM[E] EMP 22,175
SIC 4833 4832 7812 6794 2711 2721 Television broadcasting stations; Radio broadcasting stations; Television film production; Performance rights, publishing & licensing; Newspapers, publishing & printing; Magazines: publishing only, not printed on site; Trade journals: publishing only, not printed on site
CEO: Robert A Iger
*Pr: Anne M Sweeney
CFO: Michael Kirshbaum
*Ex VP: Albert Cheng
Ex VP: Marla Provencio
*Sr VP: Laurie Younger
*VP: Charissa Gilmore
VP: Herbert A Granath
Assoc Dir: Christina Tesauro
Creative D: Jeffrey Weinstock
Dir IT: Michael Dann
Board of Directors: Chris Bury, John Harney, Paul Roston, David Ruder, Al Schwartz, Seth Traxler

D-U-N-S 07-840-6855
ABC INOAC EXTERIOR SYSTEMS LLC
24175 Northwestern Hwy, Southfield, MI 48075-2532
Tel (248) 619-6057 Founded/Ownrshp 2011, 1926
Sales 131.0MM[E] EMP 435[E]
SIC 5013 Body repair or paint shop supplies, automotive

D-U-N-S 00-692-3106 IMP
ABC LIQUORS INC (FL)
A B C FINE WINE & SPIRITS
8989 S Orange Ave, Orlando, FL 32824-7996
Tel (407) 851-0000 Founded/Ownrshp 1936, 1994
Sales 269.5MM[E] EMP 1,500
SIC 5921 Liquor stores
Pr: C E Bailes
Pr: Alya Barker
*CFO: John C Eicher
*VP: Jess D Bailes
VP: Rick Hughes
VP: Brad Lewis
Exec: Luann Smith
Rgnl Mgr: Romy Nicdao
CIO: Rick Tull
IT Man: Walter Adams
S&M/VP: Andy Abernathy

ABC NISSAN
See AUTOMOTIVE INVESTMENT GROUP INC

D-U-N-S 03-125-7574
ABC PHONES OF NORTH CAROLINA INC (NC)
A WIRELESS
1290 E Arlington Blvd B, Greenville, NC 27858-7854
Tel (252) 317-0388 Founded/Ownrshp 1996, 2016
Sales 146.5MM[E] EMP 550
SIC 5999 Mobile telephones & equipment
Pr: Rich Balot
*COO: Scott Levinson
*CFO: Matthew Goodman
*Ofcr: Michael Moore
Site Mgr: Jonathan Bauman

D-U-N-S 10-990-9403
ABC PROFESSIONAL TREE SERVICES INC
201 Flint Ridge Rd, Webster, TX 77598-4362
Tel (281) 280-1100 Founded/Ownrshp 2000
Sales 57.6MM[E] EMP 1,500
SIC 0783 Tree trimming services for public utility lines
Pr: Rocio Jasso
CFO: Daniel Hernandez

ABC STORES
See MNS LTD

ABC SUPPLY CO.
See AMERICAN BUILDERS & CONTRACTORS SUPPLY CO INC

ABC WAREHOUSE
See ABC APPLIANCE INC

D-U-N-S 07-347-9834
ABCM CORP
1320 4th St Ne, Hampton, IA 50441-1104
Tel (641) 456-5636 Founded/Ownrshp 1972
Sales 189.2MM[E] EMP 2,426
SIC 8741 6519 7011 Nursing & personal care facility management; Real property lessors; Motels
CEO: Richard Allbee
CTO: Julie Hearst
IT Man: Mark Hunt

ABCO
See J&B MEDICAL SUPPLY CO INC

D-U-N-S 05-462-6437 IMP
ABCO REFRIGERATION SUPPLY CORP (NY)
4970 31st St, Long Island City, NY 11101-3114
Tel (718) 937-9000 Founded/Ownrshp 1949
Sales 262.7MM[E] EMP 225
SIC 5078 Refrigeration equipment & supplies
Ch Bd: Michael Senter
*Pr: John Gottlieb
COO: Louis Mirabal
CFO: Kenneth Brown
*CFO: Scott Stumpf
*Sec: George Moncher
Chf Mktg O: Cesiro Bob
VP: Stephen Breckenridge
VP: Hugh Drum
VP: Howard Katz
VP: Andy Kelly
Exec: Larry Kosek

ABCWUA
See ALBUQUERQUE BERNALILLO COUNTY WATER UTILITY AUTHORITY

D-U-N-S 07-863-2778
ABD INSURANCE & FINANCIAL SERVICES INC
3 Waters Park Dr Ste 100, San Mateo, CA 94403-1162
Tel (650) 488-8565 Founded/Ownrshp 2009, 2012
Sales NA EMP 140[E]
SIC 6411 Insurance agents, brokers & service
CEO: Brian M Hetherington
*Pr: Kurt De Grosz
*CFO: Michael F McCloskey
*Ex VP: Darren D Brown
*Ex VP: Andrea M Trudeau
Sr VP: Paula Choy
Sr VP: Suzette Germano
Sr VP: Robin Hendrickson
Sr VP: Frances Lisius
Sr VP: Bryan Martin
Sr VP: Yen Tanega
Sr VP: Nicole White
VP: Brian Ashworth
VP: Nancy Brown
VP: Cheryl Cohen
*VP: Edward I Cha
VP: Brian Gilmore
VP: Timothy Guzman
VP: Mandee Loney
VP: Jean Neu
VP: Martin Ogden

D-U-N-S 94-760-6042
ABDON CALLAIS OFFSHORE LLC
1300 N Alex Plisance Blvd, Golden Meadow, LA 70357-2612
Tel (985) 475-7111 Founded/Ownrshp 1945
Sales 101.2MM EMP 430[E]
SIC 4499 Piloting vessels in & out of harbors
CFO: Lionel Largared
Mktg Mgr: Corey Callais
Board of Directors: Charles Callais, Corey Callais

D-U-N-S 00-699-6144
■ ABE ENTERCOM HOLDINGS LLC
JEFFERSON-PILOT
(Suby of ENTERCOM RADIO LLC) ★
401 E City Ave Ste 809, Bala Cynwyd, PA 19004-1130
Tel (404) 239-7211 Founded/Ownrshp 1928, 2015
Sales NA EMP 1,100
SIC 6411 Insurance agents, brokers & service
CEO: Jon A Boscia
Ex VP: Mark Kopen
Sr VP: Reggie D Adamson
VP: Lisa Buckingham
VP: Dean Chatlain
VP: John D Hopkins
VP: Laura James

D-U-N-S 01-227-0745
ABE ORLANDO BUSTAMANTE
BUSTAMANTE, FRED WOOD PRODUCTS
7859 Diagonal Hwy, Longmont, CO 80503-8746
Tel (303) 652-3394 Founded/Ownrshp 1970
Sales 150.0MM EMP 1
SIC 5099 4789 4212 Firewood; Cargo loading & unloading services; Local trucking, without storage
Owner: Abe Bustamante

D-U-N-S 05-212-5404 IMP
ABEINSA HOLDING INC
(Suby of ABENGOA SA)
2929 N Cent Ave Ste 1100, Phoenix, AZ 85012
Tel (602) 265-6870 Founded/Ownrshp 2009
Sales 89.2MM[E] EMP 300[E]

SIC 1522 1542 Residential construction; Nonresidential construction
Pr: Leonardo Maccio
* *Treas:* Santiago Duran
* *Prin:* Pablo Bouvier
* *Prin:* Victor Grille

ABEKA BOOK PUBLICATIONS
See PENSACOLA CHRISTIAN COLLEGE INC

D-U-N-S 02-403-9083
ABEL CONSTRUCTION CO INC (KY)
3401 Bashford Avenue Ct, Louisville, KY 40218-3162
Tel (502) 451-2235 *Founded/Ownrshp* 1938, 1937
Sales 100.0MM *EMP* 200
SIC 1541 1542 Industrial buildings, new construction; Renovation, remodeling & repairs: industrial buildings; Commercial & office building, new construction; Commercial & office buildings, renovation & repair
CEO: William S Abel Jr
* *Pr:* John H Hays
* *VP:* Richard Banta Jr
* *VP:* Mike Gies
* *VP:* Paul Hirn
* *VP:* Jeff Nuttall
Sfty Mgr: Meghan Jacobs
Sales Exec: Bill Abel
Mktg Dir: Tonii Rizzo
Snr PM: Ed Martin

D-U-N-S 02-989-9499
ABEL OIL CO
ABEL'S QUIK SHOPS
10406 Highway 79, Louisiana, MO 63353-4159
Tel (573) 754-5595 *Founded/Ownrshp* 1940
Sales 99.5MM *EMP* 200
SIC 5171 5411 Petroleum bulk stations; Convenience stores, independent
Pr: Mark M Abel
* *CFO:* Randall L Anderson
Off Mgr: Diane Todd

D-U-N-S 15-414-2962
ABEL WOMACK INC
1 International Way, Lawrence, MA 01843-1065
Tel (978) 989-9400 *Founded/Ownrshp* 1995
Sales 84.7MM^E *EMP* 183
SIC 5084 7699 Lift trucks & parts; Materials handling machinery; Industrial machinery & equipment repair
CEO: John Croce
* *CFO:* Gary Mell
Treas: John Everts
* *VP:* Anthony Fedele
* *VP:* Michael Petinge
Natl Sales: Stephen Bronstein
Natl Sales: Ron Coan

D-U-N-S 04-342-0082 IMP
ABELL CORP (LA)
OUACHITA FERTILIZER CO DIV
2500 Sterlington Rd, Monroe, LA 71203-3047
Tel (318) 343-7565 *Founded/Ownrshp* 1955
Sales 347.0MM^E *EMP* 280
SIC 5191 3089 Farm supplies; Molding primary plastic
Pr: Dixon W Abell
Sec: Kim Coker
VP: Charles Venable
Exec: Wanda Malta
Board of Directors: G Hughes Abell

ABEL'S QUIK SHOPS
See ABEL OIL CO

ABEND-AID MARKETING COMPANY
See COMPUWARE CORP

D-U-N-S 02-136-6125 EXP
ABENGOA BIOENERGY US HOLDING LLC
(*Suby of* ABENGOA BIOENERGIA SA)
16150 Main Circle Dr # 300, Chesterfield, MO 63017-4689
Tel (478) 254-7183 *Founded/Ownrshp* 2002
Sales 127.6MM^E *EMP* 165
SIC 2869 Ethyl alcohol, ethanol
* *Pr:* Javier Benjumea Llorente
* *CEO:* Javier Garoz Neira
COO: Daniel B Allison
* *CFO:* Ignacio Garcia
CFO: Itnicio Garcia
CFO: Jose Nunez
* *Ex VP:* Joaquin Alarcon
Ex VP: Gints De Mula
* *Ex VP:* Salvador Martos
* *Ex VP:* Francisco Morillo
* *VP:* Christopher G Standlee

ABENGOA SOLAR
See TEYMA USA & ABENER ENGINEERING AND CONSTRUCTION SERVICES PARTNERSHIP

D-U-N-S 03-816-3168 IMP/EXP
▲ **ABERCROMBIE & FITCH CO**
6301 Fitch Path, New Albany, OH 43054-9269
Tel (614) 283-6500 *Founded/Ownrshp* 1892
Sales 3.5MMM *EMP* 49,000
Accts Pricewaterhousecoopers Llp Co
Tkr Sym ANF *Exch* NYS
SIC 5611 5621 5641 5632 5651 5961 Men's & boys' clothing stores; Women's clothing stores; Children's & infants' wear stores; Women's accessory & specialty stores; Family clothing stores; Catalog & mail-order houses
CEO: Jonathan E Ramsden
* *Ch Bd:* Arthur C Martinez
Pr: Stacia Andersen
CEO: Jonathan E Ramsden
CFO: Joanne C Crevoiserat
Treas: Everett Gallagher
Bd of Dir: Elizabeth M Lee
Chf Mktg O: Fran Horowitz
Ex VP: Diane Chang
Ex VP: Leslee Herro
Sr VP: Robert E Bostrom
VP: Quave Burton
VP: Ron Grzymkowski
VP: William Piper
VP: Sarah Schwartz
VP: Michael Sherman
VP: Ryan Wendt

D-U-N-S 82-884-8718
■ **ABERCROMBIE & FITCH HOLDING CORP**
(*Suby of* ABERCROMBIE & FITCH CO) ★
6301 Fitch Path, New Albany, OH 43054-9269
Tel (614) 283-6500 *Founded/Ownrshp* 1988
Sales 2.1MMM^E *EMP* 21,100
SIC 5611 Men's & boys' clothing stores
CEO: Michael S Jefferies

D-U-N-S 82-884-8601
■ **ABERCROMBIE & FITCH MANAGEMENT CO**
(*Suby of* ABERCROMBIE & FITCH HOLDING CORP) ★
6301 Fitch Path, New Albany, OH 43054-9269
Tel (614) 283-6500 *Founded/Ownrshp* 1988
Sales 2.1MMM^E *EMP* 21,000
SIC 5611 Men's & boys' clothing stores
CEO: Michael S Jeffries

D-U-N-S 82-884-8791
■ **ABERCROMBIE & FITCH STORES INC**
(*Suby of* ABERCROMBIE & FITCH MANAGEMENT CO) ★
6301 Fitch Path, New Albany, OH 43054-9269
Tel (614) 283-6500 *Founded/Ownrshp* 2000
Sales 1.6MMM^E *EMP* 20,500
SIC 5611 Men's & boys' clothing stores
CEO: Michael S Jeffries

D-U-N-S 04-015-6593 IMP/EXP
■ **ABERCROMBIE & FITCH TRADING CO** (OH)
(*Suby of* JMH TRADEMARK INC) ★
6301 Fitch Path, New Albany, OH 43054-9269
Tel (614) 283-6500 *Founded/Ownrshp* 2000, 2007
Sales 474.8MM^E *EMP* 300^E
SIC 5136 5137 5641 5621 5611 Men's & boys' clothing; Women's & children's clothing; Children's & infants' wear stores; Women's clothing stores; Men's & boys' clothing stores
Pr: Michael Jefferies
* *COO:* Seth Johnson
CFO: Michael Kramer
* *CFO:* Wesley S McDonald
Sr VP: Jim Bierbower

D-U-N-S 60-388-4524
ABERDEEN ASSET MANAGEMENT INC
(*Suby of* ABERDEEN ASSET MANAGEMENT PLC)
1735 Market St Fl 32, Philadelphia, PA 19103-7503
Tel (215) 405-5700 *Founded/Ownrshp* 1994
Sales 99.4MM^E *EMP* 180
SIC 6282 Investment advisory service
CEO: Christian Pittard
CFO: Alan Goodson
CFO: Timothy Packard
Ofcr: John McDevitt
VP: Megan Kennedy
Dir Bus: Emmanuel Piechowski
* *Prin:* Martin J Gilbert
Mng Dir: Alex Boggis
Opers Mgr: Scot Gedraitis
Mktg Dir: Piers Currie

D-U-N-S 62-325-4067
ABF DATA SYSTEMS INC
DIRECT SYSTEMS SUPPORT
9020 Kenamar Dr Ste 201, San Diego, CA 92121-2431
Tel (858) 547-8300 *Founded/Ownrshp* 1989
Sales 91.8MM^E *EMP* 35
SIC 5045 7377 Computers; Computer peripheral equipment; Computer hardware rental or leasing, except finance leasing
Pr: James Herbst
Sales Exec: Mark Wiebe

D-U-N-S 00-690-2977 IMP/EXP
■ **ABF FREIGHT SYSTEM INC** (DE)
(*Suby of* ARCBEST CORP) ★
3801 Old Greenwood Rd, Fort Smith, AR 72903-5937
Tel (479) 785-8700 *Founded/Ownrshp* 1935
Sales 1.8MMM *EMP* 1,000
SIC 4213 Trucking, except local; Less-than-truckload (LTL) transport
Pr: Tim Thorne
Ch Bd: Robert A Young III
Sr VP: Michael R Moss
VP: Richard J Beaulieu
VP: Rick Brown
VP: Tom Carlson
VP: James T Curtis
VP: Robert A Davidson
VP: Walter J Echols
VP: Randy Eller
VP: Jim Fletcher
VP: Sid Hatfield
VP: David Humphrey
VP: Jim Ingram
VP: Chanci Kasper
VP: Matthew Letter
VP: Edward G Myers
VP: Don Reynolds
VP: Donald N Reynolds
VP: Steve Riha
VP: James A Teter

D-U-N-S 07-946-2957
ABF NORTH AMERICA CORP
(*Suby of* ASSOCIATED BRITISH FOODS PLC)
7171 Goodlett Farms Pkwy, Cordova, TN 38016-4909
Tel (901) 381-3000 *Founded/Ownrshp* 2013
Sales 69.4MM^E *EMP* 2,001^E
SIC 2079 2099 Oil, hydrogenated: edible; Food preparations
Pr: Richard Rankin
* *Treas:* Steven Zaruba
* *VP:* Carmen Sciackitano

D-U-N-S 19-106-8670
ABF NORTH AMERICA HOLDINGS INC
(*Suby of* ABF NORTH AMERICA CORP) ★
7171 Goodlett Farms Pkwy, Cordova, TN 38016-4909
Tel (901) 381-3000 *Founded/Ownrshp* 2002
Sales 69.4MM^E *EMP* 1,990^E
SIC 2079 2099 Oil, hydrogenated: edible; Food preparations
Sr VP: Carmen Sciackitano

ABI
See INDIANA LLC ADVICS MANUFACTURING

D-U-N-S 02-225-2345
ABIBOW RECYCLING LLC
(*Suby of* RESOLUTE FOREST PRODUCTS INC)
14950 Hathrow Forest Pkwy, Houston, TX 77032-3847
Tel (800) 874-1301 *Founded/Ownrshp* 1998
Sales 269.3MM^E *EMP* 8,500
SIC 4212 Garbage collection & transport, no disposal
Genl Mgr: Robert Cook
* *Treas:* Pierre Rougeau
* *VP:* Luc Ranger
* *VP:* Thor Thorsteinson
* *VP:* Barry Warren
* *VP:* Darryl Wharton

D-U-N-S 07-317-1951
ABILENE CHRISTIAN UNIVERSITY INC
1600 Campus Ct, Abilene, TX 79601-3761
Tel (325) 674-2000 *Founded/Ownrshp* 2010
Sales 115.3MM *EMP* 675
Accts Davis Kinard & Co Pc Abilene
SIC 8221 University
Pr: Phil Schubert
* *Ex VP:* Allison Garrett
VP: Katie Alfson
VP: Jeff Arrington
VP: Phil Boone
VP: Billie Currey
VP: Bob Hunter
VP: Robert Hunter
VP: Larry Musick
VP: Jack Rich
VP: Kevin Roberts
VP: Charles Siburt
VP: Thomas Winter
VP: Kelly Young
Assoc Dir: Julie Treece

D-U-N-S 07-314-2846
ABILENE INDEPENDENT SCHOOL DISTRICT
241 Pine St, Abilene, TX 79601-5911
Tel (325) 677-1444 *Founded/Ownrshp* 1956
Sales 163.3MM *EMP* 2,800
Accts Davis Kinard & Co Pc Abilen
SIC 8211 Public elementary school; Public junior high school; Public senior high school
Pr: Danny Wheat
* *VP:* Randy Piersall
Board of Directors: Susan L King, Phil Morehead, Mike Sullivan, Dr Danny Wheat, Charles L Wolfe

D-U-N-S 18-119-2154
ABILENE MOTOR EXPRESS
1700 Willis Rd, North Chesterfield, VA 23237-2911
Tel (804) 275-0224 *Founded/Ownrshp* 1986
Sales 85.2MM *EMP* 258^E
Accts Dixon Hughes Goodman Llp Ches
SIC 4213 6221 4212 Trucking, except local; Commodity brokers, contracts; Local trucking, without storage
CEO: Keith H Jones
Pr: Kolen S Jones
VP: Alan K Jones
Dir IT: Russell Folk
Trfc Dir: Jamie Johnson

ABILENE REGIONAL MEDICAL CTR
See ARMC LP

D-U-N-S 07-214-7465
ABILITY BEYOND DISABILITY INC
4 Berkshire Blvd, Bethel, CT 06801-1001
Tel (203) 826-3025 *Founded/Ownrshp* 1953
Sales 68.6MM *EMP* 1,000
Accts O Connor Davies Llp Stamford
SIC 8322 8082 Rehabilitation services; Home health care services
Ch: Gregory Smith
* *Ch Bd:* Greg Smith
* *V Ch:* Robert Bedoukian
V Ch: George Mulvaney
* *CEO:* Jane Davis
* *CFO:* Lori Pasqualini
VP: Jane W Davis
Mng Dir: Kristine Foss
CIO: Laurie Dale
Dir IT: Gary Hull
Dir IT: Jacqueline Osborne

D-U-N-S 00-721-6570
ABILITY NETWORK INC
100 N 6th St Ste 900a, Minneapolis, MN 55403-1516
Tel (612) 460-4301 *Founded/Ownrshp* 2000
Sales 118.2MM^E *EMP* 355
SIC 7379 Computer related consulting services;
CEO: Mark Briggs
Pt: Dave Flesher
* *Ch Bd:* Mark A Pulido
* *Pr:* John Fraser
* *COO:* Ken Ernsting
* *CFO:* Robert Barbieri
* *CFO:* John A Gappa
* *CFO:* Jack Hauser
* *Ofcr:* Bud Meadows
Ex VP: Geoff Charron
* *Ex VP:* David Fusari
Ex VP: Justin Silver
Sr VP: Stan E Opstad
Sr VP: John Porricolo
Sr VP: Mike Tarwacki
VP: John Agostino
* *VP:* Leann Castillo
* *VP:* Amy Coulter
VP: Pat Lucyshyn
* *VP:* James O'Reilly
* *VP:* Chelle Wolley
Board of Directors: Tim Adams, Jerre L Stead

D-U-N-S 78-739-9583 IMP/EXP
ABIMAR FOODS INC
LIL' DUTCH MAID COOKIES
(*Suby of* GRUPO NUTRESA S A)
5425 N 1st St, Abilene, TX 79603-6424
Tel (325) 691-5425 *Founded/Ownrshp* 1992
Sales 113.6MM^E *EMP* 560
SIC 2052 Cookies
Pr: Miguel Moreno
* *Pr:* Steve Fehr
* *CFO:* Gerardo Duarte
CFO: George Percival
Exec: Tera Gibson
Sfty Dirs: Chris Carey
Prd Mgr: Alex Leyco

D-U-N-S 06-989-5340
ABINGTON MEMORIAL HOSPITAL INC
1200 Old York Rd, Abington, PA 19001-3788
Tel (215) 481-2000 *Founded/Ownrshp* 1913
Sales 697.6MM *EMP* 4,018
SIC 8062 Hospital, AMA approved residency
Pr: Laurence M Merlis
Chf Path: Herbert Auerbach
COO: Margaret M McGoldrick
Trst: Bette Landman
Ex VP: Jan Seip
VP: Gary R Candia
VP: Lisa Durst
* *VP:* Thomas E Mallon
VP: Meghan O'Donnell
VP: Paul V O Moore MD
VP: John Peniston
VP: Mary Thomson
Dir Risk M: Regina Sturgis
Dir Case M: Mary Theresa Mintz
Assoc Dir: Rn M Whelan Cen
Dir Rad: Kristin L Crisci
Comm Man: Jim Schmidt

D-U-N-S 82-758-4421 EXP
ABINGTON RELDAN METALS LLC
RELDAN METALS COMPANY
550 Old Bordentown Rd, Fairless Hills, PA 19030-4510
Tel (267) 316-2000 *Founded/Ownrshp* 2005
Sales 420.0MM *EMP* 135
SIC 3339 Precious metals
CEO: Howard Steinberg
* *Pr:* Alan Nadler
* *Ex VP:* Ken Federman

D-U-N-S 07-146-4853
ABINGTON SCHOOL DISTRICT
970 Highland Ave, Abington, PA 19001-4535
Tel (215) 884-4700 *Founded/Ownrshp* 1888
Sales 127.6MM *EMP* 500
Accts Maillie Llp Oaks Pennsylvani
SIC 8211 Public elementary & secondary schools; Public junior high school; Public senior high school; Public special education school
CFO: J H Baxter
Exec: Suzanne Alfonso
Orthpdst: Patrick Hurley

D-U-N-S 05-063-6737
▲ **ABIOMED INC**
22 Cherry Hill Dr, Danvers, MA 01923-2599
Tel (978) 646-1400 *Founded/Ownrshp* 1981
Sales 329.5MM *EMP* 747^E
Tkr Sym ABMD *Exch* NGS
SIC 3845 Electromedical apparatus; Pacemaker, cardiac
Ch Bd: Michael R Minogue
COO: David M Weber
CFO: Michael J Tomsicek
VP: William J Bolt
VP: Andrew J Greenfield
VP: Michael G Howley
Exec: Ramzi Hanania
QA Dir: Don Hedeman
Board of Directors: W Gerald Austen, Dorothy E Puhy, Jeannine M Rivet, Eric A Rose, Martin P Sutter, Henri A Termeer, Paul G Thomas, Christopher Van Gorder

D-U-N-S 00-655-7078 EXP
ABITIBI CONSOLIDATED SALES CORP
ABITIBI-PRICE
(*Suby of* RESOLUTE FOREST PRODUCTS INC)
55 E Camperdown Way, Greenville, SC 29601-3511
Tel (864) 656-3975 *Founded/Ownrshp* 1955, 2007
Sales 105.1MM^E *EMP* 550
SIC 5111 5113 Printing paper; Industrial & personal service paper
Pr: Breen Blain
* *Sr VP:* Collin Keeler

ABITIBI-PRICE
See ABITIBI CONSOLIDATED SALES CORP

ABL
See ARCHBROOK LAGUNA LLC

ABLE BUILDING MAINTENANCE
See CROWN BUILDING MAINTENANCE CO

ABLE CARE HOME HEALTH
See SARASOTA DOCTORS HOSPITAL INC

ABLE ENGINEERING SERVICES
See CROWN ENERGY SERVICES INC

D-U-N-S 02-934-1507
■ **ABM FACILITY SERVICES LLC**
A B M
(*Suby of* LINC GROUP) ★
152 Technology Dr, Irvine, CA 92618-2401
Tel (949) 330-1555 *Founded/Ownrshp* 2012
Sales 216.7MM^E *EMP* 1,391^E
SIC 8711 Engineering services
* *Pr:* James P McClure

D-U-N-S 14-722-1506 EXP
■ **ABM FACILITY SOLUTIONS GROUP LLC**
LINC GROUP
(*Suby of* ABM INDUSTRIES INC) ★
1201 Louisiana St, Houston, TX 77002-5600
Tel (832) 214-5500 *Founded/Ownrshp* 2010
Sales 605.5MM^E *EMP* 4,000

SIC 8744

D-U-N-S 61-685-8908 EXP
■ ABM GOVERNMENT SERVICES LLC
(*Suby of* LINC GROUP) ★
101 Walton Way, Hopkinsville, KY 42240-6833
Tel (270) 885-4642 *Founded/Ownrshp* 2010
Sales 253.6MM^E *EMP* 2,000
SIC 8748 Industrial development planning
Sfty Mgr: Doug Turner
Opers Mgr: Susan Osmer
Sls Mgr: Penny Nichols

D-U-N-S 00-691-1622
▲ ABM INDUSTRIES INC
1 Liberty Plz Fl Con1, New York, NY 10006-1404
Tel (212) 297-0200 *Founded/Ownrshp* 1909
Sales 4.9MMM *EMP* 120,000^E
Accts Kpmg Llp New York New York
Tkr Sym ABM *Exch* NYS
SIC 7349 7521 7381 8711 Building maintenance services; Janitorial service, contract basis; Window cleaning; Automobile parking; Parking lots; Parking garage; Parking structure; Security guard service; Private investigator; Burglary protection service; Mechanical engineering; Electrical or electronic engineering
Pr: Scott Salmirs
**COO:* James P McClure
**CFO:* D Anthony Scaglione
Ex VP: Martin Gjelaj
**Ex VP:* Sarah Hlavinka McConnell
**Sr VP:* Dean A Chin
Sr VP: Doug Gilbert
Sr VP: Rich Kindorf
VP: Jim Altieri
VP: Lanesha T Anderson
VP: John Bierer
VP: Kevin Bray
VP: Kecia Davison
VP: Bill Francis
VP: John Healy
VP: Rod Howery
VP: Qaiser Khan
VP: Glenn Railey
VP: Scott Robinson
VP: Anthony Scaglione
VP: Jon Schwarzbach
Board of Directors: Linda Chavez, J Philip Ferguson, Anthony G Fernandes, Thomas M Gartland, Luke S Helms, Maryellen C Herringer, William W Steele, Winifred Markus Webb

D-U-N-S 13-677-1420
■ ABM INDUSTRIES INC
ABM JANITORIAL
(*Suby of* ABM INDUSTRIES INC) ★
500 S Ewing Ave Ste A, Saint Louis, MO 63103-2944
Tel (314) 241-1975 *Founded/Ownrshp* 2003
Sales 20.3MM^E *EMP* 1,000
SIC 7349 Building & office cleaning services
Pr: Henrik C Slipsager

ABM JANITORIAL
See ABM INDUSTRIES INC

D-U-N-S 78-779-9642
■ ABM JANITORIAL SERVICES - SOUTHWEST INC
(*Suby of* ABM INDUSTRIES INC) ★
5300 S Eastern Ave, Los Angeles, CA 90040-2943
Tel (323) 720-4020 *Founded/Ownrshp* 1939
Sales 54.2MM^E *EMP* 4,168
SIC 7349 Janitorial service, contract basis
Pr: Jim McClure
**Treas:* David L Farwell
VP: Albert Failla
Brnch Mgr: Laura Heins

D-U-N-S 02-915-3558
■ ABM JANITORIAL SERVICES INC
(*Suby of* ABM INDUSTRIES INC) ★
1111 Fannin St Ste 1500, Houston, TX 77002-6996
Tel (713) 654-8924 *Founded/Ownrshp* 1948
Sales 316.1MM^E *EMP* 3,980
SIC 7349 Janitorial service, contract basis
Pr: Henrik Slipsager
Treas: Douglas Bowlus
VP: William W Steele

D-U-N-S 96-335-5313
■ ABM ONSITE SERVICES INC
A B M
(*Suby of* ABM INDUSTRIES INC) ★
1 Liberty Plz Fl 7, New York, NY 10006-1417
Tel (212) 497-0600 *Founded/Ownrshp* 2004
Sales 344.2MM^E *EMP* 22,800^E
SIC 7349 7381 7521 8711 Building maintenance services; Janitorial service, contract basis; Window cleaning; Security guard service; Automobile parking; Engineering services
Pr: James P McClure
**Ex VP:* Jan Kaupas
**Sr VP:* Robert Juestel
Counsel: Scott Flynn

D-U-N-S 04-848-8340 IMP
■ ABM PARKING SERVICES INC
AMPCO AIRPORT PARKING
(*Suby of* ABM INDUSTRIES INC) ★
1150 S Olive St Fl 19, Los Angeles, CA 90015-2479
Tel (213) 284-7600 *Founded/Ownrshp* 1966
Sales 501.0MM^E *EMP* 9,469^E
SIC 7521 7349 Parking lots; Janitorial service, contract basis; Cleaning service, industrial or commercial
CEO: Mark Muglich
**Treas:* D Anthony Scaglione
**Sr VP:* James K Alexander
**Sr VP:* Arnold Klauber
Sr VP: Rick Wilson
**VP:* Robert G Avant
**VP:* Brian Bush
**VP:* Leonard Carder
**VP:* John Coyne
**VP:* Rod Howery
**VP:* Michael Malatin

D-U-N-S 03-868-0211
ABM SECURITY SERVICES INC
A B M
(*Suby of* UNIVERSAL PROTECTION SERVICE LP) ★
3800 Buffalo Speedway # 325, Houston, TX 77098-3714
Tel (713) 928-5344 *Founded/Ownrshp* 1909
Sales 66.8MM^E *EMP* 1,500
SIC 7382 Security systems services
Pr: Christopher C Hansen
**Treas:* Diego Anthony Scaglione
**VP:* Robert G Avant

D-U-N-S 82-816-1740
ABMB-HNTB JOINT VENTURE LLC
500 Main St, Baton Rouge, LA 70801-1908
Tel (225) 765-7400 *Founded/Ownrshp* 2008
Sales 98.4MM^E *EMP* 3,500
SIC 8711 Engineering services
Ex Dir: John Kee

D-U-N-S 06-849-7064
ABN AMRO CLEARING CHICAGO LLC
(*Suby of* ABN AMRO CLEARING BANK N.V.)
175 W Jackson Blvd # 400, Chicago, IL 60604-3027
Tel (312) 604-8000 *Founded/Ownrshp* 2005
Sales 99.7MM^E *EMP* 150
SIC 6289 Security & commodity clearinghouses
Treas: Timothy Taylor
CFO: Shiven Shah
**Treas:* Tim Taylor
Ofcr: Coleen J Bannon
Ofcr: Heleen Bovekerk
Ofcr: Roberta Siewert
Sr VP: Robert Jones
VP: Justin Belt
VP: Michelle Bodenshok
VP: Giuliana Debrown
VP: Megan Flaherty
VP: Brian J Gallagher
VP: Glen Hagar
VP: John Hinkamp
VP: Maria Mancusi
VP: Craig Matthews
VP: Celine McGuire
VP: Thomas Mueller
VP: Eunice Pareja
VP: Doug Thonus
VP: Carlos Uviedo

D-U-N-S 01-275-1178
ABOFFS INC (NY)
33 Gerard St Ste 204, Huntington, NY 11743-2742
Tel (631) 427-2008 *Founded/Ownrshp* 1929, 1974
Sales 186.7MM^E *EMP* 125
SIC 5198 5231 Paints, varnishes & supplies; Paint & painting supplies
Ch Bd: Michael Aboff
**Sec:* Rod Aboff
**VP:* Donna Aboff
Genl Mgr: Susan Toczek

D-U-N-S 60-531-9987 IMP
ABOUT TIME LTD
7220 Bob Bullock Loop, Laredo, TX 78041-2058
Tel (956) 723-1198 *Founded/Ownrshp* 1991
Sales 85.2MM^E *EMP* 20
Accts Cuellar Saldana Cuellar Mor
SIC 5092 5945 Video games; Games (chess, backgammon & other durable games)
Pr: Shashi Vaswani
COO: Juan Vela
**VP:* Priya S Vaswani
IT Man: Albert Torres

D-U-N-S 19-828-5517 IMP/EXP
ABOUT TIME TECHNOLOGIES LLC
58 N 1100 W Apt 2, Payson, UT 84651-5715
Tel (801) 465-8181 *Founded/Ownrshp* 2004
Sales 188.8MM^E *EMP* 2,650
SIC 5045 7372 7375 Computer software; Business oriented computer software; Remote data base information retrieval
Off Mgr: Mandy Myers
Snr Sftwr: Kent Riley
QA Dir: Nathan Olsen

D-U-N-S 86-101-7473
■ ABOVENET INC
(*Suby of* ZAYO GROUP LLC) ★
360 Hamilton Ave, White Plains, NY 10601-1811
Tel (866) 859-6971 *Founded/Ownrshp* 2012
Sales 255.7MM^E *EMP* 500^E
SIC 4813 Local telephone communications;
Pr: Bill Laperch
COO: Joseph Ciavarella
CFO: Joseph P Ciavarella
Sr VP: Rajiv Datta
Sr VP: Nick Ridolfi
Sr VP: Jeff Rock
Sr VP: Robert Sokota
VP: Keith Alexander
Adv Bd Mbr: Bob Chan
CIO: Adam Glick
DP Exec: Nicole Martinez

D-U-N-S 93-047-0914 IMP
ABP CORP
AU BON PAIN
19 Fid Kennedy Ave, Boston, MA 02210-2427
Tel (617) 423-0629 *Founded/Ownrshp* 2005
Sales 285.8MM^E *EMP* 1,500
SIC 5461 5812 2051 Bakeries; Eating places; Bread, cake & related products
Pr: Susan Morelli
**Treas:* Michael Lynch
**Treas:* Timothy Oliveri
VP: Michael Coyle
VP: Steve Culbert
VP: Arpita Gentela
VP: Daniel Romanelli
VP: David Wilton
VP: Scott Zeitlan
Genl Mgr: Scott Aronson
Genl Mgr: Daouda Ndiaye
Board of Directors: Kenny Gateau/Operat, Jeffrey M Perlman

D-U-N-S 01-209-7883
ABQ HEALTH PARTNERS LLC
5400 Gibson Blvd Se, Albuquerque, NM 87108-4729
Tel (505) 254-6500 *Founded/Ownrshp* 2006
Sales 81.0MM *EMP* 1,300^E
SIC 8011 Clinic, operated by physicians
**CFO:* Stuart Schroeder
VP: Tina Rulo
Off Mgr: Denise Nieto
Dir IT: Bindu Purushothaman
Surgeon: Andrew Ribner
Opthamlgy: Curtis R Cornelius
Opthamlgy: Jospeh P Fammartino
Doctor: Dorothy Beach
Nrsg Dir: Sheila Jaramillo

D-U-N-S 78-311-7596
ABR PROPERTY LLC
ARIZONA BILTMORE RESORT & SPA
2400 E Missouri Ave, Phoenix, AZ 85016-3106
Tel (602) 955-6600 *Founded/Ownrshp* 2006
Sales 46.8MM^E *EMP* 1,160
SIC 7011 Hotels
Genl Mgr: Sheila Foley
Off Mgr: Jamie White
Sales Exec: Greg Waters
Natl Sales: Dave Oglesby
Sls Mgr: Heather Abram
Sls Mgr: Patrick Pilcher

D-U-N-S 15-207-0066 IMP
ABRA AUTO BODY & GLASS LP
ABRA AUTOBODY & GLASS
7225 Northland Dr N # 210, Brooklyn Park, MN 55428-1571
Tel (651) 487-2470 *Founded/Ownrshp* 2014
Sales 1.5MMM^E *EMP* 1,755
SIC 6794 7532 Franchises, selling or licensing; Body shop, automotive
Ex VP: Timothy R Adelmann
COO: Glenn Mahoney
CFO: Brent A Moen
Ex VP: Scott M Krohn
VP: Laurie Janu
Dist Mgr: David Mulder Jr
Genl Mgr: Elmer Baker
Genl Mgr: Jessica Moore
Genl Mgr: Dan Nelson
Genl Mgr: Chris Ray
Genl Mgr: Jeff Richards

ABRA AUTOBODY & GLASS
See ABRA AUTO BODY & GLASS LP

D-U-N-S 10-399-4489 IMP
ABRAMS INTERNATIONAL INC
111 Congress Ave Ste 2400, Austin, TX 78701-4083
Tel (512) 322-4000 *Founded/Ownrshp* 1977
Sales 155.1MM *EMP* 800
Accts Schmid Broaddus Nugent Gano P
SIC 1611 1622 1629 6799 7359 8742 General contractor, highway & street construction; Bridge construction; Dam construction; Real estate investors, except property operators; Aircraft rental; Management consulting services
Ch Bd: James D Abrams
**Pr:* Jon F Abrams
**Treas:* J Kelly Gallagher
**VP:* Dean Bernal
**VP:* Brad Everett

ABRASIVE LEADERS & INNOVATORS
See ALI INDUSTRIES INC

D-U-N-S 05-402-8295 IMP
ABRASIVE TECHNOLOGY INC (OH)
8400 Green Meadows Dr N, Lewis Center, OH 43035-9453
Tel (740) 548-4100 *Founded/Ownrshp* 1971
Sales 87.1MM^E *EMP* 400
SIC 3291 Abrasive stones, except grinding stones: ground or whole; Abrasive wheels & grindstones, not artificial
Pr: Loyal M Peterman Jr
**Prin:* Daryl L Peterman
Genl Mgr: Philip Teng
QA Dir: Don Dorr
IT Man: Weihong Lee
Site Mgr: Ian Watkins
Snr Mgr: Jason Hogan
Snr Mgr: Stephan Koknat

ABRAXAS YOUTH & FAMILY SVCS
See CORNELL ABRAXAS GROUP INC

D-U-N-S 82-533-3177
■ ABRAXIS BIOSCIENCE INC
(*Suby of* CELGENE CORP) ★
11755 Wilshire Blvd Fl 20, Los Angeles, CA 90025-1543
Tel (310) 883-1300 *Founded/Ownrshp* 2010
Sales 102.3MM^E *EMP* 885
SIC 2834 Pharmaceutical preparations
CEO: Bruce Wendel
**CFO:* Mitchell Fogelman
Ex VP: Edward C Geehr
QA Dir: Alice Dayoub

D-U-N-S 83-210-8497
■ ABRAXIS BIOSCIENCE LLC
(*Suby of* ABRAXIS BIOSCIENCE INC) ★
11755 Wilshire Blvd Fl 20, Los Angeles, CA 90025-1543
Tel (800) 564-0216 *Founded/Ownrshp* 2007
Sales 102.3MM^E *EMP* 794
SIC 2834 Pharmaceutical preparations

D-U-N-S 07-898-9977
■ ABRAZO CENTRAL CAMPUS
(*Suby of* VANGUARD HEALTH SYSTEMS INC) ★
2000 W Bethany Home Rd, Phoenix, AZ 85015-2443
Tel (602) 249-0212 *Founded/Ownrshp* 2000
Sales 164.0MM *EMP* 1,160
SIC 8062 General medical & surgical hospitals
CEO: Ken Howell
CFO: Alan Germany
Ofcr: Dan Jones
Dir Risk M: Julie Ritzman

Dir Rad: Ron Fulk
Pharmcst: Sandra Sutcliff

D-U-N-S 03-501-3647
ABRAZO WEST CAMPUS
13677 W Mcdowell Rd, Goodyear, AZ 85395-2635
Tel (623) 882-1500 *Founded/Ownrshp* 2008
Sales 146.2MM *EMP* 3^E
SIC 8062 General medical & surgical hospitals
CEO: Stan Holm
Dir Lab: Julie Pilkington
Dir Bus: Yancey Gaither
Snr Mgr: Arthur Sitelman

D-U-N-S 96-161-3353 IMP
ABRY PARTNERS INC
888 Boylston St Ste 1600, Boston, MA 02199-8193
Tel (617) 859-2959 *Founded/Ownrshp* 1994
Sales 525.9MM^E *EMP* 2,534
SIC 4899 2741 Data communication services; Directories: publishing & printing
CEO: Royce Yugkoff
**Pt:* Michael Ashton
**Pt:* Blake Battaglia
**Mng Pt:* Jay Grossman
**Mng Pt:* Peggy Koenig

D-U-N-S 19-622-8758
ABRY PARTNERS LLC
888 Boylston St Ste 1600, Boston, MA 02199-8193
Tel (617) 375-8800 *Founded/Ownrshp* 1989
Sales 151.1MM^E *EMP* 1,535
SIC 6799 Venture capital companies
**Pt:* Blake Battaglia
**Pt:* C J Brucato
**Pt:* John Connor
CFO: Debra Johnson
Ofcr: Kostas Sofronas
Sr VP: Michael Ashton
Sr VP: Matt Lapides
Sr VP: Christopher Turco
VP: Nathan Ott
Dir IT: James Scola

D-U-N-S 07-956-9790
ABRY PARTNERS VI LP
(*Suby of* ABRY PARTNERS LLC) ★
111 Huntington Ave Fl 30, Boston, MA 02199-7685
Tel (617) 859-2959 *Founded/Ownrshp* 2014
Sales 50.2MM^E *EMP* 1,500^E
SIC 6722 Money market mutual funds
Prin: Andrew Banks

ABS AMERICAS
See AMERICAN BUREAU OF SHIPPING INC

ABS COMPUTER TECHNOLOGIES
See MAGNELL ASSOCIATE INC

ABS CONSULTING
See ABSG CONSULTING INC

D-U-N-S 78-547-6743
ABS FINANCE CO INC
(*Suby of* ACME) ★
250 E Parkcenter Blvd, Boise, ID 83706-3940
Tel (208) 395-6200 *Founded/Ownrshp* 2002
Sales 106.1MM^E *EMP* 1^E
SIC 5141 Groceries, general line
Pr: David Boehnen

D-U-N-S 94-109-7370
ABS GROUP OF COMPANIES INC
(*Suby of* ABS AMERICAS) ★
16855 Northchase Dr, Houston, TX 77060-6006
Tel (281) 673-2800 *Founded/Ownrshp* 1987
Sales 328.7MM^E *EMP* 2,200
SIC 4785 8741 Transportation inspection services; Management services
CFO: Jeffrey Weiner
Sr VP: Robert Gilman
VP: Alex Weisselberg
Board of Directors: James Moore

ABS-AMERICAN BUILDING SUPPLY
See AMERICAN BUILDING SUPPLY INC

D-U-N-S 82-523-1616 IMP
ABS-CBN INTERNATIONAL
(*Suby of* ABS-CBN INTERACTIVE, INC.)
150 Shoreline Dr, Redwood City, CA 94065-1400
Tel (800) 527-2820 *Founded/Ownrshp* 1979
Sales 93.0MM^E *EMP* 154
SIC 4841 7822 Cable & other pay television services; Television & video tape distribution
CEO: Eugenio Lopez III
COO: Raffy Lopez
Sr VP: Zoilo D Cruz
Sr VP: Juan Manahan
VP: Edie Wasserberg
Mng Dir: Chinky Dejesus
Mng Dir: Carlo Katigbak
Mng Dir: Jo Kyle
Genl Mgr: Miguel Santos
CIO: Genemar Simpao
CTO: Sherry Supelana

D-U-N-S 03-939-0018
ABSCO LTD CORP
FIA FINANCIAL SERVICES GROUP
2740 Rte 10 E Ste 205, Morris Plains, NJ 07950-1258
Tel (973) 402-2148 *Founded/Ownrshp* 1979
Sales NA *EMP* 186
SIC 6351 6411 6211 6282 Surety insurance; Insurance claim processing, except medical; Investment bankers; Investment advisory service
Prin: Patrick J Lynch

D-U-N-S 07-523-8337
ABSG CONSULTING INC
ABS CONSULTING
(*Suby of* ABS GROUP OF COMPANIES INC) ★
16855 Northchase Dr, Houston, TX 77060-6006
Tel (281) 673-2800 *Founded/Ownrshp* 1972
Sales 223.1MM^E *EMP* 2,200
SIC 8748 Safety training service; Testing services; Systems analysis & engineering consulting services
Pr: David Walker
Pr: Adam Moilanen
**CFO:* Jeffrey Weiner

*Ch: David Weinstein
*Sr VP: David Johnson
Sr VP: William M Keogh
*Sr VP: Henrique Paula
*VP: Darrell Barker
Prgrm Mgr: Kevin Puzder
Genl Mgr: Gary Graham
IT Man: Wendi Sarrazin

ABSG-CORPORATE
See AMERISOURCEBERGEN SPECIALTY GROUP INC

D-U-N-S 00-683-5029
ABSHER CONSTRUCTION CO (WA)
1001 Shaw Rd, Puyallup, WA 98372-7437
Tel (253) 845-9544 Founded/Ownrshp 1940
Sales 171.4MM^E EMP 300^E
SIC 1542 School building construction; Hospital construction; Commercial & office building contractors
Ch Bd: Daniel R Absher
*CFO: Lane Tanabe
*Sec: Bradley C Sayre
*Ex VP: Thomas Absher
Ex VP: Greg Helle
*VP: Clark Helle
*VP: Gregory A Helle
Genl Mgr: Rebecca Purdy
CIO: Nick Belanger
Dir IT: Eric Van Guilder
Sfty Mgr: Kent Lindsay

D-U-N-S 07-951-8472
ABSOLUTE ENVIRONMENTAL SERVICES LTD LLP
11315 Dogwood Dr, Humble, TX 77338-2525
Tel (281) 319-4789 Founded/Ownrshp 2002
Sales 18.6MM^E EMP 1,200
SIC 1799 Asbestos removal & encapsulation
Pr: Thomas Montgomery
VP: Carolyn Coleen Montgomery

D-U-N-S 07-985-3695
ABSOLUTE RETURN PORTFOLIO
(Suby of PACIFIC LIFE FUND ADVISORS LLC) ★
700 Newport Center Dr, Newport Beach, CA 92660-6307
Tel (800) 800-7646 Founded/Ownrshp 2015
Sales 36.5MM^E EMP 2,235^E
SIC 6722 Money market mutual funds

ABSOPURE DIRECT
See ABSOPURE WATER CO LLC

D-U-N-S 12-328-2923 IMP
ABSOPURE WATER CO LLC
ABSOPURE DIRECT
8845 General Dr, Plymouth, MI 48170-4679
Tel (313) 898-1200 Founded/Ownrshp 1982
Sales 89.7MM^E EMP 350
SIC 5499 5149 Water: distilled mineral or spring; Water, distilled; Mineral or spring water bottling
Pr: William C Young
CFO: Dennis Zimmer
VP: Art Amelotte
IT Man: Roger Werling
Site Mgr: Timothy J Noud
Mktg Mgr: Frank Zolenski
Sls Mgr: Jamie Visger

D-U-N-S 96-425-9378
ABSTRACT ELECTRONICS INC
11526 53rd St N, Clearwater, FL 33760-4825
Tel (727) 540-0236 Founded/Ownrshp 1996
Sales 91.0MM^E EMP 120
SIC 5065 Electronic parts & equipment
Pr: Christopher A Colandrea
IT Man: Joschi Cassel

D-U-N-S 04-339-7520
ABT ASSOCIATES INC (MA)
55 Wheeler St Ste 1a, Cambridge, MA 02138-1168
Tel (617) 492-7100 Founded/Ownrshp 1965
Sales 515.8MM^E EMP 2,700
SIC 8732 Commercial nonphysical research
CEO: Kathleen L Flanagan
*Ch Bd: Stanley J Lukowski
*Ch Bd: Gary L Perlin
Pr: Diana Silimperi
*CFO: Noel N Samuel
*CFO: Richard Small
Ofcr: Bob Depalma
Ex VP: Jay L Knott
*Ex VP: Joshua Lipton
Sr VP: Mary F Maguire
VP: Lisa Ashcraft
VP: Susan Bannister
VP: Mario Bazan
VP: Stephen Bell
VP: Peter Broderick
VP: Frank Chandler
VP: Mike Conti
VP: Carlos Cullar
VP: Sheila O Dougherty
VP: Elaine Haemisegger
VP: Mary Holin

ABT ELECTRONICS & APPLIANCE
See ABT ELECTRONICS INC

D-U-N-S 02-501-8953 EXP
ABT ELECTRONICS INC (IL)
ABT ELECTRONICS & APPLIANCE
1200 Milwaukee Ave, Glenview, IL 60025-2416
Tel (847) 967-8830 Founded/Ownrshp 1936
Sales 71.8MM^E EMP 1,100
SIC 5722 5731

ABUELOS MEXICAN FOOD EMBASSY
See FOOD CONCEPTS INTERNATIONAL INC

D-U-N-S 03-006-1225
ABUNDANT LIFE HOME HEALTH INC (TX)
1900 Pecan, Brownsville, TX 78520-8336
Tel (956) 544-7714 Founded/Ownrshp 1997
Sales 24.3MM^E EMP 1,200
SIC 8082 Home health care services
Pr: Pete Gonzales
*VP: Fredrick Gonzales
*Prin: Marylou Gonzalez

D-U-N-S 09-986-7038
■ ABX AIR INC
(Suby of ATSG) ★
145 Hunter Dr, Wilmington, OH 45177-9550
Tel (937) 382-5591 Founded/Ownrshp 1980
Sales 125.1MM^E EMP 700
SIC 4513 5088 4581 8299 Letter delivery, private air; Package delivery, private air; Parcel delivery, private air; Aircraft & parts; Aircraft servicing & repairing; Flying instruction
Pr: John Starkovich
CEO: Joe Hete
CFO: Duane Kimble
Ofcr: Terry Ogilvie
VP: Capt Bob Boja
VP: Phil Flowers
VP: Robert Gray
VP: Mike Kuli
VP: Joe Payne
VP: W Joseph Payne
VP: Terry Scherz
Board of Directors: James E Bushman, James H Carey, Jeffrey A Dominick, John D Geary, Randy D Rademacher, Jeffrey J Vorholt

AC
See ANDERSON COLUMBIA CO INC

D-U-N-S 00-283-8225 IMP
AC CORP
301 Creek Ridge Rd, Greensboro, NC 27406-4421
Tel (336) 273-4472 Founded/Ownrshp 1933
Sales 108.5MM^E EMP 500
SIC 1711 1731 3556 3823 3625 3535

D-U-N-S 83-113-7638
AC FIRST LLC
20501 Seneca Meadows Pkwy, Germantown, MD 20876-7016
Tel (817) 698-6860 Founded/Ownrshp 2009
Sales 80.8MM^E EMP 2,300
SIC 8744 Facilities support services

D-U-N-S 17-665-0141
AC MOORE ARTS & CRAFTS INC
(Suby of NICOLE CRAFTS LLC) ★
130 A C Moore Dr, Berlin, NJ 08009-9500
Tel (856) 768-4930 Founded/Ownrshp 2011
Sales 500.0MM EMP 4,400
SIC 5945 Arts & crafts supplies
Pr: Adolph Pipeno
Pr: Daniel C Maguire
*COO: Rex Rambo
*CFO: Leslie H Gordon
*CFO: Katz Joins
*CFO: David Stern
*Chf Mktg O: Anthony Piperno
*Ex VP: David Abelman
*Ex VP: Joseph Scappa
*Sr VP: Amy Rhoades
VP: David M Frawley
*VP: Rodney Schriver
VP: Eric Vandenberg

D-U-N-S 11-627-5330 IMP/EXP
AC MOORE INC
(Suby of AC MOORE ARTS & CRAFTS INC) ★
130 A C Moore Dr, Berlin, NJ 08009-9500
Tel (856) 768-4930 Founded/Ownrshp 1984
Sales 379.4MM^E EMP 3,339
SIC 5945 Arts & crafts supplies
CEO: Tete Piperno
*Ch Bd: William Kaplan
*COO: Rex A Rambo
VP: Thomas Dickey
VP: Robert Martin
Dist Mgr: Ronald Last
Store Mgr: Jim Ryan
CTO: Jeff Ball
Sales Exec: Jeremy Lipham
Board of Directors: Richard Bauer, Richard Drake, Richard Lesser

AC SERVICES
See ASSOCIATED COMMUNITY SERVICES INC

AC TRANSIT
See ALAMEDA-CONTRA COSTA TRANSIT DISTRICT

D-U-N-S 06-032-5586
ACA INDUSTRIES INC
AMERICAN MAINTENANCE
385 W Main St, Babylon, NY 11702-3023
Tel (631) 587-2485 Founded/Ownrshp 1978
Sales 54.1MM^E EMP 2,000^E
SIC 7349 Building maintenance, except repairs
Ch Bd: Alexander C Alex

D-U-N-S 86-094-7126
ACA SPARROW CORP
2937 N Kenwood Ave Apt B, Indianapolis, IN 46208-5134
Tel (317) 920-1374 Founded/Ownrshp 1987
Sales 9.8MM^E EMP 1,000
SIC 6519 Real property lessors
Pr: Stephanie Murray
*CEO: Stacy Murray

D-U-N-S 00-707-5549
▲ ACACIA COMMUNICATIONS INC
3 Mill And Main Pl # 400, Maynard, MA 01754-2656
Tel (978) 938-4896 Founded/Ownrshp 2009
Sales 239.0MM EMP 257
Tkr Sym ACIA Exch NGS
SIC 3674 8999 Semiconductors & related devices; Communication services
Pr: Murugesan Shanmugaraj
Ch Bd: Eric A Swanson
CFO: John F Gavin
Founder: Mehrdad Givehchi
Founder: Christian J Rasmussen
Ofcr: Renee M Pianka
Sr VP: John P Kavanagh
VP: Janene I Asgeirsson
VP: John Lomedico
CTO: Benny P Mikkelsen
VP Sls: John J Lomedico
Board of Directors: Peter Y Chung, Stan J Reiss, John Ritchie, Vincent T Roche

ACACIA GROUP
See ACACIA LIFE INSURANCE CO

D-U-N-S 00-691-9179
ACACIA LIFE INSURANCE CO
ACACIA GROUP
(Suby of AMERITAS HOLDING CO) ★
7315 Wisconsin Ave 1000w, Bethesda, MD 20814-3218
Tel (301) 280-1000 Founded/Ownrshp 1869
Sales NA EMP 845^E
Accts Deloitte & Touche Llp Omaha
SIC 6311 6411 6035 6282 6211 Mutual association life insurance; Insurance brokers; Federal savings banks; Manager of mutual funds, contract or fee basis; Dealers, security
Pr: Haluk Ariturk
CFO: Robert C Barth
Ex VP: Robert W Clyde
Sr VP: Robert-John H Sands
VP: Jan M Connolly
VP: Arnold D Henkel
VP: Dale D Johnson
VP: William W Lester
VP: Kevin W O'Toole
VP: Janet L Schmidt

D-U-N-S 14-746-2191
ACACIA NETWORK INC
300 E 175th St, Bronx, NY 10457-5804
Tel (718) 299-1100 Founded/Ownrshp 1999
Sales 131.7MM^E EMP 275
Accts Withumsmithbrown Pc New Bruns
SIC 8399 Health & welfare council
CEO: Raul Russi
*Pr: Hector L Diaz
*COO: Pamela Mattel
CFO: Tom Del Rio
*CFO: Tomas Del Rio
VP: Adriene Rosell
Exec: Lisa Maldonado
Ex Dir: Raul Rodriguez
Dir IT: Irvin Rodriguez

D-U-N-S 84-544-2326 IMP
▲ ACACIA RESEARCH CORP
520 Newport Center Dr # 1200, Newport Beach, CA 92660-7022
Tel (949) 480-8300 Founded/Ownrshp 1993
Sales 125.0MM EMP 42^E
Tkr Sym ACTG Exch NGS
SIC 6794 Patent buying, licensing, leasing
CEO: Marvin Key
*Ch Bd: G Louis Graziadio III
CFO: Clayton J Haynes
Sr VP: Edward J Treska
Board of Directors: William S Anderson, Fred A De Boom, Edward W Frykman, Frank E Walsh III

D-U-N-S 13-882-9747
ACADEMI LLC
(Suby of CONSTELLIS HOLDINGS LLC) ★
12018 Sunrise Valley Dr # 140, Reston, VA 20191-3444
Tel (252) 435-2488 Founded/Ownrshp 2010
Sales 62.1MM^E EMP 1,000
SIC 7382 8742 Security systems services; Management consulting services
Pr: Ted Wright
*COO: Charles Thomas
*CFO: Douglas Lee
VP: Ana Bundy
VP: William Matthew
Prgrm Mgr: Ross Botson
Genl Mgr: Michael Weixel
DP Exec: Dian Wells
IT Man: Debbie Kuhn

D-U-N-S 96-931-4389
ACADEMIC ACQUISITION CORP
1615 W Chester Pike, West Chester, PA 19382-6223
Tel (484) 947-2000 Founded/Ownrshp 2011
Sales 333.2MM^E EMP 4,700^E
SIC 8211 8299 Private elementary & secondary schools; Educational services
Pr: George H Bernstein

ACADEMIES OF ANTELOPE VALLEY
See ANTELOPE VALLEY UNION HIGH SCHOOL DISTRICT

D-U-N-S 07-103-1280
ACADEMY FOR EDUCATIONAL DEVELOPMENT INC
A E D
1825 Conn Ave Nw Ste 800, Washington, DC 20009-5721
Tel (202) 884-8976 Founded/Ownrshp 1961
Sales 202.4MM EMP 1,200
Accts Kpmg Llp Mclean Va
SIC 8742 8732 Management consulting services; Educational research
Ex Dir: Stephen F Moseley
*COO: Jack Downey
*CFO: Deanna Trotter
*Chf Mktg O: Ricardo Dillega
Ofcr: Tony Davenport
Assoc Dir: Desta Kebede
Pgrm Dir: Rudi Klauss

D-U-N-S 06-509-2538 IMP/EXP
ACADEMY LTD
ACADEMY SPORTS OUTDOORS
1800 N Mason Rd, Katy, TX 77449-2897
Tel (281) 646-5200 Founded/Ownrshp 2011
Sales 1.6MMM^E EMP 7,000
SIC 5941 5699 5661 Specialty sport supplies; Camping equipment; Fishing equipment; Sports apparel; Footwear, athletic
Ch Bd: David E Gochman
*Pr: Rodney Faldyn
CFO: Michael N Arnett
CFO: Michael Arnett
CFO: David Huff
Ex VP: Ken Attaway
Ex VP: A J Blanchard
Ex VP: Len Caldwell
Ex VP: Robert Frennea
Ex VP: Howard M Frost
Ex VP: Michelle McKinney
Ex VP: Beth Menuet
Ex VP: Elise Neal
*VP: Sylvia Barrera
VP: Christina Beahm
VP: James Carcasi
VP: Kevin Chapman
VP: John Hay
VP: Joe Matthews
VP: Allen McConnell
VP: Bruce Meunier

D-U-N-S 36-381-6083
ACADEMY MORTGAGE CORP
RESIDENTIAL MORTGAGE
339 W 13490 S, Draper, UT 84020-7220
Tel (801) 233-7237 Founded/Ownrshp 1988
Sales NA EMP 1,300
Accts Allred Jackson Pc North Lo
SIC 6163 Mortgage brokers arranging for loans, using money of others
Pr: Adam Kessler
CFO: Greg Brown
Ofcr: Deidre Kay
Ofcr: Megan Lower
Ofcr: John Norman
Ex VP: Crawford Cragun
Ex VP: Rusty Hansen
Sr VP: Jerry Devlin
*VP: Duane Shaw
Dir Risk M: Paul Keefer
Dir Risk M: John Suggs

ACADEMY OF ART UNIVERSITY
See STEPHENS INSTITUTE

D-U-N-S 07-882-1642
ACADEMY OF MOTION PICTURE ARTS & SCIENCES
8949 Wilshire Blvd, Beverly Hills, CA 90211-1907
Tel (310) 247-3000 Founded/Ownrshp 1927
Sales 123.6MM EMP 174
Accts Pricewaterhousecoopers Llp I
SIC 8621 7819 8611 Professional membership organizations; Services allied to motion pictures; Business associations
CEO: Dawn Hudson
*CFO: Andy Horn
Chf Mktg O: Clay Crutchfield
Assoc Dir: Karen Barcellona
*Ex Dir: Bruce Davis
Mng Dir: Lorenza Munoz
Dir Sec: Diego Lopez
Snr Ntwrk: Les Jin
Web Dev: Patrick Waller
Software D: Yogesh Rahalkar
Opers Mgr: Deborah Cahn

D-U-N-S 07-649-0531
ACADEMY OF OUR LADY OF LOURDES INC
ASSISI HEIGHTS
1001 14th St Nw Ste 100, Rochester, MN 55901-2525
Tel (507) 282-7441 Founded/Ownrshp 1878
Sales 100.0MM EMP 100
SIC 8661 Convent
Pr: Dolore Rockers
*Treas: Jean Keniry

D-U-N-S 00-217-3136
ACADEMY SCHOOL DISTRICT 20 (CO)
1110 Chapel Hills Dr, Colorado Springs, CO 80920-3923
Tel (719) 234-1200 Founded/Ownrshp 1957
Sales 245.2MM EMP 3,000
Accts Cliftonlarsonallen Llp Green
SIC 8211 Public elementary & secondary schools
Bd of Dir: Mark Vangampleare
Ofcr: Tom Gregory
CIO: Shelley Kooser
Dir IT: Jeff Gronski
Software D: Dave Haehn
Software D: Ruth Henss
Pr Dir: Allison Cortez
Teacher Pr: Gail Kozheunikov
Psych: Sean Brotherton
Psych: Dale Sutton

ACADEMY SPORTS OUTDOORS
See ACADEMY LTD

D-U-N-S 96-874-2507
▲ ACADIA HEALTHCARE CO INC
6100 Tower Cir Ste 1000, Franklin, TN 37067-1509
Tel (615) 861-6000 Founded/Ownrshp 2005
Sales 1.7MMM EMP 26,400^E
Tkr Sym ACHC Exch NGM
SIC 8093 Specialty outpatient clinics
Ch Bd: Joey A Jacobs
Pr: Anne Kelly
Pr: Brent Turner
COO: Ron Fincher
CFO: David M Duckworth
Ex VP: Christopher L Howard
VP: Michael Drake
VP: Bryan Kaegi
VP: Robert Swinson
VP: Dwight Willingham
VP Bus Dev: Jason Campbell
Dir Bus: Patrick Quisenberry
Board of Directors: E Perot Bissell, Christopher R Gordon, Vicky B Gregg, William F Grieco, Kyle D Lattner, Wade D Miquelon, William M Petrie, Hartley R Rogers

D-U-N-S 08-555-8518 IMP
ACADIA PARISH SCHOOL DISTRICT
2402 N Parkerson Ave, Crowley, LA 70526-2015
Tel (337) 783-3664 Founded/Ownrshp 1887
Sales 86.7MM^E EMP 1,400
SIC 8211 Public elementary & secondary schools
Ofcr: Keisha Comeaux
Genl Mgr: Justin Carrier

D-U-N-S 80-872-0601
▲ ACADIA REALTY TRUST
411 Theodore Fremd Ave # 300, Rye, NY 10580-1410
Tel (914) 288-8100 Founded/Ownrshp 1993
Sales 217.2MM EMP 116

Tkr Sym AKR *Exch* NYS
SIC 6798 Real estate investment trusts
Pr: Kenneth F Bernstein
COO: Christopher Conlon
CFO: John Gottfried
Ofcr: Joseph M Napolitano
Ex VP: Joel Braun
Sr VP: Jason Blacksberg
Sr VP: Robert Masters
VP: Timothy Collier
VP: Joseph Napolitano
VP: John Swagerty
Board of Directors: Douglas Crocker II, Wendy Luscombe, William T Spitz, Lynn C Thurber, Lee S Wielansky, C David Zoba

ACADIAN AMBULANCE & A MED SVCS
See ACADIAN AMBULANCE SERVICE INC

D-U-N-S 05-652-6536
ACADIAN AMBULANCE SERVICE INC
ACADIAN AMBULANCE & A MED SVCS
130 E Kaliste Saloom Rd, Lafayette, LA 70508-8308
Tel (337) 291-3333 *Founded/Ownrshp* 1971
Sales 587.5MM[E] *EMP* 4,000
Accts Ernst & Young Llp New Orlean
SIC 4119 Ambulance service
CEO: Richard E Zuschlag
**Pr:* David A Pierce
**CFO:* David L Kelly
Ex VP: David Kelly
**Ex VP:* John Zuschlag
VP: Mike Burney
**VP:* Diane Groh
**VP:* Clay Henry
**VP:* Ross Judice
VP: Daniel Lennie
VP: Joe Lightfoot
**VP:* Tyron Picard
**VP:* Bill Vidacovich

ACADIANA HEALTH CARE LOUISIANA
See ACADIANA HEALTH CARE OF LOUISIANA INC

D-U-N-S 10-011-8343
ACADIANA HEALTH CARE OF LOUISIANA INC
ACADIANA HEALTH CARE LOUISIANA
101 La Rue France Ste 300, Lafayette, LA 70508-3138
Tel (337) 232-5044 *Founded/Ownrshp* 1997
Sales 728.6M[E] *EMP* 1,200
SIC 7363 Medical help service
CEO: Tim Howard

ACAPULCO MEXICAN REST CANTINA
See ACAPULCO RESTAURANTS INC

D-U-N-S 08-219-3889
ACAPULCO RESTAURANTS INC
ACAPULCO MEXICAN REST CANTINA
(*Suby of* EL TORITO MEXICAN RESTAURANT) ★
4001 Via Oro Ave Ste 200, Long Beach, CA 90810-1400
Tel (310) 513-7538 *Founded/Ownrshp* 1998
Sales 79.1MM[E] *EMP* 3,000
SIC 5812 5813 Mexican restaurant; Drinking places
Ch: Nick Valenti
VP: Carlos Angulo

ACB RECOVERY
See ALLTRAN FINANCIAL LP

D-U-N-S 08-871-1783
ACBL RIVER OPERATIONS LLC
AEP RIVER OPERATIONS
(*Suby of* ACL) ★
1701 E Market St, Jeffersonville, IN 47130-4755
Tel (636) 530-2100 *Founded/Ownrshp* 2015
Sales 245.9MM[E] *EMP* 2,000
SIC 4449 River transportation, except on the St. Lawrence Seaway
VP: Bob Blocker
IT Man: Cathy Hood
IT Man: Kendal D Walton

ACC
See ATLANTIC COAST COTTON INC

ACC BUSINESS
See ACC CORP

ACC CONSTRUCTION COMPANY
See ACC CONSTRUCTION CO INC

D-U-N-S 16-170-0646 EXP
ACC CONSTRUCTION CO INC
ACC CONSTRUCTION COMPANY
635 Nw Frontage Rd Ste A, Augusta, GA 30907-3679
Tel (706) 868-1037 *Founded/Ownrshp* 1986
Sales 86.3MM *EMP* 35
Accts Cherry Bekaert Llp Augusta G
SIC 1542 1541 Commercial & office building, new construction; Industrial buildings, new construction
Pr: Mason McKnight III
**CFO:* Kurt Williams
**Treas:* Lou Ann McKnight
**VP:* Mason McKnight IV
**VP:* Mathew McKnight

D-U-N-S 02-970-4822
■ ACC CORP
ACC BUSINESS
(*Suby of* AMERICAN TELEPHONE AND TELG) ★
400 West Ave Ste 3, Rochester, NY 14611-2538
Tel (585) 987-3000 *Founded/Ownrshp* 1998
Sales 222.1MM[E] *EMP* 681
SIC 4813 Local & long distance telephone communications; Long distance telephone communications; Local telephone communications
Pr: John Baker
CFO: Frank Sazdo
**VP:* M Daley
Area Mgr: Kim Noto
Dir IT: Terri McCarty
VP Opers: Erika Young
S&M/VP: Jack Barron
Mktg Dir: Bob Gorman
Sls Dir: Sandy Butler-Buchanon
Manager: Jon Day
Sls Mgr: Sherry Jenkins

D-U-N-S 96-294-3572
ACCELERATE HOLDINGS CORP
TPG CREATIVE CAPITAL
(*Suby of* TEXAS PACIFIC GROUP) ★
301 Commerce St Ste 3300, Fort Worth, TX 76102-4133
Tel (817) 871-4000 *Founded/Ownrshp* 2001
Sales 5.0MMM[E] *EMP* 500
SIC 6722 Management investment, open-end
CEO: David Bonderman

D-U-N-S 04-801-9345
ACCELERATED PRODUCTION SERVICES INC
1585 Sawdust Rd Ste 210, The Woodlands, TX 77380-2095
Tel (281) 403-5793 *Founded/Ownrshp* 2013
Sales 100.1MM[E] *EMP* 165[E]
SIC 1389 Oil field services
Pr: Brad Goebel

D-U-N-S 61-526-3543
ACCELLENT ACQUISITION CORP
(*Suby of* ACCELLENT HOLDINGS CORP) ★
100 Fordham Rd Bldg C, Wilmington, MA 01887-2168
Tel (978) 570-6900 *Founded/Ownrshp* 2012
Sales 178.2MM[E] *EMP* 3,667
SIC 3841 3317 3679 3315 3552 3089 Surgical & medical instruments; Seamless pipes & tubes; Microwave components; Wire products, ferrous/iron: made in wiredrawing plants; Dyeing, drying & finishing machinery & equipment; Injection molding of plastics
Pr: Ron Sparks
CFO: Stewart Fisher
Board of Directors: Michael Michelson

D-U-N-S 61-526-1810
ACCELLENT HOLDINGS CORP
100 Fordham Rd, Wilmington, MA 01887-2168
Tel (978) 570-6900 *Founded/Ownrshp* 2005
Sales 590.5MM[E] *EMP* 3,667
SIC 3841 3679 3315 3552 3317 3089 Surgical & medical instruments; Microwave components; Wire products, ferrous/iron: made in wiredrawing plants; Dyeing, drying & finishing machinery & equipment; Seamless pipes & tubes; Injection molding of plastics
Pr: Ron Sparks
**CFO:* Stewart Fisher
Ex VP: Kenneth Stone
VP: Finbar Crean
VP: Tom Lemker
Genl Mgr: Simon Weeks

D-U-N-S 15-223-4824
■ ACCELLENT LLC
LAKE REGION MEDICAL
(*Suby of* LAKE REGION MEDICAL INC) ★
100 Fordham Rd Bldg C, Wilmington, MA 01887-2168
Tel (978) 570-6900 *Founded/Ownrshp* 2005
Sales 394.5MM[E] *EMP* 2,130
SIC 3841 8711 Surgical & medical instruments; Engineering services
Pr: Robert E Kirby
**CFO:* Jeremy A Friedman
Dir Surg: Steve Mariano
Board of Directors: H Stephen Cookston, William Landman, Larry Pickering, Eric M Pollock, Daniel Pulver, T Quinn Spitzer Jr

D-U-N-S 78-654-3970
ACCELLOS INC
90 S Cascade Ave Ste 1200, Colorado Springs, CO 80903-1678
Tel (719) 433-7000 *Founded/Ownrshp* 2012
Sales 159.0MM[E] *EMP* 771
SIC 7373 Computer integrated systems design
CEO: Michael Cornell
**CFO:* Flint Seaton
**Chf Mktg O:* Chad Collins
Sr VP: Brian Jamieson
VP: Benoit Dubuc
VP: Jim Krantz
**Dir Sec:* Ross Elliott
Off Admin: Sara Amigo
Snr Sftwr: Joseph Zuppardo
**CTO:* Dan Radunz
Natl Sales: Bill Baker

D-U-N-S 83-002-5529
ACCENT FOOD SERVICES LLC
16209 Central Commerce Dr, Austin, TX 73301-0001
Tel (512) 251-9500 *Founded/Ownrshp* 2008
Sales 83.9MM[E] *EMP* 229[E]
SIC 5046 Commercial equipment
CEO: Thomas L Hawkins
Pr: Gregory M Barr

D-U-N-S 80-472-2114
■ ACCENT MARKETING SERVICES LLC
(*Suby of* STARTEK INC) ★
4550 Town Center Blvd, Jeffersonville, IN 47130-7136
Tel (812) 941-1112 *Founded/Ownrshp* 2015
Sales 114.5MM[E] *EMP* 3,100
SIC 7331 7389 8748 Direct mail advertising services; Telemarketing services; Business consulting
CEO: Tim Searcy
**COO:* Robert Brillhart
**COO:* Timothy S Hardin
**CFO:* Linda Ruffenach
**Ofcr:* John Hoholik
**Ex VP:* Patrick Scheen
Prgrm Mgr: April Billups
Genl Mgr: Phyllis Mayo
Netwrk Eng: Mark Schneider

D-U-N-S 15-475-2141 IMP/EXP
ACCENT PACKAGING INC
ACCENT WIRE-TIE
10131 Fm 2920 Rd, Tomball, TX 77375-8918
Tel (281) 251-3700 *Founded/Ownrshp* 1986
Sales 105.4MM[E] *EMP* 122
SIC 5051 5084 5085 Wire; Steel; Industrial machinery & equipment; Tools; Seals, industrial
Pr: William P Sims
**VP:* Carolyn Sims
**VP:* J P Sims
**VP:* Todd Sims

ACCENT WIRE-TIE
See ACCENT PACKAGING INC

D-U-N-S 80-078-5474
ACCENTCARE HOME HEALTH INC
(*Suby of* ACCENTCARE INC) ★
135 Technology Dr Ste 150, Irvine, CA 92618-2402
Tel (949) 623-1500 *Founded/Ownrshp* 2006
Sales 18.8MM[E] *EMP* 2,000
SIC 8082 Home health care services
Prin: William Comte
Sfty Dirs: Nabil Rafail

D-U-N-S 07-167-0900
ACCENTCARE INC
17855 Dallas Pkwy, Dallas, TX 75287-6852
Tel (800) 834-3059 *Founded/Ownrshp* 1999
Sales 318.9MM[E] *EMP* 8,060[E]
SIC 8082 Home health care services
CEO: Stephan S Rodgers
**COO:* Steve Jakubcanin
**CFO:* Jeff Reynolds
Admn Mgr: Rich Guertin
Brnch Mgr: Hannah Schultz
Netwrk Eng: Matt Bustamante

D-U-N-S 13-972-7148
ACCENTURE FEDERAL SERVICES LLC
ACCENTURE NATIONAL SEC SVCS
(*Suby of* ACCENTURE LLP) ★
800 N Glebe Rd Ste 300, Arlington, VA 22203-2151
Tel (703) 947-2000 *Founded/Ownrshp* 2002
Sales 228.7MM[E] *EMP* 1,200
SIC 8742 7379 Management consulting services;
**CEO:* David Moskovitz

D-U-N-S 01-085-0857
ACCENTURE INC
(*Suby of* ACCENTURE PUBLIC LIMITED COMPANY)
161 N Clark St Ste 1100, Chicago, IL 60601-3362
Tel (312) 737-8842 *Founded/Ownrshp* 1989
Sales 6.0MMM[E] *EMP* 25,482
SIC 7379 7389 8742 ;Telemarketing services; Management consulting services
Pr: Julie Sweet
**Treas:* Steven M Kupres
Exec: Richard Birhanzel
Exec: Heather Duncan
Exec: Jared Farnsworth
Exec: Kahlil Fitzgerald
Exec: Aimee Fuller
Exec: Igor Gurland
Exec: Ahmed Hassan
Exec: Geert Hermans
Exec: James Hughey
Exec: John Mahoney
Exec: Glenn Moses
Exec: Aaron Mugg
Exec: Donna Nguyen
Exec: Julu Panat
Exec: David Pierce
Exec: Gayle Rubin
Exec: Aaron Savincki
Exec: Gurminder Singh

D-U-N-S 92-799-2529
ACCENTURE LLC
(*Suby of* ACCENTURE INC) ★
161 N Clark St Ste 1100, Chicago, IL 60601-3362
Tel (312) 693-0161 *Founded/Ownrshp* 2001
Sales 3.9MMM[E] *EMP* 21,090[E]
Accts Kpmg Llp
SIC 7379 7389 8742 ;Telemarketing services; Management consulting services
Ch: Pierre Nanterme
**Ch Bd:* Joe W Forehand
**CEO:* William D Green
**COO:* Jo Deblaere
**COO:* Stephen Rohleder
**CFO:* Mike McGrath
**CFO:* David P Rowland
**Sr VP:* Pamela J Craig
Web Dev: Nicole Kato
Snr Mgr: Donald Counsell
Snr Mgr: Adriano Levi

D-U-N-S 13-782-0580 IMP
ACCENTURE LLP
(*Suby of* ACCENTURE LLC) ★
161 N Clark St Ste 1100, Chicago, IL 60601-3362
Tel (312) 693-0161 *Founded/Ownrshp* 1989
Sales 3.9MMM[E] *EMP* 21,090
SIC 8742 Management consulting services
Ofcr: Stephanie Elliott
Exec: Robert Fuhrmann
Exec: Damon Harrison
Exec: Andrew Hays
Exec: Robert Holston
Exec: Denise Machonis
Snr Sftwr: Abhinav Rakheja
CIO: Andrew Gissler
DP Exec: Julie Guill
DP Exec: Basil Hirzalla
DP Exec: Deepna Nandiga

ACCENTURE NATIONAL SEC SVCS
See ACCENTURE FEDERAL SERVICES LLC

D-U-N-S 07-870-3223
ACCENTURE SUB INC
(*Suby of* ACCENTURE LLP) ★
161 N Clark St Ste 1100, Chicago, IL 60601-3362
Tel (312) 693-0161 *Founded/Ownrshp* 2001
Sales 117.4MM[E] *EMP* 404[E]
SIC 8742 Administrative services consultant
CEO: Pierre Nanterme
**COO:* Jo Deblaere
**CFO:* David P Rowland
**Dir Sec:* Shawn Collinson

ACCESS
See RETRIEVEX ACQUISITION CORP II

D-U-N-S 61-306-1493 IMP
ACCESS BUSINESS GROUP INTERNATIONAL LLC
NUTRILITE
5600 Beach Blvd, Buena Park, CA 90621-2007
Tel (714) 521-2853 *Founded/Ownrshp* 1934
Sales 131.6MM[E] *EMP* 700
SIC 2834 Pharmaceutical preparations
VP: James Siewbertsen
VP: Jim Siewertsen
QA Dir: Gloria Anderson
Site Mgr: Bonita Kahler
QI Cn Mgr: Nellie Garcia

D-U-N-S 83-983-0713 IMP
ACCESS BUSINESS GROUP LLC
NUTRILITE
(*Suby of* ALTICOR INC) ★
7575 Fulton St E, Ada, MI 49355-0001
Tel (616) 787-6000 *Founded/Ownrshp* 1993
Sales 1.0MMM *EMP* 3,000[E]
SIC 5169 2842 5122 2833 5136 5137 Chemicals & allied products; Detergents & soaps, except specialty cleaning; Metal salts; Metal polishes; Specialty cleaning, polishes & sanitation goods; Drugs, proprietaries & sundries; Toiletries; Cosmetics, perfumes & hair products; Vitamins, natural or synthetic: bulk, uncompounded; Men's & boys' clothing; Women's & children's clothing
CFO: Michael J Cazer
VP: Jim Ayres
VP: Ken Davis
VP: Robin Dykhouse
VP: Catherine Ehrenberger
VP: Rob Hunter
VP: Farouque Khattak
Exec: Margaret Tuttle
Dir Soc: Joe Pettalia
IT Man: Terry Christopher
IT Man: Peggy Wood

D-U-N-S 01-056-2390
ACCESS COMMUNITY HEALTH NETWORK (IL)
600 W Fulton St Ste 200, Chicago, IL 60661-1262
Tel (312) 526-2200 *Founded/Ownrshp* 1984, 1990
Sales 123.8MM *EMP* 650
Accts Cliftonlarsonallen Llp Oak Br
SIC 8011 Offices & clinics of medical doctors
CEO: C Michael Savage
Pr: Laura Brown
**CEO:* Donna Thompson
**CFO:* Eduardo De Jesus
**CFO:* Mahomed Ouedraogo
Sr VP: Rosa Hernandez
**VP:* Steven Glass
**VP:* Eleva Riley
Dir IT: Abraham Miller
**Med Dir:* Dan Mukundan

D-U-N-S 92-932-4002
ACCESS DIRECT TELEMARKETING SERVICES INC
(*Suby of* PRC LLC) ★
4515 20th Ave Sw Ste B, Cedar Rapids, IA 52404-1224
Tel (319) 390-8900 *Founded/Ownrshp* 2000
Sales 35.3MM[E] *EMP* 2,000
SIC 7389 7361 Telemarketing services; Employment agencies
Pr: Tom Cardella
**Ex VP:* Mark Nelson
**VP:* Steve Brown
VP: Robert Iglehart
**VP:* Vince Ingrando
VP: James Van Housen
Oper/Mgr: Steve Hinsley
S&M/VP: Rachel Macha

D-U-N-S 80-717-5476
ACCESS GROUP INC
10 N High St Fl 4, West Chester, PA 19380-3014
Tel (484) 653-3300 *Founded/Ownrshp* 1993
Sales NA *EMP* 60
Accts Grant Thorton Llp Philadelph
SIC 6163 Loan agents
CEO: Christopher P Chapman
**Ch Bd:* Hannah R Arterian
**COO:* Charles Albano
VP: Eileen Santos-Perez
Exec: Scott Duke
Mng Dir: Amy Tien-Gordon

D-U-N-S 86-770-5584
ACCESS INDUSTRIES INC
730 5th Ave Fl 20, New York, NY 10019-4105
Tel (212) 247-6400 *Founded/Ownrshp* 1986
Sales 3.2MMM[E] *EMP* 4,211[E]
SIC 6211 Investment firm, general brokerage
CEO: Lincoln Benet
Pr: Len Blavatnik
Sr VP: Barry Dinaburg
Sr VP: Sergei Karpukhovich

D-U-N-S 87-689-7831
ACCESS INFORMATION MANAGEMENT SHARED SERVICES LLC
RHINODOX
6818 Patterson Pass Rd A, Livermore, CA 94550-4230
Tel (925) 461-5352 *Founded/Ownrshp* 2007
Sales 12.0MM *EMP* 1,500
SIC 7375 Information retrieval services
CEO: Rob Alston
**Pr:* John Chendo
**COO:* Nathan Campbell
**CFO:* Judd Feldman
**CFO:* Tony Skarupa
**Ex VP:* David Gesinger
**Ex VP:* Michael Schwab
VP: Shaun Stevens
Exec: Dede Wynne
Genl Mgr: Kim Greber
Genl Mgr: Chris Harris

D-U-N-S 92-951-0501
ACCESS INSURANCE HOLDINGS INC
3 Ravinia Dr Ste 400, Atlanta, GA 30346-2162
Tel (770) 234-3631 *Founded/Ownrshp* 1994
Sales NA *EMP* 350

SIC 6411 Insurance brokers
Pr: Michael McMenamin
**CFO:* Daniel Lazarek
VP: Donald Johnson
Software D: Jason Waters
Mktg Mgr: Hai Nguyen

D-U-N-S 02-530-3731
ACCESS INTELLIGENCE LLC
O R MANAGER
9211 Corp Blvd Fl 4, Rockville, MD 20850
Tel (301) 354-2000 *Founded/Ownrshp* 2000
Sales 95.0MM^E *EMP* 200^E
SIC 2741 2721 Miscellaneous publishing; Periodicals: publishing & printing
Pr: Donald Pazour
Ex VP: Michelle Troup
Sls Mgr: Michael Cassinelli
Assoc Ed: David Teich

D-U-N-S 80-815-7957 IMP
ACCESS INTERNATIONAL CO
(*Suby of* QUANTA INTERNATIONAL LIMITED)
45630 Northport Loop E, Fremont, CA 94538-6477
Tel (510) 226-1000 *Founded/Ownrshp* 1998
Sales 522.2MM^E *EMP* 12,100^E
SIC 5045 Computers, peripherals & software

D-U-N-S 07-966-6900
ACCESS MEDIQUIP LLC (TX)
(*Suby of* WATER STREET HEALTHCARE PARTNERS LLC) ★
255 Primera Blvd Ste 230, Lake Mary, FL 32746-2148
Tel (713) 985-4850 *Founded/Ownrshp* 1997
Sales 112.5MM^E *EMP* 135
SIC 5047 Medical equipment & supplies
Pr: Prakash Patel
COO: Jorge Amaro
CFO: Hartman Craig
CFO: Mike Duval
Ofcr: Jon Buffa
Ex VP: Carmen Fontanez
Ex VP: Buffa Jon
VP: Marcellus Davis
VP: Ruth Potts
Exec: Karen Eckhardt
Prin: Arnold Steve
Board of Directors: Steve Shulman

ACCESS PARATRANSIT
See ACCESS SERVICES

D-U-N-S 07-872-8592
■ **ACCESS PERMIAN MIDSTREAM LLC** (OK)
(*Suby of* WILLIAMS PARTNERS LP) ★
525 Central Park Dr # 1005, Oklahoma City, OK 73105-1723
Tel (877) 413-1023 *Founded/Ownrshp* 2012
Sales 35.8MM^E *EMP* 2,607^E
SIC 4922 Pipelines, natural gas
CEO: J Michael Stice
COO: Robert Purgason
CFO: David Shiels

D-U-N-S 88-330-0121
ACCESS SERVICES
ACCESS PARATRANSIT
3449 Santa Anita Ave, El Monte, CA 91731-2424
Tel (213) 270-6000 *Founded/Ownrshp* 1994
Sales 123.3MM *EMP* 80
Accts Rossi Doskocil & Finkelstein
SIC 4111 Local & suburban transit
CEO: Doran J Barnes
COO: F S Jewell
**Ex Dir:* Shelly Verrinder

D-U-N-S 82-508-1284
ACCESS STAFFING LLC
360 Lexington Ave Fl 8, New York, NY 10017-6559
Tel (212) 687-5440 *Founded/Ownrshp* 2005
Sales 131.5MM *EMP* 4,600
SIC 7361 Employment agencies
VP: Lee Caspi
VP: Jeff Freehof
VP: Jamie Grey
VP: Debra McAllen
VP: Diane Rafferty
VP: Dian Reid
VP: Tina Ruark
VP: Rachel Studdard
Exec: David Pomeroy
Assoc Dir: Audrey Moore
Mng Dir: Ric Boltz

D-U-N-S 03-204-3379 IMP
ACCESS TELECOM GROUP INC
1882 Nw 97th Ave, Doral, FL 33172-2304
Tel (305) 468-1955 *Founded/Ownrshp* 1999
Sales 110.0MM *EMP* 21
SIC 5065 5999 Telephone equipment; Telephone equipment & systems
Pr: Albert A Benhamu

D-U-N-S 96-348-4485
ACCESSDATA GROUP INC
(*Suby of* SOFTWARE FORENSICS INC) ★
588 W 400 S Ste 350, Lindon, UT 84042-1983
Tel (801) 377-5410 *Founded/Ownrshp* 2013
Sales 83.0MM *EMP* 150^E
SIC 7373 Systems software development services
Ch Bd: Victor Limongelli
Ex VP: Samuel Maccherola
VP: Abdeslam Afras
VP: Chad Gailey
VP: Nadine Weiskopf
IT Man: Farid Nabavi

D-U-N-S 94-970-2187 IMP
ACCESSORY CORP
T A C
575 8th Ave Fl 16, New York, NY 10018-3055
Tel (212) 391-8607 *Founded/Ownrshp* 1992
Sales 101.9MM^E *EMP* 1,200
SIC 3089 5199 Clothes hangers, plastic; Clothes hangers
Pr: Steven Sutton
**VP:* Jesse Sutton
**Prin:* Sharon Sutton

D-U-N-S 02-051-4530
ACCESSPOINT LLC
28800 Orchard Lake Rd # 200, Farmington Hills, MI 48334-2982
Tel (248) 504-6539 *Founded/Ownrshp* 2000
Sales 69.0MM *EMP* 1,000^E
SIC 8742 Human resource consulting services
CEO: Greg Packer
COO: Jim Mack
Ex VP: Charlie Ingram
Ex VP: Jeanne Nugent

D-U-N-S 06-417-0475 IMP
ACCIDENT FUND HOLDINGS INC
UNITED HEARTLAND
(*Suby of* BLUE CROSS AND BLUE SHIELD OF MICHIGAN) ★
200 N Grand Ave, Lansing, MI 48933-1228
Tel (866) 206-5851 *Founded/Ownrshp* 2009
Sales NA *EMP* 1,100
SIC 6331 Workers' compensation insurance
Pr: Michael K Britt
Pr: Steffani Schlinker
COO: David Frederiksen
CFO: Frank H Freund
CFO: Ronald H Schoen
Ofcr: Patrick J Walsh
Ex VP: Steven C Hess
Sr VP: William G Carney
**VP:* Linda Barnes
VP: Justin Bealhen
VP: Karin Geyer
**VP:* Al Gileczek
**VP:* Lisa Riddle
VP: Michael Sekoni
VP: Mike Seling

D-U-N-S 60-668-6095
ACCLAMATION INSURANCE MANAGEMENT SERVICES
A I M S
10445 Old Placerville Rd, Sacramento, CA 95827-2508
Tel (916) 563-1900 *Founded/Ownrshp* 1974
Sales NA *EMP* 225
SIC 6411 Insurance claim adjusters, not employed by insurance company
CEO: Dominic Russo
**CFO:* Tom Hoeberling
**Sr VP:* Lynn Cavalcanti
**VP:* Cheryl Agee
**VP:* Ralph Matthews
**VP:* Pat Nii
**VP:* Jeffrey Russo
Exec: Leonard Russo
Dir IT: Ren Johnson
Sales Exec: Jeff Head
Sls Dir: Robyn Azevedo

D-U-N-S 36-109-2450
■ **ACCLARENT INC**
(*Suby of* ETHICON INC) ★
33 Technology Dr, Irvine, CA 92618-2346
Tel (650) 687-5888 *Founded/Ownrshp* 2010
Sales 104.1MM^E *EMP* 400
SIC 3841 Surgical & medical instruments
Pr: David Shepherd
Dir IT: Praveen Chopra
Sls Dir: Lee Langford
Mktg Mgr: Jonathan Burkett
Mktg Mgr: Michael Pinder
Manager: Adam Herlevi
Snr Mgr: Kaylynn Callister

D-U-N-S 03-933-3067 IMP/EXP
▲ **ACCO BRANDS CORP**
4 Corporate Dr, Lake Zurich, IL 60047-8997
Tel (847) 541-9500 *Founded/Ownrshp* 1970
Sales 1.5MMM *EMP* 5,020
Tkr Sym ACCO *Exch* NYS
SIC 2782 3083 2761 2672 Looseleaf binders & devices; Paper ruling; Laminated plastic sheets; Computer forms, manifold or continuous; Adhesive papers, labels or tapes: from purchased material
Pr: Boris Elisman
**Ch Bd:* Robert J Keller
Pr: Christopher M Franey
Pr: Thomas W Tedford
CFO: Neal V Fenwick
Ofcr: Ralph P Hargrow
Sr VP: Gregory J McCormack
Sr VP: Joseph S Pekala
Sr VP: Kathleen D Schnaedter
Sr VP: Pamela R Schneider
VP: Joe Madormo
Board of Directors: George V Bayly, James A Buzzard, Kathleen S Dvorak, Robert H Jenkins, Thomas Kroeger, Michael Norkus, E Mark Rajkowski

D-U-N-S 12-627-8493 IMP
■ **ACCO BRANDS INC**
(*Suby of* ACCO BRANDS CORP) ★
4 Corporate Dr, Lake Zurich, IL 60047-8997
Tel (847) 541-9500 *Founded/Ownrshp* 1970
Sales 177.5MM^E *EMP* 1,484
SIC 2542 Fixtures: display, office or store: except wood
Pr: Robert J Keller
**Pr:* David Campbell
Ex VP: Neil McLachlan
Sr VP: Greg McCormack
Sr VP: Thomas P O'Neill Jr
Sr VP: Jeffrey Turofsky
VP: Rick Nelson
VP: Thomas O'Neill
VP: James Thorpe
Exec: Jessie Larson
Dir IT: Majella Tylka

D-U-N-S 00-151-9339 IMP/EXP
■ **ACCO BRANDS USA LLC**
(*Suby of* ACCO BRANDS CORP) ★
4 Corporate Dr, Lake Zurich, IL 60047-8997
Tel (800) 222-6462 *Founded/Ownrshp* 1925
Sales 1.0MMM^E *EMP* 3,000
SIC 3089 2761 3496 2675 Injection molding of plastics; Manifold business forms; Clips & fasteners, made from purchased wire; Folders, filing, die-cut: made from purchased materials
Pr: Boris Elisman
**Treas:* Laurie Keck
Ex VP: Mike Vogel
**VP:* Christopher Franey
**VP:* Jed Peters
**VP:* Thomas Tedford
IT Man: Mark E Johnson
Pdt Mgr: Gina Faso

D-U-N-S 07-848-5022
ACCO BRANDS USA LLC
4751 Hempstead Station Dr, Kettering, OH 45429-5165
Tel (937) 495-6323 *Founded/Ownrshp* 2012
Sales 59.8MM^E *EMP* 1,264
SIC 5943 Office forms & supplies
Ex VP: Neil Maclachlan
Art Dir: Maria Pasquel

ACCO CHAIN & LIFTING PRODUCTS
See FKI INDUSTRIES INC

D-U-N-S 00-690-5558
ACCO ENGINEERED SYSTEMS INC
6265 San Fernando Rd, Glendale, CA 91201-2214
Tel (818) 244-6571 *Founded/Ownrshp* 1934
Sales 841.6MM^E *EMP* 1,950
SIC 1711 7623

D-U-N-S 01-429-6407
ACCOMPLISH THERAPY LLC
1665 Palm Beach Lks, West Palm Beach, FL 33401-2121
Tel (561) 223-4332 *Founded/Ownrshp* 2010
Sales 57.0MM *EMP* 1,800
SIC 8093 Rehabilitation center, outpatient treatment
CEO: Brian Plasky

D-U-N-S 80-904-0520
ACCOR BUSINESS AND LEISURE NORTH AMERICA INC
(*Suby of* ACCOR)
245 Park Ave, New York, NY 10167-0002
Tel (972) 360-9000 *Founded/Ownrshp* 1989
Sales 28.7MM^E *EMP* 1,000
SIC 7011 Hotels
Pr: Jean-Francois Maljean
VP: Oliver Poriot
**Prin:* Armand Sebban

D-U-N-S 06-196-8517
ACCOR NORTH AMERICA INC
(*Suby of* ACCOR)
5055 Kelle Sprin Rd Ste 2, Addison, TX 75001
Tel (972) 360-9000 *Founded/Ownrshp* 1986
Sales 97.3MM^E *EMP* 2,000
SIC 7011 Hotels
Pr: James J Amorosia
**Pr:* George Lemener
CFO: Didier Bosc
**Treas:* Gregg Toon
Ex VP: Lance Miceli
Ex VP: Patrick Ollivier
Ex VP: Jeffrey Winslow
Sr VP: Christine Pouletty
VP: Michael Hucho
VP: Laurent Idrac
VP: Becky Lennard
VP: Thomas Lusk
VP: Simon McGrath
VP: Perry Ping
Exec: Cynthia Green
Exec: Peter Neber
Exec: Brian Stewart

D-U-N-S 60-422-2237 EXP
ACCORD HEALTHCARE INC
(*Suby of* INTAS PHARMACEUTICALS LIMITED)
1009 Slater Rd Ste 210b, Durham, NC 27703-8446
Tel (919) 941-7878 *Founded/Ownrshp* 2005
Sales 223.8MM *EMP* 25
Accts Jansen Valk Thompson Reahm Pc
SIC 5122 Pharmaceuticals
Pr: Gerald Price
**VP:* Burt Sullivan

D-U-N-S 92-780-0417
ACCORD HUMAN RESOURCES INC
210 Park Ave Ste 1200, Oklahoma City, OK 73102-5626
Tel (405) 232-9888 *Founded/Ownrshp* 2007
Sales 191.7MM^E *EMP* 13,000
SIC 8742 Compensation & benefits planning consultant
Pr: Dale Hageman
**CFO:* David R Baer
**VP:* Marilyn Conyer
CTO: Brklyn Flywalker
VP Sls: Peter Civello
Sls Mgr: Steve Davis

D-U-N-S 07-849-4465
ACCORD MEDICAL MANAGEMENT LP
NIX HEALTH CARE SYSTEM
(*Suby of* PROSPECT MEDICAL HOLDINGS INC) ★
414 Navarro St Ste 600, San Antonio, TX 78205-2541
Tel (210) 271-1800 *Founded/Ownrshp* 2012
Sales 134.2MM *EMP* 800
SIC 8062 General medical & surgical hospitals
CFO: Lester Surrock
CIO: Donna Thomas
Board of Directors: John A Evans, Will Ganltry Jr, Ken Newman

D-U-N-S 83-942-2342
ACCOUNT CONTROL TECHNOLOGY HOLDINGS INC
6918 Owensmouth Ave, Canoga Park, CA 91303-2003
Tel (818) 712-4999 *Founded/Ownrshp* 2012
Sales 228.1MM^E *EMP* 3,668^E
SIC 7389 Personal service agents, brokers & bureaus
CEO: Nabil Kabbani
**CFO:* Ryan Stearns
Ex VP: Tara Furiani
**CIO:* Sameer Maini

ACCOUNT SOLUTIONS GROUP
See FIRSTSOURCE SOLUTIONS USA INC

ACCOUNT SOLUTIONS GROUP
See FIRSTSOURCE ADVANTAGE LLC

D-U-N-S 05-441-2657
ACCOUNTABLE HEALTHCARE HOLDINGS CORP (FL)
999 Nw 51st St Ste 210, Boca Raton, FL 33431-4478
Tel (561) 235-7813 *Founded/Ownrshp* 2012
Sales 125.2MM^E *EMP* 1,027^E
SIC 6719 Investment holding companies, except banks
CEO: Robert Adamson
**Pr:* Kevin Little
COO: Nancy Bourg
**COO:* Lynne Mathews

D-U-N-S 07-869-6369
ACCOUNTABLE HEALTHCARE STAFFING INC
AHS-MEDREC
999 Yamato Rd Ste 210, Boca Raton, FL 33431-4478
Tel (561) 235-7810 *Founded/Ownrshp* 2011
Sales 117.4MM^E *EMP* 2,500
SIC 7363 Employee leasing service
Ch Bd: Robert Adamson
**CEO:* Kevin Little
**CFO:* Jeff Yesner

ACCOUNTANTS MEDIA GROUP
See THOMSON REUTERS (TAX & ACCOUNTING) INC

ACCOUNTS PAYABLE DEPT
See SOUTHEAST MISSOURI STATE UNIVERSITY

D-U-N-S 01-089-2311
ACCOUNTS PAYABLE MERCY ME
1221 Main St Ste 108, Holyoke, MA 01040-5396
Tel (413) 539-2692 *Founded/Ownrshp* 2009
Sales 125.7MM *EMP* 3
SIC 8011 Medical centers

D-U-N-S 12-415-3284
ACCREDITED HOME LENDERS HOLDING CO
(*Suby of* L S F 5 ACCREDITED INVESTMENTS LLC) ★
15253 Ave Of Science, San Diego, CA 92128-3437
Tel (858) 676-2100 *Founded/Ownrshp* 2007
Sales 242.7MM^E *EMP* 2,700^E
SIC 6798 Real estate investment trusts
CEO: James A Konrath
**Pr:* Joseph J Lydon
CFO: John S Buchanan
**Ex VP:* Stuart D Marvin
VP: Evan Eageloff
VP: Martyn Hughes
CIO: James M Pathman

D-U-N-S 12-253-6654
■ **ACCREDO HEALTH GROUP INC**
(*Suby of* ACCREDO HEALTH INC) ★
1640 Century Center Pkwy # 110, Memphis, TN 38134-8822
Tel (877) 222-7336 *Founded/Ownrshp* 1997
Sales 57.2MM^E *EMP* 1,500
SIC 8051 8052 8093 Skilled nursing care facilities; Intermediate care facilities; Specialty outpatient clinics
CEO: Ken Boltner
**Pr:* Steven Fitzpatrick
Treas: Peter Gaylord
Sr VP: Joel R Kimbrough
**VP:* Kevin Franko
Dir Rx: Deborah Coleman
MIS Dir: Cheryl Conlee
Dir IT: Galen Bolton
IT Man: Darrell Gentry
IT Man: Shane Waldroup
Mktg Mgr: Niketa Bryant

D-U-N-S 95-966-7585
■ **ACCREDO HEALTH INC**
(*Suby of* EXPRESS SCRIPTS HOLDING CO) ★
1640 Century Center Pkwy # 110, Memphis, TN 38134-8822
Tel (901) 373-8958 *Founded/Ownrshp* 2005
Sales 1.3MMM^E *EMP* 6,530
SIC 2835 8092 In vitro & in vivo diagnostic substances; Kidney dialysis centers
CEO: David D Stevens
**Pr:* John R Grow
COO: Steven R Fitzpatick
**CFO:* Joel Kimbrough
**Sr VP:* Thomas Bell
Sr VP: Thomas W Bell Jr
**Sr VP:* Kyle J Callahan
VP: Kirk A Cotham
VP: Janene Cromis
Nurse Mgr: Jane Jones
CIO: Kyle Truitt

D-U-N-S 14-554-0212
ACCRETIVE HEALTH INC
401 N Michigan Ave # 2700, Chicago, IL 60611-4217
Tel (312) 324-7820 *Founded/Ownrshp* 2003
Sales 117.2MM *EMP* 3,030
Accts Ernst & Young Llp Chicago I
Tkr Sym ACHI *Exch* OTO
SIC 8741 Hospital management; Nursing & personal care facility management
Pr: Joseph Flanagan
**Ch Bd:* Steven J Shulman
CFO: Peter Csapo
CFO: Christopher Ricaurte
Ex VP: Etienne Deffarges
Sr VP: Douglas A Berkson
Sr VP: Walter Ettinger Jr
Sr VP: Daniel Zaccardo
VP: Wes Arnett
VP: Jeff Blum
VP: Dan Buning
VP: Bradley Cordes
VP: Bill Falconer
VP: Jim Gaffney
VP: Stacy Gibbons
VP: Rob Hoyt
VP: Logan Johnston
VP: John Liesching
VP: Susan Lineberry

VP: Steve Meyerson
VP: Pamela Mulshine
Board of Directors: Robert V Stanek, Edgar Bronfman Jr, Mark A Wolfson, Charles J Ditkoff, Michael B Hammond, Steven N Kaplan, Arthur A Klein, Lawrence B Leisure, Stanley N Logan, Alex J Mandl, Denis J Nayden

ACCRETIVE NETWORKS
See ACCRETIVE TECHNOLOGY GROUP INC

D-U-N-S 80-924-6650
ACCRETIVE SOLUTIONS INC
1 S Wacker Dr Ste 950, Chicago, IL 60606-4670
Tel (312) 994-4600 *Founded/Ownrshp* 1983
Sales 179.1MM[E] *EMP* 1,960
SIC 8721 Accounting, auditing & bookkeeping
CEO: Kerry Barrett
**Ch Bd:* Jonathan Rosenthal
**CFO:* Joann Lilek
CFO: Joann S Lilek
**V Ch Bd:* Richard A Moran
Ex VP: Ann Hook
**Ex VP:* Mike G Reinecke
VP: Kevin Burke
VP: Maria Martindale
VP: Bill Meyer
Snr Mgr: Lilian Lin
Board of Directors: David Martin

D-U-N-S 06-946-3367
ACCRETIVE SOLUTIONS OPERATING CORP
(*Suby of* ACCRETIVE SOLUTIONS INC) ★
1 S Wacker Dr Ste 950, Chicago, IL 60606-4670
Tel (312) 994-4600 *Founded/Ownrshp* 1999
Sales 28.2MM[E] *EMP* 1,000
SIC 8721 7363 7361

D-U-N-S 02-278-3638
ACCRETIVE TECHNOLOGY GROUP INC
ACCRETIVE NETWORKS
800 Stewart St, Seattle, WA 98101-1306
Tel (206) 443-6401 *Founded/Ownrshp* 1997
Sales 366.5MM *EMP* 80[E]
Accts Gary W Lien Cpa Issaquah Wa
SIC 4813
Pr: Shawn Boday
Genl Mgr: Paul Wright

ACCRIVA DIAGNOSTICS
See INTERNATIONAL TECHNIDYNE CORP

D-U-N-S 94-750-5822
ACCRUENT LLC
(*Suby of* GENSTAR CAPITAL LLC) ★
11500 Alterra Pkwy # 110, Austin, TX 78758-3191
Tel (512) 861-0726 *Founded/Ownrshp* 2016
Sales 188.1MM[E] *EMP* 644
SIC 7372 Prepackaged software
CEO: John Borgerding
**Ch Bd:* Mark H Friedman
**COO:* Wayne Roberts
**CFO:* Van Goodrich
CFO: Bob Pape
**Ofcr:* David McCann
**Sr VP:* Melissa Sitton
VP: Jason Beem
**VP:* Carey Bettencourt
**VP:* Jeff Bolke
VP: Pascal Desmarets
VP: Tim Langan
VP: Tim McLean
VP: Jeff REA
VP: John Stockton
VP: Ning Theissen
VP: Max Thoene
VP: Ning Ning Yu

ACCS
See ASSOCIATED CLEANING CONSULTANTS AND SERVICES INC

D-U-N-S 13-389-3508
ACCT HOLDINGS LLC
1235 Westlakes Dr Ste 160, Berwyn, PA 19312-2417
Tel (610) 695-0500 *Founded/Ownrshp* 2003
Sales 347.8MM[E] *EMP* 2,300
SIC 4813 Telephone communication, except radio

ACCU-READ SERVICES
See UNIBAR SERVICES INC

D-U-N-S 11-328-4624 IMP/EXP
■ **ACCU-TECH CORP**
(*Suby of* ANIXTER INTERNATIONAL INC) ★
11350 Old Roswell Rd # 100, Alpharetta, GA 30009-2292
Tel (770) 740-2240 *Founded/Ownrshp* 1997
Sales 275.3MM[E] *EMP* 387
SIC 5065 5063 Electronic parts & equipment; Electronic wire & cable; Control & signal wire & cable, including coaxial
Pr: Dan Delavie
COO: Cameron Teeter
**CFO:* Jennifer Franklin
**CFO:* Charles Goldgeier
VP: John Burkey
VP: Bill Geary
**VP:* Randall A Guhl
**VP:* William H Lorey
Brnch Mgr: John Campbell
Brnch Mgr: Rcdd Todd Delavie
IT Man: Josh McCullough
Board of Directors: Robert Grubbs, Dennis Letham

D-U-N-S 07-888-7334
ACCUDYNE INDUSTRIES LLC
2728 N Harwood St Ste 200, Dallas, TX 75201-1579
Tel (469) 518-4777 *Founded/Ownrshp* 2012
Sales 593.9MM[E] *EMP* 1,156[E]
SIC 3463 Pump, compressor, turbine & engine forgings, except auto
CEO: Charles L Treadway

D-U-N-S 07-979-4057
ACCUIRE LLC (FL)
VFORCE STAFFING SOLUTIONS
2001 Thomasville Rd, Tallahassee, FL 32308-0733
Tel (850) 893-7710 *Founded/Ownrshp* 2014
Sales 50.0MM *EMP* 2,000
SIC 7361 Employment agencies; Placement agencies; Executive placement; Labor contractors (employment agency)

D-U-N-S 07-986-7900
ACCUMED CORP
155 Boyce Dr, Mocksville, NC 27028-4187
Tel (800) 278-6796 *Founded/Ownrshp* 2014
Sales 80.0MM[E] *EMP* 1,500
SIC 3841 Medical instruments & equipment, blood & bone work
CEO: Doughlas Constable

D-U-N-S 87-852-8165 IMP
ACCUMED TECHNOLOGIES INC
ACCUMMED INNOVATIVE TECH
160 Bud Mil Dr Ste 1, Buffalo, NY 14206-1812
Tel (716) 853-1800 *Founded/Ownrshp* 1994
Sales 302.1MM[E] *EMP* 226[E]
SIC 5047

ACCUMMED INNOVATIVE TECH
See ACCUMED TECHNOLOGIES INC

D-U-N-S 07-160-9663
ACCUPAC INC
1501 Industrial Blvd, Mainland, PA 19451
Tel (215) 256-7000 *Founded/Ownrshp* 2003
Sales 147.7MM[E] *EMP* 425[E]
SIC 7389 Packaging & labeling services
Pr: Paul H Alvater
CFO: Dave Mullen
**CFO:* Bruce Wright
**Treas:* Eileen Slawek
**VP:* Jay Jones
IT Man: Mike Gebhard

D-U-N-S 78-596-1244
▲ **ACCURAY INC**
1310 Chesapeake Ter, Sunnyvale, CA 94089-1100
Tel (408) 716-4600 *Founded/Ownrshp* 1992
Sales 398.8MM *EMP* 1,010
Tkr Sym ARAY *Exch* NGS
SIC 3841 Surgical instruments & apparatus
Pr: Joshua H Levine
**Ch Bd:* Louis J Lavigne Jr
COO: Kelly Londy
CFO: Kevin Waters
**V Ch Bd:* Elizabeth Davila
Sr VP: Alaleh Nouri
VP: Fran Jackson
Natl Sales: Lin Li
Natl Sales: Terry Reay
Mktg Dir: Peter Hoban
Mktg Dir: Takako Takeda
Board of Directors: Jack Goldstein, Richard Pettingill, Robert S Weiss, Dennis L Winger

D-U-N-S 16-177-8352
ACCURIDE CORP
(*Suby of* ARMOR PARENT CORP) ★
7140 Office Cir, Evansville, IN 47715-8235
Tel (812) 962-5000 *Founded/Ownrshp* 2016
Sales 685.5MM *EMP* 2,290
SIC 3714 3713 Wheels, motor vehicle; Wheel rims, motor vehicle; Bumpers & bumperettes, motor vehicle; Brake drums, motor vehicle; Truck bodies & parts
Pr: Richard F Dauch
Pr: David G Adams
Pr: Scott D Hazlett
Pr: Gregory A Risch
CFO: Michael A Hajost
Sr VP: Mary E Blair
Plnt Mgr: Tim Rogers
Genl Couns: Stephen A Martin

D-U-N-S 00-969-3441 IMP
ACCURIDE INTERNATIONAL INC
12311 Shoemaker Ave, Santa Fe Springs, CA 90670-4721
Tel (562) 903-0200 *Founded/Ownrshp* 1966
Sales 519.5MM[E] *EMP* 2,000
SIC 3429 Manufactured hardware (general)
CEO: Scott E Jordan
**Prin:* Jerome Barr
Dir IT: Steve Helms
Dir IT: Mario Rojas
Sls Dir: Gary Stoffer
Mktg Mgr: Claudia Tuttle
Mktg Mgr: Sue Witkowski
Sls Mgr: Nicole Notarianni
Sls Mgr: Mike Short
Pgrm Dir: Greg Rewers

D-U-N-S 07-992-8562
ACCURUS AEROSPACE CORP
222 Las Colinas Blvd W, Irving, TX 75039-5421
Tel (469) 317-6140 *Founded/Ownrshp* 2013
Sales 169.6MM[E] *EMP* 430
SIC 3728 Aircraft parts & equipment
CEO: Jim Gibson
**Pr:* Robert A Kirkpatrick
VP: Andrea Dorr
VP: Gregg Ferrell
VP: Larry Johnson
VP: Tyson Toews

D-U-N-S 08-351-0842 IMP/EXP
ACDI/VOCA (IL)
50 F St Nw Ste 1000, Washington, DC 20001-1530
Tel (202) 469-6000 *Founded/Ownrshp* 1963
Sales 176.3MM *EMP* 1,085[E]
Accts Mcgladrey Llp Mclean Virgini
SIC 8748 8641 Agricultural consultant; Civic social & fraternal associations
CEO: Bill Polidoro
COO: Jana Kurts
**CFO:* Matt Renaud
Ex VP: Philip Dipofi
**Ex VP:* Robert Fries
**Sr VP:* Paul Guenette
**Sr VP:* Marsha Moulton
Sr VP: Fred Smith

VP: Deborah Hanley
VP: John Hays
Exec: Duane Stenzel

D-U-N-S 60-710-4221
ACE AMERICAN INSURANCE CO
(*Suby of* A C E) ★
436 Walnut St, Philadelphia, PA 19106-3703
Tel (215) 640-1000 *Founded/Ownrshp* 1998
Sales NA *EMP* 2,890
SIC 6321 6331 6351 Accident & health insurance; Fire, marine & casualty insurance; Surety insurance
Pr: Brian E Dowd
CFO: Roberto Reyes
**Treas:* Kenneth R Garrett
Ex VP: Paul O'Connel
Sr VP: Lisa Humphrey
**Sr VP:* Steven Reiss
VP: Edward M Jovinelly
VP Mktg: Harry W Rambo

D-U-N-S 05-272-2196
ACE ASPHALT OF ARIZONA INC
3030 S 7th St, Phoenix, AZ 85040-1163
Tel (602) 243-4100 *Founded/Ownrshp* 1981
Sales 144.1MM[E] *EMP* 250[E]
SIC 1611 Highway & street construction
CEO: Ross Gatlin
**Pr:* Michael Moertl
CFO: Gary Keler
**CFO:* Ronald O'Connor
**VP:* Wayne Bell
Sales Exec: Bob Wade
Sls&Mrk Ex: Jeffrey Pataki

ACE ASPHALT PRODUCTS COMPANY
See EDW C LEVY CO

ACE CASH EXPRESS
See JLL PARTNERS INC

D-U-N-S 13-972-9412
ACE CASH EXPRESS INC
(*Suby of* ACE CASH EXPRESS) ★
1231 Greenway Dr Ste 600, Irving, TX 75038-2511
Tel (972) 550-5000 *Founded/Ownrshp* 2006
Sales 921.4MM[E] *EMP* 4,000
SIC 7323 6099 Credit clearinghouse; Check cashing agencies
Pr: Jay B Shipowitz
Pr: Michael J McCullough
Pr: Larry Tucker
**COO:* Ted M Eades
CFO: David Dyckman
CFO: Dave Lee
CFO: Bill McCalmont
CFO: Whitbeck Todd
**CFO:* Temple Weiss
**Chf Mktg O:* Allen J Klose
Chf Mktg O: Jake Schroepfer
Ofcr: Frank Dudowicz
Ex VP: Raymond McCarty
**Sr VP:* Joe B Edwards
Sr VP: James E Gibbs
Sr VP: Michael Nelson
Sr VP: Eric C Norrington
**Sr VP:* RB Ramsey
VP: Jason Adams
VP: Howard Beckman
VP: Denise Burch

ACE DISPOSAL
See KIMBLE COMPANIES INC

D-U-N-S 01-290-8927 IMP
ACE ENDICO CORP
LA FEDE ITALIAN FOODS
80 International Blvd, Brewster, NY 10509-2344
Tel (914) 347-3131 *Founded/Ownrshp* 1982
Sales 182.2MM[E] *EMP* 165
SIC 5141 5142 5148 Groceries, general line; Packaged frozen goods; Fresh fruits & vegetables
CEO: William A Endico
**Pr:* Murray Hertzberg
Ofcr: Maureen Hart
**Ex VP:* Thomas Recine
**VP:* Michael Endico
VP: Les Tide
Exec: Joseph Johnson
Exec: Maureen Nitka
Genl Mgr: Michael Jacobson
Dir IT: Paul Siecienski
Ql Cn Mgr: Michael Lodolce

D-U-N-S 17-062-7058
■ **ACE GAMING LLC**
(*Suby of* ATLANTIC COAST ENTERTAINMENT HOLDINGS, INC.)
8918 Spanish Ridge Ave, Las Vegas, NV 89148-1302
Tel (702) 401-5931 *Founded/Ownrshp* 2003
Sales 4.8MM[E] *EMP* 1,958
SIC 7011 Hotels; Casino hotel

ACE HARDWARE
See ROCKYS HARDWARE INC

ACE HARDWARE
See BLATCHFORDS INC

ACE HARDWARE
See NEWKIRK HOLDING CO INC

ACE HARDWARE
See WESTLAKE HARDWARE INC

D-U-N-S 00-692-8311 IMP/EXP
ACE HARDWARE CORP
2200 Kensington Ct, Oak Brook, IL 60523-2100
Tel (630) 990-6600 *Founded/Ownrshp* 1924
Sales 5.0MMM *EMP* 4,500
Accts Ernst & Young Llp Chicago I
SIC 5251 5198 5063 5074 5083 Hardware; Paints, varnishes & supplies; Paint brushes, rollers, sprayers; Electrical supplies; Light bulbs & related supplies; Lighting fixtures, residential; Batteries; Plumbing & hydronic heating supplies; Lawn & garden machinery & equipment
Pr: John Venhuizen
**Ch Bd:* David Ziegler
**CFO:* Bill Guzik
**CFO:* William Guzik

**Ch:* Jim Ackroyd
Treas: Sandra Brandt
Ex VP: Susie Batchelder
Ex VP: Graham Henderson
**Ex VP:* Rita D Kahle
Ex VP: Ruth McKelvy
Sr VP: Surane John
Sr VP: Ken Nichols
VP: Bill Bauman
VP: Lori Bossman
VP: Lori Bossmann
VP: Robert Brown
VP: Kane Calamari
VP: Mike Elmore
VP: Karen Fedyszyn
VP: Angel Garcia
VP: Howard Japlon

D-U-N-S 03-350-1701 IMP/EXP
ACE INDUSTRIES INC
CERTIFIED CRANES-HOIST
6295 Mcdonough Dr, Norcross, GA 30093-1252
Tel (770) 441-0898 *Founded/Ownrshp* 1932
Sales 146.7MM[E] *EMP* 100
SIC 5084 Industrial machinery & equipment
CEO: Joshua Arwood
**CFO:* Cheryl Rossborough
VP: Dan Arwood
VP: Andy Gurley
Brnch Mgr: Brad Grow
Dir IT: Bob Myles
IT Man: Dennis Frolov
Plnt Mgr: Paul Fleming
Sls Dir: Brad Martin
Sales Asso: Julie Newberg

D-U-N-S 07-099-3162
ACE INFO SOLUTIONS INC
ACEINFO
11490 Commerce Park Dr # 340, Reston, VA 20191-1532
Tel (703) 391-2800 *Founded/Ownrshp* 2000
Sales 116.0MM *EMP* 550
SIC 7379
CEO: Jayanth Challa
**COO:* Nar Koppula
**CFO:* John Hamilton
Prgrm Mgr: Chris Alfieri
Prgrm Mgr: Prashant Paruchuri
Prgrm Mgr: Carrie Schori
Off Mgr: Tran Kratzke
Netwrk Eng: Chuck Hoffman
Ql Cn Mgr: Fatima Aziz-Sultan
Ql Cn Mgr: Dan Boswell

D-U-N-S 02-700-4332 IMP/EXP
ACE MART RESTAURANT SUPPLY CO
2653 Austin Hwy, San Antonio, TX 78218-2049
Tel (210) 323-4400 *Founded/Ownrshp* 1975
Sales 182.8MM[E] *EMP* 200
SIC 5169 5046 Industrial chemicals; Cooking equipment, commercial; Restaurant equipment & supplies
Pr: Paul Gustafson
**Treas:* Norma Gustafson
**VP:* Carl Gustafson
Mktg Dir: Glenn Rierson
Sls Mgr: Ron Keene

ACE MOVING AND STORAGE
See BEKINS A-1 MOVERS INC

D-U-N-S 07-335-1538
ACE PARKING MANAGEMENT INC
645 Ash St, San Diego, CA 92101-3299
Tel (619) 233-6624 *Founded/Ownrshp* 1977
Sales 265.3MM[E] *EMP* 3,500
SIC 7521 Parking lots; Parking structure
Ch: Scott A Jones
**Pr:* Steve Burton
**CEO:* John Baumgardner
**CFO:* Charles Blottin
Ex VP: Matt Griesheimer
**VP:* Sasha Bradley
VP: Doug Brooks
VP: Mike Tweeten
Area Mgr: Paula Hermogenes
Area Mgr: Ryan Madsen
Area Mgr: Jason Miller

D-U-N-S 61-466-6972
ACE PROPERTY AND CASUALTY INSURANCE CO
(*Suby of* ACE LIMITED)
2 Liberty Pl 2 Liberty Place, Philadelphia, PA 19102
Tel (215) 761-1000 *Founded/Ownrshp* 1998
Sales NA *EMP* 3,330
SIC 6321 6331 6351 Accident & health insurance; Fire, marine & casualty insurance; Surety insurance
Ch Bd: Gerald A Isom
**CFO:* Robert Irvan
**Treas:* Paul Bergsteinsson
**VP:* John Murphy Jr
**VP:* James Sears
**VP:* Joseph Stagliano

ACE SANITATION
See WASTE MANAGEMENT OF MICHIGAN INC

ACE US HOLDINGS, INC.
See CHUBB US HOLDING INC

D-U-N-S 09-036-2109
ACE USA INC
A C E
436 Walnut St, Philadelphia, PA 19106-3703
Tel (215) 923-5352 *Founded/Ownrshp* 1993
Sales NA *EMP* 2,898
SIC 6411 6321 6351

D-U-N-S 00-167-8804
ACE WIRE & CABLE CO INC
7201 51st Ave, Woodside, NY 11377-7610
Tel (718) 458-9200 *Founded/Ownrshp* 1952
Sales 121.1MM[E] *EMP* 64[E]
SIC 5063 Wiring devices; Wire & cable
Pr: Jerry Firestone
**CFO:* Edwin Tyas
**Treas:* Harris Firestone
Exec: Lorette Difrenza
Sales Asso: Frank Ingoglia

Sales Asso: Nigel Martin
Sales Asso: Tom Wacaster

D-U-N-S 11-846-0802 IMP/EXP
ACE WIRELESS & TRADING INC
3031 Orange Ave Ste B, Santa Ana, CA 92707-4246
Tel (949) 748-5700 *Founded/Ownrshp* 2006
Sales 107.9MM^E *EMP* 375
SIC 5065

ACEINFO
See ACE INFO SOLUTIONS INC

D-U-N-S 07-934-6220
ACELITY LP INC
(*Suby of* CHIRON GUERNSEY HOLDINGS LP INC) ★
12930 W Interstate 10, San Antonio, TX 78249-2248
Tel (210) 524-9000 *Founded/Ownrshp* 2011
Sales 1.8MMM *EMP* 5,800^E
SIC 3841 2834 Surgical & medical instruments; Pharmaceutical preparations
Pr: Joseph F Woody
Genl Pt: Chiron G Limited
CFO: Todd Wyatt
Sr VP: John Harper
VP: Scott Jones
Sls Mgr: Diana Camp
Sls Mgr: Barry Moore
Snr Mgr: Laurel Harper
Snr Mgr: Manish Sharma
Snr Mgr: Tyler Simmons

D-U-N-S 83-150-3482
■ **ACENTIA LLC**
(*Suby of* MAXIMUS FEDERAL SERVICES INC) ★
3130 Frview Pk Dr Ste 800, Falls Church, VA 22042
Tel (703) 712-4000 *Founded/Ownrshp* 2015
Sales 202.1MM^E *EMP* 1,100^E
SIC 7371 Computer software development
CEO: Todd Stottlemyer
CFO: Sharon Pavlovsky
**CFO:* Tom Weston
Sr VP: Tricia Iveson
**Sr VP:* Richard Jacik
**Sr VP:* Danielle Johnson
**Sr VP:* Carl Rosenblatt
VP: Kim Bahrami
VP: John Dorman
VP: Steve Fite
VP: Frank Nigro
VP: Diana Poss
VP: Vincent Woody
Exec: Ed Vigil
Dir Bus: Brian Skoletsky

D-U-N-S 11-329-1769
ACER AMERICA CORP
(*Suby of* GATEWAY INC) ★
333 W San Carlos St, San Jose, CA 95110-2726
Tel (408) 533-7700 *Founded/Ownrshp* 1977
Sales 85.6MM^E *EMP* 180
SIC 7379
CEO: Emmanuel Fromont
**CFO:* Ming Wang
Prgrm Mgr: Jeff Lenz
CIO: Howard Cheung
Mktg Mgr: Nidhi Nayyar
Mktg Mgr: John Nguyen
Mktg Mgr: Sonia Vasudeva
Manager: Francisco Arroyo
Sls Mgr: Julien Bertheuil
Sls Mgr: Philip Burger
Counsel: Michael Wagner

D-U-N-S 80-848-8667
ACER AMERICAN HOLDINGS CORP
(*Suby of* BOARDWALK CAPITAL HOLDINGS LIMITED)
333 W San Carlos St # 1500, San Jose, CA 95110-2726
Tel (408) 533-7700 *Founded/Ownrshp* 2007
Sales 281.8MM^E *EMP* 1,700^E
SIC 3577 3571 Computer peripheral equipment; Electronic computers
CEO: Emmanuel Fromont
**CEO:* J T Wang
Sftwr Eng: Dan Lin

ACES POWER MARKETING
See ALLIANCE FOR COOPERATIVE ENERGY SERVICES POWER MARKETING LLC

ACET
See ADAMS COMMUNICATION & ENGINEERING TECHNOLOGY INC

D-U-N-S 00-892-1546 IMP/EXP
▲ **ACETO CORP**
4 Tri Harbor Ct, Port Washington, NY 11050-4661
Tel (516) 627-6000 *Founded/Ownrshp* 1947
Sales 558.5MM *EMP* 270^E
Accts Bdo Usa Llp Melville New Yo
Tkr Sym ACET *Exch* NGS
SIC 5122 5169 Drugs, proprietaries & sundries; Chemicals & allied products
Pr: Salvatore Guccione
**Ch Bd:* Albert L Eilender
Pr: Satish Srinivasan
COO: Walter J Kaczmarek III
CFO: Douglas Roth
Sr VP: Charles J Alaimo
Sr VP: Frank Debenedittis
Sr VP: Terry Kippley
Sr VP: Carlos Restrepo
Sr VP: Steven Rogers
Sr VP: Nicholas Shackley
VP: Raymond Bartone
Board of Directors: William N Britton, Natasha Giordano, William C Kennally III, Alan G Levin, Hans C Noetzli, Daniel B Yarosh

ACF
See A C FURNITURE CO INC

D-U-N-S 84-790-5965
ACF INDUSTRIES HOLDING CORP
(*Suby of* HIGHCREST INVESTORS LLC) ★
767 5th Ave, New York, NY 10153-0023
Tel (212) 702-4363 *Founded/Ownrshp* 1993
Sales 1.4MMM^E *EMP* 3,670
SIC 3743 4741 4789 6799 Freight cars & equipment; Tank freight cars & car equipment; Railroad equipment, except locomotives; Rental of railroad cars; Railroad car repair; Security speculators for own account
CEO: Keith Cozza
**Pr:* Carl C Icahn
**VP:* Richard T Buonato

D-U-N-S 07-873-0927
ACG SEATTLE INC
24 Roy St 442, Seattle, WA 98109-4018
Tel (206) 524-5300 *Founded/Ownrshp* 1954
Sales 98.4MM^E *EMP* 12,000
SIC 8732 Business economic service
Ex Dir: Karin Martinez
Treas: Randy Wells

D-U-N-S 60-293-6556 IMP
ACH FOAM TECHNOLOGIES INC
5250 Sherman St, Denver, CO 80216-1938
Tel (303) 297-3844 *Founded/Ownrshp* 2005
Sales 94.6MM^E *EMP* 400
SIC 3086 Insulation or cushioning material, foamed plastic
CEO: Ted Dann
**Treas:* Harry Tilden
**VP:* Todd Huempfner
**VP:* Frank Kiesecker

D-U-N-S 61-846-4036 IMP/EXP
ACH FOOD COMPANIES INC
A C H RETAIL PRODUCTS
(*Suby of* ASSOCIATED BRITISH FOODS PLC)
7171 Goodlett Farms Pkwy, Cordova, TN 38016-4909
Tel (901) 381-3000 *Founded/Ownrshp* 1995
Sales 657.2MM *EMP* 842
Accts Kpmg Llp London
SIC 2079 2099 Oil, hydrogenated: edible; Spices, including grinding; Dressings, salad: dry mixes
Pr: Richard Rankin
**CFO:* Stephen Zaruba
**Sr VP:* Carmen Sciackitano
Sr VP: Bill Wells
VP: Pete Friedman
VP: George Pastrana
Plnt Mgr: Tim Gathman
Plnt Mgr: Steve Robinson
Snr Mgr: Dave Pekol

D-U-N-S 60-360-9785
ACHEN-GARDNER INC
GDC HOMES
550 S 79th St, Chandler, AZ 85226-4706
Tel (480) 940-1300 *Founded/Ownrshp* 1986
Sales 83.7MM^E *EMP* 290
SIC 1611 1542 1521 1751 6552 Highway & street construction; Surfacing & paving; Commercial & office building, new construction; Custom builders, non-residential; New construction, single-family houses; Framing contractor; Subdividers & developers
Ch Bd: Douglas D Gardner
**Pr:* Sanders T Achen
**Treas:* Roxanne Achen
VP: Dan Spitza
Dir Risk M: Cesar Martinez
Sfty Mgr: Larry Gardner
Mktg Mgr: Lorna Tremaine

D-U-N-S 96-582-2492
■ **ACHIEVERS LLC**
(*Suby of* BLACKHAWK NETWORK HOLDINGS INC) ★
660 3rd St Ste 302, San Francisco, CA 94107-1921
Tel (888) 622-3343 *Founded/Ownrshp* 2015
Sales 110.0MM *EMP* 250
SIC 8742 Incentive or award program consultant
Genl Mgr: David Brennan
Sr VP: Paul Pedrazzi
VP: Egan Cheung
VP: David Laszewski
VP: Debbie Lillitos
VP: Brogan Taylor
VP: Dwayne Walker
VP: Aris Zakinthinos
VP Sls: Greg Brown
Pr Mgr: Jennifer Hubbard

D-U-N-S 15-583-4703
ACHIEVO CORP
1400 Terra Bella Ave E, Mountain View, CA 94043-3062
Tel (925) 498-8864 *Founded/Ownrshp* 2002
Sales 61.0MM^E *EMP* 2,002
SIC 7371 Custom computer programming services
CEO: Sandy Wai-Yan Chau
Pr: Robert P Lee
COO: Bernard Mathaisel
CFO: Julio Leung
CFO: Darryl Quan
Treas: Jennifer Chen
Sr VP: James C Li
VP: Brian K Fawkes
VP: Thomas M Mastri
VP: Gary P Silverman
Board of Directors: Terrence W Kyle, David Kynaston, Lawrence J Lau, James Schraith

D-U-N-S 10-279-8303
ACHMC INC
ARROWHEAD HOSPITAL
18701 N 67th Ave, Glendale, AZ 85308-7100
Tel (623) 561-7170 *Founded/Ownrshp* 1981
Sales 115.4MM^E *EMP* 700
SIC 8062 General medical & surgical hospitals
CEO: Jhonathan Bartlett
CFO: Brain Walton
Doctor: Cindy Moran

D-U-N-S 02-018-8793
■ **ACI WORLDWIDE CORP**
APPLIED COMMUNICATIONS
(*Suby of* ACI WORLDWIDE INC) ★
6060 Coventry Dr, Elkhorn, NE 68022-6482
Tel (402) 390-7600 *Founded/Ownrshp* 1993
Sales 342.8MM^E *EMP* 1,050
SIC 7372 5045 Business oriented computer software; Computer software
Pr: Daniel Frate
**CFO:* Scott Behrens
**Treas:* Craig Maki
VP: Amala Duggirala
VP: Kevin Long
VP: Stephen J Royer
VP: Stephen Royer
**Dir Risk M:* David Morem
Prgrm Mgr: Ryan Cole
Snr Sftwr: Steve Eschliman
Snr Sftwr: Richelle Meisinger

D-U-N-S 84-748-6990
▲ **ACI WORLDWIDE INC**
3520 Kraft Rd Ste 300, Naples, FL 34105-4957
Tel (239) 403-4600 *Founded/Ownrshp* 1993
Sales 1.0MMM *EMP* 4,576^E
Accts Deloitte & Touche Llp Omaha
Tkr Sym ACIW *Exch* NGS
SIC 7372 5045 Business oriented computer software; Computer software
Pr: Philip G Heasley
Pr: Daniel J Frate
CFO: Scott W Behrens
Treas: Craig A Maki
Ofcr: Dennis P Byrnes
Ofcr: David N Morem
Ex VP: Eve Aretakis
Ex VP: Craig Saks
Sr VP: Jan Kruger
Sr VP: Hannes Van Rensburg
VP: Ann Adams
VP: Marco Bravo
VP: Christopher Briggs
VP: David Diloreto
VP: Shesh Gorur
VP: Vivian Jimenez
VP: Ron Kitlas
VP: Charles H Linberg
VP: Brad Mullman
Exec: Anthony M Scotto Jr
Board of Directors: Janet Estep, James C Hale, James C McGroddy, Charles E Peters Jr, David A Poe, John M Shay Jr, Jan H Suwinski, Thomas W Warsop III

ACIA
See AUTO CLUB INSURANCE ASSOCIATION CO

A.C.I.P.C.O.
See AMERICAN CAST IRON PIPE CO

D-U-N-S 61-492-4397 IMP/EXP
ACK CONTROLS INC
(*Suby of* CHUO SPRING CO., LTD.)
2600 Happy Valley Rd, Glasgow, KY 42141-9063
Tel (270) 678-6200 *Founded/Ownrshp* 1989
Sales 123.1MM^E *EMP* 348
SIC 5013 3625 3357 Automotive supplies & parts; Relays & industrial controls; Automotive wire & cable, except ignition sets: nonferrous
Pr: Ryuichi Kinase
**Pr:* Takefumi Habu
**CFO:* Glenn Kenkabe
**Treas:* Hiroyuki Hamaguchi
**Genl Mgr:* Carroll Knicely

D-U-N-S 03-906-3185
■ **ACKERLEY VENTURES INC**
(*Suby of* IHEARTCOMMUNICATIONS INC) ★
1301 5th Ave Ste 3525, Seattle, WA 98101-2634
Tel (206) 624-2888 *Founded/Ownrshp* 2002
Sales 1.2MM *EMP* 1,338
Accts Miller Kaplan Arase Llp North
SIC 7941 4833 4832 7319 7312 Basketball club; Soccer club; Television broadcasting stations; Radio broadcasting stations; Transit advertising services; Outdoor advertising services
Co-Ch Bd: Gail A Ackerley
**Pr:* Chris Ackerley
Ex VP: Terry Macaluso
VP: Kim Cleworth
VP Mktg: Barry Ackerley

ACL
See AMERICAN COMMERCIAL LINES INC

D-U-N-S 78-267-3045
ACL TRANSPORTATION SERVICES LLC
(*Suby of* COMMERCIAL BARGE LINE CO) ★
1701 E Market St, Jeffersonville, IN 47130-4755
Tel (800) 899-7195 *Founded/Ownrshp* 2006
Sales 755.0MM^E *EMP* 260
SIC 4449 Canal barge operations
CEO: Mark R Holden
**Pr:* Mark Knoy
COO: Jerry Linzey
**Treas:* Robert J Joubran
Sr VP: Nick Fletcher
Sr VP: Richard Mitchell
VP: Larry Cuculic
VP: Lisa Fleming
VP: Sam George
**VP:* David Huls
VP: Nick Lonnemann
VP: Michael Monahan
VP: Michael Ryan
VP: Judith Thompson
VP: Jacques Vanier

D-U-N-S 08-019-6106
ACLARA METERS LLC
(*Suby of* METER READINGS HOLDING LLC) ★
945 Hornet Dr, Hazelwood, MO 63042-2309
Tel (800) 297-2728 *Founded/Ownrshp* 2015
Sales 221.8MM^E *EMP* 5,005^E
SIC 5045 Computer software
CEO: Allan J Connolly
**CFO:* Kurt R Bruenning

D-U-N-S 06-172-4357
ACLARA TECHNOLOGIES LLC
(*Suby of* METER READINGS HOLDING LLC) ★
945 Hornet Dr, Hazelwood, MO 63042-2309
Tel (314) 895-6400 *Founded/Ownrshp* 2012
Sales 200.0MM *EMP* 870
SIC 3824 3825 3829 7371 7373 Mechanical & electromechanical counters & devices; Instruments to measure electricity; Measuring & controlling devices; Custom computer programming services; Computer integrated systems design
Pr: Allan Connolly
**CFO:* Kurt R Bruenning
Sr VP: Robert Florence
**Sr VP:* David F Hakala
**Sr VP:* Kumi Premathilake
**Sr VP:* Richard C Riccardi
**Sr VP:* Stephen Smith
**Sr VP:* Greg Wilson
VP: Gordon Gregg
VP: Bob Richardson
VP: Daniel Sweeney
VP: Mak Tarnoff
**Exec:* Michael Garcia

ACLI AQUISITIONS COMPANY
See AAA LIFE INSURANCE CO

ACLU
See AMERICAN CIVIL LIBERTIES UNION FOUNDATION INC

ACM
See ASAMA COLDWATER MANUFACTURING INC

D-U-N-S 04-732-3693
ACM NEWSPAPERS HOLDINGS LLC
7301 State Highway 161, Irving, TX 75039-2816
Tel (214) 691-4066 *Founded/Ownrshp* 2010
Sales 89.4MM^E *EMP* 800
SIC 6719

ACME
See NEW ALBERTSONS INC

D-U-N-S 00-323-1222 IMP/EXP
ACME - MCCRARY CORP
159 North St, Asheboro, NC 27203-5411
Tel (336) 625-2161 *Founded/Ownrshp* 1961
Sales 210.8MM^E *EMP* 670
SIC 2251 Women's hosiery, except socks; Panty hose
Ch Bd: Charles W Mc Crary Jr
**Pr:* Neal Anderson
**Pr:* William Redding
**CEO:* Russell Herndon
COO: Sachin Vaidya
**CFO:* Bruce T Patram
**Ch:* Charles Mc Crary
**Treas:* S Steele Redding
**V Ch Bd:* John O H Toledano Sr
Assoc VP: Heather Bruce
VP: Ellen Silverman
**VP:* Larry Small
VP: Rod Spruill
**VP:* John O H Toledano Jr
VP: Ron Warner
Board of Directors: Diane L Donahue, Larry K Small, Virginia Weiler

ACME BRICK
See JUSTIN INDUSTRIES INC

D-U-N-S 85-872-3778 IMP
■ **ACME BRICK CO**
(*Suby of* BERKSHIRE HATHAWAY INC) ★
3024 Acme Brick Plz, Fort Worth, TX 76109-4104
Tel (817) 332-4101 *Founded/Ownrshp* 2000
Sales 747.4MM^E *EMP* 2,602
SIC 3251 5032 5211 Structural brick & blocks; Brick, except refractory; Building blocks; Brick
Pr: Dennis D Knautz
Sr VP: Stanley McCarthy
**VP:* Judy B Hunter
**VP:* Robert L Stover
Plng Mgr: Arthur Maina
IT Man: Troy Russom
Netwrk Eng: Rudy Setiawan

D-U-N-S 10-211-1309
ACME BUILDING MAINTENANCE CO INC
(*Suby of* GCA SERVICES GROUP INC) ★
941 Catherine St, Alviso, CA 95002
Tel (408) 263-5911 *Founded/Ownrshp* 2003
Sales 48.4MM^E *EMP* 1,200
SIC 7349 Building & office cleaning services; Building component cleaning service
Pr: Richard Sanchez
**Ch Bd:* Henry Sanchez
**Treas:* Solomon Wong

D-U-N-S 04-919-9573
ACME BUS CORP
3355 Vtrans Mem Hwy Ste C, Ronkonkoma, NY 11779-7626
Tel (631) 471-4600 *Founded/Ownrshp* 1960
Sales 45.4MM^E *EMP* 1,500
SIC 4151 School buses
Pr: Ronald A Baumann
**VP:* Richard Baumann Jr

D-U-N-S 04-479-3917
ACME CONSTRUCTION SUPPLY CO INC
PORTLAND FASTENERS
330 Se Salmon St, Portland, OR 97214-3357
Tel (503) 239-5230 *Founded/Ownrshp* 1979
Sales 112.5MM^E *EMP* 90
SIC 5072 Builders' hardware
Ch: Richard M Bader
**Pr:* Jordan Bader
**VP:* Jason Bader
Admn Mgr: Jim Deitz
Brnch Mgr: Mike Kutnyak
IT Man: Erin Blatter
Opers Mgr: Danny Weikel
Mktg Dir: Brian Jacobs
Manager: Jeff Faaborg
Sales Asso: Ray Gonzalez
Sales Asso: Josh Hawthorne

D-U-N-S 03-182-7439
ACME ELECTRIC MOTOR INC
TOOL CRIB OF THE NORTH
1705 13th Ave N, Grand Forks, ND 58203-2321
Tel (701) 746-2823 *Founded/Ownrshp* 1948
Sales 225.4MM^E *EMP* 200
Accts Drees Riskey & Vallager By Fax

SIC 5084 5063 5082 5072 5251 5211 Woodworking machinery; Metalworking tools (such as drills, taps, dies, files); Motors, electric; Construction & mining machinery; Hardware; Tools; Electrical construction materials
Pr: Daniel A Kuhlman
**Sec:* Steve Kuhlman
IT Man: Perry Vogel

D-U-N-S 00-722-4280 IMP/EXP
ACME ENGINEERING AND MANUFACTURING CORP (OK)
1820 N York St, Muskogee, OK 74403-1451
Tel (918) 682-7791 *Founded/Ownrshp* 1938
Sales 137.9MM[E] *EMP* 500
SIC 3564 Blowers & fans
Ch Bd: Edward Buddrus
**Pr:* Lee E Buddrus
COO: Doug Yamashta
Ex VP: John Cermak
Ex VP: Brian Combs
Ex VP: Forrest Hooks
Ex VP: B J Parker
Ex VP: Tom Walden
Dir IT: Brian Dominguez
IT Man: Michael Causey
VP Mktg: Brian Lanham

D-U-N-S 00-896-7598 IMP
ACME MARKETS INC
(*Suby of* JOAH INC) ★
75 Valley Stream Pkwy # 100, Malvern, PA 19355-1480
Tel (610) 889-4000 *Founded/Ownrshp* 1999
Sales 1.5MMM[E] *EMP* 18,000
SIC 5411 Supermarkets, chain
Pr: Carl L Jablonski
Ex VP: Andy Herring
Ex VP: Steve Jungmann
Ex VP: David Pylipow
VP: Dennis Clark
IT Man: Eve Gigis
Secur Mgr: Mike Willis
Mktg Mgr: Sherry Caldwell
Pharmcst: Julie Borlaug

D-U-N-S 19-485-2257 IMP
ACME METALS & STEEL SUPPLY INC
14930 S San Pedro St, Gardena, CA 90248-2036
Tel (310) 329-2263 *Founded/Ownrshp* 1988
Sales 93.6MM[E] *EMP* 60
Accts Howard & Howard Cpas Inc Enci
SIC 5051 Steel
CEO: Jack Goldber
**Sec:* Millee Goldberg
Sales Asso: Brien Higgins
Sales Asso: Shari Matysik

D-U-N-S 01-497-5283
ACME PACKET INC
100 Crosby Dr, Bedford, MA 01730-1438
Tel (781) 328-4400 *Founded/Ownrshp* 2013
Sales 121.2MM[E] *EMP* 880[E]
SIC 7372

D-U-N-S 02-239-4399 IMP
ACME PAPER & SUPPLY CO INC
8229 Sandy Ct, Savage, MD 20763
Tel (410) 792-2333 *Founded/Ownrshp* 1946
Sales 177.2MM[E] *EMP* 190
Accts Gross Mendelsohn & Associates
SIC 5113 5087 Industrial & personal service paper; Janitors' supplies
Pr: Edward Attman
**Treas:* Gary Attman
**VP:* David Attman

ACME STORES
See FRED W ALBRECHT GROCERY CO

D-U-N-S 05-911-8810
ACME TRUCK LINE INC
200 Westbank Expy, Gretna, LA 70053-5615
Tel (504) 368-2510 *Founded/Ownrshp* 2001
Sales 330.0MM *EMP* 3,200
Accts Laporte Apac Metairie La
SIC 4213 4212 Trucking, except local; Local trucking, without storage
Pr: Michael D Coatney
VP: Rose Cash
VP: Erin Coatney
VP: Travis Delhomme
VP: Buzz Roye
VP: Jimmie Vicknair
VP: Robin Yancoski
IT Man: Deborah Barnett
IT Man: Cathy Jones
VP Opers: John Deris
Sfty Dirs: George Hepting

D-U-N-S 00-118-0207 IMP/EXP
▲ ACME UNITED CORP
55 Walls Dr Ste 201, Fairfield, CT 06824-5163
Tel (203) 254-6060 *Founded/Ownrshp* 1867
Sales 109.8MM *EMP* 342[E]
Tkr Sym ACU *Exch* ASE
SIC 3421 2499 3842 3579 3069 3999 Scissors, hand; Shears, hand; Rulers & rules, wood; First aid, snake bite & burn kits; Pencil sharpeners; Erasers: rubber or rubber & abrasive combined; Tape measures
Ch Bd: Walter C Johnsen
**Pr:* Brian S Olschan
Ofcr: Paul G Driscoll
Ex VP: James F Farrington
VP: Ian Moreau
Board of Directors: Rex L Davidson, Richmond Y Holden Jr, Susan H Murphy

ACME-HARDESTY CO.
See JACOB STERN & SONS INC

ACMH HOSPITAL
See ARMSTRONG COUNTY MEMORIAL HOSPITAL

D-U-N-S 07-853-9668
ACN HOLDINGS INC
(*Suby of* VNU MARKETING INFORMATION INC) ★
85 Broad St, New York, NY 10004-2434
Tel (646) 654-5000 *Founded/Ownrshp* 2001, 2007
Sales 83.5MM[E] *EMP* 1,500[E]
SIC 8732 Market analysis or research; Research services, except laboratory; Survey service: marketing, location, etc.; Opinion research
Ch Bd: David L Calhoun

D-U-N-S 95-983-1579
ACNIELSEN CORP
(*Suby of* ACN HOLDINGS INC) ★
85 Broad St, New York, NY 10004-2434
Tel (646) 654-5000 *Founded/Ownrshp* 2001
Sales 89.4MM[E] *EMP* 1,500
SIC 8732 Market analysis or research; Research services, except laboratory; Survey service: marketing, location, etc.; Opinion research
Pr: Mitch Barns
Pr: Robert J Lievense
CFO: Robert J Chrenc
V Ch Bd: Michael P Connors
Ex VP: Earl H Doppelt

ACNTV
See AMERICAS COLLECTIBLES NETWORK INC

ACO HARDWARE
See ACO INC

D-U-N-S 01-681-7066 IMP
ACO INC
ACO HARDWARE
27555 Farmington Rd # 100, Farmington Hills, MI 48334-3376
Tel (248) 471-0100 *Founded/Ownrshp* 1963
Sales 281.6MM[E] *EMP* 1,400
SIC 5251 Hardware
Ch: Theodore N Traskos
Pr: Bruce M Clintock
**Treas:* Mark Vandenberg
**Ex VP:* Elaine Traskos
VP: David Gronbach
VP: J Labond
CIO: Mark Brown
Mktg Dir: Ken Papiez

D-U-N-S 11-969-9288
ACOMA BUSINESS ENTERPRISES
ACOMA LAND AND CATTLE
I 40 Exit 102, Pueblo of Acoma, NM 87034
Tel (888) 759-2489 *Founded/Ownrshp* 1800
Sales 106.7MM[E] *EMP* 450
SIC 6719 5154 Personal holding companies, except banks; Cattle
CEO: Shaun Cunningham
CFO: Tiko Charlie
**CFO:* Dennis Garcia
Ofcr: John C Ahmie
Dir IT: Skip Carlson

ACOMA LAND AND CATTLE
See ACOMA BUSINESS ENTERPRISES

D-U-N-S 93-372-0823
ACON INVESTMENTS LLC
1133 Conn Ave Nw Ste 700, Washington, DC 20036-4358
Tel (202) 454-1100 *Founded/Ownrshp* 1996
Sales 1.5MMM[E] *EMP* 11,586
SIC 6722 Management investment, open-end
Mng Pt: Daniel Jinich
Mng Pt: Aron Schwartz
CFO: Barry Johnson
Exec: Kwame Lewis
Mng Dir: Jorge Dickens

D-U-N-S 07-961-1293
ACON SUZO-HAPP LLC
1133 Conn Ave Nw Ste 700, Washington, DC 20036-4358
Tel (202) 454-1100 *Founded/Ownrshp* 2012
Sales 179.4MM *EMP* 100[E]
Accts Pricewaterhousecoopers Llp C
SIC 7389

D-U-N-S 96-384-5136 IMP
▲ ACORDA THERAPEUTICS INC
420 Saw Mill River Rd, Ardsley, NY 10502-2605
Tel (914) 347-4300 *Founded/Ownrshp* 1995
Sales 492.6MM *EMP* 535[E]
Tkr Sym ACOR *Exch* NGS
SIC 2834 8731 2836 Drugs acting on the central nervous system & sense organs; Biotechnical research, commercial; Biological products, except diagnostic
Pr: Ron Cohen
Chf Cred: Lauren M Sabella
Ofcr: Andrew Hindman
VP: Tara Stevens
Exec: Joshua Bond
Assoc Dir: Dennis Pingree
Prin: David Lawrence
Ex Dir: David Squillacote
Dir Sec: Andrew R Blight
CTO: Richard P Batycky
Info Man: Alayna Jankunis
Board of Directors: Barry Greene, Peder K Jensen, John P Kelley, Sandra Panem, Lorin J Randall, Steven M Rauscher, Ian Smith

D-U-N-S 08-152-9117
ACORN DISTRIBUTORS INC
5820 Fortune Cir W, Indianapolis, IN 46241-5503
Tel (317) 243-9234 *Founded/Ownrshp* 1976
Sales 94.7MM[E] *EMP* 84[E]
SIC 5113 5087 5169 5046 5023 Cups, disposable plastic & paper; Towels, paper; Napkins, paper; Bags, paper & disposable plastic; Restaurant supplies; Janitors' supplies; Chemicals & allied products; Commercial equipment; Home furnishings
Pr: Jennifer Rosenberg
**CEO:* Al J Wachter
CFO: Steve Biette
IT Man: Mindy Hahn
Sls Dir: Dave Baker
Sales Asso: David Adams
Sales Asso: Ramiro Campins
Sales Asso: Debbie Clark
Sales Asso: Ed Hilbert
Sales Asso: Jeffrey Hunt
Sales Asso: Adam McMinn

D-U-N-S 00-831-2423 IMP/EXP
ACORN ENGINEERING CO (CA)
MORRIS GROUP INTERNATIONAL
15125 Proctor Ave, City of Industry, CA 91746-3327
Tel (800) 488-8999 *Founded/Ownrshp* 1955
Sales 313.0MM[E] *EMP* 1,200
SIC 3448 3431 3442 Buildings, portable: prefabricated metal; Plumbing fixtures: enameled iron cast iron or pressed metal; Metal doors
Pr: Donald E Morris
**Pr:* Thomas Duddy
CFO: John Plowman
**Treas:* Charles C Fredricks
Treas: Kathryn Morris
**Ex VP:* Keith Marshall
Sr VP: Chuck Fredericks
VP: Cynthia Kahle
**VP:* Kristin E Kahle
VP: Laura Marshall
**VP:* William D Morris

D-U-N-S 04-941-7186
ACOSTA INC
ACOSTA SALES & MARKETING
6600 Corporate Ctr Pkwy, Jacksonville, FL 32216-0973
Tel (904) 332-7986 *Founded/Ownrshp* 1998
Sales 7.6MMM[E] *EMP* 37,000
SIC 5141 Food brokers
Pr: Steve Matthesen
Pt: Kathy Derenda
COO: Marshall Collins
COO: Tom Corley
COO: Gregory Delaney
Ch: Gary Chartrand
Treas: Sandra Ramsey
Ex VP: Janet Digiovanni
Ex VP: Ellen Ferguson
Ex VP: Antoinette Marsden
Ex VP: Sandra C Ramsey
Sr VP: Lauren De Simone
Sr VP: Soche Picard
Sr VP: Kelly Straub
VP: Frank Arechavala
VP: John Blizzard
VP: Raymond Clark
VP: John Clevenger
VP: Randy Coleman
VP: Vilma Consuegra
VP: Mary Cook
Board of Directors: Greg Delaney, David Moran

ACOSTA SALES & MARKETING
See ACOSTA INC

ACOSTA SALES & MARKETING
See ACOSTA SALES CO INC

D-U-N-S 07-339-0841
ACOSTA SALES & MARKETING CORP
(*Suby of* ACOSTA SALES & MARKETING) ★
3045 S Parker Rd Ste 255, Aurora, CO 80014-2905
Tel (303) 752-0030 *Founded/Ownrshp* 1959, 2008
Sales 178.4MM[E] *EMP* 2,000
SIC 5141 Food brokers
VP: Chris Neilson
Pr: David Schwinkendorf
Pr: Joseph Smalkowski
Sr VP: Carlen Hooker
**VP:* Jamie Gronowski
Dist Mgr: Dee Czopek
Telecom Ex: Annette Krelle
Sls Mgr: Elton Futrell
Sls Mgr: Douglas McDonald
Sls Mgr: Gloria Parker
Sls Mgr: Annita Phillips

D-U-N-S 06-588-8760 EXP
ACOSTA SALES CO INC
ACOSTA SALES & MARKETING
(*Suby of* ACOSTA SALES & MARKETING) ★
6600 Corporate Ctr Pkwy, Jacksonville, FL 32216-0973
Tel (904) 281-9800 *Founded/Ownrshp* 1996
Sales 1.0MMM[E] *EMP* 2,000
SIC 5149 5141 Groceries & related products; Groceries, general line
Ch Bd: Gary Chartrand
**CFO:* Gregory Delaney
**Treas:* Sandra C Ramsey
VP: Steve Christopher
VP: John Huetteman
Rgnl Mgr: Lisa Anderson
Off Mgr: Penny Baker
MIS Dir: Scott McLean
VP Opers: David Flynn
Manager: Ira Schnagel
Sls Mgr: Gilles Delaisse

ACOUNTS PAYABLE DEPT
See LAKE ELSINORE UNIFIED SCHOOL DISTRICT

D-U-N-S 00-407-7905 IMP
ACOUSTI ENGINEERING CO OF FLORIDA (FL)
4656 Sw 34th St, Orlando, FL 32811-6495
Tel (407) 425-3467 *Founded/Ownrshp* 1946, 1973
Sales 164.8MM *EMP* 900
SIC 1742 5713

D-U-N-S 80-597-3112
ACOUSTIC VENTURES LLC
ASPECT ENERGY
1775 N Sherman St # 2300, Denver, CO 80203-1100
Tel (303) 573-7011 *Founded/Ownrshp* 1993
Sales 160.0MM *EMP* 76[E]
SIC 6799 Investors
CEO: Alex Cranberg
**Pr:* Paul Favret
Pr: Lora Mays
COO: Jerry Sommer
Sr Cor Off: Roger Haston

ACPN
See TERUMO BCT INC

D-U-N-S 07-058-6858 IMP/EXP
ACPRODUCTS INC
ARMSTRONG CABINET PRODUCTS
3551 Plano Pkwy, The Colony, TX 75056-5245
Tel (214) 469-3000 *Founded/Ownrshp* 2012
Sales 159.7MM[E] *EMP* 765[E]
SIC 2434 Wood kitchen cabinets
CEO: Nick Billig
Pr: Rick Lovorne
CFO: Howard Maymon
Treas: Susan Stamper

ACPS
See ALLEGANY COUNTY PUBLIC SCHOOLS

D-U-N-S 96-626-9198
ACQUINITY INTERACTIVE LLC
2200 Sw 10th St, Deerfield Beach, FL 33442-7622
Tel (954) 312-4733 *Founded/Ownrshp* 2010
Sales 175.2MM *EMP* 2[E]
SIC 3993

D-U-N-S 82-907-0080
ACQUISITION HOLDINGS SUBSIDIARY I LLC
1177 Ave Of The Americas, New York, NY 10036-2714
Tel (212) 715-8000 *Founded/Ownrshp* 2008
Sales 112.3MM[E] *EMP* 1,000
SIC 6799 Investors

D-U-N-S 19-057-3191
ACQUISITION VEHICLE TEXAS II LLC
MINYARD GROUP
301 Commerce St Ste 3232, Fort Worth, TX 76102-4158
Tel (972) 915-2895 *Founded/Ownrshp* 2004
Sales 529.5MM[E] *EMP* 5,800
SIC 5411 5912 Grocery stores; Grocery stores, chain; Drug stores & proprietary stores
CEO: Ron Johnson
**CFO:* Wayne Peterson
Mktg Dir: Craig Reid

D-U-N-S 11-537-9000
ACRES ENTERPRISES INC
ADVANTAGE DECORATIVE PAVING
610 W Liberty St, Wauconda, IL 60084-3405
Tel (847) 526-4554 *Founded/Ownrshp* 1983
Sales 127.1MM[E] *EMP* 450
SIC 0782 0781 4959 Lawn care services; Landscape services; Snowplowing
Pr: James Schwantz
**CEO:* Jim Schwantz
IT Man: Bruce Reid

D-U-N-S 02-795-1159
ACRISURE LLC
AGENCY FLOOD RESOURCES
(*Suby of* GENSTAR CAPITAL LLC) ★
5664 Prairie Creek Dr Se, Caledonia, MI 49316-8081
Tel (800) 748-0351 *Founded/Ownrshp* 2008
Sales 104.4MM[E] *EMP* 402[E]
SIC 7389 Telemarketing services
CEO: Gregory L Williams
Pr: Jim Alton
Ofcr: Donald Collins
**Ex VP:* Ricky L Norris

A.C.R.M.D
See LIFESPIRE INC

D-U-N-S 06-958-5909
ACRO SERVICE CORP
39209 6 Mile Rd Ste 250, Livonia, MI 48152-2681
Tel (734) 591-1100 *Founded/Ownrshp* 1982
Sales 315.8MM *EMP* 4,500
SIC 7363 7371

D-U-N-S 07-932-4144
ACRO STAFFING INC
ACRO UK INC.
39209 W Six Ste 250, Livonia, MI 48152
Tel (734) 542-4204 *Founded/Ownrshp* 1993
Sales 84.2MM *EMP* 1,000
SIC 7363 Manpower pools
Pr: Chris Shahani

ACRO UK INC.
See ACRO STAFFING INC

ACROBAT STAFFING
See SE SCHER CORP

ACS
See ARVIG ENTERPRISES INC

ACS
See AEROSPACE CENTER SUPPORT

D-U-N-S 07-843-0123
ACS ACQUISITION CORP
6575 The Corners Pkwy, Norcross, GA 30092-3312
Tel (678) 268-1300 *Founded/Ownrshp* 2011
Sales 972.8MM[E] *EMP* 360[E]
SIC 5045 7374 Computers, peripherals & software; Data processing & preparation
CEO: Ted Glahn
**Pr:* Michelle Clery
**Ex VP:* Donnie Clemmons
**VP:* Robin Ormand

D-U-N-S 78-436-0781
ACS AUXILIARIES GROUP INC
ACS GROUP
(*Suby of* HARBOUR GROUP LTD) ★
1100 E Woodfield Rd # 550, Schaumburg, IL 60173-5135
Tel (847) 273-7700 *Founded/Ownrshp* 2006
Sales 167.4MM[E] *EMP* 805
SIC 8748 Business consulting
Pr: James E Holbrook
Sales Exec: Kevin Chudyk
Manager: Gary Peiss

ACS COMMERCIAL SOLUTIONS
See XEROX COMMERCIAL SOLUTIONS LLC

D-U-N-S 61-760-8476
■ ACS COMMERCIAL SOLUTIONS INC
A C S
(*Suby of* XEROX BUSINESS SERVICES LLC) ★
510 W Parkland Dr, Sandy, UT 84070-6419
Tel (801) 567-5000 *Founded/Ownrshp* 1996
Sales 1.3MMM *EMP* 5,000

SIC 7374 7389 Data entry service; Telemarketing services
CEO: Lynn Blodgett
*Mng Dir: Thomas Blodgett
IT Man: Brandon Cook
Opers Mgr: Vinton Smith
Mktg Dir: Walter McCormick

D-U-N-S 13-754-9713
■ ACS COMMUNICATIONS INC
ACS DATALINE
(Suby of BLACK BOX CORP) ★
2535 Brockton Dr Ste 400, Austin, TX 78758-4495
Tel (512) 837-4400 Founded/Ownrshp 2008
Sales 122.3MM[E] EMP 500
SIC 1731 Communications specialization; Voice, data & video wiring contractor
CEO: Michael McAndrew
VP: James T Hoover
*VP: Tim Huffmyer
MIS Mgr: Linton Jones

ACS CORPORATE
See ACS HEALTH CARE INC

ACS DATALINE
See ACS COMMUNICATIONS INC

D-U-N-S 17-414-0095
■ ACS ENTERPRISE SOLUTIONS INC
(Suby of XEROX BUSINESS SERVICES LLC) ★
2828 N Haskell Ave, Dallas, TX 75204-2909
Tel (214) 841-6111 Founded/Ownrshp 1994
Sales 113.7MM[E] EMP 4,500
SIC 7374 Data processing service
Ch Bd: Darwin Deason
*CFO: Mark A King

ACS GROUP
See ACS AUXILIARIES GROUP INC

ACS GROUP
See STERLING PRODUCTS INC

D-U-N-S 06-058-1881
■ ACS HEALTH CARE INC
ACS CORPORATE
(Suby of XEROX BUSINESS SERVICES LLC) ★
2828 N Haskell Ave, Dallas, TX 75204-2909
Tel (214) 841-6111 Founded/Ownrshp 1993
Sales 109.2MM[E] EMP 970
SIC 7376 8742 Computer facilities management; Management consulting services
Pr: Mark King
COO: Eric Sauze
*Treas: Steve Lockwood
Ex VP: Nancy Chapman
Ex VP: Randy Pond
Sr VP: Carol Leach
Sr VP: Barbara Lee
VP: Dano Bartolai
VP: Raymond Cano
VP: Matthew Dickson
VP: Kimberly Hurry
VP: Kent Miller
VP: Ricky Pope
VP: John Rexford
VP: Geoff Schenkel
Exec: Anna Campbell
Dir Soc: Craig Fela
Board of Directors: Charles Bracken, Nelly Monclus, Brett Trusko

D-U-N-S 04-729-6280
■ ACS IMAGE SOLUTIONS INC
(Suby of XEROX BUSINESS SERVICES LLC) ★
3988 N Central Expy, Dallas, TX 75204-3099
Tel (214) 818-3000 Founded/Ownrshp 1992
Sales 64.1MM[E] EMP 1,300
SIC 7389 5112 7374 7375 Microfilm recording & developing service; Data processing supplies; Optical scanning data service; Data base information retrieval
Pr: Tom Blodgett
Exec: Joseph Doherty Jr
MIS Dir: Royce Green
IT Man: Suresh Kathju

D-U-N-S 05-395-9706 IMP/EXP
ACS INDUSTRIES INC
1 New England Way Unit 1, Lincoln, RI 02865-4285
Tel (401) 769-4700 Founded/Ownrshp 2005
Sales 700.6MM[E] EMP 3,000
SIC 3291 3496 3312 3315 3569 3991 Sponges, scouring: metallic; Mesh, made from purchased wire; Wire products, steel or iron; Steel wire & related products; Gas separators (machinery); Brooms & brushes
Pr: Steven Buckler
*CFO: Paul Pimentel
*VP: Peter Botvin
*VP: Jeff Buckler
VP: Scott Mackenzie
Sls Dir: Ron Paulhus

ACS LEARNING SERVICES
See INTELLINEX LLC

ACT
See AAA COOPER TRANSPORTATION

D-U-N-S 61-158-6975
ACT 1 GROUP INC
AGILE 1
1999 W 190th St, Torrance, CA 90504-6202
Tel (310) 532-1529 Founded/Ownrshp 1978
Sales 294.4MM[E] EMP 1,350
SIC 7361 8741 Employment agencies; Administrative management
CEO: Janice B Howroyd
*Pr: Bernard Howroyd
CFO: Jeff Kornreich
*Ex VP: Carlton Bryant
VP: Patricia Bryant
*VP: Michael Hoyal
Dir Bus: Sandro Bezerra
Area Mgr: Steve Jackson
CTO: Wendy Champigny

D-U-N-S 07-972-8633
ACT COMMODITIES INC
(Suby of ACT B.V.)
437 Madison Ave Fl 19c, New York, NY 10022-7055
Tel (415) 741-2290 Founded/Ownrshp 2014
Sales 130.0MM EMP 15
SIC 6221 Commodity traders, contracts
CEO: Paul Ter Veen
CFO: Walter Kolk

ACT FASTENING SOLUTIONS
See ADVANCED CABLE TIES INC

D-U-N-S 14-952-4126
ACT FOR HEALTH INC
PRO CASE MANAGEMENT
500 E 8th Ave, Denver, CO 80203-3716
Tel (303) 253-7470 Founded/Ownrshp 1997
Sales 60.5MM[E] EMP 1,200[E]
SIC 8011 Health maintenance organization
Pr: Greg Austin
*CEO: Kevin Vollmer
*CFO: Curtis Fletcher
*Ex VP: Rick Heth

D-U-N-S 00-531-2145
ACT INC
500 Act Dr, Iowa City, IA 52243-9003
Tel (319) 337-1000 Founded/Ownrshp 1986
Sales 350.0MM EMP 1,200
Accts Mcgladrey Llp Cedar Rapids I
SIC 8748 Testing service, educational or personnel
CEO: Marten Roorda
*Ch Bd: Bob Berdahl
Pr: Lucas Kuhlmann
COO: Janet E Godwin
COO: Mehran Rahbar
COO: Tom Struve
*CFO: Thomas J Goedken
Ofcr: Richard Patz
VP: Jon L Erickson
VP: Julie Jones
VP: Debra Lyons
VP: David Zasada

D-U-N-S 07-088-8946 IMP/EXP
ACT PIPE & SUPPLY INC
6950 W Sam Houston Pkwy N, Houston, TX 77041-4023
Tel (713) 937-0600 Founded/Ownrshp 1994
Sales 250.0MM EMP 400
Accts Melton & Melton Llp Houst
SIC 5051 5085 Pipe & tubing, steel; Valves & fittings
CEO: Harry Kirk
*Pr: Andrew Zizinia
Div Mgr: Ellen Stock
IT Man: Billy Kerr
Sls Mgr: Luis Hernandez
Sls Mgr: Don Schmitt
Sales Asso: Bruce Russell
Sales Asso: Mark Thalken

D-U-N-S 09-926-2404 IMP
ACTAVIS ELIZABETH LLC
ACTAVIS US
(Suby of ACTAVIS LLC) ★
200 Elmora Ave, Elizabeth, NJ 07202-1106
Tel (908) 527-9100 Founded/Ownrshp 1979
Sales 346.1MM[E] EMP 740
SIC 2834 Pharmaceutical preparations; Druggists' preparations (pharmaceuticals)
*Pr: Sigurbar Olafsson
*CFO: R Todd Joyce
Ofcr: Deborah Penza
VP: Annie Cheung
VP: Michael R Clarke
VP: Jim Fenton
VP: Jim Huang
VP: George Long
VP: William Meury
VP: Mark Sutton
VP: Vince Warren
Assoc Dir: Michele Y Canada
Assoc Dir: Jack Milazzo
Assoc Dir: Shyam Mohan
Assoc Dir: Paul Procopio
Assoc Dir: Dhruti Thaker
Assoc Dir: Andrew Wojcik

D-U-N-S 10-693-1488 IMP/EXP
ACTAVIS LLC
(Suby of ALLERGAN PUBLIC LIMITED COMPANY)
400 Interpace Pkwy, Parsippany, NJ 07054-1120
Tel (862) 261-7000 Founded/Ownrshp 2005
Sales 8.4MMM[E] EMP 17,700
SIC 2834 5122 Pharmaceutical preparations; Pharmaceuticals
CEO: Brenton L Saunders
Pr: Sigurdur Oli Olafsson
Pr: G Frederick Wilkinson
COO: Albert Paonessa
Ofcr: Linda Bardenfleth
Ofcr: Deborah C Penza
Ofcr: Connie Truemper
Ex VP: David A Buchen
Ex VP: Bill Meury
Ex VP: Paul Navarre
Ex VP: Thomas R Russillo
Sr VP: Andy Boyer
Sr VP: Clare Carmichael
Sr VP: Maria Chow
Sr VP: Patrick J Eagan
Sr VP: Francois Menard
VP: Lynne Amato
VP: Shawn Brown
VP: Lisa M Defrancesco
VP: Patricia L Eisenhaur
VP: Sheldon V Hirt

D-U-N-S 11-972-3554
ACTAVIS PHARMA INC
(Suby of ACTAVIS LLC) ★
400 Interpace Pkwy Ste A1, Parsippany, NJ 07054-1119
Tel (862) 261-7000 Founded/Ownrshp 1993
Sales 1.1MMM[E] EMP 17,000[E]
SIC 2834 Pharmaceutical preparations
CEO: Paul M Bisaro
VP: Lisa Defrancesco
VP: Hari Sankar

Assoc Dir: May Chan-Liston
Assoc Dir: Wendy Despain
Assoc Dir: Victoria Di Santo
Assoc Dir: Mitchell Holloway
Assoc Dir: Robert Kulik
Assoc Dir: Bruce Kupfer
Assoc Dir: Sonal Shukla
Assoc Dir: Jason Zeman

ACTAVIS US
See ACTAVIS ELIZABETH LLC

D-U-N-S 07-484-9118 IMP/EXP
■ ACTERNA LLC
JDSU
(Suby of JDSU ACTERNA HOLDINGS LLC) ★
20250 Century Blvd # 100, Germantown, MD 20874-1177
Tel (301) 353-1550 Founded/Ownrshp 2003
Sales 180.2MM[E] EMP 1,700
SIC 3669 7379 3825 5065 3679 8734 Intercommunication systems, electric; Computer related consulting services; ; Instruments to measure electricity; Test equipment for electronic & electric measurement; Electronic parts & equipment; Electronic circuits; Testing laboratories
CEO: John Peeler
Prgrm Mgr: Tim Mohr
Genl Mgr: Paul Taylor
Snr Sftwr: Hermann Kontcho
Snr Sftwr: Qin Zhang
Software D: Tanumoy Pati
Snr Mgr: David Austin

D-U-N-S 61-301-6216
ACTIAN CORP
2300 Geng Rd Ste 150, Palo Alto, CA 94303-3353
Tel (650) 587-5500 Founded/Ownrshp 2005
Sales 207.3MM[E] EMP 620
SIC 7373 7372 Systems software development services; Business oriented computer software
CEO: Steve Shine
*CFO: Steven Springsteel
*Chf Mktg O: Tony Kavanagh
Sr VP: Kevin Edmiston
Sr VP: Ketan Karia
Sr VP: Bill Maimone
Sr VP: Mark Milani
VP: Chris Debiase
VP: Kevin Dunn
VP: Pamela Fowler
VP: Michael Kostow
VP: Romy Mager
VP: Steve Padgett
Dir: Joe Kronk

D-U-N-S 96-580-8236
ACTIFIO INC
333 Wyman St Ste 30, Waltham, MA 02451-1209
Tel (781) 790-7676 Founded/Ownrshp 2009
Sales 89.9MM[E] EMP 213[E]
SIC 7374 Data verification service
CEO: Ash Ashutosh
Sr Pt: Steve Egan
Pr: John Loonie
*Pr: Jim Sullivan
*CFO: Jim Kelliher
*Sr VP: David Chang
*Sr VP: Ratan Tipirneni
VP: Bob Carter
VP: Charles Godshall
VP: Kevin Hilson
VP: Michael McClurg
VP: Jim Pownell
VP: Brian Reagan
VP: Chandra Reddy
VP: Pervez Sikora
VP: Michael Warner
VP: Donna Williams

D-U-N-S 12-278-3181
ACTIMIZE INC
(Suby of NICE SYSTEMS INC) ★
1359 Broadway Fl 5, New York, NY 10018-7747
Tel (212) 643-4600 Founded/Ownrshp 2002
Sales 122.0MM[E] EMP 430[E]
SIC 7371 Computer software development
Pr: Amir Orad
COO: Yaron Shohat
CFO: Beth Gaspich
CFO: Steve Vogel
VP: Nigel Broda
VP: Michael Hughes
VP: Thomas Kwon
VP: Ido Ophir
VP: Doron Paz
VP: Keith Perry
VP: Edward Sander
Co-Founder: Boaz Pe'er
Co-Founder: David Govrin

D-U-N-S 04-547-0622
ACTION CAPITAL CORP
230 Peachtree St Nw # 810, Atlanta, GA 30303-1568
Tel (404) 524-3181 Founded/Ownrshp 1959
Sales NA EMP 17
Accts Mcgregor & Company Llp Columb
SIC 6153 Factoring services
CEO: Becky J Cronister
*CFO: John J Canning
*VP: Patrick Thom

D-U-N-S 07-986-5971
ACTION ENVIRONMENTAL GROUP INC
300 Frank W Burr Blvd, Teaneck, NJ 07666-6704
Tel (212) 564-7600 Founded/Ownrshp 2010
Sales 203.3MM[E] EMP 750[E]
SIC 4953 Recycling, waste materials
CEO: Ron Bergamini
COO: Michael Dibella
CFO: Brian Giambagno

D-U-N-S 04-103-6252
ACTION FOR BOSTON COMMUNITY DEVELOPMENT INC
A B C D
178 Tremont St, Boston, MA 02111-1006
Tel (617) 357-6000 Founded/Ownrshp 1962
Sales 157.2MM EMP 1,000
Accts Kpmg Llp Boston Ma

SIC 8399 8322 Community action agency; Individual & family services
Ch Bd: John McGahan
*Pr: John Drew
*CFO: Marjorie Lombard
*Treas: Jean M Babcock
*Treas: Patricia Washington
*Ex VP: Sharon Scott-Chandler
Sr VP: Charna Heiko
VP: Duke Hutchinson
VP: Kelly Qualman
VP: Irene Ramirez
Pgrm Dir: Stan Skowronski

D-U-N-S 13-490-1417
ACTION GYPSUM SUPPLY LP
9635 W Little York Rd, Houston, TX 77040-3319
Tel (713) 896-4002 Founded/Ownrshp 2003
Sales 101.5MM[E] EMP 61
SIC 5085 Industrial supplies
Genl Mgr: Lenin Juarez II
Mng Pt: Terri King
Div Mgr: Chris Hawkes
Sales Asso: Chris Hernandez

D-U-N-S 06-783-8680 EXP
ACTION NISSAN INC (FL)
UNIVERSAL NISSAN
12785 S Ornge Blossom Trl, Orlando, FL 32837
Tel (407) 926-7050 Founded/Ownrshp 1985, 1994
Sales 215.2MM EMP 120
SIC 5511 Automobiles, new & used
CEO: William Nero
*CFO: Bud Newberry
Sls Dir: Mark Renert
Sls Mgr: Christopher Gallagher

ACTION OUTDOOR ADVERTISING
See NEIGHBORS STORES INC

D-U-N-S 88-486-9249
ACTION RESOURCES INC
40 County Road 517, Hanceville, AL 35077-3858
Tel (256) 352-2689 Founded/Ownrshp 1995
Sales 128.0MM[E] EMP 300
SIC 4212 4213 1794 Local trucking, without storage; Trucking, except local; Excavation work
CEO: Dean Flint
Pr: Jeff Cowart
*Pr: Greg Orr
*CFO: Troy Pritchett
*Ch: Charles Corpening
*VP: John Milledge
*VP: Mark Mudryk
Opers Mgr: Cathy Anderson

D-U-N-S 01-144-3269
ACTIONET INC
2600 Park Twr Dr Ste 1000, Vienna, VA 22180
Tel (703) 204-0090 Founded/Ownrshp 1998
Sales 411.5MM EMP 1,352
Accts Aronson Llc
SIC 7379 7373 7372 7371 Computer data escrow service; Computer systems analysis & design; Word processing computer software; Custom computer programming services
Pr: Ashley W Chen
*Pr: Jeffrey D Abish
*CFO: Kendra Leser
Ex VP: Jeffrey Abish
*Sr VP: Michael L Genebach
VP: Anthony R Adoremos
VP: Tom Boyce
VP: Gerald Greer
*VP: Brian J Orourke
Prgrm Mgr: Maureen Douglas
Prgrm Mgr: Michael Giordano

D-U-N-S 18-594-6303
ACTIONLINK LLC
2279 Romig Rd, Akron, OH 44320-3823
Tel (888) 737-8757 Founded/Ownrshp 2002
Sales 53.3MM[E] EMP 1,500
SIC 8748 Business consulting
CEO: Bruce Finn
Ex VP: Cynthia Fitzgibbons
VP: Del Tanner
Opers Mgr: Brad Patterson

D-U-N-S 01-402-9677
ACTIVANT SOLUTIONS HOLDINGS INC
804 Las Cimas Pkwy, Austin, TX 78746-5150
Tel (512) 328-2300 Founded/Ownrshp 2003
Sales NA EMP 2,000
SIC 7371

D-U-N-S 13-073-2696
ACTIVAR INC
AZTEC INDUSTRIES
7808 Creekridge Cir # 200, Minneapolis, MN 55439-2615
Tel (952) 944-3533 Founded/Ownrshp 1978
Sales 160.8MM[E] EMP 480
SIC 2542 3479 3442 3429 3089 Cabinets: show, display or storage: except wood; Coating of metals with plastic or resins; Coating of metals & formed products; Hot dip coating of metals or formed products; Louver doors, metal; Builders' hardware; Novelties, plastic
CEO: James Reissner
*CFO: Joseph A Petrich

D-U-N-S 61-163-3566
■ ACTIVE AERO GROUP INC
USA JET AIRLINES
(Suby of ROADRUNNER TRANSPORTATION SYSTEMS INC) ★
2068 E St, Belleville, MI 48111-1262
Tel (734) 547-7200 Founded/Ownrshp 2014
Sales 225.0MM EMP 285
SIC 4522 Nonscheduled charter services
Ch Bd: Brian Hermadin
*Pr: Christopher Healy
*CEO: David Shcembri
*CFO: Andrew W Kirk
*CFO: Thomas Stenglein

D-U-N-S 96-753-4041
ACTIVE DAY INC
SENIOR CARE
6 Neshaminy Interplex Dr # 401, Trevose, PA 19053-6942
Tel (215) 642-6600 *Founded/Ownrshp* 2015
Sales 44.7MM^E *EMP* 1,300^E
SIC 8322 Adult day care center
CEO: Jim Donnelly
**COO:* Craig O Mehnert

ACTIVE INTEREST MEDIA
See CRUZ BAY PUBLISHING INC

D-U-N-S 14-569-2187
ACTIVE INTEREST MEDIA INC
A I M
300 Continental Blvd # 650, El Segundo, CA 90245-5067
Tel (310) 356-4100 *Founded/Ownrshp* 2005
Sales 121.7MM^E *EMP* 660^E
SIC 2721 Magazines: publishing only, not printed on site
Pr: Efrem Zimbalist
CFO: Janine Martin
CFO: Brian J Sellstrom
Ex VP: Bill Harper
**Sr VP:* Mitchell H Faigen
Sr VP: Patricia B Fox
VP: Susan McNamee
VP: Laurie Sloan
Genl Mgr: Marie Galastro
Mktg Mgr: Greg Brenton
Sls Mgr: Donna Diamond

ACTIVE INTERNATIONAL
See ACTIVE MEDIA SERVICES INC

D-U-N-S 11-749-7669
ACTIVE MEDIA SERVICES INC
ACTIVE INTERNATIONAL
1 Blue Hill Plz Ste 1705, Pearl River, NY 10965-6170
Tel (845) 735-1700 *Founded/Ownrshp* 1998
Sales 1.0MMM^E *EMP* 500
SIC 7319 4731 4789 Media buying service; Freight transportation arrangement; Cargo loading & unloading services
CEO: Alan Elkin
Pr: Rick Fuese
**Pr:* Arthur Wagner
COO: Bill Georges
CFO: Gary M Steinbeck
CFO: Richard Vendig
Bd of Dir: Irma Von Wischetski
Ofcr: Jim Por Arelli
Ofcr: Dominic Bencivenga
**Ofcr:* Alan Izenman
Ofcr: Elizabeth Topazio
Assoc VP: Lauren Depalma
Ex VP: Lisa Brown
Ex VP: Kevin Farkas
Ex VP: Karen Gabor
Ex VP: Barbara Martino
Ex VP: Jim Portarelli
Sr VP: Debra Frohlinger
Sr VP: Anat Gilad
Sr VP: Elysa Gonzalez
Sr VP: Bethany Harris
Board of Directors: Alan Brown, Deborah Fine, Steve Sommer

D-U-N-S 05-617-3364
ACTIVE NETWORK LLC
(*Suby of* VISTA EQUITY PARTNERS LLC) ★
717 N Harwood St Ste 2500, Dallas, TX 75201-6527
Tel (888) 543-7223 *Founded/Ownrshp* 2013
Sales 93.2MM^E *EMP* 1,000
SIC 8742 Management consulting services
CEO: Darko Dejanovic
**CFO:* Mark Miller
VP: Sal Despirito
VP: Stacey Fernandes
VP: Parixit Joshi
VP: Eric Richey
VP: Ray Wood
Dir Soc: Jon Ramer
**Prin:* Sejal Pietrzak
Snr Sftwr: Nancy Ellison
Snr Sftwr: Craig McLeod

ACTIVE TRANSPORT
See ACTIVE TRUCK TRANSPORT LLC

D-U-N-S 19-614-3671
ACTIVE TRUCK TRANSPORT LLC
ACTIVE TRANSPORT
(*Suby of* JHT HOLDINGS INC) ★
10801 Corporate Dr, Pleasant Prairie, WI 53158-1603
Tel (800) 558-3271 *Founded/Ownrshp* 1986
Sales 132.5MM^E *EMP* 400^E
SIC 4213 Automobiles, transport & delivery

D-U-N-S 08-000-9858
ACTIVE WELLNESS LLC
4000 Bridgeway Ste 101, Sausalito, CA 94965-4800
Tel (415) 331-1600 *Founded/Ownrshp* 2015
Sales 40.0MM *EMP* 1,400
SIC 8741 Hospital management; Nursing & personal care facility management
Ch: Jill Stevens Kinney
Pr: William Joseph McBride III
CFO: Carey White

D-U-N-S 08-026-9289
ACTIVEOPS USA INC
8300 Greensboro Dr # 800, Mc Lean, VA 22102-3605
Tel (703) 918-4918 *Founded/Ownrshp* 2015
Sales 500.0MM *EMP* 10
SIC 8741 Management services
Pr: Mark Bourgeois

D-U-N-S 09-853-3342
▲ ACTIVISION BLIZZARD INC
3100 Ocean Park Blvd, Santa Monica, CA 90405-3032
Tel (310) 255-2000 *Founded/Ownrshp* 1979
Sales 4.6MMM *EMP* 7,300
Tkr Sym ATVI *Exch* NGS
SIC 7372 Prepackaged software; Home entertainment computer software
Pr: Robert A Kotick
**Ch Bd:* Brian G Kelly
Pr: Pete Vlastelica
COO: Thomas Tippl
CFO: Dennis Durkin
Chf Cred: Brian Hodous
Ex VP: Larry Goldberg
Ex VP: Daniel Hammett
Ex VP: Michael Row
Ex VP: Ron Scott
Sr VP: Karthik Bala
Sr VP: Terri Durham
VP: Jonathan Anastas
VP: Neil Armstrong
VP: Linda Howard
VP: Shiro Lewis
VP: Julie Machock
VP: Josh Taub
Board of Directors: Robert J Corti, Hendrik J Hartong III, Barry Meyer, Robert J Morgado, Peter Nolan, Casey Wasserman, Elaine Wynn

D-U-N-S 36-149-8947
■ ACTIVISION PUBLISHING INC
(*Suby of* ACTIVISION BLIZZARD INC) ★
3100 Ocean Park Blvd, Santa Monica, CA 90405-3032
Tel (310) 255-2000 *Founded/Ownrshp* 1993
Sales 395.0MM^E *EMP* 1,306
SIC 7372 Home entertainment computer software
Pr: Michael Griffith
Ch Bd: Ron Doornink
Pr: Dave Cowling
Pr: Dan Rosensweig
Pr: Colin Schiller
CEO: Eric Hirshberg
COO: Michael Condrey
Treas: John Coyne
Ofcr: Chris Walther
Ex VP: Ronald L Scott
Sr VP: Michael Benedikt
Sr VP: Terri P Durham
Sr VP: Steve Wereb
VP: Catherine Dare
VP: Todd Harvey
VP: Peter Royea
VP: Carl Schnurr
VP: Glen A Schofield
VP: Chuck Shapiro
VP: Kristin M Southey
VP: Denise Walsh

D-U-N-S 83-969-2873 IMP
ACTRONIX INC
(*Suby of* APEX EQUITY PARTNERS INC)
476 W Industrial Prk Rd, Flippin, AR 72634
Tel (870) 453-8871 *Founded/Ownrshp* 2000
Sales 84.0MM^E *EMP* 250
SIC 3679 Harness assemblies for electronic use: wire or cable
Pr: Tim Grant
VP: Kenny Crunkleton
**VP:* Steve Orick
VP: Rhonda Troutman

D-U-N-S 07-550-1627
ACTS RETIREMENT-LIFE COMMUNITIES INC
375 Morris Rd, West Point, PA 19486
Tel (215) 699-3204 *Founded/Ownrshp* 1971
Sales 372.9MM *EMP* 5,375
SIC 8361 8051 Residential care; Convalescent home with continuous nursing care
Pr: Marvin Mashner
**Ch Bd:* Marvin D Heaps
V Ch: George R Gunn Jr
**Treas:* Donald L Davis
**Ex VP:* Gerald T Grant
**Ex VP:* J Mark Vanderbeck
**Sr VP:* Karen I Christiansen
**Sr VP:* Lori M Woodward
Pr Mgr: Colleen Wilson

D-U-N-S 94-889-9133
▲ ACTUA CORP
555 E Lancaster Ave # 640, Radnor, PA 19087-5164
Tel (610) 727-6900 *Founded/Ownrshp* 1996
Sales 133.4MM *EMP* 887
Tkr Sym ACTA *Exch* NGS
SIC 7373 Computer integrated systems design
Ch Bd: Walter W Buckley III
Pr: Douglas A Alexander
CFO: Kirk Morgan
CFO: R Kirk Morgan
Mng Dir: Vincent P Menichelli
Mng Dir: Matthew Safaii

D-U-N-S 00-658-2779
▲ ACTUANT CORP
N86w12500 Westbrook Xing, Menomonee Falls, WI 53051-3348
Tel (262) 293-1500 *Founded/Ownrshp* 1910
Sales 1.1MMM *EMP* 5,672
Tkr Sym ATU *Exch* NYS
SIC 3593 3492 3594 3625 7359 Fluid power cylinders, hydraulic or pneumatic; Fluid power valves & hose fittings; Fluid power pumps; Relays & industrial controls; Equipment rental & leasing
CEO: Randal W Baker
Pr: Mark Goldstein
CFO: Andrew G Lampereur
Ch: Robert A Peterson
Ofcr: Janessa Sidders
Ex VP: William Axline
Ex VP: Kenneth C Bockhorst
Ex VP: Sheri Grissom
Ex VP: Brian Kobylinski
Ex VP: Roger Roundhouse
Ex VP: Mark Sefcik
Ex VP: Eugene E Skogg
Ex VP: Theodore C Wozniak
VP: Dawn Boland
VP: Venkat Ganapathy
VP: Mike Mann
VP: Sam Mulabagal
VP: Ted Wozniak
Board of Directors: Robert C Arzbaecher, Danny Cunningham, E James Ferland, Thomas J Fischer, R Alan Hunter Jr,, Holly A Van Deursen, Dennis K Williams

D-U-N-S 83-785-7093
ACTUATE CORP
(*Suby of* OPENTEXT CORPORATION)
951 Mariners Island Blvd # 600, San Mateo, CA 94404-1558
Tel (650) 645-3000 *Founded/Ownrshp* 2015
Sales 134.5MM *EMP* 545^E
SIC 7372 Prepackaged software
Pr: Mark J Barrenechea
**CFO:* John Doolittle
**Chf Mktg O:* Adam Howatson
**Ofcr:* Gordon A Davies
Ofcr: Lisa Zangari
**Ex VP:* Jonathan Hunter
Sr VP: Muhi Majzoub
Sr VP: James McGourlay
Sr VP: Gary Weiss
VP: Nobby Akiha
VP: Paolo Battaglini
VP: Allen Bonde
VP: Lisa Dean
VP: Gautam Goswami
VP: Richard Guth
VP: Peter Hoopes
VP: Linda Kata
VP: Doug Koppenhofer
VP: Rajeev Raman
Comm Man: Leena Bengani

ACUA
See ATLANTIC COUNTY UTILITIES AUTHORITY

D-U-N-S 13-136-5884
ACUATIVE CORP
30 Two Bridges Rd Ste 240, Fairfield, NJ 07004-1550
Tel (862) 926-5600 *Founded/Ownrshp* 1984
Sales 120.2MM *EMP* 325
SIC 7373 5065 1731 Systems integration services; Communication equipment; Communications specialization
Pr: Vincent Sciarra
**Pr:* Rich Ackerman
**COO:* Chad Mead
**CFO:* Patrick J Danna
Ofcr: Demetrio L Guerrero
VP: Tony Carter
VP: Susan Pirzchalski
VP: Paul Prevot
Sftwr Eng: Nuno Pereira
Netwrk Eng: Ash Patel
Trfc Dir: Daria Wagner

ACUITAS DIGITAL
See BT AMERICAS INC

D-U-N-S 08-545-8508
▲ ACUITY BRANDS INC
1170 Peachtree St Ne, Atlanta, GA 30309-7649
Tel (404) 853-1400 *Founded/Ownrshp* 2001
Sales 3.2MMM *EMP* 7,800
Tkr Sym AYI *Exch* NYS
SIC 3648 3646 3645 Lighting equipment; Commercial indusl & institutional electric lighting fixtures; Residential lighting fixtures
Ch Bd: Vernon J Nagel
Pr: Peter Ngai
CFO: Richard K Reece
Ex VP: Mark A Black
Sr VP: Bill Astary
VP: Scott Butler
VP: Gene Curtin
VP: Charlie Huizenga
VP: Keith Keller
VP: Derek Nelson
VP: Karen Nocher
VP: Pete Shannin
Creative D: Risa Wilson

D-U-N-S 78-326-2520 IMP/EXP
■ ACUITY BRANDS LIGHTING INC
LITHONIA LIGHTING
(*Suby of* ACUITY BRANDS INC) ★
1 Acuity Way, Conyers, GA 30012-3957
Tel (800) 922-9641 *Founded/Ownrshp* 2001
Sales 1.4MMM^E *EMP* 6,000
SIC 3646 3645 3641

D-U-N-S 80-828-3555 EXP
ACUITY SPECIALTY PRODUCTS INC
ZEP SALES & SERVICE
(*Suby of* ZEP INC) ★
1310 Sboard Indus Blvd Nw, Atlanta, GA 30318-2825
Tel (404) 352-1680 *Founded/Ownrshp* 2007
Sales 164.0MM^E *EMP* 500
SIC 2841 2879 2842 5169 Scouring compounds; Detergents, synthetic organic or inorganic alkaline; Pesticides, agricultural or household; Degreasing solvent; Sanitation preparations; Chemicals & allied products
Pr: John K Morgan
**COO:* Ronald D Brown
**CFO:* Mark R Bachmann
**VP:* Robert Collins
**VP:* David A Korn
**VP:* Philip A Theodore
**VP:* Dr Stanley Weller
**VP:* C Francis Whitaker III

D-U-N-S 18-189-0182
ACUMEN FISCAL AGENT LLC
(*Suby of* RISE INC) ★
4542 E Inverness Ave # 210, Mesa, AZ 85206-4619
Tel (480) 497-1889 *Founded/Ownrshp* 2000
Sales 104.0MM *EMP* 3
SIC 8721 Accounting, auditing & bookkeeping; Payroll accounting service

D-U-N-S 06-122-7836
ACUMEN SOLUTIONS INC
1660 Intl Dr Ste 500, Mclean, VA 22102
Tel (703) 600-4000 *Founded/Ownrshp* 1998
Sales 98.9MM^E *EMP* 300
SIC 8748 Telecommunications consultant
Pr: David Joubran
CFO: Erfan Kabir
Mng Dir: Brian Belforte
Mng Dir: Jon Chace
Mng Dir: Chris Chatman
**Mng Dir:* Randall Fulk
Mng Dir: David Marko
Mng Dir: John McLoughlin
Mng Dir: Eric Pearsall
Mng Dir: Andy Schoka
Mng Dir: Shally B Stanley

D-U-N-S 18-364-5733 IMP
ACUMENT GLOBAL TECHNOLOGIES INC
(*Suby of* FONTANA AMERICA INC) ★
6125 18 Mile Rd, Sterling Heights, MI 48314-4205
Tel (586) 254-3900 *Founded/Ownrshp* 2014
Sales 1.8MMM^E *EMP* 7,970
SIC 3965 5072 Fasteners; Hardware
Pr: Patrick Paige
CFO: John Anslemi
CFO: Fritz Nelson
Ex VP: John Clark
Ex Dir: Rocky Pinheiro
VP Opers: Ed Bogert
Plnt Mgr: Bronston Clough
Plnt Mgr: Ryan Demont
Ql Cn Mgr: Tony Cherry
Ql Cn Mgr: Lori Lynch
Ql Cn Mgr: Tom Vehoski

D-U-N-S 03-017-1250
ACUREN INSPECTION INC
HELLIER
(*Suby of* ROCKWOOD SERVICE CORP) ★
30 Main St Ste 402, Danbury, CT 06810-3004
Tel (203) 702-8740 *Founded/Ownrshp* 1976
Sales 1.3MMM^E *EMP* 3,000
SIC 1389 8071 Testing, measuring, surveying & analysis services; Testing laboratories
Pr: Peter Scannell
**VP:* John P Lockwood

D-U-N-S 00-102-5154 IMP/EXP
■ ACUSHNET CO
(*Suby of* ACUSHNET HOLDINGS CORP) ★
333 Bridge St, Fairhaven, MA 02719-4900
Tel (508) 979-2000 *Founded/Ownrshp* 1980
Sales 1.4MMM^E *EMP* 4,600
SIC 3949 3149 2381 Balls: baseball, football, basketball, etc.; Shafts, golf club; Bags, golf; Gloves, sport & athletic: boxing, handball, etc.; Athletic shoes, except rubber or plastic; Fabric dress & work gloves
CEO: Walter R Uihlein
Pr: Edmond Abrain
Pr: James Connor
COO: Patrick McDougall
CFO: William C Burke
Treas: Dudley L Bauerlein
Treas: Mark Hausberg
Bd of Dir: Cathy Mant
Ex VP: Liz Valicenti
Sr VP: Dennis Doherty
Sr VP: Joe Nauman
Sr VP: Peg Nicholson
VP: Gerry Bellis
VP: Dennis Dorthy
VP: Jay Hill
VP: Andy Jones
VP: Brian Lucas
VP: Peter Marshall
VP: Al Martin
VP: Ken Riall
VP: Doug Robinson
Board of Directors: Dudley J Barten Jr, Hubert C Boehm, James M Connor, Thomas C Hays, Gilbert Klemann II, Craig P Omtvedt, Robert J Rukeyser, Norman Wesley

D-U-N-S 08-029-8233
■ ACUSHNET HOLDINGS CORP
(*Suby of* FILA KOREA LTD.)
333 Bridge St, Fairhaven, MA 02719-4905
Tel (800) 225-8500 *Founded/Ownrshp* 2011
Sales 1.5MMM *EMP* 5,228^E
Tkr Sym GOLF *Exch* NYS
SIC 3949 Golf equipment
Pr: Walter Uihlein
COO: David Maher
CFO: William Burke
Ofcr: Dennis Doherty
Ex VP: Joseph Nauman

D-U-N-S 87-743-1916
ACUSHNET RUBBER CO INC
PRECIX
(*Suby of* ZD USA HOLDINGS INC) ★
744 Belleville Ave, New Bedford, MA 02745-6010
Tel (508) 998-4000 *Founded/Ownrshp* 2012
Sales 128.7MM^E *EMP* 400
SIC 3053 3061 2821 Gaskets, packing & sealing devices; Mechanical rubber goods; Plastics materials & resins
CEO: David Slutz
**CFO:* Lynne Mastera
MIS Mgr: Ira Haskell
Opers Mgr: Elsie McCarty
Plnt Mgr: Alfred Goyette
Ql Cn Mgr: David Muse
Mktg Mgr: Marcy Rapaso

D-U-N-S 02-246-3293
ACUSPORT CORP
1 Hunter Pl, Bellefontaine, OH 43311-3001
Tel (937) 593-7010 *Founded/Ownrshp* 2003
Sales 346.7MM^E *EMP* 234
SIC 5091 Firearms, sporting; Archery equipment; Ammunition, sporting; Hunting equipment & supplies
Ch Bd: William L Fraim
CFO: John K Flanagan
VP: Steve Reed
CIO: Shannan Stover
QA Dir: David Crilly
QA Dir: Jordan Guck
QA Dir: Travis Patton
Dir IT: Kenneth Wright
Software D: Andrew Knapp
Software D: Michael Norgren
Opers Mgr: Julie Nystrom

ACWD
See ALAMEDA COUNTY WATER DISTRICT INC

D-U-N-S 05-196-4047
▲ ACXIOM CORP
601 E 3rd St, Little Rock, AR 72201-1709
Tel (501) 252-1000 *Founded/Ownrshp* 1969
Sales 850.0MM *EMP* 3,475
Accts Kpmg Llp Dallas Texas
Tkr Sym ACXM *Exch* NGS
SIC 7374 7375 7371 Data processing & preparation; Data processing service; Information retrieval services; On-line data base information retrieval; Custom computer programming services; Computer software development
Pr: Scott E Howe
Ch Bd: Jerry D Gramaglia
Pr: Richard E Erwin
Pr: S Travis May
Pr: Dennis D Self
CFO: Warren C Jenson
Ex VP: Jerry C Jones
Sr VP: Terilyn Juarez Monroe
VP: Mike Brewer
VP: Hailey G Dillon
VP: Julia Evan
VP: Chris Garber
VP: Craig Harrison
VP: Bonnie McEntire
VP Bus Dev: Denise Anderson
Board of Directors: John L Battelle, Timothy R Cadogan, William T Dillard II, Richard P Fox, William J Henderson, Clark M Kokich, Debora B Tomlin

ACYT
See ALABAMA CULLMAN YUTAKA TECHNOLOGIES LLC

D-U-N-S 18-410-1194 IMP/EXP
AD CORP
1551 Wewatta St, Denver, CO 80202-6173
Tel (303) 744-1911 *Founded/Ownrshp* 1997
Sales 352.1MM^E *EMP* 7,776
SIC 3634 3564 3822 3089 3714 3312 Fans, exhaust & ventilating, electric: household; Blowers & fans; Exhaust fans: industrial or commercial; Ventilating fans: industrial or commercial; Damper operators: pneumatic, thermostatic, electric; Molding primary plastic; Axles, motor vehicle; Gears, motor vehicle; Thermostats, motor vehicle; Wipers, windshield, motor vehicle; Wheels, locomotive & car: iron & steel
CEO: Anthony Reading
**CFO:* Dan Disser
**Ex VP:* John W Zimmerman
CIO: Norm Theil

D-U-N-S 00-427-9675
AD INDUSTRIES INC
6450 Poe Ave Ste 109, Dayton, OH 45414-2646
Tel (303) 744-1911 *Founded/Ownrshp* 2012
Sales NA *EMP* 7,776
SIC 3634 3564 3535 3714 3088 3089

D-U-N-S 12-152-5026
AD TRANSPORT EXPRESS INC
A D TRANSPORT
5601 Belleville Rd, Canton, MI 48188-2425
Tel (734) 397-7100 *Founded/Ownrshp* 1986
Sales 84.0MM^E *EMP* 700
SIC 4213 4212 Trucking, except local; Local trucking, without storage
Pr: Gary A Percy
**VP:* Matthew Percy
Off Mgr: Lucas Dehne
Opers Mgr: William Ogden
Opers Mgr: Art Scala
Mktg Mgr: Mary Clark

ADA SALABLE MATERIALS
See AMERICAN DENTAL ASSOCIATION

D-U-N-S 13-331-4067
■ ADA-ES INC
(*Suby of* ADVANCED EMISSIONS SOLUTIONS, INC.)
9135 Ridgeline Blvd # 200, Highlands Ranch, CO 80129-2391
Tel (303) 734-1727 *Founded/Ownrshp* 2013
Sales 95.4MM^E *EMP* 105
SIC 5075 Air pollution control equipment & supplies
Pr: Michael D Durham
**Ch Bd:* W Phillip Marcum
Pr: C Jean Bustard
Pr: Scott Terhune
**CFO:* Mark H McKinnies
Ex VP: Jonathan R Lagarenne
Ex VP: Jonathan Lagarenne
VP: Christine B Amrhein
VP: Christine Amrhein
VP: Rob Kuhta
VP: Cameron E Martin
VP: Richard Miller
VP: Richard L Miller
VP: Richard J Schlager
VP: Connie Senior
Board of Directors: Kim B Clarke, Alan Bradley Gabbard, Derek C Johnson, Robert E Shanklin, Jeffrey C Smith, Richard J Swanson

ADAC AUTOMOTIVE
See ADAC PLASTICS INC

D-U-N-S 02-088-4979 IMP
ADAC PLASTICS INC
ADAC AUTOMOTIVE
5920 Tahoe Dr Se, Grand Rapids, MI 49546-7123
Tel (616) 957-0311 *Founded/Ownrshp* 1975
Sales 226.9MM *EMP* 800
Accts Crowe Horwath Llp Grand Rapid
SIC 3089 Injection molding of plastics
Ch Bd: Kenneth G Hungerford
**Pr:* Jim Teets
**CFO:* Jeff Dolbee
Treas: Bill Powers
**Treas:* John Shape
Ofcr: Joshua Hall
**VP:* Jeff Ackerman
**VP:* Peter Hungerford
**VP:* Rick Vandekopple
Prgrm Mgr: Richard Dawson
Prgrm Mgr: Drew Fouchea

ADAMA US
See MAKHTESHIM AGAN OF NORTH AMERICA INC

D-U-N-S 83-469-8888
ADAMAR GARAGE CORP
(*Suby of* TROPICANA CASINO AND RESORT) ★
Brighton Avenue Boardwalk, Atlantic City, NJ 08401
Tel (609) 340-4000 *Founded/Ownrshp* 2016
Sales NA *EMP* 1,693^E
SIC 6162 Mortgage bankers & correspondents
Pr: Paul Rubeli

D-U-N-S 03-486-3951
ADAMS & SULLIVAN LLC
IGA
1188 N Market St, Paris, TN 38242-3206
Tel (731) 642-2752 *Founded/Ownrshp* 1963
Sales 100.4MM *EMP* 549
SIC 5411 Supermarkets, chain
Ch Bd: James L Adams
**Pr:* David E Sullivan
VP: Dwight Younger
S&M/Mgr: Mike Coley
Board of Directors: Pat Adams

D-U-N-S 06-971-4889
ADAMS 12 FIVE STAR SCHOOLS
1500 E 128th Ave, Thornton, CO 80241-2601
Tel (720) 972-4000 *Founded/Ownrshp* 1950
Sales 394.8MM *EMP* 5,040
Accts Cliftonlarsonallen Llp Broomf
SIC 8211 Public elementary school; Public junior high school; Public senior high school
Bd of Dir: Lee Peters
Ofcr: Rory Coonts
Dir Risk M: Phil Padilla
Ex Dir: Kari Cocozzella
Off Mgr: Jeanne Morrison
Off Mgr: Jodi Newby
IT Man: Vincent Ardito
Psych: Stacie Rhody
Psych: Catherine Sura
Pathlgst: Melanie Fargo
Doctor: Neil Magor

D-U-N-S 04-211-0510 EXP
ADAMS AIR & HYDRAULICS INC (FL)
7209 E Adamo Dr, Tampa, FL 33619-3427
Tel (813) 626-4128 *Founded/Ownrshp* 1960
Sales 85.2MM^E *EMP* 77^E
SIC 5084 Hydraulic systems equipment & supplies
Pr: John D Adams Jr
**Treas:* Donna S Adams
**VP:* Maurice L Thompson
VP: Reece L Thompson
Genl Mgr: Jackie Fresta
Sales Asso: Adrian Suero

D-U-N-S 60-781-1387
ADAMS AND ASSOCIATES INC
ADAMS AND ASSOCIATES OF NEVADA
10395 Double R Blvd, Reno, NV 89521-5991
Tel (775) 348-0900 *Founded/Ownrshp* 1990
Sales 233.1MM^E *EMP* 2,000
SIC 8748

ADAMS AND ASSOCIATES OF NEVADA
See ADAMS AND ASSOCIATES INC

D-U-N-S 09-209-6080
ADAMS AND REESE LLP
701 Poydras St Ste 4500, New Orleans, LA 70139-4596
Tel (504) 581-3234 *Founded/Ownrshp* 1950
Sales 89.4MM^E *EMP* 600
SIC 8111 General practice law office
Mng Pt: Jeffrey Brooks
Pt: Cannon F Allen Sr
Pt: James R Austin
Pt: Cynthia M Barnett
Pt: E G Barrios
Pt: Samuel W Bartholomew Jr
Pt: Donna L Boyce
Pt: William C Brabec
Pt: F L Butler
Pt: Jay Campbell
Pt: Paul A Carrubba
Pt: Charles A Cerise
Pt: V T Clark Jr
Pt: Alex E Cosculluela
Pt: Johnny L Domiano
Pt: Daryl G Dursum
Pt: Robert Eckinger
Pt: Christopher L Evans
Pt: Brian S Faughnan
Pt: J Bennett Fox Jr
Pt: Joel T Galanter

D-U-N-S 00-804-6331
ADAMS COMMUNICATION & ENGINEERING TECHNOLOGY INC
ACET
11637 Terrace Dr Ste 201, Waldorf, MD 20602-3708
Tel (301) 861-5000 *Founded/Ownrshp* 1999
Sales 165.2MM *EMP* 400
SIC 7379
CEO: Charles M Adams
CFO: Lanphuong Truong
**VP:* Larry Hunt
**VP:* John Pellecchia
**VP:* Michael Seldes

D-U-N-S 14-824-4387
ADAMS CONSTRUCTION CO
523 Rutherford Ave Ne, Roanoke, VA 24016-2117
Tel (540) 982-2366 *Founded/Ownrshp* 1985
Sales 130.7MM^E *EMP* 580
SIC 1611 2951

D-U-N-S 01-306-2195
ADAMS FAIRACRE FARMS INC
ADAMS POWER EQUIPMENT
765 Dutchess Tpke, Poughkeepsie, NY 12603-2000
Tel (845) 454-4330 *Founded/Ownrshp* 1965
Sales 106.2MM^E *EMP* 550
Accts Gkg Cpa S Chestnut Ridge New
SIC 5411 5261 5199 Grocery stores, independent; Garden supplies & tools; Lawnmowers & tractors; Christmas novelties
Ch Bd: Patrick Adams
**Treas:* Dale Adams
**VP:* Donald P Adams
Sales Exec: Mark U Griffin

D-U-N-S 62-434-6151
ADAMS HOMES OF NORTHWEST FLORIDA INC
3000 Gulf Breeze Pkwy, Gulf Breeze, FL 32563-5623
Tel (850) 934-0470 *Founded/Ownrshp* 1991
Sales 159.4MM^E *EMP* 200
SIC 1521 Single-family housing construction
Pr: Wayne L Adams
CFO: Don Adams
VP: Glenn Schneiter
VP: Herman Williams
Exec: Andre Jones
Rgnl Mgr: Brain Etheridge
Genl Mgr: Clay Patton
IT Man: Walter Aniels
Mktg Mgr: Marla Leger
Sls Mgr: Christina Walters

D-U-N-S 80-830-3098
ADAMS OUTDOOR ADVERTISING LIMITED PARTNERSHIP
500 Colonial Center Pkwy, Roswell, GA 30076-8856
Tel (770) 333-0399 *Founded/Ownrshp* 1992
Sales 102.0MM *EMP* 400
SIC 7312 Outdoor advertising services
Genl Pt: Kevin Gleason

ADAMS POWER EQUIPMENT
See ADAMS FAIRACRE FARMS INC

D-U-N-S 04-208-1794
ADAMS REMCO INC
2612 Foundation Dr, South Bend, IN 46628-4390
Tel (574) 288-2113 *Founded/Ownrshp* 1948
Sales 100.8MM^E *EMP* 225
SIC 5044 7629 8243 Office equipment; Copying equipment; Calculating machines; Typewriters; Business machine repair, electric; Software training, computer
Pr: Don Carlile
**Ch Bd:* Rex Carlile
CFO: Bill Fladeland
CFO: William Fladeland
**Sec:* Kathy G Riggs
**V Ch Bd:* Helen Carlile
**VP:* Dean A Carlile
**VP:* David Riggs
Exec: Jenni Boseker
Mng Dir: Phil Aitken
Dist Mgr: Steve Andrews

D-U-N-S 06-727-3649
▲ ADAMS RESOURCES & ENERGY INC
17 S Briar Hollow Ln, Houston, TX 77027-3155
Tel (713) 881-3600 *Founded/Ownrshp* 1973
Sales 1.9MMM *EMP* 809^E
Tkr Sym AE *Exch* ASE
SIC 5172 4212 1382 1311 Crude oil; Petroleum haulage, local; Oil & gas exploration services; Crude petroleum & natural gas production
Ch Bd: Thomas S Smith
COO: Sharon C Davis
Board of Directors: Larry E Bell, Murray E Brasseux, Michelle E Earley, Richard C Jenner, E C Reinauer Jr, W R Scofield

ADAMS ROBINSON CONSTRUCTION
See ADAMS-ROBINSON ENTERPRISES INC

D-U-N-S 14-038-9755 IMP
ADAMS THERMAL SYSTEMS INC
47920 W 5th St, Canton, SD 57013-5802
Tel (605) 764-1260 *Founded/Ownrshp* 2003
Sales 133.8MM^E *EMP* 625
SIC 3714 Radiators & radiator shells & cores, motor vehicle
Pr: Michael Adams
CFO: C J Jurgensen
Ex Dir: Troy Brovold
Genl Mgr: Tom Leckband
Mfg Mgr: David Barg
Mfg Mgr: Vyron Hoff
Opers Mgr: Greg Kiehn
Opers Mgr: Phil Rabinowitz
Natl Sales: Terry Danielson
Board of Directors: Thomas Deuter

D-U-N-S 00-325-1774 IMP/EXP
ADAMS-BURCH LLC
TRIMARK ADAMS-BURCH
(*Suby of* TRIMARK UNITED EAST) ★
1901 Stanford Ct, Landover, MD 20785-3219
Tel (301) 276-2000 *Founded/Ownrshp* 1896, 2016
Sales 114.4MM^E *EMP* 170
SIC 5046 5113 5087 Restaurant equipment & supplies; Industrial & personal service paper; Janitors' supplies
CEO: Daniel M Blaylock
**Pr:* Kevin McClamroch

D-U-N-S 05-656-7050
ADAMS-ROBINSON ENTERPRISES INC
ADAMS ROBINSON CONSTRUCTION
2735 Needmore Rd, Dayton, OH 45414-4207
Tel (937) 274-5318 *Founded/Ownrshp* 1983
Sales 98.9MM^E *EMP* 150
SIC 1541 Renovation, remodeling & repairs: industrial buildings
CEO: Michael Adams
**CFO:* David Miller
CFO: George Pitstick
**Sr VP:* Fred Harris
Exec: Tom Jobe
IT Man: Brenda Williams

D-U-N-S 14-805-0800 EXP
ADAPCO INC
550 Aero Ln, Sanford, FL 32771-6342
Tel (407) 330-4800 *Founded/Ownrshp* 1998
Sales 91.0MM^E *EMP* 88
SIC 5191 Pesticides
Pr: Stephen M Burt
Pr: Larry Heller
COO: Trae Etre
**CFO:* Albert P Etre
Genl Mgr: Jacky Ajalat
CIO: Donn Griffin

D-U-N-S 96-874-5661
ADAPTIS INC
999 3rd Ave Ste 1700, Seattle, WA 98104-1168
Tel (206) 521-8833 *Founded/Ownrshp* 1996
Sales 34.8MM^E *EMP* 1,300^E
SIC 7389 Personal service agents, brokers & bureaus
Pr: James Anderson
CFO: Bob Peters
Ofcr: Roya Rezai

ADAPTIVE CONSOLIDATION
See ADAPTIVE INSIGHTS INC

D-U-N-S 15-387-7720
ADAPTIVE INSIGHTS INC
ADAPTIVE CONSOLIDATION
3350 W Byshore Rd Ste 200, Palo Alto, CA 94303
Tel (800) 303-6346 *Founded/Ownrshp* 2003
Sales 144.6MM^E *EMP* 400
SIC 7372 Business oriented computer software
CEO: Thomas F Bogan
Pt: Carolee Gearhart
Ch Bd: Rob Hull
Pr: Mike Conti
CFO: Jim Johnson
CFO: David Pefley
Ofcr: Fred Gewant
Ofcr: Keith Nealon
Sr VP: Karen Pisha
Sr VP: Greg Schneider
Sr VP: Neil Thomas
VP: Tina Babbi
VP: Ethan Carlson
VP: Amy Clark
VP: Kell Forsman
VP: Michelle Herman
Dir Bus: Dave Downey
Board of Directors: Eric Dunn, Jim Kelliher, Mark Templeton

ADB AIRFIELD SOLUTIONS LLC
See ADB SAFEGATE AMERICAS LLC

D-U-N-S 82-994-8392 IMP/EXP
ADB SAFEGATE AMERICAS LLC
ADB AIRFIELD SOLUTIONS LLC
(*Suby of* ADB SAFEGATE BVBA)
977 Gahanna Pkwy, Columbus, OH 43230-6610
Tel (614) 861-1304 *Founded/Ownrshp* 2009
Sales 123.9MM^E *EMP* 300
SIC 3648 3812 Airport lighting fixtures: runway approach, taxi or ramp; Search & navigation equipment
S&M/VP: Joe Pokoj
Exec: Shelly Norman
Manager: Ben Burns
Manager: Jeff Scott
Genl Couns: Nancy Van Campenhout

ADC
See AUSTIN DIAGNOSTIC CLINIC ASSOCIATION

D-U-N-S 08-840-3233
ADCO ELECTRICAL CORP
201 Edward Curry Ave, Staten Island, NY 10314-7105
Tel (718) 494-4400 *Founded/Ownrshp* 1977
Sales 84.9MM^E *EMP* 500
Accts Grassi & Co Cpas Pc Jerich
SIC 1731 Electrical work
Ch Bd: Gina Addeo
**Ex VP:* Lisa Addeo

D-U-N-S 07-121-1887 IMP/EXP
ADCO GLOBAL INC
(*Suby of* ROYAL ELASTOMERS) ★
100 Tri State Intl # 135, Lincolnshire, IL 60069-4425
Tel (847) 282-3485 *Founded/Ownrshp* 2013
Sales 294.5MM^E *EMP* 1,000
SIC 2891 Adhesives & sealants
Prin: John Knox
**CFO:* Peter Paulsen
**VP:* Michael Graf
IT Man: Tom Konopka

D-U-N-S 00-542-2225 IMP
ADCO PRODUCTS INC
AGILE BRANDS
27615 Avenue Hopkins, Valencia, CA 91355-3493
Tel (800) 541-2326 *Founded/Ownrshp* 1955, 1982
Sales 97.3MM^E *EMP* 1,000
SIC 2393 Textile bags
Prin: Benny Blumenfeld
**Pr:* Alan Ein
**Ex VP:* Zachary Ein
**VP:* Morgan Ein
MIS Dir: Whitney Long
Sls Dir: Dwight Ford

D-U-N-S 80-227-2138
ADCS CLINICS LLC
ADVANCED DRMTLOGY CSMTC SRGERY
151 Southhall Ln Ste 300, Maitland, FL 32751-7172
Tel (407) 875-2080 *Founded/Ownrshp* 1992
Sales 120.0MM *EMP* 888
SIC 8011 Dermatologist
**Pr:* Dave Morell
**CFO:* Richard Fogle
CFO: Jusin Kuperberg
Surgeon: Alan J Bauman
Surgeon: Ivan Cohen
Surgeon: Arthur T D
Surgeon: Marcelo G D
Surgeon: Michael B D
Surgeon: Shelly Friedman
Surgeon: Sharon Keene
Surgeon: Grant F Koher

D-U-N-S 78-968-3799 EXP
ADDAX PETROLEUM US SERVICES CORP
(*Suby of* SINOPEC INTERNATIONAL PETROLEUM EXPLORATION AND PRODUCTION CORPORATION)
1301 Mckinney St Ste 2050, Houston, TX 77010-3062
Tel (713) 341-3150 *Founded/Ownrshp* 2009
Sales 110.2MM^E *EMP* 362^E

SIC 5172 Petroleum products

D-U-N-S 78-321-4773
ADDISON GROUP L L C
(*Suby of* HIRESTRATEGY) ★
901 N Lincoln Blvd # 305, Oklahoma City, OK 73104-3208
Tel (405) 235-6700 *Founded/Ownrshp* 2012
Sales 22.4MM^{E} *EMP* 1,102^{E}
SIC 7361 8742 Employment agencies; Industrial & labor consulting services

D-U-N-S 14-834-5838
■ ADDISON INSURANCE CO
(*Suby of* UFG) ★
118 2nd Ave Se, Cedar Rapids, IA 52401-1212
Tel (319) 399-5700 *Founded/Ownrshp* 1990
Sales NA *EMP* 650
SIC 6331 Fire, marine & casualty insurance & carriers; Automobile insurance
Pr: John Rife
**Treas:* Kent Baker

D-U-N-S 14-684-5594
ADDISON PROFESSIONAL FINANCIAL SEARCH LLC
HIRESTRATEGY
125 S Wacker Dr Fl 27, Chicago, IL 60606-4475
Tel (312) 424-0300 *Founded/Ownrshp* 1999
Sales 163.6MM^{E} *EMP* 1,770
SIC 7363 Help supply services
CEO: Thomas Moran
VP: Mike Biron
**VP:* John Jay Houston
**VP:* Stephen Spinner
Dir IT: Arshad Qureshi

D-U-N-S 07-809-3002
■ ADDUS HEALTHCARE INC
(*Suby of* ADDUS HOMECARE CORP) ★
2300 Warrenville Rd, Downers Grove, IL 60515-1702
Tel (630) 296-3400 *Founded/Ownrshp* 1972
Sales 206.8MM^{E} *EMP* 13,140
SIC 8082 Home health care services
Pr: W Andrew Wright
**Pr:* Mark S Heaney
Snr Sftwr: Michael Chaffee

D-U-N-S 82-985-7775
▲ ADDUS HOMECARE CORP
2300 Warrenville Rd # 100, Downers Grove, IL 60515-1717
Tel (630) 296-3400 *Founded/Ownrshp* 1979
Sales 336.8MM *EMP* 21,395^{E}
Tkr Sym ADUS *Exch* NGM
SIC 8082 8361 Home health care services; Home for the aged
Pr: R Dirk Allison
**Ch Bd:* Steven I Geringer
COO: Maxine Hochhauser
CFO: Brian Poff
Ofcr: Brenda Belger
Ex VP: Darby Anderson
CIO: James Zoccoli
Board of Directors: Simon A Bachleda, Michael Earley, Darin J Gordon, Susan T Weaver, Mark L First

D-U-N-S 09-697-2844
ADECCO EMPLOYMENT SERVICES INC
(*Suby of* ADECCO TECHNICAL) ★
175 Broadhollow Rd, Melville, NY 11747-4911
Tel (631) 844-7100 *Founded/Ownrshp* 1996
Sales 4.0MMM *EMP* 2,000
SIC 7363 7361 Temporary help service; Labor contractors (employment agency)
CEO: Robert Crouch
VP: Douglas Slack
Brnch Mgr: Matt Lauro
Mktg Dir: Cynthia Ruf
Mktg Mgr: Sarah Walls

ADECCO GOVERNMENT SOLUTIONS
See TAD PGS INC

D-U-N-S 07-911-3258
ADECCO INC
(*Suby of* ADECCO GROUP AG)
175 Broadhollow Rd # 200, Melville, NY 11747-4910
Tel (631) 391-5776 *Founded/Ownrshp* 1990
Sales 6.5MMM^{E} *EMP* 37,000^{E}
SIC 6719 Investment holding companies, except banks
CEO: Tig Gilliam
**Ex VP:* Joyce Russell
**Sr VP:* Sherry Dixon
**Sr VP:* Amy Glaser
**Sr VP:* Lauren Griffin
**Sr VP:* Daniel Masata
**Sr VP:* Andrea Sugden
**Sr VP:* Kristy Willis
CIO: Leslie Brown
CIO: Evelyn Sibilla
Mktg Dir: Karen Lee

ADECCO TECHNICAL
See ADECCO USA INC

D-U-N-S 06-161-8492
ADECCO USA INC
ADECCO TECHNICAL
(*Suby of* ADECCO INC) ★
10151 Deerwood Bldg 200, Jacksonville, FL 32256
Tel (904) 359-4710 *Founded/Ownrshp* 1972
Sales 5.5MMM^{E} *EMP* 37,000^{E}
SIC 7363 7361 8742 6794 Temporary help service; Placement agencies; Human resource consulting services; Franchises, selling or licensing
Ch Bd: Robert Crouch
V Ch: Klaus J Acobs
V Ch: Klaus Jacobs
Pr: David Alexander
Pr: Bob Cecchini
Pr: Jack Cullen
Pr: John Marshall
Pr: Jeff Rupp
CFO: Dominik De Daniel
CFO: Stephen Nolan
CFO: Felix Weber
Sr Cor Off: Bill Lafferty
Chf Mktg O: Ed Blust
Ex VP: Joyce Russell
Sr VP: George Reardon
Sr VP: Mark Rosen
Sr VP: Tyra Tutor
VP: Vimarsh Mehta
Dir Risk M: Chris Ottesen

ADEL GROCERY
See CORE-MARK DISTRIBUTORS INC

D-U-N-S 03-990-9320
ADELANTO ELEMENTARY SCHOOL DISTRICT
11824 Air Expy, Adelanto, CA 92301-1730
Tel (760) 246-8691 *Founded/Ownrshp* 1913
Sales 63.6MM^{E} *EMP* 1,000
SIC 8211 Public elementary school
Bd of Dir: Janice Dix
Bd of Dir: Sharon Inglefield
**Ofcr:* Martha Navartee
HC Dir: Donna Andrey

D-U-N-S 94-903-4110
ADELPHI ENTERPRISES LIMITED PARTNERSHIP
BREDEMANN LEXUS IN GLENVIEW
2000 Waukegan Rd, Glenview, IL 60025-1716
Tel (847) 698-3700 *Founded/Ownrshp* 1989
Sales 90.0MM *EMP* 84
SIC 5511 Automobiles, new & used
Genl Mgr: Joseph Bredemann II
Mktg Mgr: Cheryl Alvarez
Sls Mgr: Dani Serritella

D-U-N-S 06-597-2838
ADELPHI UNIVERSITY
1 S Ave Lvh 310 310 Lvh, Garden City, NY 11530
Tel (516) 877-3000 *Founded/Ownrshp* 1896
Sales 199.0MM *EMP* 1,400
Accts Grant Thornton Llp Melville
SIC 8221 University
Pr: Robert A Scott
V Ch: Carol Ammon
CFO: John N Vincent
Trst: Frank Angello
Trst: Richard Cahn
Trst: Joan Girgus
Trst: Douglas Green
Trst: Joseph Gregori
Trst: Michael Lazarus
Trst: Gerald Mahoney
Trst: Kenneth McClane
Trst: Lindsey Nederlander
Ofcr: Erin Gayron
Sr VP: Gayle D Insler
VP: Catherine Hennessy
VP: Carl J Rheins
Assoc Dir: Craig Kennedy
Assoc Dir: Jennifer Spiegel
Adv Bd Mbr: Dennis Payette

D-U-N-S 06-365-2341
ADELPHIA COMMUNICATIONS CORP
5613 Dtc Pkwy Ste 850, Greenwood Village, CO 80111-3177
Tel (814) 274-6279 *Founded/Ownrshp* 1986
Sales 3.1MMM^{E} *EMP* 26^{E}
SIC 4899 Data communication services

D-U-N-S 87-262-6411
ADELPHIA METALS I LIMITED LIABILITY CO
1930 Marlton Pike E M66, Cherry Hill, NJ 08003-2150
Tel (856) 988-8889 *Founded/Ownrshp* 2006
Sales 251.0MM *EMP* 20
Accts Goldenberg Rosenthal Llp Cpa
SIC 5051 Steel
CEO: Daniel Carlin
**Pr:* Jed Trachte

D-U-N-S 04-964-9395
ADENA HEALTH SYSTEM
GREENFIELD AREA MEDICAL CENTER
272 Hospital Rd, Chillicothe, OH 45601-9031
Tel (740) 779-7360 *Founded/Ownrshp* 1895
Sales 393.4MM *EMP* 2,500
SIC 8062 Hospital, medical school affiliated with nursing & residency
Pr: Mark Shuter
Chf Rad: Dale Hume
Chf Rad: David Magee
COO: Eric Cecava
**CFO:* Keith T Coleman
CFO: Dawn B Johnson
Treas: Tony Colby
Chf Mktg O: Diana Patterson
VP: Nick Alexander
VP: Peggy Depugh-Landrum
VP: Michael Glanzman
Exec: Brandt Lippert
Exec: Sherry Smith
Dir Risk M: Leslie Parker
Dir Rad: Dave Zanni
Dir Rx: Fred Yingling

D-U-N-S 06-651-6480
ADEPT FASTENERS INC
28709 Industry Dr, Valencia, CA 91355-5414
Tel (661) 257-6600 *Founded/Ownrshp* 2001
Sales 113.3MM^{E} *EMP* 127^{E}
SIC 5072 Miscellaneous fasteners
Pr: Gary Young
**VP:* Don List
Off Mgr: Elaine Young
IT Man: Cheryl Odermatt
Ql Cn Mgr: Dominic Cuttaia
Ql Cn Mgr: Bob Newkirk
Natl Sales: Elaine Clarke
Manager: Nichole Campion
Sales Asso: John Pierson
Board of Directors: Don List, Gary Young

D-U-N-S 07-941-1953
▲ ADEPTUS HEALTH INC
2941 Lake Vista Dr # 200, Lewisville, TX 75067-3801
Tel (972) 899-6666 *Founded/Ownrshp* 2014
Sales 373.6MM *EMP* 3,202^{E}
Accts Securities And Exchange Commis
Tkr Sym ADPT *Exch* NYS
SIC 8741 8011 Restaurant management; Freestanding emergency medical center
Ch Bd: Gregory W Scott
V Ch: Richard Covert
Pr: Graham B Cherrington
CFO: Timothy L Fielding
CFO: Frank R Williams
Chf Mktg O: Andrew Jordan
Sr VP: Traci Bowen
VP: David Pyle

ADESA AUCTIONS
See ADESA CORP LLC

D-U-N-S 85-884-8039 IMP
■ ADESA CORP LLC
ADESA AUCTIONS
(*Suby of* KAR AUCTION SERVICES INC) ★
13085 Hamilton Crossing B, Carmel, IN 46032-1412
Tel (317) 249-4550 *Founded/Ownrshp* 1992
Sales 2.0MMM^{E} *EMP* 11,915
SIC 5012 6153 Automobile auction; Financing of dealers by motor vehicle manufacturers organ.
COO: Thomas Caruso
COO: Dan Harris
COO: Bradley A Todd
CFO: Eric Loughmiller
Bd of Dir: Nancy Grace
**Ex VP:* Brenda J Flayton
Ex VP: Rebecca C Polak
Ex VP: Frank Stephens
Ex VP: Chuck Tapp
Ex VP: David Vignes
VP: Pale Ainsworth
VP: Jack Allan
VP: Jeff Bescher
VP: Warren Byrd
VP: Keith Crerar
VP: Jason Hart
VP: Dave Roach
VP: John Rogers
VP: Brett Roland
VP: Mark Thomas
Exec: Rance Rudy

D-U-N-S 02-963-9788
ADESA UTAH LLC
BRASHERS SALT LAKE AUTO AUCTN
780 S 5600 W, Salt Lake City, UT 84104-5300
Tel (801) 322-1234 *Founded/Ownrshp* 2016
Sales 91.4MM^{E} *EMP* 253^{E}
SIC 5012 5521 5084 Automobile auction; Used car dealers; Industrial machinery & equipment
Pr: Robert J Brasher
**Pr:* J L Brasher
**Sec:* Stanley G Russell
**VP:* Douglas R Brasher
Genl Mgr: Rob Brasher
Board of Directors: Justin Booth, Douglas Brasher, Jeffrey Brasher, Robert Brasher, Douglas T Brewer, Donald Rowley, Stanley Russell

ADEXIS
See FUSIONSTORM

ADF COMPANIES
See AMERICAN HUTS INC

D-U-N-S 01-904-7786
ADFITECH INC
(*Suby of* TMST INC) ★
3001 Technology Dr, Edmond, OK 73013-3734
Tel (800) 880-0456 *Founded/Ownrshp* 1983
Sales NA *EMP* 300
SIC 6162 Mortgage bankers
CEO: Samuel E Meek
**Pr:* Dru Jacobs
**Ex VP:* Sam Meek
VP: Michael Elliott
VP: Frederick Weber
VP: Robbie Williams
Dir IT: Steve Rosenhamer
Software D: Darrell Epperson

D-U-N-S 60-363-4213
ADH 702 INC
203 Lookout Pl Ste A, Maitland, FL 32751-8407
Tel (407) 629-9311 *Founded/Ownrshp* 1989
Sales 27.8MM^{E} *EMP* 2,000
SIC 5812 Restaurant, family: chain
Pr: Eric Holm
**Treas:* Diane Holm
**VP:* Doug Dannen

D-U-N-S 00-301-0345 IMP/EXP
ADHESIVES RESEARCH INC (PA)
400 Seaks Run Rd, Glen Rock, PA 17327-9500
Tel (717) 235-7979 *Founded/Ownrshp* 1961
Sales 118.0MM *EMP* 417
Accts Baker Tilly
SIC 2891 Adhesives
Pr: John Lind
V Ch: Jerry Anderson
**Pr:* George Stolakis
COO: Jim Waller
**Treas:* Erwin W Huber
**VP:* George Cramer
**VP:* Lynne Durbin
VP: Scott Huber
**VP:* Scott Knorr
Exec: John Calla
Exec: Stuart Shangraw

ADI
See AEROSPACE DYNAMICS INTERNATIONAL INC

D-U-N-S 07-955-7126
■ ADI CORPORATE
(*Suby of* HONEYWELL INTERNATIONAL INC) ★
263 Old Country Rd, Melville, NY 11747-2712
Tel (800) 233-6261 *Founded/Ownrshp* 2014
Sales 89.6MM^{E} *EMP* 98^{E}
SIC 5063 5085 Electric alarms & signaling equipment; Industrial supplies
Pr: Robert Aarnes
Brnch Mgr: Duane Westmore

D-U-N-S 95-760-7328
ADI WORLDLINK LLC
3880 Parkwood Blvd # 204, Frisco, TX 75034-1929
Tel (971) 671-3434 *Founded/Ownrshp* 1998
Sales 186.0MM *EMP* 1,000
SIC 7371 Custom computer programming services
Pr: Adil ADI
**Ofcr:* Barjis Ghadially
Sr VP: Jinwoo Kang
**VP:* Zenobia ADI
VP: Tom Jasny
**VP:* Paul Myers
VP: Rick Sharpe
VP: Jason Skinner

ADIC
See ADVANCED DIGITAL INFORMATION CORP

D-U-N-S 03-943-2976 IMP
ADIDAS AMERICA INC
ADIDAS INTERNATIONAL
(*Suby of* ADIDAS NORTH AMERICA INC) ★
5055 N Greeley Ave, Portland, OR 97217-3524
Tel (971) 234-2300 *Founded/Ownrshp* 2000
Sales 898.0MM^{E} *EMP* 1,035
SIC 5139 5136 5137 3021 2339 Footwear, athletic; Shoes; Men's & boys' clothing; Women's & children's clothing; Rubber & plastics footwear; Women's & misses' outerwear
Pr: Patrik Nilsson
**Pr:* Mark King
**CFO:* Jack Cuniff
Chf Mktg O: Hermann Deininger
Sr VP: Russ Hopcus
VP: Mark Rouse
VP: Alison Stewart
VP: Steve Vincent
Genl Mgr: Oliver Fehl
Store Mgr: Marie Aucello
Store Mgr: Sarah Johnson

ADIDAS INTERNATIONAL
See ADIDAS AMERICA INC

D-U-N-S 08-430-2152 IMP
ADIDAS NORTH AMERICA INC
(*Suby of* ADIDAS INTERNATIONAL B.V.)
5055 N Greeley Ave, Portland, OR 97217-3524
Tel (971) 234-2300 *Founded/Ownrshp* 2006
Sales 1.2MMM^{E} *EMP* 2,000
SIC 2329 Athletic (warmup, sweat & jogging) suits: men's & boys'; Men's & boys' athletic uniforms; Knickers, dress (separate): men's & boys'
CEO: Herbert Hainer
**Prin:* Glenn Bennett
**Prin:* Robin J Stalker
**Prin:* Erich Stamminger

D-U-N-S 12-565-8950 IMP
ADIENT CLANTON INC
(*Suby of* ADIENT US LLC) ★
2541 7th St S, Clanton, AL 35046-6304
Tel (205) 755-9994 *Founded/Ownrshp* 2016
Sales 243.2MM^{E} *EMP* 550
SIC 2531 Vehicle furniture
CEO: Dean Lenane
Pr: Robert Houston
VP: John Hay
VP: Tim Tow

D-U-N-S 08-045-7769
ADIENT HOLDING MEXICO LLC
49200 Halyard Dr, Plymouth, MI 48170-2481
Tel (414) 220-8900 *Founded/Ownrshp* 2016
Sales NA *EMP* 7,000
SIC 6719 Investment holding companies, except banks
Ex VP: Bruce McDonald

D-U-N-S 08-045-7629
ADIENT INC
(*Suby of* ADIENT GLOBAL HOLDINGS LTD)
49200 Halyard Dr, Plymouth, MI 48170-2481
Tel (414) 220-8900 *Founded/Ownrshp* 2015
Sales NA *EMP* 2,410
SIC 6719 Investment holding companies, except banks
Ex VP: Bruce McDonald

D-U-N-S 00-654-5438 IMP/EXP
ADIENT US LLC
(*Suby of* ADIENT PUBLIC LIMITED COMPANY)
49200 Halyard Dr, Plymouth, MI 48170-2481
Tel (734) 254-5000 *Founded/Ownrshp* 1964, 2016
Sales 1.4MMM^{E} *EMP* 2,000
SIC 3714 Motor vehicle parts & accessories
VP: Ramesh Akkala
VP: Jim Hill
DP Exec: Diedre Kutscher
Sftwr Eng: Doug Klamer
Sftwr Eng: Edward Rivera

D-U-N-S 00-131-8203 IMP/EXP
ADIR INTERNATIONAL LLC (DE)
LA CURACAO
1605 W Olympic Blvd # 405, Los Angeles, CA 90015-3836
Tel (213) 639-2100 *Founded/Ownrshp* 1976
Sales 484.7MM^{E} *EMP* 2,196
Accts Deloitte & Touche Llp
SIC 5311 Department stores
Sys Mgr: Balaji Ochoa
Netwrk Eng: Eduardo Argueta

D-U-N-S 03-736-6788 IMP
ADIRONDACK BEVERAGE CO INC
(*Suby of* POLAR BEVERAGES) ★
701 Corporation Park, Schenectady, NY 12302-1060
Tel (518) 370-3621 *Founded/Ownrshp* 1982
Sales 228.8MM^{E} *EMP* 1,000
SIC 2086 Soft drinks: packaged in cans, bottles, etc.; Pasteurized & mineral waters, bottled & canned
Ch: Angelo Mastrangelo
**Pr:* Ralph Crowley Jr
**Sec:* Michael Mulrain
**VP:* Christopher Crowley
**VP:* Douglas Martin
IT Man: David Vaughn
Plnt Mgr: Dan Dubovik

ADIRONDACK HEALTH
See ADIRONDACK MEDICAL CENTER

D-U-N-S 06-054-4657
ADIRONDACK MEDICAL CENTER
ADIRONDACK HEALTH
2233 State Route 86, Saranac Lake, NY 12983-5644
Tel (518) 891-4141 Founded/Ownrshp 1914
Sales 89.1MM EMP 650
SIC 8062 General medical & surgical hospitals
CEO: Chandler Ralph
COO: Patti Hammond
*CFO: Patrick Facteau
CFO: Mark Laramee
Exec: Mary Baker
Dir Inf Cn: Marion Tracy
Dir Lab: Steve Richardson
Ex Dir: Hannah Hanford
Telecom Ex: Paul Johnson
Netwrk Eng: Chuck Robertson
Opers Mgr: Scott Childs

D-U-N-S 07-719-8125 IMP
ADIRONDACK SCENIC INC
ADIRONDACK STUDIOS
439 County Route 45 Ste 1, Argyle, NY 12809-3514
Tel (518) 638-8000 Founded/Ownrshp 1975
Sales 180.0MM EMP 100
SIC 2599 Factory furniture & fixtures
CEO: David Thomas Lloyd
*CFO: Christopher Detmer
VP: Louis Allen
Creative D: Lara Sorensen
VP Prd: Ken Crosby
Sls Mgr: Carl Zutz

ADIRONDACK STUDIOS
See ADIRONDACK SCENIC INC

ADITYA BIRLA GROUP
See NOVELIS CORP

ADJUTANT GENERAL
See MILITARY DEPARTMENT CONNECTICUT

D-U-N-S 00-359-2743 EXP
ADJUTANT GENERAL SOUTH CAROLINA
(Suby of BUDGET & CTRL BD EXEC DIRS OFF) ★
1 National Guard Rd, Columbia, SC 29201-4766
Tel (803) 299-4308 Founded/Ownrshp 1636
Sales NA EMP 13,500
SIC 9711 National Guard;

D-U-N-S 17-673-7369
ADJUTANT GENERALS DEPARTMENT KANSAS
(Suby of EXECUTIVE OFFICE OF STATE OF KANSAS) ★
2800 Sw Topeka Blvd, Topeka, KS 66611-1287
Tel (785) 274-1000 Founded/Ownrshp 1900
Sales NA EMP 5,500
SIC 9711 National Guard;
Genl Mgr: Tod Bunting
Genl Mgr: Cheri Froetschner
*Genl Mgr: Lee Tafanelli
Genl Mgr: Jason Van Fleet
Dir IT: Jeff Howell

ADJUTANT GENERAL'S OFFICE
See DEPARTMENT OF MILITARY CALIFORNIA

ADJUTANT GENERAL'S OFFICE
See INDIANA OFFICE OF ADJUTANT GENERAL

ADJUTANT GENERAL'S OFFICE
See DEPARTMENT OF MILITARY WYOMING

ADJUTANT GENERALS OFFICE
See OKLAHOMA DEPT OF MILITARY

D-U-N-S 02-143-8569
ADLAI E STEVENSON HIGH SCHOOL DISTRICT 125
1 Stevenson Dr, Lincolnshire, IL 60069-2824
Tel (847) 415-4000 Founded/Ownrshp 1947
Sales 115.3MM EMP 550
Accts Evoy Kamschulte Jacobs & Co
SIC 8211 Public senior high school
Bd of Dir: Gary Gorson
Psych: Claire Forde
Pgrm Dir: Susan Taylor

D-U-N-S 84-968-4428 IMP/EXP
ADM ALLIANCE NUTRITION INC
1000 N 30th St, Quincy, IL 62301-3400
Tel (217) 231-2674 Founded/Ownrshp 1997
Sales 2.1MM^E EMP 1,200
SIC 2048 5154

D-U-N-S 07-924-3386 IMP/EXP
ADM COCOA INC
4666 E Faries Pkwy, Decatur, IL 62526-5678
Tel (217) 424-5200 Founded/Ownrshp 1988
Sales 127.5MM^E EMP 175^E
SIC 5169 Industrial chemicals
Pr: Patricia A Woertz
*Ex VP: Juan R Luciano
*Sr VP: Michael D Ambrose
*Sr VP: Mark A Bemis
*Sr VP: D Cameron Findlay

D-U-N-S 07-969-7511
ADM EDIBLE BEAN SPECIALTIES INC
ADM SEEDWEST
4666 E Faries Pkwy, Decatur, IL 62526-5678
Tel (217) 424-5200 Founded/Ownrshp 1978
Sales 221.8MM^E EMP 33,000
SIC 5191 Lime, agricultural

D-U-N-S 14-839-1048 EXP
■ ADM GRAIN RIVER SYSTEM INC
(Suby of ARCHER-DANIELS-MIDLAND CO) ★
4666 E Faries Pkwy, Decatur, IL 62526-5678
Tel (312) 634-8100 Founded/Ownrshp 1985
Sales 1.4MMM^E EMP 2,376
SIC 5153 Grains
Pr: Joseph Taets
*VP: Matthew D Bruns
VP: Michael Lusk

D-U-N-S 03-908-2524
■ ADM INVESTOR SERVICES INC
(Suby of ARCHER-DANIELS-MIDLAND CO) ★
141 W Jackson Blvd 2100a, Chicago, IL 60604-3002
Tel (312) 242-7000 Founded/Ownrshp 1980
Sales 153.9MM^E EMP 165
Accts Ernst & Young Llp Chicago Il
SIC 6221 Commodity brokers, contracts
Pr: Thomas R Kadlec
Ofcr: Tracy Hetherington
VP: Chris Damilatis
VP: Dennis Harding
VP: Kurt Johnson
VP: Richy Macanit
VP: John Meyer
VP: Scott Roney
VP: Scott Smith
Exec: Dennis Smith
Prin: John M Walls

D-U-N-S 05-070-2539
■ ADM MILLING CO (MN)
(Suby of ARCHER-DANIELS-MIDLAND CO) ★
8000 W 110th St Ste 300, Overland Park, KS 66210-2315
Tel (913) 491-9400 Founded/Ownrshp 1902
Sales 350.2MM^E EMP 1,500
SIC 2041 Flour mills, cereal (except rice); Grain mills (except rice)
Prin: Juan R Luciano
*Pr: Mark Kolkhorst
*VP: Mike Marsh
*VP: Loren Urquhart
*VP: Nick Weigel
Snr Mgr: Dan Carton

ADM SEEDWEST
See ADM EDIBLE BEAN SPECIALTIES INC

D-U-N-S 03-417-7154
■ ADM TRUCKING INC
(Suby of ARCHER-DANIELS-MIDLAND CO) ★
2501 N Brush College Rd, Decatur, IL 62526-5595
Tel (217) 424-5200 Founded/Ownrshp 1979
Sales 111.1MM^E EMP 650
SIC 4213 Trucking, except local
*Pr: Scott B Fredericksen

D-U-N-S 05-964-6927
ADMAR SUPPLY CO INC
1950 Brghtn Hnrietta Town, Rochester, NY 14623-2597
Tel (585) 272-9390 Founded/Ownrshp 1972
Sales 156.6MM^E EMP 225
SIC 5082 General construction machinery & equipment
Ch Bd: Joel R Dimarco
*CFO: Lawrence Keeley
*Ex VP: Richard J Dimarco
Brnch Mgr: Edward Cologie
Brnch Mgr: Matt Geren
Brnch Mgr: Frank Lippa
Genl Mgr: Rolf Witt
IT Man: Joe Posato
Sls Mgr: Shane Kiess
Sls Mgr: Jason Morris
Sales Asso: Tim Bolliger

ADMINISTAFF OF TEXAS, INC.
See INSPERITY HOLDINGS INC

ADMINISTATION DEPT
See SCHOOL BOARD OF CITY OF VIRGINIA BEACH

D-U-N-S 02-634-7760
ADMINISTRACION DE FAMILIAS Y NINOS
(Suby of SECRETARY OF COMMONWEALTH) ★
Ave Ponce De Leon Stp2, San Juan, PR 00907-3907
Tel (787) 625-4900 Founded/Ownrshp 1995
Sales NA EMP 3,500
SIC 9431

D-U-N-S 09-017-1216
ADMINISTRACION DE SERVICIOS MEDICOS DE PR
P R MEDICAL CENTER
Intersection Monacillos W, San Juan, PR 00921
Tel (787) 777-3535 Founded/Ownrshp 1962
Sales 98.4MM^E EMP 1,900
SIC 8741 Management services
Ex Dir: Ana C Rius

ADMINISTRATION
See COUNTY OF PASSAIC

ADMINISTRATION
See COUNTY OF HILLSBOROUGH

D-U-N-S 82-484-8121
ADMINISTRATION AND FINANCE MASSACHUSETTS EXECUTIVE OFFICE FOR
(Suby of EXECUTIVE OFFICE OF COMMONWEALTH OF MASSACHUSETTS) ★
24 Beacon St Ste 373, Boston, MA 02133-1099
Tel (617) 727-2040 Founded/Ownrshp 1966
Sales NA EMP 4,000
SIC 9199 9311 General government administration; ; Finance, taxation & monetary policy;

ADMINISTRATION OFFICE
See SAN FRANCISCO UNIFIED SCHOOL DISTRICT

ADMINISTRATION OFFICE
See COUNTY OF MERCER

ADMINISTRATION OFFICE
See COUNTY OF GUILFORD

ADMINISTRATION OFFICE
See COUNTY OF MUSKEGON

ADMINISTRATION OFFICE
See COUNTY OF SHASTA

ADMINISTRATION OFFICE
See OREGON DEPARTMENT OF HUMAN SERVICES

ADMINISTRATIVE BUILDING
See CITY OF COLORADO SPRINGS

D-U-N-S 01-345-8141
ADMINISTRATIVE EMPLOYER SERVICES INC (MI)
13900 Lakeside Cir 200, Sterling Heights, MI 48313-1318
Tel (586) 997-3377 Founded/Ownrshp 1998
Sales 87.1MM EMP 2,800
SIC 8742 Human resource consulting services
Pr: David Otto
Mng Pt: Don Onesi

ADMINISTRATIVE OFFICE
See COUNTY OF TULARE

ADMINISTRATIVE OFFICE
See COLORADO STATE UNIVERSITY SYSTEM

D-U-N-S 36-070-6188
ADMINISTRATIVE OFFICE OF PENNSYLVANIA COURTS
(Suby of COMMONWEALTH OF PENNSYLVANIA) ★
601 Commonwealth Ave # 1500, Harrisburg, PA 17120-0901
Tel (717) 231-3300 Founded/Ownrshp 1776
Sales NA EMP 2,250
SIC 9211 State courts;
Prin: Ralph J Cappy
Genl Mgr: Jordan Kohler
Genl Mgr: Casey Scarborough
IT Man: Denise Aylward
IT Man: Dan Hyde
Netwrk Mgr: Dave Serfass

ADMINISTRATIVE OFFICES
See COUNTY OF HARRIS

D-U-N-S 87-309-9279
ADMINISTRATIVE RESOURCES INC
801 Sunset Dr F1, Johnson City, TN 37604-3033
Tel (423) 283-0296 Founded/Ownrshp 1992
Sales 24.9MM^E EMP 1,000
SIC 8721 8741 8742 6794 Payroll accounting service; Personnel management; Personnel management consultant; Franchises, selling or licensing
Pr: Rick J Thomason
*VP Opers: Sharon Thomason

ADMINISTRATIVE SERVICES CENTER
See BURNSVILLE EAGAN SAVAGE INDEPENDENT SCHOOL DISTRICT 191

D-U-N-S 07-967-2980
ADMINISTRATIVE TRIALS & HEARINGS OFFICE OF (OATH)
(Suby of CITY OF NEW YORK) ★
100 Church St Fl 12, New York, NY 10007-2620
Tel (844) 628-4692 Founded/Ownrshp 1988
Sales NA EMP 2,420^E
SIC 9111 ; Mayors' offices

D-U-N-S 07-628-0981
ADMINISTRATORS FOR PROFESSIONS INC
(Suby of AJB VENTURES INC) ★
1800 N Blvd, Roslyn, NY 11576
Tel (516) 365-6690 Founded/Ownrshp 1981
Sales NA EMP 300
SIC 6321 Accident & health insurance
CEO: Anthony J Bonomo
*Sec: Barry F Swartz
*Ex VP: Carl Bonomo
*CTO: Bernard McArthur
*Genl Couns: Jim Tuffin

D-U-N-S 05-378-5812
ADMINISTRATORS OF TULANE EDUCATIONAL FUND (LA)
TULANE UNIVERSITY
6823 Saint Charles Ave, New Orleans, LA 70118-5665
Tel (504) 865-5000 Founded/Ownrshp 1834
Sales 949.9MM EMP 5,500
SIC 8221 8733 University; Physical research, noncommercial
Pr: Scott Cowen
*CFO: Anthony Lorino
Treas: Brent Andrus
Treas: Brent R Andus
Sr VP: Michael Bernstein
*Sr VP: Yvette M Jones
VP: John Diem
Exec: Philip Greer
Assoc Dir: Rudolf Bohm
Comm Dir: Celeste Uzee
*Prin: Tanya O'Rourke

ADMINSTRATION BLDG
See CROWLEY INDEPENDENT SCHOOL DISTRICT 912

ADMINSTRATION OFFICE
See HUNTSVILLE INDEPENDENT SCHOOL DISTRICT

ADMINSTRATIVE OFFICE OF COURTS
See JUDICIARY COURTS OF STATE OF NORTH CAROLINA

D-U-N-S 05-026-1080 IMP
ADMIRAL BEVERAGE CORP
821 Pulliam Ave, Worland, WY 82401-2325
Tel (801) 782-5072 Founded/Ownrshp 1970
Sales 610.8MM^E EMP 1,000^E
SIC 5149 2086 Soft drinks; Carbonated beverages, nonalcoholic: bottled & canned
Pr: Forrest L Clay
*Treas: William M Dimich
Sfty Mgr: Dave Lechelt
Plnt Mgr: Dave Willard

ADMIRAL DISCOUNT TOBACCO
See ADMIRAL PETROLEUM CO

D-U-N-S 12-123-1674
ADMIRAL EXPRESS INC
1823 N Yellowood Ave, Broken Arrow, OK 74012-9167
Tel (918) 249-4000 Founded/Ownrshp 1984
Sales 85.6MM^E EMP 60
SIC 5112 5021 5943 Office supplies; Office & public building furniture; Office forms & supplies
Pr: Al Yoak
*Sec: Phillip Salingue

D-U-N-S 09-909-7677
■ ADMIRAL INSURANCE CO
(Suby of W R BERKLEY CORP) ★
1000 Howard Blvd Ste 300, Mount Laurel, NJ 08054-2320
Tel (856) 429-9200 Founded/Ownrshp 1978
Sales NA EMP 205
SIC 6331 6411 6324 Fire, marine & casualty insurance & carriers; Insurance agents, brokers & service; Hospital & medical service plans
Pr: James S Carey
Pr: Steven S Zeitman
CFO: Thomas G Grilli Jr
Ch: William R Berkley Jr
Treas: Scott Barraclough
Treas: Scott R Barraclough
Ex VP: Scott Rbarraclough
Sr VP: Daniel A Macdonald
VP: Mark Brown
VP: Greg Ferrell
VP: Curt E Fletcher
VP: Michael S Howey
VP: Stephen Jones
VP: Dan Mayo
VP: Martin M Micheli
VP: Randy Myers
VP: Dan Smyrl
VP: Leah Taylor
Board of Directors: Eugene George Ballard, Martin M Michell, Edward A Thomas

D-U-N-S 01-961-4577 IMP
ADMIRAL METALS SERVICENTER CO INC
(Suby of BMH CORP) ★
11 Forbes Rd, Woburn, MA 01801-2103
Tel (781) 933-8300 Founded/Ownrshp 1950
Sales 103.5MM^E EMP 155
SIC 5051 Metals service centers & offices
Pr: James S Burstein
CFO: Dave Dasducci
CFO: Frank Feldman
CFO: David Pacucci
*CFO: David Pascucci
Sr Cor Off: Jim Bernstein
*VP: Gerald Burstein
VP: John Cruz
Telecom Ex: Kevin Quick

D-U-N-S 01-711-2434
ADMIRAL PETROLEUM CO (MI)
ADMIRAL DISCOUNT TOBACCO
(Suby of FAS MART) ★
785 W Randall St, Coopersville, MI 49404-1307
Tel (616) 837-6218 Founded/Ownrshp 1956, 2016
Sales 257.3MM^E EMP 850
SIC 5541 5411 5194 5145 Filling stations, gasoline; Convenience stores, independent; Cigarettes; Candy
Pr: Dennis Lemmen

ADMIRAL SECURITY SERVICE
See RED COATS INC

ADMIRALS PNTE NRSING RHBLTTION
See HURON HEALTH CARE CENTER INC

ADMIRATION FOODS
See SUPREME OIL CO INC

ADO STAFFING
See MPS GROUP INC

D-U-N-S 04-543-5443
ADO STAFFING INC
OLSTEN
(Suby of ADECCO TECHNICAL) ★
175 Broadhollow Rd, Melville, NY 11747-4911
Tel (631) 844-7800 Founded/Ownrshp 1968
Sales 179.5MM^E EMP 3,500
SIC 7363 6794 Temporary help service; Franchises, selling or licensing
Ch Bd: Robert Crouch
*CEO: Theron I Gilliam
*CFO: Stephen Nolan
Sr VP: Anthony J Puglisi
Off Mgr: Sarah Welch

ADOA
See ARIZONA DEPARTMENT OF ADMINISTRATION

D-U-N-S 17-481-3634
■ ADOBE MACROMEDIA SOFTWARE LLC
(Suby of ADOBE SYSTEMS INC) ★
601 Townsend St, San Francisco, CA 94103-4907
Tel (415) 832-2000 Founded/Ownrshp 2006
Sales 41.4MM^E EMP 1,445^E
SIC 7372 Prepackaged software; Publishers' computer software; Educational computer software; Home entertainment computer software
VP: Pamela Sogge

D-U-N-S 10-209-6559
▲ ADOBE SYSTEMS INC
345 Park Ave, San Jose, CA 95110-2704
Tel (408) 536-6000 Founded/Ownrshp 1982
Sales 4.8MMM EMP 13,893
Accts Kpmg Llp Santa Clara Califor
Tkr Sym ADBE Exch NGS
SIC 7372 Prepackaged software
Pr: Shantanu Narayen
*Ch Bd: Charles M Geschke
*Ch Bd: John E Warnock
COO: Bob Bringhurst
CFO: Mark Garrett
Ex VP: Michael A Dillon
Ex VP: Bryan Lamkin
Ex VP: Ann Lewnes
Ex VP: Abhay Parasnis
Ex VP: Matthew A Thompson
Sr VP: Michael Dillon
Sr VP: James J Egan
Sr VP: Bradley Rencher
Sr VP: Jim Stephens
Sr VP: Cynthia A Stoddard
Sr VP: Rob Tarkoff
VP: Colleen Berube
VP: Alan Gurock
VP: Bill Ingram
VP: Gary Kovacs
VP: Kevin Lynch

ADOLFSON & PETERSON CNSTR
See ADOLFSON & PETERSON INC

ADOLFSON & PETERSON CNSTR
See AP MOUNTAIN STATES LLC

D-U-N-S 00-977-0454
ADOLFSON & PETERSON INC
ADOLFSON & PETERSON CNSTR
6701 W 23rd St, Minneapolis, MN 55426-2855
Tel (952) 544-1561 *Founded/Ownrshp* 1953
Sales 659.2MM^E *EMP* 688
SIC 1542 Commercial & office building, new construction; School building construction; Institutional building construction
CEO: Rick Whitney
**COO:* Kent Weicht
**CFO:* Jeffrey Hanson
**Sr VP:* Brenna Mann
VP: Mark Adamson
VP: Bryan Dunn
VP: Ralph Kasper
VP: Dennis Mulvey
VP: Corbett Nichter
**VP:* Joann Stork
Exec: Randy Berner
Dir Bus: Lana Harris
Board of Directors: Brian Ferraioli

ADP
See AUTOMATIC DATA PROCESSING INC

ADP
See ADVANCED DISTRIBUTOR PRODUCTS LLC

ADP
See A D P FOUNDATION

ADP ATLANTIC, INC.
See ADP ATLANTIC LLC

D-U-N-S 61-786-1562
■ ADP ATLANTIC LLC
(*Suby of* ADP) ★
800 Delaware Ave Ste 601, Wilmington, DE 19801-1365
Tel (302) 657-4060 *Founded/Ownrshp* 1988
Sales 120.1MM^E *EMP* 1,040^E
SIC 6719 Investment holding companies, except banks
Pr: Thomas Corrigan

D-U-N-S 78-583-4131
■ ADP ATLANTIC LLC
ADP ATLANTIC, INC.
(*Suby of* ADP) ★
1 Adp Blvd Ms420, Roseland, NJ 07068-1728
Tel (605) 809-4388 *Founded/Ownrshp* 2014
Sales 11.0MMM *EMP* 60,000
SIC 8721 Payroll accounting service
Pr: Michael A Bonarti
**VP:* Lech Choroszucsa

D-U-N-S 61-933-6860
■ ADP BENEFIT SERVICES KY INC
(*Suby of* ADP) ★
11405 Bluegrass Pkwy, Louisville, KY 40299-2349
Tel (888) 421-7477 *Founded/Ownrshp* 2012
Sales 54.6MM^E *EMP* 1,000^E
SIC 8741 Administrative management
CEO: Rishabh Mehrotra
Ex VP: Jeff Lenzet

D-U-N-S 80-192-5199
■ ADP FINANCIAL INFORMATION SERVICES INC
(*Suby of* ADP) ★
110 W Park Dr, Mount Laurel, NJ 08054-1286
Tel (856) 787-8000 *Founded/Ownrshp* 1967
Sales 47.5MM^E *EMP* 1,000
SIC 7374 Data processing & preparation
Pr: Richard J Daly
CFO: Fred Koczwara
Sr VP: Donald H Totter
VP: Philip Raso
VP: Strouke Smith
Prin: John P Hogan

D-U-N-S 15-047-7545
■ ADP TOTALSOURCE GROUP INC
(*Suby of* ADP) ★
10200 Sw 72nd St, Miami, FL 33173-3033
Tel (305) 630-1000 *Founded/Ownrshp* 1984
Sales 142.2MM^E *EMP* 1,936
SIC 8742 Maintenance management consultant
CEO: Carlos A Rodriguez
**Pr:* Steve J Anenen
**CFO:* Sergio Fernandez
**VP:* Michael A Bonarti
Dist Mgr: Bruce Shetler
Off Mgr: Edette Cedo
CTO: Steffen M Fohn
Dir IT: Joseph Augustinowitz
Sales Exec: Meredith Brown
Sales Asso: Ashkan Tadaie

ADPH
See ALABAMA DEPARTMENT OF PUBLIC HEALTH

ADPLEX
See WINDWARD PRINT STAR INC

D-U-N-S 00-503-4947 EXP
ADRIAN STEEL CO (MI)
906 James St, Adrian, MI 49221-3996
Tel (517) 265-6194 *Founded/Ownrshp* 1953
Sales 139.2MM^E *EMP* 450
SIC 3496 3469 Shelving, made from purchased wire; Boxes: tool, lunch, mail, etc.: stamped metal
Pr: David E Pilmore
**Ch Bd:* Harley J Westfall
**CFO:* Joseph E Emens
VP: Lynford Baugh
Prgrm Mgr: Daryl Aschilman
Prgrm Mgr: Dalton Cheaney
Genl Mgr: Randy Marks
Genl Mgr: Wayne McElreath
Genl Mgr: Bob Southward
QA Dir: Paul Mueller
Sys/Dir: Daryl Aschliman

ADRIANNA PAPELL GROUP
See ADRIANNA PAPELL LLC

D-U-N-S 03-821-1983 IMP/EXP
ADRIANNA PAPELL LLC
ADRIANNA PAPELL GROUP
500 7th Ave Fl 10a, New York, NY 10018-0819
Tel (212) 695-5244 *Founded/Ownrshp* 1980
Sales 87.8MM^E *EMP* 145
SIC 5137

ADRONICO MARKETS
See ARLINGTON ENTERPRISES LP

ADS
See ATLANTIC DIVING SUPPLY INC

D-U-N-S 96-198-6952
ADS LOGISTICS CO LLC
ALTERNATIVE DIST SYSTEMS
(*Suby of* ODYSSEY LOGISTICS & TECHNOLOGY CORP) ★
116 E 1100 N, Chesterton, IN 46304-9675
Tel (219) 836-3900 *Founded/Ownrshp* 2014
Sales 128.4MM^E *EMP* 257
SIC 4731 Freight transportation arrangement
CEO: William Ritter
**CFO:* Jason Vavrik
VP: Mike Green
VP Opers: Matt Brinkley
Trfc Dir: Pam Olson
VP Sls: Tim Barth
Manager: Jennifer Sobek

D-U-N-S 07-885-7127
ADS TACTICAL INC
621 Lynnhven Pkwy Ste 400, Virginia Beach, VA 23452
Tel (757) 781-7758 *Founded/Ownrshp* 2009
Sales 1.4MMM^E *EMP* 386
Accts Kpmg Llp Norfolk Va
SIC 7389 Purchasing service
CEO: Jason Wallace
Pr: Kiran Rai
Ch: Luke M Hillier
VP: Bruce Dressels
VP: Kevin Hickey
VP: Charles M Salle
Sls Mgr: Benny Brown

ADSCO
See JAMAR CO

D-U-N-S 12-142-1676
ADSUMMA GROUP INC
1431 Cedar Ave, Mc Lean, VA 22101-3515
Tel (703) 883-0404 *Founded/Ownrshp* 1990
Sales 90.0MM *EMP* 500
SIC 6719 Investment holding companies, except banks
Pr: Lawrence Herbolsheimer

ADT ADVANCED INTEGRATION
See ADT SECURITY SERVICES INC

D-U-N-S 07-870-5161
ADT CORP
ADT SECURITY SERVICES
(*Suby of* PRIME SECURITY SERVICES BORROWER LLC) ★
1501 Yamato Rd, Boca Raton, FL 33431-4438
Tel (561) 988-3600 *Founded/Ownrshp* 2015
Sales 3.5MMM *EMP* 17,100^E
SIC 7381 7382 3699 Detective & armored car services; Security guard service; Security systems services; Protective devices, security; Security devices
CEO: Tim Whall
**CFO:* Michael Geltzeiler
**CFO:* Jeff Likosar
Bd of Dir: Paul Dansbury
**Chf Mktg O:* Jerri Devard
**Sr VP:* N David Bleisch
**Sr VP:* Donald Boerema
**Sr VP:* Kathleen McLean
Sr VP: Luis J Orbegoso
**Sr VP:* Arthur Orduna
VP: Andrea Bearcroft
VP: Mark Edoff
VP: Tracy Forbes
VP: Ryan Petty
VP: Ravi Tulsyan

D-U-N-S 61-839-9778
ADT HOLDINGS INC
(*Suby of* ADT SECURITY SERVICES) ★
1501 Nw 51st St, Boca Raton, FL 33431-4438
Tel (888) 298-9274 *Founded/Ownrshp* 2012
Sales 248.7MM^E *EMP* 16,000
SIC 7381 1731 Protective services, guard; Security guard service; Fire detection & burglar alarm systems specialization
Pr: Naren K Gursahaney
**Pr:* John Koch
**CFO:* Mark Edoff
**Sr VP:* Ravi Tulsyan
**VP:* Mark N Edoff
**VP:* John Kenning Vp
**Prin:* Nancy A Neal

D-U-N-S 07-849-5761
ADT LLC
ADT SECURITY SERVICES
(*Suby of* ADT SECURITY SERVICES) ★
1501 Yamato Rd, Boca Raton, FL 33431-4438
Tel (561) 988-3600 *Founded/Ownrshp* 2012
Sales 1.1MMM^E *EMP* 12,000^E
SIC 7382 Security systems services
CEO: Naren K Gursahaney
**Treas:* Ravi Tulsyan
**Sr VP:* Mark N Edoff

ADT SECURITY SERVICES
See ADT LLC

ADT SECURITY SERVICES
See ADT CORP

D-U-N-S 83-285-4165
ADT SECURITY SERVICES INC
ADT ADVANCED INTEGRATION
(*Suby of* ADT HOLDINGS INC) ★
2450 Blvd Of The Generals, Norristown, PA 19403-5288
Tel (800) 423-9637 *Founded/Ownrshp* 1981
Sales 372.1M^E *EMP* 15,994^E
SIC 7382 Security systems services
Pr: Michael F Snyder
**Treas:* William J Macarthur Jr
Treas: J W McArthur Jr
**VP:* Edward D Breen

D-U-N-S 14-787-1412 IMP
▲ ADTRAN INC
901 Explorer Blvd Nw, Huntsville, AL 35806-2807
Tel (256) 963-8000 *Founded/Ownrshp* 1986
Sales 600.0MM *EMP* 1,991^E
Tkr Sym ADTN *Exch* NGS
SIC 3661 3663 4813 Telephone & telegraph apparatus; Radio & TV communications equipment; Telephone communication, except radio; Telephone/video communications;
Ch Bd: Thomas R Stanton
CFO: Roger D Shannon
Sr VP: Michael K Foliano
Sr VP: Kevin P Heering
Sr VP: Raymond R Schansman
Sr VP: Eduard Scheiterer
Sr VP: James D Wilson Jr
VP: Tom Coch
VP: Tom Dadmun
VP: Mitch Fleming
VP: Ryan Loy
VP: Dennis McMahan
VP: Kevin W Schneider
VP: Nathan Strange
Board of Directors: H Fenwick Huss, William L Marks, Anthony J Melone, Roy J Nichols, Jacqueline Hourigan Rice, Kathryn A Walker

ADU
See ADVENTIST UNIVERSITY OF HEALTH SCIENCES INC

ADULT & CMNTY ENRICHMENT ACE
See SUNCOAST TECHNICAL COLLEGE

ADULT SWIM GAMES
See TURNER BROADCASTING SYSTEM INC

D-U-N-S 12-459-8145
ADULTS AND CHILDREN WITH LEARNING AND DEVELOPMENTAL DISABILITIES INC
A C L D
807 S Oyster Bay Rd, Bethpage, NY 11714-1030
Tel (516) 681-4500 *Founded/Ownrshp* 1957
Sales 64.8MM *EMP* 1,000^E
Accts Baker Tilly Virchow Krause Ll
SIC 8322 8331 Social services for the handicapped; Job training & vocational rehabilitation services
Pr: Joseph Ortego
CFO: Susan Shah
**CFO:* Susan Shaw
**Treas:* Gregory Licalzi
**Sec:* John J Genova
Bd of Dir: Terri Strull
Sr VP: Carine Gregory
**VP:* Richard Breuninger
**VP:* Anne Emmerson
**VP:* Donald Mitzner
Ex Dir: Robert Goldsmith

ADVACARE SYSTEMS
See UNLIMITED ADVACARE INC

D-U-N-S 17-946-9978
ADVANCE AMERICA CASH ADVANCE CENTERS INC
(*Suby of* EAGLE US SUB INC) ★
135 N Church St, Spartanburg, SC 29306-5138
Tel (864) 342-5600 *Founded/Ownrshp* 2012
Sales NA *EMP* 5,839
SIC 6141 6153 Personal credit institutions; Consumer finance companies; Short-term business credit
CEO: Patrick O'Shaughnessy
**CFO:* James A Ovenden
VP: Tim Bailey
VP: Tom Newell
VP: Carol Stewart
VP: Mark Wilcox
Exec: Hope French
Exec: Brenda Melton
Exec: Jeanetta Steward
Software D: Ginger Hunter
Netwrk Eng: Drew Pearson

ADVANCE AUTO PARTS
See ADVANCE STORES CO INC

ADVANCE AUTO PARTS
See DISCOUNT AUTO PARTS LLC

D-U-N-S 00-696-6485 IMP
▲ ADVANCE AUTO PARTS INC (DE)
5008 Airport Rd Nw, Roanoke, VA 24012-1601
Tel (877) 238-2623 *Founded/Ownrshp* 1929
Sales 9.7MMM *EMP* 73,000
Accts Deloitte & Touche Llp Charlo
Tkr Sym AAP *Exch* NYS
SIC 5531 Automobile & truck equipment & parts
CEO: Thomas R Greco
Ch Bd: Jeffrey C Smith
Pr: George E Sherman
CFO: Michael A Norona
Ex VP: Tammy M Finley
Ex VP: Charles E Tyson
Sr VP: William H Carter
Sr VP: Gregory Johnson
Sr VP: Jill A Livesay
VP: Greg Anderson
VP: Scott Bauhofer
VP: Geno Coradini
VP: Mike Cox
VP: Roger Dattilo
VP: James Doran
VP: Thomas Drapac
VP: Angela Kessler
VP: Melissa Kidwell
VP: Jonathon Milson
VP: Geraldine Ryan
VP: Walt Scott
Board of Directors: Gilbert T Ray, John F Bergstrom, Carlos A Saladrigas, John C Brouillard, O Temple Sloan III, Brad W Buss, Reuben E Slone, Fiona P Dias, Jeffrey C Smith, John F Ferraro, Jimmie L Wade, Adriana Karaboutis, Eugene I Lee Jr, William S Oglesby, J Paul Raines

D-U-N-S 04-195-4710
ADVANCE BUSINESS SYSTEMS & SUPPLY CO
10755 York Rd, Cockeysville, MD 21030-2114
Tel (410) 252-4800 *Founded/Ownrshp* 1964
Sales 93.8MM^E *EMP* 180
Accts Mcgladrey & Pullen Llp Balti
SIC 5044 Office equipment
Pr: Alan I Elkin
**COO:* Jeffrey Elkin
**CFO:* Brian Burr
**VP:* Lois Elkin
Genl Mgr: Jill Marks
Sales Asso: Spencer Anzmann

ADVANCE DESIGN & PACKAGING
See STRONGHAVEN INC

ADVANCE DISTRIBUTING COMPANY
See MCNAUGHTON-MCKAY ELECTRIC CO

D-U-N-S 00-195-8222 IMP
ADVANCE ELECTRICAL SUPPLY CO LLC (IL)
263 N Oakley Blvd, Chicago, IL 60612-2239
Tel (312) 421-2300 *Founded/Ownrshp* 1945, 2015
Sales 103.4MM^E *EMP* 85
SIC 5063 Electrical supplies
Pr: Aaron Hughes
CFO: Joe Colasuono
CFO: Anthony Santisteven
**VP:* Michael Mayworm
CTO: Michael Mals
Sales Asso: Rachel Fishback

ADVANCE ENGINEERING
See L & W INC

ADVANCE FINANCIAL
See HARPETH FINANCIAL SERVICES LLC

D-U-N-S 06-543-4946 IMP
■ ADVANCE FOOD CO INC
ADVANCEPIERRE FOODS HOLDINGS
(*Suby of* ADVANCEPIERRE FOODS HOLDINGS INC) ★
221 W Oxford Ave, Enid, OK 73701-1227
Tel (800) 969-2747 *Founded/Ownrshp* 2010
Sales 172.8MM^E *EMP* 653^E
SIC 2013 2015 2099 Cooked meats from purchased meat; Prepared beef products from purchased beef; Prepared pork products from purchased pork; Chicken, processed: cooked; Chicken, processed: frozen; Turkey, processed: cooked; Turkey, processed: frozen; Food preparations
CEO: Greg Allen
CFO: Frank Merrit
IT Man: Bruce McDowell
Sfty Dirs: Bill Eads
Mtls Mgr: Peter Ainsworth
Snr Mgr: Amy Barton
Snr Mgr: Lisa Nault

ADVANCE INSIGHTS
See HEALTH PRODUCTS RESEARCH INC

D-U-N-S 62-050-0009 IMP
ADVANCE MAGAZINE PUBLISHERS INC
CONDE NAST PUBLICATIONS
(*Suby of* ADVANCE PUBLICATIONS, INC.)
1 World Trade Ctr Fl 28, New York, NY 10007-0090
Tel (212) 286-2860 *Founded/Ownrshp* 1988
Sales 1.2MMM^E *EMP* 4,099
SIC 2721 Magazines: publishing & printing
Ch Bd: S I Newhouse Jr
Pr: Richard Beckman
Pr: Jay Felts
Pr: Daniel Lagani
Pr: Robert A Sauerberg Jr
Pr: Charles Townsend
COO: John Bellando
CFO: David Geithner
Bd of Dir: Jim Buckley
Ofcr: Mark Detroia
Ofcr: Lisa Valentino
Ex VP: Trevor Williams
Sr VP: Mitchell Fox
VP: Nancy Berger Cardone
VP: Agnes Chapski
VP: Amy Churgin
VP: Jason R Krebs
VP: Leslie Picard
Assoc Dir: Angela Byun
Assoc Dir: Wendy Kong
Assoc Dir: William Schultz

ADVANCE NEWHOUSE COMMUNICATION
See ADVANCE/NEWHOUSE COMMUNICATIONS PARTNERSHIP

ADVANCE NURSING CENTER
See GARDEN CITY HOSPITAL

D-U-N-S 00-656-5527
ADVANCE PACKAGING CORP (MI)
4459 40th St Se, Grand Rapids, MI 49512-4036
Tel (616) 949-6610 *Founded/Ownrshp* 1966, 1999
Sales 144.2MM^E *EMP* 300
SIC 2653 3412 Boxes, corrugated: made from purchased materials; Sheets, corrugated: made from purchased materials; Metal barrels, drums & pails
CEO: Carol Hoyt
**Pr:* Don Crossley
Tech Mgr: Scott Wilcox

D-U-N-S 00-828-6270 IMP
ADVANCE PAPER BOX CO
PACKAGING SPECTRUM
6100 S Gramercy Pl, Los Angeles, CA 90047-1397
Tel (323) 750-2550 *Founded/Ownrshp* 1922
Sales 89.8MM^E *EMP* 250

SIC 2653 3082 Boxes, corrugated: made from purchased materials; Boxes, solid fiber: made from purchased materials; Unsupported plastics profile shapes
CEO: Martin Gardner
**CFO:* Carlo Mendoza
**Treas:* Nick Silk
**VP:* Devan Gardner
MIS Dir: Ruben Miranda
Sfty Mgr: Susan Jacques

ADVANCE PIERRE FOODS
See ADVANCEPIERRE FOODS INC

ADVANCE SECURITY
See US SECURITY ASSOCIATES INC

D-U-N-S 92-646-0353
ADVANCE SERVICES INC
112 S Birch St, Norfolk, NE 68701-5413
Tel (402) 371-5733 *Founded/Ownrshp* 1994
Sales 134.7MM *EMP* 14,200
Accts Seim Johnson Llp Omaha Nebr
SIC 7361 Employment agencies
Pr: Paul R Sandall
CFO: Dave Warren
**VP:* Gretchen M Sandall

D-U-N-S 00-794-1529 IMP/EXP
■ ADVANCE STORES CO INC (VA)
ADVANCE AUTO PARTS
(*Suby of* ADVANCE AUTO PARTS INC) ★
5008 Airport Rd Nw, Roanoke, VA 24012-1601
Tel (540) 362-4911 *Founded/Ownrshp* 1929, 2001
Sales 4.0MMM^E^ *EMP* 30,000
SIC 5531 Automobile & truck equipment & parts
CEO: Thomas Greco
**Pr:* Jimmie L Wade
**COO:* Kevin P Freeland
Ex VP: Dave Mueller
**Ex VP:* Michael A Norona
Sr VP: Markus A Hockenson
Sr VP: Mike Marolt
**Sr VP:* Sarah E Powell
Sr VP: S Stevens
VP: Greg Blythe
VP: Greg Mace
Board of Directors: Ronald P Spoglia, Timothy C Collins, Mark J Doran, Peter J Fontaine, Paul J Liska, Stephen M Peck, Glenn Richter, John M Roth, Carlos A Saladrigas, William L Salter

D-U-N-S 12-668-1134
ADVANCE/NEWHOUSE COMMUNICATIONS PARTNERSHIP
ADVANCE NEWHOUSE COMMUNICATION
(*Suby of* ADVANCE PUBLICATIONS, INC.)
5823 Widewaters Pkwy, East Syracuse, NY 13057-3084
Tel (315) 438-4100 *Founded/Ownrshp* 2003
Sales 1.1MMM^E^ *EMP* 8,000
SIC 4841 Cable television services
Pt: Steven Miron
Pt: William Futera
Pr: Robert Miron
CFO: Bill Futera
Treas: Amy Witt
Ex VP: Nomi Bergman
VP: Mike Robertson
Assoc Dir: Christine W Carreno

D-U-N-S 61-683-1827
ADVANCED ACOUSTIC CONCEPTS LLC
A A C
425 Oser Ave Unit 1, Hauppauge, NY 11788-3676
Tel (631) 273-5700 *Founded/Ownrshp* 2006
Sales 102.7MM^E^ *EMP* 172^E^
SIC 5088 Navigation equipment & supplies
Pr: Clair Guthrie
Exec: Henry Dreyer
Genl Mgr: Linda Roger
Snr Sftwr: Danielle Miller
Snr Sftwr: Patrick Reedy
Dir IT: Mike Celauro
Sftwr Eng: Jinping Lin
VP Prd: Robert Olsen
Sls&Mrk Ex: Larry Camillo
VP Sls: Richard Lawless

D-U-N-S 07-870-4369
■ ADVANCED ATOMIZATION TECHNOLOGIES LLC
AATECH
(*Suby of* PARKER-HANNIFIN CORP) ★
124 Columbia St, Clyde, NY 14433-1049
Tel (315) 923-2341 *Founded/Ownrshp* 2012
Sales 129.3MM^E^ *EMP* 300
SIC 3724 Aircraft engines & engine parts
Genl Mgr: Leanne Collazzo
Prgrm Mgr: Ruben Colon
Manager: Christopher Paul

D-U-N-S 80-340-8124
ADVANCED BEVERAGE INC
CULINARY BEVERAGE
1835 Burnet Ave Ste 2, Union, NJ 07083-4282
Tel (908) 686-3666 *Founded/Ownrshp* 2007
Sales 94.0MM *EMP* 10
SIC 5962 Food vending machines
Pr: Thomas Dinardo
**CEO:* Joe Cirillo
**CFO:* Michael Ricca

D-U-N-S 60-698-3398
ADVANCED BIOENERGY LLC
8000 Norman Center Dr # 610, Bloomington, MN 55437-1185
Tel (763) 226-2701 *Founded/Ownrshp* 2005
Sales 152.1MM *EMP* 67^E^
SIC 2869 Ethyl alcohol, ethanol
Pr: Richard R Peterson
Bd of Dir: Earl Wisely
VP: Ty Weisendanger
Off Admin: Ashley Geiger
IT Man: John Kutz
Plnt Mgr: Tony Beam
Board of Directors: Scott A Brittenham, Daniel R Kueter, Joshua M Nelson, Troy L Otte, Bruce L Rastetter

D-U-N-S 82-834-0674 IMP
ADVANCED BIONICS CORP
(*Suby of* SONOVA HOLDING AG)
28515 Westinghouse Pl, Valencia, CA 91355-4833
Tel (661) 362-1400 *Founded/Ownrshp* 2010
Sales 127.1MM^E^ *EMP* 600^E^
SIC 3842 Hearing aids
CEO: Rainer Platz
**Sr VP:* Jeffrey Goldberg
VP: Robert Gulock
VP: Cedric Navarro
VP: Arthur Rascon
VP: Tom Santogrossi
Exec: Doreen McMuem
Exec: Upen Patel
Dir Soc: Cathleen Clark
**Prin:* Alfred Mann
Snr Sftwr: Jacob Johnston

D-U-N-S 80-390-6382
ADVANCED BIONICS LLC
A B
(*Suby of* SONOVA HOLDING AG)
12740 San Fernando Rd, Sylmar, CA 91342-3700
Tel (661) 362-1400 *Founded/Ownrshp* 1997
Sales 83.8MM^E^ *EMP* 500
SIC 3842 Hearing aids
CEO: Rainer Platz
VP: Scott Hebl
CIO: Kevin Hobson
QA Dir: Alexander Gutierrez
VP Opers: Jim EBY
QC Dir: Jeff Nickerson
Mktg Mgr: Tami Pena
Snr Mgr: Doug Colonna
Snr Mgr: Rosanne Schembri

D-U-N-S 83-762-2059 IMP
ADVANCED CABLE TIES INC
ACT FASTENING SOLUTIONS
245 Suffolk Ln, Gardner, MA 01440-1761
Tel (978) 630-3900 *Founded/Ownrshp* 1995
Sales 89.1MM^E^ *EMP* 100
SIC 5063 Wire & cable
Pr: Kenneth C Tomasetti
**Pr:* Lam Nguyen
CFO: Steven Leonard
Treas: Charles Labove
VP: Greg Riedel
IT Man: Garrett Davieau
IT Man: Chuan Phamn
IT Man: Robert R Pratt
Plnt Mgr: Ken Tomasatti
Manager: Brenda Bean
Sls Mgr: John Hollowell

D-U-N-S 96-481-1475
ADVANCED CALL CENTER TECHNOLOGIES LLC
(*Suby of* ACCT HOLDINGS LLC) ★
1235 Westlakes Dr Ste 160, Berwyn, PA 19312-2417
Tel (610) 695-0500 *Founded/Ownrshp* 1999
Sales 131.4MM^E^ *EMP* 1,700
SIC 7389 Telephone services
Prin: Joseph Lembo
Pt: James McCaughan
Chf Cred: Marc Keller
VP: Tim Dowling
IT Man: Kathy Bailey
Opers Mgr: Collette Pierce

D-U-N-S 18-850-0289
ADVANCED CENTER FOR REHABILITATION MEDICINE INC
AUDIOLOGY
24 Stevens St, Norwalk, CT 06850-3852
Tel (203) 852-2000 *Founded/Ownrshp* 1990
Sales 340.3MM *EMP* 2
SIC 5999 Hearing aids
Pr: David W Osborne
Ofcr: Keith Shuster
Ofcr: Kristen M Staikos
Exec: Stephen Winter
Mng Dir: Julie Setterlund
Pgrm Dir: Maria Grayson

D-U-N-S 60-311-1717 IMP
■ ADVANCED CIRCUITS INC
(*Suby of* COMPASS DIVERSIFIED HOLDINGS) ★
21101 E 32nd Pkwy, Aurora, CO 80011-8149
Tel (303) 576-6610 *Founded/Ownrshp* 2006
Sales 152.3MM^E^ *EMP* 563^E^
SIC 3672 Printed circuit boards
Pr: John Yacoub
**COO:* Jeff Yacoub
**VP:* Dan Chouinard
**VP:* Jim Hellmer
VP: Solder Stencil
Genl Mgr: Bobbie Callaway
CTO: Sean Cushman
QA Dir: Rob Churchill
QA Dir: Monica Garcia
Dir IT: Sean Greenwell
IT Man: Robert Fahie

D-U-N-S 11-619-3400
ADVANCED COMPUTER CONCEPTS INC
7927 Jones Branch Dr 600n, Mc Lean, VA 22102-3317
Tel (703) 276-7800 *Founded/Ownrshp* 2001
Sales 150.0MM *EMP* 48^E^
Accts Duvallwheeler Llp Manassas
SIC 5045 Computers; Computer peripheral equipment
CEO: Mandana Zarafshar Heydarian
CFO: Miriam Zand
Treas: David Coming
VP: Steve Mansoori
**VP:* Marjan Zarafshar
Exec: Alex Eslamin
Genl Mgr: Gus Khalil
Snr Ntwrk: Anurag Bajaj
Dir IT: Alberto Donoso
Dir IT: Sean Farzad
IT Man: Eslami Alex

D-U-N-S 10-350-7778
■ ADVANCED DIGITAL INFORMATION CORP
ADIC
(*Suby of* QUANTUM CORP) ★
11431 Willows Rd Ne, Redmond, WA 98052-3069
Tel (425) 881-8004 *Founded/Ownrshp* 2006
Sales 62.7MM^E^ *EMP* 1,109
SIC 3572 Computer storage devices
Ch Bd: Peter H Van Oppen
CFO: Jon Gacek
VP: Jonathan Otis
VP: Leslie Rock
VP: Rick Schulman
VP: Charles Stonecipher
VP: Chris Willis
Prgrm Mgr: Gary Zellner
IT Man: Peter Dewey

D-U-N-S 07-872-1021
■ ADVANCED DISPOSAL SERVICES INC
(*Suby of* ADVANCED DISPOSAL WASTE HOLDINGS CORP) ★
90 Fort Wade Rd Ste 200, Ponte Vedra, FL 32081-5112
Tel (904) 737-7900 *Founded/Ownrshp* 2000
Sales 1.4MMM *EMP* 5,400^E^
Tkr Sym ADSW *Exch* NYS
SIC 4953 Refuse systems; Refuse collection & disposal services; Garbage: collecting, destroying & processing
Ch Bd: Richard Burke
COO: John Spegal
**CFO:* Steven R Carn
Ofcr: William Westrate
Sr VP: Michael K Slattery
Board of Directors: Bret Budenbender, Michael Koen, John Miller, Jared Parker, Sergio Pedreiro, B Clyde Preslar, Matthew Rinklin

D-U-N-S 62-400-2445
■ ADVANCED DISPOSAL SERVICES MIDWEST LLC
(*Suby of* F/K/A VEOLIA ES SOLID WASTE) ★
90 Fort Wade Rd Ste 200, Ponte Vedra, FL 32081-5112
Tel (904) 737-7900 *Founded/Ownrshp* 2002
Sales 613.4MM^E^ *EMP* 5,697^E^
SIC 4953 Refuse systems
CEO: Richard Burke
COO: John Spegal
CFO: Steven Carn
VP: Jaime Marini

D-U-N-S 80-107-3677
■ ADVANCED DISPOSAL SERVICES SOLID WASTE MIDWEST LLC
(*Suby of* ADVANCED DISPOSAL SERVICES MIDWEST LLC) ★
90 Fort Wade Rd Ste 200, Ponte Vedra, FL 32081-5112
Tel (904) 737-7900 *Founded/Ownrshp* 2006
Sales 464.8MM^E^ *EMP* 5,400^E^
SIC 7699 4953 4959 Waste cleaning services; Medical waste disposal; Toxic or hazardous waste cleanup
Genl Mgr: Erik Hanson
**CEO:* Charles C Appleby
**CEO:* Richard Burke
**COO:* John Stegal
**CFO:* Steven Carn
**Sr VP:* Randy Arnold
**VP:* Charlie Gray
**VP:* Jaime Marini

D-U-N-S 95-866-0144
■ ADVANCED DISPOSAL SERVICES SOLID WASTE SOUTHEAST INC
(*Suby of* ADVANCED DISPOSAL SERVICES INC) ★
90 Fort Wade Rd Ste 200, Ponte Vedra, FL 32081-5112
Tel (904) 737-7900 *Founded/Ownrshp* 1998
Sales 88.9MM^E^ *EMP* 344^E^
SIC 4953 Garbage: collecting, destroying & processing; Sanitary landfill operation
CEO: Richard Burke
**CFO:* Steven Carn
Board of Directors: Charles Appleby, Christopher Beall, Bret Budenbender, Wilson Quintella Filho, John Miller, Jared Parker, Matthew Rinklin

D-U-N-S 03-231-5439
■ ADVANCED DISPOSAL SERVICES SOUTH LLC
(*Suby of* ADVANCED DISPOSAL SERVICES INC) ★
90 Fort Wade Rd Ste 200, Ponte Vedra, FL 32081-5112
Tel (904) 737-7900 *Founded/Ownrshp* 2001
Sales 1.1MMM^E^ *EMP* 4,380
Accts Pricewaterhousecoopers Llp Ja
SIC 4953 6719 Garbage: collecting, destroying & processing; Personal holding companies, except banks
CEO: Richard Burke
**COO:* John Spegal
**CFO:* Steven R Carn
**Ofcr:* Steve Carn
**Ofcr:* Bill Westrate
VP: Gerald M Allen
**VP:* Michael Slattery

D-U-N-S 07-918-5602
▲ ADVANCED DISPOSAL WASTE HOLDINGS CORP
90 Fort Wade Rd Ste 200, Ponte Vedra, FL 32081-5112
Tel (904) 737-7900 *Founded/Ownrshp* 2012
Sales 1.3MMM *EMP* 5,400
Accts Ernst & Young Llp Cpas Jacks
SIC 4953 Refuse systems; Refuse collection & disposal services; Garbage: collecting, destroying & processing
CEO: Richard Burke
**COO:* John Spegal
**CFO:* Steven R Carn

D-U-N-S 01-984-8147 IMP
■ ADVANCED DISTRIBUTOR PRODUCTS LLC
ADP
(*Suby of* LENNOX INTERNATIONAL INC) ★
1995 Air Industrial Pk Rd, Grenada, MS 38901-9561
Tel (662) 229-3000 *Founded/Ownrshp* 2000
Sales 208.0MM^E^ *EMP* 600
SIC 3585 Heating & air conditioning combination units
VP: Bob Moody

D-U-N-S 05-674-4527 EXP
▲ ADVANCED DRAINAGE SYSTEMS INC
4640 Trueman Blvd, Hilliard, OH 43026-2438
Tel (614) 658-0050 *Founded/Ownrshp* 1966
Sales 1.2MMM *EMP* 4,300
Accts Deloitte & Touche Llp Columbu
Tkr Sym WMS *Exch* NYS
SIC 3084 3086 Plastics pipe; Plastics foam products
Pr: Joseph A Chlapaty
CFO: Scott A Cottrill
Ofcr: Kevin C Talley
Ex VP: Thomas M Fussner
Ex VP: Robert M Klein
Ex VP: Ronald R Vitarelli
IT Man: Hariharan Ramakrishnan
Plnt Mgr: Mark Halepeska
Plnt Mgr: David Hicks
Board of Directors: Robert M Eversole, Alexander R Fischer, Tanya Fratto, Mark A Haney, C Robert Kidder, Carl Nelson Jr, Richard A Rosenthal, Abigail S Wexner

ADVANCED DRMTLOGY CSMTC SRGERY
See ADCS CLINICS LLC

D-U-N-S 02-119-2422 EXP
▲ ADVANCED ENERGY INDUSTRIES INC
1625 Sharp Point Dr, Fort Collins, CO 80525-9794
Tel (970) 221-4670 *Founded/Ownrshp* 1981
Sales 414.8MM *EMP* 1,382
Tkr Sym AEIS *Exch* NGS
SIC 3679 3629 3625 Power supplies, all types: static; Power conversion units, a.c. to d.c.: static-electric; Control equipment, electric
Pr: Yuval Wasserman
**Ch Bd:* Grant H Beard
CFO: Thomas Liguori
Ex VP: Thomas O McGimpsey
VP: Gary Weber
Counsel: Karen Graham
Board of Directors: Frederick A Ball, Ronald C Foster, Edward C Grady, Thomas M Rohrs, John A Roush

D-U-N-S 13-163-2973
ADVANCED EQUITIES FINANCIAL CORP
200 S Wacker Dr Ste 3200, Chicago, IL 60606-5878
Tel (312) 377-5300 *Founded/Ownrshp* 1999
Sales 130.0MM^E^ *EMP* 589
SIC 6211 Security brokers & dealers
Ch Bd: Keith Daubenspeck
**Pr:* Adam Antoniades
**CEO:* Dwight Badger
CEO: Frank L Campanale
**COO:* Joel E Marks
CFO: Gregg S Glaer
**CFO:* Gregg S Glaser
**Ex VP:* Erhard R Chorle
Ex VP: Chris Pravacek
Sr VP: Shawn D Rogers
Exec: John Galinsky

ADVANCED FOODSYSTEMS
See AFS TECHNOLOGIES INC

D-U-N-S 05-043-6364
ADVANCED HEALTH CARE CORP (ID)
215 N Whitley Dr Ste 1, Fruitland, ID 83619-2706
Tel (208) 452-6392 *Founded/Ownrshp* 2000
Sales 2.6MM^E^ *EMP* 1,500
SIC 8082 Home health care services
Pr: K Brett Nattress

D-U-N-S 07-506-8247
ADVANCED HEALTH CONCEPTS
CAPITOL HOME HEALTH
134 Mcgehee Dr, Baton Rouge, LA 70815-5012
Tel (225) 275-1660 *Founded/Ownrshp* 1979
Sales 11.0MM^E^ *EMP* 1,467
Accts Heffler Radetich & Saitta L
SIC 8082 Home health care services
Pr: Jo Ann Chiasson
**Treas:* Jackie Weber
VP: Pam Normand Bridges

D-U-N-S 01-917-5560
ADVANCED HEATING LLC
2736 12 3/4 Ave, Cameron, WI 54822-9515
Tel (715) 296-6107 *Founded/Ownrshp* 2008
Sales 176.7MM *EMP* 2^E^
SIC 1711 Heating & air conditioning contractors
Prin: Kim Scoville

ADVANCED HOME CARE
See HOME CARE OF CENTRAL CAROLINA INC

D-U-N-S 60-316-1209
ADVANCED HOME CARE INC
4001 Piedmont Pkwy, High Point, NC 27265-9402
Tel (336) 878-8950 *Founded/Ownrshp* 1986
Sales 175.4MM *EMP* 1,700
SIC 8082 5999 Home health care services; Medical apparatus & supplies
Pr: Joel C Mills
**CFO:* James P Hogan
VP: Sue Payne
VP: Janice Wilhelm
Brnch Mgr: Juanita Evans
Brnch Mgr: Tammy Wheelock
IT Man: Anthony Cipolletti
Netwrk Eng: Joel Davis
Site Mgr: John Young
Opers Mgr: Kylie Morgan
Sales Exec: Kari Sparks

D-U-N-S 05-497-1010
■ ADVANCED HOMECARE MANAGEMENT INC
ENCOMPASS HOME HEALTH
(*Suby of* HEALTHSOUTH CORP) ★
6688 N Cntrl Expy # 1300, Dallas, TX 75206-3950
Tel (214) 239-6500 *Founded/Ownrshp* 2004
Sales 185.8MM^E^ *EMP* 3,000
SIC 8082 Home health care services
Pr: April Anthony

*Treas: Robert Thompson
*VP: Peter Ehrich
VP: Stevi Taylor

D-U-N-S 07-972-8647
ADVANCED INTEGRATION TECHNOLOGY LP
2805 E Plano Pkwy Ste 300, Plano, TX 75074-7473
Tel (972) 423-8354 Founded/Ownrshp 2014
Sales 88.9MM[E] EMP 720
SIC 3728 3544 Aircraft parts & equipment; Industrial molds
Pr: Edward J Chalupa
Genl Pt: Ait GP
CFO: Matt Ptacek
Dir IT: Greg Gillham

D-U-N-S 92-952-0468 IMP
ADVANCED LIGHTING TECHNOLOGIES INC
(Suby of SARATOGA LIGHTING HOLDINGS LLC) ★
7905 Cochran Rd Ste 300, Solon, OH 44139-5471
Tel (440) 519-0500 Founded/Ownrshp 1995
Sales 218.1MM[E] EMP 1,168[E]
SIC 3641 3645 3646 3648 Electric lamps & parts for generalized applications; Residential lighting fixtures; Commercial indusl & institutional electric lighting fixtures; Lighting equipment
CEO: Wayne R Hellman
*COO: Sabu Krishnan
*CFO: Wayne J Vespoli
Ex VP: Wayne Vespoli
*VP: Lee A Bartolomei
VP: Lee A Brtolomei
VP: Lee Brtolomei
*VP: James L Schoolenberg
Genl Mgr: Lalu Chandran
CIO: Ted Sokoly
DP Exec: Lowell Davis
Board of Directors: Robert Cizik, Christian L Oberbeck, Richard A Petrocelli

ADVANCED MACHINE AND ENGRG
See GOELLNER INC

D-U-N-S 04-863-4059
▲ ADVANCED MICRO DEVICES INC
1 Amd Pl, Sunnyvale, CA 94085-3905
Tel (408) 749-4000 Founded/Ownrshp 1969
Sales 3.9MMM EMP 9,100[E]
Tkr Sym AMD Exch NAS
SIC 3674 Integrated circuits, semiconductor networks, etc.; Microprocessors; Memories, solid state; Microcircuits, integrated (semiconductor)
Pr: Lisa T Su
*Ch Bd: John E Caldwell
CFO: Devinder Kumar
Ofcr: William Edwards
Sr VP: James R Anderson
Sr VP: James A Clifford
Sr VP: Ruth Cotter
Sr VP: Darrell L Ford
Sr VP: Forrest E Norrod
Sr VP: Mark D Papermaster
Sr VP: Harry A Wolin
Sr VP: Stephen J Zelencik
VP: David Christie
VP: Robert Gama
VP: Greg Gillas
VP: Darren Grasby
VP: Gary Lloyd
VP: Frederick Mapp
VP: Michael Meeks
VP: Forrest Norrod
VP: Schultz Rich
Board of Directors: Bruce L Claflin, Nora M Denzel, Nicholas M Donofrio, Martin L Edelman, Joseph A Householder, Michael J Inglis, Ahmed Yahia

D-U-N-S 02-179-7501 IMP
ADVANCED MP TECHNOLOGY INC
1010 Calle Sombra, San Clemente, CA 92673-6227
Tel (949) 492-6589 Founded/Ownrshp 1978
Sales 143.6MM[E] EMP 274
SIC 5065 Electronic parts & equipment
CEO: Jafar Yassai
*Pr: Homayoun Shorooghi
*CFO: Mehdi Taghiei PHD
*VP: Kamran Malek
Exec: Cathy Knight
Netwrk Mgr: Khuong Huynh
QI Cn Mgr: Yahya Ashrafi
Manager: Eric Bettencourt
Manager: Lynette Singleton

D-U-N-S 02-167-5699
■ ADVANCED NEUROMODULATION SYSTEMS INC (TX)
ANS-PLANO-MANUFACTURING
(Suby of ST JUDE MEDICAL INC) ★
6901 Preston Rd, Plano, TX 75024-2508
Tel (972) 309-8000 Founded/Ownrshp 1979
Sales 93.7MM[E] EMP 529
SIC 3845 Electrotherapeutic apparatus
Pr: Eric S Fain
CFO: Bob Merrill
Ofcr: Tracy Cameron
Ofcr: Lyn Olson
Ofcr: Sandy Reif
Ex VP: Kenneth G Hawari
Ex VP: Robert Merrill
VP: Dennis Alexander
VP: James W Harrison
VP: F R Merrill III
*VP: Alan Mock
VP: Marta Munson
VP: Jennifer Olson
Exec: Lisa Cooper

ADVANCED PAYMENT SOLUTIONS
See NORTH AMERICAN BANCARD LLC

D-U-N-S 15-059-7649 IMP
ADVANCED PHYSICAL THERAPY PC
5949 W Raymond St, Indianapolis, IN 46241-4348
Tel (317) 486-2186 Founded/Ownrshp 1985
Sales 150.6MM EMP 127
SIC 8093 Rehabilitation center, outpatient treatment
CEO: Greg Steil
CFO: Nancy Butler
Ex Dir: Heather Schoen
Mktg Dir: Lisa Webber

D-U-N-S 17-782-7193 IMP
ADVANCED SCIENTIFICS INC
A S I
163 Research Ln, Millersburg, PA 17061-9402
Tel (717) 692-2104 Founded/Ownrshp 1985
Sales 104.2MM[E] EMP 320
SIC 3069 Medical & laboratory rubber sundries & related products; Tubes, hard rubber
CEO: Carl Martin
*Pr: Kent Smeltz
*VP: Jay Martin
IT Man: Steve Scott

D-U-N-S 07-857-9697 IMP
ADVANCED SPORTS ENTERPRISES INC
1 Performance Way, Chapel Hill, NC 27517-9502
Tel (919) 933-9113 Founded/Ownrshp 1987
Sales 274.9MM[E] EMP 1,083[E]
SIC 5091 Bicycle parts & accessories
CEO: Patrick Cunnane
Sr VP: Mike Starkey
Admn Mgr: Ric Ronci
IT Man: Tom Blake

D-U-N-S 09-950-0832 IMP/EXP
ADVANCED STEEL RECOVERY LLC
14451 Whittram Ave, Fontana, CA 92335-3066
Tel (909) 355-2372 Founded/Ownrshp 1999
Sales 202.5MM[E] EMP 47
SIC 5093

D-U-N-S 80-189-4549
ADVANCED STIMULATION TECHNOLOGIES INC
2903 E Interstate 20, Midland, TX 79706-4201
Tel (432) 994-0900 Founded/Ownrshp 2007
Sales 135.0MM[E] EMP 300
SIC 1389 Acidizing wells; Hydraulic fracturing wells
Pr: Robert Booth
*Ch Bd: Autry C Stephens
*Prin: Lewis Niewoehner
*Genl Mgr: Bobby Tubbs

D-U-N-S 02-517-2953
ADVANCED TECHNOLOGY INTERNATIONAL
315 Sigma Dr, Summerville, SC 29486-7790
Tel (843) 760-3200 Founded/Ownrshp 1998
Sales 385.1MM EMP 117
Accts Bdo Usa Llp Raleigh Nc
SIC 8741 Management services
Pr: Chris Van Metre
Pr: Natalie Corella
Treas: Ashley Hannah
*Treas: Julia Martin
VP: Jack Corley
VP: Dick Tiano
Exec: Ronald Glover
Prgrm Mgr: Larry Karns
Prgrm Mgr: Dennis Simon
Prgrm Mgr: Michael Stiteler
Prgrm Mgr: John Tuite

ADVANCED TECHNOLOGY MATERIALS
See ATMI INC

D-U-N-S 12-257-6192
ADVANCED TECHNOLOGY SERVICES INC
8201 N University St # 1, Peoria, IL 61615-1858
Tel (309) 693-4000 Founded/Ownrshp 1998
Sales 322.1MM[E] EMP 3,000
SIC 7699 7629 7378

D-U-N-S 18-925-4402
ADVANCED TEMPORARIES INC
5139 Fredericksburg Rd, San Antonio, TX 78229-3633
Tel (903) 561-0927 Founded/Ownrshp 1968
Sales 27.7MM[E] EMP 1,000
SIC 7363 Temporary help service
Pr: Bob G Williams
*Treas: Marty Goode
*VP: Hammond Scott Gibson
VP: Felisha Moye

ADVANCEPIERRE FOODS HOLDINGS
See ADVANCE FOOD CO INC

D-U-N-S 96-518-5437
▲ ADVANCEPIERRE FOODS HOLDINGS INC
9987 Carver Rd, Blue Ash, OH 45242-5550
Tel (800) 969-2747 Founded/Ownrshp 2008
Sales 1.6MMM EMP 4,085[E]
Tkr Sym APFH Exch NYS
SIC 2099 2013 Sandwiches, assembled & packaged: for wholesale market; Sausages & other prepared meats
Pr: John N Simons Jr
Ch Bd: Dean Hollis
Pr: Steven D Booker
Pr: James L Clough
Pr: Tony Schroder
Pr: Christopher D Sliva
COO: George F Chappelle Jr
CFO: Michael B Sims
Ofcr: Jim Clough
Sr VP: Bernie Panchot
Sr VP: John W Theis III
VP: John Morgan

D-U-N-S 04-846-5686 IMP
■ ADVANCEPIERRE FOODS INC
ADVANCE PIERRE FOODS
(Suby of ADVANCEPIERRE FOODS HOLDINGS INC) ★
9987 Carver Rd Ste 500, Blue Ash, OH 45242-5563
Tel (513) 874-8741 Founded/Ownrshp 2008
Sales 1.6MMM EMP 4,085
Accts Pricewaterhousecoopers Llp Ci
SIC 2013 2015 Prepared beef products from purchased beef; Prepared pork products from purchased pork; Chicken, processed
CEO: John N Simons
Pr: Steve Booker
Pr: Tom Lavan
Pr: Walt Thurn
*CFO: Michael B Sims
CFO: Pamela M Witters
Sr VP: George F Chappelle Jr
Sr VP: Frank Merrit
VP: Scott Benne
VP: Tom Carlson
VP: Bryan Freeman
VP: David Minx
Board of Directors: Celeste A Clark, Gary Perlin

D-U-N-S 18-350-9751 IMP/EXP
ADVANSTAR COMMUNICATIONS INC
ADVANSTAR GLOBAL
(Suby of UBM PLC)
2501 Colorado Ave Ste 280, Santa Monica, CA 90404-3754
Tel (310) 857-7500 Founded/Ownrshp 2014
Sales 146.8MM[E] EMP 1,050
SIC 7389 2721 7331

ADVANSTAR GLOBAL
See ADVANSTAR COMMUNICATIONS INC

D-U-N-S 80-848-5671
ADVANSTAR HOLDINGS CORP
(Suby of VSS-AHC CONSOLIDATED HOLDINGS CORP) ★
131 W 1st St, Duluth, MN 55802-2065
Tel (218) 740-7200 Founded/Ownrshp 2000
Sales 119.2MM[E] EMP 1,050[E]
SIC 7389 2721 7331 Trade show arrangement; Magazines: publishing only, not printed on site; Direct mail advertising services
Pr: Joseph Loggia
*CFO: Theodore S Alpert

D-U-N-S 78-787-8156
ADVANSTAR INC
(Suby of ADVANSTAR HOLDINGS CORP) ★
641 Lexington Ave Fl 8, New York, NY 10022-4503
Tel (212) 951-6600 Founded/Ownrshp 2007
Sales 119.2MM[E] EMP 1,050
SIC 2721 7389 8742

D-U-N-S 01-867-8505
ADVANTA REALTY LLC
3956 Town Ctr Blvd 329, Orlando, FL 32837-6103
Tel (407) 697-6604 Founded/Ownrshp 2011
Sales 300.0MM EMP 125
SIC 6531 Real estate brokers & agents

ADVANTAGE AUTO STORES
See HAHN AUTOMOTIVE WAREHOUSE INC

ADVANTAGE DECORATIVE PAVING
See ACRES ENTERPRISES INC

D-U-N-S 02-157-3386
ADVANTAGE HEALTH SOLUTIONS INC
9045 River Rd Ste 200, Indianapolis, IN 46240-6400
Tel (317) 573-2700 Founded/Ownrshp 2000
Sales NA EMP 270
SIC 6324 Health maintenance organization (HMO), insurance only
Pr: Vicki F Perry
*COO: Janice Teal
*CFO: Jennifer Ponski
VP: Dr Issac Myers II
VP: Doug Pearson
VP Sls: Robert Balash

D-U-N-S 62-506-2930
ADVANTAGE HEALTH SYSTEMS INC
CAREPRO MEDICAL ONE
106 Doctor Cir Ste A, Columbia, SC 29203-6503
Tel (803) 376-4190 Founded/Ownrshp 1998
Sales 14.5MM EMP 2,000
SIC 8099 Medical services organization
Pr: Paul Mitchell

D-U-N-S 96-076-9057
ADVANTAGE HUMAN RESOURCING INC
ADVANTAGE STAFFING
(Suby of ADVANTAGE STAFFING) ★
401 Thomas Rd Ste 2, West Monroe, LA 71292-7903
Tel (318) 324-8060 Founded/Ownrshp 2003
Sales 144.8MM[E] EMP 11,400
SIC 7363 Help supply services; Temporary help service
Pr: Mark Marheineke
*Ch Bd: Hitoshi Motohara
*CEO: Toshio Oka
*CFO: Reiki Muratake
Board of Directors: Mark Marheineke

D-U-N-S 79-963-8197 IMP
■ ADVANTAGE LOGISTICS SOUTHWEST INC
(Suby of SUPERVALU INC) ★
5305 W Buckeye Rd, Phoenix, AZ 85043-4715
Tel (602) 477-3100 Founded/Ownrshp 2000
Sales 2.0MMM EMP 500[E]
SIC 5141 Groceries, general line
Pr: Fred W Boehler
*Treas: John F Boyd
*VP: Kevin Holt
*VP: Todd N Sheldon
*Genl Mgr: Brent Bilquist

ADVANTAGE MED PROFESSIONALS
See ADVANTAGE MEDICAL PROFESSIONALS LLC

D-U-N-S 16-448-2390
ADVANTAGE MEDICAL PROFESSIONALS LLC
ADVANTAGE MED PROFESSIONALS
3340 Severn Ave Ste 320, Metairie, LA 70002-7410
Tel (504) 456-0073 Founded/Ownrshp 1984
Sales 35.8MM[E] EMP 1,200
SIC 7361 7363 Nurses' registry; Temporary help service
VP: Gina Cannatella
IT Man: Anthony Martin

D-U-N-S 96-175-5782
ADVANTAGE RESOURCING AMERICA INC
ADVANTAGE STAFFING
(Suby of RECRUIT HOLDINGS CO.,LTD.)
220 Norwood Park S, Norwood, MA 02062-4688
Tel (781) 251-8000 Founded/Ownrshp 2011
Sales 637.2MM[E] EMP 18,280
SIC 7361 Labor contractors (employment agency)
Ch: Hitoshi Motohara
*CFO: Reiki Muratake
Treas: Amy Saulnier
*Ex VP: Mark Marheineke
VP: Joseph Johnson
VP: Lisa Lovas
Prgrm Mgr: Janice Curry
Board of Directors: Raymond Wechsler

D-U-N-S 05-939-5061
ADVANTAGE SALES & MARKETING
BUDD MAYER OF TAMPA
(Suby of ADVANTAGE SOLUTIONS) ★
3922 Coconut Palm Dr # 300, Tampa, FL 33619-1388
Tel (813) 281-8080 Founded/Ownrshp 2011
Sales 133.9MM[E] EMP 230
SIC 5141 Groceries, general line
Ch Bd: C Michael Sunderland
*Sec: Robert Erger
*VP: Luther W Pitts Jr
VP: Ted Yeomans
Sls Mgr: Kevin Lightner
Snr Mgr: Melissa Hallett
Snr Mgr: Andrew Rhykerd

D-U-N-S 08-942-0129 IMP
ADVANTAGE SALES & MARKETING INC
ADVANTAGE SOLUTIONS
18100 Von Karman Ave # 900, Irvine, CA 92612-7195
Tel (949) 797-2900 Founded/Ownrshp 2014
Sales 13.3MMM[E] EMP 48,000
SIC 5141 Food brokers
Ch: Sonny King
CEO: Tanya Domier
COO: Mike Salzberg
COO: Brian Stevens
CFO: Andy Colombini
Treas: Robert Murray
Ex VP: Patrick Gibbons
Ex VP: Herbert Nally
Ex VP: Harry Rozelle
VP: Todd Baird
VP: George Ganzenmuller
VP: Michael O Keefe
VP: Amy Miller
VP: Luther Pitts Jr
VP: Sandy Yob

D-U-N-S 12-893-1453
ADVANTAGE SALES & MARKETING LLC
ADVANTAGE SOLUTIONS
(Suby of ADVANTAGE SOLUTIONS) ★
18100 Von Karman Ave # 900, Irvine, CA 92612-7195
Tel (949) 797-2900 Founded/Ownrshp 2006
Sales 4.4MMM[E] EMP 48,000
SIC 5141 8732 Food brokers; Commercial nonphysical research
Ch: Sonny King
CEO: Tanya Domier
COO: Brian Stevens
CFO: Brian G Stevens
Treas: Robert Murray
Ex VP: Dean Kaye
VP: Dave Arbanas
VP: Adeem Fenster
VP: Cash Frackiewicz
VP: Amy Miller
VP: Sara Riley
VP: Sheree Winslow
Board of Directors: Richard G Wolford

D-U-N-S 96-681-7020
ADVANTAGE SALES LLC
(Suby of ADVANTAGE SOLUTIONS) ★
7411 Fullerton St Ste 101, Jacksonville, FL 32256-3628
Tel (904) 292-9009 Founded/Ownrshp 2011
Sales 168.9MM[E] EMP 450[E]
SIC 5141 Food brokers
Pr: Tanya Domier
Treas: Bob Murray
VP: Todd Baird
VP: Frank Morris
Genl Mgr: Deanne Lewis
IT Man: Elanda Floyd
Snr Mgr: Robert Fischer
Board of Directors: Tanya Domier, Sonny King

ADVANTAGE SOLUTIONS
See ADVANTAGE SALES & MARKETING INC

ADVANTAGE SOLUTIONS
See ADVANTAGE SALES & MARKETING LLC

ADVANTAGE SPORTS PERFORMANCE
See DRAYER PHYSICAL THERAPY INSTITUTE LLC

ADVANTAGE STAFFING
See GCA SERVICES GROUP OF NORTH CAROLINA INC

ADVANTAGE STAFFING
See ADVANTAGE HUMAN RESOURCING INC

ADVANTAGE STAFFING
See ADVANTAGE RESOURCING AMERICA INC

ADVANTAGE TECHNICAL RESOURCES
See TECHNICAL AID CORP

D-U-N-S 02-175-0631 EXP
ADVANTAGE TRIM & LUMBER CO INC
7524 Commerce Pl, Sarasota, FL 34243-5020
Tel (941) 388-9299 Founded/Ownrshp 2004
Sales 100.0MM EMP 89
SIC 5031 5211 Lumber, plywood & millwork; Lumber products
Pr: Robert J Pelc
*VP: Betty J Pelc
Genl Mgr: Chris Foreman
Sales Exec: Jon Fletcher
Sls&Mrk Ex: Chris Hughes
VP Sls: Duane Welch

ADVANTAGE TRUCK CENTER
See YOUNGS TRUCK CENTER INC

D-U-N-S 07-845-2728
ADVANTAGE WAYPOINT LLC
13521 Prestige Pl, Tampa, FL 33635-9619
Tel (813) 358-5900 *Founded/Ownrshp* 2007
Sales 200.0MM *EMP* 1,300
SIC 5141 Food brokers
Sr VP: Craig Miller
VP: Larry Mays
Exec: Greg Rice
Genl Mgr: Mike Glaze
Genl Mgr: Greg Munger
Genl Mgr: Gary Schrank
Sls Mgr: Ginny Korte
Sales Asso: Laura Larkin

ADVANTAGE WEBCO HAWAII
See WEBCO HAWAII INC

ADVANTAGE XPO
See HIRE THINKING INC

D-U-N-S 18-063-6714 IMP
ADVANTAGE-CROWN SALES & MARKETING LLC
(*Suby of* ADVANTAGE SOLUTIONS) ★
1400 S Douglass Rd # 200, Anaheim, CA 92806-6904
Tel (714) 780-3000 *Founded/Ownrshp* 1995
Sales 285.0MM^E *EMP* 1,600
SIC 5141 Food brokers
CEO: Sonny King
CFO: Bob Vesley
Genl Mgr: Aj Stukenborg
Dir IT: Charles Choi
Snr Mgr: Keith McCracken
Snr Mgr: Scott Wolfrom

D-U-N-S 07-930-7379
ADVANTAGECARE PHYSICIANS PC
441 9th Ave Fl 8, New York, NY 10001-1623
Tel (646) 680-1563 *Founded/Ownrshp* 2013
Sales 122.5MM^E *EMP* 2,800
SIC 8011 Physicians' office, including specialists
CEO: Joseph Zeitlin

D-U-N-S 18-875-0533 IMP
ADVANTECH CORP
(*Suby of* ADVANTECH CO., LTD.)
380 Fairview Way, Milpitas, CA 95035-3062
Tel (408) 519-3800 *Founded/Ownrshp* 1987
Sales 340.0MM *EMP* 5,390
SIC 5045 7379 Computers, peripherals & software; Computer hardware requirements analysis
CEO: Ke-Cheng Liu
**Pr:* Chaney Ho
COO: Yizhong Lin
**VP:* Eric Chen
VP: Kenny Deng
**VP:* Deryu Yin
Exec: Ween Niu
CIO: Leonardo Pimenta
CIO: Bradley Rhine
DP Exec: Chung WEI
Dir IT: Victor Hernandez

D-U-N-S 08-611-5552
ADVANTEDGE BUSINESS GROUP LLC (CO)
SYNTEC CONSULTING
9777 Pyramid Ct Ste 220, Englewood, CO 80112-6046
Tel (303) 734-9424 *Founded/Ownrshp* 1997
Sales 68.3MM^E *EMP* 1,500
SIC 8741 7291 7363 Business management; Tax return preparation services; Employee leasing service

D-U-N-S 02-350-8307
ADVANTEDGE HEALTHCARE SOLUTIONS INC
AHS
30 Technology Dr Ste 1n, Warren, NJ 07059-5176
Tel (908) 279-8111 *Founded/Ownrshp* 1999
Sales 107.0MM^E *EMP* 581
SIC 8742 Management information systems consultant
Pr: David Langsam
**COO:* J Paul O'Haro
**CFO:* Michael Montemarano
**CFO:* John A Roberts
**Ex VP:* Steve G Sullivan Sr
Sr VP: Philip Bolger
Sr VP: Raymond H Cassidy
Sr VP: Jeanne A Gilreath
Sr VP: Michael Youmans
CTO: Manuel G Da Silva

ADVANTIS TECHNOLOGY
See ARCH CHEMICALS INC

D-U-N-S 13-085-0480 IMP/EXP
ADVENT INTERNATIONAL CORP
75 State St Ste 2900, Boston, MA 02109-1865
Tel (617) 951-0555 *Founded/Ownrshp* 1984
Sales 3.9MMM^E *EMP* 300
SIC 6726 Investment offices
Mng Pt: Robert E Taylor Jr
COO: Kathleen Oconnor
Treas: Janet L Hennessy
Ofcr: Heather Zuzenak
VP: Lauren Casper
VP: Mary Courtney
VP: Bert Duarte
VP: Jerry Ling
VP: Matthew Mandel
VP: William Marshall
VP: Ben Scotto

D-U-N-S 08-047-8401
ADVENT INTERNATIONAL GPE VII LLC
75 State St Fl 29, Boston, MA 02109-1827
Tel (617) 951-9493 *Founded/Ownrshp* 2012
Sales 146.8MM^E *EMP* 7,112^E
SIC 6726 Management investment funds, closed-end

D-U-N-S 11-271-3128
■ **ADVENT SOFTWARE INC**
(*Suby of* SS&C TECHNOLOGIES HOLDINGS INC) ★
600 Townsend St Fl 5, San Francisco, CA 94103-5696
Tel (415) 543-7696 *Founded/Ownrshp* 2015
Sales 335.8MM^E *EMP* 1,151^E
SIC 7371 7373 7372 6722 Custom computer programming services; Computer integrated systems design; Systems software development services; Computer systems analysis & design; Prepackaged software; Management investment, open-end
Pr: David Peter Hess Jr
**Ch Bd:* Stephanie Dimarco
**CFO:* James Cox
**Ex VP:* Todd Gottula
**Ex VP:* Chris Momsen
**Ex VP:* Anthony Sperling
**Sr VP:* John Brennan
Sr VP: David Peter F Hess
Sr VP: David Welling
Exec: Kevin McCaffrey
Snr Sftwr: Ketan Patel

D-U-N-S 80-794-8331
ADVENTIST BOLINGBROOK HOSPITAL
ADVENTIST HEALTH SYSTEM/SUNBEL
(*Suby of* ADVENTIST HLTH SYSTM SUNBELT H) ★
500 Remington Blvd, Bolingbrook, IL 60440-4988
Tel (630) 312-5000 *Founded/Ownrshp* 2003
Sales 111.9MM *EMP* 600
SIC 8062 General medical & surgical hospitals
CEO: Rick Mace
**CFO:* Mike Murrill
Dir Case M: Maureen Drumm
Dir Rx: Aleem Aziz
DP Dir: Lana Gonzales
Ansthlgy: Nicole A Boler
Ansthlgy: Joyal M Pape
HC Dir: Rosalin Johnson
HC Dir: Elizabeth Quinones

D-U-N-S 11-450-8070
ADVENTIST GLENOAKS HOSPITAL
(ADVENTIST HEALTH SYSTEM/SUNBELT, INC., ALTAMONTE SPRINGS, FL)
(*Suby of* ADVENTIST HLTH SYSTM SUNBELT H) ★
701 Winthrop Ave, Glendale Heights, IL 60139-1405
Tel (630) 545-8000 *Founded/Ownrshp* 1989
Sales 86.9MM *EMP* 550
SIC 8062 General medical & surgical hospitals
CEO: Brinsley Lewis
VP: Shawn Tyrrell
Ex Dir: William J Nelson
Rgnl Mgr: Julie Busch
Mktg Dir: Erin Gerber
Nrsg Dir: Lynn Wagner
Board of Directors: Richard Dominguez MD, Robert P Katzfey, James Kilcourse, Joe Lagattuta MD, Ron L Rowe, Joseph Shanahan Esq MD

ADVENTIST HEALTH
See PORTLAND ADVENTIST MEDICAL CENTER

ADVENTIST HEALTH
See ADVENTIST MEDICAL CENTER-HANFORD

ADVENTIST HEALTH
See SONORA REGIONAL MEDICAL CENTER

ADVENTIST HEALTH
See GLENDALE ADVENTIST MEDICAL CENTER INC

ADVENTIST HEALTH
See SIMI VALLEY HOSPITAL AND HEALTH CARE SERVICES

ADVENTIST HEALTH
See CENTRAL VALLEY GENERAL HOSPITAL

ADVENTIST HEALTH SYSTEM
See AHS/CENTRAL TEXAS INC

ADVENTIST HEALTH SYSTEM
See WHITE MEMORIAL MEDICAL CENTER INC

D-U-N-S 04-122-2019
ADVENTIST HEALTH SYSTEM GEORGIA INC
GORDON HOSPITAL
1035 Red Bud Rd Ne, Calhoun, GA 30701-6010
Tel (706) 879-4714 *Founded/Ownrshp* 1953
Sales 143.1MM *EMP* 494
SIC 8062 Hospital, affiliated with AMA residency
Pr: Pete Weber
**Pr:* Donald L Jernigan
**COO:* Steve Hannah
**COO:* Cory Reeves
Ofcr: Justina Carrick
Assoc VP: Jeni Hasselbrac
Sr VP: Carlene Jamerson
**VP:* Amy Jordon
Dir Lab: Zane Thompson
CTO: Daniel Herbard
MIS Dir: Trish Stebbins

ADVENTIST HEALTH SYSTEM SUNBEL
See FLORIDA HOSPITAL HEARTLAND MEDICAL CENTER

ADVENTIST HEALTH SYSTEM SUNBEL
See EAST ORLANDO HEALTH & REHAB CENTER INC

ADVENTIST HEALTH SYSTEM SUNBEL
See SHAWNEE MISSION MEDICAL CENTER INC

ADVENTIST HEALTH SYSTEM SUNBEL
See ADVENTIST HEALTH SYSTEM/SUNBELT INC

ADVENTIST HEALTH SYSTEM SUNBEL
See SOUTHWEST VOLUSIA HEALTHCARE CORP

D-U-N-S 96-834-1276
ADVENTIST HEALTH SYSTEM SUNBELT HEALTHCARE CORP
900 Hope Way, Altamonte Springs, FL 32714-1502
Tel (407) 357-1000 *Founded/Ownrshp* 1981
Sales 519.1MM *EMP* 78,000
SIC 5912 Drug stores
Pr: Donald Jernigan
**VP:* Robert Henderschedt
Assoc Dir: Nicole McKernan
CIO: Mark Amey
Dir IT: Trudy Wilson
Netwrk Mgr: Ruben Flores
S&M/VP: Sandra Johnson

ADVENTIST HEALTH SYSTEM/SUNBEL
See ADVENTIST BOLINGBROOK HOSPITAL

D-U-N-S 07-324-2398
ADVENTIST HEALTH SYSTEM/SUNBELT INC
ADVENTST HLTH SYSTM SUNBELT H
(*Suby of* ADVENTIST HEALTH SYSTEM SUNBELT HEALTHCARE CORP) ★
900 Hope Way, Altamonte Springs, FL 32714-1502
Tel (407) 357-1000 *Founded/Ownrshp* 1973
Sales 3.0MMM^E *EMP* 46,600
SIC 8062 8082 8051 General medical & surgical hospitals; Home health care services; Skilled nursing care facilities
Pr: Donald L Jernigan
COO: Randall Haffner
CFO: David W Evans
**CFO:* Terry D Shaw
**Treas:* David Singleton
Ofcr: Sharon Finney
VP: John Brownlow
VP: Kevin Edgerton
**VP:* Robert Henerschedt
VP: Carlene Jamerson
VP: Tim Thompson
Assoc Dir: Alice Desantola
Dir Rx: Aleem Aziz
Dir Rx: Mohammed Zakari

D-U-N-S 11-141-0861
ADVENTIST HEALTH SYSTEM/SUNBELT INC
ADVENTIST HEALTH SYSTEM SUNBEL
(*Suby of* ADVENTST HLTH SYSTM SUNBELT H) ★
1301 Wonder World Dr, San Marcos, TX 78666-7533
Tel (512) 353-8979 *Founded/Ownrshp* 1980
Sales 91.0MM *EMP* 615
SIC 8062 General medical & surgical hospitals
CEO: Sam Huenergardt
Chf Rad: Gregory Delaiglesia
**Pr:* Donald Jernigan
**CFO:* Richard D Boggess II
**CFO:* Fran Crunk
**Treas:* Terry Shaw
VP: Lisa Adams
VP: Lary A Davis
VP: Valerianna Hunt
**VP:* Paul Selivanoff
Dir Risk M: Robin Benton
Dir Risk M: Anita Herring
Dir Risk M: Deborah Lyons
Dir Risk M: Gengie Nail
Dir Risk M: Louis Prerry

D-U-N-S 07-531-3452
ADVENTIST HEALTH SYSTEM/WEST
2100 Douglas Blvd, Roseville, CA 95661-3898
Tel (916) 781-2000 *Founded/Ownrshp* 1973
Sales 251.4MM *EMP* 19,512
SIC 8062 General medical & surgical hospitals
Pr: Robert Carmen
Pr: Carrie Bannister
Pr: Roland Fargo
COO: Dag Jakobsen
CFO: Raymond Holm
CFO: Dwayne Meidenger
CFO: Terry D Shaw
**Treas:* Rodney Wehtje
Ofcr: Michael Kendall
Ex VP: Robert Carment
**Ex VP:* Scott Reiner
Sr VP: John G Raffoul
**Sr VP:* Douglas Rebok
Sr VP: Alan Rice
VP: Stan Adams
VP: Gloria Bancarz
VP: Janae Bowles
VP: Pauline Campbell
VP: Joshua Cowan
VP: Albert Deininger
VP: Randy Dodd

D-U-N-S 84-139-6802
ADVENTIST HEALTH SYSTEMS/ SUN BELT
HUGULEY MEMORIAL MEDICAL CTR
11801 South Fwy, Burleson, TX 76028-7021
Tel (817) 293-9110 *Founded/Ownrshp* 1977
Sales 123.6MM^E *EMP* 1,200^E
SIC 8062 General medical & surgical hospitals
Pr: Kenneth Finch
Chf Rad: Evan Evans
CFO: Dan Enderson
Chf Mktg O: Edward Laue
VP: Tammy Collier
Dir Inf Cn: Linda Stair
Plnt Mgr: Patrick Worley
Secur Mgr: Stan Smith
Mktg Mgr: Kurt Adamie
Psych: Ashfaq Siddiqui

D-U-N-S 08-776-4833 IMP
ADVENTIST HEALTHCARE INC
SHADY GROVE MEDICAL CENTER
820 W Diamond Ave Ste 600, Gaithersburg, MD 20878-1469
Tel (301) 315-3030 *Founded/Ownrshp* 1978
Sales 695.3MM *EMP* 5,236
Accts Baker Tilly Virchow Krause Ll
SIC 8082 8059 8062 Home health care services; Nursing home, except skilled & intermediate care facility; General medical & surgical hospitals
Pr: Terry Forde
Pr: Michael Tang
**CFO:* James Lee
Sr Cor Off: Peter Levine
Trst: Robert Fox
Trst: Mohan K Sehdev
Assoc VP: Amy Carrier
Assoc VP: Barry Lipsy
Ex VP: John Sackett
Sr VP: Gaurov Dayal
Sr VP: Marta P Rez
VP: Terryl Barnes
VP: James Brewster
VP: Edna Bruehl
VP: Tom Chan
VP: Ken De Stefano
VP: Ismael Gama
VP: Wynelle Huff
VP: Sheree P Nudd
VP: Eunmee Shim
VP: Rhodora Vaflor

ADVENTIST HLTH SYSTEM/SUNBELT
See FLORIDA HOSPITAL ZEPHYRHILLS INC

D-U-N-S 05-034-6005
ADVENTIST MEDICAL CENTER-HANFORD
ADVENTIST HEALTH
(*Suby of* ADVENTIST HEALTH SYSTEM/WEST) ★
115 Mall Dr, Hanford, CA 93230-5786
Tel (559) 582-9000 *Founded/Ownrshp* 2010
Sales 260.4MM *EMP* 41^E
SIC 8011 Medical centers
**CFO:* Eric Martinson

ADVENTIST MIDWEST HEALTH
See LA GRANGE MEMORIAL HOSPITAL INC

D-U-N-S 06-859-0447
ADVENTIST MIDWEST HEALTH
120 N Oak St, Hinsdale, IL 60521-3829
Tel (630) 856-9000 *Founded/Ownrshp* 1902
Sales 289.7MM *EMP* 2,470
SIC 8062 5947 8011 General medical & surgical hospitals; Gift shop; Physical medicine, physician/surgeon
VP: James R Garvell
Pr: Susan King
**VP:* Patricia A Sutton
**VP:* Todd S Werner Jr
Chf Nrs Of: Jann C Marks
Ex Dir: Bonnie Arnold
QA Dir: Cynthia Dougherty
QA Dir: Donita Phillips
**VP Mktg:* Steve Davis
Pathlgst: Muge Turkyilmaz

D-U-N-S 79-373-9843
ADVENTIST UNIVERSITY OF HEALTH SCIENCES INC
ADU
671 Winyah Dr, Orlando, FL 32803-1226
Tel (407) 303-7742 *Founded/Ownrshp* 1992
Sales 30.5MM *EMP* 44,000^E
SIC 8249 Medical training services
Pr: David E Greenlaw
Sr VP: Don Williams
**VP:* Lars Houmann
VP: Stephen Roche
Store Mgr: Beverly Snell
Ansthlgy: Kathleen R Wen

D-U-N-S 14-508-4583
ADVENTITY INC
(*Suby of* SUTHERLAND GLOBAL SERVICES INC) ★
444 Park Ave S Ste 1202, New York, NY 10016-7321
Tel (212) 404-2468 *Founded/Ownrshp* 2010
Sales 68.3MM^E *EMP* 2,500
SIC 7375 8742 8732 Information retrieval services; Banking & finance consultant; Business analysis; Business research service
Co-CEO: Kumar Subramanian
**COO:* Vivek Arora
**Co-CEO:* Niket Patankar
Mng Dir: Sankar Krishnan

ADVENTST HLTH SYSTM SUNBELT H
See ADVENTIST HEALTH SYSTEM/SUNBELT INC

ADVENTURES IN ADVERTISING
See AIA CORP

D-U-N-S 00-231-4446
ADVERTISING RESOURCES INC (IL)
ARI PACKAGING
11601 S Central Ave, Alsip, IL 60803-3420
Tel (708) 293-1926 *Founded/Ownrshp* 2000
Sales 86.9MM^E *EMP* 550^E
Accts Reicin Pollack & Co Ltd C
SIC 7389 Packaging & labeling services
Pr: Richard A Ehrie
**Treas:* Michael Banks
**VP:* Warren Lawson
Board of Directors: Richard Ehrie, Gary McCullough

D-U-N-S 00-228-7894
ADVERTISING SPECIALTY INSTITUTE INC (PA)
A S I
4800 E Street Rd Ste 100a, Feasterville Trevose, PA 19053-6698
Tel (215) 953-4000 *Founded/Ownrshp* 1950, 1962
Sales 86.2MM^E *EMP* 480
SIC 2721 7372 Periodicals: publishing only; Publishers' computer software
Pr: Tim Andrews
**Ch Bd:* Norman Cohn
CFO: Juan Delgado
CFO: Clem Nieto
CFO: Mark Quinn
Sr Cor Off: James La Moreaux
Sr Cor Off: Brad Nelson
**V Ch Bd:* Matthew Cohn
Chf Mktg O: Chris Matthews
**Ex VP:* Stephen F Bright
VP: Tom Augeri
VP: Linda Carretta
VP: Robert Duffy
VP: Roy Getzoff
VP: Terry Lilly
VP: Fred Oesen
VP: Stuart Rosenfield
**VP:* Stephanie Schaeffer
VP: Stephanie S Schaeffer
VP: Larry Vaughn
Creative D: Richard Angeloni

D-U-N-S 06-598-5079
■ **ADVEST GROUP INC**
(*Suby of* BANK OF AMERICA CORP) ★
90 State House Sq, Hartford, CT 06103-3708
Tel (860) 509-1000 *Founded/Ownrshp* 2005
Sales 555.9MM^E *EMP* 1,726
SIC 6211 6036 6141 6153 6282

D-U-N-S 19-656-0759 IMP
ADVICS MANUFACTURING OHIO INC
(Suby of ADVICS NORTH AMERICA INC) ★
1650 Kingsview Dr, Lebanon, OH 45036-8390
Tel (513) 934-0023 Founded/Ownrshp 2003
Sales 201.0MM^E EMP 625
SIC 3714 Motor vehicle brake systems & parts
CEO: Atsuo Matsumoto
*Pr: Geoffrey J Hearsum
CFO: Hideo Kambe
*Treas: Kaigi Ito
VP: Dave Bolton
VP: Ron Lipps
VP: Hiro Nakanishi
CTO: Tim Phipps
Dir IT: Steller Bob
Dir IT: Terrance Edwards
IT Man: Brad Koenig

D-U-N-S 17-644-0592
ADVICS NORTH AMERICA INC
(Suby of ADVICS CO.,LTD.)
1650 Kingsview Dr, Lebanon, OH 45036-8390
Tel (513) 696-5450 Founded/Ownrshp 2002
Sales 314.0MM^E EMP 1,085
SIC 8731 8742 5013 5531 Engineering laboratory, except testing; Industrial laboratory, except testing; Marketing consulting services; Automotive brakes; Automotive parts
Pr: Masahide Kato
Ql Cn Mgr: Francine Krisak
Sls Dir: Shingo Kotera

D-U-N-S 78-546-8500
ADVISOR GROUP INC
1 World Financial Ctr, New York, NY 10281-1003
Tel (866) 673-1550 Founded/Ownrshp 2016
Sales NA EMP 2,499^E
SIC 6311 Assessment life insurance agents
Pr: Erica McGinnis

D-U-N-S 06-877-9755
▲ ADVISORY BOARD CO
2445 M St Nw Ste 500, Washington, DC 20037-1448
Tel (202) 266-5600 Founded/Ownrshp 1986
Sales 768.3MM EMP 3,500
Tkr Sym ABCO Exch NGS
SIC 8732 8741 7372 Research services, except laboratory; Business management; Prepackaged software
Ch Bd: Robert W Musslewhite
*Pr: David L Felsenthal
CFO: Michael T Kirshbaum
Ex VP: Richard Schwartz
Assoc Dir: Kevin Sherman
Mng Dir: Alice Kirkpatrick
Prac Mgr: Tracy Bradley
Prac Mgr: Tracy Davis
Prgrm Mgr: Simon Newman
CTO: Mary D Van Hoose
Sftwr Eng: Zhi Zhai
Board of Directors: Peter J Grua, Nancy Killefer, Mark R Neaman, Leon D Shapiro, Leanne M Zumwalt

D-U-N-S 01-469-4685
ADVOCARE LLC
25 Lindsley Dr Ste 205, Morristown, NJ 07960-4456
Tel (973) 993-8777 Founded/Ownrshp 1950
Sales 115.7MM^E EMP 1,400
SIC 8011 General & family practice, physician/surgeon
Doctor: John M Tedeschi
*Pr: Christopher T Olivia
*CFO: Sean Porrini
*Ex VP: Roy T Santarella
*Sr VP: Frank Sorgenti
IT Man: Michael Renzi
*Doctor: Parisa Razi
*Doctor: John B Tedeschi
*Doctor: Rey Velasco

ADVOCATE , THE
See CAPITAL CITY PRESS LLC

D-U-N-S 02-559-1629
ADVOCATE CONDELL MEDICAL CENTER (IL)
ADVOCATE CONDELL MEDICAL CTR
(Suby of ADVOCATE HEALTH CARE NETWORK) ★
801 S Milwaukee Ave, Libertyville, IL 60048-3204
Tel (847) 362-2900 Founded/Ownrshp 1928, 2008
Sales 114.2MM^E EMP 2,500
SIC 8062

ADVOCATE CONDELL MEDICAL CTR
See ADVOCATE CONDELL MEDICAL CENTER

ADVOCATE GOOD SHEPHERED
See ADVOCATE NORTHSIDE HEALTH

D-U-N-S 00-322-2804
ADVOCATE HEALTH AND HOSPITALS CORP
TRINITY HOSPITAL
(Suby of ADVOCATE HEALTH CARE NETWORK) ★
3975 Highland Ave, Downers Grove, IL 60515-1515
Tel (630) 572-9393 Founded/Ownrshp 1994
Sales 4.0MMM EMP 4,110
Accts Ernst & Young Us Llp Chicago
SIC 8062 General medical & surgical hospitals
Pr: James H Skogsbergh
*VP: Patricia Smith-Calascibe
Pharmcst: Sue Marschall

D-U-N-S 94-832-4892
ADVOCATE HEALTH AND HOSPITALS CORP
ADVOCATE LUTHERAN GENERAL HOSP
1775 Dempster St, Park Ridge, IL 60068-1143
Tel (847) 723-6610 Founded/Ownrshp 1906
Sales 752.0MM EMP 4,818
SIC 8062 General medical & surgical hospitals
VP: Jim Kelley
VP: Mats Lindman
Mktg Mgr: Carl Voeleteer
Pathlgst: Miguel Gonzalez
Pathlgst: Vinubhai J Patel
Plas Surg: Russell R Eid
Plas Surg: Christopher V Pelletiere

D-U-N-S 95-691-4337
ADVOCATE HEALTH CARE NETWORK
3075 Highland Pkwy Fl 6, Downers Grove, IL 60515-5563
Tel (630) 572-9393 Founded/Ownrshp 1994
Sales 5.3MMM EMP 25,000
Accts Ernst & Young Llp Chicago Il
SIC 8621 Health association
Pr: James H Skogsbergh
Pt: Rev Delois Brown-Daniels
*COO: William P Santulli
CFO: Lawrence J Maka
*CFO: Dominic J Nakis
Ch: Tammy Lemke
Treas: Lawrence J Majka
V Ch Bd: Mary Ann Mc Dermott Rn Ed D
*Chf Mktg O: Lee B Sacks MD
Sr VP: John E Blair
Sr VP: Kelly Jo Golson
*Sr VP: Gail D Hasbrouck JD
Sr VP: Scott Powder
Sr VP: Jerry Wagenknechi
VP: Kevin R Brady
VP: Mary Ann Clemens
VP: Thomas Diederich
VP: Terry Guymon
VP: Benjamin Imdieke
VP: Larry Jackson
VP: Brian Kelly
Board of Directors: Rev Dr Jane Fisler Hoffman, David B Anderson, Abe Thomas Hughes II, Alejandro Aparicio MD, Bishop Paul R Landahl, Lynn Crump-Caine, Richard McAuliffe, John F Timmer Chairperson, Clarence Nixon Jr Phd, Jon E Christofersen MD, Michele Baker Richardson, Bruce E Creger, Julie P Schlueter, William C Graft, Joan Fowler Shaver Phd Rn, Rev Dr Donald M Hallberg, Carolyn H Smeltzer, Mark Harris, Rev Ozzie Smith Jr

D-U-N-S 09-640-4186
ADVOCATE HEALTH CENTERS INC (IL)
(Suby of ADVOCATE HEALTH CARE NETWORK) ★
2545 S Mrtn Lther King Dr, Chicago, IL 60616
Tel (312) 842-7117 Founded/Ownrshp 1970
Sales 57.0MM^E EMP 1,100
SIC 8011 Internal medicine practitioners
Pr: James Dan
Pr: Maxine Cunningham
COO: Trisha Mc Donagh
*Treas: Gail Hasbrouck
IT Man: Adam Ackerman
Doctor: Sanjay Joag MD
Doctor: Farhan Shams MD

ADVOCATE LUTHERAN GENERAL HOSP
See ADVOCATE HEALTH AND HOSPITALS CORP

D-U-N-S 10-220-0420
ADVOCATE NORTHSIDE HEALTH
ADVOCATE GOOD SHEPHERED
2025 Windsor Dr, Oak Brook, IL 60523-1586
Tel (630) 572-9393 Founded/Ownrshp 2002
Sales 500.1MM EMP 4
SIC 8062 General medical & surgical hospitals
Pr: Jim Skogsbergh

D-U-N-S 62-522-5107
ADVOCATE SOUTH SUBURBAN HOSPITAL
17800 Kedzie Ave, Hazel Crest, IL 60429-2029
Tel (708) 799-8000 Founded/Ownrshp 1988
Sales 106.1MM^E EMP 1,338
SIC 8062 General medical & surgical hospitals
Pr: Michael Englehart
*VP: Karen Clark
VP: Larry Jackson
*VP: Brian Kelly
VP: Sharon Otten
VP: Beth Purcell
Dir Lab: Mohamad G Ghosn
Dir Rad: Scott Baker
CIO: Beth Turek
QC Dir: Mary Lankford
Mtls Mgr: Marjorie Fremouw

D-U-N-S 07-960-6053
AE INDUSTRIAL PARTNERS LLC
2500 N Military Trl # 470, Boca Raton, FL 33431-6344
Tel (561) 372-7820 Founded/Ownrshp 2014
Sales 100.3MM^E EMP 576^E
SIC 3369 3324 Aerospace castings, nonferrous: except aluminum; Aerospace investment castings, ferrous
*Pt: Thomas E Brew Jr
*Pt: Wayne P Garrett

D-U-N-S 13-972-8229 IMP
■ AE SOLAR ENERGY INC
PV POWERED
(Suby of ADVANCED ENERGY INDUSTRIES INC) ★
20720 Brinson Blvd, Bend, OR 97701-7407
Tel (541) 312-3832 Founded/Ownrshp 2010
Sales 201.4MM^E EMP 850
SIC 3674 Photovoltaic devices, solid state
CEO: Gregg Patterson
*Pr: Gordon Tredger
*VP: Steve Hummel
*VP: Roger C Laubacher
*VP: Steve Levy
VP: Erick Petersen
Mfg Dir: Tucker Ruberti
Snr Mgr: Marty Fleet

D-U-N-S 04-835-2355 IMP/EXP
AEA INVESTORS LP
666 5th Ave Fl 36, New York, NY 10103-3102
Tel (212) 644-5900 Founded/Ownrshp 1968
Sales 2.6MMM^E EMP 7,193
SIC 6282 6211 Investment advisory service; Investment bankers
Pr: John Garcia
Pt: Gary A Cappeline
Pt: Glenn M Fischer
Pt: David Ryan
VP: Amy C Bevacqua
VP: Amy C Bevaqua
VP: Barbara L Burns
VP: Scott Dahnke
VP: Sandra Grinker
VP: Jessica Hodgkinson
VP: Christian Johnson
VP: Anneka Kamel
VP: Vinay Kumar
VP: Thomas Levengood
VP: Alex Mehfar
VP: James Powers
VP: Dan Schorr
VP: Todd Welsch

AEARO COMPANY
See AEARO TECHNOLOGIES LLC

D-U-N-S 61-410-1566 IMP
■ AEARO TECHNOLOGIES LLC
AEARO COMPANY
(Suby of 3M CO) ★
5457 W 79th St, Indianapolis, IN 46268-1675
Tel (317) 692-6666 Founded/Ownrshp 2008
Sales 223.6MM^E EMP 1,603
SIC 3842 3851 3643 Ear plugs; Noise protectors, personal; Protective eyeware; Plugs, electric
*Pr: Julie Bushman
VP: Rahul Kapur
*Prin: Robert D Anderson
*Prin: Brian S McGinley
Board of Directors: Robert D Anderson, Brian S McGinley

D-U-N-S 00-507-6948 IMP/EXP
AEC INC (DE)
APPLICATION ENGINEERING
(Suby of BALL & JEWELL) ★
1100 E Wdfield Rd Ste 588, Schaumburg, IL 60173
Tel (847) 273-7700 Founded/Ownrshp 1957, 1988
Sales 144.6MM^E EMP 800
SIC 3585 3823 3559 3443 3535 Refrigeration & heating equipment; Evaporative condensers, heat transfer equipment; Industrial instrmnts msrmnt display/control process variable; Temperature instruments: industrial process type; Plastics working machinery; Fabricated plate work (boiler shop); Conveyors & conveying equipment
Pr: Thomas Breslin
*Prin: Harry Anderson
Sls Mgr: Lisa Allen

AEC NARROW FABRICS
See ASHEBORO ELASTICS CORP

AECI
See ARKANSAS ELECTRIC COOPERATIVES INC

D-U-N-S 05-490-5391
AECO INTERIORS OF NEW ORLEANS
1836 Iberville St, New Orleans, LA 70112-3329
Tel (504) 301-9600 Founded/Ownrshp 2013
Sales 98.4MM^E EMP 5,000
SIC 7389 Interior design services
VP: Bill Carballo

D-U-N-S 15-356-1212
▲ AECOM
1999 Avenue Of The Stars # 2600, Los Angeles, CA 90067-6033
Tel (213) 593-8000 Founded/Ownrshp 1980
Sales 17.4MMM EMP 92,000^E
Tkr Sym ACM Exch NYS
SIC 8711 8712 Engineering services; Architectural engineering
Ch Bd: Michael S Burke
Pr: Stephen M Kadenacy
Pr: Richard Silos
Pr: Randall A Wotring
CEO: Matthew Sutton
CFO: W Troy Rudd
Treas: Gerry Ruiz
V Ch Bd: Daniel R Tishman
Ofcr: Mary E Finch
Assoc VP: Bernard Alpern
Assoc VP: David Didier
Assoc VP: Alan R Eckman
Ex VP: Carla J Christofferson
Ex VP: Judy Herman
Ex VP: Kevin A Lynch
Sr VP: Mike Brennan
Sr VP: Donald D Graul
Sr VP: James B Hilton
Sr VP: Russ Macdonald
Sr VP: Annika Moman
Sr VP: Gregory Sauter
Board of Directors: Douglas W Stotlar, John M Dionisio, Janet C Wolfenbarger, James H Fordyce, William H Frist, Linda Griego, David W Joos, William G Ouchi, Robert J Routs, William P Rutledge, Clarence T Schmitz

D-U-N-S 08-596-3908
■ AECOM C&E INC
AECOM ENVIRONMENT
(Suby of AECOM) ★
250 Apollo Dr, Chelmsford, MA 01824-3627
Tel (978) 905-2100 Founded/Ownrshp 1968
Sales 491.9MM^E EMP 2,600
SIC 8711 Engineering services
Pr: Michael S Burke
*CFO: Kerry Adams
*Ch: John M Dionisio
*VP: Christina Ching
*VP: Robert Kelleher
*Prin: Jane Chmielinski
*Prin: Daniel R Tishman
Prgrm Mgr: Mack Astorga
IT Man: Joel Farrier

AECOM DESIGN
See AECOM SERVICES INC

D-U-N-S 80-857-0415
■ AECOM E&C HOLDINGS INC
(Suby of URS HOLDINGS INC) ★
1999 Avenue Of Ste 2600, Los Angeles, CA 90067
Tel (213) 593-8000 Founded/Ownrshp 2009
Sales 5.4MMM^E EMP 10,500^E
SIC 8711 1611 1629 1623 1541 1622 Engineering services; General contractor, highway & street construction; Dams, waterways, docks & other marine construction; Industrial plant construction; Power plant construction; Pipeline construction; Industrial buildings, new construction; Bridge construction; Tunnel construction; Highway construction, elevated
CEO: Robert W Zaist
*Pr: Gary V Jandegian
Pr: Stuart I Young
*CFO: H Thomas Hicks
*Treas: Judy L Rodgers
VP: Dee Hutchison
VP: Robert E Murphy
VP: Thomas Walter
VP: Kory Wilmot
Comm Dir: Dave Tumminello
Prgrm Mgr: Frederick Schreiber

D-U-N-S 00-790-0517 IMP/EXP
■ AECOM ENERGY & CONSTRUCTION INC
(Suby of AECOM E&C HOLDINGS INC) ★
6200 S Quebec St, Greenwood Village, CO 80111-4729
Tel (303) 228-3000 Founded/Ownrshp 1918
Sales 5.3MMM^E EMP 10,500^E
SIC 1622 1629 1081 4953 Bridge, tunnel & elevated highway; Oil refinery construction; Metal mining services; Refuse systems
CEO: Thomas H Zarges
*Pr: Robert Zaist
*Treas: Judy L Rodgers
*Sr VP: Randolph J Hill
VP: Andrew Jayjack
VP: Stephen M Johnson
VP: James Loughran
VP: James Semple
Assoc Dir: Susan Wain
*Prin: H Thomas Hicks
Dir IT: Bob Jenkins

AECOM ENVIRONMENT
See AECOM C&E INC

D-U-N-S 04-327-1568 IMP/EXP
■ AECOM GLOBAL II LLC
(Suby of AECOM) ★
1999 Avenue Of The Stars, Los Angeles, CA 90067-6022
Tel (213) 593-8100 Founded/Ownrshp 1976, 2014
Sales 12.1MMM^E EMP 43,000
SIC 8711 8712 8741 Engineering services; Consulting engineer; Architectural engineering; Construction management
Pr: Tommy Bell
Pr: Rick L Randall
DP Exec: David Scripter
Dir IT: Jay Mills
IT Man: Simon Pang

D-U-N-S 11-350-0284
■ AECOM GOVERNMENT SERVICES INC
AGS
(Suby of AECOM DESIGN) ★
20501 Seneca Meadows Pkwy, Germantown, MD 20876-7016
Tel (703) 921-1600 Founded/Ownrshp 1980
Sales 1.0MMM^E EMP 4,000^E
SIC 4959 4173 4581 7299 Environmental cleanup services; Maintenance facilities for motor vehicle passenger transport; Aircraft maintenance & repair services; Station operation services
CEO: Al Konvicka
*Pr: Michael S Burke
*CEO: Michael Donnelly
Ofcr: Gregory Szynalksi

D-U-N-S 03-453-2973
■ AECOM SERVICES INC (CA)
AECOM DESIGN
(Suby of AECOM) ★
555 S Flower St Ste 3700, Los Angeles, CA 90071-2432
Tel (213) 593-8000 Founded/Ownrshp 1946, 1990
Sales 1.1MMM^E EMP 4,000
SIC 8712 8741 8711 Architectural services; Management services; Engineering services
CEO: John M Dionisio
V Ch: Daniel R Streett
*Pr: Michael S Burke
*Pr: Raymond Landy
*COO: Jane Chmielinski
COO: John Kinley
*CFO: Deborah Klem
*Ch: Richard G Newman
*Treas: Dennis Deslatte
Assoc VP: Chuck Malacarne
Assoc VP: Lupe Perez
*Ex VP: Paul Steinke
*Sr VP: Robyn Miller
Sr VP: Ed Schmeltz
VP: Brett Berra
VP: Gary Beswick
VP: Dennis Clark
VP: John Deerkoski
VP: Jeff Gaal
VP: George Gipe
*VP: Kelly Olson

D-U-N-S 60-817-9008
■ AECOM SPECIAL MISSIONS SERVICES INC
(Suby of AECOM) ★
20501 Seneca Meadows Pkwy, Germantown, MD 20876-7016
Tel (412) 367-6060 Founded/Ownrshp 2009
Sales 105.9MM^E EMP 560
SIC 8744 Facilities support services
Pr: Matthew D Schneider
*Pr: Jill Bruning
*CFO: Robert Bartolacci
*Sec: Nelson H Crooks

D-U-N-S 00-318-4462 IMP
■ AECOM TECHNICAL SERVICES INC (CA)
(Suby of AECOM) ★
300 S Grand Ave Ste 1100, Los Angeles, CA 90071-3173
Tel (213) 593-8000 Founded/Ownrshp 1970, 2008

Sales 909.2MM^E EMP 4,805
SIC 4953 8748 8742 8711 Refuse systems; Environmental consultant; Industry specialist consultants; Engineering services
CEO: Michael Burke
Sr VP: William Stead
VP: Michael J Durkin
VP: James D Weinbauer
MIS Mgr: King Nelson
Mktg Mgr: Lindsey Humphrey

D-U-N-S 17-374-7726
■ AECOM USA INC
(Suby of AECOM) ★
605 3rd Ave, New York, NY 10158-0180
Tel (212) 973-2900 Founded/Ownrshp 1990
Sales 851.5MM^E EMP 4,500
SIC 8748 Business consulting
CEO: Michael S Burke
*Ex VP: Carla Christofferson
VP Mktg: Stephen Moritz
VP Sls: John Dietrich
Board of Directors: Richard Moody

D-U-N-S 07-985-7701
AEDAN INC
27447, Sun City, CA 92586
Tel (888) 272-5505 Founded/Ownrshp 2015
Sales 200.0MM EMP 24
SIC 7371 7381 8733 3812 7382 Computer software development; Security guard service; Scientific research agency; Defense systems & equipment; Security systems services
Ch: Eric Fitzgerald
*CEO: Gong Famson

D-U-N-S 04-170-1798 IMP/EXP
■ AEE SOLAR INC
(Suby of SUNRUN SOUTH LLC) ★
775 Fiero Ln Ste 200, San Luis Obispo, CA 93401-7904
Tel (800) 777-6609 Founded/Ownrshp 2003
Sales 119.6MM^E EMP 78
SIC 5063 3645 Generators; Residential lighting fixtures
CEO: Lee Johnson
Pr: Antonio Cintra
COO: Paul Winnowski

D-U-N-S 83-116-7932
AEES INC
PKC GROUP
(Suby of PKC GROUP OYJ)
36555 Corp Dr Ste 300, Farmington Hills, MI 48331
Tel (248) 489-4700 Founded/Ownrshp 2011
Sales 4.9MMM^E EMP 17,000^E
SIC 3679 Electronic loads & power supplies
Pr: Frank Sovis
S&M/VP: Rico Mutone

D-U-N-S 61-174-9529 IMP
AEES POWER SYSTEMS LIMITED PARTNERSHIP
ENGINEERED PLASTIC COMPONENTS
(Suby of PKC GROUP) ★
999 Republic Dr, Allen Park, MI 48101-3668
Tel (248) 489-4900 Founded/Ownrshp 2009
Sales 1.0MMM^E EMP 17,000
SIC 3694 Harness wiring sets, internal combustion engines
VP: Julie Bellamy

D-U-N-S 96-257-5283
AEG MANAGEMENT TWN LLC
TARGET CENTER
(Suby of ANSCHUTZ CORP) ★
600 1st Ave N Ste Sky, Minneapolis, MN 55403-1400
Tel (612) 673-1300 Founded/Ownrshp 2007
Sales 44.6MM^E EMP 1,500
SIC 7941 Sports clubs, managers & promoters
Genl Mgr: Steve Mattson
Prd Mgr: Jerry Abell

AEGCO
See AEP GENERATING CO

D-U-N-S 08-008-8168
AEGEAN BUNKERING (USA) LLC
20 Signal Rd, Stamford, CT 06902-7909
Tel (212) 430-1100 Founded/Ownrshp 2013
Sales 1.0MMM EMP 21
SIC 2911 Oils, fuel

AEGERION PHARMACEUTICALS
See NOVELION THERAPEUTICS INC

D-U-N-S 07-828-7785
▲ AEGION CORP
17988 Edison Ave, Chesterfield, MO 63005-3700
Tel (636) 530-8000 Founded/Ownrshp 1971
Sales 1.3MMM EMP 6,200
Tkr Sym AEGN Exch NGS
SIC 1623 Water, sewer & utility lines
Pr: Charles R Gordon
*Ch Bd: Alfred L Woods
CFO: David A Martin
*V Ch Bd: Stephen P Cortinovis
Ofcr: David F Morris
Sr VP: Michael D White
VP: Robert Moorhead
Exec: Mark Wetzel
Board of Directors: Rhonda Germany Ballintyn, Christopher B Curtis, Stephanie A Cuskley, Walter J Galvin, Juanita H Hinshaw, M Richard Smith, Phillip D Wright

D-U-N-S 18-296-0047
AEGIS COMMUNICATIONS GROUP LLC
(Suby of TELEPERFORMANCE) ★
9999 Technology Blvd W, Dallas, TX 75220-4330
Tel (972) 830-1800 Founded/Ownrshp 2006
Sales 480.9MM^E EMP 12,250
SIC 7389 Telemarketing services
Pr: Sandip Sen
Pr: Joe G John
Pr: Kory Laszewski
COO: Rajiv Ahuja
*COO: Chandra Venkataramani
Ex VP: Harley Axelrod
Ex VP: Tom Franklin
Ex VP: Upendra Singh
Sr VP: Mariana Fern Ndez
Sr VP: Chandrasekar Venkataraman
VP: Jim Conway
VP: Nitin Kanade
VP: Mark Monroe
VP: Andre Silveira
Exec: Daniel Ramirez
Dir Surg: Kevin Nolan
*Dir Risk M: Neeti Khaitan

D-U-N-S 83-570-7159
AEGIS CORP
614 Dartmouth Terrace Ct, Ballwin, MO 63011-5443
Tel (636) 273-1011 Founded/Ownrshp 1995
Sales 910.0MM EMP 4,300
SIC 3699 4812 3812 3444 2326 Laser systems & equipment; Cellular telephone services; Search & navigation equipment; Sheet metalwork; Men's & boys' work clothing
Pr: David Kramer
*CFO: Marcia M Murphy
*VP: Paul Cooper

D-U-N-S 10-623-6326
AEGIS INSURANCE SERVICES INC
(Suby of ASSOCIATED ELECTRIC & GAS INSURANCE SERVICES LIMITED)
1 Meadowlands Plz Ste 300, East Rutherford, NJ 07073-2152
Tel (201) 508-2600 Founded/Ownrshp 1983
Sales NA EMP 215^E
SIC 6411 Insurance information & consulting services
Pr: Alan J Maguire
COO: Denise Keating
CFO: Mike Murphy
*Ch: Wesley W Von Schack
Ofcr: Fred Murnane
*Ex VP: John J Denman Jr
*Sr VP: William P Cullen
Sr VP: William Cullen
*Sr VP: Gilbert Gould
Sr VP: Michael Johnson
Sr VP: Bruce Rosnowski
Sr VP: Bruce Roznowski
VP: Bill Blatcher
VP: Mark Bluestein
VP: Mel Butts
VP: Simon Day
VP: Jack Denman
VP: Ladman Gary
VP: Alison Geller
VP: Thomas Joyce
VP: Karen P Larson

D-U-N-S 08-011-3693
AEGIS LIFESTYLE INC
(Suby of DENTSU AEGIS NETWORK LTD.)
32 Aveune Of The Americas, New York, NY 10013
Tel (212) 366-3400 Founded/Ownrshp 2014
Sales 139.0MM^E EMP 6,840^E
SIC 7311 7389 8743 Advertising agencies; Advertising, promotional & trade show services; Sales promotion
CEO: Charlie Horsey

AEGIS LIVING
See SENIOR AEGIS COMMUNITIES LLC

D-U-N-S 01-190-6521
AEGIS MEDIA AMERICAS INC
DENTSU AEGIS NETWORK USA
(Suby of DENTSU INC.)
150 E 42nd St, New York, NY 10017-5612
Tel (212) 591-9122 Founded/Ownrshp 1996
Sales 658.7MM^E EMP 1,700
SIC 4899 Data communication services
CEO: Jerry Buhlmann
CFO: Nick Priday
Ofcr: Roger Sant
Ex VP: Angela Courtin
Ex VP: Mitch Oscar
VP: John Bollock
VP: Pam Eleftherio
VP: Robert Freeamn
VP: Mark Hodor
VP: Lisa Johnson
VP: Thomas Meyer
VP: Vic Ruvolo
Exec: Nathan Rusell
Assoc Dir: Bree Labollita
Dir Bus: Peter Twombly

D-U-N-S 04-715-8535
AEGON DIRECT MARKETING SERVICES INC
TRANSAMERICA AFFINITY SERVICES
(Suby of AEGON USA, INC.)
100 Light St Fl B1, Baltimore, MD 21202-1098
Tel (410) 685-5500 Founded/Ownrshp 2005
Sales NA EMP 405
SIC 6311 8011 Life insurance; Medical insurance associations
Pr: Marilyn Carp
COO: Donna Black
CFO: Gregg Klocke
CFO: Martha McConnell
VP: Jake Craig
VP: Cmp E Henningsen
Dist Mgr: Jerry Sturgill
Prd Mgr: Stacey Coleman
Mktg Dir: Marcia Moore
Mktg Dir: Tawanda Saffore
Mktg Mgr: Danielle Baney

D-U-N-S 87-692-0133
AEGON DIRECT MARKETING SERVICES INC
(Suby of AEGON USA, INC.)
2700 W Plano Pkwy, Plano, TX 75075-8205
Tel (972) 881-6000 Founded/Ownrshp 2001
Sales 259.1MM^E EMP 2,250
SIC 7389 Financial services; Hotel & motel reservation service
Pr: Marilyn Carp
CFO: Robert Northam
*Treas: Susan A Peters
Treas: Sue Peterson
Sr VP: Michael Eubanks
VP: Keith Wright
CIO: Ellyn Skerkowski
Dir IT: Steve Milner
IT Man: David Fanning
Netwrk Mgr: Brian Levasseur
Software D: Cal Slayton

D-U-N-S 19-867-8849
AEGON US HOLDING CORP
(Suby of AEGON N.V.)
4333 Edgewood Rd Ne, Cedar Rapids, IA 52499-3830
Tel (319) 355-8511 Founded/Ownrshp 1986
Sales NA EMP 6,000
SIC 6311 6321 6351 6159 Life insurance carriers; Health insurance carriers; Disability health insurance; Credit & other financial responsibility insurance; Equipment & vehicle finance leasing companies
Pr: Mark W Mullin
*Pr: K J Storm
Treas: M C Fowler
*Treas: Cor H Verhagen
*Ex VP: D J Shepard
*Ex VP: Jos Streppel
*Sr VP: David L Blankenship
*VP: Kathleen Modvelewski
Exec: Vallerie Moeller

D-U-N-S 62-319-0410
AEGON USA INVESTMENT MANAGEMENT LLC
(Suby of AEGON USA, INC.)
4333 Edgewood Rd Ne, Cedar Rapids, IA 52499-3830
Tel (319) 398-8511 Founded/Ownrshp 2001
Sales 186.3MM EMP 324^E
SIC 6282 Investment advisory service
Pr: Pat Baird
Treas: H Verhagen
Bd of Dir: David Crew
Bd of Dir: Jeffry Dixon
Bd of Dir: Steven Myers
Bd of Dir: Chris Pitts
Ex VP: Kirk Buese
Ex VP: Frank E Collcchia
Ex VP: Frank E Collecchia
Ex VP: William S Cook
Ex VP: Donald Flynn
Ex VP: Daniel P Fox
Ex VP: David R Ludke
Ex VP: Jos Streppel
Ex VP: Mark Zinkula
Sr VP: Bradley J Beman
Sr VP: John T Bender
Sr VP: David L Blankenship
Sr VP: David Carney
Sr VP: David R Halfpap
Sr VP: Steven P Opp

D-U-N-S 04-580-9586
AEGON USA LLC
(Suby of AEGON US HOLDING CORP) ★
4333 Edgewood Rd Ne, Cedar Rapids, IA 52499-3830
Tel (319) 355-8511 Founded/Ownrshp 2008
Sales NA EMP 5
SIC 6311 Life insurance
CEO: Mark William Mullin
IT Man: David Dever
Netwrk Eng: Tom Hobson
Mktg Mgr: Richard Bogdon
Mktg Mgr: Lawrence Skurla

D-U-N-S 83-675-0059
AEGON USA SECURITIES INC
(Suby of AEGON USA, INC.)
570 Carillon Pkwy, Saint Petersburg, FL 33716-1294
Tel (727) 299-1800 Founded/Ownrshp 1985
Sales 100.8MM^E EMP 1,000
SIC 6211 Investment firm, general brokerage
Ch Bd: John R Kenney
*Pr: G John Hurley
*Treas: Allan Hamilton
Ofcr: Priscilla Hechler
Ofcr: Teresa Peplowski
Ofcr: David Warren
Ex VP: Bill Geiger
*Sr VP: Edie Craig
VP: Teresa Rooney
VP: Mike Scherrman
Exec: Bill Cummings

AEI
See AFFILIATED ENGINEERS INC

AEI CONSULTANTS
See ALL ENVIRONMENTAL INC

AEI RESOURCES HOLDING
See HNRC DISSOLUTION CO

D-U-N-S 16-788-1783
AEI SERVICES LLC
2929 Allen Pkwy Ste 200, Houston, TX 77019-7123
Tel (713) 345-5200 Founded/Ownrshp 2003
Sales 2.3MMM^E EMP 8,300^E
SIC 4911 Electric services
CEO: Emilio Vicens
*CFO: Tom Cimino
Sr VP: Orlando R Gonz Lez
VP: Jo O Carlos R De Albuquerque
*VP: Luis Mendez
*VP: Maureen Ryan
*VP: Alan Stringer

D-U-N-S 62-498-9112
▲ AEMETIS INC
20400 Stevens, Cupertino, CA 95014
Tel (408) 213-0940 Founded/Ownrshp 1983
Sales 146.6MM EMP 135^E
Tkr Sym AMTX Exch NGM
SIC 8731 2911 Energy research; Diesel fuels
Ch Bd: Eric A McAfee
COO: Andrew B Foster
CFO: Todd A Waltz
Ex VP: Sanjeev Gupta
VP: Satya Chillara
Board of Directors: Francis Barton, John R Block, Steven W Hutcheson, Harold Sorgenti

D-U-N-S 18-895-0745 IMP
AEON USA INC
(Suby of AEON CO., LTD.)
1 Penn Plz Fl 36, New York, NY 10119-3699
Tel (212) 946-8780 Founded/Ownrshp 1988
Sales 66.1MM^E EMP 8,000
SIC 5621 5961 2211 2391 Ready-to-wear apparel, women's; Women's apparel, mail order; Towels, dishcloths & washcloths: cotton; Sheets, bedding & table cloths: cotton; Draperies & drapery fabrics, cotton; Curtains & draperies
Prin: Isao Tsuruta
Prin: Yosuke Suzuki

AEP
See OHIO POWER CO

AEP
See SOUTHWESTERN ELECTRIC POWER CO

AEP
See AMERICAN ELECTRIC POWER CO INC

AEP
See AMERICAN ELECTRIC POWER SERVICE CORP

AEP
See INDIANA MICHIGAN POWER CO

AEP
See PUBLIC SERVICE CO OF OKLAHOMA

AEP
See APPALACHIAN POWER CO

D-U-N-S 36-152-1883
■ AEP GENERATING CO
AEGCO
(Suby of AEP) ★
1 Riverside Plz Ste 1600, Columbus, OH 43215-2355
Tel (614) 223-1000 Founded/Ownrshp 1982
Sales 1.4MMM^E EMP 9,000
SIC 4911 Generation, electric power
CEO: Nick Akins
*Pr: E L Draper Jr
CFO: Leonard Assante
Bd of Dir: James F Cordes
Bd of Dir: Stuart J Solomon
Bd of Dir: Susan Tomasky
Bd of Dir: Genevieve Tuchow
Ofcr: Marie Mohler
Ex VP: Paul Addis
Sr VP: Rodney Plimpton
VP: P J Demaria
VP: Mark A Gray
VP: Mark A Pyle
VP: Wiliam C Reed
Exec: Mannie Alvarez
Exec: Thomas Berkemeyer
Exec: Shannon Listebarger
Exec: Angela Roney
Comm Man: Bill Schalk

D-U-N-S 05-209-1683 IMP/EXP
▲ AEP INDUSTRIES INC
95 Chestnut Ridge Rd, Montvale, NJ 07645-1801
Tel (201) 641-6600 Founded/Ownrshp 1970
Sales 1.1MMM EMP 2,600
Accts Kpmg Llp Short Hills New Je
Tkr Sym AEPI Exch NGS
SIC 3081 2821 Unsupported plastics film & sheet; Plastic film & sheet; Polyethylene film; Polypropylene film & sheet; Polyvinyl chloride resins (PVC); Polyethylene resins
Ch Bd: J Brendan Barba
*Pr: John J Powers
*CFO: Paul M Feeney
Treas: James B Rafferty
Treas: James Rafferty
Ex VP: Paul C Vegliante
VP: Gary Bobko
VP: Richard Boyette
VP: Robert Covella
VP: Linda N Guerrera
VP: Lawrence R Noll
VP: Brian Ochsner
Board of Directors: Robert T Bell, Ira M Belsky, Richard E Davis, Frank P Gallagher, Lee C Stewart

D-U-N-S 95-829-8788
■ AEP POWER MARKETING INC
AMERICA ELECTRIC POWER TEXAS
(Suby of AEP) ★
1 Riverside Plz Fl 1, Columbus, OH 43215-2355
Tel (614) 716-1000 Founded/Ownrshp 1996
Sales 1.0MMM^E EMP 6,100
SIC 4911 Electric services
Pr: Michael Morris
VP: Gene Jensen
VP: William Singmon
Dir IT: Sean Parcel

AEP RIVER OPERATIONS
See ACBL RIVER OPERATIONS LLC

D-U-N-S 00-792-4772
■ AEP TEXAS CENTRAL CO
(Suby of AEP) ★
1 Riverside Plz, Columbus, OH 43215-2355
Tel (614) 716-1000 Founded/Ownrshp 1945
Sales 202.9MM^E EMP 1,224
SIC 4911 Distribution, electric power; Transmission, electric power
CEO: Nick Akins
*Ch Bd: Michael G Morris
*CFO: Holly K Koeppel
Ex VP: Nicholas K Akins
Ex VP: Venita McCellon-Allen
*Ex VP: Robert P Powers
*Ex VP: Brian X Tierney
VP: Bob Bradish
VP: Harry Gordon
VP Mktg: David Ferguson
Board of Directors: Nicholas K Akins, Carl L English, Thomas M Hagan, John B Keane, Robert P Powers, Stephen P Smith, Susan Tomasky, Dennis E Welch

AEPS
See AMERICAN EAGLE PROTECTIVE SERVICES CORP

D-U-N-S 19-690-6528
AEQUOR TECHNOLOGIES INC
377 Hoes Ln Ste 300, Piscataway, NJ 08854-4138
Tel (732) 494-4999 *Founded/Ownrshp* 1998
Sales 86.4MM^E *EMP* 500
SIC 7371 Computer software systems analysis & design, custom; Computer software development & applications; Computer software development; Software programming applications
CEO: Manmeet Virdi
Pr: Ramesh Nair
**Pr:* Kamalpreet Virdi
Dir IT: Robert Beaudet

D-U-N-S 00-750-7775 IMP
AER MANUFACTURING LP
A E R
1605 Surveyor Blvd, Carrollton, TX 75006-5103
Tel (972) 418-6499 *Founded/Ownrshp* 1973
Sales 138.8MM^E *EMP* 650
SIC 3714

D-U-N-S 09-075-5471
AERA ENERGY LLC
(*Suby of* ROYAL DUTCH SHELL PLC)
10000 Ming Ave, Bakersfield, CA 93311-1301
Tel (661) 665-5000 *Founded/Ownrshp* 1994
Sales 2.1MMM^E *EMP* 1,350
Accts Pricewaterhousecoopers Llp Ph
SIC 1381 Directional drilling oil & gas wells
Pr: Christina S Sistrunk
Chf Mktg O: Andrew Hoyer
Ex VP: Lynne Carrithers
Sr VP: Robert C Alberstadt
Sr VP: Brent D Carnahan
Sr VP: Lynne J Carrithers
Sr VP: Ronald H John
VP: Jeff Dittman
VP: John Haley
VP: Jon Hallmark
VP: Ron John
VP: Chuck Westbay

AERC RECYCLING SOLUTIONS
See AERC.COM INC

D-U-N-S 80-124-7099 IMP
AERC.COM INC
AERC RECYCLING SOLUTIONS
111 Howard Blvd Ste 108, Mount Arlington, NJ 07856-1315
Tel (973) 691-3200 *Founded/Ownrshp* 2000
Sales 103.4MM^E *EMP* 150
SIC 4953 Recycling, waste materials
CEO: Peter J Jegou
**Pr:* Robert Landmesser
CFO: Robert Szanyi
VP: William R Smith
IT Man: Eric Thompson

AERCAP US GLOBAL AVIATION LLC
See AERCAP US GLOBAL AVIATION LLC

D-U-N-S 02-606-0923
AERCAP US GLOBAL AVIATION LLC
AERCAP US GLOBAL AVIATION LLC
10250 Constellation Blvd, Los Angeles, CA 90067-6200
Tel (310) 788-1999 *Founded/Ownrshp* 2014
Sales 131.0MM^E *EMP* 367^E
SIC 3721 4581 6159 Aircraft; Airport leasing, if operating airport; Equipment & vehicle finance leasing companies
CFO: Keith Helming

AEREON
See FLARE INDUSTRIES LLC

D-U-N-S 92-922-8351
■ AERIAL COMMUNICATIONS INC
(*Suby of* T-MOBILE USA INC) ★
8410 W Bryn Mawr Ave, Chicago, IL 60631-3408
Tel (773) 399-4200 *Founded/Ownrshp* 2000
Sales 119.7MM^E *EMP* 2,054
Accts Arthur Andersen Llp
SIC 4812 Cellular telephone services
Pr: Robert Stapleton

D-U-N-S 02-111-7077
AERO CALIFORNIA AIRLINES
1960 E Grand Ave Ste 1200, El Segundo, CA 90245-5084
Tel (800) 237-6225 *Founded/Ownrshp* 1996
Sales 49.6MM^E *EMP* 2,000
SIC 4512 Air passenger carrier, scheduled
Ch Bd: Raul Arechiga

D-U-N-S 07-926-9610
AERO COMMUNICATIONS HOLDING INC
5711 Research Dr, Canton, MI 48188-2261
Tel (734) 467-8121 *Founded/Ownrshp* 2012
Sales 368.5MM^E *EMP* 1,600^E
SIC 1623 Telephone & communication line construction

D-U-N-S 07-866-4680
AERO COMMUNICATIONS INC
(*Suby of* AERO COMMUNICATIONS HOLDING INC) ★
5711 Research Dr, Canton, MI 48188-2261
Tel (734) 467-8121 *Founded/Ownrshp* 2012
Sales 364.0MM^E *EMP* 1,600^E
SIC 1623 Telephone & communication line construction
CEO: Greg McCray
COO: Jon Sirken
**VP:* Nick Zautcke

D-U-N-S 04-998-6177 IMP/EXP
AERO HARDWARE & SUPPLY INC
HYDRAULIC SUPPLY CO
300 International Pkwy, Sunrise, FL 33325-6240
Tel (954) 845-1040 *Founded/Ownrshp* 1986
Sales 129.4MM *EMP* 190
SIC 5084 5085 Pumps & pumping equipment; Industrial fittings
CEO: James H Inglis
**Pr:* Luis Abellon
**Pr:* John Serra
**CFO:* Sandra Maccarron
**VP:* Maureen Ward
Genl Mgr: David Vandenhouten
Store Mgr: Pedro Lara
Store Mgr: Jerry Miller
Opers Mgr: Greg Steffen
Mktg Mgr: Gina Menicucci
Manager: Ryan Sharkey

D-U-N-S 08-042-4516
AERO OPCO LLC
125 Chubb Ave Fl 5, Lyndhurst, NJ 07071-3504
Tel (201) 508-4500 *Founded/Ownrshp* 2016
Sales 1.0MMM *EMP* 10,000
SIC 5621 5611 Women's clothing stores; Men's & boys' clothing stores
CEO: Julian Geiger
COO: Marc Miller
CFO: David Dick

D-U-N-S 80-363-8477
AERO PRECISION INDUSTRIES LLC
(*Suby of* GREENWICH AEROGROUP INC) ★
201 Lindbergh Ave, Livermore, CA 94551-7667
Tel (925) 579-5327 *Founded/Ownrshp* 2012
Sales 126.7MM *EMP* 106
SIC 5088 Aircraft & space vehicle supplies & parts
Pr: Francis Cowle
CFO: Richard Archer
Sr VP: Joseph Massucco
VP: Angel Flores
Off Admin: Ryann Ness
QA Dir: Tayfur Yuncuoglu
Sls Dir: Sebnem Flores
Sls Dir: Pavel Slavin
Sls Dir: Tiffany Walden
Mktg Mgr: Saul Tervydis
Sls Mgr: Cengiz Ergin

D-U-N-S 19-455-0042 IMP
AERO-MED LTD
85 Commerce St, Glastonbury, CT 06033-2312
Tel (860) 659-0602 *Founded/Ownrshp* 1985
Sales 232.1MM^E *EMP* 90^E
Accts Montovani Murray Nemphos & T
SIC 5047 Veterinarians' equipment & supplies; X-ray film & supplies; Dentists' professional supplies
Pr: Daniel A Del Mastro
CFO: Peter A Donovan
Sr VP: Sam Samad
VP: Jill Garnette
VP: Sheri K Gay
VP: Jill H McGarry
VP: Daniel J Pandiscia
VP: Mark Stauffer
VP: Blair Williams
VP Opers: Donna Roberts

AEROCONTROLEX
See TRANSDIGM INC

AEROFAB
See TUBE PROCESSING CORP

D-U-N-S 79-548-0698
AEROFLEX COLORADO SPRINGS INC
COBHAM SEMICONDUCTOR SOLUTIONS
(*Suby of* COBHAM AES HOLDINGS INC) ★
4350 Centennial Blvd, Colorado Springs, CO 80907-3701
Tel (719) 594-8000 *Founded/Ownrshp* 2014
Sales 122.7MM^E *EMP* 300
SIC 3674 Integrated circuits, semiconductor networks, etc.
Pr: Jill Kale
Sec: Jon Carlson
CTO: Sharon Cooke
Sftwr Eng: Troy Noble
VP Opers: David Kerwin
Opers Mgr: Bob Labelle
Ql Cn Mgr: Gordon McManus
Sls Mgr: Janet Rosacker
Board of Directors: Brian Drzewiecki, Bud Kick

D-U-N-S 80-636-6469 EXP
AEROFLEX HOLDING CORP
(*Suby of* COBHAM HOLDINGS INC) ★
35 S Service Rd, Plainview, NY 11803-4117
Tel (516) 694-6700 *Founded/Ownrshp* 2014
Sales 528.5MM^E *EMP* 2,700^E
SIC 3674 Semiconductors & related devices
Pr: Leonard Borow
Ch Bd: Hugh Evans
CFO: John Adamovich Jr
Treas: Charles Badlato
Ex VP: John Buyko
Sr VP: Andrew F Kaminsky
Sr VP: Edward Wactlar
VP: Francis Kwan
VP: Ryan Panos
Manager: Donna Langan

D-U-N-S 00-205-0532 IMP
AEROFLEX INC
(*Suby of* AEROFLEX HOLDING CORP) ★
35 S Service Rd, Plainview, NY 11803-4117
Tel (516) 694-6700 *Founded/Ownrshp* 2007
Sales 521.4MM^E *EMP* 2,700
SIC 3812 3621 3677 3674 3496 3827 Acceleration indicators & systems components, aerospace; Torque motors, electric; Electronic coils, transformers & other inductors; Microcircuits, integrated (semiconductor); Mesh, made from purchased wire; Optical instruments & apparatus
Pr: Leonard J Borow
Ch Bd: Robert B McKeon
V Ch: Michael G Gorin
COO: Leslie Collins
CFO: John Adamovich Jr
Treas: Charles Badlato
**Ex VP:* John Buyko
Sr VP: Ed Wactlar
VP: Rafi Albarian
VP: Robert Brucato
VP: Kevin J Finnegan
VP: Andrew Kaminsky
VP: Ian Langley
VP: Sam Strang

D-U-N-S 15-557-5095
AEROFLEX PLAINVIEW INC
(*Suby of* COBHAM AES HOLDINGS INC) ★
35 S Service Rd, Plainview, NY 11803-4117
Tel (516) 694-6700 *Founded/Ownrshp* 2014
Sales 191.5MM^E *EMP* 894
SIC 3679 3621 3674 3827 Electronic circuits; Motors, electric; Microcircuits, integrated (semiconductor); Microprocessors; Optical instruments & lenses
CEO: Jill Kale
**Ch Bd:* Leonard Borow
**Sr VP:* Carl Caruso
VP: William Brown
**VP:* Kevin J Finnegan
**VP:* Rob Sichenzia
Genl Mgr: Joseph Castaldo
IT Man: Bill Brown

D-U-N-S 05-810-0074
AEROFLEX WICHITA INC
COBHAM AVCOMM
(*Suby of* IFR SYSTEMS INC) ★
10200 W York St, Wichita, KS 67215-8999
Tel (316) 522-4981 *Founded/Ownrshp* 2014
Sales 87.5MM^E *EMP* 500
SIC 4581 Aircraft servicing & repairing
VP: Jeffrey Gillum
Pr: Marv Rozner
CFO: Dan Kelly
VP: Fred Arnold
VP: Bill Martin
**VP:* Ryan Panos
VP: Jeff L Ray
Dir Lab: Mark Elzinga
Prgrm Mgr: Steve Kahler
Genl Mgr: Kimberly Taylor
Snr Sftwr: Steve White

D-U-N-S 15-109-4570
AEROGROUND INC
AIR CARGO HANDLING SERVICE
(*Suby of* MENZIES AVIATION PLC)
270 Lawrence Ave, South San Francisco, CA 94080-6817
Tel (650) 266-6965 *Founded/Ownrshp* 2006
Sales 73.2MM^E *EMP* 1,500
SIC 4581 4213 Air freight handling at airports; Trucking, except local
CEO: Anthony Bonino
Sr VP: Steven Ballard
VP: John Peery

D-U-N-S 14-784-4419 IMP/EXP
AEROGROUP INTERNATIONAL INC
AEROSOLES
201 Meadow Rd, Edison, NJ 08817-6002
Tel (732) 985-6900 *Founded/Ownrshp* 2014
Sales 491.8MM^E *EMP* 1,572
SIC 5139 5661 Shoes; Shoe stores
CEO: R Shawn Neville
**Pr:* Jules Schneider
**Ofcr:* Sandy Coviello
Sr VP: Alena Margolis
VP: Jonathan Victor
Store Mgr: Gaetano Canzano
Software D: Sumedha De Silva
Software D: Kristen Schober
Opers Mgr: Amy Rothman
Prd Mgr: Sharon Molfetta
Sls Mgr: Kelly Bowers

D-U-N-S 78-070-6300
▲ AEROHIVE NETWORKS INC
1011 Mccarthy Blvd, Milpitas, CA 95035-7920
Tel (408) 510-6100 *Founded/Ownrshp* 2006
Sales 151.6MM *EMP* 624^E
Tkr Sym HIVE *Exch* NYS
SIC 7373 Local area network (LAN) systems integrator
Ch Bd: David K Flynn
CFO: John Ritchie
Chf Mktg O: David Greene
Sr VP: Raphael Gernez
Sr VP: Efstathios Papaefstathiou
Sr VP: Thomas J Wilburn
VP: Steve Debenham
VP: Michael Lin
Snr Sftwr: Thimmayya AME
Snr Sftwr: Yuqing MAI
**CTO:* Changming Liu
Board of Directors: Remo Canessa, Curt Garner, Frank J Marshall, Conway Rulon-Miller, John Gordon Payne, Christopher J Schaepe

D-U-N-S 00-131-6330 EXP
▲ AEROJET ROCKETDYNE HOLDINGS INC
2001 Aerojet Rd, Rancho Cordova, CA 95742-6418
Tel (916) 355-4000 *Founded/Ownrshp* 1915
Sales 1.7MMM *EMP* 4,823
Tkr Sym AJRD *Exch* NYS
SIC 3812 3764 3769 6552 6519 Defense systems & equipment; Propulsion units for guided missiles & space vehicles; Guided missile & space vehicle parts & auxiliary equipment; Subdividers & developers; Real property lessors
Pr: Eileen Drake
Pr: Warren M Boley
COO: David C Hatch
COO: Mark Tucker
CFO: Kathleen E Redd
**Ch:* Warren G Lichtenstein
VP: John D Schumacher
Board of Directors: Thomas A Corcoran, James R Henderson, Warren G Lichtenstein, Lance W Lord, Merrill A McPeak, James H Perry, Martin Turchin

D-U-N-S 00-825-5853 IMP
■ AEROJET ROCKETDYNE INC
(*Suby of* AEROJET ROCKETDYNE HOLDINGS INC) ★
2001 Aerojet Rd, Rancho Cordova, CA 95742-6418
Tel (916) 355-4000 *Founded/Ownrshp* 1944
Sales 956.3MM^E *EMP* 2,700
SIC 3728 3764 3769 3761 Aircraft body & wing assemblies & parts; Propulsion units for guided missiles & space vehicles; Guided missile & space vehicle parts & auxiliary equipment; Guided missiles & space vehicles
CEO: Warren M Boley Jr
**CFO:* Kathleen E Redd
Treas: Ronald Gollmer
**Treas:* John Joy
Ofcr: Randy Rosado
VP: Michael Bright
**VP:* Christopher C Cambria
VP: John Canzio
**VP:* Chris W Conley
VP: Tyler Evans
VP: Craig M Halteran
VP: John Luddy
VP: Scott Neish
**VP:* Jose Ruiz Jr
VP: Jerry Tarnacki
Exec: Steven Flowers
Comm Dir: Timothy Murphy
Board of Directors: Douglas Greer

D-U-N-S 00-342-1310
■ AERONAUTICAL RADIO INC
(*Suby of* ROCKWELL COLLINS INFO MGT SVCS) ★
2551 Riva Rd, Annapolis, MD 21401-7435
Tel (410) 266-4000 *Founded/Ownrshp* 1929
Sales 156.6MM^E *EMP* 660
SIC 4812 4899 Radio telephone communication; Data communication services
Ch Bd: James L Pierce
**Pr:* John M Belcher
**CFO:* Richard Jones
**Treas:* James Sadler
Bd of Dir: Grant Thornton
VP: Robert E Manigold

D-U-N-S 80-971-7598 IMP/EXP
AERONAUTICAL SYSTEMS INC
(*Suby of* GENERAL ATOMICS) ★
16761 Via Del Campo Ct, San Diego, CA 92127-1713
Tel (858) 455-2810 *Founded/Ownrshp* 1991
Sales 1.1MMM^E *EMP* 7,204
SIC 3721 Aircraft
Pr: Neal Blue
**Treas:* Max D Kemp

D-U-N-S 02-626-3132 IMP/EXP
▲ AEROPOSTALE INC
AROPOSTALE
100 W 33rd St Ste 1100, New York, NY 10001-2914
Tel (646) 485-5410 *Founded/Ownrshp* 1995
Sales 1.5MMM *EMP* 20,330
Tkr Sym AROPQ *Exch* OTO
SIC 5621 5611 Ready-to-wear apparel, women's; Clothing, sportswear, men's & boys'
CEO: Julian R Geiger
**Ch Bd:* Karin Hirtler-Garvey
COO: Marc D Miller
CFO: David J Dick
Ex VP: Emilia A Fabricant
Ex VP: Mary Jo Pile
IT Man: Doug Leder
Mktg Mgr: Patricia Crespo
Board of Directors: Ronald R Beegle, Michael J Cunningham, Evelyn Dilsaver, Kenneth B Gilman, Janet E Grove, John N Haugh, John D Howard, David B Vermylen

D-U-N-S 06-081-6159
AEROQUIP-VICKERS INC
(*Suby of* EATON CORP) ★
1111 Superior Ave E, Cleveland, OH 44114-2522
Tel (216) 523-5000 *Founded/Ownrshp* 1999
Sales 1.3MMM^E *EMP* 14,568^E
SIC 3052 3492 3429 3069 3585 3728 Rubber hose; Plastic hose; Hose & tube fittings & assemblies, hydraulic/pneumatic; Clamps & couplings, hose; Keys & key blanks; Molded rubber products; Parts for heating, cooling & refrigerating equipment; Aircraft parts & equipment
Pr: A M Cutler
**CFO:* A T Dillon
Treas: R E Tarmenter
VP: J R Horst
VP: D E Kimmet
VP: J S Mitchell

AEROSOLES
See AEROGROUP INTERNATIONAL INC

AEROSPACE
See ENSIGN-BICKFORD INDUSTRIES INC

D-U-N-S 92-929-4353
AEROSPACE CENTER SUPPORT
ACS
100 Kindel Dr Ste A211, Tullahoma, TN 37389
Tel (931) 454-3000 *Founded/Ownrshp* 1995
Sales 62.4MM^E *EMP* 1,200^E
SIC 8744 Facilities support services
Pt: James L Nicholson
**Pt:* Robert Danna
**Pt:* Gary P Hobbs
**Pt:* Paul Lombari
**Pt:* Carl H McNair Jr
**Pt:* Robert E Tyner
VP: Jack R Wormington

D-U-N-S 00-955-3637
AEROSPACE CORP (CA)
2310 E El Segundo Blvd, El Segundo, CA 90245-4609
Tel (310) 336-5000 *Founded/Ownrshp* 1960
Sales 916.6MM *EMP* 3,920
Accts Deloitte & Touche Llp Los Ang
SIC 8733 8731 8711 Scientific research agency; Commercial physical research; Engineering services
Pr: Dr Wanda M Austin
**Pr:* Wanda M Austin
**CFO:* Ellen M Beatty
**Ch:* Barbara M Barrett
Treas: Thomas Oconnor
Bd of Dir: Gail Johnson
Trst: Rufus A Fulton
Ofcr: James F Jusko
Ofcr: Jeffrey Thomas
Ex VP: Michael Daugherty
**Sr VP:* Malissia Clinton
**Sr VP:* J Michael Drennan
Sr VP: Wayne H Goodman
**Sr VP:* David J Gorney
VP: Stephen Burrin
VP: Jeanne Campanella
VP: Diana Cannon

VP: Moria Cunningham
VP: Glenn Davis
VP: Mindy Dayton
VP: Shirley Dohzen
Board of Directors: Howell M Estes III, K Anne Street, Wanda M Austin, Rufus A Fulton Jr, Peter B Teets, Kevin P Chilton, Keith R Hall, Vincent Vitto, Kevin P Chilton, Dr Daniel E Hastings, Alan C Wade, Dr David M Dicarlo, Tina W Jonas, Robert S Walker, Dr David M Dicarlo, John E Mc Laughlin, Michael B Donley, Michael Montelongo, Michael B Donley, Thomas S Moorman Jr, Dr Bonnie J Dunbar, Sally K Ride, Dr Bonnie J Dunbar, Jeffrey H Smith

D-U-N-S 60-211-7954 IMP/EXP
■ AEROSPACE DYNAMICS INTERNATIONAL INC
ADI
(Suby of PCC) ★
25540 Rye Canyon Rd, Valencia, CA 91355-1169
Tel (661) 257-3535 Founded/Ownrshp 2014
Sales 183.1MM^E EMP 450
SIC 3728 Aircraft parts & equipment
CEO: Joseph I Snowden
*Pr: John T Cave II
CFO: Bill Barritt
*CFO: William S Barritt
*VP: James W Fish
VP: Ron Yazma
Exec: Trisha Preece
Off Mgr: John Marshall

D-U-N-S 07-970-6066
AEROSPACE PARTS HOLDINGS INC
CADENCE AEROSPACE
610 Nwport Ctr Dr Ste 950, Newport Beach, CA 92660
Tel (949) 877-3630 Founded/Ownrshp 2012
Sales 301.0MM EMP 1,175^E
SIC 6719 Investment holding companies, except banks
CEO: Ron Case
*COO: Mike Coburn
*CFO: Don Devore

D-U-N-S 03-927-4506 IMP
AEROSPACE PRODUCTS INTERNATIONAL INC
API
2871 Business Park Dr, Memphis, TN 38118-1556
Tel (901) 365-3470 Founded/Ownrshp 2013
Sales 115.5MM^E EMP 136
SIC 5088 4522 Transportation equipment & supplies; Air cargo carriers, nonscheduled
CEO: Aaron P Hollander
*Pr: Ahmed M Metwalli
*Pr: Andy Trosper
*CFO: James G Howell II
Sr VP: Jean-Marie Pogu
VP: Bobbie Espitia
*VP: Jim Howell
VP: Eric Waller
Prgrm Mgr: Greg Paule
Genl Mgr: Wes Bevels
CIO: David S Currence
Board of Directors: Joseph J Lhota

AEROSPACE STRUCTURES DIVISION
See ATK SPACE SYSTEMS INC

D-U-N-S 11-471-7346
AEROSPACE TESTING ALLIANCE
ATA
600 William Northern Blvd, Tullahoma, TN 37388-4729
Tel (931) 454-3000 Founded/Ownrshp 2003
Sales 1.1MM^E EMP 2,100
SIC 8711 Engineering services
Prin: Rogers F Starr
Ex Dir: Ricky L Peters
Dir IT: Mark Rigney

D-U-N-S 80-002-9451 EXP
■ AEROSTRUCTURES CORP
(Suby of TRIUMPH AEROSTRUCTURES LLC) ★
1431 Vultee Blvd, Nashville, TN 37217-2007
Tel (615) 361-2000 Founded/Ownrshp 2010
Sales 141.8MM^E EMP 201^E
SIC 3721 3728 3812 3769 Aircraft; Aircraft parts & equipment; Search & navigation equipment; Guided missile & space vehicle parts & auxiliary equipment

D-U-N-S 05-481-4959 IMP/EXP
AEROTECH INC
100 Zeta Dr, Pittsburgh, PA 15238-2897
Tel (412) 963-7470 Founded/Ownrshp 1969
Sales 83.0MM^E EMP 300
SIC 3699 3825 Electrical equipment & supplies; Galvanometers; Meters, power factor & phase angle
Pr: Mark A Botos
VP: Brian Fink
*VP: Bob Novotnak
VP: Jeff A Wisyanski
IT Man: Joseph W Garofalo
IT Man: Matthew Maurer
Sftwr Eng: Paul Duerig
Sftwr Eng: Kevin Shaffer
Mfg Mgr: Dave Holmes
Sls Mgr: Dan Hixson
Snr Mgr: Eric Baum

D-U-N-S 16-169-2074
AEROTEK INC
AEROTEK STAFFING
(Suby of ALLEGIS GROUP INC) ★
7301 Parkway Dr, Hanover, MD 21076-1159
Tel (410) 694-5100 Founded/Ownrshp 1993
Sales 5.3MMM EMP 4,200
Accts Pricewaterhousecoopers Llp B
SIC 7363 8748 8711 Temporary help service; Business consulting; Engineering services
Pr: Todd M Mohr
*CFO: Thomas B Kelly
*Treas: Paul J Bowie
Ofcr: Brittany McInnis
Ex VP: Ron Germack
*Sr VP: John Flanigan
*Sr VP: Chad Koele
VP: John Ambrose
VP: Tony Bartolucci
VP: Jeff Colvin
VP: Mark Cooper
VP: Mike Hansen
VP: Greg Jones
VP: Brad Kennedy
VP: John Rudy
VP: Marty Schager
VP: Bryan Toffey
VP: Jocelyn Villecco
VP: Brooks Wells

AEROTEK STAFFING
See AEROTEK INC

D-U-N-S 05-802-4456 IMP
▲ AEROVIRONMENT INC
800 Royal Oaks Dr Ste 210, Monrovia, CA 91016-6347
Tel (626) 357-9983 Founded/Ownrshp 1971
Sales 264.1MM EMP 663
Tkr Sym AVAV Exch NGS
SIC 3721 8711 3694 Aircraft; Gliders (aircraft); Engineering services; Energy conservation engineering; Battery charging alternators & generators
Pr: Wahid Nawabi
*Ch Bd: Timothy E Conver
CFO: Raymond D Cook
Sr VP: Cathleen S Cline
Sr VP: Doug Scott
VP: Brett Hush
Board of Directors: Charles Thomas Burbage, Arnold L Fishman, Charles R Holland, Catharine Merigold, Edward R Muller, Stephen F Page

D-U-N-S 06-231-9777 IMP
AEROVOX INC
167 John Vertente Blvd, New Bedford, MA 02745-1221
Tel (508) 994-9661 Founded/Ownrshp 1978
Sales NA EMP 1,740
SIC 3629 3675

D-U-N-S 96-168-6248
AERSALE HOLDINGS INC
121 Alhambra Plz Ste 1700, Coral Gables, FL 33134-4541
Tel (305) 764-3200 Founded/Ownrshp 2010
Sales 125.3MM^E EMP 200
SIC 5088 7359 Transportation equipment & supplies; Aircraft rental
VP: Douglas Meyer
*VP: Ron Wolf

D-U-N-S 83-291-6188 IMP
AERSALE INC
(Suby of AERSALE HOLDINGS INC) ★
121 Alhambra Plz Ste 1700, Coral Gables, FL 33134-4541
Tel (305) 764-3200 Founded/Ownrshp 2008
Sales 125.3MM^E EMP 200
SIC 5088 Aircraft engines & engine parts
CEO: Nick Finazzo
*COO: Robert Nichols
Sr VP: Bill Thompson
VP: Steven Boecker
*VP: Bill Kmiotek
VP: Vanessa Machado
*VP: Tom McFarland
*VP: Craig Wright

AES
See IPALCO ENTERPRISES INC

AES
See CILCORP INC

D-U-N-S 14-777-5733
■ AES ALAMITOS LLC
(Suby of AES CORP) ★
690 N Studebaker Rd, Long Beach, CA 90803-2221
Tel (562) 493-7891 Founded/Ownrshp 1997
Sales 200.0MM EMP 90
SIC 3621 Generators & sets, electric

D-U-N-S 04-385-7812
▲ AES CORP
4300 Wilson Blvd Ste 1100, Arlington, VA 22203-4168
Tel (703) 522-1315 Founded/Ownrshp 1981
Sales 14.9MMM EMP 21,000
Accts Ernst & Young Llp Mclean Vir
Tkr Sym AES Exch NYS
SIC 4911 Electric services; Generation, electric power; Distribution, electric power
Pr: Andres R Gluski
*Ch Bd: Charles O Rossotti
Pr: Victoria Harker
Pr: Andrew Vesey
COO: Bernerd Da Santos
COO: Nelson Vasquez
CFO: Thomas M O'Flynn
Ex VP: Brian A Miller
Sr VP: Michael Chilton
Sr VP: Elizabeth Hackenson
VP: Rosa Alvarado
VP: Lorenzo Comassetto
VP: Ramon Eulacio
VP: Paritosh Mishra
VP: Julian Nebreda
VP: Bryan Robinson
VP: Ruben Saavedra
VP: Ernest Wohnig
VP: Alison Zimlich
Board of Directors: Charles L Harrington, Kristina M Johnson, Holly K Koeppel, Philip Lader, James H Miller, John B Morse Jr, Moises Naim

D-U-N-S 07-874-0012
■ AES DPL HOLDINGS LLC
(Suby of AES CORP) ★
4300 Wilson Blvd, Arlington, VA 22203-4167
Tel (703) 522-1315 Founded/Ownrshp 2011
Sales 1.6MMM^E EMP 1,510^E
SIC 4911 Generation, electric power; Transmission, electric power; Distribution, electric power
Pr: Mary Wood
*Treas: Willard Hoagland III

D-U-N-S 07-843-0362 IMP/EXP
AES DRILLING FLUIDS LLC
(Suby of CANADIAN ENERGY SERVICES & TECHNOLOGY CORP)
11767 Katy Fwy Ste 230, Houston, TX 77079-1711
Tel (888) 556-4533 Founded/Ownrshp 2008
Sales 246.0MM^E EMP 250^E
SIC 1381 Drilling oil & gas wells
Pr: Kenneth Zinger

D-U-N-S 15-645-0186
AES ELECTRICAL INC
FREESTATE ELECTRICAL SVC CO
13335 Mid Atlantic Blvd, Laurel, MD 20708-1432
Tel (301) 770-2060 Founded/Ownrshp 2006
Sales 120.0MM EMP 650
SIC 1731 Electrical work
Pr: Michael F Dugan
*CFO: Gregg Kaderabek
*Treas: Charley Wooldridge
Sfty Dirs: Pete Courtemanche

AES OMEGA
See ASRC ENERGY SERVICES OMEGA LLC

D-U-N-S 16-016-0420 IMP
■ AES PUERTO RICO LP
(Suby of AES CORP) ★
Carretera Ste 3 Km 142 0, Guayama, PR 00784
Tel (787) 866-8117 Founded/Ownrshp 1994
Sales 347.9MM EMP 112
Accts Ernst & Young Llp San Juan
SIC 4911 Electric services
Pr: Manuel Mata
CFO: Gamaliel Rivera

AESCO MANUFACTURING SERVICES
See AIRBORN ELECTRONICS INC

D-U-N-S 60-784-1608 IMP
AESYNT INC
MCKESSON AUTOMATION HEALTHCARE
(Suby of FRANCISCO PARTNERS MANAGEMENT LP) ★
500 Cranberry Woods Dr # 400, Cranberry Township, PA 16066-5224
Tel (724) 741-8000 Founded/Ownrshp 1987
Sales 258.9MM^E EMP 850
SIC 7373 Turnkey vendors, computer systems
Pr: Kraig McEwen
CFO: Gary Bucciarelli
Sr VP: Douglas Descalzi
VP: George S Attar
VP: Stacey Bartlett
*VP: Willie C Bogan
VP: Scott Deaton
VP: Brenda Dwyer
VP: Frances Nahas
VP: Ryan Seager
Ex Dir: Neil Dibernardo

AET FILMS
See TAGHLEEF INDUSTRIES INC

AETN INTERNATIONAL
See A&E TELEVISION NETWORKS LLC

D-U-N-S 61-647-9528
■ AETNA FINANCIAL HOLDINGS LLC
(Suby of AETNA INC) ★
151 Farmington Ave, Hartford, CT 06156-0001
Tel (860) 273-0123 Founded/Ownrshp 1986
Sales 271.8MM^E EMP 33,100
SIC 8322 Referral service for personal & social problems
CEO: Mark Bertolini

D-U-N-S 18-359-8320
■ AETNA HEALTH HOLDINGS LLC
(Suby of AETNA INC) ★
151 Farmington Ave, Hartford, CT 06156-0001
Tel (860) 273-0123 Founded/Ownrshp 2002
Sales NA EMP 676
SIC 6324 6411 6321 Hospital & medical service plans; Insurance agents, brokers & service; Accident & health insurance

D-U-N-S 15-094-5132
■ AETNA HEALTH INC
(Suby of AETNA HEALTH HOLDINGS LLC) ★
151 Farmington Ave, Hartford, CT 06156-0001
Tel (800) 872-3862 Founded/Ownrshp 1987
Sales NA EMP 676
SIC 6324 Health maintenance organization (HMO), insurance only
Pr: Martha Reardon Temple
*Treas: Elaine Rose Cofrancesco
*VP: Edward Chung-I Lee
Exec: Lisa Chace
Exec: Ayde Gonzales
Exec: Kathleen Kadziolka
Snr Sftwr: David Jones
Dir IT: Marc Scheinblum
IT Man: Ty Farris
Netwrk Mgr: Julie Gonzalez
Netwrk Eng: Carolyn Brodginski

D-U-N-S 15-137-8346
■ AETNA HEALTH INC (NJ)
(Suby of AETNA INC) ★
9 Entin Rd, Parsippany, NJ 07054-5000
Tel (973) 244-3500 Founded/Ownrshp 1983
Sales NA EMP 150
SIC 6324 6321 Health maintenance organization (HMO), insurance only; Accident & health insurance
Pr: John W Coyle
Genl Mgr: Paul Kratochvil
Sls Mgr: John Lawrence
Snr Mgr: Max McDaniel

D-U-N-S 80-443-2003
■ AETNA HEALTH MANAGEMENT INC
(Suby of AETNA HEALTH HOLDINGS LLC) ★
151 Farmington Ave, Hartford, CT 06156-0001
Tel (860) 273-0123 Founded/Ownrshp 2002
Sales NA EMP 336
SIC 6324 Health maintenance organization (HMO), insurance only
Pr: Alan Munro Bennett
Sr VP: John Lowenberg
*VP: Roberta Louise Downey

D-U-N-S 14-746-0562
■ AETNA HEALTH OF CALIFORNIA INC
(Suby of AETNA HEALTH MANAGEMENT INC) ★
2409 Camino Ramon, San Ramon, CA 94583-4285
Tel (925) 543-9000 Founded/Ownrshp 1986
Sales NA EMP 300
SIC 6324 Health maintenance organization (HMO), insurance only
CEO: John Brian Ternan
VP: Pamela M Lemon
Exec: Michael L Smith
Netwrk Mgr: Denise Casner
Netwrk Mgr: Stacy Powell
Netwrk Mgr: Steven E Twinam
VP Sls: Stuart Macdonald
Counsel: Ben Diamond
Counsel: Jessica Dorazio
Snr PM: Glenn Bair
Snr PM: Sabrina De Melo

D-U-N-S 80-443-3241
■ AETNA HEALTH OF ILLINOIS INC
(Suby of AHP HOLDINGS INC) ★
100 N Riverside Plz Fl 20, Chicago, IL 60606-1501
Tel (312) 928-3000 Founded/Ownrshp 1990
Sales NA EMP 265
SIC 6324 Health maintenance organization (HMO), insurance only
Pr: Kevin F Hickey
VP: Joel Montalvo
Dir Rx: Stephen Magosin
Software D: Terri Robinson
Snr Mgr: Steven Schock

D-U-N-S 94-515-5190
▲ AETNA INC
151 Farmington Ave, Hartford, CT 06156-0001
Tel (860) 273-0123 Founded/Ownrshp 1853
Sales NA EMP 50,100
Tkr Sym AET Exch NYS
SIC 6324 6321 6371 8011 Health maintenance organization (HMO), insurance only; Accident insurance carriers; Disability health insurance; Health insurance carriers; Pensions; Medical insurance associations
Ch Bd: Mark T Bertolini
Pr: Karen S Lynch
CFO: Shawn M Guertin
Treas: Sheila M Jaskowiak
Bd of Dir: Joseph Newhouse
Bd of Dir: Sylvia V Pacquing
Bd of Dir: Cheryl Parmelee
Chf Mktg O: Harold L Paz
Top Exec: Alan Pawlak
Top Exec: Mark Robitaille
Ex VP: William J Casazza
Ex VP: Gary W Loveman
Ex VP: Margaret M McCarthy
Ex VP: Jennifer S Shick
Ex VP: Francis S Soistman Jr
Ex VP: Thomas W Weidenkopf
VP: Betty Assapimonwait
VP: Sherry Baker
VP: Michael Barski
VP: Jane L Batchelder
VP: Jerry Bellizzi
Board of Directors: Joseph P Newhouse, Fernando Aguirre, Olympia J Snowe, Frank M Clark, Betsy Z Cohen, Molly J Coye, Roger N Farah, Jeffrey E Garten, Ellen M Hancock, Richard J Harrington, Edward J Ludwig

D-U-N-S 00-691-6969
■ AETNA LIFE INSURANCE CO INC
(Suby of AETNA INC) ★
151 Farmington Ave, Hartford, CT 06156-0001
Tel (860) 273-0123 Founded/Ownrshp 2000
Sales NA EMP 27,550
SIC 6324 6321 8011 Health maintenance organization (HMO), insurance only; Accident & health insurance; Health maintenance organization
Ch: John W Rowe
Pt: Courtney Rijksen
CFO: Shawn M Guertin
CFO: Joseph M Zebretsky
*Treas: Alfred P Quirk Jr
Ex VP: Richard Di Benedetto
Ex VP: Steven B Kelmar
Ex VP: Gary W Loveman
Ex VP: Kristi Matus
Ex VP: Margaret M McCarthy
Ex VP: Thomas J Sabatino Jr
Ex VP: Fran S Soistman
Ex VP: Thomas W Weidenkopf
Sr VP: David J Mahder
*VP: Alan M Bennett
VP: Robert Kleman
VP: Joseph Petonak
VP: Dave Roberts
Exec: Carolyn Sheldon

D-U-N-S 17-567-6386
AETNA MAINTENANCE INC
AMI
101 E Kennedy Blvd G102, Tampa, FL 33602-5135
Tel (813) 621-6878 Founded/Ownrshp 1986
Sales 15.1MM^E EMP 1,000
Accts J Richard Claville Pa Bra
SIC 7349 Janitorial service, contract basis
Pr: James Green
*Sec: Mervin Hellman

D-U-N-S 15-637-3040
■ AEV INC
(Suby of OTTER TAIL CORP) ★
3030 24th Ave S, Moorhead, MN 56560-5933
Tel (218) 284-9518 Founded/Ownrshp 2002
Sales 232.3MM^E EMP 194
SIC 1731 General electrical contractor
CEO: Charles Macfarlane
*Pr: Michael Hanson
*Treas: Kevin Moug
Ex VP: Greg Ogary
*VP: Suzanne Allen
VP: Kurt Beichel

D-U-N-S 05-071-4765
AEW CAPITAL MANAGEMENT LP (DE)
AEW REAL ESTATE ADVISORS
(*Suby of* NATIXIS GLOBAL ASSET MANAGEMENT)
2 Seaport Ln, Boston, MA 02210-2021
Tel (617) 951-0812 *Founded/Ownrshp* 1996, 1981
Sales 162.1MM^E *EMP* 224
SIC 6282 6798 Investment advisory service; Real estate investment trusts
Pt: Jeffery Furver
CFO: Linda Danyluk
CFO: Linda Magee
Treas: Jeanne Caldwell
VP: Carrie Bellerby
VP: Peter Berg
VP: Alec Burleigh
VP: Michael Byrne
VP: Elizabeth Herlihy
VP: Christopher Irrera
VP: Hall J Jones
VP: Steven Kingsley
VP: Julie Kittler
VP: Mark Morrison
VP: Robert Norberg
VP: Alfred D Porta
VP: Claire Skinner
VP: Kevin M Stotts
VP: Jim Young

D-U-N-S 10-171-2958
AEW FOUNDATION
2176 Lee Hwy S, Cloverdale, VA 24077-2558
Tel (540) 992-2865 *Founded/Ownrshp* 1982
Sales 264.2MM^E *EMP* 800^E
SIC 1623 1731 Electric power line construction; General electrical contractor
Pr: B C Kimmel
**Pr:* William D Elliot
**CFO:* W Linwood Northern

AEW REAL ESTATE ADVISORS
See AEW CAPITAL MANAGEMENT LP

AF&F
See AMERICAN FIBER & FINISHING INC

AFA
See ASSOCIATION OF FLIGHT ATTENDANTS

D-U-N-S 00-991-7198
■ **AFAM ACQUISITION LLC**
(*Suby of* ALMOST FAMILY INC) ★
9510 Ormsby Station Rd, Louisville, KY 40223-4081
Tel (502) 640-9318 *Founded/Ownrshp* 2008
Sales 39.7MM^E *EMP* 2,013^E
SIC 8082 Home health care services
Prin: John Walker

AFBA
See ARMED FORCES BENEFIT ASSOCIATION

AFBIS
See AMERICAN FARM BUREAU INSURANCE SERVICES INC

D-U-N-S 00-968-7930 IMP
■ **AFC CABLE SYSTEMS INC**
(*Suby of* ATKORE INTERNATIONAL HOLDINGS INC) ★
16100 Lathrop Ave, Harvey, IL 60426-6021
Tel (508) 998-1131 *Founded/Ownrshp* 1993, 2010
Sales 501.4MM^E *EMP* 1,400
SIC 3429 3444 3599 5085 Manufactured hardware (general); Sheet metalwork; Hose, flexible metallic; Industrial supplies
Pr: John P Williamson
**Treas:* Arun Nayar
**VP:* Edward Arditte
**VP:* Carol Davidson
VP: John E Evard Jr
**VP:* James A Mallak
**VP:* Timothy Timmerman
Board of Directors: Mark Debiase, John S Jenkins

AFCO
See ASSOCIATED FUEL PUMP SYSTEMS CORP

AFCO DISTRIBUTION
See SKAGIT FARMERS SUPPLY

D-U-N-S 06-211-9771
AFCO INDUSTRIES INC (TX)
AFCO MILLWORK PRODUCTS DIV
3400 Roy Ave, Alexandria, LA 71302-4449
Tel (318) 448-1651 *Founded/Ownrshp* 1946, 1988
Sales 91.4MM^E *EMP* 385
Accts Payne Moore & Herrington Llp
SIC 3354 3083 3442 Aluminum extruded products; Laminated plastics plate & sheet; Moldings & trim, except automobile: metal
Pr: Don Fowler
**Treas:* Linda Mioton
**VP:* Michael T Hartnett
IT Man: John Synder
Plnt Mgr: Mike Attkisson
Sls Dir: Richard Pearson
Manager: Jacob Hawkins
Sls Mgr: Bryan Redding

AFCO MILLWORK PRODUCTS DIV
See AFCO INDUSTRIES INC

D-U-N-S 08-032-5234
AFF INC
7400 45th Street Ct E, Fife, WA 98424-3775
Tel (253) 926-5000 *Founded/Ownrshp* 2006
Sales 124.1MM^E *EMP* 350^E
SIC 4731 4213 7389 Freight consolidation; Trucking, except local; Relocation service
Pr: D Kevin Kelly
Sec: Christopher Paule

AFFFINITY HEALTH SYSTEM
See MERCY MEDICAL CENTER OF OSHKOSH INC

D-U-N-S 14-108-9040
AFFIGENT LLC
(*Suby of* QIVLIQ) ★
13873 Park Center Rd # 127, Herndon, VA 20171-3248
Tel (866) 977-8524 *Founded/Ownrshp* 2003
Sales 121.4MM^E *EMP* 169
SIC 5045 Computers, peripherals & software
Dir Bus: Matthew Speakes
Prin: Dennis Lucey
Prgrm Mgr: Michelle Popiel
Dir IT: Vic Berger
Snr PM: Dan Williams

AFFILIATE OF NATIONS ROOF
See NATIONS ROOF EAST LLC

AFFILIATE OF NATIONS ROOF
See NATIONS ROOF OF OHIO LLC

D-U-N-S 01-034-5189
AFFILIATED COMMUNITY MEDICAL CENTERS PA
101 Willmar Ave Sw, Willmar, MN 56201-3556
Tel (320) 231-5000 *Founded/Ownrshp* 1971
Sales 89.0MM^E *EMP* 875
SIC 8011 Clinic, operated by physicians
Pr: Ron Holmgren
**CFO:* Tom Rozendaal
Off Mgr: Dawn Gauer
Mktg Mgr: Deb Frank
Doctor: Julie Meyer
Pharmcst: Scott Hagen
Pharmcst: Laurie Hill

D-U-N-S 09-178-2953
AFFILIATED ENGINEERS INC
AEI
5802 Research Park Blvd, Madison, WI 53719-1249
Tel (608) 238-2616 *Founded/Ownrshp* 1978
Sales 89.1MM^E *EMP* 400
SIC 8711 Mechanical engineering
Pr: Jerry Schuett
Treas: Michael C Peterson
Bd of Dir: W Crawford
Dir Bus: Theresa Leahey
Mng Dir: Bill Vernon
IT Man: Brian Calabrese

D-U-N-S 00-791-8386
AFFILIATED FM INSURANCE CO
(*Suby of* FMIC HOLDINGS INC)
270 Central Ave, Johnston, RI 02919-4923
Tel (401) 275-3000 *Founded/Ownrshp* 1949
Sales 44.3MM^E *EMP* 1,200
SIC 6512 6331 Nonresidential building operators; Fire, marine & casualty insurance & carriers
Ch Bd: Shivan Subramaniam
CFO: Jeffrey A Burchill
CFO: Jeffrey Burchill
Chf Mktg O: Roberta Butler
**Sr VP:* William Stella
**VP:* Jeffrey Burchill
**VP:* Paul Fitzegerald
VP: Michael Kebovitz
VP: Gervais Landry
VP: Kenneth Lavigne
VP: Michael Lebovitz
**VP:* John J Pomeroy

D-U-N-S 04-427-6236 IMP
AFFILIATED FOODS INC
A F
1401 W Farmers Ave, Amarillo, TX 79118-6134
Tel (806) 345-7773 *Founded/Ownrshp* 1968
Sales 1.8MMM^E *EMP* 1,200^E
SIC 5141 2026 2051 5149 6153 Groceries, general line; Fluid milk; Bread, cake & related products; Groceries & related products; Mercantile financing
Pr: Randy Arceneaux
**Ch Bd:* Roger Lowe
**CFO:* Tammie Coffee
**Treas:* Lonnie Allsup
**V Ch Bd:* Dennis Porter Jr
Rgnl Mgr: Mark Miller
MIS Dir: Michael Limbley
IT Man: Michael Lindley
Netwrk Eng: Marvin Myers
Opers Mgr: Darryl Scott
Mktg Dir: David Campsey

D-U-N-S 03-509-3467
AFFILIATED FOODS MIDWEST COOPERATIVE INC
1301 W Omaha Ave, Norfolk, NE 68701-5872
Tel (402) 371-0555 *Founded/Ownrshp* 1931
Sales 1.5MMM *EMP* 850
SIC 5141 5142

D-U-N-S 10-818-0472
AFFILIATED HEALTHCARE SYSTEMS
(*Suby of* EMHS) ★
931 Union St, Bangor, ME 04401-3011
Tel (207) 973-6720 *Founded/Ownrshp* 1982
Sales 108.5MM *EMP* 443
Accts Berry Dunn Mcneil & Parker
SIC 5047 8071 8741 7322 6512 Medical equipment & supplies; Medical laboratories; Management services; Collection agency, except real estate; Nonresidential building operators
Pr: Miles Theeman
**Treas:* Daniel Coffey
**VP:* Brian Donahue
VP: John Doyle
VP: April Giard
**VP:* Don Sleight
Dir Rx: Heather Watson
Doctor: David Prescott

D-U-N-S 83-619-5925
▲ **AFFILIATED MANAGERS GROUP INC**
AMG
777 S Flagler Dr, West Palm Beach, FL 33401-6161
Tel (800) 345-1100 *Founded/Ownrshp* 1993
Sales 2.4MMM *EMP* 3,200^E
Tkr Sym AMG *Exch* NYS
SIC 6722 6282 Management investment, open-end; Investment advice
Ch Bd: Sean M Healey
Pr: Nathaniel Dalton
CFO: Jay C Horgen

AFFILIATED WITH NATIONS ROOF
See NATIONS ROOF CENTRAL LLC

AFFILIATES OF NATIONS ROOF
See NATIONS ROOF OF NEWYORK LLC

AFFINECO
See UNITED SERVICES OF AMERICA INC

D-U-N-S 07-980-7768
AFFINECO LLC
855 Main St Ste 900, Bridgeport, CT 06604-4915
Tel (203) 878-0638 *Founded/Ownrshp* 1966
Sales 69.5MM^E *EMP* 1,835^E
SIC 7349 7382 Janitorial service, contract basis; Building component cleaning service; Security systems services

D-U-N-S 62-128-4285
AFFINION GROUP HOLDINGS INC
6 High Ridge Park Bldg A, Stamford, CT 06905-1327
Tel (203) 956-1000 *Founded/Ownrshp* 1973
Sales 1.1MMM *EMP* 3,150^E
SIC 8611 6282 8748 Business associations; Investment advice; Business consulting
CEO: Todd H Siegel
**Ch Bd:* L Spencer Wells
Pr: Michele Conforti
Pr: Robert J Dudacek
Pr: Scott Lazear
COO: Robert Lyons
CFO: Gregory S Miller
Ofcr: James C Daly Jr
Ofcr: Sloane Levy
Ex VP: Brian J Dick
Ex VP: Brian J Fisher

D-U-N-S 07-934-1404
AFFINION GROUP HOLDINGS LLC
1 Manhattanville Rd # 201, Purchase, NY 10577-2128
Tel (203) 956-1000 *Founded/Ownrshp* 2005
Sales 16.6MM^E *EMP* 4,300
SIC 8611 Business associations
Ch Bd: Nathaniel J Lipman
CEO: Todd H Siegel

D-U-N-S 82-896-2642
AFFINION GROUP INC
(*Suby of* AFFINION GROUP HOLDINGS INC) ★
6 High Ridge Park Bldg A, Stamford, CT 06905-1327
Tel (203) 956-1000 *Founded/Ownrshp* 1973
Sales 1.1MMM *EMP* 3,100
Accts Deloitte & Touche Llp Stamfor
SIC 7389 5961 6321 Telephone solicitation service; Catalog & mail-order houses; Accident & health insurance
CEO: Todd H Siegel
**Ch Bd:* Nathaniel J Lipman
Pr: Michele Conforti
Pr: Robert J Dudacek
Pr: Scott Lazear
Pr: Sloane Levy
COO: Robert Lyons
CFO: Gregory S Miller
Ofcr: James C Daly Jr
Ex VP: Brian J Dick
Ex VP: Brian J Fisher
Ex VP: Michael Rauscher
VP: Kathy Barrett
VP: Clark Diehl
VP: Lee Halladay
VP: Tony Muro
VP: Julia Ryan
VP: Paul Stramoski
Comm Dir: Todd Smith
Board of Directors: Marc E Becker, Richard J Fernandes, Matthew H Nord, Michael A Reiss, David J Topper, Skip Victor, Eric L Press

D-U-N-S 61-195-5704
AFFINION GROUP LLC
(*Suby of* AFFINION GROUP HOLDINGS INC) ★
6 High Ridge Park Bldg A, Stamford, CT 06905-1327
Tel (203) 956-1000 *Founded/Ownrshp* 1997
Sales 111.6MM^E *EMP* 3,552
SIC 8699 8748 7319 7331 Personal interest organization; Business consulting; Display advertising service; Direct mail advertising services
CEO: Nathaniel J Lipman
**COO:* Robert G Rooney
CFO: James Hart
CFO: Thomas A Willims
Ofcr: Brian Dick
Ex VP: Mary Rusterholz
Ex VP: Tom Smith
Sr VP: James T Har
Sr VP: Robert L Sell
VP: Bill Stewart
VP: Paul Stramoski

AFFINITY
See UNIFIED COMMUNICATIONS INTERNATIONAL LLC

D-U-N-S 03-703-1262
AFFINITY GAMING
3755 Breakthrough Way # 300, Las Vegas, NV 89135-3052
Tel (702) 341-2400 *Founded/Ownrshp* 2010
Sales 393.3MM *EMP* 3,400^E
Accts Ernst & Young Llp Las Vegas
SIC 7011 Casino hotel
CEO: Michael Silberling
**Ch Bd:* David Reganato
COO: George Congdon
CFO: Walter Bogumil
Sr VP: Marc H Rubinstein
VP: Elizabeth Guth
VP: Vincent Lentini
VP: Matt Osa
VP: Deborah Richardson
VP: George Rogers
VP: Ken Sarnecky
VP: Robert Thursby
Dir Bus: Jonathan Stelly
Board of Directors: James A Cacioppo, Matthew A Doheney, Andrei Scrivens, Eric V Tanjeloff, James J Zenni Jr

D-U-N-S 96-822-3417
AFFINITY GAMING FINANCE CORP
(*Suby of* AFFINITY GAMING) ★
3755 Breakthrough Way # 300, Las Vegas, NV 89135-3052
Tel (702) 341-2400 *Founded/Ownrshp* 2010
Sales 197.3MM^E *EMP* 3,400^E
SIC 7011 7999 Casino hotel; Game parlor
Ch: Don R Kornstein
**Pr:* Ferenc Szony
**CEO:* David D Ross

AFFINITY GROUP
See AGI HOLDING CORP

D-U-N-S 19-692-6570
AFFINITY GROUP HOLDING LLC
GOOD SAM
(*Suby of* AFFINITY GROUP) ★
2750 Park View Ct Ste 240, Oxnard, CA 93036-5458
Tel (805) 667-4100 *Founded/Ownrshp* 1916
Sales 1.4MMM^E *EMP* 1,704
SIC 7997 2721 Membership sports & recreation clubs; Magazines: publishing only, not printed on site
Pr: Michael A Schneider
**CFO:* Thomas F Wolfe
Ex VP: Matthew Baden
Ex VP: Gerald Rich
**Sr VP:* Joseph Daquino
**Sr VP:* Laura A James
Sr VP: Brent Moody
**Sr VP:* Prabhuling Patel
Sr VP: Randall Rahe
Creative D: Robert Pfingston
**Prin:* James A Kalicki

D-U-N-S 61-484-3894
AFFINITY HEALTH PLAN INC
1776 Eastchester Rd # 202, Bronx, NY 10461-2334
Tel (718) 794-7700 *Founded/Ownrshp* 2002
Sales NA *EMP* 800
Accts Ernst & Young Us Llp Indianap
SIC 6324 Health maintenance organization (HMO), insurance only
Pr: Glenn A Macfarlane
**CEO:* Bob Allen
**CFO:* Steve Giasi
Sr VP: Abenaa Abboa-Offei
**Sr VP:* Sharon Deans
Sr VP: John A Selby
VP: Caron Cullen
VP: Claire Dematteis
**VP:* Ajhezza A Gonzalez
VP: Lisa A Keehn
Prgrm Mgr: Judy Leuchter

D-U-N-S 92-901-1997
AFFINITY HEALTH SYSTEM
(*Suby of* MINISTRY HEALTH CARE INC) ★
1570 Midway Pl, Menasha, WI 54952-1165
Tel (920) 720-1700 *Founded/Ownrshp* 1995
Sales 31.3MM *EMP* 4,000
Accts Deloitte Tax Llp Milwaukee W
SIC 8741 8062 Hospital management; Nursing & personal care facility management; General medical & surgical hospitals
CEO: William Calhoun
**COO:* Jane Curran-Meuli
COO: Michael Hanson
**CFO:* Jeff Badger
**V Ch Bd:* John Oliverio
Bd of Dir: Steve Evans
VP: Douglas Shew
Comm Man: Donna Schultz
Ex Dir: Vicki Schorse
Ex Dir: Barbara Stack
CIO: Will Wieder

D-U-N-S 12-478-2116
■ **AFFINITY HOSPITAL LLC**
TRINITY MEDICAL CENTER
(*Suby of* COMMUNITY HEALTH SYSTEMS INC) ★
3690 Grandview Pkwy, Birmingham, AL 35243-3326
Tel (205) 592-1000 *Founded/Ownrshp* 2007
Sales 234.0MM *EMP* 10
SIC 8062 8011 General medical & surgical hospitals; Medical centers
Dir Vol: Kim Munroe
**CEO:* Keith Granger
**CFO:* Julie Soekoro
Exec: Gail Hunt
Dir Case M: Cindy Watson
Dir Rad: Rick Kolaczek
Dir Rad: Brett J Lindsey
Dir Rad: Davor Luketic
Off Mgr: Lisa V Stevens
Mtls Mgr: Martha Tindol
Mktg Dir: Leisha Harris

AFFINITY MEDICAL CENTER
See DHSC LLC

AFFIRMATIVE ACTION/EEO DEPARTM
See HERBERT H LEHMAN COLLEGE

AFFIRMATIVE ACTION/EEO DEPT
See CITY UNIVERSITY OF NEW YORK

D-U-N-S 86-787-0065
AFFIRMATIVE LLC
(*Suby of* AFFIRMATIVE INSURANCE HOLDINGS INC)
2900 Westfork Dr Ste 600, Baton Rouge, LA 70827-0006
Tel (225) 928-9000 *Founded/Ownrshp* 2007
Sales NA *EMP* 422
SIC 6311 6141 Benevolent insurance associations; Consumer finance companies
CEO: Michael J McClure
IT Man: Eric Smith

D-U-N-S 07-972-8027
■ **AFFLINK HOLDING CORP**
(*Suby of* PERFORMANCE FOOD GROUP CO) ★
12500 West Creek Pkwy, Richmond, VA 23238-1110
Tel (804) 484-6217 *Founded/Ownrshp* 2015
Sales 1.1MMM^E *EMP* 889^E
SIC 5141 Groceries, general line

D-U-N-S 12-450-2873
AFFORDABLE CARE INC
AFFORDABLE DENTURES
1400 Industrial Dr, Kinston, NC 28504-4500
Tel (252) 527-6121 *Founded/Ownrshp* 2006
Sales 183.5MM^E *EMP* 625
SIC 8741 Business management
CEO: Doug Brown

*CFO: Paul Steelman
*VP: Rick Edwards
VP: Kelly B Patterson
VP: Matt Wells
Genl Mgr: Gayle Moody
Off Mgr: Marlene Newman
Netwrk Eng: Mike Levan

AFFORDABLE DENTURES
See AFFORDABLE CARE INC

AFFORDABLETOURS.COM
See CASTLES OF WORLD INC

D-U-N-S 80-468-2573
■ AFFYMETRIX INC
(Suby of THERMO FISHER SCIENTIFIC INC) ★
3420 Central Expy, Santa Clara, CA 95051-0703
Tel (408) 731-5000 Founded/Ownrshp 2015
Sales 359.7MM EMP 1,100E
Accts Ernst & Young Llp Redwood Cit
SIC 3826 Analytical instruments
Pr: Seth H Hoogasian
Ex VP: Kamalia Dam
Ex VP: Rick Runkel
VP: Chris Barbazette
VP: John Dangelo
VP: Farrell Doug
VP: Doug Farrell
VP: Peter Graf
VP: Peter Honkanen
VP: Luis Jevons
VP: Mindy Lee-Olsen
VP: Robert Lipshutz
VP: David Lockhart
VP: Lee-Olsen Mindy
VP: Sim Narasimhan
VP: Michael Nemzek
VP: Karen Petz
VP: Jeanette Schmidt
VP: Tracy Ting
VP: Annamaria Vaszko
Dir Bus: Richard Shippy

AFG WIPES
See ALBAAD USA INC

AFI
See AUTORIDAD PARA EL FINANCIAMIENTO DE LA VIVIENDA

AFI
See ARMSTRONG FLOORING INC

D-U-N-S 01-147-4087 IMP
AFI FOOD SERVICE DISTRIBUTORS INC (NJ)
PERFORMANCE FOODSERVICE-AFI
1 Ikea Dr, Elizabeth, NJ 07201-2987
Tel (908) 629-1800 Founded/Ownrshp 1997
Sales 221.8MME EMP 400
SIC 5141

D-U-N-S 08-037-4345
AFI PARTNERS LLC
158 Mercer St Frnt 2, New York, NY 10012-4292
Tel (212) 938-0016 Founded/Ownrshp 2007
Sales 41.0MME EMP 1,400
SIC 6719 Investment holding companies, except banks
Mng Pt: E J Antonio III

D-U-N-S 13-239-9507
AFJ LLC
(Suby of FLYING J) ★
1104 Country Hills Dr, Ogden, UT 84403-2400
Tel (801) 624-1000 Founded/Ownrshp 2001
Sales 704.6MM EMP 735
SIC 5541 5963 Gasoline service stations; Food service, mobile, except coffee-cart
Ch: J Phillip Adams
VP: Daniel Bohman
Opers Mgr: Dianna Norton

D-U-N-S 05-587-8185
AFL NETWORK SERVICES INC
(Suby of AMERICA FUJIKURA LTD) ★
170 Ridgeview Cnt Dr, Duncan, SC 29334
Tel (864) 433-0333 Founded/Ownrshp 2000
Sales 204.2MME EMP 1,000E
SIC 8711

D-U-N-S 13-943-7560 IMP/EXP
AFL TELECOMMUNICATIONS LLC
(Suby of FUJIKURA AMERICA INC) ★
170 Ridgeview Center Dr, Duncan, SC 29334-9635
Tel (864) 433-0333 Founded/Ownrshp 2005
Sales 615.1MME EMP 2,000
SIC 3229 1731 Fiber optics strands; Fiber optic cable installation
CEO: Jody Gallagher
Pr: Grant Burns
*Ch: Kenny Nara
Ofcr: Doug Cain
*Ex VP: Mike Booth
*VP: Steve Althoff
Ex Dir: Ron Parisi
Mng Dir: Abdel Soufiane PHD
Dir IT: Steve McEhainny
IT Man: Damien Laverty
IT Man: Gregg Miller

AFL-CIO
See AMERICAN FEDERATION OF LABOR & CONGRESS OF INDUSTRIAL ORGANZATION

AFLAC
See AMERICAN FAMILY LIFE ASSURANCE CO OF COLUMBUS

AFLAC
See AMERICAN FAMILY LIFE ASSURANCE CO OF NY (INC)

AFLAC GROUP INSURANCE
See CONTINENTAL AMERICAN INSURANCE CO

D-U-N-S 06-918-6674
▲ AFLAC INC
1932 Wynnton Rd, Columbus, GA 31999-0002
Tel (706) 323-3431 Founded/Ownrshp 1973
Sales NA EMP 9,915E
Accts Kpmg Llp Atlanta Georgia
Tkr Sym AFL Exch NYS
SIC 6321 6311 Accident insurance carriers; Health insurance carriers; Life insurance carriers
Ch Bd: Daniel P Amos
*Pr: Kriss Cloninger III
Pr: Charles D Lake II
Pr: Teresa L White
Pr: Hiroshi Yamauchi
CFO: Frederick J Crawford
Treas: Kenneth S Janke
Ex VP: Koji Ariyoshi
Ex VP: Thomas R Giddens
Ex VP: Eric M Kirsch
Ex VP: Rob Moran
Ex VP: Audrey B Tillman
Sr VP: J Todd Daniels
Sr VP: Gail A Galuppo
Sr VP: June Howard
Sr VP: Robin Y Wilkey
VP: Tyler Bennett
VP: Jay Hutchins
VP: Michele McMullin
VP: David Nelson
VP: Michel Perreault
Board of Directors: Karole F Lloyd

D-U-N-S 12-856-9055
AFN LLC
7230 N Caldwell Ave, Niles, IL 60714-4502
Tel (847) 498-8885 Founded/Ownrshp 2002
Sales 88.9MME EMP 115
SIC 4731 Foreign freight forwarding
CEO: Ryan Daube
Pr: Blaine Barnett
CFO: Chad McGinn
VP: David Koch
VP: Peter Malling
VP: Michael Peterman
VP: Adam Wakefield
VP: Oleg Yanchyk
Opers Mgr: Joe Couch
Opers Mgr: Tim Crow
Opers Mgr: Mike Link

D-U-N-S 09-258-2444
AFNI INC
404 Brock Dr, Bloomington, IL 61701-2654
Tel (309) 828-5226 Founded/Ownrshp 1965
Sales 434.5MME EMP 3,400
SIC 8742 7322 Business planning & organizing services; Adjustment & collection services
Ch Bd: Bruce F Griffin
*Pr: Ronald L Greene
CFO: Steve Czirjak
VP: John G Donnell
*VP: Michael Garner
*VP: John Mobley Jr
VP: John H Mobley
VP: John Mobley Jr
*VP: John O'Donnell
Ex Dir: Jeff Hobbs
IT Man: Mike Turnbull

D-U-N-S 05-208-9695
AFOGNAK NATIVE CORP
3909 Arctic Blvd Ste 500, Anchorage, AK 99503-5793
Tel (907) 222-9500 Founded/Ownrshp 1973
Sales 457.5MM EMP 4,450
SIC 0851

D-U-N-S 01-426-9406 IMP
AFP ADVANCED FOOD PRODUCTS LLC
(Suby of BC USA) ★
402 S Custer Ave, New Holland, PA 17557-9234
Tel (717) 355-8667 Founded/Ownrshp 2001
Sales 196.5MME EMP 600
SIC 2026 2035 2032 2099 2022 Fluid milk; Pickles, sauces & salad dressings; Puddings, except meat: packaged in cans, jars, etc.; Food preparations; Cheese spreads, dips, pastes & other cheese products
CEO: Miro Hosek
COO: Christy Oliver
VP: Bill Orban
Rgnl Mgr: Paul Gibel
Genl Mgr: Debra Macdonald
QA Dir: Matthew Brown
QI Cn Mgr: Rob Brumer
Manager: Chris Tenaglio
Snr Mgr: Katie Lauterbach

AFR FURNITURE RENTAL
See AMERICAN FURNITURE RENTALS INC

D-U-N-S 07-482-5894 EXP
AFRICARE
440 R St Nw, Washington, DC 20001-1961
Tel (202) 328-5320 Founded/Ownrshp 1970
Sales 49.2MM EMP 1,000
SIC 8399 Fund raising organization, non-fee basis
Pr: Julius Coles
*Pr: William O Kirker
CFO: Dexter Lockamy
Ex VP: Rodney E Slatr
*Sr VP: Jeannine Scott
*VP: John D Campbell
VP: Stephen Cashin
Mng Ofcr: Mikhail Brown

AFS
See AHOLD USA INC

D-U-N-S 80-672-5206
AFS TECHNOLOGIES INC
ADVANCED FOODSYSTEMS
2141 E Highland Ave # 100, Phoenix, AZ 85016-4737
Tel (602) 522-8282 Founded/Ownrshp 1997
Sales 89.0MME EMP 450
SIC 7371 Computer software development
CEO: Joe Bellini
*CFO: Todd Lawson
Ofcr: Jim Christen
VP: Jenna Beck
VP: Pamela Brunte
VP: Ajay Chidrawar
VP: Kevin Collier
VP: Tim Fortier
VP: David Franklin
VP: Jonathan Greene
VP: Kevin Hart
VP: Mark Miller
VP: Chris Mitchell
VP: Alexander Ring
VP: Tim Shorter
VP: Joann Snycer
VP: Milan Vacval

AFSC
See ARMED FORCES SERVICES CORP

AFSCME
See AMERICAN FEDERATION OF STATE COUNTY & MUNICIPAL EMPLOYEES

AFSPA
See AMERICAN FOREIGN SERVICE PROTECTIVE ASSOCIATION

D-U-N-S 84-182-3206
AFTER HOURS FAMILY CARE INC
UPPER VALLEY MEDICAL CENTER
450 N Hyatt St Ste 204, Tipp City, OH 45371-1488
Tel (937) 667-2614 Founded/Ownrshp 1981
Sales 144.1MM EMP 13
SIC 8011 Physicians' office, including specialists

D-U-N-S 07-248-1740 IMP
■ AFTER HOURS FORMALWEAR INC
(Suby of MENS WEARHOUSE INC) ★
4444 Shackleford Rd # 100, Norcross, GA 30093-2915
Tel (770) 448-8381 Founded/Ownrshp 2007
Sales 71.8MME EMP 1,700
SIC 5611 Suits, men's
Pr: Joseph Doyle
*CFO: Michael Salter
Treas: Diana M Wilson
VP: Gary Ckodre

D-U-N-S 07-873-3433
AFTER-PARTY6 INC
CLASSIC PARTY RENTALS
901 W Hillcrest Blvd, Inglewood, CA 90301-2100
Tel (310) 966-4900 Founded/Ownrshp 2014
Sales 143.3MME EMP 130
SIC 7359

D-U-N-S 07-965-8470
AFTERDARKK MEDIA SOLUTIONS LLC
271 Beach 135th St, Belle Harbor, NY 11694-1305
Tel (347) 244-6619 Founded/Ownrshp 2014
Sales 145.0MM EMP 3
SIC 7374 Computer graphics service

D-U-N-S 07-911-3348
AFTERMARKET PARTS CO LLC
NEW FLYER
(Suby of NEW FLYER INDUSTRIES INC)
3229 Sawmill Pkwy, Delaware, OH 43015-7541
Tel (888) 333-6224 Founded/Ownrshp 2013
Sales 251.6MME EMP 1,019E
SIC 5013 Motor vehicle supplies & new parts; Automotive brakes
Pr: Jim Marcotuli

D-U-N-S 05-396-9234 IMP/EXP
■ AFTON CHEMICAL CORP
(Suby of NEWMARKET CORP) ★
500 Spring St, Richmond, VA 23219-4300
Tel (804) 788-5086 Founded/Ownrshp 1975
Sales 314.9MME EMP 555
SIC 2899 2999 3999 Oil treating compounds; Waxes, petroleum: not produced in petroleum refineries; Atomizers, toiletry
CEO: Robert A Shama
Ofcr: Bruce Hazelgrove III
*Sr VP: Alexander McLean
*VP: Richard M Mendel
*VP: Marshall B Nelson
VP: Mooney J Robert
Genl Mgr: Ed Cox
Tech Mgr: Lawrence Cunningham
Opers Mgr: Alessandro Menezes
Opers Mgr: Scott Turner
Mktg Mgr: Bill Harwood

D-U-N-S 09-116-7924
AFTRA HEALTH & RETIREMENT FUND (INC)
261 Madison Ave Fl 7, New York, NY 10016-2312
Tel (212) 499-4800 Founded/Ownrshp 1954
Sales NA EMP 122
SIC 6371 8111 Welfare pensions; Legal services
CEO: Christine Dubois
*Ch Bd: James F Sirmons
*Ch Bd: Bruce York
CTO: Althea Pratt
QA Dir: Angela Miele
Dir IT: Amin Rahim
Dir IT: Rick Rubano
Opers Mgr: Cynthia Pellot

D-U-N-S 96-659-9834
AFTRA HEALTH FUND
261 Madison Ave Fl 8, New York, NY 10016-2303
Tel (212) 499-4800 Founded/Ownrshp 2011
Sales 95.8MM EMP 11E
Accts Bond Beebe Pc Bethesda Md
SIC 8099 Health & allied services
Prin: Peggy Conlon

D-U-N-S 04-640-3007 IMP
AFX INDUSTRIES LLC
AFX/TRIM
(Suby of EXCO INC) ★
1411 3rd St Ste G, Port Huron, MI 48060-5480
Tel (810) 966-4650 Founded/Ownrshp 2016
Sales 115.8MME EMP 1,300
SIC 3111 5531 Industrial leather products; Automotive parts
QI Cn Mgr: Javier Mata

AFX/TRIM
See AFX INDUSTRIES LLC

AG
See ASSOCIATED GROCERS OF FLORIDA INC

AG AGENCIES, THE
See FARM CREDIT BANK OF TEXAS

D-U-N-S 14-289-0214
AG FACILITIES OPERATIONS LLC
6380 Wilshire Blvd # 800, Los Angeles, CA 90048-5017
Tel (323) 651-1808 Founded/Ownrshp 2003
Sales 8.1MME EMP 1,000
SIC 8059 Nursing home, except skilled & intermediate care facility
CFO: Leo Krieger

AG FINANCE SOLUTIONS
See TENNESSEE FARMERS COOPERATIVE INC

AG FORTE
See WILLMAR POULTRY CO INC

D-U-N-S 60-251-5082
AG HOLDINGS INC
4601 Sheridan St Ste 500, Hollywood, FL 33021-3439
Tel (954) 987-7180 Founded/Ownrshp 1989
Sales 138.9MME EMP 3,000
Accts Moore Stephens Lovelace Pa
SIC 8051 Skilled nursing care facilities
Pr: Matan Ben-Aviv
*Treas: Harvey L Lichtman
Board of Directors: Guy Katsav, Harvey Lichtman

D-U-N-S 96-778-0797
AG MORTGAGE INVESTMENT TRUST INC
245 Park Ave Fl 26, New York, NY 10167-2699
Tel (212) 692-2000 Founded/Ownrshp 2011
Sales 141.2MM EMP 5
SIC 6798 Real estate investment trusts
Ch Bd: David N Roberts
*Pr: Jonathan Lieberman
CFO: Brian C Sigman
Dir Risk M: Andrew Parks

AG MOTION SPECIALTY GRAINS
See US COMMODITIES LLC

D-U-N-S 94-171-7720
AG PARTNERS COOP
1st And Bdwy Way, Goodhue, MN 55027
Tel (651) 345-3328 Founded/Ownrshp 1996
Sales 163.0MME EMP 69
SIC 5153 5191 Grain elevators; Fertilizer & fertilizer materials
CEO: Greg Schwanbeck
*Pr: Dale Kackman
Exec: Joel Eichelberger

D-U-N-S 17-929-6124
AG PARTNERS LLC
30 Main St, Albert City, IA 50510-1215
Tel (712) 843-2291 Founded/Ownrshp 1997
Sales 185.6MME EMP 150
SIC 5153 5191 2048 Grain elevators; Chemicals, agricultural
CEO: Troy Upah
CFO: Jay Magnussen
*VP: Jared Bruggman
*VP: Dan De Jong
*VP: Scott Lovin
*VP: Brent Low
Netwrk Mgr: Paul Schuler
Sls Mgr: Gerald Droog
Sls Mgr: Jim Van Gorp

D-U-N-S 00-798-7126
AG PLUS INC (IN)
401 N Main St, South Whitley, IN 46787-1250
Tel (260) 723-5141 Founded/Ownrshp 1912
Sales 90.4MME EMP 75
SIC 5191 2041 5153 Fertilizers & agricultural chemicals; Animal feeds; Feed; Flour & other grain mill products; Grain elevators
Ch: Kent Hoffman
*CEO: Jeff Mize
*Sec: Stanley Studebaker
*VP: Dan Bacon

AG PRO
See AG-PRO LLC

D-U-N-S 00-850-3316
AG PROCESSING INC (IA)
12700 W Dodge Rd, Omaha, NE 68154-6102
Tel (402) 496-7809 Founded/Ownrshp 1994
Sales 173.6MME EMP 1,112E
SIC 4221 Grain elevator, storage only
Pr: Reagan P Martin
*Sec: J Keith Spackler
VP: Dennis Rademacher
Sfty Mgr: Chuck Coffey

D-U-N-S 00-527-5631
AG PROCESSING INC A COOPERATIVE
AGP
12700 W Dodge Rd, Omaha, NE 68154-6102
Tel (402) 496-7809 Founded/Ownrshp 1943
Sales 4.9MMME EMP 1,456
SIC 5153 2075 2048 5999 0254 Soybeans; Grains; Grain elevators; Soybean oil mills; Soybean oil, cake or meal; Lecithin, soybean; Soybean flour & grits; Prepared feeds; Feed & farm supply; Poultry hatcheries
CEO: Martin P Reagan
Pr: Paula Markmann
*CEO: John Keith Spackler
*CFO: J Keith Spackler
*Sr VP: Gary Olsen
*VP: Robert J Flack
VP: Mike Maranell
*VP: Calvin Meyer
Exec: Richard Ingraham
Genl Mgr: Dave Christensen
CTO: Dean Nosbisch

D-U-N-S 80-848-9553 IMP
AG PROVISION LLC
277 Faison W Mcgowan Rd, Kenansville, NC 28349-8948
Tel (910) 296-0302 Founded/Ownrshp 1990
Sales 150.8MME EMP 60
SIC 5191 Chemicals, agricultural; Herbicides
Sls Dir: Greta Thompson

AG QUEST
See HARVEST LAND COOPERATIVE

D-U-N-S 78-123-0771 IMP
AG SUPERMARKET HOLDINGS LLC
(*Suby of* ANGELO GORDON & CO LP) ★
245 Park Ave, New York, NY 10167-0002
Tel (212) 692-2000 *Founded/Ownrshp* 2006
Sales 71.8MM^E *EMP* 2,500
SIC 5411 Supermarkets, chain

D-U-N-S 03-501-4653
AG VALLEY COOPERATIVE NON-STOCK
72133 State Hwy 136, Edison, NE 68936
Tel (308) 927-3681 *Founded/Ownrshp* 1953
Sales 239.5MM^E *EMP* 150
SIC 5153 5191 Grains; Fertilizer & fertilizer materials; Feed
Pr: Tom Hansen
Comm Dir: Ed Newcomb
Genl Mgr: Ron Hunter
Sls&Mrk Ex: Tim Goding

D-U-N-S 10-184-8919
AG-MART PRODUCE INC
SANTA SWEETS
4006 Airport Rd, Plant City, FL 33563-1108
Tel (877) 606-5003 *Founded/Ownrshp* 1983
Sales 800.9MM^E *EMP* 253
SIC 0171

D-U-N-S 07-884-4464
AG-PRO LLC
AG PRO
19595 Us Hwy 84, Boston, GA 31626
Tel (229) 498-8833 *Founded/Ownrshp* 2010
Sales 193.3MM^E *EMP* 512^E
SIC 3523 5082 Tractors, farm; Construction & mining machinery
CEO: James Groover

D-U-N-S 11-263-7079
AGA (VIRGINIA) INC
(*Suby of* ALLIANZ SE)
9950 Mayland Dr, Richmond, VA 23233-1463
Tel (804) 285-3300 *Founded/Ownrshp* 2000
Sales NA *EMP* 950^E
SIC 6411 4724 Insurance agents & brokers; Travel agencies
Pr: Michael J Nelson
**Pr:* Beth Godlin
COO: Hensley West
**CFO:* Mark Huntley
**CFO:* Daniel Wichels
**VP:* David Bloom
**VP:* Frederick Faett
**VP:* Mike Kunc
Software D: Eli Fernandes

D-U-N-S 79-405-5541
AGA SERVICE CO
JEFFERSON INSURANCE CO
(*Suby of* AGA (VIRGINIA) INC) ★
2805 N Parham Rd, Richmond, VA 23294-4401
Tel (804) 285-3300 *Founded/Ownrshp* 1990
Sales 202.4MM^E *EMP* 950
Accts Kpmg Llp Richmond Va
SIC 6719 Investment holding companies, except banks
CEO: Michael J Nelson
Pr: Randy Hill
COO: Pam Dufour
**CFO:* Daniel Wichels
Treas: Alphonzo Jackson
Sr Cor Off: Robert Lawther
Chf Mktg O: Joe Mason
Ofcr: Jack Zemp
VP: Chris Burroughs
VP: David Domster
**VP:* Faett Frederick
VP: Subramania Ramaswamy
VP: Jason Rice

AGAR SUPPLY CO.
See REINHART FOODSERVICE LLC

D-U-N-S 18-587-1324 IMP/EXP
AGC AMERICA INC
(*Suby of* ASAHI GLASS COMPANY,LIMITED)
11175 Cicero Dr Ste 400, Alpharetta, GA 30022-1167
Tel (404) 446-4200 *Founded/Ownrshp* 1986
Sales 729.6MM^E *EMP* 6,846
SIC 6719 3211 2869 5169 3229 Investment holding companies, except banks; Flat glass; Industrial organic chemicals; Chemicals & allied products; Pressed & blown glass
Pr: Yasuharu Takada
**Pr:* William Dankmyer
**CFO:* Steve Hughesc
**CFO:* Toshihiko Uchida
**VP:* Robert Dobie
Dir Bus: Gus Trupiano

D-U-N-S 00-337-4048 IMP/EXP
AGC FLAT GLASS NORTH AMERICA INC (GA)
(*Suby of* AGC AMERICA INC) ★
11175 Cicero Dr Ste 400, Alpharetta, GA 30022-1167
Tel (404) 446-4200 *Founded/Ownrshp* 1956, 1996
Sales 1.5MMM^E *EMP* 5,320
SIC 3231 3211 Safety glass: made from purchased glass; Flat glass
Pr: Yasuharu Takada
Pr: Marc Foguenne
CEO: Kazuhiko Ishimura
CEO: D Roger Kennedy
COO: David Lukens
CFO: Jackie Beverly
CFO: Steve Hughes
CFO: Doris Ladd
Ex VP: John Litzinger
Sr VP: Michael Antonucci
Sr VP: Alberto Trevino
VP: Robert Cobie
VP: James Collin
VP: Christopher F Correnti
VP: Randy Lantz
VP: Fred Wallin

D-U-N-S 11-870-3404
■ **AGC LIFE INSURANCE CO**
(*Suby of* AIG LIFE HOLDINGS INC) ★
American General Ctr, Brentwood, TN 37027
Tel (615) 749-1000 *Founded/Ownrshp* 1982
Sales NA *EMP* 9,000
SIC 6411 Insurance agents, brokers & service; Medical insurance claim processing, contract or fee basis
Ch Bd: Rodney Owen Martin
**Treas:* Gregory Alan Hayes
Bd of Dir: Matthew Winter
Mktg Mgr: Donald Passer
Corp Couns: Kyle Jennings

AGCO
See SUNFLOWER MANUFACTURING CO INC

D-U-N-S 61-893-8260
▲ **AGCO CORP**
4205 River Green Pkwy, Duluth, GA 30096-2584
Tel (770) 813-9200 *Founded/Ownrshp* 1990
Sales 7.4MMM *EMP* 19,600
Tkr Sym AGCO *Exch* NYS
SIC 3523 6159 Farm machinery & equipment; Tractors, farm; Combines (harvester-threshers); Haying machines: mowers, rakes, stackers, etc.; Equipment & vehicle finance leasing companies
Ch Bd: Martin H Richenhagen
CFO: Andrew H Beck
Treas: David Williams
Ofcr: Roger Batkin
Sr VP: Andr M Carioba
Sr VP: Gary L Collar
Sr VP: Robert B Crain
Sr VP: Helmut R Endres
Sr VP: Eric P Hansotia
Sr VP: Lucinda B Smith
Sr VP: Rob Smith
Sr VP: Hans-Bernd Veltmaat
Sr VP: Thomas F Welke
VP: Andy Beck
VP: Torsten Dehner
VP: Declan Hayden
VP: Debra Kuper
VP: Francesco Quaranta
VP: Boris Schoepplein
VP: Josip Tomasevic
Board of Directors: Roy V Armes, Michael C Arnold, P George Benson, Wolfgang Deml, Luiz F Furlan, George E Minnich, Gerald L Shaheen, Hendrikus Visser

D-U-N-S 14-780-5238
■ **AGCO FINANCE LLC**
(*Suby of* AGCO CORP) ★
8001 Birchwood Ct C, Johnston, IA 50131-2889
Tel (515) 251-2800 *Founded/Ownrshp* 1986
Sales NA *EMP* 69
SIC 6159 Agricultural loan companies; Equipment & vehicle finance leasing companies

D-U-N-S 15-233-7796
AGCOUNTRY FARM CREDIT SERVICES ACA
1900 44th St S, Fargo, ND 58103-7428
Tel (701) 235-9858 *Founded/Ownrshp* 1917
Sales NA *EMP* 410
Accts Pricewaterhousecoopers Llp Mi
SIC 6029 Commercial banks
CEO: Robert C Bahl
**CFO:* Jeremy Oliver
Ofcr: Jessica Bernstien
Sr VP: Howard Olson
**VP:* David Anderson
VP: Harmon Badger
VP: Bob Ellerbusch
VP: Kyle Froslie
VP: Jessica Fyre
VP: Larry Nelson
VP: Costain Richard
VP: Fronning Robert
VP: Russ Tweiten
VP: Keith Wilson

D-U-N-S 10-201-8553
AGE GOLDEN PROPERTIES LTD
DUBLINAIRE
19 Merritt St, Hawkinsville, GA 31036-4706
Tel (478) 783-1438 *Founded/Ownrshp* 1971
Sales 32.1MM^E *EMP* 1,200
SIC 8059 Nursing home, except skilled & intermediate care facility; Convalescent home
CEO: Harris A Hardin
**Sec:* Barbara Hardin

D-U-N-S 13-020-4043 IMP/EXP
AGE GROUP LTD
2 Park Ave Fl 18, New York, NY 10016-5675
Tel (212) 213-9500 *Founded/Ownrshp* 1985
Sales 84.3MM *EMP* 65
SIC 5137 Women's & children's lingerie & undergarments
Ch Bd: Harold Ebani
**VP:* Richard Adjmi
Mktg Mgr: Mallory Martell
Sls Mgr: Karen Bleistern

D-U-N-S 06-897-8105
AGE INDUSTRIES LTD
3601 County Road 316c, Cleburne, TX 76031-9098
Tel (817) 477-5266 *Founded/Ownrshp* 1982
Sales 130.1MM^E *EMP* 285
Accts Gilliam Wharram & Co Pc
SIC 2653 2655 2671 Boxes, corrugated: made from purchased materials; Fiber cans, drums & similar products; Packaging paper & plastics film, coated & laminated
Ch Bd: Cynthia Murdock
**Pr:* Donald Reynolds
**CEO:* Patricia Griswold
**COO:* Royce Drennan
Ex VP: Max Walls
Sr VP: David R Sheil
VP: Martinez Avelino
Genl Mgr: Mike Coe
Genl Mgr: Jeff Eshelman
Genl Mgr: Ralph Roman
Genl Mgr: Jimmy Toal

D-U-N-S 96-029-9691
■ **AGEE STERNE GROUP INC**
STERNE AGEE
(*Suby of* STIFEL FINANCIAL CORP) ★
800 Shades Creek Pkwy # 700, Birmingham, AL 35209-4532
Tel (205) 949-3500 *Founded/Ownrshp* 2015
Sales 297.5MM^E *EMP* 6,200
SIC 7389 Financial services
Prin: Ronald J Kruszewski
Mng Pt: Bill Parrish
COO: Patricia A Jamison
**CFO:* Jon Sanderson
Ofcr: Gigi Gant
Ofcr: Scott Satchwell
Ofcr: Ron Trout
Sr VP: Kevin Cavin
Sr VP: Lawrence T De Maria
Sr VP: Robert Dudley
**Sr VP:* Senator Steve French
Sr VP: Steve French
Sr VP: Nicholas P Heymann
Sr VP: Tricia Holbrook
Sr VP: Michael Libera
Sr VP: Larry Meding
Sr VP: John M Nadel
Sr VP: Russell Sugg
Sr VP: Laura Wainwright
VP: Krista Clarke
VP: Robert M Jones

AGENCY FLOOD RESOURCES
See ACRISURE LLC

AGENT FOR BRCLAY HSPTLITY SVCS
See ALLIANCE HOSPITALITY MANAGEMENT LLC

AGENT FOR N AMERCN VAN LINES
See BELTMANN GROUP INC

AGENT FOR UNITED VAN LINES
See MERGENTHALER TRANSFER & STORAGE CO INC

D-U-N-S 79-476-5573
■ **AGENTS ALLIANCE INSURANCE CO**
(*Suby of* GMAC) ★
3800 Sollie Rd, Mobile, AL 36619-1453
Tel (251) 665-2418 *Founded/Ownrshp* 2011
Sales NA *EMP* 1,216^E
SIC 6411 Advisory services, insurance

D-U-N-S 07-933-4523
AGERA ENERGY LLC
(*Suby of* AGERA HOLDINGS LLC) ★
555 Pleasantville Rd 107s, Briarcliff Manor, NY 10510-1966
Tel (844) 692-4372 *Founded/Ownrshp* 2014
Sales 330.0MM *EMP* 100
SIC 4911
Genl Mgr: Michael Nordlicht

D-U-N-S 07-951-1284
AGERA HOLDINGS LLC
555 Pleasantville Rd 107s, Briarcliff Manor, NY 10510-1966
Tel (914) 236-1405 *Founded/Ownrshp* 2014
Sales 228.3MM *EMP* 100
Accts Rbsm Llp New York Ny
SIC 4911

D-U-N-S 17-786-3862 IMP
AGERE SYSTEMS INC
(*Suby of* LSI CORP) ★
1110 American Pkwy Ne, Allentown, PA 18109-9117
Tel (610) 712-1000 *Founded/Ownrshp* 2000
Sales 102.8M^E *EMP* 1,500
SIC 3663 Television broadcasting & communications equipment
CEO: Richard L Clemmer
Pr: Sajol Ghoshal
CFO: Mark Greenquist
**CFO:* Peter Kelly
Bd of Dir: Rae F Sedel
Ex VP: Paul Dumas
Ex VP: Joseph O'Hare
Ex VP: Denis P Regimbal
Ex VP: Samir F Samhouri
Sr VP: Kevin P Ennington
VP: Donal Alvine
VP: Nik Bahram
VP: John Gamble Jr
VP: Cees Links
VP: Jack Molets
VP: Luc Seraphin
VP: Chuck Sperazza
VP: Mark Weaver
Dir Bus: Norberto Zayas

D-U-N-S 07-171-7631
AGERO - CHECK
CCMC
(*Suby of* CROSS COUNTRY GROUP) ★
1 Cabot Rd, Medford, MA 02155-5117
Tel (781) 393-9300 *Founded/Ownrshp* 1972
Sales 45.7MM^E *EMP* 1,800
SIC 8699 Automobile owners' association
CEO: Dave Ferrick
**Pr:* Michael Saxton
**CFO:* Peggy Ward
**Ch:* Sidney D Wolk
VP: Joseph Texeira

D-U-N-S 11-524-7835
AGERO INC
CROSS COUNTRY GROUP
1 Cabot Rd Ste 4, Medford, MA 02155-5130
Tel (781) 393-9300 *Founded/Ownrshp* 1972
Sales 246.7MM^E *EMP* 2,200
SIC 8699 Automobile owners' association
Ch: Sidney D Wolk
Pr: Rick Belsky
Pr: Michael Saxton
CEO: Dave Ferrick
COO: Christina Scalcione
CFO: Frederick Pinkham
CFO: Peggy Ward
Treas: Thomas Graham
Sr VP: Jeffrey Blecher
Sr VP: Jack Bowen
Sr VP: Mark Carbrey
Sr VP: Peter Necheles
Sr VP: Cathy Orrico
Sr VP: Bryan Sander
Sr VP: Jeffrey Wolk
VP: Frank Campolo
VP: Steve Deeb
VP: Steve Medeiros
VP: Andy Parven
VP: Chris Richard
VP: Kate Sweeney

D-U-N-S 04-797-0459 IMP
AGFA CORP
AGFA GRAPHICS
(*Suby of* AGFA-GEVAERT NV)
10 S Academy St, Greenville, SC 29601-2632
Tel (800) 526-5441 *Founded/Ownrshp* 1998
Sales 5.6MM^E *EMP* 2,093
SIC 3861 Photographic equipment & supplies; Film, sensitized motion picture, X-ray, still camera, etc.; Photographic processing chemicals
Pr: Dany Claeys
Pr: Steve White
**CFO:* Timothy Coakley
CFO: Cazelma Groomes
**Treas:* John Engeman
Mng Dir: Ruben Silva
IT Man: Michel Konings
IT Man: Mike Letherbarrow
IT Man: Kurt Vanslambrouck
Sftwr Eng: Lopamudra Patnaik
Sftwr Eng: Bo Yang

AGFA GRAPHICS
See AGFA CORP

D-U-N-S 00-797-0650 IMP
AGFINITY INC
260 Factory Rd, Eaton, CO 80615-3481
Tel (970) 454-4000 *Founded/Ownrshp* 1915
Sales 149.1MM^E *EMP* 190
SIC 5172 2048 7549 5191 Diesel fuel; Gases, liquefied petroleum (propane); Gasoline; Prepared feeds; Feed concentrates; Feed premixes; Feed supplements; Automotive maintenance services; Fertilizer & fertilizer materials
Pr: Mitch Anderson
COO: Mary Blosz
VP: Terry Kohler
Exec: William Mott
Genl Mgr: Steve Cure
Genl Mgr: Paul Dent
Genl Mgr: Tim Kiefer
Genl Mgr: Robert Mekelburg
IT Man: Chad Kuskie
IT Man: Kerri Long
IT Man: Cheryl Martin

D-U-N-S 03-010-7247
AGFIRST FARM CREDIT BANK
1901 Main St, Columbia, SC 29201-2443
Tel (803) 799-5000 *Founded/Ownrshp* 1988
Sales NA *EMP* 530
SIC 6111 Federal & federally sponsored credit agencies
CEO: Tim Amerson
**CFO:* Charl Butler
CFO: Charl L Butler
Treas: Nancy Huffstetler
Ofcr: William Melton
Ofcr: Rob Nettles
Ofcr: John W Weathers
Ex VP: Thomas S Welsh
Sr VP: Benjamin F Blakewood
VP: Neda Beal
VP: John Burnside
VP: Ricky Clark
VP: Patricia Geddings
VP: Michael Mancini
VP: Stacy Nobles
VP: Beth Ozenghar
VP: Joe Preloznik
VP: Eric Wilkowski
VP: Isvara Wilson

AGFIRST FARMERS COOP BUS OFF
See AGFIRST FARMERS COOPERATIVE

D-U-N-S 00-894-1858
AGFIRST FARMERS COOPERATIVE (SD)
AGFIRST FARMERS COOP BUS OFF
204 1st St S, Brookings, SD 57006-3003
Tel (605) 692-6216 *Founded/Ownrshp* 1913
Sales 95.2MM *EMP* 18
Accts Gardiner Thomsen Pc Sioux Fa
SIC 5191 5153 Fertilizer & fertilizer materials; Chemicals, agricultural; Feed; Seeds: field, garden & flower; Grains
CEO: Terry Knudson
**Pr:* Joel Ripley
CFO: Brian Delgado
IT Man: Nancy Nelson

D-U-N-S 62-225-8929 IMP
AGGREGATE INDUSTRIES
AGGREGATE INDUSTRIES MGT
(*Suby of* HOLCIM USA) ★
6211 N Ann Arbor Rd, Dundee, MI 48131-9527
Tel (734) 529-5876 *Founded/Ownrshp* 2011
Sales 694.5MM^E *EMP* 1,295
SIC 3273 2951 1442 1411 1771 5211 Ready-mixed concrete; Asphalt & asphaltic paving mixtures (not from refineries); Concrete, bituminous; Common sand mining; Gravel mining; Dimension stone; Concrete work; Lumber products
CEO: Nabil Bouris
**COO:* Guy Edwards
VP: Michael Refer
Tech Mgr: Scott Buchanan
Natl Sales: Heather Foo
Sls Mgr: Tom Ryan

AGGREGATE INDUSTRIES MGT
See AGGREGATE INDUSTRIES

D-U-N-S 05-388-8038
AGGREGATE INDUSTRIES-SWR INC
(*Suby of* AGGREGATE INDUSTRIES MGT) ★
3101 E Craig Rd, North Las Vegas, NV 89030-7501
Tel (702) 281-9696 *Founded/Ownrshp* 2004
Sales 165.8MM[E] *EMP* 650
SIC 1611 5032 General contractor, highway & street construction; Highway & street paving contractor; Aggregate
Pr: Patrick R Ward
**Treas:* Elizabeth McClain
Opers Mgr: Lee Motis

D-U-N-S 04-158-0643
AGGREGATE INDUSTRIES-WCR INC
(*Suby of* BARDON U S CORPORATION)
1687 Cole Blvd Ste 300, Lakewood, CO 80401-3318
Tel (303) 716-5200 *Founded/Ownrshp* 2000
Sales 167.9MM[E] *EMP* 900
SIC 1611 1442 1499 2951 Surfacing & paving; Construction sand & gravel; Asphalt (native) mining; Asphalt paving mixtures & blocks
Pr: Patrick R Ward
**VP:* Michael C Refer
Sls Mgr: Dick Gordon

D-U-N-S 96-193-7849
AGGREGATES USA LLC
3300 Cahaba Rd Ste 302, Birmingham, AL 35223-2629
Tel (205) 777-6340 *Founded/Ownrshp* 2010
Sales 112.4MM[E] *EMP* 179[E]
SIC 5032 Granite building stone; Limestone; Gravel
Plnt Mgr: Charles Varadin

D-U-N-S 16-602-2249 IMP
AGGREKO INTERNATIONAL PROJECTS
2 Northpoint Dr Ste 810, Houston, TX 77060-3200
Tel (281) 848-1400 *Founded/Ownrshp* 2004
Sales 4.3MMM[E] *EMP* 2,000
SIC 4911 Electric services
Prin: Dennis L Proctor
Area Mgr: David Cochran
Opers Mgr: Steve Leslie

D-U-N-S 07-945-3643 IMP/EXP
AGGREKO LLC
(*Suby of* AGGREKO PLC)
4610 W Admiral Doyle Dr, New Iberia, LA 70560-9134
Tel (337) 367-7884 *Founded/Ownrshp* 1986
Sales 534.7MM[E] *EMP* 800
SIC 5064 3822 Air conditioning appliances; Temperature controls, automatic
Pr: Bruce Pool
Bd of Dir: Chad Williams
VP: Ana Amicarella
Exec: Jim Kelly
Brnch Mgr: James Merry
Netwrk Mgr: Hugh Morris
Opers Mgr: Christopher Saxton

AGI
See ARCHITECTURAL GRAPHICS INC

AGI
See ANALYTICAL GRAPHICS INC

D-U-N-S 19-692-3122 IMP
AGI HOLDING CORP
AFFINITY GROUP
2575 Vista Del Mar Dr, Ventura, CA 93001-3920
Tel (805) 667-4100 *Founded/Ownrshp* 1988
Sales 1.4MMM[E] *EMP* 2,230[E]
SIC 7997 2741 Membership sports & recreation clubs; Directories: publishing & printing; Newsletter publishing
CEO: Mr Stephen Adams
**Pr:* Joe McAdams
COO: Maria Recinos
**COO:* Michael Schneider
**CFO:* Mark Boggess
Ex Dir: Sue Bray
CIO: Matthew Baden
Dir IT: Bill Myers
VP Opers: Dan Hoopes
Prd Mgr: Brenda Hutchinson
Mktg Dir: Kate Moe
Board of Directors: Lory James

D-U-N-S 18-797-3974
AGI NORTH AMERICA LLC
AGI SHOREWOOD U.S.
(*Suby of* AGI-SHOREWOOD US) ★
100 Northfield St, Greenwich, CT 06830-4618
Tel (203) 622-9138 *Founded/Ownrshp* 2012
Sales 175.2MM[E] *EMP* 3,825[E]
SIC 2671 Paper coated or laminated for packaging
Genl Mgr: Mike Ukropina

D-U-N-S 15-109-8415
AGI PUBLISHING INC
VALLEY YELLOW PAGES
1850 N Gateway Blvd # 152, Fresno, CA 93727-1600
Tel (559) 251-8888 *Founded/Ownrshp* 1985
Sales 145.7MM[E] *EMP* 450
SIC 2741 Directories, telephone: publishing only, not printed on site
CEO: Sieg A Fischer
**Treas:* Michael Schilling
Area Mgr: Bobby Bird
Area Mgr: Deborah Lassila
Area Mgr: Lou Marquez
Area Mgr: Thomas Paley
Area Mgr: Richard Rummelhart
Area Mgr: Jason Smith
VP Sls: Dominick Innocenti
Sls Mgr: Joey Barron
Sls Mgr: Lance Bussean

D-U-N-S 07-847-7824
AGI SHOREWOOD GRAVURE LLC
400 Atlantic St, Stamford, CT 06901-3512
Tel (203) 541-8100 *Founded/Ownrshp* 2011
Sales 204.2MM[E] *EMP* 3,850
SIC 2671 Packaging paper & plastics film, coated & laminated; Paper coated or laminated for packaging; Plastic film, coated or laminated for packaging; Waxed paper: made from purchased material

AGI SHOREWOOD U.S.
See AGI NORTH AMERICA LLC

D-U-N-S 01-002-6391 IMP/EXP
AGI-SHOREWOOD GROUP US LLC
(*Suby of* ATLAS HOLDINGS LLC) ★
300 Atlantic St Ste 206, Stamford, CT 06901-3514
Tel (203) 324-4839 *Founded/Ownrshp* 1966, 2011
Sales 58.0M[E] *EMP* 1,005
SIC 2671 2652 2657 Packaging paper & plastics film, coated & laminated; Setup paperboard boxes; Folding paperboard boxes
CFO: Donald K Eldert
**Treas:* Philip E Schuch
**VP:* Timothy J Facio
**VP:* Jacob D Hudson
VP: Tim S Nicholls

AGI-SHOREWOOD U.S.
See ATLAS AGI HOLDINGS LLC

AGI-SHOREWOOD U.S.
See SHOREWOOD PACKAGING HOLDINGS LLC

A.G.I.A.
See G I A A INC

AGIE CHARMILLES
See GF MACHINING SOLUTIONS LLC

AGILE 1
See ACT 1 GROUP INC

AGILE BRANDS
See ADCO PRODUCTS INC

D-U-N-S 80-053-0789
AGILE SOURCING PARTNERS INC
2385 Railroad St, Corona, CA 92880-5411
Tel (951) 279-4154 *Founded/Ownrshp* 2006
Sales 222.5MM *EMP* 180
Accts Bates Coughtry Reiss
SIC 4939 Combination utilities
Pr: Maria Thompson
VP: Courtney Gaik

D-U-N-S 08-496-3177 IMP
▲ AGILENT TECHNOLOGIES INC
5301 Stevens Creek Blvd, Santa Clara, CA 95051-7201
Tel (408) 345-8886 *Founded/Ownrshp* 1999
Sales 4.0MMM *EMP* 11,800[E]
Accts Pricewaterhousecoopers Llp Sa
Tkr Sym A *Exch* NYS
SIC 3825 3826 7372 Instruments to measure electricity; Analytical instruments; Gas testing apparatus; Instruments measuring magnetic & electrical properties; Prepackaged software
CEO: Michael McMullen
Pr: Mark Doak
CFO: Didier Hirsch
Treas: Barbara Nowaczyk
Ex VP: William Buffington
Sr VP: Bryan Anderson
Sr VP: Rick Burdsall
Sr VP: Gooi Soon Chai
Sr VP: Dominique P Grau
Sr VP: William R Hahn
Sr VP: Larry Holmberg
Sr VP: Richard D Kniss
Sr VP: Stephen R Rusckowski
Sr VP: Darlene J Solomon
Sr VP: Thomas White
VP: Rodney Gonsalves
VP: Shanya Kane
VP: Guy S N
VP: Peter Planitz
VP: Shiela Robertson
VP: Fred Strohmeier
Board of Directors: Paul N Clark, James G Cullen, Heidi Fields, Robert J Herbold, Koh Boon Hwee, Daniel K Podolsky, Sue H Rataj, George A Scangos

D-U-N-S 14-225-4072
AGILITY HEALTH LLC
AGILITY HEALTH P.T.
607 Dewey Ave Nw Ste 300, Grand Rapids, MI 49504-7335
Tel (616) 356-5000 *Founded/Ownrshp* 1999
Sales 48.4MM[E] *EMP* 1,050
SIC 8049 Physical therapist; Occupational therapist; Speech therapist
CEO: Steven N Davidson
**Pr:* Ken Scholten
**COO:* Gene Miyamoto
**CFO:* Adam Kinder
**Ofcr:* Terry Vanderkruyk
VP: Tim Hollstein
VP: Joseph F Laurent
Info Man: Pat Sagan

AGILITY HEALTH P.T.
See AGILITY HEALTH LLC

D-U-N-S 96-209-3019 IMP/EXP
AGILITY HOLDINGS INC
AGILITY LOGISTICS
(*Suby of* AGILITY LOGISTICS INTERNATIONAL B.V.)
310 Commerce Ste 250, Irvine, CA 92602-1399
Tel (714) 617-6300 *Founded/Ownrshp* 1996
Sales 451.8MM[E] *EMP* 5,700
SIC 4731 4213 4214 Domestic freight forwarding; Foreign freight forwarding; Transportation agents & brokers; Household goods transport; Heavy machinery transport; Household goods moving & storage, local
Pr: Essa Al-Saleh
V Ch: Dale Aman
Pr: John Iacouzzi
Pr: Jamie Robertson
CEO: Mark Soubry
COO: Michael Robinson
CFO: Margaret Forrester
**CFO:* James Fredholm
Treas: Linda L Williams
Ex VP: Louis Roden
VP: Margaret Churchill
VP: Jim Falanga
**VP:* Shura Kim
VP: Robert Polock
VP: Michael Thames
Exec: Sim Kiat
Dir Bus: Tim Orner
Comm Man: Vince Lipiz
Board of Directors: James Down

AGILITY LOGISTICS
See AGILITY HOLDINGS INC

D-U-N-S 06-696-6359 IMP/EXP
AGILITY LOGISTICS CORP
GLOBAL INTEGRATED LOGISTICS
(*Suby of* AGILITY LOGISTICS) ★
240 Commerce, Irvine, CA 92602-1318
Tel (714) 617-6300 *Founded/Ownrshp* 1996
Sales 422.3MM[E] *EMP* 759
SIC 4731 8742 7372 1381

D-U-N-S 03-444-6484
AGILITY PROJECT LOGISTICS INC
(*Suby of* GLOBAL INTEGRATED LOGISTICS) ★
15600 Morales Rd, Houston, TX 77032-2118
Tel (504) 465-1000 *Founded/Ownrshp* 1947
Sales 91.1MM[E] *EMP* 225
SIC 4731 4225 Foreign freight forwarding; Domestic freight forwarding; Customhouse brokers; Freight forwarding; General warehousing
CEO: Gregory R Rusovich
**Pr:* Francesc Casamitjana
**Treas:* Marty K Brogden
**Ex VP:* Richard Castaing
**VP:* Peggy A Beebe
**VP:* Nanci Laureano
**VP:* Karl Schneider
**VP:* Rosa Villarreal
**VP:* Larry Weischwill
Mng Dir: Kamal Sidawi
Board of Directors: Grant Wattman

D-U-N-S 00-445-4211
▲ AGILYSYS INC (OH)
425 Walnut St Ste 1800, Cincinnati, OH 45202-3920
Tel (770) 810-7800 *Founded/Ownrshp* 1963
Sales 120.3MM *EMP* 553[E]
Tkr Sym AGYS *Exch* NGS
SIC 5045 Computer peripheral equipment; Disk drives; Computer software
Pr: James H Dennedy
**Ch Bd:* Michael A Kaufman
CFO: Janine K Seebeck
**V Ch Bd:* Keith M Kolerus
Sr VP: Kyle C Badger
Sr VP: Larry Steinberg
Sr VP: Jimmie D Walker Jr
VP: Tim Davis
VP: Debra Dowling
Board of Directors: Donald Colvin, Melvin Keating, John Mutch

D-U-N-S 00-505-9402
■ AGL RESOURCES SERVICE CO
(*Suby of* SOUTHERN CO GAS) ★
10 Peachtree Pl Ne # 1000, Atlanta, GA 30309-4497
Tel (404) 584-9470 *Founded/Ownrshp* 1996
Sales 302.9MM[E] *EMP* 400
SIC 8742 8721 8744 4924 Human resource consulting services; Accounting, auditing & bookkeeping; Facilities support services; Natural gas distribution
CEO: Walter M Higgins
VP: John H Moldey Jr
IT Man: Kristan Kamm

AGLA
See AMERICAN GENERAL LIFE & ACCIDENT INSURANCE CO

D-U-N-S 01-822-8387
AGLAND CO-OP INC
364 Lisbon St, Canfield, OH 44406-1422
Tel (330) 533-5551 *Founded/Ownrshp* 2000
Sales 269.5MM *EMP* 129
Accts Four-Fifteen Group Canton Oh
SIC 5153 Grains
Pr: Jeffrey Osentoski

D-U-N-S 07-350-3018
AGMARK LLC
118 W Main St, Beloit, KS 67420-2745
Tel (785) 738-9641 *Founded/Ownrshp* 1999
Sales 314.0MM *EMP* 27
Accts Lindburg Vogel Pierce Faris H
SIC 4221 Farm product warehousing & storage
Opers Mgr: Derek Sandmann

D-U-N-S 00-520-6243 IMP/EXP
AGMOTION INC (MN)
US COMMODITIES
730 2nd Ave S Ste 700, Minneapolis, MN 55402-2480
Tel (612) 486-3800 *Founded/Ownrshp* 2000
Sales 221.2MM[E] *EMP* 77
SIC 5153 Grains
CEO: Rolf S Peters
**Pr:* Tim Carlson
**CFO:* Bill Hren
**VP:* Wint Ritchie

D-U-N-S 82-473-7725
▲ AGNC INVESTMENT CORP
2 Bethesda Metro Ctr # 12, Bethesda, MD 20814-6319
Tel (301) 968-9315 *Founded/Ownrshp* 2008
Sales 1.4MMM *EMP* 9[E]
Tkr Sym AGNC *Exch* NGS
SIC 6798 Real estate investment trusts
Pr: Gary D Kain
**Ch Bd:* Prue B Larocca
CFO: Peter J Federico
Chf Cred: Kenneth L Pollack
Sr VP: Bernice E Bell
Sr VP: Christopher J Kuehl

AGNESIAN HALTHCARE FOND DU LAC
See ST AGNES HOSPITAL OF FOND DU LAC WISC INC

D-U-N-S 62-424-8071
AGNESIAN HEALTHCARE INC
430 E Division St, Fond Du Lac, WI 54935-4560
Tel (920) 929-2300 *Founded/Ownrshp* 1896
Sales 339.3MM *EMP* 2,012
Accts Wipfli Llp Green Bay Wi
SIC 8069 Specialty hospitals, except psychiatric; Drug addiction rehabilitation hospital; Children's hospital; Maternity hospital
Pr: John St Peter
**Pr:* Mr Robert Fale
Sr VP: Danny Henson
VP: Debra V Zande
Dir Lab: Linda Muche
Dir Lab: Amy Zipp
Ex Dir: Rita Meidam
CIO: Maria Zahn
MIS Dir: Nancy Birschbach
QA Dir: Pam Buchholz
IT Man: Richard Daly

D-U-N-S 02-003-3335
AGORA CYBER CHARTER SCHOOL
590 N Gulph Rd, King of Prussia, PA 19406-2800
Tel (610) 230-0775 *Founded/Ownrshp* 2005
Sales 125.5MM *EMP* 3
Accts Barbacane Thornton & Company L
SIC 8211

D-U-N-S 07-264-1236
AGORA INC
14 W Mount Vernon Pl, Baltimore, MD 21201-5125
Tel (410) 783-8499 *Founded/Ownrshp* 1974
Sales 248.1MM[E] *EMP* 500
SIC 2741 7331 Newsletter publishing; Direct mail advertising services; Mailing list brokers; Mailing list management
CEO: Myles Norin
Pr: Elizabeth Bonner
CFO: Bob Compton
Treas: Matt Turner
Sec: Gregory Barnhill
Prin: William Bonner
Dir IT: Shane Enos
Dir IT: Shawn McClenahan
Dir IT: Kevin Walker
IT Man: Maria Sadecki
Netwrk Mgr: Tom Bacon

D-U-N-S 82-866-9049
AGORA MARKETING SOLUTIONS INC
8285 Bryan Dairy Rd # 150, Largo, FL 33777-1350
Tel (727) 369-2700 *Founded/Ownrshp* 2008
Sales 98.4MM[E] *EMP* 815
SIC 7331 7389 Direct mail advertising services; Subscription fulfillment services: magazine, newspaper, etc.; Telephone solicitation service
Ch: Dennis A Cahill
Mng Pt: Avy Stein
V Ch: David Moscow
**Pr:* Thomas H Ripley
COO: Dave Anderson
CFO: Harold Hale
**CFO:* Doug Lombardo
VP: Dawn Daugherty
VP: Dawn Daugherty-Kane
VP: Jack Linder
VP: Thomas Lord
**VP:* Rob Paolillo
VP: Ralph Reeser
**VP:* Karen Roberts
VP: Troy Schneider
Dir Bus: Frank Deprisco

D-U-N-S 14-577-2760
■ AGOURON PHARMACEUTICALS INC
(*Suby of* PFIZER INC) ★
10777 Science Center Dr, San Diego, CA 92121-1111
Tel (858) 622-3000 *Founded/Ownrshp* 1999
Sales 45.0MM[E] *EMP* 1,200
SIC 2834 5122 8731 Pharmaceutical preparations; Pharmaceuticals; Commercial physical research
Sr VP: Catherine Mackey PHD
VP: Gary Friedman
VP: Jeff Jensen
VP: Alex Polinsky
QC Dir: Norm Kobyashi
Snr Mgr: Thomas Tong

AGP
See AG PROCESSING INC A COOPERATIVE

D-U-N-S 86-924-9284 EXP
AGP GRAIN LTD
(*Suby of* AGP) ★
12700 W Dodge Rd, Omaha, NE 68154-6102
Tel (402) 496-7809 *Founded/Ownrshp* 1994
Sales 260.2MM[E] *EMP* 1,000
SIC 5153 Grain & field beans
Pr: Spackler J Keith
**Pr:* Cal Meyer

D-U-N-S 79-759-3238 IMP
AGRELIANT GENETICS LLC
LG SEED
1122 E 169th St, Westfield, IN 46074-9601
Tel (317) 896-5552 *Founded/Ownrshp* 2000
Sales 431.3MM[E] *EMP* 400
SIC 5191 Farm supplies; Alfalfa; Seeds & bulbs; Flower & field bulbs
Pr: Raphael Journel
COO: Christine Hartfield
CFO: Ed Germain
CFO: Edward Germain
Chf Mktg O: Craig Newman
VP: Kenneth Craig
VP: Thomas Koch
VP: Guenter Seitz
VP: Jon Wensman
Genl Mgr: Ron Bell
Dir IT: Steve Thompson

D-U-N-S 87-815-9144 IMP/EXP
AGRESERVES INC
(*Suby of* FARMLAND RESERVE INC) ★
79 S Main St Ste 1100, Salt Lake City, UT 84111-1945
Tel (801) 715-9100 *Founded/Ownrshp* 2005
Sales 169.1MM[E] *EMP* 800
SIC 0762 Farm management services
Pr: Darell Wilkendorf
**Sec:* Casey Jones
**VP:* Brent J Garlick
**VP:* Erik Jacobsen
**VP:* Glen L Lambert
**VP:* Louis S Rothey
**VP:* R Burke Teichert

IT Man: Michael Rawlings
Mktg Dir: Wayne Park

AGRESOURCE
See ARTHUR COMPANIES INC

D-U-N-S 04-524-2245 EXP
AGREX INC
FGDI
(*Suby of* MITSUBISHI CORPORATION)
10975 Grandview Dr # 200, Overland Park, KS 66210-1522
Tel (913) 851-6300 *Founded/Ownrshp* 1973
Sales 4.5MMM *EMP* 173
SIC 5153 Grain & field beans
CEO: Go Kojima
**CFO:* Takashi Matsuki
**Sr VP:* Joe Milkowski
**Sr VP:* Robert Obrock
**VP:* Amy Ashlock
**VP:* Robert Barr
**VP:* David Christofore Sr
Dir IT: Steve Carpenter

D-U-N-S 09-312-2190 IMP/EXP
AGRI BEEF CO
1555 W Shoreline Dr # 320, Boise, ID 83702-9109
Tel (208) 338-2500 *Founded/Ownrshp* 1975
Sales 323.0MM[E] *EMP* 1,000
SIC 2011 0212 Beef products from beef slaughtered on site; Beef cattle except feedlots
Pr: Robert Rebholtz Jr
**CFO:* William B Rawlings
**Treas:* Rick Stott
VP: Jim Crane
**VP:* Jeff Johnson
Exec: Terry Reynolds
Genl Mgr: Rob Miller
Genl Mgr: Jess Painter
Off Mgr: Bobbie Quick
**CIO:* Jim Hay
Sls&Mrk Ex: Nate Gilliam
Board of Directors: Dorothy Rebholtz, Paul Rebholtz

D-U-N-S 00-694-1116
AGRI INDUSTRIES INC
700 Se Dalbey Dr, Ankeny, IA 50021-3908
Tel (515) 964-2200 *Founded/Ownrshp* 1903
Sales 117.7MM[E] *EMP* 127
SIC 5153 7359 Grains; Equipment rental & leasing
Pr: Jerry Vanderkamp

D-U-N-S 08-605-4137
AGRI SERVICES OF BRUNSWICK LLC
A S B
Hwy 24 W, Brunswick, MO 65236
Tel (660) 549-3351 *Founded/Ownrshp* 1998
Sales 196.3MM *EMP* 50
Accts Wilson Toellner & Associates
SIC 5153 5191 Grains; Fertilizer & fertilizer materials

D-U-N-S 08-016-8609
AGRI TRAILS COOP INC
508 N Main St, Hope, KS 67451-9421
Tel (785) 366-7213 *Founded/Ownrshp* 2015
Sales 160.0MM *EMP* 151[E]
SIC 5999 5261 Farm equipment & supplies; Feed & farm supply; Fertilizer
Pr: Darel Anderson

D-U-N-S 13-911-5690
AGRI-AFC LLC
121 Somerville Rd Ne, Decatur, AL 35601-2659
Tel (256) 560-2848 *Founded/Ownrshp* 2003
Sales 339.3MM *EMP* 165
SIC 5159 5153 5083 5191 Peanuts (bulk), unroasted; Grains; Agricultural machinery & equipment; Farm supplies
Pr: Mike Malone
**CFO:* Jamie Bowling
Bd of Dir: Melodee Cannon
Bd of Dir: Jodi Hanson
Bd of Dir: Bob Kincade
Bd of Dir: Micki Mathiesen
Bd of Dir: Robin Pachuta
Bd of Dir: Susan Spaniol

AGRI-BUSINESS COMPLEX DIVISION
See MUSCOGEE CREEK NATION

D-U-N-S 07-914-3426 IMP/EXP
AGRI-FAB INC
809 S Hamilton St, Sullivan, IL 61951-2209
Tel (217) 728-8388 *Founded/Ownrshp* 1975, 2007
Sales 114.2MM[E] *EMP* 400
SIC 3469 3429 5083

D-U-N-S 02-171-9893 IMP/EXP
AGRI-MARK INC
100 Milk St Ste 5, Methuen, MA 01844-4665
Tel (978) 689-4442 *Founded/Ownrshp* 1980
Sales 239.8MM[E] *EMP* 900
SIC 2026 2022 Milk processing (pasteurizing, homogenizing, bottling); Cheese, natural & processed
Pr: Paul P Johnston
**COO:* Ed Townley
**Treas:* Walter Fletcher
**Ex VP:* Dr Richard Stammer
**Sr VP:* Margaret H Bertolino
VP: Val Adams
VP: Alan Dibenedetto
VP: Nancy Lafountain
VP: Richard Langworthy
VP: Robert Stoddart
**Prin:* Mike Barnes

D-U-N-S 10-167-9363
AGRICULTURAL COMMODITIES INC
2224 Oxford Rd, New Oxford, PA 17350-9643
Tel (717) 624-8249 *Founded/Ownrshp* 1983
Sales 118.7MM[E] *EMP* 80
SIC 5191 2048 2041 0723 2875

D-U-N-S 92-933-1072
■ AGRICULTURAL MARKETING SERVICE
USDA
(*Suby of* U S D A) ★
1400 Independence Ave Sw, Washington, DC 20250-0002
Tel (202) 720-8998 *Founded/Ownrshp* 1972
Sales NA *EMP* 4,000
SIC 9641 Regulation of agricultural marketing;
CIO: Marcelo Olascoaga

D-U-N-S 92-933-1197
■ AGRICULTURAL RESEARCH SERVICE
(*Suby of* U S D A) ★
5601 Sunnyside Ave, Beltsville, MD 20705-5000
Tel (301) 504-1147 *Founded/Ownrshp* 1953
Sales NA *EMP* 1,215
SIC 9641 Regulation of agricultural marketing;

D-U-N-S 80-825-6614
■ AGRIGENETICS INC
(*Suby of* MYCOGEN PLANT SCIENCE INC) ★
9330 Zionsville Rd, Indianapolis, IN 46268-1053
Tel (317) 337-3000 *Founded/Ownrshp* 2000
Sales 190.2MM[E] *EMP* 320[E]
SIC 5191 Seeds: field, garden & flower
Pr: Rolando Meninato
**VP:* Daniel R Kittle
**VP:* Dana L Mathes
**VP:* William E Root
**VP:* Gordon E Slack
**Prin:* Walter Peter Siggelko
**Genl Mgr:* Tim Kroenke

D-U-N-S 12-860-2963 IMP/EXP
AGRILIANCE LLC
5500 Cenex Dr, Inver Grove Heights, MN 55077-1721
Tel (651) 481-2031 *Founded/Ownrshp* 2000
Sales 273.3MM[E] *EMP* 2,100
SIC 5083 Agricultural machinery & equipment
Pr: George Thornton
**CFO:* Keith Peterson
VP: Steven John
VP: Pat Jones

D-U-N-S 00-947-6186
AGRILOGIC INSURANCE SERVICES LLC
1000 Ballpark Way Ste 314, Arlington, TX 76011-5171
Tel (888) 245-6442 *Founded/Ownrshp* 2009
Sales NA *EMP* 257[E]
SIC 6331 Agricultural insurance
CEO: Stephen L Stephano
Pr: Joey K Davis
CEO: Joe Davis
COO: Paul Tate
Treas: David G Pirrung
Sr VP: Michael Fanning
VP: Kenneth C Coon Sr
Board of Directors: Joe Davis

AGRIUM ADVANCED TECH US INC
See AGRIUM ADVANCED TECHNOLOGIES (US) INC

D-U-N-S 83-207-5209 IMP/EXP
AGRIUM ADVANCED TECHNOLOGIES (US) INC
AGRIUM ADVANCED TECH US INC
(*Suby of* AGRIUM INC)
2915 Rocky Mountain Ave # 400, Loveland, CO 80538-9048
Tel (970) 292-9000 *Founded/Ownrshp* 2009
Sales 176.1MM[E] *EMP* 500[E]
SIC 2873 Nitrogenous fertilizers
Pr: Andrew Mittag
CFO: Mike Cleveland
VP: J Muse
VP: Jeff Novak
Software D: Kurtis Halvorson
Software D: Chris Maxfield
VP Opers: Mike Collins
Opers Supe: Jerry R Cook
Opers Mgr: Terry Hart
Manager: Jim Davis
Sls Mgr: John McKay

D-U-N-S 80-895-7229 IMP
AGRIUM US INC
(*Suby of* AGRIUM INC)
4582 S Ulster St Ste 1700, Denver, CO 80237-2641
Tel (303) 804-4400 *Founded/Ownrshp* 1993
Sales 927.4MM[E] *EMP* 2,500
Accts Kpmg Llp Calgary Canada
SIC 2873 Nitrogenous fertilizers; Fertilizers: natural (organic), except compost; Nitrogen solutions (fertilizer); Urea
Ch: Victor J Zaleschuk
Pr: Charles V Magro
Treas: Angela Lekatsas
Ex VP: Leslie O'Donoghue
Sr VP: Stephen G Dyer
Sr VP: Andrew K Mittag
Sr VP: Michael Webb
Exec: John Leal
Dir IT: Steve Chapman
S&M/Mgr: Katie M Donald

AGRO PACIFICA
See FRESH PACIFIC FRUIT AND VEGETABLE INC

D-U-N-S 00-613-9430
AGROPUR INC
(*Suby of* AGROPUR COOPERATIVE)
3500 E Destination Dr # 200, Appleton, WI 54915-7305
Tel (920) 944-0990 *Founded/Ownrshp* 1960
Sales 172.5MM[E] *EMP* 319
SIC 2022 Natural cheese
Pr: Douglas Simon
**CFO:* Bill Diedrich
**VP:* Dan La Marche
**VP:* Chris Simon
VP: Mike Sipple

AGROPUR INGREDIENTS
See AGROPUR MSI LLC

D-U-N-S 36-255-5302 IMP
AGROPUR MSI LLC
AGROPUR INGREDIENTS
(*Suby of* AGROPUR COOPERATIVE)
2340 Enterprise Ave, La Crosse, WI 54603-1713
Tel (608) 781-2345 *Founded/Ownrshp* 2010
Sales 200.0MM[E] *EMP* 250[E]
SIC 2023

D-U-N-S 78-246-9688 IMP/EXP
AGROYCE METAL MARKETING LLC
CONCRETE REINFORCING PRODUCTS
1381 Sawgrs Corp Pkwy, Sunrise, FL 33323-2889
Tel (954) 581-3607 *Founded/Ownrshp* 2000
Sales 112.9MM[E] *EMP* 18
SIC 5051 Concrete reinforcing bars; Reinforcement mesh, wire; Steel
Pr: Ira Vernon
**Mng Pt:* Joe Kirner
**CFO:* Meghan Russell
Mktg Dir: Joanne Jacobs

AGS
See AECOM GOVERNMENT SERVICES INC

D-U-N-S 83-363-7887
AGSOUTH FARM CREDIT ACA
26 S Main St, Statesboro, GA 30458-5256
Tel (912) 764-9091 *Founded/Ownrshp* 1999
Sales NA *EMP* 226
Accts Pricewaterhousecoopers Llp Fo
SIC 6159 Farm mortgage companies; Production credit association, agricultural
Pr: William P Spigener Jr
CFO: Lisa Gunter

D-U-N-S 07-950-4441
AGSPRING IDAHO LLC
THRESHER ARTISAN WHEAT
(*Suby of* AGSPRING LLC) ★
600 Highway 169 S Ste 720, Saint Louis Park, MN 55426-1211
Tel (952) 956-6720 *Founded/Ownrshp* 2014
Sales 255.1MM[E] *EMP* 24[E]
SIC 5153 Grain elevators
CEO: Randal Linville
**COO:* Donald Wille

D-U-N-S 07-888-7090
AGSPRING LLC
5250 W 116th Pl Ste 200, Leawood, KS 66211-7826
Tel (913) 333-3035 *Founded/Ownrshp* 2012
Sales 270.0MM[E] *EMP* 60[E]
SIC 0191 8748 General farms, primarily crop; Agricultural consultant
CEO: Randal Linville
**CEO:* Dennis Krause
VP Mktg: Bradford Warner

D-U-N-S 08-767-6532
AGSTAR FINANCIAL SERVICES ACA
LOOKOUT RIDGE
1921 Premier Dr, Mankato, MN 56001-5901
Tel (507) 387-4174 *Founded/Ownrshp* 1918
Sales NA *EMP* 600
Accts Pricewaterhouse Coopers Minne
SIC 6111 Federal & federally sponsored credit agencies
Pr: Paul Debryin
**COO:* Joseph Deufel
**CFO:* Rodney Hebrink
**Sr VP:* Dave Hoelmer
VP: Donald S Farm Jr
VP: Mark Greenwood
VP: Kramer Jeffrey
VP: Tom Neher
VP: Timothy E Tracy
IT Man: Mark Rude
Mktg Dir: Cathy Riley

D-U-N-S 61-899-9515
AGT CRUNCH ACQUISITION LLC
CRUNCH FITNESS
22 W 19th St Ste 3l, New York, NY 10011-4204
Tel (212) 993-0300 *Founded/Ownrshp* 2006
Sales 18.2MM[E] *EMP* 2,000
SIC 7991 Physical fitness facilities

D-U-N-S 14-601-4423 IMP
AGU US HOLDINGS INC
(*Suby of* AGRIUM INC)
7251 W 4th St, Greeley, CO 80634-9763
Tel (970) 356-4400 *Founded/Ownrshp* 2008
Sales 146.1MM[E] *EMP* 3,100
SIC 2879 5191 Agricultural chemicals; Fertilizers & agricultural chemicals
Pr: Michael M Wilson
Pr: David R Birk
COO: David W Bullock
CFO: Jeffrey L Rutherford
Ex VP: Dean Williams
VP: Brent Smith
VP: Todd A Suko
VP: Dave Tretter
VP: Tom Warner
Prin: Michael E Ducey
Prin: Thomas R Miklich

D-U-N-S 18-207-0482
AGUA CALIENTE BAND OF CAHUILLA INDIANS
5401 Dinah Shore Dr, Palm Springs, CA 92264-5970
Tel (760) 699-6800 *Founded/Ownrshp* 1988
Sales 182.0MM[E] *EMP* 2,200[E]
SIC 8699 6552 7999 Reading rooms & other cultural organizations; Subdividers & developers; Tour & guide services
Ch: Jeff L Grubbe
**Sec:* Vincent Gonzales III
**Prin:* Larry N Olinger
Ex Dir: Kari Smith
Genl Mgr: Marc Payan
Dir IT: Ralph Kato

AGVISION
See BRANDT CONSOLIDATED INC

AGWAY
See SEEDWAY LLC

D-U-N-S 05-251-9563 IMP/EXP
AGY HOLDING CORP
A G Y
(*Suby of* KOHLBERG & CO) ★
2556 Wagener Rd, Aiken, SC 29801-9572
Tel (888) 434-0945 *Founded/Ownrshp* 2006
Sales 252.9MM[E] *EMP* 1,053[E]
SIC 2221 Fiberglass fabrics
Ch Bd: Robert Isaman
Pr: Patrick J Burns
CFO: Jay W Ferguson
Treas: Patty Baron
Ex VP: Thomas Skidmore
Prin: Samuel P Frieder
Prin: Seth H Hollander
Prin: Christopher Lacovara
Sales Asso: Julie Broome
Snr Mgr: Kelley Boetsch
Snr Mgr: Eddie McDonald
Board of Directors: Seth Hollander, Christopher Lacovara,samue

A.H. VENDING & FOOD SERVICE
See A H MANAGEMENT GROUP INC

AHA
See AMERICAN HOSPITAL ASSOCIATION

D-U-N-S 06-385-0285
AHC
121 Ne Jefferson Ave # 100, Peoria, IL 61602-1256
Tel (888) 568-3137 *Founded/Ownrshp* 2011
Sales 100.0MM *EMP* 370
SIC 7322 Collection agency, except real estate
Pr: Mark Schanck
Ex VP: Jan Draher

AHERN HEAVY EQUIPMENT
See AHERN RENTALS INC

D-U-N-S 01-690-8464
AHERN RENTALS INC
AHERN HEAVY EQUIPMENT
1401 Mineral Ave, Las Vegas, NV 89106-4342
Tel (702) 362-0623 *Founded/Ownrshp* 1953
Sales 642.9MM[E] *EMP* 1,580
SIC 7353 Heavy construction equipment rental; Cranes & aerial lift equipment, rental or leasing; Earth moving equipment, rental or leasing
Pr: Don F Ahern
**CFO:* Howard L Brown
Treas: D Kirk Hartle
Chf Inves: Mike Ertel
**Ex VP:* Evan B Ahern
Sr VP: Lorrie Covey
Sr VP: Kirk Hartle
Sr VP: Timothy N Lotspeich
VP: Chris Cavalli
VP: Arnie Lendon
VP: Rick Weaver
Board of Directors: P Enoch Stiff, Mark J Wattles

D-U-N-S 06-624-5895 IMP/EXP
■ AHF-DUCOMMUN INC
DUCOMMUN AROSTRUCTURES-GARDENA
(*Suby of* DUCOMMUN INC) ★
268 E Gardena Blvd, Gardena, CA 90248-2814
Tel (310) 380-5390 *Founded/Ownrshp* 1973
Sales 298.5MM[E] *EMP* 1,300
SIC 3728 3812 3769 3469 Aircraft body & wing assemblies & parts; Search & navigation equipment; Guided missile & space vehicle parts & auxiliary equipment; Metal stampings
Sls Mgr: John Summit

D-U-N-S 01-964-2037
AHI HOLDINGS INC
AIRXCEL HOLDINGS
3050 N Saint Francis St, Wichita, KS 67219-4045
Tel (316) 832-3484 *Founded/Ownrshp* 1991
Sales 162.1MM[E] *EMP* 1,250
SIC 3585 3444

D-U-N-S 84-707-5546 IMP
AHI INVESTMENT INC
LINZER PRODUCTS
(*Suby of* OHTSUKA BRUSH MFG.CO., LTD.)
675 Glenoaks Blvd, San Fernando, CA 91340-1471
Tel (818) 979-0030 *Founded/Ownrshp* 1989
Sales 112.7MM[E] *EMP* 1[E]
SIC 5199 3991 Broom, mop & paint handles; Paint brushes
Prin: Hisatoshi Ohtsuka
**Ex VP:* Mark Saji
**Prin:* Yuko Waki

D-U-N-S 13-910-6335
AHL SERVICES INC
102 S Union St, Alexandria, VA 22314-3324
Tel (703) 682-0729 *Founded/Ownrshp* 2003
Sales 53.6MM[E] *EMP* 8,405[E]
SIC 8742 Marketing consulting services
Pr: Clay Perfall
**CFO:* Brian Burke
Sr Cor Off: Frank Argenbright
**VP:* Matthew Fletchall

D-U-N-S 10-167-6547 IMP
AHLSTROM ATLANTA LLC
(*Suby of* AHLSTROM USA INC) ★
3820 Mansell Rd Ste 200, Alpharetta, GA 30022-1538
Tel (770) 650-2100 *Founded/Ownrshp* 1990
Sales 107.2MM[E] *EMP* 510
SIC 2621 Filter paper

D-U-N-S 06-226-4296 IMP/EXP
AHLSTROM FILTRATION LLC
(*Suby of* AHLSTROM ATLANTA LLC) ★
215 Nebo Rd, Madisonville, KY 42431-8831
Tel (270) 821-0140 *Founded/Ownrshp* 1999
Sales 95.9MM[E] *EMP* 300
SIC 2621 Specialty papers; Filter paper
**Prin:* Thomas R Bastian

D-U-N-S 03-999-3345 IMP/EXP
AHLSTROM NONWOVENS LLC
(*Suby of* AHLSTROM USA INC) ★
2 Elm St, Windsor Locks, CT 06096-2335
Tel (860) 654-8300 *Founded/Ownrshp* 2000
Sales 234.0MM[E] *EMP* 740
SIC 2297 Nonwoven fabrics
Ex VP: William Casey
V Ch: Daniel Hennessy
* *Treas:* Gary Dzioba
Ql Cn Mgr: Eugene Pellerano
Mktg Dir: Jerome Barrillon
Mktg Dir: Gary Byrom
Mktg Mgr: Gavin Gauld

D-U-N-S 79-927-1887 EXP
AHLSTROM USA INC
(*Suby of* AHLSTROM OYJ)
2 Elm St, Windsor Locks, CT 06096-2335
Tel (860) 654-8300 *Founded/Ownrshp* 2007
Sales 376.6MM[E] *EMP* 1,000
SIC 2621 Specialty or chemically treated papers
Pr: William Casey
* *Treas:* Leonard H Mirahver
* *VP:* Christopher Coates
* *VP:* David T Pluta
Opers Mgr: Jani Haimilahti

D-U-N-S 01-552-0844
AHMC GARFIELD MEDICAL CENTER LP
(*Suby of* AHMC HEALTHCARE INC) ★
525 N Garfield Ave, Monterey Park, CA 91754-1202
Tel (626) 573-2222 *Founded/Ownrshp* 2004
Sales 204.7MM *EMP* 150
SIC 8051 8062 Skilled nursing care facilities; General medical & surgical hospitals
Genl Pt: Philip Cohen
Pt: Steve Maekewa
CFO: Linda Marsh
Dir Risk M: Marie Trembath
Dir Case M: Jane Petre
Dir Lab: Wendy Lee
QA Dir: Ruth Honig
Pathlgst: Muh-Yua Y Tang
Obsttrcn: Henry Tsai
Ansthlgy: Steven Lau
Ansthlgy: Yaw Wu

D-U-N-S 17-021-5573
AHMC HEALTHCARE INC
1000 S Fremont Ave Unit 6, Alhambra, CA 91803-8836
Tel (626) 943-7526 *Founded/Ownrshp* 2004
Sales 615.4MM[E] *EMP* 6,500
SIC 8062 8641 General medical & surgical hospitals; Civic social & fraternal associations
CEO: Jonathan Wu MD
COO: Jose Ortega
Sr VP: Linda Marsh
VP: Judy Saito
Dir Rad: Mike Craig
Chf Nrs Of: Sharon Carpenter
Prgrm Mgr: Patti Metzger
Dir IT: Ann Curnutt
Dir IT: Bernie Sauer
Mktg Dir: Jeffrey Lu
Mktg Dir: Carol Yeh

AHN - ALLEGHENY HEALTH NETWORK
See HM HEALTH SOLUTIONS INC

D-U-N-S 17-327-0430
AHO CONSTRUCTION I INC
A H O CONSTRUCTION
5512 Ne 109th Ct Ste 101, Vancouver, WA 98662-6185
Tel (360) 254-0493 *Founded/Ownrshp* 1985
Sales 145.0MM *EMP* 80
SIC 1531 1521 Operative builders; Single-family housing construction
Pr: Melvin Aho
VP: Lisa Logan

D-U-N-S 18-681-5635 IMP/EXP
AHOLD USA INC
AFS
(*Suby of* KONINKLIJKE AHOLD DELHAIZE N.V.)
1385 Hancock St, Quincy, MA 02169-5103
Tel (717) 249-4000 *Founded/Ownrshp* 2001
Sales 23.1MMM[E] *EMP* 169,835
SIC 5411 Supermarkets, chain
CEO: Dick Boer
COO: Lawrence Benjamin
* *COO:* James McCann
* *CFO:* Bob Fishbune
VP: Chuck Anderson
VP: Michel De Fontaine
VP: Ed Porter
VP: Scott Tegethoff
VP: Peter Wakkie
Telecom Mg: Phil Smith
Advt Mgr: Kay Wells

D-U-N-S 87-977-6904
AHOM HOLDINGS INC (DE)
AMERICAN HOME PATIENTS
(*Suby of* COUNSEL CORPORATION)
5200 Maryland Way Ste 400, Brentwood, TN 37027-5059
Tel (615) 221-8884 *Founded/Ownrshp* 1994
Sales 12.5MM[E] *EMP* 1,891
SIC 8082 Home health care services
Pr: Joseph Ferlong

AHP
See ASSOCIATED HYGIENIC PRODUCTS LLC

D-U-N-S 55-689-7692
■ **AHP HOLDINGS INC**
(*Suby of* AETNA LIFE INSURANCE CO INC) ★
151 Farmington Ave, Hartford, CT 06156-0001
Tel (860) 273-0123 *Founded/Ownrshp* 1989
Sales NA *EMP* 500
SIC 6321 6311 8011 Accident & health insurance; Life insurance; Health maintenance organization
Ch Bd: James W Mc Lane
* *Treas:* James Mc Cauley
* *Sr VP:* Charles T Bell

AHRC NEW YORK CITY
See NYSARC

AHRC-NASSAU COUNTY CHAPTER
See NASSAU COUNTY A H R C

AHS
See ADVANTEDGE HEALTHCARE SOLUTIONS INC

D-U-N-S 96-506-1752
AHS AMARILLO HEALTH SYSTEM LLC
(*Suby of* VTR AMS, INC)
1600 Wallace Blvd, Amarillo, TX 79106-1799
Tel (806) 212-2000 *Founded/Ownrshp* 2012
Sales 31.7MM[E] *EMP* 2,600[E]
SIC 8062

D-U-N-S 96-977-0960
AHS CLAREMORE REGIONAL HOSPITAL LLC
HILLCREST HOSPITAL CLAREMORE
(*Suby of* AHS HILLCREST HEALTHCARE SYSTEM LLC) ★
1202 N Muskogee Pl, Claremore, OK 74017-3058
Tel (918) 341-2556 *Founded/Ownrshp* 2012
Sales 1.0MM[E] *EMP* 3,729[E]
SIC 8062 General medical & surgical hospitals
CEO: David Chaussard

D-U-N-S 07-849-1209
AHS HILLCREST HEALTHCARE SYSTEM LLC
(*Suby of* AHS LEGACY OPERATIONS LLC) ★
1 Burton Hills Blvd # 250, Nashville, TN 37215-6293
Tel (615) 296-3000 *Founded/Ownrshp* 2009
Sales 702.1MM[E] *EMP* 6,501[E]
SIC 8062 General medical & surgical hospitals
Pr: David T Vandewater
Snr Ntwrk: Ardent H Brad

D-U-N-S 04-907-3091
AHS HILLCREST MEDICAL CENTER LLC
(*Suby of* AHS HILLCREST HEALTHCARE SYSTEM LLC) ★
1120 S Utica Ave, Tulsa, OK 74104-4012
Tel (918) 579-1000 *Founded/Ownrshp* 2012
Sales 472.4MM *EMP* 2,126
SIC 8062 General medical & surgical hospitals
CEO: Kevin Gross
Sr VP: Stephen C Petrovich
VP: Stephanie Gibson
Dir Rx: Joe Forcum
Adm Dir: Barbara Poulter
Adm Dir: Karna Williams
Prac Mgr: Cathy Garner
Off Mgr: Kay Baldridge
Off Mgr: Carrie Bowen
Off Mgr: Pamela Johnson
Nurse Mgr: Lauren Lasley

D-U-N-S 96-246-4756
AHS HOSPITAL CORP
MORRISTOWN MEMORIAL HOSPITAL
465 South St, Morristown, NJ 07960-6442
Tel (973) 660-3100 *Founded/Ownrshp* 1996
Sales 1.6MMM *EMP* 7,300
Accts Pricewaterhousecoopers Llp F
SIC 8062 8249 General medical & surgical hospitals; Vocational schools
Pr: Joseph A Trunfio
* *CFO:* Kevin Lenahan
* *VP:* Joseph A Dipaolo
* *VP:* Andrew L Kovach
VP: New Person
VP: Linda Reed
Sfty Mgr: William Damiano
Doctor: David Bullek
Doctor: Andrew Willis

D-U-N-S 08-002-5436
AHS LEGACY OPERATIONS LLC
(*Suby of* ARDENT LEGACY ACQUISITIONS INC) ★
1 Burton Hills Blvd, Nashville, TN 37215-6293
Tel (615) 296-3000 *Founded/Ownrshp* 2015
Sales 723.1MM[E] *EMP* 7,961[E]
SIC 8069 Specialty hospitals, except psychiatric
CEO: David T Vandewater

D-U-N-S 61-222-5656
AHS OKLAHOMA HEALTH SYSTEM LLP
110 W 7th St Ste 2540, Tulsa, OK 74119-1104
Tel (918) 579-1000 *Founded/Ownrshp* 2013
Sales NA *EMP* 3,170
SIC 8062 8069 7352 6512 7389 5999

D-U-N-S 96-977-1117
AHS SOUTHCREST HOSPITAL LLC
HILLCREST HOSPITAL SOUTH
(*Suby of* AHS HILLCREST HEALTHCARE SYSTEM LLC) ★
8801 S 101st East Ave, Tulsa, OK 74133-5716
Tel (918) 294-4000 *Founded/Ownrshp* 2012
Sales 154.7MM *EMP* 5
SIC 8062 General medical & surgical hospitals

D-U-N-S 86-855-2816
AHS TULSA REGIONAL MEDICAL CENTER LLC
744 W 9th St P252, Tulsa, OK 74127-9020
Tel (918) 587-2561 *Founded/Ownrshp* 2009
Sales 44.0MM[E] *EMP* 1,225[E]
SIC 8062 General medical & surgical hospitals
CEO: Dan Sieker

AHS-MEDREC
See ACCOUNTABLE HEALTHCARE STAFFING INC

D-U-N-S 02-909-5570
AHS/CENTRAL TEXAS INC
ADVENTIST HEALTH SYSTEM
(*Suby of* ADVENTIST HEALTH SYSTEM/WEST) ★
900 Hope Way, Altamonte Springs, FL 32714-1502
Tel (407) 357-1000 *Founded/Ownrshp* 1991
Sales 206.1MM[E] *EMP* 5,404[E]
SIC 8062 General medical & surgical hospitals
Pr: Don Jernigan
* *Ex VP:* Terry D Shaw
* *Sr VP:* Robert R Henderschedt

Sr VP: Sandra Johnson
VP: David L Huffman
* *VP:* Richard K Reiner
VP: Timothy J Reiner
Assoc Dir: Nicole McKernan
Assoc Dir: Jason Sanders
Comm Man: Kevin Edgerton
Ex Dir: Carole Owens

AHT INSURANCE
See ARMFIELD HARRISON & THOMAS INC

D-U-N-S 06-958-6055
AHTNA INC
110 W 38th Ave Ste 100, Anchorage, AK 99503-5677
Tel (907) 868-8250 *Founded/Ownrshp* 1972
Sales 242.1MM[E] *EMP* 2,000
SIC 1629 7389 1542 1521

D-U-N-S 03-521-1387
AI DUPONT HOSPITAL FOR CHILDREN
1600 Rockland Rd, Wilmington, DE 19803-3607
Tel (302) 651-4620 *Founded/Ownrshp* 1940
Sales 29.3MM[E] *EMP* 4,000
SIC 8062 General medical & surgical hospitals
Pr: David Bailey MD
* *Sr VP:* Steven R Sparks
* *VP:* Gina Altieri
* *VP:* R Jay Cummings
* *VP:* Debbie I Chang

D-U-N-S 96-895-9614
AI ENTERTAINMENT HOLDINGS LLC
(*Suby of* ACCESS INDUSTRIES INC) ★
730 5th Ave Fl 20, New York, NY 10019-4105
Tel (212) 247-6400 *Founded/Ownrshp* 2011
Sales 3.2MMM[E] *EMP* 4,211[E]
SIC 2731 Book music: publishing & printing
Pr: Lincoln Benet

D-U-N-S 01-202-4741
AI FRIEDMAN LP
A I FRIEDMAN
44 W 18th St Fl 4, New York, NY 10011-4645
Tel (212) 243-9000 *Founded/Ownrshp* 1989
Sales 245.3MM[E] *EMP* 185
SIC 5199 5945 Artists' materials; Arts & crafts supplies
Pt: Jim White
CFO: Gary Charkow
CFO: Jorge Morales
Bd of Dir: Eric Ramos
Sales Asso: Mike Campbell
Sales Asso: Michelle Donahue

D-U-N-S 03-573-2973 IMP
AIA CORP
ADVENTURES IN ADVERTISING
800 W Winneconne Ave, Neenah, WI 54956-3196
Tel (920) 886-3700 *Founded/Ownrshp* 2013
Sales 93.4MM[E] *EMP* 75
SIC 5199 Advertising specialties
Pr: David Woods
* *CFO:* Thomas Lehr
VP: Jim Roccia

AIAC
See AMERICAN INDUSTRIAL ACQUISITION CORP

AIAC
See AMERICAN INDUSTRIAL ACQUISITION CORP

AICO
See AMINI INNOVATION CORP

AICPA
See AMERICAN INSTITUTE OF CERTIFIED PUBLIC ACCOUNTANTS

D-U-N-S 07-908-6911
AID HOLDINGS LLC
W140n8981 Lilly Rd, Menomonee Falls, WI 53051-2325
Tel (262) 257-8888 *Founded/Ownrshp* 2013
Sales 293.3MM[E] *EMP* 4,200
SIC 8052 8051 8059 8082 Intermediate care facilities; Skilled nursing care facilities; Personal care home, with health care; Home health care services
CEO: Jack R Callison Jr

AIDB CHILDREN & YOUTH PROGRAMS
See ALABAMA INSTITUTE FOR DEAF AND BLIND

D-U-N-S 16-146-3146
■ **AIDELLS SAUSAGE CO INC**
(*Suby of* SARA LEE FOOD & BEVERAGE) ★
2411 Baumann Ave, San Lorenzo, CA 94580-1801
Tel (510) 614-5450 *Founded/Ownrshp* 2011
Sales 174.7MM[E] *EMP* 900
SIC 2013 5147 Sausages & other prepared meats; Meats & meat products
Pr: Ernie Gabiati
Sr VP: Mike Jones
VP: Jerry Lu
Exec: Kerry Heffernan
MIS Dir: Dan Vuletich
VP Opers: Storie Johnson
Sls Dir: Kevin Heraty
Sales Asso: Jerry Kriz
Sales Asso: Erin Wood

D-U-N-S 60-796-3980 IMP
AIDS HEALTHCARE FOUNDATION
LINN HOUSE
6255 W Sunset Blvd Fl 21, Los Angeles, CA 90028-7422
Tel (323) 860-5200 *Founded/Ownrshp* 1987
Sales 1.0MMM *EMP* 2,331
Accts Vasquez & Company Llp Los Ang
SIC 5932 8093 5912 Used merchandise stores; Specialty outpatient clinics; Drug stores
CEO: Michael Arthur Weinstein
* *CFO:* Lyle Honig
* *Ch:* Rodney L Wright
* *Sr VP:* Peter Reis
Assoc Dir: Oscar Aymbinder
Dir Rx: Arlette De
Dir Rx: Maryanna Golovash
* *Prin:* Scott Carruthers
Ex Dir: Lisha Wilson

Nurse Mgr: Christina Humphrey
Off Admin: Marcelo Escobar

AIG
See WESTERN NATIONAL LIFE INSURANCE CO

AIG
See AMERICAN INTERNATIONAL GROUP INC

AIG
See AMERICAN GENERAL LIFE INSURANCE CO OF DELAWARE

D-U-N-S 62-037-1435
■ **AIG CAPITAL CORP**
(*Suby of* AIG) ★
70 Pine St Fl 11, New York, NY 10270-0001
Tel (908) 679-3150 *Founded/Ownrshp* 1983
Sales NA *EMP* 7,000[E]
SIC 6411 6799 Insurance information & consulting services; Investors
Ch Bd: William N Dooley
COO: Frank E Celli
Ofcr: Robert Colonna
* *VP:* Neil Friedman
VP: Raymond Hampel
VP: Nancy Noto
IT Man: James Sweeney
Genl Couns: Michael McKiernan

D-U-N-S 09-506-1370
■ **AIG CLAIM SERVICES INC**
(*Suby of* AIG) ★
100 Connell Dr Ste 2100, Berkeley Heights, NJ 07922-2740
Tel (973) 402-2800 *Founded/Ownrshp* 1977
Sales NA *EMP* 2,600
SIC 6411 8111 Insurance agents, brokers & service; Legal services
Ch: Robert M Sandler
Pr: Stanton F Long
COO: Anthony J Galioto
CFO: William McDonough
Treas: William M Dooley
Ofcr: Mark Neidich
Ofcr: Dheeraj Salhotra
Sr VP: Phil Rhodes
Sr VP: Mark Vanderveen
VP: Steven Allen
VP: Terri Austin
VP: Gary Gyscek
VP: David C Patch
VP: Lynn Santangelo
VP: Charles B Weber

D-U-N-S 92-698-7777
■ **AIG DIRECT INSURANCE SERVICES INC**
(*Suby of* AMERICAN GENERAL LIFE INSURANCE CO) ★
9640 Gran Rdge Dr Ste 200, San Diego, CA 92123
Tel (858) 309-3000 *Founded/Ownrshp* 2007
Sales NA *EMP* 275
SIC 6411 Insurance agents, brokers & service
CEO: Ron Harris
Treas: Robert F Herbert Jr
* *Ex VP:* Laura Huffman
VP: Richard Gravette
* *VP:* Patty Karstein
* *VP:* Kevin Wilshusen
MIS Dir: Michael Bryce
IT Man: Greg Patrick
Sls Mgr: Robert Avats

D-U-N-S 55-644-1343
■ **AIG FUNDING INC**
(*Suby of* AIG) ★
70 Pine St Fl 50, New York, NY 10270-0001
Tel (212) 770-7000 *Founded/Ownrshp* 1986
Sales NA *EMP* 1,000
SIC 6411 6153 Insurance agents, brokers & service; Purchasers of accounts receivable & commercial paper
Pr: Edward E Matthews

D-U-N-S 13-208-0826
■ **AIG GLOBAL ASSET MANAGEMENT HOLDINGS CORP**
(*Suby of* AIG CAPITAL CORP) ★
111 8th Ave, New York, NY 10011-5201
Tel (212) 709-6100 *Founded/Ownrshp* 1995
Sales 299.7MM[E] *EMP* 5,030
SIC 6722 6411 Management investment, open-end; Insurance agents, brokers & service
Pr: Bob Benmosche

D-U-N-S 01-495-0757
■ **AIG GLOBAL INVESTMENT CORP**
(*Suby of* AIG GLOBAL ASSET MANAGEMENT HOLDINGS CORP) ★
175 Water St Fl 18, New York, NY 10038-4969
Tel (212) 770-7000 *Founded/Ownrshp* 2001
Sales 295.5MM[E] *EMP* 5,030
SIC 6722 6411 Management investment, open-end; Insurance agents, brokers & service
CEO: Win Jay Neuger
VP: Guillermo P Donadini
VP: Valerie Kwong
VP: Frank Scalia
Mng Dir: Christopher Lee

D-U-N-S 80-831-9425
■ **AIG GLOBAL REAL ESTATE INVESTMENT CORP**
AIG INVESTMENTS
(*Suby of* AIG) ★
32 Old Slip Fl 28, New York, NY 10005-3500
Tel (646) 857-2300 *Founded/Ownrshp* 1988
Sales 78.3MM[E] *EMP* 2,500
SIC 6512 6411 Nonresidential building operators; Insurance agents, brokers & service
Pr: Robert G Gifford

AIG GLOBAL SERVICES, INC.
See AIG TECHNOLOGIES INC

D-U-N-S 13-209-2326
■ AIG HIGHSTAR CAPITAL LP
(*Suby of* AIG GLOBAL INVESTMENT CORP) ★
277 Park Ave Fl 45, New York, NY 10172-2903
Tel (646) 857-8700 *Founded/Ownrshp* 2010
Sales 258.5MM^E *EMP* 4,380
SIC 6722 4491 Money market mutual funds; Stevedoring
CFO: Hayden Horowitz

AIG INVESTMENTS
See AIG GLOBAL REAL ESTATE INVESTMENT CORP

D-U-N-S 00-793-0811
■ AIG LIFE HOLDINGS INC (TX)
(*Suby of* AIG) ★
2929 Allen Pkwy, Houston, TX 77019-7100
Tel (713) 522-1111 *Founded/Ownrshp* 1926, 2001
Sales NA *EMP* 11,300
SIC 6311 6321 6331 6141 6162 6153 Life insurance carriers; Health insurance carriers; Accident insurance carriers; Fire, marine & casualty insurance: stock; Consumer finance companies; Installment sales finance, other than banks; Mortgage bankers; Mercantile financing
Pr: Rodney O Martin Jr
CFO: Greg Hayes
CFO: Nicholas Rassmussen
**CFO:* Christopher J Swift
Treas: Tara S Rock
Assoc VP: Jenny Swan
Sr VP: Craig Cheyne
VP: Bruce R Abrams
VP: Scott Brown
VP: Dave Butterfield
VP: Mark Childs
VP: Robert Cicchi
VP: Brad Gabel
VP: Allen Holt
VP: Rembert Owen
Assoc Dir: Mary Midoux
Assoc Dir: John Sherman

D-U-N-S 05-522-0305
■ AIG PROPERTY CASUALTY CO
(*Suby of* AIG) ★
70 Pine St Fl 1, New York, NY 10005-1522
Tel (800) 551-0824 *Founded/Ownrshp* 1871
Sales NA *EMP* 139
SIC 6411 Insurance agents, brokers & service
VP: Patrick Foley
COO: Robert Beier
Ofcr: Mark V Veen
Sr VP: Andy Hockenhull
Sr VP: Ernest Patrikis
Sr VP: Rhonda Prussack
Sr VP: Jeff Watts
VP: Brian Bornstein
VP: Anne Brenner
**VP:* Michael Joseph Castelli
VP: Joseph D Cook
VP: Gail Culleton
VP: Joseph Demauro
VP: John Doyle
VP: Janis Dunstan
VP: Jim Galli
VP: David Garlow
VP: Martin Gilligan
VP: John Gerheart Hughes
VP: Ronald Latz
VP: Chris Lezny
Board of Directors: Maurice R Greenberg, Edwin Manton, Howard Ian Smith, William D Smith

D-U-N-S 96-544-2846
■ AIG PROPERTY CASUALTY INC
CHARTIS INSURANCE
(*Suby of* AIG) ★
175 Water St Fl 5, New York, NY 10038-4918
Tel (212) 458-5000 *Founded/Ownrshp* 2009
Sales NA *EMP* 40,000^E
SIC 6331 6321 6311 Fire, marine & casualty insurance; Accident insurance carriers; Health insurance carriers; Life insurance carriers
CEO: Peter Douglas Hancock
Pr: James E Mostofi
**V Ch Bd:* Kristian P Moor
Bd of Dir: Bill Carr
Ofcr: Tim Carter
Ex VP: Marybeth Diffley
Sr VP: Stephen Bisbee
Sr VP: Ted Devivo
Sr VP: Don Hurter
Sr VP: Joseph Puzzo
Sr VP: Greg Sterling
VP: Yussur Abrar
VP: Jim Albes
VP: Marie Ali
VP: Gerard Louis
VP: Mike McCabe
VP: Lawrence Moloney
VP: Charith Perera
VP: Karen Votta
Dir Bus: Royce Phillips

D-U-N-S 00-727-0028
■ AIG TECHNOLOGIES INC
AIG GLOBAL SERVICES, INC.
(*Suby of* AIG) ★
2 Peach Tree Hill Rd, Livingston, NJ 07039-5701
Tel (973) 597-0285 *Founded/Ownrshp* 1972
Sales 163.4MM^E *EMP* 870
SIC 8742 6411 7374 Management consulting services; Insurance agents, brokers & service; Data processing service
Pr: Lawrence W English
Treas: Carol Ann McFate
**Sr VP:* Anthony J Tesoriero
**VP:* Warren Arthur Luedecker Jr
VP: Arthur M Troccoli
Board of Directors: Edward E Matthews, Robert M Sandler, Howard I Smith, Ernest E Stemple, Thomas R Tizzio

AIG VALIC
See VARIABLE ANNUITY LIFE INSURANCE CO (INC)

D-U-N-S 04-600-0041
AIH FLINTCO LLC
(*Suby of* ALBERICI GROUP INC) ★
8800 Page Ave, Saint Louis, MO 63114-6106
Tel (314) 733-2000 *Founded/Ownrshp* 2012
Sales 770.8MM^E *EMP* 300^E
SIC 1389 1522 Construction, repair & dismantling services; Apartment building construction

D-U-N-S 07-930-9551
AIH LLC
ASTEC INTERNATIONAL HOLDING
(*Suby of* ARTESYN NORTH AMERICA LLC) ★
5810 Van Allen Way, Carlsbad, CA 92008-7300
Tel (760) 930-4600 *Founded/Ownrshp* 2003
Sales 739.4MM^E *EMP* 23,000^E
SIC 3629 3621 3679 Power conversion units, a.c. to d.c.: static-electric; Power generators; Power supplies, all types: static
CEO: Jay Geldmacher
CFO: Tom Rosenast
VP: Mark Rice

D-U-N-S 00-163-7149 IMP
AIJJ ENTERPRISES INC (NY)
RAINBOW SHOPS
1000 Pennsylvania Ave, Brooklyn, NY 11207-8417
Tel (718) 485-3000 *Founded/Ownrshp* 1990
Sales 825.8MM^E *EMP* 12,000
SIC 5621

AIKEN COUNTY PUBLIC SCHOOLS
See AIKEN COUNTY SCHOOL DISTRICT

D-U-N-S 07-799-6338
AIKEN COUNTY SCHOOL DISTRICT
AIKEN COUNTY PUBLIC SCHOOLS
1000 Brookhaven Dr, Aiken, SC 29803-2108
Tel (803) 641-2428 *Founded/Ownrshp* 1967
Sales 140.4MM^E *EMP* 3,050
SIC 8211 Public elementary & secondary schools
Pr Dir: Merryglenne Piccolino
Teacher Pr: Tomiko Smalls
HC Dir: Monica Mazzell

D-U-N-S 00-791-9020
AIKEN ELECTRIC COOPERATIVE INC (SC)
2790 Wagener Rd, Aiken, SC 29801-8126
Tel (803) 649-6245 *Founded/Ownrshp* 1938
Sales 110.4MM^E *EMP* 140
Accts Mcnair Mclemore Middlebrooks
SIC 4911 4841 Electric services; Direct broadcast satellite services (DBS)
CEO: Gary L Stooksbury
Treas: Frank Dorn
Trst: J M Dorn
VP: Charles W Prosser
Admn Mgr: Michael Campbell
Dir IT: Dell Hunnicutt
IT Man: Celine Davis
IT Man: Jef Gray

D-U-N-S 03-011-2551
■ AIKEN REGIONAL MEDICAL CENTERS LLC (SC)
AURORA PAVILION
(*Suby of* UNIVERSAL HEALTH SERVICES INC) ★
302 University Pkwy, Aiken, SC 29801-2792
Tel (803) 641-5000 *Founded/Ownrshp* 1976, 1995
Sales 186.7MM *EMP* 1,200^E
SIC 8062 General medical & surgical hospitals
CEO: Vance Reynolds
**COO:* Matthew Merrifield
**CFO:* Cynthia Long
Dir Rx: Andrew Philipp
Adm Dir: Cathy Robey-Williams
Info Man: Talmon Ayers
Mktg Dir: Melissa Summer
Pharmcst: Amanda Smith
Pharmcst: Greg Weaver

AIL
See AMERICAN INCOME LIFE

AIM AEROSPACE
See AIM GROUP USA INC

D-U-N-S 04-280-1944
AIM AEROSPACE SUMNER INC
(*Suby of* AIM AEROSPACE) ★
1502 20th St Nw, Auburn, WA 98001-3428
Tel (253) 804-3355 *Founded/Ownrshp* 1972
Sales 97.0MM^E *EMP* 700
SIC 3728 3543 Aircraft parts & equipment; Industrial patterns
CEO: Jeff Smith
**Pr:* John Feutz
**CFO:* Hans Ulland
**VP:* Brian J Retzloff
Sfty Dirs: Kirk Flannery

AIM BLUE CHIP FUNDS
See INVESCO AIM ADVISORS INC

D-U-N-S 83-011-6190
AIM GROUP INC
(*Suby of* AIM GROUP (ALBERTA) INC, THE)
9450 Grogans Mill Rd # 120, The Woodlands, TX 77380-3626
Tel (281) 847-2000 *Founded/Ownrshp* 1997
Sales 98.4MM^E *EMP* 1,700
SIC 8711 Engineering services
Pr: Dave Megson
**Ex VP:* Michael R Child
**VP:* Meredith Egan

D-U-N-S 60-603-8800
AIM GROUP USA INC
AIM AEROSPACE
705 Sw 7th St, Renton, WA 98057-2915
Tel (425) 235-2750 *Founded/Ownrshp* 1989
Sales 132.5MM^E *EMP* 999
SIC 3728 Aircraft body & wing assemblies & parts
Pr: Mark Potensky
**Ch:* Jeff Smith

D-U-N-S 07-113-0942
AIM LEASING CO
NATIONALEASE
1500 Trumbull Ave, Girard, OH 44420-3453
Tel (330) 759-0438 *Founded/Ownrshp* 1982
Sales 248.8MM^E *EMP* 2,007
SIC 7513 7538 4212 5983 Truck leasing, without drivers; General truck repair; Truck rental with drivers; Fuel oil dealers
Pr: Thomas Fleming
**Treas:* Rick Fox
**VP:* Terry Dimascio
CIO: John Reed
VP Opers: Bruce P Berger
Sfty Mgr: John Rugarber
Opers Mgr: Adam Olrich

D-U-N-S 04-669-2980 IMP
AIM MEDIA TEXAS OPERATING LLC
MONITOR, THE
1400 E Nolana Ave, McAllen, TX 78504-6111
Tel (956) 683-4000 *Founded/Ownrshp* 2012
Sales 89.6MM^E *EMP* 525^E
SIC 2711 4899 Newspapers, publishing & printing; Data communication services
CEO: Jeremy L Halbreich
**Pr:* William R Starks

AIM MUTUAL INSURANCE CO
See ASSOCIATED INDUSTRIES OF MASSACHUSETTS MUTUAL INSURANCE CO

AIM SPECIALTY HEALTH
See AMERICAN IMAGING MANAGEMENT INC

D-U-N-S 10-865-3122 IMP/EXP
AIM SPECIALTY MATERIALS USA
AMERICAN IRON & METAL
(*Suby of* COMPAGNIE AMERICAINE DE FER & METAUX INC, LA)
25 Kenney Dr, Cranston, RI 02920-4443
Tel (401) 463-5605 *Founded/Ownrshp* 1936
Sales 381.3MM^E *EMP* 2,000^E
SIC 3291 Abrasive metal & steel products
CEO: Herbert Black
**Pr:* Richard Black
**Sec:* Ronald Black

AIM SUPPLY CO
See NESTOR SALES LLC

D-U-N-S 13-047-8618
AIMBRIDGE HOSPITALITY LLC
5851 Legacy Cir Ste 400, Plano, TX 75024-5979
Tel (972) 952-0200 *Founded/Ownrshp* 2012
Sales 582.4MM^E *EMP* 5,400
SIC 8741 Hotel or motel management
Pr: Dave Johnson
Pr: Tony Maness
Pr: Richard T Sprecher
COO: Robert Burg
CFO: Judy Hendrick
Ex VP: Greg Moundas
Sr VP: Vince Cuce
Sr VP: Kevin Detz
Sr VP: Michael Johnson
Sr VP: Jack McHugh
Sr VP: Angel Phifer
Sr VP: Lynne Roberts
VP: David L Capps
VP: Lisa Holman
VP: Nolan Wrentmore
Exec: Cici Thomas

AIMCO
See APARTMENT INVESTMENT & MANAGEMENT CO

D-U-N-S 86-132-3855
AIMCO PROPERTIES LP
4582 S Ulster St Ste 1100, Denver, CO 80237-2662
Tel (303) 757-8101 *Founded/Ownrshp* 1994
Sales 981.3MM *EMP* 1,932
SIC 6798 Real estate investment trusts
Ch Bd: Terry Considine
CFO: Ernest M Freedman
Bd of Dir: Cara M Nelson

D-U-N-S 07-973-1145
■ AIMCO-GP INC
(*Suby of* AIMCO) ★
4582 S Ulster St Ste 1100, Denver, CO 80237-2662
Tel (303) 757-8101 *Founded/Ownrshp* 1995
Sales 111.4MM^E *EMP* 1,693
SIC 6798 Real estate investment trusts
Ch Bd: Terry Considine

D-U-N-S 07-850-6167
■ AIMCO-LP TRUST
(*Suby of* AIMCO) ★
4582 S Ulster St Ste 1100, Denver, CO 80237-2662
Tel (303) 757-8101 *Founded/Ownrshp* 1995
Sales 48.3MM^E *EMP* 2,640
SIC 6798 Real estate investment trusts
Ch Bd: Terry Considine

D-U-N-S 01-174-4778
AIMIA PROPRIETARY LOYALTY US INC
(*Suby of* AIMIA INC)
100 N 6th St Ste 700b, Minneapolis, MN 55403-1535
Tel (763) 445-3000 *Founded/Ownrshp* 1969
Sales 539.5MM^E *EMP* 3,800
SIC 8741

AINA HOLDINGS
See AIRBUS AMERICAS INC

D-U-N-S 06-873-0027
AINSWORTH PET NUTRITION LLC
ENHANCE
984 Water St, Meadville, PA 16335-3450
Tel (814) 724-7710 *Founded/Ownrshp* 1933
Sales 95.1MM^E *EMP* 320^E
SIC 2047

AIP AEROSPACE
See AIP/AEROSPACE HOLDINGS LLC

AIP AEROSPACE HOLDINGS
See COAST COMPOSITES LLC

D-U-N-S 62-389-8678
AIP LLC
AMERICAN INDUSTRIAL PARTNERS
330 Madison Ave Fl 28, New York, NY 10017-5018
Tel (212) 627-2360 *Founded/Ownrshp* 2002
Sales 1.3MMM^E *EMP* 3,600
SIC 6799 Investors
Pr: Larry Denbrock

D-U-N-S 07-872-2374 IMP
AIP/AEROSPACE HOLDINGS LLC
AIP AEROSPACE
330 Madison Ave Fl 28, New York, NY 10017-5018
Tel (212) 916-8142 *Founded/Ownrshp* 2012
Sales 200.0MM *EMP* 1,108
Accts Mcgladrey Llp New York Ny
SIC 3721 6799 Aircraft; Investors
CEO: Brian Williams
**CFO:* Steve Littauer
**CIO:* Rajesh Kasaraneni

D-U-N-S 83-150-0413
AIP/FW FUNDING INC
1031 E Us Highway 224, Decatur, IN 46733-2737
Tel (212) 627-2360 *Founded/Ownrshp* 2009
Sales 139.0MM^E *EMP* 600
SIC 3716 Motor homes
Pr: Dino Cusumano
**VP:* Paul Bamatter

AIPC
See AMERICAN ITALIAN PASTA CO

AIR CARGO HANDLING SERVICE
See AEROGROUND INC

D-U-N-S 15-055-3592 IMP/EXP
AIR CRUISERS CO LLC
(*Suby of* ZODIAC AEROSYSTEMS) ★
1747 State Route 34, Wall Township, NJ 07727-3935
Tel (732) 681-3527 *Founded/Ownrshp* 2004
Sales 386.2MM^E *EMP* 2,759
SIC 2531 3069 3728 2399 Seats, aircraft; Air-supported rubber structures; Fuel tanks, aircraft; Parachutes
**CFO:* John Melone
VP: T Webb
Exec: Tina Andreasson
Genl Mgr: Walid Nicro
Genl Mgr: Kelly Svihla
Dir IT: Robert Schalhoub
IT Man: Glenn Anders
VP Mfg: Neil Cavaleri
Plnt Mgr: Paul Patterson
Snr Mgr: Sherry Shepherd

D-U-N-S 07-091-1112
AIR DISTRIBUTION TECHNOLOGIES INC
(*Suby of* JOHNSON CONTROLS INC) ★
605 Shiloh Rd, Plano, TX 75074-7210
Tel (972) 943-6100 *Founded/Ownrshp* 2012
Sales 1.1MMM^E *EMP* 2,070^E
SIC 3585 Refrigeration & heating equipment

AIR EVAC SERVICES
See PHI AIR MEDICAL LLC

D-U-N-S 00-985-4241 IMP
AIR EXPRESS INTERNATIONAL USA INC
DHL GLOBAL FORWARDING
(*Suby of* DHL) ★
1801 Nw 82nd Ave, Doral, FL 33126-1013
Tel (786) 264-3500 *Founded/Ownrshp* 1983
Sales 813.6MM^E *EMP* 3,300
SIC 4731 4513

AIR FILTERS SALES & SERVICE
See PUROLATOR PRODUCTS AIR FILTRATION CO

D-U-N-S 07-845-3061
AIR INDIA LIMITED
570 Lexington Ave Rm 1401, New York, NY 10022-6841
Tel (212) 407-1400 *Founded/Ownrshp* 2007
Sales 260.0MM *EMP* 70
SIC 7363 Pilot service, aviation
Ch: Shri Rohit Nandan
Exec: Ferdoas Nagarvala
Rgnl Mgr: Rishi Tang
**Genl Mgr:* Pervin B Choksey

D-U-N-S 96-248-5723
▲ AIR LEASE CORP
2000 Avenue Of The Stars 1000n, Los Angeles, CA 90067-4734
Tel (310) 553-0555 *Founded/Ownrshp* 2010
Sales 1.2MMM *EMP* 74^E
Tkr Sym AL *Exch* NYS
SIC 7359 7389 Equipment rental & leasing; Aircraft & industrial truck rental services; Aircraft rental; Financial services
Pr: John L Plueger
**Ch Bd:* Steven F Udvar-Hazy
CFO: Gregory B Willis
Chf Cred: Carol H Forsyte
Ex VP: Marc H Baer
Ex VP: Jie Chen
Ex VP: Alex A Khatibi
Ex VP: Kishore Korde
Ex VP: Grant A Levy
Sr VP: John D Poerschke
Board of Directors: Matthew J Hart, Cheryl Gordon Krongard, Marshall O Larsen, Robert M Milton, Ian M Saines, Ronald D Sugar

D-U-N-S 17-329-3994 IMP/EXP
AIR LIQUIDE ADVANCED MATERIALS INC
(*Suby of* AIR LIQUIDE SA ETU EXPLOIT PROCE)
9811 Katy Fwy Ste 100, Houston, TX 77024-1274
Tel (713) 624-8000 *Founded/Ownrshp* 2013
Sales 86.9MM^E *EMP* 230
SIC 2813 Industrial gases
Pr: Paul Burlingame
**CFO:* Richard Hallett
QA Dir: Justine Falk
Snr Mgr: Peter Smith

D-U-N-S 79-703-1494 IMP
AIR LIQUIDE ADVANCED TECHNOLOGIES US LLC
(*Suby of* AMERICAN AIR LIQUIDE HOLDINGS INC) ★
9807 Katy Fwy, Houston, TX 77024-1275
Tel (713) 624-8000 *Founded/Ownrshp* 2011
Sales 749.6MM^E *EMP* 5,000
SIC 2813 Industrial gases
CEO: Ole Hoefelmann
**Pr:* Michael F Smith
Prin: Sabrina Kristobak

D-U-N-S 00-331-2600 IMP/EXP
AIR LIQUIDE AMERICA LP
(*Suby of* AMERICAN AIR LIQUIDE HOLDINGS INC) ★
9811 Katy Fwy Ste 100, Houston, TX 77024-1274
Tel (713) 624-8000 *Founded/Ownrshp* 1964
Sales 591.6MM^E *EMP* 600
SIC 5084 3533 2813 3569

D-U-N-S 80-843-4711 IMP/EXP
AIR LIQUIDE AMERICA SPECIALTY GASES LLC
(*Suby of* AMERICAN AIR LIQUIDE HOLDINGS INC) ★
2700 Post Oak Blvd, Houston, TX 77056-5784
Tel (800) 217-2688 *Founded/Ownrshp* 2007
Sales 182.0MM^E *EMP* 600
SIC 2911 2813 Petroleum refining; Industrial gases
Pr: David Meneses
Treas: Gregg Alexander

D-U-N-S 18-001-5278 IMP
AIR LIQUIDE ELECTRONICS US LP
(*Suby of* AMERICAN AIR LIQUIDE HOLDINGS INC) ★
9101 Lyndon B Johnson Fwy # 800, Dallas, TX 75243-1920
Tel (972) 301-5200 *Founded/Ownrshp* 2014
Sales 2.4MMM *EMP* 42,300
SIC 2813 3564 8631 2819 Industrial gases; Dust or fume collecting equipment, industrial; Labor unions & similar labor organizations; Industrial inorganic chemicals
Pr: Justin Beres
Ex VP: Leonardo Caroli
**VP:* Kevin Feeney
**Prin:* G B Alexander
Genl Mgr: Mark Ohlmeier
Dir IT: Glenda Candelaria
Plnt Mgr: Mike Crist
Plnt Mgr: Steve Jordan
Sls&Mrk Ex: Johnny Wosniack
Snr Mgr: Thomas Mnter

D-U-N-S 18-001-5336 IMP/EXP
AIR LIQUIDE INDUSTRIAL US LP
2700 Post Oak Blvd # 1800, Houston, TX 77056-5784
Tel (713) 624-8000 *Founded/Ownrshp* 2011
Sales 263.6MM^E *EMP* 1,400^E
SIC 2813

D-U-N-S 18-001-5062 IMP
AIR LIQUIDE LARGE INDUSTRIES US LP
(*Suby of* AMERICAN AIR LIQUIDE HOLDINGS INC) ★
9811 Katy Fwy Ste 100, Houston, TX 77024-1274
Tel (713) 624-8000 *Founded/Ownrshp* 2011
Sales 302.2MM^E *EMP* 600^E
SIC 2813 Industrial gases
Mng Pt: Roger Perreault
Pt: Gb Alexander
Pt: Kevin Feeney
Pr: Matt Wigle
Ex VP: Rich Jahr
Sr VP: Johnnye Wozniak
VP: Leonardo Caroli
VP: Ken Clarke
VP: Adam Peters
VP: Chip Stoicovy
IT Man: Minh Pham

D-U-N-S 19-599-5761
AIR LIQUIDE USA LLC
(*Suby of* AIR LIQUIDE AMERICA LP) ★
9811 Kepy Fwy Ste 100, Houston, TX 77024
Tel (713) 402-2221 *Founded/Ownrshp* 2004
Sales 204.1MM^E *EMP* 600^E
SIC 2813 Industrial gases
Pr: Michael J Graff
**VP:* Gregory B Alexander
VP: Scott Krapf
Exec: Jean Buono
CTO: Patti Hess
Dir IT: Sajjad Ahmed

D-U-N-S 10-849-3503
▲ AIR METHODS CORP
SAN ANTONIO AIRLIFE
7301 S Peoria St, Englewood, CO 80112-4133
Tel (303) 749-1330 *Founded/Ownrshp* 1982
Sales 1.0MMM *EMP* 4,798
Tkr Sym AIRM *Exch* NGS
SIC 4522 Air transportation, nonscheduled; Ambulance services, air
CEO: Aaron D Todd
**Ch Bd:* C David Kikumoto
Pr: David Doerr
Pr: Jim Greiner
CFO: Trent J Carman
CFO: Peter P Csapo
Chf Mktg O: David Frederick Edward Stuhlmi
Ex VP: David M Doerr
Sr VP: Crystal L Gordon
Sr VP: Leo Morrissette
VP: Mark Rambis
VP: Craig Yale
Board of Directors: Ralph J Bernstein, Mark D Carleton, John J Connolly, Jeffrey A Dorsey, Claire M Gulmi, Joseph E Whitters, Jessica L Wright

D-U-N-S 09-023-5982
AIR NATIONAL GUARD PENNSYLVANIA
(*Suby of* PA DEPARTMENT OF MILITARY AND VETERANS AFFAIRS) ★
215 S O 47 Bldg, Annville, PA 17003
Tel (717) 861-8667 *Founded/Ownrshp* 1930
Sales NA *EMP* 1,684
SIC 9711 National Guard;
Ex Dir: Col Stanley Jaworski
Genl Mgr: Gen Sollivan

AIR PREHEATER
See ARVOS INC

D-U-N-S 00-300-1070 IMP/EXP
▲ AIR PRODUCTS AND CHEMICALS INC
7201 Hamilton Blvd, Allentown, PA 18195-9642
Tel (610) 481-4911 *Founded/Ownrshp* 1940
Sales 9.5MMM *EMP* 19,700
Tkr Sym APD *Exch* NYS
SIC 2813 2842 2891 3569 Industrial gases; Oxygen, compressed or liquefied; Nitrogen; Argon; Ammonia, household; Adhesives; Gas producers, generators & other gas related equipment; Gas separators (machinery); Separators for steam, gas, vapor or air (machinery)
Ch Bd: Seifollah Ghasemi
Pr: Jeffry Byrne
Pr: Jean Dalstad
CFO: M Scott Crocco
Ofcr: John D Stanley
Ex VP: Guillermo Novo
Ex VP: Corning F Painter
Ex VP: Samir J Serhan
VP: Leslie Clay
VP: Elizabeth Klebe
VP: Caroline Lloyd
VP: Patricia Mattimore
VP: Laurie K Stewart

D-U-N-S 78-901-7688
■ AIR PRODUCTS MANUFACTURING CORP
(*Suby of* AIR PRODUCTS AND CHEMICALS INC) ★
6601 S Ridge Rd, Haysville, KS 67060-7134
Tel (316) 522-8181 *Founded/Ownrshp* 2014
Sales 192.3MM^E *EMP* 1,000
SIC 2813 2819 Industrial gases; Industrial inorganic chemicals
Pr: Pamela L Johnson

D-U-N-S 80-832-1871
AIR RESOURCES BOARD
A R B
(*Suby of* CAL/EPA) ★
1001 I St, Sacramento, CA 95814-2828
Tel (916) 322-2990 *Founded/Ownrshp* 1968
Sales NA *EMP* 1,225
SIC 9511 Environmental agencies;
Ch Bd: Allen Lloyd
Pr: Linda Smith
**CFO:* Judy Tanimoto
Ex VP: Eric Decetis
Exec: Barbara Bamberger
Exec: Aguila Brieanne
Exec: Hart Gerald
Exec: Debbie Sawaya
Counsel: Victoria Davis
Snr Mgr: Robert Fletcher
Snr Mgr: John Urkov

D-U-N-S 96-421-5156
AIR SAFETY EQUIPMENT INC
1601 State Route 27, Edison, NJ 08817-3464
Tel (732) 591-9412 *Founded/Ownrshp* 1976
Sales 54.3MM^E *EMP* 3,200
SIC 4581 Aircraft servicing & repairing
Pr: Captain Shital Rajan
**VP:* John Myer

D-U-N-S 11-237-3779
■ AIR SERV CORP
(*Suby of* ABM INDUSTRIES INC) ★
3399 Peachtree Rd Ne, Atlanta, GA 30326-1120
Tel (404) 926-4200 *Founded/Ownrshp* 2001
Sales 195.6MM^E *EMP* 1,000
Accts Bdo Usa Llp Atlanta Ga
SIC 4581 4111 Airports, flying fields & services; Airport transportation services, regular route
Ch Bd: Frank Argenbright Jr
**CEO:* Larry Parrotte
**COO:* David Lgamsey
**Sr VP:* John Montgomery
**Sr VP:* Don Ridgway
VP: Megan Jones
VP: Steve Wragg
Off Mgr: Jane Risley
Dir IT: Don Stephens
VP Opers: Michael Cox
Mktg Mgr: Harold Bailey

D-U-N-S 82-992-6794
AIR SERV SECURITY INC
INTERNATIONAL RAM ASSOCIATES
3399 Peachtree Rd Ne # 1800, Atlanta, GA 30326-1120
Tel (404) 926-4200 *Founded/Ownrshp* 2009
Sales 27.0MM *EMP* 1,200
SIC 4581 Airports, flying fields & services
Ch Bd: Frank Argenbright
**Pr:* Shannon Conklin
**Pr:* Tom Marano

D-U-N-S 08-151-8474
AIR STREAM CORP
AIR STREAM FOODS
3400 Lawson Blvd, Oceanside, NY 11572-3720
Tel (516) 763-1600 *Founded/Ownrshp* 1977
Sales 122.6MM^E *EMP* 128
SIC 5141 5148 Food brokers; Fruits, fresh
Ch Bd: Thomas Fitzsimmons
**Pr:* Robert Fitzsimmons
Opers Mgr: Dennis Reutter

AIR STREAM FOODS
See AIR STREAM CORP

D-U-N-S 02-053-5238 IMP
AIR SYSTEM COMPONENTS INC
A S C
(*Suby of* JOHNSON CONTROLS INC) ★
605 Shiloh Rd, Plano, TX 75074-7210
Tel (972) 212-4888 *Founded/Ownrshp* 2014
Sales 663.4MM^E *EMP* 2,300
SIC 3585 Air conditioning equipment, complete; Heating equipment, complete
Pr: Gordon Jones
**VP:* Jon Muckley
**VP:* Marc R Szczerba
CIO: Rich Risotti
Dir IT: Ron Davis
Plnt Mgr: Pam Young
Ql Cn Mgr: Lee Peacher

D-U-N-S 13-090-6105 IMP
AIR SYSTEMS INC
940 Remillard Ct Frnt, San Jose, CA 95122-2684
Tel (408) 280-1666 *Founded/Ownrshp* 2003
Sales 158.5MM *EMP* 500
SIC 1711 7623 Plumbing contractors; Refrigeration service & repair
CEO: Arthur Williams
**Exec:* Marty Cull
CIO: Kevin Soohoo
CTO: Michael Krommes
Sls Mgr: Paul Accinelli
Sls Mgr: Hussain Mandviwala
Snr PM: Jeff Balvanz

D-U-N-S 80-218-2852
▲ AIR TRANSPORT SERVICES GROUP INC
ATSG
145 Hunter Dr, Wilmington, OH 45177-9550
Tel (937) 382-5591 *Founded/Ownrshp* 1980
Sales 619.2MM *EMP* 2,170^E
Tkr Sym ATSG *Exch* NGS
SIC 4513 Air courier services
Pr: Joseph C Hete
**Ch Bd:* Randy D Rademacher
CFO: Quint O Turner
Chf Cred: Richard F Corrado
Bd of Dir: Jeffrey Vorholt
Sr VP: W Joseph Payne
Exec: Holly Ibaugh
Sfty Dirs: Steve Janasov
Snr Mgr: John Brown
Snr Mgr: John Vestal
Board of Directors: Richard Baudouin, Arthur J Lichte, J Christopher Teets, Jeffrey J Vorholt

D-U-N-S 62-142-7558 IMP
AIR TREATMENT CORP
640 N Puente St, Brea, CA 92821-2830
Tel (909) 869-7975 *Founded/Ownrshp* 2001
Sales 92.6MM^E *EMP* 125
SIC 5075 Electrical heating equipment; Air conditioning equipment, except room units
Pr: Mark Hartman
**CFO:* Deborah Hudson
**VP:* Greg Blackfelner
**VP:* Craig Domagala
**VP:* Tim Thomas
Off Admin: Meela Shah
Sls Mgr: Ken Mozek
Sales Asso: Lyvania Partida
Sales Asso: Renzo Segovia
Sales Asso: Elliott Spore

D-U-N-S 80-719-7819
AIR WISCONSIN AIRLINES CORP
UNITED EXPRESS
W6390 Challenger Dr # 203, Appleton, WI 54914-9120
Tel (920) 739-5123 *Founded/Ownrshp* 1993
Sales 300.9MM^E *EMP* 3,100^E
SIC 4512 Air transportation, scheduled
Pr: James P Rankin
V Ch: Bill Jordan
**COO:* Bob Frisch
**COO:* Vince Portaro
**CFO:* Christine Deister
Ofcr: Matthew Hennigan
Ofcr: Daniel Mincheff
**Sr VP:* Joel Kuplack
VP: Janet Huculak
VP: R Keith Johnson
VP: Rose Lussier
VP: Laurie Martin
VP: Gary Pratt
VP: Chris White
Dir: David Nesseler

D-U-N-S 62-208-4411
■ AIR WORLDWIDE CORP
(*Suby of* VERISK ANALYTICS) ★
131 Dartmouth St Ste 401, Boston, MA 02116-5386
Tel (617) 267-6645 *Founded/Ownrshp* 2005
Sales NA *EMP* 475^E
SIC 6411 Loss prevention services, insurance
Pr: Bill Churney
Treas: Paul Devlin
Sr VP: William Churney
Sr VP: Jay Guin
Sr VP: David Lalonde
Sr VP: Robert Nebold
Sr VP: Uday Virkud
VP: Ashish Belambe
VP: John Elbl
VP: Daniel Kaniewski
VP: Sudhir Potharaju
VP: John W Rollins

AIRAWARE
See SCHRADER-BRIDGEPORT INTERNATIONAL INC

D-U-N-S 03-424-3315
AIRBNB INC
888 Brannan St Ste 400, San Francisco, CA 94103-4932
Tel (415) 800-5959 *Founded/Ownrshp* 2008
Sales 198.1MM^E *EMP* 2,276
SIC 7041 Residence club, organization
CEO: Brian Chesky
Founder: Nathan Blecharczyk
Exec: Varsha RAO
Prgrm Mgr: Diana Wong
Tech Mgr: Gurer Kiratli
Software D: Jeff Yip
Sftwr Eng: Gil Birman
Sftwr Eng: Spike Brehm
Sftwr Eng: Stephen Bush
Sftwr Eng: Clint Kelly
Sftwr Eng: Mike Lewis

D-U-N-S 04-107-0749
AIRBORN ELECTRONICS INC
AESCO MANUFACTURING SERVICES
2230 Picton Pkwy, Akron, OH 44312-4269
Tel (330) 245-2630 *Founded/Ownrshp* 1957
Sales 107.0MM^E *EMP* 230
SIC 5065 Electronic parts
CEO: Cindy Lewis
**Pr:* Roger G Engle
Pr: Ron Gedrich
**CFO:* Robert McGehan
**Treas:* David L Glass
**Sr VP:* Dennis Daniel
Genl Mgr: Carolyn Arriaga
Genl Mgr: Marcia Bates
CTO: Jesus Lim

D-U-N-S 00-734-3429 IMP
AIRBORN INTERCONNECT INC
3500 Airborn Cir, Georgetown, TX 78626-8215
Tel (512) 863-5585 *Founded/Ownrshp* 2001
Sales 182.3MM^E *EMP* 700
SIC 3678 3679

D-U-N-S 03-144-9367
■ AIRBORNE ACQUISITION INC
(*Suby of* TRANSDIGM GROUP INC) ★
30500 Aurora Rd Ste 100, Solon, OH 44139-2776
Tel (216) 438-6111 *Founded/Ownrshp* 2009
Sales 83.8MM^E *EMP* 900^E
SIC 6726 Investment offices
CEO: Elek Puskas

AIRBORNE SYSTEMS NA
See AIRBORNE SYSTEMS NORTH AMERICA INC

D-U-N-S 13-856-4252
■ AIRBORNE SYSTEMS NORTH AMERICA INC
AIRBORNE SYSTEMS NA
(*Suby of* TRANSDIGM GROUP INC) ★
5800 Magnolia Ave, Pennsauken, NJ 08109-1309
Tel (856) 663-1275 *Founded/Ownrshp* 2013
Sales 98.5MM^E *EMP* 200
SIC 2426 3429 Textile machinery accessories, hardwood; Parachute hardware
CEO: Elek Puskas
**Pr:* Vicki Panhuise
**Pr:* Brad Pedersen
**CFO:* George Bullock
**Ex VP:* JC Berland
**Ex VP:* Mike Garten
Ex VP: Richard J Smallwood

D-U-N-S 05-061-4114 IMP
AIRBOSS FLEXIBLE PRODUCTS CO
(*Suby of* AIRBOSS OF AMERICA CORP)
2600 Auburn Ct, Auburn Hills, MI 48326-3201
Tel (248) 852-5500 *Founded/Ownrshp* 1980
Sales 121.7MM^E *EMP* 250
SIC 3069 3714 Rubber automotive products; Motor vehicle parts & accessories
Pr: Glenn Reid
Treas: Ronald J Dzierzawski
VP: Douglas L Reid

D-U-N-S 15-769-6998
AIRBUS AMERICAS INC
AINA HOLDINGS
(*Suby of* AIRBUS SAS)
2550 Wasser Ter Ste 9100, Herndon, VA 20171-6381
Tel (703) 834-3400 *Founded/Ownrshp* 2002
Sales 136.5MM^E *EMP* 240
SIC 3721 Aircraft
Pr: Barry Eccleston
Pr: Fabrice Brgier
COO: Gnter Butschek
COO: John Leahy
CFO: Harald Wilhelm
Ex VP: Gerald Weber
Ex VP: Tom Williams
Sr VP: Thomas Anderson
VP: Olivier Cauquil
VP: Charles Fletcher
VP: Mark Haisman
VP: Robert Hein
VP: Bill Heydrick
VP: Joseph Houghton
VP: Renee Martin-Nagle
VP: Ken McKenzie
VP: Julien Puyou
VP: Peter Schoonjans
VP: Andrew Shankland
VP: Terry Stone
VP: Eric Thiebault
Board of Directors: Edward Deschapell

D-U-N-S 07-480-5730 IMP
AIRBUS DEFENSE AND SPACE HOLDINGS INC
(*Suby of* AIRBUS GROUP SE)
2550 Wasser Ter Ste 9000, Herndon, VA 20171-6382
Tel (703) 466-5600 *Founded/Ownrshp* 2002
Sales 1.5MM^E *EMP* 1,702
SIC 3721 Aircraft
Pr: Michael Cosentino
Pr: Stephen Mundt
CFO: Michael Garner
Sr VP: Reinhold Lutz
VP: Marc Bouvier
VP: Dennis Burnett
VP: Andreas Groth
VP: David Haines
VP: Nathan Harvey
VP: Guy M Hicks
VP: Jim Hvizd
VP: Corinne Kaplan
VP: Steve Lowry
VP: Ted Mickevicius
VP: Terry Smith
VP: Samuel D Wyman III
Dir Bus: Timothy Gann
Board of Directors: Les Brownlee

D-U-N-S 10-317-5931
AIRBUS DEFENSE AND SPACE INC
(*Suby of* AIRBUS GROUP SE)
2550 Wasser Ter Ste 9000, Herndon, VA 20171-6382
Tel (703) 466-5600 *Founded/Ownrshp* 2014
Sales 344.5MM^E *EMP* 385
SIC 3721

D-U-N-S 04-605-7246 IMP
AIRBUS DS COMMUNICATIONS INC
(*Suby of* AIRBUS DEFENSE AND SPACE INC) ★
42505 Rio Nedo, Temecula, CA 92590-3726
Tel (951) 719-2100 *Founded/Ownrshp* 2008
Sales 111.6MM[E] *EMP* 338[E]
SIC 3661 Telephone station equipment & parts, wire
Pr: Bob Freinberg
COO: Bernhard Gerwert
**CFO:* Louis Albatro
CFO: Dave Rutan
Top Exec: Denis Gardin
VP: Kyle Brack
VP: Hans Brugger
VP: Philippe Devos
VP: Jeroen Dewitte
Dir Soc: Alicia Caddy
Prgrm Mgr: Cathy Kurnas
Board of Directors: Michael Consentino

D-U-N-S 13-416-0873 IMP/EXP
AIRBUS HELICOPTERS INC
(*Suby of* AIRBUS DEFENSE AND SPACE INC) ★
2701 N Forum Dr, Grand Prairie, TX 75052-8927
Tel (972) 641-0000 *Founded/Ownrshp* 2014
Sales 158.6MM[E] *EMP* 375
SIC 5088 7699 3721 Helicopter parts; Aircraft & heavy equipment repair services; Helicopters
Pr: Chris Emerson
**CEO:* Marc Paganini
**CFO:* Francois Bordes
**Treas:* Linda Burkett
Ex VP: Michel Farssac
VP: Andrea Bugar
VP: Kevin Cabani
**VP:* Jim Cawyer
VP: Peter Cutler
VP: Del Livingston
**VP:* Treg Manning
VP: Serge Panabiere
VP: Diane Sanderson
**VP:* Mike Spears
Board of Directors: Pierre Nardelli

D-U-N-S 79-039-1598
▲ AIRCASTLE LIMITED
300 1st Stamford Pl 9a, Stamford, CT 06902-6733
Tel (203) 504-1020 *Founded/Ownrshp* 2004
Sales 819.2MM *EMP* 103[E]
Accts Ernst & Young Llp Stamford C
Tkr Sym AYR *Exch* NYS
SIC 7359 Aircraft rental
CEO: Ron Wainshal
**Ch Bd:* Peter V Ueberroth
CFO: Michael Inglese
Chf Cred: Michael Kriedberg
Ofcr: Guy Bacigalupi
Ex VP: Howard Brewer
Ex VP: Nigel Harwood
Ex VP: Nigel A Harwood
Ex VP: Owen Roberts
Ex VP: Joseph Schreiner
VP: Sarah Clarkin
VP: Alan Godson
VP: Sergio Gonzalez
VP: Vivienne McBride
VP: Jill Saverine
Board of Directors: Ronald W Allen, Giovanni Bisignani, Michael J Cave, Douglas A Hacker, Ronald L Merriman, Agnes Mura, Charles W Pollard

D-U-N-S 07-155-6732
AIRCO MECHANICAL INC
AMI MANUFACTURING
8210 Demetre Ave, Sacramento, CA 95828-0919
Tel (916) 381-4523 *Founded/Ownrshp* 1974
Sales 112.1MM[E] *EMP* 250
SIC 1711 8711 Plumbing, heating, air-conditioning contractors; Engineering services
CEO: Wyatt Jones
**CFO:* Bruce Stimson
**VP:* Larry R Cook
**VP:* Dean Schouweiler
Dept Mgr: Stuart Thompson
Board of Directors: Roger Akers, David Cooper, Charles Jones, John Tyson

D-U-N-S 12-795-6345
AIRCRAFT FINANCE TRUST
2401 Kerner Blvd, San Rafael, CA 94901-5569
Tel (415) 485-4500 *Founded/Ownrshp* 1999
Sales 142.3MM *EMP* 3[E]
SIC 7359 Equipment rental & leasing
VP: Tong Bryant

D-U-N-S 04-312-1029 IMP/EXP
AIRCRAFT SERVICE INTERNATIONAL INC
A S I G
(*Suby of* EXECUTIVE BEECHCRAFT) ★
201 S Orange Ave Ste 1100, Orlando, FL 32801-3478
Tel (407) 648-7373 *Founded/Ownrshp* 1947, 1967
Sales 174.4MM[E] *EMP* 250
SIC 4581 5172 Airport terminal services; Aircraft fueling services
CEO: Keith P Ryan
**Pr:* Michael S Scheeringa
CFO: Jeff Hartman
**CFO:* Sami Teittinen
Treas: Jeffrey Hartman
**VP:* John A Reeves
Genl Mgr: Bary D McClain II
Genl Mgr: Al Miller
Genl Mgr: Mike Sveen
Genl Mgr: Larry Willis
Opers Mgr: Ralph Ostrand

AIRCRAFT SPRUCE
See IRWIN INTERNATIONAL INC

AIRCRAFT TECHNOLOGY
See IDAHO STATE UNIVERSITY

D-U-N-S 00-325-4844 IMP
AIRECO SUPPLY INC (MD)
8860 Gorman Rd, Laurel, MD 20723-5800
Tel (301) 953-8800 *Founded/Ownrshp* 1972, 1973
Sales 160.0MM[E] *EMP* 260
SIC 5075 5078 Warm air heating equipment & supplies; Air conditioning equipment, except room units; Refrigeration equipment & supplies
Pr: Dan Hinchman
COO: Walter Wyne
CFO: Martin Libold
**VP:* Clark Adams
VP: Paul Burke
VP: Chris Hudson
**Prin:* James F Kemp
Rgnl Mgr: Harold Bergman
Brnch Mgr: Jeremy Burroughs
Brnch Mgr: Don Denny
Brnch Mgr: Sheri McKinney

D-U-N-S 05-708-3321
AIREFCO INC
HADCO SUPPLY
18755 Sw Teton Ave, Tualatin, OR 97062-8848
Tel (503) 692-3210 *Founded/Ownrshp* 1971
Sales 93.0MM *EMP* 150
SIC 5075 Air conditioning equipment, except room units; Ventilating equipment & supplies; Warm air heating equipment & supplies
CEO: Jk Hussa
CFO: Bernard Thomas
**Sec:* Thomas C Burnard
Exec: Janet Burnard
**Prin:* Larry Riggins
IT Man: Benjamin Wanlass
Sls Mgr: Scott Lewis
Sls Mgr: Paul Luvaas
Sales Asso: Cassie Kuwahara

D-U-N-S 09-004-9008 IMP
AIREKO CONSTRUCTION LLC
Las Casas St Lot 20, Caguas, PR 00725
Tel (787) 653-6300 *Founded/Ownrshp* 1963
Sales 285.3MM[E] *EMP* 1,000[E]
SIC 1542 1541 1731 1711 Commercial & office building, new construction; Industrial buildings, new construction; General electrical contractor; Mechanical contractor
Pr: Paulino Lopez
**Treas:* Francisco Uriarte
Genl Mgr: Waldemar Toro
Board of Directors: Jose Rossi, Waldemar Tito Toro, Francisco Uriarte, Luis Uzcategui

AIRFLOW SYSTEMS GROUP
See BOSCH AUTOMOTIVE MOTOR SYSTEMS CORP

D-U-N-S 02-718-3839 IMP
AIRGAS - SOUTHWEST INC
(*Suby of* AIRGAS INC) ★
4817 Agnes St, Corpus Christi, TX 78405-3624
Tel (361) 882-1141 *Founded/Ownrshp* 1996
Sales 374.9MM[E] *EMP* 1,212
SIC 5169 5084 Industrial gases; Welding machinery & equipment
Pr: Brent Sparks
**CFO:* Monica Delagarza
CFO: Tom Podsialick
Dir IT: Brandon Marquez
Board of Directors: Monica

D-U-N-S 04-113-8371 IMP/EXP
AIRGAS CARBONIC INC
(*Suby of* AIRGAS INC) ★
2530 Sever Rd Ste 300, Lawrenceville, GA 30043-4022
Tel (770) 717-2210 *Founded/Ownrshp* 1997
Sales 106.4MM[E] *EMP* 344
SIC 2813 7359 5088 Carbon dioxide; Dry ice, carbon dioxide (solid); Equipment rental & leasing; Tanks & tank components
Pr: Phil Filer
**VP:* Sandra Fowler-Hurt
Genl Mgr: Nancy Durden
MIS Dir: Anthony Belenchia
Plnt Mgr: Paul Jankowski
Plnt Mgr: Jason Morsfield
Plnt Mgr: Nathan Thomas
Plnt Mgr: Rusty Wilson
Snr Mgr: Jim Lepage
Snr Mgr: Brian Speelman

D-U-N-S 02-449-2860 IMP/EXP
AIRGAS INC
(*Suby of* AIR LIQUIDE SA ETU EXPLOIT PROCE)
259 N Radnor Chester Rd # 100, Radnor, PA 19087-5240
Tel (610) 687-5253 *Founded/Ownrshp* 1986, 2016
Sales 5.3MMM *EMP* 17,000
Accts Kpmg Llp Philadelphia Pennsy
SIC 5169 5084 5085 2813 2819 Industrial gases; Gases, compressed & liquefied; Carbon dioxide; Dry ice; Welding machinery & equipment; Safety equipment; Welding supplies; Industrial gases; Carbon dioxide; Nitrous oxide; Dry ice, carbon dioxide (solid); Industrial inorganic chemicals; Calcium carbide
CEO: Michael L Molinini
V Ch: Michael J Graff
COO: Andrew R Cichocki
Div VP: Robert Bradshaw
VP: David Burnstein
VP: Randall Cornelius
VP: Terry Ernst
VP: Jeff Mann
VP: Braband Michael
VP: Aaron New
VP: Bill Russo
VP: Ted Schulte
VP: Wayne Wilson

D-U-N-S 80-403-7435
AIRGAS MERCHANT GASES LLC
(*Suby of* AIRGAS INC) ★
6055 Rckside Woods Blvd N, Cleveland, OH 44131-2301
Tel (800) 242-0105 *Founded/Ownrshp* 2003
Sales 103.6MM[E] *EMP* 335
SIC 5169 Industrial gases
VP: Thomas Smyth

D-U-N-S 94-141-5903 IMP/EXP
AIRGAS SAFETY INC
(*Suby of* AIRGAS INC) ★
2501 Green Ln, Levittown, PA 19057-4146
Tel (215) 826-9000 *Founded/Ownrshp* 1996
Sales 154.6MM[E] *EMP* 500
SIC 5084 5085 3561 3841 Safety equipment; Welding supplies; Cylinders, pump; Surgical & medical instruments
Pr: Donald S Carlino
CFO: Dennis Johnson
**Treas:* David Levin
**VP:* John W Smith
**VP:* Thomas M Smyth
Board of Directors: Michael L Molinini

D-U-N-S 07-830-1808
AIRGAS USA LLC
(*Suby of* AIRGAS INC) ★
259 N Radnor Chester Rd # 100, Radnor, PA 19087-5240
Tel (610) 687-5253 *Founded/Ownrshp* 1982
Sales 4.3MMM[E] *EMP* 14,000
SIC 5169 5084 5085 2813 2819 Industrial gases; Gases, compressed & liquefied; Carbon dioxide; Dry ice; Welding machinery & equipment; Safety equipment; Welding supplies; Industrial gases; Carbon dioxide; Nitrous oxide; Dry ice, carbon dioxide (solid); Industrial inorganic chemicals; Calcium carbide
CEO: Peter McCausland
COO: Michael L Molinini
CFO: David Brown
CFO: Terry Cherry
CFO: Paul Fitzgerald
CFO: Robert M McLaughlin
CFO: Jay Sullivan
Div Pres: Max D Hooper
Div Pres: Terry L Lodge
Div Pres: B Shaun Powers
Div Pres: Michael E Rohde
Sr VP: Kelly P Justice
Sr VP: Ronald J Stark
VP: Thomas M Smyth

D-U-N-S 00-231-9044 IMP
AIRLINE HYDRAULICS CORP (PA)
3557 Progress Dr, Bensalem, PA 19020-5896
Tel (610) 758-9400 *Founded/Ownrshp* 1950
Sales 201.6MM[E] *EMP* 211
SIC 5085 5084 Pistons & valves; Controlling instruments & accessories
Pr: Joseph Miceli
Recvr: David Hems
**Treas:* Joseph E Loughran
**VP:* Andrew Fedor
VP: Marc Stofle
Adv Bd Mbr: Erik Jensen
Brnch Mgr: Edmund Karam
Dir IT: Andy Gorrell
Plnt Mgr: J Wus
Ql Cn Mgr: Charles Accisano
Manager: Glen Katerson

D-U-N-S 05-736-5546
AIRLINE PILOTS ASSOCIATION INTERNATIONAL
1625 Massachusetts Ave Nw, Herndon, VA 20172
Tel (703) 689-2270 *Founded/Ownrshp* 1931
Sales 136.6MM *EMP* 369
SIC 8631 8512

AIRLINE SERVICES
See WORLDWIDE FLIGHT SERVICES INC

D-U-N-S 07-485-3201 IMP
AIRLINE TARIFF PUBLISHING CO (DC)
A T P C O
45005 Aviation Dr Ste 400, Dulles, VA 20166-7546
Tel (703) 661-7400 *Founded/Ownrshp* 2006, 1974
Sales 133.1MM[E] *EMP* 400
SIC 2721 7374 2731 Statistical reports (periodicals): publishing & printing; Data processing service; Book publishing
Pr: Bill Andres
CFO: Steve Greenagle
**CFO:* Brian Kirk
**VP:* Priscilla O'Donnell
**Prin:* Steve Daniels
**Prin:* Rolf Purzer
CIO: Theodore Frazier
QA Dir: Zoya Amanchi
IT Man: Sirisha Nagabhairava
Info Man: Leonard Howell
Web Dev: Marc Lieberman

D-U-N-S 13-025-6647
AIRLINES REPORTING CORP
ARC
3000 Wilson Blvd Ste 300, Arlington, VA 22201-3862
Tel (703) 816-8000 *Founded/Ownrshp* 1985
Sales 116.4MM[E] *EMP* 450
SIC 7389 6099 7374 Brokers' services; Regional clearinghouse associations; Data processing service
Pr: Mike Premo
**Ch Bd:* Bonnie S Reitz
**COO:* Lauri Reishus
**Ofcr:* Eric J Barger
Ofcr: Helena Hadley
**VP:* Leslie Bauer
**VP:* Randy Black
**VP:* Ann J Bruder
**VP:* Thomas F Casalino
VP: Thomas Casalino
**VP:* Dickie Oliver
Board of Directors: Karen Berry, Steven Ebbro, Brian McMenamy, Allan Muttn

D-U-N-S 00-725-9617 IMP/EXP
AIRLITE PLASTICS CO
6110 Abbott Dr, Omaha, NE 68110-2834
Tel (402) 341-7300 *Founded/Ownrshp* 1946
Sales 173.5MM[E] *EMP* 650[E]
SIC 3089 Plastic containers, except foam; Caps, plastic; Food casings, plastic
Pr: Brad Crosby
**Treas:* Patrick J Kenealy
VP: Mike Corrigan
QA Dir: Craig Wyler
Sfty Dirs: Jim Steele
Plnt Mgr: Brian Christensen
Advt Mgr: Tammy Lumbard
Mktg Mgr: Laurie Jorgensen
Manager: Scott Applegate
Manager: Michael Conway
Manager: Mike Dalzell

D-U-N-S 11-825-7484
AIRNET SYSTEMS INC
7250 Star Check Dr, Columbus, OH 43217-1025
Tel (614) 409-4900 *Founded/Ownrshp* 1996
Sales 163.3MM[E] *EMP* 640[E]
SIC 4522 4731 Air transportation, nonscheduled; Air cargo carriers, nonscheduled; Freight transportation arrangement
Owner: Joan C Makley
COO: Jeffery B Harris
CFO: Fred Deleeuw
CFO: Ray L Druseikis
CFO: Ray Druseikis
Sr VP: Larry M Glasscock Jr
Sr VP: Wynn D Peterson
VP: Tom Brennan
VP: Craig A Leach
VP: Craig Leach
VP: Michael Snyder
Exec: Shawn Wilkinson
Board of Directors: James M Chadwick, Gerald Hellerman, Thomas J Kiernan, Robert H Milbourne, Bruce D Parker, James E Riddle

D-U-N-S 78-542-3229
AIRPORT COMMISIONS
BUSINESS OF FINANCE
(*Suby of* CITY & COUNTY OF SAN FRANCISCO) ★
San Francisco Intl Arprt, San Francisco, CA 94128
Tel (650) 821-5000 *Founded/Ownrshp* 1954
Sales 33.2MM[E] *EMP* 1,121
SIC 4581 Airports, flying fields & services

AIRPORT FAST PARK
See PARKING CO OF AMERICA INC

AIRPORT MARINA FORD
See FOX HILLS AUTO INC

D-U-N-S 04-094-9667
AIRPORT TERMINAL SERVICES FOREIGN HOLDINGS CORP
(*Suby of* ATS) ★
111 West Port Plz Ste 400, Saint Louis, MO 63146-3014
Tel (314) 739-1900 *Founded/Ownrshp* 2000
Sales 22.5MM[E] *EMP* 1,301[E]
SIC 4581 Airport terminal services
Ch Bd: Richard B Hawes

D-U-N-S 06-057-3185
AIRPORT TERMINAL SERVICES INC
ATS
111 West Port Plz Ste 400, Saint Louis, MO 63146-3014
Tel (314) 739-1900 *Founded/Ownrshp* 1994
Sales 266.2MM[E] *EMP* 1,900
SIC 4581 Aircraft cleaning & janitorial service; Airport terminal services
Ch Bd: Richard B Hawes
**Pr:* Sally A Leible
**VP:* Peggy Hohl
**VP:* Brian McCormick
**VP:* Ed Vandeven
Genl Mgr: Mark Dooley
Genl Mgr: Steve Helfrich
Genl Mgr: Shawn Senkow
Sls Dir: Patricia M Lavelle
Snr Mgr: Mark Wenham

D-U-N-S 03-750-2168 IMP/EXP
■ AIRSTREAM INC
(*Suby of* THOR INDUSTRIES INC) ★
419 W Pike St, Jackson Center, OH 45334-9728
Tel (937) 596-6111 *Founded/Ownrshp* 1980
Sales 85.6MM[E] *EMP* 351
SIC 3716 3792 3714 3713 3711 Motor homes; Travel trailers & campers; Motor vehicle parts & accessories; Truck & bus bodies; Motor vehicles & car bodies
Pr: Robert Wheeler
**Ch Bd:* Lawrence J Huttle
**Ch Bd:* Peter B Orthwein
**CFO:* Dan Froehlich
**Treas:* Dominic A Romeo
**VP:* Bruce Annister
VP: Mollie Hansen
VP: Mark Wahl
**VP:* Mark Wall
**Prin:* Wade F B Thompson
Genl Mgr: Chris Burch

AIRT
See T AIR INC

D-U-N-S 80-116-9368 IMP
AIRTEX MANUFACTURING LLLP
ENGINEERED AIR
(*Suby of* AIRTEX MANUFACTURING PARTNERSHIP)
32050 W 83rd St, De Soto, KS 66018-9693
Tel (913) 583-3181 *Founded/Ownrshp* 2006
Sales 92.6MM[E] *EMP* 275
SIC 3585 5075 3564 3433 Refrigeration & heating equipment; Air conditioning & ventilation equipment & supplies; Blowers & fans; Heating equipment, except electric
Pt: Richard Rambacher
Genl Mgr: Doug Ryan
Ql Cn Mgr: Rann Mark

D-U-N-S 13-362-7815 IMP/EXP
AIRTEX PRODUCTS LP
(*Suby of* UCI-FRAM AUTOBRANDS) ★
407 W Main St, Fairfield, IL 62837-1622
Tel (618) 842-2111 *Founded/Ownrshp* 1960
Sales 418.8MM[E] *EMP* 800
SIC 5013 Automotive supplies & parts
Pt: Thomas Degnan
Pr: John Economou
VP: Andrew Kratky
Exec: Martin Walsh
IT Man: Rich Sherrick
Mfg Dir: Mark Hilliard

Plnt Mgr: Ryan Bailey
Mktg Dir: Brandon Kight

D-U-N-S 80-786-0648
■ AIRTRAN AIRWAYS INC
(*Suby of* AIRTRAN HOLDINGS INC) ★
2702 Love Field Dr, Dallas, TX 75235-1908
Tel (407) 318-5600 *Founded/Ownrshp* 1992
Sales 175.9MM^E *EMP* 2,800
SIC 4512 Air passenger carrier, scheduled
Pr: Robert Fornaro
Ex VP: Klaus Goersch
Ex VP: Stephen Kolski
Sr VP: Jack Smith
Sr VP: Rocky Wiggins

D-U-N-S 92-978-3637
■ AIRTRAN HOLDINGS INC
(*Suby of* SOUTHWEST AIRLINES CO) ★
9955 Airtran Blvd, Orlando, FL 32827-5330
Tel (407) 318-5600 *Founded/Ownrshp* 2011
Sales 176.9MM^E *EMP* 8,330^E
SIC 4512 Air passenger carrier, scheduled
Pr: Robert E Jordan
Ex VP: Klaus Goersch
Ex VP: Stephen J Kolski
Sr VP: Loral Blinde
Sr VP: Arne G Haak
Sr VP: Kevin P Healy
Sr VP: Jack Smith
Sr VP: Rocky Wiggins
VP: Peggy Sauer Clark
VP: Jeff Miller
VP: Mark W Osterberg
VP: Jim Tabor

D-U-N-S 13-329-6199
AIRTRON INC
(*Suby of* DIRECT ENERGY US HOME SERVICES INC) ★
9260 Marketpl Dr, Miamisburg, OH 45342
Tel (937) 898-0826 *Founded/Ownrshp* 2003
Sales 145.6MM^E *EMP* 900
SIC 1711 Plumbing contractors
Pr: Eric Salzer
VP: Dan Kipp
VP: Victor Ragucci

D-U-N-S 07-930-3487
■ AIRVANA LP
(*Suby of* COMMSCOPE HOLDING CO INC) ★
250 Apollo Dr, Chelmsford, MA 01824-3627
Tel (877) 855-4092 *Founded/Ownrshp* 2010
Sales 770.3MM^E *EMP* 4,653^E
SIC 4899 Communication signal enhancement network system
Pr: Richard Lowe
Sr VP: Jay Hilbert
VP: Rod Gatehouse
VP: Woojune Kim
VP: John Pagliuca
VP: Rayadurgam Ravinkath
Snr Sftwr: Minti Patel
CTO: Vedat Eyuboglu
IT Man: Mike McCullough
IT Man: Johnathan Scolastico
VP Opers: Joanne Mavroides

AIRWATCH HOLDING
See AWS HOLDINGS LLC

D-U-N-S 79-161-1630
■ AIRWATCH LLC
WANDERING WIFI
(*Suby of* AIRWATCH HOLDING) ★
1155 Perimeter Ctr # 100, Atlanta, GA 30338-5461
Tel (470) 247-4312 *Founded/Ownrshp* 2010
Sales 98.4MM^E *EMP* 750
SIC 7371 Computer software development
Ch: Alan J Dabbiere
**Pr:* John Marshall
**COO:* David Dabbiere
VP: Rick Franke
Dir Bus: Cesar Berenguer
IT Man: Michael Kanizay
Software D: Ananya Bhuyan
Netwrk Eng: Mikel Mack
Sls Dir: George Christian
Sls Dir: Tony Gomez
Mktg Mgr: Jaime Willhite

AIRWORKS
See MULTI-CRAFT CONTRACTORS INC

AIRXCEL HOLDINGS
See AHI HOLDINGS INC

D-U-N-S 60-652-9873 IMP
AIRXCEL INC
R V PRODUCTS DIV
(*Suby of* ONE ROCK CAPITAL PARTNERS LLC) ★
3050 N Saint Francis St, Wichita, KS 67219-4045
Tel (316) 832-3400 *Founded/Ownrshp* 2014
Sales 280.0MM *EMP* 940
SIC 3585 Heating & air conditioning combination units
CEO: Melvin Adams
**Pr:* Jeff Rutherford
**CFO:* Debra Jones
VP: Bill Wilson
IT Man: Mike Ramsey

D-U-N-S 01-718-8228 IMP/EXP
AIS CONSTRUCTION EQUIPMENT SERVICE CORP
600 44th St Sw, Grand Rapids, MI 49548-4128
Tel (616) 538-2400 *Founded/Ownrshp* 1961
Sales 170.2MM^E *EMP* 500
SIC 5082 Construction & mining machinery; Road construction & maintenance machinery; Excavating machinery & equipment
Ch: Larry L Behrenwald
**Pr:* Jim Behrenwald's
Exec: Karen Davis
Brnch Mgr: Steve Higgins

D-U-N-S 82-916-8116
■ AIS MANAGEMENT LLC
(*Suby of* M C C) ★
17785 Center Court Dr N # 250, Cerritos, CA 90703-8573
Tel (562) 345-4247 *Founded/Ownrshp* 2009
Sales NA *EMP* 572
SIC 6411 Insurance agents, brokers & service
Pr: Mark Ribisi
**CFO:* Chris Bremer
**VP:* Mark Casas
**VP:* Romayne Levee
**VP Opers:* Lani Elkin

D-U-N-S 00-889-2929 IMP/EXP
AISIN AUTOMOTIVE CASTING LLC (KY)
(*Suby of* A H A) ★
4870 E Highway 552, London, KY 40744-9532
Tel (606) 878-6523 *Founded/Ownrshp* 1996, 2001
Sales 228.8MM^E *EMP* 730
SIC 3363 Aluminum die-castings
COO: Simon Mortimer
Brnch Mgr: Brian Walter

D-U-N-S 12-140-0142 IMP
AISIN HOLDINGS OF AMERICA INC
A H A
(*Suby of* AISIN SEIKI CO., LTD.)
1665 E 4th Street Rd, Seymour, IN 47274-4307
Tel (812) 524-8144 *Founded/Ownrshp* 1970
Sales 1.0MMM^E *EMP* 1,300
SIC 5013 Automotive supplies & parts
Pr: Masayasu Saito
**Treas:* Atsushi Onishi
VP: Koichi Kondo
Mfg Mgr: Ivan Hayes
Sls Mgr: Gregory Hyde

D-U-N-S 11-840-6698 IMP
AISIN MFG ILLINOIS LLC
(*Suby of* AISIN USA MFG INC) ★
11000 Redco Dr, Marion, IL 62959-5889
Tel (618) 998-8333 *Founded/Ownrshp* 2001
Sales 129.6MM^E *EMP* 720
SIC 3714 Motor vehicle parts & accessories
Pr: Hiroyuki Kato
Treas: Naoki Niimi
Ex VP: Glenn Edwards

D-U-N-S 19-707-7944 IMP
AISIN USA MFG INC
(*Suby of* A H A) ★
1700 E 4th Street Rd, Seymour, IN 47274-4309
Tel (812) 523-1969 *Founded/Ownrshp* 1987
Sales 225.4MM^E *EMP* 750^E
SIC 3714 Motor vehicle parts & accessories; Brake drums, motor vehicle; Motor vehicle engines & parts
Pr: Tsukasa Ito
Ex VP: H Aiki
Ex VP: Keith Warf
**VP:* Dennis Putman
Dept Mgr: K Kayama

D-U-N-S 62-143-5239 IMP
AISIN WORLD CORP OF AMERICA
(*Suby of* A H A) ★
15300 Centennial Dr, Northville, MI 48168-8687
Tel (734) 453-5551 *Founded/Ownrshp* 2001
Sales 383.3MM^E *EMP* 1,278
SIC 5013 Automotive supplies & parts
Pr: Tsutomu Yasui
**Pr:* Don Whitsitt
**Treas:* Hisashi Hatta
VP: Toshifumi Yanai
Genl Mgr: Mark Greenawalt

D-U-N-S 09-677-6844 IMP/EXP
AIT WORLDWIDE LOGISTICS INC (CO)
701 N Rohlwing Rd, Itasca, IL 60143-1348
Tel (630) 766-0711 *Founded/Ownrshp* 1979
Sales 400.3MM^E *EMP* 760
SIC 4731 Customhouse brokers; Domestic freight forwarding; Foreign freight forwarding
CEO: Vaughn Moore
Treas: Paul Codere
**Treas:* Josephine Lisowski
**Founder:* Daniel F Lisowski
**Ex VP:* Ray Fennelly
**Ex VP:* Joe Kayser
**Ex VP:* Keith Tholan
**VP:* Herb Cohan
VP: Bill Fallon
**VP:* Albert Oliver
VP: Tony Parisi
**VP:* Bill Reichman
**VP:* Greg Weigel
Dir Surg: Michael Kohan
Dir Bus: Myung Kim
**Co-Founder:* Steven L Leturno

D-U-N-S 00-698-8729
■ AIU INSURANCE CO
(*Suby of* AIG) ★
175 Water St Fl 24, New York, NY 10038-4918
Tel (212) 770-7000 *Founded/Ownrshp* 1851, 1972
Sales NA *EMP* 250
SIC 6331 6321 Fire, marine & casualty insurance; Property damage insurance; Accident & health insurance
Pr: Evan Greenberg
**Ch Bd:* Thomas R Tizzio
**V Ch Bd:* Edward E Matthews
Ofcr: Anthony Prospie Jr
**Sr VP:* David J Walsh
VP: David S Hawksby
VP: Mark Willis
Exec: William D Loucks Jr
Tech Mgr: William Edmondson

AIU3
See ALLEGHENY INTERMEDIATE UNIT 3 FOUNDATION

A.J. WRIGHT
See CONCORD BUYING GROUP INC

D-U-N-S 00-784-4319
AJAX BUILDING CORP (FL)
1080 Commerce Blvd, Midway, FL 32343-6678
Tel (850) 224-9571 *Founded/Ownrshp* 1958
Sales 130.9MM *EMP* 130
Accts Carr Riggs & Ingram Llc Tall
SIC 1542 Commercial & office building, new construction; Commercial & office buildings, renovation & repair
Pr: William P Byrne
**COO:* Derek Gamble
**CFO:* Ken Lindlau
**Sec:* John B Smith II
VP: Thomas Crow
Opers Mgr: Lon Neuman
Opers Mgr: Mike Wilson

D-U-N-S 00-581-2276
AJAX PAVING INDUSTRIES INC
(*Suby of* HHJ HOLDINGS LIMITED) ★
1957 Crooks Rd A, Troy, MI 48084-5504
Tel (248) 244-3300 *Founded/Ownrshp* 1951
Sales 150.8MM^E *EMP* 950
SIC 1611 2951 3273 3272 Highway & street paving contractor; Concrete construction: roads, highways, sidewalks, etc.; Resurfacing contractor; Asphalt & asphaltic paving mixtures (not from refineries); Ready-mixed concrete; Concrete products
Ch Bd: Herbert H Jacob
Pr: James A Jacob
VP: Dale G Hauer
VP: Paul Selesky
Genl Mgr: Christie Alvaro
Genl Mgr: Dave Reid
Sfty Dirs: Joe Landino
Opers Mgr: Joe Minich

D-U-N-S 03-243-6479
AJAX PAVING INDUSTRIES OF FLORIDA LLC
(*Suby of* AJAX PAVING INDUSTRIES INC) ★
1 Ajax Dr, North Venice, FL 34275-3505
Tel (941) 486-3600 *Founded/Ownrshp* 1982
Sales 144.5MM^E *EMP* 950
SIC 1611 2951 Surfacing & paving; Asphalt & asphaltic paving mixtures (not from refineries)
QC Dir: Mike Curle
Opers Mgr: Clay Collins

D-U-N-S 03-482-0076
AJAX TURNER CO INC
4010 Centre Pointe Dr, La Vergne, TN 37086-4955
Tel (615) 244-2424 *Founded/Ownrshp* 1990
Sales 178.9MM^E *EMP* 220
SIC 5182 Wine & distilled beverages
Pr: Scott Turner
CFO: John Batte
**Ex VP:* Todd Williams
VP: John Keene
Exec: Eric Gibbons
Area Mgr: Jeremy Bennett
Dir IT: Boyd Neighbors
Mktg Dir: Megan Turner

D-U-N-S 78-708-9163
AJB VENTURES INC
10 Walter Ln, Manhasset, NY 11030-1652
Tel (516) 365-6690 *Founded/Ownrshp* 2006
Sales NA *EMP* 300
SIC 6321 Accident & health insurance
CEO: Anthony J Bonomo
**VP:* Gerald Dolman

D-U-N-S 88-422-7109 IMP/EXP
AJC INTERNATIONAL INC
A J C
1000 Abernathy Rd Ste 600, Atlanta, GA 30328-5647
Tel (404) 252-6750 *Founded/Ownrshp* 1972
Sales 335.5MM^E *EMP* 201^E
SIC 5144 5147 5148 5146 Poultry & poultry products; Meats & meat products; Fresh fruits & vegetables; Fish & seafoods
CEO: Gerald L Allison
Pt: John D Partington
**V Ch:* Eric J Joiner
**Pr:* Bradley J Allison
CFO: John Paitington
**CFO:* John Partington
**Chf Cred:* Evan S Davidman
VP: Thierry Murad
Genl Mgr: Coen Vrolijk
Opers Mgr: Mark Gentry
Opers Mgr: Chris Swartz

D-U-N-S 02-146-0886
AJILON LLC
(*Suby of* ADECCO TECHNICAL) ★
175 Broadhollow Rd, Melville, NY 11747-4911
Tel (631) 844-7800 *Founded/Ownrshp* 1987
Sales 165.9MM^E *EMP* 4,520
SIC 7379 8742 7374 Data processing consultant; Computer related consulting services; General management consultant; Data processing & preparation
Pr: Roy F Haggerty
Pr: Lorrina Guilmet
CFO: Tom Finnott
CFO: Roy Goldman
Sr VP: Jerry Lowe
VP: Corina Bussey
VP: Craig Coleman
VP: Michel Plouffe
VP: Dan Sims
Exec: Gene Sabyan
Rgnl Mgr: Lisa Lindberg

AJIN USA
See JOON LLC

D-U-N-S 11-417-2596 IMP/EXP
AJINOMOTO HEARTLAND INC
(*Suby of* AJINOMOTO ANIMAL NUTRITION GROUP, INC.)
8430 W Bryn Mawr Ave, Chicago, IL 60631-3473
Tel (773) 380-7000 *Founded/Ownrshp* 2011
Sales 102.9MM^E *EMP* 120
SIC 5159 Fibers, vegetable
Pr: Masami Kashiwakura
VP: Cheryl Boles
VP: Michael Chittaro
VP: Dennis Mullane
Assoc Dir: Joseph A Formanek
Genl Mgr: Chiaki Sano
Genl Mgr: Hideaki Shinada
VP Sls: Bradley Bigger

D-U-N-S 05-790-0229 IMP
AJINOMOTO NORTH AMERICA HOLDINGS INC
7124 N Marine Dr, Portland, OR 97203-6480
Tel (503) 505-5783 *Founded/Ownrshp* 2013
Sales 246.1MM^E *EMP* 2,500^E
SIC 5142 6719 2038 2037 Packaged frozen goods; Investment holding companies, except banks; Frozen specialties; Frozen fruits & vegetables
Pr: Tomoya Yoshizumi

D-U-N-S 00-185-3852 IMP/EXP
AJINOMOTO NORTH AMERICA INC
(*Suby of* AJINOMOTO CO., INC.)
400 Kelby St, Fort Lee, NJ 07024-2943
Tel (201) 292-3200 *Founded/Ownrshp* 1956, 2011
Sales 240.2MM^E *EMP* 400
SIC 5142 5169 2869 2899

D-U-N-S 96-120-0995
AJK ENTERPRISES INC
BURNS & WILCOX
30833 Northwestern Hwy, Farmington Hills, MI 48334-2551
Tel (248) 932-9000 *Founded/Ownrshp* 1996
Sales NA *EMP* 1,005
SIC 6411 Insurance brokers; Insurance agents; Property & casualty insurance agent
Pr: Alan J Kaufman

D-U-N-S 00-538-3898 IMP
AJM PACKAGING CORP
A J M
E-4111 Andover Rd, Bloomfield Hills, MI 48302
Tel (248) 901-0040 *Founded/Ownrshp* 1949
Sales 358.6MM^E *EMP* 1,000
SIC 2656 2674 Plates, paper: made from purchased material; Paper bags: made from purchased materials
Pr: Robert Epstein
**CFO:* Terry Jackson
Tech Mgr: Margaret Defrancesco
Plnt Mgr: Barry Gritton
Plnt Mgr: John Nilles
Plnt Mgr: Joe Obermeyer
Natl Sales: Keith Hardy
Mktg Mgr: Bill Baumann
Manager: David Huntley
Sales Asso: Ben Staley

D-U-N-S 60-607-2130 IMP/EXP
■ AK STEEL CORP
(*Suby of* AK STEEL HOLDING CORP) ★
9227 Centre Pointe Dr, West Chester, OH 45069-4822
Tel (513) 425-4200 *Founded/Ownrshp* 1989
Sales 2.8MMM^E *EMP* 6,200
SIC 3312 Blast furnaces & steel mills; Sheet or strip, steel, hot-rolled; Coated or plated products; Sheet or strip, steel, cold-rolled: own hot-rolled
Pr: James Wainscott
**COO:* Roger K Newport
**CFO:* Albert E Ferrara Jr
**Treas:* Dave Westcott
Ex VP: Kirk W Reich
Sr VP: Keith J Howell
**VP:* Joseph C Alter
VP: Alan H McCoy
Genl Mgr: Bill Cro
VP Sls: Douglas Gant
Board of Directors: John Brinzo, William K Gerber, Robert H Jenkins, Ralph S Michael III, Roger Newport

D-U-N-S 83-110-0995 IMP/EXP
▲ AK STEEL HOLDING CORP
9227 Centre Pointe Dr, West Chester, OH 45069-4822
Tel (513) 425-5000 *Founded/Ownrshp* 1993
Sales 6.6MMM *EMP* 8,500
Tkr Sym AKS *Exch* NYS
SIC 3312 Blast furnaces & steel mills; Sheet or strip, steel, hot-rolled; Coated or plated products; Sheet or strip, steel, cold-rolled: own hot-rolled
CEO: Roger K Newport
Pr: Kirk W Reich
CFO: Jaime Vasquez
Ex VP: Steve Boston
Sr VP: John F Kaloski
VP: Joseph C Alter
VP: Brian K Bishop
VP: Michael A Kercsmar
VP: Eric S Petersen
VP: Larry Zizzo
Exec: Mike Lehman
Board of Directors: Vicente Wright, Dennis C Cuneo, Sheri H Edison, Mark G Essig, William K Gerber, Robert H Jenkins, Gregory B Kenny, Ralph S Michael III, James A Thomson, James L Wainscott

D-U-N-S 18-237-6145
AK-CHIN INDIAN COMMUNITY DEVELOPMENT CORP
42507 W Peters & Nall Rd, Maricopa, AZ 85138-3940
Tel (520) 568-1000 *Founded/Ownrshp* 1961
Sales 156.4MM^E *EMP* 820
SIC 0131 0139 5251 7993 Cotton; Alfalfa farm; Hardware; Gambling establishments operating coin-operated machines; Gambling machines, coin-operated; Slot machines
Ch: Louis Manuel Jr
**Prin:* Delia Carlyle
**Prin:* Terry Enos
Ex Dir: Marlene Garcia

D-U-N-S 12-360-0046
AKA ENERGY GROUP LLC
(*Suby of* LAKE CAPOTE PARK) ★
65 Mercado St Ste 250, Durango, CO 81301-7317
Tel (970) 764-6650 *Founded/Ownrshp* 2002
Sales 116.8MM^E *EMP* 130
SIC 1389 Gas compressing (natural gas) at the fields
Pr: Brian Briscoe
Pr: Dennis Casto

Pr: Barbara Witman
VP: Bryant Frihart

D-U-N-S 11-311-8009
AKA WIRELESS INC
Z WIRELESS
(*Suby of* ATLANTIC STREET CAPITAL MANAGEMENT LLC) ★
7505 S Louise Ave, Sioux Falls, SD 57108-5951
Tel (605) 275-3733 *Founded/Ownrshp* 2011
Sales 206.1MM^E *EMP* 402
SIC 4813 Telephone communication, except radio
Pr: Kevin Tupy

D-U-N-S 01-771-1888
AKAL SECURITY INC (NM)
7 Infinity Loop, Espanola, NM 87532-6737
Tel (505) 753-7832 *Founded/Ownrshp* 1980
Sales 440.4MM^E *EMP* 15,000
Accts Pulaskos Cpas Pc Albuquerque
SIC 7381 Protective services, guard; Private investigator
CEO: Matthew Branigan
**Pr:* Daya Khalsa
**Pr:* Joseph Trindal
**CFO:* Dave Garlock
CFO: Singh Sukhwinder
VP: Brian Beckwith

D-U-N-S 04-777-5205
▲ **AKAMAI TECHNOLOGIES INC** (MA)
150 Broadway Ste 100, Cambridge, MA 02142-1055
Tel (617) 444-3000 *Founded/Ownrshp* 1998
Sales 2.2MMM *EMP* 6,111
Accts Pricewaterhousecoopers Llp Bo
Tkr Sym AKAM *Exch* NGS
SIC 7372 7374 Prepackaged software; Data processing & preparation
CEO: F Thomson Leighton
Ch Bd: George H Conrades
Pr: Robert W Hughes
Pr: Rick McConnell
CFO: James Benson
V Ch Bd: Paul Sagan
Chf Mktg O: Monique Bonne
Ofcr: James Gemmell
Ex VP: Robert Blumofe
Ex VP: Melanie Haratunian
VP: Mike Afergan
VP: Louis Suchy
VP: John Summers
Board of Directors: Pamela J Craig, Monte E Ford, Jill A Greenthal, Daniel R Hesse, Jonathan F Miller, Frederic V Salerno, Steven Scopellite, Naomi O Seligman

AKEBONO BRAKE
See AMAK BRAKE LLC

D-U-N-S 02-935-0613 IMP/EXP
AKEBONO BRAKE CORP
(*Suby of* AKEBONO BRAKE INDUSTRY CO., LTD.)
34385 W 12 Mile Rd, Farmington Hills, MI 48331-3375
Tel (248) 489-7400 *Founded/Ownrshp* 1998
Sales 737.7MM^E *EMP* 3,165
SIC 3714 Motor vehicle parts & accessories
Pr: Wilm Uhlenbecker
CFO: Ron Jones
CFO: Satoshi Utsugi
**Treas:* William Gleeson
Mtls Mgr: John Edwards
Sls Dir: Matt Alley

D-U-N-S 17-489-9146 IMP
AKEBONO BRAKE ELIZABETHTOWN PLANT
(*Suby of* AKEBONO BRAKE CORP) ★
300 Ring Rd, Elizabethtown, KY 42701-6778
Tel (270) 737-4906 *Founded/Ownrshp* 1986
Sales 228.8MM^E *EMP* 1,600
SIC 3714 Motor vehicle brake systems & parts
CEO: Ted Saito
**CFO:* Ron Jones
VP: Bobby Singer

AKEBONO ELIZABETHTOWN
See AMBRAKE MANUFACTURING LTD

D-U-N-S 82-506-1070 IMP
AKER SUBSEA INC
(*Suby of* AKER SOLUTIONS ASA)
3010 Briarpark Dr, Houston, TX 77042-3706
Tel (713) 685-5700 *Founded/Ownrshp* 1994
Sales 159.2MM^E *EMP* 553
SIC 3533 1389 8711 Oil field machinery & equipment; Construction, repair & dismantling services; Engineering services
CEO: Neil Holder
**Pr:* Erik Wiik
CFO: Virginia Kahnt
CFO: Sverre Slaatsveen
Snr Sftwr: John Chambless

D-U-N-S 06-024-3664
AKERMAN LLP
98 Se 7th St Ste 1100, Miami, FL 33131-3525
Tel (305) 374-5600 *Founded/Ownrshp* 2013
Sales 260.8MM^E *EMP* 1,200
SIC 8111 General practice attorney, lawyer
Ch Bd: Andrew M Smulian
COO: Patrick Murphy
CFO: Leshan Crum
CFO: Michael Ehren
**Chf Mktg O:* Jason Bovis
Exec: Fred Stanton
Mktg Mgr: Leanne Lee
Genl Couns: Thomas Casamassima
Counsel: J Cookson
Counsel: Pedro Freyre
Counsel: Michael Gennett

D-U-N-S 61-040-1754
AKIMA CORP
(*Suby of* NANA DEVELOPMENT CORP) ★
11405 N Community House R, Charlotte, NC 28277-4364
Tel (704) 552-0082 *Founded/Ownrshp* 1990
Sales 84.5MM^E *EMP* 760
SIC 8744 Facilities support services
Ch Bd: Ronald S Hadden
**Pr:* Bruce Adkins
Pr: Tom Thompson
**Treas:* Shelby Stastny
VP: Romina Fincher
VP: Scot Kramer
VP: John Lanzillotta
**VP:* Dave Nevzuroff
**VP:* John Wood
Exec: Sharon Holmes
Exec: Maria Loredo
Dir Bus: Dan Adams

D-U-N-S 14-108-1393
AKIMA LLC
QIVLIQ
(*Suby of* NANA DEVELOPMENT CORP) ★
13873 Park Center Rd 400n, Herndon, VA 20171-3271
Tel (571) 323-5200 *Founded/Ownrshp* 2003
Sales 545.2MM^E *EMP* 1,000
SIC 8741 Management services
Pr: William Monet
Treas: Khalid Khan
Genl Mgr: Peter Burgess
Genl Mgr: Terry Nelson
Dir IT: Mark Lambert
IT Man: Laura Mitchell
Netwrk Mgr: Richard Rose
Opers Mgr: Fred Smith
Sls Dir: Laura McGarry
Mktg Mgr: Robert Tozier

D-U-N-S 13-105-6868
AKIMA MANAGEMENT SERVICES LLC
(*Suby of* NANA DEVELOPMENT CORP) ★
13873 Park Center Rd 400n, Herndon, VA 20171-3271
Tel (571) 323-5200 *Founded/Ownrshp* 2003
Sales 346.5MM^E *EMP* 684
SIC 4581 Air freight handling at airports
**Sr VP:* Mia Gill
Sr VP: Dan Jenrich
VP: William J Brinkman
VP: Mike W Page
VP: Richard S Waldrop
Dir Bus: Steve Rusinko
CTO: Greg Monostori
VP Opers: Rick Craig
Snr Mgr: Jason Yu

D-U-N-S 07-837-6928
AKIN GUMP STRAUSS HAUER & FELD LLP
1333 New Hampshire Ave Nw # 400, Washington, DC 20036-1564
Tel (202) 887-4000 *Founded/Ownrshp* 1945
Sales 352.7MM^E *EMP* 2,235
SIC 8111

D-U-N-S 60-592-8246
AKIRA TECHNOLOGIES INC
1747 Penn Ave Nw Ste 600, Washington, DC 20006-4639
Tel (202) 517-7187 *Founded/Ownrshp* 2003
Sales 106.0MM *EMP* 100
SIC 7373 7379 Value-added resellers, computer systems; Computer related consulting services
CEO: Srinivas RAO Chennamaraja
Snr Mgr: Michelle Moreland

AKM
See NORTH AMERICAN KIOSK LLC

D-U-N-S 06-264-9876 IMP/EXP
▲ **AKORN INC**
1925 W Field Ct Ste 300, Lake Forest, IL 60045-4862
Tel (847) 279-6100 *Founded/Ownrshp* 1971
Sales 985.0MM *EMP* 2,172
Tkr Sym AKRX *Exch* NGS
SIC 2834 5047 Pharmaceutical preparations; Surgical equipment & supplies
CEO: Raj Rai
**Ch Bd:* John N Kapoor
COO: Bruce Kutinsky
CFO: Duane A Portwood
Ofcr: Cathy Sloan
Ex VP: Jonathon Kafer
Ex VP: Steven Lichter
Ex VP: Randall Pollard
Sr VP: Joseph Bonaccorsi
Sr VP: Rob Monahan
VP: Pati Biswajit
Board of Directors: Kenneth S Abramowitz, Adrienne L Graves, Ronald M Johnson, Steven J Meyer, Terry Allison Rappuhn, Brian Tambi, Alan Weinstein

D-U-N-S 02-486-0178
AKQA INC
(*Suby of* WPP PLC)
360 3rd St Ste 500, San Francisco, CA 94107-2165
Tel (415) 645-9400 *Founded/Ownrshp* 1990
Sales 119.5MM^E *EMP* 535
SIC 8742 Management consulting services; Marketing consulting services
CEO: Tom Bedecarre
CFO: Lester Feintuck
CFO: Veronica Kavanagh
Chf Cred: Rei Inamoto
Exec: Andy Almquist
Assoc Dir: Michael Andrew
Assoc Dir: Gearoid Oflynn
Creative D: Whitney Jenkins
Creative D: Jefferson Liu
Off Mgr: Alan Ramos
Snr Sftwr: Mark Kell

D-U-N-S 80-479-0124 EXP
AKRIMAX PHARMACEUTICALS LLC
11 Commerce Dr Ste 103, Cranford, NJ 07016-3513
Tel (908) 372-0506 *Founded/Ownrshp* 2007
Sales 85.0MM *EMP* 75
SIC 2834 Pharmaceutical preparations
Ch: Joseph Krivulka
**Pr:* Gregory Ford
**Pr:* Donald C Olsen
**Ch:* Leonard Mazur
**VP:* Mitchell Arnold
**VP:* Bernard Kijek
VP: Keith Lavan
**VP:* Keith Rotenberg
**VP:* Timothy J Soule
Exec: Timothy Soule
Exec: Justine Westrich

D-U-N-S 03-999-8992 IMP/EXP
AKROCHEM CORP
3770 Embassy Pkwy, Akron, OH 44333-8367
Tel (330) 535-2100 *Founded/Ownrshp* 1929
Sales 106.2MM *EMP* 77
SIC 5169

D-U-N-S 96-575-5986 IMP/EXP
■ **AKRON BRASS CO**
(*Suby of* AKRON BRASS HOLDING CORP) ★
343 Venture Blvd, Wooster, OH 44691-7564
Tel (330) 264-5678 *Founded/Ownrshp* 2008
Sales 115.1MM *EMP* 395
SIC 3647 3699 Vehicular lighting equipment; Electrical equipment & supplies
Pr: Sean Tillinghast
Treas: Brian Hungerman
**VP:* Joseph R Daprile
VP: David Durstine
**VP:* Steven Webb
VP: Mark Whiteling
VP: Richard Wuescher
Dist Mgr: Josh Christner
Dist Mgr: Kent Clasen
Dist Mgr: Will Leach
Dist Mgr: Steve Lynn
Board of Directors: Patrick Milbourne

D-U-N-S 08-023-2316
■ **AKRON BRASS HOLDING CORP**
(*Suby of* IDEX CORP) ★
343 Venture Blvd, Wooster, OH 44691-7564
Tel (330) 264-5678 *Founded/Ownrshp* 2016
Sales 115.1MM^E *EMP* 673^E
SIC 3647 3699 6719 Vehicular lighting equipment; Electrical equipment & supplies; Investment holding companies, except banks
Pr: Sean Tillinghast

AKRON CHILDREN'S HOSPITAL
See CHILDRENS HOSPITAL MEDICAL CENTER OF AKRON

D-U-N-S 07-774-8655
AKRON CITY HOSPITAL INC
525 E Market St, Akron, OH 44304-1698
Tel (330) 253-5046 *Founded/Ownrshp* 1890
Sales 152.2MM^E *EMP* 2,900
Accts Kpmg Peat Marwick Cpa S
SIC 8062 General medical & surgical hospitals
Pr: Albert F Gilbert
**Ch Bd:* Barbara Hiney
**Treas:* David H Wilhoite
**Ex VP:* Beth O'Brien
**VP:* James B Pickering
Pharmcst: Jackie Ewald

D-U-N-S 00-416-2962 IMP
■ **AKRON COCA-COLA BOTTLING CO**
(*Suby of* COCA-COLA REFRESHMENTS USA INC) ★
1560 Triplett Blvd, Akron, OH 44306-3306
Tel (330) 784-2653 *Founded/Ownrshp* 1985
Sales 169.8MM^E *EMP* 1,300
SIC 5149 Soft drinks
Genl Mgr: Matt Cartaglia

AKRON GENERAL HEALTH SYSTEM
See AKRON GENERAL MEDICAL CENTER INC

D-U-N-S 18-658-5683
AKRON GENERAL HEALTH SYSTEM
(*Suby of* CLEVELAND CLINIC HEALTH SYSTEM) ★
1 Akron General Ave, Akron, OH 44307-2432
Tel (330) 344-6000 *Founded/Ownrshp* 2015
Sales 544.4MM^E *EMP* 5,200^E
Accts Blue & Co Llc Columbus Oh
SIC 8741 Hospital management
Pr: Thomas L Stover
V Ch: Robert A Stefanko
COO: Cathy M Ceccio
COO: Nancy Jones
CFO: Pat McMahon
Treas: Mark C Leeson
Ofcr: Denise Myricks
Sr VP: Daniel P Cunningham
Sr VP: Anthony N Gorant
Sr VP: Phyllis B Marino
Sr VP: Richard J Streck
VP: Steve Abdenour
VP: John Agler
VP: Robert Arnold
VP: Don Corpora
VP: Joe Plavecski
VP: Richard Streck
Dir Risk M: Susan Carter
Dir Lab: Debbie Metzger

D-U-N-S 04-163-5665
AKRON GENERAL MEDICAL CENTER INC
AKRON GENERAL HEALTH SYSTEM
(*Suby of* AKRON GENERAL HEALTH SYSTEM) ★
1 Akron General Ave, Akron, OH 44307-2432
Tel (330) 344-6000 *Founded/Ownrshp* 1914
Sales 544.4MM *EMP* 875^E
Accts Lb Blue & Co Llc Columbus Oh
SIC 8062 8011 8322 8221 General medical & surgical hospitals; Offices & clinics of medical doctors; Individual & family services; Colleges universities & professional schools
Ch Bd: F William Steere
Chf Rad: Carl R Martino
V Ch: Justin Lavin
V Ch: Robert Stefanko
Chf Mktg O: Tom Neumann
Ofcr: Barbara Vimont
Ex VP: William Gardner
Sr VP: Penny Walberg
VP: Benito B Alvarez
VP: Beverly Bokovitz
VP: Christina Cyrus
VP: Debbie Gorbach
VP: Cherie Guster
VP: Carol Icsman
Dir Lab: Kenneth F Button
Dir Lab: Debbie Metzger
Dir Rad: Rick White
Mng Ofcr: Kim Self-Martter

D-U-N-S 01-084-5220
AKRON PUBLIC SCHOOLS
70 N Broadway St, Akron, OH 44308-1911
Tel (330) 761-1661 *Founded/Ownrshp* 1847
Sales 197.5MM^E *EMP* 3,937
SIC 8211 Public elementary & secondary schools
CFO: Ryan Pendleton
**Treas:* John Pierson
Ofcr: Kelly Johnson
Ofcr: Leroy Moss
VP: Bruce Alexander
**Ex Dir:* Mark Black
Prgrm Mgr: Kenneth Phares
Instr Medi: Martha Godward
Psych: Terry Bendo
Psych: Bambi Berger
Psych: Marlana Esposito

D-U-N-S 05-266-5023
AKRON SERVICES INC
17705 N Elevator Rd, Edelstein, IL 61526-9716
Tel (309) 243-7533 *Founded/Ownrshp* 1960
Sales 125.2MM *EMP* 37^E
Accts Thomas M Donald Cpa Eldora
SIC 5153 5191 Grain elevators; Fertilizer & fertilizer materials
Pr: Lawrence Wagenbach
**Sec:* Elaine Wagenbach
**Ex VP:* Timothy G Wagenbach
Genl Mgr: Jennifer Dell

D-U-N-S 01-233-3519 IMP
■ **AKT AMERICA INC**
(*Suby of* APPLIED MATERIALS INC) ★
3101 Scott Blvd Bldg 91, Santa Clara, CA 95054-3318
Tel (408) 563-5455 *Founded/Ownrshp* 1999
Sales 8.0MMM *EMP* 800
SIC 3699 Electrical equipment & supplies
VP: In Doo Kang

D-U-N-S 18-397-7487 IMP
AKZO NOBEL CHEMICALS LLC
(*Suby of* AKZONOBEL) ★
525 W Van Buren St # 1600, Chicago, IL 60607-3845
Tel (312) 544-7000 *Founded/Ownrshp* 1997
Sales 617.3MM^E *EMP* 2,100
SIC 2841 Soap & other detergents
CFO: Barbara Allen
Top Exec: Paul Nolan
VP: Blake Holder
Mng Dir: Matt Pullen
Mng Dir: Paul Radlinski
Genl Mgr: Inna Patriki
Genl Mgr: Hanni Radwan
Genl Mgr: Ali Zaman
QA Dir: Pamela Hodge
IT Man: David Thompson
Tech Mgr: Howard Chadwick

D-U-N-S 02-197-3748 IMP/EXP
AKZO NOBEL COATINGS INC
AKZONOBEL PACKAGING COATINGS
(*Suby of* AKZONOBEL) ★
8220 Mohawk Dr, Strongsville, OH 44136-1794
Tel (440) 297-5100 *Founded/Ownrshp* 1980
Sales 404.3MM^E *EMP* 2,500
SIC 2851 5198 2821

D-U-N-S 13-449-7259 IMP
AKZO NOBEL FUNCTIONAL CHEMICAL LLC
AKZONOBEL
(*Suby of* AKZO NOBEL CHEMICALS LLC) ★
525 W Van Buren St # 1600, Chicago, IL 60607-3845
Tel (312) 544-7000 *Founded/Ownrshp* 1999
Sales 157.8MM^E *EMP* 450
SIC 2869 Industrial organic chemicals
CEO: Marco Wijnands
Pr: John Wolff
VP: Ralph Sterling
Genl Mgr: Janice Lucchesi
Mktg Mgr: Mark Schroeder

D-U-N-S 06-299-9347 IMP/EXP
AKZO NOBEL INC
AKZONOBEL
(*Suby of* AKZO NOBEL N.V.)
525 W Van Buren St Fl 16, Chicago, IL 60607-3835
Tel (312) 544-7000 *Founded/Ownrshp* 1982
Sales 2.9MMM^E *EMP* 8,210
SIC 2869 2851 2834 3841 3826 2819 Industrial organic chemicals; Paints & paint additives; Lacquers, varnishes, enamels & other coatings; Pharmaceutical preparations; Hemodialysis apparatus; Analytical instruments; Industrial inorganic chemicals
CEO: Ton Bchner
Pr: Philip E Radtke
CFO: Keith Nichols
CFO: Steven Shamrock
Ofcr: John Smith
VP: Kenneth Frank
VP: Wouter Hut
VP: Larry Klar
VP: Paul Radlinski
VP: Katia Righammar
VP: Henry Vasterling
Exec: Ronald Vergouwen
Dir Rx: John Griffin
Dir Bus: Andy Nemes

D-U-N-S 15-133-4422 IMP/EXP
AKZO NOBEL PAINTS LLC
GLIDDEN PROFESSIONAL PAINT CTR
8381 Pearl Rd, Strongsville, OH 44136-1637
Tel (440) 297-8000 *Founded/Ownrshp* 2013
Sales NA *EMP* 5,000
SIC 2851 2891

D-U-N-S 02-782-2696 IMP/EXP
AKZO NOBEL POLYMER CHEM LLC
525 W Van Buren St # 1600, Chicago, IL 60607-3845
Tel (312) 544-7000 *Founded/Ownrshp* 1999
Sales NA *EMP* 2,000^E
SIC 2869

D-U-N-S 10-665-4973 IMP/EXP
AKZO NOBEL PULP AND PERFORMANCE CHEMICALS INC
(Suby of AKZO NOBEL PULP AND PERFORMANCE CHEMICALS AB)
1850 Parkway Pl Se # 1200, Marietta, GA 30067-4439
Tel (770) 578-0858 Founded/Ownrshp 2002
Sales 126.8MM[E] EMP 450
SIC 2899 2819 Sodium chloride, refined; Peroxides, hydrogen peroxide
CEO: Mario Houde
*Pr: Byron Smith
*CFO: Michel Gregoire
CFO: Corinne Hazan
Comm Man: Steve Main
Genl Mgr: Philippe Beaudet
Genl Mgr: Paul Radlinski
CTO: William Ostrozynski
Dir IT: Don Foster
IT Man: Stefan Malmsten
Tech Mgr: Britt Willskytt

D-U-N-S 82-590-1759 IMP
AKZO NOBEL SPG LLC
10 Finderne Ave Ste A, Bridgewater, NJ 08807-3365
Tel (908) 685-5000 Founded/Ownrshp 2008
Sales 146.7MM[E] EMP 472[E]
SIC 2841

AKZONOBEL
See AKZO NOBEL INC

AKZONOBEL
See AKZO NOBEL FUNCTIONAL CHEMICAL LLC

AKZONOBEL PACKAGING COATINGS
See AKZO NOBEL COATINGS INC

D-U-N-S 87-903-9790 IMP/EXP
AL DAHRA ACX GLOBAL INC
920 E Pacific Coast Hwy, Wilmington, CA 90744-2725
Tel (209) 465-3718 Founded/Ownrshp 1990
Sales 85.4MM[E] EMP 100
SIC 5191 Animal feeds
Pr: John M Gombos
*Treas: Brent Hansston

D-U-N-S 00-799-2704
AL J SCHNEIDER CO
GALT HOUSE, THE
325 W Main St Ste 1800, Louisville, KY 40202-4244
Tel (502) 584-5984 Founded/Ownrshp 1947
Sales 98.7MM[E] EMP 1,200
SIC 7011 5031 Hotels; Hotel, franchised; Lumber: rough, dressed & finished; Millwork
Pr: Scott T Shoenberger

D-U-N-S 00-304-1597 IMP
AL SHELLCO LLC
(Suby of PROPHET EQUITY LP) ★
9330 Scranton Rd Ste 600, San Diego, CA 92121-7706
Tel (570) 296-6444 Founded/Ownrshp 1953, 2009
Sales 85.0MM[E] EMP 1,800
SIC 3651 3577 Radio receiving sets; Computer peripheral equipment
*Pr: George Stelling
*CEO: Ross Gatlin
CFO: Dick Horner
*CFO: Richard P Horner
CFO: David Scchniak
Mktg Mgr: Rob Puzey

D-U-N-S 02-475-7353
AL SMITH CO INC
AL SMITH DODGE
2511 Wake Forest Rd, Raleigh, NC 27609-7835
Tel (919) 839-7481 Founded/Ownrshp 1988
Sales 86.0MM EMP 185
Accts Ernst & Young Llp Raleigh Nc
SIC 5511 5521 Automobiles, new & used; Used car dealers
Sec: David Hushek
IT Man: Jeff Williams
Netwrk Mgr: Gene Fourney

AL SMITH DODGE
See AL SMITH CO INC

D-U-N-S 04-658-4538
AL WARREN OIL CO INC
1646 Summer St, Hammond, IN 46320-2232
Tel (773) 735-6900 Founded/Ownrshp 1948
Sales 158.9MM EMP 55
SIC 5172 5541 Service station supplies, petroleum; Filling stations, gasoline
Pr: Tom Warren

D-U-N-S 07-912-1448
ALABAMA A & M UNIVERSITY
4900 Meridian St N, Huntsville, AL 35810
Tel (256) 372-5200 Founded/Ownrshp 1875
Sales 137.8MM[E] EMP 1,000[E]
SIC 8221 University
Pr: Dr Andrew Hugine Jr
Mng Pt: Douglas Turner
Ofcr: Timothy Dawkins
Ofcr: Nancy Turner
*VP: Juanita Cales
Assoc Dir: Rakesha Hines
Assoc Dir: Tarsha Lockhart
Ex Dir: Constance Adams
Prgrm Mgr: Elicia Chaverest
Off Mgr: Christian Elizer
Dir IT: Sang Han

D-U-N-S 17-637-7042
ALABAMA COMMUNITY COLLEGE SYSTEM
POSTSECONDARY EDUCATN ALA DEPT
(Suby of OFFICE OF SECRETARY STATE) ★
135 S Union St, Montgomery, AL 36130-2100
Tel (334) 262-8734 Founded/Ownrshp 1982
Sales NA EMP 1,000
SIC 9411 Administration of educational programs;
Assoc Dir: Amy Brabham
*Prin: Jane Leatherwood
IT Man: Sara Calhoun

ALABAMA CRMSNTIDE SFTBALL
See UNIVERSITY OF ALABAMA

ALABAMA CROWN DISTRIBUTING CO
See GEORGIA CROWN DISTRIBUTING CO

D-U-N-S 82-856-7557
ALABAMA CULLMAN YUTAKA TECHNOLOGIES LLC
ACYT
(Suby of CARDINGTON YUTAKA TECHNOLOGIES INC) ★
460 Al Highway 157, Cullman, AL 35058-3630
Tel (256) 739-3533 Founded/Ownrshp 2006
Sales 153.8MM[E] EMP 1[E]
SIC 3714 Motor vehicle parts & accessories
Prin: Ben Harrison

D-U-N-S 00-180-0247
ALABAMA DEPARTMENT OF LABOR
WORKERS COMPENSATION
(Suby of OFFICE OF SECRETARY STATE) ★
649 Monroe St, Montgomery, AL 36131-0001
Tel (334) 242-8055 Founded/Ownrshp 1930
Sales NA EMP 1,000[E]
SIC 9441 Administration of social & manpower programs;
Snr Mgr: David White

D-U-N-S 61-384-2061 IMP/EXP
ALABAMA DEPARTMENT OF PUBLIC HEALTH
ADPH
(Suby of OFFICE OF SECRETARY STATE) ★
201 Monroe St Ste 1050, Montgomery, AL 36104-6959
Tel (334) 206-5300 Founded/Ownrshp 1875
Sales NA EMP 4,000
SIC 9431 Administration of public health programs;
Ofcr: Allen Rowe
Ofcr: Donald E Williamson
Counsel: Samarria Dunson

D-U-N-S 92-993-3406
ALABAMA DEPT OF CONSERVATION & NATURAL RESOURCES
(Suby of OFFICE OF SECRETARY STATE) ★
64 N Union St Rm 458, Montgomery, AL 36130-3020
Tel (334) 242-3468 Founded/Ownrshp 1890
Sales NA EMP 1,200
SIC 9512 Land, mineral & wildlife conservation;
*CFO: Jack McDaniel
Genl Mgr: Bruce Lawler
Genl Mgr: Stacey Norris

D-U-N-S 83-672-3197
ALABAMA DEPT OF HUMAN RESOURCES
(Suby of OFFICE OF SECRETARY STATE) ★
50 N Ripley St, Montgomery, AL 36130-1001
Tel (334) 242-1310 Founded/Ownrshp 1996
Sales NA EMP 4,500
SIC 9441 Administration of social & manpower programs;
Prgrm Mgr: Lisa Wise
MIS Dir: Duey Kerper

D-U-N-S 92-995-6324
ALABAMA DEPT OF MENTAL HEALTH
(Suby of OFFICE OF SECRETARY STATE) ★
100 N Union St Ste 520, Montgomery, AL 36104-3719
Tel (334) 242-3107 Founded/Ownrshp 1970
Sales NA EMP 1,798
SIC 9199
Admn Mgr: Jessica Hales
Admn Mgr: Lynn Hubbard
Genl Mgr: James Perdue
IT Man: Kris Dilamaa
Genl Couns: Courtney Tarver

D-U-N-S 83-672-2991
ALABAMA DEPT OF PUBLIC SAFETY
EXECUTIVE OFFCE OF THE STATE
(Suby of OFFICE OF SECRETARY STATE) ★
301 S Ripley St, Montgomery, AL 36104-4425
Tel (334) 242-4394 Founded/Ownrshp 1935
Sales NA EMP 1,400
SIC 9229 Public safety bureau, government;
*Prin: Col W M Coppage
Admn Mgr: Michael Gillis
Admn Mgr: Scott Haga
Genl Mgr: Shaundra Morris

D-U-N-S 83-789-2371
ALABAMA DEPT OF TRANSPORTATION
EXECUTV OFC OF THE STATE OF AL
(Suby of OFFICE OF SECRETARY STATE) ★
1409 Coliseum Blvd, Montgomery, AL 36110-2060
Tel (334) 242-6258 Founded/Ownrshp 1819
Sales NA EMP 4,000[E]
SIC 9621 Transportation department: government, non-operating;
Ofcr: Gary Ray
Prgrm Mgr: Adam Foutz
Off Mgr: Sylvia Dryer
Trfc Dir: Shelby McElvaine

D-U-N-S 00-400-5898 EXP
ALABAMA FARMERS COOPERATIVE INC (AL)
BONNIE PLANTS
121 Somerville Rd Ne, Decatur, AL 35601-2659
Tel (256) 353-6843 Founded/Ownrshp 1936
Sales 651.8MM[E] EMP 3,000
SIC 5191 5153 5159 Farm supplies; Herbicides; Grains; Peanuts (bulk), unroasted
Pr: Tommy Paulk
*Pr: Rivers Myres
*COO: Roger Pangle
CFO: Jamie Bowling
*CFO: W Dan Groscost
VP: Terry Reach
CIO: Wayne Olt
Software D: Dan Truitt

D-U-N-S 00-690-0104
■ **ALABAMA GAS CORP** (AL)
ALAGASCO
(Suby of SPIRE INC) ★
2101 6th Ave N Ste 240, Birmingham, AL 35203-2789
Tel (205) 326-8100 Founded/Ownrshp 1800
Sales 368.5MM EMP 909[E]
SIC 4924 Natural gas distribution
CEO: Steven L Lindsey
*Ch Bd: Suzanne Sitherwood
Pr: Ken A Smith
*CFO: Steven P Rasche
VP: Steven Chapman
VP: Sidney Quick
VP: Kenneth A Smith
VP: Amy E Watson
Board of Directors: Mark C Darrell, Larry Craig Dowdy

D-U-N-S 00-691-9211
■ **ALABAMA GREAT SOUTHERN RAILROAD CO**
(Suby of NORFOLK SOUTHERN RAILWAY CO) ★
3 Commercial Pl, Norfolk, VA 23510-2108
Tel (540) 981-4049 Founded/Ownrshp 1895
Sales 51.2MM[E] EMP 2,562[E]
SIC 4011 Railroads, line-haul operating
Prin: Tom Mahoney
*Treas: Ronald Sink
*VP: Steven C Tobias

D-U-N-S 07-545-6699 IMP
ALABAMA INSTITUTE FOR DEAF AND BLIND
AIDB CHILDREN & YOUTH PROGRAMS
205 South St E, Talladega, AL 35160-2411
Tel (256) 761-3200 Founded/Ownrshp 1980
Sales 47.0MM[E] EMP 1,266[E]
SIC 8249 8211 Trade school; Public vocational/technical school; School for physically handicapped
Pr: John Mascia
Treas: Thomas F Hickey

D-U-N-S 07-955-6743
ALABAMA JUDICIAL BUILDING AUTHORITY
(Suby of STATE OF ALABAMA) ★
100 N Union St Rm 224, Montgomery, AL 36104-3719
Tel (334) 353-3328 Founded/Ownrshp 2014
Sales NA EMP 2,633[E]
SIC 9111
Prin: Roy Moore

D-U-N-S 00-400-3489 IMP
■ **ALABAMA METAL INDUSTRIES CORP**
AMICO
(Suby of GIBRALTAR INDUSTRIES INC) ★
3245 Fayette Ave, Birmingham, AL 35208-4822
Tel (205) 787-2611 Founded/Ownrshp 1939, 2005
Sales 250.8MM[E] EMP 900
SIC 3446 3449 3089 3441 3316 Architectural metalwork; Open flooring & grating for construction; Lath, expanded metal; Extruded finished plastic products; Fabricated structural metal; Cold finishing of steel shapes
Pr: Joseph D Smith
VP: Andrew Harwood
Telecom Mg: Jimmy Wood

D-U-N-S 60-363-6051
ALABAMA MUNICIPAL ELECTRIC AUTHORITY
AMEA
80 Technacenter Dr, Montgomery, AL 36117-6028
Tel (334) 262-1126 Founded/Ownrshp 1981
Sales 201.1MM EMP 14[E]
Accts Deloitte & Touche Llp Birming
SIC 4911 Electric services
CEO: Fred D Clark Jr
*CFO: J Marlin Wade
CFO: Marlin Wade

D-U-N-S 00-690-0120 IMP
■ **ALABAMA POWER CO** (AL)
(Suby of SOUTHERN CO) ★
600 18th St N, Birmingham, AL 35203-2200
Tel (205) 257-1000 Founded/Ownrshp 1906
Sales 5.7MMM EMP 6,986
SIC 4911 Generation, electric power; Transmission, electric power; Distribution, electric power
Ch Bd: Mark A Crosswhite
Pr: Steve R Spencer
CFO: Philip C Raymond
CFO: Philip Raymond
Ofcr: Debbie Davis
Ex VP: Greg J Barker
Ex VP: Banks Farris
Ex VP: Alan Martin
Ex VP: Georgia Power
Ex VP: Zeke W Smith
Ex VP: John Young
Sr VP: James P Heilbron
Sr VP: Robin A Hurst
Sr VP: Quentin Riggins
VP: Christopher T Bell
VP: Matthew Bowden
VP: William Bowers
VP: Larry R Grill
VP: Myrk Harkins
VP: Williamr Hathaway
VP: Robin Hurst
Board of Directors: Whit Armstrong, David J Cooper Sr, Grayson Hall Jr, Anthony A Joseph, Patricia M King, James K Lowder, Robert D Powers, Catherine J Randall, C Dowd Ritter

D-U-N-S 08-138-1568 IMP/EXP
ALABAMA RIVER CELLULOSE LLC
(Suby of GEORGIA-PACIFIC LLC) ★
2373 Lena Landegger Hwy Cnty, Perdue Hill, AL 36470
Tel (251) 575-2000 Founded/Ownrshp 1978, 2010
Sales 136.0MM[E] EMP 320
SIC 2611 Kraft (sulfate) pulp
Pr: George F Landegger
*CFO: Russell Kendrick
*Ex VP: Robert Black

D-U-N-S 09-568-7794
ALABAMA RIVER WOODLANDS INC
(Suby of ALABAMA RIVER CELLULOSE LLC) ★
2373 Lena Landegger Hwy, Perdue Hill, AL 36470
Tel (251) 575-2039 Founded/Ownrshp 1978
Sales 100.0MM EMP 26
SIC 5099 Timber products, rough
Pr: Richard Koger

D-U-N-S 04-067-2685
ALABAMA STATE UNIVERSITY (INC)
A S U
915 S Jackson St, Montgomery, AL 36104-5714
Tel (334) 229-4100 Founded/Ownrshp 1967
Sales 234.4MM EMP 3,000
SIC 8221 University
COO: John F Knight Jr
Ofcr: Melva Deramus
Assoc VP: Zillah Fluker
Prin: Clarence A Wilson
Adm Dir: Sidney Brown
Adm Dir: Anthony Flemings
Genl Mgr: Candy Capel
Genl Mgr: David Okeowo
IT Man: Larry Cobb
IT Man: Terence Thomas
Mtls Mgr: Dante Tyson-Bey

D-U-N-S 14-458-1113
ALABAMA THRIFT STORES INC
AMERICAS THRIFT
1125 Huffman Rd, Birmingham, AL 35215-7501
Tel (205) 856-1234 Founded/Ownrshp 1984
Sales 131.8MM[E] EMP 900
SIC 5331 5932 Variety stores; Used merchandise stores
CEO: J Buford Salmon
*CEO: Buford Salmon
*COO: Mike Kane
*Treas: Lillian Salmon

D-U-N-S 36-070-4134
ALABAMA UNIFIED JUDICIAL SYSTEM
SUPREME COURT
(Suby of STATE OF ALABAMA) ★
300 Dexter Ave, Montgomery, AL 36104-3741
Tel (334) 954-5000 Founded/Ownrshp 1819
Sales NA EMP 1,950
SIC 9211 State courts;
Prin: Roy F Moore

ALACER GOLD
See ALACER MANAGEMENT CORP

D-U-N-S 00-446-8196
ALACER MANAGEMENT CORP
ALACER GOLD
9635 Maroon Cir Ste 300, Englewood, CO 80112-5902
Tel (303) 292-1299 Founded/Ownrshp 2012
Sales 300.0MM EMP 19
SIC 1041 Gold ores mining
CEO: Rodney P Antal

D-U-N-S 15-647-0163
ALACHUA COUNTY PUBLIC SCHOOLS
620 E University Ave, Gainesville, FL 32601-5448
Tel (352) 955-7300 Founded/Ownrshp 1869
Sales 176.2MM[E] EMP 4,299
Accts David W Martin Cpa Tallahass
SIC 8211 Public elementary & secondary schools
CFO: Scott Ward
Exec: Will Calsam
Ex Dir: Kathy Black
Dir Sec: Scott Jamison
Opers Mgr: David Stanley
Pr Dir: Jackie Johnson
Teacher Pr: Beverly Finley
Instr Medi: Mary Hall
HC Dir: Pat Hughes

D-U-N-S 79-150-3068
ALACRITY LENDING CO
6209 Colleyville Blvd, Colleyville, TX 76034-6439
Tel (817) 481-1500 Founded/Ownrshp 2006
Sales NA EMP 65
SIC 6162 Mortgage bankers & correspondents
Pr: Steven B Holmes

D-U-N-S 12-093-0102 IMP
■ **ALADDIN MANUFACTURING CORP**
MOHAWK
(Suby of MOHAWK CARPET LLC) ★
160 S Industrial Blvd, Calhoun, GA 30701-3030
Tel (706) 629-7721 Founded/Ownrshp 1995
Sales 1.9MMM[E] EMP 17,000
SIC 2273 Finishers of tufted carpets & rugs; Smyrna carpets & rugs, machine woven
Pr: W Christopher Wellborn
Ch Bd: Jeffrey Lorberbaum
CEO: Frank Boykins
CFO: James F Brunk
Dir IT: Jebin Jensen
IT Man: Don McCurdy
Mfg Dir: Tony Swink

D-U-N-S 80-097-4735 IMP/EXP
ALADDIN TEMP-RITE LLC
(Suby of ALI SPA)
250 E Main St, Hendersonville, TN 37075-2521
Tel (615) 537-3600 Founded/Ownrshp 2002
Sales 101.6MM[E] EMP 200[E]
SIC 5047 Hospital equipment & supplies
Pr: Martin A Rothshchild
Art Dir: Rodger Crocker

ALAGASCO
See ALABAMA GAS CORP

ALAHAMBRA HIGH SCHOOL
See ALHAMBRA UNIFIED SCHOOL DISTRICT

D-U-N-S 02-444-3814 EXP
ALAMANCE FOODS INC (NC)
TRITON WATER
840 Plantation Dr, Burlington, NC 27215-6711
Tel (336) 226-6392 Founded/Ownrshp 1959
Sales 87.5MM[E] EMP 180

SIC 2026 2899 2024 2086 Milk & cream, except fermented, cultured & flavored; Distilled water; Ice cream & frozen desserts; Fruit drinks (less than 100% juice): packaged in cans, etc.
Ch: William C Scott Sr
*CEO: Bill Scott
Plnt Mgr: Gene Smith
VP Sls: Jeff Parker
Mktg Dir: Jessica Kirkland
Manager: Jerry Shumate

D-U-N-S 15-324-8091
ALAMANCE REGIONAL MEDICAL CENTER INC
ARMC HEALTH CARE
1240 Huffman Mill Rd, Burlington, NC 27215-8700
Tel (336) 538-7000 Founded/Ownrshp 1937
Sales 240.4MM EMP 1,500
Accts Stout Stuart Mcgowen & King L
SIC 8062 General medical & surgical hospitals
Pr: John G Currin Jr
Dir Vol: Gina Blackwell
*CFO: Rex A Street
CFO: Rex Street
Ofcr: Lea Gillis
*Ofcr: Preston Hammock
*Ex VP: Rex Street
*Sr VP: Robert E Byrd
VP: Robert Byrd
*VP: Lavern Delaney
*VP: Vicki Moran
Exec: Dick Donahey
Dir Lab: Marilyn Rubright
Dir Rx: Pam Brugger

D-U-N-S 79-545-7548
ALAMANCE-BURLINGTON SCHOOL DISTRICT
1712 Vaughn Rd, Burlington, NC 27217-2916
Tel (336) 570-6060 Founded/Ownrshp 1996
Sales 103.6MM[E] EMP 2,663
SIC 8211 Public elementary & secondary schools

D-U-N-S 96-186-1424
ALAMEDA ALLIANCE FOR HEALTH
1240 S Loop Rd, Alameda, CA 94502-7084
Tel (510) 747-4555 Founded/Ownrshp 1994
Sales NA EMP 135
Accts Deloitte & Touche Llp Oakland
SIC 6324 Health maintenance organization (HMO), insurance only
CEO: Ingrid Lamirault
COO: Matthew Woodruff
CFO: Robert Larue
CFO: Kelvin Quan
Dir: Carol Oosterwijk
IT Man: Angela Ingel
Info Man: Brian Bretz
Snr Mgr: Jacqueline Kelly

D-U-N-S 08-317-1488 IMP
ALAMEDA BUREAU OF ELECTRICITY IMPROVEMENT CORP
ALAMEDA MUNICPAL POWER
2000 Grand St, Alameda, CA 94501-1228
Tel (510) 748-3901 Founded/Ownrshp 1887
Sales 85.4MM[E] EMP 120
SIC 4911 4899 4841 Transmission, electric power; Distribution, electric power; Communication signal enhancement network system; Cable & other pay television services
CEO: Edwin Dankworth
*Pr: Gregory Hamm
Bd of Dir: Alameda Green
*VP: Peter Holmes
VP: Bob Mackey
VP: Ann McCormick
*VP: Margie Sherratt
Exec: Denise Connors
Exec: Chiara Hanna
Exec: Robert Orbeta
Genl Mgr: Girish Balachandran

D-U-N-S 05-877-5230
ALAMEDA COUNTY WATER DISTRICT INC
ACWD
43885 S Grimmer Blvd, Fremont, CA 94538-6375
Tel (510) 668-4200 Founded/Ownrshp 1914
Sales 150.8MM[E] EMP 217
SIC 4941 Water supply
Genl Mgr: Walt Wadlow
Dir IT: John Musser
IT Man: Jon Allsup
IT Man: Geoffry Brown
IT Man: Ariv Naqui
Plnt Mgr: Al Wagner
Prd Mgr: Kwame Agyare
Sales Exec: Debhra Conner
VP Sls: Stephanie Nevins

D-U-N-S 00-922-6937 IMP
ALAMEDA ELECTRIC SUPPLY (CA)
ALAMEDA ELECTRICAL DISTRS
3875 Bay Center Pl, Hayward, CA 94545-3619
Tel (510) 786-1400 Founded/Ownrshp 1976
Sales 106.8MM[E] EMP 68
SIC 5063 Electrical supplies
CEO: Robert E Larue
*VP: Greg Berkowitz
*VP: Criag Larue
Mktg Mgr: Jeff Wright
Sales Asso: Anne Donathan

ALAMEDA ELECTRICAL DISTRS
See ALAMEDA ELECTRIC SUPPLY

ALAMEDA MUNICPAL POWER
See ALAMEDA BUREAU OF ELECTRICITY IMPROVEMENT CORP

D-U-N-S 00-916-8824
ALAMEDA NEWSPAPERS INC
TIMES HERALD
(Suby of DIGITAL FIRST MEDIA) ★
22533 Foothill Blvd, Hayward, CA 94541-4109
Tel (510) 783-6111 Founded/Ownrshp 1985
Sales 73.1MM[E] EMP 1,055
SIC 2711 Newspapers, publishing & printing
Pr: Joh Schueler
*Pr: P Scott McKibben
*CFO: Patrick Brown
*Sr VP: Nancy Conway
*Sr VP: Dennis Miller
*VP: Colleen Brewer
*VP: James Dove
*VP: Mike Lynch

D-U-N-S 07-652-7324
ALAMEDA UNIFIED SCHOOL DISTRICT
2060 Challenger Dr, Alameda, CA 94501-1037
Tel (510) 337-7060 Founded/Ownrshp 1953
Sales 79.2MM[E] EMP 1,100
SIC 8211 8299 Public elementary & secondary schools; Public adult education school; Educational services
Treas: Wendy Mariani
Trst: Philip Hu
Exec: Timothy Erwin
Dir Rx: Patricia Murillo
Off Admin: Christina Nieves
Dir IT: Jasmina Huskic
IT Man: Janet Copeland
Opers Mgr: Wendy Huang
Opers Mgr: Julie Yosofzay
Sls Dir: James Johnson
Sls Mgr: Susan Hartle

D-U-N-S 04-323-6231 IMP
ALAMEDA-CONTRA COSTA TRANSIT DISTRICT
AC TRANSIT
1600 Franklin St, Oakland, CA 94612-2806
Tel (510) 891-4777 Founded/Ownrshp 1956
Sales 68.6MM EMP 2,210
Accts Maze & Associates Pleasant Hi
SIC 4111 Bus line operations
Genl Mgr: David J Armijo
*CFO: Lewis Clinton
Bd of Dir: Dennis Lim
Bd of Dir: Joel Young
*Ofcr: Kathleen Kelly
Exec: Kurt Destigter
Genl Mgr: Mike Hursh
*Genl Mgr: Nancy Skowbo

D-U-N-S 07-460-2749
ALAMO COMMUNITY COLLEGE DISTRICT
SAN ANTONIO COLLEGE
201 W Sheridan, San Antonio, TX 78204-1450
Tel (210) 485-0000 Founded/Ownrshp 1945
Sales 95.9MM EMP 2,134
Accts Ernst & Young Llp San Antoni
SIC 8222 Community college
Ofcr: Richard Rodriguez
VP: Maureen Matheson
VP: Erin Sherman
Adm Dir: Schoolcraft Tandy

D-U-N-S 82-645-0207
ALAMO CONCRETE PRODUCTS LTD
6055 W Green Mountain Rd, Austin, TX 78744
Tel (512) 444-2464 Founded/Ownrshp 1994
Sales 163.9MM[E] EMP 500
SIC 3272 Concrete products
COO: Kirk Taylor
CFO: Alan Leitko
VP: Al J Mandelbaum
VP: Robert Wells
Dir IT: Randy Weeks
Prd Mgr: David Johnson

D-U-N-S 04-821-1288 IMP
■ ALAMO GROUP (USA) INC
(Suby of ALAMO GROUP INC) ★
1627 E Walnut St, Seguin, TX 78155-5259
Tel (830) 379-1480 Founded/Ownrshp 1969
Sales 224.0MM[E] EMP 2,500
SIC 3523 Grounds mowing equipment
Pr: Ronald Robinson
Ex VP: Dan E Malone
*VP: Ian Burden
*VP: Robert George

D-U-N-S 02-355-5014 IMP
▲ ALAMO GROUP INC
1627 E Walnut St, Seguin, TX 78155-5259
Tel (830) 379-1480 Founded/Ownrshp 1955
Sales 879.5MM EMP 3,030
Tkr Sym ALG Exch NYS
SIC 3523 3531 Farm machinery & equipment; Grounds mowing equipment; Haying machines: mowers, rakes, stackers, etc.; Balers, farm: hay, straw, cotton, etc.; Construction machinery attachments; Backhoe mounted, hydraulically powered attachments; Subsoiler attachments, tractor mounted
Pr: Ronald A Robinson
*Ch Bd: Gary L Martin
CFO: Robert George
CFO: Dan E Malone
Treas: Robert H George
VP: Geoffrey Davies
VP: John Fisher
VP: Maurica Hewitt
VP: Keith Krichevsky
VP: Janet Pollock
VP: Richard D Pummell
VP: Edward Rizzuti
VP: Rick Solano
VP: Richard J Wehrle
Exec: Julie Edwards

ALAMO RENT A CAR
See ALAMO RENTAL (US) INC

D-U-N-S 80-700-1644
ALAMO RENTAL (US) INC
ALAMO RENT A CAR
(Suby of VANGUARD CAR RENTAL USA INC.)
600 Corporate Park Dr, Saint Louis, MO 63105-4204
Tel (314) 512-5000 Founded/Ownrshp 2003
Sales 104.9MM[E] EMP 7,487[E]
SIC 7514 Rent-a-car service
Pr: Greg Stubblefield
Opers Mgr: Joseph Long
Opers Mgr: Todd Parker
Secur Mgr: Chis Call

D-U-N-S 18-823-7580
■ ALAMO TITLE CO
(Suby of ALAMO TITLE HOLDING CO) ★
18618 Tuscany Stone, San Antonio, TX 78258-3465
Tel (210) 490-1313 Founded/Ownrshp 2013
Sales NA EMP 150
SIC 6361 Title insurance
Ch Bd: Bill Foley
CFO: David Fitzhugh
*Sec: Alan Stinson
Ofcr: Carolyn Fletcher
*Sr VP: Juan Cavazos
*Sr VP: Charles Weisenberger
*Prin: Paula Long
Dir IT: Anita Prestige

D-U-N-S 83-633-0688
■ ALAMO TITLE HOLDING CO
(Suby of FIDELITY NATIONAL FINANCIAL INC) ★
6200 Colleyville Blvd, Colleyville, TX 76034-6223
Tel (817) 428-6996 Founded/Ownrshp 1993
Sales NA EMP 363
SIC 6361 Title insurance
Ch: William Foley
*CEO: Don Still
*Ex VP: Al Stinson

D-U-N-S 05-631-3323
■ ALAMO TITLE INSURANCE CO
(Suby of ALAMO TITLE HOLDING CO) ★
434 N Loop 1604 W # 2204, San Antonio, TX 78232-1371
Tel (210) 499-5872 Founded/Ownrshp 1998
Sales NA EMP 150[E]
SIC 6361 Title insurance
Ch: William P Folley II
*Pr: Paula Long
VP: Bruce Dunbar
*VP: David Fitzhugh
Ex Dir: Raymond Quirk
CTO: Laura Londenberg

D-U-N-S 10-192-6165
■ ALAMOSA HOLDINGS INC
(Suby of SPRINT COMMUNICATIONS INC) ★
5225 S Loop 289 Ste 120, Lubbock, TX 79424-1319
Tel (806) 722-1111 Founded/Ownrshp 2006
Sales 114.6MM[E] EMP 1,300
SIC 4813 Telephone communication, except radio
Ch Bd: David E Sharbutt
*COO: Steven A Richardson
*CFO: Kendall W Cowan
*Sr VP: Loyd I Rinehart
*Sr VP: Anthony Sabatino

ALAN REVEL ENTERTAINMENT
See REVEL ENTERTAINMENT GROUP LLC

D-U-N-S 04-784-1887
ALAN RITCHEY INC
MARTINDALE FEED MILL
740 S Frontage Rd, Valley View, TX 76272-9733
Tel (940) 726-3276 Founded/Ownrshp 1959
Sales 168.5MM[E] EMP 470
SIC 7389 4213 2048 0291 Industrial & commercial equipment inspection service; Contract haulers; Livestock feeds; General farms, primarily animals
CEO: Robby Ritchey
*COO: Richard Stroup
*VP: David Allison
*VP: Lora Hinton
*VP: Charlene Ritchey
*Prin: Brad Hieb
*Counsel: Craig Brown

D-U-N-S 79-927-5370
ALANT CORP
CIRCLE PORSCHE
1850 Outer Traffic Cir, Long Beach, CA 90815-2651
Tel (562) 494-1911 Founded/Ownrshp 1986
Sales 200.0MM EMP 85
SIC 5511 Automobiles, new & used
Pr: James Speck
*VP: Michael Ernst
Genl Mgr: Tom Croxton
Sls Mgr: Raphael Borenstein
Sls Mgr: Darrin Ellis
Sls Mgr: Eric Ernst
Sales Asso: Albert Felix
Sales Asso: Kamran Haghbin

ALARIS SYSTEMS
See CAREFUSION 303 INC

D-U-N-S 10-795-4070
ALARM SECURITY GROUP LLC
ASG SECURITY
12301 Kiln Ct Ste A, Beltsville, MD 20705-6308
Tel (301) 623-4000 Founded/Ownrshp 2015
Sales 85.4MM[E] EMP 350
SIC 7382 Security systems services
Pr: Joseph Nuccio
Pr: Mike Schobel
*VP: Glenn Seaburg
Brnch Mgr: David Yarmosky
Dist Mgr: Jim Fogg
*Genl Mgr: Jeff Smith
Opers Mgr: William Foux
Sls Mgr: Matthew Manz
Sls Mgr: Raul Mendiondo
Sls Mgr: Joe Morris
Sls Mgr: George Schneck

D-U-N-S 07-984-4405
▲ ALARM.COM HOLDINGS INC
8281 Greensboro Dr # 100, Tysons Corner, VA 22102-5213
Tel (877) 389-4033 Founded/Ownrshp 2009
Sales 208.8MM EMP 507[E]
Tkr Sym ALRM Exch NGS
SIC 7382 Security systems services
Pr: Stephen Trundle
*Ch Bd: Timothy McAdam
CFO: Steve Valenzuela
Ofcr: Jeffrey Bedell
Sr VP: Daniel Ramos
CTO: Jean-Paul Martin
Tech Mgr: Neha Arora

D-U-N-S 04-459-3515
■ ALASCOM INC
AT & T ALASCOM
(Suby of AMERICAN TELEPHONE AND TELG) ★
505 E Bluff Dr, Anchorage, AK 99501-1108
Tel (907) 264-7000 Founded/Ownrshp 1995
Sales 203.8MM[E] EMP 624
SIC 4813 4833 4832 Local telephone communications; Long distance telephone communications; Voice telephone communications; Telephone cable service, land or submarine; Television broadcasting stations; Radio broadcasting stations
Pr: Tom Posey
*Pr: Michael Felix
CFO: Kathy Gleason
*Treas: Charles Allen
Genl Mgr: Wanda Wilson
CTO: Rich Mavrogeanes
IT Man: Pat Hann
Mktg Dir: Trent Long

D-U-N-S 14-844-1256
▲ ALASKA AIR GROUP INC
19300 International Blvd, Seatac, WA 98188-5304
Tel (206) 392-5040 Founded/Ownrshp 1932
Sales 5.6MMM EMP 15,143[E]
Accts Kpmg Llp Seattle Washington
Tkr Sym ALK Exch NYS
SIC 4512 4731 Air passenger carrier, scheduled; Air cargo carrier, scheduled; Freight transportation arrangement
CEO: Brad Tilden
Pr: Ben Minicucci
CFO: Brandon S Pedersen
Sr VP: Joseph A Sprague
VP: Gary Beck
VP: Kyle Levine
VP: Diana Shaw
VP: Sangita Woerner
Exec: Susan Peterson
Mng Dir: Michael Adams
Mng Dir: Laurie Sands

D-U-N-S 07-962-4443
ALASKA AIRLINES
20833 International Blvd, Seatac, WA 98198-5950
Tel (206) 392-5885 Founded/Ownrshp 2014
Sales 1.2MM[E] EMP 5,000
SIC 4512 Air passenger carrier, scheduled
CEO: Brad Tilden

D-U-N-S 00-794-2493 IMP
■ ALASKA AIRLINES INC
(Suby of ALASKA AIR GROUP INC) ★
19300 International Blvd, Seatac, WA 98188-5303
Tel (206) 433-3200 Founded/Ownrshp 1937
Sales 2.1MMM[E] EMP 10,454
SIC 4512 Air passenger carrier, scheduled; Air cargo carrier, scheduled
CEO: William S Ayer
CFO: Brandon S Pedersen
Ofcr: Dominic Balappa
Ofcr: Andrew Harrison
Ofcr: Sheryl Schultz
Sr VP: Glenn Johnson
VP: Jeff Butler
VP: Kelley Dobbs
VP: Benjamin Forrest
VP: Steve Jarvis
VP: Kurt Kinder
VP: John Kirby
VP: David Kuhl
VP: Ben Minicucci
VP: Benito Minicucci
VP: Frederick L Mohr
VP: Marilyn F Romano
VP: Andy Schneider
VP: Shane Tackett
Board of Directors: Patricia M Bedient, Mark R Hamilton, Jessie J Knight Jr, Dennis F Madsen, Byron I Mallott, Brad Tilden

D-U-N-S 08-251-0439 IMP
ALASKA COMMERCIAL CO
FRONTIER EXPEDITERS
(Suby of NORTH WEST COMPANY INC, THE)
550 W 64th Ave Ste 200, Anchorage, AK 99518-1720
Tel (907) 273-4600 Founded/Ownrshp 2010
Sales 86.3MM[E] EMP 650
SIC 5399 Country general stores
Pr: Rex Wilhelm
Treas: Reinhard Sedlacek
VP: Henry J Baldwin II
*VP Opers: Walt Pickett

D-U-N-S 09-704-4676 IMP
▲ ALASKA COMMUNICATIONS SYSTEMS GROUP INC
600 Telephone Ave, Anchorage, AK 99503-6010
Tel (907) 297-3000 Founded/Ownrshp 1998
Sales 232.8MM EMP 661[E]
Tkr Sym ALSK Exch NGS
SIC 4813 Local & long distance telephone communications; ; ; Telephone/video communications
Pr: Anand Vadapalli
*Ch Bd: Edward J Hayes Jr
Sr VP: William H Bishop
Sr VP: Laurie M Butcher
Sr VP: Randy M Ritter
Sr VP: Leonard A Steinberg
Sr VP: Michael R Todd
Exec: Foster Williams
MIS Dir: Michael Dunn
Opers Mgr: Stanley Masneri
Snr Mgr: Brian Evans
Board of Directors: Margaret L Brown, David W Karp, Peter D Ley, Brian A Ross

D-U-N-S 80-938-6790
ALASKA DEPARTMENT OF ADMINISTRATION
(Suby of OFFICE OF GOVERNOR) ★
333 Willoughby Ave, Juneau, AK 99801-1770
Tel (907) 465-2200 Founded/Ownrshp 1959
Sales NA EMP 1,797
Accts Pat Davidson Cpa Juneau Ak
SIC 9199 General government administration;

Ofcr: Becky Hultberg
Ofcr: Vern Jones

D-U-N-S 80-938-7475
ALASKA DEPARTMENT OF FISH AND GAME
(*Suby of* OFFICE OF GOVERNOR) ★
1255 W 8th St, Juneau, AK 99801-1856
Tel (907) 465-4210 *Founded/Ownrshp* 1959
Sales NA *EMP* 1,200
SIC 9512 Wildlife conservation agencies;

D-U-N-S 80-938-6543
ALASKA DEPARTMENT OF HEALTH AND SOCIAL SERVICES
(*Suby of* OFFICE OF GOVERNOR) ★
350 Main St Rm 427, Juneau, AK 99801-1149
Tel (907) 465-3030 *Founded/Ownrshp* 1959
Sales NA *EMP* 2,500
SIC 9431 9441 Administration of public health programs; ; Administration of social & manpower programs;
Dept Mgr: Sarah Brinkley

D-U-N-S 80-938-6725
ALASKA DEPARTMENT OF MILITARY AND VETERANS AFFAIRS
(*Suby of* OFFICE OF GOVERNOR) ★
49000 Army Guard Rd Ste 6, Jber, AK 99505
Tel (907) 428-6008 *Founded/Ownrshp* 1959
Sales NA *EMP* 4,300
SIC 9711 9451 National security; ; Administration of veterans' affairs;

D-U-N-S 80-938-7434
ALASKA DEPARTMENT OF TRANSPORTATION AND PUBLIC FACILITIES
(*Suby of* OFFICE OF GOVERNOR) ★
3132 Channel Dr Ste 300, Juneau, AK 99801-7814
Tel (907) 465-3900 *Founded/Ownrshp* 1978
Sales NA *EMP* 3,000
SIC 9621 Regulation, administration of transportation;
Genl Mgr: John Falvey
Sls Mgr: Pat Shillinger

ALASKA GENERAL SEAFOODS
See KANAWAY SEAFOODS INC

D-U-N-S 04-998-4305
ALASKA INDUSTRIAL HARDWARE INC
GENERAL HARDWARE DISTRIBUTORS
(*Suby of* BERING STRAITS NATIVE CORP) ★
2192 Viking Dr, Anchorage, AK 99501-1731
Tel (907) 279-6691 *Founded/Ownrshp* 2015
Sales 169.1MM[E] *EMP* 210
SIC 5072 5251 Hardware; Power tools & accessories; Hardware; Tools, power
Pr: Terry Shurtleff
**COO:* Jeff Clapp
Advt Mgr: Derek Hansen
Board of Directors: Kristin Mellinger, Gail Schubert, Rex Wilhelm

D-U-N-S 07-847-8748
ALASKA INTERNATIONAL AIRPORTS SYSTEM
5000 W Intl Airport Rd, Anchorage, AK 99502-0913
Tel (907) 266-2404 *Founded/Ownrshp* 1959
Sales 124.0MM *EMP* 499
SIC 4581 Airport leasing, if operating airport

D-U-N-S 03-926-9741
ALASKA NATIONAL CORP
ALASKA NATIONAL INSURANCE CO
7001 Jewel Lake Rd, Anchorage, AK 99502-2825
Tel (907) 248-2642 *Founded/Ownrshp* 1964
Sales NA *EMP* 253
SIC 6411 Insurance agents, brokers & service
Ch: George S Suddock
**Pr:* Craig L Nodtvedt
**Treas:* Takashi Azegami
**Sr VP:* Robert C Alexander
**Sr VP:* Kristy Bottomley
**Sr VP:* Wayne Bryan
**Sr VP:* Betty A Humphries
**Sr VP:* Terrence E Kordewick
**Sr VP:* Scott Lincoln
**Sr VP:* Roger L Moseley
**Sr VP:* Jeff Mouck
**Sr VP:* John L Ramey
VP: Joseph Gianotti
**VP:* June Hill
**VP:* Gary B Oehler
**VP:* Bernie D Raven
**VP:* Richard B Suddock

ALASKA NATIONAL INSURANCE CO
See ALASKA NATIONAL CORP

D-U-N-S 03-926-9808
ALASKA NATIONAL INSURANCE CO
(*Suby of* ALASKA NATIONAL INSURANCE CO) ★
7001 Jewel Lake Rd, Anchorage, AK 99502-2825
Tel (907) 248-2642 *Founded/Ownrshp* 1979
Sales NA *EMP* 200
Accts Kpmg Llp Anchorage Ak
SIC 6331 6351 Workers' compensation insurance; Property damage insurance; Automobile insurance; Burglary & theft insurance; Liability insurance
Pr: Craig L Nodtvedt
**Ch:* David P Jones
**Ch:* George S Suddock
**Treas:* Takashi Azegami
Ex VP: June Hill
Ex VP: Gary B Oehler
Ex VP: Bernie D Raven
Ex VP: Richard B Suddock
Sr VP: Robert C Alexander
Sr VP: Kristy Bottomley
Sr VP: Wayne Bryan
Sr VP: Betty A Humphries
Sr VP: Terrence E Kordewick
Sr VP: Scott Lincoln
Sr VP: Roger L Moseley
Sr VP: Jeff Mouck
VP: Anne Hancock
VP: Jason Jacques
**VP:* Richard Suddock

D-U-N-S 07-137-5658
ALASKA NATIVE TRIBAL HEALTH CONSORTIUM
4000 Ambassador Dr, Anchorage, AK 99508-5909
Tel (907) 729-1900 *Founded/Ownrshp* 1997
Sales 618.5MM *EMP* 1,850
Accts Bdo Usa Lp Anchorage Ak
SIC 8399 8741 Social service information exchange; Hospital management
Pr: Teuber Andy
**Bd of Dir:* Lincoln A Bean
Sr VP: Angel Dotomain
**VP:* Bean Lincoln
Dir Risk M: Leann Stubblefield
Prgrm Mgr: Sharon Corbett
Prgrm Mgr: Lakota Holman
CIO: Mary Ford
CTO: Ray Martin
Software D: Selma O Simon
Pathlgst: Lee Astle

ALASKA PACIFIC SEAFOOD
See NORTH PACIFIC SEAFOODS INC

D-U-N-S 10-287-4161
ALASKA PERMANENT FUND CORP
A P F C
801 W 10th St Ste 302, Juneau, AK 99801-1878
Tel (907) 796-1500 *Founded/Ownrshp* 1980
Sales 512.3MM *EMP* 50[E]
Accts Kpmg Llp Anchorage Ak
SIC 6733 Trusts, except educational, religious, charity: management
CEO: Angela Rodell
**COO:* Russell Read
**CFO:* Valerie Mertz
Comm Dir: Laura Achee
Comm Man: Paulyn Swanson
Prin: Chris Poag
Adm Dir: Kathy Thatcher

D-U-N-S 00-948-7042 IMP
ALASKA RAILROAD CORP
327 W Ship Creek Ave, Anchorage, AK 99501-1671
Tel (907) 265-2494 *Founded/Ownrshp* 1985
Sales 163.8MM *EMP* 775
Accts Kpmg Llp Anchorage Ak
SIC 4011 6531 Railroads, line-haul operating; Real estate managers
CEO: William G O'Leary
**COO:* Doug Engebretson
**CFO:* Barbara Amy
Ch: Linda Leary
Bd of Dir: John Binkley
Bd of Dir: John Cook
Bd of Dir: Marc Luiken
Ofcr: Stephenie Wheeler
VP: Tom Brooks
VP: Andrew Donovan
**VP:* William Hupprich
VP: James Kubitz
Exec: Emil Notti
Dir Risk M: Roberta Highstone
Board of Directors: Jack Burton, Chris Hladick, William Sheffield

ALASKA REGIONAL HOSPITAL
See GALEN HOSPITAL ALASKA INC

ALASKA UNITED
See GCI INC

D-U-N-S 07-925-8588
ALASKA USA FEDERAL CREDIT UNION
4000 Credit Union Dr, Anchorage, AK 99503-6636
Tel (907) 563-4567 *Founded/Ownrshp* 1948
Sales NA *EMP* 1,700
SIC 6061 6163 Federal credit unions; Loan brokers
CEO: William B Eckhardt
V Ch: Darrel E Cavender
**Pr:* Bobby Alexander
Pr: Crystal Peltola
COO: Frederick Miller
**CFO:* Norman P West
**Treas:* Anna Hick
Ofcr: Julie Opp
Ofcr: Steve Salvestrin
Ofcr: Kelly Schmainda
Sr VP: Kim Bassett
VP: Carol Anderson
VP: Liz Behike
VP: Jim Fish
VP: Leonna Kuntze
**VP:* Geoff Lundfelt
VP: Rachel Norman
**VP:* Lorran J Skinner
VP: Brian Spink

ALASKAN COPPER & BRASS CO
See ALASKAN COPPER COMPANIES INC

D-U-N-S 00-925-5571 IMP
ALASKAN COPPER COMPANIES INC (WA)
ALASKAN COPPER & BRASS CO
(*Suby of* ALASKAN COPPER WORKS) ★
27402 72nd Ave S, Kent, WA 98032-7366
Tel (206) 623-5800 *Founded/Ownrshp* 1913
Sales 154.0MM[E] *EMP* 375
SIC 5051 3498 3443 Metals service centers & offices; Copper; Miscellaneous nonferrous products; Steel; Fabricated pipe & fittings; Fabricated plate work (boiler shop); Heat exchangers, condensers & components; Industrial vessels, tanks & containers
Ch Bd: William M Rosen
**Pr:* Kermit Rosen Jr
**CFO:* Brian Lucarelli
**Treas:* Alan J Rosen
**VP:* Donald Rosen
**VP:* Douglas C Rosen
Genl Mgr: Arthur Grunbaum
Genl Mgr: Rob Rosen
IT Man: Roland Lamarca
Manager: Chad Gudjonson
Sls Mgr: Tom Rutter

ALASKAN COPPER WORKS
See ALCO INVESTMENT CO

D-U-N-S 01-438-6465 IMP
ALATRADE FOODS LLC
725 Blount Ave, Guntersville, AL 35976-1505
Tel (256) 571-9696 *Founded/Ownrshp* 2000
Sales 233.4MM[E] *EMP* 1,300
SIC 2015 Poultry slaughtering & processing
CEO: Davis Lee Sr
**Pr:* John Pittard
**CFO:* Patti Yancey
Off Mgr: Laura Couch

D-U-N-S 14-340-6457 IMP/EXP
ALBAAD USA INC
AFG WIPES
(*Suby of* AL-BAD MASSUOTYITZHAK LTD)
129 S Technology Dr, Reidsville, NC 27320-1563
Tel (336) 634-0091 *Founded/Ownrshp* 2003
Sales 92.9MM[E] *EMP* 202
SIC 2844 Towelettes, premoistened
CEO: Boaz Roseman
**CEO:* Ronald Gbrek
**CFO:* ADI Maor
**CFO:* Eyal Shechter
**VP:* Sam Hacohen

D-U-N-S 00-309-9298 IMP
ALBAN TRACTOR CO INC
CATERPILLAR AUTHORIZED DEALER
8531 Pulaski Hwy, Baltimore, MD 21237-3092
Tel (410) 686-7777 *Founded/Ownrshp* 1926
Sales 371.7MM[E] *EMP* 780
SIC 5082 5084 7699 General construction machinery & equipment; Engines, gasoline; Construction equipment repair
Ch: James C Alban III
CFO: Myles Snyder
**CFO:* Jim Sweeney
VP: Jeff Gould
VP: Ryan Johnson
**VP:* Michael E Lewis
**VP:* Tom Linton
**VP:* John Rodal
**VP:* James D Stewart
VP: Jim Stewart
VP Bus Dev: Joseph Dellinger
Comm Man: Gary Deluca

D-U-N-S 09-693-2520
ALBANY CITY SCHOOL DISTRICT
1 Academy Park, Albany, NY 12207-1099
Tel (518) 475-6000 *Founded/Ownrshp* 1972
Sales 105.9MM[E] *EMP* 1,600
SIC 8211 Public elementary & secondary schools
IT Man: Earl Davis
IT Man: Tim Moore
Netwrk Mgr: Timothy Schramm
Teacher Pr: Kathleen Colligan
HC Dir: Frank Owens
Board of Directors: Patrick Amodeo, John Evers, Barbara Gaffuri, Joseph McCaffrey, Theresa Portelli, Theresa Swidorski, Katherine Webb

D-U-N-S 04-991-8501
ALBANY COUNTY SCHOOL DISTRICT ONE
1948 E Grand Ave, Laramie, WY 82070-4317
Tel (307) 721-4400 *Founded/Ownrshp* 1878
Sales 91.2MM *EMP* 800
Accts Mader Tschacher Peterson & Co
SIC 8211 Public elementary & secondary schools
**Prin:* Stuart Nelson

ALBANY ELECTRIC COMPANY
See METROPOWER INC

D-U-N-S 86-116-5512
ALBANY GENERAL HOSPITAL
SAMARITAN ALBANY GENERAL HOSP
1046 6th Ave Sw, Albany, OR 97321-1999
Tel (541) 812-4000 *Founded/Ownrshp* 1924
Sales 154.4MM *EMP* 832[E]
SIC 8062 8741 General medical & surgical hospitals; Hospital management
CEO: David Triebes
**COO:* Gerald Mc Intosh
Opers Mgr: Jim Kelly
Pr Dir: Marti Cersorski

D-U-N-S 05-707-0617
ALBANY GENERAL HOSPITAL LIFELINE
FIRST CARE HEALTH
1046 W 6th St, Albany, OR 97321
Tel (541) 812-4000 *Founded/Ownrshp* 1924
Sales 153.9MM *EMP* 550
Accts Moss-Adams Llp Portland Or
SIC 8062 General medical & surgical hospitals
COO: Gerald McIntosh
**VP:* Terry Fitzpatrick

D-U-N-S 92-669-2088 IMP/EXP
ALBANY INDUSTRIES INC
504 N Glenfield Rd, New Albany, MS 38652-2214
Tel (662) 534-9800 *Founded/Ownrshp* 1993
Sales 119.8MM *EMP* 485
SIC 2512 Upholstered household furniture
Pr: Richie McClarty
**VP:* Phillip Jamieson
VP Opers: Terry Treadaway
Plnt Mgr: Terry Greer
Plnt Mgr: Sam Taylor
Mktg Mgr: Drew Daugherty

D-U-N-S 00-207-5414 IMP/EXP
▲ ALBANY INTERNATIONAL CORP
216 Airport Dr, Rochester, NH 03867-1718
Tel (518) 445-2200 *Founded/Ownrshp* 1895
Sales 709.8MM *EMP* 3,900
Accts Kpmg Llp Albany New York
Tkr Sym AIN *Exch* NYS
SIC 2221 3496 2399 2899 3089 Paper broadwoven fabrics; Fabrics, woven wire; Belting, fabric: made from purchased materials; Insulating compounds; Doors, folding: plastic or plastic coated fabric
Ch Bd: Erland E Kailbourne
V Ch: John C Standish
Pr: Joseph G Morone
CFO: John B Cozzolino
Sr VP: Robert A Hansen
VP: Richard Carlstrom
VP: Brian Coffenberry
VP: William H Dutt
VP: Edward R Hahn
VP: Clark Johnston
VP: Michael J Joyce
VP: Tom Licha
VP: Charles J Silva Jr
VP: Dawne H Wimbrow
Exec: Steve Bolen
Board of Directors: A William Higgins, Kenneth W Krueger

D-U-N-S 14-451-0203 IMP/EXP
ALBANY MEDICAL CENTER
43 New Scotland Ave, Albany, NY 12208-3478
Tel (518) 262-3125 *Founded/Ownrshp* 1982
Sales 1.1MMM *EMP* 7,000[E]
Accts Kpmg Llp Albany Ny
SIC 8062 General medical & surgical hospitals
Pr: James J Barba
Pr: Tania Allard
COO: Gary Kochem
COO: Gary J Kochem
CFO: William C Hasselbarth
Ofcr: Teresa Kundel
Ofcr: Mary Ellen Plass
Ex VP: Kim Fine
Ex VP: Steven M Frisch
Ex VP: Arthur A Gross
Ex VP: George T Hickman
Ex VP: Vincent Verdile
Sr VP: Courtney Burke
Sr VP: Kevin M Leyden
Sr VP: Bernadette Pedlow
VP: Frances Albert
VP: Dennis Delisle
VP: Jeffrey Gordon
VP: Michael Gruenthal
VP: Carol McDonald
Dir Risk M: Vickey Masta
Board of Directors: Sharon M Duker

D-U-N-S 07-312-8365
ALBANY MEDICAL CENTER HOSPITAL
(*Suby of* ALBANY MEDICAL CENTER) ★
43 New Scotland Ave, Albany, NY 12208-3478
Tel (518) 262-3125 *Founded/Ownrshp* 1982
Sales 893.2MM *EMP* 1,568[E]
Accts Kpmg Llp Albany Ny
SIC 8062 8249 Hospital, affiliated with AMA residency; Medical training services; Medical & dental assistant school
Pr: James J Barba
**COO:* Gary J Kochem
Ofcr: Teresa Kundel
Dir Risk M: Vickey Masta
Chf Nrs Of: Mary E Plass
IT Man: Jason Fliesser
Ansthlgy: Branko Furst
Doctor: Frederick Eames

D-U-N-S 19-059-2162
ALBANY MEDICAL COLLEGE
47 New Scotland Ave, Albany, NY 12208-3479
Tel (518) 262-6008 *Founded/Ownrshp* 1982
Sales 290.7MM *EMP* 1,568
Accts Kpmg Llp Albany Ny
SIC 8249 Medical & dental assistant school
Ex VP: Vincent P Verdile
**CFO:* William Hasselbarth
Ex VP: Kim Fine
VP: Donna Beebe
Doctor: Steven Fein

ALBANY MEMORIAL HOSPITAL
See MEMORIAL HOSPITAL

D-U-N-S 78-779-3900 IMP/EXP
▲ ALBANY MOLECULAR RESEARCH INC
26 Corporate Cir, Albany, NY 12203-5121
Tel (518) 512-2000 *Founded/Ownrshp* 1991
Sales 402.3MM *EMP* 2,220[E]
Tkr Sym AMRI *Exch* NGS
SIC 2836 8731 Biological products, except diagnostic; Biotechnical research, commercial
Pr: William S Marth
Ch Bd: Thomas E D'Ambra
COO: George Svokos
CFO: Felicia I Ladin
CFO: Michael Nolan
Sr VP: Steven R Hagen
Sr VP: Lori M Henderson
Mfg Dir: Eric Peterson
Corp Couns: Ben Seisler
Board of Directors: David H Deming, Gerardo Gutierrez, Kenneth P Hagen, Anthony J Maddaluna, Kevin O'connor, Arthur J Roth, Una S Ryan

D-U-N-S 00-697-5916
ALBANY STEEL INC (NY)
566 Broadway Ste 2, Menands, NY 12204-2842
Tel (518) 436-4851 *Founded/Ownrshp* 1921, 1980
Sales 90.2MM[E] *EMP* 120
SIC 5051 3441 Steel; Fabricated structural metal
Pr: Peter J Hess
Genl Mgr: Scott Bello
CIO: John Clement
Sfty Mgr: Erla Miller

D-U-N-S 82-773-3440 IMP
■ ALBANY-CHICAGO CO LLC
(*Suby of* SHILOH INDUSTRIES INC) ★
8200 100th St, Pleasant Prairie, WI 53158-2207
Tel (262) 947-7600 *Founded/Ownrshp* 2012
Sales 91.4MM[E] *EMP* 300
SIC 3363 Aluminum die-castings
CFO: Peter Floryance
**Prin:* Michael W Altschaefl
Plnt Mgr: Curt Pape
Ql Cn Mgr: Tim Collins

D-U-N-S 04-807-7101
ALBAR INDUSTRIES INC (MI)
780 Whitney Dr, Lapeer, MI 48446-2570
Tel (810) 667-0150 *Founded/Ownrshp* 1966
Sales 99.2MM[E] *EMP* 300
SIC 3089 Coloring & finishing of plastic products
Pr: Edward A May
**Sec:* Rowland Plutchak
VP: Glenn Curtis
Exec: Mark Gerics

Genl Mgr: Wayne Hellane
CIO: Mark Gericks
Mtls Mgr: David Smith
Plnt Mgr: Wayne Helland

D-U-N-S 09-872-9502 IMP
ALBAUGH LLC
1525 Ne 36th St, Ankeny, IA 50021-6754
Tel (515) 964-9444 *Founded/Ownrshp* 1979
Sales 292.2MM^E *EMP* 200
SIC 2879 Fungicides, herbicides
Rgnl Mgr: Craig Musselman

D-U-N-S 96-334-5884 IMP/EXP
ALBEA AMERICAS INC
(*Suby of* ALBEA SERVICES)
191 State Route 31 N, Washington, NJ 07882-1529
Tel (908) 689-3000 *Founded/Ownrshp* 2010
Sales 182.5MM^E *EMP* 500
SIC 3312 Pipes & tubes
Pr: Francois Luscan
**CFO:* Xavier Leclerc
**Treas:* Fabriee Beaussant
**Ex VP:* Franois Tassart
**VP:* Jose Filipe
**VP:* Herv Marion
Plnt Mgr: Douglas Jerman

D-U-N-S 85-858-6084 IMP/EXP
ALBEA COSMETICS AMERICA INC
(*Suby of* ALBEA SERVICES)
595 Madison Ave Fl 10, New York, NY 10022-1955
Tel (212) 371-5100 *Founded/Ownrshp* 1980
Sales 259.8MM^E *EMP* 2,200
SIC 3089 3911 5162 5051 Plastic containers, except foam; Precious metal cases; Plastics products; Metals service centers & offices
Pr: Jean P Imbert

D-U-N-S 07-878-3044 IMP
ALBEA THOMASTON INC
(*Suby of* ALBEA AMERICAS INC) ★
60 Electric Ave, Thomaston, CT 06787-1617
Tel (860) 283-2000 *Founded/Ownrshp* 2013
Sales 106.3MM^E *EMP* 370
SIC 2844 Cosmetic preparations
CEO: Francois Luscan
IT Man: Benny Dobruna

D-U-N-S 05-276-8327
■ ALBECCA INC (GA)
(*Suby of* BERKSHIRE HATHAWAY INC) ★
3900 Steve Reynolds Blvd, Norcross, GA 30093-3061
Tel (770) 279-5210 *Founded/Ownrshp* 1993, 2002
Sales 116.5MM^E *EMP* 2,070
SIC 2499 3499 Picture frame molding, finished; Picture frames, metal
Pr: Stephen E McKenzie
**Ch Bd:* Craig A Ponzio
V Ch: June R Ponzio
Pr: William Trimarco
CFO: Bradley R Goodson
CFO: R Bradley Goodson
Opers Mgr: Scott Howell

D-U-N-S 18-606-1131
ALBECO INC
MOLLIE STONE'S MARKET
150 Shoreline Hwy Ste 5, Mill Valley, CA 94941-3637
Tel (415) 289-5720 *Founded/Ownrshp* 1987
Sales 91.7MM^E *EMP* 600
SIC 5411 Grocery stores, independent
CEO: Mike Stone
**VP:* David Bennett

D-U-N-S 16-368-1237 IMP/EXP
■ ALBEMARLE CATALYSTS CO LP
(*Suby of* ALBEMARLE CORP) ★
13000 Baypark Rd, Pasadena, TX 77507-1104
Tel (281) 474-2864 *Founded/Ownrshp* 2004
Sales 84.3MM^E *EMP* 265
SIC 2819 Catalysts, chemical
Genl Pt: Mark Rohr
**CEO:* Luther C Luke Kissam

D-U-N-S 82-508-0096 IMP/EXP
▲ ALBEMARLE CORP
4350 Congress St Ste 700, Charlotte, NC 28209-4953
Tel (980) 299-5700 *Founded/Ownrshp* 1993
Sales 3.6MMM *EMP* 6,963
Tkr Sym ALB *Exch* NYS
SIC 2821 2834 2819 2899 2812 2869 Plastics materials & resins; Pharmaceutical preparations; Bromine, elemental; Fire retardant chemicals; Alkalies & chlorine; Industrial organic chemicals
Ch Bd: Luther C Kissam IV
**Ch Bd:* Jim W Nokes
CFO: Scott A Tozier
Ex VP: Karen G Narwold
Sr VP: Matthew K Juneau
VP: Donald J Labauve Jr
Board of Directors: William H Hernandez, Douglas L Maine, J Kent Masters, James J O'brien, Barry W Perry, John Sherman Jr, Gerald A Steiner, Harriett Tee Taggart, Alejandro D Wolff

D-U-N-S 18-985-7105
ALBEMARLE COUNTY PUBLIC SCHOOLS
401 Mcintire Rd, Charlottesville, VA 22902-4579
Tel (434) 296-5820 *Founded/Ownrshp* 1988
Sales 74.5MM^E *EMP* 1,587
SIC 8211 Public elementary & secondary schools
Pr Dir: Phil Giaramita
Teacher Pr: John Gray
Teacher Pr: Clare Keiser
Instr Medi: Robert Rejonis

D-U-N-S 07-473-8824
ALBEMARLE HOSPITAL AUTHORITY
1144 N Road St, Elizabeth City, NC 27909-3473
Tel (252) 338-0101 *Founded/Ownrshp* 1949
Sales 123.5MM *EMP* 95^E
SIC 8062 General medical & surgical hospitals
Pr: Wick Baker
CFO: John Wiggins
VP: Jay Briley
Pharmcst: Nancy Easterday

D-U-N-S 00-890-7990 IMP
ALBERICI CONSTRUCTORS INC
(*Suby of* ALBERICI GROUP INC) ★
8800 Page Ave, Saint Louis, MO 63114-6106
Tel (314) 733-2000 *Founded/Ownrshp* 2001
Sales 1.0MMM *EMP* 2,000
SIC 1541 1542 1622 Industrial buildings, new construction; Commercial & office building contractors; Bridge construction
Pr: Gregory J Kozicz
Pr: Greg Brokenshire
Pr: Bob Niemeier
**CFO:* Gregory T Hesser
Ex VP: Christopher Hermann
**VP:* John S Alberici
VP: Alan D Gough
VP: Trevor Ladner
VP: Steve Moffatt
**VP:* Leroy Stromberg
VP: Thomas A Taylor
VP: Ronald W Wiese
Dir Risk M: Joe Gallagher
Dir Bus: Kevin Bocek

D-U-N-S 15-093-7027 IMP/EXP
ALBERICI CORP
KIENLEN CONSTRUCTORS
8800 Page Ave, Saint Louis, MO 63114-6106
Tel (314) 733-2000 *Founded/Ownrshp* 1985
Sales 1.8MMM *EMP* 2,080
SIC 1541 1542 1622 1629 Industrial buildings & warehouses; Nonresidential construction; Bridge construction; Power plant construction
Pr: Gregory J Kozicz
**Ch Bd:* John S Alberici
COO: Leroy J Stromberg
Ex VP: Craig M Fesler
Sr VP: James E Frey
VP: Michael W Burke
VP: David Calcaterra
VP: Denay Davis
VP: David Gough
VP: Matt Grieshaber
VP: David M Kress
VP: Trevor Ladner
VP: Martin W Schaper
VP: Ronald W Wiese

D-U-N-S 11-166-1935
ALBERICI GROUP INC
(*Suby of* KIENLEN CONSTRUCTORS) ★
8800 Page Ave, Saint Louis, MO 63114-6106
Tel (314) 733-2000 *Founded/Ownrshp* 2000
Sales 1.1MMM *EMP* 2,000
SIC 1541 1542 1622 Industrial buildings & warehouses; Nonresidential construction; Bridge, tunnel & elevated highway
CEO: Gregory J Kozicz
**Ch Bd:* John S Alberici
**COO:* Leroy J Stromberg Jr
**VP:* Michael W Burke

D-U-N-S 00-945-0362
ALBERT C KOBAYASHI INC
94-535 Ukee St Ste 101, Waipahu, HI 96797-4275
Tel (808) 671-6460 *Founded/Ownrshp* 1997
Sales 383.4MM *EMP* 200
Accts N&K Cpas Inc Honolulu Hawa
SIC 1542 1521 1522 Commercial & office building contractors; Single-family housing construction; Multi-family dwelling construction; Condominium construction
CEO: Russell Young
**CFO:* Clyde Sugawa
**VP:* George Ballao
**VP:* Kendall Korenaga
**VP:* Warren Leong

D-U-N-S 11-052-1739
ALBERT EINSTEIN COLLEGE OF MEDICINE
(*Suby of* YESHIVA COLLEGE) ★
1300 Morris Park Ave, Bronx, NY 10461-1900
Tel (718) 430-2000 *Founded/Ownrshp* 1984
Sales 330.9M *EMP* 3,100
SIC 8221 Colleges universities & professional schools
Exec: Sean Cottman
Mng Dir: Paul Moniz
MIS Mgr: Dale Hochstein
Software D: Carlo Garcia
Pathlgst: Thomas Belbin
Pathlgst: Linda Cannizzaro
Pathlgst: Peter Davies
Pathlgst: John McKitrick
Obsttrcn: Amir Fazeoli
Obsttrcn: Nora R Miller
Doctor: Herbert H Scaumburg

D-U-N-S 07-978-3367
ALBERT EINSTEIN COLLEGE OF MEDICINE INC
1300 Morris Park Ave, Bronx, NY 10461-1975
Tel (718) 920-6758 *Founded/Ownrshp* 2014
Sales 450.0MM *EMP* 3,000^E
SIC 8249 Medical & dental assistant school
Pr: Steven Safyer
**CFO:* James Geraghty

ALBERT EINSTEIN HEALTH MED CTR
See ALBERT EINSTEIN MEDICAL ASSOCIATES INC

ALBERT EINSTEIN HEALTHCARE MED
See ALBERT EINSTEIN MEDICAL CENTER

D-U-N-S 14-840-6911
ALBERT EINSTEIN HEALTHCARE NETWORK
5501 Old York Rd, Philadelphia, PA 19141-3018
Tel (215) 456-7890 *Founded/Ownrshp* 1984
Sales 112.3MM *EMP* 5,732^E
SIC 8062

D-U-N-S 06-901-9032
ALBERT EINSTEIN MEDICAL ASSOCIATES INC (PA)
ALBERT EINSTEIN HEALTH MED CTR
5501 Old York Rd Ste 1, Philadelphia, PA 19141-3018
Tel (215) 456-7890 *Founded/Ownrshp* 1952
Sales 679.9MM^E *EMP* 5,251
SIC 8062 8051 Hospital, affiliated with AMA residency; Skilled nursing care facilities
Pr: Barry Freedman
**Pr:* Herbert S Waxman
COO: Beth Duffy
**CFO:* Brian Derrick
**Treas:* Gerard McKee
**Treas:* John Murino
Chf Mktg O: Joan Gubernick
Ofcr: Paula Jones
VP: Gerry Blainey
VP: Kenneth Levitan
**VP:* Penny Rezet
Assoc Dir: Duanne Pearson

D-U-N-S 79-992-0913
ALBERT EINSTEIN MEDICAL CENTER
ALBERT EINSTEIN HEALTHCARE MED
(*Suby of* ALBERT EINSTEIN HEALTH MED CTR) ★
5501 Old York Rd Ste 1, Philadelphia, PA 19141-3098
Tel (215) 456-7890 *Founded/Ownrshp* 1952
Sales 679.9MM *EMP* 58^E
SIC 8062 General medical & surgical hospitals
Pr: Richard Greenberg
VP: Lynn Kornblatt
Pharmcst: Debbie Hauser

ALBERT ENSTEIN HLTH CARE NTWRK
See ALBERT M HOSPICE EINSTEIN

ALBERT H HALFF ASSOCIATES
See HALFF ASSOCIATES INC

D-U-N-S 01-257-2731 IMP
ALBERT KEMPERLE INC
8400 New Horizons Blvd, Amityville, NY 11701-1153
Tel (631) 841-1241 *Founded/Ownrshp* 1940
Sales 251.3MM^E *EMP* 300
Accts Jones Little & Co East Isli
SIC 5013 Automotive supplies
Ch Bd: Ronald Kemperle
**Pr:* Albert Kemperle Jr

D-U-N-S 01-776-7161
ALBERT M HIGLEY CO
2926 Chester Ave, Cleveland, OH 44114-4414
Tel (216) 404-5783 *Founded/Ownrshp* 1925
Sales 159.0MM *EMP* 180
Accts Meaden & Moore Ltd Clevelan
SIC 1542 1541 Commercial & office building, new construction; Institutional building construction; Industrial buildings, new construction
Ch Bd: Albert M Higley Jr
**Pr:* Charles Stephenson
**Treas:* Bruce G Higley
VP: Kurt Heinicke
VP: Rex Lewers
Off Mgr: Fran Cooney
IT Man: Carlo Barone

D-U-N-S 07-737-6494
ALBERT M HOSPICE EINSTEIN
ALBERT ENSTEIN HLTH CARE NTWRK
5501 Old York Rd Ste 3, Philadelphia, PA 19141-3018
Tel (215) 456-7890 *Founded/Ownrshp* 1984
Sales 138.0MM *EMP* 30
Accts Pricewaterhousecoopers Llp Ph
SIC 8062 General medical & surgical hospitals

D-U-N-S 00-481-5924
ALBERT REECE INC (TX)
3001 Foster St, San Angelo, TX 76903-9216
Tel (325) 653-1241 *Founded/Ownrshp* 1940, 1968
Sales 94.8MM^E *EMP* 300
SIC 1611 1794 1623 1622 General contractor, highway & street construction; Excavation work; Underground utilities contractor; Bridge construction
Pr: Jack Albert
**Pr:* Roger Albert
**Ex VP:* Richard Albert
**Ex VP:* Terry Albert
VP: Albert Terrence
Admn Mgr: Karen Williams
CTO: Albert Terry
Sfty Dirs: David Hartin
Mktg Mgr: Mike Hester

D-U-N-S 02-252-1025 IMP
ALBERT S SMYTH CO INC
SMYTH JEWELERS
2020 York Rd, Lutherville Timonium, MD 21093-4244
Tel (410) 252-6666 *Founded/Ownrshp* 1933
Sales 90.5MM *EMP* 150
Accts Stegman & Company Baltimore
SIC 5944 5961 Jewelry stores; Clock & watch stores; Jewelry, precious stones & precious metals; Silverware; Jewelry, mail order; Gift items, mail order
Pr: Thomas A Smyth
**COO:* Mark Motes
**Exec:* Leonard Getschel Jr
**Prin:* Robert L Smyth Jr
Dir Sec: Keith Hannum
Dir IT: John Jackson
IT Man: Nathan Tacy
Advt Dir: Ruth Carroll
Sls Mgr: Steve Fischer

D-U-N-S 00-231-9085 IMP
ALBERT TIRE CO (PA)
39 Phoenix Dr, West Deptford, NJ 08086-2156
Tel (856) 663-0574 *Founded/Ownrshp* 1919, 1946
Sales 204.3MM^E *EMP* 55
SIC 5014 Automobile tires & tubes; Truck tires & tubes
Pr: William A Albert
**VP:* John P Cassey
Dir IT: Tom Kett

D-U-N-S 00-607-7051 IMP
ALBERT TROSTEL & SONS CO
(*Suby of* EVERETT SMITH GROUP LTD) ★
800 N Marshall St, Milwaukee, WI 53202-3911
Tel (414) 223-1560 *Founded/Ownrshp* 1858, 1983
Sales 143.6MM^E *EMP* 4,250^E
SIC 3111 Tanneries, leather
Ch: J Douglas Gray
**CFO:* James P Orth
**Treas:* Thomas J Hauske Jr
**VP:* Bruce J Betters
Board of Directors: Anders Segerdahl, Wendell F Bueche, Walter G Winding III, J Douglas Gray, Steven J Hartung, Thomas J Hauske Jr, Richard C Kleinfeldt, Charles D Krull, Wayne R Lueders, James P Orth, Randall M Perry

D-U-N-S 10-893-7061
■ ALBERTA INVESTMENTS INC
(*Suby of* US CONCRETE) ★
1445 Mac Arthur Dr Ste 13, Carrollton, TX 75007-4461
Tel (972) 242-4550 *Founded/Ownrshp* 2006
Sales 88.1MM^E *EMP* 650
SIC 3273 Ready-mixed concrete
Pr: Gerald A Berkhold

D-U-N-S 08-119-1439
ALBERTINA KERR CENTERS
KERR YOUTH & FAMILY SERVICES
424 Ne 22nd Ave, Portland, OR 97232-2809
Tel (503) 239-8101 *Founded/Ownrshp* 1907
Sales 47.1MM *EMP* 1,050
Accts Gary Mcgee & Co Llp Portlan
SIC 8052 8361 8093 Home for the mentally retarded, with health care; Residential care; Mental health clinic, outpatient
Pr: Christopher Krenk
**CFO:* Jerald Hoffert
CFO: John Lara
Ofcr: Brenda Eames
Assoc Dir: Nanda Sturm
Prgrm Mgr: Kerwin Shannon
Pr Mgr: Meghan Anderson
Pr Mgr: Stephanie Bolson

D-U-N-S 00-507-1378 IMP/EXP
ALBERTO-CULVER CO
(*Suby of* UNILEVER UNITED STATES INC) ★
800 Sylvan Ave, Englewood Cliffs, NJ 07632-3201
Tel (708) 681-2668 *Founded/Ownrshp* 2006
Sales 271.6MM^E *EMP* 2,600
SIC 2844 2842 2099 Toilet preparations; Shampoos, rinses, conditioners: hair; Hair preparations, including shampoos; Deodorants, personal; Specialty cleaning, polishes & sanitation goods; Furniture polish or wax; Seasonings & spices; Baking powder & soda, yeast & other leavening agents
Pr: Gina Boswell
Pr: Kenneth Keller Jr
**CFO:* Ralph J Nicoletti
Ex VP: David Brunswig
Sr VP: John R Berschied
**Sr VP:* Gary P Schmidt
VP: Anthony J Bender
VP: David Brownsweig
VP: J Chiakarallo
VP: Sheryl Green
VP: Mary A Oleksiuk
VP: Steve Spiegel

D-U-N-S 15-589-7226 IMP
■ ALBERTS ORGANICS INC
(*Suby of* UNITED NATURAL FOODS INC) ★
1155 Commerce Blvd, Logan Township, NJ 08085-1763
Tel (800) 899-5944 *Founded/Ownrshp* 1984
Sales 238.8MM^E *EMP* 460
SIC 5149 5148 Natural & organic foods; Fresh fruits & vegetables
CEO: Steve Spinner
Treas: Kevin Michel
VP: Kevin Lyons
VP: Rod Moyer
Div Mgr: Mario Barone
Genl Mgr: Charlie Nealis
Opers Mgr: Todd Hansen
Ql Cn Mgr: Robert Primmer
Sls Mgr: Curtis Steinback
Snr Mgr: Ron McCubbins

ALBERTSONS
See ALBERTSONS LLC

D-U-N-S 07-990-3211
ALBERTSONS COMPANIES INC
250 E Parkcenter Blvd, Boise, ID 83706-3999
Tel (208) 395-6200 *Founded/Ownrshp* 1939
Sales 58.7MMM^E *EMP* 265,000^E
SIC 5912 5499 Drug stores; Health & dietetic food stores; Health foods
Ch Bd: Robert G Miller
COO: Wayne A Denningham
CFO: Robert B Dimond
Ofcr: Shane Sampson
Ex VP: Anuj Dhanda
Ex VP: Robert A Gordon
Ex VP: Susan Morris

D-U-N-S 08-009-0774
ALBERTSONS COMPANIES LLC
(*Suby of* AB ACQUISITION LLC) ★
250 E Parkcenter Blvd, Boise, ID 83706-3999
Tel (208) 395-6200 *Founded/Ownrshp* 2015
Sales 54.3MMM^E *EMP* 138,000^E
SIC 5912 5499 Drug stores; Health & dietetic food stores; Health foods
Ch Bd: Robert G Miller

D-U-N-S 07-966-9653
ALBERTSONS HOLDINGS LLC
(*Suby of* AB ACQUISITION LLC) ★
250 E Parkcenter Blvd, Boise, ID 83706-3999
Tel (208) 395-6200 *Founded/Ownrshp* 2006
Sales 28.0MMM^E *EMP* 138,000^E
SIC 5411 Supermarkets, chain
CEO: Robert G Miller

D-U-N-S 00-692-7180 IMP/EXP
ALBERTSONS LLC
ALBERTSONS
(*Suby of* ALBERTSONS COMPANIES LLC) ★
250 E Parkcenter Blvd, Boise, ID 83706-3999
Tel (208) 395-6200 *Founded/Ownrshp* 1969
Sales 26.3MMM^E *EMP* 138,000
SIC 5499 5912 Health foods; Drug stores
**COO:* Wayne Denningham
COO: Wayne A Denningham
COO: Kelly P Griffith
COO: Jim Perkins

COO: Darin Wells
**CFO:* Robert Dimond
Bd of Dir: Paul W Klasing
Ofcr: Justin Dye
**Ex VP:* Justin Ewing
Ex VP: Barry J Libenson
Ex VP: Shane Sampson
Sr VP: James F Gentile
Sr VP: Michael McCarthy
VP: Susan Morris
VP: Matthew Muta
**Exec:* Robert Gordon
Exec: Eric Johnson

D-U-N-S 19-400-9817
ALBERTVILLE QUALITY FOODS INC
FOOD PROCESSING HOLDINGS
130 Quality Dr, Albertville, AL 35950-8554
Tel (256) 840-9923 *Founded/Ownrshp* 2010
Sales 233.9MM[E] *EMP* 1,000
SIC 2015 Chicken slaughtering & processing
CEO: Jerry Wilson
**CFO:* Kathy Ford

D-U-N-S 78-282-7575
ALBUQUERQUE BERNALILLO COUNTY WATER UTILITY AUTHORITY
ABCWUA
1 Civic Plz Nw Fl 10, Albuquerque, NM 87102-2111
Tel (505) 768-2907 *Founded/Ownrshp* 2003
Sales 85.7MM[E] *EMP* 100[E]
SIC 4941 Water supply
Ex Dir: Mark Sanchez
**COO:* John M Stomp
**CFO:* Stanley Allred
Prgrm Mgr: Jane Derose-Bamman

ALBUQUERQUE PROP MGT
See AMERICAN PROPERTY-MANAGEMENT CORP

D-U-N-S 07-341-3544
ALBUQUERQUE PUBLIC SCHOOL DISTRICT
6400 Uptown Blvd Ne, Albuquerque, NM 87110-4204
Tel (505) 880-3700 *Founded/Ownrshp* 1890
Sales 530.7MM[E] *EMP* 11,500
Accts Moss Adams Llp Albuquerque N
SIC 8211 Public elementary & secondary schools
**CFO:* Dubuy Bateman
CFO: Michael Vigil

D-U-N-S 83-135-1445
ALCAMI CAROLINAS CORP
(*Suby of* ALCAMI CORP) ★
2320 Scientific Park Dr, Wilmington, NC 28405-1800
Tel (910) 254-7000 *Founded/Ownrshp* 2016
Sales 254.6MM[E] *EMP* 701
SIC 2834 8734 8731 Pharmaceutical preparations; Product testing laboratories; Medical research, commercial
CEO: Stephan Kutzer
COO: Scott Neilson
**COO:* Ted Nolan
CFO: Eugene T Haley
**CFO:* Adam Lauber
CFO: Tom Wilcock
Treas: Thomas Aluse
**Sr Ex VP:* Syed Husain
Ex VP: Gregory S Bentley
Ex VP: Jeff Yuen
VP: Armando Cortes
VP: Kevin Flanagan
VP: Dean Shirazi
VP: Christopher Smith
**VP:* Scott Warner
Assoc Dir: Lee Danford

D-U-N-S 08-019-7709
ALCAMI CORP
(*Suby of* ALCAMI HOLDINGS LLC) ★
2320 Scientific Park Dr, Wilmington, NC 28405-1800
Tel (910) 254-7000 *Founded/Ownrshp* 2009
Sales 357.9MM[E] *EMP* 975[E]
SIC 2834 Pharmaceutical preparations
CEO: Stephan Kutzer
**COO:* Ted Dolan
**CFO:* Adam Lauber
**VP:* Syed Hyusain
Sls Dir: Vito Saccente

D-U-N-S 07-950-3880
ALCAMI HOLDINGS LLC
2320 Scientific Park Dr, Wilmington, NC 28405-1800
Tel (910) 254-7000 *Founded/Ownrshp* 2012
Sales 225.0MM *EMP* 975[E]
SIC 2834 8731 8734 Pharmaceutical preparations; Medical research, commercial; Product testing laboratories
CEO: Stephan Kutzer

D-U-N-S 05-445-2136
ALCAMI WISCONSIN CORP (WI)
(*Suby of* ALCAMI CORP) ★
W130n10497 Washington Dr, Germantown, WI 53022-4448
Tel (262) 251-5044 *Founded/Ownrshp* 1998, 2016
Sales 91.0MM *EMP* 276
SIC 8731 8734 Medical research, commercial; Product testing laboratories
CEO: Ted Dolan
**CEO:* Stephan Kutzer
CFO: Mark Abatto
**CFO:* Adam Lauber
**Sr Ex VP:* Syed Husain
VP: Armando Cortes
Assoc Dir: Christopher Seekamp
Tech Mgr: Martin Meyer
Opers Mgr: Adam Kujath

D-U-N-S 17-194-4338 IMP/EXP
ALCAN CORP
(*Suby of* RIO TINTO PLC)
6060 Parkland Blvd, Cleveland, OH 44124-4225
Tel (440) 460-3307 *Founded/Ownrshp* 2003
Sales 733.2MM[E] *EMP* 4,750
SIC 3351 3355 3496 3357 Wire, copper & copper alloy; Wire, aluminum: made in rolling mills; Miscellaneous fabricated wire products; Nonferrous wire-drawing & insulating
Pr: Tom Albanese
**Pr:* Timothy Guerra
**Treas:* Cheree N Finan
**Treas:* Robert J Mosesian
**VP:* William J Adams
**VP:* Eileen Burns Lerum
**VP:* Donald P Seberger

ALCAN PACKAGING
See CEBAL AMERICAS

D-U-N-S 17-471-7525 IMP/EXP
ALCAN PRIMARY PRODUCTS CORP
(*Suby of* ALCAN CORP) ★
6055 Rockside Woods Blvd, Independence, OH 44131-2301
Tel (440) 460-3300 *Founded/Ownrshp* 2003
Sales 125.9MM[E] *EMP* 1,228[E]
SIC 3334 Primary aluminum
Pr: Yvon Danjou
**Treas:* Pamela Schneider
**VP:* Eileen Burns Lerum
**VP:* Donald P Seberger

ALCATEL ONETOUCH
See TCT MOBILE (US) INC

D-U-N-S 08-365-4947 IMP
ALCATEL-LUCENT HOLDINGS INC
(*Suby of* ALCATEL LUCENT PARTICIPATIONS)
601 Data Dr, Plano, TX 75075-7839
Tel (972) 477-2000 *Founded/Ownrshp* 1976, 2006
Sales 1.6MMM[E] *EMP* 6,800
SIC 3661 Telephones & telephone apparatus; Switching equipment, telephone
CEO: Philippe Camus
COO: Hubert Pesouidoux
CFO: Nancy Grier
**Treas:* Glenn B Gunn
Sr VP: David L Henshaw
Sr VP: Patrick Vogeler
**VP:* Max Chyobotov
VP: David Dwyer
**VP:* Barbara Larsen
VP: Bob O'Brien
VP: James Tindall
VP: David Witte
Board of Directors: James Cocito, Barbara Larsen, Julie Liptak, Charles Marsh, Perry McGregor

D-U-N-S 93-350-3385 IMP/EXP
ALCATEL-LUCENT USA INC
(*Suby of* ALCATEL LUCENT)
600 Mountain Ave Ste 700, New Providence, NJ 07974-2008
Tel (908) 582-3275 *Founded/Ownrshp* 2006
Sales 1.1MMM[E] *EMP* 29,921
SIC 7372 3674 Prepackaged software; Integrated circuits, semiconductor networks, etc.; Hybrid integrated circuits
CEO: Michel Combes
Pr: Satoshi Fujita
Pr: Frank Noviello
COO: Tom Burns
CFO: Barbara Ristau
Ex VP: Stephen Carter
Ex VP: Soria Jose
VP: Brenton C Greene
VP: Paul Kenefick
VP: Thomas J Miller
VP: Patricia Rimo
Dir Bus: Tim Drake

D-U-N-S 07-921-9063 IMP
ALCHEMY AROMATICS LLC
621 Park East Blvd, New Albany, IN 47150-7253
Tel (812) 755-6660 *Founded/Ownrshp* 2013
Sales 100.0MM *EMP* 25
SIC 5169 5122 Aromatic chemicals; Perfumes
COO: Aaron Sorenson

D-U-N-S 10-883-9168 IMP
ALCO INDUSTRIES INC
1275 Glenlivet Dr Ste 100, Allentown, PA 18106-3107
Tel (610) 666-0930 *Founded/Ownrshp* 1983
Sales 225.9MM[E] *EMP* 630
Accts Parentebeard Llc Harrisburg
SIC 2879 2851 2842 2873 Pesticides, agricultural or household; Paints & paint additives; Coating, air curing; Waxes for wood, leather & other materials; Nitrogen solutions (fertilizer)
Pr: Andrew P Lesko
CFO: Allie Hess
CFO: John C Long
**Ch:* T Lawrence Way
**Treas:* David Disanto
Treas: David D Santo
**VP:* Cynthia K Sharo
VP: Bette J Walters

D-U-N-S 96-728-2138 IMP
ALCO INVESTMENT CO
ALASKAN COPPER WORKS
27402 72nd Ave S, Kent, WA 98032-7366
Tel (206) 623-5800 *Founded/Ownrshp* 1913
Sales 154.0MM *EMP* 375
SIC 5051 3498 3443 Metals service centers & offices; Fabricated pipe & fittings; Fabricated plate work (boiler shop)
Ch Bd: William Rosen
**Pr:* Kermit Rosen Jr
**CFO:* Brian Lucarelli
**Treas:* Alan J Rosen
**VP:* Donald Rosen
**VP:* Douglas Rosen
Mfg Dir: Judy Tangen

D-U-N-S 00-694-2353 IMP
ALCO STORES INC
751 Freeport Pkwy, Coppell, TX 75019-4411
Tel (469) 322-2900 *Founded/Ownrshp* 1901
Sales 474.0MM *EMP* 3,300[E]
SIC 5311 5331 Department stores, discount; Variety stores
CEO: Stanley B Latacha
**Ch Bd:* Robert J Sarlls
Sr VP: Ricardo Clemente
Sr VP: Brent Streit
VP: Brian Assmus
Board of Directors: John M Climaco, William L Lechtner, David W Pointer, Mark Stolper

ALCOA
See ARCONIC SECURITIES LLC

D-U-N-S 08-036-2431
▲ ALCOA CORP
390 Park Ave Fl 12, New York, NY 10022-4608
Tel (212) 518-5400 *Founded/Ownrshp* 1903
Sales 2.3MMM[E] *EMP* 16,000[E]
Tkr Sym AA *Exch* NYS
SIC 3355 3363 3297 2819 Aluminum rolling & drawing; Aluminum die-castings; Alumina fused refractories; Bauxite, refined
CEO: Roy C Harvey
**Ch Bd:* Michael G Morris
COO: Tomas Sigurosson
CFO: William F Oplinger
Ofcr: Leigh Ann C Fisher
Ex VP: Robert S Collins
Ex VP: Jeffrey D Heeter
VP: Molly Beerman

ALCOA FASTENING SYSTEMS RINGS
See HUCK INTERNATIONAL INC

ALCOA INTALCO WORKS
See INTALCO ALUMINUM LLC

D-U-N-S 07-975-2073
■ ALCOA MEXICO HOLDINGS LLC
(*Suby of* ARCONIC INC) ★
201 Isabella St, Pittsburgh, PA 15212-5858
Tel (412) 553-4545 *Founded/Ownrshp* 2000
Sales 228.8MM[E] *EMP* 10,001
SIC 3334 Primary aluminum

ALCOA POWER & PROPULSION
See HOWMET CORP

ALCOA TITANIUM ENGINEERED PDTS
See RTI INTERNATIONAL METALS INC

D-U-N-S 83-740-9671 IMP/EXP
■ ALCOA WORLD ALUMINA LLC
(*Suby of* ALCOA CORP) ★
201 Isabella St, Pittsburgh, PA 15212-5858
Tel (412) 553-4545 *Founded/Ownrshp* 2016
Sales 1.2MMM[E] *EMP* 1,001
SIC 1099 1081 4911 Bauxite mining; Metal mining services; Electric services
COO: William Oplinger
VP: Julie P Caponi
VP: John Kenna
VP: Kevin McKnight
Prin: Bill Oplinger
MIS Dir: Bob Welch
IT Man: Linda Berardelli
IT Man: Chowdary Garimella
IT Man: Brandi Grubbs
IT Man: Charles Seibert
IT Man: Paul Stamatakis

D-U-N-S 13-272-5339 IMP
ALCOHOL MONITORING SYSTEMS INC
1241 W Mineral Ave # 200, Littleton, CO 80120-5687
Tel (303) 785-7813 *Founded/Ownrshp* 1993
Sales 156.5MM[E] *EMP* 135
SIC 5169 3825 Alcohols; Test equipment for electronic & electric measurement
CEO: Michael Iiams
CFO: Mike Machens
VP: Lisa Fellows
VP: John Hennessey
VP: Janet Pierce
**VP:* Don White
Ex Dir: Kelli Tennison
Software D: Robert Vanguilder

ALCOMAT
See ALLEYTON RESOURCE CO LLC

ALCON
See CIBA VISION CORP

D-U-N-S 00-172-1302 IMP
ALCON LABORATORIES HOLDING CORP
(*Suby of* NOVARTIS AG)
6201 South Fwy, Fort Worth, TX 76134-2001
Tel (817) 293-0450 *Founded/Ownrshp* 2011
Sales 2.5MMM[E] *EMP* 24,000
SIC 2834 3841 Solutions, pharmaceutical; Ophthalmic instruments & apparatus
Pr: Robert K Warner
**CFO:* Robert Kars
**VP:* Bettina Maunz

D-U-N-S 00-801-8525 IMP
ALCON LABORATORIES INC
(*Suby of* ALCON LABORATORIES HOLDING CORP) ★
6201 South Fwy, Fort Worth, TX 76134-2001
Tel (817) 293-0450 *Founded/Ownrshp* 1947
Sales 1.6MMM[E] *EMP* 4,500
SIC 3841 2834 Ophthalmic instruments & apparatus; Solutions, pharmaceutical
Pr: Cary Rayment
Pr: Dick Siom
COO: Allen Baker
COO: Lori Barnhill
CFO: Svetlana Artyomova
CFO: Robert Kelly
CFO: Monte Smith
CFO: Andrew White
Treas: David Bass
Treas: Mike Farchild
Ofcr: Kay Cox
VP: Doug Machatton
Exec: George Neal
Assoc Dir: Mike Christensen
Assoc Dir: Cindy Milam
Assoc Dir: Andreas Minke
Assoc Dir: Onkar Singh

D-U-N-S 05-124-1615 IMP
ALCON MANUFACTURING LTD
(*Suby of* ALCON LABORATORIES HOLDING CORP) ★
6201 South Fwy, Fort Worth, TX 76134-2001
Tel (817) 293-0450 *Founded/Ownrshp* 2001
Sales 46.6MM[E] *EMP* 1,102[E]
SIC 2834 3841 Pharmaceutical preparations; Surgical & medical instruments
CFO: David Nieto
Dir Risk M: Dolores Demartini
Dir IT: Louis Morton
Sfty Mgr: Marcia Orozco
Snr Mgr: Shawn O'Neil

D-U-N-S 00-767-2236
ALCON RESEARCH LTD
(*Suby of* NOVARTIS AG)
6201 South Fwy, Fort Worth, TX 76134-2001
Tel (817) 551-4555 *Founded/Ownrshp* 2007, 2013
Sales 84.7MM[E] *EMP* 800[E]
SIC 8733 3841 2834 Research institute; Surgical & medical instruments; Pharmaceutical preparations
CEO: Cary R Rayment
**Pr:* Sergio Duplan
**CEO:* Mike Ball
**Sr VP:* Christina Ackermann
**Sr VP:* Merrick McCracken
**VP:* Bettina Maunz

D-U-N-S 19-963-2100
ALCON SURGICAL INC
(*Suby of* ALCON LABORATORIES INC) ★
6201 South Fwy, Fort Worth, TX 76134-2001
Tel (817) 293-0450 *Founded/Ownrshp* 1988
Sales 97.4MM *EMP* 3,000
SIC 3841 Ophthalmic instruments & apparatus
Pr: Gary Rayman
**CEO:* David Bass
VP: Frederic Baldowsky
Mfg Dir: Steven Thompson

ALCOSAN
See ALLEGHENY COUNTY SANITARY AUTHORITY

D-U-N-S 17-374-6231
ALCOTT GROUP INC
71 Executive Blvd Ste 1, Farmingdale, NY 11735-4709
Tel (631) 420-0100 *Founded/Ownrshp* 1987
Sales 78.1MM[E] *EMP* 4,400
SIC 7363 Employee leasing service
Pr: Louis Basso Jr
COO: Karen Williams
Treas: Staff Leasing
Dir Risk M: Robert Byrnes
Off Mgr: Patricia T Patane
IT Man: John Bradley
IT Man: Robert Castaldo

ALDEN GROUP
See ALDEN MANAGEMENT SERVICES INC

D-U-N-S 09-657-3506
■ ALDEN JOHN LIFE INSURANCE CO
ASSURANT HEALTH
(*Suby of* ASSURANT INC) ★
501 W Michigan St, Milwaukee, WI 53203-2706
Tel (414) 271-3011 *Founded/Ownrshp* 1998
Sales NA *EMP* 1,884[E]
SIC 6311 Life insurance
CEO: Adam Lamnin
**CFO:* James Elliott
**Treas:* Donald George Hamm Jr
**Sr VP:* Scott Krienke
VP: Kathy Dobrzynski
CTO: Tony Burlo
CTO: Philip Ericksen
CTO: Michael Vangerpen
IT Man: K Mertens

D-U-N-S 08-981-9965 IMP
ALDEN MANAGEMENT SERVICES INC (IL)
ALDEN GROUP
4200 W Peterson Ave # 142, Chicago, IL 60646-6818
Tel (773) 282-8183 *Founded/Ownrshp* 1977
Sales 224.8MM[E] *EMP* 4,000
SIC 8051 8741 Skilled nursing care facilities; Business management
Pr: Floyd Schlossberg
CFO: Steve Kroll
**VP:* Joan Carl
VP: Mary Smith
VP: Victoria H Wolpoff
Genl Mgr: Thomas Catania
CIO: Rick Hoffman
CIO: Joyce Young
Dir IT: Jeff Nichols

D-U-N-S 16-181-2417
ALDEN PADFIELD INC
QUALITY TIRE
(*Suby of* QUALITY TIRE SLC) ★
203 N 5500 W, Hurricane, UT 84737-3159
Tel (435) 674-9883 *Founded/Ownrshp* 1963
Sales 91.3MM[E] *EMP* 123
SIC 5014 5531 Automobile tires & tubes; Automotive tires
Pr: Alden Padfield

D-U-N-S 00-851-9316
ALDEN-WENTWORTH NURSING CENTER INC
201 W 69th St, Chicago, IL 60621-3719
Tel (773) 487-1200 *Founded/Ownrshp* 1981
Sales 6.5MM *EMP* 3,102
SIC 8051 Skilled nursing care facilities
**Pr:* Floyd Schlossberg
**VP:* Joan Robinson Carl
**VP:* Herbert Odom

D-U-N-S 83-719-6336
■ ALDERWOODS (DELAWARE) INC
(*Suby of* SCI) ★
1929 Allen Pkwy, Houston, TX 77019-2506
Tel (713) 522-5141 *Founded/Ownrshp* 2006
Sales 92.1MM[E] *EMP* 7,900
SIC 7261 6553 6311 Funeral home; Cemetery subdividers & developers; Funeral insurance
Pr: Curtis G Briggs

D-U-N-S 00-694-0423 IMP
ALDI INC (KS)
(*Suby of* ALDI GMBH & CO. KG ESSEN)
1200 N Kirk Rd, Batavia, IL 60510-1477
Tel (630) 879-8100 *Founded/Ownrshp* 1975
Sales 1.0MMM[E] *EMP* 3,000

SIC 5411 Supermarkets; Grocery stores, chain
Pr: Charles E Youngstrom
**Co-Pr:* Brent Laubaugh
VP: Jeff Baehr
VP: Joan Kavanaugh
VP: Horst Leitner
VP: Gordon Nesbit
Dist Mgr: Ben Lawrence
Dir IT: Ken Moyner
IT Man: Rich Felder
IT Man: Scott Kreyer
IT Man: Kathy Taylor

D-U-N-S 06-310-7106 IMP
ALDILA INC
(*Suby of* MITSUBISHI RAYON AMERICA INC) ★
14145 Danielson St Ste B, Poway, CA 92064-8827
Tel (858) 513-1801 *Founded/Ownrshp* 2013
Sales 109.3MM^E *EMP* 670^E
SIC 3949 3297 Shafts, golf club; Graphite refractories: carbon bond or ceramic bond
Ch Bd: Peter R Mathewson
Mng Pt: Alan B Howe
**CFO:* Scott M Bier
CFO: Scott Bier
VP: John E Oldenburg
CIO: Derek Hall
Board of Directors: Thomas A Brand, Alan B Howe, Peter H Kamin, Andrew M Leitch, Bryant R Riley, Michael J Sheldon

D-U-N-S 02-451-0836
ALDIN ASSOCIATES LIMITED PARTNERSHIP (CT)
CHUCKY'S COUNTRY STORE
77 Sterling Rd, East Hartford, CT 06108-1665
Tel (860) 282-0651 *Founded/Ownrshp* 1982
Sales 94.9MM^E *EMP* 250
SIC 5541 5411 Filling stations, gasoline; Convenience stores
Genl Pt: David Savin
COO: Ron Tateosian
IT Man: Paul Kirschner

D-U-N-S 07-389-8017
ALDINE INDEPENDENT SCHOOL DISTRICT
2520 Ww Thorne Blvd, Houston, TX 77073-3406
Tel (281) 449-1011 *Founded/Ownrshp* 1935
Sales 690.2MM *EMP* 7,000
Accts Whitley Penn Llp Houston Te
SIC 8211 Public elementary & secondary schools
Prin: Ruth Dimmick
Prin: Jeannette Ross
Dir IT: Dominic Tong
Sales Exec: Jocelyn Adams
Instr Medi: Cynthia Buchanan
HC Dir: Angela Singletary

ALDO SHOES
See ALDO US INC

D-U-N-S 12-663-8852 EXP
ALDO US INC
ALDO SHOES
(*Suby of* GROUPE ALDO INC, LE)
180 Passaic Ave, Fairfield, NJ 07004-3516
Tel (888) 818-2536 *Founded/Ownrshp* 1991
Sales 99.1MM^E *EMP* 1,000
SIC 5611 Men's & boys' clothing stores
Pr: Albert Bensadoun
CFO: Robert Raven

D-U-N-S 00-611-3906 IMP
ALDRICH CHEMICAL CO LLC
MILLIPORE SIGMA
(*Suby of* SIGMA-ALDRICH) ★
6000 N Teutonia Ave, Milwaukee, WI 53209-3645
Tel (414) 438-3850 *Founded/Ownrshp* 1951
Sales 181.1MM^E *EMP* 1,100
SIC 2869 2819 3821 7371 2741 Industrial organic chemicals; Industrial inorganic chemicals; Chemical laboratory apparatus; Computer software development; Technical manuals: publishing only, not printed on site
CEO: Rakesh Sachdev
CFO: Larry Polakowski
**Treas:* Kirk Richter
**VP:* Ali Ataei
**VP:* Jeff Thurston
Snr Mgr: Sherri Fujihira

D-U-N-S 00-554-7393 IMP
ALDRIDGE ELECTRIC INC (DE)
844 E Rockland Rd, Libertyville, IL 60048-3358
Tel (847) 680-5200 *Founded/Ownrshp* 1952
Sales 273.5MM^E *EMP* 850
SIC 2899 4789 3643 Drilling mud; Cargo loading & unloading services; Power line cable
Ch Bd: Ken Aldridge
**Pr:* Tom McLinden
**CEO:* Steven Rivi
**COO:* Alex Aldridge
VP: Daniel Galovich
VP: Paul Legg
Dir Risk M: Jeff Arnold
Prgrm Mgr: Douglas Sandner
Rgnl Mgr: Marty Bradley
Div Mgr: Randy Farmer
CIO: Patrick Laude

D-U-N-S 03-123-7065
ALDRIDGE PITE LLP
3575 Piedmont Rd Ne # 500, Atlanta, GA 30305-1623
Tel (404) 994-7400 *Founded/Ownrshp* 2009
Sales 46.4MM^E *EMP* 1,200^E
SIC 8111 Real estate law
COO: John Crane
CIO: Eric Garner
Genl Couns: Marissa Connors
Genl Couns: Judy Newberry
Snr Mgr: Ralph Tune

D-U-N-S 03-196-3734
ALE HOUSE MANAGEMENT INC
5750 Major Blvd Ste 400, Orlando, FL 32819-7971
Tel (407) 547-1120 *Founded/Ownrshp* 1994
Sales 156.2MM^E *EMP* 3,000
SIC 8741 Restaurant management
CEO: Phil Hickey
Mktg Dir: Beth Miller
Genl Couns: Michael J Burley

D-U-N-S 07-956-0086
ALE USA INC
(*Suby of* CHINA HUAXIN POST AND TELECOMMUNICATION ECONOMY DEVELOPMENT CENTER)
26801 Agoura Rd, Calabasas, CA 91301-5122
Tel (818) 878-4816 *Founded/Ownrshp* 2014
Sales 130.0MM *EMP* 550
SIC 3663 3613 Mobile communication equipment; Switchgear & switchboard apparatus
**CEO:* Michel Emelianoff
**VP:* Stan Stopka

D-U-N-S 60-542-7595
ALECTO HEALTHCARE SERVICES LLC
16310 Bake Pkwy Ste 200, Irvine, CA 92618-4684
Tel (323) 938-3161 *Founded/Ownrshp* 2012
Sales 1.0MMM^E *EMP* 4,700
SIC 8062 General medical & surgical hospitals
CEO: John A Calderone
**CFO:* Babur Ozkan
CFO: Matt Williams
Prgrm Mgr: Natalie Tran
Mktg Dir: Steve Rosenthaul
Pharmcst: Lynh Nguyen
Pharmcst: Lisa Preimesberger

D-U-N-S 07-698-3956
ALEGENT HEALTH - IMMANUEL MEDICAL CENTER
(*Suby of* CHI HEALTH) ★
6901 N 72nd St, Omaha, NE 68122-1709
Tel (402) 572-2121 *Founded/Ownrshp* 1890
Sales 250.3MM *EMP* 2,313
Accts Catholic Health Initiatives O
SIC 8062 8051 8351 Hospital, AMA approved residency; Extended care facility; Child day care services
CEO: Wayne Sensor
VP: Charles McMinn
Doctor: Timothy Burd
Doctor: Peterson Ronald I
Pharmcst: Paul L Price
Dir Health: Jim Harwood

D-U-N-S 02-018-9064
ALEGENT HEALTH MEMORIAL HOSPITAL
(*Suby of* CHI HEALTH) ★
104 W 17th St, Schuyler, NE 68661-1304
Tel (402) 352-2441 *Founded/Ownrshp* 1995
Sales 11.9MM *EMP* 8,000
Accts Lb Catholic Health Initiatives
SIC 8062 General medical & surgical hospitals
**Prin:* Merry Bryant-Cavanah

D-U-N-S 55-555-2186
ALEGENT HEALTH- BERGAN MERCY HEALTH SYSTEM
CHI
(*Suby of* CHI) ★
7500 Mercy Rd, Omaha, NE 68124-2319
Tel (402) 398-6060 *Founded/Ownrshp* 1995
Sales 543.8MM *EMP* 1^E
SIC 8062 General medical & surgical hospitals
CEO: Cliff Robertson
Pr: Lawrence Beckman
COO: Joan Neuhaus
CFO: Jeanette Wojtalewicz
Sr VP: Bonnie Burnett
VP: Leigh Bertholf

D-U-N-S 01-762-5851
■ **ALENCO HOLDING CORP**
ALL SEASONS
(*Suby of* PLY GEM INDUSTRIES INC) ★
615 W Carson St, Bryan, TX 77801-1199
Tel (979) 779-1051 *Founded/Ownrshp* 2006
Sales 106.1MM^E *EMP* 900
SIC 3442 Window & door frames
Pr: Bryan Redpath
**CFO:* Chuck Gessler
Dir IT: Mike Anderson
IT Man: Matt Bonn

D-U-N-S 78-532-0953
ALENCO INC
ALENCO MATERIALS COMPANY
(*Suby of* ENCANA CORPORATION)
16201 W 110th St, Lenexa, KS 66219-1313
Tel (913) 438-1902 *Founded/Ownrshp* 2015
Sales 242.4MM^E *EMP* 80
SIC 1521 1751 1761 Single-family housing construction; Single-family home remodeling, additions & repairs; New construction, single-family houses; Window & door (prefabricated) installation; Siding contractor
Pr: Allen Erskine
**Genl Mgr:* Abe Eller

ALENCO MATERIALS COMPANY
See ALENCO INC

D-U-N-S 19-931-7491
ALENIA AERMACCHI NORTH AMERICA INC
(*Suby of* ALENIA AERMACCHI SPA)
1235 S Clark St Ste 700, Arlington, VA 22202-4364
Tel (703) 413-2125 *Founded/Ownrshp* 2003
Sales 102.8MM^E *EMP* 30
SIC 8711 Aviation &/or aeronautical engineering
CEO: John H Young
VP: Claudio Di Gioa
IT Man: Elio D Brogna
Software D: Alberto Fantino
Genl Couns: Larissa Meli

ALENZA
See DEANGELO BROTHERS LLC

D-U-N-S 93-377-1123
■ **ALERE HEALTH LLC**
(*Suby of* OPTUMHEALTH CARE SOLUTIONS INC) ★
3200 Windy Hill Rd Se 100b, Atlanta, GA 30339-8504
Tel (770) 767-4500 *Founded/Ownrshp* 2015
Sales 147.0MM^E *EMP* 3,598
SIC 8099 Medical services organization
CEO: Craig Keyes
Pr: Martin Israelsen
Pr: Quang Nguyen
**CFO:* Joseph Blankenship
**Ex VP:* Pete Desai
**Ex VP:* Steven Kelley
**Ex VP:* Stacy Knapp
**Ex VP:* Norm Ryan
**Ex VP:* Eva Vyas
Sr VP: June Allen
Sr VP: Richard Ventimiglia
Sr VP: Robert Wittenstein
VP: Daniel Birachexecutive
VP: Marian Licata
VP: Jane Pratt
VP: Wes Rhea

D-U-N-S 09-380-3398 IMP
▲ **ALERE INC**
51 Sawyer Rd Ste 200, Waltham, MA 02453-3448
Tel (781) 647-3900 *Founded/Ownrshp* 1981
Sales 2.4MMM *EMP* 9,800^E
Tkr Sym ALR *Exch* NYS
SIC 2835 8071 8742 In vitro & in vivo diagnostic substances; In vitro diagnostics; Pregnancy test kits; Medical laboratories; Hospital & health services consultant
Pr: Namal Nawana
**Ch Bd:* Gregg J Powers
Pr: Daniella Cramp
Pr: Sanjay Malkani
Pr: AVI Pelossof
CFO: James Hinrichs
CFO: Marshall Mohr
Sr VP: Ellen Chiniara
Sr VP: Mark Gladwell
Sr VP: Melissa Guerdan
Sr VP: Robert Hargadon
Sr VP: Renuka Uppaluri
VP: Dominic B Borotto
VP: John Bridgen
VP: Daniel Childree
VP: Michael Connor
VP: F Fernandez
VP: Mike Horvath
VP: Samantha Kaiser
VP: Rich Long
VP: Keith Mason
Board of Directors: Hakan Bjorklund, Geoffrey S Ginsburg, Carol R Goldberg, John F Levy, Brian A Markison, Thomas McKillop, John A Quelch, James Roosevelt Jr

D-U-N-S 19-485-4949 IMP
■ **ALERE SAN DIEGO INC**
(*Suby of* ALERE INC) ★
9975 Summers Ridge Rd, San Diego, CA 92121-2997
Tel (858) 455-4808 *Founded/Ownrshp* 2007
Sales 228.8MM^E *EMP* 1,003
SIC 2835 In vitro & in vivo diagnostic substances
Pr: John Yonkin
Sr VP: Winton Gibbons
VP: James E Douglas
VP: Gary A King
VP: Paul McPherson
VP: Norman Paradis
VP: Robin Weiner
VP: Peter Witerzens
Assoc Dir: John McKenna
**Prin:* Mark Gladwell
QA Dir: S Elaine Walton
Board of Directors: Ellen Chiniara, Paul Hempel, Jon Russell, John Yonkin

D-U-N-S 96-478-1830
ALERIS CORP
25825 Science Park Dr # 400, Cleveland, OH 44122-7392
Tel (216) 910-3400 *Founded/Ownrshp* 2010
Sales 2.9MMM *EMP* 5,100
Accts Ernst & Young Llp Cleveland
SIC 3355 3354 Bars, rolled, aluminum; Aluminum extruded products
Pr: Sean M Stack
Pr: Jeff Hoober
Pr: John Zhu
CFO: Eric M Rychel
Ofcr: Tami Polmanteer
Ex VP: Christopher R Clegg
Sr VP: Ingrid Elisabeth Jorg
Sr VP: Mike Keown
Sr VP: Ralf Zimmermann
VP: Jeffrey A Byrd
VP: Michael J Hobey

D-U-N-S 96-479-0856 IMP
ALERIS INTERNATIONAL INC
(*Suby of* ALERIS CORP) ★
25825 Science Park Dr # 400, Beachwood, OH 44122-7392
Tel (216) 910-3400 *Founded/Ownrshp* 2004
Sales 2.0MMM^E *EMP* 5,000
SIC 3355 3354 Bars, rolled, aluminum; Aluminum extruded products
CEO: Sean M Stack
**Pr:* Roeland Baan
**CFO:* Eric M Rychel
Sr Cor Off: C Newton
**Ex VP:* Christopher R Clegg
Ex VP: Bruce Warshuaer
Sr VP: Alan K Dick
**Sr VP:* Steven A Faas
Sr VP: Ingrid Jorg
**Sr VP:* Scott A McKinley
VP: Joseph Byers
VP: Wendy Kacer
VP: Ray D Peterson
VP: Gerald K Reichelt
VP: Teresa Tan
VP: Kelly Thomas
VP: Timothy Trombetta
VP: Edward C Wingenbach
Board of Directors: Christopher M Crane, Jonathan Garfinkel, Dale V Kesler, Paul E Lego, Michael Macdougall, Lawrence W Stranghoener, G Richard Wagoner, J Steven Whisler

D-U-N-S 01-411-7387 IMP
ALERIS RECYCLING BENS RUN LLC
4203 S State Route 2, Friendly, WV 26146-9753
Tel (304) 652-1415 *Founded/Ownrshp* 2010
Sales 106.7MM^E *EMP* 797^E
SIC 3355

D-U-N-S 08-006-8656
ALERIS ROLLED PRODUCTS INC
(*Suby of* ALERIS INTERNATIONAL INC) ★
25825 Science Park Dr # 400, Beachwood, OH 44122-7323
Tel (216) 910-3400 *Founded/Ownrshp* 2010
Sales 302.7MM^E *EMP* 2,589^E
SIC 3341 Secondary nonferrous metals
CEO: Sean M Stack

D-U-N-S 07-829-3200 IMP
ALERIS ROLLED PRODUCTS LLC
(*Suby of* ALERIS ROLLED PRODUCTS INC) ★
25825 Science Park Dr # 400, Cleveland, OH 44122-7323
Tel (216) 910-3400 *Founded/Ownrshp* 2009
Sales 110.3MM^E *EMP* 1,514
SIC 3355 Aluminum rolling & drawing
CEO: Sean M Stack

D-U-N-S 00-699-8074
ALERUS FINANCIAL NATIONAL ASSN
(*Suby of* ALERUS FINANCIAL CORPORATION)
2300 S Columbia Rd, Grand Forks, ND 58201-5826
Tel (701) 795-3200 *Founded/Ownrshp* 1933
Sales NA *EMP* 299
SIC 6021 National commercial banks
Ch Bd: Randy Newman
CFO: Eric Carlson
**Sr VP:* Mike Winkel
VP: Compton Kris
IT Man: Chris Dunnigan
Sls Dir: Jeff Hoplin

D-U-N-S 02-025-6798
ALEUT CORP
4000 Old Seward Hwy # 300, Anchorage, AK 99503-6068
Tel (907) 561-4300 *Founded/Ownrshp* 1972
Sales 170.3MM^E *EMP* 705
SIC 6799 1542 8742 Real estate investors, except property operators; Commercial & office building contractors; Business consultant
Pr: Thomas Mack
CFO: Chris Lace
Sls&Mrk Ex: Ji Kim

D-U-N-S 17-072-9045
ALEUT MANAGEMENT SERVICES LLC
(*Suby of* ALEUT CORP) ★
5540 Tech Center Dr # 100, Colorado Springs, CO 80919-2332
Tel (719) 531-9090 *Founded/Ownrshp* 2004
Sales 116.3MM^E *EMP* 415
SIC 8741 Management services
Pr: Samuel L Cole
Ofcr: Carole Horst
**Sr VP:* Mike Mikita
**VP:* Brenda Gallegos
**VP:* Breke Harnagel
VP: Ken Nachbar
**VP:* Kenneth D Nachbar
**VP:* Carolyn P Smithhisler
Exec: Amelia Swenson
Dir Bus: Rafael Dejesus
Genl Mgr: Krista Ochlech

D-U-N-S 93-368-5174 EXP
ALEX AND ANI LLC
2000 Chapel View Blvd # 360, Cranston, RI 02920-3040
Tel (401) 633-1486 *Founded/Ownrshp* 2003
Sales 362.6MM^E *EMP* 634^E
SIC 3915 5944 Jewelry parts, unassembled; Jewelry, precious stones & precious metals
Prin: Carolyn Rafaelian
**Pr:* Cindy Dipietrantonio
**Pr:* Harlan M Kent

D-U-N-S 01-383-4981
ALEX E PARIS CONTRACTING CO INC
1595 Smith Township State, Atlasburg, PA 15004
Tel (724) 947-2235 *Founded/Ownrshp* 1928
Sales 99.5MM *EMP* 350
SIC 1623 1629 Underground utilities contractor; Earthmoving contractor
Pr: Emanuel A Paris
**VP:* Timothy A Paris
Genl Mgr: Gregory Cortese
Sfty Mgr: Bill Santa

D-U-N-S 18-535-8061
ALEX ENERGY INC
(*Suby of* MASSEY COAL EXPORT CO) ★
2 Jerry Fork Rd, Drennen, WV 26667
Tel (304) 872-5065 *Founded/Ownrshp* 1997
Sales 39.1MM^E *EMP* 2,200^E
SIC 1241 Coal mining services
Pr: Jon C Brown
**Treas:* G Scott Cole
**VP:* Richard R Grinnan
**Prin:* David C Hughart

D-U-N-S 79-431-6364
ALEX LEE INC
120 4th St Sw, Hickory, NC 28602-2947
Tel (828) 725-4424 *Founded/Ownrshp* 1931
Sales 2.2MMM *EMP* 9,200
Accts Mcgladrey Llp Charlotte Nc
SIC 5141 5142 5147 5148 5194 5411 Groceries, general line; Packaged frozen goods; Meats & meat products; Meats, fresh; Fresh fruits & vegetables; Tobacco & tobacco products; Supermarkets, chain
CEO: Boyd L George
V Ch: Gerald D Davis
Pr: Brian A George
**CFO:* Ronald W Knedlik
CFO: Joyce Reto
Sr VP: Michael J Greene
Sr VP: John B Orgain
Sr VP: Jay Schwarz
Sr VP: Robert Vipperman
VP: Bruce Brooking
VP: Kimberly D George
VP: Steve Hall
VP: Roger Henderson

VP: Bob McTeir
VP: Robert H McTeir
VP: Jay Schwartz
VP: Joseph Walpole
Exec: Doug King
Exec: Melissa Littlejohn
Exec: CHI Sit
Board of Directors: Joyce Corbett, Warren D Feldberg, Alice L George, H Donetta George, John R Georgius, Frederick D McClure, Ernie J Smith, William R Waddell

D-U-N-S 06-811-3703 IMP
ALEX PRODUCTS INC (OH)
19911 County Rd T, Ridgeville Corners, OH 43555
Tel (419) 267-5240 *Founded/Ownrshp* 1973
Sales 104.5MM[E] *EMP* 550
SIC 3599 Machine shop, jobbing & repair
Pr: Dave Von Deylen
COO: Kevin Bock
**CFO:* Gary Crider

D-U-N-S 07-867-4799
▲ ALEXANDER & BALDWIN INC
AB
822 Bishop St, Honolulu, HI 96813-3925
Tel (808) 525-6611 *Founded/Ownrshp* 1870
Sales 570.5MM *EMP* 1,496[E]
Tkr Sym ALEX *Exch* NYS
SIC 6512 2062 Nonresidential building operators; Cane sugar refining
Pr: Christopher J Benjamin
**Ch Bd:* Stanley M Kuriyama
CFO: Paul K Ito
Sr VP: Meredith J Ching
VP: George M Morvis
Genl Mgr: Miriam Kusuda

D-U-N-S 00-913-1228
■ ALEXANDER & BALDWIN LLC
(*Suby of* AB) ★
822 Bishop St, Honolulu, HI 96813-3925
Tel (808) 525-6611 *Founded/Ownrshp* 2012
Sales 296.7MM *EMP* 946[E]
SIC 6531 0133 0179 6552 Real estate agent, commercial; Real estate agent, residential; Sugarcane & sugar beets; Sugarcane farm; Coffee farm; Subdividers & developers; Land subdividers & developers, commercial; Land subdividers & developers, residential
Ch Bd: Stanley M Kuriyama
Pr: Christopher J Benjamin
CFO: Paul K Ito
Ofcr: Nelson NS Chun
Sr VP: Meredith J Ching
VP: Kevin L Halloran
VP: George M Morvis Jr
VP: Thomas A Wellmn
Off Mgr: Patricia Saltiban
Genl Couns: Michele S Loudermilk
Genl Couns: Michael Marks

D-U-N-S 62-323-7240
ALEXANDER GALLO HOLDINGS LLC
101 Marietta St Nw # 2700, Atlanta, GA 30303-2711
Tel (404) 495-0777 *Founded/Ownrshp* 2006
Sales NA *EMP* 2,808
SIC 7311

D-U-N-S 06-212-8400 IMP
ALEXANDER OIL CO (TX)
2993 N Hwy 123 Byp, Seguin, TX 78155-7443
Tel (830) 379-1736 *Founded/Ownrshp* 1940, 1972
Sales 100.9MM *EMP* 29
Accts Plummer & Plummer Cpa Brenha
SIC 5171 Petroleum bulk stations
Pr: Jud G Alexander
**Sec:* Barry Brandenberger
**VP:* Jay T Alexander
**VP:* Jud G Alexander Jr

D-U-N-S 80-941-5599
ALEXANDER OPEN SYSTEMS INC
A O S
12980 Foster St Ste 300, Overland Park, KS 66213-2692
Tel (913) 307-2300 *Founded/Ownrshp* 1992
Sales 217.8MM[E] *EMP* 103[E]
SIC 5045 7373 8748 7376 3577 1731 Computer peripheral equipment; Systems software development services; Local area network (LAN) systems integrator; Business consulting; Computer facilities management; Computer peripheral equipment; Electrical work
CEO: Grant Cynor
**Pr:* Matt Cussigh
**Pr:* Brad Ellingsworth
**Pr:* Elliot Fritsche
**Pr:* Dan Urzendowski
Off Mgr: Tracy Young
Sales Asso: Patrick Bernard

D-U-N-S 00-697-8480
▲ ALEXANDERS INC
210 E Rte 4, Paramus, NJ 07652-5108
Tel (201) 587-8541 *Founded/Ownrshp* 1955
Sales 207.9MM *EMP* 73[E]
Accts Deloitte & Touche Llp Parsipp
Tkr Sym ALX *Exch* NYS
SIC 6798 Real estate investment trusts
Ch Bd: Steven Roth
CFO: Joseph Macnow
CTO: Tara Jones

D-U-N-S 10-007-9318
ALEXANDRIA CITY PUBLIC SCHOOLS
1340 Braddock Pl Ste 100, Alexandria, VA 22314-1651
Tel (703) 619-8000 *Founded/Ownrshp* 1872
Sales 252.1MM *EMP* 2,300
Accts Cliftonlarsonallen Llp Arling
SIC 8211 Public elementary school; Public junior high school; Public senior high school
**CFO:* Stacey Johnson
**Ch:* Karen A Graf
Bd of Dir: William Campbell
Bd of Dir: Stephanie Kapsis
MIS Dir: Elizabeth Hoover
Pr Dir: Barbara Hunter
Teacher Pr: Kevin North
HC Dir: Barbara Novak

D-U-N-S 00-645-2916 IMP
ALEXANDRIA EXTRUSION CO (MN)
ALEXANDRIA INDUSTRIES
401 County Road 22 Nw, Alexandria, MN 56308-4974
Tel (320) 762-7657 *Founded/Ownrshp* 1968, 1997
Sales 138.4MM[E] *EMP* 350[E]
SIC 3354 Aluminum extruded products
Pr: Tom Schabel

ALEXANDRIA INDUSTRIES
See ALEXANDRIA EXTRUSION CO

D-U-N-S 82-842-7281
ALEXANDRIA INOVA HEALTH SERVICES CORP
(*Suby of* INOVA HEALTH SYSTEM) ★
8110 Gatehouse Rd 200e, Falls Church, VA 22042-1252
Tel (703) 289-2000 *Founded/Ownrshp* 2008
Sales 250.1M *EMP* 1,765[E]
Accts Reznick Group Pc Vienna V
SIC 8062 General medical & surgical hospitals
Pr: John Knox Singleton
Dir Risk M: Diane Dickerson
Doctor: Bruce Tinker

D-U-N-S 05-794-6774
ALEXANDRIA INOVA HOSPITAL
(*Suby of* ALEXANDRIA INOVA HEALTH SERVICES CORP) ★
4320 Seminary Rd, Alexandria, VA 22304-1535
Tel (703) 504-3000 *Founded/Ownrshp* 1984
Sales 369.3MM *EMP* 1,750
SIC 8062 General medical & surgical hospitals
Pr: J Knox Singleton
**CFO:* Thomas Knight
**Sec:* Richard C Magenheimer
**VP:* H Patrick Walters
VP: Patrick Walters
Info Man: Tracy Gore
HC Dir: Bonnie Greek

D-U-N-S 86-109-0074
ALEXANDRIA REAL ESTATE EQUITIES INC
385 E Colo Blvd Ste 299, Pasadena, CA 91101
Tel (626) 578-0777 *Founded/Ownrshp* 1994
Sales 843.4MM *EMP* 243
Accts Ernst & Young Llp Los Angeles
SIC 6798 Real estate investment trusts
Ch Bd: Joel S Marcus
Pr: Tim White
COO: Stephen A Richardson
CFO: Shigenaga Dean
CFO: Dean A Shigenaga
Chf Inves: Peter M Moglia
Ex VP: Thomas J Andrews
Ex VP: Jennifer J Banks
Ex VP: Daniel J Ryan
Sr VP: Vincent R Ciruzzi
Sr VP: John J Cox
Sr VP: John H Cunningham
Sr VP: Larry J Diamond
VP: Marc Binda
VP: Jonathan Dapeer
VP: Aaron Jacobson
VP: Todd Miller
VP: Terezia Nemeth
VP: Steve Pomerenke
VP: Steve Richardson
Exec: Callie Supsinskas
Board of Directors: John L Atkins III, James P Cain, Maria C Freire, Richard B Jennings, Richard H Klein, Steven R Nash, James H Richardson

D-U-N-S 07-436-9034
ALEXIAN BROTHERS HEALTH SYSTEM INC
(*Suby of* ASCENSION HEALTH) ★
3040 Salt Creek Ln, Elk Grove Village, IL 60007
Tel (847) 437-5500 *Founded/Ownrshp* 1999
Sales 99.7MM *EMP* 8,000
Accts Deloitte Tax Llp Chicago Il
SIC 8062 General medical & surgical hospitals
Pr: Mark A Frey
**Treas:* Paul Murphy
**Treas:* James Sances
**Sr VP:* Paul Belter
**VP:* Tracey Rogers
VP: Peg Wendell
Dir Sec: Eric Swanson
Software D: Eric Korte

D-U-N-S 06-620-5352 IMP
ALEXIAN BROTHERS MEDICAL CENTER INC
A B H S
800 Biesterfield Rd Fl 1, Elk Grove Village, IL 60007-3310
Tel (847) 437-5500 *Founded/Ownrshp* 1966
Sales 449.0MM *EMP* 3,500
SIC 8062 Hospital, AMA approved residency
Pr: John Werrbach
COO: Christopher Novak
**CFO:* Sherri Vincent
**Treas:* James Sances
Ofcr: Debbie Davis
Assoc VP: Susan Breier
VP: Melanie Furlan
VP: Maryann Magnifico
VP: Joan Scheffer
Exec: Nancy Hellyer
Dir OR: Ann Harie Herlehy

D-U-N-S 80-646-7101
ALEXIAN BROTHERS OF AMERICA INC
3040 W Salt Creek Ln, Arlington Heights, IL 60005-1069
Tel (847) 640-7550 *Founded/Ownrshp* 1970
Sales 108.2MM[E] *EMP* 3,000
SIC 8742 8062 8361 Business consultant; General medical & surgical hospitals; Geriatric residential care
Pr: Lawrence Krueger
**VP:* Brother Thomas Keusenkothen

D-U-N-S 78-935-9510
▲ ALEXION PHARMACEUTICALS INC
100 College St, New Haven, CT 06510-3210
Tel (203) 272-2596 *Founded/Ownrshp* 1992
Sales 2.6MMM *EMP* 2,924[E]
Tkr Sym ALXN *Exch* NGS
SIC 2834 8733 Pharmaceutical preparations; Medical research
CEO: David Brennan
**Ch Bd:* Leonard Bell
CFO: David J Anderson
CFO: Vikas Sinha
Ofcr: Clare Carmichael
Ex VP: Saqib Islam
Ex VP: Martin Mackay
Ex VP: John B Moriarty
Ex VP: Julie O'Neill
Ex VP: Carsten Thiel
Sr VP: Daniel A Bazarko
Sr VP: Nancy Motola
Sr VP: Heidi L Wagner
VP: Jordi Casals
Board of Directors: Felix J Baker, M Michele Burns, Christopher J Coughlin, John T Mollen, R Douglas Norby, Alvin S Parven, Andreas Rummelt, Ann M Veneman

ALFA AESAR
See FISHER THERMO SCIENTIFIC CHEMICALS INC

D-U-N-S 36-131-6169
ALFA CORP
(*Suby of* ALFA MUTUAL INSURANCE CO) ★
2108 E South Blvd, Montgomery, AL 36116-2015
Tel (334) 288-3900 *Founded/Ownrshp* 2008
Sales NA *EMP* 4,161
SIC 6331 6411 7389 Fire, marine & casualty insurance; Insurance agents, brokers & service; Financial services
Ch Bd: Jerry A Newby
Pr: Tammy Hackett
Pr: John C Pace
CFO: Stephen G Grutledge
Ex VP: C Lee Ellis
Ex VP: Lee Ellis
Ex VP: Herman T Watts
Sr VP: H Alscott
Sr VP: John T Jung
VP: Mark Campbell
VP: Carol Golson
VP: David Rickey
VP: Becky Taylor

D-U-N-S 01-643-7399
ALFA GENERAL INSURANCE CORP (AL)
(*Suby of* ALFA CORP) ★
2108 E South Blvd, Montgomery, AL 36116-2015
Tel (334) 288-0375 *Founded/Ownrshp* 1982
Sales NA *EMP* 3
SIC 6331 Fire, marine & casualty insurance
Ch Bd: Jerry A Newby
**CFO:* Stephen G Rutledge
**Treas:* C Lee Ellis

ALFA INSURANCE
See ALFA MUTUAL GENERAL INSURANCE CO

D-U-N-S 13-965-8983
ALFA INSURANCE CORP
(*Suby of* ALFA CORP) ★
2108 E South Blvd, Montgomery, AL 36116-2015
Tel (334) 277-6942 *Founded/Ownrshp* 1955
Sales NA *EMP* 2,500
SIC 6331 Automobile insurance; Property damage insurance
Pr: Jerry Newby
**Pr:* C Lee Ellis
**COO:* Jason Ellen
**Ex VP:* Stephen G Rutledge
**Sr VP:* Thomas Bryant
**Sr VP:* Ralph Forsythe
**Sr VP:* Carol Golsan
**Sr VP:* Jerry Johnson
**Sr VP:* John Russell
**VP:* Angela L Cooner
VP: Scott Forrest
VP: John Holley
VP: Kevin Lawrence

D-U-N-S 00-132-8236 IMP/EXP
ALFA LAVAL INC (NJ)
(*Suby of* ALFA LAVAL US HOLDING INC) ★
5400 Intl Trade Dr, Richmond, VA 23231
Tel (804) 222-5300 *Founded/Ownrshp* 1885, 1997
Sales 291.7MM[E] *EMP* 711
SIC 3491 3433 3585 3569 3821 Industrial valves; Heating equipment, except electric; Refrigeration & heating equipment; Assembly machines, non-metalworking; Laboratory apparatus & furniture
CEO: Tom Erixon
**Pr:* John Atanasio
**CFO:* Thomas Thuresson
**Treas:* Joe Lawrence
Ex VP: Lars Henriksson
Ex VP: Tan Hiong
Ex VP: Nish Patel
Ex VP: Joakim Vilson
VP: Peter Bailliere
VP: Leo Krieg
VP: Mark Larsen
VP: Marc Lerch
VP: Ruiqun Yang
Comm Man: Kimberly Dickerson
Comm Man: Meghan Henigin
Board of Directors: John Atanasio, Bill Connolly, Joe Lawrence

D-U-N-S 84-935-8692 IMP/EXP
ALFA LAVAL US HOLDING INC
(*Suby of* ALFA LAVAL USA INC) ★
5400 Intl Trade Dr, Richmond, VA 23231
Tel (804) 222-5300 *Founded/Ownrshp* 2000
Sales 428.9MM[E] *EMP* 1,511
SIC 3569 5085 Centrifuges, industrial; Valves & fittings
Ch: Nish Patel
**Pr:* John Atanasio
**Treas:* Joseph M Lawrence
**VP:* Mark Larsen
**VP:* Jeff Sharbaugh
VP: Ruiqun Yang
Exec: Vaishali Diwan
Genl Mgr: Mark Oestreich
Ql Cn Mgr: Debra Smith
Board of Directors: Thomas Thuresson

D-U-N-S 06-338-8113 IMP/EXP
ALFA LAVAL USA INC
(*Suby of* ALFA LAVAL CORPORATE AB)
5400 Intl Trade Dr, Richmond, VA 23231
Tel (804) 222-5300 *Founded/Ownrshp* 2000
Sales 428.9MM[E] *EMP* 1,700[E]
SIC 3443 3585 Finned tubes, for heat transfer; Evaporative condensers, heat transfer equipment
Ch: Nish Patel
**Pr:* John Atanasio
**VP:* Stephen D Pratt
**VP:* Jeff Sharbaugh
Exec: Jitesh Dedhia
Mng Dir: Jyrki Lindholm
Genl Mgr: Ottar Grande
IT Man: Bill Connolly
IT Man: Ebbe Lindgren
IT Man: Alan Young
Mfg Mgr: Bill Hertz

D-U-N-S 79-044-7374
ALFA MUTUAL FIRE INSURANCE CO
2108 E South Blvd, Montgomery, AL 36116-2015
Tel (334) 288-3900 *Founded/Ownrshp* 1945
Sales NA *EMP* 50
SIC 6411 Insurance agents, brokers & service
CEO: Jimmy Parnell
VP: William B Harper
VP Sls: Carol Golsan
Sls Mgr: Jerry Vincent

D-U-N-S 13-965-9601
ALFA MUTUAL GENERAL INSURANCE CO
ALFA INSURANCE
(*Suby of* ALFA CORP) ★
2108 E South Blvd, Montgomery, AL 36116-2015
Tel (334) 288-3900 *Founded/Ownrshp* 1946
Sales NA *EMP* 1,000
SIC 6331 Fire, marine & casualty insurance; Automobile insurance
CEO: Jerry Newby
CFO: Stephen G Rutledge
VP: Mark Campbell
VP: Ralph Forsythe
VP: Mona Russell
Ex Dir: Kathleen Watson
QA Dir: Amy Dubose
Netwrk Eng: Dennis Hopper

D-U-N-S 00-402-7900
ALFA MUTUAL INSURANCE CO
2108 E South Blvd, Montgomery, AL 36116-2015
Tel (334) 613-4639 *Founded/Ownrshp* 1947
Sales NA *EMP* 6,296
SIC 6411 Insurance agents, brokers & service
Pr: Jerry A Newby
**Ex VP:* Stephen G Rutledge
IT Man: James Cleckler

D-U-N-S 01-225-9813
ALFA SMARTPARKS INC
1 W Adams St Ste 200, Jacksonville, FL 32202-3643
Tel (904) 358-1027 *Founded/Ownrshp* 1999
Sales 26.7MM[E] *EMP* 2,500
SIC 7996 Theme park, amusement
Pr: Randy Drew
**Treas:* Andy Barkley
**Ex VP:* Nathan Goldman

D-U-N-S 09-991-2446
ALFALFAS MARKET INC
1651 Broadway, Boulder, CO 80302-6218
Tel (303) 449-5343 *Founded/Ownrshp* 1980
Sales 68.9MM[E] *EMP* 1,000
SIC 5499 Health foods
Pr: S M Hassan
Pr: Paul McLean
**CFO:* Caryn Ellison
VP: Jimmy Searcy
Mktg Dir: Stacee McGovern

D-U-N-S 80-854-6266
ALFATECH CAMBRIDGE GROUP GP
345 S California Ave # 3, Palo Alto, CA 94306-1866
Tel (650) 543-3030 *Founded/Ownrshp* 2006
Sales 150.0MM *EMP* 70
SIC 8741 8742 Construction management; Management engineering
Pt: William Hammerson
Pt: Jeff Fini

D-U-N-S 04-981-2563
ALFRED BENESCH & CO
205 N Michigan Ave # 2400, Chicago, IL 60601-5923
Tel (312) 565-2497 *Founded/Ownrshp* 2009
Sales 163.5MM[E] *EMP* 470
SIC 8711 Consulting engineer
Pr: John L Carrato
**Ch Bd:* Muthiah Kasi
**CFO:* Kristlina S Horn
**Ex VP:* James Blanusha
**Ex VP:* Gregory Brennan
**Ex VP:* Michael Gorman
**Ex VP:* John P Kweder Jr
**Sr VP:* Thomas Clinard
**Sr VP:* Jeffery Sockel
VP: James Canham
VP: Bill Epp
**VP:* Kevin Fitzpatrick
VP: Michael Goodkid
VP: David Morrill
VP: Gary Proskovec
VP: Daniel J Rivers
VP: Gary Westergren

D-U-N-S 00-122-4799 IMP
ALFRED DUNNER INC (NY)
1411 Broadway Fl 24, New York, NY 10018-3471
Tel (212) 478-4300 *Founded/Ownrshp* 1946, 1961
Sales 95.6MM[E] *EMP* 275

SIC 2337 2331 2339 Skirts, separate: women's, misses' & juniors'; Jackets & vests, except fur & leather: women's; T-shirts & tops, women's: made from purchased materials; Slacks: women's, misses' & juniors'; Shorts (outerwear): women's, misses' & juniors'
Ch: Joseph Aresty
**Pr:* Peter Aresty
**VP:* Jerome Aresty
Creative D: Nadia Regazzin
CIO: William Werner
Prd Mgr: Linda Gold
Sales Exec: Harry Gersten

ALFRED I DUPONT HOSPITAL FOR
See NEMOURS FOUNDATION

ALFRED I DUPONT HOSPITAL FOR C
See NEMOURS CHILDRENS HOSPITAL

D-U-N-S 80-438-0939
ALFRED IDUPONT HOSPITAL FOR CHILDREN
A I DUPONT HOSP FOR CHILDREN
(*Suby of* ALFRED I DUPONT HOSPITAL FOR) ★
1600 Rockland Rd, Wilmington, DE 19803-3607
Tel (302) 651-4000 *Founded/Ownrshp* 1995
Sales 77.3MM^E *EMP* 3,068
Accts Kpmg Llp Jacksonville Fl
SIC 8069 Children's hospital
CEO: Thomas Ferry
**CFO:* William Britton
**VP:* Stephen T Lawless
Ansthlgy: Divya Dixit
Doctor: Dianna Willis
Pharmcst: Stacey Collings
Pharmcst: Letitia Kanar
Pharmcst: Jack Lagowski
Pharmcst: Karen Marra

D-U-N-S 00-446-5381 IMP
ALFRED NICKLES BAKERY INC (OH)
26 Main St N, Navarre, OH 44662-1158
Tel (330) 879-5635 *Founded/Ownrshp* 1909
Sales 205.0MM *EMP* 1,600
Accts Maloney Novotny Llc Canton O
SIC 2051 Bread, all types (white, wheat, rye, etc): fresh or frozen
Pr: David A Gardner
**Sr VP:* Mark Sponseller
**VP:* Matthew Boxrucker
**VP:* Ernest Brideweser
**VP:* Christian Gardner
**VP:* J Wesley Webber
VP: R Weber
Brnch Mgr: Ron Fields
Sales Exec: Ernie Brideweser
VP Mktg: James Wilson

D-U-N-S 07-863-0894
ALFRED P SLOAN FOUNDATION
SLOAN INDUSTRY CENTERS
45 Rockefeller Plz # 2200, New York, NY 10111-0217
Tel (212) 649-1649 *Founded/Ownrshp* 1934
Sales 116.9MM *EMP* 25
Accts Kpmg Peat Marwick Llp
SIC 6732 Trusts: educational, religious, etc.
Pr: Paul Johnson
COO: Patti Giglio
Treas: Barbara Leff
Chf Inves: William Petersen
Ofcr: Evan Michelson
VP: Wendy Marino
VP: Petersen William
CTO: Christopher Sia
Pgrm Dir: Kathleen Christensen
Pgrm Dir: Ted Greenwood
Pgrm Dir: Gaif M Pesyna

D-U-N-S 02-475-9961 IMP
ALFRED WILLIAMS & CO
410 S Salisbury St # 200, Raleigh, NC 27601-1775
Tel (919) 832-9570 *Founded/Ownrshp* 1867
Sales 117.1MM^E *EMP* 180
SIC 5021 Office furniture
Ch Bd: J Blount Williams
COO: Edward Boiar
**CFO:* Gordon Brown
CFO: Linda McCotter
**Ex VP:* John McKinney
VP: Katherine Thomas
Exec: Kyle Ryan
Mng Dir: Susan Russell
IT Man: Jeff Russell
Sales Asso: Arlene Kierce

ALGECO SCOTSMAN
See WILLIAMS SCOTSMAN INTERNATIONAL INC

ALGOMOD TECHNOLOGIES
See AXELON SERVICES CORP

ALGONQUIN BOOKS CHAPEL HL DIV
See WORKMAN PUBLISHING CO INC

D-U-N-S 00-695-1446
■ **ALGONQUIN GAS TRANSMISSION LLC** (DE)
(*Suby of* SPECTRA ENERGY CORP) ★
5400 Westheimer Ct, Houston, TX 77056-5353
Tel (713) 627-5400 *Founded/Ownrshp* 1949, 2007
Sales 270.0MM *EMP* 151
Accts Deloitte & Touche Llp Housto
SIC 4923 Gas transmission & distribution
Pr: William T Yardley
Sr VP: Richard Kruse Jr
**VP:* John V Adams
**VP:* Frederick S Steve Bush
**VP:* Allen C Capps
**VP:* Patricia M Rice
VP Mktg: Bill Yardley

D-U-N-S 13-101-1822
ALGONQUIN POWER WINDSOR LOCKS LLC
26 Canal Bank Rd, Windsor Locks, CT 06096-2333
Tel (860) 627-6616 *Founded/Ownrshp* 2003
Sales 453.5MM^E *EMP* 400
SIC 4911

D-U-N-S 07-448-4726
ALHAMBRA SCHOOL DISTRICT 68
4510 N 37th Ave, Phoenix, AZ 85019-3206
Tel (602) 336-2920 *Founded/Ownrshp* 1910
Sales 110.3MM *EMP* 1,700
Accts Heinfeld Meech & Co Pc P
SIC 8211 Public elementary school

D-U-N-S 07-064-9793
ALHAMBRA UNIFIED SCHOOL DISTRICT
ALAHAMBRA HIGH SCHOOL
1515 W Mission Rd, Alhambra, CA 91803-1618
Tel (626) 943-3000 *Founded/Ownrshp* 1886
Sales 112.2MM^E *EMP* 1,800
SIC 8211 Public elementary & secondary schools
VP: Jane Canderson
**COO:* Cynthia Martin
**Prin:* Pat Rodriguez-Mackintosh
CTO: Ashton Potter
IT Man: Laurel Bear
Pr Dir: Jim Schofiled
Schl Brd P: Robert Gin
Psych: Stephanie Cohen

D-U-N-S 07-980-3309
ALI GROUP NORTH AMERICA CORP
(*Suby of* ALI SPA)
101 Corporate Woods Pkwy, Vernon Hills, IL 60061-3109
Tel (847) 215-6565 *Founded/Ownrshp* 2002
Sales 574.2MM^E *EMP* 1,511^E
SIC 3589 Cooking equipment, commercial
CFO: Bradford Willis
**Pr:* Filipo Berti
IT Man: Rob Anderson

D-U-N-S 00-427-8933 IMP/EXP
ALI INDUSTRIES INC
ABRASIVE LEADERS & INNOVATORS
747 E Xenia Dr, Fairborn, OH 45324-8761
Tel (937) 878-3946 *Founded/Ownrshp* 1961
Sales 85.0MM^E *EMP* 200
SIC 3291 Abrasive products
Pr: Terry Ali
**VP:* Christopher Ali
**VP Sls:* Phillip Ali

D-U-N-S 79-902-0953
ALICE BYRD TAWES NURSING HOME INC
201 Hall Hwy, Crisfield, MD 21817-1237
Tel (410) 968-1200 *Founded/Ownrshp* 1968
Sales 478.8MM *EMP* 280
Accts Scott Tawed & Associates Pa
SIC 8051 Convalescent home with continuous nursing care
CEO: Charles Pinkerman
COO: Sydney Barnes
Board of Directors: Eleanor Eberhart, Russel Ward, Dewayne Whittington Phd

ALICE C HRRIS INTRMEDIATE SCHL
See BOX ELDER SCHOOL DISTRICT

D-U-N-S 09-511-1209
ALICE INDEPENDENT SCHOOL DISTRICT
2 Coyote Trl, Alice, TX 78332-4223
Tel (361) 664-0981 *Founded/Ownrshp* 1903
Sales 55.2MM *EMP* 1,500
Accts Raul Hernandez & Company Pc
SIC 8211 Public elementary school; Public junior high school; Public senior high school
Ex Dir: Jerry Cavazos
IT Man: Debbie Jackson
IT Man: Rachel Martin

D-U-N-S 00-335-5245 IMP/EXP
ALICE MANUFACTURING CO INC (SC)
208 E 1st Ave, Easley, SC 29640-3039
Tel (864) 859-6323 *Founded/Ownrshp* 1923, 1952
Sales 126.3MM^E *EMP* 600
SIC 2211 2221 Broadwoven fabric mills, cotton; Broadwoven fabric mills, manmade
Ch: Ellison Mc Kissick III

ALICE SOUTHERN EQUIPMENT
See SELECT ENERGY SERVICES LLC

D-U-N-S 00-692-1951
▲ **ALICO INC** (FL)
10070 Daniels Interstate, Fort Myers, FL 33913-7876
Tel (239) 226-2000 *Founded/Ownrshp* 1960
Sales 144.2MM *EMP* 346^E
Accts Rsm Us Llp Orlando Florida
Tkr Sym ALCO *Exch* NGS
SIC 0174 0212 0133 6519 Citrus fruits; Beef cattle except feedlots; Sugarcane farm; Farm land leasing
Pr: Clayton G Wilson
**Ch Bd:* Henry R Slack
V Ch: Christopher Swift
CFO: Mark Humphrey
CFO: John E Kiernan
Treas: Steven C Lewis
Sr VP: Michael Rosen
Dir IT: Lindsay Krill
Board of Directors: George R Brokaw, T Greg Eisner, Benjamin D Fishman, W Andrew Krusen Jr, Remy W Trafelet

D-U-N-S 03-186-1214
ALIEF INDEPENDENT SCHOOL DISTRICT
4250 Cook Rd, Houston, TX 77072-1115
Tel (281) 498-8110 *Founded/Ownrshp* 1917
Sales 269.0MM^E *EMP* 6,000
Accts Null-Lairson Pc Houston Tx
SIC 8211 Public elementary & secondary schools
**CFO:* Deanna Wentz
Bd of Dir: John Hansen
Trst: Rick Guerrero
VP: Nghi Ho
Exec: Kathy Cherry
Exec: Lori Wyatt
Ex Dir: Kathleen Jahn
Admn Mgr: Jonell Keller
MIS Dir: Doug Brown
MIS Dir: Tabitha Carter
IT Man: Sarah Trigg

D-U-N-S 92-928-2700
ALIGN AEROSPACE HOLDING INC
(*Suby of* AVIC INTERNATIONAL HOLDING CORPORATION)
21123 Nordhoff St, Chatsworth, CA 91311-5816
Tel (818) 727-7800 *Founded/Ownrshp* 2015
Sales 277.3MM^E *EMP* 101^E
SIC 3324 Aerospace investment castings, ferrous
Pr: Jerome De Truchis
COO: You Lei
CFO: Pan Linwu
Ex VP: Chen Hongliang

D-U-N-S 96-932-9007
ALIGN AEROSPACE LLC
(*Suby of* ALIGN AEROSPACE HOLDING INC) ★
21123 Nordhoff St, Chatsworth, CA 91311-5816
Tel (818) 727-7800 *Founded/Ownrshp* 2011
Sales 277.3MM^E *EMP* 300^E
SIC 5088 Aircraft & space vehicle supplies & parts
Pr: Ashley Graeber
Treas: Rodney Shoemaker
Genl Mgr: Dean Buttress
Genl Mgr: Dan Fitch
IT Man: Mike Watts
Manager: Carol Tess
Manager: Earl Osborn

D-U-N-S 01-383-1768 IMP
▲ **ALIGN TECHNOLOGY INC**
2560 Orchard Pkwy, San Jose, CA 95131-1033
Tel (408) 470-1000 *Founded/Ownrshp* 1997
Sales 845.4MM *EMP* 4,375^E
Tkr Sym ALGN *Exch* NGS
SIC 3843 Orthodontic appliances
Pr: Joseph M Hogan
**Ch Bd:* C Raymond Larkin Jr
VP: Simon Beard
VP: John D'Angelo
VP: John Dangelo
VP: Jennifer M Erfurth
VP: Roger E George
VP: John Graham
VP: Tim Mack
VP: Timothy A Mack
VP: Eric Meyer
VP: Jennifer Olson-Wilk
VP: Raphael S Pascaud
VP: Christopher C Puco
VP: Zelko Relic
VP: Julie Tay
VP: Emory M Wright
Board of Directors: Joseph Lacob, Thomas M Prescott, Andrea L Saia, Greg J Santora, Warren S Thaler

D-U-N-S 07-993-8529
ALIGNED AG DISTRIBUTORS LLC
224b S Bell Ave, Ames, IA 50010-7719
Tel (641) 858-2341 *Founded/Ownrshp* 2015
Sales 225.0MM^E *EMP* 5
SIC 5191 Chemicals, agricultural
Pr: Steve Watts
**Treas:* Carl Hoff
**VP:* Brad Oelmann

D-U-N-S 19-407-5719 IMP/EXP
ALIMAK HEK INC
(*Suby of* ALIMAK HEK AB)
12552 Galveston Rd Ste A 160, Webster, TX 77598
Tel (713) 640-8500 *Founded/Ownrshp* 2001
Sales 84.6MM^E *EMP* 200
SIC 5084 7699 3535 3534 Elevators; Elevators: inspection, service & repair; Conveyors & conveying equipment; Elevators & moving stairways
Pr: Dale Stoddard
**CFO:* Donn McIsaac
CFO: Stefan Petersson
Treas: Michael O Sullivan
Ex VP: Fredrik Wiking
IT Man: Michael Canle
Opers Mgr: Tom Demars
Sls Dir: Tony Dragone
Manager: Paul Spadorcia
Manager: Anthony Whaley

D-U-N-S 60-846-9362
ALINDA CAPITAL PARTNERS LLC
1266 E Main St Ste 700r, Stamford, CT 06902-3507
Tel (203) 930-3800 *Founded/Ownrshp* 2005
Sales 202.3MM^E *EMP* 894^E
SIC 6726 Investment offices
Mng Pt: Chris Beale
**Pt:* Andrew Bishop
**Pt:* Alex Black
**Pt:* Sanjay Khettry
**Pt:* Jim Metcalfe
CFO: Guy Lotem
VP: Zaid Nashashibi
VP: Christopher Reid
Mng Dir: Gary Dielsi
Mng Dir: Mike Gallup

D-U-N-S 11-916-2332
ALION SCIENCE AND TECHNOLOGY CORP
1750 Tysons Blvd Ste 1300, Mc Lean, VA 22102-4220
Tel (703) 918-4480 *Founded/Ownrshp* 2001
Sales 1.0MMM^E *EMP* 2,713
SIC 8711 8731 Engineering services; Commercial physical research; Commercial physical research
Ch Bd: Bahman Atefi
Pr: Dennis Murphy
Pr: Ronals A Ross
Pr: Jeffrey White
COO: Stacy Mendler
COO: Bruce Samuelsen
CFO: Barry Broadus
CFO: Kevin L Cook
Sr VP: Christopher Amos
Sr VP: Kevin Boyle
Sr VP: John Carty
Sr VP: Robert Hirt
Sr VP: Sean Pender
Sr VP: Dave Russell
Sr VP: Terri Spoonhour
Sr VP: Ali Zandi
VP: James Armstrong
VP: Bill Carter
VP: David Colby
VP: William Crabb
VP: Rae Dehncke
Board of Directors: Leslie L Armitage, Daniel H Clare, Lewis Collens, Harold W Gehman Jr, Michael V Hayden, George A Joulwan, Michael E Ryan, Lawrence A First

D-U-N-S 84-473-7556 IMP
ALIPHCOM
99 Rhode Island St Fl 3, San Francisco, CA 94103-5233
Tel (415) 230-7600 *Founded/Ownrshp* 1998
Sales 260.8MM^E *EMP* 300^E
SIC 5065 5999 Sound equipment, electronic; Electronic parts & equipment
Ch: Alexander Asseily
**Pr:* Mindy Mount
**CEO:* Hosain Rahman
CFO: Patrick Chiang
Sr VP: Richard Drysdale
**VP:* Travis Bogard
VP: Randy Knaflic
VP: Sean Ludick
VP: Steven Rechtschaffner
VP: Max Utter
**Prin:* Marissa Mayer

D-U-N-S 12-240-3645 IMP
ALIXPARTNERS LLP
AP SERVICES
(*Suby of* SUNSET SARL)
909 3rd Ave Fl 30, New York, NY 10022-5002
Tel (212) 490-2500 *Founded/Ownrshp* 2006
Sales 119.5MM^E *EMP* 600
SIC 7311 Advertising agencies
Ch: Frederick A Crawford
**Pr:* Stefano Aversa
**CFO:* Doug Barnett
**CFO:* Kevin G Wills
Treas: Lawrence Writer
**Ofcr:* Theodore C Billies
Ex VP: Jason Marx
VP: Francesco Barosi
VP: Guillaume Bourcier
VP: Brieh Guevara
VP: Jamey Hamilton
VP: Tristan Honore
VP: Hans Lehmann
VP: Lara Nemerov
VP: Tom Studebaker
VP: Andrew Wagner
VP: Mark Wakefield
VP: Mark Wessel
Comm Dir: Roxanne Kerr
Dir Bus: Sean Dowd
Board of Directors: Michael Grindfors, Michael Ratze

D-U-N-S 94-331-7370
▲ **ALJ REGIONAL HOLDINGS INC**
244 Madison Ave, New York, NY 10016-2817
Tel (212) 883-0083 *Founded/Ownrshp* 1999
Sales 149.0MM *EMP* 4,000
Tkr Sym ALJJ *Exch* NGM
SIC 6719 Investment holding companies, except banks
Ch Bd: Jess M Ravich
**Pr:* John Scheel
CFO: Rob Christ
**CFO:* T Robert Christ

ALKCO LIGHTING COMPANY
See JJI LIGHTING GROUP INC

D-U-N-S 18-548-1132 IMP
ALKERMES INC
(*Suby of* ALKERMES PUBLIC LIMITED COMPANY)
852 Winter St, Waltham, MA 02451-1420
Tel (781) 609-6000 *Founded/Ownrshp* 2011
Sales 166.5MM^E *EMP* 570^E
SIC 2834 8731 Pharmaceutical preparations; Biotechnical research, commercial
CEO: Richard Pops
**COO:* Gordon G Pugh
CFO: Jim Crotty
**CFO:* James M Frates
Ex VP: Markus Coppel
**Sr VP:* Kathryn L Biberstein
Sr VP: Chris Burns
**Sr VP:* Elliot W Ehrich
Sr VP: Duncan Higgons
VP: Mary Bareilles
VP: Jackson Blair
VP: Tina Casteris
VP: Dan Deaver
VP: Tom Harvey
VP: Blair Jackson
VP: Stephen King
VP: Gary Liversidge
VP: David Marshall
VP: Terry Munson
VP: Rebecca Peterson
VP: Marc Somer
Board of Directors: David W Anstice, Floyd E Bloom, Robert A Breyer, Wendy L Dixon, Geraldine Henwood, Paul J Mitchell, Alexander Rich, Mark B Skaletsky, Michael A Wall

ALL A DOLLAR
See GREENBACKS INC

D-U-N-S 02-922-4083
ALL ABOARD AMERICA HOLDINGS INC
2838 Touro St, New Orleans, LA 70122-3641
Tel (800) 356-6831 *Founded/Ownrshp* 2012
Sales 84.6MM^E *EMP* 391
SIC 6719 4141 4131 4119 4111 Investment holding companies, except banks; Local bus charter service; Intercity & rural bus transportation; Sightseeing bus; Bus transportation; Commuter bus operation
Pr: Craig Lentzsch
**Treas:* Laura McBryde

D-U-N-S 96-662-4348 IMP
ALL ACCESS APPAREL INC
SELF ESTEEM
1515 Gage Rd, Montebello, CA 90640-6613
Tel (323) 889-4300 *Founded/Ownrshp* 1997
Sales 140.5MM *EMP* 134
Accts Moss Adams Llp

SIC 2331 2361 2335 Women's & misses' blouses & shirts; Girls' & children's dresses, blouses & shirts; Women's, juniors' & misses' dresses
CEO: Richard Clareman
CFO: Michael Conway
Sr Cor Off: Ben Quan
Ex VP: Andrea Rankin
Sr VP: Robert Roberts

D-U-N-S 06-370-0421
ALL AMERICA INSURANCE CO INC
CENTRAL INSURANCE COMPANIES
(*Suby of* CENTRAL INSURANCE COMPANIES) ★
800 S Washington St, Van Wert, OH 45891-2357
Tel (419) 238-1010 *Founded/Ownrshp* 1961
Sales NA *EMP* 450
SIC 6411 Insurance agents, brokers & service
Pr: Francis W Purmort III
* *Treas:* Thad Eikenbary
* *VP:* Jeffrey L Hanson
* *VP:* Michael Thompson
* *VP:* John E White
* *VP:* Paul C Woirol
* *Prin:* Jon A Rhoades
* *Prin:* Karl Waite

ALL AMERICAN AGRIGATE
See ALL AMERICAN ASPHALT

D-U-N-S 04-876-3379
ALL AMERICAN ASPHALT
ALL AMERICAN AGRIGATE
400 E 6th St, Corona, CA 92879-1521
Tel (951) 736-7600 *Founded/Ownrshp* 1969
Sales 189.5MM[E] *EMP* 400
SIC 1611 5032 Highway & street paving contractor; Brick, stone & related material
Pr: Mark Albert Luer
Ofcr: Robert Bradley
Brnch Mgr: Kim McGuire
CIO: Jim Harnetiaux

D-U-N-S 78-375-1852 IMP
ALL AMERICAN CONTAINERS INC
9330 Nw 110th Ave, Medley, FL 33178-2519
Tel (305) 887-0797 *Founded/Ownrshp* 1991
Sales 157.5MM[E] *EMP* 202
SIC 5085 5099 Pails, metal; Containers: glass, metal or plastic
Pr: Remedios Diaz Oliver
* *CEO:* Fausto Diaz-Oliver
* *CFO:* Amparo Alvarez
Ofcr: Rick Rangel
VP: Richard Cabrera
* *VP:* Maria Flores
* *Ex Dir:* Fausto G Diaz

D-U-N-S 60-534-7939 IMP
ALL AMERICAN FOODS INC
1 All American Way, North Kingstown, RI 02852-2607
Tel (401) 294-5455 *Founded/Ownrshp* 1988
Sales 90.2MM[E] *EMP* 85
SIC 5147 5146 5142 Meats & meat products; Seafoods; Frozen fish, meat & poultry
Pr: Leon Panteleos
Genl Mgr: Anthony Conti
Opers Mgr: Jim Flanagan
Sales Exec: Steven Savastano
Sls Mgr: Fred Soulliere
Sls Mgr: Fred Souulliere
Sls Mgr: Kimon Zarokostas

D-U-N-S 96-810-6521
ALL AMERICAN GROUP HOLDINGS LLC
1450 Brickell Ave # 3100, Miami, FL 33131-3444
Tel (305) 379-2322 *Founded/Ownrshp* 2010
Sales 114.2MM[E] *EMP* 615[E]
SIC 6719 Investment holding companies, except banks

D-U-N-S 00-543-3081 IMP/EXP
ALL AMERICAN GROUP INC
VIKING FORMED PRODUCTS
(*Suby of* ALL AMERICAN GROUP HOLDINGS LLC) ★
2831 Dexter Dr, Elkhart, IN 46514-8225
Tel (574) 262-0123 *Founded/Ownrshp* 1964
Sales 133.8MM[E] *EMP* 612
SIC 3716 3792 2452 3714 1521 Motor homes; Travel trailers & campers; Camping trailers & chassis; Truck campers (slide-in); Modular homes, prefabricated, wood; Motor vehicle parts & accessories; Single-family housing construction
Pr: Richard M Lavers
* *CFO:* Colleen A Zuhl
Ex VP: Del Herr
VP: James R Frahm
* *VP:* Martin L Miranda
* *Genl Couns:* W Todd Woelfer

D-U-N-S 62-112-5772
ALL AMERICAN OIL INC OF BREVARD
402 High Point Dr Ste 102, Cocoa, FL 32926-6600
Tel (321) 690-0807 *Founded/Ownrshp* 1987
Sales 95.8MM *EMP* 20
SIC 5541 5411 Filling stations, gasoline; Convenience stores
Pr: Mahesh Shah
* *Treas:* Kanan Shah
* *VP:* Rajendra Shah

D-U-N-S 06-533-2009
ALL AMERICAN QUALITY FOODS INC
FOOD DEPOT
125 Eagles Landing Pkwy, Stockbridge, GA 30281-5092
Tel (770) 474-5904 *Founded/Ownrshp* 1973
Sales 173.6MM[E] *EMP* 1,240
SIC 5411 Grocery stores, independent
CEO: Gerald Taylor

D-U-N-S 80-139-0977
ALL AMERICAN SEMICONDUCTOR LLC
3100 Nw 36th St, Miami, FL 33142-5162
Tel (305) 626-4183 *Founded/Ownrshp* 2007
Sales 102.3MM[E] *EMP* 130[E]
SIC 5065 Electronic parts & equipment
VP: Riad Nizam
Genl Mgr: Phil Wall
IT Man: Cynthia Dixon

D-U-N-S 80-808-6235 IMP
ALL AMERICAN SPORTS CORP
RIDDELL ALL AMERICAN SPORT
(*Suby of* RBG HOLDINGS CORP) ★
669 Sugar Ln, Elyria, OH 44035-6309
Tel (440) 366-8225 *Founded/Ownrshp* 2004
Sales 5.0MM *EMP* 1,000
SIC 7699 Recreational sporting equipment repair services
Pr: Don Gleisner
Mktg Mgr: Diane Golias
Sls Mgr: Tim Moran

D-U-N-S 05-510-9861
ALL AROUND ROUSTABOUT LLC
41350 County Road 33, Ault, CO 80610-9647
Tel (970) 518-2479 *Founded/Ownrshp* 2008
Sales 297.1MM[E] *EMP* 300
SIC 1389 Roustabout service

ALL CHILDREN HEALTH SYSTEM
See JOHNS HOPKINS ALL CHILDRENS HOSPITAL INC

ALL CONNECT
See INTELLIGENT CONSUMER HOLDINGS LLC

D-U-N-S 07-039-0075
ALL COPY PRODUCTS INC
4141 Colorado Blvd, Denver, CO 80216-4307
Tel (303) 373-1105 *Founded/Ownrshp* 1999
Sales 104.9MM[E] *EMP* 220
SIC 5044 5112 7371 Office equipment; Stationery & office supplies; Custom computer programming services
CEO: Brad Knepper
* *Ex VP:* Scott Dewar
Brnch Mgr: Desiree Salerno
Div Mgr: Ty Bartels
Div Mgr: Jennifer Huddle
Div Mgr: Scott Meredith
IT Man: Jim Ryan
VP Opers: Dan Dunbabin
Opers Mgr: Aaron Hill
Sales Exec: Pam Webster
VP Sls: Fred Longmore

D-U-N-S 80-008-9989
ALL ENVIRONMENTAL INC
AEI CONSULTANTS
2500 Camino Diablo, Walnut Creek, CA 94597-3998
Tel (925) 746-6000 *Founded/Ownrshp* 1992
Sales 100.6MM[E] *EMP* 153
SIC 4959 Environmental cleanup services
CEO: Craig Hertz
* *Pr:* Holly Neber
Ex VP: Peter F Millar
VP: Joe Campisi
* *VP:* Brian Cochran
* *VP:* Paul Hinkston
* *VP:* Peter McIntyre
* *VP:* Mark Nobler
Genl Mgr: Dusty Roy
Mktg Mgr: Marissa Miller

D-U-N-S 04-520-7842 EXP
ALL ERECTION & CRANE RENTAL CORP
4700 Acorn Dr, Cleveland, OH 44131-6940
Tel (216) 524-6550 *Founded/Ownrshp* 1964
Sales 94.2MM[E] *EMP* 360
SIC 7353 7359 Heavy construction equipment rental; Equipment rental & leasing
Pr: Michael C Liptak Jr
CFO: John Sivak
* *Treas:* Lawrence Liptak

ALL HALLOWS GARDEN APARTMENTS
See ALL HALLOWS PRESERVATION LP

D-U-N-S 01-335-2538
ALL HALLOWS PRESERVATION LP
ALL HALLOWS GARDEN APARTMENTS
54 Navy Rd, San Francisco, CA 94124-2825
Tel (415) 285-3909 *Founded/Ownrshp* 2007
Sales 950.0M *EMP* 3,900
SIC 6513 Apartment building operators
Sr VP: Leeann Morein
Pt: George Buchanan

D-U-N-S 79-121-1316 IMP
ALL MARKET INC
VITA COCO
250 Park Ave S Fl 7, New York, NY 10003-1402
Tel (212) 206-0763 *Founded/Ownrshp* 2004
Sales 220.0MM *EMP* 180[E]
Accts Deloitte & Touche Llp New Yor
SIC 5499 Juices, fruit or vegetable
CEO: Michael Kirban
* *CFO:* Jose Carvalho
Exec: Nicole Kereszti
Dir Bus: Joss Ford
Area Mgr: Dave Agan
Area Mgr: Chris Thompson
Off Mgr: Elana Fisher
Mktg Mgr: John McManus

D-U-N-S 15-360-9011
ALL METALS INDUSTRIES INC
4 Higgins Dr, Belmont, NH 03220-4257
Tel (603) 267-7023 *Founded/Ownrshp* 1986
Sales 84.9MM[E] *EMP* 70[E]
SIC 5051 Aluminum bars, rods, ingots, sheets, pipes, plates, etc.; Steel
Pr: Paul W Koza
* *Ch Bd:* Terry W Robinson
* *VP:* Heidi M Paiva
Sales Asso: Ron Skilton

D-U-N-S 55-712-2210 IMP
ALL ONE GOD FAITH INC
DR. BRONNER'S SOAPS
1335 Park Center Dr, Vista, CA 92081-8357
Tel (844) 937-2551 *Founded/Ownrshp* 1858
Sales 90.0MM[E] *EMP* 135[E]
SIC 2841 Soap: granulated, liquid, cake, flaked or chip
CEO: David Bronner
* *Pr:* Michael Bronner
* *CFO:* Trudy Bronner

Ofcr: Raquel Santiago
Off Mgr: Nina Vujko
Natl Sales: Mike Stacy
Mktg Dir: Christina Volgyesi
Manager: Gina Coccari

D-U-N-S 12-350-2812
■ **ALL POINTS CAPITAL CORP**
NORTH FORK EQUIPMENT LEASING
(*Suby of* CAPITAL ONE BANK) ★
275 Broadhollow Rd, Melville, NY 11747-4808
Tel (631) 531-2800 *Founded/Ownrshp* 1999
Sales NA *EMP* 2,878
SIC 6035 6159 Savings institutions, federally chartered; Equipment & vehicle finance leasing companies
VP: Aurelie Campbell

D-U-N-S 03-503-1657
ALL POINTS COOPERATIVE
120 8th St, Gothenburg, NE 69138-1006
Tel (308) 537-7141 *Founded/Ownrshp* 1927
Sales 236.0MM *EMP* 150
SIC 5153 5191 5541

ALL POINTS TRANSPORT
See EVANS DELIVERY CO INC

D-U-N-S 80-019-9325
ALL SAINTS HEALTH CARE SYSTEM INC
3801 Spring St, Mount Pleasant, WI 53405-1667
Tel (262) 687-4011 *Founded/Ownrshp* 1987
Sales 406.8MM *EMP* 2,680
SIC 8062 General medical & surgical hospitals
Pr: Ken Buser
CFO: Jim Beck

ALL SEASONS
See ALENCO HOLDING CORP

D-U-N-S 16-184-8270
ALL SEASONS SERVICES INC
ALL SEASONS VENDING
5 Campanelli Cir Ste 200, Canton, MA 02021-2436
Tel (781) 828-2345 *Founded/Ownrshp* 1996
Sales 140.8MM[E] *EMP* 1,700
SIC 5962 5812 Merchandising machine operators; Cafeteria
Pr: Mark Bruno
* *CFO:* Bill Glass
VP: Michael Nugent

ALL SEASONS VENDING
See ALL SEASONS SERVICES INC

D-U-N-S 07-658-5368
ALL STAR AUTOMOTIVE GROUP
13000 Florida Blvd, Baton Rouge, LA 70815-2955
Tel (225) 298-3210 *Founded/Ownrshp* 2001
Sales 212.9MM[E] *EMP* 580
SIC 5511 Automobiles, new & used
Ch Bd: John Noland
* *Pr:* Matthew G McKay
* *CFO:* William Lockwood
Genl Mgr: Lee Carney
Off Mgr: Betty Milton
IT Man: Sean Hallquist
Sales Asso: Larnell Davis

D-U-N-S 04-411-7372
ALL STAR DAIRY ASSOCIATION INC
1050 Monarch St Ste 101, Lexington, KY 40513-1819
Tel (859) 255-3644 *Founded/Ownrshp* 2001
Sales 458.0MM *EMP* 12
SIC 5149 5169 5113 5199 Flavourings & fragrances; Sugar, refined; Syrups, except for fountain use; Chemicals & allied products; Containers, paper & disposable plastic; Advertising specialties
Ex Dir: Jeff Sterne
* *CFO:* Jeff Hoogerheide
* *VP:* Bruce Daily
VP: Jim Sutton

D-U-N-S 07-507-0078
ALL STAR ELECTRIC INC (LA)
1032 Bert St, La Place, LA 70068-5312
Tel (985) 618-1200 *Founded/Ownrshp* 1971, 2001
Sales 103.0MM[E] *EMP* 350
SIC 1731 General electrical contractor
CEO: Todd P Trosclair Sr
* *Pr:* Timothy S Blanchard
* *COO:* Jarred Bradley
* *VP:* Harold Boydston

ALL STAR FUEL
See GARRISON FRED OIL CO

D-U-N-S 01-894-4154
ALL STATE ASSOCIATION INC
11487 San Fernando Rd, San Fernando, CA 91340-3406
Tel (877) 425-2558 *Founded/Ownrshp* 2003
Sales 120.0MM *EMP* 250
SIC 8611 Trade associations
Pr: Alfred Megrabyan
* *CEO:* Steve Avetyan
* *COO:* Armen Karibyan

D-U-N-S 00-655-3036 IMP/EXP
ALL STATE FASTENER CORP
15460 E 12 Mile Rd, Roseville, MI 48066-1839
Tel (586) 773-5400 *Founded/Ownrshp* 1963
Sales 95.5MM[E] *EMP* 190
SIC 5072 Bolts
CEO: Anthony Giorgio
* *Pr:* A O Giorgio
* *CFO:* Pamela Meyer
* *Ex VP:* N Giorgio
IT Man: John Kennedy
IT Man: Bill Nelson
QI Cn Mgr: Ted Parker
Mktg Dir: Marty Monforton
Sales Asso: Mersija Mehmedovic
Sales Asso: Elizabeth Wilson

D-U-N-S 01-965-9408
ALL STATES ASPHALT INC
ALL STATES MATERIALS GROUP
325 Amherst Rd, Sunderland, MA 01375-9311
Tel (413) 665-7021 *Founded/Ownrshp* 1957
Sales 249.6MM[E] *EMP* 225
SIC 5032 Asphalt mixture; Paving mixtures
Pr: Richard J Miller
* *Treas:* Craig S Reed
* *VP:* Seth M Hankowski
Dir Bus: Seth Hankowski
* *Prin:* David M Hankowski
Off Mgr: Bethany Martin
Opers Mgr: Phil Foley
QI Cn Mgr: Steve Goulas

ALL STATES MATERIALS GROUP
See ALL STATES ASPHALT INC

ALL TUBE DIV
See MICROGROUP INC

D-U-N-S 80-102-7280
ALL WEB LEADS INC
7300 Rm Ste 100, Austin, TX 78730
Tel (512) 349-7900 *Founded/Ownrshp* 2015
Sales NA *EMP* 118[E]
SIC 6411 Insurance agents, brokers & service
Pr: Bill Daniel
Sr VP: Charlie Brock
Off Mgr: Heather Hanssens
Sftwr Eng: Kenneth Armond
Sftwr Eng: John Chandler
Mktg Mgr: Julie Pham

D-U-N-S 03-124-1064
ALL YEAR SERVICES LLC
270 Amherst Rd, Lima, OH 45806-9756
Tel (419) 296-1699 *Founded/Ownrshp* 2009
Sales 4.5MMM *EMP* 12
SIC 6531 Real estate agents & managers

D-U-N-S 04-248-4667 EXP
ALL-AMERICAN BOTTLING CORP
(*Suby of* BROWNE BOTTLING CO INC) ★
5345 Hickory Hill Rd # 102, Memphis, TN 38141-8227
Tel (901) 369-0483 *Founded/Ownrshp* 2002
Sales 53.0MM[E] *EMP* 1,100
SIC 2086 Carbonated beverages, nonalcoholic: bottled & canned
Pr: Stephen B Browne

D-U-N-S 15-157-9851
ALL-CITY MANAGEMENT SERVICES INC
10440 Pioneer Blvd Ste 5, Santa Fe Springs, CA 90670-8238
Tel (310) 202-8284 *Founded/Ownrshp* 1985
Sales 96.9MM[E] *EMP* 1,200
SIC 8748 Traffic consultant
CEO: Baron Farwell

ALL-MED SERVICES OF FLORIDA
See UNIVITA OF FLORIDA INC

D-U-N-S 00-390-0409
ALLADDIN GAMING LLC
3667 Las Vegas Blvd S, Las Vegas, NV 89109-4331
Tel (702) 785-5555 *Founded/Ownrshp* 2005, 2009
Sales 51.4MM[E] *EMP* 1,200
SIC 7011 Resort hotel; Casino hotel
Pt: Micheal V Mecca
* *Pt:* Donna Lehman
* *Pt:* Susan Madison

ALLAN COMPANY
See CEDARWOOD-YOUNG CO

D-U-N-S 14-742-0780
ALLAN INDUSTRIES INC
ALLAN INDUSTRIES OF NEW JERSEY
270 Us Highway 46 Ste E, Rockaway, NJ 07866-3850
Tel (973) 586-9400 *Founded/Ownrshp* 2008
Sales 287.7MM[E] *EMP* 1,600
SIC 1521 7349 1799 Repairing fire damage, single-family houses; Building cleaning service; Post-disaster renovations
Pr: Michael Carroll
* *Pr:* Paul Gracyalny
* *COO:* Kevin Ginsberg
COO: Robert Greenspan
* *Treas:* Eleanor Gracyalny
VP: John Reitzen
Dir Bus: Patricia Ray
IT Man: Matty Scalera
Opers Mgr: Vinnie Gortaire
Opers Mgr: Rafael A Gutierrez
Opers Mgr: Andres Pizarro

ALLAN INDUSTRIES OF NEW JERSEY
See ALLAN INDUSTRIES INC

D-U-N-S 03-100-1857
ALLAN MYERS INC
1805 Berks Rd, Worcester, PA 19490
Tel (610) 222-8800 *Founded/Ownrshp* 1998
Sales 745.6MM *EMP* 2,000
Accts Pricewaterhousecoppers Llp Ph
SIC 1629 1794 1611 1622 3281 5032 Land preparation construction; Waste water & sewage treatment plant construction; Excavation & grading, building construction; Surfacing & paving; Bridge, tunnel & elevated highway; Bridge construction; Stone, quarrying & processing of own stone products; Brick, stone & related material
CEO: A Ross Myers
* *Pr:* Dale R Wilson
* *CFO:* Denis P Moore
Sr VP: Bob Herbein
* *Sr VP:* Robert A Herbein
VP Bus Dev: Joseph Prego
MIS Dir: J E Morris
Snr PM: Bob Rube

D-U-N-S 06-739-8685
ALLAN MYERS LP
INDEPENDENCE CONSTRUCTION MTLS
(*Suby of* ALLAN MYERS INC) ★
1805 Berks Rd, Worcester, PA 19490
Tel (610) 584-3430 *Founded/Ownrshp* 1998
Sales 322.2MM[E] *EMP* 865
SIC 1629 1794 1611 1622 Land preparation construction; Waste water & sewage treatment plant construction; Excavation & grading, building construction; Surfacing & paving; Bridge construction
Genl Pt: A Ross Myers

Pr: Dale R Wilson
Treas: Denis P Moore
VP Admn: Richard Dungan
Netwrk Eng: Edward Kordzian
Snr PM: Daniel Rieger

D-U-N-S 00-379-4807
ALLAN MYERS MATERIALS INC
(*Suby of* ALLAN MYERS INC) ★
638 Lancaster Ave, Malvern, PA 19355-1898
Tel (610) 560-7900 *Founded/Ownrshp* 1953
Sales 484.3MM^E *EMP* 1,300
SIC 1422 Crushed & broken limestone; Whiting mining, crushed & broken-quarrying; Agricultural limestone, ground
CEO: Ross Myers
**Pr:* Dale R Wilson
**Treas:* Denis P Moore
**VP:* Allan B Myers
Sfty Dirs: Steve Sereditch

D-U-N-S 07-494-8811
ALLAN MYERS MD INC
(*Suby of* ALLAN MYERS INC) ★
2011 Bel Air Rd, Fallston, MD 21047-2721
Tel (410) 879-3055 *Founded/Ownrshp* 1939
Sales 372.5MM^E *EMP* 1,000
SIC 1611 1623 Highway & street construction; Water, sewer & utility lines
CEO: A Ross Myers
**Pr:* Dale R Wilson
**Treas:* Denis P Moore
**VP:* Richard W Dungan
**VP:* Joe Prego

D-U-N-S 04-399-0464
ALLAN MYERS VA INC
(*Suby of* ALLAN MYERS INC) ★
301 Cncourse Blvd Ste 300, Glen Allen, VA 23059
Tel (804) 290-8500 *Founded/Ownrshp* 2000
Sales 111.7MM^E *EMP* 300^E
SIC 1623 1611 1542 1794 Water main construction; Sewer line construction; General contractor, highway & street construction; Nonresidential construction; Excavation work
CEO: A Ross Myers
**Treas:* Denis P Moore
**VP:* Aaron T Myers
VP: Gary Tiller
**VP:* Dale R Wilson

D-U-N-S 00-281-3343 IMP
ALLAN S GOODMAN INC (CT)
180 Goodwin St, East Hartford, CT 06108-1151
Tel (860) 289-2731 *Founded/Ownrshp* 1933
Sales 125.7MM^E *EMP* 180
SIC 5181 5182 Beer & other fermented malt liquors; Wine; Liquor
Ch: Roger S Loeb
**Pr:* David Heller

D-U-N-S 06-449-4404 EXP
ALLAN VIGIL FORD LINCOLN INC
6790 Mount Zion Blvd, Morrow, GA 30260-3102
Tel (678) 364-3675 *Founded/Ownrshp* 1985
Sales 100.3MM^E *EMP* 250^E
SIC 5511 Automobiles, new & used
Pr: Allan Vigil
**Sec:* Melissa Pinson Jones
**VP:* Michael Vigil
Sales Asso: Paul Adams
Sales Asso: Adam Hardt
Sales Asso: Tommy Lancaster
Sales Asso: Andrew Spinks

D-U-N-S 05-861-0890
■ ALLBRITTON COMMUNICATIONS CO
(*Suby of* ALLBRITTON GROUP LLC) ★
1000 Wilson Blvd Ste 2700, Arlington, VA 22209-3921
Tel (703) 647-8700 *Founded/Ownrshp* 1974
Sales 226.3MM *EMP* 805
SIC 4833 7812 Television broadcasting stations; Motion picture & video production
Ch Bd: Robert L Allbritton
**V Ch:* Frederick J Ryan Jr
CFO: Stephen P Gibson
**Ex VP:* Barbara B Allbritton
Ex VP: Barbara B Allritton
Sr VP: Jerald N Fritz

D-U-N-S 96-666-0974
■ ALLBRITTON GROUP LLC
(*Suby of* PERPETUAL CAPITAL PARTNERS LLC) ★
1000 Wilson Blvd Ste 2700, Arlington, VA 22209-3921
Tel (703) 647-8700 *Founded/Ownrshp* 1996
Sales 226.3MM^E *EMP* 814^E
SIC 4833 Television broadcasting stations
Ch Bd: Joe L Allbritton

D-U-N-S 05-945-5423 IMP
ALLCHEM INDUSTRIES HOLDING CORP
6010 Nw 1st Pl, Gainesville, FL 32607-6018
Tel (352) 378-9696 *Founded/Ownrshp* 1998
Sales 208.8MM^E *EMP* 175
SIC 5169 Chemicals & allied products
CEO: Josh Feldstein
**Pr:* Alex Olcese
**CFO:* Rebecca Prince
**VP:* James Calais

D-U-N-S 13-760-8048
ALLCO LLC
6720 College St, Beaumont, TX 77707-3309
Tel (409) 860-4459 *Founded/Ownrshp* 2008
Sales 96.8MM^E *EMP* 200
SIC 1623 1542 1541 Underground utilities contractor; Commercial & office building, new construction; Commercial & office buildings, renovation & repair; Industrial buildings, new construction; Renovation, remodeling & repairs: industrial buildings
Pr: Tom Harrison
Ex VP: Eugene R Allen
VP: Dale Harrison
Mktg Dir: Eduardo Menchaca

D-U-N-S 12-309-2749
ALLCONNECT INC
(*Suby of* ALL CONNECT) ★
980 Hammond Dr Ste 1000, Atlanta, GA 30328-8187
Tel (404) 260-2200 *Founded/Ownrshp* 2000
Sales 195.0MM^E *EMP* 700^E
SIC 4812 Cellular telephone services
CEO: Sam Howe
Pt: Christine Ellis
Pr: Sean Barry
COO: Neil J Singer
CFO: Ed Milman
CFO: Michael Picchi
Sr Cor Off: Jim Quigley
Ofcr: Glenn Goad
Ofcr: Liz Pastor
Ex VP: Scott Klinger
Ex VP: Vishy Natarajan
Ex VP: Kim Shumway
VP: Rob Caiello
VP: Johnson Jim
VP: Robert Kocerha
VP: Rich Moore
VP: Lynn Moss
VP: David Palinski
VP: Jim Rasnick
Assoc Dir: Victor Moore

D-U-N-S 07-214-9826
ALLE-KISKI MEDICAL CENTER (PA)
1301 Carlisle St, Natrona Heights, PA 15065-1152
Tel (724) 224-5100 *Founded/Ownrshp* 1908, 1983
Sales 58.4MM *EMP* 1,353
SIC 8062 Hospital, AMA approved residency
CEO: Joseph Calig
**Pr:* Cindy Schamp
Dir OR: Andrea Brown
Pharmcst: Diane Bowser
Pharmcst: Kielie Ciuchta
Pharmcst: Jane Haduch

D-U-N-S 09-631-7607
■ ALLEGAN METROPOLITAN TITLE AGENCY
(*Suby of* FIRST AMERICAN TITLE INSURANCE CO) ★
400 Water St Ste 100, Rochester, MI 48307-2089
Tel (248) 656-8686 *Founded/Ownrshp* 1979, 2003
Sales NA *EMP* 700
SIC 6361 Title insurance
CEO: Kenneth J Lingenfelter
**CFO:* Robin P Gilroy
**Sr VP:* Terry Brown
Sr VP: Carol Jones
**VP:* Dennis Lintemuth
**VP:* Tamara Yeagle

D-U-N-S 95-689-7730
ALLEGANY COUNTY PUBLIC SCHOOLS
ACPS
108 Washington St, Cumberland, MD 21502-2931
Tel (301) 759-2000 *Founded/Ownrshp* 1890
Sales 45.1MM^E *EMP* 1,300
SIC 8211 Public elementary & secondary schools
Dir Sec: Ben T Brauer
Teacher Pr: Jeffrey Blank

D-U-N-S 03-539-8442
■ ALLEGHANY CAPITAL CORP
(*Suby of* ALLEGHANY CORP) ★
7 Times Square Tower, New York, NY 10036
Tel (212) 752-1356 *Founded/Ownrshp* 2014
Sales 130.1MM^E *EMP* 1,577^E
SIC 3944 Electronic games & toys
Pr: David Van Geyzel

D-U-N-S 00-697-9652
▲ ALLEGHANY CORP
7 Times Sq Tower, New York, NY 10036
Tel (212) 752-1356 *Founded/Ownrshp* 1929
Sales NA *EMP* 3,135
Tkr Sym Y *Exch* NYS
SIC 6331 6411 6531 Fire, marine & casualty insurance; Property & casualty insurance agent; Real estate managers
Pr: Weston M Hicks
Ch Bd: Jefferson W Kirby
CFO: John L Sennott Jr
Treas: Roger B Gorham
Ex VP: Joseph P Brandon
Sr VP: Christopher K Dalrymple
VP: John Carr
Exec: Jerry Borrelli

D-U-N-S 13-369-0391
■ ALLEGHANY INSURANCE HOLDINGS LLC
(*Suby of* ALLEGHANY CORP) ★
7 Times Sq Tower Fl 17, New York, NY 10152
Tel (212) 752-1356 *Founded/Ownrshp* 1999
Sales NA *EMP* 480
SIC 6331 Fire, marine & casualty insurance

D-U-N-S 07-497-3918
ALLEGHENY COLLEGE (PA)
520 N Main St, Meadville, PA 16335-3902
Tel (814) 332-3100 *Founded/Ownrshp* 1815
Sales 123.3MM *EMP* 479
Accts Schneider Downs & Co Inc Pitt
SIC 8221 College, except junior
Pr: James H Mullen Jr
**CFO:* David McInally
Ofcr: Gerard Bey
Ofcr: Caryl Jewell
Ofcr: Philip Johnson
VP: Rachael Gottlieb
VP: Sue Stuebner
Assoc Dir: James Fitch
Dir Soc: Edward Luben
Mng Ofcr: Lawrence T Potter Jr
Off Mgr: Debra Carman

D-U-N-S 06-873-8426
ALLEGHENY COUNTY SANITARY AUTHORITY
ALCOSAN
3300 Preble Ave, Pittsburgh, PA 15233-1092
Tel (412) 732-8020 *Founded/Ownrshp* 1946
Sales 126.6MM *EMP* 350
Accts Maher Duessel Pittsburg Penn
SIC 4952 Sewerage systems
Ch: Harry A Readshaw
**Treas:* Jack Shea
**Treas:* John K Weinstein
Ofcr: Bernard Spada
Ofcr: Suzanne Thomas
Dir Lab: Betty Kindle
**Prin:* Sylvia C Wilson
**Ex Dir:* Arletta Scott Williams
Genl Mgr: Karen McCarthy
IT Man: Patricia Pritchett
MIS Mgr: Tom Johnston

D-U-N-S 01-058-3789
ALLEGHENY ELECTRIC COOP INC
212 Locust St Ste 500, Harrisburg, PA 17101-1510
Tel (717) 233-5704 *Founded/Ownrshp* 1940
Sales 155.2MM *EMP* 55
SIC 4911 8741 Distribution, electric power; Management services
Pr: Frank M Betley
**Ch:* Alston Teeter
**Treas:* Kathryn Coopers-Wint
**V Ch Bd:* Lowell Friedline
Bd of Dir: Larry S Adams

D-U-N-S 00-697-9660 IMP
■ ALLEGHENY ENERGY INC (MD)
(*Suby of* FIRSTENERGY CORP) ★
800 Cabin Hill Dr, Greensburg, PA 15601-1650
Tel (724) 837-3000 *Founded/Ownrshp* 1925, 2011
Sales 3.3MMM^E *EMP* 4,383
SIC 4911 Generation, electric power; Transmission, electric power; Distribution, electric power
Pr: Paul J Evanson
**COO:* Curtis H Davis
**CFO:* Kirk R Oliver
**VP:* David M Feinberg
VP: Thomas Kloc
VP: David W McDonald
**VP:* William F Wahl III
Genl Mgr: Ralph Cannon
Genl Mgr: Michael B Delmar
CIO: Thomas Cardner
Opers Mgr: Dennis Napier

D-U-N-S 00-172-1273
■ ALLEGHENY ENERGY SERVICE CORP (MD)
FIRSTENERGY
(*Suby of* ALLEGHENY ENERGY INC) ★
800 Cabin Hill Dr, Greensburg, PA 15601-1650
Tel (724) 837-3000 *Founded/Ownrshp* 1963, 2006
Sales 2.3MMM^E *EMP* 4,383
SIC 4911 Electric services
Ch Bd: Paul J Evanson
**CEO:* Anthony J Alexander
**COO:* Joseph Richardson
**CFO:* Philip L Goulding
**Treas:* Suzanne C Lewis
Treas: Steven R Staub
Bd of Dir: William Wahl
**Ex VP:* Mark T Clark
VP: J M Adams
VP: Richard C Arthur
VP: David C Cannon Jr
VP: Mike Dandria
VP: Rodney L Dickens
VP: George J Farah
VP: David E Flitman
VP: Thomas R Gardner
VP: Eric S Gleason
VP: Robert L Henry
VP: Peter Kotsenas
VP: David W McDonald
VP: Daniel C McIntire

D-U-N-S 10-643-8018 IMP
■ ALLEGHENY ENERGY SUPPLY CO LLC
(*Suby of* ALLEGHENY ENERGY INC) ★
800 Cabin Hill Dr, Greensburg, PA 15601-1650
Tel (724) 837-3000 *Founded/Ownrshp* 1999
Sales 113.2MM^E *EMP* 200
SIC 4911 Generation, electric power; ;
Pr: Michael P Morrell
**VP:* David C Benson
VP: James R Haney
VP: Robert L Henry
VP: Loyd Warnock

D-U-N-S 06-501-9700
ALLEGHENY FOUNDATION
301 Grant St Ste 1, Pittsburgh, PA 15219-1424
Tel (412) 392-2900 *Founded/Ownrshp* 2001
Sales 373.6MM *EMP* 3
SIC 8641 Civic social & fraternal associations
Prin: Clyde Baker

D-U-N-S 09-421-4947
ALLEGHENY GENERAL HOSPITAL INC
(*Suby of* ALLEGHENY HEALTH NETWORK) ★
320 E North Ave, Pittsburgh, PA 15212-4772
Tel (412) 359-3131 *Founded/Ownrshp* 1882
Sales 700.5MM *EMP* 5,064
SIC 8062 8051 Hospital, professional nursing school; Skilled nursing care facilities
Pr: Gregory Burfitt
Dir Recs: Linda Bridgens
Pr: Diane Nugyen
Treas: Dennis Trumble
Ofcr: Bart Metzger
VP: Karl Borgman
VP: Rick Fries
VP: Matthew Peterson
VP: John Raves
VP: Sheran Sullivan
Assoc Dir: Jennifer Lewis
Dir Rx: Edward C Seidl

D-U-N-S 03-823-5150
ALLEGHENY HEALTH NETWORK
(*Suby of* AHN - ALLEGHENY HEALTH NETWORK) ★
30 Isabella St Ste 320, Pittsburgh, PA 15212-5862
Tel (412) 330-2400 *Founded/Ownrshp* 2011
Sales 1.1MMM^E *EMP* 5,079^E
SIC 8099 Blood related health services
Prin: Cynthia Hundorfean
IT Man: Brian Bittner
Snr Mgr: Jason Maselli

D-U-N-S 03-006-4208
ALLEGHENY INTERMEDIATE UNIT 3 FOUNDATION
AIU3
475 E Waterfront Dr, Homestead, PA 15120-1144
Tel (412) 394-5700 *Founded/Ownrshp* 1971
Sales 64.9MM^E *EMP* 1,300
Accts Maher Duessel Pittsburgh Pen
SIC 8211 Public special education school; Public vocational/technical school
Ex Dir: Donna Durno
**CFO:* Stragier Barone
Bd of Dir: Glenn Beigay
Ex Dir: Donald Detemple
Dir IT: Sean McDonough
IT Man: Leslie McConnell
Web Dev: Michelle Crown
Opers Mgr: Patrice Allison
Psych: Tabitha Brown
Psych: Mary Cunningham
Psych: Marissa Deleel

D-U-N-S 02-635-2310 EXP
■ ALLEGHENY LUDLUM LLC (PA)
ATI ALLEGHENY LUDLUM
(*Suby of* ATI OPERATING HOLDINGS LLC) ★
1000 Six Ppg Pl, Pittsburgh, PA 15222
Tel (412) 394-2800 *Founded/Ownrshp* 1938, 1996
Sales 2.5MMM^E *EMP* 10,900
SIC 3312 Stainless steel; Sheet or strip, steel, cold-rolled: own hot-rolled
Pr: Richard J Harshman
Pr: Robert Arnold
**Treas:* Rose Marie Manley
Sr VP: Joe Yanik
VP: Julie Beideman
**VP:* Danny L Greenfield
**VP:* Dale G Reid
**VP:* Jeff Thompson
Sls Mgr: Bill Milon

D-U-N-S 94-926-2737 IMP/EXP
▲ ALLEGHENY TECHNOLOGIES INC
ATI
1000 Six Ppg Pl, Pittsburgh, PA 15222
Tel (412) 394-2800 *Founded/Ownrshp* 1996
Sales 3.7MMM *EMP* 9,200
Tkr Sym ATI *Exch* NYS
SIC 3312 3339 3545 Stainless steel; Primary nonferrous metals; Machine tool accessories
Ch Bd: Richard J Harshman
CFO: Patrick J Decourcy
Chf Cred: Elliot S Davis
Ofcr: Elizabeth C Powers
Ex VP: Hunter R Dalton
Ex VP: John D Sims
Ex VP: Robert S Wetherbee
VP: John Hansen
VP: Melissa Martinez
VP: Karl D Schwartz
VP: Jon D Walton
Board of Directors: John D Turner, Carolyn Corvi, Diane C Creel, James C Diggs, J Brett Harvey, Barbara S Jeremiah, David J Morehouse, John R Pipski, James E Rohr, Louis J Thomas

D-U-N-S 07-496-1020
ALLEGHENY VALLEY SCHOOL (PA)
1996 Ewings Mill Rd, Coraopolis, PA 15108-3380
Tel (412) 299-7777 *Founded/Ownrshp* 1960, 1972
Sales 53.2MM^E *EMP* 2,000
SIC 8361

D-U-N-S 06-321-6592 EXP
ALLEGHENY WOOD PRODUCTS INC
AWP
240 Airport Rd, Petersburg, WV 26847-8921
Tel (304) 257-1082 *Founded/Ownrshp* 1972
Sales 130.9MM^E *EMP* 566
SIC 2421 Sawmills & planing mills, general; Kiln drying of lumber
Ch Bd: John Crites
**Pr:* John W Crites II
**CFO:* Larry Rodgers
Ex VP: Brenda Borror
VP: Kelly Riddle
Opers Mgr: Tom Phares
Plnt Mgr: Josh Chandler
Plnt Mgr: Mark Lauer
VP Sls: Dean Alanko
Sls Dir: Bill Haver
Sls Mgr: K C Wallace

D-U-N-S 01-944-0128
▲ ALLEGIANCE BANCSHARES INC
8847 W Sam Houston Pkwy N, Houston, TX 77040-5369
Tel (281) 894-3200 *Founded/Ownrshp* 2007
Sales NA *EMP* 310
Tkr Sym ABTX *Exch* NGM
SIC 6022 State commercial banks
Ch Bd: George Martinez
**Pr:* Steven F Retzloff
Board of Directors: John B Beckworth, Frances H Jeter, David B Moulton, William S Nichols III, Thomas A Reiser, Raimundo Riojas E, Fred S Robertson, Ramon A Vitulli III

D-U-N-S 10-236-7489
■ ALLEGIANCE BENEFIT PLAN MANAGEMENT INC
CBMI
(*Suby of* CIGNA) ★
2806 S Grfield St Ste 101, Missoula, MT 59801
Tel (406) 523-3122 *Founded/Ownrshp* 2008
Sales NA *EMP* 200^E
SIC 6324 Hospital & medical service plans
Pr: Dirk C Visser
**CFO:* Rich Daniels
DP Dir: Gary Sanders
Dir IT: Robert Ball
VP Mktg: Aaron Bay

D-U-N-S 16-550-6077
ALLEGIANCE HEALTH MANAGEMENT INC
504 Texas St Ste 200, Shreveport, LA 71101-3526
Tel (318) 226-8202 Founded/Ownrshp 2002
Sales 127.1MM[E] EMP 2,000
SIC 8741 Hospital management
Pr: Rock Bordelon
*CFO: Jim Turgeon
VP: Jacob Candler
VP: Rob Lindsey Jr
VP: Scott Prouty
Off Mgr: Lesly Boyet

D-U-N-S 07-530-6332
■ ALLEGIANCE INSURANCE CO
(Suby of HORACE MANN SERVICE CORP) ★
1 Horace Mann Plz, Springfield, IL 62715-0001
Tel (217) 789-2500 Founded/Ownrshp 1994
Sales NA EMP 1[E]
SIC 6331 Fire, marine & casualty insurance
Pr: Paul Kardos
CFO: Larry K Becer
*CFO: Larry Keith Becker
*VP: Ann Mary Caparros
*VP: Robert Harding Lee

D-U-N-S 79-571-9793
ALLEGIANCE SECURITY GROUP LLC
(Suby of UNIVERSAL PROTECTION SERVICE LP) ★
2900 Arendell St Ste 18, Morehead City, NC 28557-3393
Tel (252) 247-1138 Founded/Ownrshp 2013
Sales 38.9MM[E] EMP 3,500[E]
SIC 7381 Guard services

D-U-N-S 01-921-6626
■ ALLEGIANT AIR LLC (NV)
(Suby of ALLEGIANT TRAVEL CO) ★
1201 N Town Center Dr # 110, Las Vegas, NV 89144-6305
Tel (702) 505-8888 Founded/Ownrshp 1997, 2001
Sales 91.1MM[E] EMP 2,502[E]
SIC 4512 Air transportation, scheduled
Sr VP: Scott Allard
VP: Tom Doxey
Exec: Linda Sunbury
Software D: Eric Kumik
Sftwr Eng: Andrey Voev
Sfty Dirs: Eric Gust
Pr Mgr: Kristine Cooper
Genl Couns: Laura Meagher

D-U-N-S 78-657-6293
▲ ALLEGIANT TRAVEL CO
1201 N Town Center Dr, Las Vegas, NV 89144-6307
Tel (702) 851-7300 Founded/Ownrshp 1997
Sales 1.2MMM EMP 2,846[E]
Tkr Sym ALGT Exch NGS
SIC 4512 4724 Air transportation, scheduled; Air passenger carrier, scheduled; Travel agencies
Ch Bd: Maurice J Gallagher Jr
Pr: John Redmond
COO: Jude I Bricker
CFO: Scott Sheldon
Ofcr: Alex Kopp
Sr VP: Scott M Allard
VP: Gregory C Anderson
VP: Eric Gust
Exec: Ntcia Coark
Board of Directors: Montie Brewer, Gary Ellmer, Linda A Marvin, Charles Pollard

D-U-N-S 07-921-8390
ALLEGION S&S US HOLDING CO INC
(Suby of ALLEGION PUBLIC LIMITED COMPANY)
11819 N Pennsylvania St, Carmel, IN 46032-4555
Tel (317) 810-3700 Founded/Ownrshp 2013
Sales 1.0MMM[E] EMP 3,000
SIC 3429 Locks or lock sets
CEO: David D Petratis
Pr: Anshu Mehrotra
CFO: Patrick Shannon
VP: Linda Batchelor
VP: Paul Kirkeiner
VP: Michael Wagnes
Prgrm Mgr: Kim Fill
Prgrm Mgr: Josh McCallin
Prgrm Mgr: Linda Reed
Prgrm Mgr: Helen West
CIO: Tracy Kemp

D-U-N-S 83-249-9110
ALLEGIS GLOBAL SOLUTIONS INC
ALLEGIS GROUP
(Suby of ALLEGIS GROUP INC) ★
7312 Parkway Dr, Hanover, MD 21076-1158
Tel (410) 579-3000 Founded/Ownrshp 2001
Sales 505.4MM[E] EMP 12,000[E]
SIC 7361 Employment agencies
CEO: Michael W Salandra
*Pr: Chris Hartman
Ex Dir: Maria Boyse
Ex Dir: Anne Nogami
Prgrm Mgr: Mark Cline
Off Mgr: Paige Matthews
Software D: Gail Suprik
Software D: Yan Xu
Opers Mgr: Philip Heyman
Snr Mgr: Robert Greer

ALLEGIS GROUP
See ALLEGIS GLOBAL SOLUTIONS INC

D-U-N-S 12-176-8035
ALLEGIS GROUP INC
7301 Parkway Dr, Hanover, MD 21076-1159
Tel (410) 579-3000 Founded/Ownrshp 1991
Sales 10.8MMM EMP 85,000
Accts Pricewaterhousecoopers Llp Ba
SIC 7361 Employment agencies; Executive placement
Ch: James C Davis
Sr Pt: Sean Linkson
Sr Pt: John Powell
CFO: Paul J Bowie
Sr VP: Gil Smith
VP: Michael Bison
VP: Mark Cooper
VP: Chris Hartman
VP: Rick Haviland
VP: John Markey
Ex Dir: Maria Boyse
Board of Directors: John T Carey, Michael W Salandra

D-U-N-S 62-142-0678 IMP/EXP
ALLEGRO MICROSYSTEMS LLC
(Suby of SANKEN ELECTRIC CO., LTD.)
115 Ne Cutoff, Worcester, MA 01606-1224
Tel (508) 853-5000 Founded/Ownrshp 1990
Sales 516.0MM[E] EMP 3,500
SIC 3674 Semiconductors & related devices
CEO: Dennis H Fitzgerald
V Ch: Jose Terminel
*Pr: Ravi Vig
*CFO: Mark A Feragne
*Treas: Diane Macaluso
*Ex VP: Yoshihiro Suzuki
VP: Lyndon Ambruson
VP: Vimal Gupta
*VP: Andre G Labrecque
VP: Vijay Mangtani
*VP: Steven Miles
Board of Directors: Richard R Lury, John H Mackinnon

D-U-N-S 96-976-4542
ALLEN BIOTECH LLC
ALLEN HARIM
(Suby of ALLEN HARIM FOODS LLC) ★
126 N Shipley St, Seaford, DE 19973-3100
Tel (302) 629-9136 Founded/Ownrshp 2011
Sales 219.7MM[E] EMP 1,000
SIC 2015 Poultry, processed
CEO: Joseph Moran
CFO: Brian G Hildreth
VP: Warren R Allen Jr

D-U-N-S 00-607-6863 IMP
ALLEN EDMONDS CORP (WI)
(Suby of GHJ&M) ★
201 E Seven Hills Rd, Port Washington, WI 53074-2512
Tel (262) 235-6000 Founded/Ownrshp 1922
Sales 199.9MM[E] EMP 616[E]
SIC 3143 5661 Men's footwear, except athletic; Men's shoes
CEO: Paul D Grangaard
CFO: Jay Schauer
VP: David Barber
Exec: Elizabeth Gregoire
DP Dir: Nancy Wegner
Plnt Mgr: Mark Birmingham
Mktg Dir: Kim Kuczynski
Sls Mgr: MO RAD
Board of Directors: John Becker, Andrew Fleckenstein, Donald J Schuenke, Richard Van Deuren, Bob Buchanan Ft Albert Di

ALLEN HARIM
See ALLEN BIOTECH LLC

D-U-N-S 07-850-8812
ALLEN HARIM FOODS LLC
(Suby of HARIM USA LTD) ★
126 N Shipley St, Seaford, DE 19973-3100
Tel (302) 629-9136 Founded/Ownrshp 2011
Sales 219.7MM[E] EMP 1,600
SIC 0251 Broiler, fryer & roaster chickens
CEO: Joe Moran
CFO: Brian Hildreth
Sls&Mrk Ex: Shelley Workman

ALLEN HEALTH CARE SERVICES
See HEALTH ACQUISITION CORP

D-U-N-S 10-394-8451
ALLEN HEALTH SYSTEMS INC
(Suby of ALLEN HOSPITAL) ★
1825 Logan Ave, Waterloo, IA 50703-1916
Tel (319) 235-3941 Founded/Ownrshp 1983
Sales 636.0M EMP 1,750[E]
SIC 8741 Hospital management; Nursing & personal care facility management
Pr: Pam Delagardelle

ALLEN HOSPITAL
See ALLEN MEMORIAL HOSPITAL CORP

D-U-N-S 07-984-0559
ALLEN INDEPENDENT SCHOOL DISTRICT
ALLEN ISD
612 E Bethany Dr, Allen, TX 75002-4050
Tel (972) 727-0511 Founded/Ownrshp 1883
Sales 211.8MM EMP 2,500
Accts Evans Pingleton And Howard P
SIC 8211 Public elementary school; Public junior high school; Public senior high school
Pr: Louise Master
Dir Vol: Cheryll Tallent
*VP: Susan Olinger
Dir Sec: Ernie Rodriguez
Pr Dir: Margaret Goodman
Psych: Julie Northam

D-U-N-S 07-972-9593
ALLEN INSTITUTE FOR BRAIN SCIENCE
1441 N 34th St, Seattle, WA 98103-8904
Tel (206) 548-7000 Founded/Ownrshp 2013
Sales 131.2MM EMP 58[E]
Accts Peterson Sullivan Llp Cpa S S
SIC 8733 Noncommercial research organizations

ALLEN ISD
See ALLEN INDEPENDENT SCHOOL DISTRICT

D-U-N-S 80-179-8810
ALLEN LUND CO INC
4529 Angeles Crest Hwy, La Canada Flintridge, CA 91011-3247
Tel (818) 790-8412 Founded/Ownrshp 1990
Sales 476.6MM[E] EMP 310
SIC 4731 Truck transportation brokers
Pr: David Allen Lund
*CFO: Steve Doerfler
*VP: David F Lund
*VP: Edward V Lund
*VP: Ken Lund
*VP: Theresa Walker

D-U-N-S 08-173-6738
ALLEN LUND CO LLC
(Suby of ALLEN LUND CO INC) ★
4529 Angeles Crest Hwy # 300, La Canada Flintridge, CA 91011-3247
Tel (818) 790-1110 Founded/Ownrshp 1976
Sales 457.4MM EMP 310
SIC 4731 Freight transportation arrangement; Truck transportation brokers
*CFO: Steve Doerfler
*VP: David F Lund
VP: Ed Lund
*VP: Edward V Lund
*VP: Kathleen M Lund
VP: Kenny Lund
VP Bus Dev: Doug Clark
Genl Mgr: Jeremy McGovern
Dir IT: Chetan Tandon
Netwrk Mgr: Craig Borzelliere
Opers Mgr: Leonora Winegar

D-U-N-S 07-276-0465
ALLEN MEMORIAL HOSPITAL CORP
ALLEN HOSPITAL
1825 Logan Ave, Waterloo, IA 50703-1999
Tel (319) 235-3941 Founded/Ownrshp 1862
Sales 221.0MM EMP 1,800[E]
SIC 8062 Hospital, affiliated with AMA residency
Pr: Pamela K Delagardelle
COO: Steve Slessor
*CFO: Renee Rasmussen
*Treas: Betty Steege
*Prin: Richard A Seidler
Genl Mgr: Mary Kunkle
Off Mgr: Deb Borwig
IT Man: Linnea Leto
IT Man: Kristina Wagner
Sfty Mgr: Steven Cusher
Plas Surg: Michael F Emery
Board of Directors: Carol Rankin

ALLEN OIL
See JACK A ALLEN INC

ALLEN PRODUCTS COMPANY
See NATIONAL WINE & SPIRITS INC

ALLEN SAMUELS AUTO GROUP
See ASE MOTORS HOLDING CORP

D-U-N-S 07-452-6617
ALLEN TATE CO INC
ALLEN TATE REALTORS
6700 Fairview Rd, Charlotte, NC 28210-3324
Tel (704) 365-6910 Founded/Ownrshp 1957
Sales NA EMP 1,500
SIC 6411 Insurance agents, brokers & service
Ch Bd: H Allen Tate Jr
*Pr: Patrick C Riley
*CFO: Eric Heintschel
VP: Phyllis York Brookshire
VP: Lynda Stiles
Off Admin: Veige Beeson
CIO: Sergio Gomez
Snr Mgr: Sandra Paul
Snr Mgr: Robert Smith

ALLEN TATE REALTORS
See ALLEN TATE CO INC

ALLENBERG COTTON CO.
See LOUIS DREYFUS CO COTTON LLC

ALLENMORE HOSPITAL
See MULTICARE HEALTH SYSTEM

D-U-N-S 04-579-0383 IMP/EXP
ALLENTOWN INC
165 Route 526, Allentown, NJ 08501-2017
Tel (609) 259-7951 Founded/Ownrshp 1968
Sales 95.2MM[E] EMP 340
SIC 3444 3496 5162 Sheet metalwork; Cages, wire; Plastics products
CEO: Michael A Coiro Sr
*Pr: John M Coiro
Dir IT: Steve Miller
Dir IT: Mike Pylypiak
Web Dev: Frank Bartell
VP Opers: Michele Hladick
Mktg Dir: Kevin Johnson
Mktg Mgr: Joe Romano
Sls Mgr: Scott Hoy
Sales Asso: Patrick Connahan
Sales Asso: Kelly Ham

D-U-N-S 14-479-6497 IMP
ALLERGAN INC
(Suby of ALLERGAN PUBLIC LIMITED COMPANY)
400 Interpace Pkwy Bldg D, Parsippany, NJ 07054-1120
Tel (862) 261-7000 Founded/Ownrshp 2015
Sales 4.7MMM[E] EMP 10,500
SIC 2834 3841 Solutions, pharmaceutical; Dermatologicals; Drugs acting on the central nervous system & sense organs; Proprietary drug products; Surgical & medical instruments
Ch Bd: A Robert D Bailey
Assoc Dir: Michael Ryan

ALLERGAN PHARMACY
See WATSON LABORATORIES INC

D-U-N-S 62-100-1098
ALLERGAN SALES LLC
(Suby of ALLERGAN INC) ★
2525 Dupont Dr 14th, Irvine, CA 92612-1599
Tel (714) 246-4500 Founded/Ownrshp 2002
Sales 720.3MM[E] EMP 900
SIC 5122 Pharmaceuticals
Ch Bd: David E I Pyott
*Ex VP: Raymond H Diradoorian
*Ex VP: Scott D Sherman
*Ex VP: Scott M Whitcup
*VP: Julian S Gangolli
VP: Laura Hayman
VP: Jane LI

D-U-N-S 05-300-0621
ALLERGAN SPECIALTY THERAPEUTICS INC
(Suby of ALLERGAN INC) ★
2525 Dupont Dr, Irvine, CA 92612-1599
Tel (714) 264-4500 Founded/Ownrshp 1951
Sales 117.7MM[E] EMP 1,500
SIC 2834 Pharmaceutical preparations
Pr: David Pyott
Sr VP: Sue-Jean Lin
VP: Robert Gaskin
VP: Steve Guida
VP: John Hartmann
VP: John N Hendrick
VP: Steward Morgan
VP: Lily Tu
VP: J Wielenga
IT Man: Louise D'Alessandro
Info Man: Eugene Hayden

D-U-N-S 60-321-4581
ALLERGAN USA INC
(Suby of ALLERGAN INC) ★
2525 Dupont Dr, Irvine, CA 92612-1599
Tel (714) 246-4500 Founded/Ownrshp 2007
Sales 228.8MM[E] EMP 2,000
SIC 2834 Druggists' preparations (pharmaceuticals)
Pr: F Michael Ball
CEO: David E I Pyott
CFO: Jeffrey L Edwards
Treas: James M Hindman
Sr VP: T J Hindman
VP: Lori Alarimo
VP: James Barlow
VP: Letty Burks
VP: Julian S Gangolli
VP: Robert E Grant
VP: Douglas S Ingram
VP: David Lawrence
VP: Matthew J Maletta
VP: Fidela Moreno
VP: Terilea J Wielenga

D-U-N-S 61-034-8125
ALLERGY CENTERS OF AMERICA LLC
2430 Mall Dr Ste 210, North Charleston, SC 29406-6549
Tel (843) 747-4294 Founded/Ownrshp 2005
Sales 36.5MM[E] EMP 5,070
SIC 8011 8071 Ears, nose & throat specialist: physician/surgeon; Medical laboratories

D-U-N-S 00-696-1296 IMP/EXP
▲ ALLETE INC
30 W Superior St, Duluth, MN 55802-2191
Tel (218) 279-5000 Founded/Ownrshp 1906
Sales 1.4MMM EMP 1,945[E]
Tkr Sym ALE Exch NYS
SIC 4931 4924 4941 1231 6552 Electric & other services combined; Natural gas distribution; Water supply; Anthracite mining; Subdividers & developers; Land subdividers & developers, commercial; Land subdividers & developers, residential
Ch Bd: Alan R Hodnik
CFO: Steven Q Devinck
Treas: Patrick L Cutshall
Sr VP: Robert J Adams
Sr VP: Deborah A Amberg
Sr VP: David J McMillan
Exec: Patrick Mullen
Dir IT: Steve Beck
IT Man: Paul Bergson
IT Man: Dennis Claflin
Web Dev: Nick Flint
Board of Directors: Kathryn W Dindo, Sidney W Emery Jr, George G Goldfarb, James S Haines Jr, James J Hoolihan, Madeleine W Ludlow, Douglas C Neve, Leonard C Rodman

D-U-N-S 03-482-0779
ALLEY-CASSETTY COMPANIES INC
2 Oldham St, Nashville, TN 37213-1107
Tel (615) 244-7077 Founded/Ownrshp 1964
Sales 99.7MM[E] EMP 180
Accts Puryear Hamilton Hauman And Wo
SIC 5032 5052 Masons' materials; Coal
CEO: Fred Cassetty
*Pr: Sam Strang
Opers Mgr: Bobby Brockman
Sales Asso: David Bonvino

D-U-N-S 61-271-0827
ALLEYTON RESOURCE CO LLC
ALCOMAT
(Suby of SUMMIT MATERIALS LLC) ★
755 Fm 762, Columbus, TX 78934
Tel (281) 238-1010 Founded/Ownrshp 2014
Sales 157.8MM[E] EMP 460[E]
SIC 5251 Builders' hardware
Pr: Bryan Kalbfleisch
VP: Glen Sheppard

D-U-N-S 60-939-9899
ALLFLEX USA INC
2805 E 14th St, Dallas, TX 75261
Tel (972) 456-3686 Founded/Ownrshp 1995
Sales 105.3MM[E] EMP 329
SIC 6719 Personal holding companies, except banks
Pr: Brian Bolton
*Sr VP: Glenn Fischer
Sls Mgr: Dave Lehman

D-U-N-S 08-021-4198
ALLIANCE AG AND GRAIN LLC (KS)
313 N Main, Spearville, KS 67876
Tel (620) 385-2898 Founded/Ownrshp 2015
Sales 99.9MM[E] EMP 160
SIC 0723 Crop preparation services for market
CEO: Stan Stark
CFO: Jason Murray

D-U-N-S 07-985-9942
ALLIANCE AIRCRAFT LTD
4906 Penn Ave, Reading, PA 19608-8609
Tel (888) 233-1503 Founded/Ownrshp 2000
Sales 2.0MMM EMP 10[E]
SIC 3721 Aircraft
CFO: Earl J Robinson

*COO: Joe Cox
*CFO: Scott Gaul

ALLIANCE ASSOCIATES
See ALLIANCE FOODS INC

D-U-N-S 05-825-5782 IMP
ALLIANCE BEVERAGE DISTRIBUTING CO LLC
BREAKTHRU BEVERAGE ARIZONA
(Suby of BREAKTHRU BEVERAGE GROUP LLC) ★
1115 N 47th Ave, Phoenix, AZ 85043-1801
Tel (602) 760-5500 Founded/Ownrshp 2016
Sales 400.0MM EMP 550
SIC 5182 5181 Liquor; Wine; Beer & other fermented malt liquors
Ex VP: Gary Lederer
*Ex VP: Bill Barrett
*Ex VP: John Ellington
*Ex VP: Joe Malina
*Ex VP: Chris Todd
*Ex VP: Jon Willis
*Ex VP: Steve Zawisa
VP: Kevin Smith
VP: Michael Vetrano
Div Mgr: Kari Sumney
Opers Mgr: Brett Underwood

D-U-N-S 07-881-8117
ALLIANCE BEVERAGE DISTRIBUTING LLC
4490 60th St Se, Grand Rapids, MI 49512-9631
Tel (616) 241-5022 Founded/Ownrshp 2012
Sales 150.0MM EMP 450
SIC 5181 Beer & ale
Exec: Mike Konwinski

ALLIANCE CAPITAL MARKETS
See ALLIANCE FUNDING GROUP

D-U-N-S 11-813-7108
ALLIANCE CITIZENS HEALTH ASSOCIATION
200 E State St, Alliance, OH 44601-4936
Tel (330) 596-6000 Founded/Ownrshp 1921
Sales 100.5MM EMP 1,200
SIC 8062 General medical & surgical hospitals
CEO: Stan Jonas
VP: Roger Palutsis

ALLIANCE CNSLTING GLOBL HLDNGS
See ALLIANCE GLOBAL SERVICES INC

D-U-N-S 06-454-5726 EXP
■ **ALLIANCE COAL LLC**
(Suby of ALLIANCE RESOURCE OPERATING PARTNERS LP) ★
1717 S Boulder Ave # 400, Tulsa, OK 74119-4833
Tel (918) 295-7600 Founded/Ownrshp 1999
Sales 1.1MMM^E EMP 1,400
SIC 1221 1222 Bituminous coal surface mining; Coal preparation plant, bituminous or lignite; Bituminous coal-underground mining
*Ex VP: Robert G Sachse
*Sr VP: Brian L Cantrell
*Sr VP: R Eberley Davis
*Sr VP: Thomas M Wynne
*VP: Kevin J Larkin
*VP: Brad F Shellenberger
*VP: Timothy J Whelan

D-U-N-S 07-675-1379
ALLIANCE COMMUNITY HOSPITAL
COMMUNITY CARE CENTER
200 E State St, Alliance, OH 44601-4936
Tel (330) 596-6000 Founded/Ownrshp 1900
Sales 89.2MM EMP 900
SIC 8062

D-U-N-S 05-623-1085
■ **ALLIANCE CONSULTING GLOBAL HOLDINGS INC**
(Suby of EPAM SYSTEMS INC) ★
181 Washington St Ste 350, Conshohocken, PA 19428-2080
Tel (610) 234-4301 Founded/Ownrshp 2015
Sales 63.1MM^E EMP 1,107^E
SIC 7371 Computer software systems analysis & design, custom
Pr: John Castleman
CFO: Tonya Zweier
Sr VP: John Carmody
VP: Liz Smith
CTO: David Rader

D-U-N-S 79-784-7969
▲ **ALLIANCE DATA SYSTEMS CORP**
7500 Dallas Pkwy Ste 700, Plano, TX 75024-4006
Tel (214) 494-3000 Founded/Ownrshp 1996
Sales 6.4MMM EMP 16,000
Tkr Sym ADS Exch NYS
SIC 7389 Credit card service
Pr: Edward J Heffernan
*Ch Bd: Robert A Minicucci
CFO: Charles L Horn
Ex VP: Daniel P Finkelman
Ex VP: Bryan J Kennedy
Sr VP: Joseph L Motes III
Sr VP: Laura Santillan
Sr VP: Richard E Schumacher Jr
VP: Jeff Chesnut
VP: Tom Evich
VP: Jeffrey Fair
VP: Gwen Mannarino
VP: Mike Rosello
Board of Directors: Bruce K Anderson, Roger H Ballou, Lawrence M Benveniste, D Keith Cobb, E Linn Draper Jr, Kenneth R Jensen, Laurie A Tucker

D-U-N-S 16-834-6927
ALLIANCE DEVELOPMENT GROUP LLC
DAMON'S
301 S Tryon St Ste 1500, Charlotte, NC 28282-1923
Tel (704) 973-2950 Founded/Ownrshp 2004
Sales 25.9MM^E EMP 2,016
SIC 5812 6552 American restaurant; Land subdividers & developers, commercial
VP: Larry C Fox

D-U-N-S 62-281-3087 IMP
■ **ALLIANCE DISPLAY AND PACKAGING CO**
(Suby of WESTROCK RKT CO) ★
5921 Grassy Creek Blvd, Winston Salem, NC 27105-1206
Tel (336) 661-1700 Founded/Ownrshp 2006
Sales 121.4MM^E EMP 1,000
SIC 2653 Boxes, corrugated: made from purchased materials; Display items, corrugated: made from purchased materials
VP: John Dortch

D-U-N-S 88-492-7450
■ **ALLIANCE ENERGY LLC**
(Suby of GLOBAL OPERATING LLC) ★
800 South St Ste 500, Waltham, MA 02453-1483
Tel (781) 674-7780 Founded/Ownrshp 2011
Sales 175.3MM^E EMP 1,200^E
SIC 5411 5541 Grocery stores; Gasoline service stations
Pr: Andrew Slifka
*Sr VP: Mark Cosenza
Off Mgr: Christine DOE
CIO: James Shelton
VP Mktg: Rick Disalvatore
Genl Couns: Amy Gouldm

D-U-N-S 79-682-8049
ALLIANCE ENERGY SERVICES LLC
1405 Highway 12 E, Willmar, MN 56201-3746
Tel (320) 875-2641 Founded/Ownrshp 2006
Sales 171.9MM EMP 12
SIC 5172 Gases, liquefied petroleum (propane)

D-U-N-S 04-077-3940
ALLIANCE ENTERTAINMENT HOLDING CORP
1401 Nw 136th Ave Ste 100, Sunrise, FL 33323-2854
Tel (954) 255-4000 Founded/Ownrshp 2010
Sales 367.6MM^E EMP 525^E
SIC 5199 6719 General merchandise, non-durable; Investment holding companies, except banks
CEO: Jeff Walker

D-U-N-S 96-503-6101
ALLIANCE ENTERTAINMENT LLC
(Suby of ALLIANCE ENTERTAINMENT HOLDING CORP) ★
1401 Nw 136th Ave Ste 100, Sunrise, FL 33323-2854
Tel (954) 255-4403 Founded/Ownrshp 2013
Sales 367.6MM^E EMP 525^E
SIC 5199 3651 General merchandise, non-durable; Home entertainment equipment, electronic
CEO: Jeff Walker
*CFO: George Campagna
VP: Terri Borders
*VP: Mary Flynn
VP: Karen Gilbert
VP: Greg Harris
VP: Mike Karsting
VP: Eric Schwab
CIO: Brad Gerber
VP Mktg: Victor Bello
VP Sls: Michael Donohue

ALLIANCE EXPRESS
See ALLIANCE PLASTICS INC

D-U-N-S 94-306-0491 IMP
ALLIANCE FIBER OPTIC PRODUCTS INC
275 Gibraltar Dr, Sunnyvale, CA 94089-1312
Tel (408) 736-6900 Founded/Ownrshp 1995
Sales 81.1MM EMP 1,576^E
Accts Marcum Llp San Francisco Cal
SIC 3229 3661 Fiber optics strands; Fiber optics communications equipment
Ch Bd: Peter C Chang
CFO: Anita K Ho
Ex VP: David A Hubbard
Board of Directors: Richard Black, Ray Sun, James C Yeh

D-U-N-S 04-640-3986
ALLIANCE FOODS INC
ALLIANCE ASSOCIATES
605 W Chicago Rd, Coldwater, MI 49036-8400
Tel (517) 278-2395 Founded/Ownrshp 1967
Sales 85.3MM^E EMP 400
Accts Mcgladrey & Pullen Llp Elkha
SIC 5411 5141 Grocery stores, chain; Food brokers
Pr: James Erickson
*Ch Bd: Robert T Harris
*Pr: Sal Stazzorone
*CFO: Craig Linch
MIS Dir: Ed Parsall
Dir IT: Mike Deems
Snr Mgr: Lana Tosto

D-U-N-S 10-605-5044
ALLIANCE FOR COOPERATIVE ENERGY SERVICES POWER MARKETING LLC
ACES POWER MARKETING
4140 W 99th St, Carmel, IN 46032-7731
Tel (317) 344-7000 Founded/Ownrshp 1998
Sales 137.0MM^E EMP 200
SIC 4911 Electric services
Pr: Michael T Steffes
CFO: David Claspell
Bd of Dir: Donald Gulley
Bd of Dir: Michael W Price
Bd of Dir: J S Smith
Sr VP: Michael Steffes
VP: Todd Pilcher
VP: Annette Stamatkin
VP: Scott Thompson
VP: Jeffrey Walker
MIS Dir: Chris Haas

D-U-N-S 80-594-8051
ALLIANCE FOR SUSTAINABLE ENERGY LLC
15013 Denver West Pkwy, Lakewood, CO 80401-3111
Tel (303) 275-3000 Founded/Ownrshp 2008
Sales 378.6MM EMP 1,678
Accts Eks&H Lllp Denver Co
SIC 8733 Research institute

Pr: Dr Daniel E Arvizu
*COO: Ken Powers
*CFO: Owen Barwell
*Genl Couns: Steven Sibergleid

D-U-N-S 01-967-7769
ALLIANCE FUNDING GROUP (CA)
ALLIANCE CAPITAL MARKETS
3745 W Chapman Ave # 200, Orange, CA 92868-1656
Tel (714) 940-0653 Founded/Ownrshp 1998
Sales NA EMP 80
SIC 6159 Machinery & equipment finance leasing
Pr: Brijesh Ashok Patel
*VP: Shawn M Donohue
*VP: Vishal V Masani
Sls Mgr: Christopher Shipp

ALLIANCE GAME DISTRIBUTORS
See DIAMOND COMIC DISTRIBUTORS INC

D-U-N-S 11-870-7780
■ **ALLIANCE GLOBAL SERVICES INC**
ALLIANCE CNSLTING GLOBL HLDNGS
(Suby of ALLIANCE CONSULTING GLOBAL HOLDINGS INC) ★
41 University Dr Ste 202, Newtown, PA 18940-1873
Tel (610) 234-4301 Founded/Ownrshp 2008
Sales 63.1MM^E EMP 1,105^E
SIC 7371 Computer software systems analysis & design, custom
*CFO: Tonya Zweier
Sr VP: John Carmody
Sr VP: Bill Lewallen
VP: Frank Ginfrida
Dir Bus: Manish Pandey

D-U-N-S 95-919-8230
■ **ALLIANCE GLOBAL SERVICES LLC**
(Suby of ALLIANCE CNSLTING GLOBL HLDNGS) ★
41 University Dr Ste 202, Newtown, PA 18940-1873
Tel (610) 234-4301 Founded/Ownrshp 2008
Sales 63.1MM^E EMP 1,100^E
SIC 8742 Management consulting services
Pr: John Castleman
CFO: Tonya Zweier
VP: Bob Donaldson
VP: Sreekanth Singaraju
VP: Joelle Smith
Exec: Sandhya Gaddam
Exec: SRI Kanneganti
Software D: Muqthar Basha
Sftwr Eng: Bushra Anjum
Sftwr Eng: Ramesh Govindula
Sftwr Eng: Soumya RAO

ALLIANCE HEALTH & HUMAN SVCS
See ALLIANCE HEALTH INC

D-U-N-S 79-104-0798
ALLIANCE HEALTH AND LIFE INSURANCE CO
(Suby of HEALTH ALLIANCE PLAN OF MICHIGAN) ★
2850 W Grand Blvd Fl 5, Detroit, MI 48202-2643
Tel (313) 872-8100 Founded/Ownrshp 2007
Sales NA EMP 507^E
SIC 6311 Life insurance
Pr: James Connelly

D-U-N-S 84-952-8864
ALLIANCE HEALTH CARE INC
2260 Cliff Rd, Saint Paul, MN 55122-2316
Tel (651) 895-8030 Founded/Ownrshp 1989
Sales 24.8MM^E EMP 1,300
SIC 8082 Home health care services
Pr: Alana Fiala
Dir Opers: Laurie Lamson
Pr Dir: Shalon Novak

D-U-N-S 94-452-1798
ALLIANCE HEALTH INC
ALLIANCE HEALTH & HUMAN SVCS
134 Rumford Ave Ste 306, Auburndale, MA 02466-1378
Tel (617) 332-3366 Founded/Ownrshp 1999
Sales 3.6MM EMP 1,000
Accts Cliftonlarsonallen Llp Quincy
SIC 8051 Skilled nursing care facilities
Pr: Mary A McCarthy
*Sr VP: Frank Grady

D-U-N-S 10-922-0046
▲ **ALLIANCE HEALTHCARE SERVICES INC**
100 Bayview Cir Ste 400, Newport Beach, CA 92660-2984
Tel (949) 242-5300 Founded/Ownrshp 1983
Sales 473.0MM EMP 2,430
Tkr Sym AIQ Exch NGM
SIC 8071 Medical laboratories; Ultrasound laboratory
CEO: Percy C Tomlinson
*Ch Bd: Qisen Huang
Pr: Richard A Jones
Pr: Steven M Siwek
Pr: Gregory E Spurlock
CFO: Rhonda A Longmore-Grund
*V Ch Bd: Larry C Buckelew
VP: Jennifer Bradley
VP: Christianna Rosow
Area Mgr: Tim Budrewicz
Brnch Mgr: Doug McCracken
Board of Directors: Scott A Bartos, Neil F Dimick, Edward L Samek, Paul S Viviano

D-U-N-S 62-140-1046
▲ **ALLIANCE HOLDINGS GP LP**
1717 S Boulder Ave # 400, Tulsa, OK 74119-4805
Tel (918) 295-1415 Founded/Ownrshp 2005
Sales 2.2MMM EMP 4,439
Accts Ernst & Young Llp Tulsa Okla
Tkr Sym AHGP Exch NGS
SIC 1221 1222 Bituminous coal & lignite-surface mining; Bituminous coal-underground mining
Ch Bd: Joseph W Craft III
Genl Pt: Alliance GP
COO: Thomas M Wynne
CFO: Brian L Cantrell
Ex VP: Robert G Sachse
Genl Couns: R Eberley Davis

D-U-N-S 13-342-8776
ALLIANCE HOSPITALITY MANAGEMENT LLC
AGENT FOR BRCLAY HSPTLITY SVCS
215 N Boylan Ave, Raleigh, NC 27603-1424
Tel (919) 791-1801 Founded/Ownrshp 2003
Sales 91.6MM^E EMP 1,800
SIC 7011 Hotels & motels
CEO: Rolf Tweeten
Bd of Dir: Carrie Tweeten
Ex VP: Greg Presley
Ex VP: Joe Reardon
Sr VP: Andrew Broad
*VP: Mark Antolik
*VP: Rob Cote
Genl Mgr: Barry Shatoff
Opers Mgr: Alma Emso
VP Sls: Ryan Gosdin

D-U-N-S 06-005-9440
ALLIANCE HR INC
9076 Madison Blvd Ste G, Madison, AL 35758-1741
Tel (256) 203-6432 Founded/Ownrshp 2011
Sales 42.1MM^E EMP 2,400^E
SIC 8742 Human resource consulting services
Pr: Charlie Hall
*VP: Judy Gregory

D-U-N-S 61-849-1877
ALLIANCE INSPECTION MANAGEMENT LLC
330 Golden Shore Ste 400, Long Beach, CA 90802-4217
Tel (562) 432-5050 Founded/Ownrshp 2005
Sales 591.8MM^E EMP 954
SIC 6541 Title abstract offices
Pr: James D Yates
COO: Bob Clucas
*CFO: Joseph Rakauskas
*Sr VP: Tom Gardner
*Sr VP: Eric Widmer
QA Dir: Marc Weiner
*Genl Couns: Jesse Graham

ALLIANCE INSURANCE CO
See FARMERS ALLIANCE MUTUAL INSURANCE CO

ALLIANCE INTERNATIONAL
See ALLIANCE SHIPPERS INC

D-U-N-S 14-637-8836 IMP/EXP
ALLIANCE LAUNDRY HOLDINGS LLC
221 Shepard St, Ripon, WI 54971-1390
Tel (920) 748-3121 Founded/Ownrshp 2004
Sales 726.2MM EMP 2,100
Accts Pricewaterhousecoopers Milwau
SIC 3582 3633 Commercial laundry equipment; Dryers, laundry: commercial, including coin-operated; Washing machines, laundry: commercial, incl. coin-operated; Laundry dryers, household or coin-operated; Washing machines, household: including coin-operated

D-U-N-S 01-857-5493 IMP/EXP
ALLIANCE LAUNDRY SYSTEMS LLC
(Suby of BDT CAPITAL PARTNERS LLC) ★
221 Shepard St, Ripon, WI 54971-1390
Tel (920) 748-3121 Founded/Ownrshp 1998, 2015
Sales 800.0MM EMP 1,580
Accts Pricewaterhousecoopers Milwau
SIC 3582 3633 Commercial laundry equipment; Household laundry equipment
*Pr: Rick Pyle
*CFO: Bruce Rounds
*VP: Scott L Spiller
Ex Dir: Jamie Zaffke
Genl Mgr: Kate Holmes
Genl Mgr: Susan Peppler
IT Man: Tom Formella
Sftwr Eng: Jake Beyer
Mktg Dir: Eric Quandt
Manager: Tom Fleck
Manager: Pat Havlin

D-U-N-S 96-719-7682 IMP/EXP
ALLIANCE MACHINE SYSTEMS INTERNATIONAL LLC
J & L INDUSTRIES
(Suby of H ENTERPRISES) ★
5303 E Desmet Ave, Spokane Valley, WA 99212-0915
Tel (509) 842-5104 Founded/Ownrshp 1995
Sales 114.4MM^E EMP 300
SIC 3554 Corrugating machines, paper; Folding machines, paper
CEO: Mark Duchesne
Pr: Marius Batrin
VP: Eric Helmstetter
Tech Mgr: Gary Kneale
VP Mfg: Brian Barnes
Opers Mgr: Mike Hogberg
Sls Mgr: Dave Ahrendt

D-U-N-S 10-268-8657 IMP
ALLIANCE MEDICAL PRODUCTS INC
(Suby of SIEGFRIED USA HOLDING INC) ★
9342 Jeronimo Rd, Irvine, CA 92618-1903
Tel (949) 768-4690 Founded/Ownrshp 2012
Sales 135.4MM^E EMP 800
SIC 3841 7819 Medical instruments & equipment, blood & bone work; Laboratory service, motion picture
Pr: Juan C Valdes
CFO: Dan Moore
*VP: Tom Lucas
Exec: Tina Sheramitaro
Dir Lab: Peter Mead
IT Man: Calvin Witcher
Mtls Mgr: Craig Fromm
Opers Mgr: Brian Jones

D-U-N-S 00-794-0091
▲ **ALLIANCE ONE INTERNATIONAL INC** (VA)
8001 Aerial Center Pkwy # 100, Morrisville, NC 27560-8417
Tel (919) 379-4300 Founded/Ownrshp 1910
Sales 1.9MMM EMP 3,299^E
Tkr Sym AOI Exch NYS

SIC 5159 Tobacco distributors & products; Tobacco auctioning & warehousing; Tobacco, leaf
Pr: J Pieter Sikkel
CFO: Joel L Thomas
Treas: Michael Shannon
Ex VP: Jose Maria Costa Garcia
Ex VP: Jose Garcia
Ex VP: Graham J Kayes
Board of Directors: Jeffrey A Eckmann, Joyce L Fitzpatrick, C Richard Green Jr, Carl L Hausmann, Nigel G Howard, Mark W Kehaya, John D Rice, Martin R Wade III

D-U-N-S 00-490-8216 IMP
ALLIANCE PACKAGING LLC
BEAVERTON PACKAGING
(*Suby of* SP HOLDINGS, INC.)
1000 Sw 43rd St, Renton, WA 98057-4832
Tel (425) 291-3500 *Founded/Ownrshp* 1967
Sales 106.0MM[E] *EMP* 425
SIC 2653 3086

D-U-N-S 86-902-4075
ALLIANCE PHYSICIANS INC
K M C P I
2110 Leiter Rd, Miamisburg, OH 45342-3598
Tel (937) 558-9070 *Founded/Ownrshp* 1985
Sales 108.5MM *EMP* 15
Accts Clark Schaefer Hackett & Co D
SIC 8011 Offices & clinics of medical doctors

ALLIANCE PLASTICS
See ESSENTRA POROUS TECHNOLOGIES CORP

D-U-N-S 01-683-3395 IMP/EXP
ALLIANCE PLASTICS INC
ALLIANCE EXPRESS
3123 Station Rd, Erie, PA 16510-6599
Tel (814) 899-7671 *Founded/Ownrshp* 2009
Sales 100.4MM[E] *EMP* 200
SIC 5162 5065 Plastics materials & basic shapes; Electronic parts & equipment
Pr: Mike Conley
Genl Mgr: Deb Trandel
Plnt Mgr: Ron Mensing
Manager: Bernie Slomski
Sls Mgr: Scott States

D-U-N-S 07-889-6730
ALLIANCE RESIDENTIAL LLC
2415 E Camelback Rd # 600, Phoenix, AZ 85016-9298
Tel (602) 778-2800 *Founded/Ownrshp* 2001
Sales 253.7MM[E] *EMP* 1,500
SIC 6531 Real estate agents & managers
Pr: Bruce Ward
**COO:* Bradley Cribbins
**CFO:* Jay Hiemenz
**Sr VP:* Tina Mortera
**Sr VP:* Connie Spalla
VP: Kellea Curns
VP: Tonya Decker
VP: Bruce Francis
VP: Tina Makssour
VP: Annette Thurman
Ex Dir: Jeff Krohn

D-U-N-S 95-802-3442
ALLIANCE RESOURCE HOLDINGS INC
1717 S Boulder Ave Fl 6, Tulsa, OK 74119-4805
Tel (918) 295-7600 *Founded/Ownrshp* 1996
Sales 144.5MM[E] *EMP* 1,400
SIC 1221 1222 Bituminous coal surface mining; Coal preparation plant, bituminous or lignite; Bituminous coal-underground mining

D-U-N-S 82-762-9952
■ ALLIANCE RESOURCE OPERATING PARTNERS LP
(*Suby of* ALLIANCE RESOURCE PARTNERS LP) ★
1717 S Boulder Ave # 600, Tulsa, OK 74119-4805
Tel (918) 295-7600 *Founded/Ownrshp* 2008
Sales 1.1MMM[E] *EMP* 3,859[E]
SIC 1221 Bituminous coal & lignite-surface mining
Prin: Joseph W Craft III

D-U-N-S 06-347-5552
▲ ALLIANCE RESOURCE PARTNERS LP
1717 S Boulder Ave # 400, Tulsa, OK 74119-4805
Tel (918) 295-7600 *Founded/Ownrshp* 1971
Sales 2.2MMM *EMP* 4,243
Tkr Sym ARLP *Exch* NGS
SIC 1221 1222 1241 Coal preparation plant, bituminous or lignite; Bituminous coal-underground mining; Coal mining services
Pr: Joseph W Craft III
Genl Pt: Alliance R GP
CFO: Brian L Cantrell

ALLIANCE RETAIL SERVICE GROUP
See ARSG INC

D-U-N-S 07-887-6291
ALLIANCE SECURITY INC
85 Garfield Ave, Cranston, RI 02920-7807
Tel (877) 746-2559 *Founded/Ownrshp* 2013
Sales 100.0MM *EMP* 391
SIC 7382 Security systems services
CEO: Jasjit Gotra

D-U-N-S 08-564-6859
ALLIANCE SHIPPERS INC
ALLIANCE INTERNATIONAL
516 Sylvan Ave, Englewood Cliffs, NJ 07632-3022
Tel (201) 227-0400 *Founded/Ownrshp* 1973
Sales 280.2MM[E] *EMP* 550
SIC 4731 Transportation agents & brokers
Pr: Ronald Lefcourt
Pr: Thomas Lavender
**Sec:* Mark Schwed
Ex VP: Frank Delatorre
VP: Steven M Golich
VP: Richard Gutsell
VP: Jonath A Lefcourt
VP: Jonathan Lefcourt
VP: Lou Trentacoste
Off Mgr: Jeff Salkin
IT Man: Paul Duff

ALLIANCE STEEL BLDG SYSTEMS
See ALLIANCE STEEL INC

D-U-N-S 06-543-4417 IMP
ALLIANCE STEEL INC
ALLIANCE STEEL BLDG SYSTEMS
(*Suby of* ASSOCIATED STEEL GROUP, LLC)
3333 S Council Rd, Oklahoma City, OK 73179-4410
Tel (405) 745-7500 *Founded/Ownrshp* 1978
Sales 92.8MM[E] *EMP* 214
SIC 3448 Buildings, portable: prefabricated metal
COO: George Glover
**Treas:* Lisa Stewart
Prd Mgr: John Trotter
Ql Cn Mgr: Rocky Clark

ALLIANCE TITLE
See WFG NATIONAL TITLE INSURANCE CO

D-U-N-S 93-267-5333
ALLIANCE TITLE & ESCROW CORP
(*Suby of* FUTURE FOUNDATION INC) ★
380 E Parkcenter Blvd # 105, Boise, ID 83706-3963
Tel (208) 388-8881 *Founded/Ownrshp* 1995
Sales NA *EMP* 300
SIC 6411
Pr: Larry Matney
**Pr:* Ric Eborall
Pr: Chris Phillips
CFO: Glenn Glass
Ofcr: Ingrid Davis
Ofcr: Anne Knight
Ofcr: Don Wilhelm
**Sr VP:* Paul Fritz
CIO: Jason Jacobson
Counsel: Katie Mahoney

D-U-N-S 15-014-4330
ALLIANCE TOWERS LLC
(*Suby of* AIMCO PROPERTIES LP) ★
350 S Arch Ave Apt 106, Alliance, OH 44601-2677
Tel (330) 823-1063 *Founded/Ownrshp* 2004
Sales 31.4MM[E] *EMP* 3,924
SIC 6513 Apartment building operators
Prin: David Robertson
Pt: Leeann Morein

D-U-N-S 09-299-2916
ALLIANCE WATER RESOURCES INC
206 S Keene St, Columbia, MO 65201-6622
Tel (573) 874-8080 *Founded/Ownrshp* 1976
Sales 116.4MM[E] *EMP* 250
Accts Williams Keepers Llc Columbia
SIC 4941 4952 Water supply; Sewerage systems
Pr: Dale Wagner
Treas: Mary Ann Perkins
VP: Sandy Neal

D-U-N-S 07-521-7356 IMP
■ ALLIANCEBERNSTEIN CORP
AB
(*Suby of* AXA EQUITABLE LIFE INSURANCE CO) ★
1345 Ave Of The Americas, New York, NY 10105-0302
Tel (212) 969-1000 *Founded/Ownrshp* 1987, 1991
Sales 1.0MMM[E] *EMP* 3,318[E]
SIC 6282

D-U-N-S 19-480-0694
■ ALLIANCEBERNSTEIN HOLDING LP
(*Suby of* AB) ★
1345 Ave Of The Americas, New York, NY 10105-0302
Tel (212) 969-1000 *Founded/Ownrshp* 1967
Sales 212.5MM *EMP* 3,000[E]
Tkr Sym AB *Exch* NYS
SIC 6282 Investment advice; Investment advisory service
Ch Bd: Peter S Kraus
Genl Pt: Alliancebernstein Corporation
Ch Bd: Robert P Van Brugge
Pr: Drew Harker
COO: James A Gingrich
CFO: John C Weisenseel
Sr Cor Off: Philip Kirstein
VP: Shane Bigelow
VP: Joseph Carson
VP: Frank Caruso
VP: Yun Chen
VP: Yukiko Hanai
VP: Brad Hawkins
VP: Thomas Heath
VP: Wallin James
VP: Ping Jiang
VP: Donna Joseph
VP: Stephan Kretzschmar
VP: Samantha Lau
VP: Sam Mari
VP: Scott Mortensen

D-U-N-S 04-617-0544
■ ALLIANCEBERNSTEIN LP
(*Suby of* AXA)
1345 Ave Of The Americas, New York, NY 10105-0302
Tel (212) 969-1000 *Founded/Ownrshp* 1999
Sales 3.0MMM *EMP* 3,487
Accts Pricewaterhousecoopers Llp Ne
SIC 6282 Investment research; Investment advisory service; Investment counselors
V Ch: Roger Hertog
Genl Pt: Alliancebernstein Corporation
Ch Bd: Peter S Kraus
CFO: John C Weisenseel
Chf Mktg O: John Greer
Chf Inves: Kevin Simms
Sr VP: Stanley Bogen
Sr VP: Chris Cheesman
Sr VP: Mark Gersten
Sr VP: Christopher Marx
Sr VP: Natalia Nesterova
VP: Steven Barr
VP: Carmine Devito
VP: Gershon Distenfeld
VP: Paul Gonoud
VP: Andy Hess
VP: Scott Howe
VP: Halley Love
VP: Matthew McClanahan
VP: Eva Paprocki
VP: Joseph Pucci

D-U-N-S 09-032-8290
ALLIANCEONE INC (DE)
(*Suby of* TELEPERFORMANCE USA) ★
4850 E Street Rd Ste 300, Trevose, PA 19053-6643
Tel (215) 354-5500 *Founded/Ownrshp* 1998, 2007
Sales 65.9MM[E] *EMP* 2,500
SIC 7322 Collection agency, except real estate
CEO: Timothy Casey
**Sec:* Harry M Neerenberg
VP: Cindy Bohannon
VP: Jim Digiovanni
VP: Mark Lombardo
VP: Kevin Underwood
Dir IT: Lynda Vanness
VP Opers: Jake Becker

D-U-N-S 07-688-4238
ALLIANT CREDIT UNION FOUNDATION
11545 W Touhy Ave, Chicago, IL 60666-5000
Tel (800) 328-1935 *Founded/Ownrshp* 1935
Sales NA *EMP* 300
SIC 6062 6061 State credit unions, not federally chartered; Federal credit unions
Ch: Marc Krohn
**Pr:* David W Mooney
**CFO:* Mona Leung
Chf Inves: Wayne Rosenwinkel
Ex VP: Philip Salis
VP: Jerrold Anderson
VP: Kathy Hall
VP: Jeremy Pinard
VP: Mark Trevor
**VP:* R Weidner
CIO: Alan Pitcher
Board of Directors: Laurene Bentel, Laurene Bentel, Shirley Jones, Bill Lothridge, Alex Marren, Lee Schafer, Jenny Wong

ALLIANT ENERGY
See ALLIANT INDUSTRIES INC

D-U-N-S 18-717-3612
▲ ALLIANT ENERGY CORP
4902 N Biltmore Ln # 1000, Madison, WI 53718-2148
Tel (608) 458-3311 *Founded/Ownrshp* 1981
Sales 3.2MMM *EMP* 4,070
Tkr Sym LNT *Exch* NYS
SIC 4911 4924 Generation, electric power; Distribution, electric power; Transmission, electric power; ; Natural gas distribution
CEO: Patricia L Kampling
CFO: Thomas L Hanson
Ex VP: John Kratchmer
Ex VP: Pamela J Wegner
Sr VP: James H Gallegos
Sr VP: Douglas R Kopp
Sr VP: John O Larsen
Sr VP: Wayne A Reschke
VP: Robert J Durian
VP: James Gallegos
VP: Terry Kouba
VP: Jeanine Penticoff
Board of Directors: Patrick E Allen, Michael L Bennett, Deborah B Duine, Darryl B Hazel, Thomas F O'toole, Dean C Oestreich, Carol P Sanders, Susan D Whiting

D-U-N-S 13-972-2941
■ ALLIANT HOLDINGS LLC
(*Suby of* ORBITAL ATK INC) ★
7480 Flying Cloud Dr, Eden Prairie, MN 55344-3720
Tel (952) 351-3000 *Founded/Ownrshp* 2004
Sales 3.6MMM[E] *EMP* 12,300
SIC 3764 3812 3483 3482 3489 Propulsion units for guided missiles & space vehicles; Search & navigation equipment; Warfare counter-measure equipment; Detection apparatus: electronic/magnetic field, light/heat; Ammunition, except for small arms; Mortar shells, over 30 mm.; Rockets (ammunition); Bombs & parts; Small arms ammunition; Guns, howitzers, mortars & related equipment
Prin: Dianne Deering

D-U-N-S 79-034-3081
■ ALLIANT INDUSTRIES INC
ALLIANT ENERGY
(*Suby of* ALLIANT ENERGY CORP) ★
200 1st St Se, Cedar Rapids, IA 52401-1409
Tel (398) 786-4268 *Founded/Ownrshp* 1992
Sales 42.6MM[E] *EMP* 3,945
SIC 4011 4741 4911 4924 Interurban railways; Rental of railroad cars; Generation, electric power; Natural gas distribution
CEO: Patricia Leonard Kampling
**Pr:* Kevin P Burke
**Sr VP:* James H Gallegos
**Sr VP:* Thomas L Hanson
**Sr VP:* Douglas R Kopp

D-U-N-S 07-335-7766
ALLIANT INSURANCE SERVICES INC
1301 Dove St Ste 200, Newport Beach, CA 92660-2436
Tel (949) 756-0271 *Founded/Ownrshp* 2007
Sales NA *EMP* 997
SIC 6411 8748 Insurance agents & brokers; Business consulting
Ch Bd: Thomas Corbett
Owner: Jim Castle
**V Ch:* Peter Worth
Pr: Cheryl Crittenden
Pr: Nathan Harrison
Pr: Tawnya Keith
Pr: Carol Russell
Pr: Lisa Thornton
**Pr:* Greg Zimmer
**COO:* Jerold Hall
**CFO:* Ilene Anders
Ex VP: Donna Baker
Ex VP: Peter C Carpenter
Ex VP: Bert Durel
**Ex VP:* Michael G Feinberg
Ex VP: William G Franey
Ex VP: Robert Munao
Ex VP: Bill Nellen
Ex VP: Fred T Podolsky
**Sr VP:* Joe Marchese
VP: Catia Alati

D-U-N-S 60-114-5191
ALLIANT NATIONAL TITLE INSURANCE CO INC
1831 Lefthand Cir Ste G, Longmont, CO 80501-6768
Tel (303) 682-9800 *Founded/Ownrshp* 2005
Sales NA *EMP* 30
SIC 6361 Title insurance
CEO: Robert Grubb
**Pr:* David Ginger
**COO:* Carol Mastrofini
**CFO:* Scott Hendrickson
Sr VP: Rodney Anderson
Sr VP: Dan Solomon
VP: Margaret Cook
VP: Matt Frasure
VP: Mary Howard
VP: Kyle Rank
VP: Donna Slomins
VP: Jeffry Stein
VP: Mark Szenas

D-U-N-S 93-380-0377 EXP
■ ALLIANT TECHSYSTEMS OPERATIONS LLC
(*Suby of* ALLIANT HOLDINGS LLC) ★
Hc 114, Radford, VA 24143
Tel (540) 831-4788 *Founded/Ownrshp* 2010
Sales 3.6MMM[E] *EMP* 14,000
SIC 2892 Gunpowder
Pr: Nicholas Vlchakis
**Treas:* Patrick Nolan
Ex Dir: Betty Barker
Ex Dir: Pat Brown
Ex Dir: Paula Downs
Ex Dir: Ronnie Martin
Ex Dir: Andy Morikawa
Ex Dir: Jan Reynolds
Opers Mgr: Ken Burton
Plnt Mgr: Anthony Miano
Pr Dir: Susan Seymore

D-U-N-S 96-591-3887 IMP/EXP
■ ALLIANT TECHSYSTEMS OPERATIONS LLC
(*Suby of* ORBITAL ATK INC) ★
4700 Nathan Ln N, Plymouth, MN 55442-2512
Tel (952) 351-3000 *Founded/Ownrshp* 2010
Sales 252.6MM[E] *EMP* 700
SIC 3484 Small arms
Pr: David W Thompson
**CEO:* Mark Deyoung
VP: Marynell Devaughn
VP: Scott Marston
VP: Doris K Tuura
Comm Dir: Rod Gibbons
Dept Mgr: Christopher Hayes
Genl Mgr: Steven Bills
MIS Dir: Nicholas Galati
IT Man: Mitch Powers
IT Man: Layne Wilson

D-U-N-S 07-033-7363
ALLIANZ GLOBAL ASSISTANCE (AGA) SERVICE CO
ALLIANZ GLOBAL ASSISTANCE USA
9950 Mayland Dr, Richmond, VA 23233-1463
Tel (800) 628-4908 *Founded/Ownrshp* 2014
Sales NA *EMP* 1,500
SIC 6411 Insurance agents, brokers & service
Pr: Michael J Nelson
**COO:* Jay Levine
**CFO:* Diane Babson
VP: Ryan Kern
VP: Mike Kunc
VP: Bruce Trowbridge
QA Dir: Denise Brown
Netwrk Mgr: Mark Ryder
Software D: Sreenivas Mandava
Software D: Chipsy Patel
Netwrk Eng: Preston Means

ALLIANZ GLOBAL ASSISTANCE USA
See ALLIANZ GLOBAL ASSISTANCE (AGA) SERVICE CO

D-U-N-S 61-783-3595
ALLIANZ GLOBAL INVESTORS OF AMERICA LP
FOREIGN PRNT IS ALANZ AG MNCHN
(*Suby of* ALLIANZ SE)
680 Newport Ctr Dr Ste 250, Newport Beach, CA 92660
Tel (949) 219-2200 *Founded/Ownrshp* 1990
Sales 474.4MM[E] *EMP* 1,800
SIC 6282 Investment advisory service; Manager of mutual funds, contract or fee basis
Pr: Brian Gaffney
Pt: David Flattum
COO: Greg Goldstein
CFO: John Maneyy
Sr VP: Tony Burg
Sr VP: Kari Furry
Sr VP: Graham Lambert
VP: Julie Bryant
VP: James Funaro
VP: Gautam Ghosh
VP: Seon Harry
VP: Dabei Stellt

D-U-N-S 08-111-1874 IMP
ALLIANZ GLOBAL RISKS US INSURANCE CO
(*Suby of* FIREMANS FUND INSURANCE CO) ★
2350 W Empire Ave, Burbank, CA 91504-3350
Tel (818) 260-7500 *Founded/Ownrshp* 1977
Sales NA *EMP* 425
SIC 6331 Property damage insurance; Fire, marine & casualty insurance & carriers; Workers' compensation insurance
CEO: Hugh Burgess
Pr: Phil Metz
**CFO:* Randy Renn
Sr VP: Jon Downey
VP: Edwin Van Zijll
Exec: Rick Magill
CIO: Mary Grana
Tech Mgr: Andrew Higgins
Board of Directors: Nanette

D-U-N-S 17-497-7363
ALLIANZ LIFE INSURANCE CO OF NORTH AMERICA
(*Suby of* ALLIANZ SE)
5701 Golden Hills Dr, Minneapolis, MN 55416-1297
Tel (763) 765-6500 *Founded/Ownrshp* 2000
Sales NA *EMP* 2,800
SIC 6311 Life insurance
Ch Bd: Gary C Bhojwani
Pr: Denise Brinker
Pr: Adam Brown
Pr: Clay Eschrich
Pr: Ricci Granberg
Pr: Erin Krawiecki
Pr: Dan Krueger
Pr: Andrew Mattson
Pr: Todd Petit
Pr: Mark Springett
Pr: Dave Thom
Pr: Walter White
CFO: Bill Gaumond
CFO: Giulio Terzariol
Chf Cred: Steve Koslow
Chf Mktg O: Nancy Jones
Chf Inves: Carsten Quitter
Chf Inves: Volker Stueven
Ofcr: Ivy Beebe
Ofcr: Linda Burm
Ofcr: Douglas Degrote

D-U-N-S 15-120-0094
ALLIANZ OF AMERICA INC
(*Suby of* ALLIANZ SE)
55 Greens Farms Rd Ste 1, Westport, CT 06880-6149
Tel (203) 221-8500 *Founded/Ownrshp* 1976
Sales NA *EMP* 10,706
SIC 6311 6331 Life insurance; Fire, marine & casualty insurance
Ch: Gary C Bhojwani
**Pr:* Giulio Terzariol
**CFO:* Kevin E Walker
Board of Directors: Giulio Terzariol, Kevin E Walker

ALLIED AIR ENTERPRISES
See ARMSTRONG AIR CONDITIONING INC

D-U-N-S 12-350-3158 IMP
■ **ALLIED AIR ENTERPRISES LLC**
(*Suby of* LENNOX INDUSTRIES INC) ★
215 Metropolitan Dr, West Columbia, SC 29170-2294
Tel (803) 738-4000 *Founded/Ownrshp* 2000
Sales 102.1MM[E] *EMP* 400[E]
SIC 3585 3433 5075 Heating equipment, complete; Heating equipment, except electric; Air conditioning equipment, except room units
VP: Joe Nassabi
IT Man: Ron Brown
IT Man: Paul Damon
IT Man: Duane Wisebaker
VP Sls: Todd L King
Sls Mgr: Hilary Carlin

D-U-N-S 78-955-7704 IMP/EXP
ALLIED ALLOYS LP
6002 Donoho St, Houston, TX 77033-1102
Tel (713) 643-6966 *Founded/Ownrshp* 2006
Sales 85.8MM[E] *EMP* 125
SIC 5093 Metal scrap & waste materials
VP: Mukesh Turakhia
Opers Mgr: Jean Cervantes

ALLIED ALLOYS MIDWEST
See STAINLESS STEEL MIDWEST LLC

D-U-N-S 94-902-5670
ALLIED AUTOMOTIVE GROUP INC
(*Suby of* ALLIED SYSTEMS HOLDINGS INC) ★
2302 Parklake Dr Ne # 600, Atlanta, GA 30345-2896
Tel (404) 373-4285 *Founded/Ownrshp* 1995
Sales 57.7MM[E] *EMP* 1,000
SIC 4213 Trucking, except local
Pr: Mark Gengregske
COO: Guy W Rutland IV
**Sr VP:* John Harrington
**Sr VP:* Tommy Kirkman
**Sr VP:* Keith Runtzel
**Sr VP:* Stan Weaver
**VP:* Guy Rutland IV

D-U-N-S 96-841-3323
ALLIED AVIATION LLC
4120 Higel Ave, Sarasota, FL 34242-1232
Tel (212) 868-5593 *Founded/Ownrshp* 2011
Sales 402.1MM[E] *EMP* 1,200[E]
SIC 5172 Aircraft fueling services
Pr: Robert L Rose

D-U-N-S 62-783-7958
ALLIED AVIATION SERVICES INC
(*Suby of* ALLIED AVIATION LLC) ★
462 7th Ave Fl 17, New York, NY 10018-7426
Tel (212) 868-3870 *Founded/Ownrshp* 2001
Sales 402.1MM[E] *EMP* 1,200
SIC 5172 Aircraft fueling services
Pr: Robert L Rose
**Treas:* Alice R Nicholas
**Sr VP:* Stan Czaplicki
**VP:* Gerard Biscardi
**VP:* Ron Mustain
Exec: Terry Pennino
Opers Mgr: William Lugo

ALLIED BALTIC RUBBER
See ZHONGDING SEALING PARTS (USA) INC

D-U-N-S 00-697-4943 IMP
ALLIED BEVERAGE GROUP LLC
J & J DISTR CO
600 Washington Ave, Carlstadt, NJ 07072-2902
Tel (201) 842-6200 *Founded/Ownrshp* 1934
Sales 331.7MM[E] *EMP* 815
SIC 5182 Wine; Liquor
CFO: Marvin Bartfeld
Ex VP: William Harmelin
Sr VP: John D'Attoma
VP: Steven Altschuler
VP: Jon Baker
VP: Francis Bilancio
VP: Corey Bronstein
VP: Lou Demarino
**VP:* Beth Feldman
**VP:* Myron Feldman
**VP:* Robert Harmelin
VP: Jerry Moultry
VP: Kevin Murray
Exec: Josephine Buckner
Exec: Diana Mercado

D-U-N-S 05-575-3685 IMP
ALLIED BEVERAGES INC
BEST-WAY DISTRIBUTING CO
13235 Golden State Rd, Sylmar, CA 91342-1129
Tel (818) 493-6400 *Founded/Ownrshp* 1971
Sales 231.0MM[E] *EMP* 420
Accts Hedman Partners Valencia Ca
SIC 5181 Beer & other fermented malt liquors
CEO: Kevin Williams
**CFO:* Erin S Gabler
**VP:* William L Larson
VP Sls: Steve Zulanas
Board of Directors: Claudia Joyce, Earl J Whitehead, Kevin Williams

ALLIED BUILDING PRODUCTS CO
See OLDCASTLE DISTRIBUTION INC

D-U-N-S 00-182-4655 IMP/EXP
ALLIED BUILDING PRODUCTS CORP (NJ)
(*Suby of* OLDCASTLE INC) ★
15 E Union Ave, East Rutherford, NJ 07073-2127
Tel (201) 507-8400 *Founded/Ownrshp* 1950, 1996
Sales 2.1MMM[E] *EMP* 3,123
SIC 5031 5033 Building materials, interior; Roofing, siding & insulation
CEO: Bob Feury Jr
Pr: Ron Pilla
Pr: Donald Toth
Sr Cor Off: John Rooney
**VP:* Gregory Bloom
VP: Ralph Bove
VP: Ophelia Ho
VP: Mark Peconie
Exec: Brian McCormack
Brnch Mgr: Jeff Deweese
Brnch Mgr: Jay Haddick

D-U-N-S 03-433-9101 IMP
ALLIED BUILDING STORES INC
850 Kansas Ln, Monroe, LA 71203-4776
Tel (318) 699-9100 *Founded/Ownrshp* 1965
Sales 497.7MM *EMP* 125
Accts Heard Mcelroy & Vestal Llc
SIC 5031 Lumber, plywood & millwork
Pr: Dale Mercer
**CFO:* Gary McManus
Treas: Dennis Stine
Ofcr: Henry R Bockus III
VP: Kevin Cockrel
**VP:* Kevin Cockrell
**VP:* Mike Cunningham
**VP:* Tommy Ormond
**VP:* Larry Whitmire

D-U-N-S 10-664-8652
ALLIED BUSINESS SYSTEMS LLC
4848 Mercer University Dr, Macon, GA 31210-5602
Tel (800) 727-7534 *Founded/Ownrshp* 2002
Sales 52.2MM[E] *EMP* 1,000
SIC 7371 5734 Computer software development; Computer & software stores
Pr: William Cutshaw

ALLIED CASH ADVANCE
See ALLIED CASH HOLDINGS LLC

D-U-N-S 08-172-3053
ALLIED CASH HOLDINGS LLC
ALLIED CASH ADVANCE
7755 Montgomery Rd # 400, Cincinnati, OH 45236-4197
Tel (305) 371-3141 *Founded/Ownrshp* 2009
Sales NA *EMP* 700
SIC 6099 Check cashing agencies
Pr: David Davis
**CFO:* Roger Dean
**VP:* Douglas Clark
VP: Scott Kitchen
VP: Shannon Obrien
Dir IT: Michael Fountain

D-U-N-S 00-530-5792
ALLIED CONSTRUCTION SERVICES INC
COLOR
2122 Fleur Dr, Des Moines, IA 50321-1103
Tel (515) 288-4855 *Founded/Ownrshp* 1950
Sales 117.8MM[E] *EMP* 900
SIC 1742 1752 1721 1751 1542

D-U-N-S 60-601-7101
ALLIED CONVENTION SERVICE INC
BREDE EXPOSITION SERVICES
2502 Lake Orange Dr, Orlando, FL 32837-7802
Tel (407) 851-0261 *Founded/Ownrshp* 1988
Sales 92.3MM[E] *EMP* 1,160
SIC 7389 Convention & show services; Tourist information bureau
Pr: Charles T Premone
**Treas:* Edward J McNeil
Genl Mgr: Stacy Rhodes
VP Sls: Jim Cherry
Sls Dir: Jon Mills
Sls Mgr: Dan Crawford

D-U-N-S 02-312-5289
ALLIED COOPERATIVE
540 S Main St, Adams, WI 53910-9701
Tel (608) 339-3394 *Founded/Ownrshp* 2001
Sales 195.3MM[E] *EMP* 304
SIC 5191 5171 5251 Feed; Seeds: field, garden & flower; Fertilizer & fertilizer materials; Petroleum bulk stations; Hardware
Pr: Tom Walker
**V Ch:* Paul Zastoupil
**CEO:* Tim Diemert
**Ch:* Rodger Schomberg

ALLIED CUSTOM GYPSUM
See HARRISON GYPSUM LLC

ALLIED DIE CASTING COMPANY ILL
See RCM INDUSTRIES INC

D-U-N-S 00-643-3650 IMP
ALLIED DIESEL INC
JOHN DEERE
13015 W Custer Ave, Butler, WI 53007-1113
Tel (262) 781-7100 *Founded/Ownrshp* 1958
Sales 117.6MM *EMP* 275
SIC 5084 5531 7699

D-U-N-S 78-478-3748
ALLIED DOMESTIC FORWARDING LLC
(*Suby of* ALLIED VAN LINES, INC.)
5001 Us Highway 30 W, Fort Wayne, IN 46818-9701
Tel (260) 429-2511 *Founded/Ownrshp* 1992
Sales 2.1MM *EMP* 1,938
SIC 4212 Local trucking, without storage
Pr: Michael McMahon

D-U-N-S 61-473-3525 IMP/EXP
ALLIED ELECTRONICS INC
(*Suby of* ELECTROCOMPONENTS PUBLIC LIMITED COMPANY)
7151 Jack Newell Blvd S, Fort Worth, TX 76118-7037
Tel (817) 595-3500 *Founded/Ownrshp* 1999
Sales 977.2MM[E] *EMP* 800
SIC 5065 7389 3999 Electronic parts & equipment; Packaging & labeling services; Barber & beauty shop equipment
Pr: Scott McLendon
**CFO:* Nick Hawtrey
**CFO:* Gavin Robinson
**Treas:* Graeme Hancock
VP: Dennis Cash
VP: Mike Klepikow
**VP:* Mark Simon
VP: Dan Stewart
**Prin:* Andy Jackson
Brnch Mgr: Paul Bolton
Brnch Mgr: Denise Greenwald

ALLIED FARMING COMPANY
See SUN PACIFIC FARMING COOPERATIVE INC

ALLIED FITTING AND FLANGE
See ALLIED FITTING LP

D-U-N-S 19-606-6781 IMP/EXP
ALLIED FITTING LP
ALLIED FITTING AND FLANGE
7200 Mykawa Rd, Houston, TX 77033-1122
Tel (800) 969-5565 *Founded/Ownrshp* 1965
Sales 119.6MM[E] *EMP* 80
SIC 5085 Valves, pistons & fittings; Industrial fittings
Pt: Marc Herzstein
CFO: Ricardo Ibarra
Ex VP: Dave Washko
VP: Jose Coronado
Exec: Bob Selig

D-U-N-S 04-913-8639
ALLIED GROUP INC
(*Suby of* NATIONWIDE CORP) ★
1100 Locust St, Des Moines, IA 50391-1100
Tel (515) 280-4211 *Founded/Ownrshp* 1971
Sales NA *EMP* 4,700
SIC 6331 6211 5112 Property damage insurance; Reciprocal interinsurance exchanges: fire, marine, casualty; Mortgages, buying & selling; Business forms
Pr: W Kim Austen
**Treas:* Wendell P Crosser
VP: Paul Curran
VP: Dave Thompson
Exec: Carl Hayden
S&M/VP: James Hagenbucher
Sls Mgr: Ed Adamczak

D-U-N-S 96-194-1408
ALLIED HEALTH CARE SERVICES
ALLIED REHAB HOSPITAL
475 Morgan Hwy, Scranton, PA 18508-2605
Tel (570) 348-1300 *Founded/Ownrshp* 1959
Sales 66.8MM *EMP* 1,000
SIC 8322 Individual & family services
Pr: William Conaboy
IT Man: Todd Dietrich

D-U-N-S 10-113-1217 IMP
ALLIED HEALTHCARE INTERNATIONAL INC
(*Suby of* SAGA GROUP LIMITED)
245 Park Ave Fl 39, New York, NY 10167-4000
Tel (212) 750-0064 *Founded/Ownrshp* 2011
Sales 20.5MM[E] *EMP* 1,160[E]
SIC 8082 8049 Home health care services; Nurses & other medical assistants
CEO: Alexander Young
COO: Robin Norris
CFO: Gwen Flavell
CFO: Charles F Murphy
CFO: Paul Weston
VP: Marvet Abbassi
CIO: Sarah L Eames
IT Man: Ken Matus
Board of Directors: Sophia Corona, Mark Hanley, Wayne Palladino, Jeffrey S Peris, Raymond J Playford, Ann Thornburg

ALLIED INSURANCE
See AMCO INSURANCE CO

D-U-N-S 07-762-1258
ALLIED INTERSTATE LLC
(*Suby of* INTELLIRISK MANAGEMENT CORP) ★
12755 Hwy 55 Ste 300, Plymouth, MN 55441-4676
Tel (973) 630-5720 *Founded/Ownrshp* 1998
Sales 34.8MM[E] *EMP* 1,150
SIC 7322 Collection agency, except real estate
IT Man: Wendy Kluz

ALLIED KITCHENS & BATH
See A & M SUPPLY CORP

ALLIED MERCHANDISING INDUSTRY
See CORE-MARK INTERRELATED COMPANIES INC

D-U-N-S 04-107-8106 IMP/EXP
ALLIED MINERAL PRODUCTS INC
2700 Scioto Pkwy, Columbus, OH 43221-4660
Tel (614) 876-0244 *Founded/Ownrshp* 1961
Sales 91.3MM[E] *EMP* 300
SIC 3297 Nonclay refractories
Pr: Jon R Tabor
CFO: Todd Henry
**Ex VP:* Douglas K Doza
Ex VP: Douglas Doza
**VP:* Anthony S Disaia
**VP:* John S Halsted Jr
**VP:* Paul D Jamieson
Exec: Thomas Hamm
Genl Mgr: Ben GE
Genl Mgr: Mark Rowland
Dir IT: Ana Carazo

D-U-N-S 00-706-7713 IMP
▲ **ALLIED MOTION TECHNOLOGIES INC**
495 Commerce Dr Ste 3, Amherst, NY 14228-2311
Tel (716) 242-8634 *Founded/Ownrshp* 1962
Sales 232.4MM *EMP* 1,046[E]
Accts Eks&H Llp Denver Colorado
Tkr Sym AMOT *Exch* NGM
SIC 3621 3825 Motors & generators; Rotary converters (electrical equipment); Function generators
Ch Bd: Richard S Warzala
CFO: Michael R Leach
Bd of Dir: Richard D Smith
VP: Robert P Maida
VP: Kenneth R Wyman
Creative D: Wout Liefaard
IT Man: Jim Jordan
IT Man: Tim Makai
Snr Mgr: Bjorn Karlstrom
Board of Directors: Richard D Federico, Gerald J Laber, Alexis P Michas, Richard D Smith, James J Tanous, Michael R Winter

ALLIED NEVADA GOLD
See HYCROFT MINING CORP

ALLIED OIL & GAS SERVICES
See FK DELLIA LLC

D-U-N-S 00-749-6284
ALLIED OIL & TIRE CO
ALLIED TIRE CO
2209 S 24th St, Omaha, NE 68108-3815
Tel (402) 344-4343 *Founded/Ownrshp* 1958
Sales 115.6MM *EMP* 260
Accts Frankel Zacharia Llc Omaha
SIC 5014 5172 Automobile tires & tubes; Lubricating oils & greases
Pr: R Conrad Heinson
**Pr:* Steve Phillips
**Sr VP:* Tamara Heinson Fowler
Brnch Mgr: Kory Petersen
Site Mgr: Brett Black
Opers Mgr: John Smidt
Mktg Dir: Stefanie Daigle
Sls Mgr: Chuck Buis
Sls Mgr: Conrad Heinson
Sales Asso: James Castillo
Board of Directors: Tamara Heinson Fowler, R Conrad Heinson, Debra Heinson Thiesfeld

D-U-N-S 00-116-0936 IMP/EXP
ALLIED PRINTING SERVICES INC (CT)
1 Allied Way, Manchester, CT 06042-8933
Tel (860) 643-1101 *Founded/Ownrshp* 1949
Sales 88.1MM[E] *EMP* 350[E]
SIC 2396 2752 2759 2789 2791 Automotive & apparel trimmings; Commercial printing, offset; Commercial printing; Bookbinding & related work; Typesetting
Pr: John G Sommers
**Treas:* Robert B Mc Cann
Treas: Robert B McCann
**Ex VP:* Bettina Sommers
**Ex VP:* Gerald Sommers
**VP:* Peter Swan
Sls Dir: John Troy

D-U-N-S 80-130-9337
ALLIED PROPERTY AND CASUALTY INSURANCE CO
(*Suby of* ALLIED GROUP INC) ★
1100 Locust St, Des Moines, IA 50391-1100
Tel (515) 280-4211 *Founded/Ownrshp* 1984
Sales NA *EMP* 3,000[E]
SIC 6331 Property damage insurance; Fire, marine & casualty insurance & carriers
Pr: Kim Austin
Treas: Jamie H Saffer

D-U-N-S 83-129-8489 IMP
ALLIED RECREATION GROUP INC
FLEETWOOD HOMES
(*Suby of* AIP/FW FUNDING INC) ★
1031 E Us Highway 224, Decatur, IN 46733-2737
Tel (260) 728-2121 *Founded/Ownrshp* 2013
Sales 139.0MM[E] *EMP* 510
SIC 3716 Motor homes
Pr: Jim Jacobs
**CEO:* John Draheim
**COO:* John Lowry
**CFO:* Lance Randolph
VP: Paul Bamatter
**VP:* Steve Heim
VP: Kyle McCrary
VP Opers: Luis Ortiz
Sfty Dirs: Tim Quinton
QC Dir: Jo Theart
Plnt Mgr: Jeff Newport

D-U-N-S 00-599-3571 IMP
ALLIED REFRIGERATION INC
2300 E 28th St, Signal Hill, CA 90755-2180
Tel (562) 595-5301 *Founded/Ownrshp* 1934
Sales 87.8MM[E] *EMP* 126
SIC 5075 5078 Air conditioning & ventilation equipment & supplies; Warm air heating equipment & supplies; Refrigeration equipment & supplies
Ch: Robert Nichols
**Pr:* Michael R Luther
**CEO:* Robert Nichols Jr
**CFO:* Navi Lyman

Dir Bus: Regina Binion
Sales Exec: Knute Fredholm
Sls Dir: Kevin Cross
Mktg Mgr: Scott Melton
Sales Asso: Mike Harrelson

ALLIED REHAB HOSPITAL
See ALLIED HEALTH CARE SERVICES

D-U-N-S 07-934-1141
ALLIED RESOURCES LLC (MT)
387 15th St W 366, Dickinson, ND 58601-3017
Tel (800) 677-1142 *Founded/Ownrshp* 2013
Sales 200.0MM *EMP* 10
SIC 1389 Gas field services
Pr: Mark Abell

ALLIED SALES COMPANY
See TEXAS ENTERPRISES INC

D-U-N-S 16-872-4149
ALLIED SECURITY HOLDINGS LLC
ALLIEDBARTON SECURITY SERVICES
(*Suby of* WENDEL NORTH AMERICA LLC) ★
161 Washington St Ste 600, Conshohocken, PA 19428-2083
Tel (484) 351-1300 *Founded/Ownrshp* 2015
Sales 2.1MMM *EMP* 7,010
SIC 7381 7382 Guard services; Security systems services
CEO: William C Whitmore Jr
**CFO:* William A Torzolini
**Treas:* James W Lennon
**Ex VP:* David I Buckman
VP: Paul Laconi
VP: Elizabeth Ritts
VP: Jim Smolarski
VP: Paul Stab
Off Mgr: Nicola Serasin
VP Opers: Bud E Bradly
VP Opers: Gesi McAllister
Board of Directors: Chris Swecker

D-U-N-S 00-196-8346
ALLIED SECURITY LLC
ALLIEDBARTON SECURITY SERVICES
(*Suby of* ALLIEDBARTON SECURITY SERVICES) ★
161 Washington St, Conshohocken, PA 19428-2083
Tel (610) 239-1100 *Founded/Ownrshp* 1957, 2000
Sales 207.1MM^E *EMP* 38,000
SIC 7381

D-U-N-S 18-514-5414
ALLIED SERVICES FOUNDATION INC
100 Abington Executive Pa, Clarks Summit, PA 18411-2260
Tel (570) 348-1407 *Founded/Ownrshp* 1957
Sales 3.8MM *EMP* 2,500
Accts Parentebeard Llc Philadelphia
SIC 8093 8361 Rehabilitation center, outpatient treatment; Rehabilitation center, residential: health care incidental
Ch: Louis Denaples
Pr: James L Brady
CFO: Mike Avvisato
VP: Mary L Knabel
Prgrm Mgr: Karen Roberto
CIO: John Regula

D-U-N-S 13-038-3495
ALLIED SOLUTIONS LLC
(*Suby of* SECURIAN) ★
1320 City Center Dr # 300, Carmel, IN 46032-3816
Tel (317) 706-7600 *Founded/Ownrshp* 2009
Sales NA *EMP* 100
SIC 6321 6351 6159 Accident & health insurance; Credit & other financial responsibility insurance; Automobile finance leasing
CEO: Chris Hilger
Pr: Ron Barnes
Pr: Mike Button
Pr: Pete Hilger
COO: Jeff Wisdorf
CFO: Brian Urbanski
Ofcr: Michael Clouser
Sr VP: Mike Naughton
VP: Jay Berryman
VP: Mark Bugalski
VP: Fred Caprio
VP: Joe Culloo
VP: Brian Curtis
VP: Ann D Davidson
VP: Ann Davidson
VP: Sherry Deeds
VP: Sharla Demedeiros
VP: Doug Frawley
VP: Judy Harrison
VP: Bill Haynes
VP: Kurt Kesler

D-U-N-S 06-755-0080
ALLIED STAFF AUGMENTATION PARTNERS INC
ASAP
7421 Carmel Executive Par, Charlotte, NC 28226-0400
Tel (980) 219-8477 *Founded/Ownrshp* 2011
Sales 85.0MM *EMP* 500
SIC 8711 Engineering services
Pr: Richard L Barnes
VP: Richard L Barnes Jr

D-U-N-S 78-424-0582
ALLIED STAFFING INC
4400 Buffalo Gap Rd # 4500, Abilene, TX 79606-2717
Tel (325) 695-5822 *Founded/Ownrshp* 1989
Sales 27.5MM^E *EMP* 2,800
SIC 7361 7363 Employment agencies; Employee leasing service
Pr: James McNeer
CFO: Frank Caceres
VP Opers: Shelia Clark

D-U-N-S 06-148-7781 IMP/EXP
ALLIED SYSTEMS CO
21433 Sw Oregon St, Sherwood, OR 97140-9799
Tel (503) 625-2560 *Founded/Ownrshp* 2004
Sales 132.9MM^E *EMP* 340
SIC 3531 3537 3536 Winches; Dozers, tractor mounted: material moving; Logging equipment; Stackers, power (industrial truck stackers); Cranes, industrial truck; Hoists, cranes & monorails
Pr: Lewis A Rink
CFO: Wolfgang Mann
VP: Bill Chan
Prin: Dan Laxon
VP Opers: Aaron Bruce

D-U-N-S 80-981-0179
ALLIED SYSTEMS HOLDINGS INC
2302 Parkl Dr Bldg 15ste, Atlanta, GA 30345
Tel (404) 373-4285 *Founded/Ownrshp* 2007
Sales 542.7MM^E *EMP* 5,600
SIC 4213 Automobiles, transport & delivery
Pr: Mark J Gendregske
**CFO:* Thomas H King
Treas: David S Forbes
**Ex VP:* Thomas M Duffy
**Sr VP:* Scott Macaulay
Sr VP: Guy W Rutland
Corp Couns: Jonathan B Davis
Board of Directors: Brian Cullen, Jos Opdeweegh, Ira Tochner

ALLIED TIRE CO
See ALLIED OIL & TIRE CO

D-U-N-S 08-576-7338 IMP/EXP
■ **ALLIED TRADE GROUP LLC**
ATGSTORES
(*Suby of* LOWES COMPANIES INC) ★
11410 Ne 122nd Way Ste 20, Kirkland, WA 98034-6945
Tel (425) 814-2515 *Founded/Ownrshp* 2011
Sales 160.1MM^E *EMP* 160
SIC 5063 Lighting fixtures
Pr: Michelle Newberry
Mng Pt: Donna Miller

D-U-N-S 60-734-3142
ALLIED TRANSPORTATION SERVICES INC
CHANGING LANES TRNSP BRKS
1533 Nw 2nd St, Madison, SD 57042-3806
Tel (877) 241-6237 *Founded/Ownrshp* 1984
Sales 115.0MM *EMP* 7
SIC 7363 4731 Truck driver services; Freight transportation arrangement
Pr: Brian Kringen
**CFO:* Merrell Holbrook

D-U-N-S 05-786-3847 IMP/EXP
■ **ALLIED TUBE & CONDUIT CORP**
(*Suby of* ATKORE INTERNATIONAL INC) ★
16100 Lathrop Ave, Harvey, IL 60426-6021
Tel (708) 339-1610 *Founded/Ownrshp* 2010
Sales 382.2MM^E *EMP* 750
SIC 3317 Welded pipe & tubes
Pr: William Taylor
CFO: Carl Schmidt
**VP:* Jim Hays
**VP:* Ed Kurasz
Exec: John Ashbaugh
IT Man: Brian Muick
Sfty Mgr: James Skalon

D-U-N-S 00-413-4623 IMP/EXP
ALLIED UNIVERSAL CORP (FL)
3901 Nw 115th Ave, Doral, FL 33178-1859
Tel (305) 888-2623 *Founded/Ownrshp* 1954
Sales 120.3MM^E *EMP* 159
SIC 5169 Chlorine; Chemicals, industrial & heavy
CEO: Robert Namoff
**Pr:* Bernard Epstein
**Pr:* James Palmer
**CFO:* Michael Koven
VP: Fabian Cano
**VP:* Ronald Rubin
**VP:* Todd Tucker
Rgnl Mgr: Ron Zeigler
IT Man: Prakash Lodha
Sfty Mgr: Robin Bolte
Opers Mgr: Jim Lafreniere

D-U-N-S 08-041-7901
ALLIED UNIVERSAL HOLDCO LLC
(*Suby of* ALLIED UNIVERSAL TOPCO LLC) ★
1551 N Tustin Ave Ste 650, Santa Ana, CA 92705-8664
Tel (714) 619-9700 *Founded/Ownrshp* 2015
Sales 1.5MMM^E *EMP* 88,000^E
SIC 6719 7381 Investment holding companies, except banks; Security guard service
CEO: Steve Jones

ALLIED UNIVERSAL SECURITY SVCS
See UNIVERSAL PROTECTION SERVICE LLC

D-U-N-S 08-043-7521
ALLIED UNIVERSAL TOPCO LLC
1551 N Tustin Ave, Santa Ana, CA 92705-8634
Tel (714) 619-9700 *Founded/Ownrshp* 2015
Sales 1.0MMM^E *EMP* 88,000^E
SIC 6719 7381 7349 Investment holding companies, except banks; Security guard service; Janitorial service, contract basis
CEO: Steve Jones

ALLIED WASTE INDUSTRIES
See ALLIED WASTE SERVICES OF MASSACHUSETTS LLC

D-U-N-S 01-365-2383
■ **ALLIED WASTE INDUSTRIES (ARIZONA) INC**
(*Suby of* ALLIED WASTE INDUSTRIES INC) ★
15880 N Greenway, Scottsdale, AZ 85260
Tel (480) 627-2700 *Founded/Ownrshp* 1992
Sales 120.8MM^E *EMP* 400
SIC 4953 Garbage: collecting, destroying & processing
Pr: Thomas Van Weelden
**Pr:* Jeff D Andrews
**VP:* Brian A Bales
**VP:* W T Eggleston Jr
**VP:* Timothy S Powell
**VP:* Andrew J Sweet

D-U-N-S 18-061-5429 IMP
■ **ALLIED WASTE INDUSTRIES INC**
(*Suby of* REPUBLIC SERVICES INC) ★
18500 N Allied Way # 100, Phoenix, AZ 85054-3101
Tel (480) 627-2700 *Founded/Ownrshp* 1994
Sales 3.7MMM^E *EMP* 400
SIC 4953 Refuse collection & disposal services; Sanitary landfill operation
Ch Bd: John J Zillmer
Pr: Don Slager
COO: Rob Maruster
CFO: Glenn Culpepper
CFO: Peter S Hathaway
Ex VP: Brian Bales
Ex VP: Timothy R Donovan
Ex VP: Edward A Evans
Ex VP: Jon Vander
Sr VP: Denise R Danner
Sr VP: James P Zeumer

D-U-N-S 96-403-4185
■ **ALLIED WASTE NORTH AMERICA INC**
REPUBLIC SERVICES
(*Suby of* ALLIED WASTE INDUSTRIES INC) ★
18500 N Allied Way # 100, Phoenix, AZ 85054-3101
Tel (480) 627-2700 *Founded/Ownrshp* 1996
Sales 2.4MMM^E *EMP* 100
SIC 4953 Refuse collection & disposal services; Sanitary landfill operation
CEO: Thomas Van Weelden
**Pr:* Don Slager
**CFO:* Peter Hathaway
**VP:* Tom Ryan

ALLIED WASTE SERVICES
See NATIONAL WASTE SERVICE INC

ALLIED WASTE SERVICES MEMPHIS
See BROWNING-FERRIS INDUSTRIES OF TENNESSEE INC

ALLIED WASTE SERVICES NW IND
See ILLIANA DISPOSAL SERVICE INC

D-U-N-S 15-423-2581
■ **ALLIED WASTE SERVICES OF INDEPENDENCE**
SITE 468
(*Suby of* ALLIED WASTE SYSTEMS INC) ★
1220 S Brookside Ave, Independence, MO 64052-1870
Tel (816) 254-1470 *Founded/Ownrshp* 2000
Sales 100.5MM^E *EMP* 485
SIC 4953 Refuse collection & disposal services
CEO: Brian Cunningham
**Pr:* Phil Bethel

D-U-N-S 14-023-9539
■ **ALLIED WASTE SERVICES OF MASSACHUSETTS LLC**
ALLIED WASTE INDUSTRIES
(*Suby of* ALLIED WASTE INDUSTRIES INC) ★
15880 N Hayden Rd, Scottsdale, AZ 85260-1907
Tel (480) 627-2700 *Founded/Ownrshp* 2003
Sales 130.8MM^E *EMP* 551^E
SIC 4953 Refuse collection & disposal services; Sanitary landfill operation

ALLIED WASTE SVCS FORT MILL
See CONTAINER CO OF CAROLINA

D-U-N-S 06-858-7633
■ **ALLIED WASTE SYSTEMS INC**
(*Suby of* REPUBLIC SERVICES INC) ★
18500 N Allied Way # 100, Phoenix, AZ 85054-3101
Tel (480) 627-2700 *Founded/Ownrshp* 2008
Sales 267.9MM^E *EMP* 585
SIC 4953 Refuse collection & disposal services; Sanitary landfill operation
Pr: Donald W Slager
Treas: G Thomas Rochford Jr
VP: Bob Doyle
VP: Joe Duncan
VP: James Eng
VP: Denny Marchetti
VP: Jo Lynn White
IT Man: Victoria Thompson
Sales Asso: Maribel Nieto

D-U-N-S 18-657-9173 IMP/EXP
ALLIED WIRE & CABLE INC
A W C
101 Kestrel Dr, Collegeville, PA 19426-2061
Tel (484) 928-6700 *Founded/Ownrshp* 1988
Sales 107.3MM^E *EMP* 176^E
SIC 5063 Wire & cable
Pr: Daniel Flynn
**CFO:* Matthew O Reilly
Genl Mgr: Tom Gilmore
Mktg Mgr: Natalie Beers

D-U-N-S 07-948-4365
■ **ALLIED WIRELESS COMMUNICATIONS CORP**
(*Suby of* ATN INTERNATIONAL INC) ★
600 Cummings Ctr, Beverly, MA 01915-6194
Tel (978) 619-1300 *Founded/Ownrshp* 2009
Sales 28.0MM^E *EMP* 1,000
SIC 4813 Data telephone communications
Pr: Michael T Prior

D-U-N-S 96-331-0516
ALLIED WIRELINE SERVICES LLC
3200 Wilcrest Dr Ste 170, Houston, TX 77042-3366
Tel (713) 343-7280 *Founded/Ownrshp* 2010
Sales 159.9MM^E *EMP* 105
SIC 1389 Oil field services
CEO: Larry Albert
**CFO:* Peter Brink
**CFO:* David Otte
**VP:* Scott O'Beirne
Dist Mgr: Shawn McCafferty
Off Mgr: Brittany Kerr
Off Mgr: Shannon Mendenhall

D-U-N-S 19-347-6319
ALLIED WORLD ASSURANCE CO (US) INC
ALLIED WORLD NATIONAL ASRN CO
(*Suby of* ALLIED WORLD ASSURANCE COMPANY, LTD)
2 Liberty Sq Fl 11, Boston, MA 02109-4890
Tel (857) 288-6000 *Founded/Ownrshp* 2003
Sales NA *EMP* 800^E
SIC 6411 Insurance information & consulting services
Pr: David Imhoff
CFO: Nicholas Johndrow
Chf Inves: Aimee Bornstein
Ex VP: Thomas Bradley
Sr VP: Michele B Bernstein
Sr VP: Sarah Doran
Sr VP: Gregory Sandvik
VP: Christopher J Adamec
VP: Pauline Barry
VP: Claudia Carnevale
VP: Michael P Conroy
VP: Peter Ford
VP: Cara O Gallagher
VP: Lynn Guan
VP: Carla Pantano
VP: Kyle Powal
VP: Jennifer Stevenson

D-U-N-S 02-817-5546
ALLIED WORLD ASSURANCE INC
(*Suby of* ALLIED WORLD ASSURANCE COMPANY, LTD)
1690 New Britain Ave B, Farmington, CT 06032-3361
Tel (860) 284-1300 *Founded/Ownrshp* 2010
Sales NA *EMP* 300^E
SIC 6411 Property & casualty insurance agent
Pr: John Gauthier
VP: Lynne Fletcher
VP: Jan E Haylett
VP: Carl Lythcott
VP: Marlene Mourad
**Prin:* Stephen J Sills
CIO: Glenn Gardner

ALLIED WORLD NATIONAL ASRN CO
See ALLIED WORLD ASSURANCE CO (US) INC

D-U-N-S 08-017-4588
ALLIEDBARTON AEROSPACE AND DEFENSE SERVICES LLC
(*Suby of* ALLIEDBARTON SECURITY SERVICES) ★
161 Washington St Ste 600, Conshohocken, PA 19428-2083
Tel (484) 351-1300 *Founded/Ownrshp* 2015
Sales 4.1MM^E *EMP* 2,000
SIC 7381 7382 Guard services; Security systems services
Ch Bd: William C Whitmore Jr
**CFO:* William A Torzolini
**Ex VP:* David I Buckman

ALLIEDBARTON SECURITY SERVICES
See ALLIED SECURITY LLC

ALLIEDBARTON SECURITY SERVICES
See SPECTAGUARD ACQUISITION LLC

ALLIEDBARTON SECURITY SERVICES
See ALLIED SECURITY HOLDINGS LLC

D-U-N-S 61-055-6917
ALLIEDBARTON SECURITY SERVICES LLC
(*Suby of* WENDEL)
8 Tower Bridge 161 Wshgtn, Conshohocken, PA 19428
Tel (610) 239-1100 *Founded/Ownrshp* 2015
Sales 857.3MM^E *EMP* 2,010
SIC 7381 Guard services; Security guard service
CEO: William C Whitmore
Pr: Carol Johnson
Pr: Jim Smolarski
Ofcr: Monica Beltran
Ofcr: Crystal Christian
Ofcr: Ruth Ekpo
Ofcr: James Finocchio
Ofcr: Brittany Hebert
Ofcr: Seth Hunter
Ofcr: Rafael Jimenez
Ofcr: Sylvester Joseph
Ofcr: Joshua Juliano
Ofcr: Shawn Nichols
Ofcr: Jake Scott
Ofcr: Jordan Weidenhaft
Sr VP: Mimi Lanfranchi
VP: Nancy Peterson
Exec: Caress Kennedy
Dir Bus: Taylor McDonald

D-U-N-S 11-621-3349 IMP
ALLINA HEALTH SYSTEM
ALLINA HOSPITALS & CLINICS
2925 Chicago Ave, Minneapolis, MN 55407-1321
Tel (612) 262-5000 *Founded/Ownrshp* 1983
Sales 3.6MMM *EMP* 26,400
Accts Kpmg Llp Minneapolis Mn
SIC 8062 8741 8011 General medical & surgical hospitals; Hospital management; Medical centers
Pr: Penny Wheeler
Pr: Mark S Jordahl
CFO: Duncan Gallagher
CFO: Duncan P Gallagher
Ofcr: Cindy Early
Ofcr: Heather Smith
Ex VP: Christine Bent
Ex VP: Daniel McGinty
Ex VP: Elizabeth Truesdell Smith
Ex VP: Robert Wieland
Ex VP: Robert A Wieland
Sr VP: John Church
VP: Courtney Baechler
VP: Margaret Butler
VP: John Lesser
VP: Cathy Runck
Dir Lab: Jan Skoog

ALLINA HOSPITALS & CLINICS
See ABBOTT NORTHWESTERN HOSPITAL

ALLINA HOSPITALS & CLINICS
See ST FRANCIS REGIONAL MEDICAL CENTER

ALLINA HOSPITALS & CLINICS
See ALLINA HEALTH SYSTEM

ALLIS CHALMERS
See IRONGATE ENERGY SERVICES LLC

D-U-N-S 00-607-5816
ALLIS-CHALMERS ENERGY INC
12101 Cutten Rd, Houston, TX 77066-1811
Tel (281) 301-2600 *Founded/Ownrshp* 2010
Sales 830.3MM^E *EMP* 3,174
SIC 1381 1389 7353

ALLISON TAYLOR
See FYC APPAREL GROUP LLC

D-U-N-S 96-913-2880
▲ ALLISON TRANSMISSION HOLDINGS INC
1 Allison Way, Indianapolis, IN 46222-3271
Tel (317) 242-5000 *Founded/Ownrshp* 1915
Sales 1.9MMM *EMP* 2,800^E
Tkr Sym ALSN *Exch* NYS
SIC 3714 Motor vehicle parts & accessories; Motor vehicle transmissions, drive assemblies & parts
Ch Bd: Lawrence E Dewey
Pr: David S Graziosi
Sr VP: Michael G Headly
Sr VP: Randall R Kirk
Sr VP: Jeff Mason
Sr VP: David L Parish
VP: Michael A Dick
VP: Edward L Dyer
VP: Eric C Scroggins
CIO: Dean E Ranalli

D-U-N-S 80-440-7463 IMP/EXP
■ ALLISON TRANSMISSION INC
(*Suby of* ALLISON TRANSMISSION HOLDINGS INC) ★
1 Allison Way, Indianapolis, IN 46222-3271
Tel (317) 242-5000 *Founded/Ownrshp* 2007
Sales 1.0MMM^E *EMP* 2,700^E
SIC 3714 Transmissions, motor vehicle
CEO: Lawrence E Dewey
**Pr:* David S Graziosi
Pr: Randall Kirk
**VP:* G Frederick Bohley
**VP:* Robert M Clark III
**VP:* Sharon L Dean
**VP:* Michael A Dick
VP: Edward L Dyer
VP: Edward Dyer
**VP:* David L Parish
VP: Eric Scroggins

D-U-N-S 00-580-8829
ALLISON-SMITH CO LLC
1869 S Cobb Indus Blvd Se, Smyrna, GA 30082-4909
Tel (404) 351-6430 *Founded/Ownrshp* 2001
Sales 158.5MM^E *EMP* 500
SIC 1731 7389 Electrical work; Design services
CEO: Robert Jerrell
**Ch Bd:* Lanny S Thomas
**Pr:* Joe M Satterfield
**CFO:* Todd Schirner
Sfty Dirs: Gary Brookshire

D-U-N-S 07-534-1552
■ ALLMERICA FINANCIAL LIFE INSURANCE AND ANNUITY
(*Suby of* GOLDMAN SACHS GROUP INC) ★
440 Lincoln St, Worcester, MA 01653-0002
Tel (508) 855-1000 *Founded/Ownrshp* 2005
Sales NA *EMP* 20
SIC 6411 6211 Insurance agents, brokers & service; Mutual funds, selling by independent salesperson
Pr: Michael A Reardon
COO: Kristen Park
Trst: Ranne Warner
VP: Gregory Tranter

D-U-N-S 00-508-3860 EXP
ALLMETAL INC (DE)
1 Pierce Pl Ste 900, Itasca, IL 60143-1253
Tel (630) 250-8090 *Founded/Ownrshp* 1915
Sales 94.5MM^E *EMP* 300
SIC 3699 3089 Laser welding, drilling & cutting equipment; Injection molding of plastics
CFO: Richard Allen
CFO: Allen Rick
Treas: Linda Edie
Genl Mgr: Jeff Andresen
Genl Mgr: Philip C Colin
Off Mgr: Alice Edwards
CIO: Vince Catalano
IT Man: Kevin Grenda
Board of Directors: Lisa Fulton

D-U-N-S 07-878-6182
ALLNEX USA INC
CYNEL
(*Suby of* ALLNEX BELGIUM NV)
9005 Westside Pkwy, Alpharetta, GA 30009-4783
Tel (800) 433-2873 *Founded/Ownrshp* 2012
Sales 400.0MM^E *EMP* 110
SIC 2821 Plastics materials & resins
Pr: Thomas H Kelly
**CFO:* Duncan Taylor
**VP:* Jean-Marc Durbuis
**VP:* Doug Hartman
**VP:* Franois L Thys
**VP:* Marie Van In
Mktg Mgr: Scott Auger

D-U-N-S 79-433-7662
ALLONE HEALTH RESOURCES INC
(*Suby of* HIGHMARK BLUE CRSS-BLUE SHIELD) ★
100 N Penna Ave, Wilkes Barre, PA 18701-3503
Tel (877) 720-7770 *Founded/Ownrshp* 1985
Sales NA *EMP* 300^E
SIC 6321 Accident & health insurance; Accident insurance carriers; Health insurance carriers
Pr: Denise Cesare
**VP:* Mark Destefano
Dir IT: James Michaels

D-U-N-S 83-539-3869
■ ALLOS THERAPEUTICS INC
(*Suby of* SPECTRUM PHARMACEUTICALS INC) ★
11000 Westmoor Cir # 150, Westminster, CO 80021-2733
Tel (303) 426-6262 *Founded/Ownrshp* 2012
Sales 186.0MM^E *EMP* 241^E
SIC 2834 Pharmaceutical preparations
Pr: Abraham N Oler

D-U-N-S 94-680-8136 IMP
ALLOSOURCE
6278 S Troy Cir, Centennial, CO 80111-6422
Tel (720) 873-0213 *Founded/Ownrshp* 1994
Sales 146.1MM *EMP* 160
Accts Mcgladrey Llp Davenport Ia
SIC 3841 Bone drills; Bone plates & screws; Medical instruments & equipment, blood & bone work
Pr: Thomas A Cycyota
Pr: James Czepiel
CFO: Mary L March
**CFO:* Olivia M Thompson
**Ofcr:* Kerr Holbrook
VP: Brent Atkinson
VP: Dale Binke
VP: Robert Brook
VP: Robert-Bob Bundy
VP: Dan Maye
Exec: David White

D-U-N-S 00-549-5171
ALLOY INC
ALLOY ONLINE
(*Suby of* ALLOY MEDIA HOLDINGS LLC) ★
151 W 26th St Fl 11, New York, NY 10001-6810
Tel (609) 655-8878 *Founded/Ownrshp* 1996, 2010
Sales 98.2MM^E *EMP* 602
SIC 8743 8742 7331 7312 Promotion service; Marketing consulting services; Direct mail advertising services; Billboard advertising
CEO: Matthew C Diamond
Pr: Gary Colen
**Pr:* James K Johnson Jr
CEO: Kent Haehl
**Ofcr:* Gina R Digioia
Sr VP: Wendy Wildfeuer
VP: Andy Belth
VP: Elizabeth Hellman
VP: Jodi Smith
Exec: Candace Turner
Creative D: Brian Gibbs

D-U-N-S 96-556-0407
ALLOY MEDIA HOLDINGS LLC
19 W 44th St Fl 18, New York, NY 10036-6101
Tel (212) 784-2010 *Founded/Ownrshp* 2010
Sales 98.2MM^E *EMP* 605^E
SIC 8743 Promotion service
CEO: Struass Zelnick
**VP:* Andrew Vogel

ALLOY ONLINE
See ALLOY INC

D-U-N-S 94-987-4577
ALLPLAYERS NETWORK INC
RANK ONE SPORT
4145 Belt Line Rd Ste 212, Addison, TX 75001-5866
Tel (214) 234-9770 *Founded/Ownrshp* 2013
Sales 365.0MM *EMP* 16
SIC 5941 Sporting goods & bicycle shops
CEO: Jason McKay

D-U-N-S 15-218-9726 IMP/EXP
ALLPLUS COMPUTER SYSTEMS CORP
3075 Nw 107th Ave, Doral, FL 33172-2134
Tel (305) 436-3993 *Founded/Ownrshp* 1997
Sales 164.2MM *EMP* 46
Accts Cherry Bekaert Llp Coral Gabl
SIC 5065 5045 Communication equipment; Computers, peripherals & software
Pr: Alberto M J Rodrigues
**Treas:* Eduardo Jose Rodrigues
**Genl Mgr:* Camilo Rodrigues

ALLROC BUILDING PRODUCTS
See WINROC CORP MIDWEST

D-U-N-S 07-875-3092
■ ALLSCRIPTS HEALTHCARE LLC
(*Suby of* ALLSCRIPTS HEALTHCARE SOLUTIONS INC) ★
8529 Six Forks Rd, Raleigh, NC 27615-2963
Tel (919) 847-8102 *Founded/Ownrshp* 2008
Sales 554.2MM^E *EMP* 2,300
SIC 7372 Prepackaged software
CEO: Paul Black
**Pt:* Roger L Davenport
**Pt:* John P McConnell
**Pt:* Marc Winchester
Pr: Bevey Miner
Ex VP: Archell Georgiou
Sr VP: Nicoa Dunne
Sr VP: Kelly L Ross
Sr VP: Tony Ryzinski
VP: Lisa Baker
VP: Kathy Egan
VP: Chris Horn
VP: Michael Raymer
Exec: Michael Biggs
Exec: Ed Dix
Exec: Cindy Fisher
Exec: Gray Mason
Exec: Chad Novitski

D-U-N-S 15-178-8601
▲ ALLSCRIPTS HEALTHCARE SOLUTIONS INC
222 Merchandise Mart Plz, Chicago, IL 60654-1103
Tel (312) 506-1200 *Founded/Ownrshp* 1986
Sales 1.3MMM *EMP* 6,900
Tkr Sym MDRX *Exch* NGS
SIC 7372 Prepackaged software
CEO: Paul M Black
Ch Bd: Michael A Klayko
Pr: Richard Poulton
Ex VP: James Hewitt
Sr VP: Brian Farley
Sr VP: Dennis Olis
Sr VP: Tejal Vakharia
VP: Charles Fitch
VP: Anissa Grant
VP: Mark Heron
VP: Greg Manning
VP: John Scruggs
VP: Chad Thompson
VP: Jonathan Vipperman
VP Bus Dev: Jacob Plummer
Board of Directors: Gregory Garrison, Jonathan J Judge, Yancey L Spruill, Dave B Stevens, David D Stevens, Ralph H Thurman

D-U-N-S 62-778-7153
ALLSTAFF MANAGEMENT INC
HR STRATEGIES
6650 Sugarloaf Pkwy # 300, Duluth, GA 30097-4364
Tel (770) 339-0000 *Founded/Ownrshp* 2007
Sales 49.7MM^E *EMP* 1,500
SIC 7363 Employee leasing service
CEO: James Beesley

D-U-N-S 62-282-8986 IMP/EXP
ALLSTAR MARKETING GROUP LLC
ALLSTAR PRODUCTS GROUP
2 Skyline Dr, Hawthorne, NY 10532-2142
Tel (914) 347-7827 *Founded/Ownrshp* 1998
Sales 213.7MM *EMP* 61
SIC 5023 Home furnishings
Exec: Andrea Dadio
Dir Bus: Osania Del Rio
Mktg Mgr: Teresa Dippolito

ALLSTAR PRODUCTS GROUP
See ALLSTAR MARKETING GROUP LLC

ALLSTATE
See SAM SWOPE AUTO GROUP LLC

ALLSTATE
See AMERICAN MORTGAGE SERVICE CO

D-U-N-S 03-404-7308 IMP
ALLSTATE BEVERAGE CO INC (AL)
130 6th St, Montgomery, AL 36104-1633
Tel (334) 265-0507 *Founded/Ownrshp* 1950, 1986
Sales 97.1MM^E *EMP* 158
SIC 5181 Beer & other fermented malt liquors
Pr: Charles B Grant III
**VP:* Walker Grant
IT Man: Jason Bush
IT Man: Jason Rawlinson

D-U-N-S 80-389-8469
▲ ALLSTATE CORP
2775 Sanders Rd, Northbrook, IL 60062-6110
Tel (847) 402-5000 *Founded/Ownrshp* 1931
Sales NA *EMP* 41,600
Tkr Sym ALL *Exch* NYS
SIC 6411 6351 6311 6371 Insurance agents, brokers & service; Fire insurance underwriters' laboratories; Patrol services, insurance; Mortgage guarantee insurance; Life insurance carriers; Pensions
Ch Bd: Thomas J Wilson
V Ch: Jeff Dunning
Pr: Steve Ihm
Pr: Maria McNitt
Pr: Mike Scardina
Pr: Matthew E Winter
CFO: Steven E Shebik
Treas: Bill Mann
Ofcr: John M Rhodes
Ex VP: Chris Gibbs
Ex VP: Sanjay Gupta
Ex VP: Susan L Lees
VP: Shawn Anderson
VP: Bill Ballinger
VP: Victoria Blake
VP: Ryan Briggs
VP: Peter Chafetz
VP: Laura Clark
VP: Edward Collins
VP: Luke Doebele
VP: Joseph R Eckert
Board of Directors: Kermit R Crawford, Michael L Eskew, Herbert L Henkel, Jacques P Perold, Andrea Redmond, John W Rowe, Judith A Sprieser, Mary Alice Taylor, Perry M Traquina

D-U-N-S 12-317-8878
■ ALLSTATE DISTRIBUTORS LLC
(*Suby of* ALLSTATE CORP) ★
2775 Sanders Rd, Northbrook, IL 60062-6110
Tel (847) 402-5000 *Founded/Ownrshp* 2000
Sales NA *EMP* 1,000
SIC 6411 Insurance agents, brokers & service

D-U-N-S 04-423-9085
■ ALLSTATE INDEMNITY CO (IL)
(*Suby of* ALLSTATE INSURANCE CO) ★
2775 Sanders Rd F9, Northbrook, IL 60062-6110
Tel (847) 402-5000 *Founded/Ownrshp* 1960
Sales NA *EMP* 2,500
SIC 6411 Insurance agents, brokers & service
Pr: Steven L Groot
Ch Bd: Jerry D Choate
Pr: Harriet Harty
Treas: James P Zils
Assoc VP: Richard Heneberry
Sr VP: Robert W Gary
Sr VP: Robert W Pike
Sr VP: Casey J Sylla
Sr VP: Thomas J Wilson II
VP: Karen C Gardner
VP: Samuel H Pitch
VP: Sanford C Price Jr
VP: Kevin T Sullivan
Exec: Andy Hassan

D-U-N-S 00-693-5886
■ ALLSTATE INSURANCE CO
(*Suby of* ALLSTATE CORP) ★
2775 Sanders Rd, Northbrook, IL 60062-6127
Tel (847) 402-5000 *Founded/Ownrshp* 1931
Sales NA *EMP* 25,000
SIC 6411 Insurance agents, brokers & service
Pr: Thomas J Wilson
Pr: Joan M Crockett
**CFO:* Danny L Hale
**Chf Mktg O:* Joseph V Tripodi
Ofcr: Sperrano Anthony
Ofcr: Henry Brautigam
Ofcr: Mark Bugenhagen
Ofcr: Joseph Dioguardi
Ofcr: Stephen Ehrlich
Ofcr: Brian Fitzpatrick
Ofcr: Edward Gerg
Ofcr: Matthew Huffman
Ofcr: Randall Knoll
Ofcr: Danny Marcengill
Ofcr: Frank Sarmiento
Ofcr: Garland Smith
Ofcr: Brent Walters
**Ofcr:* Anise D Wiley-Little
Ex VP: Laura Bartlett
Ex VP: Guy Hill
**Ex VP:* Robert W Pike

D-U-N-S 10-763-2861
■ ALLSTATE LIFE INSURANCE CO
(*Suby of* ALLSTATE INSURANCE CO) ★
3075 Sanders Rd, Northbrook, IL 60062-7119
Tel (847) 402-5000 *Founded/Ownrshp* 1957
Sales NA *EMP* 4^E
Accts Deloitte & Touche Llp Chicago
SIC 6411 6311 Insurance agents, brokers & service; Pension & retirement plan consultants; Life insurance
Pr: Don Civgin
**Ch Bd:* Thomas J Wilson
**CFO:* Jesse E Merten
VP: Andrew Plebanski
Div Mgr: Mary Allen
QA Dir: Sara Foster
Dir IT: Tim Rodine
IT Man: Carol Bonovich
IT Man: David Lutz
IT Man: Jim Smejkal
Software D: Funke Oladunmoye

D-U-N-S 12-316-6915
■ ALLSTATE NON INSURANCE HOLDINGS INC
(*Suby of* ALLSTATE CORP) ★
2775 Sanders Rd Ste D, Northbrook, IL 60062-6110
Tel (847) 402-5000 *Founded/Ownrshp* 1999
Sales NA *EMP* 850
SIC 6411 Insurance agents, brokers & service
VP: William Crimmins
Dir IT: Linda Rice

ALLSTATE PETERBILT GROUP
See W D LARSON COMPANIES LTD INC

D-U-N-S 12-316-7442
■ ALLSTATE TEXAS LLOYDS
(*Suby of* ALLSTATE CORP) ★
8711 Freeport Pkwy, Irving, TX 75063-2578
Tel (847) 402-3029 *Founded/Ownrshp* 1988
Sales NA *EMP* 40,000
SIC 6331 Fire, marine & casualty insurance
Pr: Thomas Clarkson
**Ch Bd:* Larry Sedillo

D-U-N-S 12-031-6711 IMP/EXP
■ ALLSTEEL INC
(*Suby of* HNI CORP) ★
2210 2nd Ave, Muscatine, IA 52761-5263
Tel (563) 272-4800 *Founded/Ownrshp* 1912
Sales 338.9MM^E *EMP* 1,600
SIC 2522 Office furniture, except wood; Office chairs, benches & stools, except wood; Office cabinets & filing drawers: except wood; Office desks & tables: except wood
Pr: Jeff Lorenger
VP: Sabine Bartzke
VP: Steve Sparks
VP: Lynda Whittle
Exec: Michael J Shelby
Opers Mgr: Randy Moberg

D-U-N-S 10-281-5537
ALLSUP ENTERPRISES INC
2112 N Thornton St, Clovis, NM 88101-4130
Tel (575) 769-2311 *Founded/Ownrshp* 1986
Sales 152.6MM^E *EMP* 1,274
SIC 5411 5541 4832 6519 5171 Convenience stores, chain; Filling stations, gasoline; Radio broadcasting stations; Farm land leasing; Petroleum bulk stations
Pr: Lonnie Allsup
**VP:* Barbara Allsup
**VP:* Mark A Allsup

D-U-N-S 04-136-9000
ALLSUPS CONVENIENCE STORES INC
(*Suby of* ALLSUP ENTERPRISES INC) ★
2112 N Thornton St, Clovis, NM 88101-4130
Tel (575) 769-2311 *Founded/Ownrshp* 1956
Sales 149.0MM^E *EMP* 1,238
SIC 5411 5541 Convenience stores, chain; Filling stations, gasoline
Pr: Lonnie Allsup
**VP:* Mark A Allsup
CIO: Gary Holmes

D-U-N-S 03-785-3744 IMP/EXP
ALLTECH INC
FORTNIGHT PRODUCTIONS
3031 Catnip Hill Rd, Nicholasville, KY 40356-9765
Tel (859) 885-9613 *Founded/Ownrshp* 1980
Sales 296.7MM^E *EMP* 600
SIC 2869 2048 3821 2819 Enzymes; Feed supplements; Laboratory apparatus & furniture; Industrial inorganic chemicals
Pr: T Pearse Lyons
CEO: Alric Blake
COO: E Michael Castle II
Sec: Nathan H Hohman
VP: Aidan Connolly
VP: Peter Karnezos
VP: Mark Lyons
Exec: Manoella Alves
Off Mgr: China S Force
Off Mgr: Ben Shafer
Off Mgr: Sylvie St-Pierre

D-U-N-S 00-790-3792
■ ALLTEL COMMUNICATIONS CORP
(*Suby of* ALLTEL CORP) ★
66 N 4th St, Newark, OH 43055-5000
Tel (740) 349-8551 *Founded/Ownrshp* 1930
Sales 89.9MM^E *EMP* 779
SIC 4813 4812 Local telephone communications; Long distance telephone communications; Radio telephone communication
Pr: Dennis Mervis
* *Treas:* Giulio Freda
* *VP:* Ken Blake
Area Mgr: Richard Mc Clain

D-U-N-S 12-218-9723
■ ALLTEL COMMUNICATIONS LLC
(*Suby of* ALLTEL CORP) ★
1 Allied Dr, Little Rock, AR 72202-2065
Tel (501) 905-8000 *Founded/Ownrshp* 1996
Sales 680.0MM^E *EMP* 3,000^E
SIC 4812 Cellular telephone services

D-U-N-S 13-974-2134
■ ALLTEL COMMUNICATIONS OF VIRGINIA INC
(*Suby of* ALLTEL CORP) ★
1 Allied Dr, Little Rock, AR 72202-2065
Tel (501) 905-8100 *Founded/Ownrshp* 1985
Sales 72.7MM^E *EMP* 1,060
SIC 4812 Cellular telephone services; Paging services
Pr: Michael T Flynn

D-U-N-S 00-790-2802 IMP
■ ALLTEL CORP
(*Suby of* AT&T INC) ★
1001 Technology Dr, Little Rock, AR 72223-5943
Tel (866) 255-8357 *Founded/Ownrshp* 2013
Sales 4.3MMM^E *EMP* 14,899
SIC 4812 5999 Cellular telephone services; Mobile telephones & equipment
Pr: Scott T Ford
Ch Bd: Francis X Frantz
Pr: Kevin L Beebe
CEO: Jeff Gardner
COO: Jeffrey Fox
CFO: Gunnar Forcier
CFO: Sharilyn S Gasaway
Treas: Matthew Ellis
Treas: Holly Larkin
Bd of Dir: Dave Massery
Ex VP: CJ Duvall Jr
Ex VP: Richard N Massey
Sr VP: John Ebner
Sr VP: John S Haley
Sr VP: Nicola Palmer
VP: Kevin Halpin

D-U-N-S 08-597-1570
ALLTRAN FINANCIAL LP
ACB RECOVERY
5800 N Course Dr, Houston, TX 77072-1613
Tel (800) 568-0399 *Founded/Ownrshp* 1977
Sales 163.6MM^E *EMP* 2,136
SIC 7322 Collection agency, except real estate
Pr: Kevin Keleghan
Pr: James Kellerher
Pr: Glenn P Osuch
CFO: George Williams
Ofcr: Michael Strachan
Ofcr: Ken Vizena
Ex VP: Michael Chandler
VP: Drew Anderson
VP: Jacqueline Berry
VP: Dale Bissette
VP: Charly Filipek
VP: Rick Hargreaves
VP: Justin Martinez
VP: Kathy Wingard

D-U-N-S 78-563-4242
■ ALLY BANK
(*Suby of* ALLY FINANCIAL INC) ★
6985 S Union Park Ctr # 435, Midvale, UT 84047-4177
Tel (801) 790-5005 *Founded/Ownrshp* 2004
Sales NA *EMP* 42
SIC 6153 6021 6311 6331 6162 Financing of dealers by motor vehicle manufacturers organ.; Installment paper; Purchasers of accounts receivable & commercial paper; National commercial banks; Life insurance carriers; Automobile insurance; Fire, marine & casualty insurance: stock; Burglary & theft insurance; Mortgage bankers
Ch Bd: Diane E Morais
CFO: James N Young
Ex VP: Jeffrey J Brown

D-U-N-S 00-698-4298 IMP
▲ ALLY FINANCIAL INC
500 Woodward Ave Fl 1, Detroit, MI 48226-3423
Tel (866) 710-4623 *Founded/Ownrshp* 1919
Sales NA *EMP* 7,100
Tkr Sym ALLY *Exch* NYS
SIC 6021 6153 6159 6311 6331 6162 National commercial banks; Financing of dealers by motor vehicle manufacturers organ.; Installment paper; Purchasers of accounts receivable & commercial paper; Automobile finance leasing; Machinery & equipment finance leasing; Truck finance leasing; Finance leasing, vehicles: except automobiles & trucks; Life insurance carriers; Automobile insurance; Fire, marine & casualty insurance: stock; Burglary & theft insurance; Mortgage bankers
CEO: Jeffrey J Brown
* *Ch Bd:* Franklin W Hobbs
CFO: Christopher Halmy
Ofcr: David Shevsky
Ex VP: Tim M Russi
VP: David Debrunner
VP: Mike Goeller
VP: William B Solomon
VP: Richard Strahota
Prgrm Mgr: James Palacios
Dir IT: Gary Schuster
Board of Directors: Kenneth J Bacon, Robert T Blakely, William H Cary, Maureen A Breakiron-Evans, Kim S Fennebresque, Marjorie Magner, John J Stack, Michael F Steib

D-U-N-S 04-636-0681
■ ALLY INSURANCE HOLDINGS INC
GMAC
(*Suby of* ALLY FINANCIAL INC) ★
500 Woodward Ave Fl 1, Detroit, MI 48226-3423
Tel (888) 737-8460 *Founded/Ownrshp* 1997
Sales NA *EMP* 3,700
SIC 6331 6141 Automobile insurance; Fire, marine & casualty insurance: stock; Personal credit institutions
Pr: Byron Storms
CFO: Michael Weiner
Ofcr: John C Beattie
Ex VP: Thomas D Callahan
Ex VP: Ronald M Judd
Sr VP: Donald McKee
VP: John Pinto
VP: Jim Porcari
VP: Brian Rogers
Snr Ntwrk: Tricia Watson
IT Man: Don Hawes

D-U-N-S 60-959-0620
■ ALLY SERVICING LLC
SEMPERIAN COLLECTION CENTER
(*Suby of* ALLY FINANCIAL INC) ★
500 Woodward Ave Fl 1, Detroit, MI 48226-3423
Tel (248) 948-7702 *Founded/Ownrshp* 1999
Sales 155.9MM^E *EMP* 3,455^E
SIC 1389 Roustabout service
Pr: Evan Noulas
* *Ex VP:* Lee G McCarty
* *Ex VP:* William C Ploog
Mng Dir: Darren Linder

ALLYN FOUNDATION, THE
See ALLYN WELCH HOLDINGS INC

D-U-N-S 00-224-0281
ALLYN WELCH HOLDINGS INC
ALLYN FOUNDATION, THE
4341 State Street Rd, Skaneateles Falls, NY 13153-5300
Tel (315) 685-4100 *Founded/Ownrshp* 1915
Sales 625.8MM^E *EMP* 2,806
SIC 3841

D-U-N-S 02-306-4996
ALM MEDIA HOLDINGS INC
120 Broadway Fl 5, New York, NY 10271-1100
Tel (212) 457-9400 *Founded/Ownrshp* 2009
Sales 190.2MM^E *EMP* 1,015
SIC 2721 2711 2741 2731 7389 Magazines: publishing only, not printed on site; Newspapers: publishing only, not printed on site; Newsletter publishing; Book publishing; Trade show arrangement
Pr: William L Pollak
Pr: Andrew Neblett
CFO: Eric Flundberg
* *CFO:* Eric F Lundberg
* *Ofcr:* Jeffrey K Whittle
* *Sr VP:* Jack Berkowitz
Sr VP: Jeffrey S Litvack
Sr VP: Eric Lundberg
* *VP:* Anup Bagaria
* *VP:* Fabio Bertoni
* *VP:* Renee Citera
* *VP:* Allison C Hoffman

D-U-N-S 02-306-5605
ALM MEDIA LLC
NEW YORK LAW JOURNAL
(*Suby of* ALM MEDIA HOLDINGS INC) ★
120 Broadway Fl 5, New York, NY 10271-1100
Tel (212) 457-9400 *Founded/Ownrshp* 1997
Sales 189.2MM^E *EMP* 800
SIC 2721 2711 2741 2731 7389 Magazines: publishing only, not printed on site; Newspapers: publishing only, not printed on site; Newsletter publishing; Book publishing; Trade show arrangement
CEO: Bill Carter
* *COO:* Kevin Michielsen
* *CFO:* Eric Lundberg
* *Chf Mktg O:* Molly Miller
Sr VP: Lenny Izzo
Sr VP: Jeff Litvack
Sr VP: John Stuttard
VP: Steven Andreazza
* *VP:* Renee Citera
VP: Michael Desiato
VP: Kenneth Gary
VP: Dan Rubinetti
VP: Stephen Wellman
VP: Jeffrey K Whittlesenior
Dir Soc: Douglas Brown
Dir Bus: Gail Cleary

D-U-N-S 11-115-9195
ALMA HEALTHCARE AND REHABILITATION CENTER LLC
ALMA HLTHCARE REHABILATION CTR
401 Heather Ln, Alma, AR 72921-5025
Tel (479) 632-4343 *Founded/Ownrshp* 2001
Sales 2.6MM^E *EMP* 8,200
SIC 8059 Nursing home, except skilled & intermediate care facility

ALMA HLTHCARE REHABILATION CTR
See ALMA HEALTHCARE AND REHABILITATION CENTER LLC

ALMA PRODUCTS COMPANY
See ETX INC

D-U-N-S 96-335-4253
ALMAC CLINICAL SERVICES LLC
(*Suby of* ALMAC GROUP INC) ★
25 Fretz Rd, Souderton, PA 18964-2610
Tel (215) 660-8500 *Founded/Ownrshp* 2007
Sales 96.6MM^E *EMP* 733
SIC 7389 Packaging & labeling services
Pr: Robert Dunlop
* *Treas:* Michael Bacon
Ofcr: Allan Armstrong
VP: Celine Bradley
VP: Charlie Morris
Assoc Dir: Robert Smith
Dir Bus: Michael Cannarsa
Dir IT: Christi Gimber
Tech Mgr: Kevin Gross
Ql Cn Mgr: Walter Beniquez
Sales Exec: Richard Shannon

D-U-N-S 82-987-9845
ALMAC GROUP INC
(*Suby of* ALMAC GROUP LIMITED)
25 Fretz Rd, Souderton, PA 18964-2610
Tel (215) 660-8500 *Founded/Ownrshp* 2002
Sales 707.4MM^E *EMP* 1,400
SIC 2834 Pharmaceutical preparations
Pr: Alan Armstrong
Pr: David Downey
* *Treas:* Kevin Stephens
VP: Karen Borda
* *VP:* Stephen Campbell
* *VP:* John Irvine
Assoc Dir: Jim Lomker
Assoc Dir: Jamie Romanowski
Assoc Dir: Robert Weney
Mng Dir: Derek Thornton
Prgrm Mgr: Ada Gurman

D-U-N-S 07-860-7239 IMP
ALMAC PHARMA SERVICES LLC
(*Suby of* ALMAC GROUP INC) ★
2661 Audubon Rd, Audubon, PA 19403-2413
Tel (610) 666-9500 *Founded/Ownrshp* 2010
Sales 567.0MM *EMP* 75
SIC 2834 Druggists' preparations (pharmaceuticals)
* *Treas:* Kevin Stevhens
VP: Celine Bradley
VP: John Dooley

ALMACENES PITUSA
See PR RETAIL STORES INC

D-U-N-S 07-940-9480
ALMATIS BURNSIDE LLC
(*Suby of* ALMATIS INC) ★
41237 Hwy 22, Burnside, LA 70738
Tel (225) 474-1700 *Founded/Ownrshp* 2013
Sales 87.3MM^E *EMP* 330
SIC 2819 Bauxite, refined
Pr: Taco Gerbranda

D-U-N-S 14-278-7600 IMP/EXP
ALMATIS INC
(*Suby of* ALMATIS B.V.)
501 W Park Rd, Leetsdale, PA 15056-1018
Tel (412) 630-2800 *Founded/Ownrshp* 2007
Sales 185.2MM^E *EMP* 330
SIC 2819 Industrial inorganic chemicals
CEO: Taco Gerbranda
VP: Peter Post
VP: Leslie Power
Sfty Mgr: Sidney Degarmo
Opers Mgr: Dinesh Moorjani
Prd Mgr: Frank Kraaijenbos
Prd Mgr: Mark Vandijk
Prd Mgr: Charles Zeigler
Manager: Pedro Garcia
Genl Couns: Nick R Elliot
Snr Mgr: Martina Novotny

D-U-N-S 04-396-7561 IMP
ALMO CORP
2709 Commerce Way, Philadelphia, PA 19154-1011
Tel (215) 698-4000 *Founded/Ownrshp* 1970
Sales 149.2MM^E *EMP* 210
SIC 5064 5063

D-U-N-S 10-553-3749 IMP/EXP
ALMOD DIAMONDS LTD
DIAMONDS INTERNATIONAL
592 5th Ave Fl 9, New York, NY 10036-4707
Tel (212) 764-6900 *Founded/Ownrshp* 1991
Sales 162.2MM^E *EMP* 140
SIC 5094 Diamonds (gems)
Ch Bd: Albert Gad
Prin: Francine Gad
Prin: Morris Gad
Prin: Joseph Hecht
Plng Mgr: Elizabeth Reda
Mktg Mgr: Alon Cohen
Mktg Mgr: Sonia Graham

ALMOND GROUP
See ALMOND JEWELERS INC

D-U-N-S 07-860-4287 IMP
ALMOND JEWELERS INC
ALMOND GROUP
16 S Maryland Ave, Port Washington, NY 11050-2913
Tel (516) 933-6000 *Founded/Ownrshp* 1975
Sales 100.0MM *EMP* 15
SIC 3911 Jewelry, precious metal
Pr: Jonathan Mandelbaum
CFO: Henry Bubrow
* *VP:* Maurice Mandelbaum

D-U-N-S 15-360-0796
▲ ALMOST FAMILY INC
9510 Ormsby Station Rd # 103, Louisville, KY 40223-4081
Tel (502) 423-4336 *Founded/Ownrshp* 1976
Sales 532.2MM *EMP* 14,200^E
Tkr Sym AFAM *Exch* NGS
SIC 8082 Home health care services
Ch Bd: William B Yarmuth
Pr: C Steven Guenthner
COO: Daniel J Schwartz
Chf Cred: Rajneesh Kaushal
Sr VP: P Todd Lyles
Board of Directors: Henry M Altman Jr, Steven B Bing, Jonathan D Goldberg, Donald G McClinton, W Earl Reed III, Tyree G Wilburn

ALMOST FAMOUS CLOTHING
See TURN ON PRODUCTS INC

D-U-N-S 04-765-3753 IMP
ALNOR OIL CO INC
70 E Sunrise Hwy Ste 418, Valley Stream, NY 11581-1233
Tel (516) 561-6146 *Founded/Ownrshp* 1969
Sales 85.0MM *EMP* 9
SIC 5199 Oils, animal or vegetable
Pr: Marjorie Klayman
* *VP:* Gordon Kaplan
* *VP:* Nancy Kaplan

D-U-N-S 07-948-2260
■ ALO ACQUISITION LLC
(*Suby of* ALBANY MOLECULAR RESEARCH INC) ★
26 Corporate Cir, Albany, NY 12203-5121
Tel (518) 464-0279 *Founded/Ownrshp* 2014
Sales 116.4MM^E *EMP* 217^E
SIC 2833 5122 8733 Medicinals & botanicals; Drugs & drug proprietaries; Research institute
Ch Bd: Thomas E D'Ambra

D-U-N-S 08-190-9046 IMP
■ ALOHA PETROLEUM LTD
ISLAND MINI MART
(*Suby of* SUSSER PETROLEUM PROPERTY CO LLC) ★
1132 Bishop St Ste 1700, Honolulu, HI 96813-2820
Tel (808) 833-3249 *Founded/Ownrshp* 2014
Sales 247.5MM^E *EMP* 500
SIC 5172 5541 5411 Lubricating oils & greases; Service station supplies, petroleum; Filling stations, gasoline; Convenience stores, independent
Pr: Richard Parry
* *Treas:* Thomas A Grimes
VP: Lois Osorno
Area Supr: Butch Galdeira
IT Man: Alton Higa
Opers Mgr: Jeff Finch

D-U-N-S 83-278-9247
■ ALON REFINING KROTZ SPRINGS INC
(*Suby of* ALON USA ENERGY INC) ★
E I 20, Krotz Springs, LA 70750
Tel (337) 594-5300 *Founded/Ownrshp* 2009
Sales 2.6MMM *EMP* 10
SIC 2911 Petroleum refining
Ch Bd: David Wiessman

D-U-N-S 02-710-3550
■ ALON USA DELAWARE LLC
(*Suby of* ALON USA INC) ★
12700 Park Central Dr # 1600, Dallas, TX 75251-1517
Tel (972) 367-3600 *Founded/Ownrshp* 2000
Sales 107.4MM^E *EMP* 286
SIC 8741 Management services
Genl Mgr: Rhonda Buras

D-U-N-S 87-666-1062
▲ ALON USA ENERGY INC
12700 Park Central Dr # 1600, Dallas, TX 75251-1517
Tel (972) 367-3600 *Founded/Ownrshp* 2000
Sales 4.3MMM *EMP* 2,860
Tkr Sym ALJ *Exch* NYS
SIC 2911 5171 5411 Petroleum refining; Asphalt or asphaltic materials, made in refineries; Petroleum bulk stations & terminals; Convenience stores, chain
Pr: Paul Eisman
* *Ch Bd:* Ezra Uzi Yemin
Pr: Josef Lipman
Pr: Kyle McKeen
CFO: Shai Even
Sr VP: Jimmy C Crosby
Sr VP: Claire A Hart
Sr VP: Alan Moret
Sr VP: Michael Oster
Sr VP: James Ranspot
Sr VP: Scott Rowe
VP: Jeff Brorman
VP: Gregg Byers
Board of Directors: Ilan Cohen, Ron W Haddock, William Kacal, Yeshayahu Pery, Zalman Segal, Mark D Smith, Franklin R Wheeler, David Wiessman

D-U-N-S 16-884-8013
■ ALON USA INC
(*Suby of* ALON USA ENERGY INC) ★
12700 Park Central Dr # 1600, Dallas, TX 75251-1517
Tel (972) 367-3600 *Founded/Ownrshp* 2000
Sales 107.7MM^E *EMP* 286
SIC 2911 Petroleum refining
* *Pr:* Paul Eisman
* *CFO:* Shai Even
CFO: Rainee Landry
* *Sr VP:* Claire Hart
* *Sr VP:* Alan Moret
VP: Scott Rowe
Exec: Eric Nystrom
Genl Mgr: Bryan Hector
IT Man: Christopher Retz
Netwrk Eng: Charlie Evano
Sales Exec: Kyle McKeen

D-U-N-S 80-662-5757
■ ALON USA LP
(*Suby of* ALON USA DELAWARE LLC) ★
12700 Park Central Dr # 1600, Dallas, TX 75251-1517
Tel (972) 367-3600 *Founded/Ownrshp* 2000
Sales 107.4MM^E *EMP* 284
SIC 2911 4612 5172 5541 2895 Petroleum refining; Gasoline; Jet fuels; Kerosene; Crude petroleum pipelines; Petroleum products; Filling stations, gasoline; Carbon black
Ch Bd: David Wiessman
CEO: Paul Eisman
CFO: Claire A Hart
Sr VP: Shai Even
Sr VP: Alan P Moret
VP: Kyle C McKeen

D-U-N-S 07-842-1052
■ ALON USA PARTNERS LP
(*Suby of* ALON USA ENERGY INC) ★
12700 Park Central Dr # 1600, Dallas, TX 75251-1517
Tel (972) 367-3600 *Founded/Ownrshp* 2012
Sales 2.1MMM *EMP* 2,860
Tkr Sym ALDW *Exch* NYS
SIC 2911 Petroleum refining; Gasoline; Oils, fuel
Pr: Paul Eisman
* *Genl Pt:* Alon U GP
* *Ch Bd:* David Wiessman

D-U-N-S 13-401-0847 IMP
ALORICA INC
PRIORITY ONE SUPPORT
5 Park Plz Ste 1100, Irvine, CA 92614-8502
Tel (949) 527-4600 *Founded/Ownrshp* 2016

Sales 4.8MMM^E *EMP* 92,000
SIC 7389 Telephone services
Pr: Andy Lee
CFO: Jack Pollock
* *Ofcr:* Gregory Hopkins
* *Ofcr:* James Molloy
* *Ex VP:* Art Dibari
Ex VP: Robert Luke
VP: Kristina Chavis
VP: Paul Collins
VP: Mark Hauge
VP: Mary Henson
VP: Robert Hosier
VP: Joyce Lee
VP: Yc Liu
VP: Derrick Latreille Od
VP: Beverly Tarnoff
VP: Todd Werner
VP: Leslie Zimprich

D-U-N-S 80-761-7618 IMP/EXP
ALOUETTE CHEESE USA LLC
FLEUR DE LAIT EAST
(*Suby of* BC USA) ★
400 S Custer Ave, New Holland, PA 17557-9220
Tel (717) 355-8500 *Founded/Ownrshp* 1976
Sales 192.4MM^E *EMP* 200^E
SIC 5143 2022 Dairy products, except dried or canned; Cheese, natural & processed
CFO: Ulrich Strietholt
QA Dir: Louise Newswanger
Ql Cn Mgr: Connie Penner
VP Sls: David Issenberg

D-U-N-S 05-786-6907 IMP/EXP
ALP LIGHTING & CEILING PRODUCTS INC
A.L.P. LIGHTING COMPONENTS
6333 W Gross Point Rd, Niles, IL 60714-3915
Tel (773) 774-9550 *Founded/Ownrshp* 1972
Sales 193.8MM^E *EMP* 669
SIC 3089 3354 5162 3496 3442 3229

A.L.P. LIGHTING COMPONENTS
See ALP LIGHTING & CEILING PRODUCTS INC

ALPCO
See ALUMINUM LINE PRODUCTS CO

D-U-N-S 03-167-2942
ALPENA REGIONAL MEDICAL CENTER
ARMC HOME CARE SERVICES
1501 W Chisholm St, Alpena, MI 49707-1498
Tel (989) 356-7390 *Founded/Ownrshp* 1940
Sales 128.8MM *EMP* 976
Accts Plante & Moran Pllc East Lan
SIC 8062 General medical & surgical hospitals
CEO: Karmon Bjella
COO: Aldean J Moe
* *VP:* George Smart
VP: Gary Weeks
Mktg Mgr: Staci Chroninger
Dir Health: Susan McConnell

D-U-N-S 00-472-9765 IMP/EXP
ALPHA APPALACHIA HOLDINGS INC
(*Suby of* ALPHA NATURAL RESOURCES INC) ★
1 Alpha Pl, Bristol, VA 24209
Tel (276) 619-4410 *Founded/Ownrshp* 1920, 1978
Sales 720.2MM^E *EMP* 7,359
SIC 1221 1222 Bituminous coal & lignite-surface mining; Bituminous coal & lignite loading & preparation; Coal preparation plant, bituminous or lignite; Bituminous coal-underground mining
CEO: Kevin S Crutchfield
* *Ex VP:* Vaughn R Groves
VP Cor Dev: Andrew Hampton
VP Sls: Steve Sears
VP Sls: Roger T Williams

D-U-N-S 09-898-0766
ALPHA BAKING CO INC
5001 W Polk St, Chicago, IL 60644-5249
Tel (773) 489-5400 *Founded/Ownrshp* 1979
Sales 229.1MM^E *EMP* 1,000
SIC 2051

D-U-N-S 05-031-1000
ALPHA BUILDING CORP
24870 Blanco Rd, San Antonio, TX 78260-6674
Tel (210) 491-9925 *Founded/Ownrshp* 1993
Sales 95.0MM^E *EMP* 115
SIC 1542 Commercial & office building contractors
Pr: Kathleen Acock
* *Ex VP:* Richard Booher
* *VP:* Jonathan Rogero

D-U-N-S 79-694-2084
ALPHA COAL WEST INC
(*Suby of* ALPHA NATURAL RESOURCES INC) ★
2273 Bishop Rd, Gillette, WY 82718-9356
Tel (307) 687-3400 *Founded/Ownrshp* 2003
Sales 188.5MM^E *EMP* 575
SIC 1221 Bituminous coal & lignite-surface mining
CEO: Shane Durgin
VP: Gary Buchan
* *Genl Mgr:* Kenneth Ferguson

D-U-N-S 00-703-7765 IMP/EXP
ALPHA CORP OF TENNESSEE (TN)
955 Highway 57, Collierville, TN 38017-5205
Tel (901) 854-2800 *Founded/Ownrshp* 1960, 1983
Sales 285.5MM^E *EMP* 560
SIC 3089 2865 Plastic processing; Dyes & pigments
Pr: Fredrick S Norman
* *CFO:* John Griggs
VP: Matther Watkins

ALPHA GROUP, THE
See ALPHA TECHNOLOGIES INC

D-U-N-S 80-673-8258 EXP
ALPHA INDUSTRIES MANAGEMENT INC
SIGMA PLASTICS GROUP, THE
Page And Schuyler Ave, Lyndhurst, NJ 07071
Tel (201) 933-6000 *Founded/Ownrshp* 1988
Sales 1.3MMM^E *EMP* 1,800
SIC 2673 Plastic & pliofilm bags
Ch Bd: Alfred Teo
CFO: John Reier
* *Ex VP:* Stanley Band
Genl Mgr: Greg Gallow

D-U-N-S 61-034-6350
ALPHA MATERIALS HANDLING INC
313 N 9th St, Midlothian, TX 76065-2701
Tel (972) 775-2555 *Founded/Ownrshp* 2005
Sales 3.7MMM *EMP* 5
SIC 5084

D-U-N-S 16-666-5831
ALPHA NATURAL RESOURCES INC
1989 E Stone Dr, Kingsport, TN 37660-4607
Tel (423) 723-8900 *Founded/Ownrshp* 2004
Sales 4.2MMM *EMP* 8,900^E
SIC 1221 1222 Bituminous coal & lignite-surface mining; Bituminous coal-underground mining
Ch Bd: Kevin S Crutchfield
CFO: Andy Eidson
Ofcr: Gary W Banbury
Ex VP: Keith Hainer
Ex VP: Mark M Manno
Ex VP: Richard H Verheij
Ex VP: Richard Verheij
Sr VP: John W Hanekamp
Sr VP: Alan W Jones Jr
VP: Mike Gisin
VP: Drew McCallister
VP: Phillip Monroe
VP: John Pearl
Board of Directors: Angelo C Brisimitzakis, William J Crowley Jr, E Linn Draper Jr, Deborah M Fretz, P Michael Giftos, L Patrick Hassey, Joel Richards III

D-U-N-S 12-376-8975
ALPHA NATURAL RESOURCES LLC
(*Suby of* ALPHA NATURAL RESOURCES INC) ★
1 Alpha Pl, Bristol, VA 24209
Tel (276) 619-4410 *Founded/Ownrshp* 2009
Sales 2.6MMM^E *EMP* 8,800
SIC 1241 Coal mining services
Ch Bd: Kevin S Crutchfield
Bd of Dir: Fox John
VP: Daniel E Horn
VP Mktg: Kroh Scott

D-U-N-S 07-141-8059
ALPHA OIL & GAS SERVICES INC
453 Tower St Nw, Clearbrook, MN 56634-4289
Tel (218) 776-2278 *Founded/Ownrshp* 2011
Sales 93.2MM^E *EMP* 79^E
SIC 5172 1623 1522 Crude oil; Gas main construction; Residential construction
Pr: Ken Pharpentier

ALPHA PACKAGING
See ALPHA PLASTICS INC

D-U-N-S 96-215-7959
ALPHA PACKAGING HOLDINGS INC
1555 Page Industrial Blvd, Saint Louis, MO 63132-1309
Tel (314) 427-4300 *Founded/Ownrshp* 2004
Sales 263.3MM^E *EMP* 770
SIC 3085 Plastics bottles
CEO: David Spence
* *COO:* Dan Creston
COO: Greg Freeman
* *CFO:* Gary Seeman
VP: Perry Craig
VP Sls: Jack Baily

D-U-N-S 06-464-3117 IMP
ALPHA PLASTICS INC
ALPHA PACKAGING
(*Suby of* ALPHA PACKAGING HOLDINGS INC) ★
1555 Page Industrial Blvd, Saint Louis, MO 63132-1309
Tel (314) 427-4300 *Founded/Ownrshp* 1985
Sales 242.6MM^E *EMP* 700
SIC 3085 Plastics bottles
Pr: David Spence
* *COO:* Dan Creston
* *CFO:* Gary Seeman
VP: Creston Dan
Telecom Ex: Jack Badolian
Netwrk Mgr: Randy Kotoucek
Sales Exec: John Woelfel
Sales Asso: Fred Venezia

D-U-N-S 14-792-7966
ALPHA RAE PERSONNEL INC
347 W Berry St Ste 700, Fort Wayne, IN 46802-2213
Tel (260) 426-8227 *Founded/Ownrshp* 1980
Sales 36.6MM^E *EMP* 1,350
SIC 8742 Human resource consulting services
Pr: Rae Pearson
COO: Alisa Pearson
* *Ex VP:* Lesley Sears

D-U-N-S 01-462-8093 IMP/EXP
ALPHA SHIRT CO
(*Suby of* BRODER BROS CO) ★
6 Neshaminy Interplex Dr # 6, Feasterville Trevose, PA 19053-6964
Tel (215) 291-0300 *Founded/Ownrshp* 1934
Sales 180.3MM^E *EMP* 750
SIC 5136 5137

D-U-N-S 06-765-0960 IMP/EXP
ALPHA TECHNOLOGIES INC (WA)
ALPHA GROUP, THE
3767 Alpha Way, Bellingham, WA 98226-8302
Tel (360) 647-2360 *Founded/Ownrshp* 1980
Sales 121.2MM^E *EMP* 190^E
SIC 8742 8711 Marketing consulting services; Engineering services
Ch: Fred Kaiser
Pr: Patrick Kosuth
Pr: Andrew Zogby
VP: Frank Albano
VP: Robert Hamlin
VP: Jim Heidenreich
VP: John O'Rourke
VP: Gerald Winters
Exec: Nikki Ghai
Rgnl Mgr: Stephen Jones
Admn Mgr: Diane Zediker

D-U-N-S 05-670-7714
ALPHA WIRE CORP
ALPHAWIRE
711 Lidgerwood Ave, Elizabeth, NJ 07202-3115
Tel (908) 259-2613 *Founded/Ownrshp* 1986
Sales 217.5MM^E *EMP* 1,050
SIC 5063 3082 3357 Wire & cable; Tubes, unsupported plastic; Shipboard cable, nonferrous
Ch Bd: Philip R Cowen
Pr: Willis E Bye
Pr: Mike Dugar
CFO: William M Mailler
Treas: Charles T Wiggins
VP: Stanton D Ose
Brnch Mgr: Michael Dugas
Dist Mgr: Steve Rensel
Dist Mgr: Tim Yontek
Dir IT: Mayur Gohil
Plnt Mgr: Joe Marciano
Board of Directors: Andrew C Cowen, David S Cowen, Ellen B Cowen

D-U-N-S 96-502-8199
■ **ALPHABET HOLDING CO INC**
(*Suby of* CARLYLE GROUP L P) ★
2100 Smithtown Ave, Ronkonkoma, NY 11779-7347
Tel (631) 200-2000 *Founded/Ownrshp* 2010
Sales 3.2MMM *EMP* 1,500^E
SIC 2833 5122 5499 5961 Vitamins, natural or synthetic: bulk, uncompounded; Vitamins & minerals; Health & dietetic food stores; Vitamin food stores; Health foods; Dietetic foods; Pharmaceuticals, mail order
CEO: Jeffrey A Nagel
* *Pr:* Sandra Horbach
* *CFO:* Dipak Golechha
* *CFO:* Harvey Kamil
* *VP:* Anita Balaji

D-U-N-S 07-994-2718
▲ **ALPHABET INC**
1600 Amphitheatre Pkwy, Mountain View, CA 94043-1351
Tel (650) 253-0000 *Founded/Ownrshp* 2015
Sales 74.9MMM *EMP* 61,814^E
Tkr Sym GOOG *Exch* NGS
SIC 7371 Custom computer programming services
CEO: Larry Page
Ch Bd: Eric E Schmidt
Pr: Sergey Brin
CFO: Ruth Porat
CFO: Ruth M Porat
Sr VP: David Carl Drummond

D-U-N-S 80-919-8588 IMP
ALPHAPET INC
(*Suby of* INDORAMA POLYMERS PUBLIC COMPANY LIMITED)
1301 Finley Island Rd, Decatur, AL 35601-7911
Tel (256) 308-1180 *Founded/Ownrshp* 2007
Sales 525.0MM^E *EMP* 125
SIC 2821 Polyethylene resins
CEO: D K Agarwal
* *COO:* G L Modi
* *CFO:* Sachin Agarwalla
* *Ch:* Aloke Lohia
* *Sr VP:* Hussam Awad
* *VP:* Yashwant Awasthi
* *VP:* Suchitra Lohia
Mfg Mgr: Sathish Seshadri

D-U-N-S 62-418-3351
▲ **ALPHATEC HOLDINGS INC**
5818 El Camino Real, Carlsbad, CA 92008-8816
Tel (760) 431-9286 *Founded/Ownrshp* 1990
Sales 185.2MM *EMP* 430^E
Tkr Sym ATEC *Exch* NGS
SIC 3841 Surgical & medical instruments
Ch Bd: Leslie H Cross
Pr: Michael Plunkett
Ex VP: Craig Hunsaker
Sr VP: Ebun Garner
Sr VP: Kristin Machacek Leary
Board of Directors: Stephen Eo'neil, R Ian Molson, Donald A Williams

D-U-N-S 60-246-5783 IMP
■ **ALPHATEC SPINE INC**
(*Suby of* ALPHATEC HOLDINGS INC) ★
5818 El Camino Real, Carlsbad, CA 92008-8816
Tel (760) 494-6610 *Founded/Ownrshp* 2006
Sales 110.2MM^E *EMP* 300
SIC 3842 8711 5047 Surgical appliances & supplies; Engineering services; Medical equipment & supplies
CEO: James M Corbett
* *Pr:* Patrick Ryan
* *COO:* Michael Plunkett
COO: M Ross Simmonds
* *CFO:* Michael O'Neill
* *Sr VP:* Thomas McLeer
* *VP:* Ebun S Garner
VP: Ebuns Garner
VP: Frances Harrison
VP: Kristin Leary
VP: Jack Timm
VP: Vernon Trimble
VP: Armin Weichert
VP: Scott Wiese
Board of Directors: Luke T Faulstick

ALPHAWIRE
See ALPHA WIRE CORP

ALPHERA FINANCIAL SERVICES
See BMW FINANCIAL SERVICES NA LLC

D-U-N-S 01-361-4615
ALPIN HAUS SKI SHOP INC (NY)
4850 State Highway 30, Amsterdam, NY 12010-7435
Tel (518) 843-4400 *Founded/Ownrshp* 1964
Sales 105.1MM^E *EMP* 231
Accts Bollam Sheedy Torani & Co L
SIC 5561 5551 5941 Travel trailers: automobile, new & used; Motor homes; Boat dealers; Skiing equipment
CEO: Andrew Heck
* *VP:* Greg Heck
Exec: Kate Osborn
DP Dir: Tom Traskos

ALPINE ACCESS CANADA
See ALPINE ACCESS INC

D-U-N-S 10-319-0398
■ **ALPINE ACCESS INC**
ALPINE ACCESS CANADA
(*Suby of* SYKES ENTERPRISES INC) ★
1290 N Broadway Ste 1400, Denver, CO 80203-5605
Tel (303) 850-3700 *Founded/Ownrshp* 2012
Sales 154.6MM^E *EMP* 4,000^E
SIC 7361 8742 8748 Employment agencies; Management consulting services; Business consulting
Prin: Christopher Carrington
* *COO:* Robert A Duncan
CFO: Rick Millett Jr
* *CFO:* Robert N Pinkerton
* *Ch:* Stephen W Schovee
VP: Kim Abery
VP: Birdy Allard
VP: Terry Bate
VP: Lynn Baumann
VP: Susan Caple
VP: Beth Capra
VP: Chuck Carlson
VP: Leha Combs
VP: Nichole Dibacco
VP: Giuliana Finn
VP: Charlotte Green
VP: King Jeff
VP: Kelly Kumse
VP: Kim Mays
VP: Susan McKinney
VP: Sherrie Moss

D-U-N-S 03-977-7941
ALPINE BANK
(*Suby of* ALPINE BANKS OF COLORADO)
2200 Grand Ave, Glenwood Springs, CO 81601-4120
Tel (970) 945-2424 *Founded/Ownrshp* 1980
Sales NA *EMP* 505
SIC 6022 State trust companies accepting deposits, commercial
V Ch: Glen Jammaron
* *Ch Bd:* Robert Young
COO: Paulette Dangler
* *CFO:* Eric Gardey
Sr VP: Jo Applegate
Sr VP: Jeff Mozingo
Brnch Mgr: Bill Sanderson
Dir IT: Doug Merrell
Opers Supe: Valerie Harju

D-U-N-S 83-036-1999
ALPINE DISPOSAL INC
ALPINE WASTE & RECYCLING
7373 Washington St, Denver, CO 80229-6301
Tel (303) 289-8019 *Founded/Ownrshp* 1999
Sales 94.5MM^E *EMP* 180
SIC 4953 Refuse collection & disposal services
Pr: John Griffith
* *CFO:* Alek Orloff
* *VP:* Brent Hildebrand
* *VP:* John Tovado
Div Mgr: Robert Gutierrez
Genl Mgr: Shannon Smith
Plnt Mgr: Tom Reed

D-U-N-S 09-401-6391 IMP
ALPINE ELECTRONICS OF AMERICA INC (CA)
(*Suby of* ALPINE ELECTRONICS, INC.)
19145 Gramercy Pl, Torrance, CA 90501-1162
Tel (310) 326-8000 *Founded/Ownrshp* 1978
Sales 379.7MM^E *EMP* 900
SIC 5064 3651 3679 Radios, motor vehicle; Household audio & video equipment; Harness assemblies for electronic use: wire or cable
CEO: Toshinori Kobayashi
* *Pr:* Isao Nagasako
* *CFO:* Masanobu Takagi
Prgrm Mgr: Jim Walter
Snr Sftwr: Dai Kawano
QA Dir: Arturo Mares
Sftwr Eng: Jun Cheng
Ql Cn Mgr: Joe Cilluffo
Manager: Joel Kaplan

D-U-N-S 11-528-5892 IMP
ALPINE FOOD DISTRIBUTING INC
2400 Se Mailwell Dr, Milwaukie, OR 97222-7328
Tel (503) 905-5201 *Founded/Ownrshp* 1983
Sales 143.0MM *EMP* 117
SIC 5142 5149 Packaged frozen goods; Dried or canned foods
Pr: Gregory Carlston

ALPINE INSULATION
See CITY WIDE INSULATION OF MADISON INC

D-U-N-S 08-025-7543
■ **ALPINE INSULATION I LLC**
(*Suby of* INSTALLED BUILDING PRODUCTS INC) ★
495 S High St Ste 50, Columbus, OH 43215-5689
Tel (614) 221-3399 *Founded/Ownrshp* 2016
Sales 30.0MM^E *EMP* 3,675
SIC 5033 5211 Insulation materials; Insulation material, building
Pr: Jeffrey W Edwards
COO: Jay P Elliott
CFO: Michael T Miller

D-U-N-S 04-321-7280
ALPINE LUMBER CO
10170 Church Ranch Way # 300, Westminster, CO 80021-6061
Tel (303) 451-8001 *Founded/Ownrshp* 1963, 1989
Sales 102.3MM^E *EMP* 390
SIC 5211

D-U-N-S 02-153-3203
ALPINE SCHOOL DISTRICT
575 N 100 E, American Fork, UT 84003-1758
Tel (801) 610-8400 *Founded/Ownrshp* 1915
Sales 364.1MM^E *EMP* 8,000
Accts Squire & Company Pc Orem Ut
SIC 8211 Public elementary school
Dir Sec: Jeanne Bates
Genl Mgr: Garrick Peterson
MIS Dir: Paul Lewis

Dir IT: Matt Johnson
Dir IT: Cody Spendlove
Pr Dir: Kevin Cox
Pr Dir: David Stephenson
Instr Medi: Jim Moon

D-U-N-S 83-695-1756
■ ALPINE VALLEY BREAD CO
(*Suby of* FLOWERS FOODS INC) ★
300 W Southern Ave, Mesa, AZ 85210-5213
Tel (480) 483-2774 *Founded/Ownrshp* 2015
Sales 104.0MM[E] *EMP* 300[E]
SIC 2051 Bread, cake & related products
Pr: Todd Wood
**VP:* Andrea Wood

ALPINE WASTE & RECYCLING
See ALPINE DISPOSAL INC

D-U-N-S 94-970-0223 IMP
ALPS ELECTRIC (NORTH AMERICA) INC
(*Suby of* ALPS ELECTRIC CO., LTD.)
3151 Jay St Ste 101, Santa Clara, CA 95054-3332
Tel (408) 361-6400 *Founded/Ownrshp* 1995
Sales 248.0MM[E] *EMP* 300
SIC 5045 5065 5013 Computer peripheral equipment; Electronic parts; Motor vehicle supplies & new parts
Pr: Dave Sato
**Pr:* Toshihiro Kuriyama
**CEO:* Hiroyuki Sato
**CFO:* Marty Sukle
VP: Shoshiro Kojima

ALRO GROUP
See ALRO STEEL CORP

D-U-N-S 04-118-2767 IMP/EXP
ALRO METALS SERVICE CENTER CORP
ALRO STEEL
(*Suby of* ALRO GROUP) ★
6200 Pk Of Commerce Blvd, Boca Raton, FL 33487-8296
Tel (561) 997-6766 *Founded/Ownrshp* 1966
Sales 90.7MM *EMP* 244
SIC 5051 5085 Steel; Industrial supplies
Ch Bd: Alvin Glick
**Pr:* Barry Glick
**VP:* Carl Glick
**VP:* Daniel R Sella

ALRO STEEL
See ALRO METALS SERVICE CENTER CORP

D-U-N-S 00-538-1447 IMP/EXP
ALRO STEEL CORP
ALRO GROUP
3100 E High St, Jackson, MI 49203-6413
Tel (517) 787-5500 *Founded/Ownrshp* 1948
Sales 1.6MMM *EMP* 2,400
SIC 5085 5162 Industrial supplies; Plastics materials
CEO: Alvin Glick
Pr: Mark Alyea
Pr: David Schmidt
CFO: Steve Laten
Treas: Jim Norman
Sr VP: Randy Glick
Sls Mgr: Greg Clanton
Sls Mgr: Jennifer Flaherty
Sales Asso: Lindsey Lamarre
Sales Asso: Nicholas Lombardo
Sales Asso: Shannon Milcherska

ALS ASSOCIATION, THE
See AMYOTROPHIC LATERAL SCLEROSIS ASSOCIATION

D-U-N-S 11-978-9191
ALS GROUP USA CORP
ALS LABORATORY GROUP
(*Suby of* ALS TESTING SERVICES GROUP INC) ★
10450 Stncliff Rd Ste 210, Houston, TX 77099
Tel (281) 530-5656 *Founded/Ownrshp* 1999
Sales 102.2MM[E] *EMP* 632[E]
SIC 8734 Testing laboratories
Pr: Gregory F Kilmister
**Sec:* Patricia Davis
**VP:* Raj Naran
Off Mgr: Lisa McGee

ALS LABORATORY GROUP
See ALS GROUP USA CORP

D-U-N-S 00-993-6498
ALS TESTING SERVICES GROUP INC
(*Suby of* ALS LIMITED)
818 W 7th St Ste 930, Los Angeles, CA 90017-3476
Tel (213) 627-8252 *Founded/Ownrshp* 1999
Sales 129.9MM[E] *EMP* 819
Accts Ernst & Young Llp
SIC 5141 5072 5084 Food brokers; Hardware; Industrial machinery & equipment
CEO: Bruce Brown

ALSAC
See AMERICAN LEBANESE SYRIAN ASSOCIATED CHARITIES INC

D-U-N-S 06-754-4262
ALSAKER CORP
SAKS
6409 E Sharp Ave, Spokane Valley, WA 99212-1255
Tel (509) 242-6327 *Founded/Ownrshp* 1986
Sales 97.8MM[E] *EMP* 260
SIC 5541 5411 Truck stops; Convenience stores, independent
Pr: Daniel Lee Alsaker
**Treas:* Anne Virginia Alsaker
**VP:* Thomas Hemingway

D-U-N-S 02-179-2101
■ ALSATE EXPLORATION INC
ALSATE MANAGEMENT AND INV CO
(*Suby of* SANDRIDGE ENERGY INC) ★
1601 Nw Expwy St Ste 400, Oklahoma City, OK 73118-1460
Tel (405) 753-5500 *Founded/Ownrshp* 2000
Sales 285.0MM *EMP* 250
SIC 1382 Oil & gas exploration services
Pr: Malone Mitchell
Treas: Alicia Johnson

ALSATE MANAGEMENT AND INV CO
See ALSATE EXPLORATION INC

D-U-N-S 00-703-9176
ALSCO INC (UT)
LINENS OF THE WEEK
505 E South Temple, Salt Lake City, UT 84102-1004
Tel (801) 328-8831 *Founded/Ownrshp* 1889
Sales 683.4MM *EMP* 16,000
SIC 7213 Uniform supply; Apron supply; Coat supply; Linen supply, non-clothing
CEO: Robert C Steiner
Pr: Kevin K Steiner
COO: Norm Underwood
CFO: James D Kearns
CFO: Steve Larson
Treas: Steven Tassey
Dir Risk M: Randy Brough
Dist Mgr: Dan Barnetson
Dist Mgr: Kevin Honeycutt
Dist Mgr: John Matchett
Dist Mgr: Brian Ulep

D-U-N-S 80-623-9422 IMP
ALSTOM GRID INC
2 International Plz # 325, Philadelphia, PA 19113-1504
Tel (724) 483-7816 *Founded/Ownrshp* 1993
Sales NA *EMP* 1,070
SIC 3613

D-U-N-S 09-826-3820 IMP/EXP
ALSTOM INC
(*Suby of* ALSTOM)
200 Great Pond Dr, Windsor, CT 06095-1564
Tel (866) 257-8664 *Founded/Ownrshp* 2001
Sales 4.6MMM[E] *EMP* 7,200
SIC 4911 6719 Generation, electric power; Public utility holding companies
Pr: Tim Curran
Pr: Pierre Gauthier
Treas: Jeff Schad
VP: Christopher Palmer
VP: J F Pereira
VP: William F Scheolwer
Pr Mgr: Beverly Boucher

D-U-N-S 12-537-7692 IMP/EXP
■ ALSTOM POWER INC
(*Suby of* GENERAL ELECTRIC CO) ★
200 Great Pond Dr, Windsor, CT 06095-1564
Tel (866) 257-8664 *Founded/Ownrshp* 1990
Sales 223.9MM[E] *EMP* 4,500
SIC 3443 3564 3621 3823 8711 Fabricated plate work (boiler shop); Blowers & fans; Motors & generators; Industrial instrmnts msrmnt display/control process variable; Engineering services
Pr: Tim Curran
**Treas:* Michael J Tolpa
**VP:* Robert L Abbott
**VP:* Richard D Austin
**VP:* Francois Berthiaume
**VP:* Bruce Moffat
**VP:* Richard Pangrazzi
**VP:* William F Schoelwer
Genl Mgr: Jonathan Wenger
Mfg Dir: Ron Konopacki

D-U-N-S 07-999-3344
■ ALSTOM RENEWABLE US LLC
(*Suby of* ALSTOM POWER INC) ★
7901 Suthpark Plz Ste 110, Littleton, CO 80120
Tel (303) 730-4000 *Founded/Ownrshp* 2013
Sales 150.0MM *EMP* 35
SIC 3621 3511 Power generators; Turbines & turbine generator sets
**Pr:* Richard Austin

D-U-N-S 00-715-1327 IMP
ALSTOM SIGNALING OPERATION LLC
TRANSPORTATION SYSTEMS GLOBA
2901 E Lake Rd Bldg 122, Erie, PA 16531-0001
Tel (800) 825-3178 *Founded/Ownrshp* 1946, 2000
Sales 1.7MMM[E] *EMP* 8,000
SIC 3669 5088 3672 3663 Railroad signaling devices, electric; Railroad equipment & supplies; Printed circuit boards; Radio broadcasting & communications equipment
CEO: David L Calhoun
CIO: Nancy Anderson
Dir IT: Robert Payne
Snr Mgr: Richard Evans

D-U-N-S 05-318-2341 IMP
ALSTOM USA INC
(*Suby of* ALSTOM)
1 Transit Dr, Hornell, NY 14843-2298
Tel (607) 324-4595 *Founded/Ownrshp* 1986
Sales 2.7MM[E] *EMP* 1,169
SIC 3321 7699 Railroad car wheels & brake shoes, cast iron; Railroad car customizing
Pr: Roelof Van Ark
**Treas:* Francois Michel
Ofcr: Lynette Yarka
VP: Jean-Francois Blanc
VP: Valerie Chardon
**VP:* Ian Desouza
Genl Mgr: Tim Buchanan
Dir IT: Colin Haynes
Sys Mgr: Philippe Michaut
VP Opers: Jean-Francois Beaudoin
**VP Sls:* Chuck Wochele

D-U-N-S 07-921-1227
ALSTOM USA INC
2000 Day Hill Rd, Windsor, CT 06095-1580
Tel (860) 285-3790 *Founded/Ownrshp* 1983
Sales 44.9MM[E] *EMP* 1,000
SIC 8711 Engineering services
VP: Jean-Marc Decloquement
Dir Soc: Belen Prieto-Flores
Dir Bus: Patrick McKenna

D-U-N-S 07-247-5205
ALSTON & BIRD LLP
1201 W Peachtree St Ne # 4000, Atlanta, GA 30309-3424
Tel (404) 881-7654 *Founded/Ownrshp* 1982
Sales 318.5MM[E] *EMP* 1,050
SIC 8111 General practice law office
Pt: Richard R Hays
Pt: James S Hutchinson
Pt: H Bryan Ives III
Mng Pt: Richard K Hays
CFO: Richard Levinson
CFO: Richard G Levinson
VP: Glenda B Darrell
Dir Bus: Barbara Bryant
CIO: Robert Marburger
Dir IT: Jeffrey R Allaman
IT Man: Rodney Miller

D-U-N-S 07-488-5034
ALSTON CONSTRUCTION CO INC
8775 Folsom Blvd Ste 201, Sacramento, CA 95826-3725
Tel (916) 340-2400 *Founded/Ownrshp* 1999
Sales 642.5MM *EMP* 200
Accts Campbell Taylor & Company Ros
SIC 1541 1542 Industrial buildings & warehouses; Commercial & office building contractors
CEO: Paul David Little
**CFO:* Adam Nickerson
Ex VP: Dave Fazekas
Ex VP: Dan Hudson
Ex VP: Jim Odewald
Ex VP: Jeff Pintar
VP: Cheryl Fusselman
**VP:* Evan Hamilton
VP: Ronald Kropke
VP: Jeff Raduechel
VP: Eric Shelton

ALSTYLE APPAREL
See A AND G INC

D-U-N-S 02-002-4472 IMP/EXP
■ ALSTYLE APPAREL & ACTIVEWEAR MANAGEMENT CO (IL)
(*Suby of* ENNIS INC) ★
1501 E Cerritos Ave, Anaheim, CA 92805-6400
Tel (714) 765-0400 *Founded/Ownrshp* 2001, 2016
Sales 529.4MM[E] *EMP* 5,600
SIC 2253 Shirts (outerwear), knit
CEO: Rauf Gajiani
**VP:* Amin Amdani
CTO: Irshad Ahmad
Sls Mgr: Scott Bloom

D-U-N-S 07-938-7022
■ ALSTYLE APPAREL LLC
(*Suby of* ALSTYLE APPAREL & ACTIVEWEAR MANAGEMENT CO) ★
1501 E Cerritos Ave, Anaheim, CA 92805-6400
Tel (714) 765-0400 *Founded/Ownrshp* 2014
Sales 71.2M[E] *EMP* 3,765[E]
SIC 2211 Apparel & outerwear fabrics, cotton

ALTA BATES SUMMIT MEDICAL CTR
See SURGERY CENTER OF ALTA BATES SUMMIT MEDICAL CENTER LLC

D-U-N-S 08-391-8714
ALTA CALIFORNIA REGIONAL CENTER INC
ALTA CALIFORNIA REGIONAL CTR
2241 Harvard St Ste 100, Sacramento, CA 95815-3332
Tel (916) 978-6400 *Founded/Ownrshp* 1970
Sales 322.2MM[E] *EMP* 487
Accts Stroub Thompson Noble Cpas Sa
SIC 8322 General counseling services
Pr: James Huyck
COO: Peter Tiedemann
Genl Mgr: Nelly Stark
Off Admin: Raeona Elston
Off Admin: Yvonne Quezada

ALTA CALIFORNIA REGIONAL CTR
See ALTA CALIFORNIA REGIONAL CENTER INC

D-U-N-S 84-891-9247
ALTA COLLEGES INC
REDSTONE COLLEGE
10249 Church Ranch Way # 100, Westminster, CO 80021-5542
Tel (303) 846-1700 *Founded/Ownrshp* 1989
Sales 78.5MM[E] *EMP* 2,500
Accts Deloitte & Touche Llp Denver
SIC 8249 Trade school
Ch: Kirk Riedinger
**Ch Bd:* Jamie Turner
**Pr:* Dean Gouin
**CFO:* Jeremy Cleaver
Bd of Dir: George Burnett
Exec: Yvonne Lott
Genl Mgr: Matt Vigil

D-U-N-S 96-246-2714
ALTA EQUIPMENT CO INC
13211 Merriman Rd, Livonia, MI 48150-1826
Tel (248) 449-6700 *Founded/Ownrshp* 2010
Sales 142.9MM[E] *EMP* 223
SIC 3537 5084 Industrial trucks & tractors; Lift trucks & parts
CEO: Steven Greenawalt
Pr: Rob Chiles
Pr: Jeremy Cionca
Brnch Mgr: Tom Colwell
Brnch Mgr: Jarrad Rose
Opers Mgr: Tom Odonnell

D-U-N-S 07-938-9942
ALTA FOREST PRODUCTS LLC
810 Nw Alta Way, Chehalis, WA 98532
Tel (360) 219-0008 *Founded/Ownrshp* 2014
Sales 138.3MM[E] *EMP* 420
SIC 2421 Sawmills & planing mills, general

ALTA GRACIA
See KNIGHTS APPAREL INC

D-U-N-S 19-644-2768
ALTA MESA HOLDINGS LP
15021 Katy Fwy Ste 400, Houston, TX 77094-1900
Tel (281) 530-0991 *Founded/Ownrshp* 1987
Sales 433.8MM *EMP* 225
Accts Bdo Usa Llp Houston Texas
SIC 1311 Crude petroleum & natural gas; Crude petroleum & natural gas production
Pr: Harlan H Chappelle
Genl Pt: Alta Mesa Holdings GP
COO: Michael E Ellis

D-U-N-S 79-643-8609
ALTA MESA RESOURCES LP
15021 Katy Fwy Ste 400, Houston, TX 77094-1900
Tel (281) 530-0991 *Founded/Ownrshp* 2005
Sales 554.5MM[E] *EMP* 9
SIC 5541 Gasoline service stations
CEO: Hal Chappelle
**CFO:* Michael McCabe
**Ch:* Mike Ellis
**VP:* David Murrell

D-U-N-S 12-097-1916 IMP
ALTA PROPERTIES INC
CTG
879 Ward Dr, Santa Barbara, CA 93111-2920
Tel (805) 967-0171 *Founded/Ownrshp* 1983
Sales 148.4MM[E] *EMP* 1,356
SIC 3264 3699 3823 3679 Porcelain electrical supplies; Underwater sound equipment; Infrared instruments, industrial process type; Transducers, electrical
CEO: Robert F Carlson
**CFO:* Paul J Downey
CFO: Franklin Richard
**VP:* Randy Copperman
**VP:* Gary Douville
**VP:* Mark Shaw
Exec: Linda Osborne
**Prin:* Kevin Ruelas
Prgrm Mgr: Tim Jock
Sfty Dirs: Jeff Golden
Mtls Mgr: Gary Irwin

D-U-N-S 83-851-2408
ALTA RESOURCES CORP
120 N Commercial St, Neenah, WI 54956-3006
Tel (877) 464-2582 *Founded/Ownrshp* 1995
Sales 138.2MM[E] *EMP* 800
SIC 7389 8742 Telemarketing services; Training & development consultant; Marketing consulting services
Pr: James Bere
**Pr:* James Goetz
**CFO:* Patrick Hawley
**Ch:* Teri Koski
VP: Patrick Nicholson
**VP:* Dnyanesh Patkar
**VP:* David H Quandt
VP: Mike Ryder
Prgrm Mgr: Pat Garrigan
Off Mgr: Danielle Johnson
**CIO:* Matt Nelson

D-U-N-S 00-850-6370
■ ALTA-DENA CERTIFIED DAIRY LLC
(*Suby of* DEAN WEST II LLC) ★
17637 E Valley Blvd, City of Industry, CA 91744-5731
Tel (626) 964-6401 *Founded/Ownrshp* 1945, 1999
Sales 183.4MM[E] *EMP* 430
SIC 2026 Fluid milk; Milk & cream, except fermented, cultured & flavored; Buttermilk, cultured; Cottage cheese
**CFO:* Jack Tewers
**VP:* Bob Pettigrew
**Genl Mgr:* Steve Schaffer

D-U-N-S 10-555-7677
ALTADIS HOLDINGS USA INC
(*Suby of* SOCIETE NATIONALE D'EXPLOITATION INDUSTRIELLE DES TABACS ET ALLUMETTES)
5900 N Andrews Ave # 1100, Fort Lauderdale, FL 33309-2354
Tel (954) 772-9000 *Founded/Ownrshp* 2000
Sales 340.6MM[E] *EMP* 7,800
SIC 6719 Personal holding companies, except banks
CEO: Gary R Ellis
**VP:* James M Parnofiello
Dir IT: Andrew Vega
Sls&Mrk Ex: Joseph Clark

D-U-N-S 04-908-2373 IMP/EXP
ALTADIS USA INC
(*Suby of* CONSOLIDATED CIGAR HOLDINGS INC) ★
5900 N Andrews Ave # 1100, Fort Lauderdale, FL 33309-2354
Tel (954) 772-9000 *Founded/Ownrshp* 1999
Sales 258.1MM[E] *EMP* 1,000
SIC 2121 Cigars
CEO: Gary R Ellis
**Pr:* Rob Wilkey
CFO: Chris Ellis
V Ch Bd: Bruno Bich
Bd of Dir: Tony Frankenberger
VP: Workman Eric
Mng Dir: Luz Reyes
Prgrm Mgr: Greg Cowart
Dist Mgr: Keith Moore
Genl Mgr: Andy Creasy
Genl Mgr: Javier Estades
Board of Directors: Tony Frankenberger

ALTAIR COMPANY, THE
See RICHARDSON TRIDENT CO LLC

D-U-N-S 13-143-0514
ALTAIR ENGINEERING INC
1820 E Big Beaver Rd, Troy, MI 48083-2031
Tel (248) 614-2400 *Founded/Ownrshp* 1985
Sales 979.3MM[E] *EMP* 15,000
SIC 8711 Structural engineering; Designing: ship, boat, machine & product
Pr: James R Scapa
Pr: Miles Mahoney
**CFO:* Howard Morof
CFO: Norma Jean Zaleski
**Sec:* George Christ
VP: Bobbi Blake
VP: Patrick Champati
VP: Doron Helfman

VP: Michael J Heskitt
VP: Michael Heskitt
VP: Michael M Humphrey
VP: Michael J Kidder
**VP:* Mark Kistner
VP: David M Mason
VP: Thomas Perring
VP: David L Simon
VP Bus Dev: Michael Hoffmann
Dir Bus: Matthias Goelke
Board of Directors: Martin Clague, Louis Crain, Marc F McMorris

ALTAIRSTRICKLAND
See REPCONSTRICKLAND INC

D-U-N-S 08-390-6024
ALTAMED HEALTH SERVICES CORP
2040 Camfield Ave, Commerce, CA 90040-1574
Tel (323) 725-8751 *Founded/Ownrshp* 1970
Sales 360.3MM *EMP* 1,230
Accts Vasquez & Company Llp Los Ang
SIC 8011 8099 Gynecologist; Pediatrician; Radiologist; Medical services organization
CEO: Castulo De La Rocha
**CFO:* Jose U Esparza
**Sr VP:* Marie S Torres
**VP:* Zoila D Escobar

D-U-N-S 07-860-6403
ALTAMONT CAPITAL PARTNERS LLC
400 Hamilton Ave Ste 230, Palo Alto, CA 94301-1834
Tel (650) 264-7750 *Founded/Ownrshp* 2011, 2012
Sales 1.0MMM^E^ *EMP* 6,420^E^
SIC 6799 Investors
VP: Iain Bridges
VP: Melissa Kennedy
VP: Kevin Mason
VP: Pete Meyerdirk
VP: Gregory Ruiz
Ex Dir: Randall Eason

ALTEC
See OHIO VALLEY ALUMINUM CO II LLC

D-U-N-S 08-669-4861 EXP
ALTEC INC
210 Inverness Center Dr, Birmingham, AL 35242-4834
Tel (205) 991-7733 *Founded/Ownrshp* 1999
Sales 683.3MM^E^ *EMP* 1,550^E^
SIC 3531 3713 3536 Derricks, except oil & gas field; Aerial work platforms: hydraulic/elec. truck/carrier mounted; Truck bodies (motor vehicles); Cranes, overhead traveling
Ch Bd: Lee J Styslinger Jr
CFO: Don Williams
**Sr VP:* J D Cox
**VP:* Tony Gann

D-U-N-S 00-400-1731 IMP/EXP
ALTEC INDUSTRIES INC (AL)
(*Suby of* ALTEC INC) ★
210 Inverness Center Dr, Birmingham, AL 35242-4834
Tel (205) 991-7733 *Founded/Ownrshp* 1929
Sales 475.9MM^E^ *EMP* 1,500
SIC 3531 3536 3713 Derricks, except oil & gas field; Aerial work platforms: hydraulic/elec. truck/carrier mounted; Cranes, overhead traveling; Truck bodies (motor vehicles)
CEO: Lee J Styslinger III
**Ch Bd:* Lee J Styslinger Jr
Treas: Jerry W Moore
Ofcr: Steve Pena
Ex VP: Allen Ritchie
Sr VP: Jon C Styslinger
Sr VP: J Donald Williams
VP: David Boger
VP: Jarrett Gandy
VP: Tony Gann
VP: Marcus Miles
VP: Bruce Starks
VP: Jon Styslinger
Board of Directors: H Corbin Day, William W Feathl eringill, John Panettieri, Samuel E Upchurch

D-U-N-S 07-833-1446
ALTEGRA HEALTH INC
(*Suby of* MEDIFAX-EDI LLC) ★
1725 N Commerce Pkwy, Weston, FL 33326-3201
Tel (305) 779-6070 *Founded/Ownrshp* 2010, 2015
Sales 229.1MM^E^ *EMP* 1,000^E^
SIC 7374 Data processing service
CEO: Kevin C Barrett
**COO:* Dan Lieber
**CFO:* Michele I Hass
**Ex VP:* Mark D Fabiano
**Ex VP:* Jarrod Mandozzi
Sr VP: Mark Filiault
Sr VP: Barbara Havens
VP: Jeff Boone
VP: Kelley Cohen
VP: Donna Jacobson
VP: Lance Scott

ALTER METAL RECYCLING
See ALTER TRADING CORP

D-U-N-S 02-350-1422 IMP
ALTER METAL RECYCLING
(*Suby of* ALTER METAL RECYCLING) ★
4400 Sycamore Ave, Madison, WI 53714-1334
Tel (608) 241-7191 *Founded/Ownrshp* 1982
Sales 127.5MM^E^ *EMP* 812
SIC 5093 Metal scrap & waste materials
VP Opers: Michael Spear
**VP:* Gary Bachus
Rgnl Mgr: Randy Bollig
Trfc Dir: Mike Lasher

D-U-N-S 14-780-5642 IMP/EXP
ALTER TRADING CORP
ALTER METAL RECYCLING
700 Office Pkwy, Saint Louis, MO 63141-7105
Tel (314) 872-2400 *Founded/Ownrshp* 2006
Sales 515.7MM^E^ *EMP* 1,325
SIC 5093 Ferrous metal scrap & waste
CEO: Robert S Goldstein
Pr: Jeffrey Goldstein
Pr: Jay Robinovitz
CFO: Timothy C Oliver

Sr VP: Robert G Ellis
Sr VP: Don Martin
VP: Brian Chamberlin
VP: Robert A Rosencrants
VP: Rick Rosga
VP: Timothy J Sasek
VP: Jon Spigel
VP: Thomas Streight

D-U-N-S 11-817-1834 IMP
■ **ALTERA CORP**
(*Suby of* INTEL CORP) ★
101 Innovation Dr, San Jose, CA 95134-1941
Tel (408) 544-7000 *Founded/Ownrshp* 2015
Sales 1.9MMM *EMP* 3,094^E^
SIC 3674 7371 Semiconductors & related devices; Computer software development & applications
Ch Bd: John P Daane
**CFO:* Ronald J Pasek
Sr VP: Scott Bibaud
**Sr VP:* Danny Biran
**Sr VP:* William Y Hata
**Sr VP:* Bradley Howe
**Sr VP:* Kevin H Lyman
**Sr VP:* Mark Nelson
Sr VP: Mark J Nelson
**Sr VP:* Katherine E Schuelke
**Sr VP:* Jeff Waters
Sr VP: Jeffrey W Waters
VP: Premal Buch
VP: Richard Cliff
VP: Bruce Euzent
VP: Martin Langhammer
VP: Bill Mazotti
VP: Thomas Murchie
VP: Erhaan Shaikh
VP: Scott Wylie
Board of Directors: A Blaine Bowman, Elisha W Finney, Kevin McGarity, T Michael Nevens, Shane V Robison, John Shoemaker, Thomas H Waechter

D-U-N-S 13-171-7332
ALTERMAN GROUP INC
14703 Jnes Maltsberger Rd, San Antonio, TX 78247-3713
Tel (210) 496-6888 *Founded/Ownrshp* 1984
Sales 116.2MM^E^ *EMP* 450
SIC 1731 General electrical contractor
Ch Bd: Don Kuykendall
**Pr:* John C Wright
**CFO:* William E Gellhausen

D-U-N-S 00-883-1521
ALTERMAN INC
(*Suby of* ALTERMAN GROUP INC) ★
14703 Jnes Maltsberger Rd, San Antonio, TX 78247-3713
Tel (210) 496-6888 *Founded/Ownrshp* 1988
Sales 99.3MM^E^ *EMP* 350
Accts Padgett Stratemann & Co Llp
SIC 1731 General electrical contractor
Ch: Don Kuykendall
**Pr:* John C Wright
**Ex VP:* Denis St Pierre
**VP:* William Gellhausen
Exec: Jerry Katz
Dir IT: Ross Martin
Snr PM: Nelson Froboese
Snr PM: Robert John

D-U-N-S 15-449-9701
ALTERNATIVE BEHAVIORAL SERVICES INC
(*Suby of* FHC HEALTH SYSTEMS INC) ★
240 Corporate Blvd, Norfolk, VA 23502-4900
Tel (757) 459-5200 *Founded/Ownrshp* 1986
Sales 150.0MM *EMP* 19^E^
SIC 8741 Hospital management
Ch Bd: Dr Ronald Dozoretz
**Treas:* Randall Little
**Treas:* Tim Mc Carthy
**VP:* Edward C Irby Jr

ALTERNATIVE BEVERAGE
See NEVADA BEVERAGE CO

ALTERNATIVE DIST SYSTEMS
See ADS LOGISTICS CO LLC

ALTERNATIVE LIVING SERVICES
See SENIOR BROOKDALE LIVING COMMUNITIES INC

D-U-N-S 08-575-3734
ALTERNATIVE OPPORTUNITIES INC
1111 S Glenstone Ave 3-100, Springfield, MO 65804-0338
Tel (417) 869-8911 *Founded/Ownrshp* 1993
Sales 88.2MM^E^ *EMP* 3,000
SIC 8322 Individual & family services
Ex Dir: Bontiea Goss
**Pr:* Keith Noble
**CEO:* Marilyn Nolan
**CFO:* Tom Goss
Exec: Sarah Schacher
Prgrm Mgr: Denise Dunn
Off Mgr: Tina Wyatt
CIO: Jack Stilgenbauer
IT Man: Martha Hurt

D-U-N-S 60-485-6450
ALTERNATIVE RESOURCES CORP
A R C
(*Suby of* POMEROY IT SOLUTIONS SALES CO INC) ★
600 Hart Rd Ste 300, Barrington, IL 60010-2610
Tel (847) 381-6701 *Founded/Ownrshp* 2004
Sales 31.2MM^E^ *EMP* 1,860
SIC 7363 Help supply services
Pr: Robert P Stanojev
Pr: David Nolan
**COO:* Victor Fricas
**CFO:* Steven Purcell
**Ex VP:* Gibbs Vandercook
**Sr VP:* Sharon A McKinney
**Sr VP:* Bill McLendon

D-U-N-S 15-782-0374
ALTERNATIVE STAFFING INC
5620 W Cermak Rd, Cicero, IL 60804-2219
Tel (708) 652-3636 *Founded/Ownrshp* 1997

Sales 39.9MM^E^ *EMP* 2,508
SIC 7361 Placement agencies
Pr: Steven Swerdloff
Genl Mgr: Julie Tracey

ALTICE USA
See NEPTUNE HOLDING US CORP

ALTICOR
See SOLSTICE HOLDINGS INC

D-U-N-S 62-510-7896
ALTICOR GLOBAL HOLDINGS INC
7575 Fulton St E, Ada, MI 49301
Tel (616) 787-1000 *Founded/Ownrshp* 2004
Sales 9.4MMM^E^ *EMP* 20,000
SIC 5169 5122 2833 5136 5137 5021 Chemicals & allied products; Detergents & soaps, except specialty cleaning; Metal salts; Metal polishes; Drugs, proprietaries & sundries; Toiletries; Cosmetics, perfumes & hair products; Vitamins, natural or synthetic: bulk, uncompounded; Men's & boys' clothing; Women's & children's clothing; Furniture
Pr: Doug Devos
**Ch Bd:* Stephen Van Andel
**COO:* Alvin Koop
VP: Roger Colman
VP: Michael Meissner
Exec: Mike Bollman
Exec: Robert Farley
Exec: Judith Ferrell
Exec: Steve Lieberman
Ex Dir: David Prescott
DP Exec: Chris Lutz

D-U-N-S 00-602-6793 IMP/EXP
ALTICOR INC (MI)
(*Suby of* ALTICOR) ★
7575 Fulton St E, Ada, MI 49355-0001
Tel (616) 787-1000 *Founded/Ownrshp* 1949
Sales 9.4MMM *EMP* 14,000
SIC 5169 5122 2833 5136 5137 5021 Chemicals & allied products; Detergents & soaps, except specialty cleaning; Metal salts; Metal polishes; Drugs, proprietaries & sundries; Toiletries; Cosmetics, perfumes & hair products; Vitamins, natural or synthetic: bulk, uncompounded; Men's & boys' clothing; Women's & children's clothing; Furniture
Ch: Steve Van Andel
**Pr:* Doug Devos
**Pr:* Richard M Devos Sr
**CFO:* Michael Cazer
**Treas:* Jeffery C Tuori
Chf Mktg O: Burt Crandey
Ex VP: Glenn Armstrong
Ex VP: Eva Chang
VP: Roger Colman
VP: Craig Datema
VP: Rob Davidson
VP: Ken Davis
VP: Richard Holwill
**VP:* Robert P Hunter
VP: Judy West
Exec: Margaret Tuttle

ALTIERI CAROL
See METROPOLITAN JEWISH HEALTH SYSTEM INC

D-U-N-S 61-005-4512
ALTIG INTERNATIONAL INC
AMERICAN INCOME LIFE INSURANCE
15440 Bel Red Rd, Redmond, WA 98052-5509
Tel (425) 885-2838 *Founded/Ownrshp* 1984
Sales NA *EMP* 285
SIC 6411 Insurance agents, brokers & service
Ch: Rick Altig
Bd of Dir: Rachel Claflin
Ex VP: James Hill
Exec: Samantha Dale
**Prin:* Richard W Altig Jr
IT Man: Grant Zurmely
Sls Dir: Dustin Venekamp

D-U-N-S 11-449-7378
ALTIMETRIK CORP
SYNOVA
1000 Town Ctr Ste 700, Southfield, MI 48075-1220
Tel (248) 281-2500 *Founded/Ownrshp* 1998
Sales 133.4MM^E^ *EMP* 1,800
SIC 7371 Custom computer programming services
CEO: Raj Vattikuti
**Pr:* Tim Manney
VP: Prasad Beesabathuni
VP: Pete Waddell
Admn Mgr: Kathy Nguyen
Snr Sftwr: Suresh Suresetti
Mktg Mgr: Robin Hood
Mktg Mgr: Mabillard Housh
Sls Mgr: Rob Cole

D-U-N-S 96-518-3853
ALTISOURCE HOLDINGS LLC
(*Suby of* ALTISOURCE PORTFOLIO SOLUTIONS SA)
1000 Abernathy Rd, Atlanta, GA 30328-5606
Tel (877) 839-7118 *Founded/Ownrshp* 2009
Sales 285.2MM^E^ *EMP* 3,500
SIC 6794 6519 Performance rights, publishing & licensing; Real property lessors
CEO: William B Shepro

D-U-N-S 07-864-0630
ALTISOURCE RESIDENTIAL CORP (MD)
36c Strand St, Christiansted, VI 00820
Tel (340) 692-1055 *Founded/Ownrshp* 2012
Sales 248.1MM *EMP* 46
Accts Deloitte & Touche Llp Atlanta
SIC 6798 Real estate investment trusts
Pr: George G Ellison
**Ch Bd:* David B Reiner
CFO: Robin N Lowe
Ofcr: Stephen H Gray
Board of Directors: Michael A Eruzione, Robert J Fitzpatrick, William P Wall

D-U-N-S 83-179-2622
ALTISOURCE SOLUTIONS INC
(*Suby of* ALTISOURCE PORTFOLIO SOLUTIONS SA)
1000 Abernathy Rd Ste 200, Atlanta, GA 30328-5604
Tel (770) 612-7007 *Founded/Ownrshp* 2009
Sales NA *EMP* 6,000^E^
Accts Deloitte & Touche Llp Atlant
SIC 6162 Mortgage bankers & correspondents
CEO: William B Shepro
**Pr:* Joseph Davila
**CEO:* Steven Nielsen
**CEO:* William Shepro
**COO:* Mark Hynes
**COO:* Shekar Sivasubramanian
**CFO:* Michelle Esterman
CFO: Robert W McCallum
VP: Stephen Hewins

ALTMAN PLANTS
See ALTMAN SPECIALTY PLANTS INC

D-U-N-S 09-838-6238 IMP
ALTMAN SPECIALTY PLANTS INC
ALTMAN PLANTS
3742 Blue Bird Canyon Rd, Vista, CA 92084-7432
Tel (760) 744-8191 *Founded/Ownrshp* 1973
Sales 583.9MM^E^ *EMP* 1,000
SIC 5193 3999 Nursery stock; Atomizers, toiletry
CEO: Ken Altman
CFO: Phyliss Schmedake
**VP:* Deena Altman
Exec: Vickie Spurlock
Genl Mgr: Dean Chaloupka
IT Man: Rod Baine
Mktg Dir: Becky Drumright
Manager: Jeff Rood

D-U-N-S 62-647-8747
ALTON MEMORIAL HOSPITAL FOUNDATION
BJC HEALTHCARE
1 Memorial Dr, Alton, IL 62002-6722
Tel (618) 463-7311 *Founded/Ownrshp* 2008
Sales 119.2MM *EMP* 1,000^E^
SIC 8062 8059 General medical & surgical hospitals; Nursing home, except skilled & intermediate care facility
Pr: David Braasch
Chf Path: Susan Rayne
Dir Vol: Irene McLaughlin
COO: Doug W Pytlinski
CFO: Brad Goascher
**Ch:* Kenneth Balsters
**Bd of Dir:* Ron Milligan
VP: David Weiss
Exec: Beth Alpers
Dir Risk M: May Grogg
Dir Lab: Cathy Storey
Dir Lab: Cathy Story

D-U-N-S 11-458-3961
ALTON OCHSNER MEDICAL FOUNDATION
1516 Jefferson Hwy # 517, New Orleans, LA 70121-2429
Tel (504) 842-3700 *Founded/Ownrshp* 1994
Sales 33.2MM^E^ *EMP* 3,000
Accts Deloitte & Touche Llp New Orl
SIC 8082 Home health care services
Prin: Edward C Frohlich
**Pr:* Patrick Quinlan
COO: Walter Thomas
Obsttrcn: Angela M Parise
Doctor: Joseph A Miceli MD

D-U-N-S 13-327-0038 IMP
ALTON STEEL INC
5 Cut St, Alton, IL 62002-1776
Tel (618) 463-4490 *Founded/Ownrshp* 2001
Sales 126.8MM^E^ *EMP* 259
SIC 3312 Blast furnaces & steel mills
**Ch Bd:* John Simmons
CFO: John Goldschmidt
**VP:* Micheal Cook
Genl Mgr: Terry Laird
Sftwr Eng: Caleb Peuterbaugh
Sfty Mgr: Steven Vaughan
Manager: Jason Buchheit
QI Cn Mgr: Craig Ralston

D-U-N-S 09-712-1677
ALTOONA AREA SCHOOL DISTRICT INC
1415 6th Ave, Altoona, PA 16602-2427
Tel (814) 946-8211 *Founded/Ownrshp* 1854
Sales 95.7MM^E^ *EMP* 1,200
Accts Young Oakes Brown & Company Pc
SIC 8211 Public elementary & secondary schools
**VP:* Maryann Joyce Bistline
Dir IT: Sidney Clark

D-U-N-S 17-961-3547
▲ **ALTRA INDUSTRIAL MOTION CORP**
300 Granite St Ste 201, Braintree, MA 02184-3950
Tel (781) 917-0600 *Founded/Ownrshp* 2004
Sales 746.6MM *EMP* 3,855^E^
Tkr Sym AIMC *Exch* NGS
SIC 3568 5085 3542 3625 Power transmission equipment; Power transmission equipment & apparatus; Brakes, metal forming; Brakes, electromagnetic; Controls for adjustable speed drives
Ch Bd: Carl R Christenson
CFO: Christian Storch
Treas: Todd B Patriacca
VP: Glenn E Deegan
VP: William Duff
VP: Gerald P Ferris
Area Mgr: Wesley Egert
VP Mktg: Craig Schuele
Sls Mgr: Michael Barrett
Sls Mgr: Dan O'Donnell
Board of Directors: Edmund M Carpenter, Lyle G Ganske, Michael S Lipscomb, Larry P McPherson, Thomas W Swidarski, James H Woodward Jr

D-U-N-S 80-516-5982
ALTRADIUS CREDIT INSURANCE INC
(*Suby of* ATRADIUS INSURANCE HOLDING N.V.)
230 Schilling Cir Ste 240, Hunt Valley, MD 21031-1409
Tel (410) 568-3850 *Founded/Ownrshp* 1993
Sales NA *EMP* 100

SIC 6351 Credit & other financial responsibility insurance
Pr: Richard Ariens
Treas: Samuel Hautot
VP: Douglas Collins
VP: Joyce E Knodell
VP: Scott Pales
VP: Risa Pickle
Board of Directors: Harry G Hayman II, Peter Ingenlath, Neil A Leary, Annette Merz, Robert M Solitro

D-U-N-S 82-991-0525
■ ALTRIA GROUP DISTRIBUTION CO
(*Suby of* ALTRIA GROUP INC) ★
6601 W Broad St, Richmond, VA 23230-1723
Tel (804) 274-2000 *Founded/Ownrshp* 2009
Sales 92.8MM[E] *EMP* 2,212[E]
SIC 5159 Tobacco distributors & products
CEO: Craig A Johnson
**Pr:* Randal Lawrence
**VP:* Peter Dicepeledi
Manager: Kim Short

D-U-N-S 14-462-8310
▲ ALTRIA GROUP INC
6601 W Broad St, Richmond, VA 23230-1723
Tel (804) 274-2200 *Founded/Ownrshp* 1919
Sales 25.4MMM *EMP* 8,800
Accts Pricewaterhousecoopers Llp Ri
Tkr Sym MO *Exch* NYS
SIC 2111 2084 Cigarettes; Wines
CEO: Martin J Barrington
Dir Recs: Lisa Hunt
COO: Howard A Willard III
CFO: William F Gifford Jr
Chf Cred: Charles N Whitaker
Ex VP: Denise F Keane
Sr VP: James E Dillard III
VP: Ivan S Feldman
VP: Michael French
VP: Rodger Rolland
Dir Risk M: Ron Allen
Board of Directors: Gerald L Baliles, John T Casteen III, Debra J Kelly-Ennis, Thomas F Farrell II, Thomas W Jones, W Leo Kiely III, Kathryn B McQuade, George Munoz, Nabil Y Sakkab

D-U-N-S 07-652-1392 IMP
ALTRU HEALTH SYSTEM
ALTRU HOSPITAL
1200 S Columbia Rd, Grand Forks, ND 58201-4044
Tel (701) 780-5000 *Founded/Ownrshp* 1970
Sales 488.1MM *EMP* 3,800
SIC 7352 8011 8062 8063 Medical equipment rental; Offices & clinics of medical doctors; General medical & surgical hospitals; Psychiatric hospitals
CEO: David Molmen
**Pr:* Casey Ryan
CEO: Eric Lunn
**COO:* Brad Wehe
**CFO:* Dwight Thompson
Ofcr: Unice Nelson
Exec: Margaret Reed
Adm Dir: Renee Axtman
Adm Dir: Kerry Carlson
Adm Dir: Kelly Hagen
Adm Dir: Joseph Myers

ALTRU HOSPITAL
See ALTRU HEALTH SYSTEM

D-U-N-S 10-362-1814
ALTURA COMMUNICATION SOLUTIONS LLC
(*Suby of* ALTURA HOLDINGS LLC) ★
1335 S Acacia Ave, Fullerton, CA 92831-5315
Tel (714) 948-8400 *Founded/Ownrshp* 2011
Sales 90.0MM[E] *EMP* 300
SIC 5065 Electronic parts & equipment
CEO: Robert Blazek
Pr: Tim Henion
**CFO:* David Key
Dir IT: Valerie Dorian
Dir IT: Lee Gray
Dir IT: Steve Lichtman
Dir IT: John Mundies
Dir IT: Courtney Saddler
Dir IT: Jacci Simms
Dir IT: Kevin Smith
Dir IT: Travis Walters

D-U-N-S 96-809-8835
ALTURA HOLDINGS LLC
(*Suby of* SILVER OAK SERVICES PARTNERS LLC) ★
1335 S Acacia Ave, Fullerton, CA 92831-5315
Tel (714) 948-8400 *Founded/Ownrshp* 2011
Sales 100.0MM[E] *EMP* 300[E]
SIC 6722 Management investment, open-end
CEO: Robert Blazek
CFO: Karen Frankenberg

ALTURA POWER
See OPTIM ENERGY TWIN OAKS LP

ALUF PLASTICS DIVISION
See API INDUSTRIES INC

D-U-N-S 03-814-5504
ALUM ROCK UNION ELEMENTARY SCHOOL DISTRICT
ARUESD
2930 Gay Ave, San Jose, CA 95127-2322
Tel (408) 928-6800 *Founded/Ownrshp* 1900
Sales 106.2MM[E] *EMP* 1,516[E]
SIC 8211
**Pr:* Dolores Marquez
**VP:* Andres Quintero
**VP:* Andrea Flores Shelton
Off Mgr: Eduarda Brasil
Off Admin: Helen Gaeta
CTO: Maribel Guizar-Maita
MIS Dir: Debbie Elliott
Dir IT: Debbie Elliot
Teacher Pr: Robert Meteau
Board of Directors: Anthony Alexander, F J Alvarez, A G Benavides, Esau Ruiz Herrera, William Horn, V Pres

ALUMA CRAFT PRODUCTS
See STYLE-VIEW PRODUCTS INC

D-U-N-S 36-296-7296
ALUMA SYSTEMS
(*Suby of* ALUMA SYSTEMS INC)
1020 Anita Ave, Antioch, IL 60002-1818
Tel (847) 838-4366 *Founded/Ownrshp* 2005
Sales 98.4MM[E] *EMP* 3,000
SIC 7359 Equipment rental & leasing
Pr: Stephen F Tisdall

D-U-N-S 05-783-0952
■ ALUMAX LLC
(*Suby of* ARCONIC INC) ★
201 Isabella St, Pittsburgh, PA 15212-5827
Tel (412) 553-4545 *Founded/Ownrshp* 1998
Sales 1.0MMM[E] *EMP* 14,400
SIC 3334 3353 3354 3449 3442 3446 Primary aluminum; Aluminum sheet, plate & foil; Coils, sheet aluminum; Plates, aluminum; Foil, aluminum; Aluminum extruded products; Miscellaneous metalwork; Curtain wall, metal; Store fronts, prefabricated, metal; Storm doors or windows, metal; Architectural metalwork; Ornamental metalwork
Pr: Russel W Porter Jr
**Treas:* William B Plummer
VP: Julie A Caponi
VP: Ronald D Dickel
VP: Richard T McCracken

ALUMCO
See SPECTRA METAL SALES INC

ALUMINUM DIV
See LE SUEUR INC

D-U-N-S 00-421-1348 IMP
ALUMINUM LINE PRODUCTS CO (OH)
ALPCO
24460 Sperry Cir, Westlake, OH 44145-1591
Tel (440) 835-8880 *Founded/Ownrshp* 1960
Sales 100.0MM *EMP* 110
SIC 5051 3365 3999 Metals service centers & offices; Aluminum foundries; Barber & beauty shop equipment
VP: Chris Harrington
**CFO:* Richard Daniel
**Treas:* Wendy L Wilson-Kieding
**Prin:* Edward Murray
Manager: Dave Livingston
Board of Directors: Charles Huffman

D-U-N-S 00-963-7513 IMP/EXP
ALUMINUM PRECISION PRODUCTS INC
3333 W Warner Ave, Santa Ana, CA 92704-5898
Tel (714) 546-8125 *Founded/Ownrshp* 1965
Sales 195.1MM[E] *EMP* 800
Accts Mcgladrey & Pullen Llp Irvin
SIC 3463 Aluminum forgings
Pr: Gregory S Keeler
**CFO:* Simona Manoiu
**VP:* Roark Keeler
VP: David P Silva
VP Bus Dev: Terry Seibert
Exec: Mary Block
Exec: Ramon Navarro
IT Man: Raymond Howard
QC Dir: Daniel McMahon
Plnt Mgr: Ron Aurey
Plnt Mgr: Jerry Boreman

D-U-N-S 04-266-7274
ALUTIIQ LLC
(*Suby of* AFOGNAK NATIVE CORP) ★
3909 Arctic Blvd Ste 500, Anchorage, AK 99503-5793
Tel (907) 222-9500 *Founded/Ownrshp* 2001
Sales 504.5MM *EMP* 4,434
SIC 8748

D-U-N-S 80-984-1898
ALUTIIQ PACIFIC LLC
(*Suby of* ALUTIIQ LLC) ★
3909 Arctic Blvd Ste 500, Anchorage, AK 99503-5793
Tel (907) 222-9500 *Founded/Ownrshp* 2008
Sales 104.2MM *EMP* 36
SIC 8742 7379 Management consulting services; Computer related consulting services

D-U-N-S 61-283-6114
ALVACO TRADING CO
12301 Nw 39th St, Coral Springs, FL 33065-2403
Tel (800) 852-8089 *Founded/Ownrshp* 1989
Sales 114.2MM[E] *EMP* 951[E]
SIC 6719 Investment holding companies, except banks
Pr: Alvarez Angel I

D-U-N-S 19-989-4817
ALVARADO HOSPITAL LLC
(*Suby of* PRIME HEALTHCARE SERVICES INC) ★
6655 Alvarado Rd, San Diego, CA 92120-5208
Tel (619) 287-3270 *Founded/Ownrshp* 2010
Sales 79.6M[E] *EMP* 1,000[E]
SIC 8062 General medical & surgical hospitals
CFO: Tracey Tally
**COO:* Darlene Wetton
CFO: Augustine Lopez
Dir Inf Cn: Kathi Foley
Dir Env Sv: Ann Boyce
Dir QC: Mario Lopez-Luna
Info Man: Don Murphy
Opthamlgy: Paul L Treger
Doctor: Philip Bajo
Doctor: Peter Berkman
Doctor: Edwin Fuller

D-U-N-S 14-934-3597
ALVAREZ & MARSAL CORPORATE PERFORMANCE IMPROVEMENT LLC
600 Madison Ave Fl 8, New York, NY 10022-1758
Tel (212) 759-4433 *Founded/Ownrshp* 2003
Sales 196.2MM[E] *EMP* 268
SIC 8748 8742 Business consulting; Financial consultant
CEO: Bryan Marsal
**CEO:* Antonio Alvarez
**COO:* John Suckow
**CFO:* Steven Cohn
CFO: Susan Robison

D-U-N-S 18-634-5062
ALVAREZ & MARSAL INC
(*Suby of* ALVAREZ & MARSAL CORPORATE PERFORMANCE IMPROVEMENT LLC) ★
600 Madison Ave Fl 8, New York, NY 10022-1758
Tel (212) 759-4433 *Founded/Ownrshp* 1983
Sales 190.7MM[E] *EMP* 268
SIC 8742 Financial consultant
Pr: Bryan Marsal
Bd of Dir: Ricardo Paes
Bd of Dir: Erik Wahl
**VP:* Antonio Alvarez
VP: Christopher Bryan
Exec: Yael Creditor
Exec: Stephen Wallace
Mng Dir: Marc Alms
Mng Dir: Rick Arrowsmith
Mng Dir: William Beer
Mng Dir: Anthony Caporrino

D-U-N-S 16-075-9135
ALVAREZ LLC
8251 Greensboro Dr # 230, Tysons Corner, VA 22102-4900
Tel (301) 830-4020 *Founded/Ownrshp* 2004
Sales 241.8MM *EMP* 28
Accts Kelly & Company Llc Tysons Co
SIC 8742 8741 7379 5044 Management consulting services; Management services; Computer related maintenance services; Office equipment
CEO: Everett Alvarez Jr
**VP:* Lee Snowberger

D-U-N-S 07-614-3205
ALVERNO COLLEGE
3400 S 43rd St, Milwaukee, WI 53219-4844
Tel (414) 382-6000 *Founded/Ownrshp* 1940
Sales 57.5MM *EMP* 1,000[E]
SIC 8221 College, except junior
Pr: Mary J Meehan
Treas: Ronald Blake
VP: Kathleen O'Brien
**VP:* James Oppermann
VP: Wendy Powers
CTO: Lauralee Guilbault
IT Man: Veronica Carrillo

D-U-N-S 80-287-4982
ALVEST (USA) INC
(*Suby of* LBO FRANCE GESTION)
812 Bloomfield Ave, Windsor, CT 06095-2340
Tel (860) 602-3400 *Founded/Ownrshp* 1991
Sales 137.4MM[E] *EMP* 250[E]
SIC 3585 3535 Air conditioning equipment, complete; Unit handling conveying systems
CEO: Mark Garlasco

D-U-N-S 07-760-0260
ALVIN INDEPENDENT SCHOOL DISTRICT
301 E House St, Alvin, TX 77511-3579
Tel (281) 388-1130 *Founded/Ownrshp* 1998
Sales 117.1MM[E] *EMP* 2,100
SIC 8211 Public elementary & secondary schools
**Prin:* Tiffany Wennerstrom
Teacher Pr: Kathy Windsor

D-U-N-S 96-329-4397
ALVOGEN GROUP INC
10 Bloomfield Ave, Pine Brook, NJ 07058-9743
Tel (973) 796-3400 *Founded/Ownrshp* 2015
Sales 319.8MM[E] *EMP* 2,300
SIC 2834 Pharmaceutical preparations
CEO: Robert Wessman
**Pr:* Darren Alkins
**COO:* Elin Gabriel
**CFO:* Kevin Bain
**Treas:* Andrew David
**Ex VP:* Georg Ingram
**Ex VP:* Chris Young
VP: Fjalar Kristjnsson
Assoc Dir: Christine Gordon
Snr Mgr: Jen Roche

D-U-N-S 00-805-7330
ALVOGEN INC
(*Suby of* ALVOGEN GROUP INC) ★
10 Bloomfield Ave Ste 3, Pine Brook, NJ 07058-9743
Tel (973) 796-3400 *Founded/Ownrshp* 2009
Sales 250.0MM *EMP* 110
SIC 2834 Pharmaceutical preparations
CFO: Kevin Bain
**Ex VP:* Lisa Graver

D-U-N-S 07-934-6294
ALVOGEN PHARMA US INC
(*Suby of* ALVOGEN GROUP INC) ★
10 Bloomfield Ave, Pine Brook, NJ 07058-9743
Tel (973) 796-3400 *Founded/Ownrshp* 2014
Sales 209.2M[E] *EMP* 1,652[E]
SIC 3559 Pharmaceutical machinery
CEO: Robert Wessman
**Pr:* Lisa Graver
**CFO:* Graham Baker

D-U-N-S 06-615-1747
ALVORD UNIFIED SCHOOL DISTRICT
9 Kpc Pkwy, Corona, CA 92879-7102
Tel (951) 509-5000 *Founded/Ownrshp* 1896
Sales 95.8MM[E] *EMP* 1,400
SIC 8211 Public elementary & secondary schools
Pr: Wendel W Tucker
**Pr:* Art Kaspereen Jr
**VP:* Greg Kraft
Prin: Beth Davis
Dir Sec: Tracy Horton
Dir IT: Steve Marx
Teacher Pr: Patrick Kellahar
Teacher Pr: Kirk Skorpanich
HC Dir: Charles Cummins

ALWAYS FRESH
See VALU MERCHANDISERS CO

ALWAYS HOME CARE
See ATTENTIVE HOME CARE AGENCY INC

D-U-N-S 04-923-1541
■ ALZA CORP
ALZA PHARMACEUTICALS
(*Suby of* JOHNSON & JOHNSON) ★
6500 Paseo Padre Pkwy, Fremont, CA 94555-3658
Tel (650) 564-5000 *Founded/Ownrshp* 2001
Sales 364.8MM[E] *EMP* 1,845
SIC 3826 Analytical instruments
CEO: Michael Jackson
CFO: Stan Abel
VP: Angela Nwaneri
Exec: Julie Folsch
Assoc Dir: Paul Hayter
Assoc Dir: Dave Killian
Assoc Dir: Barbara Pruitt
Assoc Dir: Peter Quigley
Ex Dir: Noymi Yam
QA Dir: Jen Osborne
Dir IT: Lisa Garrard

ALZA PHARMACEUTICALS
See ALZA CORP

D-U-N-S 01-145-9096 IMP
AM BEST CO INC
1 Ambest Rd, Oldwick, NJ 08858-7000
Tel (908) 439-2200 *Founded/Ownrshp* 1899
Sales 150.2MM[E] *EMP* 500
SIC 2731 2721 2732 Books: publishing only; Magazines: publishing only, not printed on site; Book printing
CEO: Arthur Snyder
Pr: Douglas Woelfel
**Treas:* Thomas Plummer
**Ex VP:* Lawrence Mayewski
**Ex VP:* Arthur Snyder III
VP: John Andre
VP: Andrew Edelsberg
VP: James Gillard
VP: Denise Gordon
VP: Donna Lagos
VP: Barbara Liebergall
VP: Anne Prisner
VP: James Snee
VP: Joan Sullivan
**VP:* Paul Tinnirello

D-U-N-S 00-325-3069
■ AM BRIGGS INC
METROPOLITAN POULTRY
(*Suby of* SYSCO CORP) ★
1920 Stanford Ct, Landover, MD 20785-3219
Tel (301) 773-2175 *Founded/Ownrshp* 1926
Sales 107.7MM[E] *EMP* 325
SIC 5147 5144 5146 Meats, fresh; Poultry: live, dressed or frozen (unpackaged); Seafoods
Pr: Scott Willard
Sls Mgr: Steven Powel

D-U-N-S 18-995-0368
AM GENERAL HOLDINGS LLC
(*Suby of* MACANDREWS & FORBES HOLDINGS INC) ★
105 N Niles Ave, South Bend, IN 46617-2705
Tel (574) 237-6222 *Founded/Ownrshp* 2004
Sales 488.7MM *EMP* 1,021[E]
SIC 3714 3711 8711 Motor vehicle parts & accessories; Military motor vehicle assembly; Engineering services
Pr: Charles M Hall
Pr: Howard Glaser
**COO:* John Ulrich
**CFO:* Paul J Cafiero
**Treas:* Brian Harshberger
**Ex VP:* Daniel J Dell'orto
Sr VP: Daniel Chien
**Sr VP:* Thomas R Douglas
Opers Mgr: Charles Huddlestun
Plnt Mgr: Paul Robinson
Ql Cn Mgr: Robert Ries

D-U-N-S 05-468-1739 IMP/EXP
AM GENERAL LLC
(*Suby of* AM GENERAL HOLDINGS LLC) ★
105 N Niles Ave, South Bend, IN 46617-2705
Tel (574) 237-6222 *Founded/Ownrshp* 1903
Sales 88.1MM[E] *EMP* 355
SIC 3711 3714 8711

D-U-N-S 82-787-7460 IMP
■ AM RETAIL GROUP INC
WILSONS LEATHER OUTLET
(*Suby of* G-III APPAREL GROUP LTD) ★
7401 Boone Ave N, Brooklyn Park, MN 55428-1007
Tel (763) 391-4000 *Founded/Ownrshp* 2008
Sales 1.8MMM[E] *EMP* 4,160[E]
SIC 3199 Leather garments
CEO: Morris Goldfarb
**Pr:* Bill Hutchison
COO: Mike Seale
**CFO:* Randy Roland
Bd of Dir: Jeffrey W Orton
**Sr VP:* Josh Burris
Sr VP: Mike Tripp
VP: Darren L Acheson
VP: William F Farley
VP: Michael J McCoy
**VP:* Jeff Montang
VP: Chad Moorefield
**VP:* Heidi Waller
VP: Ted R Weschler

A.M. TODD
See WILD FLAVORS INC

AM WAX
See CALIFORNIA BEES INC

D-U-N-S 92-616-2652 IMP
AM-MEX PRODUCTS INC
3801 W Military Hwy, McAllen, TX 78503-8810
Tel (956) 631-7916 *Founded/Ownrshp* 1989
Sales 245.1MM[E] *EMP* 3,500[E]
SIC 3714 7361 3672 Motor vehicle electrical equipment; Labor contractors (employment agency); Printed circuit boards
Pr: Donald P King
**VP:* Frank King

D-U-N-S 07-932-7916
AM/NS CALVERT LLC
1 Am Ns Way, Calvert, AL 36513
Tel (251) 289-3000 *Founded/Ownrshp* 2007
Sales 226.4MM^E *EMP* 1,001
SIC 3312 3449 Blast furnace & related products; Bars, concrete reinforcing: fabricated steel
CEO: Robrecht Himpe
Pr: Chris Richards
VP: Kai Mahnke

D-U-N-S 06-445-4531 IMP
AMA PLASTICS
1100 Citrus St, Riverside, CA 92507-1731
Tel (951) 734-5600 *Founded/Ownrshp* 1971
Sales 127.3MM^E *EMP* 393
SIC 3089 3544 Molding primary plastic; Forms (molds), for foundry & plastics working machinery
Prin: Mark Atchinson
VP: Craig Atchison
VP: Tony Mauer
CIO: Amy Halcrow
Ql Cn Mgr: Mina Mehta
Ql Cn Mgr: Davis Ngo

AMACOM
See AMERICAN MANAGEMENT ASSOCIATION INTERNATIONAL

D-U-N-S 05-381-1386 IMP
AMADA AMERICA INC
(*Suby of* AMADA HOLDINGS CO., LTD.)
7025 Firestone Blvd, Buena Park, CA 90621-1869
Tel (714) 739-2111 *Founded/Ownrshp* 1971
Sales 218.7MM^E *EMP* 500
SIC 5084 6159 Metalworking machinery; Metalworking tools (such as drills, taps, dies, files); Machinery & equipment finance leasing
CEO: Mike Guarin
CFO: KOA Nakata
Sr VP: Pablo Cervantes
Exec: Stephen Keating
Ex Dir: Charles Wittig
Rgnl Mgr: Themis Alexopoulos
Genl Mgr: Michael Beransky
Genl Mgr: Graham Dallas
Genl Mgr: Don Murphy
Genl Mgr: Rob Ochs
Genl Mgr: Tim Siple

D-U-N-S 10-094-7154
AMADEUS AMERICAS INC
(*Suby of* AMADEUS IT GROUP SOCIEDAD ANONIMA.)
3470 Nw 82nd Ave Ste 1000, Doral, FL 33122-1030
Tel (305) 499-6000 *Founded/Ownrshp* 1997
Sales 223.2MM^E *EMP* 1,353
SIC 7371 Computer software development & applications
Pr: Scott Gutz
IT Man: Guillermo Cuadrado
IT Man: Glenn Dean
IT Man: Sammed Govaria

D-U-N-S 18-198-8064
AMADEUS HOSPITALITY AMERICAS INC
NEWMARKET INTERNATIONAL, INC.
(*Suby of* NMTI HOLDINGS INC) ★
75 Nh Ave Ste 300, Portsmouth, NH 03801-2864
Tel (603) 436-7500 *Founded/Ownrshp* 2007
Sales 107.8MM^E *EMP* 275
SIC 7371 Computer software development
Pr: Lee Horgan
COO: William Sintiris
Ofcr: Tim Pelletier
Ex VP: Paul Rantilla
Ex VP: Ahmed Youssef
VP: Erin Jacobsen
VP: Kenneth Smaha
VP Inf Sys: Marc Berthiaume
QA Dir: David Turner
Dir IT: Eddie Fernandez
Software D: Roy Briscoe

D-U-N-S 17-494-2359
AMADEUS NORTH AMERICA INC
(*Suby of* AMADEUS AMERICAS INC) ★
3470 Nw 82nd Ave Ste 1000, Doral, FL 33122-1030
Tel (305) 499-6613 *Founded/Ownrshp* 1995
Sales 96.6MM^E *EMP* 550
SIC 7371 8322 Computer software systems analysis & design, custom; Computer software development; Travelers' aid
Pr: Scott Gutz
Pr: Diana Kaiser
Sr VP: John J Jarrell
Sr VP: Mary Martinez
VP: Stewart Alvarez
VP: Franaois Weissert
Exec: Syed-Sohail Ahmed
Mng Dir: Tim Russell
Prgrm Mgr: Tom Jones
Dept Mgr: Frederic Bessis
Genl Mgr: Xuan Du
Board of Directors: Ana De Pro, Holger Taubmann

D-U-N-S 01-751-1155
▲ AMAG PHARMACEUTICALS INC
1100 Winter St Fl 3, Waltham, MA 02451-1473
Tel (617) 498-3300 *Founded/Ownrshp* 1981
Sales 418.2MM *EMP* 814
Accts Pricewaterhousecoopers Llp Bo
Tkr Sym AMAG *Exch* NGS
SIC 2834 2835 Pharmaceutical preparations; In vitro diagnostics; In vivo diagnostics
CEO: William K Heiden
Ch Bd: Gino Santini
Pr: Frank E Thomas
Pr: Kenneth A Wilson
CFO: Edward Myles
Treas: Scott A Holmes
Sr VP: Tony Casciano
Sr VP: Edward P Jordan
Sr VP: Scott B Townsend
VP: Jeffrey Hart
VP: Linda Lennox
VP: Mark Stanton
VP: Joseph Vittiglio
VP: Paul Williams

Board of Directors: Barbara Deptula, John A Fallon, Brian Kelley, Robert J Perez, Lesley Russell, Davey S Scoon, James R Sulat

D-U-N-S 80-920-8577
AMAIZING ENERGY HOLDING CO LLC
2404 Highway 30, Denison, IA 51442-7595
Tel (712) 263-2676 *Founded/Ownrshp* 2006
Sales 160.0MM *EMP* 43
SIC 2869 Ethyl alcohol, ethanol
Ch Bd: Sam Cogdill
CFO: Connie Jensen

D-U-N-S 88-376-2718 IMP
AMAK BRAKE LLC
AKEBONO BRAKE
(*Suby of* AKEBONO BRAKE CORP) ★
1765 Cleveland Ave, Glasgow, KY 42141-1057
Tel (270) 678-1765 *Founded/Ownrshp* 1994
Sales 199.3MM^E *EMP* 650
SIC 3714 Motor vehicle brake systems & parts
Pr: Roy Okawa
Exec: Chris Gibbons
VP Mfg: Harold Rumple
Mtls Mgr: William Speed
Opers Mgr: Tommy Reveira
Ql Cn Mgr: Shellie Bates
Ql Cn Mgr: Scott Rucker
Sls Mgr: Mike Eldard

D-U-N-S 00-697-9769
AMALGAMATED BANK
(*Suby of* ALICO SERVICES CORPORATION)
275 7th Ave Lbby 2, New York, NY 10001-8400
Tel (212) 895-8988 *Founded/Ownrshp* 1923
Sales NA *EMP* 433
SIC 6022 State commercial banks
Pr: Edward Grebow
Pr: Stephen Buffel
Chf Cred: Michael Zahaby
Chf Mktg O: Keith Pilkington
Ex VP: Louis De Luca
Ex VP: Louis Deluca
Ex VP: Louis J Deluca
Ex VP: Gregory Fierce
Ex VP: Lawrence Fruchtman
Ex VP: Daniel A Greene
Ex VP: George Jarvis
Ex VP: Leonard Maisel
Ex VP: Anthony Pellecchia
Ex VP: John Romano
Ex VP: Gardner Semet
Sr VP: Joseph E Brunken
Sr VP: David Knopp
Sr VP: Robert O'Brien
VP: Jason Clearwaters
VP: Claude Colimon
VP: Monica Cox

D-U-N-S 96-733-9503
AMALGAMATED NATIONAL HEALTH FUND
333 Westchester Ave N101, White Plains, NY 10604-2910
Tel (914) 367-5000 *Founded/Ownrshp* 2011
Sales 174.6MM *EMP* 3
Accts Bdo Usa Llp New York Ny
SIC 8631 Labor unions & similar labor organizations
CEO: Raghubar Singh

D-U-N-S 00-907-6738 IMP
AMALGAMATED SUGAR CO LLC
WHITE SATIN SUGAR
(*Suby of* SNAKE RIVER SUGAR CO) ★
1951 S Saturn Way Ste 100, Boise, ID 83709-2924
Tel (208) 383-6500 *Founded/Ownrshp* 1896, 1897
Sales 722.4MM *EMP* 1,500
Accts Eide Bailly Llp Boise Idaho
SIC 2063 Beet sugar from beet sugar refinery; Molasses from sugar beets
Pr: Vic Jaro
COO: Joe Huff
CFO: John Landis
Ch: Duane Grant
Treas: Dave Budge
VP: John McCreedy
VP: Wayne Neeley
VP: Willie E Smith Jr
VP: Bryan Whipple
Sfty Dirs: Erv Vansickle

D-U-N-S 00-409-1146 IMP/EXP
AMALIE OIL CO
1601 Mcclosky Blvd, Tampa, FL 33605-6710
Tel (813) 248-1988 *Founded/Ownrshp* 1977
Sales 140.9MM^E *EMP* 175
SIC 2992 3085 Lubricating oils & greases; Plastics bottles
Ch Bd: Harry J Barket
Treas: Richard Barkett
VP: Anthony Barkett
VP: Dennis Madden
VP: Denny Madden
MIS Dir: Don Bryant
Dir IT: Gianni Barkett
IT Man: Chip Clark
IT Man: Dave Leedke
IT Man: Wayne Matthews
Prd Mgr: Nathaniel Ashe

D-U-N-S 61-528-0955 IMP/EXP
AMANO USA HOLDINGS INC
(*Suby of* AMANO CORPORATION)
140 Harrison Ave, Roseland, NJ 07068-1239
Tel (973) 403-1900 *Founded/Ownrshp* 1990
Sales 113.3MM^E *EMP* 387
SIC 3589 2842 3579 3559 5169 5087 Floor washing & polishing machines, commercial; Cleaning or polishing preparations; Time clocks & time recording devices; Parking facility equipment & supplies; Industrial chemicals; Floor machinery, maintenance
Pr: Tomoaki Hashimoto
Pr: Thomas M Benton
VP: Yoshio Misumi
Ex Dir: Alan Poulton
Dir IT: David Lopez
Plnt Mgr: George Sandusky
Sales Exec: Tom Moro

D-U-N-S 05-549-3340 IMP
AMARGOSA INC
EDDIE BAUER
(*Suby of* EBHI HOLDINGS INC) ★
10401 Ne 8th St Ste 500, Bellevue, WA 98004-4346
Tel (425) 755-6100 *Founded/Ownrshp* 1971
Sales 113.5MM^E *EMP* 687
SIC 5611 5699 5941 5719 5947 5961 Men's & boys' clothing stores; Sports apparel; Sporting goods & bicycle shops; Housewares; Gift shop; Clothing, mail order (except women's); Fishing, hunting & camping equipment & supplies: mail order; Furniture & furnishings, mail order; Women's apparel, mail order
Ex VP: James Cannataro
CFO: S Ronald Gaston
Chf Cred: Engle E Saez
Sr VP: Bill Bredy
VP: Michael Africa
Snr Ntwrk: Darin Mattner
Prd Mgr: Janet Malag
Ql Cn Mgr: Yifei Zhang
Mktg Mgr: Natalie Smith

D-U-N-S 80-539-4850
AMARI METALS EUROPE LTD
555 Skokie Blvd Ste 555, Northbrook, IL 60062-2854
Tel (847) 480-4690 *Founded/Ownrshp* 2004
Sales 230.0MM^E *EMP* 1,103^E
SIC 6719 Investment holding companies, except banks
Pr: David Sims

AMARILLO COLLEGE BOOKSTORE
See AMARILLO JUNIOR COLLEGE DISTRICT

D-U-N-S 08-096-6666
AMARILLO INDEPENDENT SCHOOL DISTRICT
EDUCATION SUPPORT CENTER
7200 W Interstate 40, Amarillo, TX 79106-2528
Tel (806) 326-1000 *Founded/Ownrshp* 1889
Sales 312.3MM *EMP* 3,600
Accts Connor Mcmillon Mitchell Sh
SIC 8211 Public elementary & secondary schools; Public elementary school; Public junior high school; Public senior high school
Prin: David Bishop
Exec: Holly Holder
Exec: Natashia Woolley
Telecom Ex: Barbara Hilburn
Pr Dir: Holly Shelton
Psych: Sharyn Delgado
Psych: Sharra Karrh
Psych: Nancy McKinley
HC Dir: Patricia Miranda
Pgrm Dir: Cheryl Reed

D-U-N-S 07-318-6108
AMARILLO JUNIOR COLLEGE DISTRICT
AMARILLO COLLEGE BOOKSTORE
2201 S Washington St, Amarillo, TX 79109-2411
Tel (806) 371-5000 *Founded/Ownrshp* 1929
Sales 32.6MM *EMP* 1,116
Accts Connor Mcmillon Mitchell Sh
SIC 8222 8221 Junior college; Colleges universities & professional schools
Pr: Paul Matney
Assoc VP: Patsy Lemaster
VP: Terry Berg
Genl Mgr: Jackie Smith
Tech Mgr: Brenda Veach
Mktg Dir: Cynthia Hunt

D-U-N-S 01-011-6130
AMARILLO NATIONAL BANCORP INC (TX)
Plaza One 410 S Taylor St # 1, Amarillo, TX 79101
Tel (806) 378-8000 *Founded/Ownrshp* 1982
Sales NA *EMP* 580
SIC 6021 National commercial banks
Pr: Richard C Ware II
Ofcr: Sharon Liotart
Ex VP: Bill Ware
VP: Alisha Amero
VP: John Hunt
Site Mgr: Cara Copado
Opers Mgr: Toby Ezzell

D-U-N-S 00-792-3444
AMARILLO NATIONAL BANK
(*Suby of* AMARILLO NATIONAL BANCORP INC) ★
410 S Taylor St, Amarillo, TX 79101-1555
Tel (806) 349-9760 *Founded/Ownrshp* 1892
Sales NA *EMP* 550
SIC 6021 National commercial banks
Pr: Richard C Ware II
Trst: Sheri Coleman
Ofcr: Bliss Green
Ofcr: Jerry N Ivy
Ofcr: Sharon Liotart
Ofcr: Chris Richardson
Ofcr: Ryan Roy
Ofcr: Erik Schrader
Ofcr: Lisa Wilson
Trst Ofcr: Lisa Simpson
Ex VP: Cliff Bickerstaff
Ex VP: Wade Porter
Ex VP: R Wesley Savage
Ex VP: Bill Ware
Sr VP: Gregg Jordan
Sr VP: Cory Ramsey
Sr VP: Shirley Rhea
Sr VP: Patrick C Stanley
VP: Shawna Bachman
VP: Stewart Dodson
VP: Sha Gearn

D-U-N-S 02-487-9660 IMP/EXP
AMARR CO (NC)
AMARR GARAGE DOORS
(*Suby of* ASSA ABLOY USA) ★
165 Carriage Ct, Winston Salem, NC 27105-1326
Tel (336) 744-5100 *Founded/Ownrshp* 1951
Sales 266.4MM^E *EMP* 1,000
SIC 2431 3442 5031 5211 Garage doors, overhead: wood; Garage doors, overhead: metal; Doors, garage; Garage doors, sale & installation
Ch Bd: Richard A Brenner
Pr: Jeffrey D Mick
Treas: Gary Elkins
Treas: Richard S Sears
VP: Stephen R Crawford
VP: Matthew S Hukill
Genl Mgr: Brenton Cheney
Genl Mgr: Jason Degroot
Genl Mgr: Donald Ferry
Genl Mgr: John Henderson
Genl Mgr: Jeff Henry

AMARR GARAGE DOORS
See AMARR CO

AMARR GARAGE DOORS
See GARAGE DOOR GROUP INC

AMAX COMPUTER
See AMAX ENGINEERING CORP

D-U-N-S 03-989-0892 IMP
AMAX ENGINEERING CORP
AMAX COMPUTER
1565 Reliance Way, Fremont, CA 94539-6103
Tel (510) 651-8886 *Founded/Ownrshp* 1979
Sales 194.8MM^E *EMP* 180
SIC 5045 Computer peripheral equipment; Computer software
CEO: Jerry Kc Shih
VP: Azaa Lee
VP: CHI-Lei Ni
VP: Jean Shih
VP: Edward Zheng
Creative D: Paul Sun
QA Dir: Nathaniel Castro
QA Dir: Danny Haloc
QA Dir: Kai Sun
Opers Mgr: David Chang
Sls Mgr: Matthew Thauberger

D-U-N-S 17-521-4675
AMAZING SAVINGS HOLDING LLC
20 Industry Dr, Mountainville, NY 10953
Tel (845) 534-1000 *Founded/Ownrshp* 1995
Sales 71.8MM^E *EMP* 2,492
SIC 5399 Surplus & salvage goods
Pr: Sam Friedland
VP: Jerry Hoffnung
VP: Phil Rosenblatt

D-U-N-S 83-938-3945
■ AMAZON COM DEDC LLC
(*Suby of* AMAZON.COMDEDC LLC) ★
1227 124th Ave Ne Ste 200, Bellevue, WA 98005-2111
Tel (206) 266-5363 *Founded/Ownrshp* 2000
Sales 66.4M^E *EMP* 5,007^E
SIC 5961 Catalog & mail-order houses

D-U-N-S 12-899-0418 IMP
■ AMAZON FULFILLMENT SERVICES INC
(*Suby of* AMAZON.COM INC) ★
410 Terry Ave N, Seattle, WA 98109-5210
Tel (206) 266-1000 *Founded/Ownrshp* 2002
Sales 306.2MM^E *EMP* 1,800
SIC 5735 5961 5731 5945 Records, audio discs & tapes; Video discs & tapes, prerecorded; Book & record clubs; Book club, mail order; Record &/or tape (music or video) club, mail order; Mail order house; Radio, television & electronic stores; Hobby, toy & game shops
Pr: Dave H Clark
VP: Catherine Beaudoin
VP: Jason M Bristow
VP: Stephanie Burns
VP: Brian W Calvin
VP: Timothy C Collins

D-U-N-S 96-254-8496
■ AMAZON LAB126
(*Suby of* AMAZON.COM INC) ★
1100 Enterprise Way, Sunnyvale, CA 94089-1412
Tel (650) 426-1100 *Founded/Ownrshp* 2010
Sales 92.9MM^E *EMP* 615^E
SIC 8731 Electronic research
VP: Gregg Zehr
VP: Malachy Moynihan
Exec: Jessica Staley
Dir: Chuck Desmond
Prgrm Mgr: Gavin O'Duffy
Snr Sftwr: Dmitri Khokhlov
QA Dir: Melissa Erickson
QA Dir: Anh Vu
Dir IT: Terry Lin
IT Man: Payman Armin
Sftwr Eng: Victor Francis

D-U-N-S 88-474-5530
▲ AMAZON.COM INC
410 Terry Ave N, Seattle, WA 98109-5210
Tel (206) 266-1000 *Founded/Ownrshp* 1994
Sales 107.0MMM *EMP* 230,800
Accts Ernst & Young Llp Seattle Wa
Tkr Sym AMZN *Exch* NGS
SIC 5961
Ch Bd: Jeffrey P Bezos
CFO: Brian T Olsavsky
Ex VP: Rich Williams
Sr VP: Jeffrey M Blackburn
Sr VP: Diego Piacentini
Sr VP: David A Zapolsky
VP: Amber Beckman
VP: Yvette Bohanan
VP: Chee Chew
VP: Andrew Devore
VP: Edward G Feitzinger
VP: Kathryn Giorgianni
VP: Russell Grandinetti
VP: Peter Krawiec
VP: Llew Mason
VP: Gene Pope
VP: Kim Rachmeler
VP: Shelley L Reynolds
VP: Max Safai
VP: Robert Saltzman
VP: Tim Stone
Board of Directors: Wendell P Weeks, Tom A Alberg, John Seely Brown, William B Gordon, Jamie S Gorelick, Daniel P Huttenlocher, Judith A McGrath, Jonathan J Rubinstein, Thomas O Ryder, Patricia Q Stonesifer

D-U-N-S 12-898-9188 IMP/EXP
■ **AMAZON.COMDEDC LLC**
(Suby of AMAZON.COM INC) ★
410 Terry Ave N, Seattle, WA 98109-5210
Tel (206) 266-1000 Founded/Ownrshp 2000
Sales 9.3MM[E] EMP 183,100
SIC 5961 5735 5731 5945 Book & record clubs; Book club, mail order; Record &/or tape (music or video) club, mail order; Mail order house; Records, audio discs & tapes; Video discs & tapes, prerecorded; Radio, television & electronic stores; Hobby, toy & game shops
Exec: Jeffrey Elwell
Area Mgr: Corey Blain
Area Mgr: Lisa Schade
QA Dir: Jen Diaz
QA Dir: Michael Lipp
QA Dir: Kyle Marcroft
IT Man: Shannon Lowther
Software D: Dylan Marriner
Sftwr Eng: Neeraj Agrawal
Sftwr Eng: Bibek Bhusal
Sftwr Eng: Arvind Chandrasekar

D-U-N-S 07-875-3818
AMAZON.COMINDC LLC
(Suby of AMAZON DEVELOPMENT CENTRE (INDIA) PRIVATE LIMITED)
440 Terry Ave N, Seattle, WA 98109-5210
Tel (206) 266-1000 Founded/Ownrshp 2013
Sales 96.6MM[E] EMP 169[E]
SIC 4813 5999 7371 ; Audio-visual equipment & supplies; Computer software development & applications
Pr: Jeff Bezos
Sftwr Eng: Michael Yie

D-U-N-S 12-898-9436
■ **AMAZON.COMKYDC LLC**
(Suby of AMAZON.COM INC) ★
1850 Mercer Rd, Lexington, KY 40511-1013
Tel (859) 381-2102 Founded/Ownrshp 1999
Sales 168.8MM[E] EMP 1,782[E]
SIC 4226 Special warehousing & storage
Pr: Jeffery P Bezos
*Treas: Russell Grandinetti
*VP: L Michelle Wilson

D-U-N-S 13-135-5612
▲ **AMBAC FINANCIAL GROUP INC**
1 State St Fl 15, New York, NY 10004-1484
Tel (212) 658-7470 Founded/Ownrshp 1991
Sales 644.6MM EMP 158[E]
Accts Kpmg Llp New York New York
Tkr Sym AMBC Exch NGS
SIC 6211 Investment bankers
Pr: Nader Tavakoli
*Ch Bd: Jeffrey S Stein
Pr: Venka Korsapati
Pr: Pranay Nadkarni
Pr: Yanira Vergara
CFO: David Trick
Sr Cor Off: G Yong
Chf Cred: Denise Tauriello
Ex VP: Joseph V Salzano
Ex VP: John Uhlen
VP: Valerie Anderson
VP: Robert Bose
VP: Michael Braganca
VP: Ronaldo Contreras
VP: Lee Gigante
VP: Emily He
VP: Art Heffner
VP: Charu Kanbur
VP: Michael Klaassens
VP: Justine Kong
VP: Dwight Kwa
Board of Directors: Eugene M Bullis, Alexander D Greene, Ian Haft, David Herzog, Victor Mandel, C James Prieur

D-U-N-S 18-552-0819
AMBARELLA INC
3101 Jay St, Santa Clara, CA 95054-3329
Tel (408) 734-8888 Founded/Ownrshp 2004
Sales 316.3MM EMP 640
Tkr Sym AMBA Exch NGM
SIC 3674 Semiconductors & related devices
Ch Bd: Feng-Ming Wang
CFO: George Laplante
VP: Yun-Lung Chen
*CTO: Leslie Kohn
VP Mktg: Christopher Day
Board of Directors: Christopher B Paisley, D Jeffrey Richardson, Andrew W Verhalen

D-U-N-S 06-594-2286
AMBASSADOR BOOK SERVICE INC
445 Broadhollow Rd, Melville, NY 11747-3669
Tel (631) 770-1010 Founded/Ownrshp 1973
Sales 143.9MM[E] EMP 102[E]
SIC 5192 Books
CEO: Gary Herald
*COO: Steven Blicht
CFO: Mamie Abrams

D-U-N-S 83-144-5908
AMBER HOLDING INC
(Suby of VISTA EQUITY PARTNERS FUND III LP) ★
150 California St, San Francisco, CA 94111-4500
Tel (415) 765-6500 Founded/Ownrshp 1995
Sales 23.4MM[E] EMP 1,010
SIC 7371 Computer software development; Computer software development & applications
Pr: Robert F Smith
*VP: Brian N Sheth

D-U-N-S 83-729-0667 IMP
AMBERCARE CORP
AMBERCARE HOME HEALTH
420 N Main St, Belen, NM 87002-3718
Tel (505) 861-0060 Founded/Ownrshp 1993
Sales 90.6MM[E] EMP 2,000
SIC 8082 8361 5047 7352 Home health care services; Geriatric residential care; Medical & hospital equipment; Medical equipment rental
Pr: Mike Merrell
CFO: Laura Armstrong
*Treas: Laura T Armstrong
Off Mgr: Martha Jurado
Dir IT: Barbara Crawley
Sales Exec: Nannette Sanchez
Nrsg Dir: Robert Foster

AMBERCARE HOME HEALTH
See AMBERCARE CORP

D-U-N-S 03-840-3945
AMBERJACK LTD
(Suby of STATE FARM INSURANCE) ★
3 State Farm Plz, Bloomington, IL 61791-0001
Tel (309) 766-6920 Founded/Ownrshp 1979
Sales 11.9MM[E] EMP 1,000
SIC 6512 6513 Commercial & industrial building operation; Apartment building operators
Ch Bd: Kurt G Moser
*Pr: David Graves
*Treas: John Higgins

AMBIRONTRUSTWAVE
See TRUSTWAVE CORP

D-U-N-S 60-479-2791
AMBIT ENERGY HOLDINGS LLC
1801 N Lamar St Ste 200, Dallas, TX 75202-1726
Tel (214) 461-4736 Founded/Ownrshp 2005
Sales 487.1MM[E] EMP 581[E]
SIC 4931 Electric & other services combined
CEO: Jere W Thompson Jr
CFO: Laurie Rodriguez
Chf Mktg O: Chris Chambless
CIO: John Burke

D-U-N-S 10-871-4783
AMBITECH ENGINEERING CORP
1411 Opus Pl Ste 200, Downers Grove, IL 60515-1060
Tel (630) 963-5800 Founded/Ownrshp 1982
Sales 152.6MM[E] EMP 695
SIC 8711 Designing: ship, boat, machine & product
CEO: Allan R Koenig
*Pr: G Richard Hutter
CFO: Christopher Hunt
*Ex VP: Muneer M Bachh Pe
VP: Muneer Bachh
VP: Bernie Gunn
VP: Mark Johnson
VP: Jerry Mundy
Mng Dir: Wayne Meyer
Genl Mgr: Mark Heuer
Genl Mgr: Jim Vetromila
Board of Directors: Philippa Coates, Alan English, Steven Ford, Eric Greer, G Richard Hutter, Mark Johnson, Allan Koenig, Michael Koenig

D-U-N-S 17-807-6469
AMBLING MANAGEMENT CO LLC
REA CONSTRUCTION
348 Enterprise Dr, Valdosta, GA 31601-5169
Tel (866) 777-7228 Founded/Ownrshp 1997
Sales 125.0MM[E] EMP 350
SIC 1522 6552 6531 6513 Hotel/motel & multi-family home construction; Land subdividers & developers, residential; Real estate managers; Apartment building operators
Pr: Mike Godwin
CFO: Cynamon Willis
Ex VP: Pamela Meyers
*VP: Ryan Holmes

D-U-N-S 13-165-6373
AMBOY BANCORPORATION
3590 Us Highway 9, Old Bridge, NJ 08857-2765
Tel (732) 591-8700 Founded/Ownrshp 1888
Sales NA EMP 236
SIC 6021 National commercial banks
Pr: George Scharpf
*COO: Stanley Koreyva
Ofcr: Susan G Haynes
*Sr VP: Peter Davis
VP: Patricia Broadnax
VP: Karen Casey
*VP: Shirley M Croasmun
VP: Anthony Detoro
*VP: Stanley J Koreya Jr
*VP: Domenick Margiotta
VP: George Willever
Board of Directors: Olive W Bray, Joseph J Disepio, Ernest J Scharf, George E Scharpf, Harold G Smith

D-U-N-S 00-256-8616
AMBOY BANK
(Suby of AMBOY BANCORPORATION) ★
3590 Us Highway 9, Old Bridge, NJ 08857-2765
Tel (732) 721-4200 Founded/Ownrshp 1888
Sales NA EMP 217
SIC 6021 National commercial banks
Pr: George E Scharpf
Treas: Edwin Wojtaszek
*Sr VP: Peter W Davis
*Sr VP: Stan Koreyva
VP: Edward Clemente
VP: Harry Deerfield
*VP: Peggy Dembowski
VP: Harry Gray
*VP: Domenick Margiotta
Exec: Bill Haluska
Exec: Denise Hundley

D-U-N-S 02-151-9541
AMBOY BUS CO INC
(Suby of ATLANTIC EXPRESS TRANSPORTATION CORP)
7 North St, Staten Island, NY 10302-1227
Tel (718) 442-7000 Founded/Ownrshp 1993
Sales 24.8MM[E] EMP 1,000
SIC 4151 School buses
Pr: Domenic Gatto

D-U-N-S 14-368-9706 IMP/EXP
AMBRAKE MANUFACTURING LTD
AKEBONO ELIZABETHTOWN
(Suby of AKEBONO BRAKE CORP) ★
300 Ring Rd, Elizabethtown, KY 42701-6778
Tel (270) 737-4906 Founded/Ownrshp 2003
Sales 111.1MM[E] EMP 750
SIC 3714 Motor vehicle brake systems & parts
Pt: Ronald L Jones
Plnt Mgr: Doug Morgan

AMBROSE INTERNATIONAL
See FRANK AMBROSE INC

D-U-N-S 96-356-9749
AMBROSIA GUILLEN TSVH
9650 Kenworthy St, El Paso, TX 79924-6011
Tel (915) 751-0967 Founded/Ownrshp 2010
Sales 899.8MM EMP 7[E]
SIC 8051 Skilled nursing care facilities
Prin: Ambrosio Guillen

D-U-N-S 00-929-9017 IMP
AMBU INC
KING SYSTEMS
(Suby of AMBU A/S)
15011 Herriman Blvd, Noblesville, IN 46060-4253
Tel (317) 776-6823 Founded/Ownrshp 1977, 2013
Sales 146.1MM[E] EMP 465
SIC 3841 Surgical & medical instruments; Anesthesia apparatus
CEO: Steve Davis
VP: Tony Yeh
CIO: Chad Brooks
Netwrk Mgr: Stuart Williamson
Software D: Bess Wang

D-U-N-S 10-726-0275 IMP
AMBU INC
AMBU USA
(Suby of RIIS ENTREPRISE A/S)
6230 Old Dobbin Ln # 250, Columbia, MD 21045-5955
Tel (410) 768-6464 Founded/Ownrshp 1983
Sales 220.0MM[E] EMP 575
SIC 5047 Medical equipment & supplies
Pr: Steven Block
*Pr: Frank Homa
CFO: Michael Stern
Ex VP: Mikael Worning
VP: Trent Starkes
VP Opers: Sanjay Parikh
Mfg Dir: Andy Camp
VP Mktg: John Schmitz
Mktg Mgr: John Florian

AMBU USA
See AMBU INC

D-U-N-S 92-816-1769
AMBULATORY SERVICES INC
QUEENS HEALTH CARE CENTERS
(Suby of QUEENS MEDICAL CENTER ASSOCIATES)
1301 Punchbowl St, Honolulu, HI 96813-2402
Tel (808) 538-9011 Founded/Ownrshp 2001
Sales 425.0MM EMP 5
SIC 8031 Offices & clinics of osteopathic physicians
Pr: Wendy Takeshita
Off Mgr: Laura Pladson

AMC
See TARGET SOURCING SERVICES CORP

AMC
See AMERICAN MULTI-CINEMA INC

D-U-N-S 80-863-4328
■ **AMC ENTERTAINMENT HOLDINGS INC**
(Suby of DALIAN WANDA GROUP CO., LTD.)
1 Amc Way 11500 Ash St, Leawood, KS 66211
Tel (913) 213-2000 Founded/Ownrshp 2012
Sales 2.9MMM EMP 21,300[E]
Tkr Sym AMC Exch NYS
SIC 7832 Motion picture theaters, except drive-in
Pr: Adam Aron
*Ch Bd: Lin Zhang
CFO: Craig R Ramsey
Chf Mktg O: Stephen A Colanero
Ex VP: Elizabeth Frank
Ex VP: John D McDonald
Ex VP: Mark A McDonald
Sr VP: Kevin M Connor
Sr VP: Chris A Cox
Sr VP: Carla Sanders

D-U-N-S 10-251-9584
■ **AMC ENTERTAINMENT INC**
(Suby of AMC ENTERTAINMENT HOLDINGS INC) ★
11500 Ash St, Leawood, KS 66211-7804
Tel (913) 213-2000 Founded/Ownrshp 1920
Sales 2.9MMM EMP 19,700[E]
Accts Kpmg Llp Kansas City Missour
SIC 7832 Motion picture theaters, except drive-in
Pr: Gerardo I Lopez
*Ch Bd: Lin Zhang
CFO: Craig R Ramsey
Chf Mktg O: Stephen A Colanero
Sr VP: Kevin M Connor
Sr VP: Chris A Cox
Sr VP: Alice Rogers
VP: Kathy Weekley
Genl Mgr: Daniel Huffines
Genl Mgr: Paul Lindsay
Netwrk Eng: Ryan Tobey

AMC FLORAL INTERNATIONAL
See KENNICOTT BROS CO

D-U-N-S 08-824-9420
▲ **AMC NETWORKS INC**
11 Penn Plz, New York, NY 10001-2006
Tel (212) 324-8500 Founded/Ownrshp 1980
Sales 2.5MMM EMP 2,506
Accts Kpmg Llp New York New York
Tkr Sym AMCX Exch NGS
SIC 4841 Cable & other pay television services
Pr: Joshua W Sapan
Pr: Kirk Linden
Ch Bd: Charles F Dolan
COO: Edward A Carroll
CFO: Sean S Sullivan
Ex VP: Scott Collins
Ex VP: James G Gallagher
Ex VP: John Huffman
Ex VP: Steven Pontillo
Ex VP: Lisa Schwartz
Ex VP: Christian Wymbs
Sr VP: Michele Goldstein
Sr VP: Linda Schupack
VP: Rob Berju
VP: Alysse Bezahler
VP: Robert B Bruno
VP: Michael Cagnazzi
VP: Kevin Cashman
VP: Thomas Etheridge
VP: Susie Fitzgerald
VP: Shannon M Frasier
Board of Directors: David E Van Zandt, William J Bell, Carl E Vogel, James L Dolan, Marianne Dolan Weber, Kristin A Dolan, Robert C Wright, Patrick F Dolan, Thomas C Dolan, Jonathan F Miller, Alan D Schwartz, Brian G Sweeney, Leonard Tow

AMCANE SUGAR
See SUGAR AMERICANE REFINING LLC

D-U-N-S 09-310-9528
AMCO INSURANCE CO
ALLIED INSURANCE
(Suby of ALLIED GROUP INC) ★
1100 Locust St, Des Moines, IA 50391-1100
Tel (515) 280-4211 Founded/Ownrshp 1959
Sales NA EMP 4,200
SIC 6411 Insurance agents, brokers & service; Insurance adjusters
Ch: William Jurgensen
*Pr: Kirt Walker
Ofcr: Marcus Haith
*VP: James Hagenbucher
VP: Ronald L Keer
*VP: Steven Larsen
VP: George Oleson
*VP: Stephen Rasmussen
VP: Donna Smith
Assoc Dir: Doug Hoyle
Genl Mgr: Greg Martin

AMCOL
See AMERICAN COLLOID CO

D-U-N-S 00-509-2556 IMP/EXP
■ **AMCOL INTERNATIONAL CORP**
(Suby of MTI) ★
2870 Forbs Ave, Hoffman Estates, IL 60192-3702
Tel (847) 851-1500 Founded/Ownrshp 2014
Sales 966.8MM[E] EMP 1,990
SIC 1459 5032 4213 4731 Bentonite mining; Fuller's earth mining; Clay construction materials, except refractory; Trucking, except local; Truck transportation brokers
Pr: Ryan F McKendrick
*CFO: Donald W Pearson
Sr VP: Gary L Castagna
Sr VP: Robert C Steele
VP: James W Ashley
VP: Jim Papp
Dist Mgr: Steven Dunn
Off Mgr: Terri Cardona
Snr Sftwr: Mike Sakelarios
Opers Mgr: Carl Coldren
Plnt Mgr: Wendy Anderson

D-U-N-S 15-455-9827
▲ **AMCON DISTRIBUTING CO INC**
7405 Irvington Rd, Omaha, NE 68122-1232
Tel (402) 331-3727 Founded/Ownrshp 1986
Sales 1.2MMM EMP 808[E]
Tkr Sym DIT Exch ASE
SIC 5194 5141 5145 5113 5122 Tobacco & tobacco products; Groceries, general line; Confectionery; Industrial & personal service paper; Drugs, proprietaries & sundries; Cosmetics; Hair preparations; Toilet preparations
Ch Bd: Christopher H Atayan
*Pr: Kathleen M Evans
CFO: Andrew C Plummer
CFO: Andy Plummer
Ex VP: Rick Kaupke
VP: Dave Clem
VP: Rick Vance
VP Sls: Clem O'Donnell
Mktg Mgr: Brian Beal
Sls Mgr: Mike Baldrige
Board of Directors: Raymond F Bentele, Jeremy W Hobbs, John R Loyack, Stanley Mayer, Timothy R Pestotnik

D-U-N-S 00-611-5828 IMP/EXP
AMCOR FLEXIBLES LLC
(Suby of AMCOR LTD)
1919 S Butterfield Rd, Mundelein, IL 60060-9740
Tel (847) 362-9000 Founded/Ownrshp 2003
Sales 221.2MM[E] EMP 500
SIC 2671 2621 2821 3081 3466 Plastic film, coated or laminated for packaging; Packaging paper; Plastics materials & resins; Packing materials, plastic sheet; Closures, stamped metal
CEO: K N Mackenzie
*Pr: Peter Brues
COO: Point Kim
*Treas: Candy Lewis
Dir Soc: Mary Dlugosz
Mng Dir: Gerald Blatrix
Mng Dir: Michael Orye
Genl Mgr: Kerry Turner
MIS Dir: Tom Hicks
MIS Dir: Dan Hottz
Mfg Dir: Mark Pearson

D-U-N-S 62-513-6684 IMP
AMCOR PACKAGING (USA) INC
(Suby of AMCOR LTD)
6600 Valley View St, Buena Park, CA 90620-1145
Tel (714) 562-6000 Founded/Ownrshp 1989
Sales 613.8MM[E] EMP 2,397[E]
SIC 2653 5113 Boxes, corrugated: made from purchased materials; Paper & products, wrapping or coarse
CEO: Ramiro Martinez
*Pr: Peter Brues
CFO: Mark Condron
*VP: Ron Delia
IT Man: Steven Khuu
Mktg Dir: Brad Philip

D-U-N-S 13-065-0711 IMP
AMCOR PET PACKAGING USA INC
AMCOR RIGID PLAS - ALLENTOWN
(*Suby of* AMCOR PACKAGING (USA) INC) ★
6974 Schantz Rd, Allentown, PA 18106-9399
Tel (610) 871-9000 *Founded/Ownrshp* 2003
Sales 166.9MM[E] *EMP* 1,991[E]
SIC 3089 Blow molded finished plastic products
Prin: Michael Warhola
Exec: Christopher Curtis
Ql Cn Mgr: Nick Noell

D-U-N-S 00-234-9850 IMP
AMCOR PHARMACEUTICAL PACKAGING USA LLC
(*Suby of* AMCOR LTD)
625 Sharp St N, Millville, NJ 08332-2862
Tel (856) 327-1540 *Founded/Ownrshp* 1888, 2010
Sales 472.8MM[E] *EMP* 2,500[E]
SIC 3221 3085 Cosmetic jars, glass; Medicine bottles, glass; Plastics bottles
Pr: Peter Brues
**Pr:* Peter Bruess
Pr: David White
Genl Mgr: Dick Calabro
Genl Mgr: Igor Playner
Genl Mgr: Lorenzo Salvaggio

AMCOR RIGID PLAS - ALLENTOWN
See AMCOR PET PACKAGING USA INC

AMCOR RIGID PLAS - MANCHESTER
See AMCOR RIGID PLASTICS USA LLC

D-U-N-S 96-897-1317 IMP/EXP
AMCOR RIGID PLASTICS USA LLC
AMCOR RIGID PLAS - MANCHESTER
(*Suby of* AMCOR LTD)
10521 M 52, Manchester, MI 48158-9474
Tel (734) 428-9741 *Founded/Ownrshp* 2002
Sales 203.4MM[E] *EMP* 380
SIC 3085 Plastics bottles
Pr: Michael Schmitt
**CFO:* Garry Noonan
CFO: Larry Weber
VP: Mike Bieringer
**VP:* Scott Chambery
VP: Matt Kaufman
VP: Jeff McGrory
Prgrm Mgr: Daniel Elpi
Prgrm Mgr: Thomas Seaman
Prgrm Mgr: Ron Stokes
Dist Mgr: Bill Gallagher

D-U-N-S 16-176-9591 IMP/EXP
AMCOR TOBACCO PACKAGING AMERICAS LLC
(*Suby of* AMCOR LTD)
445 Dividend Dr, Peachtree City, GA 30269-1940
Tel (770) 486-9095 *Founded/Ownrshp* 2010
Sales 118.5MM[E] *EMP* 400
SIC 2671 Packaging paper & plastics film, coated & laminated
CEO: Ken Mackenzie
**Ch Bd:* Billy Chan
**Pr:* Peter Brues
**CFO:* Keith Adkins
**Ex VP:* Ron Delia
**Ex VP:* Steve Keogh
VP: Glenn Fish
VP: Diane Frisch
**VP:* Dwight Kennedy
Comm Man: Polly Moles
VP Sls: David Stacey

D-U-N-S 02-373-6343
AMCP RETAIL ACQUISITION CORP
RUGGED WEARHOUSE
(*Suby of* RUGGED WEARHOUSE) ★
55 Scott Ave, Morgantown, WV 26508-8853
Tel (304) 292-6965 *Founded/Ownrshp* 2012
Sales 629.0MM[E] *EMP* 3,800[E]
SIC 5611 5621 Clothing, men's & boys': everyday, except suits & sportswear; Women's specialty clothing stores
CEO: Jeff Feinberg
**CFO:* Jim Kline

D-U-N-S 05-373-4169
AMCP RETAIL HOLDINGS CORP
RUGGED WEARHOUSE
55 Scott Ave, Morgantown, WV 26508-8853
Tel (304) 292-6965 *Founded/Ownrshp* 2012
Sales 567.3MM[E] *EMP* 3,815
SIC 5621 5611 Women's specialty clothing stores; Clothing, sportswear, men's & boys'
CEO: Jeff M Feinberg
**CEO:* Kurtis Kaull
**CFO:* Jim Kline

D-U-N-S 15-022-0002
AMDOCS INC
(*Suby of* AMDOCS LTD)
1390 Timberlake Manor Pkw, Chesterfield, MO 63017-6041
Tel (314) 212-7000 *Founded/Ownrshp* 1984
Sales 3.3MM *EMP* 2,015
Accts Ernst & Young Llp New York N
SIC 7372 7371 7373 Prepackaged software; Computer software systems analysis & design, custom; Computer integrated systems design
Pr: John J Horgan
**CEO:* Dov Baharav
**Treas:* Thomas G Obrien
Ofcr: Ravi Ravichandran
Sr VP: Chanan Epstein
VP: Eyal Amram
VP: Micheal Bricker
VP: Jere Calmes
VP: Moshe Raccah
Prgrm Mgr: Nicola Dilley
Genl Mgr: Osnat Vardi

D-U-N-S 00-344-6762
AME INC
2467 Coltharp Rd, Fort Mill, SC 29715-8991
Tel (803) 548-7766 *Founded/Ownrshp* 1960
Sales 141.5MM[E] *EMP* 230
SIC 1541 7353 3443 Industrial buildings & warehouses; Cranes & aerial lift equipment, rental or leasing; Fabricated plate work (boiler shop)
Pr: Gregg Campell
**Pr:* Frankie Campell
**Pr:* Erik Nelson
**CFO:* Lloyd H Case Jr
**VP:* Samantha Brindle
Div/Sub He: Michael Wylie

AMEA
See ALABAMA MUNICIPAL ELECTRIC AUTHORITY

D-U-N-S 06-663-0070
AMEC E&I HOLDINGS INC
1105 Lakewood Pkwy # 300, Alpharetta, GA 30009-7624
Tel (770) 360-0600 *Founded/Ownrshp* 2011
Sales NA *EMP* 3,100
SIC 8744 8711

D-U-N-S 17-836-6183 IMP/EXP
AMEC E&I INC
1105 Lakewood Pkwy # 300, Alpharetta, GA 30009-7624
Tel (770) 360-0600 *Founded/Ownrshp* 2000
Sales NA *EMP* 3,100
SIC 8711

D-U-N-S 86-951-3416
AMEC FOSTER WHEELER E&C SERVICES INC
(*Suby of* AMEC FOSTER WHEELER PLC)
1979 Lkeside Pkwy Ste 400, Tucker, GA 30084
Tel (770) 688-2500 *Founded/Ownrshp* 2001
Sales 125.8MM[E] *EMP* 750
SIC 8711

D-U-N-S 00-964-3354 IMP
AMEC FOSTER WHEELER ENVIRONMENT & INFRASTRUCTURE INC (NV)
(*Suby of* AMEC FOSTER WHEELER VENTURES INC) ★
1105 Lakewood Pkwy # 300, Alpharetta, GA 30009-7624
Tel (770) 360-0600 *Founded/Ownrshp* 1994, 1999
Sales 1.1MMM[E] *EMP* 4,374
SIC 8748 8711 Environmental consultant; Engineering services
CEO: Thomas J Logan
**Treas:* Kendall H Sherrill
**Sr VP:* Charles Mouzannar
**Sr VP:* Lytle C Troutt
Sr VP: Lawrence White
**VP:* David K Baxter
VP: William Beutel
VP: Rob Feighery
**VP:* Robert J Feighery
Genl Mgr: Joe Tarsavage
Board of Directors: Simon D Naylor, Steven M Toevs

D-U-N-S 07-516-0499 IMP/EXP
AMEC FOSTER WHEELER NORTH AMERICA CORP
(*Suby of* AMEC FOSTER WHEELER PLC)
Perryville Corporate Pk 5, Hampton, NJ 08827
Tel (908) 713-2891 *Founded/Ownrshp* 1992, 2014
Sales 428.6MM[E] *EMP* 97
SIC 3433 3443 3532 3569 Steam heating apparatus; Burners, furnaces, boilers & stokers; Oil burners, domestic or industrial; Gas burners, industrial; Condensers, steam; Boilers: industrial, power, or marine; Process vessels, industrial: metal plate; Coal breakers, cutters & pulverizers; Generators: steam, liquid oxygen or nitrogen
CEO: Gary Nedelka
**Pr:* Byron Roth
**CFO:* Steve Di Lauri
**Ex VP:* Peter Coppola
**Ex VP:* David Parham
**Ex VP:* Anthony Scerbo

D-U-N-S 06-810-0361
AMEC FOSTER WHEELER OIL & GAS INC
AMEC PARAGON
(*Suby of* AMEC FOSTER WHEELER PLC)
585 N Dairy Ashford Rd, Houston, TX 77079-1103
Tel (713) 929-5000 *Founded/Ownrshp* 2005
Sales 129.5MM[E] *EMP* 580
SIC 8711 8742 8741 Engineering services; Training & development consultant; Construction management
Pr: Andrew Sallis
**CFO:* Mark Miles
**Ch:* Simon Naylor
Sr VP: Chuck Kemper
**VP:* Kirk Barwick
**VP:* Joanne Karakashian
**VP:* Richard Sikora
Dir IT: Randy Oliver
Opers Mgr: Chris Smith
Sls&Mrk Ex: Andy Sallis

D-U-N-S 13-048-7143
AMEC FOSTER WHEELER USA CORP
(*Suby of* AMEC FOSTER WHEELER PLC)
585 N Dairy Ashford Rd, Houston, TX 77079-1103
Tel (713) 929-5000 *Founded/Ownrshp* 1973
Sales 343.8MM[E] *EMP* 1,310
SIC 8711 3443 1629 Engineering services; Boilers: industrial, power, or marine; Chemical plant & refinery construction; Oil refinery construction
CEO: J Kent Masters
Pr: Chris E Covert
CFO: Lee Barnett
Treas: Kevin Hagan
Sr VP: Jimmy Collins
Sr VP: Clive Vaughan
Sr VP: Bruce Young
**VP:* Jean Paul Archambault
VP: Michelle Davies
VP: Rakesh Jindal
VP: Michael Ondrias

D-U-N-S 02-652-1332
AMEC FOSTER WHEELER VENTURES INC
(*Suby of* AMEC FOSTER WHEELER PLC)
1979 Lkeside Pkwy Ste 400, Tucker, GA 30084
Tel (770) 688-2500 *Founded/Ownrshp* 1991
Sales 1.0MMM[E] *EMP* 4,374[E]
SIC 8748 8711 Environmental consultant; Engineering services
Pr: Timothy P Gelbar
Dir IT: Louise Gehl

AMEC PARAGON
See AMEC FOSTER WHEELER OIL & GAS INC

AMECO
See AMERICAN EQUIPMENT CO INC

AMEDEX
See BUPA INSURANCE CO

D-U-N-S 79-321-6198
■ **AMEDISYS HOME HEALTH INC OF FLORIDA**
(*Suby of* AMEDISYS INC) ★
5959 S Shrwood Frest Blvd, Baton Rouge, LA 70816
Tel (225) 292-2031 *Founded/Ownrshp* 2009
Sales 9.5MM[E] *EMP* 1,659[E]
SIC 8082 Home health care services
Prin: Larry Graham

D-U-N-S 79-321-6776
■ **AMEDISYS HOME HEALTH INC OF VIRGINIA**
(*Suby of* AMEDISYS INC) ★
5959 S Shrwood Frest Blvd, Baton Rouge, LA 70816
Tel (225) 292-2031 *Founded/Ownrshp* 2009
Sales 17.6MM[E] *EMP* 1,437[E]
SIC 8082 Home health care services
Pr: Larry Graham

D-U-N-S 80-850-6331
▲ **AMEDISYS INC**
3854 American Way Ste A, Baton Rouge, LA 70816-4013
Tel (225) 292-2031 *Founded/Ownrshp* 1982
Sales 1.2MMM *EMP* 16,100
Tkr Sym AMED *Exch* NGS
SIC 8082 8051 8049 8361 Home health care services; Skilled nursing care facilities; Physical therapist; Occupational therapist; Speech therapist; Rehabilitation center, residential: health care incidental
Pr: Paul B Kusserow
COO: Daniel P McCoy
CFO: Ronald A Laborde
Ofcr: Jane Carmody
Ofcr: David B Pearce
Ofcr: Larry R Pernosky
Ofcr: Stephen Seim
Ofcr: Susan Sender
VP: Kim Bromley
VP: Cami Oravetz
Off Mgr: Pam Adams

AMEDYSIS HOME HEALTH
See FAMILY HOME HEALTH CARE INC

D-U-N-S 08-471-0177
■ **AMEDYSIS HOME HEALTH INC OF SOUTH CAROLINA**
(*Suby of* AMEDISYS INC) ★
5959 S Shrwood Frest Blvd, Baton Rouge, LA 70816
Tel (225) 292-2031 *Founded/Ownrshp* 1976, 2001
Sales 401.2MM[E] *EMP* 250
SIC 8082 Home health care services
IT Man: Alison Joseph

D-U-N-S 05-213-7882
AMEGY BANK NATIONAL ASSOCIATION (TX)
4400 Post Oak Pkwy, Houston, TX 77027-3421
Tel (713) 235-8800 *Founded/Ownrshp* 2005
Sales NA *EMP* 1,534
SIC 6021

D-U-N-S 18-326-8796
AMELIA ISLAND CO
AMELIA ISLAND PLANTATION
1423 Julia St, Fernandina Beach, FL 32034-4915
Tel (904) 261-6161 *Founded/Ownrshp* 1978
Sales 44.9MM[E] *EMP* 1,100
SIC 7011 6552 7992 7991 5812 Resort hotel; Land subdividers & developers, residential; Public golf courses; Physical fitness facilities; Eating places
Pr: Jack B Healan Jr
Treas: Julie Blake
VP: Norman S Bray
**VP:* S Norman Bray
VP: Laura Palmisano
Sls Mgr: Carrie N Jones

AMELIA ISLAND PLANTATION
See AMELIA ISLAND CO

D-U-N-S 62-606-1956 IMP/EXP
AMER SPORTS CO
(*Suby of* AMER SPORTS OYJ)
8750 W Bryn Mawr Ave, Chicago, IL 60631-3655
Tel (773) 714-6400 *Founded/Ownrshp* 1989
Sales 713.3MM[E] *EMP* 2,700
SIC 3949 Sporting & athletic goods; Golf equipment; Baseball equipment & supplies, general; Tennis equipment & supplies
Pr: Gary Diehl
**Ch Bd:* Hekey Takala
**Pr:* Juha Vaisanen
Manager: Brett Jacobson

D-U-N-S 05-440-8745 IMP/EXP
▲ **AMERCO** (NV)
5555 Kietzke Ln Ste 100, Reno, NV 89511-2096
Tel (775) 688-6300 *Founded/Ownrshp* 1945
Sales 3.2MMM *EMP* 26,400[E]
Tkr Sym UHAL *Exch* NGS
SIC 7513 7519 4226 Truck rental & leasing, no drivers; Trailer rental; Household goods, warehousing
Ch Bd: Edward J Shoen
Pr: Douglas M Bell
Pr: Mark A Haydukovich
Pr: John C Taylor
Pr: Carlos Vizcarra
CFO: Jason A Berg
Treas: Gary B Horton
Genl Couns: Laurence J Derespino
Board of Directors: James E Acridge, Charles J Bayer, John P Brogan, John M Dodds, Michael L Gallagher, Daniel R Mullen, Samuel P Shoen

D-U-N-S 36-413-8990 IMP
▲ **AMEREN CORP**
1901 Chouteau Ave, Saint Louis, MO 63103-3003
Tel (314) 621-3222 *Founded/Ownrshp* 1881
Sales 6.1MMM *EMP* 8,527
Tkr Sym AEE *Exch* NYS
SIC 4911 4931 4923 Generation, electric power; Transmission, electric power; Distribution, electric power; Electric & other services combined; Gas transmission & distribution
Ch Bd: Warner L Baxter
CFO: Martin J Lyons Jr
Sr VP: Mark C Birk
Sr VP: Mary P Heger
Sr VP: Gregory L Nelson
Sr VP: Bruce A Steinke
VP: Bruce Steinke
Board of Directors: Stephen R Wilson, Catherine S Brune, J Edward Coleman, Ellen M Fitzsimmons, Rafael Flores, Walter J Galvin, Richard J Harshman, Gayle P W Jackson, James C Johnson, Steven H Lipstein

D-U-N-S 00-693-6017 IMP
■ **AMEREN ILLINOIS CO** (IL)
(*Suby of* AMEREN CORP) ★
6 Executive Dr, Collinsville, IL 62234-6120
Tel (618) 343-8150 *Founded/Ownrshp* 1923
Sales 2.4MMM *EMP* 3,133[E]
SIC 4924 4911 Natural gas distribution; Generation, electric power; Transmission, electric power; Distribution, electric power
Ch Bd: Richard J Mark
**CFO:* Martin J Lyons Jr
Sr VP: Bruce A Steinke
Board of Directors: Daniel F Cole, Craig D Nelson, Gregory L Nelson

AMEREN MISSOURI
See UNION ELECTRIC CO

D-U-N-S 96-685-1875
■ **AMEREN SERVICES CO**
(*Suby of* AMEREN CORP) ★
1901 Chouteau Ave, Saint Louis, MO 63103-3003
Tel (314) 621-3222 *Founded/Ownrshp* 1998
Sales 176.7MM[E] *EMP* 900[E]
SIC 8741 Business management
CEO: Gary L Rainwater
**Sr VP:* David A Whiteley
Exec: Cheryl Beckett
Dir IT: Chris Sewall
IT Man: Karan Henderson

D-U-N-S 60-343-9428
▲ **AMERESCO INC**
111 Speen St Ste 410, Framingham, MA 01701-2090
Tel (508) 661-2200 *Founded/Ownrshp* 2000
Sales 630.8MM *EMP* 1,037
Tkr Sym AMRC *Exch* NYS
SIC 8711 1731 Energy conservation engineering; Energy management controls
Ch Bd: George P Sakellaris
CFO: John R Granara III
**Ex VP:* David J Anderson
**Ex VP:* David J Corrsin
Ex VP: Joseph P Demanche
VP: William Cunningham
VP: Britta Macintosh
Rgnl Mgr: Grant Thorsland
Site Mgr: James McCoy
Mktg Mgr: Josh Kantor
Mktg Mgr: William Smith
Board of Directors: Douglas I Foy, Michael E Jesanis, Jennifer L Miller, Thomas S Murley, Joseph W Sutton, Frank V Wisneski

D-U-N-S 00-697-9793 IMP
AMEREX GROUP INC
AMEREX KIDS GROUP
512 Fashion Ave Fl 9, New York, NY 10018-0861
Tel (212) 221-3151 *Founded/Ownrshp* 1946
Sales 143.1MM[E] *EMP* 500
SIC 5137 5136 Women's & children's outerwear; Sportswear, women's & children's; Men's & boys' outerwear; Sportswear, men's & boys'
Ch Bd: Ira Ganger
CFO: Adam Berkman
CFO: Anthony Pisano
Ex VP: Stuart Cohen
VP: Joe Ford
VP: David Ganger
VP: Fran Metzler
Creative D: Brad Volenec
Brnch Mgr: Roxanne Cowen
Sls Mgr: Jennifer Cronin

AMEREX KIDS GROUP
See AMEREX GROUP INC

D-U-N-S 05-379-5998
■ **AMERGEN ENERGY CO LLC**
(*Suby of* EXELON CORP) ★
200 Exelon Way, Kennett Square, PA 19348-2442
Tel (215) 841-4000 *Founded/Ownrshp* 1997
Sales 235.9MM[E] *EMP* 1,300
Accts Pricewaterhousecoopers Llp
SIC 4911 Generation, electric power
Pr: Robin Jeffrey
**CEO:* John L Skolds
**V Ch Bd:* Dickinson Smith

D-U-N-S 06-831-2230 IMP
AMERHART LIMITED
2455 Century Rd, Green Bay, WI 54303-4899
Tel (920) 494-4744 *Founded/Ownrshp* 1972
Sales 160.1MM[E] *EMP* 140
SIC 5031 Lumber: rough, dressed & finished; Composite board products, woodboard; Building materials, exterior; Plywood
Pr: Mark Kasper
COO: Jim Schmit
**Treas:* Rick Johnson
**VP:* William Campion
**VP:* Dave Destiche

*VP: Michael Graume
*VP: Kenneth Hager
*VP: Jeffrey Kocken
Mktg Mgr: Jeff Verboncouer

D-U-N-S 60-960-1034 IMP
■ AMERI KART CORP
AMERI-KART CORP.
(Suby of MYERS INDUSTRIES INC) ★
17196 State Road 120, Bristol, IN 46507-9593
Tel (574) 848-7462 Founded/Ownrshp 1992
Sales 96.8MM^E EMP 475
SIC 3089 3537 2821 5162 Garbage containers, plastic; Molding primary plastic; Thermoformed finished plastic products; Tables, lift: hydraulic; Plastics materials & resins; Plastics products
CEO: Robin Johnson
*Pr: Eric Gottuso
*Pr: Dennis Roberts
Exec: Connie Jowhite
Dir IT: John Lusk
Plnt Mgr: Deborah Risner
Plnt Mgr: Robert Wagner
Sls Mgr: Doug Eck
Sls Mgr: Paul Mihojevich
Sls Mgr: Gregg Thomas

D-U-N-S 80-014-3919
AMERI-FORCE INC
9485 Regency Square Blvd, Jacksonville, FL 32225-8194
Tel (904) 633-9918 Founded/Ownrshp 1991
Sales 61.5MM^E EMP 1,400
SIC 7363 Employee leasing service; Temporary help service
Pr: Dave Enman
*Pr: James Adams
*Ch: John Arbizzani
*Treas: Don Self
Dir Risk M: John Goldberg
Brnch Mgr: Beth Callahan
Opers Mgr: Phil Wheeler
Sls Mgr: Pete Sherrill

AMERI-KART CORP.
See AMERI KART CORP

D-U-N-S 84-107-1426
AMERI-KLEEN
AMERI-KLEEN BUILDING SERVICES
119 W Beach St, Watsonville, CA 95076-4557
Tel (831) 722-8888 Founded/Ownrshp 1999
Sales 51.2MM^E EMP 1,150
SIC 7349 Janitorial service, contract basis
Pr: Brett Meyers
*Ch: Steve Meyers
Area Mgr: Albert Saldivar

AMERI-KLEEN BUILDING SERVICES
See AMERI-KLEEN

D-U-N-S 62-338-2900 EXP
AMERICA CHUNG NAM (GROUP) HOLDINGS LLC
1163 Fairway Dr, City of Industry, CA 91789-2846
Tel (909) 839-8383 Founded/Ownrshp 1993
Sales 164.5MM^E EMP 250
SIC 5093 Waste paper
CEO: Peter Wang
*CFO: Kevin Zhao
*VP: John Wong
*Prin: Ming Chung Liu
Opers Mgr: Laura Hu
Mktg Mgr: Tom Doherty
Mktg Mgr: Carrie Farley

D-U-N-S 80-825-8649 IMP/EXP
AMERICA CHUNG NAM LLC
A C N
(Suby of AMERICA CHUNG NAM (GROUP) HOLDINGS LLC) ★
1163 Fairway Dr Fl 3, City of Industry, CA 91789-2851
Tel (909) 839-8383 Founded/Ownrshp 1990
Sales 143.4MM^E EMP 200^E
SIC 5093 Waste paper
CEO: Teresa Cheung
COO: Sam Liu
CFO: Kevin Zhao
VP: Ming Liu
VP: Scott Taylor
VP: John Wong
Mng Dir: Wade Schuetzeberg
MIS Dir: John Lovely
MIS Dir: America Nam
IT Man: Eric Lum
Mktg Mgr: Justin Chiu

AMERICA ELECTRIC POWERTEXAS
See AEP POWER MARKETING INC

D-U-N-S 07-295-7699
AMERICA FIRST CREDIT UNION
AMERICA FIRST FEDERAL CR UN
1344 W 4675 S Ste 130, Ogden, UT 84405-3690
Tel (801) 627-0900 Founded/Ownrshp 1939
Sales NA EMP 2,000
SIC 6062 State credit unions, not federally chartered
Ch Bd: Linda Carver
*Pr: John Lund
CFO: Rick Britnell
*CFO: Rex Rollo
*Ch: Barney Chapman
Treas: Volker Hagen
*Treas: Glen Olpin
Treas: Dave Stacey
Ofcr: Mindrum Brice
Ofcr: Yvonne Feld
Ofcr: Casey Shaw
Ex VP: Brent Allen
Ex VP: Patrick Criss
VP: Sheryl Cox
VP: Rich Syme
Exec: Randi Kennedy

AMERICA FIRST FEDERAL CR UN
See AMERICA FIRST CREDIT UNION

D-U-N-S 19-475-9440
AMERICA FUJIKURA LTD
(Suby of FUJIKURA LTD.)
170 Ridgeview Cir, Duncan, SC 29334
Tel (864) 433-8281 Founded/Ownrshp 2005
Sales 947.9MM^E EMP 3,180^E
SIC 3661 Telephones & telephone apparatus
Pr: Jody Gallagher
*VP: Masatoshi Kuroda

D-U-N-S 60-992-0822 IMP/EXP
AMERICA II ELECTRONICS INC
2600 118th Ave N, Saint Petersburg, FL 33716-1921
Tel (727) 573-0900 Founded/Ownrshp 1989
Sales 475.4MM^E EMP 807
SIC 5065 Electronic parts & equipment; Diodes; Transistors; Semiconductor devices
CEO: Michael Galinski
*Pr: Brian Ellison
*COO: Dan Bisaillon
*VP: Michael Pointer
Genl Mgr: Toshiharu Ban
Genl Mgr: Gill Tory
Dir IT: Nelson Chow
IT Man: Tesshu Naka
Sls Mgr: Gerrard Lamothe
Sls Mgr: John McKay
Sls Mgr: Jesse Smith

D-U-N-S 09-232-2783 IMP/EXP
AMERICA PLASTICS LLC
OMEGA PLASTICS
2636 Byington Solway Rd, Knoxville, TN 37931-3213
Tel (865) 457-7000 Founded/Ownrshp 1978
Sales 102.0MM^E EMP 350^E
SIC 3089 Extruded finished plastic products
Pr: Stephen J Redwine
COO: Donna James
VP: Herb Hutchison
VP: Robert Price
Exec: Lindsey Windmiller
*Opers Mgr: Bob R Bailey
Opers Mgr: Robert Danis
S&M/VP: Brian McFerran

D-U-N-S 06-884-8051
■ AMERICA SAVING BANK
(Suby of HEI) ★
200 Kahelu Ave, Mililani, HI 96789-3915
Tel (808) 627-6900 Founded/Ownrshp 2011
Sales NA EMP 776^E
SIC 6035 Federal savings banks
CEO: Richard Wacker
*Ex VP: Tab Bowers
*Ex VP: Gabriel Lee
*Ex VP: Margaret Pettyjohn
*Ex VP: Rick Robel

D-U-N-S 01-151-3124
■ AMERICA WEST AIRLINES INC
(Suby of AMERICA WEST HOLDINGS CORP) ★
4000 E Sky Harbor Blvd, Phoenix, AZ 85034-3802
Tel (480) 693-0800 Founded/Ownrshp 1996
Sales 552.7MM^E EMP 12,400
SIC 4512 Air passenger carrier, scheduled; Air cargo carrier, scheduled
Ch Bd: Douglas W Parker
*Pr: J Scott Kirby
*COO: Robert Isom
*CFO: Derek J Kerr
*Sr VP: Janet Dhillon
VP: Elise Eberwein
VP: Kara Gin
VP: Shirley Kaufman
VP: Paul Lambert
Dir IT: Jim Templin
VP Sls: Joette Schmidt

D-U-N-S 96-648-3109
■ AMERICA WEST HOLDINGS CORP
(Suby of AMERICAN AIRLINES INC) ★
111 W Rio Salado Pkwy, Tempe, AZ 85281-2880
Tel (480) 693-0800 Founded/Ownrshp 2005
Sales 767.5MM^E EMP 12,400^E
SIC 6719 Investment holding companies, except banks
Ch Bd: W Douglas Parker
*CFO: Derek J Kerr
Ex VP: Scott J Kirby
Sr VP: Douglas W Parker
Mng Dir: Rusty Falk
Mng Dir: Joubine Motaharian
IT Man: Steve Bingham

AMERICAID COMMUNITY CARE
See AMERIGROUP NEW YORK LLC

D-U-N-S 00-314-9333 IMP/EXP
AMERICAN & EFIRD LLC
22 American St, Mount Holly, NC 28120-2150
Tel (704) 827-4311 Founded/Ownrshp 1891, 2011
Sales 160.2MM^E EMP 9,457
SIC 2284 Thread from natural fibers; Thread from manmade fibers
CEO: Les Miller
*Treas: Robert L Johnson Jr
*Ex VP: John L Miller
VP: Ron Ensley
VP: James P Guin Jr
VP: L Richard Heavener
VP: Pat Howard
VP: Albert L Irvine
VP: Millard L McGee
VP: Nelson Plant
*VP: A Knox Winget III

D-U-N-S 01-064-8921
AMERICAN ACADEMY OF FAMILY PHYSICIANS
AAFP
11400 Tomahawk Creek Pkwy, Leawood, KS 66211-2680
Tel (913) 906-6000 Founded/Ownrshp 1947
Sales 95.5MM EMP 390
Accts Bkd Llp Leawood Ks
SIC 8621 Medical field-related associations
CEO: Douglas E Henley
*Pr: John Meigs Jr
Ex VP: Jim Vavra
VP: Craig Doane
VP: Louis Gardner
VP: Clayton Hasser
VP: Norman Kahn
VP: Mickey Schaefer
VP: Gary Warren
*Prin: Wanda Filer
Adm Dir: Joe Anthuis

D-U-N-S 05-539-9364 IMP
AMERICAN ACADEMY OF PEDIATRICS
CENTER FOR CHILD HEALTH RES
141 Northwest Point Blvd, Elk Grove Village, IL 60007-1019
Tel (847) 228-5005 Founded/Ownrshp 1987
Sales 111.2MM EMP 400
Accts Plante & Moran Pllc Chicago
SIC 8621 Medical field-related associations
Pr: Robert W Block
*Pr: Thomas McInerny
*CFO: John Miller
CFO: Vickie Olson
Ex Dir: Dee Dehaas
Prgrm Mgr: Lynne R Peters
IT Man: Ruchi Teotia
Mktg Dir: Maureen Derosa
Doctor: Richard Powers

D-U-N-S 86-009-4106 IMP
AMERICAN ACHIEVEMENT CORP
AAC
(Suby of AAC GROUP HOLDING CORP) ★
7211 Circle S Rd, Austin, TX 78745-6603
Tel (512) 444-0571 Founded/Ownrshp 2004
Sales 530.1MM^E EMP 1,600^E
SIC 3911 2741 Rings, finger: precious metal; Yearbooks: publishing & printing
CEO: Steven Parr
CFO: Kris G Radhakrishnan
Ch: Donald J Percenti
Ex VP: Sherice P Bench
VP: Sherice Bench
VP: Bob McQuade
Sftwr Eng: John Langley
Sfty Dirs: Collin Bond
Mktg Dir: Kim Meeder
Board of Directors: Alan J Bowers, Myles Kleeger, Peter Lamm, Timothy P Mayhew, W Gregg Smart

D-U-N-S 80-668-0760
AMERICAN ACHIEVEMENT GROUP HOLDING CORP
(Suby of FENWAY PARTNERS LLC) ★
7211 Circle S Rd, Austin, TX 78745-6603
Tel (512) 444-0571 Founded/Ownrshp 2006
Sales 530.1MM^E EMP 1,600^E
SIC 5094 Jewelry & precious stones
Ch Bd: Steve Parr
Ex VP: Sherice P Bench

D-U-N-S 03-407-3754 IMP
AMERICAN ACRYL LP (DE)
(Suby of AMERICAN ACRYL NA LLC) ★
4631 Old Highway 146 B, Pasadena, TX 77507-1877
Tel (281) 909-2600 Founded/Ownrshp 1997
Sales 121.6MM EMP 51
Accts Pricewaterhousecoopers Llp Ho
SIC 2869 Industrial organic chemicals
Genl Mgr: Masayuki Ito
Genl Mgr: Joe Goins

D-U-N-S 01-716-6575
AMERICAN ACRYL NA LLC
4631 Old Highway 146 B, Pasadena, TX 77507-1877
Tel (281) 909-2600 Founded/Ownrshp 1997
Sales 121.6MM EMP 52
Accts Pricewaterhousecoopers Llp Ho
SIC 2869 Amines, acids, salts, esters
Ch: Leon Connor
Genl Mgr: Greg Fleming

D-U-N-S 07-738-2281
AMERICAN AGCREDIT FLCA
400 Aviation Blvd Ste 100, Santa Rosa, CA 95403-1181
Tel (707) 545-1200 Founded/Ownrshp 1925
Sales NA EMP 221
Accts Pricewaterhousecoopers Llp
SIC 6159 Agricultural credit institutions
CEO: Ron Carli
*Pr: Byron Enix
Pr: Fletcher Monroe
COO: Bruce Richardson
*CFO: Christopher Call
Bd of Dir: John Caldwell
Sr VP: Roger D Bastow
Sr VP: Alan Feit
Sr VP: Jerry Rose
Sr VP: Deb Seedorf
Sr VP: Lindsay Wurlitzer
VP: Jay Aastrup
VP: Edwin Adams
VP: Shannon Antonini
VP: Michael Balok
VP: Greg Beougher
VP: Josh Cheney
VP: Brad Collins
VP: Maryam Ghazi
VP: Alexander Klein
VP: Wynn Kollenborn

AMERICAN AIR FILTER
See AAF-MCQUAY GROUP INC

D-U-N-S 07-838-1958
AMERICAN AIR FILTER CO INC
AAF INTERNATIONAL
(Suby of DAIKIN INDUSTRIES, LTD.)
9920 Corporate Campus Dr # 2200, Louisville, KY 40223-5000
Tel (502) 637-0011 Founded/Ownrshp 2016
Sales 217.3MM^E EMP 902^E
SIC 3564 Air purification equipment
CEO: Philip Whitaker
*Pr: Peter Kurto
*Treas: Ronald J Pederson
*VP: Yasuhisa Kumada

D-U-N-S 19-608-7626
AMERICAN AIR LIQUIDE HOLDINGS INC
(Suby of AIR LIQUIDE SA ETU EXPLOIT PROCE)
2700 Post Oak Blvd, Houston, TX 77056-5784
Tel (713) 624-8000 Founded/Ownrshp 2007
Sales 4.2MMM^E EMP 7,892^E
SIC 2813 6719 Industrial gases; Investment holding companies, except banks
Plnt Mgr: Bob Collier
Plnt Mgr: Paulo Guzman
Plnt Mgr: Jay Loesch
Plnt Mgr: Isaac Nelson
Plnt Mgr: Perry Page
Plnt Mgr: Brett Phillips
Plnt Mgr: Shawn Riehle
Plnt Mgr: Roy Stamm
Plnt Mgr: John Watts

D-U-N-S 60-606-7130 IMP/EXP
AMERICAN AIR LIQUIDE INC
(Suby of AIR LIQUIDE INTERNATIONAL)
46409 Landing Pkwy, Fremont, CA 94538-6496
Tel (510) 624-4000 Founded/Ownrshp 2003
Sales 388.7MM^E EMP 4,400
SIC 2813 5084 3533 4931 Industrial gases; Welding machinery & equipment; Oil & gas drilling rigs & equipment; Electric & other services combined
Ch: Benoit Potier
*Pr: Pierre Dufour
*CFO: Scott Krapf
*Treas: Gregory Alexander
*Ex VP: Jean-Pierre Duprieu
Sr VP: Thomas Hansen
VP: Chris Clark
VP: Francois Darchis
VP: Jean De Royere
VP: Mok Kwong
VP: Jean D Royere

AMERICAN AIRLINES CENTER
See CENTER OPERATING CO LP

D-U-N-S 07-850-8314
AMERICAN AIRLINES FEDERAL CREDIT UNION INC
4151 Amon Carter Blvd, Fort Worth, TX 76155-2601
Tel (817) 963-6000 Founded/Ownrshp 1936
Sales NA EMP 500
SIC 6061 Federal credit unions
Pr: Angie Owens
Pt: Reid Bork
CFO: Todd Dunham
VP: Alice Liu
VP: Don Scott
VP: Ray Wade
Exec: Ralph Cotton
Mng Dir: Mary Francis Johnson
CIO: Joan C Kuehl
Dir IT: Tom Coady
Dir IT: Jessie Davis

D-U-N-S 07-256-0154
▲ AMERICAN AIRLINES GROUP INC
4333 Amon Carter Blvd, Fort Worth, TX 76155-2664
Tel (817) 963-1234 Founded/Ownrshp 1982
Sales 40.9MMM EMP 118,500
Tkr Sym AAL Exch NGS
SIC 4512 4581 Air passenger carrier, scheduled; Air freight handling at airports
Ch Bd: W Douglas Parker
Pr: Robert D Isom Jr
CFO: Derek J Kerr
Chf Mktg O: Andrew Nocella
Ofcr: Beverly Goulet
Ofcr: Beverly K Goulet
Ex VP: Elise R Eberwein
Ex VP: Stephen L Johnson
Ex VP: Maya Leibman
Sr VP: Kurt Stach
Sr VP: Alison Taylor
VP: Tim Ahern
VP: Bridged Blaise-Shamai
VP: Ken Gilbert
VP: Joe Mohan
VP: Vasu Raja
Creative D: David Jennings
Board of Directors: Denise M O'leary, James F Albaugh, Ray M Robinson, Jeffrey D Benjamin, Richard P Schifter, John T Cahill, Michael J Embler, Matthew J Hart, Alberto Ibarguen, Richard C Kraemer, Susan D Kronick, Martin H Nesbitt

D-U-N-S 00-697-9801
■ AMERICAN AIRLINES INC
(Suby of AMERICAN AIRLINES GROUP INC) ★
4333 Amon Carter Blvd, Fort Worth, TX 76155-2664
Tel (817) 963-1234 Founded/Ownrshp 1934
Sales 41.0MMM EMP 98,900^E
SIC 4512 4513 Air transportation, scheduled; Air cargo carrier, scheduled; Air passenger carrier, scheduled; Air courier services
CEO: W Douglas Parker
Pr: J Scott Kirby
Pr: Dale Morris
CFO: Derek J Kerr
Ex VP: Stephen L Johnson
Sr VP: Don Casey
Sr VP: Danielle Kirgan
Sr VP: Maya Leibman
Sr VP: Will Ris
Sr VP: Diann Sanchez
VP: Susan Garcia
VP: Jim R Smith
VP: Jill Surdek

D-U-N-S 80-023-2386 IMP/EXP
AMERICAN ALLOY STEEL INC
6230 N Houston Rosslyn Rd, Houston, TX 77091-3410
Tel (713) 462-8081 Founded/Ownrshp 1971
Sales 264.2MM EMP 200
Accts Bdo Usa Llp Houston Tx
SIC 3443 Fabricated plate work (boiler shop)
Pr: Arthur J Moore
*CFO: Laurie Vice
*Ex VP: James P Moore
*Sr VP: Anne Y Haynes
Sr VP: Pat Moore
*VP: Al Acock Jr
*VP: Stephen Kibling

IT Man: Robert Flores
IT Man: Greg Hilton
VP Mktg: Pat Hays
**Mktg Mgr:* Johanna Hotfelt

D-U-N-S 18-289-6514
AMERICAN APPAREL INC
107 Cecil Jackson Byp, Selma, AL 36703-9206
Tel (334) 872-6337 *Founded/Ownrshp* 1987
Sales 496.2MM^E *EMP* 1,300
SIC 2311 2385 Military uniforms, men's & youths': purchased materials; Waterproof outerwear
Ch Bd: Lash Harrison
**Pr:* James Hodo
**COO:* Chuck Lambert
CFO: Ronnie Yarborough
**Sec:* Carl Barranco
**Ex VP:* Ronald E Yarbrough
**VP:* Joan Adkison
**VP:* Jeff Bresee
VP: Jim Holdo
Genl Mgr: Roy Ezell
CTO: Rick Cippele
Board of Directors: Paris Wixon

D-U-N-S 12-710-4391 IMP/EXP
AMERICAN APPAREL LLC
747 Warehouse St, Los Angeles, CA 90021-1106
Tel (213) 488-0226 *Founded/Ownrshp* 2006
Sales 608.8MM *EMP* 10,000^E
SIC 2389 2311 2331 Men's miscellaneous accessories; Men's & boys' suits & coats; Women's & misses' blouses & shirts
CEO: Paula Schneider
**Ch Bd:* Colleen B Brown
CFO: Ken Cieply
CFO: Hassan N Natha
Sr Cor Off: Sam Lim
Bd of Dir: Robert Greene
Ofcr: Martin Bailey
Ex VP: Chelsea A Grayson
Ex VP: Glenn A Weinman
Sr VP: Cynthia Erland
Sr VP: Brian McHale
Sr VP: Kurt Wilson
VP: Aldo Aldana
VP: Michael Posner
VP: Amy Terhar

D-U-N-S 05-162-0896
AMERICAN APPRAISAL ASSOCIATES INC
(*Suby of* DUFF & PHELPS CORP) ★
411 E Wisconsin Ave # 1900, Milwaukee, WI 53202-4466
Tel (630) 541-4650 *Founded/Ownrshp* 2015
Sales 111.0MM^E *EMP* 900
SIC 8748 7389 6531 Business consulting; Appraisers, except real estate; Inventory computing service; Appraiser, real estate
CEO: Joseph Zvesper
**CFO:* Kimberly Russo
Bd of Dir: Lee Hactett
Assoc VP: Abhishek Pandey
**Ex VP:* Lee P Hackett
**Sr VP:* Richard Siladi
VP: Douglas Bing
**VP:* Dale Egan
VP: John Ferrara
VP: Kelly McCracken
VP: Hoddle Poon
VP: William Summers

AMERICAN ARBITRATION ASSN
See INTERNATIONAL CENTRE FOR DISPUTE RESOLUTION

D-U-N-S 02-031-1817
AMERICAN ARMED FORCES MUTUAL AID ASSOCIATION
AAFMAA
102 Sheridan Ave, Fort Myer, VA 22211-1110
Tel (800) 522-5221 *Founded/Ownrshp* 1879
Sales NA *EMP* 1^E
Accts Berlin Ramos & Company Pa Roc
SIC 6411 Insurance agents
Pr: Walter R Lincoln
V Ch: Jack Merritt
COO: Jim Malley
CFO: Ltc Mannell
Chf Mktg O: Kevin Kincaid
Sr Tst Off: Bonnie Humphrey
VP: Cmsgt Gruler
Sales Exec: Charles Betancourt
Sales Exec: Tim Hickey

D-U-N-S 96-301-6444
AMERICAN ASSETS TRUST INC
11455 El Camino Real # 200, San Diego, CA 92130-2047
Tel (858) 350-2600 *Founded/Ownrshp* 2011
Sales 275.6MM *EMP* 113^E
SIC 6798 Real estate investment trusts
Ch Bd: Ernest S Rady
CFO: Robert F Barton
Sr VP: Adam Wyll
VP: Jerry Gammieri
Board of Directors: Larry E Finger, Duane A Nelles, Thomas S Olinger, Robert S Sullivan

D-U-N-S 96-237-6187
AMERICAN ASSOCIATED PHARMACIES INC
AAP
201 Lnnie E Crawford Blvd, Scottsboro, AL 35769-7408
Tel (256) 574-6819 *Founded/Ownrshp* 2009
Sales 648.4MM^E *EMP* 75
Accts Gant Croft Associates Pc Sc
SIC 5122 Pharmaceuticals
Pr: Jon Copeland
Pr: Bob Vaden
**CFO:* Paul Carlin
Treas: Larry Curtis
VP: Bruce Grant
Genl Mgr: Forrest Williams
Ql Cn Mgr: Jim Giles
Sls Mgr: Wes Drake
Sls Mgr: James Lovelady
Sls Mgr: Rich Nastasi

D-U-N-S 07-779-5672
AMERICAN ASSOCIATION FOR ADVANCEMENT OF SCIENCE
AAAS
1200 New York Ave Nw, Washington, DC 20005-3928
Tel (202) 898-0873 *Founded/Ownrshp* 1848
Sales 106.9MM *EMP* 475^E
Accts Pricewaterhousecoopers Llp Wa
SIC 8621 2721 Scientific membership association; Magazines: publishing & printing
CEO: Alan I Leshner
**Pr:* Phillip A Sharp
**CFO:* Phillip Blair
**Ch:* William Press
**Treas:* David Evans Shaw
Ofcr: Elana Kimbrell
Dir Rx: Will Schweitzer
Dir IT: David Levy
Web Dev: Jimmy Marks
Sales Exec: Nancy Toema
Mktg Dir: Ian King

D-U-N-S 00-325-4810 IMP/EXP
AMERICAN AUTOMOBILE ASSOCIATION INC (CT)
AAA
1000 Aaa Dr Ms28, Heathrow, FL 32746-5060
Tel (407) 444-7000 *Founded/Ownrshp* 1910
Sales 123.0MM^E *EMP* 873
SIC 8699 Automobile owners' association
Pr: Marshall Doney
**Ch Bd:* Antonia Hernandez
**CEO:* Robert Darbelnet
**CFO:* Robert McKee
CFO: John Schaffer
CFO: Tony Spada
**Ch:* Wayne A Budd
**Treas:* John G Schaffer
Sr VP: Bill Sutherland
**VP:* Birchard Clothier
**VP:* Scott Denman
VP: Satish D Mahajan
VP: Margaret Diego Pittelko
VP: Mary Reisinger
**VP:* William Sutherland
VP: Bill Wood

D-U-N-S 07-465-4120
AMERICAN AUTOMOBILE ASSOCIATION OF NORTHERN CALIFORNIA NEVADA & UTAH
CSAA TRAVEL AGENCY
1900 Powell St Ste 1200, Emeryville, CA 94608-1814
Tel (800) 922-8228 *Founded/Ownrshp* 1907
Sales 1.1MMM^E *EMP* 3,000
SIC 8699 Automobile owners' association
CEO: Tim Condon
CFO: Amy Cocks
Bd of Dir: Edgar Grubb
Bd of Dir: Norma J Howard
Bd of Dir: Dan Whitehurst
Ex VP: Paul Gaffney
VP: Murat Erdem
CIO: Neil Jarvis
Mfg Dir: Kristen Wilson

D-U-N-S 04-476-6678 IMP/EXP
▲ **AMERICAN AXLE & MANUFACTURING HOLDINGS INC**
1 Dauch Dr, Detroit, MI 48211-1198
Tel (313) 758-2000 *Founded/Ownrshp* 1994
Sales 3.9MMM *EMP* 13,050^E
Tkr Sym AXL *Exch* NYS
SIC 3714 3711 Axles, motor vehicle; Axle housings & shafts, motor vehicle; Chassis, motor vehicle
Ch Bd: David C Dauch
Pr: Mark S Barrett
Pr: Michael J Bly
Pr: Donald L Joseph
Pr: Steven J Proctor
Pr: Alberto L Satine
Pr: Michael K Simonte
Pr: Tolga I Oal
Pr: Norman Willemse
CFO: Christopher J May
Sr VP: Timothy E Bowes
VP: David A Culton
VP: Nigel J Francis
VP: Philip R Guys
VP: Michael J Lynch
VP: Allan R Monich
VP: John S Sofia
VP: Thomas J Szymanski
Board of Directors: Elizabeth A Chappell, William L Kozyra, Peter D Lyons, James A McCaslin, William P Miller II, John F Smith, Samuel Valenti III

D-U-N-S 80-884-4567 IMP
■ **AMERICAN AXLE & MANUFACTURING INC**
AAMCO TRANSMISSIONS
(*Suby of* AMERICAN AXLE & MANUFACTURING HOLDINGS INC) ★
1 Dauch Dr, Detroit, MI 48211-1198
Tel (313) 758-3600 *Founded/Ownrshp* 1993
Sales 1.5MMM^E *EMP* 3,000
SIC 3714 Rear axle housings, motor vehicle
Pr: David C Dauch
Pr: Jon R Morrison
Pr: Tolga Oal
**CFO:* Michael K Simonte
**V Ch Bd:* Yogendra N Rahangdale
Ofcr: Michael Dorah
**Ex VP:* John J Bellanti
Sr VP: Timothy E Bowes
**Sr VP:* Alberto Satine
**Sr VP:* Terry J Woychowski
**VP:* Mark Sbarrett
VP: Mark S Barrett
VP: Marion A Cumo
VP: Thomas O Delanoy
VP: Michael C Flynn
**VP:* Nigel Francis
**VP:* Philip R Guys
VP: Curt S Howell
VP: John E Jerge
VP: Terri M Kemp
VP: Robin Kendrick
Board of Directors: Elizabeth A Chappell, Forest J Farmer, Richard C Lappin, B G Mathis, William P Miller II, Larry K Switzer, Thomas K Walker, Dr Henry T Yang

D-U-N-S 82-468-2736
AMERICAN BANK OF TEXAS
(*Suby of* NORTH AMERICAN BANCSHARES INC)
2011 Texoma Pkwy Ste 101, Sherman, TX 75090-2665
Tel (903) 893-7555 *Founded/Ownrshp* 1971
Sales NA *EMP* 285
SIC 6022 State commercial banks
Pr: Wes Shelton
**CFO:* James Parker
Bd of Dir: Kyle Beall
Ofcr: Natalia Lopez
**Ex VP:* Julie Barnes
**Ex VP:* Tim Blalock
**Ex VP:* Robert Crawley
**Ex VP:* John M Hubbert Jr
Sr VP: Brian Baumann
Sr VP: Carl Frietsch
VP: Keith Carlisle
VP: Beth Denison
VP: Annabel Fey
VP: Pam Harkins
VP: John Nikirk
VP: Holly Whittenburg

D-U-N-S 78-244-5662
■ **AMERICAN BANKERS INSURANCE CO OF FLORIDA**
(*Suby of* AMERICAN BANKERS INSURANCE GROUP INC) ★
11222 Quail Roost Dr, Miami, FL 33157-6596
Tel (305) 253-2244 *Founded/Ownrshp* 1999
Sales NA *EMP* 469^E
SIC 6411 6331 Property & casualty insurance agent; Fire, marine & casualty insurance
Sr VP: Ana Rojas-Fillibeu
VP: Katherine Greenzang
IT Man: Connie Boring

D-U-N-S 00-414-9381
■ **AMERICAN BANKERS INSURANCE GROUP INC**
(*Suby of* ASSURANT INC) ★
11222 Quail Roost Dr, Miami, FL 33157-6543
Tel (305) 253-2244 *Founded/Ownrshp* 1946
Sales NA *EMP* 3,200^E
SIC 6331 6311 6351 6321 6324 Property damage insurance; Fire, marine & casualty insurance: stock; Life insurance carriers; Credit & other financial responsibility insurance; Mortgage guarantee insurance; Accident & health insurance carriers; Group hospitalization plans
Pr: P Bruce Camacho
Ex VP: Russell H Cross
**VP:* Jerome Adkinson
**VP:* Floyd G Denison
**VP:* Arthur W Heggen
**VP:* Kathern Stoddard
IT Man: David Helvia
Sys/Mgr: Owen D Childs

D-U-N-S 00-692-2116
■ **AMERICAN BANKERS LIFE ASSURANCE CO OF FLORIDA**
(*Suby of* ASSURANT INC) ★
11222 Quail Roost Dr, Miami, FL 33157-6596
Tel (305) 253-2244 *Founded/Ownrshp* 1952
Sales NA *EMP* 3,500
SIC 6311 Life insurance
CEO: Rob Pollock
**Pr:* Bruce Camacho
**Pr:* Floyd Denison
**CFO:* Adam Lamnin
Treas: Wendall Stocker
Sr VP: Joe Erdeman
Sr VP: Allen Tuthill
VP: Bruce Altman
VP: Rosie Arias
VP: Mark Bohen
VP: Ragnhild Defranks

D-U-N-S 08-787-5159
■ **AMERICAN BANKING CO** (GA)
AMERIS
(*Suby of* AMERIS BANCORP) ★
225 S Main St, Moultrie, GA 31768-4576
Tel (229) 985-2222 *Founded/Ownrshp* 1971, 1980
Sales NA *EMP* 55^E
SIC 6022 6021 State commercial banks; National commercial banks
Pr: Ronnie Marchant
**Pr:* Brooks Sheldon
**Ch:* Willard Lasseter

D-U-N-S 04-543-5468 IMP/EXP
AMERICAN BANKNOTE CORP
2200 Fletcher Ave Ste 501, Fort Lee, NJ 07024-5016
Tel (201) 592-3400 *Founded/Ownrshp* 1993
Sales 264.2MM^E *EMP* 1,200
SIC 2759 2752 2621 Commercial printing; Cards, lithographed; Card paper
CEO: Steven G Singer
**CFO:* Steve Andrews
Treas: Brian Kudish
VP: John Ekers
VP: Rola Hamandi
**VP:* David Kober
MIS Dir: Paul Merkert

D-U-N-S 06-817-5637
AMERICAN BAPTIST HOMES OF MIDWEST
14850 Scenic Heights Rd, Eden Prairie, MN 55344-2243
Tel (952) 941-3175 *Founded/Ownrshp* 1930
Sales 56.3MM *EMP* 2,185
Accts Cliftonlarsonallen Llp Minnea
SIC 8051 8361 8052 Convalescent home with continuous nursing care; Mental retardation hospital; Rest home, with health care incidental; Home for the mentally retarded, with health care
CEO: David Zwickey
**Pr:* Robert B Inhoff
**COO:* Jim Selvy
CFO: Jeff Hongslo
Dir IT: Roger Henn

D-U-N-S 18-018-0630
AMERICAN BAPTIST HOMES OF WASHINGTON INC
JUDSON PARK RETIREMENT
23600 Marine View Dr S, Des Moines, WA 98198-7352
Tel (206) 870-6641 *Founded/Ownrshp* 1994
Sales 119.7MM *EMP* 220
SIC 8051 8059 8052 Skilled nursing care facilities; Convalescent home; Intermediate care facilities
Pr: David B Ferguson
CFO: Pamela Claassen
Ex Dir: Russel Akiyama

D-U-N-S 07-169-1307
AMERICAN BAPTIST HOMES OF WEST (CA)
6120 Stoneridge Mall Rd # 300, Pleasanton, CA 94588-3298
Tel (925) 924-7100 *Founded/Ownrshp* 1955
Sales 129.1MM *EMP* 2,500
Accts Rk Taylor & Associates Walnut
SIC 8059 Rest home, with health care
CEO: David B Ferguson
V Ch: Bruce Laycook
**Pr:* Christopher A Vito
CFO: Frank Tsai
**Ch:* Randy Stamper
Sr Cor Off: Peter Roberts
Ofcr: Randall L Stamper
**Sr VP:* Sloan Bentley
**Sr VP:* Terese Farkas
**Sr VP:* Jeff Glaze
VP: Joe Gerardi
VP: Travis Hanna
VP: Andrew Lenick

D-U-N-S 05-057-3591
AMERICAN BAR ASSOCIATION
321 N Clark St Ste Ll2, Chicago, IL 60654-7598
Tel (312) 988-5000 *Founded/Ownrshp* 1878
Sales 151.7MM *EMP* 900
Accts Grant Thornton Llp Chicago I
SIC 8621 2721 2731 Bar association; Magazines: publishing only, not printed on site; Books: publishing only
Ch Bd: Michael E Burke
Mng Pt: John W Anderson
Pr: Linda Klein
COO: Jo Saringer
CFO: Janet Gibbs
CFO: John Hanle
CFO: Kenneth Widelka
Sr Cor Off: Charles Wolf
Bd of Dir: Ryan Adams
VP: Linda Cooper
VP: William Hubbard
VP: Edward Waller
Exec: Randall McClanahan
Assoc Dir: Joseph Besharse
Dir Bus: Bill McDonough
Dir Bus: Jill Werner

D-U-N-S 60-082-8417
AMERICAN BARGE LINE CO
(*Suby of* ACL) ★
1701 E Market St, Jeffersonville, IN 47130-4755
Tel (812) 288-0100 *Founded/Ownrshp* 2004
Sales 855.2MM^E *EMP* 2,500
SIC 4449 3731 4491 Canal barge operations; Barges, building & repairing; Marine terminals
Pr: Mark Holden

D-U-N-S 05-841-8567
AMERICAN BECHTEL INC
(*Suby of* BECHTEL CORP) ★
50 Beale St, San Francisco, CA 94105-1813
Tel (415) 768-1234 *Founded/Ownrshp* 1972
Sales 41.0MM^E *EMP* 1,889
SIC 8711 Engineering services
**Sr VP:* PA Dawson
**Sr VP:* Ja Miller
VP: Chris Maslak

D-U-N-S 82-849-4802
AMERICAN BEEF PACKERS INC
13677 Yorba Ave, Chino, CA 91710-5059
Tel (909) 628-4888 *Founded/Ownrshp* 2014
Sales 200.0MM *EMP* 250
Accts Singer Traynor & Scholefield
SIC 0751 2011 5147 Slaughtering: custom livestock services; Beef products from beef slaughtered on site; Meats & meat products
Pr: Lawrence Miller
CFO: Rafael Santamaria
Sls Mgr: Henry Wong

D-U-N-S 07-480-8494
AMERICAN BEVERAGE ASSOCIATION
1101 16th St Nw Ste 700, Washington, DC 20036-4811
Tel (202) 223-4832 *Founded/Ownrshp* 1921
Sales 84.6MM *EMP* 37
Accts Calibre Cpa Group Pllc Bethes
SIC 8611 Trade associations
Pr: Susan Neely
CFO: Mark N Hammond
Treas: Ralph D Crowley Jr
Sr VP: Bill Race
VP: William M Dermody Jr
VP: Genna Gent
VP: Maia M Jack
VP: James A McGreevy
VP: Michael Redman
Board of Directors: Venus Adkins, Barbara Ferreira, Jerry Fowden, Seth Goldman, Scott Miller, J Andrew Moore, Anthony J Varni

D-U-N-S 01-748-6978 EXP
AMERICAN BEVERAGE CORP
ABC
(*Suby of* HARVEST HILL BEVERAGE CO) ★
1 Daily Way, Verona, PA 15147-1135
Tel (412) 828-9020 *Founded/Ownrshp* 2015
Sales 213.4MM^E *EMP* 550^E
SIC 2033 Fruits & fruit products in cans, jars, etc.
Pr: Fhj Koffrie
**Pr:* Kevin McGahren-Clemens
**Treas:* Edward M Levy
**VP:* Frans Eelkmanrooda
**VP:* Ken Janowitz

D-U-N-S 00-103-0493 IMP/EXP
▲ AMERICAN BILTRITE INC
57 River St Ste 302, Wellesley, MA 02481-2097
Tel (781) 237-6655 Founded/Ownrshp 1908
Sales 205.5MM EMP 600
Tkr Sym ABLT Exch OTO
SIC 3069 2672 2241 3961 5094 Rubber floor coverings, mats & wallcoverings; Heels, boot or shoe: rubber, composition or fiber; Soles, boot or shoe: rubber, composition or fiber; Tape, pressure sensitive: rubber; Coated & laminated paper; Adhesive papers, labels or tapes: from purchased material; Tape, pressure sensitive: made from purchased materials; Fabric tapes; Costume novelties; Costume jewelry, ex. precious metal & semiprecious stones; Jewelry
Ch Bd: Roger S Marcus
*Pr: Richard G Marcus
*CFO: Howard N Feist III
*Treas: William M Marcus
Ex VP: William Marcus
VP: Pat Buckley
VP: Roch Leblanc
VP: Jean Richard
*VP: Henry W Winkleman
*Prin: Leo R Breitman
*Prin: John C Garrels III

D-U-N-S 02-472-3520 IMP
AMERICAN BLOCK CO (TX)
AMERICAN BLOCK MFG CO
6311 Breen Dr, Houston, TX 77086-3836
Tel (800) 572-9087 Founded/Ownrshp 1980
Sales 124.8MM^E EMP 540
SIC 3441 3599 3533 3496 3444 3429 Fabricated structural metal; Machine & other job shop work; Oil & gas field machinery; Miscellaneous fabricated wire products; Sheet metalwork; Manufactured hardware (general)
Pr: Rajani K Shah
*Sec: Darshana Shah
*VP: Kanti Patel
Opers Mgr: Madhu Patel
Sls Dir: Mike Borg
Sls Mgr: Samuel Chellam
Sales Asso: Estefania Flores
Sales Asso: Rocquee Johnson

AMERICAN BLOCK MFG CO
See AMERICAN BLOCK CO

D-U-N-S 83-014-9634
AMERICAN BLUE RIBBON HOLDINGS LLC
VILLAGE INN RESTAURANT
(Suby of FIDELITY NEWPORT HOLDINGS LLC) ★
3038 Sidco Dr, Nashville, TN 37204-4506
Tel (615) 256-8500 Founded/Ownrshp 2009
Sales 862.3MM^E EMP 15,000
Accts Grant Thornton Llp Denver C
SIC 5812 6794 Restaurant, family: chain; Franchises, selling or licensing
CEO: Hazem Ouf
*Pr: Steve Weis
CFO: Anita Adams
Ofcr: Mark Hampton
Exec: Kirk Akerstrom
*CIO: Jeffery Kent
CIO: Jeffery V Kent
CTO: John Christopher
IT Man: Christine Adkins
Mktg Dir: Dee Cleveland
Snr Mgr: Christopher Scarborough
Board of Directors: Brent Bickett, William Foley II, Tim Janszen, Ryan Langdon, Robert Wheaton

D-U-N-S 61-644-7116 IMP
AMERICAN BOA INC
(Suby of BOA BALG- UND KOMPENSATOREN-TECHNOLOGIE GMBH)
1420 Redi Rd, Cumming, GA 30040-5892
Tel (678) 513-3348 Founded/Ownrshp 1994
Sales 144.5MM^E EMP 400
SIC 3494 Expansion joints pipe
Pr: Richard Stover
Pr: Bill Hunter
*CFO: Rune Are
VP: Ludger Brake
VP: Richard Stober
Prgrm Mgr: Jim Forton
Genl Mgr: Charles Flock
Dir IT: Lora Hopkins
IT Man: Kevin Allred
IT Man: Clyde L Anthony
IT Man: Christof Bennett

D-U-N-S 01-293-6378 IMP
AMERICAN BOOK CO
10267 Kingston Pike, Knoxville, TN 37922-3277
Tel (865) 966-7454 Founded/Ownrshp 1997
Sales 235.3MM^E EMP 225
SIC 5192 2731 Books; Book publishing
CEO: Dean Winegardner
Pr: Patrick O'Conner
Treas: Darren Raines
Trfc Mgr: Terry Wood

D-U-N-S 94-028-8553 EXP
■ AMERICAN BOTTLING CO
DR PEPPER SNAPPLE GROUP
(Suby of DR PEPPER SNAPPLE GROUP INC) ★
5301 Legacy Dr, Plano, TX 75024-3109
Tel (972) 673-7000 Founded/Ownrshp 2008
Sales 1.8MMM^E EMP 12,500^E
SIC 2086 Soft drinks: packaged in cans, bottles, etc.
CEO: Larry D Young
*CFO: Marty Ellen
*Ex VP: Jim Baldwin
Sr VP: Carolyn Ross
VP: James L Baldwin Jr
VP: Fred Cherne
VP: Kyle Currlin
VP: Wayne Lewis
VP: Elaine Nelson
VP: Arthur Swanson
Brnch Mgr: Michael Haferkamp

D-U-N-S 82-787-9631
AMERICAN BREAD CO LLC
8905 Lake Ave Fl 2, Cleveland, OH 44102-6316
Tel (216) 961-6767 Founded/Ownrshp 2001
Sales 57.1MM^E EMP 1,500
SIC 7389 Cafe

D-U-N-S 18-062-0254 IMP/EXP
AMERICAN BRIDGE CO
(Suby of AB) ★
1000 American Bridge Way, Coraopolis, PA 15108-1266
Tel (412) 631-1000 Founded/Ownrshp 1989
Sales 157.6MM^E EMP 500
SIC 1791 8711 1622 Structural steel erection; Engineering services; Bridge construction
CEO: Michael Flowers
*COO: Terry Poole
*CFO: Paul Driscoll
*Treas: Kenneth Sible
*VP: Michael Cegelis
VP: Michael D Flowers
*VP: Scott Gammon
VP: Dick Kermode
VP: Kwadwo Osei-Akoto
Off Mgr: Debbie Easton
Off Admin: Anne Royster

D-U-N-S 60-914-3086 IMP/EXP
AMERICAN BRIDGE HOLDING CO
AB
1000 American Bridge Way, Coraopolis, PA 15108-1266
Tel (412) 631-1000 Founded/Ownrshp 1989
Sales 157.6MM^E EMP 928^E
SIC 1791 1542 Structural steel erection; Commercial & office building contractors
Pr: Michael Flowers
*COO: Terry Poole
*CFO: Paul Driscoll
*Sr VP: Scott Gammon
Off Mgr: Debbie Easton

D-U-N-S 00-697-9819
■ AMERICAN BROADCASTING COMPANIES INC
ABC
(Suby of ABC HOLDING CO INC) ★
77 W 66th St Rm 100, New York, NY 10023-6298
Tel (212) 456-7777 Founded/Ownrshp 1996
Sales 1.3MMM^E EMP 8,000
SIC 4833 Television broadcasting stations
Pr: David Westin
*Sr VP: Allan N Braverman
*Sr VP: Ronald J Doerfler
*Sr VP: Walter C Liss Jr
*Sr VP: Michael P Mallardi
*Sr VP: Stephen A Weiswasser
Genl Mgr: Robert Edelman
IT Man: Peter Kurz

D-U-N-S 05-269-0047 IMP/EXP
AMERICAN BUILDERS & CONTRACTORS SUPPLY CO INC
ABC SUPPLY CO.
1 Abc Pkwy, Beloit, WI 53511-4466
Tel (608) 362-7777 Founded/Ownrshp 1982
Sales 6.7MMM^E EMP 7,299
SIC 5033 5031

D-U-N-S 05-459-4270
■ AMERICAN BUILDING MAINTENANCE CO OF ILLINOIS INC (CA)
A B M
(Suby of ABM INDUSTRIES INC) ★
420 Taylor St 200, San Francisco, CA 94102-1702
Tel (415) 351-4386 Founded/Ownrshp 1973
Sales 42.7MM^E EMP 2,600
SIC 7349 Janitorial service, contract basis
Pr: Henrik Slipsager
*Treas: Douglas Bowlus
*Sr VP: William Micheli
Sr VP: Paul C Monahan
Sr VP: Michael L Roppolo
Sr VP: Douglas E Smyers
Area Mgr: Jake Murphy
Brnch Mgr: Wendy Podkasik
Dist Mgr: Joe Annino
Genl Mgr: Leron Canup
Opers Mgr: Scott Houck

D-U-N-S 61-545-1648
■ AMERICAN BUILDING MAINTENANCE CO OF NEW YORK
(Suby of ABM INDUSTRIES INC) ★
101 California St, San Francisco, CA 94111-5802
Tel (415) 733-4000 Founded/Ownrshp 1975
Sales 39.1MM^E EMP 4,530
SIC 7349 Janitorial service, contract basis
Pr: Henrik Slipsager
*Treas: Douglas Bowlus
*Ex VP: Scott Salmirs

D-U-N-S 61-545-1622
■ AMERICAN BUILDING MAINTENANCE CO-WEST (INC)
(Suby of ABM INDUSTRIES INC) ★
75 Broadway Ste 111, San Francisco, CA 94111-1423
Tel (415) 733-4000 Founded/Ownrshp 1986
Sales 21.8MM^E EMP 3,000
SIC 7349 Janitorial service, contract basis
Pr: Henrik Slipsager
*Treas: Douglas Bowlus

D-U-N-S 02-902-0732 IMP
AMERICAN BUILDING SUPPLY INC
ABS-AMERICAN BUILDING SUPPLY
8360 Elder Creek Rd, Sacramento, CA 95828-1705
Tel (916) 503-4100 Founded/Ownrshp 1985
Sales 324.9MM^E EMP 800
SIC 5031 3231 Doors; Door frames, all materials; Doors, glass: made from purchased glass
Pr: Son Winn
*VP: Dave Baker
*VP: Jan Leonard
VP: Doug Shorey
*CTO: Son Nguyen
Software D: Mike Doescher
Prd Mgr: Junior Hill
Natl Sales: Dave Adolphson
Sls Mgr: Mike Yoas

D-U-N-S 05-864-2950 EXP
■ AMERICAN BUILDINGS CO
(Suby of NUCOR CORP) ★
1150 State Docks Rd, Eufaula, AL 36027-3344
Tel (888) 307-4338 Founded/Ownrshp 1947
Sales 237.0MM^E EMP 950
SIC 3448 Prefabricated metal buildings; Prefabricated metal components
Pr: Raymond S Napolitan
Pr: Raylene Smallwood
VP: Buck Carroll
Area Mgr: David Reed
Dist Mgr: Jim Larrimore
Dist Mgr: Brad Mayfield
Genl Mgr: Wes Brooker
Genl Mgr: Beverly Robertson
Genl Mgr: Anne M Savage
CTO: Bryan Gilbert
Software D: Chris Odom

D-U-N-S 80-831-3357
AMERICAN BULK COMMODITIES INC
R & J TRUCKING
8063 Southern Blvd, Youngstown, OH 44512-6306
Tel (330) 758-0841 Founded/Ownrshp 1992
Sales 103.2MM^E EMP 600
SIC 4212 7532 6531 7363 Local trucking, without storage; Dump truck haulage; Paint shop, automotive; Body shop, automotive; Body shop, trucks; Real estate managers; Truck driver services
Pr: Ronald Carrocce
*Treas: Troy Carrocce
*VP: Mark Carrocce

D-U-N-S 07-886-8396 IMP
AMERICAN BULK PIPE & STEEL LLC
607 Oyster Shell Ct, Missouri City, TX 77459-7562
Tel (281) 431-3473 Founded/Ownrshp 2011
Sales 120.0MM^E EMP 13^E
SIC 3317 Steel pipe & tubes

D-U-N-S 04-471-0341
AMERICAN BUREAU OF SHIPPING INC
ABS AMERICAS
16855 Northchase Dr, Houston, TX 77060-6010
Tel (281) 877-5800 Founded/Ownrshp 1970
Sales 1.2MMM^E EMP 3,000
Accts Ernst & Young Llp Houston Tx
SIC 4785 Surveyors, marine cargo
Ch Bd: Robert D Somerville
COO: Chris J Wiernicki
Sr VP: Vikki Dunn
VP: Robert Gilman
VP: Stephen Gumpel
*VP: Stewart H Wade
Exec: Andrea Guinan-Haynes
Exec: Sophia Tejada
CTO: Sonya Shears
Dir IT: Daniel Lee
IT Man: Ben Cooper

D-U-N-S 16-191-6767
▲ AMERICAN CAMPUS COMMUNITIES INC
12700 Hill Country Blvd, Austin, TX 78738-6361
Tel (512) 732-1000 Founded/Ownrshp 1993
Sales 753.3MM EMP 3,108
Tkr Sym ACC Exch NYS
SIC 6798 6531 Real estate investment trusts; Real estate agent, residential; Real estate leasing & rentals
Pr: William C Bayless Jr
*Ch Bd: Edward Lowenthal
COO: James C Hopke Jr
CFO: Jonathan A Graf
CFO: Mark Hagar
Chf Inves: William W Talbot
Ex VP: Jennifer Beese
Ex VP: Jorge De Cardenas
Ex VP: Daniel B Perry
Ex VP: Kim K Voss
Ex VP: Jamie Wilhelm
Sr VP: Daniel Perry
VP: Aaron Armstrong
VP: Larry Greenberg
VP: Brett Hahnel
VP: Kimberly Kelley
VP: Terri Schilling
VP: Dan Shoepe
VP: Bryan Storey
Board of Directors: Blake Chandlee, G Steven Dawson, Dennis G Lopez, Oliver Luck, C Patrick Oles Jr, Winston W Walker

D-U-N-S 94-178-0264
■ AMERICAN CAMPUS COMMUNITIES OPERATING PARTNERSHIP LP
(Suby of AMERICAN CAMPUS COMMUNITIES INC) ★
12700 Hill Country Blvd, Austin, TX 78738-6361
Tel (512) 732-1000 Founded/Ownrshp 2004
Sales 753.3MM EMP 570
SIC 6531 Real estate managers
Genl Pt: William Bayless
*Pt: Brian Nickel
*Ex VP: Noel Brinkman
*Ex VP: Michael Cipriano
*Ex VP: Gina Cowart
Ex VP: James C Hopke Jr
*Ex VP: William Talbot
Ex VP: Jamie Wilhelm III
Sr VP: Jennifer Beese
Sr VP: Clint Braun
Sr VP: Steve Crawford
Sr VP: Daniel Perry
Sr VP: James Sholders
Sr VP: Kim K Voss
Sr VP: Jason Wills
Sr VP: Brian Winger
Sr VP: Victor Young

D-U-N-S 03-767-0981
AMERICAN CANCER SOCIETY EAST CENTRAL DIVISION INC
Sipe Ave Rr 422, Hershey, PA 17033
Tel (717) 533-6144 Founded/Ownrshp 1944
Sales 91.7MM EMP 560
Accts Ernst & Young Us Llp Birmin
SIC 8733 Noncommercial research organizations
CEO: Gary Pincock
*Ch Bd: Stephen Swanson
*Pr: M Joyce Dienger
*Pr: Patrick Welch
*Treas: Dan Heist
VP: Teresa Gonzalez

D-U-N-S 06-305-8655
AMERICAN CANCER SOCIETY EASTERN DIVISION INC
2 Lyon Pl, White Plains, NY 10601-5402
Tel (914) 949-4800 Founded/Ownrshp 1921
Sales 93.5MM EMP 520^E
Accts Ernst & Young Us Llp Birmingh
SIC 8322 Individual & family services
CEO: Donald Distasio
*COO: James Nealy
*CFO: Jim McGovern
Treas: Janice Maloof
VP: Maureen Allex
IT Man: Gladys Rodrigues

D-U-N-S 06-120-7064
AMERICAN CANCER SOCIETY INC (GA)
250 Williams St Nw # 6000, Atlanta, GA 30303-1034
Tel (404) 320-3333 Founded/Ownrshp 1913
Sales 847.8MM EMP 1,093
SIC 8621

D-U-N-S 07-822-2577
AMERICAN CANCER SOCIETY MID-SOUTH DIVISION INC
1100 Ireland Way Ste 300, Birmingham, AL 35205-7014
Tel (205) 879-2242 Founded/Ownrshp 1945
Sales 953.5MM EMP 475
Accts Ernst & Young Llp Atlanta Ga
SIC 8733 Noncommercial research organizations
CEO: Lisa Roth
*COO: Pam Dotson
*VP: Kelly Doss

AMERICAN CAPITAL FUNDING
See WESTLEND FINANCING INC

D-U-N-S 15-190-7672
▲ AMERICAN CAPITAL LTD
2 Bethesda Metro Ctr # 14, Bethesda, MD 20814-5390
Tel (301) 951-6122 Founded/Ownrshp 1986
Sales 671.0MM EMP 346
Tkr Sym ACAS Exch NGS
SIC 6726 Investment offices; Management investment funds, closed-end
Ch Bd: Malon Wilkus
Pr: John R Erickson
Pr: Brian S Graff
Pr: Gordon J O'Brien
CFO: Bernice Bell
Chf Cred: Samuel A Flax
Top Exec: Clare Copeland
Ex VP: Tom McHale
Sr VP: Mark Lindsey
VP: Leona Clague
VP: Roland Cline
VP: Peter Dahms
VP: Cydonii Fairfax
VP: Heather French
VP: Alex Grau
VP: Michael Messersmith
VP: Ajay Nanda
VP: Adam Schatzow
Dir: Sean Bare
Board of Directors: Mary C Baskin, Neil M Hahl, Philip R Harper, Stan Lundine, Kristen L Manos, Susan K Nestegard, Kenneth D Peterson Jr, Alvin N Puryear, David G Richards

D-U-N-S 79-408-1724
AMERICAN CAPITAL PARTNERS LLC
205 Oser Ave, Hauppauge, NY 11788-3710
Tel (631) 851-0918 Founded/Ownrshp 2001
Sales 160.6MM^E EMP 3,750
SIC 6282 Investment advice
Exec: Lance Cuoco

AMERICAN CARBIDE TOOLING DIV
See PENN UNITED TECHNOLOGIES INC

D-U-N-S 19-580-4323
AMERICAN CARGO EXPRESS INC
2345 Vauxhall Rd, Union, NJ 07083-5036
Tel (908) 351-3400 Founded/Ownrshp 1988
Sales 96.8MM^E EMP 220
SIC 4789 Cargo loading & unloading services
Pr: Rick Trizano
*CFO: Christina Murray
CFO: Christina Trizano
Ex VP: Lloyd Burke
*VP: Julian Zhao
Dir IT: Ronald Schultz
IT Man: Armand Herreras
Snr Mgr: Tracey Ball

D-U-N-S 13-101-7860
AMERICAN CASINO & ENTERTAINMENT PROPERTIES LLC
(Suby of W2007/ACEP MANAGERS VOTECO LLC) ★
2000 Las Vegas Blvd S, Las Vegas, NV 89104-2507
Tel (702) 383-5242 Founded/Ownrshp 2008
Sales 373.0MM EMP 4,300^E
Accts Grant Thornton Llp Reno Neva
SIC 7011 Casino hotel
CEO: Frank V Riolo
Pr: Jim King
*CFO: Edward W Martin III
Ex VP: Phyllis Gilland
Ex VP: Ronald P Lurie
Ex VP: Ronald Lurie
Sr VP: Phyllis A Gilland
Sr VP: Mark Majetich
VP: Kevin R Ball
VP: Bill Boswell
VP: Brian Christensen
VP: Brian Lambert
VP: Marlon Ortiz
Dir Soc: Rychly Natasha
Board of Directors: Alan Kava, Peter Weidman

D-U-N-S 87-638-3907
AMERICAN CASINO & ENTERTAINMENT PROPERTIES LLC
(*Suby of* AMERICAN CASINO & ENTERTAINMENT PROPERTIES LLC) ★
1900 S Casino Dr, Laughlin, NV 89029-1513
Tel (702) 298-5111 *Founded/Ownrshp* 2007
Sales 54.5MM[E] *EMP* 1,586[E]
SIC 6512 7011 Nonresidential building operators; Hotels & motels
VP: Kathy Hilderhof
VP: Dana Kissinger
Dir Soc: Mary Evans
Dir Sec: David Snyder
Genl Mgr: Paul Hobson
MIS Dir: Rachel N Garcia
VP Mktg: Susan Murphy
VP Mktg: Denise Shinsky
Mktg Mgr: Cris Robinson

AMERICAN CASINO & ENTRMT PRPTS
See STRATOSPHERE LLC

D-U-N-S 00-339-7569 IMP/EXP
AMERICAN CAST IRON PIPE CO (AL)
A.C.I.P.C.O.
1501 31st Ave N, Birmingham, AL 35207-4101
Tel (205) 325-7856 *Founded/Ownrshp* 1905
Sales 975.9MM[E] *EMP* 2,500[E]
SIC 3491 3369 3321 3053 3317 Fire hydrant valves; Castings, except die-castings, precision; Ductile iron castings; Gaskets, all materials; Steel pipe & tubes
CEO: Van L Richey
**CFO:* Cook J M
**Treas:* John M Cook
Treas: Sue Sellers
Ex VP: Kristina Alpaugh
**VP:* J M O Brien
VP: Charles Dowling
VP: Mike Kitchens
**VP:* Frank C Pausic
**VP:* John L Woods
Rgnl Mgr: Jeanie Lawley

D-U-N-S 04-423-8780
■ AMERICAN CASUALTY CO OF READING PENNSYLVANIA INC
CNA INSURANCE
(*Suby of* CNA INSURANCE) ★
333 S Wabash Ave Fl 22, Chicago, IL 60604-4258
Tel (312) 822-5000 *Founded/Ownrshp* 1902
Sales NA *EMP* 3,000
SIC 6411 Insurance agents, brokers & service
Ch Bd: Steven Slioienthal
**CFO:* Craig Mense
**Sr VP:* Larry Boyson
**Sr VP:* Jonathan Kantor

D-U-N-S 78-140-1849
■ AMERICAN CELLULAR CORP
(*Suby of* DOBSON COMMUNICATIONS CORP) ★
14201 Wireless Way, Oklahoma City, OK 73134-2512
Tel (405) 529-8500 *Founded/Ownrshp* 2000
Sales 518.4MM *EMP* 179
SIC 4812 Cellular telephone services
CEO: Steven P Dussek
**Ch Bd:* Everett R Dobson
CFO: Bruce R Knooihuizen
**Sec:* Stephen T Dobson

D-U-N-S 14-451-9733
AMERICAN CENTURY COMPANIES INC
AMERICAN CENTURY INVESTMENTS
430 W 7th St, Kansas City, MO 64105-1407
Tel (816) 531-5575 *Founded/Ownrshp* 2005
Sales 976.5MM[E] *EMP* 1,837[E]
SIC 6282 Investment advisory service
Pr: Jonathan Thomas
Pr: William M Lyons
CFO: Patrick Bannigan
Treas: Jean Wade
Chf Inves: Keith Creveling
Chf Inves: David Hollond
Chf Inves: Scott Wittman
Chf Inves: Gregory Woodhams
Sr VP: Phillip Davidson
Sr VP: Mark Kopinski
Sr VP: Keith Kreveling
Sr VP: G David McEwen
Sr VP: Gudron Neumann
Sr VP: Peruvemba Satish
Sr VP: Victor Zhang
VP: Jim Blythe
VP: Jay Breitenkamp
VP: Brian L Brogan
VP: Alan Chingren
VP: Brad Cloverdyke
VP: Chris Doyle

D-U-N-S 02-121-3020
AMERICAN CENTURY INVESTMENT MANAGEMENT INC
IRAS MOUNIR ABANNI
(*Suby of* AMERICAN CENTURY INVESTMENTS) ★
4500 Main St, Kansas City, MO 64111-7709
Tel (816) 531-5575 *Founded/Ownrshp* 2005
Sales 155.1MM[E] *EMP* 1,443
SIC 6722 6282 Management investment, open-end; Investment advisory service
CEO: Jonathan S Thomas
**Sr VP:* Mark Kopinski
**Sr VP:* G David Macewen
**Sr VP:* Victor Zhang
VP: Niels Anderson
VP: Paul Somogye
VP: Rich Taylor
Mktg Mgr: Jennifer Pumphrey

AMERICAN CENTURY INVESTMENTS
See AMERICAN CENTURY COMPANIES INC

D-U-N-S 04-675-0063
AMERICAN CENTURY SERVICES CORP
(*Suby of* AMERICAN CENTURY INVESTMENTS) ★
4500 Main St, Kansas City, MO 64111-7709
Tel (816) 531-5575 *Founded/Ownrshp* 1956
Sales 153.0MM[E] *EMP* 1,280
SIC 7374 8741 Data processing service; Administrative management
CEO: Jonathan S Thomas
Pr: Hayden Berk
CFO: Robert Morrie
**Chf Inves:* David Hollond
**Sr VP:* Phillip Davidson
Sr VP: Mark Gilstrap
**Sr VP:* Mark Kopinski
**Sr VP:* Keith Kreveling
**Sr VP:* G David Macewen
Sr VP: Steve McClain
**Sr VP:* Scott Wittman
**Sr VP:* Victor Zhang
VP: Stacey Belford
VP: Brian Brady
VP: Jay Breitenkamp
VP: Ellen Denicola
VP: Chris Doyle
VP: Greg Garvin
VP: Gary Kostuke
VP: Yulin Long
VP: Casey McCarthy

D-U-N-S 18-892-2421 IMP
AMERICAN CHARTERED BANK
1199 E Higgins Rd, Schaumburg, IL 60173-4711
Tel (847) 517-5400 *Founded/Ownrshp* 1987
Sales NA *EMP* 387
SIC 6022 6021

D-U-N-S 00-623-3910 IMP/EXP
AMERICAN CHEMET CORP
AMERICAN CHEMET EXPORT
740 Waukegan Rd Ste 202, Deerfield, IL 60015-4400
Tel (847) 948-0800 *Founded/Ownrshp* 1946
Sales 218.2MM *EMP* 140
Accts Anderson Zurmuehlen & Co Pc
SIC 2819 2816 Copper compounds or salts, inorganic; Zinc pigments: zinc oxide, zinc sulfide
Pr: W H Shropshire
**Treas:* Brad Smith
**VP:* Daniel B Brimhall
**VP:* Kim A Klatt
IT Man: Kenneth Stringer

AMERICAN CHEMET EXPORT
See AMERICAN CHEMET CORP

D-U-N-S 04-476-0098
AMERICAN CHEMICAL SOCIETY
JOURNAL OF CHEMICAL & ENGINEER
1155 16th St Nw, Washington, DC 20036-4892
Tel (202) 872-4600 *Founded/Ownrshp* 1876
Sales 601.9MM *EMP* 2,000[E]
Accts Lb Kpmg Llp Mc Lean Va
SIC 8621 7319 Scientific membership association; Display advertising service
Prin: Thomas Connelly Jr
Mng Pt: Gary Epp
CFO: Brian A Bernstein
CFO: Brian Bernstein
CFO: Donna Ruthe
Treas: Brian Bernstein
VP: Arthur M Brener
VP: David Cochran
VP: Bill Cook
VP: Edward F Hand
VP: Jim Leonard
VP: John Loomis
VP: Mary Minette
VP: Jack Ochs
VP: Kris Rubottom
VP: Dave Russ
VP: Dean Smith
Exec: Keona Davis
Exec: Marion Mullauer
Dir Soc: Huggins Peter
Comm Dir: Jane Shure

D-U-N-S 04-603-9152
AMERICAN CHEMISTRY COUNCIL INC (DC)
CHEMSTAR DIVISION
700 2nd St Ne Fl 8-10, Washington, DC 20002-8101
Tel (202) 249-7000 *Founded/Ownrshp* 1872
Sales 116.3MM *EMP* 320
SIC 8611 8748 8621 8699

D-U-N-S 14-451-8727 IMP
AMERICAN CITY BUSINESS JOURNALS INC
STREET & SMITH SPORTS GROUP
(*Suby of* ADVANCE PUBLICATIONS, INC.)
120 W Morehead St Ste 400, Charlotte, NC 28202-1874
Tel (704) 973-1000 *Founded/Ownrshp* 1985
Sales 345.9MM[E] *EMP* 1,600
SIC 2711 2721 Newspapers: publishing only, not printed on site; Magazines: publishing only, not printed on site
Pr: Whitney R Shaw
**CFO:* George B Guthinger
Ofcr: Ed Baker
Ofcr: Mike Olivieri
Ex VP: Tim Bradbury
VP: At Castillo
**VP:* S I Newhouse Jr
**VP:* Kirk Shaw
Exec: Abe Madkour
Dir Soc: Julie Borra
Creative D: Misty Berry

D-U-N-S 84-717-8873
AMERICAN CIVIL CONSTRUCTORS HOLDINGS INC
4901 S Windermere St, Littleton, CO 80120-1021
Tel (303) 795-2582 *Founded/Ownrshp* 2011
Sales 102.6MM[E] *EMP* 200
SIC 1622 0781 Bridge construction; Landscape counseling & planning
Pr: Randy Maher
Off Mgr: Naomi Lodte

D-U-N-S 07-646-1680 IMP
AMERICAN CIVIL CONSTRUCTORS LLC
(*Suby of* AMERICAN CIVIL CONSTRUCTORS HOLDINGS INC) ★
4901 S Windermere St, Littleton, CO 80120-1021
Tel (303) 795-2582 *Founded/Ownrshp* 1999
Sales 89.2MM[E] *EMP* 200
SIC 1629 0783 0181 Land preparation construction; Earthmoving contractor; Golf course construction; Dam construction; Spraying services, ornamental bush; Removal services, bush & tree; Sod farms
Pr: Randy Maher
CFO: Jeff Rudolph
VP: Victoria Aguilar
**VP:* Cliff Barber
**VP:* Rob Barclay
**VP:* Jeff Croll
**VP:* Larry Rice
**VP:* Linda Sinclair
**VP:* Dave Wilkerson
Sls Mgr: Mike Brien

D-U-N-S 07-329-6634
AMERICAN CIVIL LIBERTIES UNION FOUNDATION INC
ACLU
125 Broad St Fl 18, New York, NY 10004-2454
Tel (212) 549-2500 *Founded/Ownrshp* 1966
Sales 94.0MM *EMP* 350
Accts Lb Mcgladrey Llp New York Ny
SIC 8699 Charitable organization
Pr: Susan N Herman
**Pr:* Nadine Strossen
CFO: Caroline Greene
Bd of Dir: Bob Goodrich
Bd of Dir: Madeline Kochen
Bd of Dir: Dick Lobenthal
Bd of Dir: Carolyn Macadam
Bd of Dir: Theresa Melendez
Bd of Dir: Bob Pettapiece
VP: Penny Beardslee
VP: Rebecca Steele
Comm Dir: Ed Yohnka

D-U-N-S 00-176-4968
AMERICAN CLEANING CO INC (MA)
94 Lincoln St, Brighton, MA 02135-1490
Tel (617) 562-4000 *Founded/Ownrshp* 1910, 1973
Sales 42.3MM *EMP* 1,800
SIC 7349 Janitorial service, contract basis
Pr: Joseph Sullivan

D-U-N-S 04-226-2449 IMP
AMERICAN COAL CO
(*Suby of* MURRAY ENERGY CORP) ★
9085 Highway 34 N, Galatia, IL 62935-2344
Tel (618) 268-6311 *Founded/Ownrshp* 1998
Sales 703.2MM[E] *EMP* 500
SIC 1222 5052 Bituminous coal-underground mining; Copper ore

D-U-N-S 06-201-7140
AMERICAN COLLEGE OF CARDIOLOGY FOUNDATION
2400 N St Nw, Washington, DC 20037-1153
Tel (202) 375-6000 *Founded/Ownrshp* 1949
Sales 88.5MM *EMP* 307
SIC 8621

D-U-N-S 06-847-8452
AMERICAN COLLEGE OF SURGEONS INC
633 N Saint Clair St # 2600, Chicago, IL 60611-5927
Tel (312) 202-5000 *Founded/Ownrshp* 1913
Sales 115.2MM *EMP* 257
Accts Grant Thornton Llp Chicago I
SIC 8621 Medical field-related associations
Pr: L D Britt
**Ch Bd:* Gerald B Healy
**CFO:* Gay Vincent
**Treas:* Andrew Warshaw
**VP:* Richard J Finley
Adm Dir: Bernadette Trubatisky
Ex Dir: David Hoyt
**Ex Dir:* Mary H Mc Grath
Prgrm Mgr: Samuel Agesilas
Prgrm Mgr: Julia McMurray
Off Mgr: D'Arcey Johnson

D-U-N-S 96-731-4691 IMP/EXP
■ AMERICAN COLLOID CO
AMCOL
(*Suby of* AMCOL INTERNATIONAL CORP) ★
2870 Forbs Ave, Hoffman Estates, IL 60192-3702
Tel (847) 851-1700 *Founded/Ownrshp* 1994
Sales 497.9MM[E] *EMP* 608
SIC 1459 2899 Bentonite mining; Chemical preparations
Pr: Gary Morrison
CFO: Ed Sieracki
**VP:* Jim Papp
Rgnl Mgr: Bob Oliver
Dir IT: Jim Butz
IT Man: Allan Prejean
IT Man: Murali Venkatraman
Mfg Dir: Jeff Campbell
Opers Mgr: Katie Laundon
Plnt Mgr: Raymond Arpin
Plnt Mgr: Jan Deigert

D-U-N-S 04-642-4776
AMERICAN COMMERCE INSURANCE CO
(*Suby of* COMMERCE INSURANCE CO) ★
3590 Twin Creeks Dr, Columbus, OH 43204-1628
Tel (614) 272-6951 *Founded/Ownrshp* 1999
Sales NA *EMP* 217
SIC 6331 6351 Automobile insurance; Property damage insurance; Liability insurance
VP: Greg Clark
Telecom Ex: John Gardner
Snr Mgr: Stephen Winston

D-U-N-S 00-693-8864
AMERICAN COMMERCIAL BARGE LINE
(*Suby of* PLATINUM EQUITY LLC) ★
1701 E Market St, Jeffersonville, IN 47130-4717
Tel (812) 288-0100 *Founded/Ownrshp* 2010
Sales 750.0MM *EMP* 2,300
SIC 4449 3731 4491 Canal barge operations; Barges, building & repairing; Marine terminals
CEO: Mark K Knoy
**COO:* Paul A Tobin
**CFO:* David J Huls
Bd of Dir: Nils E Larsen
**Sr VP:* Robert M Blocker
VP: Todd Covini
VP: Bill Foster
VP: Jeff Kindl
VP: Nick Lonnemann
VP: Chris Shepherd
Trfc Dir: Angela Boyer

D-U-N-S 60-082-7955
AMERICAN COMMERCIAL LINES INC
ACL
(*Suby of* PLATINUM EQUITY) ★
1701 E Market St, Jeffersonville, IN 47130-4755
Tel (812) 288-0100 *Founded/Ownrshp* 2010
Sales 1.1MMM[E] *EMP* 2,570
SIC 4449 3731 4491 Canal barge operations; Barges, building & repairing; Marine terminals
CEO: Mark K Knoy
**COO:* Paul A Tobin
**CFO:* Thomas R Pilholski
**Sr VP:* Robert M Blocker
**Sr VP:* David J Huls
**Sr VP:* Dawn R Landry
VP: Nick Lonnemann
Opers Mgr: Terry Phelps
Sales Asso: Anastasia Swanson
Corp Couns: Brooke Egan
Snr Mgr: Sharon Ratliff

D-U-N-S 12-732-5632
AMERICAN COMMERCIAL LINES INTERNATIONAL LLC
(*Suby of* COMMERCIAL BARGE LINE CO) ★
1701 E Market St, Jeffersonville, IN 47130-4755
Tel (800) 899-7195 *Founded/Ownrshp* 2003
Sales 22.8MM[E] *EMP* 1,267[E]
SIC 4449 Intracoastal (freight) transportation
Pr: W Norbert Whitlock

D-U-N-S 18-360-1129
■ AMERICAN COMMERCIAL SECURITY SERVICES INC
AMERICAN LOSS PREVENTION SVCS
(*Suby of* ABM INDUSTRIES INC) ★
420 Taylor St Fl 2, San Francisco, CA 94102-1702
Tel (415) 856-1020 *Founded/Ownrshp* 1983
Sales 37.0MM[E] *EMP* 5,000
SIC 7381 Security guard service; Private investigator
Pr: Larry T Smith

D-U-N-S 07-277-1892
AMERICAN COMMUNITY MUTUAL INSURANCE CO
39201 7 Mile Rd, Livonia, MI 48152-1079
Tel (734) 591-9000 *Founded/Ownrshp* 1938
Sales NA *EMP* 475
SIC 6321 6311 Accident & health insurance; Life insurance
Pr: Michel Tobin
Ch Bd: Anther Dummer
**Ch Bd:* Gerald E Meach
**Pr:* Francis Dempsey
**CFO:* David Skup
Sr VP: Jeff Erickson
Mktg Dir: Neil Spero
Board of Directors: Andrew M Jarmel, Lynn M Lalinowski, Joseph A Nathan, John P Perrot, Thomas H Ritter, Stephen A Steward, James R Temple, Michael E Tobin

D-U-N-S 08-258-5670
AMERICAN CONSTRUCTORS INC (TX)
11900 W Parmer Ln Ste 200, Cedar Park, TX 78613
Tel (512) 328-2026 *Founded/Ownrshp* 1982
Sales 95.8MM[E] *EMP* 191
SIC 1541 1542 Industrial buildings & warehouses; Commercial & office building, new construction
Pr: W A Heine
CFO: Joe Moore
**VP:* Martin Burger
VP: Justin Huling
**VP:* S R Swanson
VP Mktg: Joe Charlton

D-U-N-S 84-705-0796
AMERICAN CONTRACTORS INDEMNITY CO
HCC SURETY GROUP
(*Suby of* TOKIO MARINE HCC) ★
601 S Figueroa St # 1600, Los Angeles, CA 90017-5721
Tel (213) 330-1309 *Founded/Ownrshp* 2004
Sales NA *EMP* 227
SIC 6399 Bank deposit insurance
Pr: Adam S Pessin
Sr VP: Jon Schneider
**VP:* Michael Budnitsky
VP: Jeannie J Lee
VP: Kio Lo
VP: Paul A Yasilli
Brnch Mgr: Bruce Lowdermilk
Dir IT: Bill White
IT Man: Azniv Tashdjian
Sales Exec: Sewell Larry

AMERICAN COTTON COOP ASSN
See CALCOT LTD

AMERICAN CRAFTSMAN
See SILVER LINE BUILDING PRODUCTS LLC

AMERICAN CREW
See BEAUTYGE BRANDS USA INC

D-U-N-S 05-479-2773 IMP
AMERICAN CRYSTAL SUGAR CO
101 3rd St N, Moorhead, MN 56560-1990
Tel (218) 236-4326 *Founded/Ownrshp* 1973
Sales 1.2MMM *EMP* 1,365
Accts Clifton Larson Allen Llp Stev
SIC 2063 7359 Beet sugar from beet sugar refinery; Beet pulp, dried: from beet sugar refinery; Molasses from sugar beets; Equipment rental & leasing
Pr: David A Berg
**COO:* Joseph J Talley
**CFO:* Thomas S Astrup
Ch: Bob Vivatson
**Treas:* Samuel S M Wai
Bd of Dir: Buzz Baldwin
Bd of Dir: David Mueller
Dir Bus: David L Malmskog
Dir IT: Neil Budke

IT Man: Sean Forrester
Sftwr Eng: Nathan Lutz
Board of Directors: Curtis Knutson, Donald S Andringa, Jeff D McInnes, William Baldwin, David Mueller, John Brainard, Wayne Tang, Brian R Erickson, Neil C Widner, Dale Fischer, Steve Williams, Robert M Green, John F Gudajtes, Curtis E Haugen, William A Hejl

D-U-N-S 06-502-3959
AMERICAN CUSTOMER CARE INC
225 N Main St Fl 5, Bristol, CT 06010-4997
Tel (800) 267-0686 *Founded/Ownrshp* 2000
Sales 108.1MM[E] *EMP* 2,000
SIC 7389 Telephone services
CEO: Mark E Facey
Pr: Danilo Vanegas
CFO: Jeff Neistat
VP: Staci Kress
Dir IT: Walter Patrosky
Dir IT: Walt Petrosky
IT Man: Mitch Briggs

D-U-N-S 09-963-3919
AMERICAN CYBERSYSTEMS INC
2400 Meadowbrook Pkwy, Duluth, GA 30096-4635
Tel (770) 493-5588 *Founded/Ownrshp* 1989
Sales 428.5MM[E] *EMP* 1,000[E]
SIC 7373 7371 7372 Systems software development services; Custom computer programming services; Prepackaged software
CEO: Rajiv Sardana
**COO:* Joe McAvoy
**COO:* Barry Osson
**Sec:* Nita Sardana
**Ex VP:* Charles Halash
Sr VP: Harminder Singh
**VP:* Nick Goel
VP: Jared King
VP: Mark Zisholtz
Assoc Dir: Vimal Vijay
Off Admin: Salam Elamrani

D-U-N-S 96-249-0749
AMERICAN DAIRY INC
2275 Huntington Dr 278, San Marino, CA 91108-2640
Tel (626) 757-8885 *Founded/Ownrshp* 2010
Sales 267.8MM *EMP* 4
SIC 5451 Dairy products stores
Prin: Lui Hua
Genl Mgr: You-Bin Leng

AMERICAN DENTAL
See HU-FRIEDY MFG CO LLC

D-U-N-S 07-442-5216
AMERICAN DENTAL ASSOCIATION
ADA SALABLE MATERIALS
211 E Chicago Ave, Chicago, IL 60611-2637
Tel (312) 440-2500 *Founded/Ownrshp* 1922
Sales 132.8MM *EMP* 475[E]
Accts Crowe Horwath Llp Chicago Il
SIC 8621 Dental association
Pr: Robert A Faiella
**CFO:* Paul Sholty
CFO: Bill Zimmerman
**Treas:* Ron Lemmo
Treas: Edward Leone Jr
**Chf Cred:* Stephanie Moritz
Bd of Dir: Aditi Bagchi
Bd of Dir: Amit Batra
Bd of Dir: Antonio S Braithwaite
Bd of Dir: Alan Carr
Bd of Dir: Arun Grover
Bd of Dir: Aicha Lyazidi
Bd of Dir: Amy Marckese
Bd of Dir: Barry Margolis
Bd of Dir: Art Mowery
Bd of Dir: Albert P Nordone
Bd of Dir: Abhinav Sinha
Bd of Dir: Alice Yang
**VP:* Charles Nornam
VP: Aj Smith
Board of Directors: Hal Fair, Alexander Kogan, Alvin Rosenblum, Charles Weber, Alex Acevedo, Maxine Feinberg, Albert Lam, Alexander Rubinshtein, Gary Yonemoto, Amy Anderson, Alan J Foster, Alyssa Martin, Brian Scott, James Zenk, Alyssa Brownb, Steven Gournardes, Alex Martin, Donald Seago, Mark Zust, Terry Buckenheimer, Joseph Hagenbruch, Alex McMillan, Alan Smolen, Joseph Crowley, Glen Hall, Adriana Mora

D-U-N-S 95-688-0587
AMERICAN DENTAL PARTNERS INC
(*Suby of* ACE CASH EXPRESS) ★
401 Edgewater Pl Ste 430, Wakefield, MA 01880-6225
Tel (781) 224-0880 *Founded/Ownrshp* 2012
Sales 262.2MM[E] *EMP* 2,651[E]
SIC 8621 8742 Dental association; Management consulting services; Training & development consultant; Business planning & organizing services; Financial consultant
CEO: Kevin Trexler
COO: Michael J Vaughan
CFO: Breht T Feigh
Ch: Gregory A Serrao
Sr VP: Lee Feldman
Sr VP: Michael J Kenneally
VP: Ian H Brock
VP: Roger A Horton
VP: David Nelsen
VP: Mark W Vargo
VP: Peter Young
Board of Directors: Daniel Agroskin, Ramsey Frank, Michel Lagarde, Paul Levy

D-U-N-S 80-017-4039
AMERICAN DIRECT PROCUREMENT INC
11000 Lakeview Ave, Lenexa, KS 66219-1311
Tel (913) 677-5588 *Founded/Ownrshp* 1992
Sales 104.1MM[E] *EMP* 175
SIC 5031 Lumber, plywood & millwork; Doors & windows
Pr: Byron W Whetstone
**CFO:* Rod Beason
VP Sls: Austin Cummings
Sales Asso: David Small

AMERICAN DISPLAY & FIXTURE
See MARKETING ALLIANCE GROUP INC

D-U-N-S 01-585-9813 IMP
AMERICAN DISPLAY & FIXTURE LLC
(*Suby of* AMERICAN DISPLAY & FIXTURE) ★
3600 N Hawthorne St, Chattanooga, TN 37406-1305
Tel (423) 624-1191 *Founded/Ownrshp* 2009
Sales 112.2MM[E] *EMP* 500
SIC 2541 Display fixtures, wood
CFO: Frank Grant
VP: Rick Davis
Plnt Mgr: David Milliken

D-U-N-S 14-636-2970 IMP
AMERICAN DISPOSAL SERVICES INC
10370 Central Park Dr, Manassas, VA 20110-4196
Tel (703) 789-7935 *Founded/Ownrshp* 2003
Sales 107.3MM[E] *EMP* 350
SIC 4953 Refuse systems
Pr: Larry Edwards
**VP:* Paul Coury
Genl Mgr: Buff Mundale
Sfty Mgr: Greg Hubbell
Sls Mgr: Eli Hayes

D-U-N-S 00-693-2040
AMERICAN DRUG STORES LLC
OSCO DRUG
250 E Parkcenter Blvd, Boise, ID 83706-3940
Tel (208) 395-6200 *Founded/Ownrshp* 1999
Sales 8.9MMM[E] *EMP* 200,000
SIC 5912 Drug stores
Pr: Chris Demos
Treas: John F Boyd
VP: William H Arnold
VP: Robert K Banks
VP: Colleen R Batcheler
VP: Gerald A Bay
VP: Charles F Cole
VP: Christopher T Dimos
VP: Elizabeth S Garrett
VP: Gary D Hunstiger
VP: Linda K Massman
VP: John D McGovern
VP: Ronald T Mendes
VP: Robert J Potter
VP: Barbara G Russell
VP: Bradley M Trom
VP: Thomas J Walter
VP: Daniel J Zbonek
Board of Directors: Peter F Collins

D-U-N-S 00-141-9688 IMP/EXP
■ **AMERICAN DRYER CORP**
(*Suby of* WHIRLPOOL CORP) ★
88 Currant Rd, Fall River, MA 02720-4781
Tel (508) 678-9000 *Founded/Ownrshp* 1965, 2015
Sales 88.7MM[E] *EMP* 230
SIC 3582 Dryers, laundry: commercial, including coin-operated
Pr: Christopher Fitzgerald
CFO: Michael Davidson
Plnt Mgr: Creig Benevides
Sls Mgr: Nelson Hughes

AMERICAN EAGLE
See PIEDMONT AIRLINES INC

AMERICAN EAGLE
See FFE TRANSPORTATION SERVICES INC

AMERICAN EAGLE
See EXECUTIVE AIR LINES INC

D-U-N-S 02-237-7795
■ **AMERICAN EAGLE HOLDING LLC**
(*Suby of* AMERICAN AIRLINES GROUP INC) ★
14760 Trinity Blvd # 300, Fort Worth, TX 76155-2642
Tel (817) 963-1234 *Founded/Ownrshp* 1998
Sales 130.3M[E] *EMP* 12,300
SIC 7389 Personal service agents, brokers & bureaus
Pr: Peter Bowler
**Sr VP:* David C Kennedy
**Sr VP:* Ralph L Richardi

D-U-N-S 83-446-9876 IMP/EXP
▲ **AMERICAN EAGLE OUTFITTERS INC**
77 Hot Metal St, Pittsburgh, PA 15203-2381
Tel (412) 432-3300 *Founded/Ownrshp* 1972
Sales 3.5MMM *EMP* 37,800
Accts Ernst & Young Llp Pittsburgh
Tkr Sym AEO *Exch* NYS
SIC 5621 5611 5661 5632 Women's clothing stores; Ready-to-wear apparel, women's; Men's & boys' clothing stores; Shoe stores; Men's shoes; Women's shoes; Men's boots; Women's accessory & specialty stores; Apparel accessories
Ch Bd: Jay L Schottenstein
Pr: Jennifer M Foyle
Pr: Charles F Kessler
COO: Michael R Rempell
CFO: Scott Hurd
Chf Mktg O: Michael Leedy
Ofcr: Scott M Hurd
Ex VP: Fredrick Grover
VP: Neil Bulman
VP: Roberto Croce
VP: Josh Denton
VP: Brian Franks
VP: Dana McKean-Hayson
VP: Rick Milazzo
VP: Frank Scavetta
VP: Jeff Shelton
VP: Charles Teti
VP: Jim Thompson
VP Bus Dev: Leann Rohan
Board of Directors: Michael G Jesselson, Thomas R Ketteler, Cary D McMillan, Janice E Page, David M Sable, Noel J Spiegel

AMERICAN EAGLE PAPER MILLS
See TEAM TEN LLC

D-U-N-S 13-143-4057
AMERICAN EAGLE PROTECTIVE SERVICES CORP
AEPS
7700 Chevy Chase Dr, Austin, TX 78752-1558
Tel (512) 380-9700 *Founded/Ownrshp* 2002
Sales 86.0MM *EMP* 600
Accts Aronson Llc Rockville Maryla
SIC 8744 Facilities support services
Owner: Bredgitt Walker
**Pr:* Dan Walker
**COO:* Jeff Norman
**CFO:* David Tucker
Ofcr: Zaid Kadri

D-U-N-S 08-913-3052 IMP
AMERICAN EAGLE WHEEL CORP
5780 Soestern Ct, Chino, CA 91710-7020
Tel (909) 590-8828 *Founded/Ownrshp* 1977
Sales 230.2MM[E] *EMP* 650
SIC 5013 Wheels, motor vehicle
Pr: Ray Elbertse
**VP:* Maria Furcolon

D-U-N-S 05-470-0216
AMERICAN ECONOMY INSURANCE CO INC
(*Suby of* SAFECO INSURANCE CO OF AMERICA) ★
500 N Meridian St, Indianapolis, IN 46204-1272
Tel (317) 423-9920 *Founded/Ownrshp* 1959, 1997
Sales NA *EMP* 1,000
SIC 6331 Fire, marine & casualty insurance
Ch Bd: Robert A Anker
Ch: Roger Eigsti
Treas: Stephen Bauer
Ofcr: Michael Peters
Assoc VP: James Siegfries
Sr VP: Wayne Browne
Sr VP: Donald Chapman
Sr VP: J Kreitzer
Sr VP: Dale Lauer
Sr VP: Rod Pierson
Sr VP: Robert Taylor
VP: F E Barthel
VP: Judy Blanton
**VP:* Wayne Smith
VP: Lynda D Van Kirk

D-U-N-S 96-435-5093
AMERICAN EDUCATIONAL SERVICES CORP
(*Suby of* FEDLOAN SERVICING) ★
1200 N 7th St, Harrisburg, PA 17102-1419
Tel (717) 720-2700 *Founded/Ownrshp* 1983
Sales NA *EMP* 2,300
SIC 6111 Student Loan Marketing Association
Ex VP: Brian Lecher
Sr VP: Edward Cunningham
VP: Mary Miller

D-U-N-S 00-697-9868 IMP
▲ **AMERICAN ELECTRIC POWER CO INC**
AEP
1 Riverside Plz Fl 1, Columbus, OH 43215-2373
Tel (614) 716-1000 *Founded/Ownrshp* 1906
Sales 16.4MMM *EMP* 17,405
Accts Deloitte & Touche Llp Columbu
Tkr Sym AEP *Exch* NYS
SIC 4911 Electric services; Distribution, electric power; Generation, electric power; Transmission, electric power
Ch Bd: Nicholas K Akins
COO: Robert P Powers
CFO: Brian X Tierney
Treas: Lonni L Dieck
Ofcr: Lana L Hillebrand
Ex VP: Lisa M Barton
Ex VP: David M Feinberg
Ex VP: Mark C McCullough
Sr VP: Charles E Zebula
VP: Jeffrey Cross
VP: Stephen Haynes
VP: Raja Sundararajan
Exec: Jason Agee
Exec: Abbie Fellrath

D-U-N-S 00-697-9876 IMP
■ **AMERICAN ELECTRIC POWER SERVICE CORP** (NY)
AEP
(*Suby of* AEP) ★
1 Riverside Plz Fl 1, Columbus, OH 43215-2373
Tel (614) 716-1000 *Founded/Ownrshp* 1937
Sales 356.7MM[E] *EMP* 2,152
SIC 4911 8711 8713 8721 Electric services; Engineering services; Surveying services; Accounting services, except auditing; Auditing services; Billing & bookkeeping service
Ch Bd: Nicholas K Akins
Pr: Johnathan Powers
CFO: Holly Koeppel
Treas: Armando A Pena
Ex VP: Donald M Clements Jr
**Ex VP:* Susan Tomasky
Sr VP: J Craig Baker
Sr VP: John B Keane
VP: Mark Gray
VP: Joseph Hartsoe
VP: Anthony P Kavanagh
VP: Michael F Moore
VP: William L Scott
VP: Scott Slisher
VP: Albert M Smoak
VP: Van Der Walde

D-U-N-S 11-838-5145 IMP
AMERICAN ELECTRIC SUPPLY INC
361 S Maple St, Corona, CA 92880-6907
Tel (951) 734-7910 *Founded/Ownrshp* 1984
Sales 112.1MM[E] *EMP* 99[E]
SIC 5063 Electrical fittings & construction materials; Wire & cable; Lighting fixtures
CEO: Michael Pratt
**Treas:* Jerry Empson
IT Man: Tim Pratt
Opers Mgr: Robert Fonseca
Mktg Mgr: Shannon Winans
Sales Asso: Bill Houston
Sales Asso: Bill McDonald
Sales Asso: Pedro Moya
Sales Asso: Mica Razo
Sales Asso: Jim Vick

D-U-N-S 94-772-2351
AMERICAN ENDOWMENT FOUNDATION
1521 Georgetown Rd # 104, Hudson, OH 44236-4066
Tel (330) 655-7552 *Founded/Ownrshp* 1993
Sales 133.6MM *EMP* 5
SIC 8699 8733 Charitable organization; Noncommercial research organizations
Pr: Philip T Tobin
Treas: Gail Tobin
Ex VP: John Farren
Ex VP: John Tobin
VP: Shannon Baker
VP: Peter McCrea
VP: Mike Ryzak
**VP:* Thomas J Tobin
Sls Mgr: Lori Page

D-U-N-S 07-911-6160
AMERICAN ENERGY PARTNERS LP
301 Nw 63rd St Ste 600, Oklahoma City, OK 73116-7909
Tel (405) 418-8000 *Founded/Ownrshp* 2013
Sales 385.6MM[E] *EMP* 650[E]
SIC 1311 Natural gas production
CEO: David C Shiels
COO: Jeff Fisher
Ofcr: Traci D Cook
Sr VP: Curt Launer
Sr VP: Jeff Mobley
Snr Ntwrk: Tobin Paris

D-U-N-S 07-482-2933
AMERICAN ENTERPRISE INSTITUTE FOR PUBLIC POLICY RESEARCH
A E I
1150 17th St Nw Ste 1100, Washington, DC 20036-4603
Tel (202) 862-5800 *Founded/Ownrshp* 1943
Sales 84.6MM *EMP* 130
Accts Uhy Advisors Midatlantic Md In
SIC 8733 8732 Educational research agency; Commercial nonphysical research
Pr: Arthur C Brooks
Mng Pt: Hans Humes
V Ch: David Weinstein
**Pr:* Christopher Demuth
**CFO:* Margaret C Barth
CFO: Erin Covington
CFO: Maggie Gochal
**Chf Mktg O:* Jason Bertsch
**Ex VP:* David Gerson
VP: Danielle Pletka
Exec: Shani Rosenstock
Exec: Phillip Stucky

D-U-N-S 83-105-2709
■ **AMERICAN ENTERPRISE INVESTMENT SERVICES INC**
(*Suby of* AMERIPRISE FINANCIAL INC) ★
70400 Axp Financial Ctr, Minneapolis, MN 55474-0001
Tel (612) 671-3131 *Founded/Ownrshp* 1990
Sales 110.1MM *EMP* 199
Accts Ernst & Young Llp Minneapolis
SIC 8742 Financial consultant
Pr: Brent Wissbrod

D-U-N-S 79-712-3689
AMERICAN ENTERPRISE MUTUAL HOLDING CO
601 6th Ave, Des Moines, IA 50309-1605
Tel (515) 245-2000 *Founded/Ownrshp* 1999
Sales NA *EMP* 1,300
Accts Ernst & Young Llp Des Moines
SIC 6321 6411 Accident insurance carriers; Health insurance carriers; Insurance agents, brokers & service
CFO: Brian Felner

D-U-N-S 05-818-4227 IMP/EXP
■ **AMERICAN EQUIPMENT CO INC** (SC)
AMECO
(*Suby of* FLUOR CORP) ★
2106 Anderson Rd, Greenville, SC 29611-6096
Tel (864) 295-7800 *Founded/Ownrshp* 1971, 1984
Sales 127.0MM[E] *EMP* 1,230
SIC 7699 7359 5082 7353

D-U-N-S 95-745-2170
▲ **AMERICAN EQUITY INVESTMENT LIFE HOLDING CO**
6000 Westown Pkwy, West Des Moines, IA 50266-7711
Tel (515) 221-0002 *Founded/Ownrshp* 1995
Sales NA *EMP* 490[E]
Tkr Sym AEL *Exch* NYS
SIC 6311 Life insurance; Life insurance carriers
Pr: John M Matovina
**Ch Bd:* David J Noble
CFO: Wendy Carlson
CFO: Ted M Johnson
Ex VP: Jeffrey D Lorenzen
Ex VP: Renee D Montz
VP: Carole Hunt
VP: Scott A Samuelson
VP: Denny Southern
Counsel: Tara C Banks
Board of Directors: A J Strickland III, Joyce A Chapman, Alexander M Clark, James M Gerlach, Robert L Howe, William R Kunkel, Alan D Matula, David S Mulcahy, Gerard D Neugent, J Richardson

D-U-N-S 82-678-6365
■ **AMERICAN EQUITY INVESTMENT LIFE INSURANCE CO**
(*Suby of* AMERICAN EQUITY INVESTMENT LIFE HOLDING CO) ★
5000 Westown Pkwy Ste 440, West Des Moines, IA 50266-5921
Tel (515) 221-0002 *Founded/Ownrshp* 1995
Sales NA *EMP* 238[E]
SIC 6311 Life insurance
Pr: Lloyd R Hill
Pr: Martin Grosskopf
Dir IT: Dean Merrel
IT Man: Dean Merrel

D-U-N-S 87-851-0564
AMERICAN ESOTERIC LABORATORIES
AMERICAN PATHOLOGY
(*Suby of* SONIC HEALTHCARE USA INC) ★
2763 Summer Oaks Dr, Bartlett, TN 38134-2850
Tel (901) 937-1910 *Founded/Ownrshp* 2008
Sales 75.8MM[E] *EMP* 5,004[E]
SIC 8734 Testing laboratories
Prin: Bill Brooks

D-U-N-S 11-298-5676
AMERICAN EUROPEAN GROUP INC
605 3rd Ave Fl 9, New York, NY 10158-0180
Tel (212) 355-3310 *Founded/Ownrshp* 1986
Sales NA *EMP* 475
SIC 6331 Fire, marine & casualty insurance & carriers; Automobile insurance
Ch Bd: Nachum Stein
**Treas:* Hirsh Wolf
Chf Inves: Steve Klein
VP: Vivalde Couto

AMERICAN EX PROPERTY CSLTY
See AMERIPRISE BANK FSB

D-U-N-S 10-884-0075
AMERICAN EXPEDITING CO
801 Primos Ave, Folcroft, PA 19032-2105
Tel (484) 540-8180 *Founded/Ownrshp* 1983
Sales 90.2MM[E] *EMP* 300
SIC 4215 4513 Package delivery, vehicular; Package delivery, private air
Pr: Victor Finnegan
IT Man: Steve Schramm
Trfc Dir: Norman Johnson
Trfc Dir: Kristofer Kris
Trfc Dir: Michael A Mazzi
Trfc Dir: Maureen Reenock
Trfc Dir: Tony Sfaro
Opers Mgr: Jennifer Bunting
Opers Mgr: Tony Celender
Opers Mgr: Joe Deblase
Opers Mgr: Nancy Schreck

D-U-N-S 80-045-1325
■ **AMERICAN EXPRESS BANK FSB**
(*Suby of* AMERICAN EXPRESS TRAVEL RELATED SERVICES CO INC) ★
4315 S 2700 W, Salt Lake City, UT 84184-0001
Tel (801) 945-5000 *Founded/Ownrshp* 2005
Sales NA *EMP* 100
SIC 6029 Commercial banks
Pr: Douglas Short
Chf Cred: Todd Boren
VP: Sravanthi Agrawal
VP: Mark Gomez
VP: Jorge Guevara
VP: Samantha Hammock
VP: John McHugh
VP: Linda Worrell
Dir Risk M: Kelly Ball
Genl Mgr: Sue Boevers

AMERICAN EXPRESS BANK LTD.
See STANDARD CHARTERED INTERNATIONAL (USA) LTD

D-U-N-S 00-697-9900 IMP
▲ **AMERICAN EXPRESS CO**
200 Vesey St, New York, NY 10285-0002
Tel (212) 640-2000 *Founded/Ownrshp* 1850
Sales NA *EMP* 54,000[E]
Tkr Sym AXP *Exch* NYS
SIC 6141 7389 6282 6099 6311 6211 Personal credit institutions; Credit card service; Investment counselors; Travelers' checks issuance; Life insurance; Mutual funds, selling by independent salesperson
Ch Bd: Kenneth I Chenault
Dir Recs: Frank Nigro
V Ch: Stephen J Squeri
Pr: Douglas E Buckminster
Pr: William H Glenn
Pr: Neal Sample
Pr: Anre Williams
CFO: Jeffrey C Campbell
Treas: June Miller
Treas: Edward Monton
Treas: Kim Rosenberg
Chf Inves: William Truscott
Ofcr: L Kevin Cox
Ofcr: Ashwini Gupta
Ex VP: Kim Goodman
Ex VP: Marc D Gordon
Ex VP: John D Hayes
Ex VP: Valerie Soranno Keating
Ex VP: Katrina Lane
Ex VP: Massimo Quarra
Ex VP: Laureen E Seeger
Board of Directors: Ronald A Williams, Charlene Barshefsky, Ursula M Burns, Peter Chernin, Anne Lauvergeon, Theodore J Leonsis, Richard C Levin, Samuel J Palmisano, Daniel M Vasella, Robert D Walter

D-U-N-S 04-766-0337
■ **AMERICAN EXPRESS CREDIT CORP**
(*Suby of* AMERICAN EXPRESS TRAVEL RELATED SERVICES CO INC) ★
200 Vesey St, New York, NY 10285-0002
Tel (866) 572-4944 *Founded/Ownrshp* 1983
Sales NA *EMP* 8[E]
Accts Pricewaterhousecoopers Llp Ne
SIC 6153 Purchasers of accounts receivable & commercial paper; Credit card services, central agency collection
CEO: David L Yowan
**CFO:* Anderson Y Lee
Sr VP: Kimberly R Scardino

AMERICAN EXPRESS TRAVEL
See FIRST SIERRA FINANCIAL INC

D-U-N-S 07-784-8968
■ **AMERICAN EXPRESS TRAVEL RELATED SERVICES CO INC**
(*Suby of* AMERICAN EXPRESS CO) ★
200 Vesey St, New York, NY 10285-0002
Tel (212) 640-2000 *Founded/Ownrshp* 1982
Sales 12.5MMM[E] *EMP* 54,000[E]
SIC 4724 Travel agencies
Ch Bd: Kenneth I Chenault
**Pr:* Edward P Gilligan
**VP:* David L Yowan
CIO: Stephen S Squeri

AMERICAN FAMILY INSURANCE
See AMERICAN FAMILY MUTUAL INSURANCE CO INC

D-U-N-S 04-209-9168
■ **AMERICAN FAMILY LIFE ASSURANCE CO OF COLUMBUS** (GA)
AFLAC
(*Suby of* AFLAC INC) ★
1932 Wynnton Rd, Columbus, GA 31999-0001
Tel (706) 323-3431 *Founded/Ownrshp* 1955, 1973
Sales NA *EMP* 7,919
SIC 6311 Life insurance
Ch Bd: Daniel P Amos
**Pr:* Kriss Cloninger III
VP: Mike Bartow
Sales Exec: Mike Brown
Sales Exec: Traci Hutchinson
Counsel: Catherine Budzynski
Snr Mgr: Wassel Lewis
Board of Directors: N Phillip Foster, Kenneth S Janke Sr, Joey M Loudermilk, Henry Caplan Schwob, James Kyle Spencer

D-U-N-S 61-848-8332
■ **AMERICAN FAMILY LIFE ASSURANCE CO OF NY (INC)**
AFLAC
(*Suby of* AFLAC) ★
22 Corporate Woods Blvd, Albany, NY 12211-2374
Tel (518) 438-0764 *Founded/Ownrshp* 1986
Sales NA *EMP* 5
SIC 6321 Accident & health insurance
Pr: Daniel P Amos
COO: Stephen Purdom
Sr VP: David Hewitt
VP Mktg: Michael Chille

D-U-N-S 07-313-6269
AMERICAN FAMILY LIFE INSURANCE CO
(*Suby of* AMFAM INC) ★
6000 American Pkwy, Madison, WI 53783-0001
Tel (608) 249-2111 *Founded/Ownrshp* 1982
Sales NA *EMP* 296[E]
SIC 6411 Insurance agents, brokers & service
Ch Bd: Harvey Pierce
Pr: Dave Anderson
Treas: Brent Johnson
Ex VP: Daniel De Salvo
Ex VP: James Eldridge
Ex VP: Darnell Moore
VP: Lynn Alme
VP: William F Bahl
VP: Byrne Chapman
VP: Vicki Chuala
VP: Richard A Fetherston
VP: Bernard McCartan
VP: Alan Meyer
VP: Michelle Reserving
VP: Peter Sotos
VP: Terese A Taarud

D-U-N-S 00-794-6262
AMERICAN FAMILY MUTUAL INSURANCE CO INC
AMERICAN FAMILY INSURANCE
6000 American Pkwy, Madison, WI 53783-0001
Tel (608) 249-2111 *Founded/Ownrshp* 1927
Sales NA *EMP* 8,627
SIC 6331 6311 Fire, marine & casualty insurance: mutual; Mutual association life insurance
CEO: David R Anderson
COO: Dan Schultz
CFO: Daniel J Kelly
CFO: Jack Slazwedel
Treas: William Smith
Chf Inves: Peter C Gunder
Ofcr: David C Holman
Ex VP: James Eldridge
Ex VP: Darnell Moore
Ex VP: Daniel D Salvo
VP: Carl Ivey
Exec: Tom Kosmicki
Exec: Jeffrey Matthias
Exec: Mark Villano
Dir Risk M: Gregory Gisi
Dir Bus: Gary Stamenss
Board of Directors: Dr Jerry Sue Thornton, Craig C Culver, Dr John D Wiley, Leslie A Howard, Thomas J Zimbrick, Ted D Kellner, Thomas J Mohs, Walter M Oliver, Barbara A Parish, Harvey R Pierce, Eliot G Protsch, Richard R Renk

D-U-N-S 15-211-3002
AMERICAN FARM BUREAU INSURANCE SERVICES INC
AFBIS
1501 E Wdfeld Rd Ste 300w, Schaumburg, IL 60173
Tel (847) 969-2900 *Founded/Ownrshp* 1995
Sales NA *EMP* 74
SIC 6411 Insurance agents, brokers & service
VP: Roger Swartz

D-U-N-S 03-541-2915
AMERICAN FARMERS & RANCHERS MUTUAL INSURANCE CO
4400 Will Rogers Pkwy, Oklahoma City, OK 73108-1837
Tel (405) 218-5400 *Founded/Ownrshp* 1982
Sales NA *EMP* 140[E]
SIC 6331 Property damage insurance
Pr: Terry Detrick
**COO:* Royce Meek
**CFO:* Tara Brooks
Exec: Mary Foreman
Board of Directors: Sam Cook, Bob Nick, Bill Perrin, Ray Perryman, George Stone, Dick Stults

D-U-N-S 18-764-6294
AMERICAN FAST FREIGHT INC
AMERICAN RELOCATION SERVICES
(*Suby of* AFF INC) ★
7400 45th Street Ct E, Fife, WA 98424-3775
Tel (253) 926-5000 *Founded/Ownrshp* 2013
Sales 119.3MM[E] *EMP* 350
SIC 4731 4213 7389 4214 Freight consolidation; Trucking, except local; Relocation service; Local trucking with storage
Pr: Kevin Kelly
**CFO:* Chris Paule
**Treas:* Harry Nayyar
**Ex VP:* Tim Jacobson
**VP:* Craig Forbes
VP: Mike Porter
Dir Risk M: Don Lacey
Genl Mgr: Scott Alstrom
**CTO:* Jeff Lepage
Software D: Carl Haning
Secur Mgr: Ken Staten

D-U-N-S 05-795-1634
AMERICAN FEDERATION OF LABOR & CONGRESS OF INDUSTRIAL ORGANZATION
AFL-CIO
815 16th St Nw, Washington, DC 20006-4101
Tel (202) 637-5000 *Founded/Ownrshp* 1955
Sales 158.9MM *EMP* 380
Accts Calibre Cpa Group Pllc Bethes
SIC 8631 Labor unions & similar labor organizations
Pr: John J Sweeney
**Sec:* Richard L Trumka
**Ex VP:* Arlene Holt-Baker
Genl Mgr: Armando Olivas
Info Man: Steve Piekarec
Counsel: Donna Euben

D-U-N-S 07-781-3061
AMERICAN FEDERATION OF STATE COUNTY & MUNICIPAL EMPLOYEES
AFSCME
1625 L St Nw, Washington, DC 20036-5665
Tel (202) 429-1000 *Founded/Ownrshp* 1932
Sales 181.8MM *EMP* 450
SIC 8631 Trade union
Pr: Gerald W McEntee
**Treas:* William Lucy
Sr VP: Dick Shaner
VP: George Boncoraglio
VP: Albert Garrett
VP: Anette Johnson
Ex Dir: Anthony Casso
Ex Dir: Carl Goldman
Ex Dir: Cheryl Parisi
Sales Exec: Liz Ustaris
Sls Mgr: Tina Saxon

D-U-N-S 15-217-2029 IMP
AMERICAN FIBER & FINISHING INC
AF&F
225 N Depot St, Albemarle, NC 28001-3914
Tel (704) 983-6102 *Founded/Ownrshp* 1986
Sales 135.5MM[E] *EMP* 895
SIC 2211 3842 2844 2392 Broadwoven fabric mills, cotton; Basket weave fabrics, cotton; Surgical appliances & supplies; Toilet preparations; Household furnishings
Ch Bd: J J Kiser
**Pr:* Paul Robichaud
**CFO:* Marcus Wiebel
**VP:* Carle Shotwell
Dir IT: Christine Geise
S&M/VP: Todd Carlton

AMERICAN FIDELITY ASSURANCE
See CAMERON ENTERPRISES A LIMITED PARTNERSHIP

D-U-N-S 05-770-9339
AMERICAN FIDELITY ASSURANCE CO
(*Suby of* AMERICAN FIDELITY CORP) ★
9000 Cameron Pkwy, Oklahoma City, OK 73114-3702
Tel (405) 523-2000 *Founded/Ownrshp* 1960
Sales NA *EMP* 1,250
SIC 6321 6311 Accident insurance carriers; Health insurance carriers; Life insurance carriers
Ch: William M Cameron
**Pr:* John W Rex
Pr: David Robinson
CFO: Robert Brearton
CFO: Shirley Williams
Treas: David R Carpenter
Ofcr: Lisa Blaich
Ofcr: Linda Devine
Ofcr: Janice Farmer
Ofcr: Linda Martin
Ofcr: Rhonda Morse
Ex VP: Alfred L Litchenburg
Ex VP: Jeanette M Rice
Sr VP: Kenneth D Klehm
VP: Dave Abeln
VP: Larry Alkire
VP: Diana Bittle
VP: Timothy Bolden
VP: Shirley Brodersen
VP: Shelley Deck
VP: Joann Dickey

D-U-N-S 02-191-2639
AMERICAN FIDELITY CORP (NV)
(*Suby of* AMERICAN FIDELITY ASSURANCE) ★
2000 Classen Ctr Blvd, Oklahoma City, OK 73106
Tel (405) 523-2000 *Founded/Ownrshp* 1954
Sales NA *EMP* 1,400
SIC 6321 6311 Health insurance carriers; Life insurance carriers
Ch Bd: William M Cameron
CFO: Ken Klehm
Treas: David R Carpenter
Ex VP: John W Rex
VP: Brian Mauck
VP: Janie McCurdy
VP: Allison Regier
VP: Clinton M Schwab
VP: Brad Traynor
VP: Bob Willingham
VP: Robert Yetter

D-U-N-S 80-533-7920
AMERICAN FIDELITY GENERAL AGENCY INC
(*Suby of* AMERICAN FIDELITY ASSURANCE CO) ★
9000 Cameron Pkwy, Oklahoma City, OK 73114-3702
Tel (405) 523-2000 *Founded/Ownrshp* 1993
Sales NA *EMP* 1[E]
SIC 6321 6311 Accident & health insurance; Life insurance
CEO: Bill Cameron

D-U-N-S 79-993-9913
▲ **AMERICAN FINANCIAL GROUP INC**
301 E 4th St, Cincinnati, OH 45202-4245
Tel (513) 579-2121 *Founded/Ownrshp* 1872
Sales NA *EMP* 7,215[E]
Tkr Sym AFG *Exch* NYS
SIC 6331 6311 6321 Fire, marine & casualty insurance; Life insurance; Life insurance carriers; Accident & health insurance; Accident associations, mutual
CEO: Carl H Lindner III
Pr: S Craig Lindner
CFO: Joseph E Consolino
Ofcr: Michelle A Gillis
Ex VP: Alicia Yoo
Sr VP: Vito C Peraino
VP: Howard Baird
VP: Chester Eng
VP: Karl Grafe
VP: Ross Norstrom
IT Man: Nick Stergiopulos

D-U-N-S 02-075-7706
AMERICAN FINANCIAL NETWORK INC
10 Pointe Dr Ste 330, Brea, CA 92821-7620
Tel (909) 606-3905 *Founded/Ownrshp* 2001
Sales NA *EMP* 900
Accts Mcbride Edwards Llp Folsom
SIC 6141 Personal credit institutions
CEO: John B Sherman
**Pr:* John R Sherman

D-U-N-S 09-109-7886
AMERICAN FINANCIAL NETWORK INC
GATEWAY HOME REALTY
3110 Chino Ave Ste 290, Chino, CA 91710
Tel (909) 606-3905 *Founded/Ownrshp* 2001
Sales NA *EMP* 1,053
SIC 6162 Mortgage bankers & correspondents
Pr: John B Sherman
**VP:* John R Sherman

D-U-N-S 02-025-7023
AMERICAN FINANCIAL RESOURCES INC
E LEND
9 Sylvan Way Ste 310, Parsippany, NJ 07054-3802
Tel (973) 983-5626 *Founded/Ownrshp* 1997, 1998
Sales NA *EMP* 450
SIC 6163 Mortgage brokers arranging for loans, using money of others
CEO: Richard Dubnoff
**Pr:* Timothy Yanoti
**COO:* Laura Brandao
**CFO:* Larry Jackson
Ofcr: Bryan Mazzarisi
Ofcr: Kyle Palmer
VP: Joe Burns
Ex Dir: Kevin Darnell
**CIO:* William Packer
Natl Sales: Russell Rothstein
Sls Mgr: Andrew Allen

AMERICAN FISH AND SEAFOOD
See PROSPECT ENTERPRISES INC

D-U-N-S 93-830-7816
AMERICAN FLORIST SUPPLY INC
BAY STATE FARM DIRECT FLOWERS
1 Progress Way, Wilmington, MA 01887-4611
Tel (978) 658-2400 *Founded/Ownrshp* 2000
Sales NA *EMP* 240
SIC 6411 Insurance agents, brokers & service
Pr: John T Dickinson
Sales Exec: Bobby Dabrieo
Sls Mgr: Tonia Egan
Board of Directors: Steven Dabrio

AMERICAN FOOD
See ROLAND FOODS LLC

D-U-N-S 62-079-5591
AMERICAN FOOD & VENDING CORP
124 Metropolitan Park Dr, Liverpool, NY 13088-5593
Tel (315) 457-9950 *Founded/Ownrshp* 1990
Sales 180.8MM[E] *EMP* 1,000
SIC 5962 5812 Merchandising machine operators; Lunchrooms & cafeterias
CEO: Martin Wells
Exec: Joe Bay
**Prin:* Steven Wells
Genl Mgr: David Alexander
Genl Mgr: Michelle Bruckner
CTO: Jim Burkett
Dir IT: Jamie Butts
Genl Couns: Traci Geisler
Board of Directors: Joshua Wells

AMERICAN FOOD SERVICE
See FRESHPOINT DALLAS INC

D-U-N-S 00-585-9558 IMP
AMERICAN FOODS GROUP LLC
(*Suby of* LONG PRAIRIE PACKING) ★
500 S Washington St, Green Bay, WI 54301-4219
Tel (320) 759-5900 *Founded/Ownrshp* 1978, 2005
Sales 522.5MM[E] *EMP* 2,000
SIC 2011 Meat packing plants
Sls Mgr: Dale Prechel

D-U-N-S 19-451-2331
AMERICAN FOREIGN SERVICE PROTECTIVE ASSOCIATION
AFSPA
1620 L St Nw Ste 800, Washington, DC 20036-2902
Tel (202) 833-4910 *Founded/Ownrshp* 1929
Sales 250.4MM *EMP* 53
SIC 8621 Professional membership organizations
CEO: Paula Jakub
**COO:* Kyle Longton

AMERICAN FRIENDS OF BAR ILAN U
See BAR-ILAN UNIVERSITY IN ISRAEL

D-U-N-S 00-962-8298 IMP/EXP
■ AMERICAN FRUITS AND FLAVORS LLC
JUICE DIVISION
(Suby of MONSTER BEVERAGE CORP) ★
10725 Sutter Ave, Pacoima, CA 91331-2553
Tel (818) 899-9574 Founded/Ownrshp 1975
Sales 200.0MM EMP 190
SIC 2087 Concentrates, drink; Powders, drink; Syrups, drink
Pr: William Haddad
Ex VP: Jesus Ramerez
VP: Bill Haddad
VP Mktg: Richard Linn

D-U-N-S 01-113-4264
AMERICAN FUJI SEAL INC
(Suby of FUJI SEAL INTERNATIONAL,INC.)
1051 Bloomfield Rd, Bardstown, KY 40004-9794
Tel (502) 348-9211 Founded/Ownrshp 1975
Sales 84.3MM[E] EMP 350[E]
SIC 8748 2671 Business consulting; Packaging paper & plastics film, coated & laminated
Pr: Masayuki Shirokawa
Ofcr: John Ballard
*VP: Marty Winchell

D-U-N-S 02-474-4943 IMP/EXP
AMERICAN FURNITURE MANUFACTURING INC (MS)
604 Pontotoc County Indu, Ecru, MS 38841-8421
Tel (662) 489-2633 Founded/Ownrshp 1997, 2015
Sales 190.8MM[E] EMP 800
SIC 2519 Furniture, household: glass, fiberglass & plastic
CEO: Michael Thomas
*Pr: Randy Spak
*Treas: Robert Sussman
Exec: Dale Gray

D-U-N-S 07-710-5153
AMERICAN FURNITURE RENTALS INC
AFR FURNITURE RENTAL
720 Hylton Rd, Pennsauken, NJ 08110-1350
Tel (856) 406-1200 Founded/Ownrshp 1989
Sales 98.6MM EMP 475
SIC 7359 5712 Furniture rental; Furniture stores
CEO: Neil Scholnick
*Pr: Ray Fiorica
CFO: David Foster
*Co-CEO: Jerome Hellmann
Genl Mgr: Fran Fung
Genl Mgr: Jay Gates
Genl Mgr: Steve Wohl
MIS Dir: Dave Soster
VP Opers: Tom Molony
Opers Mgr: Robert Barnes
Opers Mgr: Patrick Cotroneo

D-U-N-S 07-645-9668 IMP
AMERICAN FURNITURE WAREHOUSE CO INC
8820 American Way, Englewood, CO 80112-7056
Tel (303) 799-9044 Founded/Ownrshp 1966
Sales 530.3MM EMP 1,900
Accts Bauerle And Company Pc Den
SIC 5712 Furniture stores
Pr: Jacob Jabs
*Sec: Lori Tielke
Comm Dir: Charlie Shaulis
Genl Mgr: Kevin Michalek
Store Mgr: Dan George
Store Mgr: Garrett Mitchell
IT Man: Chris Gibson
Mktg Mgr: Sarah Klobnak
Sls Mgr: Rich Burlingame
Sls Mgr: Anna Campbell
Sales Asso: Gordon Boucher
Board of Directors: Lori Tielke

D-U-N-S 06-438-1262
AMERICAN FUTURE SYSTEMS INC (PA)
PROGRESSIVE BUS PUBLICATIONS
370 Technology Dr, Malvern, PA 19355-1315
Tel (610) 695-8600 Founded/Ownrshp 1973, 1974
Sales 144.8MM[E] EMP 600
SIC 2741 8742 Newsletter publishing; Management consulting services
Pr: Edward M Satell
*COO: Tom Schubert
Ofcr: Derrick McNeal
*VP: James Brown
Exec: Bryan Kish
Brnch Mgr: William Townsend
Software D: Pavly Mikhael
Mktg Dir: Sharon McHugh
Mktg Dir: Edward Moore
Mktg Mgr: Thomas Busillo

D-U-N-S 04-687-1849 IMP
AMERICAN FUTURE TECHNOLOGY CORP
IBUYPOWER
529 Baldwin Park Blvd, City of Industry, CA 91746-1419
Tel (888) 462-3899 Founded/Ownrshp 1997
Sales 98.3MM[E] EMP 120
SIC 5045 Computers, peripherals & software
CEO: Alex Hou
*VP: Darren Su

D-U-N-S 07-562-3876
■ AMERICAN GENERAL ASSURANCE CO
(Suby of AIG LIFE HOLDINGS INC) ★
1000 E Wdfield Rd Ste 300, Schaumburg, IL 60173
Tel (847) 517-6000 Founded/Ownrshp 1968
Sales NA EMP 600
SIC 6311 Life insurance
Pr: Jim Weakley
*V Ch: Donald Britton
*Pr: Jim Weakly
*CFO: Richard Stanko
*Ch: Rodney Martin
*Ex VP: David Fravel
*Ex VP: David Herzog
*Ex VP: Thomas Zurek
*Sr VP: David Armstrong
*Sr VP: Henry Carpenter
*Sr VP: Larry Compton
*Sr VP: Felix Curcuru
*Sr VP: Alfred Thome
VP: Elizabeth Cloud
VP: Randy Marash
VP: Deanna D Osmonson
VP: Brian Roberson
VP: Sherri Stanton

D-U-N-S 00-792-2677
■ AMERICAN GENERAL LIFE & ACCIDENT INSURANCE CO (TN)
AGLA
(Suby of AGC LIFE INSURANCE CO) ★
2000 American General Way, Brentwood, TN 37027-4525
Tel (800) 265-5054 Founded/Ownrshp 1900, 2001
Sales NA EMP 9,000
SIC 6311 Life insurance
CEO: James A Mallon
Pr: Bob Ley
Sr Cor Off: Richard Hollar
Ex VP: David Entrekin
Sr VP: Rick Borchert
Sr VP: Craig Clark
Sr VP: Scott German
Sr VP: Gregory Hayes
Sr VP: Kenneth Juneau
Sr VP: Edmund McClure
Sr VP: Donald J Tasser
Sr VP: Steven Zimmerman
VP: Thomas Bryant
VP: Jack Everdale
VP: Charles Gibson
VP: Zimmer Mayra
VP: John Rafferty
VP: Carolyn Rowe
Exec: Gregory Carpenter
Exec: Tammy Deason
Exec: John Lagrasse
Board of Directors: Lawrence Ness

D-U-N-S 00-794-7179
■ AMERICAN GENERAL LIFE BROKERAGE GROUP
(Suby of AIG LIFE HOLDINGS INC) ★
1200 N Mayfair Rd Ste 300, Milwaukee, WI 53226-3288
Tel (414) 443-5800 Founded/Ownrshp 1910
Sales NA EMP 289
SIC 6311 6411 Life insurance carriers; Insurance agents, brokers & service
Pr: Richard A Hollar
VP: Christopher Briskie
VP: Kenneth James Griesemer
VP: David Nathan Howe
VP: Dale Henry Nauta
VP: Fredric Robert Yopps
VP: Christopher Young
Sls&Mrk Ex: Durr Sexton
Mktg Dir: Amy Dethloff
Board of Directors: Gordon Crosby Jr, Richard G Hohn, Christopher S Ruisi, William A Simpson

D-U-N-S 00-693-6041
■ AMERICAN GENERAL LIFE INSURANCE
(Suby of AIG) ★
1 Franklin Sq, Springfield, IL 62703
Tel (217) 528-2011 Founded/Ownrshp 1884
Sales NA EMP 700
SIC 6411 6321 6211 Insurance agents, brokers & service; Health insurance carriers; Brokers, security
V Ch: Gary D Reick
VP: Dale Sachtleben
VP: Richard Scott
VP: Robert Spencer

D-U-N-S 04-445-4213
■ AMERICAN GENERAL LIFE INSURANCE CO (DE)
(Suby of AGC LIFE INSURANCE CO) ★
2727 Allen Pkwy Ste A, Houston, TX 77019-2116
Tel (713) 522-1111 Founded/Ownrshp 1960, 2001
Sales NA EMP 3,500
SIC 6311 Life insurance
Pr: Ronald H Ridlehuber
Pr: Curtis W Olson
*CFO: Robert Frank Herbert Jr
CFO: David L Herzog
CFO: Zafar Rashid
Treas: Tara Rock
Ex VP: Kyle Jennings
Ex VP: Don Ward
*Sr VP: David A Fravel
*Sr VP: John V Lagrasse
VP: Ed Bacon
VP: Wayne Barnard
VP: Rebecca Campbell
VP: Craig Cheyne
VP: James Cortiglia
VP: Lisa Gerhart
VP: Edmund McClure
VP: Michael McFadden
VP: John Rafferty
*VP: Richard W Scott
Assoc Dir: Kevin Brown

D-U-N-S 04-908-2076
■ AMERICAN GENERAL LIFE INSURANCE CO
(Suby of AIG LIFE HOLDINGS INC) ★
10700 Northwest Fwy # 300, Houston, TX 77092-7323
Tel (713) 522-1111 Founded/Ownrshp 1925
Sales NA EMP 1,119
SIC 6311 Life insurance carriers
Pr: Robert M Devlin
V Ch: Frederick W Geissinger
V Ch: Rodney Martin
Pr: Richard McFarland
CFO: Terry Festervand
CFO: Robert Hebert
*CFO: Zafar Rashid
CFO: Nicholas Rassmussen
CFO: Austin Young
Ofcr: Gary D Reddick
Sr VP: Neal Goodrum
Sr VP: Susan A Jacobs
Sr VP: Robert Y Mrlik
VP: Robert Cicchi
VP: Leo Grace
VP: John Pluhowski
VP: Bill Rapp
Assoc Dir: Jason Demouy
Assoc Dir: John Sherman
Assoc Dir: Donna Talbot
Comm Man: Gregory Freeman

D-U-N-S 13-445-7365
■ AMERICAN GENERAL LIFE INSURANCE CO OF DELAWARE
AIG
(Suby of AMERICAN GENERAL LIFE INSURANCE CO) ★
2727 Allen Pkwy Ste A, Houston, TX 77019-2116
Tel (713) 522-1111 Founded/Ownrshp 2001
Sales NA EMP 360
SIC 6411 Insurance agents, brokers & service
Pr: Gerry Wyndorf
Pr: Chris Ayers
*CFO: John Oehmke
*Treas: Nicholas A O'Kulich
VP: John Deprich
VP: Thomas Heller
Assoc Dir: Ricky Bean
Assoc Dir: Jeanne Licciardo
*Prin: Robert J O'Connell
CIO: George Foulke
Dir IT: Kyle Baden

D-U-N-S 17-360-5262 IMP
■ AMERICAN GIRL BRANDS LLC
(Suby of MATTEL INC) ★
8400 Fairway Pl, Middleton, WI 53562-2548
Tel (608) 836-4848 Founded/Ownrshp 1998
Sales 206.0MM[E] EMP 1,915
SIC 5945 2731 Dolls & accessories; Book publishing
CEO: Kevin Farr
*Treas: Scott Tophem
VP: David Eley
VP: Kathy Monetti
VP: Kathleen Simpson-Taylor
Exec: Mirek Buzga
Exec: Tom Kazunas
Exec: Charles Lee
Dir Surg: Lisa Dyson
Dir Surg: Jack Woodworth
Dir Risk M: Cathy Bacher
Creative D: John Fiebelkorn

D-U-N-S 04-034-6694
AMERICAN GOLF CORP
6080 Center Dr Ste 500, Los Angeles, CA 90045-9205
Tel (310) 664-4000 Founded/Ownrshp 2003
Sales 509.6MM[E] EMP 6,000
SIC 7997 7999 5812 5941 7992 Golf club, membership; Tennis club, membership; Golf services & professionals; Eating places; Golf goods & equipment; Public golf courses
CEO: Jim Hinckley
*Pr: Paul Major
*COO: Keith Brown
*CFO: Mike Moecker
*CFO: Rick Rosen
*Sr VP: Jim Allison
*Sr VP: Craig Kniffen
*VP: Joe Stegman
VP: CAM Stephens
Exec: David Ing
Genl Mgr: Ken Davidson

D-U-N-S 00-418-0022 IMP/EXP
AMERICAN GREETINGS CORP (OH)
(Suby of CENTURY INTERMEDIATE HOLDING CO) ★
1 American Rd, Cleveland, OH 44144-2398
Tel (216) 252-7300 Founded/Ownrshp 1906, 2013
Sales 1.9MMM EMP 28,400
SIC 2771 2679 2656 2678 Greeting cards; Gift wrap, paper: made from purchased material; Cups, paper: made from purchased material; Plates, paper: made from purchased material; Stationery: made from purchased materials
Co-CEO: Zev Weiss
*Ch Bd: Morry Weiss
*Pr: John W Beeder
CFO: Gregory Steinberg
*Co-CEO: Jeffrey Weiss
Sr VP: Douglas W Rommel
Sr VP: Erwin Weiss
VP: Pat Camino
VP: Ellen Frank
VP: Christopher W Haffke
VP: Gary Hock
VP: Ken Jayjack
VP: Steven Laserson
VP: Janet Quinn
VP: Patricia Ripple
VP: Matt Stein
Board of Directors: Michael J Merriman Jr, Elie Weiss, Gary Weiss

D-U-N-S 36-098-9672
AMERICAN GUARANTY MORTGAGE LLC
2000 S Colo Blvd Ste 3700, Denver, CO 80222
Tel (303) 577-7210 Founded/Ownrshp 2004
Sales 132.0MM EMP 29
SIC 6282 Investment advice
Pr: Matt Klaess

D-U-N-S 10-661-0009 IMP
■ AMERICAN GYPSUM CO LLC
(Suby of EAGLE MATERIALS INC) ★
3811 Turtle Creek Blvd # 1200, Dallas, TX 75219-4424
Tel (214) 530-5500 Founded/Ownrshp 1994
Sales 96.4MM[E] EMP 376
SIC 3275 5031 Wallboard, gypsum; Wallboard
Pr: David House
CFO: Mark V Dendle
CFO: Arthur R Zunker
VP Opers: Peter Bauer
Sls Dir: Brad Tonkin
Manager: Tim Franklin

D-U-N-S 94-269-1734
AMERICAN HABILITATION SERVICES INC
RESCARE
9050 N Capital Of Texa, Austin, TX 78759-7268
Tel (325) 676-8992 Founded/Ownrshp 2008
Sales 29.3MM[E] EMP 1,300
SIC 8059 Home for the mentally retarded, exc. skilled or intermediate
CEO: Nancy Newberry
*COO: Sheryl Rae Baker
*CFO: Dennis R Clapp
MIS Dir: Shem Isukh

AMERICAN HEALTH & LF INSUR CO
See CITI ASSURANCE SERVICES INC

D-U-N-S 62-482-4058
AMERICAN HEALTH ASSOCIATES INC
2831 Corporate Way, Miramar, FL 33025-3972
Tel (954) 919-5005 Founded/Ownrshp 1995
Sales 82.0MM[E] EMP 1,102
SIC 8071 Blood analysis laboratory
Pr: Debbie L Martin
*COO: Jim Jackson
VP: Christopher Martin
*VP: Carlos Pages
Rgnl Mgr: Donna Berard
Off Mgr: Diana Bernet
Manager: Darrell Moore

D-U-N-S 95-627-9137
AMERICAN HEALTH CHOICE INC
8350 Nw 52nd Ter Ste 206, Doral, FL 33166-7707
Tel (305) 860-2333 Founded/Ownrshp 1996
Sales 135.0MM[E] EMP 105
SIC 8011 Offices & clinics of medical doctors; Internal medicine, physician/surgeon
Pr: Walter Janke
COO: Richard Tuten
CFO: Hugh Chang Alloy
*Prin: Miguel A Cruz

D-U-N-S 11-870-6662
AMERICAN HEALTH COMPANIES INC
A H C
1971 Tennessee Ave N, Parsons, TN 38363-5049
Tel (731) 847-6343 Founded/Ownrshp 1976
Sales 475.4MM[E] EMP 4,200
Accts Bdo Usa Llp Memphis Tn
SIC 8051 8052 8059 Skilled nursing care facilities; Intermediate care facilities; Convalescent home; Domiciliary care; Nursing home, except skilled & intermediate care facility; Personal care home, with health care
Pr: James Smith
*CFO: Anne Vise
VP: Barb Knuutila
Off Mgr: Sherry Vaughn
IT Man: Terry Sheppard

D-U-N-S 61-346-2902
AMERICAN HEALTH FOUNDATION INC
5920 Venture Dr Ste 100, Dublin, OH 43017-2236
Tel (614) 798-5110 Founded/Ownrshp 1988
Sales 28.7MM[E] EMP 1,000
Accts Hhh Cpa Group Llc Columbus O
SIC 8741 Nursing & personal care facility management
Ch Bd: John M Haemmerle
*Pr: Mark Haemmerle

AMERICAN HEALTH MEDICARE
See TRIPLE-S ADVANTAGE INC

D-U-N-S 18-174-9243
AMERICAN HEALTH NETWORK INC
PEDIATRIC PHYSICIANS OF NEWARK
2500 Corporate Exchange D, Columbus, OH 43231-7601
Tel (614) 794-4500 Founded/Ownrshp 1987
Sales 211.7MM[E] EMP 1,170
SIC 8011 Offices & clinics of medical doctors
CEO: Ben Park
Off Mgr: Jeff R Fisher

D-U-N-S 87-288-7997
AMERICAN HEALTH NETWORK INC
(Suby of PEDIATRIC PHYSICIANS OF NEWARK) ★
10689 N Pennsylvna St # 200, Indianapolis, IN 46280-1099
Tel (317) 580-6309 Founded/Ownrshp 1998
Sales 211.7MM[E] EMP 1,170
SIC 8011 General & family practice, physician/surgeon
CEO: Ben Park
CFO: Mike Kirshner
CFO: Dennis Ressler
VP: Darcy Burthay
VP: Sarah D Cotterill
Exec: Debra Burton
Dir Lab: Patsy Bauer
Ex Dir: Mary Griffin
Ex Dir: Bruce Hughes
Ex Dir: Debbie Wunder
Prac Mgr: David Barrett

D-U-N-S 87-770-7885
AMERICAN HEALTH NETWORK OF INDIANA INC
(Suby of AMERICAN HEALTH NETWORK INC) ★
10689 N Pennsylvna St # 200, Indianapolis, IN 46280-1099
Tel (317) 580-6314 Founded/Ownrshp 1985
Sales NA EMP 787[E]
SIC 6324 8011 Hospital & medical service plans; Offices & clinics of medical doctors
Pr: Ben H Park MD
*CFO: Michael Kirschner
CFO: Shelley Murdock
Sr Cor Off: Donald Hindes
Sr Cor Off: Michael Williams

D-U-N-S 07-993-6854
AMERICAN HEALTH NETWORK OF INDIANA LLC
(Suby of AMERICAN HEALTH NETWORK OF INDIANA INC) ★
10689 N Pennsylvna St # 200, Indianapolis, IN 46280-1070
Tel (317) 580-6309 Founded/Ownrshp 2014
Sales 208.1MM EMP 1,600
Accts Crowe Horwath Llp Indianapoli
SIC 8011 Physicians' office, including specialists

Prin: Ben Park
**Prin:* Linda Sundin

D-U-N-S 06-342-2018
AMERICAN HEALTHCARE LLC
3131 Electric Rd, Roanoke, VA 24018-6427
Tel (540) 774-4263 *Founded/Ownrshp* 2001
Sales 95.3MM[E] *EMP* 1,700
SIC 8052 8051 8059 Intermediate care facilities; Skilled nursing care facilities; Convalescent home
CEO: Tommy East
**Treas:* Jeffrey L Petersen
Nrsg Dir: Lance Long

AMERICAN HEART ASSN NAT CTR
See AMERICAN HEART ASSOCIATION INC

D-U-N-S 07-328-4507
AMERICAN HEART ASSOCIATION INC
AMERICAN HEART ASSN NAT CTR
7272 Greenville Ave, Dallas, TX 75231-5129
Tel (214) 373-6300 *Founded/Ownrshp* 1924
Sales 780.2MM *EMP* 3,500
SIC 8399 2721

D-U-N-S 00-692-1324
■ **AMERICAN HERITAGE LIFE INSURANCE CO INC** (FL)
(*Suby of* ALLSTATE CORP) ★
1776 Amercn Heritg Lf Dr, Jacksonville, FL 32224
Tel (904) 992-1776 *Founded/Ownrshp* 1956
Sales NA *EMP* 978[E]
SIC 6321 6311 6351 Accident & health insurance; Life insurance; Credit & other financial responsibility insurance
Pr: David A Bird
**Ex VP:* Charles C Baggs
**Ex VP:* Keith Hauschildt
Sr VP: Walter M Jones
IT Man: James Friday

D-U-N-S 04-893-1877
■ **AMERICAN HERITAGE LIFE INVESTMENT CORP**
(*Suby of* ALLSTATE CORP) ★
1776 Amercn Heritg Lf Dr, Jacksonville, FL 32224
Tel (904) 992-1776 *Founded/Ownrshp* 1968
Sales NA *EMP* 738
SIC 6311 6321 6351 7374 Life insurance carriers; Accident & health insurance carriers; Credit & other financial responsibility insurance; Data processing & preparation
Ch Bd: David A Bird
VP: Tina R Taylo

D-U-N-S 80-526-7358
AMERICAN HOLDCO LLC
EAST COAST SEAFOOD
448 Boston St, Topsfield, MA 01983-1216
Tel (978) 561-3800 *Founded/Ownrshp* 1981
Sales 129.1MM[E] *EMP* 190
SIC 5146 4213 Seafoods; Refrigerated products transport
Pr: Michael J Tourkistas
**CFO:* James Bouras
Ex VP: Willard Fehr
**VP:* Spiridon Tourkakis
CIO: David J Bows

D-U-N-S 00-697-9959
■ **AMERICAN HOME ASSURANCE CO INC**
(*Suby of* AIG) ★
70 Pine St Fl 1, New York, NY 10005-1522
Tel (212) 770-7000 *Founded/Ownrshp* 1899
Sales NA *EMP* 2,800
SIC 6331 7371 Property damage insurance; Fire, marine & casualty insurance & carriers; Computer software systems analysis & design, custom
Pr: John Doyle
**Ch Bd:* Thomas Tizzio
**COO:* Christopher A Maleno
**Ex VP:* Kristian Philip Moor
Sr VP: Sonja Ochsenkuehn
VP: John Coyle
VP: Stephen Diamond
VP: Janis Dunstan
VP: Joan Gelpi
VP: Alex Pittignano
Assoc Dir: Randy Helms

AMERICAN HOME BUILDERS
See AMERICAS HOME PLACE INC

AMERICAN HOME PATIENTS
See AHOM HOLDINGS INC (DE)

D-U-N-S 79-115-0514
■ **AMERICAN HOME SHIELD CORP**
(*Suby of* CDRSVM HOLDING LLC) ★
889 Ridge Lake Blvd, Memphis, TN 38120-9425
Tel (901) 597-8000 *Founded/Ownrshp* 1979
Sales NA *EMP* 215[E]
SIC 6351 Warranty insurance, home
Pr: Mark J Barry
Exec: Stephanie Schumacher
Mktg Dir: Jennifer Brereton
Corp Couns: Kent Lashley

D-U-N-S 09-309-0611
■ **AMERICAN HOME SHIELD INSPECTION SERVICES INC**
(*Suby of* SERVICEMASTER CONSUMER SERVICES LIMITED PARTNERSHIP) ★
860 Ridge Lake Blvd # 101, Memphis, TN 38120-9421
Tel (901) 537-8000 *Founded/Ownrshp* 1971, 1989
Sales NA *EMP* 1,600
SIC 6351 Warranty insurance, home
Pr: Mark Barry
**COO:* Ernest Mrozek
**Chf Mktg O:* Philipp Von Holtzendorff-Fehli

D-U-N-S 09-910-9766
AMERICAN HOMECARE SUPPLY LLC
101 W Elm St Ste 210, Conshohocken, PA 19428-2075
Tel (484) 530-0880 *Founded/Ownrshp* 2009
Sales NA *EMP* 1,250
SIC 5999 7352

D-U-N-S 55-628-0899
AMERICAN HOMEPATIENT INC
(*Suby of* LINCARE HOLDINGS INC) ★
5200 Maryland Way Ste 400, Brentwood, TN 37027-5059
Tel (615) 221-8884 *Founded/Ownrshp* 2016
Sales 229.3MM[E] *EMP* 2,375
SIC 8049 Inhalation therapist
Pr: Kristen Hoefer
CFO: Stephen L Clanton

D-U-N-S 07-909-5970
▲ **AMERICAN HOMES 4 RENT**
30601 Agoura Rd Ste 200, Agoura Hills, CA 91301-2148
Tel (805) 413-5300 *Founded/Ownrshp* 2012
Sales 630.5MM *EMP* 781[E]
Tkr Sym AMH *Exch* NYS
SIC 6798 Real estate investment trusts
CEO: David P Singelyn
**Ch Bd:* B Wayne Hughes
**COO:* John Corrigan
CFO: Diana M Laing
Ex VP: David Goldberg
Ex VP: Bryan Smith
Board of Directors: Douglas N Benham, Tamara Hughes Gustavson, Matthew J Hart, James H Kropp, Kenneth M Woolley

D-U-N-S 10-385-4527
AMERICAN HOMESTAR CORP
2450 S Shore Blvd Ste 300, League City, TX 77573-2997
Tel (281) 334-9700 *Founded/Ownrshp* 1983
Sales 125.5MM *EMP* 568
Accts Hein & Associates Llp Houston
SIC 2451 4213 5271 6351 6515 Mobile homes, personal or private use; Mobile homes transport; Mobile homes; Credit & other financial responsibility insurance; Warranty insurance, home; Mobile home site operators
Pr: Finis F Teeter
**COO:* Charlie Boyer
**COO:* Charles N Carney Jr
**CFO:* Craig A Reynolds
VP: F R Daily Jr
Exec: Jennifer Henry
Sls&Mrk Ex: Ronnie Richards
Board of Directors: Richard F Dahlson, Richard N Grasso, Ellis L McKinley, Nathan P Morton

D-U-N-S 06-897-1654
AMERICAN HONDA FINANCE CORP
HONDA FINANCIAL SERVICES
(*Suby of* AMERICAN HONDA MOTOR CO INC) ★
20800 Madrona Ave, Torrance, CA 90503-4915
Tel (310) 972-2239 *Founded/Ownrshp* 1980
Sales NA *EMP* 1,000
Accts Kpmg Llp Los Angeles Califor
SIC 6141 Financing: automobiles, furniture, etc., not a deposit bank; Automobile & consumer finance companies
CEO: Hideo Tamaka
**CFO:* John Weisickle
Treas: Shinji Kubaru
Treas: Mikio Yoshimi
Ofcr: David W Paul
**Sr VP:* Stephan Smith
VP: Harry Beyer
VP: Anthony Piazza
Genl Mgr: Glenn Yamamoto
Dir IT: Grace Jean
Dir IT: Tom Laymon

D-U-N-S 00-886-0389 IMP/EXP
AMERICAN HONDA MOTOR CO INC (CA)
(*Suby of* HONDA MOTOR CO., LTD.)
1919 Torrance Blvd, Torrance, CA 90501-2722
Tel (310) 783-2000 *Founded/Ownrshp* 1959, 2008
Sales 13.8MMM[E] *EMP* 26,000
SIC 5012 3732 Automobiles; Jet skis
CEO: Takuji Yamada
**Pr:* Takanobu Ito
COO: Satoshi Aoki
COO: Steve Brandon
COO: Steve Mortimer
CFO: Geoff Farmer
CFO: Stuart Lund
**CFO:* Hiroyuki Suganuma
Treas: Richard Crawford
**Treas:* H Okada
**Ex VP:* Thomas G Elliott
Ex VP: Suguru Kanazawa
**Sr VP:* Jeff Conrad
VP: Kazutoshi Nishizawa
VP: Hideki Okada
VP: Jim Roach
VP: Stephen Smith
Exec: Nicolas Nomicos
Dir Teleco: Roger Cope

D-U-N-S 78-794-6651
AMERICAN HOSPICE HOLDINGS LLC
(*Suby of* RIVERSIDE CO) ★
50 N Laura St Ste 1800, Jacksonville, FL 32202-3614
Tel (904) 493-6745 *Founded/Ownrshp* 2004
Sales 25.6MM[E] *EMP* 1,000
SIC 8059 Personal care home, with health care
CEO: Jeffrey Preuss
CFO: Richard Fogle

D-U-N-S 05-106-4566
AMERICAN HOSPITAL ASSOCIATION (IL)
AHA
155 N Wacker Dr Ste 400, Chicago, IL 60606-1719
Tel (312) 422-3000 *Founded/Ownrshp* 1920
Sales 126.3MM *EMP* 508
Accts Crowe Horwath Llp Chicago Il
SIC 2721 2731 8099 Periodicals: publishing only; Books: publishing only; Medical services organization
Ch: Jim Skogsbergh
**Pr:* Richard Umbdenstock
**CFO:* R John Evans
Trst: Ron J Anderson
**Ex VP:* Neil J Jesuele
**Ex VP:* Richard J Pollack
**Sr VP:* Lisa Allen
**Sr VP:* Anthony J Burke
**Sr VP:* Michael Guerin
Exec: Michelle Hoffman
Assoc Dir: Dorothy Cobbs

AMERICAN HOTEL FURNISHINGS
See AMERICAN HOTEL REGISTER CO

D-U-N-S 00-508-4835 IMP/EXP
AMERICAN HOTEL REGISTER CO
AMERICAN HOTEL FURNISHINGS
100 S Milwaukee Ave # 100, Vernon Hills, IL 60061-4321
Tel (847) 743-3000 *Founded/Ownrshp* 1865
Sales 927.2MM[E] *EMP* 930
SIC 5046 5023 5021 5113 Hotel equipment & supplies; Floor coverings; Draperies; Bedspreads; Beds; Public building furniture; Industrial & personal service paper
Pr: Lawrence J Morse
**Pr:* James F Leahy
**CFO:* Daniel D Potts
**Treas:* Jeffrey S Carroll
**Ex VP:* J Patrick Leahy
**Ex VP:* Thomas Leahy
VP: Hugh Armstrong
VP: Karl Baker
VP: Bill Boyle
Dir Bus: Jim Korompilas
Genl Mgr: Chris Batt

D-U-N-S 00-433-5147 IMP
■ **AMERICAN HOUSEHOLD INC** (DE)
SUNBEAM OUTDOOR PRODUCTS
(*Suby of* NEWELL BRANDS) ★
2381 Nw Executive Ctr Dr, Boca Raton, FL 33431-8560
Tel (561) 912-4100 *Founded/Ownrshp* 1900, 2005
Sales 4.5MMM[E] *EMP* 9,000
SIC 3631 2514 3421 3634 3829 3841 Barbecues, grills & braziers (outdoor cooking); Metal lawn & garden furniture; Lawn furniture: metal; Scissors, shears, clippers, snips & similar tools; Shears, hand; Clippers, fingernail & toenail; Electric housewares & fans; Hair dryers, electric; Blenders, electric; Food mixers, electric: household; Thermometers & temperature sensors; Temperature sensors, except industrial process & aircraft; Thermometers, liquid-in-glass & bimetal type; Geophysical & meteorological testing equipment; Blood pressure apparatus
Ch Bd: Jerry Levin
VP: John Frederick
VP Mktg: Steve Testut
Board of Directors: Philip Beekman, Charles M Elson, Howard Gittis, John H Klein, Howard G Kristol, Peter A Langerman, Faith Whittlesey

AMERICAN HT INCOME PRPTS REIT
See LODGING ENTERPRISES LLC

D-U-N-S 04-637-7516
AMERICAN HUTS INC
ADF COMPANIES
350 Passaic Ave, Fairfield, NJ 07004-2025
Tel (973) 808-9525 *Founded/Ownrshp* 2000
Sales 128.9MM[E] *EMP* 3,000
SIC 5812 Pizzeria, chain
Pr: Donald Harty
**Ch Bd:* Frank Levy

D-U-N-S 78-332-8396
■ **AMERICAN IMAGING MANAGEMENT INC**
AIM SPECIALTY HEALTH
(*Suby of* ANTHEM INC) ★
8600 W Bryn Mawr Ave 800s, Chicago, IL 60631-3544
Tel (773) 864-4600 *Founded/Ownrshp* 1989
Sales NA *EMP* 300
SIC 6321 Health insurance carriers
Pr: Brandon W Cady
**Chf Mktg O:* Susan Nedza
Sr VP: Michael Backus
Sr VP: Joel Cesario
Sr VP: Randy Hutchinson
Sr VP: David Soffa
Sr VP: Bob Zimmerman
VP: Richard Bergman
VP: Kevin McDermott
VP: Laticia Miller
VP: Anne Pukstys
VP: Suzanne Ross
VP: Boris Spevak
VP: Michael Stec
VP: Julie Thiel
VP: Neil Witek

D-U-N-S 05-087-2738
AMERICAN IMPLEMENT INC
JOHN DEERE AUTHORIZED DEALER
2611 W Jones Ave, Garden City, KS 67846-2514
Tel (620) 275-4114 *Founded/Ownrshp* 1970
Sales 86.5MM[E] *EMP* 350
SIC 5083 Farm implements
Pr: Duane E Koster
Off Mgr: Lisa Chester
Store Mgr: MO Pando
Sales Asso: Luther Augustine
Sales Asso: Tony Butts
Sales Asso: Dennis Ferris
Sales Asso: Ed Mildenberger

D-U-N-S 02-025-4547
AMERICAN INCOME LIFE
AIL
8820 Trinity Rd, Cordova, TN 38018-2735
Tel (901) 748-5584 *Founded/Ownrshp* 2014
Sales NA *EMP* 20
SIC 6311 Life insurance
Prin: Drew Crameans

AMERICAN INCOME LIFE INSURANCE
See ALTIG INTERNATIONAL INC

D-U-N-S 86-003-3737
AMERICAN INCOME LIFE INSURANCE
10000 Shelbyville Rd # 211, Louisville, KY 40223-2950
Tel (812) 280-1360 *Founded/Ownrshp* 1990
Sales NA *EMP* 2
SIC 6411 Insurance agents, brokers & service
Owner: William Heath

D-U-N-S 06-413-4307
■ **AMERICAN INCOME LIFE INSURANCE CO INC**
(*Suby of* GLOBE LIFE & ACCIDENT INSURANCE CO) ★
1200 Wooded Acres Dr, Waco, TX 76710-4436
Tel (254) 741-5701 *Founded/Ownrshp* 1951
Sales NA *EMP* 380
SIC 6311 Life insurance
Pr: Roger Smith
Treas: Randall David Mull
VP: Diana L Crosby
VP: Kevin Poynter
VP: Hugh Walsh
Exec: Danny Fisher
Exec: Donna Tucker
IT Man: Carolyn Fisher

AMERICAN INDEPENDENCE CORP.
See AMIC HOLDINGS INC

D-U-N-S 06-005-8021
AMERICAN INDEPENDENT INSURANCE CO INC
GOOD2GO AUTO INSURANCE
(*Suby of* INDEPENDENT INSURANCE INVESTMENTS INC) ★
1400 Union Meeting Rd # 250, Blue Bell, PA 19422-1952
Tel (610) 832-4940 *Founded/Ownrshp* 2005
Sales NA *EMP* 140
SIC 6331 6411 Automobile insurance; Property damage insurance; Insurance agents, brokers & service
Pr: William B Lockhorn
**CFO:* Mark J Keyser
VP: Bruce Arneson
VP: John Edwards
Exec: Adam Niad
Mktg Mgr: Ray Medovich
Sls Mgr: Kimberly Carney

D-U-N-S 09-227-4591
AMERICAN INDUSTRIAL ACQUISITION CORP
AIAC
1465 E Putnam Ave Ste 229, Greenwich, CT 06830
Tel (203) 698-9595 *Founded/Ownrshp* 1996
Sales 145.9MM[E] *EMP* 9,500
SIC 8741

D-U-N-S 96-583-2657
AMERICAN INDUSTRIAL ACQUISITION CORP
AIAC
250 Park Ave Fl 7, New York, NY 10177-0799
Tel (212) 572-4853 *Founded/Ownrshp* 1996
Sales 810.0MM[E] *EMP* 5,422[E]
SIC 6211 6153 Investment firm, general brokerage; Direct working capital financing
Ch Bd: Charles Anderson

D-U-N-S 06-801-1519
AMERICAN INDUSTRIAL CLEANING CO INC
10 Chelsea Pl, Great Neck, NY 11021-3244
Tel (516) 482-8424 *Founded/Ownrshp* 1963
Sales 20.5MM[E] *EMP* 1,200
SIC 7349 Building cleaning service; Building maintenance, except repairs
Pr: Myron Stempa
**VP:* Ovidio Contreras

AMERICAN INDUSTRIAL PARTNERS
See AIP LLC

D-U-N-S 83-060-1832
AMERICAN INDUSTRIAL PARTNERS CAPITAL FUND IV (PARALLEL) LP
(*Suby of* AMERICAN INDUSTRIAL PARTNERS) ★
330 Madison Ave Fl 28, New York, NY 10017-5018
Tel (212) 627-2360 *Founded/Ownrshp* 2008
Sales 206.7MM[E] *EMP* 1,045
SIC 6726 Investment offices
Pt: Kim Marvin
**Pt:* Jorge Amador
**Pt:* Eric Baroyan
**Pt:* John Becker
**Pt:* Dino Cusumano
Ex Dir: Dana Goldsmith

D-U-N-S 19-788-4992
AMERICAN INDUSTRIAL PARTNERS LP
1 Maritime Plz Ste 1925, San Francisco, CA 94111-3530
Tel (415) 788-7354 *Founded/Ownrshp* 1988
Sales 273.8MM[E] *EMP* 1,428
SIC 6282 Investment advisory service
Pt: Richard Bingham
Pt: Theodore C Rogers
Mng Dir: Al Barry

D-U-N-S 01-997-9566
■ **AMERICAN INDUSTRIAL WATER LLC**
(*Suby of* AMERICAN WATER WORKS CO INC) ★
1025 Laurel Oak Rd, Voorhees, NJ 08043-3506
Tel (856) 346-8200 *Founded/Ownrshp* 2015
Sales 124.6MM[E] *EMP* 353[E]
SIC 1629 Waste water & sewage treatment plant construction
CEO: Susan Story
CFO: Linda Sullivan
VP: Mark Chesla

D-U-N-S 09-222-4588
AMERICAN INFOSOURCE LP
5847 San Felipe St # 1200, Houston, TX 77057-3167
Tel (713) 532-8977 *Founded/Ownrshp* 2000
Sales 103.3MM[E] *EMP* 1,535
SIC 7374 Data processing & preparation
Pr: Blake Hogan
**COO:* Matt Sutherland
**CFO:* Drew Kanellopoulos
Ex VP: Matt Sutherlind
VP: Shawn Hogan
**VP:* Larque Piatt
Software D: Susan Peacock

D-U-N-S 04-681-3507 IMP
AMERICAN INSTITUTE OF CERTIFIED PUBLIC ACCOUNTANTS
AICPA
220 Leigh Farm Rd, Durham, NC 27707-8110
Tel (919) 402-0682 *Founded/Ownrshp* 1887
Sales 247.5MM *EMP* 800
Accts Cohnreznick Llp Roseland Nj
SIC 8299 8621 2721 Educational service, nondegree granting: continuing educ.; Professional membership organizations; Periodicals: publishing only
Pr: Barry C Melancon
CFO: Nisha Fredericks
CFO: Tim Laspaluto
**CFO:* Scott H Spiegel
CFO: Scott Spiegel
**Ch:* Tommye E Barie
**Ch:* Tim Kristen
Treas: Adell Battle
**Sr VP:* Lawson Carmichael
Sr VP: Susan S Coffey
**Sr VP:* Janice Maiman
**Sr VP:* Mark Peterson
Sr VP: Mark Gardner Peterson
Sr VP: Arleen R Thomas
VP: Todd Conard
VP: Kevin Henson
VP: John Hudson
VP: Edward Karl
VP: Hemchandra Nerkar
VP: Jeannie Patton
VP: Susan Pierson

D-U-N-S 07-525-6222
AMERICAN INSTITUTE OF CERTIFIED PUBLIC ACCOUNTANTS FOUNDATION
201 Plaza Three Harborsid, Jersey City, NJ 07311
Tel (903) 823-2727 *Founded/Ownrshp* 1922
Sales 213.2MM *EMP* 2^E
SIC 8399

D-U-N-S 04-173-3197
AMERICAN INSTITUTES FOR RESEARCH IN BEHAVIORAL SCIENCES
A I R
1000 Thmas Jfferson St Nw, Washington, DC 20007-3835
Tel (202) 403-5000 *Founded/Ownrshp* 1946
Sales 488.3MM *EMP* 1,700
Accts Rubino And Company Chartered
SIC 8733 Noncommercial social research organization
Ch: Patricia B Gurin
**Pr:* David Myers
COO: Lydia Quijada
**CFO:* Marijo Ahlgrimm
VP: Hans Bos
VP: Bob Holstein
VP: Mark Schneider
Snr Ntwrk: Sean Hartwell
IT Man: Nikki Sharan
IT Man: Greggory Stefanelli
Netwrk Eng: Matthew Bailey

D-U-N-S 05-325-2664
AMERICAN INSURANCE CO INC
(*Suby of* ALLIANZ SE)
1465 N Mcdowell Blvd, Petaluma, CA 94954-6516
Tel (415) 899-2000 *Founded/Ownrshp* 2007
Sales NA *EMP* 4,400
SIC 6331 Fire, marine & casualty insurance
Pr: Mike Larocco
Board of Directors: Douglas E Franklin, Jeffrey F Johnson, Sally B Narey, D Andrew Torrance, Kevin W Walker, David M Zona

D-U-N-S 07-949-5651
AMERICAN INSURANCE SERVICE INC
3 Bala Plz E Ste 300, Bala Cynwyd, PA 19004-3406
Tel (610) 664-1500 *Founded/Ownrshp* 1997
Sales NA *EMP* 250
SIC 6411 6331 Insurance agents; Fire, marine & casualty insurance & carriers
Prin: Robert Fishman
**Ch Bd:* Raymond L Freudberg
**Pr:* Seth Freudberg
**Treas:* Kevin L Tate
**VP:* Richard S March
**VP:* John Yaglenski

D-U-N-S 07-973-9901
AMERICAN INTEGRITY INSURANCE GROUP LLC (TX)
5426 Bay Center Dr # 650, Tampa, FL 33609-9902
Tel (813) 880-7000 *Founded/Ownrshp* 2006, 2015
Sales NA *EMP* 130
SIC 6331 Property damage insurance
CEO: Robert Ritchie

D-U-N-S 06-060-2554 IMP/EXP
AMERICAN INTERNATIONAL FOREST PRODUCTS LLC
(*Suby of* FOREST CITY TRADING GROUP LLC) ★
5560 Sw 107th Ave, Beaverton, OR 97005-4171
Tel (503) 641-1611 *Founded/Ownrshp* 1976
Sales 89.4MM^E *EMP* 87^E
SIC 5031 Lumber: rough, dressed & finished; Plywood; Particleboard
**Sec:* Lois Tonning
VP Sls: Bill Culver

D-U-N-S 04-469-1103 IMP/EXP
▲ **AMERICAN INTERNATIONAL GROUP INC**
AIG
175 Water St Rm 1800, New York, NY 10038-4969
Tel (212) 770-7000 *Founded/Ownrshp* 1919
Sales NA *EMP* 66,400
Tkr Sym AIG *Exch* NYS
SIC 6331 6321 6311 6324 6411 6282 Fire, marine & casualty insurance; Accident insurance carriers; Health insurance carriers; Life insurance carriers; Group hospitalization plans; Advisory services, insurance; Investment advice
Pr: Peter D Hancock
Ch Bd: Douglas M Steenland
V Ch: Thomas Tizzio
Pr: Carol Allan
Pr: Thomas Borst
Pr: Sandra Chefitz
Pr: Cathy Chen
Pr: Ross Connell
Pr: Craig Crowder
Pr: Cherie Dawson
Pr: Mauricio Donoso
Pr: Douglas Grove
Pr: Sean Guy
Pr: Willy Hammond
Pr: Allen Himmelstein
Pr: Paul Hoepfl
Pr: Sylvia Hom
Pr: Rebecca Hunt
Pr: Arthi Kasu
Pr: Gonzalo Longoria
Pr: Jim McCadden
Board of Directors: Robert S Miller, W Don Cornwell, Linda A Mills, Peter R Fisher, John A Paulson, John H Fitzpatrick, Ronald A Rittenmeyer, Suzanne Nora Johnson, Theresa M Stone, William G Jurgensen, Christopher S Lynch, Samuel J Merksamer, George L Miles Jr, Henry S Miller

D-U-N-S 04-972-7873 IMP/EXP
AMERICAN INTERNATIONAL INDUSTRIES
2220 Gaspar Ave, Commerce, CA 90040-1516
Tel (323) 728-2999 *Founded/Ownrshp* 1971
Sales 480.2MM^E *EMP* 700^E
SIC 5122 2844 Cosmetics; Toilet preparations
Pt: Zvi Ryzman
Sr VP: Jennifer Paulson
VP: Mark Moesta

D-U-N-S 80-309-4549
■ **AMERICAN INTERNATIONAL WATER SERVICES CO**
(*Suby of* AMERICAN WATER WORKS CO INC) ★
1025 Laurel Oak Rd, Voorhees, NJ 08043-3506
Tel (856) 346-8200 *Founded/Ownrshp* 1998
Sales 88.2MM^E *EMP* 250
SIC 4941 Water supply
Pr: Jeremy Pelczer
**Pr:* Jorge Carrasco
**VP:* Windall F Holland
**VP:* Howard Woods
Dir IT: Doneen Hobbs

D-U-N-S 07-971-4763
AMERICAN INVESTMENT GROUP
1549 Ne 123rd St, North Miami, FL 33161-6029
Tel (561) 714-6157 *Founded/Ownrshp* 2014
Sales 90.0MM *EMP* 50
SIC 6799 Investors
Pr: Jeff Patel

AMERICAN IRON & METAL
See AIM SPECIALTY MATERIALS USA

D-U-N-S 94-333-1496 IMP/EXP
AMERICAN IRON OXIDE CO
AMROX
Fster Plz Ste 7 661 Adrsn, Pittsburgh, PA 15220
Tel (412) 929-0177 *Founded/Ownrshp* 1995
Sales 108.8MM^E *EMP* 175^E
SIC 4953 2816 Recycling, waste materials; Iron oxide pigments (ochers, siennas, umbers)
Ch: Walter Sieckman
**VP:* Michael Sieckmann
VP: Mark Stropkaj

D-U-N-S 16-089-9605 IMP/EXP
■ **AMERICAN ITALIAN PASTA CO**
AIPC
(*Suby of* TREEHOUSE PRIVATE BRANDS INC) ★
1000 Italian Way, Excelsior Springs, MO 64024-8016
Tel (816) 502-6000 *Founded/Ownrshp* 2010
Sales 193.8MM^E *EMP* 675^E
SIC 2099 Pasta, uncooked: packaged with other ingredients
Pr: Walt George
Pr: Eric L Johnson
Ex VP: David E Watson
VP: Dennis Krause
Exec: Janice Rice
Dir Bus: Mark Gonda
VP Mktg: Rob Persaud
VP Sls: Brian Fox
Sls Mgr: Daniel Getteson
Sls Mgr: Daniel W Trott

D-U-N-S 06-822-6141 IMP
AMERICAN JEWISH JOINT DISTRIBUTION COMMITTEE INC (NY)
J.D.C.
711 3rd Ave Rm 901, New York, NY 10017-9207
Tel (212) 687-6200 *Founded/Ownrshp* 1914
Sales 352.5MM *EMP* 840
Accts Grant Thornton Llp New York
SIC 8699 Charitable organization
CEO: Alan H Gill
**Ch Bd:* Dr Irving A Smokler
**Pr:* Penny Blumenstein
CFO: Ophir Singal
Ofcr: Shaun Goldstone
Ex Dir: Michael Novick
CTO: Jennie Goldress
Dir IT: Linda Levi
Dir IT: Jason Nadell
Pr Dir: Jennifer Kraft

D-U-N-S 02-030-4440
AMERICAN KIDNEY FUND INC (DC)
11921 Rockville Pike # 300, Rockville, MD 20852-2737
Tel (301) 881-3690 *Founded/Ownrshp* 1971
Sales 265.2MM *EMP* 40
Accts Cliftonlarsonallen Llp Timoni
SIC 8399 Fund raising organization, non-fee basis
Ex Dir: Lavarne Burton
**CFO:* Donald Roy
VP: Carol Cohen
Prgrm Mgr: Dennis Cooper

D-U-N-S 03-041-1888
AMERICAN LEBANESE SYRIAN ASSOCIATED CHARITIES INC
ALSAC
501 Saint Jude Pl, Memphis, TN 38105-1905
Tel (901) 578-2150 *Founded/Ownrshp* 1957
Sales 1.1MMM *EMP* 1,200
Accts Deloitte Tax Llp Nashville T
SIC 8399 Fund raising organization, non-fee basis
CEO: Rick Shadyac Jr
**Ch Bd:* Paul J Ayoub
**CFO:* Mike Canarios
**Ex VP:* Larry E Kun
**Sr VP:* Robyn Diaz
**Sr VP:* Pam Dotson
Assoc Dir: Mandy Flood
Assoc Dir: Robet Wilson
CTO: Milu Cherian
Sftwr Eng: Roshan Shrestha
Counsel: Mark Allen

D-U-N-S 00-512-9598
AMERICAN LICORICE CO
1900 Whirlpool Dr S, La Porte, IN 46350-2594
Tel (510) 487-5500 *Founded/Ownrshp* 1914
Sales 106.0MM^E *EMP* 400
SIC 2064 Licorice candy
CEO: John R Kretchmer
**Ch Bd:* Tim Walsh
VP: Kristen Bergevin

D-U-N-S 00-691-8718
■ **AMERICAN LIFE INSURANCE CO**
METLIFE
(*Suby of* METLIFE INC) ★
1 Alico Plz, Wilmington, DE 19801-3722
Tel (302) 594-2000 *Founded/Ownrshp* 2010
Sales NA *EMP* 3,000
SIC 6411 6321 6324 Insurance agents & brokers; Accident & health insurance; Group hospitalization plans
CEO: Marlene Debel
Sr VP: Kevin Kelley
VP: Douglas P Bomberger
VP: Chris Demartine
VP: Kenneth Smith
IT Man: Tamer Issa
Sls Dir: Patrick McKenna

D-U-N-S 82-777-0819 IMP
AMERICAN LITHO INC
175 Mercedes Dr, Carol Stream, IL 60188-9409
Tel (630) 462-1700 *Founded/Ownrshp* 1994
Sales 204.0MM^E *EMP* 350
SIC 2752 Commercial printing, offset
Pr: Mike Fontana
CFO: Jackie Kieta
VP: Joe Bulgarelli
VP: Sam Dentino
**VP:* Chris Joyaux
Mng Dir: Frank Arostegui
MIS Dir: Donald Schoen
Opers Mgr: Sam Cece
Prd Mgr: Jim Severyns
Sales Exec: John Townsend
Natl Sales: Rick Ross

AMERICAN LOSS PREVENTION SVCS
See AMERICAN COMMERCIAL SECURITY SERVICES INC

D-U-N-S 96-811-6871
AMERICAN LUBEFAST LLC
1550 N Brown Rd Ste 140, Lawrenceville, GA 30043-8154
Tel (770) 995-6312 *Founded/Ownrshp* 1998
Sales 96.3MM^E *EMP* 480^E
SIC 6794 7549 Franchises, selling or licensing; Lubrication service, automotive
**CEO:* Tim Embry
**CFO:* Scott Hesprich
**VP:* Joe Johnson
Dist Mgr: Matt Duckworth

AMERICAN LUMBER CO
See BAILLIE LUMBER CO LP

AMERICAN MAINTENANCE
See ACA INDUSTRIES INC

D-U-N-S 14-048-6437
AMERICAN MANAGED CARE LLC
100 Central Ave Ste 200, Saint Petersburg, FL 33701-3324
Tel (866) 690-4842 *Founded/Ownrshp* 2002
Sales NA *EMP* 800
Accts Ernst & Young Llp Tampa Fl
SIC 6411 Medical insurance claim processing, contract or fee basis
Pr: Akshay M Desai MD
**COO:* Michael Holohan
**CFO:* Alec Mahmood
**Treas:* Steven Schaefer
**Ofcr:* Deepak Desai

D-U-N-S 06-493-0233
AMERICAN MANAGEMENT ASSOCIATION INTERNATIONAL
AMACOM
1601 Broadway Fl 7, New York, NY 10019-7420
Tel (212) 586-8100 *Founded/Ownrshp* 1923
Sales 84.4MM *EMP* 500
Accts Kpmg Llp New York Ny
SIC 8299 2731 8621 7812 2721 Educational service, nondegree granting: continuing educ.; Books: publishing only; Professional membership organizations; Video tape production; Periodicals: publishing only
Pr: Edward T Reilly
CFO: Vivianna Guzman
Trst: Charles R Craig
Sr VP: Richard J Barton
Sr VP: Jeremy Donovan
Sr VP: Arthur J Levy
Manager: Felice Artonio
Counsel: Arthur Levy

D-U-N-S 80-976-7010
AMERICAN MANAGEMENT SERVICES LLC
PINNACLE
2801 Alaskan Way Ste 200, Seattle, WA 98121-1136
Tel (206) 215-9700 *Founded/Ownrshp* 2003
Sales 88.4MM^E *EMP* 1,000
SIC 8742 Real estate consultant
Off Mgr: Amber Studer

D-U-N-S 13-518-5747
AMERICAN MANAGEMENT SERVICES WEST LLC
PINNACLE
2801 Alaskan Way Ste 200, Seattle, WA 98121-1136
Tel (206) 215-9700 *Founded/Ownrshp* 2003
Sales 192.7MM^E *EMP* 4,140
SIC 6531 Real estate agents & managers
Pr: Joel Oldham IV
Pr: Glenn Rand
CFO: John Carrosino
Bd of Dir: Stephen Sanger
Rgnl VP: Russell Peterson
VP: Lynne Shirley
**VP:* Deke Turner

D-U-N-S 04-423-8848
AMERICAN MANUFACTURERS MUTUAL INSURANCE CO
1 Kemper Dr, Long Grove, IL 60047-8955
Tel (847) 320-2000 *Founded/Ownrshp* 1912
Sales NA *EMP* 8,500
SIC 6331 Fire, marine & casualty insurance; Workers' compensation insurance
Pr: Michael A Coutu
**Treas:* Michael P Sullivan

D-U-N-S 10-145-1441 IMP/EXP
AMERICAN MANUFACTURING CORP
555 Croton Rd Ste 200, King of Prussia, PA 19406-3171
Tel (610) 962-3770 *Founded/Ownrshp* 1981
Sales 148.4MM^E *EMP* 2,200
SIC 8748 Business consulting
Ch Bd: Russell C Ball III
Pr: Robert H Strouse
CFO: Timothy J Dwyer
CFO: John F Yaglenski
Treas: Lawrence Heck
VP: Paul F Brennan
VP: Andrew K Janas

D-U-N-S 03-971-8796 IMP
■ **AMERICAN MARAZZI TILE INC**
(*Suby of* DALTILE) ★
7834 C F Hawn Fwy, Dallas, TX 75217-6529
Tel (972) 232-3801 *Founded/Ownrshp* 2013
Sales 169.7MM^E *EMP* 465
SIC 3253 Ceramic wall & floor tile
Pr: Gianni Mattiolo
VP: Dennis Patton
IT Man: Cheri Houghton
Sls Mgr: Stacy Hogan
Sls Mgr: Sara Senn
Art Dir: Brent Luecke

D-U-N-S 82-746-2636
AMERICAN MARITIME HOLDINGS INC
A M H
813 Industrial Ave, Chesapeake, VA 23324-2614
Tel (757) 961-9311 *Founded/Ownrshp* 2005
Sales 174.6MM^E *EMP* 938^E
SIC 3731 7929 Military ships, building & repairing; Entertainers & entertainment groups
Ch Bd: Gary R Brandt
**COO:* Michael Torrech
VP Sls: Victor Brannon

D-U-N-S 80-189-8073 IMP
AMERICAN MARKETING ENTERPRISES INC
(*Suby of* MAX LEATHER) ★
Empir State Bldg 350fit, New York, NY 10018
Tel (646) 839-7000 *Founded/Ownrshp* 2007
Sales 226.8MM^E *EMP* 109
SIC 5137 Women's & children's clothing; Women's & children's lingerie & undergarments
CEO: Dow Famulak
**Pr:* Victor M Azrak
**VP:* Elliott Azrak

AMERICAN MDRN SRPLS LNES INSUR
See AMERICAN MODERN HOME INSURANCE CO

AMERICAN MED SEC FROM PCF CARE
See UNITEDHEALTHCARE LIFE INSURANCE CO

D-U-N-S 16-066-9081
AMERICAN MEDIA INC
301 Yamato Rd Ste 4200, Boca Raton, FL 33431-4933
Tel (561) 997-7733 *Founded/Ownrshp* 2009
Sales 223.0MM *EMP* 2,400
Accts Deloitte & Touche Llp Boca R
SIC 2711 2741 Newspapers; Newspapers: publishing only, not printed on site; Miscellaneous publishing
Ch Bd: David Pecker
Pr: John Swider
Ofcr: Joseph Bilman
**Ofcr:* Brian Krosk
Ex VP: Barbara Harris
Ex VP: Kevin Hyson
Ex VP: Dave Leckey
Ex VP: Daniel Rotstein
Ex VP: Keller Whalen
Sr VP: Michael Esposito
Sr VP: Neil Goldstein
Sr VP: Dave Thompson
VP: Steve Aaron
VP: Robin Chang
VP: Robert Cockburn
VP: Julius Elfe
VP: Saverio Flemma
VP: Bobbie Halfin
VP: Jeffrey Laymon
VP: Ron Minutella
VP: Michelle Myers

D-U-N-S 55-593-4389
AMERICAN MEDIA OPERATIONS INC
1000 American Media Way, Boca Raton, FL 33464-1000
Tel (561) 997-7733 *Founded/Ownrshp* 1999
Sales NA *EMP* 1,389^E
SIC 2711 2741

D-U-N-S 00-521-2287
AMERICAN MEDICAL ASSOCIATION INC (IL)
A M A
330 N Wabash Ave # 39300, Chicago, IL 60611-5885
Tel (312) 464-5000 *Founded/Ownrshp* 1847
Sales 261.3MM *EMP* 1,150
Accts Deloitte Tax Llp Indianapolis
SIC 8621 2721 6321 6282 Medical field-related associations; Trade journals: publishing only, not printed on site; Reinsurance carriers, accident & health; Investment advice
CEO: James Madera
Pr: Andrew W Gurman
COO: Bernard L Hengesbaugh
CFO: Denise M Hagerty
CFO: Gregory Teague
Treas: Herman L Abromowitz
Bd of Dir: Jack Rhian
Trst: Thomas T Flahery
Ofcr: Dave Jaroszewski
Sr VP: Lee J Stillwell
Sr VP: Linn A WEI
VP: Jay Crosson
VP: Craig Ethridge
VP: Deborah Harvey
VP: Omar Hasan
VP: Robert Hobart
VP: Cae Lawler
VP: Mary J Malone
VP: Christine McMahon
VP: Lisa Obrien
Exec: Todd Hey
Board of Directors: Sarah Sanders, Benjamin Schanker, Patricia Turner, Melanie Walker

D-U-N-S 88-314-4552
■ AMERICAN MEDICAL RESPONSE
(*Suby of* ENVISION HEALTHCARE) ★
879 Marlborough Ave, Riverside, CA 92507-2133
Tel (951) 782-5200 *Founded/Ownrshp* 1997
Sales 40.3MM^E *EMP* 1,357
SIC 4119 Ambulance service
Pr: Bill Fanger

D-U-N-S 80-204-4615
■ AMERICAN MEDICAL RESPONSE AMBULANCE SERVICE INC
AMR
(*Suby of* ENVISION HEALTHCARE) ★
879 Marlborough Ave, Riverside, CA 92507-2133
Tel (303) 495-1217 *Founded/Ownrshp* 2007
Sales 6.8MM^E *EMP* 1,813
SIC 4119 Ambulance service
CEO: William A Sanger
**Pr:* Don Harvey
**VP:* Randel Owen
Off Mgr: Lynne Liko

D-U-N-S 79-146-6386
■ AMERICAN MEDICAL RESPONSE INC
ENVISION HEALTHCARE
(*Suby of* ENVISION HEALTHCARE CORP) ★
6363 S Fiddlers Green Cir # 1400, Greenwood Village, CO 80111-5024
Tel (303) 495-1200 *Founded/Ownrshp* 1992
Sales 1.6MMM^E *EMP* 10,153
SIC 4119 Ambulance service
Pr: Edward Van Horne
COO: Rich Bartus
COO: Dan O'Brien
COO: Randy Strozyk
COO: Kurt Williams
**CFO:* Randy Owen
Ofcr: Ross Ronan
Ofcr: Chris Valenzano
**Ex VP:* Steve W Ratton
**Sr VP:* Ron Thackery
VP: John J Connolly
VP: Valerie Gaither
VP: David Lindberg

D-U-N-S 01-949-9805
■ AMERICAN MEDICAL RESPONSE OF MASSACHUSETTS INC
(*Suby of* ENVISION HEALTHCARE) ★
4 Tech Cir, Natick, MA 01760-1029
Tel (508) 650-5600 *Founded/Ownrshp* 1995
Sales 60.6MM^E *EMP* 2,000
SIC 4119 Ambulance service
Genl Mgr: Brendan McNiff

D-U-N-S 00-437-5213
■ AMERICAN MEDICAL RESPONSE OF SOUTHERN CALIFORNIA
(*Suby of* ENVISION HEALTHCARE) ★
1055 W Avenue J, Lancaster, CA 93534-3328
Tel (661) 945-9310 *Founded/Ownrshp* 2000
Sales 22.3MM^E *EMP* 2,806
SIC 4119 Ambulance service
Pr: Louis Meyer
**COO:* Don Harvey
**CFO:* Randel Owen
**Ex VP:* Todd Zimmerman
**VP:* Tim Dorn

D-U-N-S 80-792-1742
■ AMERICAN MEDICAL RESPONSE WEST
AMR
(*Suby of* ENVISION HEALTHCARE) ★
400 S Fresno St, Stockton, CA 95203-3007
Tel (209) 948-5136 *Founded/Ownrshp* 1992
Sales 61.5MM^E *EMP* 3,537^E
SIC 4119 Ambulance service
Pr: William A Sanger
**Pr:* Louis K Meyer
**COO:* Don S Harvey
**CFO:* Timothy Dorn
**CFO:* Randel G Owen
Off Mgr: Lynne Liko

D-U-N-S 03-536-2495
■ AMERICAN MEDICAL SECURITY GROUP INC PAC
(*Suby of* PACIFICARE HEALTH SYSTEMS LLC) ★
3100 Ams Blvd, Green Bay, WI 54313-9700
Tel (920) 661-1111 *Founded/Ownrshp* 2004
Sales NA *EMP* 1,400^E
SIC 6321 6311 Health insurance carriers; Life insurance
Pr: Steven Deraleau
**CFO:* Gregory W Scott
**VP:* Bradford A Bowlus
**VP:* James C Modaff
**VP:* Thomas G Zielinski

D-U-N-S 96-401-3346
■ AMERICAN MEDICAL SECURITY INC
(*Suby of* AMERICAN MED SEC FROM PCF CARE) ★
3100 Ams Blvd, Green Bay, WI 54313-9700
Tel (920) 661-1111 *Founded/Ownrshp* 1996
Sales NA *EMP* 1,300^E
SIC 6324 Hospital & medical service plans
Pr: Sam Miller
CFO: Gary D Gruengerich
Ex VP: Steve De Raleau
Ex VP: Tom Zielinski

D-U-N-S 17-123-2338
AMERICAN MEDICAL SYSTEMS HOLDINGS INC
AMS
(*Suby of* ENDO HEALTH SOLUTIONS INC) ★
10700 Bren Rd W, Hopkins, MN 55343-9679
Tel (952) 930-6000 *Founded/Ownrshp* 2011
Sales 201.9MM^E *EMP* 1,255
SIC 3842 Surgical appliances & supplies
Pr: Camille Farhat
**CFO:* Mark A Heggestad
CFO: Mark Heggestad
Ex VP: James M Call
**Sr VP:* Whitney D Erickson
**Sr VP:* Maximillian D Fiore
**Sr VP:* Jeanne Forneris
**Sr VP:* Joe W Martin
**Sr VP:* John F Nealon
**Sr VP:* Derrill Palidwar
**VP:* Pam Balthazor
VP: Whitney Erickson
VP: Maximillian Fiore
VP: Larry Getlin
**VP:* Susan Thompson

D-U-N-S 12-511-1448
■ AMERICAN MEDICAL SYSTEMS LLC
BOSTON SCIENTIFIC
(*Suby of* BOSTON SCIENTIFIC CORP) ★
10700 Bren Rd W, Minnetonka, MN 55343-9679
Tel (952) 930-6000 *Founded/Ownrshp* 2014
Sales 2.8MM^E *EMP* 1,200
SIC 3842 3841 Surgical appliances & supplies; Surgical & medical instruments
Pr: Camille I Farhat
Bd of Dir: Gerhard W Sennewald
**Sr VP:* Maximillian D Fiore
**Sr VP:* Christine R Kowalski
Sr VP: Joe W Martin
**Sr VP:* John F Nealon
**VP:* Larry Getlin
**VP:* Ginger Glaser
**VP:* Brian Millberg
**VP:* Hans Neisz
VP: Thomas K Rasmussen
VP: Richard D Staples

D-U-N-S 16-169-8956 IMP
AMERICAN MEGATRENDS INC
A M I
5555 Okbrook Pkwy Ste 200, Norcross, GA 30093
Tel (770) 246-8600 *Founded/Ownrshp* 1985
Sales 129.3MM^E *EMP* 680
SIC 3572

D-U-N-S 00-490-6062
AMERICAN MERCHANTS INC
3279 Laurel Canyon Blvd, Studio City, CA 91604-4131
Tel (818) 505-1040 *Founded/Ownrshp* 2012, 2010
Sales 100.0MM *EMP* 18^E
SIC 7389 Credit card service
Owner: Jumish Walia

D-U-N-S 05-907-3288
■ AMERICAN MERCURY INSURANCE CO
(*Suby of* MERCURY GENERAL CORP) ★
7301 Nw Expressway # 200, Oklahoma City, OK 73132-1511
Tel (405) 621-6509 *Founded/Ownrshp* 1997
Sales NA *EMP* 225
SIC 6411 6331 Insurance agents; Property & casualty insurance agent; Automobile insurance; Fire, marine & casualty insurance & carriers
Pr: Gabriel Tirador
**CFO:* Theodore Stalick
**Treas:* Patricia Mullendore
**VP:* Richard L McCathron
IT Man: Judy Garrison

AMERICAN MESSAGING MOBILE
See AMERICAN MESSAGING SERVICES LLC

D-U-N-S 61-715-5809
AMERICAN MESSAGING SERVICES LLC
AMERICAN MESSAGING MOBILE
1720 Lakepointe Dr # 100, Lewisville, TX 75057-6425
Tel (888) 699-9014 *Founded/Ownrshp* 2000
Sales 420.5MM^E *EMP* 1,107^E
SIC 4812 Paging services
CEO: J Roy Pottle
**Pr:* Tom Cook
**Sr VP:* Peter Barnett
**Sr VP:* Jeffrey Chalmers
Opers Mgr: Lyle Baker
VP Sls: Rick Darling
Sls Dir: Randy Smith

D-U-N-S 80-473-1610 IMP
■ AMERICAN METALS CORP
(*Suby of* RELIANCE STEEL & ALUMINUM CO) ★
1499 Parkway Blvd, West Sacramento, CA 95691-5019
Tel (916) 371-7700 *Founded/Ownrshp* 1993
Sales 122.1MM^E *EMP* 150
SIC 5051 Iron or steel flat products; Castings, rough: iron or steel; Steel; Aluminum bars, rods, ingots, sheets, pipes, plates, etc.
CEO: Nicole Heater
CFO: Terry Stahmann
Genl Mgr: Dan Nethaway
Sfty Mgr: John Walls
Sales Asso: Troy Trosin

D-U-N-S 60-676-8265 IMP
■ AMERICAN METER HOLDINGS CORP
(*Suby of* ELSTER GMBH)
1105 N Market St Ste 1300, Wilmington, DE 19801-1241
Tel (302) 477-0208 *Founded/Ownrshp* 1987
Sales 72.2MM^E *EMP* 1,400
SIC 3824 3823 Gas meters, domestic & large capacity: industrial; On-stream gas/liquid analysis instruments, industrial
Pr: Frederick Janssen
**CFO:* Michael W Cunningham
CFO: Jeffrey Dworken

D-U-N-S 83-266-1065
▲ AMERICAN MIDSTREAM PARTNERS LP
2103 Citywest Blvd # 800, Houston, TX 77042-2834
Tel (720) 457-6060 *Founded/Ownrshp* 2009
Sales 236.3MM *EMP* 300^E
Tkr Sym AMID *Exch* NYS
SIC 4922 Natural gas transmission; Pipelines, natural gas; Storage, natural gas
Ch Bd: Lynn L Bourdon III
Genl Pt: American Midstream GP
CFO: Eric T Kalamaras

AMERICAN MITSUBA
See MITSUBA BARDSTOWN INC

D-U-N-S 61-102-8635 IMP
AMERICAN MITSUBA CORP
(*Suby of* MITSUBA CORPORATION)
2945 Three Leaves Dr, Mount Pleasant, MI 48858-4596
Tel (989) 779-4962 *Founded/Ownrshp* 1986
Sales 556.2MM *EMP* 800
Accts Plante & Moran Pllc Auburn H
SIC 3714 Motor vehicle parts & accessories
Pr: Yoshimasa Kimura
Treas: Higeki Miyazaki
**VP:* Mishel Ashtary
**VP:* Yutaka Iijima
**VP:* Shigeki Miyazaki
**VP:* Tetsuya Onai
Board of Directors: David Stevens

AMERICAN MODERN HOME INSUR CO
See AMERICAN MODERN INSURANCE GROUP INC

D-U-N-S 05-215-4119
■ AMERICAN MODERN HOME INSURANCE CO (FL)
AMERICAN MDRN SRPLS LNES INSUR
(*Suby of* AMERICAN MODERN HOME INSUR CO) ★
7000 Midland Blvd, Amelia, OH 45102-2646
Tel (513) 943-7100 *Founded/Ownrshp* 1965, 1994
Sales NA *EMP* 490^E
SIC 6331 Fire, marine & casualty insurance
Prin: Tomothy S Hogan
**Pr:* John Hayden
**Treas:* Jim Tierney
**Ex VP:* Ken Boberg
Sr VP: Patrick Gallagher
**Sr VP:* John Von Lehman
VP: Denny Robich
**Prin:* W Gary King
**Prin:* William McD Kite

D-U-N-S 80-232-7882
■ AMERICAN MODERN INSURANCE GROUP INC
AMERICAN MODERN HOME INSUR CO
(*Suby of* MIDLAND-GUARDIAN CO) ★
7000 Midland Blvd, Amelia, OH 45102-2646
Tel (513) 943-7100 *Founded/Ownrshp* 1994
Sales NA *EMP* 883
SIC 6411 6321 Accident & health insurance carriers; Insurance agents & brokers
Pr: John W Hayden
Pr: Kevin Barber
Pr: Tony Dirksing
Pr: Eric S Hunziker
Pr: Donald Marthey
Pr: Kelda Weber
Pr: Jay W Whittle
**Treas:* James P Tierney
**Chf Mktg O:* Tammy Nelson
VP: Elvia Alaniz
VP: Mike Bowen
**VP:* John Campbell
VP: Robert Capobianco
VP: Kerri Coburn
VP: Joseph G David
VP: Peter Effler
VP: Ted Fischer
VP: Brad Fisher
VP: Paul F Gelter
VP: Kevin Habash
VP: Robert Herich

D-U-N-S 08-550-5642
AMERICAN MORTGAGE SERVICE CO (OH)
ALLSTATE
7324 Kingsgate Way Ste C, West Chester, OH 45069-6514
Tel (513) 452-4120 *Founded/Ownrshp* 1975
Sales NA *EMP* 250
SIC 6162 Mortgage bankers
Ch: Edward W Wolterman
CFO: Phillip Go
**VP:* David Colliver
**VP:* Ronald Gray
VP: Bart Hanselman
Rgnl Mgr: Russ Iona
Brnch Mgr: Don Copeland
Brnch Mgr: Jim Humphries
Brnch Mgr: Rick McCreadie
Brnch Mgr: Joe Smith
Brnch Mgr: Frankie Story

D-U-N-S 06-419-2250
AMERICAN MOTELS ACQUISITION CO LLC
2101 4th Ave Ste 1020, Seattle, WA 98121-2313
Tel (206) 443-3550 *Founded/Ownrshp* 1998
Sales 10.7MM^E *EMP* 1,000^E
SIC 7011 Motels
Pr: Lawrence P Horwitz

D-U-N-S 00-692-8444
AMERICAN MOTORISTS INSURANCE CO
(*Suby of* MIDVALE INDEMNITY CO) ★
1 Kemper Dr, Long Grove, IL 60047-8955
Tel (847) 320-2000 *Founded/Ownrshp* 1926, 1989
Sales NA *EMP* 2,000
SIC 6411 Insurance agents, brokers & service
Ch Bd: David B Mathis
**Pr:* Douglas Sean Andrews
**Pr:* William Douglas Smith
**CFO:* Walter Lucas White
IT Man: Linda Orfanos
Board of Directors: Kenneth A Randall, Jerome R Coleman, Richard N Rosett, Peter B Hamilton, William D Smith, Roberta Segal Karmel, Daniel R Toll, George D Kennedy, Walter L White, Dalton L Knauss, George R Lewis, Katharine C Lyall, Gerald L Meatman, David B Mathis

D-U-N-S 05-638-7442
■ AMERICAN MULTI-CINEMA INC (MO)
AMC
(*Suby of* AMC ENTERTAINMENT INC) ★
1 Amc Way, Leawood, KS 66211
Tel (913) 213-2000 *Founded/Ownrshp* 1947, 1983
Sales 760.1MM^E *EMP* 15,200
SIC 7832 5812 8741 Motion picture theaters, except drive-in; Concessionaire; Management services
CEO: Gerardo Lopez
**Pr:* Terry Crawford
**Pr:* Robert J Lenihan
**CFO:* Craig Ramsey
**Sr VP:* Kevin M Connor
**Sr VP:* Chris A Cox

D-U-N-S 10-568-7560 IMP/EXP
AMERICAN MUNICIPAL POWER INC
AMP-OHIO
1111 Schrock Rd Ste 100, Columbus, OH 43229-1155
Tel (614) 540-1111 *Founded/Ownrshp* 1971
Sales 1.1MMM *EMP* 229
Accts Pricewaterhousecoopers Llp C
SIC 4911 Electric services
Pr: Marc Gerken
**Ch Bd:* Jon Bisher
**CFO:* Robert W Trippe
**Ofcr:* Bobby Little
**Sr VP:* John Bentine
Sr VP: Branndon Kelley
Sr VP: Scott Kiesewetter
**Sr VP:* Pam Sullivan
**Sr VP:* Jolene Thompson
Secur Mgr: David Fields

D-U-N-S 06-120-2768 IMP
AMERICAN MUSEUM OF NATURAL HISTORY
Central Park W At 79th St, New York, NY 10024
Tel (212) 769-5000 *Founded/Ownrshp* 1869
Sales 180.3MM *EMP* 1,262
Accts Grant Thornton Llp New York
SIC 8412 8221 Museum; Colleges universities & professional schools
Ch: Lewis Bernard
V Ch: Roger Altman
**Pr:* Ellen V Futter
COO: Barbara B Gunn
COO: Dawn Melton
CFO: Ellen Gallagher
Bd of Dir: Allen Turner
Ex VP: Lynn Debow
Exec: Anita Caltabiano
Exec: Cindi Hahn
Exec: Lauri Halderman
Exec: Francis Lees
Exec: Ben Oppenheimer
Exec: Beth Wildstein
Dir Lab: Lori Pendleton
Assoc Dir: Daniel Scheiner

AMERICAN NAT PROPERTY & CSLTY
See AMERICAN NATIONAL PROPERTY AND CASUALTY CO

D-U-N-S 00-749-5120
AMERICAN NATIONAL BANK
METRO LEASING COMPANY
(*Suby of* AMERICAN NATIONAL CORPORATION)
8990 W Dodge Rd Ste 1, Omaha, NE 68114-3383
Tel (402) 399-5000 *Founded/Ownrshp* 1979
Sales NA *EMP* 253
SIC 6021 National commercial banks
CEO: Steve Ritzman
**Ch Bd:* John F Kotouc
CFO: Brad Konen
Treas: Andrew Schmillen
Bd of Dir: Deb Vosika
Ex VP: Edward Kelleher
Sr VP: Richard Borst
Sr VP: James W Burns
Sr VP: Nancy J Skoda
VP: Sue Austin
VP: Jim Bauer
VP: Eric Bunderson
VP: Laura Burford
VP: Mike Gee
VP: Cory R Libis
VP: Jeffrey Rezac
VP: Stuart C Sioussat
Exec: Todd Hammock
Dir Risk M: Doug Murphy

D-U-N-S 00-794-8110
AMERICAN NATIONAL BANK OF CHEYENNE INC
(*Suby of* STURM FINANCIAL GROUP INC) ★
3033 E 1st Ave Ste 300, Denver, CO 80206-5619
Tel (303) 394-5100 *Founded/Ownrshp* 1919, 1993
Sales NA *EMP* 99
SIC 6021 National commercial banks
Pr: Tig Hallingbye

Pr: John Masur
Pr: Lonnie Parsons
CEO: Dennis Nathan
Sr VP: Judy Collins
Sr VP: Nancy Harvey
Sr VP: William L Larson
Sr VP: Judy Zezula
VP: Kathy Mawford
VP: Lisa Mills
VP: Dave Ridder
VP: Jennifer Taylor
Exec: Hugh Marshall

D-U-N-S 00-895-3564
AMERICAN NATIONAL BANK OF TEXAS
ANBTX
(*Suby of* ANB HOLDING CO LTD) ★
102 W Moore Ave Lbby, Terrell, TX 75160-3129
Tel (972) 524-3411 *Founded/Ownrshp* 1989
Sales NA *EMP* 480
SIC 6021 National commercial banks
Pr: Robert Hulsey
Ch Bd: Riter C Hulsey
CFO: Robert Messer
Ex VP: Steve Booker
Ex VP: John Davidson

D-U-N-S 00-793-0332
▲ AMERICAN NATIONAL INSURANCE CO INC (TX)
ANICO
1 Moody Plz Fl 18, Galveston, TX 77550-7999
Tel (409) 763-4661 *Founded/Ownrshp* 1905
Sales NA *EMP* 4,736
Tkr Sym ANAT *Exch* NGS
SIC 6351 6311 6321 6324 6331 Credit & other financial responsibility insurance; Life insurance carriers; Accident insurance carriers; Health insurance carriers; Group hospitalization plans; Property damage insurance; Fire, marine & casualty insurance: stock
Ch Bd: James E Pozzi
Pr: Wayne J Cucco
Pr: William Hogan
Pr: Brian Schaffer
CFO: John J Dunn Jr
Ex VP: David A Behrens
Ex VP: Johnny D Johnson
Ex VP: Gregory V Ostergren
Ex VP: James W Pangburn
Ex VP: Hoyt J Strickland
Sr VP: Frank V Broll Jr
Sr VP: William F Carlton
Sr VP: Steven Schouweiler
VP: Mark Andrews
VP: Scott Brast
VP: Linda Dennison
VP: Gordon Dixon
VP: Bruce Pavelka
VP: Kara Phillips
VP: Ronald Price
VP: Mark Walker
Board of Directors: William C Ansell, Frances A Moody-Dahlberg, Arthur O Dummer, James P Payne, Elvin Jerome Pederson, James D Yarbrough

D-U-N-S 61-346-1037
■ AMERICAN NATIONAL LIFE INSURANCE CO OF TEXAS
ANTEX
(*Suby of* ANICO) ★
1 Moody Plz Fl 8, Galveston, TX 77550-7947
Tel (409) 763-4661 *Founded/Ownrshp* 1954
Sales NA *EMP* 30
SIC 6411 6321 Insurance agents, brokers & service; Health insurance carriers
CEO: G Richard Ferdinandtsen
Sr VP: Frank Broll Jr
**Sr VP:* Ronald Jay Welch
VP: D A Behrens
Dir IT: Kim Youngblood
Sftwr Eng: Gordon Hughes

D-U-N-S 07-302-2519
■ AMERICAN NATIONAL PROPERTY AND CASUALTY CO
AMERICAN NAT PROPERTY & CSLTY
(*Suby of* ANICO) ★
1949 E Snshine Corp Cntre, Springfield, MO 65804
Tel (417) 887-0220 *Founded/Ownrshp* 1973
Sales NA *EMP* 850[E]
SIC 6411 Insurance agents
Ch Bd: Greg Ostergren
**Sr VP:* Robert Campbell Jr
**VP:* Janet Clark
VP: Michael M Croskey
**VP:* Bernard Gerwel
VP: Charles Jones
**VP:* Jerry Jones
VP: Ron Koch
**VP:* Michael Mc Croskey
VP: Jeffrey A Sonnenfeld
Mng Dir: John McCaskill
Board of Directors: Charles H Addison, George Ferdinandtsen, Erwin Herz Jr, Ross R Moody, Stephen Pavlicek, Ronald J Welch

D-U-N-S 18-297-9625
■ AMERICAN NATIONAL PROPERTY AND CASUALTY INSURANCE CO
(*Suby of* AMERICAN NAT PROPERTY & CSLTY) ★
1949 E Snshine Corp Cntre, Springfield, MO 65899-0001
Tel (417) 887-0220 *Founded/Ownrshp* 1981
Sales NA *EMP* 802
SIC 6411 Insurance agents, brokers & service
Pr: Greg Ostergren
**Sr VP:* Robert J Campbell
**VP:* Byron Smith

D-U-N-S 00-698-0015
■ AMERICAN NATURAL RESOURCES CO (DE)
(*Suby of* TRANSCANADA CORPORATION)
717 Texas St Ste 2400, Houston, TX 77002-2834
Tel (832) 320-5000 *Founded/Ownrshp* 1901, 2007
Sales 628.6MM[E] *EMP* 1,000[E]
SIC 4922 1311 1222 Pipelines, natural gas; Storage, natural gas; Natural gas production; Underground mining, semianthracite
Pr: Gregory A Lohnes

D-U-N-S 96-270-7159
AMERICAN NEIGHBOURHOOD MORTGAGE ACCEPTANCE CO LLC
ANNIE MAC HOME MORTGAGE
700 E Gate Dr Ste 400, Mount Laurel, NJ 08054-3807
Tel (856) 252-1506 *Founded/Ownrshp* 2010
Sales NA *EMP* 500
SIC 6162 Mortgage bankers
Pr: Joseph Panebianco
**Ex VP:* Matthew Buckley
Brnch Mgr: Brent Duffield

D-U-N-S 93-788-9293
AMERICAN NEWLAND COMMUNITIES LP
9820 Towne Centre Dr # 100, San Diego, CA 92121-1912
Tel (858) 455-7503 *Founded/Ownrshp* 2000
Sales 163.7MM[E] *EMP* 350
SIC 6552 Subdividers & developers
CEO: Ladonna K Monsees
Pr: Jennifer Taylor
Pr: Dave Wood
**COO:* Daniel C Van Epp
**CFO:* Vicki R Mullins
CFO: Noel Webb
Sr VP: Tim C Durie
Sr VP: Douglas Hageman
Sr VP: Keith Hurand
Sr VP: Jim Nyberg
Sr VP: William M Olson
Sr VP: Bruff L Shea
VP: Brian Cramer
VP: Gary Deletegagne
VP: Lori Henriksen
VP: Scott Jones
VP: Bill Meyer
VP: Bill Mumford
VP: Mary Ruby
Dir Risk M: Patricia A Hernandez

D-U-N-S 03-235-8645
AMERICAN NICARAGUAN FOUNDATION INC
A N F
1000 Nw 57th Ct Ste 770, Miami, FL 33126-3288
Tel (305) 374-3391 *Founded/Ownrshp* 1992
Sales 122.9MM *EMP* 4
Accts Crowe Horwath Llp Fort Laude
SIC 8399 8641 Community development groups; Civic social & fraternal associations
Ex Dir: Alvaro Pereira
Ex Dir: Armando Rodriguez

D-U-N-S 05-433-6565 IMP
AMERICAN NTN BEARING MANUFACTURING CORP
ANBM
(*Suby of* NTN USA CORP) ★
1525 Holmes Rd, Elgin, IL 60123-1205
Tel (847) 741-4545 *Founded/Ownrshp* 1990
Sales 83.5MM[E] *EMP* 450
SIC 3562 Ball bearings & parts; Roller bearings & parts
Pr: Andy Kitajima
**Pr:* Katsu Miyake
**Treas:* Hajime Kato
Genl Mgr: Mike Bilyk
Genl Mgr: John Welch

D-U-N-S 09-390-2799
AMERICAN NURSING CARE INC (OH)
(*Suby of* CHI HEALTH AT HOME) ★
1700 Edison Dr Ste 300, Milford, OH 45150-2729
Tel (513) 576-0262 *Founded/Ownrshp* 1976, 1993
Sales 96.0MM[E] *EMP* 4,400
SIC 8051 Skilled nursing care facilities
Pr: Thomas J Karpinski
CFO: Jerry McKinney

D-U-N-S 02-239-6790 EXP
AMERICAN OFFICE EQUIPMENT CO INC
309 N Calvert St, Baltimore, MD 21202-3699
Tel (410) 539-7529 *Founded/Ownrshp* 1932
Sales 119.9MM[E] *EMP* 200
SIC 5021 Office furniture
Pr: David Kuntz
**Sr VP:* Benjamin Kuntz
**Sr VP:* Michael Kuntz
VP: Ed Fleming
VP: Lou Kreiner
VP: Dennis Shea
VP: Nancy Siegel
Dir IT: Vinny Avallone
IT Man: Mike Curran
Sls Dir: Adil Desai
Sls Dir: Denise Ebert-Carlston

D-U-N-S 07-706-2727
AMERICAN ONCOLOGIC HOSPITAL INC
CHASE CANCER CENTER
(*Suby of* FOX CHASE CANCER CENTER FOUNDATION) ★
333 Cottman Ave Frnt, Philadelphia, PA 19111-2496
Tel (215) 214-3264 *Founded/Ownrshp* 1972
Sales 251.5MM *EMP* 725
SIC 8069 Cancer hospital
Pr: Michael V Seiden
**Pr:* Robert Young MD
Treas: R Leedy
Sr VP: Thomas S Albanesi
**VP:* Joseph F Hediger Sr
Netwrk Mgr: Stuart R Lessin

D-U-N-S 01-114-8157 IMP
AMERICAN ORDNANCE LLC
17575 Hwy 79, Middletown, IA 52638
Tel (319) 753-7004 *Founded/Ownrshp* 1998, 1999
Sales 21.6M *EMP* 1,502[E]
SIC 3483 Ammunition loading & assembling plant
Pr: Matt Dibas
VP: Thomas Rudy
Prgrm Mgr: Bob Wright
Genl Mgr: Brock Menold
IT Man: Craig Osborn
IT Man: Burdette Wetzel
VP Opers: Don Halferty
VP Opers: Andrew Wilson
Snr Mgr: Joseph Schilling

D-U-N-S 04-466-8515
AMERICAN ORTHODONTICS CORP
3524 Washington Ave, Sheboygan, WI 53081-6442
Tel (920) 457-5051 *Founded/Ownrshp* 1968
Sales 109.4MM[E] *EMP* 525
SIC 3843 8021

D-U-N-S 07-758-5024 IMP/EXP
AMERICAN PACIFIC CORP
AMPAC
(*Suby of* FLAMINGO PARENT CORP.)
10622 W 6400 N, Cedar City, UT 84721-9016
Tel (435) 865-5000 *Founded/Ownrshp* 2014
Sales 193.2MM[E] *EMP* 160[E]
SIC 2899 Oxidizers, inorganic
Pr: Hal Murdock
**COO:* Dave Thayer
**Treas:* Curtis Grant
**VP:* Layne Benzon
**VP:* Jeffrey Gibson
VP: Kent Richman

D-U-N-S 96-396-1099
AMERICAN PACIFIC MORTGAGE CORP
BIG VALLEY MORTGAGE
3000 Lava Ridge Ct # 200, Roseville, CA 95661-2800
Tel (916) 960-1325 *Founded/Ownrshp* 1996
Sales NA *EMP* 705
SIC 6162 Mortgage bankers & correspondents
CEO: Kurt Reisig
**Pr:* Bill Lowman
**COO:* David Mack
**CFO:* Ralph Hints
Treas: Tom Allen
Ofcr: Victoria Huynh
Sr VP: Keith Becher
VP: Leif A Boyd
**VP:* Mathew Brinitzer
VP: Ned Payant
VP: Eric Reisig

D-U-N-S 06-653-6517 IMP/EXP
AMERICAN PACKAGING CORP
FLEXOGRAPHIC PRINTING
777 Driving Park Ave, Rochester, NY 14613-1591
Tel (585) 254-9500 *Founded/Ownrshp* 1986
Sales 186.3MM[E] *EMP* 575
SIC 2673 3497 2671 2754 2674 Bags: plastic, laminated & coated; Metal foil & leaf; Paper coated or laminated for packaging; Rotogravure printing; Bags: uncoated paper & multiwall
Pr: Peter B Schottland
CFO: Phillip Brinkheide
Ch: Steven Schottland
Ex VP: Jeffery R Koch
VP: Raymond Graham
QA Dir: Ken George
QA Dir: Julie Rieck
Dir IT: Max Engel
Tech Mgr: David Arndt
Tech Mgr: Ed Connor
Tech Mgr: Stephen Rickey

D-U-N-S 12-087-0076
AMERICAN PAPER & PLASTICS INC
AMERICAN PAPER & PROVISIONS
550 S 7th Ave, City of Industry, CA 91746-3120
Tel (626) 444-0000 *Founded/Ownrshp* 1982
Sales 160.6MM[E] *EMP* 119
SIC 5113 Industrial & personal service paper
CEO: Daniel Emrani
Exec: Jacob Handy
Dir Bus: Anthony Paventi
Adv Bd Mbr: Chris Tellez
Dir IT: Marc Holzer
Dir IT: Fred Moaven
IT Man: Angel Hernandez
Opers Mgr: Bob Dohring
Sales Exec: Matthew Beskin
Sales Exec: Jonathan Fink
Sales Exec: Erin McCrink

AMERICAN PAPER & PROVISIONS
See AMERICAN PAPER & PLASTICS INC

D-U-N-S 00-405-2544
AMERICAN PAPER & TWINE CO (TN)
7400 Cockrill Bend Blvd, Nashville, TN 37209-1047
Tel (615) 350-9000 *Founded/Ownrshp* 1926
Sales 241.2MM[E] *EMP* 285
SIC 5113 5087 5112 Industrial & personal service paper; Closures, paper & disposable plastic; Janitors' supplies; Stationery & office supplies
Pr: Robert S Doochin
**Treas:* William D Morris
Genl Mgr: Justin Fahey
Genl Mgr: Jonathan Ramsey
Sls Dir: Cliff Robertson

AMERICAN PATHOLOGY
See AMERICAN ESOTERIC LABORATORIES

D-U-N-S 10-581-2325 IMP/EXP
AMERICAN PETROLEUM CO INC
AMERICAN PETROLEUM PRODUCTS
Km 0 Hm 2 Cam Rr 865, TOA Baja, PR 00949
Tel (787) 794-1985 *Founded/Ownrshp* 1982
Sales 118.3MM *EMP* 80
Accts Jimenez Vazquez & Associates
SIC 5172 Diesel fuel
Pr: Nelson Soto
Sls Mgr: William Martinez

D-U-N-S 05-627-8963
AMERICAN PETROLEUM INSTITUTE INC
API
1220 L St Nw Ste 900, Washington, DC 20005-4070
Tel (202) 682-8000 *Founded/Ownrshp* 1919
Sales 224.3MM[E] *EMP* 250
Accts Tate And Tryon Washington Dc
SIC 1389 Construction, repair & dismantling services
CEO: Jack N Gerard
**Ch Bd:* Larry Nichols
**CFO:* Brenda Hargett
**Treas:* Clarence Cazalot
Ex VP: Louis Finkel
**VP:* Jim Craig
VP: J Elder
**VP:* Jim Ford
VP: William F Keefe
VP: Stacy Linden
VP: Edward Rogers
VP: Lisa Salley
VP: Mark Watson
Exec: Howard Nusbaum
Dir Soc: Cassie A Wiltse

AMERICAN PETROLEUM PRODUCTS
See AMERICAN PETROLEUM CO INC

D-U-N-S 96-350-5453
■ AMERICAN PETROLEUM TANKERS PARENT LLC
(*Suby of* AMERICAN APT NEW INTERMEDIATE HOLDCO LLC)
1777 Sentry Pkwy W, Blue Bell, PA 19422-2207
Tel (215) 367-1804 *Founded/Ownrshp* 2010
Sales 106.2MM *EMP* 18[E]
SIC 4491 4424 Marine cargo handling; Coastwide transportation, freight
Pr: Robert K Kurz
VP: Philip Doherty

D-U-N-S 79-500-4118 IMP
AMERICAN PHOENIX INC
A P I
5500 Wayzata Blvd # 1010, Golden Valley, MN 55416-3551
Tel (763) 591-5035 *Founded/Ownrshp* 1992
Sales 114.0MM[E] *EMP* 400
SIC 3069 Custom compounding of rubber materials
Pr: Alexander Nazarenko
**COO:* Gregory A Lewis
Plnt Mgr: Industial Rubber
Sls Mgr: Mike Amis

D-U-N-S 08-073-9915
■ AMERICAN PHYSICIANS SERVICE GROUP INC (TX)
(*Suby of* PROASSURANCE CORP) ★
1221 S Mo Pac Expy # 200, Austin, TX 78746-6819
Tel (512) 328-0888 *Founded/Ownrshp* 1974, 2010
Sales 84.4MM[E] *EMP* 99
SIC 6282 6741 6411 6211 Investment advice; Management services; Insurance agents, brokers & service; Security brokers & dealers
CEO: Kenneth S Shifrin
**Pr:* Timothy L Lafrey
**CFO:* Marc J Zimmermann
**Sec:* William H Hayes
VP: Vicky Gould
Exec: Phillip Brady

D-U-N-S 18-686-7958
AMERICAN PIZZA PARTNERS LP
PIZZA HUT
7700 E Polo Dr, Wichita, KS 67206-3000
Tel (316) 634-1190 *Founded/Ownrshp* 1987
Sales 93.9MM *EMP* 1,450
SIC 5812 Pizzeria, chain
Genl Pt: Hal Mc Coy
Genl Pt: Hal W McCoy II
CFO: Terry Freund

D-U-N-S 00-810-6205 EXP
AMERICAN PLANT FOOD CORP (TX)
A P F
903 Mayo Shell Rd, Galena Park, TX 77547-3291
Tel (713) 675-2231 *Founded/Ownrshp* 1964
Sales 224.1MM *EMP* 150
Accts John E Turner Pc Houston
SIC 2875 Fertilizers, mixing only
Pr: Jerry L Newcomb
**Pr:* Donald R Ford
**CFO:* Mark A Hembree
**Ex VP:* Tobias M Hlavinka
**VP:* Phillip Kramer
Board of Directors: Kenneth E Winborn III Cha, Thomas M Gattle, Charles R Harrison, John W Jenkins, John R Suddarth, Everett B Williams, Gregory L Winborn

D-U-N-S 07-484-9688
AMERICAN POSTAL WORKERS UNION
APWU
1300 L St Nw Ste 200, Washington, DC 20005-4128
Tel (202) 842-4200 *Founded/Ownrshp* 1971
Sales 52.2MM *EMP* 1,200
Accts Calibre Cpa Group Pllc Bethes
SIC 8631 Labor unions & similar labor organizations
Pr: William Burres
Sr Cor Off: David Daniel
Ex Dir: Al Williams

AMERICAN POWER CONVERSION
See SCHNEIDER ELECTRIC IT USA INC

D-U-N-S 00-211-4643 IMP/EXP
■ AMERICAN PRECISION INDUSTRIES INC
BASCO
(*Suby of* DANAHER CORP) ★
45 Hazelwood Dr, Amherst, NY 14228-2224
Tel (716) 691-9100 *Founded/Ownrshp* 1946, 2000
Sales 211.2MM[E] *EMP* 2,026
SIC 3677 3621 3625 3443 Coil windings, electronic; Inductors, electronic; Motors & generators; Electromagnetic clutches or brakes; Heat exchangers: coolers (after, inter), condensers, etc.; Condensers, steam; Separators, industrial process: metal plate
CEO: James W Bingel

AMERICAN PREMIUM BEVERAGE
See R H BARRINGER DISTRIBUTING CO INC

D-U-N-S 00-691-1648 IMP/EXP
AMERICAN PRESIDENT LINES LTD
APL
(*Suby of* CMA CGM)
16220 N Scottsdale Rd, Scottsdale, AZ 85254-1720
Tel (602) 586-4894 *Founded/Ownrshp* 1983
Sales 534.8MM[E] *EMP* 1,265

SIC 4412 4424 4491 Deep sea foreign transportation of freight; Deep sea domestic transportation of freight; Stevedoring
CEO: Eric L Mensing
Pr: Lars Christian Kastrup
CEO: Nicholas Sartini
CFO: Serge Corbel
Ch: Rodolphe Saade
VP: Eric R Swett
Board of Directors: Edward W Aldridge, E G Frankel

D-U-N-S 07-977-4082
AMERICAN PRIDE PAPER & PLASTIC LLC
601 Prospect St, Lakewood, NJ 08701-4628
Tel (732) 367-4444 *Founded/Ownrshp* 2013
Sales 110.0MM *EMP* 100
SIC 5162 Plastics products

D-U-N-S 94-387-9320
AMERICAN PRODUCT DISTRIBUTORS INC
A P D
8350 Arrowridge Blvd, Charlotte, NC 28273-5755
Tel (704) 522-9411 *Founded/Ownrshp* 1992
Sales 121.1MME *EMP* 50
SIC 5111 5112 5047 5044 5085 5087 Printing & writing paper; Stationery & office supplies; Medical equipment & supplies; Copying equipment; Industrial supplies; Janitors' supplies
CEO: C Ray Kennedy
**Pr:* Cy Kennedy
**Sr VP:* Eva Dinion
IT Man: Darlisa King
Mktg Dir: Cynthia Mason

D-U-N-S 04-786-6033 IMP/EXP
AMERICAN PROMOTIONAL EVENTS INC
TNT FIREWORKS
4511 Helton Dr, Florence, AL 35630-6239
Tel (256) 284-1003 *Founded/Ownrshp* 1966
Sales 134.4MME *EMP* 330
SIC 5092 5999 Fireworks; Foam & foam products
CEO: Terry Anderson
**Pr:* Tommy Glasgow
Pr: Genice Nelson
CFO: Kim Kraft
VP: Jan Johnson
VP: Kathie Pendergrass
VP: Michael Shook
VP: Brian Trim
VP: Peter Yu
Area Mgr: Harlan Horvath
Genl Mgr: David Butler

D-U-N-S 04-442-3106
AMERICAN PROPERTY-MANAGEMENT CORP
ALBUQUERQUE PROP MGT
8910 University Center Ln # 100, San Diego, CA 92122-1029
Tel (858) 964-5500 *Founded/Ownrshp* 1994
Sales 142.3MME *EMP* 6,600
SIC 6531 Real estate agents & managers
Pr: Michael Gallegos
**COO:* Eric Kaplan
**CFO:* Alfred Segovia
**VP:* Kim Dailey
**Prin:* Jim Long
Genl Mgr: Victor Barothy-Langer

D-U-N-S 09-254-0962
AMERICAN PROTECTION INSURANCE CO INC
AMPICO
(*Suby of* MIDVALE INDEMNITY CO) ★
1 Kemper Dr, Long Grove, IL 60047-8955
Tel (847) 320-2000 *Founded/Ownrshp* 1973
Sales NA *EMP* 2,700
SIC 6411 Insurance agents, brokers & service
CEO: Robert L Smialek
**Pr:* Mike Coutu
**Pr:* William E Simmons
COO: Peter Imbrogno
CFO: Frederick Griffith
CFO: Murel Josephson
CFO: Ed Mullen
CFO: Keith Yoder
Treas: Andrew G Cooke
**Treas:* Robert Stacy
Ofcr: Katherine Slonina
Sr VP: Sue A Coughlin
**VP:* James S Kemper III

D-U-N-S 08-635-2101
AMERICAN PSYCHOLOGICAL ASSOCIATION INC
A P A
750 1st St Ne Ste 605, Washington, DC 20002-8009
Tel (202) 336-5500 *Founded/Ownrshp* 1892
Sales 130.4MM *EMP* 550E
Accts Bdo Usa Llp Mc Lean Va
SIC 8621 Scientific membership association
CEO: Norman B Anderson
CFO: Susan Graves
**CFO:* Archie L Turner
Assoc Dir: Garth Fowler
Assoc Dir: Tia Scales
Ex Dir: Anthony Jackson
Ex Dir: Nancy Moore
Mng Dir: Catherine Wattenberg
Genl Couns: John Dovidio
Board of Directors: Suzanne B Johnson, Michael Wertheimer

D-U-N-S 60-367-4750
▲ AMERICAN PUBLIC EDUCATION INC
APEI
111 W Congress St, Charles Town, WV 25414-1621
Tel (304) 724-3700 *Founded/Ownrshp* 1991
Sales 327.9MM *EMP* 2,210E
Tkr Sym APEI *Exch* NGS
SIC 8221 Colleges universities & professional schools; University
Pr: Wallace E Boston Jr
**Ch Bd:* Barbara G Fast
CFO: Richard W Sunderland Jr
Ofcr: Peter W Gibbons
Ex VP: Karan Powell

D-U-N-S 92-987-5615
▲ AMERICAN RAILCAR INDUSTRIES INC
ARI
100 Clark St, Saint Charles, MO 63301-2075
Tel (636) 940-6000 *Founded/Ownrshp* 1988
Sales 889.3MM *EMP* 2,407E
Tkr Sym ARII *Exch* NGS
SIC 3743 8742 Railroad equipment; Railroad equipment, except locomotives; Freight cars & equipment; Transportation consultant
Pr: Jeffrey S Hollister
**Ch Bd:* Sunghwan Cho
CFO: Luke M Williams
Sr VP: Yevgeny Fundler
VP: Harold Storz
CIO: Subbu Subramanian
Opers Mgr: Larry Culligan
Board of Directors: Jonathan Christodoro, Jonathan Frates, J Mike Laisure, James C Pontious, Harold First

D-U-N-S 04-036-5876
AMERICAN REALTY ASSOCIATES INC
801 N Brand Blvd Ste 800, Glendale, CA 91203-3237
Tel (818) 545-1152 *Founded/Ownrshp* 1991
Sales 85.3MME *EMP* 134
SIC 6282 Investment advice
CEO: Stanley L Iezman
Pr: Scott Darling
Mng Dir: Daniel Robinson
CIO: Raymond E Kivett

D-U-N-S 96-727-6416
■ AMERICAN REALTY CAPITAL HEALTHCARE TRUST INC
AR CAPITAL
(*Suby of* REALTY INCOME CORP) ★
1065 Ave Of The Amer # 23, New York, NY 10018-0976
Tel (212) 415-6500 *Founded/Ownrshp* 2011
Sales 125.3MM *EMP* 2
SIC 6798 Real estate investment trusts
CEO: Thomas P D'Arcy
**Ch Bd:* Nicholas S Schorsch
**Pr:* Michael Weil
**COO:* Edward F Lange Jr
**Ex VP:* Peter M Budko
**Sr VP:* Boris Korotkin
VP: Benjamin T Hatz
VP: Ross Sanders

D-U-N-S 08-002-9785
AMERICAN REALTY CAPITAL OPERATING PARTNERSHIP II LP
405 Park Ave Fl 15, New York, NY 10022-9406
Tel (212) 415-6500 *Founded/Ownrshp* 2015
Sales 247.5MM *EMP* 1E
SIC 6733 Trusts
CFO: Katie Kurtz

D-U-N-S 87-295-1863
▲ AMERICAN REALTY INVESTORS INC
1603 Lbj Fwy Ste 800, Dallas, TX 75234-6061
Tel (469) 522-4200 *Founded/Ownrshp* 1999
Sales 104.1MM *EMP* 361
Accts Farmer Fuqua & Huff Pc Rich
Tkr Sym ARL *Exch* NYS
SIC 6798 6162 6513 6512 Real estate investment trusts; Mortgage bankers & correspondents; Apartment building operators; Commercial & industrial building operation; Shopping center, property operation only
Pr: Daniel J Moos
**Ch Bd:* Henry A Butler
CFO: Gene S Bertcher
Ex VP: Louis J Corna
Ex VP: Alfred Crozier
Ex VP: David Starowicz
VP: Robert Waldman

D-U-N-S 00-325-5213 IMP/EXP
AMERICAN RED CROSS
431 18th St Nw, Washington, DC 20006-5304
Tel (202) 737-8300 *Founded/Ownrshp* 1881
Sales 2.4MMME *EMP* 34,978
SIC 8322

D-U-N-S 02-195-7329 IMP/EXP
AMERICAN REFINING GROUP INC
77 N Kendall Ave, Bradford, PA 16701-1726
Tel (814) 368-1200 *Founded/Ownrshp* 1976
Sales 170.2MME *EMP* 310
SIC 5171 2911

D-U-N-S 07-245-8946
AMERICAN RELIABLE INSURANCE CO
(*Suby of* GLOBAL INDEMNITY GROUP INC) ★
8655 E Via De Ventura E200, Scottsdale, AZ 85258-3390
Tel (480) 483-8666 *Founded/Ownrshp* 2015
Sales NA *EMP* 1,641E
SIC 6331 Property damage insurance
Pr: Rober Hill
Sr Pt: Dylan Place
Sr Pt: Wim D Raak
Sr VP: Doug Ulery
VP: Philip Camacho
VP: Wim Den Draak
VP: Paula Nysrom
VP: Patricia Quint
Div Mgr: Bruce Petersen
IT Man: Robert Byrd
IT Man: Chris Gatlin

AMERICAN RELOCATION SERVICES
See AMERICAN FAST FREIGHT INC

D-U-N-S 96-955-3002
▲ AMERICAN RENAL ASSOCIATES HOLDINGS INC
500 Cummings Ctr Ste 6550, Beverly, MA 01915-6539
Tel (978) 922-3080 *Founded/Ownrshp* 1999
Sales 657.5MM *EMP* 4,030E
Accts Grant Thornton Llp Boston Ma
Tkr Sym ARA *Exch* NYS
SIC 8092 Kidney dialysis centers
Ch Bd: Joseph A Carlucci
**Pr:* Syed T Kamal
COO: John J McDonough
CFO: Jonathan L Wilcox
VP: Jan S Bernardy
VP: Jason Boucher
VP: Michael R Costa
VP: Jeff Dale
Off Mgr: Stacey Jolin
Off Admin: Cindy Cosentino
CIO: Robert Laramie
Board of Directors: Michael E Boxer, Thomas W Erickson, Jared S Hendricks, John M Jureller, Patrick T Ryan, Steven M Silver

D-U-N-S 07-663-3408
■ AMERICAN RENAL ASSOCIATES LLC
(*Suby of* AMERICAN RENAL HOLDINGS INC) ★
500 Cummings Ctr Ste 6550, Beverly, MA 01915-6539
Tel (978) 922-3080 *Founded/Ownrshp* 1999
Sales 191.3MME *EMP* 1,000
SIC 8092 Kidney dialysis centers
CEO: Joseph A Carlucci
**Ch Bd:* Christopher T Ford
**Pr:* Syed T Kamal
**COO:* John McDonough
Exec: Richard Fishpaw
IT Man: John Delpero

D-U-N-S 07-875-7578
■ AMERICAN RENAL HOLDINGS INC
(*Suby of* AMERICAN RENAL ASSOCIATES HOLDINGS INC) ★
500 Cummings Ctr Ste 6550, Beverly, MA 01915-6539
Tel (978) 922-3080 *Founded/Ownrshp* 1999
Sales 192.0MME *EMP* 1,000E
SIC 8092 Kidney dialysis centers
Pr: Syed Kamal
COO: John J McDonough
CFO: Jonathan L Wilcox
**Treas:* John McDonough

D-U-N-S 04-848-1618 IMP
■ AMERICAN REPROGRAPHICS CO LLC
A R C
(*Suby of* ARC DOCUMENT SOLUTIONS INC) ★
1981 N Broadway Ste 385, Walnut Creek, CA 94596-8214
Tel (925) 949-5100 *Founded/Ownrshp* 1997
Sales 262.2MME *EMP* 1,500
SIC 8744 7334 Facilities support services; Photocopying & duplicating services
CEO: K Suriyakumar
COO: Nick Spence
**COO:* Dilantha Wijesuriya
**CFO:* John E D Toth
Bd of Dir: Kumarakulas Suriyakumar
**Ex VP:* Ted Buscaglia
**VP:* Jorge Avalos
VP: Steve Biernbaum
VP: Dennis Dillon
VP: Dick Hill
VP: Glen Prezembel

D-U-N-S 04-561-4013
AMERICAN REPUBLIC INSURANCE CO
AMERICARE
(*Suby of* AMERICAN ENTERPRISE MUTUAL HOLDING CO) ★
601 6th Ave, Des Moines, IA 50309-1695
Tel (515) 245-2000 *Founded/Ownrshp* 1929
Sales NA *EMP* 891
SIC 6324 Hospital & medical service plans
Pr: Michael E Abbott
**Treas:* Brian Sellner
Dir IT: Lyle Carpenter

D-U-N-S 07-845-1055
AMERICAN RESIDENTIAL PROPERTIES LLC
7033 E Greenway Pkwy # 210, Scottsdale, AZ 85254-2083
Tel (480) 474-4800 *Founded/Ownrshp* 2008
Sales 86.8MM *EMP* 2E
SIC 6799 Real estate investors, except property operators
Pr: Laurie Hawke
Sr VP: Jay Byce

D-U-N-S 07-053-1868
AMERICAN RESIDENTIAL SERVICES LLC
ARS OF MEMPHIS
965 Ridge Lake Blvd # 201, Memphis, TN 38120-9401
Tel (901) 271-9700 *Founded/Ownrshp* 2014
Sales 2.7MMME *EMP* 8,030
SIC 1711 Plumbing, heating, air-conditioning contractors
CEO: Don Karnes
**COO:* David Slott
**CFO:* James McMahon
Chf Mktg O: Brad Cumings
Sr VP: John J Hayes
Sr VP: Christy Luttrell
Sr VP: Frank N Meditch
VP: Terri L Hardt
VP: Tim Hill
VP: Jim McMahon
VP: Ken Peterson

D-U-N-S 93-896-3634
AMERICAN RESIDENTIAL SERVICES OF INDIANA INC
(*Suby of* ARS OF MEMPHIS) ★
10403 Baur Blvd Ste E, Saint Louis, MO 63132-1910
Tel (314) 812-6000 *Founded/Ownrshp* 1999
Sales 578.2MME *EMP* 7,500
SIC 1711 1731 1799 5722 Plumbing contractors; Heating systems repair & maintenance; Heating & air conditioning contractors; Mechanical contractor; General electrical contractor; Appliance installation; Electric household appliances
Pr: William E Le Baron
**COO:* David Slott
CFO: James T McMahon
**CFO:* Stanley J Zalik
VP: Robert H Dejong
VP: Lorne G Dillon
VP: Gary Myers
VP: Rick Pfeiffer
VP: Ed Phelan
VP: Gary Schultz
VP: David Thiessen

D-U-N-S 15-394-5860
AMERICAN RESTAURANT GROUP INC
STUART ANDERSON'S BLACK ANGUS
4410 El Camino Real # 201, Los Altos, CA 94022-1070
Tel (650) 949-6400 *Founded/Ownrshp* 1986
Sales NA *EMP* 5,000
SIC 5812 5813 Eating places; Drinking places
CEO: Meredith Taylor
COO: Bruce Macdiarmid
**CFO:* Rick Rokson
**CFO:* Bill G Taves
CFO: William G Taves
**VP:* Patrick J Kelvie
Dir IT: Joseph Trietsch

D-U-N-S 18-650-9071
▲ AMERICAN RESTAURANT PARTNERS LP
PIZZA HUT
3020 N Cypress St Ste 100, Wichita, KS 67226-4010
Tel (316) 634-1190 *Founded/Ownrshp* 1987
Sales 34.3MME *EMP* 2,100
Accts Regier Carr & Monroe Llp
Tkr Sym ICTPU *Exch* OTO
SIC 5812 Pizzeria, chain
Genl Pt: Hal W McCoy
Pt: Terry Freund
Mktg Dir: Linda Carrier

D-U-N-S 08-954-9737
■ AMERICAN RETIREMENT CORP
(*Suby of* BROOKDALE SENIOR LIVING) ★
111 Westwood Pl Ste 200, Brentwood, TN 37027-1014
Tel (615) 221-2250 *Founded/Ownrshp* 2006
Sales 223.1MME *EMP* 10,400
SIC 8051 Skilled nursing care facilities
Pr: W E Sheriff
COO: Gregory B Richard
CFO: Bryan Richardson
Ex VP: George Hicks
Ex VP: H Todd Kaestner
Ex VP: Todd Kaestner
Ex VP: James T Money
Sr VP: Tom G Downs
Sr VP: Terry Frisby
VP: Eddie Fenoglio
VP: Sheila Garner
Dir Surg: Terry Myers

D-U-N-S 05-696-3911
■ AMERICAN RIVER TRANSPORTATION CO LLC
ARTCO
(*Suby of* ARCHER-DANIELS-MIDLAND CO) ★
4666 E Faries Pkwy, Decatur, IL 62526-5630
Tel (217) 424-5200 *Founded/Ownrshp* 1971
Sales 144.7MME *EMP* 1,500
SIC 4449 River transportation, except on the St. Lawrence Seaway
Pr: Royce Wilkin
**VP:* Gene Senesac

D-U-N-S 03-685-7498
AMERICAN ROCK SALT CO LLC
3846 Retsof Rd, Retsof, NY 14539
Tel (585) 991-6878 *Founded/Ownrshp* 1997
Sales 1.0MMME *EMP* 385
SIC 1479 5169 Rock salt mining; Salts, industrial
Ch Bd: Gunther Buerman
**CFO:* Ann Blake
CFO: Ray Nartel
**Prin:* Joseph G Bucci
Genl Mgr: Justin Curley
Sls Mgr: Barb Heller

D-U-N-S 00-167-2617 IMP/EXP
AMERICAN ROLAND FOOD CORP (NY)
71 W 23rd St Ste 1500, New York, NY 10010-4103
Tel (800) 221-4030 *Founded/Ownrshp* 2013
Sales 245.0MM *EMP* 100
SIC 5149 Canned goods: fruit, vegetables, seafood, meats, etc.
Ch Bd: Charles E Scheidt
**CEO:* James Wagner
**CFO:* Richard Frame
**CFO:* Ted McCormick
Ex VP: Tyler Hawes
QA Dir: Jillian Rosenthal
Pr Dir: Lisa Kartzman

D-U-N-S 00-514-0918 IMP
AMERICAN ROLLER CO LLC
1440 13th Ave, Union Grove, WI 53182-1560
Tel (262) 878-8665 *Founded/Ownrshp* 1938
Sales 104.5MME *EMP* 310
SIC 3549 3548 Metalworking machinery; Electric welding equipment; Gas welding equipment
CEO: Charles J Tasch
Brnch Mgr: Bob Langley
Off Mgr: Joan Thompson
Off Admin: Joen Franko
Prd Mgr: Howard Sanchez
Mktg Mgr: Stephannie Crane
Manager: Rob Pierson
Sls Mgr: Jon Souder

AMERICAN RV & MARINE
See AMERICAN RV CENTERS LLC

D-U-N-S 78-453-0144
AMERICAN RV CENTERS LLC
AMERICAN RV & MARINE
(*Suby of* FREEDOMROADS LLC) ★
14303 Central Ave Nw, Albuquerque, NM 87121-7704
Tel (505) 293-1983 *Founded/Ownrshp* 2004
Sales 358.4ME *EMP* 2,283E
SIC 5561 Motor homes
Genl Mgr: Greg Doney

AMERICAN SAFETY RAZOR COMPANY
See OLD RAZOR CO LLC

D-U-N-S 87-837-4961
AMERICAN SALES AND MANAGEMENT ORGANIZATION LLC
EULEN AMERICA
7200 Corp Ctr Dr Ste 206, Miami, FL 33126
Tel (305) 269-2700 *Founded/Ownrshp* 1994
Sales 98.4MM^E *EMP* 2,005
SIC 7382 7349 7363 Security systems services; Janitorial service, contract basis; Pilot service, aviation
CEO: Luis Rodriguez Lopez
CFO: Brent Blake

D-U-N-S 80-918-3973 IMP
AMERICAN SALES CO LLC
(*Suby of* AFS) ★
4201 Walden Ave, Lancaster, NY 14086-1591
Tel (716) 686-7000 *Founded/Ownrshp* 1992
Sales 203.8MM^E *EMP* 600
SIC 5199 5122 General merchandise, non-durable; Drugs & drug proprietaries
Pr: John Rishton
**Sec:* Brian Hotarek
**Sr VP:* Steve Neeley
VP: Haberl Norman
VP: Patricia Pangel

D-U-N-S 60-231-1508
■ **AMERICAN SAVINGS BANK FSB**
(*Suby of* HEI DIVERSIFIED INC)
915 Fort Street Mall, Honolulu, HI 96813-5604
Tel (808) 627-6900 *Founded/Ownrshp* 1988
Sales NA *EMP* 375
SIC 6035 Federal savings banks
Pr: Richard Wacker
**CFO:* Heather Schwarm
**Chf Cred:* Terence Yeh
**Ex VP:* Gabriel Lee
Ex VP: Arlene Nakaamoto
Ex VP: Arlene M Nakamoto
Ex VP: Allen K Ono
**Ex VP:* Rick Robel
**Ex VP:* Natalie Taniguchi
VP: Betty Brow
VP: Susan Lau
VP: Dan Oshima

D-U-N-S 00-176-7763 IMP/EXP
■ **AMERICAN SCIENCE AND ENGINEERING INC** (MA)
(*Suby of* OSI SYSTEMS INC) ★
829 Middlesex Tpke, Billerica, MA 01821-3907
Tel (978) 262-8700 *Founded/Ownrshp* 1958, 2016
Sales 102.9MM *EMP* 245^E
SIC 7389 8734 7382 Industrial & commercial equipment inspection service; Inspection & testing services; Safety inspection service; X-ray inspection service, industrial; Security systems services; Protective devices, security
Pr: Charles P Dougherty
**CFO:* Diane J Basile
Sr VP: Kenneth Breur
Sr VP: Michael N Tropeano
VP: Joseph Callerame
VP: John Chrisos
VP: Paul Grazewski
VP: David P Hack
VP Bus Dev: Richard Mastronardi
Prgrm Mgr: Monique Faucher
Sftwr Eng: Eric Lizotte

D-U-N-S 04-364-0593 IMP/EXP
AMERICAN SEAFOODS CO LLC
(*Suby of* AMERICAN SEAFOODS GROUP LLC) ★
2025 1st Ave Ste 900, Seattle, WA 98121-2154
Tel (206) 448-0300 *Founded/Ownrshp* 2006
Sales 52.9MM^E *EMP* 1,000
SIC 0912 0921 2092 Finfish; Pollack, catching of; Whiting, catching of; Fish hatcheries; Fresh or frozen packaged fish; Fish, frozen: prepared; Fish fillets
Pr: Micheal Hyde
CIO: Dar Khaligi
CTO: Hugh Holman
QA Dir: Rich Draves
Dir IT: Mitch Stewart

D-U-N-S 13-943-8720 IMP
AMERICAN SEAFOODS GROUP LLC
(*Suby of* ASG CONSOLIDATED LLC) ★
2025 1st Ave Ste 900, Seattle, WA 98121-3123
Tel (206) 374-1515 *Founded/Ownrshp* 2000
Sales 168.9MM^E *EMP* 1,000
SIC 5421 5146 Fish & seafood markets; Fish & seafoods
Ch Bd: Bernt O Bodal
**Pr:* Inge Andreassen
**COO:* Jeffrey Davis
**CFO:* Brad Bodenman
Ofcr: Matthew Latimer
Ofcr: Jim Rosselot
VP: Sabry Hefny
Opers Mgr: Jennifer Adamski
Mktg Mgr: Dustin Carlson

D-U-N-S 80-358-9691 IMP/EXP
AMERICAN SEAFOODS LP
2025 1st Ave Ste 900, Seattle, WA 98121-3123
Tel (206) 374-1515 *Founded/Ownrshp* 2000
Sales 168.9MM^E *EMP* 1,001
SIC 5421 5146 Fish & seafood markets; Fish & seafoods
Pt: Bernt O Bodal
Pr: Inge Andreassen
CFO: Brad Bodenman
Ex VP: Scott McNair
VP: Ronald Rogness
VP: Glenn Sumida
Prin: Matthew D Latimer
IT Man: Joe Guptill

D-U-N-S 00-602-4749 IMP/EXP
AMERICAN SEATING CO (DE)
401 Amrcan Seating Ctr Nw, Grand Rapids, MI 49504-4499
Tel (616) 732-6600 *Founded/Ownrshp* 1886
Sales 122.4MM^E *EMP* 500
Accts Plante & Moran Pllc
SIC 2522 2531 Office furniture, except wood; Vehicle furniture; Stadium seating
CEO: Edward J Clark
**Pr:* Thomas E Bush
VP: Deb McDermott
**VP:* Keith A McDowell
**VP:* David B McLaughlin
VP: Sandra Mesler
VP: Fritz Owen
**VP:* Bruce R Weener
VP: Bruce Weener
CIO: Aaron Stein
Opers Mgr: John Dinsmore
Board of Directors: William J Fisher

D-U-N-S 92-952-8693 IMP/EXP
▲ **AMERICAN SECURITIES LLC**
299 Park Ave Fl 34, New York, NY 10171-3805
Tel (212) 476-8000 *Founded/Ownrshp* 1994
Sales 1.8MMM^E *EMP* 4,481
SIC 6799 Investors
CEO: Michael G Fisch
Chf Inves: Neil Goldstein
Ofcr: Jeremy Maco
Ofcr: Robert Schaefer
VP: Steve Bakerink
VP: Jamie Jacobs
VP: Michael Leamer
VP: Aaron Maeng
VP: Jim Nelles
VP: David Xu
Mng Dir: Loren Easton

D-U-N-S 05-101-4306
■ **AMERICAN SECURITY INSURANCE CO**
ASSURANT SOLUTIONS
(*Suby of* ASSURANT INC) ★
260 Interstate N Cir Se, Atlanta, GA 30339-2210
Tel (770) 763-1000 *Founded/Ownrshp* 2000
Sales NA *EMP* 1,400^E
SIC 6331 Fire, marine & casualty insurance
CEO: Gene Mergelmeyer
**Pr:* Robert Pollock
Pr: Tammy Schultz
Pr: Karen Smith
**CEO:* S Craig Lemasters
**COO:* Shawn Marcotte
CFO: R Klotz
**CFO:* Adam Lamnin
**Ex VP:* Michael D Anderson
**Ex VP:* Manuel Becerra
Ex VP: Joseph E Erdeman
Ex VP: Thomas Rocca
**Ex VP:* Gerald Tassa
**Sr VP:* Gregory Dechurch
Sr VP: Gilles Giacosa
Sr VP: Ivan L Morales
**Sr VP:* Ana Rojas-Filliben
VP: Maria Cabral
VP: Allen Cheatham
VP: Deandrea Foote
VP: Gary Mann

D-U-N-S 07-135-6208
AMERICAN SECURITY LLC
1717 University Ave W, Saint Paul, MN 55104-3687
Tel (651) 644-1155 *Founded/Ownrshp* 1976
Sales 51.3MM^E *EMP* 1,055
SIC 7381 Protective services, guard; Armored car services
CEO: Guy Mingo
Dir Sec: Kelly Boylan
Area Mgr: John Baker
Genl Mgr: John Kerr
IT Man: Lawrence May
Sales Exec: Scott Froehlich

D-U-N-S 07-846-3967
AMERICAN SECURITY OF GREENVILLE LLC
(*Suby of* AMERICAN SERVICES INC) ★
1300 Rutherford Rd, Greenville, SC 29609-3100
Tel (864) 292-7450 *Founded/Ownrshp* 2012
Sales 15.0MM^E *EMP* 1,300
SIC 7381 Security guard service
CEO: Henry C Harrison Jr

D-U-N-S 02-364-0162
AMERICAN SERVICE CENTER ASSOCIATES OF ALEXANDRIA LLC
200 S Pickett St, Alexandria, VA 22304-4702
Tel (703) 284-2490 *Founded/Ownrshp* 2002
Sales 144.4MM^E *EMP* 325
SIC 5511 7538 Automobiles, new & used; General automotive repair shops
Exec: Guadalupe Velarde
Genl Mgr: Peter Collins
Sls Mgr: Charisse Ebb
Sales Asso: AVI Baider
Sales Asso: Alvin Daniels
Sales Asso: Jay-AR Williams

D-U-N-S 03-009-4999
AMERICAN SERVICES INC (SC)
1300 Rutherford Rd, Greenville, SC 29609-3100
Tel (864) 292-7450 *Founded/Ownrshp* 1975
Sales 96.3MM^E *EMP* 4,000
SIC 7381 7349 7363 Security guard service; Detective agency; Janitorial service, contract basis; Temporary help service
CEO: Henry C Harrison
**Pr:* Jim M Ward

D-U-N-S 17-829-7297 IMP/EXP
AMERICAN SHOWA INC
(*Suby of* SHOWA CORPORATION)
707 W Cherry St, Sunbury, OH 43074-9595
Tel (740) 965-1133 *Founded/Ownrshp* 1986
Sales 141.8MM^E *EMP* 1,149
SIC 3714

D-U-N-S 80-745-4079
AMERICAN SHRINKWRAP CO
1901 Mason Ave, Daytona Beach, FL 32117-5123
Tel (800) 229-2904 *Founded/Ownrshp* 1993
Sales 192.0MM *EMP* 2
SIC 5084 Processing & packaging equipment
Pr: Caryn Cordoma

D-U-N-S 19-621-2679 EXP
AMERICAN SIGNATURE HOME
(*Suby of* VALUE CITY) ★
161 Brandon Town Ctr Dr, Brandon, FL 33511-4754
Tel (813) 315-1120 *Founded/Ownrshp* 2005
Sales 71.8MM^E *EMP* 5,007^E
SIC 5712 Furniture stores
Genl Mgr: Jay Genneari
Exec: Jesse Osborn

D-U-N-S 11-212-6573
AMERICAN SIGNATURE INC
VALUE CITY
(*Suby of* VALUE CITY) ★
4300 E 5th Ave, Columbus, OH 43219-1816
Tel (614) 449-6107 *Founded/Ownrshp* 2002
Sales 345.6MM^E *EMP* 4,000
SIC 7389 Furniture finishing
Pr: Jonathan Schottenstein
Ofcr: Steve Ditommaso
Ofcr: Tod Friedman
Ex VP: Bryan Beam
Ex VP: Bryan Woods
VP: Jim Draper
VP: Dannielle Mlynek
Exec: Craig Bigham
Rgnl Mgr: Lorraine Henicheck
Rgnl Mgr: Adam Smith
Dir IT: Fred Needham

D-U-N-S 06-185-1942
AMERICAN SMARTPHONE INC (UT)
SAYGUS
10421 S Jordan Gtwy # 500, South Jordan, UT 84095-3901
Tel (801) 748-1780 *Founded/Ownrshp* 2008
Sales 5.0MMM *EMP* 35
SIC 3663 Mobile communication equipment
Pr: Roger Yack
**CEO:* Chad Sayers
VP: Chris Baker
CTO: Tim Riker

D-U-N-S 07-327-2304
AMERICAN SOCIETY FOR PREVENTION OF CRUELTY TO ANIMALS (INC)
A S P C A
424 E 92nd St, New York, NY 10128-6804
Tel (212) 876-7700 *Founded/Ownrshp* 1866
Sales 171.6MM *EMP* 350^E
Accts Kpmg Llp New York Ny
SIC 8699 Animal humane society
Pr: Edwin J Sayres
**Ch Bd:* James L Nederlander
**Ch Bd:* Frederick Tanne
**Ch Bd:* Tim Wray
**CFO:* Julia Nelson
CFO: Eudene Stephen
**Treas:* Fredrik G Gradin
Sr VP: Gail Buchwald
Sr VP: Sarah Goodstine
Sr VP: Todd Hendricks
Sr VP: Julie Morris
Sr VP: Nancy Perry
Sr VP: Art Rios
Sr VP: Jed Rogers
Sr VP: Stacy Wolf
VP: Ann Church
VP: Elysia Howard
Comm Dir: Elizabeth Estroff
Board of Directors: Thomas Belden, Mary Jo White

D-U-N-S 07-326-9474
AMERICAN SOCIETY FOR TECHNION-ISRAEL INSTITUTE OF TECHNOLOGY INC
AMERICAN TECHNION SOCIETY
55 E 59th St Fl 14, New York, NY 10022-1710
Tel (212) 407-6300 *Founded/Ownrshp* 1940
Sales 91.6MM *EMP* 96
Accts Grant Thornton Llp New York
SIC 8399 Fund raising organization, non-fee basis
V Ch Bd: Lewis Weston
**Treas:* Robert Davidow
Treas: Nina Sabban
**Ex VP:* Melvyn H Bloom
VP: Jeffrey Sussman

D-U-N-S 14-867-4880
AMERICAN SOCIETY OF CLINICAL ONCOLOGY INC
ASCO
2318 Mill Rd Ste 800, Alexandria, VA 22314-6834
Tel (571) 483-1300 *Founded/Ownrshp* 1964
Sales 101.9MM *EMP* 220
Accts Lb Bdo Usa Llp Bethesda Md
SIC 8621 Medical field-related associations
CEO: Allen Lichter
CFO: Paul Aines
Chf Mktg O: Richard L Schilsky
Ex VP: Dina Michels
Ex Dir: Nancy Daly
IT Man: Mike Feuti
Board of Directors: Stephen S Grubbs, Michael Kosty

D-U-N-S 00-166-6619
AMERICAN SOCIETY OF COMPOSERS AUTHORS AND PUBLISHERS (NY)
ASCAP
1 Lincoln Plz Fl 6, New York, NY 10023-8105
Tel (212) 621-6000 *Founded/Ownrshp* 1995
Sales 1.0MMM *EMP* 630^E
SIC 8621 Professional membership organizations
CEO: Elizabeth Matthews
Pt: Janine Small
Ch Bd: Paul Williams
Pr: Robert Cannone
COO: Al Wallace
CFO: Paul Rourke
Treas: Arnold Broido
Ex VP: John Titta
Sr VP: Kevin Gage
Sr VP: Nancy Neil
Sr VP: Mark Sperling
VP: Michael Martin
VP: Christine Pepe
Assoc Dir: Marc Hutner
Assoc Dir: Tim Maginnis
Assoc Dir: Rachel Perkins
Assoc Dir: Ed Reyes
Assoc Dir: Etan Rosenbloom
Assoc Dir: Meena Venkataramu
Board of Directors: Zach Katz, Jon Platt

D-U-N-S 03-005-4860
▲ **AMERICAN SOFTWARE INC**
470 E Paces Ferry Rd Ne, Atlanta, GA 30305-3301
Tel (404) 261-4381 *Founded/Ownrshp* 1970
Sales 113.8MM *EMP* 420^E
Tkr Sym AMSWA *Exch* NGS
SIC 7372 Application computer software; Business oriented computer software
Pr: J Michael Edenfield
**Ch Bd:* James C Edenfield
CFO: Vincent C Klinges
VP: Michael Edenfield
VP: James R McGuone
Board of Directors: W Dennis Hogue, James B Miller Jr, Thomas L Newberry V

AMERICAN SPECIALTY CARS
See ST JAMES INC

D-U-N-S 12-477-0822 IMP
AMERICAN SPECIALTY HEALTH GROUP INC
(*Suby of* AMERICAN SPECIALTY HEALTH INC) ★
10221 Wateridge Cir # 201, San Diego, CA 92121-2702
Tel (858) 754-2000 *Founded/Ownrshp* 1987
Sales 160.6MM^E *EMP* 500
SIC 8082 Home health care services
CEO: George T Devries
**COO:* Robert White
**CFO:* William M Comer Jr
**Ex VP:* Kevin E Kujawa
**Ex VP:* R Douglas Metz
VP: Kirk Hartman

D-U-N-S 80-495-5479
AMERICAN SPECIALTY HEALTH INC
10221 Wateridge Cir # 201, San Diego, CA 92121-2702
Tel (858) 754-2000 *Founded/Ownrshp* 1999
Sales NA *EMP* 1,100^E
SIC 6411 Insurance information & consulting services
CEO: George Devries III
Pr: Joy Kleinmaier
Pr: Robert White
CFO: William Comer
Treas: William Komer Jr
Assoc VP: Kirk Hartman
Sr VP: Julie Jennings
VP: John Donaghue
VP: Debi Heck
VP: Kevin Kujawa
VP: Arthur Leighton
VP: Dianna McGonigle
VP: Jerry Nosewicz
VP: Mary Jane Osmick
Exec: Leslie Sloate
Creative D: Mike Burgos
Board of Directors: Thomas P Cooper, Jan Devries, Bud Volberding, Daniel T Yunker

D-U-N-S 19-992-3384 IMP
AMERICAN SPECIALTY RETAILING GROUP INC
DUNHAMS SPORTS
5607 New King Dr Ste 125, Troy, MI 48098-2654
Tel (248) 674-4991 *Founded/Ownrshp* 1937
Sales 362.7MM^E *EMP* 2,000
SIC 5661 5941 5699 Footwear, athletic; Sporting goods & bicycle shops; Skiing equipment; Hunting equipment; Fishing equipment; Sports apparel
CEO: Jeff Lynn
VP: Kenneth R Meehan
VP: Steven J Sander
VP: Marshall Sosne

D-U-N-S 04-270-8586 IMP
AMERICAN SPRING WIRE CORP
A S W
26300 Miles Rd, Bedford Heights, OH 44146-1072
Tel (216) 292-4620 *Founded/Ownrshp* 1968
Sales 166.1MM^E *EMP* 402
SIC 3272 3315 3316 3339 3624 Concrete products; Wire products, ferrous/iron: made in wiredrawing plants; Wire, flat, cold-rolled strip: not made in hot-rolled mills; Primary nonferrous metals; Carbon & graphite products
CEO: Timothy W Selhorst
**COO:* Greg Bokar
VP: William Snyder
**Prin:* Michael L Miller
MIS Mgr: Jan Istok
Tech Mgr: Mike Caranna
Sfty Mgr: Peter Anselmi
Ql Cn Mgr: Michael Murral

D-U-N-S 83-210-3233
AMERICAN STAFF MANAGEMENT INC
27613 Cashford Cir # 102, Wesley Chapel, FL 33544-6913
Tel (813) 994-1200 *Founded/Ownrshp* 2002
Sales 61.5MM^E *EMP* 3,000
SIC 7363 Employee leasing service
Pr: James Moran
VP: Steven Stanburg

D-U-N-S 84-790-6070 EXP
AMERICAN STAINLESS TUBING INC
129 Honeycutt Rd, Troutman, NC 28166-7610
Tel (704) 878-8823 *Founded/Ownrshp* 1994
Sales 88.6MM^E *EMP* 200
SIC 3317 Tubing, mechanical or hypodermic sizes: cold drawn stainless
**Pr:* Tommy McCoy
**VP:* Fred Lampe
Sfty Mgr: Chris Nickel
Snr Mgr: Prissy Worthington

AMERICAN STAIR AND CABINETRY
See LAMINATE CO

AMERICAN STANDARD BRANDS
See AS AMERICA INC

D-U-N-S 02-364-0589
▲ AMERICAN STATES WATER CO
630 E Foothill Blvd, San Dimas, CA 91773-1207
Tel (909) 394-3600 Founded/Ownrshp 1929
Sales 458.6MM EMP 707[E]
Accts Pricewaterhousecoopers Llp Lo
Tkr Sym AWR Exch NYS
SIC 4941 4911 Water supply; Electric services; Distribution, electric power; Generation, electric power
Pr: Robert J Sprowls
*Ch Bd: Lloyd E Ross
CFO: Eva G Tang
VP: Shengder D Chang
Board of Directors: James L Anderson, Sarah J Anderson, Diana M Bonta, John R Fielder, Anne M Holloway, James F McNulty, Janice F Wilkins

D-U-N-S 04-182-9771 IMP
AMERICAN STEEL AND ALUMINUM CORP
STEEL SALES REALTY
27 Elm St, Auburn, MA 01501-2754
Tel (508) 832-9681 Founded/Ownrshp 2012
Sales 156.0MM[E] EMP 400
SIC 5051 Steel; Aluminum bars, rods, ingots, sheets, pipes, plates, etc.
CEO: Domenico Lepore
*Pr: Corrado Degasperis
*Treas: Jim Vincent
Plnt Mgr: Greg Egan

D-U-N-S 04-627-8032 IMP
AMERICAN STEEL INC
SWIFF-TRAIN COMPANY
2500 Agnes St, Corpus Christi, TX 78405-1618
Tel (361) 883-1706 Founded/Ownrshp 1937
Sales 85.0MM[E] EMP 145
SIC 5023 5051 5084 5191 Floor coverings; Steel; Industrial machinery & equipment; Chemicals, agricultural
Pr: Lee Allen Train
CFO: Jerry Carter
*Ex VP: Kenneth E Train
*VP: Jeffrey Train

D-U-N-S 07-522-7884
AMERICAN STOCK TRANSFER & TRUST CO LLC
(Suby of PACIFIC EQUITY PARTNERS PTY LIMITED)
6201 15th Ave, Brooklyn, NY 11219-5411
Tel (718) 921-8200 Founded/Ownrshp 1971, 2008
Sales 323.9MM[E] EMP 430
SIC 6289 Stock transfer agents
Pr: Mark C Healy
Pr: Mona Hanes
COO: Robert M Carney Sr
CFO: Marty Flanigan
Ofcr: David Becker
Ofcr: Jill Spielberger
Ex VP: David H Brill
Ex VP: Julian Clark
Ex VP: Melissa A Halverson
Ex VP: Tom Kies
Ex VP: James McBride
Ex VP: Chris Terenzi
Sr VP: Matt Alden
Sr VP: John Buonomo
Sr VP: Thomas H Caruth
Sr VP: John Hammond
Sr VP: Michael Hutto
Sr VP: Miri R Landman
Sr VP: Leslie Lab
Sr VP: Josh McGinn
Sr VP: Michael Nespoli

D-U-N-S 02-571-7815
AMERICAN STRATEGIC INSURANCE CORP
A S I
1 Asi Way N, Saint Petersburg, FL 33702-2514
Tel (727) 821-8765 Founded/Ownrshp 1997
Sales NA EMP 120
SIC 6331 Fire, marine & casualty insurance
Pr: John F Auer
*Ex VP: Kevin R Milkey
*VP: Angel Bostick
VP: Philip Brubaker
*VP: Mary Frances Fournet
*VP: Tony Scognamiglio
*VP: Greg Stewart
Exec: Judy Small
Div Mgr: Adam Anderson
VP Mktg: Jeff Hannon
VP Mktg: Sophie Whitenton

AMERICAN STUDENT ASSISTANCE
See MASSACHUSETTS HIGHER EDUCATION ASSISTANCE CORP

D-U-N-S 07-057-2912 IMP/EXP
AMERICAN SUGAR REFINING INC
DOMINO SUGAR
(Suby of ASR GROUP INTERNATIONAL INC) ★
1 Federal St, Yonkers, NY 10705-1079
Tel (800) 729-4840 Founded/Ownrshp 1986
Sales 111.5MM[E] EMP 2,000
SIC 2062

D-U-N-S 18-590-4497 IMP
▲ AMERICAN SUPERCONDUCTOR CORP
64 Jackson Rd, Devens, MA 01434-4020
Tel (978) 842-3000 Founded/Ownrshp 1987
Sales 96.0MM EMP 369[E]
Accts Rsm Us Llp Boston Massachuse
Tkr Sym AMSC Exch NGS
SIC 3674 3621 Semiconductors & related devices; Motors & generators
Pr: Daniel P McGahn
*Ch Bd: John W Wood Jr
CFO: David A Henry
Ex VP: James F Maguire
VP: James Parker
VP Bus Dev: John Ulliman
Dir Bus: Andreas Thieme
Dir IT: Mike Richardson
IT Man: Michael Vasconi
Mfg Mgr: Michael Sauriol
Sls Mgr: John Wright-Smith
Board of Directors: Vikram S Budhraja, Pamela F Lenehan, David R Oliver Jr, John B Vander Sande

D-U-N-S 00-638-2857 IMP/EXP
AMERICAN SYNTHETIC RUBBER CO LLC (DE)
ASRC
(Suby of MICHELIN NORTH AMERICA INC) ★
4500 Camp Ground Rd, Louisville, KY 40216-4675
Tel (502) 449-8300 Founded/Ownrshp 1955, 2001
Sales 108.9MM[E] EMP 335
SIC 2822 2821 Butadiene rubbers, polybutadiene; Plastics materials & resins
Pr: Joel Audureau

D-U-N-S 07-779-9799
AMERICAN SYSTEMS CORP
14151 Pk Madow Dr Ste 500, Chantilly, VA 20151
Tel (703) 968-6300 Founded/Ownrshp 1997
Sales 303.1MM EMP 1,640
Accts Bdo Usa Llp Mclean Virginia
SIC 8711 1731 8742 7373 Engineering services; Fiber optic cable installation; Telephone & telephone equipment installation; Management consulting services; Computer integrated systems design
Pr: Peter L Smith
*Ch Bd: William C Hoover
Treas: Randall Toure
*Ofcr: L Kenneth Johnson
Ex VP: Finley B Foster
*Ex VP: Joseph Kopfman
VP: Stephen Bonwich
VP: Ruth Bowers
VP: Chris Braccio
VP: Ron Costella
VP: Joseph Dizinno
VP: Kevin Dodge
VP: John Dyer
VP: Paul Fields
VP: Brian Fitzpatrick
VP: Doug Gosnell
VP: Jerry Harden
VP: J R Hundley
VP: Michael Innella
VP: Bob Irelan
VP: Jeff Jancek

D-U-N-S 00-990-1059 IMP/EXP
■ AMERICAN TECHNICAL CERAMICS CORP
ATC
(Suby of AVX CORP) ★
1 Norden Ln, Huntington Station, NY 11746-2140
Tel (631) 622-4700 Founded/Ownrshp 2007
Sales 162.7MM[E] EMP 782
SIC 3672 3675 Printed circuit boards; Electronic capacitors
CEO: John Lawing
Sr VP: Richard Monsorno
Sr VP: David B Ott
VP: Bill Johnson
VP: Kathleen M Kelly
VP: Andrew R Perz
Prin: John S Gilbertson
IT Man: George Lacorte
IT Man: Stacy Melendez
IT Man: Eduardo Sayers
VP Mktg: Eric Forstner

AMERICAN TECHNION SOCIETY
See AMERICAN SOCIETY FOR TECHNION-ISRAEL INSTITUTE OF TECHNOLOGY INC

D-U-N-S 61-161-4207 IMP
AMERICAN TECHNOLOGIES INC
ATI
210 W Baywood Ave, Orange, CA 92865-2603
Tel (714) 283-9990 Founded/Ownrshp 1989
Sales 180.8MM EMP 500
Accts Moss-Adams Llp Irvine Califo
SIC 1521 1541 1742 1731 1721 1711 Single-family housing construction; Industrial buildings & warehouses; Plastering, drywall & insulation; Electrical work; Painting & paper hanging; Plumbing, heating, air-conditioning contractors
Pr: Gary Moore
CFO: Steven Pace
Ex VP: Doug Fairless
VP: Bruce Ehlers
VP: Jeff Huddleston
VP: Charles W Peacock
Rgnl Mgr: Aaron Murray
Brnch Mgr: Jeffery Jackson
Brnch Mgr: Tim Kassen
Brnch Mgr: Barry Metcalf
Genl Mgr: Kyle Pickett

AMERICAN TELEPHONE AND TELG
See AT&T CORP

AMERICAN TELEPHONE HEADQARTERS
See TELQUEST INTERNATIONAL CORP

D-U-N-S 00-433-7473 IMP/EXP
AMERICAN TEXTILE CO INC (PA)
10 N Linden St, Duquesne, PA 15110-3001
Tel (412) 948-1020 Founded/Ownrshp 1925
Sales 177.4MM[E] EMP 500
SIC 5719 2392 Bedding (sheets, blankets, spreads & pillows); Pillowcases: made from purchased materials; Mattress protectors, except rubber
Ch Bd: Jack Ouellette
*Ch Bd: Reid Ruttenberg
*Pr: Lance Ruttenberg
*CFO: John Riccio
*Ex VP: Blake Ruttenberg
Sr VP: Patrick Seiffert
VP: Jane Fischer
VP: Michael Guidry
VP: Jennifer Katz
VP: John Miller
VP: Gary Schultz
VP: Paul Stark
Exec: Nancy Sweeny
Board of Directors: Charles Bitzer, Jeff Brown, John Burke, Blake Ruttenberg

D-U-N-S 07-968-1039
AMERICAN TEXTILE HOLDINGS LLC
1926 Fm 548, Littlefield, TX 79339
Tel (806) 385-6401 Founded/Ownrshp 2014
Sales 110.2MM[E] EMP 2,400[E]
SIC 2211 Denims

D-U-N-S 02-620-2812 IMP/EXP
■ AMERICAN TILE AND STONE INC
(Suby of ACME BRICK CO) ★
2244 Luna Rd Ste 160, Carrollton, TX 75006-6542
Tel (972) 243-2377 Founded/Ownrshp 1966, 1994
Sales 114.2MM[E] EMP 230
SIC 5032 Ceramic wall & floor tile
Pr: Dennis D Knautz
*CFO: Judy Hunter
*VP: Larry Atkins

AMERICAN TIRE DEPOT
See ATV INC

D-U-N-S 36-150-4983 IMP/EXP
AMERICAN TIRE DISTRIBUTORS HOLDINGS INC
(Suby of TPG CREATIVE CAPITAL) ★
12200 Herbert Wayne Ct # 150, Huntersville, NC 28078-6335
Tel (704) 992-2000 Founded/Ownrshp 2010
Sales 5.0MMM EMP 500[E]
Accts Pricewaterhousecoopers Llp Ch
SIC 5014 5013 Tires & tubes; Automobile tires & tubes; Truck tires & tubes; Motor vehicle supplies & new parts; Wheels, motor vehicle
CEO: Stuart S Schuette
*CFO: Jason T Yaudes
*Ex VP: J Michael Gaither
*Sr VP: J David Phillips
*Sr VP: Dan Seitler
VP: Roland Boyette
Snr Sftwr: Karen Smith
Mktg Mgr: Wall Casey

D-U-N-S 00-317-3481 IMP/EXP
AMERICAN TIRE DISTRIBUTORS INC
(Suby of AMERICAN TIRE DISTRIBUTORS HOLDINGS INC) ★
12200 Herbert Wayne Ct # 150, Huntersville, NC 28078-6397
Tel (704) 992-2000 Founded/Ownrshp 1999
Sales 1.0MMM[E] EMP 3,370[E]
SIC 5014 5013

D-U-N-S 96-909-4858
▲ AMERICAN TOWER CORP
116 Huntington Ave # 1100, Boston, MA 02116-5786
Tel (617) 375-7500 Founded/Ownrshp 2011
Sales 4.7MMM EMP 2,716[E]
Tkr Sym AMT Exch NYS
SIC 4813 3663 ; Radio broadcasting & communications equipment
Ch Bd: James D Taiclet Jr
CFO: Thomas A Bartlett
CFO: Bradley E Singr
CFO: Joseph Win
Sr Cor Off: David Tomick
Ofcr: Edmund Disanto
Ex VP: Danny Agresta
Ex VP: Amit Sharma
Sr VP: Robert J Meyer Jr
VP: Mark Lee
VP: Richard Rossi
VP: Rob Sherman
Board of Directors: Gustavo Lara Cantu, Pamela Da Reeve, Raymond P Dolan, Ronald M Dykes, Robert D Hormats, Carolyn F Katz, Craig Macnab, Joann A Reed, David E Sharbutt

D-U-N-S 00-308-0215 IMP
AMERICAN TRADING AND PRODUCTION CORP (MD)
ATAPCO
1 South St Ste 2800, Baltimore, MD 21202-3335
Tel (410) 347-7150 Founded/Ownrshp 1931
Sales 159.3MM[E] EMP 300
SIC 6552 Land subdividers & developers, commercial
CEO: Daniel Hirschhorn
*CFO: Henry Koether
CFO: Kathy Wolff
*VP: Vincent Hock
*VP: Paul Huston
VP: Sanford V Schmidt
Opers Mgr: Betty Wiser
Counsel: Jonathan E Newman
Counsel: S J Yeoman

D-U-N-S 16-567-4149
■ AMERICAN TRAFFIC SOLUTIONS INC
ATSOL
(Suby of TRANSCORE LP) ★
1150 N Alma School Rd, Mesa, AZ 85201-3000
Tel (480) 443-7000 Founded/Ownrshp 1992
Sales 101.1MM[E] EMP 200[E]
SIC 7374 1731 5084 Data processing & preparation; Safety & security specialization; Safety equipment
CEO: James D Tuton
*Pr: David Roberts
Pr: John Wood
*CFO: Tricia Chiodo
*Ex VP: Adam Draizin
*Ex VP: Adam E Tuton
Sr VP: Vincent Brigidi
Sr VP: Liz Caracciolo
Sr VP: Michael Tooker
Sr VP: Nikki Woodward
VP: Craig Cheatle
VP: Ray M Martinelli
VP: Mark Priebe
VP: Philip Underhill

D-U-N-S 96-664-5306
AMERICAN TRAILER WORKS INC
(Suby of BIG TEX TRAILER MANUFACTURING INC) ★
180 State St Ste 230, Southlake, TX 76092-7619
Tel (817) 328-3686 Founded/Ownrshp 2011
Sales 385.5MM[E] EMP 1,346[E]
SIC 3715 Truck trailers
CEO: James Pearson
*CEO: Curt Howell
*CFO: Douglas Clark

AMERICAN TRANSIT INSURANCE CO
See A T I C MANAGEMENT CORP DE CORP

D-U-N-S 07-524-7601
AMERICAN TRANSIT INSURANCE CO INC
(Suby of AMERICAN TRANSIT INSURANCE CO) ★
1 Metrotech Ctr Fl 7, Brooklyn, NY 11201-3949
Tel (212) 857-8200 Founded/Ownrshp 1984
Sales NA EMP 325
SIC 6321 6331 6311 Accident & health insurance; Automobile insurance; Life insurance
Pr: Edward T McGettigan Jr
CFO: Chris Ryan
*VP: Ralph Bisceglia
VP: Heather Ritter
CIO: Israel Mendez
QC Dir: Mark Decarlo
Genl Couns: John Poklemba

D-U-N-S 84-007-4806
AMERICAN TRANSMISSION CO LLC
W234n2000 Rdgview Pky Ct, Waukesha, WI 53188-1022
Tel (262) 506-6700 Founded/Ownrshp 2000
Sales 615.8MM EMP 547
Accts Deloitte & Touche Llp Milwau
SIC 4911 Transmission, electric power
Ch Bd: Patricia Kampling
*Pr: Allen Leverett
*Pr: Gale Norton
*Pr: Michael Peters
*Pr: Gary Wolter
*CEO: John Jamar
*Ex VP: Mike Rowe
*Exec: Lawrence Borgard
*Mng Dir: Stephen Yanisch
Snr Ntwrk: Dan Marek
Dir IT: Steve Dykstra

D-U-N-S 12-609-0377
AMERICAN TRANSPORT GROUP LLC
A T G
1900 W Kinzie St, Chicago, IL 60622-6243
Tel (773) 235-9600 Founded/Ownrshp 2002
Sales 89.7MM[E] EMP 105
SIC 4731 Brokers, shipping
Software D: Adel Rafiq
Trfc Dir: Jacob Queen
Opers Mgr: Jeff Atwell
Opers Mgr: Brad Straub
Natl Sales: Joseph Bialorucki
Natl Sales: Adam Cooper
Natl Sales: Joe Curran
Natl Sales: Chris Czekaj
Natl Sales: Patrick Gliege
Natl Sales: Matthew Mueller
Sls Mgr: John Charboneau

D-U-N-S 08-521-3010
AMERICAN TRAVELER STAFFING PROFESSIONALS LLC
AMERICAN TRAVERLER
1615 S Federal Hwy # 300, Boca Raton, FL 33432-7468
Tel (561) 391-1811 Founded/Ownrshp 1999
Sales 101.3MM[E] EMP 3,200[E]
SIC 7363 7361 Temporary help service; Nurses' registry
Pr: Robert Bok
CFO: Tammy Page
*VP: Dave Bok
Genl Mgr: Brian Bok
CTO: Carlos Alberto
Dir IT: Sue Higgins
Mktg Mgr: Caterina Oliveira

AMERICAN TRAVERLER
See AMERICAN TRAVELER STAFFING PROFESSIONALS LLC

AMERICAN TRIM
See SUPERIOR METAL PRODUCTS INC

D-U-N-S 93-869-5020 IMP/EXP
AMERICAN TRIM LLC
(Suby of AMERICAN TRIM) ★
1005 W Grand Ave, Lima, OH 45801-3429
Tel (419) 228-1145 Founded/Ownrshp 1948
Sales 256.0MM[E] EMP 800
SIC 3469 Metal stampings; Porcelain enameled products & utensils; Ornamental metal stampings
CEO: Jeffrey A Hawk
*CFO: Dana Morgan
*Ch: Leo J Hawk
*VP: Rick Pfeifer
Prgrm Mgr: Michael McClure
Genl Mgr: Marcelo Gonzalez
MIS Dir: Craig Rogers
IT Man: Colin Watkins
Netwrk Eng: Greg Gross
Prd Mgr: Scott Peltier
Prd Mgr: Mike Taylor

D-U-N-S 06-950-2821
AMERICAN TRISTAR INC
(Suby of EXEL LOGISTICS) ★
525 Dunham Rd, Saint Charles, IL 60174-1490
Tel (920) 872-2181 Founded/Ownrshp 1968
Sales 355.1MM[E] EMP 1,600
SIC 2099 Food preparations
Pr: Gordon Gruszka
*VP: Ernest Shepard
*Ex Dir: Chuck Woods

D-U-N-S 02-331-3422 IMP
AMERICAN TV & APPLIANCE OF MADISON INC
AMERICAN TV OF MADISON
2404 W Beltline Hwy, Madison, WI 53713-2387
Tel (608) 515-5020 Founded/Ownrshp 1972
Sales 244.3MM[E] EMP 1,634
SIC 5731 5712 5722 Television sets; High fidelity stereo equipment; Video recorders, players, disc players & accessories; Furniture stores; Household appliance stores
Pr: Douglas G Reuhl
Ch Bd: Leonard S Mattioli
Pr: Kim Fleller
CFO: Steve Mixtacki
V Ch Bd: George A Reuhl
Sr VP: Paul Kolbert

AMERICAN TV OF MADISON
See AMERICAN TV & APPLIANCE OF MADISON INC

D-U-N-S 07-203-1487
AMERICAN UNITED LIFE INSURANCE CO INC
(*Suby of* ONEAMERICA FINANCIAL PARTNERS INC) ★
1 American Sq Ste 368, Indianapolis, IN 46282-0002
Tel (317) 285-1877 *Founded/Ownrshp* 1877
Sales NA *EMP* 1,640[E]
SIC 6371 6311 6321 Pension funds; Life insurance carriers; Health insurance carriers
Ch: Dayton H Molendorp
*Ex VP: Scott Davidson
*Sr VP: Jeff Holley
Sr VP: G David Sapp
VP: Jim Crampton
VP: James Freeman
VP: David Gatman
VP: Cheryl Gentry
VP: Brandon Kaboski
VP: Mark Luttner
VP: James Nash
VP: Mark Roller
VP: Steve Torence
VP: Kevin Weston
VP: Jay Williams

D-U-N-S 13-104-3312
AMERICAN UNITED MUTUAL INSURANCE HOLDING CO
1 American Sq, Indianapolis, IN 46282-0020
Tel (317) 285-1877 *Founded/Ownrshp* 2000
Sales 1.8MMM[E] *EMP* 13,840
SIC 6211 6311 6371 6351 6331 Mutual funds, selling by independent salesperson; Life insurance carriers; Pension funds; Surety insurance; Fire, marine & casualty insurance
Pr: Dayton Molendorp
*CFO: J Scott Davison
VP: Brian Case
Dept Mgr: Brian Wade
Genl Mgr: Steven Howen
Dir IT: Tom McCarthy
Info Man: Suzanne Conrad
Genl Couns: James Kemper
Board of Directors: Yvonne H Shaheen, Gerald L Bepko, Alpha C Blackburn, Christel Dehaan, David W Goodrich, William P Johnson, Richard L Merrill, James T Morris, R S Radcliffe, Thomas E Reilly, Jerry Semier

D-U-N-S 07-779-5060
AMERICAN UNIVERSITY
4400 Massachusetts Ave Nw, Washington, DC 20016-8200
Tel (202) 885-1000 *Founded/Ownrshp* 1891
Sales 507.1MM *EMP* 2,000
Accts Pricewaterhousecoopers Llp Ba
SIC 8221 University
Pr: Cornelius Kerwin
*Ch Bd: Gary Abramson
Pr: Kevin Grasty
Pr: Vincent Harkins
Pr: Robert Hradsky
*Pr: Neil Kerwin
Pr: Chris Moody
CFO: Douglas Kudravetz
*Treas: Donald L Myers
Trst: Gina F Adams
Trst: Stephanie M Bennett-Smith
Trst: Gary D Cohn
Trst: Pamela M Deese
Trst: David R Drobis
Trst: Marc N Duber
Trst: Hani M Farsi
Trst: Thomas A Gottschalk
Trst: Gisela B Huberman
Trst: Margery Kraus
Trst: Charles H Lydecker
Trst: Alan L Meltzer

D-U-N-S 07-774-3268
AMERICAN UNIVERSITY IN CAIRO
420 5th Ave Fl 3, New York, NY 10018-2729
Tel (212) 730-8800 *Founded/Ownrshp* 1986
Sales 186.8MM *EMP* 1,000
Accts Ernst & Young Us Llp Chicago
SIC 8221 University
Pr: Lisa Anderson
V Ch: Kim Fox
*Pr: David Arnold
Chf Inves: Michael Stambaugh
Ofcr: Michel Hebert
Ofcr: May Ramy
Ofcr: Niveen Salah
Ofcr: Hazem Zaki
Sr VP: Peter Smith
VP: Kenneth Manotti
*VP: Andrew Snaith
Assoc Dir: Khalid S Hilal
Assoc Dir: Trevor Naylor
Assoc Dir: Ramza Sedky

D-U-N-S 07-103-3294
AMERICAN UNIVERSITY OF BEIRUT INC (NY)
(*Suby of* AMERICAN UNIVERSITY OF BEIRUT - AUB)
3 Dag Hammarskjold Plz # 8, New York, NY 10017-2324
Tel (212) 583-7600 *Founded/Ownrshp* 1863
Sales 390.8MM *EMP* 4,400
Accts Deloitte & Touche Llp New Yor
SIC 8221 University
Pr: Fablo R Khuri
*Ch Bd: Phillip S Khoury
*Ch: Hutham S Olayan
*Treas: Nemeh Sabbagh
Ofcr: Barbara Rosica
Ofcr: Justin Tessier

D-U-N-S 96-933-4809
AMERICAN UNIVERSITY OF GREECE
53 N Park Ave Ste 50, Rockville Centre, NY 11570-4111
Tel (516) 766-2718 *Founded/Ownrshp* 2011
Sales 101.2MM *EMP* 22
Accts Ernst & Young Us Llp Indiana
SIC 8222 Community college

D-U-N-S 04-934-3924 IMP/EXP
▲ AMERICAN VANGUARD CORP
AVD
4695 Macarthur Ct, Newport Beach, CA 92660-1882
Tel (949) 260-1200 *Founded/Ownrshp* 1969
Sales 289.3MM *EMP* 347[E]
Tkr Sym AVD *Exch* NYS
SIC 2879 Agricultural chemicals; Pesticides, agricultural or household; Fungicides, herbicides
Ch Bd: Eric G Wintemute
COO: Ulrich G Trogele
CFO: David T Johnson
Sr VP: Cynthia B Smith
VP: Cindy Smith
Off Mgr: Debra Pruette
Board of Directors: Scott D Baskin, Lawrence S Clark, Debra F Edwards, Morton D Erlich, Alfred F Ingulli, John L Killmer, M Esmail Zirakparvar

AMERICAN W WINDMILL & SOLAR CO
See GICON PUMPS & EQUIPMENT INC

D-U-N-S 00-446-0515 EXP
■ AMERICAN WATER HEATER CO
(*Suby of* A O SMITH CORP) ★
500 Princeton Rd, Johnson City, TN 37601-2030
Tel (423) 283-8000 *Founded/Ownrshp* 2008
Sales 205.0MM[E] *EMP* 1,200
SIC 3639 Hot water heaters, household
Pr: Ajita G Rajendra
*Pr: Kevin Wheeler
*Treas: John J Kita
VP: Andy Demski
VP: Rick Shuppert
IT Man: Nick Shortridge
VP Sls: Mary Stout
Mktg Dir: Brian Wilson

D-U-N-S 00-691-8726
▲ AMERICAN WATER WORKS CO INC
1025 Laurel Oak Rd, Voorhees, NJ 08043-3597
Tel (856) 346-8200 *Founded/Ownrshp* 1886
Sales 3.1MMM *EMP* 6,700
Accts Pricewaterhousecoopers Llp Ph
Tkr Sym AWK *Exch* NYS
SIC 4941 1629 1623 Water supply; Chemical plant & refinery construction; Water, sewer & utility lines
Pr: Susan N Story
Ch Bd: George Mackenzie
Pr: Brian Bruce
Pr: Alan Deboy
Pr: Walter Lynch
Pr: Kathy Pape
COO: Walter J Lynch
CFO: Linda G Sullivan
Treas: Deborah Degillio
Treas: Deborah A Degillio
Ex VP: Michael A Sgro
Sr VP: Nick Rowe
Sr VP: Mark Strauss
VP: Greg Panagos
VP: Mark S Smith
VP: Martin Uczen

D-U-N-S 03-521-6530
AMERICAN WELDING & GAS INC
4900 Falls Of Neuse Rd, Raleigh, NC 27609-5368
Tel (406) 969-1444 *Founded/Ownrshp* 1992
Sales 125.9MM[E] *EMP* 309
SIC 3548

D-U-N-S 78-768-2269
AMERICAN WEST HOMES INC
250 Pilot Rd Ste 140, Las Vegas, NV 89119-3543
Tel (702) 736-6434 *Founded/Ownrshp* 1990
Sales 94.3MM[E] *EMP* 400
SIC 6552 Subdividers & developers
Pr: Lawrence D Canarelli
*CFO: Corey Adcock
Dir IT: Mike Ferraro
Ql Cn Mgr: Ron Reynolds
Sls&Mrk Ex: Jennifer Almeido
Sales Asso: Elizabeth Carvalho

AMERICAN WHOLESALE GROCERS
See PURITY WHOLESALE GROCERS INC

D-U-N-S 79-487-2440 IMP
AMERICAN WOOD FIBERS INC
9841 Broken Land Pkwy # 302, Columbia, MD 21046-3073
Tel (410) 290-8700 *Founded/Ownrshp* 1991
Sales 100.1MM[E] *EMP* 350
SIC 2499 Wood flour; Mulch or sawdust products, wood
CEO: Stephen Faehner
*VP: Steve Radant
Genl Mgr: Joel Haveman
IT Man: Eileen Murphy
Plnt Mgr: Pat Krish

AMERICAN WOOD MOULDING
See AWM LLC

D-U-N-S 02-145-8534 IMP/EXP
▲ AMERICAN WOODMARK CORP (VA)
3102 Shawnee Dr, Winchester, VA 22601-4208
Tel (540) 665-9100 *Founded/Ownrshp* 1980
Sales 947.0MM *EMP* 5,070
Tkr Sym AMWD *Exch* NGS
SIC 2434 Wood kitchen cabinets; Vanities, bathroom: wood
Pr: S Cary Dunston
*Ch Bd: Kent B Guichard
CFO: M Scott Culbreth
Sr VP: R Perry Campbell
Dist Mgr: Helen Ramey
Genl Mgr: Mark Barnhart
Dir IT: Pg Coverstone
Opers Mgr: Cranfill Chuck
Opers Mgr: Michael McKinney
Opers Mgr: Simon Yule
Mktg Dir: Duane Hart
Board of Directors: William F Brandt Jr, Andrew B Cogan, Martha M Dally, James G Davis Jr, Daniel T Hendrix, Carol B Moerdyk, David W Moon, Vance W Tang

AMERICAN WORKER
See BOOT BARN INC

D-U-N-S 84-733-9454 IMP/EXP
AMERICANA DEVELOPMENT INC
7095 Americana Pkwy, Reynoldsburg, OH 43068-4118
Tel (614) 866-9803 *Founded/Ownrshp* 1988
Sales 97.0MM *EMP* 450
SIC 6552 Land subdividers & developers, commercial
Pr: CHI Jen Yang

AMERICANMUSCLE.COM
See TURN 5 INC

D-U-N-S 94-290-3159
AMERICANS FOR PROSPERITY
1728 M St Nw, Washington, DC 20036-4541
Tel (866) 730-0150 *Founded/Ownrshp* 2007
Sales 115.1MM *EMP* 21[E]
SIC 8299 Educational services
Pr: Tim Phillps

D-U-N-S 15-650-7121
AMERICANWEST BANCORPORATION
41 W Rverside Ave Ste 300, Spokane, WA 99201
Tel (509) 467-6993 *Founded/Ownrshp* 1983
Sales NA *EMP* 531[E]
SIC 6022

D-U-N-S 01-526-5460
AMERICANWEST BANK
41 W Rverside Ave Ste 300, Spokane, WA 99201
Tel (509) 232-1515 *Founded/Ownrshp* 2001
Sales NA *EMP* 276
SIC 6021

AMERICARE
See AMERICAN REPUBLIC INSURANCE CO

D-U-N-S 10-725-0003 IMP/EXP
AMERICARES FOUNDATION INC
88 Hamilton Ave, Stamford, CT 06902-3100
Tel (203) 658-9500 *Founded/Ownrshp* 1982
Sales 742.0MM *EMP* 231
Accts Grant Thornton Llp New York
SIC 8322 Temporary relief service; Disaster service; First aid service
Pr: Michael Nyenhuis
Mng Pt: Jerry Leamon
*Sr VP: Richard K Trowbridge Jr

AMERICA'S 1 WIRED CITY
See CITY OF TACOMA

AMERICAS BEST CNTCTS EYGLASSES
See CONSOLIDATED VISION GROUP INC

D-U-N-S 15-091-7979
AMERICAS BEST CONTACTS & EYEGLASSES INC
(*Suby of* AMERICAS BEST CNTCTS EYGLASSES) ★
296 Grayson Hwy, Lawrenceville, GA 30046-5737
Tel (770) 822-2036 *Founded/Ownrshp* 1997
Sales 177.4MM[E] *EMP* 1,200
SIC 5995 Contact lenses, prescription; Eyeglasses, prescription
Pr: Barry H Feinberg
*CEO: L Reade Fahs
*CFO: Paul A Criscillis Jr
*CFO: Raymond C French
VP Opers: Debra Woyce

AMERICA'S BEVERAGE COMPANY
See KROGER TEXAS LP

D-U-N-S 04-454-7325
AMERICAS BUSINESS SOLUTION LLC
1070 Coolbaugh Rd, East Stroudsburg, PA 18302-7984
Tel (718) 308-1331 *Founded/Ownrshp* 2012
Sales 500.0MM *EMP* 5
SIC 8741 8742 Business management; Marketing consulting services

D-U-N-S 13-117-0987
▲ AMERICAS CAR-MART INC
802 Se Plaza Ave Ste 200, Bentonville, AR 72712-3220
Tel (479) 464-9944 *Founded/Ownrshp* 1981
Sales 567.9MM *EMP* 1,420[E]
Accts Grant Thornton Llp Tulsa Ok
Tkr Sym CRMT *Exch* NGS
SIC 5521 6141 Used car dealers; Financing: automobiles, furniture, etc., not a deposit bank
CEO: William H Henderson
*Pr: Jeffrey A Williams
VP: Hank B Henderson
Opers Mgr: Brent Jensen
Board of Directors: Daniel J Englander, Kenny Gunderman, Eddie L Hight, Robert Cameron Smith, Jim Von Gremp

D-U-N-S 18-152-1154
AMERICAS CATCH INC
46623 County Road 523, Itta Bena, MS 38941-2439
Tel (662) 254-7207 *Founded/Ownrshp* 1987
Sales 100.0MM *EMP* 375
SIC 2092 0273

D-U-N-S 80-883-2422 IMP
AMERICAS COLLECTIBLES NETWORK INC
ACNTV
9600 Parkside Dr, Knoxville, TN 37922-2201
Tel (865) 692-6000 *Founded/Ownrshp* 1993
Sales 2.1MMM[E] *EMP* 1,982
SIC 5094 Jewelry & precious stones
Pr: Tim Matthews
COO: F Hall
CFO: Robert Hall
CFO: Crawford Wagner
Ch: Charles A Wagner III
Ex VP: Harris Bagley
Sr VP: Tim Engle
VP: Burt Bagley
VP: Patrick Bryant
VP: Andy Caldwell
VP: Trisha Condra
VP: Virgil Gerin
VP: Eric Johnson
VP: Bill Kouns
VP: Kris Kulesza
VP: Natalie Parman
VP: R Pearson
VP: Randy Puryear
VP: Stephen Roth
VP: Craig Shields
VP: Gerald Sisk

D-U-N-S 05-729-8937
AMERICAS HOME PLACE INC
AMERICAN HOME BUILDERS
2144 Hilton Dr, Gainesville, GA 30501-6172
Tel (770) 532-1128 *Founded/Ownrshp* 1992
Sales 175.2MM *EMP* 285
Accts Brady Ware & Schoenfeld Atlan
SIC 1521 New construction, single-family houses
Pr: Barry G Conner
VP: Alan Cooper
VP: Ron Meares
Dir Surg: Vicki Ryan
Genl Mgr: Tom Palmer
Off Admin: Lyndi Blair
Off Admin: Rita McMahan
Opers Mgr: Crystal Brown
Prd Mgr: David Frady
Sls Dir: Linda Blake
Sls Mgr: Joshua Proctor

D-U-N-S 03-776-6875 IMP/EXP
▲ AMERICAS MINING CORP
1150 N 7th Ave, Tucson, AZ 85705-6606
Tel (520) 798-7500 *Founded/Ownrshp* 2009
Sales 6.7MMM[E] *EMP* 25,902
SIC 1021 1044 1031 1041 3331 Copper ores; Silver ores; Lead ores mining; Zinc ores mining; Gold ores; Primary copper
CEO: J Felix
*Pr: J Eduardo Gonzalez Felix
*Prin: Ernesto Duran Trinidad

D-U-N-S 05-358-2776
AMERICAS PIZZA CO LLC
201 Rue De Jean Ste 200, Lafayette, LA 70508-8510
Tel (337) 806-1100 *Founded/Ownrshp* 1998
Sales 69.2MM[E] *EMP* 2,200
SIC 5812 Pizzeria, chain
VP Opers: Jim Sill
Snr Mgr: Terrie Gibson-Sill

D-U-N-S 07-019-2625
AMERICAS POWERSPORTS INC
A P S
825 Market St Bldg M, Allen, TX 75013
Tel (214) 383-4835 *Founded/Ownrshp* 1998
Sales 170.3MM[E] *EMP* 600
SIC 5571 7941 Motorcycle dealers; Sports clubs, managers & promoters
CEO: Tom Andrus
*CFO: Blake Lawson
VP: Bill Oshields

D-U-N-S 82-529-2100 EXP
AMERICAS STYRENICS LLC
AMSTY
24 Waterway Ave Ste 1200, The Woodlands, TX 77380-3289
Tel (832) 616-7800 *Founded/Ownrshp* 2010
Sales 531.2MM[E] *EMP* 500
SIC 2821 2865 Polystyrene resins; Styrene
CEO: Bradley Crocker
*Pr: Tim Roberts
*CFO: Dan Bialkowski
*VP: Douglas R Chauveaux
*VP: Joe Hulett
*VP: Scot Mitchell
*VP: Peter Ott
*VP: Randy Pogue
*VP: Frank Wright Jr
CIO: Laura Tibodeau

AMERICAS THRIFT
See ALABAMA THRIFT STORES INC

AMERICA'S THRIFT STORES
See ATS OPERATING LLC

D-U-N-S 00-446-7387 IMP/EXP
AMERICHEM INC (OH)
2000 Americhem Way, Cuyahoga Falls, OH 44221-3303
Tel (330) 929-4213 *Founded/Ownrshp* 1941, 1958
Sales 218.7MM[E] *EMP* 620
SIC 2865 2851 2819 2816 Color pigments, organic; Paints & allied products; Industrial inorganic chemicals; Inorganic pigments
Pr: Richard C Juve
*CFO: Tom Gannon
*CFO: John Volcheck
VP: Matthew Miklos
VP: Clay Wedan
Exec: Kattie Cool
Dir Rx: Rod Manfull
Dir IT: Rob Clayton
Opers Mgr: CJ Foster
Snr Mgr: Sean Hamilton
Snr Mgr: Wil Hartong

D-U-N-S 94-916-5542
■ AMERICHOICE CORP
(*Suby of* UNITEDHEALTH GROUP INC) ★
12018 Sunrise Valley Dr # 400, Reston, VA 20191-3432
Tel (571) 262-8933 *Founded/Ownrshp* 2002
Sales NA *EMP* 1,439
Accts Deloitte & Touche Llp Cpa
SIC 6324 Health maintenance organization (HMO), insurance only
CEO: Anthony Welters
COO: Jess E Sweely
CFO: Terra Rios

D-U-N-S 84-793-3363
AMERICO LIFE INC
(*Suby of* IPFS CORP) ★
300 W 11th St, Kansas City, MO 64105-1618
Tel (816) 391-2000 *Founded/Ownrshp* 1992
Sales NA *EMP* 766

SIC 6311 6321 6331 Life insurance carriers; Accident insurance carriers; Fire, marine & casualty insurance: mutual; Automobile insurance
Pr: Gary Mullers
**Ch Bd:* Michael A Merriman
Pr: Renee Keffer
Pr: Eric Petersen
**CFO:* Mark K Fallon
Chf Mktg O: Rod Foster
Sr VP: Mark Fallon
VP: Robert Graham
VP: Ram Pulakanam
Exec: Michael McQueen
Exec: Joanetta Rembert
Dir Risk M: Kimberly Beckley

D-U-N-S 00-796-5817 IMP
AMERICOLD LOGISTICS LLC
(P&O COLD LOGISTICS, LLC)
19840 S Rancho Way, Compton, CA 90220-6320
Tel (310) 635-4993 *Founded/Ownrshp* 2005
Sales NA *EMP* 1,230
SIC 4222

D-U-N-S 05-814-9378 IMP/EXP
AMERICOLD LOGISTICS LLC
(*Suby of* AMERICOLD REALTY TRUST) ★
10 Glenlake Pkwy Ste 324, Atlanta, GA 30328-3495
Tel (678) 441-1400 *Founded/Ownrshp* 2004
Sales 4.0MMM^E *EMP* 10,600
SIC 4222 4899 8742 7389 Warehousing, cold storage or refrigerated; Data communication services; Transportation consultant; Packaging & labeling services
Pr: Fred Boehler
COO: Mike Oconnell
CFO: Edward F Lange
**CFO:* Marc Smernoff
**Chf Cred:* Keith Goldsmith
Chf Mktg O: Gary Laughlin
**Ex VP:* Jed Milstein
**Ex VP:* Thomas Musgrave
**Ex VP:* Todd Sheldon
Sr VP: Carl Fowler
**Sr VP:* Jeff Hogarth
Sr VP: Marc Levin
VP: Greg Bryan
VP: Bob Duron
VP: West Hutchison
VP: Todd Jeska
VP: Todd S Klumok
VP: Michael Nelson
VP: Doug Olmstead
VP: Fred Walker
Dir Risk M: John Ermlich

D-U-N-S 19-738-3594
AMERICOLD REALTY TRUST
(*Suby of* YUCAIPA COMPANIES LLC) ★
10 Glenlk Pkwy Ste 600, Atlanta, GA 30328
Tel (404) 394-1312 *Founded/Ownrshp* 2008
Sales 4.1MMM^E *EMP* 10,600
SIC 4222 Refrigerated warehousing & storage
CEO: Tony Schnug
**Pr:* Fred Boehler
**CFO:* Allison Aden
**CFO:* Edward F Lange Jr
**Chf Cred:* Hamid Arabzadeh
**Ofcr:* Andrea Darweesh
Sr VP: Carl Fowler
**VP:* Keith Goldsmith
**CIO:* Ronald B Hutchison

D-U-N-S 11-336-8146
AMERICRAFT CARTON INC
7400 State Line Rd # 206, Prairie Village, KS 66208-3444
Tel (913) 387-3700 *Founded/Ownrshp* 1983
Sales 191.9MM^E *EMP* 600
SIC 2657 Folding paperboard boxes
CEO: Rick N Johnson
**VP:* C Allen Booe
**VP:* Richard M Horton
Genl Mgr: James Kleinfeld
QC Dir: Doug Delong

AMERICREDIT
See GENERAL MOTORS FINANCIAL CO INC

D-U-N-S 87-690-9268
■ **AMERICREDIT FINANCIAL SERVICES INC**
(*Suby of* AMERICREDIT) ★
801 Cherry St Ste 3500, Fort Worth, TX 76102-6854
Tel (817) 302-7000 *Founded/Ownrshp* 1992
Sales NA *EMP* 3,800
SIC 6141 Financing: automobiles, furniture, etc., not a deposit bank
Pr: Daniel Berce
**COO:* Kyle Birch
**COO:* Mark Floyd
**COO:* Preston Miller
**CFO:* Chris Choate
**Ch:* Clifton H Morris Jr
**Chf Cred:* Steve Bowman
**Ex VP:* Robert Beatty
**Ex VP:* Steven P Bowman
**Ex VP:* Chris A Choate
Sr VP: Barbara Williams

D-U-N-S 78-254-6568
AMERICUS MORTGAGE CORP
6110 Pinemont Dr Ste 215, Houston, TX 77092-3216
Tel (713) 684-0725 *Founded/Ownrshp* 1993
Sales NA *EMP* 2,500
Accts Gainer Donnelly & Desroches
SIC 6162 Mortgage brokers, using own money; Mortgage bankers
Pr: Jim C Hodge
**CFO:* James Hagen
**Sr VP:* Jamey J Hodge
VP: Jim Clooney
Brnch Mgr: Maria Anderson
Brnch Mgr: Kevin Chase
Brnch Mgr: Carl Snyder
Opers Mgr: Annette Gaspar

D-U-N-S 17-734-9438
AMERIFIRST FINANCIAL CORP
AMERIFIRST HOME MORTGAGE
950 Trade Centre Way # 400, Portage, MI 49002-0493
Tel (269) 324-4240 *Founded/Ownrshp* 1986
Sales NA *EMP* 1,000
SIC 6162 Mortgage bankers
CEO: David N Gahm
**Pr:* Mark A Jones

AMERIFIRST HOME MORTGAGE
See AMERIFIRST FINANCIAL CORP

D-U-N-S 00-345-1189
AMERIFLEET TRANSPORTATION INC (NV)
1111 Alderman Dr, Alpharetta, GA 30005-2022
Tel (770) 442-0222 *Founded/Ownrshp* 1997
Sales 146.2MM^E *EMP* 750
SIC 4789 Cargo loading & unloading services
CEO: Robert Smith
**CFO:* Richard M Dennis
Treas: Ted Joens
VP: Kathy Massey
MIS Dir: Belinda Mantz
Trfc Dir: Brad Ford
VP Sls: Terri Stiffler
Sls Dir: John Cordova
Board of Directors: Ted Joens, Fred Shilling, Kerry Smith

D-U-N-S 62-638-8680 EXP
■ **AMERIFOODS TRADING CO LLC**
(*Suby of* SMART & FINAL INC) ★
600 Citadel Dr, Commerce, CA 90040-1562
Tel (323) 869-7500 *Founded/Ownrshp* 1990
Sales 88.8MM^E *EMP* 774^E
SIC 5141 Food brokers
Ch Bd: Ross E Roeder
**CFO:* Richard Phegley
**Sr VP:* Donald G Alvarado
**VP:* Robert Bishoff

D-U-N-S 14-250-6372 IMP
AMERIFORGE CORP
(*Suby of* FORGED VESSEL CONNECTIONS) ★
13770 Industrial Rd, Houston, TX 77015-6821
Tel (713) 393-4200 *Founded/Ownrshp* 1996
Sales 144.6MM^E *EMP* 267^E
SIC 3462 Automotive forgings, ferrous: crankshaft, engine, axle, etc.
Pr: Gean B Stalcup
**COO:* Guenter Karhut
**CFO:* Gabriel Faimann
**Treas:* Perry Ewing
**VP:* Brian Fontana

D-U-N-S 13-643-8327 IMP/EXP
AMERIFORGE GROUP INC
FORGED VESSEL CONNECTIONS
945 Bunker Hill Rd # 500, Houston, TX 77024-1358
Tel (713) 688-9705 *Founded/Ownrshp* 2012
Sales 212.4MM^E *EMP* 400
SIC 3462 Iron & steel forgings; Flange, valve & pipe fitting forgings, ferrous
CEO: Gean B Stalcup
**CFO:* Brian Fontana
**Treas:* Perry Ewing
Ofcr: Dave Heminger
**Ex VP:* Thomas Giles
VP: Jack Foster
VP: Sheri Zhang
Exec: Sheryl Berg
Exec: John Bergeron
Exec: Curtis Samford
VP Opers: Joe Jenkins
Board of Directors: Alan J Carr, Jonathan F Foster

D-U-N-S 01-435-4518 IMP
■ **AMERIGAS INC** (PA)
(*Suby of* UGI CORP) ★
460 N Gulph Rd Ste 100, King of Prussia, PA 19406-2815
Tel (610) 337-7000 *Founded/Ownrshp* 1959, 1995
Sales 616.5MM^E *EMP* 5,026
SIC 5984 5172 5722 2911 2813 Liquefied petroleum gas dealers; Liquefied petroleum gas, delivered to customers' premises; Gases, liquefied petroleum (propane); Gas household appliances; Petroleum refining; Industrial gases
Ch Bd: Lon R Greenberg
**Pr:* Jerry E Sheridan
Ch: John Walsh
**Treas:* Hugh J Gallagher
VP: Glenn Griffin
VP: John Iannarelli
VP: Robert Knauss
VP: Martha Lindsay
VP: David Lugar
Exec: Roger Maiolini
**Prin:* K Rick Turner
Board of Directors: Anne Pol, Jerry E Sheridan, K Rick Turner

D-U-N-S 83-540-6448
▲ **AMERIGAS PARTNERS LP**
460 N Gulph Rd Ste 100, King of Prussia, PA 19406-2815
Tel (610) 337-7000 *Founded/Ownrshp* 1994
Sales 2.3MMM *EMP* 8,500
Accts Ernst & Young Llp Philadelph
Tkr Sym APU *Exch* NYS
SIC 5984 5172 Liquefied petroleum gas, delivered to customers' premises; Propane gas, bottled; Gases, liquefied petroleum (propane)
Pr: Jerry E Sheridan
Genl Ptr: Amerigas Propane
CFO: Hugh J Gallagher
VP: Earle Compton

D-U-N-S 93-308-4212 IMP
■ **AMERIGAS PROPANE INC**
(*Suby of* AMERIGAS INC) ★
460 N Gulph Rd Ste 100, King of Prussia, PA 19406-2815
Tel (610) 337-7000 *Founded/Ownrshp* 1994
Sales 613.4MM^E *EMP* 5,000
SIC 5984 Propane gas, bottled
Pr: Eugene N V Bissell
CFO: Martha B Lindsay
CFO: Penelope Sheetzs
Ch: Lon R Greenberg
Board of Directors: John R Hartmann, Pedro A Ramos, Marvin O Schlanger, Jerry E Sheridan, K Rick Turner

D-U-N-S 83-540-6539
■ **AMERIGAS PROPANE LP**
(*Suby of* AMERIGAS PARTNERS LP) ★
460 N Gulph Rd Ste 100, King of Prussia, PA 19406-2815
Tel (610) 337-7000 *Founded/Ownrshp* 1994
Sales 1.9MMM^E *EMP* 8,500
SIC 5984 Liquefied petroleum gas dealers
Pr: Jerry Sheridan
Pr: Scott Culbertson
**CFO:* Hugh Gallagher
CFO: Martha B Lindsay
VP: John Iannarelli
VP: Greg Robey
**Prin:* Tom Niccum
Dist Mgr: Michael M McGuire
Genl Mgr: Russell Boisvert
Genl Mgr: Cassandra Curry
CTO: Steven Struthers

D-U-N-S 01-990-4241
AMERIGREEN ENERGY INC
1650 Manheim Pike Ste 201, Lancaster, PA 17601-3088
Tel (717) 945-1392 *Founded/Ownrshp* 2005
Sales 212.0MM *EMP* 22^E
Accts Trout Ebersole & Groff Llp
SIC 5172 Petroleum products
Pr: Jeffrey B Lyons
**Treas:* Robert W Obetz
**VP:* R Seth Obertz
Genl Mgr: Len Zvorsky
VP Opers: Jason Lawrence

AMERIGROUP
See MORTGAGE INVESTORS CORP

D-U-N-S 87-851-7747
■ **AMERIGROUP CORP**
(*Suby of* ANTHEM INC) ★
4425 Corp Ln Ste 160, Virginia Beach, VA 23462
Tel (757) 473-2737 *Founded/Ownrshp* 2012
Sales NA *EMP* 5,100^E
SIC 6324 Health maintenance organization (HMO), insurance only
Pr: James G Carlson
Pr: Steve Broudy
Pr: Sue Haskins
Pr: Alice Hudson
Pr: Gerald Stoner
**CEO:* Zoretic Richard C
CEO: Carolyn W Colvin
CEO: Julie C Locke
CEO: Tunde Sotunde
COO: Vincent M Ancona
COO: John Koehn
COO: James Voiland
**COO:* Richard C Zoretic
CFO: Scott Anglin
CFO: E Dunn
**CFO:* James W Truess
**Treas:* Kretschmer R David
Assoc VP: Lisa Stinson
Ex VP: William T Keena
Ex VP: John E Littel
Ex VP: Mary T McCluskey

D-U-N-S 12-610-7023
■ **AMERIGROUP FLORIDA INC**
(*Suby of* AMERIGROUP CORP) ★
4200 W Cypress St 900-1000, Tampa, FL 33607-4156
Tel (813) 830-6900 *Founded/Ownrshp* 1992
Sales NA *EMP* 313^E
SIC 6324 Health maintenance organization (HMO), insurance only
CEO: Don Gilmore
**Pr:* David Rodriguez
**Ofcr:* John Knispel
**VP:* Stanley F Baldwin

D-U-N-S 01-531-0972
■ **AMERIGROUP NEW YORK LLC**
AMERICAID COMMUNITY CARE
(*Suby of* AMERIGROUP CORP) ★
360 W 31st St Fl 5, New York, NY 10001-2727
Tel (212) 372-6900 *Founded/Ownrshp* 2005
Sales NA *EMP* 415
SIC 6324 Health maintenance organization (HMO), insurance only
CEO: Robert A Wychulis
VP Mktg: Anthony Woods
Mktg Dir: Todd Kiefer

D-U-N-S 84-741-0511
AMERIHEALTH ADMINISTRATORS INC
(*Suby of* BLUE CROSS) ★
1900 Market St Ofc 624, Philadelphia, PA 19103-3513
Tel (215) 657-8900 *Founded/Ownrshp* 1988
Sales NA *EMP* 440
SIC 6321 Health insurance carriers
Pr: Michael Sullivan
Pr: Michael Miller
**CFO:* George W Grimes
Ofcr: Daniel J Pedriani Jr
Sr VP: Linda M Taylor
VP: Gideon D Hill
VP: Michael Robak
VP: Timothy Sears
**VP:* Raymond A Stabilito
**VP:* Linda Taylor
**VP:* Leo G Watt
VP: Linda Zychowicz

D-U-N-S 10-719-0829
AMERIHEALTH CARITAS HEALTH PLAN
AMERIHEALTH CARITAS PA
200 Stevens Dr, Philadelphia, PA 19113-1520
Tel (215) 937-8000 *Founded/Ownrshp* 1996
Sales NA *EMP* 3,750
SIC 6321 Health insurance carriers
Pr: Paul A Tufano
Pr: Dwight Chenette
COO: Cindy Helling
CFO: Russ Gianforcoro
**Treas:* Steven H Bohner
**Chf Cred:* Mark T Bullock
Assoc VP: Carolyn Hayden
Assoc VP: Tonya Moody
Sr VP: Alan Krigstein
VP: Rita Juray
VP: Victor Negron
VP: Stephen Orndorff
VP: Richard Scanlon
VP: Vrajesh Shah
VP: Herbert Weldon
VP: Darlene Williams

AMERIHEALTH CARITAS PA
See AMERIHEALTH CARITAS HEALTH PLAN

D-U-N-S 18-290-1348
AMERIHEALTH INC
(*Suby of* BLUE CROSS) ★
1901 Market St Fl 32, Philadelphia, PA 19103-1465
Tel (215) 241-3019 *Founded/Ownrshp* 2008
Sales NA *EMP* 256
SIC 6411 6324 8748 Medical insurance claim processing, contract or fee basis; Insurance agents & brokers; Hospital & medical service plans; Health maintenance organization (HMO), insurance only; Employee programs administration
Pr: Daniel J Hilferty
**CFO:* John G Foos
**Sr VP:* Richard J Neeson
Exec: Susan Sendlewski
S&M/VP: Michael Munoz
Mktg Dir: Michael Zangrilli

D-U-N-S 08-017-4733
AMERIJET HOLDINGS INC
3401 Nw 72nd Ave Ste A, Miami, FL 33122-1329
Tel (800) 927-6059 *Founded/Ownrshp* 2016
Sales 248.0MM^E *EMP* 649
SIC 4512 8741 4581 4213 Air transportation, scheduled; Management services; Airports, flying fields & services; Trucking, except local
Pr: David G Bassett
**CFO:* John R Nash
CFO: John Nash
Ofcr: Fernando Rodriguez
Ofcr: John Turley
Sr VP: Mark Stewart
VP: Pamela Rollins
Snr Ntwrk: Ransford Waite
IT Man: Juana Villa
Trfc Dir: Akshy Patel
Opers Mgr: Raul Barron

D-U-N-S 09-970-3225
AMERILIFE GROUP LLC
2650 Mccormick Dr Ste 100, Clearwater, FL 33759-1061
Tel (727) 726-0726 *Founded/Ownrshp* 1971
Sales NA *EMP* 226
SIC 6411 Insurance agents, brokers & service
CEO: Timothy O North
Pr: Robert Barry
**Pr:* Heather Cranford
Pr: Lee Jay Hart
**Pr:* Gary Jenkins
Pr: Frank Tebyani
**CFO:* Patrick Tolliver
**Sr VP:* Tom Donegan
Sr VP: Mike Massrock
**VP:* Jerry Cwiok
VP: Chip Perks
VP: Kevin Smith
Exec: Erika Vrakas
Comm Dir: Wayne Shelor

D-U-N-S 06-410-7097 IMP
AMERIMARK DIRECT LLC
WINDSOR COLLECTION
(*Suby of* AMERIMARK HOLDINGS LLC) ★
6864 Engle Rd, Cleveland, OH 44130-7910
Tel (440) 826-1900 *Founded/Ownrshp* 1998
Sales 200.0MM *EMP* 575
Accts Pricewaterhousecoopers Llp Fl
SIC 4226 5961 7331 Special warehousing & storage; Mail order house; Direct mail advertising services
Pr: Louis Geisler
Treas: Richard Corey
Ex VP: Joe Albanese
VP: Steven Fortson
VP: Jill Friedman
Dir IT: Mary Vartorella
Dir IT: Maria Zinner
IT Man: Cynthia Tancer

D-U-N-S 80-898-1711
AMERIMARK HOLDINGS LLC
6864 Engle Rd, Cleveland, OH 44130-7910
Tel (440) 325-2000 *Founded/Ownrshp* 2007
Sales 368.5MM^E *EMP* 743
SIC 5961 4226 7331 Catalog sales; Mail order house; Special warehousing & storage; Direct mail advertising services
CEO: Mark Ethier
**CEO:* Gareth Giesler
**CFO:* Joe Albanese
**Ex VP:* Diane Huzar

D-U-N-S 01-433-5934 IMP
AMERIMEX MOTOR & CONTROLS LLC
610 N Milby St, Houston, TX 77003-1369
Tel (713) 225-4300 *Founded/Ownrshp* 1998
Sales 99.8MM^E *EMP* 120^E
SIC 5063 3625 7694 Motors, electric; Generators; Motor control centers; Armature rewinding shops
Pr: V Wayne Stockstill
**Sr VP:* Wade Stockstill

D-U-N-S 80-086-1312
AMERIPARK LLC
3200 Cobb Galleria Pkwy # 299, Atlanta, GA 30339-5937
Tel (404) 364-0342 *Founded/Ownrshp* 2008
Sales 52.2MM^E *EMP* 1,000
SIC 7521 7299 Parking lots; Valet parking
Pr: Travis Larrison

Pr: Will Mitchener
Rgnl Mgr: Josh Westcott
Dist Mgr: Clay Walden

D-U-N-S 13-076-1823 IMP
■ AMERIPATH HOLDINGS INC
(*Suby of* QUEST DIAGNOSTICS INC) ★
7111 Fairway Dr Ste 101, Palm Beach Gardens, FL 33418-4205
Tel (561) 845-1850 *Founded/Ownrshp* 2007
Sales 123.8MM^E *EMP* 4,300
SIC 8071 Pathological laboratory
Ch: Donald Steen
CFO: David L Redmond
Chf Mktg O: Jeffrey A Mossler MD
Telecom Ex: Theresa Eastman
Snr Sftwr: Steron Brown
CTO: Mike Saganis
IT Man: Jose Dvila Sacasas
Software D: Kalyan Reddy Akkasani
Sftwr Eng: Keith Duncan

D-U-N-S 03-244-9027 IMP/EXP
■ AMERIPATH INC
(*Suby of* AMERIPATH HOLDINGS INC) ★
7111 Fairway Dr Ste 101, Palm Beach Gardens, FL 33418-4205
Tel (561) 712-6200 *Founded/Ownrshp* 1996
Sales 123.8MM^E *EMP* 3,979
SIC 8071 Pathological laboratory
Pr: Miller Joan E
VP: Lynne Bird
* *VP:* Lukas Michael G
VP: Bob V Kliveck
VP: Will Santiago
VP: Randy Wills
CIO: Michael J Downs
Dir IT: Scott Manley
Dir IT: Marc Scheinblum
Software D: Stefano Fiorini
VP Sls: Bruce C Walton

D-U-N-S 00-696-1544 IMP
AMERIPRIDE SERVICES INC
10801 Wayzata Blvd # 100, Hopkins, MN 55305-1531
Tel (800) 750-4628 *Founded/Ownrshp* 1989
Sales 421.5MM^E *EMP* 6,025
SIC 7213 7218 Linen supply; Industrial launderers
Pr: Bill Evans
* *Ch Bd:* Lawrence G Steiner
* *COO:* Jerry E Johnson
Treas: Dan Langermeier
Sr Cor Off: Dan Meyers
Ofcr: Wendy Colins
* *Sr VP:* Curt Gray
* *Sr VP:* Brian Keegan
* *Sr VP:* Dan Lagermeier
* *Sr VP:* John Sutherland
VP: Steven John
VP: Kenneth Tippery
Comm Dir: Ben Saukko

D-U-N-S 07-114-6195
■ AMERIPRISE BANK FSB
AMERICAN EX PROPERTY CSLTY
(*Suby of* AMERIPRISE FINANCIAL INC) ★
3500 Packerland Dr, De Pere, WI 54115-9034
Tel (920) 330-5835 *Founded/Ownrshp* 1986
Sales NA *EMP* 727
SIC 6331 Automobile insurance; Property damage insurance
Pr: Kenneth J Ciak
* *Sr VP:* Diane Wilson
* *VP:* Larry W Frazier
* *VP:* Lorraine Rose Hart
* *VP:* Terry Lee Seirstad
Div Mgr: Chad Giesen
IT Man: Paul Spychalla

D-U-N-S 00-696-1999
■ AMERIPRISE CERTIFICATE CO
(*Suby of* AMERIPRISE FINANCIAL INC) ★
1099 Ameriprise Fincl Ctr, Minneapolis, MN 55474-0010
Tel (612) 671-3131 *Founded/Ownrshp* 1977
Sales 90.6MM *EMP* 3^E
SIC 6726 Face amount installment certificate issuing
Pr: Abu M Arif
CFO: Ross P Palacios
VP: David K Stewart
Sls Dir: Nick Creager
Sls Dir: David Koth
Snr Mgr: Ann Deboef

D-U-N-S 00-696-1957
▲ AMERIPRISE FINANCIAL INC
55 Ameriprise Fincl Ctr, Minneapolis, MN 55474-9900
Tel (612) 671-3131 *Founded/Ownrshp* 1894
Sales 12.1MMM *EMP* 13,000^E
Accts Pricewaterhousecoopers Llp Mi
Tkr Sym AMP *Exch* NYS
SIC 6282 7389 6411 6311 Investment advice; Investment advisory service; Manager of mutual funds, contract or fee basis; Financial services; Life insurance agents; Pension & retirement plan consultants; Life insurance; Life insurance carriers
Ch Bd: James M Cracchiolo
Assoc VP: Alan Melamed
Ex VP: Kelli A Hunter
Ex VP: John C Junek
Ex VP: Randy Kupper
Ex VP: Deirdre D McGraw
Ex VP: Pat O'Connell
Ex VP: Bill Williams
Sr VP: David K Stewart
VP: Tracy Anderson
VP: Lamont Boykins
VP: Eric Brandt
VP: Craig Brimhall
VP: Stephen Ehele
VP: William Emptage
VP: Manish Ganatra
VP: Steve Gathje
VP: Jacqueline Glockner
VP: Justin Hansen
VP: Diane Harren
VP: Paul Hoghaug
Board of Directors: Dianne Neal Blixt, Amy Digeso, Lon R Greenberg, Jeffrey Noddle, H Jay Sarles, Robert F Sharpe Jr, Christopher J Williams

D-U-N-S 07-027-1846
■ AMERIPRISE FINANCIAL SERVICES INC
(*Suby of* AMERIPRISE FINANCIAL INC) ★
500 2nd St S Ste 101, La Crosse, WI 54601-4028
Tel (608) 783-2639 *Founded/Ownrshp* 1971
Sales 2.4MMM^E *EMP* 11,100
SIC 6282 6411 6211 8742 Investment advice; Futures advisory service; Investment advisory service; Investment counselors; Insurance agents, brokers & service; Insurance agents; Security brokers & dealers; Security brokers & dealers; Brokers, security; Dealers, security; Management consulting services; Maintenance management consultant; Banking & finance consultant; Financial consultant
CEO: Jim Cracchiolo
CFO: Walter S Berman
Ex VP: Kelli Hunter
Sr VP: Mark Schwarzmann
VP: Marty Griffin
VP: Jeff McGregor
Sales Asso: Lynn Konsela

AMERIQUAL FOODS
See AMERIQUAL GROUP LLC

D-U-N-S 09-977-1198 IMP/EXP
AMERIQUAL GROUP LLC
AMERIQUAL FOODS
(*Suby of* AMERIQUAL GROUP HOLDINGS LLC)
18200 Highway 41 N, Evansville, IN 47725-9300
Tel (812) 867-1300 *Founded/Ownrshp* 1993
Sales 265.4MM^E *EMP* 650
SIC 2099 Ready-to-eat meals, salads & sandwiches
VP: Timothy Brauer
Opers Mgr: Daniel Bittner

D-U-N-S 01-074-0715
AMERIQUEST BUSINESS SERVICES INC
NATIONALEASE
457 Haddonfield Rd # 220, Cherry Hill, NJ 08002-2220
Tel (800) 608-0809 *Founded/Ownrshp* 1996
Sales 84.8MM *EMP* 222
Accts Ernst & Young Llp Philadelphi
SIC 7389 Purchasing service
Pr: Douglas Clark
* *CFO:* Mark Joyce
CFO: Mark P Joyce
Ch: Brian Hogan
Ofcr: Bea Clark
* *Ex VP:* Jim Guice
VP: Patrick Barrett
VP: Sean Bliss
VP: Robert Upton
* *VP Mktg:* Kate Freer
Sls Dir: Kevin Fessler

D-U-N-S 87-303-9564
AMERIQUEST CAPITAL CORP
1100 W Twn Cntry Rd R, Orange, CA 92868-4600
Tel (714) 564-0600 *Founded/Ownrshp* 1994
Sales NA *EMP* 10,000
SIC 6163 Mortgage brokers arranging for loans, using money of others
Pr: Aseem Mital
Exec: Steve Goldberg

D-U-N-S 08-012-6157
AMERIQUEST INC
457 Haddonfield Rd # 220, Cherry Hill, NJ 08002-2201
Tel (630) 925-7681 *Founded/Ownrshp* 1998
Sales 86.7MM *EMP* 227
Accts Ernst & Young Llp Philadelphi
SIC 7374 Data processing & preparation
Ch Bd: Douglas Clark
CFO: Mark Joyce
Ex VP: James Guice
Board of Directors: Thomas Brown, Michael Enright, John Gavin, Brian J Hogan, Kirk Tilley

D-U-N-S 87-426-7560
AMERIQUEST MORTGAGE CO
(*Suby of* AMERIQUEST CAPITAL CORP) ★
2677 N Main St Ste 140, Santa Ana, CA 92705-6659
Tel (714) 732-9100 *Founded/Ownrshp* 1994
Sales NA *EMP* 4,000^E
SIC 6162 Mortgage bankers
CEO: Michael O Gibson Jr
* *Ch Bd:* Aseem Mital
* *CFO:* Karen Christensen
* *Ex VP:* John Grazer
* *VP:* Patricia Fitzpatrick
Board of Directors: C S Mansfield, M J Mayesh, Edward Resendez

AMERIS
See AMERICAN BANKING CO

D-U-N-S 17-813-5851
▲ AMERIS BANCORP
310 1st St Se, Moultrie, GA 31768-4731
Tel (229) 890-1111 *Founded/Ownrshp* 1980
Sales NA *EMP* 1,110^E
Accts Crowe Horwath Llp Atlanta Ge
Tkr Sym ABCB *Exch* NGS
SIC 6022 State commercial banks
Pr: Edwin W Hortman Jr
* *Ch Bd:* Daniel B Jeter
COO: Andrew B Cheney
COO: Dennis J Zember Jr
Chf Cred: Jon S Edwards
Ofcr: Cindi H Lewis
Ex VP: Stephen A Melton
Board of Directors: William I Bowen Jr, R Dale Ezzell, Leo J Hill, Robert P Lynch, Elizabeth A McCague, William H Stern, Jimmy D Veal

D-U-N-S 03-633-8812
■ AMERIS BANK (GA)
(*Suby of* AMERIS BANCORP) ★
310 1st St Se, Moultrie, GA 31768-4731
Tel (800) 845-5219 *Founded/Ownrshp* 1945, 1971
Sales NA *EMP* 183
SIC 6022 State commercial banks
CEO: Edwin W Hortman Jr
* *Pr:* Andrew B Cheney
Ofcr: Tim Dollins
Ofcr: Mona Hayes
Ofcr: Jim Zimmerman
Sr VP: Marc E Demott
Sr VP: Jennifer Garizio
Sr VP: Tony Jones
Sr VP: Garry Lubi
Sr VP: Michael Pannell
VP: Candace Adkins
* *VP:* Tommy Bargeron
VP: Denise Inman
VP: Keith McAnulty
* *VP:* Lea Pate
VP: Tiffany Pearce
VP: Lori Putnam
VP: Gregory Seabaugh
VP: Terri Sherman
VP: Paula Stamand
VP: Freddie Zeh
Board of Directors: Austin L Coarsey, Buck Flowers, Raymond Fulp, Stewart Gilbert MD, Kenneth J Hunnicutt, Buddy Walker

D-U-N-S 62-339-6785
▲ AMERISAFE INC
2301 Highway 190 W, Deridder, LA 70634-6004
Tel (337) 463-9052 *Founded/Ownrshp* 1986
Sales NA *EMP* 451^E
Accts Ernst & Young Llp New Orleans
Tkr Sym AMSF *Exch* NGS
SIC 6331 Workers' compensation insurance
Pr: G Janelle Frost
* *Ch Bd:* Jared A Morris
CFO: Neal A Fuller
Ex VP: Vincent J Gagliano
Ex VP: Brendan D Gau
Sr VP: Kathryn H Shirley
VP: Ed Ennis
Board of Directors: Michael Brown, Teri Fontenot, Philip A Garcia, Millard E Morris, Daniel Phillips, Randall Roach, Austin P Young III

D-U-N-S 10-308-3817
AMERISAVE MORTGAGE CORP
3350 Peachtree Rd Ne # 1000, Atlanta, GA 30326-1040
Tel (866) 970-7283 *Founded/Ownrshp* 2002
Sales NA *EMP* 200
SIC 6163 Mortgage brokers arranging for loans, using money of others
CEO: Patrick Markert
* *Pr:* Carol Poupart
COO: Todd Vickery
* *CFO:* Andrea Watts
Ofcr: Benjamin Teasley
Ex VP: Gary Suess
Sr VP: Joseph Watts
VP: Dave Williams
Dir IT: Marion Bass
Natl Sales: Marisa Davis
VP Sls: Dustin McCain

D-U-N-S 03-927-7590
▲ AMERISOURCEBERGEN CORP
1300 Morris Dr Ste 100, Chesterbrook, PA 19087-5594
Tel (610) 727-7000 *Founded/Ownrshp* 2001
Sales 146.8MMM *EMP* 17,500
Accts Ernst & Young Llp Philadelphi
Tkr Sym ABC *Exch* NYS
SIC 5122 5047 Drugs, proprietaries & sundries; Pharmaceuticals; Drugs & drug proprietaries; Medical & hospital equipment; Medical equipment & supplies; Surgical equipment & supplies; Hospital equipment & furniture
Pr: Steven H Collis
Pr: Peyton R Howell
CFO: Tim G Guttman
Chf Mktg O: Gina K Clark
Ex VP: June B Barry
Ex VP: John G Chou
Ex VP: Dale Danilewitz
Ex VP: Michael Dicandilo
Ex VP: Lawrence C Marsh
Ex VP: David W Neu
Sr VP: Lazarus Krikorian
VP: Ncole Alvi
VP: Brian Ansay
VP: Dustin Bateman
VP: Bruce Bennett
VP: Susan Bertot
VP: Mike Biesanz
VP: Deanna L Bush
VP: Tom Byrne
VP: Kevin Conway
VP: Frank Dicenso
Board of Directors: Henry W McGee, Ornella Barra, Douglas R Conant, D Mark Durcan, Richard W Gochnauer, Richard C Gozon, Lon R Greenberg, Jane E Henney, Kathleen W Hyle, Michael J Long

D-U-N-S 00-791-4906
■ AMERISOURCEBERGEN DRUG CORP
(*Suby of* AMERISOURCEBERGEN SERVICES CORP) ★
1300 Morris Dr Ste 100, Chesterbrook, PA 19087-5594
Tel (610) 727-7000 *Founded/Ownrshp* 1985, 1988
Sales 8.8MMM^E *EMP* 3,500
SIC 5122 Drugs, proprietaries & sundries; Pharmaceuticals; Drugs & drug proprietaries
Pr: David W Neu
* *COO:* Kurt J Hilzinger
* *Treas:* Donald E Steinbacher
VP: Liz Carbon
* *VP:* Tim G Guttman

D-U-N-S 19-900-3476
■ AMERISOURCEBERGEN SERVICES CORP
(*Suby of* AMERISOURCEBERGEN CORP) ★
1300 Morris Dr Ste 100, Chesterbrook, PA 19087-5594
Tel (610) 727-7000 *Founded/Ownrshp* 2001
Sales 8.8MMM^E *EMP* 7,400
SIC 5122 5047 5199 8721 Drugs, proprietaries & sundries; Pharmaceuticals; Drugs & drug proprietaries; Cosmetics, perfumes & hair products; Medical equipment & supplies; Surgical equipment & supplies; General merchandise, non-durable; Billing & bookkeeping service
CEO: Steven H Collis
* *Ex VP:* Michael D Dicandilo
Sr VP: Gina Clark
Opers Mgr: Ron Holmes

D-U-N-S 07-846-8849
■ AMERISOURCEBERGEN SPECIALTY GROUP INC
ABSG-CORPORATE
(*Suby of* AMERISOURCEBERGEN CORP) ★
3101 Gaylord Pkwy, Frisco, TX 75034-8655
Tel (866) 408-3761 *Founded/Ownrshp* 2001
Sales 1.0MMM^E *EMP* 600^E
SIC 5122 Pharmaceuticals
CEO: Steve Collis
Ofcr: Dustin Roller
Ofcr: Richard Taylor
Sr VP: Brian Ansay
VP: Robert Sorenson
VP: William Venus
Prgrm Mgr: Greg Glaser
Prgrm Mgr: Georgios Tserotas
Genl Mgr: Neil Herson
Dir IT: Rob Vick
Dir IT: Stephanie Walsh

D-U-N-S 94-156-2936
■ AMERISTAR CASINO COUNCIL BLUFFS LLC
(*Suby of* GOLD MERGER SUB LLC) ★
2200 River Rd, Council Bluffs, IA 51501-7070
Tel (712) 328-8888 *Founded/Ownrshp* 1993
Sales 68.1MM^E *EMP* 1,250
SIC 7011 7991 5813 5812 Casino hotel; Physical fitness facilities; Drinking places; Eating places
Pr: Craig H Neilsen
CFO: Michael Shelton
* *Treas:* Thomas Steinbauer
VP: Ray Neilsen
IT Man: Jerry Davis
Mktg Mgr: Kelley Kulesa

D-U-N-S 95-616-0378
■ AMERISTAR CASINO KANSAS CITY INC
(*Suby of* GOLD MERGER SUB LLC) ★
3200 Ameristar Dr, Kansas City, MO 64161-9223
Tel (816) 414-7000 *Founded/Ownrshp* 2000
Sales 122.8MM^E *EMP* 2,200
SIC 7011 7999 Casino hotel; Gambling establishment
CEO: Gordon R Kanofsky
* *Pr:* Larry A Hodges
* *Pr:* Troy A Stremming
* *CFO:* Thomas M Steinbauer
Dir Sec: Brent Lewis
Dir Sec: Dan Redding
Genl Mgr: Stephanie Hurla
Pr Mgr: Michael Knopfel
Mktg Mgr: Lisa Culbertson

D-U-N-S 07-979-7928
■ AMERISTAR CASINO ST CHARLES INC
(*Suby of* GOLD MERGER SUB LLC) ★
1 Ameristar Blvd, Saint Charles, MO 63301-3500
Tel (636) 949-7777 *Founded/Ownrshp* 2000
Sales 11.8MM^E *EMP* 1,700
SIC 7999 7011 Gambling establishment; Gambling machines, operation; Hotels & motels; Casino hotel
Pr: Carlos A Ruisanchez
VP: Steve Peate
Dir Soc: Ashley Gaddy
Brnch Mgr: Jim Scheve

D-U-N-S 80-855-4463
■ AMERISTAR CASINO VICKSBURG INC
(*Suby of* GAMING AND LEISURE PROPERTIES INC) ★
4116 Washington St, Vicksburg, MS 39180-5288
Tel (601) 638-1000 *Founded/Ownrshp* 2011
Sales 126.3MM^E *EMP* 7,200
SIC 7999 7011 5812 Gambling establishment; Casino hotel; Eating places
Pr: Carlos A Ruisanchez
* *Pr:* Gordon R Kanofsky
* *Sec:* Thomas M Steinbauer
* *Sr VP:* Peter C Walsh
VP: Bob Forister
* *VP:* Larry A Hodges
* *VP:* Thomas Steinbauer
VP: Troy Stremming
Genl Mgr: Bruce Howard
Opers Mgr: Brady Clark
Mktg Mgr: Lori Burke
Board of Directors: Gordon R Kanofsky, Ray Sienko

D-U-N-S 82-745-2111
AMERISTAR CASINOS INC
3773 Howard Hughes Pkwy # 490, Las Vegas, NV 89169-0949
Tel (702) 567-7000 *Founded/Ownrshp* 2012
Sales NA *EMP* 7,210
SIC 7011

D-U-N-S 80-834-2153
■ AMERISTAR EAST CHICAGO HOLDINGS LLC
(*Suby of* GOLD MERGER SUB LLC) ★
777 Ameristar Blvd, East Chicago, IN 46312-1806
Tel (219) 378-3000 *Founded/Ownrshp* 2007
Sales 20.5MM^E *EMP* 1,200^E
SIC 7999 Gambling & lottery services
Prin: Tracy West

AMERISTAR FENCE PRODUCTS
See GAFP INC

D-U-N-S 05-968-8896
AMERISTAR PERIMETER SECURITY USA INC
ASSA ABLOY GROUP COMPANY
(*Suby of* ASSA ABLOY USA) ★
1555 N Mingo Rd, Tulsa, OK 74116-1506
Tel (918) 835-0898 *Founded/Ownrshp* 2013
Sales 200.0MM^E *EMP* 630
SIC 3089 3446 1799 Fences, gates & accessories: plastic; Fences, gates, posts & flagpoles; Fence construction
Pr: Mark Meek
Treas: Joe Hurley
VP: Barry Willingham

D-U-N-S 80-633-3001
AMERISURE INC
(*Suby of* AMERISURE MUTUAL INSURANCE CO) ★
26777 Halsted Rd Lbby, Farmington Hills, MI 48331-3587
Tel (248) 615-9000 *Founded/Ownrshp* 1983
Sales NA *EMP* 700
SIC 6411 Insurance agents, brokers & service
Pr: Gregory J Crabb
**Ch Bd:* James B Nicholson
Ex VP: Lisa M Barton
Sr VP: Barbara Radous
VP: Kelly Bifano
VP: Nancy Caudill
VP: Gerald Chiddick
VP: Kevin Clary
VP: Gerry Espinoza
VP: Steve Solimine
Telecom Mg: Lori Wodrich

D-U-N-S 19-534-7307
AMERISURE INSURANCE CO
(*Suby of* AMERISURE MUTUAL INSURANCE CO) ★
26777 Halsted Rd Lbby, Farmington Hills, MI 48331-3587
Tel (248) 615-9000 *Founded/Ownrshp* 1968
Sales NA *EMP* 700
SIC 6331 Workers' compensation insurance; Automobile insurance; Property damage insurance; Fire, marine & casualty insurance: mutual
Ch Bd: James B Nicholson
Pr: Mark Gromek
**Pr:* Richard Russell
**CFO:* R Douglas Kinnan
Sr VP: Dirk Olsick
**VP:* Pamela Burgess
VP: Michael M Dieterk
VP: Matthew Morrison
VP: Matt Simon
**VP:* Carol A Taylor
Netwrk Eng: Wes Zastrow
Board of Directors: John William Dwyer, Kenneth John Le Strange, Harry Austin Lomason II, Eugene Albert Miller, William Paul Panny II, Martha R Seger, Stephen William Trewhella, William Paul Vititoe

D-U-N-S 00-695-8565
AMERISURE MUTUAL INSURANCE CO (OR)
26777 Halsted Rd Lbby, Farmington Hills, MI 48331-3587
Tel (248) 615-9000 *Founded/Ownrshp* 1912
Sales NA *EMP* 700
SIC 6331 Workers' compensation insurance; Fire, marine & casualty insurance: mutual; Automobile insurance
Pr: Gregory J Crabb
**Ch Bd:* James B Nicholson
**CFO:* Matt Simon
Chf Inves: Daniel J Graf
**Ofcr:* Angela McBride
Ofcr: Angela M McBride
**Ofcr:* Todd B Ruthruff
**VP:* Pamela Burgess
VP: Tom Carlson
VP: Thomas McDaniel
**VP:* Matt Simmons
VP: Eric Spencer
VP: Jim Suchara
**VP:* Carol A Taylor
Board of Directors: Matt Bertman, Todd Harrison

D-U-N-S 78-603-7577
AMERISURE MUTUAL INSURANCE CO
(*Suby of* AMERISURE MUTUAL INSURANCE CO) ★
2160 Satellite Blvd # 200, Duluth, GA 30097-4006
Tel (770) 813-3300 *Founded/Ownrshp* 2006
Sales NA *EMP* 60
SIC 6411 Insurance agents, brokers & service
CEO: Richard Russell

D-U-N-S 04-143-0351
AMERITAS HOLDING CO
(*Suby of* AMERITAS MUTUAL HOLDING CO) ★
5900 O St, Lincoln, NE 68510-2234
Tel (402) 467-1122 *Founded/Ownrshp* 1998
Sales NA *EMP* 2,300
Accts Deloitte & Touche Llp Omaha
SIC 6311 Life insurance
Pr: Joann M Martin
**Treas:* Robert P Kocher
Bd of Dir: James Anderson
Bd of Dir: Michael Cambron
Bd of Dir: Richard Finan
Bd of Dir: Michael Fisher
Bd of Dir: Francis Mastrianna
Bd of Dir: Patricia McGuire
Bd of Dir: Floretta McKenzie
Bd of Dir: Thomas Petry
Bd of Dir: Larry Pike
Bd of Dir: Myrns Powell
Bd of Dir: Edward Quinn
Bd of Dir: D Silby
Bd of Dir: Dudley Taft
Ex VP: Haluk Ariturk
Ex VP: Gary Huffman
**VP:* Jan M Connolly
VP: Scott Corbett
**VP:* Nancy A Dalessio
**VP:* Dale D Johnson

D-U-N-S 00-696-9646
AMERITAS LIFE INSURANCE CORP
(*Suby of* AMERITAS HOLDING CO) ★
5900 O St, Lincoln, NE 68510-2234
Tel (402) 467-1122 *Founded/Ownrshp* 1887
Sales NA *EMP* 1,300
Accts Deloitte & Touche Llp Omaha
SIC 6371 6311 6211 Pension funds; Life insurance; Brokers, security
Pr: Joann M Martin
Pr: Drew Fleming
**CFO:* Robert C Barth
**Treas:* William Lester
Treas: Nanci Mayhan
Ofcr: Julie Schadt
**Sr VP:* Jan Connolly
Sr VP: Janet Schmidt
VP: Bob Barth
VP: Dave Butler
VP: Martin Hall
VP: Scott Renard
VP: Tammy Shaner
VP: Ed Swotek
VP: Mike Weckenbrock
**VP:* Sue Wilkinson
VP: Terry R Young
Exec: Barbara Lingle

D-U-N-S 04-142-5252
AMERITAS MUTUAL HOLDING CO
5900 O St, Lincoln, NE 68510-2234
Tel (402) 467-1122 *Founded/Ownrshp* 1999
Sales NA *EMP* 3,600
Accts Deloitte & Touche Llp Omaha
SIC 6311 Life insurance
Pr: Joann M Martin
Pr: Patty Reiners
Ex VP: William W Lester
**Sr VP:* Nancy A Dalessio
**Sr VP:* Dale G Johnson
Sr VP: Bruce E Mieth
**Sr VP:* Robert John H Sands
**Sr VP:* Janet L Schmidt
**Sr VP:* Richard A Wiedenbeck
**Sr VP:* Sue Wilkinson
VP: Bob Herum
VP: Dennis Kelleher
VP: Donald Lomax
VP: Bruce Meith
VP: Teresa Pegler
VP: Deb Sterns
Board of Directors: Bryan Slone

D-U-N-S 00-693-8187 IMP
■ **AMERITECH**
SBC
(*Suby of* AT&T INC) ★
240 N Meridian St, Indianapolis, IN 46204-1931
Tel (317) 265-2266 *Founded/Ownrshp* 1920, 2000
Sales 747.9MM^{E} *EMP* 4,000
SIC 4813 8721 Local & long distance telephone communications; Local telephone communications; Voice telephone communications; Data telephone communications; Billing & bookkeeping service
Pr: George S Fleetwood
VP: Jake Smith
Exec: David Jones
Exec: Michael Owens
Tech Mgr: Dave Mahlke
Tech Mgr: Donna Tuschoff
VP Sls: Timothy Skola

D-U-N-S 02-475-1591
■ **AMERITECH PAYPHONE SERVICES OF MICHIGAN INC**
SBC
(*Suby of* AT&T MIDWEST) ★
225 W Randolph St, Chicago, IL 60606-1838
Tel (708) 458-8460 *Founded/Ownrshp* 2001
Sales 103.4MM^{E} *EMP* 1,929^{E}
SIC 4813 Telephone communication, except radio
Prin: Donald Goens

D-U-N-S 10-842-0167
■ **AMERITECH PUBLISHING INC**
SBC
(*Suby of* AT&T MIDWEST) ★
23500 Northwestern Hwy, Southfield, MI 48075-3369
Tel (800) 996-4609 *Founded/Ownrshp* 1983
Sales 222.4MM^{E} *EMP* 2,955
SIC 2741 Directories, telephone: publishing only, not printed on site; Directories: publishing only, not printed on site
Pr: Edward Whittaker
**VP:* Allan Duy
**VP Mktg:* Andrew Dutton

D-U-N-S 10-217-7813
■ **AMERITECH SERVICES INC**
SBC
(*Suby of* AT&T INC) ★
208 S Lasalle St Ste 814, Chicago, IL 60604
Tel (847) 248-2000 *Founded/Ownrshp* 1996
Sales 456.3MM^{E} *EMP* 7,243
SIC 7389 4225 8742 8721 Purchasing service; General warehousing; Marketing consulting services; Accounting services, except auditing
Pr: Randall Stephenson
COO: Marvin Allums
COO: Diane Bonina
COO: Matt Gallant
COO: Pamela Holt

AMERITECH WISCONSIN
See WISCONSIN BELL INC

D-U-N-S 78-410-4957
AMERITOX LIMITED PARTNERSHIP
300 E Lombard St Ste 1610, Baltimore, MD 21202-3210
Tel (443) 220-0115 *Founded/Ownrshp* 1996
Sales 146.2MM^{E} *EMP* 486
SIC 7374 8734 8731 Data processing service; Testing laboratories; Commercial physical research
CEO: Andrew Scott Walton
Pt: Ron Backer
COO: Todd G Gardner
COO: Joel A McEndree
COO: Dan Valenti
COO: Jay B Zimmerman
CFO: Todd Gardner
CFO: John McDonough
Chf Mktg O: Thomas Smith
Sr VP: Regina Morano
Sr VP: Mike Ziegler
VP: Joel McEndree
Assoc Dir: Karl Neumann

AMERIVEST
See TD AMERITRADE CLEARING INC

AMERIWOOD INDUSTRIES, INC.
See DOREL HOME FURNISHINGS INC

AMERLUX LIGHTING SYSTEMS
See AMERLUX LLC

D-U-N-S 04-793-5531 IMP/EXP
AMERLUX LLC
AMERLUX LIGHTING SYSTEMS
178 Bauer Dr, Oakland, NJ 07436-3105
Tel (973) 882-5010 *Founded/Ownrshp* 1995
Sales 100.0MM^{E} *EMP* 200^{E}
SIC 3646 Commercial indusl & institutional electric lighting fixtures
Ch: Frank Diassi
Pr: Joe Manning
**CEO:* Chuck Campagna
**CFO:* Frank L Weston Sr
VP: Ken Heinis
**VP:* Don Knickerbocker
**VP:* John Mamo
**VP:* Christopher McQuillan
VP Opers: Eric Lannon
VP Mktg: Bill Plageman
VP Sls: Chris McQuillan

AMERON CORPORATE OFFICE
See AMERON INTERNATIONAL CORP

D-U-N-S 14-767-3354 IMP
■ **AMERON INTERNATIONAL CORP**
AMERON CORPORATE OFFICE
(*Suby of* NOV) ★
245 S Los Robles Ave, Pasadena, CA 91101-3638
Tel (626) 683-4000 *Founded/Ownrshp* 1986
Sales 646.0MM^{E} *EMP* 2,300
SIC 3272 3317 3273 1442 3084 Cylinder pipe, prestressed or pretensioned concrete; Steel pipe & tubes; Ready-mixed concrete; Construction sand & gravel; Plastics pipe
CEO: Thomas Charles Zyroll Jr
**CFO:* Gary Wagner
**Treas:* Daniel L Molinaro
**VP:* Craig C Goss
**VP:* Dwight W Rettig
VP: David Tantalean
**Prin:* James S Marlen
**Prin:* Clay C Williams
Dir IT: James Fisher
IT Man: Ketan Thanki

D-U-N-S 62-129-7563 IMP/EXP
■ **AMES COMPANIES INC**
(*Suby of* CLOPAY AMES TRUE TEMPER HOLDING CORP) ★
465 Railroad Ave, Camp Hill, PA 17011-5611
Tel (717) 737-1500 *Founded/Ownrshp* 2010
Sales 359.5MM^{E} *EMP* 1,100
SIC 3423 3799 3524 Garden & farm tools, including shovels; Shovels, spades (hand tools); Wheelbarrows; Lawn & garden equipment
Pr: Michael A Sarrica
**CFO:* Marcus Hamilton
**Treas:* Tom Gibbons
VP: Michael Doyle
VP: Bill Grambo
Exec: Joanne Fitzgerald
Prgrm Mgr: Brian Troup
Rgnl Mgr: Mike Flores
IT Man: Gary Klock
IT Man: Bryan Thompson
Tech Mgr: Mike Lupey

D-U-N-S 04-316-9309
AMES CONSTRUCTION INC (MN)
14420 County Road 5, Burnsville, MN 55306-6997
Tel (952) 435-7106 *Founded/Ownrshp* 1960
Sales 1.0MMM *EMP* 2,200
Accts Cliftonlarsonallen Llp Minnea
SIC 1611 1041 1021 1794 Airport runway construction; Highway & street paving contractor; Open pit gold mining; Open pit copper ore mining; Excavation work
Ch: Richard J Ames
**Pr:* Raymond G Ames
**CFO:* Michael J Kellen
Sr Cor Off: Stephen A Ames
VP: Mike Billing
VP: Roger L McBride
VP: Jerry Volz
Dir Risk M: Trish Campbell
Comm Dir: Ken Brandt
DP Exec: Marco Vera
Dir IT: Bob Bruckner

D-U-N-S 60-738-1142 IMP/EXP
AMESBURY ACQUISITION HOLDINGS (2) INC
BALANCE SYSTEMS
(*Suby of* TYMAN PLC)
2061 Sherrill Dr, Statesville, NC 28625-9025
Tel (704) 924-8586 *Founded/Ownrshp* 2007
Sales 264.4MM^{E} *EMP* 1,000
SIC 3272 Concrete window & door components, sills & frames
Pr: Johnnthan Petromelis

D-U-N-S 09-427-5658 IMP/EXP
AMESBURY GROUP INC
(*Suby of* BALANCE SYSTEMS) ★
57 S Hunt Rd, Amesbury, MA 01913-4422
Tel (978) 834-3233 *Founded/Ownrshp* 1981
Sales 235.7MM^{E} *EMP* 700
SIC 3053 3442 3086 2221 3089 Gaskets, packing & sealing devices; Sash, door or window: metal; Plastics foam products; Pile fabrics, manmade fiber & silk; Extruded finished plastic products
CFO: Brian Cann
CFO: James Eisenhaure
CFO: James Sluss
Mfg Mgr: Grant Marquardt
Sls Dir: Kim Kenzevich
Manager: Brian Gutzler
Board of Directors: John Garnett, G C Wilkinson

AMETEK ELECTROMECHANICAL GROUP
See AMETEK TECHNICAL & INDUSTRIAL PRODUCTS INC

D-U-N-S 00-134-5149 IMP/EXP
▲ **AMETEK INC**
AMETEK SENSOR TECHNOLOGY BUS
1100 Cassatt Rd, Berwyn, PA 19312-1177
Tel (610) 647-2121 *Founded/Ownrshp* 1930
Sales 3.9MMM *EMP* 15,400
Tkr Sym AME *Exch* NYS
SIC 3621 3823 3824 3825 Motors & generators; Motors, electric; Industrial instrmnts msrmnt display/control process variable; Temperature instruments: industrial process type; Pressure gauges, dial & digital; Controllers for process variables, all types; Vehicle instruments; Tachometer, centrifugal; Engine electrical test equipment
Ch Bd: Frank S Hermance
Pr: Brian Nash
COO: David A Zapico
CFO: Robert R Mandos
Treas: William J Burke
Treas: Robert Rausch
Sr VP: Matthew C French
Sr VP: Bruce P Wilson
VP: David W Jordan
VP: Theresaterry Kelso
VP: Prakash Mahesh
VP: Ian McGavisk
VP: Joseph A Muklevicz
VP: Jared Riddle
VP: Ken Weirman
Board of Directors: Ruby R Chandy, Anthony J Conti, Steven W Kohlhagen, James R Malone, Gretchen W McClain, Elizabeth R Varet, Dennis K Williams

D-U-N-S 00-969-2351 IMP
■ **AMETEK PROGRAMMABLE POWER INC**
(*Suby of* AMETEK SENSOR TECHNOLOGY BUS) ★
9250 Brown Deer Rd, San Diego, CA 92121-2267
Tel (858) 450-0085 *Founded/Ownrshp* 2006
Sales 106.5MM^{E} *EMP* 350^{E}
SIC 3679 Power supplies, all types: static
CEO: Timothy F Croal
**CFO:* John Molinelli
**VP:* Shawn Smith
Prgrm Mgr: Joellen Atkins
Ql Cn Mgr: Cecilia Juarez
Sls Mgr: Grant Moore

AMETEK ROTRON
See ROTRON INC

AMETEK SENSOR TECHNOLOGY BUS
See AMETEK INC

D-U-N-S 00-417-8265
■ **AMETEK TECHNICAL & INDUSTRIAL PRODUCTS INC** (MN)
AMETEK ELECTROMECHANICAL GROUP
(*Suby of* AMETEK SENSOR TECHNOLOGY BUS) ★
100 E Erie St Ste 130, Kent, OH 44240-3587
Tel (330) 677-3754 *Founded/Ownrshp* 2009
Sales 105.3MM^{E} *EMP* 145
SIC 3621 5063 3566 Motors, electric; Motors, electric; Speed changers, drives & gears
VP: Matt French
**CFO:* Peter Smith
**Treas:* William D Burke
**Genl Mgr:* Todd Schlegel
Opers Mgr: Dan Kirtz

D-U-N-S 96-736-8184 IMP
AMF AUTOMATION TECHNOLOGIES LLC
2115 W Laburnum Ave, Richmond, VA 23227-4396
Tel (804) 355-7961 *Founded/Ownrshp* 2008
Sales 143.2MM^{E} *EMP* 500^{E}
SIC 3556 Bakery machinery
COO: Margaret Shaia

D-U-N-S 96-635-1595
AMF BOWLING CENTERS HOLDINGS INC
(*Suby of* AMF BOWLING WORLDWIDE INC) ★
7313 Bell Creek Rd, Mechanicsville, VA 23111-3551
Tel (804) 417-2008 *Founded/Ownrshp* 2004
Sales 562.1MM^{E} *EMP* 8,841
SIC 7933 Duck pin center
Pr: Frederick R Hipp
**COO:* Warren Hardie
**VP:* Daniel M McCormack
**VP:* Stephen D Satterwhite

D-U-N-S 80-911-8974
AMF BOWLING CENTERS INC
(*Suby of* AMF BOWLING CENTERS HOLDINGS INC) ★
7313 Bell Creek Rd, Mechanicsville, VA 23111-3551
Tel (855) 263-7278 *Founded/Ownrshp* 1982
Sales 561.1MM^{E} *EMP* 8,841
SIC 7933 Bowling centers
Pr: Frederick R Hipp
**CFO:* Stephen D Satterwhite
VP: Harsha Bellur
**VP:* Scott W Brown
**VP:* Mark S Hatcher
**VP:* Rachel S Labrecque
**VP:* Michael S McKinley
VP: Harsha Nagaraj
**VP:* Jody Pastula
VP: Tony Ponsiglione
**VP:* Larry Ross
**VP:* Joseph F Scarnaty
**VP:* John S Shearer
**VP:* Evelyn J Walter
**VP:* Merrell C Wreden

D-U-N-S 96-634-8138 IMP/EXP
AMF BOWLING WORLDWIDE INC
(*Suby of* KINGPIN INTERMEDIATE CORP) ★
7313 Bell Creek Rd, Mechanicsville, VA 23111-3551
Tel (804) 730-4000 *Founded/Ownrshp* 2004
Sales 627.4MM^{E} *EMP* 8,841
SIC 3949 7933 Bowling equipment & supplies; Bowling pins; Bowling alleys & accessories; Billiard & pool equipment & supplies, general; Bowling centers
Pr: Frederick R Hipp
**CFO:* Stephen D Satterwhite
Treas: Usha Atluri
Treas: Tabatha Garcia
VP: William McDonnell
**VP:* Merrell C Wreden
VP Mktg: Merrell Wreden

D-U-N-S 61-055-9929
AMFAB INC
1424 Campostella Rd, Chesapeake, VA 23320-6004
Tel (757) 543-1485 Founded/Ownrshp 2003
Sales 250.0MM EMP 6
SIC 3499 Fire- or burglary-resistive products
Pr: William Proffitt

D-U-N-S 13-033-1671
■ AMFAC HAWAII LLC A HAWAII LIMITED LIABILITY CO
(Suby of KAANAPALI LAND, LLC)
700 Bishop St Ste 2002, Honolulu, HI 96813-4121
Tel (808) 543-8900 Founded/Ownrshp 1995
Sales 263.1MM^E EMP 1,000
SIC 6531 6552 0133 0179 Real estate managers; Land subdividers & developers, residential; Land subdividers & developers, commercial; Sugarcane farm; Coffee farm
Pr: Gary Grottke
Sr VP: Chester Richardson
Info Man: Joann Takamiyashiro
Board of Directors: Edward G Karl

D-U-N-S 10-829-7268
AMFAM INC
(Suby of AMERICAN FAMILY INSURANCE) ★
6000 American Pkwy, Madison, WI 53783-0001
Tel (608) 249-2111 Founded/Ownrshp 1981
Sales NA EMP 4,367
Accts Pricewaterhousecoopers Llp C
SIC 6331 6311 6141 Fire, marine & casualty insurance: stock; Life insurance; Consumer finance companies
Pr: David Anderson
*Ex VP: J Brent Johnson

D-U-N-S 14-748-4901
AMFM INC
AMFM NRSING RHABILITATION CTRS
240 Capitol St Ste 500, Charleston, WV 25301-2297
Tel (304) 344-1623 Founded/Ownrshp 1982
Sales 78.9MM^E EMP 1,000
SIC 8741 8742 Management services; Hospital & health services consultant
Pr: John R Elliot
COO: Pamela Shumate
*VP: Fonda J Elliott
VP: Tammy Painter

AMFM NRSING RHABILITATION CTRS
See AMFM INC

AMG
See AFFILIATED MANAGERS GROUP INC

AMG ADVNCED MTLLRGCAL GROUP NV
See METALLURG INC

D-U-N-S 62-347-8211
■ AMG FUNDS LLC
MANAGERS FUNDS
(Suby of AMG) ★
800 Connecticut Ave Ste 2, Norwalk, CT 06854-1628
Tel (203) 299-3500 Founded/Ownrshp 1999
Sales NA EMP 110
SIC 6141 Mutual benefit associations
CEO: Jeffrey Cerutti
COO: Keitha Kiene
Treas: Donald S Rumery
Sr VP: Steven Dunn
VP: Steven M Pires
VP: Christopher Rodzen

D-U-N-S 03-997-6196 IMP/EXP
▲ AMGEN INC
1 Amgen Center Dr, Thousand Oaks, CA 91320-1799
Tel (805) 447-1000 Founded/Ownrshp 1980
Sales 21.6MMM EMP 17,900
Tkr Sym AMGN Exch NGS
SIC 2836 Biological products, except diagnostic
Ch Bd: Robert A Bradway
*CFO: David W Meline
Treas: Loretta Joseph
*Chf Cred: Cynthia M Patton
Bd of Dir: Jonie Anderson
Bd of Dir: Erich Durchschlag
Bd of Dir: Patty Salerno
Bd of Dir: Marcus Schulte
*Ex VP: Madhavan Balachandran
Ex VP: Sean E Harper
Ex VP: Anthony C Hooper
Sr VP: Suzanne Blaug
Sr VP: Paul R Eisenberg
*Sr VP: Jonathan P Graham
Sr VP: Laura Hamill
Sr VP: Michael A Kelly
Sr VP: Corinne Le Goff
Sr VP: Brian McNamee
Sr VP: Anna S Richo
Sr VP: Esteban Santos
VP: Duane Barnes
Board of Directors: Tyler Jacks, David Baltimore, Ellen J Kullman, Frank J Biondi Jr, Judith C Pelham, Vance D Coffman, Ronald D Sugar, Francois De Carbonnel, R Sanders Williams, Robert A Eckert, Greg C Garland, Fred Hassan, Rebecca M Henderson, Frank C Herringer

D-U-N-S 78-580-0020 IMP/EXP
■ AMGEN MANUFACTURING LIMITED
(Suby of AMGEN INC) ★
6 Carr 31 Km, Juncos, PR 00777-3871
Tel (787) 656-2000 Founded/Ownrshp 1991
Sales 228.8MM^E EMP 2,100
Accts Ernst & Young Llp San Juan P
SIC 2836 Biological products, except diagnostic
Pr: Emilio Rivera
*Treas: Raul Cermeno
*VP: Robert Maroney
Ql Cn Mgr: Jessica Gonzalez
Snr Mgr: Ismael Del Pilar

D-U-N-S 01-476-7904
■ AMGEN PHARMACEUTICALS INC
(Suby of AMGEN INC) ★
1 Amgen Center Dr, Thousand Oaks, CA 91320-1799
Tel (805) 447-1000 Founded/Ownrshp 1980
Sales 95.9MM^E EMP 4,200
SIC 8733 Biotechnical research, noncommercial
Pr: Gordon Binder
Snr Mgr: Kevin Wilcox

D-U-N-S 07-971-1090
■ AMGRAM CASSELL-EAST LLC
(Suby of CIVITAS SOLUTIONS INC) ★
40020 Grand River Ave, Novi, MI 48375-2112
Tel (248) 615-6025 Founded/Ownrshp 2015
Sales 1.3MM^E EMP 5,006^E
SIC 8322 Rehabilitation services
Pr: Martha A Williams Cassell

D-U-N-S 82-876-3958
AMH HOLDINGS II INC
3773 State Rd, Cuyahoga Falls, OH 44223-2603
Tel (330) 929-1811 Founded/Ownrshp 2002
Sales 228.8MM^E EMP 8,402
SIC 3355 Coils, wire aluminum: made in rolling mills
CEO: Thomas N Chieffe
Board of Directors: Kevin M Hayes, Ira D Kleinman, Kevin C Nickelberry, Dana R Snyder, Thomas J Sullivan, Dennis W Vollmershausen

D-U-N-S 82-535-8497
AMH HOLDINGS LLC
(Suby of ASSOCIATED MATERIALS GROUP INC) ★
3773 State Rd, Cuyahoga Falls, OH 44223-2603
Tel (330) 929-1811 Founded/Ownrshp 2004
Sales 207.8MM^E EMP 2,400
SIC 3355 3444 Coils, wire aluminum: made in rolling mills; Siding, sheet metal
Pr: Thomas N Chieffe
*Ch Bd: Ira D Kleinman
*CFO: Stephen E Graham
*Sr VP: Warren J Arthur
Board of Directors: Lars C Haegg, Kevin C Nickelberry, Dana R Snyder, Dennis W Vollmershausen, Christopher D Whalen

D-U-N-S 96-826-2436
AMHERST NY BOBS INC
(Suby of H C BOBS INC) ★
160 Corporate Ct, Meriden, CT 06450-7177
Tel (203) 235-5775 Founded/Ownrshp 1993
Sales 84.9MM^E EMP 3,000
SIC 5651 5611 5699 5621 5641 5661 Family clothing stores; Clothing accessories: men's & boys'; Clothing, sportswear, men's & boys'; Sports apparel; Women's clothing stores; Children's wear; Men's shoes; Women's shoes; Children's shoes
Pr: David Farrell
*VP: Mike Zibel

D-U-N-S 07-836-3620
AMHERST PIERPONT SECURITIES LLC
245 Park Ave Fl 15, New York, NY 10167-2400
Tel (203) 428-2500 Founded/Ownrshp 2009
Sales 92.5MM^E EMP 135
SIC 6211 Security brokers & dealers
CEO: Mark B Werner
*Pr: Joseph N Walsh III
*CFO: Mike Santangelon

AMI
See MENZIES AVIATION (TEXAS) INC

AMI
See AETNA MAINTENANCE INC

AMI MANUFACTURING
See AIRCO MECHANICAL INC

D-U-N-S 11-626-2676
AMI MECHANICAL INC
12141 Pennsylvania St, Thornton, CO 80241-3115
Tel (303) 280-1401 Founded/Ownrshp 1984
Sales 84.0MM^E EMP 250
SIC 1711 Plumbing contractors; Warm air heating & air conditioning contractor
CEO: Manuel Gonzales
*Pr: Allan H Inge
*COO: Paula Wiley
*CFO: Shayne Smith
IT Man: Alejandra Spray
Sfty Dirs: Rick Brandsma
Opers Mgr: Herman Biggers
Opers Mgr: Porter May

D-U-N-S 08-583-0792 IMP
■ AMI METALS INC
(Suby of RELIANCE STEEL & ALUMINUM CO) ★
1738 Gen George Patton Dr, Brentwood, TN 37027-7901
Tel (615) 370-4917 Founded/Ownrshp 1997
Sales 182.7MM^E EMP 250
SIC 5051 Steel; Aluminum bars, rods, ingots, sheets, pipes, plates, etc.
Pr: Scott Smith
Genl Mgr: Lee Brown
Dir IT: Todd Carlig
Sales Exec: Vince Conese
VP Sls: Eric Beard
S&M/VP: Bernie Rees
Mktg Dir: Joel Moss

D-U-N-S 04-649-1577
AMI SEMICONDUCTOR INC
ON SEMICONDUCTOR
2300 W Buckskin Rd, Pocatello, ID 83201-2734
Tel (208) 233-4690 Founded/Ownrshp 2008
Sales NA EMP 2,500
SIC 3674 8711

D-U-N-S 80-173-8345
AMI-HTI TARZANA ENCINO JOINT VENTURE
A M I ENCN-TRZANA RGNAL MED CE
18321 Clark St, Tarzana, CA 91356-3501
Tel (818) 881-0800 Founded/Ownrshp 1993
Sales 14.6MM EMP 1,800
SIC 8062 General medical & surgical hospitals
Mng Pt: Dale Surowitz

D-U-N-S 00-181-0803
■ AMIC HOLDINGS INC
AMERICAN INDEPENDENCE CORP
(Suby of MADISON INVESTORS CORPORATION)
485 Madison Ave Fl 14, New York, NY 10022-5819
Tel (212) 355-4141 Founded/Ownrshp 2002, 2016
Sales NA EMP 189^E
SIC 6321 6411 Accident & health insurance; Health insurance carriers; Reinsurance carriers, accident & health; Property & casualty insurance agent
CEO: Roy T K Thung
Pr: David T Kettig
CFO: Teresa A Herbert
VP: David Melman
VP: Elena Seha
VP: Adam Vandervoort

AMICA INSURANCE
See AMICA MUTUAL INSURANCE CO

D-U-N-S 06-232-0692
AMICA MUTUAL INSURANCE CO
AMICA INSURANCE
100 Amica Way, Lincoln, RI 02865-1156
Tel (800) 992-6422 Founded/Ownrshp 1907
Sales NA EMP 3,000
SIC 6331

D-U-N-S 00-484-5225
AMICK FARMS LLC
3682 Highway 23, Monetta, SC 29105-9451
Tel (803) 532-1400 Founded/Ownrshp 2007
Sales 3.9MM^E EMP 2,000
SIC 5191 Feed
CEO: Ben Harrison

D-U-N-S 04-650-8875 EXP
AMICK FARMS LLC
(Suby of OTTO & SONS DIV) ★
2079 Batesburg Hwy, Batesburg, SC 29006-8522
Tel (803) 532-1400 Founded/Ownrshp 1941
Sales 213.2MM^E EMP 1,500^E
SIC 0751 Slaughtering: custom livestock services
Pr: Ben Harrison
Pr: Rhonda Frye
*Pr: Marcus Miller
*VP: Steve Kernen
*VP: Wes Knight
VP: Doug Smith
*VP: Fred West
QA Dir: Dustin Cave
QA Dir: Frank Wier
IT Man: Joshua Walker
Opers Mgr: Tim Enlow

AMICO
See ALABAMA METAL INDUSTRIES CORP

D-U-N-S 03-070-1308
AMIDA CARE INC
225 W 34th St Fl 2, New York, NY 10122-0300
Tel (646) 757-7000 Founded/Ownrshp 2010
Sales NA EMP 1
Accts Mcgladrey Llp New York Ny
SIC 6324 Hospital & medical service plans
Pr: Doug Wirth
*CFO: Felice Kussoy
VP: Maria Dasilva
VP: Kathy Frank-Klein
VP: Lisa Keehn
VP: Terry Leach
VP: Kevin Steffens
Dir Rx: John Moore
CIO: Alexander Shuss
VP Mktg: Teri Wade
Sls Dir: Sylvia Cowan

AMIGOS
See GROWTH MANAGEMENT CORP

D-U-N-S 87-455-6178 IMP
AMIGOS MEAT DISTRIBUTORS LP
611 Crosstimbers St, Houston, TX 77022-3936
Tel (713) 928-3111 Founded/Ownrshp 1994
Sales 270.1MM^E EMP 370
SIC 5147 Meat brokers
CEO: Max Hurtado
*Pt: Francisco Moreno
*Pt: Rafael Ortega
*CFO: Manny Rangel
Opers Mgr: Melissa Ontiveros

D-U-N-S 79-017-9915 IMP/EXP
AMINI INNOVATION CORP
AICO
8725 Rex Rd, Pico Rivera, CA 90660-6703
Tel (562) 222-2500 Founded/Ownrshp 1987
Sales 88.8MM^E EMP 110
SIC 5021 Furniture
CEO: Michael Amini
Ex VP: Martin Ploy
VP: Jeff Santanello
Dir IT: James Fang
Dir IT: Hsu Ted
Opers Mgr: Gabriel Duran

AMISH COUNTRY EGGS
See R W SAUDER INC

D-U-N-S 05-922-6795
■ AMISUB OF CALIFORNIA INC
TENET
(Suby of TENET HEALTHSYSTEM MEDICAL INC) ★
18321 Clark St, Tarzana, CA 91356-3501
Tel (818) 881-0800 Founded/Ownrshp 1973
Sales 480.0M EMP 1,300
SIC 8062 General medical & surgical hospitals
CEO: Dale Surowitz
*COO: Don Kreitz
*CFO: Nick Lymberopolous
VP: Edward Gong

D-U-N-S 80-624-3242 IMP/EXP
■ AMISUB OF SOUTH CAROLINA INC
(Suby of TENET HEALTHCARE CORP) ★
222 S Herlong Ave, Rock Hill, SC 29732-1158
Tel (803) 329-1234 Founded/Ownrshp 1996
Sales 237.8MM EMP 1,271
SIC 8062 General medical & surgical hospitals
CEO: Bill Masterton
*COO: Jim Riley
Dir Rx: Amy Bryson
Dir IT: Claudette Stemmer
Pathlgst: James Maynard
HC Dir: Anita Romano

D-U-N-S 08-247-1525
AMITY CARE LLC
GRACE LIVING CENTERS
4350 Will Rogers Pkwy, Oklahoma City, OK 73108-1826
Tel (405) 943-1144 Founded/Ownrshp 1976
Sales 143.3MM^E EMP 1,481
SIC 8741 Nursing & personal care facility management
Off Mgr: Deserae Moyer
MIS Dir: Phil Loper

D-U-N-S 01-819-8205 IMP
▲ AMKOR TECHNOLOGY INC
2045 E Innovation Cir, Tempe, AZ 85284-2005
Tel (480) 821-5000 Founded/Ownrshp 1968
Sales 2.8MMM EMP 26,700
Tkr Sym AMKR Exch NGS
SIC 3674 3825 Semiconductors & related devices; Semiconductor test equipment
Pr: Stephen D Kelley
*Ch Bd: James J Kim
CFO: Megan Faust
CFO: Ken Joyce
CFO: Joanne Solomon
Bd of Dir: Scott Varga
Ofcr: Gil C Tily
Ex VP: Jim Fusaro
Ex VP: Eric R Larson
Ex VP: Giel Rutten
VP: Alan Abrams
VP: Jungah Choi
VP: Miguel Jimarez
VP: Richard Karam
VP: Robert Lanzone
VP: Tony Martinez
VP: Barry Miles
VP: Jon Woodyard
Board of Directors: Roger A Carolin, Winston J Churchill, Susan Y Kim, John F Morse, John F Osborne, David N Watson, James W Zug

D-U-N-S 82-735-1156
■ AMLI RESIDENTIAL PROPERTIES LP
AMLI RESIDENTILAL
(Suby of MORGAN STANLEY) ★
141 W Jackson Blvd # 300, Chicago, IL 60604-3123
Tel (312) 283-4700 Founded/Ownrshp 1993
Sales 164.9MM^E EMP 800
Accts Kpmg Llp Chicago Illinois
SIC 6798 Real estate investment trusts
Ch Bd: Gregory Mutz
*Ch Bd: Gregory Mutz
*Pr: Steve Hallsey
*Treas: Charles C Kraft
*Ex VP: Philip N Tague
*Sr VP: Rosita A Lina
*Sr VP: James McCormick
*Sr VP: Ken Veltri
VP: Maria L Banks
VP: Anita V Brottonel
VP: Philip Cadwell
VP: Gerould Centergard
VP: David D Groose
VP: Joseph M Hardiman
*VP: Scott Harman
VP: Richard T Hughes
*VP: Jeffrey L Leaders
VP: Kevin Neal
VP: Connie Palacios
VP: Randall W Wosilus
Exec: Carol E Gardner
Board of Directors: Bruce P Bickner, Marc S Heilweil, Stephen G McConahey, John G Schreiber

AMLI RESIDENTILAL
See AMLI RESIDENTIAL PROPERTIES LP

D-U-N-S 01-601-1041 IMP/EXP
AMMARS INC
MAGIC MART
710 S College Ave, Bluefield, VA 24605-1600
Tel (276) 322-4686 Founded/Ownrshp 1975
Sales 66.9MM EMP 1,000
Accts Brown Edwards & Company Llp
SIC 5947 Gift shop
Ch Bd: Kaleel A Ammar Jr
*Pr: K A Ammar III
*Co-Ch Bd: Richard F Ammar
*VP: Sara Ammar Whitt
IT Man: Steve Hess

D-U-N-S 78-547-0209
■ AMN HEALTHCARE INC
(Suby of AMN HEALTHCARE SERVICES INC) ★
12400 High Bluff Dr, San Diego, CA 92130-3077
Tel (858) 792-0711 Founded/Ownrshp 1987
Sales 191.0MM^E EMP 1,700^E
SIC 8011 Primary care medical clinic
CEO: Susan R Nowakowski
Pr: Kim Howard
*Pr: Susan R Salka
CFO: David C Dreyer
Sr VP: Jeff Decker
Sr VP: Beth Machado
Sr VP: Brian McCloskey
VP: Michael Elbaz
*VP: Marcia Faller
VP: Darren Findley
*VP: Julie Fletcher
*VP: Michael Healey
*VP: Denise L Jackson

D-U-N-S 15-272-5966
▲ AMN HEALTHCARE SERVICES INC
12400 High Bluff Dr, San Diego, CA 92130-3077
Tel (866) 871-8519 Founded/Ownrshp 1985
Sales 1.4MMM EMP 2,550^E
Tkr Sym AMN Exch NYS
SIC 7363 Help supply services; Medical help service
Ch Bd: Douglas D Wheat
Pr: Diana Bowden
Pr: Ralph Henderson

*Pr: Susan R Salka
CFO: Brian M Scott
Ex VP: Hector Mon
Sr VP: Bruce R Carothers
Sr VP: Julie Fletcher
Sr VP: Denise L Jackson
VP: Darren Findley
VP Bus: Kurt Mosley
Board of Directors: Mark G Foletta, R Jeffrey Harris, Michael M E Johns, Martha H Marsh, Andrew M Stern, Paul E Weaver

D-U-N-S 82-774-8190 IMP
AMNEAL PHARMACEUTICALS LLC
400 Crossing Blvd Fl 3, Bridgewater, NJ 08807-2863
Tel (631) 952-0214 Founded/Ownrshp 2004
Sales 572.4MM^E EMP 1,200
SIC 2834 3999 Pharmaceutical preparations; Atomizers, toiletry
CEO: Chirag Patel
*CFO: Rochelle Fuhrmann
Ex VP: Nikunj Patel

D-U-N-S 12-379-7875 IMP
AMNEAL PHARMACEUTICALS OF NEW YORK LLC
(Suby of AMNEAL PHARMACEUTICALS PRIVATE LIMITED)
50 Horseblock Rd, Brookhaven, NY 11719-9509
Tel (631) 952-0214 Founded/Ownrshp 2008
Sales 110.6MM^E EMP 245
SIC 2834 5122 Pharmaceutical preparations; Pharmaceuticals
CEO: Chintu Patel
*Pr: Chirag Patel
*CFO: Rochelle Fuhrmann
*Sr VP: Johnny Mikell
*Sr VP: Sanjiv Patel
*VP: Shankar Hariharan
*VP: Jim Luce
Tech Mgr: Maja Marien

D-U-N-S 13-923-9607 IMP
■ **AMO PUERTO RICO MANUFACTURING INC**
(Suby of A M O) ★
Carr 402 Km 42 Zona Indus St Ca, Anasco, PR 00610
Tel (787) 826-2727 Founded/Ownrshp 2002
Sales 143.1MM EMP 500
Accts Ernst & Young Llp San Juan P
SIC 2834 Pharmaceutical preparations
CEO: James Mazzo
Genl Mgr: Luis Abbott

D-U-N-S 13-884-6428
■ **AMO USA INC**
(Suby of A M O) ★
1700 E Saint Andrew Pl, Santa Ana, CA 92705-4933
Tel (714) 247-8200 Founded/Ownrshp 2002
Sales 1.1MMM EMP 200
SIC 3841 3845 Surgical & medical instruments; Laser systems & equipment, medical
Pr: Tom Frinzi

AMOCO
See BP PIPELINES (NORTH AMERICA) INC

AMOCO
See BP OIL SUPPLY CO

AMOCO
See BUCKS INC

D-U-N-S 14-997-9239
AMOCO OIL HOLDING CO
(Suby of BP SHIPPING USA) ★
200 E Randolph St, Chicago, IL 60601-6436
Tel (312) 856-4650 Founded/Ownrshp 1981
Sales 27.2MM^E EMP 1,029
SIC 8699 4953 Automobile owners' association; Incinerator operation
Pr: W Doug Ford
VP: W Wishlinski
Board of Directors: R E Evans, S R Winters

AMP-OHIO
See AMERICAN MUNICIPAL POWER INC

AMPAC
See AMERICAN PACIFIC CORP

D-U-N-S 07-390-3937 IMP
AMPAC FINE CHEMICALS LLC
(Suby of FINE CHEMICALS HOLDINGS CORP.)
Highway 50 And Hazel Ave Bldg 5019, Rancho Cordova, CA 95741
Tel (916) 357-6880 Founded/Ownrshp 1946
Sales 148.6MM^E EMP 400^E
SIC 2834 Pharmaceutical preparations
Pr: Aslam Malik
*Pr: Jeff Robinson
*CFO: John Sobchak
*VP: Richard Beatty
VP: Joe Campbell
*VP: William Dubay
*VP: Patrick Park
Exec: Cleta Russo
Dir Bus: Nick Duda
VP Opers: Terence Vollrath
Plnt Mgr: Gurcharan Singh

D-U-N-S 07-099-1018 IMP/EXP
AMPAC HOLDINGS LLC
PROAMPAC
(Suby of AMPAC PACKAGING LLC) ★
12025 Tricon Rd, Cincinnati, OH 45246-1719
Tel (513) 671-1777 Founded/Ownrshp 2001, 2015
Sales 622.4MM^E EMP 875
SIC 2673 2677 3081 2674 6719 Plastic bags: made from purchased materials; Pliofilm bags: made from purchased materials; Envelopes; Unsupported plastics film & sheet; Shopping bags: made from purchased materials; Investment holding companies, except banks
*CFO: Eric Bradford
Sr VP: James Baker
Plnt Mgr: Gene Walton

D-U-N-S 07-845-1947
AMPAC PACKAGING LLC
(Suby of PROAMPAC INTERMEDIATE INC) ★
12025 Tricon Rd, Cincinnati, OH 45246-1719
Tel (513) 671-1777 Founded/Ownrshp 2006
Sales 622.4MM^E EMP 1,216^E
SIC 2673 Pliofilm bags: made from purchased materials
CEO: John Baumann
Ex VP: Andrew Dun
Prin: Tom Geyer
QA Dir: Samantha Schaeper
Natl Sales: Mark Gaffin
Natl Sales: Diane Utaski
Mktg Mgr: Max Baumann

D-U-N-S 62-516-1484 IMP
AMPAC PAPER LLC
(Suby of AMPAC HOLDCO, INC.)
30 Coldenham Rd, Walden, NY 12586-2036
Tel (845) 778-5511 Founded/Ownrshp 2001
Sales 103.5MM^E EMP 580^E
SIC 2674 2621 5162 Shopping bags: made from purchased materials; Paper mills; Plastics materials
Ch Bd: John Q Baumann
*Pr: Robert Tillis
*CFO: Jon Dill
*Ch: Leland Lewis
*Sr VP: Robert De Gregorio
Sr VP: Robert D Gregorio
VP: Linda Murphy
Exec: Rory Holmes
*VP Mfg: Tom Geyer
*VP Sls: James Baker

D-U-N-S 00-128-7911 IMP/EXP
AMPACET CORP
660 White Plains Rd # 360, Tarrytown, NY 10591-5171
Tel (914) 631-6600 Founded/Ownrshp 1954
Sales 626.9MM^E EMP 1,600
SIC 3087 Custom compound purchased resins
Ch Bd: Robert A Defalco
*CFO: Joel Slutsky
*Treas: Bennett Schwartz
Sr VP: Howard England
*Sr VP: Robert Felding
Sr VP: Robert J Fielding
*VP: Sam Bhoumik
VP: Yves Carette
VP: Christian Carnevali
Genl Mgr: Giuseppe Giusto
Genl Mgr: Alvaro Mendoza

D-U-N-S 03-970-8755 IMP
AMPAM PARKS MECHANICAL INC
17036 Avalon Blvd, Carson, CA 90746-1206
Tel (310) 835-1532 Founded/Ownrshp 1999
Sales 158.5MM^E EMP 800
SIC 1711 Plumbing contractors
CEO: Charles E Parks III
*CFO: James C Wright
*VP: John D Parks
IT Man: Phil Borough

AMPCO
See ATLANTIC METHANOL PRODUCTION CO LLC

AMPCO AIRPORT PARKING
See ABM PARKING SERVICES INC

D-U-N-S 18-081-0835
AMPCO CONTRACTING INC
1540 S Lewis St, Anaheim, CA 92805-6423
Tel (949) 955-2255 Founded/Ownrshp 2004
Sales 144.7MM^E EMP 220
SIC 4959 1795 1794 Environmental cleanup services; Wrecking & demolition work; Excavation & grading, building construction
Pr: Andrew Pennor
Pr: Bill Vitta
VP: Joe Ha
*VP: Trung Joe Q Ha
*VP: Michael King

D-U-N-S 00-432-7862 IMP
▲ **AMPCO-PITTSBURGH CORP** (PA)
726 Bell Ave Ste 301, Carnegie, PA 15106-1138
Tel (412) 456-4400 Founded/Ownrshp 1929
Sales 238.4MM EMP 1,027^E
Accts Deloitte & Touche Llp Pittsbu
Tkr Sym AP Exch NYS
SIC 3312 3561 3351 3353 Blast furnaces & steel mills; Pumps & pumping equipment; Copper & copper alloy pipe & tube; Coils, sheet aluminum
CEO: John S Stanik
*Ch Bd: Leonard M Carroll
CFO: Marliss D Johnson
CFO: Michael G McAuley
Ofcr: Rose Hoover
VP: Maria Trainor
Board of Directors: James J Abel, Michael I German, Paul A Gould, William K Lieberman, Laurence E Paul, Stephen E Paul, Carl H Pforzheimer III, Ernest G Siddons, J Fredrik Stromholm

D-U-N-S 02-473-6733 IMP
▲ **AMPHASTAR PHARMACEUTICALS INC**
11570 6th St, Rancho Cucamonga, CA 91730-6025
Tel (909) 980-9484 Founded/Ownrshp 1996
Sales 251.5MM EMP 1,460
Tkr Sym AMPH Exch NGS
SIC 2834 Pharmaceutical preparations
CEO: Jack Yongfeng Zhang
*Ch Bd: Mary Ziping Luo
*Pr: Jason B Shandell
*CFO: William J Peters
*Ex VP: Marilyn J Purchase
*Sr VP: Diane G Gerst
VP: Jenevieve Duguies
VP: Peter R Langosh
VP: Bill Peters
VP: Richard Whitlow
MIS Dir: Chen Lin
Board of Directors: Richard Koo, Howard Lee, Floyd F Petersen, Stephen B Shohet, Michael A Zasloff, Richard Prins

D-U-N-S 62-399-6472 IMP
■ **AMPHENOL AEROSPACE FRANCE INC**
(Suby of AMPHENOL CORP) ★
191 Delaware Ave, Sidney, NY 13838-1349
Tel (800) 678-0141 Founded/Ownrshp 1994
Sales 114.5MM^E EMP 93^E
SIC 5065 Connectors, electronic
CEO: Gary Anderson
Opers Mgr: Brendan Harder

D-U-N-S 87-475-2231
■ **AMPHENOL BORISCH TECHNOLOGIES INC**
BORISCH MFG
(Suby of AMPHENOL CORP) ★
4511 East Paris Ave Se, Grand Rapids, MI 49512-5314
Tel (616) 554-9820 Founded/Ownrshp 2011
Sales 161.6MM^E EMP 360
SIC 3679 3599 Harness assemblies for electronic use: wire or cable; Electronic circuits; Machine shop, jobbing & repair
Pr: Jonathan Borisch
Prgrm Mgr: Shawnie Michmerhuizen
Genl Mgr: Bill Callahan
Dir IT: Tom Borisch
IT Man: Michael Jaczkowski
Mfg Mgr: Aaron Hauter
Ql Cn Mgr: June Pellerito

D-U-N-S 17-722-0647 EXP
▲ **AMPHENOL CORP**
358 Hall Ave, Wallingford, CT 06492-3574
Tel (203) 265-8900 Founded/Ownrshp 1932
Sales 5.5MMM EMP 50,700
Tkr Sym APH Exch NYS
SIC 3678 3643 3661 Electronic connectors; Connectors & terminals for electrical devices; Fiber optics communications equipment
Pr: R Adam Norwitt
*Ch Bd: Martin H Loeffler
CFO: Craig A Lampo
CFO: Craig A Lampo
Sr VP: Richard E Schneider
Sr VP: Luc Walter
VP: Martin W Booker
VP: William J Doherty
VP: Jean-Luc Gavelle
VP: Alessandro Perrotta
VP: John Treanor
VP: Edward C Wetmore
VP: Edward Wetmore
Dir Bus: David Pearson
Board of Directors: Ronald P Badie, Stanley L Clark, David P Falck, Edward G Jepsen, Randall D Ledford, Andrew E Lietz, John R Lord, Diana G Reardon

D-U-N-S 19-704-7665 IMP
■ **AMPHENOL INTERCONNECT PRODUCTS CORP**
(Suby of AMPHENOL CORP) ★
20 Valley St, Endicott, NY 13760-3600
Tel (607) 754-4444 Founded/Ownrshp 1932
Sales 99.4MM^E EMP 500
SIC 3679 Harness assemblies for electronic use: wire or cable
Pr: Martin H Loeffler
*CEO: Richard Adam Norwitt
*CFO: Edward G Jepsen
*Treas: Diana Reardon
VP: Craig Lampo
CIO: Catherine Hostrander
CTO: Fred Barber
IT Man: Gretchen Spengler
Mktg Mgr: John Majernik

D-U-N-S 13-940-9544 IMP
■ **AMPHENOL OPTIMIZE MANUFACTURING CO**
(Suby of AMPHENOL CORP) ★
180 N Freeport Dr 10, Nogales, AZ 85621-2423
Tel (520) 397-7015 Founded/Ownrshp 1990
Sales 109.6MM^E EMP 905
SIC 3678 3643 Electronic connectors; Current-carrying wiring devices
CEO: Adam R Norwitt
*Pr: R Adam Norwitt
*Treas: David J Jositas
*Treas: Diana Reardon
*Ex VP: Edward G Jepsen
*VP: Craig A Lampo
Mfg Mgr: Gerado Soto
Plnt Mgr: Jaime Ramirez
Ql Cn Mgr: Octavio Medrano
Ql Cn Mgr: Juan Rivera

D-U-N-S 08-125-5788 IMP
■ **AMPHENOL PRINTED CIRCUITS INC**
APC PHNO
(Suby of AMPHENOL CORP) ★
91 Northeastern Blvd, Nashua, NH 03062-3141
Tel (603) 324-4500 Founded/Ownrshp 1976, 1998
Sales 295.7MM^E EMP 2,200^E
SIC 3679 3678 3672 3357 Electronic circuits; Electronic connectors; Printed circuit boards; Nonferrous wiredrawing & insulating
Pr: R Adam Norwitt
Genl Mgr: Richard Bates
IT Man: Bob McGrath
VP Opers: Jack Nolan
Mtls Mgr: Mike Beauchesne

D-U-N-S 93-209-4261 IMP
■ **AMPHENOL THERMOMETRICS INC**
GE SENSING & INSPECTION TECH
(Suby of AMPHENOL CORP) ★
967 Windfall Rd, Saint Marys, PA 15857-3333
Tel (814) 834-9140 Founded/Ownrshp 2013
Sales 116.9MM^E EMP 300
SIC 3823 Thermistors, industrial process type
CEO: Brian Palmer
*Pr: John Carter
*CFO: David Reuscher
*Treas: Richard T Maxstadt
*VP: Monica A Oconnor
Exec: Tom Abbey
Sfty Mgr: Adam Arnold

AMPHITHEATER PUBLIC SCHOOLS
See PIMA COUNTY AMPHITHEATER SCHOOLS

AMPICO
See AMERICAN PROTECTION INSURANCE CO INC

D-U-N-S 10-911-2388
AMPLIFON (USA) INC
(Suby of AMPLIFIN SPA)
5000 Cheshire Pkwy N, Plymouth, MN 55446-4103
Tel (763) 268-4000 Founded/Ownrshp 1999
Sales 340.4MM^E EMP 1,000
SIC 3842 Hearing aids
Pr: Robert Wabler
*CFO: Mario Riemma
Sr VP: Diana Beaufils
VP: Paul D'Amico
VP: Thomas Tedeschi
Dir Soc: Allison Grant
Dir IT: Atul Dua
Mktg Mgr: Ann Heinle

D-U-N-S 01-599-5710 IMP/EXP
AMPLIFY EDUCATION INC
WIRELESS GENERATION
55 Washington St Ste 900, Brooklyn, NY 11201-1071
Tel (212) 213-8177 Founded/Ownrshp 2013
Sales 168.9MM^E EMP 709
SIC 7371 8299 Computer software development; Educational services
CEO: Joel Klein
Pr: Jim Mylen
CEO: Larry Berger
COO: Shannon Kete
Sr VP: Kate Finnefrock
Sr VP: Margaret Honey
VP: Keith A Sanders
Exec: Brandon Hess
Ex Dir: Karen Castle
Ex Dir: Jessica Yin
Prgrm Mgr: Sharon Santillo

D-U-N-S 07-989-0263
▲ **AMPLIFY SNACK BRANDS INC**
500 W 5th St Ste 1350, Austin, TX 78701-3836
Tel (512) 600-9893 Founded/Ownrshp 2014
Sales 183.9MM EMP 45
Tkr Sym BETR Exch NYS
SIC 2099 2064 2096 Food preparations; Popcorn balls or other treated popcorn products; Tortilla chips
Pr: Thomas C Ennis
*Ch Bd: Jeffrey S Barber
*CFO: Brian Goldberg
*Ex VP: Jason Shiver

D-U-N-S 94-647-0127
AMPORTS INC
10201 Centurion Pkwy N # 401, Jacksonville, FL 32256-4114
Tel (904) 652-2962 Founded/Ownrshp 2003
Sales 101.7MM^E EMP 400
SIC 4491 Marine cargo handling
Pr: Steven Rand
*CFO: John Callihan

AMR
See AMERICAN MEDICAL RESPONSE AMBULANCE SERVICE INC

AMR
See AMERICAN MEDICAL RESPONSE WEST

AMR EAGLE
See ENVOY AIR INC

D-U-N-S 18-970-0206
■ **AMR EAGLE INC**
(Suby of AMERICAN AIRLINES GROUP INC) ★
4333 Amon Carter Blvd, Fort Worth, TX 76155-2605
Tel (214) 927-6016 Founded/Ownrshp 1987
Sales 14.3MM^E EMP 1,096^E
SIC 4512 Air passenger carrier, scheduled
Pr: Peter M Bowler
*CEO: Gerard Arpey
*VP: Robert W Baker
VP: Andrew Pardue

D-U-N-S 05-101-0429 IMP/EXP
AMREP INC
(Suby of ZEP INC) ★
425 Franklin Gtwy Se # 530, Marietta, GA 30067-7736
Tel (770) 590-5960 Founded/Ownrshp 2010
Sales 107.7MM^E EMP 400
SIC 2842 2079 2911 2869 2841 2819 Specialty cleaning preparations; Sanitation preparations, disinfectants & deodorants; Edible oil products, except corn oil; Greases, lubricating; Industrial organic chemicals; Soap & other detergents; Industrial inorganic chemicals
CEO: John K Morgan
*CEO: Kevin J Gallagher
COO: Joseph Seladi
*CFO: Mark R Bachmann
VP: Paul Gehrke
VP: David Leonard
VP: Jeff Miller
Genl Mgr: Ron Potts
Sales Exec: Clay Freebaren
VP Mktg: Richard Scott
VP Sls: Dan Bucci

D-U-N-S 83-260-9155
AMREST LLC
APPLEBEE'S
(Suby of AMREST HOLDINGS SE)
2045 Attic Pkwy Nw, Kennesaw, GA 30152-7610
Tel (770) 850-8816 Founded/Ownrshp 2007
Sales 95.2MM^E EMP 4,500
SIC 5812 Restaurant, family: chain

D-U-N-S 12-419-3793 IMP
■ **AMRI RENSSELAER INC**
(Suby of ALBANY MOLECULAR RESEARCH INC) ★
33 Riverside Ave, Rensselaer, NY 12144-2951
Tel (518) 433-7700 Founded/Ownrshp 1999
Sales 129.9MM^E EMP 429
SIC 5169 Industrial chemicals
CEO: Thomas D'Ambra
*VP: Michael M Nolan

*Genl Mgr: Ken Shultis
Snr Mgr: Bernie Lennon

AMROX
See AMERICAN IRON OXIDE CO

AMS
See WALNUT INVESTMENT CORP

AMS
See AVIATION & MISSILE SOLUTIONS LLC

AMS
See AMERICAN MEDICAL SYSTEMS HOLDINGS INC

D-U-N-S 62-387-6315 IMP
AMS PLASTICS INC
1530 Hilton Head Rd # 205, El Cajon, CA 92019-4655
Tel (619) 713-2000 Founded/Ownrshp 1983
Sales 103.3MM^E EMP 400
SIC 3089 Injection molding of plastics
CEO: Thomas G Plein
*Pr: James Watson

AMS SERVICES
See VERTAFORE INC

D-U-N-S 14-448-8095 IMP/EXP
AMSAFE PARTNERS INC
1043 N 47th Ave, Phoenix, AZ 85043-1817
Tel (602) 850-2850 Founded/Ownrshp 2007
Sales 91.0MM^E EMP 475
SIC 2399

D-U-N-S 96-479-7393 IMP/EXP
■ **AMSCAN HOLDINGS INC**
(Suby of PARTY CITY HOLDINGS INC) ★
80 Grasslands Rd Ste 3, Elmsford, NY 10523-1100
Tel (914) 345-2020 Founded/Ownrshp 2004
Sales 3.7MMM^E EMP 14,212
SIC 5947 2679 3089 3069 6794 Gifts & novelties; Gift wrap & novelties, paper; Plastic kitchenware, tableware & houseware; Balloons, metal foil laminated with rubber; Franchises, selling or licensing
CEO: Gerald C Rittenberg
*Pr: James M Harrison
*CFO: Michael A Correale
*Sr VP: Brent Schlosser

D-U-N-S 00-194-8520 IMP/EXP
■ **AMSCAN INC** (NY)
DECO DIVISION
(Suby of AMSCAN HOLDINGS INC) ★
80 Grasslands Rd Ste 3, Elmsford, NY 10523-1100
Tel (914) 345-2020 Founded/Ownrshp 1947
Sales 637.2MM^E EMP 2,050
SIC 2656 3089 5113 2676 Cups, paper: made from purchased material; Dishes, paper: made from purchased material; Utensils, paper: made from purchased material; Cups, plastic, except foam; Dishes, plastic, except foam; Cups, disposable plastic & paper; Dishes, disposable plastic & paper; Eating utensils, disposable plastic; Sanitary paper products
Ch Bd: Gerald C Rittenberg
Pr: Raoph Fink
Pr: James Harrison
CFO: Michael Correale
CTO: Steven Skiba
Sls Mgr: Chris Whiteside

AMSCO STEEL COMPANY LLC
See AMSCO STEEL CO LLC

D-U-N-S 00-289-4913
AMSCO STEEL CO LLC
AMSCO STEEL COMPANY LLC
3430 Mccart Ave, Fort Worth, TX 76110-3634
Tel (817) 926-3355 Founded/Ownrshp 2009
Sales 85.2MM^E EMP 75
SIC 5051 Structural shapes, iron or steel; Sheets, metal; Bars, metal; Wire
*VP: Courtney Moore
*VP: John Sikes

D-U-N-S 00-908-2173
AMSCO WINDOWS
1880 S 1045 W, Salt Lake City, UT 84104-2233
Tel (801) 972-6444 Founded/Ownrshp 1949
Sales 123.7MM^E EMP 550
SIC 3442 Metal doors, sash & trim
Pr: Bart S Naylor
*Ch Bd: R Phillip Rasmussen
VP: Steve Kettle
VP Mfg: Sean Jager
Mktg Dir: Andy Schulz

D-U-N-S 05-666-2398
■ **AMSEC CORP**
(Suby of HUNTINGTON INGALLS INDUSTRIES INC) ★
5701 Cleveland St, Virginia Beach, VA 23462-1788
Tel (757) 463-6666 Founded/Ownrshp 1981
Sales 295.8MM^E EMP 1,573
SIC 8711 Mechanical engineering; Electrical or electronic engineering; Marine engineering
Pr: Carl M Albero
*COO: Gary M Lisota
CFO: Karl W Jahn Jr
Treas: Lauren Rene Hunter
VP: Joseph L Carlini
VP: John Graf
Board of Directors: Mark Hughes, James Idell, Stephen Loftus, William Roper, Dr John H Warner Jr

D-U-N-S 07-258-1718
■ **AMSEC LLC**
(Suby of HUNTINGTON INGALLS INDUSTRIES INC) ★
5701 Cleveland St, Virginia Beach, VA 23462-1788
Tel (757) 463-6666 Founded/Ownrshp 2011
Sales 432.5MM^E EMP 2,300
SIC 8711 Engineering services
CFO: Karl Jahn Jr
Ex VP: J Carlini
Sr VP: Joseph Carlini
Sr VP: Henry C Giffin
VP: Michael Mazarr
Dir Bus: Ryan Norris

Prgrm Mgr: Thomas Bienkowski
Prgrm Mgr: Frank Chaco
Prgrm Mgr: Dana McKnight
Prgrm Mgr: Helene Siesel
Genl Mgr: Cathy Cope

D-U-N-S 05-545-7865 IMP/EXP
AMSOIL INC
925 Tower Ave, Superior, WI 54880-1582
Tel (715) 392-7101 Founded/Ownrshp 1978
Sales 124.8MM^E EMP 245
SIC 2992 3589 2873 3714 Lubricating oils & greases; Water filters & softeners, household type; Fertilizers: natural (organic), except compost; Motor vehicle parts & accessories
CEO: Ben Galili
*Ex VP: Dean Alexander
VP: Julie Jacobson
VP: Greg Sandbulte
Dir Lab: Dave Leitten
Ex Dir: Matt Konig
MIS Dir: Todd Mackey
Plnt Mgr: Mike Martin
Sales Asso: Benjamin Grembowski

AMSOUTH
See REGIONS BANK

AMSOUTH LEASING
See DE LAGE LANDEN FINANCIAL SERVICES INC

D-U-N-S 17-502-7507
AMSPEC LLC
1249 S River Rd Ste 204, Cranbury, NJ 08512-3633
Tel (908) 925-7333 Founded/Ownrshp 1997
Sales 231.0MM^E EMP 808
SIC 8734 7389 Product testing laboratories; Inspection & testing services
Pr: Matthew J Corr
COO: Malcolm Vella
CFO: Gerard O'Dell
Ch: Joseph H Wright
VP: Andy Mortensen
VP: Robert Ruggiero
VP: Simon Wright
Dir Lab: Michael Holland
Area Mgr: Courtney Vincent
QA Dir: Chris Seested
Dir IT: Raj Macwan

D-U-N-S 12-414-5561
AMSTAR MORTGAGE CORP
10851 Scarsdale Blvd # 800, Houston, TX 77089-5743
Tel (281) 481-9040 Founded/Ownrshp 2002
Sales NA EMP 1,200
SIC 6163 Mortgage brokers arranging for loans, using money of others
Pr: Howard Wayland

D-U-N-S 00-514-6667 IMP/EXP
AMSTED INDUSTRIES INC (DE)
180 N Stetson Ave, Chicago, IL 60601-6808
Tel (312) 645-1700 Founded/Ownrshp 1902, 1986
Sales 2.0MMM^E EMP 11,000^E
SIC 3443 3325 3585 3321 3743 Cooling towers, metal plate; Railroad car wheels, cast steel; Refrigeration & heating equipment; Gray & ductile iron foundries; Freight cars & equipment
Ch Bd: W Robert Reum
CFO: Thomas E Bergmann
CFO: Tomas Bergmann
Treas: Glen Chamberlain
VP: Tony Bauer
VP: Pat Forsburg
VP: Marilyn Franson
VP: Steve Obendorf
VP: Steven Obendorf
VP: Steven Smith
VP: Bryon Speice
VP: Griffin Wheel
VP: Shirley J Whitesell
Exec: John Oliver
Dir Risk M: Mary Kelly
Board of Directors: Lewis Collens, John M Dixon, J Erik Frywald, Raymond A Jean, William Moeller, Richard E Terry, Thomas H Weidemeyer

D-U-N-S 82-633-4729 IMP/EXP
AMSTED RAIL CO INC
(Suby of AMSTED INDUSTRIES INC) ★
311 S Wacker Dr Ste 5300, Chicago, IL 60606-6630
Tel (312) 922-4501 Founded/Ownrshp 1977
Sales 447.1MM^E EMP 3,597^E
SIC 3743 Railroad equipment
Pr: John Wories
Pr: Jay Monaco
CFO: Daniel Litwin
Sr VP: William O'Donnell
VP: D Fitzsimmons
VP: Wes Hodges
VP: Cameron Lonsdale
VP: Mike McDonnell
VP: Mike McDonnell
VP: Steve E Obendorf
VP: J Oliver
VP: John Oliver

D-U-N-S 00-206-6777 IMP
AMSTERDAM PRINTING & LITHO INC (MN)
(Suby of BANYAN INCENTIVES) ★
166 Wallins Corners Rd, Amsterdam, NY 12010-1899
Tel (518) 842-6000 Founded/Ownrshp 1898
Sales 95.1MM^E EMP 585
SIC 3993 2752 2761

AMSTY
See AMERICAS STYRENICS LLC

AMSURG
See SURGERY CENTER TORRANCE L P

AMSURG
See WILTON SURGERY CENTER LLC

D-U-N-S 78-605-6820
▲ **AMSURG CORP**
1a Burton Hills Bvld, Nashville, TN 37215
Tel (615) 665-1283 Founded/Ownrshp 1992
Sales 2.5MMM EMP 12,461
Tkr Sym AMSG Exch NGS

SIC 8011 Ambulatory surgical center; Occupational & industrial specialist, physician/surgeon
CEO: Christopher A Holden
*Ch Bd: Steven I Geringer
*CFO: Claire M Gulmi
Ex VP: Phillip A Clendenin
Ex VP: David L Manning
Sr VP: Kevin D Eastridge
VP: James Ciutiis
VP: Erik Hamnes
VP: Sandy C Smith
VP: Mark Wainner
VP: Kim Walsh
VP: Kathy Wilson
Dir Rx: Holly Udell
Board of Directors: Thomas G Cigarran, James A Deal, John T Gawaluck, Henry D Herr, Joey A Jacobs, Kevin P Lavender, Cynthia S Miller, John W Popp

D-U-N-S 82-715-9133
■ **AMT WARRANTY CORP**
(Suby of AMTRUST FINANCIAL SERVICES INC) ★
5800 Lombardo Ctr Ste 150, Seven Hills, OH 44131-2588
Tel (212) 220-7120 Founded/Ownrshp 2004
Sales NA EMP 505^E
SIC 6399

D-U-N-S 88-435-6429
■ **AMTEC CORP**
(Suby of NATIONAL PRESTO INDUSTRIES INC) ★
4230 Capital Cir, Janesville, WI 53546-8314
Tel (608) 752-2699 Founded/Ownrshp 2001
Sales 130.6MM^E EMP 725
SIC 3483 Arming & fusing devices for missiles
Pr: Randy Lansing
Treas: Don Jerritt
Ex VP: Todd Anderson
Mtls Mgr: David Montgomery

D-U-N-S 18-747-5132
■ **AMTECH SERVICES INC**
(Suby of ABM INDUSTRIES INC) ★
420 Taylor St 200, San Francisco, CA 94102-1702
Tel (415) 733-4000 Founded/Ownrshp 1981
Sales 16.2MM^E EMP 2,600
SIC 7349 8742 Lighting maintenance service; Marketing consulting services
Pr: J E Benton III
*Treas: Douglas Bowlus

D-U-N-S 03-575-3920
▲ **AMTECH SYSTEMS INC** (AZ)
131 S Clark Dr, Tempe, AZ 85281-3008
Tel (480) 967-5146 Founded/Ownrshp 1981
Sales 120.3MM EMP 503
Accts Mayer Hoffman Mccann Pc Pho
Tkr Sym ASYS Exch NGS
SIC 3559 Semiconductor manufacturing machinery
Pr: Fokko Pentinga
*Ch Bd: Jong S Whang
CFO: Bradley C Anderson
CFO: Bradley Anderson
Ex VP: Bradley Anderso
VP: James Hwang
CTO: Jan-Marc Luchies

D-U-N-S 09-256-6355
AMTECK OF KENTUCKY INC
2421 Fortune Dr Ste 150, Lexington, KY 40509-4126
Tel (859) 255-9546 Founded/Ownrshp 1977
Sales 158.5MM^E EMP 300
SIC 1731

D-U-N-S 00-502-8261
AMTHOR STEEL INC (PA)
1717 Gaskell Ave, Erie, PA 16503-2429
Tel (814) 452-4700 Founded/Ownrshp 1920, 1966
Sales 900.0MM^E EMP 28
SIC 3441 Fabricated structural metal
Pr: Terry Carrara
*Pr: Richard L Carrara
*VP: Patrick S Carrara
VP: Patrick Carrara

D-U-N-S 85-855-5337 IMP
AMTOPP CORP
(Suby of INTEGRATED BAGGING SYSTEMS) ★
101 Interplast Blvd, Lolita, TX 77971-4115
Tel (361) 874-3000 Founded/Ownrshp 1992
Sales 670.2M^E EMP 1,550^E
SIC 3081 Unsupported plastics film & sheet
Pr: John Young
*Ch Bd: Y C Wang
*Pr: Homer Hsieh

AMTRAK
See NATIONAL RAILROAD PASSENGER CORP

D-U-N-S 95-956-8783
AMTROL HOLDINGS INC
1400 Division Rd, West Warwick, RI 02893-2300
Tel (401) 884-6300 Founded/Ownrshp 1996
Sales 294.2MM^E EMP 1,300
SIC 3822 3585 3443 Refrigeration controls (pressure); Heating equipment, complete; Tanks, lined: metal plate
Pr: Larry T Guillemette
*Treas: Michael L Lecours
Mktg Dir: Ken Ferri
Board of Directors: Larry Guillemette, Richard Harris, Timothy Janszen, Ryan Langdon, David Spalding

D-U-N-S 00-119-2145 IMP/EXP
AMTROL INC (RI)
(Suby of AMTROL HOLDINGS INC) ★
1400 Division Rd, West Warwick, RI 02893-2300
Tel (401) 884-6300 Founded/Ownrshp 1946, 1973
Sales 277.4MM^E EMP 1,300
SIC 3443 3585 Industrial vessels, tanks & containers; Tanks, lined: metal plate; Cylinders, pressure: metal plate; Heating equipment, complete; Refrigeration equipment, complete
CEO: Larry T Guillemette
Pr: William Chohfi
CFO: Joseph L Depaula
Treas: Michael Lecours
Treas: Michael H Lecours

Bd of Dir: Tim Janszen
Sr VP: John Cooper
Sr VP: Christopher A Laus
VP: Phillip Colantonio
VP: Christopher Laus
VP: Starla Sunderland
VP: Christopher Van Haaren
VP: Christopher Vanhaaren
Exec: Peter Marafino
Comm Dir: Kieran Andre
Board of Directors: Richard Harris, Timothy Janszen, Ryan Langdon, David Spalding

AMTRUST FINANCIAL SERVICES
See AMTRUST NORTH AMERICA INC

D-U-N-S 78-436-3954
▲ **AMTRUST FINANCIAL SERVICES INC**
59 Maiden Ln Fl 43, New York, NY 10038-4639
Tel (212) 220-7120 Founded/Ownrshp 1990
Sales NA EMP 6,211^E
Tkr Sym AFSI Exch NGS
SIC 6331 Fire, marine & casualty insurance; Workers' compensation insurance; Property damage insurance
Pr: Barry D Zyskind
Pr: Thomas Harding
Pr: Julie McCann
Pr: Lindsay Santos
Pr: Christina Stone
COO: Christopher M Longo
*COO: Michael J Saxon
*CFO: Ronald E Pipoly Jr
Ex VP: Brian Fullerton
Ex VP: Adam Karkowsky
Sr VP: Gabriella Roberts
*Sr VP: Stephen B Ungar
VP: Joel Alligood
VP: Jennifer Arrogante
VP: John Bledsoe
VP: Don Cunningham
VP: Michael Frampton
VP: Hilly Gross
VP: Henry Sibley
VP: Sheryl Skolnik
VP: Eli Toron

D-U-N-S 10-951-3841
■ **AMTRUST NORTH AMERICA INC**
AMTRUST FINANCIAL SERVICES
(Suby of AMTRUST FINANCIAL SERVICES INC) ★
800 Superior Ave E # 2100, Cleveland, OH 44114-2613
Tel (216) 328-6100 Founded/Ownrshp 2001
Sales NA EMP 980
SIC 6331 6411 Workers' compensation insurance; Insurance claim processing, except medical
CEO: Barry D Zyskind
Treas: Eli Tisser
Sr VP: Robert Eisendrath
VP: Carolyn Carlson
VP: Peggy Gierlach
VP: Ryan Kollar
VP: Georjean Mottolo
VP: Matt Rispoli
VP: Jim Sawitzke
Brnch Mgr: Drew Kairis
Brnch Mgr: Delores Moore

D-U-N-S 08-341-6854 EXP
AMWAY CORP
AMWAY NORTH AMERICA
(Suby of ALTICOR INC) ★
7575 Fulton St E, Ada, MI 49355-0001
Tel (616) 787-6000 Founded/Ownrshp 1959
Sales 71.8MM^E EMP 4,000
SIC 5963

D-U-N-S 15-661-9959 IMP/EXP
AMWAY INTERNATIONAL INC
(Suby of ALTICOR INC) ★
7575 Fulton St E, Ada, MI 49355-0001
Tel (616) 787-1000 Founded/Ownrshp 1978
Sales 5.6MMM^E EMP 10,000
SIC 5169 5122 5099 5199 2099 2032 Detergents & soaps, except specialty cleaning; Toiletries; Cosmetics; Vitamins & minerals; Child restraint seats, automotive; Video & audio equipment; Gifts & novelties; Fabrics, yarns & knit goods; Food preparations; Canned specialties
Pr: Douglas Devos
*Ch Bd: Stephen Van Andel
CFO: Russ Evans
Ex VP: Eva Cheng
VP: Rajneesh Chopra
VP: Catherine Ehrenberger
VP: Ken Hake
VP: Mirna Laxton
VP: Michael Nelson
VP: Brian Smith
VP: Todd Woodward

AMWAY NORTH AMERICA
See AMWAY CORP

D-U-N-S 07-797-7721
AMWINS GROUP BENEFITS INC
NEBCO
(Suby of AMWINS GROUP INC) ★
50 Whitecap Dr, North Kingstown, RI 02852-7445
Tel (877) 739-3330 Founded/Ownrshp 1991
Sales NA EMP 455
SIC 6311 6321 Life insurance; Health insurance carriers
Pr: Sam Fleet
COO: Will Pagan
Sr VP: Donald B Sheehan
VP: Sharad Arora
VP: David Collier
*VP: Jim McCarthy
VP: Shawn Sisti
Info Man: Marty Stacheria
Software D: Andey Zhu
Mktg Mgr: Randy Stoloff

D-U-N-S 02-248-8964
AMWINS GROUP INC
4725 Piedmont Row Dr # 600, Charlotte, NC 28210-4283
Tel (704) 749-2700 Founded/Ownrshp 2005
Sales NA EMP 474

SIC 6411 8748 Insurance brokers; Economic consultant
CEO: Steven Decarlo
Owner: Geion Bright
Owner: Denise Chaussard
Pr: Emily Agramonte
Pr: Bethany Asselin
Pr: W H Cooper
Pr: James Drinkwater
Pr: John Florido
Pr: Jean Gentry
Pr: Robert V Gibson
Pr: J Scott Reynolds
Pr: Gloriajean Ricca
Pr: Justin Saunders
CEO: David Scruggs
CFO: Scott M Purviance
Div Pres: Samuel H Fleet
Bd of Dir: Michael O'Brien
Assoc VP: Amy Bishop
Ex VP: Munawar Ali
Ex VP: Sam Baig
Ex VP: Randy Bailey

D-U-N-S 04-505-7882 IMP/EXP
■ AMX LLC
HARMAN PROFESSIONAL SOLUTIONS
(*Suby of* HARMAN INTERNATIONAL INDUSTRIES INC) ★
3000 Research Dr, Richardson, TX 75082-3546
Tel (469) 624-8740 *Founded/Ownrshp* 2014
Sales 238.3MM *EMP* 602
SIC 3625 Control equipment, electric
Pr: Rashid Skap
Pr: Jim Potler
**CFO:* C Chris Apple
Ex VP: Kevin Morrison
VP: Joe Andrulis
VP: Steve Byars
VP: Lee Dodson
VP: Jeff Fink
VP: John Hanby
VP: Harold Hickey
VP: Michael Olinger
VP: Shaun G Robinson
VP: Mark Stoldt
Creative D: Kevin Spicer

D-U-N-S 62-123-6129
AMYLIN OHIO LLC
9360 Towne Centre Dr, San Diego, CA 92121-3057
Tel (858) 552-2200 *Founded/Ownrshp* 2005
Sales NA *EMP* 1,300
SIC 2834

D-U-N-S 19-687-7526 IMP
AMYLIN PHARMACEUTICALS LLC
1800 Concord Pike, Wilmington, DE 19897-0001
Tel (858) 552-2200 *Founded/Ownrshp* 2012
Sales 227.8MM^E *EMP* 1,300
SIC 2834 8731

D-U-N-S 02-127-7223
AMYOTROPHIC LATERAL SCLEROSIS ASSOCIATION
ALS ASSOCIATION, THE
1275 K St Nw Ste 250, Washington, DC 20005-6823
Tel (202) 407-8580 *Founded/Ownrshp* 1985
Sales 138.3MM *EMP* 54
Accts Windes Inc Long Beach Ca
SIC 8611 Business associations
CEO: Jane H Gilbert
**Ch Bd:* Wiliam Thoet
CFO: Gregory Mitchell
**Treas:* Luis Leon
**VP:* Lawrence Barnett

D-U-N-S 19-496-2577 IMP/EXP
AMYS KITCHEN INC
2330 Northpoint Pkwy, Santa Rosa, CA 95407-5004
Tel (707) 578-7188 *Founded/Ownrshp* 1988
Sales 300.3MM^E *EMP* 860
SIC 2038 2053 Dinners, frozen & packaged; Frozen bakery products, except bread
CEO: Andy Berliner
**CFO:* Andrew Koprel
Ex VP: Kevin Haslebacher
**VP:* Rachel Berliner
**VP:* Eleanor Goodman
VP: Kathleen Haibach
VP: John Humphires
VP: Laura Setzfand
Exec: Cindy L Gillespie
QA Dir: Juliet Basile
QA Dir: Michele Gaminde

D-U-N-S 83-143-6071
AMZ HOLDING CORP
4800 State Road 60 E, Mulberry, FL 33860-7905
Tel (863) 578-1206 *Founded/Ownrshp* 2008
Sales 129.5MM^E *EMP* 220^E
SIC 5169 Industrial chemicals
Pr: Frank Walters
**CFO:* Doug Wilson

AN AFFLIATE OF HEICO COMPANIES
See PETTIBONE LLC

AN ANTONIO AUTO AUCTION
See BA & W ENTERPRISES INC

D-U-N-S 06-693-0256 EXP
■ AN MOTORS OF PEMBROKE LLC
AUTONTION CHVRLET PMBROKE PNES
(*Suby of* AN DEALERSHIP HOLDING CORP)
8600 Pines Blvd, Pembroke Pines, FL 33024-6534
Tel (954) 433-3377 *Founded/Ownrshp* 1998
Sales 114.1MM^E *EMP* 572
SIC 5511 Automobiles, new & used; Pickups, new & used

D-U-N-S 07-888-8764
ANA GLOBAL LLC
2360 Marconi Ct, San Diego, CA 92154-7241
Tel (619) 482-9990 *Founded/Ownrshp* 2012
Sales 151.5MM^E *EMP* 800
SIC 2517 5999 Television cabinets, wood; Medical apparatus & supplies

D-U-N-S 17-292-3182
■ ANADARKO E&P ONSHORE LLC
(*Suby of* ANADARKO PETROLEUM CORP) ★
1201 Lake Robbins Dr, The Woodlands, TX 77380-1124
Tel (832) 636-1000 *Founded/Ownrshp* 2002
Sales 205.9MM^E *EMP* 11
SIC 2911 Petroleum refining
Pr: Charles A Meloy
VP: Scott Elliott
Prgrm Mgr: Alan Howard

D-U-N-S 86-705-6517 IMP
■ ANADARKO HOLDING CO
(*Suby of* ANADARKO PETROLEUM CORP) ★
17001 Northchase Dr, Houston, TX 77060-2141
Tel (832) 636-7200 *Founded/Ownrshp* 2000
Sales 455.6MM^E *EMP* 2,060^E
SIC 1311 1321 5172 4922 Crude petroleum production; Natural gas production; Natural gas liquids; Petroleum products; Pipelines, natural gas
Ch Bd: Robert J Allison Jr
**Pr:* John N Seitz
**CFO:* Michael E Rose
**Treas:* Albert L Richey
**Sr VP:* James R Larson
VP: Diane L Dickey
**VP:* J Stephen Martin
**Prin:* George Lindahl

D-U-N-S 02-640-9797 IMP/EXP
▲ ANADARKO PETROLEUM CORP
1201 Lake Robbins Dr, The Woodlands, TX 77380-1124
Tel (832) 636-1000 *Founded/Ownrshp* 1985
Sales 8.7MMM *EMP* 5,800^E
Tkr Sym APC *Exch* NYS
SIC 1311 4924 5171 1382 Crude petroleum production; Natural gas production; Natural gas distribution; Petroleum bulk stations; Oil & gas exploration services
Ch Bd: R A Walker
CFO: Robert G Gwin
Ex VP: William Bargh
Ex VP: Robert P Daniels
Ex VP: Darrell Hollek
Ex VP: Darrell E Hollek
Ex VP: Mitchell W Ingram
Ex VP: James J Kleckner
Ex VP: Ernie Leyendecker
Ex VP: Aisha Ragas
Ex VP: Robert K Reeves
Sr VP: Rex Alman III
Sr VP: Michael D Cochran
Sr VP: Mario M Coll III
Sr VP: Robert D Lawler
Sr VP: Mark L Pease
Sr VP: Richard J Sharples
Sr VP: Bruce H Stover
VP: Bob Almonte
VP: Michael O Bridges
VP: Christopher O Champion
Board of Directors: Mark C McKinley, Anthony R Chase, Eric D Mullins, Kevin P Chilton, David E Constable, H Paulett Eberhart, Peter J Fluor, Richard L George, Joseph W Gorder, John R Gordon, Sean Gourley

D-U-N-S 03-980-3176 IMP
■ ANAGRAM INTERNATIONAL INC
(*Suby of* AMSCAN HOLDINGS INC) ★
7700 Anagram Dr, Eden Prairie, MN 55344-7307
Tel (952) 949-5600 *Founded/Ownrshp* 1977
Sales 105.1MM^E *EMP* 350
SIC 3069 Balloons, advertising & toy: rubber
CEO: James Plutt

D-U-N-S 03-058-4221
ANAHEIM CITY SCHOOL DISTRICT
1001 S East St, Anaheim, CA 92805-5749
Tel (714) 517-7500 *Founded/Ownrshp* 1887
Sales 78.4MM^E *EMP* 1,100
SIC 8211 Public elementary & secondary schools
Comm Dir: Keith Sterling
Schl Brd P: Bob Gardner
Instr Medi: Brian Brooks
Psych: Mike Tincup

ANAHEIM HILTON & TOWERS
See MAKAR ANAHEIM LLC

D-U-N-S 07-930-5167
ANAHEIM REGIONAL MEDICAL CENTER
1111 W La Palma Ave, Anaheim, CA 92801-2804
Tel (714) 774-1450 *Founded/Ownrshp* 2014
Sales 209.8MM *EMP* 164^E
SIC 8069 8062 Children's hospital; General medical & surgical hospitals
CEO: Patrick Petre
**COO:* Deborah Webber
CFO: Fred Drewette
Chf Nrs Of: Phyllis Snyder
Dir IT: Jeff Desroches
IT Man: Maria Bautista
Doctor: Carlos Medina
Doctor: David Simon

D-U-N-S 06-765-3436
ANAHEIM UNION HIGH SCHOOL DIST
501 N Crescent Way, Anaheim, CA 92801-5401
Tel (714) 999-3511 *Founded/Ownrshp* 1898
Sales 365.5MM *EMP* 2,300
Accts Vavrinek Trine Day & Co Ll
SIC 8211 Public elementary & secondary schools
Exec: Terri Kipp
Genl Mgr: Bruce Saltz
Off Admin: James Goran
Off Admin: Tisha Ludeman
MIS Dir: Willie Dumas
Sls&Mrk Ex: Dayna Arbiso
Schl Brd P: Annmarie R Trejo
Teacher Pr: Brad Jackson
Psych: Christine Awadallah
Psych: Eileen Cabrera
Psych: Sandy Fernandez

ANAHUAC HEALTHCARE CENTER
See SENIOR LIVING PROPERTIES LLC

D-U-N-S 04-764-4638
ANALEX CORP
(*Suby of* VENCORE SERVICES AND SOLUTIONS INC) ★
3076 Centreville Rd # 200, Herndon, VA 20171-3737
Tel (703) 880-2800 *Founded/Ownrshp* 2007
Sales 63.8MM^E *EMP* 1,068
SIC 7371 Custom computer programming services; Computer software development
CEO: John Curtis
**CFO:* Jennifer Felix
Ex VP: S A Gordon
Sr VP: V Joseph Broadwater Jr
**Sr VP:* Stephen Costalas
Sr VP: Stephen C Matthews
VP: Denis Clements
VP: Charles W Floyd

D-U-N-S 00-141-8417 IMP/EXP
▲ ANALOG DEVICES INC (MA)
1 Technology Way, Norwood, MA 02062-2666
Tel (781) 329-4700 *Founded/Ownrshp* 1965
Sales 3.4MMM *EMP* 9,700
Tkr Sym ADI *Exch* NGS
SIC 3674 Integrated circuits, semiconductor networks, etc.; Hybrid integrated circuits
Pr: Vincent T Roche
Ch Bd: Ray Stata
COO: Del Jones
CFO: Murphy Denis
CFO: David A Zinsner
Sr VP: John Hassett
Sr VP: Rick D Hess
Sr VP: William Matson
Sr VP: Margaret K Seif
VP: John J Hassett
VP: Patrick Odoherty
VP: Jim Ryan
VP: Eileen Wynne
Exec: Phil Fraser
Board of Directors: Richard M Beyer, James A Champy, Bruce R Evans, Edward H Frank, John C Hodgson, Neil Novich, Kenton J Sicchitano, Lisa T Su

D-U-N-S 01-967-7418
▲ ANALOGIC CORP (MA)
8 Centennial Dr, Peabody, MA 01960-7987
Tel (978) 326-4000 *Founded/Ownrshp* 1967
Sales 508.8MM *EMP* 1,679
Accts Ernst & Young Llp Boston Mas
Tkr Sym ALOG *Exch* NGS
SIC 3825 3812 Instruments to measure electricity; Search & detection systems & instruments
Pr: James W Green
Recvr: Mike Russo
**Ch Bd:* Bernard Bailey
CFO: Mark Frost
CFO: Mark T Frost
Ex VP: Lothar Koob
Sr VP: Shalabh Chandra
Sr VP: Mervat Faltas
Sr VP: John J Fry
Sr VP: James P Ryan
VP: Daniel Abenaim
VP: Michael J Bourque
VP: Dan Karl
VP: Mark Laustra
VP: Farley Peechatka
VP: George Procter
VP: Eric F Zanin
Board of Directors: Jeffrey P Black, James J Judge, Michael T Modic, Steve Odland, Fred B Parks

D-U-N-S 01-291-3265
ANALYSIS & DESIGN APPLICATION CO LTD
CD-ADAPCO
(*Suby of* SIEMENS AG)
60 Broadhollow Rd, Melville, NY 11747-2504
Tel (631) 549-2300 *Founded/Ownrshp* 1980
Sales 137.5MM^E *EMP* 319^E
SIC 7371 Computer software development
Pr: Peter McDonald
Pr: Milovan Peric
Sr VP: Jean-Claude Ercolanelli
Sr VP: Tom Marinaccio
Sr VP: Wayne Smith
**VP:* Steve Feldman
VP: Stephen McIlwain
VP: Deryl Snyder
Exec: Keri Maher
Comm Man: Stephen Ferguson
Snr Sftwr: Udaya Gunasena

D-U-N-S 15-068-6301
ANALYSIS GROUP INC
111 Huntington Ave Fl 10, Boston, MA 02199-7636
Tel (617) 425-8000 *Founded/Ownrshp* 1981
Sales 128.8MM^E *EMP* 485
SIC 8732 Market analysis, business & economic research
Ch Bd: Bruce E Stangle
Mng Pt: John Jarofz
**CEO:* Martha Samuelson
CFO: Norman Gorin
CFO: Elyse Swallow
**Treas:* Michael Falvey
VP: Matthew Barrett
VP: Michael Beauregard
VP: Stephen M Benenson
VP: Stephen Cacciola
VP: Janis Carey
VP: Paul Centolella
VP: Mitch Cohen
VP: Adam Decter
VP: Robert L Earle
VP: Elizabeth Eccher
VP: Sara Filipek
VP: James A Fricano
VP: Christian Frois
VP: Arindam Ghosh
VP: Kevin Gold

D-U-N-S 06-478-0281
ANALYSTS INTERNATIONAL CORP
(*Suby of* AMERICAN CYBERSYSTEMS INC) ★
7700 France Ave S Ste 200, Minneapolis, MN 55435-5867
Tel (952) 835-5900 *Founded/Ownrshp* 2013
Sales 115.3MM^E *EMP* 871^E
SIC 7371 7379 Custom computer programming services; Computer software systems analysis & design, custom; Computer related consulting services
CEO: Rajiv Sardana
COO: Joe McAvoy
CFO: Pankaj Goel
Ofcr: Lynn Blake
Sr VP: James D Anderson
Sr VP: Sanjeev Sardana
Sr VP: Brian Soderholm
VP: Mike Brown
VP: Allison Gross
VP: Joe Thiel
Prac Mgr: Tanya Stauffer

ANALYTIC ENDODONTICS
See SYBRON DENTAL SPECIALTIES INC

D-U-N-S 09-963-7209
ANALYTIC STRESS RELIEVING INC
3118 W Pinhook Rd Ste 202, Lafayette, LA 70508-3444
Tel (337) 237-8790 *Founded/Ownrshp* 1979
Sales 277.6MM^E *EMP* 350
SIC 1389 Oil field services
Pr: David Herzog
**CFO:* Dalton Meaux
**Ch:* Paula Pennington
IT Man: Sarah McClelland
Sfty Dirs: Cindy Prejean
Opers Mgr: Butch Guidry
Opers Mgr: Patrick McNaughton
Natl Sales: Jason Tetzlaff
Sls Mgr: Dan Ciarlariello
Sls Mgr: Thomas Neale
Sls Mgr: Chase Richard

D-U-N-S 60-623-0399
ANALYTICAL GRAPHICS INC
AGI
220 Valley Creek Blvd, Exton, PA 19341-2380
Tel (610) 981-8000 *Founded/Ownrshp* 1989
Sales 96.0MM^E *EMP* 262
SIC 7372 Prepackaged software
Pr: Paul L Graziani
**Pr:* Joseph Sheehan
**COO:* Francesco F Linsalata
**CFO:* William J Broderick
VP: Travis Langster
**VP:* Scott Reynolds
VP: Rick Spinogatti
VP: Ronald E Thompson
Software D: Bill Chuba
Software D: Kevin Murray
Software D: Peter Nalyvayko

D-U-N-S 07-930-4856
ANAREN HOLDING CORP
590 Madison Ave Fl 41, New York, NY 10022-2524
Tel (212) 415-6700 *Founded/Ownrshp* 2013
Sales 280.9MM^E *EMP* 1,311^E
SIC 3663 Radio & TV communications equipment

D-U-N-S 04-235-2922 IMP
ANAREN INC
(*Suby of* ANAREN HOLDING CORP) ★
6635 Kirkville Rd, East Syracuse, NY 13057-9672
Tel (315) 432-8909 *Founded/Ownrshp* 2014
Sales 280.9MM^E *EMP* 880
SIC 3679 Electronic circuits; Microwave components
CEO: Lawrence A Sala
**V Ch:* Carl W Gerst Jr
Pr: David E Kopf
Pr: Jeff Liebl
COO: Eric Britt
**CFO:* George A Blanton
Sr VP: Mark P Burdick
Sr VP: Amy B Tewksbury
Exec: Tom Holtsbery
Genl Mgr: David Whitaker
Off Mgr: Graziella Walters

D-U-N-S 88-426-3617
ANATOLE HOTEL INVESTORS L P
WYNDHAM ANATOLE HOTEL
2201 N Stemmons Fwy, Dallas, TX 75207-2801
Tel (214) 748-1200 *Founded/Ownrshp* 1995
Sales 24.3MM^E *EMP* 1,600
SIC 7011 5813 5812 Hotels; Drinking places; Eating places
Mktg Mgr: Mark Herron

D-U-N-S 02-064-4766
ANATOLIA MINERALS DEVELOPMENT LTD
YAMAS IN TURKEY SUBSIDUARY
3721 Hwy 74 Ste 14, Evergreen, CO 80439
Tel (303) 670-9945 *Founded/Ownrshp* 1996
Sales 291.6MM *EMP* 2
SIC 1382 8748 Geological exploration, oil & gas field; Business consulting
Pr: Richard Moores
**Pt:* Rio Tinto Mining and Explorati
COO: Stewart Beckman
CFO: Mark E Murchison
**CFO:* John A Powers
Sr VP: Robert D Benbow

D-U-N-S 82-738-7221 IMP
ANAYA GEMS INC
OTC INTERNATIONAL
3100 47th Ave Unit 5, Long Island City, NY 11101-3010
Tel (718) 391-7400 *Founded/Ownrshp* 2008
Sales 153.7MM^E *EMP* 80
Accts Ft Kleiger And Company Grea
SIC 5094 3911 Jewelry & precious stones; Jewelry, precious metal
Ch Bd: Anshul A Gandhi
Pr: Lonnie Mayne
**COO:* Boaz Hirshberg
**Ch:* Ajay Gandhi
**Chf Mktg O:* Michael Sheinman
VP: Marlenie Paredes
Dir IT: Ozzy Happ
Info Man: Sammy Algerin
VP Mktg: Mark Christensen
Mktg Dir: Karen Pursch
Mktg Mgr: Wendy Blackinton

D-U-N-S 78-655-4373
ANB CORP
102 W Moore Ave Lbby Lbby, Terrell, TX 75160-3129
Tel (972) 563-2611 Founded/Ownrshp 2006
Sales NA EMP 2
Accts Jones Baggett Llp Dallas Te
SIC 6712 Bank holding companies
Prin: Robert A Hulsey

D-U-N-S 09-347-3176
ANB HOLDING CO LTD
102 W Moore Ave, Terrell, TX 75160-3140
Tel (972) 524-3411 Founded/Ownrshp 1889
Sales NA EMP 504E
SIC 6712 Bank holding companies
Pr: Robert A Hulsey
Genl Pt: Riter Hulsey

ANBM
See AMERICAN NTN BEARING MANUFACTURING CORP

ANBTX
See AMERICAN NATIONAL BANK OF TEXAS

D-U-N-S 07-871-7036
ANCESTRY US HOLDINGS INC
(Suby of ANCESTRY.COM LLC) ★
360 W 4800 N, Provo, UT 84604-5675
Tel (801) 705-7000 Founded/Ownrshp 2012
Sales 600.0MME EMP 1,000E
SIC 7375 Information retrieval services
Snr Sftwr: Jeff Brodie

D-U-N-S 07-936-4201
ANCESTRY.COM HOLDINGS LLC
360 W 4800 N, Provo, UT 84604-5675
Tel (801) 705-7000 Founded/Ownrshp 2013
Sales 619.5MME EMP 1,385E
SIC 7374 7375 Data processing & preparation; Information retrieval services
Sr VP: Kendall Hulet

D-U-N-S 06-243-6766
ANCESTRY.COM INC
(Suby of ANCESTRY US HOLDINGS INC) ★
1300 W Traverse Pkwy, Lehi, UT 84043-5373
Tel (801) 705-7000 Founded/Ownrshp 2012
Sales 600.0MM EMP 1,000
SIC 7374 Data processing & preparation
Pr: Timothy Sullivan
*COO: Howard Hochhauser
Chf Mktg O: Rob Singer
*Ex VP: Eric Shoup
*Sr VP: Jeffery Weber
Snr Sftwr: Jeff Brodie
Snr Sftwr: Jin Lee
Snr Sftwr: Bill Reid
Snr Sftwr: Ramya Rengarajan
Snr Sftwr: Chuck Reynolds
CTO: Daren Thayne

D-U-N-S 07-936-4301
ANCESTRY.COM LLC
(Suby of ANCESTRY.COM HOLDINGS LLC) ★
1300 W Traverse Pkwy, Lehi, UT 84043-5373
Tel (801) 705-7000 Founded/Ownrshp 1983
Sales 619.5MM EMP 1,385E
SIC 7374 Data processing & preparation
Pr: Timothy Sullivan
COO: Howard Hochhauser
*Ch: Bruce Chizen
Chf Mktg O: Rob Singer
CTO: Scott Sorensen
Board of Directors: Janice Chaffin, Brad Garlinghouse, Victor Parker, Brian Ruder

D-U-N-S 60-747-0064 IMP/EXP
ANCHI INC
ANCHOR HOCKING
(Suby of ANCHOR HOCKING CO) ★
1115 W 5th Ave, Lancaster, OH 43130-2938
Tel (740) 653-2527 Founded/Ownrshp 2001
Sales 154.9MME EMP 1,500
SIC 3231 Products of purchased glass
CEO: Mark R Eichhorn

D-U-N-S 79-171-3332
ANCHOR BANCORP WISCONSIN INC
25 W Main St, Madison, WI 53703-3399
Tel (608) 252-8700 Founded/Ownrshp 1992
Sales NA EMP 690E
SIC 6035
Pr: Chris M Bauer
*Ch Bd: David L Omachinski
CFO: Thomas G Dolan
Ofcr: Michael Helser
Ex VP: Mark D Timmerman
VP: Penny Armagost
VP: Ron Osterholtz
VP: Rae Valasek
VP: Linda Zirdars
Brnch Mgr: Barb Ahlgren
Brnch Mgr: Nora Brautigam
Board of Directors: Richard A Bergstrom, Holly Cremer Berkenstadt, Pat Richter

ANCHOR BLUE
See HUB DISTRIBUTING INC

D-U-N-S 11-542-9151 IMP/EXP
■ **ANCHOR COUPLING INC**
(Suby of CATERPILLAR INC) ★
5520 13th St, Menominee, MI 49858-1014
Tel (906) 863-2672 Founded/Ownrshp 1992
Sales 140.0MME EMP 550
SIC 3429 Manufactured hardware (general); Clamps & couplings, hose
Pr: Bonnie Fetch
*VP: Rick Brown
*VP: John Pressler
*Prin: Dave Bozeman
Mtls Mgr: Gail R Clark

ANCHOR DIE CAST
See MERCHANTS METALS LLC

ANCHOR DRILLING FLUIDS, USA
See ANCHOR DRILLING FLUIDS USA INC

D-U-N-S 10-904-0352
■ **ANCHOR DRILLING FLUIDS USA INC**
ANCHOR DRILLING FLUIDS, USA
(Suby of ADF HOLDINGS, INC.)
2431 E 61st St Ste 710, Tulsa, OK 74136-1211
Tel (918) 583-7701 Founded/Ownrshp 1984
Sales 205.9MME EMP 375
SIC 5169

D-U-N-S 96-647-5170 IMP/EXP
ANCHOR GLASS CONTAINER CORP
(Suby of KPS CAPITAL PARTNERS LP) ★
401 E Jackson St Ste 1100, Tampa, FL 33602-5271
Tel (813) 884-0000 Founded/Ownrshp 2014
Sales 1.1MMME EMP 2,840
SIC 3221 Glass containers
CEO: James J Fredlake
*CFO: Kenneth G Wilkes
VP: Pat Rudden
Genl Mgr: John Sode
IT Man: Mike Thompson
IT Man: Kevin Tipton
Ql Cn Mgr: Jerry Brewer
Board of Directors: Eugene I Davis

ANCHOR HOCKING
See ANCHI INC

ANCHOR HOCKING COMPANY, THE
See ANCHOR HOCKING LLC

ANCHOR HOCKING INDUS GL DIV
See GHP II LLC

D-U-N-S 79-707-2464 EXP
ANCHOR HOCKING LLC
ANCHOR HOCKING COMPANY, THE
(Suby of EVERYWARE GLOBAL INC) ★
519 N Pierce Ave, Lancaster, OH 43130-2969
Tel (740) 681-6478 Founded/Ownrshp 2007
Sales 444.9MME EMP 1,600
SIC 3229 3089 3411 3221 Tableware, glass or glass ceramic; Cooking utensils, glass or glass ceramic; Cups, plastic, except foam; Plates, plastic; Bottle caps, molded plastic; Metal cans; Glass containers
Pr: Mark Eichhorn
V Ch: John McDonough
*CFO: Mark Hedstrom
*Sr VP: Bert Filice
*Sr VP: Joe Sundberg
VP: Carolyn Jones
DP Exec: Michelle Tunno
Plnt Mgr: Greg Stark
Sls Mgr: Cheryl Brumfield
Sales Asso: Michael Moore
Snr Mgr: Dustin Burggraf

ANCHOR LAMINA AMERICA
See DAYTON LAMINA CORP

D-U-N-S 17-087-9535 IMP
ANCHOR PACKAGING INC
(Suby of HERMANN COMPANIES INC) ★
13515 Barrett Parkway Dr # 100, Ballwin, MO 63021-5870
Tel (314) 394-3701 Founded/Ownrshp 1997
Sales 146.6MME EMP 500
SIC 3086 Packaging & shipping materials, foamed plastic
Pr: Jeff Wolff Anchor
*Sr VP: David Johnson
Dist Mgr: Margie Southard
Dir IT: Andy Rikand
IT Man: Mike Kreh
VP Opers: David Taylor
Natl Sales: Eric Shaffer
VP Mktg: Mike Thaler
Mktg Dir: Marilyn Stapleton
Sls Dir: William McMillen
Mktg Mgr: Joe Pinkowski

D-U-N-S 82-770-8962
ANCHOR STAFFING INC
39209 6 Mile Rd Ste 250, Livonia, MI 48152-2681
Tel (734) 591-1100 Founded/Ownrshp 2006
Sales 58.6MM EMP 2,000E
SIC 7363 Temporary help service; Engineering help service
Pr: Chitra R Shahani

D-U-N-S 07-666-7013
ANCHORAGE MUNICIPALITY OF (INC)
632 W 6th Ave Ste 810, Anchorage, AK 99501-6312
Tel (907) 343-6610 Founded/Ownrshp 1975
Sales NA EMP 3,680
SIC 9111 City & town managers' offices;
Ofcr: Kevin Armstrong
Ofcr: Kristiana Bastian
Ofcr: Jeffrey Bell
Ofcr: Ralph Blanchard
Ofcr: John Bolen
Ofcr: James Bucher
Ofcr: Brian Burton
Ofcr: Robin Callison
Ofcr: Jack Carson
Ofcr: James Conley
Ofcr: James Dokken
Ofcr: Justin Doll
Ofcr: Richard Fern
Ofcr: John Goetz
Ofcr: Debbie Jacobson
Ofcr: Al Kennedy
Ofcr: John Kleinsmith
Ofcr: Michael Lofton
Ofcr: Kevin McDonald
Ofcr: Christopher Nelson
Ofcr: David Parker

D-U-N-S 15-040-4523
ANCHORAGE SCHOOL DISTRICT
ASD
5530 E Nthrn Lights Blvd, Anchorage, AK 99504
Tel (907) 742-4000 Founded/Ownrshp 1947
Sales 858.1MM EMP 5,039
Accts Bdo Usa Llp Anchorage Alask
SIC 8211 Public elementary & secondary schools; Kindergarten; Public elementary school; Public junior high school
MIS Dir: Mike Fleckenstein
IT Man: Dale Sheldon-Hess
Pr Dir: Heidi Embley
Pr Dir: Patti Layou
Teacher Pr: Todd Hess
Teacher Pr: Susan Schmidt
Instr Medi: Ann Morgester
HC Dir: Nancy Edtl

D-U-N-S 05-083-1106
ANCHORBANK FSB
25 W Main St Lowr, Madison, WI 53703-3329
Tel (608) 252-8700 Founded/Ownrshp 1992
Sales NA EMP 690
SIC 6036

D-U-N-S 13-952-5331
ANCIRA ENTERPRISES INC
10855 W Interstate 10, San Antonio, TX 78230-1301
Tel (210) 681-4900 Founded/Ownrshp 1983
Sales 188.5MME EMP 560
SIC 5511 New & used car dealers
Pr: Ernesto Ancira Jr
*CFO: Carolyn E Ferguson
*Ex VP: Greg Spence
Genl Mgr: Lino Liberatorf
IT Man: Elisabeth Barrera
IT Man: Elizabeth Collins
Prd Mgr: Sam Mendoza

ANCO FINE CHEESE
See SCHRATTER FOODS INC

D-U-N-S 87-827-3226
ANCO INDUSTRIES LLC
(Suby of BROCK GROUP) ★
10343 Sam Houston Park Dr # 200, Houston, TX 77064-4656
Tel (281) 807-8200 Founded/Ownrshp 2000
Sales 42.7MME EMP 1,600
SIC 1721 1799 Industrial painting; Fireproofing buildings; Insulation of pipes & boilers
Pr: Michael McGinnis
CFO: Robert Hardy

D-U-N-S 80-174-5381
ANCO INSURANCE MANAGERS INC
1111 Briarcrest Dr, Bryan, TX 77802-2793
Tel (979) 776-2626 Founded/Ownrshp 1965
Sales NA EMP 276
Accts Fisher Herbst & Kemble Pc S
SIC 6411 Insurance agents
Pr: Laura K Gregory
Sr VP: Ron Smith
VP: Sandi Hopkins
VP: John Lynn
VP: Cara O'Conor
*VP: Don A Smith
*Prin: M L Cashion
Dir IT: Craig Johnson
Mktg Dir: Patrick Croll
Board of Directors: Bill Cauthorn, Drew Cauthorn, Guy Cauthorn, Sid Cauthorn, Norman Elder, Kathy Gregory, Dick Haddox, Adrian McDonald, Steve Stevens

D-U-N-S 02-598-5946 IMP
ANCONNECT LLC (TX)
(Suby of ANDERSON MEDIA CORP) ★
421 Se 34th Ave, Amarillo, TX 79103-1702
Tel (806) 376-6251 Founded/Ownrshp 2012, 1994
Sales 3.4MMME EMP 3,000
SIC 5099 5192 Compact discs; Phonograph records; Tapes & cassettes, prerecorded; Video cassettes, accessories & supplies; Books
CEO: Bill Lardie
*Ch Bd: Joel R Anderson
*CFO: Jay R Maier
*CFO: Chuck Taylor
*Ex VP: Tony Girard
*Ex VP: Steve McClanahan
*Ex VP: Matthew Smith
*Sr VP: Jay Coile
*Sr VP: Lisa Gibson
VP: Maria Layne
Dir Rx: Bill Williams

ANCOR CAPITAL PARTNERS
See ANCOR HOLDINGS LP

D-U-N-S 87-626-8269
ANCOR HOLDINGS LP
ANCOR CAPITAL PARTNERS
100 Throckmorton St St Ste 1600, Southlake, TX 76092
Tel (817) 877-4458 Founded/Ownrshp 1994
Sales 185.3MME EMP 810E
SIC 8741 8742 Management services; Financial consultant
CEO: J Randall Keene
Pt: Timothy Mc Kibben

D-U-N-S 79-479-1251 IMP
ANDA INC
(Suby of TEVA NORTH AMERICA) ★
2915 Weston Rd, Weston, FL 33331-3627
Tel (954) 217-4500 Founded/Ownrshp 2016
Sales 767.0MME EMP 377
SIC 5122 Pharmaceuticals
Pr: Charles D Phillips
Pr: Marc Falkin
*COO: Robert Stewart
VP: Kim Bloom
VP: William Versosky
Genl Mgr: Sheila Boucher
IT Man: Jason Nodarse
Natl Sales: Gabriel Ocampo
Mktg Mgr: Anita Isabella
Mktg Mgr: Carolina Sanchez
Sls Mgr: Joseph Falzone

D-U-N-S 04-647-9986
ANDALUSIA DISTRIBUTING CO INC
A D C
117 Allen Ave, Andalusia, AL 36420-2501
Tel (334) 222-3671 Founded/Ownrshp 1956
Sales 123.1MM EMP 62
Accts White & Mcclung Llc Andalusi
SIC 5172 5113 5194 5149 Petroleum products; Industrial & personal service paper; Tobacco & tobacco products; Groceries & related products
Exec: Jody Kelley
Manager: Tonya Mount
Sales Asso: Steve Koelbel
Sales Asso: Kyle Powell

D-U-N-S 05-359-9320
ANDERSEN CONSTRUCTION CO
HA ANDERSEN COMPANY
6712 N Cutter Cir, Portland, OR 97217-3933
Tel (503) 283-6712 Founded/Ownrshp 1954
Sales 582.3MM EMP 150E
Accts Thompson Kessler Wiest & Borqu
SIC 1542 1541 Commercial & office building, new construction; Industrial buildings, new construction
Pr: David L Andersen
*CFO: Bill Eckhardt
*VP: Joel Andersen
*VP: Martin Cloe
Snr PM: Jeff Sawyer

D-U-N-S 00-616-7332 IMP/EXP
ANDERSEN CORP (MN)
100 4th Ave N, Bayport, MN 55003-1096
Tel (651) 264-5150 Founded/Ownrshp 1903
Sales 3.4MMME EMP 10,000
SIC 2431 3231 Windows, wood; Doors, wood; Products of purchased glass
Pr: Jay Lund
Pr: Dave Beeken
Pr: Michael Clark
Pr: Paul Saterbak
*CFO: Philip E Donaldson
Ex VP: Charles W Schmid
*Sr VP: Alan Bernick
*Sr VP: Holly M Boehne
Sr VP: Craig Evanich
*Sr VP: Karen Richard
VP: Lynn Burnette
VP: Grant Davis
VP: Jeanne Junker
VP: Steve Kirby
*VP: Stephen S MOG
VP: Keith Olson
VP: Jim Weglewski

D-U-N-S 09-734-0293 IMP
ANDERSEN DISTRIBUTION INC
ANDERSEN LOGISTICS
(Suby of ANDERSEN CORP) ★
100 4th Ave N, Bayport, MN 55003-1058
Tel (651) 264-5150 Founded/Ownrshp 1999
Sales 482.7MME EMP 1,500
SIC 5031 Windows; Millwork
Pr: James E Humphrey
Pr: Michael Clark
QA Dir: Dan Frederick
Opers Mgr: Larry Leach
Plnt Mgr: Tom Armstrong

ANDERSEN E SERIES
See EAGLE WINDOW & DOOR INC

ANDERSEN LOGISTICS
See ANDERSEN DISTRIBUTION INC

D-U-N-S 78-780-2719
ANDERSON AND DUBOSE INC
ANDERSON-DUBOSE CO, THE
5300 Tod Ave Sw, Warren, OH 44481-9767
Tel (440) 248-8800 Founded/Ownrshp 1995
Sales 546.8MM EMP 100
SIC 5142 5141 Packaged frozen goods; Groceries, general line
Pr: Warren Anderson
IT Man: Mark Ferrel
Opers Supe: Matt Durci

D-U-N-S 18-584-9387
ANDERSON COLUMBIA CO INC
AC
871 Nw Guerdon St, Lake City, FL 32055-4346
Tel (386) 752-7585 Founded/Ownrshp 1988
Sales 607.9MME EMP 950
SIC 1611 2951 General contractor, highway & street construction; Asphalt & asphaltic paving mixtures (not from refineries)
Ch Bd: Joe Anderson Jr
*Pr: Joe H Anderson
*Pr: Joe H Anderson III
*Treas: Harriett Anderson Wall
*VP: Tony Williams

D-U-N-S 13-621-0726
■ **ANDERSON COMPANIES INC**
ROY ANDERSON
(Suby of TUTOR PERINI CORP) ★
11400 Reichold Rd, Gulfport, MS 39503-6008
Tel (228) 896-4000 Founded/Ownrshp 2011
Sales 267.5MM EMP 475
Accts Deloitte & Touche Llp Los Ang
SIC 1542 1541 1522 Commercial & office building contractors; Industrial buildings, new construction; Multi-family dwelling construction
CEO: Roy Anderson III
CFO: David Jackson
*Treas: William B Sparks
*Treas: Robert P Vollenweider
VP: Steve Bryant
VP: Travis Coulter
VP: Trish McAllister
*VP: Steven Meilicke
VP: Roger Short
Plnt Mgr: Chip Merrigan

D-U-N-S 00-598-6054
ANDERSON COUNTY SCHOOL DISTRICT FIVE INC
400 Pearman Dairy Rd, Anderson, SC 29625-3100
Tel (864) 260-5000 Founded/Ownrshp 1952
Sales 130.8MM EMP 1,300
Accts Greene Finney & Horton Llp M
SIC 8211 Public elementary & secondary schools
*Pr: Mike Mahaffey
Treas: Christina Alexander
Treas: Pamela Hassan
VP: Mandy Glenn
VP: Donna Harrington
Snr Ntwrk: Ben Willis
Dir IT: Jennifer Diebold

Dir IT: Brad Sutton
IT Man: Wess Grand
Pr Dir: Sandra Broom

D-U-N-S 07-979-8859
ANDERSON COUNTY SCHOOLS
101 S Main St Ste 500, Clinton, TN 37716-3619
Tel (865) 463-8631 *Founded/Ownrshp* 2015
Sales 46.2MM^E *EMP* 1,008^E
SIC 8211 Public elementary & secondary schools

D-U-N-S 00-790-9955 IMP/EXP
ANDERSON EQUIPMENT CO (PA)
1000 Washington Pike, Bridgeville, PA 15017-2701
Tel (412) 343-2300 *Founded/Ownrshp* 1935
Sales 101.4MM^E *EMP* 310
SIC 5082 7699 7353 5531

D-U-N-S 00-527-8734 IMP
ANDERSON ERICKSON DAIRY CO (IA)
2420 E University Ave, Des Moines, IA 50317-6501
Tel (515) 265-2521 *Founded/Ownrshp* 1930
Sales 162.8MM^E *EMP* 520
SIC 0241 Milk production
CEO: Miriam Erickson Brown
**Ch Bd:* James W Erickson
**CFO:* Warren Erickson
**Treas:* Robert L Mahaffey
Bd of Dir: Steve Flattery
Genl Mgr: Sheryl Williamson
Sfty Dirs: Mike Peterson
Plnt Mgr: Mary Koogler
Mktg Dir: Kim Peter
Mktg Dir: Betsy Watson
Sls Mgr: Adam Buford

D-U-N-S 79-308-7925 EXP
■ **ANDERSON GROUP INC**
(*Suby of* CHARTER CONSOLIDATED LIMITED)
3411 Silverside Rd # 103, Wilmington, DE 19810-4812
Tel (302) 478-6160 *Founded/Ownrshp* 1991
Sales 268.5MM^E *EMP* 805
SIC 5047 5063 5099 7699 3443 Industrial safety devices: first aid kits & masks; Electrical apparatus & equipment; Lifesaving & survival equipment (non-medical); Hydraulic equipment repair; Cylinders, pressure: metal plate
Pr: Herbert F Gerhard
**Treas:* Mark F Fornari
**Treas:* Howard L Nelson

D-U-N-S 82-696-9052
ANDERSON GROUP LLC
111 2nd Ave Ne Ste 105, Saint Petersburg, FL 33701-3440
Tel (248) 645-8000 *Founded/Ownrshp* 2001
Sales 220.3MM^E *EMP* 200^E
SIC 6799 6719 Investors; Investment holding companies, except banks

D-U-N-S 02-730-2181 IMP/EXP
ANDERSON HAY & GRAIN CO INC (WA)
910 Anderson Rd, Ellensburg, WA 98926-9693
Tel (509) 925-9818 *Founded/Ownrshp* 1940
Sales 179.3MM^E *EMP* 250
SIC 5191 Hay; Feed
Ch Bd: Ronald T Anderson
Pr: Mark T Anderson
CFO: Steve Gordon
Sec: Rick C Galloway
Off Mgr: Derek Holland
Off Mgr: Amy Shiner
Opers Mgr: Rodney Van Orman
Opers Mgr: Matt Weston
Sls Mgr: Brian Thompson

ANDERSON HOSPITAL
See SOUTHWESTERN ILLINOIS HEALTH FACILITIES INC

ANDERSON LADD
See HALDEMAN-HOMME INC

D-U-N-S 62-159-9901 IMP
ANDERSON MEDIA CORP
265 Brookview Town Ste, Knoxville, TN 37919
Tel (865) 474-8500 *Founded/Ownrshp* 1917
Sales 4.0MMM^E *EMP* 4,000
SIC 5099 5192 Compact discs; Phonograph records; Tapes & cassettes, prerecorded; Video cassettes, accessories & supplies; Books
Ch Bd: Joel Anderson
**Pr:* Charles C Anderson Jr
**CFO:* Jay R Maier
Dist Mgr: Don Bruce
Dist Mgr: Christopher Floyd
Dist Mgr: Stephanie White
Off Mgr: Amanda Whisenhunt

D-U-N-S 07-912-7118
ANDERSON MERCHANDISERS LLC
(*Suby of* ANDERSON MEDIA CORP) ★
5601 Gran Pkwy Ste 1400, Plano, TX 75024
Tel (972) 987-5516 *Founded/Ownrshp* 2014
Sales 164.7MM^E *EMP* 3,000
SIC 7389
CEO: Bill Lardie
**Pr:* Scott McDaniel
**CFO:* John Campbell
**Ex VP:* Jeff King
VP: Andrew Stavros
Dist Mgr: Wayne Chiodo
Dist Mgr: Bill Eubanks
Dist Mgr: Gail Griffin
Dist Mgr: Kevin Kelley
Software D: Wendell Farley
Opers Mgr: Cody McCrary

ANDERSON NEWS COMPANY
See ANDERSON NEWS LLC

D-U-N-S 03-469-9728 IMP
ANDERSON NEWS LLC
ANDERSON NEWS COMPANY
265 Brookview Town Ste, Knoxville, TN 37919
Tel (865) 584-9765 *Founded/Ownrshp* 1977
Sales 219.0MM^E *EMP* 1,000
SIC 5192 Magazines; Newspapers; Books

Off Mgr: Amy Moles
DP Dir: Steve Tarwater

D-U-N-S 96-204-0130 IMP
ANDERSON PERFORATING LTD
API PERFORATING
124 Welco Rd, Albany, TX 76430
Tel (325) 762-2200 *Founded/Ownrshp* 2010
Sales 114.9MM^E *EMP* 227^E
SIC 1389 Perforating well casings
Pt: Ronnie Anderson
Pt: Donnie Anderson

D-U-N-S 07-210-5505
ANDERSON REGIONAL MEDICAL CENTER
JEFF ANDERSON REGIONAL MED CTR
2124 14th St, Meridian, MS 39301-4040
Tel (601) 553-6000 *Founded/Ownrshp* 1928
Sales 177.7MM *EMP* 1,314
SIC 8062 General medical & surgical hospitals
CEO: W Jeff Anderson
Dir Vol: Laura Jordan
**CEO:* L Ray Humphreys
Chf Mktg O: Ann Weddington
**VP:* John Anderson
**VP:* Wanda Cooper
**VP:* Denton Farr
VP: Ann Lundy
VP: Andy Miller
**VP:* Tony Rispoli
**VP:* Linda Todd
Dir Lab: Marilyn Bell
Dir Rad: Larry Schwan
Dir Rx: Adrian Page
Comm Man: Elizabeth Wiggins

D-U-N-S 62-677-4801
ANDERSON SERVICES LLC
6016 Brookvale Ln 110b, Knoxville, TN 37919-4003
Tel (865) 584-6714 *Founded/Ownrshp* 2002
Sales 66.8MM^E *EMP* 2,328
SIC 4212 Local trucking, without storage

D-U-N-S 00-977-1437
ANDERSON TRUCKING SERVICE INC
ATS
725 Opportunity Dr, Saint Cloud, MN 56301-5886
Tel (320) 255-7400 *Founded/Ownrshp* 1955
Sales 397.3MM^E *EMP* 900
SIC 4213 Trucking, except local; Heavy hauling; Building materials transport
CEO: Rollie Anderson
**COO:* Brent Anderson
**CFO:* Scott Fuller
**Treas:* Scott Anderson
VP: Joe Goering
VP: Jeff Potthoff
Exec: Gene Janssen
Rgnl Mgr: Terry Weiland
Admn Mgr: Jodi Nesland
VP Mfg: Mike Lackmann
Sfty Dirs: Jeff Stewart

ANDERSON-DUBOSE CO, THE
See ANDERSON AND DUBOSE INC

D-U-N-S 00-701-8047 EXP
ANDERSON-TULLY CO (MS)
ANDERSON-TULLY LUMBER COMPANY
(*Suby of* FORESTLAND GROUP LLC) ★
1725 N Washington St, Vicksburg, MS 39183-7696
Tel (601) 629-3283 *Founded/Ownrshp* 1980, 1979
Sales 87.7MM^E *EMP* 294
Accts Deloitte & Touche Llp Memphi
SIC 2421 0811 Sawmills & planing mills, general; Timber tracts
Pr: Chip Dickinson
CFO: Edward Coombs
**Sec:* Lin Thornton
**Ex VP:* Norman Davis
**Ex VP:* Richard Wilkerson
Sales Exec: Ej Irby

ANDERSON-TULLY LUMBER COMPANY
See ANDERSON-TULLY CO

D-U-N-S 05-321-7022
ANDERSONBRECON INC
PCI SERVICES OF ILLINOIS
(*Suby of* PACKAGING COORDINATORS LLC) ★
4545 Assembly Dr, Rockford, IL 61109-3081
Tel (815) 484-8900 *Founded/Ownrshp* 2013
Sales 212.0MM^E *EMP* 1,000
SIC 7389 Packaging & labeling services
CEO: William Mitchell
Pr: Pam Olson
VP: Chuck Aubrey
VP: Steve McNett
QA Dir: Mitch Farris
IT Man: Terry Turner
Manager: Steve Tooker
Sls Mgr: Steve Kemp

D-U-N-S 19-699-1731
▲ **ANDERSONS INC**
480 W Dussel Dr, Maumee, OH 43537-1690
Tel (419) 893-5050 *Founded/Ownrshp* 1947
Sales 4.2MMM *EMP* 3,443
Tkr Sym ANDE *Exch* NGS
SIC 5153 0723 5191 2874 4789 4741 Grain & field beans; Grains; Grain elevators; Crop preparation services for market; Cash grain crops market preparation services; Farm supplies; Fertilizers & agricultural chemicals; Seeds & bulbs; Phosphatic fertilizers; Plant foods, mixed: from plants making phosphatic fertilizer; Railroad car repair; Rental of railroad cars
Pr: Patrick E Bowe
**Ch Bd:* Michael J Anderson
CFO: John Granato
Treas: James C Burmeister
Treas: James Burmeister
Sr VP: Naran U Burchinow
VP: Charles Brown
VP: Art Depompei
VP: Richard George
VP: Anne G Rex
VP: Anne Rex
VP: Randy Thomure
VP: Phil Zulch
Exec: Roxann Brewer

Board of Directors: Gerard M Anderson, Catherine M Kilbane, Robert J King Jr, Ross W Manire, Donald L Mennel, Patrick S Mullin, John T Stout Jr, Jacqueline F Woods

D-U-N-S 07-970-6666
ANDERTON CASTINGS LLC
(*Suby of* ANDERTON INTERMEDIATE COMPANY)
222 Lely Dr, Troy, TX 76579-3714
Tel (254) 938-2541 *Founded/Ownrshp* 2014
Sales 112.5MM^E *EMP* 300^E
SIC 3465 Body parts, automobile: stamped metal

D-U-N-S 14-045-3221
ANDES INDUSTRIES INC
2260 W Broadway Rd # 101, Mesa, AZ 85202-1898
Tel (480) 813-0925 *Founded/Ownrshp* 2003
Sales 162.8MM^E *EMP* 1,400
SIC 5063 3663 3643 Wire & cable; Radio & TV communications equipment; Current-carrying wiring devices
Pr: Steven Youtsey
IT Man: Paul Gemme

ANDOVER ACADEMY
See TRUSTEES OF PHILLIPS ACADEMY

ANDOVER CO, THE
See BAY STATE INSURANCE CO

D-U-N-S 80-890-5066
ANDOVER PUBLIC SCHOOLS
TOWN OF ANDOVER
50 Bartlet St, Andover, MA 01810-3813
Tel (978) 623-8519 *Founded/Ownrshp* 2007
Sales 31.9MM^E *EMP* 1,000
SIC 8211 Public elementary & secondary schools

ANDOVER TOWNSMAN
See EAGLE-TRIBUNE PUBLISHING CO

D-U-N-S 07-737-2449
ANDRE-BOUDIN BAKERIES INC
BOUDIN SOURDOUGH BAKERY & CAFE
(*Suby of* BOUDIN HOLDINGS INC) ★
50 Francisco St Ste 200, San Francisco, CA 94133-2132
Tel (415) 882-1849 *Founded/Ownrshp* 2002
Sales 117.7MM^E *EMP* 750
SIC 2051 5812 5961 5481

D-U-N-S 07-736-8439
ANDREINI & CO
220 W 20th Ave, San Mateo, CA 94403-1339
Tel (650) 573-1111 *Founded/Ownrshp* 1951
Sales NA *EMP* 176
SIC 6411 Insurance brokers
CEO: Michael J Colzani
Mng Pt: Craig Oden
Mng Pt: Jeff Tebow
**Pr:* John Andreini
COO: Dan Centoni
Ex VP: Don Kuhns
Ex VP: Mark Mathias
Sr VP: Paul Hughes
Sr VP: Ralph Neate
Sr VP: Randy Viglienzone
VP: Laura Brugger
VP: Bill Cook
VP: Jim Denardi
VP: Kenneth Kneis
VP: Kirk Maberry
VP: Omar Perez
VP: Mike Quint
VP: Randy Reed
VP: Sean Sheets
VP: Brian Stuart
VP: Bernie Tillotson

ANDRESON COMPANY, THE
See MOUNTVILLE MILLS INC

D-U-N-S 05-322-8834
■ **ANDREW INTERNATIONAL SERVICES CORP**
(*Suby of* COMMSCOPE TECHNOLOGIES LLC) ★
2700 Ellis Rd, Joliet, IL 60433-8459
Tel (779) 435-6000 *Founded/Ownrshp* 1937
Sales 106.8MM^E *EMP* 1,400
SIC 3663 Microwave communication equipment
CEO: Marvin S Edwards
**Pr:* Ralph Faison

D-U-N-S 80-362-4931
ANDREW LAUREN CO INC
ANDREW LAUREN INTERIORS
8909 Kenamar Dr Ste 101, San Diego, CA 92121-3439
Tel (858) 793-5319 *Founded/Ownrshp* 1993
Sales 106.2MM^E *EMP* 240
Accts Douglas Wechsler Chino Hills
SIC 5023 Carpets; Floor coverings
CEO: David Dominguez
**CFO:* Jim De Laurentis

ANDREW LAUREN INTERIORS
See ANDREW LAUREN CO INC

D-U-N-S 02-037-9194
ANDREW W MELLON FOUNDATION
140 E 62nd St, New York, NY 10065-8124
Tel (212) 838-8400 *Founded/Ownrshp* 1969
Sales 331.9MM *EMP* 70
SIC 7389 Fund raising organizations
Pr: William G Bowen
**Treas:* Thomas Sanders
Trst: Walter E Massy
Ofcr: Eugene Tobin
**VP:* John Hull
VP: Patricia Irvin
VP: Marit Westermann
**VP:* Harriet Zuckerman
Counsel: Rebecca Feit

D-U-N-S 03-745-7611 IMP
ANDREWS DISTRIBUTING CO OF NORTH TEXAS LLC
2730 Irving Blvd, Dallas, TX 75207-2308
Tel (214) 525-9400 *Founded/Ownrshp* 1980
Sales 569.0MM^E *EMP* 1,310

SIC 5181 Beer & other fermented malt liquors
CEO: Barry Andrews
**Pr:* Michael McGuire
**COO:* Mike Barnes
**CFO:* Joe Jernigan
**VP:* Jim Campbell
**VP:* Bea Cisneros
VP: David Holt
VP: Don Jaresh
VP: Sean Murphy
VP: Pam Spackman
Mng Dir: Shawn Jensen

ANDREWS FABULOUS FOODS
See WHITSONS FOOD SERVICE CORP

ANDREWS FOOD SERVICE SYSTEMS
See ANDREWS PRODUCE INC

D-U-N-S 12-777-0886
ANDREWS INTERNATIONAL
(*Suby of* ANDREWS INTERNATIONAL INC) ★
200 Mansell Ct E Ste 500, Roswell, GA 30076-4852
Tel (661) 775-8400 *Founded/Ownrshp* 1989
Sales 39.3MM^E *EMP* 3,000
SIC 7381 Security guard service
Pr: Lemarque R Shepperd
**Sr VP:* Obie Moore

D-U-N-S 12-154-4472
ANDREWS INTERNATIONAL INC
(*Suby of* ANDREWS INTERNATIONAL INC) ★
5870 Trinity Pkwy Ste 300, Centreville, VA 20120-1970
Tel (703) 592-1400 *Founded/Ownrshp* 2009
Sales 57.5MM^E *EMP* 4,000
SIC 7381

D-U-N-S 14-486-0756
ANDREWS INTERNATIONAL INC
455 N Moss St, Burbank, CA 91502-1727
Tel (818) 487-4060 *Founded/Ownrshp* 1988
Sales 219.1MM^E *EMP* 5,000
SIC 7381 Protective services, guard; Private investigator
Pr: Randy Andrews
**COO:* Ty Richmond
**COO:* James Wood
**CFO:* Michael Topf
Ofcr: Francis Coates Jr
Ex VP: Obie R Moore III
Ex VP: Obie Moore
Sr VP: David Levenberg
Sr VP: Michael Stockman
**VP:* Roger Andrews
VP: Michael Cantrell
VP: Bill Flores
VP: Michael Maloof
VP: Henry Wilkins Jr

D-U-N-S 07-844-3413
ANDREWS KURTH LLP (TX)
600 Travis St Ste 4200, Houston, TX 77002-2929
Tel (713) 220-4200 *Founded/Ownrshp* 1901, 2007
Sales 159.6MM^E *EMP* 916
SIC 8111 General practice law office
Mng Pt: Bob Jewell
Pt: Howard Ayers
Pt: Jerry L Beane
Pt: Elizabeth A Campbell
Pt: Marcus W Deitz
Pt: Tonya M Gray
Pt: Diana Hudson
Pt: Robert V Jewell
Pt: Jonathan I Levine
Pt: Richard H Kronthal
Pt: Jason M Peters
Pt: Lynne M Uniman
Mng Pt: Robin Russell
**Ch:* Tom Perich
VP: Andrew Vindigni
Dir Bus: Deborah Roth Grabein

D-U-N-S 03-212-9876
ANDREWS PRODUCE INC
ANDREWS FOOD SERVICE SYSTEMS
717 E Industrial Blvd, Pueblo West, CO 81007-1592
Tel (719) 543-3846 *Founded/Ownrshp* 1926
Sales 95.4MM^E *EMP* 91
SIC 5141 5148 Food brokers; Fruits, fresh; Vegetables, fresh
Pr: George A Andrews III
**VP:* Debbie Andrews
**VP:* Rusty Disanti
**VP:* Deb Hinkle
**VP:* Jacque Ponx
Sls Mgr: David Garcia

D-U-N-S 07-866-2237
ANDREWS STAFFING INC
1834 Walden Office Sq # 150, Schaumburg, IL 60173-4281
Tel (847) 995-9300 *Founded/Ownrshp* 2010
Sales 21.8MM^E *EMP* 1,500
SIC 7363 Temporary help service
Pr: Mary Zwirn
**Treas:* Mel Zwirn

D-U-N-S 00-516-2151
ANDREWS UNIVERSITY (MI)
4150 Administration Dr, Berrien Springs, MI 49104-0001
Tel (269) 471-7771 *Founded/Ownrshp* 1874
Sales 148.7MM^E *EMP* 2,302
SIC 8221 University; Theological seminary
Pr: Niels-Erik Andreasen
**Ch Bd:* Benjamin Shoun
COO: Angelina Camren
**CFO:* Larry Shalk
Treas: Merle Bascom
**V Ch Bd:* Don Livesay
VP: Margarita Mattingly
VP: Stephen Payne
**VP:* Edward E Wines
Off Mgr: Jeanie Craig
Telecom Ex: Dan Hamstra

D-U-N-S 55-590-9746 IMP/EXP
ANDRITZ (USA) INC
(Suby of ANDRITZ AG)
5405 Windward Pkwy 100, Alpharetta, GA 30004-3894
Tel (770) 640-2500 Founded/Ownrshp 1990
Sales 480.2MM[E] EMP 1,200
SIC 3554 3523 Pulp mill machinery; Grading, cleaning, sorting machines, fruit, grain, vegetable
Pr: Timothy J Ryan
Pr: Steve Huff
CFO: Olav Bagwald
*CFO: Christopher Keays
*Treas: John Morphis
VP: Carrier Daniel
Div Mgr: Tim Orr
Genl Mgr: Tim Mahoney
Genl Mgr: Thomas Taylor
Dir IT: Aaron Leavitt
Dir IT: Scott Wiggins

D-U-N-S 00-207-5695 IMP/EXP
ANDRITZ INC (GA)
(Suby of ANDRITZ (USA) INC) ★
500 Technology Dr, Canonsburg, PA 15317-9584
Tel (724) 597-7801 Founded/Ownrshp 1992, 2001
Sales 194.2MM[E] EMP 646
SIC 3554 8711 7389 Pulp mill machinery; Industrial engineers; Design, commercial & industrial
Pr: Timothy J Ryan
CFO: Veli Pekka
*Treas: John E Morphis
*VP: Christopher Keays
VP: Keith Meyer
*VP: Jay Miele
*VP: Robert Ward
IT Man: Michael Sestrich
Sls Mgr: Allen Turner
Board of Directors: Karl Hornhofer, Humbert Koefler, Wolfgang Leitner, Eric J Oakes, Tim Ryan

D-U-N-S 11-486-6739 IMP/EXP
ANDROID INDUSTRIES LLC
2155 Executive Hills Dr, Auburn Hills, MI 48326-2943
Tel (248) 454-0500 Founded/Ownrshp 2014
Sales 558.5MM[E] EMP 1,100
SIC 5013 Motor vehicle supplies & new parts
IT Man: Jim Fisher
VP Prd: Pat Frey
Mtls Mgr: George Tuttle
Mfg Mgr: Donald Wine
Opers Mgr: Kevin Foster
Opers Mgr: Brad Rhoades
Plnt Mgr: Lou Fage
Plnt Mgr: Gerard Stanaway
Ql Cn Mgr: Angela Buford
Snr Mgr: Lara Todd

ANDROS FOODS NORTH AMERICA
See BOWMAN ANDROS PRODUCTS LLC

D-U-N-S 80-086-3201 IMP
ANDRX CORP
(Suby of ACTAVIS LLC) ★
4955 Orange Dr, Davie, FL 33314-3902
Tel (954) 585-1400 Founded/Ownrshp 2006
Sales 266.3MM[E] EMP 1,680
SIC 2834 5122 Pharmaceutical preparations; Pharmaceuticals
Sr VP: Thomas R Giordano
*Sr VP: Robert I Goldfarb
*Sr VP: Ian J Watkins
Ex Dir: John Manfredi

D-U-N-S 80-174-9953
ANDRX PHARMACEUTICALS INC
(Suby of ANDRX CORP) ★
4955 Orange Dr, Davie, FL 33314-3902
Tel (954) 581-7500 Founded/Ownrshp 1992
Sales 162.9MM[E] EMP 900
SIC 3826

D-U-N-S 02-844-9445 IMP
ANDWIN CORP
ANDWIN SCIENTIFIC
6636 Variel Ave, Woodland Hills, CA 91303-2808
Tel (818) 999-2828 Founded/Ownrshp 1986
Sales 103.2MM[E] EMP 110[E]
SIC 5113 3842 5199 5087 5047 2835 Industrial & personal service paper; Surgical appliances & supplies; Packaging materials; Janitors' supplies; Hospital equipment & furniture; In vitro & in vivo diagnostic substances
CEO: Natalie Sarraf
*Pr: Abner Levy
VP: Andrew Fox
Genl Mgr: Ryan Smith

ANDWIN SCIENTIFIC
See ANDWIN CORP

ANDY BOY
See DARRIGO BROSCOOF CALIFORNIA

D-U-N-S 13-938-2803
ANDY FRAIN SERVICES INC
761 Shoreline Dr, Aurora, IL 60504-6194
Tel (630) 820-3820 Founded/Ownrshp 1998
Sales 183.8MM[E] EMP 8,500[E]
Accts Steinberg Advisors Ltd Nort
SIC 7381 7363 Protective services, guard; Security guard service; Usher service
Pr: David H Clayton
*VP: Dane Vontobel
Dir Soc: Steve Goodrum
Dir Soc: Jackie Rutkowski
Dir Bus: Chuck Mitman
Dir Sec: William Moore
Rgnl Mgr: Kenneth Jones
Area Mgr: Cody McCollum
Brnch Mgr: Barbarito Sanudo
Off Mgr: Rosie Rivera
Dir IT: Seidel Ed
Board of Directors: Thomas Powers

D-U-N-S 00-628-1919 IMP/EXP
ANDY MARK INC (MO)
18081 Chstrfld Aprt Rd, Chesterfield, MO 63005-1116
Tel (636) 532-4433 Founded/Ownrshp 1957, 2014
Sales 238.5MM[E] EMP 500
SIC 3555 3565 Printing trades machinery; Packaging machinery
CEO: Pj Desai
CFO: Phil Reinkmeyer
VP: Dale Bunnell
VP: Don Hoelscher
VP: John Howard
VP: Roy Webb
Telecom Ex: Tom Schafer
IT Man: Josep Requena
Mfg Dir: Chris Bronikowski
Plnt Mgr: Marty Cozzi
VP Mktg: Joe Spell

D-U-N-S 09-518-4396
ANGEL BROTHERS ENTERPRISES LTD
5210 West Rd, Baytown, TX 77521-9022
Tel (281) 421-5721 Founded/Ownrshp 1972
Sales 141.8MM[E] EMP 475
SIC 1794 1611 Excavation & grading, building construction; General contractor, highway & street construction
Genl Pt: Greg Angel
Pt: Gary Angel

D-U-N-S 13-191-2789
ANGEL BROTHERS INC
5210 West Rd, Baytown, TX 77521-9022
Tel (281) 471-6730 Founded/Ownrshp 1975
Sales 44.9MM[E] EMP 1,000
SIC 1611 Concrete construction: roads, highways, sidewalks, etc.
Pr: Greg Angel
*VP: Glenn Angel

D-U-N-S 07-837-9259
ANGEL HOLDINGS LLC
ANGELO
245 Park Ave, New York, NY 10167-0002
Tel (212) 692-2000 Founded/Ownrshp 2012
Sales 610.4MM[E] EMP 3,000[E]
SIC 6282 Investment advisory service
Prin: Angela Milano

ANGEL MANAGEMENT GROUP
See HAKKASAN HOLDINGS LLC

D-U-N-S 00-629-1694
ANGELICA CORP (MO)
ANGELICA UNIFORM GROUP
(Suby of CLOTHESLINE HOLDINGS INC) ★
1105 Lakewood Pkwy # 210, Alpharetta, GA 30009-7625
Tel (678) 823-4100 Founded/Ownrshp 1878, 2008
Sales 261.9MM[E] EMP 5,500
SIC 7213 5699 5661 Linen supply; Linen supply, clothing; Linen supply, non-clothing; Uniforms; Shoe stores
CEO: David A Van Vliet
COO: Dave Van Vliet
*Treas: John Patridge
Ex VP: Larry Newman
*Sr VP: E Melton Davis
*Sr VP: Jim Ducker
*Sr VP: Twyla Gray
*Sr VP: Richard M Oliva
VP: Robert Coble
VP: Frank Dargavage
VP: Amber Edmondson
*VP: Steve Frey
*VP: Steven L Frey
VP: Leon Johnson
VP: Carol Landry
VP: Alan Wells

D-U-N-S 04-310-6988
ANGELICA TEXTILE SERVICES INC (GA)
(Suby of ANGELICA UNIFORM GROUP) ★
1105 Lakewood Pkwy # 210, Alpharetta, GA 30009-7625
Tel (678) 823-4100 Founded/Ownrshp 1960, 1969
Sales 257.4MM[E] EMP 5,500
SIC 7213 7211 Linen supply; Uniform supply; Power laundries, family & commercial
Pr: David A Van Vliet
*CFO: Lew Belote
Treas: John Partridge
Ex VP: Jim Ducker
Ex VP: Ed Ryan
*Sr VP: Frank Dargavage
*Sr VP: Twyla Gray
*Prin: Steve Frey
Genl Mgr: Jeff Hoffman
*CIO: Richard Fiorillo
IT Man: Merlin Richardson

ANGELICA UNIFORM GROUP
See ANGELICA CORP

D-U-N-S 87-862-3479
ANGELINAS PIZZERIA & PASTA INC
4005 E County Highway 30a, Santa Rosa Beach, FL 32459-6455
Tel (850) 231-2500 Founded/Ownrshp 1993
Sales 24.1MM[E] EMP 1,522
SIC 5812 Pizza restaurants
Pr: Jan Ethrich
*Pr: Carolyn Pallotta

ANGELO
See ANGEL HOLDINGS LLC

ANGELO BROTHERS CO
See WESTINGHOUSE LIGHTING CORP

D-U-N-S 36-291-5118
ANGELO GORDON & CO LP
245 Park Ave Fl 24, New York, NY 10167-0094
Tel (212) 692-2000 Founded/Ownrshp 1988
Sales 4.4MMM[E] EMP 9,583
SIC 6282 Investment advisory service
CEO: John M Angelo
CFO: Andrew Smith
Top Exec: Wilson Leung
Top Exec: Andrew Solomon
VP: Sharone Benezra
VP: Michael Chang
VP: Jason Filiberti
VP: Peter Gingold
VP: Amanda Hughes
VP: Jennifer Keating
VP: Yoon Kim
VP: Nicole Matuszewski
VP: Mary Parrinelli

D-U-N-S 01-689-6532
ANGELO IAFRATE CONSTRUCTION CO
26300 Sherwood Ave, Warren, MI 48091-4168
Tel (586) 756-1070 Founded/Ownrshp 1946
Sales 133.0MM EMP 350
Accts Uhy Llp Farmington Hills Mic
SIC 1623 1794 1611 Sewer line construction; Excavation work; Highway & street paving contractor
Pr: Robert Adcock
Treas: Don Bonaventure
*Treas: Chris Hamrick
*VP: Hal Howlett
*VP: Duane Laurilla
Board of Directors: Angelo Iafrate

D-U-N-S 07-813-7064
ANGELS BASEBALL LP (CA)
LOS ANGELES ANGELS OF ANAHEIM
2000 E Gene Autry Way, Anaheim, CA 92806-6143
Tel (714) 940-2000 Founded/Ownrshp 1996
Sales 55.2MM[E] EMP 1,000
SIC 7941 Baseball club, professional & semi-professional
Genl Pt: Dennis Kuhl
Pt: Bill Beverage
Pt: Molly Jolly
Pt: Richard McClemmy
Pt: Tim Mead
Pt: Tony Reagins
CFO: Andrew Roundtree
Ofcr: Bane Eddie
Ex VP: Robert Manfred
VP: Robert Alvarado
Sls Mgr: Michael Means

D-U-N-S 96-730-0422
▲ ANGIES LIST INC
1030 E Washington St, Indianapolis, IN 46202-3902
Tel (888) 888-5478 Founded/Ownrshp 2001
Sales 315.0MM EMP 1,730[E]
Tkr Sym ANGI Exch NGM
SIC 7311 Advertising agencies
Pr: Scott Durchslag
*Ch Bd: Thomas R Evans
CFO: Thomas R Fox
*Chf Mktg O: Angela R Hicks Bowman
Ex VP: Michael D Rutz
Sr VP: Marla Thompson
VP: Sherri Adams
VP: Anthony Palella
Creative D: Tanja Pohl
Comm Dir: Cheryl Reed
Prgrm Mgr: Jennifer Pike
Board of Directors: George Bell, Mark Britto, Thomas R Evans, Michael S Maurer, David B Mullen, H Eric Semler, Susan E Thronson

D-U-N-S 09-091-0639
▲ ANGIODYNAMICS INC
14 Plaza Dr, Latham, NY 12110-2166
Tel (518) 795-1400 Founded/Ownrshp 1988
Sales 353.8MM EMP 1,300[E]
Tkr Sym ANGO Exch NGS
SIC 3841 Surgical & medical instruments
Pr: James C Clemmer
*Ch Bd: Howard W Donnelly
CFO: Michael C Greiner
Sr VP: Gary Barrett
Sr VP: Chad Campbell
Sr VP: Christopher Crisman
Sr VP: Ben Davis
Sr VP: Barbara Kucharczyk
Sr VP: Richard Stark
Sr VP: Mark Stephens
Sr VP: Stephen A Trowbridge
Board of Directors: David Burgstahler, Jeffrey G Gold, Kevin J Gould, Wesley E Johnson Jr, Steven R Laporte, Dennis S Meteny

D-U-N-S 13-149-4846
ANGIOTECH PHARMACEUTICALS (US) INC
ROUNDTABLE HP
241 W Palatine Rd, Wheeling, IL 60090-5824
Tel (847) 637-3333 Founded/Ownrshp 2006
Sales NA EMP 1,430
SIC 3841 3541 3842 8731

D-U-N-S 16-688-7161
ANGLO-SUISSE OFFSHORE PARTNERS LLC
919 Milam St Ste 2300, Houston, TX 77002-5418
Tel (713) 358-9763 Founded/Ownrshp 2004
Sales 84.7MM[E] EMP 24
SIC 1311

D-U-N-S 62-212-3735 IMP/EXP
ANGSTROM GRAPHICS INC
4437 E 49th St, Cleveland, OH 44125-1005
Tel (216) 271-5300 Founded/Ownrshp 1989
Sales 281.1MM[E] EMP 1,015
SIC 2721 2754 2752 Magazines: publishing & printing; Commercial printing, gravure; Commercial printing, lithographic
CEO: Wayne R Angstrom
*CFO: Rachel Malakoff
Ex VP: Chip Owen
VP: Marlene Kruse
VP: Edward Lipp
Genl Mgr: John Gorman
CTO: Alejandro Rivera
Software D: Joey Pongallo
Opers Mgr: Jaime Caraballo
VP Sls: Rhonda Perry

D-U-N-S 03-460-1096 IMP/EXP
ANGUS CHEMICAL CO (DE)
DOW
(Suby of GOLDEN GATE CAPITAL LP) ★
1500 E Lake Cook Rd, Buffalo Grove, IL 60089-6556
Tel (847) 215-8600 Founded/Ownrshp 1982, 2015
Sales 188.3MM[E] EMP 500
SIC 2869 2899

ANGUS-PALM
See WORTHINGTON INDUSTRIES ENGINEERED CABS INC

D-U-N-S 13-942-2760
ANHEUSER BUSCH INVESTMENT
(Suby of ANHEUSER-BUSCH COMPANIES LLC) ★
1 Busch Pl, Saint Louis, MO 63118-1852
Tel (314) 577-2000 Founded/Ownrshp 1984
Sales 85.3MM[E] EMP 1,000
SIC 2082 Beer (alcoholic beverage)
Ch Bd: Patrick T Stokes
*Pr: Ken Reiter
Bd of Dir: Larry Hoffman
Bd of Dir: Charles Klauke
Exec: Tom Reidarson
Prgrm Mgr: Traci Batson
CTO: Michael Starkweather
IT Man: Preston Page
IT Man: Chris Stahlschmidt
IT Man: Jerry Willick
Netwrk Mgr: Lew Keathley

ANHEUSER-BUSCH
See BI WAREHOUSING INC

D-U-N-S 09-863-0254 IMP
ANHEUSER-BUSCH COMPANIES LLC
1 Busch Pl, Saint Louis, MO 63118-1852
Tel (314) 632-6777 Founded/Ownrshp 2008
Sales 19.6MMM[E] EMP 30,236
SIC 2082 3411 7996 Beer (alcoholic beverage); Near beer; Aluminum cans; Beer cans, metal; Beverage cans, metal: except beer; Theme park, amusement
Pr: August A Busch IV
Ch Bd: Patrick T Stokes
CEO: Carlos Brito
COO: Edward OH
CFO: W Randolph Baker
Ex VP: Philip Singleton
VP: Mark Broughton
VP: Sanjiv Chhatwal
VP: Blaise D'Sylva
VP: Pablo Gonzalez
VP: Donald Hartmann
VP: Lee Keathley
VP: John F Kelly
VP: Peter J Kraemer
VP: Paula Lindenberg
VP: Fued Sadala
VP: Thomas W Santel
VP: Darren Zobrist
Exec: Cheryl Cavins

D-U-N-S 14-976-0852
ANHEUSER-BUSCH INTERNATIONAL INC
(Suby of ANHEUSER-BUSCH COMPANIES LLC) ★
1 Busch Pl, Saint Louis, MO 63118-1852
Tel (314) 577-2000 Founded/Ownrshp 1980
Sales 915.4MM[E] EMP 1,348
SIC 5181 Beer & ale
Pr: Thomas W Santel
*Ch Bd: Patrick T Stokes
*VP: Joseph P Castellano
VP: John T Farrell

D-U-N-S 00-628-8799 IMP/EXP
ANHEUSER-BUSCH LLC
(Suby of ANHEUSER-BUSCH COMPANIES LLC) ★
1 Busch Pl, Saint Louis, MO 63118-1852
Tel (314) 632-6777 Founded/Ownrshp 1979
Sales 17.9MMM[E] EMP 15,000
SIC 5181 2082 Beer & other fermented malt liquors; Beer (alcoholic beverage); Near beer
Pr: Luiz Fernando Edmond
*Ch Bd: August A Busch III
Pr: Sue Becker
Pr: Sherry Brown
*Pr: Patrick T Stokes
*VP: James G Brickey
*VP: Pablo Gonzalez
*VP: Joao Guerra
*VP: James F Hoffmeister
*VP: Lee Keathley
Opers Mgr: Mark Benoit

ANICO
See AMERICAN NATIONAL INSURANCE CO INC

ANICO
See MASTERS INSURANCE AGENCY INC

D-U-N-S 80-761-3393 IMP
▲ ANIKA THERAPEUTICS INC
32 Wiggins Ave, Bedford, MA 01730-2315
Tel (781) 457-9000 Founded/Ownrshp 1983
Sales 93.0MM EMP 107[E]
Tkr Sym ANIK Exch NGS
SIC 2836 Biological products, except diagnostic
Pr: Charles H Sherwood
COO: Dana M Alexander
CFO: Sylvia Cheung
Chf Cred: Richard Hague
Chf Mktg O: Stephen R Mascioli
Ofcr: Edward Ahn
VP: Steven Cyr
Board of Directors: Joseph L Bower, Raymond J Land, Glenn R Larsen, Jeffery S Thompson, Steven E Wheeler

D-U-N-S 09-191-7211 IMP/EXP
■ ANIMAL HEALTH INTERNATIONAL INC
LEXTRON ANIMAL HEALTH
(Suby of PATTERSON COMPANIES INC) ★
822 7th St Ste 740, Greeley, CO 80631-3943
Tel (970) 353-2600 Founded/Ownrshp 1967
Sales 701.1MM[E] EMP 1,389
SIC 5122 5047 5999 5191 5083 5154

ANIMAL PLANT HLTH INSPTN SERVI
See USDA APHIS VETERINARY

D-U-N-S 18-056-9980 IMP
ANIMAL SUPPLY CO LLC
600 Las Colinas Blvd E, Irving, TX 75039-5616
Tel (972) 616-9600 Founded/Ownrshp 1987
Sales 242.0MM[E] EMP 461
SIC 5199

D-U-N-S 04-758-3851 IMP/EXP

■ ANIXTER INC
(*Subyof* ANIXTER INTERNATIONAL INC) ★
2301 Patriot Blvd, Glenview, IL 60026-8020
Tel (224) 521-8000 *Founded/Ownrshp* 1967
Sales 5.8MMM^E *EMP* 8,200
SIC 5063 4899 Electrical apparatus & equipment; Wire & cable; Control & signal wire & cable, including coaxial; Hanging & fastening devices, electrical; Data communication services
CEO: Robert J Eck
**Treas:* Dave Johnson
**Ex VP:* Giulio Berardesca
**Ex VP:* Justin C Choi
**Ex VP:* Ian R Clarke
**Ex VP:* Theodore A Dosch
**Ex VP:* William A Galvin
Ex VP: Eric Greenberg
**Ex VP:* Rodney A Smith
VP: Terry Faber
VP: Joe Healy

D-U-N-S 82-893-0375

ANIXTER INC
2301 Patriot Blvd, Glenview, IL 60026-8020
Tel (800) 323-8167 *Founded/Ownrshp* 1967
Sales 104.2MM^E *EMP* 198^E
SIC 3641

D-U-N-S 04-651-6753

▲ ANIXTER INTERNATIONAL INC
2301 Patriot Blvd, Glenview, IL 60026-8020
Tel (224) 521-8000 *Founded/Ownrshp* 1957
Sales 6.1MMM *EMP* 8,700
Accts Ernst & Young Llp Chicago Il
Tkr Sym AXE *Exch* NYS
SIC 5063 5085 Wire & cable; Electronic wire & cable; Power wire & cable; Telephone & telegraph wire & cable; Fasteners, industrial: nuts, bolts, screws, etc.
Pr: Robert J Eck
**Ch Bd:* Samuel Zell
Pr: Daisy Santos
CFO: Theodore A Dosch
Ex VP: Justin C Choi
Ex VP: Scott Ramsbottom
Ex VP: William Standish
Sr VP: Terrance A Faber
Sr VP: Ilaria Mocciaro
VP: Steven Dean
VP: Dawn Galluzzi
VP: Pat Kelliher
VP: Delroy Rhooms
Board of Directors: Stuart M Sloan, Lord James Blyth, Frederic F Brace, Linda A Walker Bynoe, Robert W Grubbs, F Philip Handy, Melvyn N Klein, George Munoz, Scott R Peppet, Valerie L Sheppard

D-U-N-S 79-204-7750

ANIXTER POWER SOLUTIONS LLC
501 W Church St Ste 100, Orlando, FL 32805-2270
Tel (407) 841-4755 *Founded/Ownrshp* 2015
Sales 1.2MMM^E *EMP* 846
SIC 5063

D-U-N-S 07-349-2415

ANKENY COMMUNITY SCHOOLS INC
ANKENY SCHLS-DMNSTRTION OFFCES
306 Sw School St, Ankeny, IA 50023-3063
Tel (515) 965-9600 *Founded/Ownrshp* 1902
Sales 127.1MM *EMP* 1,457
Accts Rsm Us Llp Des Moines Iowa
SIC 8211 Public elementary & secondary schools
CFO: Dr Craig Hansel
Dir Sec: Chad Bentzinger
MIS Dir: Brad B Johnson
Pr Dir: Samantha Kampman
Teacher Pr: Jenifer Owenson
Psych: Christine Thomson
HC Dir: Lisa Glenn

ANKENY SCHLS-DMNSTRTION OFFCES
See ANKENY COMMUNITY SCHOOLS INC

D-U-N-S 07-370-0643

ANMED HEALTH
800 Nh Fant St, Anderson, SC 29621
Tel (864) 261-1000 *Founded/Ownrshp* 1906
Sales 590.5MM *EMP* 2,600
SIC 8062 8011 General medical & surgical hospitals; General & family practice, physician/surgeon
Pr: John A Miller Jr
Dir Risk M: Tim Arellano
Nurse Mgr: John Williamson
Surgeon: Felice Moody
Obsttrcn: Mark Lacy
Obsttrcn: John Nordeen
Doctor: Timothy Malinowski

D-U-N-S 62-273-7005

ANMED HEALTH RESOURCES INC
800 N Fant St, Anderson, SC 29621-5708
Tel (864) 512-1000 *Founded/Ownrshp* 1986
Sales 98.1MM^E *EMP* 3,000
Accts Ernst & Young Llp Greenville
SIC 8062 General medical & surgical hospitals
Pr: John Miller
CFO: Jerry Parish
Nurse Mgr: Chuck Horton

D-U-N-S 07-443-8755

ANN & ROBERT H LURIE CHILDRENS HOSPITAL OF CHICAGO
225 E Chicago Ave, Chicago, IL 60611-2991
Tel (312) 227-7132 *Founded/Ownrshp* 1882
Sales 625.5MM *EMP* 2,800
SIC 8011 8069 Medical centers; Children's hospital
Pr: Patrick M Magoon
**CFO:* Paula Noble
Treas: Jessica Strausbaugh
Top Exec: Marisa S Klein-Gitelman
Sr VP: Susan H Gordon
Div/Sub He: Leon G Epstein
Surgeon: Michelle Sagan
Surgeon: Riccardo Superina
Doctor: Mark D Adler
Doctor: Risa A Alperin
Doctor: Katherine A Barsness

ANN ARBOR NEUROLOGY
See IHA HEALTH SERVICES CORP

ANN ARBOR PUBLIC SCHOOLS
See PUBLIC SCHOOLS OF CITY ANN ARBOR

D-U-N-S 19-920-2664

■ ANN INC
LOFT
(*Subyof* ASCENA RETAIL GROUP INC) ★
7 Times Sq Bsmt Sb4, New York, NY 10036-6548
Tel (212) 541-3300 *Founded/Ownrshp* 2015
Sales 2.8MMM^E *EMP* 19,800^E
SIC 5621 5632 5661 Ready-to-wear apparel, women's; Women's sportswear; Dress shops; Apparel accessories; Blouses; Costume jewelry; Handbags; Women's shoes
CEO: Katherine L Krill
**Pr:* Gary Muto
**COO:* Michael J Nicholson
**Ex VP:* Pattie Friedman
**Ex VP:* Muriel Gonzalez
**Ex VP:* Alan Hirota
Ex VP: Mark Morrison
**Ex VP:* Katherine H Ramundo
Sr VP: Liisa P Fiedelholtz
Sr VP: George Sappenfield
VP: Denise Adams
VP: Sherri Barnes
VP: Jeannette Ferran-Astorga
VP: Liisa Fiedelholtz
**VP:* Catherine Fisher
VP: Eric Germa
VP: Wade Haddad
VP: Rose Hamilton
VP: Michelle Horowitz
VP: Richard Jojo
VP: Robert Lepere

D-U-N-S 03-081-9890

ANNA JAQUES HOSPITAL
SEACOAST REGIONAL
25 Highland Ave, Newburyport, MA 01950-3894
Tel (978) 463-1000 *Founded/Ownrshp* 1884
Sales 116.6MM *EMP* 1,211
SIC 8062 General medical & surgical hospitals
Pr: Saira Naseer
Dir Vol: Cheryl Satryb
**Treas:* Mark L Goldstein
Trst: Colleen Dolan
Trst: Julie Geary
Trst: Tamara Hickey
Trst: Allison Hurteau
Trst: Tracy Martin
VP: Sarah Gnerre
VP: Gary Lee
**VP:* David Swierzewski
Dir Inf Cn: Patricia Lawrence
Dir Rx: Jeff Gwinn

ANNALLECT GROUP
See OMNICOM MEDIA GROUP

D-U-N-S 93-928-6662

▲ ANNALY CAPITAL MANAGEMENT INC
1211 Ave Of The Americas, New York, NY 10036-8701
Tel (212) 696-0100 *Founded/Ownrshp* 1997
Sales 2.1MMM *EMP* 149^E
Tkr Sym NLY *Exch* NYS
SIC 6798 Real estate investment trusts; Mortgage investment trusts
Pr: Kevin G Keyes
**Ch Bd:* Wellington J Denahan
CFO: Kathryn Fagan
CFO: Glenn A Votek
VP: Robert Calhoun
VP: Gary Gordon
VP: Michael Mulroe
VP: Nancy Murtha
VP: Eric Szabo
CIO: David L Finkelstein
Genl Couns: Melissa Shaw
Board of Directors: Francine J Bovich, Kevin P Brady, Jonathan D Green, Michael Haylon, E Wayne Nordberg, John H Schaefer, Donnell A Segalas

ANNAPOLIS AREA LIBRARY
See COUNTY OF ANNE ARUNDEL

ANNAS LINENS
See ANNAS LINENS INC

D-U-N-S 18-216-3592 IMP/EXP

ANNAS LINENS INC
ANNAS LINENS
3550 Hyland Ave, Costa Mesa, CA 92626-1438
Tel (714) 850-0504 *Founded/Ownrshp* 1987
Sales 457.8MM^E *EMP* 2,500
SIC 5719 5714 5023

D-U-N-S 06-939-8444

ANNE ARUNDEL COMMUNITY COLLEGE
AACC
101 College Pkwy, Arnold, MD 21012-1895
Tel (410) 777-2222 *Founded/Ownrshp* 1967
Sales 69.5MM *EMP* 1,245
Accts Bdo Usa Llp Mclean Va
SIC 8222 Community college
Pr: Dawn Lindsey
**V Ch Bd:* Diane R Dixon- Proctor
Ofcr: Kelly Koermer
Ex Dir: Dan Baum
Ex Dir: Charlene Templeton
Genl Mgr: Wanda Grace
Off Mgr: Gina Macklin
IT Man: Cathy Bosse
Netwrk Mgr: Nancy L Jones
Nrsg Dir: Beth A Batturs

D-U-N-S 07-492-6064

ANNE ARUNDEL COUNTY BOARD OF EDUCATION
2644 Riva Rd, Annapolis, MD 21401-7427
Tel (410) 222-5000 *Founded/Ownrshp* 1865
Sales 1.1MMM *EMP* 118^E
Accts Cliftonlarsonallen Llp Baltim
SIC 8211 School board
Pr: Stacy Korbelak

D-U-N-S 07-847-0617

ANNE ARUNDEL COUNTY PUBLIC SCHOOLS
AACPS
2644 Riva Rd, Annapolis, MD 21401-7427
Tel (410) 222-5000 *Founded/Ownrshp* 2012
Sales 210.2MM^E *EMP* 10,112^E
SIC 8211 Public elementary & secondary schools
Dir Sec: Doyle Batten
Dir Sec: Alice Swift
IT Man: Colette Preis
Info Man: Mark Thieme
Pr Dir: Bob Mosier
Teacher Pr: Florence Bozzella
Teacher Pr: William Goodman
HC Dir: Christiana Walsh
Snr Mgr: David Catrel
Snr Mgr: Bill Goodman

D-U-N-S 06-938-3289

ANNE ARUNDEL MEDICAL CENTER INC
(*Subyof* ANNE ARUNDEL MEDICAL CENTER INC) ★
2001 Medical Pkwy, Annapolis, MD 21401-3773
Tel (443) 481-1000 *Founded/Ownrshp* 1902, 1989
Sales 492.1MM *EMP* 1,890
Accts Sc&H Tax & Advisory Services L
SIC 8062 General medical & surgical hospitals
Ch Bd: Florence B Kurdle
**Pr:* Martin L Doordan
COO: Victoria Bayle
**CFO:* Bob Reilly
**Treas:* John M Suit II
**V Ch Bd:* James F McEncaney Jr
Trst: Robert E Henel
**Sr VP:* Joseph D Moser MD
**VP:* Stephen L Clarke
**VP:* Bill Hughes
**VP:* Shirley J Knelly
Dir Rad: Riccardo Pallia

D-U-N-S 61-524-1510

ANNE ARUNDEL MEDICAL CENTER INC
2001 Medical Pkwy, Annapolis, MD 21401-3773
Tel (443) 481-1000 *Founded/Ownrshp* 1989
Sales 498.5MM *EMP* 4,000
SIC 8062 8093 6732 General medical & surgical hospitals; Specialty outpatient clinics; Charitable trust management
CEO: Victoria W Bayless
**CFO:* Bob Reilly
Ofcr: Caroline Rader
**VP:* Stephen L Clarke
Dir Lab: Janet C Baxter
MIS Dir: Andy Cole
Dir IT: Chuck Daniel
Dir IT: Joan Harris
IT Man: Craig Schenkel
Netwrk Eng: Pete Nevins
Plnt Mgr: Inar Maharaj

D-U-N-S 15-511-9811

ANNETT HOLDINGS INC
TMC TRANSPORTATION
6115 Leland Ave, Des Moines, IA 50321-9624
Tel (515) 287-6380 *Founded/Ownrshp* 1972
Sales 676.2MM^E *EMP* 2,750
SIC 4213 Building materials transport; Heavy machinery transport
Ch Bd: Harrold W Annett
**Pr:* Timothy W Annett
**CFO:* Larry Clark
Sr Cor Off: Annett Harrold
Ex VP: Scott Crouse
**Ex VP:* Travis Johnson
Ex VP: Glen McCravy
Ex VP: Rod Simon
VP: Duane Boswell
VP: Joe Brannen
VP: Eric Fish
VP: Tiffany Hoeck
VP: Jeff Wisgerhof
VP Bus Dev: Jeff Floyd

D-U-N-S 15-117-9694

ANNIE E CASEY FOUNDATION INC
CASEY FAMILY SERVICES
701 Saint Paul St, Baltimore, MD 21202-2311
Tel (410) 547-6600 *Founded/Ownrshp* 1978
Sales 266.5MM *EMP* 360
SIC 8322 8361 Child related social services; Group foster home
Pr: Patrick McCarthy
Bd of Dir: Calvin E Tyler
Sr VP: Ralph Smith
VP: Lisa Hamilton
VP: Kenneth M Jones II
VP: Burt Sonenstein
Mng Dir: Henrig Dennig
Snr Mgr: Rafael Lopez

ANNIE MAC HOME MORTGAGE
See AMERICAN NEIGHBOURHOOD MORTGAGE ACCEPTANCE CO LLC

ANNIE PENN HOSPITAL
See MOSES H CONE MEMORIAL HOSPITAL

D-U-N-S 00-218-6666 IMP/EXP

ANNIN & CO
ANNIN FLAG MAKERS
105 Eisenhower Pkwy # 203, Roseland, NJ 07068-1640
Tel (973) 228-9400 *Founded/Ownrshp* 1847, 1901
Sales 163.8MM^E *EMP* 500
SIC 2399 Flags, fabric; Banners, made from fabric; Pennants
CEO: Carter Beard
**Pr:* Joseph T Lapaglia
CFO: Padi Benzing
**Ex VP:* Lindley Scarlett
VP: Joe Brennan
VP: Robert Caggiano
VP: Mary Repke
**VP:* Sandra Van Lieu
VP Opers: Rich Caramanga
Prd Mgr: Joseph Douglass
VP Sls: Randy Beard

ANNIN FLAG MAKERS
See ANNIN & CO

D-U-N-S 10-694-3863 IMP

ANNING-JOHNSON CO
(*Subyof* ANSON INDUSTRIES INC) ★
1959 Anson Dr, Melrose Park, IL 60160-1088
Tel (708) 681-1300 *Founded/Ownrshp* 1940
Sales 334.0MM *EMP* 1,200
SIC 1742 1752 1799 1761 Acoustical & ceiling work; Drywall; Floor laying & floor work; Fireproofing buildings; Siding contractor; Roofing contractor
CEO: John Andrzejewski
**Pr:* L J Domino
COO: Jason Gran
CFO: David Grueggen
**VP:* Kathy Comaska
VP: B E Morton
Creative D: Tom Barnes
Off Mgr: Sandra Hunt
IT Man: Zack Frangiadakis
Sls Mgr: John Stralka

D-U-N-S 04-053-4570 IMP/EXP

■ ANNS HOUSE OF NUTS INC
(*Subyof* TREEHOUSE FOODS INC) ★
380 Sint Pter St Ste 1000, Saint Paul, MN 55102
Tel (651) 348-4100 *Founded/Ownrshp* 1987
Sales 271.8MM^E *EMP* 500
SIC 2068 2064

D-U-N-S 17-373-7628

■ ANNTAYLOR INC
(*Subyof* LOFT) ★
7 Times Sq, New York, NY 10036-6524
Tel (212) 541-3300 *Founded/Ownrshp* 1989
Sales 695.6MM^E *EMP* 6,300
SIC 5621 5632 5661 Ready-to-wear apparel, women's; Women's sportswear; Dress shops; Apparel accessories; Blouses; Costume jewelry; Handbags; Women's shoes
Ch Bd: Kay Krill
**CFO:* Mike Nicholson
**Ex VP:* Barbara K Eisenberg
**VP:* Dominick J Reis

D-U-N-S 61-843-7011

■ ANNTAYLOR RETAIL INC
(*Subyof* ANNTAYLOR INC) ★
7 Times Sq, New York, NY 10036-6524
Tel (212) 541-3300 *Founded/Ownrshp* 2012
Sales 662.0MM^E *EMP* 6,299^E
SIC 5621 5632 5661 Ready-to-wear apparel, women's; Women's sportswear; Dress shops; Apparel accessories; Blouses; Costume jewelry; Handbags; Women's shoes
Ch Bd: Kay Krill

D-U-N-S 08-025-4824

ANOKA-HENNEPIN SCHOOL DIST NO 11
2727 N Ferry St, Anoka, MN 55303-1650
Tel (763) 506-1000 *Founded/Ownrshp* 1952
Sales 289.4MM^E *EMP* 6,100
SIC 8211 Public elementary school; Public junior high school; Public senior high school; Public combined elementary & secondary school
Ch: Tom Heidemann
**CFO:* Michelle Vargas
VP: Georgia Kedrowski

D-U-N-S 06-906-7932 IMP/EXP

ANOMATIC CORP (OH)
(*Subyof* THYSSEN'SCHE HANDELSGESELLSCHAFT MIT BESCHRANKTER HAFTUNG)
1650 Tamarack Rd, Newark, OH 43055-1359
Tel (740) 522-2203 *Founded/Ownrshp* 1974, 2016
Sales 111.7MM^E *EMP* 500^E
SIC 3471 3469 2396 Anodizing (plating) of metals or formed products; Metal stampings; Automotive & apparel trimmings
Pr: William B Rusch
Pr: Pete McCallin
COO: Greg Boatwright
**Treas:* Scott L Rusch
Ex VP: Don Perry
VP: Peter McCallin
VP: Josh Orlandi
IT Man: Matthew Offers
VP Mfg: Chris Wilson
Plnt Mgr: Casey Meyer
Snr Mgr: Joel Brown

D-U-N-S 00-695-8581 IMP/EXP

■ ANR PIPELINE CO (DE)
(*Subyof* AMERICAN NATURAL RESOURCES CO) ★
700 Louisiana St Ste 700, Houston, TX 77002-2873
Tel (832) 320-2000 *Founded/Ownrshp* 1945
Sales 627.9MM^E *EMP* 1,000
SIC 4922 Natural gas transmission; Pipelines, natural gas; Storage, natural gas
Pr: Lee Hobbs
**VP:* Gary C Charette
**VP:* Dean Patry
IT Man: Kay Dennison

ANRITSU COMPANY
See ANRITSU US HOLDING INC

D-U-N-S 00-911-5080 IMP

ANRITSU CO
(*Subyof* ANRITSU CO) ★
490 Jarvis Dr, Morgan Hill, CA 95037-2834
Tel (408) 201-1551 *Founded/Ownrshp* 1990
Sales 228.6MM *EMP* 600
SIC 5065 3825 3663 Electronic parts & equipment; Test equipment for electronic & electric measurement; Radio & TV communications equipment
Pr: Hirokazu Hashimoto
Sr Cor Off: Andrea Culler
Bd of Dir: Takanori Sumi
Ex VP: Kenji Tanaka
Sr VP: Toshihiko Takahashi
VP: Pete Alexander
VP: Peter Chalfant
VP: Wade Hulon
VP: Paul Mayer
VP: Junkichi Shirono
VP: Jessica Willmott

D-U-N-S 13-506-0478
ANRITSU US HOLDING INC
ANRITSU COMPANY
(Suby of ANRITSU CORPORATION)
490 Jarvis Dr, Morgan Hill, CA 95037-2834
Tel (408) 778-2000 Founded/Ownrshp 1990
Sales 323.5MM EMP 800
Accts Kpmg Llp Mountain View Ca
SIC 3825 3663 5065 Test equipment for electronic & electric measurement; Radio & TV communications equipment; Electronic parts & equipment
Pr: Wade Hulon

D-U-N-S 96-195-3304 IMP
ANS HOLDINGS INC
210 S Beck Ave, Chandler, AZ 85226-3311
Tel (480) 966-9630 Founded/Ownrshp 1996
Sales 155.0MM^E EMP 600^E
SIC 2834 Vitamin preparations
Pr: Jonathan Pinkus

ANS-PLANO-MANUFACTURING
See ADVANCED NEUROMODULATION SYSTEMS INC

D-U-N-S 80-387-6895
ANSA MCAL (US) INC
(Suby of ANSA MCAL LIMITED)
11403 Nw 39th St, Doral, FL 33178-4843
Tel (305) 599-8766 Founded/Ownrshp 2010
Sales 102.6MM^E EMP 25^E
Accts De La Hoz Perez & Barbeito C
SIC 7389 4731 Purchasing service; Freight forwarding
Pr: Wendell Beckels
*CFO: Veronica McGrane
CFO: Sean Ramnarine
Ex Dir: Philip Marshall
Genl Mgr: Adam Sabga

D-U-N-S 82-962-1130
ANSA MCAL TRADING INC
(Suby of ANSA MCAL (US) INC) ★
11403 Nw 39th St, Doral, FL 33178-4843
Tel (305) 599-8766 Founded/Ownrshp 2007
Sales 100.0MM EMP 22
SIC 8741 5084 5085 4731 Management services; Industrial machinery & equipment; Industrial supplies; Freight forwarding
Ch Bd: Andrew Sabga
Pr: Wendell Backles

D-U-N-S 19-201-3159 IMP/EXP
ANSALDO STS USA INC
(Suby of ANSALDO STS SPA)
1000 Technology Dr, Pittsburgh, PA 15219-3120
Tel (412) 688-2400 Founded/Ownrshp 1996
Sales 234.1MM^E EMP 700
Accts Pricewaterhousecoopers Llp Pi
SIC 3669 Railroad signaling devices, electric
Pr: Marco Fumagalli
Treas: Bradley A Pearce
*Treas: Joseph R Pozza
Ofcr: Sergio De Luca
Exec: Melissa Emrick
IT Man: Aaron Lapkis
Sftwr Eng: Ron Davis
Sftwr Eng: Ken Heburn
Sftwr Eng: Diana Rayzberg
VP Mfg: Joseph D Eiseman
Sfty Mgr: Pasquale Di Matteo

D-U-N-S 07-912-5862
ANSAR GALLERY (CA)
(Suby of ANSAR MALL)
2505 El Camino Rd, Tustin, CA 92782
Tel (949) 220-0000 Founded/Ownrshp 2013
Sales 110.6MM^E EMP 200
SIC 5141 Groceries, general line
*Pr: Hussein Saadat
Board of Directors: Ali Akbar Ferozesh, Ali Fouroozesh

D-U-N-S 80-433-6675
ANSARA RESTAURANT GROUP INC
RED ROBIN
23925 Industrial Park Dr, Farmington Hills, MI 48335-2862
Tel (248) 848-9099 Founded/Ownrshp 1961
Sales 76.8MM^E EMP 2,100
SIC 5812 5813 Restaurant, family: chain; Bars & lounges
Pr: Victor L Ansara
*Treas: Andrew Ansara Jr
*VP: Louis Ansara

D-U-N-S 87-483-1126
ANSCHUTZ CORP
555 17th St Ste 2400, Denver, CO 80202-3987
Tel (303) 298-1000 Founded/Ownrshp 1991
Sales 110.6MM^E EMP 35,000
SIC 2711 1382 7941 Newspapers; Oil & gas exploration services; Sports clubs, managers & promoters
CEO: Phillip Anschutz
Pr: Cannon Y Harvey
CFO: Wayne Barnes
Treas: Tom Kundert
Ex VP: Craig Slater
VP: Jim Bain
VP: Bruce Black
VP: Scott Carpenter
VP: Randy Fullerton
VP: Richard Jones
VP: Roxane Perruso
VP: Phyllis Spear
VP: Monica Stoeber
Dir Risk M: Linnore Gonzales

D-U-N-S 78-501-5376
ANSCHUTZ FILM GROUP
(Suby of ANSCHUTZ CORP) ★
1888 Century Park E # 1400, Los Angeles, CA 90067-1718
Tel (310) 887-1000 Founded/Ownrshp 2004
Sales 4.9MM^E EMP 5,002^E
SIC 1742

D-U-N-S 09-615-9371 IMP
■ ANSCO & ASSOCIATES LLC
(Suby of DYCOM INDUSTRIES INC) ★
736 Park North Blvd, Clarkston, GA 30021-1901
Tel (404) 508-5700 Founded/Ownrshp 1976, 1990
Sales 332.1MM^E EMP 1,115
SIC 1623 Telephone & communication line construction
Pr: George Summers
VP: Michael S Cassidy
VP: Ellis Mannis
VP: Hayden Saling

D-U-N-S 12-052-2524 IMP/EXP
ANSELL HEALTHCARE PRODUCTS LLC
(Suby of PACIFIC DUNLOP HOLDINGS (USA) LLC) ★
111 Wood Ave S Ste 210, Iselin, NJ 08830-2700
Tel (732) 345-5400 Founded/Ownrshp 1981
Sales 84.1MM^E EMP 1,900
SIC 3069 3842 2822 2326 Balloons, advertising & toy: rubber; Birth control devices, rubber; Finger cots, rubber; Surgical appliances & supplies; Synthetic rubber; Men's & boys' work clothing
CEO: Douglas Tough
*CFO: Rustom Jilla
*Ch: Glenn L L Barnes
*Sr VP: William Reilly Jr
VP: Dave Harrington
VP: Fred Marx
Assoc Dir: Tom Paolella
Assoc Dir: Bala Srinivas
Genl Mgr: Thomas Draskovics
IT Man: Scott Johnson
Software D: Mike Miedona

D-U-N-S 60-343-2162 IMP/EXP
ANSELL PROTECTIVE PRODUCTS LLC
(Suby of PACIFIC DUNLOP HOLDINGS (USA) LLC) ★
111 Wood Ave S Ste 210, Iselin, NJ 08830-2700
Tel (732) 345-5400 Founded/Ownrshp 1989
Sales 2.1MM^E EMP 1,900
SIC 3842 3069 Gloves, safety; Rubber coated fabrics & clothing; Aprons, vulcanized rubbed or rubberized fabric
Pr: Douglas Tough
*CFO: Rustom Jilla
*Sr VP: William Reed
*Sr VP: William Reilly Jr
VP: Angie Phillips
Sales Exec: Omar Shareef
Sls Dir: Raymond Morris
Sls Mgr: Jeff Dooley
Sls Mgr: Jim McBride
Sls Mgr: Bryan Solesha
Snr Mgr: Jason Kokoszka

D-U-N-S 11-211-8398 IMP
ANSEN CORP
100 Chimney Point Dr, Ogdensburg, NY 13669-2206
Tel (315) 393-3573 Founded/Ownrshp 2013
Sales 87.8MM^E EMP 351
SIC 3672 Printed circuit boards
CEO: James Kingman
*Pr: Jerry W Slusser
*Sec: Kenneth Emter

D-U-N-S 07-199-0378
ANSIRA PARTNERS INC
2300 Locust St, Saint Louis, MO 63103-1512
Tel (314) 783-2300 Founded/Ownrshp 2005
Sales 91.4MM^E EMP 296
SIC 7389 7331 Press clipping service; Direct mail advertising services
Pr: Mark Mantovani
Assoc VP: Tim St Clair
*Ex VP: Jim Badum
*Ex VP: Ernie Capobianco
*Ex VP: Marian Leonard
*Ex VP: Tom Millweard
*Ex VP: Gary Weller
Sr VP: Mary Jacoby
Sr VP: Ray Rosenbaum
Sr VP: Julia Thuman
Sr VP: Gary L Weller
VP: Andy Arnold
VP: Peggie Bayliss
VP: Heidi Brooks
VP: Logan Flatt
VP: Kay Klos
VP: Sam Monica
VP: Kelly J Sands
VP: John Traina
VP: Mary Wiesehan
VP: Jeff Wingbermuehle

D-U-N-S 00-693-4640
ANSON INDUSTRIES INC
1959 Anson Dr, Melrose Park, IL 60160-1018
Tel (708) 681-1300 Founded/Ownrshp 1940
Sales 386.4MM EMP 1,300
SIC 1742 1752 1761 1799

D-U-N-S 88-323-5913
ANSWER GROUP INC
TAG
7562 Southgate Blvd, North Lauderdale, FL 33068-1362
Tel (954) 720-4002 Founded/Ownrshp 1994
Sales 113.9MM^E EMP 3,200
SIC 7371 8748

D-U-N-S 06-374-7653
▲ ANSYS INC
2600 Ansys Dr, Canonsburg, PA 15317-0404
Tel (724) 746-3304 Founded/Ownrshp 1970
Sales 942.7MM EMP 2,800^E
Accts Deloitte & Touche Llp Pittsb
Tkr Sym ANSS Exch NGS
SIC 7372 Prepackaged software
Pr: James E Cashman III
*Ch Bd: Ronald W Hovsepian
CFO: Maria T Shields
Treas: Kristi Fenner
VP: Eric Bienvenu
VP: Vinay Carpenter
VP: Dipankar Choudhury
VP: Michael Engelman
VP: John Lee
VP: Rick Mahoney
VP: Wade Smith
Board of Directors: Guy E Dubois, William R McDermott, Bradford C Morley, Barbara V Scherer, Michael C Thurk, Patrick J Zilvitis

D-U-N-S 05-056-3832
ANTARCTIC MECHANICAL SERVICES INC
PMT
140 Tower Dr, Burr Ridge, IL 60527-5784
Tel (630) 887-7700 Founded/Ownrshp 1982
Sales 120.8MM^E EMP 300
SIC 1711 1731 Warm air heating & air conditioning contractor; Process piping contractor; Refrigeration contractor; Ventilation & duct work contractor; Electrical work
Pr: John Berzanskis
*VP: Krista Bulow
*VP: Bill Montgomery Pe
VP: Bill Montgomery
VP: Dan Panice
*VP: Michael Roberts
*VP: Richard Watters
Off Mgr: George Thomas
Dir IT: Robert Dobbins

ANTEA GROUP
See ANTEA USA INC

D-U-N-S 15-758-6827
ANTEA USA INC
ANTEA GROUP
(Suby of ORANJEWOUD N.V.)
5910 Rice Creek Pkwy, Saint Paul, MN 55126-5025
Tel (651) 639-9449 Founded/Ownrshp 2008
Sales 129.2MM^E EMP 456
Accts Stirtz Bernards Boyden Surd
SIC 8748 Environmental consultant
CEO: Gary Wisniewski
*CEO: Gerard Sanderink
*CEO: Gary M Wisniewski
*CFO: Pieter Pijper
*Ch: Robert M Karls
*Ex VP: Raimond Baumans
*Ex VP: Rosanna Ouellette
*Ex VP: John Platko

D-U-N-S 60-513-0368 IMP
■ ANTECH DIAGNOSTICS INC
(Suby of VCA INC) ★
17672 Cowan Bldg B, Irvine, CA 92614-6845
Tel (800) 745-4725 Founded/Ownrshp 1994
Sales 194.2MM^E EMP 1,000
SIC 0742 Veterinary services, specialties
CEO: Robert L Antin
*Pr: Bob Anton
Pr: Kevin Bloss
*CFO: Tomas Fuller
VP: Jim Church
VP: Stephen Elliott
VP: Paul Fisher
VP: Cathy Otto
Dir Lab: David Brown
Prin: Judi Lathrop
Genl Mgr: Fanny Bambang

D-U-N-S 00-802-4077 EXP
ANTELOPE OIL TOOL & MFG CO LLC
8807 W Sam Houston Pkwy N # 200, Houston, TX 77040-5346
Tel (832) 756-2300 Founded/Ownrshp 1960, 2013
Sales 97.8MM^E EMP 300
SIC 3533 Oil & gas field machinery
CEO: Bill Kelley
*Treas: Mark Margavio

ANTELOPE VALLEY COLLEGE
See ANTELOPE VALLEY COMMUNITY COLLEGE DISTRICT

D-U-N-S 07-414-4403
ANTELOPE VALLEY COMMUNITY COLLEGE DISTRICT
ANTELOPE VALLEY COLLEGE
(Suby of CALIFORNIA COMMUNITY COLLEGES SYSTEM) ★
3041 W Avenue K, Lancaster, CA 93536-5402
Tel (661) 722-6300 Founded/Ownrshp 1929
Sales 130.0MM^E EMP 800
SIC 8222 8221 Community college; Colleges universities & professional schools
Exec: Julie Broadwater
Exec: Terry Cleveland
Exec: Jodine Setter
Exec: Nicola Tesseneer
Adm Dir: Anne Redding
Dir IT: Calvin Madlock

ANTELOPE VALLEY HLTH CARE DST
See ANTELOPE VALLEY HOSPITAL AUXILIARY

D-U-N-S 04-034-9482
ANTELOPE VALLEY HOSPITAL AUXILIARY
ANTELOPE VALLEY HLTH CARE DST
1600 W Avenue J, Lancaster, CA 93534-2894
Tel (661) 949-5000 Founded/Ownrshp 1953
Sales 380.0MM EMP 2,200
SIC 8062 General medical & surgical hospitals
CEO: Harriet Lee
Chf Rad: Jennifer Hill
*CFO: Dennis Empey
CFO: Les Wong
*Ch: Abdallah Farrukh
Treas: Steve Fox
Ofcr: Vikki Haley
VP: Jim Flynn
VP: Shan Nathan
VP: Tom Ward
Dir Lab: Larry Walker
Dir Rad: Rick Rowe
Dir Rx: Evelyn Elliott

D-U-N-S 07-414-4346
ANTELOPE VALLEY UNION HIGH SCHOOL DISTRICT
ACADEMIES OF ANTELOPE VALLEY
44811 Sierra Hwy, Lancaster, CA 93534-3226
Tel (661) 948-7655 Founded/Ownrshp 1912
Sales 210.8MM EMP 1,500
SIC 8211

D-U-N-S 07-960-5479
ANTERO MIDSTREAM PARTNERS LP
1615 Wynkoop St, Denver, CO 80202-1106
Tel (307) 357-7310 Founded/Ownrshp 2013
Sales 387.3MM EMP 480
Tkr Sym AM Exch NYS
SIC 4922 Natural gas transmission
Ch Bd: Paul M Rady
*Pr: Glen C Warren Jr

D-U-N-S 83-100-3012
▲ ANTERO RESOURCES CORP
1615 Wynkoop St, Denver, CO 80202-1106
Tel (303) 357-7310 Founded/Ownrshp 2002
Sales 3.9MMM EMP 480^E
Tkr Sym AR Exch NYS
SIC 1311 Crude petroleum & natural gas
Ch Bd: Paul M Rady
*Pr: Glen C Warren Jr
Sr VP: Michael N Kennedy
Sr VP: Kevin J Kilstrom
Sr VP: Brian A Kuhn
Sr VP: Mark D Mauz
Sr VP: Ward D McNeilly
Sr VP: Alvyn A Schopp
VP: Troy Roach
VP Bus Dev: Steven M Woodward
Off Admin: Amanda Pros
Board of Directors: Robert J Clark, Richard W Connor, Benjamin A Hardesty, Peter R Kagan, W Howard Keenan Jr, James R Levy

D-U-N-S 96-359-0893
ANTERO RESOURCES LLC
1625 17th St Ste 300, Denver, CO 80202-5986
Tel (303) 357-7310 Founded/Ownrshp 2009
Sales 735.7MM EMP 150^E
SIC 1311

ANTEX
See AMERICAN NATIONAL LIFE INSURANCE CO OF TEXAS

D-U-N-S 14-447-6897
ANTHELIO HEALTHCARE SOLUTIONS INC
1 Lincoln Centre 5400 L, Dallas, TX 75240
Tel (214) 257-7000 Founded/Ownrshp 1999
Sales 208.0MM^E EMP 1,672^E
Accts Ernst & Young Llp Dallas Te
SIC 8741 8071 7389 Hospital management; Medical laboratories;
CEO: Asif Ahmad
Ch Bd: David R White
COO: Lawrence Schunder
CFO: Mark C Falkenberg
CFO: Parasuraman Krishnaswamy
CFO: Jeff Robertson
CFO: Dionne Viator
Ex VP: Satya Gottumukkala
Ex VP: Vicki Laurie
Ex VP: Gary Oneal
Sr VP: Kelly J Vroom
VP: David Earnshaw
VP: David Grau
VP: Belinda Wiegand
Exec: Judi Ashline
Board of Directors: Phil Incarnati, Kevin A Schulman, Charles M Young

ANTHEM EDUCATION GROUP
See HIGH-TECH INSTITUTE HOLDINGS INC

D-U-N-S 05-891-6206
■ ANTHEM HEALTH PLANS OF VIRGINIA INC
(Suby of ANTHEM SOUTHEAST INC) ★
2015 Staples Mill Rd, Richmond, VA 23230-3108
Tel (804) 354-7000 Founded/Ownrshp 2002
Sales NA EMP 3,112
SIC 6324 Group hospitalization plans
Pr: C Burke King
*Pr: R A Rankin Jr
*COO: Keith L Muth
*COO: Thomas G Snead Jr
*Treas: R David Kretschmer
*Ex VP: Manuel Deese
*Ex VP: Raymond M Sisk
*Sr VP: Richardson Grinnan
*Sr VP: Ronald M Nash
*Sr VP: Thomas A Payne
*Sr VP: Peter L Perkins
*Sr VP: Thomas H Tullidge

D-U-N-S 82-739-6990
■ ANTHEM HOLDING CORP
(Suby of ANTHEM INC) ★
120 Monument Cir Ste 200, Indianapolis, IN 46204-4902
Tel (317) 488-6000 Founded/Ownrshp 2008
Sales NA EMP 782
SIC 6321 Health insurance carriers
Pr: Wayne S Deveydt
*Treas: R David Kretschmer
IT Man: Rob Rogers

D-U-N-S 03-795-5940
▲ ANTHEM INC
120 Monument Cir Ste 200, Indianapolis, IN 46204-4902
Tel (317) 488-6000 Founded/Ownrshp 2001
Sales NA EMP 53,000^E
Tkr Sym ANTM Exch NYS
SIC 6324 6321 Hospital & medical service plans; Dental insurance; Group hospitalization plans; Health maintenance organization (HMO), insurance only; Health insurance carriers
Ch Bd: Joseph R Swedish
Pr: Krista A Bowers
Pr: Tom Byrd
Pr: Sheri Coyner
Pr: Rebecca Crown
Pr: Tracy Edmonds
Pr: Jason Gorevic
Pr: Brian Griffin
Pr: Kevin R Hayden
Pr: Morgan Kendrick
Pr: Joan Kennedy

Pr: Michael Malouf
Pr: Pamela Martin
Pr: John Martie President
Pr: Susan E Rawlings
Pr: David B Zinkerman
CFO: Wayne S Deveydt
CFO: John E Gallina
Ofcr: Gloria M McCarthy
Assoc VP: Janie Leo
Ex VP: Peter D Haytaian
Board of Directors: R Kerry Clark, Robert L Dixon Jr, Lewis Hay III, Julie A Hill, Ramiro G Peru, William J Ryan, George A Schaefer Jr, Elizabeth E Tallet

D-U-N-S 04-186-1980
■ ANTHEM INSURANCE COMPANIES INC
BLUE CROSS
(*Suby of* ANTHEM INC) ★
120 Monument Cir Ste 200, Indianapolis, IN 46204-4902
Tel (317) 488-6000 *Founded/Ownrshp* 2001
Sales NA *EMP* 14,800
SIC 6324 6411 6321 6331 6159 7371 Group hospitalization plans; Health maintenance organization (HMO), insurance only; Pension & retirement plan consultants; Insurance brokers; Health insurance carriers; Property damage insurance; Fire, marine & casualty insurance: mutual; Equipment & vehicle finance leasing companies; Computer software development
CEO: Larry C Glasscock
**Ch Bd:* L Ben Lytle
**Pr:* Wayne S Deveydt
Pr: Leon Lamoreaux
**CFO:* Michael L Smith
**Treas:* R David Kretschmer
Ex VP: Brian Griffin
VP: Amy Cheslock
VP: Keith Heckel
Prgrm Mgr: Rena Patel
**CIO:* Jane Niederberger

D-U-N-S 36-155-2149
■ ANTHEM SOUTHEAST INC
(*Suby of* ANTHEM INC) ★
120 Monument Cir Ste 200, Indianapolis, IN 46204-4902
Tel (317) 488-6000 *Founded/Ownrshp* 2002
Sales NA *EMP* 5,000^E
SIC 6411 6311 6321 Medical insurance claim processing, contract or fee basis; Life insurance carriers; Disability health insurance
Pr: Kenneth R Goulet
Treas: R David Kretschmer

D-U-N-S 04-861-1792
ANTHONY & SYLVAN POOLS CORP (OH)
3739 N Eastern Rd, Doylestown, PA 18901
Tel (215) 489-5600 *Founded/Ownrshp* 1997, 2004
Sales 171.9MM^E *EMP* 466
SIC 1799 5999 Swimming pool construction; Swimming pool chemicals, equipment & supplies
Ch Bd: Stuart D Neidus
**Pr:* Howard P Wertman
**CEO:* Mark Koide
**CFO:* Martin Iles
**Ex VP:* William J Evanson
**Ex VP:* Richard M Kelso
VP: James E Palmer
Prin: Beth A Campbell
Admn Mgr: Jeanne Jolluck
Genl Mgr: Tracy Dance

D-U-N-S 61-840-4388 IMP/EXP
■ ANTHONY DOORS INC
ANTHONY INTERNATIONAL
(*Suby of* DOVER RFRGN & FD EQP INC) ★
12391 Montero Ave, Sylmar, CA 91342-5370
Tel (818) 365-9451 *Founded/Ownrshp* 2012
Sales 644.0MM^E *EMP* 1,475
SIC 3585 Refrigeration & heating equipment
CEO: Jeffrey Clark
COO: Stan Gwizdak
**CFO:* David Lautenschaelger
**Sr VP:* Craig Little
VP: Paul Artwohl
**VP:* Michael Murth
VP: Jeff Spotts
Opers Mgr: Jose Colon
Opers Mgr: Martin Euan
Mktg Mgr: Uri Rainisch
Sls Mgr: Tim Carson

ANTHONY INTERNATIONAL
See ANTHONY DOORS INC

D-U-N-S 00-849-2878
ANTHONY MANUFACTURING CORP
145 N Grand Ave, Glendora, CA 91741-2434
Tel (626) 963-9311 *Founded/Ownrshp* 1959
Sales 51.5MM^E *EMP* 1,005
SIC 3432 Lawn hose nozzles & sprinklers
Pr: A W La Fetra
**CFO:* Arthur Ludwick

D-U-N-S 05-107-3740 IMP
ANTHONY MARANO CO
3000 S Ashland Ave # 100, Chicago, IL 60608-5348
Tel (773) 321-7500 *Founded/Ownrshp* 1961
Sales 191.5MM^E *EMP* 225
SIC 5148 Vegetables, fresh
Pr: Anthony Marano
Pr: Damon Marano
Dir IT: Chris Nowak
Sfty Mgr: Chuck Sparacino

D-U-N-S 00-633-7893
ANTHONY TIMBERLAND INC
(*Suby of* BEARDEN LEASING CO LTD) ★
111 S Plum St, Bearden, AR 71720
Tel (870) 687-3611 *Founded/Ownrshp* 1947
Sales 148.0MM *EMP* 235
SIC 2421 Lumber: rough, sawed or planed
Pr: Steven M Anthony
**Ch:* John E Anthony
**Sec:* James R Green
**Ex VP:* Rick Green
**VP:* O D Cathey
MIS Dir: Boyd Hudson

D-U-N-S 06-768-0777
ANTHONY TIMBERLANDS INC
3 Executive Cir, Arkadelphia, AR 71923-5330
Tel (870) 245-3000 *Founded/Ownrshp* 1974
Sales 170.0MM *EMP* 525
SIC 2421

D-U-N-S 03-934-6432
ANTHONY WAYNE REHABILITATION CENTER FOR HANDICAPPED AND BLIND INC
AWS
8515 Bluffton Rd, Fort Wayne, IN 46809-3022
Tel (260) 744-6145 *Founded/Ownrshp* 1959
Sales 27.6MM *EMP* 1,300
Accts Haines Isenbarger & Skiba Llc
SIC 8331 7331 3441 3412 2449 2448 Vocational rehabilitation agency; Mailing service; Fabricated structural metal; Metal barrels, drums & pails; Wood containers; Wood pallets & skids
Pr: William J Swiss
**CFO:* Mark Flegge
Comm Dir: Kalonji Bobb

ANTHONYS SEAFOOD
See MAD ANTHONYS INC

D-U-N-S 78-900-1179 IMP
■ ANTHROPOLOGIE INC
(*Suby of* URBAN OUTFITTERS INC) ★
5000 S Broad St, Philadelphia, PA 19112-1402
Tel (215) 454-4421 *Founded/Ownrshp* 1992
Sales 399.1MM^E *EMP* 2,600
SIC 5719 5621 Housewares; Women's clothing stores
CEO: Tedford Marlow
Pr: Margaret A Hayne
Pr: Richard Hayne
CFO: Frank J Conforti
Treas: Eric Artz
VP: Glen Senk
Mng Dir: Michael Robinson
Dist Mgr: Jenn Ernst
Dist Mgr: Erica Johnson
Site Mgr: Tiffany Cross
Prd Mgr: Suren Gopalakrishnan

D-U-N-S 01-340-0085
ANTIGUA ENTERPRISES INC
(*Suby of* SPORTS DIRECT INTERNATIONAL PLC)
16651 N 84th Ave, Peoria, AZ 85382-4772
Tel (623) 523-6000 *Founded/Ownrshp* 2003
Sales 147.1MM^E *EMP* 280
Accts Grant Thornton Phoenix Az
SIC 2329 Men's & boys' sportswear & athletic clothing
CEO: Ron McPherson
**CFO:* Gerald K Whitley
**VP:* Joe Blanchette

D-U-N-S 09-803-2923 IMP/EXP
ANTIGUA GROUP INC
(*Suby of* ANTIGUA ENTERPRISES INC) ★
16651 N 84th Ave, Peoria, AZ 85382-4772
Tel (623) 523-6000 *Founded/Ownrshp* 1997
Sales 147.1MM^E *EMP* 250
SIC 5137 5136 2395 2339 3993 Sportswear, women's & children's; Sportswear, men's & boys'; Pleating & stitching; Women's & misses' outerwear; Signs & advertising specialties
Pr: Ronald A Mc Pherson
**Pr:* Ron McPherson
CFO: Sherrill Maxwell
**CFO:* Gerald K Whitley
Chf Mktg O: Michele Sporrer
**VP:* Joe Blanchette
VP: Chris Devous
**VP:* Pamla Miller
CTO: Grant Thornton
IT Man: Chris Devoux
Site Mgr: John Martinez

D-U-N-S 08-015-7548
ANTIOCH PRESERVATION LP
ANTIOCH TOWERS
8920 Carnegie Ave, Cleveland, OH 44106-2923
Tel (216) 721-6100 *Founded/Ownrshp* 1976
Sales 53.7MM^E *EMP* 3,900
SIC 6513 Apartment building operators
Pt: Leeann Morein
Prin: Jennifer Hardee

ANTIOCH TOWERS
See ANTIOCH PRESERVATION LP

D-U-N-S 08-452-0725
ANTIOCH UNIFIED SCHOOL DISTRICT
510 G St, Antioch, CA 94509-1259
Tel (925) 779-7500 *Founded/Ownrshp* 1890
Sales 120.2MM^E *EMP* 1,800
SIC 8211 Public adult education school; Public elementary school; Public junior high school; Public senior high school
Prin: Mary Vinceguerra
IT Man: Mark Branson
Teacher Pr: Jessica Romeo
Psych: Jon Schlenker

D-U-N-S 04-106-4825
ANTIOCH UNIVERSITY
900 Dayton St, Yellow Springs, OH 45387-1745
Tel (937) 769-1370 *Founded/Ownrshp* 1852
Sales 65.7MM *EMP* 1,100^E
Accts Rsm Us Llp Columbus Ohio
SIC 8221 University
Dir Vol: Cindy Steffen
Treas: James McDonald
VP: Thomas Saecke
VP: Guy Smith
Exec: James Malarkey
Adm Dir: Elizabeth Allyn
Adm Dir: Julia Cline
Adm Dir: Susan Fletcher
Off Mgr: Margaret Smeltz
Tech Mgr: Brandon Capron
Snr Mgr: Barbara Stewart

D-U-N-S 13-284-6882
ANTLERS PUBLIC SCHOOLS
219 Ne A St, Antlers, OK 74523-3241
Tel (580) 298-5504 *Founded/Ownrshp* 1936
Sales 35.9MM^E *EMP* 1,936
SIC 8211 Public elementary & secondary schools
Prin: Bob Barnes

D-U-N-S 01-952-5448 IMP
ANTOLIN INTERIORS USA INC
ATREUM
(*Suby of* GRUPO ANTOLIN NORTH AMERICA INC) ★
1700 Atlantic Blvd, Auburn Hills, MI 48326-1504
Tel (248) 373-1749 *Founded/Ownrshp* 2015
Sales 788.5MM^E *EMP* 2,500
SIC 3714 Motor vehicle parts & accessories
Pr: Pablo Baroja
Ofcr: Paul Brock
Prgrm Mgr: Joe Callahan
Prgrm Mgr: Ryan Littleton
Tech Mgr: Keijo Huotari
Opers Mgr: Todd Latouf
Ql Cn Mgr: Michelle Thompson
Mktg Dir: Rhonda McNally

D-U-N-S 01-477-6249 IMP
ANTONIO ORIGLIO INC
ORIGLIO BEVERAGE
3000 Meetinghouse Rd, Philadelphia, PA 19154-1027
Tel (215) 698-9500 *Founded/Ownrshp* 1933
Sales 138.2MM^E *EMP* 200
SIC 5181 Beer & other fermented malt liquors
Pr: Dominic Origlio
**Sec:* Jeffrey Honickman
VP: Christian Origlio
Comm Dir: Maryanne Origlio
Genl Mgr: Bob Sokel
IT Man: Mark Lewis
Sfty Dirs: Thomas Milewski
Natl Sales: Fritzi Bennett
Sls Dir: Bill Castelberg
Mktg Mgr: Mike Kugler
Sls Mgr: Doreen Case

D-U-N-S 02-609-8640 IMP
ANTRONIX INC
440 Forsgate Dr, Cranbury, NJ 08512-3518
Tel (609) 860-0160 *Founded/Ownrshp* 1980
Sales 117.0MM^E *EMP* 1,500
SIC 3663 5063 Cable television equipment; Electrical apparatus & equipment
Pr: Daniel Tang
**VP:* Neil Tang
**VP:* Suphie Tang
Opers Mgr: Terri Bell
Sls Dir: Michael Scheuerman
Sls Mgr: Milton Ulua

D-U-N-S 94-310-4828 IMP/EXP
ANVIL HOLDINGS INC
(*Suby of* GILDAN ACTIVEWEAR INC)
228 E 45th St Fl 4, New York, NY 10017-3303
Tel (843) 774-8211 *Founded/Ownrshp* 2012
Sales 525.2MM^E *EMP* 5,055
SIC 5137 Women's & children's clothing
CEO: Anthony Frank Corsano
**CFO:* Frank Frramosca
**Ex VP:* Caterina A Conti
**VP:* Jacob Hollander
Natl Sales: Richard Silletto

D-U-N-S 15-461-5095 IMP
■ ANVIL INTERNATIONAL LLC
(*Suby of* MUELLER GROUP LLC) ★
2 Holland Way, Exeter, NH 03833-2937
Tel (603) 418-2800 *Founded/Ownrshp* 1999
Sales 664.3MM^E *EMP* 3,100
SIC 3498 3321 3317 3494 3429 Fabricated pipe & fittings; Gray & ductile iron foundries; Steel pipe & tubes; Valves & pipe fittings; Manufactured hardware (general)
Pr: Thomas E Fish
**Pr:* Patrick M Donovan
Treas: Dean Taylor
**VP:* Bob Arison
**VP:* Hugh Brennan
**VP:* Ken Dangelmaier
VP: Mark Demchyk
VP: Rick Laviolette
**VP:* John Martin
VP: Ronald Pound
Exec: Lou Andreano
Exec: Dawn Cardona
Exec: Brian Reef

ANVIL KNITWEAR, INC.
See GILDAN APPAREL USA INC

D-U-N-S 01-621-5282
ANWORTH MORTGAGE ASSET CORP
1299 Ocean Ave Fl 2, Santa Monica, CA 90401-1036
Tel (310) 255-4493 *Founded/Ownrshp* 1998
Sales 147.0MM *EMP* 2
Accts Rsm Us Llp Seattle Washingto
Tkr Sym ANH *Exch* NYS
SIC 6798 Real estate investment trusts
Ch Bd: Joseph Lloyd McAdams
Pr: Joseph E McAdams
CFO: Thad Brown
CFO: Charles J Siegel
Sr VP: Bistra Pashamova
Sr VP: Brett Roth

D-U-N-S 92-647-5542
ANZ LIMITED PARTNERSHIP
(*Suby of* AUSTRALIA AND NEW ZEALAND BANKING GROUP LIMITED)
1177 Ave Of The Americas, New York, NY 10036-2714
Tel (212) 801-9800 *Founded/Ownrshp* 1971
Sales NA *EMP* 582^E
SIC 6081 Branches & agencies of foreign banks
Pr: Richard McInnis
Pt: Willem L BR Cker
Genl Mgr: Scott McInnis

ANZA
See HOLIEN INC

AO SMITH
See APCOM INC

D-U-N-S 87-631-4329 IMP
AOC LLC
(*Suby of* ALPHA CORP OF TENNESSEE) ★
955 Highway 57, Collierville, TN 38017-5205
Tel (901) 854-2800 *Founded/Ownrshp* 1994
Sales 312.0MM^E *EMP* 560
SIC 2295 Resin or plastic coated fabrics
Pr: Frederick S Norman
Pr: Scott C Lane
Ex VP: Matt Watkins
VP: Edward Mirra
VP: Tom Solta
VP: Randy Weghorst
Exec: Mike Bayless
Exec: Linda Ross
Exec: Rene' Taillon
Comm Dir: Leslie Deck
Mng Dir: Jeff Holshevnikoff

D-U-N-S 13-383-5822 IMP
AOC TECHNOLOGIES INC
5960 Inglewood Dr, Pleasanton, CA 94588-8515
Tel (925) 875-0808 *Founded/Ownrshp* 1999
Sales 113.1MM^E *EMP* 315
SIC 5051 3357 Metal wires, ties, cables & screening; Fiber optic cable (insulated)
Pr: Gordon Gu

D-U-N-S 83-268-5072
■ AOL INC
(*Suby of* VERIZON COMMUNICATIONS INC) ★
770 Broadway Fl 4, New York, NY 10003-9562
Tel (212) 652-6400 *Founded/Ownrshp* 2015
Sales 1.5MMM^E *EMP* 4,350^E
SIC 7374 Data processing & preparation
CEO: Tim M Armstrong
Pr: Bob Lord
Pr: Dermot McCormack
CEO: Tim Armstrong
CFO: Karen Dykstra
CFO: Holly Hess
Bd of Dir: Ricky Blaha
Bd of Dir: Nathan Wiggins
Ofcr: Mark Connon
Ofcr: Tim Lemmon
Ofcr: Terri Zandhuis
Ex VP: Julie Jacobs
Ex VP: Julie M Jacobs
Ex VP: William Pence
Ex VP: William E Pence
Sr VP: Michael Manos
Sr VP: Bud Rosenthal
VP: Jon Abramson
VP: Caroline Campbell
VP: Seth Demsey
VP: Abigail Gray

D-U-N-S 04-335-2368
AON BENFIELD FAC INC
(*Suby of* AON RE WORLDWIDE INC)
200 E Randolph St Fl 15, Chicago, IL 60601-6426
Tel (312) 381-5300 *Founded/Ownrshp* 1988
Sales NA *EMP* 400
SIC 6321 6311 Reinsurance carriers, accident & health; Life insurance
Pr: Michael Bungerk
**COO:* Michael Wall
**CFO:* Jack Roby
Assoc VP: Thomas Neff
Ex VP: Stephen Slade
**Sr VP:* Jeffery Crouch
**Sr VP:* James Matthias
Off Mgr: Melida Skipton
Sales Exec: Susan Navarra

D-U-N-S 07-179-3657
AON BENFIELD INC
(*Suby of* AON PLC)
5600 W 83rd St Ste 1100, Minneapolis, MN 55437-1062
Tel (866) 280-3720 *Founded/Ownrshp* 1988
Sales NA *EMP* 710
SIC 6321 Reinsurance carriers, accident & health
Pr: Rod Fox
Ex VP: Kevin Traetow
Sr VP: Karl Thomforde
Sr VP: Joseph J Vitale
VP: Anthony W Fick
Snr Ntwrk: Brandon Vickers
Sls&Mrk Ex: Jan Wagener

D-U-N-S 10-155-8476
AON CONSULTING (MICHIGAN) INC
(*Suby of* AON CONSULTING INC) ★
400 Renaissance Ctr Lbby, Detroit, MI 48243-1607
Tel (313) 393-7888 *Founded/Ownrshp* 1994
Sales NA *EMP* 700
SIC 6411 Insurance brokers
Ch Bd: Daniel Quinn
**VP:* Mark Lifter

D-U-N-S 07-162-9000
AON CONSULTING INC
(*Suby of* AON PLC)
315 W 3rd St, Little Rock, AR 72201-2411
Tel (501) 374-9300 *Founded/Ownrshp* 1955, 2012
Sales 245.7MM^E *EMP* 1,987
SIC 8742 Compensation & benefits planning consultant
Ch Bd: Donald C Ingram
Pr: Linda E Amuso
Chf Mktg O: Paul Berger
Ex VP: Mark Arian
**Ex VP:* Paul G Chicos
**Ex VP:* Walter L Ogle
**Ex VP:* Robert Ryan
**Ex VP:* Roger Vaughn
Sr VP: Johan Dekeyzer
Sr VP: Andy Hiles
Sr VP: Larry Kurzner
Sr VP: Eugene Oppo
**Sr VP:* Matt Ward
VP: Eddie Franco
VP: Daniel Junk
VP: Lela Laurent
**VP:* Matthew Rice
VP: Clifford Shnier

D-U-N-S 01-462-3651
AON CONSULTING WORLDWIDE INC
(*Suby of* AON GROUP INC) ★
100 Half Day Rd 2, Lincolnshire, IL 60069-3258
Tel (312) 381-4800 *Founded/Ownrshp* 1998
Sales NA *EMP* 7,500
SIC 6311 6321 6331 8742 6411 6351 Life insurance carriers; Life reinsurance; Accident insurance carriers; Health insurance carriers; Reinsurance carriers, accident & health; Property damage insurance; Fire, marine & casualty insurance: stock; Compensation & benefits planning consultant; Policyholders' consulting service; Insurance brokers; Insurance adjusters; Credit & other financial responsibility insurance
CEO: Baljit Dail
**Ch Bd:* Andrew M Appel
**Ch Bd:* Don Ingram
CEO: Reiji Ohtaki
**CFO:* Mark Blumenthal
Sr VP: Todd Chambley
Sr VP: Joe Clouse
Sr VP: Yannick Gagne
Sr VP: Kristine Klepper
Sr VP: Barbara Weaver Lloyd
Sr VP: Daniel Russell
Sr VP: Mark Scarafone
Sr VP: Matthew Shadrick
**Sr VP:* Elizebeth Varghese
Sr VP: Nina Zazzara
VP: Suzi Anderson
VP: Timothy Copeland
VP: Lynn Devany
VP: Daniel Junk
VP: Lela Laurent
VP: Heidi Mader
Board of Directors: Michael Gulotta, Roger Vaughn

D-U-N-S 03-850-3546
AON CORP
(*Suby of* AON PLC)
200 E Randolph St, Chicago, IL 60601-6436
Tel (312) 381-1000 *Founded/Ownrshp* 1979
Sales NA *EMP* 65,000ᴱ
Accts Ernst & Young Llp Chicago Il
SIC 6411 8742 Insurance agents, brokers & service; Policyholders' consulting service; Insurance brokers; Insurance adjusters; Compensation & benefits planning consultant
Pr: Gregory C Case
COO: Mark Rochholz
CFO: Ernie Caponetti
Sr Ex VP: Michael D O'Halleran
Ex VP: Edward Dadakis
Ex VP: Peter Lieb
Sr VP: Michael Day
Sr VP: Sally Higgins
Sr VP: Maki Kawasumi
Sr VP: John Keely
Sr VP: Brian Kuhlman
Sr VP: Karen Roberts
Sr VP: Lisa Rowe
Sr VP: Brian Ruggeberg
Sr VP: John Shish
VP: Joanne Bartholomew
VP: Jo A Dragoun
VP: Kathleen Fleming
VP: Cathy Gavin
VP: Matt Gelotti
VP: Jeanne Herold

D-U-N-S 60-654-0078
AON GROUP INC
(*Suby of* AON PLC)
200 E Randolph St Fl 5, Chicago, IL 60601-6416
Tel (312) 381-2738 *Founded/Ownrshp* 2012
Sales NA *EMP* 14,000
SIC 6311 8742 6411 Life insurance carriers; Compensation & benefits planning consultant; Insurance brokers
Ch Bd: Patrick G Ryan
Pr: Michael D O'Halleran
CFO: Joseph J Prochaska Jr
Ex VP: Steve Kisor
Sr VP: Barbara Spain

D-U-N-S 06-799-9979
AON HEWITT LLC
(*Suby of* AON PLC)
200 E Randolph St Ll3, Chicago, IL 60601-6408
Tel (312) 381-1000 *Founded/Ownrshp* 1982
Sales 4.8MMMᴱ *EMP* 62,040
SIC 8742 8999 Human resource consulting services; Compensation & benefits planning consultant; Actuarial consultant
CEO: Fulvio Conti
**Pr:* Gregory C Case
**CEO:* Russell P Fradin
COO: Amit Dhadwal
CFO: J Michael Losh
CFO: Ralph R Mueller
**CFO:* Robert A Schriesheim
**Ch:* Edgar D Jannotta
**Ch:* Lester B Knight
Acting Pr: Julie S Gordon
Assoc VP: Geraldine Allen
Assoc VP: Diane Fiore
Assoc VP: Jason Swann
Ex VP: Anthony B Cochrane
**Sr VP:* Tracy S Keogh
**Sr VP:* Steven J Kyono
Sr VP: Matthew C Levin
Sr VP: Laura Zimmerman
Assoc Dir: Richard Evans
Assoc Dir: Grant Foster
Assoc Dir: Jeffrey T Landesmann

D-U-N-S 60-669-2481
AON NATIONAL FLOOD SERVICES INC
(*Suby of* AON US HOLDINGS INC) ★
555 Corporate Dr, Kalispell, MT 59901-6074
Tel (406) 756-8656 *Founded/Ownrshp* 2014
Sales NA *EMP* 800
SIC 6331 Fire, marine & casualty insurance & carriers
Pr: Keith Thomas Brown
Pr: Greg Knuffke
CFO: Michael Lemons
Chf Mktg O: Deb Coulson
VP: Marlene Freeman
VP: G Hultquist
VP: Dean Myers
MIS Dir: Gail Drew
IT Man: Troy McCabe

D-U-N-S 00-542-8875
AON RISK SERVICES COMPANIES INC (MD)
(*Suby of* AON PLC)
200 E Randolph St Fl 14, Chicago, IL 60601-6425
Tel (312) 381-1000 *Founded/Ownrshp* 1898, 1988
Sales NA *EMP* 6,000
SIC 6411 8111 Insurance brokers; Legal services
CEO: Gregory C Case
**Pr:* Stephen P McGill Acii
**Pr:* Michael D Rice II
**CFO:* Christa Davies
**Ofcr:* Gregory J Besio
**Ofcr:* Philip B Clement
**Ex VP:* Matthew Levin
**Ex VP:* Peter Lieb
**Sr VP:* Laurel Meissner
Admn Mgr: Marc Armstrong

D-U-N-S 62-319-5393
AON RISK SERVICES INC OF FLORIDA
(*Suby of* AON PLC)
13901 Sutton Park Dr S # 360, Jacksonville, FL 32224-0229
Tel (904) 724-2001 *Founded/Ownrshp* 2012
Sales NA *EMP* 300
SIC 6411 Insurance agents, brokers & service
Pr: Richard B Decoster
**Treas:* Paul A Hagy
**Mng Dir:* Terry Wilcox

D-U-N-S 08-040-5765
AON RISK SERVICES INC OF MARYLAND
(*Suby of* AON RISK SERVICES COMPANIES INC) ★
500 E Pratt St, Baltimore, MD 21202-3133
Tel (410) 547-2800 *Founded/Ownrshp* 1997
Sales NA *EMP* 1,168
SIC 6411 Insurance agents, brokers & service
Pr: Otis L Tolbert
COO: Joseph Propati
CFO: Liam P Caffrey
Treas: Paul A Hagy
Sr VP: William R Filbert Jr
Sr VP: Domingo Garcia Jr
Sr VP: James S Mackrell III
VP: Deborah Sweigart Bates
VP: Gerald W Brown
VP: Kelly Bryant
**VP:* Mary Moore Johnson
VP: Patricia A Piccinini
VP: Rosalie Poston
VP: Patricia A Rainier
VP: Kaci J Tomlinson
Board of Directors: Christopher Asher

D-U-N-S 05-829-7722
AON RISK SERVICES NORTHEAST INC
A O N
(*Suby of* AON PLC)
1660 W 2nd St, Cleveland, OH 44113-1454
Tel (216) 621-8100 *Founded/Ownrshp* 2012
Sales NA *EMP* 1,600
SIC 6411 Insurance brokers
Prin: Richard Longyhore

D-U-N-S 06-071-1207
AON RISK SERVICES SOUTHWEST INC
(*Suby of* AON RISK SERVICES COMPANIES INC) ★
5555 San Felipe St # 1500, Houston, TX 77056-2739
Tel (832) 476-6000 *Founded/Ownrshp* 2004
Sales NA *EMP* 450
SIC 6411 Insurance brokers
Pr: Bruce Jefferies
COO: Scott Lassila
CFO: Jennefer Peacock
Sr VP: Eric Viktorin
VP: Jeremy Gayser

D-U-N-S 55-690-9026
AON SOLUTIONS INC
(*Suby of* AON RISK SERVICES COMPANIES INC) ★
200 E Randolph St, Chicago, IL 60601-6436
Tel (312) 381-1000 *Founded/Ownrshp* 1898
Sales NA *EMP* 6,000
SIC 6411 Insurance brokers
Ch Bd: Pat Ryan
VP: George Nakis
Snr Sftwr: Chris Pallavicini
CIO: Rick Sandweiss

D-U-N-S 07-950-3750
AON US HOLDINGS INC
(*Suby of* AON PLC)
200 E Randolph St, Chicago, IL 60601-6436
Tel (312) 381-1000 *Founded/Ownrshp* 2014
Sales NA *EMP* 152ᴱ
SIC 6411 6799 8741 Insurance agents, brokers & service; Policyholders' consulting service; Insurance brokers; Insurance adjusters; Commodity investors; Business management

D-U-N-S 96-187-8811
AOT BEDDING INTERMEDIATE HOLDINGS LLC
(*Suby of* SERTA SIMMONS BEDDING LLC) ★
1 Concrs Pkwy Ne Ste 800, Atlanta, GA 30328-6188
Tel (770) 512-7700 *Founded/Ownrshp* 2009
Sales 120.9MMᴱ *EMP* 2,300ᴱ
SIC 2515 Mattresses, innerspring or box spring
Pr: Stephen G Fendrich

D-U-N-S 96-527-8661
AP CARIB HOLDING LTD
9 W 57th St Fl 43, New York, NY 10019-2700
Tel (212) 515-3202 *Founded/Ownrshp* 2010
Sales 34.2MMᴱ *EMP* 1,800
SIC 8741 8748 7379 Business management; Business consulting; Computer related consulting services
Prin: Marc Becker

D-U-N-S 02-156-0052 IMP/EXP
AP EMISSIONS TECHNOLOGIES LLC
300 Dixie Trl, Goldsboro, NC 27530-7119
Tel (919) 580-2000 *Founded/Ownrshp* 1927
Sales 113.4MMᴱ *EMP* 380
SIC 3714 Mufflers (exhaust), motor vehicle
CEO: Hugh Charvat
**Pr:* Chris Ostrander
CFO: Donatella Zoccolan
**VP:* Andy Proimos
CTO: Calvin Long
Mktg Dir: Gary Nix

D-U-N-S 80-978-0500
AP MIDWEST LLC
(*Suby of* ADOLFSON & PETERSON CNSTR) ★
6701 W 23rd St, Minneapolis, MN 55426-2801
Tel (952) 544-1561 *Founded/Ownrshp* 2006
Sales 124.7MM *EMP* 175
SIC 1542 Commercial & office building contractors

D-U-N-S 79-060-4057
AP MOUNTAIN STATES LLC
ADOLFSON & PETERSON CNSTR
(*Suby of* ADOLFSON & PETERSON CNSTR) ★
797 Ventura St, Aurora, CO 80011-7900
Tel (303) 363-7101 *Founded/Ownrshp* 1946
Sales 246.1MM *EMP* 240
SIC 1542 Nonresidential construction
CEO: Doug Jaeger
**COO:* Kent Weicht
**CFO:* Jeffrey Hansen
**Ex VP:* Scott Weicht
Snr PM: Tom Bailey

AP SERVICES
See ALIXPARTNERS LLP

APAC
See PREFERRED MATERIALS INC

D-U-N-S 78-564-0462
APAC CUSTOMER SERVICES INC
(*Suby of* EXPERT GLOBAL SOLUTIONS INC) ★
507 Prudential Rd, Horsham, PA 19044-2308
Tel (215) 441-3000 *Founded/Ownrshp* 1995
Sales 14.0MMᴱ *EMP* 1,007ᴱ
SIC 8741 Management services
Prin: Michael J Barrist
VP: Joshua Gindin
QA Dir: Lori Warnsley

D-U-N-S 19-699-1665
APAC HOLDINGS INC
(*Suby of* OLDCASTLE MATERIALS GROUP) ★
900 Ashwood Pkwy Ste 700, Atlanta, GA 30338-4780
Tel (770) 392-5300 *Founded/Ownrshp* 2006
Sales 716.8MMᴱ *EMP* 2,344
Accts Ernst & Young Llp Atlanta Ga
SIC 1611 3531 5032 Highway & street paving contractor; Concrete construction: roads, highways, sidewalks, etc.; Airport runway construction; Asphalt plant, including gravel-mix type; Brick, stone & related material; Sand, construction; Gravel
CEO: Kirk Randolph

D-U-N-S 03-503-7381
APAC-ATLANTIC INC
HARRISON CONSTRUCTION CO.
(*Suby of* APAC HOLDINGS INC) ★
4817 Rutledge Pike, Knoxville, TN 37914-3228
Tel (865) 983-3100 *Founded/Ownrshp* 1980, 1987
Sales 187.0MMᴱ *EMP* 700
SIC 5032 3531 3273 2951 1611 Brick, stone & related material; Asphalt plant, including gravel-mix type; Ready-mixed concrete; Asphalt paving mixtures & blocks; Highway & street paving contractor
IT Man: Danette Burchfield

D-U-N-S 04-737-2602
APAC-ATLANTIC INC
(*Suby of* OLDCASTLE MATERIALS GROUP) ★
300 S Benbow Rd, Greensboro, NC 27401-3402
Tel (336) 412-6800 *Founded/Ownrshp* 1945, 1967
Sales 179.3MMᴱ *EMP* 1,300
SIC 1611 1771 3531 5032 Highway & street paving contractor; Concrete construction: roads, highways, sidewalks, etc.; Airport runway construction; Parking lot construction; Asphalt plant, including gravel-mix type; Sand, construction; Gravel
Pr: David L Schwartz
Sec: William M Roberts
VP: E S Arthur Jr
VP: Barry L Johnson
VP: David H Kilpatrick
VP: Thomas G Kindred
VP: Otis A Vaughn
Genl Mgr: Thumper Swann
IT Man: David Schmeckpepper
Board of Directors: Christopher B Lodge, E M Mac Thomas, H W Medcalf Jr

D-U-N-S 83-311-1599
APAC-CENTRAL INC
ARKHOLA SAND & GRAVEL
(*Suby of* OLDCASTLE MATERIALS GROUP) ★
755 E Millsap Rd, Fayetteville, AR 72703-4004
Tel (417) 226-4833 *Founded/Ownrshp* 1980
Sales 122.9MMᴱ *EMP* 500ᴱ
SIC 3272 1611 Concrete products; Concrete construction: roads, highways, sidewalks, etc.; Highway & street paving contractor; Grading
Pr: Bryan C Kalbfleisch
CFO: Lee Duchanois
VP: Jerry Goodson

D-U-N-S 06-927-7150 IMP
APAC-KANSAS INC
(*Suby of* OLDCASTLE MATERIALS GROUP) ★
7415 W 130th St Ste 300, Overland Park, KS 66213-2677
Tel (913) 371-1003 *Founded/Ownrshp* 1980, 2012
Sales 183.6MMᴱ *EMP* 500
SIC 1611 1771 2951 7353 1622 Highway & street paving contractor; Airport runway construction; Parking lot construction; Asphalt & asphaltic paving mixtures (not from refineries); Cranes & aerial lift equipment, rental or leasing; Bridge, tunnel & elevated highway
Pr: David Guilluame
**Sec:* Dan R Craig

D-U-N-S 03-942-8339
APAC-MISSISSIPPI INC
(*Suby of* OLDCASTLE MATERIALS GROUP) ★
101 Riverview Dr, Richland, MS 39218-4401
Tel (601) 376-4000 *Founded/Ownrshp* 2015
Sales 118.9MMᴱ *EMP* 358
SIC 1611 1771 3531 5032 2951 Highway & street paving contractor; Concrete construction: roads, highways, sidewalks, etc.; Airport runway construction; Parking lot construction; Asphalt plant, including gravel-mix type; Sand, construction; Gravel; Asphalt paving mixtures & blocks
Pr: Dwayne H Boyd
**Sec:* Wilma G Foreman
**VP:* Michael W Bogue
**VP:* Ladell N Estes
**VP:* Joe P Pennington
**VP:* G Randy Shelton

D-U-N-S 04-187-4546
APAC-MISSOURI INC
(*Suby of* OLDCASTLE MATERIALS GROUP) ★
1591 E Prathersville Rd, Columbia, MO 65202-9614
Tel (573) 449-0886 *Founded/Ownrshp* 2012
Sales 127.8MMᴱ *EMP* 500
SIC 1611 Highway & street paving contractor
Pr: David Guilleaum
**Sec:* Cathey Spotts
**VP:* Michael J Eschelman
**VP:* Chad Girard
**VP:* John A Pasley
**VP:* Shawn Riley

D-U-N-S 01-387-2585 IMP/EXP
APAC-OKLAHOMA INC
(*Suby of* APAC HOLDINGS INC) ★
4150 S 100th East Ave # 300, Tulsa, OK 74146-3662
Tel (918) 438-2020 *Founded/Ownrshp* 1987
Sales 91.4MMᴱ *EMP* 442
SIC 1611 Surfacing & paving; Highway & street paving contractor; Airport runway construction
Pr: Jerry A Kreymer
VP: Bill J Shafer

D-U-N-S 04-123-7868 IMP
APAC-SOUTHEAST INC
(*Suby of* APAC HOLDINGS INC) ★
900 Ashwood Pkwy Ste 700, Atlanta, GA 30338-4780
Tel (770) 392-5300 *Founded/Ownrshp* 1989
Sales 188.1MMᴱ *EMP* 1,500
SIC 1611 1622 2951 Highway & street construction; Surfacing & paving; Bridge, tunnel & elevated highway; Asphalt paving mixtures & blocks
Pr: Frank D Nichols Jr
**Treas:* Pete Onuschak
**VP:* M Lee Powell III
**VP:* R Kirk Randolph
**VP:* T E Wilson III

D-U-N-S 02-234-1858
APAC-TENNESSEE INC
(*Suby of* OLDCASTLE MATERIALS GROUP) ★
1210 Harbor Ave, Memphis, TN 38113
Tel (901) 947-5600 *Founded/Ownrshp* 1980
Sales 86.5MMᴱ *EMP* 230
SIC 1611 Highway & street construction
Pr: Nicholas R Haynes
**VP:* Matt Carden
IT Man: Cris Barnes

D-U-N-S 03-993-9236 IMP/EXP
APAC-TEXAS INC
(*Suby of* OLDCASTLE MATERIALS GROUP) ★
1320 Arrow Point Dr # 600, Cedar Park, TX 78613-2167
Tel (512) 861-7100 *Founded/Ownrshp* 2012
Sales 389.1MMᴱ *EMP* 552
SIC 1611 Surfacing & paving; Highway & street paving contractor; Airport runway construction
Pr: Stephen B Robertson
**VP:* John D Armeni
**VP:* Brad W Bankston
**VP:* Joseph G Beatty
**VP:* Michael D Manning
Genl Mgr: Kirk Morris

D-U-N-S 00-696-1551 IMP
▲ APACHE CORP (DE)
2000 Post Oak Blvd # 100, Houston, TX 77056-4400
Tel (713) 296-6000 *Founded/Ownrshp* 1954
Sales 6.3MMM *EMP* 3,860
Accts Ernst & Young Llp Houston Te
Tkr Sym APA *Exch* NYS
SIC 1311 Crude petroleum production; Natural gas production
Pr: John J Christmann IV
CFO: Stephen J Riney
Ex VP: Michael S Bahorich
Ex VP: Margery M Harris
Ex VP: Robert V Johnston
Ex VP: P Anthony Lannie
Ex VP: P Lannie
Ex VP: Timothy J Sullivan
Sr VP: Timothy R Custer
VP: Grady L Ables
VP: Mark Bauer
VP: Jeffrey Bender
VP: Craig Clark
VP: Gary T Clark
VP: Matthew Dundrea
VP: James L House
VP: Rebecca A Hoyt
VP: Steven J Keenan
VP: Castlen M Kennedy
VP: Jim Kimble
VP: Cory L Loegering
Board of Directors: Annell R Bay, George D Lawrence, John E Lowe, William C Montgomery, Amy H Nelson, Rodman D Patton, Charles J Pitman, Daniel W Rabun, Peter A Ragauss

D-U-N-S 80-673-7607
■ APACHE GATHERING CO
(*Suby of* APACHE CORP) ★
2000 Post Oak Blvd # 100, Houston, TX 77056-4499
Tel (713) 296-6000 *Founded/Ownrshp* 1992
Sales 24.3MM^E *EMP* 1,000
SIC 4924 Natural gas distribution
Ch Bd: Raymond Plank
**Pr:* G Steven Farris

D-U-N-S 02-204-6270 IMP
APACHE HOSE & BELTING CO INC
4805 Bowling St Sw, Cedar Rapids, IA 52404-5021
Tel (319) 365-0471 *Founded/Ownrshp* 1989
Sales 86.1MM^E *EMP* 300
SIC 3496 3052 5085 Conveyor belts; Rubber & plastics hose & beltings; Industrial supplies; Hose, belting & packing; Industrial fittings
Pr: Thomas E Pientok
**Treas:* Randall M Walter
Board of Directors: Randy Smedstad

D-U-N-S 07-864-5071
APACHE INDUSTRIAL SERVICES INC
15423 Vantage Pkwy E, Houston, TX 77032-1937
Tel (281) 609-8800 *Founded/Ownrshp* 2010
Sales 133.1MM^E *EMP* 200^E
SIC 1629 1541 Industrial plant construction; Industrial buildings & warehouses
Ex Dir: Kim Hardin
**Pr:* Doug Lee
**CEO:* Michael Knigin
VP: Burt Hulett
**VP:* Delin Manuel
VP: David Schexnaydre
Dir IT: Raymond Tucker

D-U-N-S 05-804-0767 IMP/EXP
APACHE MILLS INC
197 Royal Dr Se, Calhoun, GA 30701-3661
Tel (706) 629-7791 *Founded/Ownrshp* 1971
Sales 126.1MM^E *EMP* 500
SIC 2273 Mats & matting
Ch Bd: Michael Wildstein
**Pr:* Stephen Wildstein
**CEO:* Art Wildstein
**VP:* Daniel Wildstein
IT Man: Ed Walraven
Mtls Mgr: Andy Friend
Sfty Mgr: Clint Davis

D-U-N-S 00-839-9263 IMP
APACHE NITROGEN PRODUCTS INC (AZ)
1436 S Apache Powder Rd, Saint David, AZ 85630-6103
Tel (520) 720-2217 *Founded/Ownrshp* 1920
Sales 96.9MM *EMP* 75
Accts Ernst & Young Llp Phoenix Az
SIC 2873 5169 2875 2819 Ammonium nitrate, ammonium sulfate; Explosives; Fertilizers, mixing only; Industrial inorganic chemicals
Pr: Jeremy Barrett
CFO: Andy Hunter
Sfty Mgr: Tony Brown

D-U-N-S 88-388-9354
APACHE OIL CO INC
WILLY'S FUELS
261 Ledyard St, New London, CT 06320-5337
Tel (860) 437-6200 *Founded/Ownrshp* 1993
Sales 300.0MM *EMP* 5
SIC 5172 5541 Petroleum products; Gasoline service stations
Pr: Christopher P Ohl
**Treas:* Warren L Wunderlich
**VP:* James H Castle

D-U-N-S 84-748-5364
▲ APARTMENT INVESTMENT & MANAGEMENT CO
AIMCO
4582 S Ulster St Ste 1100, Denver, CO 80237-2662
Tel (303) 757-8101 *Founded/Ownrshp* 1994
Sales 981.3MM *EMP* 1,591
Tkr Sym AIV *Exch* NYS
SIC 6798 Real estate investment trusts
Ch Bd: Terry Considine
CFO: Paul L Beldin
Treas: Patti K Fielding
Ofcr: Miles Cortez
Ex VP: John E Bezzant
Ex VP: Lisa R Cohn
Sr VP: John Bezzant
VP: Keith M Kimmel

D-U-N-S 00-680-6655
APARTMENTIME COM LLC
2025 Peachtree Rd Ne, Atlanta, GA 30309-1413
Tel (404) 961-0603 *Founded/Ownrshp* 1997
Sales 42.0MM *EMP* 4,000
SIC 7299 Apartment locating service

D-U-N-S 83-225-5090
APAX PARTNERS LP
(*Suby of* APAX PARTNERS LLP)
601 Lexington Ave Fl 53, New York, NY 10022-4630
Tel (212) 753-6300 *Founded/Ownrshp* 2005
Sales 1.6MMM^E *EMP* 2,075
SIC 6282 Investment advisory service
Dir Bus: Ellen De Kreij
Off Mgr: Mario A Mancheno
Dir IT: Duncan Kemp
IT Man: Neil Patel

D-U-N-S 07-327-2932 IMP
APAX PARTNERS OF NEW YORK
(*Suby of* APAX PARTNERS HOLDINGS LTD)
601 Lexington Ave Fl 53, New York, NY 10022-4630
Tel (212) 419-2447 *Founded/Ownrshp* 2005
Sales 387.6MM^E *EMP* 5,000^E
SIC 6282 5399 5199 5812 5813 Investment advisory service; Surplus & salvage goods; General merchandise, non-durable; American restaurant; Bar (drinking places)
CEO: Martin Halusa
Pt: Nicol S Bonilla
**Pt:* Marcelo Gigliani
**Pt:* Buddy Gumina
**Pt:* David Kim
**Pt:* John F Megrue
Pt: Christian J N Ther
**Pt:* Mitch Truwit
VP: Adil Haque
**Mng Dir:* Greg Case
**Mng Dir:* George Jenkins

APC PHNO
See AMPHENOL PRINTED CIRCUITS INC

D-U-N-S 17-306-4457
APC WORKFORCE SOLUTIONS LLC
ZEROCHAOS
420 S Orange Ave Ste 600, Orlando, FL 32801-4902
Tel (407) 770-6161 *Founded/Ownrshp* 2004
Sales 1.9MMM *EMP* 600
SIC 7363

D-U-N-S 12-652-0683
APCO WORLDWIDE INC
A P C O ASSOCIATES
1299 Penn Ave Nw Ste 300, Washington, DC 20004-2412
Tel (202) 638-4082 *Founded/Ownrshp* 2004
Sales 132.2MM^E *EMP* 585
SIC 8748 8742 8732 Business consulting; Foreign trade consultant; Commercial nonphysical research
CEO: Margery Kraus
V Ch: Mark Michelson
CEO: Neal Cohen
Ex VP: Mark Medish
Sr VP: Nelson Fernandez
VP: Lisa Carr
VP: Matthew Gallagher
VP: Alexandra Lazorchak
VP: Scott Milburn
VP: Chrystine Zacherau
Exec: Richard Allen
Assoc Dir: Laura Bacci
Assoc Dir: Usha Harikrishnan
Assoc Dir: Carly Ramsey
Assoc Dir: Ramon Wright

D-U-N-S 04-812-0570 IMP/EXP
■ APCOM INC
AO SMITH
(*Suby of* STATE WATER HEATERS) ★
125 Se Parkway, Franklin, TN 37064-3925
Tel (615) 794-5574 *Founded/Ownrshp* 1969
Sales 120.0MM^E *EMP* 325
SIC 3491 5064 Valves, automatic control; Water heaters, electric
Pr: Paul Dana
VP Mfg: Larry Lillard
Prd Mgr: John Myers

APD
See APPLIANCE PARTS DEPOT LP

APEI
See AMERICAN PUBLIC EDUCATION INC

D-U-N-S 08-011-9854
APERION CARE PERU LLC (IL)
1850 W Matador St, Peru, IN 46970-3711
Tel (765) 689-5000 *Founded/Ownrshp* 2014
Sales 1.2MM^E *EMP* 1,001
SIC 8051 Skilled nursing care facilities

D-U-N-S 80-347-1432
APEX CAPITAL CORP
6000 Western Pl Ste 1000, Fort Worth, TX 76107-4699
Tel (800) 511-6022 *Founded/Ownrshp* 1995
Sales NA *EMP* 210
SIC 6153 Factoring services
Pr: David Baker
**VP:* Dean A Tetirick
Exec: Shelley Sullivan
Snr Sftwr: Larry Wilson
Sftwr Eng: Dave Ashworth
Sftwr Eng: Chad Donohue
Mktg Mgr: Sherry Leigh
Snr Mgr: Brian Carlgren

D-U-N-S 07-850-2596
APEX CLEARING CORP
350 N Paul St Ste 1300, Dallas, TX 75201
Tel (214) 765-1100 *Founded/Ownrshp* 2012
Sales NA *EMP* 300
SIC 6099 7389 4813 6289 Check clearing services; Personal service agents, brokers & bureaus; Local & long distance telephone communications; Protective committees
CEO: William Capuzzi
**COO:* John Kenny
**CFO:* William Brennan
**Ofcr:* Brian Gover
Sr VP: Melissa Miller
Sr VP: Gary Wiedman
VP: Lisa Henderson
VP: Melissa Schachter

D-U-N-S 18-920-5032
APEX COMPANIES LLC
APEX ENGINEERING
15850 Crabbs Branch Way # 200, Rockville, MD 20855-2616
Tel (301) 417-0200 *Founded/Ownrshp* 1988
Sales 106.6MM *EMP* 700
Accts Aronson & Company Rockville
SIC 8744 8748 8742 ; Environmental consultant; Safety training service; Hospital & health services consultant
Ch: Peter T Young
Pr: Vincent N Direnzo Jr
CEO: Peter A Ceribelli
COO: Robert Brackett
CFO: Donald Olinger
Sr VP: Roger Nordlinger
VP: Lynn Aminzadeh
Prgrm Mgr: Peter Granholm
Prgrm Mgr: Geoffrey May
Brnch Mgr: Jeff Obrecht
Genl Mgr: Audrey Kunkler
Board of Directors: Joseph Burgess, Jeff Calhoun, Vincent Direnzo Jr, Jim Hoch, Mark Lewis, John Rando, Frank Sica, Peter Young

APEX COVANTAGE
See APEX DATA SERVICES INC

D-U-N-S 19-558-3729
APEX DATA SERVICES INC
APEX COVANTAGE
198 Van Buren St Ste 200, Herndon, VA 20170-5338
Tel (703) 709-3000 *Founded/Ownrshp* 1988
Sales 184.0MM^E *EMP* 2,500
SIC 7374 Data processing & preparation
CEO: Shashikant Gupta
CFO: Hasmik Avetisyan
**Treas:* Srini Vasan
**Ex VP:* Margaret Boryczka
Off Mgr: Melissa Sharon

APEX ENGINEERING
See APEX COMPANIES LLC

D-U-N-S 80-832-7691
APEX EPUBLISHING DATA SERVICES LLC
(*Suby of* APEX COVANTAGE) ★
198 Van Buren St Ste 120, Herndon, VA 20170-5338
Tel (703) 709-3000 *Founded/Ownrshp* 2007
Sales 15.7MM^E *EMP* 1,640^E
SIC 7373 Computer integrated systems design
Prin: Shashikant Gupta

D-U-N-S 03-618-8001
APEX HOLDING CO
8235 Forsyth Blvd Ste 400, Saint Louis, MO 63105-1621
Tel (314) 889-9600 *Founded/Ownrshp* 1979
Sales 239.4MM^E *EMP* 700
SIC 6792 4412 4226 Oil leases, buying & selling on own account; Deep sea foreign transportation of freight; Petroleum & chemical bulk stations & terminals for hire
CEO: Paul A Novelly
**CFO:* John Hank

D-U-N-S 01-522-6132 IMP
APEX INTERNATIONAL MFG INC
134 Columbia Ct, Chaska, MN 55318-2304
Tel (952) 227-3000 *Founded/Ownrshp* 1999
Sales 176.9MM^E *EMP* 400
SIC 2844 Cosmetic preparations
Pr: David Goldberg
**CFO:* Joseph Dougherty
**VP:* Eric Brichta
**VP:* Greg Poirier
QC Dir: Dan Kotecki

D-U-N-S 61-907-9775 IMP/EXP
APEX OIL CO INC
(*Suby of* APEX HOLDING CO) ★
8235 Forsyth Blvd Ste 400, Saint Louis, MO 63105-1644
Tel (314) 889-9600 *Founded/Ownrshp* 1932
Sales 234.4MM^E *EMP* 250
SIC 4412 5084 Deep sea foreign transportation of freight; Petroleum industry machinery
CEO: Paul Anthony Novelly
**Pr:* Ed Wahl
CFO: John L Hank Jr

D-U-N-S 96-266-4293
APEX RESTAURANT MANAGEMENT INC
1024 Serpentine Ln # 101, Pleasanton, CA 94566-4716
Tel (925) 233-0006 *Founded/Ownrshp* 2007
Sales 50.1MM^E *EMP* 1,495^E
SIC 5812 Fast-food restaurant, chain
CEO: Ajay Pal S Dhillon

D-U-N-S 83-819-3720
■ APEX SYSTEMS LLC
(*Suby of* ON ASSIGNMENT INC) ★
4400 Cox Rd Ste 100, Glen Allen, VA 23060-3354
Tel (804) 254-2600 *Founded/Ownrshp* 2012
Sales 113.3MM^E *EMP* 801
SIC 7363 7361

D-U-N-S 96-334-8037 IMP/EXP
APEX TOOL GROUP LLC
NICHOLSON
(*Suby of* BC MOUNTAIN HOLDINGS INC) ★
14600 York Rd Ste A, Sparks, MD 21152-9396
Tel (410) 773-7800 *Founded/Ownrshp* 2013
Sales 2.5MMM^E *EMP* 8,000^E
SIC 3423 Hand & edge tools
CEO: James J Roberts
**Pr:* John P Constantine
CFO: Kevin O'Leary
**Ch:* Thomas Wroe Jr
**Treas:* Charles A Schwertner
VP: Russ Bohart
**VP:* Ray Johnson
**VP:* Robert S Lutz
**VP:* Frank T McFaden
VP: Matthew Nuijens
**VP:* Willard A Sprang
**VP:* Ed Tetreault
VP Bus Dev: James Raskin
Exec: Jake Nichol
Creative D: Dave Roberts

D-U-N-S 55-690-5532
APEXCARE INC
1418 Howe Ave Ste B, Sacramento, CA 95825-3230
Tel (916) 924-9111 *Founded/Ownrshp* 2005
Sales 22.8MM^E *EMP* 2,000^E
SIC 8082 Home health care services
Pr: Kenneth Wang

D-U-N-S 19-156-3824
APHC INC
421 Fayetteville St # 600, Raleigh, NC 27601-1777
Tel (919) 677-2000 *Founded/Ownrshp* 2008
Sales 583.5MM^E *EMP* 2,500
SIC 8711 Consulting engineer
Pr: Mark S Wilson
**Pr:* John C Atz
**VP:* Nicholas L Ellis

D-U-N-S 83-274-3756
APHENA PHARMA SOLUTIONS HOLDINGS INC
1920 Fisk Rd, Cookeville, TN 38506-5010
Tel (215) 953-5100 *Founded/Ownrshp* 2007
Sales 102.4MM^E *EMP* 423
Accts Bdo Usa Llp Nashville Tn
SIC 7389 2834 Packaging & labeling services; Pharmaceutical preparations
Ch: Bob Allen
**CEO:* Kevin H Kerchner
VP: Greg Lane
VP: David Loy

API
See AEROSPACE PRODUCTS INTERNATIONAL INC

API
See AMERICAN PETROLEUM INSTITUTE INC

D-U-N-S 94-399-6009 IMP
API ENTERPRISES INC
4901 S I 35 Service Rd, Oklahoma City, OK 73129-7017
Tel (713) 580-4800 *Founded/Ownrshp* 1992
Sales 98.6MM^E *EMP* 180
SIC 2673 Bags: plastic, laminated & coated
**Pr:* Hiralal Chamdal
Pr: Janak Sheth
VP: Tom Nguyen
Div/Sub He: Ninh Nguyen

D-U-N-S 03-585-4939 IMP/EXP
API GROUP INC
1100 Old Highway 8 Nw, Saint Paul, MN 55112-6447
Tel (651) 636-4320 *Founded/Ownrshp* 1997
Sales 2.4MMM *EMP* 4,237
Accts Kpmg Llp Minneapolis Mn
SIC 1711 1742 7699 1799 Boiler maintenance contractor; Insulation, buildings; Boiler & heating repair services; Insulation of pipes & boilers
Pr: Russell Becker
**Ch Bd:* Lee R Anderson Sr
CFO: Gregory Keup
VP: Ronnie Davidson
VP: James Doody
Dir Risk M: Mike Leidholm
Mng Dir: John McCann
Genl Mgr: Shane Shipman
Dir IT: Keith Hansen
Plnt Mgr: Peter Kaz

D-U-N-S 07-879-1497
API HEAT TRANSFER CO
2777 Walden Ave Ste 1, Buffalo, NY 14225-4788
Tel (716) 684-6700 *Founded/Ownrshp* 2005
Sales 350.0MM^E *EMP* 1,723^E
SIC 3443 Heat exchangers: coolers (after, inter), condensers, etc.
Pr: Joseph Cordosi

D-U-N-S 14-254-3490 IMP/EXP
API HEAT TRANSFER INC
API SCHMIDT BRETTEN DIVISION
(*Suby of* API HEAT TRANSFER CO) ★
2777 Walden Ave Ste 1, Buffalo, NY 14225-4788
Tel (716) 684-6700 *Founded/Ownrshp* 2012
Sales 350.0MM^E *EMP* 1,500
SIC 5084 Heat exchange equipment, industrial
Pr: Michael Laisure
**CFO:* Bill Dunn
CFO: Dave Hoffman
CFO: Barbara Jackson
Ofcr: Fran Lounsbury
VP: Rice David
**VP:* Jill Kelly
**VP:* Jeff Lennox
**VP:* Dave Rice
Mng Dir: Calvin Chin
Mng Dir: Friedrich Schenker

D-U-N-S 08-564-5117 IMP/EXP
API INDUSTRIES INC
ALUF PLASTICS DIVISION
2 Glenshaw St, Orangeburg, NY 10962-1207
Tel (845) 365-2200 *Founded/Ownrshp* 1977
Sales 122.8MM^E *EMP* 310
SIC 2673 3081 Plastic bags: made from purchased materials; Unsupported plastics film & sheet
CEO: Susan Rosenberg
**Pr:* Reuven Rosenberg
CFO: Martin Ayrovainen
Genl Mgr: Gabriel Kahana
Off Mgr: Rivka Eichenstein
Sfty Mgr: Ezra Majerowitz
VP Sls: Greg Kampschroer

API PERFORATING
See ANDERSON PERFORATING LTD

API SCHMIDT BRETTEN DIVISION
See API HEAT TRANSFER INC

API TECHNOLOGIES
See SPECTRUM CONTROL INC

D-U-N-S 79-006-5564
API TECHNOLOGIES CORP
(*Suby of* RF1 HOLDING CO) ★
400 Nickerson Rd, Marlborough, MA 01752-4717
Tel (855) 294-3800 *Founded/Ownrshp* 2016
Sales 232.2MM *EMP* 1,942^E
SIC 3674 Semiconductors & related devices
Pr: Robert E Tavares
**CFO:* Eric F Seeton

D-U-N-S 19-636-7416
■ APIGEE CORP
(*Suby of* GOOGLE INC) ★
10 Almaden Blvd Ste 1600, San Jose, CA 95113-2275
Tel (408) 343-7300 *Founded/Ownrshp* 2016
Sales 92.0MM^E *EMP* 374
Accts Kpmg Llp Santa Clara Califor
SIC 7371 Computer software development & applications
CEO: Chet Kapoor
CFO: Tim Wan
Sr VP: Ed Anuff
VP: Bala Kasiviswanathan
VP: Simon Molenberg

VP: Shankar Ramaswamy
VP: Scott Regan
VP: Niraj Tulachan
CTO: Anant Jhingran
Board of Directors: Bob L Corey, Neal Dempsey, William D Jenkins Jr, Edmond Mesrobian, Robert Schwartz

D-U-N-S 03-755-3664 IMP/EXP
■ APIO INC
(*Suby of* LANDEC CORP) ★
4575 W Main St, Guadalupe, CA 93434-1659
Tel (800) 454-1355 *Founded/Ownrshp* 1998
Sales 488.0MM *EMP* 90
SIC 2099 0723 Food preparations; Vegetable packing services
CEO: Ron Midyett
Pr: Tim Nykoluk
Pr: Debra Vanhorsen
Ex VP: Mike Casazza
Comm Dir: Dennis Flynn
Genl Mgr: Doug Larose
CTO: Betsy Coria
MIS Dir: Stacia Skinner
IT Man: Richard Carter
Tech Mgr: Judy Davis
VP Opers: Bill Richardville

APL
See AMERICAN PRESIDENT LINES LTD

APL
See JOHNS HOPKINS UNIVERSITY APPLIED PHYSICS LABORATORY LLC

D-U-N-S 15-870-9829
APL LOGISTICS AMERICAS LTD
A P L
(*Suby of* APL LOGISTICS LTD)
16220 N Scottsdale Rd, Scottsdale, AZ 85254-1720
Tel (602) 586-4800 *Founded/Ownrshp* 1996
Sales 1.8MMM[E] *EMP* 4,205
SIC 4731 Domestic freight forwarding
CEO: William K Villalon
**Pr:* Jim McAdam
Sr VP: Danny Goh
Sr VP: Tony Zasimovich
VP: May Chew
VP: Ted Fordney
VP: David Frentzel
VP: David Goodwin
VP: Rajiv Saxena
VP: William Villalon
VP: Eddy Wouters
Exec: Claudia Brasser
Exec: Rodolfo Paiz

D-U-N-S 17-498-5791 IMP
APL LOGISTICS AMERICAS LTD
(*Suby of* A P L) ★
2649 Internationale Pkwy, Woodridge, IL 60517-4803
Tel (630) 783-0200 *Founded/Ownrshp* 2005
Sales 134.5MM[E] *EMP* 21[E]
SIC 3531 Construction machinery
Pr: Crystal Stram

D-U-N-S 10-297-0597
APL LOGISTICS LTD
(*Suby of* APL LOGISTICS LTD)
16220 N Scottsdale Rd # 300, Scottsdale, AZ 85254-1798
Tel (602) 586-4800 *Founded/Ownrshp* 1983
Sales 1.6MMM[E] *EMP* 4,782
SIC 4412 4731 4491 4011 Deep sea foreign transportation of freight; Freight transportation arrangement; Agents, shipping; Truck transportation brokers; Freight consolidation; Stevedoring; Railroads, line-haul operating
Ch: Cheng Ywai Keung
**Pr:* Kenneth Glenn
Pr: Daniel Montgomery
**Pr:* Gene Seroka
**CEO:* Ronald Dean Widdows
**COO:* Nathaniel Seeds
**CFO:* Shigeo Mori
CFO: Kam G Soh
**Treas:* Robert Sappio
Treas: William J Stuebgen
**Chf Cred:* Peter Jongepier
Ex VP: Ian Moore
Sr VP: Dave Appleton
Sr VP: Danny Goh
Sr VP: Jeff Theobald
VP: May Chew
VP: Eric Eng
VP: Pradeep Kumar
VP: Tommy Lee
VP: Bob Sappio
VP: Cindy Stoddard
Board of Directors: Ernest G Frankel, Timothy J Rhein

D-U-N-S 05-409-4693 IMP/EXP
APL LOGISTICS WAREHOUSE MANAGEMENT SERVICES INC
(*Suby of* A P L) ★
16220 N Scottsdale Rd # 300, Scottsdale, AZ 85254-1720
Tel (480) 483-0886 *Founded/Ownrshp* 2001
Sales 406.9MM[E] *EMP* 2,642
SIC 4213 4225 Trucking, except local; General warehousing
Pr: Hans Mueller- Hickler
Pr: David Frentzel
CFO: Glynis A Bryan
Treas: Neil West
VP: William K Villalon

D-U-N-S 11-157-8738
APM TERMINALS NORTH AMERICA INC
(*Suby of* MAERSK LINE) ★
9300 Arrowpoint Blvd, Charlotte, NC 28273-8136
Tel (704) 571-2768 *Founded/Ownrshp* 1996
Sales 206.7MM[E] *EMP* 1,329[E]
SIC 4491 Marine cargo handling
CEO: Kim Fejfer
**Pr:* Eric Sisco
**CFO:* Wim Lagaay
**Chf Cred:* Jonathan Goldner
**Sr VP:* John Crowley

Sr VP: Glenn Eddy
**Sr VP:* John Loeprich
**VP:* Jack Craig
**VP:* Stacey Fales
VP: Rich D Rosa
Genl Mgr: Ed McCarthy

D-U-N-S 00-196-2042 IMP/EXP
▲ APOGEE ENTERPRISES INC (MN)
4400 W 78th St Ste 520, Minneapolis, MN 55435-5446
Tel (952) 835-1874 *Founded/Ownrshp* 1949
Sales 981.1MM *EMP* 4,614
Tkr Sym APOG *Exch* NGS
SIC 3231 Products of purchased glass; Strengthened or reinforced glass
Pr: Joseph F Puishys
**Ch Bd:* Bernard P Aldrich
CFO: James S Porter
Treas: Gary R Johnson
Sr VP: John A Klein
Off Admin: Joy Keopple
Sfty Dirs: John Weddle
Board of Directors: Jerome L Davis, Sara L Hays, John T Manning, Robert J Marzec, Donald A Nolan, Richard V Reynolds, Patricia K Wagner, David E Weiss

D-U-N-S 04-887-7500
■ APOGEE WAUSAU GROUP INC
WAUSAU WINDOW AND WALL SYSTEM
(*Suby of* APOGEE ENTERPRISES INC) ★
7800 International Dr, Wausau, WI 54401-9623
Tel (715) 845-2161 *Founded/Ownrshp* 1968
Sales 106.3MM[E] *EMP* 500[E]
SIC 3479 3442 3471 3449 Painting, coating & hot dipping; Window & door frames; Sash, door or window: metal; Casements, aluminum; Plating & polishing; Miscellaneous metalwork
Pr: Rick Marshall
VP: Kevin Rell
Sfty Mgr: Doug Janz
Opers Mgr: Brian V Heuvel
Manager: Keith Lindberg
Snr Mgr: Sarah Zydzik

D-U-N-S 16-729-4094
APOGEN TECHNOLOGIES INC
(*Suby of* VENCORE SERVICES AND SOLUTIONS INC) ★
11091 Sunset Hills Rd # 200, Reston, VA 20190-5378
Tel (703) 644-6433 *Founded/Ownrshp* 2004
Sales 74.1MM[E] *EMP* 1,294
SIC 7373 7379 Computer integrated systems design; Computer related consulting services
Pr: Paul Leslie
**CFO:* Thomas W Weston Jr
Prgrm Mgr: Fatima Abugideiri

D-U-N-S 18-616-5544
■ APOGENT TECHNOLOGIES INC
(*Suby of* FISHER SCIENTIFIC INTERNATIONAL LLC) ★
81 Wyman St, Waltham, MA 02451-1223
Tel (781) 622-1300 *Founded/Ownrshp* 2004
Sales 219.8MM[E] *EMP* 7,200
Accts Deloitte & Touche Llp New Yor
SIC 3821 3229 3843 Laboratory apparatus & furniture; Laboratory heating apparatus; Scientific glassware; Dental equipment & supplies; Dental materials; Dental equipment; Orthodontic appliances
Pr: Seth H Hoogasian
**Treas:* Anthony Smith
Bd of Dir: William Binnie
Bd of Dir: Don Davis
Bd of Dir: Stephen Hadis
Bd of Dir: Stephen Hardis
Bd of Dir: R Harris
Bd of Dir: William Parfet
Bd of Dir: Mary Puma
Bd of Dir: Simon Rich
Bd of Dir: Joe Roby
Bd of Dir: Richard Vieser
Div/Sub He: Duncan Ross
Div/Sub He: Yuh Tsay

APOLLO BRANDS
See MACH SPEED HOLDINGS LLC

D-U-N-S 83-151-7284
APOLLO COMMERCIAL REAL ESTATE FINANCE INC
9 W 57th St Fl 43, New York, NY 10019-2700
Tel (212) 515-3200 *Founded/Ownrshp* 2009
Sales 192.1MM *EMP* 2
Tkr Sym ARI *Exch* NYS
SIC 6798 Real estate investment trusts
Pr: Stuart A Rothstein
**Ch Bd:* Jeffrey M Gault
CFO: Jai Agarwal
CFO: Megan B Gaul

D-U-N-S 03-908-9248
▲ APOLLO EDUCATION GROUP INC
4025 S Riverpoint Pkwy, Phoenix, AZ 85040-0723
Tel (480) 966-5394 *Founded/Ownrshp* 1973
Sales 2.1MMM *EMP* 34,000
Tkr Sym APOL *Exch* NGS
SIC 8221 8299 8748 University; Educational services; Educational consultant
CEO: Gregory W Cappelli
**Ch Bd:* Peter V Sperling
**V Ch:* Terri C Bishop
COO: J Mitchell Bowling
CFO: Gregory J Iverson
CFO: Byron Uopx
Ofcr: Matravius Avent
Ofcr: Stacey Etherington
Sr VP: Sean B W Martin
Sr VP: Frederick J Newton
VP: Ed Escobedo
VP: Alicia Miner
VP: Stacy Tucker
Exec: Preston Amsbaugh
Exec: Stacia Brocco
Exec: Eugene Duvall
Exec: Elizabeth Graney
Exec: Leslie Iverson
Exec: Ryan Munoz
Exec: Madison Reynolds
Assoc Dir: Chris Brown

Board of Directors: Dana H Born, Matthew Carter Jr, Richard H Dozer, Roy A Herberger Jr, Ann Kirschner, Robert S Murley, Manuel F Rivelo, Darby E Shupp, Allen R Weiss

D-U-N-S 96-251-9000
▲ APOLLO GLOBAL MANAGEMENT LLC
9 W 57th St Fl 43, New York, NY 10019-2700
Tel (212) 515-3200 *Founded/Ownrshp* 1990
Sales 1.0MMM *EMP* 3,615
Tkr Sym APO *Exch* NYS
SIC 6726 6282 6799 Management investment funds, closed-end; Investment advice; Investment advisory service; Real estate investors, except property operators
Ch Bd: Leon Black
CFO: Teresa Covello
CFO: Gregory Hunt
CFO: Martin Kelly
Assoc Dir: Albert Chen
Board of Directors: Michael Ducey, Paul Fribourg, Robert Kraft, Alvin Bernard Krongard, Pauline Richards

D-U-N-S 08-463-1498 IMP/EXP
APOLLO IDEMITSU CORP
(*Suby of* IDEMITSU KOSAN CO.,LTD.)
1831 16th St, Sacramento, CA 95811-6606
Tel (916) 443-0890 *Founded/Ownrshp* 1976
Sales 7.6MMM[E] *EMP* 6,941
SIC 5172 2911 Petroleum products; Crude oil; Petroleum refining
CEO: Tadashi Terauchi
**Pr:* T Kono
VP: Brian Coulson
**Prin:* Toshiaki Sagishima
IT Man: Rod Tkach
Manager: Norm Ueunten
Sls Mgr: Danielle Chavez

D-U-N-S 93-321-4892
APOLLO INC
1133 W Columbia Dr, Kennewick, WA 99336-3472
Tel (509) 586-1104 *Founded/Ownrshp* 1993
Sales 93.5MM[E] *EMP* 250
SIC 1542 Nonresidential construction
Pr: Bruce Ratchford
**Treas:* Angie Haisch
**Ex VP:* Jesse Van Schoiack
**VP:* Dan Briscoe
**VP:* Amy Jenne
Div Mgr: Mitch Ratchford
Div Mgr: Mark Vealey
Opers Mgr: Lars Refvik

D-U-N-S 78-564-0660
▲ APOLLO INVESTMENT CORP
9 W 57th St Fl 43, New York, NY 10019-2700
Tel (212) 515-3450 *Founded/Ownrshp* 2004
Sales 379.7MM *EMP* 6[E]
Tkr Sym AINV *Exch* NGS
SIC 6726 Management investment funds, closed-end
CEO: James C Zelter
**Ch Bd:* John J Hannan
Pr: Howard Widra
CFO: Gregory W Hunt
Chf Cred: Cindy Z Michel

D-U-N-S 62-395-7334
APOLLO INVESTMENT FUND VI LP
1 Manhattanville Rd # 201, Purchase, NY 10577-2100
Tel (914) 694-8000 *Founded/Ownrshp* 2007
Sales 633.7MM[E] *EMP* 13,800
SIC 6726 Investors syndicates
Pt: Mark J Rowan
Mng Dir: Jeffrey D Benjamin

D-U-N-S 82-842-8750
■ APOLLO MANAGEMENT HOLDINGS LP
(*Suby of* APOLLO GLOBAL MANAGEMENT LLC) ★
9 W 57th St Fl 43, New York, NY 10019-2706
Tel (212) 515-3200 *Founded/Ownrshp* 2007
Sales 1.6MMM[E] *EMP* 85
SIC 8741 Management services
CEO: Leon Black
Pr: Marc Spilker
CFO: Martin Kelly
Treas: John Donohoe
Mng Dir: Ayad Alhadi
Off Mgr: Brigitte Zaki
Snr Mgr: Novell Loh

D-U-N-S 88-495-7374
■ APOLLO MANAGEMENT LP
(*Suby of* APOLLO MANAGEMENT HOLDINGS LP) ★
9 W 57th St Fl 43, New York, NY 10019-2706
Tel (212) 515-3200 *Founded/Ownrshp* 1994
Sales 1.6MMM[E] *EMP* 84[E]
SIC 6799 6531 Real estate investors, except property operators; Commodity investors; Real estate managers
Prin: Marc J Rowan
Pt: Cheryl G Gordon
**Mng Pt:* Leon Black
**Mng Pt:* Joshua Harris
COO: Henry Silverman
Bd of Dir: Jordan Zaken
**Prin:* Peter Copses
**Prin:* Gerald Cruz

D-U-N-S 96-825-6227
APOLLO MANAGEMENT V LP
1 Manhattanville Rd # 201, Purchase, NY 10577-2100
Tel (914) 467-6510 *Founded/Ownrshp* 2000
Sales 221.8MM[E] *EMP* 4,370
SIC 5051 3272 3354 Metals service centers & offices; Iron & steel (ferrous) products; Aluminum bars, rods, ingots, sheets, pipes, plates, etc.; Building materials, except block or brick: concrete; Aluminum extruded products
Ch Bd: Lourenco Goncalves

D-U-N-S 05-307-0231
APOLLO OIL LLC (KY)
CUSTOM AUTO EQP SPECIALISTS
1175 Early Dr, Winchester, KY 40391-3012
Tel (859) 744-5444 *Founded/Ownrshp* 1970, 2000
Sales 193.4MM *EMP* 140

SIC 5172 5013 Engine fuels & oils; Automotive supplies
Genl Mgr: Phillip Holley
**CFO:* Ransom E Dotson
Exec: Carol Haddix
Genl Mgr: Dewayne Lee
**Genl Mgr:* William E Stevens

D-U-N-S 11-422-7929
APOLLO PROFESSIONAL SOLUTIONS INC
29 Stiles Rd Ste 302, Salem, NH 03079-5802
Tel (866) 277-3343 *Founded/Ownrshp* 1983
Sales 36.0MM *EMP* 1,135
SIC 7363 Temporary help service
Pr: Gayle Williams
**Treas:* Simpat Parnagian
**VP:* Edward Bonadio
Brnch Mgr: Jennifer Leck

D-U-N-S 96-814-6055
APOLLO RESIDENTIAL MORTGAGE INC
9 W 57th St Fl 43, New York, NY 10019-2700
Tel (212) 515-3200 *Founded/Ownrshp* 2011
Sales 160.1MM *EMP* 3[E]
SIC 6798 Real estate investment trusts
Pr: Michael A Commaroto
**Ch Bd:* Frederick N Khedouri
CFO: Teresa D Covello
CFO: Gregory W Hunt

D-U-N-S 62-564-9546
APOLLO SECURITY INTERNATIONAL INC
2150 Bston Providence Hwy, Walpole, MA 02081
Tel (508) 660-1197 *Founded/Ownrshp* 1990
Sales 35.6MM[E] *EMP* 1,365
SIC 7381 8748 Security guard service; Private investigator; Business consulting
CEO: Dennis M Crowley Jr
**Pr:* Kenneth D Jenkins
**Treas:* Margaret Crowley
VP: Steve Lisle
Area Mgr: Steve McKinnon
IT Man: Gregory Pais
Secur Mgr: Nicole Orne

D-U-N-S 05-333-8794
APOLLO SHEET METAL INC
1201 W Columbia Dr, Kennewick, WA 99336-3459
Tel (509) 586-1104 *Founded/Ownrshp* 1981
Sales 253.9MM[E] *EMP* 1,000[E]
SIC 1711 3444 Mechanical contractor; Sheet metalwork
Pr: Bruce Ratchford
Pr: Emily Castle
**Pr:* Bob Hightower
**CEO:* Angie Haisch
**Ex VP:* Jesse Van Schoack
**VP:* Dan Briscoe
VP: Dale Hollandsworth
VP: Amy Jenne
Dir Bus: Dan McCormick
Prd Mgr: Don Westfall

D-U-N-S 80-199-5809
■ APOLLO SVF MANAGEMENT LP ★
(*Suby of* AREA PROPERTY PARTNERS L P) ★
1 Manhattanville Rd # 201, Purchase, NY 10577-2128
Tel (914) 694-8000 *Founded/Ownrshp* 2006
Sales 45.5MM[E] *EMP* 1,179[E]
SIC 6726 Investment offices
CEO: James Zelter

D-U-N-S 80-199-5833
■ APOLLO VALUE MANAGEMENT LP
(*Suby of* AREA PROPERTY PARTNERS L P) ★
2 Mnhttnville Rd Fl 2, Purchase, NY 10577
Tel (914) 694-8000 *Founded/Ownrshp* 2003
Sales 87.3MM[E] *EMP* 1,886[E]
SIC 6726 Investment offices
Prin: Steven Martinez

APOLLO VALVES
See CONBRACO INDUSTRIES INC

D-U-N-S 09-231-2735 IMP
APOTHECARY PRODUCTS LLC
11750 12th Ave S, Burnsville, MN 55337-1297
Tel (800) 328-2742 *Founded/Ownrshp* 1975
Sales 107.0MM[E] *EMP* 536
SIC 2834 5122 3069 Druggists' preparations (pharmaceuticals); Pharmaceuticals; Druggists' rubber sundries; Baby pacifiers, rubber; Teething rings, rubber
Pr: Nathan Hanson
**CFO:* Darran Spence
Sls Mgr: Cindy Bleisner

D-U-N-S 07-886-5093
APP WHOLESALE LLC
3686 E Olympic Blvd, Los Angeles, CA 90023-3146
Tel (323) 980-8315 *Founded/Ownrshp* 2013
Sales 164.1MM[E] *EMP* 500
SIC 5149 Specialty food items

D-U-N-S 60-437-5287 IMP
APPA SEAFOOD INC
FAIRMONT AND CLARK
135 Klug Cir, Corona, CA 92880-5424
Tel (951) 278-2772 *Founded/Ownrshp* 1987
Sales 90.8MM[E] *EMP* 364
SIC 5411 Convenience stores; Convenience stores, chain
Pr: Thom Rindt
**VP:* Michael Rindt
Plnt Mgr: Saul Gallegos

D-U-N-S 06-539-7838 EXP
APPALACHIA HOLDING CO
MASSEY COAL EXPORT COMPANY
(*Suby of* ALPHA APPALACHIA HOLDINGS INC) ★
1 Alpha Pl, Bristol, VA 24202
Tel (276) 619-4410 *Founded/Ownrshp* 1916, 2000
Sales 711.0MM[E] *EMP* 5,407
SIC 1221 Bituminous coal surface mining; Coal preparation plant, bituminous or lignite
VP: Richard H Verheij
Treas: Philip W Nichols
**Chf Cred:* Jeffrey M Jarosinski
**Sr VP:* J Christopher Adkins

*VP: Baxter F Phillips
*VP: H Drexel Short
VP Opers: Dwayne Francisco

D-U-N-S 06-670-7605
APPALACHIAN ELECTRIC COOPERATIVE
TENNESSEE ELECTRIC COOP ASSN
1109 Hill Dr, New Market, TN 37820-3832
Tel (423) 586-4755 Founded/Ownrshp 1940
Sales 104.3MM EMP 98
Accts Pugh & Company Pc Knoxville
SIC 4911 Distribution, electric power
Pr: Robert Drinnen
COO: Conard Srye
*Sec: Charles A Catlett
*Ex VP: William A Underwood
*VP: Rody Blevins

D-U-N-S 13-471-8530
APPALACHIAN PIPELINE CONTRACTORS LLP
170 E Main St Ste D, Hendersonville, TN 37075-3952
Tel (615) 264-8775 Founded/Ownrshp 2003
Sales 103.4MM^E EMP 300
SIC 1623 Oil & gas pipeline construction
Prin: Andrew Crooks
Pt: Jana Metcalfe Crooks
Pt: Bobby A Crotts
Pt: Jimmy Crotts
Pt: Jamey Wade
Off Mgr: Hollie Durham
Mtls Mgr: Andy Baldwin
Sfty Mgr: Albert Collins

D-U-N-S 00-794-1537 IMP
■ **APPALACHIAN POWER CO** (VA)
AEP
(Suby of AEP) ★
1 Riverside Plz, Columbus, OH 43215-2355
Tel (614) 716-1000 Founded/Ownrshp 1926
Sales 2.9MMM EMP 1,967^E
SIC 4911 Electric services; Distribution, electric power; Generation, electric power; Transmission, electric power
Ch Bd: Nicholas K Akins
*CFO: Brian X Tierney
VP: Jeffery Lafleur
VP: Armando A Pe
VP: Barbara Radous
VP: Phil Wright
Board of Directors: Lisa M Barton, David M Feinberg, Lana L Hillebrand, Mark C McCullough, Robert P Powers, Dennis E Welch

D-U-N-S 05-868-5439
APPALACHIAN REGIONAL HEALTHCARE INC
2260 Executive Dr, Lexington, KY 40505-4808
Tel (859) 226-2440 Founded/Ownrshp 1955
Sales 591.0MM^E EMP 4,520
Accts Mountjoy Chilton Medley Llp L
SIC 8062 General medical & surgical hospitals
Pr: Jerry W Haynes
*Pr: Joseph L Grossman
COO: Willis Bultje
*CFO: Christopher Ellington
CFO: Judy Lykins
Trst: Mary Hall
Trst: Syam H Reddy
*VP: Joe Grossman
*VP: Danny Harris
VP: Hollie Harris
*VP: Rick King
Dir Rad: Joe Forton
Dir Rx: Pat Amburgey
Dir Rx: Leigh A Hall
Dir Rx: Don Rigdon
Dir Rx: Leann Umburger

D-U-N-S 96-489-3304
APPALACHIAN REGIONAL HEALTHCARE SYSTEM INC
336 Deerfield Rd, Boone, NC 28607-5008
Tel (828) 262-4100 Founded/Ownrshp 2010
Sales 160.9MM EMP 2,100^E
Accts Dixon Hughes Goodman Llp Roan
SIC 8062 Hospital, medical school affiliation
CEO: Richard Sparks
CFO: Kevin May
Chf Mktg O: Herman Godwin
Ofcr: Chris Benfield
Ofcr: Brandon Greer
Ofcr: Mitch Rattler
VP: Angie Hicks
VP: Maran Sigmon
Exec: Jean Johnson
Exec: Diane Wilson
Dir Lab: Ellen White
Dir Rx: Jeffrey Akers
Dir Rx: Jason Rice

D-U-N-S 15-847-5041
APPALACHIAN RESPITE CARE LTD
DAYSPRING HEALTHCARE CENTER
501 Pinecrest Dr, Beverly, OH 45715-8909
Tel (740) 984-4262 Founded/Ownrshp 2000
Sales 441.2MM EMP 75
SIC 8051 Skilled nursing care facilities
Pt: Meg Suermondt

D-U-N-S 06-629-9918
APPALACHIAN STATE UNIVERSITY INC
(Suby of OFFICE OF PRESIDENT) ★
438 Academy St Rm 340, Boone, NC 28608-0001
Tel (828) 262-2000 Founded/Ownrshp 1899
Sales 194.5MM EMP 3,390^E
Accts Beth A Wood Cpa Raleigh No
SIC 8221 Colleges universities & professional schools
Ch Bd: G A Sywassink
*Ch Bd: Alice G Roess
*V Ch Bd: James M Barnes
VP: Emily Haas
VP: Tim Hetherington
VP: Emily Lane
VP: John Misenheimer
VP: Brad Price
VP: Tyler Sawyer
VP: McRae Whitley

Dir Lab: Tim Leonard
Assoc Dir: Kathy Graham
Assoc Dir: Brad Vest
Assoc Dir: Peter Wachs

D-U-N-S 00-895-8720 IMP
APPALACHIAN TIRE PRODUCTS INC (WV)
2907 4th Ave, Charleston, WV 25387-1797
Tel (304) 744-9473 Founded/Ownrshp 1947
Sales 126.3MM^E EMP 150
SIC 5014 5531 5013 7534 Tires & tubes; Automotive tires; Automotive supplies & parts; Rebuilding & retreading tires
Ch: Walter B Dial Jr
*Pr: Jennifer Dial
*Treas: Walt E Dial Jr
*VP: Pat Graney
Site Mgr: Teddy Lambert
Sls Mgr: Keith Williams

APPALACHIAN WIRELESS
See EAST KENTUCKY NETWORK LLC

D-U-N-S 18-117-6298 IMP
APPAREL BRANDS INC
AB TEXTILES
434 Carolina Way, Highlands, NC 28741
Tel (828) 526-0167 Founded/Ownrshp 1986
Sales 37.0MM^E EMP 1,350
SIC 2325 2337 8721 Men's & boys' trousers & slacks; Women's & misses' suits & coats; Accounting, auditing & bookkeeping
CEO: Judith Y Brinson
*Pr: Jack Brinson

D-U-N-S 82-710-2190 IMP
APPAREL CONCEPTS INTERNATIONAL INC
CLH GROUP, THE
4804 Laurel Canyon Blvd # 59, Valley Village, CA 91607-3717
Tel (626) 233-9198 Founded/Ownrshp 1995
Sales 73.9MM^E EMP 1,560
SIC 5136 Men's & boys' clothing
Pr: John Vorzimer

D-U-N-S 00-128-6459 IMP/EXP
APPAREL GROUP LTD
(Suby of TAG HOLDINGS INC) ★
883 Trinity Dr, Lewisville, TX 75056-5297
Tel (214) 469-3300 Founded/Ownrshp 1934
Sales 150.0MM EMP 200
SIC 2339 2321 Sportswear, women's; Men's & boys' dress shirts; Sport shirts, men's & boys': from purchased materials
CEO: Chris Nakatani
*Pr: Thomas J Dietrich
*COO: John Liu
*CFO: Terry Lay
Sales Exec: Michelle Abernathy
Sls Mgr: Pam Wyke

D-U-N-S 96-268-0190
APPDYNAMICS INC
303 2nd St Ste N450, San Francisco, CA 94107-3636
Tel (415) 442-8400 Founded/Ownrshp 2008
Sales 119.6MM^E EMP 1,000^E
SIC 7371 Computer software development
CEO: David Wadhwani
Pr: Joe Sexton
CFO: Randy Gottfried
Founder: Jyoti Bansal
Chf Mktg O: Kendall Collins
Sr VP: Ed Rowe
VP: Jeremy Duggan
VP: Stuart Horne
VP: Brian Howie
VP: Jonah Kowall
VP: Kalyan Ramanathan
VP: Hatim Shafique
VP: Bhaskar Sunkara
VP: Dan Wright
Exec: Tom Reksten
Creative D: Shireen Afshar
Board of Directors: Jonathan C Chadwick, Ravi Mhatre, Gary M Reiner, Charles J Robel, David C Scott

APPELLATE SUPREME COURT
See UNIFIED COURT SYSTEM OF NEW YORK STATE

APPERT'S FOODSERVICE
See APPERTS INC

APPERT'S FOODSERVICE
See SYSCO WESTERN MINNESOTA INC

D-U-N-S 00-617-9089
■ **APPERTS INC**
APPERT'S FOODSERVICE
(Suby of SYSCO CORP) ★
900 Highway 10 S, Saint Cloud, MN 56304-1807
Tel (320) 251-3200 Founded/Ownrshp 2013
Sales 182.9MM^E EMP 190
SIC 5142 5141 5411 5421 2013 Packaged frozen goods; Frozen fish, meat & poultry; Groceries, general line; Grocery stores; Meat & fish markets; Frozen meats from purchased meat
Ch: Timothy Appert
*Pr: Joseph R Omann
*VP: Wayne Harrison

D-U-N-S 87-850-4856
APPIAN CORP
11955 Democracy Dr # 1700, Reston, VA 20190-5662
Tel (703) 442-8844 Founded/Ownrshp 1999
Sales 179.1MM^E EMP 450^E
SIC 7379 7371 Computer related consulting services; Computer software development & applications
Pr: Matthew W Calkins
*CFO: Mark Lynch
*Sr VP: Michael Beckley
*Sr VP: Marc Wilson
*VP: Samir Gulati
*VP: Suvajit Gupta
VP: David Metzger
VP: Garry Yeates
Comm Dir: Ben Farrell
*Prin: Harry Weller
*Mng Dir: Martijn Schilperoort
Board of Directors: Michael G Devine, Harry Weller

D-U-N-S 82-606-4060
APPIRIO INC
760 Market St Ste 1150, San Francisco, CA 94102-2306
Tel (415) 663-4433 Founded/Ownrshp 2006
Sales 180.0MM EMP 1,200
SIC 7371 7379 Computer software development & applications; Computer related consulting services
Pr: Chris Barbin
Pr: Mike Pav
CFO: Rick Gross
*CFO: Mark O'Connor
Sr VP: Ellen Humphrey
*Sr VP: Dan Lascell
Sr VP: Dave Orrico
VP: Takashi Watanabe
*CTO: Alex Castro
Opers Mgr: Kathleen Hohl
VP Sls: Dan Carayiannis
Board of Directors: Jeff Epstein, Matt Thompson

D-U-N-S 07-848-5735
APPLABS TECHNOLOGIES PVT LTD
(Suby of COMPUTER SCIENCES CORPORATION INDIA PRIVATE LIMITED)
1515 Market St Ste 1110, Philadelphia, PA 19102-1905
Tel (215) 563-9396 Founded/Ownrshp 2011
Sales 84.6MM^E EMP 2,300^E
SIC 7373 Computer integrated systems design
Pr: Michael Lawrie
Pr: William L Berg
VP: Robert Gushue
VP: Kalyana Konda
Snr Ntwrk: Jerry Steed
Sls&Mrk Ex: Shane Raut
Snr Mgr: Gopal Subrahmanyam

D-U-N-S 09-571-1524
APPLE AMERICAN GROUP LLC
APPLEBEE'S
(Suby of FLYNN RESTAURANT GROUP LLC) ★
6200 Oak Tree Blvd # 250, Independence, OH 44131-6943
Tel (216) 525-2775 Founded/Ownrshp 2001
Sales 1.1MMM EMP 5,500
Accts Pricewaterhousecoopers Llp Cl
SIC 5812 Restaurant, family: chain
COO: Brad Pettinger
Exec: Katy Sienko
Genl Mgr: Sarah Chamberland
Genl Mgr: Eddie Evans
Genl Mgr: Kenneth Tousignant
Off Mgr: Eric Pasto
CTO: Gary Simpson
Genl Couns: Melissa Griffin

D-U-N-S 86-844-7400
APPLE AMERICAN INDIANA LLC
6515 E 82nd St Ste 109, Indianapolis, IN 46250-1590
Tel (317) 577-8334 Founded/Ownrshp 1993
Sales 21.6MM^E EMP 2,000
Accts Price Waterhouse Coopers
SIC 5812 5813 Restaurant, family: chain; Bar (drinking places)

D-U-N-S 79-064-1898
APPLE AMERICAN LIMITED PARTNERSHIP OF OHIO
APPLEBEE'S
8905 Lake Ave, Cleveland, OH 44102-6315
Tel (216) 961-6767 Founded/Ownrshp 1993
Sales 31.0MM^E EMP 1,700
Accts Pricewater House Coopers Llp
SIC 5812 Restaurant, family: chain
Pt: Don Strang
Ltd Pt: Allen Musikantow

D-U-N-S 94-985-5753
APPLE AMERICAN LP OF INDIANA
APPLEBEE'S
8905 Lake Ave Fl 2, Cleveland, OH 44102-6316
Tel (216) 961-6767 Founded/Ownrshp 1996
Sales 59.1MM EMP 1,435
Accts Pricewater House Coopers Llp
SIC 5812 Restaurant, family: chain
Pr: Don Strang III

D-U-N-S 00-698-5055
APPLE BANK FOR SAVINGS
1395 Northern Blvd, Manhasset, NY 11030-3007
Tel (516) 627-1800 Founded/Ownrshp 1863
Sales NA EMP 735
SIC 6036 State savings banks, not federally chartered
Ch Bd: Alan Shamoon
*Ch Bd: Steven C B'Ush
Ofcr: Steven B'Ush
Sr VP: Vincent D Baldino
Sr VP: George Bossis
Sr VP: Bruce A Herman
Sr VP: James G Matera
Sr VP: Antonio Pietrantuono
Sr VP: Robin Thomson
VP: Joseph Sherman Dp
VP: Alex Floratos
VP: Michael Lukin
VP: Robert Sovatsky
VP: Ginetta Stroescu

D-U-N-S 62-337-0343
APPLE CORE ENTERPRISES INC
APPLEBEES NIGHORHOOD GRILL BAR
1400 31st Ave Sw, Minot, ND 58701-6965
Tel (701) 838-2822 Founded/Ownrshp 1998
Sales 59.4MM^E EMP 2,000
Accts Brady Martz & Associates Pc
SIC 5812 Restaurant, family: chain
Pr: Myron Thompson
*CFO: Robert Lamont
*VP: Shirley Thompson

D-U-N-S 02-530-2774
APPLE CORPS LP
APPLEBEE'S
1877 N Rock Rd, Wichita, KS 67206-1260
Tel (316) 683-2611 Founded/Ownrshp 1998
Sales 46.3MM^E EMP 1,300
SIC 5812 Restaurant, family: chain

Pt: Darrel Rolph
Pt: David Rolph

APPLE EIGHT
See APPLE REIT EIGHT INC

D-U-N-S 96-973-2424
APPLE EIGHT HOSPITALITY MANAGEMENT INC
(Suby of APPLE REIT EIGHT INC) ★
814 E Main St, Richmond, VA 23219-3306
Tel (804) 727-6337 Founded/Ownrshp 2007
Sales 68.9MM EMP 1,632
SIC 8741 Hotel or motel management
CEO: Justin Knight
*Treas: David McKenney
Ex VP: Nelson Knight
*VP: David Buckley
VP: Bryan Peery
*VP: Bryan Perry

D-U-N-S 15-071-1778
APPLE GOLD INC
APPLEBEES NGHBORHOOD BAR GRILL
164 Wind Chime Ct, Raleigh, NC 27615-6433
Tel (919) 846-2577 Founded/Ownrshp 1984
Sales 75.3MM^E EMP 2,200
SIC 5812 Restaurant, family: chain
Pr: Michael Olander
*Treas: John Sook
Off Mgr: Mark Rhodes
VP Opers: Paul Boyd
Genl Couns: BJ Stolz

D-U-N-S 18-537-8841
APPLE HEALTH CARE INC
APPLE REHAB
21 Waterville Rd, Avon, CT 06001-2097
Tel (860) 678-9755 Founded/Ownrshp 1986
Sales 103.6MM^E EMP 2,000
SIC 8093 Rehabilitation center, outpatient treatment
Pr: Brian J Foley
*CFO: Mark E Hambley
Treas: Curtis Breslin
*VP: Brian F Bedard
VP: Grace Flight
Dir IT: Ileene Chernoff
Dir IT: Wess Zeigenfuse
HC Dir: Shelley Okoye

D-U-N-S 82-917-1466
APPLE HOSPITALITY REIT INC
814 E Main St, Richmond, VA 23219-3306
Tel (804) 344-8121 Founded/Ownrshp 2008
Sales 898.3MM EMP 102^E
SIC 6798 Real estate investment trusts
Pr: Justin G Knight
COO: Kristian M Gathright
CFO: Bryan F Peery
Ex VP: David P Buckley
Ex VP: Nelson G Knight
Board of Directors: Glenn W Bunting, Jon A Fosheim, Bruce H Matson, Daryl A Nickel, L Hugh Redd

D-U-N-S 06-070-4780 IMP/EXP
▲ **APPLE INC**
1 Infinite Loop, Cupertino, CA 95014-2083
Tel (408) 996-1010 Founded/Ownrshp 1977
Sales 215.6MMM EMP 116,000
Accts Ernst & Young Llp San Jose C
Tkr Sym AAPL Exch NGS
SIC 3663 3571 3575 3577 3651 7372 Mobile communication equipment; Personal computers (microcomputers); Computer terminals, monitors & components; Printers, computer; Sound reproducing equipment; Operating systems computer software; Application computer software
CEO: Timothy D Cook
Ch Bd: Arthur D Levinson
Pr: Jennifer Hakes
COO: Jeffrey E Williams
CFO: Luca Maestri
Ofcr: Jonathan Ive
Ex VP: Brian Bedard
Sr VP: Angela Ahrendts
Sr VP: John Browett
Sr VP: Craig Federighi
Sr VP: Daniel Riccio
Sr VP: Philip W Schiller
Sr VP: D Bruce Sewell
Sr VP: Johny Srouji
VP: Ann Bowers
VP: Eduardo H Cue
VP: Doug Field
VP: Jennifer Henard
VP: Oconnor Niall
VP: Kevin Saul
VP: Dan Whisenhunt
Board of Directors: James A Bell, Al Gore, Robert A Iger, Andrea Jung, Ronald D Sugar, Susan L Wagner

D-U-N-S 02-720-8287
APPLE INVESTORS GROUP LLC (FL)
APPLEBEE'S
303 E Woolbright Rd, Boynton Beach, FL 33435-6010
Tel (888) 265-7402 Founded/Ownrshp 2008
Sales 60.6MM^E EMP 2,000^E
SIC 5812 Restaurant, family: chain

D-U-N-S 07-963-2411
■ **APPLE JV HOLDING CORP**
(Suby of EECO INC) ★
8000 W Florissant Ave, Saint Louis, MO 63136-1414
Tel (314) 553-2000 Founded/Ownrshp 1998, 2014
Sales 620.8MM^E EMP 2,200^E
SIC 3644 3643 3613 3446 3699 Junction boxes, electric; Electric conduits & fittings; Plugs, electric; Electric switches; Starting switches, fluorescent; Switchgear & switchgear accessories; Power circuit breakers; Panelboards & distribution boards, electric; Architectural metalwork; Extension cords
Pr: Russell S Kerstetter

D-U-N-S 05-123-9725
APPLE LEISURE GROUP
7 Campus Blvd Ste 100, Newtown Square, PA 19073-3227
Tel (610) 359-6500 Founded/Ownrshp 2010

Sales 114.5MM^E *EMP* 600^E
SIC 8699 Travel club
CEO: Alejandro Z Gorostiza
CFO: Julia Davidson
* *Ex VP:* Javier Coll De San Simon
VP: Antonio Fungairino
VP: Ryan Solomon
DP Dir: Poneet Nadkarni
Sls&Mrk Ex: Kris Potter
Mktg Dir: Colleen Caponi

APPLE MKT CONVENIENCE STORES
See FUEL USA LLC

APPLE ONE EMPLOYMENT
See HOWROYD-WRIGHT EMPLOYMENT AGENCY INC

APPLE REHAB
See CHESTERFIELDS LTD

APPLE REHAB
See APPLE HEALTH CARE INC

D-U-N-S 07-936-2386
APPLE REIT EIGHT INC
(*Suby of* APPLE HOSPITALITY REIT INC) ★
14 E Main St, Richmond, VA 23219-2110
Tel (804) 344-8121 *Founded/Ownrshp* 2014
Sales 93.0MM^E *EMP* 1,673^E
SIC 6798 Real estate investment trusts
Ch Bd: Glade M Knight
Pr: Justin Knight
COO: Kristian Gathright
CFO: Bryan Peery

D-U-N-S 79-113-8956
APPLE REIT EIGHT INC
APPLE EIGHT
814 E Main St, Richmond, VA 23219-3306
Tel (804) 344-8121 *Founded/Ownrshp* 2007
Sales 197.9MM *EMP* 6^E
SIC 7011

D-U-N-S 79-451-6794
APPLE REIT SEVEN INC
814 E Main St, Richmond, VA 23219-3306
Tel (804) 344-8121 *Founded/Ownrshp* 2005
Sales 215.9MM *EMP* 5^E
SIC 7011

D-U-N-S 78-499-7673
APPLE REIT SIX INC
345 Park Ave, New York, NY 10154-0004
Tel (804) 344-8121 *Founded/Ownrshp* 2004
Sales 260.4MM *EMP* 50^E
SIC 6798

D-U-N-S 96-404-9113
APPLE REIT TEN INC
(*Suby of* APPLE HOSPITALITY REIT INC) ★
814 E Main St, Richmond, VA 23219-3306
Tel (804) 344-8121 *Founded/Ownrshp* 2016
Sales 262.1MM *EMP* 51^E
SIC 6798 Real estate investment trusts
Pr: Justin Knight
COO: Kristian Gathright
CFO: Bryan Peery
Chf Inves: Nelson Knight
Ex VP: David Buckley

D-U-N-S 80-737-5167
APPLE SAUCE INC
APPLEBEES NGHBORHOOD GRILL BAR
741 Centre View Blvd # 100, Crestview Hills, KY 41017-5435
Tel (859) 331-3900 *Founded/Ownrshp* 1992
Sales 123.2MM^E *EMP* 3,558
SIC 5812 Restaurant, family: chain
Pr: W Curtis Smith
* *CFO:* Jerome D Kreger
* *VP:* James P Borke
VP: Barb Wells
Genl Mgr: Eric Schlieman
Mktg Dir: Mark Smith

APPLE VALLEY UNIFIED SCHL DST
See APPLE VALLEY UNIFIED SCHOOL DISTRICT PUBLIC FACILITIES CORP

D-U-N-S 05-751-9209
APPLE VALLEY UNIFIED SCHOOL DISTRICT PUBLIC FACILITIES CORP
APPLE VALLEY UNIFIED SCHL DST
12555 Navajo Rd, Apple Valley, CA 92308-7256
Tel (760) 247-7267 *Founded/Ownrshp* 1987
Sales 60.4MM^E *EMP* 1,446
SIC 8211 Public combined elementary & secondary school
MIS Dir: Jason Buchanan
HC Dir: David Wheeler

D-U-N-S 88-408-7883
APPLE-METRO INC
APPLEBEE'S
550 Mmaroneck Ave Ste 204, Harrison, NY 10528
Tel (914) 777-2331 *Founded/Ownrshp* 1993
Sales 77.6MM^E *EMP* 2,000
SIC 5812 Restaurant, family: chain
Pr: Roy Raeburn
* *Ch Bd:* Zane Tankel
* *COO:* Miguel Fernandez
* *Ex VP:* Frank Venice
* *VP:* Ken Feldman

APPLEBEE'S
See APPLE CORPS LP

APPLEBEE'S
See APPLE INVESTORS GROUP LLC

APPLEBEE'S
See SPECIALTY RESTAURANT DEVELOPMENT LLC

APPLEBEE'S
See APPLE AMERICAN GROUP LLC

APPLEBEE'S
See WHIT-MART INC

APPLEBEE'S
See GREEN APPLE LLC

APPLEBEE'S
See NEW APPLE INC

APPLEBEE'S
See GOURMET SYSTEMS OF KANSAS INC

APPLEBEE'S
See THOMAS AND KING INC

APPLEBEE'S
See CASUAL RESTAURANT CONCEPTS INC

APPLEBEE'S
See JS VENTURES INC

APPLEBEE'S
See THOMAS AND KING OF ARIZONA INC

APPLEBEE'S
See QUALITY RESTAURANT CONCEPTS LLC

APPLEBEE'S
See APPLE AMERICAN LIMITED PARTNERSHIP OF OHIO

APPLEBEE'S
See AMREST LLC

APPLEBEE'S
See ROSE CASUAL DINING INC

APPLEBEE'S
See APPLE-METRO INC

APPLEBEE'S
See APPLE AMERICAN LP OF INDIANA

D-U-N-S 19-198-8468
■ **APPLEBEES INTERNATIONAL INC**
(*Suby of* DINEEQUITY INC) ★
8140 Ward Pkwy Ste 300, Kansas City, MO 64114-2039
Tel (913) 890-0100 *Founded/Ownrshp* 1987
Sales 565.7MM^E *EMP* 33,592^E
SIC 5812 6794 Restaurant, family: chain; Mexican restaurant; Franchises, selling or licensing
Ch Bd: Julia A Stewart
CFO: Steve K Lumpkin
Sr VP: Beverly Elving
Sr VP: George Williams
VP: Rebecca R Tilden

APPLEBEES NGHBORHOOD BAR GRILL
See APPLE GOLD INC

APPLEBEES NGHBORHOOD GRILL BAR
See APPLE SAUCE INC

APPLEBEES NGHBURHOOD GRILL BAR
See CONCORD NEIGHBORHOOD CORP

APPLEBEES NIGHORHOOD GRILL BAR
See APPLE CORE ENTERPRISES INC

D-U-N-S 10-663-8786
APPLETON AREA SCHOOL DISTRICT
122 E College Ave Ste 1a, Appleton, WI 54911-5741
Tel (920) 832-6161 *Founded/Ownrshp* 1850
Sales 187.6MM *EMP* 1,425
Accts Schenck Green Bay Wisconsin
SIC 8211 Public senior high school; Public junior high school; Public elementary school
Dir Vol: Mary Greiner
* *CFO:* Don Hietpas
Ex Dir: Julie Krause
Dir IT: Jim Hawbaker
Teacher Pr: Julie King
Psych: Susan Davis
Psych: Karen Rakita

D-U-N-S 12-442-2515 IMP/EXP
APPLETON COATED LLC
(*Suby of* VIRTUS HOLDINGS LLC) ★
540 Prospect St, Combined Locks, WI 54113-1120
Tel (920) 788-3550 *Founded/Ownrshp* 1999
Sales 325.0MM *EMP* 585^E
SIC 2621 2672 Uncoated paper; Coated paper, except photographic, carbon or abrasive
CEO: Douglas Osterberg
* *Treas:* Marianne Sterr
VP: Mary Ebert
* *VP:* Ann Whalen
Ex Dir: Michael Baker
IT Man: Marsha Cortright
Opers Mgr: Tim Krause
QI Cn Mgr: Jason Long
Sls Dir: Daniel Oconnell

APPLETON GROUP
See APPLETON GRP LLC

D-U-N-S 00-512-1686 IMP
■ **APPLETON GRP LLC**
APPLETON GROUP
(*Suby of* APPLE JV HOLDING CORP) ★
9377 W Higgins Rd, Rosemont, IL 60018-4973
Tel (847) 268-6000 *Founded/Ownrshp* 1903, 1997
Sales 620.8MM^E *EMP* 2,200
SIC 3644 3643 3613 3646 3699 Junction boxes, electric; Electric conduits & fittings; Plugs, electric; Electric switches; Starting switches, fluorescent; Switchgear & switchgear accessories; Power circuit breakers; Panelboards & distribution boards, electric; Commercial indusl & institutional electric lighting fixtures; Extension cords
Pr: Ross Kerseter
* *Pr:* Scott Anderson
* *CFO:* Michael Bryant
* *VP:* Jerry Mc Quade
* *VP:* Harley M Smith
Mktg Dir: Mary Krauss
Sls Dir: Miriam Blazowski

D-U-N-S 07-478-1121
APPLETON MEDICAL CENTER INC
1818 N Meade St, Appleton, WI 54911-3496
Tel (920) 731-4101 *Founded/Ownrshp* 1988
Sales 150.1MM^E *EMP* 1,230
SIC 8062 General medical & surgical hospitals
CEO: Dean Gruner
Chf Path: Karla M Sendelbach-Eliz

* *COO:* Bob Malte
* *CFO:* Tim Olson
CFO: Timothy Olson
Sr VP: Kim Barnas
Sr VP: Jeffrey Hunter
VP: Mark G Hermans
Dir OR: Deborah Doyle
Dir Lab: Linda Mirkes
Off Mgr: Laura Schroeder

D-U-N-S 02-749-5977
■ **APPLEWAY CHEVROLET INC**
AUTONATION TOYOTA SPOKANE VLY
(*Suby of* AUTONATION MOTORS HOLDING CORP) ★
8600 E Sprague Ave, Spokane, WA 99212
Tel (509) 924-1150 *Founded/Ownrshp* 1997
Sales 87.7MM^E *EMP* 300
SIC 5511 Automobiles, new & used
* *Pr:* William Berman
* *VP:* James Murphy

D-U-N-S 06-106-8433
APPLIANCE DEALERS COOPERATIVE INC
A D C
2 Matrix Dr, Monroe Township, NJ 08831-3702
Tel (609) 235-1000 *Founded/Ownrshp* 1972
Sales 157.1MM^E *EMP* 110^E
SIC 5064 Electrical appliances, major; Electrical entertainment equipment; Air conditioning appliances
Pr: Helene R Siegel
* *VP:* Ken Kohn
* *VP:* Michael Napoletano
Ex Dir: R Siegel
Merch Mgr: Arti Tripathi

D-U-N-S 02-435-3406 EXP
APPLIANCE PARTS DEPOT LP
APD
4754 Almond Ave, Dallas, TX 75247-6402
Tel (214) 631-6331 *Founded/Ownrshp* 2001
Sales 83.7MM^E *EMP* 185
SIC 5064 5722 Appliance parts, household; Appliance parts
Pt: Gail Parker
Off Admin: Karla Jackson
Trfc Mgr: Jorge Adame
Sls Dir: Shawn Connely
Sls Mgr: Besor Fayas
Sls Mgr: Kevin York
Snr Mgr: Grant Breech

D-U-N-S 10-225-8696
▲ **APPLIANCE RECYCLING CENTERS OF AMERICA INC**
ARCA
175 Jackson Ave N Ste 102, Hopkins, MN 55343-4565
Tel (952) 930-9000 *Founded/Ownrshp* 1976
Sales 111.8MM *EMP* 335^E
Tkr Sym ARCI *Exch* NAS
SIC 5722 4953 Household appliance stores; Appliance parts; Recycling, waste materials
CEO: Tony Isaac
Pr: Bradley S Bremer
Pr: Edward R Cameron
Ex VP: Peter Hausback
Ex VP: Rachel L Holmes
VP: Todd Lein
VP: Jeffrey Woloz
VP Mktg: Bryan Bremer
Board of Directors: Richard D Butler, Dennis Gao

APPLIANCE RECYCLING OUTLET
See JACO ENVIRONMENTAL INC

D-U-N-S 06-889-3229 IMP
APPLICA CONSUMER PRODUCTS INC
601 Ray O Vac Dr, Madison, WI 53711-2460
Tel (608) 275-4562 *Founded/Ownrshp* 1999
Sales 105.2MM^E *EMP* 570
SIC 3634 3631

APPLICATION ENGINEERING
See AEC INC

D-U-N-S 03-637-0914
APPLICATIONS SOFTWARE TECHNOLOGY CORP
AST
1755 Park St Ste 100, Naperville, IL 60563-8477
Tel (630) 778-0707 *Founded/Ownrshp* 1995
Sales 86.2MM^E *EMP* 160
SIC 4813
Pr: Pravin Kumar
COO: Tony Catalano
* *COO:* Nick Vlahos
* *Ex VP:* Shaji Zechariah
VP: Prasad Nettem
Comm Dir: Melissa Sider
Prac Mgr: Abhinav Raina
Admn Mgr: Yolanda Lewis
Admn Mgr: Lucy Montana
Genl Mgr: Jennifer Ryerson
QA Dir: Navneet Ritolia

D-U-N-S 13-782-2875
APPLIED BIOSCIENCE INTERNATIONAL LLC
A B I
(*Suby of* PHARMACEUTICAL PRODUCT DEVELOPMENT LLC) ★
3151 S 17th St, Wilmington, NC 28412-6461
Tel (910) 251-0081 *Founded/Ownrshp* 2000
Sales 40.4MM^E *EMP* 3,665
SIC 8731 Commercial physical research
Pr: William Sharbaugh

D-U-N-S 00-118-4480 IMP
■ **APPLIED BIOSYSTEMS LLC** (DE)
(*Suby of* LIFE TECHNOLOGIES CORP) ★
5791 Van Allen Way, Carlsbad, CA 92008-7321
Tel (650) 638-5000 *Founded/Ownrshp* 1937, 2008
Sales 1.5MMM^E *EMP* 10,000
SIC 3826 7372 Analytical instruments; Gas chromatographic instruments; Liquid chromatographic instruments; Thermal analysis instruments, laboratory type; Prepackaged software
Ch Bd: Tony L White
Pr: Lars Holmkvist

Pr: Kathy P Ordonez
CFO: Dennis L Winger
Div Pres: Leonard Klevan
Ex VP: Mark P Stevenson
Sr VP: William B Sawch
VP: Peter Barrett
VP: Robert F G Booth
VP: Michael Fitzpatrick
VP: Vikram Jog
VP: Joseph E Malandrakis

APPLIED COMMUNICATIONS
See ACI WORLDWIDE CORP

D-U-N-S 12-116-3526
■ **APPLIED INDUSTRIAL TECHNOLOGIES - CA LLC**
(*Suby of* APPLIED INDUSTRIAL TECHNOLOGIES INC) ★
1 Applied Plz, Cleveland, OH 44115-2511
Tel (216) 426-4000 *Founded/Ownrshp* 2002
Sales 125.9MM^E *EMP* 631
SIC 5063 Power transmission equipment, electric
CEO: David L Pugh
Genl Mgr: Krysta Dodd
Genl Mgr: Tom Jindra

D-U-N-S 00-787-3045 IMP
■ **APPLIED INDUSTRIAL TECHNOLOGIES - DIXIE INC** (TN)
(*Suby of* APPLIED INDUSTRIAL TECHNOLOGIES INC) ★
1 Applied Plz, Cleveland, OH 44115-2511
Tel (216) 426-4000 *Founded/Ownrshp* 1923, 1947
Sales 417.7MM^E *EMP* 685^E
SIC 5172 5169 Lubricating oils & greases; Sealants
Ch Bd: David L Pugh
* *Pr:* Robert Christensen
* *Pr:* Michael Coticchia
* *VP:* Todd A Barlett
* *VP:* Fred Bauer
VP: T A Brtlett
* *VP:* Mark O Eisele
* *VP:* James Hopper
* *VP:* William Purser
* *VP:* Jeffrey Ramras
* *VP:* Richard C Shaw

D-U-N-S 00-790-0129 IMP
▲ **APPLIED INDUSTRIAL TECHNOLOGIES INC** (OH)
1 Applied Plz, Cleveland, OH 44115-2511
Tel (216) 426-4000 *Founded/Ownrshp* 1923
Sales 2.5MMM *EMP* 5,839
Accts Deloitte & Touche Llp Clevela
Tkr Sym AIT *Exch* NYS
SIC 5085 5169 7699 Industrial supplies; Bearings; Power transmission equipment & apparatus; Seals, industrial; Sealants; Industrial machinery & equipment repair
Pr: Neil A Schrimsher
Ch Bd: Peter C Wallace
CFO: Mark O Eisele
Ofcr: Kurt W Loring
Ofcr: Christopher Macey
VP: Todd A Barlett
VP: Fred D Bauer
VP: Michael L Coticchia
VP: Barbara Emery
VP: Warren E Hoffner
VP: Lonny Lawrence
VP: Tracie Longpre
VP: Patrick Lynham
VP: Darren Padd
VP: Jeffrey A Ramras
VP: Richard C Shaw
VP: Mark A Stoneburner
VP: Jason Vasquez
VP: Kurt Weinheimer
Board of Directors: Peter A Dorsman, Edith Kelly-Green, L Thomas Hiltz, Dan P Komnenovich, John F Meier, Vincent K Petrella, Jerry Sue Thornton

D-U-N-S 87-452-2865 EXP
APPLIED MACHINERY CORP
20105 Krahn Rd, Spring, TX 77388-4012
Tel (281) 821-0700 *Founded/Ownrshp* 1994
Sales 107.1MM^E *EMP* 400^E
SIC 3533 Drill rigs
Pr: Erik Ostrander

D-U-N-S 96-359-5579
■ **APPLIED MAINTENANCE SUPPLIES & SOLUTIONS LLC**
(*Suby of* APPLIED INDUSTRIAL TECHNOLOGIES INC) ★
12420 Plaza Dr, Parma, OH 44130-1057
Tel (216) 433-7700 *Founded/Ownrshp* 2013
Sales 104.3MM^E *EMP* 215^E
SIC 5085 Industrial supplies
VP: Robert Onorato

D-U-N-S 04-272-8840 IMP
▲ **APPLIED MATERIALS INC**
3050 Bowers Ave, Santa Clara, CA 95054-3298
Tel (408) 727-5555 *Founded/Ownrshp* 1967
Sales 10.8MMM *EMP* 14,600
Tkr Sym AMAT *Exch* NGS
SIC 3559 3674 Semiconductor manufacturing machinery; Semiconductors & related devices
Pr: Gary E Dickerson
* *Ch Bd:* Willem P Roelandts
CFO: Robert J Halliday
CFO: Larry Sparks
Chf Mktg O: Yogev Barak
Chf Mktg O: Anne Hao
Top Exec: Sali Schille
Ex VP: Sameer Deshpande
Ex VP: Franz Janken
Ex VP: Mark R Pinto
Sr VP: Gino Addiego
Sr VP: Joe Flanagan
Sr VP: Thomas F Larkins
Sr VP: Ali Salehpour
VP: Chris Belden
VP: Robert Friess
VP: Rick Gesing
VP: Steve Ghanayem
VP: Jay Kerley

VP: Manfred Kerschbaum
VP: Greg Lawler
Board of Directors: Willem P Roelandts, Judy Bruner, Robert H Swan, Eric Chen, Stephen R Forrest, Thomas J Iannotti, Susan M James, Alexander A Karsner, Adrianna Ma, Gerhard H Parker, Dennis D Powell

APPLIED MATERIALS VARIAN
See VARIAN SEMICONDUCTOR EQUIPMENT ASSOCIATES INC

D-U-N-S 07-862-6049
APPLIED MEDICAL CORP
22872 Avenida Empresa, Rcho STA Marg, CA 92688-2650
Tel (949) 713-8000 *Founded/Ownrshp* 1987
Sales 446.9MM^E *EMP* 2,250^E
Accts Grant Thornton Llp Irvine Ca
SIC 3841 Surgical & medical instruments
CEO: Said Hilal
VP: Ray Frame
VP: David Heaton
VP: Mary Stegwell
Dist Mgr: Jim Johnson
Genl Mgr: Zoran Falkenstein
CIO: Samir Tall
IT Man: Digant Gupta
IT Man: Eugene Vargas
Prd Mgr: Canh Tran
Mktg Dir: John Brustad

APPLIED MEDICAL DISTRIBUTION
See APPLIED MEDICAL RESOURCES CORP

D-U-N-S 18-712-9135 IMP
APPLIED MEDICAL RESOURCES CORP
APPLIED MEDICAL DISTRIBUTION
(*Suby of* APPLIED MEDICAL CORP) ★
22872 Avenida Empresa, Rcho STA Marg, CA 92688-2650
Tel (949) 635-9153 *Founded/Ownrshp* 1987
Sales 446.9MM *EMP* 2,250^E
SIC 3841 Surgical & medical instruments
Pr: Said S Hilal
**Pr:* Nabil Hilal
**Pr:* Gary Johnson
**Pr:* Stephen E Stanley
Pr: Michael Vaughn
**CFO:* Samir Tall
VP: Mary Jo Stegwell
Dist Mgr: Ken Hyde
Plng Mgr: Josh Lichtenstein
Off Admin: Kathleen Gwaltney
Snr Sftwr: Hank Jacobs

D-U-N-S 09-853-8341 IMP
▲ APPLIED MICRO CIRCUITS CORP
4555 Great America Pkwy # 601, Santa Clara, CA 95054-1288
Tel (408) 542-8600 *Founded/Ownrshp* 1979
Sales 159.2MM *EMP* 557^E
Tkr Sym AMCC *Exch* NGS
SIC 3674 Microcircuits, integrated (semiconductor)
Pr: Paramesh Gopi
Ch Bd: Cesar Cesaratto
CFO: Martin S McDermut
Assoc VP: Fred Tan
VP: Michael Major
VP: Annie Pham
Snr Sftwr: Samuel Wang
Sls Dir: Raj Patel
Sls Mgr: Nancy Brewster
Sls Mgr: Sandra Torres
Snr Mgr: Mohi Alvi
Board of Directors: Paul R Gray, Theodore A Shlapak, Robert F Sproull, Christopher F Zepf

D-U-N-S 00-548-5859 IMP/EXP
▲ APPLIED OPTOELECTRONICS INC
13139 Jess Pirtle Blvd, Sugar Land, TX 77478-2856
Tel (281) 295-1800 *Founded/Ownrshp* 1997
Sales 189.9MM *EMP* 2,513
Tkr Sym AAOI *Exch* NGM
SIC 3674 3827 3699 Semiconductors & related devices; Optical instruments & lenses; Electrical equipment & supplies
Ch Bd: Chih-Hsiang Lin
CFO: Stefan J Murry
Sr VP: Hung-Lun Chang
Sr VP: Shu-Hua Yeh
VP: David C Kuo
Dir IT: Thomspon Lin
IT Man: Song Jim
Board of Directors: Richard B Black, Alex Ignatiev, Alan Moore, William H Yeh

D-U-N-S 18-742-1417 IMP
APPLIED POWER PRODUCTS INC
1240 Trapp Rd, Eagan, MN 55121-1217
Tel (651) 452-2250 *Founded/Ownrshp* 1988
Sales 83.8MM^E *EMP* 130
SIC 5085 Industrial supplies; Hose, belting & packing; Power transmission equipment & apparatus
CEO: Bruce Lundeen
**Pr:* Bill Scott
**VP:* Alan Luthi
Genl Mgr: Jim Burkhardt

D-U-N-S 09-796-7608
APPLIED RESEARCH ASSOCIATES INC
ARA
4300 San Mateo Blvd Ne A220, Albuquerque, NM 87110-1295
Tel (505) 883-3636 *Founded/Ownrshp* 1979
Sales 209.0MM *EMP* 1,235
Accts Kpmg Llp Albuquerque New Mex
SIC 8731 8748 Engineering laboratory, except testing; Environmental consultant
CEO: Robert H Sues
Sr Pt: Gerri Morgas
**Ch Bd:* Jimmie L Bratton
**Ex VP:* Frank A Maestas
**Ex VP:* Lawrence A Twisdale Jr
**Sr VP:* David H Artman
**Sr VP:* Curt Beckemeyer
**Sr VP:* Scott E Blouin
**Sr VP:* David Oakley
**Sr VP:* Joseph L Smith
VP: Scott Blouin
VP: Randy Brown
VP: Larry Ghormely
VP: Lew Goldberg
VP: Jack McChesney
VP: Frank A Mests
VP: William Ratliff
Board of Directors: James P Allen, James L Drake, John Healey, Cornelius J Higgins, Steven K Ruggieri, Pete Schoomaker

D-U-N-S 96-785-1531
APPLIED RESEARCH ASSOCIATES INC
11 Villiage Club Ct, Pinehurst, NC 28374-8554
Tel (910) 246-2030 *Founded/Ownrshp* 1993
Sales 30.8MM^E *EMP* 1,308
SIC 8711 8731 Engineering services; Commercial physical research
CEO: Robert Sues

D-U-N-S 10-318-7050
APPLIED SYSTEMS INC
IVANS INSURANCE SOLUTIONS
200 Applied Pkwy, University Park, IL 60484-4131
Tel (708) 534-5575 *Founded/Ownrshp* 2014
Sales 248.0MM *EMP* 1,200
SIC 7371 7372 Computer software development; Business oriented computer software
CEO: Reid French Jr
COO: Mark Layden
COO: Mark P Layden
CFO: Ryan Hobbs
CFO: Colleen Mikuce
Chf Mktg O: Ian Hoffman
Ex VP: James R White
Sr VP: Michael Howe
Sr VP: Bob Zaczynski
VP: Chuck Brock
VP: Kathleen J Cox
VP: Kathleen Cox
VP: Bill Derienzo
VP: Tracy Gissler
VP: Jacqueline Glick
VP: Christopher Hastings
VP: Scott Johnson
VP: Doug Johnston
VP: Kathy R Lattz
VP: Buck Stimson
VP: Kathleen Tomachek-Cox

D-U-N-S 04-571-2726 IMP
APPLIED TECHNICAL SERVICES CORP
A T S
6300 Merrill Creek Pkwy A100, Everett, WA 98203-1577
Tel (425) 249-5555 *Founded/Ownrshp* 1984
Sales 100.2MM^E *EMP* 221^E
SIC 3672 Printed circuit boards
CEO: George Hamilton
COO: Don Doody
VP: Jeff Bradley
Dir Bus: Lisa Heimbigner
Prgrm Mgr: Chris Klingerman
Genl Mgr: Arnulfo Manriquez
Mtls Dir: Robert Hamlin
Ql Cn Mgr: Brandon Schurr
VP Sls: Mike Kelly

D-U-N-S 04-795-2163
APPLIED TECHNICAL SERVICES INC
1049 Triad Ct, Marietta, GA 30062-2259
Tel (770) 423-1400 *Founded/Ownrshp* 1967
Sales 140.1MM^E *EMP* 375
Accts Gross Duke & Nelson Atlanta
SIC 8734 8711 8731 Testing laboratories; Calibration & certification; Forensic laboratory; Metallurgical testing laboratory; Engineering services; Commercial research laboratory; Biotechnical research, commercial
CEO: Jim J Hills
**CFO:* Jim Britton
**Ch:* William H Lewis
**VP:* Semih Geneulu
VP: Robert D Luttrell
Exec: Vickie Armbrister
Rgnl Mgr: Todd Kupfer
Off Mgr: Angie Williams
CTO: Michael Hall
MIS Dir: Mike Murray
QA Dir: David Lubinski

D-U-N-S 00-880-0901
■ APPLIED UNDERWRITERS INC
(*Suby of* BERKSHIRE HATHAWAY INC) ★
10805 Old Mill Rd, Omaha, NE 68154-2607
Tel (402) 342-4900 *Founded/Ownrshp* 1996
Sales NA *EMP* 500
SIC 6331 8721 8741 8742 Workers' compensation insurance; Payroll accounting service; Management services; Marketing consulting services; Foreign trade consultant
Ch Bd: Sidney R Ferenc
**Pr:* Steven M Menzies

D-U-N-S 07-971-0771
APPLIED-CLEVELAND HOLDINGS INC
(*Suby of* FIRST RESERVE XII ADVISORS LLC) ★
2735 State Highway 322, Longview, TX 75603-7020
Tel (918) 358-5735 *Founded/Ownrshp* 2016
Sales 126.6MM^E *EMP* 1,405
SIC 6719 7389 Public utility holding companies; Pipeline & power line inspection service
CEO: Randy Byers
Pr: Matt Cheney
CFO: Louis Berezovsky

D-U-N-S 12-628-8724
APPLUS RTD USA INC
(*Suby of* LIBERTYTOWN USA 2 INC) ★
3 Sugar Creek Center Blvd # 600, Sugar Land, TX 77478-2213
Tel (832) 295-5000 *Founded/Ownrshp* 1981
Sales 130.0MM *EMP* 675
SIC 7389 Inspection & testing services
CEO: Philip Morrison
**Sec:* Gregory Rossmiller

D-U-N-S 80-742-3103
APPNEXUS INC
28 W 23rd St Fl 4, New York, NY 10010-5260
Tel (646) 825-6460 *Founded/Ownrshp* 2007
Sales 382.8MM^E *EMP* 810^E
SIC 4813
CEO: Brian O'Kelley
COO: Jonathan Hsu
CFO: Bruce Cooperman
Chf Mktg O: Thomas Butta
Sr VP: Andy Atherton
Sr VP: Brandon Atkinson
Sr VP: Casey Birtwell
Sr VP: Ryan Christensen
Sr VP: Michelle Dvorkin
Sr VP: Ben John
Sr VP: Jason Lynn
Sr VP: Pat McCarthy
Sr VP: ARI Paparo
VP: Doina Harris
VP: Andrew Q Kraft
VP: Mike Nolet
VP: Dave Osborn
VP: Timothy G Smith
Dir Risk M: Marcus Startzel
Board of Directors: Elisabeth Demarse, Mike Tyrrell, David Yuan

D-U-N-S 08-078-4408
APPOQUINIMINK SCHOOL DISTRICT INC
118 S 6th St, Odessa, DE 19730-2060
Tel (302) 376-4128 *Founded/Ownrshp* 1925
Sales 72.4MM^E *EMP* 1,100
SIC 8211 Public elementary & secondary schools
**CFO:* Charles Longfellow
Bd of Dir: Edna Cale
**Prin:* Charles Sheppard
Dir IT: Mike Fonders
Schl Brd P: Norman Abrams
Teacher Pr: Debbie Panchisin

D-U-N-S 00-952-9863
▲ APPROACH RESOURCES INC
6500 West Fwy Ste 800, Fort Worth, TX 76116-2178
Tel (817) 989-9000 *Founded/Ownrshp* 2002
Sales 131.3MM *EMP* 102^E
Tkr Sym AREX *Exch* NGS
SIC 1311 Crude petroleum & natural gas
Ch Bd: J Ross Craft
COO: Qingming Yang
CFO: Sergei Krylov
Ofcr: J Curtis Henderson
VP: Suzanne Ogle
Board of Directors: Alan D Bell, James H Brandi, James C Crain, Vean J Gregg III, Bryan H Lawrence, Sheldon B Lubar, Christopher J Whyte

D-U-N-S 01-490-9441
APPROVED NETWORKS INC (CA)
APPROVED OPTICS
717 Lakefield Rd Ste A, Westlake Village, CA 91361-2695
Tel (800) 590-9535 *Founded/Ownrshp* 2010
Sales 123.0MM^E *EMP* 60
SIC 3299 Art goods: plaster of paris, papier mache & scagliola
Mng Dir: Thomas Horton
COO: Kurt Dumteman
CFO: Ron Beale
IT Man: Angela Lunt

APPROVED OPTICS
See APPROVED NETWORKS INC

D-U-N-S 00-964-1603
▲ APPTIO INC
11100 Ne 8th St Ste 600, Bellevue, WA 98004-4402
Tel (425) 453-5861 *Founded/Ownrshp* 2007
Sales 129.2MM *EMP* 694^E
Tkr Sym APTI *Exch* NGM
SIC 7372 Application computer software
Pr: Sachin Gupta
**Ch Bd:* Thomas Bogan
CFO: Kurt Shintaffer
Chf Mktg O: Christopher Pick
Ofcr: Barbara Gordon
Ex VP: Ted Kummert
Ex VP: John Morrow
Ex VP: Erez Yarkoni
Dir Risk M: Lawrence Blasko
Board of Directors: Peter Klein, John McAdam, Matthew McIlwain, Ravi Mohan

D-U-N-S 16-529-5606
■ APPTIS HOLDINGS INC
(*Suby of* AECOM GLOBAL II LLC) ★
4800 Westfields Blvd # 1, Chantilly, VA 20151-4232
Tel (703) 745-6016 *Founded/Ownrshp* 2011
Sales 145.7MM^E *EMP* 1,290
SIC 7371 Computer software development & applications
CEO: Albert A Notini
Owner: Jason Madden
**COO:* Skip Nowland
Treas: William Clarke
Sr VP: Michael Carroll
Sr VP: James T Underwood
VP: Mike Marsili
Genl Mgr: Gloria Kosman
Genl Mgr: William Reynolds
CTO: Phil Horvitz

D-U-N-S 08-958-1557 IMP/EXP
APPVION INC
(*Suby of* PAPERWEIGHT DEVELOPMENT CORP) ★
825 E Wisconsin Ave, Appleton, WI 54911-3873
Tel (920) 734-9841 *Founded/Ownrshp* 1907
Sales 700.0MM^E *EMP* 1,565^E
SIC 2621 2754 Securites paper; Copy paper; Specialty papers; Fine paper; Calendar & card printing, except business: gravure; Tickets: gravure printing
CEO: Kevin M Gilligan
Pr: Kevin Gilligan
CFO: Thomas J Ferree
Treas: Richard Weahrel
Sr VP: Kerry S Arent
VP: Jeffrey J Fletcher
VP: Ethan W Haas
VP: Jason Schulist
VP: Tami L Van Straten
Exec: Charles Berth
IT Man: Jim Wranosky
Board of Directors: Stephen P Carter, Terry M Murphy, Andrew F Reardon, David A Roberts, Kathi P Seifert, Mark A Suwyn, George W Wurtz

D-U-N-S 83-293-2367 IMP/EXP
APR ENERGY LLC
(*Suby of* ACON INVESTMENTS LLC) ★
3600 Prt Jcksnvl Pkwy, Jacksonville, FL 32226-4780
Tel (904) 223-2278 *Founded/Ownrshp* 2016
Sales 158.9MM^E *EMP* 200^E
SIC 4911 Distribution, electric power
CEO: John Campion
**CEO:* Laurence Anderson
**CFO:* Lee Munro
**Chf Cred:* Steve List
VP: Wayne Friedrich
VP: Andrew Martinez
Genl Mgr: Jitendra Gurjal

D-U-N-S 78-757-2320 IMP/EXP
APRIA HEALTHCARE GROUP INC
(*Suby of* SKY ACQUISITION LLC) ★
26220 Enterprise Ct, Lake Forest, CA 92630-8405
Tel (949) 639-2000 *Founded/Ownrshp* 2008
Sales 2.4MMM *EMP* 13,700^E
SIC 8082 Home health care services
Ch Bd: John G Figueroa
CFO: Peter A Reynolds
CFO: Jodi Roseman
Treas: David Burch
Div VP: Steve Foreman
Div VP: Mike McKinney
Ex VP: Robin Barton
Ex VP: Lisa George
Ex VP: William Guidetti
Ex VP: Jeffrey W Ingram
Ex VP: Brad Kreick
Ex VP: Cameron Thompson
Sr VP: Mark Goulart
Sr VP: Mark Litkovitz
VP: Rochelle Arini-Moza
VP: Doreen R Bellucci
VP: Kirby Combs
VP: Matthew Crooks
VP: Chris Hammond
VP: Diane Koss
VP: Tyson Lee
Board of Directors: Norman C Payson MD, Neil P Simpkins, Daniel J Starck, Mike S Zafirovski

D-U-N-S 10-404-2361 IMP/EXP
APRIA HEALTHCARE LLC
(*Suby of* APRIA HEALTHCARE GROUP INC) ★
26220 Enterprise Ct, Lake Forest, CA 92630-8405
Tel (949) 616-2606 *Founded/Ownrshp* 1984
Sales 1.0MMM *EMP* 4,795
SIC 5047 7352 5999 Hospital equipment & furniture; Dental equipment & supplies; Medical equipment & supplies; Medical equipment rental; Medical apparatus & supplies
CEO: Daniel J Starck
Pr: Matt Gallagher
**Treas:* Erik Degarceau
Ofcr: Judith Valosio
VP: Ken Common
VP: Heather Patterson
Brnch Mgr: Jane Scheu
Brnch Mgr: Sandra Slentz
Brnch Mgr: James Sylte
Snr Mgr: Richard Snider

APRIL CORNELL
See CORNELL TRADING INC

D-U-N-S 04-098-2048
APRO LLC
17311 S Main St, Gardena, CA 90248-3131
Tel (310) 323-3992 *Founded/Ownrshp* 1999
Sales 968.3MM *EMP* 100
Accts Holthouse Carlin & Van Trigt
SIC 5541 Gasoline service stations

APS HEALTHCARE
See INNOVATIVE RESOURCE GROUP LLC

D-U-N-S 03-463-7947
APS HEALTHCARE BETHESDA INC
(*Suby of* PARTNERS HEALTHCARE SOLUTIONS, INC.)
44 S Broadway Ste 1200, White Plains, NY 10601-4458
Tel (800) 305-3720 *Founded/Ownrshp* 2007
Sales 21.5MM^E *EMP* 1,793
SIC 8099 Medical services organization
Pr: Jerome V Vaccaro MD
Treas: John McDonough
Exec: Christina Shean

D-U-N-S 79-691-4240
APS HEALTHCARE INC
(*Suby of* KEPRO) ★
44 S Broadway Ste 1200, White Plains, NY 10601-4458
Tel (914) 288-4700 *Founded/Ownrshp* 2015
Sales 30.7MM^E *EMP* 1,000
SIC 8099 Medical services organization
CEO: Greg Scott
CFO: John McDonough
Chf Cred: Richard Chung
Ofcr: Michael Williamson
VP: Wendy Fernandez
VP: Margaret Kelly
VP: James Oleary
VP: Stephen Schlager
IT Man: Joseph Rivera
IT Man: Luis Velasco
Opers Mgr: Robert Noble

D-U-N-S 15-827-3797 IMP
APS HEALTHCARE NORTHWEST INC
(*Suby of* PARTNERS HEALTHCARE SOLUTIONS, INC.)
44 S Broadway Ste 1200, White Plains, NY 10601-4458
Tel (800) 305-3720 *Founded/Ownrshp* 2007
Sales 12.5MM^E *EMP* 1,793

SIC 8099 Medical services organization
Pr: Jerome V Vaccaro MD
**Treas:* John McDonough

APSS
See ASSET PROTECTION & SECURITY SERVICES LP

D-U-N-S 96-758-8489
APTALIS HOLDINGS INC
(*Suby of* FRX CHURCHILL HOLDINGS, INC.)
22 Inverness Center Pkwy # 310, Birmingham, AL 35242-4887
Tel (205) 991-8085 *Founded/Ownrshp* 2014
Sales 106.3MM[E] *EMP* 637[E]
SIC 2834 Pharmaceutical preparations
CEO: Frank Verwiel MD
**Pr:* David W Mims
**CFO:* Steve Gannon

D-U-N-S 11-003-3045
APTALIS MIDHOLDINGS LLC
(*Suby of* APTALIS HOLDINGS INC) ★
22 Inverness Center Pkwy, Birmingham, AL 35242-4814
Tel (205) 991-8085 *Founded/Ownrshp* 2008
Sales 106.3MM[E] *EMP* 631[E]
SIC 2834 Pharmaceutical preparations
CEO: Frank Verwiel MD
Pr: David W Mims
CFO: Steve Gannon

D-U-N-S 82-969-6306
APTALIS PHARMA LLC
(*Suby of* APTALIS MIDHOLDINGS LLC) ★
22 Inverness Center Pkwy # 310, Birmingham, AL 35242-4887
Tel (205) 991-8085 *Founded/Ownrshp* 2008
Sales 106.3MM[E] *EMP* 875[E]
SIC 2834 Pharmaceutical preparations
Pr: Frank Verwiel
**CFO:* Steve Gannon
Chf Mktg O: Ruth Thieroff-Ekerdtmd
**Ofcr:* Richard Devleeschouwer
Ex VP: Francis Gauthier
Sr VP: Robert Becker PHD
Sr VP: Theresa Stevens
VP: Patrick Colin
Genl Mgr: Gino Giacumbo
Snr Mgr: Dianne Veljasevic
Board of Directors: David Mims

D-U-N-S 61-543-5088
APTARA INC
3110 Frview Pk Dr Ste 900, Falls Church, VA 22042
Tel (703) 352-0001 *Founded/Ownrshp* 1988
Sales 291.4MM[E] *EMP* 3,600
SIC 7379 Data processing consultant
CEO: Dev Ganesan
**Pr:* William Penders
**COO:* Scott Weeren
Bd of Dir: John Shaw
**Sr VP:* Debashis Chaudhuri
**Sr VP:* Prashant Kapoor
VP: Sushant Buttan
VP: Daren Harber
**VP:* Gearoid E Moore
Exec: Meenal Agrawal
Exec: Aman Sharma
Exec: Rasika Yalanavar

D-U-N-S 80-561-9681 IMP/EXP
▲ APTARGROUP INC
475 W Terra Cotta Ave E, Crystal Lake, IL 60014-3407
Tel (815) 477-0424 *Founded/Ownrshp* 1940
Sales 2.3MMM *EMP* 13,000[E]
Tkr Sym ATR *Exch* NYS
SIC 3089 3499 Closures, plastic; Aerosol valves, metal
Pr: Stephen J Hagge
**Ch Bd:* King W Harris
Pr: Patrick Doherty
Pr: Salim Haffar
Pr: Eldon Schaffer
CFO: Brian Cassell
CFO: Robert W Kuhn
Treas: Ralph Poltermann
VP: Matt Dellamaria
VP: Michael Wedge
VP Bus Dev: Stefan Hellbardt
Dir Bus: Kay Stanish
Comm Man: Leejay Stewart
Board of Directors: Alain Chevassus, George L Fotiades, Andreas C Kramvis, Giovanna Kampouri Monnas, Peter H Pfeiffer, Joanne C Smith, Ralf K Wunderlich

APTEAN
See CDC SOFTWARE INC

D-U-N-S 17-341-0713
APTEAN HOLDINGS INC
MADE2MANAGE SYSTEMS
(*Suby of* APTEAN INC) ★
450 E 96th St Ste 300, Indianapolis, IN 46240-3797
Tel (317) 249-1700 *Founded/Ownrshp* 2012
Sales 90.1MM[E] *EMP* 650
SIC 7371 5045 Computer software development; Computer software
CEO: Jeff Tognoni
COO: John Fraser
VP: Tim Hines
VP: Paul Ross
Genl Mgr: Mehul Davi
Genl Mgr: Perry Williams
Snr Sftwr: Mustapha Hammouti
**CTO:* Steve Bailey
Dir IT: Alan Kaska
Pr Dir: Heather Knox
Snr Mgr: Jennifer Chester
Board of Directors: Michael P Cullinane, Timothy A Davenport, Richard G Halperin, Rudolf J Hermann

D-U-N-S 07-876-6944
APTEAN INC
4325 Alexander Dr Ste 100, Alpharetta, GA 30022-3740
Tel (770) 351-9600 *Founded/Ownrshp* 2012
Sales 577.7MM[E] *EMP* 2,469[E]
SIC 5045 Computer software
CEO: Kim Eaton
**COO:* Jack Blaha
COO: Kenneth Frank
**CFO:* James Fitzgibbons
**CFO:* Bijal Patel
Ex VP: Kyle Bowker
**Sr VP:* Ronald Kolz
Sr VP: Todd Schulte
Sr VP: Steve Stanislaus
VP: Brad Debold
VP: Matt Keenan
VP: Danna Nelson
VP: Venkat Rajaji
VP: Mike Ressel
VP: David Shin
VP: Mike Stensland
VP: Leslie Workman

D-U-N-S 06-760-5154
APTOS INC
EPICOR
(*Suby of* EPICOR SOFTWARE CORP) ★
945 E Paces Ferry Rd Ne, Atlanta, GA 30326-1160
Tel (866) 493-7037 *Founded/Ownrshp* 2013
Sales 124.5MM[E] *EMP* 200[E]
SIC 5044 5045 7378 7699 Cash registers; Accounting machines using machine readable programs; Computer software; Computer & data processing equipment repair/maintenance; Cash register repair
CEO: Noel Goggin
**Ch Bd:* Kevin Parker

APTOS SHOES AND APPAREL
See WEEBS INC

D-U-N-S 80-031-2451
APTTUS CORP
1400 Fashion Island Blvd # 100, San Mateo, CA 94404-2061
Tel (650) 445-7700 *Founded/Ownrshp* 2006
Sales 7.2MM[E] *EMP* 1,150
SIC 7373 Systems software development services
CEO: Kirk Krappe
**Pr:* Neehar Giri
**CFO:* Sydney Carey
**Chf Mktg O:* Kamal Ahluwalia
Sr VP: Barbara Competello
Sr VP: Rahul Parikh
Sr VP: Nagi Prabhu
Sr VP: Jeff Santelices
Sr VP: Brian Thompson
VP: Andre Deveer
VP: Prakash Jyothi
VP: Nav Kalra
VP: Tony Klinkatsis

D-U-N-S 07-827-1530
APTUIT (SCIENTIFIC OPERATIONS) LLC
2 Greenwich Office Park, Greenwich, CT 06831-5148
Tel (203) 422-6600 *Founded/Ownrshp* 2011
Sales 92.8MM[E] *EMP* 1,725[E]
SIC 2834 Pharmaceutical preparations
CFO: Thierry Amat

D-U-N-S 07-841-0077
APTUIT LLC
2 Greenwich Office Park, Greenwich, CT 06831-5148
Tel (203) 422-6600 *Founded/Ownrshp* 2004
Sales 142.1MM[E] *EMP* 1,733[E]
SIC 8731 Biotechnical research, commercial; Commercial physical research
CEO: Jonathan Goldman
**CFO:* Kurt Dinkelacker
**Ex VP:* John Fikre
**Ex VP:* Manuela Leone
**Ex VP:* Paul Overton
Ex VP: Paul D Overton
Ex VP: Henning Steinhagen
VP Mfg: Pieter Westerduin
Sls Dir: David Lustig

APV CREPACO
See SPX FLOW TECHNOLOGY SYSTEMS INC

APW WYOTT
See ASSOCIATED AMERICAN INDUSTRIES INC

APWU
See AMERICAN POSTAL WORKERS UNION

APX ALARM SECURITY SOLUTIONS
See VIVINT INC

D-U-N-S 07-884-8120
APX GROUP HOLDINGS INC (UT)
VIVINT
(*Suby of* APX PARENT HOLDCO INC) ★
4931 N 300 W, Provo, UT 84604-5816
Tel (801) 377-9111 *Founded/Ownrshp* 2012
Sales 653.7MM *EMP* 3,700[E]
SIC 7382 5065 3822 1711 Security systems services; Security control equipment & systems; Building services monitoring controls, automatic; Solar energy contractor
CEO: Todd Pedersen
**Pr:* Alex Dunn
COO: David Bywater
CFO: Mark Davies
Treas: Dale Gerard
Chf Mktg O: Jeff Lyman
Ofcr: Todd Santiago
CIO: Jt Hwang
CTO: Jeremy Warren
Genl Couns: Nathan Wilcox

D-U-N-S 07-866-4496
APX GROUP INC
(*Suby of* VIVINT) ★
4931 N 300 W, Provo, UT 84604-5816
Tel (801) 377-9111 *Founded/Ownrshp* 2006
Sales 98.4MM[E] *EMP* 3,200
SIC 8711 3822 1711 5065 Engineering services; Electrical or electronic engineering; Energy conservation engineering; Heating & ventilation engineering; Building services monitoring controls, automatic; Energy cutoff controls, residential or commercial types; Electric heat controls; Air flow controllers, air conditioning & refrigeration; Solar energy contractor; Security control equipment & systems
CEO: Christopher Black
**Pr:* Alex Dunn
**CFO:* Mark Davies

D-U-N-S 07-984-0594
APX PARENT HOLDCO INC
(*Suby of* 313 ACQUISITION LLC) ★
4931 N 300 W, Provo, UT 84604-5816
Tel (801) 377-9111 *Founded/Ownrshp* 2012
Sales 139.1MM[E] *EMP* 3,700[E]
SIC 6719 3822 1711 8711 5065 5074 Personal holding companies, except banks; Building services monitoring controls, automatic; Energy cutoff controls, residential or commercial types; Electric heat controls; Air flow controllers, air conditioning & refrigeration; Solar energy contractor; Engineering services; Electrical or electronic engineering; Energy conservation engineering; Heating & ventilation engineering; Security control equipment & systems; Heating equipment & panels, solar
CEO: Todd Pedersen

AQUA AMERICA
See AQUA PENNSYLVANIA INC

D-U-N-S 04-834-1648
▲ AQUA AMERICA INC
762 W Lancaster Ave, Bryn Mawr, PA 19010-3402
Tel (610) 527-8000 *Founded/Ownrshp* 1968
Sales 814.2MM *EMP* 1,617[E]
Tkr Sym WTR *Exch* NYS
SIC 4941 4952 Water supply; Sewerage systems
Pr: Christopher H Franklin
**Ch Bd:* Nicholas Debenedictis
**COO:* Richard S Fox
**CFO:* David P Smeltzer
Ex VP: Daniel J Schuller
**Sr VP:* Christopher P Luning
Sr VP: William C Ross
**Sr VP:* Robert A Rubin
VP: Thomas M Cox
VP: Kimberly Joyce
Board of Directors: Carolyn J Burke, Richard H Glanton, Lon R Greenberg, William P Hankowsky, Wendell F Holland, Ellen T Ruff

AQUA GROUP
See AQUATECH INTERNATIONAL LLC

D-U-N-S 96-956-7721
■ AQUA HOTELS AND RESORTS INC
(*Suby of* ILG) ★
1850 Ala Moana Blvd, Honolulu, HI 96815-1602
Tel (808) 943-9291 *Founded/Ownrshp* 2014
Sales 49.0MM[E] *EMP* 1,400[E]
SIC 7011 Hotels & motels
Pr: Benjamin Rafter
**COO:* Matt Bailey
**CFO:* William R Farnsworth
**VP:* Veronica Saba
Sls Mgr: Kehau Amorin

D-U-N-S 00-791-0003
■ AQUA PENNSYLVANIA INC
AQUA AMERICA
(*Suby of* AQUA AMERICA INC) ★
762 W Lancaster Ave, Bryn Mawr, PA 19010-3489
Tel (610) 525-1400 *Founded/Ownrshp* 1905
Sales 567.9MM[E] *EMP* 1,309
SIC 4941 8741 4971 1623 Water supply; Management services; Irrigation systems; Water, sewer & utility lines
CEO: Nicholas Debenedictis
**Pr:* Marc Lucca
**Pr:* Steven Tagert
**CFO:* David P Smeltzer
**VP:* Anthony Donatoni
**VP:* Mark J Kropilak
**VP:* Bill Miller
**VP:* William Ross
VP Prd: Curt Steffy

D-U-N-S 04-670-4685 IMP
AQUA STAR (USA) CORP
2025 1st Ave Ste 200, Seattle, WA 98121-2115
Tel (206) 448-5400 *Founded/Ownrshp* 1990
Sales 118.2MM[E] *EMP* 125
SIC 5146 Fish & seafoods
Pr: Dirk Leuenberger
Pr: James Randazzo
**Treas:* Robert Nielsen
Chf Mktg O: Andrew Pickering
Ex VP: Bob Hooey
VP: Petro Blommaert
VP: Brendan Curran
VP: Mark Lawrence
VP: Dave Main
Genl Mgr: Scott Southern
Dir IT: Mitch Stewart

D-U-N-S 00-880-3868
■ AQUA UTILITIES FLORIDA INC (FL)
(*Suby of* AQUA AMERICA INC) ★
1000 Colour Pl, Apopka, FL 32703-7753
Tel (386) 740-7174 *Founded/Ownrshp* 1961, 2005
Sales 93.0MM *EMP* 356
Accts Pricewaterhousecoopers Llp Mi
SIC 4941 4952 Water supply; Sewerage systems
CEO: Donnie R Crandell
**Pr:* Richard S Fox
**COO:* Forrest Ludsen
**CFO:* Judith Kimball
**VP:* William D Denny
**VP:* Carlyn Kowalsky
**VP:* Ida Roberts

D-U-N-S 01-922-1697
AQUA VENTURE HOLDINGS LLC
14400 Carlson Cir, Tampa, FL 33626-3005
Tel (813) 855-8636 *Founded/Ownrshp* 2006
Sales 99.5MM[E] *EMP* 277[E]
SIC 8741 Management services
Pr: John Curtis
VP Opers: Bryan Brister

D-U-N-S 06-628-3854
■ AQUA-ASTON HOSPITALITY LLC
ASTON HOTELS & RESORTS
(*Suby of* ILG) ★
2155 Kalakaua Ave Fl 5, Honolulu, HI 96815-2351
Tel (808) 931-1400 *Founded/Ownrshp* 1967
Sales 267.6MM[E] *EMP* 1,821
SIC 7389 7011 Hotel & motel reservation service; Resort hotel
Pr: Kelvin Mark Bloom
Ofcr: Marjorie L Bray-Oshiro
Ofcr: Gary Jay Ettinger
Ofcr: Donald M Everett Jr
Ofcr: Jerry Warren Fellows
Ofcr: Beverly Kirk
Ofcr: Linda Akiko Nagasako
Ofcr: Ruth Nobuye Okada
Ofcr: Cary Yukio Okimoto
Ofcr: James Sidney Olin
Ofcr: Joanne Lynette Paahao
Ofcr: Harold Alfred Rapoza Sr
Ofcr: Jerry Robertson
Ofcr: David Kyle Selberg
Ofcr: William H Settle
Ofcr: Loren Shim
Ofcr: Kelley Buechler Standard
Ofcr: Michael Alan Tasaka
Ofcr: Andre S Tatibouet
Ofcr: Shirley Tsukano
**Sr VP:* Yuriko Ruth Shiota

AQUA-MATIC
See CAPTIVE-AIRE SYSTEMS INC

AQUAFARMS INTERNATIONAL
See MULTIEXPORT FOODS INC

D-U-N-S 09-109-8678 IMP
AQUAFIL USA INC
1 Aquafil Dr, Cartersville, GA 30120-2697
Tel (678) 605-8100 *Founded/Ownrshp* 1999
Sales 140.0MM *EMP* 350[E]
SIC 5199 Fabrics, yarns & knit goods
CEO: Giulio Bonazzi
**Pr:* Franco Rossi

D-U-N-S 05-063-3890
AQUARION WATER CO (CT)
(*Suby of* MACQUARIE BANK LIMITED)
835 Main St, Bridgeport, CT 06604-4900
Tel (800) 732-9678 *Founded/Ownrshp* 1968
Sales 260.2MM[E] *EMP* 300
SIC 4941

D-U-N-S 00-691-6530
AQUARION WATER CO OF CONNECTICUT
(*Suby of* AQUARION WATER CO) ★
200 Monroe Tpke, Monroe, CT 06468-2247
Tel (203) 445-7310 *Founded/Ownrshp* 1969
Sales 229.7MM[E] *EMP* 300[E]
SIC 4941

D-U-N-S 80-400-2111 IMP
AQUASCAPE DESIGNS INC
901 Aqualand Way, Saint Charles, IL 60174-5303
Tel (630) 659-2000 *Founded/Ownrshp* 1993
Sales 108.3MM[E] *EMP* 100
Accts Dugan & Lopatka Cpas Wheaton
SIC 5191 1629 0782 0781 Garden supplies; Pond construction; Landscape contractors; Landscape counseling & planning
Pr: Gregory G Wittstock
**Pr:* Colleen Heitzler
Sr Cor Off: T Decker

D-U-N-S 00-913-0006 IMP/EXP
AQUATECH INTERNATIONAL LLC
AQUA GROUP
1 Four Coins Dr, Canonsburg, PA 15317-1776
Tel (724) 746-5300 *Founded/Ownrshp* 1981
Sales 184.5MM[E] *EMP* 500
Accts Schneider Downs And Co Inc Pi
SIC 3589 Water treatment equipment, industrial
Pr: Venkee Sharma
CFO: M Rama Subba RAO
Ex VP: C Ravi
VP: Devesh Sharma

D-U-N-S 83-315-7105 IMP
AQUATIC CO
8101 E Kaiser Blvd # 200, Anaheim, CA 92808-2287
Tel (714) 993-1220 *Founded/Ownrshp* 1999
Sales 330.7MM[E] *EMP* 1,200
SIC 3088 Shower stalls, fiberglass & plastic
CEO: Gary Anderson
IT Man: Oscar Martinez
Natl Sales: Scott McCann
Manager: Jeremy Sharpe

AQUENT
See TRI VENTURES INC

D-U-N-S 15-727-1578
AQUENT LLC
(*Suby of* AQUENT) ★
501 Boylston St Ste 3, Boston, MA 02116-3725
Tel (617) 535-5000 *Founded/Ownrshp* 1986
Sales 396.7MM[E] *EMP* 5,615
SIC 7361

D-U-N-S 82-913-4498
AQUILEX HOLDINGS LLC
AZZ WSI
2225 Skyland Ct, Norcross, GA 30071-2960
Tel (678) 728-9100 *Founded/Ownrshp* 2014
Sales 700.3MM[E] *EMP* 7,176
SIC 7349 Cleaning service, industrial or commercial
VP: Doug Vail
VP: Ian Gilpatrick
VP: Doug Jacobs

D-U-N-S 80-587-5411
AQUILEX LLC
(*Suby of* AZZ WSI) ★
2225 Skyland Ct, Norcross, GA 30071-2960
Tel (404) 869-6677 *Founded/Ownrshp* 2008
Sales NA *EMP* 3,000
SIC 6712 Bank holding companies
Sr VP: Greg Birge

Mng Dir: Peter Jones
IT Man: Mark Horony
Snr PM: Lewis Fair

D-U-N-S 07-880-5399
■ AQUILEX SPECIALTY REPAIR AND OVERHAUL LLC
(*Suby of* ARBOR-CROWLEY INC) ★
3344 Peachtree Rd Ne, Atlanta, GA 30326-4801
Tel (800) 868-9353 *Founded/Ownrshp* 2009, 2013
Sales 180.7MM^E *EMP* 1,500^E
SIC 3699 High-energy particle physics equipment

D-U-N-S 80-863-5200
AQUILINE CAPITAL PARTNERS LLC
535 Madison Ave Fl 24, New York, NY 10022-4260
Tel (212) 624-9500 *Founded/Ownrshp* 2007
Sales 113.0MM^E *EMP* 455^E
SIC 6799 Investors
VP: Craig Wunderlich

D-U-N-S 00-894-9836
AQUINAS CORP
3900 Essex Ln Ste 1200, Houston, TX 77027-5486
Tel (713) 621-2350 *Founded/Ownrshp* 1950
Sales 295.5MM^E *EMP* 500
SIC 1542 Commercial & office building, new construction; Shopping center construction; Hospital construction
Pr: David Stueckler
**CFO:* Bill Riegler
Ex VP: John Fisher
**Ex VP:* Bill Scott
**Prin:* Chuck Greco
MIS Dir: Jason Dedonato
Mktg Dir: Sara McCarthy
Mktg Mgr: Patty Charek
Snr PM: Brent Miller
Snr PM: Thomas Richert

D-U-N-S 11-622-7505 IMP
AQUIONICS INC
(*Suby of* HALMA HOLDINGS INC) ★
1455 Jamike Ave Ste 100, Erlanger, KY 41018-3147
Tel (859) 341-0710 *Founded/Ownrshp* 1983
Sales 385.0MM *EMP* 25
SIC 5074 Water purification equipment
Pr: Oliver Lawal
**Pr:* Bill Deker
Pr: Paul Ropic
Mng Dir: Danny Burns
S&M/VP: Greg Stanley

AR CAPITAL
See AMERICAN REALTY CAPITAL HEALTHCARE TRUST INC

D-U-N-S 07-998-1438
■ AR SILVER BELL INC
(*Suby of* GRUPO MEXICO) ★
5285 E Williams Cir, Tucson, AZ 85711-4426
Tel (520) 798-7500 *Founded/Ownrshp* 1995
Sales 170.0MM^E *EMP* 212^E
SIC 1021 1044 1031 1041 3331 3339 Copper ores; Silver ores; Lead ores mining; Gold ores; Primary copper; Silver refining (primary)
Pr: Manuel Ramos
**CFO:* Oscar Gonzalez Barron
**Treas:* Scott Cole
VP: Tom Aldrich
VP: John George

ARA
See APPLIED RESEARCH ASSOCIATES INC

D-U-N-S 07-986-9508
ARA HOLDINGS INC
4300 San Mateo Blvd Ne, Albuquerque, NM 87110-1229
Tel (505) 881-8074 *Founded/Ownrshp* 2015
Sales 200.6MM *EMP* 0^E
Accts Kpmg Llp Albuquerque New Mex
SIC 6719 Holding companies
Prin: William Dass
Pr: Robert Sues

D-U-N-S 07-295-4738
ARAKELIAN ENTERPRISES INC
ATHENS SERVICES
14048 Valley Blvd, City of Industry, CA 91746-2801
Tel (626) 336-3636 *Founded/Ownrshp* 1998
Sales 150.0MM *EMP* 1,000^E
SIC 4953 Rubbish collection & disposal; Street refuse systems
CEO: Ron Arakelian Jr
**CEO:* Michael Arakelian
**COO:* Gary Clifford
COO: Anthony Davidson
**CFO:* Kevin Hanifin
**Ex VP:* Dennis Chiappetta
Off Mgr: Mary Caraballo
Netwrk Mgr: Song Voong
Opers Mgr: Eric Hollman
Sls Dir: Eric Romero

D-U-N-S 79-107-2197
▲ ARAMARK CORP
1101 Market St Ste 45, Philadelphia, PA 19107-2988
Tel (215) 238-3000 *Founded/Ownrshp* 1959
Sales 14.4MMM *EMP* 265,500
Accts Kpmg Llp Philadelphia Pennsy
Tkr Sym ARMK *Exch* NYS
SIC 5812 7218 5136 Contract food services; Food bars; Work clothing supply; Work clothing, men's & boys'
Ch Bd: Eric J Foss
Pt: Ed Snowden
Pr: Salli Darden
Pr: Brannon Transue
Pr: Todd Wells
COO: Marc Bruno
COO: Victor L Crawford
COO: Brad C Drummond
COO: Brent J Franks
COO: Harrald F Kroeker
COO: Marty Welch
CFO: Stephen P Bramlage Jr
Treas: Christian Dirx
Treas: Jenna Sawyer
Assoc VP: Brian Drew
Ex VP: Lynn B McKee
Ex VP: Stephen R Reynolds
Sr VP: Christina T Morrison
Sr VP: Joseph Munnelly
Sr VP: Joseph M Munnelly
VP: Silvana Battaglia
Board of Directors: Todd M Abbrecht, Lawrence T Babbio Jr, Lisa G Bisaccia, Leonard S Coleman Jr, Richard Dreiling, Irene M Esteves, Daniel J Heinrich, John A Quelch, Stephen I Sadove

D-U-N-S 02-293-9297
■ ARAMARK FACILITY SERVICES LLC (MD)
(*Suby of* ARAMARK SERVICES INC) ★
1101 Market St, Philadelphia, PA 19107-2934
Tel (215) 238-3000 *Founded/Ownrshp* 1984, 1932
Sales 97.1MM^E *EMP* 2,300
SIC 7349 Janitorial service, contract basis; Building maintenance, except repairs
Pr: Andrew Kerin
VP: Michael Leone

D-U-N-S 96-080-9283
■ ARAMARK HEALTHCARE SUPPORT SERVICES OF TEXAS INC
(*Suby of* ARAMARK SERVICES INC) ★
1101 Market St, Philadelphia, PA 19107-2934
Tel (215) 238-3000 *Founded/Ownrshp* 2001
Sales 53.0MM^E *EMP* 1,586
SIC 5812 Contract food services; Food bars
CEO: Eric J Foss
**Ch Bd:* Joseph Neubauer
**Pr:* John Babiarz
**Pr:* David J Carpenter
**Pr:* William Leonard
**Pr:* Brian Poplin
**Treas:* Melvin Mahoney
**Sr VP:* Mary Ann Wyman
**VP:* Laura Dabkowski
**VP:* Michael Ohara

D-U-N-S 82-520-5979
■ ARAMARK INTERMEDIATE HOLDCO CORP
(*Suby of* ARAMARK CORP) ★
1101 Market St Ste 45, Philadelphia, PA 19107-2934
Tel (215) 238-3000 *Founded/Ownrshp* 2006
Sales 13.4MMM^E *EMP* 259,000^E
SIC 5812 7218 5136 Contract food services; Food bars; Work clothing supply; Work clothing, men's & boys'
CEO: Joseph Neubauer
**Pr:* Eric Foss
**Treas:* Christopher Holland
**VP:* Michael J Ohara

D-U-N-S 79-099-2622
■ ARAMARK MANAGEMENT SERVICES LIMITED PARTNERSHIP
SERVICEMASTER
(*Suby of* ARAMARK SERVICES INC) ★
2300 Warrenville Rd, Downers Grove, IL 60515-1702
Tel (630) 271-2000 *Founded/Ownrshp* 1992
Sales 442.0MM^E *EMP* 15,000
SIC 7349 Building maintenance services
Pt: Robert F Keith
VP: Gary Hearing
Dir IT: Arthur Demarah
Sls&Mrk Ex: Jim Frost

D-U-N-S 04-328-2938
■ ARAMARK REFRESHMENT SERVICES LLC
(*Suby of* ARAMARK SERVICES INC) ★
1101 Market St, Philadelphia, PA 19107-2934
Tel (215) 238-3000 *Founded/Ownrshp* 1984
Sales 764.6MM^E *EMP* 4,500
SIC 5963 Food service, coffee-cart
Dir Surg: David Raker
Genl Mgr: Jimmy Carter
Genl Mgr: Jack Obrien
Telecom Mg: Lou Rider

D-U-N-S 00-791-3098 EXP
■ ARAMARK SERVICES INC
(*Suby of* ARAMARK INTERMEDIATE HOLDCO CORP) ★
1101 Market St Ste 45, Philadelphia, PA 19107-2988
Tel (215) 238-3000 *Founded/Ownrshp* 1959, 2007
Sales 13.4MMM^E *EMP* 259,000
SIC 5812 7218 5136

D-U-N-S 04-395-6572
■ ARAMARK SPORTS AND ENTERTAINMENT GROUP LLC
(*Suby of* ARAMARK SERVICES INC) ★
1101 Market St, Philadelphia, PA 19107-2934
Tel (215) 238-3000 *Founded/Ownrshp* 1989
Sales 1.0MMM^E *EMP* 30,000
SIC 5812 Contract food services
Pr: Liza Cartnell
VP: Gary Jacobus
VP: Bob Kline
IT Man: Bob Arena

D-U-N-S 01-727-4502 IMP/EXP
■ ARAMARK UNIFORM & CAREER APPAREL GROUP INC
(*Suby of* ARAMARK SERVICES INC) ★
1101 Market St Ste 45, Philadelphia, PA 19107-2934
Tel (215) 238-3000 *Founded/Ownrshp* 2007
Sales 1.5MMM^E *EMP* 12,000
SIC 2337 2311 5699 5961 5661 5812 Uniforms, except athletic: women's, misses' & juniors'; Men's & boys' uniforms; Uniforms & work clothing; Uniforms; Work clothing; Clothing, mail order (except women's); Women's apparel, mail order; Men's shoes; Women's shoes; Eating places
Pr: Eric J Foss
CFO: Mark Adams
**CFO:* David Solomon
Ex VP: Ron Iori
Sr VP: Mike Kruszewski
Sr VP: James Lee
**Sr VP:* Barbara Prutzman
VP: John Frasik
VP: Charles Reitmeyer
**VP:* John Ryan
VP: Philippe Villain

D-U-N-S 08-838-9739 IMP/EXP
■ ARAMARK UNIFORM & CAREER APPAREL LLC
(*Suby of* ARAMARK UNIFORM & CAREER APPAREL GROUP INC) ★
115 N First St Ste 203, Burbank, CA 91502-1857
Tel (818) 973-3700 *Founded/Ownrshp* 1976
Sales 930.6MM^E *EMP* 12,000
SIC 7218 Industrial uniform supply; Treated equipment supply: mats, rugs, mops, cloths, etc.; Wiping towel supply
Ex VP: Mike Fadden
Treas: Chris Holland
VP: Dan Craig
VP: Terry Oberbroeckling
VP: Tom Peterson
VP: Paul Schmid
Dist Mgr: Michael Berger
Dist Mgr: Eddie Gray
Dist Mgr: Jason Justus
Dist Mgr: Steve McCloud
Dir IT: Anna Collins

D-U-N-S 07-220-0694
ARAMCO SERVICES CO
ASC
(*Suby of* SAUDI ARAMCO LTD)
9009 West Loop S, Houston, TX 77096-1799
Tel (713) 432-4000 *Founded/Ownrshp* 1988
Sales 366.0MM^E *EMP* 450
SIC 8711 8742 Petroleum engineering; Management consulting services
Pr: Basil Abulhamayel
**Treas:* Debra McNamara
VP: Bader Al-Harbi
**VP:* Mark Murphy
Exec: Inga Davis
Exec: Kristina Thames
Ex Dir: Nasir Naimi
IT Man: Saleh Abdulgader
IT Man: Abdullah Al Ahmed
IT Man: Khalid Al-Ahmadi
IT Man: Adnan Al-Awwami

D-U-N-S 79-284-3336 EXP
ARAMEX NEW YORK LTD
(*Suby of* ARAMEX JORDAN LTD)
18221 150th Ave, Springfield Gardens, NY 11413-4001
Tel (718) 553-8740 *Founded/Ownrshp* 1986
Sales 222.2MM^E *EMP* 7,000
SIC 4513 Air courier services
Ch Bd: Iyad Kamal
**Pr:* Tommy Kelly
Mng Dir: Moesfiqah Lee
Admn Mgr: Brian Vandort
Genl Mgr: Mike Abufaris
Snr Mgr: Mais Rihani

D-U-N-S 04-618-5765
■ ARAMIS INC
ESTEE LAUDER
(*Suby of* ESTEE LAUDER COMPANIES INC) ★
767 5th Ave, New York, NY 10153-0023
Tel (212) 572-4200 *Founded/Ownrshp* 1967, 1987
Sales 25.5MM^E *EMP* 2,443
SIC 5122 2844 Cosmetics; Cosmetic preparations
Pr: Robert A Nielsen
S&M/VP: Sherri Gleason

D-U-N-S 79-121-7859 IMP
ARAMSCO HOLDINGS INC
1480 Grand View Ave, Thorofare, NJ 08086
Tel (856) 686-7700 *Founded/Ownrshp* 2005
Sales 231.3MM^E *EMP* 235
SIC 5085 5136 5084 5139 Industrial supplies; Work clothing, men's & boys'; Industrial machinery & equipment; Footwear
Pr: Richard Salerno
**CFO:* Curtis Massey

D-U-N-S 00-496-1140 IMP/EXP
ARAMSCO INC
(*Suby of* ARAMSCO HOLDINGS INC) ★
1480 Grandview Ave, Paulsboro, NJ 08066-1801
Tel (856) 686-7700 *Founded/Ownrshp* 1989
Sales 202.2MM^E *EMP* 235
SIC 5085 5084 5136 5139 Industrial supplies; Industrial machinery & equipment; Work clothing, men's & boys'; Footwear
Pr: Rich Salerno
**CFO:* Curt Massey
Ex VP: Steven Jaffe
VP: Anthony Petrille
Natl Sales: Todd Maxwell
VP Sls: Gaarie Breier
Mktg Dir: Anna Glover
Mktg Dir: Daphne Livingston
Sls Mgr: Deborah Johnson

D-U-N-S 00-609-3470
ARANDELL CORP (WI)
N82w13118 Leon Rd, Menomonee Falls, WI 53051-3303
Tel (262) 255-4400 *Founded/Ownrshp* 1922, 2014
Sales 228.8MM^E *EMP* 625
SIC 2752 Commercial printing, lithographic
Pr: Bradley J Hoffman
**Ch Bd:* Donald J Treis
COO: Dun Trice
VP: Thomas C Benedict
VP: Wendy Hunjadi
VP: Dennis Petersdorf
VP: Terry Tschetter
Admn Mgr: Stacie Pike
IT Man: Debbie Kescenovitz
Board of Directors: Walt Edwards, Rick Kropski, Vince Lapinski

D-U-N-S 01-186-0855
ARANON CORP
285 W 74th Pl, Hialeah, FL 33014-5058
Tel (305) 557-9004 *Founded/Ownrshp* 2009
Sales 184.7MM^E *EMP* 900
SIC 5048 Frames, ophthalmic; Lenses, ophthalmic
Pr: Phillip Wolman
**Pr:* Lisa M Wolman
**Treas:* Robert Messa
**VP:* Jeffry Martin

D-U-N-S 04-072-4981
ARAPAHOE COMMUNITY COLLEGE FOUNDATION INC
(*Suby of* COLORADO COMMUNITY COLLEGE SYS) ★
5900 S Santa Fe Dr, Littleton, CO 80120-1801
Tel (303) 797-4222 *Founded/Ownrshp* 1965
Sales 389.1M *EMP* 1,500
Accts Rubinbrown Llp Denver Co
SIC 8222 Community college
Pr: Diana M Doyle PHD
Treas: Sue Sandstrom
VP: Diane Hegeman
Exec: Jeff Broome
Exec: Allison Hagood
Exec: Sophie Mabry
Exec: Lance Rubin
Exec: Linda Sulsberger
Dir IT: Jane Binns
Telecom Mg: Rhonda Olsen

ARAPAHOE COUNTY
See COUNTY OF ARAPAHOE

D-U-N-S 00-955-5442 IMP
■ ARB INC
(*Suby of* PRIMORIS SERVICES CORP) ★
26000 Commercentre Dr, Lake Forest, CA 92630-8816
Tel (949) 598-9242 *Founded/Ownrshp* 1962
Sales 330.2MM^E *EMP* 1,200
SIC 1629 1623 Industrial plant construction; Waste disposal plant construction; Waste water & sewage treatment plant construction; Water, sewer & utility lines; Oil & gas line & compressor station construction; Water & sewer line construction; Pipeline construction
Pr: Brian Pratt
**CFO:* Alfons Theeuwes
**Sec:* John P Schauerman
**VP:* Timothy Healy
**VP:* Scott Summers

D-U-N-S 06-581-7322 IMP
ARBEE ASSOCIATES
1531 S Washington Ave # 3, Piscataway, NJ 08854-6701
Tel (908) 686-3900 *Founded/Ownrshp* 1928
Sales 107.3MM^E *EMP* 150
SIC 5021 Office furniture
Ch: Howard Berkowitz
**Pr:* Nancy Berkowitz
**Treas:* Ruth Berkowitz
**VP:* Ellen Berkowitz
IT Man: Mark Gramcko

D-U-N-S 93-111-0027
ARBELLA INC
(*Suby of* ARBELLA MUTUAL INSURANCE CO) ★
101 Arch St Ste 1860, Boston, MA 02110-1118
Tel (617) 328-2800 *Founded/Ownrshp* 1994
Sales NA *EMP* 6^E
SIC 6411 Insurance agents, brokers & service
Pr: John Donohue
COO: Douglas Jones
**Treas:* Robert Medwid

ARBELLA INSURANCE GROUP
See ARBELLA SERVICE CO INC

ARBELLA MUTUAL INSURANCE
See ARBELLA PROTECTION INSURANCE CO INC

D-U-N-S 19-970-1434
ARBELLA MUTUAL INSURANCE CO
1100 Crown Colony Dr, Quincy, MA 02169-0957
Tel (617) 328-2800 *Founded/Ownrshp* 1988
Sales NA *EMP* 1,180
SIC 6411 6331

D-U-N-S 79-786-3446
ARBELLA PROTECTION INSURANCE CO INC
ARBELLA MUTUAL INSURANCE
(*Suby of* ARBELLA INC) ★
1100 Crown Colony Dr, Quincy, MA 02169-0957
Tel (617) 328-2800 *Founded/Ownrshp* 1992
Sales NA *EMP* 1^E
SIC 6411 Insurance agents, brokers & service
Pr: Richard W Brewer
COO: John J Mooney
CFO: Robert P Medwid

D-U-N-S 05-937-8195
ARBELLA SERVICE CO INC
ARBELLA INSURANCE GROUP
(*Suby of* ARBELLA MUTUAL INSURANCE CO) ★
1100 Crown Colony Dr, Quincy, MA 02169-0957
Tel (617) 328-2800 *Founded/Ownrshp* 1997
Sales 98.4MM^E *EMP* 1,000
SIC 8742 Management consulting services
Pr: John F Donohue
**V Ch:* Francis X Bellotti
Pr: Kim Kwiatkowski
Pr: Rick Maydak
Pr: Peter O'Brien
Pr: Lynellen M Ramirez
**COO:* Janet R Corcoran
**Treas:* Christopher E Hall
**Treas:* Robert P Medwid
Sr VP: John F Kittel
VP: James S Hyatt
VP: Steven A Jcobs
VP: Christopher Martin
VP: Joe Salerno
Board of Directors: Joseph G Murphy, Brian Odwyer

D-U-N-S 84-023-8732 IMP
ARBITECH LLC
15330 Barranca Pkwy, Irvine, CA 92618-2215
Tel (949) 376-6650 *Founded/Ownrshp* 2000
Sales 103.0MM^E *EMP* 74
Accts Jlk Rosenberger Llp Irvine
SIC 5045 Computer peripheral equipment
CEO: Torin Pavia

Pr: Francisco Llaca
**COO:* Clarissa Zulick
**Ex VP:* Jimmy Whalen
VP: Mark Dunlap
VP: Frank G Llaca
**Prin:* Doug Kari
DP Dir: Jason McCarty
IT Man: Craig Tran
Sales Asso: Jennifer Chavez

D-U-N-S 01-726-6466 IMP
ARBON EQUIPMENT CORP
(*Suby of* RITE-HITE HOLDING CORP) ★
8900 N Arbon Dr, Milwaukee, WI 53223-2451
Tel (414) 355-2600 *Founded/Ownrshp* 1997
Sales 103.5MM[E] *EMP* 450
SIC 5211 Masonry materials & supplies
Pr: Steve Masters
**CFO:* Mark Kirkish
VP: Marc Sundquist
**Prin:* Terry McGushin
Genl Mgr: Tom Burrill
Genl Mgr: Carolyn Smith
Sls Mgr: Ryan Bird
Sls Mgr: Brett Demott
Sls Mgr: Edward Malinowski
Sls Mgr: John Salmon

ARBOR CARPET
See ARBOR CONTRACT CARPET INC

D-U-N-S 05-344-2844
ARBOR CONTRACT CARPET INC (TX)
ARBOR CARPET
2313 E Pioneer Dr, Irving, TX 75061-8807
Tel (972) 445-2235 *Founded/Ownrshp* 1981
Sales 85.7MM *EMP* 115
SIC 1752

D-U-N-S 07-421-8348
■ **ARBOR DRUGS INC**
CVS
(*Suby of* CVS HEALTH CORP) ★
1 Cvs Dr, Woonsocket, RI 02895-6146
Tel (401) 765-1500 *Founded/Ownrshp* 1998
Sales 336.6MM[E] *EMP* 7,000
SIC 5912 Drug stores & proprietary stores
Ch Bd: Thomas M Ryan
CFO: David Rickard
**Treas:* Philip C Galbo

ARBOR INVESTMENTS
See ARBOR PRIVATE INVESTMENT CO LLC

D-U-N-S 02-051-4134
■ **ARBOR NETWORKS INC**
(*Suby of* NETSCOUT SYSTEMS INC) ★
76 Blanchard Rd Ste 1, Burlington, MA 01803-6814
Tel (781) 362-4300 *Founded/Ownrshp* 2015
Sales 144.9MM[E] *EMP* 265
SIC 4899 Communication signal enhancement network system
CEO: Matthew Moynahan
Pr: Farnam Jahanian
CFO: Dan Brosnan
CFO: Donald W Pratt Jr
Treas: Frank T McFaden
Sr VP: Jeff Lindholm
VP: Jeff Buhl
VP: Colin Gray
VP: Mike Hare
VP: Tony King
VP: Kris Lamb
VP: Robert S Lutz
VP: Mat Mathews
VP: Jeremy Nicholls
VP: Daniel Villanueva
Exec: Carlos Morales
Dir Soc: Sharon Kebalka

D-U-N-S 07-875-1028 IMP
ARBOR PHARMACEUTICALS LLC
WILSHIRE PHARMACEUTICALS
(*Suby of* ARBOR PHARMACEUTICALS, INC.)
6 Cncurse Pkwy Ste 1800, Atlanta, GA 30328
Tel (678) 334-2420 *Founded/Ownrshp* 2013
Sales 175.0MM *EMP* 157[E]
SIC 5122 Drugs & drug proprietaries; Pharmaceuticals
Pr: Ed Schutter
Genl Couns: Leslie Zachs

D-U-N-S 07-927-3863
ARBOR PRIVATE INVESTMENT CO LLC (WA)
ARBOR INVESTMENTS
676 N Michigan Ave # 3410, Chicago, IL 60611-2883
Tel (312) 981-3770 *Founded/Ownrshp* 1999
Sales 207.2MM[E] *EMP* 389
SIC 6726 Investment offices
CEO: Gregory J Purcell
Pr: Joseph P Campolo
CFO: J David Foster
Sr VP: Roberta R McQuade
VP: Alan A Weed
Genl Couns: Jason Booth

D-U-N-S 14-200-8916
ARBOR REALTY TRUST INC
333 Earle Ovington Blvd # 900, Uniondale, NY 11553-3614
Tel (516) 506-4200 *Founded/Ownrshp* 2003
Sales 142.5MM *EMP* 37[E]
Accts Ernst & Young Llp New York N
SIC 6798 Real estate investment trusts; Mortgage investment trusts
Ch Bd: Ivan Kaufman
COO: Ron Gaither
CFO: Paul Elenio
Chf Cred: Andrew Guziewicz
Ex VP: Gene Kilgore
Ex VP: Robyn C Stern
Ex VP: Fred Weber
Sr VP: Michael House

D-U-N-S 06-353-1189
■ **ARBOR-CROWLEY INC**
(*Suby of* AZZ INC) ★
3100 W 7th St Ste 500, Fort Worth, TX 76107-8701
Tel (817) 810-0095 *Founded/Ownrshp* 1991
Sales 188.6MM[E] *EMP* 1,600[E]
SIC 3629 Battery chargers, rectifying or nonrotating
CFO: Dana Perry

D-U-N-S 03-966-4052 IMP
ARBORGEN INC
2011 Broadbank Ct, Ridgeville, SC 29472-8344
Tel (843) 851-4129 *Founded/Ownrshp* 2000
Sales 92.2MM[E] *EMP* 160
SIC 0851 Forestry services
Pr: Andrew Baum
**Ch Bd:* Edward T Shonsey
**CFO:* John Radak
Bd of Dir: Beverly Lindsey
**VP:* Warren A Banner III
VP: Wayne Barfield
VP: David Nothmann
**VP:* John Pait
Assoc Dir: Weiming Wang
Genl Mgr: Kathy Parker
Dir IT: Jim Grant

ARBY'S
See RESTAURANT MANAGEMENT INC

ARBY'S
See G Z K INC

ARBY'S
See ERIE COUNTY INVESTMENT CO

ARBY'S
See SYBRA LLC

ARBY'S
See BAILEY CO LLLP

ARBY'S
See UNITED STATES BEEF CORP

ARBY'S
See TURBO RESTAURANT LLC

ARBY'S
See CAMBRIDGE INVESTMENTS LLC

ARBY'S
See SUN HOLDINGS INC

ARBY'S
See GIESEN RESTAURANT ENTERPRISES LLC

D-U-N-S 79-577-2743
ARBYS RESTAURANT GROUP
(*Suby of* ARBYS RESTAURANT GROUP INC) ★
1155 Perimeter Ctr, Atlanta, GA 30338-5463
Tel (678) 514-4100 *Founded/Ownrshp* 2005
Sales 77.8MM[E] *EMP* 1,000
SIC 5812 Fast-food restaurant, chain
**CFO:* J David Pipes

D-U-N-S 79-731-5298
ARBYS RESTAURANT GROUP INC
(*Suby of* ARG IH CORP) ★
1155 Perimeter Ctr, Atlanta, GA 30338-5463
Tel (678) 514-4100 *Founded/Ownrshp* 2004
Sales 1.1MMM[E] *EMP* 27,930
SIC 5812 Fast-food restaurant, chain
Pr: Roland Smith
Pr: Rob M Lynch
COO: John Bowie
**COO:* Diana Petrovich-Tao
**Chf Mktg O:* Russ Klein
Ofcr: Warren Chang
**Ofcr:* Nils Okeson
**Ofcr:* Mellisa Strait
**Sr VP:* Stephen Davis
**Sr VP:* John Gray
**Sr VP:* John Todd
VP: Mary Barto
**VP:* John Dasis

ARC
See ENGHOUSE INTERACTIVE INC

ARC
See AIRLINES REPORTING CORP

ARC
See GTS TECHNOLOGY SOLUTIONS INC

D-U-N-S 14-755-1183 IMP/EXP
ARC AUTOMOTIVE INC
(*Suby of* CAP-CON AUTOMOTIVE TECHNOLOGIES LTD)
1729 Midpark Rd Ste 100, Knoxville, TN 37921-5978
Tel (865) 583-7600 *Founded/Ownrshp* 2012
Sales 473.6MM[E] *EMP* 1,458[E]
SIC 3714 Motor vehicle parts & accessories
Pr: Ali L-Haj

D-U-N-S 02-429-0947
▲ **ARC DOCUMENT SOLUTIONS INC**
1981 N Broadway Ste 385, Walnut Creek, CA 94596-8214
Tel (925) 949-5100 *Founded/Ownrshp* 1997
Sales 428.6MM *EMP* 2,600
Tkr Sym ARC *Exch* NYS
SIC 7334 7335 7374 7372 Photocopying & duplicating services; Blueprinting service; Multigraphing; Photographic studio, commercial; Computer graphics service; Prepackaged software
Ch: Kumar Suriyakumar
**Ch Bd:* Kumarakulasingam Suriyakumar
COO: Johnathan N Toler
COO: Dilantha Wijesuriya
COO: Jorge Avalos
CFO: Gwen Granet
Ex VP: Ted Buscaglia
Ex VP: Patrick Welch
Ex VP: John J Zulli III
VP: Steven Biernbaum
VP: D Jeffery Grimes
VP: Kp Reddy
VP: Bob Thomas

ARC ENTERPRISES
See ARC OF SAN DIEGO

D-U-N-S 60-241-6869
▲ **ARC GROUP WORLDWIDE INC**
810 Flight Line Blvd, Deland, FL 32724-2055
Tel (303) 467-5236 *Founded/Ownrshp* 1987
Sales 103.8MM *EMP* 600[E]
Tkr Sym ARCW *Exch* NAS
SIC 3499 3462 3812 Friction material, made from powdered metal; Machine bases, metal; Welding tips, heat resistant: metal; Flange, valve & pipe fitting forgings, ferrous; Antennas, radar or communications
CEO: Jason T Young
Ch Bd: Alan G Quasha
CFO: Drew M Kelley
Board of Directors: Todd A Grimm, Eddie W Neely, Gregory D Wallis

D-U-N-S 07-164-3266
ARC INDUSTRIES INC OF FRANKLIN COUNTY OHIO
2879 Johnstown Rd, Columbus, OH 43219-1719
Tel (614) 475-6440 *Founded/Ownrshp* 1971
Sales 10.2MM *EMP* 1,200
Accts Schneider Downs & Co Inc Colu
SIC 8331 Sheltered workshop

D-U-N-S 05-900-0497 IMP/EXP
ARC INTERNATIONAL NORTH AMERICA INC
(*Suby of* ARC HOLDINGS)
601 S Wade Blvd, Millville, NJ 08332-3550
Tel (856) 825-5620 *Founded/Ownrshp* 1966
Sales 702.2MM[E] *EMP* 4,248
SIC 5023 2821 Glassware; Plastics materials & resins
Pr: Hubert Ibled
**CFO:* Bertrand Lenglart
VP: Ron Biagi
Genl Mgr: Olivier Malpel
Dir IT: Azhar Anwar
IT Man: Drew Majeskie
VP Sls: Bernard Grigri
Mktg Dir: Jack Kontes
Sls Mgr: Clara Bacon
Snr Mgr: Irving Sedeyn
Snr Mgr: Ken Turner

D-U-N-S 07-571-8767
ARC OF NORTHERN RHODE ISLAND INC
ARCINDUSTRIES
80 Siaban St 1 Sox Ri, Woonsocket, RI 02895
Tel (401) 765-3700 *Founded/Ownrshp* 1960
Sales 1.0MM *EMP* 1,100
Accts Cayer Prescott Clune Chateller
SIC 8331 8361 Sheltered workshop; Group foster home
Pr: Robert Carl Jr
CFO: Greg Young

D-U-N-S 03-757-7855
ARC OF SAN DIEGO
ARC ENTERPRISES
3030 Market St, San Diego, CA 92102-3230
Tel (619) 685-1175 *Founded/Ownrshp* 1953
Sales 34.2MM *EMP* 2,000
Accts Moss-Adams Llp San Diego Ca
SIC 8399 8351 8361 8322 Advocacy group; Child day care services; Home for the mentally retarded; Individual & family services
CEO: David W Schneider
**COO:* Anthony J Desalis
CFO: Victoria Cendreda
**CFO:* Chad Lyle
**VP:* Rich Coppa
**VP:* Jennifer Bates Navarra

D-U-N-S 06-251-3411 IMP/EXP
ARC-COM FABRICS INC
33 Ramland Rd S, Orangeburg, NY 10962-2689
Tel (845) 365-1100 *Founded/Ownrshp* 1972
Sales 99.6MM[E] *EMP* 140
SIC 5131 Textile converters
Ch Bd: Jeffrey Layne
**VP:* Peter Layne
Rgnl Mgr: Luann Pierce
Admn Mgr: Kelli Manheimer
Genl Mgr: Sherman Pollack
Dir IT: Brian Connor
Natl Sales: Steve Andrews
VP Sls: Mary Venturino
Sls Mgr: Brian Wilson
Sales Asso: Nicole Garcia

D-U-N-S 07-962-6705
ARC3 GASES INC
1636 Us Highway 301 S, Dunn, NC 28334-6791
Tel (910) 892-4016 *Founded/Ownrshp* 2014
Sales 199.3MM[E] *EMP* 400[E]
SIC 2813 5084 5169 7359 7692 Industrial gases; Industrial machinery & equipment; Chemicals & allied products; Equipment rental & leasing; Welding repair
Ch Bd: Emmett Aldredge Jr
**COO:* Christopher Aldredge

ARC3 GASES NORTH
See ARCET EQUIPMENT CO

ARC3 GASES SOUTH
See MACHINE & WELDING SUPPLY CO

ARCA
See APPLIANCE RECYCLING CENTERS OF AMERICA INC

D-U-N-S 84-313-6680
■ **ARCADE INC**
(*Suby of* VISANT HOLDING CORP) ★
1700 Broadway Fl 25, New York, NY 10019-5925
Tel (212) 541-2600 *Founded/Ownrshp* 2004
Sales 208.0MM[E] *EMP* 1,838[E]
SIC 2752 Commercial printing, lithographic
Ch Bd: Richard Kaleta
**Sr VP:* Louis Ziafonte
VP: Jamie Ross

ARCADIA HOME CARE
See ARCADIA SERVICES INC

D-U-N-S 11-828-2250 IMP
ARCADIA INC
ARCADIA NORCAL
2301 E Vernon Ave, Vernon, CA 90058-8052
Tel (323) 269-7300 *Founded/Ownrshp* 1985
Sales 109.3MM[E] *EMP* 400
SIC 3355 Extrusion ingot, aluminum: made in rolling mills
CEO: James Schladen
**CFO:* Khan Chow
CFO: Pat Homkaew
Genl Mgr: Dan Spielberger
Sfty Mgr: Gus Sanchez
Plnt Mgr: Byron Bjork
Plnt Mgr: Jason Brinsfield
Plnt Mgr: John Gabriel
Sls Mgr: Ken Martinek
Snr PM: Nelson Bezerra

ARCADIA NORCAL
See ARCADIA INC

D-U-N-S 09-454-3980
ARCADIA SERVICES INC
ARCADIA HOME CARE
20750 Civic Center Dr # 100, Southfield, MI 48076-4129
Tel (248) 352-7530 *Founded/Ownrshp* 1978
Sales 168.8MM[E] *EMP* 3,000
SIC 7363 8082 Medical help service; Home health care services
**COO:* Cathy Sparling
Dir IT: Manni Patwalia
IT Man: Kathie Tapper
Board of Directors: Matthew Burchi, Cathy Sparling

D-U-N-S 07-707-0035
ARCADIA UNIVERSITY
450 S Easton Rd, Glenside, PA 19038-3295
Tel (215) 572-2900 *Founded/Ownrshp* 1853
Sales 121.5MM *EMP* 862
Accts Baker Tilly Virchow Krause Ll
SIC 8221 College, except junior
Pr: Nicolette Christensen
**Treas:* Len Sippel
Ofcr: Jessica Leonard
Ofcr: James Scoles
Assoc VP: Melissa Harris-Brown
Assoc VP: Gerry Zaboski
**VP:* Matthew Golden
**VP:* Mark Lapreziosa
**VP:* Mary McRae
**VP:* Barbara Nodine
**VP:* Lorna Stern
VP: Frank Vogel
Exec: Mark Farley
Assoc Dir: Will Grogan
Assoc Dir: Michelle Marano
Assoc Dir: Rob Nydick
Assoc Dir: Dru Simmons
Comm Dir: Daniel Diprinzio

D-U-N-S 05-634-6539
ARCADIS CE INC
ARCADIS MALCOLM PIRNIE
(*Suby of* ARCADIS US INC) ★
44 S Broadway Ste 1500, White Plains, NY 10601-4455
Tel (914) 694-2100 *Founded/Ownrshp* 2009
Sales 88.4MM[E] *EMP* 1,775
SIC 8711 8731 Consulting engineer; Environmental research
Pr: William P Dee
**Ch Bd:* Douglas M Owen
**CFO:* Robert S Belitz
**Treas:* Mary Ann Neidert
Bd of Dir: Geoff Baldwin
Bd of Dir: Richard Crist
Bd of Dir: Bruce Fidler
Bd of Dir: Richard Franzetti
Bd of Dir: Stephen McGowan
Bd of Dir: Raul Torres
**VP:* John Batten
VP: Paul Busch
VP: Steve Davis
VP: Dick Herriott
VP: Sean P Obrien
**VP:* John Stankunas
VP: Jeff Zdrojewski
Exec: Paul Myres

ARCADIS MALCOLM PIRNIE
See ARCADIS CE INC

D-U-N-S 08-150-9838
ARCADIS US INC
(*Suby of* ARCADIS N.V.)
630 Plaza Dr Ste 200, Highlands Ranch, CO 80129-2379
Tel (720) 344-3500 *Founded/Ownrshp* 1993
Sales 837.2MM *EMP* 5,650
SIC 8748 8711 8741 Environmental consultant; Engineering services; Pollution control engineering; Consulting engineer; Management services; Construction management
CEO: Joachim Ebert
Pr: Curt A Cramer
Pr: Chuck Dahill
**CFO:* Jan Bouten
**Treas:* Mary Ann Neidert
Sr Cor Off: Harrie Noy
Bd of Dir: Mark C Zellenrath
Ofcr: Catherine Tobiasinsky
Assoc VP: T W Holcombe
Ex VP: Hal Bouknight
Ex VP: Seth Matters
Ex VP: David Thomas
Sr VP: Steve Kramer
**Sr VP:* Kim Brown Wilmsen
Sr VP: Terry Yonkers
VP: John Alonso
VP: Scott Brown
VP: Richard Coles
VP: Frank Danchetz
VP: Mike Fleischner
VP: Robert Flowers

D-U-N-S 02-238-6135
ARCAPITA INC
1180 Peachtree St Ne # 3000, Atlanta, GA 30309-7532
Tel (404) 920-9000 *Founded/Ownrshp* 1997
Sales 462.7MM[E] *EMP* 6,014
SIC 6798 Mortgage investment trusts
CEO: John Huntz Jr
**Pr:* Charles H Ogburn

*CFO: Essa Zainal
*Ch: Mohammed Abdulaziz Aljomaih
Ex Dir: Charles L Griffith Jr
Ex Dir: Khalid Jassim
Ex Dir: Charles G Ward III
Off Mgr: Debra Baker
Opers Mgr: Tammie McGowan
Genl Couns: Jay Fortin
Board of Directors: Abdulrahman A Al-Muhanna, Karim Si-Ahmed, Mohammed A Muiz, Mustafa Aramaz, Blake Olafson, Marc Bonnassieux, Matthew Pollard, Tim Doyne, Arthur Rogers, Simon Dudley, Jonathan Squires, Charles Griffith, Martin Tan, Tom Hawkins, John Wisniewski, Jaap Kalkman, Peter Karacsonyi

D-U-N-S 09-308-2295
ARCATA ASSOCIATES INC
2588 Fire Mesa St Ste 110, Las Vegas, NV 89128-9022
Tel (702) 642-9500 Founded/Ownrshp 1975
Sales 85.7MM^E EMP 425
SIC 8711 Engineering services
CEO: Tim Wong
*Ex VP: Anthony Ng
*Ex VP: Nancy Wong
*VP: Gene Bertin
*VP: Ralph Decker
*Prin: Lawrence T Wong
Admn Mgr: James Tilley

D-U-N-S 79-987-3992 IMP
ARCATECH SYSTEMS LLC
1151 Holmes Rd, Mebane, NC 27302-7975
Tel (919) 442-5200 Founded/Ownrshp 1998
Sales 211.3MM^E EMP 500
Accts Cherry Bekaert & Holland Llp
SIC 5049 Bank equipment & supplies
CEO: Mort O'Sullivan
*Pr: Aubrey Meador
*CFO: Eric Teague
VP Sls: Fearghal McAdam

D-U-N-S 19-450-1870 IMP/EXP
▲ ARCBEST CORP
3801 Old Greenwood Rd, Fort Smith, AR 72903-5937
Tel (479) 785-6000 Founded/Ownrshp 1966
Sales 2.6MMM EMP 13,000^E
Tkr Sym ARCB Exch NGS
SIC 4213 4731 Trucking, except local; Freight transportation arrangement; Freight forwarding
Pr: Judy R McReynolds
Pr: Jim A Ingram
Pr: Timothy D Thorne
CFO: David R Cobb
Sr VP: J Lavon Morton
Sr VP: Michael E Newcity
VP: Dennis L Anderson II
VP: Walter J Echols
VP: David Humphrey
VP: Michael R Johns
VP: Daniel E Loe
VP: Danny Loe
VP: Traci L Sowersby
Board of Directors: Janice E Stipp, John W Alden, Fred A Allardyce, Eduardo Conrado, Stephen E Gorman, Michael P Hogan, William M Legg, Kathleen D McElligott, Craig E Philip, Steven L Spinner

D-U-N-S 80-227-3461 IMP/EXP
ARCELOR USA HOLDING INC
(Suby of ARCELORMITTAL SA)
1 S Dearborn St Ste 1800, Chicago, IL 60603-2308
Tel (312) 899-3400 Founded/Ownrshp 2002
Sales 342.6MM^E EMP 1,100
SIC 5051 Steel
CEO: Lou Schorch
CFO: Vaidya Sethuraman

ARCELORMITTAL
See BD LAPLACE LLC

D-U-N-S 13-178-1473 IMP/EXP
ARCELORMITTAL BURNS HARBOR LLC
(Suby of ARCELORMITTAL USA LLC) ★
250 W Us Highway 12, Burns Harbor, IN 46304-9727
Tel (219) 787-2120 Founded/Ownrshp 1964
Sales 228.8MM^E EMP 3,100
SIC 3312 Blast furnaces & steel mills
CEO: Michael Rippey
CEO: Lou Schorsch
COO: John Battisti
Ex VP: John Brett
VP: Wendell Carter
VP: Gregory Ludkovsky
VP: Madhu Ranade
Div Mgr: James Bradley
Div Mgr: Thomas Mueller
Genl Mgr: Kim Kiser
Dir IT: Wilfried Hausmann

D-U-N-S 12-237-3918 IMP
ARCELORMITTAL CLEVELAND LLC
(Suby of ARCELORMITTAL SA)
3060 Eggers Ave, Cleveland, OH 44105-1012
Tel (216) 429-6000 Founded/Ownrshp 2008
Sales 336.9MM^E EMP 1,556^E
SIC 3312 Blast furnaces & steel mills
CEO: Micheal Rippey
CEO: Louis Schorsch
CFO: Aditya Mittal
Treas: William Kuhn
Div Mgr: Mary J Csonka
Genl Mgr: Terry Fedor
VP Mfg: Mike Billotti
Sfty Mgr: Ed Breach
Opers Mgr: Dale Mindeck

D-U-N-S 14-764-5928 IMP/EXP
ARCELORMITTAL HOLDINGS LLC
(Suby of ARCELORMITTAL SA)
3210 Watling St, East Chicago, IN 46312-1716
Tel (219) 399-1200 Founded/Ownrshp 2007
Sales 3.5MMM^E EMP 22,300
SIC 3312 1011 Blast furnaces & steel mills; Iron ores
Ch Bd: Lakshmi Mittal
*CFO: Michael G Rippey
Sr Cor Off: Gus Hillenbrand
VP: Jeffrey Webb
Admn Mgr: Ron Glusac

Div Mgr: Edward Williams
DP Exec: Kevin Kramer
DP Exec: Martin Nurek
QA Dir: Peter D Southwick
Prd Mgr: Aaron Langness

ARCELORMITTAL INDIANA HARBOR W
See INDIANA ARCELORMITTAL HARBOR LLC

D-U-N-S 07-686-6128 IMP/EXP
ARCELORMITTAL MINORCA MINE INC
MITTAL STEEL -IHW- 3 SP
(Suby of ARCELORMITTAL USA LLC) ★
3210 Watling St, East Chicago, IN 46312-1716
Tel (219) 399-1200 Founded/Ownrshp 1974
Sales 391.1MM^E EMP 316
SIC 1011 Open pit iron ore mining; Iron ore pelletizing
Ch Bd: Peter D Southwick
*Pr: Madhu Ranade
*CEO: Gary Krall
COO: Vijay K Bhatnagar
COO: Malay Mukherjee
Ex VP: Michael Rippey
VP: Vaidya Sethuraman
Div Mgr: Mark Dutler
Genl Mgr: Jonathan Holmes
Opers Mgr: Randall Lewis

D-U-N-S 13-182-6427 IMP/EXP
ARCELORMITTAL PLATE LLC
(Suby of ARCELORMITTAL USA LLC) ★
139 Modena Rd, Coatesville, PA 19320-4036
Tel (610) 383-2000 Founded/Ownrshp 2005
Sales 203.9MM^E EMP 1,132
SIC 3312 Plate, steel; Stainless steel; Iron & steel: galvanized, pipes, plates, sheets, etc.
CEO: Michael G Rippey
Genl Mgr: Edward Frey
Genl Mgr: Gary Sarpen
CIO: Jean-Jacqus Aernout

D-U-N-S 12-750-5357 IMP
ARCELORMITTAL RIVERDALE INC
(Suby of ARCELORMITTAL USA LLC) ★
13500 S Perry Ave, Riverdale, IL 60827-1148
Tel (708) 849-8803 Founded/Ownrshp 2002
Sales 113.5MM^E EMP 320
SIC 3316 Strip steel, flat bright, cold-rolled: purchased hot-rolled
*Pr: Gary Norgren
Div Mgr: David Pearson
Genl Mgr: Terry Fedor
Sfty Mgr: Ryan Hill
Sales Exec: Diane Dodd

D-U-N-S 13-182-8001 IMP
ARCELORMITTAL STEELTON LLC
(Suby of ARCELORMITTAL USA LLC) ★
215 S Front St, Steelton, PA 17113-2538
Tel (717) 986-2000 Founded/Ownrshp 2003
Sales 142.0MM^E EMP 640
SIC 3312 Structural & rail mill products; Rails, steel or iron; Blooms, steel
CEO: Lakshmi Niwas Mittal
Area Mgr: Rachel Smithers

D-U-N-S 18-054-1435
ARCELORMITTAL TUBULAR PRODUCTS SHELBY LLC
(Suby of ARCELORMITTAL HOLDINGS LLC) ★
132 W Main St, Shelby, OH 44875-1475
Tel (419) 347-2424 Founded/Ownrshp 2005
Sales 95.7MM^E EMP 631
SIC 3317 3321 Steel pipe & tubes; Gray & ductile iron foundries
CEO: Edward Vore
VP: Jim Baske

D-U-N-S 16-744-4434 EXP
ARCELORMITTAL TUBULAR PRODUCTS USA LLC
(Suby of ARCELORMITTAL DOFASCO G.P.)
4 Gateway Ctr, Pittsburgh, PA 15222
Tel (419) 342-1200 Founded/Ownrshp 2005
Sales 221.0MM^E EMP 2,300
Accts Ernst & Young Llp Pittsburgh
SIC 3317 Tubes, seamless steel; Tubes, wrought: welded or lock joint
CEO: Jerome Granboulan
*Pr: William Chisholm
*Treas: Robert Nuttall
Genl Mgr: Victor Cairo
Genl Mgr: Glenn Dumoulin
Genl Mgr: Marc Leclerc
Genl Mgr: Rick Owens
IT Man: Jeff Robertson
Mtls Mgr: David Walden
S&M/VP: Tim Abbott
Mktg Mgr: Kevin Flanagan

D-U-N-S 10-797-0886 IMP/EXP
ARCELORMITTAL USA LLC
(Suby of ARCELORMITTAL SA)
1 S Dearborn St Ste 1800, Chicago, IL 60603-2308
Tel (312) 346-0300 Founded/Ownrshp 1998
Sales 4.6MMM^E EMP 15,000^E
SIC 3312 3325 3356 3316 Blast furnaces & steel mills; Rolling mill rolls, cast steel; Tin; Cold finishing of steel shapes
CEO: John L Brett
CFO: Steve Edds
Ofcr: Augustus Quiah
Ofcr: Akshay Rankawat
*Ex VP: John Brett
*Ex VP: Andrew S Harshaw
*VP: Wendell Carter
*VP: Eric Hauge
VP: Neil Messick
*VP: Vaidya Sethuraman
*Prin: Brad Davey

D-U-N-S 14-847-7115 IMP
ARCELORMITTAL WEIRTON INC
(Suby of ARCELORMITTAL USA LLC) ★
100 Pennsylvania Ave, Weirton, WV 26062-2315
Tel (304) 797-2000 Founded/Ownrshp 2004
Sales 194.5MM^E EMP 1,300^E
SIC 3316 Cold finishing of steel shapes

CEO: Michael G Rippey
COO: William McKenzie
Treas: Edward O Rourke
VP: Arthur Myers
QA Dir: William R Hurd
IT Man: Jon Haines
Sftwr Eng: Susan Magnone
Sftwr Eng: Cas Tluchowski
Snr Mgr: Rickey Wilson

D-U-N-S 00-281-2691 IMP
ARCET EQUIPMENT CO (VA)
ARC3 GASES NORTH
(Suby of ARC3 GASES INC) ★
1700 Chamberlayne Ave, Richmond, VA 23222-4808
Tel (804) 644-4521 Founded/Ownrshp 1958, 2013
Sales 95.6MM^E EMP 230
SIC 5085 5084 5169 Welding supplies; Welding machinery & equipment; Industrial gases
Pr: Parker O Dillard
CFO: Andrew Ellen
VP: Ray Dillard
IT Man: Ashley Thomas
Sls Mgr: Alan Weaver
Sales Asso: Eric Landolf

D-U-N-S 17-418-6908
ARCH ALUMINUM & GLASS CO OF ARIZONA INC
ARCH AMARLITE
1825 S 43rd Ave Ste A, Phoenix, AZ 85009-6051
Tel (602) 484-9777 Founded/Ownrshp 2011
Sales 110.8MM^E EMP 1,570
SIC 3442 1793

ARCH AMARLITE
See ARCH ALUMINUM & GLASS CO OF ARIZONA INC

ARCH AMERICA
See SHAPES/ARCH HOLDINGS LLC

D-U-N-S 12-927-9761 IMP
ARCH CAPITAL GROUP (US) INC
(Suby of ARCH REINSURANCE LTD)
1 Liberty Plz Fl 53, New York, NY 10006-1404
Tel (212) 651-6500 Founded/Ownrshp 1995
Sales NA EMP 875^E
SIC 6311 6321 Life reinsurance; Reinsurance carriers, accident & health
Pr: Mark Lyons
*Pr: Ralph E Jones
Ex VP: David Gansberg
Sr VP: William W Beardsley
Sr VP: Corey Davis
Sr VP: Pet Hartman
Sr VP: Bill Hitter
Sr VP: Donald Mobley
Sr VP: Richard Zarandona
VP: Shirish Bhadsawle
VP: Terri Davis
VP: Catherine Lally
VP: Sharon Traumuller
VP: Karen Vanterpool
VP: Jerry Wosleger

D-U-N-S 04-942-2509 IMP/EXP
ARCH CHEMICALS INC
ADVANTIS TECHNOLOGY
(Suby of LONZA GROUP AG)
1200 Bluegrass Lakes Pkwy, Alpharetta, GA 30004-0544
Tel (678) 624-5800 Founded/Ownrshp 2011
Sales 1.3MMM^E EMP 2,533
SIC 2819 2899 Industrial inorganic chemicals; Chemical preparations
Pr: Scott B Waldman
*Pr: Stephan Kutzer
*Treas: W Paul Bush
*VP: Alexander H Hoy
*VP: Joseph Lacerenza
Assoc Dir: Diana Ciccognani
*Prin: Anthony Branciforte Jr
*Prin: Bradley Luria
Genl Mgr: Paul Dandy

D-U-N-S 05-262-4962
▲ ARCH COAL INC
1 Cityplace Dr Ste 300, Saint Louis, MO 63141-7066
Tel (314) 994-2700 Founded/Ownrshp 1969
Sales 2.5MMM EMP 4,655
Tkr Sym ARCH Exch NYS
SIC 1221 1222 Bituminous coal surface mining; Coal preparation plant, bituminous or lignite; Bituminous coal-underground mining
Ch Bd: John W Eaves
*Pr: Paul A Lang
CFO: John T Drexler
Ofcr: Rick Burke
Ofcr: John A Ziegler
Ofcr: John Ziegler Jr
Sr VP: C H Besten
Sr VP: Kenneth D Cochran
Sr VP: Robert G Jones
Sr VP: Deck S Slone
VP: Tom Altmeyer
VP: Henry Besten
VP: Bill Boyle
VP: Jack Conaway
VP: Johnathan Drexler
VP: Matthew Ferguson
VP: Sam Kitts
VP: Johnathan Lorson
VP: Larry Metzroth
VP: Alexander Newman
VP: David Peugh
Board of Directors: Peter I Wold, David D Freudenthal, Patricia F Godley, Paul T Hanrahan, Douglas H Hunt, J Thomas Jones, George C Morris III, James A Sabala, Theodore D Sands, Wesley M Taylor

D-U-N-S 07-836-4658
ARCH GLOBAL PRECISION LLC
12955 Inkster Rd, Livonia, MI 48150-2212
Tel (734) 266-6900 Founded/Ownrshp 2011
Sales 88.1MM EMP 170^E
Accts Mcgladrey Llp Chicago Illino
SIC 5049 3399 Precision tools; Metal fasteners
*CFO: Don Piper
*VP: Randy Hinz

D-U-N-S 05-789-4677
ARCH INSURANCE GROUP INC
(Suby of ARCH REINSURANCE CO) ★
Harborside 3 210 Hudson S, Jersey City, NJ 07311
Tel (201) 743-4000 Founded/Ownrshp 2004
Sales NA EMP 875
SIC 6331 6351 Property damage insurance; Liability insurance
*Chf Mktg O: William Casey
Ex VP: William J Casey
Ex VP: Michael Price
Ex VP: Mark C Vonnahme
Sr VP: Vincent Kellaher
Sr VP: Mark Lange
*Sr VP: Shane McCaffey
*Sr VP: Patrick Nails
Sr VP: James Slate
Exec: John Edack
QA Dir: Mohammad Monsur

ARCH LOGISTICS
See BUNZL DISTRIBUTION MIDCENTRAL INC

ARCH MIRROR NORTH
See FLORIDA A&G CO INC

D-U-N-S 13-027-1765
ARCH REINSURANCE CO
(Suby of ARCH CAPITAL GROUP (US) INC) ★
445 South St Ste 220, Morristown, NJ 07960-6475
Tel (973) 898-9575 Founded/Ownrshp 2013
Sales NA EMP 875
SIC 6411 Property & casualty insurance agent
Pr: Jerome Halgan
*CFO: Barry Golub
Treas: Tim Forshay
*Ofcr: Joel Livingston
Exec: David Gansberg
Brnch Mgr: Ralph Jones
Genl Mgr: Alex Paspalas

D-U-N-S 03-930-5060
■ ARCH WESTERN RESOURCES LLC
(Suby of ARCH COAL INC) ★
1 Cityplace Dr Ste 300, Saint Louis, MO 63141-7066
Tel (314) 994-2700 Founded/Ownrshp 1998
Sales 2.2MMM EMP 2,900^E
SIC 1221 Surface mining, bituminous
*Pr: John W Eaves
CFO: John T Drexler
Sr VP: Robert G Jones

D-U-N-S 15-519-5951
■ ARCH WIRELESS INC
(Suby of SPOK INC) ★
6850 Versar Ctr Ste 420, Springfield, VA 22151-4148
Tel (703) 269-6850 Founded/Ownrshp 2004
Sales 65.4MM^E EMP 1,725^E
SIC 5999 4812 Telephone & communication equipment; Paging services
CEO: C Edward Baker Jr
*Pr: Lyndon R Daniels
*CFO: J Roy Pottle
*Sec: Patricia A Gray

D-U-N-S 09-648-3607
ARCH-AUTO PARTS CORP (NY)
17008 Jamaica Ave, Jamaica, NY 11432-5220
Tel (718) 657-9600 Founded/Ownrshp 1979
Sales 90.3MM^E EMP 130
SIC 5013 5531 Automotive supplies & parts; Automotive parts
*Ex Dir: Michael Lee

D-U-N-S 07-800-4686
ARCHBISHOP BERGAN MERCY AUXILIARY
BERGAN MERCY CENTER GIFT SHOP
7500 Mercy Rd, Omaha, NE 68124-2319
Tel (402) 398-6199 Founded/Ownrshp 1958
Sales 580.8MM EMP 14^E
SIC 5947 Gift shop
*Pr: Deb Bogard
*Pr: Dotti Callahan
*Treas: Mary Kay McCarthy
Off Mgr: Lisa Gubbles

D-U-N-S 07-800-5147
ARCHBISHOP BERGAN MERCY HOSPITAL
BERGAN MERCY MEDICAL CENTER
7500 Mercy Rd, Omaha, NE 68124-2386
Tel (402) 398-6060 Founded/Ownrshp 1961
Sales 90.9MM^E EMP 2,500
Accts Kpmg Llp Omaha Ne
SIC 8062 8051 General medical & surgical hospitals; Extended care facility
CEO: Richard A Hachten II
Sr VP: Joan Neuhaus
Sr VP: Scott Wooten
Dir Rad: Kimberly A Apker
Prin: Patty Vana

ARCHBOLD MEDICAL CENTER
See JOHN D ARCHBOLD MEMORIAL HOSPITAL

D-U-N-S 17-594-0832
ARCHBOLD MEDICAL CENTER INC
Gordon Ave At Mimosa Dr, Thomasville, GA 31792
Tel (229) 228-2739 Founded/Ownrshp 1983
Sales 24.6MM EMP 2,700
Accts Draffin & Tucker Llp Albany
SIC 8741 8062 Hospital management; Nursing & personal care facility management; General medical & surgical hospitals
CEO: J Perry Mustian
*Pr: Ken Beverly
COO: Kevin Taylor
CFO: Charles Hightower
VP: Amy Griffin
Dir Sec: Adam Cooney
Off Mgr: Rhonda Lewis
Doctor: Scott Lewis
Doctor: Harriett B Loehne

D-U-N-S 04-296-9543 IMP/EXP
ARCHBROOK LAGUNA LLC
ABL
(Suby of ARCHBROOK LAGUNA HOLDINGS LLC)
350 Starke Rd Ste 400, Carlstadt, NJ 07072-2113
Tel (201) 372-0304 Founded/Ownrshp 2007

Sales 88.0MM[E] EMP 220
SIC 5045 5065 Computers; Electronic parts
CEO: Mr Don Zacune
*Ex VP: Mr Jim Ristow
VP: Raymond Navarrete

ARCHCARE
See TERENCE CARDINAL COOKE HEALTH CARE CENTER

ARCHDIOCESAN ELEMENTARY
See ARCHDIOCESE OF ST LOUIS

ARCHDIOCESE OF BOSTON
See ROMAN CATHOLIC ARCHBISHOP OF BOSTON

ARCHDIOCESE OF CHICAGO
See CATHOLIC BISHOP OF CHICAGO

D-U-N-S 07-678-6987
ARCHDIOCESE OF CINCINNATI
100 E 8th St Fl 8, Cincinnati, OH 45202-2150
Tel (513) 421-3131 Founded/Ownrshp 1821
Sales 225.8MM[E] EMP 6,000
SIC 8661 8211 Catholic Church; Catholic combined elementary & secondary school
Prin: Rev Dennis M Schnurr
CFO: Richard Kelly
Treas: Howard Pecquet
Assoc Dir: Brian Doyle
Assoc Dir: Andrea Parker
Assoc Dir: Teresa Phillips
*Comm Dir: Dan Andriacco
*Prin: Stephen E Burger
CTO: Charlotte Carpenter
Dir IT: Diana Brettl
Dir IT: Jenny Long

D-U-N-S 04-969-7126
ARCHDIOCESE OF DENVER
1300 S Steele St, Denver, CO 80210-2599
Tel (303) 722-4687 Founded/Ownrshp 1900
Sales 46.5MM[E] EMP 1,600
SIC 8661 Religious organizations
*CFO: David Holden
Comm Dir: Jeannete Demelo

D-U-N-S 79-747-9180
ARCHDIOCESE OF DETROIT ED OFF
ST REGIS SCHOOL
(Suby of ROMAN CATHOLIC ARCHDIOCESE OF DETROIT) ★
3691 Lincoln Rd, Bloomfield, MI 48301-4055
Tel (248) 646-2612 Founded/Ownrshp 2007
Sales 24.3MM[E] EMP 1,461[E]
SIC 8211 Catholic elementary & secondary schools
Prin: Chris Ciagne

D-U-N-S 79-751-9902
ARCHDIOCESE OF DETROIT ED OFF
HOLY FAMILY REG SCH-S CAMPUS
(Suby of ROMAN CATHOLIC ARCHDIOCESE OF DETROIT) ★
2633 John R Rd, Rochester Hills, MI 48307-4652
Tel (248) 299-3798 Founded/Ownrshp 2012
Sales 21.7MM[E] EMP 1,299[E]
SIC 8211 Catholic elementary & secondary schools

ARCHDIOCESE OF HARTFORD, THE
See HARTFORD CATHOLIC DEVELOPMENT CORP

D-U-N-S 07-988-0217
ARCHDIOCESE OF KANSAS CITY IN KANSAS
CATHOLIC ARCHDCESE K C IN KANS
12615 Parallel Pkwy, Kansas City, KS 66109-3718
Tel (913) 721-1570 Founded/Ownrshp 1852
Sales 52.7MM[E] EMP 2,750
SIC 8661 8211 8222 2711

ARCHDIOCESE OF LOS ANGELES
See ROMAN CATHOLIC ARCHBISHOP OF LOS ANGELES

ARCHDIOCESE OF LOUISVILLE
See ROMAN CATHOLIC BISHOP OF LOUISVILLE

D-U-N-S 07-222-5014 EXP
ARCHDIOCESE OF MIAMI INC
ST MARY'S PROPERTIES
9401 Biscayne Blvd, Miami Shores, FL 33138-2970
Tel (305) 757-6241 Founded/Ownrshp 1958
Sales 146.8MM[E] EMP 3,000
SIC 8661 Religious organizations
Pr: Thomas G Wenski
*CFO: Michael Cascisto
*Treas: Joseph A Catania

D-U-N-S 07-912-9219
ARCHDIOCESE OF MOBILE
400 Government St, Mobile, AL 36602-2332
Tel (251) 434-1530 Founded/Ownrshp 1825
Sales 49.4MM[E] EMP 2,000
SIC 8661 Catholic Church
Pr: Toni Kaminski
*VP: Lena Dexter

D-U-N-S 79-455-4225
ARCHDIOCESE OF MOBILE ED OFF
ST COLUMBA PRE-SCHOOL
(Suby of ARCHDIOCESE OF MOBILE) ★
2700 W Main St, Dothan, AL 36301-6408
Tel (334) 793-6742 Founded/Ownrshp 2012
Sales 5.5MM[E] EMP 1,228[E]
SIC 8211 Catholic elementary & secondary schools
Prin: Cathy Dedmon

D-U-N-S 06-266-1269
ARCHDIOCESE OF NEW ORLEANS INC
7887 Walmsley Ave, New Orleans, LA 70125-3496
Tel (504) 861-9521 Founded/Ownrshp 1880
Sales 313.3MM[E] EMP 5,000[E]
SIC 8211 8661 Catholic elementary school; Catholic senior high school; Seminary; Catholic Church
CFO: Gregory Aymond
*CFO: John Eckholdt
Comm Dir: Sarah McDonald

D-U-N-S 07-862-9854
ARCHDIOCESE OF NEW YORK
1011 1st Ave, New York, NY 10022-4112
Tel (212) 371-1000 Founded/Ownrshp 1928
Sales 245.4MM[E] EMP 9,000
SIC 8661

D-U-N-S 04-174-9771
ARCHDIOCESE OF PHILADELPHIA
ST EDMOND'S HOME FOR CRIPPLED
222 N 17th St, Bryn Mawr, PA 19010
Tel (215) 587-3500 Founded/Ownrshp 1808
Sales 7.5MM EMP 10,500[E]
SIC 8322 Child related social services
CFO: Timothy O'Shaughnessy
Prin: Dawn Perry

D-U-N-S 07-148-9983
ARCHDIOCESE OF SAINT PAUL AND MINNEAPOLIS
226 Summit Ave, Saint Paul, MN 55102-2121
Tel (651) 291-4400 Founded/Ownrshp 1850
Sales 76.5MM[E] EMP 1,504
Accts Boulay Heutmaker Zibell & Co
SIC 8661 Catholic Church
Co-Pr: John C Nienstedt
CFO: Denise Abbott
*Treas: Rev Austin T Ward
*Co-Pr: Harry J Flynn
*VP: Rev Kevin Mc Donough
*Prin: Father Peter Laird
IT Man: Ed Grebis

D-U-N-S 05-511-4680
ARCHDIOCESE OF SAN ANTONIO (TX)
2718 W Woodlawn Ave, San Antonio, TX 78228-5195
Tel (210) 433-0411 Founded/Ownrshp 1874
Sales 53.8MM[E] EMP 1,896
SIC 8661 Catholic Church
*COO: Gustavo Garcia-Siller
CFO: David Castilleja
Assoc Dir: Ellie Krupa
Assoc Dir: Joan Weiler

ARCHDIOCESE OF SEATTLE
See CORP OF CATHOLIC ARCHBISHOP OF SEATTLE

D-U-N-S 07-992-4007
ARCHDIOCESE OF ST LOUIS
ARCHDIOCESAN ELEMENTARY
20 Archbishop May Dr, Saint Louis, MO 63119-5738
Tel (314) 633-2222 Founded/Ownrshp 1826
Sales 193.6MM[E] EMP 4,000
Accts Deloitte & Touche Llp St Lou
SIC 8661 Catholic Church
Pr: Brian O Malley
*COO: David Mueckl
CFO: Robert Bouche
*CFO: Deacon Frank Chauvin
Bd of Dir: Robert Ryan
Assoc Dir: Edith L Tierney
Dir IT: Paul Giljum
Sftwr Eng: Mike Sicking
Genl Couns: Tom Buckley
Pgrm Dir: Laura George

ARCHDIOCESE PORTLAND IN OREGON
See ROMAN CATHOLIC ARCHBISHOP OF PORTLAND IN OREGON AND SUCCESSORS A CORP SOLE

D-U-N-S 06-725-2858
ARCHDIOCESES OF BALTIMORE
320 Cathedral St Ste 1, Baltimore, MD 21201-4421
Tel (410) 547-5442 Founded/Ownrshp 1789
Sales 102.7MM[E] EMP 7,000
SIC 8211 Catholic senior high school
CEO: Archbishop William H Keeler
MIS Dir: Jim Tucker

D-U-N-S 01-051-5911
ARCHER PRESSURE PUMPING LLC
GREAT WHITE ENERGY SERVICES
(Suby of ARCHER WELL CO) ★
4500 Se 59th St, Oklahoma City, OK 73135-3326
Tel (405) 285-5812 Founded/Ownrshp 2007
Sales 263.0MM EMP 432
SIC 1381 Directional drilling oil & gas wells
Pr: Sam Daniel
CFO: Christoph Bausch
*Treas: Craig Woodruff
VP: Robert Carnes
Dist Mgr: Billy Scriber

ARCHER THE WELL COMPANY
See ARCHER WELL CO INC

D-U-N-S 07-844-2772 IMP
ARCHER WELL CO INC
ARCHER THE WELL COMPANY
(Suby of ARCHER ASSETS UK LIMITED)
10613 W Sh Pkwy N Ste 600, Houston, TX 77064
Tel (713) 856-4222 Founded/Ownrshp 2008
Sales 1.6MMM[E] EMP 1,497[E]
SIC 1381 Drilling oil & gas wells
CEO: David King
*Pr: Max Bouthillette
*VP: Robin Brice
*VP: Steve Russell
*VP: Bruce Sauers
Rgnl Mgr: Joel Johns
Dir IT: Mark Nutter
Tech Mgr: James Tankersley

D-U-N-S 96-384-9901
ARCHER WESTERN CONSTRUCTION LLC
(Suby of WALSH CONSTRUCTION GROUP LLC) ★
929 W Adams St, Chicago, IL 60607-3021
Tel (312) 563-5400 Founded/Ownrshp 2009
Sales 85.3MM[E] EMP 200[E]
Accts Wolf & Company Llp Oakbrook
SIC 1521 1622 1629 1542 Single-family housing construction; Bridge, tunnel & elevated highway; Tunnel construction; Waste water & sewage treatment plant construction; Commercial & office building, new construction
*CFO: Tim Gerken

D-U-N-S 14-499-4779 IMP
ARCHER WESTERN CONTRACTORS LLC
(Suby of WALSH GROUP CONSTRUCTION) ★
2410 Paces Ferry Rd Se # 600, Atlanta, GA 30339-1821
Tel (404) 495-8700 Founded/Ownrshp 2012
Sales 1.4MMM[E] EMP 2,000
SIC 1542 1622 1611 1629 Commercial & office building, new construction; Bridge construction; Tunnel construction; Highway & street construction; Waste water & sewage treatment plant construction
Pr: Matthew M Walsh
*Ex VP: Daniel Walsh
*VP: Donald Agillis
*VP: David Casey
Dir IT: Timothy Nottoli

ARCHER WIRELINE LLC
See QES WIRELINE LLC

D-U-N-S 00-130-7586 IMP/EXP
▲ ARCHER-DANIELS-MIDLAND CO
77 W Wacker Dr Ste 4600, Chicago, IL 60601-1667
Tel (312) 634-8100 Founded/Ownrshp 1902
Sales 67.7MMM EMP 32,360
Accts Ernst & Young Llp St Louis
Tkr Sym ADM Exch NYS
SIC 2046 2041 2075 2074 5153 2083 Wet corn milling; High fructose corn syrup (HFCS); Corn starch; Corn oil products; Wheat flour; Soybean oil mills; Cottonseed oil, cake or meal; Grain elevators; Malt; Malt byproducts
Pr: Juan R Luciano
CFO: Ray G Young
Chf Cred: Victoria Podesta
Sr VP: Mark A Bemis
Sr VP: D Cameron Findlay
VP: John P Stott
Board of Directors: Daniel Shih, Alan L Boeckmann, Kelvin R Westbrook, Mollie Hale Carter, Terrell K Crews, Pierre Dufour, Donald E Felsinger, Patrick J Moore, Antonio Maciel Neto, Francisco Sanchez, Debra A Sandler

D-U-N-S 04-389-2707
■ ARCHITECT OF CAPITOL
(Suby of CONGRESS UNITED STATES) ★
Us Capitol Bldg Rm Sb-16, Washington, DC 20515-0001
Tel (202) 228-1793 Founded/Ownrshp 1793
Sales NA EMP 2,500
SIC 9121 Legislative bodies;
CEO: Beth Plemmons
*CFO: Tom Carroll
Ofcr: Tom Gard
Comm Dir: Mamie Bittner
*Ex Dir: Stephen T Ayers
*Ex Dir: Holly H Shimizu
Netwrk Mgr: Chih Chiou
Sfty Mgr: Robert Carnevale
Merch Mgr: Jamilah Williams
Genl Couns: Kevin Mulshine
Snr Mgr: Bennie Frazier

D-U-N-S 07-948-7603
ARCHITECTURAL BLOMBERG LLC
BLOMBERG WINDOW SYSTEMS
1453 Blair Ave, Sacramento, CA 95822-3410
Tel (916) 428-8060 Founded/Ownrshp 2014
Sales 84.0MM EMP 32
SIC 3442 Window & door frames

D-U-N-S 05-190-1114 IMP
ARCHITECTURAL GLASS & ALUMINUM CO INC (CA)
6400 Brisa St, Livermore, CA 94550-2550
Tel (925) 583-2460 Founded/Ownrshp 1970
Sales 147.4MM[E] EMP 200
SIC 5051 1793 1791 3442 Aluminum bars, rods, ingots, sheets, pipes, plates, etc.; Glass & glazing work; Exterior wall system installation; Sash, door or window: metal
CEO: Joseph Brescia
*Pr: John Buckley
CFO: John Okubo
*VP: William Coll Jr
Exec: Vicki Cavaz
Snr PM: Dennis Jean

D-U-N-S 04-144-8911 IMP/EXP
ARCHITECTURAL GRAPHICS INC
AGI
2655 International Pkwy, Virginia Beach, VA 23452-7802
Tel (757) 427-1900 Founded/Ownrshp 1969
Sales 126.1MM EMP 450
SIC 3993 Signs & advertising specialties
Ch Bd: David W Ramsay
*Pr: Craig Rohde
*COO: James W Raynor III
*CFO: Michael Garafalo
*Ex VP: Chris Quigley
*Sr VP: James Bell
Sr VP: Gary Finkbeiner
VP: Nathan Bretscher
VP: David Clower
VP: Steve Finley
VP: Brian Lucas
Exec: Leanne Messenger
Exec: Patrick Waxstein
Creative D: Matthew Donlan

D-U-N-S 55-593-9305 IMP
ARCHITECTURAL WALL SYSTEMS CO
(Suby of SMI) ★
12345 University Ave # 100, Clive, IA 50325-8284
Tel (515) 255-1556 Founded/Ownrshp 2015
Sales 90.4MM[E] EMP 150
SIC 1542 Commercial & office building contractors
CEO: Mike Cunningham
*Pr: Thomas John Schlotfeldt

ARCHON HOSPITALITY
See GOLDMAN SACHS REALTY MANAGEMENT LP

D-U-N-S 80-650-6437
▲ ARCHROCK INC
16666 Northchase Dr, Houston, TX 77060-6014
Tel (281) 836-8000 Founded/Ownrshp 2007
Sales 998.1MM EMP 2,200
Accts Deloitte & Touche Llp Houston
Tkr Sym AROC Exch NYS
SIC 1389 Gas compressing (natural gas) at the fields; Gas field services; Oil field services
Pr: D Bradley Childers
Ch Bd: Gordon T Hall
COO: Robert E Rice
CFO: David S Miller
Sr VP: Donald C Wayne
VP: Donna A Henderson
VP: Jason G Ingersoll
VP: Larry Lucas
Plnt Mgr: Dustin Trautwein
Snr Mgr: Lisa Walsh
Board of Directors: Wendell R Brooks, Frances Powell Hawes, J W G Honeybourne, James H Lytal, Mark A McCollum

D-U-N-S 78-829-4903
■ ARCHROCK PARTNERS LP
(Suby of ARCHROCK INC) ★
16666 Northchase Dr, Houston, TX 77060-6014
Tel (281) 836-8000 Founded/Ownrshp 2006
Sales 656.8MM EMP 5
Tkr Sym APLP Exch NGS
SIC 4922 Natural gas transmission
Ch Bd: D Bradley Childers
CFO: David S Miller

D-U-N-S 05-424-9255
ARCHSTONE COMMUNITIES LLC
9200 E Panorama Cir # 400, Englewood, CO 80112-3481
Tel (303) 708-5959 Founded/Ownrshp 2011
Sales NA EMP 2,666
SIC 6798 6513

D-U-N-S 82-980-9057
ARCHWAY MARKETING HOLDINGS INC
19850 S Diamond Lake Rd, Rogers, MN 55374-4571
Tel (763) 428-3300 Founded/Ownrshp 2008
Sales 294.5MM[E] EMP 800
SIC 8742 Management consulting services
CEO: Doug Mann
COO: Dean Truitt
CFO: Tom Smith
Ofcr: Barry Polan
Sr VP: Walter L Caudill
VP: David Nicoletta
VP: Rob Walters
CIO: Jeff Noffsinger

D-U-N-S 82-528-1251
ARCHWAY MARKETING SERVICES INC
(Suby of ARCHWAY MARKETING HOLDINGS INC) ★
19850 S Diamond Lake Rd, Rogers, MN 55374-4571
Tel (763) 428-3300 Founded/Ownrshp 2008
Sales 254.0MM[E] EMP 800
SIC 8742 4225 Transportation consultant; General warehousing & storage
CEO: Doug Mann
CFO: Brian Burke
CFO: Tom Smith
Ofcr: Barry Polan
VP: Rita Hellewell
VP: Enrique Torroledo
VP Bus Dev: Steve White
Brnch Mgr: Bridgett Gaston
Genl Mgr: Don Plantenberg
CIO: Jeff Noffsinger
DP Exec: Harvey Viren

D-U-N-S 05-695-8812 IMP
ARCHWAY SALES LLC
4155 Manchester Ave, Saint Louis, MO 63110-3823
Tel (314) 533-4662 Founded/Ownrshp 2014
Sales 117.0MM[E] EMP 96[E]
SIC 5169

ARCINDUSTRIES
See ARC OF NORTHERN RHODE ISLAND INC

D-U-N-S 87-677-4089
ARCLIGHT CAPITAL HOLDINGS LLC
ARCLIGHT CAPITAL PARTNERS
200 Clarendon St Fl 55, Boston, MA 02116-5021
Tel (617) 531-6300 Founded/Ownrshp 2001
Sales 757.5MM[E] EMP 2,071[E]
SIC 6799 Venture capital companies

ARCLIGHT CAPITAL PARTNERS
See ARCLIGHT CAPITAL HOLDINGS LLC

D-U-N-S 78-425-2343
ARCLIGHT CAPITAL PARTNERS LLC
(Suby of ARCLIGHT CAPITAL PARTNERS) ★
200 Clarendon St Fl 55, Boston, MA 02116-5021
Tel (617) 531-6300 Founded/Ownrshp 2001
Sales 730.0MM[E] EMP 600
SIC 6799 Investors
VP: Michael Christopher

D-U-N-S 00-942-0126 IMP/EXP
ARCLIN USA LLC
(Suby of ARCLIN CAYMAN HOLDINGS LTD)
1000 Holcomb Woods Pkwy, Roswell, GA 30076-2575
Tel (678) 999-2100 Founded/Ownrshp 2010
Sales 168.4MM[E] EMP 537
SIC 2821 2891 Plastics materials & resins; Sealants
Pr: Russell C Taylor
*CFO: Scott Maynard
*Sr VP: Brad Bolduc
Sr VP: Bernie Cardella
*Sr VP: Scot Johnson
*Sr VP: Ralf D Yobp

ARCO
See BP WEST COAST PRODUCTS LLC

D-U-N-S 82-828-7784
ARCO NATIONAL CONSTRUCTION CO
900 N Rock Hill Rd, Saint Louis, MO 63119-1315
Tel (314) 963-0715 Founded/Ownrshp 2000
Sales 122.0MM EMP 84
SIC 1541 Industrial buildings & warehouses
Pr: Craig Bridell
*Pr: Richard R Arnoldy
*VP: Dave Allen
*VP: Russell Gall

*VP: Jim Keeven
*Prin: Kate Helfer

ARCO PHARMACEUTICAL
See NBTY INC

ARCONIC FSTENING SYSTEMS RINGS
See SCHLOSSER FORGE CO

ARCONIC FSTENING SYSTEMS RINGS
See ARCONIC GLOBAL FASTENERS & RINGS INC

ARCONIC FSTENING SYSTEMS RINGS
See FORGED METALS INC

D-U-N-S 08-650-3539 IMP
■ ARCONIC GLOBAL FASTENERS & RINGS INC
ARCONIC FSTENING SYSTEMS RINGS
(Suby of ARCONIC INC) ★
3990a Heritage Oak Ct, Simi Valley, CA 93063-6715
Tel (310) 530-2220 Founded/Ownrshp 2002
Sales 1.4MMM^E EMP 4,630
SIC 5085 5072 5065 Fasteners & fastening equipment; Hardware; Electronic parts & equipment
Pr: Olivier Jarrault
VP: Craig Brown
CTO: Tammy Castillo
CTO: Andy Guttierrez
Dir IT: Randy Paulson
MIS Mgr: Pete Jespersen
Sales Exec: Dan McCarthy
VP Sls: Ann Ken

D-U-N-S 00-133-9472 IMP/EXP
▲ ARCONIC INC (PA)
390 Park Ave, New York, NY 10022-4608
Tel (212) 836-2674 Founded/Ownrshp 1888
Sales 22.5MMM EMP 60,000
Accts Pricewaterhousecoopers Llp Pi
Tkr Sym ARNC Exch NYS
SIC 3334 3353 1099 Primary aluminum; Aluminum sheet & strip; Coils, sheet aluminum; Plates, aluminum; Foil, aluminum; Bauxite mining
Ch Bd: Klaus Kleinfeld
CFO: Ken Giacobbe
Ex VP: Vas Nair
VP: W Paul Myron
Board of Directors: Martin S Sorrell, Amy E Alving, Arthur D Collins Jr, Sean O Mahoney, E Stanley O'neal, John C Plant, Leo Rafael Reif, Julie G Richardson, Patricia F Russo, Ulrich R Schmidt

D-U-N-S 13-765-6039 IMP/EXP
■ ARCONIC SECURITIES LLC
ALCOA
(Suby of ARCONIC INC) ★
101 Cherry St Ste 400, Burlington, VT 05401-4405
Tel (802) 658-2661 Founded/Ownrshp 1954
Sales 141.8MM^E EMP 2,835
SIC 3353 Aluminum sheet, plate & foil
Pr: John E Wilson Jr

D-U-N-S 07-954-4416
ARCSERVE (USA) LLC
(Suby of MARLIN EQUITY PARTNERS LLC) ★
1 Ca Plz, Islandia, NY 11749-5305
Tel (866) 576-9742 Founded/Ownrshp 2014
Sales 103.0MM EMP 500
SIC 7372 Business oriented computer software
CEO: Michael Crest
*CFO: Bhadresh Sutaria
VP: Cristophe Bertrand
VP: Steve Fairbanks
VP: Louis Lautin
VP: Chris Ross
VP: Jason Shangold
VP Opers: John Ball

D-U-N-S 07-242-9947 IMP/EXP
▲ ARCTIC CAT INC
500 N 3rd St, Minneapolis, MN 55401-1202
Tel (763) 354-1800 Founded/Ownrshp 1982
Sales 632.9MM EMP 1,573^E
Accts Grant Thornton Llp Minneapoli
Tkr Sym ACAT Exch NGS
SIC 3799 2329 2339 3732 Snowmobiles; All terrain vehicles (ATV); Men's & boys' sportswear & athletic clothing; Women's & misses' athletic clothing & sportswear; Jet skis
Pr: Christopher T Metz
*Ch Bd: Kenneth J Roering
CFO: Christopher J Eperjesy
Chf Mktg O: Greg Williamson
Ofcr: Patricia L Jones
VP: Tracy J Crocker
VP: Paul A Fisher
VP: Steven Nadler
VP: Eric C Nelson
VP: Michael D Okerlund
VP: Briton Reich
Board of Directors: Kim A Brink, Tony J Christianson, Andrew S Duff, Susan E Lester, Joseph F Puishys

D-U-N-S 08-019-5404
ARCTIC GLACIER USA HOLDINGS LLC
1654 Marthaler Ln, Saint Paul, MN 55118-3516
Tel (651) 455-0410 Founded/Ownrshp 2016
Sales 120.0MM^E EMP 74^E
SIC 2097 Manufactured ice
VP: Debra Rodd

D-U-N-S 07-983-3055
ARCTIC GLACIER USA INC
(Suby of ARCTIC GLACIER USA HOLDINGS LLC) ★
1654 Marthaler Ln, Saint Paul, MN 55118-3516
Tel (204) 784-5873 Founded/Ownrshp 2012
Sales 120.0MM EMP 2,500^E
SIC 2097 Manufactured ice
CEO: Fred Smagorinski
CFO: Linda Davachi
VP: Debra Rodd

D-U-N-S 03-540-1140 IMP
ARCTIC OFFICE MACHINE INC
ARCTIC OFFICE PRODUCTS
100 W Fireweed Ln, Anchorage, AK 99503-2604
Tel (907) 276-2295 Founded/Ownrshp 1946
Sales 93.5MM^E EMP 102
SIC 5112 5021 5044 7629 Office supplies; Office furniture; Office equipment; Business machine repair, electric
Pr: William A Borchardt
*Treas: Smith Linda
VP: Greg Martin
*VP: Mari Wood
IT Man: Melissa McClelland
IT Man: Marcia Wilkes

ARCTIC OFFICE PRODUCTS
See ARCTIC OFFICE MACHINE INC

D-U-N-S 07-663-7073
ARCTIC SLOPE REGIONAL CORP
3900 C St Ste 801, Anchorage, AK 99503-5963
Tel (907) 339-6000 Founded/Ownrshp 1972
Sales 2.6MMM^E EMP 6,700
SIC 1389 2911 1623 Oil field services; Petroleum refining; Oil & gas pipeline construction
Ch: Jacob Adams
*V Ch: George Sielak
*Pr: Patsy Aamodt
*Pr: George Kaleak Sr
*Pr: Raymond Paneak
*CEO: Rex A Rock Sr
*COO: Mark Kroloff
COO: Butch Lincoln
CFO: Charlie Kozak
*CFO: Kristin Mellinger
*Treas: Crawford Patkotak
Ex VP: Denali Kemppel
Ex VP: John Suddeth
VP: Richard Glenn
VP: Teresa Imm
VP: Tara Sweeney
VP: Lisa Young
Exec: Shawn Barrows

D-U-N-S 08-303-3605
ARCTURIS INC (MO)
720 Olive St Ste 200, Saint Louis, MO 63101-2335
Tel (314) 206-7100 Founded/Ownrshp 1977
Sales 83.0MM EMP 48^E
SIC 8712 7389 Architectural services; Interior design services
Ch: Patricia Whitaker
Dir: Russ Volmert
Genl Mgr: Julie Finocchio
Off Mgr: Julie Finoccoi

D-U-N-S 62-513-0828
ARD MALLINCKRODT INC
(Suby of MALLINCKRODT PUBLIC LIMITED COMPANY)
675 Jmes S Mcdonnell Blvd, Hazelwood, MO 63042-2379
Tel (714) 786-4200 Founded/Ownrshp 2014
Sales 127.8MM^E EMP 557^E
SIC 2834 Pharmaceutical preparations
Pr: Don M Bailey
*CFO: Juergen Hermann
*Ofcr: Stephen L Cartt
*Ofcr: Raymond J Furey
*Ofcr: David Young
*Ex VP: David J Medeiros
*Ex VP: Michael H Mulroy
Sr VP: Michael Aldridge
Sr VP: Steven C Halladay
Sr VP: Eric J Liebler

D-U-N-S 92-775-6882 IMP/EXP
ARDAGH GLASS INC
VERALLIA NORTH AMERICA
(Suby of ARDAGH GROUP SA)
1509 S Macedonia Ave, Muncie, IN 47302-3664
Tel (765) 741-7000 Founded/Ownrshp 1995
Sales 1.7MMM^E EMP 300
SIC 3221 Glass containers; Bottles for packing, bottling & canning: glass
CEO: Niall Wall
Pr: Eric Dirlam
*Pr: Joseph R Grewe
Treas: James F Harkins Jr
Sr VP: Tom Duffy
*Sr VP: John M Haack
Sr VP: Steve Rhea
Sr VP: Stephen Sagebarth
VP: Tony Cappelino
*VP: Jim Keener
VP: Joel Patrick
VP: Robert Shanteau
VP: Robert Statile

D-U-N-S 08-037-6954
ARDAGH METAL BEVERAGE USA INC
8770 W Bryn Mawr Ave # 175, Chicago, IL 60631-3515
Tel (773) 399-3000 Founded/Ownrshp 2016
Sales 1.0MMM EMP 75
SIC 3411 Metal cans
CEO: Claude Marbach
*CFO: Thomas Holz

D-U-N-S 79-942-4051 IMP/EXP
ARDAGH METAL PACKAGING USA INC
(Suby of ARDAGH GROUP SA)
600 N Bell Ave Ste 200, Carnegie, PA 15106-4315
Tel (412) 923-1080 Founded/Ownrshp 2010
Sales 310.4MM^E EMP 750
SIC 3565 Packaging machinery
CEO: James H Willich
*CFO: John Boyas
Dir Bus: Robert Zanetto
Plnt Mgr: Lloyd Taylor

D-U-N-S 00-655-3143 IMP
ARDEN COMPANIES INC
(Suby of ARDEN-BENHAR MILLS) ★
30400 Telg Rd Ste 200, Bingham Farms, MI 48025
Tel (248) 415-8500 Founded/Ownrshp 1986
Sales 219.5MM^E EMP 650
SIC 2392 Cushions & pillows
CEO: Robert S Sachs
*Pr: Cecil Kearse
*CFO: Juli S Musch
VP: Fredy Granillo
Opers Mgr: Scott Gilan

D-U-N-S 03-086-6602
ARDEN GROUP INC
GELSON'S MARKETS
13833 Freeway Dr, Santa Fe Springs, CA 90670-5701
Tel (310) 638-2842 Founded/Ownrshp 2014
Sales 377.6MM^E EMP 2,151
SIC 5411 Supermarkets, chain
CEO: Bernard Briskin
*CFO: Laura J Neumann
Off Mgr: Denise Gupton
Sys Mgr: Jose Flores
Info Man: Todd Hungerford
Snr Mgr: Rajat Saxena

ARDEN HILL HOSPITAL
See ORANGE REGIONAL MEDICAL CENTER

ARDEN-BENHAR MILLS
See KRAMS ENTERPRISES INC

D-U-N-S 00-838-1915
ARDEN-MAYFAIR INC
(Suby of GELSONS MARKETS) ★
13833 Freeway Dr, Santa Fe Springs, CA 90670-5701
Tel (310) 638-2842 Founded/Ownrshp 1889
Sales 377.6MM^E EMP 2,358^E
SIC 5411 Supermarkets, chain
Pr: Bernard Briskin

ARDENT COMPANIES
See ARDENT SERVICES LLC

D-U-N-S 08-001-9617
ARDENT HEALTH PARTNERS LLC
1 Burton Hills Blvd # 250, Nashville, TN 37215-6195
Tel (615) 296-3000 Founded/Ownrshp 2015
Sales 723.1MM^E EMP 11,000
SIC 8069 8062 Specialty hospitals, except psychiatric; General medical & surgical hospitals
CEO: David T Vandewater
VP: Mark Gilliam

D-U-N-S 08-002-2384
ARDENT LEGACY ACQUISITIONS INC
(Suby of ARDENT LEGACY HOLDINGS INC) ★
1 Burton Hills Blvd, Nashville, TN 37215-6293
Tel (615) 296-3000 Founded/Ownrshp 2015
Sales 723.1MM^E EMP 7,967^E
SIC 8069 Specialty hospitals, except psychiatric
CEO: David T Vandewater

D-U-N-S 08-002-0481
ARDENT LEGACY HOLDINGS INC
(Suby of ARDENT HEALTH PARTNERS LLC) ★
1 Burton Hills Blvd, Nashville, TN 37215-6293
Tel (615) 296-3000 Founded/Ownrshp 2015
Sales 723.1MM^E EMP 7,973^E
SIC 8069 Specialty hospitals, except psychiatric
CEO: David T Vandewater

ARDENT MILLS CORPORATE
See ARDENT MILLS LLC

D-U-N-S 03-282-7243 IMP/EXP
ARDENT MILLS LLC
ARDENT MILLS CORPORATE
1875 Lawrence St Ste 1400, Denver, CO 80202-1854
Tel (800) 851-9618 Founded/Ownrshp 2001
Sales 699.1MM^E EMP 980
SIC 2041 4789 8741 Flour & other grain mill products; Cargo loading & unloading services; Management services
CEO: Dan Dye
VP: Tom Black
*VP: Dean Grossman
*VP: Mike Miller
IT Man: Dawn James
QC Dir: Brent Mann
Plnt Mgr: Don Niblock
Plnt Mgr: Jim Pulverenti

D-U-N-S 11-269-7227
■ ARDENT SERVICES LLC
ARDENT COMPANIES
(Suby of EMCOR GROUP INC) ★
170 New Camellia Blvd, Covington, LA 70433-7819
Tel (985) 792-3000 Founded/Ownrshp 2016
Sales 104.4MM^E EMP 350
SIC 1731 General electrical contractor
Pr: Albert Vallotton III
VP: Rick Bubrig
VP: Patrick Malloy
IT Man: Lilia Zepeda
Opers Mgr: Bill Bryant
Snr PM: Edward Rondey

ARE
See ARE ACCESSORIES LLC

D-U-N-S 79-579-8375 IMP
ARE ACCESSORIES LLC
ARE
(Suby of TECTUM HOLDINGS INC)
400 Nave Rd Se, Massillon, OH 44646-8898
Tel (330) 830-7800 Founded/Ownrshp 2015
Sales 206.3MM^E EMP 750
SIC 3713 Truck bodies & parts
CEO: Terry Seikel
*Pr: Todd Hoffman
*CFO: Stan Vogler
Rgnl Mgr: Ron Bostard
*CTO: Sandy Patrick
IT Man: Heather Nave
IT Man: Gena Roberts
Sfty Dirs: Robert Glasgow
Plnt Mgr: Mike Miller
Ql Cn Mgr: Gerald Pedoto
Sls Mgr: Jim Blayne

D-U-N-S 08-038-1734
ARE INC
400 Nave Rd Sw, Massillon, OH 44646
Tel (330) 830-7800 Founded/Ownrshp 1960
Sales 107.0MM EMP 518
SIC 3713 3714 3792 5013 Truck bodies & parts; Motor vehicle body components & frame; Travel trailers & campers; Motor vehicle supplies & new parts
Pr: Ralph Gatti
VP: Bill Andrea
*VP: Aden Miller
VP: Todd Roberson
Plnt Mgr: Richard Schmeltzer

D-U-N-S 87-918-4133
AREA EDUCATION AGENCY 267
9184b 265th St Ste B, Clear Lake, IA 50428-8893
Tel (641) 357-6125 Founded/Ownrshp 1974
Sales 14.0MM^E EMP 1,050
SIC 8211 Specialty education
Prin: Melissa Gilbert

D-U-N-S 00-407-1416
■ AREA PROPERTY PARTNERS L P
(Suby of ARES MANAGEMENT LLC) ★
245 Park Ave Fl 44, New York, NY 10167-4400
Tel (212) 515-3400 Founded/Ownrshp 1993, 2013
Sales 351.0MM^E EMP 7,402^E
SIC 6799 Real estate investors, except property operators
CEO: Lee Neibart
Pt: Robert Gigliotti
Pt: Henry W Haunss Jr
Pt: John R S Jacobsson
Pt: Jason Kelley
Pt: Stuart F Koenig
Pt: Richard J Mack
Pt: William McCahill
Pt: Dean Pentikis
Pt: Cindy Wenig
Pt: Steven Wolf
VP: Julie Bierman

D-U-N-S 60-343-8920
AREA TEMPS INC
1228 Euclid Ave Ste 1115, Cleveland, OH 44115-1846
Tel (216) 781-5350 Founded/Ownrshp 1986
Sales 72.5MM^E EMP 7,000
SIC 7363 Temporary help service; Office help supply service
CEO: Raymond Castelluccio
*Pr: Kent Castelluccio
VP: Gail Rodgers
Tech Mgr: Gail Enders
Mktg Dir: Sue Cornwell
Mktg Mgr: Jennifer Roberts
Sls Mgr: Karen Rosenhoffer

AREA WIDE PROTECTIVE
See AWP INC

D-U-N-S 01-095-8711
AREA WIDE PROTECTIVE INC
AWP
(Suby of AREA WIDE PROTECTIVE) ★
826 Overholt Rd, Kent, OH 44240-7530
Tel (330) 644-0655 Founded/Ownrshp 1991
Sales 106.6MM^E EMP 1,600
SIC 3669 Pedestrian traffic control equipment; Traffic signals, electric
Pr: John P Sypek
*CFO: Don Weidig
*VP: Ron Brotherton
*VP: Rusty Parrish
Genl Mgr: Sue Lynch
IT Man: Jennifer Sanicky
Opers Mgr: Howard Blevins

D-U-N-S 80-440-6929 IMP
AREAS USA INC
(Suby of AREAS SA)
5301 Blue Lagoon Dr # 690, Miami, FL 33126-7034
Tel (305) 264-1709 Founded/Ownrshp 2005
Sales 428.1MM^E EMP 3,000
SIC 5399 5812 Duty-free goods; Eating places
CEO: Xavier Rabell
*Ch Bd: Jose Gabriel Martin
*Pr: Gonsal Artigot
*VP: Fernando Martinez
*VP: Eduardo Uribe
IT Man: Guillermo Padron

D-U-N-S 11-526-7338 IMP
ARENA BRANDS INC
(Suby of HAT BRANDS HOLDING CORP) ★
601 Marion Dr, Garland, TX 75042-7930
Tel (972) 494-7133 Founded/Ownrshp 1992
Sales 115.4MM^E EMP 1,165
SIC 2353 Caps: cloth, straw & felt; Hats: cloth, straw & felt; Uniform hats & caps
Ch Bd: John R Muse
*Pr: Paul E Lavoie
*CFO: Thomas A Hough
Sr Cor Off: Kevin Hatten

D-U-N-S 11-930-9909
ARENA ENERGY LP
VALIANT ENERGY
4200 Res Frest Dr Ste 500, The Woodlands, TX 77381
Tel (281) 681-9500 Founded/Ownrshp 1999
Sales 275.8MM EMP 8^E
Accts Ernst & Young Llp
SIC 1311 Crude petroleum production; Natural gas production
Mng Dir: Stanley J Bouley
Mng Dir: Renee Kelly
Mng Dir: Todd Stone
Mng Dir: Donny Torres
Mng Dir: Jim Trocchio
Mktg Mgr: Mike McGinnis
Mktg Mgr: Bernice Norris

D-U-N-S 07-844-7111
ARENDS HOGAN WALKER LLC
JOHN DEERE AUTHORIZED DEALER
27688 E 3200 North Rd, Dwight, IL 60420-8047
Tel (217) 388-7717 Founded/Ownrshp 2012
Sales 83.5MM^E EMP 310
SIC 5999 5082 Farm equipment & supplies; Construction & mining machinery
CEO: Sean Hogan
*COO: Chad Braden
*VP: Mark Arends
IT Man: Jimmy Nees
Manager: Kent Arends
Manager: Brian Walker

D-U-N-S 07-782-0272
ARENT FOX LLP
1717 K St Nw Ste B1, Washington, DC 20006-5344
Tel (202) 857-6000 Founded/Ownrshp 2010
Sales 116.9MM^E EMP 800
SIC 8111 General practice law office
Mng Pt: Matthew J Clark
Mng Pt: Andrew I Silfen
Mng Pt: Bill Charyk
Mng Pt: Robert C O'Brien
Ch Bd: Mark Katz
CFO: Beth Munno
VP: Arnold Westerman
Exec: Timothy Brown
Ex Dir: Kurt M Salisbury
Dept Mgr: Michael A Grow
CTO: Edward Macnamara

D-U-N-S 78-424-5834
▲ ARES CAPITAL CORP
245 Park Ave Fl 44, New York, NY 10167-4400
Tel (212) 750-7300 Founded/Ownrshp 2004
Sales 1.0MMM EMP 870^E
Tkr Sym ARCC Exch NGS
SIC 6726 Management investment funds, closed-end
CEO: R Kipp Deveer
*Ch Bd: Michael J Arougheti
*Ch Bd: Bennett Rosenthal
Pr: Mitchell Goldstein
Pr: Michael L Smith
CFO: Penni F Roll
Treas: Scott C Lem
Ofcr: Miriam Krieger
VP: Joshua M Bloomstein
VP: Michael McFerran
VP: Daniel F Nguyen
VP: Michael D Weiner
VP: Irina Zilbergleyt
Board of Directors: Steve Bartlett, Ann Torre Bates, Daniel G Kelly Jr, Steven B McKeever, Robert L Rosen, Eric B Siegel

D-U-N-S 07-827-5574
ARES COMMERCIAL REAL ESTATE CORP
245 Park Ave Fl 42, New York, NY 10167-4202
Tel (212) 750-7300 Founded/Ownrshp 2011
Sales 85.4MM EMP 870
Tkr Sym ACRE Exch NYS
SIC 6798 Real estate investment trusts
Pr: John Jardine
*Ch Bd: Robert L Rosen
CFO: Tae-Sik Yoon
VP: Michael D Weiner
Board of Directors: Rand S April, Michael J Arougheti, Caroline E Blakely, William L Browning, John Hope Bryant, James E Skinner

D-U-N-S 80-772-1980
ARES CORP
ARES GOVERNMENT SERVICES
(Suby of ARES HOLDING CORP) ★
1440 Chapin Ave Ste 390, Burlingame, CA 94010-4058
Tel (505) 661-6390 Founded/Ownrshp 1992
Sales 87.2MM^E EMP 640
SIC 8711 Engineering services
Ch Bd: Richard Stuart
Pr: Robert Curbeam
Pr: Michael Jackson
*Pr: William Vantine
COO: Stan Lynch
*CFO: Douglas Schmidt
Ex VP: Dan Cooprider
VP: Brian Ginna
VP: Scott Hyman
VP: Steven Newman
Mng Dir: Allen Friberg

ARES GOVERNMENT SERVICES
See ARES CORP

D-U-N-S 96-799-4273
ARES HOLDING CORP
1440 Chapin Ave Ste 390, Burlingame, CA 94010-4058
Tel (650) 401-7100 Founded/Ownrshp 1992
Sales 133.2MM EMP 750
SIC 8711 Engineering services
CEO: Dr Richard J Stuart
*Pr: Dr William Vantine
*CFO: Douglas Schmidt
*Ex VP: Larry Shipley
*Sr VP: Stanley Lynch
Board of Directors: Stanley C Lynch, Larry E Shipley, Dr Richard J Stuart, Dr William L Vantine

D-U-N-S 96-897-1817
ARES MANAGEMENT HOLDINGS LP
2000 Avenue Of The Stars, Los Angeles, CA 90067-4700
Tel (310) 201-4100 Founded/Ownrshp 2010
Sales 1.0MMM^E EMP 40^E
SIC 6211 Investment firm, general brokerage
Pr: Tony Ressler
*Pt: David Kaplan
*Pt: John Kissick
*Pt: Greg Margolies
*Pt: Anthony Ressler

D-U-N-S 18-695-4934
■ ARES MANAGEMENT LLC
(Suby of ARES MANAGEMENT LP) ★
2000 Avenue Of The Stars, Los Angeles, CA 90067-4700
Tel (310) 201-4100 Founded/Ownrshp 2001
Sales 748.9MM^E EMP 800
SIC 6799 Venture capital companies
Sr Pt: Greg Margolies
Pr: Tom Bevan
Pr: Satya Nayak
Top Exec: David Reilly
Assoc VP: Vincent Chan
Assoc VP: Vivek Chandra
Ex VP: Janine Cristiano
Ex VP: Michael McFerran
Ex VP: Michael Weiner
Sr VP: Ken Verges
VP: Carl Deeley
VP: Cindy Fortune
VP: Katie Hahn
VP: Tara Hicks
VP: Jennifer Kroehl
VP: Jamie Kudrako
VP: Tyler Levin
VP: Lysa Ngo
VP: Peter Ogilvie
VP: Brett Pugliese
VP: Alek Roomet

D-U-N-S 05-201-8806
▲ ARES MANAGEMENT LP
2000 Avenue Of The Stars, Los Angeles, CA 90067-4700
Tel (310) 201-4100 Founded/Ownrshp 1997
Sales 814.4MM EMP 870^E
Tkr Sym ARES Exch NYS
SIC 6282 Investment advice
Ch Bd: Antony P Ressler
Genl Pt: Ares M LLC
Pr: Michael J Arougheti
Ofcr: Antonio Petrilli
Mng Dir: Paul Colatrella

D-U-N-S 07-876-6419
ARETEC GROUP INC
405 Park Ave Fl 12, New York, NY 10022-4405
Tel (866) 904-2988 Founded/Ownrshp 2012
Sales 2.1MMM EMP 1,967^E
SIC 6211 6282 6722 Security brokers & dealers; Investment advice; Investment research; Management investment, open-end
CEO: R Lawrence Roth
*Ch Bd: Robert Dineen
*CFO: Brian D Jones
Ofcr: David Orlofsky
Ex VP: Christopher W Mee
Ex VP: Sanjay Yodh
*Dir Sec: John H Grady
Counsel: James Tanaka

D-U-N-S 01-116-7509 IMP
ARETT SALES CORP
9285 Commerce Hwy, Pennsauken, NJ 08110-1201
Tel (856) 751-1224 Founded/Ownrshp 1951
Sales 122.9MM EMP 150
Accts Frendel Brown & Weissman Llp
SIC 5191 Garden supplies
Pr: Lindsey Chesbrough
COO: Patsch Timothy
CFO: Joyce Bauge
*CFO: Cathy Schappert
CFO: Cathy Shappert
*Ex VP: Mauri Librett
*VP: Neil Shainwald
Dir IT: Michael Perilli
Web Dev: Terry Murphy
Opers Mgr: Bruce Peditto
Mktg Dir: Noah Chesbrough

D-U-N-S 79-171-9982 IMP/EXP
AREVA INC
(Suby of AREVA NP)
7207 Ibm Dr, Charlotte, NC 28262-4307
Tel (704) 805-2000 Founded/Ownrshp 1987
Sales 1.3MMM^E EMP 3,400
SIC 3823 3829 8711 5085 3561 2819 Industrial instrmnts msrmnt display/control process variable; Measuring & controlling devices; Engineering services; Industrial supplies; Valves & fittings; Pumps & pumping equipment; Industrial inorganic chemicals
CEO: Gary Mignogna
CFO: Katherine Williams
*Treas: Laurie S Harris
Treas: Laurie Harris
*Chf Cred: Craig Ranson
Sr Ex VP: Veronique Rouzaud
Ex VP: Bill George
*Sr VP: George B Beam
Sr VP: Markus Birkhofer
VP: Roger Alexander
VP: Francois Bavoillot
*VP: Peter F Castine
VP: Tom Franch
VP: Steve Hamilton
VP: Jim Hicks
VP: Alexis Marincic
VP: Laurence Pernot
VP: Joe Zwetolitz

AREY JONES EDUCTL SOLUTIONS
See BROADWAY TYPEWRITER CO INC

D-U-N-S 96-871-6956
ARG HOLDING CORP
(Suby of ROARK CAPITAL GROUP INC) ★
1180 Peachtree St Ne, Atlanta, GA 30309-3531
Tel (404) 591-5200 Founded/Ownrshp 2011
Sales 1.1MMM^E EMP 27,930^E
SIC 5812 Fast-food restaurant, chain
CEO: Neal K Aronson

ARG IH CORPORATION
See ARG IH LLC

D-U-N-S 96-660-8734
ARG IH LLC
ARG IH CORPORATION
(Suby of ARG HOLDING CORP) ★
1180 Peachtree St Ne, Atlanta, GA 30309-3531
Tel (404) 591-5200 Founded/Ownrshp 2011
Sales 1.1MMM^E EMP 27,930^E
SIC 5812 Fast-food restaurant, chain
CEO: Paul J Brown
*CEO: Neal K Aronson

D-U-N-S 00-132-5877 IMP
▲ ARGAN INC
1 Church St Ste 201, Rockville, MD 20850-4181
Tel (301) 315-0027 Founded/Ownrshp 1961
Sales 413.2MM EMP 1,188^E
Tkr Sym AGX Exch NYS
SIC 4813 1623 8748 Data telephone communications; Communication line & transmission tower construction; Energy conservation consultant
Ch Bd: Rainer H Bosselmann
CFO: David H Watson
Board of Directors: Henry A Crumpton, Cynthia A Flanders, Peter W Getsinger, William F Griffin Jr, William F Leimkuhler, W G Champion Mitchell, James W Quinn, Brian R Sherras

D-U-N-S 07-272-5984
ARGENT ASSOCIATES INC
140 Fieldcrest Ave, Edison, NJ 08837-3620
Tel (732) 512-9009 Founded/Ownrshp 1999
Sales 140.3MM EMP 27
Accts Ingis & Company Pa Mahwah N
SIC 4225 General warehousing & storage
CEO: Betty Manetta
*COO: Ray Moya
*VP: William Donadio
*VP: Joyce Hart
VP Sls: Lauren Peterson

D-U-N-S 18-486-0831
ARGIX DIRECT INC
100 Middlesex Center Blvd, Jamesburg, NJ 08831-3036
Tel (732) 536-9173 Founded/Ownrshp 1977
Sales 160.6MM^E EMP 580
SIC 4213 4225 Trucking, except local; General warehousing
Pr: Kenneth Wappel
*Pr: John Vreeland
*CFO: Alan Darwick
*VP: Michael Guerriero
Dir Sec: Charles Gormley
Genl Mgr: Ralph Castagna
Genl Mgr: Jean Estenes
IT Man: Dom Damato
S&M/VP: Scot C Lindsay

D-U-N-S 10-297-1728
ARGO GROUP US INC
(Suby of ARGO GROUP INTERNATIONAL HOLDINGS, LTD.)
10101 Reunion Pl Ste 500, San Antonio, TX 78216-4156
Tel (210) 321-8400 Founded/Ownrshp 2007
Sales NA EMP 1,122
SIC 6331 Fire, marine & casualty insurance & carriers; Workers' compensation insurance
Ch Bd: Gary V Woods
Pr: John Gribbin
Pr: B Thomas Johns
Pr: Dale H Pilkington
*Pr: Kevin J Rehnberg
*CEO: Mark E Watson III
*CFO: Mark W Haushill
Sr VP: Robert J Broomall
*Sr VP: Barbara C Bufkin
*Sr VP: Ronald B Given
Sr VP: Steve Jones
*Sr VP: Byron L Leflore Jr
Sr VP: Byron Leflore
VP: Craig Comeaux
VP: Karen Meriwether
VP: Dan Platt

D-U-N-S 96-488-8697 EXP
ARGO TURBOSERVE CORP
ATC NUCLEAR
160 Chubb Ave Ste 102, Lyndhurst, NJ 07071-3526
Tel (201) 804-6200 Founded/Ownrshp 1996
Sales 320.9MM EMP 366
Accts Eisner Amper Llp Iselin New
SIC 5084 Industrial machinery & equipment
Pr: Clyde Keaton
Ch Bd: John Calicchio
Pr: Rob Bruinsma
Pr: Steve Kinnard
CFO: Wayne Ackerman
VP: Richard Lemond
QA Dir: Charles Tuozzolo

D-U-N-S 04-989-2735 IMP
ARGO-HYTOS INC
(Suby of FSP FLUID SYSTEMS PARTNERS HOLDING AG)
1835 N Research Dr, Bowling Green, OH 43402
Tel (419) 353-6070 Founded/Ownrshp 1998
Sales 221.8MM^E EMP 1,200
SIC 5084 Hydraulic systems equipment & supplies
Pr: Christian H Kienzle
*CFO: Walter Bader
*VP: Larry Gerken
Sls Dir: Patrick Green

ARGO-TECH
See EATON INDUSTRIAL CORP

D-U-N-S 14-072-7624 IMP/EXP
ARGON MEDICAL DEVICES INC
(Suby of ROUNDTABLE HEALTHCARE PARTNERS LP) ★
5151 Hdqtr Dr Ste 210, Plano, TX 75024
Tel (903) 675-9321 Founded/Ownrshp 2003
Sales 99.3MM^E EMP 395^E
SIC 3845 3842 3841 Electromedical equipment; Surgical appliances & supplies; Surgical & medical instruments
Pr: Mike Hudson
*VP: Christian Chilcott
VP: Greg Justice
*VP: Sharon McNally
*VP: Bill Morgan
*VP: Janice Russell
Genl Mgr: Belynda Daniel
QA Dir: Nirav Shah
Dir IT: Anita Younger
Plnt Mgr: Larry Negills
VP Sls: Duncan Hedley

D-U-N-S 05-860-0123 EXP
■ ARGON ST INC
(Suby of BOEING CO) ★
12701 Fair Lakes Cir # 800, Fairfax, VA 22033-4910
Tel (703) 322-0881 Founded/Ownrshp 2010
Sales 214.1MM^E EMP 895
SIC 3812 Search & navigation equipment; Navigational systems & instruments; Defense systems & equipment; Search & detection systems & instruments
VP: Kerry M Rowe
CFO: John Holt
VP: L M Buckner
VP: William Joe Carlin
Dir Rx: Lamar Day
Prgrm Mgr: John Bauer
Prgrm Mgr: John Goodman
Prgrm Mgr: John Koss
Prgrm Mgr: Theresa Kupeski
Prgrm Mgr: Dan Marini
Prgrm Mgr: Roy Tubbs

D-U-N-S 96-022-8018
ARGONAUT GOLD INC
9600 Prototype Ct, Reno, NV 89521-5976
Tel (775) 284-4422 Founded/Ownrshp 2009
Sales 186.2MM EMP 12
SIC 1081 1041 Metal mining exploration & development services; Gold ores mining
Ch: Brian J Kennedy
*Pr: Peter C Dougherty
*COO: Richard Rhoades
*CFO: Barry Dahl
*CFO: David A Ponczoch
*Ofcr: Curtis Turner
*VP: Tom H Burkhart
VP: Bob Rose
*VP: W Robert Rose
Exec: Thomas H Burkhart
*VP Opers: Thomas Bukhart

D-U-N-S 00-690-9501
ARGONAUT INSURANCE CO INC
(Suby of ARGO GROUP US INC) ★
10101 Reunion Pl Ste 500, San Antonio, TX 78216-4156
Tel (210) 321-8400 Founded/Ownrshp 1957
Sales NA EMP 1,100
SIC 6331 Workers' compensation insurance; Automobile insurance; Fire, marine & casualty insurance & carriers
Ch Bd: Mark E Watson III
CFO: Jay Bullock
Snr Sftwr: Milan Anson

D-U-N-S 13-452-1389
ARGONNE CAPITAL GROUP LLC
3060 Peachtree Rd Nw # 400, Atlanta, GA 30305-2234
Tel (404) 364-2984 Founded/Ownrshp 2002
Sales 332.6MM^E EMP 7,060^E
SIC 6799 Investors

ARGONNE NATIONAL LABORATORY
See UCHICAGO ARGONNE LLC

ARGOS CEMENT LLC
See ARGOS USA LLC

D-U-N-S 01-716-8557
ARGOS HOLDINGS INC
650 Madison Ave Fl 15, New York, NY 10022-1029
Tel (212) 891-2880 Founded/Ownrshp 2014
Sales 12.6MMM^E EMP 53,008^E
SIC 0752 Pedigree record services, pet & animal specialties
Pt: Justin Bateman
Pt: Cdric Dubourdieu

D-U-N-S 05-353-4780
ARGOS READY MIX (CAROLINAS) CORP
SOUTHERN EQUIPMENT COMPANY INC
(Suby of CEMENTOS ARGOS S A)
3610 Bush St, Raleigh, NC 27609-7511
Tel (919) 790-1520 Founded/Ownrshp 2006
Sales 88.0MM^E EMP 475
SIC 3273 Ready-mixed concrete
Pr: George Turner
Pr: J G Loftin
Treas: Henry Willey
Netwrk Eng: Jonathan Campbell

D-U-N-S 13-446-4705
ARGOS READY MIX (SOUTH CENTRAL) CORP
SOUTHERN STAR
(Suby of ARGOS USA CORP) ★
3015 Wndward Pl Dr Ste 30, Alpharetta, GA 30005
Tel (678) 368-4300 Founded/Ownrshp 2005
Sales 299.1MM^E EMP 900
SIC 3273 Ready-mixed concrete
Pr: Tommy Abbott
CFO: Robert Schmidt

D-U-N-S 19-743-6652
ARGOS USA CORP
(Suby of GRUPO ARGOS S A)
757 N Eldridge Pkwy # 525, Houston, TX 77079-4531
Tel (281) 759-7392 Founded/Ownrshp 2007
Sales 1.0MMM^E EMP 2,000
SIC 3273 Ready-mixed concrete
Pr: Jose A Velez
*Treas: Ricardo A Sierra
*VP: Eric Flesch
VP: Chip Hussey
Plnt Mgr: Bryan Fox
Ql Cn Mgr: Joseph Bernard
Mktg Dir: Kim Quinn

D-U-N-S 07-831-8694
ARGOS USA LLC
(Suby of ARGOS USA CORP) ★
3015 Windward Plz, Alpharetta, GA 30005-8715
Tel (678) 368-4300 Founded/Ownrshp 2011
Sales 193.6MM^E EMP 400^E
SIC 3272 Concrete stuctural support & building material
VP: Eric Flesch
Opers Mgr: Nick Ryan

D-U-N-S 96-996-2146 IMP/EXP
ARGOS USA LLC
ARGOS CEMENT LLC
(Suby of ARGOS USA CORP) ★
3015 Windward Plz Ste 300, Alpharetta, GA 30005-8713
Tel (678) 368-4300 Founded/Ownrshp 2011
Sales 145.6MM^E EMP 400
SIC 3272 5032 Concrete stuctural support & building material; Cement

ARGOSY RIVERSIDE CASINO
See MISSOURI GAMING CO

D-U-N-S 02-673-2255
ARGUINDEGUI OIL CO II LTD
PUMP-N-SHOP
6551 Star Ct, Laredo, TX 78041-9140
Tel (956) 722-5251 *Founded/Ownrshp* 1942
Sales 270.3MM^E *EMP* 170
SIC 5171 Petroleum bulk stations
Pr: Alfonso Arguindegui
**CFO:* Raymond Rodriguez
**Ch:* Peter Arguindegui Jr
**VP:* Carlos Arguindegui Jr
**VP:* Ray Hernandez
Exec: Patty Cardenas
Opers Mgr: Jesus Garcia
Sales Exec: Pablo Perrez

ARGUS OF COLORADO HOME HEALTH
See ARGUS OF COLORADO INC

D-U-N-S 62-327-0220
ARGUS OF COLORADO INC
ARGUS OF COLORADO HOME HEALTH
720 S Colorado Blvd 600n, Denver, CO 80246-1952
Tel (303) 322-4100 *Founded/Ownrshp* 1991
Sales 12.0MM *EMP* 1,000
SIC 8082 7361 Home health care services; Nurses' registry
Pr: Dan Sillers
**Treas:* Iva Lou Bailey

D-U-N-S 06-042-7788 IMP
ARHAUS LLC
51 E Hines Hill Rd, Hudson, OH 44236-1151
Tel (440) 439-7700 *Founded/Ownrshp* 1976
Sales 160.5MM^E *EMP* 400
SIC 5712 Furniture stores
Pr: John Reed
Chf Mktg O: Kate C Clegg
**Sr VP:* Kathy Veltri
VP: Gary Babcock
VP: Kevin Hughes
VP: Skye Westcott
Mng Ofcr: Patrice Varni
Comm Man: Rebekah Unkefer
Store Mgr: Donald Conroy
Store Mgr: Dominic Milanese
Store Mgr: Alyssa Welch

ARI
See AMERICAN RAILCAR INDUSTRIES INC

ARI PACKAGING
See ADVERTISING RESOURCES INC

ARI-AUTOMOTIVE RESOURCES INTL
See AUTOMOTIVE RENTALS INC

D-U-N-S 07-550-1312
ARIA HEALTH
TORRESDALE CAMPUS
10800 Knights Rd, Philadelphia, PA 19114-4299
Tel (215) 612-4000 *Founded/Ownrshp* 2008
Sales 432.0MM *EMP* 4,000
SIC 8062 Hospital, professional nursing school with AMA residency
CEO: Kathleen Kinslow
**Treas:* Ronald R Thomas
Bd of Dir: Ronald Thomas
VP: John Quinn
Assoc Dir: Kelly Milligan
Dir: Maureen Goudreau
Ex Dir: Richard J Galup
Dir Sec: Darryl Beard
IT Man: Louise Dougherty
Mktg Dir: Maria Sereeo-Slade
Ansthlgy: Dollie Silpasuvan

D-U-N-S 78-622-7231
▲ ARIAD PHARMACEUTICALS INC
26 Landsdowne St Ste 175, Cambridge, MA 02139-4284
Tel (617) 494-0400 *Founded/Ownrshp* 1991
Sales 118.8MM *EMP* 459^E
Tkr Sym ARIA *Exch* NGS
SIC 2836 8731 Biological products, except diagnostic; Medical research, commercial
Ch Bd: Harvey J Berger
**Ch Bd:* Alexander J Denner
Pr: Timothy P Clackson
**Pr:* Paris Panayiotopoulos
CFO: Manmeet S Soni
Chf Cred: Jennifer L Herron
Ofcr: Hugh M Cole
Sr VP: Daniel M Bollag
VP: Hugh Cole
VP: John McCabe
Assoc Dir: Tiffany Burt
Assoc Dir: Melissa A Erickson
Assoc Dir: Graeme Hodgson
Assoc Dir: Tom Malone
Assoc Dir: Sandip Mehta
Assoc Dir: Meera Tugnait
Board of Directors: George W Bickerstaff III, Jules A Haimovitz, Anna Protopapas, Norbert G Riedel, Sarah J Schlesinger

D-U-N-S 78-999-5313 IMP
ARIAT INTERNATIONAL INC
3242 Whipple Rd, Union City, CA 94587-1217
Tel (510) 477-7000 *Founded/Ownrshp* 1991
Sales 340.2MM^E *EMP* 400
SIC 3199 5139 5137 5136 Equestrian related leather articles; Boots, horse; Leather garments; Footwear; Women's & children's clothing; Men's & boys' clothing
Pr: Elizabeth Cross
CFO: Pankaj Gupta
VP: Liz Bradley
VP: Megan Iwersen
VP: Todd A Levy
VP: Brian Mignano
VP: Jake Rivas
VP: Jack Teague
VP: Pamela Vaughn
QA Dir: Sarah Guthrie
VP Mktg: Steve Panotes

D-U-N-S 96-747-7712
ARIBA INC
(*Suby of* SAP AMERICA INC) ★
3420 Hillview Ave Bldg 3, Palo Alto, CA 94304-1355
Tel (650) 849-4000 *Founded/Ownrshp* 2012
Sales 175.1MM^E *EMP* 2,432
SIC 7372 Business oriented computer software
CEO: Alex Atzberger
**CFO:* Marc Malone
**Chf Mktg O:* Alicia Tillman
VP: Mark Hamlin
Software D: Tanvi Shah
Secur Mgr: Joseph Gomez
Sls Dir: Craig Myers
Snr PM: Simon Hauser

D-U-N-S 04-901-3617
■ ARICENT INC
(*Suby of* KOHLBERG KRAVIS ROBERTS & CO LP) ★
303 Twin Dolphin Dr # 600, Redwood City, CA 94065-1422
Tel (650) 632-4310 *Founded/Ownrshp* 2009
Sales 143.6MM^E *EMP* 1,014^E
SIC 7371 Computer software development
CEO: Sudip Nandy
**Pr:* Doreen Lorenzo
Pr: Dinesh Singh
VP: Theodore Forbath
Snr Sftwr: Vikash Agarwal
Snr Sftwr: Krishna M Choudhary
Snr Sftwr: Madhavi Ginjupalli
Snr Sftwr: Nikhil Goyal
Snr Sftwr: Shilpi Jain
Snr Sftwr: Vaibhav Khare
Snr Sftwr: Neeraj Kumar

D-U-N-S 78-945-2096
■ ARICENT US INC
(*Suby of* ARICENT INC) ★
1 Tower Center Blvd Fl 18, East Brunswick, NJ 08816-1145
Tel (732) 514-6654 *Founded/Ownrshp* 2011
Sales 142.9MM^E *EMP* 1,014
SIC 7371 Computer software development
CEO: Frank Kern
Ch Bd: Joe Forehand
Pr: Sanjay Dhawan
Pr: Doreen Lorenzo
Pr: CP Murali
CFO: David Freedman
CFO: Mick Lopez
Bd of Dir: Adam H Clammer
Bd of Dir: James H Greene
Bd of Dir: Thomas J Smach
Bd of Dir: Nathaniel H Taylor
Chf Mktg O: Tim Leberecht
Ex VP: Patrick Joggerst
Sr VP: Raj Datt
VP: Ajay Gupta
VP: Yash Malhotra
VP: Deepak Mehrotra
VP: Mike Webb
Dir Bus: Shivappa Madegowda

D-U-N-S 06-357-9940 IMP/EXP
ARIEL CORP
35 Blackjack Road Ext, Mount Vernon, OH 43050-9482
Tel (740) 397-0311 *Founded/Ownrshp* 2001
Sales 114.7MM^E *EMP* 430^E
SIC 3563

D-U-N-S 00-642-3719 IMP/EXP
ARIENS CO
655 W Ryan St, Brillion, WI 54110-1072
Tel (920) 756-2141 *Founded/Ownrshp* 1933
Sales 380.9MM^E *EMP* 1,600^E
SIC 3524

D-U-N-S 01-645-9208 IMP/EXP
ARIENS SPECIALTY BRANDS LLC (WI)
STENS POWER EQUIPMENT PARTS
(*Suby of* ARIENS CO) ★
1919 Hospitality Dr, Jasper, IN 47546-6700
Tel (800) 457-7444 *Founded/Ownrshp* 1969, 1995
Sales 379.1MM^E *EMP* 500
SIC 5084 Industrial machine parts
Pr: Ralph Howard
Mtls Mgr: Suzzie Guthrie
Manager: Chris Halstead
Manager: Al Keller
Sales Asso: Erika Conrad
Sales Asso: Nick Sternberg

ARIES BUILDING SYTEMS
See RELIANT ASSET MANAGEMENT LLC

D-U-N-S 10-145-8586 EXP
■ ARINC INC
ROCKWELL COLLINS INFO MGT SVCS
(*Suby of* RADIO HOLDINGS INC) ★
2551 Riva Rd, Annapolis, MD 21401-7435
Tel (410) 266-4000 *Founded/Ownrshp* 2007
Sales 703.7MM^E *EMP* 1,857
Accts Kpmg Llp Mclean Va
SIC 8711 4899 Aviation &/or aeronautical engineering; Data communication services
Pr: Robert K Ortberg
Pr: Byung Kim
**CFO:* Patrick E Allen
Treas: James Sadler
Ofcr: Timothy R Summerville
**Sr VP:* Barry M Abzug
**Sr VP:* Robert J Perna
VP: Monte Bolt
VP: Yun Chong
VP: Bob Hanley
VP: Robert F Jefferson
VP: Dennis Lengyel
VP: Jim Martin
VP: Philip McDonough
VP: Monty Montero
VP: Robert Poole
VP: Jeffrey Standerski
VP: Stephen L Waechter
Board of Directors: Anthony J Carbone, Chris A Davis, Ralph E Eberhart, John A Edwardson, David Lilley, Andrew J Policano, Cheryl L Shavers, Jeffrey Turner

D-U-N-S 06-136-5805
■ ARINC RESEARCH CORP
(*Suby of* ROCKWELL COLLINS INFO MGT SVCS) ★
2551 Riva Rd, Annapolis, MD 21401-7461
Tel (410) 266-4000 *Founded/Ownrshp* 1958
Sales 153.7MM *EMP* 1,268
Accts Price Waterhouse Llp Washingt
SIC 8711 Engineering services
Ch Bd: James L Pierce
CFO: Richard Jones
Treas: Joan Decker
VP: Stewart Baily
VP: Robert M Covell
VP: Ruth M Hough
VP: Frederick J Jacoby
VP: Daniel E Sassi
VP: Victor S Stachelczyk
CTO: Carla Cleveland
VP Mktg: Robert F Jefferson

D-U-N-S 00-573-4363
ARINSO INTERNATIONAL INC (GA)
(*Suby of* NORTHGATEARINSO BELGIUM NV)
3965 Johns Creek Ct Ste A, Suwanee, GA 30024-1222
Tel (678) 259-0500 *Founded/Ownrshp* 1994
Sales 125.4MM^E *EMP* 2,500
SIC 7379

D-U-N-S 14-132-6111
ARION CARE SOLUTIONS LLC
1405 N Dobson Rd Ste 3, Chandler, AZ 85224-8594
Tel (480) 323-0468 *Founded/Ownrshp* 2003
Sales 4.0MM *EMP* 3,200
SIC 8082 Home health care services
CEO: Ryne Reed
**COO:* Wendi K Reed
**CFO:* Brian Deak
**VP:* Marianne Mulligan
Area Mgr: Kellan Fluckiger
Area Mgr: Ashlee Jensen
Area Mgr: Ron Martinez
Area Supr: Christianna Brimley
Area Supr: Rosa Chacon
Area Supr: Mireya Corral-Garcia
Area Supr: Heaven Dykhuizen

D-U-N-S 00-445-0987 IMP
ARIS HORTICULTURE INC
YODER TRADING COMPANY
115 3rd St Se, Barberton, OH 44203-4208
Tel (330) 745-2143 *Founded/Ownrshp* 1920
Sales 283.4MM^E *EMP* 1,100
SIC 0181 Plants, foliage & shrubberies; Florists' greens & flowers
Ch: G Ramsey Yoder
**Pr:* William Rasbach
**CFO:* Scott Schaefer
**VP:* William Riffey
Exec: Bill Rasbach
Comm Man: Christine Kelleher
**Prin:* Thomas D Doak

D-U-N-S 79-120-4857
▲ ARISTA NETWORKS INC
5453 Great America Pkwy, Santa Clara, CA 95054-3645
Tel (408) 547-5500 *Founded/Ownrshp* 2004
Sales 837.5MM *EMP* 1,200^E
Tkr Sym ANET *Exch* NYS
SIC 3577

D-U-N-S 08-747-7147
ARISTEO CONSTRUCTION CO
12811 Farmington Rd, Livonia, MI 48150-1607
Tel (734) 427-9111 *Founded/Ownrshp* 1977
Sales 289.3MM *EMP* 1,025
Accts Yeo & Yeo Ann Arbor Mi
SIC 1541 Industrial buildings & warehouses
Pr: Joseph A Aristeo
CFO: Bill Litz
**CFO:* William Litz
**VP:* James Like
**VP:* Jeff Wilkie
Exec: Kirk Peilet
Genl Mgr: Dave Hurst
Genl Mgr: Rick Lewandowski
Genl Mgr: David Nadeau
Dir IT: Travis Roy
Sfty Dirs: Kevin Robson

D-U-N-S 14-518-8897
ARISTEO INSTALLATION LLC
(*Suby of* ARISTEO CONSTRUCTION CO) ★
12811 Farmington Rd, Livonia, MI 48150-1607
Tel (734) 427-9111 *Founded/Ownrshp* 1977
Sales 88.5MM *EMP* 50
Accts Yeo & Yeo Ann Arbor Mi
SIC 1541 Industrial buildings & warehouses
CFO: William Litz
**Genl Mgr:* David Hurts

D-U-N-S 09-953-7284 IMP/EXP
ARISTOCRAT TECHNOLOGIES INC
(*Suby of* ARISTOCRAT TECHNOLOGIES AUSTRALIA PTY LIMITED)
7230 Amigo St, Las Vegas, NV 89119-4306
Tel (702) 270-1000 *Founded/Ownrshp* 1953
Sales 273.9MM^E *EMP* 800
SIC 5099 Coin-operated machines & mechanisms
Pr: Jamie Odell
CFO: Ron Deffucy
**CFO:* Toni Korsanos
**Ex VP:* Mark Dunn
**Sr VP:* Victor Blanco
VP: Jason Walbridge
VP: Clark Warren
Snr Sftwr: Curt Martin
CTO: Manjit Singh
IT Man: Robert Page
Tech Mgr: Luke Duyndam

D-U-N-S 60-757-6592 IMP
ARIZON COMPANIES INC
JOHNSON HEATER
11880 Dorsett Rd, Maryland Heights, MO 63043-2516
Tel (314) 739-0037 *Founded/Ownrshp* 1988
Sales 124.5MM^E *EMP* 467^E
SIC 3585 1711 2394 1541 1542 8611 Refrigeration & heating equipment; Heating & air conditioning contractors; Tents: made from purchased materials; Industrial buildings & warehouses; Nonresidential construction; Manufacturers' institute
Ch: Ron Scharf
**Pr:* Jan Ligas
**Pr:* Suzanne Scharf
**COO:* Tim Scharf
CFO: John Brennan
**Ofcr:* Ryan Rice
**VP:* Tom Soenhgen

ARIZONA ARMY NATIONAL GUARD
See ARIZONA DEPARTMENT OF EMERGENCY AND MILITARY AFFAIRS

D-U-N-S 96-492-5577
ARIZONA BEVERAGES USA LLC
60 Crossways Park Dr W, Woodbury, NY 11797-2018
Tel (516) 812-0300 *Founded/Ownrshp* 2010
Sales 199.9MM^E *EMP* 400
SIC 5149 Beverages, except coffee & tea

ARIZONA BILTMORE RESORT & SPA
See ABR PROPERTY LLC

ARIZONA BILTMORE RESORT & SPA
See KSL ARIZONA HOLDINGS III INC

ARIZONA BOARD OF REGENTS
See UNIVERSITY OF ARIZONA

D-U-N-S 80-634-3562
ARIZONA BOARD OF REGENTS
BRA
(*Suby of* EXECUTIVE OFFICE OF STATE OF ARIZONA) ★
2020 N Central Ave # 230, Phoenix, AZ 85004-4593
Tel (602) 229-2500 *Founded/Ownrshp* 1912
Sales 1.7MMM^E *EMP* 20,000
SIC 8221 9411 Colleges universities & professional schools; Administration of educational programs;
Pr: Eileen Klein
**Ch:* Rick Myers
Off Mgr: Stella Galaviez
CIO: Arthur Ashton

ARIZONA CHARLIES HT & CASINO
See ARIZONA CHARLIES INC

D-U-N-S 03-493-2392
ARIZONA CHARLIES INC
ARIZONA CHARLIES HT & CASINO
740 S Decatur Blvd, Las Vegas, NV 89107-3907
Tel (702) 258-5200 *Founded/Ownrshp* 2001
Sales 46.5MM^E *EMP* 1,000^E
SIC 7011 5812 5813 Casino hotel; Eating places; Bars & lounges
Pr: Carl Icahn
Chf Mktg O: Millet Pezzi
Exec: Debbie Pingul
IT Man: Lori Nelson
Mktg Dir: Ron Laurie
Pr Mgr: Mike Gilmartin

D-U-N-S 13-930-5197 IMP/EXP
ARIZONA CHEMICAL CO LLC
4600 Touchton Rd E # 1500, Jacksonville, FL 32246-1530
Tel (904) 928-8700 *Founded/Ownrshp* 2010
Sales 529.9MM^E *EMP* 1,000
SIC 2861 2911 Wood distillation products; Fractionation products of crude petroleum, hydrocarbons
Pr: Kevin M Fogarty
**CFO:* Frederic Jung
**VP:* Carl Bilgrien
**VP:* Joe Chan
**VP:* David Cowfer
VP: David B Cowfer
VP: John Marterer
VP: Mark Santangelo
VP: Joseph Segers III
Dir Risk M: Michael Gracie
CTO: David Lavy

D-U-N-S 14-892-6462
ARIZONA COMMUNITY FOUNDATION INC
2201 E Camelback Rd # 405, Phoenix, AZ 85016-3476
Tel (928) 348-9649 *Founded/Ownrshp* 1978
Sales 95.4MM *EMP* 50^E
Accts P Csiz Mhm Llc Phoenix Az
SIC 6732 Charitable trust management
Pr: Steve Seleznow
COO: Debra Whitehurst
CFO: Paul Velaski
Bd of Dir: Mark Klein
Ofcr: Anna Hurtado
Comm Man: Robbi Graham
Ex Dir: Vince Yanez
Rgnl Mgr: Kristi Edwards
Off Mgr: Ashley Miller
Off Mgr: Karen Morabito
Mktg Mgr: Michael Ponzio

D-U-N-S 08-371-4766
ARIZONA DENTAL INSURANCE SERVICE INC
DELTA DENTAL OF ARIZONA
5656 W Talavi Blvd, Glendale, AZ 85306-1876
Tel (602) 588-3617 *Founded/Ownrshp* 1972
Sales NA *EMP* 70
Accts Mayer Hoffman Mclean Pc Phoe
SIC 6324 6411 Dental insurance; Medical insurance claim processing, contract or fee basis
Pr: Bernard Glossy
**CFO:* Mark Anderson
Bd of Dir: Harold J Dias Jr
Bd of Dir: Alice Spurling
VP Sls: Barbara Crawford

D-U-N-S 80-454-5986
ARIZONA DEPARTMENT OF ADMINISTRATION
ADOA
(*Suby of* EXECUTIVE OFFICE OF STATE OF ARIZONA) ★
100 N 15th Ave Ste 401, Phoenix, AZ 85007-2636
Tel (602) 542-1500 *Founded/Ownrshp* 1912
Sales NA *EMP* 1,018

SIC 9199 General government administration;
Telecom Mg: Lawrence Heinz
IT Man: Alan Holcomb
Opers Mgr: Rob Smook

D-U-N-S 80-474-5297
ARIZONA DEPARTMENT OF EMERGENCY AND MILITARY AFFAIRS
ARIZONA ARMY NATIONAL GUARD
(*Suby of* EXECUTIVE OFFICE OF STATE OF ARIZONA) ★
5636 E Mcdowell Rd, Phoenix, AZ 85008-3455
Tel (602) 267-2700 *Founded/Ownrshp* 1912
Sales NA *EMP* 5,740
SIC 9711 National security;
Prin: David P Rataczak
Exec: Aprille Slutsky

D-U-N-S 80-474-5255
ARIZONA DEPT OF ECONOMIC SECURITY
(*Suby of* EXECUTIVE OFFICE OF STATE OF ARIZONA) ★
1717 W Jefferson St, Phoenix, AZ 85007-3202
Tel (602) 542-7166 *Founded/Ownrshp* 1912
Sales NA *EMP* 10,000
SIC 9441 Administration of social & manpower programs;

D-U-N-S 80-479-5284 IMP
ARIZONA DEPT OF TRANSPORTATION
(*Suby of* EXECUTIVE OFFICE OF STATE OF ARIZONA) ★
206 S 17th Ave, Phoenix, AZ 85007-3236
Tel (602) 712-7227 *Founded/Ownrshp* 1912
Sales NA *EMP* 4,700
SIC 9621

D-U-N-S 06-839-7876
ARIZONA ELECTRIC POWER COOPERATIVE INC
ARIZONA G&T COOPERATIVE
1000 S Highway 80, Benson, AZ 85602-7007
Tel (520) 586-3631 *Founded/Ownrshp* 1961
Sales 166.3MM *EMP* 135
SIC 4911

ARIZONA G&T COOPERATIVE
See ARIZONA ELECTRIC POWER COOPERATIVE INC

D-U-N-S 07-952-0837
ARIZONA II MERGER CORP
(*Suby of* SUNBEAM GP LLC) ★
15 Burton Hills Blvd, Nashville, TN 37215-6163
Tel (615) 665-1283 *Founded/Ownrshp* 2014
Sales 54.6MM^E *EMP* 3,000^E
SIC 6719 Investment holding companies, except banks
CEO: Christopher A Holden

D-U-N-S 07-963-3050
ARIZONA NUTRITIONAL SUPPLEMENTS LLC
210 S Beck Ave, Chandler, AZ 85226-3311
Tel (480) 966-9630 *Founded/Ownrshp* 2012
Sales 189.1MM^E *EMP* 700^E
Accts Mcgladrey Llp Phoenix Arizon
SIC 2834 Vitamin preparations
VP: Michael Hoard

D-U-N-S 10-404-0290
ARIZONA PARKING LOT SERVICE
FIELDER EQUIPMENT
1415 E Bethany Home Rd, Phoenix, AZ 85014-2082
Tel (602) 277-8007 *Founded/Ownrshp* 1963
Sales 300.5MM *EMP* 3
SIC 1799 1611 Parking lot maintenance; Surfacing & paving
Owner: Al Fielder

D-U-N-S 15-129-0731
ARIZONA PARTSMASTER INC
AZ PARTSMASTER
7125 W Sherman St, Phoenix, AZ 85043-4773
Tel (602) 233-3580 *Founded/Ownrshp* 1985
Sales 104.0MM^E *EMP* 140
Accts Donald W Stoker Pc Scottsd
SIC 5087 Cleaning & maintenance equipment & supplies
CEO: David D Schlecht
**Sec:* Jean Schlecht
**VP:* Brad L Schlecht
Sls Mgr: Scott Sherman

D-U-N-S 02-913-3030
ARIZONA PIPE LINE CO (AZ)
17372 Lilac St, Hesperia, CA 92345-5162
Tel (760) 244-8212 *Founded/Ownrshp* 1979
Sales 98.8MM *EMP* 1,000
Accts Soren Mcadam Christenson Llp
SIC 1623 Pipeline construction
CEO: Lowell D Moyers
**CEO:* Nina Moyers
**Sec:* Tom Seals
**VP:* Phyliss Moyers
Exec: Connie Borden
Exec: Jim Harris
Div Mgr: Ernie Bernard
Div Mgr: William Fregozo
Div Mgr: Charlie Manherz

ARIZONA PORTLAND CEMENT
See CALPORTLAND CO

D-U-N-S 00-690-1995 IMP
■ **ARIZONA PUBLIC SERVICE CO** (AZ)
(*Suby of* PINNACLE WEST CAPITAL CORP) ★
400 N 5th St Fl 2, Phoenix, AZ 85004-3992
Tel (602) 250-1000 *Founded/Ownrshp* 1920
Sales 3.4MMM *EMP* 6,309^E
SIC 4911 Generation, electric power; Transmission, electric power; Distribution, electric power
Ch Bd: Donald E Brandt
COO: Mark A Schiavoni
CFO: James R Hatfield
Treas: Lee Nickloy
Ofcr: Randall K Edington
Ex VP: Walter Ekstrom
Ex VP: David P Falck
Sr VP: Bob Bement
Sr VP: Daniel T Froetscher
Sr VP: Jeffrey Guldner
Sr VP: Maria Lacal
Sr VP: Nancy C Loftin
VP: Ann Becker
VP: Denise R Danner
VP: Barbara M Gomez
VP: David A Hansen
VP: Tammy McLeod
Board of Directors: Denis A Cortese, Richard P Fox, Michael L Gallagher, Roy A Herberger Jr, Dale E Klein, Humberto S Lopez, Kathryn L Munro, Bruce J Nordstrom, David P Wagener

ARIZONA REPUBLIC
See PHOENIX NEWSPAPERS INC

D-U-N-S 80-634-5658
ARIZONA STATE UNIVERSITY
300 E University Dr # 410, Tempe, AZ 85281-2061
Tel (480) 965-2100 *Founded/Ownrshp* 1885
Sales 1.3MMM *EMP* 8,000^E
Accts Debbie K Davenport Cpa Phoe
SIC 8221 Colleges universities & professional schools
Pr: Michael M Crow
**CFO:* Carol Campbell
CFO: Morgan R Olsen
**Treas:* Gerald Snyder
**Ex VP:* Elizabeth Capaldi
Opers Mgr: Catherine Skoglund

D-U-N-S 07-346-2368
ARIZONA STATE UNIVERSITY FOUNDATION FOR A NEW AMERICAN UNIVE
300 E University Dr, Tempe, AZ 85281-2061
Tel (480) 965-3759 *Founded/Ownrshp* 1955
Sales 164.8MM *EMP* 170
Accts Grant Thornton Llp San Franci
SIC 6732 Trusts: educational, religious, etc.
CEO: R F Shangraw Jr
**Pr:* Johnnie Ray
Brnch Mgr: Virgil Renzulli

D-U-N-S 13-165-9133 IMP
ARIZONA TILE LLC
8829 S Priest Dr, Tempe, AZ 85284-1905
Tel (480) 991-3066 *Founded/Ownrshp* 2000
Sales 319.0MM^E *EMP* 950
SIC 5032 Tile & clay products; Ceramic wall & floor tile
CEO: John Huarte
Pr: Robert Traxler
CFO: Gary Skarsten
Ex VP: Gary D Skarsten
VP: Mark Huarte
VP: Don Kesteloot
VP Bus Dev: Matt Huarte
Ex Dir: Lisa Wright
Brnch Mgr: Richard Armstrong
Genl Mgr: Rick Collins
Genl Mgr: Roy Kunihiro

D-U-N-S 00-690-2001
ARIZONA WATER CO (AZ)
3805 N Black Canyon Hwy, Phoenix, AZ 85015-5351
Tel (480) 982-2201 *Founded/Ownrshp* 1955, 2011
Sales 148.1MM^E *EMP* 189
SIC 4941 Water supply
Pr: Bill Garfield
COO: Tom Harrell
**Treas:* Jackie Craig
Treas: Jackie Dollarhyde
**Treas:* Joseph D Harris
**VP:* Bob Geake
VP: Ralph Kennedy
VP: Fred Schneider
**VP:* Mike Whitehead
**VP:* James Wilson
Div Mgr: Joe Mauzy

D-U-N-S 13-120-9058 IMP
ARJOHUNTLEIGH INC
(*Suby of* GETINGE AB)
2349 W Lake St Ste 250, Addison, IL 60101-6188
Tel (630) 785-4490 *Founded/Ownrshp* 1995
Sales 1.2MMM^E *EMP* 4,400
SIC 5047 Medical equipment & supplies
Pr: Philip Croxford
Pr: Rick Lytle
**CFO:* Gary Jensen
CIO: Joan Santana
Sls Dir: James Rowley

D-U-N-S 95-747-3523 EXP
■ **ARK LAS VEGAS RESTAURANT CORP**
(*Suby of* ARK RESTAURANTS CORP) ★
3790 Las Vegas Blvd S, Las Vegas, NV 89109-4338
Tel (702) 207-4498 *Founded/Ownrshp* 1996
Sales 30.3MM^E *EMP* 1,000^E
SIC 5812 American restaurant
Pr: Michael Weinstein
**VP:* Paul Gordon

D-U-N-S 14-462-2438 IMP
▲ **ARK RESTAURANTS CORP**
85 5th Ave, New York, NY 10003-3019
Tel (212) 206-8800 *Founded/Ownrshp* 1983
Sales 145.8MM *EMP* 2,028
Tkr Sym ARKR *Exch* NGM
SIC 5812 5813 Eating places; Fast food restaurants & stands; Fast-food restaurant, independent; Bars & lounges
Ch Bd: Michael Weinstein
**Pr:* Robert Stewart
**COO:* Vincent Pascal
**Sr VP:* Paul Gordon
Genl Mgr: Todd Birnbaum
Genl Mgr: Danny Phee
Board of Directors: Marcia Allen, Bruce R Lewin, Stephen Novick, Steven Shulman, Arthur Stainman

D-U-N-S 93-020-0741
ARK-LA-TEX FINANCIAL SERVICES LLC
BENCHMARK MORTGAGE LOUISIANNA
5160 Tennyson Pkwy 2000w, Plano, TX 75024-4297
Tel (972) 398-7676 *Founded/Ownrshp* 1999
Sales NA *EMP* 250
Accts Bkm Sowan Horan Llp Addison
SIC 6163 Mortgage brokers arranging for loans, using money of others
CEO: Bryan Harlan
Pt: Sean Smith
**COO:* Stewart Hunter
**Treas:* Harold Rasmussen
Ofcr: Kyle Hiers
Ofcr: Josh Morita
Ofcr: Mary White
**Ex VP:* Jim Poulin
**Ex VP:* Steve Remington
VP Bus Dev: Gib Holloway
Brnch Mgr: Jeff Beck

ARKANSAS BLUE CROSS & BLU
See PINNACLE BUSINESS SOLUTIONS INC

ARKANSAS BLUE CROSS & BLUE
See USABLE MUTUAL INSURANCE CO

ARKANSAS BLUE CROSS BLUE SHELD
See BLUE ADVANTAGE ADMINISTRATORS OF ARKANSAS

D-U-N-S 07-566-9416
ARKANSAS CHILDRENS HOSPITAL (AR)
1 Childrens Way, Little Rock, AR 72202-3500
Tel (501) 364-1100 *Founded/Ownrshp* 1912
Sales 585.6MM *EMP* 3,700
Accts Kpmg Llp Memphis Tennessee
SIC 8062 8069 General medical & surgical hospitals; Children's hospital
Ch: Tom Baxter
Dir Vol: Robin Armstrong
**Pr:* Marcy Doderer
COO: David T Berry
CFO: Jena Waynefield
**CFO:* Gena G Wingfield
**Ex VP:* Scott R Gordon
Sr VP: Tom W Bonner
**Sr VP:* Darrell Leonhardt
Sr VP: Darrell T Leonhardt
VP: Larry Beckius
VP: Pamela Brown
VP: Jayant K Deshpande
VP: Cheryl Edwards
VP: Katherine Friend
VP: Carol Hudgens
VP: Rhonda McKinnis
VP: Beth Petlak
VP: Curtis Summers
VP: Rhonda Thornton
Exec: Julie Gentry

D-U-N-S 96-962-9885
ARKANSAS CHILDRENS HOSPITAL FOUNDATION INC
1 Childrens Way, Little Rock, AR 72202-3500
Tel (501) 320-1100 *Founded/Ownrshp* 1982
Sales 536.8MM *EMP* 83^E
Accts Deloitte Tax Llp Houston Tx
SIC 8699 Charitable organization
Prin: Joe Knight

D-U-N-S 96-427-0065
ARKANSAS CITY PRESBYTERIAN MANOR INC
1711 N 4th St, Arkansas City, KS 67005-1607
Tel (620) 442-8700 *Founded/Ownrshp* 1977
Sales 511.4MM *EMP* 10
SIC 8051 Skilled nursing care facilities
Pr: Lynne Lawrence
Ex Dir: Lynne Lawrence

ARKANSAS CLARK CONTRACTORS
See CLARK CONTRACTORS LLC

D-U-N-S 04-148-1417
ARKANSAS DEMOCRAT-GAZETTE INC
(*Suby of* WEHCO NEWSPAPERS INC) ★
121 E Capitol Ave, Little Rock, AR 72201-5734
Tel (501) 378-3400 *Founded/Ownrshp* 1974
Sales 84.7MM^E *EMP* 866^E
SIC 2711 Newspapers, publishing & printing
Pr: Lynn Hamilton
**Ch Bd:* Walter E Hussman Jr
**Pr:* Nat Lea
**Pr:* Paul R Smith
**Treas:* Allen Berry
**VP:* Conan Gallaty
Web Dev: Becky Harris
Web Dev: Tim Hicks
Sls Mgr: Lisa Williams
Corp Couns: Charlie Frago

D-U-N-S 80-987-2856
ARKANSAS DEPARTMENT OF EDUCATION
EXECUTIVE OFFICE OF THE STATE
(*Suby of* GOVERNERS OFFICE) ★
4 Capitol Mall, Little Rock, AR 72201-1019
Tel (501) 682-4475 *Founded/Ownrshp* 1867
Sales NA *EMP* 2,541
SIC 9411 Administration of educational programs;
Adm Dir: Michael Simmons

D-U-N-S 80-987-3185
ARKANSAS DEPARTMENT OF HEALTH
EXECUTIVE OFFC OF AR
(*Suby of* GOVERNERS OFFICE) ★
4815 W Markham St, Little Rock, AR 72205-3867
Tel (501) 661-2000 *Founded/Ownrshp* 1913
Sales NA *EMP* 2,800
SIC 9431 Administration of public health programs;
Ofcr: Ranelle Brock
Ofcr: Brandon Harrison
Nurse Mgr: Patricia Scott
Doctor: Carolyn Ahill
Doctor: Angel Akard
Doctor: Carole Allen
Doctor: Jane Aston
**Doctor:* Joe Bates
Doctor: Bobby Bridges
Doctor: Ladonna Carey
Doctor: Carolyn Crosby

D-U-N-S 80-987-3235
ARKANSAS DEPARTMENT OF HIGHWAY AND TRANSPORTATION
(*Suby of* GOVERNERS OFFICE) ★
10324 Interstate 30, Little Rock, AR 72209-4206
Tel (501) 569-2000 *Founded/Ownrshp* 1977
Sales NA *EMP* 3,639
SIC 9621 Regulation, administration of transportation;
Prin: Scott Dennette
**CFO:* Larry Dickerson
**Ex Dir:* Dan Flowers

D-U-N-S 80-987-3268
ARKANSAS DEPARTMENT OF HUMAN SERVICES
EXECUTV OFC OF THE STATE OF AR
(*Suby of* GOVERNERS OFFICE) ★
700 Main St, Little Rock, AR 72201-4608
Tel (501) 682-1001 *Founded/Ownrshp* 1971
Sales NA *EMP* 1,023
Accts Wood And Wood Ltd Magnolia A
SIC 9441 Administration of social & manpower programs;
**CFO:* Jerry Berry
CIO: Keith K Leathers

D-U-N-S 80-959-4021
ARKANSAS DEPARTMENT OF NATIONAL GUARD
MILITARY DEPARTMENT ARKANSAS
(*Suby of* GOVERNERS OFFICE) ★
Camp Robinson Bldg 6000, North Little Rock, AR 72199-0001
Tel (501) 212-5100 *Founded/Ownrshp* 1925
Sales NA *EMP* 1,624
SIC 9711 National Guard;
**Prin:* Mark Berry

D-U-N-S 80-959-4039
ARKANSAS DEPARTMENT OF PARKS AND TOURISM
EXECUTIVE OFC OF THE STATE ARK
(*Suby of* GOVERNERS OFFICE) ★
1 Capitol Mall Ste 900, Little Rock, AR 72201-1087
Tel (501) 682-7777 *Founded/Ownrshp* 1971
Sales NA *EMP* 1,200
SIC 9512 9611 Recreational program administration, government; ; Administration of general economic programs;
Ex Dir: Richard W Davies

D-U-N-S 80-987-2872
ARKANSAS DEPT OF FINANCE AND ADMINISTRATION
EXECUTV OFC OF THE STATE OF AR
(*Suby of* GOVERNERS OFFICE) ★
1509 W 7th St, Little Rock, AR 72201-3933
Tel (501) 682-2242 *Founded/Ownrshp* 1973
Sales NA *EMP* 1,820
SIC 9311 Finance, taxation & monetary policy;
Brnch Mgr: John Greer

D-U-N-S 62-058-7514
ARKANSAS ELDER OUTREACH OF LITTLE ROCK
EASTRIDGE NURSING CENTER
12111 Hinson Rd, Little Rock, AR 72212-3410
Tel (225) 906-2274 *Founded/Ownrshp* 2007
Sales 56.0MM *EMP* 1,200
SIC 8322 Outreach program
Ex Dir: Douglas M Walsh

D-U-N-S 04-355-9699
ARKANSAS ELECTRIC COOPERATIVE CORP
1 Cooperative Way, Little Rock, AR 72209-5493
Tel (501) 570-2200 *Founded/Ownrshp* 1949
Sales 455.3MM *EMP* 220
Accts Bkd Llp Little Rock Arkansas
SIC 4911 Electric services; Generation, electric power
CEO: Gary Voigt
**Pr:* Michael W Henderson
**CEO:* Duane D Highley
**Sr VP:* Robert M Lyford
VP: Carmie Henry
**VP:* Jonathan Oliver
VP Sls: Pat McClafferty

D-U-N-S 03-554-2398
ARKANSAS ELECTRIC COOPERATIVES INC (AR)
AECI
1 Cooperative Way, Little Rock, AR 72209-5493
Tel (501) 570-2361 *Founded/Ownrshp* 1949
Sales 462.4MM *EMP* 840
Accts Bkd Llp Little Rock Arkansa
SIC 5063 1623 1629 7629 Transformers, electric; Pole line hardware; Electric power line construction; Power plant construction; Land clearing contractor; Electrical equipment repair, high voltage
Pr: Duane Highley
VP: Pat McClafferty
VP: Jonathan Oliver
VP: Doug White
Genl Mgr: Carey Woodall
Snr Ntwrk: Daniel Hardy

ARKANSAS GAZETTE, THE
See GANNETT RIVER STATES PUBLISHING CORP

D-U-N-S 94-818-0914
ARKANSAS HEART HOSPITAL LLC
(*Suby of* MEDCATH CORP) ★
1701 S Shackleford Rd, Little Rock, AR 72211-4335
Tel (501) 219-7000 *Founded/Ownrshp* 2011
Sales 144.8MM *EMP* 414^E
SIC 8062 8011 General medical & surgical hospitals; Offices & clinics of medical doctors
Pr: Bruce Murphy
**Owner:* Mary Ann Hutcherson
**Owner:* Caroline Morris
COO: Adam Head

CFO: Bryan Z Nichols
VP: Nelson Andrea
VP: Dan Caldwell
VP: Mark Hartman
Dir Inf Cn: Joanne Rausch
Dir Risk M: Inga Witcher
CIO: Neal Fendley

D-U-N-S 00-690-3058
ARKANSAS OKLAHOMA GAS CORP (AR)
(*Suby of* A O G CORP) ★
115 N 12th St, Fort Smith, AR 72901-2741
Tel (479) 784-2000 *Founded/Ownrshp* 1920
Sales 133.3MM^E *EMP* 200
SIC 4923 Gas transmission & distribution
Pr: Michael J Callan
Ex VP: Jerry Schreckhise
**VP:* Kim R Linam
**Prin:* Michael C Carter
Genl Couns: Michael Callan

D-U-N-S 07-351-0067
ARKANSAS STATE UNIVERSITY
501 Woodlane St Ste 600, Little Rock, AR 72201-1038
Tel (870) 972-2024 *Founded/Ownrshp* 1909
Sales 111.3MM *EMP* 1,582
Accts Roger A Norman Jd Cpa Cfe
SIC 5812 Pizzeria, chain
Ch: Ron Rhodes
**Ch Bd:* Dan Pierce
Treas: Philip Jackson
Treas: Judy Reed
VP: Judy Blevins
VP: Angela Smith
VP: Jennifer Smith
Genl Mgr: John Nickel
IT Man: Erin Lynn
Info Man: Sandra Petty
Netwrk Eng: Eric Barnett

D-U-N-S 02-546-9073 IMP
ARKANSAS STEEL ASSOCIATES LLC (AR)
2803 Van Dyke Rd, Newport, AR 72112-9755
Tel (870) 523-3693 *Founded/Ownrshp* 1989
Sales 94.9MM^E *EMP* 230
Accts Kpmg Llp Memphis Tn
SIC 3312 3547 Plate, steel; Billet mills
VP: Ginger Carlyle
VP: Lef Phillips
Ql Cn Mgr: Craig Rohlfing
VP Sls: Joseph Reardon

D-U-N-S 07-563-8866
ARKANSAS TECH UNIVERSITY
1605 Coliseum Dr, Russellville, AR 72801-8819
Tel (479) 968-0300 *Founded/Ownrshp* 1909
Sales 80.6MM *EMP* 1,039
Accts Roger A Norman Jd Cpa Cfe
SIC 8221 University
Pr: Robert C Brown PHD
Ofcr: Charles Moore
VP: Aj Anglin
**VP:* Jayne Jones
**VP:* David C Mosley
**VP:* Susin Nicholson
**VP:* David Underwood
**VP:* John Watson
Adm Dir: Cindy Dawson
Sales Asso: Cheryl Moody

ARKANSAS VALLEY ELECTRIC CO-OP
See ARKANSAS VALLEY ELECTRIC COOPERATIVE CORP

D-U-N-S 00-780-7068
ARKANSAS VALLEY ELECTRIC COOPERATIVE CORP
ARKANSAS VALLEY ELECTRIC CO-OP
1811 W Commercial St, Ozark, AR 72949-2905
Tel (479) 667-2176 *Founded/Ownrshp* 1937
Sales 112.6MM *EMP* 165
SIC 4911 Generation, electric power
CEO: Bill Peter
**Pr:* Williams H Peters
Ex Dir: Lirhonda Melton
Off Mgr: Jay Logan
IT Man: Amber Canada

D-U-N-S 07-193-3279
ARKEL INTERNATIONAL LLC
1048 Florida Blvd, Baton Rouge, LA 70802-4628
Tel (225) 343-0500 *Founded/Ownrshp* 1955
Sales 90.2MM^E *EMP* 250
SIC 1542 Nonresidential construction
CEO: John Moore
IT Man: Jason Rogacki
Opers Mgr: Jeffrey Hall

D-U-N-S 62-212-1697 IMP/EXP
ARKEMA DELAWARE INC
(*Suby of* ARKEMA AMERIQUES SAS)
900 First Ave, King of Prussia, PA 19406-1308
Tel (610) 205-7000 *Founded/Ownrshp* 2013
Sales 2.4MMM^E *EMP* 4,500
SIC 2812 2819 2869 2891 2899 2992 Chlorine, compressed or liquefied; Caustic soda, sodium hydroxide; Industrial inorganic chemicals; Sodium compounds or salts, inorg., ex. refined sod. chloride; Sodium sulfate, glauber's salt, salt cake; Peroxides, hydrogen peroxide; Industrial organic chemicals; Solvents, organic; Adhesives; Metal treating compounds; Lubricating oils & greases
Pr: Bernard Roche
**Treas:* Otto Takken
**VP:* Patricia McCarthy
IT Man: Jody Northrop
IT Man: Steve Rauch
Mktg Mgr: Randy Miller

D-U-N-S 00-229-0773 IMP/EXP
ARKEMA INC (PA)
(*Suby of* ARKEMA DELAWARE INC) ★
900 First Ave, King of Prussia, PA 19406-1308
Tel (610) 205-7000 *Founded/Ownrshp* 1850, 2013
Sales 2.4MMM^E *EMP* 2,400
SIC 2812

D-U-N-S 18-123-3297
■ **ARKGALV INC**
(*Suby of* AZZ INC) ★
998 Escue Dr, Prairie Grove, AR 72753-2836
Tel (479) 846-4500 *Founded/Ownrshp* 1996
Sales 88.8MM^E *EMP* 1,000
SIC 3312 Iron & steel: galvanized, pipes, plates, sheets, etc.
Pr: Davis Dingas
**VP:* Dana Perry

ARKHOLA SAND & GRAVEL
See APAC-CENTRAL INC

D-U-N-S 10-397-6544
ARKLATEX ENERGY SERVICES LLC
6913 Westport Ave, Shreveport, LA 71129-2321
Tel (318) 688-9850 *Founded/Ownrshp* 2005
Sales 114.7MM^E *EMP* 100^E
SIC 1389 Oil field services
Genl Mgr: Brian Christian
Mng Pt: Shawn Saunders
**Prin:* Randal Brooks

D-U-N-S 04-157-8634 IMP
ARLA FOODS INC
(*Suby of* ARLA FOODS A.M.B.A)
106 Allen Rd Ste 401, Basking Ridge, NJ 07920-3851
Tel (908) 604-6551 *Founded/Ownrshp* 1963
Sales 96.1MM^E *EMP* 150
SIC 5143 Cheese
Pr: Andrew Simpson
**CFO:* Jeff Brauner
Ofcr: Outi Fagerlund
Dir IT: Jon Zieman
Sales Exec: Hans Kristensen

D-U-N-S 08-013-2208
ARLANXEO USA HOLDINGS CORP
(*Suby of* ARLANXEO HOLDING B.V.)
111 Ridc Park West Dr, Pittsburgh, PA 15275-1112
Tel (412) 809-1000 *Founded/Ownrshp* 2016
Sales 98.1MM^E *EMP* 750
SIC 2821 2824 Elastomers, nonvulcanizable (plastics); Elastomeric fibers
Pr: Antonis Papadourakis

D-U-N-S 08-013-2206
ARLANXEO USA LLC
(*Suby of* ARLANXEO USA HOLDINGS CORP) ★
111 Ridc Park West Dr, Pittsburgh, PA 15275-1112
Tel (412) 809-1000 *Founded/Ownrshp* 2016
Sales 98.1MM^E *EMP* 750
SIC 2821 2824 Elastomers, nonvulcanizable (plastics); Elastomeric fibers
Pr: Antonis Papadourakis

ARLEE GROUP
See ARLEE HOME FASHIONS INC

D-U-N-S 08-062-6294 IMP
ARLEE HOME FASHIONS INC
ARLEE GROUP
261 5th Ave Fl Mezz, New York, NY 10016-7600
Tel (212) 213-0425 *Founded/Ownrshp* 1976
Sales 126.5MM^E *EMP* 500
SIC 2392 Pillows, bed: made from purchased materials; Chair covers & pads: made from purchased materials
CEO: David Frankel
Pr: Marsha Cutler
CFO: Alan Mandell
VP: Marsha Caparelli
VP: Julie Polich

D-U-N-S 96-729-9736
▲ **ARLINGTON ASSET INVESTMENT CORP**
1001 19th St N Ste 1900, Arlington, VA 22209-1720
Tel (703) 373-0200 *Founded/Ownrshp* 2003
Sales 154.5MM *EMP* 11^E
Accts Pricewaterhousecoopers Llp Mc
Tkr Sym AI *Exch* NYS
SIC 6798 6162 Real estate investment trusts; Mortgage investment trusts; Mortgage bankers & correspondents
Pr: J Rock Tonkel Jr
**Ch Bd:* Eric F Billings
CFO: Richard E Konzmann
Ofcr: Brian J Bowers
Sr VP: Mishari Al-Bader
VP: Therese Bracken
VP: Michael Robertson
VP: Shannon Small

D-U-N-S 05-190-8069
ARLINGTON AUTOMOTIVE GROUP INC
ARLINGTON TOYOTA
2095 N Rand Rd, Palatine, IL 60074-2596
Tel (847) 394-5100 *Founded/Ownrshp* 1983
Sales 90.6MM *EMP* 136
SIC 7538 5521 5511 5531 7532 General automotive repair shops; Used car dealers; Automobiles, new & used; Automotive & home supply stores; Body shop, automotive
Pr: Gary Vicari
**VP:* Scott Vicari
**Prin:* James Ashe
**Prin:* Steven Sack
Dir IT: James Brinlee
Sls Mgr: Gene Gilerman
Sls Mgr: Mike Gordon
Sls Mgr: Igor Mett
Sls Mgr: Gianni Schiaffino

D-U-N-S 05-323-6449
ARLINGTON CAPITAL PARTNERS LP
5425 Wisconsin Ave # 200, Chevy Chase, MD 20815-3577
Tel (202) 337-7500 *Founded/Ownrshp* 1998
Sales 202.3MM^E *EMP* 1,065
SIC 6726 6211 Investment offices; Security brokers & dealers
Mng Pt: Jeffrey H Freed
Genl Pt: Robert Knibb
Pt: Matthew L Altman
Pt: Michael H Lustbader
Pt: Peter M Manos
Pt: Perry W Steiner

D-U-N-S 04-667-3877
ARLINGTON CENTRAL SCHOOL DISTRICT
144 Todd Hill Rd, Lagrangeville, NY 12540-5916
Tel (845) 486-4460 *Founded/Ownrshp* 1920
Sales 90.3MM^E *EMP* 2,000
Accts Bonadio & Co Llp Syracuse
SIC 8211 Public elementary & secondary schools
Prin: Joyce Craw
Prin: Brady Fister
Prin: Edwin Fox
Prin: Linda Heitmann
Prin: Stephen Kerins
Prin: Michael Kessler
Prin: Michael Malet
Prin: Linda Roy
Prin: Eric Schetter
Genl Mgr: Lisa Barker
Teacher Pr: Margaret Muenkel

D-U-N-S 13-120-3515
ARLINGTON COMPUTER PRODUCTS INC
A C P
851 Commerce Ct, Buffalo Grove, IL 60089-2366
Tel (847) 541-2475 *Founded/Ownrshp* 1984
Sales 116.0MM^E *EMP* 90
SIC 5045 Computers, peripherals & software
CEO: Arlington Guenther
**Pr:* Karen Guenther
VP: Mark Buchek
VP: Michael Palmer
IT Man: John Gibbs
Netwrk Eng: Brian Blume
Natl Sales: Tod Folkl
Natl Sales: Lisa Kalck
Natl Sales: Scott Kleiman

D-U-N-S 00-181-8124
ARLINGTON ENTERPRISES LP
ADRONICO MARKETS
1200 Irving St Ste 2, San Francisco, CA 94122-2121
Tel (415) 753-0403 *Founded/Ownrshp* 1998
Sales 68.5MM^E *EMP* 1,100
SIC 5411 Grocery stores, independent
Pt: Demetra Andronico
Pt: Constance Adronico
Pt: William Andronico

ARLINGTON HEIGHTS PD
See DAVITA ARLINGTON HEIGHTS RENAL CENTER

D-U-N-S 07-854-4475
ARLINGTON INDEPENDENT SCHOOL DISTRICT
1203 W Pioneer Pkwy, Arlington, TX 76013-6246
Tel (682) 867-4611 *Founded/Ownrshp* 1902
Sales 613.9MM *EMP* 8,000
Accts Whitley Penn Llp Houston Tex
SIC 8211 Public elementary & secondary schools
Pr: Bowie Hogg
**VP:* Jamie Sullins
Prin: Michael Martin
Pr Dir: Leslie Johnson
Teacher Pr: Scott Kahl

ARLINGTON INDUSTRIES
See CAROLINA WHOLESALE GROUP INC

D-U-N-S 00-303-1010 IMP
ARLINGTON INDUSTRIES INC
1 Stauffer Industrial Par, Scranton, PA 18517-9620
Tel (570) 562-0270 *Founded/Ownrshp* 1961
Sales 126.0MM *EMP* 320
Accts Rosen And Glaser
SIC 1731 Electrical work; General electrical contractor
Pr: Thomas Stark
**VP:* Thomas J Gretz
VP: Joseph Sullivan
Rgnl Mgr: Dennis Gravette
Genl Mgr: Thomas Gretz
VP Mktg: Ray Kennedy
Sls Dir: Bradley Davis
Mktg Mgr: Jim Cortese
Sls Mgr: Larry Troxel
Sls Mgr: Jack White

D-U-N-S 14-326-0433 IMP
ARLINGTON INDUSTRIES INC
(*Suby of* ARLINGTON INDUSTRIES) ★
1616 S Lakeside Dr, Waukegan, IL 60085-8306
Tel (847) 689-2754 *Founded/Ownrshp* 2003
Sales 129.8MM^E *EMP* 130
SIC 5112 Stationery & office supplies
Pr: Larry L Huneycutt
**CFO:* Martin D Wilson
**Prin:* Gary Feltman
Off Mgr: Dianne Sweeney
Natl Sales: Gary Edwards
Sales Asso: Lynn Conway

D-U-N-S 06-838-5376
ARLINGTON MEMORIAL HOSPITAL ALLIANCE INC
(*Suby of* TEXAS HEALTH RESOURCES) ★
800 W Randol Mill Rd, Arlington, TX 76012-2504
Tel (817) 548-6100 *Founded/Ownrshp* 1994
Sales 212.7MM *EMP* 1,700
SIC 8062 General medical & surgical hospitals
Pr: Bohn D Allen
**VP:* Dudley D Jones
Dir Inf Cn: Sue Sebazco
Dir Lab: Pam Hicks
Dir Lab: Susan Magee
Chf Nrs Of: Donna Bertram
MIS Dir: Toni Miles
Mktg Dir: Amy McCall
Doctor: Karen Fincannon
Doctor: Scott C Tisdell

D-U-N-S 02-576-3611
ARLINGTON PUBLIC SCHOOLS
1426 N Quincy St, Arlington, VA 22207-3674
Tel (703) 228-6000 *Founded/Ownrshp* 1872
Sales 65.6MM^E *EMP* 1,000
SIC 8211 Public elementary & secondary schools
DP Exec: Pat Teske
MIS Dir: Terrance Proctor
Teacher Pr: Erin Wales-Smith

Psych: Jordan Glick
Psych: Marisol Leach
Psych: Ricia Weiner

ARLINGTON TOYOTA
See ARLINGTON AUTOMOTIVE GROUP INC

D-U-N-S 12-272-9804
ARLO TRANSPORTATION INC
(*Suby of* ARNOLD LOGISTICS LLC) ★
3811 Dixon St, Des Moines, IA 50313-3907
Tel (515) 265-6171 *Founded/Ownrshp* 2001
Sales 265.2M^E *EMP* 1,679^E
SIC 4731 Freight transportation arrangement
CEO: Brian Lutt
Pr: Scott Temple
**CFO:* Jack Ingle
VP: Frank Dagostino
VP: Marty Howard
Board of Directors: Ted Dardani, John Rachwalski

D-U-N-S 07-846-3902
ARLON FOOD AND AGRICULTURE PARTNERS LP
277 Park Ave, New York, NY 10172-0003
Tel (212) 207-5200 *Founded/Ownrshp* 2010
Sales 83.5MM^E *EMP* 56^E
SIC 6799 Investors

D-U-N-S 60-659-6450 IMP
■ **ARLON LLC**
ARLON MTL TECH MICROWAVE MTLS
(*Suby of* ROGERS CORP) ★
1100 Governor Lea Rd, Bear, DE 19701-1927
Tel (302) 834-2100 *Founded/Ownrshp* 2015
Sales 90.8MM^E *EMP* 200
SIC 2822 Silicone rubbers
Pr: Bob Carini
VP Mktg: Peter Ni

ARLON MTL TECH MICROWAVE MTLS
See ARLON LLC

D-U-N-S 79-602-3968
ARM INC
(*Suby of* ARM HOLDINGS PLC)
150 Rose Orchard Way, San Jose, CA 95134-1358
Tel (408) 576-1500 *Founded/Ownrshp* 2004
Sales 153.4MM^E *EMP* 359
SIC 3674 Integrated circuits, semiconductor networks, etc.
CEO: Simon Segars
**COO:* Graham Budd
**CFO:* Chris Kennedy
Ex VP: Tom Cronk
Ex VP: Thomas Lantzsch
Ex VP: Antonio Viana
VP: Brent Dichter
VP: R Keith Hopkins
VP: Catherine Tan
Exec: Scott Bordelon
Exec: David G Bressert

D-U-N-S 07-981-9909
ARM STRONG GROUP LLC
3960 Howard Hughes Pkwy, Las Vegas, NV 89169-5972
Tel (702) 948-8960 *Founded/Ownrshp* 2015
Sales 140.0MM *EMP* 11
SIC 5169 Specialty cleaning & sanitation preparations
Pr: Joseph Feldman

ARMA
See AUTOMATED RESOURCE MANAGEMENT ASSOCIATES INC

D-U-N-S 82-516-6528
ARMA GLOBAL CORP
2701 N Rocky Point Dr # 1150, Rocky Point, FL 33607-5556
Tel (866) 554-9333 *Founded/Ownrshp* 2008
Sales 189.2MM^E *EMP* 815
SIC 5045 8748 8742 Computers, peripherals & software; Business consulting; Management consulting services
CEO: Todd Schweitzer
**Pr:* James Fugit
**COO:* Brian Overstreet
**VP:* Charles Broms
Prgrm Mgr: Kendon Cato
Dir IT: Richard Johnson
Pgrm Dir: James Myrick

D-U-N-S 07-883-0862
▲ **ARMADA HOFFLER PROPERTIES INC**
222 Central Park Ave # 2100, Virginia Beach, VA 23462-3039
Tel (757) 366-4000 *Founded/Ownrshp* 2012
Sales 252.4MM *EMP* 139^E
Accts Ernst & Young Llp Mclean Vi
Tkr Sym AHH *Exch* NYS
SIC 6798 Real estate investment trusts
Pr: Louis S Haddad
**Ch Bd:* Daniel A Hoffler
Pr: Eric E Apperson
Pr: Anthony P Nero
CFO: Michael P O'Hara
**V Ch Bd:* A Russell Kirk

D-U-N-S 80-793-9983
ARMADA/HOFFLER PROPERTIES LLC
222 Central Park Ave # 2100, Virginia Beach, VA 23462-3039
Tel (757) 366-4000 *Founded/Ownrshp* 2000
Sales 168.0MM *EMP* 2^E
SIC 6552 Subdividers & developers; Land subdividers & developers, residential; Land subdividers & developers, commercial
Ch Bd: Dan Hoffler
**CEO:* Louis S Haddad
**CFO:* Michael P O'Hara
**Ex VP:* Alan Hunt
VP: Eric L Smith

D-U-N-S 55-671-9326
ARMAND AGRA INC
1330 Capital Blvd, Reno, NV 89502-7180
Tel (775) 322-4073 *Founded/Ownrshp* 1991

Sales 91.3MM *EMP* 153
Accts Crawford Pimentel & Corporati
SIC 0291 5147 General farms, primarily animals; Meats & meat products
Pr: Christopher J Flocchini
CFO: John Lemos
* *Treas:* Bernadette Flocchini
* *Sec:* Richard Flocchini
* *VP:* Armando Flocchini III

ARMANI EXCHANGE
See PRESIDIO INTERNATIONAL INC

D-U-N-S 12-963-7773
ARMANINO LLP
12657 Alcosta Blvd # 500, San Ramon, CA 94583-4600
Tel (925) 790-2600 *Founded/Ownrshp* 2012
Sales 90.9MM^E *EMP* 350
SIC 8721 8742 Certified public accountant; Management consulting services
Mng Pt: Andy Armanino
Pt: Linda Antonelli
Pt: Esther Ratterree
VP: Frank Siskowski
Dir IT: Doug Miller
IT Man: Jeremy Sucharski
Genl Couns: Chris Carlberg

ARMC
See ARROWHEAD REGIONAL MEDICAL CENTER

ARMC HEALTH CARE
See ALAMANCE REGIONAL MEDICAL CENTER INC

ARMC HOME CARE SERVICES
See ALPENA REGIONAL MEDICAL CENTER

D-U-N-S 86-780-7414
■ **ARMC LP**
ABILENE REGIONAL MEDICAL CTR
(*Suby of* COMMUNITY HEALTH SYSTEMS INC) ★
6250 Highway 83 84, Abilene, TX 79606
Tel (325) 428-1000 *Founded/Ownrshp* 2007
Sales 87.2MM^E *EMP* 750
SIC 8062 8093 8011 7991 General medical & surgical hospitals; Specialty outpatient clinics; Clinic, operated by physicians; Health club
CEO: Mike D Murphy
* *CFO:* Ron Bennett
Dir Case M: Rosemary Lara
Dir Lab: Michael Woodall
Dir Rad: Janie Thornhill
Adm Dir: Vishia Wilson
Nurse Mgr: Donna Mayfield
Mtls Dir: Eric Fisher
Sls&Mrk Ex: Delores Cox
Psych: Amy McClatchy
Ansthlgy: Michael Price

D-U-N-S 82-939-9687 IMP
ARMCO METALS HOLDINGS INC
1730 S Amphlett Blvd # 230, San Mateo, CA 94402-2722
Tel (650) 212-7630 *Founded/Ownrshp* 2008
Sales 124.1MM *EMP* 53^E
SIC 5051 Nonferrous metal sheets, bars, rods, etc.
Ch Bd: Kexuan Yao
CFO: Fengtao Wen

D-U-N-S 00-799-0039
ARMED FORCES BANK NATIONAL ASSOCIATION
(*Suby of* DICKINSON FINANCIAL CORP)
320 Kansas Ave, Fort Leavenworth, KS 66027-1139
Tel (913) 682-9090 *Founded/Ownrshp* 1907
Sales NA *EMP* 506
SIC 6021 National commercial banks
Ch Bd: Rick L Smalley
* *Pr:* Don Giles
* *V Ch Bd:* Robert Arter
VP: Darryl Pagel
VP: Jodie Pitsenbarger
Mktg Mgr: Laura Swisshelm

D-U-N-S 07-481-7248
ARMED FORCES BENEFIT ASSOCIATION
AFBA
909 N Washington St # 767, Alexandria, VA 22314-1555
Tel (703) 549-4455 *Founded/Ownrshp* 1947
Sales 102.5MM *EMP* 210
Accts Pricewaterhousecoopers Llp Wa
SIC 7389 Financial services
Pr: Ralph Eberhart
COO: Robert Mentelson
* *Treas:* Addie Gordon-Monroe
* *Sr VP:* David Orr
VP: Robert Bell
VP: Gary Griffin
* *VP:* Claudia Hasty
VP: A Jeanine Hoover
* *VP:* Col Scott S Pinckney
* *VP:* Keith Taylor
VP: Cap Yentsch
Board of Directors: Salvatore J Cassano

D-U-N-S 83-033-3824
■ **ARMED FORCES SERVICES CORP**
AFSC
(*Suby of* MAGELLAN HEALTHCARE INC) ★
2800 S Shirlington Rd # 350, Arlington, VA 22206-3617
Tel (571) 312-7670 *Founded/Ownrshp* 2016
Sales 62.5MM^E *EMP* 1,800
SIC 8742 Management consulting services
Pr: Geoffrey J Deutsch
VP: Nicole Bazemore
Genl Mgr: Jacky Dargan
Dir IT: Jerry Alexandratos
IT Man: Sarah Kim

D-U-N-S 15-687-9371
ARMELLINI INDUSTRIES INC
3446 Sw Armellini Ave, Palm City, FL 34990-8129
Tel (772) 287-0575 *Founded/Ownrshp* 1984
Sales 90.1MM^E *EMP* 650
Accts Harris Cotherman & Associates
SIC 4213 5193 4731 Trucking, except local; Flowers, fresh; Customhouse brokers
Ch: Jules Armellini
* *Pr:* Richard Armellini
* *COO:* James Merritt
* *Sec:* John J Nicholason
* *Exec:* David Armellini
* *Exec:* Sarah B Armellini
* *Exec:* Stephen Armellini
* *Exec:* Judith Dusharm
Software D: Geoff Guthrie
VP Opers: Jeff Jackson

D-U-N-S 06-611-2798
ARMFIELD HARRISON & THOMAS INC
AHT INSURANCE
20 S King St Ste 300, Leesburg, VA 20175-3026
Tel (703) 777-2341 *Founded/Ownrshp* 1936
Sales NA *EMP* 190
SIC 6411 Property & casualty insurance agent
Pr: David L Schaefer
* *COO:* Katherine Armfield
CFO: Michael Crilley
Sr Cor Off: Joseph Face
Ex VP: Alexander G Green III
Ex VP: Mary White
Sr VP: Dennis Gustafson
Sr VP: Ryan Murphy
Sr VP: Richard Whiteley
VP: Brett Webster
* *Prin:* George Forrester

ARMITRON WATCH DIV
See E GLUCK CORP

D-U-N-S 10-119-6504 IMP
■ **ARMKEL LLC**
(*Suby of* CHURCH & DWIGHT CO INC) ★
469 N Harrison St, Princeton, NJ 08540-3510
Tel (609) 683-5900 *Founded/Ownrshp* 2004
Sales 76.8MM^E *EMP* 1,500
SIC 2844 2835 Toilet preparations; Depilatories (cosmetic); Pregnancy test kits
Board of Directors: Philip E Berney, Michael B Goldberg, Michael B Lazar

D-U-N-S 09-316-6908
ARMON INC
2265 Carlson Dr, Northbrook, IL 60062-6705
Tel (847) 498-4800 *Founded/Ownrshp* 1977
Sales 162.8MM^E *EMP* 644
SIC 1711 7515 6552 Warm air heating & air conditioning contractor; Ventilation & duct work contractor; Plumbing contractors; Fire sprinkler system installation; Passenger car leasing; Subdividers & developers
CEO: Brian Moran
Mktg Dir: Cathy Tabor

D-U-N-S 17-107-9028
ARMOR CORRECTIONAL HEALTH SERVICES INC
4960 Sw 72nd Ave Ste 400, Miami, FL 33155-5550
Tel (305) 662-8522 *Founded/Ownrshp* 2004
Sales 154.9MM *EMP* 2,000
Accts Morrison Brown Argiz & Farra
SIC 8099 Medical services organization
CEO: Bruce A Teal
* *Pr:* Jose Armas
COO: Robert Berton
* *COO:* Kenneth M Palombo
* *Sr VP:* Angela Goehring

D-U-N-S 96-244-2138
ARMOR DOMAIN INC
235 Westlake Ctr Pmb 518, Daly City, CA 94015-1430
Tel (415) 637-1817 *Founded/Ownrshp* 2010
Sales 580.0MM *EMP* 12
SIC 7381 Armored car services
CEO: Leonard Pierce
Pr: Lila Tam

D-U-N-S 08-047-3268
ARMOR PARENT CORP
7140 Office Cir, Evansville, IN 47715-8235
Tel (812) 962-5000 *Founded/Ownrshp* 2016
Sales 70.3MM^E *EMP* 2,290^E
SIC 6719 Investment holding companies, except banks
Prin: Alex Rose

ARMORED AUTO GROUP
See ARMORED AUTOGROUP INC

D-U-N-S 96-552-3801 IMP
ARMORED AUTOGROUP INC
ARMORED AUTO GROUP
44 Old Ridgebury Rd # 300, Danbury, CT 06810-5107
Tel (203) 205-2900 *Founded/Ownrshp* 2010
Sales 298.1MM *EMP* 242
SIC 3714

D-U-N-S 07-934-2281
■ **ARMORED AUTOGROUP PARENT INC**
(*Suby of* SPECTRUM BRANDS HOLDINGS INC) ★
44 Old Ridgebury Rd # 300, Danbury, CT 06810-5107
Tel (203) 205-2900 *Founded/Ownrshp* 2010, 2015
Sales 1.1MM^E *EMP* 1,331^E
SIC 2842 2911 2899 Automobile polish; Fuel additives; Chemical preparations
CEO: Michael Klein
CFO: Andy Bolt

D-U-N-S 13-350-3743
ARMORWORKS INC
7071 W Frye Rd, Chandler, AZ 85226-3316
Tel (480) 517-1150 *Founded/Ownrshp* 1996
Sales 94.2MM^E *EMP* 401
SIC 3462 Iron & steel forgings
CFO: David Wirthlin
Genl Mgr: Chris Hanisko
Genl Mgr: Shelley Shrum
IT Man: Jeff Collins
IT Man: Theresa McElwee
Mtls Mgr: Annette Furman
Mtls Mgr: George Lloyd
Secur Mgr: Rob Hood

D-U-N-S 80-961-4477
ARMOUR RESIDENTIAL REIT INC
3001 Ocean Dr Ste 201, Vero Beach, FL 32963-1992
Tel (772) 617-4340 *Founded/Ownrshp* 2008
Sales 365.3MM *EMP* 19^E
SIC 6798 Real estate investment trusts
Pr: Jeffrey J Zimmer
* *Ch Bd:* Scott J Ulm
* *COO:* Mark Gruber
* *CFO:* James R Mountain

D-U-N-S 78-815-6920 EXP
ARMOUR-ECKRICH MEATS LLC
(*Suby of* MORRELL JOHN & CO) ★
4225 Naperville Rd # 600, Lisle, IL 60532-3699
Tel (630) 281-5000 *Founded/Ownrshp* 2006
Sales 603.3MM^E *EMP* 3,000^E
SIC 3556 Meat, poultry & seafood processing machinery
Pr: Michael Brown
Exec: Joel Miller
Dist Mgr: Larry Hawley

D-U-N-S 36-440-2719 IMP
■ **ARMSTRONG AIR CONDITIONING INC**
ALLIED AIR ENTERPRISES
(*Suby of* LENNOX INTERNATIONAL INC) ★
215 Metropolitan Dr, West Columbia, SC 29170-2294
Tel (803) 738-4000 *Founded/Ownrshp* 1988
Sales 104.0MM^E *EMP* 300
SIC 3585 Air conditioning units, complete: domestic or industrial; Heating equipment, complete
Genl Mgr: Joe Nassab
Ex Dir: Chris Burton
Board of Directors: Robert Schjerven

ARMSTRONG CABINET PRODUCTS
See ACPRODUCTS INC

ARMSTRONG CABLE SERVICES
See ARMSTRONG UTILITIES INC

D-U-N-S 07-215-4289
ARMSTRONG COUNTY MEMORIAL HOSPITAL
ACMH HOSPITAL
1 Nolte Dr, Kittanning, PA 16201-7111
Tel (724) 543-8500 *Founded/Ownrshp* 1995
Sales 109.3MM *EMP* 990
Accts Bkd Llp Springfield Mo
SIC 8062 8011 General medical & surgical hospitals; Clinic, operated by physicians
Pr: John Lewis
* *Ch Bd:* Elizabeth White
* *CFO:* Pat Burns
* *Sec:* Harry Atkins
* *Ofcr:* Dr Hal Altman
* *VP:* Anne Remaley
Exec: Monette Adamson
Dir Rx: Amy McKelvey
Nurse Mgr: Janis Reeves
Mtls Mgr: Diane Vogeley
Mktg Dir: Sharon Urban

ARMSTRONG FLOORING
See ARMSTRONG HARDWOOD FLOORING CO

ARMSTRONG FLOORING
See ARMSTRONG WOOD PRODUCTS INC

D-U-N-S 08-016-3180
▲ **ARMSTRONG FLOORING INC**
AFI
2500 Columbia Ave, Lancaster, PA 17603-4117
Tel (717) 672-9611 *Founded/Ownrshp* 2015
Sales 1.1MMM *EMP* 3,700
Tkr Sym AFI *Exch* NYS
SIC 3996 2426 Hard surface floor coverings; Hardwood dimension & flooring mills; Flooring, hardwood
Pr: Donald R Maier
* *Ch Bd:* Larry S McWilliams
CFO: John W Thompson
Chf Cred: Christopher S Parisi
Sr VP: John C Bassett
Sr VP: Joseph N Bondi
Sr VP: Charles E Grogan
Sr VP: Scott W Hess
Sr VP: Dominic C Rice
VP: Kimberly Z Boscan
Board of Directors: Michael F Johnston, Kathleen S Lane, Jeffrey Liaw, Michael W Malone, James C Melville, James J O'connor, Jacob H Welch, Richard E Wenz

D-U-N-S 08-904-2261 IMP
ARMSTRONG GARDEN CENTERS INC
ARMSTRONG GROWERS
2200 E Route 66 Ste 200, Glendora, CA 91740-4699
Tel (626) 914-1091 *Founded/Ownrshp* 1977
Sales 208.4MM^E *EMP* 1,100
SIC 5261 0782 Nurseries & garden centers; Garden maintenance services
Pr: Michael D Kunce
* *CFO:* David Weisman
VP: Monte Enright
* *Prin:* Don Rogers
Brnch Mgr: Michele St Amant
Store Mgr: Thomas Purnell
Dir IT: Emmayln Anderson
Dir IT: Allison Potter
Sls&Mrk Ex: Gary Jones
Pr Dir: Chris Greenwood
Board of Directors: Don L Rogers Jr

D-U-N-S 83-471-8389
ARMSTRONG GROUP OF COMPANIES INC
1 Armstrong Pl, Butler, PA 16001-1951
Tel (724) 283-0925 *Founded/Ownrshp* 1946
Sales 296.9MM^E *EMP* 1,327^E
SIC 4813

ARMSTRONG GROWERS
See ARMSTRONG GARDEN CENTERS INC

D-U-N-S 00-338-3072 EXP
■ **ARMSTRONG HARDWOOD FLOORING CO** (TN)
ARMSTRONG FLOORING
(*Suby of* AFI) ★
2500 Columbia Ave, Lancaster, PA 17603-4117
Tel (717) 672-9611 *Founded/Ownrshp* 1946, 1996
Sales 228.8MM^E *EMP* 955
SIC 2426 Flooring, hardwood; Parquet flooring, hardwood
Pr: Donald Maier
* *Treas:* Douglas Bingham
* *VP:* Charles J Wilson
Sls Mgr: Andrew Hash

D-U-N-S 79-690-9844
ARMSTRONG HOLDINGS INC
(*Suby of* ARMSTRONG GROUP OF COMPANIES INC) ★
1 Armstrong Pl, Butler, PA 16001-1951
Tel (724) 283-0925 *Founded/Ownrshp* 1986
Sales 237.7MM^E *EMP* 1,000
SIC 1731 5999 7382 Safety & security specialization; Fire detection & burglar alarm systems specialization; Alarm signal systems; Security systems services
Pr: Jay L Sedwick
* *CFO:* Bryan Cipoletti
VP: Dave Wittmann
Dir Bus: Justin Grew
Dir IT: Tom Nicklas
VP Opers: Don Tacik
Opers Mgr: Roger Hughes

D-U-N-S 00-506-8028 IMP
ARMSTRONG INTERNATIONAL INC (MI)
816 Maple St, Three Rivers, MI 49093-2345
Tel (269) 273-1415 *Founded/Ownrshp* 1895
Sales 112.3MM^E *EMP* 250
SIC 3491 Steam traps; Pressure valves & regulators, industrial; Regulators (steam fittings)
CEO: Patrick Armstrong
Ch Bd: Merrill H Armstrong
Pr: David M Armstrong
CFO: Stephen P Gibson
Genl Mgr: Tom Grubka
Genl Mgr: Harriett Romig
IT Man: Paul Davis
IT Man: Tim McCollum
IT Man: John Shelley
Plnt Mgr: Dan Finlay
VP Sls: Rex Scare

D-U-N-S 00-686-8582
ARMSTRONG TRANSFER AND STORAGE CO INC/ARMSTRONG RELOCATION CO MEMPHIS (TN)
UNITED VAN LINES
3927 Winchester Rd, Memphis, TN 38118-4994
Tel (901) 363-1914 *Founded/Ownrshp* 1956
Sales 137.7MM^E *EMP* 980
SIC 4213

D-U-N-S 00-436-0756
ARMSTRONG UTILITIES INC
ARMSTRONG CABLE SERVICES
1 Armstrong Pl, Butler, PA 16001-1988
Tel (724) 283-0925 *Founded/Ownrshp* 1957
Sales 171.0MM^E *EMP* 550
SIC 4841 Cable television services
Pr: William C Stewart
VP: Christopher King
* *VP:* Jay L Sedwick
Dir IT: Janice Schnell
IT Man: Melvin Black
IT Man: Ken Hoover
IT Man: Lisa Leasure
IT Man: Renee Uram

D-U-N-S 13-955-7664 IMP/EXP
■ **ARMSTRONG WOOD PRODUCTS INC**
ARMSTRONG FLOORING
(*Suby of* ARMSTRONG WORLD INDUSTRIES INC) ★
2500 Columbia Ave, Lancaster, PA 17603-4117
Tel (800) 233-3823 *Founded/Ownrshp* 1998
Sales 424.3MM^E *EMP* 4,200
SIC 2426 Flooring, hardwood
CEO: Donald Maier
* *CEO:* Thomas B Mangas
* *CEO:* Frank J Ready
* *Treas:* Thomas Waters
* *VP:* Howard J Maymon

D-U-N-S 00-130-7792 IMP/EXP
▲ **ARMSTRONG WORLD INDUSTRIES INC** (PA)
2500 Columbia Ave Bldg 5b, Lancaster, PA 17603-4117
Tel (717) 397-0611 *Founded/Ownrshp* 1891
Sales 2.4MMM *EMP* 7,600
Accts Kpmg Llp Philadelphia Pennsy
Tkr Sym AWI *Exch* NYS
SIC 3646 3296 Ceiling systems, luminous; Acoustical board & tile, mineral wool
Pr: Victor D Grizzle
* *Ch Bd:* James J O'Connor
CFO: Brian L Macneal
CFO: Brian Macneal
Chf Cred: Mark A Hershey
Bd of Dir: Liesl Morell
Sr VP: Charlie Chiappone
Sr VP: Dave Cookson
Sr VP: David S Cookson
Sr VP: Ellen R Romano
VP: Patrick Barnds
VP: Richard Born
VP: Tom Ellis
VP: Bryan Hesse
VP: Donald Maier
VP: Stephen F McNamara
Exec: Lori Rowley
Board of Directors: Stan A Askren, James J Gaffney, Larry S McWilliams, James C Melville, John J Roberts, Gregory P Spivy, Roy W Templin, Cherryl Thomas

D-U-N-S 85-859-8568 IMP
ARMSTRONG WORTHINGTON VENTURE
WAVE
101 Lindenwood Dr Ste 350, Malvern, PA 19355-1744
Tel (610) 722-1200 *Founded/Ownrshp* 1992
Sales 188.4MM^E *EMP* 415
SIC 3446 5051 Acoustical suspension systems, metal; Iron & steel (ferrous) products
Pr: Rose Mary Clyburn
CFO: Michael George
CFO: Doug Wisel

D-U-N-S 00-169-5568 IMP/EXP
■ ARMY & AIR FORCE EXCHANGE SERVICE
AAFES
(*Suby of* UNITED STATES DEPARTMENT OF DEFENSE) ★
3911 S Walton Walker Blvd, Dallas, TX 75236-1598
Tel (214) 312-2011 *Founded/Ownrshp* 1941
Sales 8.5MMM^E *EMP* 35,000^E
SIC 5399 9711 Army-Navy goods; Army; Air Force;
CEO: Thomas Counter Shull
CEO: Janine Dumond
**CEO:* Thomas C Shull
**COO:* Michael P Howard
**CFO:* Renee Figge
**Chf Mktg O:* Ana Middleton
Ofcr: John Rakestraw
Sr VP: Jack Morris
VP: Joyce Bowers
VP: Mickey Bradford
VP: Michael Farren
VP: Timothy Kelly
VP: Richard Koloski
VP: Tom Lozier
VP: Mark Morell
VP: Sean Shaw
Exec: Valerie Sanchez
Dir Surg: Jack Ormbrek
Dir Soc: Yolanda Gonzalez
Dir Soc: Ray Lamy

D-U-N-S 13-170-7213
■ ARMY FLEET SUPPORT LLC
(*Suby of* L-3 COMMUNICATIONS CORP) ★
1117 Dilly Branch Rd, Fort Rucker, AL 36362
Tel (334) 598-0400 *Founded/Ownrshp* 2003
Sales 204.8MM^E *EMP* 4,122^E
SIC 7699 Aircraft & heavy equipment repair services
VP: Mark Wentlent
VP: James Budney
VP: Lowell Green
Prgrm Mgr: Pat Thomas
Genl Mgr: Edward Claunch
Dir IT: David Haley
Opers Mgr: Teck M Matthews
Ql Cn Mgr: Michael Olive

D-U-N-S 07-884-5499
■ ARMY FORCES COMMAND UNITED STATES
FORSCOM
(*Suby of* UNITED STATES DEPARTMENT OF THE ARMY) ★
4700 Knox St, Fort Bragg, NC 28310-0001
Tel (910) 570-7200 *Founded/Ownrshp* 2013
Sales NA *EMP* 15,000
SIC 9711 Air Force
Pr: Daniel Allyn
Snr Mgr: Paul Hurley

ARMY NATIONAL GUARD, DELAWARE
See NATIONAL GUARD DELAWARE

D-U-N-S 09-023-7947
ARMY NATIONAL GUARD PENNSYLVANIA
(*Suby of* PA DEPARTMENT OF MILITARY AND VETERANS AFFAIRS) ★
14th & Calder St, Harrisburg, PA 17103
Tel (717) 787-5113 *Founded/Ownrshp* 2000
Sales NA *EMP* 2,500
SIC 9711 National Guard;

D-U-N-S 07-878-0826
■ ARMY RESERVE COMMAND UNITED STATES
USARC
(*Suby of* UNITED STATES DEPARTMENT OF THE ARMY) ★
4710 Knox St, Fort Bragg, NC 28310-0001
Tel (910) 570-8472 *Founded/Ownrshp* 2013
Sales NA *EMP* 1,063^E
SIC 9711 Army;

D-U-N-S 07-956-3599
ARNETT PHYSICIAN GROUP PC
(*Suby of* INDIANA UNIVERSITY HOSPITAL) ★
2600 Greenbush St, Lafayette, IN 47904-2477
Tel (765) 448-8000 *Founded/Ownrshp* 1922, 2011
Sales 53.4MM^E *EMP* 1,300
SIC 8011 Clinic, operated by physicians; Health maintenance organization; General & family practice, physician/surgeon
Pr: Thomas Jones MD
Ex VP: James Brunnemer
**VP:* Thomas Meyer MD
Doctor: David L Mitchefynn MD

D-U-N-S 07-781-5397
ARNOLD & PORTER LLP
601 Massachusetts Ave Nw, Washington, DC 20001-3743
Tel (202) 942-5000 *Founded/Ownrshp* 1947
Sales 287.1MM^E *EMP* 1,500
SIC 8111 General practice law office
Ex Dir: Elizabeth Respess
Pt: Thad T Dameris
Pt: Tim J Frazer
Pt: Michael B Gerrard
Pt: Judy Hurley
Pt: Timothy R Macdonald
Pt: Lisanne Morales
Pt: Douglas A Winthrop
Mng Pt: Anne P Davis
Prin: Andrew Karron
Prin: Thomas Milch

ARNOLD ADVERTISING
See ARNOLD WORLDWIDE LLC

D-U-N-S 11-617-9763 IMP/EXP
ARNOLD FOODS CO INC
GEORGE WESTON BAKERIES
(*Suby of* BIMBO BAKERIES USA INC) ★
255 Business Center Dr # 200, Horsham, PA 19044-3424
Tel (215) 672-8010 *Founded/Ownrshp* 2013
Sales 628.5MM^E *EMP* 12,000
SIC 2051 5149 Bread, cake & related products; Bread, all types (white, wheat, rye, etc): fresh or frozen; Rolls, bread type: fresh or frozen; Groceries & related products
Pr: Gary Prince
**CFO:* Bill Petersen
VP: Richard M Lee Jr
Sfty Dirs: Anthony Grosso
Sfty Mgr: Derek Jackson
**Genl Couns:* Shelly W Seligman

D-U-N-S 02-644-5914
ARNOLD LOGISTICS LLC
(*Suby of* JHCI ACQUISITION INC) ★
3811 Dixon St, Des Moines, IA 50313-3907
Tel (515) 265-6171 *Founded/Ownrshp* 2010
Sales 2.9MM^E *EMP* 1,686^E
SIC 4789 Cargo loading & unloading services
CEO: Brian Lutt

D-U-N-S 00-895-4489 IMP/EXP
ARNOLD MACHINERY CO
DITCH WITCH INTERMOUNTAIN
2975 W 2100 S, Salt Lake City, UT 84119-1273
Tel (801) 972-4000 *Founded/Ownrshp* 1929
Sales 309.7MM *EMP* 450
Accts Grant Thornton Llp Salt Lake
SIC 5082 5084 5012 5083 General construction machinery & equipment; Mining machinery & equipment, except petroleum; Road construction & maintenance machinery; Excavating machinery & equipment; Lift trucks & parts; Trailers for trucks, new & used; Cultivating machinery & equipment
Pr: Kayden W Bell
Ch Bd: Alvin Richer
Pr: Russell Fleming
VP: Rex Mecham
VP: Tom O'Byrne
VP: Matt Sierverts
Brnch Mgr: Steve Bailey
Brnch Mgr: Branch Billings
Brnch Mgr: Mike Brown
Brnch Mgr: Dave Eulberg
Brnch Mgr: Cary Finkelstein

D-U-N-S 19-477-5438 IMP
■ ARNOLD MAGNETIC TECHNOLOGIES CORP
MAGNETIC TECHNOLOGY
(*Suby of* COMPASS DIVERSIFIED HOLDINGS) ★
770 Linden Ave, Rochester, NY 14625-2716
Tel (585) 385-9010 *Founded/Ownrshp* 2012
Sales 235.3MM^E *EMP* 870^E
SIC 3264 3499 Magnets, permanent: ceramic or ferrite; Magnets, permanent: metallic
Pr: Gordon H McNeil
**CFO:* Michael D Kaser
Treas: Margaret Zminda
Genl Mgr: Michael Stachura
CIO: Jerry Morgan
**CTO:* Jeremy Morgan
IT Man: Christian Erb

ARNOLD OIL COMPANY FUELS
See ARNOLD OIL CO OF AUSTIN GP LLC

D-U-N-S 06-241-6763
ARNOLD OIL CO OF AUSTIN GP LLC
ARNOLD OIL COMPANY FUELS
5909 Burleson Rd, Austin, TX 78744-1202
Tel (512) 476-2401 *Founded/Ownrshp* 1977
Sales 149.7MM^E *EMP* 300
SIC 5013 5172 Automotive supplies & parts; Lubricating oils & greases
CFO: Ann Nelson
Treas: Rhonda Arnold
VP: Steve Voges
Genl Mgr: Gary Gregory
IT Man: Scott Slaton
Site Mgr: Robert Madsen
Manager: Jerry Hart
Opers Mgr: Ken Whitaker
Sales Exec: Betty Davis
Mktg Mgr: Kurt Filbert
Manager: Dale Metting

D-U-N-S 06-405-0115
ARNOLD TRANSPORTATION SERVICES INC
3375 High Prairie Rd, Grand Prairie, TX 75050-4228
Tel (972) 986-3154 *Founded/Ownrshp* 1936
Sales 252.0MM^E *EMP* 600
SIC 4213 Trucking, except local
Pr: Mike Driggers
**Sec:* Obed Rivera Vp Fin
VP: Glenn Guest
Genl Mgr: Bob Brown
VP Opers: Bill Yohn
Sfty Dirs: Robert Ryan
Opers Mgr: Michael J Gregerson
Board of Directors: Max Fuller, Mike Green, Ray Harlin

D-U-N-S 01-917-6932
ARNOLD WORLDWIDE LLC
ARNOLD ADVERTISING
(*Suby of* HAVAS)
10 Summer St Ste 600, Boston, MA 02110-1292
Tel (617) 587-8000 *Founded/Ownrshp* 2000
Sales 116.6MM^E *EMP* 1,000
SIC 7311 8743 Advertising agencies; Public relations & publicity
CEO: Robert Leplae
Mng Pt: Tom Guerin
Mng Pt: Woody Kay
**Ch Bd:* Ronald Lawner
**Pr:* Francis Kelly
Pr: Corey Mitchell
COO: Lauren Forman
COO: Chris Geraghty
COO: Stephen Ruby
COO: Annita Tanini
**Chf Cred:* Jim Elliott
Chf Mktg O: Lisa Unsworth
Ofcr: Angela WEI
Ex VP: Stephen Badenhop
Ex VP: Bill Boch
Ex VP: Nisha Dass
Ex VP: Wade Devers
Ex VP: Jon Drawbaugh
Ex VP: Cheryl Eklind
Ex VP: Greg Johnson
Ex VP: John Petruney

D-U-N-S 07-834-4671
ARNOT HEALTH INC
600 Roe Ave, Elmira, NY 14905-1629
Tel (607) 737-4231 *Founded/Ownrshp* 2011
Sales 275.3MM *EMP* 3,200
SIC 8062 General medical & surgical hospitals
Pr: Robert Lambert
VP Opers: Mark Dworsky
Doctor: Jeremy Lux

D-U-N-S 06-462-0750
AROGAS INC
MR FUEL
1821 Sherman Dr Ste 200, Saint Charles, MO 63303-3965
Tel (636) 947-0255 *Founded/Ownrshp* 1970
Sales 262.4MM^E *EMP* 132
Accts Brown Smith Wallace Llc St C
SIC 5172 Petroleum products; Engine fuels & oils; Gasoline; Fuel oil
Pr: T Patrick Manning
**VP:* Kevin Manning

D-U-N-S 03-771-8277
AROOSTOOK MEDICAL CENTER INC
TAMC
(*Suby of* EMHS) ★
140 Academy St, Presque Isle, ME 04769-3171
Tel (207) 768-4000 *Founded/Ownrshp* 1912
Sales 116.2MM *EMP* 1,100
Accts Berry Dunn Mcneil & Parker Ll
SIC 8062 8011 8052 General medical & surgical hospitals; General & family practice, physician/surgeon; Intermediate care facilities
CEO: Sylvia Getman
Chf Rad: John Mullen
Pr: Mark Morrow
Pr: Zaina Sovani
COO: Bill Calhoun
CFO: Bruce Sandstrom
CFO: C Bruce Sandstrom
Treas: David Djones
Ofcr: Susan Forbes
Sr VP: Jack Ginty
Sr VP: Stephen Poitras
Sr VP: Thomas Umphrey
VP: John Doyle
VP: Roland Joy

AROPOSTALE
See AEROPOSTALE INC

D-U-N-S 82-503-6189 IMP
▲ AROTECH CORP
1229 Oak Valley Dr, Ann Arbor, MI 48108-9675
Tel (800) 281-0356 *Founded/Ownrshp* 1991
Sales 96.5MM *EMP* 523^E
Accts Bdo Usa Llp Grand Rapids Mic
Tkr Sym ARTX *Exch* NGM
SIC 3691 3694 Batteries, rechargeable; Battery charging alternators & generators; Battery charging generators, automobile & aircraft
Pr: Steven Esses
**Ch Bd:* Jon B Kutler
CFO: Thomas J Paup
Board of Directors: Carol J Battershell, Kenneth W Cappell, Lawrence F Hagenbuch, Michael E Marrus, James J Quinn, Richard I Rudy

D-U-N-S 78-869-1561
ARPIN GROUP INC
ARPIN VAN LINES
99 James P Murphy Ind Hwy, West Warwick, RI 02893-2382
Tel (401) 828-8111 *Founded/Ownrshp* 1900
Sales 107.8MM^E *EMP* 555
SIC 4213 Contract haulers
**Pt:* Peter Arpin
COO: Matt Dolan
**CFO:* Michael Killoran
VP: Brian Asay
VP: Conrad Swanson
Genl Mgr: Keith Gilbert
IT Man: Donald Frasier
Mktg Dir: Ricardo Seyffert

ARPIN VAN LINES
See ARPIN GROUP INC

ARPOL
See NEXEO SOLUTIONS LLC

D-U-N-S 13-177-7328
ARR INVESTMENTS INC
A R R LEARNING CENTERS
2600 E Jackson St, Orlando, FL 32803-6314
Tel (407) 894-8401 *Founded/Ownrshp* 1996
Sales 22.9MM^E *EMP* 1,000
SIC 8351 8211 Child day care services; Catholic elementary & secondary schools
Pr: Alex Rodriguez

ARR MAZ PRODUCTS
See ARR-MAZ CUSTOM CHEMICALS INC

ARR-MAZ CUSTOM CHEMICALS
See ARR-MAZ PRODUCTS LP

D-U-N-S 03-210-4478 IMP
ARR-MAZ CUSTOM CHEMICALS INC
ARR MAZ PRODUCTS
4800 State Road 60 E, Mulberry, FL 33860-7905
Tel (863) 578-1206 *Founded/Ownrshp* 2003
Sales 93.9MM^E *EMP* 241
SIC 2869 Industrial organic chemicals
Pr: Dave Keselica
**Pr:* Patrick G Lavin
Pr: Doug Vanorsdale
**CFO:* Ronald S Lueptow
**Chf Mktg O:* Jeff Walker
Chf Mktg O: Jeffrey Walker
**Sr VP:* John Davis
**VP:* Patricia Yonker Arscott
**VP:* Paul Kern
**VP:* Jason Lewis
**VP:* Dan Partin
VP: Patricia R Scott
**VP:* Doug Van Orsdale
VP: James Vanorsdale

D-U-N-S 09-298-3139 IMP
ARR-MAZ PRODUCTS LP
ARR-MAZ CUSTOM CHEMICALS
(*Suby of* AMZ HOLDING CORP) ★
4800 State Road 60 E, Mulberry, FL 33860-7905
Tel (863) 578-1206 *Founded/Ownrshp* 1994, 2008
Sales 95.8MM^E *EMP* 220
SIC 2899 2869 Chemical preparations; Industrial organic chemicals
Pt: Hank Waters
Pt: William Cook
Pt: Ronald S Lueptow
Pt: Doug Vanorsdall
Pt: Jeffrey Walker
Pr: Patrick Lavin
VP: Chris Day
VP: Paul Kern
VP: Dan Partin
VP: Sam Sutherland
VP: Vido Vareika

D-U-N-S 00-404-7838
▲ ARRAY BIOPHARMA INC
3200 Walnut St, Boulder, CO 80301-2514
Tel (303) 381-6600 *Founded/Ownrshp* 1998
Sales 137.8MM *EMP* 177^E
Accts Securities And Exchange Commis
Tkr Sym ARRY *Exch* NGM
SIC 2834 Pharmaceutical preparations
CEO: Ron Squarer
**Ch Bd:* Kyle A Lefkoff
COO: Andrew R Robbins
CFO: Jason Haddock
Ofcr: Nicholas A Saccomano
Ofcr: Victor Sandor
VP: Gary M Clark
VP: John R Moore
VP: James Winkler
Prgrm Mgr: Tomas Kaplan
Board of Directors: Charles M Baum, Gwen A Fyfe, John A Orwin, Gil J Van Lunsen

ARRIS
See PACE AMERICAS LLC

D-U-N-S 03-762-5550
ARRIS GROUP INC
3871 Lakefield Dr Ste 300, Suwanee, GA 30024-1292
Tel (678) 473-2907 *Founded/Ownrshp* 2012
Sales 5.3MMM *EMP* 6,500
SIC 7372 3663 3357 7373 3661 Prepackaged software; Radio & TV communications equipment; Cable television equipment; Television broadcasting & communications equipment; Satellites, communications; Nonferrous wiredrawing & insulating; Fiber optic cable (insulated); Systems integration services; Telephone & telegraph apparatus
CEO: Robert J Stanzione
Pr: Ronald M Coppock
Pr: Bruce McClelland
Pr: Tim O'Loughlin
Pr: Larry Robinson
CFO: David B Potts
Sr VP: Phil Baldock
Sr VP: James R Brennan
Sr VP: Vickie Brewster
Sr VP: Patrick Macken
VP: Jim Brennan
VP: Stan Brovont
VP: John Burke
VP: Jerry Cederlund
VP: Jay Chambers
VP: Phillip Chapman
VP: Charlie Cheevers
VP: Susan George
VP: Evan Groat
VP: Elaine Guan
VP: Steve Herbst

D-U-N-S 80-719-6852 IMP
ARRIS INTERNATIONAL INC
(*Suby of* ARRIS GROUP INC) ★
3871 Lakefield Dr Ste 300, Suwanee, GA 30024-1292
Tel (678) 473-2000 *Founded/Ownrshp* 2001
Sales 133.3MM^E *EMP* 731
SIC 3663 Radio & TV communications equipment; Cable television equipment; Television broadcasting & communications equipment; Satellites, communications
Ch Bd: Robert J Stanzione
**Pr:* Ron Coppock
**Pr:* Bryant Isaacs
**Pr:* James Larkin
**Pr:* Robert Puccini
**CFO:* Lawrence A Margolis
**Treas:* Marc Geraci
**Sr VP:* David B Potts
**VP:* Debbie Marry
**VP:* Ruben Sanchez
Snr Mgr: Alan H Hoover
Board of Directors: Alex B Best, Harry L Bosco, John Ian Anderson Craig, Matthew B Kearney, William H Lambert, John R Petty

D-U-N-S 83-741-1714 IMP/EXP
ARRIS SOLUTIONS INC
(*Suby of* ARRIS GROUP INC) ★
3871 Lakefield Dr Ste 300, Suwanee, GA 30024-1292
Tel (678) 473-2000 *Founded/Ownrshp* 2007
Sales 1.2MMM^E *EMP* 6,500

SIC 3661 3663 3357 Telephone & telegraph apparatus; Radio & TV communications equipment; Cable television equipment; Television broadcasting & communications equipment; Satellites, communications; Fiber optic cable (insulated); Coaxial cable, nonferrous
Pr: Robert J Stanzione
**CFO:* David B Potts
**VP:* Ronald M Coppock
**VP:* Lawrence A Margolis
VP: Robert Puccini
**VP:* Brent Sharp

D-U-N-S 00-218-3333
ARRIS TECHNOLOGY INC
(*Suby of* ARRIS GROUP INC) ★
3871 Lakefield Dr, Suwanee, GA 30024-1292
Tel (678) 473-2907 *Founded/Ownrshp* 1997, 2013
Sales 401.4MM^E *EMP* 2,000
SIC 7372 3825 Application computer software; Network analyzers
CFO: David Potts
**Pr:* Robert J Stanzione
**Treas:* Richard C Smith
**Ex VP:* Lawrence A Margolis
VP: Mike Laraia
Ql Cn Mgr: David Miller
Sales Exec: Rob Mc Laughlin
Mktg Mgr: Zenita Henderson
Mktg Mgr: Kevin O'Leary

D-U-N-S 17-479-7944 IMP
ARRO CORP
7440 Santa Fe Dr, Hodgkins, IL 60525-5022
Tel (708) 352-8200 *Founded/Ownrshp* 1995
Sales 715.6MM^E *EMP* 400
SIC 5141 Groceries, general line
Pr: Patrick Gaughan
IT Man: Alex Alia

D-U-N-S 04-915-9957 IMP
▲ ARROW ELECTRONICS INC
9201 E Dry Creek Rd, Centennial, CO 80112-2818
Tel (303) 824-4000 *Founded/Ownrshp* 1935
Sales 23.2MMM *EMP* 18,500^E
Tkr Sym ARW *Exch* NYS
SIC 5065 5045 Electronic parts & equipment; Electronic parts; Semiconductor devices; Computer peripheral equipment
Ch Bd: Michael J Long
Pr: Sean J Kerins
Pr: Andy King
Pr: Charles F Kostalnick II
Pr: Carolyn Pisel
CFO: Paul J Reilly
CFO: Chris Stansbury
CFO: Christopher D Stansbury
Treas: Michael Taunton
Bd of Dir: Sharad Kulkarni
Ofcr: M Catherine Morris
Sr VP: Vincent P Melvin
Sr VP: Gregory P Tarpinian
Sr VP: Gretchen K Zech
VP: Bill Foster
VP: Mark Hagan
VP: Ernest Keith
VP: Raime Muhle
VP: Leonie Tipton
VP: David West
Board of Directors: Philip K Asherman, Gail E Hamilton, John N Hanson, Richard S Hill, M Fran Keeth, Andrew C Kerin, Stephen C Patrick, Barry W Perry

D-U-N-S 82-916-0865
■ ARROW ENTERPRISE COMPUTING SOLUTIONS INC
(*Suby of* ARROW ELECTRONICS INC) ★
7459 S Lima St Bldg 2, Englewood, CO 80112-3879
Tel (303) 824-7650 *Founded/Ownrshp* 1987
Sales 739.6MM^E *EMP* 99^E
SIC 5045 Computers, peripherals & software
Pr: Michael J Long
**VP:* Andrew C Kerin
VP: Sean Kerins

D-U-N-S 03-362-4909
ARROW EXTERMINATORS INC
8613 Roswell Rd Bldg 4, Atlanta, GA 30350-1827
Tel (770) 993-8705 *Founded/Ownrshp* 1978
Sales 160.0MM *EMP* 1,450
SIC 1742 7342 1521 1542 Plastering, drywall & insulation; Termite control; Pest control in structures; Single-family housing construction; Nonresidential construction
CEO: Emily Thomas Kendrick
**Ch Bd:* James Stark Thomas
**COO:* Tim Pollard
**Sec:* Michael Barry Thomas
Sr VP: Kevin Malone
**Sr VP:* Brent Purcell
VP: Tommy Giardino
VP: Glenn Glover
VP: Heather Gordy
**VP:* Joey Holland
VP: Marie Horner
VP: Chuck Longenecker
VP: Mike Malone

D-U-N-S 00-149-5746 IMP
■ ARROW FASTENER CO LLC
(*Suby of* MASCO CORP) ★
271 Mayhill St, Saddle Brook, NJ 07663-5395
Tel (201) 843-6900 *Founded/Ownrshp* 2009
Sales 125.8MM^E *EMP* 400
SIC 3579 3315 3452 3542 2891 3586 Stapling machines (hand or power); Staples, steel: wire or cut; Rivets, metal; Riveting machines; Glue; Grease guns (lubricators)
Pr: Gary Duboff
Dir IT: Ajay Kamble

D-U-N-S 11-972-3401
▲ ARROW FINANCIAL CORP
250 Glen St, Glens Falls, NY 12801-3505
Tel (518) 745-1000 *Founded/Ownrshp* 1983
Sales NA *EMP* 516^E
Accts Kpmg Llp Albany New York
Tkr Sym AROW *Exch* NGS

SIC 6021 National commercial banks
Pr: Thomas J Murphy
**Ch Bd:* Thomas L Hoy
CFO: Terry R Goodemote
Ofcr: Laura Vamvalis
Ex VP: Kathleen Kelleher
Sr VP: David S Demarco
Sr VP: David Kaiser
VP: Jim Brown
VP Mktg: Timothy Badger

D-U-N-S 00-452-4450 IMP/EXP
ARROW INTERNATIONAL INC
9900 Clinton Rd, Cleveland, OH 44144-1097
Tel (216) 961-3500 *Founded/Ownrshp* 1965
Sales 249.0MM^E *EMP* 1,161^E
SIC 3944 Board games, puzzles & models, except electronic
CEO: John E Gallagher
VP: David M Delgado
VP: Joel Horne
VP: Richard Kurman
VP: Nancy J Parker
VP: Greg Pollock
**Prin:* Edward J Maher
**Prin:* Robert E Sweeney
Snr Sftwr: Erik Mathisen
Snr Ntwrk: Brad Jones
CTO: Mac McElroy

D-U-N-S 07-283-1415 IMP
■ ARROW INTERNATIONAL INC
TELEFLEX
(*Suby of* TELEFLEX INC) ★
550 E Swedesford Rd # 400, Wayne, PA 19087-1601
Tel (610) 225-6800 *Founded/Ownrshp* 1989
Sales 863.1MM^E *EMP* 4,000
SIC 3841 3844 Catheters; Therapeutic X-ray apparatus & tubes
Pr: John E Gallagher
**Sec:* Catherine Gallagher
VP: Jim Fitzpatrick
**VP:* Dennis P Gallagher
Mfg Dir: Sandy Feick
Manager: Jeff Gauthier

D-U-N-S 19-446-1448
ARROW MOTOR & PUMP INC
629 Cent St, Wyandotte, MI 48192
Tel (734) 285-7860 *Founded/Ownrshp* 2006
Sales 200.0MM^E *EMP* 30
SIC 7694 5063 7699 5084 Electric motor repair; Motors, electric; Pumps & pumping equipment repair; Pumps & pumping equipment
Pr: Nancy Prohaska
Sls Mgr: John Prohaska

ARROW PRESCRIPTION CENTER
See FAMILYMEDS GROUP INC

D-U-N-S 15-213-0931
■ ARROW SYSTEMS INTEGRATION INC
SHARED SOLUTIONS AND SERVICES
(*Suby of* ARROW ELECTRONICS INC) ★
1820 Preston Park Blvd # 2800, Plano, TX 75093-3685
Tel (972) 462-5800 *Founded/Ownrshp* 2010
Sales 398.5MM^E *EMP* 1,000
SIC 4813 1731 5999 Data telephone communications; Local telephone communications; Long distance telephone communications; Voice telephone communications; Telephone & telephone equipment installation; Telephone equipment & systems
Pr: Mike Bevilacqua
**CFO:* Tim Kick
CFO: Denny Maunder
Ex VP: John Waenbergh
VP: Dan Herhold
VP: Kerry Jenkins
VP: Jimmie Morton
VP: Andrew Paquin
VP: Ed Root
VP: Jack Sanders
VP: Tony Verna
VP: Mark Wechsler

ARROW THOMPSON METALS
See THOMPSON STEEL CO INC

D-U-N-S 02-982-2178 EXP
ARROW TRUCK SALES INC
(*Suby of* VNA HOLDING INC) ★
3200 Manchester Trfy I-70, Kansas City, MO 64129-1336
Tel (816) 923-5000 *Founded/Ownrshp* 1950
Sales 186.2MM^E *EMP* 313
SIC 5521 5012 Trucks, tractors & trailers: used; Truck tractors; Trailers for trucks, new & used
Pr: Steven Clough
**CFO:* Ryan Sherwood
VP: Mary Frear
VP: Lee Wallace
Brnch Mgr: Kevin Buehner
Brnch Mgr: Chad Fine
Brnch Mgr: Doug Moravec
Dir IT: Mark Samuel
Mktg Dir: Don Mueller
Mktg Mgr: Lane Bartram
Sls Mgr: Billie Britton

D-U-N-S 16-878-9142
ARROW USA
1105 Highland Ct, Beaumont, CA 92223-7091
Tel (951) 845-6144 *Founded/Ownrshp* 2000
Sales 500.0MM *EMP* 75
SIC 5087 Beauty salon & barber shop equipment & supplies
Pr: Sam Chang
**Pr:* Zuhair Klenzi
**Treas:* Wen Zhang
**VP:* S Kalanzeh

D-U-N-S 15-753-7929
■ ARROWHEAD GENERAL INSURANCE AGENCY INC
(*Suby of* ARROWHEAD MANAGEMENT CO) ★
701 B St Ste 2100, San Diego, CA 92101-8197
Tel (619) 881-8600 *Founded/Ownrshp* 1983
Sales NA *EMP* 250

SIC 6331 6411 Automobile insurance; Insurance agents, brokers & service
CEO: Chris L Walker
**Genl Pt:* Peter C Arrowsmith
**Pr:* Steve Boyd
Pr: Wendy Castelo
Pr: Robert T Kingsley
**Pr:* Stephen M Lesieur
**CFO:* D McDonald Armstrong
**Founder:* Brion Applegate
Ex VP: Caroline Barwick
**Ex VP:* Steve Bouker
**Ex VP:* Gary Kadota
Ex VP: Mark Richardson
Sr VP: Ronald Barnett
**Sr VP:* Scott Marshall
VP: Chris Booker
VP: Ron Casner
VP: Brian Jirak
VP: Jason Lovell
VP: Paul McIntosh
VP: Karen Mynsted
VP: Niels Seebeck

ARROWHEAD HOSPITAL
See ACHMC INC

D-U-N-S 15-908-8772
■ ARROWHEAD MANAGEMENT CO
(*Suby of* ARROWHEAD GENERAL INSURANCE AGENCY SUPERHOLDING CORPORATION)
701 B St Ste 2100, San Diego, CA 92101-8197
Tel (800) 669-1889 *Founded/Ownrshp* 1986
Sales NA *EMP* 508
SIC 6411 8741 Insurance agents, brokers & service; Administrative management
Ch Bd: Patrick Kilkenny
**Sec:* Marianne Harmon
QA Dir: Linh Nguyen
Sftwr Eng: Mike Darnaud
Mktg Mgr: Todd Drake

D-U-N-S 84-990-5286 IMP
ARROWHEAD PRODUCTS CORP
(*Suby of* INDUSTRIAL MANUFACTURING CO LLC) ★
4411 Katella Ave, Los Alamitos, CA 90720-3599
Tel (714) 828-7770 *Founded/Ownrshp* 1968
Sales 228.8MM^E *EMP* 640
SIC 3728 Aircraft parts & equipment
CEO: Daniel P Bradford
CFO: Dick Hoff
Treas: Robert Bosi
Ex VP: David S Larner
VP: Chris Buntin
VP: John Curci
**VP:* Bill Gardner
VP: James Geringswald
VP: Bill Lyon
VP: Sherry Nemarnik
VP: Steve Schwarz
Exec: Bob Sweet

D-U-N-S 03-433-2358
ARROWHEAD REGIONAL MEDICAL CENTER
ARMC
(*Suby of* COUNTY OF SAN BERNARDINO) ★
400 N Pepper Ave, Colton, CA 92324-1819
Tel (909) 580-1000 *Founded/Ownrshp* 1952
Sales 468.9MM *EMP* 2,500
SIC 8062 General medical & surgical hospitals
Dir Lab: Theodore Friedman
Prgrm Mgr: Carol Farrell
Nurse Mgr: Claire Ciresa
Mtls Mgr: Dale Conrad
Pathlgst: Carolyn Leach
Ansthlgy: Joseph Galura
Doctor: Remy Piibe
Cert Phar: Maria L Garibaldi
Diag Rad: Chandler Shyu
Pgrm Dir: Dennis Carden

D-U-N-S 00-698-9735
ARROWOOD INDEMNITY CO
ROYAL & SUNALLIANCE
(*Suby of* ARROWPOINT CAPITAL CORP) ★
3600 Arco Corporate Dr, Charlotte, NC 28273-8100
Tel (704) 522-2000 *Founded/Ownrshp* 1910, 1978
Sales NA *EMP* 290
SIC 6331 Property damage insurance; Fire, marine & casualty insurance & carriers
CEO: John Tighe
COO: Dennis Cahill
**CFO:* Sean Beatty
CFO: Joe Fisher
CFO: Ernie Frohboese
Sr VP: George Juzdan
Sr VP: Daniel Reppert
Sr VP: Paul Stewman
VP: David Davenport
VP: Greg Madson
VP: Steve Ward

D-U-N-S 17-949-2640
ARROWPOINT CAPITAL CORP
3600 Arco Corporate Dr, Charlotte, NC 28273-8100
Tel (704) 522-2000 *Founded/Ownrshp* 2006
Sales NA *EMP* 300^E
SIC 6331 Fire, marine & casualty insurance & carriers
Pr: John Tighe
COO: Terry Broderick
**COO:* Dennis Cahill
**CFO:* Sean Beatty
CFO: Kathy Crawford
CFO: John Rzepinski
Treas: Gwyn Fuller
**Ofcr:* Julie Fortune
Ofcr: Andre Lefebvre
IT Man: Alicia Andrews
Pgrm Dir: Christine McGough
Board of Directors: Michael Crall, Edward J Muhl, Larry Simmons

D-U-N-S 80-060-6720
ARS INVESTMENT HOLDINGS LLC
965 Ridge Lake Blvd # 201, Memphis, TN 38120-9401
Tel (901) 271-9700 *Founded/Ownrshp* 2006
Sales NA *EMP* 7,700

SIC 6719 Investment holding companies, except banks
COO: David Slott
**CFO:* Jim McMahon
**VP:* Mike Noonan

ARS OF MEMPHIS
See AMERICAN RESIDENTIAL SERVICES LLC

D-U-N-S 01-103-0355
ARSENAL CAPITAL PARTNERS LP
100 Park Ave Fl 31, New York, NY 10017-5584
Tel (212) 771-1717 *Founded/Ownrshp* 2000
Sales 689.7MM^E *EMP* 1,440
SIC 6722 Management investment, open-end
Mng Pt: Terrence Mullen
Pt: Donald Deieso
Pt: Eugene Gorbach
Pt: Jeffrey Kovach
Pt: Joelle Marquis
Pt: Stephen M McLean
Pt: Frank Scrudato
Pt: John Televantos
Pt: Timothy Zappala
CFO: Joseph Croasdale
Ex VP: Mary Driscoll
VP: Eric Geveda
VP: Joe Rooney

D-U-N-S 03-485-7555
ARSENS HOME CARE INC
SARAHCARE HOME HEALTH AGENCY
101 Washington Ln Ste G6, Jenkintown, PA 19046-3532
Tel (215) 663-8090 *Founded/Ownrshp* 2010
Sales 19.0MM *EMP* 1,300
SIC 8082 Home health care services
CEO: Arsen Ustayev

D-U-N-S 83-062-0659
ARSG INC
ALLIANCE RETAIL SERVICE GROUP
3870 E Eagle Dr, Anaheim, CA 92807-1706
Tel (714) 666-6650 *Founded/Ownrshp* 2009
Sales 2.5MM *EMP* 2,000
SIC 7389 Inventory stocking service
CEO: Joseph Smith
**COO:* Tim Nelke
**CFO:* Cynthia Simms

D-U-N-S 07-798-2361 IMP
ART CENTER COLLEGE OF DESIGN INC
1700 Lida St, Pasadena, CA 91103-1999
Tel (626) 396-2200 *Founded/Ownrshp* 1932
Sales 94.1MM *EMP* 400
Accts Moss Adams Llp Stockton Ca
SIC 8221 Colleges & universities
Pr: Lorne M Buchman
CFO: Glenn Baker
CFO: Ronald C Jernigan
Trst: Maria Contreras-Sweet
Ex VP: Marvin Woods
**Sr VP:* Kit Baron
Sr VP: Michael A Bermn
**Sr VP:* George E Falardau
**Sr VP:* George Falardeau
**Sr VP:* Rich Haluschak
Sr VP: Scarlett P Osterling
VP: Nick Laes
VP: Jill Strawbridge
VP: Dyan Sublett
Exec: Michael Berman
Exec: Ross Lamanna
Assoc Dir: Laura Flower
Assoc Dir: Courtney Stricklin

D-U-N-S 06-847-8353 IMP
ART INSTITUTE OF CHICAGO
GENE SISKEL FILM CENTER
111 S Michigan Ave, Chicago, IL 60603-6488
Tel (312) 443-3600 *Founded/Ownrshp* 1879
Sales 312.8MM *EMP* 1,035
SIC 8412 8299

ART STORE CENTER
See MARYLAND INSTITUTE

D-U-N-S 02-924-9083 IMP
ART SUPPLY ENTERPRISES INC
MACPHERSON'S
1375 Ocean Ave, Emeryville, CA 94608-1128
Tel (510) 768-6633 *Founded/Ownrshp* 1906
Sales 128.4MM *EMP* 190
Accts Shea Labagh Dobberstein Cpas
SIC 5199 Artists' materials
Ch: Stuart Beattie
**Pr:* Rich Rusnack
**CEO:* Frank Stapleton
**COO:* Jim Semitekol
**VP:* Natasha Nicholson Bjerre
**VP:* Edo Van Der Burgt
**CIO:* Greg Bjerre
**VP Sls:* Steve Robinson

D-U-N-S 01-743-3988 IMP
ART VAN FURNITURE INC
6500 E 14 Mile Rd, Warren, MI 48092-1295
Tel (586) 939-2100 *Founded/Ownrshp* 1959
Sales 600.0MM *EMP* 3,000
Accts Pricewaterhousecoopers Llp De
SIC 5712 Furniture stores
CEO: Kim Yost
**Ch Bd:* Archie A Van Elslander
**Pr:* David Van Elslander
**Pr:* Gary Van Eslander
**Sec:* Mary Ann Van Elslander
Sr VP: Diana Sikes
**VP:* Michael C Bolton
VP: Steve Glucksman
VP: Jeanette McNamara
Dir Soc: Karen Gilbert
Advt Dir: Julie Kennedy

D-U-N-S 15-229-5788 EXP
ART.COM INC
2100 Powell St Fl 10th, Emeryville, CA 94608-1893
Tel (510) 879-4700 *Founded/Ownrshp* 2006
Sales 207.0MM^E *EMP* 800
SIC 5999 Posters
CEO: Geoffroy Martin

Ofcr: Ivy Ross
Sr VP: Bob Inman
Sr VP: Lesa Musatto
VP: Terry Hill
VP: Kevin Lucas
VP: Michael Marston
VP: Isis Murillo
VP: Anna Punsal
VP: Rick Salvadore
Prgrm Mgr: Youngah Lee
Board of Directors: A George Battle, Sharon McCollam

ARTCARVED
See COMMEMORATIVE BRANDS INC

ARTCO
See AMERICAN RIVER TRANSPORTATION CO LLC

D-U-N-S 78-005-3299 IMP
ARTCO (US) INC
BROOKHOLLOW
(*Suby of* OCCASIONS GROUP INC) ★
1 Stationery Pl, Rexburg, ID 83441-5000
Tel (208) 359-1000 *Founded/Ownrshp* 2006
Sales 163.3MM^E^ *EMP* 250
SIC 5112 2759 Stationery; Commercial printing
Pr: Dan Sandell
VP: Gordon Rhiger

D-U-N-S 78-804-5409
ARTECH INFORMATION SYSTEMS LLC
360 Mount Kemble Ave # 2, Morristown, NJ 07960-6662
Tel (973) 998-2500 *Founded/Ownrshp* 1999
Sales 470.2MM^E^ *EMP* 4,000
SIC 7371 7379 Computer software development; Computer related consulting services
VP: Lynel Derose
VP: Varun Mehra
VP: Dannie Wasylak
VP: Theresa Zandi
Dir Bus: Adam Weir
Ex Dir: Dianne Bogert
MIS Mgr: Rob Loglisci

D-U-N-S 07-892-8223 IMP
ARTESYN EMBEDDED COMPUTING INC
(*Suby of* ARTISAN EMBEDDED TECHNOLOGY) ★
2900 S Diablo Way Ste 190, Tempe, AZ 85282-3202
Tel (602) 438-5720 *Founded/Ownrshp* 2013
Sales 2.6MMM^E^ *EMP* 23,000
SIC 3829 Instrument board gauges, automotive: computerized
CEO: Jay L Geldmacher
**CFO:* Nate Myer
VP: Linda Craig
**VP:* Eva M Kalawski
**VP:* Mary Ann Sigler
**VP:* Brian Walsh
VP: Todd Wynia
CTO: Pam Cavey
MIS Mgr: George Matykowski

D-U-N-S 04-493-0139 IMP
ARTESYN EMBEDDED TECHNOLOGIES INC
ARTISAN EMBEDDED TECHNOLOGY
(*Suby of* PLATINUM EQUITY LLC) ★
2900 S Diablo Way Ste 190, Tempe, AZ 85282-3202
Tel (800) 759-1107 *Founded/Ownrshp* 2013
Sales 5.5MMM^E^ *EMP* 23,000
SIC 3679 3577 3571 7629 5045 Static power supply converters for electronic applications; Power supplies, all types: static; Computer peripheral equipment; Input/output equipment, computer; Data conversion equipment, media-to-media: computer; Electronic computers; Electronic equipment repair; Computers, peripherals & software
CEO: Jay L Geldmacher
**CFO:* Nate Myer
**VP:* Brian Walsh
Board of Directors: Eva M Kalawski, Jacob Kotzubei, Mary Ann Sigler

D-U-N-S 10-850-0810 IMP
ARTESYN NORTH AMERICA LLC
(*Suby of* ARTISAN EMBEDDED TECHNOLOGY) ★
7575 Market Place Dr, Eden Prairie, MN 55344-3637
Tel (952) 392-6500 *Founded/Ownrshp* 1998
Sales 924.3MM^E^ *EMP* 23,000
SIC 3679 7629 Power supplies, all types: static; Electronic equipment repair
CTO: Gary Drever

D-U-N-S 13-174-7628 IMP/EXP
ARTHREX INC
1370 Creekside Blvd, Naples, FL 34108-1945
Tel (239) 643-5553 *Founded/Ownrshp* 1991
Sales 435.6MM^E^ *EMP* 1,200
SIC 3841 Surgical & medical instruments
Pr: Reinhold D Schmieding
CFO: John Cheek
**Treas:* Kathleen D Sparrow
Sr VP: Shawn Buskey
VP: Kevin Grieff
**VP:* R Scott Price
VP Bus Dev: Paula Wegman
Exec: Francesca Miani
Dir Soc: Evelyn McCarthy
CTO: Michael Koszewnik
QA Dir: Hank Buikema

D-U-N-S 83-457-0533
ARTHROCARE CORP
(*Suby of* SMITH&NEPHEW) ★
7000 W William Cannon Dr # 1, Austin, TX 78735-8509
Tel (512) 391-3900 *Founded/Ownrshp* 2014
Sales 174.8MM *EMP* 1,840^E^
SIC 3841 Surgical & medical instruments
Pr: David Fitzgerald
**COO:* Todd Newton
**Ofcr:* Gayle Wiley
**Sr VP:* Richard Rew
**Sr VP:* Jean Woloszko
VP: John Raffle
Ql Cn Mgr: Sarah Larson
Mktg Dir: Karl Ring
Sls Mgr: Donna Brandon
Sls Mgr: Mike Cunningham
Corp Couns: Brian Szymczak

D-U-N-S 03-179-2773
ARTHUR COMPANIES INC
AGRESOURCE
429 Main St, Arthur, ND 58006
Tel (701) 967-8312 *Founded/Ownrshp* 1971
Sales 422.8MM *EMP* 100
SIC 5153

D-U-N-S 00-791-4989 IMP/EXP
ARTHUR H THOMAS CO (PA)
THOMAS SCIENTIFIC
1654 High Hill Rd, Swedesboro, NJ 08085-1780
Tel (856) 467-2000 *Founded/Ownrshp* 1900, 1943
Sales 112.4MM^E^ *EMP* 300^E^
SIC 3821 5049 Laboratory equipment: fume hoods, distillation racks, etc.; Scientific & engineering equipment & supplies
Ch: Robert D Patterson
**COO:* Paul F Seliskar
**CFO:* Craig D Kingery
Treas: Edward L Sudnick
VP: Dennis McDonough
VP: Stephen Tolmie
**Prin:* Edward B Patterson Jr
CTO: John Hughs
Mktg Dir: Brian Emmons
Mktg Mgr: Lee Smith
Manager: Stu Geisser

D-U-N-S 07-442-4540
▲ ARTHUR J GALLAGHER & CO
2 Pierce Pl, Itasca, IL 60143-1203
Tel (630) 773-3800 *Founded/Ownrshp* 1927
Sales NA *EMP* 21,542
Accts Ernst & Young Llp Chicago Il
Tkr Sym AJG *Exch* NYS
SIC 6411 6282 8741 Insurance brokers; Insurance information & consulting services; Investment advice; Financial management for business
Ch Bd: J Patrick Gallagher Jr
Pr: Joel D Cavaness
Pr: James W Durkin Jr
Pr: James S Gault
Pr: Scott R Hudson
CFO: Douglas K Howell
Ch: Thomas J Gallagher
Ofcr: Susan E Pietrucha
VP: Walter D Bay
Board of Directors: Sherry S Barrat, William L Bax, D John Coldman, Frank E English Jr, Elbert O Hand, David S Johnson, Kay W McCurdy, Ralph J Nicoletti, Norman L Rosenthal

D-U-N-S 61-296-2878
■ ARTHUR J GALLAGHER & CO (ILLINOIS)
(*Suby of* ARTHUR J GALLAGHER & CO) ★
2 Pierce Pl Ste 100, Itasca, IL 60143-1293
Tel (630) 773-3800 *Founded/Ownrshp* 1960
Sales NA *EMP* 7,100
Accts Ernst & Young Llp Chicago Il
SIC 6411 Insurance agents, brokers & service
Pr: J Patrick Gallagher
**CFO:* Doug Howell
**Treas:* Jack H Lazearo
VP: Cindy Comeaux
IT Man: Jim O"brien

D-U-N-S 00-340-7897
ARTHUR J GLATFELTER AGENCY INC (PA)
GLATFELTER INSURANCE GROUP
183 Leaders Heights Rd, York, PA 17402-4714
Tel (717) 741-0911 *Founded/Ownrshp* 1951
Sales NA *EMP* 525
SIC 6411 8742 Insurance agents, brokers & service; Management consulting services
CEO: Anthony P Campisi
**Ch Bd:* Arthur J Glatfelter
Pr: Jim Patridge
**Pr:* Mark S Schmidt
**Pr:* Arthur B Seifert
**CFO:* Thomas Clements
VP: Peggy A Amspacher
**VP:* Ray Fidler
CTO: Nichole Giedzinski
Dir IT: Cary Marion
Dir IT: Stephen Mercado
Board of Directors: Lawrence Brandon, Frank X Briel, Theodore C Flam, Thomas C Norris, Neil Schneider

D-U-N-S 01-223-4647 IMP/EXP
ARTHUR SCHUMAN INC
SCHUMAN CHEESE
40 New Dutch Ln, Fairfield, NJ 07004-2514
Tel (973) 227-0030 *Founded/Ownrshp* 1946
Sales 155.5MM^E^ *EMP* 350
SIC 2022 Cheese, natural & processed
CEO: Neal Schuman
Pr: Vincent Angiolillo
**COO:* Tom Deangelo
**CFO:* Larry Schaefer
Treas: Glenn Carrera
**VP:* Patrick O'Callaghan
Dir IT: Robert Castaldi
Manager: Jack Convery
Opers Mgr: Marta Rego-Capozzi
Ql Cn Mgr: Kevin Battel
Mktg Dir: Joan Allen

ARTIFICIAL KIDNEY CENTER RI
See BIO MEDICAL APPLICATIONS OF FLORIDA INC

D-U-N-S 00-446-9011 IMP
■ ARTIFLEX MANUFACTURING LLC
GERSTCO DIVISION
(*Suby of* WORTHINGTON INDUSTRIES INC) ★
1425 E Bowman St, Wooster, OH 44691-3185
Tel (330) 262-2015 *Founded/Ownrshp* 1860, 2011
Sales 158.1MM^E^ *EMP* 600
SIC 3465 3469 Body parts, automobile: stamped metal; Metal stampings
Pr: Erin Hoffmann
**CFO:* Ed Kurzenberger
Dir Bus: John Gloster
Prgrm Mgr: Jeremy Deemter
Prgrm Mgr: Harry Host
Mfg Dir: Steve Delmoro
QC Dir: Jeremy Boggs
Ql Cn Mgr: Kim Cardace
Ql Cn Mgr: Ruby Klotz
Ql Cn Mgr: Jim Young

ARTISAN EMBEDDED TECHNOLOGY
See ARTESYN EMBEDDED TECHNOLOGIES INC

D-U-N-S 07-876-7277
ARTISAN PARTNERS ASSET MANAGEMENT INC
875 E Wscnsin Ave Ste 800, Milwaukee, WI 53202
Tel (414) 390-6100 *Founded/Ownrshp* 1994
Sales 805.4MM *EMP* 345
Accts Pricewaterhousecoopers Llp Mi
Tkr Sym APAM *Exch* NYS
SIC 6282 Investment advice
Pr: Eric R Colson
**Ch Bd:* Andrew A Ziegler
CFO: Charles J Daley Jr
Sr VP: Gregory K Ramirez
Board of Directors: Matthew R Barger, Seth W Brennan, Stephanie G Dimarco, Jeffrey A Joerres

D-U-N-S 80-001-6289
ARTISTIC FRAME CORP
979 3rd Ave Ste 1705, New York, NY 10022-3804
Tel (212) 289-2100 *Founded/Ownrshp* 1991
Sales 104.2MM^E^ *EMP* 1,100
SIC 2426 5021 Frames for upholstered furniture, wood; Office furniture
Pr: David Stevens
Exec: Morris Sutton
IT Man: Yossi Dilmani

D-U-N-S 10-834-7381
■ ARUBA NETWORKS INC
(*Suby of* HEWLETT PACKARD ENTERPRISE CO) ★
1344 Crossman Ave, Sunnyvale, CA 94089-1113
Tel (408) 227-4500 *Founded/Ownrshp* 2015
Sales 728.9MM *EMP* 1,754
SIC 3577 3663 7371 Computer peripheral equipment; Mobile communication equipment; Computer software development
Pr: Rishi Varma
Pr: Yong Shu
**CFO:* Catherine A Lesjak
VP: Wathik Labidi
VP: Patrick Li
VP: David Miller
IT Man: Vivek Balasubramanian
IT Man: Fei Yan
Mktg Dir: Sylvia Hooks
Sls Dir: Xin Jin
Mktg Mgr: Gary Gujral

ARUESD
See ALUM ROCK UNION ELEMENTARY SCHOOL DISTRICT

D-U-N-S 83-093-6006
ARUP AMERICAS INC
(*Suby of* ARUP GROUP LIMITED)
77 Water St, New York, NY 10005-4401
Tel (212) 896-3000 *Founded/Ownrshp* 2005
Sales 160.7MM^E^ *EMP* 900^E^
SIC 8711 Engineering services
Ch Bd: Mahadev Raman
**Pr:* Greg Hodkinson
**CFO:* Alan Jennat
**VP:* Andy Howard
Assoc Dir: James Sze
**Prin:* Nigel Nicholls
DP Exec: George Perez
Snr PM: James Mallender
Snr Mgr: Mike Straughton

D-U-N-S 11-751-3135 IMP
ARUP LABORATORIES INC
ASSOCTED RGNAL UNIV PTHLOGISTS
(*Suby of* UNIVERSITY OF UTAH) ★
500 S Chipeta Way, Salt Lake City, UT 84108-1221
Tel (801) 583-2787 *Founded/Ownrshp* 1983
Sales 206.1MM^E^ *EMP* 2,700
SIC 8071 Testing laboratories
Pr: Edward R Ashwood
COO: K Ash
**COO:* Ronald L Weiss
**CFO:* Andy Theurer
Treas: Ronald McFarland
Bd of Dir: Mark E Astill
Bd of Dir: Frederic Clayton
Bd of Dir: Raymond A Daynes
Bd of Dir: Jerry Kaplan
Bd of Dir: David P Knight
Bd of Dir: C J Marshall
Bd of Dir: S F Mohammad
Bd of Dir: Gregory P Smith
**Ofcr:* Jerry W Hussong
Ofcr: Ronald Weiss
Sr VP: Peggy Ahlin
Sr VP: Sherrie Perkins
Sr VP: Khosrow Shotorbani
VP: Kathy Carlson
VP: Cheryl M Coffin
VP: Susan Garr

D-U-N-S 61-471-2875
ARUP NORTH AMERICA LIMITED
(*Suby of* ARUP AMERICAS INC) ★
560 Mission St Fl 7, San Francisco, CA 94105-0915
Tel (415) 957-9445 *Founded/Ownrshp* 1987
Sales 103.0MM^E^ *EMP* 900
SIC 8711 Engineering services
Pr: Mahadev Ramen
Ofcr: Stuart Robertson
**VP:* Andrew Howard
VP: Brian Jackson
**VP:* James Quiter
Dir IT: Keith Ali
IT Man: Mark Westerhout
Netwrk Mgr: Jeff Tranchina
Snr PM: Evan Hughes
Board of Directors: Phillip Dilley

D-U-N-S 15-014-4488
ARVADA HOUSE PRESERVATION LIMITED PARTNERSHIP
(*Suby of* AIMCO PROPERTIES LP) ★
10175 W 58th Pl Apt 402, Arvada, CO 80004-5029
Tel (303) 423-8872 *Founded/Ownrshp* 2004
Sales 39.6MM^E^ *EMP* 3,900
SIC 6513 Apartment building operators
Sr VP: Leeann Morein

D-U-N-S 00-850-8657 IMP
ARVATO DIGITAL SERVICES LLC
29011 Commerce Center Dr, Valencia, CA 91355-4195
Tel (661) 702-2700 *Founded/Ownrshp* 2007
Sales 562.6MM^E^ *EMP* 2,400
SIC 5961 7389

D-U-N-S 03-633-2567
ARVEST BANK
(*Suby of* ARVEST BANK GROUP INC) ★
1 N Mcilroy Ave, Fayetteville, AR 72701-4017
Tel (479) 575-1000 *Founded/Ownrshp* 1986
Sales NA *EMP* 270^E^
SIC 6022 State commercial banks
Pr: Donny Story
Chf Mktg O: Misty Crug-Pitchford
Ex VP: Jim Cole
**Ex VP:* Gaye Wilcox
Sr VP: Amy Bretall
Sr VP: Tom Butkus
Sr VP: Denise Cate
Sr VP: Mark Dunker
Sr VP: Steve Hull
Sr VP: Keran Lemons
Sr VP: Diane Wells
VP: Karen Anderson
VP: Ricardo Ballesteros
VP: Tim Beaver
VP: Joe Beshoner
VP: Carla Green
VP: Robin Schilling
VP: Lori R Smith

D-U-N-S 12-219-2594
ARVEST BANK GROUP INC
913 W Monroe Ave, Lowell, AR 72745-9683
Tel (479) 750-1400 *Founded/Ownrshp* 1976
Sales NA *EMP* 4,800
SIC 6712 Bank holding companies
Ch Bd: Jim C Walton
COO: Kevin K Sabin
Treas: Wayne Ardrey
**Sr VP:* Karla Payne
VP: Scott Deboer
VP: Barry Sullivan
VP: Ray Tubaugh
Dir Risk M: Debbie McCullough
Brnch Mgr: Trish Collins

ARVIG COMMUNICATION SYSTEM ACS
See EAST OTTER TAIL TELEPHONE CO

D-U-N-S 14-851-0183
ARVIG ENTERPRISES INC
ACS
150 2nd St Sw Ste 100, Perham, MN 56573-1461
Tel (218) 346-4227 *Founded/Ownrshp* 1984
Sales 161.1MM^E^ *EMP* 282
Accts Warinner Gesinger & Associate
SIC 4813 4841 Telephone communication, except radio; Cable television services
Pr: Allen Arvig
**Treas:* Rick Vyskocil
**VP:* Donna Ward
Genl Mgr: Gene Curtis
Genl Mgr: James Putnam
Dir IT: Grace Schertler

D-U-N-S 18-469-7241 IMP/EXP
ARVIN SANGO INC
A S I
2905 Wilson Ave, Madison, IN 47250-3834
Tel (812) 265-2888 *Founded/Ownrshp* 1986
Sales 216.3MM^E^ *EMP* 750
SIC 3714 Exhaust systems & parts, motor vehicle; Instrument board assemblies, motor vehicle; Motor vehicle body components & frame
Pr: Gordon Pebbles
**VP:* John Kakimoto
QC Dir: Keiji Kondo

D-U-N-S 00-340-4477 IMP/EXP
■ ARVINMERITOR EXHAUST SYSTEMS INC
(*Suby of* MERITOR INC) ★
2135 W Maple Rd, Troy, MI 48084-7121
Tel (248) 435-1000 *Founded/Ownrshp* 2000
Sales 76.3MM^E^ *EMP* 1,000
SIC 5013 Automotive supplies
Ch: Ivor J Evans

D-U-N-S 01-947-2054 IMP
■ ARVINMERITOR OE LLC
(*Suby of* MERITOR INC) ★
2135 W Maple Rd, Troy, MI 48084-7121
Tel (248) 435-1000 *Founded/Ownrshp* 1997
Sales 80.3MM^E^ *EMP* 1,201
SIC 3714 Motor vehicle parts & accessories
COO: Paul Kruse
COO: Charles Long
Ex VP: James Donlon III
VP: Rich Hanlon
Dist Mgr: Scott Burckhard
Genl Couns: Vernon Baker

D-U-N-S 06-465-7896
ARVOS HOLDING LLC
LJUNGSTRM
(*Suby of* ARVOS HOLDING GMBH)
3020 Truax Rd, Wellsville, NY 14895-9531
Tel (585) 596-2501 *Founded/Ownrshp* 2014
Sales 263.9MM^E^ *EMP* 623^E^
SIC 3494 Steam fittings & specialties
Pr: David Breckinridge
CFO: Ludger Heuberg

D-U-N-S 07-950-1668
ARVOS INC
AIR PREHEATER
(*Suby of* LJUNGSTRM) ★
3020 Truax Rd, Wellsville, NY 14895-9531
Tel (585) 593-2700 *Founded/Ownrshp* 2014
Sales 263.9MM[E] *EMP* 750[E]
SIC 3443 Fabricated plate work (boiler shop); Air preheaters, nonrotating: plate type
Pr: David Breckinridge
**CFO:* Ludger Heuberg

D-U-N-S 96-847-8664 EXP
ARYZTA HOLDINGS IV LLC
(*Suby of* ARYZTA AG)
6080 Center Dr Ste 900, Los Angeles, CA 90045-9226
Tel (310) 417-4700 *Founded/Ownrshp* 2011
Sales 1.7MMM *EMP* 5,000
SIC 2052 2053 2045 2051 Cookies & crackers; Cookies; Frozen bakery products, except bread; Bread & bread type roll mixes: from purchased flour; Breads, rolls & buns
CEO: John Yamin
**COO:* Ronan Minahan
**CFO:* Robin Jones

D-U-N-S 08-720-5746 IMP/EXP
ARYZTA LLC
(*Suby of* ARYZTA HOLDINGS IV LLC) ★
6080 Center Dr Ste 900, Los Angeles, CA 90045-9226
Tel (310) 417-4700 *Founded/Ownrshp* 2002
Sales 1.6MMM *EMP* 5,000
SIC 2052 2053 2051 Cookies; Frozen bakery products, except bread; Cakes, pies & pastries; Breads, rolls & buns
CEO: John Yamin
**COO:* Ronan Minahan
**CFO:* Robin Jones
CFO: Marian Punzalan
Sr VP: Jon Davis
VP: Brian Anderson
VP: Jeff E Dearduff
VP: Doug Freitas
VP: Matt Gabris
VP: Mike Granda
VP: Steve Mills
VP: Todd Stillwell
VP: Jim White

D-U-N-S 96-847-8524
ARYZTA US HOLDINGS I CORP
(*Suby of* ARYZTA AG)
14490 Catalina St, San Leandro, CA 94577-5516
Tel (800) 938-1900 *Founded/Ownrshp* 2006
Sales 228.8MM[E] *EMP* 9,500
SIC 2052 2053 2051 Cookies; Frozen bakery products, except bread; Cakes, pies & pastries
CEO: John Yamin
**COO:* Ronan Minahan
**CFO:* Robin Jones
Sr VP: Dan Bailey
VP Mktg: Rick Werhel
Snr Mgr: Harish Ramani

D-U-N-S 80-911-9709 IMP
AS AMERICA INC
AMERICAN STANDARD BRANDS
(*Suby of* LIXIL CORPORATION)
1 Centennial Ave Ste 101, Piscataway, NJ 08854-3921
Tel (732) 980-3000 *Founded/Ownrshp* 2013
Sales 2.0MMM[E] *EMP* 7,325
SIC 3261 3432 Vitreous plumbing fixtures; Plumbing fixture fittings & trim
Pr: Steve Delarge
Treas: Henry Johansen
Treas: Henry Johansson
VP: Nazer Ali
VP: Nick Anthony
VP: Chris Capone
VP: Victor Colon
VP: George H Kerckove
VP: Edward Manley
VP: Jean-Claude Montauze
VP: Eric Nutter
VP: Peter Rogers
VP: Barbara Sellinger

D-U-N-S 11-530-9882
AS HOLDINGS INC
TEMPCO
5120 Beck Dr, Elkhart, IN 46516-9512
Tel (574) 295-8384 *Founded/Ownrshp* 1984
Sales 105.3MM[E] *EMP* 170
SIC 5033 5169 5031 5162 Roofing & siding materials; Insulation materials; Adhesives & sealants; Building materials, exterior; Skylights, all materials; Plastics materials & basic shapes
Pr: David V Smith Jr
**VP:* Nancy B Smith

D-U-N-S 09-865-4551 IMP/EXP
ASA ELECTRONICS LLC
2602 Marina Dr, Elkhart, IN 46514-8642
Tel (574) 264-3135 *Founded/Ownrshp* 1991
Sales 83.2MM[E] *EMP* 115
Accts Grant Thornton Llp Chicago I
SIC 5099 Video & audio equipment
CFO: Julia Willis
Exec: Michelle Fioritto
Dir IT: John Pennington
Opers Mgr: Kurt Wood
Sls Mgr: Justin Garver
Sls Mgr: Patrick McCullough
Sales Asso: Darrell Robinson

D-U-N-S 78-415-2964 IMP
ASAHI KASEI PLASTICS (AMERICA) INC
ASAHI KASEI PLASTICS N AMER
1 Thermofil Way, Fowlerville, MI 48836-7936
Tel (517) 223-2000 *Founded/Ownrshp* 2000
Sales 111.0MM[E] *EMP* 376[E]
SIC 2821 Thermoplastic materials
Pr: Nobuyuki Shunaga
CFO: Dave Donie

ASAHI KASEI PLASTICS N AMER
See ASAHI KASEI PLASTICS (AMERICA) INC

D-U-N-S 00-293-5591 IMP/EXP
ASAHI KASEI PLASTICS NORTH AMERICA INC
(*Suby of* ASAHI KASEI PLASTICS N AMER) ★
1 Thermofil Way, Fowlerville, MI 48836-7936
Tel (517) 223-2000 *Founded/Ownrshp* 1993
Sales 115.1MM[E] *EMP* 200
SIC 2821 Thermoplastic materials
Pr: John Moyer
Sec: Yuta Kume
Sr VP: Fumihide Inada
VP: Michael Balow
VP: Dave Donie
QA Dir: Tucker Keith
VP Sls: Iichiro Kitsuda

D-U-N-S 07-968-1898
ASAHI REFINING USA INC
(*Suby of* ASAHI HOLDINGS, INC.)
4601 W 2100 S, Salt Lake City, UT 84120-1221
Tel (801) 972-6466 *Founded/Ownrshp* 2015
Sales 21.0MMM *EMP* 131
SIC 1041 Gold ores mining
Pr: Grant A Angwin
CFO: Scott Delorefice

D-U-N-S 96-160-1127 IMP
ASAMA COLDWATER MANUFACTURING INC
ACM
(*Suby of* ASAMA GIKEN CO.,LTD.)
180 Asama Pkwy, Coldwater, MI 49036-1590
Tel (517) 279-1090 *Founded/Ownrshp* 1996
Sales 107.3MM[E] *EMP* 340
Accts Ernst & Young Llp Troy Mich
SIC 3714 Motor vehicle steering systems & parts
Pr: Masao Yamaura
Ql Cn Mgr: Brandon Reed
Snr Mgr: Tim Arey

ASAMO CO
See ASMO GREENVILLE OF NORTH CAROLINA INC

D-U-N-S 16-146-0357
ASANTE
ASANTE HEALTH SYSTEM
2825 E Barnett Rd, Medford, OR 97504-8332
Tel (541) 789-7000 *Founded/Ownrshp* 1998
Sales 739.5MM *EMP* 4,000
SIC 8069

ASANTE HEALTH SYSTEM
See ASANTE ROGUE REGIONAL MEDICAL CENTER

ASANTE HEALTH SYSTEM
See ASANTE

D-U-N-S 05-360-6844
ASANTE ROGUE REGIONAL MEDICAL CENTER
ASANTE HEALTH SYSTEM
(*Suby of* ASANTE HEALTH SYSTEM) ★
2825 E Barnett Rd, Medford, OR 97504-8332
Tel (541) 608-4900 *Founded/Ownrshp* 1993
Sales 450.9MM *EMP* 1,779
SIC 8062

ASAP
See ALLIED STAFF AUGMENTATION PARTNERS INC

D-U-N-S 12-148-2657
■ **ASAP SOFTWARE EXPRESS INC**
(*Suby of* DELL COMPUTER) ★
850 Asbury Dr, Buffalo Grove, IL 60089-4557
Tel (847) 465-3700 *Founded/Ownrshp* 2007
Sales 362.1MM[E] *EMP* 600
SIC 5045 Computer software
Pr: Paul Jarvie
**Pr:* John Swainson
IT Man: Bob Louandowski
Sls Dir: Kory Kendziora
Sls Mgr: Anoop Elgonda
Sales Asso: Helen Esin

D-U-N-S 85-964-3686
ASAP SOLUTIONS GROUP LLC
3885 Holcomb Bridge Rd, Norcross, GA 30092-2269
Tel (770) 246-1718 *Founded/Ownrshp* 1989
Sales 98.8MM[E] *EMP* 740
Accts Rachel Taylor Sec By Fax On J
SIC 7379 8742 Computer related consulting services; Administrative services consultant
Dir IT: Jackson Jeffrey

D-U-N-S 00-132-5281 IMP
■ **ASARCO LLC**
GRUPO MEXICO
(*Suby of* AMERICAS MINING CORP) ★
5285 E Williams Cir # 2000, Tucson, AZ 85711-7711
Tel (520) 798-7500 *Founded/Ownrshp* 1899
Sales 1.7MMM[E] *EMP* 2,000
SIC 1021 1044 1031 1041 3331 3339 Copper ores; Silver ores; Lead ores mining; Zinc ores mining; Gold ores; Primary copper; Silver refining (primary); Lead smelting & refining (primary); Gold refining (primary); Zinc smelting (primary), including zinc residue
CFO: Daniel Muniz
Treas: Scott Cole
VP: Tom Aldrich
VP: Oscar G Barron
VP: John George
VP: James O'Neil
VP: Manuel Rada
Genl Mgr: Dale Dixon
Sfty Dirs: Joanna Acosta
Sales Exec: Yolanda Marquez

D-U-N-S 07-482-1208
ASBURY ATLANTIC INC
WILSON HEALTH CARE CENTER
(*Suby of* ASBURY METHODIST VILLAGE) ★
201 Russell Ave, Gaithersburg, MD 20877-2800
Tel (301) 216-4100 *Founded/Ownrshp* 1926
Sales 123.5MM *EMP* 875
SIC 8059 8051 Nursing home, except skilled & intermediate care facility; Skilled nursing care facilities
CEO: Edwin C Thomas III
**Treas:* Lawrence Bradshaw
CIO: Chip Burns
Dir IT: David Herr

D-U-N-S 94-604-4844
ASBURY ATLANTIC INC
20030 Century Blvd, Germantown, MD 20874-1111
Tel (301) 250-2100 *Founded/Ownrshp* 1945
Sales 126.1MM *EMP* 2[E]
SIC 7389 Personal service agents, brokers & bureaus
Pr: Doug Leidig

D-U-N-S 17-079-1136
■ **ASBURY AUTOMOTIVE ARKANSAS DEALERSHIP HOLDINGS LLC**
NORTHPOINT FORD
(*Suby of* ASBURY AUTOMOTIVE GROUP INC) ★
4400 Landers Rd, Little Rock, AR 72201
Tel (501) 945-1200 *Founded/Ownrshp* 1999
Sales 120.4MM[E] *EMP* 470
SIC 5511 Automobiles, new & used
Ch Bd: Thomas Mc Larty III
**Pr:* Charles R Oglesby
**CEO:* Joe Shine
Off Mgr: Cherry Johnson

D-U-N-S 00-587-0167 EXP
■ **ASBURY AUTOMOTIVE ATLANTA LLC** (GA)
NALLEY MOTOR TRUCKS
(*Suby of* ASBURY AUTOMOTIVE GROUP INC) ★
3039 Premiere Pkwy # 900, Duluth, GA 30097-5015
Tel (404) 622-1921 *Founded/Ownrshp* 1955, 1996
Sales 95.8MM[E] *EMP* 480
SIC 5511 7515 5013 6159 5521 Automobiles, new & used; Pickups, new & used; Vans, new & used; Passenger car leasing; Tools & equipment, automotive; Automobile finance leasing; Used car dealers
Pr: Charles Oglesby
CFO: Bill Salomone

D-U-N-S 04-390-5384 IMP
▲ **ASBURY AUTOMOTIVE GROUP INC**
2905 Premiere Pkwy, Duluth, GA 30097-5247
Tel (770) 418-8200 *Founded/Ownrshp* 1994
Sales 6.5MMM *EMP* 8,600[E]
Tkr Sym ABG *Exch* NYS
SIC 5511 Automobiles, new & used
Pr: Craig T Monaghan
**Ch Bd:* Thomas C Deloach Jr
COO: David W Hult
CFO: Keith R Style
Sr VP: George C Karolis
Sr VP: George A Villasana
VP: Renee McKenzie
VP: Brandi Nicholson
Exec: Casey Coffey
Genl Mgr: John Clark
Genl Mgr: Renee Huff
Board of Directors: Joel Alsfine, Dennis E Clements, Juanita T James, Eugene S Katz, Philip F Maritz, Thomas J Reddin, Scott L Thompson

D-U-N-S 10-479-3729
■ **ASBURY AUTOMOTIVE NORTH CAROLINA LLC**
CROWN AUTOMOTIVE
(*Suby of* ASBURY AUTOMOTIVE GROUP INC) ★
3633c W Wendover Ave, Greensboro, NC 27407-1507
Tel (336) 851-3500 *Founded/Ownrshp* 1997
Sales 266.1MM[E] *EMP* 1,300
SIC 5511 Automobiles, new & used
CIO: Stephen McGee

D-U-N-S 79-983-9394
■ **ASBURY AUTOMOTIVE SOUTHERN CALIFORNIA LLC**
(*Suby of* ASBURY AUTOMOTIVE GROUP INC) ★
3700 W Airport Fwy, Irving, TX 75062-5903
Tel (972) 790-6000 *Founded/Ownrshp* 1998
Sales 903.6MM[E] *EMP* 7,000
SIC 5511 Automobiles, new & used
CEO: Thomas G McCollum
**Chf Mktg O:* Allen T Levenson

D-U-N-S 09-497-0613 IMP/EXP
ASBURY CARBONS INC
103 Foulk Rd Ste 202, Wilmington, DE 19803-3742
Tel (302) 652-0266 *Founded/Ownrshp* 1895
Sales 154.0MM[E] *EMP* 300
SIC 1499 3295 1241 5051 3952 3069 Graphite mining; Graphite, natural: ground, pulverized, refined or blended; Coal mining services; Metals service centers & offices; Pencil lead: black, indelible or colored: artists'; Erasers: rubber or rubber & abrasive combined
Ch Bd: H Marvin Riddle III
**Pr:* Carol A Kalmar
**CEO:* Stephen A Riddle
**CFO:* William T Meglaughlin Jr
**VP:* Sue Rish

D-U-N-S 13-396-9803
ASBURY COMMUNITIES INC
ASBURY METHODIST VILLAGE
20030 Century Blvd # 300, Germantown, MD 20874-1111
Tel (301) 250-2100 *Founded/Ownrshp* 1994
Sales 11.0MM *EMP* 2,407
Accts Cliftonlarsonallen Llp Plymou
SIC 8361 Residential care
Pr: Edwin C Thomas III
**CFO:* Michael Connell
**Ofcr:* Ann E Gillespie
**Ofcr:* Peggy Kaplan
Sr VP: Bill Pickhardt
VP: Tara McDaniel
VP Mktg: William McDermott
Mktg Dir: Simi Brady
Mktg Dir: Katie Crane
Nrsg Dir: Janet Dykstra

ASBURY METHODIST VILLAGE
See ASBURY COMMUNITIES INC

D-U-N-S 00-216-7930 IMP
■ **ASBURY PARK PRESS INC**
HOME NEWS & TRIBUNE
(*Suby of* GANNETT CO INC) ★
3600 Route 66, Neptune, NJ 07753-2605
Tel (732) 922-6000 *Founded/Ownrshp* 1879, 2015
Sales 172.6MM[E] *EMP* 1,200
SIC 2711 2752 Commercial printing & newspaper publishing combined; Commercial printing, lithographic
Pr: Thomas M Donovan
**VP:* W Raymond Ollwerther
VP: Wayne Paragallo
Exec: Kim Klein
Exec: Jenkins Powers
Exec: Bill Tuohy
**Prin:* Robert T Collins
Off Admin: Plath Maltais
Software D: Dan Sinni
Prd Mgr: Kristen Janet Materese

ASC
See ARAMCO SERVICES CO

D-U-N-S 01-844-4241
ASC COMMUNICATIONS INC (IL)
315 Vernon Ave, Glencoe, IL 60022-2136
Tel (800) 417-2035 *Founded/Ownrshp* 1996
Sales 103.0MM *EMP* 50
SIC 4899 Data communication services
Pr: Jessica Cole
**Prin:* Laura Miller
Assoc Ed: Heather Punke

D-U-N-S 17-189-9623 IMP/EXP
ASC CONSTRUCTION EQUIPMENT USA INC
(*Suby of* ASCENDUM, S.A.)
9115 Harris Corners Pkwy # 450, Charlotte, NC 28269-3706
Tel (704) 494-8100 *Founded/Ownrshp* 2004
Sales 129.9MM[E] *EMP* 345
SIC 5082 Construction & mining machinery
VP: Ron Huibers
Pr: Joseph Bradley Stimmel
CFO: Nuno Colaco
Sr VP: James Brannon
Manager: Kelly Mackerer
Sls Mgr: Steve Brown

D-U-N-S 06-042-2193 IMP/EXP
ASC INDUSTRIES INC
(*Suby of* UCI) ★
2100 International Pkwy, North Canton, OH 44720-1373
Tel (330) 899-0340 *Founded/Ownrshp* 2006
Sales 120.0MM[E] *EMP* 237[E]
SIC 3714 Water pump, motor vehicle
CEO: William Blackerby

D-U-N-S 07-093-0946
ASC UTAH INC
CANYONS, THE
4000 Canyons Resort Dr, Park City, UT 84098-6546
Tel (435) 649-5400 *Founded/Ownrshp* 1975, 2008
Sales 54.1MM[E] *EMP* 1,500
SIC 7011 5812 Ski lodge; Eating places
Pr: Mike Goar
Ex VP: Enoch Kim
**VP:* Hal Leonard
**VP:* Gary Riness
CTO: Franklin Carey

ASCAP
See AMERICAN SOCIETY OF COMPOSERS AUTHORS AND PUBLISHERS

D-U-N-S 96-403-6383 IMP
▲ **ASCENA RETAIL GROUP INC**
933 Macarthur Blvd, Mahwah, NJ 07430-2045
Tel (551) 777-6700 *Founded/Ownrshp* 2010
Sales 7.0MMM *EMP* 48,000[E]
Tkr Sym ASNA *Exch* NGS
SIC 5621 5632 Women's specialty clothing stores; Women's sportswear; Dress shops; Ready-to-wear apparel, women's; Women's accessory & specialty stores; Apparel accessories
Pr: David Jaffe
**Ch Bd:* Elliot S Jaffe
CFO: Robb Giammatteo
Ofcr: John Pershing
Ex VP: Erin Stern
Sr VP: Duane Holloway
Sr VP: Ernest Laporte
VP: David Johns
Board of Directors: Katie J Bayne, Kate Buggeln, Steven L Kirshenbaum, Kay Krill, Randy L Pearce, Carl Rubin, Linda Yaccarino

D-U-N-S 06-770-5857
ASCEND LEARNING LLC
11161 Overbrook Rd, Leawood, KS 66211-2299
Tel (800) 667-7531 *Founded/Ownrshp* 2010
Sales 330.0MM *EMP* 850
SIC 8249 Medical training services
CEO: Greg Sebasky
Treas: Mike Pater
Sr VP: Jonathan Moulton
VP: Mark Williams-Abrams
Prgrm Mgr: Bob Kohlsaat
Snr Sftwr: Timothy Franzke
Snr Sftwr: Jason Hart
Snr Sftwr: Paul Huntington
Snr Sftwr: Bharath Parlapalli
Snr Sftwr: Geoffrey Wadsworth
Dir IT: Whit Farrington

D-U-N-S 07-844-9293
ASCEND PERFORMANCE MATERIALS HOLDINGS INC
(*Suby of* SK TITAN HOLDINGS LLC) ★
1010 Travis St Ste 900, Houston, TX 77002-5917
Tel (713) 315-5700 *Founded/Ownrshp* 2012, 2009
Sales 1.4MMM[E] *EMP* 3,100[E]
SIC 6722 Management investment, open-end
Pr: J Timothy Strehl
Pr: Phil McDivitt
**CFO:* Jeff Bird
**VP:* Dale Borths

*VP: Malcolm Oneal
*VP: Dave Pendlebury

D-U-N-S 83-023-5474 IMP/EXP
ASCEND PERFORMANCE MATERIALS OPERATIONS LLC
(Suby of ASCEND PERFORMANCE MATERIALS HOLDINGS INC) ★
1010 Travis St Ste 900, Houston, TX 77002-5917
Tel (713) 315-5700 Founded/Ownrshp 2009
Sales 1.4MMM[E] EMP 3,080
SIC 2821 2284 Plastics materials & resins; Nylon thread
Ch Bd: Barry Siadat
*Pr: J Timothy Strehl
CFO: Kevin Bartol
*CFO: Jeffrey Bird
*VP: Dale Borths
VP: Jim Hull
*VP: Jamshid Keynejad
*VP: Malcolm Oneal
*VP: Dave Pendlebury
*VP: Barry Penney
VP: Richard Prinstein
*VP: Andrew Ralston
VP: Scott Rook

D-U-N-S 06-550-2540
ASCENDA USA INC
14001 E Iliff Ave Ste 500, Aurora, CO 80014-1428
Tel (720) 399-2050 Founded/Ownrshp 2010
Sales 100.0MM EMP 2,400
SIC 7389 Telephone answering service
Pr: Greg Fettes
*COO: Jeff Fettes
*CFO: Mitul Kotecha
VP: Brad Cull

D-U-N-S 08-002-8910
■ ASCENSIA DIABETES CARE US INC
CONTOUR NEXT
(Suby of ASCENSIA DIABETES CARE HOLDINGS AG)
5 Woodhollow Rd, Parsippany, NJ 07054-2832
Tel (973) 560-6500 Founded/Ownrshp 2016
Sales 400.0MM EMP 450
SIC 5047 2835 3841 Electro-medical equipment; In vitro diagnostics; Diagnostic apparatus, medical
CEO: Michael Kloss
Pr: Tetsuyuki Watanabe
Treas: Masashi Inada
Ofcr: Peter Eckenberg
Ofcr: David Simmons
VP: Steven Lynum
VP: Hiromichi Yoshitake

ASCENSION BNFITS INSUR SLTIONS
See ASCENSION INSURANCE INC

ASCENSION BNFITS INSUR SLTIONS
See PORTAL INSURANCE AGENCY INC

D-U-N-S 07-712-6852
ASCENSION HEALTH
(Suby of ASCENSION HEALTH ALLIANCE) ★
4600 Edmundson Rd, Saint Louis, MO 63134-3806
Tel (314) 733-8000 Founded/Ownrshp 1999
Sales 4.9MMM[E] EMP 109,000[E]
Accts Deloitte Tax Llp Cincinnati
SIC 8099 Medical services organization
CEO: Robert J Henkel Fache
*Pr: Anthony R Tersigni
*CFO: Rhonda Anderson
CFO: Rhonda C Anderson
*CFO: Anthony J Speranzo
Trst: Jean Deblois
Ofcr: James K Beckman
Ex VP: Therese Gottschalk
Ex VP: David B Pryor
*Sr VP: Katherine Arbuckle
*Sr VP: Mark D Barner
Sr VP: Timothy L Glover
Sr VP: Ziad Haydar
Sr VP: Sally E Jeffcoat
Sr VP: Maureen McGuire
Sr VP: Nick Ragone
VP: Jim Beckman
VP: Phyllis Bruemer
VP: Rashaanda Cook
VP: Melissa Dill
VP: David Dowlin
Board of Directors: Regina Benjamin

D-U-N-S 07-869-3230
ASCENSION HEALTH ALLIANCE (MO)
4600 Edmundson Rd, Saint Louis, MO 63134-3806
Tel (314) 733-8000 Founded/Ownrshp 2011
Sales 21.9MMM EMP 111,489[E]
Accts Ernst & Young Llp
SIC 5912 Drug stores
Pr: Anthony R Tersigni
*CFO: Anthony J Speranzo
*Ex VP: John D Doyle
*Ex VP: Robert J Henkel
*Ex VP: Joseph R Impicciche
*Ex VP: Susan Nestor Levy
*Ex VP: Sister Maureen McGuire DC
*Ex VP: David B Pryor MD
*Exec: Sister Bernice Coreil DC
Board of Directors: Eduardo Conrado, Stephen M Dufilho, Eve J Higginbotham, Dennis H Holtschneider, Kathleen Kelly, W Stancil Starnes

D-U-N-S 07-884-0307
ASCENSION HEALTH INSURANCE LTD
(Suby of ASCENSION HEALTH) ★
4600 Edmundson Rd, Saint Louis, MO 63134-3806
Tel (314) 733-8000 Founded/Ownrshp 2013
Sales NA EMP 1,278[E]
SIC 6411 Insurance agents, brokers & service

D-U-N-S 96-726-6771
ASCENSION HEALTH WELFARE BENEFITS TRUST
11775 Borman Dr Ste 200, Saint Louis, MO 63146-4134
Tel (314) 733-8648 Founded/Ownrshp 2011
Sales 263.3MM EMP 2
Accts Deloitte Tax Llp Cincinnati
SIC 6733 Trusts

VP: Eric Feinftein

D-U-N-S 00-215-1205
ASCENSION INSURANCE INC
ASCENSION BNFITS INSUR SLTIONS
9225 Indian Creek Pkwy # 700, Overland Park, KS 66210-2010
Tel (816) 842-1332 Founded/Ownrshp 2007
Sales NA EMP 410
SIC 6411 Insurance agents, brokers & service
Ch: Leonard P Kline Jr
*Pr: Joe Tatum
*CFO: Robert Schneider
Ex VP: Robert Smith
Sr VP: Ed Bray
Sr VP: Greg Merrill
Sr VP: Michael Stallone
*VP: Daniel Brookehart
VP: Michael Makar

D-U-N-S 08-021-7442
ASCENSION INSURANCE INC
PORTAL INSURANCE AGENCY INC
1277 Treat Blvd Ste 400, Walnut Creek, CA 94597-7986
Tel (800) 404-4969 Founded/Ownrshp 2016
Sales NA EMP 450[E]
SIC 6411 Insurance agents, brokers & service
CEO: Joseph L Tatum
*Pr: Edward Nathan
*CFO: Jamie Linden

D-U-N-S 09-269-0585
ASCENSION PARISH SCHOOLS
1100 Webster St, Donaldsonville, LA 70346-2754
Tel (225) 257-2000 Founded/Ownrshp 1871
Sales 270.1MM EMP 3,300
Accts Postlethwaite & Netterville G
SIC 8211 Public elementary & secondary schools
*Pr: A J Nickens
Dir Bus: Diane Allison
IT Man: Fran Aucoin
Schl Brd P: Lorraine Wimberly

D-U-N-S 06-904-0004
ASCENSUS INC
200 Dryden Rd E Ste 1000, Dresher, PA 19025-1044
Tel (215) 648-8000 Founded/Ownrshp 2015
Sales NA EMP 700
SIC 6371 Pensions
Pr: Robert Guillocheau
*Treas: Michael Finn
Sr VP: Steven Schweitzer
VP: Anthony Bologna
VP: Donald Brenton
VP: Carl Dotger
*VP: Michael Folmer
VP: Chris Grebey
VP: Marc Jarman
VP: Ray Leavitt
VP: Jim Racine
Dir Teleco: Reed Hofmann

D-U-N-S 07-993-8307
ASCENT AEROSPACE LLC
(Suby of AIP AEROSPACE) ★
1395 S Lyon St, Santa Ana, CA 92705-4608
Tel (949) 455-0665 Founded/Ownrshp 2014
Sales 200.0MM EMP 900
SIC 3544 Special dies, tools, jigs & fixtures
CEO: Brian Williams
Pr: Michael Mahfet

D-U-N-S 82-841-7753
▲ ASCENT CAPITAL GROUP INC
5251 Dtc Pkwy Ste 1000, Greenwood Village, CO 80111-2739
Tel (303) 628-5600 Founded/Ownrshp 2008
Sales 563.3MM EMP 1,000
Accts Kpmg Llp Dallas Texas
Tkr Sym ASCMA Exch NGS
SIC 3822 7382 Building services monitoring controls, automatic; Security systems services; Burglar alarm maintenance & monitoring; Fire alarm maintenance & monitoring; Confinement surveillance systems maintenance & monitoring
Pr: William R Fitzgerald
CFO: Michael R Meyers
Ex VP: Jeffery R Gardner
Ex VP: William E Niles
Board of Directors: Philip J Holthouse, Rana Kashyap, Michael J Pohl, Charles Y Tanabe, Carl E Vogel

D-U-N-S 07-972-3279
ASCENT RESOURCES LLC
3501 Nw 63rd St, Oklahoma City, OK 73116-2223
Tel (405) 608-5544 Founded/Ownrshp 2015
Sales 92.7MM[E] EMP 100[E]
SIC 1382 6719 Oil & gas exploration services; Investment holding companies, except banks
CEO: Aubrey K McClendon
*COO: Jeff Fisher
Dir IT: Murphy Crosby

D-U-N-S 07-885-7004
ASCENT TOOLING GROUP LLC
(Suby of AIP AEROSPACE) ★
1395 S Lyon St, Santa Ana, CA 92705-4608
Tel (949) 455-0665 Founded/Ownrshp 2013
Sales 75.4MM[E] EMP 1,108
SIC 3812 Acceleration indicators & systems components, aerospace
CEO: Brian Williams
*COO: Paul Walsh
*CFO: Steve Littauer
VP: Ray Kauffmann

D-U-N-S 07-731-1728
ASCENTRIA CARE ALLIANCE
14 E Worcester St Ste 300, Worcester, MA 01604-3612
Tel (774) 343-3900 Founded/Ownrshp 1972
Sales 7.1MM EMP 1,000
Accts Cliftonlarsonallen Llp Quincy
SIC 8322 8051 8361 Individual & family services; Child related social services; Family counseling services; Convalescent home with continuous nursing care; Home for the aged
Pr: Angela Bovill

*Treas: Nick Russo
VP: Michael Alden
*VP: Lisa Cohen
VP: Ann Dancy
VP: Jodie Justofin
*VP: Dana W Ramish
Prgrm Mgr: Karen Anfield
Dir IT: Paul Halstead
Opers Mgr: Jacob Mandell

D-U-N-S 04-515-9493 IMP
ASCI HOLDINGS UK (DE) INC
(Suby of GST AUTOMOTIVE SAFETY COMPONENTS INTERNATIONAL INC) ★
40 Emery St, Greenville, SC 29605-4572
Tel (864) 240-2600 Founded/Ownrshp 1998
Sales 87.5MM[E] EMP 1,523[E]
SIC 3714 Motor vehicle parts & accessories
Pr: Stephen B Durke

ASCI READY MIX
See ASPHALT SPECIALTIES CO INC

ASCO
See AMERICAN SOCIETY OF CLINICAL ONCOLOGY INC

ASCO DISTRIBUTION CENTER
See AUTO SUPPLY CO INC

ASCO EQUIPMENT CO
See ASSOCIATED SUPPLY CO INC

D-U-N-S 84-817-5134 IMP/EXP
ASCO POWER TECHNOLOGIES LP
(Suby of CORTES NP ACQUISITION CORP) ★
50-60 Hanover Rd, Florham Park, NJ 07932-1503
Tel (973) 966-2000 Founded/Ownrshp 2016
Sales 497.4MM[E] EMP 1,050
SIC 3699 Electrical equipment & supplies
Pr: Armand Visioli
CFO: Kevin Bunting
VP: Donald McCann

D-U-N-S 16-085-7798 IMP
■ ASCO VALVE INC
ASCO VALVE MFG
(Suby of AUTOMATIC SWITCH CO) ★
50-60 Hanover Rd, Florham Park, NJ 07932-1503
Tel (973) 966-2437 Founded/Ownrshp 1999
Sales 324.5MM[E] EMP 1,300
SIC 3443 3491 3492 3625 5063 Fabricated plate work (boiler shop); Solenoid valves; Fluid power valves & hose fittings; Control equipment, electric; Switches, except electronic
Pr: John Meek
*VP: Michael Lefkowitz
*VP: Christopher G Walsh
*VP: Jean Pierre D Yaouanc
Exec: Mary Ann Kranz
S&M/VP: Robert Kemple
Mktg Mgr: Gerard Longinetti

ASCO VALVE MFG
See ASCO VALVE INC

D-U-N-S 07-099-3191 IMP
ASCOT ENTERPRISES INC
IMPERIAL FABRICS
503 S Main St, Nappanee, IN 46550-2531
Tel (877) 773-7751 Founded/Ownrshp 1976
Sales 105.1MM[E] EMP 400
SIC 2391 2591 2392 Curtains, window: made from purchased materials; Draperies, plastic & textile: from purchased materials; Window shades; Blinds vertical; Venetian blinds; Bedspreads & bed sets: made from purchased materials
CEO: Howard Yoder
*Pr: Kenneth J Manning
*CFO: Alan Sands
Sfty Dirs: Karen Koontz

ASD
See ANCHORAGE SCHOOL DISTRICT

ASD HEALTHCARE
See ASD SPECIALTY HEALTHCARE INC

D-U-N-S 16-005-9317
■ ASD SPECIALTY HEALTHCARE INC
ASD HEALTHCARE
(Suby of ABSG-CORPORATE) ★
3101 Gaylord Pkwy Fl 3, Frisco, TX 75034-8655
Tel (469) 365-8000 Founded/Ownrshp 2003
Sales 989.5MM[E] EMP 400[E]
SIC 5122 Drugs, proprietaries & sundries
Pr: Neil Herson
*Sr VP: John G Chou
*Sr VP: Tim G Guttman
VP: Richard Burk
VP: Devetta James
VP: Tamie Joeckel
*VP: Robert H Stone
Dir Bus: Fabian Cruz
Dir IT: Greg Cummings
VP Opers: Michael Gelgor
Natl Sales: Jonathan Davis

D-U-N-S 60-692-8398
■ ASE MOTORS HOLDING CORP
ALLEN SAMUELS AUTO GROUP
(Suby of AUTO CO XXVIII INC) ★
200 Sw 1st Ave, Fort Lauderdale, FL 33301-1875
Tel (954) 769-7000 Founded/Ownrshp 1988
Sales 305.7MM[E] EMP 1,200
SIC 5511 Automobiles, new & used
Ch: Mike Lowry
*Pr: Jeff Wooley
*VP: Maxine Hall

D-U-N-S 96-488-7264
ASEA AFSCME LOCAL 52 HEALTH BENEFITS TRUST
111 W Cataldo Ave, Spokane, WA 99201-3201
Tel (509) 328-0300 Founded/Ownrshp 2010
Sales 159.6MM EMP 3
Accts Anastasi & Moore Pllc Spokane
SIC 8631 Labor unions & similar labor organizations
Prin: Fred Brown

D-U-N-S 01-188-5969
ASEA BROWN BOVERI INC (DE)
A B B POWER TRANSMISSION
(Suby of ABB HOLDINGS INC) ★
501 Merritt 7, Norwalk, CT 06851-7000
Tel (203) 750-2200 Founded/Ownrshp 1978, 1998
Sales 427.3MM[E] EMP 10,634
SIC 3612 3613 5063 3511 3625 8711 Transformers, except electric; Switchgear & switchboard apparatus; Electrical apparatus & equipment; Power transmission equipment, electric; Switchgear; Steam turbine generator set units, complete; Gas turbines, mechanical drive; Relays & industrial controls; Engineering services; Chemical engineering; Petroleum engineering
Pr: Donald Aiken
CFO: Herbert Parker
Sr VP: J P Brett
Sr VP: Jeff Halsey
Sr VP: Han-Anders Nilsson
Sr VP: Chris Reinbold
VP: Richard Burt
VP: Patrick Grady
VP: Julie Guarino
VP: Danny Julian
VP: Bruce Lindl
VP: E Barry Lyon
VP: Barry Wentworth
VP: John Yost

D-U-N-S 16-060-1394
ASERACARE HOSPICE - NEW HORIZONS LLC
1 1000 Beverly Way, Fort Smith, AR 72919-0001
Tel (479) 201-2000 Founded/Ownrshp 2004
Sales 20.1MM[E] EMP 4,000
SIC 8361 Residential care
Sr VP: L Darlene Burch

D-U-N-S 78-944-6262 IMP
ASG CONSOLIDATED LLC
(Suby of AMERICAN SEAFOODS LP) ★
2025 1st Ave Ste 900, Seattle, WA 98121-3123
Tel (206) 374-1515 Founded/Ownrshp 2004
Sales 168.9MM[E] EMP 1,000
SIC 5421 5146 Fish & seafood markets; Fish & seafoods
Ch Bd: Bernt O Bodal

D-U-N-S 78-794-4227
ASG INC
(Suby of ASSURITY SECURITY GROUP INC) ★
1526 K St, Lincoln, NE 68508-2732
Tel (402) 476-6500 Founded/Ownrshp 1988
Sales NA EMP 530
SIC 6321 6311 Health insurance carriers; Life insurance
Pr: Thomas E Henning
*Treas: Marvin P Ehly

ASG SECURITY
See ALARM SECURITY GROUP LLC

D-U-N-S 18-635-5046
ASG TECHNOLOGIES GROUP INC
708 Goodlette Rd N, Naples, FL 34102-5644
Tel (239) 435-2200 Founded/Ownrshp 1986
Sales 292.0MM[E] EMP 1,000
Accts Grant Thornton Llp
SIC 7372 Business oriented computer software
Pr: Charles Sansbury
COO: Alex Derby
*CFO: Ernest J Scheidemann
CFO: Ernie Scheidemann
Treas: Thomas Kuntz
*Treas: Tom Kuntz
Ex VP: Kirk Dauksavage
*Ex VP: Derek S Eckelman
Ex VP: Richard Vance
Ex VP: Dietmar Wendt
Ex VP: Dietmar M Wendt
Ex VP: Heather F Zalar
Sr VP: Art Campana
Sr VP: Scott McCurdy
Sr VP: Natalie Oflaherty
Sr VP: Keith Richardson
VP: Nelson Barnes
VP: David Bornancin
VP: Jill Carter
VP: John Considine
VP: Richard Corning

D-U-N-S 11-529-8846
ASH BROKERAGE CORP
888 S Harrison St, Fort Wayne, IN 46802-2206
Tel (260) 459-0823 Founded/Ownrshp 1979
Sales NA EMP 185[E]
SIC 6411 Insurance brokers
CEO: Timothy E Ash
*Pr: Michael J Hefferon
*CFO: James A Krafcheck
*Treas: Cindy A Bastress
Sr Ex VP: John Duchien
*Ex VP: Jason E Grover
*Ex VP: Brett A Lotspeich
*Ex VP: Gary G Schaefer
VP: Jason Armey MBA
*VP: James D Ash
VP: Melissa Fearnow
VP: Brendon P Kelly
*VP: David Shoup
Assoc Dir: Ryan McGee

D-U-N-S 00-712-3698 IMP
ASH GROVE CEMENT CO
11011 Cody St Ste 300, Overland Park, KS 66210-1430
Tel (913) 451-8900 Founded/Ownrshp 1949
Sales 894.8MM[E] EMP 2,600
Accts Grant Thornton Llp Kansas Cit
SIC 3241 3273 1422 3271 Portland cement; Masonry cement; Ready-mixed concrete; Crushed & broken limestone; Concrete block & brick
Ch Bd: Charlie Sunderland
V Ch: George Wells
CFO: David G Meyer
Ch: James P Sunderland
Sr VP: J Randall Vance
VP: Eileen Flink
VP: Pat Gorup

VP: Stephanie James
VP: Kelley McCaffrey
VP: Fran Streitman
VP: Ron Vidergar

D-U-N-S 18-874-8131
ASH GROVE MATERIALS CORP
CENTRAL REGION
(*Suby of* ASH GROVE CEMENT CO) ★
11011 Cody St Ste 300, Overland Park, KS 66210-1430
Tel (913) 345-2030 *Founded/Ownrshp* 1988
Sales 83.5MM^E *EMP* 570
SIC 3273 3272 1411 7389 4212 Ready-mixed concrete; Concrete products; Trap rock, dimension-quarrying; Volcanic rock, dimension-quarrying; Packaging & labeling services; Local trucking, without storage
Bd of Dir: Sasha Grutman
VP: Robert B Henning
VP: Edwin S Pierce
VP: Ronald J Vidergar

ASH GROVE PACKAGING
See MATERIAL PACKAGING CORP

D-U-N-S 61-077-5798 IMP/EXP
ASHCROFT INC
(*Suby of* ASHCROFT-NAGANO KEIKI HOLDINGS INC) ★
250 E Main St, Stratford, CT 06614-5145
Tel (203) 378-8281 *Founded/Ownrshp* 2006
Sales 163.9MM^E *EMP* 988
SIC 3823 3679 3663 3625 Pressure gauges, dial & digital; Transducers, electrical; Transmitter-receivers, radio; Switches, electric power
CEO: Steve Culmone
**Ch:* Shigeru Miyashita
**Treas:* John Vuono
VP: Sam Fan
**VP:* Phil Martin
IT Man: Doug D'Addario
Info Man: Charlie Kiely
QI Cn Mgr: Stephen Sienkiewicz
Mktg Dir: Dietmar Heinen
Mktg Dir: Joana Rodrigues
Manager: Robert Blakeslee

D-U-N-S 61-779-6722
ASHCROFT-NAGANO KEIKI HOLDINGS INC
(*Suby of* NAGANO KEIKI CO., LTD.)
250 E Main St, Stratford, CT 06614-5145
Tel (203) 378-8281 *Founded/Ownrshp* 2005
Sales 180.2MM^E *EMP* 1,060
SIC 3823 3679 3663 3625 Pressure gauges, dial & digital; Transducers, electrical; Transmitter-receivers, radio; Switches, electric power
CEO: Steven A Culmone
IT Man: Jim Orzechowski
Sales Exec: Iven Kruse

D-U-N-S 15-122-9440 IMP/EXP
ASHEBORO ELASTICS CORP
AEC NARROW FABRICS
150 N Park St, Asheboro, NC 27203-5455
Tel (336) 629-2626 *Founded/Ownrshp* 1985
Sales 165.5MM^E *EMP* 660
SIC 2221 2241 Broadwoven fabric mills, manmade; Elastic narrow fabrics, woven or braided; Manmade fiber narrow woven fabrics
CEO: Larry Himes
**Pr:* Robert B Lawson
**Treas:* Jane Crisco
**VP:* Jeff Crisco
**VP:* John K Crisco Jr
**Prin:* Charles Adams
VP Mfg: Rick Grier

D-U-N-S 96-658-9215
ASHER ALADJEM
403 E 34th St Fl 3, New York, NY 10016-4972
Tel (212) 263-8360 *Founded/Ownrshp* 2011
Sales 950.0M *EMP* 10,000
SIC 8011 Offices & clinics of medical doctors
Prin: Aladjem Asher

D-U-N-S 01-679-1025
ASHEVILLE NURSING AND REHAB CENTER
91 Victoria Rd, Asheville, NC 28801-4427
Tel (828) 255-0076 *Founded/Ownrshp* 2008
Sales 733.4MM *EMP* 2
SIC 8099 Health & allied services
Pr: John O Brien

D-U-N-S 12-712-1791
ASHFIELD HEALTHCARE LLC
(*Suby of* UDG HEALTHCARE PUBLIC LIMITED COMPANY)
1 Ivybrook Blvd Ste 110, Ivyland, PA 18974-1790
Tel (215) 347-6400 *Founded/Ownrshp* 2002
Sales 85.1MM^E *EMP* 900
SIC 8742 Hospital & health services consultant
CEO: Chris Corbin
**Pr:* Mary Anne Greenberg
**CFO:* Holly Forristall
Treas: Neville Acaster
Sr VP: Kristin Ortlieb
VP: Christopher Young
Exec: Ellen Piggott
Board of Directors: Mary Anne Greenberg, Dan Piggott

ASHFORD COURT RICHMOND CI
See EVERGREEN ENTERPRISES INC

D-U-N-S 78-583-9247
■ **ASHFORD HOSPITALITY LIMITED PARTNERSHIP**
(*Suby of* ASHFORD HOSPITALITY TRUST INC) ★
14185 Dallas Pkwy # 1100, Dallas, TX 75254-1319
Tel (972) 778-9452 *Founded/Ownrshp* 2003
Sales 348.8MM^E *EMP* 2,366^E
SIC 6722 Management investment, open-end
Genl Pt: Montgomery Bennett

D-U-N-S 07-927-1103
ASHFORD HOSPITALITY PRIME INC
14185 Dallas Pkwy # 1100, Dallas, TX 75254-1319
Tel (972) 490-9600 *Founded/Ownrshp* 2013
Sales 349.5MM *EMP* 108
SIC 6798 Real estate investment trusts
CEO: Richard J Stockton
**Ch Bd:* Monty J Bennett
**Pr:* Douglas A Kessler
COO: David A Brooks
CFO: Deric S Eubanks
Ex VP: Jeremy Welter
Dir Sec: J Robison Hays III
Board of Directors: Kenneth Hopkins Fearn Jr, Curtis B McWilliams, W Micheal Murphy, Matthew D Rinaldi, Andrew L Strong

D-U-N-S 13-946-8065
ASHFORD HOSPITALITY TRUST INC
14185 Dallas Pkwy # 1100, Dallas, TX 75254-4308
Tel (972) 490-9600 *Founded/Ownrshp* 2003
Sales 794.8MM *EMP* 108^E
SIC 6798 6733 Real estate investment trusts; Trusts
Ch Bd: Montgomery J Bennett
Pr: Douglas A Kessler
COO: David A Brooks
COO: Mark Sharkey
CFO: Deric S Eubanks
Treas: Adil Eduljee
Ex VP: Jeremy Welter
Sr VP: Donald J Denzin
VP: Pia Ackerman
VP: Eric Batis
VP: Tripp Foshee
VP: Pam Golden
VP: Victor Grant
VP: Brian R Hughes
VP: Mark Matz
VP: John O'Sullivan
VP: Chris Peckham
VP: Mitch Roberts
VP: Doug Smolinski
VP: Adam Tegge
VP: Patrick Webber

D-U-N-S 07-918-1185
■ **ASHFORD UNIVERSITY LLC**
(*Suby of* BRIDGEPOINT EDUCATION INC) ★
8620 Spectrum Center Blvd # 100, San Diego, CA 92123-1427
Tel (800) 798-0584 *Founded/Ownrshp* 2013
Sales 108.4MM^E *EMP* 5,288^E
SIC 8221 Colleges & universities; University
CEO: Dr Richard L Pattenaude
**COO:* Steve Quattrociocchi
**Sr VP:* Sheri Jones
Sr VP: Bridget McGuire
**Sr VP:* Bill Ness
VP: Amber Eckert
VP: Kenneth Haight
VP: Mike Robinson
VP: Jim Smith
VP: Thad Trapp
QA Dir: Carmel Hernandez

D-U-N-S 00-121-2930 IMP
ASHGROVE HOLDINGS LLC
(*Suby of* VINCI)
12001 Sunrise Valley Dr, Reston, VA 20191-3450
Tel (703) 821-1175 *Founded/Ownrshp* 1996
Sales 167.9MM^E *EMP* 220
SIC 5032 Concrete & cinder building products
CEO: Roger Bloomfield
Dir IT: Jacques Bloomfield
Mktg Dir: Alicia Olson

ASHLAND
See INTERNATIONAL SPECIALTY PRODUCTS INC

D-U-N-S 08-033-3866
▲ **ASHLAND GLOBAL HOLDINGS INC**
50 E Rivercenter Blvd, Covington, KY 41011-1683
Tel (859) 815-3333 *Founded/Ownrshp* 2016
Sales 5.3MMM^E *EMP* 10,500^E
Tkr Sym ASH *Exch* NYS
SIC 5169 Chemicals & allied products
Ch Bd: William A Wulfsohn
Pr: Luis Fernandez-Moreno
CFO: J Kevin Willis
Ofcr: Gregory W Elliott
Ofcr: Anne T Schumann
Sr VP: Peter J Ganz
VP: J William Heitman
VP: Keith C Silverman

D-U-N-S 07-267-7636
ASHLAND HOSPITAL CORP
KING'S DAUGHTERS MEDICAL CTR
(*Suby of* KINGS DAUGHTERS HEALTH SYSTEM INC) ★
2201 Lexington Ave, Ashland, KY 41101-2843
Tel (606) 408-4000 *Founded/Ownrshp* 1941
Sales 465.2MM *EMP* 4,200
Accts Parentebeard Llc Philadelphia
SIC 8062 General medical & surgical hospitals
Pr: Fred L Jackson
Chf Path: Katalin Z Kovacs
Chf Path: Susan Prasher
Chf OB: Tony Dotson
Chf Rad: Robert Penkava
COO: Phil Campbell
COO: Andrea Mc Kay
CFO: Paul Mc Dowell
CFO: Paul McDowdil
**CFO:* Paul McDowell
CFO: Jeff Treasure
Ofcr: Nikki Smith-Kemper
Ofcr: Rob Walters
Sr VP: Philip W Fioret
VP: Larry Bosserman
VP: Philip Fioret
VP: Ray Mecca
VP: Mona Thompson
Dir Lab: Shawn Boggs

D-U-N-S 00-500-3264
■ **ASHLAND LLC**
(*Suby of* ASHLAND GLOBAL HOLDINGS INC) ★
50 E Rivercenter Blvd # 1600, Covington, KY 41011-1678
Tel (859) 815-3333 *Founded/Ownrshp* 2016
Sales 5.3MMM *EMP* 10,500^E
SIC 2899 2851 2821 2911 5169 7549 Chemical preparations; Water treating compounds; Paints & allied products; Plastics materials & resins; Polyesters; Ester gum; Heavy distillates; Oils, lubricating; Chemicals & allied products; Trailer maintenance
Ch Bd: William A Wulfsohn
CFO: J Kevin Willis
Chf Cred: Peter J Ganz
VP: Blair Boggs
VP: Peter Collette
VP: Gregory W Elliott
VP: Matt Furcolo
VP: David L Hausrath
VP: J William Heitman
VP: John Joy
VP: Sherri Nelson
VP: J M Quin
VP: Anne T Schumann
VP: Mitchell Skaggs
VP: Stan Turner
VP: Roger D Walker
Board of Directors: Vada O Manager, Brendan M Cummins, William G Dempsey, Roger W Hale, Stephen F Kirk, Barry W Perry, Mark C Rohr, George A Schaefer Jr, Janice J Teal, Michael J Ward

D-U-N-S 15-272-8887 IMP/EXP
■ **ASHLAND SPECIALTY INGREDIENTS GP**
(*Suby of* ASHLAND LLC) ★
8145 Blazer Dr, Wilmington, DE 19808
Tel (302) 594-5000 *Founded/Ownrshp* 2014
Sales 303.1MM^E *EMP* 1,180
SIC 2869 Industrial organic chemicals
Mng Pt: John Televantos
Ex VP: Richard Weinberg
Mktg Mgr: Deneen Law

D-U-N-S 93-340-4030
ASHLEY DISTRIBUTION SERVICES LTD
A D S
(*Suby of* ASHLEY FURNITURE INDUSTRIES INC) ★
1 Ashley Way, Arcadia, WI 54612-1218
Tel (608) 323-3377 *Founded/Ownrshp* 1993
Sales 91.1MM^E *EMP* 800
SIC 4213 Trucking, except local
CEO: Todd R Wanek
Treas: Shari Wagner
**Ex VP:* John Leighty
**VP:* Larry Corey
Trfc Dir: Mary Knutson
Trfc Dir: Barbara Montagne

ASHLEY FURNITURE HOMESTORE
See RBLS INC

ASHLEY FURNITURE HOMESTORE
See HILL COUNTRY FURNITURE PARTNERS LTD

D-U-N-S 05-273-8531 IMP/EXP
ASHLEY FURNITURE INDUSTRIES INC
1 Ashley Way, Arcadia, WI 54612-1200
Tel (608) 323-3377 *Founded/Ownrshp* 1970
Sales 5.3MMM^E *EMP* 16,300
SIC 2512 2511 Upholstered household furniture; Wood upholstered chairs & couches; Wood household furniture; Kitchen & dining room furniture; Wood bedroom furniture
Ch Bd: Ronald G Wanek
**Pr:* Todd Wanek
Ofcr: Mike Jungwirth
Ex VP: Fred Bellio
Ex VP: Robert White
VP: Emad Barakat
VP: Cribbs David
VP: Brenda Dillon
VP: Paul Dotta
VP: Keri Durkin
VP: Archie Hall
VP: Bo Harvey
VP: Karen Helgeson
VP: Harry Janke
VP: Scott Kruger
VP: Jon Kuerschner
VP: Tony Laplante
VP: John Leighty
VP: Tommylicurgo Licurgo
VP: Al Maicki
VP: Tamara Matchey

D-U-N-S 05-486-7155 IMP/EXP
ASHLEY MEDICAL SUPPLY INC
1911 Church St, Nashville, TN 37203-2313
Tel (615) 329-3150 *Founded/Ownrshp* 2015
Sales 362.4MM^E *EMP* 175
SIC 5047

ASHMAN MEDALS & RECYCL COMANY
See GAMTEX INDUSTRIES LP

D-U-N-S 07-111-5620
ASHTABULA COUNTY COMMISSIONERS
25 W Jefferson St, Jefferson, OH 44047-1027
Tel (440) 576-3649 *Founded/Ownrshp* 1811
Sales NA *EMP* 1,220
SIC 9121 County commissioner;
**Prin:* Albert J Dispenza

D-U-N-S 07-774-7947
ASHTABULA COUNTY MEDICAL CENTER
2420 Lake Ave, Ashtabula, OH 44004-4970
Tel (440) 997-2262 *Founded/Ownrshp* 1902
Sales 110.4MM *EMP* 900
SIC 8062 General medical & surgical hospitals
CEO: Michael Habowski
Pr: Kenneth Philibin
COO: Kathy Crawford
CFO: Don Kepner
Ch: Joe Giangola
Sec: Bill Dingledine
Trst: Ashok Kondru
VP: Lew Hutchison
VP: Jordan Javier
Dir OR: Lu Bruno
Dir Rx: Frank Caputo

D-U-N-S 87-948-6165
ASHTEAD HOLDINGS LLC
(*Suby of* ASHTEAD US HOLDINGS INC) ★
2341 Deerfield Dr, Fort Mill, SC 29715-8298
Tel (803) 578-5811 *Founded/Ownrshp* 1990
Sales 3.3MMM^E *EMP* 8,262
SIC 7353 7359 5082 Heavy construction equipment rental; Equipment rental & leasing; Construction & mining machinery
Sls Mgr: Vaughn Nelson

D-U-N-S 07-994-5579
ASHTEAD US HOLDINGS INC
(*Suby of* ASHTEAD HOLDINGS PUBLIC LIMITED COMPANY)
401 S Tryon St, Charlotte, NC 28202-1934
Tel (803) 578-5811 *Founded/Ownrshp* 2014
Sales 3.3MMM^E *EMP* 8,263
SIC 7353 7359 5082 Heavy construction equipment rental; Equipment rental & leasing; Construction & mining machinery
CEO: Brendan C Horgan
Ch Bd: Geoffrey Drabble
Treas: John Schoenberger

D-U-N-S 17-770-7916 IMP
ASI COMPUTER TECHNOLOGIES INC
A S I
48289 Fremont Blvd, Fremont, CA 94538-6510
Tel (510) 226-8000 *Founded/Ownrshp* 1987
Sales 1.5MMM^E *EMP* 700
Accts Marcum Llp San Francisco Ca
SIC 5045 3577 Disk drives; Keying equipment; Printers, computer; Terminals, computer; Computer output to microfilm units
CEO: Christine Liang
**Ch Bd:* Marcel Liang
Ex VP: Brian Clark
Ex VP: Orlando Lopez
Genl Mgr: Steve Vangellow
Genl Mgr: Pendora Wong
Snr PM: Jon Norris

D-U-N-S 60-183-8209 IMP
ASI CONSTRUCTORS INC
A S I
1850 E Platteville Blvd, Pueblo West, CO 81007-1030
Tel (719) 647-2821 *Founded/Ownrshp* 2005
Sales 94.7MM^E *EMP* 110^E
SIC 1629 Dam construction
Pr: John Bowen
**VP:* Lee Schermerhorn

D-U-N-S 62-408-8444
ASI SYSTEM INTEGRATION INC
48 W 37th St Fl 4, New York, NY 10018-7322
Tel (212) 695-7970 *Founded/Ownrshp* 2005
Sales 115.5MM^E *EMP* 395
SIC 7379 Computer related consulting services
Ch: Sonny Chabra
**Pr:* Chris Mammano
**COO:* Narinder Chabra
**CFO:* Ravi Thakur
VP: Tom Beer

D-U-N-S 13-736-9740 IMP/EXP
ASIA CHEMICAL CORP INC
11950 Airline Dr Ste 300, Houston, TX 77037-1024
Tel (281) 445-1793 *Founded/Ownrshp* 1985
Sales 148.6MM^E *EMP* 45
SIC 5162 Plastics resins; Plastics materials
CEO: George C Yang
**VP:* Ken Yang

D-U-N-S 07-463-2001 IMP/EXP
ASIA FOUNDATION
465 California St Fl 9, San Francisco, CA 94104-1892
Tel (415) 982-4640 *Founded/Ownrshp* 1954
Sales 120.5MM *EMP* 700
Accts Clark Nuber Ps Bellevue Wa
SIC 6732 Charitable trust management
Pr: David D Arnold
**COO:* Suzanne Siskel
**CFO:* Ken Krug
Ofcr: Nadia Ali
Ofcr: Diana Alvord
Ofcr: Kate Bollinger
Ofcr: Julia Chen
Ofcr: Oliver Petzold
Ofcr: Yupa Phusahas
Ofcr: Sunil Pillai
Ofcr: Wendy Rockett
**VP:* Richard H Fuller
**VP:* Gordon Hein
VP: Nancy Yuan
Assoc Dir: Eileen Pennington

D-U-N-S 84-875-3182
ASIAINFO-LINKAGE INC
(*Suby of* ASIAINFO TECHNOLOGIES(CHINA), INC.)
5201 Great America Pkwy # 356, Santa Clara, CA 95054-1127
Tel (408) 970-9788 *Founded/Ownrshp* 1994
Sales 481.0MM *EMP* 1,500
SIC 4813
CEO: Steve Zhang
**CFO:* Ying Han
CFO: Michael Wu
**Ex VP:* Yadong Jin
VP: Jie Li
VP: WEI LI
**VP:* Lihua Yan
Prin: Tom Manning
Ex Dir: Tao Long
Ex Dir: Yungang Lu
Ex Dir: Edward Tian

D-U-N-S 06-798-0797 IMP/EXP
ASICS AMERICA CORP (CA)
ASICS TIGER
(*Suby of* ASICS CORPORATION)
80 Technology Dr, Irvine, CA 92618-2301
Tel (949) 453-8888 *Founded/Ownrshp* 1973
Sales 206.2MM^E *EMP* 195
SIC 5139 5136 5137 2369 2339 2321 Footwear, athletic; Sportswear, men's & boys'; Men's & boys' furnishings; Sportswear, women's & children's; Women's & children's accessories; Girls' & children's outerwear; Women's & misses' outerwear; Men's & boys' furnishings
CEO: Kevin Wulff
**Ch Bd:* Seiho Gohashi
**Pr:* Richard Bourne

VP: Andrew Richard
Dir IT: Anthony Mancao
IT Man: Craig Lindsay
Opers Mgr: Leo Ghazarian
Mktg Mgr: Stefanie Daniel

ASICS TIGER
See ASICS AMERICA CORP

D-U-N-S 96-437-8454 IMP/EXP
ASK CHEMICALS LP
(*Suby of* ASK CHEMICALS GMBH)
495 Metro Pl S Ste 250, Dublin, OH 43017-5319
Tel (614) 763-0384 *Founded/Ownrshp* 2010
Sales 105.4MM^E *EMP* 150
SIC 2899 Chemical preparations
CEO: Frank Coenen
COO: Scott Hoertz
Ch: Stefan Sommer
Sr VP: Daniel Salak
IT Man: Peter Mothes
Opers Mgr: Linda Kilby
Opers Mgr: Raymond Vanboven
Mktg Mgr: Charlie Hoertz

ASK.COM
See IAC SEARCH & MEDIA INC

ASKINARD
See A&S SERVICES GROUP LLC

D-U-N-S 08-170-7325 IMP
ASM AMERICA INC
(*Suby of* ASM INTERNATIONAL N.V.)
3440 E University Dr, Phoenix, AZ 85034-7255
Tel (602) 470-5700 *Founded/Ownrshp* 1980
Sales 99.5MM^E *EMP* 577
SIC 3559

D-U-N-S 07-483-5299
ASM RESEARCH LLC
(*Suby of* ACCENTURE NATIONAL SEC SVCS) ★
4050 Legato Rd Ste 1100, Fairfax, VA 22033-2895
Tel (703) 645-0420 *Founded/Ownrshp* 2013
Sales 91.5MM^E *EMP* 450
SIC 7371 8731

D-U-N-S 11-478-3041 IMP
ASML US INC
(*Suby of* ASML NETHERLANDS B.V.)
2650 W Geronimo Pl, Chandler, AZ 85224-4994
Tel (480) 696-2888 *Founded/Ownrshp* 1984
Sales 1.0MMM^E *EMP* 1,277^E
SIC 5065 7629 Electronic parts & equipment; Electrical repair shops
CEO: Eric Meurice
**Pr:* Martin Van Den Brink
**Pr:* Jerry Drube
**CEO:* Peter Wennink
**COO:* Frederic Schneider Maunoury
**Treas:* Michael D Holdaway
**Ex VP:* Frits Van Hout
Exec: Vallorie Gribschaw
Genl Mgr: Kimberlee Rose
Snr Mgr: Keith Gronlund

ASML USA
See CYMER LLC

D-U-N-S 88-498-1002 IMP
ASMO GREENVILLE OF NORTH CAROLINA INC
ASAMO CO
(*Suby of* ASMO NORTH AMERICA LLC) ★
1125 Sugg Pkwy, Greenville, NC 27834-9009
Tel (252) 754-1000 *Founded/Ownrshp* 1994
Sales 145.8MM^E *EMP* 463
SIC 3594 Fluid power motors
Pr: Isamu Sam Tada
**Treas:* Makoto Sugiura
Prd Mgr: Todd Winkler

D-U-N-S 15-193-3934 EXP
ASMO MAUNFACTURING INC
A M I
(*Suby of* ASMO NORTH AMERICA LLC) ★
500 Fritz Keiper Blvd, Battle Creek, MI 49037-7306
Tel (269) 441-2040 *Founded/Ownrshp* 1999
Sales 127.8MM^E *EMP* 700^E
SIC 3621 3089 Motors, electric; Plastic & fiberglass tanks
Pr: Yoneo Wada
**Treas:* Tadashi Ito
Plnt Mgr: Stan Hurn

D-U-N-S 05-431-3080 IMP
ASMO NORTH AMERICA LLC
(*Suby of* ASMO CO.,LTD.)
470 Crawford Rd, Statesville, NC 28625-8545
Tel (704) 872-2319 *Founded/Ownrshp* 1999
Sales 502.5MM^E *EMP* 2,000
SIC 3089 3621 Plastic & fiberglass tanks; Motors, electric
Pr: Nobuharu Mizuno

D-U-N-S 83-443-9887 IMP/EXP
ASMO NORTH CAROLINA INC
(*Suby of* ASMO NORTH AMERICA LLC) ★
470 Crawford Rd, Statesville, NC 28625-8545
Tel (704) 878-6663 *Founded/Ownrshp* 1995
Sales 228.8MM^E *EMP* 1,300
SIC 3519 3621 Gasoline engines; Motors & generators
Pr: Yutaka Kuroyanagi
**Treas:* Takashi Suzuki
**Ex VP:* Kazu Suzuki
VP: Robby Wilson
CIO: Fuzuki Kawai
QA Dir: Avery Burnett
QA Dir: Lauren Howard
QA Dir: Chris Pepino
Mfg Dir: Roy Cronce
Prd Mgr: Lorenzo Watts
Ql Cn Mgr: Gregory Chappell

D-U-N-S 08-025-0142
ASP BLADE INTERMEDIATE HOLDINGS INC
299 Park Ave Fl 34, New York, NY 10171-3805
Tel (212) 476-8000 *Founded/Ownrshp* 2015
Sales 911.4MM^E *EMP* 4,400^E
SIC 3531 3523 6719 Construction machinery; Forestry related equipment; Farm machinery & equipment; Cutters & blowers, ensilage; Tractors, farm; Investment holding companies, except banks
Pr: Loren S Easton

D-U-N-S 07-883-9211
ASP HHI HOLDINGS INC
2727 W 14 Mile Rd, Royal Oak, MI 48073-1712
Tel (248) 597-3800 *Founded/Ownrshp* 2012
Sales 101.1MM^E *EMP* 3,000
SIC 3462 Automotive & internal combustion engine forgings
CFO: Mike Johnson

D-U-N-S 07-947-4986
ASP MD HOLDINGS INC
47659 Halyard Dr, Plymouth, MI 48170-2429
Tel (734) 207-6200 *Founded/Ownrshp* 2012
Sales 1.2MMM^E *EMP* 6,600
SIC 5013 Automotive supplies & parts; Automotive engines & engine parts; Automotive hardware; Automotive supplies
CEO: Thomas A Amato
**Treas:* Jan Van Dijk

D-U-N-S 16-142-1532
ASP WESTWARD LP
HOUSTON COMMUNITY NEWSPAPER
523 N Sam Houston Pkwy E # 600, Houston, TX 77060-4053
Tel (713) 256-0953 *Founded/Ownrshp* 2002
Sales 116.6MM^E *EMP* 450
SIC 2711 Newspapers, publishing & printing
CEO: James W Hopson
Bd of Dir: Michael Sudhalter
Ex Dir: Marc Hoy
S&M/VP: Jim Pollard

ASPECT ENERGY
See ACOUSTIC VENTURES LLC

D-U-N-S 96-851-3429
ASPECT SOFTWARE GROUP HOLDINGS LTD
2325 E Camelback Rd # 700, Phoenix, AZ 85016-3422
Tel (602) 282-1500 *Founded/Ownrshp* 1981
Sales 436.7MM *EMP* 1,900^E
SIC 7373 Computer integrated systems design; Systems software development services; Computer-aided system services
Ch Bd: Stewart M Bloom
CFO: Robert Krakauer
Chf Mktg O: James Freeze
Sr VP: Stephen Beaver
Sr VP: Guido De Koning
VP: Rusty Coleman
VP: Kenneth Ewell

D-U-N-S 05-780-2209
ASPECT SOFTWARE INC
LINGUASYS
(*Suby of* ASPECT SOFTWARE GROUP HOLDINGS LTD) ★
2325 E Camelback Rd # 700, Phoenix, AZ 85016-3422
Tel (978) 250-7900 *Founded/Ownrshp* 2004
Sales 413.7MM^E *EMP* 1,800
SIC 7371 Computer software development
CEO: Stewart M Bloom
**Ch Bd:* Jim Foy
Pr: Chris Koziol
CEO: Mohamad Ali
**CEO:* Stewart Bloom
**CFO:* Bob Krakauer
CFO: Michael J Provenzano III
Ex VP: Michael Sheridan
**Sr VP:* Stephen Beaver
Sr VP: Mike Bourke
Sr VP: Gwen Braygreen
Sr VP: Laurie Cairns
Sr VP: Guido De Koning
**Sr VP:* Kenneth Ewell
Sr VP: Joe Gagnon
**Sr VP:* Jim Haskin
Sr VP: David Herzog
Sr VP: Mark King
**Sr VP:* Spence Mallder
Sr VP: Laura Clayton McDonnell
Sr VP: David Reibel

D-U-N-S 01-292-4069
▲ ASPEN AEROGELS INC
30 Forbes Rd Bldg B, Northborough, MA 01532-2501
Tel (508) 691-1111 *Founded/Ownrshp* 2001
Sales 122.5MM *EMP* 275^E
Tkr Sym ASPN *Exch* NYS
SIC 2899 Insulating compounds
Pr: Donald R Young
**Ch Bd:* Mark L Noetzel
CFO: John F Fairbanks
Sr VP: Corby C Whitaker
VP: George L Gould
VP Opers: Jeffrey Ball
Ql Cn Mgr: Craig Macinnis
Sls Dir: Chris Towry
Sls Mgr: Sean Grimes
Corp Couns: Poongs Muthukumaran
Board of Directors: P Ramsay Battin, Robert M Gervis, Craig A Huff, Steven R Mitchell, William P Noglows, Richard F Reilly

D-U-N-S 04-208-9128
ASPEN DENTAL MANAGEMENT INC
281 Sanders Creek Pkwy, East Syracuse, NY 13057-1307
Tel (315) 454-6000 *Founded/Ownrshp* 1999
Sales 139.2MM^E *EMP* 808
SIC 8021 8072 6794 Dental clinic; Dental laboratories; Franchises, selling or licensing
Ch Bd: Robert A Fontana
COO: Rob Connor
CFO: Geoff Lewis
Ofcr: Mark Weisberger
VP: Ryan Murdock
Rgnl Mgr: Scott Malarkey
Off Mgr: Jess Eppler
Off Mgr: Kris Rhoades
Ql Cn Mgr: Scott Purdy

D-U-N-S 17-828-0202
■ ASPEN EDUCATION GROUP INC
(*Suby of* CRC HEALTH CORP) ★
17777 Center Court Dr N # 300, Cerritos, CA 90703-9320
Tel (562) 467-5500 *Founded/Ownrshp* 2006
Sales 56.4MM^E *EMP* 1,913
SIC 8741 8322 Management services; General counseling services
CEO: Elliot A Sainer
**COO:* Jim Dredge
**CFO:* Kyle Wescoat
Bd of Dir: Bob Finzi
Bd of Dir: Janet A Hickey
VP: Peter Mair
Ex Dir: Laura Mack

D-U-N-S 78-958-3247
ASPEN ELECTRIC AND SUPPLY INC
LIGHTWORKS OF STEAMBOAT
1890 Loggers Ln Unit C, Steamboat Springs, CO 80487-5120
Tel (970) 879-3905 *Founded/Ownrshp* 1985
Sales 116.2MM *EMP* 7
SIC 5719 1731 Lighting fixtures; Electrical work
Pr: Richard Schwanke
**Sec:* Nancy Schwanke

ASPEN GROUP
See FBI BUILDINGS INC

D-U-N-S 00-888-1609
■ ASPEN HOLDINGS INC
FIRSTCOMP
(*Suby of* MARKEL CORP) ★
222 S 15th St Ste 1500n, Omaha, NE 68102-1656
Tel (402) 926-0099 *Founded/Ownrshp* 1996, 2010
Sales 85.8MM^E *EMP* 550^E
SIC 6719 Investment holding companies, except banks
Pr: Luke Yaransian
VP: Scott Emery
VP: Emily Huneke
VP: Jim O'Halloran
Dir IT: Brent Fay
Sls Mgr: Joshua Bjorkman
Sls Mgr: Vanessa Bloom

D-U-N-S 07-645-3711
ASPEN INSTITUTE
1 Dupont Cir Nw Ste 700, Washington, DC 20036-1133
Tel (202) 736-5800 *Founded/Ownrshp* 1949
Sales 96.4MM *EMP* 300
Accts Raffa Pc Washington Dc
SIC 8299 Educational service, nondegree granting: continuing educ.
Ch: Robert Steel
**Pr:* Elliot Gerosm
**Pr:* Walter Isaacson
**Pr:* Peter Reiling
**Pr:* Susan Sherwin
**CFO:* Dolores Gorgone
**Ch:* James S Crown
**Ch:* Leonard Lauder
**Sec:* Amy Margerum
Ex VP: Namita Khasat
Prgrm Mgr: David Mitchell

D-U-N-S 17-624-7161
■ ASPEN MARKETING SERVICES LLC
(*Suby of* EPSILON DATA MANAGEMENT LLC) ★
1240 W North Ave, West Chicago, IL 60185-1087
Tel (630) 293-9600 *Founded/Ownrshp* 2011
Sales 115.6MM^E *EMP* 750
SIC 8743 8748 5199 Sales promotion; Employee programs administration; Advertising specialties
Pr: Patrick J O'Rahilly
**COO:* Cathy Lang
**CFO:* Donald Danner
Ex VP: Jim Huston
Ex VP: John Tufo
VP: Jim Carroll
VP: Denny Dee
**VP:* Cathy Horn
VP: Kevin Huck
VP: Carrin Kapecki
VP: Cindy Lappetito
VP: Mary Schlafly
VP: Kimberly Tebbs
VP: Jullie Welsh
VP: Mark Wollney
Exec: Robin Burgett
Exec: Paul Stringer
Creative D: Scott Hart

D-U-N-S 08-679-2116 IMP/EXP
ASPEN PRODUCTS INC
4231 Clary Blvd, Kansas City, MO 64130-2328
Tel (816) 921-0234 *Founded/Ownrshp* 1968
Sales 130.8MM^E *EMP* 600^E
SIC 2674 Bags: uncoated paper & multiwall
Pr: William P Biggins Jr

D-U-N-S 02-768-0821 IMP
■ ASPEN SURGICAL PRODUCTS INC
(*Suby of* HILL-ROM INC) ★
6945 Southbelt Dr Se, Caledonia, MI 49316-7664
Tel (616) 698-7100 *Founded/Ownrshp* 2014
Sales 132.2MM^E *EMP* 285
SIC 5047 Medical equipment & supplies
Pr: Terry O Rourke
CFO: Terry O'Rourke
Sr VP: Claude Grant
Dir IT: Mark Seyfried
Ql Cn Mgr: Richard Gridley
Natl Sales: Kristi Schelhaas
Sls Mgr: Brooke Steighorst

D-U-N-S 04-551-4031
▲ ASPEN TECHNOLOGY INC
20 Crosby Dr, Bedford, MA 01730-1402
Tel (781) 221-6400 *Founded/Ownrshp* 1981
Sales 472.3MM *EMP* 1,377^E
Accts Kpmg Llp Boston Massachuset
Tkr Sym AZPN *Exch* NGS
SIC 7371 7372 Custom computer programming services; Prepackaged software; Application computer software
Pr: Antonio J Pietri
Ch Bd: Robert M Whelan Jr
CFO: Karl E Johnsen
CFO: Mark P Sullivan
Ex VP: Bill Griffin
Ex VP: Paul Taylor
Sr VP: Michael Catt
Sr VP: John W Hague
Sr VP: Frederic G Hammond
Sr VP: Richard Packwood
Sr VP: Suresh Sundaram
Sr VP: Hedwig Veith Whitney
VP: Chauchyun Chen
VP: Clint Clemans
VP: Jeffrey Duni
VP: James Hintlian
VP: Matthew Holland
VP: Basil Joffe
VP: John Lamountain
VP: Andy Lui
VP: Valdimir Mahalec

D-U-N-S 16-629-2917
ASPHALT AND FUEL SUPPLY LLC
4200 E Skelly Dr Ste 600, Tulsa, OK 74135-3210
Tel (918) 488-1339 *Founded/Ownrship* 2003
Sales 147.5MM^E *EMP* 75
SIC 5172 Petroleum products
Sls Mgr: Matt Roberts

D-U-N-S 00-642-0160
ASPHALT MATERIALS INC
5400 W 86th St, Indianapolis, IN 46268-1537
Tel (317) 872-6010 *Founded/Ownrshp* 1957
Sales 314.7MM^E *EMP* 590
SIC 2951 1442 Asphalt & asphaltic paving mixtures (not from refineries); Sand mining; Gravel mining
**Pr:* David N Blackburn
**Treas:* John P Vercruysse
VP: Jim Coplan
VP: Eric Werner
CIO: Brad Hudson
Plnt Mgr: Randy Foley
Board of Directors: Tom Fehsenfeld, James C Fehsenfeld, Nick Rutigliano, Nancy Smith

D-U-N-S 79-653-7439
ASPHALT SPECIALTIES CO INC
ASCI READY MIX
10100 Dallas St, Henderson, CO 80640-8491
Tel (303) 289-8555 *Founded/Ownrshp* 1991
Sales 90.1MM^E *EMP* 256^E
SIC 1611

D-U-N-S 17-794-5995
ASPHALT SURFACE TECHNOLOGIES CORP
ASTECH
8348 Ridgewood Rd, Saint Joseph, MN 56374-9443
Tel (320) 363-8500 *Founded/Ownrshp* 1986
Sales 93.6MM^E *EMP* 65
Accts Kern Dewenter Viere Ltd St
SIC 1611 4959 Resurfacing contractor; Snowplowing
Pr: Bruce B Batzer
**VP:* Mary L Popp
**VP:* Dale R Strandberg

D-U-N-S 08-007-7351
ASPIRE HOLDINGS LLC
ENDEAVOUR
811 Main St Ste 2100, Houston, TX 77002-6128
Tel (713) 307-8700 *Founded/Ownrshp* 2015
Sales 300.0MM *EMP* 20
SIC 6719 Investment holding companies, except banks
Treas: Kelley Pruetz
**CFO:* Cathy Stubbs

D-U-N-S 07-148-2236
ASPIRE OF WESTERN NEW YORK INC
ASPIRE OF WNY
2356 N Forest Rd, Getzville, NY 14068-1224
Tel (716) 505-5500 *Founded/Ownrshp* 1948
Sales 65.6MM *EMP* 1,400
Accts Dopkins & Company Llp Buffalo
SIC 8322 Association for the handicapped
Pr: Thomas Sy
Pr: John Ballow
**CFO:* Edward Handschumaker Jr
Assoc Dir: Melissa Roth
Genl Mgr: Kathleen Kennedy

ASPIRE OF WNY
See ASPIRE OF WESTERN NEW YORK INC

D-U-N-S 01-224-0342
ASPIRE PUBLIC SCHOOLS
1001 22nd Ave Ste 100, Oakland, CA 94606-5232
Tel (510) 251-1660 *Founded/Ownrshp* 1999
Sales 151.4MM *EMP* 1,400
Accts Gilbert Associates Inc Sacram
SIC 8211 Public elementary & secondary schools
CEO: James Willcox
VP: Bess Kennedy
Genl Mgr: Yvonne Parker
Off Mgr: Susie Estrada
Off Mgr: Elvira Iniguez
Psych: Hugo Vazquez

D-U-N-S 79-707-7604
ASPIRUS EMPLOYEE ASSISTANCE
3000 Westhill Dr Ste 102, Wausau, WI 54401-3795
Tel (715) 847-2772 *Founded/Ownrshp* 1990
Sales 91.1MM *EMP* 4
Accts Wipfli Llp Wausau Wi
SIC 8011 Offices & clinics of medical doctors
Prin: Duane L Erwin

D-U-N-S 15-084-7895
ASPIRUS INC
ASPIRUS WAUSAU HOSP GIFT SP
425 Pine Ridge Blvd # 300, Wausau, WI 54401-4124
Tel (715) 847-2121 *Founded/Ownrshp* 1979
Sales 562.0MM^E *EMP* 3,900

Accts Wipfli Llp Wausau Wisconsin
SIC 8062 General medical & surgical hospitals
CEO: Matthew Heywood
Dir Vol: Yolanda Voigt
CFO: Sidney Sczygelski
VP: Margaret Anderson
VP: Jean Burgener
VP: Sara Lusignan
VP: Todd Richardson
VP: Lisa Rowe-Peplinski
Dir OR: Patty Aho
Ex Dir: Kalynn Pempek
Mktg Dir: Catherine Leifeld

ASPIRUS WAUSAU HOSP GIFT SP
See ASPIRUS INC

D-U-N-S 07-476-9324
ASPIRUS WAUSAU HOSPITAL INC
(*Suby of* ASPIRUS WAUSAU HOSP GIFT SP) ★
425 Pine Ridge Blvd # 1, Wausau, WI 54401-4122
Tel (715) 847-2121 *Founded/Ownrshp* 1970
Sales 369.8MM *EMP* 3,500
Accts Wipfli Llp Wausau Wi
SIC 8062 General medical & surgical hospitals
CEO: Duane Erwin
Chf Rad: Ian Kurth
Chf Rad: Stephen Stine
**Pr:* Darrell Lentz
COO: Dean Danner
CFO: Sidney Sczygelsky
Sr VP: Mike Conway
Sr VP: Cari Logemann
VP: Michelle Boyland
VP: Brenda Erdman
Dir OR: Susan Tobin
Mng Ofcr: Amanda Krueger

D-U-N-S 00-791-1753 IMP/EXP
ASPLUNDH TREE EXPERT CO (PA)
708 Blair Mill Rd, Willow Grove, PA 19090-1701
Tel (215) 784-4200 *Founded/Ownrshp* 1946
Sales 5.4MMM^E *EMP* 30,000
SIC 0783 1629 1623 1611 6411 Ornamental shrub & tree services; Tree trimming services for public utility lines; Removal services, bush & tree; Spraying services, ornamental tree; Railroad & subway construction; Land clearing contractor; Underground utilities contractor; Electric power line construction; Telephone & communication line construction; Highway & street sign installation; Highway & street maintenance; Insurance agents, brokers & service
Ch Bd: Christopher B Asplundh
**Pr:* Scott M Asplundh
**Treas:* Joseph P Dwyer
Bd of Dir: James Crosby
Bd of Dir: Bill Fowler
Ex VP: Bill Catalfio
Ex VP: Pat Pinelli
VP: Robbie Adkins
VP: Holland Art
**VP:* Brent D Asplundh
VP: Shannon Barrett
**VP:* Stephen S Bostock
VP: Bud Branham
VP: Mark Fecteau
VP: Trevor Gardiner
**VP:* Douglas L Gober
**VP:* George E Graham Jr
VP: Tom Hadley
VP: Patrick Hislop
VP: Henry Jinks
VP: Larry Jones

D-U-N-S 02-964-7904
ASPLUNDISH TREE EXPERT CO
(*Suby of* ASPLUNDH TREE EXPERT CO) ★
4070 North Point Rd, Baltimore, MD 21222-3622
Tel (443) 242-6666 *Founded/Ownrshp* 2013
Sales 6.5MM^E *EMP* 1,370^E
SIC 0783 Ornamental shrub & tree services

D-U-N-S 13-190-3945 IMP/EXP
ASR GROUP INTERNATIONAL INC
(*Suby of* FLORIDA CRYSTALS CORP) ★
1 Federal St, Yonkers, NY 10705-1079
Tel (914) 963-2400 *Founded/Ownrshp* 1998
Sales 111.5MM^E *EMP* 2,000
SIC 2062 Cane sugar refining; Granulated cane sugar from purchased raw sugar or syrup
Co-Pr: Antonio Contreras Jr
**CFO:* Gregory H Smith
**Co-Pr:* Antonio L Contreras Jr
**Co-Pr:* Luis Fernandez
**VP:* Gregory A Maitner
**VP:* Armando A Tabernilla

ASRC
See AMERICAN SYNTHETIC RUBBER CO LLC

D-U-N-S 00-443-5470 IMP
ASRC AEROSPACE CORP
(*Suby of* ASRC FEDERAL HOLDING CO LLC) ★
7000 Muirkirk Meadows Dr # 100, Beltsville, MD 20705-6351
Tel (301) 837-5500 *Founded/Ownrshp* 1999
Sales 111.3MM^E *EMP* 803
SIC 3812 7371 7373 5088 Search & navigation equipment; Custom computer programming services; Computer integrated systems design; Transportation equipment & supplies
Pr: Charles Bengston
**CFO:* Carl Werner
Sr VP: Michele Bond
Sr VP: Cliff Greenblatt
Sr VP: Cass Panciocco
VP: Al Casper
VP: David Clark
VP: Elizabeth Malone
Comm Dir: Angel Brandt
Prin: Kevin Kelly
Prgrm Mgr: Kent Colwell

D-U-N-S 13-940-8244
ASRC COMMUNICATIONS LTD
(*Suby of* ASRC FEDERAL HOLDING CO LLC) ★
7000 Muirkirk Meadows Dr, Beltsville, MD 20705-6350
Tel (301) 837-5500 *Founded/Ownrshp* 2007
Sales 91.2MM^E *EMP* 314
SIC 4813 Telephone communication, except radio
Pr: Matthew Allard
COO: Donald Finnegan
Prgrm Mgr: Nancy Anderson
Prgrm Mgr: Larry Tuttle
Prgrm Mgr: Lakeisha Webb
Dir IT: Charles Wright

D-U-N-S 06-768-8028
ASRC ENERGY SERVICES LLC
(*Suby of* ARCTIC SLOPE REGIONAL CORP) ★
3900 C St Ste 701, Anchorage, AK 99503-5969
Tel (907) 339-6200 *Founded/Ownrshp* 1985
Sales 1.6MMM^E *EMP* 3,500
SIC 1389 Oil & gas wells: building, repairing & dismantling
Pr: Jeff Kinneeveauk
**CFO:* Jens Beck
**CFO:* Michael Reed
**Sr VP:* Mark D Nelson
VP: Bob Anderson
VP: Wyche Ford
**VP:* Don Gray
**VP:* Sam Hill
VP: Mark Mueller
**VP:* Daniel Wuthrich
Sftwr Eng: David Simmons
Board of Directors: Rex Allen Rock Sr, Doug Smith

D-U-N-S 60-603-4049
ASRC ENERGY SERVICES OMEGA LLC
AES OMEGA
(*Suby of* ASRC ENERGY SERVICES LLC) ★
4418 Pesson Rd, New Iberia, LA 70560-8750
Tel (337) 365-6028 *Founded/Ownrshp* 1998
Sales 236.2MM^E *EMP* 500
SIC 1389 3533 Building oil & gas well foundations on site; Oil field machinery & equipment
Pr: Gary Bucchanan
**Pr:* Jeff Kinneeveauk
**COO:* Mark D Nelson
**Sr VP:* Jens Beck
**VP:* Sam Hill
**VP:* Daniel Wuthrich
Prin: Angela Granger
Sfty Mgr: Todd Labac
Corp Couns: Shelley D Cordova

D-U-N-S 13-590-8783
ASRC FEDERAL HOLDING CO LLC
(*Suby of* ARCTIC SLOPE REGIONAL CORP) ★
7000 Muirkirk Meadows Dr # 100, Beltsville, MD 20705-6351
Tel (301) 345-4500 *Founded/Ownrshp* 2003
Sales 729.1MM^E *EMP* 3,281
SIC 7379 Computer related maintenance services
Pr: Mark Gray
Pr: Shawn Graves
**COO:* Greg Resutek
**CFO:* Gordon Foster
**Chf Cred:* Cliff Greenblatt
Sr VP: Bridget Mederios
VP: Fiona Barshow
VP: Michelle Howell
VP: Elizabeth Malone
Prgrm Mgr: Kate Burk
Prgrm Mgr: Kent Colwell

D-U-N-S 07-541-2031 IMP/EXP
ASSA ABLOY ENTRANCE SYSTEMS US INC
BESAM ENTRANCE SOLUTION
(*Suby of* ASSA ABLOY ENTRANCE SYSTEMS AB)
1900 Airport Rd, Monroe, NC 28110-7396
Tel (704) 290-5520 *Founded/Ownrshp* 1962
Sales 133.1MM^E *EMP* 490
SIC 3699 1796 3442 Door opening & closing devices, electrical; Installing building equipment; Metal doors
Pr: Michael McCaslin
**CFO:* Michael Drury
**VP:* Michael Fisher
**VP:* Michael W Griffin
VP Mktg: Keren Maslow

ASSA ABLOY GROUP COMPANY
See AMERISTAR PERIMETER SECURITY USA INC

D-U-N-S 60-916-1294 IMP/EXP
ASSA ABLOY INC
ASSA ABLOY USA
(*Suby of* ASSA ABLOY AB)
110 Sargent Dr, New Haven, CT 06511-5918
Tel (203) 624-5225 *Founded/Ownrshp* 1996
Sales 2.2MMM^E *EMP* 7,572
SIC 5065 5072 3699 3429 Security control equipment & systems; Security devices, locks; Security control equipment & systems; Keys, locks & related hardware
Pr: Thanasis Molokotos
V Ch: Ben Fellows
CFO: Steve Cavanna
**CFO:* Jeff Mereschuk
**Treas:* Joseph P Hurley
Bd of Dir: Bob Cook
Ex VP: Tomas Eliasson
Ex VP: Michael McGorty
Ex VP: Tim Shea
VP: John Davenport
VP: Paul Hodges
VP: Chris Holloway
VP: Joe Hynds
VP: Leslie Saunders
VP: Dominick Viscuso
Dir Bus: Ben Sultze
Board of Directors: Johan Fant, Otto Hansen, Hans Johansson, Johan Molin, Matti Virtaala, Carolina Dybeck Happe

ASSA ABLOY USA
See SARGENT MANUFACTURING CO

ASSA ABLOY USA
See ASSA ABLOY INC

ASSESSMENT SERVICES
See FRONTIER HEALTH

D-U-N-S 13-892-7632
■ **ASSET ACCEPTANCE CAPITAL CORP**
AACC
(*Suby of* ENCORE CAPITAL GROUP INC) ★
320 E Big Beaver Rd, Troy, MI 48083-1238
Tel (800) 505-5166 *Founded/Ownrshp* 2013
Sales NA *EMP* 1,128^E
SIC 6153 7322 Purchasers of accounts receivable & commercial paper; Collection agency, except real estate
Pr: Rion B Needs
**CFO:* Reid E Simpson
**Sr VP:* Deborah L Everly
VP: Deanna Hatmaker
**VP:* Edwin L Herbert
**VP:* Todd C Langusch
VP: Barbara Sinsley
VP: Ambrish Sundaram
Genl Couns: Lynn Martin

D-U-N-S 60-553-4028
ASSET ACCEPTANCE HOLDINGS LLC
320 E Big Beaver Rd, Troy, MI 48083-1238
Tel (586) 939-9600 *Founded/Ownrshp* 2002
Sales NA *EMP* 1,500
SIC 6141 Personal credit institutions
Pr: Nathaniel Bradley

D-U-N-S 83-619-5289
ASSET ACCEPTANCE LLC
(*Suby of* ASSET ACCEPTANCE HOLDINGS LLC) ★
320 E Big Beaver Rd, Troy, MI 48083-1238
Tel (586) 939-9600 *Founded/Ownrshp* 1994
Sales NA *EMP* 1,400
SIC 6141 Personal credit institutions
Pr: Rion Needs
**CFO:* Reid Simpson
CTO: Darnetta Leak
IT Man: Nigel Adkins

D-U-N-S 07-980-5106
ASSET CHURCHILL MANAGEMENT LLC
TEACHERS INSRN & ANNUITY ASSOC
(*Suby of* TIAA-CREF) ★
430 Park Ave Ste 701, New York, NY 10022-3531
Tel (212) 478-9207 *Founded/Ownrshp* 2015
Sales 39.7MM^E *EMP* 2,507^E
SIC 6799 Venture capital companies
Pr: Ken Kencel
CFO: Alastair Merrick
Sr VP: Keith Ryan

D-U-N-S 02-528-8262
ASSET MANAGEMENT OUTSOURCING RECOVERIES INC
5655 Peachtree Pkwy # 213, Norcross, GA 30092-2812
Tel (678) 259-9600 *Founded/Ownrshp* 1997
Sales 54.7MM^E *EMP* 1,000
SIC 8741 Management services
CEO: Sravan Vellanki
**Pr:* Sarat Vemuri
**CFO:* Scott Tsanos
VP: Richard Black
VP: Joe Lustek
Dir IT: Aaron Burke

D-U-N-S 16-180-5205
ASSET PLUS CORP
950 Corbindale Rd Ste 300, Houston, TX 77024-2849
Tel (713) 782-5800 *Founded/Ownrshp* 1990
Sales 95.1MM^E *EMP* 1,100
SIC 7011 Hotels & motels
Pr: Michael S McGrath
Pr: Stacy Sapio
Pr: Gina Thompson
**COO:* Julie Bonnin
**COO:* M Ryan McGrath
CFO: Monica Morrison
Sr VP: Ruth Ford
Sr VP: Mark Gregory
Sr VP: Karen Hefner
Sr VP: Barrett Kirk
**Sr VP:* Jeff Knowles
VP: Kirk Barrett
VP: Peter Carton
VP: Jenny Cortez
VP: Jason Mermis
VP: Wanda Norrick
VP: Stacy Padon
VP: Sharon Pheris

D-U-N-S 00-974-1828
ASSET PROTECTION & SECURITY SERVICES LP
APSS
5502 Burnham Dr, Corpus Christi, TX 78413-3855
Tel (361) 906-1552 *Founded/Ownrshp* 1994
Sales 84.3MM *EMP* 800
SIC 7381 Security guard service
Genl Pt: Charles S Mandel
**Pt:* Thelma G Garza
**Pt:* Scott Mandel
CFO: Thelma Mandel
VP: Thelma Garza
VP: Brian Mandel
Mktg Mgr: Ssol Delagarza

ASSISI HEIGHTS
See ACADEMY OF OUR LADY OF LOURDES INC

D-U-N-S 87-714-9690
ASSISTED LIVING CONCEPTS LLC
ENLIVANT
(*Suby of* AID HOLDINGS LLC) ★
330 N Wabash Ave Ste 3700, Chicago, IL 60611-7605
Tel (888) 252-5001 *Founded/Ownrshp* 2013
Sales 265.6MM^E *EMP* 4,200
SIC 8052 8051 8059 8082 Intermediate care facilities; Skilled nursing care facilities; Personal care home, with health care; Home health care services
CEO: Jack R Callison Jr
**Pr:* Akhil Sharma
**COO:* Dan Guill
**Ex VP:* Peter Tarsney
Sr VP: Richard L Bertrand
**Sr VP:* Gregory Goins
Sr VP: Nancy Gorshe
**Sr VP:* Meg Ostrom
VP: Steve Baker
VP: Roch Carter
VP: John Sattelmayer
Creative D: Julia Devos

D-U-N-S 00-997-3798
ASSISTIVE TECHNOLOGY GROUP INC
NUMOTION
(*Suby of* NUMOTION) ★
1111 Cromwell Ave Ste 601, Rocky Hill, CT 06067-3455
Tel (860) 257-3443 *Founded/Ownrshp* 1999
Sales 450.0MM *EMP* 726
SIC 5047 Medical equipment & supplies
CEO: Mike Swinford
COO: Warren Degraff
CFO: Tamas Feitel
Ofcr: Jennie D Hanson
VP: David Hess
VP: Jack Pivar
Area Mgr: Rob Regner
Genl Mgr: Bob Lang
Genl Mgr: Kathy Lindsey
IT Man: Craig Flood
IT Man: Julie Kellar

ASSOC FOR HELP
See NYSARC INC

ASSOCIATE EVERETT CLINIC PS
See NORTH PUGET SOUND CENTER FOR SLEEP DISORDERS LLC

ASSOCIATE VP OF RESEARCH
See TEXAS STATE UNIVERSITY-SAN MARCOS

ASSOCIATED AIR FREIGHT
See ASSOCIATED GLOBAL SYSTEMS INC

D-U-N-S 96-953-8529 IMP/EXP
■ **ASSOCIATED AMERICAN INDUSTRIES INC**
APW WYOTT
(*Suby of* STANDEX INTERNATIONAL CORP) ★
1307 N Watters Rd, Allen, TX 75013-5537
Tel (214) 421-7366 *Founded/Ownrshp* 2007
Sales 111.2MM^E *EMP* 520
SIC 3914 3634 3469 3639 Stainless steel ware; Electric household cooking appliances; Toasters, electric: household; Teakettles, electric; Heating units, for electric appliances; Household cooking & kitchen utensils, metal; Kitchen fixtures & equipment: metal, except cast aluminum; Trash compactors, household
Pr: Kevin Clark
**Treas:* Thomas D Debyle
**VP:* Roger L Fix
**VP:* Deborah A Rosen
VP: Brian Rosenbloom
VP Sls: Jim Hoverman

D-U-N-S 02-393-8426
ASSOCIATED ASPHALT INC
130 Church Ave Sw, Roanoke, VA 24011-1906
Tel (540) 345-8867 *Founded/Ownrshp* 1976
Sales 84.6MM^E *EMP* 80
SIC 5032 Asphalt mixture

ASSOCIATED BAG COMPANY
See ASSOCIATED SALES & BAG CO

D-U-N-S 07-477-0363
■ **ASSOCIATED BANC-CORP**
ASSOCIATED BANK
(*Suby of* ASSOCIATED BANK) ★
1305 Main St Ms7722, Stevens Point, WI 54481-2830
Tel (715) 341-0400 *Founded/Ownrshp* 1983
Sales NA *EMP* 1,750
SIC 6035 Federal savings banks
Pr: Paul Vitamine
Assoc VP: Kari Christoph
Sr VP: Lorraine Avery
VP: Gabriel Chappell
VP: Jennifer Fox
VP: Eric Grandusky
Snr Ntwrk: Kory Kitowski
Telecom Mg: Joe Higgins
IT Man: Sue Nigon
Tech Mgr: Terry Tank

D-U-N-S 07-478-8803
▲ **ASSOCIATED BANC-CORP**
ASSOCIATED BANK
433 Main St, Green Bay, WI 54301-5114
Tel (920) 491-7500 *Founded/Ownrshp* 1969
Sales NA *EMP* 4,383^E
Accts Kpmg Llp Chicago Illinois
Tkr Sym ASB *Exch* NYS
SIC 6022 State commercial banks; State trust companies accepting deposits, commercial
Pr: Philip B Flynn
Pr: Kenneth Alburg
Pr: Beverly Bourazak
Pr: Brandon Brown
Pr: Bret Kuether
Pr: Adam Puzach
Pr: Emily Radl
Pr: Jason Smith
Pr: Peg Yanke
CFO: Christopher J Del Moral
Chf Cred: Scott S Hickey
Chf Mktg O: Christopher C Piotrowski
Ofcr: Joanne Breunig
Ofcr: Anthony Checkalski
Ofcr: Judith M Docter
Ofcr: Laura Jahns
Ofcr: Tim Oliver
Ofcr: Jason Stoll
Ofcr: Timothy Vos
Trst Ofcr: Philip Gatien
Ex VP: William M Bohn
Board of Directors: J Douglas Quick, John F Bergstrom, Karen T Van Lith, Ruth M Crowley, John B Williams, R Jay Gerken, William R Hutchinson, Robert A Jeffe, Eileen A Kamerick, Gale E Klappa, Richard T Lommen, Cory L Nettles

ASSOCIATED BANK
See ASSOCIATED BANC-CORP

ASSOCIATED BANK
See ASSOCIATED BANC-CORP

D-U-N-S 12-648-5820
■ ASSOCIATED BANK NA
(*Suby of* ASSOCIATED BANK) ★
303 S 1st Ave, Wittenberg, WI 54499
Tel (715) 845-4301 *Founded/Ownrshp* 1982
Sales NA *EMP* 60
SIC 6022 State commercial banks
Pr: John P Evans
VP: Alfred Nakhla
**VP:* Milton W Voelz

D-U-N-S 00-794-5967
■ ASSOCIATED BANK NATIONAL ASSOCIATION
(*Suby of* ASSOCIATED BANK) ★
200 N Adams St, Green Bay, WI 54301-5174
Tel (920) 433-3200 *Founded/Ownrshp* 1874, 1966
Sales NA *EMP* 715
SIC 6021 6211 National commercial banks; Investment firm, general brokerage
Ch Bd: Robert C Gallagher
**V Ch:* Mark J McMullen
**Pr:* Paul S Beideman
Pr: Dennis Deloye
Ofcr: Jim Heberer
**Ex VP:* Randall J Erickson
Sr VP: Al Banach
Sr VP: Anthony Baumgardt
Sr VP: William Carroll
Sr VP: Justin Elshire
Sr VP: Kevin Jordan
Sr VP: Chris Lefever
Sr VP: Nancy Pozo
Sr VP: Jenni L Roudebush
Sr VP: Tom Schlehuber
Sr VP: Mary Thompson
Sr VP: Doug Vitek
VP: Andrew Brueggeman
VP: Jessie Bushmaker
VP: Mary Christensen
VP: Darren Dewing

D-U-N-S 03-530-2918
ASSOCIATED BRIGHAM CONTRACTORS INC
A B C STRUTURAL CONCRETE
75 N 900 W, Brigham City, UT 84302-2059
Tel (435) 723-8529 *Founded/Ownrshp* 1959
Sales 85.6MM *EMP* 335
Accts Davis & Bott Cpa Lc Brigham
SIC 1541 1771 Industrial buildings & warehouses; Concrete work
Pr: Michael J Bradshaw
**CFO:* Dennis Racine
**VP:* Kent K McBride
VP: Edgar T Valenine
Genl Mgr: Brett Schultz
Sfty Dirs: Bruce McFarland

D-U-N-S 08-055-9461
ASSOCIATED CATHOLIC CHARITIES INC
CATHOLIC CHARITIES BALTIMORE
320 Cathedral St, Baltimore, MD 21201-4421
Tel (410) 561-6363 *Founded/Ownrshp* 1923
Sales 106.0MM[E] *EMP* 2,000
Accts Ernst & Young Llp Baltimore
SIC 8322 Social service center
Ch Bd: Archbishop William H Keeler
**Ch Bd:* William E Lori
**Pr:* Kathleen M Ryan Lekin
**Treas:* Michael L Falcone
Ofcr: Derek Coelho
**VP:* Paul J Bowie
Ex Dir: Jan Lewis
Ex Dir: David Mactas
Ex Dir: Leilani Thomas
Prgrm Mgr: Karly Howell
Prgrm Mgr: Samantha Taylor
Board of Directors: William E Lori

D-U-N-S 06-561-3200
ASSOCIATED CLEANING CONSULTANTS AND SERVICES INC
ACCS
431 Davidson Rd, Pittsburgh, PA 15239-1733
Tel (412) 795-9200 *Founded/Ownrshp* 1970
Sales 23.6MM[E] *EMP* 1,502
SIC 7349 8742 Janitorial service, contract basis; Management consulting services
Pr: Leslie Riems
**Treas:* Jeffrey Riems
**Prin:* Jerome Riems

D-U-N-S 12-645-9937
ASSOCIATED COMMUNITY SERVICES INC
AC SERVICES
23800 W 10 Mile Rd # 200, Southfield, MI 48033-3199
Tel (248) 352-2600 *Founded/Ownrshp* 1999
Sales 82.9MM[E] *EMP* 1,000
SIC 7389 Telemarketing services
CEO: William Burland
**Pr:* Richard Cole

D-U-N-S 02-398-7415 IMP
ASSOCIATED DISTRIBUTORS LLC
BREAKTHRU BEVERAGE VIRGINIA
5800 Technology Blvd, Sandston, VA 23150-5035
Tel (757) 424-6300 *Founded/Ownrshp* 2005
Sales 104.4MM[E] *EMP* 295
SIC 5182 Wine
Pr: Dale Farino
**VP:* Ray Fields
VP: Tom Kirkpatrick
**VP:* Bob Kovalcheck
**VP:* John Lohr
MIS Dir: Robert Carr
VP Sls: Aubrey James
Sls Mgr: Brian McCann

D-U-N-S 05-407-7672
ASSOCIATED ELECTRIC COOPERATIVE INC
2814 S Golden Ave, Springfield, MO 65807-3213
Tel (417) 881-1204 *Founded/Ownrshp* 1962
Sales 1.1MMM *EMP* 600
Accts Kpmg Llp Kansas City Missour
SIC 4911 Electric services; Distribution, electric power; Generation, electric power; Transmission, electric power
CEO: James J Jura
**CFO:* David W McNabb
VP: Dale Reinhart
Ex Dir: Toby Schaefer
Off Admin: Emily Graaf
CIO: Brent W Bossi
Dir IT: Johnathan Douglas
Dir IT: Roderick Dubree
Dir IT: David Strong
Sftwr Eng: Andy Dettmer
Opers Supe: Ryan Mayo

D-U-N-S 06-603-8449
ASSOCIATED ESTATES REALTY CORP
1 Aec Pkwy, Richmond Heights, OH 44143-1500
Tel (216) 261-5000 *Founded/Ownrshp* 1993
Sales 194.0MM *EMP* 400[E]
SIC 6798 1531

D-U-N-S 05-616-2811 IMP
ASSOCIATED FEED & SUPPLY CO
FARWEST TRADING
5213 W Main St, Turlock, CA 95380-9413
Tel (209) 667-2708 *Founded/Ownrshp* 1971
Sales 121.9MM[E] *EMP* 125[E]
SIC 5191 Animal feeds
Pr: Matt Swanson
**Ex VP:* Jim Hyer
**VP:* Kurt Hertlein

D-U-N-S 07-972-8481
■ ASSOCIATED FINANCIAL GROUP LLC
(*Suby of* ASSOCIATED BANK NATIONAL ASSOCIATION) ★
12600 Whitewater Dr # 100, Minnetonka, MN 55343-9449
Tel (952) 945-0200 *Founded/Ownrshp* 2003
Sales NA *EMP* 195
SIC 6411 Insurance agents, brokers & service
Pr: William Bohn
Ofcr: Rebecca Kellner
Ex VP: Debbie Svihovec
VP: Joe Berlinerblau
VP: James Berry
VP: Greg Biese
VP: Scott Hairston
VP: Bob Kotecki
VP: Jennifer Nigl
VP: Winnie Norris
VP: Eric Nuytten
VP: Barry Schiefelbein
VP: Jay Scott
VP: Paul Stevens
VP: Steve Strege
VP: Rick Thill
VP: Patrick Tollefsrud
VP: Mark Zilavy
Dir Risk M: Calvin B Baker
Dir Risk M: Amy Roth
Dir Bus: Scott Fuller

D-U-N-S 00-907-9831 IMP
ASSOCIATED FOOD STORES INC (UT)
1850 W 2100 S, Salt Lake City, UT 84119-1304
Tel (801) 973-4400 *Founded/Ownrshp* 1940
Sales 1.9MMM[E] *EMP* 300[E]
Accts Deloitte & Touche Llp Salt L
SIC 5141 5147 5142 5148 5122 5023 Groceries, general line; Meats & meat products; Packaged frozen goods; Fresh fruits & vegetables; Druggists' sundries; Home furnishings
CEO: Neil Berube
Treas: Bob Obray
Treas: John Richards
**Ofcr:* Zulema Wiscovitch
**VP:* Brian T Duff
**VP:* Wade Judd
**VP:* Bob King
VP: Steven Nicholes
**VP:* Bill Price
**VP:* David Rice
VP: Troy Thomas
Dir Rx: Ed Hagen

D-U-N-S 03-847-8587 IMP/EXP
ASSOCIATED FUEL PUMP SYSTEMS CORP
AFCO
1100 Scotts Bridge Rd, Anderson, SC 29621-7629
Tel (864) 224-0012 *Founded/Ownrshp* 1989
Sales 123.1MM[E] *EMP* 350
SIC 3714 3561 Fuel pumps, motor vehicle; Pumps & pumping equipment
Pr: Ryo Nagasaka
CFO: Gary Saunders
**Ex VP:* Andreas Abbing
Sales Exec: Carl Heinz

D-U-N-S 00-591-0922 IMP/EXP
ASSOCIATED GLOBAL SYSTEMS INC
ASSOCIATED AIR FREIGHT
(*Suby of* NIPPON EXPRESS USA INC) ★
3333 New Hyde Park Rd # 207, New Hyde Park, NY 11042-1205
Tel (516) 627-8910 *Founded/Ownrshp* 2012
Sales 103.9MM[E] *EMP* 250
SIC 4731 Domestic freight forwarding; Foreign freight forwarding
CEO: James Tucci
**Sr VP:* Michael Occhicone
VP: Mike Hess
VP: Paul Moschetti
VP: Mike Occhicone
VP: Anthony Patch
**VP:* Scott Richter
**VP:* Frank Ryan
VP: Ed Young
Rgnl Mgr: Jared Lehnick
Dist Mgr: Sam Bowser

ASSOCIATED GROCERS
See ASSOCIATED WHOLESALE GROCERS INC

D-U-N-S 00-385-1441
ASSOCIATED GROCERS INC
8600 Anselmo Ln, Baton Rouge, LA 70810-1209
Tel (225) 444-1000 *Founded/Ownrshp* 1950
Sales 706.4MM *EMP* 680[E]
Accts Postlethwaite & Netterville A
SIC 5141 Groceries, general line
Pr: Emile R Breaux
CFO: Barin Arceneous
**Treas:* Douglas Drummond
VP: Steve Miller
IT Man: Sandra Moss
Opers Supe: Montrell Howard
Opers Supe: Ed Huey
Sfty Mgr: Chad Burgess
Sls Mgr: Sam Canova

D-U-N-S 00-794-2535 IMP
ASSOCIATED GROCERS INC
3301 S Norfolk St, Seattle, WA 98118-5648
Tel (206) 762-2100 *Founded/Ownrshp* 1987
Sales 221.8MM[E] *EMP* 800
SIC 5141 5147 5143 5122 5148 5142 Groceries, general line; Meats, fresh; Meats, cured or smoked; Dairy products, except dried or canned; Drugs & drug proprietaries; Druggists' sundries; Fresh fruits & vegetables; Packaged frozen goods
Pr: Craig Palm
**VP:* Steve Numata

D-U-N-S 00-692-2140
ASSOCIATED GROCERS OF FLORIDA INC
AG
1141 Sw 12th Ave, Pompano Beach, FL 33069-4614
Tel (954) 876-3000 *Founded/Ownrshp* 1945
Sales 165.1MM[E] *EMP* 500
SIC 8699 Food co-operative
CEO: Calvin J Miller
**Pr:* Christopher Miller
**COO:* Chris C Lavoy
**Sec:* Louis F Moore
Ex VP: Jose Capellades
Ex VP: Lou Moore
**Sr VP:* Georgina Perez
VP: Gary Bausch
VP: Larry Gherardini
VP: Luzmary Jimenez
VP Bus Dev: Amaury Portella

D-U-N-S 01-901-4679
ASSOCIATED GROCERS OF MAINE INC
LITTLE YANKEE
(*Suby of* PINE STATE BEVERAGE CO) ★
190 Water St, Gardiner, ME 04345-2109
Tel (207) 596-0636 *Founded/Ownrshp* 1953, 2011
Sales 98.1MM[E] *EMP* 300[E]
SIC 5141 5147 5148 5122 Groceries, general line; Meats, fresh; Fruits, fresh; Vegetables, fresh; Druggists' sundries
Ch: John Robichaud
**Pr:* Mike Westort
**CEO:* Craig Burgess
**Treas:* Vernon Seile
**VP:* Tom Barber
**VP:* John Beaupre
**Prin:* David Allenson

D-U-N-S 00-697-1246
ASSOCIATED GROCERS OF NEW ENGLAND INC
11 Cooperative Way, Pembroke, NH 03275-3251
Tel (603) 223-6710 *Founded/Ownrshp* 1946
Sales 581.7MM[E] *EMP* 625
SIC 5141 Groceries, general line
Pr: Michael C Bourgione
**Ch Bd:* Thomas E Bradbury
**CFO:* Steven N Murphy
**Sr VP:* Mike Violette
VP: Rick Wheeler
Board of Directors: Philip Tucker

D-U-N-S 00-402-7108
ASSOCIATED GROCERS OF SOUTH INC
3600 Vanderbilt Rd, Birmingham, AL 35217-4256
Tel (205) 841-6781 *Founded/Ownrshp* 1928
Sales 221.8MM[E] *EMP* 370
SIC 5141 5411 Groceries, general line; Co-operative food stores
**CFO:* Jackie Plott
VP: Ron Burke
VP: Tom Keller
**VP:* Leland Slay
VP: Larry Wilson
Snr Sftwr: Jonathan Ary

D-U-N-S 00-396-7633
ASSOCIATED GROUP HOLDINGS LLC
30 S Wacker Dr Ste 1600, Chicago, IL 60606-7432
Tel (312) 662-5488 *Founded/Ownrshp* 2012
Sales 141.4MM[E] *EMP* 215
SIC 3448 Prefabricated metal buildings
CEO: Tim Ritchie
CFO: Jim Hanson
Sr VP: Jeffrey Hyman
VP: Bradley Dame

D-U-N-S 82-755-1404
■ ASSOCIATED GROUP INC
(*Suby of* BLUE CROSS) ★
120 Monument Cir Ste 200, Indianapolis, IN 46204-4902
Tel (317) 488-6000 *Founded/Ownrshp* 2008
Sales NA *EMP* 3,331[E]
SIC 6324 Group hospitalization plans
Prin: L Ben

D-U-N-S 62-718-2801
■ ASSOCIATED HOME CARE LLC
(*Suby of* AMEDISYS INC) ★
991 Osgood St, North Andover, MA 01845-1801
Tel (978) 682-0745 *Founded/Ownrshp* 2016
Sales 4.4MM[E] *EMP* 1,500[E]
SIC 8082 Visiting nurse service
CEO: Michael Trigilio
Pr: Nancy Aldrich
COO: Robert Dean
CFO: Douglas May
Ofcr: Bob Dean
Rgnl Mgr: Maureen Wilkinson

D-U-N-S 11-282-3208 IMP
ASSOCIATED HYGIENIC PRODUCTS LLC
AHP
(*Suby of* DOMTAR CORPORATION)
1029 Old Creek Rd, Greenville, NC 27834-8178
Tel (770) 476-3594 *Founded/Ownrshp* 2013
Sales 206.9MM[E] *EMP* 630
SIC 2676 Diapers, paper (disposable): made from purchased paper; Napkins, sanitary: made from purchased paper
CEO: George H Jackson III
VP: Robert A Newmn
IT Man: Dale Hanshaw

D-U-N-S 05-169-0782
ASSOCIATED INDEMNITY CORP
(*Suby of* FIREMANS FUND INSURANCE CO) ★
1465 N Mcdowell Blvd # 100, Petaluma, CA 94954-6516
Tel (415) 899-2000 *Founded/Ownrshp* 1922
Sales NA *EMP* 2,498
SIC 6311 6321 6331 6351 Life insurance carriers; Accident insurance carriers; Health insurance carriers; Fire, marine & casualty insurance & carriers; Surety insurance
Ch: D Andrew Torrance
CFO: Jill E Paterson
CFO: Kevin Walker
Treas: Linda E Wright
Sr VP: Cynthia L Pevehouse
Board of Directors: Douglas E Franklin, Jeffery F Johnson, Sally B Narey, Kevin E Walker, David M Zona

D-U-N-S 62-416-6609
ASSOCIATED INDUSTRIES OF MASSACHUSETTS MUTUAL INSURANCE CO
AIM MUTUAL INSURANCE CO
(*Suby of* ASSOCIATED INSURANCE MANAGEMENT LLC) ★
54 3rd Ave, Burlington, MA 01803-4414
Tel (781) 221-1600 *Founded/Ownrshp* 1988
Sales NA *EMP* 167
Accts Ernst & Young Boston Ma
SIC 6331 Workers' compensation insurance
Pr: John Myers
**Treas:* Gregory R Shah
Sr VP: Adelaide Lincoln
**VP:* Bob Cella
**VP:* Thomas J Crupi
**VP:* Michael P Kelley
VP: Mike Standing
CTO: Larry Winship
Info Man: Gregory Shaw

D-U-N-S 07-269-0642
ASSOCIATED INSURANCE MANAGEMENT LLC (MA)
54 3rd Ave, Burlington, MA 01803-4414
Tel (781) 221-1600 *Founded/Ownrshp* 1989
Sales 130.5MM[E] *EMP* 167
SIC 8741 Administrative management
Pr: John Myers
VP: Allan Brecher

ASSOCIATED INTEGRATED SUPPLY
See ASSOCIATED MATERIAL HANDLING INDUSTRIES INC

D-U-N-S 10-693-8723 IMP
ASSOCIATED MATERIAL HANDLING INDUSTRIES INC
ASSOCIATED INTEGRATED SUPPLY
133 N Swift Rd, Addison, IL 60101-1447
Tel (630) 588-8800 *Founded/Ownrshp* 1997
Sales 223.6MM[E] *EMP* 400
Accts Miller Cooper & Co Ltd De
SIC 5084 7699 7353 Industrial machinery & equipment; Materials handling machinery; Industrial machinery & equipment repair; Heavy construction equipment rental; Cranes & aerial lift equipment, rental or leasing
Pr: Michael B Romano
CFO: Jeff Pudela
Treas: John F Everts
Admn Mgr: Tony Cesarini
Genl Mgr: Brandon Hodge
Genl Mgr: Kevin Mason
IT Man: Cheryl Flood
Trfc Dir: Stefanie Scorzo
Natl Sales: Dave Camp
Mktg Dir: Gordon Demaine
Mktg Mgr: Shari Sellers
Board of Directors: Timothy Combs, Patrick J McManus

D-U-N-S 96-525-5073
ASSOCIATED MATERIALS GROUP INC
1 Maritime Plz Fl 12, San Francisco, CA 94111-3502
Tel (415) 788-5111 *Founded/Ownrshp* 2010
Sales 1.5MMM[E] *EMP* 3,000[E]
SIC 3089 5033 5031 3442 Plastic hardware & building products; Siding, plastic; Windows, plastic; Fences, gates & accessories: plastic; Roofing & siding materials; Siding, except wood; Roofing, asphalt & sheet metal; Insulation materials; Windows; Kitchen cabinets; Metal doors, sash & trim

D-U-N-S 06-524-6113
ASSOCIATED MATERIALS HOLDINGS LLC
(*Suby of* ASSOCIATED MATERIALS GROUP INC) ★
3773 State Rd, Cuyahoga Falls, OH 44223-2603
Tel (330) 929-1811 *Founded/Ownrshp* 2010
Sales 201.6MM[E] *EMP* 2,000
SIC 3089 5033 5031 5063 3442 Plastic hardware & building products; Siding, plastic; Windows, plastic; Fences, gates & accessories: plastic; Roofing & siding materials; Siding, except wood; Roofing, asphalt & sheet metal; Insulation materials; Windows; Kitchen cabinets; Wire & cable; Metal doors, sash & trim
Ch Bd: Ira D Kleinman
CFO: Stephen Graham
CFO: Keith D Lavanway
CIO: Ray Capotosta
VP Opers: Scott Harcek

D-U-N-S 96-525-4662
ASSOCIATED MATERIALS INC
(*Suby of* ASSOCIATED MATERIALS GROUP INC) ★
1 Maritime Plz Fl 12, San Francisco, CA 94111-3502
Tel (415) 788-5111 *Founded/Ownrshp* 2010
Sales 1.1MMM[E] *EMP* 3,000
SIC 3089 5033 5031 3442 Plastic hardware & building products; Siding, plastic; Windows, plastic; Fences, gates & accessories: plastic; Roofing & siding materials; Siding, except wood; Roofing, asphalt & sheet metal; Insulation materials; Windows; Kitchen cabinets; Metal doors, sash & trim
Pr: Erik D Ragatz

D-U-N-S 10-730-1319
ASSOCIATED MATERIALS LLC
(*Suby of* ASSOCIATED MATERIALS INC) ★
3773 State Rd, Cuyahoga Falls, OH 44223-2603
Tel (330) 929-1811 *Founded/Ownrshp* 2010
Sales 1.1MMM *EMP* 3,000[E]
SIC 3089 5033 5031 3442 Plastic hardware & building products; Siding, plastic; Windows, plastic; Fences, gates & accessories: plastic; Roofing & siding materials; Siding, except wood; Roofing, asphalt & sheet metal; Insulation materials; Windows; Kitchen cabinets; Metal doors, sash & trim
Pr: Brian C Strauss
**Ch Bd:* Erik D Ragatz
CFO: Scott F Stephens
Chf Mktg O: Dana A Schindler
Ofcr: Curtis J Dobler
Ofcr: David L King
Ex VP: William L Topper
Sr VP: Philippe Bourbonniere
Sr VP: Adam D Casebere
VP: Chris Kline
Board of Directors: Lawrence M Blackburn, Charles A Carroll, Adam B Durrett, Dana R Snyder

D-U-N-S 04-322-5507
ASSOCIATED MILK PRODUCERS INC
A M P I
315 N Brdwy St, New Ulm, MN 56073
Tel (507) 354-8295 *Founded/Ownrshp* 1969
Sales 1.6MMM *EMP* 1,400
SIC 2023 2022 2021 2024 2026 5143 Dry, condensed, evaporated dairy products; Cheese, natural & processed; Creamery butter; Ice cream, bulk; Fermented & cultured milk products; Milk
CEO: Donn Develder
**CEO:* Donn De Velder
**CEO:* Ed Welch
**CFO:* Patricia Radloff
**Treas:* Brad Nevin
**Treas:* Greg Zwald
**Sec:* Bruce Brockshus
**V Ch Bd:* Roger Lyon
**Sr VP:* Sheryl Meshke
VP: Marshall Reece
Comm Dir: Sarah Schmidt

D-U-N-S 08-583-2376 EXP
ASSOCIATED PACKAGING INC
435 Calvert Dr, Gallatin, TN 37066-5448
Tel (615) 452-2131 *Founded/Ownrshp* 1977
Sales 160.0MM *EMP* 165
SIC 5199 5084 Packaging materials; Processing & packaging equipment
CEO: Joe Smith
**Pr:* Kevin Miller
COO: Roy Smith
**CFO:* Michael Boyette
CFO: Robert Brannon
**Ex VP:* Gene Turner
VP: Mack Greene
VP: Mark Russell
Telecom Mg: Jill Harris
Opers Mgr: Carol Biggs
VP Sls: Jerry Gilley

D-U-N-S 18-763-2682
ASSOCIATED PHARMACIES INC
(*Suby of* AAP) ★
211 Lonnie Crawford Blvd, Scottsboro, AL 35769
Tel (256) 574-6819 *Founded/Ownrshp* 1987
Sales 642.6MM *EMP* 60
SIC 5122

D-U-N-S 00-793-0852
ASSOCIATED PIPE LINE CONTRACTORS INC (TX)
(*Suby of* NW PIPELINE INC) ★
3535 Briarpark Dr Ste 135, Houston, TX 77042-5233
Tel (713) 789-4311 *Founded/Ownrshp* 1946, 2010
Sales 153.6MM[E] *EMP* 500[E]
Accts Grant Thorton Llp Houston T
SIC 1623 Oil & gas pipeline construction
CEO: Paul Somerville
**Pr:* Ralph C Pendarvis
CFO: David Hollaway
**CFO:* Dan Latter
VP: Gene Bell
**VP:* Clyde Fowler
**VP:* Thomas Wilson

D-U-N-S 00-698-0395
ASSOCIATED PRESS
450 W 33rd St Fl 16, New York, NY 10001-2626
Tel (212) 621-1500 *Founded/Ownrshp* 1848
Sales 568.0MM *EMP* 3,533
Accts Ernst & Young Llp New York N
SIC 7383 4822 News reporting services for newspapers & periodicals; Telegraph & other communications
Pr: Gary Pruitt
V Ch: Mary E Junck
CFO: Kenneth Dale
Treas: Lawrence Brando
Sr VP: Lorraine Cichowski
VP: Ian Cameron
VP: Claude Erbsen
VP: Fernando Ferre
VP: Tom Jones
VP: Srinandan Kasi
VP: David Ledford
VP: John Petrovich
VP: Lois Posimato
VP: Barry Renfrew
VP: Danny Spriggs
VP: James R Williams
VP: James Williams
Dir Soc: Warren Levinson

D-U-N-S 00-608-8330 IMP/EXP
ASSOCIATED SALES & BAG CO
ASSOCIATED BAG COMPANY
400 W Boden St, Milwaukee, WI 53207-6274
Tel (414) 769-1000 *Founded/Ownrshp* 1994
Sales 123.9MM[E] *EMP* 196
SIC 5113 Industrial & personal service paper
Pr: Herbert Rubenstein
Prgrm Mgr: Kathy Stack
Genl Mgr: Scott Pietila
Telecom Ex: Ron Borkowski
IT Man: Laura Galusha
IT Man: Craig Gorski
Info Man: Kathy Stevens
Mktg Mgr: Rich Bubik
Sls Mgr: Ed Braun
Sls Mgr: Courtney Brown
Sls Mgr: Chandra Bryant

D-U-N-S 08-601-4172
ASSOCIATED STUDENTS OF SAN DIEGO STATE UNIVERSITY
MISSION BAY AQUATIC CENTER
5500 Campanile Dr, San Diego, CA 92182-0001
Tel (619) 594-0234 *Founded/Ownrshp* 1897
Sales 25.1MM *EMP* 1,120
Accts Mcgladrey Llp Los Angeles Ca
SIC 8699 Automobile owners' association
Ex Dir: Christina Brown
IT Man: Carlos Careaga

D-U-N-S 04-744-8329
ASSOCIATED STUDENTS UCLA
UCLA BOOKSTORE
308 Westwood Plz, Los Angeles, CA 90095-8355
Tel (310) 825-4321 *Founded/Ownrshp* 1919
Sales 40.5MM *EMP* 2,016
Accts Kpmg Llp Los Angeles Ca
SIC 8399 5942 Council for social agency; Book stores
CFO: Rich Delia
Bd of Dir: Moises Roman
Exec: Kelly Ryan
Assoc Dir: Samantha West
Dir Soc: Ella Gogel
Ex Dir: Frank Lee
CIO: Annelie Rugg
Dir IT: Jack Schwab
IT Man: John Talbert
Mktg Dir: Lisa Perez
Psych: Blanca Orellana

D-U-N-S 02-676-8275 IMP
ASSOCIATED SUPPLY CO INC
ASCO EQUIPMENT CO
2102 E Slaton Rd, Lubbock, TX 79404-6800
Tel (806) 745-2000 *Founded/Ownrshp* 1961
Sales 138.4MM[E] *EMP* 258
SIC 5084 5082 7353 Materials handling machinery; Construction & mining machinery; Heavy construction equipment rental
CEO: William B Wright
**Pr:* John S Wright
**CFO:* Nathan Swindle
**Sec:* Paula Key
Brnch Mgr: Mark Hobart
Genl Mgr: Don Norton
Store Mgr: Jarrod Schwalk
CIO: Steve Jenkins
CTO: Kris Hankins
IT Man: Drew Baker
IT Man: Dan Gobin

D-U-N-S 00-694-3062 IMP/EXP
ASSOCIATED WHOLESALE GROCERS INC (KS)
ASSOCIATED GROCERS
5000 Kansas Ave, Kansas City, KS 66106-1135
Tel (913) 288-1000 *Founded/Ownrshp* 1926
Sales 8.9MMM *EMP* 5,500
SIC 5141 5143 5142 5147 5146 5148 Groceries, general line; Dairy products, except dried or canned; Packaged frozen goods; Meats & meat products; Meats, fresh; Fish, fresh; Fish, frozen, unpackaged; Fresh fruits & vegetables
Ch: Bob Hufford
**Pr:* Jerry Garland
**CFO:* Robert Z Walker
**V Ch Bd:* Don Woods Jr
Ex VP: Jean Lapointe
**Sr VP:* Frances Puhl
VP: Jim Richter
IT Man: Mike Harman

D-U-N-S 00-281-2055
ASSOCIATED WHOLESALERS INC (PA)
AWI
336 E Penn Ave, Robesonia, PA 19551-8902
Tel (610) 693-3161 *Founded/Ownrshp* 1962
Sales NA *EMP* 2,100
SIC 5141 5147 5122 5142 5148 5411

D-U-N-S 04-834-1846
■ **ASSOCIATES CORP OF NORTH AMERICA**
(*Suby of* ASSOCIATES FIRST CAPITAL CORP) ★
250 E John Carpenter Fwy, Irving, TX 75062-2806
Tel (972) 652-4000 *Founded/Ownrshp* 2000
Sales NA *EMP* 18,000
SIC 6141 6153 6159 6311 6321 6331 Consumer finance companies; Installment sales finance, other than banks; Buying of installment notes; Mercantile financing; Machinery & equipment finance leasing; Truck finance leasing; Finance leasing, vehicles: except automobiles & trucks; Life insurance carriers; Accident insurance carriers; Health insurance carriers; Property damage insurance; Fire, marine & casualty insurance: stock
Ch Bd: Keith W Hughes
CFO: Roy A Guthrie
Treas: John F Hughes
V Ch Bd: Harold D Marshall
Ex VP: Chester D Longenecker
Sr VP: Janet M Smith
Sr VP: John F Stillo
Sr VP: Jannette A Zabransky

D-U-N-S 06-119-3918
■ **ASSOCIATES FIRST CAPITAL CORP**
(*Suby of* CITIGROUP INC) ★
4000 Regent Blvd, Irving, TX 75063-2246
Tel (800) 922-6235 *Founded/Ownrshp* 2000
Sales NA *EMP* 31,706
SIC 6162 6021 6141 6159 6153 Mortgage bankers; National commercial banks; Consumer finance companies; Financing: automobiles, furniture, etc., not a deposit bank; Installment sales finance, other than banks; Industrial loan banks & companies, not a deposit bank; Automobile finance leasing; Finance leasing, vehicles: except automobiles & trucks; Machinery & equipment finance leasing; Purchasers of accounts receivable & commercial paper; Mercantile financing
Ch Bd: Keith W Hughes
**CFO:* Roy A Guthrie
Sr VP: Janet Smith
Board of Directors:

ASSOCIATION FOR INVESTMENT
See CFA INSTITUTE

D-U-N-S 06-928-7779
ASSOCIATION OF AMERICAN MEDICAL COLLEGES (IL)
AAMC
655 K St Nw Ste 100, Washington, DC 20001-2399
Tel (202) 828-0400 *Founded/Ownrshp* 1876
Sales 214.2MM *EMP* 450
Accts Kpmg Llp Mc Lean Va
SIC 8621 Education & teacher association
CEO: Darrell G Kirch
Pr: Robert Dickler
**CFO:* Bernard Jarvis
CFO: Bernard K Jarvis
CFO: David Roe
Ofcr: Gabrielle V Campbell
Ofcr: Constance M Filling
Ofcr: Atul Grover
Ofcr: Sue Jablonski
Ofcr: Yvonne Massenburg
Ofcr: Marc Nivet
Ofcr: Alexander Ommaya
Ofcr: Janis M Orlowski
Ofcr: Elisa Siegel
Ofcr: Charles Terrell
Ofcr: Frank R Trinity
Assoc VP: Diane Magrane
**Ex VP:* Carol Aschenbrener
Ex VP: Kathleen Kane
Sr VP: Robert W Davis
Sr VP: Robert M Dickler

D-U-N-S 07-484-0927
ASSOCIATION OF FLIGHT ATTENDANTS
AFA
501 3rd St Nw Fl 10, Washington, DC 20001-2750
Tel (202) 387-1968 *Founded/Ownrshp* 1973
Sales 83.0MM[E] *EMP* 1,500
SIC 8631 Trade union
Pr: Patricia Friend
**Sec:* Paul G Mac Kinnon
**Ex VP:* George M Donahue
VP: Deborah Sutor

D-U-N-S 05-790-5887
ASSOCIATION OF UNIVERSITIES FOR RESEARCH IN ASTRONOMY INC
AURA
1212 New York Ave Nw # 450, Washington, DC 20005-3912
Tel (202) 483-2101 *Founded/Ownrshp* 1957
Sales 264.3MM *EMP* 1,000
Accts Cliftonlarsonallen Llp Beltsv
SIC 8611 Business associations; Junior Chamber of Commerce; Chamber of Commerce
Pr: William S Smith
**Pr:* Charles Moulton
Ofcr: Harvey Bass
Ofcr: Karen Godzyk
Ofcr: Deborah Gronet
VP: Hh Hammel
VP: Richard Margison
**VP:* Deborah Narcisso
Dir Risk M: Tammie Lavoie
VP Admn: Harry W Feinstein
Admn Mgr: Alvaro Soms

D-U-N-S 08-684-0964
ASSOCIATION OF UNIVERSITY PHYSICIANS
UNIVERSITY WASH PHYSICIANS
701 5th Ave Ste 700, Seattle, WA 98104-7028
Tel (206) 520-5388 *Founded/Ownrshp* 1962
Sales 177.0MM *EMP* 200[E]
Accts Clark Nuber Ps Bellevue Wa
SIC 8621 Medical field-related associations
Assoc Dir: Marv Whitson
Comm Dir: Paul Stark
Ex Dir: Terry Briscoe

D-U-N-S 96-849-0727
ASSOCIATION OF WASHINGTON CITIES
1076 Franklin St Se, Olympia, WA 98501-1346
Tel (360) 753-4137 *Founded/Ownrshp* 2011
Sales 217.1MM *EMP* 9[E]
SIC 8621 Professional membership organizations
Prin: Kathy Turner

D-U-N-S 62-082-9346
ASSOCIATIONS INC
5401 N Central Expy # 300, Dallas, TX 75205-3348
Tel (214) 953-3009 *Founded/Ownrshp* 1979
Sales 1.0MMM[E] *EMP* 8,000
SIC 6531 Condominium manager
CEO: John J Carona
**Pr:* Patrick Brensinger
Pr: Joey Corona
Ofcr: Chelle O'Keefe
Ex VP: Andrew Brock
Ex VP: Helen Eden
Ex VP: Juan Fontanes
Sr VP: John Ingenito
Sr VP: Brian Kruppa
Sr VP: Tom Larkin
Sr VP: Craig Lubaczewski
Sr VP: Jose Bosco Maldonado
Sr VP: Michael Packard
Sr VP: Paul Reyes
VP: Ronald Duprey
VP: Katie Foell
VP: Mark Knudsen
VP: Trung Pham
VP: Shannon Streenz
VP: George Zalitis
Exec: Paul Little

ASSOCTED RGNAL UNIV PTHLOGISTS
See ARUP LABORATORIES INC

D-U-N-S 07-535-2815
ASSUMPTION COLLEGE
500 Salisbury St, Worcester, MA 01609-1296
Tel (508) 767-7000 *Founded/Ownrshp* 1904
Sales 108.4MM *EMP* 490
SIC 8221 College, except junior
Ch Bd: Frederick Bayon
**Pr:* Francesco Cesareo
**Treas:* Christian McCarthy
Trst: Ralph Crowley
Trst: Therese Duross
Trst: Mike Gravel
Trst: Thomas Manning
Trst: James Oconnor
Trst: James Paugh
Trst: Daniel Reilly
Trst: Michael Tsotsis
Ofcr: Gale Racine
Ex VP: Michael Rubino
VP: Francis Gurley
VP: Catherine M Woodbrooks
Dir Lab: Jeff Logee
Assoc Dir: Stephanie McCaffrey

D-U-N-S 05-379-0736
■ **ASSURAMED INC**
(*Suby of* CARDINAL HEALTH INC) ★
1810 Summit Commerce Park, Twinsburg, OH 44087-2300
Tel (330) 963-6998 *Founded/Ownrshp* 2013
Sales 104.8MM[E] *EMP* 185[E]
SIC 5047 Medical & hospital equipment
CEO: Michael B Petras Jr
**COO:* Kurt Packer
**VP:* Chris Lindroth
VP: Steven Schultz
**VP:* Mark Wells
IT Man: Shivani Marwaha
Manager: Jonathan Maag

D-U-N-S 10-762-4355
ASSURANCE AGENCY LTD
1750 E Golf Rd, Schaumburg, IL 60173-5835
Tel (847) 944-9087 *Founded/Ownrshp* 1961
Sales NA *EMP* 200[E]
SIC 6411 Insurance agents
CEO: Anthony D Chimino
**Pr:* Dan Klaras
COO: Jackie Gould
**CFO:* David Suchomski
Bd of Dir: Karl Felber
Chf Mktg O: Steven Handmaker
Sr VP: Paul Bartman
Sr VP: Michele McDermott
Sr VP: Gary Peterson
VP: Matt Buol
VP: Rich Cordova
VP: Bryan Figola
VP: Laura Gamperl
**VP:* Kim Jeschke
VP: Glenn Morrison
VP: Christopher Rode
VP: Mike Roseri
VP: Donna Wright
Exec: Kathleen Stewart

D-U-N-S 06-933-8820
ASSURANCE TECHNOLOGY CORP
84 South St, Carlisle, MA 01741-1596
Tel (978) 369-8848 *Founded/Ownrshp* 1969
Sales 97.4MM[E] *EMP* 250
Accts Vitale Caturano & Company Ltd
SIC 8711 3629 Consulting engineer; Power conversion units, a.c. to d.c.: static-electric
Pr: H Larue Renfroe
**CFO:* John J Leonard
Ex VP: Laurel Jackson
Ex VP: Gary Mullen
Ex VP: Bert Plourde
**VP:* Cosmo Diciaccio
**VP:* Fredrick A Lund
**VP:* William C Place
Dir Sec: Edward Spradlin
Snr Sftwr: Bill Grove
IT Man: Dan Maclellan

ASSURANT HEALTH
See ALDEN JOHN LIFE INSURANCE CO

ASSURANT HEALTH
See TIME INSURANCE CO

D-U-N-S 05-290-8241 IMP
▲ **ASSURANT INC**
28 Liberty St Fl 41, New York, NY 10005-1449
Tel (212) 859-7000 *Founded/Ownrshp* 1969
Sales NA *EMP* 16,950
Tkr Sym AIZ *Exch* NYS
SIC 6311 6399 6331 Life insurance; Warranty insurance, automobile; Warranty insurance, product; except automobile; Fire, marine & casualty insurance & carriers
Pr: Alan B Colberg
**Ch Bd:* Elaine D Rosen
Pr: Michael D Anderson
CFO: Richard S Dziadzio
Ofcr: Gene E Mergelmeyer
Ofcr: Christopher J Pagano
Ofcr: Robyn Price Stonehill
Ex VP: Robert A Lonergan
Ex VP: Francesca Luthi
Ex VP: Ajay Waghray
Sr VP: John A Sondej
Board of Directors: Howard L Carver, Juan N Cento,

Elyse Douglas, Lawrence V Jackson, Charles J Koch, Paul J Reilly, Robert W Stein

ASSURANT SOLUTIONS
See AMERICAN SECURITY INSURANCE CO

D-U-N-S 96-914-6898
ASSURED GUARANTY CORP
(*Suby of* ASSURED GUARANTY LTD)
31 W 52nd St Fl 26, New York, NY 10019-6161
Tel (212) 974-0100 *Founded/Ownrshp* 2011
Sales NA *EMP* 145[E]
SIC 6411 Insurance agents, brokers & service
Pr: Dominic J Frederico
CFO: Robert A Bailenson
Ofcr: Amanda Meehan
VP: Nicholas Banai
VP: Adam Bibi
VP: Ashweeta Durani
VP: Ray Geiger
VP: Joelle Israel
VP: Jason Margnelli
VP: Christine Ohara
VP: Marina Plechtchitser
VP: Joyah Pugh
VP: Alana Sevachko
VP: Jonathan Stutz
VP: Elli Wang
Dir Risk M: Howard W Albert
Dir Risk M: James Wong
Dir Soc: Jill Deangelo

D-U-N-S 14-929-3248
ASSURED GUARANTY US HOLDINGS INC
(*Suby of* ASSURED GUARANTY LTD)
31 W 52nd St Fl 26, New York, NY 10019-6161
Tel (212) 974-0100 *Founded/Ownrshp* 2004
Sales NA *EMP* 125[E]
SIC 6311 Life reinsurance
CEO: Dominique Federico
**Pr:* San W McCarthy
**Sr VP:* John Meehan

D-U-N-S 06-341-5630
ASSURED NL INSURANCE AGENCY INC
NEACE LUKENS
(*Suby of* ASSUREDPARTNERS INC) ★
2305 River Rd, Louisville, KY 40206-1010
Tel (502) 894-2100 *Founded/Ownrshp* 2011
Sales NA *EMP* 754
SIC 6411 Insurance agents, brokers & service
CEO: John Neace
Pr: Larry Schaefer
CFO: Gerald Budde
Ofcr: Claudette Doyle
Sr VP: Eric Anderson
Sr VP: David Berman
Sr VP: Michael Fishel
Sr VP: Kim Robson
Sr VP: Paul Vredenburg
VP: John Davis
VP: Chris Hancock
VP: Lee Lurton
Exec: Amy Anderson

D-U-N-S 07-937-2791
ASSUREDPARTNERS GULF COAST INSURANCE AGENCY LLC
(*Suby of* ASSUREDPARTNERS INC) ★
200 Colonial Center Pkwy, Lake Mary, FL 32746-4705
Tel (407) 804-5222 *Founded/Ownrshp* 2014
Sales NA *EMP* 1,159[E]
SIC 6321 Accident & health insurance carriers
Pr: Tom Riley

D-U-N-S 96-959-4352
ASSUREDPARTNERS INC
200 Colonial Center Pkwy, Lake Mary, FL 32746-4705
Tel (407) 804-5222 *Founded/Ownrshp* 2015
Sales NA *EMP* 1,044[E]
SIC 6411 Insurance brokers
CEO: Jim Henderson
Pr: Eric Anderson
Pr: Tom Riley
CFO: Dean Curtis
Ofcr: Paul Vredenburg
Ex VP: Steve Deal
Ex VP: Walter Smith
Counsel: Stan Kinnett

D-U-N-S 78-794-4169
ASSURITY SECURITY GROUP INC
1526 K St, Lincoln, NE 68508-2732
Tel (402) 476-6500 *Founded/Ownrshp* 1999
Sales NA *EMP* 533
SIC 6321 6311 Health insurance carriers; Life insurance
Ch Bd: Thomas E Henning
**Treas:* Marvin P Ehly
IT Man: Jack Wilbur
Manager: Christine Harpster

AST
See APPLICATIONS SOFTWARE TECHNOLOGY CORP

D-U-N-S 60-543-8423 IMP/EXP
ASTEC AMERICA LLC
(*Suby of* ASTEC INTERNATIONAL HOLDING) ★
2900 S Diablo Way Ste 190, Tempe, AZ 85282-3202
Tel (602) 438-5720 *Founded/Ownrshp* 2013
Sales NA *EMP* 23,000
SIC 3679 3629 3621 Power supplies, all types: static; Power conversion units, a.c. to d.c.: static-electric; Power generators
Pr: Jay L Geldmacher
CFO: Nate Myer
VP: Brian Walsh
Genl Mgr: Scott Ziffra

D-U-N-S 88-414-5798 IMP/EXP
■ ASTEC INC
(*Suby of* ASTEC INDUSTRIES INC) ★
4101 Jerome Ave, Chattanooga, TN 37407-2915
Tel (423) 867-4210 *Founded/Ownrshp* 1994
Sales 228.8MM[E] *EMP* 700
SIC 3531 3433 3443 Construction machinery; Bituminous, cement & concrete related products & equipment; Asphalt plant, including gravel-mix type; Pavers; Burners, furnaces, boilers & stokers; Oil burners, domestic or industrial; Heat exchangers, condensers & components
Ch Bd: Don Brock
**Pr:* Benjamin Brock
**Pr:* Malcolm Swanson
**Ex VP:* Steve Claude
Ex VP: Gail Mize
**VP:* Tom Baugh
Exec: Alan Darr
Exec: George Francisco

D-U-N-S 06-130-8649 IMP/EXP
▲ ASTEC INDUSTRIES INC
1725 Shepherd Rd, Chattanooga, TN 37421-2947
Tel (423) 899-5898 *Founded/Ownrshp* 1972
Sales 983.1MM *EMP* 3,920
Tkr Sym ASTE *Exch* NGS
SIC 3531 3433 3533 Construction machinery; Bituminous, cement & concrete related products & equipment; Asphalt plant, including gravel-mix type; Pavers; Burners, furnaces, boilers & stokers; Oil burners, domestic or industrial; Water well drilling equipment
Pr: Benjamin G Brock
Pr: Steven L Claude
Pr: Chris Colwell
Pr: Richard A Patek
**COO:* Richard J Dorris
**CFO:* David C Silvious
**V Ch Bd:* W Norman Smith
**VP:* Stephen C Anderson
VP: Jeffery J Elliott
Netwrk Eng: Jim Montgomery
Board of Directors: James B Baker, William G Dorey, Daniel K Frierson, William D Gehl, Charles F Potts, William B Sansom, Glen E Tellock

ASTEC INTERNATIONAL HOLDING
See AIH LLC

ASTECH
See ASPHALT SURFACE TECHNOLOGIES CORP

D-U-N-S 07-837-0429
ASTEELFLASH USA CORP
(*Suby of* ASTEELFLASH GROUP)
4211 Starboard Dr, Fremont, CA 94538-6427
Tel (510) 440-2840 *Founded/Ownrshp* 2011
Sales 114.3MM[E] *EMP* 300[E]
SIC 3672 3679 Printed circuit boards; Electronic circuits
Pr: Gilles Benhamou
**CFO:* Claude Savard
**Ex VP:* Pierre Laboisse
**Ex VP:* Vince Pradia
**Ex VP:* Albert Yanez
Dir Sec: Johnson Wu
Dir IT: Rubinder Chadda
Sls Mgr: Debbie Tilbury

D-U-N-S 60-576-4828 IMP
ASTELLAS PHARMA US INC
(*Suby of* ASTELLAS US HOLDING INC) ★
1 Astellas Way, Northbrook, IL 60062-6111
Tel (800) 888-7704 *Founded/Ownrshp* 2005
Sales 736.6MM[E] *EMP* 1,082[E]
SIC 5122 Drugs, proprietaries & sundries
Pr: Masao Yoshida
**Pr:* Yoshi Hatanaka
**CFO:* Shinichiro Katayanagi
**Treas:* Yasumasa Masuda
Ofcr: Tatjana Dragovic
VP: Peter Carberry
VP: Joseph Devaney
VP: Stephen Eck
VP: Doug Geiger
VP: Marty Golden
VP: Masataka Katsuma
VP: James Kellerman
VP: Steve Knowles
VP: Richard Miller
VP: Karen Reeves
VP: Mark Reisenauer
VP: Peter Sandor
Assoc Dir: Gary Kaiser
Assoc Dir: Anna Podsiadlo
Assoc Dir: Christopher Young

D-U-N-S 61-300-6415
ASTELLAS US HOLDING INC
(*Suby of* ASTELLAS PHARMA INC.)
1 Astellas Way, Northbrook, IL 60062-6111
Tel (224) 205-8800 *Founded/Ownrshp* 2007
Sales 901.9MM[E] *EMP* 785[E]
SIC 2834 Pharmaceutical preparations
CEO: Yoshihiko Hatanaka

D-U-N-S 00-226-5981 IMP
ASTENJOHNSON INC (DE)
4399 Corporate Rd, North Charleston, SC 29405-7445
Tel (843) 747-7800 *Founded/Ownrshp* 1931
Sales 569.4MM[E] *EMP* 1,925
SIC 2221 2281 2299 Broadwoven fabric mills, manmade; Manmade & synthetic fiber yarns, spun; Pressed wool felts
Prin: Kevin Frank
**CFO:* Steve Polston
VP: Tom Griffin
VP: C H Johnson
VP: Neil Johnson
VP: Keith A Kemp
VP: Doug McIlvaine
VP: Don Stewart
CIO: Rich Bermudez
Plnt Mgr: Ron Meckenna
S&M/VP: Bubba Livingston

ASTON HOTELS & RESORTS
See AQUA-ASTON HOSPITALITY LLC

D-U-N-S 06-695-8166
■ ASTORIA BANK
(*Suby of* ASTORIA FINANCIAL CORP) ★
1 Astoria Federal Plz, Lake Success, NY 11042
Tel (516) 535-9000 *Founded/Ownrshp* 1888
Sales NA *EMP* 1,602[E]
SIC 6035 Federal savings & loan associations
Pr: Monte N Redman
**Ch Bd:* Ralph F Palleschi
Pr: Michael Riviezzo
CFO: Monte Adermen
Ofcr: Hugh J Donlon
Ofcr: William Stowell
Sr Ex VP: Frank Fusco
Ex VP: Thomas W Drennan
Ex VP: Arnold K Greenberg
Ex VP: Stephen Sipola
Sr VP: James Drum
Sr VP: Peter Finn
Sr VP: Neil Ganessingh
Sr VP: Robert Harder
Sr VP: Raymond Kurzum
Sr VP: Robert McKenna
Sr VP: Richard Saybolt
Sr VP: James Thompson
Sr VP: Davi Tserpelis
Sr VP: Pam Werner
VP: Gregory Alzner

D-U-N-S 80-884-7966
▲ ASTORIA FINANCIAL CORP
1 Astoria Bank Plz, New Hyde Park, NY 11042-1085
Tel (516) 327-3000 *Founded/Ownrshp* 1993
Sales NA *EMP* 1,601[E]
Tkr Sym AF *Exch* NYS
SIC 6035 Savings institutions, federally chartered
Pr: Monte N Redman
Sr Pt: Sarwant Singh
**Ch Bd:* Ralph F Palleschi
Pr: Gloria Clarke
Pr: Bonnie Margulies
**COO:* Gerard C Keegan
CFO: Frank E Fusco
Ex VP: Josie Callari
Ex VP: Robert J Destefano
Ex VP: Brian T Edwards
Ex VP: Stephen J Sipola
VP: Joseph Caltagirone
VP: Jonathan Cheris
VP: Michael Devoe
VP: Daniel Dougherty
VP: Dina Girvan
VP: Michael Lechleider
VP: Marsha Marangiello
Exec: Alan P Eggleston
Board of Directors: John R Chrin, John J Corrado, Robert Giambrone, Brian M Leeney, Patricia M Nazemetz

D-U-N-S 05-430-1678
ASTORIA GENERATING CO LP
(*Suby of* USPOWERGEN) ★
300 Atlantic St Ste 500, Stamford, CT 06901-3524
Tel (212) 792-0800 *Founded/Ownrshp* 1999
Sales 106.3MM[E] *EMP* 1[E]
SIC 4911 Distribution, electric power
CEO: Mark Sudbey

D-U-N-S 07-945-7591
ASTRA CAPITAL MANAGEMENT LLC
1900 K St Nw Ste 1130, Washington, DC 20006-1110
Tel (202) 779-9044 *Founded/Ownrshp* 2014
Sales 92.7MM[E] *EMP* 331[E]
SIC 6211 Security brokers & dealers

D-U-N-S 79-476-0889 IMP/EXP
ASTRA OIL CO LLC
TRANSCOR ASTRA GROUP
5847 San Felipe St # 2850, Houston, TX 77057-3439
Tel (713) 357-0640 *Founded/Ownrshp* 2006
Sales 335.3MM[E] *EMP* 53[E]
SIC 5172 Diesel fuel
VP: Irenseusz Kotula
**CFO:* Kari Burke
**Treas:* Kristi Shaw

D-U-N-S 15-042-7099
ASTRACO LLC
1411 E Hidalgo Ave, Phoenix, AZ 85040-3548
Tel (602) 931-2981 *Founded/Ownrshp* 2004
Sales 1.2MM *EMP* 6,500
SIC 5136 5699 Men's & boys' robes, nightwear & undergarments; T-shirts, custom printed; Stockings: men's, women's & children's
Pr: Syed Ali
**Mng Dir:* Sayed Omar Ali

D-U-N-S 78-539-5237 IMP
ASTRAZENECA LP
(*Suby of* ASTRAZENECA PHARMACEUTICALS LP) ★
1800 Concord Pike, Wilmington, DE 19803-2910
Tel (302) 886-3000 *Founded/Ownrshp* 1988
Sales 1.8MMM[E] *EMP* 8,000
SIC 2834 Pharmaceutical preparations
CEO: Antony Zook
CFO: Mark Atkins
CFO: Eduardo Neira
Treas: James Reid
Ofcr: Trudy Tan
Ex VP: Briggs Morrison
VP: Christine Emmons
VP: Mark Lelinski
VP: Curt Petrucelli
VP: Karen Smith
Exec: Nancy Deiley
Exec: Elizabeth Lewis
Exec: Jay Merenda
Assoc Dir: Neerja Banka
Comm Dir: Terri Ford

D-U-N-S 87-651-6568 IMP/EXP
ASTRAZENECA PHARMACEUTICALS LP
(*Suby of* ASTRAZENECA PLC)
1800 Concord Pike, Wilmington, DE 19803-2910
Tel (302) 886-3000 *Founded/Ownrshp* 1998
Sales 3.8MMM[E] *EMP* 11,000
SIC 2834 5122 Pharmaceutical preparations; Pharmaceuticals
CEO: Pascal Soriot
**Pt:* David V Elkins
**Pt:* Glenn M Engelmann
**Pt:* Mark Mallon
**Pt:* Kenneth L Murtha
**Pt:* Anthony P Zook
CFO: Graham Baker
CFO: John McKenna
**Ofcr:* Trudy Tan
Ex VP: Tony Zook
VP: Topher Brooke
VP: Rich Buckley
VP: Amy Dinning
VP: Mary Dwyer
VP: Johan Hoegstedt
VP: Bob Holland
VP: Greg Keenan
VP: Gerard Kennealey
VP: Kathy Monday
VP: David P Nicoli
VP: David Snow

D-U-N-S 05-466-1202
ASTRO SHAPES INC
65 Main St, Struthers, OH 44471-1942
Tel (330) 755-1414 *Founded/Ownrshp* 1971
Sales 104.1MM[E] *EMP* 325[E]
SIC 3354 3086 Aluminum extruded products; Insulation or cushioning material, foamed plastic
Pr: Paul Cene
**Ex VP:* James Dibacco
**VP:* Robert Cene Jr
Genl Mgr: Leo Flecton
Sls Mgr: Frank Beato

D-U-N-S 87-826-5990 IMP
ASTRODYNE CORP
36 Newburgh Rd, Hackettstown, NJ 07840-3904
Tel (908) 850-5088 *Founded/Ownrshp* 2008
Sales 100.0MM[E] *EMP* 408[E]
SIC 3625 3621 3613 Switches, electric power; Motors & generators; Switchgear & switchboard apparatus
Pr: Peter Murphy
**CFO:* Lisa Gorman
VP: Ken Ogden
VP: Bob Singh
IT Man: Jim Herlihy
**S&M/VP:* Peter Resca
Manager: Joyce Brennick
Board of Directors: Alfred Corvello, Peter Resca

ASTRODYNE TDI
See TRANSISTOR DEVICES INC

D-U-N-S 00-609-5921
ASTRONAUTICS CORP OF AMERICA (WI)
4115 N Teutonia Ave, Milwaukee, WI 53209-6731
Tel (414) 449-4000 *Founded/Ownrshp* 1959
Sales 390.6MM[E] *EMP* 1,550
SIC 3812 3571 3572 3769 Navigational systems & instruments; Warfare counter-measure equipment; Heads-up display systems (HUD), aeronautical; Automatic pilots, aircraft; Electronic computers; Computer storage devices; Guided missile & space vehicle parts & auxiliary equipment
Ch Bd: Dr Ronald E Zelazo
**Pr:* Michael Russek
**CFO:* Stephen Givant
CFO: Steven Givant
Ofcr: Taner Kimball
Ex VP: Jim Muench
Sr VP: John Middleton
VP: Dan Jinar
VP: Norma Paige
**VP:* Holly Russek
VP: Dan Ryan
VP: Dan Wade
VP Bus Dev: Robert Seinfeld
Exec: David Jones

D-U-N-S 18-539-8273 IMP
ASTRONICS ADVANCED ELECTRONIC SYSTEMS CORP
ASTRONICS-AES
12950 Willows Rd Ne, Kirkland, WA 98034-8769
Tel (425) 881-1700 *Founded/Ownrshp* 2005
Sales 197.1MM[E] *EMP* 380
SIC 3825 Instruments to measure electricity
Pr: Peter Gundermann
**Pr:* Mark A Peabody
**CFO:* Dave Burney
**Ex VP:* James S Kramer
VP: Johns Frank
**VP:* David Meisinger
VP: Richard M Miller
**VP:* Diana Suzuki
Exec: Lianne Hurst
Prgrm Mgr: Michael Ballas

D-U-N-S 04-982-9302 IMP
▲ ASTRONICS CORP
130 Commerce Way, East Aurora, NY 14052-2164
Tel (716) 805-1599 *Founded/Ownrshp* 1968
Sales 692.2MM *EMP* 2,300[E]
Tkr Sym ATRO *Exch* NGS
SIC 3728 3647 Aircraft parts & equipment; Aircraft lighting fixtures
Pr: Peter J Gundermann
**Ch Bd:* Kevin T Keane
CFO: David C Burney
Ex VP: James S Kramer
Ex VP: Mark A Peabody
Prgrm Mgr: Michael Hall
Prgrm Mgr: Ray Moravec
Snr Sftwr: Alan Thieman
Dir IT: Greg Bennett
Dir IT: John Mussel
Info Man: Lianne Foote
Board of Directors: Raymond W Boushie, Robert T Brady, John B Drenning, Jeffry D Frisby, Warren C Johnson, Neil Kim, Robert J McKenna

D-U-N-S 07-931-9176 IMP/EXP
■ ASTRONICS TEST SYSTEMS INC
(*Suby of* ASTRONICS CORP) ★
4 Goodyear, Irvine, CA 92618-2002
Tel (800) 722-2528 *Founded/Ownrshp* 2014
Sales 107.1MM[E] *EMP* 350
SIC 3825 Test equipment for electronic & electric measurement
Pr: James Mulato
**Sec:* David Burney
Sr VP: Ulrike Steinhorst
Sftwr Eng: Ioan Zolog

ASTRONICS-AES
See ASTRONICS ADVANCED ELECTRONIC SYSTEMS CORP

D-U-N-S 04-798-6898 IMP
▲ ASTRONOVA INC
600 E Greenwich Ave, West Warwick, RI 02893-7526
Tel (401) 828-4000 *Founded/Ownrshp* 1969
Sales 94.6MM *EMP* 329^E
Tkr Sym ALOT *Exch* NGM
SIC 3577 3829 Printers, computer; Magnetic ink & optical scanning devices; Bar code (magnetic ink) printers; Measuring & controlling devices
Pr: Gregory A Woods
**Ch Bd:* Hermann Viets
CFO: John P Jordan
CFO: Joseph P O'Connell
VP: Thomas W Carll
VP: Erik J Mancyak
VP: Michael M Morawetz
VP: Michael J Natalizia
VP: Stephen M Petrarca
VP: Eric E Pizzuti
CTO: Michael Sullan
Board of Directors: Graeme Macletchie, April L Ondis, Everett V Pizzuti, Mitchell I Quain, Harold Schofield

D-U-N-S 62-800-0937
ASURION INSURANCE SERVICES INC
(*Suby of* ASURION LLC) ★
648 Grassmere Park # 300, Nashville, TN 37211-3663
Tel (615) 837-3000 *Founded/Ownrshp* 1991
Sales NA *EMP* 3,000
SIC 6411 Insurance brokers
CEO: Steve Ellis
**Pr:* Cindy Christy
**CEO:* Kevin Taweel
**Ch:* Bret Comolli
VP: Nancy Gilby
Exec: Linda Hall
Dir IT: Vic Arms
Dir IT: Rick Devey
Snr PM: Frederick Cawthon

D-U-N-S 02-939-3514
ASURION LLC
(*Suby of* NEW ASURION CORP) ★
648 Grassmere Park # 300, Nashville, TN 37211-3667
Tel (615) 837-3000 *Founded/Ownrshp* 1999
Sales NA *EMP* 6,200
SIC 6399 Warranty insurance, product; except automobile
Ch Bd: Bret Comolli
**Pr:* Cindy Christy
COO: Chris Carrado
**CFO:* Mark Gunning
**Ch:* Kevin Taweel
Chf Mktg O: Byron Smith
Ex VP: Colleen Bucholtz
**Sr VP:* Tony Detter
Sr VP: Tom Manger
Sr VP: Sean McKinle
Sr VP: Stuart Smith
Sr VP: Barry Vandevier
VP: Read Dupriest
VP: C Forbes
VP: Mike Jernigan
VP: John Jones
VP: Antony Kong
VP: Robert Lefkowitz
VP: Jason Martin
VP: Kaizer Siraj
VP: Jaye Thomas

D-U-N-S 07-027-9067
ASURION PROTECTION SERVICES LLC
(*Suby of* ASURION LLC) ★
8880 Ward Pkwy Fl 5, Kansas City, MO 64114-2782
Tel (816) 237-3000 *Founded/Ownrshp* 2006
Sales NA *EMP* 1,500
SIC 6411 Insurance claim processing, except medical
Dir IT: Hsing Liu
Web Dev: Saurabh Malviya
Software D: Martin Reed
Snr Mgr: Tim Thompson

D-U-N-S 94-220-9297 IMP
ASUS COMPUTER INTERNATIONAL INC
(*Suby of* ASUSTEK COMPUTER INCORPORATION)
800 Corp Way, Fremont, CA 94539
Tel (510) 739-3777 *Founded/Ownrshp* 1994
Sales 191.7MM^E *EMP* 130
SIC 5045 3577 Computer peripheral equipment; Computer peripheral equipment
CEO: Steve Chang
**Pr:* Ivan Hoe
**VP:* Raymond Chen
VP: Albert Wang
Dir IT: Markus Wierzoch
IT Man: Maurice Reed
Natl Sales: Jessica Alvarez

ASV
See REV GROUP INC

D-U-N-S 10-297-1777
■ ASYST TECHNOLOGIES INC
(*Suby of* CROSSING AUTOMATION INC) ★
46897 Bayside Pkwy, Fremont, CA 94538-6572
Tel (408) 329-6661 *Founded/Ownrshp* 2009
Sales 48.4MM^E *EMP* 1,002^E
SIC 3674 Semiconductors & related devices
Pr: Dr Stephen S Schwartz
COO: Paula C Lupriore
CFO: James Mc Cormick
CFO: James McCormick
Sr VP: Thomas R Leitzke
Sr VP: David Schoenthal
VP: Randy Clegg
VP: Steve Debenham
VP: Warren Kocmond
VP: Frank Kohoutek
VP: Tim Lenihan
VP: May Su
Board of Directors: Stanley J Grubel, Robert A McNamara, Anthony E Santelli, William Simon, Walter W Wilson

AT & T ALASCOM
See ALASCOM INC

AT & T WIRELESS SERVICE
See AB CELLULAR HOLDING LLC

D-U-N-S 04-916-6635
AT HOLDINGS CORP
(*Suby of* EATON CORP) ★
23555 Euclid Ave, Cleveland, OH 44117-1703
Tel (216) 692-6000 *Founded/Ownrshp* 2007
Sales 95.3MM^E *EMP* 736
SIC 3724 3728 6512 Pumps, aircraft engine; Aircraft parts & equipment; Commercial & industrial building operation
Ch Bd: Michael S Lipscomb
**CFO:* Frances S St Clair
**VP:* David Scaife

D-U-N-S 07-975-7372
▲ AT HOME GROUP INC
1600 E Plano Pkwy, Plano, TX 75074-8124
Tel (972) 265-6227 *Founded/Ownrshp* 1979
Sales 622.1MM *EMP* 2,941
Tkr Sym HOME *Exch* NYS
SIC 5719 5945 Kitchenware; Hobby & craft supplies
Pr: Lewis L Bird III
**Ch Bd:* Martin C Eltrich III
COO: Peter S G Corsa
CFO: Judd T Nystrom
Ofcr: Alissa M Ahlman
Ofcr: Valerie L Davisson
Ofcr: Becky Haislip
Ofcr: Norman E McLeod
Ofcr: Jennifer S Warren
Board of Directors: Wendy A Beck, Elisabeth Charles, Geoffrey G Clark, Philip L Francis, Brian R Hoesterey, Allen I Questrom, Larry D Stone

D-U-N-S 09-509-8778 IMP
■ AT HOME STORES LLC
GARDEN RIDGE POTTERY
(*Suby of* AT HOME GROUP INC) ★
1600 E Plano Pkwy, Plano, TX 75074-8124
Tel (972) 265-6227 *Founded/Ownrshp* 1995, 2009
Sales 567.3MM^E *EMP* 2,682
SIC 5719 5992 5999 5947 5945 Kitchenware; Flowers, fresh; Artificial flowers; Party favors; Hobby & craft supplies
Ch Bd: Armand Shapiro
Pr: Lewis L Bird III
CFO: Jane Arbuthnot
Chf Mktg O: Jennifer Warren
Ex VP: Cal Eller
Ex VP: Rich Nawrot
Ex VP: Gary Ramsey
Sr VP: Kevin Rutherford
VP: Dennis Dye
VP: Jay Nayak
Genl Mgr: Rick Fukano
Board of Directors: Philip L Francis

AT&T
See SOUTHWESTERN BELL TELECOMMUNICATIONS INC

AT&T
See SOUTHERN NEW ENGLAND TELECOMMUNICATIONS CORP

AT&T AUTHORIZED RETAILER
See PRIME COMMUNICATIONS LP

D-U-N-S 16-094-4666
■ AT&T COMMUNICATIONS AMERICAS INC
(*Suby of* AMERICAN TELEPHONE AND TELG) ★
900 Us Highway 202 206, Bedminster, NJ 07921-2691
Tel (404) 861-9188 *Founded/Ownrshp* 1986
Sales 960.2MM^E *EMP* 7,600^E
SIC 5065 Communication equipment
Pr: David Dorman
VP: Bruce Cooper
VP: Mark Francis
Dist Mgr: Ted Jamer
IT Man: Jacqueline Harvey
Software D: Tom Minor

D-U-N-S 00-698-0080 IMP/EXP
■ AT&T CORP (NY)
AMERICAN TELEPHONE AND TELG
(*Suby of* AT&T INC) ★
1 At&T Way, Bedminster, NJ 07921
Tel (800) 403-3302 *Founded/Ownrshp* 1885, 2005
Sales 33.0MMM^E *EMP* 47,600
SIC 4813 4822 7375 Telephone communication, except radio; ;Voice telephone communications; Data telephone communications; Cable, telegram & telex services; Electronic mail; Facsimile transmission services; Information retrieval services
Ch: Ralph De La Vega
**Pr:* Geisse Andrew M
Pr: Beth Adcock Shiroishi
Sr VP: Chris Rooney
Sr VP: Randy J Tomlin
VP: Kevin Peters
Assoc Dir: Annette Metraux
Assoc Dir: Heath Simpson
**Prin:* Paul Stephens
Ex Dir: Cameron Coursey
Area Mgr: Deborah Dorsey

D-U-N-S 07-305-4095
■ AT&T GLOBAL NETWORK SERVICES LLC
AT&T SYSTEMS
(*Suby of* AMERICAN TELEPHONE AND TELG) ★
3405 W Dr Martin Lthr Kng, Tampa, FL 33607-6212
Tel (813) 878-3000 *Founded/Ownrshp* 1999
Sales 622.3MM^E *EMP* 3,500^E
SIC 4899 Communication signal enhancement network system
Dist Mgr: Francisco Lugo
Snr Mgr: Dwight Anderson

D-U-N-S 00-968-3442
■ AT&T GOVERNMENT SOLUTIONS INC
(*Suby of* AMERICAN TELEPHONE AND TELG) ★
1900 Gallows Rd Ste 105, Vienna, VA 22182-3865
Tel (703) 506-5000 *Founded/Ownrshp* 2000
Sales 264.4MM^E *EMP* 1,338
SIC 5999 8742 7373 7371 Mobile telephones & equipment; General management consultant; Computer integrated systems design; Computer software development
Pr: Timothy S Harden
**CFO:* Tim Halsey
Ex VP: Casey Coleman
Sr VP: Don Herring
**Sr VP:* Paul Ilg
Sr VP: Robert E Larned
VP: Michael Heath
VP: Michael Leff
VP: Marvy Moore
VP: Stacy Schwartz
VP: Jill T Singer
VP: Chris Smith
**VP:* John Sutton

AT&T ILLINOIS
See ILLINOIS BELL TELEPHONE CO

D-U-N-S 10-802-4050 IMP/EXP
▲ AT&T INC
208 S Akard St, Dallas, TX 75202-4295
Tel (210) 821-4105 *Founded/Ownrshp* 1983
Sales 146.8MMM *EMP* 281,000
Tkr Sym T *Exch* NYS
SIC 4813 4812 3663 3661 2741 Telephone communication, except radio; Local & long distance telephone communications; Cellular telephone services; Cellular radio telephone; Pagers (one-way); Telephone & telegraph apparatus; Telephones & telephone apparatus; Directories, telephone: publishing & printing
CEO: Randall L Stephenson
Pr: Karen S Baer
Pr: Jarrod S Barnes
Pr: Betsy Brady
Pr: Albert Burke
Pr: Jamie Butcher
Pr: Ron Cloutier
Pr: Fletcher Cook
Pr: Gloria Corey
Pr: John Donovan
Pr: Jeff Fancher
Pr: Brooks Fitzsimmons
Pr: Thomas Fleming
Pr: Suzanne Galvanek
Pr: Mark R Graham
Pr: Joe Greer
Pr: Mike Hargrove
Pr: Blake Haydon
Pr: Cindy Irons
Pr: Robert Kafka
Pr: Phil Law

AT&T INTERACTIVE
See YP.COM LLC

D-U-N-S 60-285-6353
■ AT&T LABS INC
SBC
(*Suby of* AT&T INC) ★
9505 Arboretum Blvd, Austin, TX 78759-6337
Tel (512) 372-5000 *Founded/Ownrshp* 1988
Sales 58.6MM^E *EMP* 1,206
SIC 8748 Telecommunications consultant
Pr: Charles Roesslein
Exec: Melissa Engman
Assoc Dir: Jack Villada
Ex Dir: David Hartman
Ex Dir: Eric Puetz
Genl Couns: Umesh M Desai

D-U-N-S 62-663-5627
■ AT&T MESSAGING LLC
(*Suby of* AT&T INC) ★
4801 Nw Loop 410 Ste 850, San Antonio, TX 78229-5337
Tel (210) 523-4300 *Founded/Ownrshp* 1990
Sales 85.0MM^E *EMP* 414
SIC 4813 Voice telephone communications
Pr: Albert Porta

AT&T MICHIGAN
See MICHIGAN BELL TELEPHONE CO

AT&T MIDWEST
See AT&T TELEHOLDINGS INC

AT&T MOBILITY
See NEW CINGULAR WIRELESS SERVICES INC

AT&T MOBILITY
See CELLULAR COMMUNICATIONS OF PUERTO RICO INC

D-U-N-S 00-354-8489
■ AT&T MOBILITY LLC (GA)
(*Suby of* AT&T INC) ★
1025 Lenox Park Blvd Ne, Brookhaven, GA 30319-5309
Tel (425) 580-6014 *Founded/Ownrshp* 2000
Sales 27.1MMM^E *EMP* 43,350^E
SIC 4812 4813 5999 Radio telephone communication; Telephone communication, except radio; Telephone & communication equipment
Pr: Ralph De La Vega
**Pr:* Leann Priebe
Pr: Edgar L Reynolds
**Pr:* Stephen F Sitton
**CFO:* Peter A Ritcher
Chf Mktg O: Virginia L Vann
**Ex VP:* Joaquin R Carbonell III
Sr VP: Rickford D Bradley
VP: Jim Jacot
VP: Stephanie Joyce
VP: Tim Klein
VP: Kristin Rinne
VP: George Sloan
VP: Todd Waskelis
VP: Jim Wood
VP Bus Dev: Larry Blenk
Exec: Mike Abdul
Board of Directors: Richard G Lindner, John Stankey, Randall L Stephenson

D-U-N-S 94-142-0804 IMP
■ AT&T MOBILITY PUERTO RICO INC
(*Suby of* CENTENNIAL COMMUNICATIONS CORP.)
996 Calle San Roberto, Rio Piedras, PR 00926-2735
Tel (787) 717-9600 *Founded/Ownrshp* 1982
Sales 263.3MM^E *EMP* 1,500
SIC 4813 4812 ; Cellular telephone services
Pr: Carlos Blanko
Ofcr: Gina Gulapa
Assoc VP: Juan Medero
Assoc VP: Fred Travis
VP: Luis Miranda
**Prin:* Carlos Rivera
**Prin:* Marnaon Roya
Sftwr Eng: Greg Conley
VP Sls: Enrique Niggemann
Sls Mgr: John Holbrook

AT&T NEVADA
See NEVADA BELL TELEPHONE CO

AT&T OHIO
See OHIO BELL TELEPHONE CO

D-U-N-S 02-502-7256 IMP
■ AT&T SERVICES INC
(*Suby of* AT&T INC) ★
208 S Akard St Ste 110, Dallas, TX 75202-4209
Tel (210) 821-4105 *Founded/Ownrshp* 1996
Sales 2.2MMM^E *EMP* 37,321^E
SIC 4813 Telephone communication, except radio
Pr: John Donovan
Bd of Dir: James H Blanchard
Chf Mktg O: David Christopher
VP: Greg Beck
Exec: Pat Kruge
**Prin:* William M Daley
Area Mgr: Elizabeth Burkley
Mktg Mgr: Candace Savard

D-U-N-S 07-985-1555
■ AT&T SERVICES INC
(*Suby of* AT&T COMMUNICATIONS AMERICAS INC) ★
200 S Laurel Ave, Middletown, NJ 07748-1998
Tel (732) 420-3131 *Founded/Ownrshp* 2006
Sales 55.5MM^E *EMP* 1,000
SIC 3669 Communications equipment
CEO: Randall Stephensen

AT&T SYSTEMS
See AT&T GLOBAL NETWORK SERVICES LLC

D-U-N-S 10-333-0684
■ AT&T TELEHOLDINGS INC
AT&T MIDWEST
(*Suby of* AT&T INC) ★
30 S Wacker Dr Fl 34, Chicago, IL 60606-7413
Tel (800) 257-0902 *Founded/Ownrshp* 1999
Sales 6.8MMM^E *EMP* 65,345^E
SIC 4813 4812 2741 5065 6159 7382 Telephone communication, except radio; Local telephone communications; Long distance telephone communications; Cellular telephone services; Paging services; Directories, telephone: publishing only, not printed on site; Telephone equipment; Machinery & equipment finance leasing; Security systems services
Ch Bd: Edward Whitacre Jr
**Pr:* Andrew M Geisse
CFO: William Craft
IT Man: Jeannie Balsam

D-U-N-S 61-919-3543
■ AT&T WIRELESS SERVICES OF CALIFORNIA LLC
(*Suby of* AT&T MOBILITY) ★
7277 164th Ave Ne, Redmond, WA 98052-7823
Tel (425) 827-4500 *Founded/Ownrshp* 1990
Sales 100.5MM^E *EMP* 60^E
SIC 4812 4833 Radio telephone communication; Television broadcasting stations
Ch Bd: Craig O Mc Caw
Pr: Brian Shay
Ex Dir: Christopher Hall
Brnch Mgr: Bobby Evans
Dir IT: Gopalan Ramanujam
Dir IT: Laurence Seifert
IT Man: Brian Daly
Info Man: Signe Jackson
Netwrk Eng: Richard Jackson
VP Mktg: Mike Woodward
Mktg Dir: Terry Brush

D-U-N-S 06-786-8612 IMP
ATA AIRLINES INC
7337 W Washington St, Indianapolis, IN 46231-1328
Tel (317) 898-3110 *Founded/Ownrshp* 2007
Sales 59.9MM^E *EMP* 2,012
SIC 4581

D-U-N-S 62-605-2419 IMP
ATA RETAIL SERVICES LLC
7133 Koll Center Pkwy # 100, Pleasanton, CA 94566-3203
Tel (925) 621-4700 *Founded/Ownrshp* 1991
Sales 418.8MM^E *EMP* 1,000
SIC 5199 General merchandise, non-durable
CEO: Sumner Bennett
**Pr:* Ty Bennett
VP: Elena Bennett
CIO: Steve Raizes
Manager: Kathleen Ottaviano

D-U-N-S 00-698-0445 IMP/EXP
ATALANTA CORP
CELEBRITY FOODS
1 Atlanta Plz Ste 3, Elizabeth, NJ 07206-2120
Tel (908) 351-8000 *Founded/Ownrshp* 1972
Sales 231.5MM^E *EMP* 220
Accts Mc Gladrey & Pullen Llp New
SIC 5143 5149 5142 Cheese; Canned goods: fruit, vegetables, seafood, meats, etc.; Fish, frozen: packaged; Meat, frozen: packaged
Ch Bd: George Gellert
**Pr:* Andrew Gellert
COO: Kevin Kelly
**CFO:* Tom Decarll
**VP:* Joseph Denicholas

*VP: Robert Gellert
VP: Al Pish
VP: Carrol Stitt
MIS Dir: Carol Skitt
Dir IT: Carl Dangelo
Dir IT: Karl Deangelo

ATAPCO
See AMERICAN TRADING AND PRODUCTION CORP

ATC
See AMERICAN TECHNICAL CERAMICS CORP

A.T.C
See ABBOUD TRADING CORP

D-U-N-S 14-651-4430 IMP
■ ATC DRIVETRAIN LLC
(Suby of GENCO-ATC) ★
9901 W Reno Ave, Oklahoma City, OK 73127-7140
Tel (405) 350-3600 Founded/Ownrshp 2012
Sales 113.8MM^E EMP 1,000
SIC 3714 4731 Motor vehicle transmissions, drive assemblies & parts; Freight transportation arrangement
Pr: Michael Lepore
COO: Mike Hague-Morgan
VP: Greg Shuler

D-U-N-S 79-476-3636
ATC GROUP HOLDINGS LLC
A T C ASSOCIATES
221 Rue De Jean Ste 300, Lafayette, LA 70508-3283
Tel (337) 324-8777 Founded/Ownrshp 2005
Sales 126.2MM^E EMP 1,588
Accts Kpmg Llp Brisbane
SIC 8711 8732 8731 8249 8748 Engineering services; Commercial nonphysical research; Commercial physical research; Vocational schools; Business consulting
Pr: Bobby Toups
*CFO: Paul J Grillo
*Sr VP: Ellen B Miller
VP: Timothy G Swanson
Brnch Mgr: Fred Lyke
Snr PM: Keith Thompson

D-U-N-S 03-493-0156 IMP
ATC GROUP SERVICES LLC
(Suby of A T C ASSOCIATES) ★
221 Rue De Jean Ste 200, Lafayette, LA 70508-3283
Tel (337) 234-8777 Founded/Ownrshp 1987
Sales 126.2MM^E EMP 1,588
Accts Kpmg Brisbane
SIC 8711 8734 8731 8249 8748 Sanitary engineers; Pollution control engineering; Testing laboratories; Environmental research; Engineering laboratory, except testing; Vocational schools; Environmental consultant
Pr: Robert Toups
Pr: Donald W Beck
Pr: Wendell Lattz
CFO: Paul J Grillo
CFO: Graham Yerbury
Sr VP: Alan C Agadoni
VP: Donald Beck
VP: Ellen B Miller
Genl Mgr: Paul Gardiner
Genl Mgr: Trevor Johnson
Genl Mgr: Kylie Sprott

D-U-N-S 09-893-5257
ATC HEALTHCARE SERVICES INC
1983 Marcus Ave Ste E122, New Hyde Park, NY 11042-1029
Tel (516) 345-9928 Founded/Ownrshp 1978
Sales 218.9MM^E EMP 4,000
SIC 7363 Medical help service; Temporary help service
CEO: David Savitsky
*Ch Bd: Stephen Savitsky
COO: Ed Teixeira
*CFO: David Kimbell
*VP: Willard Derr
Dir Bus: Irv Braun
Ex Dir: John Frasse
Pgrm Dir: Jerry Bishop
Board of Directors: Gerald P Halpern, Jonathan J Halpert Phd, Martin Schiller

D-U-N-S 10-296-1880 IMP
■ ATC LOGISTICS & ELECTRONICS INC
GENCO ATC
(Suby of GENCO-ATC) ★
13500 Independence Pkwy, Fort Worth, TX 76177-4010
Tel (817) 491-7700 Founded/Ownrshp 2005
Sales 273.1MM^E EMP 2,400
SIC 4225 3714 3694 General warehousing & storage; Rebuilding engines & transmissions, factory basis; Motor vehicle transmissions, drive assemblies & parts; Engine electrical equipment
CEO: Todd R Peters
*Pr: Anthony Francis
*VP: Dan Gardner
VP: Frank Salerno
*VP: Marc Sherman
*VP Opers: Randy Engel
*VP Opers: Arthur Smuck

ATC NUCLEAR
See ARGO TURBOSERVE CORP

D-U-N-S 15-405-2245
ATC STAFFING SERVICES INC
(Suby of ATC HEALTHCARE SERVICES INC) ★
1983 Marcus Ave Ste E122, New Hyde Park, NY 11042-1029
Tel (516) 326-1396 Founded/Ownrshp 1994
Sales 61.4MM^E EMP 4,000
SIC 7361 8093 8011 Nurses' registry; Respiratory therapy clinic; Medical centers
Pr: David Savitsky
*Ch Bd: Stephen Savitsky
*COO: Ed Teixeira
*CFO: David Kimbell

D-U-N-S 87-743-7343 IMP/EXP
■ ATC TECHNOLOGY CORP
GENCO-ATC
(Suby of GENCO ATC) ★
100 Papercraft Park, Pittsburgh, PA 15238-3200
Tel (412) 820-3700 Founded/Ownrshp 1994
Sales 307.3MM EMP 2,700^E
SIC 1541 3694 4225 Industrial buildings & warehouses; Engine electrical equipment; General warehousing & storage
Pr: Todd R Peters
*Pr: Andy Smith
*COO: Art Smuck
*CFO: John M Pinkerton
*CFO: Rick Roadarmel
*Ex VP: John J Machota
*Sr VP: Bradley Peacock
*VP: Mary T Ryan
*VP: Joseph Salamunovich

D-U-N-S 07-982-0859
■ ATC TOWER SERVICES LLC
(Suby of AMERICAN TOWER CORP) ★
116 Huntington Ave # 1100, Boston, MA 02116-5786
Tel (617) 375-7500 Founded/Ownrshp 2015
Sales 171.4MM^E EMP 2,716
SIC 4813 3663 Telephone communication, except radio; Radio & TV communications equipment
Prin: Edmund Disanto
*Ch Bd: James D Taiclet Jr

D-U-N-S 00-602-2271 IMP/EXP
ATCO RUBBER PRODUCTS INC
7101 Atco Dr, Fort Worth, TX 76118-7098
Tel (817) 589-7035 Founded/Ownrshp 1961
Sales 314.6MM^E EMP 1,200
SIC 3443 3084 3585 3444 3083 Ducting, metal plate; Plastics pipe; Refrigeration & heating equipment; Sheet metalwork; Laminated plastics plate & sheet
Ch Bd: Charles B Anderson
*Pr: Ramesh Bhatia
*CFO: Randall Calaway
VP: Marvin Koerber
Exec: Mel Davis

D-U-N-S 96-162-4249
ATERIAN INVESTMENT PARTNERS LP
11 E 44th St Rm 1803, New York, NY 10017-3670
Tel (212) 547-2806 Founded/Ownrshp 2010
Sales 117.0MM^E EMP 550^E
SIC 3398 Metal heat treating
Pt: Michael Fieldstone
Pt: Eric Dieckman
VP: Daniel Phan
Off Mgr: Nadine Michel

D-U-N-S 07-973-2109
ATG / USM HOLDINGS LLC
NUMOTION
101 Huntington Ave, Boston, MA 02199-7603
Tel (860) 257-3443 Founded/Ownrshp 2013
Sales 450.0MM EMP 2,386
SIC 5999 Wheelchair lifts
CEO: Michael Swinford
CFO: Tamas Feitel
Board of Directors: Mary Hawkins

D-U-N-S 83-234-1932
ATG HOLDINGS INC
NUMOTION
(Suby of NUMOTION) ★
1111 Cromwell Ave Ste 601, Rocky Hill, CT 06067-3455
Tel (860) 257-3443 Founded/Ownrshp 1998
Sales 98.8MM^E EMP 726^E
SIC 5047 Medical equipment & supplies
CEO: Paul Bergantino

ATGSTORES
See ALLIED TRADE GROUP LLC

D-U-N-S 10-595-6986
▲ ATHENAHEALTH INC
311 Arsenal St Ste 14, Watertown, MA 02472-2785
Tel (617) 402-1000 Founded/Ownrshp 1997
Sales 924.7MM EMP 4,668^E
Accts Deloitte & Touche Llp Boston
Tkr Sym ATHN Exch NGS
SIC 7372 Prepackaged software; Business oriented computer software
Ch Bd: Jonathan Bush
COO: Ed Park
Ofcr: Kristi A Matus
Sr VP: Kyle Armbrester
Sr VP: Daniel H Orenstein
VP: Christopher Davis
VP: Jeremy Delinsky
VP: Evan Grossman
VP: Dan Haley
VP: Karl Stubelis
VP: Mark Swan

ATHENE ANNUITY & LF ASRN CO NY
See PRESIDENTIAL LIFE CORP

D-U-N-S 00-791-9780
ATHENE ANNUITY & LIFE ASSURANCE CO
(Suby of ATHENE HOLDING LTD.)
2000 Wade Hampton Blvd, Greenville, SC 29615-1037
Tel (864) 609-1000 Founded/Ownrshp 2011
Sales 217.0MM EMP 120^E
SIC 6719 Personal holding companies, except banks
CEO: James R Belardi
Pr: Chip Smith
CFO: David Attaway
Ex VP: Matthew Easley
Ex VP: Christopher Grady
Sr VP: Rod Mims
VP: Steven Harris
VP: Christine Kapteyn
VP: Eric Lund
VP: Keith Pinkley
VP: Jeffrey Robinson
VP: Jay Rosencrance

D-U-N-S 07-272-7910
ATHENE ANNUITY & LIFE ASSURANCE CO OF NEW YORK
PRESIDENTIAL LIFE INSURANCE CO
(Suby of ATHENE ANNUITY & LF ASRN CO NY) ★
69 Lydecker St, Nyack, NY 10960-2103
Tel (845) 358-2300 Founded/Ownrshp 1969
Sales NA EMP 99
SIC 6311 Life insurance
Ch Bd: Herbert Kurz
*Pr: Don Barnes
*Treas: Charles Snyder
*Ex VP: Mark Abrams
IT Man: Michael Underwood
VP Mktg: Linda Burger

D-U-N-S 79-862-5083
ATHENE ANNUITY AND LIFE CO
(Suby of ATHENE HOLDING LTD.)
7700 Mills Civic Pkwy, West Des Moines, IA 50266-3862
Tel (888) 266-8489 Founded/Ownrshp 2013
Sales NA EMP 1,400
SIC 6311 Life insurance
CEO: Grant Kvalheim
*Pr: Christopher J Littlefield
*Pr: Guy H Smith
*Treas: Brenda J Cushing
*Ex VP: David C Attaway
*Ex VP: Christopher Grady
*Ex VP: Gerhard Recker
*Ex VP: Christopher Welp
Sr VP: Megan Claypool
Sr VP: George Eldridge
Sr VP: Alain Mutricy
*Sr VP: David M Wingert
*VP: Erik H Askelsen
VP: Scott Ducar
VP: Eric Henderson
VP: Tom Mullen
VP: Sandy Stokley
VP: Christian Walker
*VP: Ron Wittenwyler

D-U-N-S 00-694-1017
ATHENE USA CORP
(Suby of ATHENE HOLDING LTD.)
7700 Mills Civic Pkwy, West Des Moines, IA 50266-3862
Tel (515) 342-3413 Founded/Ownrshp 2013
Sales NA EMP 1,400
SIC 6311 Life insurance
Pr: Christopher J Littlefield
CFO: Philip Easter
Chf Inves: Joseph W Wittrock
Ex VP: Gregory D Boal
Ex VP: Michael D Boltz
Ex VP: Brian J Clark
Ex VP: Michael H Miller
Ex VP: Roby Shay
Ex VP: Christopher R Welp
VP: Ron Wittenwyler
Exec: Chris Carney

D-U-N-S 04-221-0260
ATHENS DISPOSAL CO INC
14048 Valley Blvd, La Puente, CA 91746-2801
Tel (626) 336-3636 Founded/Ownrshp 1958
Sales 290.4MM^E EMP 515
SIC 4953 Rubbish collection & disposal
Pr: Ron Arakelian Sr
*VP: Ron Arakelian Jr
VP: Greg Huntingthon
Genl Mgr: Pete Branda
Off Mgr: Mary Caraballo

D-U-N-S 04-293-7227 IMP
ATHENS PAPER CO INC (TN)
1898 Elm Tree Dr, Nashville, TN 37210-3729
Tel (615) 889-7900 Founded/Ownrshp 1952, 1968
Sales 396.1MM^E EMP 300
SIC 5111 Printing paper
Ch Bd: W Donald Jenkins Jr
*CFO: Harold Sparks
Ex VP: Bill Blair
VP: Bill Gravely
VP: Tommy Harston
VP: Donald Jenkins
Exec: Dottie McCormick
Div Mgr: Bill Garvey
Div Mgr: Priester Mark
MIS Dir: Dona Winkowski
IT Man: Bobby Dodson

ATHENS REGIONAL HEALTH SYSTEM
See PIEDMONT ATHENS REGIONAL MEDICAL CENTER INC

ATHENS SERVICES
See ARAKELIAN ENTERPRISES INC

D-U-N-S 07-160-1074
ATHLETIC DEALERS LLC
ATHLETIC DEALERS OF AMERICA
5423 Village Dr, Viera, FL 32955-6570
Tel (321) 254-0091 Founded/Ownrshp 2007
Sales 218.0MM EMP 5
SIC 8611 Merchants' association
Pr: Peter A Schneider

ATHLETIC DEALERS OF AMERICA
See ATHLETIC DEALERS LLC

D-U-N-S 07-887-0137
ATHLON ENERGY INC
(Suby of ALENCO MATERIALS CO) ★
420 Throckmorton St # 1200, Fort Worth, TX 76102-3728
Tel (817) 984-8200 Founded/Ownrshp 2014
Sales 242.4MM^E EMP 40
SIC 1311 Crude petroleum & natural gas
Pr: Robert C Reeves
CFO: William B D Butler
Sr VP: Jennifer Palko
Sr VP: Nelson K Treadway
VP: John C Souders
Dir IT: Charles Fisher

ATI
See AMERICAN TECHNOLOGIES INC

ATI
See ALLEGHENY TECHNOLOGIES INC

ATI ALLEGHENY LUDLUM
See ALLEGHENY LUDLUM LLC

D-U-N-S 07-916-8906
■ ATI ALLEGHENY LUDLUM INC (MA)
ATI FLAT ROLLED PRODUCTS
(Suby of ATI ALLEGHENY LUDLUM) ★
1357 E Rodney French Blvd, New Bedford, MA 02744-2124
Tel (508) 992-4067 Founded/Ownrshp 2013
Sales 205.9MM^E EMP 50^E
SIC 3316 Strip steel, cold-rolled: from purchased hot-rolled; Sheet, steel, cold-rolled: from purchased hot-rolled
Prin: Marissa P Earnest

ATI FLAT ROLLED PRODUCTS
See ATI ALLEGHENY LUDLUM INC

ATI FUNDING
See A T I FUNDING CORP

D-U-N-S 61-904-9070
ATI HOLDINGS LLC
ATI PHYSICAL THERAPY
790 Remington Blvd, Bolingbrook, IL 60440-4909
Tel (630) 296-2222 Founded/Ownrshp 2016
Sales 287.3MM^E EMP 3,180
SIC 8049 Physical therapist
CEO: Dylan Bates
COO: Brent Mack
Chf Mktg O: Mark Lupo
Sr VP: Ralph Franceschini
Sr VP: Chris Noga
CIO: Rebecca Ruettiger
Dir IT: Anthony Valenti
VP Mktg: Kelly Roth

ATI LADISH FORGING
See ATI LADISH LLC

D-U-N-S 00-608-5401 IMP/EXP
■ ATI LADISH LLC (WI)
ATI LADISH FORGING
(Suby of ATI) ★
5481 S Packard Ave, Cudahy, WI 53110-2244
Tel (414) 747-2611 Founded/Ownrshp 1985, 2011
Sales 661.8MM^E EMP 1,637
SIC 3462 3463 Iron & steel forgings; Nonferrous forgings
CEO: Gary J Vroman
Pr: John Minich
VP: Wayne E Larsen
VP: Vicki Mallas
VP: Jim Meudt
IT Man: Mike Lohmen
Mtls Mgr: Jim Sorenson
Sfty Mgr: Richard Bizek

D-U-N-S 07-853-4457
■ ATI OPERATING HOLDINGS LLC
(Suby of ATI FUNDING) ★
1000 Six Ppg Pl, Pittsburgh, PA 15222
Tel (412) 394-2800 Founded/Ownrshp 2011
Sales 3.6MMM^E EMP 5,854^E
SIC 3462 Iron & steel forgings
CEO: Richard J Harshman
COO: Dylan Bates
CFO: John Egofske
Sr VP: Sheila Denman
VP: Christopher SL Pussey

ATI PHYSICAL THERAPY
See ATI HOLDINGS LLC

D-U-N-S 00-316-3359 IMP/EXP
■ ATI PRODUCTS INC (NC)
A & I PRODUCTS
(Suby of DEERE & CO) ★
5100 W WT Harris Blvd H, Charlotte, NC 28269-2157
Tel (800) 438-0660 Founded/Ownrshp 1959, 1956
Sales 111.0MM^E EMP 318
SIC 5083 5084 5085 Mowers, power; Chainsaws; Industrial supplies
Ch: Robert W Lane
*Pr: Robert Hove
*CEO: Tommy Morgan
*Treas: Robert D Barbour
*VP: Gary Davis
*VP: Mario Leone

ATI ROWLEY OPERATIONS
See ATI TITANIUM LLC

ATI SPECIALTY MATERIALS
See TDY INDUSTRIES LLC

D-U-N-S 00-598-8951
ATI SYSTEMS INTERNATIONAL INC (CA)
BROOKS ARMORED CAR
(Suby of CORPORATION DE SECURITE GARDA WORLD)
2000 Nw Corp Blvd Ste 101, Boca Raton, FL 33431-7304
Tel (561) 939-7000 Founded/Ownrshp 1947, 2007
Sales 1.2MMM^E EMP 12,700
SIC 7381 4513 4215 Armored car services; Security guard service; Air courier services; Courier services, except by air
Pr: Stephan Cretier
*Pr: Chris W Jamroz
*CFO: Patrick Prince
Genl Mgr: Terrence Freeman

D-U-N-S 82-822-8614 IMP
■ ATI TITANIUM LLC
ATI ROWLEY OPERATIONS
(Suby of ATI SPECIALTY MATERIALS) ★
12633 N Rowley Rd, Grantsville, UT 84029
Tel (801) 443-9958 Founded/Ownrshp 2012
Sales 228.8MM^E EMP 1,200
SIC 3462 Iron & steel forgings
Pr: Richard J Harshman
CFO: Dennis P Kelly
VP Opers: Bill Knauss

ATIF
See ATTORNEYS TITLE INSURANCE FUND INC

D-U-N-S 10-951-6802
■ ATK ELKTON LLC
(*Suby of* ORBITAL ATK INC) ★
55 Thiokol Rd, Elkton, MD 21921-4755
Tel (410) 392-6890 *Founded/Ownrshp* 2003
Sales 84.4MM^E *EMP* 500
SIC 3764 Rocket motors, guided missiles
CEO: Mark W Deyoung
VP: Jed Holzapfel
Prgrm Mgr: Brian Garvey
Genl Mgr: Bruce Dewitt
IT Man: Rosemary Berkowitz

D-U-N-S 00-224-1164
■ ATK LAUNCH SYSTEMS INC
ATK LAUNCH SYSTEMS-PROMONTORY
(*Suby of* ORBITAL ATK INC) ★
9160 N Highway 83, Corinne, UT 84307-9501
Tel (801) 251-2512 *Founded/Ownrshp* 1929
Sales 997.0MM^E *EMP* 16,000
SIC 3764 Guided missile & space vehicle propulsion unit parts; Propulsion units for guided missiles & space vehicles
Pr: Blake Larson
**Pr:* Jeffrey O Foote
VP: Stanley Graves
**VP:* Steven Mahon
VP: Charlie Precourt
Ql Cn Mgr: Mike Myers

ATK LAUNCH SYSTEMS-PROMONTORY
See ATK LAUNCH SYSTEMS INC

D-U-N-S 02-020-5647
■ ATK SPACE SYSTEMS INC
(*Suby of* ORBITAL ATK INC) ★
7130 Miramar Rd Ste 100b, San Diego, CA 92121-2340
Tel (937) 490-4145 *Founded/Ownrshp* 2003
Sales 119.7MM^E *EMP* 800
SIC 3769 Guided missile & space vehicle parts & auxiliary equipment
Prin: James P Gormican
COO: Robert Bernhardt
VP: James Gormican
Prin: Barbara McVeigh
Genl Mgr: Gary Van Gorder
Dir IT: Neal Haskins
IT Man: Audrey Clark
Web Prj Mg: Dan Osborne
VP Mktg: John Marks

D-U-N-S 03-251-6361
■ ATK SPACE SYSTEMS INC
(*Suby of* ORBITAL ATK INC) ★
11310 Frederick Ave, Beltsville, MD 20705-2005
Tel (301) 595-5500 *Founded/Ownrshp* 2007
Sales 117.6MM^E *EMP* 900
SIC 8711 Engineering services
Pr: Blake Larson
CFO: James Tooley
VP: Greg Maxwell
VP: Thomas Wilson
Genl Mgr: Tom Wilson
IT Man: Keith Bergman
IT Man: Wyvette Johnson

D-U-N-S 13-128-8391 IMP/EXP
■ ATK SPACE SYSTEMS INC
SPACE COMPONENTS
(*Suby of* ORBITAL ATK INC) ★
6033 Bandini Blvd, Commerce, CA 90040-2968
Tel (323) 722-0222 *Founded/Ownrshp* 1992
Sales 106.3MM^E *EMP* 550
SIC 3443 Fabricated plate work (boiler shop)
CEO: Daniel J Murphy
**Sr VP:* Ronald D Dittemore
**VP:* James Armor
VP: Gary Kawahara
**VP:* Thomas R Wilson
Prgrm Mgr: Joe Benton
Sftwr Eng: Sarah Laurenson

D-U-N-S 60-784-8251 IMP
■ ATK SPACE SYSTEMS INC
AEROSPACE STRUCTURES DIVISION
(*Suby of* ORBITAL ATK INC) ★
Freeport Ctr Bldg A15, Clearfield, UT 84016
Tel (801) 775-1141 *Founded/Ownrshp* 2002
Sales 212.1MM^E *EMP* 1,950
SIC 3728 3769 Aircraft parts & equipment; Guided missile & space vehicle parts & auxiliary equipment
Pr: Blake E Larson
**VP:* Joyce Delisser

D-U-N-S 60-598-9560
ATK SPORTING GROUP
2299 Snake River Ave, Lewiston, ID 83501-9685
Tel (208) 746-2351 *Founded/Ownrshp* 2005
Sales 221.8MM^E *EMP* 818
SIC 5099 Ammunition, except sporting
Pr: Mark W Deyoung
**CFO:* Neal Cohen
Bd of Dir: Don Preussler
**VP:* Steven J Cortese
Opers Mgr: Doug Lenz
Opers Mgr: John J Zeller

D-U-N-S 78-554-0774
ATKINS ENERGY GOVERNMENT GROUP INC
(*Suby of* ENERGY SOLUTIONS) ★
545 Oak Ridge Tpke, Oak Ridge, TN 37830-7187
Tel (865) 481-6300 *Founded/Ownrshp* 2006
Sales 300.6MM^E *EMP* 623
SIC 4959 Environmental cleanup services
CEO: David Lockwood
**Ex VP:* Greg Wood
Dir IT: Daryl Grantham

D-U-N-S 61-276-5636
ATKINS NORTH AMERICA HOLDINGS CORP
(*Suby of* WS ATKINS PLC)
4030 W Boy Scout Blvd, Tampa, FL 33607-5713
Tel (813) 282-7275 *Founded/Ownrshp* 2010
Sales 453.9MM *EMP* 2,952
SIC 8712 6519 8711 Architectural engineering; Real property lessors; Engineering services
CEO: L Joe Boyer
CFO: David D Quinn Sr
Treas: Heather McFall
**Sr VP:* C Ernest Edgar IV
Sr VP: Lawrence H Hentz
**Sr VP:* Michael M Newton
VP: Marvin Fisher
Snr PM: Gary Self
Board of Directors: Keith E F Clarke

D-U-N-S 05-043-9223
ATKINS NORTH AMERICA INC
(*Suby of* ATKINS NORTH AMERICA HOLDINGS CORP) ★
2001 Nw 107th Ave, Doral, FL 33172-2507
Tel (813) 282-7275 *Founded/Ownrshp* 1973
Sales 448.6MM *EMP* 2,790
Accts Pricewaterhousecoopers Llp Ta
SIC 8711 Engineering services
CEO: L Joe Boyer
**COO:* Barry J Schulz
**CFO:* David D Quinn Sr
**Sr VP:* Thomas F Barry Jr
**Sr VP:* Martin H Brown
**Sr VP:* David J Carter
**Sr VP:* C Ernest Edgar IV
VP: Olga Acosta-Cardenas
**VP:* Judith Aldrovandi
**VP:* Humberto P Alonso Jr
**VP:* Kevin W Brown
**VP:* Olga Acosta Cardenas
**VP:* Diego J Clavijo
**VP:* Lourdes T Fernandez
VP: Jayanth Jayaram
VP: Donald McEvoy
**VP:* Rene De Los Rios
**VP:* Jack S Schnettler
VP: Jack Schnettler
Exec: Samara Flores
Comm Dir: Carol Hobbs
Board of Directors: L Joe Boyer, C Ernest Edgar IV, Michael M Newton

D-U-N-S 96-715-6576
▲ ATKORE INTERNATIONAL GROUP INC
16100 Lathrop Ave, Harvey, IL 60426-6021
Tel (708) 339-1610 *Founded/Ownrshp* 2015
Sales 1.5MMM *EMP* 3,200
Accts Deloitte & Touche Llp Chicago
Tkr Sym ATKR *Exch* NYS
SIC 3441 1791 3446 3448 3496 Fabricated structural metal; Structural steel erection; Architectural metalwork; Prefabricated metal buildings; Miscellaneous fabricated wire products
Pr: John P Williamson
CFO: James A Mallak
VP: Kevin P Fitzpatrick
VP: Keith Whisenand
Board of Directors: James G Berges, Jeri L Isbell, Philip W Knisely, Scott H Muse, Nathan K Sleeper, William R Vanarsdale, A Mark Zeffiro, Jonathan L Zrebiec

D-U-N-S 96-715-8267
■ ATKORE INTERNATIONAL HOLDINGS INC
(*Suby of* ATKORE INTERNATIONAL GROUP INC) ★
16100 Lathrop Ave, Harvey, IL 60426-6021
Tel (708) 225-2051 *Founded/Ownrshp* 2010
Sales 1.4MMM *EMP* 3,000
SIC 6719 3441 1791 3446 3448 3496 Investment holding companies, except banks; Fabricated structural metal; Structural steel erection; Architectural metalwork; Prefabricated metal buildings; Miscellaneous fabricated wire products
Pr: John P Williamson
**Pr:* Bob Pereira
**Pr:* Mike Schulte
**Pr:* William Waltz
**Pr:* John P Williamson
**CEO:* John Williamson
**CFO:* James A Mallak
CFO: James Mallak
**CFO:* Karl J Schmidt
**Sr VP:* Rodney Long
**VP:* Kevin P Fitzpatrick
**VP:* Daniel Kelly
Comm Dir: Lisa Winter

D-U-N-S 96-665-1502 IMP
■ ATKORE INTERNATIONAL INC
(*Suby of* ATKORE INTERNATIONAL HOLDINGS INC) ★
16100 Lathrop Ave, Harvey, IL 60426-6021
Tel (708) 339-1610 *Founded/Ownrshp* 2010
Sales 1.1MMM^E *EMP* 3,000
SIC 3317 Steel pipe & tubes
Pr: John P Williamson
Pr: Steve Elsdon
Pr: Ed Kurasz
Pr: Bob Pereira
**CFO:* James A Mallak
Treas: Chuck Cohrs
VP: James W Hays
VP: James I Pinto
**VP:* Daniel Kelly
VP: Edward T Kurasz
VP: Susan C Nutson
**VP:* Steve Robins
VP: Roger Vaught
**Exec:* Kevin P Fitzpatrick
Comm Dir: Lisa Winter
Board of Directors: Mark Armstrong, Jim Berges, Nelda Connors, Phil Knisely, Arun Nayar, George Oliver, Nate Sleeper, J L Zrebiec

D-U-N-S 03-350-5181 IMP
ATLANTA BEVERAGE CO
5000 Fulton Indus Blvd Sw, Atlanta, GA 30336-2231
Tel (404) 699-6700 *Founded/Ownrshp* 1992
Sales 147.3MM^E *EMP* 300
SIC 5181 Beer & other fermented malt liquors
CEO: C Mark Pirrung
**Sr VP:* Greg Elliott
Brnch Mgr: Kelly Akins
Brnch Mgr: Roger Bligh
Brnch Mgr: Tony House
Mktg Dir: Justin Ferna
Sls Dir: Chris Green
Sls Mgr: Joey Dixon

D-U-N-S 06-921-0649
ATLANTA BOARD OF EDUCATION (GA)
130 Trinity Ave Sw, Atlanta, GA 30303-3626
Tel (404) 802-3500 *Founded/Ownrshp* 1969
Sales 174.7MM^E *EMP* 288^E
SIC 8211 School board
Pr: Courtney English
VP: Valerie Bond
Ex Dir: Glynis Lee
Off Mgr: Rita Ingram
Dir IT: Buster Barnett
Dir IT: Dan Crawford
Dir IT: Jerome Oberlton
Dir IT: Coleman Seth
Dir IT: John Williams
Pr Dir: Terreta Scope
Psych: Shaketha Blankenship

D-U-N-S 06-532-5177
ATLANTA CLARK UNIVERSITY INC
223 James P Brawley Dr Sw, Atlanta, GA 30314-4385
Tel (404) 880-8000 *Founded/Ownrshp* 1865
Sales 114.6MM *EMP* 1,150^E
Accts Grant Thornton Llp Atlanta G
SIC 8221 University
CEO: Dr Colton Brown
Pr: Narendra H Patel
COO: Lucille H Maug
**CFO:* Lucille Mauge
**Treas:* Meka Owens
Trst: Alexander B Cummings
Trst: Salvador Diaz-Verson
Trst: Harold E Doley
Trst: Eric Mintz
Trst: William E Shack
Trst: Isaac J Snype
Trst: Ruby Thompson
Trst: Leonard Walker
Top Exec: Lawanda Pearson
VP: Lucille Mauga
VP: Edward Patrick
VP: Jeffrey Phillips
Exec: Ann Clarke
Exec: Susan Kossak
Exec: Donnita Raglin

D-U-N-S 05-103-9394 IMP
ATLANTA COMMERCIAL TIRE INC
5067 Old Kennedy Rd, Forest Park, GA 30297
Tel (404) 351-8016 *Founded/Ownrshp* 1990
Sales 156.0MM^E *EMP* 150
SIC 5014 5531 Tires & tubes; Truck tires & tubes; Automotive tires
CEO: Joe Geeslin
**Pr:* Dennis Stough
**CFO:* Mary Ann Snow

D-U-N-S 04-272-7412
ATLANTA COMMUNITY FOOD BANK INC
732 Jseph E Lwery Blvd Nw, Atlanta, GA 30318-6658
Tel (404) 892-9822 *Founded/Ownrshp* 1979
Sales 103.0MM *EMP* 2
Accts Warren Averett Atlanta Ga
SIC 8322 4783 Individual & family services; Packing goods for shipping
Pr: Kyle Waide
Dir Vol: Stephen Holland
COO: Rob Johnson
**CFO:* Debra Shoaf
VP: Julie Fisher
**Assoc Dir:* David Smith
Dir IT: Torrey Williams
Mktg Mgr: Daphne Hill
Snr Mgr: Cameron Turner

D-U-N-S 00-692-4708
■ ATLANTA GAS LIGHT CO (GA)
ATLANTA GAS LIGHT RESOURCES
(*Suby of* SOUTHERN CO GAS) ★
10 Peachtree Pl Ne # 1000, Atlanta, GA 30309-4415
Tel (630) 388-2781 *Founded/Ownrshp* 1856
Sales 1.5MMM^E *EMP* 2,000
SIC 4924 Natural gas distribution
CEO: Henry P Linginfelter
**CFO:* Andrew Evans
Treas: Sara Adkins
**Ex VP:* Kevin Madden
**Sr VP:* Suzanne Sitherwood
Mktg Mgr: Michelle Fallon

ATLANTA GAS LIGHT RESOURCES
See ATLANTA GAS LIGHT CO

D-U-N-S 79-435-8218
ATLANTA HILL RESTAURANT CORP
TABOR AND MC COURTE
(*Suby of* CRAWDADDYS) ★
4155 E La Palma Ave # 250, Anaheim, CA 92807-1857
Tel (714) 579-3900 *Founded/Ownrshp* 1981
Sales 14.4MM^E *EMP* 1,302^E
SIC 5812 Eating places
Pr: David C Tallichet Jr
**VP:* Cecilia T Tallichet

ATLANTA JOURNAL & CONSTITUTION
See COX NEWSPAPERS INC

D-U-N-S 19-590-8624
■ ATLANTA MEDICAL CENTER
(*Suby of* TENET HEALTHCARE CORP) ★
303 Parkway Dr Ne, Atlanta, GA 30312-1239
Tel (404) 265-4000 *Founded/Ownrshp* 1998
Sales 347.0MM *EMP* 1,500
SIC 8062 General medical & surgical hospitals
CEO: William Moore
Chf Path: Steven Bondell
CFO: Lisa Napier
**CFO:* Jay Tennisson
Ofcr: Janet Palmer
Sr VP: Susan Davidson
Sr VP: Teresa Finch
Dir Rx: Michael Bendinelli
Dept Mgr: Rita Brown
Tech Mgr: William Liggins
Sfty Dirs: Jamey Moore

D-U-N-S 04-100-6974 IMP
■ ATLANTA NATIONAL LEAGUE BASEBALL CLUB INC
MISSISSIPPI BRAVES
(*Suby of* LIBERTY MEDIA CORP) ★
755 Hank Aaron Dr Sw, Atlanta, GA 30315-1120
Tel (404) 522-7630 *Founded/Ownrshp* 2013
Sales 109.1MM^E *EMP* 1,700
SIC 7941 Baseball club, professional & semi-professional
Pr: Terence F McGuirk
Pr: Jason Parker
**CFO:* Chip Moore
**V Ch Bd:* William Bartholomay
**Sr VP:* Henry L Aaron
VP: Scott Norwood
VP: Mike Port
Mktg Dir: Joe Clemente

D-U-N-S 93-181-7027 EXP
ATLANTA NETWORK TECHNOLOGIES INC
A N T
710 Morgan Falls Rd, Atlanta, GA 30350-5806
Tel (877) 293-9797 *Founded/Ownrshp* 1995
Sales 100.0MM *EMP* 35
SIC 5045 5065 Computers, peripherals & software; Electronic parts & equipment
Pr: Charles Comerford
**CFO:* Nancy Comerford

D-U-N-S 13-132-0822 IMP
ATLANTA ORIENTAL FOOD WHOLESALE CO
BUFORD HIGHWAY FARMERS MARKET
5600 Buford Hwy Ne, Atlanta, GA 30340-1240
Tel (770) 455-0770 *Founded/Ownrshp* 1984
Sales 107.6MM^E *EMP* 300
SIC 5146 5421 5046 5719

D-U-N-S 83-841-7751
ATLANTA OUTPATIENT PEACHTREE DUNWOODY CENTER
(*Suby of* NORTHSIDE HOSPITAL-ATLANTA) ★
5730 Glenridge Dr Ste 400, Atlanta, GA 30328-7700
Tel (404) 847-0893 *Founded/Ownrshp* 2009
Sales 1.5MM^E *EMP* 1,104^E
SIC 8093 Specialty outpatient clinics

D-U-N-S 07-979-8754
ATLANTA PUBLIC SCHOOLS
130 Trinity Ave Sw, Atlanta, GA 30303-3626
Tel (404) 802-3500 *Founded/Ownrshp* 2015
Sales 95.1MM^E *EMP* 6,500^E
SIC 8211 Public elementary & secondary schools
Exec: Linda Maddox
Ex Dir: Olufemi Aina
Dir Sec: Marquenta Sands
Dir IT: Barbara Reid
Pr Dir: Pat Sinclair
Teacher Pr: Pamela Hall
HC Dir: Tujuana Glenn
Pgrm Dir: Michelle Smith

ATLANTA SYMPHONY ORCHESTRA
See ROBERT W WOODRUFF ARTS CENTER INC

ATLANTA TITLE LOANS
See SELECT MANAGEMENT RESOURCES LLC

D-U-N-S 04-758-4941
▲ ATLANTIC AMERICAN CORP
4370 Peachtree Rd Ne # 200, Brookhaven, GA 30319-3000
Tel (404) 266-5500 *Founded/Ownrshp* 1968
Sales NA *EMP* 147^E
Tkr Sym AAME *Exch* NGM
SIC 6311 6321 6331 Life insurance; Health insurance carriers; Fire, marine & casualty insurance
Ch Bd: Hilton H Howell Jr
CFO: John G Sample Jr
Board of Directors: Robin R Howell, Mark E Preisinger, Harriet J Robinson, Joseph M Scheerer, Scott G Thompson, D Keehln Wheeler

D-U-N-S 15-534-3528 EXP
ATLANTIC AUTOMOTIVE CORP
MILE ONE
1 Olympic Pl Ste 1210, Towson, MD 21204-4106
Tel (410) 602-6177 *Founded/Ownrshp* 1986
Sales 535.5MM^E *EMP* 1,800
SIC 5511 7538 7515 New & used car dealers; General automotive repair shops; Passenger car leasing
CEO: Steven B Fader
Ch Bd: Samuel Bongiovano
**Pr:* Jerome F Fader
CFO: Louis S Richards
Ex VP: Jan Davis
Ex VP: James Gordon
Genl Mgr: Barry Lurie
Genl Mgr: Constantine Spivak
Snr Ntwrk: Orlan Marquez
CIO: Henry Lederer
CTO: Barbara Schildt

D-U-N-S 01-102-8438
■ ATLANTIC AVIATION CORP
(*Suby of* MACQUARIE INFRASTRUCTURE CORP) ★
6652 Pinecrest Dr Ste 300, Plano, TX 75024-2942
Tel (972) 905-2500 *Founded/Ownrshp* 1927, 2000
Sales 122.8MM^E *EMP* 350
SIC 4581 5088 5172 6331 6159 4522 Airports, flying fields & services; Aircraft servicing & repairing; Aircraft storage at airports; Airport hangar rental; Aircraft & parts; Aircraft fueling services; Property damage insurance; Fire, marine & casualty insurance: stock; Equipment & vehicle finance leasing companies; Flying charter service

CEO: Louis T Pepper
Pr: Glen Gross
Genl Mgr: Brice Allen
Genl Mgr: Theresa Doane
Genl Mgr: Gregory Wain
Genl Mgr: Josh Yahoudy
Dir IT: Rob Davis
VP Opers: Todd Baker
Opers Mgr: Steven Polonsky
Opers Mgr: Bob Popper
VP Sls: Sue Sommers

D-U-N-S 60-781-6928
■ ATLANTIC AVIATION FBO HOLDINGS LLC
(*Suby of* MACQUARIE INFRASTRUCTURE CORP) ★
600 5th Ave Fl 21, New York, NY 10020-2315
Tel (212) 548-6538 *Founded/Ownrshp* 2008
Sales 99.4MM[E] *EMP* 1,567[E]
SIC 4581 4785 1731 Aircraft maintenance & repair services; Toll road operation; Energy management controls
CEO: Louis T Pepper
CFO: David Mitchell

D-U-N-S 06-594-4733
■ ATLANTIC AVIATION HOLDING CORP
(*Suby of* MACQUARIE INFRASTRUCTURE CORP) ★
6652 Pinecrest Dr Ste 300, Plano, TX 75024-2942
Tel (972) 905-2500 *Founded/Ownrshp* 2005
Sales 130.3MM[E] *EMP* 400
SIC 5599 Aircraft dealers
Pr: Louis Pepper
COO: John Newcomb
Rgnl Mgr: Jay Hamby
Genl Mgr: Al Archuleta
Genl Mgr: John Butterworth
Genl Mgr: Joel Estelle
Genl Mgr: David Madden
Genl Mgr: Jeff Miller
Genl Mgr: Robert Pinedo
Genl Mgr: Joe Tazio
IT Man: Brian Myers

ATLANTIC BANK DIVISION
See NEW YORK COMMERCIAL BANK

D-U-N-S 96-611-3649
ATLANTIC BAY MORTGAGE GROUP LLC
596 Lynnhven Pkwy Ste 102, Virginia Beach, VA 23452
Tel (757) 498-6789 *Founded/Ownrshp* 1996
Sales 136.5MM[E] *EMP* 250
SIC 6211 Mortgages, buying & selling
Pr: Patti Bratton
Pr: Cory Alexander
Pr: Emily Farley
VP: Bob Dineen
VP: Alex Hampton
VP: Brandon Kimball
VP: Morgan Wise
Brnch Mgr: Robert Dineen
Dir IT: Barry Mason
Web Dev: Corey Shelton
Opers Mgr: David Dillard

D-U-N-S 00-529-5639
ATLANTIC BOTTLING CO
COCA-COLA
4 E 2nd St, Atlantic, IA 50022-1103
Tel (515) 987-1931 *Founded/Ownrshp* 1909
Sales 90.3MM[E] *EMP* 230
SIC 2086 Bottled & canned soft drinks
Ch Bd: James R Tyler
**Pr:* Kirk J Tyler
**VP:* John Otterbeck
**VP:* Dorothy M Tyler

D-U-N-S 80-203-8872
ATLANTIC BROADBAND FINANCE LLC
(*Suby of* COGECO COMMUNICATIONS INC)
1 Pine Hill Dr Ste 205, Quincy, MA 02169-7485
Tel (617) 786-8800 *Founded/Ownrshp* 2012
Sales 101.2MM[E] *EMP* 662[E]
SIC 4841 4813 Cable & other pay television services; Telephone communication, except radio
CEO: David J Keefe
**COO:* Edward T Holleran
**CFO:* Patrick Bratton
**Sr VP:* Leslie Brown
**VP:* Dan Feiertag
**VP:* David Isenberg
**VP:* Almis Kuolas
**VP:* Richard Shea

D-U-N-S 13-713-9072
ATLANTIC BROADBAND MANAGEMENT LLC
1 Pine Hill Dr Ste 205, Quincy, MA 02169-7485
Tel (617) 786-8800 *Founded/Ownrshp* 2004
Sales 175.7MM[E] *EMP* 600
Accts Pricewaterhousecoopers Llp Bo
SIC 4841 Cable & other pay television services
CEO: Edward T Holleran Jr
COO: Richard Shea
**CFO:* Patrick Bratton
**Sr VP:* Leslie Brown
**Sr VP:* David Isenberg
**VP:* Dan Feiertag
VP: Heather McCallion
Creative D: June Bryan
Dir Bus: Debbie Eblen
Genl Mgr: Chap Hanley
Genl Mgr: Earnest Lee

D-U-N-S 11-921-0656 IMP/EXP
ATLANTIC CAPES FISHERIES INC
985 Ocean Dr, Cape May, NJ 08204-1855
Tel (609) 884-3000 *Founded/Ownrshp* 1984
Sales 163.2MM *EMP* 185[E]
SIC 5146 Fish & seafoods
Pr: Daniel Cohen
Pr: Jim Mullin
Genl Mgr: Stephanie Kadison
Genl Mgr: John Tirello
Off Mgr: Sandy Bergeron
QA Dir: Matthew Grolnic
IT Man: Sandra Simmerman
Sls Mgr: Peter Hughes

D-U-N-S 17-346-3167
ATLANTIC CITY BOARD OF EDUCATION
1300 Atlantic Ave Ste 500, Atlantic City, NJ 08401-7213
Tel (609) 343-7200 *Founded/Ownrshp* 1890
Sales 187.2MM *EMP* 870
SIC 8211 School board
Pr: John Devlin
Prin: Carmen Brock
Prin: Gabrielle Caldwell
Prin: Charles Gregg
Prin: Ernest Harper
Prin: Rosetta Johnson
Prin: Sarah King
Prin: Herman Laing
Prin: Diane M Saunders
Prin: Oscar Torres
Prin: Charles Wilson

D-U-N-S 00-697-1618
■ ATLANTIC CITY ELECTRIC CO (NJ)
(*Suby of* CONECTIV LLC) ★
500 N Wakefield Dr Fl 2, Newark, DE 19702-5440
Tel (202) 872-2000 *Founded/Ownrshp* 1924
Sales 1.3MMM *EMP* 544
SIC 4911 Distribution, electric power; Transmission, electric power
Pr: David M Velazquez
COO: Thomas S Shaw
**CFO:* Frederick J Boyle
Board of Directors: Joseph M Rigby

D-U-N-S 17-883-5414
ATLANTIC CITY PUBLIC SCHOOL
1300 Atlantic Ave, Atlantic City, NJ 08401-7207
Tel (609) 343-0086 *Founded/Ownrshp* 2005
Sales 10.3MM[E] *EMP* 1,135[E]
SIC 8211 Public elementary & secondary schools

D-U-N-S 15-413-0736
ATLANTIC CITY SHOWBOAT INC
(*Suby of* SHOWBOAT HOTEL & CASINO) ★
801 Boardwalk, Atlantic City, NJ 08401-7509
Tel (609) 343-4000 *Founded/Ownrshp* 1997
Sales 21.2MM[E] *EMP* 2,500
SIC 7011 Casino hotel
CEO: Jay Snowden

D-U-N-S 17-338-4223
ATLANTIC COAST COTTON INC
ACC
14251 John Marshall Hwy, Gainesville, VA 20155-1607
Tel (703) 753-7000 *Founded/Ownrshp* 1986
Sales 143.6MM[E] *EMP* 189
SIC 5136 5137 Men's & boys' outerwear; Sportswear, men's & boys'; Sportswear, women's & children's
CEO: Richard H Sacks
**Pr:* Mitchell G Gittler
Mktg Mgr: Nathan Lucrisia

D-U-N-S 07-872-7133
ATLANTIC COAST DINING INC
4701 Cox Rd Ste 345, Glen Allen, VA 23060-6802
Tel (804) 747-5050 *Founded/Ownrshp* 1992
Sales 92.5MM *EMP* 3,000
SIC 8741 Restaurant management
Ch Bd: William H Vaughn
**Pr:* Anthony Grillo
**Sec:* Davis Wood
**VP:* Linwood Miller

D-U-N-S 80-033-7946 IMP
ATLANTIC COAST MEDIA GROUP LLC
ATLANTIC CST MDIA GRP HOLDINGS
100 Town Square Pl Fl 6, Jersey City, NJ 07310-2778
Tel (201) 942-3400 *Founded/Ownrshp* 2006
Sales 124.8MM *EMP* 81[E]
Accts Keiter Glen Allen Virginia
SIC 5961 5999 Cosmetics & perfumes, mail order; Cosmetics
CEO: Andrew Surwilo
**CEO:* Thomas Shipley
COO: Darek Hrynkiewicz
**CFO:* John Ende
CFO: Peter Maclearie
Sr VP: Rick Weinstock
VP: Steve Brita
VP: Mindy Goldstein
VP: Tammy Yaiser
CIO: Abhishek Jain
IT Man: Chris Fatzer

D-U-N-S 01-661-7225
ATLANTIC COAST MERCHANDISING LLC
599 Wood Hollow Rd, Taylorsville, NC 28681-7631
Tel (910) 300-9231 *Founded/Ownrshp* 2008
Sales 3.5MM *EMP* 6,000
SIC 8742 7389 Merchandising consultant;

D-U-N-S 79-011-9163 IMP
ATLANTIC COFFEE INDUSTRIAL SOLUTIONS LLC
ATLANTIC COFFEE SOLUTIONS
3900 Harrisburg Blvd, Houston, TX 77003-2638
Tel (713) 228-9501 *Founded/Ownrshp* 2006
Sales 135.8MM[E] *EMP* 350
SIC 2095 Roasted coffee
Pr: Jorge Esteve
Pr: David Martinez
CFO: James Dunn
Treas: Cindy Parrish
VP: Tony Jones
Opers Supe: Steven Reyna
Opers Mgr: Scotty Jones
Sls Dir: Randall Christman

ATLANTIC COFFEE SOLUTIONS
See ATLANTIC COFFEE INDUSTRIAL SOLUTIONS LLC

D-U-N-S 12-973-9046 IMP
ATLANTIC CONSTRUCTORS INC
1401 Battery Brooke Pkwy, North Chesterfield, VA 23237-3021
Tel (804) 222-3400 *Founded/Ownrshp* 2003
Sales 177.4MM[E] *EMP* 750
SIC 1796 1711 3444 Machinery installation; Plumbing contractors; Heating & air conditioning contractors; Ducts, sheet metal
Ch Bd: Arthur M Hungerford III
**Pr:* Terrence W Kerner
COO: David Hodges
CFO: David Tuttle
**Sec:* Teresa Kulinowski
CTO: Bill Stout
Dir IT: Howard Clark
IT Man: James Dondanville
Sfty Mgr: Brian Sober
Sfty Mgr: Marty Walters
Mktg Dir: Kenny Blankenship

D-U-N-S 80-442-2012
ATLANTIC CONTAINER LINE AB
A C L
50 Cardinal Dr, Westfield, NJ 07090-1019
Tel (908) 518-5300 *Founded/Ownrshp* 1994
Sales 85.7MM[E] *EMP* 360
SIC 4412 Deep sea foreign transportation of freight
CEO: Olav Rakkenes
**CFO:* Dan Axel Rosen
**Ex VP:* Andrew Abbott
**VP:* Conrad De Zego
**VP:* Paul Gross

D-U-N-S 03-752-6297
ATLANTIC CORP
ATLANTIC PACKAGING
806 N 23rd St, Wilmington, NC 28405-1802
Tel (910) 343-0624 *Founded/Ownrshp* 1946
Sales 159.4MM[E] *EMP* 900[E]
SIC 2671 Paper coated or laminated for packaging; Plastic film, coated or laminated for packaging
Pr: Steven C Quidley
VP: Eric Farmer
VP: Brad Fields
VP: Jim Friesinger
VP: Ed Turlington
Genl Mgr: Jay Gibble
Dir IT: John Codington
IT Man: Robbie Walker
Opers Mgr: Karl Day
Plnt Mgr: Lanny Wilson
Prd Mgr: Lonnie Howard

D-U-N-S 00-319-3919 IMP/EXP
ATLANTIC CORP OF WILMINGTON INC (NC)
806 N 23rd St, Wilmington, NC 28405-1802
Tel (910) 343-0624 *Founded/Ownrshp* 1946
Sales 465.2MM[E] *EMP* 557
SIC 5113 2621 2679 Industrial & personal service paper; Paper mills; Paper products, converted
Pr: Russell Carter
Treas: Susan Carter
VP: Henry Boon
VP: Roger Teague
Dist Mgr: Linda Jacobs

ATLANTIC COUNTY GOVERNMENT
See COUNTY OF ATLANTIC

D-U-N-S 07-710-6094
ATLANTIC COUNTY UTILITIES AUTHORITY
ACUA
6700 Delilah Rd, Egg Harbor Township, NJ 08234-5623
Tel (609) 272-6950 *Founded/Ownrshp* 1969
Sales 160.5MM[E] *EMP* 250
Accts Ford Scott & Associates Ll
SIC 4953 4952 Refuse systems; Sewerage systems
Pr: Richard S Dovey
**CFO:* Maria Mento
**VP:* Brian Leske
VP: Joseph Pantalone
**VP:* Eugene Petitt
Dir Lab: Harry Dalladher
Dir Lab: Mike Gille
Dir Bus: Sandy Bourguinon
IT Man: Sandy Bourguignon
Sls&Mrk Ex: Monica Coffey

ATLANTIC CST MDIA GRP HOLDINGS
See ATLANTIC COAST MEDIA GROUP LLC

D-U-N-S 07-870-4681 IMP
ATLANTIC DETROIT DIESEL ALLISON LLC
180 Route 17 South, Lodi, NJ 07644-3809
Tel (201) 489-5800 *Founded/Ownrshp* 1988
Sales 112.8MM *EMP* 378
SIC 5084 7538 7389

D-U-N-S 02-707-9776 IMP/EXP
ATLANTIC DIVING SUPPLY INC
ADS
(*Suby of* ADS TACTICAL INC) ★
621 Lynnhven Pkwy Ste 400, Virginia Beach, VA 23452
Tel (757) 481-7758 *Founded/Ownrshp* 1997
Sales 1.4MMM *EMP* 360
SIC 5091 Diving equipment & supplies
CEO: Jason Wallace
**Ch Bd:* Luke M Hillier
COO: Jason S Wallace
CFO: Patricia Bohlen
**CFO:* Kiran Rai
**VP:* John Dunn
**VP:* Charles M Salle

ATLANTIC DOMINION DISTRIBUTORS
See OLD DOMINION TOBACCO CO INC

D-U-N-S 84-206-2937
ATLANTIC EXPRESS OF PENNSYLVANIA INC
(*Suby of* ATLANTIC EXPRESS TRANSPORTATION CORP)
7 North St, Staten Island, NY 10302-1205
Tel (718) 442-7000 *Founded/Ownrshp* 1993
Sales 53.7MM[E] *EMP* 3,000[E]
SIC 4151 4142 School buses; Bus charter service, except local
Pr: Domenic Gatto

D-U-N-S 04-781-9748
ATLANTIC EXPRESS TRANSPORTATION GROUP INC
7 North St, Staten Island, NY 10302-1227
Tel (718) 442-7000 *Founded/Ownrshp* 1994
Sales 252.0MM[E] *EMP* 7,150
SIC 4151 4141 5012 School buses; Local bus charter service; Buses
Pr: Domenic Gatto
**Sec:* Nat Schlenker
Sr VP: Laura Avakian
Sr VP: Nicholas Bergan
Sr VP: Kirsten Dixson
Sr VP: Lynne Zappone
VP: Pradip Achjarya
VP: Keith Andersen
VP: Warden Andrews
VP: Brad Barackman
VP: Mary Blankenship
VP: Lynne Bulmer
VP: Steven Callahan
VP: Wayne Carroll
VP: Steve Dark
VP: Leonid Davydov
VP: Ashraf Dimitri
VP: Julie Ellis
VP: Karla Ellishyde
VP: Frank Flanagan
VP: Tansil Graham

D-U-N-S 55-593-5394 IMP/EXP
ATLANTIC FOREST PRODUCTS LLC
240 W Dickman St, Baltimore, MD 21230-5005
Tel (410) 752-8092 *Founded/Ownrshp* 2014
Sales 130.0MM *EMP* 50
SIC 5031 Lumber: rough, dressed & finished; Plywood
Pr: John Chisholm
VP: Hettinger Bob
**VP:* Robert Hettinger
**VP:* Christopher McCarthy
**VP:* Richard Spallone
Rgnl Mgr: Jack Butler
Off Mgr: Blake Galvin
Off Admin: Jennifer Silva
MIS Dir: George Augins
Info Man: Bunnie Stevenson
Sls Mgr: Matt Hubbard

D-U-N-S 79-512-4494
ATLANTIC GENERAL HOSPITAL CORP
9733 Healthway Dr, Berlin, MD 21811-1156
Tel (410) 641-1100 *Founded/Ownrshp* 1993
Sales 108.5MM *EMP* 750
SIC 8062

D-U-N-S 04-002-4890
ATLANTIC HEALTH
FAMILY HEALTH CENTER
(*Suby of* MORRISTOWN MEMORIAL HOSPITAL) ★
200 South St, Morristown, NJ 07960-5370
Tel (973) 683-0104 *Founded/Ownrshp* 1999
Sales 960.6MM *EMP* 5
SIC 8011 Offices & clinics of medical doctors
Dir IT: Joe Trunio
IT Man: Barbara Barba
IT Man: Bob Grumka
IT Man: Johany Johan

D-U-N-S 07-583-7125
ATLANTIC HEALTH SYSTEM INC
(*Suby of* MORRISTOWN MEMORIAL HOSPITAL) ★
475 South St, Morristown, NJ 07960-6459
Tel (973) 660-3100 *Founded/Ownrshp* 1995
Sales 2.1MMM *EMP* 221[E]
Accts Lb Ernst & Young Us Llp India
SIC 8249 8062 Medical training services; General medical & surgical hospitals
Pr: Brian Gragnolati
COO: Rene Kessler
COO: Genevieve Maduabum
CFO: Kevin Shaley
VP: Madeline Ferraro
Ex Dir: Linda Dimario
CIO: Robert Killi
Dir IT: Seth Meidenman
IT Man: Bill Daniels
IT Man: Robin Davis
IT Man: Richard Hendricks

D-U-N-S 96-475-0769
ATLANTIC HOLDINGS I INC
(*Suby of* BROCK GROUP INC) ★
10343 Sam Houston Park Dr, Houston, TX 77064-4656
Tel (281) 807-8200 *Founded/Ownrshp* 2008
Sales 111.6MM[E] *EMP* 2,716[E]
SIC 1721 1799 Industrial painting; Fireproofing buildings; Insulation of pipes & boilers
Pr: Michael McGinnis
**CFO:* Robert Hardy

D-U-N-S 96-475-2070
ATLANTIC HOLDINGS II INC
(*Suby of* ATLANTIC HOLDINGS I INC) ★
10343 Sam Houston Park Dr, Houston, TX 77064-4656
Tel (281) 807-8200 *Founded/Ownrshp* 2008
Sales 111.6MM[E] *EMP* 2,716[E]
SIC 1721 1799 Industrial painting; Fireproofing buildings; Insulation of pipes & boilers
Pr: Michael McGinnis
**CFO:* Robert Hardy

D-U-N-S 62-427-8474
ATLANTIC INDUSTRIAL LLC
(*Suby of* ATLANTIC HOLDINGS II INC) ★
10343 Sam Houston Park Dr, Houston, TX 77064-4656
Tel (281) 807-8200 *Founded/Ownrshp* 2004
Sales 54.8MM[E] *EMP* 2,716[E]
SIC 1721 1799 Industrial painting; Fireproofing buildings; Insulation of pipes & boilers
Pr: Michael McGinnis
**CFO:* Robert Hardy

D-U-N-S 04-166-8195 IMP
■ ATLANTIC INERTIAL SYSTEMS INC
GOODRICH SENSORS AND INTEGRATE
(*Suby of* GOODRICH ARCFT WHEELS & BRAKES) ★
250 Knotter Dr, Cheshire, CT 06410-1137
Tel (203) 250-3500 *Founded/Ownrshp* 2000
Sales 123.1MM[E] *EMP* 800
SIC 3812 Gyroscopes; Navigational systems & instruments
Pr: Justin Robert Keppy
**VP:* Richard S Caswell

Exec: Tom Krajewski
Genl Mgr: Zenon Melnyk
Dir IT: Jeffrey Lane
IT Man: Susan Crowley

ATLANTIC INTERNATIONAL PDTS
See RLE CORP

D-U-N-S 01-573-1953
■ ATLANTIC MEDICAL CENTER
COLUMBIA HCA
(*Suby of* HOSPITAL COPORATION OF AMERICA) ★
303 N Clyde Morris Blvd, Daytona Beach, FL 32114-2709
Tel (386) 239-5001 *Founded/Ownrshp* 1996
Sales 457.1MM *EMP* 4,000[E]
SIC 8062 8011 General medical & surgical hospitals; Offices & clinics of medical doctors
CEO: Ron Rees
COO: Steven Harrell
**CFO:* Edward J Heverin
VP Mktg: Gary Meredith
Obsttrcn: Ramon A Castillo

D-U-N-S 00-452-6500 IMP/EXP
ATLANTIC METHANOL PRODUCTION CO LLC
AMPCO
16945 Northchase Dr # 1950, Houston, TX 77060-2142
Tel (281) 872-8324 *Founded/Ownrshp* 1998
Sales 376.9MM *EMP* 500
Accts Bdo Usa Llp Houston Texas
SIC 2869 Methyl alcohol, synthetic methanol
Ch: Marcus Allen
**Pr:* Paul Moschell
**VP:* Jim O Casek
**VP:* Edson S Jones
**VP:* Jeff Schultz
Opers Mgr: Carmen Santangelo
Genl Couns: Andrew Costa

ATLANTIC PACIFIC AUTOMOTIVE
See DYK AUTOMOTIVE LLC

D-U-N-S 05-932-9482 IMP/EXP
ATLANTIC PACIFIC MARINE CORP
MOLLER SUPPLY SERVICES
(*Suby of* MAERSK LINE) ★
2500 City W Blvd Ste 1850, Houston, TX 77042
Tel (713) 346-4300 *Founded/Ownrshp* 1971
Sales 100.0MM *EMP* 10
SIC 1389 Oil & gas wells: building, repairing & dismantling
Pr: Andrea Jones

ATLANTIC PACKAGING
See ATLANTIC CORP

D-U-N-S 13-920-6254
ATLANTIC PETROLEUM CORP
SUNOCO
1801 Market St Ste 1500, Philadelphia, PA 19103-1608
Tel (215) 977-3000 *Founded/Ownrshp* 2012
Sales NA *EMP* 4,178
SIC 5541 5172 2911 4612

D-U-N-S 09-428-0856 IMP
■ ATLANTIC PLANT MAINTENANCE INC
(*Suby of* VICEROY INC) ★
3225 Pasadena Blvd, Pasadena, TX 77503-3101
Tel (713) 475-4500 *Founded/Ownrshp* 2000
Sales 108.8MM[E] *EMP* 510
SIC 1629 Power plant construction
Pr: Rick Rives
**Treas:* Gary Madsen
VP: Mark Buchanan
VP: Richard Maxstadt
VP: Joseph P Patin II
**VP:* Neal Rose

D-U-N-S 07-170-4621
ATLANTIC PLYWOOD CORP
8 Roessler Rd, Woburn, MA 01801-6258
Tel (781) 933-1932 *Founded/Ownrshp* 1974
Sales 106.0MM[E] *EMP* 270
SIC 5031 5198 Building materials, interior; Plywood; Structural assemblies, prefabricated: wood; Stain; Varnishes
Pr: Paul Vella
**Sec:* John Blakeney
Brnch Mgr: Eric Brooks
Brnch Mgr: Steve Ciecura
Brnch Mgr: Justin Krasinski
Off Admin: Scott Keller
S&M/VP: Martin Wojick
Mktg Dir: Emily Vella
Sls Mgr: Kevin Chouinard
Sales Asso: Wayne Dunbar
Sales Asso: David Monks
Board of Directors: Dave Johnson, Wayne Moriarty, William C Ughetta Jr

D-U-N-S 83-769-2941
▲ ATLANTIC POWER CORP
3 Allied Dr Ste 220, Dedham, MA 02026-6148
Tel (617) 977-2400 *Founded/Ownrshp* 2004
Sales 420.2MM *EMP* 291
Tkr Sym AT *Exch* NYS
SIC 4911 3621 Generation, electric power; Power generators
Pr: James J Moore Jr
**Ch Bd:* Irving R Gerstein
CFO: Terrence Ronan
Ex VP: Joseph E Cofelice

D-U-N-S 13-920-6197
■ ATLANTIC REFINING & MARKETING CORP
(*Suby of* SUNOCO INC) ★
1801 Market St, Philadelphia, PA 19103-1628
Tel (215) 977-3000 *Founded/Ownrshp* 2013
Sales 49.8MM[E] *EMP* 1,000
SIC 2911 5171 5541 5411 Petroleum refining; Petroleum terminals; Gasoline service stations; Convenience stores, chain
Pr: Robert W Owens
**Pr:* Deborah M Fretz
**Treas:* Paul A Mulholland
**VP:* S Blake Heinemann

D-U-N-S 06-112-2156 IMP
■ ATLANTIC RESEARCH CORP (DE)
(*Suby of* KOLLSMAN INSTRUMENT DIVISION) ★
5945 Wellington Rd, Gainesville, VA 20155-1633
Tel (703) 754-5000 *Founded/Ownrshp* 1968
Sales 85.9MM[E] *EMP* 1,213
SIC 3764 3694 Guided missile & space vehicle engines, research & devel.; Rocket motors, guided missiles; Propulsion units for guided missiles & space vehicles; Automotive electrical equipment
Pr: John J Quicke
Pr: Armand F Lauzen
CFO: Pat Jenkins
Treas: Kenneth A Drucker
Treas: James P Langelotti
VP: Paul Barchie
VP: Steven R Lowson
Sls&Mrk Ex: Jim Davis
VP Sls: Rick Yezzi

D-U-N-S 04-542-6723 IMP
ATLANTIC RICHFIELD CO INC
A R C O
(*Suby of* BP AMERICA INC) ★
4 Centerpointe Dr Ste 200, La Palma, CA 90623-1074
Tel (800) 333-3991 *Founded/Ownrshp* 2000
Sales 2.3MMM[E] *EMP* 11,200
SIC 5541 1321 2911 Filling stations, gasoline; Natural gas liquids; Petroleum refining
Pr: Robert A Malone
**CFO:* Ian Springett
Board of Directors: Robert D Agdern Chairman, James G Nemeth, Donald E Packham

ATLANTIC SAFETY AND SUPPLY
See MAINE OXY-ACETYLENE SUPPLY CO

D-U-N-S 03-893-8395
ATLANTIC SCAFFOLDING CO LLC
(*Suby of* ATLANTIC INDUSTRIAL LLC) ★
1217 Georgia Ave, Deer Park, TX 77536-6704
Tel (281) 807-8200 *Founded/Ownrshp* 1980
Sales 49.7MM[E] *EMP* 1,117
SIC 1721 1799 Industrial painting; Fireproofing buildings; Insulation of pipes & boilers
CFO: Robert Hardy

ATLANTIC SCRAP & PROCESS
See OMNISOURCE SOUTHEAST LLC

D-U-N-S 60-793-5269
■ ATLANTIC STATES INSURANCE CO
(*Suby of* DONEGAL GROUP INC) ★
1195 River Rd, Marietta, PA 17547-1628
Tel (717) 426-1931 *Founded/Ownrshp* 1986
Sales NA *EMP* 300
SIC 6331 Fire, marine & casualty insurance
Ch Bd: Philip Hughes Glatfelter
**Pr:* Donald H Nikolaus
**Treas:* Daniel J Wagner
**Sr VP:* Ralph G Spontak

D-U-N-S 78-783-9005
ATLANTIC STREET CAPITAL MANAGEMENT LLC
281 Tresser Blvd Fl 6, Stamford, CT 06901-3246
Tel (203) 428-3150 *Founded/Ownrshp* 2006
Sales 278.5MM[E] *EMP* 480[E]
SIC 6799 Commodity investors
Mng Dir: Peter Shabecoff
**CFO:* Iris Rosken
**VP:* Brian Cooper
VP: Phillip Druce
VP: Grant Marcks
VP: Sarah Robson

D-U-N-S 00-418-9692 IMP
ATLANTIC TOOL & DIE CO INC (OH)
19963 Progress Dr, Strongsville, OH 44149-3211
Tel (440) 238-6931 *Founded/Ownrshp* 1947
Sales 146.3MM[E] *EMP* 476
SIC 3469 3544 Metal stampings; Special dies, tools, jigs & fixtures
Pr: Frank Mehwald
CFO: Dan Prugar
Ex VP: Ernest Mehwald
Genl Mgr: Paul Durant
Genl Mgr: Russ Haid
Genl Mgr: Michael Spence
Genl Mgr: Michael Spencee
CIO: Ron Kress
DP Dir: Collette Stewart
Plnt Mgr: Chris Aviles
Ql Cn Mgr: Dan Wotring

D-U-N-S 01-110-9386 IMP/EXP
ATLANTIC TRACK & TURNOUT CO
400 Broadacres Dr Ste 415, Bloomfield, NJ 07003-3174
Tel (973) 748-5885 *Founded/Ownrshp* 1989
Sales 123.1MM[E] *EMP* 95
SIC 5088 Railroad equipment & supplies
Pr: Peter Hughes
COO: Elaine Robertson
**CFO:* Doreen Kallensee
**VP:* Charles Killeen
VP Opers: Thomas Jones

D-U-N-S 05-853-3324 IMP/EXP
■ ATLANTIC TRADING & MARKETING INC
TOTSA
(*Suby of* TOTAL HOLDINGS USA INC) ★
5847 San Felipe St # 2100, Houston, TX 77057-3193
Tel (713) 243-2200 *Founded/Ownrshp* 2000
Sales 198.5MM[E] *EMP* 43
SIC 5172 Crude oil; Gasoline; Kerosene; Fuel oil
Pr: Eric Montfajon
**Treas:* Dan Tan
**VP:* Vince Ewing
**VP:* Cedric Rigodon
Genl Mgr: Natalie Engineer
Genl Mgr: Olivier Richemont
IT Man: Stefano Dotta
IT Man: Vincent Vadot

D-U-N-S 13-984-7433
ATLANTIC TRUST CO NA
(*Suby of* CANADIAN IMPERIAL BANK OF COMMERCE)
1555 Peachtree St Ne # 1100, Atlanta, GA 30309-2493
Tel (404) 881-3400 *Founded/Ownrshp* 2003
Sales 105.3MM *EMP* 8
SIC 6733 Trusts
CEO: John S Markwalter Jr
Pr: Eric Propper
Ofcr: Bret A Farris
Ofcr: Bradley Fincher
Ofcr: Kimberly Kaltreider
Ofcr: Clint Ward
Ofcr: Denise C Whennen
Assoc VP: Joseph Beauchaine
Assoc VP: Sean Brophy
Assoc VP: Damara Jones
Assoc VP: Tim Mello
Assoc VP: Lisa Oconnor
Assoc VP: Inda Royall
Assoc VP: Amy Scofield
Assoc VP: Lauren Snee
Assoc VP: Erika Valle
Ex VP: Robert P McNeill
Sr VP: Dan Carter
Sr VP: Ryan Christine Coulson
Sr VP: J Timothy Delaney
Sr VP: Martina R Frangis

D-U-N-S 15-694-0918 IMP/EXP
ATLANTIC WOOD INDUSTRIES INC
405 E Perry St, Savannah, GA 31401-4000
Tel (912) 966-7008 *Founded/Ownrshp* 1919
Sales 87.8MM[E] *EMP* 275
SIC 2491 3272 Wood products, creosoted; Concrete products, precast
Pr: William L Crossman
**CFO:* Bruce Douglas Fina
**VP:* Ross Worsham
VP Sls: Randy Kelly

D-U-N-S 82-563-1575
ATLANTICARE HEALTH SYSTEM INC
(*Suby of* GEISINGER MEDICAL CENTER) ★
2500 English Creek Ave, Egg Harbor Township, NJ 08234-5549
Tel (609) 407-2300 *Founded/Ownrshp* 2014
Sales 66.3MM *EMP* 5,000
Accts Withumsmithbrown Pc Morristown
SIC 8071 8082 Medical laboratories; Home health care services
CEO: David Tilton
Pr: Larisa Goganzer
Pr: Liz Readeau
Ofcr: Frank King
Sr VP: Dominic Moffa
**Sr VP:* James P Nolan
VP: David Desimone
VP: Terri Schieder
Off Mgr: Dana Lisicki
Dir IT: Sandy Gilpin
VP Mktg: Rene Bunting

D-U-N-S 19-629-5641
ATLANTICARE REGIONAL MEDICAL CENTER
(*Suby of* ATLANTICARE HEALTH SYSTEM INC) ★
65 W Jimmie Leeds Rd, Pomona, NJ 08240-9102
Tel (609) 652-1000 *Founded/Ownrshp* 2005
Sales 706.8MM *EMP* 249
SIC 8062 General medical & surgical hospitals
CEO: David Tilton
**COO:* Lori Herndon
CIO: Daniel Morreale
Obsttrcn: Blair Bergen

D-U-N-S 06-905-1241
ATLANTICARE REGIONAL MEDICAL CENTER INC
1925 Pacific Ave, Atlantic City, NJ 08401-6713
Tel (609) 345-4000 *Founded/Ownrshp* 1993
Sales 368.1MM[E] *EMP* 3,500
SIC 8062 General medical & surgical hospitals
Ch: Michael Neustadter
**Pr:* David P Tilton
**CEO:* Lori Herndon
**CFO:* Walter Griner
Chf Mktg O: Maureen Donzuso
Assoc VP: Cathy Iocona
**VP:* Theresa Camillo
**VP:* Michael Walsh
Off Admin: Teri Bennett
Ql Cn Mgr: Kelly Vasquez
Pathlgst: Nicole Miller

ATLANTIS CASINO RESORT
See GOLDEN ROAD MOTOR INN INC

D-U-N-S 14-426-6975
ATLANTIS PETROLEUM LLC
998 Old Eagle School Rd # 1205, Wayne, PA 19087-1805
Tel (610) 265-8081 *Founded/Ownrshp* 2004
Sales 71.8MM[E] *EMP* 1,100
SIC 5411 5541 Convenience stores; Gasoline service stations

D-U-N-S 80-803-8694
ATLANTIS SEAFOOD LLC
SEACATCH SEAFOODS
10501 Valley Blvd # 1820, El Monte, CA 91731-2461
Tel (626) 626-4900 *Founded/Ownrshp* 2008
Sales 144.7MM[E] *EMP* 85
Accts Kwan & Co Cpa Inc Alhambra
SIC 2092 Seafoods, frozen: prepared; Seafoods, fresh: prepared

D-U-N-S 12-193-5642
ATLANTIX GLOBAL SYSTEMS LLC
1 Sun Ct, Norcross, GA 30092-2851
Tel (770) 248-7700 *Founded/Ownrshp* 2015
Sales 98.4MM[E] *EMP* 160
SIC 8731 Computer (hardware) development
Pr: Brian Glahn
Sr Cor Off: Sheila Crane
**Ex VP:* Jason Jellie
**Sr VP:* Kevin Kiernan
**VP:* Amy Grant

**VP:* Kevin Uptegraph
Dir Bus: Bo Hamby
IT Man: Sean Guerreso
IT Man: Billy Weeks
Software D: Marc Passmoor
Opers Mgr: Brian Stevens

D-U-N-S 07-844-2820 EXP
ATLAS AGI HOLDINGS LLC
AGI-SHOREWOOD U.S.
100 Northfield St, Greenwich, CT 06830-4618
Tel (203) 622-9138 *Founded/Ownrshp* 2010
Sales 282.5MM[E] *EMP* 3,860[E]
SIC 2671 Packaging paper & plastics film, coated & laminated

D-U-N-S 79-777-0773 IMP
■ ATLAS AIR INC
(*Suby of* ATLAS AIR WORLDWIDE HOLDINGS INC) ★
2000 Westchester Ave, Purchase, NY 10577-2543
Tel (914) 701-8000 *Founded/Ownrshp* 1993
Sales 262.8MM[E] *EMP* 1,200
Accts Ernst & Young Llp
SIC 4512 Air cargo carrier, scheduled
Ch Bd: William J Flynn
**Ch Bd:* Linda Chowdry
**Pr:* Jeffrey Erickson
**COO:* Scott Dolan
COO: Toni Telfer
**Treas:* Bill Bradley
**Sr VP:* Ron Lane
Sr VP: Thomas G Scott
VP: William S Allen
Exec: Dominick Principe
Dir Surg: David Bradford
Board of Directors: Lawrence W Clarkson, Richard Galbraith, Stephen Greene, Brian Rowe, Joseph Steuert

D-U-N-S 01-075-4542
▲ ATLAS AIR WORLDWIDE HOLDINGS INC
2000 Westchester Ave, Purchase, NY 10577-2530
Tel (914) 701-8000 *Founded/Ownrshp* 2000
Sales 1.8MMM *EMP* 1,998[E]
Tkr Sym AAWW *Exch* NGS
SIC 4522 4512 7359 Air cargo carriers, nonscheduled; Air cargo carrier, scheduled; Aircraft rental
Pr: William J Flynn
**Ch Bd:* Frederick McCorkle
COO: John W Dietrich
CFO: Olivier Alexandroff
CFO: Spencer Schwartz
Chf Cred: Michael T Steen
Ex VP: Adam R Kokas
VP: Layne Grindal
VP: Keith H Mayer
VP: Vamshi Rokkam
CIO: Bill Dowling
Board of Directors: Robert F Agnew, Timothy J Bernlohr, James S Gilmore III, Bobby J Griffin, Carol B Hallett, Duncan J McNabb, John K Wulff

D-U-N-S 60-622-0630 IMP/EXP
ATLAS BOX AND CRATING CO INC
223 Wrcster Prvdence Tpke, Sutton, MA 01590-2905
Tel (508) 865-1155 *Founded/Ownrshp* 1987
Sales 100.4MM[E] *EMP* 250
SIC 2441 2448 2653 Boxes, wood; Wood pallets & skids; Corrugated & solid fiber boxes
Pr: Arthur Mahassel
Ofcr: Steve Hughes
Dir IT: Michael Latour
IT Man: Melissa McGovern

ATLAS BRADFORD DIVISION
See GRANT PRIDECO INC

D-U-N-S 02-172-5213 IMP/EXP
ATLAS COPCO COMPRESSORS LLC
(*Suby of* ATLAS COPCO NORTH AMERICA LLC) ★
1800 Overview Dr, Rock Hill, SC 29730-7463
Tel (803) 817-7000 *Founded/Ownrshp* 1980
Sales 262.7MM[E] *EMP* 1,253
SIC 3563 3999 Air & gas compressors; Atomizers, toiletry
Pr: Paul Hense
Pr: Paul Humphreys
COO: Krista Groleau
VP: Brian Dove
VP: Alfredo Piccolo
Exec: Robert Archambeault
Exec: Heidi Oram
Mng Dir: Ernest Bate
Genl Mgr: Mark McGinn
Genl Mgr: Derek Samaroo
CIO: Paul Callow

D-U-N-S 05-298-3723 IMP/EXP
ATLAS COPCO COMPTEC LLC
(*Suby of* ATLAS COPCO AB)
46 School Rd, Voorheesville, NY 12186-9696
Tel (518) 765-3344 *Founded/Ownrshp* 1970, 1989
Sales 134.2MM[E] *EMP* 350
SIC 3563 Air & gas compressors including vacuum pumps
Pr: Peter Wagner
**Prin:* Holly Simboli
Genl Mgr: Weston Greenman
IT Man: Darlene Kusaywa
IT Man: Tom Pinkowski
Netwrk Eng: Scott Meade
Site Mgr: Paul Burdick
Opers Mgr: Charles Batcher
Plnt Mgr: Bill Volk
Sls Mgr: Tom Pinlowski

D-U-N-S 80-877-4801 IMP/EXP
ATLAS COPCO CONSTRUCTION MINING TECHNIQUE USA LLC
11825 W Carmen Ave, Milwaukee, WI 53225-2293
Tel (414) 760-1193 *Founded/Ownrshp* 2007
Sales 88.7MM[E] *EMP* 2,500
SIC 1521 Single-family housing construction

D-U-N-S 15-323-3460 IMP/EXP
ATLAS COPCO DRILLING SOLUTIONS LLC
(*Suby of* ATLAS COPCO NORTH AMERICA LLC) ★
2100 N 1st St, Garland, TX 75040-4102
Tel (972) 496-7258 *Founded/Ownrshp* 2004

Sales 631.3MM^E *EMP* 2,500
SIC 3541 Drilling & boring machines
COO: Chris Lybaert
VP: Jon Myers
VP: Wayne Timmins
Area Mgr: Dennis Geary
IT Man: Daniel Van Tassell
Sfty Dirs: Demarcus Smith
Prd Mgr: Juan Cordova
Mktg Mgr: Alex Grant
Manager: Todd Francis
Sls Mgr: Tom Lyttleton

D-U-N-S 62-072-2335
ATLAS COPCO NORTH AMERICA LLC
(*Suby of* ATLAS COPCO USA HOLDINGS INC) ★
7 Campus Dr Ste 200, Parsippany, NJ 07054-4413
Tel (973) 397-3400 *Founded/Ownrshp* 2006
Sales 1.1MMM^E *EMP* 3,060
SIC 3312 Tool & die steel
Opers Mgr: Chris Schlicht

D-U-N-S 79-649-6524
ATLAS COPCO USA HOLDINGS INC
(*Suby of* ATLAS COPCO AB)
7 Campus Dr Ste 200, Parsippany, NJ 07054-4413
Tel (973) 397-3432 *Founded/Ownrshp* 2006
Sales 1.2MMM^E *EMP* 3,060^E
SIC 6722 6159 7699 Management investment, open-end; Loan institutions, general & industrial; Industrial equipment services
Ch: William Thomas
**Pr:* Mark Cohen
**Pr:* Jim Levitt
**Treas:* Peter Billgert
**VP:* Eric Moore
VP: Anders Osterberg
VP: Carl Pierce
Area Mgr: Dave Farmer
Genl Mgr: Per-Arne Lindqvist
Dir IT: Jackie Malouf
IT Man: Heinrich Bunbicka

D-U-N-S 07-972-7107
▲ ATLAS ENERGY GROUP LLC
1000 Commerce Dr Ste 400, Pittsburgh, PA 15275-1033
Tel (412) 489-0006 *Founded/Ownrshp* 2011
Sales 753.4MM *EMP* 619^E
Tkr Sym ATLS *Exch* OTC
SIC 1311 4922 Crude petroleum & natural gas; Natural gas transmission
Pr: Edward E Cohen
**Ch Bd:* Jonathan Z Cohen
Pr: Daniel C Herz
CFO: Jeffrey M Slotterback

ATLAS ENERGY, L.P.
See TARGA ENERGY LP

D-U-N-S 04-287-0664
▲ ATLAS FINANCIAL HOLDINGS INC
150 Northwest Point Blvd # 3, Elk Grove Village, IL 60007-1015
Tel (847) 472-6700 *Founded/Ownrshp* 2009
Sales NA *EMP* 214
Tkr Sym AFH *Exch* NAS
SIC 6331 Automobile insurance
Pr: Scott Wollney
**Ch Bd:* Gordon G Pratt
CFO: Paul A Romano
VP: Leslie Dimaggio
VP: Bruce Giles
VP: Joseph Shugrue
Board of Directors: John T Fitzgerald, Jordan M Kupinsky, Larry Swets Jr

D-U-N-S 96-506-7239 IMP/EXP
ATLAS HOLDING INC
(*Suby of* ENERGEXTUBE) ★
1855 E 122nd St, Chicago, IL 60633-2401
Tel (773) 646-4500 *Founded/Ownrshp* 2006
Sales 91.4MM^E *EMP* 350^E
SIC 3317 Tubes, seamless steel
CEO: Barry Zekelman
Pr: Dave Seeger
CFO: John Feenan
VP: Andrew Klaus
VP: Michael McNamara
Plnt Mgr: Jeff Cole

D-U-N-S 19-564-9236
ATLAS HOLDINGS LLC
100 Northfield St, Greenwich, CT 06830-4618
Tel (203) 622-9138 *Founded/Ownrshp* 2006
Sales 1.7MMM^E *EMP* 3,950^E
SIC 5031 2491 5039 5153 Paneling, wood; Wood products, creosoted; Prefabricated structures; Grain & field beans
VP: Troy Schirk
VP: Philip Schuch
Mng Dir: Tim Fazio
Sls Dir: Christy Manor

D-U-N-S 00-955-4122
ATLAS HOTELS INC
TOWN AND COUNTRY
500 Hotel Cir N, San Diego, CA 92108-3005
Tel (619) 291-2232 *Founded/Ownrshp* 1958
Sales NA *EMP* 1,023
SIC 7011 5812 5813

D-U-N-S 02-427-2762
ATLAS INDUSTRIAL CONTRACTORS LLC
(*Suby of* GMG HOLDINGS, LLC)
5275 Sinclair Rd, Columbus, OH 43229-5042
Tel (614) 841-4500 *Founded/Ownrshp* 2012
Sales 130.0MM *EMP* 450
SIC 1731 3498 1796 Electrical work; Fabricated pipe & fittings; Machine moving & rigging
Pr: George Ghanem
**CFO:* Timothy Seils
VP: Greg Aliotta
VP: Peter Lamonica
Rgnl Mgr: Clay Perry
Div Mgr: Jeff Forgey
Div Mgr: Dallas Gerwig
Off Mgr: Therese Offerman
Sfty Dirs: Dan Hodge

Trfc Dir: Loell Thomas
Opers Mgr: Doug Elliott

D-U-N-S 00-504-2288 IMP
ATLAS INDUSTRIES INC (OH)
1750 E State St, Fremont, OH 43420-4056
Tel (419) 355-1000 *Founded/Ownrshp* 1938, 1943
Sales 165.3MM^E *EMP* 1,001
SIC 3599 Crankshafts & camshafts, machining; Custom machinery
Pr: Jerald F Clark
**COO:* Stephen Clark
**CFO:* Maurice O Clark
**VP:* James T Clark
**Prin:* Roman G Burnor Jr
**Prin:* J S Heyman
**Prin:* Merwyn G Leatherman
Genl Mgr: Donald E Sullivan
IT Man: Shane Estep
IT Man: Dave Handthorn

D-U-N-S 85-954-4749
ATLAS MANAGEMENT INC
(*Suby of* SKF MOTION TECHNOLOGIES) ★
103 Foulk Rd, Wilmington, DE 19803-3742
Tel (302) 576-2749 *Founded/Ownrshp* 1994
Sales 634.2MM^E *EMP* 1,531^E
SIC 6726 Investment offices; Management investment funds, closed-end
Pr: Brian J Duffy
**VP:* Andrew Panaccione

D-U-N-S 00-506-9349 IMP
■ ATLAS MATERIAL TESTING TECHNOLOGY LLC
SOUTH FLORIDA TEST SERVICE DIV
(*Suby of* AMETEK SENSOR TECHNOLOGY BUS) ★
1500 Bishop Ct, Mount Prospect, IL 60056-6039
Tel (773) 327-4520 *Founded/Ownrshp* 1917, 2010
Sales 115.2MM^E *EMP* 349
SIC 3823 3569 3599 8734 3825 3821 Temperature measurement instruments, industrial; Testing chambers for altitude, temperature, ordnance, power; Machine shop, jobbing & repair; Product testing laboratory, safety or performance; Instruments to measure electricity; Laboratory apparatus & furniture
Pr: Larry W Masters
CFO: Donald Eldert
VP: Tom Kulawiak
Genl Mgr: Larry Bond
Off Mgr: Lori Webb
QA Dir: Youthapol Sathornkich
IT Man: Oscar Cordo
IT Man: Helen Reed
Sftwr Eng: Paula Henn
Mfg Mgr: Allen Manojlovic
Ql Cn Mgr: James Meindl

D-U-N-S 14-735-6463
ATLAS OIL CO
24501 Ecorse Rd, Taylor, MI 48180-1641
Tel (313) 292-5500 *Founded/Ownrshp* 1985
Sales 577.9MM^E *EMP* 110
Accts Ernst & Young Llp Detroit M
SIC 5172 5171 Gasoline; Diesel fuel; Lubricating oils & greases; Petroleum terminals
CEO: Sam Simon
**Pr:* Michael Evans
Pr: Jitesh Shah
Chf Mktg O: Bill Versen
Ofcr: Edwin Herbert
**Ex VP:* Kirk Haggarty
**Ex VP:* Bob Kenyon
**VP:* Satish Kalala
VP: A Kari
**VP:* Kari Lawry
**VP:* Daniel Ravid
VP: Joseph E Rivera
**VP:* Michael Ruehring
VP: Bill Shaver
VP: Fawzi Simon
VP: Victor Simon
Exec: Dan Macdonell

D-U-N-S 02-039-8186 IMP
ATLAS PAPER MILLS LLC
(*Suby of* RESOLUTE FP FLORIDA INC) ★
3301 Nw 107th St, Miami, FL 33167-3714
Tel (800) 562-2860 *Founded/Ownrshp* 2014
Sales 96.0MM^E *EMP* 199
SIC 2621 Toilet tissue stock; Absorbent paper
Pr: Jim Brown
VP: Don Grondin
Info Man: Florin Gradinar
VP Opers: David Demarzo

ATLAS PIPELINE
See TARGA PIPELINE MID-CONTINENT LLC

ATLAS PIPELINE OPER PARTNR LP
See TARGA PIPELINE OPERATING PARTNERSHIP LP

D-U-N-S 07-854-2101
ATLAS RESOURCE PARTNERS LP
1000 Commerce Dr Ste 400, Pittsburgh, PA 15275-1033
Tel (800) 251-0171 *Founded/Ownrshp* 2011
Sales 740.0MM *EMP* 619^E
SIC 1381

D-U-N-S 00-454-6859 EXP
ATLAS ROOFING CORP (MS)
(*Suby of* HOOD COMPANIES INC) ★
802 Highway 19 N Ste 190, Meridian, MS 39307-5815
Tel (601) 484-8900 *Founded/Ownrshp* 1982
Sales 449.4MM^E *EMP* 1,350
SIC 3086 2952 Insulation or cushioning material, foamed plastic; Roofing materials
Pr: Kenneth Farrish
**Ch Bd:* Warren A Hood Jr
CFO: Jeffery Fricks
**CFO:* John Johnson
**VP:* James W Hood
VP: Kirk Villar
VP: Kirk R Villar
Exec: Tony Smith
Dist Mgr: Al Castaeda

VP Mfg: Dale Rushing
QC Dir: Meldren Collins

D-U-N-S 16-625-0696
ATLAS STAFFING INC
189 7th Pl E, Saint Paul, MN 55101-2344
Tel (651) 222-5894 *Founded/Ownrshp* 1994
Sales 51.8MM^E *EMP* 4,000
SIC 7363 7361 Employee leasing service; Employment agencies
Pr: Greg Soffee
Genl Mgr: Ben Riley
Off Mgr: Kristina Sisterman

ATLAS TOYOTA MATERIAL HANDLING
See LIFT SOURCE INC

D-U-N-S 83-074-4467 EXP
ATLAS TUBE (CHICAGO) LLC
ATLAS TUBE CHICAGO INC.
(*Suby of* ENERGEXTUBE) ★
1855 E 122nd St, Chicago, IL 60633-2401
Tel (773) 646-4500 *Founded/Ownrshp* 2005
Sales 173.3MM^E *EMP* 500
SIC 3317 3644 Pipes, seamless steel; Electric conduits & fittings
CEO: Barry Zekelman
**Pr:* Tom Muth
**Pr:* David Seager
**VP:* Tony Frabotta

ATLAS TUBE CHICAGO INC.
See ATLAS TUBE (CHICAGO) LLC

D-U-N-S 08-730-8045 IMP
ATLAS TUBULAR LLC
1710 S Highway 77, Robstown, TX 78380-4550
Tel (361) 387-7505 *Founded/Ownrshp* 2002
Sales 125.0MM^E *EMP* 239
SIC 5051 3498 Pipe & tubing, steel; Fabricated pipe & fittings
**VP:* Matt Hubbard
Exec: David Ness
**Admn Mgr:* Tracey Barrett
Dir IT: Aaron Lee
Sales Exec: Ryan Kutzik
Manager: Pete Newkirk

D-U-N-S 83-635-2492
ATLAS WORLD GROUP INC
1212 Saint George Rd, Evansville, IN 47711-2364
Tel (812) 424-2222 *Founded/Ownrshp* 1994
Sales 845.1MM *EMP* 726
Accts Ernst & Young Llp Indianapoli
SIC 4213 4731 Household goods transport; Freight forwarding
Ch Bd: Glen E Dunkerson
CFO: Donald Breivogel

D-U-N-S 78-192-0558 IMP
ATLS MEDICAL SUPPLY INC
8881 Liberty Ln, Port Saint Lucie, FL 34952-3477
Tel (772) 398-5842 *Founded/Ownrshp* 2013
Sales 848.0M^E *EMP* 1,600
SIC 5961 Mail order house
Pr: Frank A Harvey
**COO:* Keith Jones
CFO: Jonathan Strar
**Prin:* Laizer Kornwasser
IT Man: Brandi Hanna
Info Man: Tammi Meyers

ATM SERVICES GROUP
See PAYMENT ALLIANCE INTERNATIONAL INC

D-U-N-S 12-138-5264
■ ATMEL CORP
(*Suby of* MICROCHIP TECHNOLOGY INC) ★
1600 Technology Dr, San Jose, CA 95110-1382
Tel (408) 441-0311 *Founded/Ownrshp* 2015
Sales 1.1MMM *EMP* 5,200^E
Accts Kpmg Llp Sana Clara Californ
SIC 3674 3714 3545 Microcircuits, integrated (semiconductor); Memories, solid state; Solid state electronic devices; Motor vehicle electrical equipment; Wheel turning equipment, diamond point or other
Pr: Steven Laub
COO: Jalil Shaikh
CFO: Stephen A Skaggs
**CFO:* Steve Skaggs
**Ofcr:* Scott M Wornow
**Ex VP:* Tsung-Ching Wu
Sr VP: Shahin Sharifzadeh
**Sr VP:* Stanley A Swearingen
Sr VP: Robert Valiton
VP: Sander Arts
VP: Nuri Dagdeviren
VP: Rafael Fried
VP: Jing Lial
VP: Mike McLane
VP: Tom Roff
VP: Steve Schumann
VP: Vegard Wollan
VP: Yang Chiah Yee
VP: Suzanne Zoumaras

D-U-N-S 15-725-4749 IMP/EXP
■ ATMI INC
ADVANCED TECHNOLOGY MATERIALS
(*Suby of* ENTEGRIS INC) ★
7 Commerce Dr, Danbury, CT 06810-4169
Tel (952) 942-0855 *Founded/Ownrshp* 2014
Sales 242.6MM^E *EMP* 817
SIC 3674 Semiconductors & related devices; Thin film circuits
Ch Bd: Douglas A Neugold
**CFO:* Timothy C Carlson
Ofcr: Tory Oneill
**Ofcr:* Patrick J Shima
Ex VP: Tod Higinbotham
Ex VP: Tod A Higinbotham
Sr VP: Stephen Curtis
**Sr VP:* Lawrence H Dubois
Sr VP: Paul J Hohlstein
**Sr VP:* Kathleen G Mincieli
VP: Duncan Brown
VP: Sung Han
VP: Tom McGowan
VP: Jim Oneill

VP: Mike Tischler
**VP:* David M Ward

D-U-N-S 60-395-4025 IMP
■ ATMI MATERIALS LTD
(*Suby of* ADVANCED TECHNOLOGY MATERIALS) ★
706 Houston Clinton Dr, Burnet, TX 78611-4533
Tel (512) 715-5343 *Founded/Ownrshp* 2000
Sales 95.1MM^E *EMP* 700
SIC 3674 Semiconductors & related devices
Pr: Doug Neugold
**Ex VP:* Tim Carlson
**Ex VP:* Tod Higinbotham
**Ex VP:* Dan Sharkey
**Sr VP:* Mario Philips

D-U-N-S 10-820-3241
▲ ATMOS ENERGY CORP
5430 Lbj Fwy Ste 1800, Dallas, TX 75240-2615
Tel (972) 934-9227 *Founded/Ownrshp* 1906
Sales 3.3MMM *EMP* 4,753
Tkr Sym ATO *Exch* NYS
SIC 4924 4922 1629 Natural gas distribution; Storage, natural gas; Industrial plant construction
CEO: Kim R Cocklin
**Ch Bd:* Robert W Best
**Pr:* Michael E Haefner
CFO: Bret J Eckert
Sr VP: Louis P Gregory
Sr VP: Marvin L Sweetin
VP: Chris Felan
VP: Bill Greer
VP: David Hebert
VP: Mark H Johnson
VP: Mark Martin
VP: John McDill
VP: William J Senter
Board of Directors: Stephen R Springer, Kelly H Compton, Richard Ware II, Richard W Douglas, Ruben E Esquivel, Rafael G Garza, Richard K Gordon, Robert C Grable, Thomas C Meredith, Nancy K Quinn, Richard A Sampson

D-U-N-S 00-792-7130 IMP
■ ATMOS PIPELINE AND STORAGE LLC
(*Suby of* ATMOS ENERGY CORP) ★
5420 Lyndon B Johnson Fwy, Dallas, TX 75240-6222
Tel (972) 934-9227 *Founded/Ownrshp* 1909, 2004
Sales 193.1MM^E *EMP* 514^E
SIC 4911 4922 4923 Electric services; Distribution, electric power; Generation, electric power; Transmission, electric power; Natural gas transmission; Gas transmission & distribution
Pr: Richard A Erskine

D-U-N-S 19-729-5090 IMP
ATMOSPHERE COMMERCIAL INTERIORS LLC
(*Suby of* A & M BUSINESS INTERIOR SVCS) ★
81 S 9th St Ste 350, Minneapolis, MN 55402-3226
Tel (612) 343-0868 *Founded/Ownrshp* 2015
Sales 150.0MM *EMP* 170
SIC 5021 5023 7389

D-U-N-S 18-356-5613
▲ ATN INTERNATIONAL INC
500 Cummings Ctr Ste 2450, Beverly, MA 01915-6146
Tel (978) 619-1300 *Founded/Ownrshp* 1987
Sales 355.3MM *EMP* 1,200^E
Tkr Sym ATNI *Exch* NGS
SIC 4813 4812 1711 Local telephone communications; Long distance telephone communications; ; Cellular telephone services; Solar energy contractor
Pr: Michael T Prior
**Ch Bd:* Cornelius B Prior Jr
CFO: Justin D Benincasa
Sr VP: Barry C Fougere
Sr VP: William F Kreisher
Sr VP: Leonard Q Slap
Board of Directors: Martin L Budd, Bernard J Bulkin, Michael T Flynn, Liane J Pelletier, Charles J Roesslein

D-U-N-S 10-118-8514 IMP/EXP
ATOS IT SOLUTIONS AND SERVICES INC
(*Suby of* ATOS SE)
2500 Westchester Ave Fl 3, Purchase, NY 10577-2578
Tel (914) 881-3000 *Founded/Ownrshp* 2011
Sales 2.6MMM^E *EMP* 36,000
SIC 7379 Computer related maintenance services
Ch Bd: Chad Harris
Pr: John E Evers Jr
CFO: Jeffrey S Choll
Ch: Paul Stodden
Sr VP: Dan E Curtis
Sr VP: Dileep Srinivasan
VP: Jeffrey P Cohen
VP: William J McNamara
**VP:* Shirley Mehta

D-U-N-S 62-141-1289
ATOS ORIGIN INC
18062 Fm 529 Rd Ste 215, Cypress, TX 77433-1168
Tel (914) 881-3000 *Founded/Ownrshp* 2000
Sales 155.3MM^E *EMP* 750
SIC 7373 7374 7376 7379

D-U-N-S 82-618-3287 IMP
ATP OIL & GAS CORP
26219 Oak Ridge Dr, Spring, TX 77380-1960
Tel (713) 622-3311 *Founded/Ownrshp* 1991
Sales 687.2MM *EMP* 68
SIC 1311 1382

D-U-N-S 07-838-3775
ATP TOUR INC
201 Atp Tour Blvd, Ponte Vedra Beach, FL 32082-3211
Tel (904) 285-9886 *Founded/Ownrshp* 1972
Sales 107.0MM *EMP* 80^E
Accts Ernst & Young Us Llp Greenvil
SIC 8621 Professional membership organizations
CEO: Mark Young
**Pr:* Adam Helsant
CFO: Flip Galloway
**CFO:* Phillip B Galloway
Ex VP: G Bradshaw
VP: Linda Clark
VP: David Massey
Exec: Kerry Cleek

Web Dev: Chris Debelen
Pr Dir: Nanette Duxin
Pr Dir: Fabrizio Sestini

D-U-N-S 36-140-8578
ATR INTERNATIONAL INC
1230 Oakmead Pkwy Ste 110, Sunnyvale, CA 94085-4026
Tel (408) 328-8000 *Founded/Ownrshp* 1988
Sales 88.3MM *EMP* 1,250
Accts Petrivonich Pugh & Company Ll
SIC 7361 Employment agencies
Pr: Jerry Brenholz
**CFO:* Maria C Novoa Brenholz
**VP:* Thresa Seigfried
**VP:* Wendy Sun
Sls&Mrk Ex: Charles Neal
Board of Directors: Andrea Brenholz

D-U-N-S 08-000-3741
ATRENNE INTEGRATED SOLUTIONS INC
9210 Science Center Dr, New Hope, MN 55428-3621
Tel (763) 533-3533 *Founded/Ownrshp* 2014
Sales 100.0MM *EMP* 496[E]
SIC 8711 5065 Engineering services; Connectors, electronic
CEO: Jan Erik Mathiesen
**CFO:* Robert J Gold

ATREUM
See ANTOLIN INTERIORS USA INC

D-U-N-S 00-613-3784
▲ ATRICURE INC
7555 Innovation Way, Mason, OH 45040-9695
Tel (513) 755-4100 *Founded/Ownrshp* 2000
Sales 129.7MM *EMP* 430[E]
Tkr Sym ATRC *Exch* NGM
SIC 3841 Surgical instruments & apparatus; Clamps, surgical
Pr: Michael H Carrel
**Ch Bd:* Richard M Johnston
COO: Douglas J Seith
CFO: M Andrew Wade
Sr VP: Andrew L Lux
Sr VP: Justin J Noznesky
Board of Directors: Mark A Collar, Scott W Drake, Michael D Hooven, Elizabeth D Krell, Mark R Lanning, Karen P Robards, Sven Wehrwein, Robert S White

ATRION, A CAROUSEL COMPANY
See ATRION INC

D-U-N-S 11-920-2877 IMP
▲ ATRION CORP
1 Allentown Pkwy, Allen, TX 75002-4206
Tel (972) 390-9800 *Founded/Ownrshp* 1950
Sales 145.7MM *EMP* 489[E]
Tkr Sym ATRI *Exch* NGS
SIC 3841 Surgical & medical instruments
Pr: David A Battat
**Ch Bd:* Emile A Battat
CFO: Jeffery Strickland
Sls Mgr: Traci Grover
Board of Directors: Hugh J Morgan Jr, Ronald N Spaulding, Roger F Stebbing, John P Stupp Jr

D-U-N-S 17-815-7095
ATRION INC
ATRION, A CAROUSEL COMPANY
(*Suby of* CAROUSEL INDUSTRIES OF NORTH AMERICA INC) ★
125 Metro Center Blvd, Warwick, RI 02886-1768
Tel (401) 736-6400 *Founded/Ownrshp* 2016
Sales 118.9MM[E] *EMP* 200
Accts Piccerelli Gilstein & Co Ll
SIC 7373 5065 Computer integrated systems design; Communication equipment
Pr: Oscar T Hebert
**COO:* Michelle Pope
**CFO:* Marianne Caserta
VP: Don Harrington
VP: Gary Hazard
VP: Tom Maresca
Exec: Jason Brownhill
Exec: Ken Norberg
Exec: John Pyle
Exec: Alison Rossi
Exec: Mark Roy
Creative D: Keith Sereby
Dir Bus: Adam Sugarman
Board of Directors: Robert Fanch, David Mayer, Miguel Rey

ATRIUM BOUTIQUE
See BROMENN SERVICE AUXILIARY GIFT SHOP

D-U-N-S 04-813-5243 IMP
ATRIUM BUYING CORP
DAVID HIRSH
1010 Jackson Hole Dr # 100, Blacklick, OH 43004-6050
Tel (740) 966-8200 *Founded/Ownrshp* 1995
Sales 100.0MM *EMP* 100
SIC 5137 Handbags
Pr: David Hirsh
**CFO:* Douglas Tu
**CFO:* Jason Tu

D-U-N-S 19-042-6841
ATRIUM CAPITAL CORP
3000 Sand Hill Rd 2-130, Menlo Park, CA 94025-7142
Tel (650) 233-7878 *Founded/Ownrshp* 1991
Sales 117.3MM[E] *EMP* 1,505
SIC 6211 Investment firm, general brokerage
Mng Dir: Russell B Pyne
Prin: Andy Baumbusch
Off Mgr: Judy Hyrne
Mktg Dir: Kelly Macmillan

D-U-N-S 01-952-9515 IMP
ATRIUM CORP
13355 Noel Rd Ste 1250, Dallas, TX 75240-6836
Tel (214) 583-1543 *Founded/Ownrshp* 2006
Sales 1.3MMM[E] *EMP* 4,000
SIC 3442 Metal doors, sash & trim
CEO: Robert Kirby
COO: Brian Slobodow
COO: Robert Willison
CFO: Bob Hess
Sr VP: Nancy Litzler
Sr VP: John E Matuska Jr
Sr VP: Steve Monks
Sr VP: Scott Wilson
VP: Carl Gentile
VP: Cary Mailandt
VP: Gareth Raab
VP: Jamey Rentfrow
Exec: John Griffin

D-U-N-S 08-001-6444
ATRIUM HOSPITALITY LP
(*Suby of* JOHN Q HAMMONS HOTELS) ★
12735 Morris Road Ext # 400, Alpharetta, GA 30004-8904
Tel (678) 762-0005 *Founded/Ownrshp* 2015
Sales 593.0MM *EMP* 5,000
SIC 7011 Hotels & motels; Hotels
Pt: Jonathan Eilian
Pt: Ron Brown

D-U-N-S 87-796-9295
ATRIUM HOTELS INC
HOLIDAY INN
300 S John Q Hammons Pkwy # 900, Springfield, MO 65806-2550
Tel (417) 864-4300 *Founded/Ownrshp* 1994
Sales 126.8MM[E] *EMP* 6,000
SIC 7011 Hotels & motels
CEO: Jacqueline Dowdy
**Pt:* Ron Brown
**Pt:* Jonathan Eilian
**Pr:* Phill Burgess
**Sr VP:* Greggory Groves
**Sr VP:* Joe Morrissey
**Sr VP:* Christopher Smith
Sr VP: L Scott Tarwater
IT Man: Mike Morgan

D-U-N-S 03-535-8851
ATRIUM MEDICAL CENTER
1 Medical Center Dr, Middletown, OH 45005-1066
Tel (937) 499-9596 *Founded/Ownrshp* 2010
Sales 233.0MM *EMP* 1,600
SIC 8099 Blood related health services
Pr: Carol Turner

D-U-N-S 07-677-4868
ATRIUM MEDICAL CENTER
1 Medical Center Dr, Middletown, OH 45005-1066
Tel (513) 424-2111 *Founded/Ownrshp* 1983
Sales 214.1MM *EMP* 1,500
SIC 8062

D-U-N-S 05-179-8999 IMP/EXP
ATRIUM MEDICAL CORP
(*Suby of* MAQUET MEDICAL SYSTEM USA) ★
5 Wentworth Dr, Hudson, NH 03051-4929
Tel (603) 880-1433 *Founded/Ownrshp* 2011
Sales 133.0MM[E] *EMP* 592
SIC 3842 3841 Surgical appliances & supplies; Prosthetic appliances; Surgical & medical instruments
CEO: Steve Herweck
**Pr:* Trevor Carlton
**Treas:* Paul Lelievre
**VP:* Ted Karwoski
Prgrm Mgr: Joanne Krawczyk
VP Mktg: Chad Carlton
Snr Mgr: Dee Gagne

D-U-N-S 05-313-3658 IMP
ATRIUM WINDOWS AND DOORS INC
(*Suby of* ATRIUM CORP) ★
3890 W Northwest Hwy # 500, Dallas, TX 75220-8108
Tel (214) 956-8031 *Founded/Ownrshp* 1953, 1996
Sales 1.0MMM[E] *EMP* 4,000
SIC 3442 2431 3089 3354 7629 Metal doors, sash & trim; Window & door frames; Doors & door parts & trim, wood; Windows & window parts & trim, wood; Windows, plastic; Window frames & sash, plastic; Doors, folding: plastic or plastic coated fabric; Extruded finished plastic products; Aluminum extruded products; Tool repair, electric
CEO: Robert Kirby
**Pr:* Scott St Clair
COO: Bob Burns
**COO:* Robert E Burns
COO: Douglas C Ross
**COO:* Brian Slobodow
**CFO:* Chris Guinn
**CFO:* Robert Hess
CFO: Paul Lelievre
**Sr VP:* Nancy Litzler
**Sr VP:* John E Matuska Jr
**Sr VP:* Steve Monks
**Sr VP:* Robert M Reed Jr
**Sr VP:* Scott Wilson
Sr VP: Craig Zimmerman
VP: Bill Drake
**VP:* Carl Gentile
VP: Bill Jannott
**VP:* Cary Mailandt
VP: Bo Venerdi
Exec: Joann Williams

D-U-N-S 14-782-8946
ATRIUS HEALTH INC
275 Grove St Ste 3-300, Auburndale, MA 02466-2274
Tel (617) 559-8000 *Founded/Ownrshp* 2002
Sales 27.0MM[E] *EMP* 3,906[E]
SIC 8099 8062

D-U-N-S 83-785-5790
ATRIUS HEALTH INC
275 Grove St Ste 3-300, Auburndale, MA 02466-2274
Tel (617) 559-8444 *Founded/Ownrshp* 1997
Sales 28.6MM *EMP* 3,906
Accts Pkf Pc Quincy Ma
SIC 8011 Offices & clinics of medical doctors
CEO: Steven Strongwater
COO: Christian N Lebrun
COO: Glenn N Lewis
COO: Carole N Martin
**CFO:* Leland J Stacy
CFO: Samuel N Wells
Ofcr: Dan Michaud
VP: Beth Honan
VP: Marie S Lodi
VP: Kimberly Nelson
VP: Bud Stacy

ATS
See ANDERSON TRUCKING SERVICE INC

ATS
See AIRPORT TERMINAL SERVICES INC

ATS
See AVIATION TECHNICAL SERVICES INC

D-U-N-S 15-642-5873 IMP
ATS ASSEMBLY AND TEST INC
(*Suby of* ATS AUTOMATION TOOLING SYSTEMS INC)
313 Mound St, Dayton, OH 45402-8370
Tel (937) 222-3030 *Founded/Ownrshp* 1994
Sales 108.6MM[E] *EMP* 400[E]
SIC 3599 Machine shop, jobbing & repair
Ch Bd: David McAusland
Snr Sftwr: Tim Stahl
Sfty Mgr: John Donaldson

ATS CLOUD
See AUTOMATED TELECOMMUNICATION SERVICES LP

D-U-N-S 16-524-9293
ATS NORTHEAST TOW INC
2010 N Figueroa St, Los Angeles, CA 90065-1022
Tel (323) 342-0342 *Founded/Ownrshp* 1988
Sales 368.9MM *EMP* 24
SIC 7549 5012 Towing service, automotive; Automobile auction
Pr: Art Mercer
**VP:* Delores Mercer

ATS OHIO
See AUTOMATION TOOLING SYSTEMS INC

D-U-N-S 01-479-1943
ATS OPERATING LLC
AMERICA'S THRIFT STORES
1900 Crestwood Blvd, Irondale, AL 35210-2051
Tel (205) 215-9829 *Founded/Ownrshp* 1984
Sales 39.5M[E] *EMP* 1,100
SIC 5932 5331 Used merchandise stores; Variety stores
CEO: Kenneth Sobaski
**COO:* Sean Minnick
Mktg Mgr: Christi Newman

D-U-N-S 17-328-0603 IMP
ATS SYSTEMS OREGON INC
(*Suby of* ATS AUTOMATION TOOLING SYSTEMS INC)
425 Enterprise Dr, Lewis Center, OH 43035-9424
Tel (541) 738-0932 *Founded/Ownrshp* 1996
Sales 111.2MM[E] *EMP* 300
SIC 3569 5084 Robots, assembly line: industrial & commercial; Industrial machinery & equipment
CEO: Anthony Caputo
**Pr:* Maria Perrella
CFO: Ron Dorman
Mktg Mgr: Barry Rahimian

ATSG
See AIR TRANSPORT SERVICES GROUP INC

ATSOL
See AMERICAN TRAFFIC SOLUTIONS INC

D-U-N-S 10-337-7503
ATTACHMATE CORP
ATTACHMATE WRQ
(*Suby of* MICRO FOCUS INTERNATIONAL PLC)
705 5th Ave S Ste 1000, Seattle, WA 98104-4450
Tel (206) 217-7100 *Founded/Ownrshp* 2014
Sales 491.9MM[E] *EMP* 4,300
SIC 7373 7371 7372 Systems integration services; Systems software development services; Computer software development; Prepackaged software
CEO: Jeff Hawn
Pt: Stephanie Frank
Pr: Vern Gustafson
**Pr:* Kathleen Owens
COO: Marc Andrews
**CFO:* Charles Sansbury
Sr VP: John Sena
Sr VP: Logan Wray
Sr VP: Dilip Yupmanyu
VP: David Bennett
VP: Chris Buckingham
VP: Shettleroe Jennifer
VP: Larry Schuiski
VP: Dave Wilkes
VP: Dohsung Yum

D-U-N-S 78-335-9602
ATTACHMATE GROUP INC
705 5th Ave S Ste 1100, Seattle, WA 98104-4426
Tel (206) 217-7100 *Founded/Ownrshp* 2004
Sales 422.3MM[E] *EMP* 4,300[E]
SIC 7371 7372 7373

ATTACHMATE WRQ
See ATTACHMATE CORP

ATTEA APPLIANCE
See MARTIN ATTEA

D-U-N-S 02-770-2117
ATTEBURY GRAIN LLC
HITCHLAND GRAIN CO
3905 Bell St Ste A, Amarillo, TX 79109-4281
Tel (806) 335-1639 *Founded/Ownrshp* 1980
Sales 198.7MM[E] *EMP* 124
SIC 5153 Grains
CEO: Susan Boyd
**CFO:* David Gadry
Treas: Bobby Richardson
VP: Dunn Lehmer
**Genl Mgr:* Benjamin Smith
Opers Mgr: Scott Day
Genl Couns: Wendell Davies

D-U-N-S 05-220-0074
ATTENTIVE HOME CARE AGENCY INC
ALWAYS HOME CARE
3131 Coney Island Ave, Brooklyn, NY 11235-6468
Tel (718) 843-8430 *Founded/Ownrshp* 2013
Sales 8.5MM[E] *EMP* 1,000
SIC 8082 Home health care services
CEO: Yelena Pustilnik

ATTERRO HUMAN CAPITAL GROUP
See ATTERRO INC

D-U-N-S 07-420-5030
ATTERRO INC
ATTERRO HUMAN CAPITAL GROUP
(*Suby of* ADVANTAGE STAFFING) ★
730 2nd Ave S Ste 520, Minneapolis, MN 55402-2447
Tel (612) 373-2600 *Founded/Ownrshp* 2015
Sales 254.7MM[E] *EMP* 4,500
SIC 7363 7361 Temporary help service; Employment agencies; Placement agencies
CEO: Clay E Morel
**CFO:* Michael J Kennedy
**Ex VP:* Michael E Morris
**Sr VP:* Greg D Jensen
Sr VP: Laura Kelley
**Sr VP:* Susan Y Rylance
VP: Chip Gabbey
VP: Doug Karr
VP: Deanne Schreifels
**VP:* Paul D Sharps
**VP:* Candice A Winterringer
VP Bus Dev: Candice Winterringer
Creative D: Steve T Brentlinger
Board of Directors: David A Loeser

ATTORNEY GEN NEW YORK STATE
See ATTORNEY GENERAL NEW YORK STATE

ATTORNEY GENERAL
See FLORIDA DEPARTMENT OF LEGAL AFFAIRS

ATTORNEY GENERAL
See OREGON DEPARTMENT OF JUSTICE

D-U-N-S 60-381-5440
ATTORNEY GENERAL CALIFORNIA OFFICE OF
(*Suby of* CALIFORNIA DEPARTMENT OF JUSTICE) ★
1300 I St Ste 1101, Sacramento, CA 95814-2952
Tel (916) 445-9555 *Founded/Ownrshp* 1989
Sales NA *EMP* 3,655
SIC 9222 Attorney General's office;

D-U-N-S 04-254-3087
ATTORNEY GENERAL NEW YORK STATE
ATTORNEY GEN NEW YORK STATE
(*Suby of* EXECUTIVE OFFICE OF STATE OF NEW YORK) ★
The Capitol, Albany, NY 12224
Tel (518) 776-2000 *Founded/Ownrshp* 1999
Sales NA *EMP* 3,200[E]
SIC 9222 Attorney General's office;

D-U-N-S 80-903-1883
ATTORNEY GENERAL OF OHIO
FINANCE DEPARTMENT
(*Suby of* EXECUTIVE OFFICE STATE OF OHIO) ★
30 E Broad St Fl 17, Columbus, OH 43215-3414
Tel (614) 466-6963 *Founded/Ownrshp* 1803
Sales NA *EMP* 1,400
SIC 9222 Attorney General's office;
Snr Mgr: Jonathan R Fulkerson

D-U-N-S 80-910-0019
ATTORNEY GENERAL OFFICE OF
(*Suby of* STATE OF WASH OFFICE OF GVRNOR) ★
1125 Washington St Se, Olympia, WA 98501-2283
Tel (360) 753-6200 *Founded/Ownrshp* 1889
Sales NA *EMP* 1,100
SIC 9222 Attorney General's office;

D-U-N-S 80-678-0789
ATTORNEY GENERAL TEXAS
EXECUTIVE OFFICE OF THE STATE
(*Suby of* EXECUTIVE OFFICE OF STATE OF TEXAS) ★
300 W 15th St, Austin, TX 78701-1649
Tel (512) 475-4375 *Founded/Ownrshp* 1845
Sales NA *EMP* 4,200[E]
SIC 9222
Ex Dir: Ken Paxton
**CFO:* Greg Herbert
Ofcr: Donna Brown
Ofcr: Kara Hester
Ofcr: Stephanie Mock
Ofcr: Crystal Pardo
Ofcr: David Smotek
Ofcr: Janet Thompson
Ofcr: Kimberly Tyler
Ofcr: Carrie Walsh
Off Mgr: Linda Velasquez

D-U-N-S 05-594-6792
ATTORNEYS TITLE INSURANCE FUND INC
ATIF
6545 Corp Center Blvd # 100, Orlando, FL 32822-1548
Tel (407) 240-3863 *Founded/Ownrshp* 1947
Sales NA *EMP* 847
Accts Mcgladrey & Pullen Llp Orlan
SIC 6361 Real estate title insurance
Pr: John H Simmons
Bd of Dir: Ana M Camacho
**VP:* Connie J Clark
VP: Norwood Gay III
**VP:* Robert F Macconnell
VP: Charles Richardson
Dir IT: Steve Fleur
IT Man: Max Sanchez
Sales Exec: Isabell Insua
VP Sls: Sharon Priest

D-U-N-S 78-594-0495 IMP
ATV INC
AMERICAN TIRE DEPOT
14407 Alondra Blvd, La Mirada, CA 90638-5504
Tel (562) 977-8565 *Founded/Ownrshp* 1994
Sales 348.3MM[E] *EMP* 600
Accts Agopian & Baboghli Torrance

SIC 5531 7538 Automotive tires; General automotive repair shops
CEO: ARA Tchaghlassian
CFO: Patrick Karapetian

D-U-N-S 00-118-8754 IMP
ATW COMPANIES INC (RI)
125 Metro Center Blvd # 3001, Warwick, RI 02886-1785
Tel (401) 244-1002 *Founded/Ownrshp* 1886
Sales 88.3MM[E] *EMP* 390
SIC 3674 3498 Semiconductors & related devices; Fabricated pipe & fittings
Ch Bd: Frederick G Frost III
**Pr:* Peter C Frost
**CFO:* Caryn E Mitchell
**VP:* Duane Ottolini
Dir IT: Juan Hicks
Opers Mgr: Mike Jasmin
Plnt Mgr: Anthony Girard
QI Cn Mgr: Blair Sulak
Sales Exec: Karen Martin
Mktg Mgr: Lee Becton
Board of Directors: Malcolm G Chace, Carl Gibbs, V Duncan Johnson, Kenneth N Kermes, John W Wall

D-U-N-S 96-185-4259
ATWELL LLC
2 Towne Sq Ste 700, Southfield, MI 48076-3737
Tel (248) 447-2000 *Founded/Ownrshp* 2009
Sales 86.2MM *EMP* 446[E]
Accts Baker Tilly Virchow Krouse Ll
SIC 8999 8713 8748 8711 Earth science services; Surveying services; Environmental consultant; Engineering services; Construction & civil engineering; Civil engineering
CEO: Brian Wenzel
CFO: Roderick Petschauer
VP: Timothy Augustine
VP: David A Bartz
VP: Robert Beaugerand
VP: Robert W Beaugrand
VP: Matthew Bissett
VP: Alan N Harris
VP: William Henderson
VP: Daniel McNulty
VP: Ted Northrop
VP: Theodore Northrop

D-U-N-S 03-293-0513 IMP
ATWOOD DISTRIBUTING LP
ATWOODS RANCH & HOME
500 S Garland Rd, Enid, OK 73703-1137
Tel (580) 233-3702 *Founded/Ownrshp* 1962
Sales 299.0MM[E] *EMP* 1,000
SIC 5261 5251 5531 5311 Lawn & garden equipment; Hardware; Automotive parts; Automotive accessories; Department stores
Ch Bd: Gary A Atwood
VP: Jeff Gwin
Rgnl Mgr: David Arnold

D-U-N-S 12-270-6570 IMP
ATWOOD MOBILE PRODUCTS INC
1120 N Main St, Elkhart, IN 46514-3203
Tel (574) 264-2131 *Founded/Ownrshp* 1999
Sales 142.1MM[E] *EMP* 875
SIC 3714 Motor vehicle parts & accessories
Pr: Theresa Skotak
COO: Duane Vanderwerf
Exec: Judy Miller
IT Man: Bob Devreese
Mtls Mgr: George Garrett
Opers Mgr: Chris Jackson
Manager: Geoff Newman
Plnt Mgr: Brian Goethel
Plnt Mgr: Dennis Ruben
Plnt Mgr: Jeff Tomlinson
Sales Exec: Kit Ellis

D-U-N-S 80-837-2275 IMP
ATWOOD MOBILE PRODUCTS LLC
ATWOOD SOLUTIONS
(*Suby of* DOMETIC GROUP) ★
1120 N Main St, Elkhart, IN 46514-3203
Tel (574) 264-2131 *Founded/Ownrshp* 2014
Sales 266.7MM[E] *EMP* 875
SIC 3714 Motor vehicle parts & accessories
Mtls Mgr: George Garrett
Opers Mgr: Chris Jackson
Prd Mgr: David Zobrosky
QI Cn Mgr: Scott Murphy
Sales Exec: Will Troyer
Sales Asso: Duane Vanderwerf

D-U-N-S 04-821-9539
▲ ATWOOD OCEANICS INC
15011 Katy Fwy Ste 800, Houston, TX 77094-0011
Tel (281) 749-7800 *Founded/Ownrshp* 1968
Sales 1.0MMM *EMP* 1,868[E]
Tkr Sym ATW *Exch* NYS
SIC 1381 Drilling oil & gas wells
Pr: Robert J Saltiel
**Ch Bd:* George S Dotson
CFO: Mark W Smith
Treas: Evelyn A Nordin
Sr VP: Walter A Baker
Sr VP: Arthur M Polhamus
Sr VP: Barry M Smith
VP: John K Gidley
VP: Geoffrey C Wagner
VP Mktg: Mark K Monroe
Board of Directors: Deborah A Beck, Jack E Golden, Hans Helmerich, Jeffrey A Miller, James R Montague, Phil D Wedemeyer

ATWOOD SOLUTIONS
See ATWOOD MOBILE PRODUCTS LLC

ATWOODS RANCH & HOME
See ATWOOD DISTRIBUTING LP

D-U-N-S 07-841-1210
ATWORK FRANCHISE INC (TN)
ATWORK PERSONNELL SERVICES
3215 W Gov J Sevier Hwy, Knoxville, TN 37920-5540
Tel (865) 609-6911 *Founded/Ownrshp* 1992
Sales 132.3MM[E] *EMP* 1,000[E]
SIC 6794 8742 8721 Franchises, selling or licensing; Franchising consultant; Accounting, auditing & bookkeeping
CEO: John D Hall Jr

ATWORK PERSONNEL SERVICE
See PROFESSIONAL PERSONNEL SERVICE INC

ATWORK PERSONNELL SERVICES
See ATWORK FRANCHISE INC

ATX NORTH AMERICA
See SIRIUS XM CONNECTED VEHICLE SERVICES INC

AU BON PAIN
See ABP CORP

D-U-N-S 13-590-3867
AU MEDICAL CENTER INC
1120 15th St, Augusta, GA 30912-0004
Tel (706) 721-6569 *Founded/Ownrshp* 1994
Sales 445.1MM[E] *EMP* 3,095[E]
SIC 8062 Hospital, medical school affiliation
Pr: Donald Snell
**COO:* Patricia Sodomka
**CFO:* Dennis R Roemer
**VP:* Dudley Harrington
VP: Sheila Oneal
VP: R Swift
Off Mgr: Don Wicklund
MIS Dir: Kathleen Herald
Ansthlgy: Eugene K Betts
Doctor: Emily M Cribb
Doctor: Sharad A Ghamande MD

AUBREY MANUFACTURING
See BROAN-NUTONE LLC

D-U-N-S 05-622-0460
AUBREY SILVEY ENTERPRISES INC
371 Hamp Jones Rd, Carrollton, GA 30117-9492
Tel (770) 834-0738 *Founded/Ownrshp* 1971
Sales 163.2MM[E] *EMP* 300
SIC 1629 1541 3643 7389 3699 5063 Power plant construction; Industrial buildings, new construction; Connectors & terminals for electrical devices; Design, commercial & industrial; Electrical equipment & supplies; Electrical fittings & construction materials
Pr: Tommy C Muse
**Ch Bd:* T Aubrey Silvey
**CFO:* Michael A Vines
VP: Stephen Hodge
VP: Chip Long
VP: Vann Pelt
VP: Lee Thomason
VP: Ken Tuggle
Exec: Renee Mason
Exec: Gregory Webb
Netwrk Mgr: Chris Hancock

AUBURN ALUMNI CENTER
See AUBURN UNIVERSITY FOUNDATION

D-U-N-S 00-208-6478
AUBURN CITY SCHOOL DISTRICT
855 E Samford Ave, Auburn, AL 36830-6147
Tel (334) 887-2100 *Founded/Ownrshp* 1960, 1961
Sales 86.2MM *EMP* 238
Accts Machen Mcchesney Llp Auburn
SIC 8211 Public elementary & secondary schools; School board
Bd of Dir: Melanie Chambless
Bd of Dir: Katie Daniel
Bd of Dir: Leah Meadows
Bd of Dir: Tracey Oprandy
Bd of Dir: Jennifer Spencer
Top Exec: Helen Whaley
Prin: Debbie Cimo
Prin: Nancy Golson
Prin: Lilli Land
Prin: Debbie Smith
Prin: Karen Spencer

D-U-N-S 04-158-7593
AUBURN COMMUNITY HOSPITAL
FINGERLAKES CENTER FOR LIVING
17 Lansing St, Auburn, NY 13021-1983
Tel (315) 255-7011 *Founded/Ownrshp* 1879
Sales 93.6MM *EMP* 870
Accts Fust Charles Chambers Llp Syr
SIC 8062 8051 General medical & surgical hospitals; Skilled nursing care facilities
CEO: Scott Berlucchi
Chf Path: John Riccio
Pr: Richard Erali
COO: Brendan McGrath
**CFO:* Patrick Facteau
CFO: David Plaviak
Treas: Peter Emerson
Treas: Anthony Franceschelli
VP: Annie Doran
**VP:* Thomas Filiak
**VP:* Ann E McMahon
VP: Tammy Sunderlin
Exec: Colleen McLaughlin
Dir Inf Cn: Donna Wrobel
Dir Lab: John Bagenski
Dir Lab: Donna Bristol
Dir Lab: Tom Filliak

AUBURN GENERAL HOSPITAL
See AUBURN REGIONAL MEDICAL CENTER INC

D-U-N-S 10-334-9924
■ AUBURN REGIONAL MEDICAL CENTER INC
AUBURN GENERAL HOSPITAL
(*Suby of* UNIVERSAL HEALTH SERVICES INC) ★
Plz 1 202 N Div St, Auburn, WA 98001
Tel (253) 833-7711 *Founded/Ownrshp* 1981
Sales 166.0MM *EMP* 560
SIC 8062 General medical & surgical hospitals
Pr: Marvin Pember
COO: Robert Dickens
**CFO:* Dale Guffey
CFO: Cheryl Lovelace
**Treas:* Cheryl K Ramgano
**VP:* Steve Filton
Off Mgr: Courtney Eileich
MIS Dir: Andrew Swanson
Mtls Mgr: Dennis Uler
Doctor: Anne Casey
Doctor: Jan Tibbett

D-U-N-S 10-002-8620
AUBURN SCHOOL DEPARTMENT
DEPARTMENT OF EDUCATION
60 Court St Fl 4, Auburn, ME 04210-5983
Tel (207) 784-6431 *Founded/Ownrshp* 2010
Sales 42.1MM[E] *EMP* 1,000
SIC 8211 Elementary & secondary schools
Schl Brd P: Larry Pelletier

D-U-N-S 01-312-3237
AUBURN SCHOOL DISTRICT
915 4th St Ne, Auburn, WA 98002-4499
Tel (253) 931-4900 *Founded/Ownrshp* 1890
Sales 80.1MM[E] *EMP* 1,641
Accts Brian Sonntag Cgfm State Aud
SIC 8211 Public elementary & secondary schools
COO: Pam Smith
Dir IT: Ed Dunaway
Netwrk Eng: Lawrence Boyd
Pr Dir: Vicky Alonzo
Psych: Monica Clark

D-U-N-S 06-647-0972
AUBURN UNIVERSITY
107 Samford Hall, Auburn, AL 36849-0001
Tel (334) 844-4539 *Founded/Ownrshp* 1885
Sales 203.0MM *EMP* 6,000
Accts Pricewaterhousecoopers Llp Bi
SIC 8221 University
Pr: Jay Gogue
Treas: India Napier
Trst: Dwight L Carlisle
Trst: Byron P Franklin
Trst: Robert E Lowder
Trst: Paul J Spina Jr
Trst: Virginia N Thompson
Top Exec: John S Jahera Jr
**Ex VP:* Donald L Large Jr
VP: Kaitlin Byerly
**VP:* Mary Ellen Mazey
VP: Jeff McNeill
VP: Daniela Munoz
VP: Jane D Parker
Exec: Dinah Decker
Dir Lab: Nancy Capps
Dir Lab: Tom Carrington
Dir Lab: Hank Fijolek
Assoc Dir: Steve Nelson
Creative D: Shannon Bryant-Hankes

D-U-N-S 86-722-5328
AUBURN UNIVERSITY FOUNDATION
AUBURN ALUMNI CENTER
317 S College St, Auburn, AL 36849-5149
Tel (334) 844-1124 *Founded/Ownrshp* 1993
Sales 86.0MM *EMP* 90
Accts Wilson Price Cpa Montgomery
SIC 7389 8641 Fund raising organizations; Civic social & fraternal associations
Pr: James Difolco Parker
Prin: Neeta Likins

D-U-N-S 15-550-0346
AUCTION BROADCASTING CO LLC
ABC
1919 S Post Rd, Indianapolis, IN 46239-9429
Tel (317) 862-7325 *Founded/Ownrshp* 1999
Sales 86.6MM[E] *EMP* 400
SIC 5012 Automobile auction
CFO: David Newcomer
Genl Mgr: Jason Brinkley
Genl Mgr: Todd Ritter
CIO: Jeffrey Watson
Dir IT: Daniel Cayetano
Software D: Richard Bowens
Opers Mgr: Sarah Ruth
VP Sls: Joe Mappes

AUCTION.COM
See TEN-X LLC

AUDAEXPLORE
See AUDATEX NORTH AMERICA INC

D-U-N-S 80-959-3924
AUDATEX NORTH AMERICA INC
AUDAEXPLORE
(*Suby of* SOLERA HOLDINGS INC) ★
15030 Ave Of Ste 100, San Diego, CA 92128
Tel (858) 946-1900 *Founded/Ownrshp* 1980
Sales 139.5MM[E] *EMP* 807
SIC 7372 Business oriented computer software
CEO: Tony Aquila
**CFO:* Jack Pearlstein
CFO: Cory Woolf
VP: Floyd Beadle
VP: Seth Mullady
VP: Patrick Schmidlin
**VP:* Don Tartre
Snr Sftwr: John Fitzpatrick
Dir IT: Peter White
Software D: Asrar Hussain
Software D: Jacob Moe

D-U-N-S 09-026-9437
AUDAX GROUP LP
101 Huntington Ave # 2450, Boston, MA 02199-7625
Tel (617) 859-1500 *Founded/Ownrshp* 1999
Sales 1.9MMM[E] *EMP* 4,114
SIC 6726 3646 Investment offices; Commercial indusl & institutional electric lighting fixtures
CEO: Geoffrey S Rehnert
Pt: Marc B Wolpow
Pr: Kevin Smith
COO: Richard T Joseph
Sr VP: Alexander A Casale
VP: Robert Connors
VP: Brian Doherty
VP: Asheesh Gupta
VP: David Montague
VP: David Winterle
Mng Dir: Ryan Benedict

AUDI MINNEAPOLIS
See GOLDEN VALLEY TCA A LLC

AUDI OF AMERICA
See VOLKSWAGEN GROUP OF AMERICA INC

D-U-N-S 07-930-0032
AUDIA GROUP LLC (PA)
450 Racetrack Rd, Washington, PA 15301-8935
Tel (724) 228-1260 *Founded/Ownrshp* 2008
Sales 275.3MM[E] *EMP* 648
SIC 5169 Synthetic resins, rubber & plastic materials
CEO: Robert Andy
**CFO:* William Stough

D-U-N-S 07-979-7300
AUDIA INTERNATIONAL INC
(*Suby of* AUDIA GROUP LLC) ★
450 Racetrack Rd, Washington, PA 15301-8935
Tel (724) 228-1260 *Founded/Ownrshp* 2012
Sales 275.3MM[E] *EMP* 648[E]
SIC 2821 Polypropylene resins; Polyethylene resins
CEO: Robert Andy
**CFO:* William Stough

D-U-N-S 86-137-2006
■ AUDIENCE INC
(*Suby of* KNOWLES CORP) ★
331 Fairchild Dr, Mountain View, CA 94043-2200
Tel (650) 254-2800 *Founded/Ownrshp* 2015
Sales 102.0MM[E] *EMP* 349[E]
SIC 3674 Semiconductors & related devices; Microprocessors
Pr: Jeffrey Niew
**Pr:* Paul Dickinson
**Pr:* Christian Scherp
**Pr:* Gordon Walker
**Pr:* David Wightman
**COO:* Daniel Giesecke
**CFO:* John Anderson
Sr VP: Mike Adell
**Sr VP:* Ray Cabrera
**Sr VP:* Thomas Jackson
**CTO:* Alexis Bernard

D-U-N-S 05-692-6470 IMP
AUDIO AMERICA INC
15132 Park Of Commerce Bl, Jupiter, FL 33478-6438
Tel (561) 863-7704 *Founded/Ownrshp* 1993
Sales 129.7MM[E] *EMP* 50
SIC 5099 Video & audio equipment; Video cassettes, accessories & supplies
Ch: Ryan Munder
**Pr:* Mike Cronin
**CEO:* Jonathan Elster
CTO: Bob Albert
Web Dev: Jon Abrams
Sls Mgr: Doreen McQuade
Sls Mgr: Shane Mullikin
Sales Asso: Chris Baronoff

D-U-N-S 36-258-4328 IMP/EXP
AUDIO AND VIDEO LABS INC
AVL DIGITAL GROUP
(*Suby of* STEPHENS CAPITAL PARTNERS LLC) ★
7905 N Crescent Blvd, Pennsauken, NJ 08110-1402
Tel (856) 663-9030 *Founded/Ownrshp* 2013
Sales 119.4MM[E] *EMP* 450
SIC 3652 5099 7389 3651 Compact laser discs, prerecorded; Compact discs; Music copying service; Packaging & labeling services; Music distribution apparatus
CEO: Tony Van Veen
**Ch Bd:* Morris Ballen
**Pr:* Brian Felsen
COO: Kathy Chevoor
VP: Jered Gallagher
VP: Jeff Korhammer
Exec: Mark Giffen
Mng Dir: Jackie Boggi
IT Man: Carmen Molina
IT Man: Narendra Wadhwa
Info Man: Jonathan Slobodinsky

D-U-N-S 02-389-2201
AUDIO FIDELITY COMMUNICATIONS CORP
WHITLOCK GROUP, THE
12820 West Creek Pkwy, Richmond, VA 23238-1111
Tel (804) 273-9100 *Founded/Ownrshp* 1956
Sales 519.8MM[E] *EMP* 400
SIC 5044 5065 Office equipment; Video equipment, electronic
CEO: Douglas S Hall
**Pr:* John D Whitlock
**COO:* Roger Patrick
**CFO:* Mark C Baker
**Ex VP:* Julian Phillips
**Ex VP:* John Steinhauer
**VP:* Michael Dennis

D-U-N-S 62-545-3550 IMP
AUDIO VIDEO COLOR CORP
AVC
17707 S Santa Fe Ave, Compton, CA 90221-5419
Tel (424) 213-7500 *Founded/Ownrshp* 1990
Sales 93.4MM[E] *EMP* 300[E]
SIC 2671 Packaging paper & plastics film, coated & laminated
CEO: Kali J Limath
Pr: Jim Hardiman
**Ex VP:* Guy Marrom
Dir: Chris Rudder
Prgrm Mgr: Maribel Solano
IT Man: Andres Bedon
IT Man: Amanda Knechtel
VP Opers: Vipul Doshi
Mktg Dir: Thomas Kozlowski
Sls Mgr: K C Finley

D-U-N-S 03-729-3974 EXP
AUDIO VISUAL INNOVATIONS INC
A V I
(*Suby of* AVI-SPL INC) ★
6301 Benjamin Rd Ste 101, Tampa, FL 33634-5115
Tel (813) 884-7168 *Founded/Ownrshp* 1979
Sales 389.7MM[E] *EMP* 1,188[E]

SIC 3669 5064 3861 3663 3651 5043 Intercommunication systems, electric; Electrical appliances, television & radio; Photographic equipment & supplies; Radio & TV communications equipment; Household audio & video equipment; Projection apparatus, motion picture & slide
CEO: John Zettel
Pr: Tim Riek
**CFO:* Peter Grabowski
**Ex VP:* Steve Benjamin
VP: Randy Bonham
VP: Stephanie Scanlon
Dir IT: Doug Delashmutt
Opers Mgr: Robert Richardson
Snr PM: Carlos Raven

D-U-N-S 62-222-2560
AUDIO VISUAL SERVICES GROUP INC
PSAV PRESENTATION SERVICES
(*Suby of* CARIBINER GROUP) ★
5100 River Rd Ste 300, Schiller Park, IL 60176-1058
Tel (847) 222-9800 *Founded/Ownrshp* 1998
Sales 643.3MM[E] *EMP* 2,400
SIC 7359 Audio-visual equipment & supply rental
Pr: Mike McLlwain
Pr: Sony Jacob
Pr: Sam Silverman
**COO:* Sky Cunningham
**CFO:* Ben Erwin
Sr VP: Greg Dyke
**Sr VP:* Whit Markowitz
Sr VP: Spencer Williams
VP: Bob Caldrone
**VP:* Brian Lagestee
VP: Joseph Loftus
Exec: Rian Pierce

D-U-N-S 79-345-6617
AUDIO VISUAL SERVICES GROUP INC
CARIBINER GROUP, THE
111 Ocean Beach Blvd Ste 1110, Long Beach, CA 90802
Tel (562) 366-0620 *Founded/Ownrshp* 1989
Sales 677.8MM[E] *EMP* 2,400
SIC 7389 7812 7359 Advertising, promotional & trade show services; Audio-visual program production; Audio-visual equipment & supply rental
CEO: Digby J Davies
VP: Robert B Caldrone
Dir Soc: Elizabeth Lachall
Netwrk Eng: Rick Bieber
Opers Mgr: Arnie Desroches
Sls Dir: Bill Foote
Sls Dir: Juan Marichal
Sls Dir: Jason Mueller
Manager: Julie Power
Sls Mgr: John Johnson
Sls Mgr: Maya McGeathey

D-U-N-S 06-409-1465 IMP
AUDIO-TECHNICA US INC
(*Suby of* AUDIO-TECHNICA CORPORATION)
1221 Commerce Dr, Stow, OH 44224-1760
Tel (330) 686-2600 *Founded/Ownrshp* 1974
Sales 108.6MM[E] *EMP* 115[E]
SIC 5065 5731 Sound equipment, electronic; Consumer electronic equipment
Ch Bd: K Matsushita
**Pr:* Philip Cajka
CFO: Bruce Vanzo
VP: Michael Edwards
**VP:* Marc Lee Shannon
**VP:* Richard Sprunlgle
Exec: Karla U Kakias
Creative D: Peter Baker
VP Mktg: Greg Pinto

AUDIOLOGY
See ADVANCED CENTER FOR REHABILITATION MEDICINE INC

D-U-N-S 96-975-9294
AUDIOLOGY DISTRIBUTION LLC
HEARUSA
(*Suby of* SIVANTOS INC) ★
10455 Riverside Dr, Palm Beach Gardens, FL 33410-4237
Tel (561) 478-8770 *Founded/Ownrshp* 2011
Sales 132.5MM[E] *EMP* 542[E]
SIC 5999 Hearing aids
CEO: Scott Klein
Pr: Richard Whitman
VP: Kevin Beninati
Off Mgr: Laura Klindt
VP Opers: Jill Botkin
Opers Mgr: Susan Nicolopoulos
Mktg Dir: Lisa Demarinis

AUDITOR CONTROLLER
See COUNTY OF MADERA

AUDITOR OFFICE
See COUNTY OF LUCAS

AUDITORS OFFICE
See COUNTY OF TRAVIS

D-U-N-S 00-694-6412
■ **AUDUBON INSURANCE CO**
CHARTIS INSURANCE
(*Suby of* CHARTIS US INC) ★
4000 S Shrwd Frst Blvd Ste 401, Baton Rouge, LA 70816
Tel (225) 293-5900 *Founded/Ownrshp* 1946, 1982
Sales NA *EMP* 579
SIC 6331 6411 Assessment associations: fire, marine & casualty insurance; Property damage insurance; Insurance agents, brokers & service
Pr: D W Alligood
Sr VP: Robert P Hubbard
Sr VP: Williams P Kane
VP: M A Soileau

D-U-N-S 07-870-3051
■ **AUDUBON MATERIALS LLC**
CENTRAL PLAINS CEMENT COMPANY
(*Suby of* EAGLE MATERIALS INC) ★
15100 E Crtney Athrton Rd, Sugar Creek, MO 64058-3307
Tel (816) 257-4040 *Founded/Ownrshp* 2012
Sales 86.6MM[E] *EMP* 240
SIC 2891 Cement, except linoleum & tile
Pr: David Challacomb
**Ex VP:* Paul Anderson
**Sr VP:* Craig Kesler

D-U-N-S 95-666-5970 IMP
AUDUBON METALS LLC
(*Suby of* KOCH ENTERPRISES INC) ★
3055 Ohio Dr, Henderson, KY 42420-4394
Tel (270) 830-6622 *Founded/Ownrshp* 1995
Sales 389.6MM *EMP* 248
SIC 3341 Aluminum smelting & refining (secondary)
CEO: Jim Butkus
**CFO:* Keith Schultheis
VP: James W Butkus
**VP:* Rob Harris
**VP:* Brian Hawkes
**VP:* Marty Wohadlo
Dir IT: Brandon Aken
Plnt Mgr: Mike Willett

AUGE INTERNATIONAL
See AUGE MEDIA CORP

D-U-N-S 07-911-0940
AUGE MEDIA CORP
AUGE INTERNATIONAL
2029 Century Park E Fl 14, Los Angeles, CA 90067-2901
Tel (310) 739-8000 *Founded/Ownrshp* 1951
Sales 50.0MM *EMP* 6,000
SIC 2741 7812 Miscellaneous publishing; Educational motion picture production, television
Pr: Sean Lourdes

D-U-N-S 07-867-9347
AUGSBURG COLLEGE
2211 Riverside Ave, Minneapolis, MN 55454-1350
Tel (612) 330-1000 *Founded/Ownrshp* 1872
Sales 105.7MM *EMP* 623
Accts Cliftonlarsonallen Llp Minnea
SIC 8221 College, except junior
Pr: Paul Pribbenow
VP: Julie Edstrom
VP: Anne Garvey
Exec: Frankie Shackelford
Assoc Dir: Liz Bassani
Ex Dir: Tom Morgan
CIO: Leif Anderson
Mktg Dir: Jodi Collen
Mktg Dir: Lance Schwartz
Mktg Mgr: Mark Chamberlain

D-U-N-S 08-043-1873
AUGUST TECHNIC CORP CO
8 The Grn Ste 4934, Dover, DE 19901-3618
Tel (302) 223-5215 *Founded/Ownrshp* 2016
Sales 1.0MMM *EMP* 10
SIC 5065 5045 7389 Mobile telephone equipment; Computers, peripherals & software;
Pr: Ll Zhang

AUGUSTA CHRONICLE, THE
See SOUTHEASTERN NEWSPAPERS CO LLC

D-U-N-S 18-435-4512
AUGUSTA COUNTY SCHOOL BOARD
18 Government Center Ln, Verona, VA 24482-2639
Tel (540) 245-5100 *Founded/Ownrshp* 2015
Sales 18.0MM[E] *EMP* 1,333[E]
SIC 8211 School board
Bd of Dir: Timothy Quillen

D-U-N-S 07-587-2267 EXP
AUGUSTA FIBERGLASS COATINGS INC
86 Lake Cynthia Dr, Blackville, SC 29817-4126
Tel (803) 284-2246 *Founded/Ownrshp* 1974
Sales 92.0MM[E] *EMP* 300
SIC 3089 Plastic & fiberglass tanks
Pr: John Boyd
Prd Mgr: James Whittington
Ql Cn Mgr: Fred Templeton
S&M/VP: Ryan West
Mktg Dir: Gerald Meggs
Sls Mgr: Barbara Howlett
Genl Couns: John D Powell

D-U-N-S 95-608-1483
AUGUSTA HEALTH CARE FOR WOMEN
70 Medical Center Cir, Fishersville, VA 22939-2273
Tel (540) 245-7007 *Founded/Ownrshp* 1995
Sales 130.7MM *EMP* 20[E]
SIC 8011 Obstetrician; Gynecologist
Pt: Daniel McMillan MD
Pt: Amy Keatts MD

D-U-N-S 36-068-2249
AUGUSTA HEALTH CARE INC
AUGUSTA MEDICAL CENTER
78 Medical Center Dr, Fishersville, VA 22939-2332
Tel (540) 332-4000 *Founded/Ownrshp* 1994
Sales 254.1MM *EMP* 2,100
SIC 8062 General medical & surgical hospitals
Pr: Mary N Mannix
Dir Vol: Cheryl McKay
**Ch Bd:* Stewart Crow
**Pr:* Richard H Graham
**CFO:* John Heider
Bd of Dir: Arona Richard
Bd of Dir: Victor Santos
VP: David Chernoff
Exec: Marvella REA
Dir Pat Ca: Lisa Cline
Comm Dir: Vicki Kirby
Comm Man: Wayne Davis

AUGUSTA MEDICAL CENTER
See AUGUSTA HEALTH CARE INC

D-U-N-S 03-357-5663 IMP
AUGUSTA NEWSPRINT CO EMPLOYEES RECREATION ASSOCIATION INC
(*Suby of* RESOLUTE FOREST PRODUCTS INC)
2434 Doug Barnard Pkwy, Augusta, GA 30906-8719
Tel (706) 798-3440 *Founded/Ownrshp* 1968
Sales 102.6MM[E] *EMP* 340[E]
SIC 2621 Newsprint paper
CEO: Rich Zgol
**CFO:* Barbara Cole
**Treas:* David Pierce
Netwrk Eng: Ben Nelson
Sfty Mgr: Diane Austin
Sfty Mgr: Jim Herrman

D-U-N-S 08-481-5018 IMP/EXP
AUGUSTA SPORTSWEAR INC (GA)
(*Suby of* KELSO & COMPANY, L.P.)
425 Park 20 W, Grovetown, GA 30813-3214
Tel (706) 860-4633 *Founded/Ownrshp* 1977, 2012
Sales 113.5MM[E] *EMP* 1,208[E]
SIC 2329 2339 2393 2399 Men's & boys' sportswear & athletic clothing; Sportswear, women's; Canvas bags; Aprons, breast (harness)
CEO: Jon Letzler
**Pr:* Brian Marks
**CFO:* W Pat Harris
Exec: Jackie Glover
Dir: Scott Newland
Creative D: Wes Childers
Genl Mgr: Sheri Galvin

D-U-N-S 96-774-0445
AUGUSTA UNIVERSITY
GEORGIA REGENTS UNIVERSITY
(*Suby of* GEORGIA BOARD OF REGENTS) ★
1120 15th St, Augusta, GA 30912-0004
Tel (706) 721-0011 *Founded/Ownrshp* 2013
Sales 522.5MM *EMP* 5,000
Accts Greg S Griffin Atlanta Geor
SIC 8221 University
Pr: Ricardo Azziz
**CFO:* James Jones
**CFO:* Stephen Lamb
Sr VP: Mark Hamrick
VP: Susan Barcus
VP: David Barron

D-U-N-S 79-986-9128
AUGUSTANA CARE
1007 E 14th St, Minneapolis, MN 55404-1314
Tel (612) 238-5101 *Founded/Ownrshp* 1991
Sales 114.7MM *EMP* 2,000
Accts Cliftonlarsonallen Llp Minnea
SIC 6513 8051 Retirement hotel operation; Skilled nursing care facilities
CEO: Tim Tucker
**CFO:* Craig Kippelson
Bd of Dir: Heather Kraft
VP: Kay Gudmestad
**VP:* Tim Middendorf
VP Mktg: Dave Saemrow
Mktg Dir: Erica Hanson
Nrsg Dir: Patti Boller
Nrsg Dir: Cathy Iverson
HC Dir: Lavonne Lundquist

D-U-N-S 10-919-9794
AUI CONTRACTORS LLC
4775 North Fwy, Fort Worth, TX 76106-2315
Tel (817) 926-4377 *Founded/Ownrshp* 2008
Sales 134.2MM *EMP* 315
SIC 1542 1623 1771 Commercial & office building, new construction; Commercial & office buildings, renovation & repair; Underground utilities contractor; Concrete work
Pr: Doug Alumbaugh
Ex VP: Glenn Strother
VP: Mario Carbone
VP: Charles Plumhoff

D-U-N-S 19-973-6174
AULTCARE CORP
2600 6th St Sw, Canton, OH 44710-1702
Tel (330) 363-6360 *Founded/Ownrshp* 1986
Sales NA *EMP* 300
SIC 6324 Group hospitalization plans
Pr: Rick Haines
**Pr:* Allen Rovner MD
CFO: George Film
**Treas:* Robert Mann
VP: Andrea Finley
VP: Frank Getz
Dir IT: Robert Schlechirt
IT Man: Dora Oshell
Opers Mgr: Paula Angari
Mktg Dir: Michael Furcolow
Pgrm Dir: Ben Kim

D-U-N-S 94-172-2126
AULTCARE INSURANCE CO
2600 6th St Sw, Canton, OH 44710-1702
Tel (330) 363-6360 *Founded/Ownrshp* 1989
Sales NA *EMP* 400
SIC 6321 Health insurance carriers
Pr: Rick Haines
**VP:* Melissa Shelton
IT Man: Syed Fayyaz

D-U-N-S 15-727-6999
AULTMAN HEALTH FOUNDATION
2600 6th St Sw, Canton, OH 44710-1702
Tel (330) 452-9911 *Founded/Ownrshp* 1891
Sales 1.1MM *EMP* 3,000
Accts Bruner Cox Llp Canton Oh
SIC 8011 Health maintenance organization
CEO: Christopher Remark
Chf Rad: Michael Soehnlen
V Ch: Joseph R Halter Jr
Ofcr: Lani Drozda
Ofcr: Barbara McGill
Ofcr: Tim Regula
Assoc VP: Kimberly Bricker
VP: Elizabeth Edmunds
VP: Anne Gunther
VP: Vicki Haines
VP: Lori Mertes
VP: Tony Snyder
VP: Timothy M Teynor
Dir Rad: Christine Donato

D-U-N-S 06-041-2509
AULTMAN HOSPITAL (OH)
2600 6th St Sw, Canton, OH 44710-1799
Tel (330) 452-9911 *Founded/Ownrshp* 1891, 1984
Sales 307.5MM *EMP* 3,027
SIC 8062 8069 8221 General medical & surgical hospitals; Specialty hospitals, except psychiatric; Colleges universities & professional schools
CEO: Christopher E Remark
Pr: Edward J Roth III
CFO: Mark Wright
Ofcr: Steven Mueller
Assoc VP: Janine Stackhouse
Adm Dir: Carol Young
Prac Mgr: Douglas Lauby
CIO: Dane Ficco
Software D: Jessica Dray
Software D: Brian Harbert
Surgeon: Giovanni Ciuffo

AUNT MID PRODUCE CO.
See RIGGIO DISTRIBUTION CO

AUNT MILLIE'S BAKERIES
See PERFECTION BAKERIES INC

D-U-N-S 78-760-0816
AUNTIE ANNES INC
(*Suby of* CINNABON) ★
48-50 W Chestnut St # 200, Lancaster, PA 17603-3791
Tel (717) 435-1435 *Founded/Ownrshp* 2010
Sales 186.3MM[E] *EMP* 339[E]
SIC 6794 2051 5461 Franchises, selling or licensing; Bread, cake & related products; Pretzels
Pr: William P Dunn Jr
**Pr:* Russel Umphenour
**Treas:* Grant Markley
**Treas:* James H Moss
VP: Scot Crain
**VP:* Lenore Krentz
**VP:* Dom Portanova
**VP:* Rich Sauder
**VP:* Dale Smucker
Mktg Dir: Meredith Wenz
Snr Mgr: Tina Cabry

AUNTIE EM'S BAKERY
See QUALITY DAIRY CO

AURA
See ASSOCIATION OF UNIVERSITIES FOR RESEARCH IN ASTRONOMY INC

AURAMET INTERNATIONAL
See AURAMET TRADING LLC

D-U-N-S 16-563-8938
AURAMET TRADING LLC
AURAMET INTERNATIONAL
300 Frank W Burr Blvd # 24, Teaneck, NJ 07666-6712
Tel (201) 905-5000 *Founded/Ownrshp* 2004
Sales 9.3MMM *EMP* 17
SIC 3339 Precious metals
CEO: James Verraster III
**COO:* Justin Sullivan
**CFO:* Mark Edelstein

AUREON NETWORK SERVICES
See IOWA NETWORK SERVICES INC

D-U-N-S 06-852-1126 IMP/EXP
AURIGA POLYMERS INC
(*Suby of* INDORAMA VENTURES PUBLIC COMPANY LIMITED)
1550 Dewberry Rd, Spartanburg, SC 29307-4349
Tel (864) 579-5570 *Founded/Ownrshp* 2010
Sales 379.0MM[E] *EMP* 430
SIC 2821 Polyesters
**Pr:* Michael Greene
**Prin:* Mark D Holden
Opers Mgr: Mike Ginn

D-U-N-S 14-488-3142 IMP
AUROBINDO PHARMA USA INC
(*Suby of* AUROBINDO PHARMA LIMITED)
6 Wheeling Rd, Dayton, NJ 08810-1526
Tel (732) 839-9400 *Founded/Ownrshp* 2006
Sales 263.3MM[E] *EMP* 218
SIC 5122 Pharmaceuticals
CEO: Robert G Cunard
CFO: Gangadhar Gorla
Ofcr: Srinivas Vadluri
VP: Bapuji Akula
VP: Madhu M Sundar
VP: Bvann Varma
Ex Dir: K R Ramachandran
Genl Mgr: Rajeev Tl
Off Mgr: Maryann Borkar
QA Dir: Mary Villalona
Ql Cn Mgr: Sandra Martinez

D-U-N-S 07-850-9103
AURORA BAYCARE MEDICAL CENTER
2845 Greenbrier Rd, Green Bay, WI 54311-6519
Tel (920) 288-8000 *Founded/Ownrshp* 2012
Sales 375.6MM *EMP* 131[E]
SIC 8011 Physical medicine, physician/surgeon
Pr: Daniel Meyer
VP: Kathy A Becker
**VP:* Gwendolyn Christensen
**VP:* J Richard Ludgin MD JD
**VP:* Heather Schroeder
Dir OR: Maria Klim
IT Man: Patrick Lynch
Plas Surg: James Zasuly
Doctor: Toby Cohen
Genl Couns: Shelly Hart

D-U-N-S 05-783-2602 IMP/EXP
AURORA BEARING CO
901 Aucutt Rd, Montgomery, IL 60538-1338
Tel (630) 897-8941 *Founded/Ownrshp* 1971
Sales 100.1MM[E] *EMP* 252
SIC 3568 Bearings, plain
Pr: David Richard
**Ch Bd:* Jesse F Maberry
CFO: Zinser John
**VP:* Harvey Sterkel
CTO: Scott Black
IT Man: Tony Dodaro
Sls Mgr: Don Schroder

AURORA CAPITAL GROUP
See AURORA CAPITAL PARTNERS LP

D-U-N-S 55-628-8587
AURORA CAPITAL PARTNERS LP
AURORA CAPITAL GROUP
10877 Wilshire Blvd # 2100, Los Angeles, CA 90024-4378
Tel (310) 551-0101 *Founded/Ownrshp* 1990
Sales 2.2MMM[E] *EMP* 9,815
SIC 6726 Investment offices
Pt: Gerald L Parsky
Pt: Richard Crowell
Pt: Fred Elsea
Pt: Timothy J Hart
Pt: Josh R Klinefelter
Pt: John T Mapes
Pt: Richard Roeder
Pt: Steven D Smith
VP: Jared Epstein
VP: Robert Fraser
VP: Matthew Laycock
VP: Zach Mager
VP: Andrew Wilson

D-U-N-S 00-749-1392
AURORA COOPERATIVE ELEVATOR CO (NE)
2225 Q St, Aurora, NE 68818-1304
Tel (402) 694-2106 *Founded/Ownrshp* 1908
Sales 578.4MM[E] *EMP* 300
SIC 5153 5191 Grains; Farm supplies; Feed
Ch Bd: William Schuster
**Pr:* George Hohwieler
**COO:* Chris Vincent
**CFO:* Robert Brown
**VP:* Chad Carlson
**VP:* Chris Decker
**VP:* Kelly Grossnicklaus

D-U-N-S 62-248-3121 EXP
AURORA DAIRY CORP
AURORA ORGANIC DAIRY
1919 14th St Ste 300, Boulder, CO 80302-5321
Tel (720) 564-6296 *Founded/Ownrshp* 2003
Sales 162.7MM[E] *EMP* 300
SIC 0241 Milk production
CEO: Marc B Peperzak
**Ch Bd:* Mark Retzloff
**CFO:* Cammie Muller
**Ex VP:* Scott McGinty
VP: Dan Placke
VP: Sonja Tuitele
IT Man: Merritt Horn
IT Man: Gail Shirey
QC Dir: Peggy Colfelt
Plnt Mgr: John Beutler

D-U-N-S 83-101-9562
AURORA DIAGNOSTICS HOLDINGS LLC
11025 Rca Center Dr # 300, Palm Beach Gardens, FL 33410-4269
Tel (561) 626-5512 *Founded/Ownrshp* 2006
Sales 263.7MM *EMP* 935[E]
SIC 8071 Pathological laboratory
CEO: Daniel D Crowley
**COO:* Bruce Walton
**Ex VP:* Michael J Null
**Sr VP:* Fred Ferrara
**VP:* Anne M Horstmann

D-U-N-S 60-471-7165 IMP
AURORA FLIGHT SCIENCES CORP
9950 Wakeman Dr, Manassas, VA 20110-2702
Tel (703) 369-3633 *Founded/Ownrshp* 1994
Sales 111.2MM[E] *EMP* 292
Accts Argy Wiltse & Robinson Pc
SIC 3721 Research & development on aircraft by the manufacturer
CEO: John S Langford
**Pr:* Mark C Cherry
**CFO:* Tim Crossno
**CFO:* Ralph Koch
**VP:* Tom Clancy
**VP:* Matt Hutchison
VP: Jean Led
VP: Kris Miller
**VP:* Kristine Miller
Exec: Teressa Hofmann
Prgrm Mgr: Larry Reid
Board of Directors: Martin E Dandridge, Kenneth J Krieg, Darryll J Pines, Norton A Schwartz, Ellen O'kane Tauscher, Anthony J Tether, John W Warner

AURORA HEALTH CARE
See AURORA MEDICAL GROUP INC

D-U-N-S 96-775-0923
AURORA HEALTH CARE CENTRAL INC
3031 W Montana St, Milwaukee, WI 53215-3627
Tel (414) 647-3211 *Founded/Ownrshp* 2011
Sales 114.8MM *EMP* 50[E]
SIC 8099 Health & allied services
VP: Mary A Tierney
Snr Sftwr: Keith Crager
Snr Ntwrk: Kevin Frinizi
IT Man: Stephen Guenther
Netwrk Mgr: Dan Klug
Sftwr Eng: Jim Lunde

D-U-N-S 13-018-5960
AURORA HEALTH CARE INC
750 W Virginia St, Milwaukee, WI 53204-1539
Tel (414) 647-3000 *Founded/Ownrshp* 1983
Sales 3.9MMM *EMP* 30,000
Accts Lb Deloitte Tax Llp Chicago
SIC 8741 8062 Hospital management; Nursing & personal care facility management; General medical & surgical hospitals; Hospital, affiliated with AMA residency
Pr: Nicholas Turkal
**Ch Bd:* Joanne Disch
Ch Bd: John Dragisic
COO: Gerard Coleman
CFO: David Eager
CFO: Gail Hanson
CFO: Michael Panosh
Treas: Walter Kipp
Ofcr: George Hinton
Ex VP: Loren Anderson
Ex VP: Jeffrey W Bailet
Ex VP: Mollie Bartelt
Ex VP: Patrick Falvey
Ex VP: Cristy Garcia
Ex VP: Lorelle Mahoney
Sr VP: Kevin Moore
VP: Gwen Baumel
VP: Michael Brophy
VP: Diane Ekstrand
VP: Mark Huber
VP: Karlene Kerfoot PHD
Board of Directors: John Daniels Jr

D-U-N-S 05-410-3742
AURORA HEALTH CARE METRO INC
AURORA ST LUKES MEDICAL CENTER
(*Suby of* AURORA HEALTH CARE INC) ★
2900 W Oklahoma Ave, Milwaukee, WI 53215-4330
Tel (414) 649-6000 *Founded/Ownrshp* 2000
Sales 327.5MM[E] *EMP* 4,000
SIC 8062 General medical & surgical hospitals
Pr: Marie Golanowski
CFO: Anita Jarvis
**VP:* David Yeager
Dir Rad: Donna Lawien
Pr Mgr: Mary Fields
Doctor: Sara Planton
Pharmcst: Tim Strane
Phys Thrpy: Carolynn Glocka

D-U-N-S 01-592-1686
AURORA HEALTH CARE SOUTHERN LAKES INC (WI)
AURORA MEDICAL CENTER SUMMIT
(*Suby of* AURORA HEALTH CARE INC) ★
36500 Aurora Dr, Gleason, WI 54435
Tel (262) 434-1000 *Founded/Ownrshp* 2009
Sales 114.6MM *EMP* 308[E]
SIC 8099 Health & allied services
Prin: Eugene S Arnett
Surgeon: Todd T Hannula
Obsttrcn: Meridith Derrig

D-U-N-S 96-887-8889
AURORA MEDICAL CENTER GRAFTON LLC
975 Port Washington Rd, Grafton, WI 53024-9204
Tel (262) 329-2723 *Founded/Ownrshp* 2011
Sales 189.9MM *EMP* 99
SIC 8049 Physical therapist
Prin: Eugene Monroe

D-U-N-S 14-664-6240
AURORA MEDICAL CENTER OSHKOSH
855 N Westhaven Dr, Oshkosh, WI 54904-7668
Tel (920) 303-8730 *Founded/Ownrshp* 2005
Sales 126.3MM *EMP* 62[E]
SIC 8011 Medical centers
Pr: Fran Finley
Podiatrist: Camille J Zizzo

AURORA MEDICAL CENTER SUMMIT
See AURORA HEALTH CARE SOUTHERN LAKES INC

D-U-N-S 80-955-6400
AURORA MEDICAL GROUP INC
AURORA HEALTH CARE
(*Suby of* AURORA HEALTH CARE INC) ★
750 W Virginia St, Milwaukee, WI 53204-1539
Tel (414) 299-1781 *Founded/Ownrshp* 1990
Sales 294.4MM[E] *EMP* 6,384
SIC 8011 Offices & clinics of medical doctors
Pr: Jeffrey W Bailet
**CEO:* Nick Turkal
VP: Susan Buettner
VP: Robert Devermann
VP: Scott Novogoratz

D-U-N-S 12-071-4535 IMP/EXP
AURORA NETWORKS INC
(*Suby of* ARRIS GLOBAL LTD.)
1764 Automation Pkwy, San Jose, CA 95131-1873
Tel (408) 428-9500 *Founded/Ownrshp* 2013
Sales 85.2MM[E] *EMP* 250[E]
SIC 3229 Fiber optics strands
Pr: Guy Sucharczuk
CFO: Craig Mc Collam
**CFO:* Craig McCollam
CFO: Mahesh Nalavade
VP: Michael Sparkman
VP: Scott Weinstein
**VP:* Michael Yost
VP Bus Dev: Glenn Miller

AURORA ORGANIC DAIRY
See AURORA DAIRY CORP

D-U-N-S 13-767-3849 IMP
AURORA PARTS & ACCESSORIES LLC
500 S Enterprise Blvd, Lebanon, IN 46052-8307
Tel (765) 483-5622 *Founded/Ownrshp* 2015
Sales 145.8MM[E] *EMP* 125
SIC 5013 Trailer parts & accessories; Truck parts & accessories
Pr: David Clarke
CFO: Brad Fulkerson
VP: Bob Lueken
Rgnl Mgr: Phil Dowden
VP Sls: Mike Conley

AURORA PAVILION
See AIKEN REGIONAL MEDICAL CENTERS LLC

D-U-N-S 79-299-2729
AURORA PHARMACY INC
(*Suby of* AURORA HEALTH CARE INC) ★
12500 W Bluemound Rd # 201, Elm Grove, WI 53122-2600
Tel (262) 787-2136 *Founded/Ownrshp* 1992
Sales 91.6MM[E] *EMP* 750
SIC 5912 Drug stores
Pr: James Moore
Dist Mgr: Sally Fongaro

D-U-N-S 01-062-1852
AURORA PUBLIC SCHOOLS
15701 E 1st Ave Ste 106, Aurora, CO 80011-9037
Tel (303) 365-5810 *Founded/Ownrshp* 1885
Sales 451.1MM *EMP* 6,000
Accts Bkd Llp Denver Colorado
SIC 8211 Public combined elementary & secondary school; Public vocational/technical school
COO: Anthony Sturges
CFO: Adrienne Bradshaw
Bd of Dir: Mary Lewis
Bd of Dir: Dawn Mills
VP: Willie Jones
VP: Dianna Ludwig
VP: Amy Prince
Off Mgr: Gale Bankstein
Off Mgr: Kathy Rewalt
MIS Dir: Pam Barilla
MIS Dir: Sherry Davidson

D-U-N-S 18-297-0434
AURORA SINAI MEDICAL CENTER INC
(*Suby of* AURORA HEALTH CARE INC) ★
945 N 12th St, Milwaukee, WI 53233-1305
Tel (414) 219-2000 *Founded/Ownrshp* 1987
Sales 111.4MM[E] *EMP* 1,871
SIC 8062 Hospital, affiliated with AMA residency
CEO: Nick Turkal MD
**CFO:* Gail Hanson
**VP:* Jeffrey W Bailet
**VP:* Patrick Falvey PHD
**VP:* Keith Kieffer
**VP:* Mary Beth Kingston
VP: Sally Sermersheim
Dir Lab: Michelle Belmore
Dir Rx: Arlene Iglar
Off Mgr: Sandy Jensen
VP Mktg: Jeffrey Garland

AURORA ST LUKES MEDICAL CENTER
See AURORA HEALTH CARE METRO INC

D-U-N-S 07-384-1967
AURORA WEST ALLIS MEDICAL CENTER
(*Suby of* AURORA HEALTH CARE INC) ★
8901 W Lincoln Ave, Milwaukee, WI 53227-2409
Tel (414) 328-6000 *Founded/Ownrshp* 1961
Sales 189.2MM[E] *EMP* 2,000
SIC 8062 General medical & surgical hospitals
Chf Rad: Richard Weekes
**COO:* Steve Bablitch
**CFO:* Gail Hanson
VP: Carl J Knauer
Dir Risk M: Sue A Bevsek
Dir Rx: Angela D Ianni
Plnt Mgr: Mike Pabich
Ansthlgy: Robert A Corish
Ansthlgy: Mark A Nelson

D-U-N-S 02-143-0467
AURORA WEST SCHOOL DISTRICT 129
WEST AURORA SCHOOL DISTRICT 12
1877 W Downer Pl Ste 100, Aurora, IL 60506-7336
Tel (630) 301-5000 *Founded/Ownrshp* 1860
Sales 186.5MM *EMP* 1,200
Accts Crowe Horwath Llp Oak Brook
SIC 8211 Public elementary & secondary schools
CFO: Kevin Wegner
Dir IT: Stacy Stout
Pr Dir: Tony Martinez
Teacher Pr: Michael Smith

D-U-N-S 11-878-9361 IMP
AURUBIS BUFFALO INC
(*Suby of* AURUBIS AG)
70 Sayre St, Buffalo, NY 14207-2225
Tel (716) 879-6700 *Founded/Ownrshp* 2011
Sales 219.0MM[E] *EMP* 639[E]
SIC 3351 Copper rolling & drawing
Pr: Raymond Mercer
Exec: Doug Zimmerman
CTO: Dick Fisher
DP Exec: Butterworth Jamie
IT Man: Helen Mason
VP Mktg: Todd Heusner
Mktg Mgr: Joseph Smolen
Manager: Dave Mislin
Sls Mgr: Paul Schubert

D-U-N-S 80-835-2780 IMP
AUSTAL USA LLC
(*Suby of* AUSTAL LIMITED)
1 Dunlap Dr, Mobile, AL 36602-8009
Tel (251) 434-8000 *Founded/Ownrshp* 1999
Sales 228.8MM[E] *EMP* 1,400
SIC 3731 Shipbuilding & repairing
CEO: Joseph J Rella
Pr: Terry O'Brien
Netwrk Eng: Graham Wooden
Sls Mgr: Brett Reed

D-U-N-S 01-815-3356
AUSTEN GROUP LLC
(*Suby of* RUFFALO NOEL LEVITZ LLC) ★
679 Founders Ave, Eagle, CO 81631
Tel (970) 331-2965 *Founded/Ownrshp* 2001, 2013
Sales 42.0MM[E] *EMP* 2,353[E]
SIC 8732 Educational research
Pr: Mike Williams
Ex VP: Larry Stone
Ex Dir: Andrew Sallee

AUSTIN AMERICAN STATESMAN
See COX TEXAS NEWSPAPERS LP

D-U-N-S 16-091-0949
AUSTIN BANCORP INC
200 E Commerce St, Jacksonville, TX 75766-4904
Tel (903) 586-1526 *Founded/Ownrshp* 1984
Sales NA *EMP* 402
Accts Payne & Smith Llc Dallas Tx
SIC 6021 6211 6022 National commercial banks; Investment bankers; Dealers, security; State commercial banks
Ch: Jeff Austin Jr
CFO: Keith Chambers
**Treas:* Todd Burton
VP: Glenda Johnson

D-U-N-S 00-895-0552
AUSTIN BANK TEXAS N A
(*Suby of* AUSTIN BANCORP INC) ★
200 E Commerce St, Jacksonville, TX 75766-4904
Tel (903) 586-1526 *Founded/Ownrshp* 1909
Sales NA *EMP* 330
Accts Payne & Smith Llc Dallas Tx
SIC 6021 National commercial banks
Pr: John Williams
**Ch Bd:* Jeff Austin Jr
**CFO:* Keith Chambers
Ex VP: Todd Burton
Sr VP: Kent Bryson
**VP:* Sissy Austin
VP: Curtis Sparks
Adm Dir: Crystal Bateman
Board of Directors: Barry T Hughes, Jeff Austin III, Bill Mc Rae, Gene Blumbow, Robert W Nichols, Billy B Campbell, Dwight Phifer, Curtis M Carroll, Eddie Smith, Jane Chapman, H G Tilley, Charles H Creed DDS, Don L Dacus, Glen Hamilton, Chuck Hopson

D-U-N-S 00-896-4033
AUSTIN BRIDGE & ROAD INC
(*Suby of* AUSTIN INDUSTRIES DEL) ★
6330 Commerce Dr Ste 150, Irving, TX 75063-6016
Tel (214) 596-7300 *Founded/Ownrshp* 1992
Sales 230.6MM[E] *EMP* 800
SIC 1611 1622 Highway & street paving contractor; Bridge construction; Highway construction, elevated
Pr: Benard Hewett
**Treas:* Patricia Jones
**Sr VP:* Richard Mills
**VP:* Dale C Stubblefield
VP: Steven D Vincent
Off Mgr: Rhonda Ewing

D-U-N-S 11-201-6956 IMP
AUSTIN BRIDGE & ROAD LP
(*Suby of* AUSTIN BRIDGE & ROAD INC) ★
6330 Commerce Dr Ste 150, Irving, TX 75063-6016
Tel (214) 596-7300 *Founded/Ownrshp* 1999
Sales 179.1MM[E] *EMP* 800
SIC 1622 1611 Bridge, tunnel & elevated highway; Highway & street construction
Pr: Benard Hewett

D-U-N-S 61-734-2212
AUSTIN BUILDING AND DESIGN INC
AUSTIN COMPANY, THE
(*Suby of* KAJIMA INTERNATIONAL INC) ★
6095 Parkland Blvd # 100, Cleveland, OH 44124-6139
Tel (440) 544-2600 *Founded/Ownrshp* 2006
Sales 131.7MM[E] *EMP* 197
Accts S S & G Financial Services Inc
SIC 1541 1542 8742 8711 8712 Industrial buildings, new construction; Commercial & office building, new construction; Institutional building construction; Management consulting services; Engineering services; Architectural engineering
Pr: Michael G Pierce
CFO: Glen Hobratschk
**Ch:* Noriaki Ohashi
**Treas:* Mitsuyoshi Tamura
**Sr VP:* Mark Phillips
VP: D Berthlsen
VP: Matthew Eddleman
VP: James Moore
VP: Dennis Saymond
VP: Don C Schjeldahl
VP: C Wendell
Exec: Ed Wright

AUSTIN COMPANY, THE
See AUSTIN BUILDING AND DESIGN INC

D-U-N-S 05-392-4106
■ **AUSTIN COCA-COLA BOTTLING CO**
(*Suby of* COCA-COLA REFRESHMENTS USA INC) ★
1 Coca Cola Pl, San Antonio, TX 78219-3712
Tel (210) 225-2601 *Founded/Ownrshp* 1987
Sales 158.8MM[E] *EMP* 2,000
SIC 2086 Bottled & canned soft drinks
Pr: Joan Aom
VP: Sid Hodges
**VP:* David Van Houten
VP: David Vanhouten

D-U-N-S 19-939-6086 IMP
AUSTIN COMMERCIAL INC
(*Suby of* AUSTIN INDUSTRIES DEL) ★
3535 Travis St Ste 300, Dallas, TX 75204-1444
Tel (214) 443-5700 *Founded/Ownrshp* 1989
Sales 462.4MM[E] *EMP* 931
SIC 1542 Commercial & office building, new construction; Hospital construction
Pr: Brad Brown
**Treas:* Patricia Jones
Sr VP: Chuck Cleaveland
Dir Risk M: Peter Durbin

D-U-N-S 10-191-6091
AUSTIN COMMERCIAL LP
AUSTIN INDUSTRIES
(*Suby of* AUSTIN COMMERCIAL INC) ★
3535 Travis St Ste 300, Dallas, TX 75204-1444
Tel (214) 443-5700 *Founded/Ownrshp* 1999
Sales 207.6MM[E] *EMP* 700[E]
SIC 1542 Commercial & office building contractors; Commercial & office building, new construction; Commercial & office buildings, renovation & repair
Pr: Brad Brown

D-U-N-S 07-849-3517
AUSTIN COMMUNITY COLLEGE
5930 Middle Fiskville Rd, Austin, TX 78752-4390
Tel (512) 223-7000 *Founded/Ownrshp* 1972
Sales 88.5MM *EMP* 4,200
Accts Padgett Stratemann & Co Ll
SIC 8222 Community college
Pr: Richard M Rhodes
CFO: Ben Ferrell
Trst: Jeffrey Richard
Ofcr: Rachel McElroy
Ofcr: Gabriel Romero
Psych: Hilda Gartzke
Psych: Kristie Porter
Pgrm Dir: Mariah Lossing

AUSTIN CONTRACTOR SERVICES
See WILLIAMS INSULATION CO OF AUSTIN INC

D-U-N-S 07-850-0972
AUSTIN DIAGNOSTIC CLINIC ASSOCIATION
ADC
12221 N Mo Pac Expy, Austin, TX 78758-2401
Tel (512) 901-1111 *Founded/Ownrshp* 1952

Sales 90.9MM[E] *EMP* 820
SIC 8011 Clinic, operated by physicians; Internal medicine practitioners
CEO: Robert Spurck Jr
CFO: John Ratcliff
Sr VP: Brenda Forbes
**VP:* David Joseph
Genl Mgr: Lyn Castillo
CIO: Thomas Thrower
Telecom Mg: Vicci Coffman
IT Man: Jason Johnson
Opers Mgr: Marie Dunham
Surgeon: Louis Corne
Surgeon: Randy Honish

D-U-N-S 07-693-3746
AUSTIN INDEPENDENT SCHOOL DISTRICT (INC)
1111 W 6th St, Austin, TX 78703-5399
Tel (512) 414-1700 *Founded/Ownrshp* 1945
Sales 392.2MM[E] *EMP* 9,200
Accts Padgett Stratemann & Co Llp
SIC 8211 Public elementary & secondary schools
COO: Lawrence Fryer
Bd of Dir: Ave Wahrmund
Trst: Robert Schneider
Ofcr: Ed Richter
Exec: Jerry Barnard
Ex Dir: John Alawneh
Ex Dir: Shirley M Heitzman
Ex Dir: Maria Whisett
Dir Sec: Eric Mendez
Admn Mgr: Catherine Acuna
Admn Mgr: James Cogdell

D-U-N-S 10-583-4857 IMP
AUSTIN INDUSTRIAL INC
AUSTIN INDUSTRIES
(*Suby of* AUSTIN INDUSTRIES DEL) ★
2801 E 13th St, La Porte, TX 77571-9633
Tel (713) 641-3400 *Founded/Ownrshp* 1988
Sales 803.2MM[E] *EMP* 3,500
SIC 1629 Dams, waterways, docks & other marine construction
CEO: David Walls
**Pr:* Barry W Babyak
**Treas:* Brenda Schertz
**VP:* Oger L Gossett
**Prin:* Ronald J Gafford
IT Man: Moises Gonzalez
Mktg Dir: Stan Spears

AUSTIN INDUSTRIES
See AUSTIN COMMERCIAL LP

AUSTIN INDUSTRIES
See AUSTIN INDUSTRIAL INC

AUSTIN INDUSTRIES DEL
See AUSTIN INDUSTRIES INC

D-U-N-S 06-895-5640 IMP
AUSTIN INDUSTRIES INC
AUSTIN INDUSTRIES DEL
3535 Travis St Ste 300, Dallas, TX 75204-1444
Tel (214) 443-5500 *Founded/Ownrshp* 1986
Sales 2.2MMM[E] *EMP* 7,000
SIC 1542 1629 1611 1622 Commercial & office building, new construction; Industrial plant construction; Highway & street construction; Highway & street paving contractor; Bridge construction
Pr: David B Walls
V Ch: Charles M Solomon
V Ch: Charles M Soloon
**Pr:* Jt Fisher
**Ch:* Rhys J Best
**Treas:* Patricia Jones
**VP:* Barry W Babyak
VP: Mike Scott
Off Mgr: Helen Miller
Info Man: Chris Fant
VP Opers: Steve Warnick

D-U-N-S 09-759-0392
AUSTIN JACK DE COSTER
DE COSTER EGG FARMS
Plains Rd, Turner, ME 04282
Tel (207) 224-8222 *Founded/Ownrshp* 1960
Sales 114.0MM *EMP* 320
SIC 0252 0213 0723 Chicken eggs; Hogs; Feed milling custom services
Owner: Austin Jack De Coster

D-U-N-S 10-569-6582 IMP
AUSTIN MAINTENANCE & CONSTRUCTION INC
(*Suby of* AUSTIN INDUSTRIES) ★
2801 E 13th St, La Porte, TX 77571-9633
Tel (713) 641-3400 *Founded/Ownrshp* 2003
Sales 221.9MM[E] *EMP* 1,050[E]
SIC 1629 Industrial plant construction
Pr: Barry W Babyak
**Treas:* Brenda Schertz

D-U-N-S 07-858-9564
AUSTIN MATERIALS LLC
RAMMING PAVING COMPANY
(*Suby of* SUMMIT MATERIALS LLC) ★
9020 N Cpitl Of Texas Hwy, Austin, TX 78759-7279
Tel (512) 251-3713 *Founded/Ownrshp* 2011
Sales 140.7MM[E] *EMP* 410[E]
SIC 1611 5032 Concrete construction: roads, highways, sidewalks, etc.; Paving materials
**Pr:* Chuck Fuller
**VP:* Dean Lundquist
**Genl Mgr:* John Ramming
VP Opers: Lance Townsend
Mtls Mgr: Clint Blackmon
Sls Mgr: Joe Cruz
Snr Mgr: Padraic Dillon

AUSTIN NURSING CENTER
See CENTURY CARE OF AMERICA INC

D-U-N-S 00-415-9653 IMP
AUSTIN POWDER CO
(*Suby of* AUSTIN POWDER HOLDINGS CO) ★
25800 Science Park Dr # 300, Cleveland, OH 44122-7386
Tel (216) 464-2400 *Founded/Ownrshp* 1986
Sales 491.0MM[E] *EMP* 1,200
SIC 2892 Explosives
Ch Bd: William Jack Davis
**Pr:* David M Gleason
Treas: Randy Wicks
**VP:* David True
Dir IT: Larry Domzalski
IT Man: Theresa Aspenwall
Software D: Scott Galinac
Sfty Dirs: Molly Thomas

D-U-N-S 93-264-1988 IMP/EXP
AUSTIN POWDER HOLDINGS CO
(*Suby of* DAVIS MINING & MANUFACTURING INC) ★
25800 Science Park Dr # 300, Cleveland, OH 44122-7311
Tel (216) 464-2400 *Founded/Ownrshp* 1837
Sales 459.9MM[E] *EMP* 1,700
SIC 2892 Explosives
Ch Bd: William Jack Davis
**Pr:* David M Gleason
**COO:* Michael Gleason

D-U-N-S 04-626-9296
AUSTIN TACALA CORP
TACO BELL
(*Suby of* TACO BELL) ★
500 N Capitl Of Texas Hwy, Austin, TX 78746-3302
Tel (512) 327-4654 *Founded/Ownrshp* 2013
Sales 69.2MM[E] *EMP* 2,300
SIC 5812 Fast-food restaurant, chain
**CFO:* David G Polis
**VP:* Marian A Dozier
VP: Jonnie Lowry

D-U-N-S 13-182-8493
AUSTIN VENTURES LP
300 W 6th St Ste 2300, Austin, TX 78701-3912
Tel (512) 485-1900 *Founded/Ownrshp* 1984
Sales 177.9MM[E] *EMP* 642
SIC 6799 2038 Venture capital companies; Frozen specialties
Genl Pt: Joe Aragona
**Genl Pt:* Thomas Ball
**Genl Pt:* Ken Deangelis
**Genl Pt:* Basil Horangic
**Genl Pt:* Chris Pacitti
**Genl Pt:* Venu Shamapant
**Genl Pt:* Phil Siegel
**Genl Pt:* John Thornton
Pt: Michael Bennet
Pt: Mike Bennett
Pt: Shelby H Carter Jr
Pt: Jim Clardy
Pt: Russ Cockrell
Pt: Mike Dodd
**Pt:* Scott Donaldson
Pt: Mark Feighner
Pt: Chris Grafft
Pt: Michael Hathaway
**Pt:* David Lack
Pt: John McHale
Pt: Mark Melliar-Smith

AUSTIN-POWELL-LANKES AGENCY
See LIGHTHOUSE INSURANCE GROUP INC

D-U-N-S 10-000-0074
AUTAUGA COUNTY SCHOOL BOARD OF EDUCATION
153 W 4th St, Prattville, AL 36067-3011
Tel (334) 365-5706 *Founded/Ownrshp* 1930
Sales 48.2MM[E] *EMP* 1,100
Accts Ronald L Jones Montgomery A
SIC 8211 School board
Pr: Jeffrey Keith

D-U-N-S 07-979-9697
AUTAUGA COUNTY SCHOOL SYSTEM
153 W 4th St, Prattville, AL 36067-3011
Tel (334) 365-5706 *Founded/Ownrshp* 2015
Sales 11.1MM[E] *EMP* 1,212[E]
SIC 8211 Public elementary & secondary schools
Teacher Pr: Nancy Jackson
HC Dir: Sandie Manscill

D-U-N-S 96-367-8516
AUTHENTIC BRANDS GROUP LLC
JONES NEW YORK
1411 Broadway Fl 4, New York, NY 10018-3410
Tel (212) 760-2410 *Founded/Ownrshp* 2010
Sales 607.0MM[E] *EMP* 1,310[E]
SIC 6794 Copyright buying & licensing
CEO: James Salter
Mng Pt: Paul Cohen
Pr: John Erlandson
**Pr:* Perry Wolfman
**CFO:* Kevin Clarke
Chf Mktg O: Tim Pogue
Chf Mktg O: Nick Woodhouse
**Sr VP:* Noah Gelbart
VP: Katie Jones
VP: Corey Salter
Creative D: Juan Ogando

D-U-N-S 17-823-5821 IMP
AUTHENTIC LIFESTYLE PRODUCTS LLC
CAMPERS WORLD APPAREL GROUP
485 S Broadway Ste 11, Hicksville, NY 11801-5071
Tel (212) 354-2170 *Founded/Ownrshp* 2002
Sales 112.6MM *EMP* 18[E]
Accts Marks Paneth Llp Woodbury Ny
SIC 5399 Catalog showrooms
**CFO:* Farokh Hirjibehedin

D-U-N-S 60-121-9876 IMP/EXP
AUTO AIR EXPORT INC
OMEGA ENVIRONMENTAL TECH
1401 Valley View Ln # 100, Irving, TX 75061-3603
Tel (972) 812-7000 *Founded/Ownrshp* 1989
Sales 153.6MM[E] *EMP* 152[E]
SIC 5075 3585 5531 Air conditioning equipment, except room units; Air conditioning, motor vehicle; Automobile air conditioning equipment, sale, installation
CEO: Peter Butterfield
**CFO:* Mary Anne McLaren
CFO: Guntur Wilyono
**VP:* Dominick Ferraro
**VP:* Gary Wrench
Sales Exec: Valerie Rowe

D-U-N-S 07-204-5805
AUTO CLUB ENTERPRISES
3333 Fairview Rd Msa451, Costa Mesa, CA 92626-1610
Tel (714) 850-5111 *Founded/Ownrshp* 1912
Sales NA *EMP* 2,200
SIC 6321 Accident & health insurance
CEO: Robert T Bouttier
**Pr:* Thomas Mc Kernon
**Treas:* John F Boyle
Sr VP: Neiman Sharon
VP: Filomena Andre
**VP:* Avery Brown
VP: Waldo H Burnside
**VP:* James Gilmartin
VP: David Lang
VP: Stephen E Lenzi
VP: Peter R McDonald

D-U-N-S 07-313-1062
AUTO CLUB GROUP
AAA MICHIGAN
1 Auto Club Dr, Dearborn, MI 48126-4213
Tel (313) 336-1234 *Founded/Ownrshp* 1997
Sales 580.4MM[E] *EMP* 8,066
SIC 8699

D-U-N-S 07-278-6957
AUTO CLUB INSURANCE ASSOCIATION CO
ACIA
1 Auto Club Dr, Dearborn, MI 48126-4213
Tel (313) 336-1234 *Founded/Ownrshp* 1922
Sales NA *EMP* 2,005
SIC 6331 Automobile insurance
CEO: Charles H Podowski
Pr: Steven D Monahan
CFO: J Terry Mc Elroy
Sr VP: Steven Wagner
VP: Ann Federich

D-U-N-S 92-747-4804
AUTO CLUB SOUTH INSURANCE CO
(*Suby of* A A A TRAVEL AGENCY) ★
14055 Riveredge Dr # 500, Tampa, FL 33637-2091
Tel (800) 289-1325 *Founded/Ownrshp* 2008
Sales NA *EMP* 487[E]
SIC 6411 Insurance agents, brokers & service
Pr: John A Tomlin

D-U-N-S 08-033-3376
■ AUTO CO XXVIII INC
(*Suby of* AUTONATION INC) ★
200 Sw 1st Ave, Fort Lauderdale, FL 33301-1875
Tel (954) 769-7000 *Founded/Ownrshp* 2014
Sales 305.7MM[E] *EMP* 1,200[E]
SIC 5511 New & used car dealers

AUTO EDGE SOLUTIONS
See MOC PRODUCTS CO INC

AUTO PARTS GROUP
See PICK AND PULL AUTO DISMANTLING INC

D-U-N-S 80-984-5436 IMP
AUTO PARTS MANUFACTURING MISSISSIPPI INC
(*Suby of* TOYOTA AUTO BODY CO.,LTD.)
100 Tab Way, Guntown, MS 38849-8001
Tel (662) 365-3082 *Founded/Ownrshp* 2007
Sales 93.9MM[E] *EMP* 330
SIC 3089 3465 Automotive parts, plastic; Automotive stampings
Pr: Masaaki Fujii
**Sec:* Kiyoshi Tsuchiya
Genl Mgr: Yasuhiko Isohata
Counsel: Alison Goodman

AUTO PARTS WAREHOUSE
See EASTERN WAREHOUSE DISTRIBUTORS INC

AUTO PILOT
See HORNERXPRESS-SOUTH FLORIDA INC

AUTO PLUS
See UNI-SELECT USA INC

AUTO STOP
See S/S/G CORP

D-U-N-S 10-349-3094
AUTO SUPPLY CO INC
ASCO DISTRIBUTION CENTER
3740 N Patterson Ave, Winston Salem, NC 27105-3540
Tel (336) 661-6113 *Founded/Ownrshp* 1986
Sales 88.6MM[E] *EMP* 330[E]
SIC 5013

AUTO TRANSPORT TECHNICAL CTR
See URS MIDWEST INC

D-U-N-S 01-203-6640 IMP/EXP
AUTO TRUCK GROUP LLC
AUTO TRUCK GRP WYN FLT EQUIPME
(*Suby of* ARI-AUTOMOTIVE RESOURCES INTL) ★
1420 Brewster Creek Blvd, Bartlett, IL 60103-1695
Tel (630) 860-5600 *Founded/Ownrshp* 2010
Sales 220.0MM *EMP* 700
SIC 3713 1541 Truck bodies & parts; Truck & automobile assembly plant construction
Pr: James Dondlinger
**VP:* Brad Blanco
Opers Mgr: John Smulski
Manager: Bill Sammons
Sls Mgr: Matt McGowan

AUTO TRUCK GRP WYN FLT EQUIPME
See AUTO TRUCK GROUP LLC

AUTO VALUE
See METROPOLITAN AUTOMOTIVE WAREHOUSE

AUTO VALUE OF BAD AXE
See AWI HOLDINGS INC

D-U-N-S 04-133-4335
AUTO WAREHOUSING CO INC
A W C
2810 Marshall Ave Ste B, Tacoma, WA 98421-3135
Tel (253) 719-1700 *Founded/Ownrshp* 1990
Sales 131.6MM[E] *EMP* 1,000
SIC 4226 Automobile dead storage
Pr: Stephen Seher
**CFO:* Dennis Matteo
CFO: Judy Miller
Sr VP: Ian McRae
Sr VP: Ben Seher
**VP:* Julie Macdonald
VP: Brett Witzig
QA Dir: Tim Benson
IT Man: Josh Warren
Netwrk Mgr: Gary Huff
Info Man: Nancy Cook

D-U-N-S 06-340-0656
AUTO WORLD CAR WASH LLC
(*Suby of* CALIFORNIA SECURED INVESTMENTS, LLC)
15951 Los Gatos Blvd, Los Gatos, CA 95032-3428
Tel (408) 345-6532 *Founded/Ownrshp* 2011
Sales 2.7MM[E] *EMP* 1,597[E]
SIC 7542 Carwashes
CEO: Jeff Locastro

D-U-N-S 00-696-0017
AUTO-OWNERS INSURANCE CO
6101 Anacapri Blvd, Lansing, MI 48917-3994
Tel (517) 323-1200 *Founded/Ownrshp* 1916
Sales NA *EMP* 3,400
SIC 6331 Fire, marine & casualty insurance & carriers
Pr: Thomas E Froman
Pr: Mitch Lawens
Pr: Jeff Pierce
Pr: Ted Reinbold
Pr: Bill Woodbury
**CEO:* J F Harrold
**COO:* Jeffrey Scott Tagsold
**CFO:* Eileen Kay Fhaner
CFO: Eileen Fhaner
**Ex VP:* Daniel J Thelen
Sr VP: Bob Buchanan
VP: John Anderson
VP: Robert Buchanan
VP: Mike Martin
VP: Rodney Rupp
VP: Greg Shell
VP: Dan Thelan
VP: Ian Ward
VP: Scott Wilder
VP: Jon Williams
VP: Jonathan Williams
Board of Directors: J F Anderton IV, Herman J Arends, T J Buda Jr, Gregg L Cornell, P V Frederickson, Mark E Hooper, Lori Ann McAllister

D-U-N-S 78-744-6988
AUTO-OWNERS LIFE INSURANCE CO
(*Suby of* AUTO-OWNERS INSURANCE CO) ★
6101 Anacapri Blvd, Lansing, MI 48917-3968
Tel (517) 323-1200 *Founded/Ownrshp* 2002
Sales NA *EMP* 1,600
SIC 6411 6331 Insurance agents, brokers & service; Automobile insurance
CEO: Herman Arends
**Prin:* Jeff Harrold

D-U-N-S 08-015-0149
AUTO-WARES GROUP INC
440 Kirtland St Sw, Grand Rapids, MI 49507-2398
Tel (616) 243-2125 *Founded/Ownrshp* 2016
Sales 78.6MM[E] *EMP* 1,700
SIC 3559 Automotive related machinery
CEO: Barry Hill
**Pr:* Timothy Lee
**Ch:* Fred Bunting

D-U-N-S 13-946-4804 IMP/EXP
AUTOALLIANCE MANAGEMENT CO
1 International Dr, Flat Rock, MI 48134-9401
Tel (734) 782-7800 *Founded/Ownrshp* 1985
Sales 228.8MM[E] *EMP* 3,200
SIC 3711 Motor vehicles & car bodies
Pr: Tim Young
**CFO:* Rodney Haynes

D-U-N-S 09-189-0764
AUTOBAHN INC
AUTOBAHN INPORTS
3000 White Settlement Rd, Fort Worth, TX 76107-1338
Tel (817) 336-0885 *Founded/Ownrshp* 1980
Sales 93.4MM[E] *EMP* 250
SIC 5511 Automobiles, new & used
Pr: John S Chase
**VP:* Robert M Bass

AUTOBAHN INPORTS
See AUTOBAHN INC

AUTOBODY DEPOT
See TCP GLOBAL CORP

D-U-N-S 92-637-3085
▲ AUTOBYTEL INC
18872 Macarthur Blvd # 200, Irvine, CA 92612-1448
Tel (949) 225-4500 *Founded/Ownrshp* 1995
Sales 133.2MM *EMP* 148[E]
Accts Moss Adams Llp Los Angeles C
Tkr Sym ABTL *Exch* NGM
SIC 7375 Information retrieval services; On-line data base information retrieval
Pr: Jeffrey H Coats
**Ch Bd:* Michael J Fuchs
CFO: Kimberly S Boren
CFO: John M Markovich
Ofcr: Lee Sage
Ex VP: Grant Ahearn
Ex VP: Dennis Benner
Ex VP: Phillip Dupree
Ex VP: William A Ferriolo
Ex VP: Glenn E Fuller
Ex VP: Donald Perkins Jr
Sr VP: Lawrence Brogan
Sr VP: Jon Rosen
Sr VP: John J Skocilic Jr

VP: Rick Cabral
VP: Karen Howe
VP: Steerman John
VP: Russell Lbartlett
VP: Leonard McGinley
VP: John Skocilic
VP: John Steerman
Board of Directors: Michael A Carpenter, Mark N Kaplan, Jeffrey M Stibel, Janet MThompson

D-U-N-S 10-163-9599 IMP
■ AUTOCAM CORP
AUTOCAM PRCSION CMPNENTS GROUP
(Suby of NN INC) ★
4180 40th St Se, Kentwood, MI 49512-4122
Tel (616) 698-0707 *Founded/Ownrshp* 2014
Sales 401.2MM^E *EMP* 1,300
SIC 3714 3572 3841 5084 Motor vehicle parts & accessories; Motor vehicle brake systems & parts; Computer disk & drum drives & components; Surgical & medical instruments; Fuel injection systems
Pr: Richard Holder
**COO:* John R Buchan
**CFO:* Warren A Veltman
Off Mgr: Shane Kukla
Ql Cn Mgr: Paul Babosh
Sls Mgr: Mike Hand

AUTOCAM PRCSION CMPNENTS GROUP
See AUTOCAM CORP

D-U-N-S 12-762-6245 IMP
AUTOCAR LLC
(Suby of GVW HOLDINGS) ★
551 S Washington St, Hagerstown, IN 47346-1557
Tel (765) 489-5499 *Founded/Ownrshp* 2002
Sales 93.9MM^E *EMP* 200
SIC 3713 Garbage, refuse truck bodies
Ch: Andrew Taitz
**Pr:* Jim Johnston
VP: Bob Atkins
VP: Paul Blanchard
VP: Trevor Bridges
VP: Dereck Case
VP: Randy Dennis
VP: Bill Dolesch
Exec: Mike Thompson
Dir Bus: Eric Schwartz
Ex Dir: Joe Laspina

D-U-N-S 06-970-1282 IMP
▲ AUTODESK INC
111 Mcinnis Pkwy, San Rafael, CA 94903-2700
Tel (415) 507-5000 *Founded/Ownrshp* 1982
Sales 2.5MMM *EMP* 9,500
Tkr Sym ADSK *Exch* NGS
SIC 7372 Application computer software
Pr: Carl Bass
**Ch Bd:* Crawford W Beveridge
Treas: Kathleen Kewley
Sr VP: Andrew Anagnost
Sr VP: Jan Becker
Sr VP: Pascal W Di Fronzo
Sr VP: Amar Hanspal
VP: Steven Blum
VP: Joseph Chen
VP: David J Harrington
VP: Ray Savona
VP: Roberto Sigona
VP: Brian Singer
VP: Chris Snyder
VP: Lloyd Taylor
Board of Directors: Jeff Clarke, Scott Ferguson, Thomas Georgens, Richard S Hill, Mary T McDowell, Lorrie M Norrington, Betsy Rafael, Stacy J Smith, Steven M West

AUTODIRECT SOLUTIONS
See FRIEDKIN COMPANIES INC

AUTOJET TECHNOLOGIES
See SPRAYING SYSTEMS CO

D-U-N-S 60-251-1248 IMP/EXP
■ AUTOLIV ASP INC
AUTOLIV NORTH AMERICA
(Suby of AUTOLIV INC) ★
3350 Airport Rd, Ogden, UT 84405-1563
Tel (801) 625-4800 *Founded/Ownrshp* 1989
Sales 2.8MMM *EMP* 7,250
Accts Ernst & Young Llp Salt Lake C
SIC 3714 3563 Motor vehicle parts & accessories; Tire inflators, hand or compressor operated
CEO: Jan Carlson
**Pr:* George Chang
**VP:* Henrik Arrland
**VP:* Steve Fredin
**VP:* Thomas Jnsson

D-U-N-S 07-685-4327 IMP/EXP
▲ AUTOLIV INC
3350 Airport Rd, Ogden, UT 84405-1563
Tel (801) 629-9800 *Founded/Ownrshp* 1953
Sales 9.1MMM *EMP* 54,600
Tkr Sym ALV *Exch* NYS
SIC 3714 Motor vehicle parts & accessories
Ch Bd: Jan Carlson
Pr: Chang Ket Leong
Pr: Frank Melzer
Pr: Jonas Nilsson
CFO: Mats Backman
VP: Henrik Arrland
VP: Lars A Sj Bring
VP: Jesse Crookston
VP: Karin Eliasson
VP: Steven Fredin
VP: Johan L Fvenholm
VP: Thomas Jonsson
VP: Johan Lofvenholm
VP: Svante Mogefors
VP: Lars Sjobring
Exec: Dave Allen
Board of Directors: Robert W Alspaugh, Leif Johansson, David E Kepler, James M Ringler, Wolfgang Ziebart

D-U-N-S 08-011-1853
■ AUTOLIV NISSIN BRAKE SYSTEMS AMERICA LLC
(Suby of AUTOLIV NORTH AMERICA) ★
2001 Industrial Dr, Findlay, OH 45840-5444
Tel (419) 425-6725 *Founded/Ownrshp* 2015
Sales 150.0MM *EMP* 450
SIC 3714 Motor vehicle brake systems & parts
Pr: Robert Bisciotti

AUTOLIV NORTH AMERICA
See AUTOLIV ASP INC

D-U-N-S 80-402-7142 IMP
AUTOMANN INC
AUTOMANN USA
850 Randolph Rd, Somerset, NJ 08873-1288
Tel (201) 529-4996 *Founded/Ownrshp* 1994
Sales 100.1MM^E *EMP* 250^E
SIC 5013 3715 Truck parts & accessories; Truck trailer chassis
Pr: Thanwant Khanduja
VP: C Khanduja
**VP:* Chiranjeev Khanduja
Genl Mgr: Verinder Caruso
Ql Cn Mgr: Guerrier Binot
Manager: Timothy Hubler

AUTOMANN USA
See AUTOMANN INC

D-U-N-S 08-482-6304 IMP/EXP
■ AUTOMATED LOGIC CORP
A L C
(Suby of UNITED TECHNOLOGIES CARRIER) ★
1150 Roberts Blvd Nw, Kennesaw, GA 30144-3618
Tel (770) 429-3000 *Founded/Ownrshp* 1980
Sales 162.5MM^E *EMP* 501
SIC 3822 Temperature controls, automatic
CEO: Mead Rusert
CFO: Marc Rosenberg
VP: George Biskup
VP: Troy Maeder
Ex Dir: Mitch Zawacki
Area Mgr: Bill Gregory
Snr Sftwr: Wayne Nelson
QA Dir: Darryl Hirschler
Dir IT: Ward Whitaker
Sftwr Eng: Owais Akbany
Sftwr Eng: Chris Hampton

D-U-N-S 07-674-2071 IMP
AUTOMATED PACKAGING SYSTEMS INC
10175 Philipp Pkwy, Streetsboro, OH 44241-4041
Tel (330) 528-2000 *Founded/Ownrshp* 1963
Sales 186.1MM^E *EMP* 700
SIC 3081 3565

D-U-N-S 62-510-4419
AUTOMATED RESOURCE MANAGEMENT ASSOCIATES INC
ARMA
962 Wayne Ave Ste 320, Silver Spring, MD 20910-4460
Tel (301) 587-7077 *Founded/Ownrshp* 1990
Sales 408.2MM *EMP* 35
SIC 7379 Computer related maintenance services
Pr: Tomi Bannister

D-U-N-S 15-693-5590
AUTOMATED TELECOMMUNICATION SERVICES LP
ATS CLOUD
13355 Noel Rd Ste 2100, Dallas, TX 75240-6837
Tel (972) 233-9614 *Founded/Ownrshp* 2000
Sales 85.9MM^E *EMP* 642
SIC 3572 Computer storage devices
Pr: Steve Levine
**Genl Pt:* Ats General LLC
**Pt:* Nathan A Levine
**COO:* Alex Shapira
**CFO:* Douglas K Bridges

D-U-N-S 00-191-5172
▲ AUTOMATIC DATA PROCESSING INC
ADP
1 Adp Blvd Ste 1, Roseland, NJ 07068-1728
Tel (973) 974-5000 *Founded/Ownrshp* 1949
Sales 11.6MMM *EMP* 55,000
Tkr Sym ADP *Exch* NGS
SIC 7374 Data processing & preparation; Data processing service
Pr: Carlos A Rodriguez
**Ch Bd:* John P Jones
Pr: John Ayala
Pr: Mark D Benjamin
Pr: Maria Black
Pr: Thomas Perrotti
Pr: Douglas Politi
Pr: Greg Rowe
CFO: Jan Siegmund
Treas: Michael C Eberhard
Bd of Dir: David Birsner
Bd of Dir: Joe Charielli
Ofcr: Joe Timko
Div VP: Chris Brantman
Div VP: Nancy McCarthy
Ex VP: Edward B Flynn III
VP: Jeffrey Abdool
VP: Chris Backer
VP: Christina Badawy
VP: David Blanchard
VP: Michael A Bonarti
Board of Directors: Peter Bisson, Richard T Clark, Eric C Fast, Linda R Gooden, R Glenn Hubbard, William J Ready

AUTOMATIC ROLLS OF NEW YORK
See NORTHEAST FOODS INC

D-U-N-S 00-214-1778 IMP
■ AUTOMATIC SWITCH CO (DE)
(Suby of EMERSON ELECTRIC (US) HOLDING CORP) ★
50-60 Hanover Rd, Florham Park, NJ 07932-1591
Tel (973) 966-2000 *Founded/Ownrshp* 1906
Sales 424.4MM^E *EMP* 2,000
SIC 3491 3625 3677 3674 3613 3492 Solenoid valves; Control equipment, electric; Electronic coils, transformers & other inductors; Semiconductors & related devices; Switchgear & switchboard apparatus; Fluid power valves & hose fittings
Pr: Jean-Pierre Yaouanc
Pr: Gregory C Schreiber
CFO: Michael Lefkowitz
VP: John Hanifin
VP: Don McCann
VP: Armand Visioli
VP Mktg: Jan Japushinsky
VP Sls: Bill Reagan

AUTOMATION CONTROLS DIRECT
See INNOVATIVE IDM LLC

D-U-N-S 78-625-8665
AUTOMATION PERSONNEL SERVICES INC
LAW MED PERSONNEL
401 Southgate Dr, Pelham, AL 35124-1186
Tel (205) 733-3700 *Founded/Ownrshp* 1990
Sales 182.0MM *EMP* 4,200
Accts Barfield Murphy Shank & Smit
SIC 7363 Temporary help service
Pr: Steve Nordness
COO: David Soileau
**VP:* Leslie Cannella Nordness
**VP:* Randy Watts
Brnch Mgr: Brigitte Jones
Brnch Mgr: Bethany Raygoza
Brnch Mgr: Theresa Rief
Brnch Mgr: Tracy Todd
Off Mgr: Carol Glass

D-U-N-S 62-221-7297 IMP
AUTOMATION TOOLING SYSTEMS INC
ATS OHIO
(Suby of ATS AUTOMATION TOOLING SYSTEMS INC)
425 Enterprise Dr, Lewis Center, OH 43035-9424
Tel (614) 781-8063 *Founded/Ownrshp* 1987
Sales 399.4MM^E *EMP* 3,500
SIC 3569 Assembly machines, non-metalworking; Robots, assembly line: industrial & commercial
Prin: Joe Moreno
Sr VP: Dawn Martinski
Genl Mgr: Wayne Uhl
Dir IT: Mike Picklesheimer
Manager: Steve Hoenig

D-U-N-S 80-993-9275 IMP
AUTOMATIONDIRECT.COM INC
(Suby of KOYO ELECTRONICS INDUSTRIES CO.,LTD.)
3505 Hutchinson Rd, Cumming, GA 30040-5860
Tel (770) 889-2858 *Founded/Ownrshp* 1993
Sales 126.1MM^E *EMP* 230^E
SIC 5084 Controlling instruments & accessories
CEO: Thomas C Hohmann
Software D: Renwei Liou
Sfty Dirs: Chris Adams
Sls&Mrk Ex: Joan Welty
Art Dir: Steve Emery

AUTOMBILE CLB INTR-NSRNCE EXCH
See CLUB EXCHANGE CORP

AUTOMBILE DRIVING INSTRUCTIONS
See MID-CITY TRUCK DRIVING ACADEMY INC

D-U-N-S 07-696-9369
AUTOMOBILE CLUB OF MISSOURI
AAA OF MISSOURI
12901 N 40 Dr, Saint Louis, MO 63141-8699
Tel (314) 523-7350 *Founded/Ownrshp* 1902
Sales 120.2MM^E *EMP* 1,200
Accts Ernst & Young Llp Los Angeles
SIC 8699 4724 Automobile owners' association; Travel agencies
Pr: Arthur W Johnson
**Pr:* James J McGrath
VP: Daniel Hill
Rgnl Mgr: Don Crutchfield
Dir IT: William Wolf
Sftwr Eng: Randall Karpan
VP Sls: Steve Schone

D-U-N-S 00-955-4429
AUTOMOBILE CLUB OF SOUTHERN CALIFORNIA
A A A AUTOMOBILE CLUB SO CAL
2601 S Figueroa St, Los Angeles, CA 90007-3294
Tel (213) 741-3686 *Founded/Ownrshp* 1900
Sales NA *EMP* 8,051
SIC 6411 8699 Insurance agents; Automobile owners' association
V Ch: Willis B Wood
**Pr:* Zoo Babies
**Sr VP:* Peter R McDonald
VP: Brian Deephouse
VP: Galen Grillo
Prgrm Mgr: Donna Pagliuca
Prgrm Mgr: Dave Skaien
Brnch Mgr: Nicholas Beas
IT Man: Paula Muscat
Software D: Jesse Waldrip
Netwrk Eng: Brian Holzinger

D-U-N-S 14-975-4731
■ AUTOMOBILE INSURANCE CO OF HARTFORD CONNECTICUT
(Suby of STANDARD FIRE INSURANCE CO) ★
1 Tower Sq, Hartford, CT 06183-0001
Tel (860) 277-0111 *Founded/Ownrshp* 1968
Sales NA *EMP* 27
SIC 6331 Automobile insurance
Pr: Robert Irving Lipp
**Ch:* Brian William Maclean
**Ex VP:* Charles Joseph Clarke
**Ex VP:* James David Gibbs
**Ex VP:* Joseph Patrick Kiernan
**Ex VP:* Glenn David Lammey
**Ex VP:* Robert Paul Restrepo Jr
**Ex VP:* Alan Mark Silberstein
**Sr VP:* Lames Michael Michener
**VP:* Ronald Edward Foley Jr
VP: James M Michener

D-U-N-S 14-759-2489
AUTOMOBILE PROTECTION CORP-APCO
6010 Atlantic Blvd, Norcross, GA 30071-1303
Tel (678) 225-1001 *Founded/Ownrshp* 1984
Sales NA *EMP* 385^E
SIC 6411 Insurance information & consulting services
Ch Bd: Larry I Dorfman
**Pr:* John E Lee
**COO:* Micheal Curran
**CFO:* John Marks
Dir IT: Monte Pinkett

D-U-N-S 07-942-3240
AUTOMOTIVE DISTRIBUTORS CO INC
AUTOMOTIVE DISTRIBUTORS WAREHO
2981 Morse Rd, Columbus, OH 43231-6098
Tel (614) 476-1315 *Founded/Ownrshp* 1985
Sales 115.4MM *EMP* 195
SIC 5013 Automotive supplies & parts
Pr: Robert I Yeoman
Treas: Joseph Clay
**VP:* Frank Schmidt
IT Man: Doug Biesinger
Opers Mgr: Jim Ballweg
Sales Exec: Ron Eikins
Sales Asso: Rich Raymond

AUTOMOTIVE DISTRIBUTORS WAREHO
See AUTOMOTIVE DISTRIBUTORS CO INC

D-U-N-S 17-735-3406
■ AUTOMOTIVE FINANCE CORP
(Suby of ADESA AUCTIONS) ★
13085 H Croning Blvd 3 Ste 300, Carmel, IN 46032
Tel (317) 815-9645 *Founded/Ownrshp* 1997
Sales NA *EMP* 488
SIC 6153 Short-term business credit
**Pr:* Jim Money
**CEO:* John Hammer
Sr VP: Joe Keadle
VP: Mark Nelson
VP: Howard Price
Rgnl Mgr: Rob Podshadley
Rgnl Mgr: Dave Roach
Area Mgr: Jim Oliver
Brnch Mgr: Bob Bumpus
Brnch Mgr: Ryan Mackert
VP Opers: Joel Garcia

AUTOMOTIVE GROUP
See ROBERT BOSCH LLC

D-U-N-S 18-108-4526 EXP
AUTOMOTIVE INVESTMENT GROUP INC
ABC NISSAN
1300 E Camelback Rd, Phoenix, AZ 85014-3312
Tel (602) 264-2332 *Founded/Ownrshp* 1986
Sales 122.6MM^E *EMP* 275^E
SIC 5511 Automobiles, new & used
Pr: Larry Van Tuyl
VP: Phil Brawner
**VP:* Patricia Van Tuyl
Genl Mgr: Jay Carley
Genl Mgr: Travis Holt
Sales Exec: Richard Sieck
VP Sls: Simon Thomas
Sls Mgr: Anthony Guerrero
Sls Mgr: Dave Warren

D-U-N-S 05-323-1515
AUTOMOTIVE LIGHTING LLC
AUTOMOTIVE LIGHTING NORTH AMER
(Suby of FIAT CHRYSLER AUTOMOBILES N.V.)
3900 Automation Ave, Auburn Hills, MI 48326-1788
Tel (248) 418-3000 *Founded/Ownrshp* 1998
Sales 120.0MM^E *EMP* 495
SIC 8711 3647 Engineering services; Headlights (fixtures), vehicular
Pr: Eugenio Razelli
Prgrm Mgr: Todd Henderson
Sls Mgr: Beatrix Sadek

AUTOMOTIVE LIGHTING NORTH AMER
See AUTOMOTIVE LIGHTING LLC

AUTOMOTIVE MFG & INDUS PDT
See FLORIDA PRODUCTION ENGINEERING INC

D-U-N-S 02-301-4343
AUTOMOTIVE PARTS HEADQUARTERS INC
CARQUEST
2959 Clearwater Rd, Saint Cloud, MN 56301-5950
Tel (320) 252-5411 *Founded/Ownrshp* 1976
Sales 296.3MM^E *EMP* 650
SIC 5013 Automotive supplies & parts
CEO: John P Bartlett
**Pr:* John P Bartlett Jr
**Treas:* Corey Bartlett
**VP:* Rita Bartlett
VP: Larry Lavigne
VP: Rich Vierkant
CIO: Dean Ritter
Info Man: John J Burski
Sls Dir: Phil Bahl

D-U-N-S 00-250-4553 EXP
AUTOMOTIVE RENTALS INC (NJ)
ARI-AUTOMOTIVE RESOURCES INTL
(Suby of HOLMAN FORD) ★
4001 Leadenhall Rd, Mount Laurel, NJ 08054-4611
Tel (856) 778-1500 *Founded/Ownrshp* 1948
Sales 285.2MM^E *EMP* 1,900
SIC 7513 7515 7549

AUTOMOTIVE SOLUTIONS GROUP
See A123 SYSTEMS LLC

D-U-N-S 60-638-0293
AUTOMOTIVE SUPPLY ASSOCIATES INC
SANEL AUTO PARTS
129 Manchester St, Concord, NH 03301-5100
Tel (603) 225-4000 *Founded/Ownrshp* 1945
Sales 189.5MM^E *EMP* 445
SIC 5013 7539 5531 5169 5015 Automotive supplies & parts; Machine shop, automotive; Automotive parts; Chemicals & allied products; Motor vehicle parts, used
Pr: David T Segal

Treas: Robert Segal
IT Man: Tom Piper

AUTOMOTIVE TRANSPORT TECH CTR
See UNITED ROAD SERVICES INC

AUTOMTIVE TRNSCTION SVCS GROUP
See TRINITY BAY CITY HOLDINGS LLC

AUTONATION CHEVROLET HIGHWAY 6
See MIKE HALL CHEVROLET INC

D-U-N-S 08-033-3424
■ **AUTONATION ENTERPRISES INC**
(*Suby of* AUTO HOLDING, LLC)
200 Sw 1st Ave Ste 1700, Fort Lauderdale, FL 33301-2074
Tel (954) 769-7000 *Founded/Ownrshp* 1995
Sales 3.9MMM^E *EMP* 8,000^E
SIC 5511 New & used car dealers
Bd of Dir: Donna L Parlapiano
VP: Denise Foley
VP: Scott May
Genl Mgr: Brandon Busse
Genl Mgr: Kevin Deporter
Genl Mgr: David Durrill
Genl Mgr: Leith Ledger
CIO: Mayra Regalado
Mktg Dir: Teri Suhyda
Sls Mgr: Tom Carlton
Sls Mgr: Jason Kirste

AUTONATION HONDA COLUMBUS
See GA H IMPORTS LLC

D-U-N-S 04-589-3054 IMP/EXP
▲ **AUTONATION INC**
200 Sw 1st Ave Ste 1700, Fort Lauderdale, FL 33301-2074
Tel (954) 769-6000 *Founded/Ownrshp* 1999
Sales 20.8MMM *EMP* 26,000
Accts Kpmg Llp Fort Lauderdale Flo
Tkr Sym AN *Exch* NYS
SIC 5511 5521 New & used car dealers; Used car dealers
Ch Bd: Michael J Jackson
COO: William R Berman
COO: Mike Sharp
CFO: Cheryl Miller
CFO: Brian Muff
CFO: Cheryl Scully
Ofcr: Guillermo Pernas
Ex VP: Roy Bridges
Ex VP: Jonathan P Ferrando
Ex VP: Kenneth Kirk
Ex VP: Charles Lydecker
Sr VP: David L Koehler
Sr VP: Alan J McLaren
Sr VP: Donna Parlapiano
Sr VP: Allan Stejskal
VP: Jill Bilanchone
VP: Christopher R Cade
Exec: Mike Brown
Exec: Michael Cunningham
Exec: John Morford
Comm Man: Jamie Levin
Board of Directors: Robert J Brown, Rick L Burdick, David B Edelson, Karen C Francis, Robert R Grusky, Michael Larson, Carlos A Migoya, G Mike Mikan, Alison H Rosenthal

D-U-N-S 08-033-3442
■ **AUTONATION MOTORS HOLDING CORP**
(*Suby of* AUTONATION INC) ★
200 Sw 1st Ave, Fort Lauderdale, FL 33301-1875
Tel (954) 769-7000 *Founded/Ownrshp* 2001
Sales 117.9MM^E *EMP* 300^E
SIC 5511 New & used car dealers

AUTONATION TOYOTA SPOKANE VLY
See APPLEWAY CHEVROLET INC

D-U-N-S 00-510-3874 IMP
AUTONEUM NORTH AMERICA INC
(*Suby of* AUTONEUM HOLDING AG)
38555 Hills Tech Dr, Farmington Hills, MI 48331-3423
Tel (570) 784-4100 *Founded/Ownrshp* 1995
Sales 552.1MM^E *EMP* 2,200
SIC 3714 Motor vehicle parts & accessories
Pr: Richard Derr
**CFO:* Robert Larney
**CFO:* John Lenga
**VP:* Timothy Judy
VP: Timothy J Judy
VP: Hameed Khan
**Prin:* Jian Pan
QC Dir: Tom Glavas
S&M/VP: Dan Dugan

AUTONOMY INTERWOVEN
See INTERWOVEN INC

AUTONTION CHVRLET PMBROKE PNES
See AN MOTORS OF PEMBROKE LLC

D-U-N-S 01-968-5767 IMP
■ **AUTOPART INTERNATIONAL INC**
(*Suby of* ADVANCE AUTO PARTS INC) ★
192 Mansfield Ave, Norton, MA 02766-1306
Tel (781) 784-1111 *Founded/Ownrshp* 1959
Sales 231.3MM^E *EMP* 1,735
SIC 5013 5531 Automotive supplies & parts; Automotive parts
CEO: James T Durkin
Pr: Mike Creedon
COO: Thomas M O'Reilly
**VP:* Michael A Norona
VP: Sarah E Powell
Brnch Mgr: Bill Oleksiak
Brnch Mgr: Michael Paulus
Dist Mgr: Hiram Cruz
Dist Mgr: Tom Fitzgerald
Dist Mgr: Troy Ginter
Dist Mgr: Kevin Williams
Board of Directors: Kevin P Freeland Chairman, Darren R Jackson, Roger A Patkin

D-U-N-S 96-876-9948
AUTOPARTS HOLDINGS LTD
1900 W Field Ct, Lake Forest, IL 60045-4828
Tel (203) 830-7800 *Founded/Ownrshp* 2011
Sales 105.3MM^E *EMP* 2,400
SIC 3714 Motor vehicle parts & accessories

AUTORDAD DE EDIFICIOS PUBLICOS
See PUBLIC BUILDING AUTHORITY

D-U-N-S 09-038-2854
AUTORIDAD DE ACUEDUCTOS Y ALCANTARILLADOS DE PR
PUERTO RICO AQEDUCT SEWER AUTH
604 Ave Barbosa, San Juan, PR 00917-4314
Tel (787) 620-2482 *Founded/Ownrshp* 1945
Sales NA *EMP* 7,000^E
SIC 9511
Ex Dir: Jorge Rodriguez

D-U-N-S 09-028-7293
AUTORIDAD DE CARRETERAS
Calle De Diego C, San Juan, PR 00923
Tel (787) 723-1390 *Founded/Ownrshp* 1965
Sales NA *EMP* 2,720
Accts Ernst & Young Llp Hato Rey P
SIC 9621 Bureau of public roads

AUTORIDAD DE PUERTOS DE PR
See PUERTO RICO PORTS AUTHORITY

D-U-N-S 09-014-4015
AUTORIDAD METROPOLITANA DE AUTOBUSES
(*Suby of* COMMONWEALTH OF PUERTO RICO) ★
Bo Monacillos 37 Ave De D 37th, San Juan, PR 00919
Tel (787) 767-7979 *Founded/Ownrshp* 1959
Sales 29.4MM^E *EMP* 1,050
Accts Pannell Kerr Forster Cpa
SIC 4111 Local & suburban transit
Pr: Adaline Torres Santiago

D-U-N-S 08-003-8926
AUTORIDAD PARA EL FINANCIAMIENTO DE LA VIVIENDA
AFI
Ave Barbosa 606pisos St Ave Barbo, Hato Rey, PR 00917
Tel (787) 765-7577 *Founded/Ownrshp* 2001
Sales 12.8MM^E *EMP* 2,000
SIC 7389 Financial services
Ex Dir: Jose Sierra

D-U-N-S 00-136-5865 IMP
AUTOSPLICE INC (NY)
10431 Wtridge Cir Ste 110, San Diego, CA 92121
Tel (858) 535-0077 *Founded/Ownrshp* 1954
Sales 103.2MM^E *EMP* 800
SIC 3643 Electric connectors
CEO: Santosh RAO
**COO:* Kevin Barry
**CFO:* Jeffrey Cartwright
Dir IT: Brendan Lydon
Ql Cn Mgr: Mark Saunders
**VP Mktg:* Ken Krone
Sls Mgr: Bob Autosplice
Sls Mgr: Tony Autosplice

D-U-N-S 03-801-7406 IMP
■ **AUTOTOTE SYSTEMS INC**
SCIENTIFIC GAMES AND RACING
(*Suby of* SCIENTIFIC GAMES CORP) ★
1500 Bluegrass Lakes Pkwy, Alpharetta, GA 30004-7712
Tel (770) 664-3700 *Founded/Ownrshp* 1989
Sales 130.1MM^E *EMP* 1,300
SIC 3578 7373 7359 8711 Betting machines, pari-mutuel; Computer integrated systems design; Business machine & electronic equipment rental services; Engineering services
VP: Jerry Scheinbach
CTO: Glenn Kelling
IT Man: Dave Lane

D-U-N-S 04-101-0682
AUTOTRADER.COM INC (GA)
COX AUTOMOTIVE
(*Suby of* COX ENTERPRISES INC) ★
3003 Summit Blvd Fl 200, Brookhaven, GA 30319-1469
Tel (404) 568-8000 *Founded/Ownrshp* 1997
Sales 1.0MMM^E *EMP* 3,100
SIC 5521 Used car dealers
CEO: Sandy Schwartz
**Pr:* Jared Rowe
**CEO:* Victor A Perry IV
COO: Alan Smith
CFO: Dallas S Clement
**Sr VP:* James Franchi
Sr VP: Steven A Smith
**VP:* David B Amundsen
VP: Peter C Cassat
Dir Bus: Jeff Carter
Genl Mgr: Rob Huting

D-U-N-S 15-723-3511
▲ **AUTOZONE INC**
123 S Front St, Memphis, TN 38103-3618
Tel (901) 495-6500 *Founded/Ownrshp* 1979
Sales 10.6MMM *EMP* 81,000
Accts Ernst & Young Llp Memphis Te
Tkr Sym AZO *Exch* NYS
SIC 5531 5734 Automotive parts; Automotive accessories; Software, business & non-game
Ch Bd: William C Rhodes III
CFO: William T Giles
Ex VP: Mark Finestone
Ex VP: Bill Graves
Ex VP: Thomas B Newbern
Ex VP: Tom Newbern
Sr VP: Phil Daniele
Sr VP: Mark A Finestone
Sr VP: Ronald B Griffin
Sr VP: Bill Hackney
Sr VP: Rod Halsell
Sr VP: Charlie Pleas III
Sr VP: Larry M Roesel
Sr VP: Albert Saltiel
Sr VP: Rick Smith
Sr VP: Daisy L Vanderlinde
Sr VP: Michael A Womack
Sr VP: Kristen C Wright
VP: Jon Bascom
VP: William W Graves
Board of Directors: Douglas H Brooks, Linda A Goodspeed, Sue E Gove, Earl G Graves Jr, H R Hyde III, D Bryan Jordan, W Andrew McKenna, George R Mrkonic Jr, Luis P Nieto

AUTUMN CARE
See AUTUMN CORP

D-U-N-S 09-511-6455
AUTUMN CORP
AUTUMN CARE
451 N Winstead Ave, Rocky Mount, NC 27804-2230
Tel (252) 443-6265 *Founded/Ownrshp* 1979
Sales 37.8M *EMP* 2,600
SIC 8059 8051 Nursing home, except skilled & intermediate care facility; Extended care facility
Pr: Gerald P Cox
**VP:* Sam Marsh
IT Man: Irene Westall
VP Opers: Steve Haggerty

D-U-N-S 12-454-0944 IMP
AUX SABLE LIQUID PRODUCTS LP
6155 E Us Route 6, Morris, IL 60450-9020
Tel (815) 941-5800 *Founded/Ownrshp* 1997
Sales 96.0MM^E *EMP* 90
SIC 1321 Natural gas liquids production
Pt: William McAdam
**Pt:* Katherine Dodds
COO: Jeff White
CFO: Clint White
Sfty Dirs: Dave Skaggs
Sfty Mgr: Jeffery Finch
Plnt Mgr: Dean Hudson
Sales Exec: Mike Vanwinkle

AUXI HEALTH
See HARDEN HOME HEALTH LLC

D-U-N-S 96-965-1194
AUXILIARY BOARD OF FAIRVIEW GENERAL HOSPITAL
(*Suby of* CLEVELAND CLINIC HEALTH SYSTEM) ★
18101 Lorain Ave, Cleveland, OH 44111-5612
Tel (216) 476-7000 *Founded/Ownrshp* 2011
Sales 62.0M *EMP* 1,256^E
SIC 8062 General medical & surgical hospitals

D-U-N-S 01-075-6278
AUXILIARY SERVICES STATE UNIVERSITY COLLEGE AT OSWEGO INC
VENDING SERVICES
7060 Route 104, Oswego, NY 13126
Tel (315) 312-2106 *Founded/Ownrshp* 1951
Sales 26.4MM *EMP* 1,013
Accts Dermody Burke & Brown Cpas Llc
SIC 5812 5942 5962 5441 Cafeteria; College book stores; Food vending machines; Candy
Pr: Deborah F Stanley

D-U-N-S 61-475-2728
AUXILIO MUTUO HOSPITAL
TRANSPLANT SOCIETY
735 Ave Ponce De Leon, San Juan, PR 00917-5022
Tel (787) 761-6600 *Founded/Ownrshp* 2005
Sales 224.7MM *EMP* 6
SIC 8011 8062 Offices & clinics of medical doctors; General medical & surgical hospitals
Pr: Eduardo A Santiago Delpin

D-U-N-S 00-774-6469
AUXILIUM PHARMACEUTICALS INC
(*Suby of* ENDO INTERNATIONAL PUBLIC LIMITED COMPANY)
1400 Atwater Dr, Malvern, PA 19355-8701
Tel (484) 321-5900 *Founded/Ownrshp* 1999, 2015
Sales 208.1MM^E *EMP* 639^E
SIC 2834 Pharmaceutical preparations; Hormone preparations
Pr: Adrian Adams
**CFO:* Andrew Saik
**Chf Mktg O:* James P Tursi
Ex VP: Andrew Koven
Sr VP: Benjamin Deltito
Sr VP: Mark A Glickman
VP: Betty Jean
Assoc Dir: Brian Cohen
Assoc Dir: Diane McCaul
Ex Dir: Jason Krentz
Area Mgr: Daniel R Bennett

D-U-N-S 07-943-4175
AV COOLING SOLUTIONS INC
AV COOLING SUPPLY
803 E Donegan Ave, Kissimmee, FL 34744-1938
Tel (407) 572-8739 *Founded/Ownrshp* 2013
Sales 150.0MM *EMP* 1
SIC 5999 Alcoholic beverage making equipment & supplies
Pr: Mayra Hernandez-Rodriguez
**VP:* Benjamin Hernandez-Hernandez

AV COOLING SUPPLY
See AV COOLING SOLUTIONS INC

D-U-N-S 04-526-0007
▲ **AV HOMES INC**
8601 N Scottsdale Rd # 220, Scottsdale, AZ 85253-2727
Tel (480) 214-7400 *Founded/Ownrshp* 1970
Sales 517.7MM *EMP* 308
Accts Ernst & Young Llp Phoenix Ar
Tkr Sym AVHI *Exch* NGS
SIC 1531 Operative builders
Pr: Roger A Cregg
CFO: Michael S Burnett
Ex VP: Michael F Levy
Ex VP: Joseph C Mulac III
Ex VP: S Gary Shullaw
VP: Lucas Morris

D-U-N-S 82-850-4431
AV THOMAS PRODUCE INC
3900 Sultana Ave, Atwater, CA 95301-9605
Tel (209) 394-7514 *Founded/Ownrshp* 1960
Sales 85.1MM *EMP* 8
Accts Atherton & Associates Llp Mod
SIC 0161 Vegetables & melons
CFO: Dana Miller
VP: Carlos Vieira
**VP:* Rick Vieira

D-U-N-S 17-512-1078
AVA PORK PRODUCTS INC
383 W John St Unit A, Hicksville, NY 11801-1046
Tel (516) 750-1500 *Founded/Ownrshp* 1984
Sales 214.2MM^E *EMP* 300
Accts Grassi & Co Cpas Pc Jericho
SIC 5147 Meat brokers
CEO: Albert L Girgenti
**Pr:* Mark Greenberg
**CFO:* Stephen O'Donnel
**CFO:* Mark Small
**Ex VP:* Leonard Lombardi
VP: Domenic Capul

D-U-N-S 60-313-2460 IMP/EXP
AVAD LLC
5805 Sepulvda Blvd # 750, Sherman Oaks, CA 91411-2546
Tel (818) 742-4800 *Founded/Ownrshp* 2016
Sales 444.4MM^E *EMP* 400
SIC 5065 7359 Electronic parts; Audio-visual equipment & supply rental
CEO: Tom Jacoby
Pr: Fred Farrar
CFO: Kurt Kilgast
Sr Cor Off: Bob Rossum
Ex VP: Wally Whinna
VP: Lindsay Davis
Brnch Mgr: Tom Aird
Brnch Mgr: Mike Hanrahan
Brnch Mgr: Keith Steinkoenig
Sales Asso: Mark Smith

D-U-N-S 60-837-4406
AVAGO TECHNOLOGIES US INC
1320 Ridder Park Dr, San Jose, CA 95131-2313
Tel (800) 433-8778 *Founded/Ownrshp* 2005
Sales 318.6MM^E *EMP* 5,272
SIC 3674 Semiconductors & related devices; Semiconductor diodes & rectifiers; Integrated circuits, semiconductor networks, etc.
Pr: Hock E Tan
**Ch Bd:* Dick Chang
**CFO:* Douglas R Bettinger
Treas: Boon Ooi
**Sr VP:* Jeff Henderson
**Sr VP:* Bryan Ingram
VP: Dave Allen
**VP:* Tze Siong Chong
**VP:* Philip Gadd
**VP:* Fatt Lun Ho
**VP:* Hassan Hussain
VP: Todd Metcalf
VP: Chong Mien
VP: Andy Nallappan
VP: Ivy Pong
Board of Directors: Simon E Brown, Adam H Clammer, James A Davidson, Kenneth Hao

D-U-N-S 61-071-9465
AVAGO TECHNOLOGIES WIRELESS (USA) INC
BROADCOM
4380 Ziegler Rd, Fort Collins, CO 80525-9790
Tel (970) 288-2575 *Founded/Ownrshp* 2005
Sales 1.2MMM^E *EMP* 5,272
SIC 3674 Semiconductors & related devices
CEO: Hock E Tan
Pr: Greg Dix
**COO:* Brian Ingram
**CFO:* Anthony Maslowski
**Sr VP:* Boon Chye Ooi
**VP:* Tze Siong Chong
Dir IT: David Leary
Opers Mgr: Eric Griego
Opers Mgr: Troy Sterk
Snr Mgr: Toni Bermudez

D-U-N-S 00-503-6722 IMP
AVALANCHE STRATEGIES LLC
THINK FASTTOYS.COM
144 Dixon St, Selbyville, DE 19975-3053
Tel (302) 436-7060 *Founded/Ownrshp* 2012
Sales 158.6MM^E *EMP* 180
SIC 5092 5945 Toys & hobby goods & supplies; Toys & games
CEO: William Spraul
**Pr:* Stu Eisenman
COO: Cyrus Giroir
**VP:* Felecia Benzakan
**VP:* Cyrus Jiroir
**VP:* Ksenia Litvinova

D-U-N-S 17-311-1365 IMP
AVALON APPAREL LLC
2520 W 6th St Ste 101, Los Angeles, CA 90057-3177
Tel (323) 581-3511 *Founded/Ownrshp* 2004
Sales 100.0MM^E *EMP* 175
SIC 2361 Girls' & children's dresses, blouses & shirts

AVALON FLOORING
See SOVEREIGN DISTRIBUTORS INC

D-U-N-S 01-807-2678
AVALON FOODSERVICE INC (OH)
1 Avalon Dr, Canal Fulton, OH 44614-8893
Tel (330) 854-4551 *Founded/Ownrshp* 1957, 1995
Sales 188.3MM^E *EMP* 120
SIC 5142 5149 5169 5113 8322 5812 Packaged frozen goods; Canned goods: fruit, vegetables, seafood, meats, etc.; Chemicals & allied products; Industrial & personal service paper; Individual & family services; Eating places
Pr: Andrew Schroer
Pr: Jeff Fix
Pr: John Holdren
Pr: Tim Weisend
Ex VP: Keith Kilgore
VP: Jeff Cockerham
VP: Alan Dade
VP: Alan Durell
VP: Len Meuti
VP: Dave Soos

VP: Scott Van Spaaentak
VP: Doug Yaecker

AVALON HEALTH CARE GROUP
See AVALON HEALTH CARE INC

D-U-N-S 14-501-7443
AVALON HEALTH CARE INC
AVALON HEALTH CARE GROUP
206 N 2100 W Ste 300, Salt Lake City, UT 84116-4741
Tel (801) 596-8844 Founded/Ownrshp 1988
Sales 491.1MM[E] EMP 3,900
SIC 8741 8051 Nursing & personal care facility management; Skilled nursing care facilities
CEO: Randy Kirton
Pr: Kirton Hyrum
CFO: Thomas E Pagt
*CFO: Anne Stuart
Sr Cor Off: James Mason
*Ofcr: Nate Ruden
*Sr VP: Scott Carpenter
*VP: William Di Sera
*VP: Christie Franklin
*VP: Linda Gaddie
*VP: Nani Gray
VP: Schuyler Hollingsworth
VP: Faye Lincoln
*VP: Denis Morrill
VP: Matthew Strange

AVALON PROPERTIES
See AVALONBAY COMMUNITIES INC

AVALON WATERWAYS
See GROUP VOYAGERS INC

D-U-N-S 10-210-1557
▲ AVALONBAY COMMUNITIES INC
AVALON PROPERTIES
671 N Glebe Rd Ste 800, Arlington, VA 22203-2138
Tel (703) 329-6300 Founded/Ownrshp 1995
Sales 1.8MMM EMP 2,981
Tkr Sym AVB Exch NYS
SIC 6798 Real estate investment trusts
Ch Bd: Timothy J Naughton
COO: Sean J Breslin
CFO: Kevin P Oshea
Chf Inves: Matthew H Birenbaum
Ofcr: Leo S Horey
Ex VP: Michael M Feigin
Ex VP: Matthew Fry
Ex VP: William M McLaughlin
Ex VP: Charlene Rothkopf
Ex VP: Edward M Schulman
Ex VP: Stephen W Wilson
Sr VP: Sean Clark
Sr VP: James R Liberty
Sr VP: J Richard Morris
Sr VP: Kevin P O'Shea
VP: Frederick Harris
VP: Sarah Mathewson
VP: Christopher Payne
Board of Directors: Glyn F Aeppel, Terry S Brown, Alan B Buckelew, Lance R Primis, Peter S Rummell, H Jay Sarles, W Edward Walter

D-U-N-S 00-323-1797
AVAMERE HEALTH SERVICES LLC
25115 Sw Parkway Ave A, Wilsonville, OR 97070-8891
Tel (503) 570-3405 Founded/Ownrshp 1996
Sales 353.6MM[E] EMP 3,000
SIC 8741 8051 8052 8093 Nursing & personal care facility management; Skilled nursing care facilities; Intermediate care facilities; Specialty outpatient clinics
CEO: Rick Miller
*CEO: John Morgan
*CFO: Ron Odermott
CTO: Adam Beyer
Pr Dir: Beverly Glas
Pr Dir: Candice Marcks
HC Dir: Bill Macy

D-U-N-S 13-693-7104
AVANADE INC
(Suby of ACCENTURE LLP) ★
818 Stewart St Ste 400, Seattle, WA 98101-3332
Tel (206) 239-5600 Founded/Ownrshp 2000
Sales 672.0MM[E] EMP 3,900[E]
SIC 7379 8742 ; Management information systems consultant
CEO: Adam Warby
*Ch Bd: Paul Daugherty
*Pr: Tyson Hartman
*Pr: Ian Jordan
Pr: Aziz Virani
*COO: Dave Seybold
*CFO: Ken Guthrie
CFO: Steve Wolf
*Chf Mktg O: Stella Goulet
Ex VP: Stephen Kelly
Ex VP: Joe Mendel
Ex VP: David Oskandy
Sr VP: Scott Rodgers
VP: Mark Barrett
VP: Tom Bishop
VP: Patrick Cimprich
VP: Alexander Eck
VP: Stephen Gallagher
VP: Erika B King
VP: Sung Lee
VP: Yoonsung Lee
Board of Directors: Judson Althoff, Pamela J Craig, Basilio Rueda, Michael J Salvino, Simon Witts

D-U-N-S 05-284-6614
AVANGATE INC
3500 Lenox Rd Ne Ste 710, Atlanta, GA 30326-4229
Tel (650) 249-5280 Founded/Ownrshp 2013
Sales 89.8MM[E] EMP 250
SIC 7373 Value-added resellers, computer systems
CEO: Alex Hart
*CFO: Jeff Hodges
*CFO: Gregor Morela
*Treas: James Bryant
Sr VP: Len Eschweiler
Sr VP: John Keating
*Dir Risk M: Erich Litch

D-U-N-S 00-697-7763
■ AVANGRID INC
(Suby of IBERDROLA, SOCIEDAD ANONIMA)
157 Church St, New Haven, CT 06510-2100
Tel (207) 688-6363 Founded/Ownrshp 2008
Sales 4.3MMM EMP 6,809
Accts Ernst & Young Llp New York
Tkr Sym AGR Exch NYS
SIC 4911 4922 4924 Distribution, electric power; Generation, electric power; Transmission, electric power; Natural gas transmission; Natural gas distribution
CEO: James P Torgerson
*Ch Bd: Ignacio Sanchez Galan
Pr: Robert D Kump
CEO: Frank Burkhartsmeyer
CFO: Richard J Nicholas
Chf Cred: R Scott Mahoney
Sr VP: Daniel Alcain
Sr VP: Sheila Duncan
Sr VP: Ignacio Estella
Board of Directors: Juan Carlos Rebollo Liceag, Jose Sainz Armada, Alan D Solomont, Alfredo Elias Ayub, Elizabeth Timm, John E Baldacci, Pedro Azagra Blazquez, Arnold L Chase, Felipe De Jesus Calderon H, Carol L Folt, Santiago Martinez Garrido, John L Lahey

D-U-N-S 83-264-2693
■ AVANGRID RENEWABLES HOLDINGS INC
AVANGRID RNWABLES HOLDINGS INC
(Suby of IBERDROLA, SOCIEDAD ANONIMA)
1125 Nw Couch St Ste 700, Portland, OR 97209-4129
Tel (503) 796-7000 Founded/Ownrshp 2003
Sales 236.5MM[E] EMP 220[E]
SIC 4932 4931 Gas & other services combined; Electric & other services combined
Pr: Martin Mugica

D-U-N-S 94-737-6422 IMP
■ AVANGRID RENEWABLES LLC
IBERDROLA RENEWABLES, LLC
(Suby of AVANGRID RNWABLES HOLDINGS INC) ★
1125 Nw Couch St Ste 700, Portland, OR 97209-4129
Tel (503) 796-7179 Founded/Ownrshp 2007
Sales 236.3MM[E] EMP 220[E]
SIC 4932 4931 Gas & other services combined; Electric & other services combined
Pr: Martin Mugica
Pr: John McStravick
*CEO: Frank Burkhartsmeyer
VP: Gene Jensen
VP: Mary Smith
VP: Barrett Stambler
VP Bus Dev: Rany Raviv
Dir Risk M: Alfred Frakes
Mng Dir: John Hull
Mng Dir: Dickson Koo
Mng Dir: Gareth Walker

AVANGRID RNWABLES HOLDINGS INC
See AVANGRID RENEWABLES HOLDINGS INC

D-U-N-S 19-841-3080
AVANIR PHARMACEUTICALS INC
(Suby of OTSUKA PHARMACEUTICAL CO., LTD.)
30 Enterprise Ste 400, Aliso Viejo, CA 92656-7114
Tel (949) 389-6700 Founded/Ownrshp 2015
Sales 136.8MM[E] EMP 484[E]
SIC 2834 Pharmaceutical preparations
Pr: Rohan Palekar
Sr VP: Gregory J Flesher
Sr VP: Richard Malamut
Sr VP: Michael E McFadden
Sr VP: Joao Siffert
VP: Jim Beitel
VP: Gregory Flesher
Assoc Dir: Tom Witt
IT Man: Michael Cruse
Sls Mgr: Christie Thibault
Snr Mgr: Keith Katkin
Board of Directors: Keith A Katkin, Robert S Sedor

AVANT CREDIT
See AVANT INC

D-U-N-S 07-937-2638
AVANT INC
AVANT CREDIT
222 N Lsalle St Ste 1700, Chicago, IL 60601
Tel (312) 448-8685 Founded/Ownrshp 1993
Sales NA EMP 450[E]
SIC 6141 Personal credit institutions
Pr: Albert Goldstein
*CFO: Suketu Shaah
*Chf Cred: John Sun
VP: Robert Levy
VP: Raj Vora
Exec: Suketu Shah
Dept Mgr: Michael Ehrlichman
Dept Mgr: John Lanctot
QA Dir: Maja Grzeszkowiak
Mktg Dir: Donald Richman
Mktg Mgr: Caroline Wetmore
Board of Directors: Sheila Bair

D-U-N-S 00-946-3507
AVANTI HEALTH SYSTEM LLC (NV)
222 N Sepulveda Blvd # 950, El Segundo, CA 90245-5627
Tel (310) 356-0550 Founded/Ownrshp 2008
Sales 123.9MM[E] EMP 446[E]
SIC 8742 Hospital & health services consultant

D-U-N-S 92-781-9359
AVANTI HEALTH SYSTEMS INC
300 Villa Dr, Hurley, WI 54534-1523
Tel (715) 561-3200 Founded/Ownrshp 1985
Sales 27.6MM[E] EMP 1,200
SIC 8399 Health systems agency
Prin: Lawrence Kutz Jr
*Prin: Joe Simonich

D-U-N-S 07-828-3375
AVANTI HOSPITALS LLC
222 N Splvd Blvd Ste 950, El Segundo, CA 90245
Tel (310) 356-0550 Founded/Ownrshp 2011
Sales 139.1MM[E] EMP 2,000
SIC 7011 Hotels & motels
CEO: Edward Mirzibergin
*Owner: Hollister Holdings
*Prin: Poe Corn
*Prin: Jamey Edwards
*Prin: Joel Freedman
*Prin: Jamie Macpherson

D-U-N-S 07-861-1762
AVANTOR PERFORMANCE MATERIALS HOLDINGS LLC
3477 Corp Pkwy Ste 200, Center Valley, PA 18034
Tel (610) 573-2600 Founded/Ownrshp 2010
Sales 80.8MM[E] EMP 1,701
SIC 2819 Chemicals, high purity: refined from technical grade
CEO: Michael Stubblefield
Ch Bd: Rajiv L Gupta
*CFO: Mark P Armstrong
Ex VP: Bjorn Hofman
Ex VP: Dawn Howard
Ex VP: Ashish K Kulkarni
Ex VP: Devashish Ohri
Ex VP: Corey Walker

D-U-N-S 00-121-3487 IMP/EXP
AVANTOR PERFORMANCE MATERIALS INC
3477 Corp Pkwy Ste 200, Center Valley, PA 18034
Tel (610) 573-2600 Founded/Ownrshp 2010
Sales 436.2MM[E] EMP 1,700
SIC 2819 Chemicals, high purity: refined from technical grade
CEO: Michael Stubblefield
Ch Bd: Rajiv L Gupta
COO: Bjorn Hofman
CFO: Richard Gaynor
Ofcr: Roland Ae Heinrich
Ofcr: Barbara Ring
Ex VP: Helen Evans
Ex VP: Devashish Ohri
Ex VP: Michael F Rettig
Ex VP: Marc Strijbos
Ex VP: Richard White
VP: Steve Daley
VP: Jeremy How
VP: Roger K McFillin
VP: Paul Smaltz
Board of Directors: David Julien

D-U-N-S 07-974-1030
AVANZAR INTERIOR SYSTEMS LLC
(Suby of ADIENT US LLC) ★
1 Lone Star Pass Bldg 41, San Antonio, TX 78264-3645
Tel (210) 271-2400 Founded/Ownrshp 2016
Sales 101.4MM[E] EMP 7[E]
SIC 5013 Automotive supplies & parts

D-U-N-S 17-170-8485 IMP
AVANZAR INTERIOR TECHNOLOGIES LTD
(Suby of AVANZAR INTERIOR SYSTEMS LLC) ★
1 Lone Star Pass Bldg 41, San Antonio, TX 78264-3645
Tel (210) 271-2300 Founded/Ownrshp 2016
Sales 101.4MM[E] EMP 6
SIC 3559 Automotive related machinery
Pt: Henry Cisneros
Pt: Miguel Alvarez
Pt: Heriberto Guerra Jr
Pt: Oliver Isaac
Pt: Brian Kesseler
Pt: Victor Miramontes
Pt: John T Tauer
Pt: Paul Van Hoof
Pt: Keith Wandell

D-U-N-S 80-828-4181
AVAYA HOLDINGS CORP
4655 Great America Pkwy, Santa Clara, CA 95054-1233
Tel (908) 953-6000 Founded/Ownrshp 2007
Sales 4.0MMM EMP 11,701[E]
Accts Pricewaterhousecoopers Llp Fl
SIC 3661 7372 Telephone & telegraph apparatus; Telephones & telephone apparatus; Telephone dialing devices, automatic; Prepackaged software
Pr: Kevin J Kennedy
*Ch Bd: Charles H Giancarlo
CFO: David Vellequette
Chf Mktg O: Morag Lucey
Sr VP: Fariborz Ebrahimi
Sr VP: Amy Fliegelman Olli

D-U-N-S 12-533-7134 IMP/EXP
AVAYA INC
(Suby of AVAYA HOLDINGS CORP) ★
4655 Great America Pkwy, Santa Clara, CA 95054-1233
Tel (908) 953-6000 Founded/Ownrshp 2007
Sales 4.0MMM EMP 11,701
SIC 3661 7372 7371 Telephone & telegraph apparatus; Business oriented computer software; Custom computer programming services
Pr: Kevin J Kennedy
*Ch Bd: Charles H Giancarlo
CFO: David Vellequette
Ex VP: James M Chirico Jr
Sr VP: Gary E Barnett
Sr VP: Amy Fliegelman Olli
Sr VP: Laurent Philonenko
Sr VP: Marc J Randall
VP: Mark Castleman
VP: Jerry Dotson
VP: Daniel Kovacs
VP: Dave Vellequette
VP: Terri Zimmerman
Board of Directors: Mary Henry, John W Marren, Greg K Mondre, Ronald Rittenmeyer, Gary B Smith

D-U-N-S 01-486-7154
■ AVB INC
NATURE BAKE
(Suby of FLOWERS FOODS INC) ★
5209 Se International Way, Portland, OR 97222-4603
Tel (503) 335-8077 Founded/Ownrshp 2015
Sales 104.0MM[E] EMP 300
SIC 2051 2052 Bakery: wholesale or wholesale/retail combined; Bread, all types (white, wheat, rye, etc): fresh or frozen; Cookies & crackers
Pr: John Tucker

AVC
See AUDIO VIDEO COLOR CORP

AVD
See AMERICAN VANGUARD CORP

D-U-N-S 07-135-2058 IMP
■ AVEDA CORP
AVEDA EXPERIENCE CENTRES
(Suby of ESTEE LAUDER COMPANIES INC) ★
4000 Pheasant Ridge Dr Ne, Blaine, MN 55449-7106
Tel (763) 783-4250 Founded/Ownrshp 1997
Sales 17.8MM[E] EMP 1,700
SIC 2844 7231 Shampoos, rinses, conditioners: hair; Face creams or lotions; Lipsticks; Perfumes, natural or synthetic; Cosmetology school
Pr: Dominique Consiel
Treas: Terence R Stack
Sr VP: Charles Weaver
VP: Harish Bhandari
VP: Ben Melendez
VP: Russ Moorehead
VP: Sue Trondson
Creative D: Ricardo Dinis
Ex Dir: Susan Headley
Ex Dir: Angie Nieland
Dir IT: Sandy Collins

AVEDA EXPERIENCE CENTRES
See AVEDA CORP

D-U-N-S 04-950-3949
AVEMCO CORP
AVEMCO GROUP
(Suby of TOKIO MARINE HCC) ★
8490 Progress Dr Ste 100, Frederick, MD 21701-4994
Tel (301) 694-5700 Founded/Ownrshp 1997
Sales NA EMP 480
SIC 6331 6321 6399 6411 7372 Fire, marine & casualty insurance; Accident & health insurance; Deposit insurance; Insurance claim adjusters, not employed by insurance company; Prepackaged software
Pr: Michael Schell
Board of Directors: Michael Collins, H Lowell Davis, J Hanna, Arnold H Johnson, Steve Markel, Thomas J Schwab, Rachel Trender

AVEMCO GROUP
See AVEMCO CORP

D-U-N-S 05-442-5293
AVEMCO INSURANCE CO (MD)
(Suby of AVEMCO GROUP) ★
8490 Progress Dr Ste 100, Frederick, MD 21701-4994
Tel (301) 694-5700 Founded/Ownrshp 1960
Sales NA EMP 195
SIC 6321 6331 Accident & health insurance; Fire, marine & casualty insurance
Pr: Michael J Schell
CFO: Edward H Ellis
Exec: Linda Eyler
IT Man: Tom Fraley

D-U-N-S 00-933-7895
AVENDRA LLC
AVENDRA REPLENISHMENT
702 King Farm Blvd # 600, Rockville, MD 20850-5842
Tel (301) 825-0500 Founded/Ownrshp 2000
Sales 96.1MM[E] EMP 230[E]
SIC 8741 Management services
Pr: Dennis Baker
*COO: Wolfram Schaefer
*CFO: Robert Heaton
*Sr VP: Eileen Adenan
*Sr VP: Jerome J Kraisinger
*Sr VP: Walt Sheffler
VP: Ed Hawkins
VP: Sally Martin
VP: George Pfeiffer
VP: Herman Schumacher
VP: Craig Selwitz
VP: Mike Shutts
VP: Eleanor Waddell

AVENDRA REPLENISHMENT
See AVENDRA LLC

D-U-N-S 78-122-9872
■ AVENTINE RENEWABLE ENERGY HOLDINGS LLC
(Suby of PACIFIC ETHANOL INC) ★
1300 S 2nd St, Pekin, IL 61554-5402
Tel (309) 347-9200 Founded/Ownrshp 2015
Sales 93.5MM[E] EMP 348[E]
SIC 2869 Ethyl alcohol, ethanol
CEO: Mark Beemer
CFO: Brian Steenhard

AVENTINE RNWBLE ENRGY HOLDINGS
See PACIFIC ETHANOL PEKIN INC

D-U-N-S 78-732-1004 IMP
AVENTIS INC
(Suby of SANOFI)
55 Corporate Dr, Bridgewater, NJ 08807-1265
Tel (800) 981-2491 Founded/Ownrshp 2006
Sales 511.0MM[E] EMP 1,358
SIC 2834 Pharmaceutical preparations
Pr: Joseph Palladino
*Treas: Richard Thomson
*VP: Gregory Irace
Netwrk Mgr: Stewart Samuels

AVENTURA HOSPITAL AND MED CTR
See MIAMI BEACH HEALTHCARE GROUP LTD

D-U-N-S 82-794-4526
AVENUE CAPITAL GROUP LLC
399 Park Ave Fl 6, New York, NY 10022-5074
Tel (212) 878-3500 Founded/Ownrshp 2001
Sales 122.1MM[E] EMP 250[E]
SIC 6282 6159 Investment advice; Finance leasing, vehicles: except automobiles & trucks
CEO: Marc Lasry
Ofcr: Ty Oyer

Ofcr: Eric Ross
VP: Nish Arnold
VP: David Leinwand
VP: Neil Mahajan
VP: Kiran Ramineni
VP: Trent Spiridellis
VP: Matt Stuparidge
Prin: David K Martin
Prin: Robert J Martin

D-U-N-S 07-845-8381 IMP
AVENUE STORES LLC
(*Suby of* VERSA CAPITAL MANAGEMENT LLC) ★
365 W Passaic St Ste 230, Rochelle Park, NJ 07662-3017
Tel (201) 845-0880 *Founded/Ownrshp* 2012
Sales 405.7MM[E] *EMP* 3,000
SIC 5621 Ready-to-wear apparel, women's
CEO: Elizabeth Williams
Sls Dir: Garrett Regelman

D-U-N-S 03-077-1583
AVEPOINT INC
3 Plaza Ten, Jersey City, NJ 07311-1116
Tel (201) 793-1111 *Founded/Ownrshp* 1999
Sales 72.0MM *EMP* 1,400
SIC 7371 Computer software development; Computer software systems analysis & design, custom
CEO: Kai Gong
COO: Ken Shiomitsu
CFO: Jim Caci
Sr VP: WEI Chen
VP: Taylor Davenport
VP: Sabrina Deoliveira
VP: Chris Foreman
VP: John Hodges
VP: John Peluso
VP: Sarju Raja
VP: Dana Simberkoff
VP: Randy Wang
VP: Dylan Zhang

D-U-N-S 12-201-2529
AVERA HEALTH
3900 W Avera Dr, Sioux Falls, SD 57108-5717
Tel (605) 322-4700 *Founded/Ownrshp* 1982
Sales 134.8MM *EMP* 2,450
Accts Eide Badly Llp Minneapolis M
SIC 8741 8721 Hospital management; Accounting, auditing & bookkeeping
Ex Dir: John T Porter
Ofcr: David Flicek
Ex VP: James J Breckenridge
Ex VP: Richard Molseed
Ex VP: Joan Reichelt
Sr VP: Judy Blauwet
**Sr VP:* Jim Breckenridge
Sr VP: David Erickson
Sr VP: David Kapaska
Sr VP: Michelle Lavallee
Sr VP: Jean Reed
Sr VP: Mary Thomas
Sr VP: Richard Thompson
Sr VP: Jim Veline
VP: Rob Bates
VP: Mary Davis
VP: Geoff Durst
VP: Kimberly Enebo
VP: John Healy
VP: Curt Hohman
VP: Monica Kapinski

AVERA HEART HOPSITAL SD
See HEART HOSPITAL OF SOUTH DAKOTA LLC

D-U-N-S 09-468-6748
AVERA MCKENNAN
CENTER FOR RURAL HEALTH
(*Suby of* AVERA MCKENNAN HOSPITAL MEDICAL STAFF) ★
3900 W Avera Dr, Sioux Falls, SD 57108-5717
Tel (605) 322-7300 *Founded/Ownrshp* 1977
Sales 809.2MM[E] *EMP* 12[E]
Accts Eide Bailly Llp Minneapolis
SIC 7389 Contractors' disbursement control
Pr: Dave Kapaska
**Sr VP:* Judy Blauwet
**Sr VP:* Michael Elliott
VP: Julie Benz
**VP:* Tom Bosch
**VP:* John Healy
Exec: Michelle Walter
Ex Dir: Rhonda Roesler
Pathlgst: Roy Burt
Pathlgst: Kim M Lorenzen
Pathlgst: Bruce R Pouse

D-U-N-S 06-864-7668
AVERA MCKENNAN HOSPITAL MEDICAL STAFF (SD)
(*Suby of* AVERA HEALTH) ★
1325 S Cliff Ave, Sioux Falls, SD 57105-1007
Tel (605) 322-8000 *Founded/Ownrshp* 1911
Sales 809.2MM[E] *EMP* 2,290
SIC 8062 Hospital, medical school affiliation
CEO: Fredrick W Slunecka
Sr VP: Sheryl Johnson
Sr VP: Richard Molseed
VP: Brenda Hanson
VP: Thomas Ripperda
Exec: Drew Laberis
Dir Lab: Mary Doolittle
Dir Lab: Leo Serrano
Dir Lab: Cheryl Wildermuth
Genl Mgr: Teri Roark
Off Mgr: Tricia Lohr

D-U-N-S 80-515-8896
AVERA QUEEN OF PEACE
AVERA QUEEN OF PEACE HEALTH SE
525 N Foster St, Mitchell, SD 57301-2999
Tel (605) 995-2000 *Founded/Ownrshp* 1905
Sales 97.8MM *EMP* 750
SIC 8062

AVERA QUEEN OF PEACE HEALTH SE
See AVERA QUEEN OF PEACE

AVERA QUEEN OF PEACE HEALTH SE
See AVERA QUEEN OF PEACE HOSPITAL

D-U-N-S 96-961-1727
AVERA QUEEN OF PEACE HOSPITAL
AVERA QUEEN OF PEACE HEALTH SE
525 N Foster St, Mitchell, SD 57301-2999
Tel (605) 995-2000 *Founded/Ownrshp* 2011
Sales 107.7MM *EMP* 46[E]
Accts Eide Bailly Llp Minneapolis
SIC 8062 General medical & surgical hospitals
CFO: Will Flett
Ofcr: Vicki S Lehrman
Pharmcst: Ron Johnson

AVERA SACRED HEART HOSPITAL
See SACRED HEART HEALTH SERVICES

D-U-N-S 06-816-2304
AVERA ST LUKES
AVERA ST LUKE'S HOSPITAL
(*Suby of* AVERA HEALTH) ★
305 S State St, Aberdeen, SD 57401-4527
Tel (605) 622-5000 *Founded/Ownrshp* 1943
Sales 166.4MM *EMP* 1,203
SIC 8062 5912 General medical & surgical hospitals; Drug stores
CEO: Todd Forkel
Chf Rad: Stephen Peters
**Pr:* Ron Jacobson
CFO: Mary Davis
**CFO:* Jeff Durst
VP: Geoff Dursdt
**VP:* Sister Edmund Walsh
Dir Lab: Deb Neitzel
Dir Rx: Alvin Haugen
Dir Sec: Bill Roth
Dir IT: Josie Hornaman

AVERA ST LUKE'S HOSPITAL
See AVERA ST LUKES

AVERITT AIR
See AVERITT INC

D-U-N-S 05-649-2606 IMP/EXP
AVERITT EXPRESS INC
(*Suby of* AVERITT AIR) ★
1415 Neal St, Cookeville, TN 38501-4328
Tel (931) 526-3306 *Founded/Ownrshp* 1986
Sales 1.0MMM *EMP* 8,208
Accts Duncan Wheeler & Wilkerson P
SIC 4214 4213 Local trucking with storage; Trucking, except local
Pr: Gary D Sasser
COO: Wayne Spain
CFO: George Johnson
Ex VP: Phil Pierce
VP: Mark Davis
Opers Mgr: Ronald Bates

D-U-N-S 60-245-6428
AVERITT INC
AVERITT AIR
1415 Neal St, Cookeville, TN 38501-4328
Tel (931) 526-3306 *Founded/Ownrshp* 1971
Sales 1.1MMM *EMP* 8,210[E]
Accts Duncan Wheeler & Wilkerson P
SIC 4213 Trucking, except local
**Ex VP:* George Johnson
**Ex VP:* Phil Pierce
VP: Johnny Fields

D-U-N-S 00-825-6364 IMP/EXP
▲ AVERY DENNISON CORP
207 N Goode Ave Fl 6, Glendale, CA 91203-1364
Tel (626) 304-2000 *Founded/Ownrshp* 1946
Sales 5.9MMM *EMP* 25,000[E]
Accts Pricewaterhousecoopers Llp Lo
Tkr Sym AVY *Exch* NYS
SIC 2672 3081 3497 2678 Adhesive papers, labels or tapes: from purchased material; Gummed paper: made from purchased materials; Coated paper, except photographic, carbon or abrasive; Unsupported plastics film & sheet; Metal foil & leaf; Notebooks: made from purchased paper
Ch Bd: Dean A Scarborough
Pr: Mitchell R Butier
CFO: Anne L Bramman
Treas: Joao Adao
Treas: Leopolo Lomeli
Ofcr: Anne Hill
Sr VP: Susan C Miller
VP: Vikas Arora
VP: Lori Bondar
VP: Carmen Chua
VP: Ed Lee
VP: Dave Skrzyniarz
Exec: Larry Gargano
Board of Directors: Bradley A Alford, Anthony K Anderson, Peter K Barker, Ken C Hicks, David E I Pyott, Patrick T Siewart, Julia A Stewart, Martha N Sullivan

D-U-N-S 07-884-0476
AVERY PRODUCTS CORP
(*Suby of* CCL LABEL) ★
50 Pointe Dr, Brea, CA 92821-3652
Tel (714) 675-8500 *Founded/Ownrshp* 2012
Sales 311.2MM[E] *EMP* 883[E]
SIC 2678 3951 2672 2891 Notebooks: made from purchased paper; Markers, soft tip (felt, fabric, plastic, etc.); Labels (unprinted), gummed: made from purchased materials; Adhesives
Pr: Geoff Martin
**VP:* Jeff Lattanzio
VP Sls: Amy Ladwig
Snr Mgr: Cindy Didomenico
Snr Mgr: Mark McAndrews

D-U-N-S 05-672-8819 IMP/EXP
■ AVERY WEIGH-TRONIX LLC
DILLON
(*Suby of* ILLINOIS TOOL WORKS INC) ★
1000 Armstrong Dr, Fairmont, MN 56031-1439
Tel (507) 238-4461 *Founded/Ownrshp* 2008
Sales 778.6MM[E] *EMP* 5,500
SIC 3596 5083 Weighing machines & apparatus; Agricultural machinery & equipment
Dir IT: Logan Martinez
IT Man: Gareth Arnold
Tech Mgr: Jon Riggs
Opers Mgr: Darrel Drevlow
Ql Cn Mgr: Carla Nagel

D-U-N-S 78-398-2093 IMP
AVEVA DRUG DELIVERY SYSTEMS INC
(*Suby of* PERMACEL-AUTOMOTIVE) ★
3250 Commerce Pkwy, Miramar, FL 33025-3907
Tel (954) 430-3340 *Founded/Ownrshp* 2003
Sales 129.5MM[E] *EMP* 230
SIC 2834 Pharmaceutical preparations
Pr: Jeremy Desai
**Pr:* Wallace K Reams
**VP:* Robert J Bloder
**VP:* Thomas Byrnes
Ql Cn Mgr: Brando Grillet

D-U-N-S 02-082-9396
AVFUEL CORP (MI)
(*Suby of* CRS ACQUISITION CORPORATION)
47 W Ellsworth Rd, Ann Arbor, MI 48108-2278
Tel (734) 663-6466 *Founded/Ownrshp* 1975, 1984
Sales 313.1MM[E] *EMP* 170
SIC 5172 Aircraft fueling services
Pr: Craig R Sincock
Treas: Stephanie Doll
**Ofcr:* C R Sincock II
VP: Joel Hirst
VP: Russ Standefer
Dist Mgr: Daniel Bull
Dist Mgr: Dean Hornig
CIO: Mark Haynes
IT Man: Mike Kormos
Ql Cn Mgr: Randy Harrison
Sales Exec: Pat Loughman

D-U-N-S 84-729-0418
AVG ADVANCED TECHNOLOGIES LP
UTICOR TECHNOLOGY
343 Saint Paul Blvd, Carol Stream, IL 60188-1851
Tel (630) 668-3900 *Founded/Ownrshp* 1975
Sales 72.3MM[E] *EMP* 1,000
SIC 3672 3661 3824 3822 3625 Printed circuit boards; Telephones & telephone apparatus; Fluid meters & counting devices; Auto controls regulating residntl & coml environmt & applncs; Relays & industrial controls
CEO: Shalabh Kumar
Genl Pt: Electronic Support Systems Cor

D-U-N-S 00-468-5835 IMP
AVGOL AMERICA INC
AVGOL NONWOVENS
(*Suby of* AVGOL INDUSTRIES 1953 LTD)
178 Avgol Dr, Mocksville, NC 27028-2558
Tel (336) 751-5007 *Founded/Ownrshp* 2001
Sales 93.9MM[E] *EMP* 140
SIC 2297 Nonwoven fabrics
CEO: Shlomo Liran
Pr: Tom Dort
**Pr:* Nir Peleg
**Treas:* Shachar Rachim
VP: Nadia Tiagounov
Genl Mgr: Ronnie Batchler
Opers Mgr: Rashanna Liles
Ql Cn Mgr: Stephanie Hinz

AVGOL NONWOVENS
See AVGOL AMERICA INC

D-U-N-S 01-840-9615
AVI FOOD SYSTEMS INC (OH)
2590 Elm Rd Ne, Warren, OH 44483-2997
Tel (330) 372-6000 *Founded/Ownrshp* 1960, 1964
Sales 663.5MM[E] *EMP* 3,000[E]
SIC 5962 5812 8742 Merchandising machine operators; Caterers; Food & beverage consultant
Ch Bd: John Payiavlas
**Pr:* Patrice Kouvas
Pr: Robert A Sunday
**CEO:* Anthony J Payiavlas
CFO: Nick Mavrogianis
Ex VP: John Coker
Sr VP: Dick Martin
VP: Julie Davis
VP: Ralph Sanese
VP: Douglas Stoll
Exec: Brian Hartley

D-U-N-S 02-047-6370
AVI SYSTEMS INC
9675 W 76th St Ste 200, Eden Prairie, MN 55344-3707
Tel (952) 949-3700 *Founded/Ownrshp* 1979
Sales 182.1MM *EMP* 498
Accts Eide Bailly Llp Bismarck Nor
SIC 5065 7622 8748 1799 Electronic parts & equipment; Communication equipment repair; Video repair; Television repair shop; Telecommunications consultant; Service & repair of broadcasting stations
Pr: Joseph Stoebner
**Pr:* Jeff Stoebner
**CFO:* Randi Borth
VP: Brian Yandell
Brnch Mgr: Carol Ternes
Sales Asso: Matt Johnson

D-U-N-S 82-687-2694 EXP
AVI-SPL EMPLOYEE EMERGENCY RELIEF FUND INC
AVI-SPL TAMPA SERVICE
(*Suby of* AVI-SPL HOLDINGS INC) ★
6301 Benjamin Rd Ste 101, Tampa, FL 33634-5115
Tel (813) 884-7168 *Founded/Ownrshp* 2008
Sales 228.8MM[E] *EMP* 2,000
SIC 3669 3861 3663 3651 5043 5064 Intercommunication systems, electric; Photographic equipment & supplies; Radio & TV communications equipment; Household audio & video equipment; Projection apparatus, motion picture & slide; Electrical appliances, television & radio
CEO: John Zettel
**COO:* Jeff Davis
**CFO:* Raj Dani
Sr VP: Tom Bigliani
Sr VP: Rhonda Wingate
VP: John Babcock
VP: Mike Garvy
VP: Rodney Laney
VP: Felix Robinson
Prgrm Mgr: Jacob Ayers
Prgrm Mgr: Eric Braverman

D-U-N-S 82-687-2983 EXP
AVI-SPL HOLDINGS INC
6301 Benjamin Rd Ste 101, Tampa, FL 33634-5115
Tel (866) 708-5034 *Founded/Ownrshp* 2008
Sales 672.9MM[E] *EMP* 2,000[E]
Accts Ernst & Young Llp Tampa Fl
SIC 3669 3861 3663 3651 1731 5064 Intercommunication systems, electric; Photographic equipment & supplies; Radio & TV communications equipment; Household audio & video equipment; Voice, data & video wiring contractor; Electrical appliances, television & radio
Treas: Jean Constant
VP: Randy Bonham

D-U-N-S 07-986-9466
AVI-SPL INC
(*Suby of* AVI-SPL HOLDINGS INC) ★
6301 Benjamin Rd Ste 101, Tampa, FL 33634-5115
Tel (866) 708-5034 *Founded/Ownrshp* 2008
Sales 444.0MM[E] *EMP* 2,877[E]
SIC 7359 5999 Audio-visual equipment & supply rental; Audio-visual equipment & supplies
CEO: John Zettel
COO: Jeff Davis
CFO: Raj Dani
Ex VP: Steve Benjamin
VP: Frank Mehr
Exec: Jeremy Blanton
Mng Dir: James Shanks
Opers Mgr: Roy Crandall
Sales Exec: Gregg Coapman
Sales Exec: Kyle Morgan
Sales Asso: Audrey Warren

AVI-SPL TAMPA SERVICE
See AVI-SPL EMPLOYEE EMERGENCY RELIEF FUND INC

D-U-N-S 06-788-6192 IMP/EXP
AVIAGEN INC
(*Suby of* ERICH WESJOHANN VERMOGENSVERWALTUNGS GMBH & CO. KG)
920 Explorer Blvd Nw, Huntsville, AL 35806-2808
Tel (256) 890-3800 *Founded/Ownrshp* 1996, 1986
Sales 217.9MM[E] *EMP* 600
SIC 2015 Poultry slaughtering & processing
CEO: Randall Ennis
**Pr:* Ben Thompson
CFO: Chris Hill
Sr VP: WY Chiang
Sr VP: Bill Souther
VP: Frank Dougherty
VP: Bryan Fancher
**VP:* B Paige Graham
VP: Ken Laughlin
VP: Jason Mack
VP: Jeffrey Schlaman
VP: Ricardo Valle

D-U-N-S 80-997-9529 IMP/EXP
■ AVIALL INC
(*Suby of* BOEING CO) ★
2750 Rgent Blvd Dfw Arprt Dfw Airport, Dallas, TX 75261
Tel (972) 586-1000 *Founded/Ownrshp* 2006
Sales 1.3MMM[E] *EMP* 1,200
SIC 5088 Aircraft engines & engine parts; Aircraft equipment & supplies
CEO: Eric Strafel
Pr: Ed Dolanksi
Pr: Paul E Fulchino
CFO: Colin M Cohen
CFO: John Meersman
Treas: Robert Kiehnle
Treas: Verett A Mims
Sr VP: William Ampofo
Sr VP: Joseph Lacik
Sr VP: James T Quinn
Sr VP: Terry Scott
Sr VP: Scott Shadle
Sr VP: Eric D Strafel
VP: Michael Booen
VP: Margaret Bouline
VP: Curt Brusto
VP: Jacqueline Collier
VP: John Guasto
VP: Louis F Koch
VP: Allison McCullough
VP: James Quinn

D-U-N-S 80-996-8902 IMP/EXP
■ AVIALL SERVICES INC
DFW AIRPORT
(*Suby of* AVIALL INC) ★
2750 Regent Blvd, Dfw Airport, TX 75261-4405
Tel (972) 586-1000 *Founded/Ownrshp* 1993
Sales 1.0MMM[E] *EMP* 1,200
SIC 5088 7699 Aircraft & space vehicle supplies & parts; Aircraft & heavy equipment repair services
**CFO:* John Meersman
Sr VP: Charley Kienzle
**Sr VP:* Terry Scott
Sr VP: Scott Shadle
**Sr VP:* Kim Stollar
**Sr VP:* Eric D Strafel
VP: William Ampofo
**VP:* Curtis W Brusto
**VP:* Jacqueline K Collier
**VP:* Robin L Everly
VP: Steve Hussey
VP: Betsy Lewis
**VP:* Eric Nelson

D-U-N-S 14-219-8493
AVIANDS LLC
1751 County Road B W # 300, Roseville, MN 55113-4081
Tel (651) 631-0940 *Founded/Ownrshp* 2003
Sales 98.4MM[E] *EMP* 1,900
SIC 8742 Restaurant & food services consultants
Sfty Mgr: Len Stoskopf

D-U-N-S 03-301-3447
AVIARA FSRC ASSOCIATES LIMITED
(Suby of PARK HYATT AVIARA RESORT) ★
7100 Aviara Resort Dr, Carlsbad, CA 92011-4908
Tel (760) 603-6800 Founded/Ownrshp 1995
Sales 12.7MM^E EMP 1,200
SIC 7011 Resort hotel
Genl Mgr: Robert Cima
*Genl Pt: Aviara Resort Club
*Genl Pt: Hef IV LLC

D-U-N-S 61-275-6551
AVIARA RESORT ASSOCIATES LIMITED PARTNERSHIP A CALIFORNIA LIMITED PARTNERSHIP
PARK HYATT AVIARA RESORT
7100 Aviara Resort Dr, Carlsbad, CA 92011-4908
Tel (760) 448-1234 Founded/Ownrshp 1989
Sales 64.8MM^E EMP 2,100
SIC 7011 Hotels & motels
Genl Pt: Maritz Wolff

D-U-N-S 79-093-9081 IMP
▲ AVIAT NETWORKS INC
860 N Mccarthy Blvd, Milpitas, CA 95035-5110
Tel (408) 941-7000 Founded/Ownrshp 2006
Sales 268.6MM EMP 740^E
Tkr Sym AVNW Exch NGS
SIC 3663 Radio & TV communications equipment; Radio broadcasting & communications equipment; Antennas, transmitting & communications
Pr: Michael A Pangia
*Ch Bd: John Mutch
CFO: Ralph S Marimon
Ofcr: Shaun McFall
Ofcr: Heinz H Stumpe
Sr VP: Meena Elliott
Sr VP: Ola Gustafsson
VP: Roberto Angeles
VP: Tam Dam
VP: Meena Elliot
VP: Paul Kennard
VP: Gerry Kinder
VP: Yves Plante
VP: Asif Rahman
VP: Kevin Renaud
VP: Brian Tucker
Dir Bus: Randy Jenkins
Board of Directors: William A Hasler, James R Henderson, Robert G Pearse, John J Quicke, James C Stoffel

D-U-N-S 11-329-9986
■ AVIAT US INC
(Suby of AVIAT NETWORKS INC) ★
860 N Mccarthy Blvd, Milpitas, CA 95035-5110
Tel (408) 941-7100 Founded/Ownrshp 2007
Sales 133.7MM^E EMP 542
SIC 3663 3661 Radio broadcasting & communications equipment; Transmitter-receivers, radio; Mobile communication equipment; Fiber optics communications equipment
Pr: Michael A Pangia
*Ch Bd: John Mutch
*CFO: Ralph Marimon
CFO: Carl A Thomsen
*Chf Mktg O: Shaun McFall
*Sr VP: Meena L Elliott
*VP: John J Madigan
Exec: Sarah Dudash
*Dir Sec: Heinz H Stumpe
Netwrk Eng: Ray Huang
Genl Couns: Juan B Otero

D-U-N-S 09-026-0089
AVIATION & MISSILE SOLUTIONS LLC
AMS
1000 Explorer Blvd Nw, Huntsville, AL 35806-2806
Tel (256) 713-5900 Founded/Ownrshp 1999
Sales 91.0MM EMP 9
SIC 7363 Engineering help service
CTO: Paula Cushman

D-U-N-S 02-512-9458
■ AVIATION COMMUNICATION & SURVEILLANCE SYSTEMS LLC
L-3 COMMUNICATION & THALES
(Suby of L-3 COMMUNICATIONS CORP) ★
19810 N 7th Ave, Phoenix, AZ 85027-4741
Tel (623) 445-7030 Founded/Ownrshp 2000
Sales 89.0MM EMP 239
SIC 8711 Aviation &/or aeronautical engineering
COO: Cole Hadden
CFO: Deena Cunningham
*VP: Ozzie Hager
*VP: Kimberly Murdoch
*VP: Jake Olds
Snr Ntwrk: Mario Velez

D-U-N-S 11-150-4895
AVIATION TECHNICAL SERVICES INC
ATS
3121 109th St Sw, Everett, WA 98204-1318
Tel (425) 347-3030 Founded/Ownrshp 2016
Sales 332.0MM^E EMP 1,285^E
SIC 4581 8711 Aircraft maintenance & repair services; Engineering services
CEO: Matt Yerbic
*Pr: Brian Hirshman
*CFO: Donald J Cook
Treas: Gary Neisinger
*Treas: Bruce Stewart
VP: Bryan Dawson
Genl Mgr: Michael Beck
Dir IT: Clark Graves
Sls Dir: Troy Daman
Snr Mgr: Josh McCracken

D-U-N-S 13-208-1592
■ AVIATION TECHNOLOGIES INC
(Suby of AEROCONTROLEX) ★
1301 E 9th St Ste 3000, Cleveland, OH 44114-1871
Tel (216) 706-2960 Founded/Ownrshp 2007
Sales 158.2MM^E EMP 611
SIC 3643 3678 3679 3728 3812 3648 Contacts, electrical; Electronic connectors; Liquid crystal displays (LCD); Aircraft parts & equipment; Search & navigation equipment; Lighting equipment
CEO: W Nicholas Howley
CFO: Russell Fleetwood
*CFO: Gregory Ruful

D-U-N-S 00-829-9257 IMP
■ AVIBANK MFG INC
(Suby of PCC SPS FASTENER DIVISION) ★
11500 Sherman Way, North Hollywood, CA 91605-5827
Tel (818) 392-2100 Founded/Ownrshp 1945, 2000
Sales 87.0MM^E EMP 400
SIC 3452 Bolts, nuts, rivets & washers
Pr: Dan Welter
CFO: Gundy Tollefson
*VP: John Duran
Netwrk Mgr: Ken Brown
Ql Cn Mgr: Peter Shea
Mktg Mgr: Dave Ladin

D-U-N-S 01-562-3119 IMP
■ AVID MEDICAL INC
(Suby of MEDICAL ACTION INDUSTRIES INC) ★
9000 Westmont Dr, Toano, VA 23168-9351
Tel (757) 566-3510 Founded/Ownrshp 1998
Sales 198.4MM^E EMP 355
SIC 5047 Surgical equipment & supplies
CEO: Meringolo Paul
*Pr: Chapman Paul
*VP: Baker Brian

D-U-N-S 19-988-0659 IMP
▲ AVID TECHNOLOGY INC
75 Network Dr, Burlington, MA 01803-2756
Tel (978) 640-6789 Founded/Ownrshp 1987
Sales 505.6MM EMP 1,522
Tkr Sym AVID Exch NGS
SIC 3861 7372 Editing equipment, motion picture: viewers, splicers, etc.; Sound recording & reproducing equipment, motion picture; Prepackaged software
Ch Bd: Louis Hernandez Jr
CFO: Ilan Sidi
Ofcr: Jeff Rosica
VP: Jason A Duva
Board of Directors: Robert M Bakish, Paula E Boggs, Elizabeth M Daley, Nancy Hawthorne, John H Park, Peter Westley

D-U-N-S 01-816-9083 IMP/EXP
■ AVINTIV INC
(Suby of BERRY PLASTICS GROUP INC) ★
9335 Harris Corners Pkwy, Charlotte, NC 28269-3818
Tel (704) 697-5100 Founded/Ownrshp 2015
Sales 903.2MM^E EMP 4,000^E
SIC 2297 Nonwoven fabrics
Pr: J Joel Hackney Jr
Pr: David Wang
VP: Rain Tian
VP: David Whitaker
IT Man: Mitchell Harris
Sls Mgr: Gary Ellis
Sls Mgr: Richard Gibson

D-U-N-S 79-705-0598 IMP/EXP
■ AVINTIV SPECIALTY MATERIALS INC
(Suby of BERRY PLASTICS GROUP INC) ★
9335 Harris Corners Pkwy, Charlotte, NC 28269-3818
Tel (704) 697-5100 Founded/Ownrshp 2011
Sales 1.8MMM EMP 4,000
SIC 2297 2392 Nonwoven fabrics; Towels, dishcloths & dust cloths; Slip covers & pads
Pr: J Joel Hackney Jr
Pr: Robert Dale
Pr: Barry Murash
*CFO: Dennis Norman
*Sr VP: Daniel Guerrero
*Sr VP: Daniel L Rikard
*Sr VP: Mary Tomasello
VP: Peter Bourgeois
VP: Tim Huskey
VP: Jorge Islas
CTO: Angela Mayfield
Board of Directors: James S Alder, Peter N Foss, Jason Giordano, Veronica Hagen, Christine St Clare, Mike S Zafirovski

D-U-N-S 96-512-9323 IMP
AVIO INC
270 Sylvan Ave Ste 130, Englewood Cliffs, NJ 07632-2545
Tel (201) 816-2720 Founded/Ownrshp 1990
Sales 1.3MMM EMP 34
SIC 3724

D-U-N-S 06-250-6134 IMP/EXP
▲ AVIS BUDGET GROUP INC
6 Sylvan Way Ste 1, Parsippany, NJ 07054-3826
Tel (973) 496-4700 Founded/Ownrshp 1946
Sales 8.5MMM EMP 30,000^E
Tkr Sym CAR Exch NGS
SIC 7514 7513 6794 Passenger car rental; Truck rental & leasing, no drivers; Franchises, selling or licensing
Pr: Ronald L Nelson
Pr: David B Wyshner
CEO: Larry D De Shon
Chf Cred: Michael K Tucker
Bd of Dir: John D Hardy
Bd of Dir: Eduardo Mestre
Ofcr: Edward P Linnen
Ex VP: W Scott Deaver
Ex VP: Gerard Insall
Ex VP: Patric Siniscalchi
Sr VP: Joseph A Ferraro
Sr VP: Ned Linnen
VP: Joe Biondo
VP: Robert Bouta
VP: Gina Bruzzichesi
VP: Glenn Burke
VP: Clive Burton
VP: David Calabria
VP: Michael Caron
VP: David Crowther
VP: Jeff Eisenbarth
Board of Directors: Brian J Choi, Mary C Choksi, Leonard S Coleman, Jeffrey H Fox, John D Hardy Jr, Lynn Krominga, Eduardo G Mestre, F Robert Salerno, Stender E Sweeney

D-U-N-S 36-425-9861
■ AVIS GROUP HOLDINGS LLC
(Suby of AVIS BUDGET GROUP INC) ★
6 Sylvan Way Ste 1, Parsippany, NJ 07054-3826
Tel (973) 496-4328 Founded/Ownrshp 2001
Sales 823.5MM EMP 28,000
SIC 7514 Rent-a-car service
Pr: F Robert Salern
Treas: John Logan
Chf Mktg O: Jeannine Haas
*Ex VP: Michael P Collins
Ex VP: Thomas M Gartland
VP: Paul Ford
VP: Tom Hocker
VP: Martin Mylott
VP: Neal Zamore
Dir Risk M: Barbara Vitale
QA Dir: Denise Slater

D-U-N-S 00-535-4568 IMP
AVIS INDUSTRIAL CORP
1909 S Main St, Upland, IN 46989
Tel (765) 998-8100 Founded/Ownrshp 1959, 1983
Sales 278.9MM^E EMP 1,179
SIC 3429 3462 3312 3531 3714 3569 Locks or lock sets; Iron & steel forgings; Tubes, steel & iron; Construction machinery; Cranes, locomotive; Fuel pumps, motor vehicle; Baling machines, for scrap metal, paper or similar material
CEO: Larita R Boren
*Pr: Leland E Boren
*V Ch Bd: Richard T Doermer
IT Man: Karl Goy

D-U-N-S 00-195-4387 IMP/EXP
■ AVIS RENT A CAR SYSTEM INC
(Suby of AVIS GROUP HOLDINGS LLC) ★
6 Sylvan Way Ste 1, Parsippany, NJ 07054-3826
Tel (973) 496-3500 Founded/Ownrshp 1956, 1996
Sales 769.5MM^E EMP 18,000
SIC 7514 Rent-a-car service
Pr: F Robert Salerno
CFO: David B Wyshner
*Ex VP: Michael P Collins
Ex VP: Larry De Shon
Ex VP: Michael K Tucker
Sr VP: Gerard Insall
VP: Ted Deutsch
Info Man: John Hoke
Opers Mgr: Donald Henson
Pr Dir: Bob Muhs
Sls Dir: Jenny Copas

D-U-N-S 04-046-8543
AVIS RENTAL CAR SYSTEMS
CENDARE
6 Sylvan Way Ste 1, Parsippany, NJ 07054-3826
Tel (973) 496-3000 Founded/Ownrshp 2001
Sales 60.6MM^E EMP 2,000^E
SIC 7514 Rent-a-car service
Pr: Robert Sarlerno

D-U-N-S 60-256-0216
AVISTA CAPITAL HOLDINGS LP
65 E 55th St Fl 18, New York, NY 10022-3309
Tel (212) 593-6900 Founded/Ownrshp 2005
Sales 689.1MM^E EMP 1,335
SIC 6799 Investors
Mng Pt: Thompson Dean
*Pt: David Burgstahler
*Pt: David Durkin
*Pt: Ohsong Kwon
*Pt: Steven Webster
*Pt: Arthur Zuckerman
Mng Pt: Dean Thompson
VP: Robert Girardi

D-U-N-S 00-794-3764 IMP/EXP
▲ AVISTA CORP (WA)
1411 E Mission Ave, Spokane, WA 99202-1902
Tel (509) 489-0500 Founded/Ownrshp 1889
Sales 1.4MMM EMP 1,938
Accts Deloitte & Touche Llp Seattl
Tkr Sym AVA Exch NYS
SIC 4911 4924 3499 Distribution, electric power; Generation, electric power; ; ; Natural gas distribution; Boxes for packing & shipping, metal
Ch Bd: Scott L Morris
CFO: Mark T Thies
Treas: Diane Thoren
Chf Cred: Marian M Durkin
Sr VP: Karen S Feltes
Sr VP: Dennis P Vermillion
VP: Kevin J Christie
VP: James M Kensok
VP: Ryan L Krasselt
VP: William Wofford
Snr Sftwr: Markus Rissmann
Board of Directors: Erik J Anderson, Donald C Burke, John F Kelly, Rebecca A Klein, Marc F Racicot, Heidi B Stanley, R John Taylor, Janet D Widmann

D-U-N-S 01-113-0205
■ AVISTA UTILITIES INC
(Suby of AVISTA CORP) ★
1411 E Mission Ave, Spokane, WA 99202-1902
Tel (509) 489-0500 Founded/Ownrshp 1889
Sales 715.0MM^E EMP 1,500
SIC 4939 Combination utilities
Pr: Scott L Morris
*VP: Don Kopczynski
VP: David Meyer
*VP: Kelly Norwood
*VP: Christy Smith
VP: Roger Woodworth

D-U-N-S 96-695-1001
AVIV HEALTHCARE PROPERTIES LIMITED PARTNERSHIP
303 W Madison St, Chicago, IL 60606-3309
Tel (312) 855-0930 Founded/Ownrshp 2011
Sales 184.0MM EMP 7^E
Accts Ernst & Young Llp Chicago I
SIC 8099 Medical services organization
Prin: Leticia Chavez

D-U-N-S 82-833-9411
AVIV REIT INC
303 W Madison St Ste 2400, Chicago, IL 60606-3335
Tel (312) 855-0930 Founded/Ownrshp 2010
Sales 184.0MM EMP 28^E
SIC 6798

AVIZENT
See FRANK GATES SERVICE CO

AVL DIGITAL GROUP
See AUDIO AND VIDEO LABS INC

D-U-N-S 78-422-5935 IMP
AVM INDUSTRIES LLC
3108 W Highway 76, Marion, SC 29571-7508
Tel (843) 464-5406 Founded/Ownrshp 2006
Sales 100.2MM^E EMP 300^E
SIC 3714 Motor vehicle parts & accessories
Ql Cn Mgr: Shelton Collins
Mktg Dir: Rodney Morrison

D-U-N-S 02-054-3633
AVMED INC
(Suby of SANTAFE HEALTHCARE INC) ★
4300 Nw 89th Blvd Fl 2, Gainesville, FL 32606-5674
Tel (352) 372-8400 Founded/Ownrshp 1986
Sales NA EMP 829
Accts Pricewaterhousecoopers Llp Ja
SIC 6324 Health maintenance organization (HMO), insurance only
Pr: Michael P Gallagher
*Pr: James M Repp
COO: Douglas Cueny
*CFO: Randall L Stuart
*Sr VP: Catherine Ayers
*Sr VP: Robert B Bentley
*Sr VP: Steven M Biegler
*Sr VP: Susan Knapp Pinnas
*Sr VP: James Simpson
*Sr VP: Ann O Wehr
VP: Kay Ayers
VP: R Bradford Bentley
VP: Vienzo Serro
*VP: Steven M Ziegler
Dir Rx: Shawn Barger

D-U-N-S 13-117-2777
■ AVNET ELECTRONICS MARKETING
(Suby of AVNET INC) ★
2211 S 47th St, Phoenix, AZ 85034-6403
Tel (480) 643-2000 Founded/Ownrshp 2006
Sales 92.7MM^E EMP 450
SIC 5065 Electronic parts
Sr VP: Kevin Yapp
VP: Dennis Bourque

D-U-N-S 00-699-5419 IMP/EXP
▲ AVNET INC (NY)
2211 S 47th St, Phoenix, AZ 85034-6403
Tel (480) 643-2000 Founded/Ownrshp 1955
Sales 26.2MMM EMP 17,705
Accts Kpmg Llp Phoenix Arizona
Tkr Sym AVT Exch NYS
SIC 5065 5045 7379 Electronic parts; Semiconductor devices; Connectors, electronic; Capacitors, electronic; Computers, peripherals & software; Computers; Computer peripheral equipment; Computer related consulting services
CEO: William J Amelio
Ch Bd: William H Schumann III
CFO: Kevin Moriarty
Ofcr: Peter Bartolotta
Ofcr: Therese Bassett
Ofcr: Maryann Miller
Sr VP: Michael D Buseman
Sr VP: Gerard W Fay
Sr VP: Erin Lewin
Sr VP: Steven R Phillips
Sr VP: Patrick Zammit
VP: Bob Bowen
VP: Bryan Brady
VP: Megan Carr
VP: John Clark
VP: Trisha Cooke
VP: Bill Crowell
VP: Rich Fitzgerald
VP: Marco Gonzalez
VP: Robert Gracz
VP: Frank Hardin
Board of Directors: Rodney C Adkins, J Veronica Biggins, Michael A Bradley, R Kerry Clark, James A Lawrence, Ray M Robinson

AVOCADO PACKER & SHIPPER
See WEST PAK AVOCADO INC

D-U-N-S 00-312-6724 IMP
AVOCENT CORP (TX)
(Suby of VERTIV) ★
4991 Corporate Dr Nw, Huntsville, AL 35805-6201
Tel (256) 430-4000 Founded/Ownrshp 2000, 2016
Sales 265.9MM^E EMP 950
SIC 3575 3577 7373 Computer terminals; Keyboards, computer, office machine; Computer peripheral equipment; Computer integrated systems design
CEO: Steve Hassell
Pr: Doyle C Weeks
CFO: Edward H Blankenship
Chf Mktg O: Kay E Kienast
Ex VP: Samuel F Saracino
Ex VP: Christopher L Thomas
Sr VP: Steve Daly
Sr VP: Thomas C Davis
VP: Andy Baldin
VP: Alan Bednarski
VP: Blake Carlson
VP: Dudley Devore
VP: Steve Geffin
VP: Bob Hamilton
VP: Mills Karl
VP: Richard Moore
VP: Steven Yellen

D-U-N-S 10-554-0272 IMP
AVOCENT HUNTSVILLE CORP
AVOCENT-HUNTSVILLE
(Suby of AVOCENT CORP) ★
4991 Corporate Dr Nw, Huntsville, AL 35805-6201
Tel (256) 430-4000 Founded/Ownrshp 1993

Sales 165.0MM[E] *EMP* 1,000
SIC 3577 Computer peripheral equipment
Pr: Doyle C Weeks
CFO: Edward Blankenship
Ex VP: Douglas E Pritchett
Ex VP: Bamb Raickas
Ex VP: Sam Saracino
Ex VP: Christopher L Thomas
VP: Steve Merrifield
Prgrm Mgr: Richard Blais
Genl Mgr: Scott Wehring

AVOCENT-HUNTSVILLE
See AVOCENT HUNTSVILLE CORP

D-U-N-S 78-507-6717 IMP
AVON AUTOMOTIVE HOLDINGS INC
(*Suby of* MGI COUTIER)
603 7th St, Cadillac, MI 49601-1344
Tel (231) 775-6571 *Founded/Ownrshp* 2009
Sales 165.4MM[E] *EMP* 500
SIC 3061 3089 Mechanical rubber goods; Injection molded finished plastic products
Pr: Leland Richards
**COO:* David Nielsen
**CFO:* William C Dircks
**VP:* Scott Maresh
Dir Bus: Trevor Kenny
CIO: Steve Haines
Dir IT: Steve Healey
VP Opers: Dave Nielsen

D-U-N-S 05-050-6153
AVON COMMUNITY SCHOOL CORP (IN)
7203 E Us Highway 36, Avon, IN 46123-7967
Tel (317) 272-2920 *Founded/Ownrshp* 1962
Sales 88.7MM[E] *EMP* 1,100
Accts State Board Of Accountants In
SIC 8211 Public elementary & secondary schools
Treas: Brenda Stipp

D-U-N-S 00-146-8693 IMP/EXP
▲ AVON PRODUCTS INC (NY)
777 3rd Ave, New York, NY 10017-1401
Tel (212) 282-5000 *Founded/Ownrshp* 1886
Sales 6.1MMM *EMP* 28,300
Tkr Sym AVP *Exch* NYS
SIC 2844 3961 5961 5023 5137 Toilet preparations; Cosmetic preparations; Perfumes & colognes; Toilet preparations; Necklaces, except precious metal; Bracelets, except precious metal; Earrings, except precious metal; Rings, finger: gold plated wire; Catalog sales; Cosmetics & perfumes, mail order; Jewelry, mail order; Glassware; Stainless steel flatware; Decorating supplies; Women's & children's clothing; Lingerie; Blouses; Sweaters, women's & children's
CEO: Sherilyn S McCoy
**Ch Bd:* Chan W Galbato
Pr: Fernando Acosta
Pr: John P Higson
Pr: David Legher
Pr: Pablo Munoz
Pr: Nilesh Patel
COO: James S Scully
Ofcr: Susan Ormiston
Ex VP: Fernando J Acosta
Sr VP: Jeff Benjamin
VP: Susan Liddie
VP: Robert Loughran
VP: Louise Scott
VP: Eddie Silcock
Exec: Betty Petrequin
Board of Directors: Jose Armario, W Don Cornwell, Nancy Killefer, Susan J Kropf, Steven F Mayer, Helen McCluskey, Charles H Noski, Cathy D Ross, Michael F Sanford

D-U-N-S 10-762-9560 IMP/EXP
AVON RUBBER & PLASTICS INC
(*Suby of* AVON RUBBER P.L.C.)
503 8th St, Cadillac, MI 49601-1370
Tel (231) 779-6290 *Founded/Ownrshp* 1982
Sales 110.7MM[E] *EMP* 500
SIC 3089 3061

D-U-N-S 79-014-3614 EXP
■ AVONDALE INDUSTRIES OF NEW YORK INC
(*Suby of* HUNTINGTON INGALLS INDUSTRIES INC) ★
5100 River Rd, Avondale, LA 70094-2706
Tel (504) 654-5254 *Founded/Ownrshp* 2011
Sales 1.0MMM[E] *EMP* 5,400
SIC 3731 Barges, building & repairing
Pr: George Yaunt

D-U-N-S 00-894-7087 IMP
AVT GROCERY INC
CARNIVAL
(*Suby of* MINYARD GROUP) ★
777 Freeport Pkwy, Coppell, TX 75019-4449
Tel (972) 241-2184 *Founded/Ownrshp* 2004
Sales 511.0MM[E] *EMP* 5,200
SIC 5411 5912

D-U-N-S 00-927-3434 IMP/EXP
■ AVTECHTYEE INC
A DIVISION OF TRANSDIGM GROUP
(*Suby of* AVIATION TECHNOLOGIES INC) ★
6500 Merrill Creek Pkwy, Everett, WA 98203-5860
Tel (206) 695-8000 *Founded/Ownrshp* 2003
Sales 137.6MM[E] *EMP* 300
SIC 3728 3648 3812 Aircraft parts & equipment; Lighting equipment; Search & navigation equipment
Ch Bd: R Jack Decrane
**Pr:* Jorge Valladares
VP: Donna Miller
Genl Mgr: Kelli Kruse
Mfg Mgr: Abe Khoury
Mfg Mgr: Rachel Kosmin
Ql Cn Mgr: Guy Anderson
Ql Cn Mgr: Brandon Schurr
Ql Cn Mgr: Brian Wolz
Sls Dir: Jon M Kasten

D-U-N-S 05-889-5921 IMP/EXP
■ AVX CORP
(*Suby of* KYOCERA CORPORATION)
1 Avx Blvd, Fountain Inn, SC 29644-9039
Tel (864) 967-2150 *Founded/Ownrshp* 1972
Sales 1.2MMM *EMP* 10,200[E]
Accts Pricewaterhousecoopers Llp Na
Tkr Sym AVX *Exch* NYS
SIC 3675 5065 3678 Electronic capacitors; Semiconductor devices; Electronic connectors
Ch Bd: John S Gilbertson
**Ch Bd:* Tetsuo Kuba
**Pr:* John Sarvis
CFO: Kurt P Cummings
CFO: Curt Cummins
CFO: Kurt Kulkarni
Sr VP: Kathleen M Kelly
Sr VP: John Lawing
Sr VP: Peter Venuto
VP: Peter Collis
VP: Carl Eggerding
VP: Alan Gordon
VP: Willing King
VP: Pete Venuto
Board of Directors: Shoichi Aoki, Donald B Christiansen, David A Decenzo, Kazuo Inamori, Joseph Stach

D-U-N-S 80-777-5858
AW HOLDINGS LLC
8515 Bluffton Rd, Fort Wayne, IN 46809-3022
Tel (260) 744-6145 *Founded/Ownrshp* 2007
Sales 28.5MM[E] *EMP* 3,000
SIC 8331 Vocational rehabilitation agency
CEO: William Swiss

D-U-N-S 00-797-2409 IMP
AW INDUSTRIES INC (MD)
SERTA MATTRESS CO
8415 Ardwick Ardmore Rd, Landover, MD 20785-2302
Tel (301) 322-1000 *Founded/Ownrshp* 1931, 1962
Sales 92.6MM *EMP* 300
Accts Ellin & Tucker Chartered Balt
SIC 2515 Mattresses & foundations
Pr: Stuart Bannett
**VP:* Alan Privot
MIS Dir: April Rogers
Sls&Mrk Ex: Charles Gilroy
Board of Directors: Robert Malin, Wanda Privot, Douglas Wolf

D-U-N-S 11-239-0773 IMP/EXP
AW NORTH CAROLINA INC
(*Suby of* AISIN AW CO.,LTD.)
4112 Old Oxford Rd, Durham, NC 27712-9428
Tel (919) 620-5500 *Founded/Ownrshp* 1998
Sales 706.0MM[E] *EMP* 3,600
SIC 3714 Transmissions, motor vehicle
Pr: Susumu Kasai
**Treas:* Takashi Eto
**Treas:* Noriaki Kamimuki
Genl Mgr: Mike Dickey
Genl Mgr: Josh Humphrey
QA Dir: Douglas Baker
QA Dir: Erica Lewis
Mfg Mgr: Kenny Lewis
Ql Cn Mgr: Jordan Best
Ql Cn Mgr: Nathan M Johnson
Snr Mgr: Christopher Davis

D-U-N-S 10-658-4188
AWARE INC
205 E Park Ave, Anaconda, MT 59711-2340
Tel (406) 563-5229 *Founded/Ownrshp* 1976
Sales 35.7MM *EMP* 1,400
Accts Anderson Zurmuehlen & Co Pc B
SIC 8361 8331 Residential care; Vocational training agency
CEO: Larry Noonan
**Pr:* Jack Haffey
CFO: Geri Francisco-Wyant
**CFO:* Geri F Wyant
Dir Bus: John Cote
**Prin:* John O'Donnell
Board of Directors: Bryan Noonan

D-U-N-S 96-691-8245
AWARE INTEGRATED INC
3535 Blue Cross Rd, Saint Paul, MN 55122-1154
Tel (651) 662-8000 *Founded/Ownrshp* 1995
Sales NA *EMP* 3,490
SIC 6324 Hospital & medical service plans
CEO: Andrew Czajkowski
**Sr VP:* Mark W Banks MD
**Sr VP:* Mark Durishan
**Sr VP:* Richard M Niemiec
**VP:* Roger W Kleppe
VP: Karen Soupir

D-U-N-S 04-775-5871 IMP
AWC INC
6655 Exchequer Dr, Baton Rouge, LA 70809-5148
Tel (225) 752-3939 *Founded/Ownrshp* 1977
Sales 156.8MM[E] *EMP* 241
Accts Hannis T Bourgeois Llp Bato
SIC 1731 Electrical work
CEO: Bob Wenyon
CFO: J D Honeycutt
**Treas:* David Honeycutt
**VP:* Phil Crigler
**VP:* George Plaeger
**VP:* Pam Trepagnier
Exec: Nan Davis
Div Mgr: Rick Gandy
CIO: Brian Sabolik
Tech Mgr: Fred Maynard
Sls Mgr: Scott Bryant

D-U-N-S 06-881-6214 IMP
AWC LIQUIDATING CO
GENEVA WATCH GROUP
(*Suby of* BINDA ITALIA SRL)
1407 Brdwy Ste 400, New York, NY 10018
Tel (212) 221-1177 *Founded/Ownrshp* 2008
Sales 89.2MM[E] *EMP* 140
SIC 5112 5199 3873 5094 Writing instruments & supplies; Advertising specialties; Watches & parts, except crystals & jewels; Watches & parts; Clocks
CEO: Jeffrey L Gregg
CFO: John Cuccurullo
**VP:* Nicholas Lancellotti
VP Sls: Charlie Kreite
Mktg Mgr: Heather Gayatgay

AWI
See ASSOCIATED WHOLESALERS INC

D-U-N-S 01-709-6421 IMP
AWI HOLDINGS INC (MI)
AUTO VALUE OF BAD AXE
440 Kirtland St Sw, Grand Rapids, MI 49507-2331
Tel (616) 243-2125 *Founded/Ownrshp* 1951, 1976
Sales 612.6MM[E] *EMP* 1,600
SIC 5013 5531 Automotive supplies & parts; Automotive parts; Automotive accessories
CEO: Fred A Bunting
**Pr:* Steve Donovan
**CFO:* Gregory D Hinkle
**VP:* Barry Hill
Dir IT: Steve Gold
Mktg Dir: James Harthorn
Mktg Dir: Jim Hawthorne

AWIZEBUY.COM
See GLOBAL AGGREGATE LLC

D-U-N-S 06-898-5456 IMP
AWM LLC
AMERICAN WOOD MOULDING
1800 Washington Blvd # 140, Baltimore, MD 21230-1701
Tel (916) 387-7317 *Founded/Ownrshp* 1996
Sales 112.4MM[E] *EMP* 660
SIC 5031 Lumber: rough, dressed & finished; Millwork
**CFO:* Jeff Sim
CIO: Brad Arrington

AWP
See AREA WIDE PROTECTIVE INC

AWP
See ALLEGHENY WOOD PRODUCTS INC

D-U-N-S 02-731-6504
AWP INC
AREA WIDE PROTECTIVE
826 Overholt Rd, Kent, OH 44240-7530
Tel (330) 644-0655 *Founded/Ownrshp* 2015
Sales 146.6MM[E] *EMP* 2,400
SIC 7381 Security guard service
Pr: William A Fink
**CFO:* Larry McKay
**VP:* Doug Naeding
Opers Mgr: Augusto Sikaffy
Opers Mgr: Todd Young

AWS
See ANTHONY WAYNE REHABILITATION CENTER FOR HANDICAPPED AND BLIND INC

D-U-N-S 07-930-6419
■ AWS HOLDINGS LLC
AIRWATCH HOLDING
(*Suby of* VMWARE INC) ★
1155 Perimeter Ctr # 100, Atlanta, GA 30338-5463
Tel (404) 478-7500 *Founded/Ownrshp* 2014
Sales 98.4MM[E] *EMP* 756[E]
SIC 7371 Computer software development & applications
CEO: John Marshall
COO: David Dabbiere

D-U-N-S 78-246-3582
AWS/GB CORP
2929 Walker Dr, Green Bay, WI 54311-8312
Tel (920) 406-4000 *Founded/Ownrshp* 1986
Sales 363.6MM[E] *EMP* 1,132[E]
SIC 5031 2431 3442 5033 1542 1541 Lumber, plywood & millwork; Millwork; Metal doors, sash & trim; Roofing, siding & insulation; Nonresidential construction; Commercial & office buildings, renovation & repair; Industrial buildings & warehouses; Renovation, remodeling & repairs: industrial buildings
Pr: Arnold W Schmidt
**Pr:* Daniel A Schmidt
**CFO:* Ronn Kleinschmidt
**VP:* Gloria J Schmidt

D-U-N-S 08-585-9213 IMP
■ AWW 10 INC
(*Suby of* ANIXTER INTERNATIONAL INC) ★
1441 N Wood Dale Rd, Wood Dale, IL 60191-1078
Tel (630) 595-0000 *Founded/Ownrshp* 2008
Sales 199.2MM[E] *EMP* 280
SIC 3452 5072

D-U-N-S 19-472-8200
■ AXA ADVISORS LLC
A X A
(*Suby of* AXA EQUITABLE LIFE INSURANCE CO) ★
1290 Ave Of Amrcs Fl Cnc1, New York, NY 10104
Tel (212) 554-1234 *Founded/Ownrshp* 1985
Sales 690.0MM[E] *EMP* 3,999
SIC 7389 Financial services
CEO: Mark Pearson
Mng Pt: J Verchot
Pr: Erik Pedersen
Pr: Mendy Reichman
Pr: Terri Trusskey
**COO:* Kevin Murray
**CFO:* Anders Malmstrom
Sr Cor Off: Mayur Dalal
Ofcr: Leanne Ogburn
Ofcr: Vincent F Parascandola
Sr Ex VP: Anthony Sages
Ex VP: Bill McDermott
Ex VP: Hiram Ramirez-Rangel
Ex VP: Amy Schlager
VP: Erik Aden
VP: Troy Barrentine
VP: Erik Carlson
**VP:* Jeff Coomes
VP: Stephen B Dunbar
**VP:* R Eric
VP: Karen Farley

D-U-N-S 00-698-3365 IMP
■ AXA EQUITABLE LIFE INSURANCE CO
(*Suby of* AXA FINANCIAL INC) ★
1290 Avenue Of The Americ, New York, NY 10104-0105
Tel (212) 554-1234 *Founded/Ownrshp* 1859
Sales NA *EMP* 7,077[E]
Accts Pricewaterhousecoopers Llp Ne
SIC 6311 6411 6282 Life insurance carriers; Insurance agents, brokers & service; Investment advice; Investment research; Manager of mutual funds, contract or fee basis
Ch Bd: Mark Pearson
Pt: Joanne Pietrini-Smith
**Ch Bd:* -Mark Pearson
Pr: Dan Bergman
Pr: Jerry Green
Pr: Lou Kyriacou
Pr: Jenna Langel
Pr: Michael Lordi
Pr: Jenna Malkin
Pr: Andrew McMahon
Pr: Rob Muller
Pr: Rich Olewnik
Pr: Alina Pogrob
Pr: Mendy Reichman
Pr: James Shepherdson
Pr: Laura Wiggers
COO: Sharon Ritchey
CFO: Anders Malmstrom
Chf Inves: Kevin R Byrne
Ofcr: Shaun Dooley
Ofcr: William McDermott
Board of Directors: Lorie A Slutsky, Henri De Castries, Richard C Vaughan, Ramon De Oliveira, Barbara Fallon-Walsh, Denis Duverne, Danny L Hale, Anthony J Hamilton, Daniel G Kaye, Peter S Kraus, Kristi A Matus, Bertram L Scott

D-U-N-S 79-080-2383
■ AXA FINANCIAL INC
(*Suby of* AXA)
1290 Ave Of The Am Fl Con, New York, NY 10104
Tel (212) 554-1234 *Founded/Ownrshp* 1992
Sales NA *EMP* 9,509
SIC 6311 6211 6552 6531 6371 6221 Life insurance carriers; Investment bankers; Brokers, security; Dealers, security; Mutual funds, selling by independent salesperson; Subdividers & developers; Real estate agents & managers; Pensions; Commodity contracts brokers, dealers
Pr: Mark Pearson
V Ch: Stanley B Tulin
Pr: Kathleen Decelie
Pr: Andrew J McMahon
Pr: Merril Tesler
CFO: Richard S Dziadzio
CFO: Kenneth Kozlowski
Ofcr: Carmen Abreu
Ofcr: Kevin Byrne
Ofcr: Shaun Dooley
Ofcr: David Held
Ofcr: Katherine Lee
Ex VP: Jennifer L Blevins
Ex VP: Pascal Dumesnil
Ex VP: Robert Garber
Ex VP: Jerald Hampton
Ex VP: Bill Levine
Ex VP: Thomas Long
Ex VP: Raghib Muhammad
Ex VP: Kevin E Murray
Sr VP: William Casill
Board of Directors: Andrew J McMahon, Henri De Castries, Scott D Miller, Ramon De Oliveira, Lorie A Slutsky, Denis Duverne, Ezra Suleiman, Danny L Hale, Peter J Tobin, Anthony J Hamilton, Richard C Vaughan, James F Higgins, Daniel G Kaye, Peter S Kraus, Kristi A Matus

D-U-N-S 07-861-1267
■ AXALTA COATING SYSTEMS LLC
(*Suby of* AXALTA COATING SYSTEMS LTD) ★
2001 Market St Fl 36a, Philadelphia, PA 19103-7105
Tel (215) 255-7932 *Founded/Ownrshp* 2013
Sales 258.9MM[E] *EMP* 250[E]
SIC 2851 3479 Polyurethane coatings; Painting, coating & hot dipping
Ch Bd: Charles W Shaver
Pr: Luke Lu
**CFO:* Robert Bryant
Ex VP: Robert Heffner
**Sr VP:* Michael A Cash
**Sr VP:* Michael F Finn
**VP:* Nigel Budden
**VP:* Michael Crickenberger
VP: Daniel Key
VP: Christopher Mecray
VP: Rajeev RAO

D-U-N-S 07-952-4986
▲ AXALTA COATING SYSTEMS LTD
2001 Market St Ste 3600, Philadelphia, PA 19103-7044
Tel (855) 547-1461 *Founded/Ownrshp* 2012
Sales 4.1MMM *EMP* 12,800[E]
Tkr Sym AXTA *Exch* NYS
SIC 2851 Paints & allied products
Ch Bd: Charles W Shaver
Pr: Michael A Cash
Pr: Steven R Markevich
CFO: Robert W Bryant
Chf Cred: Michael F Finn
Ofcr: Joseph F McDougall
VP: Rajeev RAO
Natl Sales: Spencer Stigall
Mktg Dir: Michael J Bennett
Board of Directors: Wesley T Bieligk, Orlando A Bustos, Mark Garrett, Deborah K Kissire, Andreas C Kramvis, Gregory S Ledford, Robert M McLaughlin, Lori J Ryerkerk, Samuel L Smolik

D-U-N-S 78-813-7867 IMP/EXP
■ AXALTA POWDER COATING SYSTEMS USA INC
DUPONT COATING SOLUTIONS
(*Suby of* AXALTA COATING SYSTEMS BELGIUM BVBA)
9800 Genard Rd, Houston, TX 77041-7624
Tel (800) 247-3886 *Founded/Ownrshp* 2013
Sales 100.1MM[E] *EMP* 250[E]

SIC 2851 Paints & allied products
Pr: Florian Girthofer
**Treas:* Ines Taboada
Plnt Mgr: Kevin Cadien

D-U-N-S 16-044-3177 IMP
▲ AXCELIS TECHNOLOGIES INC
108 Cherry Hill Dr, Beverly, MA 01915-1066
Tel (978) 787-4000 *Founded/Ownrshp* 1978
Sales 301.5MM *EMP* 808[E]
Tkr Sym ACLS *Exch* NGS
SIC 3559 3829 Semiconductor manufacturing machinery; Ion chambers
Pr: Mary G Puma
**Ch Bd:* Patrick H Nettles
CFO: Kevin J Brewer
Ex VP: John E Aldeborgh
Ex VP: William Bintz
Ex VP: Lynnette C Fallon
Ex VP: Douglas A Lawson
Ex VP: Russell Low
VP: Stephen Bassett
VP: Bintz Bill
VP: Marvin Farley
Board of Directors: Richard J Faubert, R John Fletcher, Arthur L George Jr, Joseph P Keithley, John T Kurtzweil, Barbara J Lundberg, Thomas St Dennis

D-U-N-S 12-630-2848
AXCESS FINANCIAL SERVICES INC
(*Suby of* CHECK N GO) ★
7755 Montgomery Rd # 400, Cincinnati, OH 45236-4197
Tel (513) 336-7735 *Founded/Ownrshp* 1996
Sales NA *EMP* 200
SIC 6141 Personal finance licensed loan companies, small
Pr: David Davis
CFO: Roger Dean
Ofcr: Roger Craig
VP: Douglas Clark
**VP:* Jared Davis
VP: Rick Pennington
VP: David Strano
VP: Keith Weyler
**Prin:* Robert M Beck Jr
Opers Mgr: Scott Pearson
Snr Mgr: Krista Darkins

D-U-N-S 14-784-8113 IMP
AXEL JOHNSON INC
(*Suby of* LEXA INTERNATIONAL CORP) ★
155 Spring St Fl 6, New York, NY 10012-5254
Tel (646) 291-2445 *Founded/Ownrshp* 1920
Sales 201.1MM[E] *EMP* 1,200[E]
Accts Ernst & Young Llp New York N
SIC 5171 Petroleum bulk stations & terminals
Pr: Michael D Milligan
Ch Bd: Antonia Axson Johnson
CFO: Ben J Hennelly
Ex VP: John Pascale
VP: Timothy Grier
VP: Clare Peeters
Prin: Sally Sarsfield
VP Opers: Riaz Rahman
Snr Mgr: Elias Flessas

AXELACARE HEALTH CARE
See AXELACARE HOLDINGS INC

D-U-N-S 94-887-0840
AXELACARE HOLDINGS INC
AXELACARE HEALTH CARE
15529 College Blvd, Lenexa, KS 66219-1351
Tel (877) 342-9352 *Founded/Ownrshp* 2008
Sales 79.9MM[E] *EMP* 1,800
SIC 8082 Home health care services
Pr: Michele Tamene
CFO: Larry Freni
Chf Mktg O: David Schaefer

D-U-N-S 05-868-8607
AXELON SERVICES CORP
ALGOMOD TECHNOLOGIES
44 Wall St Fl 18, New York, NY 10005-2408
Tel (877) 711-8700 *Founded/Ownrshp* 1977
Sales 103.4MM[E] *EMP* 1,100[E]
SIC 7379

D-U-N-S 79-914-9807 EXP
AXEON MARKETING LLC
2338 N Loop 1604 W, San Antonio, TX 78248-4521
Tel (210) 918-2000 *Founded/Ownrshp* 2007
Sales 92.1MM[E] *EMP* 40
SIC 1311 Crude petroleum & natural gas
CEO: Michael F Pesch
**Ch Bd:* Bill Greehey
**Sr VP:* Bradley C Barron
**Sr VP:* Paul W Brattlof
Off Mgr: Esther Salinas

D-U-N-S 80-920-2653
AXEON REFINING LLC
NUSTAR
(*Suby of* AXEON SPECIALTY PRODUCTS LLC) ★
750 Wshngton Blvd Ste 600, Stamford, CT 06901
Tel (210) 249-9988 *Founded/Ownrshp* 2007
Sales 425.0MM *EMP* 210
SIC 2911 Petroleum refining
Sr VP: Bradley C Barron
**Sr VP:* Mary Rose Brown

D-U-N-S 07-882-8213
AXEON SPECIALTY PRODUCTS LLC
(*Suby of* LINDSAY GOLDBERG LLC) ★
750 Wshngton Blvd Ste 600, Stamford, CT 06901
Tel (855) 378-4958 *Founded/Ownrshp* 2012
Sales 449.0MM[E] *EMP* 210
SIC 2911 Petroleum refining
CEO: David Kirshner
Pr: Darius Sweet
CFO: Amy Orr
VP: Rick Bird
CIO: Bruce Lewis

D-U-N-S 19-334-4632 IMP/EXP
AXH AIR-COOLERS LLC
401 E Lowry Rd, Claremore, OK 74017-3542
Tel (918) 283-9200 *Founded/Ownrshp* 2004
Sales 138.2MM[E] *EMP* 500
SIC 3443 Heat exchangers: coolers (after, inter), condensers, etc.
Off Mgr: Linda Skillern

D-U-N-S 12-095-7840
■ AXIALL CORP
(*Suby of* WESTLAKE CHEMICAL CORP) ★
1000 Abernathy Rd # 1200, Atlanta, GA 30328-5606
Tel (770) 395-4500 *Founded/Ownrshp* 2016
Sales 3.3MMM *EMP* 6,000[E]
SIC 2812 2821 2865 2861 2873 Alkalies & chlorine; Caustic soda, sodium hydroxide; Chlorine, compressed or liquefied; Plastics materials & resins; Vinyl resins; Polyesters; Plasticizer/additive based plastic materials; Phenol, alkylated & cumene; Acetone, natural; Methanol, natural (wood alcohol); Ammonia liquor
Pr: Albert Chao
Ch Bd: James Chao
COO: Ronnie Smith
**CFO:* M Steven Bender
Ofcr: George J Mangieri
Sr VP: Robert Buesinger
Sr VP: Michael J Mattina
Sr VP: Lawrence Teel
VP: Tim Cobaugh
VP: L Benjamin Ederington
VP: Andrew Kenner

D-U-N-S 02-205-5712
AXIALL LLC
11 Stanwix St Ste 1900, Pittsburgh, PA 15222-1312
Tel (412) 515-8149 *Founded/Ownrshp* 2014
Sales 11.5MM[E] *EMP* 1,000
SIC 2899 Chemical preparations

D-U-N-S 55-585-3949 EXP
■ AXIALL LLC
(*Suby of* AXIALL CORP) ★
1000 Abernathy Rd # 1200, Atlanta, GA 30328-5606
Tel (770) 395-4500 *Founded/Ownrshp* 1999
Sales 827.3MM[E] *EMP* 3,000[E]
SIC 2821 Plastics materials & resins
CFO: Gregory Thompson
**Ex VP:* Joseph C Breunig
VP Inf Sys: Steve Mowry

D-U-N-S 08-027-6809
AXIOM METALS INC
401 Penn Ave, Pittsburgh, PA 15221-2135
Tel (412) 243-8000 *Founded/Ownrshp* 2016
Sales 90.0MM *EMP* 16
SIC 5093 Nonferrous metals scrap
CEO: Glen S Gross
**Pr:* Steven C Derer
**CFO:* Mark Weis

D-U-N-S 13-022-5589 IMP/EXP
AXIP ENERGY SERVICES LP
1301 Mckinney St Ste 900, Houston, TX 77010-3066
Tel (832) 294-6500 *Founded/Ownrshp* 2002
Sales 1.2MMM[E] *EMP* 750
SIC 5084 7699 Industrial machinery & equipment; Compressors, except air conditioning; Compressor repair
CEO: Peter R Lane
Pr: Steve Hyche
CFO: Mark Dutcher
Treas: Dean Castleberry
Sr VP: Daniel B Cannon
Sr VP: Tanmay Desai
Sr VP: Kerry Galvin
Sr VP: Patricia Martinez
Sr VP: Scott McKinnon
VP: Awni Ayoubi
Area Mgr: Ray Cox

D-U-N-S 82-520-4188
AXIS SPECIALTY US HOLDINGS INC
(*Suby of* AXIS SPECIALTY GLOBAL HOLDINGS LIMITED)
11680 Great Oaks Way # 500, Alpharetta, GA 30022-2460
Tel (678) 746-9000 *Founded/Ownrshp* 2013
Sales 157.2MM[E] *EMP* 1,092
SIC 6719 Investment holding companies, except banks
CEO: Carlton W Maner
Sr VP: Peter Griffin
VP: Chris Howe
Snr Ntwrk: Stephen Simpson
VP Opers: Janice Ratliff

D-U-N-S 13-047-6240
AXIS SPECIALTY US SERVICES INC
(*Suby of* AXIS SPECIALTY US HOLDINGS INC) ★
11680 Great Oaks Way # 500, Alpharetta, GA 30022-2460
Tel (678) 746-9000 *Founded/Ownrshp* 2003
Sales NA *EMP* 1,000
SIC 6331 Fire, marine & casualty insurance & carriers
CEO: Carlton W Maner
CFO: Cheryl L Treas
CTO: Glen Gardener

D-U-N-S 96-835-0301
AXIUM PLASTICS LLC
9005 Smiths Mill Rd, New Albany, OH 43054-6650
Tel (614) 706-5955 *Founded/Ownrshp* 2011
Sales 135.0MM *EMP* 700
SIC 3089

D-U-N-S 60-130-7171
■ AXLE HOLDINGS INC
(*Suby of* KAR AUCTION SERVICES INC) ★
2 Westbrook Corporate Ctr, Westchester, IL 60154-5702
Tel (708) 492-7000 *Founded/Ownrshp* 2005
Sales 77.8MM[E] *EMP* 1,110
SIC 5012 Automobile auction; Automobiles
CEO: Thomas C Obrien
Treas: Sidney Kerley

D-U-N-S 14-394-6171
AXON SOLUTIONS INC
HCL AXON
(*Suby of* HCL TECHNOLOGIES LIMITED)
1 Evertrust Plz Ste 501, Jersey City, NJ 07302-3087
Tel (201) 680-7000 *Founded/Ownrshp* 2001
Sales 215.5MM *EMP* 1,000
Accts Sr Batliboi & Co Llp Gurga
SIC 8742 Management information systems consultant; Business consultant
CEO: Steve Peck
**Pr:* Richard Minney
**CFO:* Stephen Srivastava
**Treas:* Mark Leeson
**VP:* Dominic Brennan
VP: Ajay Chava
**VP:* Steve Grimes
**VP:* Simon Hopkins
**CTO:* Paul Conway
**CTO:* Adam Woollerson
Corp Couns: Carl Ailara

D-U-N-S 19-674-1979 IMP
▲ AXT INC
4281 Technology Dr, Fremont, CA 94538-6339
Tel (510) 438-4700 *Founded/Ownrshp* 1986
Sales 77.5MM *EMP* 1,045
Tkr Sym AXTI *Exch* NGS
SIC 3674 Semiconductors & related devices; Diodes, solid state (germanium, silicon, etc.)
CEO: Morris S Young
**Ch Bd:* Jesse Chen
CFO: Gary L Fischer
Ofcr: Philip C Yin
VP: Raymond Abbott
VP: Gary Fischer
VP: Robert G Ochrym
VP Bus Dev: Bob Ochrym
Sls Dir: Keith Lyall

D-U-N-S 83-984-9932
AXWAY INC
AXWAY SOFTWARE
6811 E Mayo Blvd Ste 400, Phoenix, AZ 85054-3132
Tel (480) 627-1800 *Founded/Ownrshp* 2012
Sales 152.7MM[E] *EMP* 541
SIC 7372 Prepackaged software
CEO: Christophe Fabre
**COO:* Christophe Ruilaud
**CFO:* Patrick Donovan
Chf Mktg O: Paul Fowler
Ex VP: Laurent Bride
**Ex VP:* Nick Ferrante
**Ex VP:* Roland Royer
Sr VP: Franck Kelogianian
Sr VP: Marcelo Ramos
Sr VP: Dave Robinson
Sr VP: Pat Ryan
Sr VP: Paul Shortell
VP: Gary Bachelor
VP: Mike Dayton
VP: Scott Hausman
VP: Charles Hoppensteadt
VP: Rob Nault
VP: Antoine Rizk
VP: Byron Wheeler
Exec: Laurent Menard

AXWAY SOFTWARE
See AXWAY INC

D-U-N-S 83-197-0400
■ AXYGEN BIOSCIENCE INC
(*Suby of* CORNING INC) ★
838 North St, Tewksbury, MA 01876-1256
Tel (978) 442-2200 *Founded/Ownrshp* 2009
Sales 35.9MM[E] *EMP* 1,200
SIC 3089 Injection molding of plastics

AY MCDONALD MFG CO
See A Y MCDONALD INDUSTRIES INC

AYC
See YAZAKI NORTH AMERICA INC

D-U-N-S 00-347-5254
AYCO CAFE
25 British American Blvd, Latham, NY 12110-1405
Tel (518) 782-5080 *Founded/Ownrshp* 2007
Sales 159.4MM[E] *EMP* 36[E]
SIC 5812 Cafe
Prin: Abigail Sroka
Exec: Allen Kummu

D-U-N-S 07-722-1448 IMP
■ AYCO CO L P
(*Suby of* GOLDMAN SACHS GROUP INC) ★
321 Broadway, Saratoga Springs, NY 12866-4110
Tel (518) 886-4000 *Founded/Ownrshp* 1994
Sales NA *EMP* 1,100
SIC 6411 6282 8742 7291

D-U-N-S 11-884-0284 IMP/EXP
AYCO FARMS INC
1501 Nw 12th Ave, Pompano Beach, FL 33069-1730
Tel (954) 788-6800 *Founded/Ownrshp* 1998
Sales 97.4MM *EMP* 40
SIC 5148 0161 Fresh fruits & vegetables; Melon farms
Pr: AVI Nir
Opers Mgr: Jacob Yishay

AYERCO CONVENIENCE CENTERS
See AYERS OIL CO

D-U-N-S 00-890-6224
AYERS OIL CO
AYERCO CONVENIENCE CENTERS
401 N 4th St, Canton, MO 63435-1351
Tel (573) 288-4464 *Founded/Ownrshp* 1972
Sales 136.1MM[E] *EMP* 220
SIC 5171 5411 5541 5172 Petroleum bulk stations; Convenience stores, independent; Filling stations, gasoline; Petroleum products
Ch: Robert E Ayers
**Pr:* Steven Ayers
**Sec:* James Crane
VP: Charles Nystrom
VP: Charles Porcelli

AYRSHIRE ELECTRONICS
See CDR MANUFACTURING INC

AZ DPS
See PUBLIC SAFETY ARIZONA

D-U-N-S 96-492-6153
AZ METRO DISTRIBUTORS LLC
60 Crossways Park Dr W # 400, Woodbury, NY 11797-2018
Tel (516) 812-0300 *Founded/Ownrshp* 2010
Sales 111.4MM *EMP* 210
SIC 5064 Electrical appliances, television & radio
CEO: David Menashi
**Ch:* Don Rultaggio

AZ PARTSMASTER
See ARIZONA PARTSMASTER INC

AZAMARA CRUISES
See CELEBRITY CRUISES INC

D-U-N-S 00-614-3994
AZCO INC (WI)
AZCO INTEGRATED CONSTRUCTION
806 Valley Rd, Menasha, WI 54952-1120
Tel (920) 734-5791 *Founded/Ownrshp* 1949, 1998
Sales 237.3MM *EMP* 517
Accts Grant Thornton Llp Appleton
SIC 1629 Industrial plant construction
Pr: John Trottier
CFO: Gregory Stock
Ex VP: Thomas Martin
VP: Pawe Barski
VP: Robert Brockington
VP: Dale Coenen
VP: Jenny Morrow
VP: Marjanne Prins

AZCO INTEGRATED CONSTRUCTION
See AZCO INC

AZCO STEEL
See BUSHWICK METALS LLC

D-U-N-S 05-785-3769
AZELIS AMERICAS INC
(*Suby of* AZELIS BENELUX NV)
262 Harbor Dr, Stamford, CT 06902-7438
Tel (203) 274-8691 *Founded/Ownrshp* 2015
Sales 162.6MM[E] *EMP* 77[E]
SIC 5085 5046 5169 Industrial supplies; Commercial equipment; Chemicals & allied products
Pr: Frank Bergonzi
CFO: Terry Moriarty

D-U-N-S 19-033-5794 EXP
AZKU INC
KHUDAIRI GROUP
1616 S Voss Rd Ste 550, Houston, TX 77057-2620
Tel (713) 782-1080 *Founded/Ownrshp* 2010
Sales 100.0MM *EMP* 150
SIC 5082 8711 General construction machinery & equipment; Oil field equipment; Building construction consultant
Pr: Aziz S Khudairi
**VP:* Mohammed Khudairi
**VP:* Sawsen Khudairi
Opers Mgr: Ibrahim Kubaisi
Opers Mgr: Laurent Nocca
Corp Couns: Brittainy Boessel

D-U-N-S 80-824-8517
■ AZTAR INDIANA GAMING CO LLC
CASINO AZTAR
(*Suby of* TROPICANA ENTERTAINMENT INC) ★
421 Nw Riverside Dr, Evansville, IN 47708-1047
Tel (812) 433-4000 *Founded/Ownrshp* 2010
Sales 54.5MM[E] *EMP* 1,407
SIC 7011 Casino hotel
VP: Lynn Strickland
Exec: Sara Lipking
Genl Mgr: Jason Gregorec
Mktg Dir: Stacey McNeill
Advt Mgr: Andy Herbertz

AZTEC
See XSE GROUP INC

AZTEC FACILITY MANAGEMENT
See AZTEC FACILITY SERVICES INC

D-U-N-S 05-219-1061
AZTEC FACILITY SERVICES INC
AZTEC FACILITY MANAGEMENT
11000 S Wilcrest Dr Ste 1, Houston, TX 77099-4351
Tel (281) 668-9000 *Founded/Ownrshp* 1981
Sales 54.8MM[E] *EMP* 1,000
SIC 7349 Building maintenance, except repairs
CEO: Sherra Aguirre
**COO:* Ernest Jaffarian
**CFO:* Rick Silverman
Genl Mgr: Bill Widman

AZTEC INDUSTRIES
See ACTIVAR INC

D-U-N-S 03-571-3130 IMP
AZTEC WELL SERVICING CO
300 Legion Rd, Aztec, NM 87410-4543
Tel (505) 334-6194 *Founded/Ownrshp* 1963
Sales 90.0MM[E] *EMP* 500[E]
SIC 1381 4213 Drilling oil & gas wells; Trucking, except local
Pr: Jerry W Sandel
**VP:* Stewart Peterson
**VP:* Jason Sandell

D-U-N-S 02-526-2510 IMP
AZTECA MILLING LP (TX)
(*Suby of* MISSION FOODS) ★
1159 Cottonwood Ln # 100, Irving, TX 75038-6108
Tel (972) 232-5339 *Founded/Ownrshp* 1980, 1996
Sales 180.4MM[E] *EMP* 403
Accts Coopers & Lybrand
SIC 0723 Flour milling custom services
Off Mgr: Elsa Maria Garza
Sls Mgr: Randy Hobert

AZTLAN GRAPHICS
See GONZALES ENTERPRISES INC

D-U-N-S 10-247-7817
AZTX CATTLE CO LTD
311 E Park Ave, Hereford, TX 79045-4307
Tel (806) 364-8871 *Founded/Ownrshp* 1983
Sales 169.2MM[E] *EMP* 180
SIC 0211

D-U-N-S 78-892-8000
AZURE FARMS INC
AZURE STANDARD
79709 Dufur Valley Rd, Dufur, OR 97021-3108
Tel (971) 200-8350 *Founded/Ownrshp* 1956
Sales 84.6MM[E] *EMP* 153[E]
SIC 5149 0723 2099 Organic & diet foods; Vegetable crops market preparation services; Food preparations
CEO: David Stelzer
Mill Mgr: Joe Isitt
Opers Mgr: Nathan Stelzer

AZURE STANDARD
See AZURE FARMS INC

D-U-N-S 07-624-5851
AZUSA PACIFIC UNIVERSITY
901 E Alosta Ave, Azusa, CA 91702-2701
Tel (626) 969-3434 *Founded/Ownrshp* 1899
Sales 297.2MM *EMP* 1,545
Accts Lb Capin Crouse Llp Brea Ca
SIC 8221 University
Pr: Jon R Wallace
**CFO:* Bob Johansen
**CFO:* Joan Singleton
**VP:* David Bixby
VP: Wanda Calnon
VP: David Dufault-Hunter
VP: Terry Franson
VP: Thomas Hunt
VP: Robert L Johansen
**VP:* John Reynolds
VP: Marcela Rojas
VP: Junine Schoen
Assoc Dir: Yuriko Bassett

D-U-N-S 07-983-6497
AZUSA UNIFIED SCHOOL DISTRICT
546 S Citrus Ave, Azusa, CA 91702-5932
Tel (626) 967-6211 *Founded/Ownrshp* 2015
Sales 10.8MM[E] *EMP* 1,300[E]
SIC 8211 Public elementary & secondary schools
Dir IT: Susie Vasquez
Pr Dir: Alicia Torres-Sharp
Teacher Pr: Steve Falkinburg

D-U-N-S 07-881-5719
AZUSA UNIFIED SCHOOL DISTRICT FACILITIES CORP
546 S Citrus Ave, Azusa, CA 91702-5932
Tel (626) 858-6159 *Founded/Ownrshp* 1961
Sales 59.5MM[E] *EMP* 1,092
SIC 8211 Public elementary & secondary schools
CEO: Burke Hamilton
Bd of Dir: Lisa Harrington
**VP:* Rosemary Garcia

AZZ GALVANIZING SERVICES
See NORTH AMERICAN GALVANIZING & COATINGS INC

D-U-N-S 00-801-2148
▲ AZZ INC (TX)
3100 W 7th St Ste 500, Fort Worth, TX 76107-8701
Tel (817) 810-0095 *Founded/Ownrshp* 1956
Sales 903.1MM *EMP* 3,538
Tkr Sym AZZ *Exch* NYS
SIC 3699 3613 3494 3312 Electrical equipment & supplies; Switchgear & switchboard apparatus; Valves & pipe fittings; Blast furnaces & steel mills; Coated or plated products
Pr: Tom E Ferguson
**Ch Bd:* Kevern R Joyce
CFO: Paul W Fehlman
Ofcr: Tara Mackey
VP: Matt V Emery
VP: William Estes
VP: Christopher Izzo
VP: Trey Quinn
VP: Robert J Steines
Rgnl Mgr: Mike Stroia
Site Mgr: Don Blair
Board of Directors: Venita McCellon-Allen, Daniel E Berce, Martin C Bowen, H Kirk Downey, Paul Eisman, Daniel R Feehan, Peter A Hegedus, Stephen E Pirnat, Steven R Purvis

AZZ WSI
See AQUILEX HOLDINGS LLC

D-U-N-S 09-580-6667 IMP/EXP
■ AZZ WSI LLC
(*Suby of* AQUILEX SPECIALTY REPAIR AND OVERHAUL LLC) ★
2225 Skyland Ct, Norcross, GA 30071-2960
Tel (678) 728-9200 *Founded/Ownrshp* 2008
Sales 154.0MM[E] *EMP* 900
SIC 1799

B

D-U-N-S 07-138-1289
B & B CONSULTANTS INC
SONIC DRIVE-IN
750 N 17th St, Las Cruces, NM 88005-4153
Tel (575) 524-8998 *Founded/Ownrshp* 1977
Sales 69.2MM[E] *EMP* 2,000
SIC 5812 Drive-in restaurant
Ch Bd: Bobby J Merritt
**Pr:* Barbara Stammer
CFO: Leslie Berriman
**VP:* Mike G Paulowsky

D-U-N-S 03-693-4248
B & B PLASTICS RECYCLERS INC
3040 N Locust Ave, Rialto, CA 92377-3706
Tel (909) 829-3606 *Founded/Ownrshp* 1998
Sales 155.3MM[E] *EMP* 180[E]
SIC 5093 2673 Scrap & waste materials; Bags: plastic, laminated & coated
Pr: Baltasar Mejia
**VP:* Bacilio Mejia

B & C AUTO
See REPUBLIC AUTOMOTIVE PARTS SALES INC

B & D INDUSTRIAL
See BEARINGS & DRIVES INC

D-U-N-S 17-480-7789
B & E RESOURCES LTD CO
39772 Us Highway 96 S, Buna, TX 77612-3520
Tel (409) 994-2653 *Founded/Ownrshp* 2004
Sales 158.5MM[E] *EMP* 600
SIC 1799 Insulation of pipes & boilers
Pr: Jimmy Branch
VP Sls: Ryllee Tettleton

D-U-N-S 07-950-6968
B & G ELECTRICAL CONTRACTORS OF NY INC (NY)
(*Suby of* B&G INDUSTRIES, LTD.)
7100 New Horizons Blvd, Amityville, NY 11701-1149
Tel (631) 669-6000 *Founded/Ownrshp* 1992
Sales 92.1MM *EMP* 250
SIC 1731 Electric power systems contractors
Pr: James Giorgio Jr
**VP:* Anthony Giorgio

D-U-N-S 16-563-7976
B & G FOOD ENTERPRISES INC
TACO BELL
1430 Sandra St, Morgan City, LA 70380-2136
Tel (985) 384-3333 *Founded/Ownrshp* 1982
Sales 45.3MM[E] *EMP* 1,300
Accts Darnall Sikes Gardes & Freder
SIC 5812 Fast-food restaurant, chain
Pr: Gregory Hamer
**Sec:* Brenda Hamer
Ex VP: Paul Woodberry
Exec: Tim McConnell
Genl Mgr: Joey Macnamara

D-U-N-S 12-415-7111
B & G FOOD ENTERPRISES OF TEXAS LLC
TACO BELL
(*Suby of* TACO BELL) ★
1430 Sandra St, Morgan City, LA 70380-2136
Tel (985) 384-3333 *Founded/Ownrshp* 1989
Sales 12.2MM *EMP* 1,000
Accts Darnall Sikes Gardes & Frede
SIC 5812 Fast-food restaurant, chain

B & H CONSTRUCTION
See B & H MAINTENANCE AND CONSTRUCTION INC

D-U-N-S 11-601-2659 IMP/EXP
B & H FOTO & ELECTRONICS CORP
B&H PHOTO-VIDEO
420 9th Ave, New York, NY 10001-1644
Tel (212) 239-7500 *Founded/Ownrshp* 1973
Sales 2.6MMM[E] *EMP* 1,001[E]
Accts Cohn & Reznick Llp Roseland
SIC 5946 5731 5961 Photographic supplies; Video cameras, recorders & accessories; Catalog & mail-order houses
Ch Bd: Herman Schreiber
Pr: Sam Goldstein
CFO: Israel Lebovits
Info Man: Jeremy Lavitt
Sls Dir: Henry Posner
Mktg Mgr: Barry Eisdenberg
Sls Mgr: John Pace

D-U-N-S 04-612-4574
■ B & H MAINTENANCE AND CONSTRUCTION INC
B & H CONSTRUCTION
(*Suby of* WILLBROS GROUP INC) ★
S Loop 207, Eunice, NM 88231
Tel (575) 394-2588 *Founded/Ownrshp* 2010
Sales 85.5MM[E] *EMP* 337
SIC 1623

B & H PUBLISHERS
See LIFEWAY CHRISTIAN RESOURCES OF SOUTHERN BAPTIST CONVENTION

D-U-N-S 00-442-8157
B & I CONTRACTORS INC
2701 Prince St, Fort Myers, FL 33916-5597
Tel (239) 344-3213 *Founded/Ownrshp* 1960
Sales 98.9MM[E] *EMP* 185
SIC 1711 1731 Warm air heating & air conditioning contractor; Plumbing contractors; Electrical work
Pr: Gary Griffin
Bd of Dir: Dave Johnson
**VP:* Jason Grabowski
Info Man: Joe Cherry
Snr Mgr: Matt Mason

D-U-N-S 82-633-9103
B & J FOOD SERVICE EQUIPMENT INC
236 N 7th St, Kansas City, KS 66101-3202
Tel (913) 621-6165 *Founded/Ownrshp* 1993
Sales 114.8MM[E] *EMP* 38[E]
SIC 5046 Restaurant equipment & supplies
CEO: Nancy Mosburg
**Pr:* Bill Mosburg
**Sr VP:* Robert Pickering
**VP:* Scott Mosburg

D-U-N-S 01-308-9362
B & L WHOLESALE SUPPLY INC (NY)
70 Hartford St, Buffalo, NY 14206
Tel (716) 853-2600 *Founded/Ownrshp* 1950
Sales 127.4MM[E] *EMP* 230
SIC 5033 5031 Roofing & siding materials; Roofing, asphalt & sheet metal; Shingles, except wood; Doors & windows
Pr: Donald R Tomeny
**Treas:* Arthur Finocchario
**VP:* Robert Latour
Brnch Mgr: Jason Koehler
Opers Mgr: Brian Lauffer
Opers Mgr: Andrew Shilling
Sls Mgr: Bob Castiglione
Sales Asso: Stephen Graves
Sales Asso: Dan Kent

D-U-N-S 08-595-5219
B & M OIL CO INC (OK)
5731 S 49th West Ave, Tulsa, OK 74107-8818
Tel (918) 445-0725 *Founded/Ownrshp* 1977
Sales 145.8MM *EMP* 52
SIC 5171 Petroleum bulk stations
Pr: James R Beavers
**VP:* Harold Musgrove

B & M RACING
See B&M RACING & PERFORMANCE PRODUCTS INC

D-U-N-S 03-506-1829
B & R STORES INC
RUSS SUPERMARKETS
4554 W St, Lincoln, NE 68503-2831
Tel (402) 423-9602 *Founded/Ownrshp* 1961
Sales 333.2MM[E] *EMP* 2,200
SIC 5411 Supermarkets
Pr: Patrick Raybould
**Ch Bd:* Russell W Raybould
**CFO:* Kipp Utemark
**Sec:* Anita C Raybould
Ofcr: Marty Dlouhy
**VP:* Tom Schulte
Dir IT: Kevin Martin
Mktg Dir: Eric Schafers
Sls Dir: Larry Elias
Pharmcst: Susan Irvin

D-U-N-S 06-663-7307 IMP/EXP
B & S PLASTICS INC
WATERWAY PLASTICS
2200 Sturgis Rd, Oxnard, CA 93030-8978
Tel (805) 981-0262 *Founded/Ownrshp* 1977
Sales 228.8MM[E] *EMP* 700
SIC 3089 Injection molding of plastics
CEO: Bill Spears
**Sec:* Sandy Spears

B & W
See EQUITY INTERNATIONAL INC

B A C
See BALTIMORE AIRCOIL CO INC

B A E S
See BROKEN ARROW ELECTRIC SUPPLY INC

D-U-N-S 00-658-7426 IMP
B A E SYSTEM
2101 W 10th St, Anniston, AL 36201-4223
Tel (256) 235-9671 *Founded/Ownrshp* 2011, 1999
Sales 99.9MM[E] *EMP* 85[E]
SIC 5051 Iron & steel (ferrous) products
Ch: Sir Richard Olver
Ql Cn Mgr: Tim Adams

D-U-N-S 00-239-7347 IMP/EXP
B BRAUN MEDICAL INC (PA)
(*Suby of* B BRAUN OF AMERICA INC) ★
824 12th Ave, Bethlehem, PA 18018-3524
Tel (610) 691-5400 *Founded/Ownrshp* 1957, 1979
Sales 954.6MM[E] *EMP* 4,099
SIC 3841 Surgical & medical instruments; Catheters
Ch Bd: Caroll H Neubauer
COO: Willem J Degoede
**COO:* Frank Katona
COO: Robert Kutteh
**CFO:* Bruce Heugel
CFO: Bruce A Heugel
**Ch:* Wes Cetnarowski MD
**Chf Mktg O:* Rob Albert
Ofcr: Charles Dinardo
Ex VP: Al Kiani
**Sr VP:* Cathy L Codrea
Sr VP: Charles A Dinardo
**Sr VP:* Joe Grispo Jr
VP: Rex Boland
VP: Cathy Codrea
VP: Chris Donigan
VP: Joseph Hugehes
VP: Joe Hughes
VP: Yenni Lim
VP: Isabelle Manier
VP: Greg Piatek

D-U-N-S 04-478-7661
B BRAUN OF AMERICA INC
(*Suby of* B. BRAUN NORDAMERIKA VERWALTUNGSGES. MBH)
824 12th Ave, Bethlehem, PA 18018-3524
Tel (610) 691-5400 *Founded/Ownrshp* 1997
Sales 672.5MM[E] *EMP* 4,099
SIC 6719 3841 Investment holding companies, except banks; Surgical & medical instruments
Ch Bd: Caroll H Neubauer

D-U-N-S 92-708-7163
B C C S INC
SOUTH BAY CONSTRUCTION COMPANY
1711 Dell Ave, Campbell, CA 95008-6904
Tel (408) 379-5500 *Founded/Ownrshp* 2004
Sales 90.7MM[E] *EMP* 136[E]
SIC 1542 Commercial & office buildings, prefabricated erection
Pt: Richard Furtado
VP: Wayne Smith
Dir Bus: Martin Tiscareno
Off Mgr: Linda Lipsius
Sfty Mgr: Jerry Fournier

B C D
See BCD TRAVEL USA LLC

B C I
See BREHM COMMUNICATIONS INC

B C I
See BUCKEYE CORRUGATED INC

D-U-N-S 01-059-6450
B C S INSURANCE CO
(*Suby of* BCS INSURANCE CO) ★
676 N Saint Clair St # 1500, Chicago, IL 60611-2927
Tel (312) 371-6006 *Founded/Ownrshp* 1952
Sales NA *EMP* 60
SIC 6321 Reinsurance carriers, accident & health
Pr: Daniel P Ryan
**Ch Bd:* Edward Baran
**VP:* Wendell H Berg

D-U-N-S 00-693-0465
B C S LIFE INSURANCE CO (INC) (IL)
(*Suby of* BCS INSURANCE CO) ★
2 Mid America Plz Ste 200, Oakbrook Terrace, IL 60181-4712
Tel (630) 472-7700 *Founded/Ownrshp* 1981
Sales NA *EMP* 35
SIC 6321 6311 Accident insurance carriers; Health insurance carriers; Life insurance carriers
Pr: Dan Ryan
**CFO:* William Dodge
**Treas:* Dale E Palka
**Sr VP:* Wendell H Berg
VP: Jack Doyle

D-U-N-S 93-291-4609
B C S S LTD
LOU BACRODT CHEVY MAZDA
1801 W Atlantic Blvd, Pompano Beach, FL 33069-2720
Tel (954) 971-3000 *Founded/Ownrshp* 1994
Sales 135.0MM *EMP* 300
SIC 5511 Automobiles, new & used
Genl Pt: Louis C Bachrodt III

B D & A
See BENSUSSEN DEUTSCH & ASSOCIATES LLC

D-U-N-S 01-131-1057 IMP/EXP
B D AMERICAN CO
OPICIWINES
25 De Boer Dr, Glen Rock, NJ 07452-3301
Tel (201) 689-1200 *Founded/Ownrshp* 1934
Sales 90.0MM[E] *EMP* 140
SIC 5182 Wine
Ch Bd: Hubert Opici
**Pr:* Dina Opici
**Ex VP:* Tom Deregibus
**VP:* Linda Opici
Sls Mgr: Jeff Burdge

B D I
See BEARING DISTRIBUTORS INC

B DT BEVERAGE
See BDT BEVERAGE LLC

B DALTON BOOKSELLER
See BARNES & NOBLE BOOKSELLERS INC

D-U-N-S 05-237-3966
■ B E & K ENGINEERING CO (INC)
(*Suby of* B E & K INC) ★
2000 International Pk Dr, Birmingham, AL 35243-4221
Tel (205) 972-6000 *Founded/Ownrshp* 1980
Sales 32.9MM[E] *EMP* 1,040
SIC 8711 Construction & civil engineering
CEO: Ted Kennedy
**Treas:* Doug Joehl

D-U-N-S 05-862-8074 IMP
■ B E & K INC
(*Suby of* KBR INC) ★
2000 International Pk Dr, Birmingham, AL 35243-4221
Tel (205) 972-6000 *Founded/Ownrshp* 2008
Sales 2.5MMM[E] *EMP* 11,000
SIC 1541 8711 1796 1711 Industrial buildings, new construction; Construction & civil engineering; Machinery installation; Mechanical contractor
Pr: David L Zimmerman
Pr: Randy Evans
Pr: Susan Steele
**CFO:* Clyde M Smith
**Ex VP:* John W Redmon
Dir IT: Mike Davison

B E P
See BUREAU OF ENGRAVING AND PRINTING

D-U-N-S 03-623-0956
B F FT MYERS INC (FL)
WENDY'S
(*Suby of* WENDYS) ★
3309 Collins Ln, Louisville, KY 40245-1629
Tel (502) 254-7130 *Founded/Ownrshp* 1998
Sales 37.5MM *EMP* 1,100
SIC 5812 Fast-food restaurant, chain
Pr: Ulysses L Bridgeman

D-U-N-S 03-482-4490 IMP
B F NASHVILLE INC
WENDY'S
(*Suby of* WENDYS) ★
1101 Kermit Dr Ste 310, Nashville, TN 37217-5103
Tel (615) 399-9700 *Founded/Ownrshp* 1994
Sales 16.0MM[E] *EMP* 1,116[E]
SIC 5812 Fast-food restaurant, chain
Pr: Ulysses Bridgeman
**VP:* Paul Thompson

D-U-N-S 00-692-0342
B F SAUL CO
7501 Wisconsin Ave, Bethesda, MD 20814-6519
Tel (301) 986-6000 *Founded/Ownrshp* 1892
Sales 90.4MM[E] *EMP* 1,820
SIC 6531 6411 Real estate managers; Real estate leasing & rentals; Property & casualty insurance agent
Pr: Steven Brand
Sr VP: Philip D Caraci
VP: Don Hachey
VP: Mary Mayer
CIO: Doug Hoyles
CTO: Ted Koutris
Opers Mgr: Mark Carrier

D-U-N-S 05-518-9385
B F SAUL REAL ESTATE INVESTMENT TRUST
7501 Wscnsin Ave Ste 1500, Bethesda, MD 20814
Tel (301) 657-2619 *Founded/Ownrshp* 1964
Sales 1.4MMM *EMP* 4,143
SIC 6512 6513 Nonresidential building operators; Apartment building operators

Ch Bd: B Francis Saul III
CFO: Stephen R Halpin Jr
Treas: Kenneth D Shoop
**Sr VP:* Philip D Caraci
Sr VP: Patrick Connors
VP: Scott Armstrong
VP: Scott Campbell
VP: Steven Corey
VP: Don Hachey
VP: Tom McLaughlin
VP: Carol Thomas
VP: Karen Walsh
Board of Directors: Gilbert M Grosvenor, George M Rogers Jr, John R Whitmore

D-U-N-S 78-200-9559 EXP
B F SOUTH INC
WENDY'S
3309 Collins Ln, Louisville, KY 40245-1629
Tel (502) 254-7130 *Founded/Ownrshp* 1996
Sales 105.3MM^E *EMP* 3,300
SIC 5812 Fast-food restaurant, chain
Pr: Ulysses Bridgeman

B FERNANDEZ & HERMANOS
See B FERNANDEZ & HNOS INC

D-U-N-S 08-030-5792
B FERNANDEZ & HNOS INC
Urb Luchetti Calle B, Bayamon, PR 00960
Tel (787) 288-7272 *Founded/Ownrshp* 1888
Sales 398.0MM *EMP* 365
SIC 5169 Food additives & preservatives
Pr: Angel Vasquez

D-U-N-S 09-000-1983 IMP
B FERNANDEZ & HNOS INC
B FERNANDEZ & HERMANOS
Carr 5 305 Urb Rr St Ca, Bayamon, PR 00961
Tel (787) 288-7272 *Founded/Ownrshp* 1954
Sales 338.2MM^E *EMP* 350
SIC 5181 5141 5182 Beer & other fermented malt liquors; Groceries, general line; Liquor
CEO: B Fernndez
**Pr:* At B Fernandez
VP: Reinaldo Aponte
VP: Mildred Garcia
VP: Mario Somoza
**VP:* Angel Vazquez
Genl Mgr: Hector Rivera
Genl Mgr: Damaris Torres
IT Man: Frances Vallejo

D-U-N-S 09-582-6731 IMP
B FOUR CORP
BALL'S SUPER FOOD STORES
3734 Pear St, Saint Joseph, MO 64503-1507
Tel (913) 321-4223 *Founded/Ownrshp* 1978
Sales 555.5MM^E *EMP* 4,000
SIC 5912 Drug stores
CEO: Michael J Beal
**Pr:* John Ball
**Sec:* Joann Ball

D-U-N-S 00-797-2730
B FRANK JOY LLC (DC)
5355 Kilmer Pl, Hyattsville, MD 20781-1034
Tel (301) 779-9400 *Founded/Ownrshp* 1917
Sales 86.3MM^E *EMP* 200
SIC 1623 Underground utilities contractor
Ch Bd: T Kenneth Joy
**Pr:* Melissa P Koehler
VP: James Mancuso
**VP:* Mike R Roche
MIS Dir: Dale Worley

B G
See BURROW GLOBAL LLC

B G SERVICE SOLUTIONS
See ISS WORLDWIDE

D-U-N-S 00-799-5996
B GREEN & CO INC (MD)
FOOD DEPOT
1300 S Monroe St Ste 1, Baltimore, MD 21230-1739
Tel (410) 783-7777 *Founded/Ownrshp* 1941
Sales 125.7MM^E *EMP* 200
SIC 5141 Groceries, general line
Owner: Benjamin Green
**COO:* Rick Rodgers
CFO: Mike Flanagan
**VP:* Benjamin L Sigman
Genl Mgr: Towanna Brown

B H
See BEAVERS HOLDINGS LLC

D-U-N-S 14-719-7008
B H C SERVICES INC
BRASON'S WILLCARE
26250 Euclid Ave Ste 901, Euclid, OH 44132-3696
Tel (216) 289-5300 *Founded/Ownrshp* 1985
Sales 11.0MM *EMP* 2,000
SIC 8082 Visiting nurse service
Pr: David Brason
**Prin:* Todd Brason

D-U-N-S 96-910-1018
B H P MINERALS INTERNATIONAL INC
BHP BILLITON
300 W Arrington Ste 101, Waterflow, NM 87421
Tel (505) 598-4200 *Founded/Ownrshp* 2011
Sales 39.1MM^E *EMP* 1,200
SIC 1481 Mine & quarry services, nonmetallic minerals
Pr: Patrick Risner

B H S
See BUFFALO HOSPITAL SUPPLY CO INC

D-U-N-S 83-596-4149 IMP/EXP
■ B H SHOE HOLDINGS INC
(*Suby of* BERKSHIRE HATHAWAY INC) ★
124 W Putnam Ave Ste 1, Greenwich, CT 06830-5317
Tel (203) 661-2424 *Founded/Ownrshp* 1992
Sales 360.3MM^E *EMP* 1,300
SIC 3143 Men's footwear, except athletic
Pr: James Issler
**VP:* Marc Hamburg

D-U-N-S 00-325-1113
■ B JOHNSON NASA/LYNDON SPACE CENTER
(*Suby of* NASA) ★
2101 Nasa Pkwy, Houston, TX 77058-3696
Tel (281) 483-0123 *Founded/Ownrshp* 1965
Sales NA *EMP* 3,121
SIC 9661 Space flight operations, government; Space research & development, government;
Dir Vol: Susan Bagerman
Pr: Gary Ash
CFO: John Corbett
Comm Man: Tom Randolph
Prgrm Mgr: Samuel Russell
Prgrm Mgr: Eugene Stansbery
Dept Mgr: Thomas Florio
Dept Mgr: Todd Holloway
Telecom Mg: Clifton McCarra
IT Man: Scott Guzman
IT Man: Kim Vaughn

B KWIK FOOD MART
See BUFFALO SERVICES INC

B L P MOBILE PAINT STORES
See MOBILE PAINT MANUFACTURING CO OF DELAWARE INC

B M D
See BUILDING MATERIAL DISTRIBUTORS INC

D-U-N-S 10-581-7472
B M J FOODS PR INC
PONDEROSA STEAKHOUSE
Carr 175 Km 0 2 Bo Rio Ca St Ca, Caguas, PR 00725
Tel (787) 286-7040 *Founded/Ownrshp* 1993
Sales 29.0MM^E *EMP* 1,615
Accts Kevane Grant Thornton San Jua
SIC 5812 Steak restaurant
Pr: Samuel Jove Fontan
**Treas:* Joanne Caceres
**Treas:* Luis Jove Rios
**Treas:* Nelsa Zequeira
**VP:* Samuel Jove Rios

B M W OF RIVERSIDE
See DAVID A CAMPBELL CORP

B MANISCHEWITZ COMPANY
See TMCI HOLDINGS INC

D-U-N-S 02-619-4469
■ B N S F INC
(*Suby of* BURLINGTON NORTHERN SANTA FE LLC) ★
616 S Boyd Ave, Newton, KS 67114-5227
Tel (316) 284-3260 *Founded/Ownrshp* 1876
Sales 34.6MM^E *EMP* 1,000
SIC 4011 Railroads, line-haul operating
Pr: Matt Rose
Sls Mgr: Dean Smith

B NY NATIONAL COMMUNITY
See BANK OF NEW YORK MELLON

B O C E S
See CAPITAL REGION BOCES

D-U-N-S 03-271-9630
■ B OF I FEDERAL BANK
BOFI FEDERAL BANK
(*Suby of* BOFI HOLDING INC) ★
4350 La Jolla Village Dr # 140, San Diego, CA 92122-1244
Tel (858) 350-6200 *Founded/Ownrshp* 1998
Sales NA *EMP* 50
SIC 6141 6163 Financing: automobiles, furniture, etc., not a deposit bank; Loan brokers
CEO: Greg Garrabants
**CFO:* Andrew Micheletti
Chf Mktg O: Eduardo Urdapilleta
Ofcr: Bill Baluka
Ofcr: Angie Sussner
**Ex VP:* Eshel Bar-Adon
**Ex VP:* Tom Constantine
**Ex VP:* Brian Swanson
Ex VP: Adriaan Van Zyl
Ex VP: Adriaan V Zyl
Sr VP: Robert Armstrong
Sr VP: Kyle Kolsky
Sr VP: Liz Nutting
Sr VP: Kristi Procopio
Sr VP: Salvatore Salzillo
VP: Pete Bauer
VP: Randall Becker
VP: Daniel Conley
VP: Jan Durrans
VP: Barbara Fronek
VP: Lisa Goodwin

B P
See BP LUBRICANTS USA INC

B P AMOCO BUSINESS SERVICES
See BP CORP NORTH AMERICA INC

D-U-N-S 01-835-0355
B P L CORP
BIG BOY RESTAURANT
27476 Holiday Ln, Perrysburg, OH 43551-3345
Tel (419) 874-1933 *Founded/Ownrshp* 1952
Sales 26.9MM^E *EMP* 1,500
SIC 5812 Restaurant, family: chain
Pr: David Bennett
**CFO:* Mark Wuertz
**Ch:* Milton W Bennett
**Ex VP:* Rob Armstrong
**VP:* Susan Baer
Off Mgr: Bobby Beasley

D-U-N-S 18-113-3174 IMP/EXP
B P OIL PIPELINE CO
(*Suby of* BP) ★
28301 Ferry Rd, Warrenville, IL 60555-3018
Tel (630) 420-5111 *Founded/Ownrshp* 1986
Sales 109.2MM^E *EMP* 3,000
SIC 4612 Crude petroleum pipelines
Pr: Ross Pilladi
Exec: Ian Davis

B P UPSTREAM TECHNOLOGY, DIV
See BP ENERGY CO

D-U-N-S 00-796-8068 IMP
B R FUNSTEN & CO (CA)
TOM DUFFY COMPANY DIVISION
5200 Watt Ct Ste B, Fairfield, CA 94534-4209
Tel (209) 825-5375 *Founded/Ownrshp* 1956
Sales 138.1MM^E *EMP* 325
SIC 5023 Resilient floor coverings: tile or sheet; Carpets; Wood flooring
CEO: Jim Funsten
**COO:* Curt Thompson
**CFO:* Judy Bruce
**VP:* Donna Lagano
**VP:* Bob Ramos
**VP:* Rick Wagner

B R S
See BRUCKMANN ROSSER SHERRILL & CO INC

D-U-N-S 03-407-4633
B R WILLIAMS TRUCKING INC (AL)
2339 Al Highway 21 S, Oxford, AL 36203-2906
Tel (256) 831-5580 *Founded/Ownrshp* 1958, 1966
Sales 83.1MM^E *EMP* 270
SIC 4213 4225 Contract haulers; General warehousing
Ch Bd: Gregory D Brown
**Pr:* Dee W Brown
Treas: Dee W Bron
**VP:* Kaye W Perry

D-U-N-S 83-104-5013
▲ B RILEY FINANCIAL INC
21860 Burbank Blvd, Woodland Hills, CA 91367-6477
Tel (818) 884-3737 *Founded/Ownrshp* 1973
Sales 112.5MM *EMP* 220^E
Tkr Sym RILY *Exch* NAS
SIC 7389 Financial services; Merchandise liquidators
Ch Bd: Bryant R Riley
Pr: Andrew Gumaer
**Pr:* Thomas J Kelleher
COO: Phillip J Ahn
Ex VP: Alan N Forman
Ex VP: David Seiden
Sr VP: Howard Weitzman
VP: Craig Fox
VP: Jennie Kim
Exec: Sharon Kopman
Snr PM: Celine Hur
Board of Directors: Robert D'agostino, Andrew Gumaer, Richard L Todaro, Mikel H Williams, Kenneth M Young

B S A
See BAPTIST ST ANTHONYS HOSPITAL CORP

B S A HEALTH SYSTEM
See BAPTIST/ST ANTHONYS HEALTH SYSTEM

B S I
See BUILDING SERVICE

D-U-N-S 02-365-0208
■ B S I HOLDINGS INC
(*Suby of* MASCO CORP) ★
100 Clock Tower Pl # 200, Carmel, CA 93923-8774
Tel (831) 622-1840 *Founded/Ownrshp* 2001
Sales 44.4MM^E *EMP* 2,000
SIC 1742

D-U-N-S 62-214-1919
B S W INC
WBS, INC.
(*Suby of* BASIN HOLDINGS US LLC) ★
111 Naida St, Pampa, TX 79065-6901
Tel (806) 669-1103 *Founded/Ownrshp* 1992
Sales 124.1MM^E *EMP* 160
SIC 5082 5084 Oil field equipment; Oil well machinery, equipment & supplies
Pr: Ronald G Hess
VP Sls: Reene Hotz

B T S
See BUSINESS TELECOMMUNICATIONS SERVICES INC

B V
See BLACK & VEATCH CORP

D-U-N-S 02-479-0552
B V HEDRICK GRAVEL & SAND CO (NC)
GROVE STONE & SAND DIVISION
120 1/2 N Church St, Salisbury, NC 28144-4311
Tel (704) 633-5982 *Founded/Ownrshp* 1924
Sales 337.4MM^E *EMP* 400
SIC 1442 7359 6512 3273 1541 1542 Construction sand mining; Gravel mining; Equipment rental & leasing; Commercial & industrial building operation; Ready-mixed concrete; Industrial buildings, new construction; Commercial & office building, new construction
Pr: Jeffrey V Goodman
**Ch Bd:* Frances H Johnson
**Sec:* Joanne Johnson
**VP:* Jane B Arnold
Board of Directors: Alma H Brady, Enoch A Goodman Jr

B W I
See BRIDGEWATER WHOLESALERS INC

D-U-N-S 61-545-3057
■ B WILLIAMS HOLDING CORP
(*Suby of* PITNEY BOWES INC) ★
1403 Foulk Rd Ste 200, Wilmington, DE 19803-2788
Tel (302) 656-8596 *Founded/Ownrshp* 1995
Sales 1.3MMM^E *EMP* 31
SIC 3579 3661 3861 7359 7629 6159 Mailing machines; Postage meters; Facsimile equipment; Photocopy machines; Business machine & electronic equipment rental services; Business machine repair, electric; Machinery & equipment finance leasing
Pr: Kenneth Kubacki

D-U-N-S 83-122-1580
B&C HOLDING CO LLC
351 Peabody Ave, Cabool, MO 65689-7415
Tel (417) 962-2300 *Founded/Ownrshp* 2006
Sales 124.7MM^E *EMP* 1,200^E
SIC 4212 4213 Liquid haulage, local; Trucking, except local

D-U-N-S 00-926-9445
▲ B&G FOODS INC
4 Gatehall Dr Ste 110, Parsippany, NJ 07054-4522
Tel (973) 401-6500 *Founded/Ownrshp* 1996
Sales 966.3MM *EMP* 2,003^E
Accts Kpmg Llp Short Hills New Je
Tkr Sym BGS *Exch* NYS
SIC 2013 2032 2033 2035 2099 Canned meats (except baby food) from purchased meat; Beans & bean sprouts, canned, jarred, etc.; Mexican foods: packaged in cans, jars, etc.; Canned fruits & specialties; Pickles, sauces & salad dressings; Syrups; Seasonings & spices
Pr: Robert C Cantwell
**Ch Bd:* Stephen C Sherrill
CFO: Thomas P Crimmins
Ofcr: Scott E Lerner
Ex VP: James Brown
Ex VP: Eric H Hart
Ex VP: William F Herbes
Ex VP: Vanessa Maskal
Ex VP: Vanessa E Maskal
Ex VP: Michael Sands
Ex VP: William H Wright
VP: Erin Lifeso
VP: Anthony Pacelli
VP: Bill Wright
Board of Directors: Deann L Brunts, Charles F Marcy, Cheryl M Palmer, Alfred Poe, David L Wenner

B&H PHOTO-VIDEO
See B & H FOTO & ELECTRONICS CORP

D-U-N-S 01-527-5899 IMP
B&M RACING & PERFORMANCE PRODUCTS INC
B & M RACING
100 Stony Point Rd # 125, Santa Rosa, CA 95401-4117
Tel (707) 544-4761 *Founded/Ownrshp* 2000, 2006
Sales 126.9MM^E *EMP* 200
SIC 5013 Automotive engines & engine parts; Automotive supplies & parts
Pr: Brian Applegate
CFO: Steve Potter
Prin: Jonathan Miller
VP Mktg: Bob Ritzman

D-U-N-S 09-455-9473
B&R OIL CO INC
(*Suby of* ATLAS OIL CO) ★
2147 S 3rd St, Niles, MI 49120-4007
Tel (269) 687-9642 *Founded/Ownrshp* 1978
Sales 577.9MM^E *EMP* 30
Accts Ernst & Young Llp Detroit M
SIC 5172 Petroleum products
CEO: Sam R Simon
Genl Mgr: Jeff Smith

D-U-N-S 07-848-1417
B&V - GENSLER JV
6800 W 115th St Ste 2200, Overland Park, KS 66211-2420
Tel (913) 458-6650 *Founded/Ownrshp* 2012
Sales 18.1MM^E *EMP* 1,000
SIC 8711 Engineering services
Pt: James Wallace
Pt: Douglas Anderson

D-U-N-S 96-290-5837
B&V-BAKER GUAM JV
6601 College Blvd, Overland Park, KS 66211-1504
Tel (913) 458-4300 *Founded/Ownrshp* 2010
Sales 98.4MM^E *EMP* 4,500
SIC 8711 Engineering services
Pt: Robert S Kulash
Pt: Black Veatch Corp
Pt: David M Martin

B&W Y-12
See BABCOCK & WILCOX TECHNICAL SERVICES Y-12 LLC

B-CCIWLA
See BETHESDA-CHEVY CHASE CHAPTER IZAAK WALTON LEAGUE OF AMERICA

D-U-N-S 96-469-3266
B-G WESTERN INC
1141 S 10th St, Watertown, WI 53094-6740
Tel (920) 261-0660 *Founded/Ownrshp* 1994
Sales 280.4MM^E *EMP* 1,487^E
SIC 3443 3469 3444 Industrial vessels, tanks & containers; Helmets, steel; Sheet metalwork
Pr: Tom Hall

D-U-N-S 04-412-7439
▲ B/E AEROSPACE INC
1400 Corporate Center Way, Wellington, FL 33414-2105
Tel (561) 791-5000 *Founded/Ownrshp* 1987
Sales 2.7MMM *EMP* 10,057
Accts Deloitte & Touche Llp Miami
Tkr Sym BEAV *Exch* NGS
SIC 2531 3728 3647 Seats, aircraft; Aircraft parts & equipment; Aircraft lighting fixtures
Ch Bd: Amin J Khoury
Pr: Werner Lieberherr
CFO: Joseph T Lower
Treas: Eric J Wesch
Chf Cred: Ryan M Patch
Bd of Dir: Michael Senft
VP: Doug A Armstrong
VP: Michelle Beck
VP: Sean J Cromie
VP: Douglas Debrecht
VP: Wayne Exton
VP: Jean-Pierre Foulon
VP: Matthias Funke
VP: Brian Hackler
VP: Keith Hagerich
VP: Leslie Hunt

VP: Robert Manning
VP: Pete Meister
VP: Edmund Moriarty
VP: Saul Pacheco
VP: Wynn Parrish
Board of Directors: James F Albaugh, David J Anderson, Richard G Hamermesh, Jonathan M Schofield, Mary M Vandeweghe, John T Whates

D-U-N-S 13-752-2962
■ B27 LLC
(*Suby of* DXP ENTERPRISES INC) ★
1417 Gables Ct Ste 201, Plano, TX 75075-7648
Tel (972) 244-4350 *Founded/Ownrshp* 2014
Sales 204.0MM[E] *EMP* 342
SIC 8741 5084 Management services; Pumps & pumping equipment

D-U-N-S 17-138-3305 IMP
B2B COMPUTER PRODUCTS LLC
IT SAVVY
313 S Rohlwing Rd, Addison, IL 60101-3029
Tel (630) 627-1400 *Founded/Ownrshp* 2004
Sales 240.1MM[E] *EMP* 105[E]
SIC 5045 Computers, peripherals & software
CEO: Michael Theriault
VP: Bill Dykema
VP: Jeff Greenberg
VP: Chris Kurpeikis
VP: Scott Rose
Genl Mgr: Roy Langhamer
VP Opers: Jim Morrow
Sales Exec: Jim Mundall
Mktg Dir: Jeremy Ecenbarger
Mktg Dir: Steve Theriault
Sls Dir: Kit Schmierer

D-U-N-S 04-384-4984
B4 TRAVEL GROUP INC
CARLSON WAGONLIT TRAVEL
701 Carlson Pkwy, Minnetonka, MN 55305-5240
Tel (763) 212-5000 *Founded/Ownrshp* 2008
Sales NA *EMP* 12,000
SIC 4724

D-U-N-S 13-045-2506 IMP
B456 SYSTEMS INC
(*Suby of* NEC CORPORATION)
200 West St, Waltham, MA 02451-1121
Tel (617) 778-5700 *Founded/Ownrshp* 2001
Sales 281.2MM[E] *EMP* 1,983[E]
SIC 3691 Storage batteries
Pr: David Vieau
COO: Chris Eisenhart
VP: Mujeeb Ijaz
VP: Don Kaiser
VP: David Pantano
Dir Lab: Kapila Wadumesthrige
Prgrm Mgr: Johnna Osgood
Prgrm Mgr: Rex Withers
Genl Mgr: Jesus Alvarez
Snr Sftwr: Keith Haynes
Snr Sftwr: Ed Suckstorff

D-U-N-S 11-868-4534
BA & W ENTERPRISES INC
AN ANTONIO AUTO AUCTION
13510 Toepperwein Rd, Live Oak, TX 78233-4004
Tel (361) 767-4100 *Founded/Ownrshp* 1991
Sales 170.0MM *EMP* 93
SIC 5012 Automobile auction
Pr: Wade Walker
**Pr:* Patty Walker
Genl Mgr: Brandon Walston

D-U-N-S 96-755-9774
BA HOLDINGS
(*Suby of* LUXFER GROUP 2000 LIMITED)
3016 Kansas Ave Bldg 1, Riverside, CA 92507-3445
Tel (951) 684-5110 *Founded/Ownrshp* 1985
Sales 97.7MM[E] *EMP* 400
SIC 3443 3728 Cylinders, pressure: metal plate; Aircraft parts & equipment
CEO: John S Rhodes

D-U-N-S 11-595-9744
■ BA MERCHANT SERVICES
NPC SALES
(*Suby of* BANK OF AMERICA CORP) ★
1231 Durrett Ln, Louisville, KY 40213-2041
Tel (502) 315-2000 *Founded/Ownrshp* 2004
Sales 73.9MM[E] *EMP* 1,700
SIC 7374 Data processing service
Pr: Mark D Pyke
**CFO:* David E Fountain
**Ex VP:* Robert C Robins

D-U-N-S 14-353-0892
■ BA MERCHANT SERVICES LLC
(*Suby of* NPC SALES) ★
1231 Durrett Ln, Louisville, KY 40213-2041
Tel (502) 315-2000 *Founded/Ownrshp* 2000
Sales 18.2MM[E] *EMP* 1,550
SIC 7374 Data processing service

D-U-N-S 15-083-0271
BABCOCK & BROWN HOLDINGS INC
(*Suby of* BABCOCK & BROWN INTERNATIONAL PTY LTD)
1 Pier Ste 3, San Francisco, CA 94111-2028
Tel (415) 512-1515 *Founded/Ownrshp* 2004
Sales 138.4MM[E] *EMP* 806
SIC 6211 Investment bankers
Ch: James V Babcock
Board of Directors: James Fantaci

D-U-N-S 78-502-5292
BABCOCK & BROWN RENEWABLE HOLDINGS INC
(*Suby of* BABCOCK & BROWN HOLDINGS INC) ★
1 Letterman Dr Ste 216, San Francisco, CA 94129-1495
Tel (415) 512-1515 *Founded/Ownrshp* 2006
Sales 125.4MM[E] *EMP* 806[E]
SIC 8711 Energy conservation engineering
Pr: Karen R Fagerstrom

D-U-N-S 00-128-9065 IMP/EXP
■ BABCOCK & WILCOX CO
(*Suby of* BABCOCK & WILCOX ENTERPRISES INC) ★
20 S Van Buren Ave, Barberton, OH 44203-3585
Tel (330) 753-4511 *Founded/Ownrshp* 1967, 2015
Sales 1.7MMM[E] *EMP* 2,000
SIC 1629 1711 3443 7699 8741 3822 Industrial plant construction; Power plant construction; Plumbing, heating, air-conditioning contractors; Fabricated plate work (boiler shop); Boilers: industrial, power, or marine; Boiler & heating repair services; Management services; Auto controls regulating residntl & coml environmt & applncs
Ch: E James Ferland
Pr: Gregory Calvin
**Treas:* Mark A Carano
Bd of Dir: Richard A Worden
**Sr VP:* Leslie C Kass
**Sr VP:* Mark S Low
**Sr VP:* Ken Zak
VP: Michael J Grady
VP: Craig Hansen
VP: Pamela A Horning
VP: James Kulig
VP: Walter Nischt

D-U-N-S 12-282-7819
■ BABCOCK & WILCOX CONSTRUCTION CO INC
(*Suby of* BABCOCK & WILCOX CO) ★
74 Robinson Ave, Barberton, OH 44203-2630
Tel (330) 860-6301 *Founded/Ownrshp* 1978
Sales 432.9MM[E] *EMP* 2,900
SIC 1629 Power plant construction
CEO: E James Ferland
**CFO:* Jenny L Apker
**Sr VP:* Mark S Low
**Sr VP:* D Paul Scavuzzo

D-U-N-S 07-981-4371
▲ BABCOCK & WILCOX ENTERPRISES INC
13024 Ballantyne Corporat, Charlotte, NC 28277-0496
Tel (704) 625-4900 *Founded/Ownrshp* 1867
Sales 1.7MMM *EMP* 12,700
Tkr Sym BW *Exch* NYS
SIC 3621 3829 Power generators; Nuclear instrument modules
Ch Bd: E James Ferland
CFO: Jenny L Apker
Treas: Mark A Carano
Ofcr: Wendy S Radtke
Ofcr: Paul Scavuzzo
Sr VP: Elias Gedeon
Sr VP: Jimmy B Morgan
Sr VP: James J Muckley
Board of Directors: Thomas A Christopher, Cynthia S Dubin, Brian K Ferraioli, Stephen G Hanks, Anne R Pramaggiore, Larry L Weyers

D-U-N-S 14-195-2312
■ BABCOCK & WILCOX TECHNICAL SERVICES Y-12 LLC
B&W Y-12
(*Suby of* BWXT) ★
301 Bear Creek Rd, Oak Ridge, TN 37830-2504
Tel (865) 574-1000 *Founded/Ownrshp* 2000
Sales 1.2MMM[E] *EMP* 4,600[E]
SIC 3483 3761 Missile warheads; Fin assemblies: mortar, bomb, torpedo, etc.; Guided missiles & space vehicles
VP: Dave Beck
IT Man: Jim Harvey

BABCOCK POWER
See THERMAL ENGINEERING INTERNATIONAL (USA) INC

D-U-N-S 12-436-4279 IMP/EXP
BABCOCK POWER INC
6 Kimball Ln Ste 210, Lynnfield, MA 01940-2684
Tel (978) 646-3300 *Founded/Ownrshp* 2002
Sales 627.7MM *EMP* 1,119
Accts Deloitte & Touche Llp Hartford
SIC 3443 3569 3433 Fuel tanks (oil, gas, etc.): metal plate; Air coolers, metal plate; Condensers, steam; Generators: steam, liquid oxygen or nitrogen; Burners, furnaces, boilers & stokers
Pr: Michael D Leclair
CFO: Donna Anderson
**CFO:* Anthony Brandano
Ex VP: Andrew C Allen
Ex VP: William J Ferguson Jr
Ex VP: Kumar Gopathi
Ex VP: John Hefferman
Sr VP: Edward C Dean
Sr VP: Xavier A Dorai
Sr VP: James D Dougherty
Sr VP: Stephen Kapsalis
VP: Daniel Buffone
VP: Rafael Cohen
VP: Douglas J Harding
VP: Angelos Kokkinos
VP: Scott H Leeman
VP: Fred Pyne
VP: Richard R Rochester
VP: Dudley B Spencer

BABCOCK SCHOOL OF BUSINESS
See WAKE FOREST UNIVERSITY

BABCOCK WLCOX TECH SVCS PANTEX
See CONSOLIDATED NUCLEAR SECURITY LLC

D-U-N-S 00-815-9634
BABEN MANAGEMENT LLC
3400 Industrial Park, Houma, LA 70363-3919
Tel (985) 879-2487 *Founded/Ownrshp* 1943, 2001
Sales 111.0MM[E] *EMP* 140[E]
SIC 5084 3599 Oil well machinery, equipment & supplies; Machine shop, jobbing & repair
VP: N B Nuel Jr
Off Mgr: Ray Robichaux
QC Dir: Pat Knight

BABIES "R" US
See TOYS "R" US-DELAWARE INC

BABSON CAPITAL MANAGEMENT LLC
See BARINGS LLC

D-U-N-S 07-657-6461 IMP
BABSON COLLEGE
231 Forest St, Babson Park, MA 02457
Tel (781) 235-1200 *Founded/Ownrshp* 1919
Sales 192.3MM *EMP* 750
Accts Pricewaterhousecoopers Llp Bo
SIC 8221 College, except junior
Pr: Kerry Murphy Healey
Ch Bd: Joseph Winn
Pr: Dennis Ringland
CFO: Philip Shapiro
Trst: Roland Jeannet
Chf Mktg O: Sarah Sykora
Ex VP: Erin Janklow
Sr VP: Edward Chiu
VP: Shayan Assar
VP: Eric Burns
VP: Yin Chen
VP: Jane Edmonds
VP: Brooke Greiner
VP: Shruthi Harve
VP: Caitlin Howard-Gomez
VP: Shafaat Khan
VP: Phillip Knutel
VP: Seth Kurlinski
VP: Marc Labbe
VP: Hanna Letts
VP: Wingkai Li

BABY PHAT GIRLZ
See PARIGI GROUP LTD

D-U-N-S 09-000-8855 IMP/EXP
BACARDI CORP (DE)
(*Suby of* BACARDI INTERNATIONAL LIMITED)
Km 2/6 Carretera 165 Rd S St, Catano, PR 00962
Tel (787) 788-1500 *Founded/Ownrshp* 1862, 1943
Sales 167.3MM[E] *EMP* 674
SIC 2085 Applejack (alcoholic beverage)
Pr: Joaquin Bacardi III
**VP:* Martin Guzman
VP Sls: Maggie Matias

D-U-N-S 00-414-9274 IMP
BACARDI USA INC
(*Suby of* BACARDI INTERNATIONAL LIMITED)
2701 S Le Jeune Rd, Coral Gables, FL 33134-5809
Tel (305) 573-8600 *Founded/Ownrshp* 1944
Sales 309.2MM[E] *EMP* 475
SIC 5182 Wine & distilled beverages
CEO: Robert Furniss-Roe
Pr: John P Esposito
CFO: Michael Misiorski
VP: Hector Ortiz
VP: Todd Prybylski
VP: Fredrick J Wilson III
Comm Dir: Amy Federman
IT Man: Omar Andujar
VP Mktg: Shane Graber
Mktg Mgr: Andrea Eastaugh
Counsel: Martin Voke

D-U-N-S 06-274-6300
BACE MANUFACTURING INC
SPM
(*Suby of* MEDPLAST GROUP INC) ★
3125 E Coronado St, Anaheim, CA 92806-1915
Tel (714) 630-6002 *Founded/Ownrshp* 2000
Sales 80.3MM[E] *EMP* 1,000
SIC 3089 Injection molding of plastics; Molding primary plastic
Pr: Richard R Harris
**VP:* Shannon White
Genl Mgr: Dough Bennett

D-U-N-S 02-287-5082 IMP/EXP
BACHMANS INC
FLOWERS BY BACHMAN'S
6010 Lyndale Ave S, Minneapolis, MN 55419-2289
Tel (612) 861-7600 *Founded/Ownrshp* 1991
Sales 81.5MM *EMP* 1,000
SIC 5992 5261 0181 5193 7359 Plants, potted; Flowers, fresh; Nurseries & garden centers; Ornamental nursery products; Nursery stock; Live plant rental
Ch Bd: Dale Bachman
Pr: Paul Bachman
Pr: Lesli Rauch
VP: Bachman Lee
CIO: Siebold Siebol
IT Man: Doug Johnson
IT Man: Jim Stokes
IT Man: Patrick Warden
IT Man: Richard Willoughby
VP Mktg: Kim Antonfon
VP Mktg: Lisa Paschke
Board of Directors: Alan Bachman, Dale Bachman, Lee Bachman, Paul Bachman, Martha Baker, Debra Hopp, John Johannson, Randall Tagawa, Susan Bachman West

D-U-N-S 19-888-5654
BACK TO SCHOOL ACQUISITION LLC
(*Suby of* STONINGTON PARTNERS, INC.)
540 Madison Ave Fl 25, New York, NY 10022-3242
Tel (212) 339-8500 *Founded/Ownrshp* 2003
Sales 9.2MM[E] *EMP* 3,207
SIC 8222 Technical institute
Mng Dir: Alexis Michas

D-U-N-S 62-113-2187 IMP/EXP
BACKCOUNTRY.COM LLC
WHISKEYMILITIA.COM
1678 Redstone Center Dr # 210, Park City, UT 84098-7612
Tel (801) 746-7580 *Founded/Ownrshp* 2015
Sales 678.0MM[E] *EMP* 500[E]
SIC 5091 4813 Sporting & recreation goods;
CEO: Jonathan Nielsen
**CFO:* Bill Mitchell
**Ex VP:* Ted Forbes
**Ex VP:* Pete Labore
VP: Jessica Kaing
VP: Justin Sibley
Prgrm Mgr: Michael Burleson
Prgrm Mgr: Nicole Greco
Snr Sftwr: Cory Hanson
**CTO:* CJ Singh
Dir IT: Jim Cody

D-U-N-S 96-963-1584 IMP/EXP
BACKER EHP INC
BACKER-SPRINGFIELD
4700 John Bragg Hwy, Murfreesboro, TN 37127-7599
Tel (615) 907-6900 *Founded/Ownrshp* 2011
Sales 232.5MM[E] *EMP* 781
Accts Bkd Llp Bowling Green Ky
SIC 3567 3585 Heating units & devices, industrial: electric; Heating & air conditioning combination units
CEO: Thomas Egerstrom
Dir IT: Rick Smith

BACKER-SPRINGFIELD
See BACKER EHP INC

D-U-N-S 15-118-4082
BACKUS CORP
326 Washington St, Norwich, CT 06360-2740
Tel (860) 823-6330 *Founded/Ownrshp* 1983
Sales 55.9M *EMP* 1,447
Accts Bkd Llp Kansas City Mo
SIC 8741 Hospital management
Pr: Thomas P Pipicelli

BACKYARD DISCOVERY
See LEISURE TIME PRODUCTS LLC

D-U-N-S 79-133-6824 IMP
BACKYARD PRODUCTS LLC
HANDY HOME
1000 Ternes Dr, Monroe, MI 48162-5224
Tel (734) 242-6900 *Founded/Ownrshp* 2009
Sales 243.1MM[E] *EMP* 432
SIC 2452 2511 Prefabricated wood buildings; Play pens, children's: wood
CFO: Daniel Smoke
Mktg Mgr: Brennan Deitsch

D-U-N-S 36-121-0086
BACKYARD STORAGE SOLUTIONS LLC
HEARTLAND INDUSTRIES
(*Suby of* HANDY HOME) ★
1000 Ternes Dr, Monroe, MI 48162-5224
Tel (734) 242-6900 *Founded/Ownrshp* 2005
Sales 84.1MM[E] *EMP* 225[E]
SIC 2452 Prefabricated buildings, wood
CEO: Thomas Van Der Meulen
IT Man: Andrew Elias

D-U-N-S 94-626-8281
BACO RATON COMMUNITY HOSPITAL INC
LYNN REGIONAL CANCER INSTITUTE
800 Meadows Rd, Boca Raton, FL 33486-2368
Tel (561) 955-5966 *Founded/Ownrshp* 1962
Sales 270.0MM *EMP* 2,000[E]
SIC 8093 Rehabilitation center, outpatient treatment
Ch: Richard Schmidt
**Pr:* Gary Strack
Dir Rx: Gary Dalin
Ex Dir: Brian Altschuler
CIO: Robin Hildwein
Mktg Dir: Lisa Cook

BACOME INSURANCE AGENCY
See JAMES G PARKER INSURANCE ASSOCIATES

BADCOCK HOME FURNITURE & MORE
See WS BADCOCK CORP

D-U-N-S 00-615-3142 IMP
BADGER CORRUGATING CO (WI)
1801 West Ave S, La Crosse, WI 54601-6239
Tel (608) 788-0100 *Founded/Ownrshp* 1903
Sales 138.6MM[E] *EMP* 165
SIC 5031 Building materials, exterior; Building materials, interior
Pr: Michael Sexauer
Opers Mgr: David Scidmore
Sls Mgr: Pari Sexauer
Sales Asso: Slade Hendrikson
Sales Asso: Garret Prince

D-U-N-S 10-643-0734
BADGER DAYLIGHTING CORP
(*Suby of* BADGER DAYLIGHTING USA INC) ★
8930 Motorsports Way, Brownsburg, IN 46112-2519
Tel (317) 456-1432 *Founded/Ownrshp* 1998
Sales 192.0MM *EMP* 51
SIC 1389 Hydraulic fracturing wells
Pr: Paul Vanderberg
**COO:* John Kelly
**CFO:* Gerald Schiefelbein

D-U-N-S 12-341-1659
BADGER DAYLIGHTING USA INC
(*Suby of* BADGER DAYLIGHTING LTD)
8930 Motorsports Way, Brownsburg, IN 46112-2519
Tel (317) 456-1050 *Founded/Ownrshp* 2001
Sales 192.0MM[E] *EMP* 60
SIC 1389 Hydraulic fracturing wells
Pr: Tor Wilson
**VP:* Greg Kelly
Area Mgr: David Oberg
Opers Supe: Alicia Wollinger
Natl Sales: Dustin Culverhouse

D-U-N-S 08-254-9916
BADGER FARMS INC (IL)
MURPHY FOODSERVICE
652 N Western Ave, Chicago, IL 60612-1216
Tel (773) 278-9100 *Founded/Ownrshp* 1953
Sales 92.6MM[E] *EMP* 60
SIC 5143 5149 5147 5144 5142 5087 Butter; Cheese; Crackers, cookies & bakery products; Meats & meat products; Poultry products; Eggs; Packaged frozen goods; Service establishment equipment
Pr: Jay F Nichols
**Pr:* Jay Nichols
Genl Mgr: Dave Fleming
Genl Mgr: Kevin Joyce
Sales Exec: Larry Dorfman

D-U-N-S 05-291-1849 IMP
BADGER LIQUOR CO INC (WI)
850 Morris St, Fond Du Lac, WI 54935-5649
Tel (920) 923-8160 *Founded/Ownrshp* 1958, 1970
Sales 113.5MM[E] *EMP* 300
SIC 5182 Liquor; Wine
Pr: Gary Sadoff

*VP: Thomas Griffin
Dir IT: Ed Brushaser

BADGER LIQUOR-MADISON
See FRANK LIQUOR CO INC

D-U-N-S 00-606-9710 IMP
▲ BADGER METER INC (WI)
4545 W Brown Deer Rd, Milwaukee, WI 53223-2479
Tel (414) 355-0400 Founded/Ownrshp 1905
Sales 377.7MM EMP 1,514
Tkr Sym BMI Exch NYS
SIC 3824 3491 3823 Water meters; Industrial valves; Process control regulator valves; Flow instruments, industrial process type; Gas flow computers, industrial process type; Controllers for process variables, all types
Ch Bd: Richard A Meeusen
CFO: Richard E Johnson
VP: William R A Bergum
VP: Ronald Dix
VP: Horst E Gras
VP: Stephanie Riewer
VP: Beverly L P Smiley
VP: Daniel D Zandron
VP Bus Dev: Gregory O Gomez Jr
Exec: Jay Herb
Rgnl Mgr: Rick Green
Board of Directors: Ronald H Dix, Thomas J Fischer, Gale E Klappa, Gail A Lione, Andrew J Policano, Steven J Smith, James F Stern, Todd J Teske

D-U-N-S 09-302-9007 IMP/EXP
BADGER MINING CORP
BMC
409 S Church St, Berlin, WI 54923-2114
Tel (920) 361-2388 Founded/Ownrshp 1978
Sales 690.6MM^E EMP 180
SIC 1446 Industrial sand
Pr: Timothy J Wuest
*CEO: Michael C Hess
CFO: Bob Brooks
*Sec: Robert Brooks
Bd of Dir: Vicky Wuest
Ex VP: Stephen Hart
Ex VP: Cody Wickersheim
VP: Erica Grant
*VP: Sara Joyce
VP: Dan Valiquette
Opers Supe: Ralph Taylor

D-U-N-S 00-388-5561
■ BADLANDS POWER FUELS LLC
(Suby of NUVERRA ENVIRONMENTAL SOLUTIONS INC) ★
3711 4th Ave Ne, Watford City, ND 58854-7027
Tel (701) 842-3618 Founded/Ownrshp 2012
Sales 183.5MM^E EMP 1,000
SIC 2869 Fuels
CEO: Mark D Johnsrud
*CFO: Jay Parkinson
Dist Mgr: Bob Watterud

D-U-N-S 07-900-4032 IMP
BAE SYSTEMS
(Suby of BAE SYSTEMS PLC)
7822 S 46th St, Phoenix, AZ 85044-5313
Tel (602) 643-7233 Founded/Ownrshp 1975, 2013
Sales 255.1MM^E EMP 1,500
SIC 2531 Seats, aircraft; Vehicle furniture; Seats, railroad
Pr: Bradley P Forst
*CFO: John A Jenson
*Ex VP: Joseph W Coltman
VP: Leila Duguay
Exec: Lisa Bell
Prgrm Mgr: James Olofsson
Snr Sftwr: David Sheh
Dir IT: Mike McDermott
Site Mgr: Bill Chapman
Opers Mgr: Jonilyn Martinez
Sls&Mrk Ex: Laura Neel

D-U-N-S 04-586-0756 IMP/EXP
BAE SYSTEMS AH INC
SAFARILAND
13386 International Pkwy, Jacksonville, FL 32218-2383
Tel (904) 741-5400 Founded/Ownrshp 2007
Sales 1.0MMM^E EMP 8,175
SIC 3711 3842 3312 3728

D-U-N-S 04-318-3123 IMP
BAE SYSTEMS CONTROLS INC
(Suby of BAE SYSTEMS INC) ★
1098 Clark St, Endicott, NY 13760-2815
Tel (607) 770-2000 Founded/Ownrshp 2000
Sales 397.2MM^E EMP 2,450
SIC 3812 Aircraft/aerospace flight instruments & guidance systems
Pr: Thomas A Asrseneault
Dir Bus: Frank McBride
Dir Bus: Ian Wilson
Prin: Joyce Sherwood
Prgrm Mgr: Steven Johnston
Prgrm Mgr: Rick Polhamus
Prgrm Mgr: Jeff Travis
Prgrm Mgr: Allison Vaughan
Prgrm Mgr: Mike Waters
Genl Mgr: Katelyn Warren
MIS Dir: Victor Gac

D-U-N-S 87-686-1790 IMP/EXP
BAE SYSTEMS HOLDINGS INC
(Suby of BAE SYSTEMS PLC)
1101 Wilson Blvd Ste 2000, Arlington, VA 22209-2293
Tel (703) 312-6100 Founded/Ownrshp 1999
Sales 12.2MMM^E EMP 51,813
SIC 3699 3728 3812 Electrical equipment & supplies; Electronic training devices; Aircraft parts & equipment; Search & navigation equipment
CEO: Ian King
Pr: Douglas Belair
Pr: Dennis Morris
Pr: Scott Obrien
Pr: Richard Schieffelin
VP: Richard J Millies
VP: Ted Spilman
DP Exec: James Williams
Genl Couns: Philip Bramwell

D-U-N-S 78-642-9894 EXP
BAE SYSTEMS INC
(Suby of BAE SYSTEMS HOLDINGS INC) ★
1101 Wilson Blvd Ste 2000, Arlington, VA 22209-2293
Tel (703) 312-6100 Founded/Ownrshp 1999
Sales 12.0MMM^E EMP 51,499
SIC 3812 3728 Search & detection systems & instruments; Navigational systems & instruments; Radar systems & equipment; Missile guidance systems & equipment; Countermeasure dispensers, aircraft; Chaff dispensers, aircraft
Pr: Gerard J Demuro
Pr: Dan Gobel
Pr: Deette Gray
COO: Thomas A Arseneault
COO: Linda Hudson
CFO: Roy E Perkins
Treas: Guy Montminy
Treas: Terence Shaw
Bd of Dir: Robert Natter
Ex VP: Sheila C Cheston
Ex VP: Brian Jones
Sr VP: Kristie Cunningham
*Sr VP: Ian T Graham
Sr VP: Steve Hanau
VP: Bill Anderson Anderson
VP: Rick Anderson
VP: Chuck Brummund
VP: Doug Coffey
VP: Gordon Eldridge
VP: Duncan Greene II
VP: Jerry Hammonds
Board of Directors: Ellen Tauscher, John F Campbell, Michael G Vickers, Michael Chertoff, Jonathan W Greenert, Lee Hamilton, Richard J Kerr, Ian Graham King, Peter John Lynas, Robert Natter, Frank Ruggiero

D-U-N-S 00-514-9120
BAE SYSTEMS INFORMATION AND ELECTRONIC SYSTEMS INTEGRATION INC (DE)
(Suby of BAE SYSTEMS INC) ★
65 Spit Brook Rd, Nashua, NH 03060-6909
Tel (603) 885-4321 Founded/Ownrshp 1951, 2000
Sales 2.1MMM^E EMP 7,600^E
SIC 3812 Search & navigation equipment
Pr: Tom Arseneault
VP: Rich Ashooh
VP: Douglas Coleman
VP: Don Donovan
VP: John F Lydiard III
VP: Jeff Markel
VP: Alan Stiley
VP: Mark Supko
Prgrm Mgr: Steve Danielson
Prgrm Mgr: Dennis Hart
Prgrm Mgr: Jamie A Hoffpauir

D-U-N-S 04-582-8282
BAE SYSTEMS INFORMATION SOLUTIONS INC
(Suby of BAE SYSTEMS TECHNOLOGY SOLUTIONS & SERVICES INC) ★
8201 Greensboro Dr # 1200, Mc Lean, VA 22102-3846
Tel (703) 847-5820 Founded/Ownrshp 1981
Sales 478.8MM^E EMP 6,500
SIC 8742 Quality assurance consultant
Pr: Deette D Gray
*Treas: Robert L Taylor
*VP: Jennifer H Allen
VP: Lawrence Lyons
Dir Surg: Sherri Carmichael
VP Opers: Richard Schieffelin
VP Mktg: Bill Shernit

BAE SYSTEMS LAND & ARMAMENTS
See BAE SYSTEMS SHIP REPAIR INC

D-U-N-S 82-482-5459 IMP
BAE SYSTEMS LAND & ARMAMENTS INC
(Suby of BAE SYSTEMS INC) ★
2000 15th Nw, Arlington, VA 22201
Tel (703) 907-8200 Founded/Ownrshp 2005
Sales 620.2MM^E EMP 7,700
SIC 3721 3795 Aircraft; Tanks & tank components
Pr: Erwin Bieber
Treas: James M Blue
VP: Dennis A Wagner

D-U-N-S 05-445-6657 IMP/EXP
BAE SYSTEMS LAND & ARMAMENTS LP
(Suby of BAE SYSTEMS INC) ★
2000 15th Nw Fl 11, Arlington, VA 22201
Tel (703) 312-6100 Founded/Ownrshp 1994
Sales 688.2MM^E EMP 4,577
SIC 3795 3812 Tanks & tank components; Search & navigation equipment
CEO: Linda Hudson
VP: Jennifer Allen
VP: Elmer Doty
Netwrk Eng: Terry Daniels
Genl Couns: Trish Byrne
Genl Couns: Catherine K Ronis
Counsel: Alexandra Fowler
Counsel: Gregory Reece

D-U-N-S 79-703-2372 IMP
BAE SYSTEMS NATIONAL SECURITY SOLUTIONS INC
10920 Technology Pl, San Diego, CA 92127-1874
Tel (858) 592-5000 Founded/Ownrshp 1998
Sales 228.8MM^E EMP 2,200
SIC 3825 7373 3812

D-U-N-S 00-317-5072 IMP/EXP
BAE SYSTEMS NORFOLK SHIP REPAIR INC (VA)
NORSHIPCO
(Suby of BAE SYSTEMS LAND & ARMAMENTS) ★
750 W Berkley Ave, Norfolk, VA 23523-1032
Tel (757) 494-4000 Founded/Ownrshp 1915
Sales 228.8MM^E EMP 1,200
SIC 3731 3732 7699 Shipbuilding & repairing; Barges, building & repairing; Lighters, marine: building & repairing; Ferryboats, building & repairing; Yachts, building & repairing; Nautical repair services
CEO: Ian King
*Pr: William Clifford
*VP: Thomas Seitz
VP Sls: George H Curtis
Board of Directors: Moseley Erin R-President, Allen Jennifer H-Vice Preside, Shaw Terry L-Treasurer

D-U-N-S 04-947-8725
BAE SYSTEMS ORDNANCE SYSTEMS INC
(Suby of BAE SYSTEMS HOLDINGS INC) ★
4509 W Stone Dr, Kingsport, TN 37660-1048
Tel (423) 578-6000 Founded/Ownrshp 1999
Sales 154.8MM^E EMP 450
SIC 3483 Chemical warfare projectiles & components
CEO: Linda Hudson
*CEO: Ian King
*Treas: Donald Neff
*Sec: D Mark Baker
*VP: K Bruce Hamilton

D-U-N-S 09-248-5390 IMP
BAE SYSTEMS POWER INC
(Suby of BAE SYSTEMS RESOLUTION INC) ★
5840 Dahlia St, Commerce City, CO 80022-3707
Tel (303) 287-7441 Founded/Ownrshp 2007
Sales 108.3MM^E EMP 696
SIC 5084 3531 3999 3569 Engines & parts, diesel; Road construction & maintenance machinery; Wheelchair lifts; Gas generators
Pr: Mike Grimes
Treas: Pat O'Rourke
VP: Cindy R Bergstrom
VP: Lawrence Wilson
Div Mgr: Jim Keeley

D-U-N-S 80-754-5538 IMP/EXP
BAE SYSTEMS PROTECTION SYSTEMS INC
(Suby of BAE SYSTEMS) ★
7822 S 46th St, Phoenix, AZ 85044-5313
Tel (602) 643-7233 Founded/Ownrshp 1993
Sales 176.7MM^E EMP 1,000^E
SIC 3721 2353 3795 3842 Aircraft; Hats, caps & millinery; Tanks & tank components; Surgical appliances & supplies
Genl Mgr: Don Dutton
*Pr: Erin R Moseley
*Treas: Patrick L Cristofari
*VP: Jennifer H Allen
*VP: Doug Coleman
VP: George Stringer
DP Dir: Norm Latino

D-U-N-S 00-793-2783 IMP/EXP
BAE SYSTEMS RESOLUTION INC (TX)
(Suby of STEWART & STEVENSON LLC) ★
1000 La St Ste 4950, Houston, TX 77002
Tel (713) 868-7700 Founded/Ownrshp 1902
Sales 141.8MM^E EMP 1,139^E
SIC 3713 5084 3711 7699 3351 3829 Van bodies; Dump truck bodies; Industrial machinery & equipment; Scout cars (motor vehicles), assembly of; Universal carriers, military, assembly of; Wreckers (tow truck), assembly of; Industrial equipment services; Nautical repair services; Construction equipment repair; Tubing, copper & copper alloy; Seismographs
Pr: Max L Lukens
Ch Bd: Howard Wolf
Pr: Ian T Graham
CFO: L Scott Biar
Sr VP: Carl B King
VP: Britt Davis
VP: James W Lajeunesse

D-U-N-S 08-091-1274 IMP
BAE SYSTEMS SAN DIEGO SHIP REPAIR INC (CA)
(Suby of BAE SYSTEMS LAND & ARMAMENTS) ★
2205 E Belt St Foot Of S, San Diego, CA 92113
Tel (619) 238-1000 Founded/Ownrshp 1976, 1997
Sales 228.8MM^E EMP 1,365
SIC 3731 Shipbuilding & repairing; Barges, building & repairing; Lighters, marine: building & repairing; Ferryboats, building & repairing
Pr: Erwin Bieber
*VP: James M Blue
*VP: Alice M Eldridge
VP: Thena Fantasia
VP: Bob Koerber
VP Bus Dev: Usn Camacho
Prgrm Mgr: Sara Madrid
Prgrm Mgr: Joe Wiederholt
Genl Mgr: Irene Falo
Snr Sftwr: Michael Panlasigui
Snr Sftwr: Duyen Phan
Board of Directors: Allan M Holt, Raymond A Whiteman

BAE SYSTEMS SE SHIPYARDS
See BAE SYSTEMS SOUTHEAST SHIPYARDS AMHC INC

D-U-N-S 04-355-4364
BAE SYSTEMS SHIP REPAIR INC
BAE SYSTEMS LAND & ARMAMENTS
(Suby of BAE SYSTEMS LAND & ARMAMENTS INC) ★
750 W Berkley Ave, Norfolk, VA 23523-1032
Tel (757) 494-4000 Founded/Ownrshp 2005
Sales 520.4MM^E EMP 2,570
SIC 3731 3732 Shipbuilding & repairing; Barges, building & repairing; Lighters, marine: building & repairing; Ferryboats, building & repairing; Yachts, building & repairing
Pr: Moseley Erin
*VP: Herr David
VP: Geneva Lee
*VP: Brad Moyer
Opers Mgr: Robert Penley
Snr Mgr: Jim Thomas

D-U-N-S 19-997-0039
BAE SYSTEMS SOUTHEAST SHIPYARDS ALABAMA LLC
(Suby of BAE SYSTEMS SE SHIPYARDS) ★
Mn Gate Dunlap Dr, Mobile, AL 36652
Tel (251) 690-7100 Founded/Ownrshp 1916
Sales 104.5MM^E EMP 600
SIC 3731 Shipbuilding & repairing
VP: Richard McCreary
Genl Mgr: Kent Purser

D-U-N-S 19-463-4457 IMP
BAE SYSTEMS SOUTHEAST SHIPYARDS AMHC INC
BAE SYSTEMS SE SHIPYARDS
(Suby of BAE SYSTEMS INC) ★
8500 Heckscher Dr, Jacksonville, FL 32226-2434
Tel (904) 251-3111 Founded/Ownrshp 2010
Sales 206.0MM^E EMP 1,200^E
SIC 3731 Cargo vessels, building & repairing; Barges, building & repairing; Tankers, building & repairing; Tugboats, building & repairing
CEO: Linda Hudson
*VP: Paul W Cobb Jr
*VP: Douglas Coleman
*VP: John Marinucci
*VP: Dan Welch
Genl Mgr: James Canfield
Genl Mgr: Dennis Rials

D-U-N-S 10-393-3453
BAE SYSTEMS TECHNOLOGY SOLUTIONS & SERVICES INC
(Suby of BAE SYSTEMS INC) ★
520 Gaither Rd, Rockville, MD 20850-6198
Tel (301) 738-4880 Founded/Ownrshp 1999
Sales 1.6MMM^E EMP 7,000
SIC 8711 Engineering services
Pr: Deette D Gray
Treas: Bruce Jarvie
Ofcr: Tom Arseneault
Sr VP: Anthony Ellis
VP: Mark Baker
VP: Michael Belki
VP: Michael Christie
VP: Alfred Crews Jr
VP: Susan Finkel
VP: Richard Henrichsen
VP: Carroll Marcus Jr
VP: Herb Muktarian
VP: Darrell Philpot
VP: John Sputz
VP Bus Dev: Michael Lewis

D-U-N-S 04-491-9884 EXP
BAERS FURNITURE CO INC
1589 Nw 12th Ave, Pompano Beach, FL 33069-1734
Tel (954) 946-8001 Founded/Ownrshp 1949
Sales 196.8MM EMP 437
Accts Jacobs & Company Llp West Pal
SIC 5712 Furniture stores
Pr: Allan E Baer
*CEO: Robert M Baer
*Treas: Michael W Baer
*VP: Ira J Baer
IT Man: Pedro Cedeno
Sales Asso: Jane Moulton

BAFO TECHNOLOGIES
See QUALITY COMPUTER ACCESSORIES INC

D-U-N-S 16-138-4052
BAGBY AND RUSSELL ELECTRIC CO INC
5500 Plantation Rd, Theodore, AL 36582-1702
Tel (251) 344-5987 Founded/Ownrshp 1965
Sales 180.0MM^E EMP 140
SIC 1731 General electrical contractor
CEO: Frank D Russell
*Pr: Richard Russell
*CFO: Art Walsh
Mktg Dir: Tommy Lawshe

BAGCRAFT
See PACKAGING DYNAMICS CORP

D-U-N-S 00-507-1253 IMP
BAGCRAFTPAPERCON I LLC
PACKAGING DYNAMICS
(Suby of BAGCRAFTPAPERCON LLC) ★
3900 W 43rd St, Chicago, IL 60632-3490
Tel (620) 856-2800 Founded/Ownrshp 1998
Sales 215.6MM^E EMP 940
SIC 2671 2674 2673 3497 2759 Packaging paper & plastics film, coated & laminated; Paper bags: made from purchased materials; Bags: plastic, laminated & coated; Metal foil & leaf; Commercial printing
*CEO: Phil Harris
CFO: Mike Arduino
CFO: David Wartner
Ex VP: Tom Ellsworth
*VP: Richard Cote
*VP: Chuck Hathaway
VP: Mike Klaes
VP: Mark W Linkedin
VP: Jim Roberts
*VP: Grady Wetherington
*VP: Mark Wilcox
VP: Tom Wolf

D-U-N-S 82-676-2671
BAGCRAFTPAPERCON LLC
(Suby of BAGCRAFT) ★
3900 W 43rd St, Chicago, IL 60632-3490
Tel (773) 843-8000 Founded/Ownrshp 2006
Sales 215.9MM^E EMP 940^E
SIC 8741 Business management
CEO: Roger Prevot
*VP: Chuck Hathaway
VP: Tim Love
*VP: Dan Vice
*VP: Grady Wetherington
*VP: Mark Wilcox
VP: Don Wolski
QA Dir: Michael Myers
Opers Mgr: Lonnie Turner
Ql Cn Mgr: Brandon Cox

D-U-N-S 18-782-1496
BAGGAGE AIRLINE GUEST SERVICES INC
6751 Forum Dr Ste 200, Orlando, FL 32821-8089
Tel (407) 447-5547 *Founded/Ownrshp* 2001
Sales 91.1MM^E *EMP* 1,500
SIC 4212 Baggage transfer
Pr: Craig C Mateer
**VP:* Dan Sherfield

D-U-N-S 05-861-7739 IMP
BAGMAKERS INC
6606 S Union Rd, Union, IL 60180-9535
Tel (815) 923-2247 *Founded/Ownrshp* 1981
Sales 130.8MM^E *EMP* 400
SIC 2673 2674 Plastic bags: made from purchased materials; Paper bags: made from purchased materials
CEO: Maribeth Sandford
Pr: Jeremy Bayness
**Pr:* Chuck Sandford
CFO: Scott McFadden
Sr VP: Christopher Duffy
Sr VP: Bayness Roger
VP: Roger Bayness
VP: Paul Fleming
Exec: Angie Ortiz
Web Dev: Frankie Carter
VP Sls: Chuck Sanford

D-U-N-S 36-427-8028
BAHA INDUSTRIES CORP
OPEN SYSTEMS TECHNOLOGIES
462 7th Ave Fl 15, New York, NY 10018-7429
Tel (212) 273-1921 *Founded/Ownrshp* 1997
Sales 405.9MM *EMP* 300
Accts Rosenblat Radezky Schiff & T
SIC 8748 Business consulting
Ch Bd: Harold Herling
**CFO:* Kevin Seltzer
Sr VP: Rick Ryan
VP: Brian Bavosa
VP: Mark Catanese
**VP:* Steve Young
Exec: Patrick Minton
Assoc Dir: Radhika Arora
Mng Dir: Michael Katz
Mng Dir: Glenn Lavender
Mng Dir: Nate Resnick

D-U-N-S 00-895-6807
BAHAKEL SPORTS INC (NC)
1 Television Pl, Charlotte, NC 28205-7038
Tel (704) 372-4434 *Founded/Ownrshp* 1947
Sales 84.7MM^E *EMP* 600
SIC 4833 4832 Television broadcasting stations; Radio broadcasting stations
Pr: Cy N Bahakel
**CFO:* Louis Spitzer
**VP:* Lou Poston
**VP:* Anna Rufty

D-U-N-S 78-947-9602
■ **BAHNSON HOLDINGS INC**
(*Suby of* EMCOR GROUP INC) ★
4731 Commercial Park Ct, Clemmons, NC 27012-8700
Tel (336) 760-3111 *Founded/Ownrshp* 2011
Sales 214.6MM^E *EMP* 1,003^E
SIC 8711 1711 3585 3564 Heating & ventilation engineering; Warm air heating & air conditioning contractor; Ventilation & duct work contractor; Heating equipment, complete; Air conditioning equipment, complete; Blowers & fans
Pr: Timothy J Whitener
**Treas:* Lisa J Cunningham
Ex VP: Hugh McPherson

D-U-N-S 62-608-8447
■ **BAHNSON INC**
(*Suby of* BAHNSON HOLDINGS INC) ★
4731 Commercial Park Ct, Clemmons, NC 27012-8700
Tel (336) 760-3111 *Founded/Ownrshp* 2011
Sales 214.6MM^E *EMP* 1,000
Accts Dixon Hughes Pllc
SIC 8711 1711 Heating & ventilation engineering; Warm air heating & air conditioning contractor; Ventilation & duct work contractor
Pr: Tim Whitener
**CFO:* Lisa Cunningham
**CFO:* Katie Overton
**VP:* Hugh O McPherson

D-U-N-S 96-326-3954 IMP/EXP
BAI BRANDS LLC
1800 E State St Ste 153, Trenton, NJ 08609-2020
Tel (609) 586-0500 *Founded/Ownrshp* 2009
Sales 131.6MM^E *EMP* 173^E
SIC 2086 Soft drinks: packaged in cans, bottles, etc.
CEO: Ben R Weiss
**Pr:* Ken Kurtz
**COO:* Barak Bar-Cohen
**CFO:* ARI Soroken
**CFO:* Justin Timberlake
**Ofcr:* Michael J Pengue
VP: Barney Acselrod
Dist Mgr: Martin Chung
Div Mgr: Brad Luft
Off Mgr: Denise Nosko
Mktg Mgr: Christina McCarthy

D-U-N-S 00-291-0974
BAIERL CHEVROLET INC
BAIERL HONDA
10432 Perry Hwy, Wexford, PA 15090-9241
Tel (724) 935-3711 *Founded/Ownrshp* 1961
Sales 117.5MM^E *EMP* 265
SIC 5511 5013 Automobiles, new & used; Trucks, tractors & trailers: new & used; Automotive supplies & parts
Pr: Lee W Baierl
**Treas:* William R Baierl
**Prin:* Thomas Hull
Store Mgr: Brian Kuttesch

BAIERL HONDA
See BAIERL CHEVROLET INC

D-U-N-S 03-482-2015 IMP
BAILEY CO INC
501 Cowan St, Nashville, TN 37207-5617
Tel (615) 242-0351 *Founded/Ownrshp* 1952
Sales 114.1MM^E *EMP* 300
SIC 5084 Materials handling machinery
**Pr:* Bert Bailey
**Pr:* Gordon Morrow
**Prin:* Bruce Largent

D-U-N-S 04-781-0031
BAILEY CO LLLP
ARBY'S
601 Corporate Cir, Golden, CO 80401-5607
Tel (303) 384-0200 *Founded/Ownrshp* 1968
Sales 27.5MM^E *EMP* 1,300
SIC 5812 Fast-food restaurant, chain
Pt: Geoffrey R Bailey
VP: Lynn Modisette

D-U-N-S 06-952-5632
BAILEY LUMBER & SUPPLY CO
FRIERSON BAILEY BUILDING
813 E Pass Rd, Gulfport, MS 39507-3307
Tel (228) 896-6071 *Founded/Ownrshp* 1951
Sales 94.8MM^E *EMP* 500
SIC 5211 5031 Lumber & other building materials; Lumber products; Lumber, plywood & millwork
CEO: H C Bailey Jr
**Pr:* Sherwood R Bailey Jr
**Pr:* Woody Bailey
**COO:* Richard Kostal
Store Mgr: Robin Bond

D-U-N-S 00-645-3880 IMP/EXP
BAILEY NURSERIES INC (MN)
1325 Bailey Rd, Newport, MN 55055-1502
Tel (651) 459-9744 *Founded/Ownrshp* 1905
Sales 346.6MM^E *EMP* 1,000
SIC 5193 Flowers & nursery stock
Ch Bd: Gordon J Bailey
**Pr:* Terri McEnaney
**Treas:* John Bailey
VP: Vern Black

D-U-N-S 00-213-0953 IMP/EXP
BAILLIE LUMBER CO LP
AMERICAN LUMBER CO
4002 Legion Dr, Hamburg, NY 14075-4599
Tel (800) 950-2850 *Founded/Ownrshp* 1923, 1963
Sales 273.2MM^E *EMP* 510
SIC 5211 Lumber products
Pr: Donald L Meyer
VP: James Dills
VP: Sean Karn
**VP:* Doris Meyer
VP: Jeff Meyer
Dept Mgr: Lynn Langdon
Genl Mgr: Jeff Lisk
Genl Mgr: Bob Zandi
CIO: John Vitale
Trfc Dir: Jeffrey Stanes
Trfc Mgr: Bonita Brown

BAILY CO
See BAILY INTERNATIONAL OF ATLANTA INC

D-U-N-S 00-292-1828 IMP
BAILY INTERNATIONAL OF ATLANTA INC
BAILY CO
3312-B N Berkeley Lk Rd, Duluth, GA 30096-3253
Tel (770) 452-8212 *Founded/Ownrshp* 1997
Sales 84.7MM *EMP* 103^E
Accts Galeano Li Lei & Villegas C
SIC 5087 Restaurant supplies
CEO: Jeff Tsai
**Pr:* Frank Tsai
**CFO:* Emily Tsai

D-U-N-S 06-660-6237
BAIN & CO INC
131 Dartmouth St Ste 901, Boston, MA 02116-5145
Tel (617) 572-2000 *Founded/Ownrshp* 1991
Sales 594.5MM^E *EMP* 2,400
SIC 8742 Management consulting services
Ch: Orit Gadiesh
Sr Pt: David Bellaire
Pt: Mark Horwitch
Mng Pt: Michael Thorneman
**Pr:* William W Bain Jr
**Pr:* Steve Ellis
**CFO:* Leonard C Banos
**CFO:* Kelt Kindick
**Treas:* Andrew J Frommer
**Treas:* Gary B Wilkinson
**Treas:* Graeme Williamson
VP: Neto Alexander
VP: Mark Kovac

D-U-N-S 19-988-2911
BAIN CAPITAL LP
200 Clarendon St, Boston, MA 02116-5021
Tel (617) 516-2000 *Founded/Ownrshp* 2000
Sales 19.1MMM^E *EMP* 58,583
SIC 6282 Investment advisory service
CFO: Jay Corrigan
Ex VP: Cecilia Chao
Ex VP: Beth Clymer
Ex VP: Jennifer Deason
Ex VP: Francois Gilbart
Ex VP: Brian Hirschfeld
VP: Graham Blackwell
VP: Max De Groen
VP: David Godfrey
VP: Travis Hartnett
VP: Lisa Hersh
VP: Shunsuke Nakahama
VP: David Spiller
VP: Masashi Suekane

D-U-N-S 61-254-9915
BAIN CAPITAL PARTNERS LLC
(*Suby of* BAIN CAPITAL LP) ★
200 Clarendon St, Boston, MA 02116-5021
Tel (617) 516-2000 *Founded/Ownrshp* 2000
Sales 2.3MMM^E *EMP* 31,500
SIC 6799 Venture capital companies
Mng Dir: Stephen G Pagliuca
**Pt:* Cecilia Chao
CFO: Jay Corrigan
Ofcr: Alan Halfenger
Ex VP: Andrew Carlino
Ex VP: Jon Desimone
Ex VP: Yvonne Hao
Ex VP: Jeffrey Hawkins
Ex VP: Susan Lynch
Ex VP: Jeff Robinson
Sr VP: Tim Barns
Sr VP: Michael Ewald
Sr VP: Dave Hamilton
Sr VP: Kim Harris
Sr VP: Susan Lock
Sr VP: David McCarthy
Sr VP: Natalie Wright
**VP:* Graham Blackwell
VP: James Boudreau
VP: Viva Hyatt
VP: Viva Jeffrey

D-U-N-S 61-733-9960
BAIRD FINANCIAL CORP
(*Suby of* BAIRD HOLDING CO) ★
777 E Wisconsin Ave, Milwaukee, WI 53202-5300
Tel (414) 765-3500 *Founded/Ownrshp* 1919
Sales 185.3MM^E *EMP* 2,335
SIC 6719 Investment holding companies, except banks
Mng Dir: Glen Hackmann
**COO:* Steve Booth
**CFO:* Leonard M Rush
**Mng Dir:* Michael Schroeder

D-U-N-S 61-670-7589
BAIRD HOLDING CO
777 E Wisconsin Ave, Milwaukee, WI 53202-5300
Tel (414) 765-3500 *Founded/Ownrshp* 2001
Sales 700.0MM^E *EMP* 4,752
SIC 6719 Investment holding companies, except banks
Pr: Paul E Purcell
**Pr:* Steven G Booth
**COO:* Russell P Schwei
**CFO:* Dominick P Zarcone
**Ch:* William W Mahler
Sr VP: James P Harkins
VP: Teresa Dahl
**Mng Dir:* Glen Hackmann
Mktg Dir: Geoff Mackey

D-U-N-S 17-620-6092
BAIRDS MRS BAKERIES BUSINESS TRUST
7301 South Fwy, Fort Worth, TX 76134-4004
Tel (817) 615-3100 *Founded/Ownrshp* 1997
Sales 351.1MM^E *EMP* 3,400
SIC 2051 Bread, cake & related products
Pr: Juan Muldoon
**CFO:* Darrell Miller
VP: Lecia Laswell
VP: Larry McLaughlin
VP: Gregory Stehr
CTO: Richard Bay
CTO: Juan Essa
CTO: Mike Sullivan
VP Opers: Moises Hurtada
VP Sls: John Foley
Mktg Dir: Dan Larson

BAJA DUTY FREE
See FAIRN & SWANSON INC

D-U-N-S 94-572-0845
BAJA FRESH WESTLAKE VILLAGE INC
(*Suby of* FRESH ENTERPRISES, LLC)
100 Moody Ct Ste 200, Thousand Oaks, CA 91360-6082
Tel (805) 495-4704 *Founded/Ownrshp* 1992
Sales 34.8MM^E *EMP* 1,500
SIC 5812 Mexican restaurant
Pr: Greg Dollarhyde
COO: Sally Abshire
**CFO:* Don Breen
Sr VP: Natascha Kogler
VP: Bonita Williams
QA Dir: Peter J Whitwell
Sls&Mrk Ex: Jerry Delucia
Mktg Dir: Mead Wildrick
Genl Couns: Michael Conway
Snr Mgr: Margie Dietz

D-U-N-S 06-203-4451 IMP/EXP
BAJAJ CONEAGLE LLC
(*Suby of* BAJAJ STEEL INDUSTRIES LIMITED)
1900 Market St, Millbrook, AL 36054-4234
Tel (334) 517-6139 *Founded/Ownrshp* 2012
Sales 184.0MM^E *EMP* 1,600
SIC 3523 Planting, haying, harvesting & processing machinery
VP: David Mrozinski

D-U-N-S 00-825-9152 IMP/EXP
BAKEMARK USA LLC
(*Suby of* CSM BAKERY SOLUTIONS LLC) ★
7351 Crider Ave, Pico Rivera, CA 90660-3705
Tel (562) 949-1054 *Founded/Ownrshp* 1992
Sales 370.2MM^E *EMP* 1,000
SIC 2045 5149 3556 2099 Flours & flour mixes, from purchased flour; Bakery products; Food products machinery; Food preparations
Pr: Jim Parker
VP: Jeffrey Barnhart
VP: Mark Phillips
**VP:* Ken Sparks
Genl Mgr: Mario Barone
Genl Mgr: Gene Russo
Genl Mgr: Ben Smith
Genl Mgr: John Smith
Genl Mgr: Tom Sousae
Genl Mgr: Steve Weltzin
VP Mfg: John Kupniewski

D-U-N-S 07-075-6788
BAKER & HOSTETLER LLP
127 Public Sq Ste 2000, Cleveland, OH 44114-1214
Tel (216) 621-0200 *Founded/Ownrshp* 1916
Sales 333.2MM^E *EMP* 1,771
SIC 8111 Legal services; Bankruptcy law; Labor & employment law; Real estate law
Mng Pt: Ronald G Linville
**Pt:* Richard T Fulton
Mng Pt: Christopher M Arena
Mng Pt: G Thomas Ball
Mng Pt: John F Cermak
Mng Pt: James V Etscorn
Mng Pt: David G Holcombe
Mng Pt: Joseph Lucci
Mng Pt: George T Mooradian
Mng Pt: Ronald S Okada
Mng Pt: Jeffrey H Paravano
Mng Pt: Lisa H Pennington
Mng Pt: Hewitt B Shaw Jr
Mng Pt: George A Stamboulidis
Mng Pt: Raymond L Sutton Jr
Mng Pt: Michael J Swope
Ch Bd: John M Gherlein
Ch Bd: John H Weber
Ch Bd: W Ray Whitman
**CFO:* Kevin L Cash
Trst: Irving Picard

D-U-N-S 07-442-5455
BAKER & MCKENZIE LLP
300 E Randolph St # 5000, Chicago, IL 60601-6342
Tel (312) 861-8000 *Founded/Ownrshp* 1949
Sales 1.0MMM^E *EMP* 8,000
SIC 8111 General practice law office
Ch: Eduardo C Leite
Pt: Beatriz P De ARA Jo
Pt: Rafael Jim Nez-Gusi
CFO: Charles Kessler
Exec: Janice Wilkins
Dir Bus: Courtney Woolridge
Adm Dir: Nancy A Rader
Admn Mgr: Maggie Lo
CTO: Simon King
IT Man: Jacalyn Vazquez
Counsel: Glen F White

D-U-N-S 80-789-3016
BAKER & TAYLOR ACQUISITIONS CORP
(*Suby of* CASTLE HARLAN PARTNERS IV LP) ★
2550 W Tyvola Rd Ste 300, Charlotte, NC 28217-4579
Tel (704) 998-3100 *Founded/Ownrshp* 2003
Sales 5.4MMM^E *EMP* 3,600
SIC 2731 Book publishing
CEO: George F Coe
**Pr:* M Arnie Wight
**CFO:* Jeffrey S Leonard
**Ex VP:* Matt Carroll

D-U-N-S 07-995-4862
BAKER & TAYLOR FULFILLMENT INC
(*Suby of* BAKER & TAYLOR MARKETING SVC) ★
2550 W Tyvola Rd Ste 300, Charlotte, NC 28217-4579
Tel (704) 998-3154 *Founded/Ownrshp* 2002
Sales 163.1MM^E *EMP* 3,573
SIC 5192 5045 7822 5065 Books; Computer software; Television tape distribution; Tapes, audio & video recording
CEO: George F Coe
**Sr VP:* Pete Chepul

D-U-N-S 08-071-0481 IMP
BAKER & TAYLOR HOLDINGS LLC
BAKER & TAYLOR MARKETING SVC
(*Suby of* BAKER & TAYLOR ACQUISITIONS CORP) ★
2550 W Tyvola Rd Ste 300, Charlotte, NC 28217-4579
Tel (704) 998-3100 *Founded/Ownrshp* 1991, 2006
Sales 5.4MMM^E *EMP* 3,573
SIC 5192 7822 5065 5045 Books; Television tape distribution; Tapes, audio & video recording; Computer software
CEO: George F Coe
**Pr:* David Cully
**CFO:* Jeff Leonard
**Ex VP:* Matt Carroll
**Ex VP:* Kimberly Kuo
Ex VP: Bob Nelson
Ex VP: Robert Nelson
**Ex VP:* Sydney Stanley
**Sr VP:* Gary Dayton
**Sr VP:* Beth Simonetti
VP: Bradley Lucas

D-U-N-S 78-772-4772 IMP
BAKER & TAYLOR LLC
(*Suby of* FOLLETT CORP) ★
2550 W Tyvola Rd Ste 300, Charlotte, NC 28217-4579
Tel (704) 998-3100 *Founded/Ownrshp* 2016
Sales 3.7MMM^E *EMP* 3,250
SIC 5192 7822 5065 5045 5099 Books; Television tape distribution; Tapes, audio & video recording; Computer software; Video & audio equipment
Pr: George Coe
**Ch Bd:* M Arnie Wight
Pr: David Cully
**CFO:* Jeff Leonard
Ex VP: Kimberly Kuo
Sr VP: Gary Dayton
**Sr VP:* Bradley D Murchison
VP: John Lindsay
**CIO:* Matthew Carroll
Mktg Dir: Chris Kouzes
Sales Asso: Robert Rodriguez
Board of Directors: Daniel A Daniello, Philip Dolan, Patrick W Gross, Joseph R Wright Jr

BAKER & TAYLOR MARKETING SVC
See BAKER & TAYLOR HOLDINGS LLC

D-U-N-S 00-842-5894
BAKER BOTTS LLP
910 Louisiana St Ste 3200, Houston, TX 77002-4911
Tel (713) 229-1234 *Founded/Ownrshp* 1840
Sales 225.9MM^E *EMP* 1,582
SIC 8111 Corporate, partnership & business law
Mng Pt: Andrew M Baker
COO: Nick Peacock
CFO: Lydia Companion
Chf Mktg O: Gillian Ward

D-U-N-S 05-567-1879
BAKER COLLEGE
BAKER COLLEGE OF MUSKEGEON
1050 W Bristol Rd, Flint, MI 48507-5508
Tel (810) 767-7600 *Founded/Ownrshp* 1909
Sales 93.7MM *EMP* 3,000
SIC 8222 8221 Junior college; College, except junior
Pr: F James Cummins
Ofcr: Crystal Crowe

Ofcr: Ralph Oestman
**VP:* Tiffany Davi
VP: Richard Delong
VP: Mike Helsen
VP: Gerald McCartyii
VP: Ellis Salim
Dir IT: Michael Heberling
IT Man: Malee Levitt
Pgrm Dir: Rita Atikian

BAKER COLLEGE OF MUSKEGEON
See BAKER COLLEGE

D-U-N-S 00-825-2496 EXP
BAKER COMMODITIES INC
4020 Bandini Blvd, Vernon, CA 90058-4274
Tel (323) 268-2801 *Founded/Ownrshp* 1984
Sales 200.8MM[E] *EMP* 700
SIC 2077 2048 Tallow rendering, inedible; Poultry feeds
Pr: James M Andreoli
**Ex VP:* Denis Luckey
**VP:* Mitchell Ebright
VP: James L Friend
Ex Dir: Betsy Inglis

D-U-N-S 05-910-3481 IMP/EXP
BAKER CONCRETE CONSTRUCTION INC
900 N Garver Rd, Monroe, OH 45050-1277
Tel (513) 539-4000 *Founded/Ownrshp* 1972
Sales 1.0MMM[E] *EMP* 2,500
SIC 1771 1611 Concrete work; Concrete construction: roads, highways, sidewalks, etc.
Pr: Daniel L Baker
**CFO:* Thomas Bell
**Treas:* Robert Baker
Treas: John Groth
**VP:* Gary L Benson
**VP:* Steven A Lydy
**VP:* Stephen E Martin
**VP:* Dennis W Phillips
**VP:* Michael J Schneider
Genl Mgr: Jon Chastain
MIS Dir: Tj McDermott

D-U-N-S 00-797-3696 EXP
■ BAKER DISTRIBUTING CO LLC
CONSOLIDATED COMFORT GROUP
(*Suby of* WATSCO INC) ★
14610 Breakers Dr Ste 100, Jacksonville, FL 32258-6468
Tel (904) 407-4500 *Founded/Ownrshp* 1945, 1997
Sales 612.0MM[E] *EMP* 1,200
SIC 5075 5078 Warm air heating & air conditioning; Refrigeration equipment & supplies
Pr: Al Lendino
CFO: Jack Johannesmeyer
VP: Robert Blades
VP: Bill Connelly
VP: Brian Silva
Rgnl Mgr: Brian Feuer
Brnch Mgr: Terry Dorminey
Brnch Mgr: Charley Kim
Brnch Mgr: Willis Mason
Genl Mgr: Daniel Sotelo
Store Mgr: Rick Campbell
Board of Directors: Barry S Logan, Ana M Menendez

D-U-N-S 07-354-8919
BAKER DONELSON BEARMAN CALDWELL & BERKOWITZ
165 Madison Ave Ste 2000, Memphis, TN 38103-2752
Tel (901) 526-2000 *Founded/Ownrshp* 1911
Sales 173.7MM[E] *EMP* 1,300
SIC 8111 General practice law office
CEO: Ben Adams
**Pr:* Jerry Sausser
Bd of Dir: Kristin Dunavant
Bd of Dir: Melissa Egan
Bd of Dir: Sue Porter
Off Mgr: Joyce Rose
Off Admin: Melissa Tokar
MIS Dir: John Green
Netwrk Eng: Jason Kopacko
Counsel: Stephen Azia
Counsel: Robert Bass

D-U-N-S 83-293-0320
BAKER DRYWALL LTD
(*Suby of* BAKER TRIANGLE) ★
401 Hwy 80 E, Mesquite, TX 75150-5826
Tel (972) 285-8878 *Founded/Ownrshp* 2006
Sales 69.1MM[E] *EMP* 1,500
SIC 8741 Management services
CEO: Stephen Baker
CFO: Scott Abegg
VP: Jesse Shaw

D-U-N-S 08-154-3597
BAKER DRYWALL MANAGEMENT LLC
BAKER TRIANGLE
(*Suby of* BAKER TRIANGLE) ★
401 Us Highway 80 E, Mesquite, TX 75150-5826
Tel (972) 285-8878 *Founded/Ownrshp* 2006
Sales 95.7MM[E] *EMP* 1,500
SIC 8741 Management services
COO: Doug Conter
**CFO:* Scott Abegg
CFO: James Purser
**Treas:* Carol D Baker
VP: Debbie Brocker
VP: Bryan Craft
**VP:* Mark Streetman
VP: Michael Vickery
**VP:* Nichael Vickery
Snr PM: Jeff Schilling

D-U-N-S 83-167-3335
BAKER DRYWALL PARTNERSHIP LLP
BAKER TRIANGLE
401 Us Highway 80 E, Mesquite, TX 75150-5826
Tel (972) 288-9275 *Founded/Ownrshp* 2006
Sales 164.8MM[E] *EMP* 1,902[E]
SIC 1742 Plastering, drywall & insulation
CFO: Scott Abegg
CFO: Jerry Conder
VP: Brad Bryant
Info Man: Kay Schultz

D-U-N-S 00-782-0913
BAKER ELECTRIC INC
(*Suby of* ELECTRO MANAGEMENT CORP) ★
111 Jackson Ave, Des Moines, IA 50315-1200
Tel (515) 288-6774 *Founded/Ownrshp* 1925
Sales 107.5MM[E] *EMP* 500
SIC 1731 General electrical contractor
CEO: Britt Baker
**Pr:* Dave Hearn
**CFO:* Patty Skokan
**VP:* John Layland
**VP:* Don Stockton
IT Man: Jennifer Carrillo
IT Man: Joseph Henkels

D-U-N-S 00-955-5087
BAKER ELECTRIC INC
1298 Pacific Oaks Pl, Escondido, CA 92029-2900
Tel (760) 745-2001 *Founded/Ownrshp* 1937
Sales 152.7MM[E] *EMP* 250
SIC 1731 8711

BAKER GROUP
See BAKER MECHANICAL INC

D-U-N-S 17-293-4556
BAKER HALL
BAKER VICTORY SERVICES
780 Ridge Rd, Lackawanna, NY 14218-1629
Tel (716) 828-9515 *Founded/Ownrshp* 1851
Sales 49.3MM[E] *EMP* 1,300
SIC 8361 8211 8322 Home for the emotionally disturbed; High school, junior or senior; Adoption services
CEO: James J Casion
Genl Mgr: Jeffrey Bell
Pgrm Dir: Meg Battenfeld

D-U-N-S 17-498-7909 IMP/EXP
▲ BAKER HUGHES INC
17021 Aldine Westfield Rd, Houston, TX 77073-5101
Tel (713) 439-8600 *Founded/Ownrshp* 1986
Sales 15.7MMM *EMP* 43,000
Accts Deloitte & Touche Llp Houston
Tkr Sym BHI *Exch* NYS
SIC 3533 3561 Oil & gas field machinery; Oil field machinery & equipment; Gas field machinery & equipment; Bits, oil & gas field tools: rock; Pumps, oil well & field
Ch Bd: Martin S Craighead
Pr: Khaled Nouh
Pr: Arthur L Soucy
Pr: Richard Ward
Pr: Richard L Williams
CFO: Kimberly A Ross
Bd of Dir: James Stewart
Bd of Dir: Becky Tice
Ofcr: Andrew C Esparza
Ofcr: Jay G Martin
Ofcr: Derek Mathieson
Sr VP: Alan R Crain
VP: Ralph Crabtree
VP: Archana Deskus
VP: Alan J Keifer
VP: William D Marsh
Comm Man: Robin Swanger
Board of Directors: J Larry Nichols, Larry D Brady, James W Stewart, Gregory D Brenneman, Charles L Watson, Clarence P Cazalot Jr, William H Easter III, Lynn L Elsenhans, Anthony G Fernandes, Claire W Gargalli, Pierre H Jungels, James A Lash

D-U-N-S 17-785-7823 IMP
■ BAKER HUGHES OILFIELD OPERATIONS INC
(*Suby of* BAKER HUGHES INC) ★
1333 Corporate Dr Ste 300, Irving, TX 75038-2535
Tel (972) 988-0111 *Founded/Ownrshp* 1973
Sales 157.5MM[E] *EMP* 350
SIC 1389 Oil field services; Perforating well casings; Well logging
CEO: Martin S Craighead
**Pr:* Stephen K Ellison
**VP:* Joseph W Brice III
Dist Mgr: John Gillespie
Software D: Steve Easton

D-U-N-S 61-515-7625 IMP
■ BAKER HUGHES OILFIELD OPERATIONS INC
BAKER HUGHES SOLUTIONS
(*Suby of* BAKER HUGHES INC) ★
17021 Aldine Westfield Rd, Houston, TX 77073-5101
Tel (713) 439-8600 *Founded/Ownrshp* 1981
Sales 5.0MMM[E] *EMP* 4,923
SIC 1381 1311 1389 2899 Drilling oil & gas wells; Crude petroleum & natural gas production; Servicing oil & gas wells; Chemical preparations
CEO: Martin Craighead
**Pr:* Maria Claudia Borras
**Pr:* Belgacem Chariag
**CFO:* Peter Ragauss
Ofcr: David Huber
**Sr VP:* Alan Crain
**VP:* Didier Charreton
**Prin:* Richard L Williams
Area Mgr: Mark Boyes
Dist Mgr: Dean Robinson
Opers Mgr: Carl Currie

BAKER HUGHES SOLUTIONS
See BAKER HUGHES OILFIELD OPERATIONS INC

D-U-N-S 02-987-9210 IMP
BAKER IMPLEMENT CO
915 Homecrest St, Kennett, MO 63857-1590
Tel (573) 888-4646 *Founded/Ownrshp* 1942
Sales 104.8MM[E] *EMP* 190
SIC 5083 7699 Farm implements; Tractors, agricultural; Farm equipment parts & supplies; Farm machinery repair
Pr: Jerry Combs
**Sec:* Anetha J Combs

D-U-N-S 88-333-7313 IMP
BAKER INDUSTRIES INC
BAKER MACHINING & MOLDTECH
16936 Enterprise Dr, Macomb, MI 48044-1006
Tel (586) 286-4900 *Founded/Ownrshp* 1992
Sales 98.1MM[E] *EMP* 220[E]
SIC 3544 Forms (molds), for foundry & plastics working machinery
Pr: Kevin M Baker
CFO: Brian Baker
VP: Scott Baker

BAKER MACHINING & MOLDTECH
See BAKER INDUSTRIES INC

D-U-N-S 00-531-1725
BAKER MECHANICAL INC (IA)
BAKER GROUP
4224 Hubbell Ave, Des Moines, IA 50317-4527
Tel (515) 262-4000 *Founded/Ownrshp* 1963
Sales 158.5MM[E] *EMP* 330
SIC 1711 3444 Plumbing contractors; Warm air heating & air conditioning contractor; Sheet metalwork
CEO: Bernard J Baker III
**Pr:* Gary Bridgewater
**COO:* Kathy Ladd
**CFO:* Randy Helm
VP: Jim Cooper
IT Man: Bob Rahto
Opers Mgr: Rob Cross

BAKER MEDIA SERVICES
See BOB BAKER ENTERPRISES INC

D-U-N-S 06-564-1409 IMP
BAKER MICHAEL INTERNATIONAL INC
(*Suby of* MICHAEL BAKER INTERNATIONAL HOLDCO CORP) ★
500 Grant St Ste 5400, Pittsburgh, PA 15219-2523
Tel (412) 269-6300 *Founded/Ownrshp* 1940
Sales 260.5MM[E] *EMP* 3,200
SIC 8711 8741 Civil engineering; Management services
CEO: Kurt Bergman
CEO: Michael Zugay
Assoc VP: Michael Arens
Assoc VP: Mary Anne Buvens
Assoc VP: R Joseph Chaffin
Assoc VP: Kurt D Fritz
Assoc VP: Hayden R Gellineau
Assoc VP: Peter Hankovszky
Assoc VP: Burton Johnson
Ex VP: Edward L Wiley
Sr VP: Scott R Armstrong
Sr VP: David W McFayden
Sr VP: Bonnie D Shepard
Sr VP: Thomas J Zagorski
VP: Dennis Wiehl AIA
VP: Steven L Barber
VP: Dwight A Beranek
VP: Richard T Bernet
VP: Greg Cerminara
VP: Travis Clark
VP: Michael Conaboy

D-U-N-S 61-042-5360
BAKER MICHAEL JR INC
(*Suby of* MICHAEL BAKER INTERNATIONAL HOLDCO CORP) ★
810 Hesters Crossing Rd # 163, Round Rock, TX 78681-7838
Tel (512) 248-8651 *Founded/Ownrshp* 2005
Sales 1.2MM[E] *EMP* 3,000
SIC 8711 Acoustical engineering
Pr: Kurt Bergman
**VP:* Louis Levner
VP: William P Macon
VP: Richard C Mobley

D-U-N-S 13-268-0625
BAKER NORTON US INC
(*Suby of* IVAX CORP) ★
74 Nw 176th St, Miami, FL 33169-5043
Tel (305) 575-6000 *Founded/Ownrshp* 1986
Sales 127.9MM[E] *EMP* 2,000
SIC 2834 Pharmaceutical preparations
Pr: Thomas Beier
**Treas:* RAO Uppaluri
Board of Directors: Thomas Beier, Neil Flanzraich

D-U-N-S 00-835-2387 IMP/EXP
■ BAKER PETROLITE LLC
NEW PHASE TECHNOLOGIES
(*Suby of* BAKER HUGHES SOLUTIONS) ★
12645 W Airport Blvd, Sugar Land, TX 77478-6120
Tel (281) 276-5400 *Founded/Ownrshp* 1930, 1977
Sales 800.5MM[E] *EMP* 2,550
SIC 2899 2869 Chemical preparations; Water treating compounds; Industrial organic chemicals
Pr: Edwin C Howell
VP: Chris P Beaver
VP: J W Brice
VP: Patrick A Marfone
Dist Mgr: Steve A Green
Manager: Travis J Harris
Manager: Ernestine L Wilkinson
Sls Mgr: Sam Farooki

D-U-N-S 02-474-5853
BAKER ROOFING CO
517 Mercury St, Raleigh, NC 27603-2341
Tel (919) 828-2975 *Founded/Ownrshp* 1946
Sales 346.8MM[E] *EMP* 800
SIC 1761 1799 Roofing contractor; Sheet metalwork; Waterproofing
Ch Bd: W Prentiss Baker III
**Pr:* Mark Lee
Pr: Ronald Ratliffe
**CEO:* R L Baldwin
CFO: Allen Estep
Treas: Blair Hatcher
**Ex VP:* John Matthews
**Sr VP:* Frank Baker
VP: Steve Allington
**VP:* Dylan Baker
VP: Toby Boyles
VP: Chris Brackin
VP: Keith Gregory

VP: Tyler Poole
Dir Bus: Peter Williams

D-U-N-S 07-616-1934
BAKER TILLY VIRCHOW KRAUSE LLP
205 N Michigan Ave # 2800, Chicago, IL 60601-5942
Tel (312) 729-8000 *Founded/Ownrshp* 2000
Sales 282.1MM[E] *EMP* 1,093
SIC 8721 Certified public accountant
CEO: Alan Whitman
Pt: Evin Heppner
Pt: Ed Offterdinger
Pt: Thomas Walker
COO: Brandon Andries
CFO: Jean Mathews
Dir IT: Heidi Simmons
Mktg Mgr: Bryan Besco
Snr Mgr: David Freund
Snr Mgr: Jackie Hensgen
Snr Mgr: Bree Himmelstein

BAKER TRIANGLE
See BAKER DRYWALL MANAGEMENT LLC

BAKER TRIANGLE
See BAKER DRYWALL PARTNERSHIP LLP

BAKER VICTORY SERVICES
See BAKER HALL

D-U-N-S 02-840-3228
BAKERCORP
(*Suby of* FTT HOLDINGS INC) ★
3020 Old Ranch Pkwy # 220, Seal Beach, CA 90740-2765
Tel (562) 430-6262 *Founded/Ownrshp* 1996
Sales 230.6MM[E] *EMP* 750
SIC 7359 Equipment rental & leasing
Pr: Bob Craycraft
Pr: Neal Crost
**COO:* Raymond Aronoff
**CFO:* David Ignata
VP: Mehrzad Emanuel
VP: Richard Schroebel
Mng Dir: Jurgen Verschoor
Brnch Mgr: Kevin Kerezsi
Brnch Mgr: Colin Linn
Brnch Mgr: Sam Mills
Brnch Mgr: Jeff Riddle

D-U-N-S 07-928-5437
BAKERCORP INTERNATIONAL HOLDINGS INC
320 Park Ave, New York, NY 10022-6815
Tel (212) 386-7480 *Founded/Ownrshp* 2011
Sales 332.3MM[E] *EMP* 1,068[E]
SIC 7359 Equipment rental & leasing

D-U-N-S 07-938-0351
BAKERCORP INTERNATIONAL INC
(*Suby of* BAKERCORP INTERNATIONAL HOLDINGS INC) ★
7800 Dallas Pkwy Ste 500, Plano, TX 75024-4087
Tel (888) 882-4895 *Founded/Ownrshp* 1942, 2011
Sales 332.3MM *EMP* 1,068[E]
SIC 7359 Equipment rental & leasing
Pr: Robert Craycraft
COO: Raymond Aronoff
Ofcr: Melanie Barth
VP: Amy M Paul
CIO: Carla Rolinc
Board of Directors: Richard Carey, John Coyle, Philip Green, Gerard Holthaus, Henry Minello

BAKER'S STORE, THE
See KING ARTHUR FLOUR CO INC

D-U-N-S 04-213-5103
BAKERS SUPERMARKETS INC
KROGER
4509 S 143rd St Ste 4, Omaha, NE 68137-4521
Tel (402) 397-4321 *Founded/Ownrshp* 1927, 2004
Sales 168.0MM[E] *EMP* 3,200[E]
SIC 5411 Supermarkets, chain
Pr: John Bays
VP: Ron Anderson
VP: Richard Heyman
VP: George Kapalczynski

D-U-N-S 03-039-5487
BAKERSFIELD CITY SCHOOL DISTRICT EDUCATIONAL FOUNDATION
BCSD
1300 Baker St, Bakersfield, CA 93305-4326
Tel (661) 631-4600 *Founded/Ownrshp* 1887
Sales 27.4M *EMP* 2,700
SIC 8211 Public elementary & secondary schools
**CEO:* Don Vereen
Pr Dir: Irma Cervantes
Pr Dir: Maria Matthews
Sls Dir: Don Fenske
HC Dir: Rebecca Ruiz

D-U-N-S 01-070-8006
BAKERSFIELD MEMORIAL HOSPITAL
MEMORIAL CENTER
(*Suby of* DIGNITY HEALTH) ★
420 34th St, Bakersfield, CA 93301-2237
Tel (661) 327-1792 *Founded/Ownrshp* 1987
Sales 423.2MM *EMP* 1,100
SIC 8062 General medical & surgical hospitals
CEO: Jon Van Boening
**Ch Bd:* Gordon K Foster
VP: R Mark R Root
Dietician: Rachel Larsen

D-U-N-S 06-774-0720 IMP/EXP
BAKERSFIELD PIPE AND SUPPLY INC
IMPERIAL PIPE & SUPPLY
3301 Zachary Ave, Shafter, CA 93263-9424
Tel (661) 589-9141 *Founded/Ownrshp* 1968
Sales 206.6MM[E] *EMP* 225
Accts Barbich Hooper King Dill Hoffm
SIC 5051 5085 Pipe & tubing, steel; Valves & fittings
Ch: Dwight Byrumm
**Pr:* Dan Byrum
**COO:* John Byrum
**CFO:* Cary Evans
Ex VP: Ted Armenta
**VP:* Kevin Hashim

Brnch Mgr: Tim Potter
Brnch Mgr: Jeremy Smith
Genl Mgr: Bob Smith
Mktg Dir: Richard Mangan
Mktg Dir: Lisa Razzari

D-U-N-S 12-653-2811
BAKERY & CONFECTIONERY UNION & INDUSTRY INTERNATIONAL PENSION FUND
10401 Conn Ave Ste 210, Kensington, MD 20895-3960
Tel (301) 468-3700 *Founded/Ownrshp* 1955
Sales NA *EMP* 79
Accts Bond Beebe - A Professional Co
SIC 6371 Pension funds

BAKERY CHEF
See RALCORP FROZEN BAKERY PRODUCTS INC

D-U-N-S 00-425-7770 IMP/EXP
BAKERY CRAFTS LLC (MN)
(*Suby of* DECOPAC INC) ★
3500 Thurston Ave 100, Anoka, MN 55303-1061
Tel (513) 942-0862 *Founded/Ownrshp* 1971, 2015
Sales 96.7MM^E *EMP* 150
SIC 5046 5149 2064 Bakery equipment & supplies; Bakery products; Cake ornaments, confectionery
CEO: Sam Guttman
IT Man: Aaron Haucke
VP Opers: Dan Guttman
VP Sls: Deborah Ridenour

D-U-N-S 36-455-0301 IMP
BAKKAVOR FOODS USA INC
(*Suby of* BAKKAVOR USA LIMITED)
18201 Central Ave, Carson, CA 90746-4007
Tel (310) 533-0190 *Founded/Ownrshp* 2008
Sales 146.6MM^E *EMP* 415
SIC 2051 5149 Bread, cake & related products; Groceries & related products
CEO: Ivan Clingan
**Pr:* John Gorman
CFO: David Trinkle
Exec: Ira Scott
CIO: Joe Alonso
Sfty Dirs: Lupe Alvarado
Plnt Mgr: Gautier Galtero
Ql Cn Mgr: Harry Randhawa

D-U-N-S 09-472-8920 IMP
BAL SEAL ENGINEERING INC (CA)
19650 Pauling, Foothill Ranch, CA 92610-2610
Tel (949) 334-8500 *Founded/Ownrshp* 1959
Sales 122.8MM^E *EMP* 460^E
SIC 3495 Wire springs
CEO: Richard Dawson
Pr: Jeff Huber
CFO: Bart Badard
CFO: Sean McCarthy
Ch: Peter J Balsells
Ch: Jacques Naviaux
VP: Jim Jones
VP: Gary Stoffer
Exec: Roland Reichert
Mng Dir: Marco Dekker
Mng Dir: Joseph Mok

BALANCE SYSTEMS
See AMESBURY ACQUISITION HOLDINGS (2) INC

D-U-N-S 92-932-3541
BALANCED CARE CORP
BCC
5000 Ritter Rd Ste 202, Mechanicsburg, PA 17055-6922
Tel (412) 487-6925 *Founded/Ownrshp* 1999
Sales 67.1MM^E *EMP* 2,400
SIC 8741 Nursing & personal care facility management
Ch Bd: Gary Goodman
**CEO:* Jim Fields
**CFO:* Fred Zullinger
Treas: Diane Borger
Sr VP: Robin Barber
Sr VP: Michael Kelly

D-U-N-S 18-915-3646
BALBOA CAPITAL CORP
575 Anton Blvd Fl 12, Costa Mesa, CA 92626-7169
Tel (949) 756-0800 *Founded/Ownrshp* 1988
Sales NA *EMP* 230
SIC 6141 Automobile & consumer finance companies
CEO: Patrick Byrne
Pr: Phil Silva
COO: Robert Rasmussen
Dir Bus: Paul Knapp
Dir Bus: Bill Uchic
Mng Dir: Michael Curtis
Rgnl Mgr: Mark Kelly
Rgnl Mgr: Robert Shafer
Brnch Mgr: Peter T Nguyen
IT Man: Matt Edenhoffer
Mktg Dir: Drew Henderson

D-U-N-S 04-199-2728 IMP/EXP
▲ BALCHEM CORP
52 Sunrise Park Rd, New Hampton, NY 10958-4703
Tel (845) 326-5600 *Founded/Ownrshp* 1967
Sales 552.4MM *EMP* 875^E
Tkr Sym BCPC *Exch* NGS
SIC 2869 2899 Industrial organic chemicals; Methyl alcohol, synthetic methanol; Propylene, butylene; Chemical preparations
Pr: Theodore L Harris
**Ch Bd:* Dino A Rossi
CFO: William A Backus
Treas: Francis J Fitzpatrick
VP: Frank J Fitzpatrick
VP: David F Ludwig
Board of Directors: Paul D Coombs, David B Fischer, Edward L McMillan, Perry W Premdas, John Y Televantos, Matthew D Wineinger

D-U-N-S 14-747-2872 IMP/EXP
■ BALCO INC
BALCO-METALINES
(*Suby of* CAPITAL SOUTHWEST CORPORATION)
2626 S Sheridan Ave, Wichita, KS 67217-1341
Tel (800) 767-0082 *Founded/Ownrshp* 1996
Sales 111.7MM^E *EMP* 183^E
SIC 3441 3089 3496 3446 3443 Expansion joints (structural shapes), iron or steel; Plastic hardware & building products; Bearings, plastic; Mats & matting; Architectural metalwork; Fabricated plate work (boiler shop)
CEO: Ronnie Lenard
**VP:* Ron Knak
IT Man: Melissa Maser
VP Sls: Steve Cooper
Sls Mgr: Karly Hakes

BALCO-METALINES
See BALCO INC

BALCONES RECYCLING
See BALCONES RESOURCES INC

D-U-N-S 82-519-7601 EXP
BALCONES RESOURCES INC
BALCONES RECYCLING
9301 Johnny Morris Rd, Austin, TX 78724-1523
Tel (512) 472-3355 *Founded/Ownrshp* 1994
Sales 96.6MM^E *EMP* 125
SIC 4953 Recycling, waste materials
CEO: Kerry R Getter
**Treas:* Adam Vehik

D-U-N-S 00-633-8537 IMP/EXP
BALDOR ELECTRIC CO
BALDOR MOTORS AND DRIVE
(*Suby of* ABB INC) ★
5711 Rs Boreham Jr St, Fort Smith, AR 72901-8394
Tel (479) 646-4711 *Founded/Ownrshp* 2011
Sales 1.0MMM^E *EMP* 300
SIC 3621 3566 3463 3366 Electric motor & generator parts; Motors, electric; Speed changers, drives & gears; Drives, high speed industrial, except hydrostatic; Gears, power transmission, except automotive; Torque converters, except automotive; Pump, compressor, turbine & engine forgings, except auto; Bearing & bearing race forgings, nonferrous; Bushings & bearings
Pr: Ronald E Tucker
Pr: Russell Budzileni
CFO: George E Moeschner
Treas: Bryant G Dooly Jr
Treas: John Woodson
Bd of Dir: Michelle Snelling
Ex VP: Randy Colip
Ex VP: Randy L Colip
Ex VP: Gene Hagedorn
Ex VP: Amy Lakin
Ex VP: Tom Mascari
Ex VP: George E Moschner
Ex VP: William Ramsbey
VP: Dave Bell
VP: Randy Brueax
VP: Roger V Bullock
VP: Tom Chetrick
VP: Michael D Gray
VP: Jason Green
VP: Jeff Hines
VP: Roy Johnson

D-U-N-S 05-660-1606
BALDOR ELECTRIC CO
6040 Ponders Ct, Greenville, SC 29615-4601
Tel (864) 991-8492 *Founded/Ownrshp* 1989
Sales 129.0MM^E *EMP* 490^E
SIC 3599 Amusement park equipment
Pr: Gerardo Quinones
Sales Asso: Carol Kunkel

BALDOR GENERATORS
See GENERAC POWER SYSTEMS INC

BALDOR MOTORS AND DRIVE
See BALDOR ELECTRIC CO

D-U-N-S 55-595-0310 IMP/EXP
BALDOR SPECIALTY FOODS INC
INTERNATIONAL PRODUCE EXCHANGE
155 Food Center Dr Ste 1, Bronx, NY 10474-7136
Tel (718) 860-9100 *Founded/Ownrshp* 1991
Sales 211.4MM^E *EMP* 500^E
SIC 5141

D-U-N-S 04-282-3336
▲ BALDWIN & LYONS INC
111 Congressional Blvd # 500, Carmel, IN 46032-5663
Tel (317) 636-9800 *Founded/Ownrshp* 1930
Sales NA *EMP* 438^E
Tkr Sym BWINA *Exch* NGM
SIC 6331 6411 Fire, marine & casualty insurance; Property damage insurance; Insurance agents, brokers & service
Pr: W Randall Birchfield
**Ch Bd:* Steven A Shapiro
COO: Michael J Case
CFO: William C Vens
Treas: Michael B Edwards
Dir Soc: Katina Kaisher
Mktg Mgr: Scott Stclair
Sales Asso: Justin Poole
Counsel: Luke Hodgin
Snr Mgr: Jeffrey Ucchino
Board of Directors: Norton Shapiro, Stuart D Bilton, Robert Shapiro, Otto N Frenzel IV, Gary W Miller, Philip V Moyles Jr, John M O'mara, Thomas H Patrick, John A Pigott, Kenneth D Sacks, Nathan Shapiro

D-U-N-S 09-856-9593
BALDWIN & SHELL CONSTRUCTION CO INC
1000 W Capitol Ave, Little Rock, AR 72201-3004
Tel (501) 374-8677 *Founded/Ownrshp* 1946
Sales 104.6MM^E *EMP* 178
SIC 1541 1542 Industrial buildings & warehouses; Commercial & office building, new construction; Commercial & office buildings, renovation & repair
**Pr:* Jim Wilson

**VP:* John S Copas
**VP:* Henry L Johns

BALDWIN BRASS
See BALDWIN HARDWARE CORP

D-U-N-S 00-330-5059
BALDWIN COUNTY BOARD OF EDUCATION (AL)
2600a Hand Ave, Bay Minette, AL 36507-4180
Tel (251) 937-0306 *Founded/Ownrshp* 1900
Sales 312.7MM *EMP* 50
Accts Ronald L Jones Montgomery A
SIC 8211 School board
Pr: Shannon Cauley

D-U-N-S 00-985-0892
BALDWIN COUNTY ELECTRIC MEMBERSHIP CORP
19600 State Highway 59, Summerdale, AL 36580-3016
Tel (251) 989-6247 *Founded/Ownrshp* 1937
Sales 148.2MM *EMP* 186
Accts Gruenloh & Associates Pc R
SIC 4911 Distribution, electric power
Ex VP: E A Jackins
CFO: Alaen Schotp
Ex VP: Ea Jenkins
VP: Aubrey Fuller
VP: Tom Page
CTO: Joe Sopr

D-U-N-S 07-846-2505
BALDWIN COUNTY PUBLIC SCHOOLS
2600a Hand Ave, Bay Minette, AL 36507-4180
Tel (251) 937-0306 *Founded/Ownrshp* 2012
Sales 6.2MM^E *EMP* 3,237^E
SIC 8211 Elementary & secondary schools
Pr Dir: Terry C Wilhite
Teacher Pr: Jennifer Sinclair
HC Dir: Linda W Jones

D-U-N-S 00-727-3865 IMP/EXP
■ BALDWIN FILTERS INC
(*Suby of* CLARCOR INC) ★
4400 Highway 30 E, Kearney, NE 68847-0724
Tel (800) 822-5394 *Founded/Ownrshp* 1981
Sales 313.6MM^E *EMP* 1,300
SIC 3714 3564 Filters: oil, fuel & air, motor vehicle; Blowers & fans
CEO: Norman Johnson
**Pr:* Sam Ferrise
Ex VP: Bill McKenzie
VP: Mike Allibone
VP: Hans Alpsteg
**VP:* Dave Amato
VP: Steve Merritt
VP: Jeff Vasichek
Dir Lab: Dan Arens
Off Mgr: Michaela Lewis
MIS Dir: Nancy Newman

D-U-N-S 00-235-0833 IMP
■ BALDWIN HARDWARE CORP
BALDWIN BRASS
(*Suby of* RAYOVAC) ★
19701 Da Vinci, Foothill Ranch, CA 92610-2622
Tel (949) 672-4000 *Founded/Ownrshp* 1944, 2012
Sales 82.3MM^E *EMP* 1,033
SIC 3429 Builders' hardware; Locks or lock sets; Cabinet hardware
CEO: David R Lumley

D-U-N-S 96-751-0582
BALDWIN JANITORIAL & PAPER LLC
18260 County Road 12 S, Foley, AL 36535-3760
Tel (251) 943-7570 *Founded/Ownrshp* 2011
Sales 100.0MM *EMP* 4
SIC 7349 Janitorial service, contract basis
Genl Mgr: Bily Johnson

D-U-N-S 01-263-7849
BALDWIN PARK UNIFIED SCHOOL DISTRICT
3699 Holly Ave, Baldwin Park, CA 91706-5327
Tel (626) 939-4000 *Founded/Ownrshp* 1960
Sales 125.8MM^E *EMP* 1,800
SIC 8211 Public elementary & secondary schools
Adm Dir: Sally Alvarez
Prgrm Mgr: Maria Gaytan
MIS Dir: James Wickham
Snr Mgr: Christina Barreras

D-U-N-S 09-662-1347
BALDWIN PAVING CO INC
BP
1014 Kenmill Dr Nw, Marietta, GA 30060-7911
Tel (770) 425-9191 *Founded/Ownrshp* 1979
Sales 110.0MM^E *EMP* 340
SIC 1611 2951 Highway & street paving contractor; Asphalt & asphaltic paving mixtures (not from refineries)
Pr: Ernest L Baldwin
**Pr:* John Harrison
**CFO:* John Friedel
VP: Mike Demery
VP: Nick Karamis
VP: Michael Travelstead
**VP:* Mary Wade
**VP:* Walter Dean White
Sfty Mgr: Stephanie Ware
Opers Mgr: Angie Wheatley
Plnt Mgr: Jim York

D-U-N-S 10-069-4921
BALDWIN PIANO INC
(*Suby of* GIBSON USA) ★
309 Plus Park Blvd, Nashville, TN 37217-1005
Tel (615) 277-2190 *Founded/Ownrshp* 2001
Sales 32.3MM^E *EMP* 1,000^E
SIC 3931 Pianos, all types: vertical, grand, spinet, player, etc.
CEO: Henry Juszkiewicz
**VP:* David Davis
**VP:* Donald Kremer
VP: David Mahanes
Sftwr Eng: Scott Sturgis

D-U-N-S 79-882-2222
BALDWIN RICHARDSON FOODS CO
1 Tower Ln, Oakbrook Terrace, IL 60181-4671
Tel (815) 464-9994 *Founded/Ownrshp* 1992
Sales 97.2MM^E *EMP* 302
SIC 2024 Dairy based frozen desserts
Pr: Eric Johnson
**CFO:* Evelyn White
**VP:* Pamela Johnson
QA Dir: Rachael Elrod

D-U-N-S 18-337-9239 IMP
BALDWIN TECHNOLOGY CO INC
(*Suby of* FORSYTH BALDWIN LLC) ★
8040 Forsyth Blvd, Saint Louis, MO 63105-1707
Tel (314) 726-2152 *Founded/Ownrshp* 2012
Sales 89.0MM^E *EMP* 512^E
SIC 3555 Printing trades machinery
Pr: Kyle Chapman
**Ch Bd:* Gerald A Nathe
**CFO:* Ivan R Habibe
CFO: Martin Moore
VP: James M Rutledge
**VP:* Steffen Weisser
Exec: Mark Baldwin
Mng Dir: Alain Fouque
Mng Dir: John Leek
Rgnl Mgr: Rusty Allen
Genl Mgr: Ryohei Maeda

D-U-N-S 09-237-4164
BALDWIN UNION FREE SCHOOL DISTRICT
960 Hastings St, Baldwin, NY 11510-4738
Tel (516) 377-9312 *Founded/Ownrshp* 1992
Sales 117.6MM *EMP* 1,000
Accts Cullen & Danowski Llp Cpas
SIC 8211 Public elementary school; Public junior high school; Public senior high school
**Pr:* Melissa Howell Manning
**Treas:* Sharon Moon Knoernschild
**VP:* Susan Fixler Aksionoff
Pr Dir: Christina Schmohl

D-U-N-S 06-040-8796
BALDWIN WALLACE UNIVERSITY (OH)
275 Eastland Rd, Berea, OH 44017-2005
Tel (440) 826-2900 *Founded/Ownrshp* 1845, 1914
Sales 147.5MM *EMP* 1,108^E
Accts Kpmg Llp Cleveland Ohio
SIC 8221 College, except junior
Pr: Robert C Helmer
**Ch Bd:* John Kropf
**Pr:* Richard Durst
**Treas:* Clyde E Bartter
Ofcr: Nicholas W Chalkley
**Sr VP:* Richard L Fletcher
Sr VP: Richard Fletcher
VP: Patrick Dunlavy
VP: William J Spiker
Exec: Gary Jameyson
Exec: Samuel Stansfield
Assoc Dir: Jeff Miller
Board of Directors: Carmen Castrorivera, Lisa Tomlin-Houston, Janet Leonard, Rebecca Shaw, Karen Stenger

BALFORD FARMS
See MILK INDUSTRY MANAGEMENT CORP

D-U-N-S 96-255-6739
BALFOUR BEATTY COMMUNITIES LLC
(*Suby of* BALFOUR BEATTY PLC)
1 Country View Rd Ste 100, Malvern, PA 19355-1439
Tel (610) 355-8100 *Founded/Ownrshp* 2008
Sales 150.7MM *EMP* 1,500^E
SIC 6531 Real estate agent, residential
Pr: Chris Williams
Sr VP: Kellie Ajjan
Sr VP: Steven Curtis
Sr VP: Sean Kent
Sr VP: Mark Lavin
Sr VP: Ron Nestor
Sr VP: Anne-Marie Niklaus
VP: Leslie Cohn
VP: Holly Costello
VP: Lisa Dailey
VP: Denise Hauck
VP: Jim Jefferson
VP: Dan Savoia
VP: Inez Whittington
Exec: Rosemary Phillips

D-U-N-S 04-331-3394
BALFOUR BEATTY CONSTRUCTION GROUP INC
(*Suby of* BALFOUR BEATTY LLC) ★
3100 Mckinnon St Fl 10, Dallas, TX 75201-7007
Tel (214) 451-1000 *Founded/Ownrshp* 2007
Sales 3.8MMM *EMP* 2,200
Accts Deloitte & Touche Llp Dallas
SIC 1542 1541 Commercial & office building, new construction; Commercial & office buildings, renovation & repair; Hospital construction; Industrial buildings, new construction; Renovation, remodeling & repairs: industrial buildings
Ch Bd: Mark Layman
**CFO:* Richard Jaggers
**Ex VP:* Glenn Burns
**Ex VP:* Doug Jones
**Ex VP:* Eric Stenman
**Ex VP:* John Tarpey
**Ex VP:* John Woodcock
**Sr VP:* John Parolisi
**VP:* Mark Crouser
VP: Sean Holliday

D-U-N-S 17-497-8630
BALFOUR BEATTY CONSTRUCTION LLC
(*Suby of* BALFOUR BEATTY CONSTRUCTION GROUP INC) ★
3100 Mckinnon St Fl 10, Dallas, TX 75201-7007
Tel (214) 451-1000 *Founded/Ownrshp* 2004
Sales 3.9MMM *EMP* 2,190
Accts Deloitte & Touche Llp Dallas
SIC 1542 1541 Commercial & office building, new construction; Commercial & office buildings, renovation & repair; Hospital construction; Industrial buildings, new construction
Ch Bd: Mark Layman

Bd of Dir: Brice Hill
Ofcr: Steve Holt
VP: Tony Stoneking
Dir Bus: Mark Harris
Prgrm Mgr: Amit Parikh
Rgnl Mgr: Phillip Jordan
Snr PM: Mark Chappell

D-U-N-S 78-305-9074 IMP/EXP
BALFOUR BEATTY INFRASTRUCTURE INC
FRU-CON CONSTRUCTION
(*Suby of* BALFOUR BEATTY LLC) ★
999 Peachtree St Ne # 900, Atlanta, GA 30309-3915
Tel (404) 875-0356 *Founded/Ownrshp* 1990
Sales 517.8MM *EMP* 1,100
Accts Deloitte & Touche Llp Dallas
SIC 1611 General contractor, highway & street construction
Pr: Ray Bond
Pr: Christine M Canney
CFO: Mark Birch
VP: Crandall Bates
VP: David Confer
VP: Michael R Fischer
VP: Todd Folk
VP: Mark Johnnie
VP: Drew Leist
VP: Christine McAnney
VP: Joseph Reed
VP: John Rempe
VP: Peter Winder

D-U-N-S 96-702-8429
BALFOUR BEATTY INVESTMENTS INC
(*Suby of* BALFOUR BEATTY PLC)
1 Country View Rd Ste 100, Malvern, PA 19355-1439
Tel (610) 355-8100 *Founded/Ownrshp* 2008
Sales 114.7MM^E *EMP* 1,500^E
SIC 6531 8748 1731 8999 8741 Real estate agent, residential; Energy conservation consultant; Electrical work; Geological consultant; Construction management
Pr: Rick Taylor
**CFO:* Denise Hubley
**Ex VP:* Leslie S Cohn
**Ex VP:* Richard C Taylor
Sr VP: Louis Derogatis
**Sr VP:* Marina Dikos
Sr VP: James Selmser
Sr VP: Jim G Short
VP: Amy Aponte
**VP:* Mark Jennings
VP: Josh E Smith

D-U-N-S 15-189-8053 IMP/EXP
BALFOUR BEATTY LLC
(*Suby of* BALFOUR BEATTY PLC)
1011 Centre Rd Ste 322, Wilmington, DE 19805-1266
Tel (302) 573-3873 *Founded/Ownrshp* 2001
Sales 4.6MMM *EMP* 2,200
Accts Deloitte & Touche Llp Dallas
SIC 1542 8712 8741 Commercial & office building contractors; Architectural engineering; Management services
Pr: Mark Crouser
**Treas:* Barry Crozier
**VP:* Joanne Bonfiglio
**VP:* Leslie Cohn
**VP:* Peter Zinkin

D-U-N-S 10-338-6939
BALFOUR BEATTY MILITARY HOUSING LLC
(*Suby of* BALFOUR BEATTY COMMUNITIES LLC) ★
1 Country View Rd, Malvern, PA 19355-1438
Tel (610) 355-8100 *Founded/Ownrshp* 2002
Sales 112.4MM^E *EMP* 1,500^E
SIC 1522 1542 Residential construction; Nonresidential construction
VP: Leslie Cohn
Off Mgr: Rebeka Zanarstel

D-U-N-S 12-560-1174
BALFOUR BEATTY MILITARY HOUSING MANAGEMENT LLC
(*Suby of* BALFOUR BEATTY MILITARY HOUSING LLC) ★
1 Country View Rd Ste 100, Malvern, PA 19355-1439
Tel (610) 355-8100 *Founded/Ownrshp* 2005
Sales 38.1MM^E *EMP* 1,500
SIC 6531 Real estate agent, residential
Pr: Christopher Williams

BALISE HONDA
See BALISE MOTOR SALES CO

D-U-N-S 00-686-9606
BALISE MOTOR SALES CO
BALISE HONDA
400 Riverdale St, West Springfield, MA 01089-4608
Tel (413) 733-8604 *Founded/Ownrshp* 1989
Sales 244.0MM^E *EMP* 650
SIC 5511 Automobiles, new & used
Pr: James E Balise Jr
Recvr: Telly Alvaro
**CFO:* Steven Mitus
**VP:* Michael D Balise
**VP:* William Canon Jr
**VP:* Michael J Dubois
**VP:* John Dubosh
Ex Dir: Marcelo Fazolin
Sls Mgr: Noah Cahillane
Sales Asso: Joseph Cukier
Sales Asso: Manuel Ortiz

D-U-N-S 00-693-7767 IMP
■ **BALKAMP INC**
NAPA BALKAMP
(*Suby of* GENUINE PARTS CO) ★
2601 S Holt Rd, Indianapolis, IN 46241-5700
Tel (317) 244-7241 *Founded/Ownrshp* 1936
Sales 726.6MM^E *EMP* 608
SIC 5013 Automotive supplies & parts; Automotive supplies
Pr: Donald Tollison
**Treas:* Mary Knudsen
**VP:* Frank Amato
**VP:* Ryan Maxwell
**Rgnl Mgr:* Debbie Stickley

Dept Mgr: Kris Hoopingarner
QA Dir: Joe Augsburger
Dir IT: Tom Davis
IT Man: David Evans
Info Man: Jeff Atchley
Opers Mgr: Darlene Noel

BALL & JEWELL
See STERLING INC

D-U-N-S 92-645-1519
■ **BALL AEROSPACE & TECHNOLOGIES CORP**
(*Suby of* BALL CORP) ★
1600 Commerce St, Boulder, CO 80301-2734
Tel (303) 939-4000 *Founded/Ownrshp* 1956
Sales 755.8MM^E *EMP* 3,000
SIC 3812 Aircraft/aerospace flight instruments & guidance systems; Defense systems & equipment; Navigational systems & instruments; Antennas, radar or communications
Pr: Robert D Strain
**VP:* John D Campbell
**VP:* Scott Chrisbacher
VP: Drew Crouch
**VP:* Thomas M Deany
**VP:* Frederick J Doyle Jr
VP: Sherri Fike
VP: Robert Freedman
VP: Alan Frohbieter
VP: William D Gibson Jr
VP: Vonna Weir Heaton
VP: Dave Kaufman
VP: Carol Lane
VP: Debra Facktor Lepore
VP: Cary W Ludtke
VP: Don Martin
VP: Alison Medbery
VP: Arthur Morrissey
VP: Jim Oschmann
VP: Jeff Osterkamp
VP: Jeffrey Osterkamp

D-U-N-S 16-940-2059 IMP/EXP
BALL BOUNCE AND SPORT INC
HEDSTROM FITNESS
1 Hedstrom Dr, Ashland, OH 44805-3586
Tel (419) 759-3838 *Founded/Ownrshp* 2004
Sales 141.3MM^E *EMP* 305
SIC 5092 5091 3089 Toys; Fitness equipment & supplies; Plastic processing
CEO: James Braeunig
**CFO:* Michael Kelly
VP: John McWilliams
VP: John Williams
Exec: Rae Wessler
Sales Exec: Phil Maggard
Board of Directors: Robert H Elman, Jack D Furst

BALL COR
See BALL METAL FOOD CONTAINER LLC

D-U-N-S 00-641-9147 IMP/EXP
▲ **BALL CORP**
10 Longs Peak Dr, Broomfield, CO 80021-2510
Tel (303) 469-3131 *Founded/Ownrshp* 1880
Sales 8.0MMM *EMP* 15,200
Tkr Sym BLL *Exch* NYS
SIC 3411 3085 3812 3679 Food & beverage containers; Aluminum cans; Beer cans, metal; Beverage cans, metal: except beer; Plastics bottles; Aircraft/aerospace flight instruments & guidance systems; Defense systems & equipment; Navigational systems & instruments; Antennas, radar or communications; Cryogenic cooling devices for infrared detectors, masers
Ch Bd: John A Hayes
COO: Daniel W Fisher
CFO: Scott C Morrison
Bd of Dir: Chris Barkley
Sr VP: Lisa A Pauley
VP: Neil Anderson
VP: Charles E Baker
VP: Shawn M Barker
VP: Dave Bode
VP: Andrew Crouch
VP: Sherri Fike
VP: John Friedery
VP: David Heller
VP: Michael O'Brien
VP: James N Peterson
Board of Directors: Robert W Alspaugh, Michael J Cave, Daniel J Heinrich, R David Hoover, Georgia R Nelson, Cynthia A Niekamp, George M Smart, Theodore M Solso, Stuart A Taylor II

D-U-N-S 12-090-6185
BALL HEALTHCARE SERVICES INC
1 Southern Way, Mobile, AL 36619-1210
Tel (251) 432-5800 *Founded/Ownrshp* 1988
Sales 56.2MM^E *EMP* 1,100
Accts Self Maples & Copeland Pc
SIC 8051 Skilled nursing care facilities
Pr: Clarence Ball Jr
COO: Thelma Hoffman
**VP:* John D Schutt

D-U-N-S 00-693-6322 IMP/EXP
BALL HORTICULTURAL CO
PAN AMERICAN SEED COMPANY
622 Town Rd, West Chicago, IL 60185-2698
Tel (630) 231-3600 *Founded/Ownrshp* 1905
Sales 710.6MM^E *EMP* 3,000
SIC 0181 Flowers grown in field nurseries
Pr: Anna C Ball
**CFO:* Todd Billings
**CFO:* Allen Davidson
**Sec:* Todd Frauendorfer
**Sr VP:* Cornelis A Boonman
VP: Doreen Anderson
VP: Lee Griesbach
VP: Tim Kich
**VP:* Diane Szmurlo
VP: Gary Szmurlo
Exec: Bill Doeckel
Exec: Bill Doedkel

D-U-N-S 60-335-2402 IMP
BALL INC
REXAM INC.
(*Suby of* REXAM LIMITED)
4201 Congress St Ste 340, Charlotte, NC 28209-4640
Tel (704) 551-1500 *Founded/Ownrshp* 1987
Sales 1.1MMM^E *EMP* 7,000
SIC 3411 Aluminum cans
Pr: Frank Brown
**Treas:* Clint Tumlin
VP: Richard Downes
**VP:* Ron Glasshoff
**VP:* Lisa Hysko
VP: Lisa R Lamoe-Hysko
**VP:* Charlotte Reily
Exec: Charlotte Reilly
Exec: Joe Sasso
Dir IT: Darrell Vanhoy
Tech Mgr: Oscar Suarez

D-U-N-S 84-162-2793 IMP/EXP
■ **BALL METAL BEVERAGE CONTAINER CORP**
(*Suby of* BALL CORP) ★
9300 W 108th Cir, Westminster, CO 80021-3682
Tel (303) 469-5511 *Founded/Ownrshp* 1995
Sales 1.0MMM^E *EMP* 3,700^E
SIC 3411 Aluminum cans
Pr: Micheal Herdman
**VP:* Charles Bates
VP: Doug Bradford

D-U-N-S 02-162-0161
■ **BALL METAL FOOD CONTAINER LLC**
BALL COR
(*Suby of* BALL CORP) ★
9300 W 108th Cir, Westminster, CO 80021-3682
Tel (303) 469-3131 *Founded/Ownrshp* 1982
Sales 85.6MM^E *EMP* 252^E
SIC 3411 Food containers, metal
CEO: John A Hayes
**VP:* Charles E Baker
**VP:* Shawn M Barker
**VP:* Douglas K Bradford
**VP:* Jeff A Knobel

D-U-N-S 96-198-0856 EXP
■ **BALL PACKAGING LLC**
BALL PACKAGING OPERATIONS
(*Suby of* BALL CORP) ★
9300 W 108th Cir, Westminster, CO 80021-3682
Tel (303) 469-5511 *Founded/Ownrshp* 1995
Sales 204.5MM^E *EMP* 800
SIC 3411 Food & beverage containers
CEO: John A Hayes
**Pr:* Larry J Green
**Treas:* Scott C Morrison
**VP:* Charles E Baker
**VP:* Shawn M Barker
**VP:* Douglas K Bradford
**VP:* Jeff A Knobel
**VP:* Raymond J Seabrook
**VP:* David A Westerlund

BALL PACKAGING OPERATIONS
See BALL PACKAGING LLC

D-U-N-S 06-554-0726
BALL STATE UNIVERSITY
2000 W University Ave, Muncie, IN 47306-0002
Tel (765) 289-1241 *Founded/Ownrshp* 1918
Sales 388.6MM^E *EMP* 6,426
Accts State Board Of Accounts India
SIC 8221 University
Pr: Paul Ferguson
Pr: Melissa Ginotti
**Pr:* Jo Ann M Gora
Bd of Dir: Bill Jenkins
Ofcr: Mathew Galligan
Sr VP: Sonja Markwell
VP: Ana Batres
VP: Ben E Hancock
VP: Terry S King
**VP:* Thomas J Kinghorn
**VP:* Douglas Mc Conkey
VP: Bruce E Morgan
**VP:* Donald Park PHD
VP: Phil Repp
**VP:* Philip Repp
VP: O'Neal H Smitherman
**VP:* Warren Vanderhill PHD
VP: Marie Williams
Assoc Dir: Ellen Lucas

D-U-N-S 11-479-8080
■ **BALLANTRAE INC**
DELCO REMY AMERICA
(*Suby of* BORG WARNER) ★
600 Corporation Dr, Pendleton, IN 46064-8610
Tel (800) 372-3555 *Founded/Ownrshp* 1999
Sales 228.8MM^E *EMP* 3,990^E
SIC 3714 3694 Motor vehicle parts & accessories; Engine electrical equipment
CFO: Raj Sahah
VP: Krishnaswami Subramanian
VP: Allen R Wilkie
Web Prj Mg: Babcock Randy
Netwrk Mgr: Joseph D Wilson
Mktg Dir: Stan Saunders
Mktg Mgr: Joe Tori

D-U-N-S 08-582-6485 IMP
▲ **BALLANTYNE STRONG INC**
11422 Miracle Hills Dr # 300, Omaha, NE 68154-5310
Tel (402) 453-4444 *Founded/Ownrshp* 1932
Sales 92.8MM *EMP* 316
Tkr Sym BTN *Exch* ASE
SIC 3861 3648 Motion picture apparatus & equipment; Stage lighting equipment
Ch Bd: D Kyle Cerminara
Pr: Ray F Boegner
Pr: Stephen L Schilling
**CFO:* Nathan D Legband
Treas: Kevin Herrmann
VP: Dave Barker
VP: Chris A Horsley
VP: Ryan Turner
Board of Directors: Samuel C Freitag, William J Gerber, Lewis M Johnson, Charles T Lanktree, Robert J Roschman, James C Shay

D-U-N-S 80-017-0771
BALLARD PETROLEUM HOLDINGS LLC
845 12th St W, Billings, MT 59102-5406
Tel (406) 259-8790 *Founded/Ownrshp* 1996
Sales 137.4MM *EMP* 37
Accts Wipfli Llp Billings Montana
SIC 1311 Crude petroleum & natural gas
Treas: Craig Marshall
Sr VP: Jeff Ballard

D-U-N-S 08-481-7910 IMP
BALLARD POWER SYSTEMS CORP
(*Suby of* SUPERIOR PLUS CORP)
15001 N Commerce Dr, Dearborn, MI 48120-1226
Tel (313) 583-5980 *Founded/Ownrshp* 1998
Sales 97.2MM^E *EMP* 1,100
SIC 3621 Electric motor & generator parts
CEO: John Sheridan
Exec: Raymond Ong

D-U-N-S 07-551-8092
BALLARD SPAHR LLP
1735 Market St Fl 51, Philadelphia, PA 19103-7507
Tel (215) 665-8500 *Founded/Ownrshp* 1886
Sales 218.1MM^E *EMP* 1,100
SIC 8111 General practice law office
Ch Bd: Mark S Stewart
Pt: John H Estey
Pt: Stephanie Franklin-Suber
Pt: Lawrence J Gartner
Pt: Geoffrey A Kahn
Pt: Beth Moskow-Schnoll
Pt: Kathryn H S Pett
Pt: Michael W Skojec
Pt: John Delli Venneri
Pt: Naomi Young
Mng Pt: David Sampson
Mng Pt: Stephen Savage
Mng Pt: Raymond G Truitt
CFO: Neeraj K Aggarwal
VP: Marla Hamilton
VP: Brian Pedrow
VP: Tom Sager
Exec: Stanley Parry
Exec: Harry Weiss

BALLAST PT BREWING & SPIRITS
See HOME BREW MART INC

D-U-N-S 19-945-4765
BALLENGER CONSTRUCTION CO
24200 N Fm 509, Harlingen, TX 78550-2192
Tel (956) 421-9500 *Founded/Ownrshp* 1937
Sales 106.9MM^E *EMP* 550^E
SIC 1542 Nonresidential construction
Pr: Joe C Ballenger Sr
**VP:* Hank Frailing

D-U-N-S 09-004-6111 IMP/EXP
BALLESTER HERMANOS INC
Carr 869 Parq, Catano, PR 00962
Tel (787) 788-4110 *Founded/Ownrshp* 1914
Sales 605.4MM^E *EMP* 600
Accts Bdo Puerto Rico Psc San Juan
SIC 5141 5182 Groceries, general line; Liquor
CEO: Alfonso F Ballester
**Pr:* Alejandro M Ballester
**CFO:* Romulo Carrada
**Treas:* Jose F Ballester
**VP:* Luis A Ballester
**VP:* Reuben Medina
**VP:* Jorge V Prats
**VP:* Jaime Rodriguez

BALL'S SUPER FOOD STORES
See B FOUR CORP

D-U-N-S 07-110-3188
BALLSTON SPA CENTRAL SCHOOL DISTRICT
70 Malta Ave, Ballston Spa, NY 12020-1599
Tel (518) 884-7195 *Founded/Ownrshp* 1900
Sales 89.8MM *EMP* 700
Accts Marvin And Company Pc Lath
SIC 8211 Public elementary & secondary schools
Pr: Jeanne Obermayer
VP: Jerri Cummings
VP: Lynn Lantz
**VP:* Kevin Schaefer
Genl Mgr: Susan Andi
CIO: Gail Mathias
Psych: Kevin Flores
Psych: Nicole Stehle
Psych: Lyndsey Wilcox

D-U-N-S 03-495-4198
■ **BALLY GAMING INC**
(*Suby of* BALLY GAMING INTERNATIONAL INC) ★
6601 Bermuda Rd, Las Vegas, NV 89119-3622
Tel (702) 532-7700 *Founded/Ownrshp* 1991
Sales 149.4MM^E *EMP* 568^E
SIC 3999 Slot machines
Pr: Derik Mooberry
Tech Mgr: Dan Lewis

D-U-N-S 78-266-4387 IMP
■ **BALLY GAMING INTERNATIONAL INC**
(*Suby of* BALLY TECHNOLOGIES INC) ★
6601 Bermuda Rd, Las Vegas, NV 89119-3622
Tel (702) 584-7700 *Founded/Ownrshp* 1996
Sales 222.8MM^E *EMP* 1,300
SIC 3999 Coin-operated amusement machines; Slot machines
Pr: Richard Haddrill
**Treas:* Robert Caller
Treas: Scott Schweinfurth
**VP:* Mark Lerner

D-U-N-S 07-723-4177 IMP
■ **BALLY TECHNOLOGIES INC**
(*Suby of* SCIENTIFIC GAMES CORP) ★
6601 Bermuda Rd, Las Vegas, NV 89119-3605
Tel (770) 420-2388 *Founded/Ownrshp* 1988
Sales 1.2MMM^E *EMP* 4,000^E

SIC 3999 7999 7993 7372 Coin-operated amusement machines; Slot machines; Gambling establishment; Gambling establishments operating coin-operated machines; Prepackaged software
Pr: Derik Mooberry
*Treas: Scott Schweinfurth
Chf Mktg O: Ricco Novero
Sr VP: Paul Lofgren
Sr VP: Marcus Prater
VP: Craig Bullis
VP: Marc Comella
VP: Tina Kilmer
VP: Chuck Miller
VP: Christine Taylor
VP: Nathan Wadds
VP: Warren White

D-U-N-S 06-858-2659 IMP
BALLY TOTAL FITNESS CORP
(Suby of BALLY TOTAL FITNESS HOLDING CORP) ★
12440 Imperial Hwy # 300, Norwalk, CA 90650-3178
Tel (562) 484-2000 Founded/Ownrshp 1983
Sales 150.3MM^E EMP 12,340
SIC 7991 Health club
CEO: Marc Tascher
*Pr: Lee Hillman
*CFO: John Dwyer
*Sr VP: Cary A Gaan

D-U-N-S 14-717-6986
BALLY TOTAL FITNESS HOLDING CORP
8700 W Bryn Mawr Ave 620n, Chicago, IL 60631-3560
Tel (773) 380-3000 Founded/Ownrshp 1983
Sales 295.8MM^E EMP 19,200
SIC 7991 Health club
Ch Bd: Don R Kornstein
*COO: Michael A Feder
CFO: John Dwyer
*CFO: Ronald G Eidell
*Chf Mktg O: John H Wildman
*Sr VP: Marc D Bassewitz
Sr VP: Thomas S Massimino
VP: Julie Adams
VP: Guy Thier
Area Mgr: John Rodgers
Area Mgr: Paul Spatz
Board of Directors: Eric Langshur Charles J B, Barry R Elson

D-U-N-S 07-250-6223
BALLY TOTAL FITNESS OF CALIFORNIA INC
(Suby of BALLY TOTAL FITNESS CORP) ★
12440 Imperial Hwy # 300, Norwalk, CA 90650-8309
Tel (562) 484-2000 Founded/Ownrshp 1963
Sales 2.8MM^E EMP 1,800
SIC 7991 Health club
CEO: Barry Elson

BALLYS LAS VEGAS
See PARBALL CORP

BALLYS LAS VEGAS
See CAESARS LICENSE CO LLC

D-U-N-S 08-293-9737 IMP
■ **BALLYS PARK PLACE INC** (DE)
(Suby of HARRAHS) ★
1900 Pacific Ave, Atlantic City, NJ 08401-6714
Tel (609) 340-2000 Founded/Ownrshp 1979, 1985
Sales 220.3MM^E EMP 7,480^E
SIC 7011 Casino hotel
Pr: Mark P Frissora
*Pr: Wallace R Barr
*Pr: Ken Condon
*Treas: Donna M Graham
Ofcr: Richard Negro
*Sr VP: Robert Conover
Sr VP: Steve Hann
*Sr VP: Dennis P Venuti

D-U-N-S 79-697-7122
■ **BALLYS PARK PLACE INC**
(Suby of HARRAHS) ★
1721 Boardwalk, Atlantic City, NJ 08401-6810
Tel (609) 340-2000 Founded/Ownrshp 2005
Sales 54.5MM^E EMP 5,300
SIC 6512 5812 Nonresidential building operators; Eating places
COO: Wallace R Barr
*Pr: Kenneth Condon

BALLY'S TUNICA
See RIH ACQUISITIONS MS II LLC

D-U-N-S 07-866-2572
BALMORAL FUNDS LLC
11150 Santa Monica Blvd, Los Angeles, CA 90025-3380
Tel (310) 473-3065 Founded/Ownrshp 2011
Sales 96.6MM^E EMP 750^E
SIC 6282 Investment advisory service

D-U-N-S 00-720-9539 IMP
BALON CORP
3245 S Hattie Ave, Oklahoma City, OK 73129-6697
Tel (405) 677-3321 Founded/Ownrshp 1965
Sales 228.8MM^E EMP 850
SIC 3491 3494 5085 Industrial valves; Valves & pipe fittings; Industrial supplies
Pr: Phil Scaramucci
*Pr: Domer Scaramucci Jr
CFO: Danny Williams
*Treas: Larry Wells
Rgnl Mgr: Scott Hayden
Trfc Mgr: Larry Wedman
Sales Asso: John Ferguson

D-U-N-S 06-134-7050 IMP
BALTEK INC
(Suby of 3A COMPOSITES USA INC) ★
5240 National Center Dr, Colfax, NC 27235-9719
Tel (336) 398-1900 Founded/Ownrshp 2009
Sales 148.4MM^E EMP 977
SIC 2436 Softwood veneer & plywood
CEO: Roman Thomassin
*Pr: Georg Reif

D-U-N-S 04-993-5307 IMP/EXP
BALTIMORE AIRCOIL CO INC
BAC
(Suby of AMSTED INDUSTRIES INC) ★
7600 Dorsey Run Rd, Jessup, MD 20794-9328
Tel (410) 799-6200 Founded/Ownrshp 1985
Sales 261.3MM^E EMP 572^E
SIC 3585 3443 Evaporative condensers, heat transfer equipment; Coolers, milk & water: electric; Heat exchangers: coolers (after, inter), condensers, etc.; Cooling towers, metal plate
Pr: Don Fetzer
*Treas: G E Chamberlin
*Sr VP: T E Bergmann
*VP: T Buzby
VP: Brad Considine
*VP: W E Dietrich
*VP: T P Facius
*VP: R D Liming
*VP: P J Ostman
VP: Darlene Pence
*VP: W O Rector
*VP: L A Rubino
*VP: M A Tignor

BALTIMORE CITY CMNTY COLLEGE
See STATE OF MARYLAND

D-U-N-S 00-697-2470
BALTIMORE CITY PUBLIC SCHOOL SYSTEMS (INC)
BALTIMORE CITY PUBLIC SCHOOLS
200 E North Ave, Baltimore, MD 21202-5910
Tel (410) 222-5000 Founded/Ownrshp 1997
Sales 1.4MMM EMP 10,800^E
Accts Cliftonlarsonallen Llp Baltim
SIC 8211 Public elementary & secondary schools
CEO: Sonja B Santelises
*CEO: Bonnie S Copeland
*Ofcr: Karl E Perry
Ofcr: Dawn Wood
Ex Dir: Rebekah Ghosh
Pr Dir: Edie H Foster
Teacher Pr: Deray McKesson
Psych: Esther Kiffel

BALTIMORE CITY PUBLIC SCHOOLS
See BALTIMORE CITY PUBLIC SCHOOL SYSTEMS (INC)

D-U-N-S 06-614-4570
BALTIMORE COUNTY PUBLIC SCHOOLS
BCPS
6901 N Charles St, Towson, MD 21204-3780
Tel (410) 887-4554 Founded/Ownrshp 2016
Sales 375.8MM^E EMP 17,067^E
SIC 8211 Public elementary & secondary schools

D-U-N-S 00-694-9713 IMP
■ **BALTIMORE GAS AND ELECTRIC CO** (MD)
BGE
(Suby of EXELON ENERGY DELIVERY CO LLC) ★
110 W Fayette St, Baltimore, MD 21201-3708
Tel (410) 234-5000 Founded/Ownrshp 1906, 2012
Sales 3.1MMM EMP 3,303^E
SIC 4931 Electric & other services combined
CEO: Calvin G Butler Jr
*Ch Bd: Christopher M Crane
Pr: Jeffrey Relf
Pr: Stephen J Woerner
CFO: Carim V Khouzami
CFO: Jonathan W Thayer
Chf Cred: Robert D Biagiotti
Sr VP: Jeannette Mills
VP: A C Burton
VP: J Dodge
VP: Daniel P Gahagan
VP: Albert Kirby
VP: David M Vahos
Board of Directors: Ann C Berzin, Michael E Cryor, James R Curtiss, Joseph Haskins Jr,, Denis P O'brien, Maria Harris Tildon

D-U-N-S 00-694-9721
BALTIMORE LIFE INSURANCE CO INC
10075 Red Run Blvd # 175, Owings Mills, MD 21117-4871
Tel (410) 581-6600 Founded/Ownrshp 1882
Sales NA EMP 416
SIC 6311 Life insurance
Ch Bd: Joseph E Blair Jr
*Pr: L John Pearson
CFO: Richard Spencer
*Treas: Thomas Cranston
*Ex VP: David S Sachs
*Sr VP: Jeffrey Marshall
VP: Michael Hydanus
Sales Exec: Robert Kehring
Sls Mgr: Marianne Block

D-U-N-S 12-134-5136
■ **BALTIMORE SUN CO**
MORNING SUN
(Suby of TRONC INC) ★
501 N Calvert St, Baltimore, MD 21278-1000
Tel (410) 539-7700 Founded/Ownrshp 2014
Sales 466.4MM^E EMP 2,017
SIC 2711 Newspapers, publishing & printing
Pr: Timothy Ryan
VP: Amy Powers
Dir IT: Matthew Baise
Pr Dir: Nick Madigan
Mktg Mgr: Geoff Peckham
Mktg Mgr: Denisa Protani

BALTIMORE WASHINGTON MED CTR
See BALTIMORE WASHINGTON MEDICAL SYSTEM INC

D-U-N-S 06-137-7644
BALTIMORE WASHINGTON MEDICAL SYSTEM INC (MD)
BALTIMORE WASHINGTON MED CTR
301 Hospital Dr, Glen Burnie, MD 21061-5803
Tel (410) 787-4000 Founded/Ownrshp 1993
Sales 355.4MM EMP 2,676
SIC 8062 General medical & surgical hospitals
Pr: Karen Olscamp
*Ch Bd: Melvin L Kelly
*Pr: James R Walker
*CFO: Alfred Pietsch
*Treas: Ronald C McGuirk
*Sr VP: Ronald Andro
Sr VP: Lawrence S Linder
VP: Mary Jozwik
VP: Colleen Roach
VP: Susan Ward
Dir Inf Cn: Donna Lemmert
Dir Risk M: Kristen Sapienza
Dir Lab: Garry G Fritz
Dir Lab: Kim Keller
Dir Rad: James Cary

D-U-N-S 00-722-0817 IMP
BAMA COMPANIES INC (OK)
BAMA PIE
2745 E 11th St, Tulsa, OK 74104-3913
Tel (918) 592-0778 Founded/Ownrshp 1937
Sales 280.8MM^E EMP 1,150
SIC 2053 2041 2051 Frozen bakery products, except bread; Pies, bakery: frozen; Pizza dough, prepared; Biscuits, baked: baking powder & raised
Pr: Paula Marshall
*Ch Bd: Lilah B Marshall
VP: Helen Inbody
VP: Kevin McKenna
VP: Randy Roark
Exec: Adele Lofton
CTO: Lisa Holtsinger
QA Dir: Tom Black
QA Dir: Ernst Hill
QA Dir: Kevin Shows
Sfty Mgr: Joeseph Defalco

D-U-N-S 93-838-9426
BAMA FROZEN DOUGH LLC
(Suby of BAMA PIE) ★
2435 N Lewis Ave, Tulsa, OK 74110-2121
Tel (918) 732-2600 Founded/Ownrshp 1995
Sales 100.0MM^E EMP 700
SIC 5142 Packaged frozen goods
Treas: Stephan Wendl
Bd of Dir: John Marshall
Ql Cn Mgr: Russ Wells

BAMA PIE
See BAMA COMPANIES INC

D-U-N-S 80-479-9807 EXP
BAMBERGER POLYMERS CORP
2 Jericho Plz Ste 109, Jericho, NY 11753-1681
Tel (516) 622-3600 Founded/Ownrshp 1993
Sales 291.2MM^E EMP 155
SIC 5162 Resins
Co-CEO: Steve Goldberg
*CFO: Paul Coco
*Co-CEO: Dennis Don
*Ex VP: Theodore Dwyer
*VP: Michael Pignataro
Off Mgr: Andrea Eisenberg

D-U-N-S 95-865-1853 IMP/EXP
BAMBERGER POLYMERS INC
(Suby of BAMBERGER POLYMERS CORP) ★
2 Jericho Plz Ste 109, Jericho, NY 11753-1681
Tel (516) 622-3600 Founded/Ownrshp 1993
Sales 151.1MM^E EMP 90
SIC 5162 Resins
*CFO: Paul Coco
*Ex VP: Steve Goldberg
*VP: Christine Levy
*VP: Michael Pignataro

BANA BOX
See BANA INC

D-U-N-S 05-020-7059
BANA INC
BANA BOX
624 E Mcleroy Blvd, Saginaw, TX 76179-4603
Tel (817) 232-3750 Founded/Ownrshp 1969
Sales 111.4MM^E EMP 150
SIC 5085 2441 2448 Packing, industrial; Boxes, wood; Wood pallets & skids
Pr: David R Boenker
*VP: Gregory T Boenker
*VP: Angela Dill
*VP: Linda D Wansing

D-U-N-S 09-488-2602 IMP/EXP
■ **BANANA REPUBLIC LLC**
(Suby of GAP INC) ★
2 Folsom St, San Francisco, CA 94105-1205
Tel (650) 952-4400 Founded/Ownrshp 1983
Sales 642.9MM^E EMP 8,000
SIC 5651 Family clothing stores
CEO: Art Perck
Pr: Jack Calhoun
MIS Mgr: Kevin Darling

BANC BOSTON
See BANCBOSTON CAPITAL INC

BANC HOME LOANS
See BANC OF CALIFORNIA NATIONAL ASSOCIATION

D-U-N-S 86-816-8246
■ **BANC OF AMERICA MORTGAGE CAPITAL CORP**
(Suby of BANK OF AMERICA CORP) ★
100 N Tryon St Ste 4700, Charlotte, NC 28202-4003
Tel (800) 876-4496 Founded/Ownrshp 1998
Sales NA EMP 1,150
Accts Price Waterhouse Llp
SIC 6411 Insurance agents, brokers & service
CEO: Lewis Coleman
*V Ch: William L Maxwell
*Pr: Richard Gross
*Ofcr: Charles R Brama
Board of Directors: Edward J Brown III, Thomas W Bunn, Louis W Coleman, William A Hodges, Robert L Kahan, Kent A Logan, Joseph M Schell, John K Skeen

D-U-N-S 11-907-6011
▲ **BANC OF CALIFORNIA INC**
18500 Von Karman Ave # 1100, Irvine, CA 92612-0546
Tel (949) 236-5436 Founded/Ownrshp 2002
Sales NA EMP 1,384
Tkr Sym BANC Exch NYS
SIC 6021 National commercial banks
Ch Bd: Steven A Sugarman
Pr: Heidi Johnson
Pr: Aida Rodriguez
COO: Tricia Bailey
CFO: James J McKinney
CFO: Ronald J Nicolas Jr
CFO: Ronald Nicolas Jr
Chf Cred: Hugh F Boyle
Ofcr: Matthew A March
Ofcr: Subir Prasad
Ex VP: Gary S Dunn
Ex VP: John C Grosvenor
Ex VP: Brian P Kuelbs
Ex VP: Chang Liu
Ex VP: Fred Mahintorabi
Ex VP: Ken Plummer
Ex VP: Jay Sanders
Ex VP: Tony Sisca
Ex VP: Diane M Summers
Sr VP: John Chung
Sr VP: Samantha Haugh
Board of Directors: Chad T Brownstein, Eric L Holoman, Jeffrey Karish, Jonah F Schnel, Robert D Sznewajs

D-U-N-S 07-918-1703
■ **BANC OF CALIFORNIA NATIONAL ASSOCIATION**
BANC HOME LOANS
(Suby of BANC OF CALIFORNIA INC) ★
18500 Von Karman Ave, Irvine, CA 92612-0504
Tel (877) 770-2262 Founded/Ownrshp 1967
Sales NA EMP 107^E
SIC 6035 Federal savings banks
Pr: Robert Franko
*Prin: Sean Casey
Brnch Mgr: Dominique Love
Brnch Mgr: Sean Wickersham

D-U-N-S 00-100-1924
■ **BANC ONE CAPITAL MARKETS INC**
(Suby of JP MORGAN SECURITIES LLC) ★
1 Bank One Plz, Chicago, IL 60670-0001
Tel (800) 992-7169 Founded/Ownrshp 1981, 2004
Sales 109.5MM^E EMP 1,352
SIC 6211 6282 Brokers, security; Investment bankers; Investment advice
Ch Bd: David H Schabes
Pr: W Robert Felker
CFO: William R Romani
Treas: Nancy M Amicangelo

D-U-N-S 01-060-8834
■ **BANC ONE FINANCIAL LLC**
(Suby of JPMORGAN CHASE & CO) ★
1 Chase Tower, Chicago, IL 60670-0001
Tel (312) 732-5531 Founded/Ownrshp 1998
Sales 250.8MM^E EMP 2,800
SIC 6211 6153 Security brokers & dealers; Short-term business credit
Treas: Charlie Peruski
*CFO: Heidi Miller
CFO: Charles J Wooding
VP: Bernard Delrey

D-U-N-S 12-453-4223
■ **BANC ONE SERVICES CORP**
(Suby of JPMORGAN CHASE & CO) ★
1111 Polaris Pkwy Ste B3, Columbus, OH 43240-2031
Tel (614) 248-5800 Founded/Ownrshp 1988
Sales 129.0MM^E EMP 3,690
SIC 7389 Financial services
Sr VP: Neil Williams
Netwrk Mgr: Rob Holt

D-U-N-S 36-186-5306
■ **BANCBOSTON CAPITAL INC**
BANC BOSTON
(Suby of BANK OF AMERICA CORP) ★
100 Federal St Ste 1m, Boston, MA 02110-1898
Tel (617) 434-2509 Founded/Ownrshp 2004
Sales 90.2MM^E EMP 1,309
SIC 6799 Investors
Pr: William Parent

D-U-N-S 36-191-9640
■ **BANCFIRST**
(Suby of BANCFIRST CORP) ★
101 N Broadway Ave # 1110, Oklahoma City, OK 73102-8416
Tel (405) 270-1000 Founded/Ownrshp 1989
Sales NA EMP 800^E
SIC 6022 State commercial banks
CEO: David Rainbolt
*Ch Bd: H E Rainbolt
*Treas: Richard A Reich
*V Ch Bd: K Gordon Greer
*V Ch Bd: William O Johnstone
*V Ch Bd: Ralph McCalmont
Ofcr: Sharon Lewis-Williams
Trst Ofcr: Jackie Gates
Trst Ofcr: Brenda Reeder
Ex VP: Dennis Murphy
Sr VP: Brad Cfa
Sr VP: Jean Clark
Sr VP: Steve Culbertson
Sr VP: Monty Curry
Sr VP: Mark C Demos
Sr VP: Sandy Hall
Sr VP: Brian Harris
Sr VP: Pat Hensley
Sr VP: John Huff
Sr VP: Bob Neville
Sr VP: Brian Renz

D-U-N-S 14-495-6158
▲ **BANCFIRST CORP**
101 N Broadway Ave # 1110, Oklahoma City, OK 73102-8416
Tel (405) 270-1086 Founded/Ownrshp 1984
Sales NA EMP 1,744^E
Tkr Sym BANF Exch NGS
SIC 6022 State commercial banks; State trust companies accepting deposits, commercial
Pr: David E Rainbolt
*Ch Bd: H E Rainbolt

Pr: Sara Denizot
Pr: Kristin Haynes
CFO: Randy P Foraker
CFO: Kevin Lawrence
**V Ch Bd:* Dennis L Brand
**V Ch Bd:* James R Daniel
**V Ch Bd:* William O Johnstone
Bd of Dir: Anita Patterson
Ofcr: Kelly Foster
Trst Ofcr: Carolyn Pollock
Ex VP: Scott Copeland
Ex VP: Paul Fleming
Ex VP: Randy Foraker
Ex VP: Janet Gotwals
Ex VP: Sean Shadid
Sr VP: Jennifer Weast
VP: Gene Alexander
VP: Terry Anson
VP: Adam Brown
Board of Directors: Michael S Samis, C L Craig Jr, Natalie Shirley, William H Crawford, Michael K Wallace, F Ford Drummond, Gregory G Wedel, Frank Keating, G Rainey Williams Jr, Dave R Lopez, J Ralph McCalmont, Tom H McCasland III, Ronald J Norick, Paul B Odom Jr

BANCO INTERAMERICANO DE DESAR
See INTER-AMERICAN DEVELOPMENT BANK

D-U-N-S 09-027-2576
■ BANCO POPULAR DE PUERTO RICO (INC)
(*Suby of* POPULAR INC) ★
Popular Ctr, San Juan, PR 00918-1000
Tel (787) 765-9800 *Founded/Ownrshp* 1917, 1985
Sales NA *EMP* 6,666
SIC 6022 6159 6141 State commercial banks; Automobile finance leasing; Personal finance licensed loan companies, small
CEO: Richard L Carrion
**Pr:* David H Chafey
Ofcr: Eduardo Negron
**Ex VP:* Roberto R Herencia
**Ex VP:* Larry Kesler
**Ex VP:* Humberto Martin
**Ex VP:* Gilberto F Monzn
**Ex VP:* Nstor O Rivera
**Sr VP:* Brunilda Santos De Alvarez
Sr VP: Pablo Irizarry
Sr VP: Ana Pagan
VP: Jorege Escalera
VP: Rosita Galguera
VP: Nicole Loubriel
VP: Maribel Marrero
VP: Robert Sands
**Exec:* Jorge A Junquera
**Exec:* Emilio Pinero
Exec: Lorna Ramirez
**Exec:* Carlos J Vazquez

D-U-N-S 06-847-0236
■ BANCO POPULAR NORTH AMERICA INC
(*Suby of* POPULAR INC) ★
P.O. Box 4906 (33014-0906)
Tel (847) 994-5400 *Founded/Ownrshp* 1991
Sales NA *EMP* 1,716
SIC 6022 State commercial banks
Pr: Carlos J Vzquez
Sr Cor Off: Ariel Blanco
Sr Cor Off: Daisy Jimenez
Assoc VP: Julie Tomenbang
Ex VP: Gilberto Monz
Ex VP: Eduardo J Negr
**Sr VP:* James Boyd
VP: Joseph Fradelos
Mktg Mgr: John Gannon

D-U-N-S 80-768-7780
■ BANCO SANTANDER INTERNATIONAL
(*Suby of* BANCO SANTANDER SA)
1401 Brickell Ave Ste 200, Miami, FL 33131-3502
Tel (305) 530-2900 *Founded/Ownrshp* 2006
Sales NA *EMP* 414[E]
SIC 6029 Commercial banks
Mng Dir: Francisco Pardo
CFO: Eloina Franco-Espinosa
**Treas:* Ted Ferdeza
Ofcr: Maria Cortezo
Ofcr: Vania Cruz
Ofcr: Steve Lo
Ofcr: Keila Nunez
Sr VP: Carlos Antequera
Sr VP: Leonardo Couto
Sr VP: Victor Cuenca
Sr VP: Ted Fernandez
Sr VP: Mario Jimenez
Sr VP: James McGrath
Sr VP: Rafael Moreno
Sr VP: Francisco Salt
Sr VP: Rivka Steinmetz
Sr VP: Julio Zapata
VP: Ricardo Avila
VP: Flavio Barbosa
VP: James Bathon
VP: Armando Blancq

D-U-N-S 09-057-5739
■ BANCO SANTANDER-PUERTO RICO INC
(*Suby of* BANCO SANTANDER SA)
207 Ave Ponce De Leon, San Juan, PR 00917-1818
Tel (787) 274-7200 *Founded/Ownrshp* 2005
Sales NA *EMP* 1,810
SIC 6022 State commercial banks
Pr: Juan Arenado Arsuaga
**Sr VP:* Jose Antonio Cambas
**Sr VP:* Salvador Marin
Sr VP: Fredy Molfino
**VP:* Maria Leticia Garcia

D-U-N-S 96-687-0727
BANCOMER TRANSFER SERVICES INC
(*Suby of* BBVA BANCOMER, S.A., INSTITUCION DE BANCA MULTIPLE, GRUPO FINANCIERO BBVA BANCOMER)
16825 Northchase Dr Ste 1, Houston, TX 77060-6024
Tel (281) 765-1500 *Founded/Ownrshp* 1995
Sales NA *EMP* 60[E]
SIC 6099 Electronic funds transfer network, including switching
Ch Bd: Aurora Garza Hagan
CFO: Jennifer N Cao
**CFO:* Jason Lundell
**Ch:* Gabriel Palafox
Ex VP: Lane Kerns
Ex VP: Eduardo Vieyra
**Sr VP:* Ruben Torres
**VP:* Mark Dennis
VP: Marco Flores
VP: Juan Lavalle
**VP:* Estella Resendeg

D-U-N-S 11-058-1787
■ BANCORP BANK
BANCORP.COM
(*Suby of* BANCORP INC) ★
409 Silverside Rd Ste 105, Wilmington, DE 19809-1771
Tel (302) 385-5000 *Founded/Ownrshp* 2004
Sales NA *EMP* 140
SIC 6022 State commercial banks
CEO: Betsy Z Cohen
**Ch Bd:* Daniel G Cohen
**Pr:* Frank M Mastrangelo
**CFO:* Marty Egan
Ex VP: Steven Turowski
VP: Kate Godwin
VP: Shannon Granahan
VP: Lauren Martin
VP: Paula Mathews
VP: Dawn Murphy
VP: Robert Rinicella
VP: Nancy Sjogren
VP: Ej Tumolo

D-U-N-S 15-749-2005
▲ BANCORP INC
409 Silverside Rd Ste 105, Wilmington, DE 19809-1771
Tel (302) 385-5000 *Founded/Ownrshp* 1999
Sales NA *EMP* 762[E]
Tkr Sym TBBK *Exch* NGS
SIC 6021 National commercial banks
CEO: Damian Kozlowski
**Ch Bd:* Daniel G Cohen
COO: Gail S Ball
COO: Hugh McFadden
CFO: Paul Frenkiel
Ofcr: Donald F McGraw Jr
Ofcr: Steven Turowski
Ex VP: Scott R Megargee
Ex VP: Ron Wechsler
Sr VP: Jeremy L Kuiper
Sr VP: Jeff Nager
Sr VP: Thomas G Pareigat
VP: Robert Edwards
VP: Genevieve Johnson
VP: Bernard McCabe
VP: Michael Schreiber
VP: Darin Wipf
Board of Directors: Walter T Beach, Michael J Bradley, John H Chrystal, Matthew Cohn, Hersh Kozlov, William H Lamb, James McEntee

BANCORP.COM
See BANCORP BANK

D-U-N-S 00-696-4878
■ BANCORPSOUTH BANK
(*Suby of* BANCORPSOUTH INC) ★
201 S Spring St, Tupelo, MS 38804-4811
Tel (662) 680-2000 *Founded/Ownrshp* 1982
Sales NA *EMP* 3,820
SIC 6022 State trust companies accepting deposits, commercial
Ch Bd: Aubrey B Patterson
Pr: Kyle Gilliam
Pr: James V Kelley
CEO: James D Rollins III
CFO: Nash Allen
Sr Cor Off: James Kelley
Ex VP: Clyde Hubbard
Ex VP: Gordon R Lewis
Ex VP: Bill Prater
Ex VP: Frank Riley
Ex VP: W James Threadgill Jr
Sr VP: Gary Bonds
Sr VP: Jack V McFerrin
VP: Laura Young
Board of Directors: Grace Clark, Thomas H Turner

D-U-N-S 10-629-1446
▲ BANCORPSOUTH INC
201 S Spring St, Tupelo, MS 38804-4811
Tel (662) 680-2000 *Founded/Ownrshp* 1982
Sales NA *EMP* 4,002[E]
Tkr Sym BXS *Exch* NYS
SIC 6022 State commercial banks
Ch Bd: James D Rollins III
Pr: Chris Bagley
CFO: William L Prater
Chf Cred: James Ronald Hodges
Ex VP: Gordon R Lewis
Exec: Cathy S Freeman
Board of Directors: Thomas R Stanton, Gus J Blass III, Larry G Kirl Guy W Mitche, Shannon A Brown, James E Campbell III, Deborah M Cannon, W G Holliman Jr, Warren A Hood Jr, Keith J Jackson, Robert C Nolan, Alan W Perry

D-U-N-S 06-795-2098
■ BANCORPSOUTH INSURANCE SERVICES INC
(*Suby of* BANCORPSOUTH BANK) ★
201 W Main St Fl 2, Tupelo, MS 38804-3917
Tel (662) 680-2000 *Founded/Ownrshp* 1997
Sales NA *EMP* 597
SIC 6411 Insurance agents, brokers & service
Pr: Markham McKnight
Pr: Kerry Drake
**COO:* Scott Naugle
CFO: Nash Allen Jr
**CFO:* Beverly Choppin
**Chf Mktg O:* Chris Boone
**Ofcr:* Mike Halter
**Ofcr:* Julia Kramer
Ofcr: Thomas D Murry
**CIO:* Scott Ishmael

D-U-N-S 00-651-1399
BANCPLUS CORP
1068 Highland Colony Pkwy, Ridgeland, MS 39157-8807
Tel (601) 898-8300 *Founded/Ownrshp* 1981
Sales NA *EMP* 2
SIC 6712 Bank holding companies
Pr: William Thompson

D-U-N-S 00-817-8030 IMP/EXP
BANCROFT BAG INC
425 Bancroft Blvd, West Monroe, LA 71292-5703
Tel (318) 387-2550 *Founded/Ownrshp* 1924
Sales 149.6MM[E] *EMP* 600
SIC 2674 Paper bags: made from purchased materials
Ch Bd: Thomas O Bancroft Jr
**Pr:* Bonnie Woods
**VP:* Walter Moore
**VP Mfg:* Dale Mercer
VP Sls: Dennis Pace
Manager: John Powell
Manager: Richard Simpson
Board of Directors: Lee Velten

D-U-N-S 07-374-9517
BANCROFT NEUROHEALTH A NEW JERSEY NONPROFIT CORP
1255 Caldwell Rd, Cherry Hill, NJ 08034-3220
Tel (856) 348-1183 *Founded/Ownrshp* 1883
Sales 127.5MM *EMP* 1,600
Accts Ernst & Young Llp Philadelphi
SIC 8361 8299 8211 Residential care; Educational services; Specialty education
Pr: Toni Pergolin
**CFO:* Thomas J Burke
Ofcr: Kathy Ross
**VP:* Rex Carney
VP: James Powers
Prin: Colleen Rowan-Valentino
Prin: Matthew Sharp

D-U-N-S 96-485-5766
BANCROFT REHABILITATION SERVICES A NEW JERSEY NONPROFIT CORP
1255 Caldwell Rd, Cherry Hill, NJ 08034-3220
Tel (856) 348-1183 *Founded/Ownrshp* 1990
Sales 3.3MM[E] *EMP* 5,000[E]
Accts Ernst & Young Us Llp Indianap
SIC 8322 Rehabilitation services
Pr: Toni Pergolin
**COO:* Charles McLister
Chf Mktg O: Judi London
**Sr VP:* Kurt Micelim
**Sr VP:* Josefina Nash
**Sr VP:* Regina Widdows
VP: Kurt Geiger
Comm Dir: Lori Shaffer
Ex Dir: Cynthia Boyer
Ex Dir: Eric M Eberman
Ex Dir: Dennis J Hinkel

D-U-N-S 06-411-2683 IMP
BANCTEC INC
(*Suby of* SOURCEHOV HOLDINGS INC) ★
2701 E Grauwyler Rd, Irving, TX 75061-3414
Tel (972) 821-4000 *Founded/Ownrshp* 2014
Sales 417.2MM[E] *EMP* 1,949
SIC 7389 Document storage service; Financial services
CEO: Jim Reynolds
**Pr:* Mark D Fairchild
**CFO:* Jeffrey D Cushman
Ofcr: Holash Terry
Assoc VP: Percy Nazareth
**Sr VP:* Stephen J Downey
Sr VP: Michael Fallin
**Sr VP:* Stephen Link
**Sr VP:* Mark Trivette
VP: Maria L Allen
VP: Pamela Bower
VP: David Cochrane
VP: Dave Conklin
VP: Steve Downey
VP: Harry Dugas
VP: Steve Elston
VP: Mark Fairchild
VP: John Fiala
VP: Ladonna Gibbs
VP: Nello Mariani
VP: Mike Peplow

BANCVUE
See KASASA LTD

BANDAG EQUIPMENT COMPANY
See BRIDGESTONE BANDAG LLC

D-U-N-S 62-783-9376 IMP
BANDAI NAMCO ENTERTAINMENT AMERICA INC
NDGA
(*Suby of* BANDAI NAMCO HOLDINGS USA INC) ★
2051 Mission College Blvd, Santa Clara, CA 95054-1519
Tel (408) 235-2000 *Founded/Ownrshp* 1990
Sales 182.5MM[E] *EMP* 200
SIC 5092 Video games
CEO: Kenji Hisatsune
**Pr:* Masaaki Tsuji
**COO:* Hide Irie
**CFO:* Shuji Nakata
VP: Eric Hartness
VP: Roger Hector
**VP:* Robert Stevenson
Dir Soc: Jason Cline
Mng Dir: Shigeichi Nakamura
**Genl Mgr:* Graeme Bayless
Mktg Dir: Darby Lunceford

D-U-N-S 95-736-5240 IMP
BANDAI NAMCO HOLDINGS USA INC
(*Suby of* BANDAI NAMCO HOLDINGS INC.)
2120 Park Pl Ste 120, El Segundo, CA 90245-4824
Tel (714) 816-9500 *Founded/Ownrshp* 1994
Sales 179.9M *EMP* 2,409
SIC 3999 7993 Coin-operated amusement machines; Arcades
CEO: Masayuki Matsuo
VP: Robert Stevenson
**VP:* Keiji Tanaka
VP Mktg: Catherine Fowler

BANDERA
See HILLSTONE RESTAURANT GROUP INC

D-U-N-S 19-387-6869 IMP/EXP
BANDIT INDUSTRIES INC
6750 W Millbrook Rd, Remus, MI 49340-9662
Tel (989) 561-2270 *Founded/Ownrshp* 1988
Sales 196.0MM[E] *EMP* 400
SIC 3531 5082 Chippers: brush, limb & log; Logging & forestry machinery & equipment
Pr: Jerry M Morey
**CFO:* Richard Curtiss
**VP:* Dianne C Morey
IT Man: Manny Lopez
Sfty Mgr: Kelly Zielinski
Plnt Mgr: Scott Parks
Mktg Dir: Paula Balhorn
Advt Mgr: Paula Boyer
Manager: Donald Wiseman
Sls Mgr: Dawn Cook
Sls Mgr: Cory Gross

BANDSTAND BOOKS & ART
See VERMONT COUNTRY STORE INC

D-U-N-S 02-083-4284
BANDWIDTH.COM INC
900 Main Campus Dr # 400, Raleigh, NC 27606-5177
Tel (800) 808-5150 *Founded/Ownrshp* 2001
Sales 206.6MM *EMP* 360
Accts Ernst & Young Llp
SIC 4813 Telephone communications broker
CEO: David Morken
**Pr:* John Murdock
**COO:* Chris Chuang
**CFO:* Jeff Hoffman
Sr VP: Ken Greick
VP: Steve Lacoff
VP: Jon Schniepp
VP: Nick Sgroi
VP Bus Dev: Cameron McCrindle
Off Mgr: Tyler Williams
QA Dir: De'shaun Simmons

BANFIELD PET HOSPITAL
See A CARING DOCTOR (TEXAS) PC

BANFIELD PET HOSPITAL
See A CARING DOCTOR MINNESOTA PA

BANFIELD PET HOSPITAL
See MEDICAL MANAGEMENT INTERNATIONAL INC

BANG PRINTING
See D & J PRINTING INC

D-U-N-S 80-789-4758
BANGOR BANCORP MHC
BANGOR SAVINGS BANK
3 State St, Bangor, ME 04401-5103
Tel (207) 942-5211 *Founded/Ownrshp* 2007
Sales NA *EMP* 2[E]
SIC 6712 Bank holding companies
Prin: David Carlisle

BANGOR HYDRO ELECTRIC
See BHE HOLDINGS INC

BANGOR SAVINGS BANK
See BANGOR BANCORP MHC

D-U-N-S 00-694-9010
BANGOR SAVINGS BANK (ME)
99 Franklin St, Bangor, ME 04401-4911
Tel (207) 942-3300 *Founded/Ownrshp* 1852
Sales NA *EMP* 300
SIC 6029 Commercial banks
Ch Bd: David Carlisle
**Pr:* James Conlon
Pr: Diane Hunnewell
Pr: Becky Macdonald
Pr: Mary Rogan-Gordon
Pr: Sue Rogers
**CFO:* Bruce Nickerson
CFO: Bruce G Nickerson
Ofcr: Morgan Laidlaw
Ofcr: Liz Monaghan
Ofcr: Lilly Weatherbee
Trst Ofcr: Janet Pratt
Ex VP: John A Edwards
Ex VP: Joyce Clark Sarnacki
Ex VP: Susan B Snowden
Sr VP: Scott S Blake
VP: Karl Anderson
VP: Christine Bosse
VP: Michael Chamberlain
VP: Bruce Clay
VP: Diane Donaldson

BANK ATLANTIC
See FIRST INTERNATIONAL EXCHANGE GROUP

D-U-N-S 87-655-4374
BANK EQUIPMENT SYSTEMS INC
8086 S Yale Ave Ste 103, Tulsa, OK 74136-9003
Tel (918) 630-4133 *Founded/Ownrshp* 1998
Sales 120.0MM *EMP* 1
SIC 7382 Security systems services
Owner: Don Mee

D-U-N-S 80-877-6442
BANK FUND STAFF FCU
1725 I St Nw Ste 300, Washington, DC 20006-2423
Tel (202) 429-9180 *Founded/Ownrshp* 2007
Sales NA *EMP* 1
SIC 6062 State credit unions, not federally chartered
Prin: Nawal Abouelala
CFO: Chip Harwood
VP: Stephen Breed

D-U-N-S 12-230-2839
BANK FUND STAFF FEDERAL CREDIT UNION
BANK-FUND STAFF FEDERAL CREDIT
1725 I St Nw Ste 150, Washington, DC 20006-2406
Tel (202) 212-6400 *Founded/Ownrshp* 1947
Sales NA *EMP* 170

SIC 6061 Federal credit unions
CEO: Eli Vazquez
**Pr:* Kenneth M Miranda
**CEO:* George W West
**COO:* Stephanie G Day
**Treas:* Nestor V Santiago
Bd of Dir: Richard Osius
Ofcr: John Dean
Ex VP: Hilda M Ochoa
VP: Turner Bruce
Exec: Amanda Tamborino
Dir Risk M: Cynthia Ryan

D-U-N-S 62-775-0961
BANK LEUMI LE-ISRAEL CORP
(*Suby of* BANK LEUMI LE-ISRAEL LTD.)
579 5th Ave Lbby 1, New York, NY 10017-8822
Tel (917) 542-2343 *Founded/Ownrshp* 1983
Sales NA *EMP* 492
SIC 6022 State commercial banks
Ch: Eitan Roff
VP: David Chesir
VP: Stanley Karp
**VP:* James McCrink
VP: John P McGann
VP: Yair Talmor
IT Man: Jeff Gelman
VP Opers: Dan Hoffman
Mktg Dir: Debra Bar

D-U-N-S 05-453-3864 IMP
BANK LEUMI USA
(*Suby of* BANK LEUMI LE-ISRAEL CORP) ★
579 5th Ave Frnt A, New York, NY 10017-1917
Tel (917) 542-2343 *Founded/Ownrshp* 1968, 1983
Sales NA *EMP* 393
SIC 6022 7359 State commercial banks; Equipment rental & leasing
Pr: Avner Mendelson
Pr: Shlomi Halevy
Pr: Kevin Jessup
Pr: Robert Maichin
Pr: Sivan Maseng
Pr: Stephanie Oliveri
Pr: Shellee Price
Pr: Theresa Savo
Pr: Andrew Schulman
CEO: Aharon Kacherginski
COO: Sidney Gottesman
**Ch:* Steven H Lavin
**V Ch Bd:* Zalman Segal
Chf Cred: Ira Romaff
Bd of Dir: Simon Jawitz
Ofcr: Ruth Anidjar
Ofcr: Georgi Avramov
Ofcr: Lilian Baghdasarian
Ofcr: Raymond P Cooney
Ofcr: David Leib
Ofcr: Christopher Polito
Board of Directors: E Donald Shapiro, Frederick Fetzeli, Larry Silverstein, Theodore P Glueck, Francis X Stankard, Jacob E Goldman, James R Greene, Shlomo Handel, Donald Howard, Richard Kane, Robert K Lifton, Zeev Nahari

BANK MIDWEST
See NBH BANK

D-U-N-S 07-476-9845
■ **BANK MUTUAL**
(*Suby of* BANK MUTUAL CORP) ★
4949 W Brown Deer Rd, Milwaukee, WI 53223-2421
Tel (414) 354-1500 *Founded/Ownrshp* 2000
Sales NA *EMP* 719
SIC 6036 6163 6029 6022 State savings banks, not federally chartered; Loan brokers; Commercial banks; State commercial banks
Ch Bd: Michael T Crowley Jr
**Pr:* David A Baumgarten
**CFO:* Michael W Dosland
CFO: Snl Extra
CFO: Gene Mauer
Ofcr: Brian Czarnecki
Ofcr: Carolyn Sumpter
Ofcr: Jon Wait
Assoc VP: David Kern
VP: Robert A Bladorn
VP: Rick Colberg
VP: Bruce W Hake
VP: Joseph Martin
VP: Joel Prunty
VP: Diane Selfworth
Board of Directors: David C Boerke, Richard A Brown, Howard M Frankenthal, Thomas J Lopina, Robert Olson, Richard C Smits, J Gus Swoboda

D-U-N-S 16-938-8092
▲ **BANK MUTUAL CORP**
4949 W Brown Deer Rd, Milwaukee, WI 53223-2421
Tel (414) 354-1500 *Founded/Ownrshp* 2003
Sales NA *EMP* 1,400
Tkr Sym BKMU *Exch* NGS
SIC 6036 Savings institutions, not federally chartered
Pr: David A Baumgarten
**Ch Bd:* Michael T Crowley Jr
CFO: Michael W Dosland
VP: James P Carter
VP: Richard L Schroeder
Board of Directors: David C Boerke, Richard A Brown, Thomas H Buestrin, Mark C Herr, Lisa A Mauer, William H Mielke, Robert B Olson, Mike I Shafir

BANK OF AMERICA
See BANKAMERICA FINANCIAL INC

D-U-N-S 05-516-9452
▲ **BANK OF AMERICA CORP**
100 N Tryon St Ste 220, Charlotte, NC 28202-4031
Tel (704) 386-5681 *Founded/Ownrshp* 1968
Sales NA *EMP* 213,000^E
Tkr Sym BAC *Exch* NYS
SIC 6021 6022 6211 6091 6162 6159 National commercial banks; State commercial banks; Brokers, security; Underwriters, security; Traders, security; Nondeposit trust facilities; Mortgage bankers; Equipment & vehicle finance leasing companies
Ch Bd: Brian T Moynihan
Pr: Malik Ahmed
Pr: Jon Aiello
Pr: Amalia All
Pr: Rishu Bansal
Pr: Georgiana Barrow
Pr: Matthew Benson
Pr: John Binkley
Pr: Tasha Bondurant
Pr: Kolette Boykin
Pr: Cynthia Branson
Pr: Joshua Bunting
Pr: Bonnie Burris
Pr: Scott Cassity
Pr: Eddy Castillo
Pr: Mario Castro
Pr: David Cintron
Pr: Lisa A Colbert
Pr: Simon Cook
Pr: Jessica Crawford
Pr: Amanda Cunningham
Board of Directors: Lionel L Nowell III, Sharon L Allen, Michael D White, Susan S Bies, Thomas D Woods, Jack O Bovender Jr, R David Yost, Frank P Bramble Sr, Pierre J P De Weck, Arnold W Donald, Linda P Hudson, Monica C Lozano, Thomas J May

D-U-N-S 80-848-5739
■ **BANK OF AMERICA MORTGAGE SECURITIES INC**
(*Suby of* BANK OF AMERICA NA) ★
101 S Tryon St Ste 1000, Charlotte, NC 28280-0010
Tel (704) 386-5681 *Founded/Ownrshp* 2011
Sales NA *EMP* 4,920
SIC 6162 6163 Mortgage bankers & correspondents; Loan brokers
Prin: Andy Woodward

D-U-N-S 07-959-3409
BANK OF AMERICA N A
401 N Tryon St Ste 300, Charlotte, NC 28202-2123
Tel (800) 432-1000 *Founded/Ownrshp* 2014
Sales NA *EMP* 271^E
SIC 6021 National commercial banks
Pr: William Estridge
Ofcr: Mike Delaney
Sr VP: Todd Barnett
Sr VP: Joy Bartholomew
Sr VP: Len Clamp
Sr VP: Rhonda Depetrillo
Sr VP: Karina Glass
Sr VP: Katherine Horrigan
Sr VP: Shaun Hunter
Sr VP: Robert Kelly
Sr VP: Lee Martinec
Sr VP: Robert Mossbacher
Sr VP: Donald Parker
Sr VP: Cathy Santich
Sr VP: Dan Stephenson
Sr VP: Denise Tracey
Sr VP: Roy Woodham
Sr VP: Karen Yanick
VP: Srikanth Balagangadhar
VP: Renee Berry
VP: Angela Cabrera

BANK OF AMERICA, N.A.
See BANK OF AMERICA NATIONAL ASSOCIATION

D-U-N-S 00-691-1747 IMP
■ **BANK OF AMERICA NATIONAL ASSOCIATION**
BANK OF AMERICA, N.A.
(*Suby of* BANK OF AMERICA CORP) ★
101 S Tryon St, Charlotte, NC 28280-0002
Tel (704) 386-5681 *Founded/Ownrshp* 1904
Sales NA *EMP* 182,284
SIC 6021 National commercial banks
CEO: Brian T Moynihan
**Treas:* Bruce R Thompson
Ex VP: Robert Hunt
Ex VP: James Miller
Ex VP: Richard Warner
Sr VP: Paul Baalman
Sr VP: Brek Benson
Sr VP: Gregory Bjorndahl
Sr VP: David Blanchfield
Sr VP: Yvonne Brooks
Sr VP: David Cashman
Sr VP: Robert Huss
Sr VP: Paul O'Brien
Sr VP: James Robinson
Sr VP: David Ruiz
Sr VP: Janice Walker
Sr VP: Nick Whalen
VP: Stanley Chiu
VP: Carol Critch
VP: Carolyn Dillingham
VP: Scott Enscoe

D-U-N-S 07-324-7462
■ **BANK OF AMERICA PVT WEALTH MANAGEMENT**
U.S. TRUST, BANK OF AMERICA
(*Suby of* BANK OF AMERICA CORP) ★
114 W 47th St Ste C-1, New York, NY 10036-1592
Tel (800) 878-7878 *Founded/Ownrshp* 2007
Sales 306.4MM^E *EMP* 1,941
SIC 6282 6022 6099 6733 Investment advice; Manager of mutual funds, contract or fee basis; State commercial banks; Fiduciary agencies other than real estate or trust; Trusts; Personal investment trust management
CEO: Peter K Scaturro
**Ch Bd:* Charles R Schwab
Pr: Frances Aldrich Sevilla-Sacasa
CFO: Linda S Huber
CFO: Brink Mann
Bd of Dir: Christine Delvecchio
Ofcr: Allan Maragh
Ofcr: Karen Wong
Trst Ofcr: Lori Nichols
Assoc VP: James Colabelli
Ex VP: Gerard A Callaghan
Ex VP: Noland Cheng
Ex VP: Donald Cregg
Ex VP: John M Deignan
Sr VP: Trinh Doan
Sr VP: Robert Haskins
Sr VP: Cynthia Legette
Sr VP: Robert Lovas
Sr VP: Christopher Woolley
VP: Brent Considine
VP: Angela Graham

D-U-N-S 08-798-5222
■ **BANK OF CASCADES**
(*Suby of* CASCADE BANCORP) ★
1100 Nw Wall St, Bend, OR 97703-1935
Tel (541) 617-3500 *Founded/Ownrshp* 1990
Sales NA *EMP* 399
SIC 6022 State commercial banks
CEO: Terry E Zink
Pr: Charles N Reeves
COO: Michael J Delvin
CFO: Gregory D Newton
Treas: Jon Lorberau
Chf Cred: Daniel J Lee
Ofcr: Amy Berger
Ofcr: Becky Gregory
Ofcr: Christopher J Ray
Assoc VP: Molly Rigby
Ex VP: Debbie Amerongen
Ex VP: Peggy L Biss
Ex VP: Walter O Krumbholz Jr
Ex VP: Julie A Miller
Ex VP: Frank Weis
Sr VP: Anna Bifano
Sr VP: Robert L Countryman
Sr VP: Shane Hahn
Sr VP: Art Hiemstra
Sr VP: Ted Johnson
Sr VP: Greg Newton
Board of Directors: J Lamont Keen

D-U-N-S 00-742-7594
BANK OF COLORADO
COLORADO BANK, THE
(*Suby of* COLORADO BANK) ★
1609 E Harmony Rd, Fort Collins, CO 80525-3238
Tel (970) 206-1159 *Founded/Ownrshp* 1900
Sales NA *EMP* 493
SIC 6022 State commercial banks
Ch Bd: Chris Dinsdale
Pr: Michael Bellus
Pr: Christian Bordewick
Pr: Jeff Franklin
Pr: Christina Kraft
Pr: Matthew Pieper
Ofcr: Christina Newton
Sr VP: Clayton Collier
Sr VP: Gaye Cox
Sr VP: Bill Deter
Sr VP: Joe Kusar
Sr VP: Tonya Malcom
Sr VP: Jason Portz
Sr VP: Sue Wagner
VP: Wendy Fritzler
VP: Todd Kirkman
VP: Paul Knapp
VP: Jacki Lawson
VP: Jill Marvin
VP: Tony McCune
VP: Lon Rathmell

D-U-N-S 03-633-2518
BANK OF ENGLAND (AR)
123 S Main St, England, AR 72046-1851
Tel (501) 842-2555 *Founded/Ownrshp* 1898
Sales NA *EMP* 33
SIC 6022 6021 State commercial banks; National commercial banks
Pr: Gary Canada
CFO: Amanda Mullins
VP: Joey Adams

D-U-N-S 00-692-6752
■ **BANK OF HAWAII** (HI)
(*Suby of* BANK OF HAWAII CORP) ★
130 Merchant St, Honolulu, HI 96813-4405
Tel (888) 643-3888 *Founded/Ownrshp* 1897
Sales NA *EMP* 574^E
SIC 6022 6411 6211 State commercial banks; Insurance agents, brokers & service; Security brokers & dealers
COO: David W Thomas
Pr: Peter S Ho
CFO: Kent Lucien
V Ch Bd: Donna A Tanoue
VP: Helene B Davis
VP: Nicole Dupont
VP: Marjie Malilay
VP: Janine McFarlane
VP: Craig Warren
VP: Chris Yamamoto
Board of Directors: Barbara J Tanabe, S Haunani Apoliona, Robert W Wo Jr, Mary G F Bitterman, Michael J Chun, Clinton R Churchill, David A Heenan, Robert A Huret, Kent T Lucien, Martin A Stein, Donald M Takaki

D-U-N-S 06-291-4437
▲ **BANK OF HAWAII CORP**
130 Merchant St, Honolulu, HI 96813-4405
Tel (888) 643-3888 *Founded/Ownrshp* 1897
Sales NA *EMP* 2,200^E
Tkr Sym BOH *Exch* NYS
SIC 6022 State commercial banks
Ch Bd: Peter S Ho
Pr: Paula Boyce
Pr: Kaleo Kekoolani
**CFO:* Kent T Lucien
CFO: Penny Tong
Bd of Dir: Raymie Camara
Ofcr: Peter M Biggs
Ofcr: Mark A Rossi
VP: Kelli Adams
VP: Santander Alvin
VP: Jen Baker
VP: Roberta Chu
VP: Jason D'Olier
VP: Anthony Desanctis
VP: Natalie Fogle
VP: Robert Gardiner
VP: Pat Hulaton
VP: Lai Janis
VP: Edison Kobayashi
VP: Donovan Koki
VP: Christian Look
Board of Directors: Robert W Wo, S Haunani Apoliona, Mary G F Bitterman, Mark A Burak, Michael J Chun, Clinton R Churchill, Robert Huret, Victor K Nichols, Barbara J Tanabe, Raymond P Vara Jr

D-U-N-S 60-884-7919
■ **BANK OF HOPE**
(*Suby of* HOPE BANCORP INC) ★
3731 Wilshire Blvd # 400, Los Angeles, CA 90010-2830
Tel (213) 639-1700 *Founded/Ownrshp* 1985
Sales NA *EMP* 336
SIC 6021 National commercial banks
CEO: Kevin S Kim
Pr: Min J Kim
**V Ch Bd:* Scott Yoon-Suk Whang
Ex VP: Mark Lee
Ex VP: Brian Van Dyk
Sr VP: Young Lee
Sr VP: Christine Y OH
VP: John Aragon
VP: Arindam Bose
VP: James Hong
VP: Melanie Horton
VP: Jenna Ju
VP: Sally Rodriguez

D-U-N-S 08-235-6317
BANK OF KENTUCKY FINANCIAL CORP
111 Lookout Farm Dr, Crestview Hills, KY 41017-4712
Tel (859) 371-2340 *Founded/Ownrshp* 1995
Sales NA *EMP* 349^E
SIC 6035

D-U-N-S 84-728-9568
BANK OF NEVADA
2700 W Sahara Ave Ste 100, Las Vegas, NV 89102-1712
Tel (702) 248-4200 *Founded/Ownrshp* 1994
Sales NA *EMP* 380
SIC 6022

D-U-N-S 00-698-5873 IMP
■ **BANK OF NEW YORK MELLON**
B N Y NATIONAL COMMUNITY
(*Suby of* BNY MELLON) ★
225 Liberty St, New York, NY 10281-1048
Tel (212) 495-1784 *Founded/Ownrshp* 1784, 1989
Sales NA *EMP* 17,302
SIC 6153 6211 6282 6082 Purchasers of accounts receivable & commercial paper; Security brokers & dealers; Investment research; Foreign trade & international banking institutions
Ch Bd: Thomas A Renyi
V Ch: Donald E Doles
**Pr:* Gerald L Hassell
COO: Stephen Richardson
Treas: Robert Hurni
Bd of Dir: Paul Miners
Chf Mktg O: Richard Kaleel
Top Exec: John M Dowd
Top Exec: Joseph F Murphy
Trst Ofcr: Mudassir Mohamed
Assoc VP: Chris Pitera
Ex VP: Paul Bodart
Ex VP: Robert R Field
Ex VP: Richard G Genin
Ex VP: Mark A Hemenetz
Ex VP: James B Joyce
Ex VP: Woddy Kerr
Ex VP: Ralph Mastrangelo
Ex VP: John R Mohr
Ex VP: Dennis P Neumann
Ex VP: Karen B Peetz

D-U-N-S 05-155-0713 IMP
▲ **BANK OF NEW YORK MELLON CORP**
BNY MELLON
225 Liberty St, New York, NY 10281-1048
Tel (212) 495-1784 *Founded/Ownrshp* 1784
Sales NA *EMP* 51,200
Accts Kpmg Llp New York New York
Tkr Sym BK *Exch* NYS
SIC 6022 State commercial banks
Ch Bd: Gerald L Hassell
Pr: Mark Gaulin
Pr: Richard Knoof
Pr: Jeremy Marroncelli
Pr: Kenneth K Newman
Pr: Karen B Peetz
Pr: Larry Perdeus
Pr: Remy Quito
Pr: Kim Zbilut
CFO: Thomas P Gibbons
Ch: David Cruikshank
Treas: Scott Freidenrich
Ofcr: Monique R Herena
Ofcr: Mark Musi
Ex VP: Barb Londono
Ex VP: John R Mohr
Sr VP: Sam Gentile
Sr VP: Peter Johnson
VP: Raymond Bugay
VP: Douglas Chapman
VP: Robert Dawson
Board of Directors: Mark A Nordenberg, Linda Z Cook, Catherine A Rein, Nicholas M Donofrio, Elizabeth Robinson, Joseph J Echevarria, Samuel C Scott III, Edward P Garden, Jeffrey A Goldstein, John M Hinshaw, Edmund F Kelly, John A Luke Jr, Jennifer B Morgan

D-U-N-S 62-435-6101
■ **BANK OF NORTH CAROLINA**
(*Suby of* BNC BANCORP) ★
831 Julian Ave, Thomasville, NC 27360-5848
Tel (336) 476-9200 *Founded/Ownrshp* 1991
Sales NA *EMP* 59
SIC 6022 State commercial banks
Pr: W Swope Montgomery Jr
**Ch Bd:* Thomas R Sloan
**Ofcr:* Bill McKendry
Ex VP: Curtis Weaver
**Sr VP:* Richard D Callicutt
Sr VP: Rob Ellenburg
Sr VP: Ronald Gorczynski
**Sr VP:* Sharon S Scott
Sr VP: Karen Sirls
**VP:* Emma L Allbright
VP: Jason Bradley
VP: Larry Brown
VP: Jack Davis
VP: Nisha Desai
VP: Douglas Ford

VP: Walter Hoffman
**VP:* Janie S Kennedy
VP: Martha Patterson
VP: Ginny Smith
VP: Annette Staley
VP: Dustin Van Weerdhuizen

D-U-N-S 00-227-4314
■ BANK OF NORTH GEORGIA
SYNOVUS
(*Suby of* SYNOVUS FINANCIAL CORP) ★
8025 Westside Pkwy # 150, Alpharetta, GA 30009-2139
Tel (770) 569-9660 *Founded/Ownrshp* 1998
Sales NA *EMP* 552
SIC 6022 State commercial banks
CEO: Donald D Howard
**Pr:* Rob Garcia
**CFO:* Diane Boston
Ex VP: Paige Collier
Ex VP: Frank Roedl
Sr VP: Scott Hall
Sr VP: Beth Kornegay-Tyler
Sr VP: Matt McClure
Sr VP: Michael O'Connor
Sr VP: Mark Romzick
VP: Pamela Culberson
VP: Sherron Davis
VP: Michelle Leak
VP: William Wideman
VP: Cory W Work
VP: Frankie Wright

D-U-N-S 14-031-8093
BANK OF OKLAHOMA FINANCIAL CORP
6424 E 41st St, Tulsa, OK 74135
Tel (918) 619-1578 *Founded/Ownrshp* 2003
Sales NA *EMP* 3,600
SIC 6022 State commercial banks
CEO: Stan Liearger
**Pr:* Gearge Kaiser
Pr: Anthony Phillips
VP: Corrine Castro
VP: Levi Lura

D-U-N-S 13-973-8611
▲ BANK OF OZARKS INC
17901 Chenal Pkwy, Little Rock, AR 72223-5831
Tel (501) 978-2265 *Founded/Ownrshp* 1981
Sales NA *EMP* 1,642[E]
Tkr Sym OZRK *Exch* NGS
SIC 6022 State commercial banks; State trust companies accepting deposits, commercial
Ch Bd: George Gleason
Pr: Suzanne Cole
CFO: Greg McKinney
V Ch Bd: Dan Thomas
Ofcr: Rhonda Clark
Ofcr: Marcus Galloway
Ofcr: Karen R Ruckle
Ofcr: Thomas Small
Ofcr: Tyler Vance
Ex VP: Tim Hicks
Ex VP: Greg Newman
VP: Wes Anderson
VP: Chris Bragg
VP: Adam Carter
VP: Jeff Cooper
VP: Malcolm Hicks
VP: Jeremy McAlister
VP: Steven Reynolds
VP: Jeff Starke
VP: Barry Steele
VP: Debbie Townsend
Board of Directors: Walter J Mullen III, Nicholas Brown, Robert Proost, Paula Cholmondeley, John Reynolds, Richard Cisne, Ross Whipple, Robert East, Catherine B Freedberg, Linda Gleason, Peter Kenny, William A Koefoed Jr, Henry Mariani

D-U-N-S 00-691-4329
BANK OF STOCKTON
(*Suby of* 1867 WESTERN FINANCIAL CORP)
301 E Miner Ave, Stockton, CA 95202-2501
Tel (209) 929-1600 *Founded/Ownrshp* 1988
Sales NA *EMP* 370
SIC 6022 State commercial banks
Pr: Robert M Eberhardt
Pr: John Morrison
COO: Jose Avalos
COO: Thomas H Shaffer
Bd of Dir: Madeline Hall
Ofcr: Linda Fyffe
Trst Ofcr: Annette Gail-Stone
Ex VP: Thomas Schaffer
Sr VP: Sarah Thompson
VP: Nick Aninag
VP: Angela Brusa
VP: Mel Caldwell
VP: Teresa Carrigan
VP: Steven Castellanos
VP: Kelly Christian
**VP:* John Dentoni
VP: Gina French
VP: Luanne Lewis
VP: Vincent Lo
VP: Vincent Low
VP: Ray Perry

D-U-N-S 07-465-3759
■ BANK OF WEST
(*Suby of* BNP PARIBAS)
180 Montgomery St # 1400, San Francisco, CA 94104-4297
Tel (415) 765-4800 *Founded/Ownrshp* 1978
Sales NA *EMP* 10,000
SIC 6022 State commercial banks
CEO: J Michael Shepherd
Pr: Randy Arnold
Pr: Nicole Auyang
Pr: Stephanie Beggs
Pr: Teresa Casselberry
Pr: Brandon Chavez
Pr: Leigh Clouston
Pr: Brian Cohen
Pr: Norm Duncan
Pr: Richard Dupree
Pr: Sergey Fedosov
Pr: Sheri Flister
Pr: Lynda Forthe
Pr: Lorena Garcia
Pr: Ryan Giammona
Pr: Jon Grady
Pr: Jing Guan
Pr: Jackie Hagerman
Pr: Jimmy Hakansson
Pr: Thanh Huynh
Pr: Brent Kelley

D-U-N-S 00-790-7124
■ BANK SNB
STILLWATER NAT BNK & TR CO
(*Suby of* SOUTHWEST BANCORP INC) ★
608 S Main St, Stillwater, OK 74074-4059
Tel (405) 372-2230 *Founded/Ownrshp* 1894, 1983
Sales NA *EMP* 402
SIC 6021 6163 National commercial banks; Loan brokers
Ch Bd: Robert Rodgers
**CEO:* Rick Green
**CFO:* Laura Robertson
Ofcr: Brandon Shearer
**Ex VP:* Steve Gobel
Ex VP: Gregg Jaynes
Sr VP: Priscilla Barnes
Sr VP: Bill Glover
Sr VP: Lori Jackson
Sr VP: Patrick King
Sr VP: Deborah Pippin
Sr VP: Fawn Sachleben
Sr VP: David Sine
VP: Kelly Danyluk
**VP:* Linda Darrow
VP: Elaine Hood
VP: Kathleen Laubhan
VP: Matthew Pollock
VP: Debbie Whiley
Board of Directors: Thomas D Berry, Patrice Douglas, Betty Kerns, Russ Teubner

BANK-FUND STAFF FEDERAL CREDIT
See BANK FUND STAFF FEDERAL CREDIT UNION

D-U-N-S 04-672-2140
BANK-FUND STAFF FEDERAL CREDIT UNION
1722 I St Nw Ste 200, Washington, DC 20006-3710
Tel (202) 458-4350 *Founded/Ownrshp* 2010
Sales NA *EMP* 9
SIC 6062 State credit unions
Prin: Peter Grimm
CFO: Frank D Vassallo
Dir Risk M: Cynthia S Ryan
Sls&Mrk Ex: Kingsley Lee

D-U-N-S 55-672-2403
■ BANKAMERICA FINANCIAL INC
BANK OF AMERICA
(*Suby of* BANK OF AMERICA CORP) ★
315 Montgomery St, San Francisco, CA 94104-1856
Tel (415) 622-3521 *Founded/Ownrshp* 1992
Sales NA *EMP* 1,700
SIC 6153 6141 6282 Factors of commercial paper; Consumer finance companies; Investment advisory service
Pr: James A Dern
**Ch Bd:* Lewis W Teel
V Ch: Marty Stein
Treas: Michael K Riley
Sr VP: John Carson
Sr VP: Paul Ogorzelec
VP: Claudia Chan-Schaffer
VP: Dana Flynn
VP: Patricia Fukami
VP: Jane Monnette
VP: Lisa Trygg
Board of Directors: James Westfall, M Faye Wilson

D-U-N-S 11-867-9679
BANKERS FINANCIAL CORP
(*Suby of* BANKERS INTERNATIONAL FINANCIAL CORP) ★
11101 Roosevelt Blvd N, Saint Petersburg, FL 33716-2340
Tel (727) 823-4000 *Founded/Ownrshp* 1982
Sales NA *EMP* 955
SIC 6411 Insurance agents, brokers & service
CEO: Dr John A Strong
**Ch Bd:* Robert M Menke
**Pr:* Brian Kesneck
**Pr:* David K Meehan
Pr: Mark Winkler
**CFO:* Jim D Albert
**CFO:* Anna C Arena
**CFO:* Preston Kavanagh
**CFO:* James E Tait
VP: Ian Barber
VP: Lisa Basta
VP: Tim Fellabaum
VP: Paige Gorman
VP: Nathan Schroeder
Creative D: Rusty Smart

D-U-N-S 82-541-9419
BANKERS HEALTHCARE GROUP LLC
10234 W State Road 84, Davie, FL 33324-4202
Tel (954) 384-9119 *Founded/Ownrshp* 1992
Sales NA *EMP* 246
SIC 6153 Direct working capital financing
CEO: Albert C Crawford
Pr: Robert Castro
COO: Eric Castro
CFO: Edmund Durant
Ex VP: Joe Valeo
Sr VP: Thomas Badolato
Sr VP: Nicole Boodram
Sr VP: Ammad Clegg
Sr VP: Louise Stuenzi
Sr VP: Melissa Whelan

D-U-N-S 08-068-3238
BANKERS INSURANCE CO
(*Suby of* BANKERS INSURANCE GROUP INC) ★
11101 Roosevelt Blvd N, Saint Petersburg, FL 33716-2340
Tel (727) 823-4000 *Founded/Ownrshp* 1976
Sales NA *EMP* 300
SIC 6331 Fire, marine & casualty insurance & carriers
Ch Bd: Robert M Menke
**Ch Bd:* Dr John Strong
**Pr:* Brian Keefer
**Pr:* David K Meehan
**Treas:* Edwin C Hussemann
VP: Lisa Basta

D-U-N-S 10-186-5665
BANKERS INSURANCE GROUP INC
(*Suby of* BANKERS FINANCIAL CORP) ★
11101 Roosevelt Blvd N, Saint Petersburg, FL 33716-2340
Tel (727) 823-4000 *Founded/Ownrshp* 1976
Sales NA *EMP* 944
SIC 6411 Insurance agents, brokers & service
CEO: John A Strong
**Ch Bd:* Robert G Menke
**Pr:* Wilbur L Martin IV
CFO: Lydia Boakye
**CFO:* Steven W Brandt
CFO: Svetlana Townsend
**Treas:* B Bradford Martz
Sr Cor Off: John Bilchak
Ex VP: Claudette Cope
Ex VP: Melvin Parker
Ex VP: John Stalfort
VP: Lisa Bage
**VP:* Ian B Barber
VP: Steve Messina
VP: Don Roberts
VP: Tim Stroble

D-U-N-S 80-004-5866
BANKERS INTERNATIONAL FINANCIAL CORP
(*Suby of* BANKERS INTERNATIONAL FINANCIAL CORPORATION LTD)
11101 Roosevelt Blvd N, Saint Petersburg, FL 33716-2340
Tel (727) 823-4000 *Founded/Ownrshp* 1983
Sales NA *EMP* 955[E]
SIC 6411 Insurance agents, brokers & service
Pr: John A Strong

D-U-N-S 00-692-8659
■ BANKERS LIFE & CASUALTY CO
(*Suby of* CICH INC) ★
111 E Wacker Dr Ste 2100, Chicago, IL 60601-4508
Tel (312) 396-6000 *Founded/Ownrshp* 1880
Sales NA *EMP* 450
SIC 6321 6311 6324 Health insurance carriers; Accident insurance carriers; Life insurance; Hospital & medical service plans
Pr: Scott L Goldberg
**CFO:* John M Squarok
Ex VP: Stuart Simon
Sr VP: Susan Morisato
VP: Christopher Campbell
VP: Loretta Jacobs
VP: James Lemire
VP: Anthony Monderine
VP: Michael Plazony
VP: James Valdez
VP: David Vega
VP: Joseph Violetta
Dir Teleco: Deborah Berres

D-U-N-S 00-694-0977
BANKERS TRUST CO
453 7th St, Des Moines, IA 50309-4110
Tel (515) 245-2863 *Founded/Ownrshp* 1917
Sales NA *EMP* 450
SIC 6022 State commercial banks
Ch Bd: John Ruan III
Pr: Heather Bahe
Pr: Terri Doyle
**Pr:* Suku Radia
**CFO:* Kip Albertson
**Treas:* Kermit J Albertson
Ofcr: Chris Baker
Ofcr: Ben Miller
Ofcr: Danielle Russo
Ofcr: Jason Snitker
Ofcr: Doug Wurth
Trst Ofcr: Connie Koehn
Trst Ofcr: Susan Martin
Ex VP: Robert Dewaay
**Sr VP:* Don Coffin
**Sr VP:* Paul Erickson
**Sr VP:* Renee Hardman
VP: Patricia Ashbaugh
VP: Jenny Carter
VP: Simon Clement-Davies
VP: Denyce Doubleday

D-U-N-S 80-285-8923
BANKNEWPORT
184 John Clarke Rd, Middletown, RI 02842-7633
Tel (401) 846-3400 *Founded/Ownrshp* 2007
Sales NA *EMP* 270[E]
SIC 6035 Savings institutions, federally chartered
COO: Sandra J Pattie
**Pr:* Thomas Kelly
**CFO:* Andrew Hewitt
Ofcr: Scott Bartlett
Ofcr: Nicholas Derosa
Ofcr: Angela Loomis
Ofcr: Gian Mallozzi
Ofcr: Leland Merrill
Ofcr: Evan Rose
Sr VP: Kenneth R Burnett
**Sr VP:* Wayne Long
**Sr VP:* Robert Maddock
Sr VP: Colleen Medeiros
**Sr VP:* Timothy Pigott
**Sr VP:* Fulton Pontes
Sr VP: Susan Replogle
Sr VP: Christopher Sheehan
**Sr VP:* Nicholas Vrabel
VP: Thomas Beauchene
VP: Lesley Behan
VP: Joseph Bell

BANKPLUS
See CITIZENS FINANCIAL CORP

D-U-N-S 00-705-3689
BANKPLUS
(*Suby of* BANKPLUS) ★
202 E Jackson St, Belzoni, MS 39038-3524
Tel (601) 898-8300 *Founded/Ownrshp* 1909
Sales NA *EMP* 174
SIC 6022 State trust companies accepting deposits, commercial
CEO: Bill Ray
**COO:* Eloise Patridge
**CFO:* Ann Southerland
**Ch:* Thomas Peaster
Sr VP: Jim Beidleman
VP: Lisa Tanner
VP: Wilda Thames
VP: Lindsay Tomlinson
**Exec:* William Thompson
**Exec:* Max Yates
VP Sls: Saul Keeton

D-U-N-S 79-431-6653
▲ BANKRATE INC
1675 Broadway Fl 2, New York, NY 10019-5852
Tel (917) 368-8600 *Founded/Ownrshp* 1996
Sales 370.5MM *EMP* 517[E]
Tkr Sym RATE *Exch* NYS
SIC 7389 Financial services
Pr: Kenneth S Esterow
**Ch Bd:* Peter C Morse
COO: Simon Mosk-Aoyama
CFO: Steven D Barnhart
Sr VP: James R Gilmartin
Sr VP: Daniel P Hoogterp
Sr VP: Michael J Ricciardelli
VP: Janet Gunzburg
VP: Tony Orokos
VP Mktg: Tracy White
Board of Directors: Seth Brody, Michael J Kelly, Christine Peterson, Richard J Pinola, Mitch Truwit

D-U-N-S 00-978-7086
BANKS CONSTRUCTION CO
4902 Banco Rd, North Charleston, SC 29418-5973
Tel (843) 744-8261 *Founded/Ownrshp* 1948
Sales 86.2MM[E] *EMP* 250
SIC 1611

D-U-N-S 96-699-5412
▲ BANKUNITED INC
14817 Oak Ln, Miami Lakes, FL 33016-1517
Tel (305) 569-2000 *Founded/Ownrshp* 2009
Sales NA *EMP* 1,741[E]
Tkr Sym BKU *Exch* NYS
SIC 6022 State commercial banks
Ch Bd: John A Kanas
Pr: Latasha McGee
**COO:* Rajinder P Singh
CFO: Leslie N Lunak
Ofcr: Sally Daisomont
Ex VP: Steve Redlich
Sr VP: Shane Sweet
VP: Paul Dupuis
VP: Mireya Foster
VP: Paige Homan
VP: John Kenyon
VP: Theresa Schuman
VP: Delphine Wharton
Board of Directors: Tere Blanca, Eugene F Demark, Michael J Dowling, Douglas J Pauls, A Gail Prudenti, Sanjiv Sobti, A Robert Towbin, Lynne Wines

D-U-N-S 02-024-5940
■ BANNER BANK (WA)
(*Suby of* BANNER CORP) ★
10 S 1st Ave, Walla Walla, WA 99362-1942
Tel (800) 272-9933 *Founded/Ownrshp* 1890, 1995
Sales NA *EMP* 900
SIC 6022 State commercial banks
Ch: Gary L Irmon
Pr: Paul Folz
Pr: D Michael Jones
Ofcr: Jeff Enrico
Ofcr: Stephanie Foster
Ofcr: Janele Haan
Ofcr: Joseph Timmons
Ex VP: Richard Barton
Ex VP: Douglas Bennett
Ex VP: Kayleen Kohler
Ex VP: Craig Milelr
Ex VP: Cynthia D Purcell
Sr VP: Curt Clausen
Sr VP: Matt Drown
Sr VP: Dianne Larsen
Sr VP: Gregg Marsicano
Sr VP: Marcelo Pomato
Sr VP: Kirk Quillin
Sr VP: Jim Reed
Sr VP: Anne Wuesthoff
Sr VP: Ian Zimmerman

BANNER BAYWOOD MEDICAL CENTER
See BANNER HEALTH SYSTEM

D-U-N-S 94-287-5568
▲ BANNER CORP
10 S 1st Ave, Walla Walla, WA 99362-1942
Tel (509) 527-3636 *Founded/Ownrshp* 1998
Sales NA *EMP* 1,193[E]
Tkr Sym BANR *Exch* NGS
SIC 6022 6036 State commercial banks; Savings institutions, not federally chartered
Pr: Mark J Grescovich
**Ch Bd:* Gary Sirmon
Pr: Nancy Piestrack
CFO: Lloyd W Baker
**V Ch Bd:* Jesse G Foster
Ofcr: Richard B Barton
Ofcr: Judy Steiner
Ex VP: Richard B Arton
Ex VP: Douglas M Bennett
Ex VP: Tyrone J Bliss
Ex VP: John R Neill
Ex VP: Cynthia D Purcell
Ex VP: Gary W Wagers
Sr VP: Pat Carlin
VP: Campbell Daniel
VP: Bill Endress
VP: Davis Jeff
VP: Walter McLaughlin
VP: Michael Thomas

VP: Scott Witt
Exec: James T Reed Jr
Board of Directors: Constance H Kravas, Robert D Adams, John R Layman, Doyle L Arnold, David I Matson, Gordon E Budke, Brent A Orrico, Connie R Collingsworth, Michael M Smith, Spencer Fleischer, Michael J Gillfilan, Roberto R Herencia, D Michael Jones, David A Klaue

BANNER DEL E WEBB MEDICAL CENT
See BANNER HEALTH

D-U-N-S 00-619-9400 IMP
BANNER ENGINEERING CORP (MN)
9714 10th Ave N, Minneapolis, MN 55441-5093
Tel (763) 544-3164 *Founded/Ownrshp* 1966
Sales 201.7MM^E *EMP* 600
SIC 3674 Radiation sensors
Ch Bd: Robert W Fayfield
Pr: Neal G Schumacher
COO: Larry Evans
Area Mgr: Mark Brooks
Area Mgr: Dan Patzer
QA Dir: Roger Birnbaum
Dir IT: Kelly Christensen
Tech Mgr: Mike Carlson
Sftwr Eng: Charles Osborn
Ql Cn Mgr: Daniel Kolles
Mktg Mgr: Chris Dales

BANNER HEALTH
See NORTH COLORADO MEDICAL CENTER FOUNDATION INC

D-U-N-S 07-175-3982
BANNER HEALTH
BANNER RESEARCH INSTITUTE
2901 N Central Ave # 160, Phoenix, AZ 85012-2702
Tel (602) 747-4000 *Founded/Ownrshp* 1938
Sales 6.9MMM *EMP* 35,000
Accts Ernst & Young Llp
SIC 8062 8051 8082 7361 8011 8093 General medical & surgical hospitals; Extended care facility; Home health care services; Nurses' registry; Ambulatory surgical center; Rehabilitation center, outpatient treatment
Pr: Peter S Fine
Chf Path: Mary Fietz
Chf Rad: Joel Rainwater
Pr: Michael Cherry
CFO: Stanley Adams
CFO: Jeff Buehrle
**CFO:* Dennis Dahlen
CFO: Stephanie Kaul
CFO: Greg Wojtal
**Chf Mktg O:* John Hensing
**Ex VP:* Rebecca Kuhn
Sr VP: David M Bixby
Sr VP: Ryan Smith
VP: Tricia Barger
**VP:* Kathy Bollinger
VP: Laura Brunner
VP: Twila Burdick
VP: Kip Edwards
VP: Steve Eiss
VP: Samantha Endsley
VP: Mary Hubenthal

D-U-N-S 07-827-7566
BANNER HEALTH
BANNER DEL E WEBB MEDICAL CENT
14502 W Meeker Blvd, Sun City, AZ 85375-5282
Tel (623) 524-4000 *Founded/Ownrshp* 1988
Sales 277.9MM *EMP* 1,700
SIC 8062 General medical & surgical hospitals
CEO: John Harrington
Exec: Michelle Daniels
Off Mgr: Lori Conlow
Pharmcst: William Mostow
HC Dir: Barbara Stone

D-U-N-S 13-910-4678
BANNER HEALTH SYSTEM
BANNER BAYWOOD MEDICAL CENTER
6644 E Baywood Ave, Mesa, AZ 85206-1747
Tel (480) 321-2000 *Founded/Ownrshp* 2003
Sales 272.3MM *EMP* 52^E
SIC 8062 General medical & surgical hospitals
CEO: Laura Robertson
Chf Rad: Steven Maxfield
Ex VP: Dianne Pillen
Doctor: Steve Peasley
Nrsg Dir: Cathy Townsend
Snr Mgr: Kathryn Stamadianos

D-U-N-S 80-699-7276
BANNER HEALTH SYSTEM
FAIRBANKS MEMORIAL HOSPITAL
1650 Cowles St, Fairbanks, AK 99701-5907
Tel (907) 452-8181 *Founded/Ownrshp* 2003
Sales 225.7MM *EMP* 1,000^E
SIC 8082 Home health care services
CEO: Mike Powers
Treas: Peggy Macdonald
Dir Lab: Jennifer Schuler
Chf Nrs Of: Kent Grassi
IT Man: Stephen Eikenberry
Pathlgst: Andy Evanger

BANNER HEART HOSPITAL
See LUTHERAN HEART HOSPITAL

D-U-N-S 00-691-9799
BANNER LIFE INSURANCE CO
(*Suby of* LEGAL & GENERAL AMERICA INC) ★
3275 Bennett Creek Ave, Frederick, MD 21704-7608
Tel (301) 279-4800 *Founded/Ownrshp* 1981
Sales NA *EMP* 250
SIC 6311 6411 Life insurance; Insurance agents, brokers & service
Pr: David S Lenaburg
Pr: Debbie Posin
**Ex VP:* Gene R Gilbertson
Mktg Mgr: Sabine Barclay

BANNER RESEARCH INSTITUTE
See BANNER HEALTH

BANNER RESEARCH INSTITUTE
See CASA GRANDE COMMUNITY HOSPITAL

D-U-N-S 82-728-0699
BANNER-UNIVERSITY MEDICAL CENTER SOUTH CAMPUS LLC
(*Suby of* BANNER RESEARCH INSTITUTE) ★
2800 E Ajo Way, Tucson, AZ 85713-6204
Tel (520) 874-2000 *Founded/Ownrshp* 2008
Sales 68.0MM^E *EMP* 5,181^E
SIC 8062 General medical & surgical hospitals
CEO: Karen Mlawsky
Pr: Michael Waldrum
CFO: Misty Hansen
Ofcr: Sarah Frost
Sr VP: Lynn Schneider Grennan
VP: Michele Barnard
VP: Mary Donahoe
Dir Lab: Michael Tucker

D-U-N-S 07-991-1337
BANNER-UNIVERSITY MEDICAL CENTER TUCSON CAMPUS LLC
(*Suby of* BANNER RESEARCH INSTITUTE) ★
1501 N Campbell Ave, Tucson, AZ 85724-0001
Tel (520) 694-0111 *Founded/Ownrshp* 2014
Sales 218.5MM^E *EMP* 3,000^E
SIC 8062 General medical & surgical hospitals; Hospital, medical school affiliated with nursing & residency
Pr: Peter S Fine
Off Mgr: Janette De Jonghe
Web Dev: Bill Fu
Surgeon: Christopher L Morgan
Doctor: Paul Fenster

D-U-N-S 14-836-8194
BANNER-UNIVERSITY MEDICAL GROUP
2901 N Central Ave, Phoenix, AZ 85012-2700
Tel (602) 747-4000 *Founded/Ownrshp* 1983
Sales 144.7MM^E *EMP* 1,818
Accts Beach Fleischman Pc Tucson A
SIC 8011 Offices & clinics of medical doctors
CEO: Peter Fine
**Pr:* Kathy Bollinger
**Pr:* James Ferando
**Pr:* Rebecca Kuhn
**Treas:* Patricia Block
Ofcr: Jeffrey Macewen
**Ex VP:* Ronald Bunnell
**Ex VP:* John Hensing
**Sr VP:* David Bixby
**Sr VP:* Edward Oxford
**Sr VP:* Mike Warden
**VP:* Dennis Dahlen

D-U-N-S 82-984-5549
BANORTE USA CORP
(*Suby of* BANCO MERCANTIL DEL NORTE, S.A., INSTITUCION DE BANCA MULTIPLE, GRUPO FINANCIERO BANORTE)
540 Madison Ave Fl 36, New York, NY 10022-3224
Tel (212) 484-5200 *Founded/Ownrshp* 2006
Sales NA *EMP* 205
SIC 6029 Commercial banks
Ch Bd: Carlos I Garza

D-U-N-S 00-607-6525 IMP/EXP
■ **BANTA CORP**
R R DONNELLEY
(*Suby of* RR DONNELLEY) ★
1457 Earl St, Menasha, WI 54952-1416
Tel (312) 326-8000 *Founded/Ownrshp* 1901
Sales 786.0MM^E *EMP* 8,400
SIC 2759 8742 Commercial printing; Business consultant
Pr: Padraic Allen
Pr: Michael Allen
Pr: Kimberly Williams
CFO: Geoffrey J Hibner
Ex VP: Gerald A Henseler
VP: David F Engelkemeyer
VP: Ronald D Kneezel
VP: Dennis J Meyer
VP: John E Tiffany
Plnt Mgr: Robert A Riggleman

D-U-N-S 80-855-4062 IMP
■ **BANTA GLOBAL TURNKEY LTD**
(*Suby of* RR DONNELLEY) ★
1600 Disk Dr, Plover, WI 54467-3131
Tel (715) 341-0544 *Founded/Ownrshp* 2001
Sales 228.8MM^E *EMP* 2,500
SIC 3577 Computer peripheral equipment
Pr: Thomas J Quinlan III

D-U-N-S 04-773-7549
BANYAN AIR SERVICES INC
5360 Nw 20th Ter, Fort Lauderdale, FL 33309-2727
Tel (954) 491-3170 *Founded/Ownrshp* 1986
Sales 116.6MM^E *EMP* 145
SIC 5172 4581 5088 4522 Aircraft fueling services; Aircraft servicing & repairing; Aircraft equipment & supplies; Air transportation, nonscheduled
Pr: Donald A Campion
COO: Craig Huston
**CFO:* James M Barcel
**Sr VP:* Michael D O Keeffe
Snr Mgr: Johnny Gomez

D-U-N-S 62-714-1869 IMP
BANYAN INCENTIVES
(*Suby of* TAYLOR CORP) ★
4875 White Bear Pkwy, Saint Paul, MN 55110-3325
Tel (651) 426-1667 *Founded/Ownrshp* 2005
Sales 89.6MM^E *EMP* 595
SIC 2759 Commercial printing
Pr: Tim Broadhead
**Pr:* Paul Griffiths

D-U-N-S 01-439-3743
BAPTIST AND PHYSICIANS LOCAL SERVICES BUREAU INC
BAPTIST MEMORIAL HEALTH CARE
350 N Humphreys Blvd, Memphis, TN 38120-2177
Tel (901) 227-5117 *Founded/Ownrshp* 1995
Sales 556.8MM *EMP* 500
SIC 8741 Hospital management
Pr: Stephen C Reynolds
**VP:* Bob Gordon

**VP:* David Hogan
IT Man: Kim Chriswell

D-U-N-S 96-188-5816
BAPTIST EASLEY HOSPITAL
200 Fleetwood Dr, Easley, SC 29640-2022
Tel (864) 442-7200 *Founded/Ownrshp* 2009
Sales 99.9MM^E *EMP* 865
SIC 8062 General medical & surgical hospitals
CEO: Michael Batchelor
Chf Rad: John Cooper
CFO: J L Pope
Dir Lab: Joan Clardy
Nurse Mgr: Angela Neeley
QA Dir: Dale Garrett
Pr Dir: Andrea Segal
Ansthlgy: Lee D Meeder
Diag Rad: John H Fulcher
HC Dir: Cynthia Ellenburg

BAPTIST HEALTH
See BAPTIST MEDICAL CENTER OF BEACHES INC

D-U-N-S 04-355-6760
BAPTIST HEALTH (AR)
11001 Executive Center Dr # 200, Little Rock, AR 72211-4393
Tel (501) 202-2000 *Founded/Ownrshp* 1921, 1965
Sales 836.9MM *EMP* 7,000
Accts Bkd Llp Little Rock Arkansa
SIC 8051 Skilled nursing care facilities
Pr: Russ Harrington
**Pr:* Missy Lewis
COO: Jennifer Payton
**Sr VP:* Allen Smith
Sr VP: Troy Wells
VP: Marsha Cunningham
VP: Todd Hart
VP: Anthony Kendall
VP: Jill Massiet
VP: Chris Parker
VP: Douglas Weeks
Exec: Kathy Roberts
Dir Risk M: Julie Hyett
Dir Lab: Sharon Morgan
Dir Lab: Valerie Wood
Dir Rx: John Norris

D-U-N-S 07-210-3104
BAPTIST HEALTH
HEALTHCARE AUTH FOR BPTST HLTH
301 Brown Springs Rd, Montgomery, AL 36117-7005
Tel (334) 273-4217 *Founded/Ownrshp* 1982
Sales 248.3MM^E *EMP* 2,473
SIC 8062 General medical & surgical hospitals
CEO: Russell Tyner
**COO:* Robin Barca
CFO: Joe Denton
CFO: Melissa Johnson
**CFO:* Guy Laprad
VP: Tony Kendall
Dir Rx: Clint Peevy

BAPTIST HEALTH CARE
See BAPTIST HOSPITAL INC

D-U-N-S 10-755-9163
BAPTIST HEALTH CARE CORP
1000 W Moreno St, Pensacola, FL 32501-2316
Tel (850) 434-4080 *Founded/Ownrshp* 1983
Sales 43.6MM *EMP* 5,200
Accts Lb Bkd Llp Pensacola Fl
SIC 8741 Hospital management; Nursing & personal care facility management
Ch: Marcus E Paul
**Pr:* Mark Faulkner
COO: Rich Gilmartin
**CFO:* Joseph Felkner
CFO: Sharon Nobles
**Treas:* Edward M Gray
Bd of Dir: Jodie Butler
Bd of Dir: Kyler Cole
Bd of Dir: Eugene Franklin
Bd of Dir: Sue Halfhill
Bd of Dir: Bill Pullum
Bd of Dir: Dennis Williams
Ex VP: Emily Altazan
Ex VP: Edna Williams
**Sr VP:* Ava Abney
**VP:* Gary Bembry
VP: David Di Loreto
VP: Mark T Faulkner
VP: Robert E Gowing
**VP:* H Britt J Landrum
VP: Melba Powell

BAPTIST HEALTH FLOYD
See FLOYD MEMORIAL HOSPITAL AND HEALTH SERVICES

D-U-N-S 07-132-7894
BAPTIST HEALTH MADISONVILLE INC
TROVER HEALTH SYSTEM
(*Suby of* BAPTIST HOSPITAL EAST) ★
900 Hospital Dr, Madisonville, KY 42431-1644
Tel (270) 825-5100 *Founded/Ownrshp* 2012
Sales 182.5MM *EMP* 2,100
Accts Ernst & Young Us Llp Cincinna
SIC 8011 8062 Offices & clinics of medical doctors; Physical medicine, physician/surgeon; General medical & surgical hospitals
Pr: Mike Baumgartner
**VP:* Kim Ashby
Prac Mgr: Ann Cain
Off Mgr: Kim Price
QA Dir: Judy Martin
IT Man: Kate Fuller
Doctor: William Crump
Doctor: Deepak Kapadia
Doctor: Mark J Littlehale
Doctor: William Logan
Pgrm Dir: Margo N Ashby

D-U-N-S 36-101-3530
BAPTIST HEALTH MEDICAL CENTER
9601 Baptist Health Dr # 109, Little Rock, AR 72205-6323
Tel (501) 887-3000 *Founded/Ownrshp* 2005
Sales 470.6MM *EMP* 200^E
Accts Bkd Llp Little Rock Arkansa
SIC 8062 General medical & surgical hospitals

CEO: Edward Lacy
IT Man: Kathlyn Burch
Pathlgst: Dianne Johnson
**Nrsg Dir:* Holly Langster

D-U-N-S 84-749-8938 IMP
BAPTIST HEALTH SOUTH FLORIDA INC
6855 S Red Rd, South Miami, FL 33143-3647
Tel (305) 596-1960 *Founded/Ownrshp* 1990
Sales 2.2MMM *EMP* 16,000
Accts Deloitte & Touche Llp
SIC 8062 8011 8082 General medical & surgical hospitals; Ambulatory surgical center; Home health care services
Pr: Brian E Keeley
Chf Path: Andrew Renshaw
**Ch Bd:* George E Cadman III
**COO:* Fred M Messing
**CFO:* Ralph E Lawson
**Treas:* H Robert Berry
**Treas:* Jack A Ziffer
Trst: Tony Alonso
Trst: Calvin H Babcock
Trst: Wendell R Beard
Trst: James Carr
Trst: William L Chambers III
Trst: George M Corrigan
Trst: William H Dickinson
Trst: Robert L Dub
Trst: Herbert H Greene
Trst: George P Harth
Trst: Jay A Hershoff
Trst: Charles Hood
Trst: Charles M Hood III
Trst: Gary Johnson

D-U-N-S 06-945-2373
■ **BAPTIST HEALTH SYSTEM**
(*Suby of* VHS SAN ANTONIO PARTNERS LLC) ★
215 E Quincy St Ste 200, San Antonio, TX 78215-2032
Tel (210) 297-1000 *Founded/Ownrshp* 2003
Sales 996.5MM^E *EMP* 9,932
SIC 8062 Hospital, AMA approved residency
Pr: Graham Reeve
COO: Eric R Schmacker
COO: Bettina White
CFO: Fabian Borrego
**CFO:* David Williamson
Ex VP: Shirley Parker
VP: Shan Largoza
VP: Lyn Mild
VP: Don Ryden
Dir Rad: Willie Arvuthnot
Dir Rad: Xavier Silva
Comm Man: Susan Moore

D-U-N-S 87-768-7517
BAPTIST HEALTH SYSTEM FOUNDATION INC
841 Prudential Dr # 1300, Jacksonville, FL 32207-8329
Tel (904) 202-2919 *Founded/Ownrshp* 1983
Sales 19.1MM *EMP* 8,000
Accts Ernst & Young Llp Jacksonvil
SIC 8322 Individual & family services
Pr: Carol Thompson
**VP:* Marlene Spalten
IT Man: John Erstling

D-U-N-S 07-051-8782
BAPTIST HEALTH SYSTEM INC
1130 22nd St S Ste 1000, Birmingham, AL 35205-2881
Tel (205) 715-5000 *Founded/Ownrshp* 1975
Sales 565.7MM *EMP* 4,300
Accts Warrent Averett Llc Birmingh
SIC 8011 8741 8082 8059 Medical centers; Health maintenance organization; Hospital management; Home health care services; Convalescent home
CEO: Keith Parrott
**CFO:* Greg Johnston
**Chf Mktg O:* Elizabeth Ennis
VP: Hugh McMurry
VP: Marcia A Twitty
Dir Rx: David Martin
Mng Dir: Tiffany Lewis
Dir Pat Ac: Tina Burgett
**CIO:* Chris Davis
**CIO:* Scott Fenn
Dir IT: Walt Haywood

D-U-N-S 07-210-6305
BAPTIST HEALTH SYSTEM INC
SHELBY BAPTIST MEDICAL CENTER
1000 1st St N, Alabaster, AL 35007-8703
Tel (205) 620-8100 *Founded/Ownrshp* 1959
Sales 162.6MM *EMP* 850
SIC 8062 General medical & surgical hospitals
Pr: David C Wilson
Chf OB: George M Zaharias
**CFO:* James Riddle
Ofcr: Claire Owens
Dir Rx: Karen Rutland
Ansthlgy: Michael L Lathem
HC Dir: Lisa Wilkerso

D-U-N-S 61-856-6673
BAPTIST HEALTH SYSTEM INC
800 Prudential Dr, Jacksonville, FL 32207-8202
Tel (904) 202-2000 *Founded/Ownrshp* 2002
Sales 957.1MM^E *EMP* 7,000
Accts Ernst & Young Llp Jacksonvil
SIC 8741 Hospital management; Nursing & personal care facility management
Pr: A Hugh Greene
**COO:* John Willbanks
**CFO:* Michael Lukaszewski
Ex VP: Melanie Husk
Ex VP: Sanjay Saha
Ex VP: Carol Thompson
Sr VP: William McLear
VP: Michael Lanier
VP: Diane Rains
VP: Marlene M Spalten
VP: Scott Wooten
Comm Man: Cindy Hamilton

D-U-N-S 13-026-1803
■ BAPTIST HEALTH SYSTEM OF EAST TENNESSEE INC
(*Suby of* TENNOVA HEALTHCARE) ★
137 E Blount Ave Ste 1b, Knoxville, TN 37920-1601
Tel (865) 632-5011 *Founded/Ownrshp* 1983
Sales 125.3MM^E *EMP* 2,691
SIC 8062 General medical & surgical hospitals
Mng Dir: Trent Nessler

D-U-N-S 15-057-0232
BAPTIST HEALTHCARE AFFILIATES INC
BAPTIST HOSPITAL NORTHEAST
(*Suby of* BAPTIST HOSPITAL EAST) ★
2701 Eastpoint Pkwy, Louisville, KY 40223-4166
Tel (502) 896-5008 *Founded/Ownrshp* 1992
Sales 92.7MM *EMP* 415
Accts Ernst & Young Us Llp Columbus
SIC 8062 General medical & surgical hospitals
Ch Bd: Gayle Johnson
**Pr:* Stephen C Hanson
**Pr:* Tommy J Smith
**CFO:* Carl G Herde
**VP:* Dennis Johnson
**VP:* Chris Roty

D-U-N-S 05-583-5003
BAPTIST HEALTHCARE SYSTEM INC
BAPTIST HOSPITAL EAST
2701 Eastpoint Pkwy, Louisville, KY 40223-4166
Tel (502) 896-5000 *Founded/Ownrshp* 1918
Sales 1.4MMM *EMP* 12,601
Accts Ernst & Young Us Llp Cincinna
SIC 8062 8011 8741 General medical & surgical hospitals; Medical centers; Hospital management
CEO: Stephen C Hanson
Pr: William A Brown
CFO: Stephen R Oglesby
Chf Mktg O: Timothy Jahn
Ofcr: Jennifer Hale
VP: David Gray
VP: Steve Rudolf
VP: Bonnie Schrock
VP: Andy Sears
VP: William Sisson
VP: Catherine Zoeller
Dir Risk M: Connie Barker
Dir Rx: Paul Lucas

BAPTIST HOSPITAL EAST
See BAPTIST HEALTHCARE SYSTEM INC

D-U-N-S 01-039-5739 IMP
BAPTIST HOSPITAL INC
BAPTIST HEALTH CARE
1000 W Moreno St, Pensacola, FL 32501-2316
Tel (850) 434-4011 *Founded/Ownrshp* 1951
Sales 278.6MM *EMP* 1,652
SIC 8062 General medical & surgical hospitals
Pr: Alfred G Stubblefield
**Pr:* Mark Faulkner
**CFO:* Joseph Felkner
CFO: Kent Skolrog
**CFO:* Kerry Vermillion
**Sr VP:* Gary Bembry
**Sr VP:* Brian Matson
**Sr VP:* Scott Raynes
**Sr VP:* Kent Skolrood
**VP:* Bob Harriman
VP: Allison Hill
**VP:* Sandy Rogers
VP: Daphne Scordato
**VP:* David Wildebrandt
Dir OR: Donna Morris

BAPTIST HOSPITAL NORTHEAST
See BAPTIST HEALTHCARE AFFILIATES INC

D-U-N-S 07-489-2233
BAPTIST HOSPITAL OF EAST TENNESSEE INC (TN)
MERCY RIVERSIDE
137 E Blount Ave, Knoxville, TN 37920-1601
Tel (865) 632-5200 *Founded/Ownrshp* 1944, 1983
Sales 47.2MM^E *EMP* 2,000
SIC 8062 General medical & surgical hospitals
Prin: Jeffrey A Ashin
Sr VP: Steve Clapp
Off Mgr: Tim Osterholm
IT Man: Bob Hart
Nutrtnst: Peter Lanois
Doctor: Alan Galloway
Doctor: Diane Neely
Doctor: David T Watson MD

D-U-N-S 07-601-6948
BAPTIST HOSPITAL OF MIAMI INC
(*Suby of* BAPTIST HEALTH SOUTH FLORIDA INC) ★
8900 N Kendall Dr, Miami, FL 33176-2197
Tel (786) 596-1960 *Founded/Ownrshp* 1960
Sales 889.4MM *EMP* 4,200
SIC 8062 General medical & surgical hospitals
COO: Wayne Brackin
COO: Randy Lee
**CFO:* Ralph Lawson
**Ch:* Calvin Babcock
**Treas:* Manuel Lasaga
VP: Becky Montesino
VP: Mimi Taylor
Exec: Sandra Repinski
Prgrm Mgr: Peter Guter
Nurse Mgr: Celia Hoffing
Cmptr Lab: Ofelia Alvarez

D-U-N-S 12-270-5929
■ BAPTIST HOSPITAL WEST INC
(*Suby of* HMA) ★
10820 Parkside Dr, Knoxville, TN 37934-1911
Tel (865) 218-7011 *Founded/Ownrshp* 2011
Sales 77.5MM^E *EMP* 2,000
SIC 8062 General medical & surgical hospitals
CEO: Lance Jones
**VP:* Martha Chill
Sales Exec: Alicia Kitts

D-U-N-S 01-078-7653
BAPTIST HOSPITALS OF SOUTHEAST TEXAS
MEMORIAL HERMANN BAPTIST BEAUM
3080 College St, Beaumont, TX 77701-4686
Tel (409) 212-5000 *Founded/Ownrshp* 1990
Sales 255.8MM *EMP* 1,759
Accts Bkd Llp Dallas Tx
SIC 8062 General medical & surgical hospitals
CEO: David Parmer
CFO: Louise Ferguson
CFO: Gary Troutman
Ofcr: Sarah Horner
Exec: Linda Brinkley
Chf Nrs Of: Gerald Bryant
Adm Dir: Aily Powell
IT Man: Joe Mangrum
Info Man: Roland Anderson
Info Man: Julie Boothman
Mktg Dir: Linda Gaudio

D-U-N-S 06-591-6447
BAPTIST MEDICAL CENTER OF BEACHES INC
BAPTIST HEALTH
1350 13th Ave S, Jacksonville, FL 32250-3203
Tel (904) 247-2900 *Founded/Ownrshp* 1961
Sales 123.2MM *EMP* 535
SIC 8062 Hospital, affiliated with AMA residency
Pr: Michael Mayo
CFO: Sheri Logan
CFO: John F Wilbanks
Brnch Mgr: Linda Duncan
CIO: Craig Solberg
DP Exec: Cindy Lamb
Mktg Dir: Janice Kiernen
Doctor: Darlene M Bartilucci
Doctor: Abraham Rogozinski
Dir Health: Shelly Hoy

D-U-N-S 96-631-7609
BAPTIST MEDICAL CENTER OF BEACHES INC
3563 Phillips Hwy, Jacksonville, FL 32207-5663
Tel (704) 202-1797 *Founded/Ownrshp* 2011
Sales 124.0MM *EMP* 21^E
SIC 8062 General medical & surgical hospitals
VP: Edward Sim

BAPTIST MEDICAL CENTER OKLA
See INTEGRIS BAPTIST MEDICAL CENTER INC

BAPTIST MEDICAL CENTER SOUTH
See HEALTHCARE AUTHORITY FOR BAPTIST HEALTH AND AFFILIATE OF UAB HEALTH SYSTEM

BAPTIST MEMORIAL HEALTH CARE
See BAPTIST AND PHYSICIANS LOCAL SERVICES BUREAU INC

BAPTIST MEMORIAL HEALTH CARE
See BAPTIST MEMORIAL HOSPITAL-DESOTO INC

D-U-N-S 14-824-4890
BAPTIST MEMORIAL HEALTH CARE CORP
350 N Humphreys Blvd, Memphis, TN 38120-2177
Tel (901) 227-2727 *Founded/Ownrshp* 1912
Sales 1.8MMM *EMP* 9,877
Accts Deloitte & Touche Llp Memphis
SIC 8062 8011 8741 5047 General medical & surgical hospitals; Clinic, operated by physicians; Management services; Hospital equipment & supplies
Pr: Jason Little
Dir Recs: Karen Miller
Pr: Susan Butler
COO: David Hogan
COO: David C Hogan
CFO: Monique Hart
CFO: Cyndi Pittman
**CFO:* Don Pounds
Ofcr: Edward Todd
VP: Richard Drewry Jr
VP: Greg Duckett
VP: Bill Griffin
VP: Randy King
VP: Val Lopez
VP: Keith Norman
VP: William Tuttle
Exec: Lori Goode
Dir Risk M: Serita Kirkwood
Dir Lab: Bobby Abbott
Dir Soc: Diane Thomas

D-U-N-S 00-704-9125
BAPTIST MEMORIAL HOSPITAL (TN)
(*Suby of* BAPTIST MEMORIAL HEALTH CARE CORP) ★
6019 Walnut Grove Rd, Memphis, TN 38120-2113
Tel (901) 226-5000 *Founded/Ownrshp* 1912
Sales 691.0MM *EMP* 6,000
SIC 8062 General medical & surgical hospitals
Ex VP: David Hogan
**CEO:* Jason Little
**CFO:* Don Pounds
**Ex VP:* Robert Gordon
Exec: Kristie Brown
Exec: Jeff Miller
Chf Nrs Of: Dana Dye
Chf Nrs Of: Sharon Harris
CTO: Terry Crider
CTO: Beverly Parrish
Dir IT: Lenny Goodman

D-U-N-S 07-351-3970
BAPTIST MEMORIAL HOSPITAL - NORTH MISSISSIPPI INC
(*Suby of* BAPTIST MEMORIAL HEALTH CARE CORP) ★
2301 S Lamar Blvd, Oxford, MS 38655-5373
Tel (662) 232-8100 *Founded/Ownrshp* 1989
Sales 201.9MM *EMP* 860
SIC 8062 General medical & surgical hospitals
CEO: William C Henning
Pr: Roger Holmes
CFO: Dana Williams
Dir Lab: Sonya Brewer
Prin: Peyton Warrington
Nurse Mgr: Judy Leeton
Telecom Ex: Terri Campbell
Dir IT: Linda Britt

Plnt Mgr: Don Ruby
Ql Cn Mgr: Betty Tolbert
Obsttrcn: Randy White

D-U-N-S 19-217-8671
BAPTIST MEMORIAL HOSPITAL-DESOTO INC
BAPTIST MEMORIAL HEALTH CARE
(*Suby of* BAPTIST MEMORIAL HEALTH CARE CORP) ★
7601 Southcrest Pkwy, Southaven, MS 38671-4739
Tel (662) 772-4000 *Founded/Ownrshp* 1988
Sales 322.2MM *EMP* 600
SIC 8062 General medical & surgical hospitals
CEO: Randy King
Pharmcst: Paul Wadsworth

D-U-N-S 07-547-3892
BAPTIST MEMORIAL HOSPITAL-GOLDEN TRIANGLE INC
2520 5th St N, Columbus, MS 39705-2008
Tel (662) 244-1000 *Founded/Ownrshp* 1993
Sales 193.1MM *EMP* 1,100
Accts Deloitte Tax Llp Nashville T
SIC 8062 General medical & surgical hospitals
CEO: Paul Cade
**Pr:* Joseph H Powell
**CFO:* David Webb
**Sr VP:* Charles R Baker
**Sr VP:* John Robbins
VP: Megan Brandt
**Prin:* Mary Ellen Sumral
CIO: Sheila Bardwell
QA Dir: Kim Kelly-Rhinewalt
Doctor: Gordon Jones
HC Dir: Tony Meinert

D-U-N-S 06-638-5733
BAPTIST ST ANTHONYS HOSPITAL CORP
B S A
(*Suby of* B S A HEALTH SYSTEM) ★
1600 Wallace Blvd, Amarillo, TX 79106-1799
Tel (806) 212-2000 *Founded/Ownrshp* 1996
Sales 472.8M^E *EMP* 2,500^E
Accts Ernst & Young Llp Dallas Tex
SIC 8062 General medical & surgical hospitals
Pr: John D Hicks
**CFO:* Elizebeth Pulliam
**VP:* Michael Cruz
**VP:* Belinda Gibson
**VP:* Kenneth Johnston MD
**VP:* Robert D Williams
Nrsg Dir: Sharon Hutchinson

D-U-N-S 07-304-5080
■ BAPTIST-LUTHERAN MEDICAL CENTER
HCA MIDWEST
(*Suby of* HOSPITAL COPORATION OF AMERICA) ★
6601 Rockhill Rd, Kansas City, MO 64131-1118
Tel (816) 276-7000 *Founded/Ownrshp* 2003
Sales 42.8MM^E *EMP* 1,500
SIC 8062 8731 General medical & surgical hospitals; Medical research, commercial
CEO: Darrell W Moore
**CFO:* Jim Brown
**VP:* Kevin Mc Grath
CTO: Mike Rodgers
MIS Dir: Tim Schwab

D-U-N-S 13-956-2375
BAPTIST/ST ANTHONYS HEALTH SYSTEM
B S A HEALTH SYSTEM
1600 Wallace Blvd, Amarillo, TX 79106-1799
Tel (806) 212-2000 *Founded/Ownrshp* 2013
Sales 491.7M *EMP* 2,600
Accts Ernst & Young Us Llp Austin
SIC 8062 General medical & surgical hospitals
CEO: Bob Williams
Dir Recs: Pam Biggers
Dir Vol: Ray Johnson
**Pr:* Craig Sanders
CFO: James Taylor
VP: Kenneth Johnston MD
VP: Robert D Williams
Dir Rx: Lori Henke
QA Dir: Terry Long
Info Man: Taylor Weems
Opers Mgr: Mike Higgins

BAPTISTAL HOSPITAL OF SE TEXAS
See MEMORIAL HERMANN BAPTIST HOSPITAL

D-U-N-S 17-507-7924 IMP
BAR HARBOR LOBSTER CO INC
BAR HARBOR SEAFOOD
2000 Premier Row, Orlando, FL 32809-6208
Tel (407) 851-4001 *Founded/Ownrshp* 1986
Sales 85.5MM^E *EMP* 200
SIC 5146 5812 Fish, fresh; Seafoods; Seafood shack
Pr: Jeffrey P Hazell
**CFO:* Len Lesterance
CFO: Dennis McGrath
VP Opers: Jim Harris
VP Sls: Alonzo Campillo
S&M/VP: Diane Anderson

BAR HARBOR SEAFOOD
See BAR HARBOR LOBSTER CO INC

BAR LOUIE
See BL RESTAURANT OPERATIONS LLC

D-U-N-S 13-804-7634
BAR-ILAN UNIVERSITY IN ISRAEL
AMERICAN FRIENDS OF BAR ILAN U
160 E 56th St Fl 5, New York, NY 10022-3609
Tel (212) 906-3900 *Founded/Ownrshp* 1966
Sales 363.0MM *EMP* 30
Accts Grant Thornton Llp New York
SIC 8399 Fund raising organization, non-fee basis
Pr: Moshel Straus
**CEO:* Matthew J Maryles
**CFO:* Stacy Goodman

D-U-N-S 04-880-4504 EXP
BAR-S FOODS CO
(*Suby of* SIGMA ALIMENTOS EXTERIOR SLU)
5090 N 40th St Ste 300, Phoenix, AZ 85018-2185
Tel (602) 264-7272 *Founded/Ownrshp* 1981
Sales 502.1MM^E *EMP* 1,600
SIC 2013 Sausages & other prepared meats; Prepared pork products from purchased pork; Sausages & related products, from purchased meat
Pr: Timothy T Day
Pr: Carlos Urueta
Div VP: Rasool Rabbani
**Ex VP:* Warren J Panico
CTO: Dan Schaefer
IT Man: Dave Maceldowney
Board of Directors: Alejandro Elizondo Barraga, Rodrigo Fernandez, Alvaro Fernandez Garza, Mario H Paez Gonzalez, Armando Garza Sada

D-U-N-S 06-883-5099
BARBARA ANN KARMANOS CANCER INSTITUTE (MI)
MICHIGAN CANCER FOUNDATION
4100 John R St, Detroit, MI 48201-2013
Tel (800) 527-6266 *Founded/Ownrshp* 1947
Sales 90.2MM^E *EMP* 310
SIC 8733 8093 Medical research; Rehabilitation center, outpatient treatment
CEO: Ann G Schwartz
**Ch Bd:* Alan S Schwartz
**Pr:* Gerold Bepler
Pr: Margaret Dimond
**COO:* Paul Broughton
CFO: William G Bennett
**CFO:* Brian Gamble
Treas: Meyer Prentis
**V Ch Bd:* Randolph J Agley
**Ofcr:* Justin Klamerus
Sr VP: Kathleen Carolin
VP: Nicolas Karmanos
VP: Anne Payne

D-U-N-S 80-280-6583
BARBEQUE INTEGRATED INC
SMOKEY BONE'S BAR & FIRE GRILL
(*Suby of* SUN CAPITAL PARTNERS INC) ★
4000 Hollywood Blvd, Hollywood, FL 33021-6751
Tel (407) 355-5800 *Founded/Ownrshp* 2007
Sales 85.0MM^E *EMP* 2,000
SIC 5812 Steak & barbecue restaurants
CEO: Chris Artinian

D-U-N-S 01-904-6465
■ BARBER FOODS
(*Suby of* ADVANCE PIERRE FOODS) ★
56 Milliken St, Portland, ME 04103-1530
Tel (207) 482-5500 *Founded/Ownrshp* 1955
Sales 88.2MM^E *EMP* 653
SIC 2015 Poultry, processed: frozen
Pr: David Barber
CFO: James Glover
**CFO:* Vicki Mann
**Treas:* Bruce Codgeshell
VP: Robert Lowe
CTO: Frank Davis
QC Dir: Herb Rau

D-U-N-S 00-428-5037
BARBERS HILL INDEPENDENT SCHOOL DISTRICT EDUCATION FOUNDATION (TX)
9600 Eagle Dr, Mont Belvieu, TX 77580
Tel (281) 576-2221 *Founded/Ownrshp* 1935
Sales 91.2MM *EMP* 450
Accts Weaver And Tidwell Llp Co
SIC 8211 School board
Ex VP: Abby McManus
**VP:* Fred Skinner
Exec: Dustin Hardin
Exec: Andrew Locklin
Exec: Nicole Naivar
Assoc Dir: Kent Summerour
Schl Brd P: Benny May

D-U-N-S 79-029-8058 IMP
BARCEL USA LLC
(*Suby of* GRUPO BIMBO, S.A.B. DE C.V.)
301 S Nrthpint Dr Ste 100, Coppell, TX 75019
Tel (972) 607-4500 *Founded/Ownrshp* 2009
Sales 214.5MM *EMP* 240
SIC 5145 Confectionery; Snack foods
VP: Milton Mattus

D-U-N-S 04-875-9208
BARCELO CRESTLINE CORP
(*Suby of* BARCELO CORPORACION EMPRESARIAL, SA)
3950 University Dr # 301, Fairfax, VA 22030-2565
Tel (571) 529-6000 *Founded/Ownrshp* 2002
Sales 69.1MM^E *EMP* 3,677
SIC 6513 6531 Apartment building operators; Real estate leasing & rentals
Pr: James A Carroll
**Ch Bd:* Bruce D Wardinski
CFO: Jim Carroll
Treas: Larry Harvey
**Ex VP:* Pierre M Donahue
**Ex VP:* David L Durbin
Sr VP: Victor J Perea
VP: Raphael La Vega
VP: Roberto Garrido Sanchez
Ex Dir: Jacci Duncan
Genl Mgr: Gia Mariggio

BARCLAYCARD US
See BARCLAYS FINANCIAL CORP

D-U-N-S 10-941-7209
BARCLAYS BANK DELAWARE
(*Suby of* BARCLAYCARD US) ★
100 S West St, Wilmington, DE 19801-5015
Tel (302) 255-8000 *Founded/Ownrshp* 2000
Sales NA *EMP* 349
SIC 6035 Federal savings banks
Pr: James Stewart
CFO: Gerald Pavelich
Chf Cred: Michael Mayer
VP: Elizabeth Agosto
IT Man: Peter Engime
IT Man: Rich Menuchi
Netwrk Mgr: Joe Aalbregtse

D-U-N-S 18-643-0021
BARCLAYS CAPITAL INC
(Suby of BARCLAYS GROUP US INC) ★
745 7th Ave, New York, NY 10019-6801
Tel (212) 526-7000 Founded/Ownrshp 1980
Sales 2.0MMM^E EMP 1,624
Accts Pricewaterhousecoopers Llp
SIC 6211 Dealers, security
Pr: Gerard Larocca
COO: Alastair Blackwell
CFO: Joe Busuttil
Treas: Thomas McGuire
Ofcr: Scott Coya
Top Exec: Jean-Francois Astier
VP: Jeremy Barnes
VP: Stephen Barnitz
VP: Nicholas Cirilli
VP: David Fintzen
VP: Roland Jarquio
VP: Jody Pantoliano
Dir Risk M: Chris Holliman

D-U-N-S 80-002-3843
BARCLAYS CAPITAL REAL ESTATE HOLDINGS INC
(Suby of BARCLAYS CAPITAL INC) ★
1301 Ave Of The Americas, New York, NY 10019-6022
Tel (212) 581-1628 Founded/Ownrshp 2004
Sales NA EMP 1,400^E
SIC 6162 Mortgage bankers & correspondents
VP: Ming Ng
VP: Lisa Valentino
Dir IT: Courtney Ferrare

D-U-N-S 14-275-7496
BARCLAYS FINANCIAL CORP
BARCLAYCARD US
(Suby of BARCLAYS PLC)
125 S West St, Wilmington, DE 19801-5014
Tel (302) 622-8990 Founded/Ownrshp 2004
Sales 2.2MMM^E EMP 1,100
SIC 7389 6282 6211 Credit card service; Investment advice; Security brokers & dealers
CEO: Curt Hess
COO: Sheila Monroe
*COO: Joe Purzycki
*COO: Patrick Wright
*CFO: Gerald Pavelich
*Chf Mktg O: Peggy Maher
VP: Chamblin Rooney
VP: Denny Suh
Mng Dir: Kevin Murphy
Snr Mgr: Rita Friday

D-U-N-S 83-569-5610
BARCLAYS GROUP US INC
(Suby of BARCLAYS BANK PLC)
745 7th Ave, New York, NY 10019-6801
Tel (212) 412-4000 Founded/Ownrshp 1999
Sales NA EMP 2,600^E
SIC 6712 Bank holding companies
VP: Mary A Byrne
*CEO: Damon Lembi
VP: Daniel Gabbay
VP: Jim Kerner
*VP: Michael J Mattera
VP: Jigar Patel
VP: Wes Reese
VP: David Rosu
VP: Jim Wise
Mng Dir: ARI Berger
Mng Dir: Kerrie Cohen

D-U-N-S 00-417-7270
BARCLAYS USA INC
(Suby of BARCLAYS BANK PLC)
200 Park Ave Fl 3w, New York, NY 10166-0398
Tel (212) 412-4000 Founded/Ownrshp 1984
Sales 455.8MM^E EMP 1,460
SIC 6211 Security brokers & dealers
Prin: Tom Kalaris
*CFO: Mike Montgomery
Treas: Solomon Moremong
VP: Chirag Mirani
*Prin: Blaine Short
Dir IT: George Andrus

D-U-N-S 62-254-1746 IMP
BARCO INC
(Suby of BARCO NV)
3059 Premiere Pkwy # 400, Duluth, GA 30097-4905
Tel (408) 400-4100 Founded/Ownrshp 1986
Sales 172.0MM^E EMP 580
SIC 3575 3669 Computer terminals, monitors & components; Visual communication systems
CEO: Herman Daems
*Pr: H David Scott
*COO: Filip Pintelon
*CFO: Carl Peeters
*Ch: Erik Van Zele
*Sec: Belinda Kidwell
VP: Jed Deame
*VP: Kurt Verheggen
Exec: Joel Woodruff
Genl Mgr: Dirk Hendrickx
IT Man: George Lovett

D-U-N-S 80-046-1134 EXP
BARCODES LLC
200 W Monroe St Ste 1050, Chicago, IL 60606-5122
Tel (312) 588-5960 Founded/Ownrshp 2010
Sales 152.5MM^E EMP 90
SIC 5065 Electronic parts
Pr: Dan Nettesheim
*VP: William Daly
Web Dev: Brian Clark
Sls Mgr: Juancarlos Barrera
Sls Mgr: Peter Issa
Sls Mgr: Dan Nettesheim
Sls Mgr: Derek Schroeder

D-U-N-S 04-461-1812 IMP
■ **BARD ACCESS SYSTEMS INC**
(Suby of C R BARD INC) ★
605 N 5600 W, Salt Lake City, UT 84116-3738
Tel (801) 522-5000 Founded/Ownrshp 1989
Sales 119.7MM^E EMP 519
SIC 3841 Catheters
Pr: James C Beasley
*VP: David C Hemink
*VP: Jean F Holloway
*VP: Scott T Lowry
VP: Roman Ricart
*VP: John H Weiland
Exec: Bob Mellen
Prgrm Mgr: Luis Ayllon
Prgrm Mgr: John Evans
Prgrm Mgr: Ryan Lemon
Info Man: Eric Homer

D-U-N-S 08-228-2989 IMP
BARD COLLEGE
30 Campus Rd, Annandale On Hudson, NY 12504-9800
Tel (845) 758-7518 Founded/Ownrshp 1860
Sales 226.9MM^E EMP 525
Accts Saxbst Llp Albany Ny
SIC 8221 College, except junior
Pr: Leon Botstein
*Ex VP: Dimitri Papadimitriou
VP: Deanna Cochran
VP: Michele D Dominy
*VP: Michelle Dominy
VP: James Prudvig
Assoc Dir: Greg Armbruster
Assoc Dir: Tamara Telberg
Ex Dir: James Johnson
Mng Dir: Susan Tveekrem
Prgrm Mgr: Judi Smith

D-U-N-S 84-106-6934
BARD COLLEGE PUBLICATIONS
Annandale Rd, Annandale On Hudson, NY 12504
Tel (845) 758-7417 Founded/Ownrshp 2000
Sales 181.6MM EMP 15
SIC 8999 2759 5311 Writing for publication; Publication printing; Department stores
Ex VP: Dimitri B Papadimitriou
Dir IT: Marina Kostalevsky

D-U-N-S 13-505-7938 IMP
■ **BARD PERIPHERAL VASCULAR INC**
(Suby of C R BARD INC) ★
1625 W 3rd St, Tempe, AZ 85281-2438
Tel (480) 894-9515 Founded/Ownrshp 1974
Sales 83.9MM^E EMP 300
SIC 3842 Prosthetic appliances
Pr: Steven S Williamson
*Pr: Jim Beasley
*Treas: Scott T Lowry
VP: Kimberly Hammond
Genl Mgr: Annette Everette
Ql Cn Mgr: Jon Conaway
Ql Cn Mgr: Jason Seiger
Ql Cn Mgr: Nicole Simmons
VP Sls: Brian Doherty
VP Sls: Robert Lerma
Sls Mgr: Matt Fermanich

D-U-N-S 94-268-8797
BARDEN COMPANIES INC
MAJESTIC STAR CASINO
400 Renaissance Ctr # 2400, Detroit, MI 48243-1676
Tel (313) 496-2900 Founded/Ownrshp 1992
Sales 63.8MM^E EMP 1,600
SIC 7371 7372 Computer software development; Educational computer software
Ch Bd: Don H Barden
VP: Michelle R Sherman

D-U-N-S 00-116-3732 IMP
BARDEN CORP (CT)
(Suby of SCHAEFFLER GROUP USA INC) ★
200 Park Ave, Danbury, CT 06810-7587
Tel (203) 744-2211 Founded/Ownrshp 1942, 1946
Sales 107.0MM^E EMP 600
SIC 3562 3469 3842 3089 3399 Ball bearings & parts; Machine parts, stamped or pressed metal; Surgical appliances & supplies; Injection molded finished plastic products; Steel balls
CEO: Peter J Enright
*Treas: Timothy U Zygmont
*VP: Robert Hillstrom
Dir IT: Carlos Romero
Software D: Fred Anderson

BARDEN MISSISSIPPI GAMING, LLC
See MAJESTIC MISSISSIPPI LLC

D-U-N-S 02-254-5987 IMP
BARDES CORP
ILSCO
4730 Madison Rd, Cincinnati, OH 45227-1426
Tel (513) 533-6200 Founded/Ownrshp 1996
Sales 90.8MM^E EMP 500
SIC 3643 Electric connectors
CEO: David Fitzgibbon
*Ch Bd: Merrilyn Q Bardes
*Pr: Andrew Quinn
*Treas: James E Valentine

D-U-N-S 96-326-8656 IMP
BARE ESCENTUALS BEAUTY INC
(Suby of BARE ESCENTUALS INC) ★
71 Stevenson St Fl 22, San Francisco, CA 94105-2979
Tel (415) 489-5000 Founded/Ownrshp 1999
Sales 331.8MM^E EMP 2,700
SIC 5999 Toiletries, cosmetics & perfumes
CEO: Simon Cowell
*CFO: Mike Gray
VP: Wanda MA
VP: Jing Zhu
*Prin: Leslie A Blodgett
IT Man: Deborah Taylor
Software D: Srinivas Javvadi
Software D: Bareerah N Khan
Sfty Dirs: Jennifer Everett
Opers Mgr: Anthony Rice
Snr Mgr: Emily Fan

D-U-N-S 08-700-8363 IMP
BARE ESCENTUALS INC
(Suby of SHISEIDO COMPANY, LIMITED)
71 Stevenson St Fl 22, San Francisco, CA 94105-2979
Tel (415) 489-5000 Founded/Ownrshp 2010
Sales 516.1MM^E EMP 2,779
SIC 5999 Toiletries, cosmetics & perfumes
CEO: Leslie A Blodgett
Pr: Michael Dadario
*COO: Myles B McCormick
*CFO: Mike Gray
VP: Monica Arnaudo
*VP: Kevin J Bradshaw
VP: Kathleen McCarthy
VP: Wanda MA
Snr Ntwrk: Lekshmi Sudha
IT Man: Andrew Molloy
Web Dev: Kira Roher

BARE WIRE DIV
See OMEGA WIRE INC

BARE WIRE DIVISION
See INTERNATIONAL WIRE GROUP INC

BAREFOOT
See TRUGREEN LIMITED PARTNERSHIP

D-U-N-S 04-769-9774
BARFLY VENTURES LLC
WALDRON PUBLIC HOUSE
35 Oakes St Sw Ste 400, Grand Rapids, MI 49503-3137
Tel (616) 965-9780 Founded/Ownrshp 2008
Sales 34.0MM EMP 1,200
SIC 5812 American restaurant
Mktg Mgr: Brigette O'Leary

D-U-N-S 03-066-4916
BARGAIN BARN INC
UNITED GROCERY OUTLET
2924 Lee Hwy, Athens, TN 37303-5063
Tel (423) 746-0746 Founded/Ownrshp 1974
Sales 113.6MM EMP 700
Accts Gr Rush & Company Pllc Cha
SIC 5411 5141 Grocery stores; Grocery stores, chain; Groceries, general line
Pr: Michael Tullock
*Ch Bd: L Doug Tullock
Sr Cor Off: Gary Buchanan

BARGAIN HUNT CORPORATE
See ESSEX TECHNOLOGY GROUP INC

BARGAIN WHOLESALE
See 99 CENTS ONLY STORES LLC

BARGE WAGGONER SUMNER & CANNON
See BARGE WAGGONER SUMNER AND CANNON INC

D-U-N-S 04-426-7599
BARGE WAGGONER SUMNER AND CANNON INC
BARGE WAGGONER SUMNER & CANNON
211 Commerce St Ste 600, Nashville, TN 37201-1815
Tel (615) 254-1500 Founded/Ownrshp 1955
Sales 97.7MM^E EMP 315
SIC 8711 Civil engineering
CEO: Robert B Higgins Jr
*COO: R Randolph Ferguson
*CFO: Cendy Dodd
*Chf Mktg O: Paula E Harris
Ex VP: Jason Hill
*VP: Paula Harris
Dir IT: Paul Dougherty

D-U-N-S 02-753-0310 IMP/EXP
BARGREEN-ELLINGSON INC
6626 Tacoma Mall Blvd B, Tacoma, WA 98409-9002
Tel (253) 475-9201 Founded/Ownrshp 1960
Sales 135.4MM^E EMP 250
SIC 5046 2541 Restaurant equipment & supplies; Store & office display cases & fixtures
Pr: Paul G Ellingson
VP: Eric Ellingson
*VP: Richard Ellingson
Genl Mgr: Neal Bradley
Genl Mgr: Ron Waddell
Genl Mgr: Matthew Wicks
VP Opers: Thomas Murphy
Opers Mgr: Duane Jones
Opers Mgr: Venus Steele
Sales Exec: Spence Hanson
Sales Exec: Lindsay Smith

D-U-N-S 07-994-4890
BARI HOME CORP
1215 Livingston Ave Ste 4, North Brunswick, NJ 08902-3840
Tel (973) 713-0591 Founded/Ownrshp 2014
Sales 86.0MM EMP 12
SIC 2273 Floor coverings, textile fiber
CEO: Ather Bari
Sr VP: Daniel Harris

BARING DISTRIBUTORS
See BDI INC

D-U-N-S 05-782-4294
BARINGS LLC
BABSON CAPITAL MANAGEMENT LLC
(Suby of MASSMUTUAL MORTGAGE FINANCE LLC) ★
470 Atlantic Ave Fl 9, Boston, MA 02210-2246
Tel (617) 225-3800 Founded/Ownrshp 1995
Sales 90.6MM^E EMP 151
SIC 6282 Investment counselors
CEO: Tom Finke
*Pr: Thomas Finke
*Treas: Deanne B Dupont
*V Ch Bd: Clifford Noreen
Exec: Tom Cresswell
Dir Risk M: Mike Neilsen
Assoc Dir: Shamafa Ali
Assoc Dir: Pam Barber
Assoc Dir: Faith Bigda
Assoc Dir: Shea Chris
Assoc Dir: Chris Collins
Assoc Dir: Christopher Dowd
Assoc Dir: Christina Emery
Assoc Dir: Amy Galasso
Assoc Dir: Dominic Grew
Assoc Dir: Cindy Merrill
Assoc Dir: Daniel Mick
Assoc Dir: Freddie Pereira
Assoc Dir: Justin Preftakes

D-U-N-S 00-100-8747 IMP
BARKER STEEL LLC
55 Sumner St Ste 1, Milford, MA 01757-1679
Tel (508) 473-8484 Founded/Ownrshp 2007
Sales 122.1MM^E EMP 587
SIC 3449 Bars, concrete reinforcing: fabricated steel
CFO: Russell Macmannis
VP: Paul Locore
IT Man: Joseph Sikora
Sfty Mgr: Tom Buckley
Plnt Mgr: Nathan Holland
VP Sls: Cynthia Dube

D-U-N-S 08-143-0191 IMP/EXP
BARLOWORLD HANDLING LLC
7621 Little Ave Ste 201, Charlotte, NC 28226-8366
Tel (704) 588-1300 Founded/Ownrshp 1979
Sales NA EMP 1,011
SIC 5084

D-U-N-S 62-088-4577 IMP/EXP
BARLOWORLD USA INC
(Suby of BARLOWORLD UK LIMITED)
1105 N Market St Ste 1300, Wilmington, DE 19801-1241
Tel (302) 427-2765 Founded/Ownrshp 1979
Sales 158.2MM^E EMP 2,246
SIC 5084 7699 7359 Materials handling machinery; Industrial machinery & equipment repair; Equipment rental & leasing
Pr: Alwyn P Smith
CFO: Courts Holland
VP: Andrew Bannister
VP: Eugene L Smith

BARNABAS HEALTH
See KIMBALL MEDICAL CENTER INC

D-U-N-S 07-828-7817
BARNABAS HEALTH INC
(Suby of BARNABAS RWJ HEALTH INC) ★
95 Old Short Hills Rd, West Orange, NJ 07052-1008
Tel (973) 322-4018 Founded/Ownrshp 2016
Sales 161.7MM^E EMP 106^E
SIC 8082 8099 Home health care services; Blood related health services
Sr VP: Nancy Holecek
Ex VP: Lou Lasalle
VP: Peter Angelo
Mng Dir: Dennis Wilson
Nurse Mgr: Leanne Sanabria
Dir IT: Jack Hernandez
IT Man: Kevin Sebelle
VP Opers: Michael Perdoni

D-U-N-S 08-025-6802
BARNABAS RWJ HEALTH INC
95 Old Short Hills Rd, West Orange, NJ 07052-1008
Tel (973) 322-4000 Founded/Ownrshp 2015
Sales 161.9MM^E EMP 113^E
SIC 8399 Health systems agency
Pr: Kirk Tice
Pr: Joshua M Bershad
COO: Jay Picerno
*CFO: Peter Bihuniak
CFO: Brian M Reilly
Ex VP: Michellene Davis
VP: James Karaman
VP: Kevin Kramer
VP: Barbara Mullery
VP: Ann Marie Shears
Chf Nrs Of: Lori A Colineri

D-U-N-S 06-811-9601
BARNARD COLLEGE
3009 Broadway Frnt 1, New York, NY 10027-6598
Tel (212) 854-7732 Founded/Ownrshp 1889
Sales 203.7MM EMP 650
SIC 8221

D-U-N-S 01-037-3165 IMP
BARNARD CONSTRUCTION CO INC (MT)
701 Gold Ave, Bozeman, MT 59715-2453
Tel (406) 586-1995 Founded/Ownrshp 1974
Sales 235.0MM^E EMP 400
Accts Moss-Adams Llp
SIC 1623 1629 1611 1622 Water, sewer & utility lines; Oil & gas pipeline construction; Earthmoving contractor; Dam construction; Highway & street construction; Bridge construction
CEO: Jeffery L Higgins
*Pr: Paul Franzen
*Sec: Jim Tilleman
VP: Zach Bowler
*VP: Jeff Higgins
*VP: Michael E Jenkins
*VP: Joseph P Nelson
VP: Robert Reseigh
*VP: Dan Schall
*VP: Neil W Van Amburg
Sfty Mgr: Chad Brinkerhoff

D-U-N-S 03-187-9596 IMP
■ **BARNES & NOBLE BOOKSELLERS INC**
B DALTON BOOKSELLER
(Suby of BARNES & NOBLE INC) ★
1166 Ave Of Amer 18, New York, NY 10036
Tel (212) 403-2580 Founded/Ownrshp 1992
Sales 2.0MMM^E EMP 28,000
SIC 5942 5994 5999 5735 Book stores; Magazine stand; Maps & charts; Audio tapes, prerecorded
Ch Bd: Leonard Riggio
*CEO: Stephen Riggio
*COO: Mitchell S Klipper
*VP: Mary Keating
VP: Lawrence S Zilavy
Div/Sub He: Thomas Christopher
Mktg Mgr: Laura Ross

D-U-N-S 01-211-2496 IMP
■ **BARNES & NOBLE COLLEGE BOOKSELLERS LLC**
(Suby of BARNES & NOBLE EDUCATION INC) ★
120 Mountainview Blvd A, Basking Ridge, NJ 07920-3454
Tel (908) 991-2665 Founded/Ownrshp 2015
Sales 1.7MMM^E EMP 5,300
Accts Ernst & Young Llp New York

SIC 5942 5943 5947 College book stores; School supplies; Writing supplies; Souvenirs
CEO: Max J Roberts
Pt: Michael N Rosen
**Pr:* Patrick Maloney
**Ex VP:* Bill Maloney
**VP:* Barry Brover
VP: Stephen Culver
VP: Vivian Fernandez
VP: Joel Friedman
VP: Gerard Kickul
**VP:* Lisa Malat
VP: Celeste Schwartz

D-U-N-S 07-989-1851
▲ BARNES & NOBLE EDUCATION INC
120 Mountainview Blvd A, Basking Ridge, NJ 07920-3454
Tel (908) 991-2665 *Founded/Ownrshp* 2012
Sales 1.8MMM *EMP* 5,500ᴱ
Accts Ernst & Young Llp Metropark
Tkr Sym BNED *Exch* NYS
SIC 5942 Book stores
CEO: Max J Roberts
**Ch Bd:* Michael P Huseby
COO: Patrick Maloney
CFO: Barry Brover
Treas: Thomas D Donohue
Ofcr: Lisa Malat
Ofcr: Kanuj Malhotra
Ofcr: Seema C Paul
Ex VP: William Maloney
VP: Stephen Culver
VP: Joel Friedman
VP: Philip O'Reilly
Board of Directors: Daniel A Dematteo, David G Golden, John R Ryan, Jerry Sue Thornton, David A Wilson

D-U-N-S 18-671-6668 IMP
▲ BARNES & NOBLE INC
122 5th Ave Fl 2, New York, NY 10011-5693
Tel (212) 633-3300 *Founded/Ownrshp* 1986
Sales 4.1MMM *EMP* 33,000
Tkr Sym BKS *Exch* NYS
SIC 5942 5961 5945 Book stores; Books, mail order (except book clubs); Hobby, toy & game shops
Ch Bd: Leonard Riggio
Pr: Jaime Carey
COO: Demos Parneros
CFO: Allen W Lindstorm
Treas: Thomas Donohue
Bd of Dir: Lawrence Zilavy
Ofcr: Mary Amicucci
Ex VP: Patrick Maloney
Sr VP: Mary Ellen Keating
VP: Mark Bottini
VP: David S Deason
VP: Bradley A Feuer
VP: Peter M Herpich
VP: Michael Ladd
VP: Davide Rowland
Board of Directors: George Campbell Jr, Mark D Carleton, Scott S Cowen, William Dillard II, Paul B Guenther, Patricia L Higgins

D-U-N-S 03-309-3659 IMP
■ BARNES & NOBLE PURCHASING INC
(*Suby of* BARNES & NOBLE INC) ★
122 5th Ave Fl 2, New York, NY 10011-5693
Tel (212) 633-4068 *Founded/Ownrshp* 1986
Sales 792.1MMᴱ *EMP* 200ᴱ
SIC 5192 Books
Ch Bd: Leonard Riggio
CFO: Nicholas Occhifinto
**Ex VP:* Gary King
**Ex VP:* Carl Rosendorf
**VP:* William F Duffy
**VP:* Brenda Marsh
CTO: Silvano Nino

D-U-N-S 08-927-2157
BARNES & THORNBURG LLP
11 S Meridian St Ste 1313, Indianapolis, IN 46204-3519
Tel (317) 236-1313 *Founded/Ownrshp* 1980
Sales 150.2MMᴱ *EMP* 665
SIC 8111 General practice law office
Mng Pt: Alan Levin
Pt: Bradford G Addison
Pt: Nathan A Baker
Pt: Rebecca L Ball
Pt: Bruce Donaldson
Pt: Stanley C Fickle
Pt: Addison Bradford G
Pt: David R Gillay
Pt: Abeska Timothy J
Pt: Bart A Karwath
Pt: William Moreau Jr
Pt: Robert H Reynolds
Pt: Claudia V Swhier
Mng Pt: David Angeles
Mng Pt: Randall Brown
Mng Pt: Robert T Grand
Mng Pt: Stuart C Johnson
Mng Pt: Tracy T Larsen
Mng Pt: Karen A McGee
Mng Pt: William A Nolan
Mng Pt: Mark E Rust

D-U-N-S 00-114-5481 IMP/EXP
▲ BARNES GROUP INC
123 Main St, Bristol, CT 06010-6376
Tel (860) 583-7070 *Founded/Ownrshp* 1857
Sales 1.1MMM *EMP* 4,700ᴱ
Accts Pricewaterhousecoopers Llp Ha
Tkr Sym B *Exch* NYS
SIC 3724 3495 3469 Aircraft engines & engine parts; Precision springs; Stamping metal for the trade
Pr: Patrick J Dempsey
**Ch Bd:* Thomas O Barnes
**CFO:* Christopher J Stephens Jr
**Sr VP:* Richard R Barnhart
**Sr VP:* James P Berklas Jr
**Sr VP:* Dawn N Edwards
**Sr VP:* Scott A Mayo
VP: Paul Cestari
Board of Directors: Gary G Benanav, Francis J Kramer, William J Morgan, Joanna L Sohovich

D-U-N-S 05-171-7478
BARNES HOSPITAL (INC)
Barnes Hospital Plz, Saint Louis, MO 63110
Tel (314) 362-5000 *Founded/Ownrshp* 1890
Sales 76.4MMᴱ *EMP* 5,358
SIC 8062 General medical & surgical hospitals; Hospital, medical school affiliation; Hospital, professional nursing school
Ch Bd: Charles F Knight
**Pr:* John J Finan Jr

D-U-N-S 02-487-3135
BARNES MOTOR & PARTS CO INC (NC)
NAPA AUTO PARTS
2728 Forest Hills Rd Sw, Wilson, NC 27893-4433
Tel (252) 243-2161 *Founded/Ownrshp* 1923, 1949
Sales 83.0MMᴱ *EMP* 250
Accts Anthony & Tabb Pa Wilson
SIC 5531 Automotive & home supply stores
Pr: Henry Walston
Treas: Alan Hinnant
**VP:* Robert Kirkland III
IT Man: Pat Stallings
Sales Asso: Mike Browder

D-U-N-S 94-949-2417 IMP
BARNES-JEWISH HOSPITAL
(*Suby of* BJC HEALTHCARE) ★
216 S Kingshwy Blvd 140, Saint Louis, MO 63110-1026
Tel (314) 747-3000 *Founded/Ownrshp* 2003
Sales 676.9MMᴱ *EMP* 7,500
SIC 8062 General medical & surgical hospitals
Pr: Richard J Liekweg
Pr: Mike Manno
VP: Robert Cannon
VP: Edward Carter
VP: Tim Mislan
Dir Rx: David Ritchie
Genl Mgr: Crystal Ford-Weaver
CIO: Matthew Schulte
Pr Mgr: Gail Watkins
Orthpdst: Stephanie Otis
Plas Surg: John Holds

D-U-N-S 96-552-3538
BARNES-JEWISH HOSPITAL
1 B J Hospital Plaza Dr, Saint Louis, MO 63110
Tel (314) 747-3000 *Founded/Ownrshp* 2013
Sales 1.6MMM *EMP* 27ᴱ
SIC 8062 General medical & surgical hospitals
Pr: Robert W Cannon
VP: Edward Carter
VP: Mark Krieger
Dir Rad: Colin Derdeyn
Dir Sec: Margie Brine
Prgrm Mgr: Christi Longnecker
IT Man: Robert Kennedy
Sfty Dirs: Debbie Mays
Mktg Mgr: Kay Franks
Obsttrcn: Juliana C Verticchio
Doctor: Aimee James

D-U-N-S 09-966-6497
BARNES-JEWISH ST PETERS HOSPITAL INC
BJC HEALTHCARE
(*Suby of* BARNES-JEWISH HOSPITAL) ★
10 Hospital Dr, Saint Peters, MO 63376-1659
Tel (636) 916-9000 *Founded/Ownrshp* 1988
Sales 108.5MM *EMP* 690
SIC 8062 General medical & surgical hospitals
CEO: Steven H Lipstein
Treas: Alan Brook
**Ex VP:* Richard J Liekweg
**Sr VP:* Rhonda Brandon
**Sr VP:* Michael A Dehaven
**Sr VP:* Kevin Roberts
VP: Ann Abad
VP: Jill Skyles
Exec: Cynde Huber
Dir Lab: Judy Berhle
Dir Lab: Judy Wolfe

D-U-N-S 07-195-4382
BARNES-JEWISH WEST COUNTY HOSPITAL
BJC HEALTHCARE
(*Suby of* BJC HEALTHCARE) ★
12634 Olive Blvd, Saint Louis, MO 63141-6337
Tel (314) 996-8000 *Founded/Ownrshp* 1989
Sales 107.7MM *EMP* 500
SIC 8062 General medical & surgical hospitals
Prin: Mary Mantese
COO: Lawrence Tracy
CFO: Diane Glen
Dir Inf Cn: Cathy Carroll
Dir Rad: Mike Walker
Dir Rx: Emily Martinez
Dir IT: Jennifer Arvin
Ansthlgy: Mitchell R Platin
HC Dir: Mary Jellinek

D-U-N-S 07-874-3457
■ BARNEY & BARNEY INC
LOSS AND RISK ADVISORS
(*Suby of* MARSH & MCLENNAN AGENCY LLC) ★
9171 Twne Cntre Dr 500, San Diego, CA 92122
Tel (800) 321-4696 *Founded/Ownrshp* 1970, 2014
Sales NA *EMP* 200ᴱ
SIC 6411 Property & casualty insurance agent; Life insurance agents
CEO: Paul Hering
**Pr:* Hal Dunning
CFO: Steven Berk
Bd of Dir: Christine Schindewolf
VP: Peter Epstine
Dir IT: Wayne Pages
Sls Dir: Bill Murphy
Pgrm Dir: Jim O'Connell

D-U-N-S 00-698-0783 IMP
BARNEYS INC (NY)
BARNEYS NEW YORK CORP OFFS
(*Suby of* BARNEYS NEW YORK INC) ★
575 5th Ave Fl 11, New York, NY 10017-2434
Tel (212) 450-8700 *Founded/Ownrshp* 1927
Sales 173.8MMᴱ *EMP* 1,200
SIC 5611 5621 5632 5932 5947 6794 Men's & boys' clothing stores; Ready-to-wear apparel, women's; Apparel accessories; Antiques; Gift shop; Franchises, selling or licensing
Ch Bd: Mark Lee
Creative D: Simon Doonan
Sls Dir: Tom Oconnor

BARNEYS NEW YORK CORP OFFS
See BARNEYS INC

D-U-N-S 08-245-8295 IMP
BARNEYS NEW YORK INC
575 5th Ave Fl 11, New York, NY 10017-2434
Tel (212) 450-8700 *Founded/Ownrshp* 1998
Sales 249.3MMᴱ *EMP* 1,400
SIC 5651 Unisex clothing stores
Pr: Mark Lee
CFO: Steven Feldman
Treas: Vincent Phelan
Ex VP: Kevin Hill
Ex VP: Tom Kalenderian
Ex VP: Josh Lieberman
Ex VP: David New
Ex VP: Marc H Perlowitz
Ex VP: Jennifer Sunwoo
Ex VP: Daniella Vitale
VP: Judith Bowens
VP: Dawn Brown
VP: Melissa Gallagher
VP: Josephine Geiger
VP: Lauren Kim
VP: Alfonsina Messina
VP: Rich Nasser
VP: Mark Polackov
VP: John Totolis

D-U-N-S 00-314-8285 IMP/EXP
BARNHARDT MANUFACTURING CO (NC)
NCFI
1100 Hawthorne Ln, Charlotte, NC 28205-2918
Tel (704) 376-0380 *Founded/Ownrshp* 1900, 1987
Sales 247.1MMᴱ *EMP* 520
SIC 0131 3086

D-U-N-S 18-992-9649
BARNHART CRANE AND RIGGING CO
2163 Airways Blvd, Memphis, TN 38114-5208
Tel (901) 775-3000 *Founded/Ownrshp* 1986
Sales 154.0MMᴱ *EMP* 350ᴱ
Accts Thompson Dunavant Plc Memphis
SIC 7353 4213 1796 Cranes & aerial lift equipment, rental or leasing; Trucking, except local; Machine moving & rigging
Pr: Alan Barnhart
**CFO:* Michael Honan
**Sec:* Eric Barnhart
VP: Gene Kaercher
Brnch Mgr: Jeff Bailey
Brnch Mgr: Barry Carroll
Brnch Mgr: John Clark
Brnch Mgr: Brandi Ellerbrock
Brnch Mgr: Chris Howe
Brnch Mgr: Steve Mousseau
Brnch Mgr: Rob Myers

D-U-N-S 05-450-5458 IMP/EXP
BARNHART INC
10620 Treena St Ste 300, San Diego, CA 92131-1141
Tel (858) 635-7400 *Founded/Ownrshp* 2010
Sales 162.9MMᴱ *EMP* 291
SIC 1542 8741

D-U-N-S 02-482-9988
BARNHILL CONTRACTING CO INC
800 Tiffany Blvd Ste 200, Rocky Mount, NC 27804-1807
Tel (252) 823-1021 *Founded/Ownrshp* 1949
Sales 500.5MMᴱ *EMP* 1,150
SIC 1771 1541 Blacktop (asphalt) work; Industrial buildings, new construction
Pr: Robert E Barnhill Jr III
CFO: William F Davis
Ex VP: William Lee Cooper
Sr VP: J Allen Barnhill
VP: Mark Collins
VP: Scott Fisher
VP: Carl L Groescheen
VP: Jimmie Highes Jr
VP: Brew M Johensoen
VP: Kermit L Moaser
VP: James Partington IV
VP: Chris Stroud
VP: Carey M Swann III

BARNIES COFFEE & TEA CO
See BARNIES COFFEE & TEA CO INC

D-U-N-S 03-967-7760
BARNIES COFFEE & TEA CO INC
BARNIES COFFEE & TEA CO
29 S Orange Ave, Orlando, FL 32801-2605
Tel (407) 854-6600 *Founded/Ownrshp* 2001
Sales 94.5MMᴱ *EMP* 800
SIC 5499 5812 Coffee; Tea; Carry-out only (except pizza) restaurant
Pr: Jonathan Smiga
**Ch Bd:* Neil Leach
**CFO:* Tricia Relvini
**Sr VP:* Robert Kalafut
**VP:* Bob Kalafut
**VP:* Glorian Leach
**VP:* Scott Uguccioni
**VP:* Anne Valdez
**VP:* Sonya Wahl
IT Man: Kevin Keller
IT Man: Fred Weber

D-U-N-S 11-744-7177 IMP
BARNSCO INC
(*Suby of* GEORGECO INC) ★
2609 Willowbrook Rd, Dallas, TX 75220-4422
Tel (214) 352-9091 *Founded/Ownrshp* 1984
Sales 116.3MMᴱ *EMP* 109
SIC 5032 Brick, stone & related material
Pr: Jeffrey L Barnes
**VP:* Gary A Barnes
Dir IT: Marcus Miller

D-U-N-S 84-792-2432
BARNWELL COUNTY NURSING HOME
31 Wren St, Barnwell, SC 29812-1528
Tel (803) 259-5547 *Founded/Ownrshp* 1969
Sales 232.0MMᴱ *EMP* 45
SIC 8051 8052 Skilled nursing care facilities; Intermediate care facilities
COO: Todd Bedenbaugh

D-U-N-S 19-143-2090
BARONA RESORT & CASINO
1932 Wildcat Canyon Rd, Lakeside, CA 92040-1553
Tel (619) 443-2300 *Founded/Ownrshp* 2005
Sales 118.6MMᴱ *EMP* 3,500
SIC 7011 Resort hotel; Casino hotel
Sr VP: Dean Allen
Ex VP: Nick Dillon
Ex VP: Troy Simpson
Sr VP: Linda Jordan
Sr VP: Dana Sass
Exec: Jeffty Connelly
Exec: Ryan Hall
Exec: Zac Moore
Exec: Vinh Quach
Exec: Eduardo Torres
Ex Dir: Thomas Dullien

D-U-N-S 00-167-2237 IMP
BARR & BARR INC (NY)
460 W 34th St Fl 10, New York, NY 10001-2320
Tel (212) 563-2330 *Founded/Ownrshp* 1927
Sales 200.8MMᴱ *EMP* 300
SIC 1542 1541 Hospital construction; School building construction; Industrial buildings & warehouses
CEO: Keith W Stanisce
**Pr:* Donald M Barr
**Treas:* Thomas D Barr
Ex VP: Keith Stanisce
VP: William Aquadro
**VP:* Stephen L Killian
**VP:* Thomas J Lepage
VP: Thomas Lepage
VP: Jesse Schultz
VP: Angelo Tempesta
Exec: Anthony Cucio
**Exec:* John A Decina
**Exec:* Glenn W Kiefer
Dir Bus: Jim Crawford

D-U-N-S 04-724-7945
BARR ENGINEERING CO
4300 Marketpointe Dr # 200, Minneapolis, MN 55435-5423
Tel (952) 832-2600 *Founded/Ownrshp* 1961
Sales 194.9MMᴱ *EMP* 800
SIC 8711

D-U-N-S 05-630-6780 IMP/EXP
BARR LABORATORIES INC
TEVA
(*Suby of* TEVA PHARMACEUTICAL INDUSTRIES LIMITED)
1090 Horsham Rd, North Wales, PA 19454-1505
Tel (215) 591-3000 *Founded/Ownrshp* 2008
Sales 1.6MMMᴱ *EMP* 8,900
SIC 2834 Pharmaceutical preparations; Proprietary drug products
CEO: William Marth
Pr: Mike Bogda
CEO: Christines Mundkur
**CFO:* William T McKee
Ex VP: Timothy Sawyer
**Sr VP:* Sigurd Kirk
VP: Darren Alkins
VP: Ken Domagalski
**VP:* Frederick J Killion
VP: Charlene Good Polino
VP: Jamie Warner
Exec: Nancy Austin
Exec: Jane Luebbe
Assoc Dir: James Chovan
Assoc Dir: Michael Karukin
Assoc Dir: Jennifer King
Assoc Dir: Michelle Merkelt
Assoc Dir: Denise Wayne

D-U-N-S 14-519-8490
▲ BARRACUDA NETWORKS INC
3175 Winchester Blvd, Campbell, CA 95008-6557
Tel (408) 342-5400 *Founded/Ownrshp* 2003
Sales 320.1MM *EMP* 1,491
Tkr Sym CUDA *Exch* NYS
SIC 7372 7373 Prepackaged software; Computer integrated systems design
Pr: William D Jenkins Jr
CFO: Dustin Driggs
**Chf Mktg O:* Michael D Perone
**Ex VP:* Zachary S Levow
Sr VP: Diane C Honda
Sr VP: Michael D Hughes
Sr VP: Hatem Naguib
Sr VP: Chris Ross
VP: James Forbes-May
Genl Mgr: Stephen Pao
Board of Directors: Jeffry T Allen, James J Goetz, David R Golob, John H Kispert, Gordon L Stitt

D-U-N-S 02-504-5972 IMP/EXP
BARREL ACCESSORIES AND SUPPLY CO INC
BASCO UNIVERSITY PARK WHSE
2595 Palmer Ave, University Park, IL 60484-3115
Tel (708) 534-0900 *Founded/Ownrshp* 1991
Sales 95.1MMᴱ *EMP* 62
SIC 5085 5084 Industrial supplies; Barrels, new or reconditioned; Pails, metal; Plastic bottles; Industrial machinery & equipment
Pr: Richard Rudy
CFO: Renee Weiss
Exec: Trish Carlson
Dir IT: Donna Tickman
IT Man: Jim Dinsmore
Prd Mgr: Joseph Joyce
Mktg Dir: Clifford Kowalski

BARREL O' FUN
See BARREL OFUN SNACK FOODS CO LLC

D-U-N-S 19-456-8044 IMP/EXP
BARREL OFUN SNACK FOODS CO LLC
BARREL O' FUN
(*Suby of* SHEARERS FOODS LLC) ★
400 Lakeside Dr, Perham, MN 56573-2202
Tel (218) 346-7000 *Founded/Ownrshp* 2015
Sales 191.7MM[E] *EMP* 600
SIC 2096 Potato chips & other potato-based snacks; Popcorn, already popped (except candy covered); Corn chips & other corn-based snacks
CEO: Christopher Fraleigh
Ex Dir: Gary Ebeling
Sls Mgr: Randy Johnson

D-U-N-S 12-521-7745
BARREN RIVER DEVELOPMENT COUNCIL INC
177 Graham Ave, Bowling Green, KY 42101-9175
Tel (270) 781-2381 *Founded/Ownrshp* 1974
Sales 92.8M *EMP* 1,950
Accts Hilliare And Fisher Cpa
SIC 8748 Urban planning & consulting services
Ofcr: Sharon Woods
Ex Dir: Gene Becker

D-U-N-S 08-745-9558
▲ BARRETT BUSINESS SERVICES INC
BBSI
8100 Ne Parkway Dr # 200, Vancouver, WA 98662-6735
Tel (360) 828-0700 *Founded/Ownrshp* 1965
Sales 740.8MM *EMP* 103,250[E]
Tkr Sym BBSI *Exch* NGS
SIC 7361 8742 Employment agencies; Human resource consulting services
Pr: Michael L Elich
**Ch Bd:* Anthony Meeker
COO: Gerald R Blotz
COO: Gregory R Vaughn
CFO: Gary Kramer
Board of Directors: Thomas J Carley, Tom Cusick, James B Hicks, Roger L Johnson, Jon L Justesen

D-U-N-S 01-948-6679 IMP
BARRETT DISTRIBUTION CENTERS INC
15 Freedom Way, Franklin, MA 02038-2586
Tel (508) 528-1747 *Founded/Ownrshp* 1984
Sales 98.4MM[E] *EMP* 225
SIC 4225 General warehousing & storage
Pr: Arthur F Barrett
COO: Timothy J Barrett
Sr VP: Lewis Frazer
Sr VP: Scott Hothem
Sr VP: Bob Willert
VP: Mike O'Donnell
Opers Mgr: George Bell
Opers Mgr: Tom Stad

D-U-N-S 55-758-1993
BARRETT INDUSTRIES CORP
(*Suby of* COLAS INC) ★
3 Becker Farm Rd Ste 307, Roseland, NJ 07068-1726
Tel (973) 533-1001 *Founded/Ownrshp* 2003
Sales 288.1MM[E] *EMP* 250
SIC 1611 2951 4213 1799 1794 Highway & street paving contractor; Road materials, bituminous (not from refineries); Trucking, except local; Building site preparation; Excavation work
VP: Zach Green
**Pr:* Georges Ausseil
**CFO:* Fred Shelton
Sr VP: Jack Schweber
IT Man: Robert Mikalouskas

D-U-N-S 09-926-8468 IMP/EXP
BARRETT PAVING MATERIALS INC
(*Suby of* BARRETT INDUSTRIES CORP) ★
3 Becker Farm Rd Ste 307, Roseland, NJ 07068-1726
Tel (973) 533-1001 *Founded/Ownrshp* 1989
Sales 152.6MM[E] *EMP* 250
Accts Pricewaterhousecoopers Llp
SIC 1611 2951 4213 1799 1794 Highway & street paving contractor; Road materials, bituminous (not from refineries); Trucking, except local; Building site preparation; Excavation work
Pr: Robert Doucet
CFO: Fred Shelton
VP: Robert Pomton
Genl Mgr: Michael Abbondandolo
Plnt Mgr: Mark Hudson
Prd Mgr: Michael Szymborski

D-U-N-S 11-294-8252
BARRETT SOTHEBYS INTERNATIONAL REALTY
33 Walden St, Concord, MA 01742-2504
Tel (978) 369-6453 *Founded/Ownrshp* 2007
Sales 500.0MM *EMP* 50
SIC 6531 Real estate brokers & agents
Pr: Laurie Cadigan

BARRETTE OUTDOOR LIVING
See US FENCE INC

D-U-N-S 03-728-7091 IMP/EXP
BARRETTE OUTDOOR LIVING INC
(*Suby of* ENTREPRISES BARRETTE LTEE, LES)
7830 Freeway Cir, Middleburg Heights, OH 44130-6307
Tel (440) 891-0790 *Founded/Ownrshp* 1999
Sales 391.6MM[E] *EMP* 1,050[E]
SIC 3315 Fence gates posts & fittings: steel
Pr: Jean Desautels
**CFO:* Luc Dufour
**Prin:* Neil W Gurney
**Prin:* James M Moore
Genl Mgr: Peter Fickinger
IT Man: Shannon Byrd
IT Man: Bob Howe
Mtls Mgr: Christine McPike
Opers Mgr: Monica Summers
Plnt Mgr: Danny West
Ql Cn Mgr: Marcella Horner

D-U-N-S 09-161-7019
BARRICK ENTERPRISES INC
BARRICK OIL CO
4338 Delemere Blvd, Royal Oak, MI 48073-1807
Tel (248) 549-3737 *Founded/Ownrshp* 1977
Sales 552.8MM *EMP* 35
Accts Doeren Mayhew Troy Michigan
SIC 5541 Filling stations, gasoline
Pr: Robert L Barrick

D-U-N-S 02-091-7170
BARRICK GOLD OF NORTH AMERICA INC
BARRICK MANAGEMENT
(*Suby of* BARRICK GOLD CORPORATION)
460 W 50 N Ste 500, Salt Lake City, UT 84101-1025
Tel (416) 861-9911 *Founded/Ownrshp* 1984
Sales 111.7MM[E] *EMP* 550
SIC 8741 1041 Business management; Gold ores mining
Pr: Richie Haddock
**Ch Bd:* Peter Munk
**CEO:* Jamie C Sokalsky
**CFO:* Ammar Al-Joundi
**Treas:* Deni Nicoski
**Ex VP:* Kelvin Dushnisky
**Ex VP:* Sybil Veenman
**Sr VP:* Rob Krcmarov
**Sr VP:* Rick McCreary
**Sr VP:* Ivan Mullany
**Sr VP:* Don Ritz
VP: Craig Ross

D-U-N-S 00-222-5618 IMP
BARRICK GOLDSTRIKE MINES INC
(*Suby of* BARRICK GOLD CORPORATION)
905 W Main St, Elko, NV 89801-2727
Tel (775) 748-1001 *Founded/Ownrshp* 1973
Sales 808.1MM[E] *EMP* 1,650[E]
SIC 1041 Gold ores
CEO: Randall Oliphant
**CFO:* Jamie Solkowski
**VP:* Steve Lang
Dir IT: James Meek
Dir IT: Jim Palmer

BARRICK MANAGEMENT
See BARRICK GOLD OF NORTH AMERICA INC

BARRICK OIL CO
See BARRICK ENTERPRISES INC

D-U-N-S 06-124-8944
BARRIERE CONSTRUCTION CO LLC
1 Galleria Blvd Ste 1650, Metairie, LA 70001-7595
Tel (504) 581-7283 *Founded/Ownrshp* 1965
Sales 105.4MM[E] *EMP* 304[E]
SIC 1611 1629

D-U-N-S 08-293-8077
BARRINGTON 220 COMMUNITY UNIT SCHOOL DISTRICT
310 James St, Barrington, IL 60010-3329
Tel (847) 381-6300 *Founded/Ownrshp* 1972
Sales 158.9MM *EMP* 1,115
Accts Baker Tilly Oak Brook Il
SIC 8211 Public elementary & secondary schools
**CFO:* Gary Firsch
CFO: Tim Neubauer
Dir Sec: Joseph Malloy
Genl Mgr: Jon Sander
Netwrk Mgr: Russ V Mey
Mktg Dir: Ana Ruiz
Psych: Lynn M Cobb
Psych: Brian Turcotte

D-U-N-S 96-448-0826
■ BARRINGTON BANK & TRUST CO NATIONAL ASSOCIATION
(*Suby of* WINTRUST FINANCIAL CORP) ★
201 S Hough St, Barrington, IL 60010-4321
Tel (847) 842-4500 *Founded/Ownrshp* 1996
Sales NA *EMP* 285[E]
SIC 6022 State commercial banks
Pr: W Bradley Stetson
**Pr:* Jon Stickney
Ofcr: Steve Callahan
Ofcr: Sophia Delgado
Ofcr: Kosa Pasajlic
VP: Norma Ahlstrand
VP: Russell Botwin
VP: Paul Ebert
VP: Burke Groom
VP: Susan Krcik
VP: Patricia Mitchell
VP: Christine Sherman

D-U-N-S 80-741-3435
BARRINGTON BROADCASTING LLC
(*Suby of* PILOT GROUP LP) ★
500 W Higgins Rd Ste 880, Hoffman Estates, IL 60195
Tel (847) 884-1877 *Founded/Ownrshp* 2003
Sales 120.0MM[E] *EMP* 738
SIC 4833 Television broadcasting stations
CEO: K James Yager

D-U-N-S 05-801-9352
BARRINGTON VENTURE HOLDING CO LLC (IL)
GARLANDS OF BARRINGTON, THE
6000 Garlands Ln Ste 120, Barrington, IL 60010-6029
Tel (847) 756-3000 *Founded/Ownrshp* 1996
Sales 118.9MM[E] *EMP* 200
SIC 6552 Subdividers & developers
**Pr:* Bill Brown
**VP:* Ed Gansz
VP: Kurt R Wessel
Exec: Barbara Smolenski
Admn Mgr: Joan Kerkla

D-U-N-S 18-388-4121
BARROW COUNTY BOARD OF EDUCATION
179 W Athens St, Winder, GA 30680-1779
Tel (770) 867-4527 *Founded/Ownrshp* 1980
Sales 144.3MM[E] *EMP* 2,000
Accts Russell W Hinton Cpa Cgfm
SIC 8211 School board
Ch Bd: Mark Still
Netwrk Mgr: John Stclair
Psych: Heather Lundy

D-U-N-S 07-937-4373
BARROW COUNTY SCHOOL SYSTEM
179 W Athens St, Winder, GA 30680-1779
Tel (770) 867-4527 *Founded/Ownrshp* 2014
Sales 70.7MM[E] *EMP* 1,727[E]
SIC 8211 Public elementary & secondary schools
Ex Dir: Jan Masingill
Genl Mgr: Chris Griner
MIS Dir: Jamie Gordon
Pr Dir: Kenneth Greene
Teacher Pr: Tasha Grisham

D-U-N-S 85-930-7501 IMP/EXP
BARRY CALLEBAUT USA LLC
(*Suby of* BARRY CALLEBAUT AG)
600 W Chicago Ave Ste 860, Chicago, IL 60654-2530
Tel (312) 496-7491 *Founded/Ownrshp* 2003
Sales 618.4MM *EMP* 2,000
SIC 2066 8741 Chocolate; Administrative management
Pr: David S Johnson
CFO: Ben Deschryver
CFO: Yvan Dorier
**CFO:* James Hagedorn
**VP:* James G Hagedorn
VP: Eric Schmoyer
Dir Risk M: Jonathan Osborn
Dir Lab: Luc Rooms
Genl Mgr: Willy Geeraerts
Genl Mgr: Jesus Valencia
IT Man: Richard Tang

D-U-N-S 04-603-3999
BARRY UNIVERSITY INC (FL)
11300 Ne 2nd Ave, Miami Shores, FL 33161-6695
Tel (305) 899-3050 *Founded/Ownrshp* 1940
Sales 215.6MM *EMP* 1,407
Accts Capin Crouse Llp Lawrencevill
SIC 8221 University
Pr: Sister Linda Bevilacqua
Pr: Traci Simpson
Treas: Beverly Coulter
**Treas:* Bruce D Edwards
Trst: Mary A Culfield
Trst: Susan B Domrowsky
Trst: Albert E Dotson
Trst: Nadine Foley
Trst: Dan Paul
Trst: Rosa M Pena
Trst: Donald S Roenberg
VP: Jennifer Boyd-Pugh
**VP:* Nicole Diaz
VP: Marge Macivor
**VP:* Linda Petersen
**Exec:* Susan Rosenthal

D-U-N-S 00-628-8120 IMP/EXP
BARRY-WEHMILLER COMPANIES INC
(*Suby of* BARRY-WEHMILLER GROUP INC) ★
8020 Forsyth Blvd, Saint Louis, MO 63105-1707
Tel (314) 862-8000 *Founded/Ownrshp* 1989
Sales 1.1MMM[E] *EMP* 2,420
SIC 3565 3535 3554 8711

D-U-N-S 55-677-6755 IMP/EXP
BARRY-WEHMILLER CONTAINER SYSTEMS INC
BW CONTAINER SYSTEMS
(*Suby of* BARRY-WEHMILLER COMPANIES INC) ★
1305 Lakeview Dr, Romeoville, IL 60446-3900
Tel (630) 759-6800 *Founded/Ownrshp* 1991
Sales 137.7MM[E] *EMP* 450
Accts Ernst & Young Llp St Louis
SIC 3535 Conveyors & conveying equipment
CEO: Pete Carlson
**Pr:* Phillip G Ostapowicz
**Ch:* Robert H Chapman
**VP:* David M Gianini
**VP:* James W Lawson
VP: Carlson Pete
Dir IT: Dave Eash
VP Sls: Neal McConnellogue
Mktg Dir: Lee Dearing

D-U-N-S 61-300-9687 IMP/EXP
BARRY-WEHMILLER GROUP INC
8020 Forsyth Blvd, Saint Louis, MO 63105-1707
Tel (314) 862-8000 *Founded/Ownrshp* 1989
Sales 1.7MMM[E] *EMP* 4,500
Accts Ernst & Young Llp St Louis M
SIC 3565 3535 3554 8711 Bottle washing & sterilizing machines; Bottling machinery: filling, capping, labeling; Canning machinery, food; Conveyors & conveying equipment; Paper industries machinery; Engineering services
CEO: Robert H Chapman
**CFO:* James W Lawson
**Treas:* Mike Zaccarrallo
**VP:* Gregory L Coonrod
VP: Jim Webb
Opers Mgr: Eddie Mun
Board of Directors: Marjorie E Abernathy, Richard F Ford, Brian W Hotarek, Robert J Lanigan, Warren M Shapleigh, Louis F Umsted, William F Ward, W M Windsor

D-U-N-S 12-672-3753 IMP/EXP
BARRY-WEHMILLER PAPERSYSTEMS INC
BW PAPERSYSTEMS
(*Suby of* BARRY-WEHMILLER COMPANIES INC) ★
1300 N Airport Rd, Phillips, WI 54555-1527
Tel (314) 862-8000 *Founded/Ownrshp* 2002
Sales 240.2MM[E] *EMP* 875
Accts Ernst & Young Llp St Louis M
SIC 3554 Paper industries machinery; Corrugating machines, paper
CEO: Robert H Chapman
**Pr:* Timothy Sullivan
**CFO:* James W Lawson
**Treas:* Michael D Zaccarello
**VP:* Gregory L Coonrod
**VP:* David Gianini
**VP:* William Stabler
VP: William Stotler
Exec: Sean Guzinski
VP Opers: John Walter
Plnt Mgr: Jay Deets

BART
See SAN FRANCISCO BAY AREA RAPID TRANSIT DISTRICT

D-U-N-S 03-877-3644
BARTECH GROUP INC
(*Suby of* IMPELLAM GROUP PLC)
27777 Franklin Rd Ste 600, Southfield, MI 48034-8282
Tel (201) 970-0605 *Founded/Ownrshp* 2015
Sales 295.4MM[E] *EMP* 2,500
SIC 7363 Temporary help service; Engineering help service; Office help supply service; Medical help service
CEO: David W Barfield
**CFO:* James Hanrahan
Sr VP: Brian Salkowski
VP: Bartech Dacey
VP: Kevin Dacey
VP: Lou Giampicclo
VP: Karen Gonzalez
VP: Jenifer Kihm
VP: Mark Sawicki
VP: William Sebra
VP: Gordy Steele
VP Bus Dev: Brian Soderholm
Exec: Wilmer Gonzalez
Exec: Connie Proctor

D-U-N-S 00-794-2543 IMP
BARTELL DRUG CO (WA)
BARTELL DRUGS
4025 Delridge Way Sw # 400, Seattle, WA 98106-1273
Tel (206) 763-2626 *Founded/Ownrshp* 1890
Sales 426.6MM[E] *EMP* 1,600
SIC 5912 Drug stores
Ch Bd: George D Bartell
**Pr:* Brian Unmacht
VP: Steve Nash
Store Mgr: Heidi Heath
Store Mgr: Kathy Porter
Site Mgr: Alfred Young
Pharmcst: Alice Chong

BARTELL DRUGS
See BARTELL DRUG CO

BARTELS FARMS
See BARTELS PACKING INC

D-U-N-S 06-695-8855
BARTELS PACKING INC
BARTELS FARMS
706 Oscar St, Eugene, OR 97402-5322
Tel (541) 344-4177 *Founded/Ownrshp* 1988
Sales 97.2MM *EMP* 161
SIC 2011 Meat packing plants
Pr: Christopher J Bartels
**VP:* Stephen Nee

BARTHCO INTERNATIONAL, INC.
See GEODIS USA INC

D-U-N-S 07-206-7846
BARTHOLOMEW CONSOLIDATED SCHOOL FOUNDATION INC
EDUCATION SERVICE CENTERS RISK
1200 Central Ave, Columbus, IN 47201-6001
Tel (812) 376-4234 *Founded/Ownrshp* 1955
Sales 146.2M *EMP* 1,400
Accts Blue & Co Llc Columbus In
SIC 8399 Fund raising organization, non-fee basis
Pr: Marsha Van Nahmen
**Treas:* Nancy Coons
**Treas:* Jonas Howell
**Treas:* Dr William Riley
**VP:* Jim Weeter

D-U-N-S 00-696-5370 IMP/EXP
BARTLETT AGRI ENTERPRISES INC (MO)
BARTLETT AND COMPANY
4900 Main St Ste 1200, Kansas City, MO 64112-2807
Tel (816) 753-6300 *Founded/Ownrshp* 1907
Sales 600.1MM[E] *EMP* 720
SIC 5153 5154 2041 Grains; Cattle; Flour
Ch Bd: James B Hebenstreit
Pr: William J Fellows
CFO: Charlie Deis
CFO: Michael J Koeppen
Software D: Sara Lienau
Sfty Mgr: Brian T Grimm
Opers Mgr: Dustin Bevard
Opers Mgr: Jeremy White
Board of Directors: Marilyn Hebenstreit

BARTLETT AND COMPANY
See BARTLETT AGRI ENTERPRISES INC

D-U-N-S 04-975-1043
BARTLETT COCKE GENERAL CONTRACTORS LLC
BARTLETT COCKE GENERAL CONTRS
8706 Lockway St, San Antonio, TX 78217-4837
Tel (210) 655-1031 *Founded/Ownrshp* 1959
Sales 205.3MM[E] *EMP* 300
SIC 1542

BARTLETT COCKE GENERAL CONTRS
See BARTLETT COCKE GENERAL CONTRACTORS LLC

D-U-N-S 62-422-3442
BARTLETT DAIRY INC
9004 161st St Ste 609, Jamaica, NY 11432-6103
Tel (718) 658-2299 *Founded/Ownrshp* 1990
Sales 137.0MM[E] *EMP* 171[E]
SIC 5143 5141 Dairy products, except dried or canned; Milk; Groceries, general line
Pr: Thomas A Malave
Exec: Julianne Rode
Genl Mgr: Michael Becht
Dir IT: Josh Kanis
Trfc Dir: Sean Bradley
Mktg Mgr: Michael Malave

D-U-N-S 80-202-9400
BARTLETT HOLDINGS INC
BHI ENERGY
97 Libbey Industrial Pkwy # 400, Weymouth, MA 02189-3110
Tel (800) 225-0385 *Founded/Ownrshp* 2003

Sales 93.3MM^E EMP 7,000^E
SIC 1311 Crude petroleum & natural gas
Pr: Ali A Azad
Pr: Chris Messier
COO: Jimmy B Morgan
Ex VP: Bob Beckman
Sr VP: Steven C Smith
VP: Christopher Wend
Tech Mgr: Fred Campbell
Mktg Mgr: Lauren Buckman

D-U-N-S 03-834-3075 IMP
BARTLETT NUCLEAR INC
97 Libbey Industrial Pkwy # 400, East Weymouth, MA 02189-3110
Tel (508) 746-6464 Founded/Ownrshp 1979
Sales 150.0MM^E EMP 2,500
SIC 7389 8734

BARTLETT TREE EXPERTS
See F A BARTLETT TREE EXPERT CO

D-U-N-S 00-281-3475 IMP
BARTON BRESCOME INC (CT)
(Suby of QUAKER EQUITIES LTD) ★
69 Defco Park Rd, North Haven, CT 06473-1129
Tel (203) 239-4901 Founded/Ownrshp 1936
Sales 231.9MM^E EMP 320
SIC 5182 5181 Liquor; Wine; Beer & ale
CEO: Gennaro Sepe
*COO: Kevin Kranzler
CFO: Mark Messier
*Ex VP: Robert A Sussler
Rgnl Mgr: Rachel Torre
MIS Dir: Steve Lentz
Dir IT: Nate Flynn
Opers Mgr: Ron Devine
Mktg Dir: Dan Miller
Mktg Mgr: Glenn Ackerman
Manager: Gary Buckman

D-U-N-S 07-377-9019
BARTON HEALTHCARE SYSTEM (CA)
2170 South Ave, South Lake Tahoe, CA 96150-7026
Tel (530) 541-3420 Founded/Ownrshp 1960
Sales 162.4MM EMP 850
Accts Moss Adams Llp San Francisco
SIC 8062 General medical & surgical hospitals
CEO: John Williams
*CFO: Dick Derby
Exec: Gary F Willen
Dir Bus: Barry Keil
DP Dir: Michelle Feeney
IT Man: Brian Laforce
Sfty Dirs: Jeff Long
Plnt Mgr: Richard Belli
Nutrtnst: Becky Fry
Doctor: Matthew Barulich
Doctor: Jeffrey V Behar

D-U-N-S 05-498-5555
BARTON HOSPITAL
2170 South Ave, South Lake Tahoe, CA 96150-7026
Tel (530) 543-5685 Founded/Ownrshp 2014
Sales 80.4M^E EMP 1,200
SIC 8062 General medical & surgical hospitals
CEO: Clint Purvance
*VP: Darcy Wallace

BARTON INTERNATIONAL
See BARTON MINES CO LLC

D-U-N-S 05-749-6135 IMP/EXP
BARTON LEASING INC
BARTON SUPPLY
14800 E Moncrieff Pl, Aurora, CO 80011-1211
Tel (303) 576-2200 Founded/Ownrshp 1998
Sales 149.8MM^E EMP 180
SIC 5032 Concrete & cinder building products; Concrete building products
CEO: Steve Swinney
*VP: Don Barton
*VP: E S Barton
*VP: Joe Barton
VP: Mark Stubbert
Sls Mgr: Cody Brooks
Sls Mgr: Dan Smith

D-U-N-S 00-653-6569
BARTON MALOW CO (MI)
(Suby of BARTON MALOW ENTERPRISES INC) ★
26500 American Dr, Southfield, MI 48034-2252
Tel (248) 436-5000 Founded/Ownrshp 1924, 1986
Sales 1.7MMM EMP 1,600
Accts Grant Thornton Llp Southfield
SIC 8741 Construction management
Pr: Ryan Maibach
COO: Therese Pandi
COO: Lester Snyder
*Ch: Ben C Maibach III
VP: Jeff Baxa
VP: Joe Benvenuto
VP: Jennifer U Brown
VP: Rod Creach
VP: Don Davis
VP: Blair Engle
VP: Alex Ivanikiw
VP: Todd Ketola
VP: Dan Kovoch
VP: Rick Leven
VP: Glenn Little
VP: Len Moser
VP: Harvey Oliva
VP: Tom Porter
VP: Michael Stobak
VP: Ron Torbert
VP: Ronald Torbert

D-U-N-S 14-423-6775
BARTON MALOW ENTERPRISES INC
26500 American Dr, Southfield, MI 48034-2252
Tel (248) 436-5000 Founded/Ownrshp 1986
Sales 1.7MMM EMP 1,815^E
Accts Grant Thornton Llp Southfield
SIC 8741 1542 1541 Construction management; Hospital construction; Commercial & office building, new construction; School building construction; Institutional building construction; Industrial buildings & warehouses; Factory construction; Truck & automobile assembly plant construction; Industrial buildings, new construction
Pr: Benjamin C Maibach III
CFO: Michael F Dishaw
Ex VP: Douglas L Maibach
VP: Ronald J Torbert
Mktg Dir: Jordan Garren

D-U-N-S 11-028-2936
BARTON MEMORIAL HOSPITAL
2170 South Ave, South Lake Tahoe, CA 96150-7008
Tel (530) 541-3420 Founded/Ownrshp 1980
Sales 114.2MM EMP 554^E
SIC 8062 8051 General medical & surgical hospitals; Skilled nursing care facilities
Pr: Clint Purvance
*CFO: Dick Derby
*Chf Mktg O: Rhonda Sneeringer
*VP: Sue Fairley
Chf Nrs Of: Mary Bittner
MIS Dir: Jason Roberts
Pr Dir: Monica Scuito
Ansthlgy: Jim Stansbury
Cert Phar: John Ellis
Cert Phar: Michelle Murphy
Snr Mgr: Holly Kenyon
Board of Directors: Keith Swanson MD, Pat Baghdikian MD, Jeff Tillman, Mike Bradford, John Cefalu, Abby Killebrew, Kirk Ledbetter, Rhonda McFarlane, Terrence Orr MD, Chuck Scharer, Dena Schwarte

D-U-N-S 00-699-3331 IMP/EXP
BARTON MINES CO LLC
BARTON INTERNATIONAL
6 Warren St, Glens Falls, NY 12801-4531
Tel (518) 798-5462 Founded/Ownrshp 1996
Sales 166.4MM^E EMP 200
SIC 1499 3291 5085 Garnet mining; Coated abrasive products; Abrasives
Ch Bd: Charles Bracken Jr
Pr: William Flint
CFO: Barton Mines
Exec: Melissa Smith
CTO: Charles R Barton
IT Man: John Coulter
Sls&Mrk Ex: John Swertner

BARTON SAND & GRAVEL
See TILLER CORP

D-U-N-S 00-530-6717
BARTON SOLVENTS INC (IA)
1920 Ne 46th Ave, Des Moines, IA 50313-2656
Tel (515) 265-7998 Founded/Ownrshp 1938
Sales 138.7MM^E EMP 178
SIC 5169 Chemicals & allied products
Pr: David M Casten
*COO: Douglas E Casten
*Treas: D K Smith
Ex VP: Edward Walsh
VP: Dave Richards
*VP: E J Walsh
Opers Mgr: A J Stone
Sales Exec: Chris Gander

BARTON SUPPLY
See BARTON LEASING INC

BARTON'S
See E C BARTON & CO

D-U-N-S 07-594-0957
BARTOW COUNTY BOARD OF EDUCATION
65 Gilreath Rd Nw, Cartersville, GA 30121-5016
Tel (770) 606-5800 Founded/Ownrshp 1920
Sales 75.8MM^E EMP 1,891
Accts Mauldin & Jenkins Cpa Llc At
SIC 8211 School board
Ch: Anna Sullivan
*V Ch: John Howard

D-U-N-S 07-979-8978
BARTOW COUNTY SCHOOL SYSTEM
65 Gilreath Rd Nw, Cartersville, GA 30121-5016
Tel (770) 606-5800 Founded/Ownrshp 2015
Sales 35.8MM^E EMP 1,810^E
SIC 8211 Public elementary & secondary schools
Dir Sec: Dan Knowles
Teacher Pr: Macy Defnall

D-U-N-S 12-907-2125 IMP/EXP
BASALITE CONCRETE PRODUCTS LLC
(Suby of PACIFIC COAST BUILDING PRODUCTS INC) ★
605 Industrial Way, Dixon, CA 95620-9779
Tel (707) 678-1901 Founded/Ownrshp 1979
Sales 175.7MM^E EMP 650
Accts Boden Klein & Sneesby Rosevil
SIC 3272 Concrete products
Pr: Scott Weber
*CFO: Dallas Barrett
*Bd of Dir: Richard Blickensderfer
*Bd of Dir: Alfred Mueller
*Bd of Dir: Fredrick Nelson
VP Mfg: Ronald Mulligan
Opers Mgr: Amanda Hall
Ql Cn Mgr: Traci Rodriguez

D-U-N-S 96-327-0657
BASCIANI FOODS INC
8876 Gap Newport Pike, Avondale, PA 19311-9749
Tel (610) 268-3610 Founded/Ownrshp 1996
Sales 186.6MM^E EMP 200^E
SIC 5148 Vegetables, fresh
Pr: Mario J Basciani
*Sec: Michael Basciani
*VP: Rich Basciani
DP Exec: Joann Regester
Opers Mgr: Greg Reynolds

BASCO
See AMERICAN PRECISION INDUSTRIES INC

BASCO UNIVERSITY PARK WHSE
See BARREL ACCESSORIES AND SUPPLY CO INC

D-U-N-S 08-089-7457 IMP
BASEBALL CLUB OF SEATTLE LLLP
SEATTLE MARINERS BASEBALL CLUB
1250 1st Ave S, Seattle, WA 98134-1216
Tel (206) 346-4000 Founded/Ownrshp 1992
Sales 113.6MM^E EMP 1,800^E
SIC 7941 Baseball club, professional & semi-professional
Pt: Howard Lincoln
Pt: Charles Armstrong
Pt: Bob Aylward
Pt: Kevin Mather
Ex VP: Jeff Zduriencik
CTO: Witherspoo Larry
IT Man: Oliver Roy
Software D: Shelley Separovich
VP Sls: Frances Traisman
Mktg Mgr: Camden Finney
Genl Couns: Melissa Mathews

D-U-N-S 82-906-7169
BASELINEAGENT INC
3960 Howard Hughes Pkwy # 500, Las Vegas, NV 89169-5972
Tel (813) 435-6244 Founded/Ownrshp 2008
Sales 120.0MM EMP 27
SIC 7941 Manager of individual professional athletes
Pr: Ramesh Nathan
CFO: Hema Nathan

D-U-N-S 09-929-0629 IMP/EXP
BASF CATALYSTS LLC
ENGELHARD
(Suby of BASF CORP) ★
25 Middlesex Tpke, Iselin, NJ 08830-2721
Tel (732) 205-5000 Founded/Ownrshp 2006
Sales 339.2MM^E EMP 583
SIC 2819 2816 5094 3339 Catalysts, chemical; Inorganic pigments; White pigments; Color pigments; Bullion, precious metals; Precious metals; Platinum group metal refining (primary); Silver refining (primary); Gold refining (primary)
CFO: Fried-Walter M Nstermann
Genl Mgr: Prabodh Chobe

D-U-N-S 15-134-5444 IMP/EXP
BASF CONSTRUCTION CHEMICALS LLC
DEGUSSA CONSTRUCTION
(Suby of BASF CORP) ★
23700 Chagrin Blvd, Cleveland, OH 44122-5506
Tel (216) 831-5500 Founded/Ownrshp 2001
Sales 346.9MM^E EMP 2,300
SIC 2899 2851 1799 Concrete curing & hardening compounds; Epoxy coatings; Vinyl coatings, strippable; Caulking (construction); Waterproofing
Pr: John Salvatore
*Treas: Donald Kehr
Sls Mgr: Mike Allen

D-U-N-S 00-130-7032 IMP/EXP
BASF CORP
(Suby of BASFIN CORP) ★
100 Park Ave, Florham Park, NJ 07932-1089
Tel (973) 245-6000 Founded/Ownrshp 1958, 1985
Sales 7.5MMM^E EMP 15,000^E
SIC 2869 2819 2899 2843 2834 2879 Industrial organic chemicals; Industrial inorganic chemicals; Antifreeze compounds; Surface active agents; Pharmaceutical preparations; Vitamin preparations; Agricultural chemicals
CEO: Wayne T Smith
Ch Bd: Timea Marsalko
*Pr: Frank A Bozich
*CFO: Andre Becker
*CFO: Dr Hans-Ulrich Engel
*CFO: Fried-Walter Muenstermann
CFO: Fried-Walter M Nstermann
Treas: Mark Kerschner
*Treas: Malone Robert
Bd of Dir: Jay Hofer
*Ex VP: Beate Ehle
*Sr VP: Matt Lepore
Sr VP: Paul REA
*Sr VP: David Stryker
VP: Tom Chizmadia
VP: Markus Heldt
VP: Otto III
*VP: Ansbacher Keith
VP: Cenan A Ozmeral
Exec: Janice Lee
Dir Rx: Gerald P Flood

D-U-N-S 07-101-4385 IMP
BASFIN CORP
(Suby of BASF SE)
100 Campus Dr Ste 301, Florham Park, NJ 07932-1006
Tel (973) 245-6000 Founded/Ownrshp 2006
Sales 7.5MMM^E EMP 17,331
SIC 2869 2819 2899 2843 2879 2834 Industrial organic chemicals; Industrial inorganic chemicals; Antifreeze compounds; Surface active agents; Agricultural chemicals; Pharmaceutical preparations
Pr: Peter Oakley
*Pr: Frank A Bozich
*Ch: Dr Kurt Bock
*Treas: Philip Kaplan
*Sr VP: David Stryker
*VP: Beate Ehle
*VP: Fried-Walter Mnstermann
*Prin: Dr Martin Brudermller
*Prin: Dr Hans-Ulrich Engel
*Prin: Joseph Falsone

D-U-N-S 00-690-1805
BASHAS INC
BASHAS' MARKETS
22402 S Basha Rd, Chandler, AZ 85248-4908
Tel (480) 883-6131 Founded/Ownrshp 1953
Sales 2.4MMM^E EMP 10,330
SIC 5411 5149 5148 5147 6512 Supermarkets, chain; Groceries & related products; Fresh fruits & vegetables; Meats, fresh; Commercial & industrial building operation
Ch Bd: Edward N Basha III
COO: Darl J Andersen
Sr VP: Edward R Felix
VP: Cisco Echeverria
MIS Dir: Shannon Fitzgerald
MIS Mgr: Gary Kroupa
Software D: Mike Chorak

BASHAS' MARKETS
See BASHAS INC

BASIC AMERICAN FOODS
See BASIC AMERICAN INC

D-U-N-S 00-914-9477 EXP
BASIC AMERICAN INC
BASIC AMERICAN FOODS
2185 N Calif Blvd Ste 215, Walnut Creek, CA 94596-3566
Tel (925) 472-4000 Founded/Ownrshp 1986
Sales 445.1MM^E EMP 1,500
SIC 2034 2099 Potato products, dried & dehydrated; Vegetables, dried or dehydrated (except freeze-dried); Potatoes, peeled for the trade
Pr: Bryan Reese
*CFO: Jim Collins
Treas: Sally Smedal
*VP: Gulbin Hoeberechts
*VP: Todd Peretti
*VP: Michael Villano
VP: Mike Villano
IT Man: Josh Levine
VP Mktg: Leslie Steller
Manager: Kelly Mizell
Snr Mgr: Dean Veurink

D-U-N-S 04-501-9163
■ **BASIC AMERICAN MEDICAL INC**
(Suby of HOSPITAL COPORATION OF AMERICA) ★
1 Park Plz, Nashville, TN 37203-6527
Tel (615) 344-9551 Founded/Ownrshp 1974
Sales 201.3MM^E EMP 4,300
SIC 5912 2599 8093 Drug stores; Hospital beds; Hospital furniture, except beds; Rehabilitation center, outpatient treatment
Sr VP: Richard A Schweinhart
*Sr VP: Stephen T Braun
Sr VP: Joseph D Moore

D-U-N-S 00-984-2949
▲ **BASIC ENERGY SERVICES INC**
801 Cherry St Unit 2, Fort Worth, TX 76102-6886
Tel (817) 334-4100 Founded/Ownrshp 1992
Sales 805.6MM EMP 3,900
Tkr Sym BAS Exch NYS
SIC 1389 1794 Servicing oil & gas wells; Swabbing wells; Excavation & grading, building construction
Pr: Thomas M Patterson
*Ch Bd: Steven A Webster
CFO: Alan Krenek
Sr VP: James F Newman
VP: John Cody Bissett
VP: William T Dame
VP: Lanny T Poldrack
VP: Brett J Taylor
VP Mktg: Douglas B Rogers
Board of Directors: William E Chiles, James S D'agostino Jr, Robert F Fulton, Antonio O Garza Jr, Kenneth V Huseman, Sylvester P Johnson IV, Thomas P Moore Jr

D-U-N-S 79-331-9930
■ **BASIC ENERGY SERVICES LP**
BASIC OIL & GAS WELL SERVICES
(Suby of BASIC ENERGY SERVICES LP, LLC)
801 Cherry St Unit 2, Fort Worth, TX 76102-6886
Tel (817) 334-4100 Founded/Ownrshp 2000
Sales 1.4MMM^E EMP 2,900
SIC 1389 Oil & gas wells: building, repairing & dismantling
Pt: Steven A Webster
*Pt: James J Carter
*Pt: Dub Harrison
*Pt: Ken V Huseman
*Pt: Charles Swift
*CEO: T M Roe Patterson
*Sr VP: Alan Krenek
*Sr VP: Jim Newman
*VP: Jim Tyner
Exec: David Crutcher
Area Mgr: Santiago Zubia

BASIC OIL & GAS WELL SERVICES
See BASIC ENERGY SERVICES LP

D-U-N-S 06-611-4331 IMP
BASIC RESOURCES INC
928 12th St Ste 700, Modesto, CA 95354-2330
Tel (209) 521-9771 Founded/Ownrshp 1973
Sales 244.2MM^E EMP 437
SIC 1611 3273 2951 3532 3531 Highway & street paving contractor; Ready-mixed concrete; Asphalt & asphaltic paving mixtures (not from refineries); Mining machinery; Construction machinery
CEO: Jeffrey Reed
*Pr: Wendell Reed

D-U-N-S 80-011-0314 IMP
BASIC SPORTS APPAREL INC
301 Williams St, El Paso, TX 79901-1813
Tel (915) 532-0561 Founded/Ownrshp 1992
Sales 105.7MM^E EMP 300
SIC 5136 Sportswear, men's & boys'
Pr: Hilel Chowaiki
*VP: David Chowaiki

D-U-N-S 00-386-8007 IMP
BASIN ELECTRIC POWER COOPERATIVE (ND)
1717 E Interstate Ave, Bismarck, ND 58503-0564
Tel (701) 223-0441 Founded/Ownrshp 1961
Sales 1.4MMM EMP 1,527
Accts Deloitte & Touche Llp Minneap
SIC 4911 1311 Generation, electric power; Transmission, electric power; Distribution, electric power; Coal gasification
Ch Bd: Wayne Peltier
*CEO: Paul M Sukut
*CFO: Steve Johnson
*Treas: Kermit Pearson
*Sr VP: Claire Olson

Sr VP: Michael Risan
VP: Ellen Holt
VP: Floyd Robbi
Brnch Mgr: Dean F Rohrich
Dir IT: Vernon Laning
IT Man: MarkThurn
Board of Directors: Allan Thiesen, Don Applegate, Paul Baker, Leo Brekel, Gary Drost, Arden Fuher, Charles Gilbert, Mike McQuistion, Kermit Pearson, Roberta Rohrer

D-U-N-S 94-069-4839
BASIN GOLD COOPERATIVE
5802 N Industrial Way C, Pasco, WA 99301-9302
Tel (509) 545-4161 *Founded/Ownrshp* 1994
Sales 105.0MM *EMP* 10
Accts Cliftonlarsonallen Llp Tri-Ci
SIC 5148 Fresh fruits & vegetables
Pr: Richard Betz
**CFO:* Tim Mackey
**Treas:* Patrick Connors
**VP:* Matthew Wardenaar

D-U-N-S 07-910-3692
BASIN HOLDINGS US LLC
200 Park Ave Fl 58, New York, NY 10166-5899
Tel (212) 695-7376 *Founded/Ownrshp* 2011
Sales 143.3MM[E] *EMP* 240[E]
SIC 3533 Oil & gas field machinery
CEO: John Fitzgibbons
**CFO:* Tyler Hassen
Ex VP: Gail Coleman

D-U-N-S 00-628-8872 IMP/EXP
BASLER ELECTRIC CO (IL)
12570 State Route 143, Highland, IL 62249-1074
Tel (618) 654-2341 *Founded/Ownrshp* 1947
Sales 156.8MM[E] *EMP* 1,000[E]
SIC 3679 3612 3672

BASS BROS ENTERPRISES
See BASS ENTERPRISES PRODUCTION CO

D-U-N-S 00-894-8440 IMP
BASS ENTERPRISES PRODUCTION CO
BASS BROS ENTERPRISES
201 Main St Ste 2700, Fort Worth, TX 76102-3195
Tel (817) 698-0200 *Founded/Ownrshp* 1960
Sales 1.1MMM[E] *EMP* 700
SIC 1311 1382 Crude petroleum production; Oil & gas exploration services
Pr: Sid R Bass
Ch Bd: Perry R Bass
VP: Robert Cottham
VP: W H Medary

D-U-N-S 96-195-5502
BASS PRO GROUP LLC
2500 E Kearney St, Springfield, MO 65898-0002
Tel (417) 873-5000 *Founded/Ownrshp* 2005
Sales 183.5MM[E] *EMP* 445[E]
SIC 5941 Sporting goods & bicycle shops

D-U-N-S 08-213-0378 IMP
BASS PRO LLC
BASS PRO SHOPS
2500 E Kearney St, Springfield, MO 65898-0002
Tel (417) 873-5000 *Founded/Ownrshp* 1999
Sales 3.3MMM[E] *EMP* 12,000
SIC 5961 5941 5551 5661 Catalog & mail-order houses; Sporting goods & bicycle shops; Motor boat dealers; Shoe stores
CFO: William Nunes
Treas: Curt Skotnicki
VP: Jim Broekhoven
VP: Ken Crame
VP: Rich Dalton
VP: Tad Moseley
VP: Larry Wilcher
Exec: Ken Burroughs
Exec: Sherrie Freyer
Exec: Jesse Knapp
Exec: Michele Little
Exec: Mike Ryglewicz

BASS PRO SHOPS
See BASS PRO LLC

D-U-N-S 00-312-4617 IMP/EXP
▲ **BASSETT FURNITURE INDUSTRIES INC**
3525 Fairystone Park Hwy, Bassett, VA 24055-4444
Tel (276) 629-6000 *Founded/Ownrshp* 1902
Sales 430.9MM *EMP* 2,237
Accts Ernst & Young Llp Richmond V
Tkr Sym BSET *Exch* NGS
SIC 2511 2512 5021 5712 Wood household furniture; Upholstered household furniture; Furniture; Furniture stores
Pr: Robert H Spilman Jr
CFO: J Michael Daniel
Sr VP: John E Bassett III
Sr VP: Bruce R Cohenour
Sr VP: Mark S Jordan
VP: Jason Camp
VP: Bill Dalton
VP: Jay R Hervey
VP: Dennis Hoy
VP: Tommy McGuire
VP: Louis Mossotti
VP: Stanley Payne
VP: Ronda Wilson
VP: Ann Zaccaria
Board of Directors: William C Warden Jr, John R Belk, Peter W Brown, Kristina K Cashman, Paul Fulton, Howard H Haworth, George W Henderson III, J Walter McDowell, Dale C Pond, William C Wampler Jr

D-U-N-S 04-104-3027 IMP/EXP
■ **BASSETT FURNITURE INDUSTRIES OF NORTH CAROLINA LLC**
WEIMAN COMPANY DIVISION
(*Suby of* BASSETT FURNITURE INDUSTRIES INC) ★
3525 Fairystone Park Hwy, Bassett, VA 24055-4444
Tel (276) 629-6000 *Founded/Ownrshp* 1967
Sales 96.9MM[E] *EMP* 1,329[E]
SIC 2511 2512 Wood household furniture; Tables, household: wood; Wood bedroom furniture; Club room furniture: wood; Upholstered household furniture

VP: Dennis Hoy

BASSETT MEDICAL CENTER
See MARY IMOGENE BASSETT HOSPITAL

D-U-N-S 02-641-2346 IMP
BASSHAM WHOLESALE EGG CO INC
BASSHAM WHOLESALE FOODS
5409 Hemphill St, Fort Worth, TX 76115-4411
Tel (817) 921-1600 *Founded/Ownrshp* 1953
Sales 136.9MM[E] *EMP* 99
Accts Marc E Foreman Fort Worth T
SIC 5144 5143 5141 5147 Poultry: live, dressed or frozen (unpackaged); Poultry products; Dairy products, except dried or canned; Groceries, general line; Meats, fresh
Pr: Ronnie Bassham
**COO:* Todd Hoffman
**CFO:* Adrian Smith
**VP:* Randy Bassham
**VP:* Wesley Bassham

BASSHAM WHOLESALE FOODS
See BASSHAM WHOLESALE EGG CO INC

D-U-N-S 08-574-3458
BAST HATFIELD INC
1399 Vischers Ferry Rd, Clifton Park, NY 12065
Tel (518) 373-2000 *Founded/Ownrshp* 1977
Sales 104.3MM[E] *EMP* 290
SIC 1542 1541 8741 Commercial & office building, new construction; Commercial & office buildings, renovation & repair; Industrial buildings, new construction; Renovation, remodeling & repairs: industrial buildings; Construction management
VP: Thomas W Vandish
**Ex VP:* Christopher O Bast Jr
VP: Megan Bast
VP: Jim Hendrickson
Genl Mgr: Michael Garvey
Off Admin: Lea Springstead

D-U-N-S 19-680-8112
BASTIAN AUTOMATION ENGINEERING LLC
BASTIAN SOLUTIONS
(*Suby of* BASTIAN SOLUTIONS LLC) ★
2155 Fields Blvd, Greenfield, IN 46140-3012
Tel (317) 467-2583 *Founded/Ownrshp* 2003
Sales 99.6MM[E] *EMP* 60
SIC 3579 7699 Forms handling equipment; Industrial equipment services
CEO: William A Bastian II

BASTIAN SOLUTIONS
See BASTIAN AUTOMATION ENGINEERING LLC

BASTIAN SOLUTIONS
See HALO LLC

D-U-N-S 00-604-3723
BASTIAN SOLUTIONS LLC
(*Suby of* BASTIAN SOLUTIONS) ★
10585 N Meridian St Fl 3, Indianapolis, IN 46290-1069
Tel (317) 575-9992 *Founded/Ownrshp* 1992
Sales 229.3MM *EMP* 450
Accts Katz Sapper & Miller
SIC 8711 Engineering services
CEO: Bill Bastian II
**Pr:* Aaron Jones
**Pr:* Damir Kantardzic
**VP:* Eric Cameron
**VP:* Gregg Durham
Brnch Mgr: Jon Tilmon

D-U-N-S 02-155-8937
BASTROP INDEPENDENT SCHOOL DISTRICT
BISD
906 Farm St, Bastrop, TX 78602-3310
Tel (512) 321-2292 *Founded/Ownrshp* 1894
Sales 100.3MM *EMP* 1,100
Accts Belt Harris Pechacek Lllp Bel
SIC 8211 Public elementary & secondary schools
CFO: Sandra Callahan
Ofcr: Jesus Delgadillo
Netwrk Mgr: Richard Salazar
Pr Dir: Melinda Marquez
Psych: Laura Andrade

BATES SALES COMPANY
See PURVIS INDUSTRIES LTD

D-U-N-S 00-425-4876 IMP/EXP
■ **BATESVILLE CASKET CO INC**
BATESVILLE MANAGEMENT SERVICES
(*Suby of* HILLENBRAND INC) ★
1 Batesville Blvd, Batesville, IN 47006-9229
Tel (812) 934-7500 *Founded/Ownrshp* 1884, 1969
Sales 688.6MM[E] *EMP* 3,200
SIC 3995 Burial caskets
Pr: Kimberly K Ryan
Pr: Bob Pristash
**Pr:* Joe Raver
**CFO:* Douglas Kunkel
CFO: Christopher H Trainor
**Treas:* Theodore S Haddad Jr
Treas: Mark R Lanning
Chf Mktg O: Troy Brake
Ofcr: Crol Caroll
Ofcr: Tucholski Greg
Ofcr: Greg Lewis
Sr VP: Ken Allen
Sr VP: Douglas P Wilson
Sr VP: P D Wilson
VP: Keith Ashby
VP: Michael Babich
VP: Diane Bohman
VP: Tom Brewer
VP: William Canady
VP: Carol Davis
VP: Kim Dennis
Board of Directors: Patrick D Demaynadier, Kimberly K Dennis, Gregory N Miller

BATESVILLE MANAGEMENT SERVICES
See BATESVILLE CASKET CO INC

D-U-N-S 04-351-8211
■ **BATESVILLE SERVICES INC**
(*Suby of* HILLENBRAND INC) ★
1 Batesville Blvd, Batesville, IN 47006-7756
Tel (812) 934-7000 *Founded/Ownrshp* 1998, 2013
Sales 81.9MM[E] *EMP* 1,000
SIC 3995 Burial caskets
Pr: Kimberly K Ryan
CIO: Darryl Maslar

D-U-N-S 09-390-5479 IMP
BATESVILLE TOOL & DIE INC
(*Suby of* BTD MANUFACTURING INC) ★
177 Six Pine Ranch Rd, Batesville, IN 47006-9540
Tel (812) 934-5616 *Founded/Ownrshp* 1978
Sales 114.9MM[E] *EMP* 450[E]
SIC 3469 3544 Metal stampings; Special dies & tools; Jigs & fixtures
Pr: Jody Fledderman
VP: Lance Green
VP: Bob Holtel
VP: Robert Holtel
VP: Jerry Kretschmann
VP: Jorge Lopez
VP: James Wintz
Ex Dir: Anna Ibold
IT Man: Sam Wintz
VP Mfg: Jay Fledderman
Sfty Mgr: Urban Brackman

D-U-N-S 87-895-2845 IMP/EXP
■ **BATH & BODY WORKS LLC**
(*Suby of* L BRANDS) ★
7 Limited Pkwy E, Reynoldsburg, OH 43068-5300
Tel (614) 856-6000 *Founded/Ownrshp* 1990
Sales 2.7MMM[E] *EMP* 20,000
SIC 5999 2844 Toiletries, cosmetics & perfumes; Toilet preparations
CEO: Nicholas Coe
Pr: Tony Mendoza
Pr: Mark Peters
**CFO:* Tom Fitzgerald
**Treas:* Patrick Hectorne
Chf Mktg O: Anne Martin-Vachon
Chf Mktg O: Edward Razek
Ex VP: Becky Mick
VP: Dein Boyle
VP: Bernadette David
VP: Sheena Foley
VP: Ron Ford
VP: Shannon Glass
VP: Steve Lange
VP: Sharon M Leite
VP: Sharon Lessard
**VP:* Timothy B Lyons
VP: Camille McDonald
VP: Luciana Ramsey
VP: Herman Steve
Exec: Marisa Muzatko

BATH & KITCHEN BY CRAWFORD
See CRAWFORD SUPPLY GROUP INC

D-U-N-S 04-595-3718 IMP
■ **BATH IRON WORKS CORP**
(*Suby of* GENERAL DYNAMICS CORP) ★
700 Washington St Stop 1, Bath, ME 04530-2556
Tel (207) 443-3311 *Founded/Ownrshp* 1995
Sales 339.3MM[E] *EMP* 900[E]
SIC 3731 8711 Combat vessels, building & repairing; Consulting engineer
Ch: Jay L Johnson
**Pr:* Jeffrey S Geiger
**Pr:* Phebe N Novakovic
Chf Mktg O: Joe Kuklewicz
**VP:* Thomas A Brown
VP: Thomas Egan
VP: Charles Griebel
VP: John Komer
VP: Walter Oliver
VP: Patrick Thomas
Exec: Dustin Brown
Exec: Clifford Rider

D-U-N-S 83-265-5125
BATHXCESSORIES INC
1481 N Larrabee St, Chicago, IL 60610-1101
Tel (312) 951-2885 *Founded/Ownrshp* 2009
Sales 2.8MMM *EMP* 2
Accts Enc Inc Manorville New Yor
SIC 5099 Toilets, portable
Pr: Kenneth Spoor

BATON ROUGE GENERAL
See GENERAL HEALTH SYSTEM

BATON ROUGE GENERAL HEALTH CEN
See BATON ROUGE GENERAL MEDICAL CENTER

D-U-N-S 06-589-2136
BATON ROUGE GENERAL MEDICAL CENTER
8490 Picardy Ave Ste 200, Baton Rouge, LA 70809-3733
Tel (225) 237-1547 *Founded/Ownrshp* 2014
Sales 406.2MM *EMP* 12[E]
SIC 3949 Batons
CEO: Mark F Slyter
**CFO:* Kendal Johnson

D-U-N-S 15-580-5971
BATON ROUGE GENERAL MEDICAL CENTER
BATON ROUGE GENERAL HEALTH CEN
3600 Florida Blvd, Baton Rouge, LA 70806-3842
Tel (225) 387-7000 *Founded/Ownrshp* 1937
Sales 363.6MM *EMP* 394
Accts Postlethwaite & Netterville B
SIC 8062 General medical & surgical hospitals
CEO: Milton Siepman
Pharmcst: Michael Barton

BATON ROUGE SOUTHERN RAILROAD
See WATCO COMPANIES LLC

BATORY FOODS
See TOTAL SWEETENERS INC

D-U-N-S 96-849-5171
BATS GLOBAL MARKETS INC
8050 Marshall Dr Ste 120, Lenexa, KS 66214-1572
Tel (913) 815-7000 *Founded/Ownrshp* 2010
Sales 1.7MMM *EMP* 286[E]
SIC 6231 Security & commodity exchanges
Pr: Chris Concannon
Ch Bd: Joe Ratterman
CEO: Mark Hemsley
CFO: Brian N Schell
Ex VP: Tony Barchetto
Ex VP: Bryan Harkins
Ex VP: Chris Isaacson
Ex VP: Tami Schademann
Ex VP: Eric Swanson
VP: Anthony Barchetto
VP: Bryan Christian
VP: Kapil Rathi
VP: Randy Williams
Board of Directors: Alan H Freudenstein, Robert W Jones, John McCarthy, Chris Mitchell, Frank Reardon, Michael Richter

D-U-N-S 00-332-1833
BATSON-COOK CO (GA)
BATSON-COOK CONSTRUCTION
(*Suby of* KAJIMA INTERNATIONAL INC) ★
817 4th Ave, West Point, GA 31833-1504
Tel (706) 643-2500 *Founded/Ownrshp* 1915, 2008
Sales 244.1MM[E] *EMP* 350
SIC 1542 5211 1541 Commercial & office building contractors; Lumber & other building materials; Industrial buildings, new construction
Pr: Raymond L Moody Jr
**Pr:* R Randy Hall
**Sec:* Cecil G Hood
Sr VP: David A Barksdale
Sr VP: Scott C Evers
Sr VP: Frank Nelson
Sr VP: Scott Thompson
VP: Randall Thompson
Mktg Dir: Allana Garrison
Snr PM: Scott Hudson
Snr PM: Peter Martin

BATSON-COOK CONSTRUCTION
See BATSON-COOK CO

D-U-N-S 04-423-1850 IMP
BATTAGLIA DISTRIBUTING CORP INC (IL)
2500 S Ashland Ave, Chicago, IL 60608-5321
Tel (312) 738-1111 *Founded/Ownrshp* 1966, 1993
Sales 221.8MM[E] *EMP* 200
SIC 5141 Groceries, general line
Pr: Austin W Battaglia
VP: Joseph L Battagia
**VP:* Ernie Battaglia
**VP:* Frederick P Battaglia
**VP:* Joseph L Battaglia Sr
MIS Dir: Barbara Winter
IT Man: Joe Gariti

BATTELLE ECOLOGY
See NATIONAL ECOLOGICAL OBSERVATORY NETWORK INC

D-U-N-S 15-202-0629
BATTELLE ENERGY ALLIANCE LLC
BEA
(*Suby of* BATTELLE MEMORIAL INSTITUTE INC) ★
2525 Fremont Ave, Idaho Falls, ID 83402-1509
Tel (208) 533-7606 *Founded/Ownrshp* 2004
Sales 524.5MM[E] *EMP* 4,000[E]
SIC 8731 7382 Energy research; Security systems services
Pr: John J Grossenbacher
**Pr:* Jerome R Bahlmann
Ofcr: Brady Jensen
**Ex VP:* I Martin Inglis
**Sr VP:* Leonard K Peters
**Sr VP:* Jeffrey Wadsworth
Snr Sftwr: Paul Forbord
QA Dir: Evert Mouser
Sftwr Eng: Michelle Stewart
Opers Mgr: Ken Schreck
Board of Directors: Brian Morishita

D-U-N-S 08-564-2994
BATTELLE LIBRARY
505 King Ave, Columbus, OH 43201-2693
Tel (614) 424-6302 *Founded/Ownrshp* 2001
Sales 92.2MM *EMP* 8
SIC 8733 Research institute
CTO: Matthew Christensen
CTO: Keith Dalrymple
CTO: Lynn Davidson
CTO: Denzel Fisher
CTO: John Irwin
CTO: Daniel Miller
Dir IT: Jean Hayward
Dir IT: Erin Pratt
Dir IT: Brent Stacey

D-U-N-S 03-298-7476
BATTELLE MEMORIAL INSTITUTE
PACIFIC NW NATIONAL
(*Suby of* BATTELLE MEMORIAL INSTITUTE INC) ★
900 Battelle Blvd, Richland, WA 99354-1793
Tel (509) 371-7608 *Founded/Ownrshp* 1926
Sales 98.4MM[E] *EMP* 4,500
SIC 8733 Research institute
CEO: Dr Jeffrey Wadsworth
**COO:* Martin Inglis
**Sr VP:* Russell Austin
**Sr VP:* Tom Snowberger
**VP:* L M Inglis
Prgrm Mgr: Kenneth Ames
Prgrm Mgr: Mark Dillner
Dir IT: Robert Gates
Sls Mgr: Bruce Simanton

D-U-N-S 00-790-1598 IMP
BATTELLE MEMORIAL INSTITUTE INC (OH)
505 King Ave, Columbus, OH 43201-2681
Tel (614) 424-6424 *Founded/Ownrshp* 1925
Sales 4.7MMM[E] *EMP* 7,457
Accts Deloitte & Touche Llp Columb

SIC 8731 Commercial physical research; Medical research, commercial; Environmental research; Electronic research
Ch Bd: John K Welch
CEO: Jeffrey Wadsworth
COO: Troy A Capers
COO: Tom Hickey
COO: Martin Inglis
CFO: Dave Evans
CFO: I Martin Inglis
Treas: M W Kontos
Treas: Judith L Mobley
Treas: Gwendolyn C Vonholten
Bd of Dir: Joseph Swann
Ofcr: Richard Adams
Ofcr: Elizabeth Cutie
Ofcr: Donald P Mc Connell
Ofcr: Dwayne Taliaferro
Ex VP: Gregory L Frank
Ex VP: Gregory A Horowitz
Ex VP: Douglas Olesen
Ex VP: Benjamin Ritchey
Ex VP: James Sonnett
Sr VP: Russell Austin
Board of Directors: Vicky A Bailey, Kirkland Donald, Frank L Douglas, Michael Gasser, Lester Lyles, Michael G Morris, Sean C O'keefe, Suzanne Vautrinot, John K Welch

BATTERY ASSIST
See CLUB ASSIST US LLC

D-U-N-S 05-831-0967 IMP
BATTERY SYSTEMS INC
12322 Monarch St, Garden Grove, CA 92841-2909
Tel (310) 667-9320 *Founded/Ownrshp* 2003
Sales 100.0MM *EMP* 450
SIC 5013 Automotive batteries
Pr: Brad Streelman
Brnch Mgr: Erich Heidemeyer
Brnch Mgr: Dave McMains
Manager: Dave Brickey
Manager: Kurt Facile
Manager: Eric Johnsen
Manager: Jason Martel
Manager: Randy Rushing
Sls Mgr: Ian Blomgren
Sls Mgr: Josh Brumm

D-U-N-S 00-729-7278
BATTLE CREEK FARMERS COOPERATIVE NON-STOCK
FARMERS PRIDE
83755 Highway 121, Battle Creek, NE 68715-5004
Tel (402) 675-2375 *Founded/Ownrshp* 1934
Sales 146.1MM *EMP* 90
Accts Gardiner Thomsen Lincoln Ne
SIC 5153 5191 5172 5541 5411 Grains; Feed; Fertilizer & fertilizer materials; Diesel fuel; Gasoline; Truck stops; Convenience stores, independent
CEO: Dean Thernes
**Ch:* Jerry Dolesh - Tilden

BATTLE GROUND PUBLIC SCHOOLS
See BATTLE GROUND SCHOOL DISTRICT

D-U-N-S 06-876-1873
BATTLE GROUND SCHOOL DISTRICT
BATTLE GROUND PUBLIC SCHOOLS
11104 Ne 149th St, Brush Prairie, WA 98606-9565
Tel (360) 885-5300 *Founded/Ownrshp* 1909
Sales 91.8MM[E] *EMP* 1,200
SIC 8211 Public elementary school; Public junior high school; Public senior high school
VP: Monty Anderson
Genl Mgr: Meagan Hayden
IT Man: Lynette Hofer
Pr Dir: Rita Sanders

D-U-N-S 01-494-6115 IMP
BATTLEGROUND RESTAURANT GROUP INC (NC)
TRIPPS
1337 Winstead Pl, Greensboro, NC 27408-8024
Tel (336) 272-9355 *Founded/Ownrshp* 1980
Sales 53.5MM[E] *EMP* 1,500
SIC 5812

D-U-N-S 82-744-9328
BATTMANN HOLDINGS INC
2480 Long Lake Rd, Saint Paul, MN 55113-2534
Tel (651) 639-2800 *Founded/Ownrshp* 2001
Sales 201.5MM[E] *EMP* 634
SIC 4214 Local trucking with storage; Household goods moving & storage, local
CEO: Dann Battina
**Pr:* Marc Van Kley
**Sec:* Paul A Zagaria

D-U-N-S 00-794-5785 IMP
BAUER BUILT INC (WI)
BAUER BUILT TIRE
1111 W Prospect St, Durand, WI 54736-1061
Tel (715) 672-8300 *Founded/Ownrshp* 1944
Sales 190.5MM[E] *EMP* 450
SIC 5531 5014 7534 5171 Automotive tires; Automobile tires & tubes; Truck tires & tubes; Rebuilding & retreading tires; Petroleum bulk stations
Pr: Jerome M Bauer
**Ex VP:* Tad M Bauer
**Ex VP:* James N Fenn
**Ex VP:* Steve Spindler
**Ex VP:* Dave Stordahl
**VP:* Larry Hildebrandt

BAUER BUILT TIRE
See BAUER BUILT INC

D-U-N-S 10-867-9317 IMP/EXP
BAUER HOCKEY INC
(*Suby of* BPS US HOLDINGS INC.)
100 Domain Dr Ste 1, Exeter, NH 03833-2996
Tel (603) 430-2111 *Founded/Ownrshp* 1979
Sales 170.9MM[E] *EMP* 423[E]
SIC 3949 Sporting & athletic goods; Helmets, athletic
Pr: Kevin Davis
VP: Michael Floros
VP: Michael Wall
Dir Rx: Robert Osterhammer
CIO: Paul Dachsteiner
Mktg Dir: Darryl Hughes
Counsel: Michelle Hanson

D-U-N-S 60-915-7854 IMP/EXP
BAUHAUS FURNITURE GROUP LLC
1 Bauhaus Dr, Saltillo, MS 38866-6974
Tel (662) 869-2664 *Founded/Ownrshp* 2014
Sales 94.1MM[E] *EMP* 500
SIC 2512 Upholstered household furniture
CEO: James Al Wiygul
**Pr:* Britt Allred
CFO: Todd Campbell
**CFO:* Blair Taylor
**VP:* Louis M Riccio Jr
IT Man: James Fancher
IT Man: Kobe Smith
Opers Mgr: Anthony Walker
VP Sls: Jeffrey Jones

D-U-N-S 07-909-9019
BAUSCH & LOMB HOLDINGS INC
(*Suby of* VALEANT PHARMACEUTICALS INTERNATIONAL CORP) ★
450 Lexington Ave, New York, NY 10017-3904
Tel (585) 338-6000 *Founded/Ownrshp* 2013
Sales 2.7MMM[E] *EMP* 4,213[E]
SIC 3851 2834 Ophthalmic goods; Pharmaceutical preparations
Ch Bd: Gerald M Ostrov
**CEO:* Brent L Saunders

D-U-N-S 00-220-7751 IMP/EXP
BAUSCH & LOMB INC
(*Suby of* BAUSCH & LOMB HOLDINGS INC) ★
1400 N Goodman St, Rochester, NY 14609-3596
Tel (585) 338-6000 *Founded/Ownrshp* 2013
Sales 2.7MMM[E] *EMP* 11,000
SIC 3851 2834 3841 Ophthalmic goods; Contact lenses; Magnifiers (readers & simple magnifiers); Pharmaceutical preparations; Solutions, pharmaceutical; Druggists' preparations (pharmaceuticals); Vitamin preparations; Ophthalmic instruments & apparatus
Ch Bd: Fred Hassan
**Ch Bd:* Brenton L Saunders
**Pr:* Robert Bertolini
**CFO:* Brian J Harris
Sr Cor Off: Colleen Gleason
**Chf Cred:* Susan A Roberts
Bd of Dir: John Brown
**Chf Mktg O:* Calvin W Roberts
**Ex VP:* Alan H Farnsworth
**VP:* Robert D Bailey
VP: Dave Exall
VP: George Grobe
VP: Jim Johnson
VP: Craig E Larson
VP: Tom Moore
VP: Barry Rhein
VP: Joseph Salamone
VP: Christopher Simmons
VP: Sharon Tonetta
Exec: Christine Oliver
Exec: Frank Shields

D-U-N-S 05-802-0496 IMP/EXP
BAX GLOBAL INC
DB SCHENKER
(*Suby of* DB US HOLDING CORP) ★
1305 Executive Blvd # 200, Chesapeake, VA 23320-3676
Tel (866) 744-7282 *Founded/Ownrshp* 2009
Sales 148.4MM[E] *EMP* 1,500
SIC 4731 Domestic freight forwarding; Foreign freight forwarding; Customhouse brokers
Pr: Heiner Murmann
Pr: Tom Donahue
Sr VP: Denes Roveti
VP: Jay Arnold III
Exec: Christine Difebo
CIO: Allen Weeks
VP Sls: Jason Bergman

D-U-N-S 07-976-0780
BAXALTA INC
(*Suby of* SHIRE PLC)
1200 Lakeside Dr, Bannockburn, IL 60015-1243
Tel (224) 940-2000 *Founded/Ownrshp* 2016
Sales 6.1MMM *EMP* 17,000[E]
SIC 2834 Pharmaceutical preparations; Intravenous solutions
CEO: Flemming Ornskov
Pr: Brian Goff
Pr: Jacopo Leonardi
Pr: David D Meek
Pr: Dagmar Rosa-Bjorkeson
Pr: Patrice Zagame
CFO: Jeffrey Poulton
Ex VP: Anne-Marie Law
Sr VP: John Furey
VP: John Vlasak
Div/Sub He: Ritu Shah
Assoc Dir: Lisa Meckley
Assoc Dir: Caresa Ward

D-U-N-S 07-970-8982
BAXALTA US INC
(*Suby of* BAXALTA INC) ★
1 Baxter Pkwy, Deerfield, IL 60015-4625
Tel (224) 948-2000 *Founded/Ownrshp* 2015
Sales 241.9MM[E] *EMP* 4,700[E]
SIC 7389 Personal service agents, brokers & bureaus
CEO: Dr Ludwig N Hanton
**CFO:* Robert J Hombach

D-U-N-S 12-020-0423 IMP
BAXTER COUNTY REGIONAL HOSPITAL INC
BAXTER REGIONAL MEDICAL CENTER
624 Hospital Dr, Mountain Home, AR 72653-2955
Tel (870) 508-1000 *Founded/Ownrshp* 1963
Sales 167.4MM *EMP* 1,358[E]
SIC 8062 General medical & surgical hospitals
Dir Vol: Becky Rose
**CFO:* Ivan Holleman
Bd of Dir: Greg Wood
Ofcr: Estella Tullgren
Dir Lab: Debbie Williams
Off Mgr: Brandee Litty
Off Mgr: Donna McMullen
QA Dir: Sue Rodden
QC Dir: Karla Rainwater
Pathlgst: Christopher Webb
Doctor: Shawn D Bogle

D-U-N-S 80-181-4047
BAXTER CREDIT UNION
BCU
340 N Milwaukee Ave, Vernon Hills, IL 60061-1533
Tel (847) 522-8600 *Founded/Ownrshp* 1981
Sales NA *EMP* 223
SIC 6062 State credit unions
CEO: Mike Valentine
**COO:* Bob McKay
VP: Ken Dryfhout
CIO: Jeff Johnson

BAXTER HEALTH SYSTEMS
See BAXTER HEALTHCARE CORP

D-U-N-S 00-508-3209 IMP/EXP
■ BAXTER HEALTHCARE CORP
BAXTER HEALTH SYSTEMS
(*Suby of* BAXTER INTERNATIONAL INC) ★
1 Baxter Pkwy, Deerfield, IL 60015-4625
Tel (224) 948-2000 *Founded/Ownrshp* 1966
Sales 2.1MMM[E] *EMP* 23,030
SIC 3841 2835 2389 3842 5047

D-U-N-S 00-514-6311
▲ BAXTER INTERNATIONAL INC
1 Baxter Pkwy, Deerfield, IL 60015-4634
Tel (224) 948-2000 *Founded/Ownrshp* 1931
Sales 9.9MMM *EMP* 66,000
Accts Pricewaterhousecoopers Llp Ch
Tkr Sym BAX *Exch* NYS
SIC 2834 3841 2835 3842 Pharmaceutical preparations; Intravenous solutions; Solutions, pharmaceutical; Surgical & medical instruments; Catheters; Medical instruments & equipment, blood & bone work; Surgical instruments & apparatus; Blood derivative diagnostic agents; Surgical appliances & supplies
Pr: Jose E Almeida
CFO: James K Saccaro
VP: Lou Amendola
VP: Kathy Azuara
VP: Sebastian J Bufalino
VP: Ludwin N Hantson
VP: Russ Holscher
VP: Faye Katt
VP: Irina Konstantinovsky
VP: Paul E Martin
VP: Jeanne K Mason
VP: Joe Novicki
VP: Marcus Schabacker
VP: David P Scharf
VP: Lien-Lung Sheu
VP: Karenann Terrell
Assoc Dir: Chris Stolzenbach
Board of Directors: Thomas F Chen, John D Forsyth, James R Gavin III, Peter S Hellman, Michael F Mahoney, Carole J Shapazian, Thomas T Stallkamp, Albert Pl Stroucken

BAXTER REGIONAL MEDICAL CENTER
See BAXTER COUNTY REGIONAL HOSPITAL INC

D-U-N-S 10-217-4950
■ BAXTER WORLD TRADE CORP
(*Suby of* BAXTER INTERNATIONAL INC) ★
1 Baxter Pkwy, Deerfield, IL 60015-4625
Tel (224) 948-2000 *Founded/Ownrshp* 1979
Sales 143.4MM[E] *EMP* 1,500
SIC 2834 3841 Intravenous solutions; Blood transfusion equipment; Hemodialysis apparatus; Diagnostic apparatus, medical; Needles, suture
Pr: Robert Parkinson

BAY
See BERRY CONTRACTING LP

BAY & BAY BROKERAGE
See BAY & BAY TRANSFER CO INC

D-U-N-S 03-001-4989
BAY & BAY TRANSFER CO INC (MN)
BAY & BAY BROKERAGE
3686 140th St E, Rosemount, MN 55068-2746
Tel (800) 273-0366 *Founded/Ownrshp* 1940, 1989
Sales 133.9MM[E] *EMP* 300
SIC 4213 4212 Trucking, except local; Local trucking, without storage
CEO: Sam Anderson
**Pr:* Lois A Anderson
Ex VP: Eric Lien
Ex VP: Aaron Thompson
**VP:* David B Anderson
Exec: Rob Adams

D-U-N-S 82-652-8197
BAY & BAY TRANSPORTATION SERVICES INC
(*Suby of* BAY & BAY BROKERAGE) ★
2905 W Svc Rd Ste 2000, Eagan, MN 55121
Tel (651) 480-7961 *Founded/Ownrshp* 2007
Sales 91.2MM[E] *EMP* 290
SIC 4731 Freight transportation arrangement
CEO: Sam Anderson
Ex VP: Eric Lien
VP: Jeff O'Conner
**VP:* Jeff Oconnor
**Prin:* Lois A Anderson
VP Sls: Justin Johnson

D-U-N-S 02-877-6060 IMP
BAY ALARM CO
S A S
60 Berry Dr, Pacheco, CA 94553-5601
Tel (925) 935-1100 *Founded/Ownrshp* 1946
Sales 160.6MM[E] *EMP* 500
SIC 1731 7382 5063 Fire detection & burglar alarm systems specialization; Burglar alarm maintenance & monitoring; Fire alarm maintenance & monitoring; Electrical apparatus & equipment
Ch Bd: Bruce A Westphal
CEO: Roger L Westphal
Co-Pr: Graham Westphal
VP: Shane Clary
VP: Tim Westphal
Brnch Mgr: Ryan Steiger
Off Mgr: Mary Gutierrez
Off Mgr: Kathy Hundorf
Off Mgr: Jasmine Phu
Off Admin: Mindy Beckman
CTO: Kevin Feeney

BAY AREA BEVERAGE
See T F LOUDERBACK INC

D-U-N-S 06-060-0533
BAY AREA HEALTH DISTRICT
BAY AREA HOSPITAL
1775 Thompson Rd, Coos Bay, OR 97420-2125
Tel (541) 269-8111 *Founded/Ownrshp* 1952
Sales 149.6MM *EMP* 1,020
SIC 8062 8082 General medical & surgical hospitals; Home health care services
Ch Bd: Thomas McAndrew
**Pr:* Paul Janke
CFO: Sam Patterson
VP: Benjamin Pfau
Dir Inf Cn: Katie Griffith
Dir Lab: Vickie Montgomery
Dir Rx: Chuck Axelton
Genl Mgr: Patty Clark
Plnt Mgr: Karl Delzotti
Pr Dir: Barbara Bauder
Pathlgst: Lamont Wettstein

D-U-N-S 05-573-1181
■ BAY AREA HEALTHCARE GROUP LTD
DOCTORS REGIONAL CAMPUS
(*Suby of* HOSPITAL COPORATION OF AMERICA) ★
3315 S Alameda St, Corpus Christi, TX 78411-1820
Tel (361) 761-1400 *Founded/Ownrshp* 1991
Sales 128.4MM[E] *EMP* 1,800[E]
SIC 8062 8063 8069 8093 General medical & surgical hospitals; Psychiatric hospitals; Specialty hospitals, except psychiatric; Specialty outpatient clinics
CEO: Jay Woodall
**Pt:* Howard Ainsley
**Pt:* Steve Woerner
**CFO:* Kris Nicosia
Dir Lab: Gilbert Gonzalez
Chf Nrs Of: Melonie Kelley
**Prin:* Donna Quinn
**Prin:* Kathy Rubano
Nurse Mgr: Michelle Holt
Dir IT: Brian Brown
Doctor: James Dinn

BAY AREA HOSPITAL
See BAY AREA HEALTH DISTRICT

BAY AREA KENWORTH
See SSMB PACIFIC HOLDING CO INC

D-U-N-S 07-479-0981
BAY AREA MEDICAL CENTER INC (WI)
3100 Shore Dr, Marinette, WI 54143-4297
Tel (715) 735-4200 *Founded/Ownrshp* 1939, 1985
Sales 90.0MM *EMP* 700[E]
SIC 8062 General medical & surgical hospitals
CEO: Edward Harding
CFO: C Carlson
**CFO:* Daniel Carlson
VP: Shelly Spaude
CIO: Pete Eisenzoph
CTO: Jenny Rasner
Opers Mgr: Nicole Klingbeil
Mktg Mgr: Mariah Harris
Doctor: Qefli Neziri
Pharmcst: Karen Hines

BAY CITY DIVISION
See NEWCOR INC

D-U-N-S 12-840-6449
BAY CLUB LOS ANGELES INC
15759 San Pedro Ave, San Antonio, TX 78232-3726
Tel (210) 490-1980 *Founded/Ownrshp* 1999
Sales 14.0MM[E] *EMP* 1,000
SIC 7991 Physical fitness facilities
Pr: Matthew Stevens
**CEO:* Anthony M Rockhill

D-U-N-S 03-950-2142
BAY COUNTY HEALTH SYSTEM LLC
BAY MEDICAL CTR SACRED HEART
615 N Bonita Ave, Panama City, FL 32401-3623
Tel (850) 769-1511 *Founded/Ownrshp* 2013
Sales 204.1MM *EMP* 52[E]
SIC 8011 Offices & clinics of medical doctors
V Ch: Harold Bazzel
Bd of Dir: Jerry Sowell

D-U-N-S 04-944-4565
BAY COVE HUMAN SERVICES INC
66 Canal St, Boston, MA 02114-2002
Tel (617) 371-3000 *Founded/Ownrshp* 1973
Sales 87.8MM *EMP* 1,128
Accts Kevin P Martin Associates Pc
SIC 8052 8093 8361 Home for the mentally retarded, with health care; Substance abuse clinics (outpatient); Mental health clinic, outpatient; Home for the emotionally disturbed
Pr: Stanley P Connors
**CEO:* Bill Sprague
**Sr VP:* Kerry Horgos
**Sr VP:* Jim Laprade
Sr VP: Nancy Mahan
VP: Clarissa Erving
Prgrm Mgr: Katie Nadeau
Dir IT: Hilary Croach
Mktg Dir: Melbourne Henry
Pgrm Dir: Alice Andrews
Pgrm Dir: Natalia Levin

D-U-N-S 10-001-2624
BAY DISTRICT SCHOOL BOARD
1311 Balboa Ave, Panama City, FL 32401-2080
Tel (850) 767-4100 *Founded/Ownrshp* 1930
Sales 196.5MM[E] *EMP* 5,000
SIC 8211 School board
**CFO:* Jess Snyder
Ofcr: Tim Kitts

D-U-N-S 07-979-8980
BAY DISTRICT SCHOOLS
1311 Balboa Ave, Panama City, FL 32401-2080
Tel (850) 767-4101 *Founded/Ownrshp* 2015
Sales 31.3MM^E *EMP* 4,206^E
SIC 8211 Public elementary & secondary schools
Ex Dir: Karen Hall
Dir Sec: Michael Jones
MIS Dir: David Smith
Pr Dir: Karen Tucker
Teacher Pr: Sharon Michalik
Instr Medi: Rob Tindel

D-U-N-S 06-267-2142
BAY FOODS INC
ROSE HILL FARM
1021 Noell Ln, Rocky Mount, NC 27804-1761
Tel (252) 937-2000 *Founded/Ownrshp* 1972
Sales 389.1MM *EMP* 850
Accts Ernst & Young Llp Raleigh No
SIC 5812 Fast-food restaurant, chain
Pr: William M Boddie
**Sec:* Douglas Anderson

D-U-N-S 15-730-3959 EXP
BAY INDUSTRIES INC
(*Suby of* AWS/GB CORP) ★
2929 Walker Dr, Green Bay, WI 54311-8312
Tel (920) 406-4000 *Founded/Ownrshp* 1986
Sales 250.5MM^E *EMP* 300
SIC 5031 5033 Doors, garage; Insulation materials
Pr: Arnold W Schmidt
CFO: Ronn Kleinschmidt
Treas: Sally Firman
**VP:* Gloria Schmidt
Dist Mgr: Jeff Knight
Dist Mgr: Steve Ungrodt
Genl Mgr: Mike McLain
Genl Mgr: Eric Paye
Plnt Mgr: Shawn Barrington
Plnt Mgr: John Paxton

D-U-N-S 06-854-6485 IMP/EXP
BAY ISLAND SPORTSWEAR INC (SC)
1415 Emerald Rd, Greenwood, SC 29646-9559
Tel (864) 229-1298 *Founded/Ownrshp* 1999
Sales 185.0MM^E *EMP* 1,500^E
SIC 2253 2339 T-shirts & tops, knit; Sportswear, women's
Pr: Sam Simchon
Sr VP: Matt Vander Wyden
**VP:* Renee Simchon
Genl Mgr: Mike McGarvey

BAY LIMITED
See BERRY HOLDINGS LP

D-U-N-S 18-005-6350
BAY MEDICAL CENTER
615 N Bonita Ave, Panama City, FL 32401-3623
Tel (850) 769-1511 *Founded/Ownrshp* 1949
Sales 223.4MM^E *EMP* 2,000
SIC 8062 8011 General medical & surgical hospitals; Offices & clinics of medical doctors
Pr: Barry Keel
Chf Path: David Weinrach
Chf OB: Yvonne Bullard
CFO: Sherry Bradshaw
**CFO:* Chris Brooks
CFO: Deborah Edgeworth
Treas: Jimmy Barr
**VP:* Donna Baird
VP: Anne Dick
**VP:* Paul Horn
**VP:* Tammy Newton
Exec: Belinda Hofer
Dir Rad: Glen Bailey
Dir Rad: Emily Billingsley

BAY MEDICAL CTR SACRED HEART
See BAY COUNTY HEALTH SYSTEM LLC

D-U-N-S 07-277-1140
BAY REGIONAL MEDICAL CENTER
BAY REGIONAL MEDICAL CENTER AMBULANCE
(*Suby of* MCLAREN HEALTH CARE CORP) ★
1900 Columbus Ave, Bay City, MI 48708-6831
Tel (989) 894-3000 *Founded/Ownrshp* 1972
Sales 278.8MM *EMP* 1,800
SIC 8062 General medical & surgical hospitals
Pr: Alice Gerard
**Pr:* Clarence Sevian
CFO: R Townsend
Bd of Dir: David B Mikolajczak
VP: John Way
Dir Rx: Dick Boon
Admn Mgr: Dan Hatten
Genl Mgr: Jim Boudon
CIO: P J Julian
IT Man: Kurt Valley
Ansthlgy: Garry Bundy

BAY REGIONAL MEDICAL CENTER AMBULANCE
See BAY REGIONAL MEDICAL CENTER

BAY SHIPBUILDING
See FINCANTIERI MARINE GROUP LLC

BAY SHORE SCHOOLS
See BAY SHORE UNION FREE SCHOOL DISTRICT

D-U-N-S 09-331-4086
BAY SHORE UNION FREE SCHOOL DISTRICT
BAY SHORE SCHOOLS
75 Perkal St, Bay Shore, NY 11706-6642
Tel (631) 968-1100 *Founded/Ownrshp* 1898
Sales 58.2MM^E *EMP* 1,600
SIC 8211 Public elementary & secondary schools; Public elementary school; Public senior high school
Treas: Rosanne Albanese
Bd of Dir: Mary Cohen
**Ofcr:* Maureen Virsinger
VP: Laura S Glynn
Dir Sec: Joseph Hodoski
Pr Dir: Krystyna Baumgartner
Pr Dir: Sonia Bonilla
Teacher Pr: Lisa Giacoia

BAY STATE FARM DIRECT FLOWERS
See AMERICAN FLORIST SUPPLY INC

D-U-N-S 06-934-0214
■ **BAY STATE GAS CO** (MA)
(*Suby of* NISOURCE INC) ★
4 Technology Dr, Westborough, MA 01581-1791
Tel (508) 836-7000 *Founded/Ownrshp* 1847
Sales 370.9MM^E *EMP* 757
SIC 4923 Gas transmission & distribution
Pr: Stephen H Bryant
Treas: Jose Soares
**Treas:* David J Vajda
VP: Richard Cencini
VP: Donald N Gershuy
VP: Gail W Haroski
VP: Scott C Madonald
VP: Barbara S McKay
VP: David A Monte
VP: Charles E Shafer
Prin: Mary Kneeland

D-U-N-S 05-532-4248
BAY STATE INSURANCE CO
ANDOVER CO, THE
(*Suby of* STATE FIRE INSURANCE CO) ★
95 River Rd, Andover, MA 01810-1000
Tel (978) 475-3300 *Founded/Ownrshp* 1955
Sales NA *EMP* 240
SIC 6331 Fire, marine & casualty insurance
Pr: William Nichols
VP: Alan Kober
**VP:* Donald Vose
Mktg Dir: Heather Terry

BAY STATE MEDICAL CENTER
See MARYLANE HOSPITAL

D-U-N-S 00-615-4736 IMP/EXP
BAY STATE MILLING CO
100 Congress St Ste 2, Quincy, MA 02169-0906
Tel (617) 328-4423 *Founded/Ownrshp* 1960
Sales 156.0MM^E *EMP* 344
SIC 2041 Flour
CEO: Brian G Rothwell
**Pr:* Peter F Levangie
**CFO:* Peter Banat
**Ch:* Bernard J Rothwell III
**Ex VP:* James D Wilmes
VP: Douglas Dewitt
VP: Walker Humphires
VP: Kevin Kavanaugh
VP: Michael H Pate
VP: Jennifer Robinson
VP: Jim Tomaszewski

D-U-N-S 00-103-1459
BAY STATE POOL SUPPLIES INC
BAYSTATE POOL SUPPLIES
691 Concord Ave, Cambridge, MA 02138-1050
Tel (617) 547-9145 *Founded/Ownrshp* 1968
Sales 276.0MM^E *EMP* 150
SIC 5169 5091 Chemicals & allied products; Swimming pools, equipment & supplies
Pr: Charles P Arakelian
**Sec:* John A Arakelian
**VP:* Chuck Hamilton
**VP:* Gary Najarian
Mktg Mgr: Ron Ossen

D-U-N-S 00-612-7708 IMP/EXP
■ **BAY VALLEY FOODS LLC**
(*Suby of* TREEHOUSE FOODS INC) ★
3200 Riverside Dr Ste A, Green Bay, WI 54301-1644
Tel (800) 558-4700 *Founded/Ownrshp* 2005
Sales 543.7MM^E *EMP* 1,000
SIC 2099 Vegetables, peeled for the trade; Packaged combination products: pasta, rice & potato; Pancake syrup, blended & mixed; Pie fillings, except fruit, meat & vegetable
Pr: Christopher D Sliva
VP: Greg Lewandowski
VP: Chris Purdy
VP: Gary Tritt
Prin: Jill Westrich
Genl Mgr: Tim Hatfield
QA Dir: Maria Konetes
QA Dir: Dustin Krause
QA Dir: Dawn Moriarity
QA Dir: Vanessa Pongnon
QA Dir: Chuck Robatisin
Board of Directors: Howard M Dean Jr, Barbara Kline, Bill Luegurs

BAY WEST PAPER
See WAUSAU PAPER TOWEL & TISSUE LLC

D-U-N-S 07-554-4478
BAYADA HOME HEALTH CARE INC
290 Chester Ave, Moorestown, NJ 08057-3306
Tel (856) 231-1000 *Founded/Ownrshp* 1975
Sales 577.7MM^E *EMP* 17,000
SIC 8082 Visiting nurse service
Pr: J Mark Baiada
COO: Linda Siessel
**CFO:* Tom Sibson
Assoc Dir: Michelle Bloch
Assoc Dir: Denise Kelemen
Assoc Dir: Mellene Palmer
IT Man: Christopher Broschard
IT Man: Craig Petrosky
Opers Mgr: Ellen White
Mktg Mgr: Donna Buhosky
Snr Mgr: Mark Wallace

D-U-N-S 09-120-0266
BAYBEACH HOTELS LLC
BAYBEACH INN
51 Gulf Breeze Pkwy, Pensacola, FL 32507
Tel (850) 932-2214 *Founded/Ownrshp* 2002
Sales 200.0MM *EMP* 60
SIC 7011 Hotels
Genl Mgr: Jana Brewer

BAYBEACH INN
See BAYBEACH HOTELS LLC

BAYCARE EDUCATION SERVICES
See BAYCARE HEALTH SYSTEM INC

BAYCARE EDUCATION SERVICES
See WINTER HAVEN HOSPITAL INC

D-U-N-S 02-907-9022
BAYCARE HEALTH SYSTEM INC
BAYCARE EDUCATION SERVICES
2985 Drew St, Clearwater, FL 33759-3012
Tel (727) 519-1200 *Founded/Ownrshp* 1987
Sales 463.9MM *EMP* 20,000
SIC 8741 Hospital management; Nursing & personal care facility management
Pr: Steve Mason
CFO: Tremonti Carl
CFO: Susan Olds
VP: Stewart Schafferq
Mng Ofcr: Christopher Yarnold
Comm Man: Debra Brooks
Comm Man: Alan Figga
**Prin:* Stewart Schaffer
Ex Dir: Emily Callaway
Off Mgr: Vicki Pine
Pr Mgr: Beth Hardy

D-U-N-S 01-450-2863
BAYCARE HEALTH SYSTEMS LLC (WI)
164 N Broadway, Green Bay, WI 54303-2728
Tel (920) 490-9046 *Founded/Ownrshp* 1996
Sales 84.7MM^E *EMP* 1,076
SIC 8011 Offices & clinics of medical doctors
CEO: Chris Augustian
Netwrk Eng: Jeffrey Bitney
Doctor: Zambrano Isidoro

D-U-N-S 79-404-6607
BAYCARE HOME CARE INC
(*Suby of* BAYCARE EDUCATION SERVICES) ★
8452 118th Ave, Largo, FL 33773-5007
Tel (727) 394-6461 *Founded/Ownrshp* 1999
Sales 5.6MM^E *EMP* 2,000
Accts Ernst & Young Us Llp Atlanta
SIC 8082 7352 Home health care services; Medical equipment rental
Pr: Denton W Crockett
**Treas:* Thomas W Ribble
**VP:* Stephen R Mason
**VP:* Daniel E Sweeney
Nurse Mgr: Jacqueline McGuane
Off Admin: Erica Smith
Sls&Mrk Ex: Nancy Castor
Nrsg Dir: Margaret Gross
Pharmcst: Lisa Hicks

D-U-N-S 12-143-4773 IMP/EXP
BAYCO PRODUCTS INC
640 Sanden Blvd, Wylie, TX 75098-4922
Tel (214) 342-0288 *Founded/Ownrshp* 1983
Sales 179.3MM^E *EMP* 200
SIC 5063 Lighting fixtures, commercial & industrial
Pr: Bijan Bayat
Opers Mgr: Greg Mayfield
Opers Mgr: Cheryl Sun
Natl Sales: Steve Lynch
Natl Sales: Rick Rochambeau
Sls Dir: Peter Fodero
Mktg Mgr: Russell Hoppe
Mktg Mgr: Jeff Rooker

D-U-N-S 11-211-7853
BAYER BUSINESS AND TECHNOLOGY SERVICES LLC
BBTS
(*Suby of* BAYER CORP) ★
100 Bayer Rd, Pittsburgh, PA 15205-9707
Tel (412) 777-2000 *Founded/Ownrshp* 2002
Sales 103.2MM^E *EMP* 800^E
SIC 8742 Business planning & organizing services
CEO: Claudio F Abreu
**Pr:* Helmut Hegger
Top Exec: Stephen Burke
Sr VP: Joerg Ohle
VP: Guy Kingwill
Exec: Hans Bishop
Opers Mgr: Leela Dasari

D-U-N-S 06-496-0248 EXP
BAYER CORP
(*Suby of* BAYER AG)
100 Bayer Rd, Pittsburgh, PA 15205-9741
Tel (412) 777-2000 *Founded/Ownrshp* 1973
Sales 4.7MMM^E *EMP* 16,300
SIC 2821 2879 2819 2834 3841 Polypropylene resins; Pesticides, agricultural or household; Industrial inorganic chemicals; Pharmaceutical preparations; Surgical & medical instruments
Pr: Klaus H Risse
COO: Kurt De Ruwe
**Treas:* Jon R Wyne
VP: Martin Beuck
VP: Christine Bryant
VP: Julie Cheng
VP: Mike Cockrill
VP: Diderico Eyl
VP: Edwin Hemwall
VP: Stefan Hesse
VP: Steinz Heumeller
VP: Chris Loder
VP: Lori McDonald
VP: Johannes Michaelis
VP: Malini Moorthy
VP: Sean O'Dowd
VP: Thomas Panzer
VP: Todd Paporello
VP: Roger Rumer
VP: K Sekhar
**VP:* Melvyn A Silver

D-U-N-S 00-135-0263 IMP/EXP
BAYER CROPSCIENCE LP
(*Suby of* BAYER CORP) ★
2 Tw Alexander Dr, Durham, NC 27709-0198
Tel (919) 549-2000 *Founded/Ownrshp* 1999
Sales 381.1MM^E *EMP* 2,400
SIC 2879 5191

BAYER HEALTHCARE
See BAYER MEDICAL CARE INC

D-U-N-S 11-211-7283 IMP/EXP
BAYER HEALTHCARE LLC
(*Suby of* BAYER CORP) ★
100 Bayer Blvd, Whippany, NJ 07981-1544
Tel (862) 404-3000 *Founded/Ownrshp* 1941
Sales 1.9MMM^E *EMP* 7,000
SIC 2834 8731 3845 3841 Pharmaceutical preparations; Commercial physical research; Electromedical equipment; Surgical & medical instruments
CEO: Gregory S Babe
**Pr:* Erica L Mann
**Pr:* Joerg Ohle
**Pr:* Mark Trudeau
Ofcr: Assi Christelle
Ofcr: Sona Grossova-Garie
Top Exec: Janice Brunetti II
**Sr VP:* Joerg Heidrich
VP: Steve Neumann
Exec: Stacey Wilson
Assoc Dir: Vicki Colman
Assoc Dir: Lillian Kirk
Assoc Dir: Joseph Poth

D-U-N-S 09-317-0199 IMP
BAYER HEALTHCARE PHARMACEUTICALS INC
(*Suby of* BERLIN SCHERING INC) ★
100 Bayer Blvd, Whippany, NJ 07981-1544
Tel (862) 404-3000 *Founded/Ownrshp* 2008
Sales 652.9MM^E *EMP* 1,975
SIC 2834 3841 Drugs affecting neoplasms & endrocrine systems; Drugs acting on the central nervous system & sense organs; Drugs acting on the cardiovascular system, except diagnostic; Surgical & medical instruments
Ofcr: Daniel Apel
**Pr:* Habib Dable
VP: Jon Stelzmiller

D-U-N-S 04-967-3973 EXP
BAYER MEDICAL CARE INC
BAYER HEALTHCARE
(*Suby of* BERLIN SCHERING INC) ★
1 Bayer Dr, Indianola, PA 15051-9702
Tel (724) 940-6800 *Founded/Ownrshp* 2006
Sales 364.2MM^E *EMP* 1,226
SIC 3841 Surgical & medical instruments
Pr: San Ll Ang-
**Pr:* San Ll Ang
**CFO:* Michael T Howard
**Sr VP:* Joseph B Havrilla
**Sr VP:* James F Kessing
**Sr VP:* Clifford E Kress
VP: Doni George
**VP:* John R Tedeschi
Ex Dir: Giles Lieb
Mng Dir: Peter Cleber
Prgrm Mgr: Erik Larson
Board of Directors: Dr Hubertus Erlen, Dr Marlin S Heilman, Wolfgang Kunze, Christian Nowak, H Michael Rook, Thomas H Witmer

BAYFRONT CANCER CENTER
See BAYFRONT MEDICAL CENTER INC

BAYFRONT HEALTH ST PETERSBURG
See BAYFRONT HMA MEDICAL CTR LLC

D-U-N-S 03-431-1830
BAYFRONT HMA MEDICAL CTR LLC (FL)
BAYFRONT HEALTH ST PETERSBURG
701 6th St S, Saint Petersburg, FL 33701-4814
Tel (727) 823-1234 *Founded/Ownrshp* 2013, 2012
Sales 316.9MM *EMP* 83^E
SIC 8011 Medical centers

D-U-N-S 07-322-4370
■ **BAYFRONT MEDICAL CENTER INC**
BAYFRONT CANCER CENTER
(*Suby of* COMMUNITY HEALTH SYSTEMS INC) ★
701 6th St S, Saint Petersburg, FL 33701-4891
Tel (727) 893-6111 *Founded/Ownrshp* 1968
Sales 163.3MM *EMP* 2,018
SIC 8062 General medical & surgical hospitals
CEO: Sue Brody
**Pr:* Kathryn Gillette
CFO: Eric Smith
Obsttrcn: Astrid Mondaca

D-U-N-S 78-901-6136
BAYFRONT REGIONAL DEVELOPMENT CORP
(*Suby of* HAMOT HEALTH FOUNDATION) ★
201 State St, Erie, PA 16550-0002
Tel (814) 877-7000 *Founded/Ownrshp* 1981
Sales 1.2MM^E *EMP* 2,000
SIC 8011 Medical centers
CEO: John Malone

D-U-N-S 83-183-6668
BAYHEALTH MEDICAL CENTER INC
640 S State St, Dover, DE 19901-3530
Tel (302) 422-3311 *Founded/Ownrshp* 1925
Sales 570.1MM *EMP* 2,790^E
Accts Grant Thornton Llp Philadelph
SIC 8062 General medical & surgical hospitals
Pr: Terry Murphy
COO: Mike Metzing
Bd of Dir: Harjinder Grewal
Ofcr: Bonnie Millman
Sr VP: Gary Siegelman
VP: Terry Feinour
VP: Eric Gloss
VP: Gary Shaw
Off Mgr: Trudy Beckett
CIO: Lynn Gold
MIS Dir: David Walczak

D-U-N-S 93-160-5208
BAYLEY CONSTRUCTION A GENERAL PARTNERSHIP
8005 Se 28th St Ste 100, Mercer Island, WA 98040-2911
Tel (206) 621-8884 *Founded/Ownrshp* 1997
Sales 94.6MM^E *EMP* 125

SIC 1542 1541 Commercial & office building, new construction; Commercial & office buildings, renovation & repair; Shopping center construction; Industrial buildings, new construction; Renovation, remodeling & repairs: industrial buildings
CEO: Ron Bayley
Mng Pt: John Pietromonaco
Pr: Steve Grasso
VP: Joan C Bayley
VP: Brandon Etnyre
VP: Mark Florer
VP: Warren Johnsonm
VP: Jim Lansciardi
Sfty Dirs: Joseph Chandler

D-U-N-S 15-470-7954
BAYLOR ALL SAINTS MEDICAL CENTER
(*Suby of* BHCS) ★
1400 8th Ave, Fort Worth, TX 76104-4110
Tel (817) 926-2544 *Founded/Ownrshp* 2002
Sales 347.7MM *EMP* 1,800
SIC 8062 General medical & surgical hospitals
Pr: Steve Newton
**Pr:* David G Klein
COO: Sandra Aaron
VP: Leigh Anne Gates
Dir Lab: Flora McCright
Doctor: Mohammad Ashfaq MD
Pharmcst: Trang Nguyen
Phys Thrpy: Sharon Cheng
HC Dir: Luisa Corley

D-U-N-S 05-111-3330 IMP
BAYLOR COLLEGE OF MEDICINE (TX)
1 Baylor Plz, Houston, TX 77030-3498
Tel (713) 798-4951 *Founded/Ownrshp* 1969
Sales 1.6MMM *EMP* 10,684
SIC 8221

D-U-N-S 10-260-9997 IMP
BAYLOR HEALTH CARE SYSTEM
BHCS
(*Suby of* BAYLOR SCOTT & WHITE HEALTH) ★
3500 Gaston Ave, Dallas, TX 75246-2088
Tel (214) 820-0111 *Founded/Ownrshp* 2013
Sales 2.4MMM^E *EMP* 20,000
Accts Pricewaterhousecoopers Llp D
SIC 8062 8082 1542 General medical & surgical hospitals; Home health care services; Hospital construction
Pr: Joel T Allison
COO: Gary Brock
CFO: Lydia Jumonville
CFO: Fredrick Savelsberg
Chf Cred: Robert Michalski
Chf Mktg O: Irving Prengler
Ex VP: M Timothy Parris
Sr VP: David Ballard
Sr VP: Jennifer Coleman
Sr VP: Keith Holtz
Sr VP: Rosemary Luquire
Sr VP: John McWhorter III
Sr VP: Robert Pickton
Sr VP: William Roberts
VP: John Allen
VP: Bernard Brigonnet
VP: Kevin Croy
VP: Monica Frazer
VP: Kristi Sherrill Hoyl
VP: John B McWhorter III
VP: Joseph Schneider

BAYLOR HEALTH CARE SYSTEMS
See BAYLOR REGIONAL MEDICAL CENTER AT PLANO

D-U-N-S 07-488-4115
BAYLOR HEALTH ENTERPRISES LP
(*Suby of* BHCS) ★
411 N Washington Ave # 7200, Dallas, TX 75246-1713
Tel (214) 820-2492 *Founded/Ownrshp* 1984
Sales 157.2MM^E *EMP* 464
SIC 5122 7011 7991 Pharmaceuticals; Hotels; Physical fitness facilities
Pr: John McWhorter
VP: Jan Baldwin
**VP:* Jennifer Colon
Snr PM: Jim McSweeney

D-U-N-S 02-374-7459
BAYLOR MEDICAL CENTER AT CARROLLTON
BHCS
(*Suby of* BHCS) ★
4343 N Josey Ln, Carrollton, TX 75010-4603
Tel (972) 492-1010 *Founded/Ownrshp* 1953
Sales 158.2MM *EMP* 270
SIC 8062

BAYLOR MEDICAL CENTER AT FRISC
See FRISCO MEDICAL CENTER LLP

D-U-N-S 07-508-9052
BAYLOR MEDICAL CENTER AT GARLAND
PRIORITY SYSTEMS FOR EMPLOYEES
(*Suby of* BHCS) ★
2300 Marie Curie Dr, Garland, TX 75042-5706
Tel (972) 487-5000 *Founded/Ownrshp* 1958, 1991
Sales 189.2MM *EMP* 915
SIC 8062 8082 8011 8093 Hospital, affiliated with AMA residency; Home health care services; Offices & clinics of medical doctors; Mental health clinic, outpatient
Pr: Tom Trenary
**CFO:* Rhonda D Chatham
Dir Soc: Angela Bennett
**Ex Dir:* John Mc Whorter
IT Man: Lynn Fair
IT Man: Robert Freeman
VP Sls: Janet Stuart
Pharmcst: Anila Thachet

D-U-N-S 00-528-1246
BAYLOR MEDICAL CENTER AT IRVING (TX)
BHCS
(*Suby of* BHCS) ★
1901 N Macarthur Blvd, Irving, TX 75061-2220
Tel (972) 579-8100 *Founded/Ownrshp* 1964
Sales 252.9MM *EMP* 1,500^E
SIC 8062 General medical & surgical hospitals
Pr: Cindy Schamp
**VP:* Mitchell Mulvehill
Dir Rad: Penny Tessing
Dir Rx: Garry Green
Phys Thrpy: Cathy Thut

D-U-N-S 07-858-5255
BAYLOR MEDICAL CENTER AT MCKINNEY
5252 W University Dr, McKinney, TX 75071-7822
Tel (469) 764-4600 *Founded/Ownrshp* 2012
Sales 148.4MM *EMP* 41^E
SIC 8011 Medical centers
Pr: Scott Peek
**COO:* Melissa Winter
**CFO:* Steve Roussel

D-U-N-S 07-837-4402
BAYLOR MEDICAL CENTER AT WAXAHACHIE
BHCS
(*Suby of* BHCS) ★
1405 W Jefferson St, Waxahachie, TX 75165-2231
Tel (972) 923-7000 *Founded/Ownrshp* 1983
Sales 110.1MM *EMP* 486
SIC 8062 General medical & surgical hospitals
Pr: Jay Fox
**COO:* Cindy Murray
**VP:* Cheryl McMullen
Mktg Mgr: Sheryl Sullivan
Nrsg Dir: Elaine Nelson
Board of Directors: Ronald P Hudspeth

D-U-N-S 07-315-4338
BAYLOR REGIONAL MEDICAL CENTER AT GRAPEVINE (TX)
BAYLOR SCOTT & WHITE
(*Suby of* BAYLOR SCOTT & WHITE HEALTH) ★
1650 W College St, Grapevine, TX 76051-3565
Tel (817) 481-1588 *Founded/Ownrshp* 1967, 1981
Sales 257.5MM *EMP* 450
SIC 8062 General medical & surgical hospitals
Pr: Scott Peek
Dir OR: Sheldrick Streete
Dir Rad: Roy Thomas
**Ex Dir:* Mark Hood
Opers Mgr: Donna Grace
Pharmcst: Melissa Scott
HC Dir: Terry Clarke

D-U-N-S 19-299-9717
BAYLOR REGIONAL MEDICAL CENTER AT PLANO
BAYLOR HEALTH CARE SYSTEMS
4700 Alliance Blvd, Plano, TX 75093-5323
Tel (469) 814-2000 *Founded/Ownrshp* 2002
Sales 194.9MM *EMP* 800
SIC 8062 General medical & surgical hospitals
CEO: Joel Allison
**Pr:* Jerri Garison
CFO: Robert Knowlton
Nrsg Dir: Ellen Pitcher
Occ Thrpy: Jill Bass

D-U-N-S 96-961-1719
BAYLOR REGIONAL MEDICAL CENTER AT PLANO
2001 Bryan St Ste 2200, Dallas, TX 75201-3024
Tel (214) 820-4135 *Founded/Ownrshp* 2011
Sales 216.3MM *EMP* 4^E
SIC 8011 Offices & clinics of medical doctors

BAYLOR SCOTT & WHITE
See BAYLOR REGIONAL MEDICAL CENTER AT GRAPEVINE

BAYLOR SCOTT & WHITE
See SCOTT & WHITE CLINIC

D-U-N-S 07-916-2757
BAYLOR SCOTT & WHITE HEALTH
3500 Gaston Ave, Dallas, TX 75246-2088
Tel (214) 820-1075 *Founded/Ownrshp* 2013
Sales 13.2MMM^E *EMP* 20,300^E
SIC 8082 8062 Home health care services; General medical & surgical hospitals
CEO: Joel Allison
**CFO:* Fred Savelsbergh
**Chf Cred:* Robert Michalski
**Chf Mktg O:* Bob Pryor
**Ofcr:* David J Ballard
**Ofcr:* Stephen Boyd
**Ofcr:* Kristi Sherrill Hoyl
**Ofcr:* Kristi Hoyl
**Ofcr:* Robert Michalsk
**Ofcr:* J James Rohack
**Ofcr:* Jim Rohack
**Ofcr:* Steve Sullivan
VP: Blake Allison
Exec: Marilyn Hulse

D-U-N-S 07-952-9107
BAYLOR SCOTT & WHITE HOLDINGS (TX)
(*Suby of* BAYLOR SCOTT & WHITE HEALTH) ★
350 N Saint Paul St # 2900, Dallas, TX 75201-4240
Tel (214) 820-3151 *Founded/Ownrshp* 2014
Sales 7.5MMM *EMP* 1^E
Accts Pricewaterhousecoopers Llp Da
SIC 8062 General medical & surgical hospitals
Ex Dir: Paul E Madeley

D-U-N-S 00-751-6735
BAYLOR UNIVERSITY (TX)
700 S University Parks Dr, Waco, TX 76706-1003
Tel (254) 710-1561 *Founded/Ownrshp* 1845
Sales 558.9MM *EMP* 2,500
Accts Grant Thornton Llp Dallas Te
SIC 8221 University
Pr: Robert Sloan PHD
**Pr:* Ken Starr
**VP:* John M Barry
**VP:* Elizabeth Davis
**VP:* Tommye Lou Davis
Off Mgr: Charlotte Angeletti
Off Mgr: Rita Massey
Off Mgr: Melissa Perry
CTO: Denny Kramer
IT Man: Scott Huggins
VP Prd: Taylor Pfeiffer

D-U-N-S 13-103-9331 IMP
BAYLOR UNIVERSITY MEDICAL CENTER
(*Suby of* BAYLOR SCOTT & WHITE HEALTH) ★
2001 Bryan St Ste 2200, Dallas, TX 75201-3024
Tel (214) 820-3151 *Founded/Ownrshp* 1903
Sales 692.3MM^E *EMP* 5,003
SIC 8062 Hospital, medical school affiliation
Pr: Jon Skinner
Chf Rad: Joseph Hise
**Pr:* T Douglas Lawson
**Pr:* John McWhorter
**Pr:* Michael Ramsay
**Pr:* Nancy Vish
**Pr:* Chris York
VP: Stephen Boyd
VP: Mairead Geary
VP: Alok Pareek
VP: Ellen Parri
VP: Irving D Prengler
**VP:* Fred Salvesbergh
Assoc Dir: Robert Perrillo

BAYMONT INN & SUITES
See COLFIN JIH AHI OPCO LLC

BAYONNE MEDICAL CENTER
See IJKG LLC

BAYONNE MEDICAL CENTER
See IJKG OPCO LLC

D-U-N-S 03-026-0467 EXP
BAYONNE MEDICAL CENTER INC
(*Suby of* CAREPOINT HEALTH MANAGEMENT ASSOCIATES LLC) ★
29th Street At Ave E, Bayonne, NJ 07002
Tel (201) 858-5000 *Founded/Ownrshp* 1988
Sales 176.9MM *EMP* 1^E
SIC 8062 General medical & surgical hospitals
CEO: Paul Mimmick
**Pr:* Daniel Kane
**COO:* Marvin Apsel
CFO: Gary Bryant
**CFO:* Gary Perrinoni
CFO: Alfred Setter
Assoc VP: Sabina Sallon
VP: Dara Quinn
VP: Maryanne Sabol
Dir Rx: Daniel Shifrin
DP Exec: Edward Kaczka

D-U-N-S 07-980-6900
BAYONNE SCHOOL DISTRICT
669 Avenue A, Bayonne, NJ 07002-1851
Tel (201) 858-5814 *Founded/Ownrshp* 2015
Sales 135.5MM *EMP* 2,745^E
Accts Donohue Gironda Doria & Tomk
SIC 8211 Public elementary & secondary schools
MIS Dir: Melissa Sisk
Schl Brd P: William Lawson

D-U-N-S 04-734-1052
BAYOU GRAIN & CHEMICAL CORP
P.O. Box 67 (71661-0067)
Tel (870) 473-2281 *Founded/Ownrshp* 1966
Sales 132.5MM *EMP* 17
Accts Howland & Norris Cpa Little
SIC 4221 2873 5153 Elevator storage; Nitrogenous fertilizers; Grain & field beans
Pr: James W Johnson
**Treas:* William J Currie
**VP:* Richard Stock
Genl Mgr: Ron Miller
Genl Mgr: Justin Towery

D-U-N-S 03-996-3384 IMP
■ **BAYOU HOLDINGS OF NEW IBERIA LLC**
(*Suby of* INSITUFORM TECHNOLOGIES LLC) ★
5200 Curtis Ln, New Iberia, LA 70560-0449
Tel (337) 369-3761 *Founded/Ownrshp* 2009
Sales 104.4MM^E *EMP* 160^E
SIC 1389 Oil field services; Gas field services
CTO: Shea Jimmy
IT Man: Charles Shea
Sfty Dirs: David Bourgeois

BAYPOINT TRADING
See BTIG LLC

D-U-N-S 61-290-2536
BAYSHORE COMMUNITY HEALTH SERVICES INC
BAYSHORE COMMUNITY HOSPITAL
727 N Beers St, Holmdel, NJ 07733-1514
Tel (732) 739-5900 *Founded/Ownrshp* 1972
Sales 139.8MM *EMP* 1,512
SIC 8062 8741 General medical & surgical hospitals; Hospital management
Pr: Timothy J Hogan
**Pr:* Timothy Jhogan
**COO:* Anthony Cava
**Ex VP:* Laurence Gumina
VP: Wendy Brown
**VP:* Kelli O'Brien
**VP:* Joseph Reichman
**VP:* Edward Rittweger
**VP:* Linda Walsh
**Prin:* Thomas Goldman
Ex Dir: Mike Schwartz

BAYSHORE COMMUNITY HOSPITAL
See BAYSHORE COMMUNITY HEALTH SERVICES INC

D-U-N-S 06-870-3636
BAYSHORE COMMUNITY HOSPITAL (NJ)
727 N Beers St, Holmdel, NJ 07733-1598
Tel (732) 739-5900 *Founded/Ownrshp* 1962
Sales 123.8MM *EMP* 1,450
SIC 8062 General medical & surgical hospitals
Pr: Timothy J Hogan
**COO:* Anthony Cava
VP: Wendy Brown
**VP:* Linda Walsh
Off Mgr: Rose Sembler

BAYSHORE MEDICAL CENTER
See PASADENA BAYSHORE HOSPITAL INC

D-U-N-S 18-438-7210
BAYSIDE CAPITAL INC
1450 Brickell Ave Fl 31, Miami, FL 33131-3460
Tel (305) 379-8686 *Founded/Ownrshp* 2004
Sales 442.6MM^E *EMP* 3,510
SIC 6799 Investors
Pr: Anthony Tamer
Ofcr: Ed Boyd
**Prin:* Sami Mnaymneh
Mng Dir: John Bolduc
Mng Dir: Craig Jackson
Mng Dir: Duncan Priston
Mng Dir: Andrew Scotland
Sls Mgr: Nikoleta Angelova

D-U-N-S 01-248-9696
BAYSIDE FUEL OIL CORP
1776 Shore Pkwy, Brooklyn, NY 11214-6546
Tel (718) 622-2900 *Founded/Ownrshp* 1937
Sales 142.0MM *EMP* 37
Accts Margolin Winer And Evens Llp
SIC 5171 Petroleum bulk stations; Petroleum terminals
Pr: Sergio Allegretti
**Prin:* Bartolo Allegretti

D-U-N-S 01-248-9704
BAYSIDE FUEL OIL DEPOT CORP
(*Suby of* BAYSIDE FUEL OIL CORP) ★
1776 Shore Pkwy, Brooklyn, NY 11214-6546
Tel (718) 372-9800 *Founded/Ownrshp* 2001
Sales 276.4MM *EMP* 36
Accts Margolin Winer & Evens Llp P
SIC 5171 Petroleum bulk stations; Petroleum terminals
Pr: Sergio Allegretti
**Treas:* Bartollo Allegretti
**Sr VP:* Vincent Allegretti
VP: Bart Allegretti

D-U-N-S 07-923-7988
BAYSTATE HEALTH INC
BAYSTATE MEDICAL CENTER
759 Chestnut St, Springfield, MA 01199-1001
Tel (413) 784-0000 *Founded/Ownrshp* 1983
Sales 1.0MMM *EMP* 4,691
SIC 8062 8221 8249 Hospital, professional nursing school with AMA residency; Colleges universities & professional schools; Vocational apprentice training
CEO: Mark R Tolosky
Chf Path: Richard Friedburg
**Pr:* Mark A Keroack MD
**CFO:* Dennis W Chalke
**Ex VP:* Greg Harb Fache
**Sr VP:* Evan M Benjamin
VP: Mark Gorrel
VP: Keith Holtz
VP: Rick Oliveri
VP: Paula Squires
VP: Joel Vengco
Exec: Danica Larivera
Dir Rad: Patrick Giordano

D-U-N-S 10-899-9004
BAYSTATE HEALTH SYSTEM HEALTH SERVICES INC
280 Chestnut St, Springfield, MA 01199-1000
Tel (413) 794-9939 *Founded/Ownrshp* 1983
Sales 736.1MM^E *EMP* 5,000
SIC 8741 8062 6324 6512

BAYSTATE MEDICAL CENTER
See BAYSTATE HEALTH INC

D-U-N-S 82-770-6008
BAYSTATE MEDICAL PRACTICES INC
759 Chestnut St, Springfield, MA 01199-1001
Tel (413) 794-0000 *Founded/Ownrshp* 2011
Sales 236.5MM *EMP* 2
Accts Deloitte Tax Llp Jericho Ny
SIC 8099 Health & allied services
Prin: Kwan Mew

BAYSTATE POOL SUPPLIES
See BAY STATE POOL SUPPLIES INC

D-U-N-S 82-731-8973
BAYVIEW CADILLAC NEW CARS & SERVICE LLC
1240 N Federal Hwy, West Palm Beach, FL 33403
Tel (954) 537-6200 *Founded/Ownrshp* 1975
Sales 71.8MM^E *EMP* 1,500
SIC 5511 Automobiles, new & used

D-U-N-S 03-868-7430
BAYVIEW FINANCIAL HOLDINGS LP
BAYVIEW FINANCIAL MORTGAGE
4425 Ponce De Leon Blvd # 500, Coral Gables, FL 33146-1873
Tel (305) 854-8880 *Founded/Ownrshp* 1995
Sales 516.9MM *EMP* 1,600
SIC 6211 Investment bankers
COO: Richard Jolis
Treas: John Fischer
Treas: Laura Mischel
Ofcr: Robert Pondolfi
Sr VP: Richard Obrien
Sr VP: Dayle Rosen
Sr VP: Michael Sorenson
VP: David Briggs
VP: Curt Chittenden
VP: Charleston Ellen
VP: Madelin Florence
VP: Ken Gill
VP: Emron Goolcharran
VP: Robert Hall
VP: Matt Jurgaitis
VP: Amit Kenig
VP: Darin Phillips
VP: Louis Piper
VP: Jack Silver
VP: Joann Snyder

BAYVIEW FINANCIAL MORTGAGE
See BAYVIEW FINANCIAL HOLDINGS LP

D-U-N-S 80-884-7888
BAYVIEW LENDING GROUP LLC
(*Suby of* BAYVIEW FINANCIAL MORTGAGE) ★
4425 P De Leon Blvd Fl 3, Coral Gables, FL 33146
Tel (305) 854-8880 *Founded/Ownrshp* 2007
Sales 116.7MM[E] *EMP* 1,480
SIC 6211 Security brokers & dealers

D-U-N-S 01-999-3848
BAYVIEW PRESERVATION LP
5 Commer Ct, San Francisco, CA 94124-2713
Tel (415) 285-7344 *Founded/Ownrshp* 2008
Sales 30.3MM[E] *EMP* 3,900
SIC 6513 Apartment building operators
Sr VP: Leeann Morein
Pt: Jennifer Hardee
Pt: David Robertson

D-U-N-S 60-674-6217 IMP
▲ BAZAARVOICE INC
10901 Stonelake Blvd, Austin, TX 78759-5749
Tel (512) 551-6000 *Founded/Ownrshp* 2005
Sales 199.7MM *EMP* 756
Accts Pricewaterhousecoopers Llp A
Tkr Sym BV *Exch* NGM
SIC 7372 Prepackaged software; Application computer software
Pr: Gene Austin
**Ch Bd:* Thomas J Meredith
CFO: James R Offerdahl
Chf Mktg O: Sara Spivey
Ofcr: Jaime Loera
Ofcr: Elizabeth Ritzcovan
Ofcr: Ryan D Robinson
Ex VP: Gary G Allison
VP: Andy North
VP: John Stockton
VP: Philip Ziman
Exec: Marie Tarpley
Exec: Ashley Wallace
Board of Directors: Steven H Berkowitz, Sydney L Carey, Jeffrey S Hawn, Jared Kopf, Mary T McDowell

D-U-N-S 04-964-7118
BAZELL OIL CO INC
14371 State Route 328, Logan, OH 43138-9449
Tel (740) 385-5420 *Founded/Ownrshp* 1972
Sales 123.0MM *EMP* 35
SIC 5172 5983 Fuel oil; Petroleum brokers; Fuel oil dealers
Pr: Joseph Michael Bazell
**Sec:* Donald D Poling
VP: Janet S Bazell

D-U-N-S 79-834-0725
BAZON-COX AND ASSOCIATES INC
1244 Executive Blvd B113, Chesapeake, VA 23320-2878
Tel (757) 410-2128 *Founded/Ownrshp* 1992
Sales 289.8MM *EMP* 40
SIC 7373 Systems integration services
CEO: Gerald Lynn Brooks
**Pr:* Anderson Cox
**Pr:* John L Lentini
VP Opers: Paul Murray

BB &T CAPITAL MARKETS
See SCOTT & STRINGFELLOW LLC

D-U-N-S 19-859-6640
■ BB &T FINANCIAL FSB A FEDERAL SAVINGS BANK
(*Suby of* BB&T CORP) ★
4 Bradley Park Ct Ste 1c, Columbus, GA 31904-3649
Tel (706) 653-7885 *Founded/Ownrshp* 2001
Sales 367.2MM *EMP* 34
SIC 8742 Financial consultant
Prin: Lynn Gooch
CFO: Jimi H Pope

BB&T
See BRANCH BANKING AND TRUST CO

BB&T
See BRANCH BANKING AND TRUST CO HEALTH CARE PLAN

D-U-N-S 00-313-6327
BB&T
COLONIAL BANK
8214 Westchester Dr # 100, Dallas, TX 75225-6100
Tel (214) 234-7750 *Founded/Ownrshp* 1998
Sales NA *EMP* 200[E]
SIC 6021
Pr: Malcolm Holland
Sr VP: Gail Fuller
Sr VP: Angela Harper
VP: Michael Catapano
Netwrk Eng: Jan Haley

D-U-N-S 80-684-2519
■ BB&T CAPITAL TRUST IV
(*Suby of* BB&T CORP) ★
200 W 2nd St Ste 1800, Winston Salem, NC 27101-4049
Tel (336) 733-2000 *Founded/Ownrshp* 2007
Sales NA *EMP* 374[E]
SIC 6021 National commercial banks
CEO: Kelly S King
VP: Sandra Camastra
VP: Terry Yim
Snr Mgr: William Collins

D-U-N-S 07-557-6306 IMP
▲ BB&T CORP
200 W 2nd St Ste 260, Winston Salem, NC 27101-4049
Tel (336) 733-2000 *Founded/Ownrshp* 1968
Sales NA *EMP* 37,200
Tkr Sym BBT *Exch* NYS
SIC 6021 6311 6035 6211 National commercial banks; Life insurance; Federal savings & loan associations; Security brokers & dealers
Pr: Kelly S King
Pr: Don Bowie
Pr: Leigh Bradley
Pr: Emily Brown
Pr: Ricky K Brown
Pr: Heath Campbell
Pr: Sarah Creed
Pr: Chevol Davis
Pr: Dane Dunkel
Pr: Connie Eubanks
Pr: Melissa Hopp
Pr: Debbie Hunt
Pr: Andrew Hurwich
Pr: Willie Karnes
Pr: Mala Kasthurirangan
Pr: Carl Kurth
Pr: Jeff Molesa
Pr: Jason Morehouse
Pr: Susanne Pearce
Pr: Penney Potts
Pr: Christina Powers
Board of Directors: William J Reuter, Jennifer S Banner, Christine Sears, K David Boyer Jr, Thomas E Skains, Anna R Cablik, Thomas Thompson, James A Faulkner, Edwin H Welch, I Patricia Henry, Stephen T Williams, Eric C Kendrick, Louis B Lynn, Edward C Milligan, Charles A Patton

D-U-N-S 07-916-4626
■ BB&T INSURANCE HOLDINGS INC
(*Suby of* BB&T) ★
200 W 2nd St, Winston Salem, NC 27101-4019
Tel (336) 733-2500 *Founded/Ownrshp* 2000
Sales NA *EMP* 1,309[E]
SIC 6021 National commercial banks
CEO: Kelly S King
**CFO:* Daryl Bible

D-U-N-S 03-686-0070
■ BB&T INSURANCE SERVICES INC
KEMPER INSURANCE
(*Suby of* BB&T) ★
3605 Glenwood Ave Ste 190, Raleigh, NC 27612-3908
Tel (919) 716-9907 *Founded/Ownrshp* 2006
Sales NA *EMP* 2,405
SIC 6411 Insurance agents, brokers & service
Pr: H Wade Reece
Treas: Mary W Peele
VP: Camille Smith

BBA AVIATION GROUP
See BBA US HOLDINGS INC

D-U-N-S 60-435-3524
BBA US HOLDINGS INC
BBA AVIATION GROUP
(*Suby of* BBA OVERSEAS HOLDINGS LIMITED)
201 S Orange Ave Ste 1425, Orlando, FL 32801-5006
Tel (407) 648-7230 *Founded/Ownrshp* 1994
Sales 95.7MM[E] *EMP* 732
SIC 3728 2399 3052 Aircraft parts & equipment; Belting, fabric: made from purchased materials; Rubber belting
Pr: Joseph I Goldstein
**Treas:* Daniel Marcinik

BBAHC
See BRISTOL BAY AREA HEALTH CORP

D-U-N-S 08-617-1873
BBAM LLC
(*Suby of* BABCOCK & BROWN RENEWABLE HOLDINGS INC) ★
50 California St Fl 14, San Francisco, CA 94111-4683
Tel (415) 512-1515 *Founded/Ownrshp* 1999
Sales 137.9MM[E] *EMP* 805
SIC 6211 Investment bankers
CEO: Steve Zissis
**Pt:* James V Babcock
**Pt:* James Fantaci
**Pt:* James D Jaworski
**Pt:* F Jan Blaustein Scholes
**CFO:* Rob Tomczak
Bd of Dir: Ian M Faicd
Bd of Dir: Elizabeth Nosworthy
Ex Dir: Martin Rey
IT Man: Tillman Dickson

D-U-N-S 36-269-2113 IMP
BBB INDUSTRIES LLC
LTD PARTS
29627 Renaissance Blvd, Daphne, AL 36526-9596
Tel (800) 280-2737 *Founded/Ownrshp* 2004
Sales 953.5MM[E] *EMP* 5,000
SIC 3694 3714 Engine electrical equipment; Motor vehicle parts & accessories
CEO: Joseph Ceretta
CFO: Ross Bratlee
CFO: Jeremy Dwidwell
CFO: William Read
Treas: William Jackson
Ex VP: John Smart
VP: Glenn Barco
VP: Bruce Bigler
VP: John Boyer
VP: Gilbert Estrada
VP: Joe Feicelli
VP: Don Garrett
VP: Matthew Knott

D-U-N-S 61-438-0199
BBB TANK SERVICES INC
162 Independence Pkwy N, Baytown, TX 77520-1033
Tel (832) 695-2132 *Founded/Ownrshp* 2001
Sales 95.1MM[E] *EMP* 108
Accts Weaver And Tidwell Llp Da
SIC 1389 Lease tanks, oil field: erecting, cleaning & repairing
Pr: Robert E Swain
**CFO:* Jacob Swain
**Treas:* Gary Thompson
**VP:* Roy Dennis

D-U-N-S 02-682-6628 IMP
BBC WORLDWIDE AMERICAS INC
(*Suby of* BBC WORLDWIDE LIMITED)
1120 Ave Of The Amrcas, New York, NY 10036-6700
Tel (212) 705-9300 *Founded/Ownrshp* 1984
Sales 117.9MM[E] *EMP* 300
SIC 4833 Television broadcasting stations
Pr: Herb Scannell
**COO:* Ann Sarnoff
**CFO:* Andrew Bott
Ex VP: David Boyle
Ex VP: Soumya Sriraman
Sr VP: Matt Stein
Sr VP: Danette Trosclair
Sr VP: Carol Turner
VP: Christine Black
VP: Valerie Bruce
VP: Gregg Brussel
VP: Stella Creasey
VP: Tracy Forsyth
VP: Melissa Green
VP: Devin Johnson
VP: Emily Powers
VP: Michael Thomson
Comm Man: Patricia Blanco-Ramos

BBCF BUILDING-BAPTIST EAST
See BOSTON BASKIN CANCER FOUNDATION INC

D-U-N-S 15-157-7723 IMP
BBCN BANK
CALIFORNIA CENTER BANK
3731 Wilshire Blvd # 1000, Los Angeles, CA 90010-2828
Tel (213) 251-2222 *Founded/Ownrshp* 2011
Sales NA *EMP* 704
SIC 6021

D-U-N-S 00-698-0825
■ BBDO WORLDWIDE INC
(*Suby of* OMNICOM GROUP INC) ★
1285 Ave Of The Amer, New York, NY 10019-6069
Tel (212) 459-5000 *Founded/Ownrshp* 1928
Sales 667.4MM[E] *EMP* 10,000[E]
SIC 7311 Advertising agencies
Pr: Andrew Robertson
Pr: John B Osborn
CFO: James Cannon
Ofcr: Elana Firestone
Ofcr: David Lubars
Ex VP: Michael Aimette
Ex VP: John Berg
Ex VP: Stacie Boney
Ex VP: Marc Burns
Ex VP: Gina Christie
Ex VP: Simon Marlow
Ex VP: Rob McKinley
Ex VP: Jim Reath
Ex VP: Richard Santiago
Ex VP: Mark Tillinghast
Sr VP: Connie Eggert
Sr VP: Eric Harkna
Sr VP: Joyce Pedretti
Sr VP: Davis Sheron
VP: Misty Baker
VP: Mike Boulia

D-U-N-S 96-286-5452
BBHI HOLDINGS LLC
(*Suby of* CABLEVISION) ★
1111 Stewart Ave, Bethpage, NY 11714-3533
Tel (516) 803-2300 *Founded/Ownrshp* 2010
Sales NA *EMP* 1,105
SIC 6719 Investment holding companies, except banks
Pr: James L Dolan
**Treas:* Kevin Watson

D-U-N-S 10-330-6465
BBL LLC
302 Washington Ave, Albany, NY 12203-1027
Tel (518) 452-8200 *Founded/Ownrshp* 1996
Sales 100.7MM[E] *EMP* 251
SIC 1542 1541 1521 1622 8741 Commercial & office building, new construction; Commercial & office buildings, renovation & repair; Industrial buildings, new construction; Renovation, remodeling & repairs: industrial buildings; New construction, single-family houses; General remodeling, single-family houses; Bridge construction; Construction management
**VP:* Jon Deforest
VP: John Kellogg
VP: John Wodoslawsky
Off Mgr: Patty Baxter

BBNC
See BRISTOL BAY NATIVE CORP

BBS
See BIRNIE BUS SERVICE INC

BBSI
See BARRETT BUSINESS SERVICES INC

BBTS
See BAYER BUSINESS AND TECHNOLOGY SERVICES LLC

D-U-N-S 80-878-7733 IMP/EXP
BBU INC
(*Suby of* GRUPO BIMBO, S.A.B. DE C.V.)
255 Business Center Dr # 200, Horsham, PA 19044-3424
Tel (215) 347-5500 *Founded/Ownrshp* 1993
Sales 10.8MMM[E] *EMP* 26,000
SIC 2051 Bread, cake & related products
Pr: Fred Penny
Treas: H Darrell Miller
VP: Ruben Herrera
**VP:* Stephen J Mollick
**VP:* Shelly W Seligman
CIO: John Scalia
IT Man: Netty Pavel
Opers Mgr: Steve Batey
VP Mktg: Steven Zamichow
Board of Directors: Rick Lee

D-U-N-S 05-986-4702
BBVA COMPASS BANCSHARES INC
COMPASS BANK
(*Suby of* COMPASS BANK) ★
2200 Post Oak Blvd Fl 18, Houston, TX 77056-4786
Tel (205) 297-3000 *Founded/Ownrshp* 1971
Sales NA *EMP* 8,000
SIC 6022 State commercial banks
CEO: Gary Hegel
**Ch Bd:* Jose M Garcia
Pr: Cedric Buchanon
Pr: Will Leonard
Pr: Everett Orrick
Pr: Brad Parker
Pr: Katie Sharon
Pr: Shawn J Thompson
**COO:* Rafael Bustillo
COO: Cecilia Rodriguez
COO: Clark Tucker
Chf Cred: James Muston
Bd of Dir: Ben Hardman
**Ofcr:* Caleb Merriman
Ofcr: David S Neel
Ex VP: Peter Bauer
Ex VP: David Davis
Ex VP: David Erwin
Ex VP: Scott Flowers
Ex VP: James Heslop
Ex VP: Jonathan P Mulkin

D-U-N-S 84-923-8902
■ BBX CAPITAL CORP
(*Suby of* HOFFMANS CHOCOLATES) ★
401 E Las Olas Blvd, Fort Lauderdale, FL 33301-2210
Tel (954) 940-4000 *Founded/Ownrshp* 1994
Sales 131.4MM *EMP* 651[E]
Tkr Sym BBX *Exch* NYS
SIC 6798 6035 Real estate investment trusts; Savings institutions, federally chartered
Ch Bd: Jarett S Levan
CFO: Raymond S Lopez
**V Ch Bd:* John E Abdo
Ex VP: Seth M Wise
VP: Brick Kerge

D-U-N-S 82-523-4735 IMP
BC INTERNATIONAL GROUP INC
922 Riverview Dr, Totowa, NJ 07512-1127
Tel (973) 826-1140 *Founded/Ownrshp* 1993
Sales 90.8MM[E] *EMP* 800
Accts Patrizio & Zhao Llc Parsippa
SIC 5632 Fur apparel, made to custom order
Ch Bd: Chris Spyropoulos
Pr: John Alciviades
**CFO:* Savvy Asprou
Sr VP: Peter Levin
Sr VP: Tom Rice
S&M/VP: Ken O'Day

D-U-N-S 07-974-6429
BC MOUNTAIN HOLDINGS INC
(*Suby of* BAIN CAPITAL LP) ★
14600 York Rd Ste A, Sparks, MD 21152-9396
Tel (800) 763-1233 *Founded/Ownrshp* 2012
Sales 2.5MMM[E] *EMP* 8,000[E]
SIC 3423 Hand & edge tools
CEO: Tom Wroe

BC USA
See ZAUSNER FOODS CORP

D-U-N-S 60-969-3874 IMP/EXP
BCBG MAX AZRIA GROUP LLC
2761 Fruitland Ave, Vernon, CA 90058-3607
Tel (323) 589-2224 *Founded/Ownrshp* 1989
Sales 1.9MMM[E] *EMP* 2,650
SIC 5137 5621 2335 Women's & children's clothing; Women's clothing stores; Women's, juniors' & misses' dresses
CEO: Max Azria
CFO: Daniell Duclon
**CFO:* Brian Fleming
**Chf Cred:* Lubov Azria
**Ex VP:* Martine Melloul
Exec: Carrie Dempsey
Creative D: Lissa Marie
Brnch Mgr: Lydia Miner
Dist Mgr: Kendra Sacca
CIO: Nader Karimi
Web Prj Mg: Melissa Dickson

BCBSA
See BLUE CROSS & BLUE SHIELD ASSOCIATION

D-U-N-S 00-621-2997
BCBSM INC (MN)
BLUE CROSS AND BLUE SHIELD
(*Suby of* AWARE INTEGRATED INC) ★
3535 Blue Cross Rd, Saint Paul, MN 55122-1154
Tel (651) 662-8000 *Founded/Ownrshp* 1933
Sales NA *EMP* 3,400
SIC 6321 6324 Accident & health insurance; Hospital & medical service plans
Pr: Michael J Guyette
CEO: Tina Holmes
CEO: Elizabeth Moran
**COO:* James Eppel
**CFO:* Jay Matushack
CFO: Jay Matushak
**CFO:* Pamela Sedmak
**Chf Mktg O:* William Gerardi
**Ex VP:* Michael Morrow
**Sr VP:* James Egan
**Sr VP:* Richard M Niemiec
Sr VP: Jamison Rice
VP: Diana Crowell
VP: Dana Erickson
VP: Sandy Hill
VP: Rochelle Myers
VP: Lori Nelson
**VP:* Jason Newman
VP: Erin Satterwhite
VP: Maryann Stump
VP: Janelle Waldock

BCC
See BALANCED CARE CORP

BCCI BUILDERS
See BCCI CONSTRUCTION CO

D-U-N-S 15-766-1083
BCCI CONSTRUCTION CO
BCCI BUILDERS
1160 Battery St Ste 250, San Francisco, CA 94111-1216
Tel (415) 817-5100 *Founded/Ownrshp* 1986
Sales 92.2MM[E] *EMP* 140[E]
Accts Shea Labagh Dobberstein Cpas
SIC 1542 Commercial & office buildings, renovation & repair
Pr: Michael Scribner
**CFO:* Hisham Mushasha
Sr VP: Bill Groth
**VP:* Michael Dean
**VP:* William Groth
**VP:* Dominic Sarica

**VP:* Todd Swartz
Mktg Dir: Wendy Bryant

D-U-N-S 11-849-9610
BCD TRAVEL USA LLC
B C D
6 Concourse Pkwy Ste 2400, Atlanta, GA 30328-6120
Tel (678) 441-5200 *Founded/Ownrshp* 1996
Sales 559.2MM^E *EMP* 6,050
SIC 4724 7372 Travel agencies; Business oriented computer software
Pr: John Snyder
Pr: Mark Johnson
**CFO:* Stephan Baars
**Ex VP:* David Coppens
Sr VP: Kathy M Bedell
Sr VP: April Bridgeman
**Sr VP:* Christian Dahl
Sr VP: John McDowell
Sr VP: Lori Popiolkowski
Sr VP: Leithia Warren
VP: Dixie Akins
VP: Rose B Aquino
VP: Kathy Bedell
VP: Julie Carroll
VP: Jorge Cruz
VP: Joseph Dooley
VP: Deborah Elbaum
VP: Reggie McNeil
VP: Reggie McNeill
VP: Rob McTeague
VP: Andy Pierce

BCFORWARD
See BUCHER AND CHRISTIAN CONSULTING INC

D-U-N-S 06-945-9576
BCFS HEALTH AND HUMAN SERVICES
1506 Bexar Crossing St, San Antonio, TX 78232-1587
Tel (210) 832-5000 *Founded/Ownrshp* 1944
Sales 197.2MM *EMP* 500^E
Accts Bkd Llp San Antonio Texas
SIC 8322 Individual & family services
Pr: Kevin C Dinnin
**Treas:* Claudia M Oliveira

BCG
See BOSTON CONSULTING GROUP INC

D-U-N-S 08-137-0421
BCH MECHANICAL INC
EXPRESS METALS
6354 118th Ave, Largo, FL 33773-3728
Tel (727) 546-3561 *Founded/Ownrshp* 2000
Sales 109.2MM^E *EMP* 450
SIC 1711 3444 Plumbing, heating, air-conditioning contractors; Sheet metalwork
Pr: D W Blume
**Pr:* Daryl Bloom
COO: Dan Allen
**Treas:* John Fields
VP Sls: Brain Wilkinson

BCI
See BLOCK COMMUNICATIONS INC

D-U-N-S 00-828-9373 IMP/EXP
■ BCI COCA-COLA BOTTLING CO OF LOS ANGELES
(*Suby of* COCA-COLA REFRESHMENTS USA INC) ★
1334 S Central Ave, Los Angeles, CA 90021-2210
Tel (213) 746-5555 *Founded/Ownrshp* 1986
Sales 443.2MM^E *EMP* 4,200
SIC 2086 Bottled & canned soft drinks
Genl Mgr: Terry Fitch
**Genl Mgr:* William O'Brien

BCIU
See BERKS COUNTY INTERMEDIATE UNIT

BCPS
See BALTIMORE COUNTY PUBLIC SCHOOLS

D-U-N-S 01-348-9380
BCS FINANCIAL CORP
BCS INSURANCE COMPANY
2 Mid America Plz, Oakbrook Terrace, IL 60181-4451
Tel (630) 472-7700 *Founded/Ownrshp* 1949, 1985
Sales NA *EMP* 104
SIC 6331 6311 6211 Property damage insurance; Life insurance carriers; Security brokers & dealers
Pr: H F Beacham III
Pr: Joe Castellon
Pr: Elias Georgopoulos
Pr: Vanessa Jacobs
Chf Mktg O: Peter Costello
VP: Rich Behrens
VP: Sharon Dold
VP Admn: Yvonne Lee
QA Dir: Sue Wilk
Telecom Mg: Joyce Marshall
Sales Exec: Mike Murphy

BCS INSURANCE COMPANY
See BCS FINANCIAL CORP

BCS SERVICES
See BEST CONTRACTING SERVICES INC

BCSD
See BAKERSFIELD CITY SCHOOL DISTRICT EDUCATIONAL FOUNDATION

BCU
See BAXTER CREDIT UNION

D-U-N-S 09-268-2129 IMP/EXP
BD LAPLACE LLC
ARCELORMITTAL
138 Highway 3217, La Place, LA 70068-8821
Tel (985) 652-4900 *Founded/Ownrshp* 2016
Sales 252.0MM^E *EMP* 620
SIC 3312 Blast furnaces & steel mills; Structural & rail mill products; Structural shapes & pilings, steel; Billets, steel
CEO: Robert Simon
**Pr:* Alton Davis
Genl Mgr: Ray Hawkins
IT Man: Stephane Brochu
VP Sls: Jim Howe

D-U-N-S 00-890-1568 IMP
BD VINTON LLC
METAL PROCESSING
I-10 Vinton Rd, Canutillo, TX 79835
Tel (915) 886-2000 *Founded/Ownrshp* 2016
Sales 248.6MM^E *EMP* 450
SIC 5051 3312 3449 3316 Metals service centers & offices; Bars & bar shapes, steel, hot-rolled; Miscellaneous metalwork; Cold finishing of steel shapes
CEO: Robert Simon
Pr: Alton Davis
VP Opers: Juan Delgado
VP Opers: Miguel Franco
VP Sls: Jim Howe

D-U-N-S 82-868-4014
BDF HOLDING CORP
428 Tolland Tpke, Manchester, CT 06042-1765
Tel (860) 474-1200 *Founded/Ownrshp* 2014
Sales 551.0MM^E *EMP* 1,800^E
SIC 5712 Furniture stores
CEO: Ted English
**Pr:* Mike Skirvin

D-U-N-S 10-315-5656 IMP
BDI INC
BARING DISTRIBUTORS
8000 Hub Pkwy, Cleveland, OH 44125-5731
Tel (216) 642-9100 *Founded/Ownrshp* 1935
Sales 477.2MM^E *EMP* 500^E
SIC 1389 Oil sampling service for oil companies
CEO: Frank L Bystricky
COO: Chris Hawkins
VP: Kenneth Miko
**VP:* Bud Thayer
**Prin:* Mike Fryz
Brnch Mgr: Larry Carr
Brnch Mgr: Byron Kempf
Brnch Mgr: Tom Ornell

D-U-N-S 04-768-4840
BDO USA LLP
130 E Randolph St # 2800, Chicago, IL 60601-6207
Tel (312) 240-1236 *Founded/Ownrshp* 2010
Sales 611.7MM^E *EMP* 3,193
SIC 8721 Certified public accountant
CEO: Wayne Berson
Mng Pt: Rocco Dibartolo
CFO: Lynn Calhoun
Prin: Matthew K Becker
Prin: Stephanie Giammarco
Prin: Christopher J Orella
Adm Dir: Martin McLaughlin
Ex Dir: Ken A Mooney
Off Admin: Elizabeth Shapiro-Loser
Dir IT: Greg Sasso
Sales Exec: Carolyn Brown

D-U-N-S 06-903-7802
BDP INTERNATIONAL INC
BDP TRANSPORT
510 Walnut St Fl 14, Philadelphia, PA 19106-3690
Tel (215) 629-8900 *Founded/Ownrshp* 1972
Sales 1.0MMM^E *EMP* 3,355
SIC 4731 Freight forwarding; Customhouse brokers; Transportation agents & brokers
Pr: Richard J Bolte Jr
Sr Pt: Joann Boccia
**Pr:* Mike Andaloro
**Treas:* Francis X Bolte
Treas: Roseanna Dalessandro
**Ofcr:* Lance Malesh
Top Exec: James Fenaroli
VP: Peter Annese
VP: John Clark
VP: Michael Ford
VP: Raffelina Giove
VP: Thomas Janssens
VP: Edward Kane
VP: Thomas Keene
VP: Tom Lynch
VP: Joseph Messick
VP: Hugh R Parrish
VP: Rob Parrish
VP: Kenneth M Wensel
VP: Michael Wilson
Exec: Andria Dipresso

BDP TRANSPORT
See BDP INTERNATIONAL INC

D-U-N-S 13-192-8285
BDS MARKETING INC
10 Holland, Irvine, CA 92618-2504
Tel (949) 472-6700 *Founded/Ownrshp* 1984
Sales 120.9MM^E *EMP* 1,100
SIC 7311 8743 8732 Advertising agencies; Promotion service; Commercial nonphysical research
Prin: Mark Dean
Mng Pt: Kristen Cook
**Ex VP:* Mike Britton
VP: Larry Dorr
VP: Jeffrey Hull
VP: Khalid Kakish
VP: Paul Spadino
Ex Dir: George Hoffman
Sls Mgr: Joe Pearson

BD'S MONGOLIAN GRILL
See MONGOLIAN OPERATING CO LLC

D-U-N-S 02-881-8701
BDT BEVERAGE LLC
B D T BEVERAGE
2712 Westwood Dr, Nashville, TN 37204-2712
Tel (615) 742-3771 *Founded/Ownrshp* 2001
Sales 97.9MM^E *EMP* 70
SIC 5149 Beverages, except coffee & tea
Rgnl Mgr: Casey Lane
Off Mgr: Catherine Miller

D-U-N-S 07-969-2306
BDT CAPITAL PARTNERS LLC
401 N Michigan Ave # 3100, Chicago, IL 60611-4251
Tel (312) 660-7311 *Founded/Ownrshp* 2009
Sales 800.0MM^E *EMP* 1,580^E
SIC 6799 Tax liens: holding, buying & selling

BE THE MATCH
See NATIONAL MARROW DONOR PROGRAM INC

D-U-N-S 19-651-9412
■ BE&K BUILDING GROUP LLC
(*Suby of* PERNIX BUILDING GROUP LLC) ★
201 E Mcbee Ave Ste 400, Greenville, SC 29601-2894
Tel (864) 250-5000 *Founded/Ownrshp* 2004
Sales 284.6MM^E *EMP* 408^E
SIC 1542 1541 1522 Commercial & office building contractors; Specialized public building contractors; Institutional building construction; Stadium construction; Industrial buildings & warehouses; Food products manufacturing or packing plant construction; Industrial buildings, new construction; Pharmaceutical manufacturing plant construction; Hotel/motel & multi-family home construction; Renovation, hotel/motel
Pr: Mac Carpenter
Treas: Douglas M Joehl
VP: Shawn Rodwell

BEA
See BATTELLE ENERGY ALLIANCE LLC

D-U-N-S 83-755-6844
■ BEA SYSTEMS INC
(*Suby of* ORACLE CORP) ★
2315 N 1st St, San Jose, CA 95131-1010
Tel (650) 506-7000 *Founded/Ownrshp* 2008
Sales 160.8MM^E *EMP* 4,278
SIC 7371 7372 Computer software development; Prepackaged software
Ch Bd: Alfred S Chuang
Pt: Alan Button
Pr: Ted Kimes
CFO: William Kline
Chf Mktg O: John Knightlys
Chf Mktg O: Judith Sim
Ex VP: Mark T Carges
Ex VP: Richard Geraffo
Ex VP: Olivier Helleboid
Ex VP: William Klein
Ex VP: David Logan
Ex VP: Wai M Wong
Sr VP: Galit Appo
Sr VP: Rich Geraffo
VP: Nobby Akiha
VP: Matthew Androski
VP: Laurie Cremona
VP: Joe Dachuk
VP: Mercedes Ellison
VP: Michael Goldstein
VP: Stephen Heilig

D-U-N-S 04-338-7976
BEACH CO
211 King St Ste 300, Charleston, SC 29401-3173
Tel (843) 722-2615 *Founded/Ownrshp* 1975
Sales 240.3MM^E *EMP* 425
SIC 6552 8741 1542 Subdividers & developers; Management services; Commercial & office building, new construction
Ch Bd: Charles S Way Jr
Pr: Stephanie Czerwinski
**Pr:* John C Darby
COO: Mark Taylor
CFO: J Reyna
**Treas:* Pat McDermott
VP: Judy G McCann
VP: Kevin Oneill
VP: Mike Stallings
Sales Exec: Glenn Hollis
Mktg Dir: Karen Bacot

D-U-N-S 06-295-2080 IMP
BEACH MOLD & TOOL INC
999 Progress Blvd, New Albany, IN 47150-7221
Tel (812) 945-2688 *Founded/Ownrshp* 1972
Sales 92.2MM^E *EMP* 600
SIC 3089 3544

D-U-N-S 10-141-0413 EXP
BEACH TRADING CO INC
BEACHCAMERA.COM
80 Carter Dr, Edison, NJ 08817-2094
Tel (800) 572-3224 *Founded/Ownrshp* 1983
Sales 200.0MM *EMP* 100
SIC 3861 5731 Photographic equipment & supplies; Video cameras, recorders & accessories
Pr: Raymond R Mosseri
**Sec:* Sol Mosseri
**VP:* Albert R Mosseri

D-U-N-S 05-373-9905 IMP
BEACHBODY LLC
PRODUCT PARTNERS
3301 Exposition Blvd Fl 3, Santa Monica, CA 90404-5082
Tel (310) 883-9000 *Founded/Ownrshp* 1999
Sales 151.5MM^E *EMP* 230^E
SIC 7313 7999 Electronic media advertising representatives; Physical fitness instruction
**Ofcr:* William E Wheeler
VP: Louise Bak
Dir: Jonathan Cook
Art Dir: Brian Woldman

BEACHCAMERA.COM
See BEACH TRADING CO INC

BEACHLAWN MORTGAGE COMPANY
See COLD HEADING CO

D-U-N-S 62-189-6430
BEACHNER GRAIN INC
2600 Flynn Dr, Parsons, KS 67357-7448
Tel (620) 449-8500 *Founded/Ownrshp* 1986
Sales 138.5MM^E *EMP* 160
SIC 5153 Grains
CEO: Gary Breachner
**Pr:* Eugene C Beachner
CFO: Dan Plake
**Sec:* Robert T Beachner
**VP:* Jerry Beachner

BEACHSIDE SERVICES
See SWS ENVIRONMENTAL SERVICES

BEACHWOOD NRSING HALTHCARE CTR
See EZRA HEALTH CARE INC

D-U-N-S 00-695-1529
BEACON COMPANIES INC (MA)
2 Center Plz Ste 700, Boston, MA 02108-1906
Tel (617) 574-1100 *Founded/Ownrshp* 1995
Sales 103.6MM^E *EMP* 800
SIC 1522 6531 1542 Hotel/motel, new construction; Multi-family dwellings, new construction; Real estate managers; Commercial & office building, new construction
Pr: Howard Earl Cohen
**Pr:* Timothy Donovan
**Ch:* Edwin N Sidman
**Treas:* Timothy J Cowles
**VP:* David Greenblatt
Ex Dir: Karen Baker
VP Sls: Reesa Fischer

D-U-N-S 08-819-2141
BEACON HEALTH OPTIONS INC (TX)
(*Suby of* FHC HEALTH SYSTEMS INC) ★
240 Corporate Blvd # 100, Norfolk, VA 23502-4971
Tel (757) 459-5100 *Founded/Ownrshp* 1987
Sales NA *EMP* 3,000
SIC 6324 8322 6411 Hospital & medical service plans; Individual & family services; Medical insurance claim processing, contract or fee basis
CEO: Timothy Murphy
CEO: Jason Bearden
COO: Bob Esposito
COO: Nancy Lane
CFO: Scott M Tabakin
CFO: Douglas Thompson
Ex VP: Harold A Levine
Ex VP: Kyle A Raffaniello
Ex VP: Daniel M Risku
Ex VP: Terry Young
VP: Renee Abdou-Malta
VP: Watkins Bracey
VP: Lucy Buckner
VP: Lisa M Clements
VP: Cathy Gilbert
VP: Maria Hester
VP: Deborah Hirschfelder
VP: Doug Miller
VP: Izhar Mujaddidi
VP: Dale Rehkamp
VP: John Straus

BEACON HEALTH SYSTEM
See ELKHART GENERAL HOSPITAL INC

D-U-N-S 07-922-8770
BEACON HEALTH SYSTEM INC
MEMORIAL HOSPITAL SOUTH BEND
615 N Michigan St, South Bend, IN 46601-1033
Tel (574) 647-1000 *Founded/Ownrshp* 2011
Sales 67.2MM *EMP* 1,900^E
SIC 8741 8399 8082 Hospital management; Nursing & personal care facility management; Health systems agency; Home health care services
Prin: Philip Newbold
Ofcr: Kevin Slaughter
Ofcr: Carla Wagner
Exec: Steven Eller
Ex Dir: Matt Krathwohl
Off Admin: Anna Marvel
Off Admin: Emily Richards
Dir IT: Mark Oyer
Surgeon: Joseph Schnittker
Doctor: Melissa Bunton
Cert Phar: David Hills

BEACON HILL
See ROBERT ALLEN GROUP INC

BEACON HILL APARTMENTS
See BEACON HILL PRESERVATION LIMITED DIVIDEND HOUSING ASSOCIATION LIMITED PARTNERSHIP

D-U-N-S 83-290-1818
BEACON HILL PRESERVATION LIMITED DIVIDEND HOUSING ASSOCIATION LIMITED PARTNERSHIP
BEACON HILL APARTMENTS
32 E Carleton Rd, Hillsdale, MI 49242-1675
Tel (517) 437-2177 *Founded/Ownrshp* 2008
Sales 30.4MM^E *EMP* 3,900
SIC 6513 Apartment building operators

D-U-N-S 14-537-5908
BEACON HILL STAFFING GROUP LLC
BEACON HILL TECHNOLOGIES
152 Bowdoin St, Boston, MA 02108-2702
Tel (617) 326-4000 *Founded/Ownrshp* 2000
Sales 348.0MM *EMP* 475
SIC 7361 Labor contractors (employment agency)
CEO: Andrew Wang
Ex Dir: Joe Kanka
Mng Dir: Mark Howell
Mng Dir: Jeff McLaren
Mng Dir: John Tarbox
Div Mgr: Tim Bolduc
Div Mgr: Heather Harrold
Off Mgr: Jennifer McDonald
IT Man: Marti White
Software D: Ammar Totonchy

BEACON HILL TECHNOLOGIES
See BEACON HILL STAFFING GROUP LLC

D-U-N-S 07-827-5116 EXP
BEACON HOLDING INC
25 Research Dr, Westborough, MA 01581-3680
Tel (774) 512-7400 *Founded/Ownrshp* 2011
Sales 5.4MMM^E *EMP* 24,800^E
SIC 5399 5541 Warehouse club stores; Filling stations, gasoline
Mng Pt: Ashley Ingle

BEACON HOSPICE AN AMEDISYS CO
See BEACON HOSPICE INC

D-U-N-S 01-864-9876
■ BEACON HOSPICE INC
BEACON HOSPICE AN AMEDISYS CO
(*Suby of* AMEDISYS INC) ★
529 Main St Ste 126, Charlestown, MA 02129-1248
Tel (617) 242-4872 *Founded/Ownrshp* 2004
Sales 30.0MM *EMP* 13,000

SIC 8051 Skilled nursing care facilities
Pr: Paul Kusserow
**VP:* Debby Allen
CTO: Scott Noonan
VP Opers: Bette Meins

D-U-N-S 60-258-8837 IMP/EXP
BEACON MARITIME INC
BEACON OFFSHORE
96 W Front St, Orange, TX 77630-5810
Tel (409) 670-1060 *Founded/Ownrshp* 1999
Sales 122.0MM^E *EMP* 550
SIC 1629 3731 Marine construction; Shipbuilding & repairing
Pr: Russell Covington
**VP:* Guy Covington
**VP:* Elizabeth Jackson
Opers Mgr: Mike Dolan

D-U-N-S 12-209-0160
BEACON MEDICAL GROUP INC
MEMORIAL HOSPITAL
(*Suby of* MEMORIAL HOSPITAL SOUTH BEND) ★
615 N Michigan St, South Bend, IN 46601-1033
Tel (574) 647-1000 *Founded/Ownrshp* 1982
Sales 106.7MM *EMP* 1,900
SIC 8741 8399 8082 Hospital management; Nursing & personal care facility management; Health systems agency; Home health care services
Pr: Philip A Newbold
**Treas:* Larry Harding
Bd of Dir: Carol George
Ofcr: Paul Davis
Ex VP: Daniel E Neufelder
Exec: Matt Dickinson
Assoc Dir: Janel Charlton
Nurse Mgr: Patricia Ridenour
Doctor: Daniel E Dquist MD
Pgrm Dir: Dale Patterson
Pgrm Dir: Robert Riley

D-U-N-S 79-244-3095
BEACON MUTUAL INSURANCE CO
1 Beacon Ctr Ste 100, Warwick, RI 02886-1378
Tel (401) 825-2667 *Founded/Ownrshp* 1990
Sales NA *EMP* 180
SIC 6331 Workers' compensation insurance
Ch Bd: Richard De Rienzo
**Pr:* James Rosati
**COO:* Clifford Leo Parent Jr
CFO: Cynthia Lee Lawlor
**VP:* Rob Deorsey
VP: Robert G Deorsey
**VP:* Jeffrey Johnson
**VP:* Michael Lynch
Dir IT: Jim Moody
Software D: Ashik Kannan
Software D: Christy Sherman

BEACON OFFSHORE
See BEACON MARITIME INC

D-U-N-S 36-192-1752 IMP/EXP
BEACON PRINTING & GRAPHICS INC
PAGE/NTRNTIONAL COMMUNICATIONS
(*Suby of* NWAS) ★
2748 Bingle Rd, Houston, TX 77055-1135
Tel (713) 464-8484 *Founded/Ownrshp* 1998
Sales 107.3MM^E *EMP* 469
SIC 2752 2791 2789 Commercial printing, lithographic; Typesetting; Bookbinding & related work
CEO: Carl L Norton
**Sr VP:* Jerry L Hyde

D-U-N-S 79-947-4010
BEACON RESIDENTIAL MANAGEMENT LIMITED PARTNERSHIP
2 Center Plz Ste 700, Boston, MA 02108-1906
Tel (617) 574-1100 *Founded/Ownrshp* 1997
Sales 135.0MM^E *EMP* 420
SIC 6531 Real estate agents & managers
CEO: Pam Goodman
Ch Bd: Howard Cullan
Pr: Jeff Baker
CTO: Robert Mello

D-U-N-S 02-489-1926
▲ BEACON ROOFING SUPPLY INC
505 Huntmar Park Dr # 300, Herndon, VA 20170-5152
Tel (571) 323-3939 *Founded/Ownrshp* 1928
Sales 4.1MMM *EMP* 3,366
Tkr Sym BECN *Exch* NGS
SIC 5033 5031 Roofing, siding & insulation; Roofing & siding materials; Siding, except wood; Insulation materials; Lumber, plywood & millwork; Windows
Pr: Paul M Isabella
**Ch Bd:* Robert R Buck
CFO: Joseph M Nowicki
Ex VP: Ross D Cooper
VP: Gregory T Jorgensen
VP: Chris Nelson
Snr Mgr: Matthew Pittinaro

D-U-N-S 06-218-6630 IMP
■ BEACON SALES ACQUISITION INC
(*Suby of* BEACON ROOFING SUPPLY INC) ★
50 Webster Ave, Somerville, MA 02143-4199
Tel (877) 645-7663 *Founded/Ownrshp* 1997
Sales 538.0MM^E *EMP* 3,000
SIC 5033 5031

D-U-N-S 07-875-6213
BEAGLE PARENT CORP
3055 Lebanon Pike # 1000, Nashville, TN 37214-2230
Tel (615) 932-3000 *Founded/Ownrshp* 2011
Sales 1.4MMM^E *EMP* 3,300
SIC 7374 Data processing service
Pr: Neil E De Crescenzo
**CFO:* Randy Giles
**VP:* Jeff Kerley

BEAL BANK
See BEAL FINANCIAL CORP

D-U-N-S 11-041-7909
BEAL BANK
(*Suby of* BEAL BANK) ★
6000 Legacy Dr, Plano, TX 75024-3601
Tel (469) 467-5000 *Founded/Ownrshp* 1985
Sales NA *EMP* 349^E
SIC 6029 Commercial banks
Ch: Andrew Beal
Pr: David Meek
Pr: Raymond Morton
Pr: Apryl Strass
CEO: Margaret Jaques
CFO: Nancy Richardson
Treas: David Riemer
CIO: Gary Powers
Mktg Dir: Nathan Lee
Mktg Dir: Sherrie Scott
Mktg Mgr: Ben Royal
Board of Directors: Robert D McTeer

D-U-N-S 18-319-8949
BEAL BANK USA
(*Suby of* BEAL BANK) ★
1970 Vlg Ctr Cir Ste 1, Las Vegas, NV 89134-6241
Tel (702) 242-8846 *Founded/Ownrshp* 2004
Sales NA *EMP* 46^E
SIC 6036 Savings institutions, not federally chartered
Pr: D Andrew Beal

D-U-N-S 83-861-9625
BEAL FINANCIAL CORP
BEAL BANK
6000 Legacy Dr, Plano, TX 75024-3601
Tel (469) 467-5000 *Founded/Ownrshp* 1993
Sales NA *EMP* 105
SIC 6036 Savings & loan associations, not federally chartered
Ch Bd: Andrew Beal
CFO: Geoffroy Petit
CFO: Nancy Richardson
Sr VP: Jim Chambless
**Sr VP:* Molly Curl
**Sr VP:* Clark Enright
**Sr VP:* James W Lewis
**Sr VP:* William Saurenmann
Sr VP: Shawn D Ward
**VP:* Stephen Costas
VP: Will Lewis
VP: Sherrie Scott

D-U-N-S 01-072-7506
■ BEALL CONCRETE ENTERPRISES LTD
READY MIX CONCRETE
(*Suby of* US CONCRETE) ★
331 N Main St, Euless, TX 76039-3636
Tel (817) 835-4100 *Founded/Ownrshp* 2000
Sales 102.0MM^E *EMP* 460
SIC 1611 1771 Concrete construction: roads, highways, sidewalks, etc.; Concrete work
CEO: Gene Martineau
**Pr:* Scott Evan
Chf Mktg O: Lorrie Smithers

D-U-N-S 79-695-5821 IMP/EXP
BEALLS DEPARTMENT STORES INC
(*Suby of* BEALLS INC) ★
1806 38th Ave E, Bradenton, FL 34208-4700
Tel (941) 747-2355 *Founded/Ownrshp* 1982
Sales 541.7MM *EMP* 3,400
SIC 5311 5651 5947 Department stores; Family clothing stores; Gift, novelty & souvenir shop
Ch Bd: Stephen Knopik
Ch Bd: Robert M Beall II
Pr: Daniel Love
Pr: Lorna E Nagler
COO: Brian Hallagan
Chf Mktg O: Sean Sondreal
VP: Gwen Bennett
VP: Rick Edgar
VP: Darrell Gold
VP: Joe Iannello
VP: Jerry Izzi
VP: Michael Maddaloni
VP: Bill Simpson
VP: Jim Simpson
VP: Jack Wurzbacher
Exec: Dan Doyle

D-U-N-S 06-967-4018 IMP/EXP
BEALLS INC
1806 13th Ave E, Bradenton, FL 34208
Tel (941) 747-2355 *Founded/Ownrshp* 1915
Sales 1.3MMM *EMP* 9,700
Accts Christopher Smith Leonard B
SIC 5311 5719 5651 5947 Department stores; Housewares; Family clothing stores; Gift, novelty & souvenir shop
CEO: Stephen Knopik
Ch Bd: Robert M Beall II
Pr: Dan Love
CEO: Stephen M Knopik
COO: Terry Bailey
COO: Pamela Redding
COO: Marisela Saenz
CFO: Brian Crowley
CFO: Jeff Fudge
CFO: Julie Harris
CFO: Pam Murphy
CFO: Kathleen Zehr
Sr VP: Dave Massey
VP: Brian Hallagan
Exec: Lanna Bozonie
Board of Directors: Edward Albertian, Clarence Anthony, Robert M Beall III, Tom Cole, Evelyn Follit, W Andrew Krusen, Conrad Szymanski, Mark Szymanski, Clifford Walters

D-U-N-S 10-648-7812 IMP/EXP
BEALLS OUTLET STORES INC
(*Suby of* BEALLS INC) ★
1806 38th Ave E, Bradenton, FL 34208-4700
Tel (941) 747-2355 *Founded/Ownrshp* 1987
Sales 513.4MM^E *EMP* 5,200
SIC 5611 5621 5661 5719 Men's & boys' clothing stores; Women's clothing stores; Shoe stores; Housewares
Ch Bd: Stephen Knopik
**Pr:* Dave Alves
**Ofcr:* Robert M Beall II
Board of Directors: Mark Szymanski

D-U-N-S 03-218-8138
BEALLS WEST GATE CORP
1806 38th Ave E, Bradenton, FL 34208-4700
Tel (941) 744-4330 *Founded/Ownrshp* 1984
Sales 141.1MM *EMP* 800^E
SIC 5651 5661 5719 Family clothing stores; Shoe stores; Wicker, rattan or reed home furnishings
CEO: Stephen M Knopik
CIO: David Massey
Board of Directors: Beverly Beall, Matt Beall, Geoff Szymanski, Steve Szymanski, William Webster

D-U-N-S 04-409-2350
BEAM ASSOCIATES LLC
301 Commerce Blvd Ste 2, Oldsmar, FL 34677-2806
Tel (813) 855-5695 *Founded/Ownrshp* 2012
Sales 335.5MM^E *EMP* 350^E
SIC 3585 Refrigeration & heating equipment

D-U-N-S 00-772-4057 IMP/EXP
BEAM GLOBAL SPIRITS & WINE LLC
BEAM SUNTORY
(*Suby of* BEAM SUNTORY INC) ★
510 Lake Cook Rd, Deerfield, IL 60015-4971
Tel (847) 948-8888 *Founded/Ownrshp* 1899
Sales 396.1MM^E *EMP* 1,789
SIC 2085 Distilled & blended liquors; Bourbon whiskey; Gin (alcoholic beverage); Vodka (alcoholic beverage)
Pr: Matthew Shattock
Pr: Alonzo Johnson
COO: Tom V Wilen
CFO: Robert Probst
Sr Cor Off: Ronald Kapolnek
Ex VP: David Tanner
Sr VP: Jeffrey J Buresh
Comm Man: Gail Hansche
Mng Dir: Torsten Helbig
Mng Dir: Harish Moolchandani
Div Mgr: Chuck Shaw

BEAM SUNTORY
See BEAM GLOBAL SPIRITS & WINE LLC

D-U-N-S 00-126-5768 IMP/EXP
BEAM SUNTORY INC
(*Suby of* SUNTORY HOLDINGS LIMITED)
510 Lake Cook Rd, Deerfield, IL 60015-4971
Tel (847) 948-8888 *Founded/Ownrshp* 2014
Sales 1.4MMM^E *EMP* 3,400
SIC 2085 Distilled & blended liquors; Bourbon whiskey; Gin (alcoholic beverage); Vodka (alcoholic beverage)
Pr: Matthew J Shattock
**Pr:* Albert Baladi
**Pr:* Nicholas Fink
**Pr:* Atsushi Koizumi
**Pr:* Bill Newlands
**CEO:* Yasuhiro Fukuyama
COO: Ronald Waters
**Chf Mktg O:* Kevin George
Sr VP: Sheri Grissom
Sr VP: Christopher Klein
**Sr VP:* John Owen
**Sr VP:* Kenton R Rose
VP: Michael Goldberg
VP: Brian Lantz
VP: Tom McPartlin
**VP:* Leo A Mierzwicki
VP: Steve Robertson
VP: Elif Sagsen-Ercel
VP: Gary Tobison
VP: Edward Wiertel
Exec: Charles Hansen

D-U-N-S 03-482-2411
BEAMAN MOTOR CO
BEAMAN SCION COMPANY
1525 Broadway, Nashville, TN 37203-3121
Tel (615) 251-8430 *Founded/Ownrshp* 1946
Sales 107.5MM^E *EMP* 275
SIC 5511 7538 Automobiles, new & used; General automotive repair shops
CEO: Lee A Beaman
**Pr:* Doug Mc Clanahan
**CFO:* Ruthie Keene
Sls Mgr: Mark McVey

BEAMAN SCION COMPANY
See BEAMAN MOTOR CO

D-U-N-S 01-505-3606 EXP
BEANS-CLASS FORD MERCURY INC
NEW HOLLAND FORD ISUZU
508 W Main St, New Holland, PA 17557-1121
Tel (717) 354-4901 *Founded/Ownrshp* 1981
Sales 144.0MM^E *EMP* 155
SIC 5511 Automobiles, new & used
Pr: Geoffrey H Class
**VP:* Matt Fagnani

D-U-N-S 14-752-6743
BEAR CONSTRUCTION CO
1501 Rohlwing Rd, Rolling Meadows, IL 60008-1336
Tel (847) 222-1900 *Founded/Ownrshp* 1984
Sales 129.0MM *EMP* 202
Accts Remy Vitale Maines Llc Oak B
SIC 1542 Commercial & office building, new construction; Commercial & office buildings, renovation & repair; Institutional building construction
Pr: Nicholas T Wienold
**Pr:* James S Wienold
**CEO:* George H Wienold
CFO: Bret M Bush
Ex VP: James S Weinold
VP: Michael A Colliander
Exec: Timothy Kosogof
Exec: Joseph Malfeo
Exec: Joe Nieckula
Exec: William Ziemek
Off Mgr: Vicky Bee

BEAR COUNTY HOSPITAL DISTRICT
See UNIVERSITY HEALTH SYSTEM

D-U-N-S 08-010-8778
BEAR PARENT INC
(*Suby of* SYCAMORE PARTNERS MANAGEMENT LP) ★
9 W 57th St Ste 3100, New York, NY 10019-2701
Tel (212) 796-8500 *Founded/Ownrshp* 2015
Sales 4.6MMM^E *EMP* 34,350^E
SIC 5311 Department stores, discount
Prin: Peter Morrow

D-U-N-S 08-531-6495
BEAR RIVER MUTUAL INSURANCE CO
778 E Winchester St, Salt Lake City, UT 84107-7565
Tel (801) 267-5000 *Founded/Ownrshp* 1909
Sales NA *EMP* 70
SIC 6331 6411 Property damage insurance; Insurance agents, brokers & service
Pr: Don H Adams
COO: Eric R Ericksen
**Sec:* Duffy E Pingree
**VP:* Sheryl Boehme
**VP:* Adrene Coleman
**VP:* Craig Densley
**VP:* Kathy Jensen
CIO: Doug Golder
CTO: Brent Hansen
Netwrk Mgr: Adam Deason
Software D: David Horton

D-U-N-S 07-867-6143
▲ BEAR STATE FINANCIAL HOLDINGS LLC
900 S Shackleford Rd # 200, Little Rock, AR 72211-3817
Tel (501) 320-4862 *Founded/Ownrshp* 2010
Sales 168.3MM^E *EMP* 1,003^E
SIC 6799 Investors
CEO: Richard N Massey

D-U-N-S 14-464-7336
■ BEAR STEARNS COMPANIES LLC
(*Suby of* JPMORGAN CHASE & CO) ★
383 Madison Ave, New York, NY 10179-0001
Tel (212) 272-2000 *Founded/Ownrshp* 2008
Sales 2.0MMM^E *EMP* 14,153^E
SIC 6211 6282 6221 6099 6091 6289 Security brokers & dealers; Investment bankers; Traders, security; Underwriters, security; Investment advisory service; Investment research; Futures brokers & dealers, commodity; Commodity traders, contracts; Fiduciary agencies other than real estate or trust; Nondeposit trust facilities; Security & commodity clearinghouses; Financial reporting
Pr: Michael J Cavanagh
Pr: Henry Tsang
CEO: John Moore
CEO: Michel Peretie
COO: Samuel L Molinaro Jr
Ch: Jeffrey Bruce Lane
Ch: Arlene Semaya
Treas: Lisa F Others
Ex VP: Sam Buttigieg
Ex VP: J C Hoeffel
Ex VP: Jeffrey Mayer
Ex VP: Samuel Molinaro Jr
Sr VP: Shelley Bergman
Sr VP: Jeffrey M Farber
VP: Fernando Castanheira
VP: Peter D Cherasia
VP: Kathleen O'Halloran
VP: Benjamin Rouah
Assoc Dir: Alexander Dean

D-U-N-S 05-385-7368 EXP
BEARCOM GROUP INC (TX)
4009 Dist Dr Ste 200, Garland, TX 75041
Tel (214) 340-8876 *Founded/Ownrshp* 1983, 1985
Sales 131.2MM^E *EMP* 410
SIC 5999 5065 Communication equipment; Communication equipment
Pr: Jerry Denham
**CFO:* Gerald Noonan
**Ex VP:* Brent Bisnar
**Prin:* Greg Yearsley

D-U-N-S 10-651-4805 EXP
BEARCOM OPERATING LLC
(*Suby of* BEARCOM GROUP INC) ★
4009 Dist Dr Ste 200, Garland, TX 75041
Tel (214) 765-7100 *Founded/Ownrshp* 1995
Sales 99.2MM^E *EMP* 410
SIC 4812 5065 Cellular telephone services; Communication equipment; Telephone equipment
CFO: Gerald Noonan

D-U-N-S 02-492-0233
BEARD IMPLEMENT CO (INC)
216 W Frederick St, Arenzville, IL 62611-3588
Tel (217) 997-5514 *Founded/Ownrshp* 1937
Sales 84.5MM *EMP* 40
Accts Zumbahlen Eyth Surrat Foote &
SIC 5083 7699 Farm implements; Farm machinery repair
Pr: Gerald Lee Beard
**Sec:* Jeremy M Beard
**VP:* Kyle M Schumacher
Off Mgr: Ann Brockhouse

D-U-N-S 05-196-2330
BEARDEN LEASING CO LTD
111 S Plum St, Bearden, AR 71720
Tel (870) 687-2246 *Founded/Ownrshp* 1945
Sales 148.0MM^E *EMP* 250
SIC 7359 0811 Equipment rental & leasing; Timber tracts
Pt: John E Anthony
**Pt:* Garland Anthony Sr Estate
**Pt:* Steven Anthony
**Pt:* Susan P Anthony
**Pt:* Oliver Anthony Trust

D-U-N-S 00-397-8277 IMP/EXP
BEARING DISTRIBUTORS INC (OH)
B D I
(*Suby of* FORGE INDUSTRIES INC) ★
8000 Hub Pkwy, Cleveland, OH 44125-5788
Tel (216) 642-9100 *Founded/Ownrshp* 1935, 1966
Sales 583.0MM^E *EMP* 896

SIC 5085 Bearings; Gears; Power transmission equipment & apparatus
Pr: Carl G James
**CFO:* Dan Maisonville
**VP:* Steve Kieffer
**VP:* John Ruth
VP: William Shepard
**VP:* Bud Thayer
Brnch Mgr: David Wilkerson
IT Man: Bob Ruester
Opers Mgr: Blake Blacklidge
Ql Cn Mgr: Robert Maddox

BEARING HEADQUARTERS CO
See HEADCO INDUSTRIES INC

D-U-N-S 01-409-7146
BEARINGPOINT INC
100 Crescent Ct Ste 700, Dallas, TX 75201-2112
Tel (214) 459-2770 *Founded/Ownrshp* 2000
Sales 452.0MM^E *EMP* 15,200
Accts Ernst & Young Llp Mclean Vi
SIC 8748 Business consulting
CEO: F Edwin Harbach
**Ch Bd:* Roderick C McGeary
COO: David Hunter
CFO: Kenneth A Hiltz
Ch: Keith Burgess
Ex VP: Rod Lineberger
Sr VP: S Singh Mecker
Sr VP: Michael Reuschel
VP: Joy Boatwright
VP: Jose Garcia
VP: Louis Katz
VP: Mark Lee
VP Bus Dev: Bettina Smilo
Board of Directors: Douglas C Allred, Betsy J Bernard, Frederic F Brace, Wolfgang H Kemna, Albert L Lord, Jill S Kanin-Lovers, Eddie R Munson, J Terry Strange

D-U-N-S 00-331-8334 IMP
BEARINGS & DRIVES INC
B & D INDUSTRIAL
607 Lower Poplar St, Macon, GA 31201-3521
Tel (478) 746-7623 *Founded/Ownrshp* 1947
Sales 265.0MM^E *EMP* 362
SIC 5085 Power transmission equipment & apparatus; Bearings
Pr: Andrew H Nations
**Ch:* John D Nations
**Sec:* Michael T Nations
VP: Linda Miller
**VP:* Harold Sharp
Brnch Mgr: Keith Boutwell
Brnch Mgr: Philip Hamby
Brnch Mgr: Randy Horn
Brnch Mgr: Steve Patat
CIO: Whitey Price
Sfty Dirs: Russ Klingemier

BEARPAW SHOES
See ROMEO & JULIETTE INC

D-U-N-S 08-018-3601
▲ BEASLEY BROADCAST GROUP INC
3033 Riviera Dr Ste 200, Naples, FL 34103-2748
Tel (239) 263-5000 *Founded/Ownrshp* 1961
Sales 105.9MM *EMP* 1,673^E
Tkr Sym BBGI *Exch* NGM
SIC 4832 Radio broadcasting stations
Ch Bd: George G Beasley
**Pr:* Bruce G Beasley
**CEO:* Caroline Beasley
**V Ch Bd:* Allen B Shaw
Dir IT: John Brown
Sls Mgr: INA Cartrette
Pgrm Dir: Kris Fisher
Board of Directors: Brian E Beasley, Joe B Cox, Mark S Fowler, Herbert W McCord

BEATS BY DRE
See BEATS ELECTRONICS LLC

D-U-N-S 96-723-1601 IMP
■ BEATS ELECTRONICS LLC
BEATS BY DRE
(*Suby of* APPLE INC) ★
8600 Hayden Pl, Culver City, CA 90232-2902
Tel (424) 326-4679 *Founded/Ownrshp* 2014
Sales 152.3MM^E *EMP* 500^E
SIC 3651 3679 Speaker systems; Headphones, radio
CEO: Timothy Cook

BEAU RIVAGE RESORT & CASINO
See BEAU RIVAGE RESORTS INC

D-U-N-S 92-628-2583 IMP
■ BEAU RIVAGE RESORTS INC
BEAU RIVAGE RESORT & CASINO
(*Suby of* MGM RESORTS) ★
875 Beach Blvd, Biloxi, MS 39530-4241
Tel (228) 386-7111 *Founded/Ownrshp* 1995
Sales 157.6MM^E *EMP* 3,145
SIC 7011 Casino hotel
Pr: George Perez
**CFO:* Todd Raziano
CFO: Courtney Wenleder
Ofcr: Chris Viverette
VP: Peter Brascia
VP: Shay Malpass
**VP:* Jorge Perez
VP: Jeff Segan
VP: Jake S Vanderlei
Exec: Lou Canillo
Ex Dir: Troy Douglas

BEAUDRY HONDA
See BEAUDRY MOTOR CO

D-U-N-S 03-595-8727 IMP
BEAUDRY MOTOR CO
BEAUDRY HONDA
4600 E 22nd St, Tucson, AZ 85711-5712
Tel (520) 750-1264 *Founded/Ownrshp* 1940, 1953
Sales 168.1MM^E *EMP* 885
SIC 5511 5561 Automobiles, new & used; Motor homes
Pr: Robert M Beaudry
**CEO:* Thomas P Sylvester
**COO:* Dennis Bene
**COO:* Robert Burden
Genl Mgr: Cliff Allison

D-U-N-S 09-157-1810
BEAUFORT COUNTY BOARD OF EDUCATION
321 Smaw Rd, Washington, NC 27889-3937
Tel (252) 946-6593 *Founded/Ownrshp* 1900
Sales 62.1MM *EMP* 1,400
Accts Dixon Hughes Goodman Llp Pine
SIC 8211 School board
Ch Bd: Terry Williams

D-U-N-S 07-370-7432
BEAUFORT COUNTY MEMORIAL HOSPITAL
BEAUFORT MEMORIAL HOSPITAL
955 Ribaut Rd, Beaufort, SC 29902-5441
Tel (843) 522-5200 *Founded/Ownrshp* 1945
Sales 188.1MM *EMP* 1,300
SIC 8062 General medical & surgical hospitals
Pr: Richard Toomey
**CFO:* Jeff White
Chf Mktg O: Timothy Pearce
Ofcr: Lavane Barnes
**VP:* Karen Carroll
VP: Pat Foulger
**VP:* David Homyk
Exec: Eric Sayers
Assoc Dir: Cynthia Mims
**Ex Dir:* Alice Beddingfield Moss
Telecom Ex: Tammy Cieplowski

D-U-N-S 06-933-3227
BEAUFORT COUNTY SCHOOL DISTRICT
2900 Mink Point Blvd, Beaufort, SC 29902-5873
Tel (843) 322-2300 *Founded/Ownrshp* 1919
Sales 259.5MM *EMP* 2,600
Accts Elliott Davis Llc Charleston
SIC 8211 Public elementary & secondary schools
Dir Sec: David Grissom

D-U-N-S 07-979-9688
BEAUFORT COUNTY SCHOOLS (NC)
321 Smaw Rd, Washington, NC 27889-3937
Tel (252) 946-6593 *Founded/Ownrshp* 2015
Sales 24.0MM^E *EMP* 1,323^E
SIC 8211 Public elementary & secondary schools
VP: Jessica Adams
Pr Dir: Sarah Hodges
Instr Medi: Wendy Petteway
Psych: Kim Reel
HC Dir: Nicole Howard

BEAUFORT MEMORIAL HOSPITAL
See BEAUFORT COUNTY MEMORIAL HOSPITAL

D-U-N-S 02-979-2376 IMP/EXP
BEAULIEU GROUP LLC
BLISS
1502 Coronet Dr, Dalton, GA 30720-2664
Tel (706) 259-4511 *Founded/Ownrshp* 1996
Sales 2.5MMM^E *EMP* 6,000
SIC 2273 2281 Carpets, hand & machine made; Manmade & synthetic fiber yarns, spun
CEO: Ralph J Boe
**Pr:* James Lsslie
CFO: Lawrence A Swanson
**Prin:* Peter N Farley
**Prin:* Farley Peter N

D-U-N-S 08-697-1363 IMP/EXP
BEAULIEU OF AMERICA INC
BEAULIEU RESIDENTIAL
(*Suby of* BLISS) ★
1502 Coronet Dr, Dalton, GA 30720-2664
Tel (706) 278-6666 *Founded/Ownrshp* 1978
Sales 1.1MMM^E *EMP* 4,500
SIC 2273 Carpets, hand & machine made
CEO: Carl M Bouckaert
**CFO:* Del Land
**CFO:* David A Marr
Ex VP: Danny Wade
**VP:* Peter N Farley
Board of Directors: Carl M Bouckaert

BEAULIEU RESIDENTIAL
See BEAULIEU OF AMERICA INC

BEAUMONT BOTSFORD OAKWOOD HEAL
See ZIEGER HEALTH CARE CORP

BEAUMONT BOTSFORD OAKWOOD HLTH
See BEAUMONT HEALTH

D-U-N-S 05-998-6429
BEAUMONT HEALTH
BEAUMONT BOTSFORD OAKWOOD HLTH
3601 W 13 Mile Rd, Royal Oak, MI 48073-6712
Tel (248) 898-5000 *Founded/Ownrshp* 2014
Sales 2.7MMM^E *EMP* 31,182^E
SIC 8062 General medical & surgical hospitals
Ch Bd: John Lewis
Ch Bd: Paul Lacasse
Pr: Brian Connolly
**CEO:* Gene Michalski
**CFO:* John Keuten
CFO: Nickolas A Vitale
Ofcr: Margaret Casey
Ofcr: Doug Clarkston
Ofcr: Peggy Dehaven
Ofcr: Subra Sripada
Assoc VP: Laura Charbonneau
Ex VP: Ananias C Diokno
VP: Valentina Gokenbach
VP: Edward Grima
VP: Jay Holden
VP: Paula Levesque
VP: John Peetz
VP: Colette Stimmell
VP: Kent Teeters

BEAUMONT HEALTH SYSTEM
See WILLIAM BEAUMONT HOSPITAL

BEAUMONT HOSP - FRMNGTON HILLS
See BOTSFORD GENERAL HOSPITAL

D-U-N-S 07-392-3146
BEAUMONT INDEPENDENT SCHOOL DISTRICT
3395 Harrison Ave, Beaumont, TX 77706-5009
Tel (409) 617-5000 *Founded/Ownrshp* 1913
Sales 134.7MM^E *EMP* 2,700
Accts Gayle W Botley & Associates
SIC 8211 Public senior high school; Public junior high school; Public elementary school; Public special education school
Ofcr: Robert Zingelman
Genl Mgr: Preston Shaw
MIS Dir: Jarod Parnell
Cmptr Lab: Carol Siler
Pr Dir: Nakisha Myles
Doctor: Debra Williams

D-U-N-S 09-916-5458
BEAUMONT UNIFIED SCHOOL DISTRICT
350 W Brookside Ave, Cherry Valley, CA 92223-4073
Tel (951) 845-1631 *Founded/Ownrshp* 1950
Sales 586.9M *EMP* 11,000
SIC 8211 Public elementary & secondary schools
Off Mgr: Wilma Grimes
MIS Dir: John Lewis

D-U-N-S 05-187-9112
BEAUREGARD ELECTRIC COOPERATIVE INC
1010 E 1st St, Deridder, LA 70634-4302
Tel (800) 367-0275 *Founded/Ownrshp* 1939
Sales 87.3MM *EMP* 125
Accts Schmidt & Company Llc Lees Su
SIC 4911 Distribution, electric power
Pr: Kevin Turner
Pr: Kevin Aycock
**Pr:* Dale Peterson
CFO: Ronny Marshal
VP: Mark Royer
VP: Rex Waggener
Dir IT: Ali Daniali
IT Man: Leslie Hooks
IT Man: Margaretta Mayes
IT Man: Margaretta Mays
VP Mktg: Fox Kay

D-U-N-S 16-159-0658 IMP
BEAUTY 21 COSMETICS INC
L A GIRL
2021 S Archibald Ave, Ontario, CA 91761-8535
Tel (909) 945-2220 *Founded/Ownrshp* 1985
Sales 92.2MM^E *EMP* 105
SIC 5122 2844 Cosmetics, perfumes & hair products; Toilet preparations
CEO: Lan Jack Yu
**VP:* Mahon Yu
Mktg Dir: Jessica Talancon
Mktg Dir: Greg Verbeck

D-U-N-S 95-865-5284
BEAUTY BRANDS LLC
BEAUTY BRNDS SLON SPA SPRSTORE
4600 Madison Ave Ste 400, Kansas City, MO 64112-3001
Tel (816) 531-2266 *Founded/Ownrshp* 2013
Sales 440.0MM^E *EMP* 1,850
SIC 5999 7231 Toiletries, cosmetics & perfumes; Hairdressers
CEO: Lyn Kirby
**Pr:* Rich Bos
Snr Mgr: Cynthia Lasala

BEAUTY BRNDS SLON SPA SPRSTORE
See BEAUTY BRANDS LLC

D-U-N-S 80-121-9796 IMP
■ BEAUTY SYSTEMS GROUP LLC
COSMOPROF
(*Suby of* SALLY HOLDINGS LLC) ★
3001 Colorado Blvd, Denton, TX 76210-6802
Tel (940) 297-2000 *Founded/Ownrshp* 1996
Sales 1.5MMM^E *EMP* 10,330^E
SIC 5999 5122 5087 Cosmetics; Cosmetics; Service establishment equipment
VP: Pat Hills
Sales Asso: R J Oswald

D-U-N-S 96-869-3056 EXP
■ BEAUTYGE BRANDS USA INC
AMERICAN CREW
(*Suby of* BEAUTYGE PARTICIPATIONS S.L.)
1515 Wazee St Ste 200, Denver, CO 80202-1674
Tel (800) 598-2739 *Founded/Ownrshp* 1996
Sales 199.3MM^E *EMP* 390
SIC 5122 2844 Hair preparations; Toilet preparations
CFO: Roberto Simon
**Pr:* Martn Garca
**VP:* Sennen Pamich

D-U-N-S 07-614-2215
BEAVER DAM COMMUNITY HOSPITALS INC
HILLSIDE MANOR
707 S University Ave, Beaver Dam, WI 53916-3027
Tel (920) 887-7181 *Founded/Ownrshp* 1972
Sales 91.3MM *EMP* 830
SIC 8062 8051 General medical & surgical hospitals; Skilled nursing care facilities
CEO: Kim Miller
**COO:* David Corso
COO: Mark Manson
COO: Mark Monson
**CFO:* Donna Hutchinson
**Ex VP:* Pat Tuckwell
**VP:* Jane Belongie
**VP:* Joe Bonnett
VP: George Dumontier
Dir Lab: Trinity Pulvermacher
Adm Dir: John Sweeney

D-U-N-S 00-446-4541
BEAVER EXCAVATING CO (OH)
2000 Beaver Place Ave Sw, Canton, OH 44706-1963
Tel (330) 478-2151 *Founded/Ownrshp* 1953
Sales 187.7MM *EMP* 600^E
SIC 1794 1611 1771 1623

D-U-N-S 00-164-5147
BEAVER EXPRESS SERVICE LLC
4310 Oklahoma Ave, Woodward, OK 73801-3841
Tel (580) 256-6460 *Founded/Ownrshp* 2002
Sales 145.4MM^E *EMP* 425
SIC 4213 Trucking, except local; Less-than-truckload (LTL) transport
VP: Mike Kirtley
Board of Directors: Louis Thompson

D-U-N-S 00-407-9364 IMP/EXP
BEAVER STREET FISHERIES INC
BEAVER STREET FOODS
1741 W St Beaver, Jacksonville, FL 32209
Tel (904) 354-5661 *Founded/Ownrshp* 1950
Sales 263.2MM^E *EMP* 350
SIC 5142 5141 Packaged frozen goods; Fish, frozen: packaged; Meat, frozen: packaged; Groceries, general line
Ch Bd: Hans Frisch
**Pr:* Benjamin Frisch
**Ex VP:* Mark Frisch
VP: Harry Frisch
Genl Mgr: Greg Tison
Genl Mgr: Charles Trager
CIO: Scott Lane
QA Dir: Ryan Gill
QA Dir: David Mantilla
QA Dir: Jorge Rodriguez
Telecom Mg: Mike Harlow

BEAVER STREET FOODS
See BEAVER STREET FISHERIES INC

D-U-N-S 82-864-2921
BEAVERS HOLDINGS LLC
B H
3550 Hobson Rd Fl 3, Woodridge, IL 60517-5456
Tel (630) 963-2736 *Founded/Ownrshp* 2008
Sales 83.7MM^E *EMP* 148
SIC 8741 6531 Management services; Real estate agent, commercial
**CEO:* Robert M Beavers Jr
**VP:* Jim Barker
**Ex Dir:* Kathy Spano

BEAVERTON HONDA
See LANPHERE ENTERPRISES INC

BEAVERTON PACKAGING
See ALLIANCE PACKAGING LLC

D-U-N-S 01-072-7956
BEAVERTON SCHOOL DISTRICT
16550 Sw Merlo Rd, Beaverton, OR 97003-5179
Tel (503) 591-8000 *Founded/Ownrshp* 1963
Sales 513.9MM *EMP* 4,000
Accts Grove Mueller & Swank Pc
SIC 8211 Public combined elementary & secondary school
**CFO:* Janice Essenberg
CFO: Claire Hertz
Bd of Dir: Craig Irwin
Ofcr: Maureen Wheeler
**CIO:* Stephen Langford
IT Man: Lori Morgan
Psych: Andre Abraham
Psych: Dori Beals

D-U-N-S 80-762-1164
BEAVEX INC
2120 Powers Ferry Rd Se, Atlanta, GA 30339-7206
Tel (404) 260-0961 *Founded/Ownrshp* 1989
Sales 371.0MM^E *EMP* 400
SIC 4215 4513 Courier services, except by air; Package delivery, private air
Pr: Richard Boland
**CFO:* Doug Duskin
**CFO:* Ryan O Neal
VP: Paul Calabro
VP: Rick Kolpinski
VP: Ed Masiello
CTO: Steven Smith
Dir IT: Timothy A Stanley
IT Man: Jeanette Sanchez
Opers Mgr: Kevin Long
Opers Mgr: Terry Okeeffe

D-U-N-S 18-151-8531
■ BEAZER HOMES CORP
(*Suby of* BEAZER HOMES USA INC) ★
1000 Abernathy Rd, Atlanta, GA 30328-5606
Tel (770) 829-3700 *Founded/Ownrshp* 1996
Sales 255.5MM^E *EMP* 250
SIC 1531 Speculative builder, single-family houses
COO: Michael Furlow
Ex VP: Allan P Merrill
Sr VP: Robert L Salomon

D-U-N-S 17-442-4994
▲ BEAZER HOMES USA INC
1000 Abernathy Rd Ste 260, Atlanta, GA 30328-5648
Tel (770) 829-3700 *Founded/Ownrshp* 1985
Sales 1.8MMM *EMP* 1,100
Accts Deloitte & Touche Llp Atlant
Tkr Sym BZH *Exch* NYS
SIC 1521 1522 New construction, single-family houses; Multi-family dwelling construction; Multi-family dwellings, new construction
Pr: Allan P Merrill
**Ch Bd:* Stephen P Zelnak Jr
CFO: Robert L Salomon
Ex VP: Kenneth F Khoury

D-U-N-S 78-032-2702
BEAZLEY INSURANCE CO INC
(*Suby of* BEAZLEY GROUP LIMITED)
30 Batterson Park Rd, Farmington, CT 06032-2579
Tel (860) 677-3700 *Founded/Ownrshp* 2005
Sales NA *EMP* 800
SIC 6331 Fire, marine & casualty insurance
CEO: Andrew Horton
**Pr:* Andrew Frederick Beazley
**COO:* Ian Fantozzi
**Treas:* Ellen Lombard
**Ex VP:* Martin Bride
**VP:* Mark Bernacki
**VP:* Jerry Sullivan
Ex Dir: Ken Sroka

IT Man: Matt Fitch
Sls Mgr: James Lannon
Board of Directors: Mark Bernacki, Martin Bride, Jonathan Gray, Andrew Horton, Richard Kelley, Jerry Sullivan

D-U-N-S 05-459-4957 IMP/EXP
▲ **BEBE STORES INC** (CA)
400 Valley Dr, Brisbane, CA 94005-1210
Tel (415) 715-3900 *Founded/Ownrshp* 1976
Sales 393.5MM *EMP* 2,924
Tkr Sym BEBE *Exch* NGS
SIC 2331 Women's & misses' blouses & shirts
Ch Bd: Manny Mashouf
Pr: Walter Park
Pr: Tara Poseley
CFO: Kerry Flynn
Ex VP: Brigitte Bogart
Sr VP: Lawrence Smith
VP: Tim Millen
VP: Richard Pierson
VP: Susan Powers
VP: Lawrence R Smith
Exec: Kimberly Eaton
Dir Risk M: Helyn Hoffman
Dir Soc: Susie Im
Board of Directors: Brett Brewer, Robert Galvin, Seth Johnson

D-U-N-S 15-588-0029 IMP
BECARRO INTERNATIONAL CORP
SONDRA ROBERTS
1730 Corporate Dr, Boynton Beach, FL 33426-6662
Tel (561) 737-5585 *Founded/Ownrshp* 2000
Sales 120.0MM *EMP* 50
SIC 3171 Handbags, women's
Pr: Robert Camche
**VP:* Glenn Camche
Sls Mgr: Leesha Ragbeer

D-U-N-S 36-116-1367
BECHTEL CAPITAL MANAGEMENT CORP
(*Suby of* BECHTEL GROUP INC) ★
50 Beale St, San Francisco, CA 94105-1813
Tel (415) 768-1234 *Founded/Ownrshp* 1987
Sales 53.3MM[E] *EMP* 2,000
SIC 8741 Financial management for business
Ch: Riley Bechtel
Pr: Brendan Bechtel
CEO: Bill Dudley
CFO: Peter Dawson
Treas: Anshul Maheshwari
Board of Directors: J D Carter, W L Friend, D J Gunther, C W Hull, J Neerhout Jr, Adrian Zaccaria

D-U-N-S 88-474-1141
BECHTEL CONSTRUCTION OPERATIONS INC
(*Suby of* BECHTEL CORP) ★
50 Beale St Bsmt 1, San Francisco, CA 94105-1819
Tel (415) 768-1234 *Founded/Ownrshp* 1994
Sales 646.5MM *EMP* 1,740
Accts Pricewaterhousecoopers
SIC 1541 1629 1623 8741 7353 Industrial buildings, new construction; Power plant construction; Chemical plant & refinery construction; Water, sewer & utility lines; Construction management; Heavy construction equipment rental
Ch Bd: Riley P Bechtel
**V Ch Bd:* Adrian Zaccaria

D-U-N-S 09-487-8998
BECHTEL CORP
(*Suby of* BECHTEL GROUP INC) ★
50 Beale St, San Francisco, CA 94105-1813
Tel (415) 768-1234 *Founded/Ownrshp* 1898
Sales 6.7MMM[E] *EMP* 29,000
Accts Pricewaterhousecoopers Llp
SIC 8711 1629 8742 Civil engineering; Industrial plant construction; Power plant construction; Construction project management consultant
CEO: Bill Dudley
**Ch Bd:* Riley Bechtel
**Pr:* Brendan Bechtel
Pr: Steve Katzman
COO: Ken Wood
**CFO:* Peter Dawson
**Treas:* Kevin Leader
Ex VP: How Bechtel
Ex VP: Lee McIntire
Ex VP: G Mumm
**Sr VP:* P A Dawson
**Sr VP:* J A Miller
**Sr VP:* T D Statton
VP: John Deshong
VP: Mark Seely
VP: Ralph Zimmermann
Dir Bus: Craig Walker
Comm Man: Jeff Berger
Board of Directors: W F Woolen

D-U-N-S 09-995-6971
BECHTEL ENERGY CORP
(*Suby of* BECHTEL POWER CORP) ★
50 Beale St Bsmt 1, San Francisco, CA 94105-1819
Tel (415) 768-1234 *Founded/Ownrshp* 1979
Sales 36.0MM[E] *EMP* 1,588[E]
SIC 8711 8741 Construction & civil engineering; Construction management
Ch: R P Bechtel
**Sr VP:* G C Proctor

D-U-N-S 09-487-8980
BECHTEL GROUP INC
50 Beale St Bsmt 1, San Francisco, CA 94105-1819
Tel (415) 768-1234 *Founded/Ownrshp* 1980
Sales 7.0MMM[E] *EMP* 52,700
SIC 8711 1629 8742 Engineering services; Civil engineering; Industrial plant construction; Construction project management consultant
V Ch: Bill Dudley
Pr: Brendan Bechtel
Pr: Adrian Zaccaria
CFO: Peter Dawson
CFO: Georgeann Proctor
Ch: Riley Bechtel
Ex VP: John D Carter
Ex VP: Jack Futcher
Sr VP: John T Mitchell
Sr VP: V P Unruh
Sr VP: W Foster Wollen
VP: Kc Choi
VP: Van Prooyen
Board of Directors: John W Weiser, A M Dachs, William L Friend, Frederick W Gluck, H J Haynes, C W Hull, J P Laspa, David J O'reilly, G P Shultz, M L Thiele

D-U-N-S 17-189-3886
BECHTEL JACOBS CO LLC
(*Suby of* BECHTEL GROUP INC) ★
E Tennessee Techn 58, Oak Ridge, TN 37831
Tel (865) 241-1151 *Founded/Ownrshp* 1997
Sales 43.8MM[E] *EMP* 1,309
SIC 8744

D-U-N-S 82-633-6344
BECHTEL MARINE PROPULSION CORP
(*Suby of* BECHTEL NATIONAL INC) ★
12011 Sunset Hills Rd, Reston, VA 20190-5918
Tel (301) 228-6000 *Founded/Ownrshp* 2008
Sales 317.2MM[E] *EMP* 6,100[E]
SIC 8731 Commercial physical research
Ch: J Scott Obilvie
**CEO:* Morgan N Smith

D-U-N-S 08-917-6176
BECHTEL NATIONAL INC
(*Suby of* BECHTEL NUCLEAR SECURITY & ENVIRONMENTAL INC) ★
5275 Westview Dr, Frederick, MD 21703-8306
Tel (415) 768-1234 *Founded/Ownrshp* 1989
Sales 1.3MMM[E] *EMP* 14,085
SIC 8711 1629 8742 Civil engineering; Industrial plant construction; Construction project management consultant
Pr: Bill Dudley
**Pr:* Tyrone P Troutman
**CFO:* Mike Adams
Ofcr: Doris Heim
Ex VP: James Nolan
VP: David Blaisdell
Prgrm Mgr: Duane Kelsey
Rgnl Mgr: Aaron How
Genl Mgr: Adrian Johnpillai
QA Dir: Raj Jolly
IT Man: Eric Isaacson

D-U-N-S 83-788-1895
BECHTEL NEVADA CORP
2621 Losee Rd, North Las Vegas, NV 89030-4129
Tel (702) 295-1000 *Founded/Ownrshp* 2005
Sales NA *EMP* 2,200
SIC 8711 1629

D-U-N-S 96-387-6305
BECHTEL NUCLEAR SECURITY & ENVIRONMENTAL INC
(*Suby of* BECHTEL CORP) ★
12021 Sunset Hills Rd, Reston, VA 20190-5854
Tel (415) 768-1234 *Founded/Ownrshp* 1898
Sales 1.3MMM[E] *EMP* 14,435
Accts Pricewaterhousecoopers
SIC 8711 1629 8742 Civil engineering; Industrial plant construction; Construction project management consultant
Ch Bd: Riley Bechtel
Pr: Bill Dudley
CFO: Mike Adams
VP: Shirley Douglas
VP: Carol B Duke
Prin: Michael Bailey

D-U-N-S 80-105-5489 IMP
BECHTEL OIL GAS AND CHEMICALS INC
3000 Post Oak Blvd, Houston, TX 77056-6580
Tel (713) 235-2000 *Founded/Ownrshp* 2011
Sales 1.2MMM[E] *EMP* 4,000
SIC 1629 Oil refinery construction; Chemical plant & refinery construction
Ch Bd: Riley Bechtel
**Pr:* John E Futcher
**CEO:* Bill Dudley
**COO:* Brendan Bechtel
**CFO:* Mike Adams
**CFO:* Peter Dawson
CFO: Steve Kuxhausen
**Sr VP:* Amos A Avidan
**Sr VP:* Michael C Bailey
**Sr VP:* Maria K Brady
Ql Cn Mgr: Iris Betancourt

D-U-N-S 09-398-3034
BECHTEL PLANT MACHINERY INC
BPMI
(*Suby of* BECHTEL NATIONAL INC) ★
3500 Technology Dr, Monroeville, PA 15146-8300
Tel (412) 829-8626 *Founded/Ownrshp* 2005
Sales 86.0MM[E] *EMP* 850[E]
SIC 8711 Engineering services
Pr: Michael E Stango
Ofcr: Nellie F Mells
**VP:* Raymond E Boyer
Genl Mgr: Mike McCoy

D-U-N-S 06-299-5907
BECHTEL POWER CORP
(*Suby of* BECHTEL GROUP INC) ★
50 Beale St Bsmt 2, San Francisco, CA 94105-1819
Tel (415) 768-1234 *Founded/Ownrshp* 1972
Sales 242.7MM[E] *EMP* 1,902
Accts Pricewaterhousecoopers
SIC 8711 8742 1629 Civil engineering; Construction project management consultant; Industrial plant construction; Power plant construction
Pr: Alasdair I Cathcart
**Treas:* Kevin C Leader
**Sr VP:* P A Dawson
**Sr VP:* J A Miller

D-U-N-S 80-865-3195
BECHTEL-JACOBS JOINT VENTURE
3000 Post Oak Blvd, Houston, TX 77056-6580
Tel (713) 235-2000 *Founded/Ownrshp* 2007
Sales NA *EMP* 2,500
SIC 8711

D-U-N-S 78-480-0914
BECK & MASTEN PONTIAC-GMC INC
11300 Fm 1960 Rd W, Houston, TX 77065-3698
Tel (281) 469-5222 *Founded/Ownrshp* 1983
Sales 1.8MMM *EMP* 280
SIC 5511 Automobiles, new & used
Owner: James L Masten
**Owner:* John A Beck
**Sec:* Roni L Dippel
Genl Mgr: Pete Trammell
Sls Dir: Parrish Hadley

BECK GRAPHICS
See COLORGRAPHX INC

BECK GROUP, THE
See BECK INTERNATIONAL LLC

D-U-N-S 11-347-9633
BECK INTERNATIONAL LLC
BECK GROUP, THE
1807 Ross Ave Ste 500, Dallas, TX 75201-8006
Tel (214) 303-6200 *Founded/Ownrshp* 1991
Sales 537.1MM[E] *EMP* 500
SIC 1542 8712 Commercial & office building contractors; Architectural services
Mng Pt: Peter Beck
Pt: Kip Daniel
Pt: Rick Del Monte
Pt: Sam Ellison
Pt: Jim Gettman
Pt: Paul Higgins
Pt: Mark House
CEO: Brad Phillips
CFO: Mark Collins
Mktg Mgr: Summer Hudson
Snr PM: Joe Saatkamp

D-U-N-S 01-803-4017
BECK SUPPLIERS INC
FRIENDSHIP FOOD STORES
1000 N Front St, Fremont, OH 43420-1921
Tel (419) 332-5527 *Founded/Ownrshp* 1963
Sales 234.8MM[E] *EMP* 250
SIC 5171 5541 5411 5984 1542 Petroleum bulk stations; Filling stations, gasoline; Convenience stores; Liquefied petroleum gas dealers; Commercial & office building contractors
CEO: Daryl Becker
**CFO:* Loren Owens
**Ch:* Robert Becker
**Treas:* Marcia Becker
**VP:* Rochelle Becker

BECKER ELECTRIC SUPPLY
See JOHN A BECKER CO

D-U-N-S 07-292-3808
■ **BECKER PROFESSIONAL DEVELOPMENT CORP**
BECKER PROFESSIONAL EDUCATION
(*Suby of* DEVRY GROUP) ★
3005 Highland Pkwy # 700, Downers Grove, IL 60515-5798
Tel (630) 515-7700 *Founded/Ownrshp* 1996
Sales 36.4MM[E] *EMP* 3,506
SIC 8299 Tutoring school
Pr: John Roselli
**CEO:* Daniel Hamburger
**Sr VP:* Rick Gunst
Mktg Dir: Sue Burns

BECKER PROFESSIONAL EDUCATION
See BECKER PROFESSIONAL DEVELOPMENT CORP

D-U-N-S 03-125-0756
BECKER TIRE & TREADING INC (KS)
904 Washington St, Great Bend, KS 67530-4939
Tel (620) 793-5414 *Founded/Ownrshp* 1954, 1975
Sales 116.5MM[E] *EMP* 158
SIC 5014 5531 Tires & tubes; Automotive tires
CEO: Gary Albright
**Pr:* Steven Burhenn
**VP:* Willy Allen
**VP:* Paul Doll
Off Mgr: Darlene Klug

D-U-N-S 00-825-4708 IMP/EXP
■ **BECKMAN COULTER INC**
(*Suby of* DANAHER CORP) ★
250 S Kraemer Blvd, Brea, CA 92821-6232
Tel (714) 993-5321 *Founded/Ownrshp* 2011
Sales 2.5MMM[E] *EMP* 11,900
SIC 3826 3841 3821

D-U-N-S 07-861-5792
BECKMAN PRODUCTION SERVICES INC
3786 Beebe Rd Ne, Kalkaska, MI 49646-8014
Tel (231) 258-9524 *Founded/Ownrshp* 2003
Sales 85.0MM[E] *EMP* 50[E]
SIC 1382 Oil & gas exploration services
Sfty Mgr: Ed Sarin

D-U-N-S 02-717-6833
BECKMAN RESEARCH INSTITUTE OF CITY OF HOPE
1500 Duarte Rd, Duarte, CA 91010-3012
Tel (626) 359-8111 *Founded/Ownrshp* 1979
Sales 298.9MM *EMP* 250
Accts Lb Ernst & Young Us Llp Irvin
SIC 8733 Medical research
CEO: Michael A Friedman
**Pr:* Robert Stone
**CEO:* Harlan Levine
**COO:* William Sargeant
**CFO:* Terry Blackwood
**CFO:* Ric Magnuson
CFO: Dennis Rusch
Comm Dir: Roy Alt

D-U-N-S 00-791-5416
BECKWITH MACHINERY CO INC
(*Suby of* CLEVELAND BROTHERS HOLDINGS INC) ★
4565 William Penn Hwy, Murrysville, PA 15668-2003
Tel (724) 327-1300 *Founded/Ownrshp* 1907
Sales 162.8MM[E] *EMP* 680
SIC 5082 5084 7629 7353 Front end loaders; Road construction & maintenance machinery; Tractors, construction; Excavating machinery & equipment; Industrial machinery & equipment; Electrical repair shops; Heavy construction equipment rental
Ch Bd: James S Beckwith III
**Pr:* G Nicholas Beckwith III
Treas: Thomas Fleury
**VP:* Paul Counahan
**VP:* Robert Fredrickson

BECO GROUP, THE
See MESSINA GROUP INC

BECTON COLLEGE ARTS & SCIENCES
See FAIRLEIGH DICKINSON UNIVERSITY

D-U-N-S 00-129-2192 IMP/EXP
▲ **BECTON DICKINSON AND CO**
1 Becton Dr, Franklin Lakes, NJ 07417-1880
Tel (201) 847-6800 *Founded/Ownrshp* 1897
Sales 12.4MMM *EMP* 49,517
Tkr Sym BDX *Exch* NYS
SIC 3841 3842 3829 3826 3821 Hypodermic needles & syringes; IV transfusion apparatus; Catheters; Surgical knife blades & handles; Gloves, safety; Surgical appliances & supplies; Elastic hosiery, orthopedic (support); Thermometers & temperature sensors; Analytical instruments; Blood testing apparatus; Hemoglobinometers; Laboratory apparatus & furniture; Pipettes, hemocytometer
Ch Bd: Vincent A Forlenza
Pr: Gilberto Bulcao
Pr: A John Hanson
Pr: Deborah J Neff
Pr: Rex C Valentine
Pr: James R Wessel
COO: William A Kozy
Treas: John E Gallagher
Ofcr: Pierre Boisier
Ofcr: Jerome V Hurwitz
Ofcr: Christopher R Reidy
Ex VP: Richard J Naples
Ex VP: Nabil Shabshab
Ex VP: Jeffrey S Sherman
Ex VP: Stephen Sichak
Ex VP: Ellen R Strahlman
Sr VP: Jane Jerbasi
VP: Glenn Barbi
VP: Scott Binder
VP: Jean-Marc Dageville
VP: Bob Ferrigno
Board of Directors: Rebecca W Rimel, Basil L Anderson, Bertram L Scott, Catherine M Burzik, Claire M Fraser, Christopher Jones, Marshal O Larsen, Gary A Mecklenburg, James F Orr, Willard J Overlock Jr, Claire Pomeroy

D-U-N-S 09-363-6368 EXP
■ **BECTON DICKINSON INFUSION THERAPY HOLDINGS INC**
(*Suby of* BECTON DICKINSON AND CO) ★
9450 S State St, Sandy, UT 84070-3234
Tel (801) 565-2300 *Founded/Ownrshp* 2000
Sales 70.3MM[E] *EMP* 1,425
SIC 3841 3842 Catheters; Surgical appliances & supplies
Pr: Robert Adrion

D-U-N-S 19-446-1919 IMP/EXP
■ **BECTON DICKINSON INFUSION THERAPY SYSTEMS INC**
(*Suby of* BECTON DICKINSON INFUSION THERAPY HOLDINGS INC) ★
9450 S State St, Sandy, UT 84070-3234
Tel (801) 565-2300 *Founded/Ownrshp* 1986
Sales 63.4MM[E] *EMP* 1,425
SIC 3841 3842 Catheters; Surgical appliances & supplies
Pr: William Marshall
VP: Cal Alexander
**VP:* Mark H Borofsky
**VP:* Raymond P Ohlmuller

BECU
See BOEING EMPLOYEES CREDIT UNION

D-U-N-S 05-812-7986
▲ **BED BATH & BEYOND INC**
650 Liberty Ave, Union, NJ 07083-8107
Tel (908) 688-0888 *Founded/Ownrshp* 1971
Sales 12.1MMM *EMP* 62,150
Accts Kpmg Llp Short Hills New Jer
Tkr Sym BBBY *Exch* NGS
SIC 5719 5947 5999 Beddings & linens; Gift, novelty & souvenir shop; Toiletries, cosmetics & perfumes
Ch Bd: Warren Eisenberg
Ch Bd: Leonard Feinstein
CEO: Steven H Temares
COO: Eugene A Castagna
CFO: Susan E Lattmann
Treas: Gene Castagna
Chf Mktg O: Arthur Stark
Sr VP: Matthew Fiorilli
VP: Kenneth Bradley
VP: Kim Campbell
VP: Lisa Cavanagh
VP: Ronald Curwin
VP: Robyn D'Elia
VP: Pete Daleiden
VP: David Eckert
VP: Kenneth Frankel
VP: Jim Halliday
VP: Nancy Katz
VP: Tim Kirchner
VP: Ed Kopil
VP: Jeffrey Macak

D-U-N-S 79-731-1875
■ **BED N BATH STORES INC**
(*Suby of* BED BATH & BEYOND INC) ★
650 Liberty Ave Ste 2, Union, NJ 07083-8107
Tel (908) 688-0888 *Founded/Ownrshp* 1986
Sales 353.5MM[E] *EMP* 6,600[E]
SIC 6719 Investment holding companies, except banks
Pr: Warren Eisenberg
**Treas:* Ronald Curwin
**VP:* Leonard Feinstein

Genl Mgr: Todd Day
Snr Mgr: Sharon Smith

D-U-N-S 62-154-1259
BEDFORD COUNTY SCHOOL DISTRICT
310 S Bridge St, Bedford, VA 24523-2706
Tel (540) 586-1045 *Founded/Ownrshp* 1974
Sales 68.8MM^E *EMP* 1,700
Accts Brown Edwards & Company Ll
SIC 8211 Public elementary & secondary schools
Bd of Dir: John Hicks
Dir Sec: Gary Lowry

BEDFORD FAIR APPAREL
See ORCHARD BRANDS CORP

D-U-N-S 04-178-5387 IMP/EXP
BEDFORD INDUSTRIES INC
1659 Rowe Ave, Worthington, MN 56187-8700
Tel (507) 376-4136 *Founded/Ownrshp* 1966
Sales 124.3MM^E *EMP* 275
SIC 2671 2759 Plastic film, coated or laminated for packaging; Flexographic printing
Ch Bd: Robert Ludlow
**Pr:* Kim Milbrandt
**CFO:* Dave Reker
**Sec:* Sarah Milbrandt
Genl Mgr: Jeff Tschetter
CIO: Beth Radloff
CTO: Tom Macklin

BEDFORD LABORATORIES
See BEN VENUE LABORATORIES INC

BEDFORD RENT A CAR
See NISSAN GRUBBS MID-CITIES LTD

D-U-N-S 04-707-4505
BEDIVERE INSURANCE CO
ONEBEACON
(*Suby of* COMMERCIAL UNION/ ONEBEACON) ★
605 Hwy 169th N Ste 800, Plymouth, MN 55441
Tel (952) 852-2431 *Founded/Ownrshp* 2001
Sales NA *EMP* 1,500
SIC 6331 6282 6159 7389 Fire, marine & casualty insurance & carriers; Automobile insurance; Burglary & theft insurance; Workers' compensation insurance; Investment advisory service; Equipment & vehicle finance leasing companies; Financial services
CEO: Frank J Coyne
**Ch Bd:* Ray Barrette
**CEO:* Mike Miller
**CFO:* Paul McDonough
**Treas:* John J Naughton
**Ex VP:* Dennis Crosby
**Ex VP:* Paul Romano
**Sr VP:* Kevin Rehnberg
**VP:* Michael E McLoone
VP: Joseph Topale
VP: Jessica Wiley

BEDROSIAN'S TILES & STONE
See PARAGON INDUSTRIES INC

D-U-N-S 13-595-2609 IMP/EXP
BEE BUMBLE FOODS LLC
BUMBLE BEE
(*Suby of* BEE BUMBLE HOLDINGS INC) ★
280 10th Ave, San Diego, CA 92101-7406
Tel (858) 715-4000 *Founded/Ownrshp* 2010
Sales 178.5MM^E *EMP* 500
SIC 2091 Tuna fish: packaged in cans, jars, etc.
Prin: Christopher Lischew
**CEO:* Christopher Lischewski
VP: Scott Cameron
VP: Michael Fairman
VP: Dan Gerlach
VP: Chris Russell
Exec: Chris Fuller
Off Mgr: Michelle Lester
Snr Ntwrk: Steve Steinmetz
CIO: Tony Costa
CTO: Jerry Schwartz

D-U-N-S 00-326-6012 IMP/EXP
BEE BUMBLE HOLDINGS INC (GA)
(*Suby of* BUMBLE BEE PARENT INC) ★
280 10th Ave, San Diego, CA 92101-7406
Tel (858) 715-4000 *Founded/Ownrshp* 1926, 2010
Sales 178.5MM^E *EMP* 550
SIC 2013 2032 2033 Beef stew from purchased meat; Canned meats (except baby food) from purchased meat; Frozen meats from purchased meat; Chili with or without meat: packaged in cans, jars, etc.; Vegetables & vegetable products in cans, jars, etc.
Ch Bd: Robert P Kirby
CFO: Richard J Sosnoski
Treas: David J Carmany
Sr VP: Peter D Lemahieu
VP: Lester Florence
VP: Stephen J Kowalski
VP: David F Melbourne
MIS Mgr: Leon Connors

D-U-N-S 78-244-8484
■ **BEE CEE INC**
(*Suby of* NBC UNIVERSAL LLC) ★
30 Rockefeller Plz Fl 31, New York, NY 10112-0015
Tel (212) 664-4444 *Founded/Ownrshp* 1994
Sales 2.3MM^E *EMP* 2,000^E
SIC 4833 Television broadcasting stations
Pr: Steven Burke

BEEBE MEDICAL CENTER HOME HEAL
See BEEBE MEDICAL CENTER INC

D-U-N-S 06-988-5374
BEEBE MEDICAL CENTER INC
BEEBE MEDICAL CENTER HOME HEAL
424 Savannah Rd, Lewes, DE 19958-1462
Tel (302) 645-3300 *Founded/Ownrshp* 1916, 1935
Sales 325.7MM *EMP* 1,600
Accts Pricewaterhousecoopers Llp Ph
SIC 8062 General medical & surgical hospitals
Chf Rad: Frances Esposito
**Pr:* Jeffrey M Fried
VP: Bruce Leshine
VP: Gerald Smith
VP: Donna Streletzky
Dir Risk M: Teena Crane
Dir Lab: Mark Lamastra
Dir Lab: Rosemarie Rosmarin
Dir Rx: Samuel Roberts
Ex Dir: Cherrie Rich
Nurse Mgr: Margaret Porter

D-U-N-S 17-348-9899
BEECH FORK PROCESSING INC
Rr 292, Lovely, KY 41231
Tel (606) 395-6841 *Founded/Ownrshp* 1987
Sales 97.3MM^E *EMP* 281
SIC 1222 Bituminous coal-underground mining
Pr: James Booth
**Sec:* Roy Collier
**VP:* Ted Mc Ginnis

D-U-N-S 82-753-3571 IMP/EXP
BEECH-NUT NUTRITION CO
(*Suby of* HERO AG)
1 Nutritious Pl, Amsterdam, NY 12010-8105
Tel (518) 839-0300 *Founded/Ownrshp* 2012
Sales 112.7MM^E *EMP* 300
SIC 2032 Baby foods, including meats: packaged in cans, jars, etc.
Pr: Jeffrey Boutelle
VP: Shen-Youn Chang
Exec: Amy McGrath
Exec: Debra Quackenbush
VP Sls: Stephen La Magna
Mktg Mgr: Patrick Haughton
Manager: Monica Davis
Sls Mgr: Bruce Williams

D-U-N-S 00-748-2011 IMP
■ **BEECHCRAFT CORP**
TEXTRON AVIATION
(*Suby of* BEECHCRAFT HOLDINGS LLC) ★
10511 E Central Ave, Wichita, KS 67206-2557
Tel (316) 676-7111 *Founded/Ownrshp* 2007
Sales 2.1MMM^E *EMP* 5,650^E
SIC 3728 3721 Aircraft parts & equipment; Airplanes, fixed or rotary wing; Research & development on aircraft by the manufacturer
Ch: Sanjeev K Mehra
**Ch Bd:* William Boisture
**Pr:* Russ Bartlett
**CEO:* Robert Steve Miller
CFO: Briant Lewis
CFO: James Sanders
**CFO:* Karin-Joyce Tjon
**Treas:* George M Sellew
**Ex VP:* William E Brown
Ex VP: William Brown
VP: Brian Campbell
VP: Chris Charnley
**VP:* Bill James
**VP:* James D Knight
**VP:* Gail Lehman
VP: Dick Norwood
**VP:* Dave Rosenberg
VP: Bob Sill
Board of Directors: Jack Daly, David Hirsch, Seth Mersky

D-U-N-S 79-544-8567
■ **BEECHCRAFT HOLDINGS LLC**
(*Suby of* TEXTRON AVIATION INC) ★
10511 E Central Ave, Wichita, KS 67206-2557
Tel (316) 676-7111 *Founded/Ownrshp* 2015
Sales 2.1MMM^E *EMP* 7,400^E
SIC 3721 3728 6719 Airplanes, fixed or rotary wing; Aircraft parts & equipment; Investment holding companies, except banks
Pr: Robert S Miller
**CFO:* Karin-Joyce Tjon Sien Fat
**VP:* Gina E Vascsinec

D-U-N-S 14-434-9607
■ **BEECHER CARLSON HOLDINGS INC**
(*Suby of* BROWN & BROWN INC) ★
6 Concourse Pkwy Ste 2300, Atlanta, GA 30328-6185
Tel (404) 460-1400 *Founded/Ownrshp* 2013
Sales NA *EMP* 435
SIC 6411 Insurance brokers
Ch: Dan Donovan
**CEO:* Steve Denton
CFO: David Gamsey
Treas: John Gable
Sr VP: Jennifer Antrobus
Sr VP: Souwei Brune
Sr VP: Tim Cooper
Sr VP: Rick Craig
Sr VP: Dennis Doherty
Sr VP: Christian Florence
Sr VP: Richard Huntington
Sr VP: Geraldine Kerrigan
Sr VP: Matt Mautz
Sr VP: Carl Phillips
Sr VP: Nicholas Polo
Sr VP: Jason Richardson
Sr VP: Michael Stern
Sr VP: Robert Storey
Sr VP: Kyle Strand
VP: Dan Degrange
VP: Ross Downing
Board of Directors: Manu Rana, Blaine Wesner

D-U-N-S 11-410-8244 IMP
BEECHWOOD DISTRIBUTORS INC
BEECHWOOD SALES AND SERVICE
(*Suby of* GREAT BREWERS) ★
5350 S Emmer Dr, New Berlin, WI 53151-7365
Tel (262) 717-2831 *Founded/Ownrshp* 1987
Sales 91.0MM^E *EMP* 200
SIC 5181 Beer & other fermented malt liquors
Pr: John Sheehan
CFO: Eileen Rossmiller
Area Mgr: Cliff Kaplan
VP Sls: David Hock
Mktg Mgr: Scott McConeghy
Sls Mgr: Tom Holen
Sls Mgr: Mikal Stoltenberg
Sales Asso: Justin Wellington

D-U-N-S 08-689-9932 IMP/EXP
BEECHWOOD MOUNTAIN LLC
500 Broadway Ste A, Brooklyn, NY 11211-1741
Tel (718) 418-3205 *Founded/Ownrshp* 1998
Sales 136.2MM^E *EMP* 1,200^E
SIC 5021 Furniture
Ex Dir: Alex Gross
Mktg Dir: Malky Katz

BEECHWOOD SALES AND SERVICE
See BEECHWOOD DISTRIBUTORS INC

D-U-N-S 10-155-1310
BEECKEN PETTY OKEEFE & CO LLC
131 S Dearborn St Ste 122, Chicago, IL 60603-5581
Tel (312) 435-0300 *Founded/Ownrshp* 1996
Sales 129.6MM^E *EMP* 2,150
SIC 6799 3841 Venture capital companies; Surgical & medical instruments
VP: Peter Magas
VP: Grant Patrick
Off Mgr: Debbie Wahl

BEEF PRODUCTS
See BPI TECHNOLOGY INC

BEEHIVE CLOTHING
See CORP OF PRESIDING BISHOP OF CHURCH OF JESUS CHRIST OF LATTER-DAY SAINTS

D-U-N-S 80-803-5625
BEELINE.COM INC
(*Suby of* MODIS INC) ★
12724 Gran Bay Pkwy W # 200, Jacksonville, FL 32258-9485
Tel (904) 527-5700 *Founded/Ownrshp* 2000
Sales 98.4MM^E *EMP* 5,112^E
SIC 7371 Computer software development
Pr: Doug Leeby
Prgrm Mgr: Jeff McCartney
Off Mgr: Kelly Stancil
CTO: Richard Rislove

D-U-N-S 00-781-4825
BEELMAN TRUCK CO
1 Racehorse Dr, East Saint Louis, IL 62205-1001
Tel (618) 646-5300 *Founded/Ownrshp* 1978
Sales 101.2MM^E *EMP* 450
SIC 4214

D-U-N-S 05-286-6951 IMP
BEER CAPITOL DISTRIBUTING INC
(*Suby of* BADGER LIQUOR-MADISON) ★
W222n5700 Miller Way, Sussex, WI 53089-3988
Tel (262) 932-2337 *Founded/Ownrshp* 2016
Sales 185.5MM^E *EMP* 370
SIC 5181 Beer & other fermented malt liquors
CEO: Aldo Madrigrano
**Pr:* Mike Merriman
Opers Mgr: Eric Werner
Sls Mgr: Ken Zeman

D-U-N-S 07-828-7145
■ **BEF FOODS INC** (OH)
(*Suby of* BOB EVANS FARMS LLC) ★
8111 Smiths Mill Rd, New Albany, OH 43054-1183
Tel (800) 272-7675 *Founded/Ownrshp* 2011
Sales 94.4MM^E *EMP* 800^E
SIC 5963 Food services, direct sales
Pr: Mike Townseley
**VP:* Kevin C O'Neil
Plnt Mgr: Eugene Smith

BEGREEN
See GREEN MOUNTAIN ENERGY CO

D-U-N-S 09-919-6073
BEHAVIORAL HEALTH NETWORK INC
CHILD GUIDANCE CLINIC OF SPRIN
417 Liberty St Ste 1, Springfield, MA 01104-3739
Tel (413) 747-0705 *Founded/Ownrshp* 1992
Sales 65.2MM *EMP* 1,400
Accts Alexander Aronson Finning & Co
SIC 8093 8322 Mental health clinic, outpatient; Child related social services
Pr: Katherine B Wilson
Sr VP: Susan West
VP: Richard Follett
VP: Steven Winn
Prgrm Mgr: Jeffrey Kassis
Prgrm Mgr: Meg Mastriana
Off Mgr: Juliet Hansen
Off Mgr: Roberta Krause
Off Mgr: Nilda Rivera
Off Mgr: Amy Wilson
Dir IT: Ken Lawless

D-U-N-S 96-673-4340
BEHAVORIAL HEALTHCARE INC
155 Inverness Dr W, Englewood, CO 80112-5095
Tel (720) 490-4400 *Founded/Ownrshp* 2011
Sales 90.2MM *EMP* 2
Accts Kundinger Corder & Eng E Pc D
SIC 8099 Health & allied services
Prin: Terry Andrews

BEHLEN CAFETERIA
See BEHLEN MKTG CO

D-U-N-S 11-506-6292 IMP/EXP
BEHLEN MFG CO
INDUSTRIAL PRODUCTS
(*Suby of* BEHLEN CAFETERIA) ★
4025 E 23rd St, Columbus, NE 68601-9944
Tel (402) 564-3111 *Founded/Ownrshp* 1984
Sales 268.2MM^E *EMP* 945
SIC 3523 3448 4213 3556 3496 3443 Farm machinery & equipment; Hog feeding, handling & watering equipment; Cattle feeding, handling & watering equipment; Crop storage bins; Prefabricated metal buildings; Farm & utility buildings; Silos, metal; Panels for prefabricated metal buildings; Trucking, except local; Food products machinery; Miscellaneous fabricated wire products; Fabricated plate work (boiler shop)
Pr: John Underwood
**Ch:* Tony Raimondo
Sr VP: Dick Casey
**VP:* Lyle Burbach
VP: Allen Cooke
VP: Dave Slusarski
Creative D: Mike Krzycki
Dist Mgr: Eric McVey
MIS Dir: Don Luby
Info Man: Lee Easton
QI Cn Mgr: Rick Pfeiffer

D-U-N-S 78-202-0077 IMP
BEHLEN MKTG CO
BEHLEN CAFETERIA
4025 E 23rd St, Columbus, NE 68601-3448
Tel (402) 564-3111 *Founded/Ownrshp* 1984
Sales 272.9MM^E *EMP* 1,200
SIC 3523 3448 4213 Farm machinery & equipment; Cattle feeding, handling & watering equipment; Prefabricated metal buildings; Trucking, except local
Pr: Anthony F Raimondo
**Treas:* CT Burton

D-U-N-S 00-890-1522
BEHLER-YOUNG CO
JOHNSON CONTRLS AUTHORIZED DLR
4900 Clyde Park Ave Sw, Wyoming, MI 49509-5118
Tel (616) 531-3400 *Founded/Ownrshp* 1927
Sales 132.8MM^E *EMP* 225
SIC 5075 5051 5074 Warm air heating & air conditioning; Air conditioning & ventilation equipment & supplies; Warm air heating equipment & supplies; Sheets, metal; Plumbing & hydronic heating supplies
Ch Bd: Richard W Young
**CEO:* Douglas R Young
**CFO:* Joseph E Hrabovsky
Brnch Mgr: Bob Compton
Brnch Mgr: Jim Kemper
Brnch Mgr: Steve Nagel
Mktg Mgr: Naomi Bistline
Sls Mgr: Brent Bunce

D-U-N-S 96-203-1795
BEHLMANN AUTOMOTIVE HOLDING CO INC
820 Jmes S Mcdonnell Blvd, Hazelwood, MO 63042-2306
Tel (314) 895-1600 *Founded/Ownrshp* 1996
Sales 90.4MM^E *EMP* 377
SIC 5511 Pickups, new & used
Pr: Kenneth Behlmann

BEHR HOLDINGS
See BEHR PAINT CORP

BEHR IRON & METAL
See JOSEPH BEHR & SONS INC

D-U-N-S 00-204-0793
■ **BEHR PAINT CORP** (CA)
BEHR HOLDINGS
(*Suby of* MASCO CORP) ★
3400 W Segerstrom Ave, Santa Ana, CA 92704-6405
Tel (714) 545-7101 *Founded/Ownrshp* 1948, 1993
Sales 720.9MM^E *EMP* 2,000^E
SIC 2851 Paints & paint additives; Stains: varnish, oil or wax
CEO: Jeffrey D Filley
**CFO:* Jonathan M Sullivan
**Sr VP:* Anthony Demiro
VP: Irene Arredondo
VP: John Sznewajs

D-U-N-S 96-256-9575 IMP
■ **BEHR PROCESS CORP**
(*Suby of* MASCO CORP) ★
3400 W Segerstrom Ave, Santa Ana, CA 92704-6405
Tel (714) 545-7101 *Founded/Ownrshp* 1999
Sales 762.6MM^E *EMP* 1,298^E
SIC 2851 Paints & paint additives; Stains: varnish, oil or wax; Varnishes
CEO: Jeffrey D Filley
Pr: Greg Brod
Pr: Beth Galliher
**Sr VP:* Jonathan Sullivan
VP: Barry Friedman
VP: Eugene A Gargaro Jr
**VP:* Lawrence F Leaman
VP: Richard Maus
**VP:* Jerry W Mollien
**VP:* John G Sznewajs
VP: Pam Van Bogaert

D-U-N-S 79-301-3798
BEHRMAN CAPITAL LP
126 E 56th St Fl 27, New York, NY 10022-3694
Tel (212) 980-5419 *Founded/Ownrshp* 1992
Sales 354.9MM^E *EMP* 4,490
SIC 6799 Venture capital companies; Security speculators for own account
Pt: Grant Behrman
Pt: Robert E Flaherty
Mng Pt: William M Matthes
Ofcr: Lexi Terrero
VP: Michael Rapport
VP: Pradyut Shah
Dir IT: Darlene Baerga

BEI HAWAII
See PHOENIX V LLC

BEI INDUSTRIAL ENCODERS
See BEI SENSORS & SYSTEMS CO LLC

D-U-N-S 79-972-2327 IMP
BEI SENSORS & SYSTEMS CO LLC
BEI INDUSTRIAL ENCODERS
(*Suby of* SENSATA TECHNOLOGIES INC) ★
1461 Lawrence Dr, Thousand Oaks, CA 91320-1311
Tel (805) 968-0782 *Founded/Ownrshp* 2015
Sales 159.3MM^E *EMP* 1,000
SIC 3679 Electronic circuits
CEO: Eric Pilaud
**Treas:* Jean-Yves Mouttet
VP: Bob Ciurzzak
VP: Vincent Inendino
Genl Mgr: JD Agustas
**CTO:* Jean-Yves Vo
Mktg Mgr: Scott Orlosky
Sls Mgr: James Barrett

D-U-N-S 00-117-7906 IMP
BEIERSDORF INC (DE)
(*Suby of* BEIERSDORF NORTH AMERICA INC) ★
45 Danbury Rd, Wilton, CT 06897-4405
Tel (203) 563-5800 *Founded/Ownrshp* 1928

Sales 195.4MM^E *EMP* 525
SIC 2844 Face creams or lotions
CFO: Joerg Disseld
**VP:* Amy Nenner
**VP:* Kathy Shea

D-U-N-S 11-496-2108 IMP
BEIERSDORF NORTH AMERICA INC
(*Suby of* BEIERSDORF AG)
45 Danbury Rd, Wilton, CT 06897-4405
Tel (203) 563-5800 *Founded/Ownrshp* 1998
Sales 195.4MM^E *EMP* 535
SIC 2844 5122 3842 2841 2672 Face creams or lotions; Antiseptics; Bandages & dressings; Stockinette, surgical; Soap: granulated, liquid, cake, flaked or chip; Tape, pressure sensitive: made from purchased materials
CEO: James A Kenton
**Pr:* Bill Graham
COO: Manfred Fink
**CFO:* Raymond Engelbrecht
**Ch:* Stefan Heidenreich
**VP:* Tina Jackse
**VP:* Magnus Jonsson
VP: Alexandra Kowcz
VP: Thomas Mc
VP: Horst Wenck
VP: Clemens Woehrle
Dir Teleco: Kris Abate
Dir Risk M: Ed Brill
Dir Bus: Irene Valles

D-U-N-S 00-300-7267 IMP/EXP
BEISTLE CO (PA)
1 Beistle Plz, Shippensburg, PA 17257-9684
Tel (717) 532-2131 *Founded/Ownrshp* 1900
Sales 97.3MM^E *EMP* 500
SIC 2679 3993 2675 2657 2631 2621 Novelties, paper: made from purchased material; Signs & advertising specialties; Die-cut paper & board; Folding paperboard boxes; Paperboard mills; Paper mills
CEO: H R Luhrs
**Pr:* Patricia D Lacy
**CFO:* Christopher Keegan
**VP:* Kenneth E Shoap
**VP:* Alan R Weist
Genl Mgr: Mark Sullivan
IT Man: Randy Arnold
IT Man: Jacob Rosenberry
Sftwr Eng: Kevin Myers
Sftwr Eng: Russell Wiest
VP Prd: Doug Wilson

D-U-N-S 05-152-5129 IMP/EXP
BEKAERT CORP
(*Suby of* BEKAERT NORTH AMERICA MANAGEMENT CORP) ★
3200 W Market St Ste 303, Fairlawn, OH 44333-3326
Tel (330) 867-3325 *Founded/Ownrshp* 1994
Sales 689.9MM^E *EMP* 1,927
SIC 3315 Wire & fabricated wire products; Fencing made in wiredrawing plants
CEO: Matthew Taylor
**CFO:* Bruno Humblet
Ex VP: Geert V Haver
**Ex VP:* Lieven Larmuseau
Ex VP: Dominique Neerinck
Ex VP: Piet V Riet
**Ex VP:* Piet Van Riet
**Ex VP:* Curd Vandekerckhove
Ex VP: Frank Vromant
VP: Peter Ramaut
VP: Briggs Whitfield
Exec: Peter Andries
Exec: Therese Crapanzano

D-U-N-S 08-650-6354 IMP/EXP
BEKAERT NORTH AMERICA MANAGEMENT CORP
(*Suby of* BEKAERT SA NV)
3200 W Market St Ste 303, Fairlawn, OH 44333-3326
Tel (330) 867-3325 *Founded/Ownrshp* 1996
Sales 689.9MM^E *EMP* 1,987^E
Accts Deloitte
SIC 3315 Wire & fabricated wire products
Pr: Rick McWhirt
**CFO:* David Best
**Ch:* Bert Degraeve

D-U-N-S 80-564-5959 IMP/EXP
BEKAERT TEXTILES USA INC
240 Business Park Dr, Winston Salem, NC 27107-6538
Tel (336) 747-4900 *Founded/Ownrshp* 1992
Sales 186.9MM^E *EMP* 190
SIC 5021 2211

D-U-N-S 03-842-7258
BEKINS A-1 MOVERS INC
ACE MOVING AND STORAGE
125 Stewart Rd, Hanover Township, PA 18706-1462
Tel (570) 793-2586 *Founded/Ownrshp* 1997
Sales 93.3MM^E *EMP* 300
SIC 4213 Trucking, except local
CEO: David A Caruso
**Pr:* Terry Kostoff
CFO: Steve Pisaneschi
VP: Gary Grote
Brnch Mgr: Adam Morgan
**Off Mgr:* Beverly Jone
Off Mgr: Beverly Jones
Mktg Dir: Tonya Vrba

BEL AIR MARKETS
See RALEYS

D-U-N-S 06-498-3646 IMP
BEL BRANDS USA INC
(*Suby of* FROMAGERIES BEL)
30 S Wacker Dr Ste 3000, Chicago, IL 60606-7459
Tel (312) 462-1500 *Founded/Ownrshp* 1971
Sales 113.6MM^E *EMP* 350
SIC 2022 Natural cheese; Processed cheese
Pr: Lance Chambers
VP: Didier Aziza
VP Sls: Heather Rewiski
Manager: John Cryer
Manager: Brandon Fontenot
Manager: Kevin Sharp
Manager: Jeffrey Smith

Board of Directors: Philippe Deloffre, Didier Lesur, M Troussier

D-U-N-S 00-132-1389 IMP
▲ BEL FUSE INC (NJ)
206 Van Vorst St, Jersey City, NJ 07302-4421
Tel (201) 432-0463 *Founded/Ownrshp* 1949
Sales 567.0MM *EMP* 7,971^E
Accts Deloitte & Touche Llp New Yor
Tkr Sym BELFA *Exch* NGS
SIC 3679 3674 3613 3677 Cores, magnetic; Semiconductors & related devices; Modules, solid state; Fuses, electric; Inductors, electronic
Pr: Daniel Bernstein
Treas: Colin Dunn
VP: Dennis Ackerman
VP: Raymond Cheung
Snr Mgr: Dean Wang
Board of Directors: Norman Yeung, Howard B Bernstein, Avi Eden, Peter Gilbert, John S Johnson, Eric Nowling, Mark B Segall, Robert H Simandl, John F Tweedy, Vincent Vellucci

D-U-N-S 00-201-5196 IMP
BEL-AQUA POOL SUPPLY INC (NY)
20 Commerce Dr, New Rochelle, NY 10801-5214
Tel (914) 235-2200 *Founded/Ownrshp* 1955
Sales 125.3MM^E *EMP* 70^E
SIC 5091 Swimming pools, equipment & supplies
Pr: Martin Silver
**VP:* Susan Wisan
Mktg Mgr: Shanna Leuchter
Sls Mgr: Greg Parker

BEL-CAPRI
See LOSURDO FOODS INC

D-U-N-S 07-836-3436
BELAIR HD STUDIOS LLC
2233 S Throop St, Chicago, IL 60608-5002
Tel (312) 254-5188 *Founded/Ownrshp* 2001
Sales 180.0MM *EMP* 30
SIC 7335 2711 Commercial photography; Commercial printing & newspaper publishing combined
CEO: Clyde Scott

D-U-N-S 00-974-7015
BELCAN ENGINEERING GROUP LLC
(*Suby of* BELCAN LLC) ★
10200 Anderson Way, Blue Ash, OH 45242-4718
Tel (513) 891-0972 *Founded/Ownrshp* 1991
Sales 327.0MM *EMP* 3,000
SIC 8711 Engineering services
CEO: Lance Kwasniewski
Exec: George Pirtle
Snr Sftwr: David M Bry
Snr Sftwr: Mark Farver
IT Man: Pat Callahan
Sftwr Eng: Jason Anyalebechi
Sftwr Eng: Kyle Bowerman
Sftwr Eng: Shannon Cozens
Ql Cn Mgr: Russell Lubik
Board of Directors: Candace McCaw, Mike McCaw

D-U-N-S 05-510-5399
BELCAN LLC
10200 Anderson Way, Blue Ash, OH 45242-4718
Tel (513) 891-0972 *Founded/Ownrshp* 2015
Sales 825.0MM^E *EMP* 10,215
SIC 7363 8711 Engineering help service; Engineering services
CEO: Lance H Kwasneiwski
CFO: Colin Cohen
CFO: Michael Wirth
Sr VP: Rick Schneider
VP: Kerry Byrne
VP: Steve Houghtaling
VP: Mehran Jouhari
VP: Neal Montour
VP: Eugene Vaughn
Brnch Mgr: M D Cwayna
Brnch Mgr: Shannon Herrell

D-U-N-S 18-432-2725
BELCAN SERVICES GROUP LIMITED PARTNERSHIP
(*Suby of* BELCAN LLC) ★
10200 Anderson Way, Blue Ash, OH 45242-4718
Tel (513) 891-0972 *Founded/Ownrshp* 1958
Sales 260.6MM *EMP* 3,000
SIC 7363 Engineering help service
Genl Pt: Candace McCaw
Pt: Arnold Johnson
Pt: John Kuprionis
Pt: Michael McCaw
CFO: Mike Wirth
IT Man: Curtis Shreve

D-U-N-S 00-602-6710 IMP
BELCO INDUSTRIES INC
9138 W Belding Rd, Belding, MI 48809-1768
Tel (616) 794-0410 *Founded/Ownrshp* 1959
Sales 87.0MM^E *EMP* 395
SIC 3567 5084 3541 3535 3444 Paint baking & drying ovens; Industrial machinery & equipment; Machine tools, metal cutting type; Conveyors & conveying equipment; Sheet metalwork
CEO: Thomas F Kohn
**Pr:* Mike Kohn
Off Mgr: Sandra Menke
Dir IT: Michael MA
Sls Mgr: Kevin Wilson
Sales Asso: Kyle Kohn

D-U-N-S 80-918-2579 IMP
■ BELDEN 1993 LLC
(*Suby of* BELDEN INC) ★
1 N Brentwood Blvd # 1500, Saint Louis, MO 63105-3925
Tel (314) 854-8000 *Founded/Ownrshp* 1993
Sales 562.2MM^E *EMP* 2,000^E
SIC 3357 Communication wire; Coaxial cable, nonferrous; Fiber optic cable (insulated)
Pr: John S Stroup
**Ch Bd:* Bryan C Cressey
**Treas:* Stephen H Johnson
**VP:* Gray Benoist
**VP:* Kevin L Bloomfield

BELDEN CDT ELECTRONICS DIV
See BELDEN WIRE & CABLE CO LLC

D-U-N-S 00-917-8666 IMP/EXP
▲ BELDEN INC
1 N Brentwood Blvd # 1500, Saint Louis, MO 63105-3925
Tel (314) 854-8000 *Founded/Ownrshp* 1988
Sales 2.3MMM *EMP* 8,200
Tkr Sym BDC *Exch* NYS
SIC 3357 Nonferrous wiredrawing & insulating; Communication wire; Fiber optic cable (insulated)
Ch Bd: John S Stroup
CFO: Henk Derksen
Bd of Dir: Judy Brown
Ex VP: Christoph Gusenleitner
Ex VP: Glenn Pennycook
Ex VP: Dhrupad Trivedi
Ex VP: Roel Vestjens
Sr VP: Brian E Anderson
Sr VP: Dean McKenna
Sr VP: Ross Rosenberg
VP: John Norman
VP: Douglas R Zink
Dir Bus: Leifeng Xu
Board of Directors: David J Aldrich, Lance C Balk, Steven W Berglund, Judy L Brown, Bryan Cressey, Jonathan C Klein, George Minnich, John M Monter

D-U-N-S 80-943-0325 IMP/EXP
■ BELDEN WIRE & CABLE CO LLC
BELDEN CDT ELECTRONICS DIV
(*Suby of* BELDEN INC) ★
2200 Us Highway 27 S, Richmond, IN 47374-7437
Tel (765) 983-5200 *Founded/Ownrshp* 1993
Sales 561.9MM^E *EMP* 1,999
SIC 3357

D-U-N-S 07-956-3332
■ BELEN MEADOWS HEALTHCARE AND REHABILITATION CENTER LLC
(*Suby of* GENESIS HEALTHCARE LLC) ★
1831 Camino Del Llano, Belen, NM 87002-2619
Tel (505) 864-1600 *Founded/Ownrshp* 2007
Sales 7.7MM^E *EMP* 3,283^E
SIC 8051 Skilled nursing care facilities
CEO: George V Hagaer Jr

D-U-N-S 03-345-9186
BELFLEX STAFFING NETWORK LLC
11591 Goldcoast Dr, Cincinnati, OH 45249-1633
Tel (513) 488-8588 *Founded/Ownrshp* 1998
Sales 110.1MM *EMP* 4,200
Accts Clark Schaefer Hackett & Co
SIC 7361 7363 Employment agencies; Help supply services
Ch: Candace McCaw
Pr: Todd Cross
CEO: Mike McCaw
CFO: Tim Mueller
VP: Bob Baer

D-U-N-S 61-038-9707
BELFOR HOLDINGS INC
185 Oakland Ave Ste 300, Birmingham, MI 48009-3481
Tel (248) 594-1144 *Founded/Ownrshp* 2006
Sales 1.0MMM *EMP* 6,000
Accts Price Waterhouse
SIC 6719 Investment holding companies, except banks
Pr: Sheldon Yellen
COO: Mike N Yellen
**CFO:* Joe Ciolino
Treas: Chris Jones
**Ex VP:* Theresa Williams Brownd
VP: John Stagl
VP: Matt Wetzel
Genl Mgr: Chris Davis
Genl Mgr: Steve Delillo
Genl Mgr: Dave Dellinger
Genl Mgr: Greg French

BELFOR PROPERTY RESTORATION
See BELFOR USA GROUP INC

D-U-N-S 84-262-0338 IMP
BELFOR USA GROUP INC
BELFOR PROPERTY RESTORATION
(*Suby of* BELFOR HOLDINGS INC) ★
185 Oakland Ave Ste 150, Birmingham, MI 48009-3430
Tel (248) 594-1144 *Founded/Ownrshp* 1998
Sales 939.8MM *EMP* 5,064
SIC 1799 Post-disaster renovations
Pr: Sheldon Yellen
**CFO:* Joe Ciolino
CFO: Joe Schalino
Exec: Summer Jenkins
Exec: Megan O'Gorman
Prgrm Mgr: Tony Marino
Genl Mgr: Steve Mahoney
Genl Mgr: Gerry McGonagle
Genl Mgr: John Rybski
Genl Mgr: Tricia Sarrazin
Off Mgr: Kelly Chernault

D-U-N-S 09-343-2243 IMP
BELGIOIOSO CHEESE
BELGIOIOSO CHEESE COMPANY
4200 Main St, Green Bay, WI 54311-9614
Tel (920) 863-2123 *Founded/Ownrshp* 1979, 1993
Sales 102.8MM^E *EMP* 180
SIC 2022 Natural cheese
Pr: Errico Auricchio
**CFO:* Thomas J Krueger
CFO: Thomas Krueger
VP: Brad S Siebold
VP: Francis Wall
Exec: Lisa Cumbers
QA Dir: Helen Schmude
VP Opers: Mark Schleitwiler
Opers Mgr: Francesca Elfner
Opers Mgr: Brett Laronge
Plnt Mgr: Gianni Toffolon

BELGIOIOSO CHEESE COMPANY
See BELGIOIOSO CHEESE

D-U-N-S 07-106-1386
BELK FINANCE CO INC
2801 W Tyvola Rd, Charlotte, NC 28217-4525
Tel (704) 357-1000 *Founded/Ownrshp* 1961
Sales 22.6MM^E *EMP* 1,205
SIC 8741 Financial management for business
Pr: Thomas M Belk
Pr: John R Belk
Pr: McKay Belk
Pr: Tim Belk
Treas: James Berry
Off Mgr: John Walker
Board of Directors: Irwin Belk

D-U-N-S 01-683-6160 IMP
BELK INC
(*Suby of* BEAR PARENT INC) ★
2801 W Tyvola Rd, Charlotte, NC 28217-4500
Tel (704) 357-1000 *Founded/Ownrshp* 2015
Sales 4.6MMM^E *EMP* 24,350
SIC 5311 Department stores, discount
CEO: Thomas M Belk Jr
Treas: James Cook
Chf Mktg O: David Zant
Ex VP: Brian Marley
Ex VP: Ralph A Pitts
Sr VP: Barbara Schrantz
VP: Shawn Blair
VP: Cynthia Nester
VP: Tom Nystrom
VP: Ilene Shleffar
Exec: Melissa Valero

BELKIN COMPONENTS
See BELKIN INTERNATIONAL INC

D-U-N-S 06-510-7708 IMP/EXP
BELKIN INTERNATIONAL INC
BELKIN COMPONENTS
12045 Waterfront Dr, Playa Vista, CA 90094-2999
Tel (310) 751-5100 *Founded/Ownrshp* 1983
Sales 613.9MM^E *EMP* 1,300
SIC 5065 5045 Intercommunication equipment, electronic; Communication equipment; Computers & accessories, personal & home entertainment
Pr: Chester J Pipkin
**CFO:* George C Platisa
**Sec:* Janice Pipkin
VP Mktg: Miki Yamanaka
Mktg Dir: Daisy Su

BELKNAP WHITE ALCCO
See BELKNAP WHITE GROUP INC

D-U-N-S 00-196-3586 IMP
BELKNAP WHITE GROUP INC
BELKNAP WHITE ALCCO
111 Plymouth St, Mansfield, MA 02048-2073
Tel (508) 337-2700 *Founded/Ownrshp* 1986
Sales 86.1MM^E *EMP* 135
SIC 5023 Floor coverings
CEO: Raymond Mancini Jr
Pr: Bill Prescott
VP: Neal Coughlin
VP: Stephen Mancini
VP: Craig McLean
Brnch Mgr: Roger Oetman
Opers Mgr: Brad Fye
VP Mktg: Scott Wodicka
Manager: Steve Hilton
Sls Mgr: Paul Allen

D-U-N-S 05-067-0256
BELL & ASSOCIATES CONSTRUCTION LP (TN)
BELL CONSTRUCTION
255 Wilson Pike Cir, Brentwood, TN 37027-5207
Tel (615) 373-4343 *Founded/Ownrshp* 1997
Sales 110.2MM^E *EMP* 300
SIC 1622 1541 1542 Bridge construction; Warehouse construction; Commercial & office building, new construction; Hospital construction; School building construction
Pr: Keith Pyle
CFO: Jody Evans
VP: Darek Bell
Dir Bus: Allan Cox
CIO: Don Stillman

BELL & EVANS
See FARMERS PRIDE INC

D-U-N-S 18-818-7439
BELL AMERICAN GROUP LLC
TACO BELL
(*Suby of* FLYNN RESTAURANT GROUP LLC) ★
8930 Bash St Ste L, Indianapolis, IN 46256-1285
Tel (317) 788-0374 *Founded/Ownrshp* 2012
Sales 49.7MM^E *EMP* 1,326
SIC 5812 Fast-food restaurant, chain
CEO: Greg Flynn
**Pr:* Craig E Fenneman
CFO: Lorin Cortina
**VP:* Charles W Brown

D-U-N-S 96-867-3835 IMP
BELL AND HOWELL LLC
(*Suby of* CONTRADO BBH HOLDINGS LLC) ★
3791 S Alston Ave, Durham, NC 27713-1880
Tel (919) 767-4401 *Founded/Ownrshp* 2011
Sales 341.5MM^E *EMP* 1,400^E
SIC 3579 Envelope stuffing, sealing & addressing machines; Mailing machines; Address labeling machines; Voting machines
CEO: Ramesh Ratan
COO: Larry Blue
CFO: Lior Yahalomi
VP: Jim Feely
VP: Wayne Quesnelle
Exec: Lisa Swank
Ex Dir: Peter Dutka
Ex Dir: Phil Ehardt
Ex Dir: Warren Phillips
CIO: Ronald Ridge

D-U-N-S 12-267-9749 IMP
■ BELL ATLANTIC GLOBAL WIRELESS INC
(*Suby of* VERIZON COMMUNICATIONS INC) ★
1717 Arch St Fl 33, Philadelphia, PA 19103-2751
Tel (215) 246-9494 *Founded/Ownrshp* 2008
Sales 241.5MM^E *EMP* 1,846
SIC 4813 4812 5065 7379 Long distance telephone communications; Cellular telephone services; Paging services; Mobile telephone equipment; Paging & signaling equipment; Computer related maintenance services
Pr: Dennis Strigl
**CFO:* Dermott O Murphy
**VP:* Stephen B Heimann
**VP:* Gary C Ridge

D-U-N-S 18-507-1594
■ BELL ATLANTIC INVESTMENT DEVELOPMENT CORP
VERIZON
(*Suby of* VERIZON COMMUNICATIONS INC) ★
1717 Arch St Fl 22, Philadelphia, PA 19103-2740
Tel (215) 963-6000 *Founded/Ownrshp* 2008
Sales 91.8MM^E *EMP* 1,650
SIC 1731 Computer installation
Ch: William Albertini
**CFO:* J Kevin Cauley

D-U-N-S 04-671-1735
BELL BANK
(*Suby of* STATE BANKSHARES INC) ★
3100 13th Ave S, Fargo, ND 58103-3507
Tel (701) 298-1500 *Founded/Ownrshp* 1989
Sales NA *EMP* 300
SIC 6022 State commercial banks
CEO: Michael Solberg
Treas: Bob Buth
Ofcr: Sarah Crompton
Ofcr: Mark Hengel
Ofcr: Melanie Keltgen
Ofcr: Dan Peters
Ofcr: Kathy Radermacher
Sr Tst Off: Dick Brudvik
Ex VP: Rodney Jordahl
Ex VP: Bill Russell
Sr VP: Patrick Chaffee
Sr VP: Eric Fischer
Sr VP: Warren Hilde
Sr VP: Richard Kadry
Sr VP: Diane Kaiser
Sr VP: Rebecca Kronlund
Sr VP: Blake Nelson
VP: Heidi Bye
VP: Kelly Fenno
VP: Eric Halvorson
VP: Brandy Harris

D-U-N-S 61-298-0789
BELL CO LLC
1340 Lexington Ave, Rochester, NY 14606-3010
Tel (585) 277-1000 *Founded/Ownrshp* 1986
Sales 196.9MM^E *EMP* 350
SIC 1541 1542 Industrial buildings & warehouses; Commercial & office building contractors
Pr: Steve Reuther
**CFO:* Jim Dreier
**Ex VP:* Michael Benulis
**Ex VP:* Andrew Carayiannis
VP: Robert E Bell

BELL CONSTRUCTION
See BELL & ASSOCIATES CONSTRUCTION LP

D-U-N-S 04-542-5735
BELL COUNTY TEXAS
101 E Central Ave, Belton, TX 76513
Tel (254) 933-5115 *Founded/Ownrshp* 2010
Sales NA *EMP* 1,000
SIC 9111 Executive offices
Prin: John Burrows

D-U-N-S 11-828-5360
BELL GARDENS BICYCLE CLUB INC
BICYCLE CLUB CASINO
888 Bicycle Casino Dr, Bell Gardens, CA 90201-7617
Tel (562) 806-4646 *Founded/Ownrshp* 1984
Sales 33.9MM^E *EMP* 1,300
SIC 7999 5812 Card rooms; Coffee shop
Pr: George Hardie
Pr: Jim Griffo
**Pr:* George G Hardie
Chf Mktg O: Kelley O'Hara
VP: Joy Harn
Mktg Mgr: Kelley O'Harra

D-U-N-S 06-292-3321 IMP/EXP
■ BELL HELICOPTER TEXTRON INC
(*Suby of* TEXTRON INC) ★
3255 Bell Helicopter Blvd, Fort Worth, TX 76118-7630
Tel (817) 280-2011 *Founded/Ownrshp* 1981
Sales 1.8MMM^E *EMP* 5,100
SIC 3728 5088 3721 Aircraft parts & equipment; Transportation equipment & supplies; Helicopters; Motorized aircraft
Pr: Mitchell L Snyder
**COO:* Gunnar Kleveland
**COO:* Cathy Smith
Ex VP: Sue Gove
**Ex VP:* Felipe Gumucio
Ex VP: Barry Kohler
Ex VP: Jeffrey Lowinger
Ex VP: Danny Maldonado
**Ex VP:* Peter Riley
**Ex VP:* Anthony A Viotto
Sr VP: Cathy Ferrie
Sr VP: Matt Hasik
**Sr VP:* Martha May
Sr VP: Larry D Roberts
Sr VP: Mary Simmerman
VP: Richard Harris
VP: Ken Hudson
VP: Kevin Kett
VP: John Klopfer
VP: Darrell Pate
VP: Mark Rudeseal

D-U-N-S 00-690-5533
BELL INDUSTRIES INC
(*Suby of* NEWCASTLE CAPITAL MANAGEMENT LP) ★
4400 W 96th St, Indianapolis, IN 46268-2912
Tel (866) 782-2355 *Founded/Ownrshp* 1979
Sales 109.2MM^E *EMP* 700
SIC 7379 5734 ; Computer & software stores
CEO: Clinton J Coleman
IT Man: Jon Adams
Opers Mgr: Kellie Pumphrey
Sales Asso: Lisa Goolsby

D-U-N-S 02-704-3693
BELL INTEGRATOR INC
800 W El Camino Real, Mountain View, CA 94040-2567
Tel (650) 603-0988 *Founded/Ownrshp* 2014
Sales 38.4MM^E *EMP* 2,000^E
SIC 7373 7389 Systems integration services;
CEO: Andrey Korobitsyn
**COO:* Eugene Pozdnikov

D-U-N-S 06-351-8831 IMP/EXP
BELL LABORATORIES INC
MOTOMCO
3699 Kinsman Blvd, Madison, WI 53704-2598
Tel (608) 241-0202 *Founded/Ownrshp* 1973
Sales 97.1MM^E *EMP* 630
SIC 2879 Pesticides, agricultural or household
Pr: Steve Levy
**VP:* Linda Stack Hughes
Exec: Kent Gutzmer
Rgnl Mgr: Arnaud Valle
CTO: Michelle Bailey
Opers Mgr: Craig Kail
Opers Mgr: Robert Radix
Mktg Mgr: John Schwerin
Manager: Daniel De Poli
Sls Mgr: Mike Bowler
Sls Mgr: Jeremy Davis

D-U-N-S 00-620-6403
BELL LUMBER & POLE CO (MN)
(*Suby of* BELL LUMBER & POLE CANADA, ULC)
778 1st St Nw, New Brighton, MN 55112-3216
Tel (651) 633-4334 *Founded/Ownrshp* 1909, 1970
Sales 100.9MM^E *EMP* 163
SIC 5099 2411 Logs, hewn ties, posts & poles; Logging
Pr: Thomas Bell
**CFO:* Pat Tymkiw
Treas: Tom Brix
Dir Bus: Jeff Whiteside
Div Mgr: Todd Brown
Genl Mgr: Precious Johnson
Genl Mgr: Leigh Skeeles
IT Man: Jason Sixsmith
Opers Mgr: Dave Imholte
Plnt Mgr: Rick Bleskey
Sales Exec: Mark Von-Grey

D-U-N-S 08-142-9060
BELL PARTNERS INC
300 N Greene St Ste 1000, Greensboro, NC 27401-2173
Tel (336) 232-1900 *Founded/Ownrshp* 1976
Sales 62.0MM^E *EMP* 1,600
SIC 6513 Apartment hotel operation
Ch: Steven D Bell
Pr: Lili F Dunn
CEO: Jon D Bell
COO: Gwyneth J Cote
COO: Robert H Slater
CFO: John E Tomlinson
Ex VP: Durant Bell
Ex VP: E Durant Bell
Sr VP: Erin J Ditto
Sr VP: Anne Ossewaarde
Sr VP: Rebecca Shaffrey
VP: James Hamrick
VP: Steve Hancock
VP: Allison Ray
VP: Tammy Siegner
VP: Adrienne Smith

D-U-N-S 01-867-8235 IMP
BELL PUMP SERVICE CO
JOHNSON CONTRLS AUTHORIZED DLR
29 Lafayette St, Hartford, CT 06106-1508
Tel (860) 525-6678 *Founded/Ownrshp* 1940
Sales 122.6MM^E *EMP* 250
SIC 5075 5078 5074 Air conditioning & ventilation equipment & supplies; Oil burners
Pr: Floran J Boland
VP: Steve Ambrose
VP: Mike Stevens
Off Mgr: Eunice Noble
IT Man: David Caley
Sales Exec: Wayne Lopes

D-U-N-S 61-013-1161 IMP
BELL SPORTS CORP
(*Suby of* BRG SPORTS INC) ★
6333 N State Highway 161 # 300, Irving, TX 75038-2218
Tel (469) 417-6600 *Founded/Ownrshp* 2004
Sales 337.6MM *EMP* 1,368
SIC 3949 3751 5091 Helmets, athletic; Protective sporting equipment; Bicycles & related parts; Bicycle parts & accessories
COO: Dona Flood
CFO: Jeffrey Gregg
CFO: Paul Lehman
CFO: Paul Lehmanc
CFO: Mark Tripp
CFO: Terry Tuttle
VP: Bill Mote
Comm Man: Mike Canter
Sls Dir: Scott Oliver

D-U-N-S 00-838-9322 IMP/EXP
BELL SPORTS INC
EASTON BELL SPORTS
(*Suby of* BELL SPORTS CORP) ★
6333 N State Highway 161 # 300, Irving, TX 75038-2218
Tel (469) 417-6600 *Founded/Ownrshp* 1989
Sales 174.3MM^E *EMP* 578
SIC 3949 3751 Helmets, athletic; Bicycles & related parts
COO: Dona Flood
Exec: Jackie Werblo

D-U-N-S 62-059-8735 IMP
BELL SUPPLY CO LLC
SYNERGY ENERGY HOLDINGS
(*Suby of* SYNERGY ENERGY HOLDINGS LLC) ★
114 E Foreline St, Gainesville, TX 76240-3320
Tel (940) 612-0612 *Founded/Ownrshp* 2006
Sales 257.3MM^E *EMP* 500
SIC 5084 Oil well machinery, equipment & supplies

D-U-N-S 01-728-4420
BELL TECHLOGIX INC
(*Suby of* BELL INDUSTRIES INC) ★
4400 W 96th St, Indianapolis, IN 46268-2912
Tel (317) 333-7777 *Founded/Ownrshp* 2008
Sales 98.4MM^E *EMP* 700
SIC 7379
CEO: Clinton Coleman
**Pr:* Anthony D Ambrosi
**CEO:* Ron S Frankenfield
Sr VP: Dan Dempsey
Sr VP: Don Imaizumi
Sr VP: Elizabeth Kubycheck
VP: Jack Mansfield
**VP:* Steve Shannon
Prgrm Mgr: Robert Sonday
Genl Mgr: David Stearns
IT Man: Todd Brown

BELL TRANSPORTATION
See WHITTLESEA BLUE CAB CO

D-U-N-S 00-912-5642 IMP/EXP
BELL-CARTER FOODS INC
BELL-CARTER OLIVE COMPANY
3742 Mt Diablo Blvd, Lafayette, CA 94549-3601
Tel (925) 284-5933 *Founded/Ownrshp* 1912
Sales 165.3MM^E *EMP* 450^E
SIC 2033 Olives: packaged in cans, jars, etc.
CEO: Timothy T Carter
**CFO:* John Toth
**VP:* Paul McGinty
VP: Robin Robinson
Genl Mgr: Margo Llyod
QA Dir: Tammy Neyhard
Plnt Mgr: Steve Henderson
Snr Mgr: Shawn Heitland

BELL-CARTER OLIVE COMPANY
See BELL-CARTER FOODS INC

D-U-N-S 12-888-4793
BELLA FOUR BAKERY INC
NATURE'S BAKERY
1150 Trademark Dr Ste 101, Reno, NV 89521-2999
Tel (775) 883-2253 *Founded/Ownrshp* 2002
Sales 138.8MM^E *EMP* 330^E
SIC 2064 5461 Candy & other confectionery products; Bakeries
Pr: David B Marson
**Treas:* Jan T Marson
VP: Jon Wesson
Mktg Dir: Andrew Strolin

D-U-N-S 09-014-6465 IMP/EXP
BELLA INTERNATIONAL CORP
HONDA DE SAN JUAN
Ave Kennedy Sector Bechar, San Juan, PR 00921
Tel (787) 620-7010 *Founded/Ownrshp* 1963
Sales 84.9MM^E *EMP* 385
SIC 5511 Automobiles, new & used
Ch Bd: Jeronimo Esteve Abril
**Pr:* Carlos Lopez-Lay
**Treas:* Mary Pineda
**Sr VP:* Enrique Tormos
VP: Santos Antonetti
**VP:* Maria Isabel Esteve
VP Sls: Jose Carlos Villares

BELLACANVAS
See COLOR IMAGE APPAREL INC

D-U-N-S 09-766-2746
BELLCO CREDIT UNION
7600 E Orchard Rd 400n, Greenwood Village, CO 80111-2522
Tel (303) 689-7800 *Founded/Ownrshp* 1936
Sales NA *EMP* 250
SIC 6061 Federal credit unions
Pr: Douglas A Ferraro
Ofcr: Sean Fitzhugh
Ex VP: Sandra Blogett
Exec: Dan Cass
Assoc Dir: Debra Hicks
Brnch Mgr: Lynneil Campbell
Brnch Mgr: Ben Franklin
Brnch Mgr: Scott Greene
Brnch Mgr: Betsy Madden
Brnch Mgr: Stacie Zidan
IT Man: Sharon Maas

D-U-N-S 00-385-4999
BELLCO DRUG CORP
BELLCO HEALTH
5500 New Horizons Blvd, Amityville, NY 11701-1156
Tel (631) 789-6900 *Founded/Ownrshp* 1960
Sales 1.2MMM^E *EMP* 1,805
SIC 5122 5047

BELLCO HEALTH
See BELLCO DRUG CORP

D-U-N-S 01-683-0705 IMP
BELLE TIRE DISTRIBUTORS INC (MI)
1000 Enterprise Dr, Allen Park, MI 48101-3029
Tel (888) 462-3553 *Founded/Ownrshp* 1945, 1988
Sales 391.4MM^E *EMP* 1,100
SIC 5531 5014 Automotive tires; Automotive accessories; Automobile tires & tubes; Truck tires & tubes
Pr: Don Barnes Jr
**CFO:* Daniel T Light
**VP:* Robert Barnes
VP: Jennifer Smith
Exec: Scott Gallup

D-U-N-S 18-511-3255
BELLEHOFF CORP
PONDEROSA STEAKHOUSE
405 S Mission St, Mount Pleasant, MI 48858-2878
Tel (989) 772-2902 *Founded/Ownrshp* 1987
Sales 49.3MM^E *EMP* 4,200
SIC 5812 Steak restaurant
CEO: Douglas La Belle
**CFO:* Thomas Binder
**Sec:* Barton W La Belle

D-U-N-S 00-627-7974 IMP
BELLEVILLE BOOT CO
100 Premier Dr, Belleville, IL 62220-3423
Tel (618) 233-5600 *Founded/Ownrshp* 1904
Sales 116.7MM^E *EMP* 705
SIC 3143 Men's footwear, except athletic; Work shoes, men's
Ch Bd: Homer W Weidmann

D-U-N-S 08-993-7353
BELLEVUE COLLEGE FOUNDATION (WA)
3000 Landerholm Cir Se, Bellevue, WA 98007-6484
Tel (425) 564-1000 *Founded/Ownrshp* 1966
Sales 1.6MM *EMP* 1,808
Accts Smith Bunday Berman Britton Ps
SIC 8222 8221 Community college; Colleges universities & professional schools
Pr: Sarah Langton
**Treas:* Chad Wall
Ofcr: Mark Knight
VP: Lucy P Macneil
VP: Andrea Torres
Assoc Dir: Teri Hull
Assoc Dir: Joy Prosise
**Ex Dir:* Jennifer Strother
Prgrm Mgr: Deron Dahlke
Prgrm Mgr: Nicholas Michiels
Admn Mgr: Carol Deehr

D-U-N-S 07-803-3982
BELLEVUE PUBLIC SCHOOLS
2600 Arboretum Dr, Bellevue, NE 68005-3501
Tel (402) 293-4000 *Founded/Ownrshp* 1876
Sales 2.1MM *EMP* 1,100
Accts Hsmc Orizon Llc Omaha Ne
SIC 8299 8748 8211 Educational services; Business consulting; Public elementary school
**Pr:* Doug Cook
**Pr:* Frank Kumor
**Treas:* Mary Kay Davenport
Treas: Carrie Smoots
Trst: Mike Kinney
Trst: Lisa Rybar
Ex Dir: Kim Bodensteiner
IT Man: Frank Harwood
Teacher Pr: Julee Sauer
Teacher Pr: Sharra Smith
Psych: Lisa Olsen

D-U-N-S 07-004-9218
BELLEVUE SCHOOL DISTRICT
12111 Ne 1st St, Bellevue, WA 98005-3181
Tel (425) 456-4000 *Founded/Ownrshp* 1942
Sales 90.1MM^E *EMP* 2,000
SIC 8211 Public elementary school; Public junior high school; Public senior high school; Public special education school
Bd of Dir: Mike Bartz
Bd of Dir: Judy Buckmaster
Bd of Dir: Tricia Gundersen
Bd of Dir: Deborah Kraft
Bd of Dir: Linda Peterson
Bd of Dir: Krischanna Roberson
Bd of Dir: Bjorn Unneland
Bd of Dir: Denise Vance
Dir Sec: Mike Dorman
Genl Mgr: Brian Flynn
MIS Dir: Jason Goleck

D-U-N-S 07-191-3719
BELLFLOWER UNIFIED SCHOOL DISTRICT
16703 Clark Ave, Bellflower, CA 90706-5245
Tel (562) 866-9011 *Founded/Ownrshp* 1946
Sales 73.6MM^E *EMP* 1,200
Accts Vavrinek Trine Day & Co Ll
SIC 8211 Public elementary & secondary schools

D-U-N-S 60-382-6132
BELLIN HEALTH SYSTEMS INC
BELLIN MEMORIAL HOSPITAL
744 S Webster Ave, Green Bay, WI 54301-3505
Tel (920) 433-3500 *Founded/Ownrshp* 1983
Sales 502.4MM *EMP* 2,300
Accts Wipfli Llp Green Bay Wiscons
SIC 8062 8063 7352 General medical & surgical hospitals; Hospital, professional nursing school; Psychiatric hospitals; Medical equipment rental
Pr: George Kerwin
COO: Chris Woleske
**CFO:* Jim Dietsche
Ofcr: Jeremy Nelson
VP: Amy Dettman
VP: James Dietsche
VP: Amy Stlaurent
Dir OR: Amanda Sosnosky
Dir Sec: Ron Hieronimczak
Software D: Tara Shank
Opers Mgr: Jody Wilmet
Board of Directors: Barb Braun, Michael Frohna, Anne Ledvina

BELLIN HOSPITAL
See BELLIN MEMORIAL HOSPITAL INC

BELLIN MEMORIAL HOSPITAL
See BELLIN HEALTH SYSTEMS INC

D-U-N-S 07-477-9430
BELLIN MEMORIAL HOSPITAL INC (WI)
BELLIN HOSPITAL
(*Suby of* BELLIN MEMORIAL HOSPITAL) ★
744 S Webster Ave, Green Bay, WI 54301-3581
Tel (920) 433-3500 *Founded/Ownrshp* 1908
Sales 462.8MM *EMP* 1,725^E
Accts Wipfli Llp Green Bay Wiscons
SIC 8062 General medical & surgical hospitals
Pr: George Kerwin
Chf Rad: Robert Monette

*CFO: Jim Dietsche
Bd of Dir: Larry Weyers
VP: Jacquelyn Hunt
VP: Lori Rexses
VP: John Rocheleau
Dir Inf Cn: Carol Bess
Dir Risk M: Mary Mueller
QA Dir: Colleen Obrien
Dir IT: Troy Schiesl

D-U-N-S 96-791-1269
BELLINGHAM PUBLIC SCHOOLS
1306 Dupont St, Bellingham, WA 98225-3118
Tel (360) 676-6400 Founded/Ownrshp 2011
Sales 14.7MM^E EMP 1,022^E
SIC 8211 Elementary & secondary schools
Opers Supe: Danielson Christian
Pr Dir: Tanya Rowe
Teacher Pr: Nora Klewiada

D-U-N-S 04-018-8419
BELLINGHAM SCHOOL BOARD
1306 Dupont St, Bellingham, WA 98225-3118
Tel (360) 676-6400 Founded/Ownrshp 1942
Sales 104.3MM EMP 1,170^E
SIC 8211 School board
Pr: Kelly Bashaw

D-U-N-S 01-952-1344
BELLISIO FOODS FOODSERVICE
1201 Hennepin Ave, Minneapolis, MN 55403-1707
Tel (952) 469-2000 Founded/Ownrshp 2008
Sales 169.0MM^E EMP 1,385
SIC 5141 Groceries, general line

D-U-N-S 61-675-2069 IMP/EXP
BELLISIO FOODS INC
YU SING
(Suby of CENTRE PARTNERS MANAGEMENT LLC) ★
525 S Lake Ave Ste 201, Duluth, MN 55802-2300
Tel (218) 723-5555 Founded/Ownrshp 2011
Sales 716.3MM^E EMP 2,092
SIC 2038 Dinners, frozen & packaged; Ethnic foods, frozen; Snacks, including onion rings, cheese sticks, etc.
CEO: Joel Conner
Ex VP: Charlie Postnay
*Sr VP: Danette Bucsko
*Sr VP: Charles Pountney
VP: Joel Spoonheim
Sys Mgr: Jim Engel
Sfty Mgr: Tom Austin
Sls Dir: Stephen Shockley
Sls Mgr: Derald Walker

D-U-N-S 17-831-6253 IMP
BELLOFRAM CORP
MARSH BELLOFRAM COR
8019 Ohio River Blvd, Newell, WV 26050
Tel (304) 387-1200 Founded/Ownrshp 1986
Sales 107.3MM^E EMP 475
SIC 3612 3829 3625 Transformers, except electric; Pressure transducers; Actuators, industrial; Positioning controls, electric
Ch Bd: A B Siemer
*CFO: Roger Bailey
Natl Sales: Jeff Gamble
Sls Dir: Tim Webb
Manager: John Koniski

BELLSOUTH
See YP ADVERTISING & PUBLISHING LLC

D-U-N-S 95-820-2756
■ **BELLSOUTH BUSINESS SYSTEMS INC**
(Suby of BELLSOUTH TELECOMMUNICATIONS INC) ★
2180 Lake Blvd Ne, Brookhaven, GA 30319-6004
Tel (404) 829-8000 Founded/Ownrshp 1992
Sales 347.3MM^E EMP 2,000
SIC 4813 4812 Local & long distance telephone communications; Radio telephone communication
CEO: Phil S Jacobs
VP: Larry Gill
*VP: Paul Harmon

D-U-N-S 05-691-2207 IMP
■ **BELLSOUTH COMMUNICATION SYSTEMS LLC**
(Suby of AMERICAN TELEPHONE AND TELG) ★
1936 Blue Hills Dr Ne, Roanoke, VA 24012-8611
Tel (540) 983-6000 Founded/Ownrshp 2006
Sales 222.6MM^E EMP 2,000
SIC 5065 4813 4812 Telephone equipment; Telephone communication, except radio; Radio telephone communication
Pr: John Foote
Sls&Mrk Ex: Douglas Holcomb

D-U-N-S 10-667-8006 IMP
■ **BELLSOUTH CORP**
(Suby of AT&T INC) ★
675 W Peach St Ste 4300, Atlanta, GA 30375-0001
Tel (404) 420-6126 Founded/Ownrshp 1983
Sales 13.1MMM^E EMP 63,000
SIC 4813 4812 2741 5065 Telephone communication, except radio; Local telephone communications; Voice telephone communications; Data telephone communications; Cellular telephone services; Directories, telephone: publishing only, not printed on site; Telephone & telegraphic equipment; Telephone equipment
CEO: Andrew M Geisse
Pr: Rex Adams
Pr: Richard A Anderson
*Pr: Mark L Feidler
Pr: Harry Lightsey
Pr: David Scobey
*CEO: F Duane Ackerman
*CEO: Robert D Daniel
CFO: Frank Dunn
*CFO: Jonathan P Klug
*CFO: Pat Shannon
Treas: Linda S Harty
Ofcr: Keith O Cowan
Ofcr: Ronald E Frieson
*Ex VP: Francis A Dramis Jr
VP: Robert M Airasian
VP: Barry Boniface
VP: Suzanne Detlefs
VP: Jan Funderburg
*VP: Marc Gary
VP: Lori Groves

D-U-N-S 00-692-5333
■ **BELLSOUTH TELECOMMUNICATIONS INC**
(Suby of BELLSOUTH CORP) ★
675 W Peach St Ne St Ne, Atlanta, GA 30375-0001
Tel (912) 526-3440 Founded/Ownrshp 1983
Sales 2.9MMM^E EMP 10,000
Accts Pricewaterhousecoopers Llp
SIC 4813 4812 2741 5065 Telephone communication, except radio; Local telephone communications; Voice telephone communications; Data telephone communications; Radio telephone communication; Directories, telephone: publishing only, not printed on site; Telephone & telegraphic equipment
CFO: Guy Cochran
Pr: Joseph P Lacher
Pr: Carl E Swearingen
CEO: Robert D Daniel
CFO: Tom Koch
Treas: Jerry W Robinson
VP: William Smith
QI Cn Mgr: Porscha Rankine

D-U-N-S 80-354-4899
■ **BELLVILLE TUBE CO LP**
(Suby of LONE STAR TECHNOLOGIES INC) ★
141 Miller Rd E, Bellville, TX 77418-7096
Tel (979) 865-9111 Founded/Ownrshp 2000
Sales 170.6MM^E EMP 1,900
SIC 3312 Tubes, steel & iron
Genl Pt: Micheal Chddick
Exec: Rebecca Janish
Exec: Leslie Melnar
VP Opers: Bently Munson

D-U-N-S 08-617-9199 IMP
BELMARK INC
600 Heritage Rd, De Pere, WI 54115-2444
Tel (920) 336-2848 Founded/Ownrshp 1977
Sales 218.0MM EMP 650
SIC 2759 2657 2671 Labels & seals: printing; Folding paperboard boxes; Packaging paper & plastics film, coated & laminated
Ch: Bruce Bell
*Pr: Karl A Schmidt
*CFO: Cindy Schultz
Sales Asso: Mariah A Pizzo

BELMONT PARK
See NYRA INC

D-U-N-S 07-538-3638
BELMONT UNIVERSITY
1900 Belmont Blvd, Nashville, TN 37212-3757
Tel (615) 460-6000 Founded/Ownrshp 1949
Sales 261.8MM EMP 600^E
Accts Crowe Horwath Llp Brentwood
SIC 8221 University
Ch Bd: Marty Dickens
*Pr: Robert C Fisher
Treas: Caleb L Bumbaugh
Ofcr: Freida Sage
VP: Dodd Lake
VP: Jason Rogers
VP: Bettel Thomas
*VP: Susan West
Dir Rx: Michael McGuire
Off Mgr: Lissa Edwards
Off Mgr: Antonette Gardner

D-U-N-S 00-734-0078 IMP
■ **BELO CORP**
BELO FOUNDATION
(Suby of TEGNA INC) ★
7950 Jones Branch Dr, Mc Lean, VA 22102-3302
Tel (703) 854-6000 Founded/Ownrshp 2013
Sales 1.0MMM^E EMP 2,696^E
SIC 4833 Television broadcasting stations
Pr: Dunia A Shive
Pr: Albert Brown
Pr: Peter L Diaz
Pr: Mario A Hewitt
Pr: Mark A Higgins
Pr: Robert A Klingle
Pr: Patti Smith
CFO: Carey P Hendrickson
Ex VP: Guy H Kerr
Sr VP: Colleen B Rown
VP: Janice Bryant
VP: R Paul Fry
VP: Sergio H Salinas
VP: Joe Weir

BELO FOUNDATION
See BELO CORP

BELOIT HEALTH SYSTEM
See BELOIT MEMORIAL HOSPITAL FOUNDATION INC

D-U-N-S 96-502-4099
BELOIT HEALTH SYSTEM INC
1969 W Hart Rd, Beloit, WI 53511-2298
Tel (608) 364-5011 Founded/Ownrshp 1971
Sales 211.2MM EMP 1,400^E
SIC 8062 General medical & surgical hospitals
Pr: Gregory Britton
Dir Vol: Roberta Henning
*Sr VP: Timothy McKevett
*VP: Kristinn Armann
*VP: Leland From
*VP: William Groeper
VP: Doris Mulder
Exec: Tom Sullivan

D-U-N-S 96-653-5606
BELOIT MEMORIAL HOSPITAL FOUNDATION INC
BELOIT HEALTH SYSTEM
1969 W Hart Rd, Beloit, WI 53511-2230
Tel (608) 363-5724 Founded/Ownrshp 1988
Sales 211.2MM EMP 2
Accts Wipfli Llp Milwaukee Wiscons
SIC 6733 Trusts
Ex Dir: Ann Sitrick

D-U-N-S 07-613-9690 IMP
BELOIT MEMORIAL HOSPITAL INC
1969 W Hart Rd, Beloit, WI 53511-2230
Tel (608) 364-5011 Founded/Ownrshp 1928
Sales 209.5MM EMP 1,400
SIC 8062 8011 General medical & surgical hospitals; Offices & clinics of medical doctors
V Ch: Gregory K Britton
Chf Rad: Thomas Lisk
*Pr: Timothy McKevett
Treas: Steve M Eldred
Sr VP: Timothy M McKevett
*VP: Kristinn Armann
*VP: Leland From
VP: Kenneth Klein
VP: Linda Lynch
VP: Doris R Mulder
VP: Susan K Scheiber
Exec: Thomas Sullivan

D-U-N-S 01-762-0899 IMP
BELTING CO OF CINCINNATI
CBT COMPANY
5500 Ridge Ave, Cincinnati, OH 45213-2516
Tel (513) 621-9050 Founded/Ownrshp 1921
Sales 122.9MM^E EMP 119
SIC 5085 5063 Bearings; Power transmission equipment, electric
Pr: James E Stahl Jr
CFO: Ben Corbett
Chf Mktg O: Alex C Kepley
VP: Jerry Reichert
Mng Dir: Daryl A Albrecht
Genl Mgr: Pat Cullen
Genl Mgr: Jerry Perkins
IT Man: Dan Corbett
IT Man: Dan Turner
Sales Asso: Bob Bauman
Sales Asso: Chris Reinstatler

D-U-N-S 00-285-5336 IMP/EXP
BELTMANN GROUP INC (MN)
AGENT FOR N AMERCN VAN LINES
(Suby of BATTMANN HOLDINGS INC) ★
2480 Long Lake Rd, Saint Paul, MN 55113-2534
Tel (651) 639-2800 Founded/Ownrshp 1933
Sales 208.2MM^E EMP 634
SIC 4213 4214 Trucking, except local; Household goods transport; Local trucking with storage; Household goods moving & storage, local
CEO: Dann Battina
*Pr: Marc Van Kley
*Sec: Paul A Zagaria
Ex VP: Paul Zagaria
VP: Carol Kennedy
VP: Cheryl Wencl
Genl Mgr: Rhonda Hurt
CIO: Eric Yancy
Dir IT: Jon Smart
IT Man: Douglas Longworth
Sfty Dirs: Kenny Gamblin

D-U-N-S 07-761-7967
BELTON INDEPENDENT SCHOOL DISTRICT
BELTON ISD
400 N Wall St, Belton, TX 76513-3143
Tel (254) 215-2000 Founded/Ownrshp 1926
Sales 105.7MM EMP 1,300
Accts Pattillo Brown & Hill Llp W
SIC 8211 Public elementary & secondary schools
*CFO: Eric Banfield
*VP: Penny Digby
Ex Dir: Manuela Challis
MIS Dir: John Greiner
Pr Dir: Kyle Debeer
Psych: Sara Cregan
Psych: Christy Fairey
Psych: Melodi Howard
Psych: Scott Ivy
Nutrtnst: Danielle Rombold

BELTON ISD
See BELTON INDEPENDENT SCHOOL DISTRICT

D-U-N-S 04-884-4542 IMP/EXP
BELTSERVICE CORP
4143 Rider Trl N, Earth City, MO 63045-1102
Tel (314) 344-8500 Founded/Ownrshp 1969
Sales 88.0MM EMP 275
SIC 3052

D-U-N-S 82-885-5713
BELV PARTNERS LP
PEABODY ORLANDO, THE
9801 International Dr, Orlando, FL 32819-8104
Tel (407) 352-4000 Founded/Ownrshp 1986
Sales 30.1MM^E EMP 1,200
SIC 7011 Hotels & motels
Pr: Alan C Villaverde
VP: Gregg J Herning

D-U-N-S 00-311-4931 IMP/EXP
■ **BELVAC PRODUCTION MACHINERY INC**
(Suby of DOVER RFRGN & FD EQP INC) ★
237 Graves Mill Rd, Lynchburg, VA 24502-4203
Tel (434) 239-0358 Founded/Ownrshp 1993
Sales 105.0MM EMP 200
SIC 3565 Canning machinery, food
Pr: Richard S Steigerwald
*Ex VP: David J Mammolenti
VP: Joseph Schill
VP: Anthony Zellars
Tech Mgr: Rod Ellis
Mktg Mgr: Jeff Watts
Board of Directors: Graham Mc Mahon

D-U-N-S 15-723-3172
BELZ HOTEL GROUP LLC
PEABODY HOTEL GROUP
(Suby of SOUTH PLAZA CO) ★
5118 Park Ave Ste 245, Memphis, TN 38117-5708
Tel (901) 762-5466 Founded/Ownrshp 1983
Sales 99.2MM^E EMP 2,400
SIC 8741 8721 Hotel or motel management; Accounting, auditing & bookkeeping
Ch: Martin S Belz
*CFO: Michael K Craft
*Sec: Jimmy Williams
*Ex VP: David Shamoian
*VP: Ronald A Belz
VP: Timothy Gonser
VP: Mohamed Hakimian

D-U-N-S 00-102-5865 IMP/EXP
BEMIS ASSOCIATES INC
1 Bemis Way, Shirley, MA 01464-2527
Tel (978) 425-6761 Founded/Ownrshp 1940
Sales 114.9MM^E EMP 300
SIC 2891 2851 3479 Adhesives; Lacquers, varnishes, enamels & other coatings; Painting, coating & hot dipping
Pr: Stephen Howard
*Treas: David R Riggert
Genl Mgr: George Skinner
Dir IT: Mark Erickson
VP Mfg: Eric Longo
Mfg Dir: Thomas Decolfmacker
Plnt Mgr: David Pott
Prd Mgr: Michael Huebsch
QI Cn Mgr: David Martin
Board of Directors: John Mc Carthy, Neil Mc Phail, Howard Nichols

D-U-N-S 00-647-7061
▲ **BEMIS CO INC** (MO)
1 Neenah Ctr Fl 4, Neenah, WI 54956-3087
Tel (920) 527-5000 Founded/Ownrshp 1858
Sales 4.0MMM EMP 17,500
Accts Pricewaterhousecoopers Llp Mi
Tkr Sym BMS Exch NYS
SIC 2671 2672 Paper coated or laminated for packaging; Plastic film, coated or laminated for packaging; Adhesive papers, labels or tapes: from purchased material
Pr: William F Austen
*Ch Bd: Timothy M Manganello
CFO: Michael B Clauer
Treas: Melanie E R Miller
Sr VP: James W Ransom
VP: Sheri H Edison
VP: Jerry Hauerwas
VP: William E Jackson
VP: Jerry S Krempa
VP: Wim Van Smissen
Exec: Jeff Hopp
Exec: Linda Le Clair
Dir Bus: Edward Gentile
Board of Directors: Ronald J Floto, Adele M Gulfo, David S Haffner, William L Mansfield, Arun Nayar, Edward N Perry, David T Szczupak, Holly A Van Deursen, Philip G Weaver

D-U-N-S 00-614-4737 IMP/EXP
■ **BEMIS HEALTHCARE PACKAGING INC**
BEMIS NORTH AMERICA
(Suby of BEMIS CO INC) ★
3500 N Main St, Oshkosh, WI 54901-1233
Tel (920) 527-7464 Founded/Ownrshp 1965
Sales 561.4MM^E EMP 3,500
SIC 2671 3565 Packaging paper & plastics film, coated & laminated; Thermoplastic coated paper for packaging; Packaging machinery
Ch: James Ransom
*Pr: Thomaz Gruber
*VP: James Mitchell
VP: Don Nimis
VP: Dave Vierthaler
VP Opers: Tim Ferguson
Sfty Mgr: Scott Reineck
Plnt Mgr: Kint Sikorski
Plnt Mgr: Sam Smith
Mktg Dir: Chris Nimis
Mktg Mgr: Matt Mengel

D-U-N-S 11-846-9865 IMP/EXP
■ **BEMIS HEALTHCARE PACKAGING INC**
(Suby of BEMIS CO INC) ★
3500 N Main St, Oshkosh, WI 54901-1233
Tel (920) 527-3000 Founded/Ownrshp 1996
Sales 242.4MM^E EMP 820
SIC 2671 Packaging paper & plastics film, coated & laminated
Pr: Paul Verbeten
CFO: Mike Brown
*Treas: Jerry S Krempa
*VP: Melanie Miller
Area Mgr: Jonathan Smith
Mfg Dir: Mark Keenan
Mfg Dir: Don Zaiki
Opers Mgr: Luis Silva
VP Sls: Doug Latreille
Sls Dir: Michael Obrien
Board of Directors: Jerry S Krempa

BEMIS JASON
See PACON CORP

D-U-N-S 00-607-2078 IMP/EXP
BEMIS MANUFACTURING CO INC (WI)
CHURCH SEAT CO
300 Mill St, Sheboygan Falls, WI 53085-1807
Tel (920) 467-4621 Founded/Ownrshp 1899, 1901
Sales 588.1MM^E EMP 2,000
SIC 3089 Injection molded finished plastic products; Molding primary plastic; Extruded finished plastic products; Plastic processing
CEO: Peter F Bemis
*Pr: Richard A Bemis
COO: Norman Giertz
*CFO: James Kertscher
Treas: Frank J Poja
VP: Wayne Laning
Netwrk Mgr: Jeff Meyer
Mtls Mgr: Kimberly Eibs
Mfg Mgr: Ignacio Beaver
Opers Mgr: Ryan Schmidt
QI Cn Mgr: John Cutting
Board of Directors: James Kroscher, Robert Melzer, Richard D Pauls, James Schreiber, Jeffrey J Trowbridge

BEMIS NORTH AMERICA
See BEMIS HEALTHCARE PACKAGING INC

BEMIS NORTH AMERICA
See BEMIS PACKAGING INC

D-U-N-S 06-187-0101
■ BEMIS PACKAGING INC
BEMIS NORTH AMERICA
(*Suby of* BEMIS CO INC) ★
3550 Moser St, Oshkosh, WI 54901-1255
Tel (920) 527-2300 *Founded/Ownrshp* 1990
Sales 227.9MM^E *EMP* 1,075
SIC 2671 Packaging paper & plastics film, coated & laminated
VP: Gregory J Derhaeg
**Treas:* Jerry S Krempa
**VP:* Sheri H Edison
**VP:* Kent F Kreul
VP: Bob Simpson
Dir IT: Rusty Witthuhn
Tech Mgr: Scott Schneider
Sfty Mgr: Renee Hoffman
Mfg Mgr: Wilton Brown
Plnt Mgr: John Seider
Mktg Mgr: Robert Krause

D-U-N-S 04-268-4902 IMP
BEN & JERRYS HOMEMADE INC
BEN & JERRY'S ICE CREAM
(*Suby of* UNILEVER PLC)
30 Community Dr Ste 1, South Burlington, VT 05403-6828
Tel (802) 846-1500 *Founded/Ownrshp* 1977
Sales 123.0MM^E *EMP* 841
SIC 2024 5812 6794

BEN & JERRY'S ICE CREAM
See BEN & JERRYS HOMEMADE INC

D-U-N-S 87-941-4696 IMP/EXP
BEN ARNOLD-SUNBELT BEVERAGE CO OF SOUTH CAROLINA L P
BEVERAGE SOUTH CAROLINA
101 Beverage Blvd, Ridgeway, SC 29130-9785
Tel (803) 337-3500 *Founded/Ownrshp* 1993
Sales 128.6MM^E *EMP* 400
SIC 5182

D-U-N-S 02-741-4572
■ BEN BRIDGE - JEWELER INC
(*Suby of* BERKSHIRE HATHAWAY INC) ★
2901 3rd Ave Ste 200, Seattle, WA 98121-1004
Tel (206) 448-8800 *Founded/Ownrshp* 2000
Sales 168.9MM^E *EMP* 750
SIC 5944 7631 Jewelry stores; Watch, clock & jewelry repair
Ch Bd: Herbert M Bridge
**CEO:* Jonathan Bridge
CFO: Jerome Jerry Gronfien
**Co-Ch Bd:* Robert L Bridge
VP: Lisa Bridge
**VP:* MaryTodd-Mc Ginnis
**VP:* Cathy Hall
VP Mktg: Steven Davolt

D-U-N-S 00-792-9748 IMP
BEN E KEITH CO (TX)
BEN E KEITH FOODS
601 E 7th St, Fort Worth, TX 76102-5501
Tel (817) 877-5700 *Founded/Ownrshp* 1906
Sales 3.5MMM^E *EMP* 4,000
SIC 5181 5141 Beer & other fermented malt liquors; Groceries, general line
Ch Bd: Robert G Hallam
**Pr:* Howard Hallam
**CFO:* Gordon Crow
Treas: Matt McLin
Top Exec: Phil Brandt
Ex VP: Nolan Cleaves
Sr VP: Ron Boyd
VP: Andy McCaskill
**VP:* Mike Roach
VP: Jim Stone
Exec: Shane Henderson

BEN E KEITH FOODS
See BEN E KEITH CO

D-U-N-S 00-408-7284 IMP
BEN HILL GRIFFIN INC
GRIFFIN FERTILIZER CO
700 S Scenic Hwy, Frostproof, FL 33843-2443
Tel (863) 635-2281 *Founded/Ownrshp* 1943
Sales 90.6MM *EMP* 300
Accts Randolph Swain Tallent & White
SIC 2875 0174 2033 Fertilizers, mixing only; Citrus fruits; Fruits: packaged in cans, jars, etc.
Ch Bd: Ben Hill Griffin III
**Pr:* Ben Hill Griffin IV
**CFO:* Stewart Hurst
**Ex VP:* Eugene Mooney

D-U-N-S 00-685-1521
BEN HUR CONSTRUCTION CO (MO)
3783 Rider Trl S, Earth City, MO 63045-1114
Tel (314) 298-8007 *Founded/Ownrshp* 1909
Sales 121.1MM^E *EMP* 300
SIC 1542 1791 1541 3441 Nonresidential construction; Structural steel erection; Industrial buildings & warehouses; Building components, structural steel
Ch Bd: John Brown
**CEO:* William W Brown
**Treas:* Thomas Schmidt
**VP:* Randy Boettler
**VP:* Mark Douglas
**VP:* John Vogt
Sfty Dirs: Chris Wolf

D-U-N-S 06-666-1588 IMP/EXP
BEN MYERSON CANDY CO INC
WINE WAREHOUSE
6550 E Washington Blvd, Commerce, CA 90040-1822
Tel (800) 331-2829 *Founded/Ownrshp* 1973
Sales 342.6MM^E *EMP* 550
SIC 5182 5023 Wine; Glassware
Pr: James P Myerson
V Ch: Donald Schiff
Pr: Linda Perez
**Sec:* James Myerson
Sr VP: Trevor Thiret
Rgnl Mgr: Rick Alles
Rgnl Mgr: Diana Cely
Rgnl Mgr: Robert Fogarty
Rgnl Mgr: Betsy Galdamez
Area Mgr: Justin Lewis
Sales Exec: Jim Lilly

D-U-N-S 07-143-8329 IMP
BEN TIRE DISTRIBUTORS LTD
NEAL TIRE & AUTO SERVICE
203 E Madison St, Toledo, IL 62468-1126
Tel (800) 252-8961 *Founded/Ownrshp* 1969
Sales 109.9MM *EMP* 380
Accts Harding Shymanski & Company
SIC 5014 5013 5531 7534 Tires & tubes; Automotive batteries; Automotive tires; Batteries, automotive & truck; Tire repair shop
Pr: Burnham Neal
**Pr:* Terry Carlon
**VP:* Cerry Carlinn

D-U-N-S 00-432-7953 IMP
BEN VENUE LABORATORIES INC
BEDFORD LABORATORIES
(*Suby of* BOEHRINGER INGELHEIM CORP) ★
300 Northfield Rd, Bedford, OH 44146-4650
Tel (800) 989-3320 *Founded/Ownrshp* 1938, 1998
Sales 110.5MM^E *EMP* 1,336
SIC 2834

D-U-N-S 01-301-5268
BEN WEITSMAN AND SON INC
(*Suby of* WEITSMAN RECYCLING, LLC)
15 W Main St, Owego, NY 13827-1569
Tel (607) 687-2780 *Founded/Ownrshp* 2012
Sales 139.0MM^E *EMP* 209^E
SIC 5051 5093 3341 Metals service centers & offices; Scrap & waste materials; Secondary nonferrous metals
Pr: Adam Weitsman
**Pr:* Harold Weitsman

BENCH MARK EQUIPMENT COMPANY
See BENCHMARK HOSPITALITY INC

D-U-N-S 62-394-3453 IMP
BENCHMARK BRANDS INC
1375 Peachtree St Ne Fl 6, Atlanta, GA 30309-3173
Tel (770) 242-1254 *Founded/Ownrshp* 1989
Sales 204.9MM^E *EMP* 350
SIC 5139

BENCHMARK CONTRACTORS
See MORLEY BUILDERS INC

D-U-N-S 17-911-9268 IMP
■ BENCHMARK ELECTRONICS HUNTSVILLE INC
HUNTSVILLE DIVISION
(*Suby of* BENCHMARK ELECTRONICS INC) ★
4807 Bradford Dr Nw, Huntsville, AL 35805-1948
Tel (256) 722-6000 *Founded/Ownrshp* 1999
Sales 125.6MM^E *EMP* 650
SIC 3699 Electrical equipment & supplies
CEO: Donald E Nigbor
VP: Paul Snapp
Exec: Noli Zarate
**Prin:* Pam Blasing
Snr Sftwr: Ken Fuchs

D-U-N-S 02-479-2194 IMP
▲ BENCHMARK ELECTRONICS INC (TX)
3000 Technology Rd, Angleton, TX 77515-2599
Tel (979) 849-6550 *Founded/Ownrshp* 1979
Sales 2.5MMM *EMP* 10,500^E
Accts Kpmg Llp Houston Texas
Tkr Sym BHE *Exch* NYS
SIC 3672 3679 Printed circuit boards; Electronic circuits
Pr: Paul J Tufano
**Ch Bd:* David W Scheible
CFO: Donald F Adam
Ex VP: Greg W Cominos
Ex VP: Jon J King
VP: Ken Hendrickson
VP: Jessica Lin
VP: Scott R Peterson
VP: Shabnam Shaghafi
Prgrm Mgr: Cathy Atchley
Prgrm Mgr: Dale Herman
Board of Directors: Michael R Dawson, Douglas G Duncan, Kenneth T Lamneck, Paul J Tufano, Clay C Williams

D-U-N-S 16-127-3545
■ BENCHMARK ELECTRONICS MANUFACTURING SOLUTIONS (MOORPARK) INC
(*Suby of* BENCHMARK ELECTRONICS MANUFACTURING SOLUTIONS INC) ★
200 Science Dr, Moorpark, CA 93021-2003
Tel (805) 532-2800 *Founded/Ownrshp* 1986
Sales 83.4MM^E *EMP* 523
SIC 3679 Electronic circuits

D-U-N-S 00-828-8813 IMP
■ BENCHMARK ELECTRONICS MANUFACTURING SOLUTIONS INC
(*Suby of* BENCHMARK ELECTRONICS INC) ★
5550 Hellyer Ave, San Jose, CA 95138-1005
Tel (408) 754-9800 *Founded/Ownrshp* 2013
Sales 140.3MM^E *EMP* 549
SIC 3672 Printed circuit boards
VP: Robert Miller
Genl Mgr: Tom Dineen

D-U-N-S 05-982-9226 IMP
■ BENCHMARK ELECTRONICS PHOENIX INC
(*Suby of* BENCHMARK ELECTRONICS INC) ★
2222 W Pinnacle Pk Rd # 310, Phoenix, AZ 85027-1231
Tel (619) 397-2400 *Founded/Ownrshp* 2013
Sales 377.7MM^E *EMP* 1,510
SIC 3577 3672 Computer peripheral equipment; Printed circuit boards
Sr VP: Michael W Ebin
VP: Carolyn Davis
**VP:* Rod Gunther
VP: Michael Oliveri
**VP:* Michael Seltzer
Genl Mgr: Roger White

D-U-N-S 62-512-2531 IMP
BENCHMARK ENERGY PRODUCTS LP
(*Suby of* ROCKWATER ENERGY SOLUTIONS) ★
4113 W Industrial Ave, Midland, TX 79703-7704
Tel (432) 697-8171 *Founded/Ownrshp* 2002
Sales 190.1MM^E *EMP* 115
SIC 5169 Oil additives
Pt: E Wayne Kinsey III
**Pt:* Mark Kinsey

D-U-N-S 61-203-3134
BENCHMARK HOSPITALITY INC
BENCH MARK EQUIPMENT COMPANY
4 Waterway Square Pl # 300, The Woodlands, TX 77380-3854
Tel (281) 367-5757 *Founded/Ownrshp* 1986
Sales 320.4MM^E *EMP* 6,300
SIC 8741 5046 Management services; Hotel or motel management; Hotel equipment & supplies
Pr: Burt Cabanas
Mng Pt: Maritza Montiel
**CFO:* Brad Hayden
**CFO:* Kirk Jones
Ofcr: Mary Watson-Delauder
VP: Barry Anderson
VP: Alex Caba As
VP: Giorgi Di Lemis
**VP:* Scott Mc Minn
VP: Kim Nugent
VP: Harold Powell
**VP:* Esther Rodriguez
VP: Lisa Maria Stice
VP: Lisa Stice

BENCHMARK MORTGAGE LOUISIANNA
See ARK-LA-TEX FINANCIAL SERVICES LLC

D-U-N-S 19-596-9837 EXP
BENCHMARK PERFORMANCE GROUP INC
ROCKWATER ENERGY SOLUTIONS
(*Suby of* ROCKWATER ENERGY SOLUTIONS INC) ★
2801 Post Oak Blvd, Houston, TX 77056-6136
Tel (713) 986-2500 *Founded/Ownrshp* 1986
Sales 267.6MM^E *EMP* 287
SIC 5169 Oil additives
Pr: E Wayne Kinsey III
**Pr:* Mark Kinsey
**CEO:* Holli Ladhani
**CFO:* Sheila Buchanan
**Sec:* Mary K Harvey
**Ex VP:* David N Harry
**Ex VP:* Harlan B Naylor III
**Sr VP:* Danny F Wilson
**VP:* Duane Sales
**VP:* R Duane Sales
Off Mgr: Verna Hagen
Board of Directors: David Baldwin, Larry O'donnell, Logan Walters

D-U-N-S 10-319-6718 IMP
BENCHMASTER FURNITURE LLC
1481 N Hundley St, Anaheim, CA 92806-1323
Tel (714) 414-0240 *Founded/Ownrshp* 2001
Sales 122.0MM *EMP* 300
SIC 5021 Furniture
**Pr:* Eugene V Trobaugh
**VP:* Emmy Chen

D-U-N-S 01-510-8087 IMP
BENCO DENTAL SUPPLY CO
295 Centerpoint Blvd, Pittston, PA 18640-6136
Tel (570) 602-7781 *Founded/Ownrshp* 1930
Sales 557.0MM^E *EMP* 1,385
Accts Cohen And Co Cleveland Ohio
SIC 5047 Dental equipment & supplies; Medical equipment & supplies
Mng Dir: Charles F Cohen
**Treas:* Donald Stephens
**VP:* Terry Barrett
VP: William Brodie
**VP:* Paul Jackson
**VP:* Lou Mangino
**VP:* George Rable
**Mng Dir:* Richard S Cohen
Board of Directors: Charles F Cohen, Lawrence E Cohen, Richard S Cohen, Chris Mellon, Sheila Riggs, Lawrence Rosenfeld, David A Smith, Marcy Syms

BENCO MANUFACTURING
See DIEOMATIC INC

BEND-LA PINE SCHOOLS
See BEND-LAPINE SCHOOLS

D-U-N-S 04-486-8149
BEND-LAPINE SCHOOLS
BEND-LA PINE SCHOOLS
520 Nw Wall St, Bend, OR 97703-2608
Tel (541) 383-6000 *Founded/Ownrshp* 1910
Sales 77.7MM^E *EMP* 1,600
Accts Greermahr & Associates Llp Be
SIC 8211 Public combined elementary & secondary school; Kindergarten
Prin: Peter Miller

D-U-N-S 00-415-5941 IMP/EXP
BENDIX COMMERCIAL VEHICLE SYSTEMS LLC
(*Suby of* NEW YORK AIR BRAKE) ★
901 Cleveland St, Elyria, OH 44035-4153
Tel (440) 329-9000 *Founded/Ownrshp* 1990
Sales 1.1MMM^E *EMP* 2,110
SIC 5013 8711 Automotive supplies & parts; Engineering services
Ch Bd: Joseph J McAleese
Pr: Christian Fischer
CEO: Berend Bracht
COO: Carlos Hungria
CFO: Arnfred Kulenkampff
VP: Claus Beyer
VP: Scott Burkhart
VP: Patricia Destefano
VP: Thomas Doll
VP: Mark McCollough
VP: Bill Mossing

D-U-N-S 14-445-0269
BENECARD SERVICES INC
BENERX
3131 Princeton Pike 2-B103, Lawrenceville, NJ 08648-2206
Tel (609) 219-0400 *Founded/Ownrshp* 1989
Sales NA *EMP* 150^E
SIC 6411 Policyholders' consulting service
CEO: Micheal Perry
Ch: Richard O Ullman
Ofcr: La' Quay Dansby
VP: Richard Grey
VP: John McMullen
VP: Gregory Rhu
VP: Frank Schiraldi
Exec: Mark Sofia

D-U-N-S 62-679-8177
BENEDICTINE HEALTH SYSTEM
503 E 3rd St Ste 400, Duluth, MN 55805-1907
Tel (218) 786-2370 *Founded/Ownrshp* 1985
Sales 348.5MM^E *EMP* 8,000
SIC 8059 Personal care home, with health care
Pr: Dale Thompson
**Ch Bd:* Mary Frances Scala
Ofcr: Garry Woessner
VP: Jim Glynn
Dir Case M: Annette Lundy
Ex Dir: Chris Kerns
CTO: Becky Kofoed
Dir IT: Jody Gudvangen
Dir IT: Tammy Ness
Netwrk Mgr: Jon Danielson
Web Dev: Jeff Anderson

D-U-N-S 06-995-7298
BENEDICTINE UNIVERSITY
5700 College Rd, Lisle, IL 60532-0900
Tel (630) 829-6000 *Founded/Ownrshp* 1887
Sales 137.3MM *EMP* 350^E
Accts Bkd Llp Villa Park Il
SIC 8221 College, except junior; University
Ex Dir: William Carroll
**Treas:* Paul R Gauvreau
Adm Dir: Jean Geisheker
Off Admin: Cathy Gaddis

D-U-N-S 07-952-5471
▲ BENEFICIAL BANCORP INC
1818 Market St, Philadelphia, PA 19103-3638
Tel (215) 864-6000 *Founded/Ownrshp* 2014
Sales NA *EMP* 809^E
Tkr Sym BNCL *Exch* NGS
SIC 6035 Savings institutions, federally chartered
Pr: Gerard P Cuddy
CFO: Thomas D Cestare
Board of Directors: Edward G Boehne, Karen Dougherty Buchholz, Michael J Donahue, Frank A Farnesi, Donald F Gayhardt Jr, Elizabeth H Gemmill, Thomas J Lewis, Roy D Yates

BENEFICIAL BANK
See BENEFICIAL MUTUAL SAVINGS BANK

D-U-N-S 00-691-8783
BENEFICIAL CO LLC
(*Suby of* HSBC FINANCE CORP) ★
1421 W Shure Dr Ste 100, Arlington Heights, IL 60004-7818
Tel (708) 453-6502 *Founded/Ownrshp* 1998
Sales NA *EMP* 1,600
SIC 6141 6351 6162 6021 6552 6311 Consumer finance companies; Installment sales finance, other than banks; Financing: automobiles, furniture, etc., not a deposit bank; Credit & other financial responsibility insurance; Mortgage bankers; National commercial banks; Subdividers & developers; Life insurance carriers
Ch Bd: William F Aldinger
**Pr:* David J Farris
**Pr:* Andrew C Halvorsen
CFO: B B Moss
Treas: Daniel W Anderson
Treas: Samuel F McMillan
**Ex VP:* James H Gilliam Jr
Sr VP: Jonathan Macey
VP: D Chiesa
VP: M A Deluca
VP: John T Greene
VP: Gregory T Zelman

BENEFICIAL FINANCIAL GROUP
See BENEFICIAL LIFE INSURANCE CO

D-U-N-S 00-793-8814
BENEFICIAL LIFE INSURANCE CO (UT)
BENEFICIAL FINANCIAL GROUP
(*Suby of* CHURCH OF JSUS CHRST OF LD STS) ★
55 N 300 W Ste 375, Salt Lake City, UT 84101-3502
Tel (801) 933-1272 *Founded/Ownrshp* 1905, 1985
Sales NA *EMP* 273
SIC 6311 Life insurance carriers
Pr: Kent Cannon
Ofcr: David Pearce
Sr VP: Hardi Jenkins
Sr VP: Seth Vance
VP: Ted Lewis
Dir IT: Brad Hess
IT Man: Brent Burgen
Info Man: Douglas Hancock
Netwrk Eng: David Simpson
Board of Directors: Nolan E Karras, Woodruff Kirton Jr, William R Walker, Maryanne Quinn Wood, Harold C Yancey

D-U-N-S 80-259-0757
BENEFICIAL MUTUAL BANCORP INC
(*Suby of* BENEFICIAL SAVINGS BANK MHC) ★
1818 Market St, Philadelphia, PA 19103-3638
Tel (215) 864-6000 *Founded/Ownrshp* 2004
Sales NA *EMP* 875
SIC 6035

D-U-N-S 00-791-3197 IMP/EXP
BENEFICIAL MUTUAL SAVINGS BANK
BENEFICIAL BANK
(*Suby of* BENEFICIAL SAVINGS BANK MHC) ★
1818 Market St Fl 8, Philadelphia, PA 19103-3610
Tel (888) 742-5272 *Founded/Ownrshp* 1853, 1965

Sales NA *EMP* 837
SIC 6036 State savings banks, not federally chartered
CEO: Gerard P Cuddy
**CFO:* Thomas Cestare
Treas: Joseph P Mc Cauley
Ex VP: Paul Driscoll
**Sr VP:* Robert Bush
Sr VP: Robert B Sadoff
VP: James F Bonner
VP: Bill Casey
VP: James Fecca
VP: Thomas F Howley
VP: Joseph Juliano
VP: Tina Malek
VP: Brian Miller
VP: Kerry Sczepkowski
VP: Joseph Vetter
Exec: Lisa Smalley
Dir Bus: Michael Gallagher

D-U-N-S 96-950-5499
BENEFICIAL SAVINGS BANK MHC
1818 Market St Fl 8, Philadelphia, PA 19103-3610
Tel (215) 864-6000 *Founded/Ownrshp* 2011
Sales NA *EMP* 966[E]
SIC 6411 Insurance agents, brokers & service
Pr: Gerard P Cuddy
Ex VP: Denise Kassekert
Sr VP: Bill Kline

D-U-N-S 06-892-2160
BENEFIS HOSPITALS INC
1101 26th St S, Great Falls, MT 59405-5161
Tel (406) 455-5000 *Founded/Ownrshp* 1897
Sales 363.4MM *EMP* 2,419
SIC 8062 8051 General medical & surgical hospitals; Skilled nursing care facilities
CEO: John Goodnow
Chf Rad: Ronald Eagan
Pr: Alexander N Chung
Pr: Mary Davis
**Pr:* Laura Goldhahn
COO: Laura Goldhahn-Konen
Ofcr: Kathie Avis
Ofcr: Joe Duca
Ofcr: Kathy Hill
**VP:* Steven Ballock
VP: John Preston
Dir OR: Janelle Nelson
Dir Pat Ca: Vicki Robinson
Dir Inf Cn: Pam Webb
Dir Risk M: Deb McCracken
Dir Rx: Nickolas Casellnova
Dir Rx: David Runkel

D-U-N-S 01-204-8663
■ **BENEFITFOCUS INC**
(*Suby of* BENEFITFOCUS INC) ★
1016 Woods Crossing Rd, Greenville, SC 29607-6834
Tel (864) 234-2827 *Founded/Ownrshp* 2013
Sales 106.3MM[E] *EMP* 833[E]
SIC 7371 Computer software development
CEO: Shawn A Jenkins
**COO:* Andrew L Howell
**CFO:* Milton A Alpern
**Sr VP:* Joel Wilhite
**Prin:* Mason R Holland Jr

D-U-N-S 07-914-0342
▲ **BENEFITFOCUS INC**
100 Benefitfocus Way, Daniel Island, SC 29492-8378
Tel (843) 849-7476 *Founded/Ownrshp* 2000
Sales 185.1MM *EMP* 1,450[E]
Tkr Sym BNFT *Exch* NGM
SIC 7372 Prepackaged software
CEO: Shawn A Jenkins
Ch Bd: Mason R Holland Jr
Pr: Raymond A August
CFO: Jeffrey Laborde
CTO: James P Restivo
Board of Directors: Douglas A Dennerline, Joseph P Disabato, Ann H Lamont, Francis J Pelzer V, Stephen M Swad

BENEFITMALL
See CENTERSTONE INSURANCE AND FINANCIAL SERVICES INC

D-U-N-S 05-515-5410
BENEFITMALL INC
4851 Freeway Ste 100, Dallas, TX 75244
Tel (469) 791-3300 *Founded/Ownrshp* 1998
Sales NA *EMP* 1,324
SIC 6411 8742 7375

BENERX
See BENECARD SERVICES INC

D-U-N-S 78-320-5933 IMP
BENETEAU INC
(*Suby of* BENETEAU)
1313 W Highway 76, Marion, SC 29571-6614
Tel (843) 629-5300 *Founded/Ownrshp* 1985
Sales 109.2MM[E] *EMP* 780
SIC 3732 Sailboats, building & repairing
Pr: Annette Roux

D-U-N-S 15-550-1658
BENEVIS LLC
KOOL SMILES
1090 Northchase Pkwy Se, Marietta, GA 30067-6405
Tel (770) 916-9000 *Founded/Ownrshp* 2001
Sales 94.1MM[E] *EMP* 500[E]
SIC 8741 7389 Business management; Financial services
CEO: Kevin Miller
CFO: Tom Nance
VP: Rajat Duggal
VP: Ryan Lindgren
VP: Paul O Walker
Off Admin: Roxanne Steely
Mktg Dir: Aldo Benedetto

D-U-N-S 06-248-2070 IMP/EXP
BENIHANA INC
(*Suby of* ANGELO GORDON & CO LP) ★
21500 Biscayne Blvd # 100, Miami, FL 33180-1255
Tel (305) 593-0770 *Founded/Ownrshp* 2012
Sales 318.5MM[E] *EMP* 6,900
SIC 5812 6794 Japanese restaurant; Franchises, selling or licensing
Pr: Thomas J Baldwin
**COO:* Christopher P Ames
CFO: David Flanery
**CFO:* J David Flanery
VP: Michael Burris
VP: Juan Compos
VP: Leiala Whattoff
Genl Mgr: Christopher Catledge
Genl Mgr: Steven Huang
Genl Mgr: Christopher Shaw
Snr Ntwrk: David Schwartzberg

D-U-N-S 79-701-6701 IMP
BENJAMIN FOODS LLC
1001 S York Rd, Hatboro, PA 19040-4035
Tel (215) 437-5000 *Founded/Ownrshp* 2003
Sales 130.7MM[E] *EMP* 95
Accts Gitomer & Berenholz Pc
SIC 5141 8741 Groceries, general line; Restaurant management
CEO: Howard Klayman
CFO: Mark Oltman
**VP:* David Klayman
Exec: John Hindman
Dir Bus: Matthew Fitzgerald
Genl Mgr: Lisa Barash

D-U-N-S 00-121-0715 IMP/EXP
■ **BENJAMIN MOORE & CO**
(*Suby of* BERKSHIRE HATHAWAY INC) ★
101 Paragon Dr, Montvale, NJ 07645-1727
Tel (201) 573-9600 *Founded/Ownrshp* 1891
Sales 1.3MMM[E] *EMP* 3,151
SIC 2851 5231 Paints & allied products; Paints: oil or alkyd vehicle or water thinned; Enamels; Varnishes; Paint, glass & wallpaper
Pr: Michael Searles
CFO: Donald Devine
Ofcr: Talia M Griep
Ex VP: Dan Calkins
Ex VP: Barry Chadwick
VP: Michael L Behringer
VP: Bart Fingan
VP: Keri Fleming
VP: Susan Freije
VP: Julianne Maguire
Exec: Tom Jozefowicz

BENJAMIN NEWS GROUP
See NORTHWEST NEWS CO INC

D-U-N-S 08-912-6007 IMP/EXP
BENNETT AUTO SUPPLY INC
3141 Sw 10th St, Pompano Beach, FL 33069-4828
Tel (954) 335-8700 *Founded/Ownrshp* 1977
Sales 184.7MM[E] *EMP* 325
SIC 5531 5013 3711 Automotive parts; Automotive supplies & parts; Automobile assembly, including specialty automobiles
Pr: Harold Bennett
CFO: Todd Donaghue
**CFO:* Brad Fondiler
**VP:* Barry Bennett
Dist Mgr: Darrell Smith
Sls Mgr: Art Aleman

D-U-N-S 07-757-5868
BENNETT ENTERPRISES INC
HAMPTON INN
27476 Holiday Ln, Perrysburg, OH 43551-3345
Tel (419) 874-1933 *Founded/Ownrshp* 1960
Sales 63.0MM[E] *EMP* 1,500
SIC 7011 5812 Hotels & motels; Restaurant, family: independent
Pr: David Bennett
**Treas:* Milton W Bennett
Exec: Mark Wuertz
**Prin:* Robert W Talburt
**Prin:* M A Wood
Area Supr: Paula Duran
IT Man: David Schalitz

D-U-N-S 88-497-9493 IMP/EXP
BENNETT INTERNATIONAL GROUP LLC
1001 Industrial Pkwy, McDonough, GA 30253-7330
Tel (770) 957-1866 *Founded/Ownrshp* 1993
Sales 564.0MM[E] *EMP* 670
SIC 4213

D-U-N-S 08-860-6280
BENNETT MOTOR EXPRESS LLC
(*Suby of* BENNETT INTERNATIONAL GROUP LLC) ★
1001 Industrial Pkwy, McDonough, GA 30253-7330
Tel (770) 957-1866 *Founded/Ownrshp* 1993
Sales 90.3MM[E] *EMP* 140
SIC 4213 4212 4215

BENNIGAN'S
See METROMEDIA CO

BENNIGAN'S
See HOMESTYLE DINING LLC

BENNINGTON
See PONTOON BOAT LLC

D-U-N-S 00-787-4530 IMP
BENNYS INC (RI)
340 Waterman Ave, Smithfield, RI 02917-2559
Tel (401) 231-0965 *Founded/Ownrshp* 1924, 1929
Sales 239.2MM[E] *EMP* 500
SIC 5531 Automotive & home supply stores
Pr: Malcolm C Bromberg
**VP:* Arnold Bromberg
**VP:* Howard Bromberg
VP: Judith Rosenstein

D-U-N-S 93-765-7930 IMP
BENORE LOGISTIC SYSTEMS INC
TOTAL LOGISTICS
2500 E Erie Rd, Erie, MI 48133-9760
Tel (734) 848-2046 *Founded/Ownrshp* 1994
Sales 161.3MM[E] *EMP* 700
SIC 4225 General warehousing & storage
Pr: Jeffery M Benore
**VP:* David A Benore
**VP:* Joan Benore

D-U-N-S 11-891-6097
BENSCO INC
5800 Airline Dr, Metairie, LA 70003-3876
Tel (210) 349-6200 *Founded/Ownrshp* 1965
Sales 201.0MM[E] *EMP* 675
SIC 5511 New & used car dealers
Pr: R Tom Roddy
**V Ch:* Renee Benson
**Ch:* Tom Benson
**Treas:* Charlotte Troxler
**Sr VP:* Don Zander
**VP:* Grace Benson

D-U-N-S 02-674-0340
BENSON - SABIN INC
STAR TOYOTA
2112 Gulf Fwy S, League City, TX 77573-5142
Tel (281) 338-9700 *Founded/Ownrshp* 1987
Sales 94.9MM *EMP* 102
SIC 5511 7538 Automobiles, new & used; General automotive repair shops
Pr: Carolyn S Hibbard
Sr VP: David Pham
**Prin:* Royce B Casey
Board of Directors: Royce B Casey, Carolyn Hibbard, Carolyn S Hibbard

D-U-N-S 02-770-9476 IMP
■ **BENSON INDUSTRIES INC**
(*Suby of* MITEK USA INC) ★
1650 Nw Naito Pkwy # 250, Portland, OR 97209-2597
Tel (503) 226-7611 *Founded/Ownrshp* 1926
Sales 429.8MM[E] *EMP* 621
SIC 5031 1793 3231 3211 Window frames, all materials; Door frames, all materials; Glass & glazing work; Products of purchased glass; Flat glass
CEO: Lou S Niles
**Pr:* Thomas J Manenti
VP Sls: Bryan Sullivan

D-U-N-S 17-543-2491 IMP
BENSUSSEN DEUTSCH & ASSOCIATES LLC
B D & A
15525 Woodinville Rdmnd, Woodinville, WA 98072-6977
Tel (425) 492-6111 *Founded/Ownrshp* 1984
Sales 413.7MM[E] *EMP* 375
SIC 5199 5136 5137 Advertising specialties; Sportswear, men's & boys'; Sportswear, women's & children's
CEO: Jay Deutsch
**Pr:* Eric Bensussen
**COO:* Rob Martin
**CFO:* Jared Collinge
**Ex VP:* Barry Deutsch
CTO: Paul Wagner
IT Man: Ashley Kinghorn
Mktg Dir: James Szubski
Sls Dir: Warren Cook

D-U-N-S 11-283-6044 IMP
BENTELER AUTOMOTIVE CORP
(*Suby of* BENTELER BUSINESS SERVICES GMBH)
2650 N Opdyke Rd Ste B, Auburn Hills, MI 48326-1954
Tel (248) 364-7190 *Founded/Ownrshp* 1980
Sales 641.0MM[E] *EMP* 2,500
SIC 3714 3465 3999 Manifolds, motor vehicle; Automotive stampings; Atomizers, toiletry
Pr: Joachim Perske
CFO: Jim Dostine
**CFO:* Ulf M Kranz
Ex VP: Martin Weidlich
VP: Martin Becker
VP: Keith Carpentier
**VP:* Ulrike Hildebrand
VP: Robert Smart
Info Man: Michael Lindner
Mtls Mgr: Shannon Littrell
Plnt Mgr: Scott Callow

D-U-N-S 07-862-8887 IMP
BENTELER NORTH AMERICA CORP
BENTLER AUTOMOTIVE
(*Suby of* BENTELER INTERNATIONAL AKTIENGESELLSCHAFT)
2650 N Opdyke Rd Ste B, Auburn Hills, MI 48326-1954
Tel (248) 377-9999 *Founded/Ownrshp* 2012
Sales 358.7MM[E] *EMP* 400
SIC 5051 Steel
Prin: Steffen Tutschka
QC Dir: Rajnish Karan

D-U-N-S 17-955-1395 IMP
BENTELER STEEL & TUBE
ROTHRIST TUBE
(*Suby of* BENTLER AUTOMOTIVE) ★
3050 Post Oak Blvd # 1130, Houston, TX 77056-6523
Tel (713) 629-9111 *Founded/Ownrshp* 2011
Sales 358.7MM *EMP* 22
Accts Kpmg Llp Windsor Canada
SIC 5051 Steel
CEO: Michael Herminghaus
**CEO:* Corne Buijs
Counsel: Logan Anderson

BENTLER AUTOMOTIVE
See BENTELER NORTH AMERICA CORP

D-U-N-S 09-946-0388 IMP/EXP
BENTLEY MILLS INC
14641 Don Julian Rd, City of Industry, CA 91746-3106
Tel (626) 333-4585 *Founded/Ownrshp* 1993
Sales 237.3MM[E] *EMP* 350
SIC 2273 2299 Carpets, textile fiber; Batting, wadding, padding & fillings
CEO: Ralph Grogan
**COO:* Jim Harley
**CFO:* Eric Petty
**Sr VP:* Ray Willoch
**VP:* David Moore
VP: Rosa Solis
VP Bus Dev: George Maibach
Genl Mgr: Melanie Taylor
IT Man: Bo Bartlett
IT Man: Mark Bumstead

D-U-N-S 13-109-7651
BENTLEY SYSTEMS INC
685 Stockton Dr, Exton, PA 19341-1151
Tel (610) 458-5000 *Founded/Ownrshp* 1984
Sales 755.0MM[E] *EMP* 2,774
SIC 7372 7373 Application computer software; Computer integrated systems design
Ch Bd: Gregory Bentley
Pr: Alton B Cleveland Jr
Pr: Jeffrey Hollings
Pr: David Nation
COO: James W Breyer
COO: Malcolm Walter
COO: Malcolm S Walter
CFO: David Hollister
CFO: Paul Lamparski
Treas: Richard Fiery
Ofcr: Keith Bentley
Ofcr: Florence Zheng
Ex VP: Jeff Amerine
Ex VP: Barry Bentley
Ex VP: Raymond B Bentley
Ex VP: Richard Bentley
Sr VP: George Church
Sr VP: Ted Lamboo
Sr VP: Jean-Baptiste Monnier
Sr VP: John Riddle
Sr VP: Bhupinder Singh

D-U-N-S 06-516-3503
BENTLEY UNIVERSITY
175 Forest St, Waltham, MA 02452-4713
Tel (781) 891-2000 *Founded/Ownrshp* 1917
Sales 288.1MM *EMP* 911
Accts Kpmg Llp Boston Ma
SIC 8221 College, except junior
Pr: Gloria Larson
**CFO:* Paul Clemente
Trst: George W Carmany
Trst: Andrew J Hajducky
Ofcr: Robert Aurilio
Ofcr: Jillian Proia
VP: Jean Bedard
VP: Kenneth B Cody
VP: Gerald A Madek
VP: Roxanne Martinez
VP: Joann C McKenna
VP: Joann McKenna
VP: Michael J Page
Assoc Dir: Carla Berg
Assoc Dir: Audra Boni
Assoc Dir: Karen Peters
Assoc Dir: Jason Shumaker
Assoc Dir: Kristine Vidic
Dir Bus: Jack Pini

D-U-N-S 61-971-9560
BENTLEY WORLD-PACKAGING LTD
4080 N Port Washington Rd, Milwaukee, WI 53212-1132
Tel (414) 967-8000 *Founded/Ownrshp* 1942
Sales 169.6MM[E] *EMP* 500
SIC 4783 5199 Packing goods for shipping; Packaging materials
Ch Bd: Tom Bentley III
CFO: Angela Damon
**Ex VP:* Todd Bentley
**VP:* Dean Mowery
Off Mgr: Pat Hotton
Plnt Mgr: Andy Roberts
Plnt Mgr: Todd Wrobbel
Prd Mgr: Michael Kujawa
Sales Exec: Jeff Hawthorne

D-U-N-S 16-368-5600 IMP/EXP
■ **BENTLY NEVADA INC**
GE ENERGY
(*Suby of* GENERAL ELECTRIC CO) ★
1631 Bently Pkwy S, Minden, NV 89423-4119
Tel (775) 782-3611 *Founded/Ownrshp* 2001
Sales 178.9MM[E] *EMP* 900
SIC 3829 Measuring & controlling devices
CEO: Steve Bolze
Pr: Venkat Kannan
**CFO:* Lynn Calpeter
**VP:* Jeff Connelly
**Genl Mgr:* Ganesh Bell
Tech Mgr: Clair Forland
Sftwr Eng: Scott Roby
Snr Mgr: Paul Manzano
Snr Mgr: Dennis Mills

BENTON EXPRESS
See BENTON GLOBAL LLC

D-U-N-S 00-303-9286
BENTON FOUNDRY INC
5297 State Route 487, Benton, PA 17814-7641
Tel (570) 925-6711 *Founded/Ownrshp* 1887
Sales 84.2MM[E] *EMP* 250
SIC 3321 Gray iron castings; Ductile iron castings
Pr: Alfred B Hall
**VP:* Thomas Brown
**VP:* Jeff Hall
Netwrk Eng: Matthew Sabol
Ql Cn Mgr: Carl Stackhouse
Sls Mgr: Bob Kover

D-U-N-S 00-388-7437
BENTON GLOBAL LLC (GA)
BENTON EXPRESS
1045 S Rver Indus Blvd Se, Atlanta, GA 30315
Tel (404) 267-2200 *Founded/Ownrshp* 2012
Sales 151.2MM[E] *EMP* 540
SIC 4213

D-U-N-S 00-491-8322
BENTONVILLE SCHOOL DISTRICT 6
500 Tiger Blvd, Bentonville, AR 72712-4208
Tel (479) 254-5000 *Founded/Ownrshp* 1841
Sales 144.8MM *EMP* 1,600
Accts Beall Barclay & Company Plc
SIC 8211 Public elementary & secondary schools
Pr Dir: Paul Stolt
Schl Brd P: Travis Riggs
Teacher Pr: Dena Ross
HC Dir: Debrah Keith
HC Dir: Zoe Morton

D-U-N-S 13-736-9468
BEP COLORADO RESTAURANTS LLC
BLACK-EYED PEA RESTAURANT
304 Inverness Way S # 305, Englewood, CO 80112-5828
Tel (303) 671-7333 *Founded/Ownrshp* 1983
Sales NA *EMP* 1,050
SIC 5812

D-U-N-S 07-845-6596
BEP/LYMAN LLC
LYMAN LUMBER COMPANY
(*Suby of* US LBM HOLDINGS LLC) ★
520 3rd St Ste 200, Excelsior, MN 55331-1928
Tel (952) 470-3600 *Founded/Ownrshp* 2011
Sales 270.3MM^E *EMP* 509^E
SIC 5031 5211 Lumber, plywood & millwork; Lumber & other building materials
Pr: Dale Carlson
**Treas:* Brian Balcer
**VP:* Tim Liester
Sales Asso: Chris Johnson

D-U-N-S 06-736-3622
BERAT CORP
SHOP RITE OF LAUREL HILL
1230 Blckwood Clmenton Rd, Clementon, NJ 08021-5632
Tel (856) 627-6501 *Founded/Ownrshp* 1972
Sales 161.0MM^E *EMP* 2,100
SIC 5411 Supermarkets, chain
Ch Bd: George Zallie Sr
Pr: Pat Rodgers
CFO: Kenneth Gorman

D-U-N-S 08-381-8781 IMP
BERBERIAN ENTERPRISES INC
JON'S MARKETPLACE
5315 Santa Monica Blvd, Los Angeles, CA 90029-1105
Tel (323) 460-4646 *Founded/Ownrshp* 1978
Sales 192.3MM^E *EMP* 1,100
SIC 5411 Supermarkets, independent
Pr: John Berberian
**CFO:* Steve Stork
CFO: Steven Stork
**VP:* Jack Berberian
MIS Mgr: Joe Alisy

D-U-N-S 00-196-0566
BEREA COLLEGE (KY)
BEREA COLLEGE STUDENT INDS
101 Chestnut St, Berea, KY 40403-1516
Tel (859) 985-3000 *Founded/Ownrshp* 1855
Sales 114.1MM *EMP* 550
Accts Crowe Horwath Llp Lexington
SIC 8221 College, except junior
Pr: Lyle D Roelofs
Pr: Cheryl Daulton
**VP:* Jeff Amburgey
VP: Tammy Morgeson
Assoc Dir: Erin Connor
Assoc Dir: Linda Cooper
Assoc Dir: John Kim
Assoc Dir: Christopher Miller
Assoc Dir: Darla Pearson
CIO: Huapei Chen
CTO: Bill Ramsey

BEREA COLLEGE STUDENT INDS
See BEREA COLLEGE

D-U-N-S 03-312-1641 IMP
BERENDSEN FLUID POWER INC
(*Suby of* MIDCON INVESTORS INC) ★
401 S Boston Ave Ste 1200, Tulsa, OK 74103-4013
Tel (918) 592-3781 *Founded/Ownrshp* 2000
Sales 172.2MM^E *EMP* 700
SIC 5084

D-U-N-S 16-106-4993 IMP
BERENFIELD CONTAINERS INC
(*Suby of* MAUSER USA LLC) ★
4555 Lake Forest Dr # 205, Blue Ash, OH 45242-3785
Tel (513) 618-3780 *Founded/Ownrshp* 2016
Sales 84.8MM^E *EMP* 300
SIC 3412 2655 Drums, shipping: metal; Drums, fiber: made from purchased material
Pr: Leonard H Berenfield
**CFO:* Tony Boscarino
**Ex VP:* Gregory N Berenfield
Sr VP: Anthony V Boscarino
Sr VP: Robert W Okra
VP: Thomas Ernst
VP: Ken Fowler
VP: Keith Singleton
Prin: Don Anglim
Area Mgr: Patrick O'Neal
Genl Mgr: Gregory Okra

D-U-N-S 05-629-4879 IMP/EXP
BERETTA USA CORP
(*Suby of* BERETTA HOLDING SPA)
17601 Beretta Dr, Accokeek, MD 20607-9566
Tel (301) 283-2191 *Founded/Ownrshp* 1977
Sales 117.2MM^E *EMP* 325
SIC 5091 3484 Firearms, sporting; Pistols or pistol parts, 30 mm. & below
Pr: Ugo Gussalli Beretta
COO: Jeff Cooper
Treas: Marie Catterton
Ex VP: Franco Gussali Beretta
Ex VP: Christopher Merritt
VP: Chris Recchia
Mktg Mgr: Lee Colquitt

D-U-N-S 04-280-5879
BEREXCO LLC
2020 N Bramblewood St, Wichita, KS 67206-1094
Tel (316) 265-3311 *Founded/Ownrshp* 1978
Sales 563.7MM^E *EMP* 100
SIC 1382 1311

D-U-N-S 01-098-6648 IMP
BERG SPIRAL PIPE CORP
(*Suby of* EUROPIPE GMBH)
900 Paper Mill Rd, Mobile, AL 36610-2516
Tel (251) 330-2900 *Founded/Ownrshp* 2012
Sales 101.4MM^E *EMP* 173
SIC 3317 Steel pipe & tubes
Pr: Ingo Riemer
CFO: Murray Davenport
VP: Peter Borgards
VP: Dimitris D Dimopoulos
VP: Andy Hicks
Sls Mgr: Jessica Waddell

BERGAN MERCY CENTER GIFT SHOP
See ARCHBISHOP BERGAN MERCY AUXILIARY

BERGAN MERCY MEDICAL CENTER
See ARCHBISHOP BERGAN MERCY HOSPITAL

D-U-N-S 05-666-7249 IMP
BERGDORF GOODMAN INC
(*Suby of* NEIMAN MARCUS GROUP LLC) ★
754 5th Ave, New York, NY 10019-2581
Tel (800) 558-1855 *Founded/Ownrshp* 1987
Sales 71.8MM^E *EMP* 1,200
SIC 5621 5632 5611 Ready-to-wear apparel, women's; Women's accessory & specialty stores; Clothing, sportswear, men's & boys'
Pr: Joshua Schulman
Bd of Dir: Shane Feeney
Ex VP: Ginny Hershey-Lambert
Sr VP: Michael Crotty
Sr VP: Linda Fargo
Sr VP: Margaret Spaniolo
VP: Daphnie Au
VP: Michael Castro
VP: Bill Cournoyer
VP: Leonard Hankin
VP: Jodi Kaplan
VP: Adain Kemp
VP: Andrew Mandell
VP: Christine Nakaoka
VP: David Percha
VP: Fred Richardson
VP: Barb Stec
VP: Burton Tansky
VP: Brooks Thomas
Exec: Sherri Ackerman
Exec: Katherine Harned
Board of Directors: David Barr, Ronald Beegle, Bill Brobston, Jonathan Coslet, James Coulter, John Danhakl, Sidney Lapidus, Burton Tansky, Carrie Wheeler

D-U-N-S 03-587-3991 EXP
BERGE FORD INC (AZ)
460 E Auto Center Dr, Mesa, AZ 85204-6500
Tel (480) 497-7600 *Founded/Ownrshp* 1950
Sales 149.4MM^E *EMP* 350
SIC 5511 Automobiles, new & used
Pr: Craig M Berge
Sales Exec: Steve Countryman
Sls Mgr: Tom Smith
Sales Asso: Laura Alvarez

D-U-N-S 02-845-8826 IMP
BERGELECTRIC CORP
5650 W Centinela Ave, Los Angeles, CA 90045-1501
Tel (310) 337-1377 *Founded/Ownrshp* 1964
Sales 507.6MM *EMP* 2,100
Accts Moss Levy & Hartzheim Llp B
SIC 1731 General electrical contractor
Ch Bd: Thomas R Anderson
**Pr:* Alan Mashburn
**CEO:* William Wingrning
**Ex VP:* William M Wingerning
**Sr VP:* Edward P Billig
**Sr VP:* Ronald Wood
**VP:* Steve Buhr
VP: Douglas Crumby
**VP:* William Sorber
VP: William Wingerning
Off Mgr: Lynn Baker

D-U-N-S 62-367-1307
BERGEN BRUNSWIG DRUG CO
4000 W Metropolitan Dr # 200, Orange, CA 92868-3503
Tel (714) 385-4000 *Founded/Ownrshp* 2001
Sales 179.7MM^E *EMP* 2,845
SIC 5122 Drugs, proprietaries & sundries; Pharmaceuticals; Cosmetics; Toiletries
Pr: Brent Martini
**CFO:* John H Mc Alpine

D-U-N-S 07-667-7822
BERGEN COMMUNITY COLLEGE
400 Paramus Rd Ste A330-C, Paramus, NJ 07652-1508
Tel (201) 447-7100 *Founded/Ownrshp* 1965
Sales 680.0M *EMP* 1,054
SIC 8222 Junior college; Community college
Pr: Judith Winn
V Ch: James M Carroll
**Pr:* Dr B Kaye Walter
CFO: Ellen Aramini
Bd of Dir: Vivian Brown-Carman
Trst: Robert L Poifroni
VP: R Harvison
VP: Yun K Kim
VP: David Levinson
**VP:* James R Miller
VP: Michael D Remon
Dir Teleco: Andrew Chiang

D-U-N-S 13-137-0512
BERGEN RECORD CORP
RECORD THE
(*Suby of* MACROMEDIA INC) ★
150 River St, Hackensack, NJ 07601-7110
Tel (201) 646-4000 *Founded/Ownrshp* 1895
Sales 52.7MM^E *EMP* 1,193
SIC 2711 Newspapers, publishing & printing
Ch Bd: Malcolm A Borg
**Pr:* Robert Sapanara
**CFO:* Charles W Gibney
Dir IT: Richard Henning
Board of Directors: Sandra A Borg

D-U-N-S 01-094-9188
BERGEN REGIONAL MEDICAL CENTER LP (NJ)
230 E Ridgewood Ave, Paramus, NJ 07652-4142
Tel (201) 967-4000 *Founded/Ownrshp* 1916, 1998
Sales 207.5MM *EMP* 1,856
SIC 8062 General medical & surgical hospitals
Pr: Susan Mendelowitz
Chf Rad: Susan Rubinoff
Dir Vol: Gita Patel
COO: Kamelia Kameli
CFO: Connie Magdangal
CFO: Robert Pudlack
Ch: V Robert Salazar
VP: Donnalee Corrieri
VP: Debbie Greenip
VP: Herman Lindenbaum
VP: Amelia Reyes
VP: Matt Stopler
VP: Anthony Tesoriero
Assoc Dir: George Piltz
Assoc Dir: Virginia Tan
Dir Rad: Andrew S Laer

D-U-N-S 18-533-4810
BERGENSONS PROPERTY SERVICES INC
SOLVE ALL FACILITY SERVICES
3605 Ocean Ranch Blvd # 200, Oceanside, CA 92056-2695
Tel (760) 631-5111 *Founded/Ownrshp* 1984
Sales 52.1MM^E *EMP* 2,000
SIC 7349 Building maintenance, except repairs; Janitorial service, contract basis
CEO: Mark M Minasian
**Pr:* Aram Minasian
CFO: James Braun
Ex VP: James Henley
Ex VP: Dan Watkins
VP: Nelson Antezana
VP: Cathy Opaczewski
VP: Graham Powers
Exec: Gina Middleton
Rgnl Mgr: Luther Davis
Rgnl Mgr: Mark Grieco

BERGER ALLIED
See BERGER TRANSFER & STORAGE INC

D-U-N-S 78-909-2293
BERGER GROUP HOLDINGS INC
111 Market Pl, Baltimore, MD 21202-4035
Tel (410) 468-4054 *Founded/Ownrshp* 1990
Sales 415.1MM^E *EMP* 6,000
SIC 8711 8732 8712 Consulting engineer; Economic research; Architectural services
Ch Bd: Fredric S Berger
**Pr:* Thomas G Lewis
**COO:* Claudette Fisher
**CFO:* Luke McKinnon

D-U-N-S 00-881-7652 IMP
BERGER TRANSFER & STORAGE INC (MN)
BERGER ALLIED
2950 Long Lake Rd, Saint Paul, MN 55113-1000
Tel (651) 639-2260 *Founded/Ownrshp* 1910, 1949
Sales 118.6MM *EMP* 425
Accts Clifton Larson Allen
SIC 4731 4213 4214 Truck transportation brokers; Household goods transport; Local trucking with storage
Pr: William K Dircks
CFO: Thomas J Boehme
**Ch:* William R Dircks Sr
VP: Rick Goffin
**VP:* Don Schrooten
VP: Brad Vetter
Genl Mgr: Doug Morhland
Dir IT: Dick Wagner
Netwrk Mgr: Randy Underwood
Sfty Mgr: Mary Smith
Opers Mgr: Kevin Dunlevy

BERGEY'S FUEL CENTER
See BERGEYS INC

D-U-N-S 00-248-5860
BERGEYS INC (PA)
BERGEY'S FUEL CENTER
462 Harleysville Pike, Souderton, PA 18964-2153
Tel (215) 721-3430 *Founded/Ownrshp* 1924, 1973
Sales 171.7MM^E *EMP* 396
SIC 5511 5531 7538 5013 5014 Automobiles, new & used; Automotive tires; General automotive repair shops; Automotive supplies; Automobile tires & tubes
Pr: Lester Bergey
**CFO:* P Scott Heckler
**Treas:* Henry Bergey
**Sec:* Henry B Bergey
**VP:* Duane L Bergey
**VP:* Mark Bergey
IT Man: Dan Frustino
VP Mktg: Timothy Keeler
Mktg Mgr: Robert Yoters

D-U-N-S 00-542-8537
BERGLUND CONSTRUCTION CO (IL)
8410 S South Chicago Ave, Chicago, IL 60617-1992
Tel (773) 374-1000 *Founded/Ownrshp* 1911, 1981
Sales 153.2MM^E *EMP* 375
SIC 1542 Commercial & office building, new construction
Pr: Fred Berglund
Sr VP: Thomas Sicinski
Exec: Lucian Cioata

D-U-N-S 07-179-1503 IMP/EXP
BERGQUIST CO
(*Suby of* HENKEL AG & CO. KGAA)
18930 W 78th St, Chanhassen, MN 55317-8728
Tel (952) 835-2322 *Founded/Ownrshp* 2014
Sales 214.0MM *EMP* 824
Accts Mcgladrey Llp Minneapolis Mi
SIC 5731 5063 3645 3646 2822 Consumer electronic equipment; Lighting fixtures; Residential lighting fixtures; Commercial indusl & institutional electric lighting fixtures; Synthetic rubber
CEO: Benoit Pouliquen
**Ch:* Carl R Bergquist II
VP: Sarah Black
Area Mgr: Trent Johnson
QA Dir: Cuong Hoang
Dir IT: Amy Powell
IT Man: Henning Pubanz
Opers Mgr: Brian Merkel
Ql Cn Mgr: Douglas Hoffman
Ql Cn Mgr: Emily Schock
Ql Cn Mgr: Michael Switzer
Board of Directors: Carl R Bergquist II

BERGSTROM AUTOMOTIVE
See BERGSTROM CORP

D-U-N-S 05-272-2030
BERGSTROM CHEVROLET-BUICK-CADILLAC INC
BERGSTROM OF NEENAH
(*Suby of* BERGSTROM AUTOMOTIVE) ★
150 N Green Bay Rd, Neenah, WI 54956-2243
Tel (866) 575-8036 *Founded/Ownrshp* 1982
Sales 407.4MM^E *EMP* 1,500
SIC 5511

D-U-N-S 07-997-4462
BERGSTROM CLIMATE SYSTEMS LLC
(*Suby of* BERGSTROM INC) ★
2390 Blackhawk Rd, Rockford, IL 61109-3605
Tel (815) 874-7821 *Founded/Ownrshp* 1998
Sales 277.0MM *EMP* 538
SIC 3585 Air conditioning units, complete: domestic or industrial
**Pr:* Jack Shaffer

D-U-N-S 07-386-0058
BERGSTROM CORP
BERGSTROM AUTOMOTIVE
1 Neenah Ctr Ste 700, Neenah, WI 54956-3053
Tel (920) 725-4444 *Founded/Ownrshp* 1974
Sales 612.2MM^E *EMP* 1,500
SIC 5511 New & used car dealers
CEO: John F Bergstrom
**Pr:* Richard A Bergstrom
**COO:* Tim Bergstrom
COO: Timothy Bergstrom
VP: Jake Bergstom
**VP:* John Hogerty
VP: John Minarick
**VP:* Mark Snyder
Exec: Karen Krause
Genl Mgr: Robin Auth
Genl Mgr: Greg Daggett

D-U-N-S 00-546-9580 IMP
BERGSTROM INC (IL)
2390 Blackhawk Rd, Rockford, IL 61109-3605
Tel (815) 874-7821 *Founded/Ownrshp* 1949, 1964
Sales 435.3MM^E *EMP* 1,920
SIC 3531 Cabs, for construction machinery
Ch Bd: David Rydell
Pr: J B Shaffer
CFO: Dan Giovannetti
Treas: Steve Balsley
Ofcr: Mark Meegan
VP: Steven L Boyle
CTO: George Lamoureuz
Dir IT: Bruce Lauager
IT Man: John Buchwald

BERGSTROM OF NEENAH
See BERGSTROM CHEVROLET-BUICK-CADILLAC INC

D-U-N-S 07-664-1612
BERING STRAITS NATIVE CORP
110 Front St Ste 300, Nome, AK 99762
Tel (907) 443-5252 *Founded/Ownrshp* 1972
Sales 326.0MM *EMP* 280
Accts Mcgladrey Llp Frederick Mary
SIC 1081 Exploration, metal mining; Mine development, metal
CEO: Gail Schubert
**Pr:* Carolyn Crowder
**Ch:* Henry Ivanoff
**Sec:* Clara Langton
**Bd of Dir:* Tim Towarak
Ofcr: Marilyn Koezuna-Irelan
**Ex VP:* Moriah Sallaffie
**VP:* Jerald Brown
VP: Bill Mendenhall
VP: Jenette Paulson
VP Admn: Peggy Hoogendorn

D-U-N-S 00-151-3704 IMP
BERJE INC (NY)
700 Blair Rd, Carteret, NJ 07008-1221
Tel (973) 748-8980 *Founded/Ownrshp* 1950, 1949
Sales 87.1MM^E *EMP* 125
SIC 5169 2869 Aromatic chemicals; Perfumes, flavorings & food additives
CEO: Kim Bleimann
**Pr:* Dave Herbst
**CFO:* Brian Hart
VP: Jill Moats
VP: John D Virgillio

D-U-N-S 14-540-7404 EXP
BERK-TEK LLC
(*Suby of* NEXANS USA INC) ★
132 White Oak Rd, New Holland, PA 17557-8303
Tel (717) 354-6200 *Founded/Ownrshp* 2000
Sales 166.8MM^E *EMP* 1^E
SIC 3357 Coaxial cable, nonferrous
Pr: Paul Trunk
Treas: Jean-Francois Pirot
VP: Stephanie Ward

D-U-N-S 83-210-9420
BERKADIA COMMERCIAL MORTGAGE LLC
323 Norristown Rd Ste 300, Ambler, PA 19002-2758
Tel (215) 328-3200 *Founded/Ownrshp* 2009
Sales NA *EMP* 1,035
SIC 6162 Mortgage bankers & correspondents
CEO: Justin Wheeler
**Pr:* Randall Jenson
**Pr:* Mark E McCool
**CEO:* Don Hendricks
**COO:* Linda Pickles
Ex VP: Robert Ballard
**Ex VP:* Thomas Miraglia
Sr VP: David Blake
Sr VP: Christopher Blechschmidt
Sr VP: Russ Callahan
Sr VP: Brian Campbell
Sr VP: Andrea Dauphinee
Sr VP: John Dicrocco
Sr VP: Clare C Dooley

Sr VP: Clare Dooley
Sr VP: Matt Greer
Sr VP: Ernest Katai
Sr VP: Jeffery Kinney
Sr VP: Robert Lipson
Sr VP: John Lucerne
Sr VP: Donald Marshall

D-U-N-S 03-119-7221 EXP
BERKEL & CO CONTRACTORS INC
2649 S 142nd St, Bonner Springs, KS 66012-9459
Tel (913) 422-5125 *Founded/Ownrshp* 1959
Sales 218.4MM^E *EMP* 700
Accts Bkd Llp Kansas City Mo
SIC 1771 1741 Foundation & footing contractor; Concrete repair; Foundation & retaining wall construction
Pr: Alan R Roach
CFO: Mary Darr
**CFO:* Grant D White
**Ch:* Charles J Berkel
**Treas:* Greg Welicky
**Sr VP:* Dominic A Cerasi
**Sr VP:* David J Weatherer
**VP:* Keith Blum
**VP:* Joseph Brand
**VP:* Tracy T Brettmann
**VP:* Gregory K Righter
**VP:* Randy Thomas

D-U-N-S 00-815-9220
BERKELEY COUNTY SCHOOL DISTRICT
229 E Main St, Moncks Corner, SC 29461-3767
Tel (843) 899-8600 *Founded/Ownrshp* 1900
Sales 222.9MM^E *EMP* 4,000
Accts Greene Finney & Horton Llp Ma
SIC 8211 Public elementary & secondary schools
Sls&Mrk Ex: Amy Kovach
Pr Dir: Susan Haire
Schl Brd P: Jim Hayes
Schl Brd P: Kent Murray

D-U-N-S 06-936-6136
BERKELEY COUNTY SCHOOLS
401 S Queen St, Martinsburg, WV 25401-3233
Tel (304) 267-3500 *Founded/Ownrshp* 1933
Sales 84.6MM^E *EMP* 2,000
SIC 8211 Academy
Exec: Archie Franchini
Ex Dir: Susan Starliper
IT Man: James Butts
Board of Directors: Todd Beckwith, Bernice Collis, Bill Norris, Dr Bill Queen, Bill Sonnik

D-U-N-S 09-840-0203
BERKELEY COUNTY WATER AND SANITATION AUTHORITY
212 Oakley Plantation Dr, Moncks Corner, SC 29461-5036
Tel (843) 761-8817 *Founded/Ownrshp* 1973
Sales 105.1MM^E *EMP* 223
Accts Greene Finney & Horton Mauldi
SIC 4941 4953 Water supply; Sanitary landfill operation
Prin: Colin L Martin
Telecom Ex: Jerri Christmas

D-U-N-S 00-279-7876
BERKELEY ELECTRIC COOPERATIVE INC (SC)
551 Rmbert C. Dnnis Blvd, Moncks Corner, SC 29461
Tel (843) 761-8200 *Founded/Ownrshp* 1940
Sales 217.4MM *EMP* 237
SIC 4911 Distribution, electric power
CEO: Dwayne Cartwright
**Pr:* E E Strickland Jr
**VP:* Anthony J Capobianco
**VP:* Mark Gaddy
**VP:* H Eddie McKnight
**VP:* J Scott Shepherd
S&M/VP: Eddie Plowden

D-U-N-S 05-750-1173 IMP
■ **BERKELEY FARMS LLC**
(*Suby of* DEAN FOODS CO) ★
25500 Clawiter Rd, Hayward, CA 94545-2739
Tel (510) 265-8600 *Founded/Ownrshp* 2013
Sales 553.0MM^E *EMP* 625
SIC 5143 2026 0241 Dairy products, except dried or canned; Butter; Cheese; Ice cream & ices; Fluid milk; Dairy farms

BERKELEY MEDICAL CENTER
See CITY HOSPITAL INC

D-U-N-S 96-242-9069
BERKELEY RESEARCH GROUP LLC
2200 Powell St Ste 1200, Emeryville, CA 94608-1833
Tel (510) 285-3300 *Founded/Ownrshp* 2010
Sales 137.2MM^E *EMP* 704^E
SIC 8748 Business consulting
Ch: David Teece
**Pr:* Marvin Tenenbaum
COO: Sebastien Belanger
**CFO:* Kimberly Starr
Ex VP: David Salat
Sr VP: Eric Miller
VP: Chip Goodman
Assoc Dir: Dennis Jasinski
Assoc Dir: Joanna Martin
Assoc Dir: Caroline H Neuhaus
**Prin:* Norman Boyter
Board of Directors: Ned Barnes, G Anthony Lopez, Robert Maclaverty, Stuart McCrary, Paul Rowe, Mark Schankerman, Carl J Schramm

D-U-N-S 07-168-1811
BERKELEY UNIFIED SCHOOL DISTRICT
2020 Bonar St Rm 202, Berkeley, CA 94702-1793
Tel (510) 644-4500 *Founded/Ownrshp* 1879
Sales 157.2MM *EMP* 1,230
Accts Crowehorwath Llp Sacramento
SIC 8211 Public elementary & secondary schools; Public adult education school
CFO: George Sirogrannis
Exec: Myratta Whitaker
Dir Risk M: Inez Reed
Off Mgr: Erica Johnson
CTO: Jay Nitscke

Dir IT: Jay Schab
Pr Dir: Charles Burress

D-U-N-S 07-172-4884
BERKLEE COLLEGE OF MUSIC INC
1140 Boylston St, Boston, MA 02215-3693
Tel (617) 266-1400 *Founded/Ownrshp* 1933
Sales 259.5MM *EMP* 1,082^E
Accts Kpmg Llp Boston Ma
SIC 8221 College, except junior
Pr: Roger H Brown
**CFO:* Richard M Hisey
Trst: Robert Morrison
**Sr VP:* Cindy Albert Link
**Sr VP:* David Mash
**VP:* Lawrence E Bethune
VP: Christopher Kandus-Fisher
VP: David S Mash
VP: Lee Whitmore
Exec: Dave Buda
Assoc Dir: Karen Pinette
Assoc Dir: Hugo Sanchez
Creative D: Audrey Harrer

D-U-N-S 08-074-3318
■ **BERKLEY MID-ATLANTIC GROUP LLC**
(*Suby of* W R BERKLEY CORP) ★
4820 Lake Brook Dr # 300, Glen Allen, VA 23060-9285
Tel (804) 285-2700 *Founded/Ownrshp* 2007
Sales NA *EMP* 212
SIC 6411 Insurance agents, brokers & service
Pr: Kevin W Nattrass
**Pr:* Susan N Grady
Pr: Leonard T Hampton
**CFO:* Allen R Latimer
CFO: Allen Latimer
**Sr VP:* Nancy Newmister
**VP:* Jeffrey E Bouton
**VP:* William T Gardner
**VP:* Bernie Kurtzweil
VP: James E Lange Jr
**VP:* J Michael Lent
VP: Jamie Osborne
**VP:* Vickie Price
**VP:* Laura L Thorne
**VP:* William Yount

D-U-N-S 80-004-1329
■ **BERKLEY REGIONAL INSURANCE CO**
(*Suby of* W R BERKLEY CORP) ★
475 Steamboat Rd Fl 1, Greenwich, CT 06830-7144
Tel (203) 629-3000 *Founded/Ownrshp* 1996
Sales NA *EMP* 400
Accts Kpmg Llp Des Moines Iowa
SIC 6331 Fire, marine & casualty insurance: mutual
VP: Karen Horvath
**Pr:* William R Berkley
**Treas:* Robert Buehler
VP: Donna J Latham

D-U-N-S 15-177-2480
■ **BERKLEY RISK ADMINISTRATION CO LLC**
(*Suby of* W R BERKLEY CORP) ★
222 S 9th St Ste 2700, Minneapolis, MN 55402-3365
Tel (612) 766-3000 *Founded/Ownrshp* 1997
Sales NA *EMP* 856
SIC 6411 3052 3432 Insurance agents & brokers; Rubber hose; Lawn hose nozzles & sprinklers
Pr: John M Goodwin
**Ch Bd:* J Michael Foley
**Pr:* Robert W Berkley Jr
Pr: Dave Kyllo
VP: Joyce Krech
VP: Doug Olson
Mng Dir: Jon M Paulsen
Dir IT: Kevin Conway
IT Man: Tom Houghtling
IT Man: Keith H Johnson
IT Man: Bob Kleiber

D-U-N-S 06-587-8936
BERKOT LTD
BERKOT SUPER FOODS
11333 W 159th St, Orland Park, IL 60467-5659
Tel (708) 590-4088 *Founded/Ownrshp* 1981
Sales 120.0MM^E *EMP* 800
SIC 5411 Grocery stores, independent
Pr: John Kotara

BERKOT SUPER FOODS
See BERKOT LTD

BERKS COUNTY CLERK OF COURTS
See COUNTY OF BERKS

D-U-N-S 01-058-0041
BERKS COUNTY INTERMEDIATE UNIT
BCIU
1111 Commons Blvd, Reading, PA 19605-3334
Tel (610) 987-2248 *Founded/Ownrshp* 1971
Sales NA *EMP* 1,100^E
SIC 9411 Administration of educational programs;
Ex Dir: Dr John J George
**CFO:* Carl D Blessing
VP: Robert Quinter Jr
Ex Dir: Stanley H Kita Jr
MIS Dir: William F Miller
Teacher Pr: Rob Rosenberry
Psych: Christine Devine
Psych: Michael Houck

D-U-N-S 00-791-6778
BERKS PRODUCTS CORP (PA)
167 Berks Products Dr, Leesport, PA 19533-8686
Tel (610) 374-5131 *Founded/Ownrshp* 1896, 1984
Sales 98.4MM^E *EMP* 325
SIC 5031 3273 5983 5172 2439 1711

D-U-N-S 00-695-5579
■ **BERKSHIRE BANK**
(*Suby of* BERKSHIRE HILLS BANCORP INC) ★
24 North St, Pittsfield, MA 01201-5157
Tel (413) 443-5601 *Founded/Ownrshp* 1846
Sales NA *EMP* 290^E
SIC 6035 Federal savings banks
Pr: Michael P Daly
Pr: Mike Ferry
**Pr:* Richard Marotta

**COO:* Sean Gray
CFO: Josephine Iannelli
**CFO:* James M Moses
**Treas:* Kevin P Riley
Ofcr: Nicholas Dicaprio
Ofcr: Suzanne Direnzo
Ofcr: Paula Hilchey
Ofcr: Moriah Lonczak
Ofcr: Ryan Melle
Ofcr: Beth Nolan
Ofcr: Michael O'Donnell
Ofcr: Kimberly Rainey
Ofcr: Carly Remington
Ofcr: Samantha Tanner
Ofcr: Christine Turley
Ofcr: Karen Worcester
Ofcr: Lee Zucco
Ex VP: John J Howard
Board of Directors: Peter J Lafayette, Anne E Wojtkowski, Wallace W Altes, Edward G Mc Cormick, John W Altmeyer, Catherine B Miller, Thomas O Andrews, Michael G Miller, Geno Auriemma, Raymond B Murray, Thoms R Dawson, Louis J Oggiani, J Williar Dunlaevy, David E Phelps, Henry D Granger, Barton D Raser, A Allen Gray, Robert S Raser, John Kittredge, William E Williams

D-U-N-S 02-984-7109
■ **BERKSHIRE HATHAWAY AUTOMOTIVE INC**
VAN TUYL GROUP, LLC
(*Suby of* BERKSHIRE HATHAWAY INC) ★
8333 Royal Ridge Pkwy # 100, Irving, TX 75063-2868
Tel (972) 536-2900 *Founded/Ownrshp* 2015
Sales 110.8MM^E *EMP* 255^E
SIC 7549 5511 Automotive maintenance services; New & used car dealers
CEO: Jeffrey C Rachor
VP: Patricia Van Tuyl
Web Dev: Brandon Cecil

D-U-N-S 96-300-8388
■ **BERKSHIRE HATHAWAY ENERGY CO**
(*Suby of* BERKSHIRE HATHAWAY INC) ★
666 Grand Ave Ste 500, Des Moines, IA 50309-2511
Tel (515) 242-4300 *Founded/Ownrshp* 2000
Sales 17.3MMM *EMP* 20,900^E
SIC 4911 4924 6531 Electric services; Transmission, electric power; Distribution, electric power; Natural gas distribution; Real estate agents & managers
Ch Bd: Gregory E Abel
CFO: Patrick J Goodman
Ofcr: Maureen E Sammon
Ex VP: Douglas L Anderson
VP: Maureen Sammon
VP: Mark Sherwood
VP: Jonathan Weisgall
Exec: Barbara Anderson
Genl Mgr: Ted Davis
MIS Dir: Dominic Dittman
Dir IT: Jane M Burt
Board of Directors: Warren E Buffett, Marc D Hamburg, Walter Scott Jr

BERKSHIRE HATHAWAY HOME
See GET SOLD REALTY INC

BERKSHIRE HATHAWAY HOME
See HOMESERVICES OF ILLINOIS LLC

D-U-N-S 00-102-4314
▲ **BERKSHIRE HATHAWAY INC**
3555 Farnam St Ste 1440, Omaha, NE 68131-3378
Tel (402) 346-1400 *Founded/Ownrshp* 1889
Sales NA *EMP* 331,000
Tkr Sym BRKA *Exch* NYS
SIC 6331 6321 4911 4924 6531 5963 Property damage insurance; Fire, marine & casualty insurance: stock; Reinsurance carriers, accident & health; Electric services; Natural gas distribution; Real estate brokers & agents; Food services, direct sales
Ch Bd: Warren E Buffett
CFO: Marc D Hamburg
**V Ch Bd:* Charles T Munger
Bd of Dir: Thomas Murphy
VP: Daniel J Jaksich

D-U-N-S 10-661-7434
BERKSHIRE HEALTH SYSTEMS INC
725 North St, Pittsfield, MA 01201-4109
Tel (413) 447-2000 *Founded/Ownrshp* 2013
Sales 516.9MM *EMP* 3,000
SIC 8062 General medical & surgical hospitals
Pr: David E Phelps
**Treas:* Darlene Rodowicz
**VP:* Michael Cullen
VP: Thomas Romeo
Nrsg Dir: Karen Hagmaier
Phys Thrpy: Nicole Cook

D-U-N-S 00-466-0346
▲ **BERKSHIRE HILLS BANCORP INC**
24 North St, Pittsfield, MA 01201-5106
Tel (413) 443-5601 *Founded/Ownrshp* 2000
Sales NA *EMP* 1,221^E
Accts Pricewaterhousecoopers Llp B
Tkr Sym BHLB *Exch* NYS
SIC 6022 6411 State commercial banks; Insurance agents, brokers & service
Pr: Michael P Daly
**Ch Bd:* William J Ryan
Pr: Levante Gregg
CFO: James M Moses
Ex VP: Michael D Carroll
Ex VP: Tami F Gunsch
Ex VP: Allison P O'Rourke
VP: Patricia Nebosky
VP: Justin Priddle
Exec: Sean A Gray
Exec: Richard M Marotta

D-U-N-S 00-695-5595
BERKSHIRE LIFE INSURANCE CO OF AMERICA
(*Suby of* GUARDIAN LIFE INSURANCE CO OF AMERICA) ★
700 South St, Pittsfield, MA 01201-8285
Tel (413) 395-4321 *Founded/Ownrshp* 2001
Sales NA *EMP* 435

SIC 6321 Accident insurance carriers; Health insurance carriers
Pr: Gordon Griffith Dinsmore
CFO: Henry W Glass Jr
VP: Carl Desrochers
VP: Larry Hazzard
Exec: Joelle Benoit
Exec: Amanda Carpenter
Dir IT: Craig Kleiner
IT Man: Christine Decarlo
IT Man: Brian Staubach
Software D: Bill Mallory
Opers Mgr: Albert J Baldassarri

D-U-N-S 02-067-3778
BERKSHIRE MEDICAL CENTER INC
V N A OF THE BERKSHIRES
(*Suby of* BERKSHIRE HEALTH SYSTEMS INC) ★
725 North St, Pittsfield, MA 01201-4124
Tel (413) 447-2000 *Founded/Ownrshp* 1982
Sales 424.7MM *EMP* 1,375
SIC 8062 General medical & surgical hospitals
Pr: David E Phelps
Chf Rad: Mal Kani
Pr: John Rogers
COO: Amela Nerey
CFO: Paula Bush
CFO: Michael Cullen
**Treas:* Michael R Cullen
Trst: Ann Barrett
Trst: John Kearns
Trst: Joan McFalls
Trst: Carole Siegal
Ofcr: George Ritter
VP: Thomas Romeo
Dir Lab: Terry Bills
Dir Rx: Dee Aberdale
Dir Rx: Jeff Mizia

D-U-N-S 15-359-9907
BERKSHIRE PARTNERS LLC
200 Clarendon St Ste 3500, Boston, MA 02116-5040
Tel (617) 227-0050 *Founded/Ownrshp* 1984
Sales 236.4MM^E *EMP* 1,372
SIC 6211 6726 8741 Investment firm, general brokerage; Investment offices; Management services
CFO: Julia Selvig
Exec: Joshua Friedman

D-U-N-S 19-433-5576 IMP/EXP
BERLIN PACKAGING LLC
525 W Monroe St Ste 1400, Chicago, IL 60661-3648
Tel (312) 876-9292 *Founded/Ownrshp* 2014
Sales 336.3MM^E *EMP* 303
SIC 5085 Commercial containers; Crowns & closures, metal
CEO: Andrew T Berlin
COO: Larry Rydzewski
CFO: Neil Schwab
QA Dir: Bridget Fitzpatrick
IT Man: Jennifer O'Donnell
Opers Mgr: Shawn Cochrane
Snr Mgr: Paul Mansour

D-U-N-S 05-217-9490 IMP
BERLIN SCHERING INC
(*Suby of* BAYER HEALTHCARE LLC) ★
100 Bayer Blvd, Whippany, NJ 07981-1544
Tel (862) 404-3000 *Founded/Ownrshp* 1986
Sales 1.0MMM^E *EMP* 1,975
SIC 2834 3841 Drugs affecting neoplasms & endrocrine systems; Drugs acting on the central nervous system & sense organs; Drugs acting on the cardiovascular system, except diagnostic; Surgical & medical instruments
Ofcr: Daniel Apel

D-U-N-S 15-632-6167
BERLITZ CORP
(*Suby of* BENESSE CORPORATION)
7 Roszel Rd Fl 3, Princeton, NJ 08540-6257
Tel (207) 828-3768 *Founded/Ownrshp* 1989
Sales 101.9MM^E *EMP* 6,015
SIC 8299 8748 Language school; Test development & evaluation service
Pr: Yukako Uchinaga
CFO: Michael Mockler
CFO: Ron Starch
Ex VP: Bettina Neidhardt
VP: Alistair Gatoff
Dir Bus: Dan Bolger
Ex Dir: Anne Kelly
Prgrm Mgr: Susanne Koch
Prgrm Mgr: Ian McCallum
Prgrm Mgr: Maggie Pelka
Prgrm Mgr: Ivana Zecevic

D-U-N-S 10-327-0161
BERLITZ LANGUAGES (UNITED STATES) INC
BERLITZ LANGUAGES, INC.
(*Suby of* BERLITZ CORP) ★
7 Roszel Rd Fl 3, Princeton, NJ 08540-6257
Tel (609) 759-5371 *Founded/Ownrshp* 2007
Sales 100.5MM^E *EMP* 5,594
SIC 8299 7389 2731 Language school; Translation services; Books: publishing only
CEO: Yukako Uchinaga
Ex VP: Mark W Harris
VP: Paul Weinstein
Dir Bus: Christopher Ekvall
Board of Directors: Kenichi Arai, Carol Trinca-Bautista, Edward G Nelson, Robert L Purdum, Donna Russomano, Hiroyuki Yagi

BERLITZ LANGUAGES, INC.
See BERLITZ LANGUAGES (UNITED STATES) INC

BERMAN GLASS
See FORMS AND SURFACES INC

D-U-N-S 09-003-7383 IMP/EXP
BERMUDEZ LONGO DIAZ-MASSO LLC
Km 0 5 Cupey Rr 845, San Juan, PR 00926
Tel (787) 761-3030 *Founded/Ownrshp* 2007
Sales 119.8MM^E *EMP* 800
Accts Horwath Velez & Co Psc Guayb
SIC 1731 1711 Electrical work; Mechanical contractor
Pr: Francisco Daz Mass

*VP: Damaso Bermudez
*VP: Lizette Mass
*VP: Jaime Vasquez

D-U-N-S 07-221-6336 IMP/EXP
BERNARD EGAN & CO
DNE WORLD FRUIT
1900 N Old Dixie Hwy, Fort Pierce, FL 34946-1423
Tel (772) 465-7555 Founded/Ownrshp 1977
Sales 128.5MM^E EMP 190
SIC 0723 8741 0174 Fruit (fresh) packing services; Management services; Citrus fruits
Pr: Greg Nelson
*Treas: Jeffrey A Hurwitz
*VP: Richard Carnell
*VP: Jean Jacques Gilet
MIS Dir: Debbie Wood
Dir IT: Carmen Capezzuto
Opers Mgr: Joe Crosby
VP Sls: Mark Hanks

BERNARD MITCHELL HOSPITAL
See UNIVERSITY OF CHICAGO MEDICAL CENTER

D-U-N-S 07-726-2525
BERNARDS BROS INC
555 1st St, San Fernando, CA 91340-3051
Tel (818) 898-1521 Founded/Ownrshp 1974
Sales 165.5MM^E EMP 270
SIC 1542 1541

BERNATELLO'S FOODS
See BERNATELLOS PIZZA INC

D-U-N-S 01-047-2314
BERNATELLOS PIZZA INC (MN)
BERNATELLO'S FOODS
200 Congress St W, Maple Lake, MN 55358-3525
Tel (320) 963-6191 Founded/Ownrshp 1982
Sales 115.3MM^E EMP 470^E
Accts Larson Allen Weishair & Co
SIC 2038 Pizza, frozen
CEO: William Ramsey
*Sec: James Cousin
*VP: Dave Ramsey
Prd Mgr: Candy Triplett

D-U-N-S 00-523-6856
BERNER FOOD & BEVERAGE LLC
BERNER FOODS
2034 E Factory Rd, Dakota, IL 61018-9736
Tel (815) 563-4222 Founded/Ownrshp 2015
Sales 135.4MM^E EMP 300
SIC 2022 2026 2095 2086 2033 Cheese spreads, dips, pastes & other cheese products; Dips, cheese-based; Dips, sour cream based; Instant coffee; Soft drinks: packaged in cans, bottles, etc.; Spaghetti & other pasta sauce: packaged in cans, jars, etc.
CEO: Stephen A Kneubuehl
Pr: Bill Marchido
COO: Edward Kneubuehl
CIO: Troy Grove
Prd Mgr: Zachary Kneubuehl
Ql Cn Mgr: James Humphrey

BERNER FOODS
See BERNER FOOD & BEVERAGE LLC

BERNHARDT DESIGN
See BERNHARDT FURNITURE CO INC

BERNHARDT FURNITURE COMPANY
See BERNHARDT INDUSTRIES INC

D-U-N-S 00-315-8979 IMP/EXP
BERNHARDT FURNITURE CO INC (NC)
BERNHARDT DESIGN
(Suby of BERNHARDT FURNITURE CO) ★
1839 Morganton Blvd Sw, Lenoir, NC 28645-5338
Tel (828) 758-9811 Founded/Ownrshp 1889
Sales 369.1MM^E EMP 1,250
SIC 2511 2512 2521 2522 Dining room furniture: wood; Wood bedroom furniture; Couches, sofas & davenports: upholstered on wood frames; Chairs: upholstered on wood frames; Desks, office: wood; Chairs, office: padded, upholstered or plain: wood; Filing cabinets (boxes), office: wood; Tables, office: wood; Chairs, office: padded or plain, except wood
Pr: G Alex Bernhardt Jr
*Ch Bd: G Alexander Bernhardt Sr
*V Ch: Anne H Bernhardt
*Pr: J Rountree Collett Jr
*Pr: Jerry Helling
*CFO: Peter Craymer
*Ex VP: William Collett
*Ex VP: Harland Dick
VP: William B Collett
Exec: Heather Eidenmiller
Adm Dir: Diane Reid

D-U-N-S 00-193-6699 IMP/EXP
BERNHARDT INDUSTRIES INC
BERNHARDT FURNITURE COMPANY
1839 Morganton Blvd Sw, Lenoir, NC 28645-5338
Tel (828) 758-9811 Founded/Ownrshp 1927
Sales 369.1MM^E EMP 777^E
SIC 2511 2521 2512 2522 Wood household furniture; Wood office furniture; Chairs, office: padded, upholstered or plain: wood; Upholstered household furniture; Office furniture, except wood
Pr: Alex Bernhardt Jr
*COO: J Rountree Collett Jr
*CFO: Peter W Craymer
*Ex VP: William B Collett
*Ex VP: Harland Dick
Board of Directors: Alex Bernhardt Sr, Anne H Bernhardt

BERNIE & PHYL'S FURNITURE
See CONVERTIBLE CASTLE INC

BERNINA OF AMERICA
See MIZAR HOLDING CO INC

BERRA CONSTRUCTION
See J H BERRA HOLDING CO INC

D-U-N-S 00-277-7050
BERRY BROS GENERAL CONTRACTORS INC (LA)
1414 River Rd, Berwick, LA 70342-3020
Tel (985) 384-8770 Founded/Ownrshp 1956, 1975
Sales 83.2MM^E EMP 140
SIC 1629 4959 Dredging contractor; Pile driving contractor; Oil spill cleanup
Ch: Doyle G Berry
*Pr: Joe'al S Berry
*Sec: Lloyd Aucoin
*VP: Ricky Thibodeaux
Exec: Shawn Price
Mfg Mgr: Weldon Miller

D-U-N-S 06-450-1000
BERRY COLLEGE INC
2277 Martha Berry Hwy Nw, Rome, GA 30161-9707
Tel (706) 232-5374 Founded/Ownrshp 1902
Sales 132.7MM EMP 550
SIC 8221 College, except junior
Pr: Stephen R Briggs
COO: Brianne Smedley
Ofcr: Jean Druckenmiller
*VP: Brian Erb
VP: Debbie Heida
Off Mgr: Kerrie Dalrymple
IT Man: John Rix
Board of Directors: Debbie Emory

D-U-N-S 06-356-9230
BERRY COMPANIES INC
BERRY TRACTOR & EQUIPMENT CO
3223 N Hydraulic St, Wichita, KS 67219-3893
Tel (316) 838-3321 Founded/Ownrshp 1957
Sales 277.5MM^E EMP 520
Accts Kennedy & Coe Llc Wichita K
SIC 5082 7353 7699 5084 Construction & mining machinery; General construction machinery & equipment; Heavy construction equipment rental; Industrial machinery & equipment repair; Industrial machinery & equipment
Pr: Walter Berry
Ch Bd: Fred F Berry Jr
Treas: Judy Worrell
Ex VP: Dan Scheer
VP: John Engels
VP: Bob Young
Brnch Mgr: Paul Hall
Brnch Mgr: Travis Krueger
Dir IT: Wayne Becker
IT Man: Brian Curtis
Info Man: Rod Opliger

D-U-N-S 96-747-4946
BERRY CONTRACTING LP
BAY
1414 Corn Product Rd, Corpus Christi, TX 78409-3020
Tel (361) 693-2100 Founded/Ownrshp 2000
Sales 542.5MM^E EMP 3,000^E
SIC 2911 1611 Petroleum refining; Highway & street construction
VP: Robert C Blair
*Sr VP: John Dill
*VP: J Jones

D-U-N-S 03-808-9038 IMP
BERRY ECLIPSE FARMS LLC
11812 San Vicente Blvd # 250, Los Angeles, CA 90049-6632
Tel (310) 207-7879 Founded/Ownrshp 1999
Sales 85.8MM^E EMP 100
SIC 0171 5148 Berry crops; Fresh fruits & vegetables
Bd of Dir: Norman Gilfenbain
*Genl Mgr: Robert Wiviott

BERRY FAMILY OF NURSERIES
See BFN OPERATIONS LLC

D-U-N-S 60-315-8325 IMP
BERRY FRESH LLC
BERRY FRESH PRODUCE
19640 S Rancho Way, Rancho Dominguez, CA 90220-6039
Tel (310) 637-2401 Founded/Ownrshp 2005
Sales 133.7MM EMP 41
SIC 5148 Fruits
Prd Mgr: Patrick Garrison

BERRY FRESH PRODUCE
See BERRY FRESH LLC

D-U-N-S 00-813-3340
BERRY GP INC (TX)
1414 Corn Product Rd, Corpus Christi, TX 78409-3020
Tel (361) 693-2100 Founded/Ownrshp 1952, 1962
Sales 583.3MM EMP 3,000
SIC 1541 1611 3498 Industrial buildings & warehouses; Highway & street construction; Highway & street paving contractor; General contractor, highway & street construction; Fabricated pipe & fittings
Pr: Edward A Martin
*Pr: Ken Luhan
*CFO: Johnna Jones
*Sr VP: Dj Smith
*VP: Charles Vanaman

D-U-N-S 05-043-6872 IMP
BERRY HOLDINGS LP
BAY LIMITED
1414 Corn Product Rd, Corpus Christi, TX 78409-3020
Tel (361) 693-2100 Founded/Ownrshp 1981
Sales 562.4MM EMP 3,000
SIC 1541 1611 3498 Industrial buildings & warehouses; Highway & street paving contractor; Fabricated pipe & fittings
CEO: Edward Martin
Pr: Ken Luhan
CFO: Johnna Jones
VP: Jeremy Baker
VP: David Carlin
VP: Randy Feikls
VP: Charles Vanaman
Exec: Paul Caldwell
Area Mgr: Max Oneill
Off Admin: Ginette Asselin
CIO: Jim Bliss
Board of Directors: David Carlin, Wayne Coleman

D-U-N-S 00-690-4684 IMP
■ **BERRY KNOTTS FARM LLC**
KNOTT'S BERRY FARM
(Suby of CEDAR FAIR LP) ★
8039 Beach Blvd, Buena Park, CA 90620-3225
Tel (714) 827-1776 Founded/Ownrshp 1920, 1997
Sales 102.2MM^E EMP 600
SIC 2099 Syrups
Pt: Jack Falfas
CFO: Sandy Blackstone
VP: Larry Daniel
VP: Jeff Gahagan
VP: John Goodnight
VP: Raffi Kaprelyan
VP: Jason Kimball
VP: Greg Picon
VP: Dick Rohrback
Area Mgr: Ian Barnette
Area Mgr: Mary A Gomez

D-U-N-S 15-132-1411
■ **BERRY PETROLEUM CO LLC**
(Suby of LINN ACQUISITION CO LLC) ★
600 Travis St Ste 5100, Houston, TX 77002-3092
Tel (281) 840-4000 Founded/Ownrshp 2013
Sales 641.6MM EMP 3^E
SIC 1311 Crude petroleum production; Natural gas production
Pr: Mark E Ellis
*CFO: David B Rottino
*VP: Darren R Schluter

D-U-N-S 62-332-7731 IMP/EXP
■ **BERRY PLASTICS CORP**
(Suby of BERRY PLASTICS GROUP INC) ★
101 Oakley St, Evansville, IN 47710-1252
Tel (812) 424-2904 Founded/Ownrshp 2006
Sales 3.7MMM^E EMP 15,000
SIC 3089 3081 Plastic containers, except foam; Cups, plastic, except foam; Bottle caps, molded plastic; Caps, plastic; Unsupported plastics film & sheet
Ch Bd: Jonathan D Rich
Pr: Randall J Becker
Pr: Bob Kiely
CFO: James M Kratochvil
CFO: David Smith
Ex VP: Brett Bauer
Ex VP: Ed Stratton
VP: Vike Engh
VP: Michael Harris
VP: Jennye Scott
VP: Jeffrey Thompson
Exec: Amy Morphew
Board of Directors: Anthony M Civale, Robert V Seminara

D-U-N-S 79-544-8062 EXP
▲ **BERRY PLASTICS GROUP INC**
101 Oakley St, Evansville, IN 47710-1252
Tel (812) 424-2904 Founded/Ownrshp 1967
Sales 6.4MMM EMP 20,500
Accts Ernst & Young Llp Indianapoli
Tkr Sym BERY Exch NYS
SIC 3089 3085 2673 3081 3083 Plastic containers, except foam; Cups, plastic, except foam; Bottle caps, molded plastic; Caps, plastic; Plastics bottles; Trash bags (plastic film): made from purchased materials; Plastic film & sheet; Laminated plastics plate & sheet
Ch Bd: Jonathan D Rich
Pr: William J Norman
Pr: Thomas E Salmon
CFO: Mark W Miles
Ex VP: Scott Farmer
Ex VP: Rodgers Greenawalt
Ex VP: Jason K Greene
Ex VP: Rodgers K Greenwalt
Ex VP: Jeffrey D Thompson
Ex VP: James M Till
VP: Brett C Bauer

BERRY SEED & FEED
See A L GILBERT CO

BERRY TRACTOR & EQUIPMENT CO
See BERRY COMPANIES INC

D-U-N-S 80-269-5221 IMP
BERRYVILLE GRAPHICS INC
(Suby of BERTELSMANN INC) ★
25 Jack Enders Blvd, Berryville, VA 22611-1501
Tel (540) 955-2750 Founded/Ownrshp 1998
Sales 217.9MM^E EMP 750
SIC 2732 2752 2789 Book printing; Commercial printing, offset; Bookbinding & related work
CEO: David Liess
*Ch: Bertram Stausberg
*Treas: Jared Verano
*Ex VP: Mitchel Weiss
Sfty Mgr: Paul Ehlers
VP Mktg: Donna Dempsey

D-U-N-S 15-281-1600 IMP
BERTELSMANN INC
(Suby of BERTELSMANN SE & CO. KGAA)
1745 Broadway Fl 20, New York, NY 10019-4640
Tel (212) 782-1000 Founded/Ownrshp 1975
Sales 1.4MMM^E EMP 13,000
SIC 2731 2721 7819 3652 6512 Books: publishing & printing; Magazines: publishing & printing; Trade journals: publishing & printing; Video tape or disk reproduction; Compact laser discs, prerecorded; Commercial & industrial building operation
CEO: Jaroslaw Gabor
*Ch Bd: Thomas Rabe
V Ch: Gerd Schulte-Hillen
Pr: Joshua Kraus
COO: Peter Blobel
CFO: Joe Gorman
Ex VP: Jasmine Borhan
Sr VP: Steve Redmond
VP: Bernhard Derlath
*VP: William Tung
Dir Bus: Nihar Malaviya
Board of Directors: Siegfried Luther

D-U-N-S 07-279-5982
BERTELSMANN PUBLISHING GROUP INC
(Suby of BERTELSMANN INC) ★
1540 Broadway Fl 24, New York, NY 10036-4039
Tel (212) 782-1000 Founded/Ownrshp 1974
Sales 80.1MM^E EMP 2,000
SIC 2731 2721 Books: publishing only; Magazines: publishing only, not printed on site
Ch Bd: Hans-Martin Sorge
*Pr: Peter Olson
*CEO: Thomas Middelhoff
*CEO: Robert J Sorrentino
*Treas: Bernhard U Derlath
IT Man: Joe Blow

BERTRAM FOODS
See S BERTRAM INC

D-U-N-S 00-525-3519
BERTSCHI NORTH AMERICA INC (TX)
(Suby of BERTSCHI AG)
16902 El Cmno Real 3b Ste 3, Houston, TX 77058
Tel (281) 751-8800 Founded/Ownrshp 2012
Sales 91.1MM^E EMP 2,500
SIC 4731 Freight transportation arrangement
*Mng Dir: Eloy Ramos

BERTUCCI'S BRICK OVEN PIZZERIA
See BERTUCCIS CORP

D-U-N-S 15-105-5555
BERTUCCIS CORP
BERTUCCI'S BRICK OVEN PIZZERIA
155 Otis St Ste 3, Northborough, MA 01532-2454
Tel (508) 351-2500 Founded/Ownrshp 1998
Sales 290.1MM^E EMP 6,500
SIC 5812 Pizzeria, chain
CEO: David Lloyd
*Ch Bd: Benjamin R Jacobsen
*CEO: David G Lloyd
*COO: Francis Christman
*CFO: Brian P Connell
VP: Bob Burns
VP: Kir Schnaubel
VP: Christopher Snyder
VP Mktg: Maria Feizht
VP Mktg: Kathy Kiely
Sls Mgr: Nicole Mutters
Board of Directors: Maria Fisch, Jim Lux, Jim Moriaty, Dave Nace, Kevin Quinlen, Bryan Schwanke, Chris Snyder

D-U-N-S 07-992-1992
BERWIND CONSOLIDATED HOLDINGS INC
(Suby of BERWIND CORP) ★
3000 Ctr Sq W 1500 Mkt St 1500 W, Philadelphia, PA 19102
Tel (215) 563-2800 Founded/Ownrshp 2015
Sales 220.0MM^E EMP 1,200
SIC 6722 Management investment, open-end
CEO: Mike McLelland
*Treas: Ray Baran

D-U-N-S 00-791-3213 IMP/EXP
BERWIND CORP (PA)
3000 Ctr Sq W 1500 Mkt St 1500 W, Philadelphia, PA 19102
Tel (215) 563-2800 Founded/Ownrshp 1870
Sales 3.1MMM^E EMP 4,500
SIC 6519 5052 4789 3625 3669 2899

D-U-N-S 62-787-9968
BERWIND INDUSTRIES INC
(Suby of BERWIND CORP) ★
3000 Ctr Sq W 1500 Mkt St, Philadelphia, PA 19102
Tel (215) 563-2800 Founded/Ownrshp 1990
Sales 97.8MM^E EMP 339
SIC 7389 Personal service agents, brokers & bureaus
Pr: James L Hamling

BESAM ENTRANCE SOLUTION
See ASSA ABLOY ENTRANCE SYSTEMS US INC

BESCO
See BROADWAY ELECTRIC SERVICE CORP

D-U-N-S 11-306-7946
BESSEMER GROUP INC
BESSEMER TRUST
100 Woodbridge Center Dr, Woodbridge, NJ 07095-1162
Tel (732) 694-5500 Founded/Ownrshp 1981
Sales 558.6MM^E EMP 657
SIC 6282 Investment research
Ch: Stuart S Janny III
Pr: Karen A Zebro
CEO: Marc D Stern
VP: Jeff Gannon
Mng Dir: Stephen Kutz

BESSEMER TRUST
See BESSEMER GROUP INC

D-U-N-S 07-522-0889
BESSEMER TRUST CO NA
(Suby of BESSEMER TRUST) ★
45 Rockefeller Plz 600b, New York, NY 10111-0227
Tel (212) 708-9100 Founded/Ownrshp 1981
Sales NA EMP 170
SIC 6022 State trust companies accepting deposits, commercial
Pr: John A Hilton Jr
*CFO: John G Macdonald
Chf Inves: Rebecca Patterson
Assoc VP: Lisa Fox
Assoc VP: Jeff Gattens
Assoc VP: Ryan Gillespie
Assoc VP: Bradley Marschalk
Assoc VP: John McQuade
Assoc VP: Julie Pardue
Assoc VP: Robyn Polansky
Assoc VP: Donna Tuen
Assoc VP: Delroy Wright
Ex VP: G Clapp
Ex VP: John Trott
Sr VP: Ricardo Best
Sr VP: Robert Cermeli
Sr VP: Daniel Hayes
Sr VP: Hisham Mohamed
Sr VP: Richard Ober

Sr VP: Richard Shaw
Sr VP: WEI Wang

D-U-N-S 00-531-9173 IMP/EXP
BESSER CO (MI)
801 Johnson St, Alpena, MI 49707-1897
Tel (989) 354-4508 *Founded/Ownrshp* 1897
Sales 249.1MM[E] *EMP* 800
SIC 3531 3559 3564 3443 Concrete plants; Concrete products machinery; Dust or fume collecting equipment, industrial; Fabricated plate work (boiler shop)
CEO: Kevin L Curtis
**CFO:* Juli S Musch
S&M/VP: Rodney Lang
Sls Dir: Gary Ericson
Cust Svc D: Kari Schellie
Board of Directors: George Kuehn, Joseph McCullogh, Richard Muzzy, James Park, Kim Park

D-U-N-S 05-450-0434 IMP/EXP
BEST BRANDS CORP
CSM BAKERY SUPPLIES NORTH AMER
111 Cheshire Ln Ste 100, Saint Paul, MN 55121
Tel (952) 404-7500 *Founded/Ownrshp* 2000
Sales 219.9MM[E] *EMP* 1,000
SIC 5149 2045 2053 2052 2051

D-U-N-S 02-305-8159 IMP
▲ BEST BUY CO INC
7601 Penn Ave S, Richfield, MN 55423-3683
Tel (612) 291-1000 *Founded/Ownrshp* 1966
Sales 39.5MMM *EMP* 125,000[E]
Accts Deloitte & Touche Llp Minneap
Tkr Sym BBY *Exch* NYS
SIC 5731 5734 5735 5712 5722 Radio, television & electronic stores; Television sets; Video cameras, recorders & accessories; Consumer electronic equipment; Computer & software stores; Printers & plotters: computers; Software, computer games; Personal computers; Record & prerecorded tape stores; Video discs & tapes, prerecorded; Customized furniture & cabinets; Electric household appliances
Ch Bd: Hubert Joly
Pr: Shari L Ballard
Pr: Mary Lou Kelley
Ofcr: Paula F Baker
Ofcr: Sharon L McCollam
Ofcr: R Michael Mohan
Ofcr: Greg Revelle
Ex VP: David Morrish
Sr VP: Dave Williams
VP: Eva Mui
VP: Mathew R Watson
Board of Directors: Lisa M Caputo, J Patrick Doyle, Russell P Fradin, David W Kenny, Karen McLoughlin, Thomas L Millner, Claudia F Munce, Kathy J Higgins Victor

D-U-N-S 78-609-5484
■ BEST BUY ENTERPRISE SERVICES INC
(*Suby of* BEST BUY CO INC) ★
7601 Penn Ave S, Minneapolis, MN 55423-3683
Tel (612) 291-1000 *Founded/Ownrshp* 2002
Sales 1.3MMM[E] *EMP* 2[E]
SIC 8742 Management consulting services
CEO: Susan Hoff

BEST BUY MOBILE FAIRFAX CO
See BEST BUY STORES LP

D-U-N-S 62-487-4249 IMP
■ BEST BUY STORES LP
BEST BUY MOBILE FAIRFAX CO
(*Suby of* BBC PROPERTY CO)
7601 Penn Ave S, Richfield, MN 55423-3683
Tel (612) 291-3979 *Founded/Ownrshp* 2004
Sales 177.4MM[E] *EMP* 5,993[E]
SIC 5961 General merchandise, mail order
Pt: Brian's Whiteboard
Sls Mgr: Jason Leist
Snr Mgr: Jill Jasper

D-U-N-S 00-639-7772 IMP/EXP
BEST CHAIRS INC
COUNTY LINE DIVISION
1 Best Dr, Ferdinand, IN 47532-9233
Tel (812) 367-1761 *Founded/Ownrshp* 1962
Sales 183.4MM[E] *EMP* 875
Accts Nonte & Company Llc Jasper
SIC 2512 Chairs: upholstered on wood frames
CEO: Glenn A Lange
Pr: Brian L Lange
CFO: Steven M Wahl
Ch: Clement M Lange Jr
VP: Stuart C Curtis
VP: Joseph L Lange
VP: Mary C Lange
VP: Gregory K Sicard
VP: Sheila M Wendholt
CIO: Ronald G Swick
Netwrk Eng: Lucas Kluemper

D-U-N-S 11-312-3483 IMP
BEST CONTRACTING SERVICES INC
BCS SERVICES
19027 S Hamilton Ave, Gardena, CA 90248-4408
Tel (310) 328-6969 *Founded/Ownrshp* 1982
Sales 88.0MM[E] *EMP* 500
SIC 1761 Roofing contractor
Pr: Modjtaba Tabazadeh
**CEO:* Sean Tabazadeh
**Treas:* Fatemeh Tabazadeh
Genl Mgr: Penni Barnes
Genl Mgr: Mohammad Beigi
Genl Mgr: Sean Taba
Dir IT: Myris Guballa
IT Man: Andrew Dorman
Opers Mgr: Anne Tuliau

D-U-N-S 07-988-5318
BEST DOCTORS INSURANCE HOLDINGS LLC
5201 Blue Lagoon Dr # 300, Miami, FL 33126-2064
Tel (305) 269-2521 *Founded/Ownrshp* 2006
Sales 135.0MM[E] *EMP* 150
SIC 8011 6719 Medical insurance plan; Investment holding companies, except banks

BEST EQUIPMENT / PUMPWORKS
See BEST EQUIPMENT SERVICE & SALES CO LLC

D-U-N-S 09-351-6474
■ BEST EQUIPMENT SERVICE & SALES CO LLC
BEST EQUIPMENT / PUMPWORKS
(*Suby of* BEST HOLDINGS, LLC)
8885 Monroe Rd, Houston, TX 77061-5226
Tel (713) 956-2002 *Founded/Ownrshp* 1978
Sales 118.3MM[E] *EMP* 124
SIC 5084 Pumps & pumping equipment
Manager: Hussni Omar
Board of Directors: Ron L Wall

D-U-N-S 12-128-4181 IMP
BEST FOOD SERVICES INC
7131 W 61st St, Chicago, IL 60638-3925
Tel (773) 966-1123 *Founded/Ownrshp* 2002
Sales 115.0MM[E] *EMP* 60[E]
SIC 5149 Specialty food items
CEO: Tom Tung
**Pr:* Jimmy HEI San Kowk
Genl Mgr: Eric Kwok

D-U-N-S 07-057-6665
BEST FRIENDS PET CARE INC
19717 62nd Ave S Ste F103, Kent, WA 98032-1153
Tel (253) 981-3998 *Founded/Ownrshp* 2001
Sales 241.7MM[E] *EMP* 800
SIC 0752 0742 5999 Animal specialty services; Veterinarian, animal specialties; Pet food
Pr: John A Heyder
Ch Bd: Thomas E Martin
COO: Joan Manienan
CFO: John Hyder
Prin: Dennis Doland
Genl Mgr: Tami Chandler
Genl Mgr: Sue Sullivan
Genl Mgr: Angela Wood
Genl Mgr: Kim Young
Advt Dir: Barb Sauers

BEST LINE EQUIPMENT
See BEST LINE LEASING INC

D-U-N-S 15-379-9291
BEST LINE LEASING INC
BEST LINE EQUIPMENT
140 Hawbaker Indus Dr, State College, PA 16803-2318
Tel (814) 237-9050 *Founded/Ownrshp* 1985
Sales 124.2MM[E] *EMP* 380
SIC 5082 General construction machinery & equipment
Pr: Michael Houseknecht
**COO:* Michael Getz
Genl Mgr: Adam Houseknecht
Genl Mgr: Ryan Walk
Sfty Dirs: Kevin Gern
Mktg Dir: Robert J Henry
Sls Mgr: Craig Grove
Sls Mgr: Chris Stemler
Sales Asso: Wayne Lawrence
Sales Asso: Bob Sanso

BEST LOCK
See STANLEY SECURITY SOLUTIONS INC

D-U-N-S 02-274-6804
BEST OIL CO
LITTLE STORE , THE
30 N 8th St, Cloquet, MN 55720-1669
Tel (218) 879-0201 *Founded/Ownrshp* 1961
Sales 199.7MM[E] *EMP* 250
SIC 5171 5172 5013 5983 5541 5411 Petroleum bulk stations & terminals; Lubricating oils & greases; Motor vehicle supplies & new parts; Fuel oil dealers; Gasoline service stations; Convenience stores, chain
Pr: John Mc Kinney
CFO: Tyler Olson
**Treas:* Bruce Larson
**VP:* Christopher Mc Kinney

D-U-N-S 62-069-8357 IMP
BEST PETROLEUM CORP
Km 20 Hm 5 Rr 2, TOA Baja, PR 00951
Tel (787) 251-6218 *Founded/Ownrshp* 1986
Sales 479.6MM *EMP* 130
Accts Jesus Oyola Cuadrado Bayamon
SIC 5172 Petroleum products
Pr: Antonio De Jesus Nieves
Genl Mgr: Oscar Nieves

D-U-N-S 00-169-5758 IMP/EXP
BEST PLUMBING SUPPLY INC
BEST PLUMBING TILE & STONE
49 Route 138, Somers, NY 10589-2700
Tel (914) 232-2020 *Founded/Ownrshp* 1960
Sales 103.5MM[E] *EMP* 100
SIC 5074 5999 Plumbing & hydronic heating supplies; Heating equipment (hydronic); Plumbing fittings & supplies; Plumbing & heating supplies
Ch Bd: Jess Weiner
**Pr:* Melvin Weiner
**VP:* Jonas Weiner
IT Man: Steven Toth

BEST PLUMBING TILE & STONE
See BEST PLUMBING SUPPLY INC

D-U-N-S 00-192-6864
BEST SAND CORP (OH)
(*Suby of* FAIRMOUNT MINERALS) ★
11830 Ravenna Rd, Chardon, OH 44024-7006
Tel (440) 285-3132 *Founded/Ownrshp* 1938, 1986
Sales 129.5MM[E] *EMP* 62
SIC 1446 1442

BEST SOFTWARE SMALL BUS DIV
See PEACHTREE SOFTWARE INC

BEST TILE DISTRIBUTORS
See EAST COAST TILE IMPORTS INC

D-U-N-S 08-003-1796
BEST TRUCKING LOGISTICS INC
126 Pine Meadow Dr, Pooler, GA 31322-9353
Tel (912) 349-6869 *Founded/Ownrshp* 2013
Sales 185.5MM *EMP* 4
SIC 4789 Pipeline terminal facilities, independently operated
CEO: Moon C Kang

D-U-N-S 04-580-7195
BEST WESTERN INTERNATIONAL INC
6201 N 24th Pkwy, Phoenix, AZ 85016-2023
Tel (602) 957-4200 *Founded/Ownrshp* 1957
Sales 295.8MM[E] *EMP* 1,015
Accts Mukai Greenlee & Company Pc
SIC 7389 7311 5046 8743 Hotel & motel reservation service; Advertising agencies; Hotel equipment & supplies; Sales promotion
Pr: David Kong
**Ch Bd:* Pg West
V Ch: Raymond Johnston
V Ch: Terry Porter
Pr: Sudhir Sinha
**CFO:* Mark Straszynski
**Treas:* Julie Montmaneix
Ofcr: Greg Adams
Sr VP: Barbara Bras
Sr VP: Dorothy Dowling
**VP:* Lawrence Cuculic
VP: David Velasquez
VP: Suzi Yoder
Board of Directors: Terrance 'terry' J Bichse, Beth Campbell

BEST WSTN LK BENA VISTA RESORT
See WW LBV INC

D-U-N-S 07-941-8363
BEST YET MARKET INC
1 Lexington Ave, Bethpage, NY 11714-3121
Tel (516) 570-5300 *Founded/Ownrshp* 2013
Sales 88.4MM *EMP* 1,900
SIC 5411 Co-operative food stores
Ch Bd: Aviv Raitses
CFO: Jeffrey Yonkers
Store Mgr: John Bello
Advt Dir: Joe Sender

D-U-N-S 04-734-4429
BEST-WADE PETROLEUM INC (TN)
EXPRESS STORE
(*Suby of* EXPRESS SHOPS) ★
201 Dodge Dr, Ripley, TN 38063-8073
Tel (731) 635-9661 *Founded/Ownrshp* 1982, 2001
Sales 121.7MM[E] *EMP* 250
SIC 5171 5541 5411 Petroleum bulk stations & terminals; Gasoline service stations; Convenience stores
Pr: Maurice Gaines
**VP:* David Jennings
**VP:* Lin Thompson
Genl Mgr: Charles Hyde
VP Opers: Morris Gaines
Sls Mgr: Jeff Windham
Sales Asso: Shawn Ripley

BEST-WAY DISTRIBUTING CO
See ALLIED BEVERAGES INC

D-U-N-S 06-191-6094
BESTCARE INC (NY)
3000 Hempstead Tpke # 205, Levittown, NY 11756-1406
Tel (516) 731-3535 *Founded/Ownrshp* 1981
Sales 97.5MM[E] *EMP* 3,300
SIC 8082 Home health care services
Ch Bd: Lawrence Wiener
**Pr:* Bernhard Schiel
COO: Richard Feliciano
Dir IT: Weitzner Lynn

D-U-N-S 61-492-6962 IMP/EXP
BESTCO HOLDINGS INC
288 Mazeppa Rd, Mooresville, NC 28115-7928
Tel (704) 664-4300 *Founded/Ownrshp* 1990
Sales 127.7MM[E] *EMP* 424
SIC 2064 Candy & other confectionery products
CEO: Richard Zulman
Pr: Tim Condron
CFO: Scott Wattenberg
Ex VP: Steve Berkowitz
Ex VP: Mark Knight
Mfg Dir: Justin Shingleton

D-U-N-S 00-214-9136 IMP
BESTCO INC
(*Suby of* BESTCO HOLDINGS INC) ★
288 Mazeppa Rd, Mooresville, NC 28115-7928
Tel (704) 664-4300 *Founded/Ownrshp* 2013
Sales 106.4MM[E] *EMP* 400[E]
SIC 2023 Dietary supplements, dairy & non-dairy based
CEO: Richard Zulman
Pr: Paul Hervey
**CFO:* Victor Clark
**Ex VP:* Stephen Berkowitz
**Ex VP:* Jonathan Zulman
VP: Mark Knight
VP: Kathy Powell
Prgrm Mgr: Kelly Spang
IT Man: Elizabeth Bach
Mktg Mgr: Joe Senos
Snr Mgr: Mark Gilreath

D-U-N-S 00-708-5715 IMP/EXP
BESTOP INC
(*Suby of* MAGNA INTERNATIONAL INC)
333 Centennial Pkwy B, Louisville, CO 80027-1269
Tel (303) 465-1755 *Founded/Ownrshp* 1953, 1986
Sales 114.9MM[E] *EMP* 450
SIC 2394 3714 Convertible tops, canvas or boat: from purchased materials; Motor vehicle parts & accessories
CEO: John Larson
**CFO:* Jeff Green
VP: Daniel R Getzchman
VP: Kenneth L Holbrook
VP: Mark Nussbaumer
Sls Mgr: Brad Bricker
Sls Mgr: Richard Sabourin

BESTREADGUIDE.COM
See MORRIS COMMUNICATIONS CO LLC

BET CABLE NETWORK
See BLACK ENTERTAINMENT TELEVISION LLC

D-U-N-S 05-910-3994 IMP
BETA LASERMIKE INC
Z- MIKE
8001 Technology Blvd, Dayton, OH 45424-1568
Tel (937) 233-9935 *Founded/Ownrshp* 2005
Sales 115.0MM *EMP* 115
SIC 3545

D-U-N-S 83-896-1550 IMP
BETA STEEL LLC
6300 Hughes Dr, Sterling Heights, MI 48312-2634
Tel (586) 698-9200 *Founded/Ownrshp* 1999
Sales 83.0MM *EMP* 40[E]
SIC 5051 Steel
**Off Mgr:* Frank Spiga

D-U-N-S 00-505-0158 IMP
BETCO CORP (OH)
400 Van Camp Rd, Bowling Green, OH 43402-9062
Tel (419) 241-2156 *Founded/Ownrshp* 1950
Sales 138.2MM[E] *EMP* 250
SIC 6719 Investment holding companies, except banks
CEO: Paul C Betz
COO: Greg Chesnutt
COO: Terry Huber
**CFO:* Tony Lyons
CFO: Sharon Murdock
Sr VP: Robert Gail
Sr VP: Denise Lennard
VP: Dan Carr
VP: Jeff Iverson
VP: John Reed
CIO: Carol Hoffman

D-U-N-S 07-992-0435
BETH ABRAHAM HEALTH SERVICES
BETHCO
(*Suby of* CENTERLIGHT HEALTHCARE INC) ★
2540 Barker Ave Ofc, Bronx, NY 10467-7482
Tel (718) 519-5831 *Founded/Ownrshp* 1920
Sales 157.1MM[E] *EMP* 3,000
Accts Loeb & Troper Llp New York N
SIC 8059 8351 8082 Nursing home, except skilled & intermediate care facility; Child day care services; Home health care services
Pr: Michael Fassler
**Pr:* Michael S Fassler
**CFO:* Ira Green
**Ch:* Marvin Factor
**Ch:* Michael R Potack
**Treas:* Stephen Mann
Bd of Dir: Linda Murray
VP: Karen Eastmond
Dir Soc: Robin Tucker
Sys/Dir: William Frohlich
Sys/Dir: Paul B Wigsten Jr

D-U-N-S 06-979-2648
BETH ISRAEL DEACONESS HOSPITAL - MILTON INC
199 Reedsdale Rd, Milton, MA 02186-3926
Tel (617) 696-4600 *Founded/Ownrshp* 1903
Sales 84.5MM *EMP* 77[E]
Accts Deloitte Tax Llp Jericho Ny
SIC 8011 Medical centers
Pr: Peter J Healy

D-U-N-S 86-743-8061
BETH ISRAEL DEACONESS HOSPITAL - PLYMOUTH INC
275 Sandwich St, Plymouth, MA 02360-2183
Tel (508) 746-2000 *Founded/Ownrshp* 1901
Sales 187.1MM *EMP* 3[E]
SIC 8082 Home health care services
Pr: Peter J Holden
COO: Margaret Oconnor
COO: Denise Smith
CFO: Jason Radzevich
Treas: Kevin Feeney
**Treas:* Joseph Iannoni
Chf Mktg O: Bernard Durante
Ofcr: Peter W Holden Jr
VP: Lisa L Mennonna
Dir Lab: Bob Hardy
Dir Rad: Justino Fernandes
Dir Rad: James Galvin
Dir Rad: Ken Kelly

D-U-N-S 07-172-3621 IMP
BETH ISRAEL DEACONESS MEDICAL CENTER INC
BIDMC
(*Suby of* CAREGROUP INC) ★
330 Brookline Ave, Boston, MA 02215-5400
Tel (617) 667-7000 *Founded/Ownrshp* 1996
Sales 1.2MMM *EMP* 6,500
SIC 8062 General medical & surgical hospitals; Hospital, medical school affiliation
Pr: Kevin Tabb
Pr: Eric Buehrens
COO: Nancy Formella
CFO: Steve Fischer
CFO: Steven Fischer
Treas: Allan Bufferd
Ofcr: Karen Foulkrod
Ofcr: Marsha Maurer
Ofcr: Patricia Thurston
Sr VP: Paul Donovan
Sr VP: John D Halamka
Sr VP: Kristine Laping
Dir Bus: Brian Connolly
Comm Man: Patrice Taddonio

D-U-N-S 07-525-5364 IMP
BETH ISRAEL MEDICAL CENTER
BETH ISRAEL SCHOOL OF NURSING
First Ave 16th St, New York, NY 10003
Tel (212) 420-2806 *Founded/Ownrshp* 1890
Sales 1.0MMM[E] *EMP* 8,100
Accts Pricewaterhousecoopers Llp Ne
SIC 8062 8063 General medical & surgical hospitals; Psychiatric hospitals
Pr: Robert G Newman MD
CFO: Frank Cracolici

Trst: Edwin Levy
Ofcr: John Collura
Ofcr: Lou Schenkel
**Ex VP:* Thomas J Hayes
VP: Hope Bellingham
VP: Marc Hall
VP: Barbara King
VP: Mitchell Leone
Prin: Marisa Steffers

BETH ISRAEL SCHOOL OF NURSING
See BETH ISRAEL MEDICAL CENTER

D-U-N-S 08-035-0796
BETHANY CHRISTIAN SERVICES
901 Eastern Ave Ne, Grand Rapids, MI 49503-1201
Tel (616) 224-7550 *Founded/Ownrshp* 1945
Sales 12.8MM *EMP* 1,100
Accts Bethany Christian Services Gr
SIC 8322 Individual & family services
CEO: William J Balcquiere
IT Man: Robert Van Putten
Pgrm Dir: Rich Gritter
Board of Directors: Marvin Auchtung, Cortez Cooper, Gary Kuyper, Jack V Ploeg, Jack Van Der

D-U-N-S 08-039-6515
BETHANY CHRISTIAN SERVICES USA LLC
(*Suby of* BETHANY CHRISTIAN SERVICES) ★
901 Eastern Ave Ne, Grand Rapids, MI 49503-1295
Tel (616) 224-7610 *Founded/Ownrshp* 2011
Sales 15.8MM^E *EMP* 1,000^E
SIC 8322 Individual & family services

D-U-N-S 07-405-8918
BETHANY CIRCLE OF KINGS DAUGHTERS OF MADISON INDIANA INC
KINGS DAUGHTERS HEALTH
1373 E Sr 62, Madison, IN 47250-7328
Tel (812) 801-0800 *Founded/Ownrshp* 1899
Sales 102.2MM *EMP* 1,000
SIC 8062 8011 8082 General medical & surgical hospitals; Medical centers; Home health care services
VP: Lisa Morgan
Ofcr: Joy Yager
**VP:* Denine Fallis-Hallgarth
VP: Denine Hallgarth
VP: Larry Keith
**VP:* Holly Robinson
Genl Mgr: Nadja Boone
Genl Mgr: Stacy Dennings
Off Mgr: Denine Hallgrath
Off Admin: Julie Applegate
Off Admin: Laurie Livorno

BETHCO
See BETH ABRAHAM HEALTH SERVICES

D-U-N-S 08-519-6053
BETHEL SCHOOL DISTRICT
516 176th St E, Spanaway, WA 98387-8335
Tel (253) 683-6000 *Founded/Ownrshp* 1950
Sales 228.4MM *EMP* 2,000
SIC 8211 Public elementary & secondary schools
**CFO:* Harvey Erickson
**VP:* Stanley E Chapin
**VP:* Brenda Rogers
Genl Mgr: Wendy Howard
Psych: Michael Kirlin
Snr Mgr: Michael Rushton

D-U-N-S 03-940-8547
BETHEL UNIVERSITY
325 Cherry Ave, Mc Kenzie, TN 38201-1769
Tel (731) 352-4000 *Founded/Ownrshp* 1842
Sales 93.4MM *EMP* 117
SIC 8221 5942 College, except junior; College book stores
Pr: Walter Butler
CFO: Joey Stoner
VP: Rus Andrews
Assoc Dir: Terika Anderson
Assoc Dir: Gina Evans
Assoc Dir: Barry McBride
**Prin:* Robert Prosser
Genl Mgr: Sandra Ashley
Off Mgr: Jennifer Bolin
Store Mgr: Dawn Ervin
Dir IT: Wanda McMackin

D-U-N-S 07-177-7692
BETHEL UNIVERSITY
3900 Bethel Dr, Saint Paul, MN 55112-6902
Tel (651) 638-6400 *Founded/Ownrshp* 1871
Sales 103.4MM *EMP* 720
Accts Clifton Larson Allen Llp Minn
SIC 8221 College, except junior; Theological seminary
Pr: James Barnes
CFO: John Bergeson
Ofcr: Harrison Hitt
Assoc Dir: Terry Morris
Cmptr Lab: Robert Ramgren
IT Man: Joseph Herter
IT Man: Gavin House
Netwrk Eng: Ray Lu
Prd Mgr: Michele Hamersma
Pr Mgr: Joe Laluzerne
Pgrm Dir: Laura Gilbertson

BETHESDA CARE
See GENESIS HEALTHCARE SYSTEM

D-U-N-S 06-463-8190
BETHESDA HEALTH GROUP INC
BETHESDA SENIOR LIVING
1630 Des Peres Rd Ste 290, Saint Louis, MO 63131-1800
Tel (314) 800-1900 *Founded/Ownrshp* 1889
Sales 74.6MM *EMP* 1,121
Accts Clifton Larson Allen Llp Sain
SIC 8052 Personal care facility
Pr: Joseph Brinker
Sr VP: Roger Byrne
**Sr VP:* Katherine Joslin
Sr VP: Patricia Kapsar
**Sr VP:* Al Poelker
**Sr VP:* Amy Trau
VP: Scott Middelkamp
Ex Dir: Tom Miskle

Genl Mgr: Michelle Glass
CIO: Larry Hickman
IT Man: Jill Roethler

D-U-N-S 07-135-8519
BETHESDA HEALTHEAST HOSPITAL
HEALTHEAST CORPORATE
(*Suby of* HEALTHEAST CORPORATE) ★
559 Capitol Blvd Fl 6, Saint Paul, MN 55103-2101
Tel (651) 232-2000 *Founded/Ownrshp* 1895
Sales 81.2MM *EMP* 5,500
SIC 8062 8741 8069 General medical & surgical hospitals; Hospital management; Nursing & personal care facility management; Specialty hospitals, except psychiatric
Pr: Timothy Hanson
**VP:* Robert Gill
CIO: Mac McClurkan
CIO: Darlene McDonough

D-U-N-S 05-286-1614
BETHESDA HOSPITAL ASSOCIATION INC
2951 Maple Ave, Zanesville, OH 43701-1465
Tel (740) 454-4000 *Founded/Ownrshp* 1983
Sales 187.4M *EMP* 1,100
Accts Plante & Moran Pllc Columbus
SIC 8062 8063 8082 General medical & surgical hospitals; Psychiatric hospitals; Home health care services
Pr: Thomas Sieber
**COO:* Charles Hunter
**CFO:* Paul Masterson

D-U-N-S 07-288-2756
BETHESDA HOSPITAL INC
TRIHEALTH HOSPITAL
(*Suby of* TRIHEALTH HOSPITAL) ★
619 Oak St, Cincinnati, OH 45206-1690
Tel (513) 569-6100 *Founded/Ownrshp* 1896
Sales 551.9MM *EMP* 3,000
Accts Bkd Llp Cincinnati Oh
SIC 8062 General medical & surgical hospitals
Pr: John Prout
Chf OB: Alan P Oltman
COO: Sher A Mc Clanahan
**CFO:* Craig Rucker
Surgeon: Nicholas S Mirkopoulos
Ansthlgy: Elizabeth Burgess
Corp Couns: Donna Nenaber

D-U-N-S 13-210-4829
BETHESDA HOSPITAL INC
BETHESDA HOSPITAL WEST
(*Suby of* BETHESDA HEALTH, INC.)
2815 S Seacrest Blvd, Boynton Beach, FL 33435-7995
Tel (561) 737-7733 *Founded/Ownrshp* 1959
Sales 287.5MM *EMP* 304
SIC 8062 General medical & surgical hospitals
Pr: Roger L Kirk
**CFO:* Joanne Aquilina
Sec: Elizabeth Rivera-Vazquez
VP: Al Beihl
**VP:* Robert Broadway
VP: Mary E McClory
VP: Robert Taylor
Dir Rad: Lori Jalens
Adm Dir: Valerie Coniglio
Adm Dir: Frances T Lutz
Ex Dir: Scott E Classen

BETHESDA HOSPITAL WEST
See BETHESDA HOSPITAL INC

D-U-N-S 11-288-6429
BETHESDA INC
TRIHEALTH HOSPITAL
(*Suby of* CHI) ★
619 Oak St 7n, Cincinnati, OH 45206-1613
Tel (513) 569-6400 *Founded/Ownrshp* 1982
Sales 17.6MM *EMP* 5,543
Accts Bkd Llp Cincinnati Oh
SIC 8062 General medical & surgical hospitals
Pr: J James Pearce Jr
**Treas:* William A Tsacalis
**VP:* Chip Crowther

D-U-N-S 78-640-6793
BETHESDA INVESTMENT HOLDING CO INC
JAME COLEMAN CADILLAC
10400 Auto Park Ave, Bethesda, MD 20817-1006
Tel (301) 469-6600 *Founded/Ownrshp* 1989
Sales 109.9MM^E *EMP* 212^E
SIC 5511 7539 5013 5531 Automobiles, new & used; Automotive repair shops; Motor vehicle supplies & new parts; Automobile & truck equipment & parts
Pr: James R Coleman
**Ch Bd:* William H Coleman Jr
Genl Mgr: Greg Raynor
Genl Mgr: Kurt Rodgers

D-U-N-S 07-384-3419
BETHESDA LUTHERAN COMMUNITIES INC
600 Hoffmann Dr, Watertown, WI 53094-6223
Tel (920) 261-3050 *Founded/Ownrshp* 1904
Sales 126.5MM *EMP* 3,106
Accts Baker Tilly Virchow Krause Llp
SIC 8361 Residential care
CEO: Mike Thirtle
**CFO:* Jack Tobias
**VP:* Jeff Kaczmarski

BETHESDA SENIOR LIVING
See BETHESDA HEALTH GROUP INC

D-U-N-S 02-094-9485
BETHESDA-CHEVY CHASE CHAPTER IZAAK WALTON LEAGUE OF AMERICA (MD)
B-CCIWLA
20601 Izaak Walton Way, Poolesville, MD 20837
Tel (301) 972-8913 *Founded/Ownrshp* 2008
Sales 844.9M *EMP* 1,000
Accts Michael Meyer & Associates Pc
SIC 8641 Environmental protection organization
Prin: Byron Ricketts
**Pr:* Ernest W Smith

D-U-N-S 07-361-5668
BETHLEHEM AREA SCHOOL DISTRICT
EDUCATION CENTER
1516 Sycamore St, Bethlehem, PA 18017-6037
Tel (610) 807-5571 *Founded/Ownrshp* 1890
Sales 114.5MM^E *EMP* 1,650
Accts Gorman & Associates Pc Nor
SIC 8211 Public elementary & secondary schools
Psych: Lori Skripek
HC Dir: Kathy Hawkins

D-U-N-S 06-803-5161
BETHPAGE FEDERAL CREDIT UNION INC
899 S Oyster Bay Rd, Bethpage, NY 11714-1031
Tel (516) 349-6700 *Founded/Ownrshp* 1941
Sales NA *EMP* 309
SIC 6061 Federal credit unions
Ch: Philip Gandolfo
COO: Wayne Gross
**CFO:* Brian Clarke
**Treas:* Don Balducci
Assoc VP: Thomas Layer
Sr VP: Robert Hoppenstedt
VP: Diane Krieger
VP: Tamika Mendoza
VP: Jerry Schmitt
VP: Linda Ward
Exec: Michelle Latorre
Exec: Peter Letizia
Assoc Dir: Arnold Sparr

D-U-N-S 06-472-2945
BETHPAGE UNION FREE SCHOOL DISTRICT
10 Cherry Ave, Bethpage, NY 11714-1501
Tel (516) 644-4100 *Founded/Ownrshp* 1927
Sales 84.1MM *EMP* 575
Accts Cullen & Danowski Llp Port J
SIC 8211 Public elementary school; Public junior high school; Public senior high school
**Treas:* Laurie Baum
Bd of Dir: Micheal Kelly
Prin: Angelita Cintado

D-U-N-S 07-831-5918
BETHUNE-COOKMAN UNIVERSITY INC (FL)
640 Dr Mary Mcleod Bethun, Daytona Beach, FL 32114-3012
Tel (386) 481-2000 *Founded/Ownrshp* 1904
Sales 91.9MM *EMP* 600
Accts Cross Fernandez & Riley Llp O
SIC 8221 College, except junior
Pr: Edison O Jackson
**Pr:* Trudie Kibbe Reed
VP: Clara Acker
VP: Pamela Browne
VP: Valerie Collman
**VP:* Ronald Dowdy
VP: Dorcas McCoy
VP: Shelly Rice
VP: Willis Walter
Off Mgr: Mary J Drayton
CIO: Franklin G Patterson

BETMAR
See BOLLMAN HAT CO

BETSON ENTERPRISES DIVISION
See H BETTI INDUSTRIES INC

BETSY JOHNSON REGIONAL HOSPITA
See HARNETT HEALTH SYSTEM INC

D-U-N-S 80-431-3633
BETT-A-WAY TRAFFIC SYSTEMS INC
BETTAWAY
110 Sylvania Pl, South Plainfield, NJ 07080-1448
Tel (908) 222-2500 *Founded/Ownrshp* 1982
Sales 104.7MM^E *EMP* 50
SIC 4731 Truck transportation brokers
Prin: Betty Vaccaro
**Treas:* June Delaney
Dir IT: Anthony Vaccaro
Opers Mgr: Dennis Yost

BETTAWAY
See BETT-A-WAY TRAFFIC SYSTEMS INC

BETTE & CRING CNSTR GROUP
See BETTE & CRING LLC

D-U-N-S 08-797-3439 IMP
BETTE & CRING LLC
BETTE & CRING CNSTR GROUP
22 Century Hill Dr # 201, Latham, NY 12110-2137
Tel (518) 213-1010 *Founded/Ownrshp* 1999
Sales 120.0MM *EMP* 350
SIC 1541 1542 1622 1611 Industrial buildings & warehouses; Commercial & office building contractors; Institutional building construction; Bridge construction; Highway & street construction
CFO: Ralph Silipo
Exec: Jean Derouin
Genl Mgr: John Moynihan
Prd Mgr: Tony Corradi
Snr PM: Michael Russo
Snr PM: Mark Scott

D-U-N-S 04-982-7884
BETTER BAKED FOODS INC
(*Suby of* NE FOODS INC) ★
56 Smedley St, North East, PA 16428-1632
Tel (814) 725-8778 *Founded/Ownrshp* 1988
Sales 88.3MM^E *EMP* 350
SIC 2051 Bread, cake & related products
Ch Bd: Christopher R Miller
Pr: Joseph Pacinelli
VP: Brad Harrison
IT Exec: Jim Zaranek

BETTER BRANDS
See GREAT STATE BEVERAGES INC

D-U-N-S 11-531-0013
■ **BETTER WAY PARTNERS LLC**
BETTER WAY PRODUCTS
(*Suby of* CANA) ★
70891 County Road 23, New Paris, IN 46553-9771
Tel (574) 831-3340 *Founded/Ownrshp* 2015
Sales 109.5MM^E *EMP* 420
SIC 3089 Laminating of plastic

BETTER WAY PRODUCTS
See BETTER WAY PARTNERS LLC

D-U-N-S 05-643-6751
BETTERAVIA FARMS LLC
1850 W Stowell Rd, Santa Maria, CA 93458-9719
Tel (805) 925-2585 *Founded/Ownrshp* 1963
Sales 267.6MM^E *EMP* 250^E
SIC 0161

BETTERECYCLING
See BETTEROADS ASPHALT CORP

D-U-N-S 09-000-9002 IMP/EXP
BETTEROADS ASPHALT CORP
BETTERECYCLING
Edif Empresas Diaz, San Juan, PR 00926
Tel (787) 760-1050 *Founded/Ownrshp* 1954
Sales 92.7MM^E *EMP* 500
Accts Jorge Torres Valles San Juan
SIC 1611 2951 Highway & street paving contractor; Asphalt paving mixtures & blocks
Pr: Jorge Diaz
**Pr:* Arturo Diaz Jr
VP: Miguel Guerra

D-U-N-S 15-525-4618 IMP
BEVERAGE DISTRIBUTORS CO LLC
PINNACLE DISTRIBUTING COMPANY
14200 E Moncrieff Pl, Aurora, CO 80011-1647
Tel (303) 371-3421 *Founded/Ownrshp* 1999
Sales 248.4MM^E *EMP* 400
SIC 5182 Liquor; Wine
Pr: Joseph Marotta
COO: Brian Boronkay
**CFO:* Justin Voigts
**VP:* Don Kiwor
**VP:* Mark Krantz
**VP:* Jeremy Tostrup
Sls Mgr: Stephen Anzalone
Sls Mgr: Craig Judge
Sls Mgr: Nancy Thibodeau
Doctor: Marne Obenauer MD

BEVERAGE SOUTH CAROLINA
See BEN ARNOLD-SUNBELT BEVERAGE CO OF SOUTH CAROLINA L P

D-U-N-S 82-851-7560 IMP
BEVERAGE-AIR CORP
BEVERAGE-AIR'S
(*Suby of* ALI SPA)
3779 Champion Blvd, Winston Salem, NC 27105-2667
Tel (336) 245-6400 *Founded/Ownrshp* 2008
Sales 292.8MM^E *EMP* 350
SIC 5078 Beverage coolers
CEO: Filippo Berti
**Pr:* Rob August
VP: Bill Siskar
VP: Jennifer Ward
Dir IT: Laurie O'Neil
IT Man: Rob Anderson
Sls Dir: Erica Motes

BEVERAGE-AIR'S
See BEVERAGE-AIR CORP

D-U-N-S 82-694-3268 IMP
BEVERAGES & MORE INC
BEVMO
(*Suby of* BEVMO HOLDINGS LLC) ★
1401 Willow Pass Rd # 900, Concord, CA 94520-7982
Tel (925) 609-6000 *Founded/Ownrshp* 2007
Sales 134.5MM^E *EMP* 50
SIC 5921 5499 5993 Liquor stores; Beverage stores; Gourmet food stores; Cigar store
CEO: Dimitri Haloulos
**CEO:* James R Simpson
**CFO:* Mandy Fields
**Ofcr:* Tamara Pattison
**Ex VP:* David Richards
Sr VP: Frank Braudrick
**Sr VP:* Peter Grossman
Sr VP: Michael Hester
**Sr VP:* Steven R McLaren
VP: Keymonica Johnson
Genl Mgr: Brian O'Neill

D-U-N-S 60-388-6651
BEVERAGES HOLDINGS LLC
10300 Alliance Rd Ste 500, Blue Ash, OH 45242-4767
Tel (513) 483-3300 *Founded/Ownrshp* 2004
Sales 138.5MM^E *EMP* 860^E
SIC 2086 2037 Fruit drinks (less than 100% juice): packaged in cans, etc.; Carbonated beverages, nonalcoholic: bottled & canned; Fruit juice concentrates, frozen
CEO: Billy William B Cyr
Software D: David Daiker
VP Mfg: Daniel Sileo
Mktg Mgr: Geoff Randolph
Snr Mgr: Sherry Kinzalow

D-U-N-S 07-415-0459
BEVERLY COMMUNITY HOSPITAL ASSOCIATION
BEVERLY HOSPITAL
309 W Beverly Blvd, Montebello, CA 90640-4308
Tel (323) 726-1222 *Founded/Ownrshp* 1949
Sales 176.9MM *EMP* 995^E
SIC 8062 General medical & surgical hospitals
CEO: Gary Kiff
Chf Rad: Karen Ragland
Pr: Luis Sanchez
CFO: Narci Egan
CFO: Larry Pugh
**Treas:* Renee D Martinez
Sr VP: Wendy Beesley
VP: Marlene Burnett
Dir Inf Cn: Rita Willis
Dir Rx: Wayne Campbell
CIO: Roney Cobarrubias

BEVERLY CRAFTS & FABRICS
See BEVERLY FABRICS INC

D-U-N-S 03-927-0199
BEVERLY ENTERPRISES - ALABAMA INC
BEVERLY HEALTH CARE
(*Suby of* GOLDEN LIVING CTRS COMMUNITIES) ★
One Thousand Beverly Way, Fort Smith, AR 72919-0001
Tel (479) 201-2000 *Founded/Ownrshp* 1982
Sales 5.1MM[E] *EMP* 1,000
SIC 8082 8051 Home health care services; Skilled nursing care facilities
Pr: Bill Floyd
**Sr VP:* Schuyler Hollingsworth Jr
**VP:* John Grobmyer
**VP:* Steven Hammer
**VP:* John Mackenzie
**VP:* Fredric Mass
**VP:* David Merrel
IT Man: Bridger Carroll

D-U-N-S 78-324-5137
BEVERLY ENTERPRISES - ARKANSAS INC
(*Suby of* GOLDEN LIVING CTRS COMMUNITIES) ★
1000 Fianna Way, Fort Smith, AR 72919-9008
Tel (479) 636-6285 *Founded/Ownrshp* 1982
Sales 55.9MM[E] *EMP* 5,086
SIC 8051 Skilled nursing care facilities
CEO: Salvatore F Salamone
Genl Couns: Doug Babb

D-U-N-S 08-926-6076
BEVERLY ENTERPRISES - INDIANA INC
(*Suby of* GOLDEN LIVING CTRS COMMUNITIES) ★
1000 Fianna Way, Fort Smith, AR 72919-9008
Tel (479) 201-2000 *Founded/Ownrshp* 1982
Sales 15.8MM[E] *EMP* 1,000
SIC 8051 Skilled nursing care facilities
Pr: Julianne Williams-Vink
**Ch Bd:* David R Banks
**VP:* Robert Pommerville
**VP:* John B Pool
**VP:* James T Williams

D-U-N-S 03-927-3235
BEVERLY ENTERPRISES - MINNESOTA LLC
HILLCREST REHAB HLTH CARE CTR
(*Suby of* GOLDEN LIVING CTRS COMMUNITIES) ★
650 Ramer Ave S, Rush City, MN 55069
Tel (320) 358-4765 *Founded/Ownrshp* 2002
Sales 20.6MM[E] *EMP* 1,000
SIC 8051 Skilled nursing care facilities
Pr: David R Devereaux
VP: John R Gobmye
**VP:* John R Grobmyer
**VP:* Dwight C Kouri
**VP:* David G Merrell
**VP:* Kevin M Roberts

D-U-N-S 08-410-4827
BEVERLY ENTERPRISES - MISSOURI INC
(*Suby of* GOLDEN LIVING CTRS COMMUNITIES) ★
1000 Fianna Way, Fort Smith, AR 72919-9008
Tel (479) 201-2000 *Founded/Ownrshp* 1982
Sales 15.0MM[E] *EMP* 1,400
SIC 8051 8059 Extended care facility; Convalescent home

D-U-N-S 03-927-1684
BEVERLY ENTERPRISES - VIRGINIA INC
(*Suby of* GOLDEN LIVING CTRS COMMUNITIES) ★
1 1000 Beverly Way, Fort Smith, AR 72919-0001
Tel (479) 201-2000 *Founded/Ownrshp* 1982
Sales 8.7MM[E] *EMP* 1,200
SIC 8082 8051 Home health care services; Skilled nursing care facilities
Pr: William Floyd

D-U-N-S 02-335-4186
BEVERLY ENTERPRISES - WISCONSIN INC
FIELDVIEW MANOR
(*Suby of* GOLDEN LIVING CTRS COMMUNITIES) ★
1000 Fianna Way, Fort Smith, AR 72919-9008
Tel (479) 201-2000 *Founded/Ownrshp* 1983
Sales 17.1MM[E] *EMP* 2,925
SIC 8051 Skilled nursing care facilities
CEO: Salvatore F Salamone

D-U-N-S 04-933-4683
BEVERLY ENTERPRISES INC
BEVERLY HEALTHCARE
(*Suby of* GOLDEN LIVING) ★
1000 Fianna Way, Fort Smith, AR 72919-9008
Tel (479) 201-2000 *Founded/Ownrshp* 2006
Sales 119.0M[E] *EMP* 34,300
Accts Ernst & Young Llp Rogers Ar
SIC 8741 8051 8082 Nursing & personal care facility management; Skilled nursing care facilities; Home health care services
Pr: Neil Kurtz
CFO: Darlene Burch
Treas: Shelly Henson
Treas: Michael Morton
Ex VP: Douglas J Babb
Ex VP: Jerald T Moore
Sr VP: Patrice K Acosta
Sr VP: Teresa Keller
Sr VP: Belinda Marcotte
VP: Michael Jeffries
VP: William Meenan

D-U-N-S 11-856-4871
BEVERLY ENTERPRISES-OHIO INC
(*Suby of* GOLDEN LIVING CTRS COMMUNITIES) ★
1 Thousand Beverly Way, Fort Smith, AR 72919-0001
Tel (479) 201-2000 *Founded/Ownrshp* 1982
Sales 6.7MM[E] *EMP* 1,250
SIC 8059 Convalescent home
Pr: David R Banks
Ch Bd: Diana Franklin
**CFO:* Scott Tabakin

D-U-N-S 78-324-5681
BEVERLY ENTERPRISES-PENNSYLVANIA INC
(*Suby of* GOLDEN LIVING CTRS COMMUNITIES) ★
1000 Fianna Way, Fort Smith, AR 72919-9008
Tel (479) 201-2000 *Founded/Ownrshp* 1994
Sales 59.9MM[E] *EMP* 4,000
SIC 8051 Convalescent home with continuous nursing care
CEO: Randy Churchey
**Treas:* Richard Skelly

D-U-N-S 04-372-7999 IMP/EXP
BEVERLY FABRICS INC (CA)
BEVERLY CRAFTS & FABRICS
9019 Soquel Dr Ste 175, Aptos, CA 95003-4056
Tel (831) 684-4220 *Founded/Ownrshp* 1968
Sales 102.6MM[E] *EMP* 750
SIC 5945 5949 Arts & crafts supplies; Sewing, needlework & piece goods
CEO: Robert Sleeper
**Pr:* Donald Sleeper
**CFO:* Kristi Zuniga
VP: Bruce Bostock
**VP:* Beverly Sleeper
Exec: Cathy Sleeper
IT Man: Jerry McCorkle
Board of Directors: Richard Sleeper

BEVERLY HEALTH CARE
See BEVERLY ENTERPRISES - ALABAMA INC

BEVERLY HEALTHCARE
See HOMECARE PREFERRED CHOICE INC

BEVERLY HEALTHCARE
See BEVERLY ENTERPRISES INC

D-U-N-S 01-115-6150 IMP
BEVERLY HILLS BANCORP INC
333 S Grand Ave Ste 4070, Los Angeles, CA 90071-1544
Tel (818) 223-8084 *Founded/Ownrshp* 1996
Sales NA *EMP* 47
SIC 6022 State commercial banks
Ch Bd: Larry B Faigin
CFO: Takeo K Sasaki
Exec: Kathleen Rosenberg
CTO: John Kardos
Board of Directors: Howard Amster, Stephen P Glennon, Kathleen L Kellogg, William D King, John J Lannan

BEVERLY HOSPITAL
See NORTHEAST HOSPITAL CORP

BEVERLY HOSPITAL
See BEVERLY COMMUNITY HOSPITAL ASSOCIATION

BEVERLY HOSPITAL
See NORTHEAST HEALTH SYSTEMS INC

BEVERLY HOSPITAL
See STEVEN LAVERTY

D-U-N-S 00-598-6690 IMP/EXP
BEVERLY RICARDO HILLS INC (WA)
6329 S 226th St Unit 101, Kent, WA 98032-4817
Tel (425) 207-1900 *Founded/Ownrshp* 1980
Sales 95.0MM *EMP* 50[E]
SIC 5099

BEVMO
See BEVERAGES & MORE INC

D-U-N-S 79-665-1300
BEVMO HOLDINGS LLC
(*Suby of* TOWERBROOK CAPITAL PARTNERS LP) ★
1470 Civic Ct Ste 1600, Concord, CA 94520-5242
Tel (925) 609-6000 *Founded/Ownrshp* 2007
Sales 143.2MM[E] *EMP* 1,111
SIC 5921 5499 5993 Liquor stores; Beverage stores; Cigar store
Pr: James Rsimpson
CFO: Daniel Carter
**Chf Mktg O:* Michelle Farabaugh
Ex VP: Douglas J Ratto
Sr VP: Peter Chai
Sr VP: Janet Tucker
VP: Bob Graham
Prgrm Mgr: Jason Pappas
Genl Mgr: Craig Chan
Dir IT: Aaron Deruntz

D-U-N-S 01-052-8560
BEXAR COUNTY BOARD OF TRUSTEES FOR MENTAL HEALTH MENTAL RETARDATION
CENTER FOR HEALTH CARE SVCS
3031 W Interstate 10, San Antonio, TX 78201-5159
Tel (210) 261-1000 *Founded/Ownrshp* 1965
Sales 91.5MM *EMP* 625
Accts Garza/Gonzales & Associates S
SIC 8361 8093 Home for the physically handicapped; Home for the mentally retarded; Specialty outpatient clinics; Mental health clinic, outpatient
CEO: Leon Evans
VP: Allison Greer
Off Mgr: Nancy Villarreal
Ql Cn Mgr: Joaquin Martinez
Psych: Rudy Rodriguez
Doctor: Brian Clark

D-U-N-S 96-674-2921
BEXAR COUNTY CLINICAL SERVICES INC
2801 Via Fortuna Ste 500, Austin, TX 78746-7573
Tel (512) 899-3995 *Founded/Ownrshp* 2006
Sales 86.4MM *EMP* 2
Accts Mikeska Monahan & Peckham Pc
SIC 8072 8071 Dental laboratories; Medical laboratories

D-U-N-S 06-944-6656 IMP
BEXAR COUNTY HOSPITAL DISTRICT
UNIVERSITY HEALTH SYSTEM
4502 Medical Dr Ms651, San Antonio, TX 78229-4402
Tel (210) 358-4000 *Founded/Ownrshp* 1955
Sales 496.9MM[E] *EMP* 3,998
SIC 8062 8011 General medical & surgical hospitals; Medical centers
Pr: George B Hernndez Jr
Dir Vol: Tracey Carrizales
Dir Vol: Ericka Garcia
**CEO:* Tim Brierty
**CFO:* Peggy Demming
CFO: David Salisbury
**Ex VP:* Bryan Alsip
**Ex VP:* Christann Vasquez
VP: Sergio Farrell
VP: Sherry Johnson
VP: Leni Kirkman
VP: Mary Mote
VP: Allen Strickland
VP: Roberto Villarreal
VP: Mark Webb
Dir Lab: Kathleen Born
Dir Lab: Vivian Mahony

D-U-N-S 07-100-4993
BEXAR COUNTY MARKETS INC
HANDY ANDY
(*Suby of* 2ML REAL ESTATE INTERESTS INC) ★
340 Enrque M Barrera Pkwy, San Antonio, TX 78237-1849
Tel (210) 227-8755 *Founded/Ownrshp* 2000
Sales 126.3MM[E] *EMP* 1,000
SIC 5411 Supermarkets; Co-operative food stores

D-U-N-S 05-631-0097
BEXAR METROPOLITAN WATER DISTRICT PUBLIC FACILITY CORP
BEXARMET WATER DISTRICT
2047 W Malone Ave, San Antonio, TX 78225-2017
Tel (210) 233-2335 *Founded/Ownrshp* 1945
Sales 130.4MM[E] *EMP* 476
Accts Garza/Gonzales & Assocites Cp
SIC 4941 Water supply
Pr: Guatalupe Lopez
CFO: Jerry Gonzales
**CFO:* Jesse Morin
VP: Dean Perry
Genl Mgr: F G Olivares

BEXARMET WATER DISTRICT
See BEXAR METROPOLITAN WATER DISTRICT PUBLIC FACILITY CORP

BEYER, DON VOLVO
See BEYER MOTORS INC DON

D-U-N-S 06-677-2898
BEYER MOTORS INC DON
BEYER, DON VOLVO
118 Gordon Rd, Falls Church, VA 22046-4605
Tel (703) 237-5000 *Founded/Ownrshp* 1974
Sales 112.5MM[E] *EMP* 300
SIC 5511 Automobiles, new & used
Pr: Michael S Beyer
Sr Cor Off: Robin Bruner
VP: Donald S Beyer Jr
Exec: Michelle Blackburn
Exec: Ileana Ghergu
Genl Mgr: Jared Beyer
Genl Mgr: Jordy Coho
Off Mgr: Sandy Proteau
IT Man: Bruce Bortle
IT Man: Andrey Martinkov
Sales Exec: Mike Turner

D-U-N-S 06-982-5461
BEZTAK CO (INC)
BEZTAK PROPERTIES
31731 Northwstrn Hwy 25 Ste 250W, Farmington Hills, MI 48334
Tel (248) 855-5400 *Founded/Ownrshp* 1972
Sales 120.4MM[E] *EMP* 306
SIC 6552 Land subdividers & developers, commercial; Land subdividers & developers, residential
Pr: Elizabeth J Carlson
**Ex VP:* Bob Goyette
**VP:* Rita Nelson
**Prin:* Harold Beznos
**Prin:* Nina D Luptak

BEZTAK PROPERTIES
See BEZTAK CO (INC)

BF GOODRICH AVIONICS SYS
See L-3 COMMUNICATIONS AVIONICS SYSTEMS INC

D-U-N-S 07-781-1990
BF SAUL PROPERTY CO
(*Suby of* B F SAUL CO) ★
7501 Wisconsin Ave, Bethesda, MD 20814-6519
Tel (301) 986-6000 *Founded/Ownrshp* 1974
Sales 45.4MM[E] *EMP* 1,600[E]
SIC 6531 6519 1542 152 Real estate managers; Real property lessors; Commercial & office building, new construction; Apartment building construction
Treas: Joel R Friedman
VP: Bryon Barlow
Mktg Dir: Sarah Deam

D-U-N-S 05-991-0968
▲ BFC FINANCIAL CORP
HOFFMAN'S CHOCOLATES
401 E Las Olas Blvd # 800, Fort Lauderdale, FL 33301-4284
Tel (954) 940-4900 *Founded/Ownrshp* 1980
Sales NA *EMP* 6,108[E]
Tkr Sym BFCF *Exch* OTO
SIC 6035 6531 6552 Federal savings & loan associations; Real estate agents & managers; Subdividers & developers
Pr: Jarett S Levan
CFO: Raymond S Lopez
V Ch Bd: John E Abdo
Ex VP: Seth M Wise
Board of Directors: Darwin Dornbush, Alan J Levy, Joel Levy, William Nicholson, Neil Sterling

D-U-N-S 01-756-1721 IMP/EXP
BFG SUPPLY CO LLC
TRICOR PACIFIC CAPITAL PARTNER
(*Suby of* TRICOR PACIFIC CAPITAL PARTNERS (FUND IV) US LP) ★
14500 Kinsman Rd, Burton, OH 44021-9423
Tel (440) 834-1883 *Founded/Ownrshp* 2000
Sales 164.1MM[E] *EMP* 190
SIC 5191 5261 Garden supplies; Garden supplies & tools
Pr: Rob Glockner
Pr: Doug Scott
CFO: Dave Daily
**Treas:* Jim Smeltzer
**VP:* Nicole Krizner
IT Man: Trisha Faris
IT Man: Dough Wolg
Sales Asso: Howard McCall

D-U-N-S 07-936-3531
▲ BFI CO LLC
300 Frank W Burr Blvd # 21, Teaneck, NJ 07666-6704
Tel (201) 329-7300 *Founded/Ownrshp* 2006
Sales 751.5MM[E] *EMP* 1,200[E]
SIC 6211 Investment firm, general brokerage

D-U-N-S 13-193-5582
■ BFI WASTE SERVICES OF PENNSYLVANIA LLC
SITE 264
(*Suby of* ALLIED WASTE INDUSTRIES INC) ★
73 Noblestown Rd Ste A, Carnegie, PA 15106-1669
Tel (412) 429-2600 *Founded/Ownrshp* 2001
Sales 94.0MM[E] *EMP* 306
SIC 4953 Refuse collection & disposal services
Prin: Dennis Lytle
Dist Mgr: Brad Greene
Genl Mgr: Dennis Marchetti

D-U-N-S 78-720-4312 IMP
■ BFI WASTE SYSTEMS OF NORTH AMERICA INC
(*Suby of* BROWNING-FERRIS INDUSTRIES INC) ★
2394 E Camelback Rd, Phoenix, AZ 85016-3429
Tel (480) 627-2700 *Founded/Ownrshp* 1991
Sales 1.4MMM[E] *EMP* 3,000
SIC 4953 Refuse collection & disposal services
CEO: Thomas H Weelden
**Pr:* Donald W Slager

D-U-N-S 00-316-2336 IMP
BFI WIND DOWN INC
BROYHILL FURNITURE
815 Visionary St, Lenoir, NC 28645-8365
Tel (828) 759-8000 *Founded/Ownrshp* 2011
Sales NA *EMP* 1,000
SIC 5712 2512

D-U-N-S 79-819-2910 IMP
BFN OPERATIONS LLC
BERRY FAMILY OF NURSERIES
8700 Freport Pkwy Ste 100, Irving, TX 75063
Tel (972) 819-5030 *Founded/Ownrshp* 2010
Sales 229.1MM[E] *EMP* 1,100
SIC 0181

D-U-N-S 05-235-1095 IMP
BFPE INTERNATIONAL INC
7512 Connelley Dr, Hanover, MD 21076-1688
Tel (410) 768-2200 *Founded/Ownrshp* 1970
Sales 136.3MM[E] *EMP* 375
SIC 1731 7382 7389 Safety & security specialization; Security systems services; Fire extinguisher servicing
Pr: Pam Boyer
**VP:* Shelley Boyer
Genl Mgr: George Hill
IT Man: Richard Boyd
IT Man: Linda Herb
Opers Mgr: Jeff Jenkins
Sales Exec: Sherry Flannery
Sls Mgr: Chuck Fusco
Sales Asso: Justin Erdman
Sales Asso: Brian Goldman
Sales Asso: Howard Salan

D-U-N-S 13-083-3887
BFS DIVERSIFIED PRODUCTS INC
FIRESTONE BUILDING PRODUCTS CO
(*Suby of* FIRESTONE METAL PRODUCTS) ★
250 W 96th St Ste 150, Indianapolis, IN 46260-1318
Tel (317) 575-7000 *Founded/Ownrshp* 2003
Sales 127.2MM[E] *EMP* 500
SIC 5031 5013 5169 Building materials, exterior; Automotive supplies & parts; Chemicals & allied products
Pr: Michael Gorey

BFS FOODS
See BRUCETON FARM SERVICE INC

D-U-N-S 00-796-0206
BFW LIQUIDATION LLC
(*Suby of* LONE STAR FUND IV (US) LP) ★
1800 Intl Pk Dr Ste 500, Birmingham, AL 35243
Tel (205) 853-2663 *Founded/Ownrshp* 1946, 2005
Sales 671.9MM[E] *EMP* 11,470
SIC 5411 5912 5921 Supermarkets, chain; Drug stores; Liquor stores

D-U-N-S 96-433-3756 IMP/EXP
BG BRASILIA LLC
BG GROUP
(*Suby of* BG GROUP LIMITED)
910 Louisiana St, Houston, TX 77002-4916
Tel (713) 599-4000 *Founded/Ownrshp* 2005
Sales 110.3MM[E] *EMP* 206[E]
SIC 1311 Crude petroleum & natural gas production
CEO: Chris Finlayson
Pr: Wajih Effendi
COO: David Freeman
Ex VP: Matt Schatzman
Comm Man: Sandra Shurie
Snr Mgr: Angus McCallum

BG GROUP
See BG BRASILIA LLC

D-U-N-S 80-789-2786
BG HOLDING LLC
2275 Res Blvd Ste 600, Rockville, MD 20850
Tel (301) 987-9200 *Founded/Ownrshp* 2006
Sales 265.1MM[E] *EMP* 6,600
SIC 0781 0782 Landscape services; Landscape contractors

D-U-N-S 80-790-8061
BG INTERMEDIATE CORP
(*Suby of* BG HOLDING LLC) ★
18227 Flower Hill Way, Gaithersburg, MD 20879-5334
Tel (301) 987-9200 *Founded/Ownrshp* 2006
Sales 41.8MM[E] *EMP* 6,600

SIC 0782 0781 Lawn & garden services; Horticulture services
VP: John M Baumer

D-U-N-S 05-836-0434 IMP
BG NORTH AMERICA LLC
(*Suby of* BG GROUP LIMITED)
811 Main St Ste 3400, Houston, TX 77002-6131
Tel (713) 426-2786 *Founded/Ownrshp* 1998
Sales 245.3MM^E *EMP* 300^E
SIC 1311 Crude petroleum & natural gas production
Pr: M Houston
Sr VP: Betsy Spomer
**VP:* J Boardman
VP: Joel Disatell
VP: David Keane
**VP:* Anita Odedra
Dir Risk M: Paige Glass
Ex Dir: John Hood
Ex Dir: Robert Wilson
Genl Mgr: Gordon Dempster
Genl Mgr: Barbara Heim

D-U-N-S 00-696-8762 EXP
■ BG RETAIL LLC
BROWN SHOE CLOSET
(*Suby of* CALERES INC) ★
8300 Maryland Ave, Saint Louis, MO 63105-3645
Tel (314) 854-4000 *Founded/Ownrshp* 1916
Sales 762.6MM^E *EMP* 5,984
SIC 5661 Shoe stores
VP: Robert D Pickle
Ex VP: Harry Rich
**Sr VP:* Russ Hammer
**Sr VP:* Douglas W Koch
**Sr VP:* Michael I Oberlander
VP: Bill Berberich
**VP:* William S Frederick
**VP:* Mark Schmitt
VP: Robert E Stadler Jr
Brnch Mgr: Paul Shapiro
Dir IT: Ray Chrisler

D-U-N-S 96-211-3945
▲ BG STAFFING INC
5850 Granite Pkwy Ste 730, Plano, TX 75024-0035
Tel (972) 692-2400 *Founded/Ownrshp* 2007
Sales 217.5MM *EMP* 240^E
Tkr Sym BGSF *Exch* ASE
SIC 7363 Temporary help service
Pr: L Allen Baker Jr
COO: Beth Garvey
CFO: Dan Hollenbach
Board of Directors: C David Allen Jr, Richard L Baum Jr, Douglas E Hailey, Paul A Seid

D-U-N-S 07-870-2963
■ BG STAFFING LLC
(*Suby of* BG STAFFING INC) ★
14900 Landmark Blvd, Dallas, TX 75254-6783
Tel (972) 692-2400 *Founded/Ownrshp* 2010
Sales 139.4MM^E *EMP* 783^E
SIC 7361 Employment agencies
Pr: Tod Grice
**CFO:* Michael Rutledge
Opers Mgr: Christina Alfaro

D-U-N-S 17-438-2254
▲ BGC PARTNERS INC
499 Park Ave, New York, NY 10022-1240
Tel (212) 610-2200 *Founded/Ownrshp* 1972
Sales 2.5MMM *EMP* 7,841
Tkr Sym BGCP *Exch* NGS
SIC 6211 Security brokers & dealers; Bond dealers & brokers; Brokers, security; Dealers, security
Ch Bd: Howard W Lutnick
Pr: Shaun D Lynn
COO: Sean A Windeatt
CFO: Steve McMurray
Ofcr: Paul M Pion
Ex VP: Stephen M Merkel
Ex VP: Thierry Vergeau
VP: James Byrne
VP: Borys Harmaty
VP: Regis Laboubee
VP: Steve Loizou
VP: Jason McGruder
VP: Dan Taylor
VP: Mark Thompson
VP: Matt Wyant
Board of Directors: Linda A Bell, Stephen T Curwood, John H Dalton, William J Moran

BGE
See BALTIMORE GAS AND ELECTRIC CO

D-U-N-S 83-512-3746
■ BGE HOME PRODUCTS AND SERVICES INC
(*Suby of* CONSTELLATION ENERGY RESOURCES LLC) ★
1409 Tangier Dr Ste A, Baltimore, MD 21220-2878
Tel (410) 918-5600 *Founded/Ownrshp* 1999
Sales 84.9MM^E *EMP* 486^E
SIC 5722 Household appliance stores
Pr: Kevin A Klages
**Ch:* Thomas F Brady
**Treas:* Thomas H Ruszin Jr
Area Mgr: David Doremus
IT Man: Anita Schott
Mktg Mgr: Dean W Bush
Sales Asso: Lawrence Kinsey

D-U-N-S 18-695-2156 IMP/EXP
BGF INDUSTRIES INC
(*Suby of* NVH INC) ★
3802 Robert Porcher Way, Greensboro, NC 27410-2190
Tel (843) 537-3172 *Founded/Ownrshp* 1988
Sales 252.7MM^E *EMP* 864
SIC 2221 3624 2241 2295 Glass broadwoven fabrics; Fibers, carbon & graphite; Glass narrow fabrics; Mats, varnished glass
Ch Bd: Philippe Porcher
Pr: Robby Dunnagan
CFO: Philippe R Dorier
Treas: Kathy Andrews
Sr VP: Philippe Dorier
VP: Ed Cardille
VP: Robert Dunnagan
Dept Mgr: Ed Carille
Dept Mgr: Bobby Stone
CIO: James M Pierce
IT Man: Redwine Johnny

D-U-N-S 83-279-9857
BH HOTELS HOLDCO LLC
HILTON WORLDWIDE
7930 Jones Branch Dr, Mc Lean, VA 22102-3388
Tel (703) 883-1000 *Founded/Ownrshp* 2007
Sales 44.2MM^E *EMP* 7,500^E
SIC 7011 Hotels & motels

D-U-N-S 00-722-1237
■ BH MEDIA GROUP HOLDINGS INC
TULSA WORLD
(*Suby of* BH MEDIA GROUP INC) ★
315 S Boulder Ave, Tulsa, OK 74103-3401
Tel (918) 583-2161 *Founded/Ownrshp* 1906, 2013
Sales 102.6MM^E *EMP* 800
SIC 2711

D-U-N-S 07-852-1489
■ BH MEDIA GROUP HOLDINGS INC
(*Suby of* BH MEDIA GROUP INC) ★
Omaha World Herald Bldg 1, Omaha, NE 68102
Tel (402) 444-1000 *Founded/Ownrshp* 2012
Sales 109.3MM^E *EMP* 3,200
SIC 2711 7379 Newspapers; Computer related consulting services
CEO: Doug Heimstra
**Ch:* Terry Kroeger
**Treas:* Duane Polodna

D-U-N-S 07-851-7228
■ BH MEDIA GROUP INC
(*Suby of* BERKSHIRE HATHAWAY INC) ★
Omaha Wrld Hrld Bldg 1314, Omaha, NE 68102
Tel (402) 444-1000 *Founded/Ownrshp* 2013
Sales 750.3MM^E *EMP* 4,000^E
SIC 2711 7379 Newspapers; Computer related consulting services
Pr: Terry Kroeger
**Sr VP:* Duane Polodna
**VP:* Doug Hiemstra
**VP:* Scott Searl
VP: Alex Skovgaard

D-U-N-S 07-924-1358
■ BHA ALTAIR LLC
CLARCOR INDUSTRIAL AIR
(*Suby of* CLARCOR INC) ★
11501 Outlook St Ste 100, Overland Park, KS 66211-1810
Tel (816) 356-8400 *Founded/Ownrshp* 2013
Sales 168.8MM^E *EMP* 700
SIC 3564 Air purification equipment
Pr: Kieth White
CFO: Christopher L Ferraro
VP: Christopher Conway
IT Man: Teresa Moore
VP Opers: John Porter

D-U-N-S 78-707-8786
■ BHC FAIRFAX HOSPITAL INC
(*Suby of* PSYCHIATRIC SOLUTIONS INC) ★
10200 Ne 132nd St, Kirkland, WA 98034-2831
Tel (425) 821-2000 *Founded/Ownrshp* 1998
Sales 142.2MM^E *EMP* 9,810
SIC 8063 Psychiatric hospitals
CEO: Ron Escarda

BHCS
See BAYLOR MEDICAL CENTER AT IRVING

BHCS
See BAYLOR MEDICAL CENTER AT CARROLLTON

BHCS
See BAYLOR MEDICAL CENTER AT WAXAHACHIE

BHCS
See BAYLOR HEALTH CARE SYSTEM

BHCS
See TEXAS HEART HOSPITAL OF SOUTHWEST LLP

BHDDH
See DEPARTMENT OF BEHAVIORAL HEALTHCARE DEVELOPMENTAL DISABILITIES AND HOSPITALS

D-U-N-S 12-261-2497
BHE HOLDINGS INC
BANGOR HYDRO ELECTRIC
(*Suby of* EMERA INCORPORATED)
21 Telcom Dr, Bangor, ME 04401-3392
Tel (207) 947-2414 *Founded/Ownrshp* 2001
Sales 254.9MM^E *EMP* 423
SIC 4911 Transmission, electric power; Distribution, electric power; Generation, electric power;
Ch Bd: Robert S Briggs

BHEP
See BLACK HILLS EXPLORATION AND PRODUCTION INC

D-U-N-S 07-929-3708
BHG HOLDINGS LLC
5001 Spring Valley Rd 600e, Dallas, TX 75244-8217
Tel (214) 365-6100 *Founded/Ownrshp* 2007
Sales 39.8MM^E *EMP* 1,000
SIC 8093 Rehabilitation center, outpatient treatment

BHI ENERGY
See BARTLETT HOLDINGS INC

BHP BILLITON
See B H P MINERALS INTERNATIONAL INC

D-U-N-S 96-890-8488 IMP
BHP BILLITON PETROLEUM (ARKANSAS) INC
(*Suby of* BHP BILLITON LIMITED)
1360 Post Blvd Ste 150, Houston, TX 77056
Tel (713) 961-8500 *Founded/Ownrshp* 2011
Sales 4.3MMM^E *EMP* 41,000
SIC 4922 1311 Natural gas transmission; Crude petroleum & natural gas production
Pr: J Michael Yeager

D-U-N-S 00-678-3021 IMP/EXP
BHP BILLITON PETROLEUM (NORTH AMERICA) INC
BHP BLLITON PETRO AMERICAS INC
(*Suby of* BHP BILLITON LIMITED)
1360 Post Oak Blvd # 150, Houston, TX 77056-3030
Tel (713) 961-8500 *Founded/Ownrshp* 1963
Sales 2.3MMM^E *EMP* 1,198
SIC 1311 4922 Crude petroleum production; Natural gas production; Pipelines, natural gas
Pr: J Michael Yeager
**CEO:* Mr Chip Goodyear
**CFO:* David D Powell
Treas: Clay Morel
**VP:* Julye Nugent
**VP:* Michael Wyle

BHP BLLITON PETRO AMERICAS INC
See BHP BILLITON PETROLEUM (NORTH AMERICA) INC

D-U-N-S 00-896-6731
BHP COPPER INC
SAN MANUEL MINING DIVISION
(*Suby of* BHP HOLDINGS (RESOURCES) INC) ★
1360 Post Oak Blvd # 150, Houston, TX 77056-3030
Tel (713) 961-8500 *Founded/Ownrshp* 2001
Sales 819.8MM^E *EMP* 1,657
SIC 1021 3341 1041 Underground copper ore mining; Open pit copper ore mining; Copper ore milling & preparation; Copper smelting & refining (secondary); Gold ores mining
Pr: J Burgess Winter
**Pr:* L Wayne Isaacs
**CFO:* Douglas J Purdom
Treas: Jeff Fraser
Bd of Dir: Jose Cervantes
Sr VP: Bill Walls
**VP:* Andrew A Brodkey
**VP:* Linda Broughton
**VP:* John F Champagne
**VP:* Bradford A Mills
**VP:* Harry C Smith
**VP:* Nelis Theron

D-U-N-S 19-719-4058
BHP HOLDINGS (RESOURCES) INC
(*Suby of* BHP BILLITON LIMITED)
1360 Post Oak Blvd # 150, Houston, TX 77056-3030
Tel (713) 961-8500 *Founded/Ownrshp* 1998
Sales 824.4MM^E *EMP* 1,657
SIC 1021 3341 1041 Underground copper ore mining; Open pit copper ore mining; Copper ore milling & preparation; Copper smelting & refining (secondary); Gold ores mining
CEO: J Burgess Winter
VP: Edwin W Parker II

D-U-N-S 00-691-3347 IMP/EXP
BHP MINERALS INTERNATIONAL INC
(*Suby of* BHP BILLITON LIMITED)
1360 Post Oak Blvd # 150, Houston, TX 77056-3030
Tel (713) 961-8500 *Founded/Ownrshp* 1956, 2000
Sales 1.2MMM^E *EMP* 2,000
SIC 1222 1011 1021 Bituminous coal-underground mining; Underground iron ore mining; Copper ores
Pr: Earl K Moore
**Treas:* Daivd Braley

D-U-N-S 79-802-1176 IMP/EXP
BHS CORRUGATED - NORTH AMERICA INC
(*Suby of* BHS CORRUGATED MASCHINEN- UND ANLAGENBAU GMBH)
9103 Yellow Brick Rd N, Baltimore, MD 21237-4703
Tel (410) 574-1550 *Founded/Ownrshp* 1992
Sales 259.7MM^E *EMP* 1,600^E
SIC 5084 7699 3316 Paper manufacturing machinery; Printing trades machinery & equipment repair; Cold finishing of steel shapes
Ch Bd: Christian Engel
**CFO:* Scott Purrington
Opers Mgr: Chris Wilson
Sales Exec: Pat Ciambruschini
Sls Mgr: Brad Johnson

D-U-N-S 62-015-9467 IMP
■ BHSF INC
(*Suby of* BERKSHIRE HATHAWAY INC) ★
1440 Kiewit Plz, Omaha, NE 68131
Tel (402) 346-1400 *Founded/Ownrshp* 1986
Sales 384.2MM^E *EMP* 4,909
SIC 3635 3563 2731 3715 Household vacuum cleaners; Air & gas compressors including vacuum pumps; Books: publishing & printing; Truck trailers
Ch: Warren E Buffett
**Treas:* William W T Stephans
**VP:* Marc D Hamburg
**VP:* Patricia M Scanlon
Prgrm Mgr: Brady Peikert

D-U-N-S 01-871-3495
BI RETAIL INC
(*Suby of* AMHERST NY BOBS INC) ★
160 Corporate Ct, Meriden, CT 06450-7177
Tel (203) 235-5775 *Founded/Ownrshp* 1965
Sales 202.6MM^E *EMP* 2,750^E
SIC 5651 5611 5699 5621 5641 5661 Family clothing stores; Clothing accessories: men's & boys'; Clothing, sportswear, men's & boys'; Sports apparel; Women's clothing stores; Children's wear; Men's shoes; Women's shoes; Children's shoes
Pr: David Farrell

D-U-N-S 10-922-4089 IMP
BI TECHNOLOGIES CORP
TT ELECTRONICS
(*Suby of* TT ELECTRONICS PLC)
4200 Bonita Pl, Fullerton, CA 92835-1051
Tel (714) 447-2300 *Founded/Ownrshp* 1984
Sales 193.4MM^E *EMP* 2,000
SIC 3679 5065 8711

D-U-N-S 04-870-5669
BI WAREHOUSING INC
ANHEUSER-BUSCH
5404 Pacific St, Rocklin, CA 95677-2714
Tel (916) 624-0654 *Founded/Ownrshp* 1992
Sales 126.1MM^E *EMP* 350
SIC 5531 5013 7539 Automotive parts; Automotive supplies & parts; Machine shop, automotive
CEO: Bart W Riebes
**VP:* Mel Todd

BI WORLDWIDE
See SCHOENECKERS INC

D-U-N-S 05-993-9660
BI-CON SERVICES INC
BSI GROUP, THE
10901 Clay Pike Rd, Derwent, OH 43733-9900
Tel (740) 685-2542 *Founded/Ownrshp* 1971
Sales 171.4MM *EMP* 400
SIC 1623 3498 3443

D-U-N-S 05-251-3511
BI-LO HOLDING FINANCE LLC
WINN-DIXIE
(*Suby of* SOUTHEASTERN GROCERS LLC) ★
5050 Edgewood Ct, Jacksonville, FL 32254-3601
Tel (904) 783-5000 *Founded/Ownrshp* 2013
Sales 5.9MMM^E *EMP* 47,014^E
SIC 5411 Convenience stores, chain
Pr: R Randall Onstead

D-U-N-S 80-056-3590
BI-LO HOLDING LLC
(*Suby of* WINN-DIXIE) ★
5050 Edgewood Ct, Jacksonville, FL 32254-3601
Tel (904) 783-5000 *Founded/Ownrshp* 2010
Sales 5.9MMM^E *EMP* 47,009^E
SIC 5411 Supermarkets, chain
VP: Terri Cull
VP: Charles Williams

D-U-N-S 00-690-1375
BI-LO HOLDINGS FOUNDATION INC (FL)
WINN-DIXIE
(*Suby of* MARKETPLACE) ★
5050 Edgewood Ct, Jacksonville, FL 32254-3601
Tel (904) 783-5000 *Founded/Ownrshp* 1946, 1954
Sales 3.2MMM *EMP* 14,000
SIC 5411 Convenience stores, chain
Pr: Kellmanson Mary
**Treas:* Byrum D Michael

D-U-N-S 03-615-7964 EXP
BI-LO LLC
(*Suby of* BI-LO HOLDING LLC) ★
8928 Prominence Pkwy # 200, Jacksonville, FL 32256-8264
Tel (904) 783-5000 *Founded/Ownrshp* 2005
Sales 5.5MMM^E *EMP* 47,007
SIC 5411 Supermarkets, chain
CEO: Randal Onstead
**Pr:* Michael Byars
**CFO:* Brian Carney
Ex VP: Marshall Collins
Ex VP: Frank Curci
Ex VP: Donald Wilken
VP: Terri Cull
VP: Harold P Hunt
Opers Mgr: Richard Sigmon
Snr Mgr: Jennifer Franklin
Snr Mgr: Tim Swan
Board of Directors: Peter J Van Dun

D-U-N-S 05-596-4576 IMP/EXP
BI-MART ACQUISITION CORP
220 Seneca Rd, Eugene, OR 97402-2725
Tel (541) 344-0681 *Founded/Ownrshp* 1996
Sales 850.5MM^E *EMP* 3,300
Accts Deloitte & Touche Llp Portlan
SIC 5912 5399 Drug stores; Country general stores
CEO: Marty W Smith
**Pr:* Richard Truett
**CFO:* Dan Chen
VP Mktg: Don Leber

D-U-N-S 02-763-0078 IMP
BI-MART CORP
(*Suby of* BI-MART ACQUISITION CORP) ★
220 S Seneca Rd, Eugene, OR 97402-2725
Tel (541) 344-0681 *Founded/Ownrshp* 1988
Sales 850.5MM^E *EMP* 3,300
SIC 5399 Warehouse club stores
CEO: Marty W Smith
**Pr:* Richard Truett
**CFO:* Dan Chen
VP: Barbara Boegl
VP: Barbara Kim
VP: Rich Truett
Genl Mgr: Randy Dunn
Genl Mgr: Kevin Helgeson
Genl Mgr: Linda Hossman
MIS Dir: Holly Plummer
MIS Dir: Joel Rosenberg

BI-RITE FOODSERVICE DISTRS
See BI-RITE RESTAURANT SUPPLY CO INC

D-U-N-S 04-131-5532 IMP/EXP
BI-RITE RESTAURANT SUPPLY CO INC
BI-RITE FOODSERVICE DISTRS
123 S Hill Dr, Brisbane, CA 94005-1203
Tel (415) 656-0187 *Founded/Ownrshp* 1941
Sales 321.6MM^E *EMP* 300
SIC 5141 5147 5148 5023 5046 5963 Groceries, general line; Meats & meat products; Fresh fruits & vegetables; Kitchenware; Linens, table; Towels; Commercial equipment; Direct selling establishments
CEO: William Barulich
**Pr:* Steve Barulich
**CFO:* Zachary Barulich
**CFO:* Zack Barulich
**VP:* Nathan Barulich
Dist Mgr: David Flavel
Dir IT: Ben Li
Sls Mgr: Karen Powell

D-U-N-S 00-649-0569
BI-STATE DEVELOPMENT AGENCY OF MISSOURI-ILLINOIS METROPOLITAN DISTRICT (INC)
ST LOUIS DOWNTOWN AIRPORT
211 N Broadway Ste 700, Saint Louis, MO 63102-2759
Tel (314) 982-1400 *Founded/Ownrshp* 1949
Sales 210.1MM^E *EMP* 2,100
Accts Mayer Hoffman Mccann Pc St
SIC 4111 4581 Commuter bus operation; Local railway passenger operation; Airport
CEO: John Nations
COO: Raymond Friem
CFO: Kathy Klevorn
Sr VP: Jennifer Nixon
IT Man: Mark Vago
Sfty Dirs: Ed Kramer
Mktg Dir: Ted Zimmerman
Genl Couns: Barbara Enneking

D-U-N-S 06-994-3801
BI-STATE PACKAGING INC
(*Suby of* GROUP O INC) ★
4905 77th Ave E, Milan, IL 61264-3250
Tel (309) 736-8500 *Founded/Ownrshp* 1974, 1992
Sales 96.3MM *EMP* 25
Accts Crippen Reid & Bowen Llc
SIC 5199 5084 Packaging materials; Packaging machinery & equipment
Ch: Robert Ontiveros
**Pr:* Gregg Ontiveros
**CFO:* Robert Marriott
**VP:* Christopher Ontiveros
Genl Mgr: Mark Bohman

BIA
See BUREAU OF INDIAN AFFAIRS

BIAGGIS
See BIAGGIS RISTORANTE ITALIANO LLC

D-U-N-S 08-943-7250
BIAGGIS RISTORANTE ITALIANO LLC
BIAGGIS
1705 Clearwater Ave Ste A, Bloomington, IL 61704-2458
Tel (309) 664-2148 *Founded/Ownrshp* 1998
Sales 59.2MM^E *EMP* 2,000
SIC 5812 Italian restaurant
CEO: Todd Hovenden
Mng Pt: Mark Borowiak
Mng Pt: Christopher Farney
Mng Pt: Jeff Jenkins
Mng Pt: Scott Miller
Mng Pt: Troy Nelson
Mng Pt: Mark Rumscheidt
Mng Pt: Donna Townsend
**Pr:* John McDonnell
Exec: Mark McCain
Dir Soc: Stephanie Roof

D-U-N-S 09-995-0115
BIAGI BROS INC
787 Airpark Rd, NAPA, CA 94558-7515
Tel (707) 745-8115 *Founded/Ownrshp* 1977
Sales 106.1MM^E *EMP* 450
SIC 4213 4225 Trucking, except local; General warehousing & storage
Pr: Fred Biagi
**CFO:* Mark Parnell

D-U-N-S 07-586-6301
BIBB COUNTY BOARD OF EDUCATION
484 Mulberry St Ste 300, Macon, GA 31201-7928
Tel (478) 765-8711 *Founded/Ownrshp* 1872
Sales 265.0MM^E *EMP* 4,200
Accts Mauldin & Jenkins Llc Macon
SIC 8211 School board
Pr: Thelma Dillard
**CFO:* Ron Collier

D-U-N-S 83-151-6807
BIBB COUNTY SCHOOL DISTRICT
484 Mulberry St Ste 300, Macon, GA 31201-7928
Tel (478) 765-8711 *Founded/Ownrshp* 2009
Sales 265.0MM *EMP* 8,405^E
Accts Mauldin & Jenkins Cpa Llc Mac
SIC 8211 Public elementary & secondary schools
VP: Jason Downey
Pr Dir: Stephanie Hartley

D-U-N-S 00-116-6586 IMP
BIC CORP (CT)
(*Suby of* SOCIETE BIC)
1 Bic Way Ste 1, Shelton, CT 06484-6223
Tel (203) 783-2000 *Founded/Ownrshp* 1958, 2005
Sales 1.6MMM^E *EMP* 5,985
SIC 3951 2899 3999 3421 5091 3952 Ball point pens & parts; Correction fluid; Cigarette lighters, except precious metal; Razor blades & razors; Watersports equipment & supplies; Lead pencils & art goods
Ch Bd: Bruno Bich
Pr: Pauline Dantas
**CEO:* Mario Guevara
CFO: James Dipietro
Sr Cor Off: ISA Al Khalifa
Chf Cred: Paul Floridia
Ex VP: Stuart Phillips
**Sr VP:* Thomas M Kelleher
**Sr VP:* Chris Mills
**Sr VP:* Paul Russo
**VP:* Francois Bich
**VP:* Marie-Aime Bich-Dufour
VP: Steven A Burkhart
Exec: Cheryl Dubois
Exec: Alison James
Exec: Susan Lanzarotto

D-U-N-S 12-869-4093 IMP
BIC USA INC
(*Suby of* BIC CORP) ★
1 Bic Way Ste 1, Shelton, CT 06484-6223
Tel (203) 783-2000 *Founded/Ownrshp* 1999
Sales 152.4MM^E *EMP* 800
SIC 3951 2899 3999 3421 Ball point pens & parts; Correction fluid; Cigarette lighters, except precious metal; Razor blades & razors
Pr: Chris Mills
**VP:* Steven A Burkhart
VP: Dorothy H Dupree
**VP:* Barry Johnson
**VP:* David T Kimball
**Genl Couns:* Thomas M Kelleher

D-U-N-S 02-185-2702 IMP/EXP
BICARA LTD
1611 S Catalina Ave, Redondo Beach, CA 90277-5255
Tel (310) 316-6222 *Founded/Ownrshp* 1979
Sales 96.6MM^E *EMP* 300^E
SIC 5147 5146 5141 Meats & meat products; Seafoods; Groceries, general line
CEO: William Jeffrey Hughes
**Pr:* William D Hughes
CFO: Gene Matsuda
VP: Eugene Matsuda
**VP:* Raymond Rosenthal

BICYCLE CLUB CASINO
See BELL GARDENS BICYCLE CLUB INC

BID CONSTRUCTION
See BID GROUP CONSTRUCTION US INC

D-U-N-S 08-020-5957
BID GROUP CONSTRUCTION US INC
BID CONSTRUCTION
(*Suby of* B.I.D. CONSTRUCTION LTD)
5154 Highway 78, Saint George, SC 29477-7930
Tel (843) 563-7070 *Founded/Ownrshp* 2015
Sales 100.0MM *EMP* 18
SIC 1542 Commercial & office building, new construction

BIDMC
See BETH ISRAEL DEACONESS MEDICAL CENTER INC

D-U-N-S 00-952-6022
BIDMC TELECOMMUNICATIONS
(*Suby of* CAREGROUP INC) ★
1 Jimmy Fund Way, Boston, MA 02115-6007
Tel (617) 278-6351 *Founded/Ownrshp* 2009
Sales 54.5MM^E *EMP* 1,182^E
SIC 4813 Telephone communication, except radio
Prin: Judith Judson

D-U-N-S 01-813-5046 IMP
BIERY CHEESE CO
6544 Paris Ave, Louisville, OH 44641-9544
Tel (330) 875-3381 *Founded/Ownrshp* 1953
Sales 83.3MM^E *EMP* 250^E
SIC 2022 Cheese, natural & processed
Pr: Dennis Biery
CFO: Chris Greenfelder
**VP:* Benjamin Biery
QA Dir: Mark Batson
QA Dir: Lisa Corbin
QA Dir: David Ebel
IT Man: Dave Dearth
IT Man: Dana Martinak
IT Man: Daniel Whelan
Snr Mgr: Mike Clapper
Snr Mgr: Tom Jaeb

D-U-N-S 04-475-1493 IMP
BIEWER LUMBER LLC
PINE RIVER GROUP
812 S Riverside Ave, Saint Clair, MI 48079-5393
Tel (810) 326-3930 *Founded/Ownrshp* 1980
Sales 113.2MM^E *EMP* 300
SIC 2491 Structural lumber & timber, treated wood; Pilings, treated wood
CFO: Gary Olmstead
VP: Tim Biewer
Info Man: George Noble
Sls Mgr: Les White
Sales Asso: Michael Bark

D-U-N-S 01-510-8738
BIG 12 CONFERENCE INC
400 E John Carpenter Fwy, Irving, TX 75062-3955
Tel (469) 524-1000 *Founded/Ownrshp* 2009
Sales 267.7MM *EMP* 2
Accts Caton Consulting Group Pc Irv
SIC 7941 7997 Sports field or stadium operator, promoting sports events; Membership sports & recreation clubs
Prin: Dan Beebe
**CFO:* Steve Pace
Exec: Dayna Scherf
**Prin:* Tim Allen
**Prin:* Dru Hancock
**Prin:* Tim Weiser

D-U-N-S 62-316-7459 EXP
BIG 3 HOLDING CO INC
1625 N Valley Mills Dr, Waco, TX 76710-2552
Tel (254) 772-8850 *Founded/Ownrshp* 1984
Sales 98.6MM^E *EMP* 120
SIC 5511 5571 New & used car dealers; Motorcycle dealers
Pr: Allen Samuels
**VP:* Robert Steakley III

D-U-N-S 02-807-7113 IMP
■ **BIG 5 CORP**
BIG 5 SPORTING GOODS
(*Suby of* BIG 5 SPORTING GOODS CORP) ★
2525 E El Segundo Blvd, El Segundo, CA 90245-4632
Tel (310) 536-0611 *Founded/Ownrshp* 1992
Sales 101.5MM^E *EMP* 450
SIC 5941 Sporting goods & bicycle shops
Pr: Steven G Miller
Pr: Luke Thompson
Ex VP: Richard A Johnson
Sr VP: Boyd Clark
**Sr VP:* Gary S Meade
VP: John Lucero
Store Mgr: Rnen Olivas
CTO: Michael Shinagawa

BIG 5 SPORTING GOODS
See BIG 5 CORP

D-U-N-S 80-472-3989
▲ **BIG 5 SPORTING GOODS CORP**
2525 E El Segundo Blvd, El Segundo, CA 90245-4642
Tel (310) 536-0611 *Founded/Ownrshp* 1955
Sales 1.0MMM *EMP* 9,000
Tkr Sym BGFV *Exch* NGS
SIC 5941 Sporting goods & bicycle shops
Ch Bd: Steven G Miller
CFO: Barry D Emerson
Sr VP: Boyd O Clark
Sr VP: Jeffrey L Fraley
Sr VP: Michael P Marrone
Sr VP: Gary S Meade
Sr VP: Shane O Starr
Sr VP: Luke D Thompson
VP: Michael J Shinagawa
IT Man: Paul Caballero
Board of Directors: Sandra N Bane, Dominic C Demarco, Nicholas Donatiello Jr, Jennifer H Dunbar, Robert C Galvin, Van B Honeycutt, David R Jessick

D-U-N-S 02-638-4164
BIG 8 FOODS LTD
P & N BIG 8 SUPERMARKET
1480 George Dieter Dr, El Paso, TX 79936-7601
Tel (915) 857-6080 *Founded/Ownrshp* 1948
Sales 110.7MM^E *EMP* 1,410
SIC 5411 Supermarkets, chain
Pt: Ronald Powell
Genl Mgr: Jim Hinson
Genl Mgr: Joel Quezada

BIG BOY RESTAURANT
See B P L CORP

BIG BOY RESTAURANT MANAGEMENT
See BIG BOY RESTAURANTS INTERNATIONAL LLC

D-U-N-S 02-167-8474
BIG BOY RESTAURANTS INTERNATIONAL LLC
BIG BOY RESTAURANT MANAGEMENT
4199 Marcy St, Warren, MI 48091-1733
Tel (586) 759-6000 *Founded/Ownrshp* 2001
Sales 80.6MM^E *EMP* 1,500
SIC 5812 2099 Restaurant, family: chain; Food preparations
CEO: Keith E Sirois
VP: Jeniffer Bourgoin
S&M/VP: William Hadden

D-U-N-S 00-489-2683
BIG CREEK CONSTRUCTION LTD
1617 Old Waco Temple Rd, Lorena, TX 76655-3651
Tel (254) 857-3200 *Founded/Ownrshp* 1997
Sales 100.0MM^E *EMP* 150
SIC 1611 Highway & street maintenance
Pr: John Miller
CFO: Chris Wolf
Ql Cn Mgr: Robbie Roberts

D-U-N-S 02-435-9291
BIG D OIL CO
3685 Sturgis Rd, Rapid City, SD 57702-0321
Tel (605) 342-6777 *Founded/Ownrshp* 1934
Sales 84.5MM^E *EMP* 225
SIC 5541 5172 8741 Filling stations, gasoline; Petroleum products; Management services
Pr: Don Policky
**Sec:* Kathryn Policky
VP Mktg: Paul McArthur

BIG DOG SPORTSWEAR
See WALKING CO HOLDINGS INC

D-U-N-S 60-973-2412
■ **BIG FISH GAMES INC**
(*Suby of* CHURCHILL DOWNS INC) ★
333 Elliott Ave W Ste 200, Seattle, WA 98119-4113
Tel (206) 213-5753 *Founded/Ownrshp* 2014
Sales 92.4MM^E *EMP* 550^E
SIC 5734 Software, computer games
Pr: John Holland
**CFO:* Robert J Chamberlain
VP: Eric Hull
VP: Jeff Nemecek
VP: Toby Ragaini
VP: Wibe Wagemans
VP: Pat Wylie
Exec: Sean Clark
**Dir Sec:* Paul J Thelen
Snr Sftwr: Jack Kern
**CTO:* Ian Hurlock-Jones

D-U-N-S 19-448-1576 IMP
BIG GEYSER INC
5765 48th St, Maspeth, NY 11378-2015
Tel (718) 821-2200 *Founded/Ownrshp* 1986
Sales 404.8MM^E *EMP* 300
SIC 5149 Beverages, except coffee & tea
CEO: Lewis Hershkowitz
**Pr:* Irving Hershkowitz
**COO:* Jerry Reda
**CFO:* Richard Richer
**VP:* Carl Galio
**VP:* Steven Hershkowitz
**Prin:* Harold Baron
Dir IT: Michael Bartz
Sales Exec: Hal Hershkowitz
Sales Asso: Anthony Gucciardo

D-U-N-S 60-917-0790 IMP/EXP
■ **BIG HEART PET BRANDS**
(*Suby of* SPF HOLDINGS II LLC) ★
1 Maritime Plz Fl 2, San Francisco, CA 94111-3407
Tel (415) 247-3000 *Founded/Ownrshp* 2011
Sales 2.1MMM *EMP* 2,500
SIC 2047 Dog & cat food
CEO: Richard K Smucker
**Pr:* David J West
CFO: Mark R Belgya
CFO: Larry E Bodner
Ex VP: Asad Husain
Sr VP: Barry C Dunaway
Sr VP: David McLain
Sr VP: Robert G Schroeck
VP: Matt Miller
VP: Jill Penrose
VP: Denise Spencer
VP: Michael West
Board of Directors: Vincent C Byrd

D-U-N-S 09-775-1887
BIG JACK ULTIMATE HOLDINGS LP
JACK'S FAMILY RESTAURANTS
124 W Oxmoor Rd, Birmingham, AL 35209-6303
Tel (205) 945-8167 *Founded/Ownrshp* 2015
Sales 88.3MM^E *EMP* 1,966^E
SIC 5812 Family restaurants
Ch: Benny M Larussa
Pr: Charles Mizerany
VP: Billy Wentz
Area Mgr: Walter Kirkland
Area Supr: Vijay Hardit

BIG JOHN'S TREE FARM
See J A M T LEYDEN ENTERPRISES INC

D-U-N-S 12-198-0783
▲ **BIG LOTS INC**
300 Phillipi Rd, Columbus, OH 43228-5311
Tel (614) 278-6800 *Founded/Ownrshp* 1967
Sales 5.1MMM *EMP* 35,900
Accts Deloitte & Touche Llp Dayton
Tkr Sym BIG *Exch* NYS
SIC 5331 Variety stores
Pr: David J Campisi
**Ch Bd:* Philip E Mallott
Chf Mktg O: Lisa M Bachmann
Ofcr: Timothy A Johnson
Ofcr: Andrew D Stein
Sr VP: Ronald A Robins Jr
Sr VP: Stewart Wenerstrom
VP: Michelle Christensen
VP: Craig Hart
VP: Gary E Huber
VP: Deborah Kelley
VP: Kevin Kuehl
VP: Brenda McKnight
VP: Ronald Robins
VP: Carlos Rodriguez
VP: Michael A Schlonsky
VP: Michael Watts
Board of Directors: Jeffrey P Berger, James R Chambers, Marla C Gottschalk, Cynthia T Jamison, Nancy A Reardon, Wendy L Schoppert, Russell E Solt

D-U-N-S 01-788-5351 IMP
■ **BIG LOTS STORES INC**
(*Suby of* BIG LOTS INC) ★
300 Phillipi Rd, Columbus, OH 43228-5311
Tel (614) 278-6800 *Founded/Ownrshp* 1986
Sales 4.5MMM^E *EMP* 35,000
SIC 5331 Variety stores
CEO: David J Campisi
**CFO:* Tim Johnson
**Ex VP:* Richard Chene
Board of Directors: Jeffrey P Berger, Sheldon M Berman, David T Kollat, Brenda J Lauderback, Phillip E Mallott, Russell Solt, James R Tener, Dennis B Tishkoff

BIG O TIRES
See TBC SHARED SERVICES INC

BIG R STORES
See WATSEKA RURAL KING SUPPLY INC

D-U-N-S 07-830-5637
BIG RIVER RESOURCES BOYCEVILLE LLC
N10185 370th St, Boyceville, WI 54725-5122
Tel (715) 643-2602 *Founded/Ownrshp* 2011
Sales 117.5MM *EMP* 32
Accts Christianson & Associates Pll
SIC 5169 Organic chemicals, synthetic
CEO: Raymond E Defenbaugh

D-U-N-S 61-024-7681
BIG RIVER RESOURCES GALVA LLC
(*Suby of* BIG RIVER RESOURCES WEST BURLINGTON LLC) ★
1100 Se 2nd St, Galva, IL 61434-8907
Tel (309) 932-2033 *Founded/Ownrshp* 2005
Sales 247.6MM *EMP* 238
Accts Christianson & Associates Pll
SIC 2869 Ethyl alcohol, ethanol
Pr: Ray Defenbaugh

D-U-N-S 80-916-3152
BIG RIVER RESOURCES LLC
15210 103rd St, West Burlington, IA 52655-8697
Tel (319) 753-1100 *Founded/Ownrshp* 1992
Sales 863.5MM *EMP* 238
Accts Christianson & Associates Pll
SIC 2869 Fuels
**Treas:* Les Allen
**Sec:* Matt Dutton
Bd of Dir: Dave Reinhart
**VP:* Andy Brader
VP: Christine Denisar
Genl Mgr: Jim Leiting
Sfty Mgr: Randy Clark
Plnt Mgr: Marc Awtrey
Plnt Mgr: Stan Janson
Plnt Mgr: Duane Salmon
Prd Mgr: John Wolf

D-U-N-S 14-363-5113
BIG RIVER RESOURCES WEST BURLINGTON LLC
(*Suby of* BIG RIVER RESOURCES LLC) ★
15210 103rd St, West Burlington, IA 52655-8697
Tel (319) 753-1100 *Founded/Ownrshp* 2002
Sales 272.4MM *EMP* 238
Accts Christianson & Associates Pll
SIC 2869 Fuels
Pr: Ray Defenbaugh
**Treas:* Les Allen
**VP:* Andy Brader
**Genl Mgr:* Jim Leiting
Genl Mgr: Edgar Seward

D-U-N-S 83-197-5219
BIG RIVER UNITED ENERGY LLC
(*Suby of* BIG RIVER RESOURCES LLC) ★
3294 Vine Rd, Dyersville, IA 52040-8714
Tel (563) 875-5500 *Founded/Ownrshp* 2006
Sales 246.5MM *EMP* 50
Accts Christianson & Associates Pll
SIC 2869 Industrial organic chemicals

Ch: Andy Brader
**Treas:* Raymond E Defenbaugh

D-U-N-S 00-486-0730
BIG RIVERS ELECTRIC CORP
201 3rd St, Henderson, KY 42420-2979
Tel (270) 827-2561 *Founded/Ownrshp* 1961
Sales 562.4MM *EMP* 599E
Accts Kpmg Llp Philadelphia Pa
SIC 4911 Transmission, electric power
CEO: Robert Berry
CFO: Lindsay Barron
**Ch:* Wayne Elliott
**Treas:* Paul Edd Butler
Bd of Dir: Lee Bearden
Bd of Dir: Bill Denton
VP: Michael Chambliss
VP: Tom Davis
VP: Eric Robeson
VP: Albert Yockey
Dir Risk M: Sharla Austin-Darnell
Board of Directors: Lee Bearden, Paul Edd Butler, William Denton

D-U-N-S 36-080-5126
BIG RIVERS ELECTRIC CORP
(*Suby of* BIG RIVERS ELECTRIC CORP) ★
9000 Hwy 2096, Robards, KY 42452
Tel (270) 827-2561 *Founded/Ownrshp* 1979
Sales 297.8MME *EMP* 200
SIC 4911 Transmission, electric power
**Pr:* Robert Berry
**Ch:* James Sills
Prd Mgr: Jeffrey Francis

D-U-N-S 96-541-7017 IMP/EXP
BIG ROCK SPORTS LLC
BIG ROCK SPORTS MARKETING
158 Little Nine Rd, Morehead City, NC 28557-8482
Tel (252) 808-3500 *Founded/Ownrshp* 1996
Sales 565.6MME *EMP* 550
SIC 5091 Sporting & recreation goods; Fishing tackle
CEO: Ed Small
**Pr:* Brian Phillips
**Sr VP:* Patrick Harve
VP: Wayne Decker
VP: Bob Hunter
VP: Ryan Link
VP: Casey Ramm
CTO: Mark Suber
Opers Mgr: Greg Clack
Mktg Dir: Mitch Mitchell
Sls Mgr: Bob Leis

BIG ROCK SPORTS MARKETING
See BIG ROCK SPORTS LLC

D-U-N-S 80-910-9296
BIG SANDY DISTRIBUTION INC
BIG SANDY SUPERSTORES
8375 Gallia Pike, Franklin Furnace, OH 45629-8989
Tel (740) 574-2113 *Founded/Ownrshp* 2000
Sales 158.7MME *EMP* 700
SIC 4225 General warehousing & storage
Ch: Robert Van Hoose Jr
**Pr:* Rober Vanhoose III
**Treas:* Laura Timberlake
Dist Mgr: Daniel Evans

BIG SANDY SUPERSTORES
See BIG SANDY DISTRIBUTION INC

D-U-N-S 00-401-6648 IMP
BIG SPRINGS INC
COCA-COLA
2700 Meridian St N, Huntsville, AL 35811-1846
Tel (256) 532-4545 *Founded/Ownrshp* 2006
Sales 139.9MME *EMP* 180E
SIC 5149 Soft drinks
Ch Bd: John Wynn
**Pr:* Paul Fowler
**CEO:* Russell Isom
**Sr VP:* Rusty Isoem

BIG STAR
See KOOS MANUFACTURING INC

D-U-N-S 00-288-3205 IMP/EXP
BIG SUR WATERBEDS INC
SOFA MART
(*Suby of* FURNITURE ROW LLC) ★
5603 Brdwy, Denver, CO 80216
Tel (303) 566-8700 *Founded/Ownrshp* 1972
Sales 306.2MME *EMP* 1,900
SIC 5712 2515 2511

D-U-N-S 03-089-4596
BIG TEN CONFERENCE INC
5440 Park Pl, Des Plaines, IL 60018-3732
Tel (847) 696-1010 *Founded/Ownrshp* 1895
Sales 448.7MM *EMP* 25
Accts Mcgladrey Llp Chicago Il
SIC 8699 Athletic organizations
CFO: Brad Traviola
**Treas:* Brad Traviolia
Assoc Dir: Kerry B Kenny
Assoc Dir: Stephanie Kirby
Assoc Dir: Brett McWethy
Assoc Dir: Joshua Munk
Dir IT: Brandon Winbush

D-U-N-S 10-920-8918
BIG TEX TRAILER MANUFACTURING INC
950 Interstate Hwy 30 E, Mount Pleasant, TX 75455-7711
Tel (903) 575-0300 *Founded/Ownrshp* 1985
Sales 537.7MME *EMP* 450
SIC 3523 5013 5599 Trailers & wagons, farm; Trailer parts & accessories; Utility trailers
Pr: Richard W Baker
**COO:* Randy Homer
**Ex VP:* Lynn Beal
**VP:* Stan Garrett

D-U-N-S 11-903-1495 IMP
BIG TIME PRODUCTS LLC
2 Wilbanks Rd Se, Rome, GA 30161-8475
Tel (706) 295-3770 *Founded/Ownrshp* 2002
Sales 140.0MME *EMP* 110
SIC 2259 Work gloves, knit

CEO: Harry Pierce
Pr: Richard Chambers

BIG VALLEY MORTGAGE
See AMERICAN PACIFIC MORTGAGE CORP

D-U-N-S 15-901-6364
BIG WEST OIL LLC
(*Suby of* FLYING J) ★
333 W Center St, North Salt Lake, UT 84054-2805
Tel (801) 624-1000 *Founded/Ownrshp* 2001
Sales 251.1MME *EMP* 460
SIC 2911 5172 Gasoline; Diesel fuels; Gasoline; Diesel fuel
Pr: Fred L Greener

D-U-N-S 01-931-8732 IMP
BIG Y FOODS INC
2145 Roosevelt Ave, Springfield, MA 01104-1650
Tel (413) 784-0600 *Founded/Ownrshp* 1936
Sales 2.1MMME *EMP* 10,098
SIC 5411 Supermarkets, chain; Supermarkets, 55,000-65,000 square feet (superstore)
CEO: William Mahoney
Pr: Charles L D'Amour
CFO: Herbert Dotterer
CFO: Bill Mahoney
Ch: Donald H D'Amour
Treas: Dwight Merriman
Treas: Jeremy P Payson
VP: Mathieu D'Amour
VP: Claire M D'Amour-Daley
VP: Michael Damour
VP: William Hogan
VP: Mike Tami

D-U-N-S 02-776-8452
BIG-D CAPITAL CORP
(*Suby of* BIG-D CONSTRUCTION CORP) ★
420 E South Temple, Salt Lake City, UT 84111-1319
Tel (801) 415-6086 *Founded/Ownrshp* 1998
Sales 172.0MME *EMP* 141E
SIC 1521 Single-family housing construction
Prin: Jack Livingood

D-U-N-S 04-711-4848
BIG-D CONSTRUCTION CORP
404 W 400 S, Salt Lake City, UT 84101-1108
Tel (801) 415-6000 *Founded/Ownrshp* 1980
Sales 640.8MM *EMP* 574
Accts Grant Thornton Llp Salt Lake
SIC 1541 1542 Industrial buildings, new construction; Renovation, remodeling & repairs: industrial buildings; Commercial & office building, new construction
CEO: Larry C Worrell
**Pr:* Robert Moore
CFO: Larry Worrell
**Ex VP:* Forrest McNabb
**Sr VP:* Dale R Satterthwaite
VP: Jim Allison
VP: Jeff Arnold
VP: Michael Kerby
Dir Bus: Josh Caldwell
Board of Directors: Jack Livingood, Forrest McNabb, Cory Moore, Dale Satterthwaite, Larry Worrell

BIGELOW TEA
See RC BIGELOW INC

D-U-N-S 00-691-3693 IMP/EXP
BIGGE CRANE AND RIGGING CO (CA)
10700 Bigge St, San Leandro, CA 94577-1032
Tel (510) 638-8100 *Founded/Ownrshp* 1916
Sales 93.3MME *EMP* 200
SIC 1796

D-U-N-S 00-692-8105
▲ BIGLARI HOLDINGS INC
17802 W Ih 10 Ste 400, San Antonio, TX 78257-2509
Tel (210) 344-3400 *Founded/Ownrshp* 1934
Sales 861.4MM *EMP* 22,958E
Tkr Sym BH *Exch* NYS
SIC 5812 6794 Restaurant, family: chain; Steak restaurant; Franchises, selling or licensing
Ch Bd: Sardar Biglari
**V Ch:* Philip L Cooley
VP: Kevin Beauchamp
VP: Robert L Grimm
VP: William Hart
VP: Elson Lynn
Board of Directors: Kenneth R Cooper, William L Johnson, James P Mastrian, Ruth J Person

D-U-N-S 08-029-1754
BIGMOUTHBEN CONVENIENCE STORE LLC (GA)
370 Auburn Ave Ne Ste A, Atlanta, GA 30312-1883
Tel (404) 331-3973 *Founded/Ownrshp* 2014
Sales 91.0MM *EMP* 2
SIC 5411 5947 Convenience stores; Souvenirs

D-U-N-S 82-943-0474
BILFINGER INDUSTRIAL SERVICES INC
(*Suby of* BILFINGER SE)
15933 Clayton Rd Ste 305, Ballwin, MO 63011-2172
Tel (636) 391-4500 *Founded/Ownrshp* 2013
Sales 396.2MME *EMP* 2,500E
Accts Ernst & Young Llp St Louis
SIC 1541 1731 1796 8711 8744 Industrial buildings & warehouses; Electrical work; Installing building equipment; Engineering services; Facilities support services
CEO: Boudewijn Van Lent
COO: John Herrin
CFO: Henrick Bormann
IT Man: Dan Bauman
IT Man: Connie Smith
Opers Mgr: Carlos Lange
Snr Mgr: Sean Agans

D-U-N-S 94-172-0567 IMP
BILFINGER TEPSCO INC
(*Suby of* BILFINGER SE)
2909 Aaron St, Deer Park, TX 77536-7626
Tel (281) 604-0309 *Founded/Ownrshp* 2004
Sales 338.7MME *EMP* 1,000
SIC 1623 Oil & gas pipeline construction
Pr: Hans Hansen

CFO: Darren Austin
CFO: Eric Kahn
VP: Oliver Puskac
QA Dir: Jimmy Lee

D-U-N-S 83-832-5954
BILFINGER WESTCON INC
WESTCON INDUSTRIES
(*Suby of* BILFINGER SE)
7401 Yukon Dr, Bismarck, ND 58503-9755
Tel (701) 222-0076 *Founded/Ownrshp* 1981
Sales 119.1MME *EMP* 1,500
SIC 1542 Commercial & office building contractors
Pr: Mark C Peterson
VP: Dave Hoff
VP: Mark Keller
QI Cn Mgr: Larry Rhinehart

D-U-N-S 12-725-6381
BILL & MELINDA GATES FOUNDATION
440 5th Ave N, Seattle, WA 98109-4631
Tel (206) 709-3100 *Founded/Ownrshp* 1997
Sales 6.7M *EMP* 1,376
SIC 8699 Charitable organization
CEO: Sue Desmond-Hellmann
**Ch Bd:* Bill Gates Sr
**Pr:* Christopher Elias
**Pr:* Patty Stonesifer
**COO:* Sylvia Mathews
COO: Gwen Sherman
Ofcr: MPH Amy Adelberger
Ofcr: Vincent Ahonkhai
Ofcr: Tom Vander Ark
Ofcr: Niranjan Bose
Ofcr: Connie Collingsworth
Ofcr: Janice Culpepper
Ofcr: Gina Dallabetta
Ofcr: Allison Davis
Ofcr: Elvis Fraser
Ofcr: Rob Horsch
Ofcr: Julie Jacobson
Ofcr: Regina Kapinga
Ofcr: Steve Landry
Ofcr: Deborah Lans
Ofcr: Elisa Mandell

D-U-N-S 03-598-6967
BILL ALEXANDER FORD LINCOLN MERCURY INC
801 E 32nd St, Yuma, AZ 85365-3432
Tel (928) 344-2200 *Founded/Ownrshp* 1980
Sales 90.4MM *EMP* 166
SIC 5511 New & used car dealers; Automobiles, new & used
Pr: Ryan Hancocl
**Treas:* Jeff Fritz
Sls Mgr: Chad Pierson

D-U-N-S 10-669-5203
▲ BILL BARRETT CORP
1099 18th St Ste 2300, Denver, CO 80202-1939
Tel (303) 293-9100 *Founded/Ownrshp* 2002
Sales 207.8MM *EMP* 139E
Tkr Sym BBG *Exch* NYS
SIC 1311 Crude petroleum & natural gas; Crude petroleum & natural gas production; Natural gas production
Pr: R Scot Woodall
**Ch Bd:* Jim W Mogg
Sr VP: William M Crawford
Sr VP: David R Macosko
Sr VP: Troy L Schindler
Sr VP: Kenneth A Wonstolen
Off Admin: Amber Martinez
Board of Directors: William F Owens, Edmund P Segner III, Randy I Stein, Michael E Wiley

D-U-N-S 08-416-4102
BILL CLARK HOMES LLC (NC)
200 E Arlington Blvd A, Greenville, NC 27858-5020
Tel (252) 355-5805 *Founded/Ownrshp* 1977
Sales 120.0MM *EMP* 103
SIC 1522 Residential construction
CEO: William H Clark
COO: Dan Koch
**CFO:* Kathryn Smith
CFO: Kathy Smith

D-U-N-S 03-277-1180
BILL CURRIE FORD INC
5815 N Dale Mabry Hwy, Tampa, FL 33614-5697
Tel (813) 872-5555 *Founded/Ownrshp* 1960
Sales 143.6MME *EMP* 312
SIC 5511 7538 Automobiles, new & used; Pickups, new & used; General automotive repair shops
Pr: Wilmer E Currie IV
**Treas:* Bruce Slusher
**Sec:* Alberto Diaz
**VP:* Jennifer L Currie Bellomo
**Genl Mgr:* Tim Joslin
Sales Asso: Mario Mirabal

D-U-N-S 04-252-7812
BILL DORAN CO
ROCKFORD INTL IMPORTERS
707 W Jefferson St, Rockford, IL 61101-6603
Tel (815) 965-8791 *Founded/Ownrshp* 1961
Sales 93.5MME *EMP* 251
SIC 5193 Flowers, fresh; Artificial flowers; Florists' supplies
Pr: William D Lafever
**Pr:* Patricia J La Fever

D-U-N-S 10-548-4724
BILL HILLARY & CHELSEA CLINTON FOUNDATION
1200 Prsident Clinton Ave, Little Rock, AR 72201-1749
Tel (501) 748-0471 *Founded/Ownrshp* 1997
Sales 148.8MM *EMP* 400
Accts Pricewaterhousecoopers Llp Ne
SIC 8399 Advocacy group
Pr: Bruce R Lindsey
**CFO:* Andrew Kessel
Comm Man: Ben Thielemier

D-U-N-S 17-481-5621 IMP
BILL JACOBS MOTORSPORT HOLDINGS INC
JACOBS, BILL BMW
1564 W Ogden Ave, Naperville, IL 60540-3957
Tel (630) 357-1200 *Founded/Ownrshp* 1985
Sales 98.4MME *EMP* 300
SIC 5511 5521 Automobiles, new & used; Used car dealers
Ch: William Jacobs
**Pr:* Denise Guardino
**VP:* John Martino
Store Mgr: Joe Hart
VP Mktg: Nancy Chafin
Sls Mgr: Ivan Corak
Sales Asso: Brian Kosanovich

D-U-N-S 03-257-2331 EXP
BILL USSERY MOTORS BODY SHOP INC
MERCEDES-BENZ OF CORAL GABLES
300 Almeria Ave, Coral Gables, FL 33134-5812
Tel (305) 445-8593 *Founded/Ownrshp* 1990
Sales 168.1MME *EMP* 485
SIC 5511 7538 Automobiles, new & used; General automotive repair shops
CEO: Robert W Brockway
**Pr:* Greg Barnes
**Treas:* Ronit Canet
**VP:* Paula Brockway

BILLABONG U S A
See BURLEIGH POINT LTD

D-U-N-S 07-979-9296
BILLERICA PUBLIC SCHOOLS
365 Boston Rd, Billerica, MA 01821-1892
Tel (978) 528-7900 *Founded/Ownrshp* 2015
Sales 18.6MME *EMP* 1,299E
SIC 8211 Public elementary & secondary schools
HC Dir: David Lezenski

D-U-N-S 06-892-0065
BILLINGS CLINIC (MT)
2800 10th Ave N, Billings, MT 59101-0703
Tel (406) 657-4000 *Founded/Ownrshp* 1917, 1993
Sales 565.5MM *EMP* 3,300
SIC 8062 General medical & surgical hospitals
CEO: Nicholas Wolter MD
**Ch Bd:* J Scott Millikan
**Pr:* Michael Schaer
CFO: Connie F Prewitt
**Treas:* Joy Ott
**VP:* Lyle R Knight
VP: Chris Stevens
**VP:* Maria Valandra
VP: Peggy Wharton
Dir Rad: Douglas Bell
MIS Dir: Scott Millikan
Board of Directors: William W Ballard, David Brown, Elizabeth Fulton, C H McCracken III MD, Joy N Ott, Aaron Sparboe

BILLINGS PUBLIC SCHOOLS
See BILLINGS SCHOOL DISTRICT 2

D-U-N-S 06-892-7722
BILLINGS SCHOOL DISTRICT 2 (MT)
BILLINGS PUBLIC SCHOOLS
415 N 30th St, Billings, MT 59101-1298
Tel (406) 281-5000 *Founded/Ownrshp* 1885
Sales 147.7MM *EMP* 2,000
Accts Eide Bailly Llp Billings Mo
SIC 8211 Public elementary school; Public junior high school; Public senior high school; Public vocational/technical school
**CFO:* Michael Arnold
Ex Dir: Brenda Koch
Ex Dir: Jeana Lervick

D-U-N-S 08-550-3147 IMP
BILLION TOWER INTL LLC
MACHINE CLOTHING COMPANY
989 6th Ave Fl 8, New York, NY 10018-0871
Tel (212) 220-0608 *Founded/Ownrshp* 1999
Sales 122.0MM *EMP* 15
SIC 2326 5136 Men's & boys' work clothing; Men's & boys' clothing

D-U-N-S 87-888-7876
BILLOWS ELECTRIC SUPPLY CO INC
1813 Underwood Blvd, Delran, NJ 08075-1232
Tel (215) 332-9700 *Founded/Ownrshp* 1990
Sales 243.0MME *EMP* 200
SIC 5063 3679 3621 3643 3644 Electrical supplies; Lighting fixtures; Electronic circuits; Motors & generators; Current-carrying wiring devices; Noncurrent-carrying wiring devices
CEO: John P Ruszel II
Pr: Jeff Billow
COO: Bob White
CFO: Scott Pressler
VP: Mitch Billows
VP: Mike Cucinotta
CIO: Wayne Kessler

BILL'S AUTO SERVICE
See TOWN AND COUNTRY CO-OP INC

D-U-N-S 00-506-2947
BILLY GRAHAM EVANGELISTIC ASSN
1 Billy Graham Pkwy, Charlotte, NC 28201-0001
Tel (704) 401-2432 *Founded/Ownrshp* 2008
Sales 85.6MM *EMP* 18E
Accts Cherry Beckaert & Holland Llp
SIC 8661 Covenant & Evangelical Church
Pr: Franklin Graham
Pr: Kathy Yokeley
Sr VP: Kenneth Barun

D-U-N-S 82-867-7109
■ BILOXI HMA LLC
(*Suby of* HMA) ★
150 Reynoir St, Biloxi, MS 39530-4130
Tel (228) 432-1571 *Founded/Ownrshp* 2008
Sales 142.6MME *EMP* 450E
SIC 8062 General medical & surgical hospitals
Ch: William J Schoen
Chf Rad: Douglas Cosentino
**Pr:* Joseph V Vumbacco

VP: John P Vollmer
HC Dir: Barbara Breal

D-U-N-S 78-848-8740
■ BILOXI REGIONAL MEDICAL CENTER INC
(*Suby of* BILOXI HMA LLC) ★
150 Reynoir St, Biloxi, MS 39530-4199
Tel (228) 432-1571 *Founded/Ownrshp* 1981
Sales 142.6MM *EMP* 450
SIC 8062 Hospital, AMA approved residency
CEO: Monte Bostwick
**Pr:* Joseph V Vumbacco
**COO:* Joshua Self
**COO:* Joan Strayham
**CFO:* Mark Wack
**Ch:* William J Schoen
Ex VP: Lori Bickel

BILT-RITE MASTEX
See MUTUAL INDUSTRIES NORTH INC

D-U-N-S 00-316-8655 IMP
BILTMORE CO
BILTMORE ESTATE
1 Lodge St, Asheville, NC 28803-2662
Tel (828) 225-6776 *Founded/Ownrshp* 1932
Sales 138.8MM^E *EMP* 1,900
SIC 7999 5947 5812 Tourist attraction, commercial; Gift shop; Souvenirs; Restaurant, family: independent; Snack bar
CEO: Bill Cecil
V Ch: Steve Miller
**Pr:* William Cecil Jr
**CFO:* Stephen Watson
**Ch:* Diana Cecil Pickering
**Sr VP:* Stephen Miller
**Sr VP:* George Pickering II
Sr VP: Steve Watson
**VP:* Ann Ashley
**VP:* Mary Cecil
VP: Ted Katsigianis
**VP:* Diana Pickering
Exec: Richard Boyer
Creative D: Shuler Russell

BILTMORE ESTATE
See BILTMORE CO

D-U-N-S 00-524-5345 IMP/EXP
BIMBA MANUFACTURING CO INC
25150 S Governors Hwy, University Park, IL 60484
Tel (708) 534-8544 *Founded/Ownrshp* 1969
Sales 134.8MM^E *EMP* 488
SIC 3593 Fluid power cylinders, hydraulic or pneumatic
Ch Bd: Charles W Bimba Jr
**Pr:* Patrick J Ormsby
**CFO:* William Gorski
Ofcr: Scott Szafasz
**VP:* Mary Fote
Rgnl Mgr: Adam Schrank
Genl Mgr: Darren Burrell
Dir IT: David Gillhouse
Sfty Mgr: Michael Maziur
QI Cn Mgr: Jatin Rai
Mktg Dir: Tom Wood

BIMBO BAKERIES USA
See BIMBO FOODS BAKERIES INC

D-U-N-S 12-909-4921 IMP
BIMBO BAKERIES USA INC
(*Suby of* BBU INC) ★
255 Business Center Dr # 200, Horsham, PA 19044-3424
Tel (215) 347-5500 *Founded/Ownrshp* 1993
Sales 10.8MMM^E *EMP* 26,000
SIC 2051 Bakery: wholesale or wholesale/retail combined
Pr: Alfred Penny
Sr VP: Jim Brennan
Sr VP: Andy Lang
VP: Joe Dangelmaier
VP: Jack French
VP: Len Heflich
VP: Sharon Hoyle
VP: Michelle Knibbs
VP: John Lee
VP: Juan Muldoon
VP: Greg Stehr

D-U-N-S 96-237-3510 IMP
BIMBO FOODS BAKERIES INC
BIMBO BAKERIES USA
(*Suby of* BIMBO BAKERIES USA INC) ★
40 Harold Ct, Bay Shore, NY 11706-2220
Tel (631) 273-6000 *Founded/Ownrshp* 2009
Sales 2.0MMM^E *EMP* 15,000
SIC 2051

D-U-N-S 01-180-6452 IMP/EXP
BINDER MACHINERY CO INC (NJ)
2820 Hamilton Blvd, South Plainfield, NJ 07080-2597
Tel (908) 561-9000 *Founded/Ownrshp* 1957
Sales 110.8MM^E *EMP* 177
SIC 5082 5084 7353 7699 General construction machinery & equipment; Tractors, construction; Excavating machinery & equipment; Compaction equipment; Heavy construction equipment rental; Construction equipment repair; Tractor repair; Hydraulic equipment repair
Ch Bd: Robert C Binder
**Pr:* Brendan Binder
**CFO:* Joseph Vazzano
**VP:* William Kretschmer
Genl Mgr: Armand Pizza

BINDLEY WESTERN DRUG
See CARDINAL HEALTH 100 INC

D-U-N-S 92-769-1063 IMP/EXP
BINEX LINE CORP
19515 S Vermont Ave, Torrance, CA 90502-1121
Tel (310) 416-8600 *Founded/Ownrshp* 1995
Sales 94.4MM^E *EMP* 160
Accts C And Y Accountants Inc Los
SIC 4731 4513 Freight transportation arrangement; Air courier services
Pr: David Paek

COO: James Yoon
**CFO:* Hyun K Cho
**VP:* Tim Park
Genl Mgr: Jan Mercado

D-U-N-S 03-393-3193
BINGHAM COOPERATIVE INC
FARM MART 11755
477 W Highway 26, Blackfoot, ID 83221-5521
Tel (208) 785-3440 *Founded/Ownrshp* 1939
Sales 115.1MM^E *EMP* 80
SIC 5191 5171 5541 Fertilizer & fertilizer materials; Chemicals, agricultural; Petroleum bulk stations; Filling stations, gasoline
Pr: Lance Gardener
CFO: Daryn Brasher
**VP:* Mark Beck

BINGHAM MEMORIAL HOSPITAL
See BMH INC

BINGHAMTON GENERAL HOSPITAL
See UNITED HEALTH SERVICES HOSPITAL INC

D-U-N-S 02-196-8495
BINGHAMTON UNIVERSITY
(*Suby of* SUNY ADMINISTRATION) ★
4400 Vestal Pkwy, Binghamton, NY 13902-4600
Tel (607) 777-2000 *Founded/Ownrshp* 1946
Sales 142.6MM^E *EMP* 1,500^E
SIC 8221 9411 Colleges universities & professional schools; Administration of educational programs;
Pr: Harvey Stenger
Pr: Gail Glover
Ofcr: Sheila Cheevers
Ex VP: Brandon Evans
VP: George S Bobinski
VP: Jeffrey B Donahue
VP: Lawrence Roma
VP: Brian Rose
VP: Gerald Sonnenfeld
Assoc Dir: Jeff Hadley
Assoc Dir: Jennifer Keegin
Assoc Dir: Jim Norris
Assoc Dir: Dave Simek
Comm Dir: Katie Ellis

D-U-N-S 62-513-2097
BINGO POTAWATOMI
POTAWATOMI BINGO CASINO
1721 W Canal St, Milwaukee, WI 53233-2655
Tel (414) 645-6888 *Founded/Ownrshp* 1991
Sales 54.8MM^E *EMP* 1,500
SIC 7999 5812 5947 Bingo hall; Gambling & lottery services; Cafeteria; Gift shop
Genl Mgr: Mike Goodrich
COO: Nancy Ziolkowski
Ofcr: Jason Corbin
Ofcr: Paul Lurenz
Exec: Tom Holtz
Exec: Jennifer Spaeth
Mktg Dir: Lee Harden
Mktg Dir: Kip Ritchie
Pr Mgr: Colleen Moore
Sls Mgr: Megan Moore
Sls Mgr: Lisa Pederson

D-U-N-S 01-166-0610
BINSKY & SNYDER LLC
BINSKY & SNYDER MECH CONTRS
281 Centennial Ave Ste 1, Piscataway, NJ 08854-3949
Tel (732) 885-0700 *Founded/Ownrshp* 2005
Sales 127.1MM^E *EMP* 400
Accts Max Bussel And Company South
SIC 1711 8711 Mechanical contractor; Heating & ventilation engineering
Pr: Robert B Snyder Sr
**Treas:* Frank J Sullivan
Ofcr: Robert Colon
Ofcr: Michael Duffy
**VP:* Phillip J Andreoli
VP: John Collins
**VP:* William J Mc Kean
VP: William J McKean
Off Admin: Melissa Lash
Dir IT: Chris Snyder
IT Man: Micky Hunt

BINSKY & SNYDER MECH CONTRS
See BINSKY & SNYDER LLC

BIO DOMES HEADGEAR
See BIO WORLD MERCHANDISING INC

D-U-N-S 05-634-0722 IMP/EXP
BIO MEDIC CORP
742 Sussex Ave, Seaford, DE 19973-2057
Tel (302) 628-4300 *Founded/Ownrshp* 1971
Sales 116.2MM^E *EMP* 550
SIC 5049 3821 3496 3914 3661 Laboratory equipment, except medical or dental; Laboratory apparatus & furniture; Cages, wire; Cutlery; Telephones & telephone apparatus
Ch Bd: George Gabriel
**VP:* Frank Marinaccio
**VP:* Edmond Silverberg

D-U-N-S 07-568-4324 IMP
BIO MEDICAL APPLICATIONS OF FLORIDA INC (DE)
ARTIFICIAL KIDNEY CENTER RI
(*Suby of* FRESENIUS MEDICAL CARE BETEILIGUNGSGES. MBH)
920 Winter St Ste A, Waltham, MA 02451-1519
Tel (781) 699-9000 *Founded/Ownrshp* 1971
Sales 85.6MM^E *EMP* 700^E
SIC 8092 Kidney dialysis centers
CEO: Ronald Kuerbitz
**Pr:* Nicholas R Brownlee
CFO: Kelly George
CFO: Chris Peter
**Ex VP:* Simon Castellanos
**VP:* Heinz Schmidt
Ex Dir: Stanley Buck
Area Mgr: Catherine Quinn
Brnch Mgr: Dan Stephenson
Genl Mgr: Steve Johnson
CTO: Kim Rick

D-U-N-S 08-760-7334 IMP/EXP
BIO WORLD MERCHANDISING INC
BIO DOMES HEADGEAR
2111 W Walnut Hill Ln, Irving, TX 75038-4406
Tel (888) 831-2138 *Founded/Ownrshp* 1998
Sales 215.6MM *EMP* 240^E
Accts Bkd Llp Dallas Texas
SIC 2353 3161 2253 5199 3021 Hats & caps; Clothing & apparel carrying cases; Hats & headwear, knit; Leather goods, except footwear, gloves, luggage, belting; Rubber & plastics footwear
Pr: Rajeev Malik
**Treas:* Mona Malik
**Ex VP:* Omar Cantu
VP: Brad Coleman
VP: Jerry Koske
IT Man: Brian Fenner
IT Man: Patrick Flanagan
Natl Sales: David Bowsher
Sls&Mrk Ex: Mayes Jason
Sls&Mrk Ex: Jason Mayes
Snr Mgr: Shawn Stauffer

D-U-N-S 01-617-1444 EXP
BIO-ENGINEERED SUPPLEMENTS & NUTRITION INC
BSN
(*Suby of* GLANBIA PUBLIC LIMITED COMPANY)
5901 Broken Sound Pkwy Nw, Boca Raton, FL 33487-2773
Tel (561) 994-8335 *Founded/Ownrshp* 2001, 2011
Sales 91.4MM^E *EMP* 130
SIC 5122 5499 Vitamins & minerals; Health & dietetic food stores
Pr: Christopher Ferguson
**VP:* Scott James

D-U-N-S 00-328-6218 EXP
BIO-LAB INC (GA)
(*Suby of* KIK DANVILLE) ★
1725 N Brown Rd, Lawrenceville, GA 30043-8119
Tel (678) 502-4000 *Founded/Ownrshp* 1955, 2014
Sales 453.4MM^E *EMP* 800
SIC 2812 2819 2899 Alkalies; Chlorine, compressed or liquefied; Elements; Chemical preparations
CEO: Jon Viner
VP: Jean Hildesheim
Comm Dir: Brian Payseno
Mng Dir: Benny Bien
CIO: Honghong GE
Opers Mgr: Sherri Lanham
Plnt Mgr: Gary Miligan
Sales Exec: Allen Schnaak
Mktg Mgr: Ryan Andersen
Mktg Mgr: Joe Defuria
Sls Mgr: Tim Berry

D-U-N-S 07-951-6589
BIO-MEDICAL APPLICATIONS MANAGEMENT CO INC
(*Suby of* NATIONAL MEDICAL CARE INC) ★
95 Hayden Ave, Lexington, MA 02421-7942
Tel (781) 402-9000 *Founded/Ownrshp* 1971
Sales 302.1MM^E *EMP* 16,078
SIC 8092 Kidney dialysis centers
Pr: Rice Powell
**CFO:* Angelo Moesslang
**Treas:* Mark Fawcett
**Ex VP:* Ronald J Kuerbitz
**VP:* Douglas G Kott
**VP:* Robert McGorty
**VP:* Joseph J Ruma

D-U-N-S 83-157-2776
BIO-MEDICAL APPLICATIONS OF CALIFORNIA INC
(*Suby of* BIO-MEDICAL APPLICATIONS MANAGEMENT CO INC) ★
920 Winter St, Waltham, MA 02451-1521
Tel (781) 699-4404 *Founded/Ownrshp* 2009
Sales 16.6MM^E *EMP* 1,104^E
SIC 8092 Kidney dialysis centers
Pr: Ben J Lipps

D-U-N-S 83-158-9788
BIO-MEDICAL APPLICATIONS OF NORTH CAROLINA INC
(*Suby of* BIO-MEDICAL APPLICATIONS MANAGEMENT CO INC) ★
920 Winter St, Waltham, MA 02451-1521
Tel (781) 699-4404 *Founded/Ownrshp* 1990
Sales 27.6MM^E *EMP* 1,540^E
SIC 8092 Kidney dialysis centers
Pr: Rice Powell
**Treas:* Mark Fawcett
**VP:* Robert McGorty

D-U-N-S 00-912-7663 IMP/EXP
▲ BIO-RAD LABORATORIES INC
1000 Alfred Nobel Dr, Hercules, CA 94547-1898
Tel (510) 724-7000 *Founded/Ownrshp* 1952
Sales 2.0MMM *EMP* 7,770^E
Tkr Sym BIO *Exch* NYS
SIC 3826 3845 2835 Analytical instruments; Electrophoresis equipment; Chromatographic equipment, laboratory type; Spectrometers; Electromedical equipment; In vitro & in vivo diagnostic substances
Ch Bd: Norman Schwartz
COO: John Goetz
CFO: Christine A Tsingos
Treas: Ronald W Hutton
Ex VP: Michael Crowley
Ex VP: Giovanni Magni
Ex VP: Janie Ramirez
Ex VP: Shawn M Soderberg
VP: Richard Danielson
VP: Leo Kaabi
VP: James Stark
Board of Directors: Louis Drapeau, Robert M Malchione, Joel McComb, Deborah J Neff, Alice N Schwartz

D-U-N-S 12-157-1798 IMP
■ BIO-REFERENCE LABORATORIES INC
(*Suby of* OPKO HEALTH INC) ★
481 Edward H Ross Dr, Elmwood Park, NJ 07407-3128
Tel (201) 791-2600 *Founded/Ownrshp* 2015
Sales 442.3MM^E *EMP* 4,347
SIC 8071 8734 Medical laboratories; Testing laboratories
CEO: Marc D Grodman
Pr: Gregory Henderson
COO: Howard Dubinett
COO: Dean Gaalaas
CFO: Nicholas Papazicos
Chf Mktg O: James Weisberger
Sr VP: Wendy Chung
Sr VP: Richard Faherty
Sr VP: Richard L Faherty
Sr VP: Charles T Todd Jr
VP: Maryanne Amato
VP: Nick Cetani
VP: Joe Donahue
VP: Scott Fein
VP: Sally Howlett
VP: Brian T Jones
VP: David Liss
VP: John Littleton
VP: Michael Molinaro
VP: Thomas Pasko
VP: Azmy Awad PH
Board of Directors: Joseph Benincasa, Harry Elias, Gary Lederman, John Roglieri

D-U-N-S 19-668-7362
▲ BIO-TECHNE CORP
614 Mckinley Pl Ne, Minneapolis, MN 55413-2610
Tel (612) 379-8854 *Founded/Ownrshp* 1976
Sales 499.0MM *EMP* 1,560^E
Accts Kpmg Llp Minneapolis Minneso
Tkr Sym TECH *Exch* NGS
SIC 2835 8731 Microbiology & virology diagnostic products; Hemotology diagnostic agents; Commercial physical research
Pr: Charles R Kummeth
**Ch Bd:* Robert V Baumgartner
CFO: James T Hippel
**V Ch Bd:* Roger C Lucas
Bd of Dir: Howard Oconnell
Sr VP: Brenda S Furlow
Sr VP: Robert Gavin
Sr VP: Kevin Gould
VP: David Eansor
VP: Karen Padgett
CTO: J Fernando Bazan
Board of Directors: Charles A Dinarello, John L Higgins, Karen A Holbrook, Randolph C Steer, Harold Wiens

D-U-N-S 78-807-9473
BIOCLINICA INC
2005 S Easton Rd Ste 304, Doylestown, PA 18901-7101
Tel (267) 757-3000 *Founded/Ownrshp* 2016
Sales 143.0MM^E *EMP* 757^E
Accts Pricewaterhousecoopers Llp Ph
SIC 8734 Testing laboratories
Pr: John Hubbard
Pr: Mukhtar Ahmed
Pr: Peter S Benton
Pr: David S Herron
Pr: Elizabeth Thiele
COO: Ross Mason
CFO: Ted I Kaminer
Ex VP: Carmella Griffin
Ex VP: Garry D Johnson
Ex VP: Maria Krus
Ex VP: David Peters
Sr VP: Andrew Masters
Sr VP: Angelo Stortini
VP: Dawn Flitcraft
VP: Paul Hopper
VP: Cheryl Schneider
Assoc Dir: Shaomin Yao

D-U-N-S 13-839-6739
BIOCON INC
125 May St, Edison, NJ 08837-3264
Tel (732) 661-0202 *Founded/Ownrshp* 2003
Sales 26.2MM^E *EMP* 1,100^E
SIC 8731 Biotechnical research, commercial
Pr: Bruce Stroever
**CFO:* Michael Kawas
**Ex VP:* Martha Anderson
**Ex VP:* Arthur A Gertzman
**Ex VP:* George A Oram
VP: Hans Burchardt
VP: Michael Schuler
VP: Joe Yaccarino
Off Mgr: Pat Archambault

D-U-N-S 55-691-5205
BIOFIRE DEFENSE LLC
79 W 4500 S Ste 14, Salt Lake City, UT 84107-2863
Tel (801) 262-3592 *Founded/Ownrshp* 1990
Sales 135.9MM^E *EMP* 300
SIC 3829 3826 6794 Measuring & controlling devices; Analytical instruments; Patent buying, licensing, leasing
VP: Kim David
Sls Mgr: Christina Flowers
Sls Mgr: Cameron Gundry
Sls Mgr: Kathleen Stewart
Board of Directors: Herm Rosenman

D-U-N-S 03-348-9186
■ BIOFUSION LLC
(*Suby of* KROGER SPECIALTY PHARMACY HOLDINGS I INC) ★
19110 Van Ness Ave, Torrance, CA 90501-1101
Tel (310) 803-8100 *Founded/Ownrshp* 2010
Sales 85.0MM *EMP* 80
SIC 8011 Medical centers
CFO: Dominic Meffe
Pr: Dinesh Patel
CFO: Vincent Cook
Ex Dir: Bob Rabone
Sls Dir: Viki Figge

D-U-N-S 12-137-6230 IMP/EXP
▲ BIOGEN INC
225 Binney St, Cambridge, MA 02142-1031
Tel (617) 679-2000 Founded/Ownrshp 1985
Sales 9.7MMM EMP 7,350
Tkr Sym BIIB Exch NGS
SIC 2834 2836 8731 Pharmaceutical preparations; Biological products, except diagnostic; Biological research
CEO: George A Scangos
*Ch Bd: Stelios Papadopoulos
CFO: Paul J Clancy
Treas: Michael Dambach
Ofcr: Michael F Maclean
Ex VP: John G Cox
Ex VP: Kenneth Di Pietro
Ex VP: Kenneth Dipetrio
Ex VP: Michael D Ehlers
Ex VP: Scott Handren
Ex VP: Adriana Karaboutis
Ex VP: Tony Kingsley
Ex VP: Alfred W Sandrock Jr
Ex VP: Michel Vounatsos
Sr VP: Paul Grint
VP: Andrew Allen
VP: Gary Bloomgren
VP: Katja Buller
VP: Olivier Danos
VP: Scott Dreyer
VP: Thorsten Eickenhorst
Board of Directors: Alexander J Denner, Caroline D Dorsa, Nancy L Leaming, Richard C Mulligan, Robert W Pangia, Brian S Posner, Eric K Rowinsky, Lynn Schenk, Stephen A Sherwin

D-U-N-S 03-833-9180 IMP
■ BIOGEN MA INC
(Suby of BIOGEN INC) ★
133 Boston Post Rd, Weston, MA 02493-2525
Tel (617) 679-2000 Founded/Ownrshp 2003
Sales 209.9MM^E EMP 500
SIC 2836 8731 Biological products, except diagnostic; Commercial research laboratory
CEO: George A Scangos
*CFO: Paul J Clancy
*Ex VP: Susan H Alexander
*Ex VP: John G Cox
*Ex VP: Kenneth Dipietro
*Ex VP: Steven H Holtzman
*Sr VP: Spyros Artavanis Tsakonas
VP: Michael Gilman
VP: Robert A Hamm
VP: Michael D Kowolenko
VP: Mark W Leuchtenberger

D-U-N-S 04-115-6514 IMP
BIOLA UNIVERSITY INC
TALBOT SCHOOL OF THEOLOGY
13800 Biola Ave, La Mirada, CA 90639-0001
Tel (562) 903-6000 Founded/Ownrshp 1908
Sales 161.5MM EMP 1,000^E
Accts Grant Thornton Llp Los Angele
SIC 8221 University
Pr: Barry H Corey
VP: Gregory Balsano
VP: Lisa Boulanger
VP: Sean Connally
VP: Gary Deweese
VP: Rebecca Hope
*VP: Carl Schreiber
VP: Scott Sevier
VP: Micah Snell
VP: Dr Wesley Willmer
Dir Surg: Donald B Sims Jr

D-U-N-S 13-541-7215
■ BIOLAB WATER ADDITIVES
(Suby of GREAT LAKES CHEMICAL CORP) ★
N Brown Rd, Lawrenceville, GA 30045
Tel (678) 502-4699 Founded/Ownrshp 2003
Sales 100.0MM^E EMP 4^E
SIC 5169 Chemical additives
Pr: Mark Bulriss
VP: Helmut Baker

D-U-N-S 04-750-1788
BIOLIFE PLASMA SERVICES LP
203 N Center Dr, North Brunswick, NJ 08902-4246
Tel (732) 422-4200 Founded/Ownrshp 2001
Sales 510.1MM^E EMP 1,200
SIC 5122 Blood plasma
Pr: Joseph Rosen
VP: Frank Bergonzi
Dir IT: Gary Dietz

D-U-N-S 16-790-6627
BIOLIFE PLASMA SERVICES LP
(Suby of BAXALTA INC) ★
1435 Lake Cook Rd, Philadelphia, PA 19182-0001
Tel (847) 940-5559 Founded/Ownrshp 2015
Sales 280.5MM^E EMP 3,000
SIC 5122 8099 Blood plasma; Plasmapherous center
Genl Pt: Dennis Young

D-U-N-S 00-700-4745
▲ BIOMARIN PHARMACEUTICAL INC
770 Lindaro St, San Rafael, CA 94901-3991
Tel (415) 506-6700 Founded/Ownrshp 1997
Sales 889.9MM EMP 2,158
Tkr Sym BMRN Exch NGS
SIC 2834 2835 Pharmaceutical preparations; Enzyme & isoenzyme diagnostic agents
Ch Bd: Jean-Jacques Bienaime
CFO: Daniel Spiegelman
Chf Mktg O: Henry J Fuchs
Ofcr: Jeff Ajer
Ex VP: Robert A Baffi
Ex VP: G Eric Davis
Ex VP: Daniel K Spiegelman
VP: Shripad Bhagwat
VP: Luisa Bigornia
VP: Karen Kistler
VP: Louis Kyjovsky
VP: Brian R Mueller
VP: Brian Mueller
VP: Patrick Pallansch
Board of Directors: Dennis J Slamon, Willard Dere, Kathryn E Falberg, Michael G Grey, Elaine J Heron, Pierre Lapalme, V Bryan Lawlis, Alan J Lewis, Richard A Meier, David Pyott

D-U-N-S 18-957-8800 IMP
BIOMAT USA INC
(Suby of GRIFOLS SHARED SERVICES NORTH AMERICA INC) ★
2410 Lillyvale Ave, Los Angeles, CA 90032-3514
Tel (323) 225-2221 Founded/Ownrshp 2007
Sales 147.1MM^E EMP 1,500
SIC 8099 Plasmapherous center
CEO: Gregory Rich
CFO: Jerry L Burdick
CFO: Max Debrouwer
Treas: Javier Chagoyen
*Ex VP: Shinji Wada
*VP: David Bell
VP: Eric Segal
Genl Mgr: Dan Davis
Board of Directors: Alfredo Arroyo, Tomas Daga, Thomas Glanzmann Chb, Victor Grifols, Ramon Riera, Dr Marla Salmon, Juan Ignacio Twose

D-U-N-S 15-632-6063
BIOMED REALTY LP
(Suby of BIOMED REALTY TRUST INC) ★
17190 Bernardo Center Dr, San Diego, CA 92128-7030
Tel (858) 485-9840 Founded/Ownrshp 2004
Sales 674.6MM EMP 247^E
SIC 6798 6531 Real estate investment trusts; Real estate brokers & agents
VP: Kent Griffin

D-U-N-S 15-952-9572
BIOMED REALTY TRUST INC
17190 Bernardo Center Dr, San Diego, CA 92128-7030
Tel (858) 485-9840 Founded/Ownrshp 2004
Sales 674.6MM EMP 235
Accts Kpmg Llp San Diego Californ
SIC 6798 Real estate investment trusts
Ch Bd: Alan D Gold
Pr: R Kent Griffin Jr
CFO: Kent R Griffin
CFO: Greg N Lubushkin
Ex VP: Gary A Kreitzer
Ex VP: Matthew G McDevitt
Ex VP: Karen A Sztraicher
Ex VP: John Wilson
Sr VP: John P Bonanno
Sr VP: Daniel C Cramer
Sr VP: Anne Hoffman
VP: David Hsiao
VP: Janice Kameir
VP: Kevin M Simonsen
VP: Robert Sistek

D-U-N-S 18-475-0008
BIOMEDICAL RESEARCH FOUNDATION OF NORTHWEST LOUISIANA
2031 Kings Hwy, Shreveport, LA 71103-3600
Tel (318) 716-4100 Founded/Ownrshp 1986
Sales 502.5MM EMP 50
Accts Postlethwaite & Netterville B
SIC 8733 8732 Scientific research agency; Medical research; Economic research
Ch Bd: Stephen F Skrivanos
*Treas: Arthur Thompson
Ofcr: Stephen Lokitz
*VP: James D Dean
*VP: Dennis Lower
*Prin: John F George Jr
Ex Dir: John Miralles
Admn Mgr: Khris Engel
Pharmcst: Frank Watson
Med Dir: David L D
Corp Couns: Hilary Wooley

D-U-N-S 08-678-5110 IMP
BIOMERIEUX INC
(Suby of BIOMERIEUX SA)
100 Rodolphe St, Durham, NC 27712-9402
Tel (919) 620-2000 Founded/Ownrshp 1988
Sales 312.4MM^E EMP 1,000
SIC 3845 8071 3841 3826 Automated blood & body fluid analyzers, except laboratory; Medical laboratories; Surgical & medical instruments; Analytical instruments
Pr: Marc Mackowiak
*CFO: Brian Armstrong
CFO: Lynne Hohlfeld
Ofcr: Linh Le
VP: Phyllis Granados
VP: Stan Gregory
VP: Nadia Hammad
VP: Jocelyne Latour
Ex Dir: John Klecker
CTO: Ronald Altman
CTO: Scott McKeel

D-U-N-S 18-612-7825 EXP
■ BIOMET 3I LLC
3I IMPLANT INNOVATIONS
(Suby of ZIMMER BIOMET) ★
4555 Riverside Dr, Palm Beach Gardens, FL 33410-4200
Tel (561) 775-9928 Founded/Ownrshp 1987
Sales 150.2MM^E EMP 600
SIC 3843 Dental materials
Sr VP: Renaat Vermeulen
QC Dir: Tammy Igo
Prd Mgr: James Scott

BIOMET BONE HEALING TECH
See EBI LLC

D-U-N-S 08-678-2224 IMP/EXP
■ BIOMET INC
ZIMMER BIOMET
(Suby of LVB ACQUISITION INC) ★
56 E Bell Dr, Warsaw, IN 46582-6924
Tel (574) 267-6639 Founded/Ownrshp 1977, 2007
Sales 3.2MMM EMP 9,279
SIC 3842 3841 3845 Surgical appliances & supplies; Supports: abdominal, ankle, arch, kneecap, etc.; Surgical appliances & supplies; Implants, surgical; Surgical & medical instruments; Medical instruments & equipment, blood & bone work; Surgical instruments & apparatus; Suction therapy apparatus; Electromedical equipment; Electromedical apparatus; Ultrasonic medical equipment, except cleaning
Pr: Daniel P Florin
Pr: Thomas R Allen
Ofcr: Belinda Bowman
Ex VP: Carolyn Knight
Sr VP: Robin T Barney
Sr VP: Adam R Johnson
Sr VP: Steven F Schiess
Sr VP: Bradley J Tandy
VP: Matt Abernethy
VP: Tony W Collins
VP: Ross Erickson
VP: Natasha Gladstone
VP: Jonathan Grandon
VP: Brad Hall
VP: Mark Leuchtenberger
VP: Daniel Williamson
Dir Lab: Kelly Howard
Board of Directors: Chad F Phipps

D-U-N-S 12-927-8169
■ BIOMET ORTHOPEDICS LLC
(Suby of ZIMMER BIOMET HOLDINGS INC) ★
56 E Bell Dr, Warsaw, IN 46582-6924
Tel (574) 267-6639 Founded/Ownrshp 2015
Sales 228.8MM^E EMP 2,500
SIC 3842 Implants, surgical
Pr: Jeffrey R Binder
Sr Pt: Gary England
CFO: Richard Fradette
Ex VP: Nancy Cooper
Ex VP: Brian Linneman
Ex VP: Gregg Seibert
Off Mgr: Kaye Pentz

D-U-N-S 96-781-3267
■ BIOMETRICS IDENTITY MANAGEMENT AGENCY
(Suby of OFFICE OF THE SECRETARY OF DEFENSE) ★
340 Washington Ave, Clarksburg, WV 26301-2922
Tel (304) 326-3000 Founded/Ownrshp 2011
Sales NA EMP 5,011^E
SIC 9711 National security;

D-U-N-S 14-722-7730
BIORELIANCE CORP
(Suby of MILLIPORE SIGMA) ★
14920 Broschart Rd, Rockville, MD 20850-3304
Tel (301) 738-1000 Founded/Ownrshp 2012
Sales 114.0MM^E EMP 700^E
SIC 8734 8731 Testing laboratories; Biological research
Ch Bd: David A Dodd
Pr: Charles Harwood
CFO: John Green
CFO: David S Walker
Ofcr: David E Onions
VP: David Bellitt
VP: Darryl L Goss
VP: James J Kramer
VP: Philip A Theodore
VP: Michael E Wiebe PHD
Dir Lab: Jason Andrew
Dir Lab: Andrew Kerr

D-U-N-S 16-514-1289
■ BIORX LLC
THRIVERX
(Suby of DIPLOMAT PHARMACY INC) ★
7167 E Kemper Rd, Cincinnati, OH 45249-1028
Tel (866) 442-4679 Founded/Ownrshp 2015
Sales 112.1MM^E EMP 200^E
SIC 5122 8748 2834 5047 8051 Pharmaceuticals; Business consulting; Pharmaceutical preparations; Intravenous solutions; Medical & hospital equipment; Medical equipment & supplies; Skilled nursing care facilities; Extended care facility; Convalescent home with continuous nursing care
Treas: Lisa McEvoy
VP: Jennifer Arms
Dir Rx: Chris Ball
Dir Bus: Julie Winton
Mtls Mgr: Derrick Loudermilk
Mktg Dir: John Louis
Sls Dir: Courtney Remley
Sls Mgr: Cynthia Hale
Sales Asso: Alexis Dever
Pharmcst: Brian Baker
Pharmcst: Kristen Goetz

D-U-N-S 95-712-6931 IMP
▲ BIOSCRIP INC
1600 Broadway Ste 700, Denver, CO 80202-4967
Tel (720) 697-5200 Founded/Ownrshp 1996
Sales 982.2MM EMP 2,286^E
Tkr Sym BIOS Exch NGS
SIC 8059 6411 Personal care home, with health care; Medical insurance claim processing, contract or fee basis
Pr: Richard M Smith
COO: Chris Luthin
CFO: Jeffrey M Kreger
Sr VP: David Evans
Sr VP: Betty Jang
Sr VP: C Britt Jeffcoat
Sr VP: Brian Stiver
Board of Directors: Michael Bronfein, David W Golding, Michael Goldstein, Tricia Nguyen, R Carter Pate, Christopher S Shackelton

D-U-N-S 94-145-4936
■ BIOSCRIP INFUSION SERVICES LLC
(Suby of BIOSCRIP INC) ★
102 The American Rd, Morris Plains, NJ 07950-2443
Tel (973) 597-0444 Founded/Ownrshp 2000
Sales 9.4MM^E EMP 2,000
SIC 5047 Medical equipment & supplies
CEO: Richard M Smith
CFO: Donna Glessing
*Sr VP: David Evans
*Sr VP: Chris Luthin
*Sr VP: Kathryn Stalmack
*VP: Jeffrey M Kreger
Exec: Annette Immella
Sales Exec: Sal Rafanelli

D-U-N-S 80-569-8438
■ BIOSCRIP PHARMACY INC
(Suby of BIOSCRIP INC) ★
10050 Crosstown Cir # 300, Eden Prairie, MN 55344-3344
Tel (952) 979-3600 Founded/Ownrshp 2005
Sales 344.7MM^E EMP 2,000
SIC 5912 Drug stores & proprietary stores
Pr: Richard M Smith
*Ch Bd: Richard Freedman
*Ch Bd: Myron Holubiak
COO: Tom Ordeman
COO: Anthony Zappa
CFO: John Ciuffo
*CFO: Hai Tran
Treas: Gregory H Keane
Sr VP: Russel J Corvese
*Sr VP: David Evans
Sr VP: David J Evans
Sr VP: Colleen M Lederer
*Sr VP: Thomas Pettit
*Sr VP: Vito Ponzio Jr
VP: Dan Colucci
VP: Mary Jalwan
VP: Meen Kang
VP: Billy Kim
VP: Faye Major
VP: Jim Melancon
VP: Patrick Randall

D-U-N-S 02-016-3218 IMP
■ BIOSENSE WEBSTER INC
(Suby of JOHNSON & JOHNSON) ★
3333 S Diamond Canyon Rd, Diamond Bar, CA 91765-4701
Tel (909) 839-8500 Founded/Ownrshp 1996
Sales 175.4MM^E EMP 565
SIC 3845 3841 Electromedical apparatus; Surgical & medical instruments
CEO: Shlomi Nachman
Pr: David Shepherd
CFO: Mary Rex
VP: Tom Turley
QA Dir: Ilan Hadida
IT Man: Scott Bourne
Pgrm Dir: Yang Gao

BIOTANE PUMPING
See IMPERIAL WESTERN PRODUCTS INC

D-U-N-S 80-020-1118 IMP/EXP
BIOTECH MEDICAL INC
7800 Whipple Ave Nw, Canton, OH 44767-0001
Tel (330) 494-5504 Founded/Ownrshp 2006
Sales 98.8MM^E EMP 800
SIC 5047 Medical & hospital equipment
CFO: Michael Giorgio
IT Man: Robin Bacopoulos

BIOTECH RESEARCH LABORATORIES
See PHILOSOPHY INC

D-U-N-S 07-884-6112
▲ BIOTELEMETRY INC
1000 Cedar Hollow Rd, Malvern, PA 19355-2300
Tel (610) 729-7000 Founded/Ownrshp 2013
Sales 178.5MM EMP 938^E
Tkr Sym BEAT Exch NGM
SIC 3845 8093 Electromedical equipment; Specialty outpatient clinics
Pr: Joseph H Capper
*Ch Bd: Kirk E Gorman
CFO: Heather C Getz
Sr VP: Fred Broadway III
Sr VP: Peter Ferola
Sr VP: George Hrenko
Sr VP: Daniel Wisniewski
Board of Directors: Anthony J Conti, Joseph A Frick, Colin Hill, Rebecca W Rimel, Robert J Rubin

D-U-N-S 80-902-1095
BIOTEST PHARMACEUTICALS CORP
(Suby of BIOTEST AG)
5800 Pk Of Commerce Blvd, Boca Raton, FL 33487-8222
Tel (561) 989-5800 Founded/Ownrshp 2007
Sales 102.8MM^E EMP 400
SIC 8731 2834 Biological research; Medical research, commercial; Pharmaceutical preparations
CEO: Jordan Siegel
*Pr: Michael Ramroth
*CEO: Rainer Pabst
*Sec: Alexander Schenk
VP: Gary Horwith
VP: Robert Lefebvre
VP: Douglas Loock
Rgnl Mgr: Kevin Bucholz
MIS Dir: Maureen Barrett
Software D: Joseph Keri
Opers Mgr: Bob Levesque

D-U-N-S 80-863-4849
BIOTIX HOLDINGS INC
PELICAN LIFE SCIENCES
9880 Mesa Rim Rd, San Diego, CA 92121-2979
Tel (858) 875-7681 Founded/Ownrshp 2005
Sales 83.6MM^E EMP 400
SIC 6719 Personal holding companies, except banks
CEO: Paul Nowak

D-U-N-S 08-319-3409
BIOTRONIK INC
6024 Jean Rd Ste C8, Lake Oswego, OR 97035-5599
Tel (503) 635-3594 Founded/Ownrshp 1973, 2001
Sales 221.8MM^E EMP 425
SIC 5047 Medical & hospital equipment
Pr: Jake Langer
Ofcr: Allan Call
Ex VP: Larry Stotts
VP: Jon Brumbaugh
VP: Ooaf Dippel
VP: Robert Erb
VP: Mike Iverson
VP: Kevin Mitchell

VP: Rex Richmond
VP: Volker Schoewel
VP: Erik Trip
Exec: Angela McGonigle

D-U-N-S 78-704-5892 IMP
BIOURJA TRADING LLC
1080 Eldridge Pkwy # 1175, Houston, TX 77077-2582
Tel (832) 775-9000 *Founded/Ownrshp* 2006
Sales 3.2MMM^E *EMP* 42
Accts Carr Riggs & Ingram Llc Houst
SIC 5172 Petroleum products
CEO: Amit Bhandari
**VP:* Arpita Bhandari
**VP:* Nathalie De Vos Burchart
**Pr:* Abhi Shek Jain
**VP:* Dushyant Kansara

D-U-N-S 03-316-7201
BIRCH COMMUNICATIONS INC (GA)
320 Interstate North Pkwy, Atlanta, GA 30339-2205
Tel (866) 424-5100 *Founded/Ownrshp* 1996
Sales 1.9MMM^E *EMP* 3,485
SIC 4813 5045 Local & long distance telephone communications; ; Computer software
Pr: Tony Tomae
**Ch Bd:* R Kirby Godsey
Pr: Daniel Gaston
COO: Glen Burford
**COO:* Jim O'Brien
COO: Luther Pennell
CFO: Robert Agler
CFO: Rocky Davidson
CFO: Susan Grother
**CFO:* Scott Murphy
Bd of Dir: Thomas Canfield
**Ofcr:* Michelle Ansley
**Ofcr:* Shawn Murray
**Sr VP:* Gordon Williams
VP: Chris Bunce
VP: David Gibson
VP: Joseph Haines
VP: Kristen Ritchie
VP: Tom Stachowiak
VP: Grant Williams
Exec: Josh Gilstrap

D-U-N-S 12-075-1362
BIRCH TELECOM INC
(*Suby of* BIRCH COMMUNICATIONS INC) ★
2323 Grand Blvd Ste 925, Kansas City, MO 64108-2675
Tel (816) 300-3000 *Founded/Ownrshp* 2008
Sales 337.3MM^E *EMP* 1,600
SIC 4813 7375 4812 Long distance telephone communications; Local telephone communications; Information retrieval services; Radio telephone communication
CFO: Edward James
**COO:* Chris Aversano
CFO: Tom Peterson
VP: Apryle Ovell
VP: Christopher Ramsey
VP: Tom Stachowiak
Dir IT: Mark Richardson

BIRCHWOOD MANUFACTURING CO
See FOREST BESSE PRODUCTS INC

D-U-N-S 14-043-7893
BIRCHWOOD POWER PARTNERS LP
10900 Birchwood Dr, King George, VA 22485-6653
Tel (540) 775-6303 *Founded/Ownrshp* 1991
Sales 106.0MM *EMP* 2
SIC 4911 Generation, electric power
Genl Pt: William Hutchins

BIRCHWOOD TRANSPORT
See KENOSHA BEEF INTERNATIONAL LTD

D-U-N-S 07-924-3765
■ **BIRD BLUE CORP**
(*Suby of* AMERICAN SECURITIES LLC) ★
402 Bluebird Blvd, Fort Valley, GA 31030-5088
Tel (478) 822-2801 *Founded/Ownrshp* 2013, 2016
Sales 932.0MM *EMP* 1,762^E
Tkr Sym BLBD *Exch* NGM
SIC 3713 Truck & bus bodies; Bus bodies (motor vehicles)
Pr: Phil Horlock
COO: John Kwapis
CFO: Phil Tighe
Treas: Paul Yousif
Chf Mktg O: Mark Terry
Ex VP: Mike Horne
Ex VP: Jay McDuffie
VP: Mike Beck
VP: Dean Coulson
VP: Trey Jenkins
VP: Bill Landreth
VP: Normand Paquet
VP: Betsy Phillips
VP: Barry Wilder
Board of Directors: Dennis Donovan, Chan Galbato, Adam Gray, Daniel J Hennessy, Alan H Schumacher

BIRD ELECTRON BEAM
See BODYCOTE THERMAL PROCESSING INC

D-U-N-S 93-231-9304
BIRD TECHNOLOGIES GROUP INC
30303 Aurora Rd, Solon, OH 44139-2743
Tel (440) 248-1200 *Founded/Ownrshp* 1995
Sales 95.7MM^E *EMP* 300
SIC 3825 3669 Test equipment for electronic & electric measurement; Intercommunication systems, electric
Pr: Mark I Johnson
**CFO:* Dennis Morgan
**VP:* Edward J Bartos Jr
**VP:* Terrence C Grant
**VP:* Thomas L Kuklo
Snr Sftwr: Afif Bouhenni
Prd Mgr: Dean Downing
Prd Mgr: Bill Toth
Ql Cn Mgr: Michael R Otcasek
Sales Asso: Nancy Black
Snr Mgr: Charles Spencer

D-U-N-S 00-221-2611 IMP/EXP
■ **BIRDS EYE FOODS INC** (DE)
(*Suby of* PINNACLE FOODS GROUP LLC) ★
121 Woodcrest Rd, Cherry Hill, NJ 08003-3620
Tel (585) 383-1850 *Founded/Ownrshp* 1961, 2009
Sales 340.5MM^E *EMP* 1,585
SIC 2037 2096 2052 2038 2035 Frozen fruits & vegetables; Vegetables, quick frozen & cold pack, excl. potato products; Potato chips & other potato-based snacks; Corn chips & other corn-based snacks; Cheese curls & puffs; Cookies & crackers; Pretzels; Whipped topping, frozen; Pickles, sauces & salad dressings; Dressings, salad: raw & cooked (except dry mixes); Mayonnaise; Pickled fruits & vegetables
Pr: Neil Harrison
Pr: David Hogbert
**CFO:* Chris Puma
**Sr VP:* Robert G Montgomery
VP: John Blough
**VP:* Carl W Caughran
VP: David Piko
MIS Dir: Paulett Kuehnert

D-U-N-S 11-882-5103
BIRDS EYE HOLDINGS INC
(*Suby of* VESTAR/AGRILINK HOLDINGS LLC)
90 Linden Park, Rochester, NY 14625
Tel (585) 383-1850 *Founded/Ownrshp* 2002
Sales 150.1MM^E *EMP* 2,960
SIC 2033 2013 2035 2096 Fruits & fruit products in cans, jars, etc.; Fruit pie mixes & fillings: packaged in cans, jars, etc.; Canned meats (except baby food) from purchased meat; Beef stew from purchased meat; Pickles, vinegar; Dressings, salad: raw & cooked (except dry mixes); Potato chips & other potato-based snacks; Cheese curls & puffs

D-U-N-S 06-890-7236
■ **BIRDSALL INC**
(*Suby of* SOUTHERN CO GAS) ★
5 E 11th St, Riviera Beach, FL 33404-7598
Tel (561) 881-3900 *Founded/Ownrshp* 2014
Sales 871.0MM^E *EMP* 1,150^E
SIC 4412 Deep sea foreign transportation of freight
Pr: John W Somerhalder II
**Treas:* Stephen Cave
**Ex VP:* Paul R Shlanta

D-U-N-S 07-856-2550
BIRDVILLE INDEPENDENT SCHOOL DISTRICT (TX)
6125 E Belknap St, Haltom City, TX 76117-4204
Tel (817) 547-5700 *Founded/Ownrshp* 1850
Sales 577.7M^E *EMP* 3,109
Accts Lynn A Sudbury Cpa Pllc North
SIC 8211 Public elementary & secondary schools
**Pr:* Whitney Harding
**Pr:* Ralph Kunkel
Bd of Dir: Richard Davis
**VP:* Brad Greene
VP: Amy Painter
VP: Dolores Webb
Dir Sec: Chris Reese
IT Man: Scott Forester
Software D: Dora Thrash
Sftwr Eng: George Lin
Trfc Dir: Helen Kemp

D-U-N-S 02-577-4555
BIRKEYS FARM STORE INC
2102 W Park Ct, Champaign, IL 61821-2986
Tel (217) 693-7200 *Founded/Ownrshp* 1979
Sales 230.5MM *EMP* 400
Accts Cliftonlarsonallen Llp Champa
SIC 5083 5082 5511 Farm implements; Excavating machinery & equipment; Automobiles, new & used
Pr: Michael Hedge
**Ch Bd:* Ronald Birkey
**VP:* Michael Carley
**VP:* Jeffrey Hedge
Sales Asso: Gregg Kromphardt

BIRLA CARBON
See COLUMBIAN CHEMICALS CO

D-U-N-S 88-326-1588 IMP
BIRLASOFT INC
(*Suby of* BIRLASOFT (INDIA) LIMITED)
399 Thornall St Ste 8, Edison, NJ 08837-2238
Tel (732) 287-5000 *Founded/Ownrshp* 2004
Sales 147.4MM *EMP* 600
SIC 7371

D-U-N-S 11-984-0916
BIRMINGHAM CITY SCHOOLS
2015 Park Pl, Birmingham, AL 35203-2705
Tel (205) 231-4600 *Founded/Ownrshp* 1883
Sales 242.7MM^E *EMP* 4,500
SIC 8211 Public elementary & secondary schools
**VP:* Sherman Collins Jr
Dir Sec: Walter Williams
Teacher Pr: Kimberly Washington

D-U-N-S 03-826-9338 IMP/EXP
BIRMINGHAM FASTENER & SUPPLY INC
931 Avenue W, Birmingham, AL 35214-6255
Tel (205) 595-3511 *Founded/Ownrshp* 1980
Sales 107.0MM *EMP* 265
SIC 5085 3452 Fasteners, industrial: nuts, bolts, screws, etc.; Nuts, metal; Bolts, metal; Screws, metal
Pr: Howard P Tinney
**CEO:* Brad Tinney
**Sec:* Retha Tinney
Genl Mgr: Mike Bethel
Genl Mgr: Joe Birmingham
Genl Mgr: Joseph Speights

BIRMINGHAM PUBLIC SCHOOLS
See SCHOOL DISTRICT OF CITY OF BIRMINGHAM

BIRMINGHAM WATER WORKS BOARD
See WATER WORKS BOARD OF CITY OF BIRMINGHAM

D-U-N-S 04-854-8135
BIRNIE BUS SERVICE INC
BBS
248 Otis St, Rome, NY 13441-4810
Tel (315) 336-3950 *Founded/Ownrshp* 1947
Sales 102.3MM^E *EMP* 1,500
SIC 4151 4119 4141 4111 School buses; Local passenger transportation; Local bus charter service; Local & suburban transit
Ch: Timothy Birnie
VP: John Warren
Genl Mgr: Nicole Podkowka

D-U-N-S 02-715-7307
BIRST INC
45 Fremont St Ste 1800, San Francisco, CA 94105-2219
Tel (415) 766-4800 *Founded/Ownrshp* 2005
Sales 109.9MM^E *EMP* 300^E
SIC 7371 Computer software development
CEO: Jay Larson
CFO: Samuel Wolff
Chf Mktg O: Carl Tsukahara
Ofcr: Brad Peters
Ofcr: Paul Staelin
VP: David Dyer
VP: David Gray
VP: Southard Jones
VP: John Pierson
VP: Junaid Saiyed
VP: Alex Saleh
VP: Rick Spickelmier
Board of Directors: Young J Chung, John Hummer, Jay Larson, Douglas Leone, John McMahon, Doug Merritt, Brad Peters

D-U-N-S 06-440-9220 IMP
■ **BISCO INDUSTRIES INC**
FASTCOR
(*Suby of* EACO CORP) ★
1500 N Lakeview Ave, Anaheim, CA 92807-1819
Tel (714) 876-2400 *Founded/Ownrshp* 1974
Sales 87.1MM^E *EMP* 250
SIC 5065

BISD
See BASTROP INDEPENDENT SCHOOL DISTRICT

BISD
See BROWNSVILLE INDEPENDENT SCHOOL DISTRICT

D-U-N-S 07-635-8142
BISHOP CONSTRUCTION INC
3374 S Center Rd Ste C, Burton, MI 48519-1958
Tel (810) 744-4550 *Founded/Ownrshp* 1974
Sales 5.0MMM^E *EMP* 22
SIC 1521 1542 Repairing fire damage, single-family houses; Commercial & office buildings, renovation & repair
Prin: Larry Baker
**VP:* Peggy Green

D-U-N-S 15-321-6507 IMP/EXP
BISHOP LIFTING PRODUCTS INC
(*Suby of* BLP SETTLEMENT CO) ★
125 Mccarty St, Houston, TX 77029-1135
Tel (713) 674-2266 *Founded/Ownrshp* 1984
Sales 168.7MM^E *EMP* 710
SIC 1799 3531 Rigging & scaffolding; Crane carriers
Pr: Derrick Deakins
CFO: Mike Reese
VP: John Hellums
VP: Jack Shreffler
Area Mgr: Billy Anderson
Genl Mgr: David Mosley
Opers Mgr: Glenn Lindley
VP Mktg: David M Moseley
Mktg Dir: Teresa Massaro

D-U-N-S 02-656-7073
■ **BISON BUILDING MATERIALS OF TEXAS INC**
(*Suby of* BMC EAST LLC) ★
1445 W Sam Houston Pkwy N, Houston, TX 77043-3110
Tel (713) 467-6700 *Founded/Ownrshp* 1962
Sales 115.8MM^E *EMP* 700
SIC 5031 Lumber, plywood & millwork; Lumber: rough, dressed & finished
Pr: Pat W Bierschwale
**COO:* Tom Tolleson
**Genl Mgr:* Phil Moody

BISON PRODUCTS
See UPSTATE NIAGARA COOPERATIVE INC

BISSELL DATA SYSTEMS
See BISSELL INC

D-U-N-S 79-032-8210 IMP/EXP
BISSELL HOMECARE INC
(*Suby of* BISSELL DATA SYSTEMS) ★
2345 Walker Ave Nw, Grand Rapids, MI 49544-2597
Tel (616) 453-4451 *Founded/Ownrshp* 1876
Sales 192.4MM^E *EMP* 800^E
SIC 3635 Household vacuum cleaners
Pr: Mark J Bissell
**Treas:* Timothy E Bosscher
Sr VP: Claudette Hampton
VP: David Andersen
VP: Manoj Chadha
VP: Kevin J Veltman
VP: Kevin Veltman
Ex Dir: Robert Spass
Prd Mgr: Tom Benham
VP Sls: Michael F Best
VP Sls: James Burggraaf

D-U-N-S 00-602-2800 IMP/EXP
BISSELL INC (MI)
BISSELL DATA SYSTEMS
2345 Walker Ave Nw, Grand Rapids, MI 49544-2597
Tel (616) 453-4451 *Founded/Ownrshp* 1876
Sales 295.4MM^E *EMP* 825
SIC 3589 2842 3635

D-U-N-S 01-754-2536
BISTATE BISTRO ASSOCIATES LP
TGI FRIDAY'S
4 Boston Crest Ct, O Fallon, MO 63366-7548
Tel (636) 537-9777 *Founded/Ownrshp* 1991
Sales 43.0MM *EMP* 1,300
SIC 5812 Restaurant, family: chain
Genl Pt: Steve Bell
Pt: Brad Bax
Pt: Mike Gallagher

D-U-N-S 36-371-3124
BISTRO MANAGEMENT INC
TGI FRIDAY'S
5803 Mariemont Ave, Cincinnati, OH 45227-4217
Tel (513) 271-2349 *Founded/Ownrshp* 1989
Sales 94.3MM^E *EMP* 3,500
SIC 5812 Restaurant, family: chain
Ch: Robert Conway Jr
**CFO:* Kathleen C Bell
**Treas:* Eric Goedde
Genl Mgr: Louis Jenks

BIT SYSTEMS
See SIX3 ADVANCED SYSTEMS INC

D-U-N-S 18-510-1136
■ **BITCO CORP**
(*Suby of* OLD REPUBLIC INTERNATIONAL CORP) ★
3700 Market Square Cir, Davenport, IA 52807-2309
Tel (309) 786-5401 *Founded/Ownrshp* 1987
Sales NA *EMP* 500
SIC 6411 6331 Insurance agents, brokers & service; Fire, marine & casualty insurance
Ch Bd: Greg Ator
Treas: Robert D Rainey
Exec: Janine K Happ
Board of Directors: John H Binning, Fred Frey, Al Johnson, Peter Lardner, John W Popp, Arnold Steiner, Aldo C Zucaro

BITCO INSURANCE COMPANY
See BITCO NATIONAL INSURANCE CO

D-U-N-S 00-292-1815
■ **BITCO NATIONAL INSURANCE CO**
BITCO INSURANCE COMPANY
(*Suby of* BITCO CORP) ★
3700 Market Square Cir, Davenport, IA 52807-2309
Tel (309) 786-5401 *Founded/Ownrshp* 1963
Sales NA *EMP* 420
SIC 6331 Automobile insurance; Property damage insurance
CEO: Vince Lamb
Treas: Dennis Vandervinne
VP: Robert EBY
VP: Christine Kruse
VP: Donald Olson

D-U-N-S 80-907-5414
BITTITAN INC
3933 Lk Wa Blvd Ne # 200, Kirkland, WA 98033-7806
Tel (206) 428-6030 *Founded/Ownrshp* 2006
Sales 103.0MM *EMP* 120^E
SIC 7372 Prepackaged software
CEO: Geeman Yip
VP: Mark Kirstein
VP: Jennifer Martin
VP: Rocco Seyboth
Board of Directors: Steve Hamerslag

D-U-N-S 00-693-5779
■ **BITUMINOUS CASUALTY CORP**
BITUMINOUS INSURANCE
(*Suby of* BITCO CORP) ★
320 18th St, Rock Island, IL 61201-8716
Tel (309) 786-5401 *Founded/Ownrshp* 1928
Sales NA *EMP* 480
Accts Kpmg Llp Chicago Illinois
SIC 6331 Automobile insurance; Workers' compensation insurance; Property damage insurance
Pr: Robert Gregory Ator
**Pr:* Vince Lamb
**Treas:* Robert D Rainey
**Sr VP:* Janine Happ
VP: Lawrence E Gorman
VP: Lori S Paulus
**VP:* Dennis V Vinne
Mng Dir: Dennis Vendervine
IT Man: Craig Mowry
Netwrk Mgr: Todd Gray
Sftwr Eng: Mark Troutwine

BITUMINOUS INSURANCE
See BITUMINOUS CASUALTY CORP

D-U-N-S 02-287-7609
BIX PRODUCE CO LLC
1415 L Orient St, Saint Paul, MN 55117-4067
Tel (651) 487-8000 *Founded/Ownrshp* 2015
Sales 115.0MM *EMP* 242
SIC 5148 5143 Fruits; Vegetables; Dairy products, except dried or canned
CFO: Ken Fechtner
CFO: Jean Kolstad
Sls Mgr: Steve Pagel
Snr Mgr: Algirdas Vosylius

BIZFI FUNDING
See MERCHANT CASH AND CAPITAL LLC

BIZLAND
See ENDURANCE INTERNATIONAL GROUP INC

D-U-N-S 05-093-4306 IMP/EXP
BJ ALAN CO
PHANTOM FIREWORKS
555 Mrtin Lther King Blvd, Youngstown, OH 44502-1102
Tel (330) 746-1064 *Founded/Ownrshp* 1972
Sales 112.0MM^E *EMP* 350
SIC 5092

D-U-N-S 62-540-9289
BJ HOLDINGS CORP
BOJANGLE'S
(*Suby of* BOJANGLES) ★
9432 Southern Pine Blvd, Charlotte, NC 28273-5553
Tel (704) 527-2675 *Founded/Ownrshp* 1998

Sales 69.4MM^E EMP 4,500
Accts Bdo Seidman
SIC 5812 6794 Fast-food restaurant, chain; Franchises, selling or licensing
Sr VP: Eric M Newman
VP: Randall Poindexter
Dir Surg: Glenn Gulledge
Board of Directors: Charles Lynch Restauant E, Daniel L Skaff Chb Sienna, Clay F Smith, James R Parish Private Co, Alexander Seaver Partner

D-U-N-S 79-820-5308 IMP
BJ SERVICES CO USA LP
5500 Nw Central Dr # 100, Houston, TX 77092-2040
Tel (713) 462-4239 Founded/Ownrshp 2013
Sales NA EMP 3,500
SIC 1389

D-U-N-S 80-966-6878
BJC HEALTH SYSTEM
BJC HEALTHCARE
4901 Forest Park Ave, Saint Louis, MO 63108-1402
Tel (314) 286-2000 Founded/Ownrshp 1992
Sales 4.2MMM EMP 27,000
SIC 8741

BJC HEALTHCARE
See BARNES-JEWISH WEST COUNTY HOSPITAL

BJC HEALTHCARE
See BARNES-JEWISH ST PETERS HOSPITAL INC

BJC HEALTHCARE
See ALTON MEMORIAL HOSPITAL FOUNDATION

BJC HEALTHCARE
See PROGRESS WEST HEALTHCARE CENTER

BJC HEALTHCARE
See BJC HEALTH SYSTEM

D-U-N-S 09-471-9804
▲ **BJS RESTAURANTS INC** (CA)
7755 Center Ave Ste 300, Huntington Beach, CA 92647-3084
Tel (714) 500-2400 Founded/Ownrshp 1978
Sales 919.6MM EMP 20,500^E
Tkr Sym BJRI Exch NGS
SIC 5812 Pizza restaurants
Pr: Gregory A Trojan
*Ch Bd: Gerald W Deitchle
CFO: Gregory S Levin
Chf Mktg O: Kevin E Mayer
Ofcr: Gregory S Lynds
Ex VP: Lon F Ledwith
Ex VP: Kevin Mayer
Sr VP: Brian S Krakower
Sr VP: Kendra D Miller
Sr VP: Alexander M Puchner
VP: Robert Deliema
VP: AME Hull
VP: Mel Landuyt
VP: Mike Langford
VP: Roger Ortiz
VP: Moe Robiglio
Exec: Blair Miller
Board of Directors: Peter A Bassi, Larry D Bouts, Noah A Elbogen, Wesley A Nichols, Lea Anne S Ottinger, James A Dal Pozzo, Patrick D Walsh

D-U-N-S 15-908-2692 IMP/EXP
BJS WHOLESALE CLUB INC
(Suby of BEACON HOLDING INC) ★
25 Research Dr, Westborough, MA 01581-3680
Tel (774) 512-7400 Founded/Ownrshp 2011
Sales 5.4MMM^E EMP 24,800
SIC 5399 Warehouse club stores
CEO: Laura Sen
Pr: Ted Bell
Pr: Laurie Bysiewicz
Pr: Tanya Cavanaugh
Pr: Russ Kiser
Pr: Laurie Lee
Pr: Maureen McCann
Pr: Melissa Mips
Pr: John Rohland
Pr: Jill Rouleau
Pr: Susan Wadowski
*CFO: Robert Eddy
*Ex VP: Cornel Catuna
*Ex VP: Christina M Neppl
Sr VP: Peter Amalfi
Sr VP: Paul Bass
Sr VP: Cristina Iaboni
*Sr VP: Carol G Stone
VP: Steve Allocco
VP: Michael Atkinson
VP: George Bomann

D-U-N-S 06-717-8491 IMP/EXP
BJT INC
MUTUAL DISTRIBUTING COMPANY
2233 Capital Blvd, Raleigh, NC 27604-1421
Tel (919) 828-3842 Founded/Ownrshp 1946
Sales 245.0MM EMP 650
SIC 5182 5149 5181 Wine; Mineral or spring water bottling; Juices; Beer & other fermented malt liquors
Pr: W T Kennedy
*Ch Bd: William Kennedy
*VP: James Burkhardt
*VP: James Enzor
Exec: Molly McClure
Genl Mgr: Greg Baker
Sfty Mgr: Glenn Pleasant
Mktg Dir: Bill Leone

D-U-N-S 00-737-3004 IMP/EXP
BJT PROPERTIES INC
CARDELL CABINETRY
12770 Coit Rd Ste 1100, Dallas, TX 75251-1329
Tel (210) 225-0290 Founded/Ownrshp 1965
Sales 109.0MM^E EMP 850^E
SIC 2434 Wood kitchen cabinets; Vanities, bathroom: wood
Pr: Billy J Tidwell
*CEO: Bryan W Tidwell
*Treas: Bill Beardsley
*Ex VP: Art Torres

D-U-N-S 07-306-9437
BKD LLP
910 E Saint Louis St # 400, Springfield, MO 65806-2570
Tel (417) 865-8701 Founded/Ownrshp 1923
Sales 387.8MM^E EMP 2,148
SIC 8721

D-U-N-S 18-333-6291
BKH ACQUISITION HOLDCO I LLC
150 E 58th St Bsmt, New York, NY 10155-0099
Tel (787) 474-7762 Founded/Ownrshp 2004
Sales 494.5MM^E EMP 6,000^E
SIC 6799 Investors

D-U-N-S 88-464-3487
BKRY PHYSICIAN GROUP INC
(Suby of STERLING HEALTHCARE) ★
1000 Park Forty Plz # 500, Durham, NC 27713-5249
Tel (919) 383-0355 Founded/Ownrshp 2002
Sales 490.9MM^E EMP 1,956
SIC 8741 8742 Hospital management; Hospital & health services consultant
Ch Bd: Robert J Bunker
*Pr: Charles R Goldstein
CFO: Jim Douthitt
*Ex VP: G Scott Dillon
*Sr VP: Kimberly Licata
Genl Couns: Eugene F Dauchert

D-U-N-S 86-704-9488
■ **BL DEVELOPMENT CORP**
HARRAHS GRAND
(Suby of CAESARS ENTERTAINMENT CORP) ★
13615 Old Highway 61 N, Robinsonville, MS 38664-9739
Tel (662) 357-3097 Founded/Ownrshp 2005
Sales 43.9MM^E EMP 3,000
SIC 7011 Casino hotel
Prin: Patrick Brown
CFO: Michael Capparelli
Genl Mgr: Ricki Busey
Genl Mgr: Sheri Pucci
Genl Mgr: Bill Rice

D-U-N-S 14-737-1236
BL HARBERT HOLDINGS LLC
820 Shades Creek Pkwy # 3000, Birmingham, AL 35209-4564
Tel (205) 802-2800 Founded/Ownrshp 2001
Sales 958.5MM^E EMP 2,000^E
Accts Pearce Bevill Leesburg Moor
SIC 1542 Nonresidential construction
CEO: Billy Harbert
*CFO: R Alan Hall
*Treas: John Rives
*Chf Cred: William Lalor
*VP: James Stewart

D-U-N-S 11-977-8806 EXP
BL HARBERT INTERNATIONAL LLC
(Suby of BL HARBERT HOLDINGS LLC) ★
820 Shades Creek Pkwy # 3000, Birmingham, AL 35209-4564
Tel (205) 802-2800 Founded/Ownrshp 1999
Sales 958.5MM EMP 1,400
SIC 1542 Commercial & office building contractors
CEO: Billy Harbert
CFO: Alan R Hall
*CFO: R Alan Hall
*Treas: John Rives
*Chf Cred: William Lalor
VP: Elizabeth Rutherford
*VP: James Stewart
Dir IT: Bruce Johnson
Snr PM: Mark Bounds

D-U-N-S 96-983-6696
BL RESTAURANT OPERATIONS LLC
BAR LOUIE
(Suby of SUN CAPITAL PARTNERS INC) ★
4550 Beltway Dr, Addison, TX 75001-3707
Tel (972) 386-5567 Founded/Ownrshp 2009
Sales 165.5MM^E EMP 2,792
SIC 5812 5813 6794 Eating places; Bars & lounges; Franchises, selling or licensing
CEO: John Neitzel
*CFO: Tamara Bebb
Creative D: Chris McDonald
Dir IT: Troy Eichelberger
IT Man: David Adamoski

BLACK & DECKER
See FIDELITONE INC

D-U-N-S 09-867-0151 IMP
■ **BLACK & DECKER (US) INC**
(Suby of STANLEY BLACK & DECKER INC) ★
1000 Stanley Dr, New Britain, CT 06053-1675
Tel (410) 716-3900 Founded/Ownrshp 1978
Sales 1.1MMM^E EMP 5,000
SIC 3546 3634 Power-driven handtools; Electric household cooking appliances; Electric household cooking utensils; Electric household fans, heaters & humidifiers
Pr: Nolan D Archibald
*CFO: Michael D Mangan
*Treas: Mark M Rothleitner
*Sr VP: Charles E Fenton
*Sr VP: Barbara B Lucas
VP: Christina M McMullen
VP: Pete Morris
VP: Bud Schreiber
VP: Kirk Stinson
Rgnl Mgr: Michael Napoli
Area Mgr: John Bailey

D-U-N-S 00-131-7189 IMP
■ **BLACK & DECKER CORP** (MD)
(Suby of STANLEY BLACK & DECKER INC) ★
701 E Joppa Rd, Towson, MD 21286-5502
Tel (410) 716-3900 Founded/Ownrshp 1910, 2010
Sales 4.7MMM^E EMP 16,000
SIC 3546 3553 3541 3634 3452 Power-driven handtools; Drills, portable, except rock: electric or pneumatic; Saws, portable & handheld: power driven; Sanders, hand: electric; Woodworking machinery; Saws, power: bench & table, except portable: woodworking; Planers, woodworking machines; Sanding machines, except portable floor sanders: woodworking; Home workshop machine tools, metalworking; Electric housewares & fans; Toasters, electric: household; Ovens, portable: household; Food mixers, electric: household; Bolts, nuts, rivets & washers
Ch Bd: Nolan D Archibald
Pr: Bruce W Brooks
Pr: Ian Carter
*Pr: James M Loree
Pr: Christopher T Metz
Pr: Edward J Scanlon
Pr: John W Schiech
*CEO: John F Lundgren
*CFO: Donald Allan Jr
CFO: Trish Pieper
CFO: Stephen F Reeves
CFO: Pat Robinson
Bd of Dir: Paul Gustafson
Ex VP: Andres Cerda
Ex VP: Joseph Galli
*Sr VP: Charles E Fenton
VP: Ray Brusca
VP: Les H Ireland
VP: Carl C Liebert
VP: Vishak Sankaran
VP: Thomas M Schoewe

D-U-N-S 09-488-6207
■ **BLACK & DECKER INC**
(Suby of BLACK & DECKER CORP) ★
1423 Kirkwood Hwy, Newark, DE 19711
Tel (302) 738-0250 Founded/Ownrshp 1989
Sales 178.6MM^E EMP 3,194
SIC 3429 3452 3579 3423 3949 Manufactured hardware (general); Locks or lock sets; Door locks, bolts & checks; Bolts, nuts, rivets & washers; Rivets, metal; Nuts, metal; Screws, metal; Stapling machines (hand or power); Garden & farm tools, including shovels; Shafts, golf club
Pr: Don Graber
*Treas: Charles Fenton

D-U-N-S 09-225-5939 IMP
BLACK & VEATCH CORP
BV
(Suby of BLACK & VEATCH HOLDING CO) ★
11401 Lamar Ave, Overland Park, KS 66211-1598
Tel (913) 458-2000 Founded/Ownrshp 1998
Sales 1.6MMM^E EMP 4,065
SIC 8711 Engineering services
CEO: Steven L Edwards
Mng Pt: W Hall
*Pr: John Chevrette
Pr: Christopher Ruddle
Pr: Timothy W Triplett
Pr: Cindy Wallis-Lage
*CFO: Karen L Daniel
CFO: David Kerns
Treas: Ken Williams
Chf Cred: Peter Loftspring
Ofcr: Jim Lewis
Assoc VP: Adrienne Mickells
Assoc VP: Christopher Mueller
Assoc VP: Carl Petz
Assoc VP: Norman Song
*Ex VP: Hoe Wai Cheong
Ex VP: Ed Walsh
Sr VP: John G Voeller
VP: April Anderson-Higgs
VP: Hilary Berndt
VP: Richard Boynton
Board of Directors: Andrew G McMaster Jr

D-U-N-S 78-894-8115
BLACK & VEATCH HOLDING CO
(Suby of BVH INC) ★
11401 Lamar Ave, Overland Park, KS 66211-1598
Tel (913) 458-2000 Founded/Ownrshp 1999
Sales 2.9MMM EMP 8,495^E
Accts Kpmg Llp Kansas City Mo
SIC 8711 8741 Consulting engineer; Sanitary engineers; Construction management
Ch Bd: Steven L Edwards
Pr: John Chevrette
CFO: Karen L Daniel
Treas: Angela L Hoffman
Ofcr: James Lewis
Ex VP: Timothy W Triplett
Sr VP: Wai C Hoe
Sr VP: Jim Spenceley
VP: Jason Abiecunas
VP: Ralph J Dyro
VP: Corrine U Smith
VP: Jeffrey J Stamm
VP: James Waller
VP: Bob Welch
Board of Directors: T M Buck Jr, W P Campbell, Martha W Gilliland, H P Goldfield, Steven H Wunning

BLACK BEAR CASINO
See FOND DU LAC RESERVATION

BLACK BEAR DELI MEATS
See DIETZ & WATSON INC

BLACK BEAR DINER
See SUNWEST RESTAURANT CONCEPTS INC

BLACK BEAUTY MINING DIV
See PEABODY MIDWEST MINING LLC

D-U-N-S 06-461-7301 IMP/EXP
▲ **BLACK BOX CORP**
1000 Park Dr, Lawrence, PA 15055-1018
Tel (724) 746-5500 Founded/Ownrshp 1976
Sales 912.6MM EMP 3,631
Accts Bdo Usa Llp Chicago Illinois
Tkr Sym BBOX Exch NGS
SIC 3577 3679 3661 5045 5065 5063 Computer peripheral equipment; Electronic switches; Harness assemblies for electronic use: wire or cable; Modems; Computer peripheral equipment; Modems, computer; Electronic parts; Electrical apparatus & equipment; Electronic wire & cable
Pr: Eslie C Sykes
Pt: Doug Oathout
*Ch Bd: Thomas G Greig
CFO: Timothy C Huffmyer
CFO: Anthony J Massetti
Ex VP: Ronald Basso
VP: Julie Lyda
VP: Jeff Murray
Exec: Damon Griffin
IT Man: Eugene Miller
Opers Mgr: Pat Kruswicki

D-U-N-S 08-225-4871
■ **BLACK BOX CORP OF PENNSYLVANIA**
BLACK BOX NETWORK SERVICES
(Suby of BLACK BOX CORP) ★
1000 Park Dr, Lawrence, PA 15055-1018
Tel (724) 746-5500 Founded/Ownrshp 1976
Sales 243.4MM^E EMP 995
SIC 5045 5063 5065 3577 3679 3661 Computer peripheral equipment; Electrical apparatus & equipment; Electronic wire & cable; Modems, computer; Electronic parts; Computer peripheral equipment; Electronic switches; Harness assemblies for electronic use: wire or cable; Modems
CEO: Terry Blakemore
VP: Tim Huffmyer
Brnch Mgr: Sharon Jackson
Tech Mgr: Phil Schwartz
Opers Mgr: Harry Brown
VP Sls: Cindy Gannon
Mktg Dir: Chris Allen
Snr PM: Diarmuid Ryan
Board of Directors: Thomas G Greig Chb, Michael McAndrew, Francis Wertheimber

BLACK BOX NETWORK SERVICES
See NORSTAN COMMUNICATIONS INC

BLACK BOX NETWORK SERVICES
See BLACK BOX CORP OF PENNSYLVANIA

BLACK BOX NETWORK SERVICES
See NEXTIRAONE FEDERAL LLC

D-U-N-S 80-594-3755
BLACK CREEK HOLDINGS LTD
2400 Dallas Pkwy Ste 230, Plano, TX 75093-4371
Tel (972) 398-7100 Founded/Ownrshp 2005
Sales 86.7MM^E EMP 1,303
SIC 3955 3861 Ribbons, inked: typewriter, adding machine, register, etc.; Carbon paper for typewriters, sales books, etc.; Toners, prepared photographic (not made in chemical plants)
Pt: John P Rochon
Pt: Alan S Lockwood

BLACK DIAMOND
See DIAMOND BLACK INC

D-U-N-S 07-382-9863
■ **BLACK EARTH TELEPHONE CO LLC**
TDS
(Suby of TDS TELECOMMUNICATIONS CORP) ★
1125 Mills St, Black Earth, WI 53515-9454
Tel (608) 767-2229 Founded/Ownrshp 1974
Sales 853.0MM EMP 2,700
SIC 4813 Local telephone communications

D-U-N-S 01-205-1697
BLACK ELK ENERGY OFFSHORE OPERATIONS (TX)
842 W Sam Houston Pkwy N # 500, Houston, TX 77024-4588
Tel (832) 973-4230 Founded/Ownrshp 2007
Sales 258.0MM EMP 10
SIC 1389 Oil field services; Gas field services
CEO: John Hoffman
*CFO: James Hagemeier
*Ex VP: Terry Clark
Opers Mgr: Troy Mouret

D-U-N-S 09-869-8269 IMP
■ **BLACK ENTERTAINMENT TELEVISION LLC**
BET CABLE NETWORK
(Suby of VIACOM INC) ★
1235 W St Ne, Washington, DC 20018-1101
Tel (202) 526-4927 Founded/Ownrshp 2005
Sales 160.0MM^E EMP 350
SIC 4841 Cable television services
Ch Bd: Debra L Lee
Pr: Monte Ivey
COO: Joe Franlin
CFO: Scott Mills
*CFO: Michael Pickrum
Ex VP: Raymond D Goulbourne
Ex VP: Janet Roll
VP: Michelle Bailey
VP: Matthew Barnhill
Creative D: Myrna Dobken
Off Mgr: Jennifer Pena

BLACK GOLD FARMS
See BLACK GOLD POTATO SALES INC

D-U-N-S 09-391-2863
BLACK GOLD FARMS
4320 18th Ave S, Grand Forks, ND 58201-3735
Tel (701) 792-3414 Founded/Ownrshp 1967
Sales 391.5MM^E EMP 717
SIC 0134 0191 Irish potatoes; General farms, primarily crop
Pr: Greg Halverson
*Ex VP: Eric Halverson
*VP: Danielle Golden
*VP: John Halverson
*VP: John Nordgaard

D-U-N-S 18-104-2797
BLACK GOLD POTATO SALES INC
BLACK GOLD FARMS
4320 18th Ave S, Grand Forks, ND 58201-3735
Tel (701) 248-3788 Founded/Ownrshp 1985
Sales 121.9MM EMP 11
SIC 5141 Food brokers
Pr: Gregg Halverson
*CFO: Bob Hoffert
*Ex VP: Danielle Golden

*Ex VP: John Nordgaard
Off Admin: Jennifer Elizondo
Off Admin: April Loken

D-U-N-S 00-792-0333 IMP
▲ BLACK HILLS CORP (SD)
625 9th St, Rapid City, SD 57701-2601
Tel (605) 721-1700 Founded/Ownrshp 1941
Sales 1.3MMM EMP 2,003
Accts Deloitte & Touche Llp Minneap
Tkr Sym BKH Exch NYS
SIC 4911 4923 1241 Distribution, electric power; Generation, electric power; Transmission, electric power; ; Gas transmission & distribution; Coal mining services
Ch Bd: David R Emery
Pr: Linden R Evans
CFO: Richard W Kinzley
Chf Cred: Steven J Helmers
Ofcr: Robert A Myers
Sr VP: Scott A Buchholz
Sr VP: Brian G Iverson
VP: John Benton
VP: Robert Myers
Exec: Lynn Brown
Exec: Karen Zandstra
Board of Directors: Michael H Madison, Linda K Massman, Steven R Mills, Gary L Pechota, Rebecca B Roberts, Mark A Schober, John B Vering, Thomas J Zeller

BLACK HILLS ENERGY
See BLACK HILLS UTILITY HOLDINGS INC

BLACK HILLS ENERGY
See BLACK HILLS/COLORADO ELECTRIC UTILITY CO LP

BLACK HILLS ENERGY
See BLACK HILLS/IOWA GAS UTILITY CO LLC

BLACK HILLS ENERGY
See BLACK HILLS/NEBRASKA GAS UTILITY CO LLC

D-U-N-S 09-469-0336
■ BLACK HILLS EXPLORATION AND PRODUCTION INC
BHEP
(Suby of BLACK HILLS NON-REGULATED HOLDINGS LLC) ★
1515 Wynkoop St Ste 500, Denver, CO 80202-2062
Tel (720) 210-1300 Founded/Ownrshp 2003
Sales 91.0MM^E EMP 40
SIC 1382 Oil & gas exploration services
CEO: David R Emery
CFO: Mark T Thies
Treas: Richard T Ashbeck
Ofcr: Russell L Cohen
Sr VP: James M Mattern
Int Pr: John Vering
Genl Mgr: Niklas Christolon
Genl Mgr: Brian Mazeski
Genl Couns: Steven Jhelmers

D-U-N-S 80-767-2311
■ BLACK HILLS GAS HOLDINGS LLC
(Suby of BLACK HILLS CORP) ★
600 12th St Ste 300, Golden, CO 80401-6142
Tel (303) 243-3400 Founded/Ownrshp 2016
Sales 266.5MM^E EMP 565
SIC 4924 Natural gas distribution
Pr: Michael Noone
*CFO: Bentley W Breland

D-U-N-S 82-819-1341 IMP
■ BLACK HILLS NON-REGULATED HOLDINGS LLC
(Suby of BLACK HILLS CORP) ★
625 9th St Ste 200, Rapid City, SD 57701-2601
Tel (605) 721-1700 Founded/Ownrshp 2008
Sales 93.9MM^E EMP 72^E
SIC 4911 4923 Generation, electric power; Gas transmission & distribution
Pr: Thomas Ohlmacher

D-U-N-S 11-667-6813
■ BLACK HILLS POWER INC
(Suby of BLACK HILLS CORP) ★
625 9th St, Rapid City, SD 57701-2601
Tel (605) 721-1700 Founded/Ownrshp 1941
Sales 277.8MM EMP 326^E
Accts Deloitte & Touche Llp Minneap
SIC 4911 Electric services; Generation, electric power; Transmission, electric power; Distribution, electric power
Ch Bd: David R Emery
CFO: Richard W Kinzley
VP: Scott Buchholz
VP: Robert Myers
Opers Supe: Alan Van Bochove
Opers Mgr: Lonny Warne
Board of Directors: Roxann R Basham, Jeffrey B Berzina, Scott A Buchholz, Anthony S Cleberg, Linden R Evans, Steven J Helmers, Brian G Iverson, Robert A Myers

D-U-N-S 80-902-4784
■ BLACK HILLS UTILITY HOLDINGS INC
BLACK HILLS ENERGY
(Suby of BLACK HILLS CORP) ★
625 9th St Ste 200, Rapid City, SD 57701-2601
Tel (605) 721-1700 Founded/Ownrshp 2007
Sales 120.3MM^E EMP 255^E
Accts Deloitte & Touche Llp
SIC 4911 4923 Distribution, electric power; Generation, electric power; Transmission, electric power; Gas transmission & distribution
Pr: David Emery
*Sr VP: Steven Helmers

D-U-N-S 82-505-3882
■ BLACK HILLS/COLORADO ELECTRIC UTILITY CO LP
BLACK HILLS ENERGY
(Suby of BLACK HILLS CORP) ★
105 S Victoria Ave, Pueblo, CO 81003-3432
Tel (719) 546-6589 Founded/Ownrshp 2007
Sales 94.3MM^E EMP 200
SIC 4911 Distribution, electric power
VP: Stuart Wevik
*Genl Pt: Black Hills Corporation
Adm/Dir: Donald Perkins
Plnt Mgr: Kevin Hall

D-U-N-S 82-948-2111
■ BLACK HILLS/IOWA GAS UTILITY CO LLC
BLACK HILLS ENERGY
(Suby of BLACK HILLS CORP) ★
1205 Sw 37th St, Grimes, IA 50111-4947
Tel (515) 224-1404 Founded/Ownrshp 2008
Sales 96.7MM^E EMP 205
Accts Deloitte & Touche Llp
SIC 4924 Natural gas distribution
VP: Tracy Peterson

D-U-N-S 82-948-2251
■ BLACK HILLS/NEBRASKA GAS UTILITY CO LLC
BLACK HILLS ENERGY
(Suby of BLACK HILLS CORP) ★
1600 Windhoek Dr, Lincoln, NE 68512-1272
Tel (402) 437-1705 Founded/Ownrshp 2008
Sales 114.1MM^E EMP 242^E
Accts Deloitte & Touche Llp
SIC 4924 Natural gas distribution
VP: Dan Mechtenburg

D-U-N-S 09-642-3699
BLACK HORSE CARRIERS INC (IL)
150 Village Ct, Carol Stream, IL 60188-1860
Tel (630) 690-8900 Founded/Ownrshp 1999, 1880
Sales 134.5MM^E EMP 600
SIC 4212 5159 Local trucking, without storage; Horses
Pr: Gerald Niedert
Pr: Jim Isaacson
COO: Steve Prusa
*VP: Dave Anderson
Brnch Mgr: Tad Buckley
Off Mgr: Art Flonyea
VP Opers: Mike Arzich

D-U-N-S 07-967-0259
▲ BLACK KNIGHT FINANCIAL SERVICES INC
601 Riverside Ave, Jacksonville, FL 32204-2946
Tel (904) 854-5100 Founded/Ownrshp 2014
Sales 930.7MM EMP 4,100^E
Tkr Sym BKFS Exch NYS
SIC 7372 Prepackaged software
Pr: Thomas J Sanzone
*Ch Bd: William P Foley II
Pr: Andy Lee
COO: Anthony Orefice
COO: Dan Scheuble
CFO: Kirk T Larsen
Ex VP: Michael L Gravelle
Ex VP: Michael Gravelle
Sr VP: Shaimaa Elk
VP: Lisa Atkinson
VP: Ryan Massey
VP: JC Wells
Board of Directors: Thomas M Hagerty, David K Hunt, Richard N Massey, John D Rood

D-U-N-S 07-932-1441
■ BLACK KNIGHT FINANCIAL SERVICES LLC
(Suby of BLACK KNIGHT HOLDINGS INC) ★
601 Riverside Ave, Jacksonville, FL 32204-2946
Tel (904) 854-8100 Founded/Ownrshp 2013
Sales NA EMP 3,748^E
SIC 6361 6331 6531 8741 Title insurance; Fire, marine & casualty insurance; Escrow agent, real estate; Restaurant management
CTO: Ben Graboske

D-U-N-S 07-931-9130
■ BLACK KNIGHT HOLDINGS INC
(Suby of FIDELITY NATIONAL FINANCIAL INC) ★
601 Riverside Ave, Jacksonville, FL 32204-2946
Tel (904) 854-8100 Founded/Ownrshp 2013
Sales NA EMP 3,796^E
SIC 6361 6331 6531 8741 Title insurance; Fire, marine & casualty insurance; Escrow agent, real estate; Restaurant management
CEO: Raymond R Quirk

D-U-N-S 82-651-8438
■ BLACK KNIGHT INFOSERV LLC
(Suby of FIDELITY NATIONAL FINANCIAL INC) ★
601 Riverside Ave, Jacksonville, FL 32204-2946
Tel (904) 854-5100 Founded/Ownrshp 2014
Sales 1.3MMM^E EMP 7,800^E
SIC 7389 7374 Financial services; Data processing & preparation
CEO: Hugh R Harris
Pr: Shannon Graham
*COO: Daniel T Scheuble
*CFO: Thomas L Schilling
*Ex VP: Todd C Johnson
*Ex VP: Joseph M Nackashi
Ex VP: Michael Weathers
*Sr VP: Christopher P Breakiron
Sr VP: Dan Burnett
Sr VP: Lynn Hatfield
Sr VP: Adam MA
Sr VP: Thomas Palmer
Sr VP: Tom Peterson
Sr VP: Darlene Strickland
Sr VP: Vicki Vidal
VP: Kevin Creedon
VP: Stuart Driggs
VP: Pebbles Folsom
VP: Bill Gellerstedt
VP: Randy Gillis
VP: Patti Graham
Board of Directors: Dan R Carmichael, Alvin R Carpenter, Philip G Heasley, David K Hunt, James K Hunt, Lee A Kennedy, Susan E Lester, John W Snow

BLACK RIVER DISPLAY GROUP
See D & S CREATIVE COMMUNICATIONS INC

D-U-N-S 07-982-0797
BLACK STONE MINERALS LP
1001 Fannin St Ste 2020, Houston, TX 77002-6715
Tel (713) 658-0647 Founded/Ownrshp 2014
Sales 392.9MM EMP 117
Accts Bdo Usa Llp Houston Texas
Tkr Sym BSM Exch NYS
SIC 1311 Crude petroleum & natural gas
Ch Bd: Thomas L Carter Jr
Genl Pt: Black Stone Minerals GP
CFO: Marc Carroll
VP: Brent Collins

BLACK THUNDER MINE
See THUNDER BASIN COAL CO LLC

D-U-N-S 13-679-4257
BLACK VIPER ENERGY SERVICES LTD
11220 W County Road 127, Odessa, TX 79765-9413
Tel (432) 561-8801 Founded/Ownrshp 2003
Sales 83.5MM^E EMP 107^E
SIC 1381

BLACK-EYED PEA RESTAURANT
See BEP COLORADO RESTAURANTS LLC

BLACK-EYED PEAS RESTAURANTS
See DYNAMIC RESTAURANTS LLC

D-U-N-S 10-121-9228
▲ BLACKBAUD INC
2000 Daniel Island Dr, Daniel Island, SC 29492-7541
Tel (843) 216-6200 Founded/Ownrshp 1981
Sales 637.9MM EMP 3,095^E
Tkr Sym BLKB Exch NGS
SIC 7372 8748 Prepackaged software; Business consulting
Pr: Michael P Gianoni
*Ch Bd: Andrew M Leitch
Pr: Brian E Boruff
Pr: Russ Cobb
Pr: Tim Hill
Pr: Kevin W Mooney
*CFO: Anthony W Boor
CFO: Andy McMillin
Treas: Alice Taylor
*Ex VP: Charles T Cumbaa
Ex VP: Kevin McDearis
*Ex VP: John J Mistretta
VP: Jana Eggers
Board of Directors: Timothy Chou, George H Ellis, David G Golden, Peter J Kight, Sarah E Nash, Joyce M Nelson

D-U-N-S 15-596-4732 IMP
BLACKBERRY CORP
(Suby of BLACKBERRY LIMITED)
3001 Bishop Dr, San Ramon, CA 94583-5005
Tel (972) 650-6126 Founded/Ownrshp 1999
Sales 84.7MM^E EMP 336^E
SIC 5999 3661 4812 Mobile telephones & equipment; Telephones & telephone apparatus; Cellular telephone services
Pr: Roger Witteveen
*CEO: Thorsten Heins
VP: Peter Broughall
VP: Don McMurtry
Ex Dir: Efrem Colmenero
CTO: Patricia Miele
Snr Mgr: Paul Koch

D-U-N-S 01-613-1430
BLACKBOARD INC
(Suby of BLACKBOARD (UK) LIMITED)
1111 19th St Nw, Washington, DC 20036-3603
Tel (202) 463-4860 Founded/Ownrshp 1997
Sales 650.6MM^E EMP 1,934
SIC 7372 Educational computer software; Business oriented computer software
CEO: William L Ballhaus
Pr: Michael L Chasen
CFO: Bill Davis
CFO: Lisa Mayr
Ofcr: Matthew H Small
Sr VP: Katie Blot
Sr VP: David Marr
Sr VP: Mark Strassman
VP: Traci Burgess
VP: Craig Greenseid
VP: Steve Kann
VP: William Lewis
VP: Paul Terry
Assoc Dir: Olivia Spain

D-U-N-S 16-983-0002
BLACKBRUSH OIL & GAS LP
BLACKBRUSH TEXSTAR
18615 Tuscany Stone, San Antonio, TX 78258-3486
Tel (210) 495-5577 Founded/Ownrshp 2004
Sales 126.1MM^E EMP 105
SIC 1311 Crude petroleum & natural gas production
CEO: Scott Martin
COO: Phillip M Mezey
CFO: Eric Friedrichs
Sr VP: Mark A Norville
VP: Phillip Mezey

BLACKBRUSH TEXSTAR
See BLACKBRUSH OIL & GAS LP

BLACKEAGLE ENERGY SERVICES
See DESCO ACQUISITION LLC

D-U-N-S 00-581-6848
BLACKFOOT TELEPHONE COOPERATIVE INC
1221 N Russell St, Missoula, MT 59808-1898
Tel (406) 541-2121 Founded/Ownrshp 1954
Sales 111.2MM^E EMP 214^E
SIC 4813 Telephone communication, except radio
CEO: Bill Squires
*Pr: Tom Eggensperger
*CFO: Theodore Otis
*VP: Frank Creasia
*VP: Jason Williams

D-U-N-S 00-794-9584
BLACKFORD CAPITAL LLC
190 Monroe Ave Nw Ste 6, Grand Rapids, MI 49503-2637
Tel (616) 233-3101 Founded/Ownrshp 2000
Sales 111.0MM^E EMP 420^E
SIC 6726 Investment offices
Mng Dir: Jeffrey Johnson
Mng Dir: Jack Kolodny
Mktg Dir: Amanda Passage

D-U-N-S 13-636-4002
BLACKHAWK HEALTHCARE LLC
6836 Fm 2244 Rd Ste 202, Austin, TX 78746-5090
Tel (512) 617-6363 Founded/Ownrshp 2003
Sales 96.6MM^E EMP 275
SIC 8741 Nursing & personal care facility management
CEO: Matthew Q Hainline
*Pr: Todd Biederman
*CFO: John D Russell

D-U-N-S 96-636-8602 IMP/EXP
BLACKHAWK INDUSTRIAL DISTRIBUTION INC
DUNCAN INDUSTRIAL SOLUTIONS
1501 Sw Expressway Dr, Broken Arrow, OK 74012-1773
Tel (918) 663-3252 Founded/Ownrshp 2009
Sales 450.1MM^E EMP 580^E
SIC 5085 3561 5084 Industrial supplies; Pumps & pumping equipment; Industrial machinery & equipment
Pr: Bill Scheller
*CFO: Parker Strickland
VP: Bryan Collins
CIO: Stephen Burns
IT Man: Cindy Schauer

D-U-N-S 07-871-7390
BLACKHAWK MINING LLC
3228 Summit Square Pl # 180, Lexington, KY 40509-2637
Tel (859) 543-0515 Founded/Ownrshp 2010
Sales 198.1MM^E EMP 363^E
SIC 1241 Coal mining services
CEO: Mitch Potter
*Pr: Nick Glancy
Sfty Mgr: Tim Smith

D-U-N-S 61-895-1680
▲ BLACKHAWK NETWORK HOLDINGS INC
6220 Stoneridge Mall Rd, Pleasanton, CA 94588-3260
Tel (925) 226-9990 Founded/Ownrshp 2001
Sales NA EMP 2,331
Tkr Sym HAWK Exch NGS
SIC 6099 Electronic funds transfer network, including switching
Pr: Talbott Roche
*Ch Bd: William Y Tauscher
Ofcr: Jerry N Ulrich
Sr VP: Christopher C Crum
Sr VP: Sachin Dhawan
Sr VP: David C Tate
VP Sls: Jayson Berg
Sls Dir: Kathryn Keller
Board of Directors: Anil D Aggarwal, Richard H Bard, Steven A Burd, Robert L Edwards, Mohan Gyani, Paul Hazen, Arun Sarin, Jane J Thompson

D-U-N-S 07-911-5815
■ BLACKHAWK NETWORK INC
(Suby of BLACKHAWK NETWORK HOLDINGS INC) ★
6220 Stoneridge Mall Rd, Pleasanton, CA 94588-3260
Tel (925) 226-9990 Founded/Ownrshp 2005
Sales NA EMP 1,860
SIC 6099 Electronic funds transfer network, including switching
Pr: Talbott Roche
Pr: Mike Gionfriddo
Pr: Ben King
Pr: Tom Neale
Pr: Jeff Pomeroy
CFO: Jerry Ulrich
Sr VP: David Tate
VP: Chris Crum
VP: Jaime Gonzalez
Creative D: Michael Carrow
Dir Bus: Ryan Koop
Dir Bus: Kate Sullivan

D-U-N-S 79-204-1670
■ BLACKHAWK PARENT LLC
(Suby of BLACKSTONE GROUP L P) ★
345 Park Ave, New York, NY 10154-0004
Tel (212) 583-5000 Founded/Ownrshp 1985
Sales 103.3MM^E EMP 700^E
SIC 6798 6531 Realty investment trusts; Real estate agent, commercial
Pr: Stephen A Schwarzman
*Ch: J Tomilson Hill

D-U-N-S 06-955-5940
BLACKHAWK SPECIALTY TOOLS LLC (TX)
11936 Brittmoore Park Dr, Houston, TX 77041-7225
Tel (713) 466-4200 Founded/Ownrshp 2008
Sales 168.1MM^E EMP 150
SIC 1382 Oil & gas exploration services
CEO: Billy Brown
Exec: Chris Glankler
Dist Mgr: Joe Chenier

D-U-N-S 06-245-0425
▲ BLACKLINE INC
21300 Victory Blvd Fl 12, Woodland Hills, CA 91367-7734
Tel (818) 223-9008 Founded/Ownrshp 2013
Sales 83.6MM EMP 490^E
Tkr Sym BL Exch NGS
SIC 7371 Computer software systems analysis & design, custom
CEO: Therese Tucker
*Ch Bd: John Brennan
CFO: Mark Partin
*Chf Mktg O: Mario Spanicciati
Ofcr: Karen Flathers
Ofcr: Max Solonski

Dir Risk M: Chris Murphy
CTO: Alain Avakian

D-U-N-S 00-892-1595 IMP
BLACKMAN PLUMBING SUPPLY CO INC
900 Sylvan Ave, Bayport, NY 11705-1012
Tel (631) 823-4300 *Founded/Ownrshp* 1934
Sales 416.0MM^E *EMP* 320
SIC 5074 5075 Heating equipment (hydronic); Plumbing fittings & supplies; Air conditioning & ventilation equipment & supplies; Warm air heating equipment & supplies
Pr: Richard Blackman
CFO: Robert Nannheimar
Ofcr: Diane Nardone
**VP:* Kevin Sossin
Rgnl Mgr: Sean Mulderig
Brnch Mgr: Victor Marco
Opers Mgr: Rene Jones
Mktg Dir: Kevin Gordon
Mktg Dir: Mark Schmittzeh
Sales Asso: Juan Reyes
Sales Asso: Matthew Vazquez
Board of Directors: Sue Cook

BLACKROCK ASSET MANAGEMENT
See BLACKROCK HOLDCO 2 INC

D-U-N-S 79-002-2904
▲ BLACKROCK CAPITAL INVESTMENT CORP
40 E 52nd St, New York, NY 10022-5911
Tel (212) 810-5800 *Founded/Ownrshp* 2005
Sales 129.4MM *EMP* 16^E
Tkr Sym BKCC *Exch* NGS
SIC 6211 Security brokers & dealers
Ch Bd: Steven Sterling
CFO: Donna Milia
CFO: Corinne Pankovcin
Chf Cred: Charles C S Park
VP: Anne Ackerley
VP: Peter Campagna
VP: Kimberly Crittenden
VP: Robert Shearer
Mng Dir: Joseph Auriemma
Mng Dir: ARA Basil
Mng Dir: Jodi Berman

D-U-N-S 78-276-7099
■ BLACKROCK FINANCIAL MANAGEMENT INC
BLACKROCK FINANCIAL MGMT
(*Suby of* BLACKROCK ASSET MANAGEMENT) ★
40 E 52nd St Fl 2, New York, NY 10022-5929
Tel (212) 810-5300 *Founded/Ownrshp* 1999
Sales 332.2MM^E *EMP* 900
SIC 6282 Investment advisory service
Ch Bd: Laurence D Fink
**Pr:* Robert S Kapito
**COO:* Rob Goldstein
CFO: Neal Andrews
**CFO:* Gary S Shedlin
VP: Lili Forouraghi
VP: Jamie Hill
VP: Paul Horowitz
VP: Navneet Kumar
VP: Edward Lee
VP: Nicholas Marino
VP: Anand Salagundi
VP: Raymond Shivers

BLACKROCK FINANCIAL MGMT
See BLACKROCK FINANCIAL MANAGEMENT INC

D-U-N-S 93-848-3237
■ BLACKROCK GLOBAL INVESTORS
(*Suby of* BLACKROCK INC) ★
400 Howard St, San Francisco, CA 94105-2618
Tel (415) 670-2000 *Founded/Ownrshp* 2009
Sales 144.7MM^E *EMP* 1,100
SIC 6282 Investment advisory service
CEO: Patricia Dunn
VP: Sapna Sardana
VP: Kota Shivaranjan
**Prin:* Blake Grossman
**Prin:* Carter Lyons
Telecom Ex: James Levinson
Dir IT: Donald Luskin
Dir IT: Rachel Ogorman
Dir IT: Cesar Oland
Dir IT: Marty Quintanilla
Dir IT: Michael Valenza

D-U-N-S 04-686-4385
■ BLACKROCK HOLDCO 2 INC
BLACKROCK ASSET MANAGEMENT
(*Suby of* BLACKROCK INC) ★
40 E 52nd St, New York, NY 10022-5911
Tel (212) 754-5300 *Founded/Ownrshp* 2006
Sales 346.7MM^E *EMP* 2,151
SIC 6282 Investment advice; Manager of mutual funds, contract or fee basis
CEO: Laurence D Fink
**Pr:* Ralph L Schlosstein
**Act CFO:* Paul L Audet
Chf Mktg O: Grace Sette
Ex VP: Tom Craven
VP: Christopher Aiken
VP: Blair Alleman
VP: Saba Anvar
VP: Doug Baker
VP: Keiran Breslin
VP: Raymond Butti
VP: Robert Chiolan
VP: Thomas Creaven
VP: Ken Daponte
VP: Vincent Dellaglio
VP: Viola Dunne
VP: Gina Forziati
VP: David Gagliardotto
VP: Jeff Greenblatt
VP: Jamie Hill
VP: Vijay Kasarabada

D-U-N-S 78-698-7052
▲ BLACKROCK INC
55 E 52nd St Fl 11, New York, NY 10055-0003
Tel (212) 810-5300 *Founded/Ownrshp* 1988
Sales 11.4MMM *EMP* 13,000
Tkr Sym BLK *Exch* NYS
SIC 6282 6211 Investment advice; Investment firm, general brokerage
Ch Bd: Laurence D Fink
V Ch: Barbara G Novick
**Pr:* Robert S Kapito
**COO:* Robert L Goldstein
**CFO:* Gary S Shedlin
Treas: Abhijit Chandra
Treas: Andre July
Ex VP: Nick Hutton
Ex VP: Apoorva Shah
Ex VP: Clinton Soose
VP: Lee Adkins
VP: Neil Blundell
VP: Richard Bravery
VP: Ed Cannon
VP: Danielle Costantino
VP: Sareena Dalla
VP: Paul Dearman
VP: Kameka Dempsey
VP: Wendy Dooley
VP: Eugene Drozdetski
VP: Whitney Ehrlich
Board of Directors: Deryck Maughan, Pamela Daley, Cheryl D Mills, William S Demchak, Gordon M Nixon, Marco Antonio Slim Domit, Thomas H O'brien, Jessica Einhorn, Ivan G Seidenberg, Fabrizio Freda, John S Varley, Murry S Gerber, Susan L Wagner, James Grosfeld, David H Komansky, Catherine A Lynch

D-U-N-S 14-992-4094
■ BLACKROCK INSTITUTIONAL TRUST CO NATIONAL ASSOCIATION
ISHARES
(*Suby of* BLACKROCK INC) ★
400 Howard St, San Francisco, CA 94105-2618
Tel (415) 597-2000 *Founded/Ownrshp* 2009
Sales 1.5MMM *EMP* 800
SIC 6722 Management investment, open-end
CEO: Laurence D Fink
**Pr:* Robert S Kapito
**Pr:* James Parsons
VP: Eric Braithwaite
Mng Dir: Scott Thompson
Natl Sales: David Denby
Board of Directors: Katrina Gil

BLACKS TIRE & AUTO SERVICE
See S BLACK TIRE SERVICE INC

D-U-N-S 96-757-4935
■ BLACKSTONE CAPITAL PARTNERS V LP
(*Suby of* BLACKSTONE GROUP L P) ★
345 Park Ave, New York, NY 10154-0004
Tel (212) 583-5000 *Founded/Ownrshp* 2005
Sales 1.5MMM^E *EMP* 19,000^E
SIC 6719 Investment holding companies, except banks
CEO: Stephen A Schwarzman
VP: Blackstone G Michael
Mng Dir: Sylvia Moss

D-U-N-S 79-019-4799
BLACKSTONE CONSULTING INC
11726 San Vicente Blvd # 550, Los Angeles, CA 90049-5089
Tel (310) 826-4389 *Founded/Ownrshp* 1991
Sales 135.0MM^E *EMP* 480^E
SIC 8742 Management consulting services
Pr: Ronald Joseph Blackstone
Sr Pt: Sean Dundon
COO: James Brown
Sr VP: Jim Strife
VP: Anna Chavez
Genl Mgr: Joe Blackstone
Genl Mgr: Michael Robinson
Snr PM: Amy Stanton

BLACKSTONE GROUP
See GSO CAPITAL PARTNERS LP

BLACKSTONE GROUP
See GRAND SLAM HOLDINGS LLC

D-U-N-S 60-318-2577
■ BLACKSTONE GROUP HOLDINGS LLC
(*Suby of* BLACKSTONE GROUP L P) ★
345 Park Ave Ste 1100, New York, NY 10154-1703
Tel (212) 583-5000 *Founded/Ownrshp* 1987
Sales 541.7MM^E *EMP* 2,000^E
SIC 6211 Security brokers & dealers
Sr VP: Lacxon Chan
VP: Cynthia Bombara
VP: Mike Carruthers
VP: Brian Caslin
VP: Richard Dziurzynski
VP: Bonnie Gleason
VP: Melissa Herland
VP: John Taggart
VP: Jimmy Wang
Ex Dir: Amit Dalmia
Ex Dir: Jeffrey Overly

D-U-N-S 14-463-0571
▲ BLACKSTONE GROUP L P
345 Park Ave Ste 1100, New York, NY 10154-1703
Tel (212) 583-5000 *Founded/Ownrshp* 1985
Sales 4.6MMM *EMP* 2,060
Tkr Sym BX *Exch* NYS
SIC 6282 6211 Investment advisory service; Manager of mutual funds, contract or fee basis; Investment research; Investment bankers
Ch Bd: Stephen A Schwarzman
Genl Pt: Blackstone G C
Pr: Samantha Fleary
Pr: Hamilton E James
Pr: Daniel Nolan
Pr: Anna Ryvkov
Bd of Dir: Fadwa Abousselham
Sr VP: Jeffrey Wilkie
VP: Sarah Acott
VP: Allan Barja
VP: John Beberus
VP: Amy Blake
VP: Damiano Buffa
VP: Daniel Chang
VP: Byung U Choi
VP: Tim Choi
VP: Walter Dinsmore
VP: Jana Douglas
VP: Andy Drasites
VP: Esther Friedman
VP: Justin Hall

D-U-N-S 00-494-3341 IMP/EXP
BLACKSTONE GROUP LLC
570 Broad St Ste 1606, Newark, NJ 07102-4532
Tel (973) 624-6300 *Founded/Ownrshp* 1996
Sales 152.0MM *EMP* 25
SIC 1542 1522 1541 Commercial & office building, new construction; Multi-family dwelling construction; Industrial buildings & warehouses
Pr: Airaj Hasan
VP: Bryan Shelby
Exec: Aleksandar Erdeljan
CTO: Dee Jackson
Opers Mgr: Gary Newman

D-U-N-S 60-102-3674
BLACKSTONE MORTGAGE TRUST INC
345 Park Ave Fl 42, New York, NY 10154-0004
Tel (212) 655-0220 *Founded/Ownrshp* 1966
Sales 410.6MM *EMP* 8^E
SIC 6798 Realty investment trusts
Pr: Stephen D Plavin
**Ch Bd:* Michael B Nash
CFO: Paul D Quinlan
Treas: Douglas N Armer
VP: Anthony F Marone Jr
Mng Dir: Randall S Rothschild
Mktg Dir: Jeremy Fitzgerald

D-U-N-S 07-913-2845
BLACKSTONE REAL ESTATE PARTNERS VI LP
345 Park Ave, New York, NY 10154-0004
Tel (212) 583-5000 *Founded/Ownrshp* 2002
Sales 98.4MM^E *EMP* 20,000
SIC 8741 6531 Financial management for business; Rental agent, real estate
CEO: Stephen A Schwarzman
**Pr:* Hamilton E James

D-U-N-S 78-424-7012
BLACKSTREET CAPITAL MANAGEMENT LLC
5425 Wisconsin Ave # 701, Chevy Chase, MD 20815-3562
Tel (240) 223-1330 *Founded/Ownrshp* 2006
Sales 157.3MM^E *EMP* 1,130
SIC 6726 5149 5145 5961 Management investment funds, closed-end; Specialty food items; Candy; Popcorn & supplies; Catalog & mail-order houses
CFO: Caroline J Miller
VP: Andy Anderson
VP: Angel I Donchev
VP: David A Hartman
VP: Jonathan Tipton
Mng Dir: Lawrence Berger
Snr Mgr: Caroline Miller

D-U-N-S 09-967-2750
BLACKWELL BALDWIN CHEVROLET GEO OLDSMOBILE CADILLAC INC
BLACKWELL-BALDWIN OLDSMOBILE
621 S Westwood Blvd, Poplar Bluff, MO 63901-5525
Tel (573) 785-0893 *Founded/Ownrshp* 1990
Sales 180.0MM *EMP* 60
SIC 5511 Automobiles, new & used
Pr: Harry Blackwell
**VP:* Roger Baldwin
Genl Mgr: Garry Lunsford
Sales Asso: Joe Bissette
Sales Asso: Andy Earls
Sales Asso: Alan King

BLACKWELL-BALDWIN OLDSMOBILE
See BLACKWELL BALDWIN CHEVROLET GEO OLDSMOBILE CADILLAC INC

D-U-N-S 09-025-1666 IMP
BLADES TECHNOLOGY INTERNATIONAL INC (GA)
8801 Macon Rd, Columbus, GA 31908
Tel (706) 568-5900 *Founded/Ownrshp* 1995
Sales 116.8MM^E *EMP* 560
SIC 3728 Blades, aircraft propeller: metal or wood
Pr: Amos Grunbaum

D-U-N-S 02-327-1463 IMP
BLAIN SUPPLY INC
BLAIN'S FARM & FLEET
3507 E Racine St, Janesville, WI 53546-2320
Tel (608) 754-2821 *Founded/Ownrshp* 1955
Sales 186.6MM^E *EMP* 300
SIC 5083 5072 5039 5013 5023 5198

D-U-N-S 04-947-1451
BLAINE CONSTRUCTION CORP
(*Suby of* YATES COMPANIES INC) ★
6510 Deane Hill Dr, Knoxville, TN 37919-6005
Tel (865) 693-8900 *Founded/Ownrshp* 1991
Sales 100.1MM *EMP* 200
SIC 1541 1542

D-U-N-S 07-296-7763
BLAINE LARSEN FARMS INC
2650 N 2375 E, Hamer, ID 83425-5038
Tel (208) 662-5501 *Founded/Ownrshp* 1990
Sales 879.1MM^E *EMP* 687
SIC 5148 2099 0111 0139 Potatoes, fresh; Food preparations; Wheat; Hay farm
Pr: Blaine Larsen
**CFO:* Blaik Sharp

BLAIN'S FARM & FLEET
See BLAIN SUPPLY INC

BLAIR E BTSON HOSP FOR CHLDREN
See UNIVERSITY OF MISSISSIPPI MEDICAL CENTER RESEARCH DEVELOPMENT

D-U-N-S 00-791-7560 IMP
BLAIR LLC
(*Suby of* BEDFORD FAIR APPAREL) ★
220 Hickory St, Warren, PA 16366-0002
Tel (814) 723-3600 *Founded/Ownrshp* 1924
Sales 273.1MM^E *EMP* 1,200
SIC 5961 Women's apparel, mail order; Clothing, mail order (except women's); Furniture & furnishings, mail order
Ch Bd: Craig N Johnson
**CFO:* Larry Pitorak
Ex VP: Giles Schutte
**Sr VP:* David N Elliott
Sr VP: David Elliott
VP: Cynthia Dziendziel
VP: Rhonda Hollabaugh
VP: Lawrence Vicini
Telecom Mg: Todd Fitch
Software D: Paul Williams
VP Advt: John A Lasher

D-U-N-S 10-968-6352
BLAIR MEDICAL ASSOCIATES
(*Suby of* WEB:WWWALTOONAHOSPITALORG) ★
1414 9th Ave, Altoona, PA 16602-2452
Tel (814) 944-0202 *Founded/Ownrshp* 2008
Sales 4.5MM^E *EMP* 1,195^E
SIC 8011 8043 Offices & clinics of medical doctors; Offices & clinics of podiatrists
CEO: Dave Duncan
CEO: John Brown
Podiatrist: Harry L Penny DPM

D-U-N-S 01-867-8508
BLAKE GROUP HOLDINGS INC (CT)
4 New Park Rd, East Windsor, CT 06088-9689
Tel (860) 243-1491 *Founded/Ownrshp* 1925, 1967
Sales 162.7MM^E *EMP* 150
SIC 5074 5084 7699 8741 Boilers, power (industrial); Water heaters, except electric; Pumps & pumping equipment; Boiler repair shop; Management services
Pr: Fred B Cuda
**VP:* David Birdsey
**VP:* Richard Cuda
VP: Bob Klybas
VP: Jim Paulhus
Div Mgr: Kimberly Garcia
Sales Asso: Bill Fisher
Sales Asso: Mark Henderson

D-U-N-S 82-951-4111 IMP
BLAKE INTERNATIONAL USA RIGS LLC
410 S Van Ave, Houma, LA 70363-6759
Tel (985) 274-2200 *Founded/Ownrshp* 2008
Sales 203.3MM^E *EMP* 300^E
SIC 1381 Drilling oil & gas wells
Ch Bd: Michael Blake
Trfc Dir: Drake Dufrene
VP Sls: Jeff Kessler

BLAKEWOOD APARTMENTS
See BLAKEWOOD PROPERTIES ASSOCIATES

D-U-N-S 83-287-9725
BLAKEWOOD PROPERTIES ASSOCIATES
BLAKEWOOD APARTMENTS
620 E Olliff St, Statesboro, GA 30458-4628
Tel (912) 764-3330 *Founded/Ownrshp* 2009
Sales 35.7MM^E *EMP* 3,900
SIC 6531 Real estate brokers & agents
Pr: Russell Fleming
**CFO:* Deedra Burroughs

D-U-N-S 00-692-3239 IMP/EXP
BLANCHARD MACHINERY CO
CATERPILLAR AUTHORIZED DEALER
3151 Charleston Hwy, West Columbia, SC 29172-2723
Tel (803) 791-7100 *Founded/Ownrshp* 1982
Sales 340.2MM^E *EMP* 575
SIC 5082 7353 Construction & mining machinery; Heavy construction equipment rental
Pr: Joseph R Blanchard
**CFO:* Kelly Jones
**VP:* Joan Deal
VP: Mike Love
VP: Chris Pierson
Admn Mgr: Carolyn Cash
Genl Mgr: Chad Tackett
CTO: Bob Gourley
Sfty Mgr: Scott Esposito
Opers Mgr: Jim Johnston
Opers Mgr: Greg Lovejoy

D-U-N-S 06-372-2029
BLANCHARD VALLEY HEALTH SYSTEM
1900 S Main St, Findlay, OH 45840-1214
Tel (419) 423-4500 *Founded/Ownrshp* 1891
Sales 31.1MM *EMP* 1,700
Accts Bkd Llp Fort Wayne In
SIC 8741 7349 Hospital management; Building maintenance, except repairs
Pr: Scott Malaney
**CFO:* John Bookmyer
CFO: Dave Cylik
**Ch:* Duane Jebbett
**Treas:* Kurt Geisheimer
**VP:* Chris Keller
VP: Patrick Milostan
**VP:* Barbara Pasztor
Dir Lab: Bonnie Vanschoik
Dir Rx: Karen Gerardi
Dir IT: Marcy Nonnamaker

BLANCHARD VALLEY HOSPITAL
See BLANCHARD VALLEY REGIONAL HEALTH CENTER

D-U-N-S 19-629-2627 IMP
BLANCHARD VALLEY REGIONAL HEALTH CENTER
BLANCHARD VALLEY HOSPITAL
(*Suby of* BLANCHARD VALLEY HEALTH SYSTEM) ★
1900 S Main St, Findlay, OH 45840-1214
Tel (419) 423-4500 *Founded/Ownrshp* 1891
Sales 222.2MM *EMP* 1,000
SIC 8062 General medical & surgical hospitals
COO: John Bookmyer
Pathlgst: Heidi Budke
Pharmcst: Rhonda Siefker
HC Dir: Connie Wenzinger
Board of Directors: Will Sturgen, Marlene Brunkswick, Kim Thomas, Robin Cramer, Roxanne Williams, Martin Hanawalt, Sherry Winegardner, Randy Hunt,

Mark Johannigman, Steve Linville, Sue Schutz, Kelly Shroll, Sandy Shutt

D-U-N-S 00-615-8943 IMP
BLANDIN PAPER CO
UPM BLANDIN PAPER
(*Suby of* UPM-KYMMENE OYJ)
115 Sw 1st St, Grand Rapids, MN 55744-3699
Tel (218) 327-6200 *Founded/Ownrshp* 1901, 1997
Sales 226.4MM[E] *EMP* 860
SIC 2621 2672 Printing paper; Coated & laminated paper
CEO: Rebecca Norris
**Pr:* Brend Eikens
**CEO:* Joe Maher
Dir Bus: Anthony Kehoe
Mng Dir: Kevin Lydon
Dist Mgr: John Deakin
Genl Mgr: Thomas Waltasaari
Mtls Mgr: Pekka Noppari

D-U-N-S 07-549-4054
BLANK ROME LLP
1 Logan Sq, Philadelphia, PA 19103-6998
Tel (215) 569-5500 *Founded/Ownrshp* 1936
Sales 152.9MM *EMP* 515
SIC 8111 General practice law office
Pt: Alan J Hoffman
Pt: Michael L Cioffi
Pt: Michael D Debaecke
Pt: Barry H Genkin
Pt: Andrew Hart
Pt: Brooke T Iley
Pt: Albert B Krachman
Pt: Michael H Leeds
Pt: Peter Mills
Pt: Robert J Mittman
Pt: Stephen M Orlofsky
Pt: Michael A Rodriguez
Pt: Michael Rowe
Pt: Kristi Lynn Swartz
Pt: Jon K Waldron
Mng Pt: Fred Blume
COO: Patrick O Cavanaugh
CFO: John Seifarth
**Ch:* T Michale Dyer
Chf Mktg O: Catherine Bishop
Chf Mktg O: Adam B SC

D-U-N-S 01-673-9880
BLARNEY CASTLE OIL CO (MI)
12218 West St, Bear Lake, MI 49614-9432
Tel (231) 864-3111 *Founded/Ownrshp* 1941
Sales 525.9MM *EMP* 700
Accts Hungerford Nichols Grand Rapi
SIC 5541 5411 5171 Filling stations, gasoline; Convenience stores, chain; Petroleum bulk stations
Pr: Dennis E Mc Carthy
CFO: Joe Taraskavage
**VP:* William J Mc Carthy
Store Mgr: Joe Haight
VP Sls: Shawn Gray

D-U-N-S 80-170-1368 IMP/EXP
BLASER SWISSLUBE HOLDING CORP
(*Suby of* KORAS AG)
31 Hatfield Ln, Goshen, NY 10924-6712
Tel (845) 294-3200 *Founded/Ownrshp* 1981
Sales 84.3MM[E] *EMP* 40[E]
SIC 2992 Lubricating oils & greases
CEO: Peter Blaser
**Pr:* Ulrich Krahenbuhl
**VP:* Richard Surico
Area Mgr: Bob Green

D-U-N-S 02-432-9302
BLATCHFORDS INC (DE)
ACE HARDWARE
207 S Chicago St, Hot Springs, SD 57747-2321
Tel (605) 745-5173 *Founded/Ownrshp* 1935, 1978
Sales 124.8MM *EMP* 13
SIC 5251 5712 5531 5947 5722 Hardware; Furniture stores; Automotive accessories; Gift shop; Electric household appliances, major
Pr: John T Blatchford Sr
**VP:* John T Blatchford Jr

D-U-N-S 96-358-6792
BLATTNER ENERGY INC
392 County Road 50, Avon, MN 56310-8684
Tel (320) 356-7351 *Founded/Ownrshp* 2008
Sales NA *EMP* 1,200
SIC 1731 General electrical contractor
CEO: Scott Blattner
CFO: John Blattner
Dir IT: Naser Ayyub

D-U-N-S 00-101-2954 IMP/EXP
BLAUER MANUFACTURING CO INC (MA)
20 Aberdeen St, Boston, MA 02215-3800
Tel (617) 536-6606 *Founded/Ownrshp* 1936
Sales 580.5MM[E] *EMP* 235
SIC 5099 3842 2337 Safety equipment & supplies; Clothing, fire resistant & protective; Uniforms, except athletic: women's, misses' & juniors'
Pr: Charles Blauer
**Pr:* Michael A Simons
CFO: Tim Coakley
**Sr VP:* Michael Blauer
Mktg Mgr: Greg Bogosian

D-U-N-S 10-689-1195
BLEDSOE COAL CORP
(*Suby of* JAMES RIVER COAL CO) ★
901 E Byrd St Ste 1140, Richmond, VA 23219-4070
Tel (606) 878-7411 *Founded/Ownrshp* 1976
Sales 66.3MM[E] *EMP* 1,018
SIC 1221 Bituminous coal & lignite-surface mining
Pr: Tim Frasure
Treas: Elmer Ison
Exec: Linda Dowe
Exec: Linda Downes
IT Man: Nancy Ibenberg

BLESSED SACRAMENT SCHOOL
See ROMAN CATHOLIC BISHOP OF PROVIDENCE (INC)

D-U-N-S 09-417-8654
BLESSEY ENTERPRISES INC
1515 River Oaks Rd E, Harahan, LA 70123-2167
Tel (504) 734-1156 *Founded/Ownrshp* 1978
Sales 168.4MM *EMP* 807[E]
SIC 4449

D-U-N-S 18-839-9950
BLESSEY MARINE SERVICE INC
1515 River Oaks Rd E, Harahan, LA 70123-2167
Tel (504) 734-1156 *Founded/Ownrshp* 1978
Sales 90.9MM[E] *EMP* 550
SIC 4492 Marine towing services
CEO: Walter Blessey Jr
**Pr:* Clark Todd
**CFO:* Patrick Voss
VP: Jim Clendenon
Opers Mgr: Jack Haskell
Sales Exec: Bob Shea

D-U-N-S 96-940-3323
BLESSING CORPORATE SERVICES INC
BLESSING HEALTH SYSTEM
Broadway At 11th, Quincy, IL 62305
Tel (217) 223-1200 *Founded/Ownrshp* 1982
Sales 49.1MM *EMP* 1,152[E]
Accts Gray Hunter Stenn Llp Quincy
SIC 8741 Management services
Prin: Rhonda Marsh

BLESSING HEALTH SYSTEM
See BLESSING CORPORATE SERVICES INC

BLESSING HOME CARE
See BLESSING HOSPITAL

D-U-N-S 07-992-9733
BLESSING HOSPITAL
BLESSING HOME CARE
(*Suby of* BLESSING HEALTH SYSTEM) ★
Broadway At 11th St, Quincy, IL 62301
Tel (217) 223-1200 *Founded/Ownrshp* 1875
Sales 316.3MM *EMP* 2,500
Accts Gray Hunter Stenn Llp Quincy
SIC 8062 General medical & surgical hospitals
CEO: Maureen A Kahn
**Ch Bd:* Thomas H Miller
V Ch: Timothy D Koontz
COO: B Bradford Billings
CFO: Patrick Gerveler
CFO: Emma Lane
Trst: Nancy A Bluhm
Trst: Jean A Disseler
Trst: Michael J Foster
Trst: Lynn P House
Trst: Michael R Hulsen
Trst: Joseph A Kuhlman
Ofcr: Kevin Wesey
VP: Nicole Ginsberg
VP: Betty Kasparie
VP: Jay R Kelley
VP: Rick Kempe
Exec: Bob Dickson
Exec: Patton Joleen
Dir Risk M: Carolin Bailey
Dir Lab: Phillip Smith

D-U-N-S 17-335-3558
BLETHEN CORP
1120 John St, Seattle, WA 98109-5321
Tel (206) 464-2471 *Founded/Ownrshp* 1956
Sales 174.6MM[E] *EMP* 1,590
SIC 2711 Newspapers, publishing & printing
Pr: Frank A Blethen
VP: Alayne Fardella
VP: Eileen Takeuchi
VP: Bill Yerous
Genl Mgr: Ken Hatch
Netwrk Mgr: Paul Dewees
VP Mktg: Bob Blethen
Mktg Mgr: Tim Williams
Sls Mgr: Neil Johnson

D-U-N-S 05-343-9634 IMP
BLEVINS INC
NONE
421 Hart Ln, Nashville, TN 37216-2003
Tel (615) 226-6453 *Founded/Ownrshp* 1971
Sales 136.0MM[E] *EMP* 275
SIC 5075 Warm air heating & air conditioning; Air conditioning & ventilation equipment & supplies; Warm air heating equipment & supplies
Pr: Brad Blevins
**Ch Bd:* James W Blevins
**Pr:* William B Blevins
**CFO:* Tim Kentner
**Sec:* Melba Blevins
**VP:* Jim Carper
**VP:* Jim Eades

BLICK DICK ART MATERIALS STORE
See DICK BLICK CO

BLIMPIE
See KAHALA BRANDS LTD

D-U-N-S 00-824-4068 EXP
BLINDS TO GO (US) INC
(*Suby of* BLINDS TO GO INC)
101 E State Rt 4, Paramus, NJ 07652-2635
Tel (201) 441-9260 *Founded/Ownrshp* 1994
Sales 91.4MM[E] *EMP* 500
SIC 2591 Drapery hardware & blinds & shades
Pr: Stephen Shiller
**CFO:* Lucy Modesti
IT Man: Hitesh Barot
Mktg Mgr: Ashish Vachhani
Sls Mgr: Ramneeta Taluja

D-U-N-S 07-844-4817
BLINN COLLEGE
902 College Ave, Brenham, TX 77833-4098
Tel (979) 830-4000 *Founded/Ownrshp* 1883
Sales 70.8MM *EMP* 1,190
SIC 8221 8222 Colleges universities & professional schools; Junior college
Pr: Mary Hensley
Dir IT: Don Cotton

D-U-N-S 00-694-2445
BLISH-MIZE CO
223 S 5th St, Atchison, KS 66002-2801
Tel (913) 367-1250 *Founded/Ownrshp* 1871
Sales 162.7MM[E] *EMP* 175
Accts Bkd Llp Kansas City Mo
SIC 5072 Hardware; Builders' hardware; Hand tools
CEO: Jonathan Mize
**Pr:* Jonathan D Mize
**CFO:* Tom Hottovy
Bd of Dir: Patti Beien
**Ex VP:* Lydia Funk
**Sr VP:* Greg Lutz
**VP:* Amy Hennis
VP: Cindy Kane
**VP:* Doug Long
**VP:* Wayne Lueckenhoff
VP: Wayne Luekenhoff
VP: Kevin Zeit

BLISS
See BEAULIEU GROUP LLC

D-U-N-S 00-607-4611
BLISS COMMUNICATIONS INC (WI)
JANESVILLE GAZETTE
1 S Parker Dr, Janesville, WI 53545-3928
Tel (608) 741-6650 *Founded/Ownrshp* 1845
Sales 128.3MM[E] *EMP* 625
SIC 2711 4832 Newspapers, publishing & printing; Radio broadcasting stations
Pr: Sidney H Bliss
Pr: Dan White
**CFO:* Robert J Lisser
Treas: Keith Kloos
VP: Tony Smithson
VP: Mary J Villa
Exec: Jenny Revels
MIS Dir: Debbie King

D-U-N-S 07-742-7396 IMP
BLISS WORLD LLC
BLISSDISTRIBUTION
(*Suby of* STEINER LEISURE LIMITED)
200 Vesey St Fl 25, New York, NY 10281-1025
Tel (212) 931-6383 *Founded/Ownrshp* 1999, 2009
Sales 128.5MM[E] *EMP* 600
SIC 5999 Spas & hot tubs
CEO: Meri Baregamian
**Pr:* Michael Indursky
**CFO:* Mike Miller

BLISSDISTRIBUTION
See BLISS WORLD LLC

D-U-N-S 17-384-8990
■ **BLIZZARD ENTERTAINMENT INC**
(*Suby of* ACTIVISION BLIZZARD INC) ★
16215 Alton Pkwy, Irvine, CA 92618-3616
Tel (949) 955-1380 *Founded/Ownrshp* 2008
Sales 99.5MM[E] *EMP* 125
SIC 7372 5734 7819 Prepackaged software; Software, computer games; Reproduction services, motion picture production
Pr: Mike Morhaime
**Pr:* Paul Sams
Ex VP: Frank Pearce
**Sr VP:* Chris Metzen
VP: Denise Dunlap-Alpert
VP: Justin Osborne
VP: Rob Pardo
**VP:* Todd Pawlowski
Creative D: Erik Jensen
Snr Sftwr: Chris Allsopp
Snr Sftwr: Joel Deaguero

BLMGTN
See KATUN CORP

D-U-N-S 00-503-8021
BLOCK COMMUNICATIONS INC (OH)
BCI
405 Madison Ave Ste 2100, Toledo, OH 43604-1224
Tel (419) 724-6212 *Founded/Ownrshp* 1965
Sales 632.1MM[E] *EMP* 2,900
SIC 4841 4833 2711 Cable television services; Television broadcasting stations; Newspapers, publishing & printing
Pr: Walter H Carstensen
**Ch Bd:* Allan J Block
**Treas:* Sara Labudda
**V Ch Bd:* John R Block
**VP:* Jodi Miehls
VP: Joseph H Zerbey IV
Dir Risk M: Jacqueline Porter
**Prin:* T P Brown
**Prin:* J K Hamilton
**Prin:* A P Miller
CIO: Malcolm Edge

D-U-N-S 80-123-1507
■ **BLOCK FINANCIAL CORP**
(*Suby of* H&R BLOCK INC) ★
4400 Main St, Kansas City, MO 64111-1812
Tel (816) 753-6900 *Founded/Ownrshp* 2001
Sales 209.5MM[E] *EMP* 1,275
SIC 8741 Financial management for business
Pr: Frank L Salizzoni
**Pr:* David J Kasper
COO: Jeffery Yabuki
Ex VP: Thomas P Fitzgerald
Exec: Thea Wiley
Brnch Mgr: Richard Dullnig
Off Mgr: Alberta Afoko

BLOCK HOUSE
See M BLOCK & SONS INC

D-U-N-S 96-840-0890 IMP/EXP
■ **BLOCKBUSTER LLC**
(*Suby of* DISH NETWORK CORP) ★
9601 S Meridian Blvd, Englewood, CO 80112-5905
Tel (702) 262-0703 *Founded/Ownrshp* 2011
Sales 15.9MM[E] *EMP* 19,000
SIC 7841 5735 Video disk/tape rental to the general public; Video tapes, prerecorded
CEO: James W Keyes
Sr VP: Jeff Gordon
Mktg Mgr: Daryn Donato
Mktg Mgr: Stephanie Kopet

BLOMBERG WINDOW SYSTEMS
See ARCHITECTURAL BLOMBERG LLC

BLOOD CENTER, THE
See GULF COAST REGIONAL BLOOD CENTER

D-U-N-S 00-690-2498
BLOOD SYSTEMS INC (AZ)
UNITED BLOOD SERVICES
6210 E Oak St, Scottsdale, AZ 85257-1101
Tel (480) 946-4201 *Founded/Ownrshp* 1943
Sales 966.8MM *EMP* 3,900
Accts Grant Thornton Llp Phoenix A
SIC 8099 Blood bank; Blood donor station
Pr: J Daniel Connor
**Pr:* David Green
**CFO:* Susan L Barnes
Treas: Lage Anderson
Ofcr: Mary Beth Bassett
Ex VP: Patrick Holt
Ex VP: Scott M Nelson
Ex VP: Ralph R Vassallo
VP: Linda J Blessing
VP: Michael Lamb
VP: Terrina Yamamoto

D-U-N-S 05-716-3172
BLOODCENTER OF WISCONSIN INC
638 N 18th St, Milwaukee, WI 53233-2121
Tel (414) 933-5000 *Founded/Ownrshp* 1946
Sales 155.6MM *EMP* 850
Accts Grant Thornton Llp Milwaukee
SIC 8099 Blood related health services
Pr: Jacquelyn Fredrick
COO: Bryan Quesenberry
**CFO:* Jeffrey Allen Sr
**Ch:* Richard S Gallagher
**Treas:* Robert Manegold
Ex VP: Gilbert White
**Sr VP:* Thomas Abshire
**VP:* Lynne Briggs
**VP:* Jay Campbell
VP: Leslie Smith
Ex Dir: Paul Pejsa

D-U-N-S 07-377-4952
BLOODSOURCE INC
10536 Peter A Mccuen Blvd, Mather, CA 95655-4128
Tel (916) 456-1500 *Founded/Ownrshp* 1948
Sales 88.1MM *EMP* 497
Accts Gilbert Associates Inc Sacram
SIC 8099 Blood bank
CEO: Michael J Fuller
**CFO:* Jim Eldridge
**VP:* Dirk Johnson
Dir IT: Cindy Enloe
Board of Directors: Leslie Botos, Tom Hulsman, Kathy King

D-U-N-S 09-288-1085
BLOODWORKS
PUGET SOUND BLOOD CENTER AND P
921 Terry Ave, Seattle, WA 98104-1239
Tel (206) 292-6500 *Founded/Ownrshp* 1977
Sales 175.7MM *EMP* 750
Accts Moss Adams Llp Seattle Wa
SIC 8071 8099 8733 8732 Biological laboratory; Blood bank; Medical research; Commercial nonphysical research
CEO: James P Aubuchon
Dir Vol: Elizabeth Page
**COO:* Linda S Barnes
**CFO:* Bob Gleason
Trst: Stephen Adamek
Trst: Steve Nicholes
Trst: Susan Peck
Ofcr: Jos A L Pez
VP: Jhune Rosario
Exec: Toni Allen-Ellingson
Dir Lab: Debbie Johnson
Assoc Dir: Paul Warner

D-U-N-S 12-253-7686 IMP
BLOOM ENERGY CORP
1299 Orleans Dr, Sunnyvale, CA 94089-1138
Tel (408) 543-1500 *Founded/Ownrshp* 2001
Sales 378.2MM[E] *EMP* 1,200
SIC 3674 Fuel cells, solid state
CEO: Kr Sridhar
COO: Susan Brennan
CFO: Randy Furr
Chf Mktg O: Matt Ross
Ex VP: Bill Thayer
Ex VP: Venkat Venkataraman
Sr VP: Jim Cook
VP: David Barber
VP: Peter Gross
VP: Bijan Moslehi
Off Mgr: Suzie Shark

D-U-N-S 07-867-3408
■ **BLOOM LAKE IRON ORE MINE LTD**
(*Suby of* CLIFFS NATURAL RESOURCES INC) ★
200 Public Sq, Cleveland, OH 44114-2316
Tel (216) 694-5700 *Founded/Ownrshp* 2012
Sales 57.6MM[E] *EMP* 7,404
SIC 1011 Iron ore mining
Pr: Joseph A Carrabba
**Pr:* Laurie Brlas
**Pr:* Donald Gallagher
**CEO:* Joe Carrabba
**CFO:* Terrance Paradie
**VP:* Clifford Smith

BLOOMBERG BNA
See BUREAU OF NATIONAL AFFAIRS INC

BLOOMBERG BUSINESSWEEK
See BLOOMBERG LP

D-U-N-S 96-709-8463
BLOOMBERG FAMILY FOUNDATION INC
909 3rd Ave, New York, NY 10022-4731
Tel (212) 205-0100 *Founded/Ownrshp* 2011
Sales 1.3MMM *EMP* 2
Accts Geller & Company Llc New York
SIC 8699 Charitable organization
Prin: Steve Fadem

D-U-N-S 05-244-3892
BLOOMBERG LP
BLOOMBERG BUSINESSWEEK
731 Lexington Ave Fl Ll2, New York, NY 10022-1346
Tel (212) 318-2000 *Founded/Ownrshp* 1982
Sales 3.6MMM^E *EMP* 15,000
SIC 7383 News syndicates; News reporting services for newspapers & periodicals
Ch: Peter T Grauer
*Pt: Maureen A McGuire
*Pt: Peter Taylor
V Ch: Thomas Secunda
*CEO: Andrew R Lack
CEO: Andrew Lack
CEO: Greg McCaffery
*COO: Caswell Holloway
*COO: Beth Mazzeo
Treas: Richard Mourdock
*V Ch Bd: Thomas F Secunda
Chf Cred: Joseph Zangri
Ofcr: John Byrne
Ofcr: John Forster
*Ofcr: Jason Schechter
*Ofcr: Paul Wood
VP: Gianpaolo G Albanese
VP: Miryam Bechtle
VP: Jacqueline Bianco
VP: Kevin Bunkley
VP: John Camp

D-U-N-S 82-904-0992
BLOOMBERG TRADEBOOK LLC
(*Suby of* BLOOMBERG BUSINESSWEEK) ★
731 Lexington Ave, New York, NY 10022-1331
Tel (212) 617-7070 *Founded/Ownrshp* 1996
Sales 201.2MM^E *EMP* 2,500
SIC 6211 Security brokers & dealers
Exec: James Tedford
CTO: Chris Hall
Dir IT: Rich Gubitosi
Netwrk Mgr: Guy Gioia
Netwrk Mgr: Gary Roberts
Info Man: John Carey
Software D: ARI Berjian
Software D: Ajay Malik
Sftwr Eng: Manny Farber
Sftwr Eng: Steven Hecker
Sftwr Eng: Matthew Heritage

D-U-N-S 07-998-1558
BLOOMER HOLDINGS INC
OPTIMUM PLASTICS
1710 N Industrial Dr, Bloomer, WI 54724-1480
Tel (800) 638-0479 *Founded/Ownrshp* 2012
Sales 110.0MM *EMP* 150
SIC 2371 Mounting heads on fur neckpieces
Pr: Kevin Keneally
*CFO: Carl Kubas

D-U-N-S 60-547-1978 EXP
■ **BLOOMFIELD BAKERS**
(*Suby of* TREEHOUSE PRIVATE BRANDS INC) ★
10711 Bloomfield St, Los Alamitos, CA 90720-2503
Tel (626) 610-2253 *Founded/Ownrshp* 1992
Sales 131.6MM^E *EMP* 600
SIC 2052 2064 Cookies & crackers; Candy & other confectionery products
Genl Pt: William R Ross
Genl Pt: Maggie Acquisition Corp
Pt: Aiko Acquisition Corp
Brnch Mgr: Gary Marx
CTO: Abdul Halim
Sfty Mgr: Humberto Gomez
Plnt Mgr: Umberto Gomez
Ql Cn Mgr: Steve Huber
Natl Sales: John Getteridge

D-U-N-S 07-637-8330
BLOOMFIELD HILLS SCHOOL DISTRICT
7273 Wing Lake Rd Ste A, Bloomfield Hills, MI 48301-3774
Tel (248) 341-5400 *Founded/Ownrshp* 1900
Sales 53.6MM^E *EMP* 1,000
Accts Yeo & Yeo Pc Saginaw Mich
SIC 8211 Public elementary & secondary schools
Pr: Grat Dalton
Trst: Howard Baron
Genl Mgr: Karen Hildebrandt
Dir IT: Don Delong
Trfc Dir: Janet Heslet
Psych: Claudia N Goldenthal
Psych: Laura N Hollyer Madis
Psych: Carla Palazzi

D-U-N-S 96-464-9821
BLOOMFIELD HOMES LP
1050 E State Hwy Ste 210, Southlake, TX 76092
Tel (817) 416-1572 *Founded/Ownrshp* 2004
Sales 172.0MM^E *EMP* 26^E
Accts Meredith & Associates Irving
SIC 1521 New construction, single-family houses
Genl Pt: Don Dykstra
Dir IT: Lyle Sharp
VP Opers: Tim Stewart

D-U-N-S 80-082-2178
▲ **BLOOMIN BRANDS INC**
OUTBACK STEAKHOUSE
2202 N West Shore Blvd # 500, Tampa, FL 33607-5747
Tel (813) 282-1225 *Founded/Ownrshp* 1987
Sales 4.4MMM *EMP* 100,000
Tkr Sym BLMN *Exch* NGS
SIC 5812 Steak restaurant
Ch Bd: Elizabeth A Smith
Mng Pt: Paul Hassing
Pr: Mike Kappitt
Pr: Gregg Scarlett
Ofcr: Christopher Brandt
Ofcr: David J Deno
Ex VP: Donagh M Herlihy
Ex VP: Donagh Herlihy
Ex VP: Dave Pace
Ex VP: Sukhdev Singh
VP: Bill Allen
VP: Monte B Batson
VP: Rick Beach
VP: John Cooper
VP: Kirk R Crowder
VP: Heather Hollander
VP: Richard L Renninger
VP: Ryan M Sinclair
VP: Jeff Smith
Exec: Mark Adair
Board of Directors: James R Craigie, David R Fitzjohn, Mindy Grossman, Tara Walpert Levy, John J Mahoney, Chris T Sullivan

BLOOMINGDALE'S
See MACYS CORPORATE SERVICES INC

D-U-N-S 36-067-1333 IMP/EXP
■ **BLOOMINGDALES INC**
(*Suby of* MACYS RETAIL HOLDINGS INC) ★
1000 3rd Ave, New York, NY 10022-1230
Tel (212) 705-2000 *Founded/Ownrshp* 1992
Sales 1.6MMM^E *EMP* 10,500
SIC 5311 2389 Department stores, non-discount; Apparel for handicapped
Ch Bd: Michael Gould
*Pr: Edwin J Holman
Chf Mktg O: Peter Sachse
Ex VP: Frank Berman
Ex VP: David Fisher
Ex VP: Jack Hruska
Ex VP: Joe Laneve
Ex VP: Christine Miller
Sr VP: William Baer
Sr VP: Anne Keating
Sr VP: Francine Klein
Sr VP: Pamela Tookool
Sr VP: John Vitale
VP: Charles Anderson
VP: Stephen Berman
VP: Roger Blazek
VP: Arif Boysan
VP: Anne Bridges
VP: Bruce Buck
VP: Jim Coia
VP: Gloria Craighead

BLOOMINGTON CHRYSLER JEEP
See REID ENTERPRISES INC

BLOOMINGTON PUB SCHL DST 271
See INDEPENDENT SCHOOL DISTRICT 271

D-U-N-S 07-599-1430
BLOOMSBURG UNIVERSITY FOUNDATION INC
400 E 2nd St, Bloomsburg, PA 17815-1301
Tel (570) 389-4000 *Founded/Ownrshp* 2011
Sales 7.8MM^E *EMP* 1,100
Accts Brewer & Company Llc Bloomsb
SIC 8221 9411 University; Administration of educational programs;
Ex Dir: Jerome Dvorak
Ofcr: Christine Gay
VP: Ira Blake
VP: Juli Miller
Exec: Mary Vezendy
Assoc Dir: Amanda L Kishbaugh
Adm Dir: Valerie Sanute
Dir IT: Jeff Cragle
IT Man: Vince Kozlek
IT Man: Melanie Mills
Web Dev: Judy Ohl

D-U-N-S 00-821-2987
BLOSSMAN COMPANIES INC (MS)
BLOSSMAN GAS COMPANIES
809 Washington Ave, Ocean Springs, MS 39564-4637
Tel (228) 875-2261 *Founded/Ownrshp* 1951
Sales 96.9MM^E *EMP* 512
Accts Carr Riggs & Ingram Llc Roi
SIC 5984 5722 Liquefied petroleum gas dealers; Gas household appliances
Ch Bd: John Blossman
*Pr: Stewart D Weidie
*Treas: Randy Doyle
VP: Al Allen
*VP: Jesse W Johnson
IT Man: Marty Beech

BLOSSMAN GAS COMPANIES
See BLOSSMAN COMPANIES INC

D-U-N-S 07-979-8788
BLOUNT COUNTY SCHOOLS
831 Grandview Dr, Maryville, TN 37803-5312
Tel (865) 984-1212 *Founded/Ownrshp* 2015
Sales 21.0MM^E *EMP* 3,031^E
SIC 8211 Public elementary & secondary schools

D-U-N-S 01-857-3949 IMP
BLOUNT FINE FOODS CORP
630 Currant Rd, Fall River, MA 02720-4713
Tel (774) 888-1300 *Founded/Ownrshp* 1946
Sales 86.8MM^E *EMP* 225
SIC 2092 2038 Fresh or frozen packaged fish; Soups, frozen
Pr: Ted Blount
Pr: Nelson Blount II
CFO: Michael Mistrot
Treas: Frederick N Blount
VP: Jonathan Arena
VP: William Bigelow
VP: Todd W Brown
Dir Surg: Veronica King
Dir IT: Phil Pitzer
Ql Cn Mgr: Steven Churchill
VP Sls: Bob Sewall

D-U-N-S 05-863-8040 IMP/EXP
BLOUNT INC
BLOUNT OUTDOOR SPORTS GROUP
(*Suby of* BLOUNT INTERNATIONAL INC) ★
4909 Se International Way, Portland, OR 97222-4679
Tel (503) 653-8881 *Founded/Ownrshp* 1999
Sales 600.4MM^E *EMP* 3,100
SIC 3546 3568 7699 3495 Chain saws, portable; Drives, chains & sprockets; Knife, saw & tool sharpening & repair; Wire springs
Pr: David A Willmott
*CFO: Calvin E Jenness
*Sr VP: Richard H Irving III

D-U-N-S 00-713-9231 IMP
BLOUNT INTERNATIONAL INC
OREGON PRODUCTS
(*Suby of* BLOUNT INTERNATIONAL INC) ★
10331 Nw Transcon Dr, Kansas City, MO 64153-1001
Tel (816) 231-5007 *Founded/Ownrshp* 1949
Sales 95.3MM^E *EMP* 190
SIC 5083 3524 3469 Lawn machinery & equipment; Lawn & garden mowers & accessories; Metal stampings
Genl Mgr: David Parish
Netwrk Eng: Randy Price

D-U-N-S 09-984-4185 IMP/EXP
BLOUNT INTERNATIONAL INC
(*Suby of* ASP BLADE INTERMEDIATE HOLDINGS INC) ★
4909 Se International Way, Portland, OR 97222-4679
Tel (503) 653-8881 *Founded/Ownrshp* 2016
Sales 911.4MM^E *EMP* 4,000^E
Accts Kpmg Llp Portland Oregon
SIC 3531 3523 Construction machinery; Forestry related equipment; Farm machinery & equipment; Cutters & blowers, ensilage; Tractors, farm
Ch Bd: Joshua L Collins
Pr: Jerry Johnson
*Pr: David A Willmott
CFO: Mike Blacker
CFO: Calvin E Jenne
*CFO: Calvin E Jenness
Sr VP: Dave P Gillrie
Sr VP: David P Gillrie
Sr VP: Andrew W York
VP: William C Alford
*VP: Mark V Allred
VP: Russell German
VP: Dave Parrish
*VP: Chad E Paulson
VP: Kevin M Trepa
Board of Directors: Robert E Beasley, Ronald Cami, Andrew C Clarke, Nelda J Connors, Thomas Fruechtel, E Daniel James, Max L Lukens, Daniel J Obringer

D-U-N-S 07-491-1181
BLOUNT MEMORIAL HOSPITAL INC
907 Lamar Alexander Pkwy, Maryville, TN 37804-5015
Tel (865) 983-7211 *Founded/Ownrshp* 1946
Sales 218.8MM *EMP* 2,060
SIC 8062 General medical & surgical hospitals
CEO: Don Heinemann
Chf Rad: John Niethammer
*Pr: Robert Redwine
*VP: Ted Flickinger
Dir Lab: Sandy Tarkletoen
Off Admin: Michelle Ritchey
CIO: Clay Pubaett
Mktg Dir: Ann Crytser
Pathlgst: John R Hilsenbeck
Pathlgst: Jim Vinson
Doctor: Alan Smuckler

BLOUNT OUTDOOR SPORTS GROUP
See BLOUNT INC

D-U-N-S 87-798-6000
BLOUNT-STRANGE FORD LINCOLN MERCURY INC
4000 Eastern Blvd, Montgomery, AL 36116-2642
Tel (334) 613-5000 *Founded/Ownrshp* 1991
Sales 90.0MM *EMP* 175
SIC 5511 Automobiles, new & used
Pr: Todd R Strange
*Ch Bd: Winton Blount III
*Pr: Tim Nix
*Pr: Gordon Trawick

D-U-N-S 08-851-4187 IMP
BLOWER-DEMPSAY CORP
PAK WEST PAPER & PACKAGING
4042 W Garry Ave, Santa Ana, CA 92704-6300
Tel (714) 481-3800 *Founded/Ownrshp* 1973
Sales 184.4MM^E *EMP* 253
SIC 5111 Printing & writing paper
Pr: James F Blower
*CFO: Serge Poirier
Sls&Mrk Ex: Michael Mann

D-U-N-S 11-738-0543 IMP/EXP
BLP SETTLEMENT CO
(*Suby of* SBP HOLDING LP) ★
125 Mccarty St, Houston, TX 77029-1135
Tel (713) 674-2266 *Founded/Ownrshp* 1984
Sales 228.3MM^E *EMP* 711
SIC 5085 3496 Industrial supplies; Slings, lifting: made from purchased wire
Pr: Jeff Bishop
*Sec: Rebecca Bishop Piro
*VP: Derrick J Deakins

BLU ECIGS
See FONTEM US INC

D-U-N-S 94-673-2997
▲ **BLUCORA INC**
10900 Ne 8th St Ste 800, Bellevue, WA 98004-4420
Tel (425) 201-6100 *Founded/Ownrshp* 1996
Sales 117.7MM *EMP* 772^E
Tkr Sym BCOR *Exch* NGS
SIC 7375 7374 Information retrieval services; Online data base information retrieval; Data processing & preparation
Pr: William J Ruckelshaus
Ch Bd: John E Cunningham IV
Pr: John S Clendening
CFO: Eric M Emans
Chf Mktg O: Mathieu Stevenson
Ex VP: Brett J Clark-Bolt
Ex VP: Todd Mackay
Ex VP: Amit Seshan
Web Dev: Kimberlee Weller
Sftwr Eng: Melvin Lervick
Sftwr Eng: Anna Terp
Board of Directors: David H S Chung, Lance G Dunn, Steven W Hooper, Elizabeth J Huebner, Andrew M Snyder, Christopher W Walters, Mary S Zappone

D-U-N-S 14-361-2971
BLUE ADVANTAGE ADMINISTRATORS OF ARKANSAS
ARKANSAS BLUE CROSS BLUE SHELD
(*Suby of* ARKANSAS BLUE CROSS & BLUE) ★
320 W Capitol Ave Ste 500, Little Rock, AR 72201-3557
Tel (501) 378-3600 *Founded/Ownrshp* 2004
Sales NA *EMP* 1^E
SIC 6321 Health insurance carriers
Ch: James Adamson
Ex VP: David Bridges
Sr VP: Jim Bailey
VP: Steve Abell
Prgrm Mgr: Jennifer Melton

BLUE ANCHOR LINE
See KUEHNE + NAGEL INC

D-U-N-S 07-887-5161
BLUE APRON INC
5 Crosby St, New York, NY 10013-3154
Tel (888) 278-4349 *Founded/Ownrshp* 2013
Sales 96.4MM^E *EMP* 200^E
SIC 5961 Catalog & mail-order houses
CEO: Matthew Salzberg
Sr VP: Pablo Cussatti
VP: Kate Muzzatti
VP: Tim Smith
Manager: Evan Schwartz
VP Mktg: Jared Cluff
Mktg Mgr: Joanna Ehrenreich
Genl Couns: Benjamin Singer
Snr Mgr: Karen Bredehoeft
Snr Mgr: Kristen Caldwell

BLUE BEACON TRUCK WASHES
See BLUE BEACON USA LP II

D-U-N-S 03-060-5190
BLUE BEACON USA LP II
BLUE BEACON TRUCK WASHES
500 Graves Blvd, Salina, KS 67401-4306
Tel (785) 825-2221 *Founded/Ownrshp* 1976
Sales 54.9MM^E *EMP* 1,800
SIC 7542

D-U-N-S 07-860-4067
BLUE BELL CREAMERIES INC
1101 S Blue Bell Rd, Brenham, TX 77833-4413
Tel (817) 560-1980 *Founded/Ownrshp* 2000
Sales 0.5 *EMP* 2,500
SIC 2024 Ice cream & frozen desserts
CEO: Paul Kruse

D-U-N-S 00-809-8196
BLUE BELL CREAMERIES LP
1101 S Blue Bell Rd, Brenham, TX 77833-4413
Tel (979) 836-7977 *Founded/Ownrshp* 1907
Sales 1.0MMM^E *EMP* 2,660
SIC 2024 5143

D-U-N-S 78-473-5875 IMP/EXP
BLUE BELL CREAMERIES USA INC
1101 S Blue Bell Rd, Brenham, TX 77833-4413
Tel (979) 836-7977 *Founded/Ownrshp* 2000
Sales 216.2MM^E *EMP* 2,800
SIC 2024 Ice cream & frozen desserts
Pr: Paul W Kruse
*Pr: Howard W Kruse
CFO: William Rankin
*Treas: Bill Rankin
*VP: Melvin Ziegenbein
Sales Exec: Matt Glaves

D-U-N-S 00-327-9627 IMP/EXP
BLUE BIRD BODY CO
(*Suby of* BLUE BIRD GLOBAL CORP) ★
402 Bluebird Blvd, Fort Valley, GA 31030-5088
Tel (478) 825-2021 *Founded/Ownrshp* 1999
Sales 273.2MM^E *EMP* 1,550
SIC 4111 Bus transportation
Pr: Phil Horlock
*CFO: Wayne Hunnell
*CFO: John Kwapis
*Treas: Paul Yusif
Bd of Dir: Gerald Armstrong
VP: Mike Beck
MIS Dir: Rodney Snider
Dir IT: Jamie Vance

D-U-N-S 78-832-7260 EXP
BLUE BIRD GLOBAL CORP
(*Suby of* THE TRAXIS GROUP B.V.)
402 Bluebird Blvd, Fort Valley, GA 31030-5088
Tel (478) 822-2811 *Founded/Ownrshp* 2006
Sales 473.6MM^E *EMP* 1,800
SIC 3713 3711 Bus bodies (motor vehicles); Chassis, motor vehicle
Pr: Phil Horlock
*COO: John Kwapis
CFO: Keith Hernando
*CFO: Wayne Hunnell
*CFO: Keith Romundo
*CFO: Phil Tighe
*Treas: Tony R Showman
Sr VP: Roger Howsmon
*Sr VP: Dale Wendell
VP: Mark Copping
*VP: Mike McCurdy
*VP: Paul Yousif

D-U-N-S 13-251-6985
■ **BLUE BUFFALO CO LTD**
(*Suby of* BLUE BUFFALO PET PRODUCTS INC) ★
11 River Rd Ste 103, Wilton, CT 06897-6011
Tel (203) 762-9751 *Founded/Ownrshp* 2012
Sales 435.8MM^E *EMP* 1,300^E
SIC 2047 5149 Dog & cat food; Pet foods
Ch: Bill Bishop
CEO: Kurt Schmidt
CFO: Mike Nathenson
Sr VP: Tom Morton
Sr VP: Steven Raleigh
Sr VP: Jennifer Stites
VP: Phil De Bruyn
Prin: William Bishop
Off Mgr: Carey Nevin
CIO: George Lesko
VP Opers: Peter J McLaughlin

Board of Directors: Michael Eck, Frances Frei, Amy Schulman

D-U-N-S 07-986-9383
▲ BLUE BUFFALO PET PRODUCTS INC
11 River Rd Ste 103, Wilton, CT 06897-6011
Tel (203) 762-9751 *Founded/Ownrshp* 2002
Sales 1.0MMM *EMP* 1,700[E]
Tkr Sym BUFF *Exch* NGS
SIC 2048 Prepared feeds; Canned pet food (except dog & cat); Dry pet food (except dog & cat); Frozen pet food (except dog & cat)
CEO: Kurt Schmidt
**Ch Bd:* William Bishop
CFO: Michael Nathenson
Sr VP: Greg Reinhart

D-U-N-S 01-123-1891
BLUE CARE NETWORK OF MICHIGAN (MI)
(*Suby of* BLUE CROSS AND BLUE SHIELD OF MICHIGAN) ★
20500 Civic Center Dr, Southfield, MI 48076-4115
Tel (248) 799-6400 *Founded/Ownrshp* 1981, 1983
Sales NA *EMP* 1,600
SIC 6324 Group hospitalization plans
Pr: Kevin James Klobucar
COO: Laurie Westfall
**CFO:* Susan Kluge
**Sr VP:* Marc Keshishian

D-U-N-S 04-115-7769
■ BLUE CHIP STAMPS
(*Suby of* BERKSHIRE HATHAWAY INC) ★
301 E Colo Blvd Ste 300, Pasadena, CA 91101
Tel (626) 585-6700 *Founded/Ownrshp* 1978
Sales 620.4MM[E] *EMP* 3,074
SIC 5051 Steel
CEO: Robert H Bird
CEO: Charles T Munger
**CFO:* Jeffrey L Jacobson
VP: Kenneth E Wittmeyer

D-U-N-S 08-028-3251
■ BLUE COAT INC
(*Suby of* SYMANTEC CORP) ★
384 Santa Trinita Ave, Sunnyvale, CA 94085-3911
Tel (408) 220-2200 *Founded/Ownrshp* 2016
Sales 733.3MM[E] *EMP* 1,583[E]
SIC 7372 Prepackaged software
CEO: Greg Clark
Pr: Michael Fey
CFO: Thomas Seifert
Ex VP: Fran Rosch
Ex VP: Scott Taylor
Ex VP: Balaji Yelamanchili
Sr VP: Amy Cappellanti-Wolf
Sr VP: Roxane Divol
Sr VP: Sheila Jordan
Sr VP: Samir Kapuria
Sr VP: Stephen Trilling

D-U-N-S 00-957-9892 IMP
■ BLUE COAT SYSTEMS LLC
(*Suby of* BLUE COAT INC) ★
384 Santa Trinita Ave, Sunnyvale, CA 94085-3911
Tel (408) 220-2200 *Founded/Ownrshp* 1996
Sales 733.3MM[E] *EMP* 1,583
SIC 7372 Prepackaged software
CEO: Gregory S Clark
Pr: Donald W Alford
**Pr:* Michael Fey
Pr: David Yntemai
**CFO:* Thomas Seifert
**Chf Mktg O:* Steve Daheb
**Chf Mktg O:* Hugh Thompson
**Ex VP:* Scott Taylor
Sr VP: Marc B Andrews
Sr VP: Marc Andrews
**Sr VP:* Betsy E Bayha
Sr VP: Kevin T Biggs
Sr VP: David L Cox
Sr VP: Gregg Hampton
Sr VP: Rich Holstein
Sr VP: Anil Khatri
Sr VP: Janet Matsuda
Sr VP: Steve Schoenfeld
Sr VP: Steve Shillingford
Sr VP: Ali Tabrizi
**Sr VP:* Stephen Trilling

BLUE CROSS
See INDEPENDENCE HOSPITAL INDEMNITY PLAN INC

BLUE CROSS
See ANTHEM INSURANCE COMPANIES INC

BLUE CROSS
See LOUISIANA HEALTH SERVICE AND INDEMNITY CO

D-U-N-S 06-948-5795
BLUE CROSS & BLUE SHIELD ASSOCIATION
BCBSA
225 N Michigan Ave Fl 5, Chicago, IL 60601-7658
Tel (312) 297-6000 *Founded/Ownrshp* 1948
Sales 362.3MM[E] *EMP* 1,880
SIC 8621 6324 Health association; Hospital & medical service plans
Ch Bd: Alphonso O'Neil-White
V Ch: John Benjamin
V Ch: Randall Clark
V Ch: Geoffrey Davis
V Ch: Deborah Freund
V Ch: David Griffith
V Ch: David Reh
V Ch: Casper Sedgwick
**Pr:* Scott Serota
CFO: Mark R Bartlett
CFO: James H Dickerson
Bd of Dir: Robert F Calise
Bd of Dir: Patrick Devlin
Bd of Dir: James B Foster
Bd of Dir: Margaret Piper
Bd of Dir: Iris Salters
Ex VP: Keith Bushardt
Ex VP: Andrew Dreyfus
Ex VP: Karen Frush
VP: Calvin Anderson
VP: Paul F Brown

D-U-N-S 06-368-9954
BLUE CROSS & BLUE SHIELD OF ALABAMA
450 Riverchase Pkwy E, Hoover, AL 35244-2858
Tel (205) 988-2200 *Founded/Ownrshp* 1936
Sales NA *EMP* 2,533
Accts Ernst & Young Llp Birmingham
SIC 6321 6324 Accident & health insurance; Hospital & medical service plans
CEO: G Phillip Pope
**Pr:* Charles Hartsell
**CEO:* Terry D Kellogg
**CFO:* Cynthia Mizell
**Sr VP:* Patrick E Ryce
VP: Joe Dunsmore
VP: Eddie Harris
VP: Jim Hill
VP: Sherrie Lemier
VP: John Lyda
VP: Koko Mackin
VP: Robert Orr
VP: Cindi Vice
VP: Tim Vines
VP: Brandon Ward

D-U-N-S 07-790-9752
BLUE CROSS & BLUE SHIELD OF MISSISSIPPI A MUTUAL INSURANCE CO (MS)
3545 Lakeland Dr, Jackson, MS 39232-9799
Tel (601) 932-3704 *Founded/Ownrshp* 1947
Sales NA *EMP* 1,000
SIC 6324 Hospital & medical service plans
Pr: Rick Hale
CFO: Douglas Garrett
VP: William V Morris III
VP: John H Proctor III
VP: John Trifone
Genl Mgr: Derek Grey
IT Man: Emily Smith

D-U-N-S 02-017-4736
BLUE CROSS & BLUE SHIELD OF NEBRASKA
1919 Aksarben Dr, Omaha, NE 68180-0001
Tel (402) 982-7000 *Founded/Ownrshp* 1939
Sales NA *EMP* 1,100
SIC 6324 6311 Group hospitalization plans; Dental insurance; Life insurance carriers
Pr: Steven S Martin
Pr: Lianne Stevens
CFO: Jerry Byers
CFO: Dwayne Wilson
Treas: David Anderson
Ofcr: Rosa Norman
**Ex VP:* Steven H Grandfield
Ex VP: Steven Grandfield
**Ex VP:* Lewis E Trowbridge
**Sr VP:* Patrick J Bourne
**Sr VP:* Gerald Byers
Sr VP: Susan Courtney
VP: Daniel Alm
VP: John Blacketer
VP: Pat Bourne
VP: Mark Dolsky
VP: Debra Esser
VP: Jerry Feilmeier
VP: Don Gray
VP: Thomas Jenkins
VP: Lynda Leahy

D-U-N-S 07-312-8407
BLUE CROSS & BLUE SHIELD OF RHODE ISLAND
500 Exchange St, Providence, RI 02903-2699
Tel (401) 459-1000 *Founded/Ownrshp* 1939
Sales NA *EMP* 1,100[E]
SIC 6324 Hospital & medical service plans; Dental insurance; Health maintenance organization (HMO), insurance only
Pr: Kim Keck
**Pr:* Peter Andruszkiewicz
Pr: Brian Kerwin
Pr: Michele B Ledererg
Pr: Jeannine Paquette
**COO:* William Ray
CFO: Michael Hudson
CFO: Bill Wilbur
**Ofcr:* Brian O'Malley
Ofcr: Bob Wolfkiel
Assoc VP: Jim Kenney
Ex VP: Thomas Boyd
Ex VP: Michele B Lederberg
Ex VP: William K Wray
Sr VP: Melissa Cummings
Sr VP: Gus Manocchia
Sr VP: Lynne A Urbani
VP: Matt Grannigan
VP: James Kenny
VP: Charley Kineke
VP: Ej Sunderland
Board of Directors: Charles F Locurto

D-U-N-S 00-220-6386
BLUE CROSS & BLUE SHIELD OF ROCHESTER
(*Suby of* EXCELLUS HEALTH PLAN INC) ★
165 Court St, Rochester, NY 14647-0001
Tel (585) 454-1700 *Founded/Ownrshp* 1999
Sales NA *EMP* 4,000
SIC 6324 Group hospitalization plans
Pr: Chris Booth
VP: Patricia Bomba
VP: Charlene Dickman
VP: James Haefner
VP: Cindy Langston
VP: Lynn Persi
VP: Marie Philippe
Prgrm Mgr: Maclean Lazik
Prgrm Mgr: Dan Shire
Netwrk Eng: William Gates
Sales Exec: John R Lynch

D-U-N-S 03-043-9285
BLUE CROSS & BLUE SHIELD OF WYOMING
4000 House Ave, Cheyenne, WY 82001-1446
Tel (307) 634-1393 *Founded/Ownrshp* 1945
Sales NA *EMP* 205
SIC 6321 Health insurance carriers
Pr: Tim Crilly
**VP:* John McBride
VP: Karen Rich
Dir Rx: Kevin Shryack
Ex Dir: Arthur Abbey
DP Dir: Gary Metzger
VP Mktg: Richard Schum
Sls Dir: Lee Shannon
Sls Mgr: Dan Myers

BLUE CROSS AND BLUE SHIELD
See BCBSM INC

BLUE CROSS AND BLUE SHIELD
See HEALTH CARE SERVICE CORP A MUTUAL LEGAL RESERVE CO

D-U-N-S 05-353-3964
BLUE CROSS AND BLUE SHIELD NORTH CAROLINA
4615 University Dr, Durham, NC 27707-3458
Tel (919) 489-7431 *Founded/Ownrshp* 1968
Sales NA *EMP* 4,397
SIC 6324 Group hospitalization plans; Dental insurance
Pr: Robert J Greczyn Jr
**Pr:* Jim Broderick
CFO: Daniel Glacer
**CFO:* Daniel E Glaser
Treas: Geoff Clasper
Trst: Andrea Bazan-Manson
Trst: Felix C Mdaniel
Trst: Andrea Baz N
Trst: James R Talton
Trst: James T Williams
**Chf Mktg O:* Bob Harris
Sr VP: Norman Phelps
**Sr VP:* J Bradley Wilson
**VP:* Fred Goldwater
VP: Bob Miglarese
VP: Daniel Risku
**VP:* John Roos
**VP:* John Sternbergh
**VP:* Bob Vavrina

D-U-N-S 04-301-8100
BLUE CROSS AND BLUE SHIELD OF ARIZONA INC
2444 W Las Palmaritas Dr, Phoenix, AZ 85021-4860
Tel (602) 864-4100 *Founded/Ownrshp* 1939
Sales NA *EMP* 1,278
SIC 6324 Hospital & medical service plans
Pr: Richard L Boals
**Ch Bd:* Gary L Trujillo
CFO: Karen Abraham
CFO: Tony M Astorga CPA
Treas: Kathryn Baker
**V Ch Bd:* Bill Post
Ofcr: Gilbert Ward
Ex VP: Sandra Lee Gibson
Ex VP: Sandy Gibson
Ex VP: Susan Golino
Ex VP: Susan H Navran
Sr VP: Karen Abraham
Sr VP: H Jody Chandler
Sr VP: Richard M Hannon
Sr VP: Vishu Jhaveri
Sr VP: Gary D Smethers
Sr VP: Jeff Stelnik
VP: Gail Damico
VP: Sue Glawe
VP: Marty Laurel
VP: Marcus Montoya
Board of Directors: Barbara J Ralston

D-U-N-S 06-591-6355
BLUE CROSS AND BLUE SHIELD OF FLORIDA INC
4800 Deerwood Campus Pkwy, Jacksonville, FL 32246-8273
Tel (904) 905-0000 *Founded/Ownrshp* 1944
Sales NA *EMP* 11,500
SIC 6324 Group hospitalization plans; Health maintenance organization (HMO), insurance only
Ch: Charles S Joseph
CEO: Patrick Geraghty
CFO: Chris R Doerr
CFO: Armando Luna
Treas: Charles Divita
Ex VP: Steve Booma
Ex VP: Thomas G Kuntz
Sr VP: Jonathan Gavras
Sr VP: Sharon Wamble King
Sr VP: Joyce Kramzer
Sr VP: Prudence Kuai
Sr VP: Craig Thomas
Sr VP: Jon Urbanek
Sr VP: Bob Wall
VP: Liz Barnett
VP: Colleen Brennan
VP: Juan Chaluja
VP: Luisa Charbonneau
VP: Tim Cronin
VP: Edward Garcia
VP: Stephanie Germann
Board of Directors: W D Frederick Jr, Robert M Beall II, Steven T Halverson, Henry H Beckwith, Walther S Mc Lin III, Catherine P Bessant, John B Ramil, Edward L Boykin, Frank P Scruggs Jr, Hugh M Brown, Barbara S Thomas, Yank D Coble Jr MD, Mary H Cross, Gonzalo F Valdes-Fauli, Gonzalo F Valdes-Fauli

D-U-N-S 05-952-4827
■ BLUE CROSS AND BLUE SHIELD OF GEORGIA INC
(*Suby of* CERULEAN COMPANIES INC) ★
3350 Peachtree Rd Ne # 300, Atlanta, GA 30326-1048
Tel (404) 842-8000 *Founded/Ownrshp* 2008
Sales NA *EMP* 176[E]
SIC 6324 6321 Health maintenance organization (HMO), insurance only; Accident & health insurance
Pr: John Watts
Pr: Stacy Brinkley
**CFO:* Randall A Edwards
**Ex VP:* Richard A Steinhausen
**Ex VP:* Robert A Yungk
**Sr VP:* Michael L Burks
**Sr VP:* Michelle D Johnson
VP: Randy Axelrod
VP: Sandra Hinds
VP: Wayne Hoffman
VP: Ron Ragland
VP: Josh Valdez
Exec: Pamela Windham

D-U-N-S 01-064-1157
BLUE CROSS AND BLUE SHIELD OF KANSAS CITY
2301 Main St, Kansas City, MO 64108-2442
Tel (816) 395-2222 *Founded/Ownrshp* 1982
Sales NA *EMP* 1,000
SIC 6321 Accident & health insurance
Prin: Danette Wilson
V Ch: William C Nelson
Pr: Judy Bond
COO: Dana Walstrom
Bd of Dir: Thomas McCullough
Bd of Dir: Michael Morrissey
VP: Shelley Bowen
VP: Nancy Creasy
VP: Salvatore S Nigro
VP: Tama Putthoff
VP: Kastner Richard
VP: Jeff Shipley
Exec: Bryan Camerlinck

D-U-N-S 07-305-3076
BLUE CROSS AND BLUE SHIELD OF KANSAS INC
1133 Sw Topeka Blvd, Topeka, KS 66629-0001
Tel (785) 291-7000 *Founded/Ownrshp* 1942
Sales NA *EMP* 1,294
SIC 6321 6324 Accident & health insurance; Hospital & medical service plans
CEO: Andrew C Corbin
V Ch: Robert Mullen
V Ch: Gary D Shorman
**Pr:* Michael Mattox
COO: Douglas Scott
CFO: Ann Shelton
**Treas:* Donald Lynn
VP: Matthew All
VP: Andrew Corbin
VP: Julie Hinrichsen
VP: Michael McNeive
VP: Shelley Pittman
VP: Ralph Weber
Exec: Stephanie Reynolds

D-U-N-S 05-781-5201
BLUE CROSS AND BLUE SHIELD OF MASSACHUSETTS INC
101 Huntington Ave # 1300, Boston, MA 02199-7603
Tel (617) 246-5000 *Founded/Ownrshp* 1937
Sales NA *EMP* 2,800
SIC 6321 8741 6324 Accident & health insurance; Management services; Hospital & medical service plans; Group hospitalization plans; Health maintenance organization (HMO), insurance only
CEO: Andrew Dreyfus
**Ch Bd:* Phyllis R Yale
V Ch: Sinclair Weeks
**COO:* Bruce M Bullen
**CFO:* Andreana Santangelo
Chf Mktg O: Alan Rosenberg
Ex VP: Patrick Gilligan
**Sr VP:* John Fallon
Sr VP: John A Fallon
**Sr VP:* Sarah Iselin
**Sr VP:* Stephanie Lovell
VP: Richard Greenhalgh
VP: Pat Washington
Dir Rx: Thomas Kowalski

D-U-N-S 00-191-0793
BLUE CROSS AND BLUE SHIELD OF MICHIGAN
600 E Lafayette Blvd, Detroit, MI 48226-2927
Tel (313) 225-9000 *Founded/Ownrshp* 1939
Sales NA *EMP* 8,546
Accts Deloitte & Touche Llp Detroi
SIC 6321 6324 Accident & health insurance; Group hospitalization plans
Pr: Daniel J Loepp
**CFO:* Mark Bartlett
CFO: James Dickerson
Sr VP: Susan L Barkell
Sr VP: Lynda M Rossi
VP: Joseph J Ashton
VP: Gary Harvey
VP: Brent Stanley
Ex Dir: David Pankotai
CIO: Raymond Khan
CTO: Ray Kahs

D-U-N-S 05-588-6303
BLUE CROSS AND BLUE SHIELD OF MISSOURI INC
(*Suby of* BCBSA) ★
1831 Chestnut St, Saint Louis, MO 63103-2275
Tel (314) 923-4444 *Founded/Ownrshp* 1936
Sales NA *EMP* 1,800
SIC 6321 Accident & health insurance
CEO: Stuart Campbell
Dir Teleco: Amelia McKay
MIS Dir: Dale Schulz
IT Man: Ed Folks
Pgrm Dir: Laura Ross

D-U-N-S 04-783-6275
BLUE CROSS AND BLUE SHIELD OF TEXAS INC
1001 E Lookout Dr, Richardson, TX 75082-4144
Tel (972) 766-6900 *Founded/Ownrshp* 1939
Sales NA *EMP* 2,500[E]
Accts Tx Dept Of Insurance
SIC 6324 6311 Hospital & medical service plans; Life insurance
Pr: Martin Foster
**Pr:* Dr Rogers K Coleman
Pr: Donna Otto

COO: Colleen Reitan
Treas: Cindy Jhonson
Treas: Dee Moore
**Chf Mktg O:* Dan McCoy
**Ofcr:* Mark Clanton
Ex VP: Jeff Ellerman
**Sr VP:* Patricia Hemmingway-Hall
Sr VP: Jan R Newsom
Sr VP: James E Ward
**Sr VP:* Lelia Wright
VP: Gary Brantz
VP: Jackie Hamilton
VP: Joanne Martucci
VP: Joe Taylor
Board of Directors: G Brint Ryan

D-U-N-S 14-398-4516
BLUE CROSS AND BLUE SHIELD OF VERMONT
445 Industrial Ln, Montpelier, VT 05602-4415
Tel (802) 223-6131 *Founded/Ownrshp* 1980
Sales NA *EMP* 350
SIC 6321 Accident & health insurance
Pr: Don George
**CFO:* Ruth K Greene
Treas: Seth Abeni
VP: Renee Cooley
**VP:* Christopher R Gannon
**VP:* Kevin Goddard
**VP:* Catherine Hamilton
VP: Robin Stone
Exec: Alison Partridge
Exec: Connie Warren
Comm Dir: Beth Edmonds
Comm Dir: Beth Lewis
Comm Man: William Germer

BLUE CROSS BLUE SHIELD ND
See NORIDIAN MUTUAL INSURANCE CO

D-U-N-S 05-591-4089
BLUE CROSS BLUE SHIELD OF SOUTH CAROLINA
I-20 Alpine Rd, Columbia, SC 29219-0001
Tel (803) 788-3860 *Founded/Ownrshp* 1946
Sales NA *EMP* 11,000
SIC 6321 Health insurance carriers
Ch Bd: M Edward Sellers
Pr: Thomas G Faulds
Pr: William Horton
Pr: Keith Killian
Pr: Charles M Potok
Pr: Shirley Scruggs
Pr: Michael J Skarupa
Pr: Susan Stursberg
CEO: David Pankau
CFO: Teresa Kinard
CFO: Robert A Leichtle
Treas: David Cote
Ofcr: John M Little Jr
Ofcr: Shawn Stinson
Assoc VP: Jason Taylor
Sr VP: James A Deyling
Sr VP: W Michael Griggs
Sr VP: James Hart
Sr VP: Stephen K Wiggins
VP: Judith M Davis
VP: Mike Harris
Board of Directors: Bill Amick, Minor Mickel Shaw

BLUE CROSS BLUE SHIELD WSTN NY
See HEALTHNOW NEW YORK INC

D-U-N-S 79-932-0098
■ BLUE CROSS OF CALIFORNIA
(*Suby of* WELLPOINT CALIFORNIA SERVICES INC) ★
4553 La Tienda Rd, Westlake Village, CA 91362-3800
Tel (805) 557-6050 *Founded/Ownrshp* 1992
Sales NA *EMP* 220^E
SIC 6324 6411 Health maintenance organization (HMO), insurance only; Insurance agents, brokers & service
Pr: Mark Morgan
**CFO:* Kenneth C Zurek
VP: Ivan Jeffrey
VP: Josh Valdez
VP Mktg: Angela Braly

D-U-N-S 07-884-0229
BLUE CROSS OF IDAHO CARE PLUS INC
3000 E Pine Ave, Meridian, ID 83642-5995
Tel (208) 345-4550 *Founded/Ownrshp* 2013
Sales NA *EMP* 3
SIC 6321 Accident & health insurance
CEO: Zelda Geyer-Sylvia
**Sec:* Steve Tobiason

D-U-N-S 07-297-4926
BLUE CROSS OF IDAHO HEALTH SERVICE INC
3000 E Pine Ave, Meridian, ID 83642-5995
Tel (208) 331-7408 *Founded/Ownrshp* 1945
Sales NA *EMP* 900
SIC 6321 Accident & health insurance; Indemnity plans health insurance, except medical service
Pr: Zelda Geyer-Sylvia
Ch: Jack Gustavel
Sr VP: Thomas B Assler
Sr VP: Thomas Bassler
VP: Sharon Heindel
VP: Debra Henry
VP: Dennis Warren
VP: Kendra Witt
Dir IT: Jim Larson
Dir IT: Ron Sater
Web Dev: Alex Holtry

BLUE DIAMOND
See MICHIGAN SEAMLESS TUBE LLC

BLUE DIAMOND MATERIALS
See SULLY-MILLER CONTRACTING CO INC

D-U-N-S 11-435-5613 IMP
■ BLUE DOLPHIN ENERGY CO
LAZARUS ENERGY SERVICES
(*Suby of* LAZARUS ENERGY SERVICES) ★
801 Travis St Ste 2100, Houston, TX 77002-5705
Tel (713) 568-4725 *Founded/Ownrshp* 2012
Sales 221.7MM *EMP* 44
Tkr Sym BDCO *Exch* OTO
SIC 1311 1382 4612 4922 Crude petroleum production; Natural gas production; Oil & gas exploration services; Crude petroleum pipelines; Pipelines, natural gas
Ch Bd: Jonathan P Carroll
COO: John S Clark
CFO: Tommy L Byrd

D-U-N-S 07-924-8297
BLUE EAGLE HOLDINGS LP
6465 E Johns Xing, Johns Creek, GA 30097-1580
Tel (678) 584-4000 *Founded/Ownrshp* 2013
Sales 283.2MM^E *EMP* 1,450^E
SIC 7389 7374 8742 Telephone services; Data processing & preparation; Marketing consulting services

D-U-N-S 01-396-4277
BLUE GOLD EQUITIES LLC
SEASONS
6818 Main St, Flushing, NY 11367-1325
Tel (718) 268-6469 *Founded/Ownrshp* 2010
Sales 6.0MM^E *EMP* 1,000^E
SIC 5411 5311 Supermarkets; Department stores

D-U-N-S 02-987-4794
BLUE GRASS ENERGY COOPERATIVE CORP
1201 Lexington Rd, Nicholasville, KY 40356-9437
Tel (859) 885-4191 *Founded/Ownrshp* 1937
Sales 131.4MM *EMP* 117
Accts Alan Zumst Lexington Ky
SIC 4911 Electric services
Pr: Daniel Brewer
Bd of Dir: Brad Marshall
**Sr VP:* Michael Williamson
**VP:* Chris Brewer
VP: Jim Kendrick
VP: Donna Miller
**VP:* Donald Smothers
VP: Beonka Sytock
Dist Mgr: Robert Farmer
Dist Mgr: Carol Higdon
IT Man: Ken Cooper

D-U-N-S 82-812-3195
■ BLUE ISLAND HOSPITAL CO LLC
METROSOUTH MEDICAL CENTER
(*Suby of* QUORUM HEALTH CORP) ★
12935 Gregory St, Blue Island, IL 60406-2428
Tel (708) 597-2000 *Founded/Ownrshp* 2016
Sales 134.2MM *EMP* 450
SIC 8062 General medical & surgical hospitals
Pr: Brian Sinotte
CEO: Enrique Beckmann
Ex VP: Robert G Porter
Off Mgr: Patty Mancuso

D-U-N-S 14-892-0668
BLUE LINE DISTRIBUTION
BLUE LINE FOOD SERVICE
(*Suby of* LITTLE CAESARS) ★
2250 Spiegel Dr Ste P, Groveport, OH 43125-9131
Tel (614) 497-9610 *Founded/Ownrshp* 2012
Sales 161.7MM^E *EMP* 1^E
SIC 5141 Groceries, general line
Prin: Keith Jones

BLUE LINE FOOD SERVICE
See BLUE LINE DISTRIBUTION

BLUE MOUNTAIN SKI AREA
See TUTHILL CORP

D-U-N-S 13-348-5594
▲ BLUE NILE INC
411 1st Ave S Ste 700, Seattle, WA 98104-3847
Tel (206) 336-6700 *Founded/Ownrshp* 1999
Sales 480.0MM *EMP* 335
Tkr Sym NILE *Exch* NGS
SIC 5944 Jewelry stores; Jewelry, precious stones & precious metals
Ch Bd: Harvey Kanter
Ofcr: David Binder
Dir Risk M: Jon Sainsbury
Board of Directors: Chris Bruzzo, Scott Howe, Leslie Lane, Mindy Meads, Michael Potter, Elaine Rubin, Robert Van Schoonenberg

BLUE PLUS
See HMO MINNESOTA

BLUE RIBBON
See TALL TREE FOODS HOLDINGS INC

D-U-N-S 02-395-1411 IMP
BLUE RIDGE BEVERAGE CO INC
4446 Barley Dr, Salem, VA 24153-8542
Tel (540) 380-2000 *Founded/Ownrshp* 1938
Sales 104.8MM^E *EMP* 250
SIC 5181 5182 Beer & other fermented malt liquors; Wine
Pr: Robert Archer
**Ch Bd:* Regine N Archer
**Pr:* Robert A Archer
**COO:* James E Archer
**CFO:* Jacqueline L Archer
**VP:* Paul C Archer
Sls Mgr: Gary Herald
Sales Asso: Phil Martinez

BLUE RIDGE CANDLE COMPANY
See SMITH MOUNTAIN INDUSTRIES OF VIRGINIA INC

D-U-N-S 00-792-0135
BLUE RIDGE ELECTRIC COOPERATIVE INC (SC)
734 W Main St, Pickens, SC 29671-2116
Tel (800) 240-3400 *Founded/Ownrshp* 1940
Sales 135.7MM *EMP* 149
Accts Mcnair M Lem Middlebrooks & C
SIC 4911 Electric services
Pr: Charles Dalton
Ex Dir: William Elrod
Opers Mgr: Sam McMillan

D-U-N-S 03-362-6289
BLUE RIDGE ELECTRIC MEMBERSHIP CORP
1216 Blowing Rock Blvd, Lenoir, NC 28645-3649
Tel (828) 758-2383 *Founded/Ownrshp* 1936
Sales 148.2MM *EMP* 1
Accts Adams Jenkins Cheatham Pc Mid
SIC 4911 Electric services
CEO: Doug Johnson
**Treas:* Lee Chase
Bd of Dir: Rachel Jolly
Comm Man: Renee Whitener
Dist Mgr: Wongalee Thomas
Opers Mgr: Steve Woodring

D-U-N-S 07-106-8589
BLUE RIDGE HEALTHCARE HOSPITALS INC (NC)
(*Suby of* CAROLINAS HEALTHCARE SYSTEM) ★
2201 S Sterling St, Morganton, NC 28655-4044
Tel (828) 580-5000 *Founded/Ownrshp* 1908
Sales 191.0MM *EMP* 1,400^E
SIC 8062 General medical & surgical hospitals
Pr: Kathy C Bailey
CFO: Robert Fritts
Treas: Jeff Carswell
VP: Laura Lambeth
VP: Jon Mercer
Dir Lab: Barry Street
Off Mgr: Cindy Cook
IT Man: Pam Long
Ansthlgy: Lucia S Parvan
Doctor: Autumn Fincher
Doctor: Amanda Ford

D-U-N-S 78-009-5340
BLUE RIDGE HEALTHCARE SYSTEM INC
2201 S Sterling St, Morganton, NC 28655-4044
Tel (828) 580-5580 *Founded/Ownrshp* 1908
Sales 7.4MM *EMP* 1,200^E
Accts Cliftonlarsonallen Llp Charlo
SIC 8062 General medical & surgical hospitals
Pr: Kenneth W Wood
CFO: Jackie Garner
Sfty Dirs: Thomas Logan

BLUE RIDGE HOLDINGS, INC.
See CERTUSHOLDINGS INC

D-U-N-S 19-407-8838 IMP/EXP
BLUE RIDGE METALS CORP
(*Suby of* CENTRAL YOSHIDA CO.,LTD.)
180 Mills Gap Rd, Fletcher, NC 28732-8548
Tel (828) 687-2525 *Founded/Ownrshp* 1988
Sales 85.0MM *EMP* 160
SIC 3399 3315 Aluminum atomized powder; Fencing made in wiredrawing plants
Ch Bd: Kazumasa Yoshida
**Pr:* Isao Yoshida
**Sr VP:* Shigero Goda
CTO: Guy Anthony
Mktg Mgr: Doug Rich
S&M/Mgr: Ron Schaffer

D-U-N-S 00-797-7747 IMP
BLUE RIDGE MOUNTAIN ELECTRIC MEMBERSHIP CORP (GA)
BLUE RIDGE MOUNTAIN EMC
875 Main St, Young Harris, GA 30582-4133
Tel (706) 379-3121 *Founded/Ownrshp* 1938
Sales 83.0MM *EMP* 197
Accts Henderson Hutcherson & Mccullo
SIC 4911 Distribution, electric power
Pr: Steven Phillip
**Treas:* Chris Logan
**VP:* Mickey Cummings
Genl Mgr: Dan Brewer
Off Mgr: Arbina Moss
Off Mgr: Patricia Young
IT Man: Dwayne Long
Mktg Dir: Tony Denton
Merch Mgr: Rick Britt

BLUE RIDGE MOUNTAIN EMC
See BLUE RIDGE MOUNTAIN ELECTRIC MEMBERSHIP CORP

D-U-N-S 04-395-9431 EXP
BLUE RIDGE PAPER PRODUCTS INC
EVERGREEN PACKAGING
(*Suby of* EVERGREEN PACKAGING INC) ★
41 Main St, Canton, NC 28716-4331
Tel (828) 454-0676 *Founded/Ownrshp* 1999
Sales 428.2MM^E *EMP* 2,000
SIC 2621 Fine paper; Kraft paper
Pr: John Rooney
CFO: Ricardo Alvergue
**Treas:* Allen Philip Hugli
Sr VP: Eduardo Sosa
**VP:* Phillip Bowen
**VP:* Joseph B Hanks
**VP:* Terry Huskey
**VP:* Robert Shanahan
**VP:* John Wadsworth
**Prin:* Richard Lozyniak
Mktg Mgr: Dan McMann

D-U-N-S 12-510-1696
BLUE SAGE CAPITAL LP
114 W 7th St Ste 820, Austin, TX 78701-3012
Tel (512) 536-1900 *Founded/Ownrshp* 2002
Sales 146.2MM^E *EMP* 808
SIC 6726 Investment offices
Pt: Jim McBride
Pt: Peter Huff
VP: Jonathan Pearce
VP: Eric Weiner

BLUE SHIELD OF CALIFORNIA
See CALIFORNIA PHYSICIANS SERVICE

D-U-N-S 07-463-7836
BLUE SHIELD OF CALIFORNIA LIFE & HEALTH INSURANCE CO
(*Suby of* BLUE SHIELD OF CALIFORNIA) ★
50 Beale St Ste 2000, San Francisco, CA 94105-1849
Tel (415) 229-5000 *Founded/Ownrshp* 1954
Sales NA *EMP* 4,000
Accts Deloitte & Touche Llp San Fra
SIC 6311 6321 Life insurance carriers; Accident insurance carriers; Health insurance carriers
CEO: Paul Markovich
CFO: Paul Swenson
Ex VP: Juan Davila
Sr VP: Seth Jacobs
Sr VP: Mary Ohara
Sr VP: Lisa Rubino
Sr VP: Michelle Simpson
VP: Doug Biehn
VP: Laura Gordon
VP: Bonnie Wait
Exec: Mark Morgan
Dir Rx: Richard Lieblich

D-U-N-S 08-604-7743
BLUE SPRINGS R-IV SCHOOL DISTRICT
BLUE SPRINGS R-IV SCHOOL DST
1801 Nw Vesper St, Blue Springs, MO 64015-3219
Tel (816) 224-1300 *Founded/Ownrshp* 1949
Sales 166.3MM *EMP* 1,676
Accts Novak Birks Pc Kansas City
SIC 8211 Public elementary school; Public junior high school; Public senior high school
Pr Dir: Erika Beebe
Pr Dir: Katie Woolf
Psych: Carolyn Courtney
Psych: Stacy Scalfaro

BLUE SPRINGS R-IV SCHOOL DST
See BLUE SPRINGS R-IV SCHOOL DISTRICT

BLUE SPRUCE CONSTRUCTION
See WESTCON INC

D-U-N-S 10-330-0849
BLUE STAR JETS LLC
880 3rd Ave Fl 11, New York, NY 10022-5088
Tel (212) 446-9037 *Founded/Ownrshp* 2001
Sales 100.0MM *EMP* 200
SIC 7389 Brokers' services
CEO: Richard Sitomer
Mng Pt: Jeffrey Honigman
Mng Pt: Caroline G Ingram
**Pr:* Todd Rome
COO: Howard Moses
CFO: Adam Hertz
Treas: Ted Mackay
VP: Ryan Auer
VP: Henk Westerduin
Mng Dir: Richard Berger
Mng Dir: Ken Lane

BLUE TEAM
See WESTERN NEVADA SUPPLY CO

D-U-N-S 12-170-1957
BLUE TECH INC
4025 Hancock St Ste 100, San Diego, CA 92110-5167
Tel (619) 497-6060 *Founded/Ownrshp* 1985
Sales 190.0MM *EMP* 40
SIC 5045

D-U-N-S 00-896-6335 IMP/EXP
BLUE TEE CORP
BROWN STRAUSS STEEL DIVISION
387 Park Ave S Fl 5, New York, NY 10016-8810
Tel (212) 598-0880 *Founded/Ownrshp* 1986
Sales 203.3MM^E *EMP* 900
Accts Deloitte & Touche Llp New Yo
SIC 3533 3589 5093 3715 3823 5051 Water well drilling equipment; Garbage disposers & compactors, commercial; Ferrous metal scrap & waste; Semitrailers for truck tractors; Water quality monitoring & control systems; Structural shapes, iron or steel
Pr: William M Kelly
**Ch Bd:* David P Alldian
**Ex Dir:* Annette Marino D'Arienzo

D-U-N-S 18-396-1361
■ BLUE WATER FINANCE & INSURANCE
(*Suby of* BRUNSWICK CORP) ★
5041 New Cntre Dr Ste 212, Wilmington, NC 28403
Tel (877) 934-9393 *Founded/Ownrshp* 2004
Sales 175.0MM *EMP* 14
SIC 7389 Financial services
Pr: Troy A Tiedeman
VP Opers: Ryan Tinkle
VP Sls: John Couture

D-U-N-S 96-811-5712
BLUE WOLF CAPITAL FUND II LP
1 Liberty Plz Fl 52, New York, NY 10006-1404
Tel (212) 488-1340 *Founded/Ownrshp* 2008
Sales 100.6MM *EMP* 398^E
SIC 6726 Investment offices
**Pt:* Charles Miller
VP: Haran Narulla
VP: Nilesh Parikh
VP: Aakash Patel
**Prin:* Bob Sharp
**Prin:* Josh Wolf-Powers
Mng Dir: Mike Musuraca

D-U-N-S 05-123-2523
■ BLUE WOLF GROUP LLC
(*Suby of* IBM) ★
11 E 26th St Fl 21, New York, NY 10010-1413
Tel (866) 455-9653 *Founded/Ownrshp* 2016
Sales 93.6MM^E *EMP* 550
SIC 7372 Prepackaged software; Business oriented computer software
Prin: Tim Anderson

D-U-N-S 05-248-3435 IMP
BLUEBONNET ELECTRIC COOPERATIVE INC
155 Electric Ave, Bastrop, TX 78602
Tel (800) 842-7708 *Founded/Ownrshp* 1939
Sales 207.3MM *EMP* 265
Accts Bolinger Segars Gilbert & Mo
SIC 4911 Distribution, electric power
CEO: Mark Rose
**Pr:* Richard Schmidt
**CFO:* Elizabeth Kana
CFO: Greg Wolf
**Sec:* James B Kershaw
**VP:* Ben Flencher

CIO: Grant Gutierrez
Dir IT: Nathan Flory
Sfty Mgr: Allen Anderson
Opers Mgr: Eric Kocian
VP Sls: Pam Chaddock

BLUEBONNET MOTORS
See KAHLIG ENTERPRISES INC

BLUECARE
See BLUECROSS BLUESHIELD OF TENNESSEE INC

D-U-N-S 03-894-5157
BLUECROSS AND BLUESHIELD OF AZ
2410 W Royal Palm Rd, Phoenix, AZ 85021-4966
Tel (602) 864-4100 *Founded/Ownrshp* 2010
Sales NA *EMP* 2
SIC 6324 Hospital & medical service plans
Prin: Shawn Aaron Fried
Mktg Mgr: Mike Chaisson

D-U-N-S 07-490-1380
BLUECROSS BLUESHIELD OF TENNESSEE INC (TN)
BLUECARE
1 Cameron Hill Cir, Chattanooga, TN 37402-2555
Tel (423) 535-5600 *Founded/Ownrshp* 1945
Sales NA *EMP* 5,373
SIC 6324 Hospital & medical service plans; Health maintenance organization (HMO), insurance only
CEO: JD Hickey
CEO: Bill Gracey
VP: Jennifer Butler
VP: Harold H Cantrell Jr
Prin: Janice Cove
Prin: April McCormick
Advt Mgr: Ginger Pettway
Genl Couns: William A Hullender
Snr Mgr: Frank Martinez

D-U-N-S 86-931-9269
BLUEGRASS FAMILY HEALTH
651 Perimeter Dr Ste 300, Lexington, KY 40517-4136
Tel (859) 269-4475 *Founded/Ownrshp* 1993
Sales NA *EMP* 225
SIC 6321 6411 Accident & health insurance; Insurance agents
CEO: James Fritz
**COO:* Carl Felix
**CFO:* Art Lowe
VP: Richard Busch
VP: Dale Fisher
Dir IT: Preston Gorman
Sls Mgr: Ronda Stewart-Wilcox
Ansthlgy: Jaudon E Behrman
Pharmcst: Scott Mason
Assoc Ed: Bobi Conn

D-U-N-S 07-785-5245
BLUEGRASSORG
1351 Newtown Pike, Lexington, KY 40511-1275
Tel (859) 253-1686 *Founded/Ownrshp* 1966
Sales 112.0MM *EMP* 1,200
Accts Deming Malone Livesay & Ostrof
SIC 8322 Association for the handicapped
CEO: Paul R Beatrice
CFO: Tambara Nalle
**CFO:* Dana Royse
**VP:* Dee Werline
QC Dir: Terry Wilson
Nrsg Dir: Bobbi Poston
Nrsg Dir: Chris Williamson

D-U-N-S 06-129-9855
■ **BLUEGREEN CORP**
(*Suby of* WOODBRIDGE HOLDINGS LLC) ★
4960 Conference Way N # 100, Boca Raton, FL 33431-4413
Tel (561) 912-8000 *Founded/Ownrshp* 2013
Sales 329.0MM^E^ *EMP* 4,040
SIC 6531 6552 Time-sharing real estate sales, leasing & rentals; Land subdividers & developers, residential
Pr: John M Maloney Jr
V Ch: John E Abdo
Pr: Barbara Stillman
**CFO:* Anthony M Puleo
Ofcr: Sheila Beauchesne
**Ofcr:* Susan J Saturday
Ofcr: Devin Sullivan
**Ex VP:* David L Pontius
**Sr VP:* David Bidgood
Sr VP: Daniel C Koscher
Sr VP: Susan Saturday
VP: John Boone
VP: Leslie Branham
VP: Paula Carls
VP: Charlie Cobb
VP: Terry Dodd
VP: Allan Herz
VP: Valarie Koshman
VP: Susan Milanese
VP: Wendy Poe
VP: Craig Robbins

D-U-N-S 80-033-6856
▲ **BLUEKNIGHT ENERGY PARTNERS LP**
201 Nw 10th St Ste 200, Oklahoma City, OK 73103-3928
Tel (405) 278-6400 *Founded/Ownrshp* 2007
Sales 180.0MM *EMP* 480^E^
Tkr Sym BKEP *Exch* NGM
SIC 4612 4226 Crude petroleum pipelines; Liquid storage; Petroleum & chemical bulk stations & terminals for hire
CEO: Mark A Hurley
Genl Pt: Blueknight E P
CFO: Alex G Stallings
VP: Jake Everett
VP: Brian Melton
Genl Couns: Joel Kanvik
Snr Mgr: Scott Richardson

D-U-N-S 14-340-3470 IMP
BLUELINE RENTAL LLC
8401 New Trils Dr Ste 150, The Woodlands, TX 77381
Tel (832) 299-7515 *Founded/Ownrshp* 2014
Sales 958.6MM^E^ *EMP* 2,300
SIC 7353 4789 Oil equipment rental services; Cargo loading & unloading services
CEO: Phillip H Hobson
**COO:* Barry Natwick
**CFO:* Evan Brumm
**Sr VP:* Klas Magnusson
**VP:* Bud Howard
VP: Jeff Reid
Brnch Mgr: Eric Eng
Genl Mgr: Andrew Murray
Sales Asso: Michael Malone
Sales Asso: Roxanne Owens

D-U-N-S 01-558-5404 IMP
■ **BLUELINX CORP**
BLUELINX SERVICES
(*Suby of* BLUELINX HOLDINGS INC) ★
4300 Wildwood Pkwy, Atlanta, GA 30339-8440
Tel (770) 953-7000 *Founded/Ownrshp* 2004
Sales 1.2MMM^E^ *EMP* 1,700
SIC 5031 Lumber, plywood & millwork
CEO: Mitchell B Lewis
Pr: Ken Black
Pr: Mark L Wasson
**CFO:* Susan O'Farrell
VP: Jim Herbig
VP: Kenneth H Kerns
VP: Whitney Patterson
VP: Scott Phillips
Genl Mgr: Robert Norman
Dir IT: Richard Grant
Opers Supe: Carl Bearden

D-U-N-S 14-508-9889
■ **BLUELINX HOLDINGS INC**
(*Suby of* CERBERUS ABP INVESTOR LLC) ★
4300 Wildwood Pkwy, Atlanta, GA 30339-8440
Tel (770) 953-7000 *Founded/Ownrshp* 2004
Sales 1.9MMM *EMP* 1,600
Tkr Sym BXC *Exch* NYS
SIC 5031 5211 Lumber, plywood & millwork; Lumber & other building materials
Pr: Mitchell B Lewis
**Ch Bd:* Roy W Haley
CFO: Susan C O'Farrell
Sr VP: Shyam K Reddy

BLUELINX SERVICES
See BLUELINX CORP

D-U-N-S 01-301-5722
BLUEOX CORP (NY)
38 N Canal St, Oxford, NY 13830-4250
Tel (607) 843-2583 *Founded/Ownrshp* 1963, 1940
Sales 132.1MM^E^ *EMP* 175
SIC 5172 5411 5541 Fuel oil; Convenience stores, independent; Gasoline service stations
Ch Bd: Neil R Bartle
**COO:* David Martin

D-U-N-S 79-931-5523
BLUEPEARL FLORIDA LLC
VETERINARY SPECIALTY
3000 Busch Lake Blvd, Tampa, FL 33614-1862
Tel (813) 933-8944 *Founded/Ownrshp* 1996
Sales 162.2MM^E^ *EMP* 3,000
SIC 0742 Animal hospital services, pets & other animal specialties
COO: David Gersholowitz
**CFO:* Clint Werts
**Chf Mktg O:* Jennifer Welser
Genl Mgr: Liezl Dale
Dir IT: Jeff Fox
Mktg Mgr: Jessica Camara

BLUES CITY BREWERY
See CITY BREWING CO LLC

D-U-N-S 83-077-0587 IMP/EXP
BLUESCOPE BUILDINGS NORTH AMERICA INC
(*Suby of* VSMA INC) ★
1540 Genessee St, Kansas City, MO 64102-1069
Tel (816) 245-6000 *Founded/Ownrshp* 2010
Sales 408.4MM^E^ *EMP* 350
SIC 1542 Commercial & office building, new construction
Prin: Douglas Engel
VP: Mike Sirna

D-U-N-S 05-290-1469 EXP
BLUESCOPE CONSTRUCTION INC
HEAVY STRUCTURES
(*Suby of* BLUESCOPE BUILDINGS NORTH AMERICA INC) ★
1540 Genessee St, Kansas City, MO 64102-1069
Tel (816) 245-6000 *Founded/Ownrshp* 1970
Sales 99.3MM^E^ *EMP* 150
Accts Ernst & Young Llp Kansas City
SIC 1542 Commercial & office building, new construction
Pr: Matthew Threadgill
**CFO:* Kerry Domke
Treas: Connie Schwada
VP: Greg Pasley
Exec: Richard Vanauken
Area Mgr: Kris Kutterer
Tech Mgr: Gary Williams
Sfty Dirs: Pat Bleyhl
Snr PM: Greg Fitzsimmons

D-U-N-S 82-523-2841
BLUESCOPE STEEL NORTH AMERICA CORP
(*Suby of* BLUESCOPE STEEL LIMITED)
1540 Genessee St, Kansas City, MO 64102-1069
Tel (816) 968-1700 *Founded/Ownrshp* 1978
Sales 1.3MMM^E^ *EMP* 3,520
SIC 1542 3448 Commercial & office building, new construction; Prefabricated metal buildings
Pr: Mark Vassella
COO: Morey Anderson
**CFO:* Adam Watson
VP: Douglas Lange
VP: Austin Laurenson
Comm Man: Lucinda Grove
Mktg Mgr: Craig Miller
Sales Asso: Laurie Holt

BLUESTAR USA
See UNITED RADIO INC

D-U-N-S 03-718-5571 IMP
BLUESTEM BRANDS INC
FINGERHUT
(*Suby of* BLUESTEM GROUP INC) ★
7075 Flying Cloud Dr, Eden Prairie, MN 55344-3532
Tel (952) 656-4037 *Founded/Ownrshp* 2002
Sales 1.3MMM^E^ *EMP* 3,900
SIC 5961 Arts & crafts equipment & supplies, mail order
CEO: Steven Nave
**COO:* Vince Jones
**CFO:* Mark Wagener
**Ofcr:* Saby Sengupta
Ofcr: Erica C Street
**Ex VP:* Chidam Chidambaram
Ex VP: Gail Crepeau
**Ex VP:* Marc Sieger
**Ex VP:* Gina Sprenger
**Sr VP:* Shawn Moren
VP: Brad Atkinson
VP: Ben Barras
VP: Scott Carter
VP: Karen Hartje
VP: Jennifer Morgans
VP: Margaret Ostrowski
VP: Randy Rudolph

D-U-N-S 36-154-6687
BLUESTEM GROUP INC
7505 Flying Cloud Dr, Eden Prairie, MN 55344
Tel (952) 656-3700 *Founded/Ownrshp* 2011
Sales 1.4MMM^E^ *EMP* 3,900
SIC 6799 7389 Real estate investors, except property operators; Financial services
Pr: Jay N Levine
Ch Bd: Dennis D Dammerman
Pr: William C Gallagher
CFO: Gregory J McManus
Ex VP: Thomas L Fairfield
Ex VP: Linda A Pickles
Sr VP: Chris Blechschmidt
Sr VP: Shawn Henry
IT Man: Tom Reynolds

D-U-N-S 07-844-0561
BLUESTREAM PROFESSIONAL SERVICES LLC
(*Suby of* KGP LOGISTICS) ★
3305 Highway 60 W, Faribault, MN 55021-4869
Tel (678) 355-6200 *Founded/Ownrshp* 2012
Sales 136.5MM^E^ *EMP* 800^E^
SIC 1731 Fiber optic cable installation; Telephone & telephone equipment installation
CEO: Kathleen Putrah
**Pr:* Trevor Putrah
**COO:* Matt Glass
**CFO:* Stuart Romenesko
Genl Mgr: Bill Davison
Genl Mgr: Paul Schultz
Board of Directors: Kathleen Putrah, Trevor Putrah

D-U-N-S 18-577-5582 IMP
BLUEWATER DEFENSE INC
Corozal Ind Pk Carr 159, Corozal, PR 00783
Tel (787) 746-5020 *Founded/Ownrshp* 1987
Sales 425.1MM^E^ *EMP* 1,403
SIC 2393 2326 3842 2325 Knapsacks, canvas: made from purchased materials; Overalls & coveralls; Clothing, fire resistant & protective; Men's & boys' trousers & slacks
Ch: Diego Jacobson
**CEO:* Eric Spackey
**Treas:* Olga Bonnin
Genl Mgr: Luis Falizciano

D-U-N-S 08-367-8235 IMP
BLUM INC
(*Suby of* JULIUS BLUM GMBH)
7733 Old Plank Rd, Stanley, NC 28164-7774
Tel (704) 827-1345 *Founded/Ownrshp* 1977
Sales 170.3MM^E^ *EMP* 400
SIC 3429 Furniture hardware
Pr: Karl Rudisser
Pr: Ralf Atzor
**Treas:* Donna Springs
**Ex VP:* Stephen Regele
Exec: Donna York
Area Mgr: Damian Barbieri
CIO: Wolfgang Kueng
Netwrk Mgr: Franz Hufnagl
Info Man: Tim Glover
QI Cn Mgr: Bojan Popovic
VP Sls: David Sanders

D-U-N-S 07-843-9758 IMP
BLUMAR USA LLC
(*Suby of* SALMONES BLUMAR S.A.)
6303 Blue Lagoon Dr 385, Miami, FL 33126-6002
Tel (305) 261-2417 *Founded/Ownrshp* 2011
Sales 150.0MM *EMP* 7
SIC 5146 5142 Fish & seafoods; Seafoods; Fish, fresh; Fish, frozen, unpackaged; Fish, frozen: packaged
Pr: Sebastian Goycoolea

D-U-N-S 00-190-2592 IMP
BLUMBERG INDUSTRIES INC (FL)
FINE ART LAMPS
5770 Miami Lakes Dr E, Miami Lakes, FL 33014-2418
Tel (305) 821-3850 *Founded/Ownrshp* 1941, 1970
Sales 96.6MM^E^ *EMP* 580
SIC 3645 3646 Residential lighting fixtures; Commercial indusl & institutional electric lighting fixtures
Ch Bd: Max Blumberg
**Pr:* Laura Goldblum
COO: Mark McDowell
VP Opers: Rene Quintana
Opers Mgr: Roberto Perez
QI Cn Mgr: Ozzie Hernandez
Mktg Mgr: Jacqueline Hessler

BLYTH HOME SCENTS INTL
See CAROLINA DESIGNS LTD

D-U-N-S 07-906-6825 IMP
BLYTHE CONSTRUCTION INC (NC)
(*Suby of* HUBBARD GROUP INC) ★
2911 N Graham St, Charlotte, NC 28206-3535
Tel (704) 375-8474 *Founded/Ownrshp* 1949, 1998
Sales 209.3MM^E^ *EMP* 480
Accts Deloitte & Touche Llp Orlando
SIC 1611 1622 2951 Highway & street paving contractor; Bridge construction; Asphalt & asphaltic paving mixtures (not from refineries)
Pr: Bill Carphardt
**Pr:* Alan Cahill
CFO: Fred Oday
**CFO:* Fred Odea
**VP:* J McBryde
Area Mgr: Shane Clark
Off Mgr: Suzanne Rimer
Sfty Mgr: Ross Peters
Opers Mgr: Roger Keene
QI Cn Mgr: Darren Hedrick
VP Mktg: Jennifer White

D-U-N-S 62-235-2847
BLYTHE DEVELOPMENT CO
1415 E Westinghouse Blvd, Charlotte, NC 28273-5801
Tel (704) 588-0023 *Founded/Ownrshp* 1989
Sales 159.3MM *EMP* 800
Accts Greerwalker Llp Charlotte Nc
SIC 1611 Grading; Sidewalk construction
Pr: Luther J Blythe Sr
**CFO:* Joey Dodson
Sfty Mgr: Bruce Poling

BMC
See BOSTON MEDICAL CENTER CORP

BMC
See BADGER MINING CORP

BMC
See BUILDING MATERIALS HOLDING CORP

BMC BAYVIEW MEDICAL CENTER
See JOHNS HOPKINS BAYVIEW MEDICAL CENTER INC

BMC CONSTRUCTION
See SELECTBUILD CONSTRUCTION INC

D-U-N-S 00-318-5774 IMP/EXP
■ **BMC EAST LLC** (NC)
(*Suby of* BMC STOCK HOLDINGS INC) ★
8020 Arco Corp Dr Ste 400, Raleigh, NC 27617
Tel (919) 431-1000 *Founded/Ownrshp* 1922, 2009
Sales 377.7MM^E^ *EMP* 2,300
SIC 5211 2431 5031 5713 5251 Millwork & lumber; Millwork; Lumber: rough, dressed & finished; Floor covering stores; Builders' hardware
Pr: Jeff REA
**CFO:* James F Major Jr
**Ex VP:* Lisa Hamblet
**Ex VP:* Jim Major
Sr VP: Joseph J Appelmann
**Sr VP:* James F Drexinger
**Sr VP:* Stephen R Short
VP: Joe Applemann
VP: Stephen G Eisner
VP: Kurt W Hans
VP: Timothy P Meyer
VP: Anne P Phillips
VP: Ian Weingarten
Board of Directors: Steve Edwards, Gary Robinette, Richard Rose, Jake Thomas, John Young

BMC HEALTHNET PLAN
See BOSTON MEDICAL CENTER HEALTH PLAN INC

D-U-N-S 07-658-8326
BMC PARTNERS LLP (MA)
1 Federal St, Boston, MA 02110-2012
Tel (617) 951-8000 *Founded/Ownrshp* 1891
Sales NA *EMP* 2,224
SIC 8111

D-U-N-S 01-158-9751 IMP
BMC SOFTWARE INC
(*Suby of* BOXER PARENT CO INC) ★
2103 Citywest Blvd # 2100, Houston, TX 77042-2857
Tel (713) 918-8800 *Founded/Ownrshp* 2013
Sales 2.1MMM^E^ *EMP* 6,900
SIC 7372 7371 Prepackaged software; Custom computer programming services
Ch: Bob Beauchamp
Pr: Michelle Carbone
Pr: Terry Gast
Pr: Bob Lewis
COO: William D Miller
CFO: Stephen B Solcher
Ofcr: Chief C Behnia
Ofcr: Nick Utton
Ex VP: Paul Appleby
Ex VP: Brian Bergdoll
Sr VP: Jerome Adams
Sr VP: Paul Avenant
Sr VP: Kenneth W Berryman
Sr VP: Darroll Buytenhuys
Sr VP: D Stephen Goddard Jr
Sr VP: Jeffrey S Hawn
Sr VP: Cosmo Santullo
Sr VP: Dan Streetman
Sr VP: Kirill Tatarinov
VP: Jason Andrew
VP: Gene Austin

D-U-N-S 83-121-1177
▲ **BMC STOCK HOLDINGS INC**
980 Hammond Dr Ste 500, Atlanta, GA 30328-8186
Tel (678) 222-1219 *Founded/Ownrshp* 1922
Sales 1.5MMM *EMP* 9,600
Accts Pricewaterhousecoopers Llp R
Tkr Sym BMCH *Exch* NGS
SIC 5211 2431 5031 5713 5251 Lumber & other building materials; Millwork & lumber; Millwork; Lumber: rough, dressed & finished; Floor covering stores; Builders' hardware
Pr: Peter C Alexander
**Ch Bd:* David Bullock
CFO: James F Major Jr
Div Pres: Walter Philip Randolph
Div Pres: Duff R Wakefield
Div Pres: Steven W Wilson
Ofcr: Bryan J Yeazel
Ex VP: Lisa M Hamblet
Sr VP: C Lowell Ball

Sr VP: Noah Gay
VP: Michael Farmer
Board of Directors: Barry J Goldstein, David L Keltner, Michael Miller, James O'leary, Jeffrey G Rea, Carl R Vertuca Jr

BMCA
See STANDARD INDUSTRIES INC

D-U-N-S 10-425-8566
BMCA HOLDINGS CORP
BUILDING MATERIALS CORP AMER
(*Suby of* G A F) ★
1361 Alps Rd, Wayne, NJ 07470-3700
Tel (973) 628-3000 *Founded/Ownrshp* 1999
Sales 1.6MMM^E *EMP* 3,701^E
SIC 2493 Insulation & roofing material, reconstituted wood
Sr VP: Daniel Goldstein
**Ch Bd:* Robert Tasaro
**Treas:* John Maitner
CIO: Adam Noble
Manager: Tom Horan
Sls Mgr: Aj Steele

D-U-N-S 02-389-3142 IMP
BMG METALS INC
(*Suby of* DESCOURS ET CABAUD SA)
950 Masonic Ln, Richmond, VA 23223-5545
Tel (804) 226-1024 *Founded/Ownrshp* 2012
Sales 121.7MM^E *EMP* 190
SIC 5051 Metals service centers & offices
CEO: Kingsbery Gay Jr
**Pr:* Thomas Gay
**Ch:* Alain Morvand
**Sec:* William C Gay
Brnch Mgr: Corey Calder
Brnch Mgr: Ron Robinson
Sales Asso: Joshua McKinney

D-U-N-S 11-524-1606 IMP
BMH CORP
11 Forbes Rd, Woburn, MA 01801-2103
Tel (781) 933-8300 *Founded/Ownrshp* 1983
Sales 1.3MMM *EMP* 155
SIC 5051 Metals service centers & offices
CEO: James S Burstein
**Ch Bd:* Maxwell Burstein
**Treas:* David Pascucci
**VP:* Gerald D Burstein
Off Mgr: Barbara Welsh
Sls&Mrk Ex: Long Joacj

D-U-N-S 07-310-0539 IMP
BMH INC
BINGHAM MEMORIAL HOSPITAL
98 Poplar St, Blackfoot, ID 83221-1758
Tel (208) 785-4100 *Founded/Ownrshp* 2006
Sales 88.6MM *EMP* 550
SIC 8062 8051 General medical & surgical hospitals; Skilled nursing care facilities
CEO: Louis Kraml
**COO:* Dan Cochran
CFO: Charles Button
**CFO:* D Jeff Daniels
**CFO:* Jeff Daniels
Dir Rad: Lisa Wells
Adm Dir: Shane Robinson
Off Mgr: Sue Goodman
Dir IT: Jack York
Surgeon: Jonathan Godfrey
Surgeon: Kenneth Newhouse

D-U-N-S 01-378-7917
BMM LOGISTICS INC
209 W Jackson Blvd # 903, Chicago, IL 60606-6905
Tel (312) 730-7495 *Founded/Ownrshp* 2008
Sales 100.0MM *EMP* 30
SIC 4731 Truck transportation brokers
Pr: Marjan Stanojevic
**CEO:* Mike Stan

D-U-N-S 05-943-7400
BMO BANKCORP INC
(*Suby of* BMO FINANCIAL CORP) ★
111 W Monroe St, Chicago, IL 60603-4096
Tel (312) 461-2121 *Founded/Ownrshp* 1984
Sales NA *EMP* 6,680
SIC 6021 6211 National commercial banks; Security brokers & dealers
CEO: Christopher Begy
V Ch: Peter B McNitt
Pr: Timothy Crane
Pr: William Downe
Pr: Jeff Patton
Pr: Adam Schabes
CFO: Pamela Pairowski
CFO: Pamela Piarowski
CFO: Pamela C Piarowski
Chf Inves: Jack A Ablin
Ofcr: Peter R Janczak
Assoc VP: Paula Davault
Ex VP: Yasmin T Bates
Ex VP: Lewis Lanwermeyer
Ex VP: Cecily Mistarz
Ex VP: Charles R Tonge
Sr VP: Amy Burk
Sr VP: Ty Garver
Sr VP: John Howard
Sr VP: Timothy Moran
Sr VP: Henry Munez
Board of Directors: Richard E Terry, Martin R Castro, James O Webb, F Anthony Comper, Susan T Congalton, Wilber H Gantz, James J Glasser, Dr Leo M Henikoff, Richard M Jaffe, Edward W Lyman Jr, Charles H Shaw

D-U-N-S 60-262-7051
BMO CAPITAL MARKETS CORP
(*Suby of* BMO FINANCIAL CORP) ★
3 Times Sq, New York, NY 10036-6564
Tel (212) 885-4000 *Founded/Ownrshp* 2003
Sales 137.7MM^E *EMP* 2,300
SIC 7389 Financial services
CEO: Thomas V Milroy
Mng Pt: Terrance S McGovern
**Pr:* Eric C Tripp
CFO: Diane Carey
Top Exec: Jack Blackstock
Ex VP: Rick King
Mng Dir: Tod Benton
Mng Dir: Bruce Eatroff
Mng Dir: Jim Goll
Mng Dir: Louis Nardi
Mng Dir: Erik Van Nispen

D-U-N-S 61-505-8914 IMP
BMO FINANCIAL CORP
(*Suby of* BANK OF MONTREAL)
111 W Monroe St Ste 1200, Chicago, IL 60603-4014
Tel (312) 461-2121 *Founded/Ownrshp* 1984
Sales NA *EMP* 8,175
SIC 6021 6082 6211 National commercial banks; Foreign trade & international banking institutions; Security brokers & dealers
Prin: Bill Downe
Ofcr: Mikael Jorgensen
Top Exec: Thomas Oneill
Ex VP: Ann M Benschoter
Ex VP: David R Casper
Ex VP: Bradley D Chapin
Sr VP: Jeff Ellis
VP: Mark Gawron
VP: Christy Horn
VP: Jim Kappel
VP: Alan G McNally
VP: Marybeth Mrowka
VP: Amy Patel
VP: Bill Schlesser
VP: Tammy Tamlin

D-U-N-S 01-449-0404 IMP/EXP
BMP INTERNATIONAL INC (FL)
5139 W Idlewild Ave, Tampa, FL 33634-8023
Tel (727) 458-0544 *Founded/Ownrshp* 2007
Sales 100.0MM *EMP* 25
SIC 1542 Commercial & office building contractors
Pr: Linna Shi
VP: Xianbin Meng

D-U-N-S 36-258-7185
BMP SUNSTONE CORP
(*Suby of* SANOFI)
3711 Kennett Pike Ste 200, Wilmington, DE 19807-2161
Tel (610) 940-1675 *Founded/Ownrshp* 2011
Sales 61.2MM^E *EMP* 1,198
SIC 5122 Drugs, proprietaries & sundries
CEO: David Gao
Pr: Zhijun Tong
COO: Yanping Zhao
CFO: Fred M Powell

D-U-N-S 07-315-6630
BMS ENTERPRISES INC
5718 Airport Fwy, Haltom City, TX 76117-6005
Tel (817) 730-1948 *Founded/Ownrshp* 1974
Sales 155.2MM *EMP* 900
Accts Mcgladrey Llp Dallas Texas
SIC 7349 Building maintenance services
CEO: Kirk Blackmon
**COO:* Greg Blackmon
**CFO:* William G Blackmon
**CFO:* Robert D Smith
Genl Mgr: James Price
Opers Supe: Salvador Zambrano
Sls Mgr: Jason Bean
Board of Directors: Greg Blackmon, Kirk Blackmon, William G Blackmon

D-U-N-S 09-998-6028 IMP/EXP
BMW (US) HOLDING CORP
(*Suby of* BAYERISCHE MOTOREN WERKE AG)
300 Chestnut Ridge Rd, Woodcliff Lake, NJ 07677-7731
Tel (201) 307-4000 *Founded/Ownrshp* 1973
Sales 1.8MMM^E *EMP* 6,500
SIC 5511

D-U-N-S 09-366-2398
BMW BANK OF NORTH AMERICA
(*Suby of* ALPHERA FINANCIAL SERVICES) ★
2735 E Parleys Way # 301, Salt Lake City, UT 84109-1666
Tel (801) 461-6415 *Founded/Ownrshp* 1999
Sales NA *EMP* 42
Accts Bdo Usa Llp Spokane Washing
SIC 6022 State commercial banks
Pr: Kenneth Petersen
**VP:* William Donnelly
Dir Risk M: Robert Brown
Off Mgr: Dianne Murphy
Genl Couns: Walker Kennedy

D-U-N-S 79-402-4216
BMW FINANCIAL SERVICES NA LLC
ALPHERA FINANCIAL SERVICES
(*Suby of* BMW GROUP) ★
5550 Britton Pkwy, Hilliard, OH 43026-7456
Tel (614) 718-6900 *Founded/Ownrshp* 1933
Sales NA *EMP* 550
SIC 6159 Automobile finance leasing
CEO: Ed Robinson
VP: David Brubaker
VP: Ian Smith
Exec: Stephanie Augenstein
Genl Mgr: Steven Swecker
Snr Sftwr: Jen Hatten
Snr Sftwr: Doug McMillan
DP Exec: Presila Copeland
Dir IT: Kevin Smith
Tech Mgr: Dennis Mull
Software D: Robb Rexroad

BMW GROUP
See BMW OF NORTH AMERICA LLC

D-U-N-S 01-206-3822 EXP
BMW OF NORTH AMERICA LLC
BMW GROUP
(*Suby of* BMW (US) HOLDING CORP) ★
300 Chestnut Ridge Rd, Woodcliff Lake, NJ 07677-7731
Tel (201) 307-4000 *Founded/Ownrshp* 1975
Sales 1.6MMM^E *EMP* 2,200
SIC 5013 3751 5012 3711 Automotive supplies & parts; Motorcycles, bicycles & parts; Automobiles; Motor vehicles & car bodies
CEO: Ludwig Willisch
Pr: Craig Helsing
CFO: Ralph Hagemann
**CFO:* Dr Gunter Niedernhuber
CFO: Robert Nitto
CFO: Stefan Sengewald
Treas: Joachim Herr
Treas: Norbert Mayer
Ex VP: Brian Eastey
Ex VP: Chris Koenders
Ex VP: Stefan Walmrath
Ex VP: Thomas Wittig
VP: Rainer Feurer
VP: Jochen Goller
VP: Amanda Henke
VP: Bryan Jacobs
VP: Carsten Regent
Exec: Adrienne Betar
Exec: Marty Caulfield
Exec: Mike Demarco
Exec: Joostu Meij

BMW OF SAN FRANCISCO
See GERMAN MOTORS CORP

D-U-N-S 14-636-4570
BMWC GROUP INC
1740 W Michigan St, Indianapolis, IN 46222-3855
Tel (317) 267-0400 *Founded/Ownrshp* 2002
Sales 219.2MM^E *EMP* 1,500^E
SIC 1629 Industrial plant construction; Chemical plant & refinery construction; Power plant construction
Ch Bd: Thomas E Obrien
**Pr:* Brian Acton
**VP:* David Clements
**VP:* Steven D Thompson

D-U-N-S 00-190-3736
BNBUILDERS INC (WA)
2601 4th Ave Ste 350, Seattle, WA 98121-1283
Tel (206) 382-3443 *Founded/Ownrshp* 2000
Sales 104.6MM^E *EMP* 130
SIC 1542 Nonresidential construction
Pr: Brad Bastian
**Treas:* Tim O'Brien
**VP:* Jeffrey Nielse

D-U-N-S 12-860-0298
▲ BNC BANCORP
3980 Premier Dr Ste 210, High Point, NC 27265-8411
Tel (336) 476-9200 *Founded/Ownrshp* 2002
Sales NA *EMP* 850^E
Tkr Sym BNCN *Exch* NAS
SIC 6021 National commercial banks
Pr: Richard D Callicutt II
**Ch Bd:* Thomas R Sloan
CFO: David B Spencer
**V Ch Bd:* W Swope Montgomery Jr
Ex VP: Ronald J Gorczynski
Board of Directors: Richard F Wood, James T Bolt Jr, Joseph M Coltrane Jr, Charles T Hagan III, Elaine M Lyerly, John S Ramsey Jr, Thomas R Smith, Robert A Team Jr, G Kennedy Thompson, D Vann Williford

D-U-N-S 61-802-6970
BNG AMERICA LLC
(*Suby of* ENERGY SOLUTIONS) ★
1235 S Clark St Ste 700a, Arlington, VA 22202-4364
Tel (703) 412-2500 *Founded/Ownrshp* 2006
Sales 20.8MM^E *EMP* 1,000
SIC 8711 8741 4953 2819 Engineering services; Management services; Refuse systems; Industrial inorganic chemicals
CEO: Philip Strawbridge
Ofcr: John Christian

D-U-N-S 00-533-5922
BNP MEDIA INC (MI)
2401 W Big Beaver Rd # 700, Troy, MI 48084-3333
Tel (248) 362-3700 *Founded/Ownrshp* 1926
Sales 175.4MM^E *EMP* 550
SIC 2721 Trade journals: publishing only, not printed on site
Ch: Jim Henderson
**Pr:* Harper Henderson
**VP:* Taggart Henderson
Dir Soc: Adriene Cooper
Creative D: Dave Zibell
Brnch Mgr: Ellyn Fishman
Prd Dir: Mary Wray
Prd Mgr: Jennifer Allen
Prd Mgr: Jeff Bagwell
Prd Mgr: Nann Barkiewicz
Prd Mgr: Janet Beatty

D-U-N-S 07-867-7480
■ BNP PARIBAS ASSET MANAGEMENT INC
(*Suby of* BNP PARIBAS INVESTMENT PARTNERS PAR ABREVIATION BNPP IP)
200 Park Ave Rm 4520, New York, NY 10166-0005
Tel (212) 681-3000 *Founded/Ownrshp* 1979
Sales 150.8MM^E *EMP* 1,684^E
SIC 6726 Management investment funds, closed-end
Pr: Robert Harrison
**CEO:* Sharad Kumar Sharma
Ex Dir: David Tufts

D-U-N-S 82-984-1597
■ BNP PARIBAS NORTH AMERICA INC
(*Suby of* BNP PARIBAS)
787 7th Ave Fl 27, New York, NY 10019-6083
Tel (212) 841-2000 *Founded/Ownrshp* 1977
Sales 84.3MM^E *EMP* 78^E
SIC 6211 Security brokers & dealers
Ch Bd: Everett Schenk
**CFO:* Arnaud Remy

D-U-N-S 14-738-8235 IMP
■ BNP PARIBAS SECURITIES CORP
(*Suby of* PARIBAS PROPERTIES INC) ★
787 7th Ave Fl 27, New York, NY 10019-6083
Tel (212) 841-3000 *Founded/Ownrshp* 1984
Sales 381.2MM^E *EMP* 612^E
Accts Pricewaterhousecoopers Llp
SIC 6211 Brokers, security; Dealers, security
CEO: David Brunner
COO: Milind Kulkarni
COO: Bertrand Meyer
CFO: Meirav Klein
Assoc VP: Lissa Malley
Sr VP: Chetan Shah
VP: George Allen
VP: Rob Bruen
VP: Derrick Dobert
VP: Arnold Mendelsohn
VP: Lorelle Minninger
VP: Claire B Paul
VP: Christophe Poulmarck
VP: Rene Ramkishun
VP: Julien Ramone
VP: Fred Scheier
Assoc Dir: Peter Monks
Assoc Dir: Stephanie Wong

D-U-N-S 00-119-1246 IMP/EXP
BNS HOLDING INC
61 E Main St Ste B, Los Gatos, CA 95030-6947
Tel (408) 399-6498 *Founded/Ownrshp* 2004, 2006
Sales 43.6MM^E *EMP* 1,001^E
SIC 3711 3713 3531 Ambulances (motor vehicles), assembly of; Bus & other large specialty vehicle assembly; Specialty motor vehicle bodies; Bulldozers (construction machinery)
Pr: Michael Warren
**Ch Bd:* Kenneth N Kermes

D-U-N-S 10-330-7968
■ BNSF LOGISTICS LLC
(*Suby of* BURLINGTON NORTHERN SANTA FE LLC) ★
2710 S 48th St, Springdale, AR 72762-6809
Tel (479) 927-5570 *Founded/Ownrshp* 2002
Sales 178.9MM^E *EMP* 600
Accts Deloitte & Touche Llp Fort Wo
SIC 4731 Truck transportation brokers
Pr: Ray Greer
Opers Mgr: Bridgette Lashlee
Opers Mgr: Catrina Morgan
Opers Mgr: Doug Snyder

D-U-N-S 06-362-4324
■ BNSF RAILWAY CO
(*Suby of* BURLINGTON NORTHERN SANTA FE LLC) ★
2650 Lou Menk Dr, Fort Worth, TX 76131-2830
Tel (800) 795-2673 *Founded/Ownrshp* 2010
Sales 21.4MMM *EMP* 1,800
SIC 4731 4011 Freight transportation arrangement; Railroads, line-haul operating
Pr: Carl R Ice
**Ch Bd:* Matthew K Rose
CFO: Julie A Piggott
Ex VP: Stevan B Bobb
Ex VP: Gregory C Fox
Ex VP: Gregory B Richard
VP: Jon I Stevens
CIO: Jeffery Campbell
Sales Exec: Dennis Sweat
Sls Mgr: Jennifer Walsh
Snr Mgr: Howard Rosas
Board of Directors: Stevan B Bobb, Gregory C Fox, Roger Nober

BNY MELLON
See BANK OF NEW YORK MELLON CORP

D-U-N-S 00-791-6018
■ BNY MELLON NATIONAL ASSOCIATION
(*Suby of* BNY MELLON) ★
1 Mellon Center Ste 3831, Pittsburgh, PA 15258-0001
Tel (412) 234-5000 *Founded/Ownrshp* 1869, 2006
Sales NA *EMP* 7,662
SIC 6021 6733 National commercial banks; Personal investment trust management
V Ch: Steven G Elliott
V Ch: John Chesko
**CEO:* Curtis Y Arledge
COO: Janet Cholewinski
**CFO:* Michael A Bryson
Treas: Leo Au
Ex VP: John Obrist
**Ex VP:* Timothy P Robison
Ex VP: Mark P Sparano
Sr VP: Michael Bichler
Sr VP: John Pritchett
Sr VP: David Thompson
Sr VP: Ginny Volponi
VP: Jan Bamford
VP: James A Basnight
VP: Steve Bernacki
VP: Dave Brown
VP: Paula Comella
VP: Tom Daniels
VP: Dan Gluckman
VP: Deborah Grizzanti

D-U-N-S 02-604-8645 IMP
BO-MAC CONTRACTORS LTD
(*Suby of* HEICO COMPANIES L L C) ★
1020 Lindbergh Dr, Beaumont, TX 77707-3623
Tel (409) 842-2125 *Founded/Ownrshp* 1966
Sales 90.3MM^E *EMP* 500
SIC 1629 1771

BOARD GOVERNORS GENERAL OFFICE
See BOARD OF GOVERNORS STATE UNIVERSITY SYSTEM OF FLORIDA

BOARD MHNING CNTY CMMISSIONERS
See MAHONING COUNTY

BOARD OF COMMISSIONERS
See COUNTY OF DEKALB

BOARD OF COMMISSIONERS
See COUNTY OF STARK

D-U-N-S 07-367-6678
BOARD OF COOP EDUC SERVICES OF 2ND SUPERVISORY DISTRICT OF MONROE & ORLEANS COUNTIES
MONROE 2-ORLEANS BOCES
3599 Big Ridge Rd, Spencerport, NY 14559-1709
Tel (585) 352-2412 *Founded/Ownrshp* 1955
Sales 97.1MM *EMP* 700
SIC 8211 Public elementary & secondary schools
Pr: Diane Choromanskis

Treas: Jeanine Gallina
Bd of Dir: John Abbott
Bd of Dir: John Heise
Bd of Dir: Dennis Laba
Exec: Jill Slavny
MIS Dir: Mark Laubacher
Teacher Pr: Karen Brown
Psych: Amanda Young

D-U-N-S 06-802-0718
BOARD OF COOPERATIVE EDUCATIONAL SERVICES
JAMES HINES ADMINISTRATIVE CTR
201 Sunrise Hwy W, Patchogue, NY 11772-1868
Tel (631) 289-2200 Founded/Ownrshp 1948
Sales 93.6MM[E] EMP 2,500
Accts Miller Lilly & Pearce Llp Cpa
SIC 8249 Vocational schools
Ofcr: Windy Scully
Genl Mgr: Dawn Delvecchio

D-U-N-S 07-368-8947
BOARD OF COOPERATIVE EDUCATIONAL SERVICES FIRST SUPERVISORY DISTRICT OF MONROE COUNTY
BOCES
41 Oconnor Rd, Fairport, NY 14450-1327
Tel (585) 377-4660 Founded/Ownrshp 1956
Sales 105.0MM EMP 1,300
SIC 8211 Public special education school; Public vocational/technical school
COO: Larry Conte
Treas: Sharon Fairbanks
Pr Dir: John Walker

BOARD OF COUNTY COMMISSIONERS
See COUNTY OF PINELLAS

BOARD OF COUNTY COMMISSIONERS
See COUNTY OF ORANGE

BOARD OF COUNTY COMMISSIONERS
See COUNTY OF CUYAHOGA

BOARD OF COUNTY COMMISSIONERS
See COUNTY OF BROWARD

BOARD OF COUNTY COMMISSIONERS
See COUNTY OF CLAY

BOARD OF CTY COMM CALVERT CNTY
See COUNTY OF CALVERT

D-U-N-S 07-500-2691
BOARD OF DIRECTORS OF WITTENBERG COLLEGE
WITTENBERG UNIVERSITY
200 W Ward St, Springfield, OH 45504-2120
Tel (937) 327-6231 Founded/Ownrshp 1845
Sales 97.0MM EMP 476
Accts Bkd Llp Indianapolis In
SIC 8221 University
Pr: Lurie Joyner
*Treas: Glan Collier
VP: Darrell Kitchen
Assoc Dir: Lindsey Stevens
Dir Sec: Carl Loney
Off Admin: Joann Berry
CTO: Kevin Evans

BOARD OF EDCATN OF CY ST LOUIS
See ST LOUIS PUBLIC SCHOOLS

D-U-N-S 96-184-3877
BOARD OF EDUC OF OGDEN CITY SD
1950 Monroe Blvd, Ogden, UT 84401-0619
Tel (801) 737-8000 Founded/Ownrshp 1964
Sales 116.1MM EMP 50
SIC 8211 Public elementary & secondary schools

BOARD OF EDUCATION
See UNIFIED SCHOOL DISTRICT 383

BOARD OF EDUCATION
See COMMUNITY UNIT SCHOOL DISTRICT 205

D-U-N-S 07-967-6854
BOARD OF EDUCATION FAYETTE COUNTY KY
701 E Main St Ste 107, Lexington, KY 40502-1670
Tel (859) 381-4141 Founded/Ownrshp 1890
Sales 448.9MM EMP 5,800
Accts Strothman And Company Louisvi
SIC 8211 Public elementary & secondary schools; Public junior high school; Public senior high school
*CFO: Mary Browning

D-U-N-S 10-001-3408
BOARD OF EDUCATION FOR CITY OF SAVANNAH AND COUNTY OF CHATHAM (INC)
SAVANNAH-CHATHAM BOARD OF EDUC
208 Bull St, Savannah, GA 31401-3997
Tel (912) 395-1000 Founded/Ownrshp 1866
Sales 478.9MM EMP 4,781
Accts Krt Cpas Pc Savannah Georg
SIC 8211 School board
Pr: Jolene Byrne

D-U-N-S 07-741-3011
BOARD OF EDUCATION OF ALLEGANY COUNTY MD INC
108 Washington St, Cumberland, MD 21502-2931
Tel (301) 722-6013 Founded/Ownrshp 1870
Sales 123.3MM EMP 87[E]
Accts Huber Michaels & Company Cum
SIC 8211 School board
Pr: Laurie Marchini

D-U-N-S 08-398-1449
BOARD OF EDUCATION OF CARROLL COUNTY
125 N Court St, Westminster, MD 21157-5192
Tel (410) 751-3000 Founded/Ownrshp 1870
Sales 358.0MM EMP 132[E]
Accts Cliftonlarsonallen Llp Baltim
SIC 8211 School board
Pr: James L Doolan

D-U-N-S 05-465-4588
BOARD OF EDUCATION OF CITY OF CHICAGO
CHICAGO PUBLIC SCHOOL
125 S Clark St Fl 14, Chicago, IL 60603-4013
Tel (773) 553-2760 Founded/Ownrshp 1996
Sales 5.7MMM EMP 41,498
SIC 8211 Public elementary & secondary schools
CEO: Barbara Byrd-Bennett

D-U-N-S 06-746-4487
BOARD OF EDUCATION OF CITY OF CHICAGO
CHICAGO PUBLIC SCHOOLS
42 W Madison St Fl 2, Chicago, IL 60602-4309
Tel (773) 553-1000 Founded/Ownrshp 1883
Sales 2.8MMM[E] EMP 43,000
Accts Mcgladrey Llp Chicago Illino
SIC 8211 Elementary & secondary schools;
Pr: Frank Clark
Treas: Teresa Parker
Top Exec: Eddy Ramirez
Exec: Patricia Dougherty
Exec: Amy Oconnor
Exec: Terrence Oreilly
Exec: Christine Zelenka
IT Man: Karen Montemayor
Psych: Jarren Strotter

D-U-N-S 07-634-0843
BOARD OF EDUCATION OF CITY OF DETROIT
3011 W Grand Blvd Fl 6, Detroit, MI 48202-3096
Tel (313) 873-7860 Founded/Ownrshp 1842
Sales 206.1MM[E] EMP 6,586
SIC 8211 School board
Pr: Herman Davis
Ex Dir: Douglas M Gniewek
Sales Asso: Monica Edwards
Psych: Doris Dixon
Psych: Lossie Pearson
Genl Couns: Anothony Adams

D-U-N-S 07-516-8146
BOARD OF EDUCATION OF CITY OF PASSAIC INC
PAYROLL DEPT
101 Passaic Ave, Passaic, NJ 07055-4879
Tel (973) 470-5244 Founded/Ownrshp 1930
Sales 61.8MM[E] EMP 1,300
SIC 8211 Public elementary & secondary schools
HC Dir: Edward Rowbotham

D-U-N-S 09-714-4281
BOARD OF EDUCATION OF CITY OF SANTA FE (INC)
SANTA FE MUNICPL SCHOOLS DST C
610 Alta Vista St, Santa Fe, NM 87505-4149
Tel (505) 467-2000 Founded/Ownrshp 1961
Sales 121.5MM[E] EMP 1,700
SIC 8211 Public elementary & secondary schools
*Pr: Frank Montao
VP: Karen Snow
*VP: Linda Trujillo
Netwrk Mgr: Steve Marteniz

D-U-N-S 06-989-1984
BOARD OF EDUCATION OF CITY OF TRENTON (INC) (NJ)
108 N Clinton Ave, Trenton, NJ 08609-1014
Tel (609) 656-4900 Founded/Ownrshp 1900
Sales 155.3MM[E] EMP 2,400
SIC 8211 School board
Pr: Jason Redd

D-U-N-S 01-010-0139
BOARD OF EDUCATION OF FREDERICK COUNTY MD (INC)
191 S East St, Frederick, MD 21701-5918
Tel (301) 696-6850 Founded/Ownrshp 1838
Sales 550.3MM EMP 106[E]
Accts Sb & Company Llc Hunt Valley
SIC 8211 School board
Pr: Brad Young
*Sec: Theresa Alban
*VP: Liz Barrett
Board of Directors: Deborah Aughenbaugh, Gordon M Cooley, Anne Hooper V Chb, Maureen Lapsa, Ronald Peppe, Jean Smith Pres, Earlene Thornton

D-U-N-S 07-304-2053
BOARD OF EDUCATION OF KANSAS CITY KS (INC)
2010 N 59th St, Kansas City, KS 66104-2800
Tel (913) 551-3200 Founded/Ownrshp 1887
Sales 114.0MM[E] EMP 3,500
SIC 8211 School board
Pr: Evelyn Hill
Genl Mgr: Amanda Chavez
IT Man: Bridgette Desmet
Sls&Mrk Ex: Christal Watson

D-U-N-S 10-066-3186
BOARD OF EDUCATION OF SOUTH ORANGE-MAPLEWOOD
525 Academy St, Maplewood, NJ 07040-1311
Tel (973) 378-9613 Founded/Ownrshp 1900
Sales 115.6MM EMP 900
Accts Noke And Heard Llp Summit
SIC 8211 Public elementary & secondary schools; High school, junior or senior

D-U-N-S 07-494-8670
BOARD OF EDUCATION OF ST MARYS COUNTY (MD)
23160 Moakley St Ste 101, Leonardtown, MD 20650-2933
Tel (301) 475-5511 Founded/Ownrshp 1879
Sales 227.3MM EMP 138[E]
Accts Mcgladrey Frederick Maryland
SIC 8211 School board
Ch Bd: Karin Bailey

D-U-N-S 07-041-4156
BOARD OF EDUCATION OF TOMS RIVER SCHOOLS (INC)
1144 Hooper Ave Ste 304, Toms River, NJ 08753-8361
Tel (732) 505-5500 Founded/Ownrshp 1852
Sales 37.6MM[E] EMP 2,100
SIC 8211 Public elementary & secondary schools
Pr: Joseph Torrone
*Treas: Matthew Varley

D-U-N-S 00-483-5112
BOARD OF EDUCATION OF TOWNSHIP OF UNION
2369 Morris Ave, Union, NJ 07083-5712
Tel (908) 810-0492 Founded/Ownrshp 1910
Sales 58.7MM[E] EMP 1,200
SIC 8211 Public elementary & secondary schools; School board; Secondary school
HC Dir: Linda Ionta

D-U-N-S 08-326-3558 IMP/EXP
BOARD OF EDUCATION-MEMPHIS CITY SCHOOLS
SHELBY COUNTY SCHOOLS
160 S Hollywood St, Memphis, TN 38112-4801
Tel (901) 416-5300 Founded/Ownrshp 1848
Sales 1.1MMM EMP 12,015
SIC 8211

BOARD OF GOV OF THE FED RESRVE
See FEDERAL RESERVE BANK OF ATLANTA

D-U-N-S 00-195-9410
BOARD OF GOVERNORS OF FEDERAL RESERVE SYSTEM
FEDERAL RESERVE SYSTEM, THE
20th St Cnsttution Ave Nw, Washington, DC 20551-0001
Tel (202) 452-3000 Founded/Ownrshp 1913
Sales NA EMP 21,000[E]
Accts Deloitte & Touche Llp Mclean
SIC 6011 Federal reserve banks
Ch: Ben S Bernanke
Pr: Kori Connelly
Ex VP: Jeffrey Fuhrer
VP: Jeffrey Blye
VP: Bruce Grinnell
VP: Diane Holloway
VP: Evan Koenig
VP: Vish P Viswanathan
Assoc Dir: Christine Fields
Assoc Dir: Arthur Lindo
Assoc Dir: Trevor Reeve

D-U-N-S 15-962-1697
BOARD OF GOVERNORS STATE UNIVERSITY SYSTEM OF FLORIDA
BOARD GOVERNORS GENERAL OFFICE
325 W Gaines St Ste 1625, Tallahassee, FL 32399-6533
Tel (850) 245-0466 Founded/Ownrshp 1965
Sales 4.6MMM[E] EMP 64,932
SIC 8221 Colleges universities & professional schools

BOARD OF GOVRS STATE UNIV
See FLORIDA INTERNATIONAL UNIVERSITY

BOARD OF GOVS OF FED RESERVE S
See FEDERAL RESERVE BANK OF KANSAS CITY (INC)

BOARD OF GOVS OF THE FED RESRV
See FEDERAL RESERVE BANK OF SAN FRANCISCO

BOARD OF GOVS OF THE FED RESRV
See FEDERAL RESERVE BANK OF BOSTON

BOARD OF GOVS STATE UNIV SYSTM
See FLORIDA A & M UNIVERSITY

BOARD OF HIGHER EDUCATION
See OREGON UNIVERSITY SYSTEM

BOARD OF LEGISLATORS
See ST LAWRENCE COUNTY

D-U-N-S 00-302-7567
BOARD OF LIGHTS AND WATER
MARIETTA POWER
675 N Marietta Pkwy Ne, Marietta, GA 30060-1528
Tel (770) 794-5150 Founded/Ownrshp 1906
Sales 110.0MM[E] EMP 201
Accts Moore & Cubbedge Llp Ga
SIC 4911 4941 Electric services; Water supply
Ch Bd: Mayor Ansley L Meaders
*Ch Bd: Mayor William B Dunnaway
Bd of Dir: Harlon D Crimm

D-U-N-S 18-570-7924
BOARD OF PENSIONS OF EVANGELICAL LUTHERAN CHURCH IN AMERICA
PORTICO BENEFIT SERVICES
800 Marquette Ave # 1050, Minneapolis, MN 55402-2892
Tel (612) 333-7651 Founded/Ownrshp 1987
Sales NA EMP 204
Accts Pwc Minneapolis Mn
SIC 6371 Pensions
Pr: Jeffrey Thiemann
CFO: Nancy Fuchs
CFO: Stacy A Kruse
Treas: Christina Skelton
Trst: Emried D Cole
*VP: David G Adams
*VP: Curtis G Fee
*VP: Ronald T Glusenkamp
*VP: Cliford M Goldberg
VP: Robert Procaccini
*VP: Robert H Rydland
VP: Robert Rydland
*VP: Terry J Ticey
*VP: Steven A Willems

D-U-N-S 07-710-6151
BOARD OF PENSIONS OF PRESBYTERIAN CHURCH USA
2000 Market St Fl 4, Philadelphia, PA 19103-3298
Tel (800) 773-7752 Founded/Ownrshp 1717
Sales NA EMP 207
Accts Deloitte & Touche Llp Philade
SIC 6371 Pension funds
Ch Bd: Earldine Robbins
Pr: Robert Maggs
COO: Frances Milano
CFO: Nancy Fuchs
Treas: Judith D Freyer
Treas: Bob Greco
Ex VP: Kurt Fee
Ex VP: Francis E Maloney
Ex VP: Robert Pelliciari
VP: Rev George Adams
VP: John McFayden
VP: Margaret Mellen
VP: Hy Rudin
Comm Dir: Monica Maeyer
Comm Man: Linda Svensk

D-U-N-S 07-498-7330
BOARD OF PUBLIC EDUCATION SCHOOL DISTRICT OF PITTSBURGH (INC)
341 S Bellefield Ave, Pittsburgh, PA 15213-3516
Tel (412) 622-3500 Founded/Ownrshp 1911
Sales 631.0MM EMP 5,573
Accts Maher Duessel Pittsburgh Pen
SIC 8211 School board
Pr: Thomas Sumpter
Dir Sec: George Brown

D-U-N-S 09-837-7336
BOARD OF REGENTS NEVADA SYSTEM OF HIGHER EDUCATION
UNIVERSITY NEVADA - LAS VEGAS
(Suby of NSHE) ★
4505 S Maryland Pkwy, Las Vegas, NV 89154-9900
Tel (702) 895-4727 Founded/Ownrshp 2010
Sales 85.6MM[E] EMP 5,000
SIC 8221 9411 Colleges universities & professional schools;
Prin: R David Paul
Exec: John Ayers
Pgrm Dir: James Pollard

D-U-N-S 06-866-2618 IMP
BOARD OF REGENTS OF UNIVERSITY OF NEBRASKA
3835 Holdrege St, Lincoln, NE 68503-1435
Tel (402) 472-2111 Founded/Ownrshp 1869
Sales 1.4MMM EMP 15,200
Accts Nebraska Auditor Of Public Acc
SIC 8221 University
Ch: Timothy Clare
Pr: Gabrielle Banick
*Pr: James B Milliken
COO: Xiao Qing
VP: Walter Aude
VP: Elbert Dickey
VP: Ronnie D Green
VP: Bruce W Haley
VP: Janet Means
VP: Mary Niemiec
VP: Jackie Ostrowicki
VP: John C Owens
VP: Joel Pedersen
Board of Directors: David Solheim, Randy Ferlic, Bob Whitehouse, Chuck Hasselbrook, Charles Wilson MD, Howard Hawks, Amber Lewis, Jim McClurg, Curtis McKnight, Bob Phares, Kent Schroeder, Lucas Seiler

D-U-N-S 96-690-8522
BOARD OF REGENTS OF UNIVERSITY OF OKLAHOMA-OU PHYSICIANS
1122 Ne 13th St St236, Oklahoma City, OK 73117-1039
Tel (405) 271-1515 Founded/Ownrshp 2011
Sales 40.6MM[E] EMP 1,000
SIC 8011 Offices & clinics of medical doctors
CEO: Brian Maddy

D-U-N-S 18-065-5748
BOARD OF REGENTS OF UNIVERSITY SYSTEM OF GEORGIA
GEORGIA BOARD OF REGENTS
270 Washington St Sw Fl 7, Atlanta, GA 30334-9009
Tel (404) 962-3050 Founded/Ownrshp 1932
Sales 4.7MMM EMP 40,000
SIC 8221 University
Assoc Dir: Lisa Baldwin
Ex Dir: Sherea Frazer
Ex Dir: Debra Lasher
Ex Dir: Denise Samples
Off Mgr: Martha Sosebee
IT Man: Barry Greeson
Software D: Danielle Pyle
Software D: Gareth Sheppard
Software D: Jessica Stewart
Software D: Brittany Stotler
Mktg Dir: John Vanchella

BOARD OF REGENTS, SOUTH DAKOTA
See SOUTH DAKOTA BOARD OF REGENTS

BOARD OF RGNTS OF THE UNVRSTY
See KENNESAW STATE UNIVERSITY

D-U-N-S 01-041-1197
BOARD OF SCHOOL COMMISSIONERS OF MOBILE COUNTY
JEROME KING
1 Magnum Pass, Mobile, AL 36618-3412
Tel (251) 221-3084 Founded/Ownrshp 1835
Sales 372.0MM[E] EMP 7,965
SIC 8211 School board
Pr: Don Stringfellow
*Prin: Robert Battles
*Prin: Reginald Crenshaw
*Prin: William Foster

D-U-N-S 00-553-2221
■ **BOARD OF TRADE OF CITY OF CHICAGO** (IL)
(Suby of CBOT HOLDINGS INC) ★
141 W Jackson Blvd 756, Chicago, IL 60604-2992
Tel (312) 435-3500 Founded/Ownrshp 1848
Sales 91.2MM[E] EMP 695
SIC 6231 Commodity contract exchanges
Pr: Bernard Dan
Pr: Richard Myers

CFO: Glen M Johnson
Ex VP: Farrow William
Sr VP: Bob W Ray
VP: Jim Amaral
*VP: James Brady
VP: Clifford M Lewis
Dir Bus: Jeff Campbell
IT Man: David Bauman
IT Man: Melissa Bukovsky

BOARD OF TRUSTEE NORTH KANSAS
See NORTH KANSAS CITY HOSPITAL

BOARD OF TRUSTEES
See PITT COMMUNITY COLLEGE

D-U-N-S 07-443-6742
BOARD OF TRUSTEES OF COMMUNITY COLLEGE DISTRICT 508 (INC)
CITY COLLEGES OF CHICAGO
226 W Jackson Blvd # 103, Chicago, IL 60606-6960
Tel (312) 553-2752 Founded/Ownrshp 1911
Sales 3.8MM EMP 3,500
Accts Deloitte Tax Llp Chicago Il
SIC 8221 8222 Colleges universities & professional schools; Junior college
*Ch Bd: Gery Chico
CFO: Abe Eshkenazi
Dir Rx: Stephen Brooks
Ex Dir: Genny Boesen
CIO: Louis Herman
CTO: Sterling Burke
DP Exec: Charles Mc Cleanon
Dir IT: Steve Dorrner
Dir IT: Joe Labadessa
Dir IT: Null M Marga
Dir IT: Ken Martin

D-U-N-S 96-056-1942
BOARD OF TRUSTEES OF COMMUNITY-TECHNICAL COLLEGE
61 Woodland St Ste 2, Hartford, CT 06105-2366
Tel (860) 723-0011 Founded/Ownrshp 1995
Sales NA EMP 3,700
SIC 8221

D-U-N-S 00-189-8142
BOARD OF TRUSTEES OF ILLINOIS STATE UNIVERSITY
COMPTROLLER'S OFFICE
302 Hovey Hall, Normal, IL 61790-0001
Tel (309) 438-2111 Founded/Ownrshp 1857
Sales 328.5MM EMP 3,441
Accts Bkd Llp Decatur Illinois
SIC 8221 University
Pr: Larry Dietz
Pr: Matthew Helm
*VP: Greg Alt
VP: Troy Johnson
*VP: Janet Krejci
*VP: Brent Paterson
VP: Greta Schapmire
VP: Deb Smitley
*VP: Pat Vickerman
Exec: Dale Birkenholz
Exec: Edward Mockford

D-U-N-S 02-365-9365
BOARD OF TRUSTEES OF STATE INSTITUTIONS OF HIGHER LEARNING
MISSISSIPPI INSTITUTIONS OF HL
3825 Ridgewood Rd, Jackson, MS 39211-6453
Tel (601) 432-6198 Founded/Ownrshp 1801
Sales 2.3MMM EMP 65
SIC 8611 Regulatory associations
Dir Rx: Paul Sumrall
Genl Mgr: Holly Johnson

D-U-N-S 06-967-4281
BOARD OF TRUSTEES ST PETERSBURG COLLEGE
ST PETERSBURG COLLEGE
6021 142nd Ave N, Clearwater, FL 33760-2822
Tel (727) 341-3329 Founded/Ownrshp 1927
Sales 52.1MM EMP 2,980
SIC 8221 Colleges universities & professional schools
Pr: William D Law Jr
V Ch: Deveron Gibbons
Ofcr: Denotra Showers
Assoc VP: Catherine Kennedy
VP: Carney Conferlete
*VP: Amy Lockhart
VP: Frances Neu
Prin: David Laborde
VP Admn: Douglas Duncan
Dir Sec: Daniel Barto
IT Man: Patrick Petrick

D-U-N-S 07-791-6880 IMP
BOARD OF WATER AND SEWER COMMISSIONERS OF CITY OF MOBILE
MOBILE AREA WATER & SEWER SYS
207 N Catherine St, Mobile, AL 36604-1504
Tel (251) 694-3100 Founded/Ownrshp 1951
Sales 98.4MM EMP 390
Accts Wilkins Miller Llc Mobile A
SIC 4952 4941 Sewerage systems; Water supply
Ex Dir: Charles Hyland
*Pr: Sally Berry
Ofcr: Mahir Butt
Dir IT: Paul Wan
Plnt Mgr: Ricky Pickett

D-U-N-S 07-770-1035
BOARD OF WATER SUPPLY (HI)
630 S Beretania St, Honolulu, HI 96843-0001
Tel (808) 748-5100 Founded/Ownrshp 1929
Sales 216.5MM EMP 589
Accts Accuity Llp Honolulu Hawaii
SIC 4941 Water supply
Treas: Daniel Bender
IT Man: Kenrick Wong

D-U-N-S 61-042-1484
■ **BOARDWALK PIPELINE PARTNERS LP**
(Suby of LOEWS CORP) ★
9 Greenway Plz Ste 2800, Houston, TX 77046-0926
Tel (866) 913-2122 Founded/Ownrshp 2005
Sales 1.2MMM EMP 1,260[E]
Tkr Sym BWP Exch NYS
SIC 4922 Natural gas transmission; Pipelines, natural gas; Storage, natural gas
Pr: Stanley C Horton
Genl Pt: Boardwalk GP LP
Pr: Patrick Giroir
Sr VP: Jamie L Buskill
VP: Stephen Bienvenu
VP: Thomas Frobase
VP: Thomas Jackson
VP: Daniel Mitchell
VP: Kimberly Tarr

D-U-N-S 80-854-4675
■ **BOARDWALK PIPELINES HOLDING CORP**
(Suby of LOEWS CORP) ★
610 W 2nd St, Owensboro, KY 42301-0739
Tel (270) 926-8686 Founded/Ownrshp 2003
Sales 695.0MM[E] EMP 1,260[E]
SIC 4922 4923 Pipelines, natural gas; Gas transmission & distribution
Pr: Stanley Horton
*CFO: Jamie L Buskill
VP: Steven A Barkauskas
VP: Roger Haycraft
*VP: James Jones
Board of Directors: Andrew H Tisch

D-U-N-S 13-182-7888
■ **BOARDWALK PIPELINES LP**
(Suby of BOARDWALK PIPELINE PARTNERS LP) ★
9 Greenway Plz Ste 2800, Houston, TX 77046-0926
Tel (713) 479-8000 Founded/Ownrshp 2008
Sales 607.6MM EMP 901[E]
SIC 4922 4923 Pipelines, natural gas; Gas transmission & distribution
Pt: Dean Jones
CFO: Jamie L Buski
CFO: Jamie L Buskill
Treas: Suzy Lamar
VP: Mercy Carrasco
VP: Tom Frobese
VP: David Goodwin
VP: Young Randy
Genl Mgr: Tom M Rolf Gafvert
Corp Couns: Patrick Byrd
Corp Couns: Adina Owen

BOARS HEAD
See FRANK BRUNCKHORST CO LLC

D-U-N-S 00-137-4297 IMP
BOARS HEAD PROVISIONS CO INC
1819 Main St Ste 800, Sarasota, FL 34236-5926
Tel (941) 955-0994 Founded/Ownrshp 2001, 1905
Sales 1.4MMM[E] EMP 2,100
SIC 5147 Meats & meat products
Pr: Michael Martella
*CFO: Steve Kourelakos
*Treas: Alex Baruch
Treas: Frank Brunkhorst
Ex VP: Stephen Slade
VP: Dominick Favalora
Dir Bus: Steve Silva
Comm Man: Elizabeth Ward
Rgnl Mgr: Bill George
QA Dir: Nicholas Hefferan
QA Dir: Davidfrancis Obrien

D-U-N-S 00-625-2845 IMP/EXP
BOART LONGYEAR CO
(Suby of LONGYEAR HOLDINGS INC) ★
2570 W 1700 S, Salt Lake City, UT 84104-4268
Tel (801) 972-6430 Founded/Ownrshp 1890, 2005
Sales 4.8MMM[E] EMP 9,464
SIC 1481 3532 3559 1771 Test boring for nonmetallic minerals; Drills & drilling equipment, mining (except oil & gas); Concrete products machinery; Grouting work
Pr: Fabrizio Roland Rasetti
*Ch Bd: Michael H Moore
*Pr: Craig Kipp
CEO: Nancy Allen
COO: Soren Soe
*CFO: Robert L Martin
*CFO: Joe Ragan
Bd of Dir: Tanya Fratto
*Sr VP: Brad Baker
Sr VP: Kent Hoots
*VP: Mike Birch
VP: Frank Clement
VP: Holm Oostveen
*VP: Alan Sides

D-U-N-S 08-012-9584
BOART LONGYEAR MANUFACTURING AND DISTRIBUTION INC
2640 W 1700 S, Salt Lake City, UT 84104-4269
Tel (801) 972-6430 Founded/Ownrshp 2013
Sales 57.6MM[E] EMP 5,001
SIC 1381 5084 3533 Service well drilling; Drilling equipment, excluding bits; Water well drilling equipment
VP: Alan Sides

D-U-N-S 05-794-5164
■ **BOAT AMERICA CORP** (VA)
BOAT U.S.
(Suby of BERKSHIRE HATHAWAY INC) ★
880 S Pickett St, Alexandria, VA 22304-4606
Tel (703) 823-0984 Founded/Ownrshp 1966
Sales NA EMP 425[E]
SIC 6331 Fire, marine & casualty insurance & carriers
Ch: Richard Schwartz
*Pr: Chris Edmonston
*Pr: William M Oakerson
*Pr: Margaret Podlich
*CEO: Brian T Wesselman
*CFO: Felix Pomponi
*Treas: Aguerrevere Cecilia L
Sr VP: John Condon
*VP: James Holler
VP: Sohan Jain
VP: Stan Johnson
VP: Mike Pellerin
*VP: Ann T Vignerot
Exec: Paula Scholl

BOAT U.S.
See BOAT AMERICA CORP

BOAT US MARINE CENTER
See WEST MARINE PRODUCTS INC

D-U-N-S 10-916-1067
BOB BAKER ENTERPRISES INC
BAKER MEDIA SERVICES
591 Camino De La Reina # 1100, San Diego, CA 92108-3113
Tel (619) 683-5591 Founded/Ownrshp 1984
Sales 156.2MM[E] EMP 740
SIC 5511 Automobiles, new & used
Pr: Robert H Baker
*Treas: Tom Solomon
*VP: Joseph Hertel
*VP Opers: Michael Baker
Counsel: Laurie Tibbit

D-U-N-S 05-852-5536 IMP/EXP
BOB BARKER CO INC
134 N Main St, Fuquay Varina, NC 27526-1934
Tel (800) 235-8586 Founded/Ownrshp 1972
Sales 203.7MM[E] EMP 260
SIC 5131 5122 2392 5136 3441 Linen piece goods, woven; Toiletries; Household furnishings; Uniforms, men's & boys'; Fabricated structural metal
CEO: Robert J Barker Sr
Pr: Robert Barker
CFO: Mike Hart
Ex VP: Patricia M Barker
Genl Mgr: Bettina Morgan
IT Man: Maria Gomez
IT Man: Joan Harding
VP Opers: David Sears
Ql Cn Mgr: Jim Storey
Mktg Dir: Pam Abernethy
Sls Dir: Dale Griffith

D-U-N-S 00-428-6407
▲ **BOB EVANS FARMS INC**
8111 Smiths Mill Rd, New Albany, OH 43054-1183
Tel (614) 491-2225 Founded/Ownrshp 1948
Sales 1.3MMM EMP 30,625
Tkr Sym BOBE Exch NGS
SIC 5812 2011 2099 2035 Restaurant, family: chain; Sausages from meat slaughtered on site; Salads, fresh or refrigerated; Pickles, sauces & salad dressings
Pr: Saed Mohseni
*Ch Bd: Douglas N Benham
CFO: Mark E Hood
Treas: T Alan Ashworth
Ex VP: Colin M Daly
Ex VP: Richard D Hall
Sr VP: Beth A Rauschenberger
VP: George Allen
VP: Mark Baldwin
VP: Kevin C O'Neil
VP: Scott C Taggart
VP: Ken Wood
Exec: David Eisel
Board of Directors: Charles M Elson, Mary Kay Haben, David W Head, Kathleen S Lane, Eileen A Mallesch, Larry S McWilliams, Kevin M Sheehan, Michael F Weinstein, Paul S Williams

D-U-N-S 07-952-9600
■ **BOB EVANS FARMS LLC**
(Suby of BOB EVANS FARMS INC) ★
8111 Smiths Mill Rd, New Albany, OH 43054-1183
Tel (614) 491-2225 Founded/Ownrshp 1985
Sales 732.1MM[E] EMP 32,341[E]
SIC 5812 Restaurant, family: chain
CEO: Mark Hood

D-U-N-S 09-588-7386
BOB FRINK MANAGEMENT INC (CA)
RPM MANAGEMENT
5112 Madison Ave Ste 201, Sacramento, CA 95841-3000
Tel (916) 338-7333 Founded/Ownrshp 1977
Sales 122.3MM EMP 424[E]
SIC 8741 5511 Management services; New & used car dealers
Ch Bd: Robert L Frink
*Pr: Patrick Frink
Exec: Chris Harris

D-U-N-S 04-563-4235
BOB JONES UNIVERSITY INC OF GREENVILLE S C
1700 Wade Hampton Blvd, Greenville, SC 29614-1000
Tel (864) 242-5100 Founded/Ownrshp 1927
Sales 139.3MM[E] EMP 1,660
SIC 8221 8211 8231 8062 5942 0191 University; Private elementary school; College or university library; General medical & surgical hospitals; Book stores; General farms, primarily crop
Pr: Steve Pettit
Creative D: Chris Hartzler
Genl Mgr: Casey Wren
Off Mgr: Cheryl Rude
IT Man: Dave Ivey
Advt Mgr: Will Meadows
Dir Health: Ellen M Allister
Art Dir: David Schuppert

D-U-N-S 62-099-7317
BOB MOORE AUTO GROUP LLC
101 N Robinson Ave # 820, Oklahoma City, OK 73102-5518
Tel (405) 605-2350 Founded/Ownrshp 2000
Sales 244.7MM[E] EMP 750
SIC 5511 New & used car dealers
Pr: Michael A Womble
*Pr: Mark Moore
*CFO: Curtis L Hayes
*Treas: Shannon Hutton
Sls Mgr: John Gullett
Sales Asso: Nick Larson

D-U-N-S 00-799-1557
BOB MOORE CADILLAC INC
13020 Broadway Ext, Oklahoma City, OK 73114-2243
Tel (888) 876-9554 Founded/Ownrshp 1992
Sales 108.9MM[E] EMP 285
SIC 5511 Automobiles, new & used
Pr: Ted Davis
*Genl Mgr: Jeff Powell
Sls Mgr: John Gullett
Sls Mgr: Will Perry
Sales Asso: Robert Walker

BOBBIE STVES AUTO WRLD RCHFELD
See ROBERT A WILLIAMS ENTERPRISES

BOBBY JONES SPORTSWEAR
See XMH-HFI INC

BOBCAT COMPANY
See CLARK EQUIPMENT CO

D-U-N-S 83-766-0810
BOBCAT CONTRACTING LLC
1721 Hcr 3106, Hillsboro, TX 76645-4092
Tel (254) 582-0205 Founded/Ownrshp 1993
Sales 237.2MM[E] EMP 250[E]
SIC 1389 Construction, repair & dismantling services
Pr: Roy M Young
Sfty Dirs: Joel Chesser
Genl Couns: Lee Sanders

BOBCAT WEST
See PAPE MATERIAL HANDLING INC

D-U-N-S 78-420-4042 IMP
BOBS DISCOUNT FURNITURE LLC
(Suby of BDF HOLDING CORP) ★
428 Tolland Tpke, Manchester, CT 06042-1765
Tel (860) 474-1200 Founded/Ownrshp 1991
Sales 551.0MM[E] EMP 1,800
SIC 5712 Furniture stores
Pr: Michael Skirvin
*COO: Steven Caprario
*CFO: John Sullivan
*Sr VP: William C Ballou
VP: Michael Bannon
*Prin: Robert Kaufman

BOB'S HEATING & AIR
See WASHINGTON ENERGY SERVICES CO

BOB'S STORES DISTRIBUTION CTR
See BS LIQUIDATING LLC

BOBST GROUP USA
See BOBST NORTH AMERICA INC

D-U-N-S 09-185-3564 IMP
BOBST NORTH AMERICA INC
BOBST GROUP USA
(Suby of BOBST MEX SA)
146 Harrison Ave, Roseland, NJ 07068-1239
Tel (973) 226-8000 Founded/Ownrshp 1978, 2007
Sales 90.7MM[E] EMP 264
SIC 5084 Packaging machinery & equipment
CEO: Jean-Pascal Bobst
*Pr: Robert J Pordon
*CFO: Attilio Tissi
*Ex VP: Thierry De Kalbermatten
VP: Michael D Angelo
*VP: Michael D'Angelo
*VP: Joseph Fuchs
*VP: Alain-Roger Jendly
*VP: Christopher Raney
IT Man: Giancarlo Cattaneo

D-U-N-S 14-463-6503 IMP
BOC GROUP INC
(Suby of B O C HOLDINGS)
575 Mountain Ave, New Providence, NJ 07974-2078
Tel (908) 665-2400 Founded/Ownrshp 1987
Sales 358.4MM[E] EMP 4,578
SIC 2813 3569 3559 3561 3511 3823 Industrial gases; Oxygen, compressed or liquefied; Nitrogen; Argon; Gas producers, generators & other gas related equipment; Cryogenic machinery, industrial; Pumps & pumping equipment; Turbines & turbine generator sets; Flow instruments, industrial process type
Pr: Trevor J Burt
Genl Pt: Suzanne Jurkovic
Genl Pt: Sandra Newnham
Genl Pt: John Ward
CFO: Gary McAtee
Treas: David L Brooks
Treas: Robert A Symnski
Top Exec: Louise Bakos
Assoc VP: Ian Macefield
VP: John Occhipinti
Mng Dir: Mike S Huggon
Board of Directors: Kevin L Baudhuin, Patrick Flannery, Brian Williams

D-U-N-S 17-026-6089
BOCA PHARMACAL LLC
150 Vintage Dr Ne, Huntsville, AL 35811-8216
Tel (800) 444-4011 Founded/Ownrshp 2014
Sales 110.0MM EMP 3
SIC 2834

BOCA RATON COMMUNITY HOSPITAL
See BRRH CORP

BOCA RATON HOTEL
See PANTHERS BRHC LLC

D-U-N-S 07-987-1968
BOCA RATON REGIONAL HOSPITAL INC
LYNN REGIONAL CANCER CENTER OF
800 Meadows Rd, Boca Raton, FL 33486-2304
Tel (561) 395-7100 Founded/Ownrshp 1962
Sales 386.7MM EMP 1,917
Accts Crowe Horwath Llp Fort Lauder
SIC 8062 Hospital, medical school affiliated with nursing & residency
Ofcr: Mary Matthews-Martin
VP: Miguel Brito
VP: Alex Eremia
*VP: Dawn Javersack
*VP: Mindy Raymond
VP: Dan Sacco
Dir Risk M: Kim Dillon
Dir Risk M: Judy Westhouse
Ex Dir: Denise Caccioppo
CIO: Robin Hildwein
Telecom Mg: Lee Murphy

BOCA RATON RESORT AND
See BRE/BATON OPERATING LESSEE LLC

D-U-N-S 11-206-4050
■ BOCA RESORTS INC
(*Suby of* BLACKSTONE GROUP L P) ★
501 E Camino Real, Boca Raton, FL 33432-6127
Tel (888) 543-1277 *Founded/Ownrshp* 2004
Sales 125.8MM[E] *EMP* 1,585
SIC 7011 Resort hotel
Co-Pr: Jean-Jacques Pergant
Pr: Jonathan D Gray
CFO: Wayne Moor
Treas: Robert L Friedman
Co-Pr: Joe Berger
Sr VP: Richard L Handley
VP: Maryjo Finocchiaro
VP: William J Stein

D-U-N-S 18-385-3977 IMP/EXP
BOCCARD PIPE FABRICATORS INC
BOCCARD USA
(*Suby of* BOCCARD)
2500 Galveston Rd, Houston, TX 77017-1925
Tel (713) 643-0681 *Founded/Ownrshp* 1989
Sales 84.7MM[E] *EMP* 300
SIC 3498 Pipe sections fabricated from purchased pipe; Pipe fittings, fabricated from purchased pipe
Ch Bd: Bruno Boccard
Ofcr: Sidney Frazier
VP: Ed Allahverdian
**VP:* Larry Fulcher
**VP:* Pascal Riu
Exec: Tim Macdavid

BOCCARD USA
See BOCCARD PIPE FABRICATORS INC

BOCCHI LABORATORIES
See SHADOW HOLDINGS LLC

BOCES
See BOARD OF COOPERATIVE EDUCATIONAL SERVICES FIRST SUPERVISORY DISTRICT OF MONROE COUNTY

D-U-N-S 05-640-3454
BODDIE-NOELL ENTERPRISES INC (NC)
HARDEE'S
1021 Noell Ln, Rocky Mount, NC 27804-1761
Tel (252) 937-2000 *Founded/Ownrshp* 1962
Sales 381.3MM *EMP* 12,000
SIC 5812 6552 Mexican restaurant; Land subdividers & developers, commercial; Land subdividers & developers, residential
CEO: Bill Boddie
Ch Bd: Ben Mayo Boddie
V Ch: Nick B Oddie
Pr: Michael W Boddie
CEO: William L Boddie
CFO: Craig Worthy
CFO: W Craig Worthy
Ex VP: Douglas E Anderson
Ex VP: Michael H Hancock
Sr VP: Robert W Crumley
VP: Nanette Herbert
VP: Bob Larimer
VP: David Schmitt
VP: Kathy Trusch
Comm Man: Jenna Green

D-U-N-S 00-762-2194
BODEGA LATINA CORP
EL SUPER
(*Suby of* GRUPO COMERCIAL CHEDRAUI, S.A.B. DE C.V.)
14601b Lakewood Blvd, Paramount, CA 90723-3602
Tel (562) 616-8800 *Founded/Ownrshp* 1995
Sales 1.1MMM[E] *EMP* 5,000
SIC 5411 Grocery stores
CEO: Carlos A Smith
CIO: Jesus Mathus
IT Man: Frank Aguirre
Genl Couns: Joe Angulo

D-U-N-S 06-900-6179 EXP
BODEK AND RHODES INC
(*Suby of* BRODER BROS CO) ★
2951 Grant Ave, Philadelphia, PA 19114-1087
Tel (215) 673-6767 *Founded/Ownrshp* 2015
Sales 833.3MM[E] *EMP* 400
SIC 5136 5137 Men's & boys' clothing; Women's & children's clothing
Pr: Michael Rhodes
**Sec:* Hal D Rhodes

D-U-N-S 06-146-3675
BODELL CONSTRUCTION CO INC (UT)
586 W Fine Dr, Salt Lake City, UT 84115-4244
Tel (801) 261-4343 *Founded/Ownrshp* 1972
Sales 89.3MM[E] *EMP* 200
SIC 1542 1541

D-U-N-S 00-627-5127 IMP
BODINE ALUMINUM INC
TOYOTA MOTOR ENGINEERING MANUF
(*Suby of* T E M A) ★
2100 Walton Rd, Saint Louis, MO 63114-5893
Tel (314) 423-8200 *Founded/Ownrshp* 1912
Sales 161.7MM[E] *EMP* 800
SIC 3363 Aluminum die-castings
Pr: Robert W Lloyd

D-U-N-S 00-506-9224 IMP
BODINE ELECTRIC CO (IL)
201 Northfield Rd, Northfield, IL 60093-3311
Tel (773) 478-3515 *Founded/Ownrshp* 1905, 1914
Sales 147.3MM[E] *EMP* 450
SIC 5063 3625 3621 Motors, electric; Motor controls, electric; Motors, electric
Pr: John R Bodine
CFO: Jeff Stahl
**CFO:* Jeffrey Stahl
**Ex VP:* Jeffrey Bodine
VP: Rich Meserve
Genl Mgr: Archelle Manliguez
Opers Mgr: Miguel Rivera
Manager: Joseph Chiarella
Snr Mgr: Jon Welu
Board of Directors: Kathleen Bodine, Michael Bodine, Cheryl Kuczek, Ted Kuczek, James Sima

BODINE ELECTRIC OF DECATUR
See RATHJE ENTERPRISES INC

D-U-N-S 01-230-2330
BODY CENTRAL CORP
6225 Powers Ave, Jacksonville, FL 32217-2215
Tel (904) 737-0811 *Founded/Ownrshp* 1972
Sales 283.5MM *EMP* 3,901
SIC 5621 5961

D-U-N-S 15-196-2479 IMP
BODY CENTRAL STORES INC
BODY SHOP
1883 W State Road 84 # 106, Fort Lauderdale, FL 33315-2232
Tel (904) 737-0811 *Founded/Ownrshp* 2006
Sales 432.5MM[E] *EMP* 2,500
SIC 5999 Perfumes & colognes
CEO: Brian P Woolf
CFO: Thomas Stoltz
Bd of Dir: John K Haley
Bd of Dir: Jerrold Rosenbaum
Bd of Dir: John H Turner
**Sr VP:* Charles Carstens
**Sr VP:* Michael Millonzi
CTO: Ray Eubanks
Dir IT: Doug Chester
Dir IT: Doug Chichester

BODY SHOP
See BODY CENTRAL STORES INC

BODY SHOP
See BUTH-NA-BODHAIGE INC

D-U-N-S 18-695-8740 IMP
BODY SHOP INC
(*Suby of* THE BODY SHOP INTERNATIONAL PLC)
5036 One World Way, Wake Forest, NC 27587-7732
Tel (919) 554-4900 *Founded/Ownrshp* 1987
Sales 441.4MM[E] *EMP* 2,625
SIC 5999 6794 2844 Toiletries, cosmetics & perfumes; Hair care products; Perfumes & colognes; Cosmetics; Franchises, selling or licensing; Toilet preparations
Ch Bd: Peter Saunders
**Pr:* Peter Ridler
CFO: Kim Mattoon
VP: Elizabeth Arsham
**VP:* Anthea Borum
VP: Heather Hartford
VP: Tara Odonnell
VP: Thomas G Roddick
Dir Risk M: Chris Sysum
Dist Mgr: Niki Ababio
Genl Mgr: Janet Bawobrs

BODYCOTE INTERNATIONAL, INC.
See BODYCOTE USA INC

D-U-N-S 00-598-2046 IMP
BODYCOTE THERMAL PROCESSING INC
BIRD ELECTRON BEAM
(*Suby of* BODYCOTE INTERNATIONAL INC) ★
12700 Park Central Dr # 700, Dallas, TX 75251-1518
Tel (214) 904-2420 *Founded/Ownrshp* 2007
Sales 420.2MM[E] *EMP* 1,596
SIC 3398 Metal heat treating; Brazing (hardening) of metal; Tempering of metal
CEO: David F Landless
**Div Pres:* Thomas J Gibbons
**VP:* Stephanie L Edgar
**VP:* David Hamilton
**VP:* David E Starkie
Board of Directors: Tracy Glende, V Pres/Dir David Hamilton, V Pres, N American Oprs, V Pres, V Pres, V Pres of Finance

D-U-N-S 03-652-8487 IMP/EXP
BODYCOTE USA INC
BODYCOTE INTERNATIONAL, INC.
(*Suby of* BODYCOTE PLC)
12700 Park Central Dr # 700, Dallas, TX 75251-1500
Tel (214) 904-2420 *Founded/Ownrshp* 1992
Sales 439.9MM[E] *EMP* 4,100
SIC 8721 Accounting, auditing & bookkeeping
Pr: Tracy Glende
**Pr:* Dan McCurdy
**CFO:* David E Starkie
**Treas:* Stephanie Edgar
**VP:* David Landless
Genl Mgr: Joe Dyer
Genl Mgr: Christian Garcia
Ql Cn Mgr: Kelly Kegg

D-U-N-S 07-270-1865 IMP/EXP
BOEHRINGER INGELHEIM CORP
(*Suby of* BOEHRINGER INGELHEIM USA CORP) ★
900 Ridgebury Rd, Ridgefield, CT 06877-1058
Tel (203) 798-9988 *Founded/Ownrshp* 2009
Sales 1.1MMM[E] *EMP* 3,000
SIC 2834 6221 Medicines, capsuled or ampuled; Veterinary pharmaceutical preparations; Commodity traders, contracts
Prin: Paul Fonteyne
Pr: Hans-Peter Grau
COO: Thomas Murphy
**CFO:* Stefan Rinn
Top Exec: John Adamou
Sr VP: Frank Ternes
VP: Kerry Blanchard
VP: Adrian J Carter
VP: Kathleen Dowd
VP: Jennifer Laux
VP: Michael Mark
VP: Christine Marsh
VP: Michael Morris
VP: Tunde Otulana
VP: Marla S Persky
VP: Peter Piliero
VP: Chris H Senanayake
VP: Werner Worf
Assoc Dir: Bethe Bogues
Assoc Dir: Damon Daulerio
Assoc Dir: Chris Grygon

D-U-N-S 60-317-5944 IMP
BOEHRINGER INGELHEIM PHARMACEUTICALS INC
(*Suby of* BOEHRINGER INGELHEIM CORP) ★
900 Ridgebury Rd, Ridgefield, CT 06877-1058
Tel (203) 798-9988 *Founded/Ownrshp* 1971
Sales 260.5MM[E] *EMP* 1,796
SIC 2834 Drugs acting on the cardiovascular system, except diagnostic; Drugs acting on the respiratory system
CEO: Paul Fonteyne
**Pr:* Andreas Barner
VP: Ralf Gorniak
**VP:* Stefan Rinn Sr
VP: Thor Voigt
Assoc Dir: Craig Conoscenti
Assoc Dir: Michael Duggan
Assoc Dir: Wendy Tennant-Beebe
Assoc Dir: Zheng Yang
Comm Dir: Jon Hearson
Ex Dir: Veronika Kohlbrenner

D-U-N-S 83-101-9760 IMP
BOEHRINGER INGELHEIM USA CORP
(*Suby of* BOEHRINGER INGELHEIM AUSLANDS-BETEILIGUNGS GMBH)
900 Ridgebury Rd, Ridgefield, CT 06877-1058
Tel (203) 798-9988 *Founded/Ownrshp* 2006
Sales 1.1MMM[E] *EMP* 3,000[E]
SIC 2834 Medicines, capsuled or ampuled; Veterinary pharmaceutical preparations
Ch Bd: Andreas Barner
**CEO:* Paul Fonteyne
**CFO:* Stefan Rinn
**Sr VP:* Marla S Persky
Assoc Dir: Daniel Coleman
Assoc Dir: Nicole Maddox
Snr Ntwrk: Michael Schimenti
Board of Directors: Walter Poerschmann

D-U-N-S 00-713-4091 IMP
BOEHRINGER INGELHEIM VETMEDICA INC
(*Suby of* BOEHRINGER INGELHEIM CORP) ★
2621 N Belt Hwy, Saint Joseph, MO 64506-2002
Tel (800) 325-9167 *Founded/Ownrshp* 1917
Sales 450.2MM[E] *EMP* 1,913
SIC 2836 2834 5191 Serums; Vaccines; Pharmaceutical preparations; Insecticides
Pr: Albrecht Kissel
VP: Dr Phillip Hayes
Assoc Dir: Toby Yager
Ex Dir: R Michael Herrman
Ex Dir: Jim Kroman
Ex Dir: Steve Muenks
QA Dir: James Flaska
Sftwr Eng: Mark McClain
VP Opers: Bernd Eichenmueller
S&M/VP: Timothy Bettington
Mktg Mgr: Wayne Cole

D-U-N-S 08-518-8316
■ BOEING AEROSPACE OPERATIONS INC
(*Suby of* BOEING CO) ★
6001 S Air Depot Blvd, Oklahoma City, OK 73135-5922
Tel (405) 622-6000 *Founded/Ownrshp* 1972
Sales 231.2MM[E] *EMP* 2,800
SIC 8711 8249 Engineering services; Aviation school
Pr: Mark Sullivan
**Treas:* Richard B Stone
Dir IT: Katherine Barker

D-U-N-S 00-925-6819 IMP/EXP
▲ BOEING CO
100 N Riverside Plz, Chicago, IL 60606-2016
Tel (312) 544-2000 *Founded/Ownrshp* 1916
Sales 96.1MMM *EMP* 161,400[E]
Tkr Sym BA *Exch* NYS
SIC 3721 3663 3761 3764 3812 3728 Airplanes, fixed or rotary wing; Helicopters; Research & development on aircraft by the manufacturer; Airborne radio communications equipment; Guided missiles, complete; Guided missiles & space vehicles, research & development; Propulsion units for guided missiles & space vehicles; Guided missile & space vehicle engines, research & devel.; Search & navigation equipment; Defense systems & equipment; Aircraft control systems, electronic; Navigational systems & instruments; Aircraft body & wing assemblies & parts
Ch Bd: Dennis A Muilenburg
Pr: Bertrand-Marc Allen
Pr: Christopher M Chadwick
Pr: Raymond L Conner
CFO: Eric Evanson
Treas: Renee Jarvi
Bd of Dir: Bill Crawford
Bd of Dir: Ed Dreyer
Bd of Dir: George Durham
Bd of Dir: Kurt Hintze
Bd of Dir: Nancy Kaatman
Bd of Dir: Jon Tuvey
Ex VP: Michael Caimona
Ex VP: Pete Desalvo
Ex VP: Gary Fitzmire
Ex VP: Rich Hoffman
Ex VP: J Michael Luttig
Ex VP: Gregory D Smith
Sr VP: Heidi B Capozzi
Sr VP: Ted Colbert
Sr VP: Thomas J Downey
Board of Directors: Randall L Stephenson, Robert A Bradway, Ronald A Williams, David L Calhoun, Mike S Zafirovski, Arthur D Collins Jr, Kenneth M Duberstein, Edmund P Giambastiani Jr, Lynn J Good, Lawrence W Kellner, Edward M Liddy, Susan C Schwab

D-U-N-S 05-730-6110
BOEING EMPLOYEES CREDIT UNION
BECU
12770 Gateway Dr S, Tukwila, WA 98168-3309
Tel (206) 439-5700 *Founded/Ownrshp* 1935
Sales NA *EMP* 900
SIC 6062 6061 State credit unions, not federally chartered; Federal credit unions
Pr: Benson Porter
CFO: Brad Canfield
CFO: Stacy Hyle
Treas: Michael Sweeney
Bd of Dir: David A Yonce
VP: Gregg Kats
VP: Pam O'Conner
VP: Mike Quamma
VP: Patricia Smith
VP: Melanie Walsh
VP: Howie Wu
Exec: Susan Kydd
Dir Bus: Helene Cox

D-U-N-S 88-451-0124
■ BOEING IRVING CO
(*Suby of* BOEING CO) ★
100 N Riverside Plz Fl 35, Chicago, IL 60606-2016
Tel (312) 544-2000 *Founded/Ownrshp* 1934
Sales 127.0MM[E] *EMP* 1,001
SIC 3663 Airborne radio communications equipment
Pr: James A Bell

D-U-N-S 92-898-9730 IMP/EXP
■ BOEING SATELLITE SYSTEMS INC
(*Suby of* BOEING CO) ★
900 N Sepulveda Blvd, El Segundo, CA 90245-2710
Tel (310) 791-7450 *Founded/Ownrshp* 2000
Sales 781.9MM[E] *EMP* 7,500
SIC 3663 Satellites, communications; Space satellite communications equipment
Pr: Craig R Cooning
**VP:* Dave Ryan
**VP:* Charles Toups
Dir Bus: Mohammad Sadjadpour
Prd Mgr: Robert Johnson
Counsel: Natalie Walters
Snr Mgr: John Eng

D-U-N-S 07-487-5162
■ BOEING SERVICE CO
(*Suby of* BOEING CO) ★
6200 J S Mcdonnell Blvd, Saint Louis, MO 63134-1939
Tel (972) 705-8000 *Founded/Ownrshp* 1996
Sales 117.1MM[E] *EMP* 1,600
SIC 8741 8711 Industrial management; Engineering services
Pr: Greg J Deiter
**VP:* Scott Livesay
Genl Mgr: Marilyn Kister

D-U-N-S 00-643-6299 IMP/EXP
BOELTER COMPANIES INC
N22 W23685 Rdgview Pkwy W, Waukesha, WI 53188-1013
Tel (262) 523-6200 *Founded/Ownrshp* 1929
Sales 245.9MM[E] *EMP* 300
SIC 5113 5046 7389 5087

D-U-N-S 19-410-0921
BOETHING TREELAND FARMS INC
23475 Long Valley Rd, Woodland Hills, CA 91367-6006
Tel (818) 883-1222 *Founded/Ownrshp* 1953
Sales 84.2MM[E] *EMP* 700
SIC 0811 5261 Tree farm; Nurseries
CEO: Bruce Edgar Pherson
**CFO:* Marji Boething
Dir IT: Nelson Chia
Sls Dir: Susie Henderson

BOFI FEDERAL BANK
See B OF I FEDERAL BANK

D-U-N-S 17-530-7359
▲ BOFI HOLDING INC
4350 La Jolla Village Dr, San Diego, CA 92122-1243
Tel (858) 350-6200 *Founded/Ownrshp* 1999
Sales NA *EMP* 467[E]
Accts Bdo Usa Llp San Diego Califo
Tkr Sym BOFI *Exch* NGS
SIC 6035 Federal savings banks
Pr: Gregory Garrabrants
Ch Bd: Theodore C Allrich
CFO: Andrew J Micheletti
V Ch Bd: Nicholas A Mosich
Ex VP: Adriaan V Zyl

D-U-N-S 16-510-2380 IMP
BOGE RUBBER & PLASTICS USA LLC
(*Suby of* CSR NEW MATERIAL TECHNOLOGIES GMBH)
1102 Aviation Blvd, Hebron, KY 41048-9332
Tel (859) 689-5900 *Founded/Ownrshp* 2014
Sales 130.0MM *EMP* 215
SIC 5013 Automotive supplies & parts
COO: Mickey Maier
Plnt Mgr: Sam Sato

D-U-N-S 14-344-2577 IMP
BOGOPA ENTERPRISES INC
FOOD BAZAAR
650 Fountain Ave, Brooklyn, NY 11208-5306
Tel (718) 346-6500 *Founded/Ownrshp* 1999
Sales 390.3MM[E] *EMP* 1,200
SIC 5141 Groceries, general line
CEO: Whee Ill An

D-U-N-S 01-476-3077 IMP
BOGOPA SERVICE CORP
FOOD BAZAAR
(*Suby of* FOOD BAZAAR) ★
650 Fountain Ave, Brooklyn, NY 11208-5306
Tel (718) 257-7801 *Founded/Ownrshp* 1988
Sales 181.4MM[E] *EMP* 1,100
SIC 5411 4225 5149 Supermarkets; General warehousing & storage; Groceries & related products
Sr VP: Jae Kim
Off Mgr: Daniel Kim
IT Man: David Chung

D-U-N-S 00-694-7386 IMP
BOH BROS CONSTRUCTION CO LLC
730 S Tonti St, New Orleans, LA 70119-7551
Tel (504) 821-2400 *Founded/Ownrshp* 1909
Sales 612.1MM[E] *EMP* 1,450
SIC 1611 1622 1629 1623

D-U-N-S 06-779-2705
BOHICA LIQUIDATION INC
HOT DOG ON A STICK
5942 Priestly Dr, Carlsbad, CA 92008-8839
Tel (760) 930-0456 *Founded/Ownrshp* 1946, 1991
Sales 51.4MM[E] *EMP* 1,500
SIC 5812

D-U-N-S 00-170-8981 IMP
BOHLER-UDDEHOLM CORP
(*Suby of* UDDEHOLMS AB)
2505 Millennium Dr, Elgin, IL 60124-7815
Tel (877) 992-8764 *Founded/Ownrshp* 2009
Sales 120.6MM[E] *EMP* 280
SIC 5051 Steel
Ch Bd: Al Pilli
**Pr:* Erik Svendsen
**CEO:* Reinhard Nobauer
**VP:* Don Ochitwa
Ql Cn Mgr: Roni Sarkar
S&M/VP: Kevin Rochford
Mktg Mgr: Ulf Wisen

BOILER TUBES OF TEXAS
See CLEAVER-BROOKS SALES AND SERVICE INC

D-U-N-S 07-304-8704
BOILERMAKER BLACKSMITH NATIONAL PENSION TRUST
BOILERMAKERS NATIONAL FUNDS
754 Minnesota Ave Ste 522, Kansas City, KS 66101-2725
Tel (913) 342-6555 *Founded/Ownrshp* 1960
Sales NA *EMP* 125
SIC 6371 Union trust funds; Union welfare, benefit & health funds

BOILERMAKERS NATIONAL FUNDS
See BOILERMAKER BLACKSMITH NATIONAL PENSION TRUST

D-U-N-S 07-972-0573
BOILERMAKERS NATIONAL HEALTH AND WELFARE FUND
754 Minnesota Ave Ste 424, Kansas City, KS 66101-2724
Tel (866) 342-6555 *Founded/Ownrshp* 2014
Sales 292.5MM *EMP* 2[E]
Accts Cliftonlarsonallen Llp Minnea
SIC 6722 Money market mutual funds
Prin: Gary Brammer

D-U-N-S 03-939-4775
▲ BOINGO WIRELESS INC
10960 Wilshire Blvd Fl 23, Los Angeles, CA 90024-3809
Tel (310) 586-5180 *Founded/Ownrshp* 2001
Sales 139.6MM *EMP* 286
Tkr Sym WIFI *Exch* NGS
SIC 4813 ;
Ch Bd: David Hagan
CFO: Peter Hovenier
Chf Mktg O: Dawn Callahan
Sr VP: Derek Peterson
Sr VP: Tom Tracey
VP: Scot Hester
VP: Bill Leinert
Dir Bus: Tom Williams
Sftwr Eng: Yu Feng
Opers Mgr: Vivian Thai
Sls Mgr: Patrick Magnarelli
Board of Directors: Mary Austin, Charles Boesenberg, David Cutrer, Chuck Davis, Michael Finley, Terrell Jones, Kathleen Misunas, Lance Rosenzweig

D-U-N-S 17-000-9265 IMP
▲ BOISE CASCADE CO
1111 W Jefferson St # 300, Boise, ID 83702-5383
Tel (208) 384-6161 *Founded/Ownrshp* 2004
Sales 3.6MMM *EMP* 5,910
Accts Kpmg Llp Boise Idaho
Tkr Sym BCC *Exch* NYS
SIC 2421 Building & structural materials, wood
CEO: Thomas K Corrick
**Ch Bd:* Thomas E Carlile
CFO: Wayne M Rancourt
Ex VP: Daniel G Hutchinson
Ex VP: Nick Stokes
Sr VP: John T Sahlberg
VP: Frank Elfering
VP: Kelly E Hibbs
VP Sls: Dennis R Huston
VP Sls: Rich Viola
Board of Directors: Steven C Cooper, Richard H Fleming, Karen E Gowland, David H Hannah, Mack L Hogans, Duane C McDougall, Christopher J McGowan

D-U-N-S 17-074-8235 IMP/EXP
BOISE CASCADE HOLDINGS LLC
(*Suby of* FOREST PRODUCTS HOLDINGS LLC) ★
1111 W Jefferson St # 300, Boise, ID 83702-5383
Tel (208) 384-6161 *Founded/Ownrshp* 2004
Sales 714.9MM[E] *EMP* 4,470
SIC 5031 8744

D-U-N-S 14-806-9854 IMP/EXP
■ BOISE CASCADE WOOD PRODUCTS LLC
(*Suby of* BOISE CASCADE CO) ★
1111 W Jefferson St # 300, Boise, ID 83728-0071
Tel (208) 384-6161 *Founded/Ownrshp* 2004
Sales 544.0MM[E] *EMP* 690[E]
SIC 5099 Wood & wood by-products
CEO: Thomas Carlile
Pr: Stanley Bell
CFO: Wayne Rancourt
Ch: Duane McDougall
Sr VP: John Sahlberg
VP: Kelly Hibbs

D-U-N-S 80-668-9548 IMP/EXP
■ BOISE INC
(*Suby of* PACKAGING CORP OF AMERICA) ★
1111 W Jefferson St # 50, Boise, ID 83702-5386
Tel (208) 384-7000 *Founded/Ownrshp* 2013
Sales 1.8MMM[E] *EMP* 5,300[E]
SIC 2671 2621 2631 Packaging paper & plastics film, coated & laminated; Paper coated or laminated for packaging; Paper mills; Printing paper; Paperboard mills
Pr: Mark W Kowlzan
COO: Robert A Warren
Treas: Wayne Rancourt
**Ex VP:* Judith M Lassa
**Sr VP:* Karen E Gowland
**Sr VP:* Robert E Strenge
**Sr VP:* Richard B West
VP: Virginia Aulin
VP: Samuel Cotterell
VP: Rick Grant
**VP:* Bernadette M Madarieta
VP: Robert Tracy

D-U-N-S 82-665-3276 EXP
■ BOISE PAPER HOLDINGS LLC
(*Suby of* BOISE INC) ★
1111 W Jefferson St # 200, Boise, ID 83702-5383
Tel (208) 384-7501 *Founded/Ownrshp* 2008
Sales 118.3MM[E] *EMP* 689[E]
Accts Kpmg Llp Boise Idaho
SIC 2621 Packaging paper
**Ex VP:* Judy Lassa
**Sr VP:* Sam Cotterell

BOISE SCHOOL DISTRICT
See INDEPENDENT SCHOOL DISTRICT OF BOISE CITY

D-U-N-S 07-299-5848 IMP
BOISE STATE UNIVERSITY (ID)
1910 University Dr, Boise, ID 83725-0002
Tel (208) 426-1011 *Founded/Ownrshp* 1932
Sales 207.7MM *EMP* 1,879
Accts Moss-Adams Llp Eugene Oregon
SIC 8221 University
CEO: Bob Kustra
Pr: Matthew Ewing
Pr: Kenneth Kline
**Pr:* Robert Kusta
Ofcr: Bernard Garrigues
VP: John Garner
VP: Lisa Harris
**VP:* Michael Laliberte
VP: John McGuire
Assoc Dir: Debra Alvord
Assoc Dir: Jim Carnahan
Assoc Dir: Teresa Church
Assoc Dir: Kris Kamann

D-U-N-S 14-806-9359 EXP
■ BOISE WHITE PAPER LLC
(*Suby of* BOISE INC) ★
1111 W Jefferson St # 200, Boise, ID 83702-5383
Tel (208) 384-7000 *Founded/Ownrshp* 2008
Sales 243.4MM[E] *EMP* 500[E]
SIC 2621 Paper mills
CEO: W Thomas Stephens
**CFO:* Tom Carlisle
**Treas:* Wayne Rancourt
Sr VP: Stanley Bell
VP: Robert Egan
VP: Nick Stokes
VP: Bob Tracy
Off Mgr: Adeld Peppe

D-U-N-S 82-954-0298
■ BOISE WHITE PAPER LLC
(*Suby of* BOISE INC) ★
31831 W Hwy 12, Wallula, WA 99363
Tel (509) 545-3318 *Founded/Ownrshp* 2004
Sales 144.9MM[E] *EMP* 420
SIC 2621 Paper mills

BOJANGLE'S
See BOJANGLES HOLDINGS INC

BOJANGLE'S
See BOJANGLES INC

BOJANGLE'S
See BOJANGLES RESTAURANTS INC

BOJANGLE'S
See BJ HOLDINGS CORP

D-U-N-S 05-954-6684
BOJANGLES HOLDINGS INC
BOJANGLE'S
(*Suby of* FALFURRIAS CAPITAL PARTNERS LP) ★
9432 Southern Pine Blvd, Charlotte, NC 28273-5553
Tel (704) 527-2675 *Founded/Ownrshp* 2007
Sales 116.8MM[E] *EMP* 4,500
SIC 5812 Fast-food restaurant, chain
Pr: Tom Lewison
**CFO:* Dane Reynolds
Sr VP: Mike Bearss
VP: Tony Hopson
Exec: Keith Haywood
Prin: Bob O'Shea
CIO: John Peterson
VP Opers: Kenny Avery
Corp Couns: Laura Roberts
Counsel: Joseph Marek

D-U-N-S 07-982-6204
▲ BOJANGLES INC
BOJANGLE'S
9432 Southern Pine Blvd, Charlotte, NC 28273-5553
Tel (704) 527-2675 *Founded/Ownrshp* 1977
Sales 488.2MM *EMP* 9,520[E]
Tkr Sym BOJA *Exch* NGS
SIC 5812 Fast-food restaurant, chain
Pr: Clifton Rutledge
**Ch Bd:* James R Kibler
COO: Kenneth E Avery
CFO: M John Jordan
VP: Laura Roberts

D-U-N-S 08-686-6647
■ BOJANGLES RESTAURANTS INC
BOJANGLE'S
(*Suby of* BOJANGLES) ★
9432 Southern Pine Blvd, Charlotte, NC 28273-5553
Tel (704) 527-2675 *Founded/Ownrshp* 2011
Sales 219.5MM[E] *EMP* 4,500
SIC 5812 6794 Fast-food restaurant, chain; Franchises, selling or licensing
CEO: Randy Kibler
**CEO:* Christine W Ipledge
**CFO:* John Jordan
**CFO:* Eric Newman
VP: Bill Easterling
CIO: Bill Lukie
**VP Opers:* Jeff McKimmie

BOK FINANCIAL
See BOKF NATIONAL ASSOCIATION

D-U-N-S 78-054-2882
▲ BOK FINANCIAL CORP
320 S Boston Ave, Tulsa, OK 74103-3706
Tel (918) 588-6000 *Founded/Ownrshp* 1910
Sales NA *EMP* 4,789[E]
Tkr Sym BOKF *Exch* NGS
SIC 6021 National commercial banks
Pr: Steven G Bradshaw
**Ch Bd:* George B Kaiser
Pr: Andrea Myers
CFO: Jim Huntzinger
CFO: Steven E Nell
Treas: Brad Emmons
Chf Cred: Marc C Maun
Ofcr: Stephen D Grossi
Assoc VP: Gordon Rudd
Sr Ex VP: Steven Bradshaw
Ex VP: Aaron Azari
Ex VP: Coy Gallatin
Ex VP: Scott Grauer
Ex VP: Stacy Kymes
Ex VP: Patrick Piper
Ex VP: Joann Schaub
Ex VP: Jennifer S Thomas
Sr VP: John Anderson
Sr VP: James A Dietz
Sr VP: James Haus
Sr VP: Levy Larry
Board of Directors: E Carey Joullian IV, Alan S Armstrong, Robert J Lafortune, C Fred Ball Jr, Stanley A Lybarger, Sharon J Bell, Steven J Malcolm, Peter C Boylan III, E C Richards, Chester E Cadieux III, Michael C Turpen, John W Gibson, R A Walker, David F Griffin, Joseph W Craft III, V Burns Hargis, Douglas D Hawthorne

D-U-N-S 04-907-2564 IMP
■ BOKF NATIONAL ASSOCIATION
BOK FINANCIAL
(*Suby of* BOK FINANCIAL CORP) ★
1 One Williams Ctr Bsmt 1, Tulsa, OK 74172-0172
Tel (918) 588-6000 *Founded/Ownrshp* 1991
Sales NA *EMP* 2,421
SIC 6021 National commercial banks
Pr: Stanley A Lybarger
**Ch Bd:* George B Kaiser
COO: John D Higginbotham
**Ex VP:* Gene A Harris
Sr VP: Randy Blattner
Sr VP: James Dietz
Sr VP: Brian Dugan
Sr VP: Janelle McGinnis
Sr VP: John Merritt
Sr VP: Sharon Moore
Sr VP: James Quillian
Sr VP: Don Wiechmann
VP: Ron Acree
VP: Donna Allred
VP: Lauren Baker
VP: Bruce Bottomley
VP: Shelly Connolly
VP: Buddy Friesner
VP: Greg Kittle
VP: Steven Nell
VP: Carrie Porter
Board of Directors: Francis Rooney III, W Wayne Allen, Glenn A Cox, Dr Robert H Donaldson, James O Goodwin, D Joseph Graham, V Burns Hargis, Eugene Harris, Carey Joullian IV, Frank McPherson

BOLAND SERVICES
See BOLAND TRANE SERVICES INC

D-U-N-S 02-265-8231
BOLAND TRANE SERVICES INC
BOLAND SERVICES
30 W Watkins Mill Rd # 300, Gaithersburg, MD 20878-4006
Tel (240) 306-3000 *Founded/Ownrshp* 1961
Sales 221.8MM[E] *EMP* 307
SIC 5075 Ventilating equipment & supplies; Air conditioning & ventilation equipment & supplies
Pr: James M Boland
**CFO:* Lawrence J Cain Jr
Treas: Michale Rohrer
**VP:* Louis J Boland Jr
VP: Peter W Cunningham
VP: James A Fusco
**VP:* Sarah Heitkemper
**VP:* Jerry Scanlan
Exec: Aileen Kippel

BOLCOF PLASTIC MATERIALS
See PORT PLASTICS INC

D-U-N-S 00-280-9721 IMP
BOLDT CO
(*Suby of* BOLDT GROUP INC) ★
2525 N Roemer Rd, Appleton, WI 54911-8623
Tel (920) 739-6321 *Founded/Ownrshp* 1889
Sales 975.4MM *EMP* 1,500
SIC 1542

D-U-N-S 11-752-7424
BOLDT GROUP INC
2525 N Roemer Rd, Appleton, WI 54911-8623
Tel (920) 739-7800 *Founded/Ownrshp* 1984
Sales 978.7MM *EMP* 1,500
SIC 1542 Nonresidential construction
Pr: Oscar C Boldt
**VP:* Thomas J Boldt
VP: Todd Brink
Dir Risk M: Mark Bray
Sls Mgr: Daren Mazier

D-U-N-S 09-316-6080 IMP/EXP
BOLER CO
500 Park Blvd Ste 1010, Itasca, IL 60143-1285
Tel (630) 773-9111 *Founded/Ownrshp* 1980
Sales 997.3MM[E] *EMP* 3,000
SIC 3714 3493 Motor vehicle parts & accessories; Axles, motor vehicle; Bumpers & bumperettes, motor vehicle; Leaf springs: automobile, locomotive, etc.
Pr: Matthew J Boler
**Ex VP:* Nancy B Coons
VP: Perry Bahr
**VP:* Michael J Boler
VP: Dave Templeton
Dir IT: Ralph Spevere

D-U-N-S 11-276-9117
BOLLINGER CALCASIEU LLC
8086 Global Dr, Sulphur, LA 70665-8807
Tel (337) 583-7383 *Founded/Ownrshp* 1963
Sales NA *EMP* 1,800
SIC 3731

D-U-N-S 06-751-9942
■ BOLLINGER INC
BOLLINGER INSURANCE AGENCY
(*Suby of* JPGAC, LLC)
200 Jefferson Park, Whippany, NJ 07981-1054
Tel (800) 526-1379 *Founded/Ownrshp* 2013
Sales NA *EMP* 444
SIC 6411 Insurance agents
Pr: John A Windolf
Mng Pt: Robin Baldassarre
Pr: Angela Canfora
Pr: Cathy Fonseca
Pr: Rob Leonard
Pr: Debbie Osberg
COO: G Alex Crispo
CFO: Dan Izraeli
Sr Ex VP: George Morville
Ex VP: John Betz
Ex VP: Douglas T Cook
Ex VP: Jim Gorga
Ex VP: Donald Jenkins
Ex VP: Bivianne Lee
Ex VP: Robert Linnett
Ex VP: Susan L Monahan
Ex VP: Christopher H Wetzel
Sr VP: Alex G Crispo
Sr VP: Joe Mignon
VP: Ronda J Ashley
VP: Donna Bailey

BOLLINGER INSURANCE AGENCY
See BOLLINGER INC

D-U-N-S 11-276-6923 IMP
BOLLINGER MARINE FABRICATORS INC
(*Suby of* BOLLINGER SHIPYARDS LOCKPORT LLC) ★
816 Bollinger Ln, Amelia, LA 70340
Tel (985) 631-5300 *Founded/Ownrshp* 1997
Sales 116.5MM[E] *EMP* 396
SIC 3731 Shipbuilding & repairing
Ch Bd: Donald T Bollinger
**Pr:* Richard N Bollinger
**COO:* Michael C Ellis
**Sec:* T Walter Berry
VP: Lynn Falgout

D-U-N-S 07-325-3309 IMP
BOLLINGER SHIPYARDS LLC
8365 Highway 308, Lockport, LA 70374-3954
Tel (985) 532-2554 *Founded/Ownrshp* 1998
Sales 964.2MM[E] *EMP* 2,900
SIC 3731 3599 Shipbuilding & repairing; Machine shop, jobbing & repair
Ch Bd: Ben Bordelon
**CFO:* Andrew Fc Germain
**Ex VP:* Charlotte A Bollinger
Ex VP: Charlotte Bollinger
**Ex VP:* Craig P Roussel
**Ex VP:* Marc L Stanley
VP: Michael Ellis
Opers Mgr: Jon Degruise
VP Sls: Eric Bollinger

D-U-N-S 00-816-3842 IMP
BOLLINGER SHIPYARDS LOCKPORT LLC
(*Suby of* BOLLINGER SHIPYARDS LLC) ★
8365 Highway 308, Lockport, LA 70374-3954
Tel (985) 532-2554 *Founded/Ownrshp* 1946
Sales 276.1MM[E] *EMP* 1,850
SIC 3731 Shipbuilding & repairing
Sr Cor Off: Andrew St Germain
**Prin:* Christopher B Bollinger

D-U-N-S 06-388-0421 IMP
BOLLMAN HAT CO
BETMAR
110 E Main St, Adamstown, PA 19501-5009
Tel (717) 484-4361 *Founded/Ownrshp* 1868
Sales 312.5MM[E] *EMP* 985
SIC 2353 5136 Hats: cloth, straw & felt; Hats, men's & boys'
Pr: Donald Rongione
COO: Dave Huber
Ex VP: Jeff Clair
Ex VP: Chris Fitterling
VP: Mark Craley
VP: Angus Macleod
VP: Christopher Swan
Genl Mgr: John Wescott
Natl Sales: Leah Andrus
Natl Sales: Jay Rubin
Mktg Mgr: Christine Distasio

D-U-N-S 80-115-6159 IMP/EXP
BOLLORE LOGISTICS USA INC
SDV USA
(*Suby of* BOLLORE)
15010 132nd Ave, Jamaica, NY 11434-3500
Tel (718) 276-3907 *Founded/Ownrshp* 2007
Sales 319.9MM *EMP* 480
Accts Constantin Associates Llp Ne
SIC 4731 Foreign freight forwarding; Customhouse brokers
CEO: Thomas Duplan
COO: Sanjay Goel
CFO: Pascal Coustar

**Sec:* Jean Claude Gailhard
**VP:* Pierre Malet
**VP:* Eric Steinbock
Off Mgr: Cathy Tatesure
Sls Mgr: Terrence Brown

D-U-N-S 14-072-4530 IMP/EXP
■ BOLTHOUSE FARMS
(*Suby of* WM BOLTHOUSE FARMS INC) ★
3200 E Brundage Ln, Bakersfield, CA 93304
Tel (661) 366-7205 *Founded/Ownrshp* 1915
Sales 24.3MM^E *EMP* 2,300
SIC 0161 Carrot farm
Owner: William Bolthouse
Mktg Mgr: Bob Borda

D-U-N-S 06-308-9673
■ BOLTHOUSE HOLDING CORP
(*Suby of* BF BOLTHOUSE HOLDCO, LLC)
7200 E Brundage Ln, Bakersfield, CA 93307-3016
Tel (310) 566-8350 *Founded/Ownrshp* 2012
Sales 617.1MM^E *EMP* 4,566^E
SIC 0161 2099 Carrot farm; Ready-to-eat meals, salads & sandwiches
Pr: Jeff Dunn

D-U-N-S 07-725-4779
BOLTON & CO
3475 E Foothill Blvd # 100, Pasadena, CA 91107-6024
Tel (626) 799-7000 *Founded/Ownrshp* 1931
Sales NA *EMP* 143
SIC 6411

D-U-N-S 03-522-3445 IMP
BOLTTECH MANNINGS INC
(*Suby of* GREY MOUNTAIN PARTNERS LLC) ★
501 Mosside Blvd, North Versailles, PA 15137-2552
Tel (724) 872-4873 *Founded/Ownrshp* 2009
Sales 95.0MM^E *EMP* 294
SIC 3546 5072 3599 7359 3545 3423 Power-driven handtools; Power tools & accessories; Machine & other job shop work; Equipment rental & leasing; Machine tool accessories; Hand & edge tools
Pr: Ed Komoski
CFO: Dave Pecore
**Treas:* Chuck Heider
Sr VP: Aidan Graham
VP: Robert Davidson
Exec: Al Stasko
QA Dir: Robert Gerlach
Sfty Dirs: Bob Carr
Opers Mgr: Jeff Fontaine
Opers Mgr: Bill Jensen
Opers Mgr: Eric Schmid
Board of Directors: Jerry Jurkiewicz

D-U-N-S 80-981-6663 IMP/EXP
BOMAG AMERICAS INC
HYPAC
(*Suby of* BOMAG GMBH)
125 Blue Granite Pkwy, Ridgeway, SC 29130-7428
Tel (803) 337-0700 *Founded/Ownrshp* 2006
Sales 116.0MM^E *EMP* 270
SIC 3531 2951 Soil compactors: vibratory; Crushers, grinders & similar equipment; Road construction & maintenance machinery; Asphalt & asphaltic paving mixtures (not from refineries)
Pr: Jorg Unger
**Pr:* Walter Link
**VP:* Stephan Adam
**VP:* Chris Cyr
VP: Jullie Jackson
**Mng Dir:* Ralf Junker
Genl Mgr: Gregory Shipley
Ql Cn Mgr: Hugh Hill
Sales Exec: Greg Shipley
S&M/VP: Rob Mueckler

D-U-N-S 02-749-5894
■ BOMBARD ELECTRIC LLC
(*Suby of* MDU CONSTRUCTION SERVICES GROUP INC) ★
3570 W Post Rd, Las Vegas, NV 89118-3866
Tel (702) 263-3570 *Founded/Ownrshp* 2005
Sales 124.3MM^E *EMP* 400
SIC 1731 General electrical contractor
CFO: Marsha Divechio
**VP:* Terry Bombard
Genl Mgr: Terry Ellis
Snr PM: Dick Pendleton

D-U-N-S 78-205-8960 IMP
BOMBARDIER AEROSPACE CORP
(*Suby of* BOMBARDIER INC)
3400 Waterview Pkwy # 400, Richardson, TX 75080-1476
Tel (972) 960-3810 *Founded/Ownrshp* 1977
Sales 584.8MM^E *EMP* 1,129
SIC 5088 3721 Aircraft & parts; Aircraft
Pr: Pierre Beaudoin

BOMBARDIER AVIATION SERVICES
See LEARJET INC

D-U-N-S 01-021-8572
BOMBARDIER LEARJET INC
1 Learjet Way, Wichita, KS 67209-2924
Tel (316) 946-2000 *Founded/Ownrshp* 2008
Sales 228.8MM^E *EMP* 3,000
SIC 3721 Airplanes, fixed or rotary wing
VP: John Dieker

D-U-N-S 19-418-5468 IMP/EXP
BOMBARDIER TRANSPORTATION (HOLDINGS) USA INC
BOMBARDIER TRNSP SYSTEMS
(*Suby of* BOMBARDIER INC)
1501 Lebanon Church Rd, Pittsburgh, PA 15236-1491
Tel (412) 655-5700 *Founded/Ownrshp* 2001
Sales 362.8MM^E *EMP* 1,366
SIC 3743 3315 3823 Interurban cars & car equipment; Steel wire & related products; Industrial instrmnts msrmnt display/control process variable
Pr: Lutz Bertling
Pr: Romuald Ponte
**CFO:* Pierre Alary
**Treas:* Keith Orton
**Sr VP:* Richard Bradeen
**Sr VP:* ME Daniel Desjardin
Sr VP: Edward Gordon
**Sr VP:* John Paul Macdonald
Sr VP: Paul Overby
Sr VP: William Smoyer
**VP:* Tomas Bjorkman
**VP:* Matthew Gardner
**VP:* A J Jost
Exec: Debbie Kaspereit

BOMBARDIER TRNSP SYSTEMS
See BOMBARDIER TRANSPORTATION (HOLDINGS) USA INC

D-U-N-S 09-757-1731
BOMEL CONSTRUCTION CO INC
8195 E Kaiser Blvd, Anaheim, CA 92808-2214
Tel (714) 921-1660 *Founded/Ownrshp* 1970
Sales 125.3MM^E *EMP* 220
SIC 1541 Industrial buildings & warehouses
CEO: Kent Matranga
CFO: Lisa Matranga
**CFO:* Lisa McGinnis
VP: Shawn Devine
**VP:* James Ure
Exec: Gordon Crane
Exec: Mike Lucio
IT Man: Matt Meehan
Sales Exec: Darrel McGinnis
Snr PM: Keith Dodson

D-U-N-S 02-232-2846 IMP
BOMGAARS SUPPLY INC
SHOPPERS SUPPLY
1805 Zenith Dr, Sioux City, IA 51103-5208
Tel (712) 226-5000 *Founded/Ownrshp* 1944
Sales 126.0MM^E *EMP* 400
SIC 5311 5999 5651 Department stores, non-discount; Farm machinery; Feed & farm supply; Family clothing stores
Pr: Roger Bomgaars
**COO:* Dave Meyer
**CFO:* Torrey Wingert
**VP:* Jane Bomgaars
**VP:* Pam Winebrinner
Mktg Dir: Lon Noble

D-U-N-S 15-172-6536 IMP
BOMIN BUNKER OIL CORP
(*Suby of* BOMINFLOT BUNKERGESELLSCHAFT FUR MINERALOLE MIT BESCHRANKTER HAFTUNG)
333 Clay St Ste 2400, Houston, TX 77002-4116
Tel (713) 952-5151 *Founded/Ownrshp* 1984
Sales 970.0MM *EMP* 30
SIC 5172 Petroleum products
Pr: Gene Owen
**CFO:* Philip Chesson
VP: Eugene Owen
Rgnl Mgr: Jan Christensen

D-U-N-S 02-177-6745 IMP
BON APPETIT MANAGEMENT CO
(*Suby of* COMPASS GROUP USA INVESTMENTS LLP) ★
100 Hamilton Ave Ste 400, Palo Alto, CA 94301-1651
Tel (650) 798-8000 *Founded/Ownrshp* 2002
Sales 364.6MM^E *EMP* 8,000
SIC 8741

D-U-N-S 00-300-4405 IMP
■ BON L MANUFACTURING CO
(*Suby of* TREDEGAR CORP) ★
25 Bonnell St, Newnan, GA 30263-1603
Tel (770) 253-2020 *Founded/Ownrshp* 1949, 1955
Sales 142.3MM^E *EMP* 1,000
SIC 3354 Aluminum extruded products
CEO: Norman Scher
**CFO:* Kevin A O'Leary
**VP:* Nancy Taylor
Opers Mgr: Timmy McGruder

BON SECOURS
See CARE ALLIANCE HEALTH INC

D-U-N-S 07-474-4905
BON SECOURS - DEPAUL MEDICAL CENTER INC
(*Suby of* BON SECOURS HEALTH SYSTEM INC) ★
150 Kingsley Ln, Norfolk, VA 23505-4602
Tel (757) 889-5000 *Founded/Ownrshp* 1996
Sales 187.3MM *EMP* 1,400^E
Accts Deloitte Tax Llp Atlanta Ga
SIC 8062 General medical & surgical hospitals
Pr: Pat Heath
**CFO:* Greg Fimia
Dir Rad: Tom Walsh

D-U-N-S 04-014-3737 IMP
BON SECOURS - ST MARYS HOSPITAL OF RICHMOND INC
BON SECOURS SAINT MARYS HOSP
5801 Bremo Rd, Richmond, VA 23226-1907
Tel (804) 288-5415 *Founded/Ownrshp* 1985
Sales 125.6MM^E *EMP* 1,745
SIC 8062 General medical & surgical hospitals; Hospital, medical school affiliated with nursing & residency
CEO: Peter J Bernard
**CFO:* Peter Gallagher
**Sr VP:* Sister Anne Marie Mack
VP: Thomas Kornig
CIO: Anna L Evans
Ansthlgy: James C Meadows
Doctor: Xuezhong Yang
Pharmcst: Marissa Djukanovic

D-U-N-S 78-780-0382
BON SECOURS BALTIMORE HEALTH CORP
(*Suby of* BON SECOURS HEALTH SYSTEM INC) ★
2000 W Baltimore St, Baltimore, MD 21223-1558
Tel (410) 362-3000 *Founded/Ownrshp* 1985
Sales 72.9MM^E *EMP* 1,700^E
SIC 8062 General medical & surgical hospitals; Hospital, AMA approved residency
Doctor: Samuel L Ross
**Pr:* Sister Anne Lutz
**CFO:* Richard Bramm
**Ch:* Carleslo Boyle

D-U-N-S 78-808-2212
BON SECOURS BALTIMORE HEALTH SYTEM
(*Suby of* BON SECOURS HEALTH SYSTEM INC) ★
2000 W Baltimore St, Baltimore, MD 21223-1558
Tel (410) 362-3000 *Founded/Ownrshp* 1999
Sales 29.1MM^E *EMP* 1,200
SIC 8051 Skilled nursing care facilities
CEO: Percy Allen II
Ex Dir: Matthew Ansel

D-U-N-S 07-969-8849
BON SECOURS CHARITY HEALTH SYSTEM INC
255 Lafayette Ave, Suffern, NY 10901-4812
Tel (845) 368-5000 *Founded/Ownrshp* 2015
Sales 502.5MM *EMP* 2
SIC 8099 Blood related health services
CEO: Mary Leahy
**Sr VP:* Jeff Reilly
**Sr VP:* Pam Tarulli
**VP:* Clare Brady
**VP:* Deborah Marshall

D-U-N-S 07-271-4249
BON SECOURS COMMUNITY HOSPITAL
(*Suby of* BON SECOURS HEALTH SYSTEM INC) ★
160 E Main St, Port Jervis, NY 12771-2253
Tel (845) 858-7000 *Founded/Ownrshp* 1915
Sales 73.5MM *EMP* 1,285
SIC 8062 General medical & surgical hospitals
CEO: Philip A Patterson
**VP:* Lela Cerkzenik
**VP:* Crew Lerman
Dir Rx: Peter Barber
Psych: Dru Buesing

D-U-N-S 03-335-8438
BON SECOURS COTTAGE HEALTH SERVICES
(*Suby of* BON SECOURS HEALTH SYSTEM INC) ★
159 Kercheval Ave, Grosse Pointe Farms, MI 48236-3610
Tel (313) 640-1000 *Founded/Ownrshp* 2007
Sales 18.0MM^E *EMP* 1,540
SIC 8062 General medical & surgical hospitals
CEO: Richard Van Lith
Dir Risk M: Barbara Stemmer

D-U-N-S 03-772-3665
BON SECOURS HEALTH SYSTEM INC
1505 Marriottsville Rd, Marriottsville, MD 21104-1301
Tel (410) 442-5511 *Founded/Ownrshp* 1983
Sales 2.5MMM^E *EMP* 19,000
Accts Kpmg Llp Baltimore Md
SIC 8062 8099 General medical & surgical hospitals; Medical services organization
Pr: Richard J Statuto
Ch Bd: Patricia Eck
CEO: Philip A Patterson
CFO: Katherine A Arbuckle
Chf Mktg O: Marlon L Priest MD
Sr VP: Skip Hubbard
VP: Shelly Buck-Turner
VP: Melinda Hancock
VP: Pat Heath
VP: Patricia Heath
VP: Sheila Kuenzle
VP: Rose Leo
VP: Pam Phillips
VP: Johnna S Reed
VP: Jennifer Scholtz
Dir: Ashley W Kelly

D-U-N-S 04-628-2893 IMP
BON SECOURS HOSPITAL BALTIMORE INC
(*Suby of* BON SECOURS HEALTH SYSTEM INC) ★
2000 W Baltimore St, Baltimore, MD 21223-1558
Tel (410) 362-3000 *Founded/Ownrshp* 1920
Sales 130.5MM *EMP* 1,120
Accts Lb Deloitte Tax Llp Atlanta
SIC 8062 Hospital, medical school affiliated with residency
CEO: Samuel L Ross
Treas: Mohan Amlani
CTO: Mitchell Perlin

BON SECOURS MARY
See MARY IMMACULATE HOSPITAL INC

BON SECOURS SAINT MARYS HOSP
See BON SECOURS - ST MARYS HOSPITAL OF RICHMOND INC

BON SECOURS VENICE HOSPITAL
See VENICE REGIONAL HOSPITAL

D-U-N-S 07-792-7077
BON SECOURS-MEMORIAL REGIONAL MEDICAL CENTER INC
MEMORIAL MEDICAL CENTER
(*Suby of* BON SECOURS HEALTH SYSTEM INC) ★
8260 Atlee Rd Ste 1203, Mechanicsville, VA 23116-1844
Tel (804) 764-1253 *Founded/Ownrshp* 1998
Sales 363.9MM *EMP* 1,975
Accts Deloitte Tax Llp Atlanta Ga
SIC 8062 8071 General medical & surgical hospitals; Hospital, professional nursing school; X-ray laboratory, including dental
CEO: Michael K Kerner
Pr: Michael D Robinson
Treas: Melinda Hancock
Nurse Mgr: Renieta Brown

D-U-N-S 78-053-8930
BON SUISSE INC
THRIFTY ICE CREAM
11860 Cmnty Rd Ste 100, Poway, CA 92064
Tel (858) 486-0005 *Founded/Ownrshp* 1988
Sales 87.9MM^E *EMP* 75
SIC 5143 Dairy products, except dried or canned
CEO: Majid N Najm
**VP:* Elena Kassner
Genl Mgr: David Taylor
Opers Mgr: Mike Butler
Ql Cn Mgr: Tim Briggs

BON WORTH FACTORY OUTLETS
See WORTH BON INC

D-U-N-S 00-791-8048 IMP
▲ BON-TON STORES INC (PA)
2801 E Market St Ofc C, York, PA 17402-2420
Tel (717) 757-7660 *Founded/Ownrshp* 1898
Sales 2.7MMM *EMP* 24,100
Accts Kpmg Llp Harrisburg Pennsylv
Tkr Sym BONT *Exch* NGS
SIC 5311 Department stores, non-discount
Pr: Kathryn Bufano
**Ch Bd:* Tim Grumbacher
COO: William Tracy
CFO: Nancy A Walsh
**V Ch Bd:* Michael L Gleim
Chf Mktg O: Luis Fernandez
Ex VP: Stephen R Byers
Ex VP: Jimmy Mansker
VP: Dennis Clouser
VP: Cindy Hupf
VP: Denise Potter
VP: Tracey Smeltzer
VP: Leigh A Staley
Creative D: Kevin Kennedy
Board of Directors: Lucinda M Baier, Philip M Browne, Todd C McCarty, Daniel T Motulsky, Paul E Rigby, Jeffrey B Sherman, Steven B Silverstein, Debra K Simon

D-U-N-S 05-290-0586 IMP/EXP
BONAKEMI USA INC
(*Suby of* BONA AB)
2550 S Parker Rd Ste 600, Aurora, CO 80014-1678
Tel (303) 371-1411 *Founded/Ownrshp* 1981
Sales 155.4MM^E *EMP* 120
SIC 5198 5169 5023 2851 Stain; Waxes, except petroleum; Floor coverings; Paints & allied products
CEO: Kerstin Lindell
COO: Kirk Roberts
CFO: Brad Stone
VP: Enos Farnsworth
**Mng Dir:* John Rauvola
IT Man: Bob Fritze
Plnt Mgr: Marv Neu
Sls Mgr: Dee Lenston
Sls Mgr: Darin Nesline

D-U-N-S 02-955-7097
BONANDER PONTIAC INC
BONANDER PONTIAC-BUICK-GMC
231 S Center St, Turlock, CA 95380-4995
Tel (209) 632-8871 *Founded/Ownrshp* 1937
Sales 240.0MM^E *EMP* 95
SIC 5511 7539 5012 Automobiles, new & used; Automotive repair shops; Trailers for trucks, new & used
Pr: Donald E Bonander
Genl Mgr: Jerry Russell

BONANDER PONTIAC-BUICK-GMC
See BONANDER PONTIAC INC

D-U-N-S 03-493-1311 IMP
BONANZA BEVERAGE CO
6333 Ensworth St, Las Vegas, NV 89119-3210
Tel (702) 361-4166 *Founded/Ownrshp* 1961
Sales 127.2MM^E *EMP* 220
SIC 5181 Beer & other fermented malt liquors
Pr: Babe Gialketsis
**Treas:* William G Gialketsis
**VP:* William Babe Gialketsis
Comm Man: Teresa Van Tuyl
Comm Man: Teresa Vantuyl
Sls Mgr: Paul Phelan

D-U-N-S 96-718-9296
▲ BONANZA CREEK ENERGY INC
410 17th St Ste 1400, Denver, CO 80202-4427
Tel (720) 440-6100 *Founded/Ownrshp* 2010
Sales 292.6MM *EMP* 282^E
Tkr Sym BCEI *Exch* NYS
SIC 1311 Crude petroleum & natural gas
Pr: Richard J Carty
**Ch Bd:* James A Watt
COO: Anthony G Buchanon
Sr VP: Curt Moore
VP: Wade E Jaques
VP: Ryan Zorn
Board of Directors: Kevin A Neveu Gregory P R, Jeff E Wojahn

D-U-N-S 00-607-2621
BONANZA PRODUCTIONS INC (CA)
4000 Warner Blvd, Burbank, CA 91522-0001
Tel (818) 954-4212 *Founded/Ownrshp* 1991
Sales 13.6MM^E *EMP* 1,000
SIC 7929 Entertainment group
CEO: John A Rogovin

BONAR, INC
See LOW & BONAR INC

D-U-N-S 01-908-9077
BOND AUTO PARTS INC
272 Morrison Rd, Barre, VT 05641-8646
Tel (802) 479-0571 *Founded/Ownrshp* 1956, 1980
Sales 136.2MM^E *EMP* 341
SIC 5013 5531 Automotive supplies & parts; Automobile & truck equipment & parts
Pr: George Bond
**Ch:* William Bond
**Treas:* Andrew Bond
**Sr VP:* Christopher Bond
**Sr VP:* W Mark Mast
**Sr VP:* Greg Pecue
**VP:* Roger Bisson
**VP:* Craig Bond
Rgnl Mgr: Mark Harper
Brnch Mgr: Jeff Deforge
Brnch Mgr: David Skibniowsky

D-U-N-S 00-799-8115
BOND BROTHERS INC (MA)
145 Spring St, Everett, MA 02149-4517
Tel (617) 387-3400 *Founded/Ownrshp* 1907
Sales 266.3MM^E *EMP* 350
SIC 1542 Commercial & office building contractors
CEO: Edward A Bond Jr
**Pr:* Robert C Murray
**CFO:* Daniel Flannery

*VP: Thomas Baillie
*VP: Francis X Hayes
Exec: Wayne Arruda
Exec: Ken Johnson
Exec: Paul Rollins
Dir IT: Kevin Noval
Sfty Dirs: James Keefe
Sfty Mgr: Greg Hogg

D-U-N-S 61-495-2778
■ BOND DRUG CO OF ILLINOIS LLC
WALGREENS
(Suby of WALGREENS) ★
200 Wilmot Rd, Deerfield, IL 60015-4620
Tel (847) 914-2500 Founded/Ownrshp 1949
Sales 2.8MMM^E EMP 90,000
SIC 5912 Drug stores
Pr: Gregory D Wasson

D-U-N-S 05-619-8161 IMP/EXP
BOND MANUFACTURING CO INC
1700 W 4th St, Antioch, CA 94509-1008
Tel (925) 252-1135 Founded/Ownrshp 1955
Sales 114.5MM EMP 50^E
Accts Johnston Gremaux & Rossi Llp
SIC 5083 3272 Lawn & garden machinery & equipment; Garden machinery & equipment; Fireplaces, concrete
CEO: Daryl Merritt
*CEO: Ronald Merritt
*CFO: Tom Schloessmann
CFO: Tom Schooessmann
*Prin: Cameron Jenkins
VP Mktg: Nikki Merit

BONDED ABRASIVES
See SAINT-GOBAIN ABRASIVES INC

D-U-N-S 05-618-8063
■ BONDED MAINTENANCE CO
(Suby of ABM INDUSTRIES INC) ★
75 Broadway Ste 111, San Francisco, CA 94111-1423
Tel (415) 733-4000 Founded/Ownrshp 1959
Sales 22.9MM^E EMP 5,000
SIC 7349 Janitorial service, contract basis
Pr: Henrik Slipsager
*Treas: David Farwell
Treas: Karen Hewitt

D-U-N-S 05-165-0922
■ BONEFISH GRILL INC
(Suby of OUTBACK STEAKHOUSE) ★
2202 N West Shore Blvd # 5, Tampa, FL 33607-5747
Tel (813) 282-1225 Founded/Ownrshp 2001
Sales 92.9MM^E EMP 2,500
SIC 5812 Grills (eating places)
CEO: A William Allen III
Mng Pt: Neal Kelly
*Pr: John Cooper
*CFO: Dirk A Montgomery
*Ex VP: Joseph J Kadow
*VP: Timothy V Curci
*VP: Timothy Gannon
VP: Clifford Pleau
*Prin: Robert D Basham

D-U-N-S 80-886-1470
BONERTS INC
BONERT'S SLICE OF PIE
273 S Canon Dr, Beverly Hills, CA 90212-4006
Tel (714) 540-3535 Founded/Ownrshp 1993
Sales 132.3MM^E EMP 80
SIC 5142 Bakery products, frozen
CEO: Michael Bonert
CFO: Robert Erickson
CFO: Harry Kaplan
CFO: Maria Munoz
VP Sls: Art Heeg

BONERT'S SLICE OF PIE
See BONERTS INC

D-U-N-S 00-615-3712 IMP/EXP
BONGARDS CREAMERIES (MN)
13200 County Road 51, Norwood, MN 55368-9743
Tel (952) 466-5521 Founded/Ownrshp 1908
Sales 141.4MM^E EMP 350
Accts Eide Bailly Llp Minneapolis
SIC 2023 2022 5451 2021 Powdered whey; Natural cheese; Processed cheese; Cheese; Creamery butter
Ch Bd: Brent Ziegler
CFO: John Phillips
Sr VP: Scott Tomes
Genl Mgr: Nancy Coleman
IT Man: Justin Ruud
Mktg Mgr: Karissa Meyers
Sls Mgr: Vikki Anderson

D-U-N-S 07-414-4080
BONITA UNIFIED SCHOOL DISTRICT
115 W Allen Ave, San Dimas, CA 91773-1437
Tel (909) 971-8200 Founded/Ownrshp 1958
Sales 67.1MM^E EMP 1,083
Accts Nigro & Nigro Pc Murrieta Ca
SIC 8211 Public elementary school; Public junior high school; Public elementary & secondary schools
Pr: Patti Latourelle
*Pr: Chuck Coyne
*VP: Diane Koach
Adm Dir: Cheryl Seifert
MIS Dir: Aaron Weatherby
Dir IT: Kris Boneman
Dir IT: Kathleen Thurman
IT Man: Barbara Leigh

D-U-N-S 15-749-7181
BONITZ CONTRACTING CO INC
BONITZ FLOORING GROUP
(Suby of BONITZ INC) ★
645 Rosewood Dr, Columbia, SC 29201-4699
Tel (803) 799-0181 Founded/Ownrshp 1987
Sales 83.0MM^E EMP 525
SIC 1742 1752 1761 1542 1541 Drywall; Acoustical & ceiling work; Carpet laying; Roofing contractor; Commercial & office buildings, renovation & repair; Renovation, remodeling & repairs: industrial buildings
Ch Bd: George W Rogers
*Pr: Thomas A Edens III
*Treas: Stephen E Lee
*VP: Thomas B Banks
VP: Jean Chabot
VP: Gerald T Davis
*VP: W Wayne Green
Exec: Kelly Still
Genl Mgr: Bill West
Dir IT: Jay Hammermeister
Sftwr Eng: Joe Fohner

BONITZ FLOORING GROUP
See BONITZ CONTRACTING CO INC

D-U-N-S 15-749-7124
BONITZ INC
645 Rosewood Dr, Columbia, SC 29201-4699
Tel (803) 799-0181 Founded/Ownrshp 1987
Sales 178.7MM EMP 850
Accts Davis And Company Columbia S
SIC 3448 1542 1742 1541 1761 1752 Panels for prefabricated metal buildings; Commercial & office buildings, renovation & repair; Drywall; Renovation, remodeling & repairs: industrial buildings; Roofing contractor; Carpet laying
Pr: Thomas B Banks
*CFO: Stephen E Lee
*Ch: George W Rogers
*Ex VP: W Wayne Green
Opers Mgr: Dan Rhodes
Prd Mgr: Ryan Livingston

BONNELL ALUMINUM
See WILLIAM L BONNELL CO INC

D-U-N-S 00-485-7660
BONNEVILLE INTERNATIONAL CORP (UT)
K S L
(Suby of CHURCH OF JSUS CHRST OF LD STS) ★
55 N 300 W, Salt Lake City, UT 84101-3502
Tel (801) 575-5555 Founded/Ownrshp 1964
Sales 285.2MM^E EMP 1,242
SIC 4832 Radio broadcasting stations
Pr: Jeffery Simpson
*Ch Bd: James B Jacobson
*COO: Robert A Johnson
*CFO: Melanie Fairman
CFO: Delon Williams
*Sr VP: David K Redd
VP: Russell Banz
VP: Mike Dowdle
VP: Scarlett Pate
Genl Mgr: Joe Kjar
IT Man: Ryan Williams

D-U-N-S 87-901-6822
BONNEVILLE JOINT SCHOOL DISTRICT NO 93
3497 N Ammon Rd, Idaho Falls, ID 83401-1301
Tel (208) 525-4400 Founded/Ownrshp 1950
Sales 69.1MM EMP 1,300
Accts Galusha Higgins & Galusha P
SIC 8211 Public elementary & secondary schools
Ch: Craig Lords
Treas: Randy Haws
Treas: Windy Horman
Treas: Amy Landers
Trst: Jeff Bird
Trst: Greg Calder
*Prin: Wendy Horman
*Prin: Annette Winchester
Dir Sec: Jhn Pymm
Genl Mgr: Joey Hodgson
Pr Dir: Phil Campbell

D-U-N-S 04-300-3334
■ BONNEVILLE POWER ADMINISTRATION
(Suby of UNITED STATES DEPT OF ENERGY) ★
905 Ne 11th Ave, Portland, OR 97232-4169
Tel (503) 230-3000 Founded/Ownrshp 1937
Sales NA EMP 3,100
Accts Pricewaterhousecoopers Llp Po
SIC 9631 Regulation, administration of utilities
*COO: Claudia Andrews
COO: Ruth Bennett
*COO: Christine Hutchkin
CFO: Don Carbonari
CFO: Nancy M Mitman
Ofcr: Brad Bea
Ofcr: Samuel A Cannady
Ex VP: Mary Jensen
Sr VP: Richard Shaheen
VP: G Bell
VP: Kim A Leathley
VP: Charles E Meyer
VP: Alexandra Smith
VP: Michael J Weedall

D-U-N-S 05-583-6075
BONNIE BERSCHEID
800 N Lewis Ave, Sioux Falls, SD 57103-1011
Tel (605) 359-8208 Founded/Ownrshp 2010
Sales 161.0MM EMP 1
SIC 4214 Local trucking with storage
Owner: Bonnie Berscheid

BONNIE PLANTS
See ALABAMA FARMERS COOPERATIVE INC

D-U-N-S 60-448-8762 IMP
BONNIE PLANTS INC
(Suby of BONNIE PLANTS) ★
1727 Highway 223, Union Springs, AL 36089-4789
Tel (334) 738-3104 Founded/Ownrshp 1975
Sales 235.0MM EMP 3,000^E
SIC 0191 General farms, primarily crop
Pr: Stan Cope
*Treas: Tricia Arnold
*VP: Tim Trussell

D-U-N-S 78-492-6201
BONNIER CORP
(Suby of BONNIER AB)
460 N Orlando Ave Ste 200, Winter Park, FL 32789-2988
Tel (407) 622-1014 Founded/Ownrshp 2007
Sales 269.2MM^E EMP 898
SIC 2721 Magazines: publishing only, not printed on site
CEO: Terry Snow
*Ch Bd: Jonas Bonnier
*CEO: Dave Freygang
*COO: Lisa Earlywine
*CFO: Randy Koubek
*Ex VP: Eric Zinczenko
VP: John Driscoll
VP: Dean Turcol
Assoc Dir: Sadie Huemmer
Ex Dir: Brenda Oliveri
Genl Mgr: Garrett Kai

D-U-N-S 00-314-9457 IMP/EXP
BONSAL AMERICAN INC
(Suby of OLDCASTLE INC) ★
625 Griffith Rd Ste 100, Charlotte, NC 28217-3576
Tel (704) 525-1621 Founded/Ownrshp 1895, 2001
Sales 316.8MM^E EMP 831
SIC 3272 1442 3253 2899 Dry mixture concrete; Construction sand & gravel; Ceramic wall & floor tile; Chemical preparations
Pr: David J Maske
*COO: Bill Ashton
*Treas: Barry Hirsch
*VP: Daniel Benigni
*VP: Andy Brinkmeier
*VP: Gil Seco
Genl Mgr: Lisa Dunlap
Genl Mgr: Dan Webb
Mtls Mgr: Steve Simmons

D-U-N-S 60-856-6675 IMP/EXP
BONSET AMERICA CORP
(Suby of C. I. KASEI COMPANY, LIMITED)
6107 Corporate Park Dr, Browns Summit, NC 27214-8301
Tel (336) 375-0234 Founded/Ownrshp 1989
Sales 85.7MM EMP 130
Accts Deloitte & Touche Llp Charlot
SIC 3081 Packing materials, plastic sheet
Pr: Keije Yamane
*CEO: Hitoshi Nakamura
CFO: Jeff Winters
Tech Mgr: Willard Adkins
Plnt Mgr: Richard Tunstall
Ql Cn Mgr: Tobias Peacock
Sales Asso: Jessica Bailey

BOOK OF THE MONTH CLUB
See FILMED ENTERTAINMENT INC

D-U-N-S 00-590-1806 IMP/EXP
BOOKAZINE CO INC
75 Hook Rd, Bayonne, NJ 07002-5006
Tel (201) 339-7777 Founded/Ownrshp 1928
Sales 433.6MM^E EMP 180^E
SIC 5192 2741 Books; Catalogs: publishing only, not printed on site
CEO: Robert Kallman
*Ch Bd: Irwin Kallman
CFO: Bruce Morgenstern
Ofcr: John Cordero
*VP: Richard Kallman

D-U-N-S 09-763-2087
BOOKLAND CAYCE SCHOOL DISTRICT NO 2
LEXINGTON COUNTY SCHOOL DST 2
715 9th St, West Columbia, SC 29169-7169
Tel (803) 739-4057 Founded/Ownrshp 1952
Sales 92.3MM EMP 1,173
Accts Burkett Burkett & Burkett Wes
SIC 8211 Public elementary & secondary schools
VP: Audie Reymolds
Exec: Dawn Fertick
Exec: Paulette Keaton
Exec: Connie Lastinger
Exec: Sandra Mims
Exec: Janet Renehan
Dir Lab: Tammy Lucas
*Prin: Elizabeth Dickerson Branham
*Prin: Glen M Conwell
*Prin: Cynthia M Cindy Kessler
*Prin: Tom Siler

D-U-N-S 03-159-5309 IMP
BOOKS-A-MILLION INC
(Suby of FAMILY ACQUISITION HOLDINGS, INC.)
402 Industrial Ln, Birmingham, AL 35211-4465
Tel (205) 942-3737 Founded/Ownrshp 1917
Sales 474.0MM EMP 5,400
SIC 5942 5994 5947 5999 Book stores; Magazine stand; Gift, novelty & souvenir shop; Communication equipment; Electronic parts & equipment
Ch Bd: Clyde B Anderson
Pr: Terrance G Finley
CFO: R Todd Noden
CFO: Todd Noden
Ex VP: James F Turner
VP: Stephen Allums
VP: Mary Gallagher
VP: Dennis Lyons
Dist Mgr: Rob Everett
Dist Mgr: Gail Sanborn
Dist Mgr: Edith Yarbrough

D-U-N-S 01-885-8614 IMP
BOOMERANG TUBE LLC
14567 North Outer 40 Rd # 500, Chesterfield, MO 63017-5759
Tel (636) 534-5555 Founded/Ownrshp 2008
Sales 202.4MM^E EMP 309
SIC 3317 Steel pipe & tubes
Pr: Kevin Nystron
*COO: Sudhakar Kanthamneni
*CFO: Jason Roberts
VP: Mike Cullen
*VP: Kelly Hanlon

BOOMTOWN BELLE CASINO
See LOUISIANA I GAMING LP

D-U-N-S 09-928-9840
BOON GROUP INC
6300 Bridge Point Pkwy 3-500, Austin, TX 78730-5088
Tel (512) 339-4441 Founded/Ownrshp 1999
Sales NA EMP 300
SIC 6411 Insurance agents
CEO: R Sterling Boon
Pr: James Patton
Pr: Reni Sakos
Ex VP: Glenna Burleson
VP: Glenna Gallagher
Prin: Mary Catherine Sakos
Sales Asso: Taylor Boon

BOONE COUNTY ALTERNATIVE CTR
See BOONE COUNTY SCHOOLS

D-U-N-S 08-186-5370
BOONE COUNTY BOARD OF EDUCATION
8330 Us Highway 42, Florence, KY 41042-9286
Tel (859) 283-1003 Founded/Ownrshp 1900
Sales 192.7MM EMP 1,900
Accts Barnes Dennig & Co Ltd Cr
SIC 8211 School board
Ch Bd: Bonnie Rickert

D-U-N-S 96-935-1241
BOONE COUNTY SCHOOLS
BOONE COUNTY ALTERNATIVE CTR
8330 Us Highway 42, Florence, KY 41042-9286
Tel (859) 283-1003 Founded/Ownrshp 2011
Sales 70.6MM^E EMP 2,226^E
SIC 8211 Public elementary & secondary schools
Dir Sec: Mike Hall
Pr Dir: Barbara Brady
Teacher Pr: Phil Sheehy
HC Dir: Joan Fitzsimmons

D-U-N-S 12-260-3327
BOONE HOSPITAL CENTER
1600 E Broadway, Columbia, MO 65201-5897
Tel (573) 815-8000 Founded/Ownrshp 2008
Sales 284.3MM EMP 3,150
SIC 8062 General medical & surgical hospitals
Pr: Paul Machuk
*Pr: Jim Sinek
COO: Randy M Morrow
Dir Risk M: Mary Kingsley
Dir Lab: Rebecca Hennessy
Doctor: Larry Scroggins

D-U-N-S 15-579-0538
BOONE NEWSPAPERS INC
1060 Fairfax Park Ste B, Tuscaloosa, AL 35406-2837
Tel (205) 330-4100 Founded/Ownrshp 1982
Sales 112.4MM^E EMP 560
SIC 2711 Newspapers
Pr: James B Boone Jr
Off Mgr: Mary Ann Robertson

D-U-N-S 07-957-0395
▲ BOOT BARN HOLDINGS INC
15345 Barranca Pkwy, Irvine, CA 92618-2216
Tel (949) 453-4400 Founded/Ownrshp 1978
Sales 569.0MM EMP 2,900^E
Tkr Sym BOOT Exch NYS
SIC 5661 5641 Shoe stores; Men's boots; Women's boots; Children's wear
Pr: James G Conroy
*Ch Bd: Peter Starrett
CFO: Gregory V Hackman
Chf Mktg O: Laurie Grijalva

D-U-N-S 03-949-9850 IMP
■ BOOT BARN INC
AMERICAN WORKER
(Suby of BOOT BARN HOLDINGS INC) ★
11251 Beech Ave Ste 200, Irvine, CA 92618
Tel (714) 288-8181 Founded/Ownrshp 2011
Sales 111.3MM^E EMP 300
SIC 5699 5661 Western apparel; Men's boots
CEO: James G Conroy

D-U-N-S 87-905-9822
BOOTH WALTZ ENTERPRISES INC
G H BERLIN OIL CO, THE
42 Rumsey Rd, East Hartford, CT 06108-1133
Tel (860) 289-7800 Founded/Ownrshp 1994
Sales 116.2MM^E EMP 44
SIC 5172 Lubricating oils & greases

D-U-N-S 83-788-8486 IMP
■ BOOTS & COOTS LLC
(Suby of HALLIBURTON CO) ★
3000 N Sam Houston Pkwy E, Houston, TX 77032-3219
Tel (281) 871-2699 Founded/Ownrshp 2010
Sales 244.3MM^E EMP 672^E
SIC 1389 Fire fighting, oil & gas field
CEO: Jerry L Winchester
*COO: Dewitt Edwards
*CFO: Cary Baetz
*Sr VP: Allen Duke
*Sr VP: John Hebert

D-U-N-S 19-274-0384
BOOTS SMITH OILFIELD SERVICES LLC
2501 Airport Dr, Laurel, MS 39440-4719
Tel (601) 649-1220 Founded/Ownrshp 2003
Sales 258.0MM^E EMP 550
SIC 1623 Pipeline construction
*CFO: Joe Riley
*Treas: Mary Sanford
Sfty Dirs: John Nail

D-U-N-S 05-836-4254
BOOTS SMITH PIPELINE SERVICES LLC
500 Dennis Rd, Weatherford, TX 76087-9098
Tel (601) 682-0761 Founded/Ownrshp 2014
Sales 150.0MM EMP 200
SIC 1623 Oil & gas pipeline construction

D-U-N-S 07-591-6762
■ BOOZ ALLEN HAMILTON ENGINEERING SERVICES LLC
(Suby of BOOZ ALLEN HAMILTON INC) ★
900 Elkridge Landing Rd # 100, Linthicum, MD 21090-2931
Tel (703) 902-5000 Founded/Ownrshp 2012
Sales 82.7MM^E EMP 1,000^E
SIC 8711 Engineering services
Pr: William Purdy
*VP: Kevin L Cook
*VP: Mario Montero Jr
*VP: Horacio D Rozanski
*VP: Samuel R Strickland

D-U-N-S 96-472-5688
▲ BOOZ ALLEN HAMILTON HOLDING CORP
8283 Greensboro Dr, Mc Lean, VA 22102-3830
Tel (703) 902-5000 *Founded/Ownrshp* 1914
Sales 5.4MMM *EMP* 22,600[E]
Tkr Sym BAH *Exch* NYS
SIC 8742 Management consulting services
Pr: Horacio D Rozanski
**Ch Bd:* Ralph W Shrader
CFO: Kevin L Cook
CFO: Lloyd W Howell Jr
Treas: Michelle Boucher
Ofcr: Joseph W Mahaffee
Ex VP: James Allen
Ex VP: Karen M Dahut
Ex VP: Karen Dahut
Ex VP: Michael A Farber
Ex VP: Michael W Jones
Ex VP: Gary D Labovich
Ex VP: Christopher Ling
Ex VP: Joseph Logue
Ex VP: Joe Mahaffee
Ex VP: Susan L Penfield
Ex VP: Bill A Thoet
Ex VP: Betty Thompson
Ex VP: Gregory G Wenzel
VP: Timothy Andrews
VP: Fred K Blackburn
Board of Directors: Joan Lordi C Amble, Melody C Barnes, Peter Clare, Ian Fujiyama, Mark Gaumond, Arthur E Johnson, Gretchen W McClain, Philip A Odeen, Charles O Rossotti

D-U-N-S 00-692-8857
■ BOOZ ALLEN HAMILTON INC
(*Suby of* BOOZ ALLEN HAMILTON HOLDING CORP) ★
8283 Greensboro Dr # 700, Mc Lean, VA 22102-3838
Tel (703) 902-5000 *Founded/Ownrshp* 1973, 2008
Sales 2.8MMM[E] *EMP* 24,500[E]
SIC 8742 Management consulting services
CEO: Ralph W Shrader
Mng Pt: Carlos Ammann
Mng Pt: Alan Gemes
CFO: Martha Clark-Goth
**CFO:* Samuel R Strickland
**Ofcr:* Horacio D Rozanski
Top Exec: Niklas Eidmann
Ex VP: Francis Henry
Ex VP: Lloyd Howell Jr
**Ex VP:* Nancy Laben
Ex VP: Joseph Logue
Ex VP: Jack D Maye
Ex VP: Rick Saunders
Sr VP: Roger Cressey
Sr VP: Nicola Herpers
Sr VP: Camilla Jarl
Sr VP: Gary D Mather
Sr VP: Betty Thompson
VP: Stefan Eikelmann
VP: Gregory Harrison
VP: Donald L Pressey

D-U-N-S 00-327-5682 IMP
BORAL BRICKS INC (GA)
BORAL BRICKS STUDIO
(*Suby of* BORAL USA) ★
200 Mansell Ct E Ste 310, Roswell, GA 30076-4972
Tel (770) 645-4500 *Founded/Ownrshp* 1899, 1981
Sales 599.6MM[E] *EMP* 1,900
SIC 3251 5211 3271 Brick & structural clay tile; Brick; Concrete block & brick
CEO: David Mariner
**CFO:* Alan Spear
Counsel: Janet McDanel

BORAL BRICKS STUDIO
See BORAL BRICKS INC

D-U-N-S 02-638-9254 IMP/EXP
BORAL INDUSTRIES INC
BORAL USA
(*Suby of* BORAL LIMITED)
200 Mansell Ct E Ste 310, Roswell, GA 30076-4972
Tel (770) 645-4500 *Founded/Ownrshp* 1978
Sales 921.1MM[E] *EMP* 2,600
SIC 3251 3272 3275 5032 3271 2899 Brick clay: common face, glazed, vitrified or hollow; Building tile, clay; Roofing tile & slabs, concrete; Wallboard, gypsum; Brick, stone & related material; Concrete block & brick; Chemical preparations
CEO: Mike Kane
CFO: Ros Ng
CFO: Andrew Poulter
**VP:* Dennis Brown
VP: Keith Depew
VP: Ron Henley
**VP:* T Micheal Lewis
**VP:* Ernest C McLean
VP: J Scoggan
**Prin:* Dr Bob Every
Rgnl Mgr: Rodney Cunningham

D-U-N-S 18-347-6969 IMP
BORAL MATERIAL TECHNOLOGIES LLC
(*Suby of* BORAL LIMITED)
45 Ne Loop 410 Ste 700, San Antonio, TX 78216-5831
Tel (210) 349-4069 *Founded/Ownrshp* 1997
Sales 85.8MM[E] *EMP* 140
SIC 5169 Concrete additives
Pr: Gary Peterson
**Pr:* Terrence J Peterson
**Ch:* Al Borm
Treas: Lynn M Turner
**VP:* Ernest C McLean III
**VP:* Oren Post
**VP:* John K Scoggan
**VP:* Gary D Shelton
Rgnl Mgr: David Ditta
Mktg Mgr: James Oquin

D-U-N-S 00-222-8711 IMP/EXP
BORAL ROOFING LLC
(*Suby of* BORAL USA) ★
7575 Irvine Center Dr # 100, Irvine, CA 92618-2987
Tel (949) 756-1605 *Founded/Ownrshp* 1997, 2010
Sales 222.0MM[E] *EMP* 375
SIC 1761 3272 3259 Roofing, siding & sheet metal work; Roofing tile & slabs, concrete; Architectural clay products
Off Admin: Micki Roche
IT Man: Adrian Cooper
Manager: Corey Montez

BORAL USA
See BORAL INDUSTRIES INC

D-U-N-S 10-691-4349 IMP/EXP
BORBET ALABAMA INC
(*Suby of* BORBET GMBH)
979 W Veterans Blvd, Auburn, AL 36832-6930
Tel (334) 502-9400 *Founded/Ownrshp* 2008
Sales 113.4MM[E] *EMP* 250
SIC 3714 Wheels, motor vehicle
CEO: Ulf Kramv
**Prin:* Mark Gardner
Mtls Mgr: Ann Thomas

D-U-N-S 00-402-3412
BORDEN DAIRY CO OF ALABAMA LLC
(*Suby of* NATIONAL DAIRY LLC) ★
509 S Craft Hwy, Mobile, AL 36617-3603
Tel (251) 456-3381 *Founded/Ownrshp* 1950
Sales 149.5MM[E] *EMP* 700
SIC 5143 Dairy products, except dried or canned; Milk
Off Mgr: Stephanie Miller

D-U-N-S 60-581-5349
BORDEN DAIRY CO OF FLORIDA LLC
VELDA FARMS DAIRIES
(*Suby of* NATIONAL DAIRY LLC) ★
308 Avenue G Sw, Winter Haven, FL 33880-3433
Tel (863) 297-7300 *Founded/Ownrshp* 2001
Sales 311.8MM[E] *EMP* 660
SIC 5143 2026 2024 2022 2021 Dairy products, except dried or canned; Fluid milk; Fermented & cultured milk products; Ice cream & frozen desserts; Cheese, natural & processed; Creamery butter
Dir Surg: Tim Long
CFO: Bill White
Genl Mgr: Dave Kachelriess

D-U-N-S 10-739-1083
BORDEN DAIRY CO OF KENTUCKY LLC
FLAV-O-RICH DAIRIES
(*Suby of* NATIONAL DAIRY LLC) ★
221 W Highway 80, London, KY 40741-1043
Tel (606) 878-7301 *Founded/Ownrshp* 2001
Sales 204.7MM[E] *EMP* 289[E]
SIC 5143 Dairy products, except dried or canned
Sls Mgr: Donald Creech
IT Man: Gina Hopkins

D-U-N-S 61-210-8340 IMP
BORDER APPAREL LAUNDRY LTD
6969 Industrial Ave, El Paso, TX 79915-1107
Tel (915) 772-7170 *Founded/Ownrshp* 1987
Sales 217.6MM[E] *EMP* 1,500
SIC 2326 7211 Men's & boys' work clothing; Power laundries, family & commercial
Pt: Enrique Cervantes
Pt: Jesus Cervantes
Admn Mgr: Saul Cervantes
Genl Mgr: Diana Jaso

D-U-N-S 62-152-9882 IMP
BORDER FOODS INC
TACO BELL
5425 Boone Ave N, Minneapolis, MN 55428-3614
Tel (763) 559-7338 *Founded/Ownrshp* 1990
Sales 109.7MM[E] *EMP* 3,250
SIC 5812 Fast-food restaurant, chain
Owner: Lee J Engler

BORDER STATES ELECTRIC SUPPLY
See BORDER STATES INDUSTRIES INC

D-U-N-S 80-624-3619
BORDER STATES ELECTRIC SUPPLY OF MINNESOTA INC
BSC
(*Suby of* BORDER STATES ELECTRIC SUPPLY) ★
105 25th St N, Fargo, ND 58102-4002
Tel (701) 258-6060 *Founded/Ownrshp* 2007
Sales 865.3MM[E] *EMP* 1,200
SIC 5063 Electrical supplies
CEO: Tammy Miller
**Pr:* Gary Miller
**CFO:* Jeremy Welsand
**Sr VP:* Gerald Poke Buck
**VP:* Brian Becker
**VP:* Matthew Eddleman

D-U-N-S 80-624-4369 IMP
BORDER STATES ELECTRIC SUPPLY OF TEXAS INC
(*Suby of* BORDER STATES ELECTRIC SUPPLY) ★
105 25th St N, Fargo, ND 58102-4002
Tel (701) 293-5834 *Founded/Ownrshp* 2006
Sales 298.9MM[E] *EMP* 1,200
SIC 5063 Electrical supplies
CEO: Tammy Miller
**Pr:* Gary Miller
**VP:* Brian Becker

D-U-N-S 04-725-5799 IMP
BORDER STATES INDUSTRIES INC
BORDER STATES ELECTRIC SUPPLY
105 25th St N, Fargo, ND 58102-4002
Tel (701) 293-5834 *Founded/Ownrshp* 1984
Sales 1.6MMM *EMP* 1,500
SIC 5063

D-U-N-S 05-964-6724
■ BORDERFREE INC
(*Suby of* PITNEY BOWES INC) ★
292 Madison Ave, New York, NY 10017-6307
Tel (212) 299-3500 *Founded/Ownrshp* 2015
Sales 112.9MM[E] *EMP* 231
SIC 8742 4731 7312

D-U-N-S 84-068-6237 IMP
BORETS US INC
(*Suby of* PK BORETS, OOO PROIZVODSTVENNAYA KOMPANIYA BORETS, OOO)
1600 N Garnett Rd, Tulsa, OK 74116-1633
Tel (918) 439-7000 *Founded/Ownrshp* 2007
Sales 147.7MM[E] *EMP* 364[E]
SIC 3533 Oil & gas field machinery
CEO: Keith Russell

BORG WARNER
See REMY INC

BORGATA HOTEL CASINO & SPA
See MARINA DISTRICT FINANCE CO INC

BORGATA HOTEL CASINO AND SPA
See MARINA DISTRICT DEVELOPMENT CO LLC

D-U-N-S 14-775-8189
BORGESS HEALTH ALLIANCE INC
1521 Gull Rd, Kalamazoo, MI 49048-1640
Tel (269) 226-7000 *Founded/Ownrshp* 1980
Sales 2.6MM *EMP* 4,000
Accts Deloitte Tax Llp Cincinnati
SIC 8062 General medical & surgical hospitals
CEO: Paul A Staude
Mng Pt: Frank Saltiel
Pr: Deddie Loomis
CFO: Tom Bedeck
CFO: Rich Felbinger
CFO: Karri Fouler
CFO: Ken Holst
Ex VP: Patrick J Dyson
VP: Robert Hill
Exec: Luis Toledo
Mng Ofcr: Earnest Lanier

BORGESS MED CTR INPATIENT PHRM
See BORGESS MEDICAL CENTER

D-U-N-S 07-257-6556
BORGESS MEDICAL CENTER
BORGESS MED CTR INPATIENT PHRM
1521 Gull Rd, Kalamazoo, MI 49048-1666
Tel (269) 226-7000 *Founded/Ownrshp* 1927
Sales 382.7MM *EMP* 2,200
SIC 8062 General medical & surgical hospitals
Pr: Paul Spaude
Chf Path: Steven Soper
Treas: Susan Pozo
VP: Jason Nicolai
Exec: Jeff Way
Ex Dir: Terry Hluchyj
Ex Dir: Tony McDonnell
Ex Dir: Jeannette Prochazka
Ex Dir: Amy Shipley
Dir Sec: Ron Gipson
Prac Mgr: Liza Rivera

BORGWARNER AUTOMOTIVE
See BORGWARNER THERMAL SYSTEMS INC

D-U-N-S 94-840-8257 IMP
■ BORGWARNER EMISSIONS SYSTEMS OF MICHIGAN INC
BORGWRNER TRBO EMSSION SYSTEMS
(*Suby of* BORGWARNER INC) ★
3800 Automation Ave # 200, Auburn Hills, MI 48326-1781
Tel (248) 754-9600 *Founded/Ownrshp* 1996
Sales 619.5MM[E] *EMP* 5,386
SIC 3714 Transmissions, motor vehicle
Pr: Roger J Wood

D-U-N-S 13-946-9787
▲ BORGWARNER INC
3850 Hamlin Rd, Auburn Hills, MI 48326-2872
Tel (248) 754-9200 *Founded/Ownrshp* 1987
Sales 8.0MMM *EMP* 30,000[E]
Accts Pricewaterhousecoopers Llp De
Tkr Sym BWA *Exch* NYS
SIC 3714 Motor vehicle parts & accessories; Transmissions, motor vehicle; Transmission housings or parts, motor vehicle; Clutches, motor vehicle
Pr: James R Verrier
CFO: Ronald T Hundzinski
Treas: Jan Bertsch
Treas: Thomas J McGill
Ofcr: Jerry Roberts
VP: Thomas Babineau
VP: Todd Bennington
VP: Marco Caputo
VP: Steven G Carlson
VP: John J Gasparovic
VP: David Hasson
VP: Brad Lafaive
VP: Wouter Nijenhuis
VP: Patrick Nolan
VP: Andre Rothfuss
Board of Directors: Thomas R Stallkamp, Jan Carlson, Dennis C Cuneo, Jere A Drummond, Michael S Hanley, John R McKernan Jr, Alexis P Michas, Ernest J Novak Jr, Vicki L Sato, Richard O Schaum

D-U-N-S 05-892-1107 IMP
■ BORGWARNER MORSETEC INC
(*Suby of* BORGWARNER INC) ★
800 Warren Rd, Ithaca, NY 14850-1266
Tel (607) 257-6700 *Founded/Ownrshp* 1987
Sales 223.2MM[E] *EMP* 699[E]
SIC 3714 3462 3568 Motor vehicle parts & accessories; Iron & steel forgings; Power transmission equipment
Pr: James R Verrier
**Pr:* Ronald M Ruzic
**CFO:* Ronald T Hundzinski
**Ch:* Timothy M Manganello
**Treas:* Thomas J McGill
**VP:* Steve G Carlson
**VP:* Tony Hensel

D-U-N-S 07-971-1502
■ BORGWARNER PDS (INDIANA) INC
(*Suby of* BORGWARNER INC) ★
600 Corporation Dr, Pendleton, IN 46064-8610
Tel (800) 372-3555 *Founded/Ownrshp* 2014, 2015
Sales 2.1MMM[E] *EMP* 13,408
SIC 3694 3714 Battery charging alternators & generators; Motor vehicle engines & parts; Motor vehicle transmissions, drive assemblies & parts; Motor vehicle electrical equipment
Pr: Ronald T Hundzinski
COO: Victor Polen
CFO: Al Vandenbergh
Treas: Thomas J McGill
Sr VP: David Krall
Sr VP: Shawn Pallagi
VP: Barbara Bitzer
VP: John J Gasparovic
IT Man: Michael Lombardo
IT Man: Iris Salcewicz

D-U-N-S 09-238-9472 IMP
■ BORGWARNER THERMAL SYSTEMS INC
BORGWARNER AUTOMOTIVE
(*Suby of* BORGWARNER INC) ★
1507 S Kalamazoo Ave, Marshall, MI 49068-8310
Tel (269) 781-1228 *Founded/Ownrshp* 1999
Sales 176.4MM[E] *EMP* 900
SIC 3625 Control equipment, electric
CEO: James R Verrier
**Ch:* Timothy M Manganello
**Ex VP:* Robin J Adams
**VP:* Jamal M Farhat
**VP:* Anthony D Hensel

D-U-N-S 00-268-6905 IMP
■ BORGWARNER TORQTRANSFER SYSTEMS INC
(*Suby of* BORGWARNER INC) ★
3850 Hamlin Rd, Auburn Hills, MI 48326-2872
Tel (248) 754-9600 *Founded/Ownrshp* 1995
Sales 214.5MM[E] *EMP* 2,000
SIC 3714 Motor vehicle parts & accessories
Pr: James R Verrier
**CFO:* Ronald T Hundzinski
**Treas:* Thomas J McGill
**VP:* Steve G Carlson

D-U-N-S 02-914-3315 IMP
■ BORGWARNER TRANSMISSION SYSTEMS INC
(*Suby of* BORGWARNER INC) ★
3800 Automation Ave # 500, Auburn Hills, MI 48326-1781
Tel (248) 754-0200 *Founded/Ownrshp* 1995
Sales 729.8MM[E] *EMP* 4,000
SIC 3714 Transmissions, motor vehicle
Pr: Bob Welding
Pr: John G Sanderson

BORGWRNER TRBO EMSSION SYSTEMS
See BORGWARNER EMISSIONS SYSTEMS OF MICHIGAN INC

BORISCH MFG
See AMPHENOL BORISCH TECHNOLOGIES INC

BORO CONSTRUCTION
See BORO DEVELOPERS INC

D-U-N-S 06-008-5776
BORO DEVELOPERS INC
BORO CONSTRUCTION
400 Feheley Dr Ste B, King of Prussia, PA 19406-2666
Tel (610) 272-7400 *Founded/Ownrshp* 1974
Sales 101.4MM[E] *EMP* 185
SIC 1542 Specialized public building contractors
Pr: Frederick Shapiro
CFO: Thomas J Baker
Sec: Bruce H Shapiro
Prgrm Mgr: Tina Distefano
Sfty Dirs: Wayne Eik
Sfty Dirs: Rob Stanley
Sales Exec: George Shapiro
Snr Mgr: Joelle Newell

D-U-N-S 78-476-3471
BORO OF MANHATTAN COMMUNITY CO
(*Suby of* AFFIRMATIVE ACTION/EEO DEPT) ★
199 Chambers St, New York, NY 10007-1044
Tel (212) 220-8000 *Founded/Ownrshp* 2000
Sales 880.3M *EMP* 1,024
Accts P Boyd Cpa Pllc Brooklyn Ny
SIC 8231 College or university library
Prin: Cynthia Murphy
VP: Joseph Spadaro

D-U-N-S 16-130-1205 IMP
BORROUGHS CORP
3002 N Burdick St, Kalamazoo, MI 49004-3458
Tel (800) 748-0227 *Founded/Ownrshp* 1991
Sales 93.6MM[E] *EMP* 200
SIC 5044 Bank automatic teller machines
Pr: Tim Tyler
**VP:* Zac Sweetland
**VP Opers:* Greg Worsnop
Board of Directors: Robert Humphrey, Peter Metros, James C Tyler

D-U-N-S 07-878-6278 IMP
BORUSAN MANNESMANN PIPE US INC
(*Suby of* BORUSAN MANNESMANN BORU SANAYI VETICARET ANONIM SIRKETI)
363 N Sam H Pkwy E Ste 63, Houston, TX 77060
Tel (832) 399-6000 *Founded/Ownrshp* 2008
Sales 199.6MM *EMP* 140
Accts Pricewaterhousecoopers Llp Ho
SIC 3317 Steel pipe & tubes
CEO: Joel Johnson
**COO:* Hakan Duman
**CFO:* Eric Diehl
Chf Inves: Erol Akgullu
**Ofcr:* Josh Croix
IT Man: Armagan Unal

BOS PADRES
See CYCLONE ENTERPRISES INC

D-U-N-S 83-495-9686 IMP
BOSAL INDUSTRIES-GEORGIA INC
BOSAL INTERNATIONAL NORTH AMER
(*Suby of* BOSAL NEDERLAND B.V.)
1476 Seaver Way, Ypsilanti, MI 48197-8300
Tel (734) 547-7022 *Founded/Ownrshp* 1995
Sales 148.1MM[E] *EMP* 555

SIC 3714 Exhaust systems & parts, motor vehicle
CEO: Aad Goudriaan
Pr: Steve Steeden
**CEO:* Spencer Sterling
CFO: Bale Nagasuresh
Mng Dir: Andrew McCrae
Rgnl Mgr: Philip De Bruyn
Plnt Mgr: Jon Baucher
Plnt Mgr: Clibe Smith
Ql Cn Mgr: Barry Millarda
Ql Cn Mgr: Stuart Mills
Sls Dir: John Beattie

BOSAL INTERNATIONAL NORTH AMER
See BOSAL INDUSTRIES-GEORGIA INC

D-U-N-S 06-826-3200
BOSCH AUTOMOTIVE AFTER MARKET SERVICE SOLUTIONS
1385 N Weber Rd, Romeoville, IL 60446-4307
Tel (815) 407-3903 *Founded/Ownrshp* 2013
Sales 250.0MM *EMP* 100
SIC 5013 Tools & equipment, automotive
Off Mgr: Eric Ansell

D-U-N-S 04-784-2422
BOSCH AUTOMOTIVE MOTOR SYSTEMS CORP
AIRFLOW SYSTEMS GROUP
(*Suby of* AUTOMOTIVE GROUP) ★
38000 Hills Tech Dr, Farmington Hills, MI 48331-3418
Tel (248) 553-9000 *Founded/Ownrshp* 1990
Sales 200.0MM *EMP* 60
SIC 3714 Motor vehicle engines & parts
Pr: David Robinson
Ofcr: Laura Papenhagen
**VP:* Leslie Gray
VP: Michael Marcus
Board of Directors: J Berner

D-U-N-S 10-867-7212 IMP
BOSCH PACKAGING TECHNOLOGY INC
(*Suby of* AUTOMOTIVE GROUP) ★
869 S Knowles Ave, New Richmond, WI 54017-1745
Tel (715) 246-6511 *Founded/Ownrshp* 1983
Sales 90.1MM^E *EMP* 260
SIC 3565 Packaging machinery
Pr: Alexander Schmitz
IT Man: Eric Elkin
Sftwr Eng: Joe Franek
Opers Mgr: Alfons Lesch
Opers Mgr: Mary Walter
Sales Exec: Mike Wilcox
Board of Directors: Dr Christian Sturzenegger

D-U-N-S 04-513-3600 IMP
BOSCH REXROTH CORP
INDRAMAT DIV
(*Suby of* BOSCH REXROTH AG)
14001 S Lakes Dr, Charlotte, NC 28273-6791
Tel (847) 645-3600 *Founded/Ownrshp* 1967
Sales 639.8MM^E *EMP* 1,996
Accts Ernst & Young Llp
SIC 3594 Fluid power pumps & motors; Pumps, hydraulic power transfer; Pumps, hydraulic, aircraft; Motors, pneumatic
CEO: Paul Cooke
**CFO:* Steve Roberts
**Ex VP:* Ken Hank
**VP:* Nancy Gustitus
VP: Manfred Hahn
VP: Scott Hibbard
VP: Ernst Iseli
VP: Mike McCormick
VP: Erwin Wieckowski
CTO: Jason Hill
Dir IT: David Wollberton

D-U-N-S 04-561-0110 IMP/EXP
BOSCH SECURITY SYSTEMS INC
130 Perinton Pkwy, Fairport, NY 14450-9107
Tel (585) 223-4060 *Founded/Ownrshp* 2001
Sales 121.7MM^E *EMP* 632
SIC 3669 3699 3826 3825 3823 3625

D-U-N-S 06-653-4611 IMP/EXP
BOSCH SECURITY SYSTEMS INC
(*Suby of* AUTOMOTIVE GROUP) ★
12000 Portland Ave, Burnsville, MN 55337-1522
Tel (952) 884-4051 *Founded/Ownrshp* 1968
Sales 324.2MM^E *EMP* 1,800
SIC 1731 3669 3679 Access control systems specialization; Fire detection systems, electric; Headphones, radio
Pr: Raymond V Malpocher
Pr: Jeffrey Swan
Ofcr: Laura Papenhagen
VP: Dennis Petricoin
Tech Mgr: Gail Former
QC Dir: Christine Devey
Manager: Jerry Albrecht
Manager: Lloyd Apricio

D-U-N-S 86-113-8253 IMP/EXP
BOSCH THERMOTECHNOLOGY CORP
(*Suby of* BOSCH THERMOTECHNIK GMBH)
50 Wentworth Ave, Londonderry, NH 03053-7475
Tel (603) 552-1100 *Founded/Ownrshp* 1993
Sales 120.2MM^E *EMP* 282
SIC 5075 Warm air heating & air conditioning
Pr: Ervin Cash
CFO: Carl Zeiss
**Treas:* Mark Gilmour
**VP:* Roger Meinert

D-U-N-S 83-196-9089
BOSCOVS DEPARTMENT STORE LLC
(*Suby of* BOSCOVS INC) ★
4500 Perkiomen Ave, Reading, PA 19606-3946
Tel (610) 779-2000 *Founded/Ownrshp* 2008
Sales 638.4MM^E *EMP* 5,800
SIC 8741 5311 Management services; Department stores, non-discount
CEO: James Boscov
Pr: Samuel Flamholtz
Pr: Samuel Flamholz
Pr: Burton C Krieger
Co-Pr: Burton Krieger
Sr VP: Russel Diehm
Sr VP: Russell C Diehm
Sr VP: Ray Douglass
Sr VP: Tj Javier
Sr VP: Peter Lakin
Sr VP: Joe McGrath
Sr VP: Dean Sheaffer
VP: Jim Boscov
VP: John Young
Exec: Toni Miller

D-U-N-S 82-920-0992
BOSCOVS INC
4500 Perkiomen Ave, Reading, PA 19606-3946
Tel (610) 779-2000 *Founded/Ownrshp* 2000
Sales 1.1MMM *EMP* 10,003
Accts Kpmg Llp Philadelphia Pennsy
SIC 8741 5311 Business management; Department stores, non-discount
CEO: Albert Boscov
**Pr:* Kenneth S Lakin
**Treas:* Russell C Diehm
**Ex VP:* Toni Miller
Sr VP: T Javier
**VP:* Peter D Lakin
Dir Risk M: Michael Conaway
Rgnl Mgr: Angie Fegley
Opers Mgr: Mel Cappel

D-U-N-S 00-257-9431 IMP/EXP
BOSE CORP
100 The Mountain, Framingham, MA 01701-8863
Tel (508) 879-7330 *Founded/Ownrshp* 1978
Sales 3.0MMM^E *EMP* 8,000
SIC 3651 5731 Household audio equipment; Radio, television & electronic stores
CEO: Bob Maresca
**Pr:* Robert L Maresca
CFO: Herbert W Batchelder
**Treas:* Mario J Cornacchio
**VP:* Deborah Aubee
VP: Clint Byford
**VP:* Bryan K Fontaine
VP: Lisa Kawakami
**VP:* Nicholaas Merks
**VP:* Sumiyoshi Sakura
Exec: Tim Saeger
Creative D: Susan Hamilton
Dir Rx: Vickey Koul

D-U-N-S 05-801-7401 IMP
BOSKOVICH FARMS INC
711 Diaz Ave, Oxnard, CA 93030-7247
Tel (805) 487-2299 *Founded/Ownrshp* 1915
Sales 89.0MM^E *EMP* 350
SIC 0723 5812 0161 Crop preparation services for market; Eating places; Rooted vegetable farms; Lettuce & leaf vegetable farms
CEO: George S Boskovich Jr
**Pr:* Philip J Boskovich Jr
QA Dir: Loy Durham
IT Man: Andrew Costales
Ql Cn Mgr: Roxy Ostrem
Sales Exec: Brian Donovan
Sales Exec: Peter Oill
Sales Exec: Russ Weiderburg
Sls Dir: Brian Lombardi

BOSS
See NORSTAR OFFICE PRODUCTS INC

D-U-N-S 02-212-1735 IMP/EXP
BOSSARD NORTH AMERICA INC
(*Suby of* BOSSARD HOLDING AG)
6521 Production Dr, Cedar Falls, IA 50613-7433
Tel (319) 268-3700 *Founded/Ownrshp* 1998
Sales 87.3MM^E *EMP* 215
SIC 5085

BOSSELMAN BOSS SHOPS
See BOSSELMAN INC

D-U-N-S 80-966-8866
BOSSELMAN ENERGY INC
3123 W Stolley Park Rd B, Grand Island, NE 68801-7228
Tel (308) 381-6900 *Founded/Ownrshp* 1989
Sales 863.9MM^E *EMP* 2,000
SIC 5172 Petroleum products
Pr: Fred Bosselman
**Pr:* Krisha Bosselman
**CFO:* Travis Hasselmann

D-U-N-S 03-503-2671 IMP
BOSSELMAN INC
BOSSELMAN BOSS SHOPS
3123 W Stolley Park Rd, Grand Island, NE 68801-7228
Tel (308) 381-2800 *Founded/Ownrshp* 1967
Sales 170.8MM^E *EMP* 420
SIC 5541 5411 5812 7011 5172 5084 Truck stops; Filling stations, gasoline; Convenience stores, chain; Family restaurants; Motels; Fuel oil; Industrial machinery & equipment; Water pumps (industrial)
Pr: Charles D Bosselman
CFO: Ron Bulger
CFO: Brian Larson
**VP:* Fred A Bosselman
Mktg Dir: Harlon Hasselman

D-U-N-S 07-137-4375
BOSSIER PARISH SCHOOL BOARD INC
410 N Sibley St, Benton, LA 71006-9534
Tel (318) 549-5000 *Founded/Ownrshp* 1918
Sales 192.0MM *EMP* 3,000
SIC 8211 School board
Pr: Sandra Samm Darby
Psych: Barbara Axelson
Doctor: Sundi Littleton

D-U-N-S 07-980-2438
BOSSIER PARISH SCHOOLS
410 N Sibley St, Benton, LA 71006-9534
Tel (318) 549-5000 *Founded/Ownrshp* 2015
Sales 73.9MM^E *EMP* 2,509^E
SIC 8211 Public elementary & secondary schools
Dir Sec: Danny Dison
Genl Mgr: Jack Adger
Genl Mgr: Frank Rougeau
Pr Dir: Sonja Bailes
Teacher Pr: Janiene Batchelor
HC Dir: Ginger Hughes

D-U-N-S 07-125-5822
BOST INC
FORT SMITH SKILL TRAINING CTR
7701 S Zero St, Fort Smith, AR 72903-6644
Tel (479) 478-5600 *Founded/Ownrshp* 1960
Sales 31.3MM^E *EMP* 1,000
Accts Little Shaneyfelt Marshall & C
SIC 8331 8351 Vocational training agency; Preschool center
Pr: Tammy Chase
COO: William Gaphercole
**CFO:* Susan Steffens
**Treas:* Stephanie Riffle
**VP:* Roger Young
**Ex Dir:* Kent C Jones
Mfg Dir: Mike Burdick

D-U-N-S 17-755-2643 IMP
BOSTIK FINDLEY F S C INC
11320 W Wtertown Plank Rd, Milwaukee, WI 53226-3413
Tel (414) 774-2250 *Founded/Ownrshp* 1973
Sales 97.4MM^E *EMP* 160
SIC 5085

D-U-N-S 00-608-3364 IMP/EXP
BOSTIK INC
BOSTIK USA
(*Suby of* ARKEMA INC) ★
11320 W Wtertown Plank Rd, Wauwatosa, WI 53226-3413
Tel (414) 774-2250 *Founded/Ownrshp* 1901, 2015
Sales 175.3MM^E *EMP* 700
SIC 2891

BOSTIK USA
See BOSTIK INC

D-U-N-S 00-695-1610
BOSTON AND MAINE CORP
PANAM RAILWAYS
(*Suby of* PAN AM RAILWAYS INC) ★
1700 Iron Horse Park, North Billerica, MA 01862-1641
Tel (978) 663-1130 *Founded/Ownrshp* 1833, 1983
Sales 119.7MM^E *EMP* 800
SIC 3531 Road construction & maintenance machinery
Ch Bd: David A Fink
**Pr:* David Armstrong
**CFO:* Eric Lawer

D-U-N-S 06-451-3579
BOSTON BASKIN CANCER FOUNDATION INC
BBCF BUILDING-BAPTIST EAST
80 Humphreys Center Dr # 330, Memphis, TN 38120-2353
Tel (901) 226-5000 *Founded/Ownrshp* 2011
Sales 18.9MM^E *EMP* 1,825^E
SIC 8062 Hospital, medical school affiliated with residency
Pr: Thomas W Ratliff
**VP:* Jim Boswell

D-U-N-S 83-710-5725 IMP/EXP
▲ BOSTON BEER CO INC
1 Design Center Pl # 850, Boston, MA 02210-2300
Tel (617) 368-5000 *Founded/Ownrshp* 1984
Sales 959.9MM *EMP* 1,429^E
Tkr Sym SAM *Exch* NYS
SIC 2082 Malt beverages; Beer (alcoholic beverage); Ale (alcoholic beverage)
Pr: Martin F Roper
**Ch Bd:* C James Koch
CFO: Frank H Smalla
CFO: Bill Urich
Ofcr: John C Geist
Sr VP: Quincy B Troupe
VP: David L Grinnell
VP: Kathleen H Wade
Exec: Justin Cruz
Exec: Robert Kercher
Dir Risk M: Andrew Luscombe
Dir Risk M: Michaela Powers
Dir Lab: Amy Gregory
Board of Directors: David A Burwick, David P Fialkow, Cynthia A Fisher, Jay Margolis, Michael Spillane, Gregg A Tanner

D-U-N-S 07-866-7507
■ BOSTON BEER CORP
(*Suby of* BOSTON BREWING CO INC) ★
1 Design Center Pl # 850, Boston, MA 02210-2300
Tel (617) 368-5000 *Founded/Ownrshp* 2014
Sales 145.3MM^E *EMP* 1,000
SIC 2082 Beer (alcoholic beverage)
Pr: Martin F Roper
CFO: William F Urich
Sec: Kathleen H Wade
Board of Directors: Jim Koch

D-U-N-S 88-309-7602
■ BOSTON BREWING CO INC
(*Suby of* BOSTON BEER CO INC) ★
1 Design Center Pl # 850, Boston, MA 02210-2313
Tel (617) 368-5250 *Founded/Ownrshp* 1984
Sales 145.3MM^E *EMP* 1,013^E
SIC 8741 Business management
Pr: Martin F Roper
**Pr:* Charles James Koch

BOSTON CEDAR
See US LUMBER GROUP LLC

D-U-N-S 03-223-2139
BOSTON CHILDRENS HEALTH PHYSICIANS LLP
(*Suby of* CHILDRENS HOSPITAL BOSTON) ★
40 Sunshine Cottage Rd, Valhalla, NY 10595-1524
Tel (914) 594-2100 *Founded/Ownrshp* 1997
Sales 129.4MM *EMP* 780^E
Accts William J Camera & Company M
SIC 8011 General & family practice, physician/surgeon
Pt: Leonard J Newman
**Pt:* Michael H Gewitz

D-U-N-S 04-706-4183
■ BOSTON CO INC
(*Suby of* BNY MELLON) ★
1 Boston Pl Ste 2100, Boston, MA 02108-4405
Tel (617) 722-7000 *Founded/Ownrshp* 2007
Sales NA *EMP* 4,200
SIC 6022 6282 State trust companies accepting deposits, commercial; Investment advisory service; Manager of mutual funds, contract or fee basis
Pr: David Lamere
Ex VP: James Gockley
Sr VP: Kevin Duggan
VP: Gregory A Cook
VP: Guy Holappa
Plas Surg: Sean Doherty
Board of Directors: Robert P Mastrovita, Dwight L Allison Jr, George Putnam, William G Burns, Charles W Schmidt, Howard L Clark Jr, C Vincent Vappi, Charles C Cunningham Jr, Hans H Estin, Avram J Goldberg, Kenneth A Himmel, Johnathan S Linen, Claudine B Malone

BOSTON COACH
See FTM CORP

D-U-N-S 17-892-3314
BOSTON COACH CORP
(*Suby of* HARRISON GLOBAL LLC) ★
69 Norman St Ste 13, Everett, MA 02149-1946
Tel (800) 672-7676 *Founded/Ownrshp* 2013
Sales 78.5MM^E *EMP* 1,260
SIC 4119 8741 Limousine rental, with driver; Management services
Pr: Lawrence Moulter
Mng Pt: David Marcou
**Pr:* Russell Cooke
**COO:* Mark Munoz
**CFO:* Hilary Simons
VP: Mike Franbach
Dir Soc: Lissa Chavarria
Dir Soc: Susan Eaton
Brnch Mgr: Blake Stephan
Genl Mgr: Keith Carmichael
Dir IT: Pat Whyte

D-U-N-S 79-841-2094
BOSTON COACH-WASHINGTON CORP
(*Suby of* BOSTON COACH) ★
5775c General Wash Dr, Alexandria, VA 22312-2418
Tel (703) 813-6280 *Founded/Ownrshp* 1991
Sales 20.8MM^E *EMP* 1,493^E
SIC 4119 Automobile rental, with driver
Pr: Russell Cooke
**CEO:* Michael B Fox

D-U-N-S 04-276-8267
BOSTON CONSULTING GROUP INC
BCG
1 Beacon St Fl 10, Boston, MA 02108-3120
Tel (617) 850-3700 *Founded/Ownrshp* 1967
Sales 786.7MM^E *EMP* 2,025
SIC 8742

D-U-N-S 01-920-1383
BOSTON CULINARY GROUP INC
THEATER MERCHANDISING
(*Suby of* CENTERPLATE INC) ★
55 Cambridge Pkwy Ste 200, Cambridge, MA 02142-1218
Tel (617) 225-0005 *Founded/Ownrshp* 2010
Sales 71.8MM^E *EMP* 11,000
SIC 5812 5145 Concessionaire; Snack bar; Candy
CEO: Joseph O'Donnell
**Pr:* Joseph Armstrong
**Treas:* Paul Glinski
Genl Mgr: Mark Wisniewski

D-U-N-S 07-170-3409
BOSTON FINANCIAL DATA SERVICES INC (MA)
2000 Crown Colony Dr, Quincy, MA 02169-0953
Tel (617) 483-5000 *Founded/Ownrshp* 1973
Sales 646.4MM^E *EMP* 2,300
SIC 6211 6289 6282 Mutual funds, selling by independent salesperson; Stock transfer agents; Investment advice
Pr: Terrence L Metzger
Pr: Deborah Andwood
**Ch:* A Edward Allinson
Treas: Stacy Rich
**Treas:* Jay A Shuman
Ofcr: Marianne Demello-Smith
Ofcr: Joan M Dowd
Ofcr: Tom Farmer
Ofcr: Jennifer Hilton
**Ofcr:* Craig Hollis
Ofcr: Corey Knopf
Ofcr: Patrick Leary
Ofcr: Bill McMahon
VP: Kevin Boivin
VP: Barbara Browne
VP: Bob Chabot
VP: Frances Corcoran
VP: Joe Filardo
VP: Don Foberg
VP: Linda Graden
VP: Corky Harris

BOSTON FLOATING HOSPITAL
See TUFTS MEDICAL CENTER PARENT INC

D-U-N-S 03-081-1855
BOSTON FOUNDATION INC
75 Arlington St Fl 10, Boston, MA 02116-3992
Tel (617) 338-1700 *Founded/Ownrshp* 1915
Sales 128.4MM *EMP* 100
Accts Kpmg Llp Boston Ma
SIC 6733 Trusts, except educational, religious, charity: management
Ch: Michael Keating
**Pr:* Paul Grogan
Ofcr: Alexandra Auguste
VP: Ruben Ordua A
VP: Jessica Allen
VP: Robert Lewis Jr
VP: Ann McQueen
Comm Man: Sandy Kendall
**Prin:* Ray Hammond

Ex Dir: Marybeth Campbell
Dist Mgr: Sean O'Hanlon

D-U-N-S 00-695-1586
BOSTON GAS CO
(*Suby of* KEYSPAN CORP) ★
40 Sylvan Rd, Waltham, MA 02451-1120
Tel (781) 907-3646 *Founded/Ownrshp* 1823, 1969
Sales 191.4MM^E *EMP* 399
SIC 4924 4922 Natural gas distribution; Storage, natural gas
Pr: Marcy L Reed
**CFO:* Kenneth D Daly
**Treas:* David B Doxsee
**Sr VP:* Colin Owyang
**VP:* Robert Ganem
**VP:* Martin Wheatcroft

D-U-N-S 07-955-4351
BOSTON GLOBE LLC
135 Wiliam T Mrrssey Blvd, Boston, MA 02125-3338
Tel (617) 929-2684 *Founded/Ownrshp* 2013
Sales 163.7MM^E *EMP* 2,200
SIC 2711 Commercial printing & newspaper publishing combined
CEO: Michael Sheehan
**CFO:* James Levy
**Mng Dir:* Linda Pizzuti Henry

BOSTON LE GOURMET PIZZA
See ZANCANELLI MANAGEMENT CORP

D-U-N-S 60-531-2651 EXP
BOSTON MARKET CORP
(*Suby of* BOSTON MARKET HOLDING CORP) ★
14103 Denver West Pkwy # 100, Lakewood, CO 80401-3124
Tel (800) 340-2836 *Founded/Ownrshp* 1999
Sales 643.8MM^E *EMP* 15,041
SIC 5812 Fast-food restaurant, chain
Pr: George Michel
Pr: Robert Karisny
CFO: Greg Uhing
Ch: T Scott King
Sr VP: Keith L Robinson
VP: Marie Bahlinger
VP: Stephen Elop
VP: Bill Forgione
VP: J Randal Miller
Dir Surg: Greg Tornsick
Rgnl Mgr: Ayman Megala

D-U-N-S 00-843-9133
BOSTON MARKET HOLDING CORP
14103 Denver West Pkwy # 100, Lakewood, CO 80401-3124
Tel (303) 278-9500 *Founded/Ownrshp* 2007
Sales 643.8MM^E *EMP* 15,100
SIC 5812 Fast-food restaurant, chain
CEO: George Michel
**Pr:* Larry Hohl
**VP:* Marie Bahlinger
VP: Anthony Buford
VP: Gregory S Uhing
Netwrk Eng: Tom Corwin

D-U-N-S 00-549-2160 IMP/EXP
BOSTON MEDICAL CENTER CORP
BMC
1 Boston Medical Ctr Pl # 1, Boston, MA 02118-2999
Tel (617) 414-5000 *Founded/Ownrshp* 1996
Sales 1.0MMM *EMP* 4,200^E
SIC 8062 General medical & surgical hospitals
CEO: Kate Walsh
COO: Alastair Bell
CFO: Richard Silveria
Treas: Marybeth Begley
**Treas:* Richard W Siveria
Chf Mktg O: David Coleman
Ofcr: Mary K Fisher
Ofcr: Nancy Gaden
Top Exec: Jeffrey H Spiegel
Sr VP: Ravin Davidoff
Sr VP: Stanley Hochberg
VP: Thomas Daley
VP: Mary Glover
VP: Michael Krugman
VP: Stephanie Lee
VP: Robert Levin
VP: Joanna Norbrun
VP: Laurie Pohl
VP: Anthony Rossetti
VP: Clara Safi

D-U-N-S 10-315-6092
BOSTON MEDICAL CENTER HEALTH PLAN INC
BMC HEALTHNET PLAN
(*Suby of* BMC) ★
2 Copley Pl Ste 600, Boston, MA 02116-6568
Tel (617) 748-6000 *Founded/Ownrshp* 1997
Sales NA *EMP* 300
Accts Pricewaterhousecoopers Llp Bo
SIC 6324 Health maintenance organization (HMO), insurance only
Chf Mktg O: Susan Coakley
**COO:* Eric Hunter
**CFO:* Laurie Doran
**Chf Mktg O:* Karen Boudreau
VP: Lisa Feingold
VP: Michael Guerriere
Exec: Kim Graham
Dir Rx: Phuong Pham
CIO: Kim Sinclair
QA Dir: John Schultheis
Dir QC: Kimberly Polk
Board of Directors: John Cragin

D-U-N-S 00-695-1644
BOSTON MUTUAL LIFE INSURANCE CO
120 Royall St Ste 1, Canton, MA 02021-1098
Tel (781) 828-7000 *Founded/Ownrshp* 1891
Sales NA *EMP* 305
SIC 6311 Life insurance carriers
CEO: Paul E Petry
VP: Kitty Boyle
VP: Susan Gardner
**VP:* Walter Gorski
VP: Charles Mabry
VP: David Mitchell
VP: Linda Smith
VP: William Wahl
Off Mgr: Terri Carter
Off Admin: Theresa Nugent
MIS Dir: Mike Nagle

D-U-N-S 00-260-7377
■ **BOSTON PRIVATE BANK & TRUST CO**
(*Suby of* BOSTON PRIVATE FINANCIAL HOLDINGS INC) ★
10885 Ne 4th St Ste 100, Bellevue, WA 98004-5584
Tel (425) 586-5038 *Founded/Ownrshp* 1998
Sales NA *EMP* 50
SIC 6022 State commercial banks
Pr: Marty Steele
**CFO:* Richard Darrow
Ex VP: Alan Fulp
**Ex VP:* Alan Sulp
VP: Terry Peterson
VP: Robert Raile

D-U-N-S 17-483-2931
■ **BOSTON PRIVATE BANK & TRUST CO**
(*Suby of* BOSTON PRIVATE FINANCIAL HOLDINGS INC) ★
10 Post Office Sq Lbby F, Boston, MA 02109-4627
Tel (617) 912-1931 *Founded/Ownrshp* 1982
Sales NA *EMP* 200
SIC 6022 State commercial banks
Pr: Mark D Thompson
Pr: Anne Tirrell
Pr: Mark Travers
COO: Mary Fischer
COO: Henrique Meirelles
COO: George G Schwartz
Treas: Jeremy F Parker
Treas: George Schwartz
Ofcr: Ken Courtney
Ofcr: Jill Howland
Ofcr: Jennie Lanza
Ofcr: Anne Lasalvia
Ofcr: Nigel Smithson
Trst Ofcr: John J Sullivan
Assoc VP: Michael Fiske
Ex VP: James C Brown
Ex VP: James D Henderson
Sr VP: Thomas K Anderson
Sr VP: John A Beccia III
Sr VP: Robert Buffum
Sr VP: Torrance Childs
Board of Directors: Gloria C Larson, Kimberly S Stevenson

D-U-N-S 61-163-0435
▲ **BOSTON PRIVATE FINANCIAL HOLDINGS INC**
10 Post Office Sq, Boston, MA 02109-4603
Tel (617) 912-1900 *Founded/Ownrshp* 1987
Sales NA *EMP* 890^E
Tkr Sym BPFH *Exch* NGS
SIC 6022 6722 6282 State commercial banks; Management investment, open-end; Investment advice
Pr: Clayton G Deutsch
**Ch Bd:* Stephen M Waters
Pr: Jill Amato
Ofcr: Martha T Higgins
Ofcr: David J Kaye
Ex VP: Margaret W Chambers
Ex VP: W Timothy Macdonald
VP: Maureen McCarthy
VP: Stephen Mead
CTO: Timothy L Vaill
Board of Directors: Mark F Furlong, Joseph C Guyaux, Deborah F Kuenstner, Gloria C Larson, John Morton III, Daniel P Nolan, Kimberly S Stevenson, Donna C Wells, Lizabeth H Zlatkus

D-U-N-S 07-381-5011
■ **BOSTON PROPERTIES INC**
(*Suby of* MEAG MUNICH ERGO ASSETMANAGEMENT GMBH)
800 Boylston St Ste 1900, Boston, MA 02199-8103
Tel (617) 236-3300 *Founded/Ownrshp* 2016
Sales 2.4MMM *EMP* 760^E
Accts Pricewaterhousecoopers Llp Bo
Tkr Sym BXP *Exch* NYS
SIC 6798 Real estate investment trusts
CEO: Owen D Thomas
Pr: Douglas T Linde
CFO: Michael E Labelle
Ex VP: Peter D Johnston
Ex VP: Bryan J Koop
Ex VP: Robert E Pester
Ex VP: John F Powers
Ex VP: Raymond A Ritchey
VP: Frank Burt
Board of Directors: Carl B Einiger, Jacob A Frenkel, Joel I Klein, Matthew J Lustig, Alan J Patricof, Ivan G Seidenberg, Martin Turchin, David A Twardock, Mortimer B Zuckerman

D-U-N-S 13-912-2290
■ **BOSTON PROPERTIES LIMITED PARTNERSHIP**
(*Suby of* BOSTON PROPERTIES INC) ★
800 Boylston St Ste 1900, Boston, MA 02199-8103
Tel (617) 236-3300 *Founded/Ownrshp* 1997
Sales 2.4MMM *EMP* 750
Accts Pricewaterhousecoopers Llp Bo
SIC 6798 Real estate investment trusts
CEO: Owen D Thomas
Genl Pt: Boston Properties
Pr: Douglas T Linde

D-U-N-S 13-461-2899
BOSTON PUBLIC SCHOOLS
2300 Washington St, Roxbury, MA 02119-3213
Tel (617) 635-9000 *Founded/Ownrshp* 1900
Sales 286.8MM^E *EMP* 9,000
SIC 8211 Public elementary & secondary schools
COO: Kim Rice
Ex Dir: Carroll Blake
Dir Sec: Eric Weston
Dir IT: Joe McLaughlin
Dir IT: Catherine Meany
IT Man: David Nagle
Pr Dir: Richard Weir
Schl Brd P: Elizabeth Reilinger
Teacher Pr: Ross Wilson
Instr Medi: Deborah Froggatt
Pgrm Dir: Kathleen Bateman

D-U-N-S 00-102-7382
BOSTON SAND & GRAVEL CO INC (MA)
100 N Washington St Fl 2, Boston, MA 02114-1712
Tel (617) 227-9000 *Founded/Ownrshp* 1914, 1945
Sales 117.6MM^E *EMP* 450
SIC 3273 1442 Ready-mixed concrete; Construction sand mining; Gravel mining
Ch Bd: Dean M Boylan Sr
COO: Kevin Verrill
CFO: David McNeil
**Sec:* Dean M Boylan Jr
**Sr VP:* David B McNeil
**VP:* Jeanne-Marie Boylan
IT Man: Arthur Cohan
Info Man: Tracy-Lee Burke
Opers Mgr: Olly Demacedo
Sales Asso: Diana Morselli

BOSTON SCIENTIFIC
See AMERICAN MEDICAL SYSTEMS LLC

D-U-N-S 02-171-7889
▲ **BOSTON SCIENTIFIC CORP**
300 Boston Scientific Way, Marlborough, MA 01752-1291
Tel (508) 683-4000 *Founded/Ownrshp* 1960
Sales 7.4MMM *EMP* 26,088^E
Tkr Sym BSX *Exch* NYS
SIC 3841 3842 3845 Surgical & medical instruments; Diagnostic apparatus, medical; Catheters; Gastroscopes, except electromedical; Surgical appliances & supplies; Grafts, artificial: for surgery; Electromedical equipment
CEO: Michael F Mahoney
Pr: Stephen F Moreci
CFO: Daniel J Brennan
Chf Mktg O: Keith D Dawkins
Ofcr: Timothy A Pratt
Sr VP: Wendy Carruthers
Sr VP: John B Sorenson
VP: Sean Aherne
VP: Francisco Ascencion
VP: Mike Blastick
VP: Terrance Brick
VP: Vance Brown
VP: Rosaleen Burke
VP: Prabal Chakraborty
VP: Samuel Conaway
VP: Patrick Crotteau
VP: John Crowley
VP: John Donohue
VP: Bruce Fiedler
VP: Peter Gafner
VP: Tim Girton
Board of Directors: Nelda J Connors, Charles J Dockenforff, Donna A James, Kristina M Johnson, Edward J Ludwig, Stephen P Macmillan, David J Roux, John E Sununu

D-U-N-S 15-019-6558 EXP
■ **BOSTON SCIENTIFIC MIAMI CORP**
(*Suby of* BOSTON SCIENTIFIC CORP) ★
8600 Nw 41st St, Doral, FL 33166-6202
Tel (305) 597-4000 *Founded/Ownrshp* 1996
Sales 92.5MM^E *EMP* 1,000
SIC 3841 Surgical & medical instruments
Pr: Robert Sparasser
Dir Rx: Raymond Almeida
IT Man: Marc Burke
MIS Mgr: Andrew Mossberg
Opers Mgr: Thomas H Norman
VP Mktg: Karen Passafaro

D-U-N-S 00-176-7441 IMP
BOSTON SYMPHONY ORCHESTRA INC
TANGLEWOOD
301 Massachusetts Ave, Boston, MA 02115-4511
Tel (617) 266-1492 *Founded/Ownrshp* 1881
Sales 100.6MM *EMP* 350
SIC 7929 Symphony orchestras
Pr: Mark Volpe
**Treas:* Theresa M Stone
Ofcr: Joe Chart
Ofcr: Francis Rogers
Ofcr: Heather Scott
Assoc Dir: Karen Leopardi
Assoc Dir: Michael Nock
Assoc Dir: Kathleen Sambuco
Dir: Peter Minichiello
CTO: Douglas McKinnie
Dir IT: Jon Doyle

D-U-N-S 07-848-7802
BOSTON UNIVERSITY
DEPT OF PHYSICS
590 Commonwealth Ave # 255, Boston, MA 02215-2521
Tel (617) 353-2000 *Founded/Ownrshp* 2012
Sales 206.1MM^E *EMP* 20,000
SIC 8221 Colleges universities & professional schools
Pr: Robert Brown
**CFO:* Martin Howard
VP: Elana Goldberg
**VP:* Todd Klipp
Assoc Dir: David Janey
Assoc Dir: Debbie Miller
Assoc Dir: Chris Russell
Adm Dir: Caroline Lyman
Admn Mgr: Linda Parlee
CTO: Thomas Szabo
Dir IT: Julia Burstein

D-U-N-S 00-101-2079 IMP/EXP
■ **BOSTON WHALER INC**
(*Suby of* BRUNSWICK CORP) ★
100 Whaler Way, Edgewater, FL 32141-7221
Tel (386) 428-0057 *Founded/Ownrshp* 1961, 1958
Sales 118.3MM^E *EMP* 400
SIC 3732 Boat building & repairing
Pr: John Ward
Pr: Ron Berman
VP: James Menzies
Prgrm Mgr: Spencer Traynom
Genl Mgr: Jennifer Butera
IT Man: Julio Valencia
Mfg Dir: Paul Bartholomew
Sfty Mgr: Chris Carver
Plnt Mgr: Jim Barclay
VP Sls: Ben Cast
VP Sls: Jeff Vaughn

D-U-N-S 14-795-5223
BOSTON-WYMAN INC
BURGER KING
110 Breeds Hill Rd Ste 8, Hyannis, MA 02601-1864
Tel (508) 778-5044 *Founded/Ownrshp* 1970
Sales 32.2MM^E *EMP* 1,000
SIC 5812 Fast-food restaurant, chain
Pr: Maurice B Wyman
**Pr:* Maurice Wyman
**Treas:* Michael Wyman
CIO: Reid Wyman
VP Opers: Reed Wyman

BOSTONIAN SHOE CO
See C & J CLARK AMERICA INC

D-U-N-S 09-723-7895 IMP
BOSTWICK-BRAUN CO
7349 Crossleigh Ct, Toledo, OH 43617-3108
Tel (419) 259-3600 *Founded/Ownrshp* 1980
Sales 198.9MM^E *EMP* 281
SIC 5072 5084 5063 5083 5023 Builders' hardware; Industrial machinery & equipment; Electrical apparatus & equipment; Lawn & garden machinery & equipment; Home furnishings
Pr: Mike Dastoli
Dir IT: George Thiel
Sls&Mrk Ex: Ken Orzechowski
Sls Mgr: Mike Deerwester
Sales Asso: Josh Goatley

BOTNICK CHEVROLET
See BOTNICK/5 VENTURES INC

D-U-N-S 01-077-0386
BOTNICK/5 VENTURES INC
BOTNICK CHEVROLET
159 Front St 163, Binghamton, NY 13905-3103
Tel (607) 723-8971 *Founded/Ownrshp* 1968
Sales 94.8MM^E *EMP* 300
SIC 5511 7218 Automobiles, new & used; Industrial launderers
Ch Bd: Richard W Botnick
**VP:* Matthew Botnick

D-U-N-S 07-423-9344
BOTSFORD GENERAL HOSPITAL
BEAUMONT HOSP - FRMNGTON HILLS
(*Suby of* BEAUMONT BOTSFORD OAKWOOD HLTH) ★
28050 Grand River Ave, Farmington Hills, MI 48336-5933
Tel (248) 471-8000 *Founded/Ownrshp* 1965
Sales 283.5MM *EMP* 1,859
SIC 8062 Hospital, medical school affiliated with residency
CEO: Paul E Lacasse
CFO: David L Marceino
**CFO:* David L Marcellino
VP: Margaret Hasler
VP: Ellis Siefer
Exec: Kathy Alfien
Dir Risk M: Lisa Garner
Dir Rad: Gilbert Davis
Dir Rad: Andrew Mizzi
Off Admin: Amy Bone
Off Admin: David S Landmesser

D-U-N-S 00-823-1672
■ **BOTTLING GROUP LLC**
PEPSI BEVERAGES COMPANY
(*Suby of* PEPSICO) ★
1111 Westchester Ave, White Plains, NY 10604-3525
Tel (800) 789-2626 *Founded/Ownrshp* 1932, 1992
Sales 127.0MM^E *EMP* 400
SIC 2086 Carbonated beverages, nonalcoholic: bottled & canned; Soft drinks: packaged in cans, bottles, etc.
Pr: James B Lindsey Jr
**Sec:* Marjorie Lindsey
**VP:* Dick Graeber
Genl Mgr: Graig Reese
Plnt Mgr: Joe Fonseca
Mktg Mgr: Kurt Groseclose
Sls Mgr: Marty Tovaas

D-U-N-S 17-637-8487 IMP/EXP
■ **BOTTLING GROUP LLC**
PEPSI BEVERAGES COMPANY
(*Suby of* PEPSICO INC) ★
1111 Westchester Ave, White Plains, NY 10604-3525
Tel (914) 767-6000 *Founded/Ownrshp* 1999
Sales 7.0MMM^E *EMP* 66,800^E
SIC 2086 Bottled & canned soft drinks; Carbonated soft drinks, bottled & canned; Carbonated beverages, nonalcoholic: bottled & canned
CEO: Albert P Carey
**Pr:* Zein Abdalla

D-U-N-S 19-788-7268 IMP
BOTTOM LINE FOOD PROCESSORS INC
MICHAEL ANGELO'S GOURMET FOODS
200 Michael Angelo Way, Austin, TX 78728-1200
Tel (512) 218-3500 *Founded/Ownrshp* 1981
Sales 124.0MM^E *EMP* 400
SIC 2038 Dinners, frozen & packaged; Lunches, frozen & packaged
Ch Bd: Michael Angelo Renna
COO: Alfred Leblanc
CFO: Linda Naselli
Ex VP: Mike Stieger
VP: Sara Agnello
VP: Dan Hammer
VP: Bruce McNeill
VP: Gina Murphy
VP: Richard Price
Ex Dir: Lisa Jefferson
VP Opers: Marty Markovich

BOTTOM LINE RV
See JAYCO INC

D-U-N-S 60-814-3251
▲ BOTTOMLINE TECHNOLOGIES (DE) INC
325 Corporate Dr Ste 300, Portsmouth, NH 03801-6847
Tel (603) 436-0700 *Founded/Ownrshp* 1989
Sales 343.2MM *EMP* 1,500E
Tkr Sym EPAY *Exch* NGS
SIC 7372 Prepackaged software
Pr: Robert A Eberle
**Ch Bd:* Joseph L Mullen
CFO: Richard D Booth
Chf Mktg O: Christine M Nurnberger
Ex VP: Andrew J Mintzer
Ex VP: David G Sweet
Sr VP: Eric K Morgan
VP: Kevin Ashworth
VP: Matt Carey
VP: David Hunkele
VP: John Kass
VP: Gregory Park
VP: Mike Vigue
Board of Directors: James W Zilinski, Joseph L Barry Jr, Michael J Curran, Kenneth J D'amato, Peter Gibson, Jennifer M Gray, Jeffrey C Leathe, James L Loomis, Daniel M McGurl, Benjamin E Robinson III

D-U-N-S 07-323-4163
BOUCHARD INSURANCE INC
101 Starcrest Dr, Clearwater, FL 33765-3225
Tel (727) 447-6481 *Founded/Ownrshp* 2004
Sales NA *EMP* 190
SIC 6411 Insurance agents
Pr: J Raymond Bouchard
COO: Andy Davis
**CFO:* Doug Bishop
**CFO:* Matt Elsey
Ex VP: Michael D Hamby
VP: Nick Amaro
VP: Cathy Chafin
VP: Todd George
VP: Craig Holland
VP: Michael Matthews
Netwrk Mgr: Penny Pyers

D-U-N-S 82-493-7234
BOUDIN HOLDINGS INC
221 Main St Ste 1230, San Francisco, CA 94105-1929
Tel (415) 287-1709 *Founded/Ownrshp* 2005
Sales 117.8MME *EMP* 750
SIC 5461 Bakeries
CEO: David Wolfgram
**Co-Founder:* Jeff Drake

BOUDIN SOURDOUGH BAKERY & CAFE
See ANDRE-BOUDIN BAKERIES INC

D-U-N-S 61-953-1424 IMP
■ BOULDER BRANDS INC
(*Suby of* PINNACLE FOODS INC) ★
1600 Pearl St Ste 300, Boulder, CO 80302-5457
Tel (303) 652-0521 *Founded/Ownrshp* 2016
Sales 583.0MME *EMP* 900E
SIC 2096 6719 Potato chips & similar snacks; Potato chips & other potato-based snacks; Investment holding companies, except banks
CEO: Robert J Gamgort
VP: Gerald Edel
VP: Kelley M Maggs
Off Admin: Caitlyn Ruffus

D-U-N-S 07-500-1420 IMP/EXP
■ BOULDER BRANDS USA INC
(*Suby of* BOULDER BRANDS INC) ★
1600 Pearl St Ste 300, Boulder, CO 80302-5457
Tel (201) 568-9300 *Founded/Ownrshp* 2004
Sales 534.6MME *EMP* 600
SIC 5149 Health foods
CEO: Stephen B Hughes
**CFO:* Christine Sacco
**Ofcr:* Tim Kraft
**Ex VP:* Norman J Matar

D-U-N-S 07-575-9969
BOULDER CITY OF (INC)
CITY ADMINISTRATION
1777 Broadway, Boulder, CO 80302-6220
Tel (303) 441-3090 *Founded/Ownrshp* 1917
Sales NA *EMP* 1,600
Accts Bkd Llp Denver Colorado
SIC 9111 9224 9221 9511 City & town managers' offices; ; Fire protection; Police protection; Water control & quality agency, government
Comm Dir: Patrick Von Keyserling
Ex Dir: Maureen Rait
Plng Mgr: Wendy Schwartz
IT Man: Sharon Danson

D-U-N-S 05-749-4676
BOULDER COMMUNITY HEALTH
BOULDER COMMUNITY HOSPITAL
1100 Balsam Ave, Boulder, CO 80304-3404
Tel (303) 440-2273 *Founded/Ownrshp* 1922
Sales 298.0MM *EMP* 1,680
SIC 8069

BOULDER COMMUNITY HOSPITAL
See BOULDER COMMUNITY HEALTH

BOULDER COUNTY
See COUNTY OF BOULDER

D-U-N-S 84-703-5458
BOULDER STATION INC
(*Suby of* STATION CASINOS LLC) ★
4111 Boulder Hwy, Las Vegas, NV 89121-2573
Tel (702) 432-7777 *Founded/Ownrshp* 1994
Sales 68.0MME *EMP* 1,600
SIC 7011 7389 Casino hotel; Convention & show services
CEO: Frank Fertitta III
**Pr:* Lorezo Fertitta
**COO:* William Warner
**Ex VP:* Tom Friel
**Ex VP:* Scott M Nielson
IT Man: Andrew Santos

D-U-N-S 01-972-0887
BOULDER VALLEY SCHOOL DISTRICT RE-2
TECHNOLOGY
6500 Arapahoe Rd, Boulder, CO 80303-1407
Tel (303) 447-1010 *Founded/Ownrshp* 1860
Sales 318.0MM *EMP* 3,815
Accts S&G Swanhorst & Company Llc G
SIC 8211 Public elementary & secondary schools
**Treas:* Linda Clausen
Comm Dir: Briggs Gamblin
Dir Sec: Chris Wilderman
Genl Mgr: Shere Holleman
Psych: Ken McLaughlin
HC Dir: Susan Rowley

BOULEVARD TERR REHAB & NURSIN
See BOULEVARD TERRACE LLC

D-U-N-S 07-920-3586
BOULEVARD TERRACE LLC
BOULEVARD TERR REHAB & NURSIN
6 Cadillac Dr Ste 310, Brentwood, TN 37027-5080
Tel (615) 896-4505 *Founded/Ownrshp* 2011
Sales 30.1MME *EMP* 2,061
SIC 8051 Skilled nursing care facilities

BOULEVARD TIRE CENTER
See EARL W COLVARD INC

D-U-N-S 00-485-3461
BOUMA CORP (MI)
DIRECT DISTRIBUTORS
(*Suby of* BOUMA GROUP INC) ★
4101 Roger B Chaffee Mem, Grand Rapids, MI 49548-3469
Tel (616) 538-3600 *Founded/Ownrshp* 1951, 1950
Sales 158.9MME *EMP* 400
SIC 1542 1752 1742 Commercial & office building contractors; Floor laying & floor work; Drywall; Plastering, plain or ornamental; Acoustical & ceiling work
Pr: Daniel W Deryke
Mng Pt: Bob Kehoe
**CEO:* Doug Bouma
**CFO:* Paul Lemly
**Ch:* John Bouma Sr
**VP:* Ed Bruursema

D-U-N-S 82-812-8939
BOUMA GROUP INC
4101 Roger B Chaffee Mem, Grand Rapids, MI 49548-3443
Tel (616) 538-3600 *Founded/Ownrshp* 2004
Sales 180.6MME *EMP* 400
Accts Crowe Chizek And Company Llc
SIC 1542 1752 1742 Commercial & office building contractors; Floor laying & floor work; Drywall; Plastering, plain or ornamental; Acoustical & ceiling work
CEO: Douglas Bouma
**Ch Bd:* John Bouma Sr
**COO:* Paul Lemley
**CFO:* Daniel De Ryke

BOUMATIC
See MADISON ONE HOLDINGS LLC

D-U-N-S 07-055-6204 IMP
BOUND TREE MEDICAL LLC
(*Suby of* SARNOVA INC) ★
5000 Tuttle Crossing Blvd, Dublin, OH 43016-1534
Tel (614) 760-5000 *Founded/Ownrshp* 2008
Sales 91.5MME *EMP* 150
SIC 5047 Medical equipment & supplies
VP: Andrew Love
Exec: Cindy Dahl
IT Man: Tim Brown
Sales Asso: Brandon Kindell

D-U-N-S 03-886-0859 IMP/EXP
BOUNTY FRESH LLC
CHESTNUT HILL FARMS
806 S Douglas Rd Ste 580, Coral Gables, FL 33134-3157
Tel (305) 592-6969 *Founded/Ownrshp* 1998
Sales 86.0MME *EMP* 30
Accts Appelrouth Farah & Co Coral
SIC 5148 Fruits, fresh
CEO: Trond S Jensen
**Pr:* Romero Raul
CFO: Jose Ferreyra
**CFO:* Fernando Lopez
**Genl Mgr:* Federico Obando
Opers Mgr: Daniel Gonzalez

BOUNTY HUNTER METAL DETECTORS
See FIRST TEXAS PRODUCTS LLC

D-U-N-S 02-691-3848
BOURLAND & LEVERICH SUPPLY CO LLC
11707 Highway 152, Pampa, TX 79065-1414
Tel (806) 665-0061 *Founded/Ownrshp* 1935
Sales 100.0MM *EMP* 60
SIC 3317

D-U-N-S 00-825-5754 IMP/EXP
BOURNS INC
1200 Columbia Ave, Riverside, CA 92507-2129
Tel (951) 781-5500 *Founded/Ownrshp* 1952
Sales 1.5MMME *EMP* 5,293
SIC 3677 3676 3661 3639 3679 Electronic transformers; Electronic resistors; Telephone & telegraph apparatus; Major kitchen appliances, except refrigerators & stoves; Electronic circuits
CEO: Gordon L Bourns
**Pr:* Erik Meijer
**CFO:* James Heiken
CFO: Bournshr Riv
**Ex VP:* Gregg Gibbons
VP: Charles Macbeth
VP: Bill McKenna
VP: Karen Smarr
Genl Mgr: Craig Shipley
IT Man: Ian Harvey
VP Sls: Stan Henson
Board of Directors: Linda Bourns Hill, Anita Bourns Macbeth, Denise Bourns Moyles

D-U-N-S 07-174-9923 IMP
BOWDOIN COLLEGE
5600 College Sta, Brunswick, ME 04011-8447
Tel (207) 725-3000 *Founded/Ownrshp* 1794
Sales 154.1MM *EMP* 949
Accts Kpmg Llp Boston Ma
SIC 8221 College, except junior
Pr: Clayton Rose
Ofcr: Hector Casas
Ofcr: Chris Gager
Ofcr: Paul Joyce
Ofcr: Albert Lappin
Ofcr: Evan McDuff
Ofcr: Robert Moore
Ofcr: Matt Ryan
Ofcr: Jack Stiles
Ofcr: Paul Tierney
Ofcr: Angelo Toscano
VP: S C Longley
VP: Luke Maur
VP: Liam Nicoll
VP: Megan Retana
VP: David Sperber
Assoc Dir: Todd Herrmann
Assoc Dir: Rami Husseini
Assoc Dir: Andrew Lardie
Assoc Dir: David Profit
Assoc Dir: Michael Pulju

D-U-N-S 12-436-3370 IMP
BOWE BELL + HOWELL HOLDINGS INC
BOWEBELLHOWELL
760 S Wolf Rd, Wheeling, IL 60090-6232
Tel (312) 541-9300 *Founded/Ownrshp* 2013
Sales 225.5MME *EMP* 1,710
SIC 3579 Mailing, letter handling & addressing machines; Address labeling machines
CEO: Leslie F Stern
COO: Larry Blue
CFO: Steve Burke
CFO: Michael Wilhelm
VP: Woodall Beth
VP: Hendrik Fischer
VP: Hank Martin
Ex Dir: Gerard Derome
Prgrm Mgr: Dan Parenti
Snr Sftwr: Steven Seburn
CIO: Gary Stedale

BOWEBELLHOWELL
See BOWE BELL + HOWELL HOLDINGS INC

D-U-N-S 04-186-1758
BOWEN ENGINEERING CORP
8802 N Meridian St Ste X, Indianapolis, IN 46260-5319
Tel (219) 661-9770 *Founded/Ownrshp* 1967
Sales 396.2MME *EMP* 700
Accts Blue & Co Llc Carmel In
SIC 1629 1623 1541 Waste water & sewage treatment plant construction; Sewer line construction; Industrial buildings, new construction
CEO: A Douglas Bowen III
**CFO:* Scot Evans Sr
**VP:* Jim Ankrum Sr
**VP:* Jeff Chinn Sr
VP: Todd Lemen
VP: Ed Storrs
Exec: Bill Fyffe
Exec: Brian Stater
Exec: Eric Stevenson
Dir IT: Michael Browning
Dir IT: Matt Gentry

BOWEN MICLETTE & BRITT INSUR
See BOWEN MICLETTE & BRITT INSURANCE AGENCY LLC

D-U-N-S 09-980-2837
BOWEN MICLETTE & BRITT INSURANCE AGENCY LLC
BOWEN MICLETTE & BRITT INSUR
1111 North Loop W Ste 400, Houston, TX 77008-4712
Tel (713) 802-6100 *Founded/Ownrshp* 1980
Sales NA *EMP* 168
SIC 6411 Insurance agents
CEO: Edward Britt Jr
**Ch Bd:* David G Miclette
**Pr:* Ed Britt
**CFO:* Larry Karren
**Treas:* Samuel F Bowen
Ex VP: Lenita W Wright
VP: Jim Drew
VP: Ray Falk
VP: Keith Kimmick
VP: Barry K McCord
Mng Dir: David Gorney

D-U-N-S 07-948-2807
BOWIE RESOURCE PARTNERS LLC
6100 Dutchmans Ln Ste 902, Louisville, KY 40205-3348
Tel (502) 584-6022 *Founded/Ownrshp* 2013
Sales 442.4MME *EMP* 785
SIC 1221 Bituminous coal & lignite-surface mining
Ch: John J Siegel
CEO: Manie Dreyer
COO: Eugene Diclaudil
CFO: James J Wolff
Sr VP: Brian S Settles

D-U-N-S 16-956-8565
BOWIE RESOURCES LLC
(*Suby of* BOWIE RESOURCE PARTNERS LLC) ★
6100 Dutchmans Ln Ste 902, Louisville, KY 40205-3348
Tel (502) 584-6022 *Founded/Ownrshp* 2008
Sales 171.4MME *EMP* 150E
SIC 1221 Bituminous coal surface mining
**CFO:* James J Wolff
**Sr VP:* Bruce Lindsay
Sr VP: Brian Settles
**VP:* Renee S Grossman

D-U-N-S 79-691-9553
BOWLES CORPORATE SERVICES INC
335 Broad St, Clifton, NJ 07013-1371
Tel (973) 773-0699 *Founded/Ownrshp* 1992
Sales 25.4MME *EMP* 2,500
SIC 7381 7389 7361 Security guard service; Private investigator; Mailing & messenger services; Courier or messenger service; Placement agencies
CEO: Jon Singer
**COO:* Albert Barette
Off Mgr: Vivan Rosas

D-U-N-S 15-685-2720 IMP
BOWLING GREEN METALFORMING LLC
(*Suby of* MAGNA INTERNATIONAL INC)
111 Cosma Dr, Bowling Green, KY 42101-8047
Tel (270) 901-1555 *Founded/Ownrshp* 2003
Sales 228.8MME *EMP* 1,500
SIC 3499 3715 Aerosol valves, metal; Truck trailer chassis
Pr: John Farrell
VP: Pat McCann
Snr Mgr: Matt Blanford

D-U-N-S 04-134-9010
BOWLING GREEN STATE UNIVERSITY
110 Mcfall Ctr, Bowling Green, OH 43403-0001
Tel (419) 372-2311 *Founded/Ownrshp* 1910
Sales 208.3MME *EMP* 2,600
SIC 8221 University
Pr: Mary Ellen Mazey
CFO: Sherideen Stoll
VP: Lindy Bobbitt
**Prin:* Sidney Ribeau PHD
Adm Dir: Kathy Rahrig
Dir IT: Mike Good
Info Man: Eric Zahnle
Opers Mgr: Jack Taylor

D-U-N-S 09-977-6148
BOWLING GREEN-WARREN COUNTY COMMUNITY HOSPITAL CORP
MEDICAL CENTER, THE
(*Suby of* C H C) ★
250 Park St, Bowling Green, KY 42101-1760
Tel (270) 745-1000 *Founded/Ownrshp* 1926
Sales 284.8MM *EMP* 1,900
SIC 8062 General medical & surgical hospitals
CEO: Connie D Smith
**Ex VP:* Ronald Sowell
**Sr VP:* Chris Roszman
VP: Mark Robison
Mktg Dir: Sandy Feria

D-U-N-S 07-909-1424
BOWLMOR AMF CORP
222 W 44th St, New York, NY 10036-3906
Tel (212) 777-2214 *Founded/Ownrshp* 2013
Sales 266.1MME *EMP* 7,600
SIC 7933 Bowling centers
Pr: Tom Shannon
**CFO:* Brett Parker
Sls Dir: Joanna Green

D-U-N-S 00-306-9812 IMP/EXP
BOWMAN ANDROS PRODUCTS LLC
ANDROS FOODS NORTH AMERICA
(*Suby of* ANDROS)
10119 Old Valley Pike, Mount Jackson, VA 22842-9565
Tel (540) 217-4100 *Founded/Ownrshp* 1939
Sales 150.0MM *EMP* 500
SIC 2033 2099 2037 Fruits & fruit products in cans, jars, etc.; Apple sauce: packaged in cans, jars, etc.; Fruit juices: fresh; Jams, jellies & preserves: packaged in cans, jars, etc.; Food preparations; Frozen fruits & vegetables
CEO: Terry Stoehr
**Pr:* Jean-Luc Heymans
Ex VP: Tim Proctor
**VP:* Julian Lahaye
Genl Mgr: Hobert Harvey
Mtls Mgr: Adam Sharp
Plnt Mgr: Gordon Bowman
Plnt Mgr: Teddy Helsley
Plnt Mgr: Ann Jones
Trfc Mgr: Dick Neese
Board of Directors: Bruno Chapoulart, Eric Duchene, George Pace, Gilles Rapp

D-U-N-S 94-559-0859
BOWMAN CONSULTING GROUP LTD
3863 Centerview Dr # 300, Chantilly, VA 20151-3287
Tel (703) 464-1000 *Founded/Ownrshp* 1995
Sales 105.0MME *EMP* 367
SIC 8711 8713 Consulting engineer; Surveying services
Pr: Gary P Bowman
Pr: Frank Quante
CFO: Robert Hickey
CFO: Bruce Labovitz
Ex VP: Trish Hollar
Ex VP: Feroz Nathani
VP: John Barnard
VP: Clif Dayton
VP: Clifton Ladd
VP: Andrew Vinisky
VP: Derek Williams
Dir: Donavon Corum

D-U-N-S 07-311-4431
BOX ELDER COUNTY SCHOOL DISTRICT
960 S Main St Ste 1, Brigham City, UT 84302-3139
Tel (435) 734-4800 *Founded/Ownrshp* 1907
Sales 93.7MM *EMP* 1,800
Accts Wiggins & Co Pc Brigham Cit
SIC 8211 Public elementary & secondary schools
Pr: Connie Archibald
**CFO:* Ronald Frandsen
VP: Wade Hyde
VP: Clark Siddoway
**VP:* Bryan Smith
Admn Mgr: Darin Nielson
Admn Mgr: Karl Starr
CIO: Darin Nielsen
IT Man: Susan Thompson
Netwrk Eng: Damian Portillo
Psych: Dee Duncan
Board of Directors: Lynn Capener, Karen Cronin, James Fuller, Nancy Kennedy, Heather Young

D-U-N-S 93-302-0703
BOX ELDER SCHOOL DISTRICT
ALICE C HRRIS INTRMEDIATE SCHL
515 N 800 W, Tremonton, UT 84337-2500
Tel (435) 257-2560 *Founded/Ownrshp* 1995
Sales 91.0MM *EMP* 800
Accts Wiggins & Co Pc Brigham City
SIC 8211 8742 Public elementary & secondary schools; School, college, university consultant
Prin: Keith Klein
Bd of Dir: Tina Fulgham

D-U-N-S 00-416-8010
▲ BOX INC
900 Jefferson Ave, Redwood City, CA 94063-1837
Tel (877) 729-4269 *Founded/Ownrshp* 2005
Sales 302.7MM *EMP* 1,370E
Accts Ernst & Young Llp San Franci
Tkr Sym BOX *Exch* NYS
SIC 7372 Prepackaged software
Ch Bd: Aaron Levie
**Pr:* Dan Levin
**CFO:* Dylan Smith
Chf Mktg O: Carrie Palin
Ex VP: Jim Herbold
Ex VP: Graham Younger
Sr VP: Peter McGoff
VP: Tom Addis
VP: Stuart Gammon
VP: Lori Jima
VP: Lori Jimenez
VP: David Leeb
VP: Jeff Mannie
VP: Rand Wacker
VP: Niall Wall
Dir Bus: Roger Murff
Board of Directors: Dana Evan, Steven Krausz, Rory O'driscoll, Gary Reiner, Josh Stein, Bryan Taylor

D-U-N-S 05-737-2765 IMP
BOX MAKER INC
6412 S 190th St, Kent, WA 98032-2191
Tel (425) 251-0655 *Founded/Ownrshp* 1981
Sales 128.5MME *EMP* 175
SIC 5113 2653 2672 3086 5199 2631

D-U-N-S 07-916-1545
BOXER PARENT CO INC
2101 Citywest Blvd, Houston, TX 77042-2829
Tel (713) 918-8800 *Founded/Ownrshp* 2013
Sales 2.1MMME *EMP* 6,900E
SIC 7372 Prepackaged software
Pr: Ian Loring
**CFO:* Stephen Solcher
**VP:* Prescott Ashe
**VP:* David Humphrey
**VP:* Corey Walsh

D-U-N-S 08-870-2980 IMP
BOXES OF ST LOUIS INC
1833 Knox Ave, Saint Louis, MO 63139-3082
Tel (314) 781-2600 *Founded/Ownrshp* 1977
Sales 83.2MME *EMP* 208
SIC 2653 Boxes, corrugated: made from purchased materials
Pr: Michael W Patton
MIS Dir: Shirley Dlanhantis

D-U-N-S 00-794-1545
BOXLEY MATERIALS CO (VA)
(*Suby of* SUMMIT MATERIALS LLC) ★
15418 W Lynchburg, Blue Ridge, VA 24064
Tel (540) 777-7600 *Founded/Ownrshp* 1923, 2016
Sales 143.1MME *EMP* 417
SIC 1422 1423 Crushed & broken limestone; Crushed & broken granite
Pr: Abney S Boxley III
COO: Jeff Perkins
Treas: John A Rourke
Sec: Thomas T Johnson
VP: Gwaltney Walter
IT Man: Sue Rourke
Ql Cn Mgr: Frank Saul
Sls Mgr: Delin Kirks

D-U-N-S 00-190-2220 IMP
BOY SCOUTS OF AMERICA
1325 W Walnut Hill Ln, Irving, TX 75038-3096
Tel (972) 580-2000 *Founded/Ownrshp* 1910
Sales 221.6MME *EMP* 2,800
Accts Pricewaterhousecoopers Llp Da
SIC 8641 5136 5091 2721 Boy Scout organization; Uniforms, men's & boys'; Camping equipment & supplies; Magazines: publishing only, not printed on site
CEO: C W Brock
Pr: Robert M Gates
Pr: Rex W Tillerson
CEO: Robert Mazzuca
CFO: Michael Ashline
VP: Terrence Dunn
Exec: Gary P Butler
Exec: Michael Surbaugh
Store Mgr: Laurie Bambas
Store Mgr: Gail Karas
Store Mgr: Delores Theodore

BOYD
See LTI HOLDINGS INC

D-U-N-S 03-155-4033
BOYD BROS TRANSPORTATION INC (DE)
BOYD LOGISTICS
(*Suby of* DASEKE INC) ★
3275 Highway 30, Clayton, AL 36016-3003
Tel (800) 633-1502 *Founded/Ownrshp* 1956, 2013
Sales 212.6MME *EMP* 947
SIC 4213 Trucking, except local
CEO: Gail B Cooper
**Pr:* Richard C Bailey
**COO:* Chris Cooper
VP: David Baker
VP: Dwight Bassett
VP: Wayne Fiquette
VP: Gary Jones
VP: Elaine Maund
VP: Gary Robinson
VP: Frank Stokes
VP: Lee Wagner

D-U-N-S 83-186-7341
BOYD CO LLC
1400 Cecil Ave, Louisville, KY 40211-1626
Tel (502) 774-4441 *Founded/Ownrshp* 2008
Sales 596.3MME *EMP* 1,300
SIC 5082 General construction machinery & equipment
**CFO:* Joseph A Yoerg
VP: Frank Lewis

D-U-N-S 00-905-2218 IMP
BOYD COFFEE CO (OR)
BOYD INTERNATIONAL FOODS
19730 Ne Sandy Blvd, Portland, OR 97230-7310
Tel (503) 666-4545 *Founded/Ownrshp* 1929
Sales 169.5MME *EMP* 400
SIC 2095 5499 5141 3634 2099 Roasted coffee; Coffee; Gourmet food stores; Groceries, general line; Electric housewares & fans; Food preparations
Pr: Jeffrey Newman
VP: Randy Layton
Mktg Mgr: Melissa Mackay

BOYD CORPORATION
See A B BOYD CO

D-U-N-S 61-736-9335
▲ BOYD GAMING CORP
3883 Howard Flr 9, Las Vegas, NV 89169
Tel (702) 792-7200 *Founded/Ownrshp* 1975
Sales 2.2MMM *EMP* 18,895
Tkr Sym BYD *Exch* NYS
SIC 7011 Casino hotel
Pr: Keith E Smith
Ch Bd: William S Boyd
CFO: Josh Hirsberg
V Ch Bd: Marianne Boyd Johnson
Ex VP: Theodore A Bogich
Ex VP: Robert L Boughner
Ex VP: Brian A Larson
Ex VP: Steve Thompson
VP: James Adams
VP: Kerrie Burke
VP: Trevor Busche
VP: Jim Carter
VP: Dave Farland
VP: David Farlin
VP: Denny Frey
VP: Denny Fry
VP: Anthony D McDuffie
VP: Vince Schwartz
VP: Kevin Sullivan
VP: Glenda Zuhse
Exec: Bill Boyd
Board of Directors: John R Bailey, William R Boyd, Richard E Flaherty, Christine J Spadafor, Peter M Thomas, Paul W Whetsell, Veronica J Wilson

D-U-N-S 06-372-2723
BOYD GROUP U S INC
(*Suby of* BOYD GROUP INC,THE)
500 W Lake St Ste 1, Elmhurst, IL 60126-1425
Tel (630) 832-0670 *Founded/Ownrshp* 2013
Sales 54.7MME *EMP* 1,206E
SIC 7549 7538 High performance auto repair & service; Engine repair
Ch: Allan Davis
**Pr:* Tim O'Day
**CEO:* Brock Bulbuck

BOYD INTERNATIONAL FOODS
See BOYD COFFEE CO

BOYD LOGISTICS
See BOYD BROS TRANSPORTATION INC

D-U-N-S 96-995-6882 IMP
BOYD LTI
(*Suby of* SENTINEL CAPITAL PARTNERS LLC) ★
600 S Mcclure Rd, Modesto, CA 95357-0520
Tel (800) 554-0200 *Founded/Ownrshp* 2011
Sales 93.8MME *EMP* 766
SIC 3549 3053 8711 Metalworking machinery; Gaskets, packing & sealing devices; Industrial engineers
Pr: Mitch Aiello
**CFO:* Kurt Wetzel

D-U-N-S 93-150-1118
■ BOYD TUNICA INC
SAM'S TOWN GMBLING HALL CASINO
(*Suby of* BOYD GAMING CORP) ★
1477 Csno Strip Res Blvd, Robinsonville, MS 38664
Tel (662) 363-0711 *Founded/Ownrshp* 1993
Sales 57.2MME *EMP* 1,594
SIC 7011 Casino hotel
Pr: Keith Smith
CIO: Willaim Boyd

D-U-N-S 01-490-3769
BOYERS FOOD MARKETS INC
301 S Warren St, Orwigsburg, PA 17961-2119
Tel (570) 366-1477 *Founded/Ownrshp* 1949
Sales 143.8MME *EMP* 900
Accts Reinsel Kentz Lesher Llp Wyom
SIC 5411 Supermarkets, chain
Pr: Dean Walker
**CFO:* Matthew Kase
**VP:* John Boyer
Store Mgr: Michael Casella
Store Mgr: Brian Clemson
Store Mgr: Derek Frantz
Store Mgr: Justin Hunsicker
Store Mgr: Matthew Pogar

D-U-N-S 07-120-3301
BOYERTOWN AREA SCHOOL DISTRICT
911 Montgomery Ave, Boyertown, PA 19512-9699
Tel (610) 367-6031 *Founded/Ownrshp* 1957
Sales 100.8MM *EMP* 1,200
Accts Barbacane Thornton & Company
SIC 8211 Public elementary school; Public junior high school; Public senior high school
Pr: Steve Elsier
Instr Medi: Rebecca Hart

BOYETT PETROLEUM
See STAN BOYETT & SON INC

BOYNE MOUNTAIN
See BOYNE USA INC

D-U-N-S 04-192-5611
BOYNE USA INC
BOYNE MOUNTAIN
1 Boyne Mountain Rd, Boyne Falls, MI 49713-9658
Tel (231) 549-6000 *Founded/Ownrshp* 1948
Sales 234.5MME *EMP* 2,400
Accts Moss Adams Llp Seattle Washi
SIC 7011 7992 7032 Resort hotel; Public golf courses; Sporting & recreational camps
Pr: John E Kircher
**Ch Bd:* Amy Kircher
**Pr:* Steve Kircher
**CFO:* Paul Jorgensen
Exec: Roland Andreasson
Exec: Ken Griffin
Dir Soc: Jessica White
Area Mgr: Joe Breighner
Brnch Mgr: Paulo Rocha
Dir IT: Dale Burmeister
Dir IT: Chris Colston

D-U-N-S 07-523-6133
BOYS & GIRLS CLUBS OF AMERICA (DC)
1275 Peachtree St Ne # 500, Atlanta, GA 30309-3509
Tel (404) 527-7100 *Founded/Ownrshp* 1906
Sales 170.8MM *EMP* 360
Accts Kpmg Llp Greensboro Nc
SIC 8322 Youth self-help agency
Pr: James Clark
**Ch Bd:* Ronald Gidwitz
Pr: Duane Hinshaw
CFO: Paul Sansone
Bd of Dir: David W Anderson
Bd of Dir: Gerald W Blakeley
Bd of Dir: Don H Davis
Bd of Dir: Ken Griffey
Ex VP: Trent Germano
Sr VP: Kevin McCartney
Sr VP: Evan McElroy
Sr VP: Ed Mishrell
Sr VP: Lorraine Orr
Sr VP: Julie Teer
Sr VP: Damon Williams
VP: Suzanne Arnold
VP: Dan Casner
VP: Tony McWhorter
**VP:* M V Prasad
Board of Directors: Rick Goings

BOYS TOWN
See FATHER FLANAGANS BOYS HOME

D-U-N-S 07-140-7050
BOZEMAN DEACONESS HEALTH SERVICES (MT)
BOZEMAN DEACONESS HOSPITAL
915 Highland Blvd, Bozeman, MT 59715-6999
Tel (406) 585-5000 *Founded/Ownrshp* 1911, 1916
Sales 212.5MM *EMP* 701
SIC 8062 8059 General medical & surgical hospitals; Rest home, with health care
Ch: Julie Jackson
**Pr:* John Hill
Pr: Elizabeth Lewis
**CFO:* Gordon Davidson
Treas: Janet Colombo
**Treas:* Dennis Munson
VP: Bill Pfingsten
Mktg Dir: Connie Martin
Surgeon: Martin Gelbke
Doctor: Tracy M Fairbanks MD

BOZEMAN DEACONESS HOSPITAL
See BOZEMAN DEACONESS HEALTH SERVICES

D-U-N-S 15-296-8525
BOZZUTO & ASSOCIATES INC
6406 Ivy Ln Ste 700, Greenbelt, MD 20770-1441
Tel (301) 220-0100 *Founded/Ownrshp* 1988
Sales 387.6MME *EMP* 1,006
SIC 6513 1522 6552

BOZZUTO BUILDING COMPANY
See BOZZUTO CONSTRUCTION CO INC

D-U-N-S 87-499-3058
BOZZUTO CONSTRUCTION CO INC
BOZZUTO BUILDING COMPANY
(*Suby of* BOZZUTO & ASSOCIATES INC) ★
6406 Ivy Ln Ste 700, Greenbelt, MD 20770-1441
Tel (301) 220-0100 *Founded/Ownrshp* 1988
Sales 255.8MM *EMP* 100
SIC 1522 1542

D-U-N-S 82-981-8488
BOZZUTO CONTRACTING CO
(*Suby of* BOZZUTO & ASSOCIATES INC) ★
6406 Ivy Ln, Greenbelt, MD 20770-1441
Tel (301) 220-0100 *Founded/Ownrshp* 2008
Sales 83.6MME *EMP* 20
Accts Cohnreznick Llp Baltimore Ma
SIC 1521 1542 General remodeling, single-family houses; Commercial & office building contractors
Pr: Mike Schlegel

D-U-N-S 00-167-7954 IMP
BOZZUTOS INC (CT)
275 Schoolhouse Rd, Cheshire, CT 06410-1257
Tel (203) 272-3511 *Founded/Ownrshp* 1945
Sales 6.0MMME *EMP* 3,100
Accts Federman Lally & Remis Llc F
SIC 5141 5411 Groceries, general line; Supermarkets
Pr: Michael A Bozzuto
VP: Jayne A Bozzuto
VP: Stephen Methvin
VP: Robert H Wood

BP
See STANDARD OIL CO

BP
See ROBERTS-GIBSON INC

BP
See BALDWIN PAVING CO INC

D-U-N-S 03-959-6507 IMP
BP AMERICA INC
(*Suby of* BP P.L.C.)
4101 Winfield Rd Ste 200, Warrenville, IL 60555-3523
Tel (630) 420-5111 *Founded/Ownrshp* 1998
Sales 11.9MMME *EMP* 22,100
SIC 2911 5171 4612 4613 4424 Petroleum refining; Petroleum bulk stations & terminals; Crude petroleum pipelines; Refined petroleum pipelines; Deep sea domestic transportation of freight
Ch Bd: H Lamar McKay
Ex VP: Graham Dudley
Ex VP: Jennifer Johnson
Sr VP: Henry Ball
Sr VP: Ashkan Samimi
VP: Matthew Amend
VP: Nicole Beaubrun-Toby
VP: John Coggeshall
VP: Jennifer Dolphin
VP: Bruce Gourd
VP: Steven Lyall
VP: Mark Smith
VP: Maureen Strobel
VP: Paul Wallace
VP: Joe Wasicka

D-U-N-S 00-896-6889 IMP/EXP
BP AMERICA PRODUCTION CO
(*Suby of* BP COMPANY NORTH AMERICA INC.)
501 Westlake Park Blvd, Houston, TX 77079-2604
Tel (281) 366-2000 *Founded/Ownrshp* 1930
Sales 14.2MMME *EMP* 10,300
SIC 1311 1321 Crude petroleum production; Natural gas production; Natural gas liquids
CEO: Bob Dudley
**COO:* Bernard Looney
**CFO:* Brian Gilvary
**Ex VP:* Katrina Landis
**Ex VP:* Helmut Schuster
Sr VP: Angus Walker
VP: Donald Cochran
VP: J Farnsworth
VP: James R Grant
VP: Morag Watson
**VP:* David F Work
**Exec:* Jerry M Brown
**Exec:* J C Burton

D-U-N-S 00-512-3195 IMP/EXP
BP AMOCO CHEMICAL CO
(*Suby of* B P AMOCO BUSINESS SERVICES) ★
150 W Warrenville Rd, Naperville, IL 60563-8473
Tel (630) 420-5111 *Founded/Ownrshp* 1945
Sales 380.2MME *EMP* 14,700
SIC 2221 2821 2869 2819 2865 Broadwoven fabric mills, manmade; Styrene resins; Industrial organic chemicals; Industrial inorganic chemicals; Cyclic organic crudes
Pr: NC Dunn
Pr: Glenn Perrine
**Pr:* Lm Sierra
Pr: Judy Ventura
Top Exec: Issam Dairanieh
Top Exec: David Hwang
Sr VP: Anne Cody
Sr VP: Cinthia Witty
VP: Frank Molina
Prgrm Mgr: Nancy Ray
Tech Mgr: Richard Farmer

D-U-N-S 00-134-4258 IMP/EXP
BP CORP NORTH AMERICA INC
B P AMOCO BUSINESS SERVICES
(*Suby of* BP AMERICA INC) ★
501 Westlake Park Blvd, Houston, TX 77079-2604
Tel (281) 366-2000 *Founded/Ownrshp* 1889, 1998
Sales 569.0MM *EMP* 22,000
SIC 2911 5541 5171 1311 4613 4612 Petroleum refining; Gasoline; Jet fuels; Diesel fuels; Filling stations, gasoline; Petroleum bulk stations & terminals; Crude petroleum production; Natural gas production; Refined petroleum pipelines; Crude petroleum pipelines
Pr: John C Minge
**Treas:* Michael C Mroz
**VP:* Donette Dewar

D-U-N-S 62-527-5755 IMP/EXP
BP ENERGY CO
B P UPSTREAM TECHNOLOGY, DIV
(*Suby of* BP AMERICA PRODUCTION CO) ★
501 Westlake Park Blvd, Houston, TX 77079-2604
Tel (281) 679-9584 *Founded/Ownrshp* 1985
Sales 193.7MME *EMP* 150
SIC 4924 Natural gas distribution
CEO: Bob Dudley
**Pr:* Brian Frank
**CFO:* Jim Dewar
**CFO:* Brian Gilvary
VP: Shlinda Bell
Pr Mgr: Annie Smith
Counsel: Gaston E Mejia

D-U-N-S 06-133-8489 IMP/EXP
BP LUBRICANTS USA INC
B P
(*Suby of* BP AMERICA INC) ★
1500 Valley Rd, Wayne, NJ 07470-2040
Tel (973) 633-2200 *Founded/Ownrshp* 2001
Sales 287.1MME *EMP* 600
SIC 2992 Lubricating oils & greases
CEO: Marci Brand
VP: Marianne Geuss
VP: Peter Meola
VP: Donna Young
Prgrm Mgr: Louis Rossi
Genl Mgr: Robert Meyers
IT Man: Jo Cubelo
IT Man: Corey Taylor
Opers Mgr: Natasha Olivo
Opers Mgr: Juan Pinedo
Sls&Mrk Ex: Volker Clasen

D-U-N-S 01-963-7727 IMP
BP OIL SUPPLY CO
AMOCO
(*Suby of* BP TRANSPORTATION (ALASKA) INC) ★
28100 Torch Pkwy, Warrenville, IL 60555-3938
Tel (630) 836-5000 *Founded/Ownrshp* 1979

Sales 126.5MM[E] *EMP* 410
SIC 5172 Filling stations, gasoline
Pr: D Wight
**VP:* Phiroz Darukhanavala
VP: Rick Dorazil
VP: Roger Humphreville
VP: Nancy Sheats
VP: Gretchen H Watkins
Genl Mgr: Graham Rose
Dir IT: Mike Elliot
IT Man: Soumya Banerjee
IT Man: Robert Kasper
IT Man: Sharmi Madaboosi

D-U-N-S 00-790-7975 IMP
BP PIPELINES (NORTH AMERICA) INC (ME)
AMOCO
(*Suby of* BP COMPANY NORTH AMERICA INC.)
28100 Torch Pkwy Ste 600, Warrenville, IL 60555-3938
Tel (630) 836-5100 *Founded/Ownrshp* 1916, 2001
Sales 121.3MM[E] *EMP* 900
SIC 4612 4613 Crude petroleum pipelines; Refined petroleum pipelines
Pr: D Wight
Pr: Jim Lamanna
VP: J L Wales

D-U-N-S 00-514-4332 IMP/EXP
BP PRODUCTS NORTH AMERICA INC
BP SHIPPING USA
(*Suby of* BP P.L.C.)
501 Westlake Park Blvd, Houston, TX 77079-2604
Tel (281) 366-2000 *Founded/Ownrshp* 1980
Sales 5.4MMM[E] *EMP* 13,800
SIC 5541 5171 4613 Filling stations, gasoline; Petroleum bulk stations & terminals; Refined petroleum pipelines
Pr: Steve Cornell
VP: Michael Zakarian
Dir Bus: Vispi Mistry
**Prin:* Susan Baur
**Prin:* Michael C Mroz
Counsel: Mary Haskins
Board of Directors: S R Winters

D-U-N-S 78-734-5107
BP PRUDHOE BAY ROYALTY TRUST INC
101 Barclay St, New York, NY 10007-2550
Tel (212) 815-6908 *Founded/Ownrshp* 1989
Sales 126.7MM *EMP* 2
Accts Kpmg Llp Dallas Texas
SIC 6733 Trusts
Prin: James Hutchinson
**Co-Trst:* F James Hutchinson

BP SHIPPING USA
See BP PRODUCTS NORTH AMERICA INC

D-U-N-S 15-146-2066 IMP
BP TRANSPORTATION (ALASKA) INC
(*Suby of* BP) ★
900 E Benson Blvd, Anchorage, AK 99508-4254
Tel (907) 561-5111 *Founded/Ownrshp* 1983
Sales 831.7MM[E] *EMP* 1,502
SIC 1311 Crude petroleum production
Pr: A N Bolea
**Pr:* John Minje
**CFO:* Ian Springett
**Treas:* M C Mroz
**VP:* K A Brown
**VP:* R J Novaria

D-U-N-S 09-720-0401 IMP/EXP
BP WEST COAST PRODUCTS LLC
ARCO
(*Suby of* BP P.L.C.)
4519 Grandview Rd, Blaine, WA 98230-9640
Tel (310) 549-6204 *Founded/Ownrshp* 2001
Sales 340.0MM[E] *EMP* 1,000
SIC 5541 Filling stations, gasoline
CFO: Brian Gilvary
Ex VP: Bernard Looney
Brnch Mgr: Stacey McDaniel

BPD PARKERSBURG OFFICE
See BUREAU OF THE PUBLIC DEBT

BPG
See BUCCINI/POLLIN GROUP INC

BPI
See BUILDING PLASTICS INC

D-U-N-S 07-874-0104
BPI HOLDINGS INTERNATIONAL INC
4400 Prime Pkwy, McHenry, IL 60050-7003
Tel (815) 363-9000 *Founded/Ownrshp* 2012
Sales 600.0MM *EMP* 5,600
SIC 3714 Motor vehicle brake systems & parts
Pr: David Overbeeke
**CFO:* Phil Cutting
**VP:* Mike Caruso

D-U-N-S 04-156-0848 IMP/EXP
BPI TECHNOLOGY INC
BEEF PRODUCTS
891 Two Rivers Dr, Dakota Dunes, SD 57049-5391
Tel (605) 217-8000 *Founded/Ownrshp* 1993
Sales 203.8MM[E] *EMP* 1,400
SIC 2011

BPMI
See BECHTEL PLANT MACHINERY INC

D-U-N-S 07-829-5159
■ **BPREX CLOSURES LLC**
(*Suby of* BERRY PLASTICS CORP) ★
101 Oakley St, Evansville, IN 47710-1237
Tel (812) 424-2904 *Founded/Ownrshp* 2011
Sales 95.6MM[E] *EMP* 760[E]
SIC 3089 Bottle caps, molded plastic

D-U-N-S 79-034-3867 IMP
■ **BPREX HEALTHCARE BROOKVILLE INC**
REXAM CLOSURE SYSTEMS
(*Suby of* BERRY PLASTICS CORP) ★
1899 N Wilkinson Way, Perrysburg, OH 43551-1685
Tel (847) 541-9700 *Founded/Ownrshp* 2014
Sales 225.5MM[E] *EMP* 800
SIC 3089 Caps, plastic; Closures, plastic
CEO: Steve Wirrig
Exec: Ron Riemer

D-U-N-S 83-284-3655
■ **BPREX HEALTHCARE PACKAGING INC**
REXAM
(*Suby of* BERRY PLASTICS CORP) ★
600 Deerfield Pkwy, Buffalo Grove, IL 60089-7050
Tel (800) 537-0178 *Founded/Ownrshp* 2014
Sales 1.9MMM[E] *EMP* 15,000[E]
SIC 3565 Packaging machinery
CEO: Frank C Brown
VP: Tom Holz

D-U-N-S 92-732-2875
■ **BPREX PLASTIC PACKAGING INC**
OI PLASTIC PRODUCTS FTS INC
(*Suby of* BERRY PLASTICS CORP) ★
1 Seagate Ste 10, Toledo, OH 43604-1563
Tel (419) 247-5000 *Founded/Ownrshp* 2014
Sales 77.2MM[E] *EMP* 1,600
SIC 3221 3089 Glass containers; Food containers, glass; Bottles for packing, bottling & canning: glass; Medicine bottles, glass; Plastic containers, except foam; Cases, plastic; Jars, plastic; Closures, plastic
CEO: Joseph Lemieux
Prin: Kenneth Hicks
Prin: Lisa Hysko

BPU
See KANSAS CITY BOARD OF PUBLIC UTILITIES

BPZ ENERGY
See BPZ RESOURCES INC

D-U-N-S 80-287-2564
BPZ RESOURCES INC
BPZ ENERGY
10497 Town And Country Wa, Houston, TX 77024-1135
Tel (281) 556-6200 *Founded/Ownrshp* 2001
Sales 83.9MM *EMP* 100
SIC 1311 Crude petroleum & natural gas
Prin: Manuel Zuniga-Pflucker
**Ch Bd:* James B Taylor
**Pr:* Manuel Pablo Zuniga-Pflucker
CFO: Richard S Menniti

BRA
See ARIZONA BOARD OF REGENTS

D-U-N-S 02-287-8979
BRAAS CO
7970 Wallace Rd, Eden Prairie, MN 55344-2232
Tel (952) 937-8902 *Founded/Ownrshp* 1964
Sales 167.9MM[E] *EMP* 147
SIC 5084

D-U-N-S 03-605-7487
BRABHAM OIL CO INC
525 Midway St, Bamberg, SC 29003-1934
Tel (803) 245-2471 *Founded/Ownrshp* 1962
Sales 435.0MM[E] *EMP* 500
SIC 5171 5541 5411 5921 Petroleum bulk stations; Filling stations, gasoline; Convenience stores, independent; Liquor stores
Pr: Clarence B McCully
Sls Mgr: Joe Norman

D-U-N-S 84-923-4661 IMP
BRACCO DIAGNOSTICS INC
(*Suby of* BRACCO USA INC) ★
259 Prospect Plains Rd, Monroe Township, NJ 08831-3820
Tel (609) 514-2200 *Founded/Ownrshp* 1994
Sales 160.1MM[E] *EMP* 375
SIC 2835 In vitro & in vivo diagnostic substances
Pr: Vittorio Puppo
COO: Anthony Lombardo
VP: William Berrek
QA Dir: Laura Masini
Mktg Dir: Jeff Cushner
Mktg Dir: Lakshmi Sundar
Snr Mgr: Richard Cubbage
Snr Mgr: Carolyn Johnson

D-U-N-S 03-635-9917 IMP
BRACCO USA INC
(*Suby of* BRACCO SPA)
259 Prospect Plains Rd, Monroe Township, NJ 08831-3820
Tel (609) 514-2200 *Founded/Ownrshp* 1993
Sales 168.7MM[E] *EMP* 380
SIC 2835 In vitro & in vivo diagnostic substances
Pr: Diana Bracco
**Treas:* Alberto Sana Maria

D-U-N-S 07-987-0933
BRACE INC
14950 Heathrow Forest Pkw, Houston, TX 77032-3855
Tel (281) 749-1020 *Founded/Ownrshp* 1991
Sales 136.0MM[E] *EMP* 1,500
SIC 6719 Investment holding companies, except banks
Pr: J Brendan Logue

D-U-N-S 04-156-8596
BRACE INDUSTRIAL GROUP INC
(*Suby of* BRACE INC) ★
14950 Heathrow Fore, Houston, TX 77032-3847
Tel (281) 749-1020 *Founded/Ownrshp* 2013
Sales 93.1MM[E] *EMP* 400[E]
SIC 8748 Business consulting
CEO: Hans Petter-Hansen
**Pr:* Craig Kaple
**CFO:* J Brendan Logue

D-U-N-S 08-000-0004
BRACE INTEGRATED SERVICES INC
(*Suby of* BRACE INC) ★
14950 Heathrow Frst, Houston, TX 77032-3847
Tel (281) 749-1020 *Founded/Ownrshp* 2015
Sales 13.4MM[E] *EMP* 1,500
SIC 8748 Business consulting
CEO: Steve Ragiel
**Pr:* Williamson T Hough
**Pr:* Todd Rouw
**COO:* Craig Kaple
**CFO:* J Brendan Logue
**VP:* Shirley Risen

D-U-N-S 07-221-0958
BRACEWELL LLP (TX)
711 Louisiana St Ste 2300, Houston, TX 77002-2770
Tel (713) 223-2300 *Founded/Ownrshp* 1992
Sales 296.0MM[E] *EMP* 900
SIC 8111 General practice law office
Mng Pt: Mark C Evans
Pt: Jeffrey J Ansley
Pt: John H Barr
Pt: W Stephen Benesh
**Pt:* Greg M Bopp
Pt: Sanford M Brown
Pt: Carol Elder Bruce
Pt: Robert T Carey
Pt: John A Couch
Pt: Joseph M Cox
Pt: Shane Egan
Pt: Kevin Ewing
Pt: Joseph Moody Ford
Pt: Christopher B Gilbert
Pt: Randall K Glover
Pt: Dewey J Gonsoulin Jr
Pt: Lacey Gourley
**Pt:* Paul Grabowski
Pt: Sheryl A Gussett
Pt: Elizabeth A Hall
Pt: Amy Karff Halwvy

D-U-N-S 11-879-3819
■ **BRACOR INC**
WILLCARE
(*Suby of* NATIONAL HEALTH INDUSTRIES INC) ★
346 Delaware Ave, Buffalo, NY 14202-1804
Tel (716) 856-7500 *Founded/Ownrshp* 2015
Sales 34.6MM[E] *EMP* 1,700
SIC 8082 8071 7361 Home health care services; Medical laboratories; Nurses' registry
Pr: Eric Armenat
CFO: David Brason

D-U-N-S 08-004-4844
BRAD HENRY FRIEDMUTTER & ASSOCIATES LTD
FRIEDMUTTER GROUP
4022 Dean Martin Dr, Las Vegas, NV 89103-4134
Tel (702) 736-7477 *Founded/Ownrshp* 1992
Sales 12.8MM[E] *EMP* 1,992
SIC 8712 7389 Architectural services; Interior design services
Pr: Brad Henry Friedmutter
**VP:* Anna Hawkins

D-U-N-S 03-348-4635
BRAD LANIER OIL CO INC
611 W Roosevelt Ave, Albany, GA 31701-2150
Tel (229) 436-0131 *Founded/Ownrshp* 1965
Sales 127.1MM *EMP* 85
Accts Draffin & Tucker Llp Albany
SIC 5171 5541 5411 Petroleum bulk stations; Filling stations, gasoline; Convenience stores, independent
Pr: Hans D Pomeroy
**VP:* Jeff Lanier

D-U-N-S 01-107-7385 EXP
BRADCO SUPPLY CORP
WICKES LUMBER DIVISION
34 Engelhard Ave, Avenel, NJ 07001-2217
Tel (732) 382-3400 *Founded/Ownrshp* 1966
Sales 1.6MMM *EMP* 2,600
SIC 5033 5211

D-U-N-S 80-958-0996 IMP
BRADEN PARTNERS LP A CALIFORNIA LIMITED PARTNERSHIP
PACIFIC PULMONARY SERVICES CO
(*Suby of* TEIJIN PHARMA USA LLC) ★
773 San Marin Dr Ste 2230, Novato, CA 94945-1366
Tel (415) 893-1518 *Founded/Ownrshp* 1978
Sales 101.3MM[E] *EMP* 1,115
SIC 8082 Home health care services
CEO: Jane Thomas
**Ch Bd:* Tsutomu Igawa
Sr VP: Alan Winters
VP: Jon Alsterlind
VP: Jim Doty
VP: Chris Kane
VP: Nancy Murr
VP: Debbie Shotwell
Genl Mgr: Joshua Stoltzfus
CIO: Mark Williams
Dir IT: Wing Yu

D-U-N-S 06-438-5784 IMP/EXP
BRADFORD EXCHANGE LTD (IL)
VAN HYGAN & SMYTHE
9333 N Milwaukee Ave, Niles, IL 60714-1392
Tel (847) 966-2770 *Founded/Ownrshp* 1962
Sales 127.4MM[E] *EMP* 600
SIC 5961 5199 Collectibles & antiques, mail order; Art goods
Pr: Richard W Tinberg
**CFO:* James D Liggett
**Sr VP:* James Gallagher
VP: Robert Botta
**VP:* Joel R Platt
Creative D: Beth Dewall
Creative D: Stephanie Greenberg
Creative D: Linda Lin
Prgrm Mgr: Judy Chupinsky
CTO: Allen King
QA Dir: Natalya Kodaneva

D-U-N-S 17-171-7833
BRADFORD HOLDING CO INC
4646 Corona Dr Ste 105, Corpus Christi, TX 78411-4383
Tel (361) 852-6392 *Founded/Ownrshp* 2000
Sales 134.0MM *EMP* 3,400
Accts Tranbarger & Company Llp Corp
SIC 7363 Employee leasing service
Ch Bd: Garry Bradford
**CFO:* Rick Delano
**Ex VP:* Rebecca Bradford
**VP Mktg:* Greg Maisel

D-U-N-S 78-557-1212 EXP
BRADFORD SOAP INTERNATIONAL INC
200 Providence St, West Warwick, RI 02893-2511
Tel (401) 821-2141 *Founded/Ownrshp* 1967
Sales 199.7MM[E] *EMP* 900
SIC 2841 Soap & other detergents
Ch: John H Howland
Ex VP: Jimmy Curran

D-U-N-S 15-729-7540 IMP/EXP
BRADFORD-WHITE CORP
725 Talamore Dr, Ambler, PA 19002-1873
Tel (215) 641-9400 *Founded/Ownrshp* 1985
Sales 14.2MM *EMP* 1,219
SIC 3433 1711 Heating equipment, except electric; Plumbing, heating, air-conditioning contractors
Ch Bd: A Robert Carnevale

D-U-N-S 15-639-6793 IMP
BRADKEN - ATCHISON/ST JOSEPH INC
400 S 4th St, Atchison, KS 66002-2886
Tel (913) 367-2121 *Founded/Ownrshp* 2003
Sales 218.1MM[E] *EMP* 749
SIC 3325

BRADKEN ENGINEERED PRODUCTS
See BRADKEN INC

D-U-N-S 14-187-4821 IMP
BRADKEN INC
BRADKEN ENGINEERED PRODUCTS
(*Suby of* BRADKEN LIMITED)
12200 N Ambassador Dr # 647, Kansas City, MO 64163-1203
Tel (816) 270-0700 *Founded/Ownrshp* 2008
Sales 389.2MM[E] *EMP* 1,015
SIC 3325 3321 3312 Steel foundries; Gray & ductile iron foundries; Stainless steel
COO: Tom Armstrong
**COO:* Kevin T McDermed
**CFO:* Dennis Rippe
VP: John Derossi
**VP:* Steve Gear
CIO: Dan Harris
CTO: John Saad
Tech Mgr: Clary Rick
Opers Mgr: Steve Hall
Ql Cn Mgr: Stan Truselo
VP Sls: Nathan Heisler

D-U-N-S 07-210-9838
BRADLEY ARANT BOULT CUMMINGS LLP
1819 5th Ave N Ste 200, Birmingham, AL 35203-2119
Tel (205) 521-8000 *Founded/Ownrshp* 1977
Sales 106.0MM[E] *EMP* 395
SIC 8111 General practice attorney, lawyer
Genl Pt: Beau Grenier
Pt: John B Hardcastle Jr
Mng Pt: John D Bond III
Mng Pt: Philip H Butler
Mng Pt: Margaret O Cupples
Mng Pt: Kimberly B Martin
Mng Pt: Douglas L Patin
COO: Joseph P Wood
Exec: Luke Martin

D-U-N-S 01-178-0152 IMP/EXP
BRADLEY CALDWELL INC
200 Kiwanis Blvd, West Hazleton, PA 18202-1160
Tel (570) 455-7511 *Founded/Ownrshp* 1930
Sales 254.3MM[E] *EMP* 435
SIC 5191 5199 5072 Farm supplies; Equestrian equipment; Garden supplies; Pet supplies; Hardware
Pr: James L Bradley
CFO: Brian Herring
**VP:* Michael Doto
IT Man: Nelson Herr
IT Man: Michael Seidel
Sls Mgr: Joseph Doto
Sales Asso: Jim Cahill
Sales Asso: Erin Flanagan
Sales Asso: Steve Laronde
Sales Asso: Frank Nagy

D-U-N-S 00-607-8307 IMP
BRADLEY CORP (WI)
W142n9101 Fountain Blvd, Menomonee Falls, WI 53051-2348
Tel (262) 251-6000 *Founded/Ownrshp* 1921
Sales 187.1MM[E] *EMP* 624
SIC 3431 3272 Metal sanitary ware; Wash foundations, precast terrazzo
Ch Bd: Donald H Mullett
**COO:* Mike Sipek
Treas: Jim Oldenburg
**Treas:* Mark Umhoefer
Chf Mktg O: Jon Dommisse
VP: Bryan Mullett
**VP:* Steve Zingsheim
Genl Mgr: Michael Vickery
IT Man: Kurt Kaestner
**VP Mfg:* Larry K Stover
Mfg Dir: Lloyd Leurquin

D-U-N-S 00-332-6733 IMP
BRADLEY PLYWOOD CORP (GA)
DIXIE PLYWOOD & LBR CO ATLANTA
204 Old West Lathrop Ave, Savannah, GA 31415-1757
Tel (912) 447-7000 *Founded/Ownrshp* 1944
Sales 94.5MM[E] *EMP* 120
SIC 5031 Lumber: rough, dressed & finished; Plywood
Ch Bd: W Waldo Bradley
**Pr:* Daniel H Bradley
**COO:* Danny Bachman
**CFO:* T Mark Gentry

D-U-N-S 04-913-0768
BRADLEY UNIVERSITY
1501 W Bradley Ave, Peoria, IL 61625-0003
Tel (309) 677-3150 *Founded/Ownrshp* 1896
Sales 122.2MM[E] *EMP* 1,000
Accts Cliftonlarsonallen Llp Peoria
SIC 8221 University
Ch: Robert E Turner
**Pr:* Joanne K Glasser
VP: Gary M Anna
VP: Paul Current
VP: Kyle Peck

VP: Zach Singleton
VP: Jobie Skaggs
Assoc Dir: Jennifer Jones
Ex Dir: Robert Farquhar
Ex Dir: Nial Johnson
Ex Dir: Jack Russel

D-U-N-S 05-734-5043 IMP/EXP
BRADSHAW INTERNATIONAL INC
9409 Buffalo Ave, Rancho Cucamonga, CA 91730-6012
Tel (909) 476-3884 Founded/Ownrshp 2010
Sales 400.0MM[E] EMP 414
SIC 5023 Kitchenware
CEO: Michael Rodrigue
*Pr: Brett R Bradshaw
Pr: Julie Hayes
*CFO: Jerry Vigliotti
Chf Mktg O: Julie Lawson
Ex VP: Jeff Megorden
VP: Scott Bradshaw
VP: Troy Schuler
VP: Scott Stephenson
Exec: Tammy Peterson
VP Admn: Susan Chesbrough

D-U-N-S 00-607-3027 IMP/EXP
▲ BRADY CORP
6555 W Good Hope Rd, Milwaukee, WI 53223-4634
Tel (414) 358-6600 Founded/Ownrshp 1914
Sales 1.1MMM EMP 6,560
Tkr Sym BRC Exch NYS
SIC 3993 2672 3695 3577 Signs & advertising specialties; Name plates: except engraved, etched, etc.: metal; Signs, not made in custom sign painting shops; Tape, pressure sensitive: made from purchased materials; Adhesive papers, labels or tapes: from purchased material; Labels (unprinted), gummed: made from purchased materials; Audio range tape, blank; Video recording tape, blank; Optical disks & tape, blank; Computer peripheral equipment
Pr: J Michael Nauman
*Ch Bd: Conrad G Goodkind
Pr: Thomas J Felmer
Pr: Russell R Shaller
CFO: Aaron J Pearce
Treas: Paul T Meyer
Sr VP: Louis T Bolognini
Sr VP: Helena R Nelligan
VP: Bentley N Curran
VP: Katie Milbeck
VP: Linda Toplikar
Board of Directors: Patrick W Allender, Gary S Balkema, Elizabeth P Bruno, Nancy L Gioia, Frank W Harris, Bradley C Richardson, Harold L Sirkin

D-U-N-S 03-493-2657 IMP
BRADY INDUSTRIES INC
7055 Lindell Rd, Las Vegas, NV 89118-4703
Tel (702) 876-3990 Founded/Ownrshp 1950
Sales 648.8MM[E] EMP 987
SIC 5169 5087 5999 5023 5064 Sanitation preparations; Janitors' supplies; Laundry equipment & supplies; Cleaning equipment & supplies; Linens & towels; Clothes dryers, electric & gas; Washing machines
CEO: William D Brady
*Pr: Travis Brady
*Sec: Eric Brady

D-U-N-S 04-451-1582
BRADY SALES AND SERVICE INC
(Suby of BRADY SERVICES) ★
1915 N Church St, Greensboro, NC 27405-5631
Tel (336) 378-0670 Founded/Ownrshp 1963
Sales 183.1MM[E] EMP 250
SIC 5075 Air conditioning & ventilation equipment & supplies
Pr: Donald J Brady
CFO: Wayne Thompson
*Treas: R Wayne Hutchins
Snr Mgr: Jeff Crum

BRADY SERVICES
See BRADY TRANE SERVICE INC

D-U-N-S 06-743-6550
BRADY TRANE SERVICE INC
BRADY SERVICES
1915 N Church St, Greensboro, NC 27405-5631
Tel (919) 781-0458 Founded/Ownrshp 1966
Sales 183.1MM[E] EMP 250
SIC 5075 1711 7623 Air conditioning equipment, except room units; Plumbing, heating, air-conditioning contractors; Air conditioning repair
Ch: Donald J Brady
*Treas: R Wayne Hutchins
*VP: James E Brady
IT Man: Karen Branson
VP Opers: Patrick Tonker
Snr Mgr: Jeff Smith

D-U-N-S 78-718-6691 IMP/EXP
■ BRADY WORLDWIDE INC
ELECTROMARK COMPANY
(Suby of BRADY CORP) ★
6555 W Good Hope Rd, Milwaukee, WI 53223-4634
Tel (414) 358-6600 Founded/Ownrshp 1991
Sales 549.0MM[E] EMP 2,556
SIC 3999 Identification badges & insignia
CEO: J Michael Nauman
*CFO: Aaron J Pearce
*Sr VP: Helena Nelligan
*VP: Matthew O Williamson
Netwrk Mgr: John Pearson
Sls Mgr: Kevin Doyle

BRAGG CRANE & RIGGING
See BRAGG INVESTMENT CO INC

D-U-N-S 15-282-2060
BRAGG INVESTMENT CO INC
BRAGG CRANE & RIGGING
6251 N Paramount Blvd, Long Beach, CA 90805-3713
Tel (562) 984-2400 Founded/Ownrshp 1946
Sales 278.7MM[E] EMP 1,000
SIC 7389 7353 1791 Crane & aerial lift service; Heavy construction equipment rental; Structural steel erection
CEO: Marilynn Bragg
*Sec: Mary A Pool
Ofcr: Michael Willer
*Sr VP: Mike Roy
*VP: Scott Bragg
VP: Jim Hulse
VP: Joe Vilardi
Exec: Susan Graham
Genl Mgr: Bob Weyers
Off Admin: Sheree Gardner
MIS Dir: Gary Wilhelm

D-U-N-S 14-045-5663
BRAHMA GROUP
(Suby of TERRA MILLENNIUM CORP) ★
1132 S 500 W, Salt Lake City, UT 84101-3018
Tel (801) 521-5200 Founded/Ownrshp 2002
Sales 194.9MM EMP 400
Accts Armanino Llp San Ramon Calif
SIC 1791 Structural steel erection
Pr: Sean G Davis
*CFO: Michael P Elam
*VP: Sean Davis
Rgnl Mgr: Mike Curtis
Rgnl Mgr: John Haas
Off Mgr: Karen Morris
IT Man: Roger Street

D-U-N-S 00-191-7426 IMP/EXP
BRAIFORM ENTERPRISES INC (NY)
PLASTI-FORM
(Suby of SPOTLESS PLASTICS (USA) INC) ★
237 W 35th St Ste 504, New York, NY 10001-1905
Tel (800) 738-7396 Founded/Ownrshp 1962, 1987
Sales 111.8MM[E] EMP 650
SIC 3089 Clothes hangers, plastic; Injection molded finished plastic products
Ch Bd: Graeme Andrew S Rutherford
*Pr: Peter Wilson
*Ch: Josef Farnik
*Ex VP: Stanley Gouldson
*VP: Chuck Kelly
VP: Chuck Nicholson
Dir IT: Doug Hernandez

D-U-N-S 14-419-8491
BRAIN HURRICANE LLC
2510 S Christiana Ave, Chicago, IL 60623-4039
Tel (312) 577-0066 Founded/Ownrshp 2002
Sales 16.1MM[E] EMP 2,050[E]
SIC 8299 Educational services
Prin: Mellinee L Thompson
Off Mgr: Elena Ramo
Off Admin: Janeth Mendoza

D-U-N-S 84-319-0971
BRAINERD PUBLIC SCHOOLS
I S D 181 COMMUNITY EDUCATION
804 Oak St, Brainerd, MN 56401-3755
Tel (218) 454-6900 Founded/Ownrshp 1980
Sales 85.9MM EMP 225
Accts Larsonallen Llp Brainerd Min
SIC 8211 Public elementary & secondary schools
Pr Dir: Cori Reynolds
HC Dir: Amy Jambor

D-U-N-S 01-400-3573 IMP
BRAINLAB INC
(Suby of BRAINLAB AG)
5 Westbrook Corp Ctr, Westchester, IL 60154-5749
Tel (800) 784-7700 Founded/Ownrshp 1998
Sales 200.4MM[E] EMP 227
SIC 5047 3841 Medical equipment & supplies; Surgical & medical instruments
CEO: Stefan Vilsmeier
*Pr: Sean Clark
COO: Stephan Holl
*Treas: Heidi King
*VP: Joseph Doyle
VP: Joel Fuchs
VP: Alexander Schwiersch
Exec: Pecky Schmidt
Dir Soc: Kristina Kreiling
Dir Soc: Rose Markovic
Comm Man: Bettina Rapperstorfer

D-U-N-S 07-973-7718
BRAINTREE HOTEL OPERATOR INC
215 Wood Rd, Braintree, MA 02184-2407
Tel (781) 380-3300 Founded/Ownrshp 2012
Sales 3.1MM[E] EMP 2,012
SIC 7011 Hotel, franchised
Pr: Michael Medzigian
*Treas: George Gudgeon

D-U-N-S 60-623-0449 IMP/EXP
BRAKE PARTS INC LLC
(Suby of BPI HOLDINGS INTERNATIONAL INC) ★
4400 Prime Pkwy, McHenry, IL 60050-7033
Tel (815) 363-9000 Founded/Ownrshp 1988
Sales 546.2MM[E] EMP 5,098
SIC 3714 Motor vehicle brake systems & parts; Brake drums, motor vehicle
Pr: H David Overbeeke
Chf Mktg O: Ken Myers
VP: Don Boeckenstedt
VP: Kevin Judge
VP: David Sather
VP: Stephanie Slatkin
Snr Ntwrk: Patrick Hoffman
MIS Mgr: Ed Wolff

D-U-N-S 01-627-9911 IMP/EXP
BRAKE SUPPLY CO INC
(Suby of KOCH ENTERPRISES INC) ★
5501 Foundation Blvd, Evansville, IN 47725-9653
Tel (812) 467-1000 Founded/Ownrshp 1986
Sales 105.8MM[E] EMP 285
SIC 5082 5084 5088 5013 3532

D-U-N-S 00-643-7966 IMP
BRAKEBUSH BROTHERS INC
N4993 6th Dr, Westfield, WI 53964-8200
Tel (608) 296-2121 Founded/Ownrshp 1983
Sales 220.9MM[E] EMP 400
SIC 2013 2015 Sausages & other prepared meats; Poultry slaughtering & processing
Pr: Carl Brakebush
COO: Dave Robinson
*CFO: Thomas Ludwig
*Treas: Nancy Brakebush
QA Dir: Christy Haefner
Mktg Mgr: Bob Jelenchick
Manager: Joe Burnett
Manager: Adam Green
Manager: Steve Male
Manager: Rick McMillen
Manager: Cindy Nathe

BRAMAN HONDA OF PALM BEACH
See BRAMAN MOTOR CARS

D-U-N-S 05-254-9136 IMP/EXP
BRAMAN MOTOR CARS
BRAMAN HONDA OF PALM BEACH
2901 Okeechobee Blvd, West Palm Beach, FL 33409-4013
Tel (561) 615-4800 Founded/Ownrshp 1982
Sales 140.0MM[E] EMP 316
SIC 5511 Automobiles, new & used
Ch: Norman Braman
*Pr: Richard S Hellawell
*Treas: Robert Bernstein
*VP: Ed Lebowitz
Dir IT: Don Rollfing
IT Man: Don Rolling
Mktg Dir: Danny Bayard
Sls Mgr: Raj Alexander
Sls Mgr: Ronald Bacak
Sls Mgr: Fred Castellano
Sls Mgr: Willie Orth

D-U-N-S 60-532-2817
BRAMBLES USA INC (DEL)
(Suby of BIP INDUSTRIES LIMITED)
180 Technology Pkwy # 600, Norcross, GA 30092-2977
Tel (770) 776-1900 Founded/Ownrshp 2006
Sales 642.9MM[E] EMP 1,750
SIC 4953 4212 7353 8741 7359 Hazardous waste collection & disposal; Refuse collection & disposal services; Non-hazardous waste disposal sites; Incinerator operation; Hazardous waste transport; Heavy construction equipment rental; Management services; Administrative management; Office management; Equipment rental & leasing
Pr: Melissa Schmidt

D-U-N-S 00-694-5133 IMP/EXP
BRAMCO INC
1801 Watterson Trl, Louisville, KY 40299-2431
Tel (502) 493-4300 Founded/Ownrshp 1908
Sales 174.1MM[E] EMP 450
SIC 5082 7353 General construction machinery & equipment; Heavy construction equipment rental
Ch: Joseph A Paradis III
*Pr: Charles Leis
*CEO: Jay Paradis
*CFO: Michael Brennan
Bd of Dir: Becky Frye
*VP: Mike Paradis
Ex Dir: Ann Campbell

D-U-N-S 06-973-6239
BRAMMER ENGINEERING INC (LA)
400 Texas St Ste 600, Shreveport, LA 71101-3546
Tel (318) 429-2345 Founded/Ownrshp 1968, 1995
Sales 128.7MM[E] EMP 110
SIC 1389 Gas field services
Pr: Keith Evans
*CFO: Stephen G Moran
VP: Robert Kyle
VP: Larry Richardson
*VP: Richard West

D-U-N-S 18-792-7355
BRANCH & ASSOCIATES INC
(Suby of BRANCH GROUP INC) ★
5732 Airport Rd Nw, Roanoke, VA 24012-1122
Tel (540) 989-5215 Founded/Ownrshp 1974
Sales 193.0MM EMP 90
Accts Kpmg Llp Roanoke Virginia
SIC 1542 Commercial & office building, new construction; Institutional building construction
Pr: Craig Floyd
COO: Mike Quinn
CFO: Freddy McGuire
*Treas: Melanie Wheeler
*VP: Tony Brown
VP: Dave Kapp
*VP: Terry Keffer
*VP: Catherine Underwood
*VP: Michael Vos
Dir Bus: Hugo Amelink
MIS Dir: Kevin Collie

D-U-N-S 00-699-7704 IMP
■ BRANCH BANKING AND TRUST CO (NC)
BB&T
(Suby of BB&T CORP) ★
200 W 2nd St, Winston Salem, NC 27101-4019
Tel (336) 733-2000 Founded/Ownrshp 1974
Sales NA EMP 12,362
SIC 6022 6021 State commercial banks; National commercial banks
CEO: Kelly S King
COO: Bob Feuerbach
COO: Christopher L Henson
CFO: Scott E Reed
Treas: Daryl N Bible
Ofcr: Kathy Tant
Ex VP: Paul Johnson
Ex VP: Jim Sherrick
Ex VP: Clarke R Starnes III
Sr VP: James N Ashby
Sr VP: Barbara F Duck
Sr VP: Todd Hannah
Sr VP: Carl Leppert
Sr VP: Randy McGann
Sr VP: Riley Moody
Sr VP: Benjamin Sharpe
Sr VP: Manny Tavares
Sr VP: Karl Tweardy
VP: Michael Brenan
VP: Ricky K Brown
VP: Grist David

D-U-N-S 07-848-4572
BRANCH BANKING AND TRUST CO HEALTH CARE PLAN
BB&T
P.O. Box 1215 (27102-1215)
Tel (336) 733-2411 Founded/Ownrshp 2012
Sales 294.7MM EMP 12[E]
SIC 6733 Trusts
Prin: Dianna Pietrzak

D-U-N-S 02-393-5984
BRANCH GROUP INC
442 Rutherford Ave Ne, Roanoke, VA 24016-2116
Tel (540) 982-1678 Founded/Ownrshp 1963
Sales 392.4MM EMP 800[E]
Accts Kpmg Llp Roanoke Virginia
SIC 1542 1611 1711 1731 1541 Commercial & office building contractors; School building construction; Institutional building construction; General contractor, highway & street construction; Mechanical contractor; General electrical contractor; Industrial buildings, new construction
CEO: J William Karbach
*COO: Steve Aud
COO: Tomlinson Mike
*CFO: Melanie Wheeler
*Ex VP: Tony Brown
*Ex VP: Larry Dickenson
*VP: Terry Keffer

D-U-N-S 11-913-5770
BRANCH GROUP INC
REXEL
1049 Prince Georges Blvd, Upper Marlboro, MD 20774-7427
Tel (301) 249-5005 Founded/Ownrshp 2000
Sales NA EMP 1,200
SIC 5063 5211

D-U-N-S 17-810-9294
BRANCH HIGHWAYS INC
(Suby of BRANCH GROUP INC) ★
442 Rutherford Ave Ne, Roanoke, VA 24016-2116
Tel (540) 982-1678 Founded/Ownrshp 1963
Sales 113.9MM EMP 250
Accts Kpmg Llp Roanoke Virginia
SIC 1611 Highway & street construction; Grading
Pr: J William Karbach
*Treas: Melanie Wheeler
VP: Larry Dickenson
*VP: Mike Higgins
*VP: Terry Keffer
VP: Thomas Partridge
Sfty Dirs: Danny Minnix

D-U-N-S 07-247-1618
BRAND BANKING CO
(Suby of BRAND GROUP HOLDINGS, INC.)
106 Crogan St, Lawrenceville, GA 30046-4942
Tel (770) 963-9224 Founded/Ownrshp 1905
Sales NA EMP 288
SIC 6036 State savings banks, not federally chartered
CEO: Bartow Morgan Jr
Pr: Chris Smith
CFO: Rob Cochran
Sr VP: Chris Gruehn
VP: Barbara Mahaffey
IT Man: Mike Shaw
Snr Mgr: David Bybee

D-U-N-S 95-697-0052
BRAND ENERGY & INFRASTRUCTURE HOLDINGS INC
(Suby of CLAYTON DUBILIER & RICE LLC) ★
1325 Cobb Intl Dr Nw A1, Kennesaw, GA 30152-8243
Tel (678) 285-1400 Founded/Ownrshp 2013
Sales 1.1MMM[E] EMP 6,000[E]
SIC 1799 Scaffolding construction
CEO: Paul T Wood
*Treas: CHI N Swallow

D-U-N-S 13-108-9034 IMP
BRAND ENERGY & INFRASTRUCTURE SERVICES INC
(Suby of BRAND ENERGY & INFRASTRUCTURE HOLDINGS INC) ★
1325 Cobb Intl Dr Nw A1, Kennesaw, GA 30152-8243
Tel (678) 285-1400 Founded/Ownrshp 1996
Sales 1.1MMM[E] EMP 6,000
SIC 1799 Scaffolding construction
CEO: Paul T Wood
Pr: David J Witsken
CFO: CHI Nguyen
Ex VP: James R Billingsley Jr
Ex VP: Jamie Ha
VP: William Dean Ryan
Dist Mgr: Eric Hogan
Genl Mgr: Jason Corbello
Off Mgr: Dee Dee Husted
IT Man: Jennifer Bryden
IT Man: Chris Gauthier

D-U-N-S 86-134-0859 IMP/EXP
BRAND ENERGY SOLUTIONS LLC
(Suby of BRAND ENERGY & INFRASTRUCTURE SERVICES INC) ★
1325 Cobb International D, Kennesaw, GA 30152-8243
Tel (678) 285-1400 Founded/Ownrshp 2005
Sales 747.9MM[E] EMP 6,000
SIC 1751 1742 1799 1721 Carpentry work; Insulation, buildings; Scaffolding construction; Residential painting
*CEO: Paul T Wood
CFO: Jeff Peterson
*Ex VP: CHI Nguyen
Snr Ntwrk: Tony Pickett

BRAND ENRGY INFRSTRUCTURE SVCS
See BRAND SERVICES LLC

Section I Businesses Alphabetically

D-U-N-S 02-397-9508 IMP
BRAND SERVICES LLC
BRAND ENRGY INFRSTRUCTURE SVCS
(*Suby of* BRAND ENERGY & INFRASTRUCTURE SERVICES INC) ★
1325 Cobb Intl Dr Nw A1, Kennesaw, GA 30152-8243
Tel (678) 285-1400 *Founded/Ownrshp* 2008
Sales 321.7MM[E] *EMP* 2,500
SIC 1799 Scaffolding construction
CEO: Paul T Woodd
CFO: Anthony Rabb

BRAND USA, THE
See CORP FOR TRAVEL PROMOTION

D-U-N-S 62-083-7450
BRANDED ENTERTAINMENT NETWORK INC
710 2nd Ave Ste 200, Seattle, WA 98104-1703
Tel (206) 373-6000 *Founded/Ownrshp* 1989
Sales 115.0MM[E] *EMP* 1,012
SIC 7335 Commercial photography
CEO: Gary Shenk
**CFO:* Joe Schick
Sr VP: Greg Isaacs
Sr VP: Chris Karl
**Sr VP:* Jim Mitchell
Sr VP: Barak Ronen
VP: Colleen Lillie
VP: Ingvar Peturrson
VP: Corey Silverman
Dir Bus: Rich Reiter
**CTO:* Brian Cohee

D-U-N-S 05-598-6020
BRANDEIS UNIVERSITY
415 South St Ms110, Waltham, MA 02453-2700
Tel (781) 736-8318 *Founded/Ownrshp* 1937
Sales 313.9MM *EMP* 1,200[E]
Accts Kpmg Llp Boston Ma
SIC 8221 University
Pr: Frederick M Lawrence
**COO:* Steven S Manos
CFO: Frances A Drolette
**Treas:* Marianne Cwalina
Trst: John M Connors
Trst: Stephen Kay
Ofcr: Deborah F Kuenstner
**Sr VP:* David A Bunis
Sr VP: Mark J Collins
**Sr VP:* Andrew Flagel
**Sr VP:* Judy Glasser
**Sr VP:* Lisa M Lynch
Sr VP: Judith R Sizer
**Sr VP:* Nancy Winship
Sr VP: Nancy K Winship
VP: Scot Bemis
VP: Mark Collins
VP: Cely De Barros
VP: Dan Feldman
VP: Daniel Feldman
VP: Emilia Feldman

D-U-N-S 17-788-1687
BRANDENBURG INDUSTRIAL SERVICE CO
2625 S Loomis St, Chicago, IL 60608-5400
Tel (312) 326-5800 *Founded/Ownrshp* 1968
Sales 177.1MM *EMP* 750
Accts Miller Cooper & Co Ltd De
SIC 4959 1795 5093 Environmental cleanup services; Wrecking & demolition work; Scrap & waste materials
Pr: Thomas J Little
Treas: Lynn Somers
**Sec:* Lynn M Jasinowski
**VP:* Jack A Jasinowski
Div Mgr: Gary Basford
MIS Dir: Steve Janett
Mtls Mgr: Jeff Fritz
Sfty Mgr: Daniel Charles
Sfty Mgr: Andrew Youpel
Opers Mgr: Laura Baron
Ql Cn Mgr: Jessica Zvyak
Board of Directors: Thomas J Little

D-U-N-S 04-410-8199
BRANDES INVESTMENT PARTNERS INC
11988 El Cmino Real Ste 6, San Diego, CA 92130
Tel (858) 755-0239 *Founded/Ownrshp* 1974
Sales 97.4MM[E] *EMP* 300[E]
SIC 6282 Investment counselors
Ch Bd: Charles H Brandes
Pt: Christopher Garrett
**CEO:* Brent V Woods
**Ex Dir:* Jeffrey A Busby
**Ex Dir:* Glenn R Carlson
Snr Ntwrk: Steven Lengua
Dir IT: Paul Tartre
Prd Mgr: Katie Henry

D-U-N-S 17-426-1693
BRANDI BOB STATIONS INC
PITT STOP
279 Cedarcrest Dr, Lexington, SC 29072-3813
Tel (803) 957-3096 *Founded/Ownrshp* 1974
Sales 83.1MM[E] *EMP* 600
SIC 5411 5172 Convenience stores, independent; Petroleum brokers
Pr: Robert Brandi
**VP:* Janice Stuerke
Genl Mgr: John Tronetti

D-U-N-S 80-832-6693
BRANDING IRON HOLDINGS INC
1682 Sauget Business Blvd, Sauget, IL 62206-1454
Tel (618) 337-8400 *Founded/Ownrshp* 2007
Sales 85.7MM[E] *EMP* 90
SIC 2013 5147 Sausages & other prepared meats; Meats & meat products
CEO: R Scott Hudspeth
**Pr:* Michael H Holten
CFO: Craig Allen
QA Dir: Jennifer Meese

D-U-N-S 83-056-0475
BRANDMAN UNIVERSITY
16355 Laguna Canyon Rd, Irvine, CA 92618-3801
Tel (949) 341-9800 *Founded/Ownrshp* 2007
Sales 101.0MM *EMP* 99[E]
SIC 8221 Colleges universities & professional schools
CEO: Gary Brahm

D-U-N-S 60-839-7894
BRANDMOTION LLC
21518 Bridge St, Southfield, MI 48033-4073
Tel (734) 619-1250 *Founded/Ownrshp* 2005
Sales 400.0MM *EMP* 20
SIC 5013 Motor vehicle supplies & new parts

BRANDSMART USA
See INTERBOND CORP OF AMERICA

BRANDSMART U.S.A.
See INTERBOND HOLDING CORP

D-U-N-S 00-750-8120 IMP
BRANDT COMPANIES LLC
1728 Briercroft Ct, Carrollton, TX 75006-6400
Tel (972) 241-9411 *Founded/Ownrshp* 2007
Sales 398.4MM *EMP* 1,500
Accts Payne & Smith Llc Dallas Tx
SIC 1711 1731 7623 Plumbing, heating, air-conditioning contractors; Plumbing contractors; Heating & air conditioning contractors; Mechanical contractor; General electrical contractor; Air conditioning repair
Pr: Arnold Picon
VP: Christian Beasley
VP: John Dunn
VP: Jimmy Hurley
Exec: Andre Burnthon
Opers Mgr: Oscar Garza
VP Mktg: Brad Rogers
Genl Couns: Kelly Lyttle

D-U-N-S 02-575-8475 EXP
BRANDT CONSOLIDATED INC
AGVISION
2935 S Koke Mill Rd, Springfield, IL 62711-9651
Tel (217) 547-5800 *Founded/Ownrshp* 1967
Sales 172.6MM[E] *EMP* 165
Accts Kerber Eck & Braeckel Llp S
SIC 2875 5191 Fertilizers, mixing only; Farm supplies
Pr: Rick C Brandt
**Ch Bd:* Glen A Brandt
**COO:* Tim McArdle
**CFO:* Joe Brummel
**Sec:* Evelyn Thomas
**Ex VP:* Bill Engel
**VP:* Fred Rice
Rgnl Mgr: Glen Kitson
Dir IT: Scott Crawford
Plnt Mgr: Thomas Wurmnest
Mktg Mgr: Shawn Thicksten

D-U-N-S 08-003-4368
BRANDT ENGINEERING CO INC (TX)
1728 Briercrest Dr, Dallas, TX 75229
Tel (972) 395-6000 *Founded/Ownrshp* 1952
Sales 350.0MM *EMP* 1,833
SIC 1711 8711 Heating & air conditioning contractors; Mechanical engineering
Owner: Mark Zilverman
**Owner:* Barry Moore
Dir Bus: Phillip Hogue
Sfty Dirs: Kerry Roney

BRANDT, RAY NISSAN-DODGE
See RAY BRANDT NISSAN INC

D-U-N-S 18-283-7039
■ **BRANDYWINE GLOBAL INVESTMENT MANAGEMENT LLC**
(*Suby of* LEGG MASON INC) ★
2929 Arch St Ste 700, Philadelphia, PA 19104-2861
Tel (215) 609-3500 *Founded/Ownrshp* 1998
Sales 150.0MM *EMP* 145
SIC 6282 Investment advice
Ofcr: Mark Glassman
Ofcr: Chris Marzullo
Sr VP: Michael T Dieschbourg
Sr VP: Nedra Hadley
Sr VP: Richard Lawrence
VP: Mark Juelis
VP: David Monahan
VP: Mark Solomon
VP: Stephen Waddell
VP: Steven Waltman
VP: Greg Zavoyna
Dir Risk M: Luz Carey
Dir Bus: Theodore Fetter

BRANDYWINE HOSPITAL
See COATESVILLE HOSPITAL CORP

D-U-N-S 13-812-4032
BRANDYWINE OPERATING PARTNERSHIP LP
(*Suby of* BRANDYWINE REALTY TRUST) ★
555 E Lancaster Ave # 100, Radnor, PA 19087-5158
Tel (610) 325-5600 *Founded/Ownrshp* 1996
Sales 596.9MM *EMP* 424
Accts Pricewaterhousecoopers Llp Ph
SIC 6798 Real estate investment trusts
Pr: Gerard H Sweeney
**Ch Bd:* M Walter D'Alessio
CFO: Thomas E Wirth
VP: Daniel A Palazzo
Board of Directors: James C Diggs, Wyche Fowler, Michael J Joyce, Anthony A Nichols Sr, Charles P Pizzi

D-U-N-S 15-650-7485
BRANDYWINE REALTY TRUST
555 E Lancaster Ave # 100, Radnor, PA 19087-5166
Tel (610) 325-5600 *Founded/Ownrshp* 1986
Sales 596.9MM *EMP* 406[E]
SIC 6798 Real estate investment trusts
Pr: Gerard H Sweeney
**CFO:* Thomas E Wirth
Ex VP: George D Johnstone
**Ex VP:* Brad A Molotsky
Ex VP: William D Redd
Ex VP: George D Sowa
Sr VP: George S Hasenecz
Sr VP: Anthony S Rimikis Sr
VP: George Johnstone
VP: Philip Odonnell
**VP:* Daniel Palazzo
VP: Stephen Rush
VP: Suzanne Stumpf
VP: Jeffrey Weinstein

D-U-N-S 87-829-7902
BRANDYWINE SCHOOL DISTRICT
1311 Brandywine Blvd, Wilmington, DE 19809-2306
Tel (302) 793-5000 *Founded/Ownrshp* 1995
Sales 86.8MM[E] *EMP* 1,200
SIC 8211 Public elementary & secondary schools
VP: Ralph Ackerman
VP: James Gise
VP: Karen Gordon
VP: Bob Maffia
Prin: Virginia M Burns-Ferrara
Prin: Gene A Capers
Prin: Mark H Frankel
Prin: Gregg P Robinson
Prin: Kristina J Viar
Ex Dir: Andy Ricketts
CIO: Dawn Hoover

D-U-N-S 12-773-5749
BRANDYWINE SENIOR LIVING MANAGEMENT LLC
525 Fellowship Rd Ste 360, Mount Laurel, NJ 08054-3406
Tel (856) 778-6100 *Founded/Ownrshp* 2006
Sales 195.9MM[E] *EMP* 3,500
SIC 8361 8051 Rehabilitation center, residential: health care incidental; Convalescent home with continuous nursing care
Pr: Brenda J Bacon
**COO:* Kenneth C Segarnick
**CFO:* Steve Carmine
**CFO:* Keith Phillips
**Ex VP:* Peter J Burke Jr
Sr VP: Jan Jedliskowski
VP: Thomas Decker
**VP:* Steve Heaney
VP: Todd Morgano
Pr Dir: Nicole Greco
Pr Dir: Rona Siaca

BRANFORD HALL CAREER INSTITUTE
See PREMIER EDUCATION GROUP LIMITED PARTNERSHIP

BRANNAN READY-MIX DIVISION
See BRANNAN SAND AND GRAVEL CO LLC

D-U-N-S 00-691-5045
BRANNAN SAND AND GRAVEL CO LLC
BRANNAN READY-MIX DIVISION
2500 Brannan Way, Denver, CO 80229-7029
Tel (303) 534-1231 *Founded/Ownrshp* 1994
Sales 133.4MM[E] *EMP* 350
SIC 1611 5032

D-U-N-S 07-946-3904
BRANSCUM CONSTRUCTION CO/ROBINS & MORTON A JOINT VENTURE
90 Key Village Rd, Russell Springs, KY 42642-4511
Tel (270) 866-5107 *Founded/Ownrshp* 2012
Sales 21.8MM[E] *EMP* 1,127
SIC 1541 8741 1542 Industrial buildings & warehouses; Construction management; Nonresidential construction
Pr: Stephen Branscum
VP: Phil Yance

D-U-N-S 00-173-8699 IMP
■ **BRANSON ULTRASONICS CORP** (GA)
(*Suby of* EMERSON ELECTRIC (US) HOLDING CORP) ★
41 Eagle Rd Ste 1, Danbury, CT 06810-4179
Tel (203) 796-0400 *Founded/Ownrshp* 1946, 1984
Sales 169.3MM[E] *EMP* 530
SIC 3699 3548 3541 Welding machines & equipment, ultrasonic; Cleaning equipment, ultrasonic, except medical & dental; Welding apparatus; Machine tools, metal cutting type
Pr: E Joe Dillon
Pr: Jon Piasecki
Sr VP: David Beittel
VP: Ed Boone
VP: Bob Brown
**VP:* Robert Tibbetts
VP: Steven Willensky
Rgnl Mgr: Mark Cragin
Genl Mgr: Edward Topolski
Genl Mgr: Johan Tuijp
CIO: Jeffrey Hilgert

D-U-N-S 01-232-5759 IMP/EXP
BRANT INDUSTRIES INC
WHITE BIRCH PAPER COMPANY
80 Field Point Rd, Greenwich, CT 06830-6416
Tel (203) 863-1200 *Founded/Ownrshp* 1941
Sales 241.6MM[E] *EMP* 2,360
SIC 2621 Paper mills
Pr: Peter M Brant
**Pr:* Christopher Brant
CFO: Tim Butler
Sr VP: Bruno Antonios
Sr VP: Russell Lowder
**VP:* Jay Epstein
**VP:* Edward D Sherrick

D-U-N-S 07-968-8534
BRANTNER HOLDING CO
(*Suby of* TE CONNECTIVITY MOG INC) ★
501 Oakside Ave, Redwood City, CA 94063-3800
Tel (650) 361-5292 *Founded/Ownrshp* 2014
Sales 96.8MM[E] *EMP* 1,000[E]
SIC 3678 Electronic connectors
Pr: Harold Barksdale

D-U-N-S 00-507-4302 IMP
BRASFIELD & GORRIE LLC
3021 7th Ave S, Birmingham, AL 35233-3502
Tel (205) 328-4000 *Founded/Ownrshp* 1997
Sales 1.9MMM[E] *EMP* 2,495
Accts Pricewaterhousecoopers Llp B
SIC 1542 Commercial & office building, new construction; Hospital construction; Garage construction
Ch: M Miller Gorrie
**CEO:* M James Gorrie
COO: Jeff Stone
**CFO:* Randall J Freeman
Ofcr: Tom Garrett
**VP:* Tracey Renner Sibley
VP: Tracey Sibley
Exec: Kim Spenney
Dir Bus: Jason Lewis
Dir Bus: Pat Mooney
Rgnl Mgr: Emily Cannon

BRASHERS SALT LAKE AUTO AUCTN
See ADESA UTAH LLC

D-U-N-S 16-166-9049
BRASKEM AMERICA INC
BRASKEM PP AMERICAS
(*Suby of* BRASKEM S/A.)
1735 Market St Fl 28, Philadelphia, PA 19103-7534
Tel (215) 841-3100 *Founded/Ownrshp* 2010
Sales 721.3MM[E] *EMP* 1,100
SIC 2821 2865 2869 Polypropylene resins; Polyesters; Acrylic resins; Plasticizer/additive based plastic materials; Cyclic crudes & intermediates; Phenol, alkylated & cumene; Aniline, nitrobenzene; Diphenylamines; Acetone, synthetic; Alcohols, non-beverage
CEO: Bruce D Rubin
**Treas:* Uy McHarmian
**VP:* Rachel Celiberti
**VP:* Srivatsan Iyer
Mktg Dir: John Carroll
Mktg Dir: Joseph Paolucci

BRASKEM PP AMERICAS
See BRASKEM AMERICA INC

BRASON'S WILLCARE
See B H C SERVICES INC

BRASS CRAFT MFG CO
See BRASSCRAFT MANUFACTURING CO

D-U-N-S 00-531-7524 IMP
■ **BRASSCRAFT MANUFACTURING CO** (MI)
BRASS CRAFT MFG CO
(*Suby of* MASCO CORP) ★
39600 Orchard Hill Pl, Novi, MI 48375-5331
Tel (248) 305-6000 *Founded/Ownrshp* 1946
Sales 194.4MM[E] *EMP* 680
SIC 3432 Plumbing fixture fittings & trim; Plumbers' brass goods: drain cocks, faucets, spigots, etc.; Plastic plumbing fixture fittings, assembly
Pr: Rick Mejia
**CFO:* Scott Kay
**Sr VP:* Wade Henderson
**VP:* Dawn Rowley
MIS Dir: Mark Labadie
IT Man: Susan Green
Ql Cn Mgr: Danny Chilton
Board of Directors: Eugene A Gargaro Jr, Wayne B Lyon, Richard G Mosteller

BRASSELER USA DENTAL
See PETER BRASSELER HOLDINGS LLC

D-U-N-S 19-643-8683 IMP/EXP
■ **BRASSTECH INC**
NEWPORT BRASS
(*Suby of* MASCO CORP) ★
2001 Carnegie Ave, Santa Ana, CA 92705-5531
Tel (949) 417-5207 *Founded/Ownrshp* 2002
Sales 159.5MM[E] *EMP* 340
SIC 3432 Plumbing fixture fittings & trim
CEO: John V Halso
VP: John Crvarich

BRATRUD MIDDLETON INSURANCE
See MIDDLETON BRATRUD INSURANCE BROKERS INC

BRAUM'S BAKERY
See W H BRAUM INC

BRAUM'S ICE CREAM & DAIRY
See BRAUMS INC

D-U-N-S 79-887-1559
BRAUMS INC
BRAUM'S ICE CREAM & DAIRY
3000 Ne 63rd St, Oklahoma City, OK 73121-1202
Tel (405) 478-1656 *Founded/Ownrshp* 1933
Sales 555.1MM[E] *EMP* 6,500
SIC 5411 5812 Grocery stores; Ice cream, soft drink & soda fountain stands; Fast food restaurants & stands
CEO: Drew Braum
**Pr:* Drew M Braum
**CFO:* Mark Godwin
**Ch:* William H Braum
**VP:* Paul Clark
**VP:* William P Ricks
Dist Mgr: Laura Clark
Dist Mgr: Amy Maxey
Genl Mgr: Megan Ganze
Genl Mgr: Kelly Hoeffel
Genl Mgr: Brian Nitz

D-U-N-S 06-157-2335 EXP
BRAUN CORP
BRAUN LIFT
(*Suby of* PATRICIA INDUSTRIES AB)
631 W 11th St, Winamac, IN 46996-1245
Tel (574) 946-6153 *Founded/Ownrshp* 2015
Sales 177.2MM[E] *EMP* 650
SIC 3999 Wheelchair lifts
Pr: Nick Gutwein
**Treas:* Thomas Eastman
Ex VP: Jeff Hermanson
Ex VP: Kevin B McMahon
VP: Greg Kiser
Dir Risk M: Barry Wolff
Area Mgr: Joseph Young
IT Man: Anthony Catalano
IT Man: Steven Sommers
Tech Mgr: Adam Smith
Software D: Brandi Larkin

BRAUN EXPORT
See HARLAND M BRAUN & CO INC

D-U-N-S 78-240-3463
BRAUN INTERTEC CORP
11001 Hampshire Ave S, Minneapolis, MN 55438-2424
Tel (952) 995-2000 Founded/Ownrshp 1957
Sales 180.8MM^E EMP 500
Accts Boulay Heutmaker Zibell & Co
SIC 8711 8734 Professional engineer; Testing laboratories; Welded joint radiographing; X-ray inspection service, industrial; Product testing laboratories
CEO: Jon Carlson
*Pr: Robert J Janssen
*CFO: Carmen M Borgeson
VP: Michael Bratrud
VP: Marvin C Denne
VP: Michael M Heuer
VP: Daniel R Holte
VP: Ray A Huber
VP: Steve Nagle
Comm Man: Kara Pritchett
Prin: Michelle Bissonnette

BRAUN LIFT
See BRAUN CORP

D-U-N-S 01-886-7742 IMP
BRAVADO INTERNATIONAL GROUP MERCHANDISING SERVICES INC
(Suby of BRAVADO INTERNATIONAL GROUP LIMITED)
1755 Broadway Fl 2, New York, NY 10019-3743
Tel (212) 445-3400 Founded/Ownrshp 1997
Sales 150.2MM^E EMP 100
SIC 5136 5137 5611 5621 Men's & boys' clothing; Women's & children's clothing; Men's & boys' clothing stores; Women's clothing stores
CEO: Lucian C Grainge
*Ch Bd: Tom Bennett
*CFO: Pete D'Auria
Sr VP: Tracy Nurse
VP: Joseph Marziotto
Genl Mgr: Mickela Mallozzi

D-U-N-S 83-733-5041
▲ BRAVO BRIO RESTAURANT GROUP INC
777 Goodale Blvd Ste 100, Columbus, OH 43212-3862
Tel (614) 326-7944 Founded/Ownrshp 1987
Sales 423.9MM EMP 9,500
Tkr Sym BBRG Exch NGS
SIC 5812 Italian restaurant; American restaurant
Pr: Brian T O'Malley
*Ch Bd: Alton F Doody III
COO: Khanh Collins
CFO: James J O'Connor
Board of Directors: Thomas J Baldwin, James S Gulmi, David B Pittaway, Harold O Rosser II, Fortunato N Valenti

D-U-N-S 18-842-7835
BRAVO BUILDING SERVICES INC
BRAVO GROUP SERVICES
29 King George Rd, Green Brook, NJ 08812-1711
Tel (732) 465-0707 Founded/Ownrshp 1997
Sales 63.1MM EMP 3,000^E
Accts Ross Rosenthal & Company Llp
SIC 7349 Janitorial service, contract basis
Pr: Karen J Martinez
Ex Dir: Alan Skolnik
IT Man: Trupti Shah
VP Opers: Rene Brunal

BRAVO GROUP SERVICES
See BRAVO BUILDING SERVICES INC

BRAVO HEALTH, INC.
See BRAVO HEALTH LLC

D-U-N-S 83-745-6243
■ BRAVO HEALTH LLC
BRAVO HEALTH, INC.
(Suby of NEWQUEST LLC) ★
3601 Odonnell St, Baltimore, MD 21224-5238
Tel (800) 235-9188 Founded/Ownrshp 2010
Sales NA EMP 983
SIC 6321 Health insurance carriers
CEO: Jeffrey M Folick
Pr: Louise McCagg
CFO: Scott Tabakin
Ex VP: Scott Ptacek
Ex VP: Thomas Rekart
VP: Benjy Green
VP: Ted Pantaleo
Co-Founder: David D Carliner
Co-Founder: Michael R Steele
Prgrm Mgr: Nate Johnson
Prgrm Mgr: Caroline Wilson

D-U-N-S 06-290-5406
BRAVOGRAND INC
BURGER KING
(Suby of BURGER KING) ★
4220 Edison Lakes Pkwy # 300, Mishawaka, IN 46545-1462
Tel (574) 271-4600 Founded/Ownrshp 2001
Sales 39.4MM^E EMP 2,000
SIC 5812 Fast-food restaurant, chain
Pr: Daniel B Fitzpatrick
*COO: Gerald Fitzpatrick
*Treas: John C Firth
*VP: James K Fitzpatrick
*VP Opers: William Lee

D-U-N-S 17-370-6367
BRAWLER INDUSTRIES LLC
WEST TEXAS PLASTICS
(Suby of TAILWIND CAPITAL) ★
11701 County Rd W 125 125 W, Midland, TX 79711
Tel (432) 563-4005 Founded/Ownrshp 1987
Sales 176.3MM^E EMP 120
SIC 5162 Plastics products
CEO: John Keating
*VP: Tim Kohn
Off Mgr: Laura Stanley

BRAY CONTROLS USA
See BRAY INTERNATIONAL INC

D-U-N-S 14-849-8512 IMP/EXP
BRAY INTERNATIONAL INC
BRAY CONTROLS USA
13333 Westland East Blvd, Houston, TX 77041-1219
Tel (281) 894-7979 Founded/Ownrshp 1986
Sales 182.8MM^E EMP 400
SIC 3491 Industrial valves; Automatic regulating & control valves
Ch Bd: Frank J Raymond Jr
*Pr: Craig C Brown
Pr: Brindesh Dhruva
CFO: Debbie Huff
VP: Robert Bloem
VP: Kenny Docherty
VP: Ron Warren
Genl Mgr: Steve Drollinger
CIO: David Gerber
Opers Mgr: Bill Bagby
Ql Cn Mgr: David W Davis

D-U-N-S 00-503-5910 IMP
BRAZEWAY INC
2711 E Maumee St, Adrian, MI 49221-3586
Tel (517) 265-2121 Founded/Ownrshp 1946
Sales 215.8MM^E EMP 1,200
SIC 3354 3353 Tube, extruded or drawn, aluminum; Aluminum sheet, plate & foil
Ch Bd: Stephen L Hickman
Pr: Stephanie Hickman Boyse
CFO: Terence R Sheehan
VP: Michael Adams
VP: John P Benzing
VP: Emory M Schmidt
Plnt Mgr: John Armstrong
Snr Mgr: Nathan Richey

BRAZIL IRRIGATION SYSTEMS
See COLEEN M MCCORMICK

BRAZOS ELECTRIC COOPERATIVE
See BRAZOS ELECTRIC POWER COOPERATIVE INC

D-U-N-S 00-377-2290 IMP
BRAZOS ELECTRIC POWER COOPERATIVE INC (TX)
BRAZOS ELECTRIC COOPERATIVE
7616 Bagby Ave, Waco, TX 76712-6924
Tel (254) 750-6500 Founded/Ownrshp 1941
Sales 943.8MM^E EMP 366
Accts Pricewaterhousecoopers Llp Ka
SIC 4911 Generation, electric power
Ch: Larry Corbett
*Pr: John Hartgraves
*Pr: Dennis McWhorter
CFO: Bret Fox
*Sec: Audie Morris
*Ex VP: Clifton D Karnei
*Sr VP: Loyd Jackson
*VP: Khaki Bordovsky
VP: Lynn Gustafson
*VP: Rick Haile
*VP: Hugh Lenox
*VP: David Murphy
*VP: Ronnie Robinson
*VP: Johnny York

BRAZOS ROCK ENERGY SERVICES
See BRAZOS ROCK INC

D-U-N-S 84-325-2748
BRAZOS ROCK INC
BRAZOS ROCK ENERGY SERVICES
1813 Banks Dr, Weatherford, TX 76087-9431
Tel (817) 594-0772 Founded/Ownrshp 2004
Sales 160.0MM EMP 500^E
SIC 1623 Oil & gas line & compressor station construction; Natural gas compressor station construction; Oil & gas pipeline construction
CEO: Chad Chester
*Pr: Shelley Chester
*CFO: Peter Doemel
*VP: Curtis Chester

BRAZOS VALLEY HEALTH NETWORK
See HILLCREST BAPTIST MEDICAL CENTER

BRAZOSPORT FACTS
See SOUTHERN NEWSPAPERS INC

D-U-N-S 07-013-6791
BRAZOSPORT INDEPENDENT SCHOOL DISTRICT (INC)
301 W Brazoswood Dr, Clute, TX 77531-3520
Tel (979) 730-7000 Founded/Ownrshp 1944
Sales 89.9MM^E EMP 1,400
Accts Belt Harris Pechacek Lllp Ho
SIC 8211 Public elementary & secondary schools
Bd of Dir: Pam Davis
Ex Dir: Becky Rinehart
Pr Dir: Tami Sophia
Snr Mgr: Kelli McBrayer

D-U-N-S 83-331-1124
BRAZOSPORT MEMORIAL HOSPITAL
194 Abner Jackson Pkwy, Lake Jackson, TX 77566-5160
Tel (979) 299-2882 Founded/Ownrshp 2010
Sales 94.9MM EMP 13^E
SIC 8062 General medical & surgical hospitals
Prin: Charla R Little

D-U-N-S 14-793-0978 IMP
BRC RUBBER & PLASTICS INC
BRC RUBBER GROUP
1029a W State Blvd, Fort Wayne, IN 46808-3165
Tel (260) 693-2171 Founded/Ownrshp 1973
Sales 171.4MM^E EMP 500
SIC 3061 3714 3053 Automotive rubber goods (mechanical); Motor vehicle parts & accessories; Gaskets, packing & sealing devices
CEO: Charles Chaffee
Pr: Joe Dickason
Pr: Dena England
*CFO: Paul Bouza
CFO: Eric Dohrman
*Sec: Karen J Chaffee
*Ex VP: Mike Meyer
*VP: Clifford Chaffee
VP: Mike Cornwell
VP: Steven M Koenig
VP: Lisa Wigger

BRC RUBBER GROUP
See BRC RUBBER & PLASTICS INC

D-U-N-S 07-876-9437
BRE PROPERTIES INC (MD)
525 Market St Fl 4, San Francisco, CA 94105-2712
Tel (415) 445-6530 Founded/Ownrshp 1970
Sales 404.0MM EMP 617
SIC 6798

D-U-N-S 78-730-9553
BRE RETAIL CENTERS HOLDINGS LP
345 Park Ave, New York, NY 10154-0004
Tel (212) 583-5000 Founded/Ownrshp 2015
Sales 130.3MM^E EMP 39^E
SIC 6513 6722 Apartment building operators; Management investment, open-end

D-U-N-S 07-883-2817
BRE SELECT HOTELS CORP
345 Park Ave, New York, NY 10154-0004
Tel (212) 583-5000 Founded/Ownrshp 2012
Sales 287.0MM EMP 6
Accts Deloitte & Touche Llp Miami
SIC 6722 Management investment, open-end
Pr: Ed Weiss

D-U-N-S 07-928-2820
BRE SELECT HOTELS OPERATING LLC
CROWNE PLAZA SAN ANTONIO ARPRT
(Suby of BRE SELECT HOTELS CORP) ★
501 E Camino Real, Boca Raton, FL 33432-6127
Tel (973) 503-9733 Founded/Ownrshp 2013
Sales 275.0MM EMP 4
SIC 7011 Hotels & motels
VP: Ed Weiss
Prin: Maria Monroe

D-U-N-S 07-974-5836
BRE SPADE VOTECO LLC
345 Park Ave Fl 42, New York, NY 10154-0004
Tel (212) 583-5000 Founded/Ownrshp 2014
Sales 528.5MM^E EMP 4,400^E
SIC 6799 Investors

D-U-N-S 07-962-5504
BRE/BATON OPERATING LESSEE LLC
BOCA RATON RESORT AND
501 E Camino Real, Boca Raton, FL 33432-6127
Tel (561) 447-3000 Founded/Ownrshp 2004
Sales 53.1MM^E EMP 1,800^E
SIC 7011 7997 Resort hotel; Country club, membership
Pr: Richard Hayduk

D-U-N-S 87-847-3383
BREADS OF WORLD LLC
PANERA BREAD
2127 Innerbelt Business C, Saint Louis, MO 63114-5700
Tel (314) 965-3304 Founded/Ownrshp 1997
Sales 98.4MM^E EMP 2,800
Accts Bkd Llp St Louis Mo
SIC 5812 5461 Cafe; Bakeries

BREAKERS, THE
See FLAGLER SYSTEM INC

BREAKTHRU BEVERAGE ARIZONA
See ALLIANCE BEVERAGE DISTRIBUTING CO LLC

BREAKTHRU BEVERAGE GROUP
See SUNBELT BEVERAGE CO LLC

D-U-N-S 08-006-9044
BREAKTHRU BEVERAGE GROUP LLC
60 E 42nd St Ste 1915, New York, NY 10165-6230
Tel (212) 699-7000 Founded/Ownrshp 2015
Sales 601.7MM^E EMP 2,690^E
SIC 5182 Wine & distilled beverages
Pr: Greg Baird
*CFO: Gene Luciana
*Ofcr: Ann Giambusso
Ex VP: Robert Catalani
*Ex VP: Arlyn Miller
Ex VP: Arlyn B Miller
Ex VP: Kevin Roberts
*Ex VP: Arthur Wirtz

D-U-N-S 08-018-5802
BREAKTHRU BEVERAGE ILLINOIS LLC
WIRTZ BEVERAGE
(Suby of BREAKTHRU BEVERAGE GROUP LLC) ★
3333 S Laramie Ave, Cicero, IL 60804-4520
Tel (708) 298-3333 Founded/Ownrshp 2016
Sales 27.5MM^E EMP 1,020
SIC 5182 Wine & distilled beverages
Dist Mgr: Alex Kanelos
Dir IT: Bob Broz
Sls Mgr: Brian Kienzler
Sales Asso: Matt Casale
Sales Asso: Neil Ciaccio
Sales Asso: Laura Hoefert
Sales Asso: Jessica Phelan

BREAKTHRU BEVERAGE MARYLAND
See RELIABLE CHURCHILL LLLP

BREAKTHRU BEVERAGE NEW JERSEY
See R & R MARKETING LLC

BREAKTHRU BEVERAGE VIRGINIA
See ASSOCIATED DISTRIBUTORS LLC

BRECKENRIDGE INSURANCE SVCS
See BRECKENRIDGE IS INC

D-U-N-S 96-313-1896
BRECKENRIDGE IS INC
BRECKENRIDGE INSURANCE SVCS
245 Townpark Dr Nw # 200, Kennesaw, GA 30144-5570
Tel (678) 322-3536 Founded/Ownrshp 2009
Sales NA EMP 175^E
SIC 6411 Insurance agents, brokers & service
CEO: Tracey Carragher
*COO: Jino Masone
*Ex VP: Bill Chesley
Ex VP: Joe Filardo
Ex VP: Peter Foley
*Ex VP: James Robertson
Ex VP: Scott Severson
Sr VP: Jack Roberts
*Sr VP: Craig Rubin
Sr VP: Vernon Southerland
*Prin: Larry Overby

BREDE EXPOSITION SERVICES
See ALLIED CONVENTION SERVICE INC

BREDEMANN LEXUS IN GLENVIEW
See ADELPHI ENTERPRISES LIMITED PARTNERSHIP

D-U-N-S 05-437-0157
BREECH REGIONAL MEDICAL CENTER
100 Hospital Dr, Lebanon, MO 65536-9210
Tel (417) 533-6026 Founded/Ownrshp 2009
Sales 104.5MM EMP 4
SIC 8011 Medical centers
Prin: Michael J Gillen

BREEZE INDUSTRIAL PRODUCTS
See NORMA PENNSYLVANIA INC

D-U-N-S 00-955-7935 IMP
■ BREEZE-EASTERN LLC
(Suby of TRANSDIGM GROUP INC) ★
35 Melanie Ln, Whippany, NJ 07981-1638
Tel (973) 602-1001 Founded/Ownrshp 2015
Sales 89.7MM EMP 216
SIC 3728 3563 3531 Aircraft parts & equipment; Aircraft armament, except guns; Air & gas compressors including vacuum pumps; Winches
Bd of Dir: Frederick Wasserman
Ofcr: Russ Heller
VP: Mike Koons
VP: Gary Olson
Exec: Reed Jacobsen
Exec: Fred Willms
Prgrm Mgr: Bryan Delia
Prgrm Mgr: Anthony Rubinich
IT Man: Patricia Bieksha
IT Man: Mary Shebell
Mktg Dir: Christine Hawk

D-U-N-S 07-858-1206
BREF HR LLC
250 Vesey St Fl 15, New York, NY 10281-1053
Tel (212) 417-7265 Founded/Ownrshp 1995
Sales 193.8MM EMP 1,363^E
SIC 7011 Hotels & motels
CEO: William W Warner
*CFO: Chad Konrad

D-U-N-S 07-924-5260
BREF HR MANAGEMENT LLC
250 Vesey St Fl 11, New York, NY 10281-1053
Tel (212) 417-7265 Founded/Ownrshp 2011
Sales 3.7MM^E EMP 1,441
SIC 7011 Hotels & motels

D-U-N-S 00-193-3738
BREHM COMMUNICATIONS INC
B C I
16644 W Bernardo Dr # 300, San Diego, CA 92127-1901
Tel (858) 451-6200 Founded/Ownrshp 1919
Sales 215.7MM^E EMP 200^E
SIC 2752 2711 Commercial printing, offset; Commercial printing & newspaper publishing combined
Pr: Bill Brehm Jr
*Ch: W J Brehm
*VP: Tom Taylor

D-U-N-S 78-652-8740
BREITBURN ENERGY PARTNERS LP
707 Wilshire Blvd # 4600, Los Angeles, CA 90017-3612
Tel (213) 225-5900 Founded/Ownrshp 2006
Sales 1.1MMM EMP 833
SIC 1311 Crude petroleum & natural gas; Crude petroleum & natural gas production
CEO: Halbert S Washburn
Genl Pt: Breitburn GP LLC
Pr: Mark L Pease
CFO: James G Jackson
Treas: Bruce D McFarland
Ex VP: Gregory C Brown
Sr VP: Thomas E Thurmond
Sr VP: W Jackson Washburn
VP: Lawrence C Smith
VP: Ray Vassallo
Snr Mgr: Mirella Fernandez

D-U-N-S 80-675-1087 IMP/EXP
BREMBO NORTH AMERICA INC
BREMBO RACING
(Suby of FRENI BREMBO SPA)
47765 Halyard Dr, Plymouth, MI 48170-2429
Tel (734) 416-1275 Founded/Ownrshp 1989
Sales 186.9MM^E EMP 430
SIC 3714 5013 Motor vehicle parts & accessories; Motor vehicle supplies & new parts; Automotive supplies & parts; Automotive supplies
Pr: Daniel Sandberg
*CFO: Cristian Baretti
Mktg Dir: Caroline Fallara
Snr Mgr: Marco Pagni
Board of Directors: Giovanni Canavotto, Paolo Ferrari, Matteo Tiraboschi

BREMBO RACING
See BREMBO NORTH AMERICA INC

D-U-N-S 00-546-1447
BREMEN CASTINGS INC
500 N Baltimore St, Bremen, IN 46506-1138
Tel (574) 546-2411 Founded/Ownrshp 1939
Sales 96.8MM^E EMP 220
SIC 3321 Gray iron castings
CEO: James E Brown
*Pr: James L Brown
*CFO: Frederick Bachman
*VP: Geoffrey Meester
Ql Cn Mgr: Scott Gerber

D-U-N-S 05-607-3711
BREMER FINANCIAL CORP
(*Suby of* OTTO BREMER FOUNDATION) ★
380 Sint Peter St Ste 500, Saint Paul, MN 55102
Tel (800) 908-2265 *Founded/Ownrshp* 1943
Sales NA *EMP* 1,652
SIC 6022 6712 State commercial banks; Bank holding companies
Ch Bd: Terry M Cummings
Pr: Stan K Dardis
CEO: Patrick Donovan
CFO: Stuart Bradt
CFO: Robert B Buck
CFO: Gary Schuette
Ex VP: Randy Wolf
Sr VP: Meghan Harris
Sr VP: Tami K Klimpel
Sr VP: Erickson Russell
VP: Annette Bleninger
VP: Jason Eyberg
VP: Greg Hohlen
VP: Charlotte S Johnson
VP: Rita Juul
VP: Ginny Kremer
VP: Matt Laubach
VP: Cindy Maanum
VP: Angie Olson
VP: Todd Olson
VP: Daniel C Reardon

D-U-N-S 15-452-4789 EXP
■ BREMNER FOOD GROUP INC
(*Suby of* TREEHOUSE PRIVATE BRANDS INC) ★
800 Market St Ste 2900, Saint Louis, MO 63101-2509
Tel (314) 877-7000 *Founded/Ownrshp* 1998
Sales 2.8MM^E *EMP* 1,550
SIC 2052 Crackers, dry; Cookies
CEO: Kevin Hunt
**Pr:* Richard R Koulouris
**CFO:* Joe Micheletto
Treas: T C Oviatt
VP: James Nichols
Genl Mgr: Arrell Ingram
IT Man: Thomas Spalding

BRENHAM WHOLESALE CONVENIENCE
See BRENHAM WHOLESALE GROCERY CO INC

D-U-N-S 00-191-1338
BRENHAM WHOLESALE GROCERY CO INC
BRENHAM WHOLESALE CONVENIENCE
602 W First St, Brenham, TX 77833-4017
Tel (979) 836-7925 *Founded/Ownrshp* 1973
Sales 203.4MM^E *EMP* 165
SIC 5194 5147 5142 5141 5148 Tobacco & tobacco products; Meats, fresh; Packaged frozen goods; Groceries, general line; Fresh fruits & vegetables
Pr: William J Ehlert Jr
**VP:* Robert Kolkhorst Jr
**VP:* John B Schaer
**Prin:* Stephen Miller
IT Man: Lloyd Schwarze
Opers Mgr: Dana McCann
Sls Mgr: John Ehlert

D-U-N-S 15-530-4371
BRENN DISTRIBUTION INC
QUALITEST PHARMACEUTICALS
(*Suby of* APAX PARTNERS HOLDINGS LTD)
130 Vintage Dr Ne, Huntsville, AL 35811-8216
Tel (256) 859-4011 *Founded/Ownrshp* 2007
Sales 128.5MM^E *EMP* 986
SIC 5122 Drugs & drug proprietaries
Pr: Marvin Sampson
VP: Phil Cupero
Exec: Nick West

D-U-N-S 06-539-5170
BRENNER HOLDINGS INC
CSI ROANOKE CI
(*Suby of* GERDAU LONG STEEL NORTH AMER) ★
2580 Broadway Ave Sw, Roanoke, VA 24014-1620
Tel (540) 981-1211 *Founded/Ownrshp* 2013
Sales 103.6MM^E *EMP* 188
SIC 4953 5093 3341 3231 Recycling, waste materials; Ferrous metal scrap & waste; Nonferrous metals scrap; Metal scrap & waste materials; Secondary nonferrous metals; Products of purchased glass
Ch: Bruce Brenner
Site Mgr: Desiree Derrow
Opers Mgr: Richard Gallegos
Board of Directors: Joan Brenner, Laura Brenner

D-U-N-S 04-368-2137
BRENNER OIL CO (MI)
DOUGLAS GAS & OIL
12948 Quincy St, Holland, MI 49424-9262
Tel (616) 399-9742 *Founded/Ownrshp* 1975, 1997
Sales 141.7MM^E *EMP* 95
SIC 5172 4212 Gasoline; Petroleum haulage, local
Pr: Douglas Brenner
COO: Walt Majcher
**Treas:* Brad Bartels
**VP:* Jerry Brenner
Off Mgr: Teresa Degracia
IT Man: Todd Leistra
Sfty Dirs: Don Wilcutt

D-U-N-S 00-610-9748 IMP
■ BRENNER TANK LLC (WI)
BRENNER TANK SERVICES
(*Suby of* WALKER GROUP HOLDINGS LLC) ★
450 Arlington Ave, Fond Du Lac, WI 54935-5571
Tel (920) 922-4530 *Founded/Ownrshp* 1900, 2007
Sales 103.2MM^E *EMP* 449^E
SIC 3715 3714 3443 Semitrailers for truck tractors; Motor vehicle parts & accessories; Fabricated plate work (boiler shop)
VP: Tom Ballon
Genl Mgr: Todd Schaefer
Genl Mgr: Mike Thorpe
IT Man: Ray Kautz
Info Man: Merlin Woltersdorff
VP Mfg: Dave Hodorff
Sales Exec: Bryan Watson
S&M/VP: John F Cannon
S&M/VP: Jim Miller
Sls Mgr: Pamela Hardee

BRENNER TANK SERVICES
See BRENNER TANK LLC

D-U-N-S 04-245-4228 IMP
BRENNTAG GREAT LAKES LLC
(*Suby of* BRENNTAG SOUTHEAST) ★
4420 N Hrley Davidson Ave, Milwaukee, WI 53225-4311
Tel (262) 252-3550 *Founded/Ownrshp* 2002
Sales 357.2MM^E *EMP* 280
SIC 5169 Chemicals & allied products
Pr: Jim Holcomb

D-U-N-S 06-727-5370 IMP/EXP
BRENNTAG LATIN AMERICA INC
(*Suby of* BRENNTAG HOLDING GMBH)
5300 Memorial Dr Ste 1100, Houston, TX 77007-8250
Tel (713) 880-5400 *Founded/Ownrshp* 1992
Sales 141.6MM^E *EMP* 59^E
SIC 5169 Industrial chemicals
CEO: Steven E Holland
**COO:* German Torres
**CFO:* Markus Klahn
**VP:* Alejandro Fernandez
**Prin:* Adrian Medina
Rgnl Mgr: Marcus Brocker
Dir IT: Ron Veillon

D-U-N-S 12-262-5064 IMP/EXP
BRENNTAG MID-SOUTH INC
(*Suby of* BRENNTAG SOUTHEAST) ★
1405 State Route 136 W, Henderson, KY 42420-9662
Tel (270) 827-3545 *Founded/Ownrshp* 1955
Sales 479.3MM^E *EMP* 275
SIC 5169 Industrial chemicals

D-U-N-S 14-586-5148 IMP/EXP
BRENNTAG NORTH AMERICA INC
BRENNTAG SOUTHEAST
(*Suby of* BRENNTAG PACIFIC INC) ★
5083 Pottsville Pike, Reading, PA 19605-9724
Tel (610) 926-6100 *Founded/Ownrshp* 2004
Sales 2.9MMM^E *EMP* 10
SIC 5169 Industrial chemicals
Pr: Markus Klaehn
**COO:* Steve Pozzi
**CFO:* H Edward Boyadjian
Ex VP: James Doyle Sr
**Sr VP:* Tom Corcoran
Sr VP: Moser Robert
**VP:* Robert Winslow
Mng Dir: Emilio Colomer

D-U-N-S 00-236-1764 IMP
BRENNTAG NORTHEAST INC (DE)
(*Suby of* BRENNTAG SOUTHEAST) ★
81 W Huller Ln, Reading, PA 19605-9728
Tel (610) 926-4151 *Founded/Ownrshp* 1919
Sales 281.4MM^E *EMP* 190
SIC 5169 Industrial chemicals
Pr: Scott Leibowitz
**Pr:* Markus Klaehn
CFO: Victoria Kochman
Treas: H E Boyadjian Sr
**Treas:* Robert Winslow
VP: Tom Crain
VP: Kevin Kessing
**VP:* Paul Rodrigo
Sls Mgr: Eric Egan

D-U-N-S 14-524-5192 IMP
BRENNTAG PACIFIC INC
(*Suby of* BRENNTAG SOUTHEAST) ★
10747 Patterson Pl, Santa Fe Springs, CA 90670-4043
Tel (562) 903-9626 *Founded/Ownrshp* 2003
Sales 497.7MM^E *EMP* 528^E
SIC 5169 Chemicals, industrial & heavy
CEO: William A Fidler
Pr: Steven Pozzi
CFO: H Edward Boyadjian
Sls Mgr: Bruce Pieper

D-U-N-S 17-462-4762 IMP
BRENNTAG PACIFIC INC
(*Suby of* BRENNTAG AG)
4199 Lathrop St, Fairbanks, AK 99701-7460
Tel (907) 452-1555 *Founded/Ownrshp* 2006
Sales 2.9MMM^E *EMP* 12^E
SIC 5169 Chemicals & allied products
Pr: Steve Clark
**VP:* Ken Drey

BRENNTAG SOUTHEAST
See BRENNTAG NORTH AMERICA INC

D-U-N-S 10-833-9032 IMP
BRENNTAG SOUTHWEST INC
(*Suby of* BRENNTAG SOUTHEAST) ★
610 Fisher Rd, Longview, TX 75604-5201
Tel (903) 241-7117 *Founded/Ownrshp* 2004
Sales 338.4MM^E *EMP* 10^E
SIC 5169 Chemicals & allied products
CEO: Thomas M Corcoran
**VP:* Wade M Clay
**VP:* Carol Ray
**VP:* James H Taylor

D-U-N-S 00-137-5294 IMP/EXP
BRENNTAG SPECIALTIES INC
(*Suby of* BRENNTAG SOUTHEAST) ★
1000 Coolidge St, South Plainfield, NJ 07080-3805
Tel (800) 732-0562 *Founded/Ownrshp* 2003
Sales 232.7MM^E *EMP* 135
SIC 5169 2816 2899 Chemicals & allied products; Color pigments; Chemical preparations
Pr: Steve Brauer
CFO: H E Boyadjian Sr
**Treas:* Brad Owens
**Ex VP:* Ted Hubbard
**Ex VP:* Jeff Kenton
**VP:* Brendan Cullinan
**VP:* Bob Przybylowski

D-U-N-S 16-795-2639
BRENT SCARBROUGH & CO INC
155 Robinson Dr, Fayetteville, GA 30214-6902
Tel (770) 461-8603 *Founded/Ownrshp* 1982
Sales 130.7MM^E *EMP* 210
SIC 1623 Pipeline construction
CEO: Brent Scarbrough
**VP:* Shane Waters
Genl Mgr: Robert Fant
Dir IT: Frank James
Info Man: Lance Thomas
Sfty Dirs: Chris West

D-U-N-S 05-050-7144 IMP/EXP
BRENTWOOD INDUSTRIES INC (PA)
500 Spring Ridge Dr, Reading, PA 19610-1069
Tel (610) 374-5109 *Founded/Ownrshp* 1965, 1975
Sales 121.8MM^E *EMP* 700
SIC 3089 Molding primary plastic
Pr: Peter Rye
Treas: Pete Pellicano
**Treas:* Peter Pellicano
VP: Linette Miller
VP: Rob Ulrich
Dir Bus: Chris Bowman
Genl Mgr: Lisa Peterson
Genl Mgr: Carl Staples
CIO: Chef C Kitchen
Plnt Mgr: Jim Rigo
VP Sls: Mike Whittmore

D-U-N-S 04-525-6484 IMP
BRENTWOOD ORIGINALS INC
20639 S Fordyce Ave, Carson, CA 90810-1019
Tel (310) 637-6804 *Founded/Ownrshp* 1968
Sales 196.3MM^E *EMP* 650
SIC 2392 Cushions & pillows
Pr: Loren Sweet
**CFO:* Joel Fierberg
**Treas:* Gerald M Bronstein
**Sr VP:* Bill Bronstein
**VP:* Mark Levy
**VP:* Sigrid Simonson
MIS Dir: James Yang
Plnt Mgr: Jaime Luna
Natl Sales: Ryan Meinhardt
VP Sls: Tom Rose
Board of Directors: Herbert Hill

BRENTWOOD PLACE
See CANTEX HEALTH CARE CENTERS LLC

D-U-N-S 06-806-9640
BRENTWOOD UNION FREE SCHOOL DISTRICT
52 3rd Ave, Brentwood, NY 11717-4651
Tel (631) 434-2335 *Founded/Ownrshp* 1856
Sales 134.2MM^E *EMP* 2,500
Accts Coughlin Foundotos Cullen & Da
SIC 8211 Public elementary & secondary schools; Kindergarten
CEO: Dr Levy McIntyre
Schl Brd P: Helen Moss
Teacher Pr: John Agostini
Instr Medi: Lisa Catenbella
Board of Directors: Deborah Credidito

D-U-N-S 18-640-4869
■ BRER AFFILIATES INC
PRUDENTIAL
(*Suby of* PRUDENTIAL INSURANCE CO OF AMERICA) ★
18500 Von Karman Ave # 400, Irvine, CA 92612-0511
Tel (949) 794-7900 *Founded/Ownrshp* 1987
Sales 116.7MM^E *EMP* 1,811
SIC 6794 6531 Franchises, selling or licensing; Real estate agents & managers
Ch Bd: John Vanderwall
Sr VP: Larry Goebel
**Sr VP:* Patti Ray
VP: David S Beard
Sales Asso: Justin Cullinan
Sales Asso: Pauline Draper
Sales Asso: Irene Gasser
Sales Asso: Alan Hausch
Sales Asso: Larry Hayes
Sales Asso: Fred Horn
Sales Asso: Betty Jeninga

D-U-N-S 02-532-7007
BRER SERVICES INC
(*Suby of* BROOKFIELD ASSET MANAGEMENT INC)
16260 N 71st St, Scottsdale, AZ 85254-1591
Tel (949) 794-7900 *Founded/Ownrshp* 1988
Sales 100.6MM^E *EMP* 900
SIC 6794 Franchises, selling or licensing
VP: Shannon Casey

D-U-N-S 00-645-7340
BRERA CAPITAL PARTNERS LLC
244 5th Ave, New York, NY 10001-7604
Tel (212) 230-5495 *Founded/Ownrshp* 1997
Sales 196.2MM^E *EMP* 3,400
SIC 6799 Investors

D-U-N-S 12-976-8656
■ BRESNAN BROADBAND HOLDINGS LLC
OPTIMUM WEST
(*Suby of* CHARTER COMMUNICATIONS OPERATING LLC) ★
1111 Stewart Ave, Bethpage, NY 11714-3533
Tel (516) 803-2300 *Founded/Ownrshp* 2013
Sales 210.0MM^E *EMP* 1,102
SIC 1623 Cable television line construction

D-U-N-S 12-091-5371
■ BRESNAN COMMUNICATIONS LLC
(*Suby of* OPTIMUM WEST) ★
1111 Stewart Ave, Bethpage, NY 11714-3533
Tel (516) 803-2300 *Founded/Ownrshp* 2002
Sales 209.9MM^E *EMP* 1,100
SIC 4841 Cable & other pay television services
CFO: Kenneth Stone
Sr VP: Robert V Bresnan
Sr VP: Terry St Marie
Ex Dir: Suzanne Belser
Ex Dir: Mark Higdon
Admn Mgr: Deborah Chaplin
Dir IT: Quentin Fleurat
Netwrk Eng: Mike Eggert
Pgrm Dir: Robert Toole

D-U-N-S 09-181-8047
BRETHREN MUTUAL INSURANCE CO
149 N Edgewood Dr, Hagerstown, MD 21740-6599
Tel (800) 621-4264 *Founded/Ownrshp* 1897
Sales NA *EMP* 140
SIC 6331 6411 Property damage insurance; Fire, marine & casualty insurance & carriers; Insurance agents, brokers & service
Ch Bd: Edward L Buchanan IV
**Pr:* Charles Flickinger
Pr: John Snyder
**CFO:* Tammy Aaron
VP: Karen Felichko
**VP:* Snyder John
Dir IT: Michael W Brashears
Dir IT: Joseph Hays
IT Man: Sue Grams
Sls Mgr: Rebecca Marshall

D-U-N-S 06-785-0438
BREVARD COUNTY CO
2725 Jdge Fran Jmeson Way, Viera, FL 32940-6605
Tel (321) 633-2046 *Founded/Ownrshp* 1854
Sales NA *EMP* 9,500
SIC 9111

D-U-N-S 07-979-9756
BREVARD COUNTY SCHOOLS
2700 Jdge Fran Jmeson Way, Viera, FL 32940-6601
Tel (321) 633-1000 *Founded/Ownrshp* 2015
Sales 81.8MM^E *EMP* 9,031^E
SIC 8211 Public elementary & secondary schools
**Prin:* Jennifer Tifft
**Prin:* Jackie Wyatt

D-U-N-S 07-324-1028
BREVARD NORTH COUNTY HOSPITAL
PARRISH MEDICAL CENTER
951 N Washington Ave, Titusville, FL 32796-2163
Tel (321) 268-6333 *Founded/Ownrshp* 1958
Sales 127.8MM *EMP* 980
SIC 8062 General medical & surgical hospitals
CEO: George Mikitarian
Chf Rad: Robert Anderson
COO: Lisa Finley
**CFO:* Tim Skeldon
Treas: Herman A Cole Jr
Ofcr: Lori Duester
Ofcr: Anual Jackson
**Sr VP:* Chris McAlpine
**VP:* Lisa Alexander
VP: Edwin Loftin
**VP:* George Edwin Loftin Jr
**VP:* Bill Moore
Dir Risk M: John Kofil
Dir Rx: Frances Androsko

D-U-N-S 07-873-0549
■ BREWER HOLDCO INC
(*Suby of* WELLTOWER INC) ★
4500 Dorr St, Toledo, OH 43615-4040
Tel (419) 247-2800 *Founded/Ownrshp* 2012
Sales 1.7MMM^E *EMP* 476^E
SIC 6798 Real estate investment trusts
CEO: George L Chapman

D-U-N-S 78-549-1163 IMP
BREWERS SUPPLY GROUP INC
800 1st Ave W, Shakopee, MN 55379-1148
Tel (952) 224-1380 *Founded/Ownrshp* 2004
Sales 91.9MM^E *EMP* 141^E
SIC 5149 Malt; Malt extract
Pr: Gary V Lee
**VP:* JD Dempsey
**Prin:* Ian Ward
VP Sls: Marc Worona

D-U-N-S 00-446-3956
BREWSTER CHEESE CO (OH)
800 Wabash Ave S, Brewster, OH 44613-1464
Tel (330) 767-3492 *Founded/Ownrshp* 1984
Sales 111.6MM^E *EMP* 325
SIC 2022 Cheese, natural & processed; Whey, raw or liquid
CEO: Fritz Leeman
**Pr:* Thomas Murphy
**CFO:* Emil Alecusan
CIO: Dale Britton
Dir IT: Dale Brittan
IT Man: James Dahan

D-U-N-S 07-926-2564
BREWSTER HEIGHTS PACKING & ORCHARDS LP (WA)
GEBBERS FARMS
25985 Hwy 97, Brewster, WA 98812-9548
Tel (509) 689-3424 *Founded/Ownrshp* 1973, 1885
Sales 163.4MM *EMP* 415^E
SIC 0723

BREWSTER WALLCOVERING
See BREWSTER WALLPAPER CORP

D-U-N-S 00-197-9459 IMP/EXP
BREWSTER WALLPAPER CORP (MA)
BREWSTER WALLCOVERING
67 Pacella Park Dr, Randolph, MA 02368-1755
Tel (781) 963-4800 *Founded/Ownrshp* 1954, 1935
Sales 159.0MM^E *EMP* 400
SIC 5198 Wallcoverings
Pr: Kenneth Grandberg
**CFO:* Peter Ciaccia
VP: David Ju
S&M/VP: L J Housman
S&M/VP: Mike Landau
Sls Mgr: Laura Bears

D-U-N-S 06-987-3420
■ BREYUT CONVALESCENT CENTER INC (NJ)
GENESIS
(*Suby of* GENESIS ELDERCARE NATIONAL CENTERS INC) ★
2240 Whthrse Mrcrville Rd, Trenton, NJ 08619-2640
Tel (609) 586-7500 *Founded/Ownrshp* 1969, 1997
Sales 12.2MM *EMP* 5,048^E
SIC 8051 8069 Skilled nursing care facilities; Specialty hospitals, except psychiatric

D-U-N-S 07-929-6217
BRFHH SHREVEPORT LLC
UNIVERSITY HEALTH SHREVEPORT
1541 Kings Hwy, Shreveport, LA 71103-4228
Tel (318) 675-5000 *Founded/Ownrshp* 2013
Sales 426.8MM *EMP* 148ᴱ
SIC 8062 General medical & surgical hospitals
Ch: Stephen Skrivanos

D-U-N-S 16-878-6353 IMP
BRG SPORTS INC
(*Suby of* RBG HOLDINGS CORP) ★
9801 W Higgins Rd, Rosemont, IL 60018-4704
Tel (831) 461-7500 *Founded/Ownrshp* 2003
Sales 785.6MMᴱ *EMP* 2,370ᴱ
Accts Ernst & Young Llp Los Angele
SIC 3949 3751 Helmets, athletic; Pads: football, basketball, soccer, lacrosse, etc.; Protective sporting equipment; Bicycles & related parts
CEO: Dan Arment
**Pr:* Timothy P Mayhew
Pr: Chris Zimmerman
COO: Tony Donofrio
CFO: Mark A Tripp
Ex VP: Thomas T Merrigan
Sr VP: Jackelyn E Werblo
VP: Ric Kern
VP: Thom Parks
Admn Mgr: Yanira Hernandez
CTO: Andrea Glagola
Board of Directors: Peter V Uerberroth, William L Beane III, Richard E Wenz, Andrew J Claerhout, James L Easton, Edward C Forst, Mary George, Dennis E Glazer, Peter D Lamm, David A Perdue, James C Shillito

BRI FREE TOURS
See DREAMERS TRAVELS LLC

D-U-N-S 19-681-3166
BRIAD CORP
BRIAD GROUP, THE
78 Okner Pkwy, Livingston, NJ 07039-1604
Tel (973) 597-6433 *Founded/Ownrshp* 1987
Sales 214.8MMᴱ *EMP* 7,000
SIC 5812 Fast-food restaurant, chain; Ice cream stands or dairy bars
CEO: Brad Honigfeld
**Pr:* Rick Barbrick
**Sr VP:* Dave Cahill
VP: Paul Blough
VP: Robert Fix
VP: Marlene Laveman
VP: Louis J Meyer
VP: Dan Shea
Dist Mgr: Bob Layman
Dist Mgr: Brian Triolo
Genl Mgr: Susan Fierros

BRIAD GROUP, THE
See BRIAD CORP

D-U-N-S 78-335-7481
BRIAD MAIN STREET INC
78 Okner Pkwy, Livingston, NJ 07039-1604
Tel (973) 597-6433 *Founded/Ownrshp* 2006
Sales 63.8MMᴱ *EMP* 7,000
SIC 5812 Restaurant, family: chain
CEO: Brad Honigfeld

D-U-N-S 92-878-8280
BRIAD RESTAURANT GROUP LLC
TGI FRIDAY'S
78 Okner Pkwy, Livingston, NJ 07039-1604
Tel (973) 597-6433 *Founded/Ownrshp* 1995
Sales 216.4MMᴱ *EMP* 6,489
SIC 5812 Restaurant, family: chain
Dir Risk M: Alicia Cherniak

BRIAN CENTER HEALTH/RETIREMENT
See SSC WINSTON-SALEM OPERATING CO LLC

D-U-N-S 01-453-3536
BRIAN CENTER REHAB
(*Suby of* SAVA SENIOR CARE) ★
78 Weaver Blvd, Weaverville, NC 28787-9322
Tel (828) 645-4297 *Founded/Ownrshp* 2010
Sales 662.3Mᴱ *EMP* 1,385ᴱ
SIC 8059 Nursing home, except skilled & intermediate care facility

D-U-N-S 09-139-7547
BRICK TOWNSHIP BOARD OF EDUCATION
101 Hendrickson Ave, Brick, NJ 08724-2574
Tel (732) 785-3000 *Founded/Ownrshp* 1850
Sales 158.3MM *EMP* 52ᴱ
Accts Jump Perry And Company Llp
SIC 8211 School board
Pr: Sharon Cantillo

D-U-N-S 00-323-7281
BRICK TOWNSHIP PUBLIC SCHOOL BOARD
101 Hendrickson Ave, Brick, NJ 08724-2574
Tel (732) 785-3000 *Founded/Ownrshp* 2000
Sales 100.8MMᴱ *EMP* 120
SIC 8211 School board
Pr: Sharon Cantillo
VP: Susan Penrod

D-U-N-S 07-941-1785
BRICKMAN ACQUISITION HOLDINGS INC
(*Suby of* BRICKMAN PARENT LP) ★
2275 Res Blvd Ste 600, Rockville, MD 20850
Tel (240) 683-2000 *Founded/Ownrshp* 2013
Sales 3.7MMMᴱ *EMP* 10,000
Accts Pricewaterhousecoopers Llp Mc
SIC 0781 Landscape services
**CFO:* William J Janetschek
**VP:* Brian Bull
**VP:* Terence Gallagher
**Genl Couns:* David Sorkin

D-U-N-S 12-732-6697
BRICKMAN GROUP HOLDINGS INC
2275 Res Blvd Ste 700, Rockville, MD 20850
Tel (301) 987-9200 *Founded/Ownrshp* 2007
Sales 844.3MM *EMP* 6,600
SIC 0782 4959

D-U-N-S 07-940-7937
BRICKMAN PARENT LP
2275 Res Blvd Ste 600, Rockville, MD 20850
Tel (240) 683-2000 *Founded/Ownrshp* 2013
Sales 914.0MM *EMP* 10,000
SIC 0781 Landscape services
VP: Robert Tyler

D-U-N-S 92-735-1122
BRICKSTREET MUTUAL INSURANCE CO
400 Quarrier St, Charleston, WV 25301-2010
Tel (304) 941-1000 *Founded/Ownrshp* 2006
Sales NA *EMP* 411
SIC 6321 6331 Accident & health insurance; Disability health insurance; Property damage insurance
Pr: Gregory A Burton
COO: T J Obrokta Jr
CFO: Chris Howat
Treas: J Christopher Howat
Sr VP: Jeff Benintendi
Sr VP: Tony Laska
Sr VP: Phil Shimer
VP: David Ashcraft
VP: Fred Boothe
VP: Bob Crossan
VP: Bill McGee
Dir Rx: Kirk Aguirre
Board of Directors: Marty Becker, Thomas V Flaherty, David Rader, Stephen Roberts, Steven F White

D-U-N-S 61-506-4334
▲ BRIDGE BANCORP INC
2200 Montauk Hwy, Bridgehampton, NY 11932-4001
Tel (631) 537-1000 *Founded/Ownrshp* 1989
Sales NA *EMP* 433ᴱ
Tkr Sym BDGE *Exch* NGS
SIC 6021 National commercial banks
Pr: Kevin M O'Connor
**Ch Bd:* Marcia Z Hefter
CFO: John M McCaffery
**V Ch Bd:* Dennis A Suskind
Ex VP: James J Manseau
Sr VP: Thomas H Simson
VP: Aidan Wood
**Exec:* Howard H Nolan

D-U-N-S 01-232-1274 IMP
BRIDGE BANK NATIONAL ASSOCIATION
55 Almaden Blvd Ste 200, San Jose, CA 95113-1619
Tel (408) 423-8500 *Founded/Ownrshp* 2001
Sales NA *EMP* 70ᴱ
SIC 6022 8742

D-U-N-S 10-214-4805
BRIDGE INVESTMENT GROUP PARTNERS LLC
5295 S Commerce Dr # 100, Salt Lake City, UT 84107-4754
Tel (801) 716-4500 *Founded/Ownrshp* 1997
Sales 63.6MMᴱ *EMP* 1,000ᴱ
SIC 6513 6531 Apartment building operators; Real estate agents & managers
**V Ch:* Dean Allara
COO: Kiernan Pusey
Chf Inves: James Chung
Sr VP: Robert Hallock
Sr VP: Kelley Hansen
VP: Matt Burkett
VP: Lisa Dubeck
VP: Matthew Jensen
VP: Danuel Stanger
Mng Dir: Micah Brown
Mng Dir: D Minnick

D-U-N-S 96-827-3040
BRIDGECREST ACCEPTANCE CORP
1720 W Rio Salado Pkwy, Tempe, AZ 85281-6590
Tel (602) 770-1940 *Founded/Ownrshp* 2003
Sales 305.2MMᴱ *EMP* 265ᴱ
SIC 7389 Financial services
Pr: Gregory Sax
**Treas:* Kurt Wood

D-U-N-S 06-801-6658
■ BRIDGEHAMPTON NATIONAL BANK
(*Suby of* BRIDGE BANCORP INC) ★
2200 Montauk Hwy, Bridgehampton, NY 11932-4001
Tel (631) 602-3005 *Founded/Ownrshp* 1989
Sales NA *EMP* 113
SIC 6021 National commercial banks
CEO: Kevin O'Conner
Pr: ST Garrett
COO: Howard Nolan
Bd of Dir: Maria Fontana
Ofcr: James Manseau
Ofcr: Robert Rossetti
Ex VP: John McCaffery
Sr VP: Stephen Sheridan
Sr VP: John P Vivona
VP: Seamus Doyle
VP: Stan J Glinka
VP: Claudia Pilato
VP: Thomas Sullivan
VP: Dawn Turnbull
Dir Risk M: Maureen Mougios
Board of Directors: Raymond A Nielsen

D-U-N-S 60-304-8802
BRIDGEMAN FOODS II INC
WENDYS OLD FASHIONED REST
(*Suby of* WENDYS) ★
2025 Ws Branch Blvd, Oak Creek, WI 53154
Tel (502) 254-7130 *Founded/Ownrshp* 1987
Sales 46.9MMᴱ *EMP* 1,050
SIC 5812 Fast-food restaurant, chain
Pr: Ulysses L Bridgeman Jr

D-U-N-S 14-717-4523
▲ BRIDGEPOINT EDUCATION INC
13500 Evening Creek Dr N, San Diego, CA 92128-8104
Tel (858) 668-2586 *Founded/Ownrshp* 1999
Sales 561.7MM *EMP* 6,960ᴱ
Tkr Sym BPI *Exch* NYS
SIC 8221 Colleges universities & professional schools; Professional schools
Pr: Andrew S Clark
**Ch Bd:* Patrick T Hackett
COO: Christopher M Henn
CFO: Kevin Royal
Chf Mktg O: Ross L Woodard
Ofcr: Marc Brown
Ex VP: Thomas Ashbrook
Ex VP: Jane McAuliffe
Ex VP: Vickie Schray
Ex VP: Diane L Thompson
Sr VP: Anurag Malik
Sr VP: Vickie L Schray
VP: Jennifer Bruce
VP: Rocky Sheng
VP: Bryan Talbot
VP: Thad Trapp
Assoc Dir: Carrissa M Gonzales
Assoc Dir: Dana Lafleur
Assoc Dir: Ryan Lewis
Dir Soc: Alison Conklin
Board of Directors: Ryan Craig, Dale Crandall, Robert D Hartman, Victor K Nichols

D-U-N-S 08-368-6685
BRIDGEPOINT HEALTHCARE LLC
4601 Martin Luther Jr, Washington, DC 20032-1131
Tel (202) 741-4174 *Founded/Ownrshp* 2015
Sales 91.1MMᴱ *EMP* 1,000
SIC 8062 General medical & surgical hospitals
Pr: Marc Ferrell

D-U-N-S 02-348-3035
BRIDGEPORT CITY SCHOOL DISTRICT
45 Lyon Ter, Bridgeport, CT 06604-4023
Tel (203) 576-7291 *Founded/Ownrshp* 1875
Sales 126.5MMᴱ *EMP* 2,262
SIC 8211 Public elementary & secondary schools
Ofcr: Robert Pascone
Ofcr: Carla Remele
Ofcr: Bernard Webb
Dir Sec: James Denton
MIS Dir: Peter Karaffa
Teacher Pr: Katherine Jaeger
HC Dir: Elizabeth Petrocelli

D-U-N-S 05-674-6464
BRIDGEPORT HOSPITAL
(*Suby of* YALE NEW HAVEN HEALTH SYSTEM) ★
267 Grant St, Bridgeport, CT 06610-2870
Tel (203) 384-3000 *Founded/Ownrshp* 1878
Sales 466.0MM *EMP* 200
SIC 8062 Hospital, medical school affiliated with residency
Pr: William M Jennings
Chf Path: Young Choi
Chf Rad: Alan D Kaye
**Sr VP:* Bruce Mc Donald MD
Sr VP: Christine Winn
**VP:* Joseph E Janell
Dir Case M: Linda Gomes
Dir Rad: Charles I Heller
Dir Rad: Dana S Chwartz
Dir Rad: Kenneth Zinn
Prin: Kumuthini Partheepan

BRIDGESTONE AMERICAS CENTER
See BRIDGESTONE RESEARCH LLC

D-U-N-S 10-147-9322 IMP/EXP
BRIDGESTONE AMERICAS INC
BRIDGESTONE AMERICAS SOURCING
(*Suby of* BRIDGESTONE CORPORATION)
535 Marriott Dr, Nashville, TN 37214-5092
Tel (615) 937-1000 *Founded/Ownrshp* 2001
Sales 16.6MMMᴱ *EMP* 45,000
SIC 3011 3493 2952 2822 3229 Tires & inner tubes; Steel springs, except wire; Asphalt felts & coatings; Synthetic rubber; Pressed & blown glass
Pr: Gary Garfield
V Ch: Mizuochi Shoji
Pr: Joseph Saoud
Pr: Brian Zempel
**Treas:* Jose Anes
Div VP: Patricia B James
Ex VP: Shoshi Arakawa
Ex VP: Donna Barron
Ex VP: Hank Hara
Ex VP: Shigehisa Sano
Ex VP: Mick Suzuki
VP: Giacomo Bertaina
VP: Gary Crigger
VP: James Demouy
VP: Linda Ferguson
VP: Mike Fujimura
VP: William Grein
VP: Bob Handlos
VP: Amber Holm
VP: Christine Karbowiak
VP: Alan Lindsey
Board of Directors: Gabriel Asbun, Philip Dobbs, Gary A Garfield, Christine Karbowiak, Gordon Knapp Eduardo Mina, William Thompson

BRIDGESTONE AMERICAS SOURCING
See BRIDGESTONE AMERICAS INC

D-U-N-S 00-128-8109 IMP/EXP
BRIDGESTONE AMERICAS TIRE OPERATIONS LLC
TIRE WHOLESALE WAREHOUSE
(*Suby of* BRIDGESTONE AMERICAS SOURCING) ★
535 Marriott Dr, Nashville, TN 37214-5092
Tel (615) 937-1000 *Founded/Ownrshp* 2001
Sales 4.4MMMᴱ *EMP* 14,088
SIC 3011 5531 Tires & inner tubes; Automobile tires, pneumatic; Truck or bus tires, pneumatic; Agricultural tires, pneumatic; Automotive & home supply stores; Automotive tires; Automotive parts; Automotive accessories
Ch Bd: Gordon Knapp
Pr: Tj Higgins
Pr: Alan Lindsey
COO: Eduardo Minardi
Chf Mktg O: Philip R Dobbs
VP: David Laubie
VP: John McQuade
VP: Matthew Stevenson
Ex Dir: Philip Pacsi
Prgrm Mgr: John Humphrey
Store Mgr: James Roth

D-U-N-S 18-692-8255 IMP
BRIDGESTONE APM CO
(*Suby of* BRIDGESTONE CORPORATION)
2030 Production Dr, Findlay, OH 45840-5449
Tel (419) 423-9552 *Founded/Ownrshp* 1987
Sales 89.6MMᴱ *EMP* 736
SIC 3061

D-U-N-S 00-526-9758 IMP/EXP
BRIDGESTONE BANDAG LLC (IA)
BANDAG EQUIPMENT COMPANY
(*Suby of* BRIDGESTONE AMERICAS SOURCING) ★
2000 Bandag Dr, Muscatine, IA 52761-5371
Tel (563) 262-2511 *Founded/Ownrshp* 1957, 2007
Sales 454.2MMᴱ *EMP* 3,788
SIC 7534 3559 5014 3011 7549 6794 Tire retreading & repair shops; Tire retreading machinery & equipment; Tires & tubes; Tread rubber, camelback for tire retreading; Retreading materials, tire; Lubrication service, automotive; Franchises, selling or licensing
Ch Bd: Saul Solomon
CFO: Warren W Heidbreder
Treas: David W Dahms
VP: Timothy T Chen
VP: Dennis M Fox
Exec: Josh Canada

D-U-N-S 60-945-2636 IMP
BRIDGESTONE GOLF INC
(*Suby of* BRIDGESTONE SPORTS CO.,LTD.)
15320 Indsrial Pk Blvd Ne, Covington, GA 30014
Tel (770) 787-7400 *Founded/Ownrshp* 2005
Sales 99.7MMᴱ *EMP* 225
Accts Deloitte & Touche Llp Atlanta
SIC 5091 3949 Golf equipment; Golf equipment
Pr: Angel Ilagan
**CFO:* Takashi Tanimura
MIS Dir: John Defoor
Mktg Mgr: Koji Takahashi
Manager: Mike Sparks
Manager: Robert Su
Sls Mgr: Randy Eaton
Sls Mgr: Steve Henry
Sls Mgr: Todd Wilcox

D-U-N-S 62-153-9097 IMP
BRIDGESTONE HOSEPOWER LLC
MASTHEAD HOSE & SUPPLY
50 Industrial Loop N, Orange Park, FL 32073-6258
Tel (904) 264-1267 *Founded/Ownrshp* 1990
Sales 102.0MMᴱ *EMP* 100
SIC 5085 3542 Pistons & valves; Crimping machinery, metal
Pr: John P Clarkson
**CFO:* Tom Henry
CFO: Sharyn Nix
VP: Mike Watts

D-U-N-S 80-590-7961 IMP/EXP
BRIDGESTONE INDUSTRIAL PRODUCTS AMERICA INC
(*Suby of* BRIDGESTONE CORPORATION)
402 Bna Dr Ste 212, Nashville, TN 37217-2530
Tel (615) 365-0600 *Founded/Ownrshp* 1994
Sales 101.5MM *EMP* 28
Accts Deloitte & Touche Llp Nashvi
SIC 5085 8711 Bearings; Engineering services
Pr: Andrew Minwegen

D-U-N-S 92-893-0882 IMP/EXP
BRIDGESTONE METALPHA USA INC
(*Suby of* BRIDGESTONE AMERICAS SOURCING) ★
570 International Blvd, Clarksville, TN 37040-5310
Tel (931) 552-2112 *Founded/Ownrshp* 2013
Sales 131.8MMᴱ *EMP* 375
SIC 2296 Steel tire cords & tire cord fabrics
Pr: Ken Yamasaki
**CFO:* Nao Kiriyama

D-U-N-S 08-040-8959
BRIDGESTONE PROCUREMENT HOLDINGS USA INC
(*Suby of* BRIDGESTONE CORPORATION)
381 W Wilbeth Rd, Akron, OH 44301-2465
Tel (337) 882-1200 *Founded/Ownrshp* 2009
Sales 198.4MMᴱ *EMP* 1,161
SIC 2822 Synthetic rubber
CEO: Gene Lavengco
**Ch Bd:* Yuji Mochizuki
**CFO:* Tinus Grobbrlaar
**Ofcr:* Greg Defrates
**Ofcr:* Cheryl Finch

D-U-N-S 82-849-7417
BRIDGESTONE RESEARCH LLC
BRIDGESTONE AMERICAS CENTER
(*Suby of* TIRE WHOLESALE WAREHOUSE) ★
1655 S Main St, Akron, OH 44301-2035
Tel (330) 379-7570 *Founded/Ownrshp* 2004
Sales 98.4MMᴱ *EMP* 3,587ᴱ
SIC 8731 Commercial physical research
Pr: H Mouri
Ex VP: Hank Hara
VP: Yutaka Yamaguchi
Comm Man: Dave Jacobs

D-U-N-S 11-560-9021 IMP/EXP
BRIDGESTONE RETAIL OPERATIONS LLC
TEAM TIRES PLUS
(*Suby of* BRIDGESTONE AMERICAS SOURCING) ★
333 E Lake St Ste 300, Bloomingdale, IL 60108-1193
Tel (630) 259-9000 *Founded/Ownrshp* 2001
Sales 6.7MMMᴱ *EMP* 17,044
SIC 5531 7534 5014 Automotive tires; Tire retreading & repair shops; Tires & tubes
Pr: Larry Magee
CFO: Thomas Studer
Ex VP: Matt Hoskins
VP: Jim Downing
**Prin:* Donald Delande
Ex Dir: David Gorodetski
Dist Mgr: Jim Fogelquist
CTO: Creed Mooneyhan
IT Man: Ann Leary
Mktg Mgr: Al Schretter

D-U-N-S 07-440-9004
BRIDGEVIEW BANK GROUP
(*Suby of* BRIDGEVIEW BANCORP, INC.)
7940 S Harlem Ave, Bridgeview, IL 60455-1598
Tel (708) 594-7400 *Founded/Ownrshp* 1983
Sales NA *EMP* 280
SIC 6022 State trust companies accepting deposits, commercial
Ch Bd: Peter J Haleas
Pr: Debbie Stouffer
CEO: William L Conaghan
COO: Contessa Flemons
CFO: David Alteteter
CFO: Donald Benziger
Ex VP: Randy Curtis
Sr VP: Dave Grzenia
Sr VP: Mark Kosiek
Sr VP: Tom Meyer
VP: Jamie Arthurs
VP: David Fagen
VP: Mark Majdecki
VP: Brigid Murphy
VP: Joe Rubinas
VP: Andrew Trippi
Exec: Christopher Paige
Exec: John Taflan

D-U-N-S 07-488-2358
BRIDGEWATER ASSOCIATES LP
1 Glendinning Pl, Westport, CT 06880-1242
Tel (203) 226-3030 *Founded/Ownrshp* 1975
Sales 399.2MME *EMP* 1,200
SIC 6282 8742 Investment advisory service; Management consulting services
Pr: David McCormick
Pr: Ben Goldner
Ofcr: Peter La Tronica
**VP:* Peter Latronica
VP: Molly Vanassche
Exec: Theodore M Yang
**Prin:* Giselle Wagner
Opers Mgr: John Sorbo
VP Mktg: Jennifer M Peterson
Corp Couns: Helene T Glozer

D-U-N-S 01-388-1706 IMP
BRIDGEWATER INTERIORS LLC
(*Suby of* ADIENT US LLC) ★
4617 W Fort St, Detroit, MI 48209-3208
Tel (313) 842-3300 *Founded/Ownrshp* 1998, 2016
Sales 269.0MME *EMP* 800
Accts Plante & Moran Southfield Mi
SIC 5013 2531 Motor vehicle supplies & new parts; Public building & related furniture
Pr: Ron Hall
COO: Cassandra Alston-Childs
CFO: John Cloud
Sr Cor Off: Ann Proctor
Ex VP: Carrie Tingle

D-U-N-S 87-804-3421
BRIDGEWATER STATE UNIVERSITY
(*Suby of* MASSACHUSETTS BOARD OF HIGHER EDUCATION SYSTEM) ★
131 Summer St Rm 109, Bridgewater, MA 02325-0001
Tel (508) 531-1000 *Founded/Ownrshp* 1840
Sales 117.5MM *EMP* 695E
Accts Wolf & Company Pc Boston Ma
SIC 8221 9199 College, except junior;
Ch: Louis M Ricciardi
**Pr:* Dana Mohler-Faria
Ofcr: Robert McEvoy
VP: Gary Boothey
VP: David Ostroth
Assoc Dir: Tracey Connell
Assoc Dir: Dwight Cook
Assoc Dir: Darlene Marks
Ex Dir: Nicole Mantville
Genl Mgr: Brian Jones
Dir IT: Chandra Gudena

D-U-N-S 12-215-0881 IMP
BRIDGEWATER WHOLESALERS INC
B W I
210 Industrial Pkwy, Branchburg, NJ 08876-3450
Tel (908) 526-7555 *Founded/Ownrshp* 1982
Sales 167.4MME *EMP* 450
SIC 2431 5031 Doors & door parts & trim, wood; Doors & windows; Molding, all materials
Ch: Susan Schumer
**Pr:* Jack Cortese
**COO:* Simon Sikora
**VP:* Brock Ryall
**Exec:* Paula Waters
DP Exec: Maria Infante
Mill Mgr: Melanio Cano
Mill Mgr: Keith Dursharm
Mill Mgr: Keith Dusharm
Mill Mgr: John Nagel
**Sfty Mgr:* Dave Gelchion

D-U-N-S 07-514-2901
BRIDGEWATER-RARITAN REGIONAL SCHOOL DISTRICT (NJ)
836 Newmans Ln, Bridgewater, NJ 08807
Tel (908) 685-2777 *Founded/Ownrshp* 1865
Sales 159.5MM *EMP* 1,200
Accts Nisivoccia Llp Mt Arlington
SIC 8211 Public elementary & secondary schools

D-U-N-S 82-695-6323
BRIDGEWATER-RARITAN REGIONAL SCHOOL DISTRICT
836 Newmans Ln, Bridgewater, NJ 08807
Tel (908) 685-2777 *Founded/Ownrshp* 2011
Sales 145.2MM *EMP* 1,000
Accts Suplee Clooney & Company Wes
SIC 8211 Elementary & secondary schools
MIS Dir: Andres Ospina
Teacher Pr: Marc Gaswirth
HC Dir: Brian Henry

D-U-N-S 12-186-3468
BRIDGEWELL INC
471 Broadway, Lynnfield, MA 01940-1401
Tel (781) 599-4240 *Founded/Ownrshp* 1958
Sales 50.0MM *EMP* 1,100
Accts Kevin P Martin & Associates Pc
SIC 8361 8093 Home for the mentally handicapped; Home for the mentally retarded; Mental health clinic, outpatient
Ex Dir: Robert Sterins
**CEO:* James Cowdell
**COO:* Anita Shipman
**CFO:* Keith Brainnfield
Pgrm Dir: Melissa Bridges-Pata
Pgrm Dir: Kevin Dodier
Pgrm Dir: Valerie Passerini
Pgrm Dir: Nicole Saccone

D-U-N-S 96-239-6003
BRIDGEWELL RESOURCES HOLDINGS LLC
(*Suby of* ATLAS HOLDINGS LLC) ★
1 Sound Shore Dr Ste 302, Greenwich, CT 06830-7251
Tel (203) 622-9138 *Founded/Ownrshp* 2010
Sales 192.0MME *EMP* 190E
SIC 5031 2491 5039 5153 Paneling, wood; Wood products, creosoted; Prefabricated structures; Grain & field beans
Pr: Andrew M Bursky
VP: Edward Fletcher
VP: Philip Schuch

D-U-N-S 96-182-3874 IMP
BRIDGEWELL RESOURCES LLC
(*Suby of* BRIDGEWELL RESOURCES HOLDINGS LLC) ★
10200 Sw Greenburg Rd # 500, Tigard, OR 97223-5510
Tel (503) 872-3566 *Founded/Ownrshp* 2010
Sales 192.0MME *EMP* 190E
SIC 5031 5039 5153 5159 Lumber, plywood & millwork; Architectural metalwork; Grain & field beans; Nuts & nut by-products
CEO: Patrick McCauley
**CFO:* Jay Wilson

BRIDGFORD FOODS
See BRIDGFORD INDUSTRIES INC

D-U-N-S 00-850-6768
■ **BRIDGFORD FOODS CORP**
(*Suby of* BRIDGFORD FOODS) ★
1308 N Patt St, Anaheim, CA 92801-2551
Tel (714) 526-5533 *Founded/Ownrshp* 1932
Sales 130.4MM *EMP* 507E
Tkr Sym BRID *Exch* NGM
SIC 2045 2099 2015 2013 2022 2038 Biscuit dough, prepared: from purchased flour; Doughs, frozen or refrigerated: from purchased flour; Sandwiches, assembled & packaged: for wholesale market; Salads, fresh or refrigerated; Poultry sausage, luncheon meats & other poultry products; Snack sticks, including jerky: from purchased meat; Cheese, natural & processed; Dips, cheese-based; Frozen specialties
Ch Bd: William L Bridgford
**Pr:* John V Simmons
**CFO:* Raymond F Lancy
Bd of Dir: Paul Zippwald
VP: Allan L Bridgford Jr
VP: Hugh Wm Bridgford
VP: Bob Delong
Exec: David Vandervoort
Rgnl Mgr: Rex Wilcken
VP Mfg: Joe Dealcuaz
Plnt Mgr: Jose Chavez
Board of Directors: Todd C Andrews, Bruce H Bridgford, D Gregory Scott, Paul R Zippwald

D-U-N-S 07-702-8553 IMP
■ **BRIDGFORD FOODS CORP**
BRIDGFORD MARKETING
(*Suby of* BRIDGFORD FOODS CORP) ★
170 N Green St, Chicago, IL 60607-2313
Tel (312) 733-0300 *Founded/Ownrshp* 1976
Sales 96.4MME *EMP* 375
SIC 2013 Prepared pork products from purchased pork; Prepared beef products from purchased beef; Sausages from purchased meat; Sausages & related products, from purchased meat
CEO: Allan L Bridgford Sr
**Ch Bd:* H W Bridgford
**Pr:* John V Simmons
**COO:* Barren Bridgford
**CFO:* Raymond F Lancy
**Ch:* William L Bridgford
Sfty Dirs: Richard Bridgford

D-U-N-S 19-773-2642
▲ **BRIDGFORD INDUSTRIES INC**
BRIDGFORD FOODS
1601 S Good Latimer Expy, Dallas, TX 75226
Tel (214) 428-1535 *Founded/Ownrshp* 1962
Sales 133.8MME *EMP* 539E
SIC 2045 2099 2015 2013 2022 2038 Biscuit dough, prepared: from purchased flour; Doughs, frozen or refrigerated: from purchased flour; Sandwiches, assembled & packaged: for wholesale market; Salads, fresh or refrigerated; Poultry sausage, luncheon meats & other poultry products; Snack sticks, including jerky: from purchased meat; Cheese, natural & processed; Dips, cheese-based; Frozen specialties
Pr: John Simmons
**CFO:* Raymond F Lancy
**Ch:* William L Bridgford
**Sr VP:* Daniel R Yost
Plnt Mgr: Rafael Cornejo
Prd Mgr: Brent Stevens

BRIDGFORD MARKETING
See BRIDGFORD FOODS CORP

D-U-N-S 06-132-9017 IMP/EXP
BRIDON-AMERICAN CORP
(*Suby of* BRIDON INTERNATIONAL LTD.)
C280 New Commerce Blvd, Wilkes Barre, PA 18706
Tel (570) 822-3349 *Founded/Ownrshp* 2014
Sales 369.2MME *EMP* 1,000
SIC 3533 3532 5084 Oil & gas field machinery; Mining machinery; Cranes, industrial
CEO: Chris Dugan
**CFO:* Joseph Simkulak
Snr Mgr: Bill Youngblood

BRIGGEMAN DISPOSAL SERVICE
See CONSOLIDATED DISPOSAL SERVICE LLC

D-U-N-S 00-608-2531 IMP/EXP
▲ **BRIGGS & STRATTON CORP** (WI)
12301 W Wirth St, Wauwatosa, WI 53222-2110
Tel (414) 259-5333 *Founded/Ownrshp* 1908
Sales 1.8MMM *EMP* 5,480
Tkr Sym BGG *Exch* NYS
SIC 3519 3524 Internal combustion engines; Gasoline engines; Lawn & garden equipment; Lawn & garden mowers & accessories; Blowers & vacuums, lawn; Snowblowers & throwers, residential
Ch Bd: Todd J Teske
CFO: Mark A Schwertfeger
Treas: Andrea L Golvach
Sr VP: Harold L Redman
Sr VP: William H Reitman
Sr VP: David J Rodgers
Sr VP: Edward J Wajda
VP: Kathryn M Buono
VP: David G Debaets
VP: David Frank
VP: Daniel B Kennedy
Board of Directors: Jeffrey R Hennion, James E Humphrey, Frank M Jaehnert, Patricia L Kampling, Keith R McLoughlin, Henrik C Slipsager, Brian C Walker

D-U-N-S 02-440-9372 IMP/EXP
■ **BRIGGS & STRATTON POWER PRODUCTS GROUP LLC**
(*Suby of* BRIGGS & STRATTON CORP) ★
12301 W Wirth St, Wauwatosa, WI 53222-2110
Tel (414) 259-5333 *Founded/Ownrshp* 2001
Sales 186.6MME *EMP* 1,000E
SIC 3621 Generator sets: gasoline, diesel or dual-fuel
Prin: Dennis Siebenaller
Prin: Gary J Lato
VP Opers: David Mauer

D-U-N-S 83-803-1177 IMP/EXP
BRIGGS EQUIPMENT INC
(*Suby of* SAMMONS ENTERPRISES INC) ★
10540 N Stemmons Fwy, Dallas, TX 75220-2425
Tel (214) 630-0808 *Founded/Ownrshp* 2007
Sales 233.6MME *EMP* 600
SIC 5084

D-U-N-S 10-734-2321 IMP
BRIGGS MEDICAL SERVICE CO
DMS HOLDINGS
7300 Westown Pkwy Ste 100, West Des Moines, IA 50266-2527
Tel (515) 327-6400 *Founded/Ownrshp* 1983
Sales 150.0MM *EMP* 300
SIC 5047 Medical equipment & supplies
CEO: Bruce Dan
**Pr:* Merwyn E Dan
Pr: Brad Mueller
**CFO:* Thomas J Young
Sr VP: Jeff Pigott

D-U-N-S 07-656-9144
BRIGHAM AND WOMENS FAULKNER HOSPITAL INC
(*Suby of* BRIGHAM AND WOMENS/FAULKNER) ★
1153 Centre St, Boston, MA 02130-3446
Tel (617) 983-7000 *Founded/Ownrshp* 1996
Sales 137.7MME *EMP* 1,535
SIC 8062 General medical & surgical hospitals
Sr VP: Michael E Conklin Jr
Dir Recs: Lawanda Dixon
**Pr:* Elizabeth Nabel
**Treas:* Peter K Markell
**Treas:* Cynthia Taft
Off Mgr: Nova South
Telecom Mg: John Wright
Mtls Mgr: Jack Coyle
Ansthlgy: Matthew G Bloch
Ansthlgy: Cynthia C Espanola
Ansthlgy: Vladimir V Kazakin

D-U-N-S 61-161-1922
BRIGHAM AND WOMENS HEALTH CARE INC
BRIGHAM AND WOMEN'S/FAULKNER
(*Suby of* PARTNERS HEALTHCARE SYSTEM INC) ★
75 Francis St, Boston, MA 02115-6110
Tel (617) 732-5500 *Founded/Ownrshp* 1994
Sales 1.9MMME *EMP* 10,000
SIC 8741 Hospital management
Pr: Gary Gottlieb
Opers Supe: Jackie Borne
Opers Mgr: Sharon Khaw
Ansthlgy: Stewart L Chritton
Ansthlgy: Lisa J Crossley
Doctor: Jane A Leopold

D-U-N-S 06-999-0880 IMP
BRIGHAM AND WOMENS HOSPITAL INC
BRIGHAM WMNS/FULKNER HOSPITALS
(*Suby of* BRIGHAM AND WOMENS/FAULKNER) ★
75 Francis St, Boston, MA 02115-6106
Tel (617) 732-5500 *Founded/Ownrshp* 1996
Sales 1.8MMM *EMP* 8,376
SIC 8062 General medical & surgical hospitals
Pr: Elizabeth G Nabel
V Ch: David Faxon
COO: Ron M Walls
CFO: Owen Robbins
Sr VP: Paul J Anderson
Sr VP: Richard W Fernandez
Sr VP: Julia Sinclair
Sr VP: Jackie Somerville
Sr VP: Steven Thompson
Dir Risk M: Ann Collins
Dir Risk M: David Seaver

BRIGHAM AND WOMEN'S/FAULKNER
See BRIGHAM AND WOMENS HEALTH CARE INC

BRIGHAM EXPLORATION COMPANY
See STATOIL EXPLORATION CO

BRIGHAM WMNS/FULKNER HOSPITALS
See BRIGHAM AND WOMENS HOSPITAL INC

D-U-N-S 00-909-4012 IMP
BRIGHAM YOUNG UNIVERSITY (UT)
CORPORATION OF PRES OF THE
(*Suby of* CHURCH OF JSUS CHRST OF LD STS) ★
A 41 Asb Brgham Yung Univ, Provo, UT 84602
Tel (801) 422-1211 *Founded/Ownrshp* 1875
Sales 491.7MME *EMP* 3,767
SIC 8221 University
Pr: Kevin Worthen
**Treas:* Richard P White
VP: Elaine Alger
VP: Edward Blaser
VP: Katherine Johnson
VP: Darin Perry
IT Man: J Potier

D-U-N-S 12-948-9808
BRIGHAM YOUNG UNIVERSITY-HAWAII
(*Suby of* CHURCH OF JSUS CHRST OF LD STS) ★
55-220 Kulanui St, Laie, HI 96762-1266
Tel (808) 293-3211 *Founded/Ownrshp* 1955
Sales 81.8MME *EMP* 1,500
SIC 8221 Colleges universities & professional schools
Pr: Steven C Whellwright
**Pr:* Michael B Bliss
**Pr:* Max Checketts
Pr: William Neal
CFO: Kirk Evans
VP: Isileli Kongaika
**VP:* David A Lewis
**VP:* Debbie Hippolite Wright
Exec: Keith Lane
Assoc Dir: Monte Marshall
Ex Dir: Yen Su

D-U-N-S 06-980-7691
BRIGHAM YOUNG UNIVERSITY-IDAHO
(*Suby of* CHURCH OF JSUS CHRST OF LD STS) ★
525 S Center St, Rexburg, ID 83460-0004
Tel (208) 496-1901 *Founded/Ownrshp* 1888
Sales 293.3MM *EMP* 2,129
SIC 8221 University
CEO: Kim B Clark
**CFO:* Shane Webster
**VP:* Charles N Andersen
**VP:* Fenton L Broadhead
Exec: Rex Barzee
Exec: Fred Free
Exec: Gloria Horrocks
Exec: Michael McLaughlin
Exec: Mark Olaveson
Exec: Steven Rigby
Off Admin: Jamie Andersen

D-U-N-S 55-625-5438
BRIGHT HEALTH PHYSICIANS
15725 Whittier Blvd # 500, Whittier, CA 90603-2350
Tel (562) 947-8478 *Founded/Ownrshp* 1991
Sales 120.5MM *EMP* 200
SIC 8011 Physicians' office, including specialists
Ch Bd: William H Stimmler MD
**Pr:* Keith Miyamoto MD
Prin: Don T Eli
Doctor: Yu-Chen Kuo

D-U-N-S 18-312-0120
■ **BRIGHT HORIZONS CHILDRENS CENTERS LLC**
(*Suby of* BRIGHT HORIZONS FAMILY SOLUTIONS LLC) ★
200 Talcott Ave, Watertown, MA 02472-5705
Tel (617) 673-8000 *Founded/Ownrshp* 1986
Sales 743.8M *EMP* 8,000
SIC 8351 Group day care center
CFO: Sheila Grayson
Sr VP: Dave Shaby
VP: Arlene Johnson
VP: Jackie Legg
Ex Dir: Joanna Stamp
Board of Directors: Joshua Bekenstein, Gabrielle Greene, Marguerite Sallee

D-U-N-S 07-873-4723
▲ **BRIGHT HORIZONS FAMILY SOLUTIONS INC**
200 Talcott Ave, Watertown, MA 02472-5705
Tel (617) 673-8000 *Founded/Ownrshp* 1986
Sales 1.4MMM *EMP* 26,000
Tkr Sym BFAM *Exch* NYS
SIC 8351 Child day care services
CEO: David H Lissy
**Ch Bd:* Linda Mason
Pr: Stephen H Kramer
CFO: Elizabeth J Boland
Ofcr: Mandy Berman
Ofcr: Danroy T Henry Sr
Ex VP: Stephen I Dreier
VP: Javed Ikbal
VP: Daniel Lenyo
VP: Ann Pickens
Dir IT: Caron Lewis
Board of Directors: Mary Ann Tocio, Lawrence M Alleva, Josh Bekenstein, Roger H Brown, E Townes Duncan, Jordan Hitch, David Humphrey, Marguerite Kondracke, Sara Lawrence-Lightfoot, Cathy E Minehan

D-U-N-S 03-112-0541
■ **BRIGHT HORIZONS FAMILY SOLUTIONS LLC**
(*Suby of* BRIGHT HORIZONS FAMILY SOLUTIONS INC) ★
200 Talcott Ave, Watertown, MA 02472-5705
Tel (617) 673-8000 *Founded/Ownrshp* 2008
Sales 397.5MME *EMP* 19,384E
SIC 8351 Group day care center; Preschool center
CEO: David Lissy
Pr: Cheryl Partida
Pr: Mary Ann Tocio
COO: Mary Lou Burke Afonso
CFO: Elizabeth J Boland
CFO: Elizabeth Boland
Ofcr: Danroy T Henry Sr
Ex VP: Mandy Berman
Sr VP: Mary L Burke
Sr VP: Gary Oneil

VP: Angella Schroller
Adv Bd Mbr: Josu Cruz

BRIGHT IDEAS GIFT SHOP
See CAPE MEMORIAL HOSPITAL INC

BRIGHT IDEAS GIFT SHOP
See LEE MEMORIAL HEALTH SYSTEM FOUNDATION INC

BRIGHT LIGHTS
See COLONIAL ELECTRIC SUPPLY CO

BRIGHT NOW DENTAL
See SMILE BRANDS GROUP INC

D-U-N-S 00-941-2875 IMP/EXP
BRIGHT WOOD CORP
335 Nw Hess St, Madras, OR 97741-9485
Tel (541) 475-2234 *Founded/Ownrshp* 1960
Sales 150.0MM[E] *EMP* 950
SIC 2431

D-U-N-S 19-926-5070
▲ BRIGHTCOVE INC
290 Congress St Fl 4, Boston, MA 02210-1005
Tel (888) 882-1880 *Founded/Ownrshp* 2004
Sales 134.7MM *EMP* 413[E]
Tkr Sym BCOV *Exch* NGM
SIC 4813 7372 ; Prepackaged software
CEO: David Mendels
**Ch Bd:* Gary Haroian
Pr: Andrew Feinberg
CFO: Kevin R Rhodes
Chf Mktg O: Neil Lieberman
Ofcr: Christopher Stagno
Sr VP: Caren Cioffi
Sr VP: Jon Corley
Sr VP: Anil Jain
Sr VP: David Plotkin
VP: Tomer Azenkot
VP: Mark Blair
VP: Katie Kulikoski
VP: Mark Stanton
Creative D: Colin Henson

D-U-N-S 07-278-5348
BRIGHTON AREA SCHOOL DISTRICT
125 S Church St, Brighton, MI 48116-1652
Tel (810) 299-4000 *Founded/Ownrshp* 1900
Sales 48.6MM[E] *EMP* 1,100
Accts Plante & Moran Pllc East Lan
SIC 8211 Public elementary & secondary schools; High school, junior or senior
Teacher Pr: Shelly Kennedy

D-U-N-S 04-851-0929 IMP
BRIGHTON COLLECTIBLES LLC
BRIGHTON FOOTWEAR
14022 Nelson Ave, City of Industry, CA 91746-2638
Tel (626) 961-9381 *Founded/Ownrshp* 1969, 2013
Sales 354.7MM[E] *EMP* 2,500
SIC 5632

D-U-N-S 96-662-7148
BRIGHTON COMMUNITY HOSPITAL ASSOCIATION
PLATTE VALLEY MEDICAL CENTER
1600 Prairie Center Pkwy, Brighton, CO 80601-4006
Tel (303) 498-1600 *Founded/Ownrshp* 1958
Sales 109.7MM *EMP* 700
Accts Bkd Llp Colorado Springs Co
SIC 8099 Childbirth preparation clinic
Pr: Marcie Demchuk
**VP:* Harold Dupper
**VP Opers:* Kurt Gensert

BRIGHTON FOOTWEAR
See BRIGHTON COLLECTIBLES LLC

BRIGHTON GARDENS
See SUNRISE SENIOR LIVING LLC

D-U-N-S 01-200-3513
BRIGHTON MARINE HEALTH CENTER INC
77 Warren St Fl 7, Brighton, MA 02135-3601
Tel (617) 562-5222 *Founded/Ownrshp* 1981
Sales 142.9MM *EMP* 28
Accts Gerald T Reilly & Company Mil
SIC 6531 Real estate managers
Pr: Kent Mathews
**Ch:* Maurice R Dumas
**Treas:* John Doyle
VP Admn: Marlene Calisi

D-U-N-S 00-390-7110 IMP/EXP
BRIGHTON-BEST INTERNATIONAL INC (CA)
(*Suby of* SUNLAND SHUTTERS) ★
5855 Obispo Ave, Long Beach, CA 90805-3715
Tel (562) 808-8000 *Founded/Ownrshp* 1965
Sales 158.5MM[E] *EMP* 260
SIC 5072 Screws
CEO: Jun Xu
**Pr:* Robert Shieh
VP: Steve Andrasik
VP: Richard Ripley
Brnch Mgr: Melissa Miller
Genl Mgr: Gary Schottlander

D-U-N-S 07-998-9928
BRIGHTPOINT HEALTH
71 W 23rd St Fl 8, New York, NY 10010-3509
Tel (718) 681-8700 *Founded/Ownrshp* 2015
Sales 2.5MM[E] *EMP* 1,000
SIC 8099 Health & allied services
Owner: Paul Vitale
IT Man: Sara Gillen

D-U-N-S 61-199-1373 IMP
■ BRIGHTPOINT INC
(*Suby of* INGRAM MICRO INC) ★
501 Airtech Pkwy, Plainfield, IN 46168-7408
Tel (317) 707-2355 *Founded/Ownrshp* 2012
Sales 797.8MM[E] *EMP* 4,008[E]
SIC 5065 Electronic parts & equipment; Telephone equipment; Mobile telephone equipment
Pr: Bashar Nejdawi
Pr: Eric Hamburger
**CEO:* Shailendra Gupta
COO: J Howell
COO: Sriram Subrahmanyam
CFO: Kari Dimler
**CFO:* Vincent Donargo
CFO: John J Ludwig
Ofcr: Jorge Reyes
**Ex VP:* John Alexander Du Plessis Curr
Ex VP: Ed Rounsville
**Sr VP:* Robert L Colin
VP: Bill Casey
VP: Robert Hanley
VP: Jeremy Murchland
VP: Eric Proctor
VP Bus Dev: Tom Cherryhomes
VP Bus Dev: Dana Hicks

D-U-N-S 05-806-4663 IMP
■ BRIGHTPOINT NORTH AMERICA LLC
(*Suby of* INGRAM MICRO INC) ★
501 Airtech Pkwy, Plainfield, IN 46168-7408
Tel (317) 707-2355 *Founded/Ownrshp* 2012
Sales 403.2MM[E] *EMP* 1,600[E]
SIC 5065 Communication equipment
Pr: Bashar Nejdawi
CEO: Robert J Laikin
CFO: Karen Smith
Treas: Erik Smolders
Ex VP: Vincent Donargo
VP: Treana Fields
VP: Scott Pelance
Prin: J Mark Howell

D-U-N-S 83-306-8104
■ BRIGHTPOINT NORTH AMERICA LP
(*Suby of* INGRAM MICRO INC) ★
501 Airtech Pkwy, Plainfield, IN 46168-7408
Tel (317) 707-2355 *Founded/Ownrshp* 2012
Sales 614.5MM *EMP* 1,810
SIC 5065 Communication equipment
CEO: Robert J Laikin
Ex VP: Craig Carpenter
Ex VP: Jac Currie
Sr VP: Doug Pasquale
VP: Frank Boyle
VP: William Casey
VP: Tom Cherryhomes
VP: Dana Hicks
VP: John Mroch
VP: Scott Pelance
Prgrm Mgr: Andrew Dietz

D-U-N-S 78-784-5598 IMP
BRIGHTSOURCE ENERGY INC
1999 Harrison St Ste 2150, Oakland, CA 94612-3500
Tel (510) 550-8161 *Founded/Ownrshp* 2006
Sales 123.6MM[E] *EMP* 336[E]
SIC 1629 Power plant construction
CEO: H David Ramm
Ch Bd: Richard Kelly
CFO: Jack Jenkins-Stark
Sr VP: Joe Desmond
Sr VP: Thomas P Doyle
Sr VP: Charlie Ricker
Sr VP: Stephen Wiley
VP: Yasser Dib
VP: Catherine Johnson
VP: Scott Rossbrooke
Genl Mgr: Yvonne Huang
Board of Directors: Thomas O'flynn

D-U-N-S 83-967-7150 IMP/EXP
■ BRIGHTSTAR CORP
(*Suby of* SOFTBANK GROUP CORP.)
9725 Nw 117th Ave Ste 105, Medley, FL 33178-1213
Tel (305) 421-6000 *Founded/Ownrshp* 2014
Sales 12.1MMM *EMP* 4,100
SIC 5065 Telephone & telegraphic equipment; Mobile telephone equipment
CEO: Jaymin Patel
Pr: Juan Carlos Archila
Pr: Harry Lagad
Pr: Oscar Rojas
Pr: Benoit Scheen
Pr: Mark Shockley
CEO: Deval Parikh
**COO:* Alan Eland
COO: David J Mizwicki
**CFO:* Reza Taleghani
**Ch:* Ronald D Fisher
**Treas:* Noel Gerald Marsden
Treas: Noel Marsden
Treas: Natasha Medina
Treas: Enrique Rodriguez
**Chf Mktg O:* Emer Timmons
Ofcr: Veronica Sulja
Ofcr: Suman Wahi
Ex VP: Andrea Bradshaw
Ex VP: Vincent Donargo
**Ex VP:* Catherine Smith

D-U-N-S 04-007-9209
■ BRIGHTSTAR DEVICE PROTECTION LLC
(*Suby of* BRIGHTSTAR CORP) ★
2325 Lkeview Pkwy Ste 700, Alpharetta, GA 30009
Tel (843) 548-0120 *Founded/Ownrshp* 2011
Sales NA *EMP* 250
SIC 6411 Insurance agents & brokers
CEO: Fraser Parker
Pr: Daniel Currie
**CFO:* Tim Kristof
Chf Mktg O: Jennifer Taylor
Sr VP: Guru Kashyap
**VP:* Stephen Bracy
CTO: Julio Palacio
Dir IT: Carlos Rodrigues

D-U-N-S 09-896-9939 IMP
■ BRIGHTSTAR US INC
(*Suby of* BRIGHTSTAR CORP) ★
850 Technology Way, Libertyville, IL 60048-5350
Tel (847) 573-2600 *Founded/Ownrshp* 2000
Sales 4.4MMM *EMP* 225
SIC 5065 Telephone & telegraphic equipment
Pr: Jeff Gower

D-U-N-S 05-079-6176 IMP/EXP
BRIGHTVIEW COMPANIES LLC
(*Suby of* BRIGHTVIEW ENTP SLTONS BRCKMAN) ★
24151 Ventura Blvd, Calabasas, CA 91302-1449
Tel (818) 223-8500 *Founded/Ownrshp* 2015
Sales 3.7MMM[E] *EMP* 8,160
SIC 1629 0782 0781 Golf course construction; Lawn & garden services; Landscape services; Landscape planning services
CEO: Rofer Zino
CEO: Roger Zino
COO: Andrew Brennan
CFO: Gareth Asten
CFO: Andrew Mandell
Sr VP: Michael Dingman
VP: William Cumberland
VP: Charles Gonzalez
VP: Greg Harbison
VP: William Leathers
VP: Jeff Lennon
VP: Robert McDonnell
VP: Howard Mees
VP: Joe Parinella
VP: Wayne Shiveley
VP: Mark Wesel

D-U-N-S 83-478-1473
BRIGHTVIEW COMPANIES LLC
2275 Research Blvd, Rockville, MD 20850-3268
Tel (240) 683-2000 *Founded/Ownrshp* 2015
Sales 258.8MM[E] *EMP* 492[E]
SIC 0781 0782 Landscape services; Landscape contractors
CEO: Andrew Kerin
Pr: Roger Zino

BRIGHTVIEW ENTP SLTONS BRCKMAN
See BRIGHTVIEW LANDSCAPES LLC

D-U-N-S 02-948-5224
BRIGHTVIEW GOLF MAINTENANCE INC
VALLEYCREST GOLF CRSE MINT INC
(*Suby of* BRIGHTVIEW COMPANIES LLC) ★
24151 Ventura Blvd, Calabasas, CA 91302-1449
Tel (818) 223-8500 *Founded/Ownrshp* 1965
Sales 140.5MM[E] *EMP* 965
SIC 1629 Golf course construction
Ch Bd: Burton Sperber
**Ch Bd:* Richard A Sperber
**Pr:* Gregory Pieschala
**CFO:* Andrew Mandell
**Ch:* Michael L Dingman
**VP:* Stanley Colton
Mktg Mgr: Lorraine Dibacco

D-U-N-S 04-115-8981 IMP/EXP
BRIGHTVIEW LANDSCAPE DEVELOPMENT INC
(*Suby of* BRIGHTVIEW COMPANIES LLC) ★
24151 Ventura Blvd, Calabasas, CA 91302-1449
Tel (818) 223-8500 *Founded/Ownrshp* 1949
Sales 592.9MM[E] *EMP* 3,059
SIC 0781 Landscape counseling & planning
CEO: Thomas Donnelly
Pr: Thomas C Donelly
Pr: Kenneth L Hutcheson
COO: Andrew J Brennan
VP: Pamela L Stark
Sales Exec: Issac Alford

D-U-N-S 06-625-4509 IMP/EXP
BRIGHTVIEW LANDSCAPE SERVICES INC
(*Suby of* BRIGHTVIEW COMPANIES LLC) ★
24151 Ventura Blvd, Calabasas, CA 91302-1449
Tel (818) 223-8500 *Founded/Ownrshp* 1970
Sales 965.9MM[E] *EMP* 8,160
SIC 0781 Landscape services
CEO: Roger Zino
**CFO:* Anthony Garruto
**Bd of Dir:* Richard A Sperber
Ex VP: Andrew Mandell
VP: William N Cohe
VP: Stanley Colton
VP: Tom Powell
Brnch Mgr: Julie Bramlett
Brnch Mgr: Scott Godfrey
Brnch Mgr: Brandon Steene
Brnch Mgr: Samuel Wells

D-U-N-S 14-478-0863
BRIGHTVIEW LANDSCAPES LLC
BRIGHTVIEW ENTP SLTONS BRCKMAN
(*Suby of* BRICKMAN ACQUISITION HOLDINGS INC) ★
2275 Res Blvd Ste 600, Rockville, MD 20850
Tel (301) 987-9200 *Founded/Ownrshp* 2015
Sales 3.7MMM[E] *EMP* 10,000
SIC 0781 0782 Landscape services; Landscape contractors
CEO: Andrew Kerin
CFO: Timothy Pease
Treas: Kevin J Hargrove
Sr VP: Kurt Bratton
Dir Bus: Jason Lewis
Dir Bus: Brad Shaffer
Prin: Damien Dowtin
Rgnl Mgr: Michael Stewart
Rgnl Mgr: John Vesko
Brnch Mgr: Lori Declement
Brnch Mgr: Dante Demaria

BRIGHTWOOD COLLEGE
See EDUCATION CORP OF AMERICA

BRIKMANN J BAXTER INTL
See J BAXTER BRINKMANN INTERNATIONAL CORP

D-U-N-S 12-213-2301 IMP/EXP
■ BRILLION IRON WORKS INC
(*Suby of* GREDE HOLDINGS LLC) ★
200 Park Ave, Brillion, WI 54110-1196
Tel (920) 756-2121 *Founded/Ownrshp* 2016
Sales 146.0MM[E] *EMP* 690[E]
SIC 3321 Gray iron castings; Ductile iron castings
Pr: Douglas J Grimm
Snr Mgr: Gary Kabat

D-U-N-S 83-020-7796
BRIM HEALTHCARE OF TEXAS LLC
WADLEY REGIONAL MEDICAL CENTER
1000 Pine St, Texarkana, TX 75501-5100
Tel (903) 798-8000 *Founded/Ownrshp* 2009
Sales 39.1MM[E] *EMP* 1,285
SIC 8062 General medical & surgical hospitals
CEO: Thomas Gilbert
COO: Phillip J Mazzuca
CFO: John M Doyle
VP: William A Stokes

D-U-N-S 15-223-2836
BRIM HOLDINGS INC
(*Suby of* IASIS HEALTHCARE CORP) ★
105 Westwood Pl Ste 300, Brentwood, TN 37027-5038
Tel (615) 309-6053 *Founded/Ownrshp* 2010
Sales 154.1MM[E] *EMP* 1,566
SIC 8741 Hospital management
CEO: Dave Widland
**Pr:* Philip J Mazzuca
**CFO:* Lynn Lambert
Treas: Richard Gore

D-U-N-S 80-541-5783
■ BRINDERSON LP
(*Suby of* AEGION CORP) ★
19000 Macarthur Blvd # 800, Irvine, CA 92612-1461
Tel (714) 466-7100 *Founded/Ownrshp* 2013
Sales 322.6MM[E] *EMP* 1,500
SIC 8711 1629 Engineering services; Dams, waterways, docks & other marine construction
VP: Ian Cairns
Prgrm Mgr: Chris Lamb
Genl Mgr: Kris Schramm
Sfty Mgr: Jimmy Lumpkins
Ql Cn Mgr: Jeffrey Barksdale
Mktg Mgr: Janet Amant

D-U-N-S 02-332-8248
▲ BRINKER INTERNATIONAL INC
6820 Lbj Fwy, Dallas, TX 75240-6511
Tel (972) 980-9917 *Founded/Ownrshp* 1977
Sales 3.2MMM *EMP* 53,000
Tkr Sym EAT *Exch* NYS
SIC 5812 6794 Eating places; Ethnic food restaurants; Italian restaurant; Mexican restaurant; Franchises, selling or licensing
Pr: Wyman T Roberts
**Ch Bd:* Joseph M Depinto
Pr: Steve Provost
Pr: Kelli Valade
CFO: Thomas J Edwards Jr
Treas: Pauline Greenwell
Chf Mktg O: Krista Gibson
Ofcr: Tony A Bridwell
Ex VP: Roger F Thomson
Sr VP: David R Doyle
Sr VP: David Doyle
Sr VP: Scarlett May
VP: Wade Allen
VP: Krista M Gibson
VP: Krista Gibson
VP: Donald L Reyburn
Board of Directors: Elaine M Boltz, Harriet Edelman, Michael A George, William T Giles, Gerardo I Lopez, Jon L Luther, George R Mrkonic, Jose Luis Prado

D-U-N-S 80-003-2120
■ BRINKER RESTAURANT CORP
(*Suby of* BRINKER INTERNATIONAL INC) ★
6820 Lbj Fwy, Dallas, TX 75240-6511
Tel (972) 980-9917 *Founded/Ownrshp* 2014
Sales 207.2MM[E] *EMP* 10,000
SIC 5812 Grills (eating places)
Ch Bd: Douglas H Brooks

BRINKMAN CONSTRUCTORS
See R G BRINKMANN CO

BRINKMANN PET
See NATIONAL CONSUMER OUTDOORS CORP

D-U-N-S 00-698-9081
▲ BRINKS CO
1801 Bayberry Ct Ste 400, Richmond, VA 23226-3771
Tel (804) 289-9600 *Founded/Ownrshp* 1859
Sales 3.0MMM *EMP* 59,900
Tkr Sym BCO *Exch* NYS
SIC 7382 7381 Burglar alarm maintenance & monitoring; Armored car services
CEO: George I Stoeckert
CFO: Ronald J Domanico
CFO: Joseph W Dziedzic
Ofcr: Rohan Pal
Ofcr: Holly R Tyson
Ex VP: Michael F Beech
Ex VP: Amit Zukerman
VP: McAlister C Marshall II
Opers Mgr: Michael Petrakis
Corp Couns: Austin Reed
Board of Directors: Betty C Alewine, Paul G Boynton, Ian D Clough, Susan E Docherty, Peter A Feld, Reginald A Hedgebeth, Michael J Herling, George I Stoeckert

BRINK'S HOME TECHNOLGIES
See BROADVIEW SECURITY INC

D-U-N-S 00-692-8923 IMP/EXP
■ BRINKS INC
(*Suby of* BRINKS CO) ★
1801 Bayberry Ct Ste 400, Richmond, VA 23226-3771
Tel (804) 289-9600 *Founded/Ownrshp* 1859, 1956
Sales 2.3MMM[E] *EMP* 45,000
SIC 7381 Armored car services
Pr: Frank T Lennon
**CFO:* Joseph W Dziedzic
Prin: Tracy Wright

BRISK WATERPROOFING COMPANY
See WESTERN WATERPROOFING CO INC

D-U-N-S 09-052-9285
BRISTLECONE INC (CA)
(*Suby of* MAHINDRA AND MAHINDRA LIMITED)
10 Almaden Blvd Ste 600, San Jose, CA 95113-2226
Tel (650) 386-4000 *Founded/Ownrshp* 1998, 2005
Sales 55.0MM[E] *EMP* 1,300
SIC 7371 8742 Software programming applications; Management consulting services
Pr: Irfan A Khan
CFO: Zhooben Bhiwandiwala
Bd of Dir: Nadir Godrej
Bd of Dir: Joerg Sperling
VP: Sankha Bhowmick
VP: Gary Botta
VP: Jessie Chimni

VP: Michael Gunn
**VP:* Naresh Hingorani
VP: Kemal Koeksal
VP: Theodore Kyriazis
VP: Nikhil Nayak
**VP:* Kulashekar Raghavan
**VP:* Bhaskar Ramanasundaram
**VP:* Tom Rauch
**VP:* Ramesh Sivakaminathan
VP: Shanmuga Sundaram

D-U-N-S 08-148-8264
BRISTOL BAY AREA HEALTH CORP
BBAHC
6000 Kanakanak Rd, Dillingham, AK 99576
Tel (907) 842-5201 *Founded/Ownrshp* 1973
Sales 88.0MM *EMP* 425
Accts Bdo Usa Llp Anchorage Ak
SIC 8062 8011 General medical & surgical hospitals; Clinic, operated by physicians
CEO: Robert J Clark
COO: Lorraine Jewett
CFO: Gary Hale
**CFO:* Lucrecia Scotford
Chf Mktg O: Deb Dahlberg
**VP:* Lorraine M Jewett
Genl Mgr: Susan Dunson
Off Mgr: Joann Livermont
IT Man: Kyle Hardin
Opers Mgr: Jennifer Gardiner
Opers Mgr: Shawn Sedgwick

D-U-N-S 06-003-6357
BRISTOL BAY NATIVE CORP
BBNC
111 W 16th Ave Ste 400, Anchorage, AK 99501-6299
Tel (907) 563-0013 *Founded/Ownrshp* 1972
Sales 1.3MMM[E] *EMP* 1,022
SIC 7011 Hotels & motels
Pr: Marie Paul
CFO: Jeff Simz
CFO: Jeffery Sinz
**Treas:* Gregory French
Ofcr: Denis Consey
**VP:* Ferguson April
**VP:* Jerry Liboff
**VP:* Torrison Scott
Admn Mgr: Inez Webb
DP Exec: Frank Okamoto
IT Man: Lisa Svendsen

D-U-N-S 88-301-8301 IMP/EXP
BRISTOL COMPRESSORS INTERNATIONAL LLC
15185 Industrial Park Rd, Bristol, VA 24202-3711
Tel (276) 466-4121 *Founded/Ownrshp* 2012
Sales 230.0MM[E] *EMP* 750
SIC 3585 Refrigeration & heating equipment; Compressors for refrigeration & air conditioning equipment
CEO: Edward Gniewek
**CFO:* Vicky Kiser
CFO: Doug Moore
**Sr VP:* Joel Moseley
**VP:* Robbie Eades
**VP:* Kevin Mumpower
Sfty Mgr: Archer Skeens
Mktg Dir: Barry Rust

D-U-N-S 06-141-1534
BRISTOL FARMS
(*Suby of* ENDEAVOUR CAPITAL FUND LIMITED PARTNERSHIP) ★
915 E 230th St, Carson, CA 90745-5005
Tel (310) 233-4700 *Founded/Ownrshp* 2010
Sales 94.5MM[E] *EMP* 300
SIC 5411 Grocery stores, chain
Pr: Edmund K Davis
Ex Dir: David Favorite

D-U-N-S 06-924-2436
BRISTOL HOSPITAL INC (CT)
41 Brewster Rd, Bristol, CT 06010-5141
Tel (860) 585-3000 *Founded/Ownrshp* 1920
Sales 133.3MM *EMP* 1,600
SIC 8062 Hospital, medical school affiliation
Pr: Kurt Darwis
Dir Recs: Janice Nowak
**Sr VP:* Sheila Kempf
**Sr VP:* Kenneth Rhee
VP: Leonard Banco MD
**VP:* George Eighmy
VP: David Racklif
**VP:* Jeanine F Reckdenwald
VP: Jeanine Reckdenwald
DP Exec: Joan Barney
IT Man: Marques Nelson

D-U-N-S 88-353-3465
BRISTOL HOTEL & RESORTS INC
(*Suby of* I H G) ★
3 Ravinia Dr Ste 100, Atlanta, GA 30346-2121
Tel (770) 604-2000 *Founded/Ownrshp* 1998
Sales 101.1MM[E] *EMP* 14,000
SIC 8741 Hotel or motel management
Ch Bd: Thomas Oliver
**CFO:* Andrew Mc Farlane
**Ex VP:* Doug Lewis
**VP:* Robert Hill
VP: Eric Pearson

D-U-N-S 05-268-7662 IMP
■ **BRISTOL INC** (DE)
EMERSON RMOTE AUTOMTN SOLUTION
(*Suby of* EMERSON ELECTRIC CO) ★
1100 Buckingham St, Watertown, CT 06795-6602
Tel (860) 945-2200 *Founded/Ownrshp* 1980, 2006
Sales 97.2MM[E] *EMP* 370
SIC 3823 Industrial process control instruments; Industrial process measurement equipment; Digital displays of process variables
Pr: Craig T Llewlyn
**Treas:* Teresa A Burnett
**VP:* Warren Howard
Dir IT: Brian Lamothe
Board of Directors: Robert Beeston

D-U-N-S 05-365-8555 IMP
BRISTOL LASALLE CORP
LASALLE BRISTOL
(*Suby of* ARRAN ISLE LIMITED)
601 County Road 17, Elkhart, IN 46516-9568
Tel (574) 295-4400 *Founded/Ownrshp* 1993
Sales 320.0MM[E] *EMP* 550
SIC 5023 5021 5051 5033 3645 3089 Floor coverings; Carpets; Resilient floor coverings: tile or sheet; Household furniture; Aluminum bars, rods, ingots, sheets, pipes, plates, etc.; Siding, except wood; Residential lighting fixtures; Ducting, plastic
Pr: Richard W Karcher
CFO: Don Boboy
CFO: Richard Sneider
VP: Mike Caffrey
VP: Brad Hurst
**Prin:* William J Schmuhl Jr
Brnch Mgr: Mike Petersen
DP Exec: Bill Schmuhl
Mktg Dir: Gil Brown

D-U-N-S 00-337-4790 IMP
■ **BRISTOL METALS LLC**
BRISTOL PIPING SYSTEMS
(*Suby of* SYNALLOY CORP) ★
390 Bristol Metals Rd, Bristol, TN 37620-9049
Tel (423) 968-2151 *Founded/Ownrshp* 1996
Sales 170.7MM[E] *EMP* 400
SIC 3312 Pipes, iron & steel
Pr: J Kyle Pennington
**Ex VP:* John C Tidlow
**VP:* Barry Newberry
**VP:* Rob Yepsen
VP: John Zelinski
Plnt Mgr: Dennis O'Neal

BRISTOL PIPING SYSTEMS
See BRISTOL METALS LLC

D-U-N-S 06-988-2777
BRISTOL TOWNSHIP SCHOOL DISTRICT AUTHORITY
6401 Mill Creek Rd, Levittown, PA 19057-4014
Tel (215) 943-3200 *Founded/Ownrshp* 1900
Sales 128.8MM *EMP* 1,500
SIC 8211 Public elementary & secondary schools
Pr: Frank Koziol
IT Man: Dan Delorenzo
IT Man: Bob Pfeu
Schl Brd P: Angela M Nober

D-U-N-S 14-154-0505
BRISTOL WEST HOLDINGS INC
(*Suby of* FARMERS INSURANCE) ★
5701 Stirling Rd, Davie, FL 33314-7429
Tel (954) 316-5200 *Founded/Ownrshp* 2007
Sales NA *EMP* 1,154
SIC 6331 Automobile insurance
Pr: Robert Sadler
COO: Simon J Noonan
Sr VP: Alexis S Oster
VP: James R Fisher
Snr PM: David Gusman

BRISTOL WEST INSURANCE GROUP
See BRISTOL WEST INSURANCE SERVICE INC

D-U-N-S 94-585-1954 EXP
BRISTOL WEST INSURANCE SERVICE INC
BRISTOL WEST INSURANCE GROUP
(*Suby of* BRISTOL WEST HOLDINGS INC) ★
5701 Stirling Rd, Davie, FL 33314-7429
Tel (954) 316-5200 *Founded/Ownrshp* 1998
Sales NA *EMP* 650
SIC 6411 Insurance agents, brokers & service
Pr: Jeffrey Rosner
**Pr:* Jeffrey Dailey
VP: Ron Latva
Prgrm Mgr: Ralph Czekalinski
Netwrk Eng: Jason V Norman
Snr Mgr: Brian Laplante

D-U-N-S 00-128-8497
▲ **BRISTOL-MYERS SQUIBB CO**
345 Park Ave Bsmt Lc3, New York, NY 10154-0028
Tel (212) 546-4000 *Founded/Ownrshp* 1887
Sales 16.5MMM *EMP* 25,000
Tkr Sym BMY *Exch* NYS
SIC 2834 Pharmaceutical preparations; Drugs acting on the cardiovascular system, except diagnostic; Antibiotics, packaged; Drugs acting on the central nervous system & sense organs
CEO: Giovanni Caforio
Ch Bd: Lamberto Andreotti
Pr: Beatrice Cazala
Pr: John Celentano
Pr: Carlo De Notaristefani
Pr: Anthony Hooper
CFO: Charles Bancroft
CFO: Charles A Bancroft
Treas: Jeffrey Galik
Treas: Ron West
Ofcr: Murdo Gordon
Ofcr: Quentin L Roach
Ex VP: Francis Cuss
Ex VP: Sandra Leung
Sr VP: Paul Biondi
Sr VP: Joseph C Caldarella
Sr VP: George P Kooluris
Sr VP: Ann Powell
Sr VP: Paul Von Autenried
VP: Robin Edwards
VP: Amy Lyons
Board of Directors: Peter J Arduini, Laurie H Glimcher, Michael Grobstein, Alan J Lacy, Thomas J Lynch Jr, Vicki L Sato, Gerald L Storch

D-U-N-S 09-108-2651 IMP
■ **BRISTOL-MYERS SQUIBB PUERTO RICO INC**
(*Suby of* BRISTOL-MYERS SQUIBB CO) ★
6 Calle Tabonuco, Guaynabo, PR 00968
Tel (787) 774-2800 *Founded/Ownrshp* 1990
Sales 103.7MM[E] *EMP* 879
SIC 2834 Pharmaceutical preparations
Pr: Francisco Hidalgo

D-U-N-S 05-377-3487
▲ **BRISTOW GROUP INC**
2103 City West Blvd Fl 4, Houston, TX 77042
Tel (713) 267-7600 *Founded/Ownrshp* 1969
Sales 1.7MMM *EMP* 4,777[E]
Tkr Sym BRS *Exch* NYS
SIC 4522 Helicopter carriers, nonscheduled
Pr: Jonathan E Baliff
**Ch Bd:* Thomas C Knudson
CFO: L Don Miller
Chf Cred: Chet Akiri
Ofcr: Hilary S Ware
Sr VP: William Collins
VP: Brian J Allman
QA Dir: Ken Turner
Dir IT: Bobby Joseph
IT Man: Ratnakar M Muppaneni
Sfty Mgr: Carol Taylor
Board of Directors: Thomas N Amonett, Lori A Gobillor, Ian A Godden, David C Gompert, Stephen A King, Mathew Masters, Bruce H Stover

D-U-N-S 11-675-9445
■ **BRISTOW US LLC**
(*Suby of* BRISTOW GROUP INC) ★
4605 Industrial Dr, New Iberia, LA 70560-9124
Tel (337) 365-6771 *Founded/Ownrshp* 1997
Sales 153.3MM[E] *EMP* 915
SIC 4522 Helicopter carriers, nonscheduled
Pr: Jonathan E Baliff
**Sr VP:* Jeremy Akel
**Sr VP:* John H Briscoe
**Sr VP:* Hilary S Ware
**VP:* Michael Imlach
Off Admin: Leslie Jones
Genl Couns: Edmund H Underwood

D-U-N-S 05-137-4431
BRITISH PETROLEUM
4519 Grandview Rd, Blaine, WA 98230-9640
Tel (360) 371-1300 *Founded/Ownrshp* 2015
Sales 38.1MM[E] *EMP* 1,000
SIC 1629 Oil refinery construction

D-U-N-S 14-567-0266
BRITT FORD SALES INC TED
4175 Auto Park Cir, Chantilly, VA 20151-1224
Tel (703) 673-2300 *Founded/Ownrshp* 2004
Sales 85.7MM[E] *EMP* 300
SIC 5511 Automobiles, new & used
Pr: Gardner Britt
**Pr:* M G Britt Jr
**Sec:* Michael R Andress
**VP:* John Adamson
**VP:* Gardner M Britt III

BRITT, TED FORD
See BRITT TRANSPORTATION ENTERPRISES INC TED

D-U-N-S 02-372-3257
BRITT TRANSPORTATION ENTERPRISES INC TED
BRITT, TED FORD
11165 Fairfax Blvd, Fairfax, VA 22030-5049
Tel (703) 591-8484 *Founded/Ownrshp* 1959
Sales 250.0MM[E] *EMP* 400
SIC 5511 Automobiles, new & used
Ch Bd: M Gardener Britt Jr
**Sec:* Michael R Andress
Genl Mgr: John Adamson
Sales Asso: Dan Akers
Sales Asso: Alexander Assefa
Sales Asso: Jason Hoptiak
Sales Asso: Matt Mayfield

D-U-N-S 10-902-7870
BRITTHAVEN INC
1435 Highway 258n, Kinston, NC 28504-7208
Tel (252) 939-4131 *Founded/Ownrshp* 1982
Sales 9.1MMM[E] *EMP* 5,000
SIC 8051 8059 Skilled nursing care facilities; Mental retardation hospital; Rest home, with health care
Pr: Steven Hill
CFO: Steve Farrar
**CFO:* Stephen Ferrar
**Sec:* Lucy Hill
**VP:* Greg Hill
**VP:* Robert Hill Jr
MIS Mgr: Allen Seagal
Counsel: Nancy Mason

D-U-N-S 78-999-1148
BRITTHAVEN OF DAVIDSON INC
(*Suby of* BRITTHAVEN INC) ★
706 Pineywood Rd, Thomasville, NC 27360-2753
Tel (336) 475-9116 *Founded/Ownrshp* 1982
Sales 949.0MM *EMP* 110
SIC 8051 8052 Skilled nursing care facilities; Intermediate care facilities
Pr: Robert Hill
**Sec:* Lucy Hill
**VP:* Gregg Hill
**VP:* Robert Hill Jr
**VP:* Steven Hill
Nrsg Dir: April Hoover

D-U-N-S 79-022-3317
BRITTHAVEN OF EDENTON INC
(*Suby of* BRITTHAVEN INC) ★
1341 Paradise Rd, Edenton, NC 27932-8503
Tel (252) 482-7481 *Founded/Ownrshp* 1982
Sales 611.0MM *EMP* 185
SIC 8051 8052 Skilled nursing care facilities; Intermediate care facilities
Pr: Robert Hill Jr
**Sec:* Lucy Hill
**VP:* Gregg Hill

D-U-N-S 78-999-1361
BRITTHAVEN OF GOLDSBORO INC
(*Suby of* BRITTHAVEN INC) ★
2401 Wayne Memorial Dr, Goldsboro, NC 27534-1727
Tel (919) 736-2121 *Founded/Ownrshp* 1982
Sales 1.3MMM *EMP* 160
SIC 8051 8052 Skilled nursing care facilities; Intermediate care facilities
VP: Robert Hill Jr

**Sec:* Lucy Hill
**VP:* Gregg Hill

D-U-N-S 08-231-3420
BRITTHAVEN OF KENTUCKY INC
BRITTHAVEN OF PROSPECT
(*Suby of* BRITTHAVEN INC) ★
6301 Bass Rd, Prospect, KY 40059-9384
Tel (502) 228-9440 *Founded/Ownrshp* 1983
Sales 580.6MM *EMP* 90
SIC 8051 Skilled nursing care facilities
Prin: Jim Kennedy
**Treas:* Lucy Hill
**Prin:* Ray Dicknson

D-U-N-S 78-998-9944
BRITTHAVEN OF MADISON INC
(*Suby of* BRITTHAVEN INC) ★
1721 Bald Hill Loop, Madison, NC 27025-7624
Tel (336) 548-9658 *Founded/Ownrshp* 1982
Sales 925.6MM *EMP* 100
SIC 8051 8052 Skilled nursing care facilities; Intermediate care facilities
Pr: Robert Hill
Dir Recs: Jane White
**Sec:* Lucy Hill
**VP:* Gregg Hill
**VP:* Robert Hill Jr
**VP:* Steven Hill
Exec: Angela Mortez
Dir Soc: Melanie Murphy
HC Dir: Kaneesha Glover

D-U-N-S 78-999-0785
BRITTHAVEN OF NEW BERN INC
(*Suby of* BRITTHAVEN INC) ★
2600 Old Cherry Point Rd, New Bern, NC 28560-6778
Tel (252) 637-4730 *Founded/Ownrshp* 1982
Sales 524.5MM *EMP* 140
SIC 8051 Skilled nursing care facilities
Pr: Robert Hill
**Sec:* Lucy Hill
**VP:* Gregg Hill

D-U-N-S 78-998-8946
BRITTHAVEN OF ONSLOW INC
(*Suby of* BRITTHAVEN INC) ★
1839 Onslow Dr, Jacksonville, NC 28540-5997
Tel (910) 455-3610 *Founded/Ownrshp* 1982
Sales 630.9MM *EMP* 95
SIC 8051 8052 Skilled nursing care facilities; Intermediate care facilities
Pr: Robert Hill

BRITTHAVEN OF PROSPECT
See BRITTHAVEN OF KENTUCKY INC

D-U-N-S 78-999-2468
BRITTHAVEN OF SMITHFIELD INC
(*Suby of* BRITTHAVEN INC) ★
515 Barbour Rd, Smithfield, NC 27577-7698
Tel (919) 934-6017 *Founded/Ownrshp* 1984
Sales 1.1MMM *EMP* 250
SIC 8051 8052 Skilled nursing care facilities; Intermediate care facilities
Pr: Robert Hill

D-U-N-S 78-999-2096
BRITTHAVEN OF SNOW HILL INC
(*Suby of* BRITTHAVEN INC) ★
1304 Se 2nd St, Snow Hill, NC 28580-2014
Tel (252) 747-8126 *Founded/Ownrshp* 1982
Sales 658.5MM *EMP* 80
SIC 8051 8052 Skilled nursing care facilities; Intermediate care facilities
Pr: Robert Hill
**Sec:* Lucy Hill
**VP:* Gregg Hill
VP: Jim Kennedy
Dir Soc: Amber Wolfe

D-U-N-S 78-999-1346
BRITTHAVEN OF WILKESBORO INC
(*Suby of* BRITTHAVEN INC) ★
1016 Fletcher St, Wilkesboro, NC 28697-9472
Tel (336) 667-9261 *Founded/Ownrshp* 1981
Sales 1.1MMM *EMP* 225
SIC 8051 Skilled nursing care facilities
Dir Recs: Polly Dimmette
QA Dir: Jennifer Brown
HC Dir: Clarissa Mastin
HC Dir: Angie Vanhoy

D-U-N-S 78-999-0181
BRITTHAVEN OF WILSON INC
(*Suby of* BRITTHAVEN INC) ★
403 Crestview Ave Sw, Wilson, NC 27893-4505
Tel (252) 237-0724 *Founded/Ownrshp* 1982
Sales 660.0MM *EMP* 125
SIC 8051 8052 Skilled nursing care facilities; Intermediate care facilities
Pr: Robert Hill Jr
**Sec:* Lucy Hill
**VP:* Gregg Hill

D-U-N-S 15-082-6436 IMP
BRITZ FERTILIZERS INC
(*Suby of* BRITZ INC) ★
3265 W Figarden Dr, Fresno, CA 93711-3912
Tel (559) 448-8000 *Founded/Ownrshp* 1991
Sales 102.7MM[E] *EMP* 250
SIC 5191 Chemicals, agricultural; Fertilizer & fertilizer materials
CEO: David Britz
**VP:* Martin Britz
**VP:* Bob Glassman
Dir IT: Chris Oday

D-U-N-S 00-914-8404
BRITZ INC (CA)
3265 W Figarden Dr, Fresno, CA 93711-3912
Tel (559) 448-8000 *Founded/Ownrshp* 1947, 1991
Sales 367.4MM[E] *EMP* 300
SIC 0723 0724 0191

D-U-N-S 05-949-5614 IMP
BRIX GROUP INC
PANA-PACIFIC
838 N Laverne Ave, Fresno, CA 93727-6868
Tel (559) 457-4700 *Founded/Ownrshp* 1973
Sales 146.9MM^E *EMP* 300
SIC 5065 5013 Mobile telephone equipment; Paging & signaling equipment; Motor vehicle supplies & new parts
CEO: Harrison Brix
**Pr:* Kristina Reed
**Pr:* John Trenberth
CIO: A J Olsen
Software D: Ricky Delisle
Software D: Attila Erzeybek
Mktg Mgr: Susan Freuler
Sls Mgr: Veronica Estall
Sls Mgr: Katy Jakus
Sls Mgr: Orlando Uranga

D-U-N-S 36-194-9225
BRIXMOR LLC
(*Suby of* BRIXMOR PROPERTY GROUP INC) ★
450 Lexington Ave Fl 13, New York, NY 10017-3956
Tel (212) 869-3000 *Founded/Ownrshp* 2007
Sales 197.1MM^E *EMP* 456
Accts Ernst & Young Llp
SIC 6798 Real estate investment trusts
**Pr:* Michael Pappagallo
COO: Graham Terry
**CFO:* Tiffanie Fisher
**Ex VP:* Dean Bernstein
**Ex VP:* Timothy Bruce
**Ex VP:* Steven Siegel
Sr VP: Tom Litzler
VP: Stacy Lipschitz
VP: Michael Wood
Dir IT: Shane McConnell
IT Man: Hector Toscano

BRIXMOR PROPERTY GROUP
See KOP KLINE PLAZA LLC

D-U-N-S 00-399-9531
BRIXMOR PROPERTY GROUP INC (MD)
450 Lexington Ave Fl 13, New York, NY 10017-3956
Tel (212) 869-3000 *Founded/Ownrshp* 2011
Sales 1.1MMM *EMP* 1,256^E
SIC 6798 Real estate investment trusts
CEO: Daniel Hurwitz
**Ch Bd:* John G Schreiber
Pr: Kelly A Franzino
Pr: Cathy Mancari
CFO: Tiffanie Fisher
CFO: Barry Lefkowitz
Ex VP: Steven F Siegel
Ex VP: Steven Siegel
Sr VP: Thomas W Litzler
VP: Nick Andreadis
VP: Samantha Didrikson
VP: Tyson Fraser
VP: Greg Levine
VP: Jason Mahoney
VP: Daren Moss
VP: Christine Shields
VP: Praneet Talukdar
VP: Lisa Tronzano
VP: Tom Wellman
Board of Directors: A J Agarwal, Michael Berman, Sheryl M Crosland, Anthony W Deering, Thomas W Dickson, William D Rahm, William J Stein, Gabrielle Sulzberger

D-U-N-S 79-331-7173 IMP/EXP
■ **BRK BRANDS INC**
FAMILY GARD/BRK
(*Suby of* FIRST ALERT INC) ★
3901 Liberty St, Aurora, IL 60504-8122
Tel (630) 851-7330 *Founded/Ownrshp* 1992
Sales 410.0MM^E *EMP* 1,100
SIC 3669 Fire detection systems, electric
Pr: Thomas Russo
**CFO:* William B Brock
CFO: Arlene Hachney
CFO: Arlene Hackney
**Treas:* Ian G H Ashken
VP: Mark Devine
VP: Doug Kellam
VP: Brian Strasma
VP: Rich Timmons
VP: Edward Tyranski
CTO: Michael Paxston
Board of Directors: John Albers, Anthony J Di Novi, David V Harkins, Scott A Schoen, Peter Wood

D-U-N-S 62-354-4785
BROAD INSTITUTE INC
BROAD INSTITUTE OF MIT AND HAR
415 Main St, Cambridge, MA 02142-1027
Tel (617) 714-7000 *Founded/Ownrshp* 2002
Sales 355.1MM *EMP* 800^E
Accts Pricewaterhousecoopers Llp Bo
SIC 8733 Noncommercial research organizations
Pr: Eric Lander
**COO:* Samantha Singer
**Chf Cred:* Clare Midgley
Bd of Dir: Susan Hockfield
**Ex VP:* Alan Fein
Dir Lab: Michael Yim
**Prin:* Derek Martyn
**Dir Sec:* Todd Golub
Snr Sftwr: Pei Lin
IT Man: David Heiman
IT Man: Barbara Weir

BROAD INSTITUTE OF MIT AND HAR
See BROAD INSTITUTE INC

D-U-N-S 19-711-8743
BROADBAND TELECOM INC
8002 Kew Gardens Rd # 1040, Kew Gardens, NY 11415-3600
Tel (718) 261-0148 *Founded/Ownrshp* 2005
Sales 109.0MM^E *EMP* 204
Accts M Hassanali Cpa Llc New Yo
SIC 4813
CEO: Bankim Brahmbhatt
Ofcr: Jigar Bhatt
VP: Chirayu Patel

D-U-N-S 79-643-7874
BROADCAST MEDIA PARTNERS HOLDINGS INC
(*Suby of* UNIVISION HOLDINGS INC) ★
605 3rd Ave Fl 12, New York, NY 10158-1299
Tel (212) 455-5200 *Founded/Ownrshp* 2014
Sales 2.4MMM^E *EMP* 8,515^E
SIC 4833 4813 7389 Television broadcasting stations; Television translator station; ; Music recording producer
Pr: Ray Rodriguez
**CFO:* Andrew W Hobson
**Ex VP:* Douglas C Kranwinkle

D-U-N-S 00-178-9494
BROADCAST MUSIC INC (NY)
250 Greenwich St, New York, NY 10007-2140
Tel (212) 220-3000 *Founded/Ownrshp* 1966
Sales 171.3MM^E *EMP* 608
SIC 6794 Music licensing & royalties; Performance rights, publishing & licensing
Pr: Michael O'Neill
Pr: Dennis Marr
**CFO:* Bruce Esworthy
**Sr VP:* Alison Smith
Sr VP: Ann Sweeney
VP: Cane Barbara
VP: John Barnett
VP: Dennis Ditraglia
VP: Charles Feldman
VP: John A Marsillo
Exec: Diana Johnston
Assoc Dir: Kent Glaser
Assoc Dir: Jim Lasseter
Assoc Dir: Elizabeth Mosley
Assoc Dir: Barbara Quinn
Assoc Dir: Calvin Rosekrans
Board of Directors: Greg Ashlock, Rebecca Campbell, Albert Cheng, Dave Lougee, Michael O'neill

D-U-N-S 10-506-6075
■ **BROADCASTING BOARD OF GOVERNORS**
VOICE OF AMERICA
(*Suby of* EXECUTIVE OFFICE OF UNITED STATES GOVERNMENT) ★
330 Independence Ave Sw # 3360, Washington, DC 20237-0002
Tel (202) 203-4000 *Founded/Ownrshp* 1999
Sales NA *EMP* 1,840
Accts Clarke Leiper Pllc Alexandria
SIC 9721
Ch: Jeffrey Shell
CFO: Mary C Pfeffner
Bd of Dir: Thomas C Korologos
Ofcr: Piero Ciancio
VP: Gregory Kuhn
Assoc Dir: Stephen Smith
Off Mgr: Larry Bullard
Dir IT: Gary Thatcher
IT Man: Douglas Zabransky
Sls&Mrk Ex: Asfaw Meraf
Mktg Mgr: Natasha Stewart

BROADCOM
See AVAGO TECHNOLOGIES WIRELESS (USA) INC

BROADCOM
See NETLOGIC MICROSYSTEMS LLC

D-U-N-S 79-987-0605 IMP
BROADCOM CORP
(*Suby of* BROADCOM LIMITED)
5300 California Ave, Irvine, CA 92617-3038
Tel (949) 926-5000 *Founded/Ownrshp* 1991
Sales 7.5MMM^E *EMP* 12,550^E
SIC 3674 Semiconductors & related devices
Pr: Hock E Tan
Pr: Katherine Lim
Pr: Carole Yum
CFO: Anthony Maslowski
Sr VP: Charlie Kawwas
VP: Nicolas Alexopoulos
VP: Mark Brazeal
VP: Greg Fischer
VP: Nelson Sollenberger
Snr Ntwrk: Anthony Pace
CIO: David Hass

D-U-N-S 08-026-8025
BROADCOM LIMITED
1320 Ridder Park Dr, San Jose, CA 95131-2313
Tel (408) 433-8000 *Founded/Ownrshp* 2016
Sales 139.5MM^E *EMP* 10,001
SIC 3674 Semiconductors & related devices

D-U-N-S 15-585-9700
BROADLANE GROUP INC
(*Suby of* BROADLANE HOLDINGS, LLC)
13727 Noel Rd Ste 1400, Dallas, TX 75240-1370
Tel (972) 813-7500 *Founded/Ownrshp* 2008
Sales 212.0MM^E *EMP* 660
SIC 5047 Medical equipment & supplies
CEO: Patrick T Ryan
**Pr:* Thomas Sherry
COO: Cheryl Anderson
**CFO:* Laurie L Jackson
Sr VP: Deanna Herrin
Sr VP: David Hixon
VP: Keith Gregory
VP: Gregory Keith
VP: Bryan Manning
VP: William Martin
VP: Eric Shaw
VP: Bill Shepley
VP: Glenn Sherman
VP: Kerry Tucker
Exec: Debbie Croff

BROADLAWN MNNER NURSG CARE CTR
See LONG ISLAND HOME

BROADLAWNS HOSPITAL
See BROADLAWNS MEDICAL CENTER GUILD

D-U-N-S 07-348-2739
BROADLAWNS MEDICAL CENTER GUILD
BROADLAWNS HOSPITAL
1801 Hickman Rd, Des Moines, IA 50314-1505
Tel (515) 282-2200 *Founded/Ownrshp* 1924
Sales 180.8MM^E *EMP* 1,000
SIC 8062 General medical & surgical hospitals
Ch Bd: Janet Metcalf
Chf Path: Jeffrey J Rissman
**Pr:* Jody Jenner
**CFO:* Karl Vilums
Bd of Dir: Julie Deuel
Bd of Dir: Jamel Kirby
Bd of Dir: Joann Mackey
Sr VP: Vincent Mandracchia
Exec: Michelle A Phillips
Dir Risk M: Rick Barrett
Dir Rx: David Seiler
Board of Directors: Mary Fuller, Cynthia Gray, Dave Harkness, Jean Logan, Charles Montgomery, Michael D Treinen

D-U-N-S 00-691-4857 IMP
BROADMOOR HOTEL INC
(*Suby of* DAILY OKLAHOMAN) ★
1 Lake Ave, Colorado Springs, CO 80906-4269
Tel (719) 634-7711 *Founded/Ownrshp* 1932
Sales 133.5MM^E *EMP* 2,800
SIC 7011 5812 5813 7992 7999 7389 Resort hotel; Eating places; Cocktail lounge; Public golf courses; Ice skating rink operation; Saddlehorse rental; Convention & show services
CEO: Edward L Gaylord
**Pr:* Stephen Bartolin
**Treas:* R Thayer Tutt Jr
VP: Jack Damioli
Dir Risk M: Sandra Garcia
Comm Man: Kevin Meyer

D-U-N-S 12-101-2418
BROADREACH CAPITAL PARTNERS LLC
248 Homer Ave, Palo Alto, CA 94301-2722
Tel (650) 331-2500 *Founded/Ownrshp* 2002
Sales 406.6MM^E *EMP* 4,010
SIC 6211 Investment firm, general brokerage

D-U-N-S 00-749-3729
■ **BROADRIDGE CUSTOMER COMMUNICATIONS CENTRAL LLC**
DST OUTPUT CENTRAL, LLC
(*Suby of* BROADRIDGE CUSTOMER COMMUNICATIONS LLC) ★
2600 Southwest Blvd, Kansas City, MO 64108-2349
Tel (816) 221-1234 *Founded/Ownrshp* 2003
Sales 117.0MM^E *EMP* 50
SIC 7331 Mailing service

D-U-N-S 78-485-5017
■ **BROADRIDGE CUSTOMER COMMUNICATIONS LLC**
(*Suby of* BROADRIDGE OUTPUT SOLUTIONS INC) ★
2600 Southwest Blvd, Kansas City, MO 64108-2349
Tel (816) 221-1234 *Founded/Ownrshp* 2016
Sales 170.1MM^E *EMP* 85
SIC 7389 2759 7374 7331 2752 7336 Microfilm recording & developing service; Laser printing; Data processing & preparation; Data processing service; Direct mail advertising services; Commercial printing, lithographic; Graphic arts & related design
Pr: Steven J Towle
Treas: Ken Hager
Ex VP: Thomas Mc Cullough
MIS Dir: David Lagreca
Software D: David Gascich

D-U-N-S 60-853-7960
▲ **BROADRIDGE FINANCIAL SOLUTIONS INC**
5 Dakota Dr Ste 300, New Hyde Park, NY 11042-1109
Tel (516) 472-5400 *Founded/Ownrshp* 1962
Sales 2.9MMM *EMP* 7,400^E
Tkr Sym BR *Exch* NYS
SIC 7374 7372 Data processing & preparation; Business oriented computer software
Pr: Richard J Daly
Ch Bd: Leslie A Brun
V Ch: Salvatore F Sodano
COO: Timothy C Gokey
CFO: James M Young
Ofcr: Julie R Taylor
Assoc VP: Nishant Bhatnagar
Sr VP: Robert Schifellite
VP: Zakir Abrahim
VP: Luz Alcantara
VP: Adam D Amsterdam
VP: Yokasta Arriaza
VP: Chuck Callan
VP: Richard Chern
VP: Steven Crombie
VP: Marc Curtis
VP: Lyell Dampeer
VP: Geoff Delesseps
VP: Ben Eva
VP: Regan Fantry
VP: Robert Fusaro
Board of Directors: Robert N Duelks, Richard J Haviland, Brett A Keller, Stuart R Levine, Maura A Markus, Thomas J Perna, Alan J Weber

D-U-N-S 08-031-6669
■ **BROADRIDGE OUTPUT SOLUTIONS INC**
(*Suby of* BROADRIDGE FINANCIAL SOLUTIONS INC) ★
5 Dakota Dr Ste 300, New Hyde Park, NY 11042-1109
Tel (516) 472-5400 *Founded/Ownrshp* 2001
Sales 163.4MM^E *EMP* 85^E
SIC 7374 Data processing & preparation
Pr: Richard J Daly
VP: Jittu Lulla

D-U-N-S 12-417-8521
▲ **BROADSOFT INC**
9737 Washingtonian Blvd # 350, Gaithersburg, MD 20878-7387
Tel (301) 977-9440 *Founded/Ownrshp* 1998
Sales 278.8MM *EMP* 1,282
Tkr Sym BSFT *Exch* NGS
SIC 7372 7371 8748 Prepackaged software; Custom computer programming services; Business consulting
Pr: Michael Tessler
**Ch Bd:* John D Markley Jr
Pr: Eric Wilkens
CFO: James A Tholen
Chf Mktg O: Taher G Behbehani
Ofcr: Jeff Kahn
VP: Gabriel Albani
VP: John Burgess
VP: Volgenau Cole
VP: Alex Dobson
VP: Michael Duke
VP: Michael Fox
VP: Robert Lafrance
VP: Ken Rokoff
VP: Nathan Stratton
VP: Robert Weidenfeller
Board of Directors: David Bernardi, Jane A Dietze, Eva M Sage-Gavin, John J Gavin Jr, Andrew M Geisse, Paul J Magelli, Douglas L Maine

D-U-N-S 07-858-2044
BROADSPECTRUM DOWNSTREAM SERVICES INC
TRANSFIELD SERVICES
(*Suby of* BROADSPECTRUM PTY LTD)
1330 Post Oak Blvd # 1250, Houston, TX 77056-3031
Tel (713) 964-2800 *Founded/Ownrshp* 2007
Sales 57.6MM^E *EMP* 2,000
SIC 1382 Oil & gas exploration services
Pr: Phil Wratt
**CFO:* Steve Whitman
CIO: Stephen Phillips

D-U-N-S 14-410-0757
BROADSPIRE SERVICES INC
(*Suby of* CRAWFORD & CO) ★
1391 Nw 136th Ave, Sunrise, FL 33323-2800
Tel (954) 452-4000 *Founded/Ownrshp* 2006
Sales 68.2MM^E *EMP* 2,150
SIC 8099 6331 Medical services organization; Workers' compensation insurance; Automobile insurance; Fire, marine & casualty insurance & carriers; Property damage insurance
CEO: Danielle Lisenbey
COO: Peter Imbrogno
Treas: Joseph R Caporaso
Ex VP: Allen W Nelson
Sr VP: Patrick Scullion
VP: Tom Yodice
Snr Sftwr: Bryan Foster
Snr Sftwr: Tresa Schultz
Dir IT: Kelly Leeds

D-U-N-S 07-279-6543
BROADSTONE GROUP INC
156 W 56th St Ste 1604, New York, NY 10019-3878
Tel (212) 333-2100 *Founded/Ownrshp* 1981
Sales 58.4MM *EMP* 2,025
SIC 6552 7011 8741 Subdividers & developers; Hotels & motels; Management services; Hotel or motel management
Ch Bd: Paul F Wallace
Treas: Lawrence Lopater
VP: Judith Bory

D-U-N-S 16-619-3425
■ **BROADSTREET PARTNERS INC**
(*Suby of* STATE AUTO FINANCIAL CORP) ★
580 N 4th St Ste 450, Columbus, OH 43215-2125
Tel (614) 993-3009 *Founded/Ownrshp* 1980
Sales 165.5MM^E *EMP* 184
SIC 6211 Investment firm, general brokerage
Pr: Richard Miley

D-U-N-S 95-845-5925
BROADVIEW NETWORKS HOLDINGS INC
800 Westchester Ave Ste N, Rye Brook, NY 10573-1354
Tel (914) 922-7000 *Founded/Ownrshp* 1996
Sales 291.1MM *EMP* 800^E
SIC 4813 4899 Local & long distance telephone communications; ; Data communication services
Pr: Michael K Robinson
**COO:* Brian P Crotty
COO: Scott Magee
**CFO:* Corey Rinker
**Ex VP:* Terrence J Anderson
**Ex VP:* Charles C Hunter
Sr VP: Jeff Blackey
VP: David Dickson
VP: Jim Lennon
VP: Paul Mumm
VP: Sanjay Patel
Board of Directors: Anthony M Abate, John R Brecker, Jeffrey A Brodsky, James N Chapman, James V Continenza, Richard J Santagati

D-U-N-S 87-738-8041 IMP
BROADVIEW NETWORKS INC
(*Suby of* BROADVIEW NETWORKS HOLDINGS INC) ★
800 Westchester Ave N501, Rye Brook, NY 10573-1336
Tel (914) 922-7000 *Founded/Ownrshp* 1997
Sales 213.9MM^E *EMP* 650
SIC 4813 Telephone communication, except radio
Ch Bd: Michael Robinson
Mng Pt: Lorin Stoner
**COO:* Brian Crotty
**CFO:* Corey Rinker
**Ex VP:* Terrance Anderson
Ex VP: Mario Deriggi
Ex VP: David Georgeadis
Sr VP: Patricia Kamertz
**Sr VP:* Donna Wenk
VP: David Dickson
Mng Dir: Kaushik Bhanderi

D-U-N-S 10-132-7898 IMP
BROADVIEW SECURITY INC
BRINK'S HOME TECHNOLGIES
8880 Esters Blvd, Irving, TX 75063-2406
Tel (972) 871-3500 *Founded/Ownrshp* 2010
Sales NA *EMP* 3,300
SIC 7382

BROADVOX
See INFOTELECOM HOLDINGS LLC

BROADWAY ACROSS AMERICA
See JOHN GORE ORGANIZATION INC

BROADWAY AUTO BODY SP & PNT SP
See BROADWAY AUTOMOTIVE - GREEN BAY INC

BROADWAY AUTOMOTIVE
See BROADWAY FORD-HYUNDAI INC

BROADWAY AUTOMOTIVE
See BROADWAY ENTERPRISES INC

D-U-N-S 00-895-9967
BROADWAY AUTOMOTIVE - GREEN BAY INC (WI)
BROADWAY AUTO BODY SP & PNT SP
(*Suby of* BROADWAY AUTOMOTIVE) ★
2700 S Ashland Ave, Green Bay, WI 54304-5303
Tel (920) 498-6666 *Founded/Ownrshp* 1916, 1993
Sales 112.4MM *EMP* 170
Accts Wipfli Llp Green Bay Wiscons
SIC 5511 New & used car dealers
Pr: Kevin J Cuene
**CFO:* Nick Lanser
**Sec:* David M Cuene
**VP:* Michael T Cuene

D-U-N-S 08-243-9662
BROADWAY BANCSHARES INC (TX)
BROADWAY NATIONAL BANK
1177 Ne Loop 410, San Antonio, TX 78209-1517
Tel (210) 283-6500 *Founded/Ownrshp* 1981
Sales NA *EMP* 600[E]
Accts Padgett Stratemann & Co Ll
SIC 6021 National commercial banks
Pr: James D Goudge
**CFO:* Chris Bannwolf
Ofcr: Diana Barron
Ofcr: Margaret Below
Ofcr: Sandy Nielsen
VP: Sherry Gonzalez
VP: Carrie Jett
VP: Michelle Pair
VP: Fernando Ramirez
**VP:* Megan Rutledge
VP: Bob Sarratt

BROADWAY CENTRAL MARKET
See HEB GROCERY CO LP

BROADWAY ELECTRIC
See COCHRAN INC

D-U-N-S 00-338-8402
BROADWAY ELECTRIC SERVICE CORP (TN)
BESCO
1800 N Central St, Knoxville, TN 37917-5411
Tel (865) 524-1851 *Founded/Ownrshp* 1950, 1958
Sales 127.7MM[E] *EMP* 630
SIC 1731 General electrical contractor
Pr: Wayne Wojciechowski
**Ch Bd:* Rodney E Napier Jr
VP: Rick Aarts
**VP:* Michael Holloway
**VP:* Jerry F Large
VP: Dottie White
Off Mgr: Kristi Cosner
Sales Asso: Kelsey Smith

D-U-N-S 87-758-1462
BROADWAY ENTERPRISES INC
BROADWAY AUTOMOTIVE
1106 S Military Ave, Green Bay, WI 54304-2119
Tel (920) 429-6249 *Founded/Ownrshp* 1993
Sales 247.7MM *EMP* 375
Accts Wipfli Llp Greenbay Wisconsi
SIC 5511 7514 Automobiles, new & used; Trucks, tractors & trailers: new & used; Passenger car rental
Pr: David M Cuene
**Treas:* Michael T Cuene
**VP:* Kevin J Cuene

D-U-N-S 02-325-3602
BROADWAY FORD-HYUNDAI INC
BROADWAY AUTOMOTIVE
(*Suby of* BROADWAY AUTOMOTIVE) ★
1010 S Military Ave, Green Bay, WI 54304-2117
Tel (920) 499-3131 *Founded/Ownrshp* 2004
Sales 143.4MM *EMP* 110[E]
Accts Wipfli Llp Green Bay Wiscon
SIC 7515 5511 7513 5521 5012 Passenger car leasing; Automobiles, new & used; Pickups, new & used; Truck rental & leasing, no drivers; Used car dealers; Automobiles & other motor vehicles
Pr: Michael T Cuene
**Sec:* David Cuene
**VP:* Kevin Cuene

D-U-N-S 07-239-6906
BROADWAY MANOR NURSING HOME
1622 E Broadway St, Muskogee, OK 74403-4601
Tel (918) 683-2851 *Founded/Ownrshp* 1960
Sales 494.6MM *EMP* 100
SIC 8052 8051 Intermediate care facilities; Skilled nursing care facilities
Pt: Michael T Scott
Off Mgr: Linda Long

BROADWAY NATIONAL BANK
See BROADWAY BANCSHARES INC

D-U-N-S 00-793-6016
BROADWAY NATIONAL BANK (TX)
EISENHOWER BANK
(*Suby of* BROADWAY NATIONAL BANK) ★
1177 Ne Loop 410, San Antonio, TX 78209-1517
Tel (210) 283-6500 *Founded/Ownrshp* 1941, 1982
Sales NA *EMP* 600
SIC 6021 National commercial banks
**Ch Bd:* James D Goudge
**Pr:* Pam Parish
**CFO:* Chris Bannwolf
CFO: Wes Dorman
Bd of Dir: Suzanne Goudge
Ofcr: Tamara E Amin
Ofcr: Angela Martin
Ex VP: Jeff Foote
Ex VP: Randy Rouse
Sr VP: Roger Bott
Sr VP: Sharon Brodbeck
Sr VP: Rebecca Cotton
Sr VP: Kyle Gubernator
Sr VP: Patricia Houston
Sr VP: Shawn Hughes
Sr VP: Josh Loden
Sr VP: Bruce McMillan
Sr VP: Jeff Nelson
Sr VP: Michelle Pair
Sr VP: Bob Waller
VP: Wendy Albers

D-U-N-S 10-145-9360
BROADWAY SERVICES INC
JOHNS HOPKINS REAL ESTATE
(*Suby of* JOHNS HOPKINS REAL ESTATE) ★
3709 E Monument St, Baltimore, MD 21205-2910
Tel (410) 563-6900 *Founded/Ownrshp* 1982
Sales 72.6MM *EMP* 1,300[E]
Accts Kpmg Llp Baltimore Md
SIC 7349 7381 7521 6512 4119 Hospital housekeeping; Cleaning service, industrial or commercial; Security guard service; Parking lots; Nonresidential building operators; Local passenger transportation
Pr: Peter Seidl
Pr: H Thomas Mc Gown
CFO: P Michael Kastendike
Dir Sec: Jack Long
Genl Mgr: Donte Alexander

D-U-N-S 06-310-9607
BROADWAY TYPEWRITER CO INC (CA)
AREY JONES EDUCTL SOLUTIONS
1055 6th Ave Ste 101, San Diego, CA 92101-5229
Tel (619) 645-0253 *Founded/Ownrshp* 1968, 1972
Sales 111.8MM *EMP* 80
Accts Matranga & Company San Diego
SIC 5045 7378 Computers, peripherals & software; Computer maintenance & repair
Pr: Michael Scarpella
**CFO:* David Scarpella
**VP:* Peter Scarpella

D-U-N-S 79-542-0491
▲ BROADWIND ENERGY INC
3240 S Central Ave, Cicero, IL 60804-3939
Tel (708) 780-4800 *Founded/Ownrshp* 1996
Sales 199.1MM *EMP* 680[E]
Tkr Sym BWEN *Exch* NAS
SIC 3511 Turbines & turbine generator sets; Turbines & turbine generator sets & parts; Turbines & turbine generator set units, complete
Pr: Stephanie K Kushner
**Ch Bd:* David P Reiland
VP: David W Fell
VP: Erik W Jensen
VP: Robert R Rogowski
Board of Directors: Charles H Beynon, Terence P Fox, Thomas A Wagner, Cary B Wood

BROADWIND HEAVY INDUSTRIES
See BROADWIND TOWERS INC

D-U-N-S 15-973-0097 IMP
■ BROADWIND TOWERS INC
BROADWIND HEAVY INDUSTRIES
(*Suby of* BROADWIND ENERGY INC) ★
101 S 16th St, Manitowoc, WI 54220-3873
Tel (920) 684-5531 *Founded/Ownrshp* 2003
Sales 117.1MM[E] *EMP* 400
SIC 3511 Turbines & turbine generator sets & parts
Ex VP: Stephanie Kushner

D-U-N-S 17-925-8892 IMP
■ BROADWING CORP
(*Suby of* LEVEL 3 COMMUNICATIONS LLC) ★
1122 Capital Of Texas Hwy, West Lake Hills, TX 78746-7175
Tel (512) 742-3700 *Founded/Ownrshp* 1997
Sales 139.5MM[E] *EMP* 1,661
SIC 3661 Fiber optics communications equipment
CFO: Gary Neill
Sr VP: Mike Jones
VP: Shane Brown
VP: Bryan Mayo
VP: Henry Ward
Dir Surg: Kristin Moya
Admn Mgr: David Searcy
CIO: Imohy J Naramore
CIO: David Spencer
Sls&Mrk Ex: Lisa Kimmel
Sls&Mrk Ex: Danny Maccallon

D-U-N-S 00-606-9330 IMP/EXP
BROAN-NUTONE LLC
AUBREY MANUFACTURING
(*Suby of* NORTEK INC) ★
926 W State St, Hartford, WI 53027-1066
Tel (262) 673-4340 *Founded/Ownrshp* 1981
Sales 709.0MM[E] *EMP* 3,200[E]
SIC 3634 3699 3635 3639 2514 3669 Fans, exhaust & ventilating, electric: household; Wall heaters, electric: household; Chimes, electric; Household vacuum cleaners; Trash compactors, household; Medicine cabinets & vanities: metal; Intercommunication systems, electric
CEO: David L Pringle
CFO: John Pendergrass
VP: Eliot Duncan
VP: Stpehen Swenerton
QC Dir: Bill Gregg
VP Mktg: Richard Palmersheim
Mktg Mgr: Bernadette Long
Mktg Mgr: Patrick Nielsen
Manager: Frank C Kinsley
Manager: George Lawrence
Manager: James Shaw

D-U-N-S 92-777-5478
▲ BROCADE COMMUNICATIONS SYSTEMS INC
130 Holger Way, San Jose, CA 95134-1376
Tel (408) 333-8000 *Founded/Ownrshp* 1995
Sales 2.3MMM *EMP* 5,588
Accts Kpmg Llp Santa Clara Califor
Tkr Sym BRCD *Exch* NGS
SIC 3577 4813 Computer peripheral equipment;
CEO: Lloyd A Carney
Ch Bd: David L House
V Ch: Vitaly Artemiev
COO: Gale England
CFO: Daniel W Fairfax
Sr VP: Ken Cheng
Sr VP: Ken K Cheng
Sr VP: Parviz Ghalambor
Sr VP: Christine Heckart
Sr VP: Kelly M Herrell
Sr VP: Jeffrey Lindholm
Sr VP: Jason Nolet
VP: Bill Bentley
VP: Michael Bushong
VP: Genhwa Chiang
VP: Michael Dorsey
VP: Marc Jaffan
VP: Raymond Lee
VP: Hadi Nahari
VP: Mark Nasiff
VP: Neil O'Donnell
Board of Directors: Judy Bruner, Renato A Dipentima, Alan L Earhart, John W Gerdelman, Kim Goodman, L William Krause, David E Roberson, Sanjay Vaswani

BROCK GROUP, THE
See BROCK HOLDINGS III INC

BROCK GROUP, THE
See MIKEN SPECIALTIES LTD

D-U-N-S 96-473-1702
BROCK GROUP INC
(*Suby of* BROCK HOLDINGS I LLC) ★
10343 Sam Houston Park Dr, Houston, TX 77064-4656
Tel (281) 807-8200 *Founded/Ownrshp* 2010
Sales 1.5MMM[E] *EMP* 15,666[E]
SIC 1721 1799 Industrial painting; Fireproofing buildings; Insulation of pipes & boilers
CEO: Michael E McGinnis
**Ch Bd:* Jeff Davis
V Ch: Brad Brock
**Pr:* Bob Pragada
**CFO:* Jon Grant
CFO: Heidi B Phillips
**Sr VP:* Tony Huval
**Sr VP:* Pamela Kunkemoeller

D-U-N-S 96-473-3013
BROCK HOLDINGS I LLC
10343 Sam Houston Park Dr # 200, Houston, TX 77064-4656
Tel (281) 807-8200 *Founded/Ownrshp* 2006
Sales 1.5MMM[E] *EMP* 15,666[E]
SIC 1721 1799 7359 Industrial painting; Fireproofing buildings; Insulation of pipes & boilers; Rigging & scaffolding; Scaffolding construction; Equipment rental & leasing
CEO: Jeff Davis
**Pr:* Michael McGinnis
**CFO:* Robert Hardy

D-U-N-S 96-473-3468
BROCK HOLDINGS II INC
(*Suby of* BROCK GROUP INC) ★
10343 Sam Houston Park Dr, Houston, TX 77064-4656
Tel (281) 807-8200 *Founded/Ownrshp* 2006
Sales 1.5MMM[E] *EMP* 11,220
SIC 1721 1799 Industrial painting; Fireproofing buildings; Insulation of pipes & boilers
Pr: Michael McGinnis
**CFO:* Robert Hardy

D-U-N-S 09-160-4327
BROCK HOLDINGS III INC
BROCK GROUP, THE
(*Suby of* BROCK HOLDINGS II INC) ★
10343 Sam Houston Park Dr, Houston, TX 77064-4656
Tel (281) 807-8200 *Founded/Ownrshp* 2007
Sales 1.4MMM[E] *EMP* 11,219
SIC 1721 7349 Industrial painting; Building maintenance services
Sr VP: Matt Boucher
Sr VP: Pamela Kunkemoeller

D-U-N-S 00-283-9751
BROCK INDUSTRIAL SERVICES LLC
(*Suby of* BROCK GROUP) ★
2210 Oak Leaf St, Joliet, IL 60436-1894
Tel (815) 730-3350 *Founded/Ownrshp* 1977
Sales 229.1MM[E] *EMP* 1,441
SIC 1721 1799 Industrial painting; Fireproofing buildings; Insulation of pipes & boilers
Pr: Jerry Stolarz
**Pr:* James Dreyer
**CFO:* Robert Hardy

D-U-N-S 96-476-4463
BROCK SERVICES HOLDINGS LLC
(*Suby of* BROCK GROUP) ★
10343 Sam Houston Park Dr # 200, Houston, TX 77064-4656
Tel (281) 807-8200 *Founded/Ownrshp* 2006
Sales 123.8MM[E] *EMP* 9,477
SIC 1721 1799 Industrial painting; Fireproofing buildings; Insulation of pipes & boilers
Pr: Michael McGinnis
**CFO:* Robert Hardy

D-U-N-S 03-451-8345
BROCK SERVICES LLC
(*Suby of* BROCK GROUP) ★
10343 Sam Houston Park Dr # 200, Houston, TX 77064-4656
Tel (281) 807-8200 *Founded/Ownrshp* 1995
Sales 904.1MM[E] *EMP* 9,477[E]
SIC 1721 1799 Industrial painting; Fireproofing buildings; Insulation of pipes & boilers
Ch: Jeff Davis
Pt: Travis Brisco
Pt: Brad Brock
Pt: Robert Hardy
CEO: Robert Pragada
Sr VP: Matt Boucher
Sr VP: Roger Peterson
VP: Russell Klinegardner
IT Man: Paul Manuel

D-U-N-S 15-216-0461
BROCKTON HOSPITAL INC
(*Suby of* SIGNATR HLTHCR BRCTN HSPTL) ★
680 Centre St, Brockton, MA 02302-3395
Tel (508) 941-7000 *Founded/Ownrshp* 1983
Sales 248.5MM *EMP* 1,500
SIC 8062 General medical & surgical hospitals
Ch: David R Wolohojian
**Pr:* Dale J Ellenberg
**Pr:* Kim Hollon
VP: Don Anderson
VP: Charlene Pontbinarg
VP: Eleanor Soeffing
MIS Dir: Christine Craven
IT Man: Harlow Sires
Netwrk Mgr: Paul Iacadoro
Mtls Mgr: Brian Murphy
Surgeon: Stephen Maloney

D-U-N-S 06-088-3456 IMP/EXP
BROCKWAY MORAN & PARTNERS INC
225 Ne Mizner Blvd # 700, Boca Raton, FL 33432-4007
Tel (561) 750-2000 *Founded/Ownrshp* 1998
Sales 127.6MM[E] *EMP* 665
SIC 5812 3599 3728 Fast-food restaurant, chain; Machine shop, jobbing & repair; Aircraft parts & equipment
Pr: Peter C Brockway
**Pt:* Patrick J Boroian
**Pt:* James R Davis Jr
**Pt:* Peter Klein
**Pt:* Lawrence I Shagrin
**Pt:* Michael E Moran
**Pt:* Richard J Wandoff
VP: Andrew Boswell
VP: David S Spinola

D-U-N-S 00-695-1719 IMP/EXP
BROCKWAY-SMITH CO
BROSCO
35 Upton Dr Ste 100, Wilmington, MA 01887-1073
Tel (978) 475-7100 *Founded/Ownrshp* 1890
Sales 186.1MM[E] *EMP* 775
SIC 5031 Millwork; Doors; Windows; Window frames, all materials
Pr: Charles F Smith
**Pr:* Mark Rieser
CFO: Paul Zacco
**CFO:* Paul Zocco
**VP:* Almon F Dirth Jr
IT Man: David Vanhorn
**VP Sls:* Timothy A Lyons
Sls Mgr: Bill Wells

D-U-N-S 10-804-8612 IMP/EXP
BRODART CO
MCNAUGHTON BOOK SERVICE
500 Arch St, Williamsport, PA 17701-4471
Tel (570) 326-2461 *Founded/Ownrshp* 1983
Sales 504.9MM[E] *EMP* 600
SIC 5192 5942 2752 2782 2789 2531 Books; Book stores; Commercial printing, lithographic; Library binders, looseleaf; Bookbinding & related work; Public building & related furniture; School furniture; Library furniture
Pr: Joseph Largen
**CFO:* Richard Dill
**VP:* Franck Chenet
**VP:* Tim Gage
**VP:* Gretchen Herman
**VP:* Randall Mackenzie
**VP:* Steven Uzupis
Exec: Chris Frantz
Genl Mgr: Joanie Hill
Genl Mgr: Tara Miller
Dir IT: Tom Bennett

D-U-N-S 00-538-1652 IMP/EXP
BRODER BROS CO
6 Neshaminy Interplex Dr, Trevose, PA 19053-6964
Tel (215) 291-0300 *Founded/Ownrshp* 1919
Sales 2.0MMM[E] *EMP* 1,326
SIC 5136 5137 Sportswear, men's & boys'; Sportswear, women's & children's
CEO: Norman Hullinger
**Pr:* Thomas Myers
CFO: Martin Matthews
**Sec:* Martin J Matthews
Ex VP: Henry E Harrell
**Sr VP:* Girisha Chandraraj
VP: Claude Chouinard
**VP:* Richard Emrich
VP: Paula Lindstrom
Snr Sftwr: Joe Kane
Dir IT: Gary Kozwoolski
Board of Directors: Richard Emrich, Edward Conard, David Heath, Michael Lundin

D-U-N-S 09-369-2267 IMP
BROETJE ORCHARDS LLC
FIRST FRUITS MARKETING WASH
1111 Fishook Park Rd, Prescott, WA 99348-9618
Tel (509) 749-2217 *Founded/Ownrshp* 1968
Sales 57.6MM[E] *EMP* 1,100
SIC 0175 Apple orchard; Cherry orchard
Pr: Ralph Broetje
VP: Julie Burtech
Sls Mgr: Robin Erickson

BROIN COMPANIES
See POET LLC

D-U-N-S 14-807-3518
BROKEN ARROW COMMUNICATIONS INC
8316 Corona Loop Ne, Albuquerque, NM 87113-1665
Tel (505) 877-2100 *Founded/Ownrshp* 2004
Sales 83.0MM[E] *EMP* 200
SIC 4899 1623 Communication signal enhancement network system; Communication line & transmission tower construction; Transmitting tower (telecommunication) construction
Pr: Nick Denton
**CFO:* Mark Cordova
**VP:* Edward Mason
Genl Mgr: Matt Stewart
Off Mgr: Elena Quilter

D-U-N-S 08-059-9970 IMP
BROKEN ARROW ELECTRIC SUPPLY INC
BAES
2350 W Vancouver St, Broken Arrow, OK 74012-1172
Tel (918) 258-3581 *Founded/Ownrshp* 1977
Sales 164.7MM[E] *EMP* 133
SIC 5063 Electrical apparatus & equipment

CEO: Bruce Garner
COO: R Banfield
**COO:* David Edkins
**CFO:* Kim Bryan
Brnch Mgr: Russ Carnes
Brnch Mgr: Tom Craig
Brnch Mgr: Michael Hayes
IT Man: Joe Banfield
Opers Mgr: Jesse Andrews
Opers Mgr: Misty White
Sales Asso: Rusty Davis

D-U-N-S 07-427-0034
BROKEN ARROW INDEPENDENT SCHOOL
701 S Main St, Broken Arrow, OK 74012-5528
Tel (918) 259-5700 *Founded/Ownrshp* 1903
Sales 122.7MM *EMP* 1,650
Accts Sanders Bledsoe & Hewett Bro
SIC 8211 Public elementary & secondary schools; Public elementary school; Seminary; Public senior high school
CFO: Brenda Charles
Genl Mgr: Sharon Moore
Pr Dir: Shelli Holland-Handy
Instr Medi: Keith Isbell

D-U-N-S 84-890-0382
BROKER SOLUTIONS INC
NEW AMERICAN FUNDING
14511 Myford Rd Ste 100, Tustin, CA 92780-7057
Tel (800) 450-2010 *Founded/Ownrshp* 2007
Sales 1373MM^E^ *EMP* 1,500
SIC 8742 6162 Financial consultant; Bond & mortgage companies
CEO: Rick Arvielo
**Pr:* Enrico Arvielo
**Pr:* Patricia Arvielo
**COO:* Christy Bunce
Sr VP: Sam Ellsworth
VP: Brigitte Ataya
VP: Frank Fuentes
VP: Cayce Macias
VP: Chris Macnaughton
VP: Jason Obradovich
Mktg Dir: Jennette Landrum

BROKERAGE SOUTHWEST
See TEAM REAL ESTATE INC

D-U-N-S 07-838-8730
BROMENN REGIONAL MEDICAL CENTER
1304 Franklin Ave, Normal, IL 61761-3558
Tel (309) 454-1400 *Founded/Ownrshp* 2012
Sales 163.1MM *EMP* 32^E^
SIC 8093 Weight loss clinic, with medical staff
Prin: Penny Cermak
Mktg Dir: Steve Holman

D-U-N-S 05-765-9112
BROMENN SERVICE AUXILIARY GIFT SHOP (IL)
ATRIUM BOUTIQUE
Franklin Ave Virginia St, Normal, IL 61761
Tel (309) 454-1400 *Founded/Ownrshp* 1956
Sales 191.6MM *EMP* 2
SIC 5947 5641 5621 Gift shop; Children's wear; Ready-to-wear apparel, women's
Treas: Lawrence Gratkins
VP Opers: Patricia Thornton
Sls&Mrk Ex: Michael Ray
Doctor: Dory Jarzabkowski
Doctor: Ramaprasad D Konanur
Doctor: Srinivas S Morampudi

D-U-N-S 78-869-1280
BRONTAPES INC
875 W Ellsworth Ave, Denver, CO 80223-1689
Tel (303) 534-2002 *Founded/Ownrshp* 1977
Sales 108.5MM^E^ *EMP* 200
SIC 5085 Industrial supplies
Pr: James Flynn
Sls Mgr: Ken Bachellor

D-U-N-S 06-886-1202 IMP/EXP
BRONCO WINE CO
CLASSIC WINES OF CALIFORNIA
6342 Bystrum Rd, Ceres, CA 95307-6652
Tel (209) 538-3131 *Founded/Ownrshp* 1973
Sales 165.9MM^E^ *EMP* 300
SIC 5182 2084

D-U-N-S 19-653-2832
BRONSON BATTLE CREEK HOSPITAL
(*Suby of* BRONSON HEALTH CARE GROUP INC) ★
300 North Ave, Battle Creek, MI 49017-3396
Tel (269) 966-8000 *Founded/Ownrshp* 2011
Sales 159.1MM *EMP* 1,882
SIC 8062 8063 8051 General medical & surgical hospitals; Psychiatric hospitals; Skilled nursing care facilities
CEO: Frank J Sardone
Dir Vol: Dawn Craig
**Sr VP:* Sue Reinoehl
**VP:* Paul Peabody
**VP:* Christine Sangalli
Dir Rad: Steven Miltz-Mille
Dir Rad: James Timmons
Dir Rad: Robert Zick
Nurse Mgr: Heather West
IT Man: Julianne Langford
Netwrk Mgr: David McClain

D-U-N-S 11-283-5053
BRONSON HEALTH CARE GROUP INC
301 John St, Kalamazoo, MI 49007-5295
Tel (269) 341-6000 *Founded/Ownrshp* 1982
Sales 941.8MM^E^ *EMP* 4,180^E^
SIC 8741 Hospital management; Nursing & personal care facility management
Pr: Frank Sardone
**CFO:* Kenneth L Taft
**Sr VP:* James B Falahee
Sr VP: John L Jones
VP: James Falahee
VP: Katie Harrelson
VP: Mac McClurkan
VP: Mike Way
Exec: Beth Farho
Exec: Sarah Shelley
Exec: Keitha Tigues

D-U-N-S 11-283-5525
BRONSON MANAGEMENT SERVICES CORP
BRONZON HEALTHCARE GROUP
(*Suby of* BRONSON HEALTH CARE GROUP INC) ★
1 Healthcare Plz, Kalamazoo, MI 49007-5339
Tel (269) 341-6000 *Founded/Ownrshp* 1982
Sales 71.3MM^E^ *EMP* 4,000
Accts Richard Hudson
SIC 8082 Home health care services
Pr: Frank Sardone
Ex VP: Kenneth Taft
VP: James Falahee
Ex Dir: Traci Haddock
QA Dir: Jane Jansen

D-U-N-S 07-258-1812
BRONSON METHODIST HOSPITAL INC
(*Suby of* BRONSON HEALTH CARE GROUP INC) ★
601 John St Ste E-012, Kalamazoo, MI 49007-5346
Tel (269) 341-7654 *Founded/Ownrshp* 1984
Sales 686.4MM *EMP* 2,861
Accts Plante & Moran Pllc Chicago
SIC 8062 General medical & surgical hospitals
CEO: Frank J Sardone
Chf Path: Nigel Bramwell
**COO:* Kenneth Taft
**CFO:* Mary Meitz
VP: Cheryl Knapp
VP: Mac McClurkan
Dir Risk M: Chris Sangalli
Dir Lab: Carol Bradley
Dir Rad: Brook Ward
Prin: Mark Atkinson
Prin: Joshua Burnett

D-U-N-S 04-248-6212
BRONSON PEDIATRIC NEUROLOGY SERVICE
601 John St Ste M-460, Kalamazoo, MI 49007-5355
Tel (269) 341-8383 *Founded/Ownrshp* 1997
Sales 156.3MM *EMP* 4
SIC 8011 Neurologist
VP: Mary Meitz
Off Mgr: Diana Allor

D-U-N-S 78-565-7420
BRONSON PHYSICIAN SERVICES INC
(*Suby of* BRONSON METHODIST HOSPITAL INC) ★
601 John St Ste W002, Kalamazoo, MI 49007-5341
Tel (269) 341-6000 *Founded/Ownrshp* 1987
Sales 173.0MM *EMP* 25
SIC 8011 Physicians' office, including specialists
Pr: Frank Sardone

BRONTE NURSING HOME
See EAST COKE COUNTY HOSPITAL DISTRICT

D-U-N-S 07-325-8493
BRONX LEBANON HOSPITAL CENTER (INC)
1276 Fulton Ave, Bronx, NY 10456-3499
Tel (718) 590-1800 *Founded/Ownrshp* 1890
Sales 631.3MM *EMP* 4,000
SIC 8062 General medical & surgical hospitals
Pr: Miguel Fuentes
**COO:* Steven Anderman
COO: Pauline Marks
**Ch:* Christopher Chang
Sr VP: Andrew Blackwood
VP: Lisa Bronikowski
VP: Selena Griffin-Mahon
VP: Milton Gumbs
VP: Sheldon Orstman
VP: Errol C Shneer
VP: Samuel Shutman
Assoc Dir: Emma Fattakhov
Dir Soc: Andrew Benjam
Dir Rx: Larry Schiller

BRONZON HEALTHCARE GROUP
See BRONSON MANAGEMENT SERVICES CORP

D-U-N-S 07-825-5593
BROOKDALE COMMUNITY COLLEGE INC
WBJB FM
765 Newman Springs Rd, Lincroft, NJ 07738-1599
Tel (732) 842-1900 *Founded/Ownrshp* 1967
Sales 63.9MM^E^ *EMP* 1,500
Accts Suplee Clooney & Company Wes
SIC 8222 Community college
Pr: Maureen Murphy
**Pr:* Peter Burnham PHD
**Ch:* Father Brian Butch
**Ex VP:* Margaret McMenamin
VP: Maureen Lawrence
**VP:* James Sulton
**VP:* Webster Trammell
Prgrm Mgr: Kacey Roy
Off Admin: Linda Massaro
Dir IT: Andrew Chiang

D-U-N-S 06-386-4656
BROOKDALE HOSPITAL CENTER HOUSING CO INC
BROOKDALE UNIV HOSP & MED CTR
1 Brookdale Plz, Brooklyn, NY 11212-3198
Tel (718) 240-5000 *Founded/Ownrshp* 1985
Sales 548.5MM^E^ *EMP* 3,725
Accts Kbl Llp Brooklyn Ny
SIC 8062 General medical & surgical hospitals
Ch Bd: Alexander Rovt
Pr: William Dugan
Pr: Renee Minutello
**CEO:* James Porter
**CEO:* Mark E Toney
**CFO:* Mounirf Doss
CFO: Steven Korf
Chf Mktg O: Louise Feeley
**VP:* Khari Edwards
**VP:* Catherine Gallogly-Simon
VP: Omar Ishmael
VP: Barbara Piascik
VP: Diana Sullivan
Exec: Laurel Esty
Exec: Ana Maloney

D-U-N-S 94-320-2226
BROOKDALE HOSPITAL CENTER HOUSING CO INC
(*Suby of* BROOKDALE UNIV HOSP & MED CTR) ★
10101 Avenue D, Brooklyn, NY 11236-1902
Tel (718) 240-5000 *Founded/Ownrshp* 1965
Sales 3.4MM *EMP* 3,508
Accts Kpmg Llp New York Ny
SIC 8082 Home health care services
IT Man: Bruce Klein

D-U-N-S 08-011-2211
BROOKDALE HOSPITAL MEDICAL CENTER
1 Brookdale Plz, Brooklyn, NY 11212-3198
Tel (718) 240-5000 *Founded/Ownrshp* 1914
Sales 476.5MM *EMP* 3^E^
SIC 8011 8062 Pediatrician; General medical & surgical hospitals

BROOKDALE SENIOR LIVING
See EMERITUS CORP

D-U-N-S 19-815-4994
▲ BROOKDALE SENIOR LIVING
111 Westwood Pl Ste 400, Brentwood, TN 37027-5057
Tel (615) 221-2250 *Founded/Ownrshp* 1978
Sales 4.9MMM *EMP* 82,000
Tkr Sym BKD *Exch* NYS
SIC 8059 8361 8051 Convalescent home; Domiciliary care; Personal care home, with health care; Nursing home, except skilled & intermediate care facility; Geriatric residential care; Skilled nursing care facilities; Convalescent home with continuous nursing care; Extended care facility
Pr: T Andrew Smith
**Ch Bd:* Daniel A Decker
Pr: Sheila Garner
COO: Labeed S Diab
CFO: Lucinda M Baier
Treas: George T Hicks
Ofcr: Glenn O Maul
Ofcr: Bryan D Richardson
Ex VP: H Todd Kaestner
Ex VP: Mary Sue Patchett
VP: Tim Barresi
VP: Chris Bird
VP: Jack Carney
VP: Cindy Chastulik
VP: Karen Doering
VP: Susannah Dwyer
VP: Pamela Engle
VP: Kim Estes
VP: Sheri Garrett
VP: David Hammonds
VP: Ming-Fang Jiang
Board of Directors: Frank M Bumstead, Jackie M Clegg, Jeffrey R Leeds, Mark J Parrell, William G Petty Jr, James R Seward, Lee S Wielansky

BROOKDALE UNIV HOSP & MED CTR
See BROOKDALE HOSPITAL CENTER HOUSING CO INC

D-U-N-S 07-995-1619
BROOKDALE UNIVERSITY HOSPITAL & MEDICAL CENTER
1 Brookdale Plz, Brooklyn, NY 11212-3139
Tel (718) 240-5000 *Founded/Ownrshp* 2015
Sales 3.2MM^E^ *EMP* 3,000
SIC 8011 6324 Medical centers; Hospital & medical service plans
CEO: Mark E Toney
**CFO:* Paul Goldberg
**Ch:* Alexander Rovt

D-U-N-S 78-998-6809
BROOKE HOLDINGS INC
205 F St, Phillipsburg, KS 67661-1943
Tel (785) 543-3199 *Founded/Ownrshp* 1988
Sales NA *EMP* 671
SIC 6411 Insurance agents
Pr: Robert Orr
**Treas:* Leland Orr

D-U-N-S 80-872-7221
BROOKESTONE VILLAGE INC
(*Suby of* HERITAGE OF GERING) ★
4330 S 144th St, Omaha, NE 68137-1051
Tel (402) 614-4000 *Founded/Ownrshp* 2000
Sales 1.1MMM *EMP* 150
SIC 8051 Skilled nursing care facilities
Pr: Jack Vetter

D-U-N-S 62-346-8886
BROOKFIELD ASSET MANAGEMENT (US) INC
(*Suby of* BROOKFIELD ASSET MANAGEMENT INC)
Brookfield Pl 250 Vesey S, New York, NY 10281
Tel (212) 417-7000 *Founded/Ownrshp* 2005
Sales 246.6MM^E^ *EMP* 6,000
SIC 8741 Business management
CEO: Harry Goldgut
Mng Pt: Tim Formuziewich
COO: Kevin English
COO: George Myhal
CFO: Brian Lawson
Sr VP: Bryan Davis
Sr VP: Lori Pearson
Sr VP: Kathrine Vyse
Sr VP: Andrew Willis
VP: Merope Pentogenis
Genl Mgr: Mable Wakamatsu

D-U-N-S 96-174-5713
BROOKFIELD ASSET MANAGEMENT INC
(*Suby of* BROOKFIELD ASSET MANAGEMENT (US) INC) ★
3 World Financial Ctr, New York, NY 10281-1013
Tel (212) 417-7000 *Founded/Ownrshp* 2010
Sales 130.5MM^E^ *EMP* 4,420^E^
SIC 8741 Management services
CEO: J Bruce Flatt
Mng Pt: Barry Blattman
Mng Pt: Alexander D Greene
Mng Pt: Aj Silber
CFO: Jon Tyras
Ofcr: Ronald Fisher-Dayn
Sr VP: Andrew W Osborne
VP: Roselyn A Hernandez
VP: Brad Hyler
VP: Sarah Pontius
VP: Ian Turnbull

BROOKFIELD FARMS
See NATIONWIDE FOODS INC

D-U-N-S 14-414-4862
BROOKFIELD GLOBAL RELOCATION SERVICES LLC
(*Suby of* BROOKFIELD ASSET MANAGEMENT INC)
150 Harvester Dr Ste 201, Burr Ridge, IL 60527-6692
Tel (630) 972-2250 *Founded/Ownrshp* 1998
Sales 136.7MM^E^ *EMP* 900
SIC 7389 Relocation service
CEO: Traci Morris
**Ex VP:* Maggie Ryan
Ex VP: Cindy Salter
**Ex VP:* Scott T Sullivan
Ex VP: Scott Sullivan
**Sr VP:* Michel Bonin
**Sr VP:* Nancy Brickwood
**Sr VP:* Matt Brownlee
**Sr VP:* Andrew Pierce
**Sr VP:* Eric Stern
**Sr VP:* Kim Trepkowski
VP: James Dotoratos
VP: Ian Johnson
VP: Joe Logudic
VP: Dan Mack
VP: Brian McEleney
VP: Chris Murphy
VP: Tara Nielsen
VP: Suzy Patton
**VP:* Jules Taylor
VP: Sally Tomte

D-U-N-S 12-614-6252
BROOKFIELD HOMES CORP
(*Suby of* BROOKFIELD ASSET MANAGEMENT INC)
3201 Jermantown Rd # 150, Fairfax, VA 22030-2875
Tel (703) 270-1400 *Founded/Ownrshp* 2002
Sales 130.0MM^E^ *EMP* 291
SIC 1521 1522 New construction, single-family houses; Hotel/motel & multi-family home construction
Pr: Ian G Cockwell
CFO: Craig J Laurie
Ex VP: William B Seith
IT Man: Rick Henson

D-U-N-S 93-101-4161
BROOKFIELD RELOCATION INC
PRUDENTIAL
(*Suby of* BRER SERVICES INC) ★
3333 Michelson Dr # 1000, Irvine, CA 92612-0625
Tel (949) 794-7900 *Founded/Ownrshp* 2001
Sales 100.6MM^E^ *EMP* 900
SIC 6794 Franchises, selling or licensing
VP: Brian McEleney
VP: Dave Benivengo
Dir IT: Marty Capaun
Dir IT: Mohammad Kahn
Dir IT: Mike Zeffiro
IT Man: Vincent Dejulio
IT Man: Chris Jacobson

D-U-N-S 00-929-5095
BROOKHAVEN MEMORIAL HOSPITAL
656 Bourdois Ave, Bellport, NY 11713-1631
Tel (631) 654-7770 *Founded/Ownrshp* 2007
Sales 17.2MM^E^ *EMP* 3,000
SIC 8062 General medical & surgical hospitals
Prin: Richard Margulis

D-U-N-S 06-196-4896
BROOKHAVEN MEMORIAL HOSPITAL MEDICAL CENTER INC (NY)
101 Hospital Rd, East Patchogue, NY 11772-4870
Tel (631) 654-7100 *Founded/Ownrshp* 1957
Sales 254.1MM *EMP* 2,100
SIC 8062 General medical & surgical hospitals
CEO: Richard T Margulis
Chf Rad: Kenneth Schwartz
Chf Rad: Michael Slattery
**Pr:* Thomas Ockers
**CEO:* Robert W Schwarz
**Treas:* Jeffrey Mayer
Trst: Gary Brown
Trst: Felix J Grucci Jr
Trst: Walter F Ladick Jr
Trst: William Lehmann
Trst: Lisa Lourie
Trst: Ernest Smith
Chf Mktg O: Walter Ladick
**VP:* Kevin Conroy
**VP:* Brenda Farrell
**VP:* Ronald A Giraulo
VP: Seth Mankes
**VP:* Kim Mendez
**VP:* Ron Stephenson
Dir Rad: Almas Abbasi
Dir Rad: Edmond Balakhane

BROOKHAVEN NATIONAL LABORATORY
See BROOKHAVEN SCIENCE ASSOCIATES LLC

D-U-N-S 02-757-9460
BROOKHAVEN SCIENCE ASSOCIATES LLC
BROOKHAVEN NATIONAL LABORATORY
2 Center St, Upton, NY 11973-9700
Tel (631) 344-8000 *Founded/Ownrshp* 1998
Sales 623.8MM^E^ *EMP* 3,000^E^
SIC 8733 Noncommercial research organizations
**Pr:* Doon Gibbs
Ofcr: Jil Clough-Johnston
Ofcr: Mark Sakitt
Dir Lab: Peter Paul
Assoc Dir: Fritz Henn
Assoc Dir: Gerald Stokes
Admn Mgr: Diane Hatton
Dir IT: Duffin Susan
Opers Mgr: R Ernst
Opers Mgr: Stephen McAlary
Ql Cn Mgr: Roy Lebel

BROOKHOLLOW
See ARTCO (US) INC

D-U-N-S 04-320-3645 IMP
BROOKINGS INSTITUTION (DC)
1775 Massachusetts Ave Nw, Washington, DC 20036-2103
Tel (202) 797-6000 *Founded/Ownrshp* 1916
Sales 106.3MM *EMP* 400[E]
Accts Mcgladrey Llp Gaithersburg M
SIC 8733 2741 8621 Noncommercial social research organization; Miscellaneous publishing; Professional membership organizations
Pr: Stroube Talbott
Pr: Betsy Biern
Pr: Carol Graham
CFO: Julie Englund
**Treas:* Fred Silbernagal
Ofcr: Christine Jacobs
Ex VP: Martin Indyk
Ex VP: Cathryn Poff
VP: Val Broadie
VP: Robert Faherty
VP: Richard Fawal
VP: Ted Gayer
VP: Bruce Katz
VP: Dl McNeal
VP: Steven Pifer
VP: Sue Tillotson
VP: Stewart Uretsky
Assoc Dir: Ona Dosunmu
Dir Soc: Anna Goodbaum

D-U-N-S 02-200-1197
▲ BROOKLINE BANCORP INC
131 Clarendon St, Boston, MA 02116-5131
Tel (617) 425-4600 *Founded/Ownrshp* 1997
Sales NA *EMP* 720[E]
Tkr Sym BRKL *Exch* NGS
SIC 6035 Federal savings & loan associations
Pr: Paul A Perrault
**Ch Bd:* Joseph J Slotnik
COO: James M Cosman
CFO: Carl M Carlso
Chf Cred: M Robert Rose
VP: Peter Lennon
Dir Risk M: Michael W McCurdy
Brnch Mgr: Polina Frenklakh

D-U-N-S 00-695-3590
■ BROOKLINE BANK
(*Suby of* BROOKLINE BANCORP INC) ★
131 Clarendon St, Boston, MA 02116-5131
Tel (617) 425-4625 *Founded/Ownrshp* 1871, 1998
Sales NA *EMP* 130
SIC 6036 State savings banks, not federally chartered
CEO: Paul Perrault
**Pr:* Charles H Peck
**CFO:* Paul Bechet
Ofcr: Lisa Lorgeree
Ofcr: Mark Sills
Sr VP: Darryl Fess
Sr VP: James Horrigan
Sr VP: Jane Wolchonok
VP: Peter Lennon
Exec: Sarah P Merritt
Brnch Mgr: Bryan Manandhar

BROOKLINE PUBLIC SCHOOLS
See BROOKLINE SCHOOL DISTRICT

D-U-N-S 10-003-0972
BROOKLINE SCHOOL DISTRICT
BROOKLINE PUBLIC SCHOOLS
333 Washington St, Brookline, MA 02445-6853
Tel (617) 730-2401 *Founded/Ownrshp* 1995
Sales 41.9MM[E] *EMP* 1,200
SIC 8211 Public elementary & secondary schools
Psych: Lauren Ashbaugh
Psych: Linda Kelly

D-U-N-S 07-657-7014
BROOKLINE TOWN OF (INC)
333 Washington St, Brookline, MA 02445-6853
Tel (617) 730-2000 *Founded/Ownrshp* 1705
Sales NA *EMP* 1,250[E]
Accts Powers & Sullivan Llc Wakefi
SIC 9111 City & town managers' offices;
Ch: Ken Goldstein
Bd of Dir: Neil Wishinsky
**Prin:* Betsy Dewitt

D-U-N-S 00-861-3320
BROOKLYN DEVELOPMENT CENTER
888 Fountain Ave, Brooklyn, NY 11239-5907
Tel (718) 642-6002 *Founded/Ownrshp* 2000
Sales 21.4MM[E] *EMP* 1,300
SIC 8051 Mental retardation hospital

D-U-N-S 04-155-5665 IMP
BROOKLYN HOSPITAL CENTER
121 Dekalb Ave, Brooklyn, NY 11201-5493
Tel (718) 250-8000 *Founded/Ownrshp* 1845
Sales 345.8MM *EMP* 3,300
SIC 8062 General medical & surgical hospitals
Ch Bd: Carlos P Naudon
Pr: Rubin Diaz
**Pr:* Jonathan M Weld
CFO: Joseph J Guarracino
**Ex VP:* Trent Crable
Sr VP: Stacy Friedman
**Sr VP:* Joseph Guarracino
**Sr VP:* Bill Moran
**Sr VP:* Gary Almedo Stephens
Sr VP: Ira Warm
**Sr VP:* Patricia Winston
VP: Karen Milano
VP: Debbie Niederhoffer
Dir Risk M: Donna Russell

D-U-N-S 06-828-9800
BROOKLYN LAW SCHOOL (NY)
250 Joralemon St, Brooklyn, NY 11201-3798
Tel (718) 625-2200 *Founded/Ownrshp* 1901
Sales 97.2MM *EMP* 230
Accts Mcgladrey Llp New York Ny
SIC 8221 Colleges universities & professional schools
Pr: Joan Wexler
Ch Bd: Stuart Subotnick
Treas: Shoshanna Campbell
Assoc Dir: Mary Fitzpatrick
Ex Dir: Paul Gangsei
Genl Mgr: Maryann Good
CIO: Gloria Barlow
Pr Mgr: John Mackin

D-U-N-S 07-435-3707 IMP
BROOKLYN PUBLIC LIBRARY
280 Cadman Plz W, Brooklyn, NY 11201-2798
Tel (718) 230-2100 *Founded/Ownrshp* 1892, 1989
Sales 107.3MM *EMP* 1,700
Accts Eisneramper Llp New York Ny
SIC 8231 Public library
CEO: Linda E Johnson
Ex VP: Brett Robinson
VP: Selvon Smith
**Ex Dir:* Dionne Mack-Harvin
Brnch Mgr: Jay Filan
Genl Mgr: David Pasteelnick
IT Man: Piotr Jurski
Web Dev: Pam Bloomfield
Web Dev: Pamela Bloomfield
VP Mktg: Robin Kenton

BROOKS ARMORED CAR
See ATI SYSTEMS INTERNATIONAL INC

D-U-N-S 03-369-0082
BROOKS AUTO PARTS INC
NAPA AUTO PARTS
402 Peterson Ave S, Douglas, GA 31533-5250
Tel (912) 384-7818 *Founded/Ownrshp* 1937
Sales 118.1MM[E] *EMP* 350
SIC 5531 Automotive & home supply stores
CEO: Elton D Brooks Jr
Sec: Terry Moore
VP: Wayne Marsh

D-U-N-S 60-319-9688
▲ BROOKS AUTOMATION INC
15 Elizabeth Dr, Chelmsford, MA 01824-4111
Tel (978) 262-2400 *Founded/Ownrshp* 1978
Sales 560.3MM *EMP* 1,426[E]
Accts Bdo Usa Llp Boston Massachu
Tkr Sym BRKS *Exch* NGS
SIC 3559 3563 3823 7699 Semiconductor manufacturing machinery; Vacuum pumps, except laboratory; Thermal conductivity instruments, industrial process type; Industrial equipment services
CEO: Stephen S Schwartz
Pr: James F Gentilcore
Pr: Mark D Morelli
Pr: Michael Pippins
Pr: Maurice Tenney III
Pr: Ralf Wuellner
COO: Greg Marvell
CFO: Lindon G Robertson
Bd of Dir: Larry Heath
Ofcr: Steven E Hebert
Ex VP: Franz Janker
Ex VP: Mark Morelli
Ex VP: Brian Quirk
Ex VP: Mitch Rowe
Ex VP: Patricio Tapia
Sr VP: David C Gray
Sr VP: Chris Hofmeister
Sr VP: David E Jarzynka
Sr VP: Thomas R Leitzke
VP: Mitchell Drew
VP: Carol Goyette
Board of Directors: A Clinton Allen, Robyn C Davis, Joseph R Martin, John K McGillicuddy, Kirk P Pond, Alfred Woollacott III, Mark S Wrighton, Ellen M Zane

D-U-N-S 92-794-7374 IMP/EXP
BROOKS BROTHERS GROUP INC
346 Madison Ave, New York, NY 10017-3788
Tel (212) 309-7765 *Founded/Ownrshp* 1998
Sales 929.4MM[E] *EMP* 5,000
SIC 5651 5632 Family clothing stores; Apparel accessories
Pr: Claudio Del Vecchio
Recvr: Patti Del Grosso
Pr: Paige Havens
Pr: Glen Hoffs
Pr: Brian Lane
**COO:* Mauro Calderan
**CFO:* Brian Baumann
**Chf Mktg O:* Vivien Kronengold
Ex VP: Lou Amendola
**Ex VP:* Steve Goldaper
Ex VP: Mary Pytko
Sr VP: Michelle Lavallee
VP: Ghislaine Bousquet
**VP:* Eugene Feola

D-U-N-S 17-373-7339 IMP
BROOKS BROTHERS INC
346 Madison Ave, New York, NY 10017-3788
Tel (212) 682-8800 *Founded/Ownrshp* 2001
Sales NA *EMP* 3,500
SIC 5611 5621 5651

BROOKS, CAROLYN E
See MEDICAL WEST COMMUNITY HEALTH

D-U-N-S 00-578-4913
BROOKS CONSTRUCTION CO INC
6525 Ardmore Ave, Fort Wayne, IN 46809-9504
Tel (260) 478-1990 *Founded/Ownrshp* 1909
Sales 100.0MM *EMP* 350
Accts Baden Gage & Schroeder Llc F
SIC 1611 Highway & street paving contractor
Pr: John R Brooks
**CFO:* Cindy Riebersal
**Treas:* Bill Stevens
**VP:* Jack Billings
**VP:* Steve Koble
Genl Mgr: Roger Kuehnert
Ql Cn Mgr: Pam Sievers

D-U-N-S 08-094-0984
BROOKS COUNTY HOSPITAL AUTHORITY
903 N Court St, Quitman, GA 31643-1315
Tel (229) 263-4171 *Founded/Ownrshp* 1935
Sales 9.7MM *EMP* 3,132
SIC 8062 General medical & surgical hospitals
VP: Toole Don
Dir Lab: Cristy Woodell

BROOKS HEALTH SYSTEM
See GENESIS HEALTH INC

BROOKS REHABILITATION
See GENESIS REHABILITATION HOSPITAL INC

BROOKS ROCK N ROLL MARATHON
See BROOKS SPORTS INC

D-U-N-S 05-150-0098 IMP
■ BROOKS SPORTS INC
BROOKS ROCK N ROLL MARATHON
(*Suby of* BERKSHIRE HATHAWAY INC) ★
3400 Stone Way N Ste 500, Seattle, WA 98103-8996
Tel (425) 488-3131 *Founded/Ownrshp* 2004
Sales 224.1MM[E] *EMP* 205
SIC 5139 Footwear, athletic
Pr: Jim Weber
**Ch:* Ann Iverson
VP: Anne Cavassa
VP: Pete Humphrey
VP: Mark McKelvey
VP: Rick Wilhelm
Creative D: Maade Seddiki
Ex Dir: Amalia Borsi
IT Man: David Deluhery
IT Man: George Lewis
Mktg Mgr: Lisa Murray

D-U-N-S 00-580-8811
BROOKS-BERRY-HAYNIE & ASSOCIATES INC (GA)
600 Discovery Pl, Mableton, GA 30126-4680
Tel (770) 874-1162 *Founded/Ownrshp* 1953, 1997
Sales 85.9MM *EMP* 175[E]
Accts Hlb Gross Collins Pc Atlanta
SIC 1731 Electrical work
Pr: Alex Owen
**Pr:* Jason A Owen
**COO:* Andy O'Kelly
**CFO:* Tim McCarty

D-U-N-S 00-793-4276
BROOKSHIRE BROTHERS LTD (TX)
1201 Ellen Trout Dr, Lufkin, TX 75904-1233
Tel (936) 634-8155 *Founded/Ownrshp* 1921
Sales 1.0MMM[E] *EMP* 6,300
SIC 5411 Grocery stores, chain
Ch: Milton Hixson
CEO: Jerry Johnson
VP: John Alston
VP: Ricky Moulder
VP: Sumner Osgood
VP: Eric Rich
Dir Rx: Mike Choate
Store Dir: Joe Williams
Telecom Ex: Royce Adkison
IT Man: Debbie Childs
IT Man: Dan Huerta

BROOKSHIRE FOOD STORES
See BROOKSHIRE GROCERY CO INC

D-U-N-S 00-895-3663 IMP
BROOKSHIRE GROCERY CO INC (TX)
BROOKSHIRE FOOD STORES
1600 W Southwest Loop 323, Tyler, TX 75701-8532
Tel (903) 534-3000 *Founded/Ownrshp* 1926, 1950
Sales 2.9MMM[E] *EMP* 12,295
SIC 5411 5983 Supermarkets, chain; Fuel oil dealers
CEO: Bradley W Brookshire
**CEO:* Marvin S Massey Jr
CFO: Carolyn Hutson
**Treas:* Carolyn Hudson
Ex VP: Kevin Albritton
Ex VP: Russ Cooper
Ex VP: Greg Nordyke Sr
Sr VP: Rick Ellis
Sr VP: Aven Nelson
VP: John D Anna
VP: Shannon Buell
**VP:* Donald P Gilbreath
**VP:* Brian Johnson
**VP:* Christopher L Kelsay
**VP:* David J Krause
**VP:* Andrew G Newberry
**VP:* Gladen G Smith

D-U-N-S 80-780-8493
BROOKSIDE LIVING CENTER LLC
208 James St, Anderson, SC 29625-2942
Tel (864) 226-3427 *Founded/Ownrshp* 2007
Sales 651.9MM *EMP* 99
SIC 8051 Skilled nursing care facilities
CFO: John F Swift

BROOKSOURCE
See TECHNICAL YOUTH LLC

D-U-N-S 01-975-1809 IMP
BROOKSTONE CO INC
(*Suby of* BROOKSTONE HOLDINGS CORP) ★
1 Innovation Way, Merrimack, NH 03054-4873
Tel (866) 576-7337 *Founded/Ownrshp* 2014
Sales 309.3MM[E] *EMP* 2,449
SIC 5947 5399 5331 5961 Gift shop; Army-Navy goods; Variety stores; Catalog sales
Pr: Steven Goldsmith
CFO: Valen Tong
Sr VP: Stephen A Gould
VP: Kevin Blossom
VP: David Figler
VP: Susan McGrath
VP: Neal Panza
VP: Dana Schwartz
VP: Kiran Smith
Board of Directors: Ron Sim Chye Hock, Nigel Roger Thomas Jones, Margaret Lui, Adam L Smith, Jackson Tai, William E Watts

D-U-N-S 79-121-1662
BROOKSTONE HOLDINGS CORP
1 Innovation Way, Merrimack, NH 03054-4873
Tel (603) 880-9500 *Founded/Ownrshp* 2014
Sales 324.2MM[E] *EMP* 3,176
SIC 5947 5961 Gift, novelty & souvenir shop; Catalog & mail-order houses
Pr: Tom Via
**CFO:* Valen Tong
**VP:* Thomas Moynihan
Genl Couns: Stephen A Gould

D-U-N-S 15-089-8138 IMP/EXP
BROOKSTONE INC
1 Innovation Way, Merrimack, NH 03054-4873
Tel (603) 880-9500 *Founded/Ownrshp* 2014
Sales 966.3MM[E] *EMP* 3,176
SIC 5961 5947

BROOKSVILLE REGIONAL HOSPITAL
See HERNANDO HEALTHCARE INC

D-U-N-S 62-196-1671 IMP
■ BROOKWOOD BAPTIST MEDICAL CENTER
BROOKWOOD MEDICAL CENTER
(*Suby of* TENET HEALTHSYSTEM MEDICAL INC) ★
2010 Brookwood Med Ctr Dr, Birmingham, AL 35209-6804
Tel (205) 877-1000 *Founded/Ownrshp* 1967
Sales 350.4MM *EMP* 2,218
SIC 8011 Offices & clinics of medical doctors
CEO: Garry Gause
**COO:* Kerry R Tirman
**CFO:* Joe Benton
Dir Lab: Michael Reymann
Orthpdst: David McLain
Pharmcst: Shondra Sholar

D-U-N-S 36-075-2448 IMP/EXP
BROOKWOOD COMPANIES INC
BROOKWOOD ROLL GOODS DIV
(*Suby of* HALLWOOD GROUP INC) ★
485 Madison Ave Frnt 5, New York, NY 10022-5833
Tel (212) 551-0100 *Founded/Ownrshp* 1989
Sales 387.6MM[E] *EMP* 400
Accts Deloitte & Touche Llp Dallas
SIC 5131 Textile converters; Notions
CEO: Amber M Brookman
**Pr:* Joanne Gallonio
**CFO:* William E C King III
**VP:* Matthew Morris
**VP:* Nathan Yahya

BROOKWOOD MEDICAL CENTER
See BROOKWOOD BAPTIST MEDICAL CENTER

BROOKWOOD ROLL GOODS DIV
See BROOKWOOD COMPANIES INC

D-U-N-S 07-160-2791
BROOME COUNTY (NY)
60 Hawley St, Binghamton, NY 13901-6699
Tel (607) 778-2452 *Founded/Ownrshp* 1840
Sales NA *EMP* 2,503
Accts Bonadio & Co Llp Albany Ne
SIC 9111 County supervisors' & executives' offices;
Pr: Kevin Drumm
CFO: Jerry Knebel
Ofcr: Aaron Martin
Exec: Tammy Cozak
**Prin:* Debbie Preston

D-U-N-S 07-730-5894
BROOME-TIOGA BOARD OF COOPERATIVE EDUCATIONAL SERVICES
BROOME-TIOGA BOCES
435 Glenwood Rd, Binghamton, NY 13905-1606
Tel (607) 763-3618 *Founded/Ownrshp* 1958
Sales 50.1MM[E] *EMP* 1,200
SIC 8299 Educational services
Netwrk Eng: Philip Sage

BROOME-TIOGA BOCES
See BROOME-TIOGA BOARD OF COOPERATIVE EDUCATIONAL SERVICES

D-U-N-S 03-469-0792
BROS MANAGEMENT INC
MCDONALD'S
2501 E Magnolia Ave, Knoxville, TN 37914-5311
Tel (865) 523-2157 *Founded/Ownrshp* 1960
Sales 51.0MM[E] *EMP* 1,500
SIC 5812 Fast-food restaurant, chain
**Pr:* Tom Cochran
**VP:* Jo Ann Huddleston

BROSCO
See BROCKWAY-SMITH CO

D-U-N-S 08-674-4182 IMP
BROSE NORTH AMERICA INC
(*Suby of* BROSE FAHRZEUGTEILE GMBH & CO. KG, COBURG)
3933 Automation Ave, Auburn Hills, MI 48326-1788
Tel (248) 339-4000 *Founded/Ownrshp* 1977
Sales 1.5MMM[E] *EMP* 8,000
SIC 5015 Motor vehicle parts, used
CEO: Jrgen Otto
**Pr:* Jan Kowal
VP: Mike Brosseau
Prgrm Mgr: Matthew Dissette
Prgrm Mgr: Troy Husk
IT Man: Gerardo Calderon
Sftwr Eng: Stephen Nawrocki
Prd Mgr: John Stanaj
Ql Cn Mgr: Lorrie Surchik
Mktg Dir: Eveline Perry
Snr Mgr: Stefan Krug

BROSHCO FABRICATED PRODUCTS
See JAY INDUSTRIES INC

D-U-N-S 01-942-6204 IMP/EXP
■ BROSNA INC
KOO KOO ROO
(*Suby of* LUBYS INC) ★
5700 S Mo Pac Expy # 300, Austin, TX 78749-1461
Tel (512) 936-7600 *Founded/Ownrshp* 1995
Sales 70.9MM[E] *EMP* 2,074[E]
SIC 5812 Fast-food restaurant, chain
CEO: Peter Large
COO: Christine Dekkers
**COO:* Ralph Flannery
**CFO:* Gregor Grant
CFO: Philip Parsons
CFO: Keith Shutz
Treas: Jan Cuypers
Sr VP: Rich Hendrie

Sr VP: Lola Legget
VP: Danielle Dawley
VP: Eddie Delvale
VP: David Donald
VP: Steve Riddick
VP: Steve Zimmerman

D-U-N-S 17-352-8407 IMP/EXP
BROTHER INDUSTRIES (USA) INC
(*Suby of* BROTHER INTERNATIONAL CORP) ★
7819 N Brother Blvd, Memphis, TN 38133-2763
Tel (901) 377-7777 *Founded/Ownrshp* 1986
Sales 228.8MM^E *EMP* 1,200
SIC 3579 Typewriters & parts; Word processing equipment
Pr: Toru Uchibayashi

D-U-N-S 06-499-2902 IMP/EXP
BROTHER INTERNATIONAL CORP
(*Suby of* BROTHER INDUSTRIES, LTD.)
200 Crossing Blvd, Bridgewater, NJ 08807-2861
Tel (908) 704-1700 *Founded/Ownrshp* 1954
Sales 1.7MMM^E *EMP* 2,000
SIC 5044 3579 3559 5084 5064 5065 Office equipment; Typing & word processing machines; Typewriters & parts; Word processing equipment; Sewing machines & hat & zipper making machinery; Sewing machines & attachments, industrial; Sewing machines, industrial; Sewing machines, household: electric; Electronic parts & equipment; Facsimile equipment
Pr: Kazufumi Ikeda
Ch Bd: Tadashi Ishiguro
CFO: Anthony Melfi
Sr VP: Donald Cummins
Sr VP: Roger T Nakagawa
Sr VP: Dean F Shulman
Sr VP: Brian Vincent
VP: Jeff Conway
VP: David Crist
VP: Suleman Madha
VP: Frank Sannazzaro
Board of Directors: Patrick T Gilmore, H Kurachi

D-U-N-S 07-889-8319
BROTHERHOOD MUTUAL INSURANCE CO
6400 Brotherhood Way, Fort Wayne, IN 46825-4251
Tel (260) 482-8668 *Founded/Ownrshp* 1935
Sales NA *EMP* 250
SIC 6331 Fire, marine & casualty insurance: mutual; Automobile insurance
Ch: Mark A Robison
**Ch Bd:* James A Blum
**Sr VP:* Mark Robison
**VP:* Michael J Allison
VP: Nathan Anguiano
**VP:* Scott Figgins
VP: Scott A Figgins
**VP:* Kathleen Turpin Johnson
**VP:* Daryl Pannabecker
**VP:* Tom Rozema
Dir IT: Beng Ong

D-U-N-S 08-063-6319
BROTHERS BROTHER FOUNDATION
1200 Galveston Ave, Pittsburgh, PA 15233-1604
Tel (412) 321-3160 *Founded/Ownrshp* 1958
Sales 244.6MM *EMP* 12^E
Accts Schneider Downs & Co Inc Pitt
SIC 8399 Health & welfare council
Pr: Luke L Hingson
**Ch:* Charles Sout
**Treas:* Charles Stout
Bd of Dir: Walter Fowler
**Trst:* Rachel Allen
**Trst:* Roy Dorrance
Trst: Paul Euwer
Trst: Chester A Hobert
**Trst:* Chip Lambert MD
Trst: William A Sante
**VP:* Bill Davis

D-U-N-S 03-967-4833
BROTHERS PRODUCE INC
3173 Produce Row, Houston, TX 77023-5813
Tel (713) 924-4196 *Founded/Ownrshp* 1980
Sales 104.3MM^E *EMP* 110
Accts Fiducial Business Centers Inc
SIC 5148 Fresh fruits & vegetables
CEO: Martin Erenwert
**Pr:* Barry Erenwert
CFO: Alex Bando
**Treas:* Debbie Erenwert
**VP:* Brent Erenwert
VP: Ernest Munoz
Genl Mgr: Mike Blanchard
Genl Mgr: Lois Carlisle

D-U-N-S 15-296-8236
■ **BROTHERS PROPERTY CORP**
(*Suby of* GREAT AMERICAN INSURANCE CO) ★
2 Alhambra Plz Ste 1280, Coral Gables, FL 33134-5237
Tel (305) 285-1035 *Founded/Ownrshp* 1987
Sales 24.9MM^E *EMP* 1,375
SIC 6512 Nonresidential building operators
Pr: Victor Fuller
**VP:* Stephen Fuller

D-U-N-S 09-650-3883 IMP/EXP
BROTHERS TRADING CO INC
VICTORY WHOLESALE GROCERS
400 Victory Ln, Springboro, OH 45066-3046
Tel (937) 746-1010 *Founded/Ownrshp* 1985
Sales 278.0MM^E *EMP* 450
SIC 5141 5122 5149 Groceries, general line; Drugs, proprietaries & sundries; Groceries & related products
Pr: David Kantor
Sr Cor Off: Steve Messer
**VP:* Richard Kantor
**VP:* Scott Mattis
Snr Sftwr: Brucken Pete

BROTMAN MEDICAL PARTNERS
See SOUTHERN CALIFORNIA HOSPITAL AT CULVER CITY

D-U-N-S 03-399-7305
BROULIMS SUPER MARKET INC
BROULIMS THRIFTWAY
182 N State St, Rigby, ID 83442-1444
Tel (208) 745-9201 *Founded/Ownrshp* 1966
Sales 97.5MM^E *EMP* 600
SIC 5912 Drug stores
Pr: C Richard Broulim
**Pr:* James Hansen
CFO: Wade Snedaker
Ofcr: Ian Martinson
**VP:* Vonnie Lue Broulim
Store Dir: Brad Bischoff

BROULIMS THRIFTWAY
See BROULIMS SUPER MARKET INC

D-U-N-S 07-602-3225
BROWARD COLLEGE
111 E Las Olas Blvd, Fort Lauderdale, FL 33301-2206
Tel (954) 201-7400 *Founded/Ownrshp* 2004
Sales 5.2MM *EMP* 2,588
SIC 8222 Community college
Pr: J David Armstrong Jr
Assoc VP: Jennifer Machado
Assoc VP: Rigoberto Rincones-Gomez
VP: Edna Chun
**VP:* Thom Olliff

D-U-N-S 08-027-3995
BROWARD COUNTY PUBLIC SCHOOLS
600 Se 3rd Ave, Fort Lauderdale, FL 33301-3125
Tel (754) 321-0000 *Founded/Ownrshp* 2016
Sales 247.1MM^E *EMP* 31,174
SIC 8211 Public elementary & secondary schools
Bd of Dir: Ann Murray
Exec: Teresa Simmons
CTO: Larry Rivera

BROWARD FACTORY SERVICE
See HERD ENTERPRISES INC

D-U-N-S 10-395-0296
BROWARD GENERAL MEDICAL CENTER
BROWARD HEALTH MEDICAL CENTER
1600 S Andrews Ave, Fort Lauderdale, FL 33316-2510
Tel (954) 355-4400 *Founded/Ownrshp* 2002
Sales 458.8MM *EMP* 98^E
SIC 8011 Medical centers
CEO: James Thaw
Chf Path: Peter S Johnson
Chf Rad: Jon Guben
Exec: Dionne Wong
Netwrk Mgr: Yari Mann
Pathlgst: Guillermo Anido
Pathlgst: Francessca Brettschneider
Pathlgst: Raymund Dala
Pathlgst: Albert Fay
Pathlgst: Julian Garcia
Pathlgst: Larry Hirschfield

BROWARD HEALTH MEDICAL CENTER
See NORTH BROWARD HOSPITAL DISTRICT

BROWARD HEALTH MEDICAL CENTER
See BROWARD GENERAL MEDICAL CENTER

D-U-N-S 07-128-9243
■ **BROWER INSURANCE AGENCY LLC**
(*Suby of* MARSH & MCLENNAN AGENCY LLC) ★
409 E Monu Ave Ste 400, Dayton, OH 45402
Tel (937) 228-4135 *Founded/Ownrshp* 2012
Sales NA *EMP* 125
SIC 6411 Insurance agents & brokers; Property & casualty insurance agent; Life insurance agents
Sr VP: Jim G Gray
Sr VP: Paul Marshall
Sr VP: Charles Murlin
VP: Marc Reynolds
Telecom Ex: John Jackson
IT Man: Rob Johnson
Mktg Dir: Scott Egbers
Snr Mgr: Brenda Taylor

D-U-N-S 00-901-0307
■ **BROWN & BROWN CHEVROLET INC** (AZ)
(*Suby of* AUTONATION ENTERPRISES INC) ★
145 E Main St, Mesa, AZ 85201-7466
Tel (480) 833-3456 *Founded/Ownrshp* 1937, 2015
Sales 107.3MM^E *EMP* 500^E
SIC 5511 5521 5012 Automobiles, new & used; Used car dealers; Automobiles & other motor vehicles
CIO: Steve Fuller
MIS Dir: Lars Nielson

D-U-N-S 00-442-9478 IMP/EXP
▲ **BROWN & BROWN INC** (ND)
220 S Ridgewood Ave # 180, Daytona Beach, FL 32114-4300
Tel (386) 252-9601 *Founded/Ownrshp* 1939
Sales NA *EMP* 7,807^E
Accts Deloitte & Touche Llp Miami
Tkr Sym BRO *Exch* NYS
SIC 6411 Property & casualty insurance agent
Ch Bd: J Hyatt Brown
Pr: J Powell Brown
CFO: R Andrew Watts
Div Pres: Chris Walker
Ofcr: Richard Freebourn Sr
Rgnl VP: P Barrett Brown
Ex VP: Sam R Boone Jr
Ex VP: Robert W Lloyd
Ex VP: J Scott Penny
Ex VP: Scott J Penny
Ex VP: Michael Riordan
Sr VP: J Neal Abernathy
Sr VP: Decker Youngman
VP: Julie Aai
VP: Janice Alexander
VP: Sharon Alexander
VP: Ty Beba
VP: Ann Brandt
VP: P Brown
VP: Kathy Colangelo
VP: Gayle Donaldson-Reitz

D-U-N-S 96-350-6923
BROWN ADVISORY HOLDINGS INC
901 S Bond St Ste 400, Baltimore, MD 21231-3340
Tel (410) 537-5400 *Founded/Ownrshp* 1998
Sales 102.0MM^E *EMP* 401^E
SIC 6282 Investment advisory service
Pr: Michael D Hankin
Board of Directors: Beatrice Hollond, Robert Murley

D-U-N-S 07-843-0256
BROWN ADVISORY LLC
901 S Bond St Ste 400, Baltimore, MD 21231-3340
Tel (410) 537-5487 *Founded/Ownrshp* 2007
Sales 105.6MM^E *EMP* 240
SIC 6211 Investment firm, general brokerage
CFO: Shannon Pierce
Bd of Dir: Gordon Rainey
Ofcr: Ryan Yu
VP: Darin Lang
Exec: Christine Baranowski
CTO: Tiffany Ernest
Sales Asso: Michael Delaney

D-U-N-S 02-916-4357
BROWN AND CALDWELL
201 N Civic Dr Ste 115, Walnut Creek, CA 94596-3865
Tel (925) 937-9010 *Founded/Ownrshp* 1944
Sales 514.2MM^E *EMP* 1,500
SIC 8711 Civil engineering; Sanitary engineers; Consulting engineer
CEO: Craig Goehring
**Pr:* Richard D' Amanto
**V Ch Bd:* James Miller
**Ofcr:* Cindy Paulson
VP: Leofwin Clark
VP: Christine Marks
VP: Victor Occiano
VP: Tracy Stigers
Sys Mgr: Bill Persich
Sls Dir: Dan Goodburn
Sls Mgr: Luci Cobb

D-U-N-S 03-786-4402
BROWN AND RIDING INSURANCE SERVICES INC
777 S Figueroa St # 2550, Los Angeles, CA 90017-5800
Tel (213) 452-7060 *Founded/Ownrshp* 1980
Sales NA *EMP* 190
SIC 6411 Insurance brokers
Ch: Chris Brown
**Pr:* Jeff Rodriguez
Bd of Dir: Nick Kuchulis
**Ex VP:* Shaida Monshi
Sr VP: Dana Cross
Sr VP: Suzanne Jensen
Sr VP: Lucy Lyons
VP: Mike Boseman
VP: Lynne Byrne
VP: George Chamblee
VP: Barbara Higgins
**VP:* Ramon C Howing
VP: Jeffrey Jarboe
**VP:* Jeff Keul
VP: Paul Nowak
VP: Guy Rawlins

D-U-N-S 10-190-5305
BROWN AUTOMOTIVE GROUP LTD
MID ATLANTIC CARS
12500 Fair Lakes Cir # 375, Fairfax, VA 22033-3804
Tel (703) 352-5555 *Founded/Ownrshp* 1983
Sales 171.6MM^E *EMP* 523
SIC 5511 Automobiles, new & used
Pr: Daniel L Legge
**Sec:* Charles S Stringfellow Jr
VP: Jeffrey Best
Sales Asso: Shane Thackston

D-U-N-S 05-502-1166
BROWN BOTTLING GROUP INC
PEPSICO
591 Highland Colony Pkwy, Ridgeland, MS 39157-8784
Tel (601) 607-3011 *Founded/Ownrshp* 1971
Sales 112.5MM^E *EMP* 300
SIC 5149

D-U-N-S 00-698-1310
BROWN BROTHERS HARRIMAN & CO
BROWN BROTHERS HARRIMAN INTL
140 Brdwy, New York, NY 10005
Tel (212) 483-1818 *Founded/Ownrshp* 1818
Sales NA *EMP* 3,000
SIC 6091 6211 Nondeposit trust facilities; Dealers, security
Pt: Glenn Edward Baker Cfa
Genl Pt: Peter Bartlett
**Pt:* Thomas E Berk
**Pt:* John J Borland
**Pt:* Timothy J Connelly
**Pt:* Geoffrey Cook
Mng Pt: Douglas A Donahue Jr
Pr: Daniel Brewer
Pr: Arun Chakraborty
Pr: John Finn
Pr: Allison Gottfried
Pr: John Kenny
Pr: Catherine O'Leary
Pr: Tammy Pittman
Pr: Dan Raines
Pr: Casey Schnurr
Pr: Gillian Whelan
COO: Annabelle Bexiga
CFO: William E Meyer
Treas: Richard Roth
Bd of Dir: Eugene Beard

BROWN BROTHERS HARRIMAN INTL
See BROWN BROTHERS HARRIMAN & CO

D-U-N-S 07-155-8787
BROWN CONSTRUCTION INC
1465 Entp Blvd Ste 100, West Sacramento, CA 95691
Tel (916) 374-8616 *Founded/Ownrshp* 2001
Sales 198.0MM^E *EMP* 71
Accts Gallina Llp Rancho Cordova
SIC 1522 1542 Apartment building construction; Nonresidential construction
Pr: Ron Brown
**CFO:* Matt Carota
**Treas:* Kathryn Mc Guire
**VP:* Matt Defazio

**VP:* Liz McCapes
Mktg Dir: Stacy Rhodes

BROWN COUNTY
See COUNTY OF BROWN

D-U-N-S 15-731-2323
BROWN COUNTY MSA CELLULAR LIMITED PARTNERSHIP
CELLCOM
(*Suby of* NSIGHT TELESERVICES) ★
1580 Mid Valley Dr, De Pere, WI 54115-8193
Tel (920) 339-4004 *Founded/Ownrshp* 1987
Sales 129.0MM^E *EMP* 400^E
SIC 4812 5999 Cellular telephone services; Telephone equipment & systems
Pt: Pat Riordan
Pr: Jim Lienau
CFO: Mark Naze
Store Mgr: Kim Pigeon
Store Mgr: Chad Vincent
IT Man: Bubb Lidke
Pr Dir: Brighid Riordan
Pr Mgr: Bonnie Cayemberg
Sls Mgr: Heather Bernhardt
Sales Asso: Adam Geiser
Sales Asso: Andrew Hecht

D-U-N-S 02-389-5246 IMP/EXP
BROWN DISTRIBUTING CO INC
1300 Allendale Rd, West Palm Beach, FL 33405-1085
Tel (561) 655-3791 *Founded/Ownrshp* 1954
Sales 131.6MM^E *EMP* 310
SIC 5181 Beer & other fermented malt liquors
Pr: Jason Brown
Treas: Reid Brown
Treas: Larry G Vaughn
VP: Jason A Brown

D-U-N-S 02-601-2203 IMP
BROWN DISTRIBUTING CO LTD
8711 Johnny Morris Rd, Austin, TX 78724-2006
Tel (512) 478-9353 *Founded/Ownrshp* 2000
Sales 153.4MM^E *EMP* 350
SIC 5181 Beer & other fermented malt liquors
CEO: Dan Brown
Pt: Scott Brown
Pt: Gayle Nixon
Pt: Laurie Watson
CFO: Hector Montes
Sales Exec: Dave Smith

BROWN FOOD SERVICE
See BROWN FOODSERVICE INC

D-U-N-S 02-416-1408
BROWN FOODSERVICE INC (KY)
BROWN FOOD SERVICE
500 E Clayton Ln, Louisa, KY 41230-8621
Tel (606) 638-1139 *Founded/Ownrshp* 1939, 1959
Sales 170.4MM^E *EMP* 150
Accts Smith Goolsby Artis & Reams
SIC 5142 5141 5084 5087 Packaged frozen goods; Groceries, general line; Food industry machinery; Janitors' supplies
CEO: John F Brown
**Pr:* Wayne Brown
Rgnl Mgr: Bill Burns
Mktg Dir: Angela Horn
Manager: Michael Warren

BROWN FORMAN BEVERAGES WORLDWI
See BROWN-FORMAN CORP

D-U-N-S 07-088-4663
BROWN FOUNDATION INC
2217 Welch St, Houston, TX 77019-5617
Tel (713) 523-6867 *Founded/Ownrshp* 1951
Sales 92.5MM *EMP* 10
SIC 6732 Charitable trust management; Educational trust management
**Ch:* Macoenda O'Connor
Bd of Dir: Katherine Dobelman
IT Man: Chereze Therkildsen

D-U-N-S 87-479-3730 IMP
BROWN INDUSTRIES INC
BROWN PRINTING
205 W Industrial Blvd, Dalton, GA 30720-7534
Tel (706) 277-1977 *Founded/Ownrshp* 1994
Sales 123.1MM^E *EMP* 400
SIC 2759 5131 2273 3552 3315 2671

D-U-N-S 07-865-0946
BROWN INTEGRATED LOGISTICS INC
6908 Chapman Rd, Lithonia, GA 30058-5246
Tel (770) 482-6521 *Founded/Ownrshp* 2007
Sales 216.2MM *EMP* 1,070^E
Accts Grant Thornton Llp Atlanta G
SIC 4225 4213 4731 7359 General warehousing & storage; Trucking, except local; Freight transportation arrangement; Industrial truck rental; Garage facility & tool rental
CEO: Brian Kinsey
**CFO:* Barbara A Leasure

D-U-N-S 04-848-7292 IMP/EXP
BROWN JORDAN CO (DE)
(*Suby of* BROWN JORDAN CO LIMITED PARTNERSHIP) ★
20 Kingbrook Pkwy, Simpsonville, KY 40067-5625
Tel (323) 686-0951 *Founded/Ownrshp* 1949, 1995
Sales 109.3MM^E *EMP* 475
SIC 2514 2511 Metal lawn & garden furniture; Wood lawn & garden furniture
CEO: Gene Moriarty
Div Pres: James B Hardy
VP: James Fornear
VP: George Gondrezick
**VP:* Frank Taff
VP: Micky Wolk
VP: Patty Zabala

D-U-N-S 94-779-6249 IMP/EXP
BROWN JORDAN CO LIMITED PARTNERSHIP
(*Suby of* WINSTON FURNITURE CO ALA) ★
9860 Gidley St, El Monte, CA 91731-1138
Tel (626) 443-8971 *Founded/Ownrshp* 2001

Sales 109.3MM^E *EMP* 500
SIC 2511 2514 Wood lawn & garden furniture; Metal lawn & garden furniture
Pt: Bruce Albertson
Prin: Brown Jordan
Opers Mgr: John Whitlock

D-U-N-S 87-970-4773 IMP/EXP
BROWN JORDAN INTERNATIONAL INC
WINSTON FURNITURE COMPANY ALA
475 W Town Pl Ste 200, Saint Augustine, FL 32092-3653
Tel (336) 622-2201 *Founded/Ownrshp* 1999
Sales 533.3MM^E *EMP* 2,000
SIC 2512 2514 Chairs: upholstered on wood frames; Couches, sofas & davenports: upholstered on wood frames; Metal household furniture; Metal lawn & garden furniture; Metal kitchen & dining room furniture
Pr: Gene J Moriarty
**V Ch:* James R Malone
Pr: Dave Biancofiore
Pr: Chris Carmicle
Pr: Bill Echols
**Pr:* William Echols
Pr: Jerry Shilling
Pr: Craig Watts
**COO:* Frederick King
**CFO:* Vincent A Tortorici
Ch: Jim Pepping
**Ex VP:* John Conely
Ex VP: Randy Danielson
**Ex VP:* John W Frederick
VP: James Hall
**VP:* Willard Kennedy
Board of Directors: James D Carreker, Robert H Dickinson, Peter Vandenberg Jr

BROWN PRINTING
See BROWN INDUSTRIES INC

BROWN SHOE CLOSET
See BG RETAIL LLC

D-U-N-S 80-854-7272
BROWN STRAUSS INC
BROWN STRAUSS STEEL
2495 Uravan St, Aurora, CO 80011-3539
Tel (303) 371-2200 *Founded/Ownrshp* 2016
Sales 83.1MM^E *EMP* 240
SIC 5051 Steel
Pr: Ryan Secrist
**CFO:* Michael Dorsey
**VP:* Ren Showalter
Genl Mgr: Chris Gunderson
**Genl Mgr:* Jay Kessler
Opers Mgr: Rick Geller
**VP Sls:* Robert Beall
Sls Mgr: Bob Beall
Sls Mgr: Matt McClain
Sls Mgr: Leslie Northrup
Sales Asso: Ken White

BROWN STRAUSS STEEL
See BROWN STRAUSS INC

BROWN STRAUSS STEEL DIVISION
See BLUE TEE CORP

D-U-N-S 00-178-5542 IMP
BROWN UNIVERSITY IN PROVIDENCE IN STATE OF RHODE ISLAND AND PROVIDENCE PLANTATIONS
1 Prospect St, Providence, RI 02912-9127
Tel (401) 863-1000 *Founded/Ownrshp* 1764
Sales 771.3MM *EMP* 5,100
Accts Kpmg Llp Providence Ri
SIC 8221 University
CEO: Christina Paxson
**Pr:* Shelia Blumstein
Ofcr: Alan Daniels
Ofcr: Ahmad Daraghmeh
Ofcr: David Dewolfe
Ofcr: Joshua Giaccotto
Ofcr: Elizabeth Goldberg
Ofcr: Emily Murphy
Ofcr: Drew Nagle
Ofcr: Jennifer Rosenberg
Ofcr: Jennifer Scruggs
Ofcr: Jennifer Trayner
Ofcr: Christine Wang
Ofcr: Cynthia Yang
**Ex VP:* Russell Carey
Ex VP: Russell C Carey
**Ex VP:* Barbara Chernow
Ex VP: Elizabeth C Huidekoper
**Sr VP:* Patricia A Watson
VP: Maria Boccardi
VP: Cass Cliatt

BROWN-DAUB CHRYSLERG JEEP DDGE
See BROWN-DAUB INC

D-U-N-S 01-404-5751
BROWN-DAUB INC
BROWN-DAUB CHRYSLERG JEEP DDGE
3903 Hecktown Rd, Easton, PA 18045-2363
Tel (610) 253-3521 *Founded/Ownrshp* 1936
Sales 139.9MM^E *EMP* 370
SIC 5511

D-U-N-S 00-637-9812 IMP/EXP
▲ BROWN-FORMAN CORP
BROWN FORMAN BEVERAGES WORLDWI
850 Dixie Hwy, Louisville, KY 40210-1038
Tel (502) 585-1100 *Founded/Ownrshp* 1870
Sales 4.0MMM *EMP* 4,400
Tkr Sym BFB *Exch* NYS
SIC 2085 2084 2449 Bourbon whiskey; Rye whiskey; Brandy & brandy spirits; Wine cellars, bonded: engaged in blending wines; Barrels, wood: coopered
CEO: Paul C Varga
Ch Bd: George Garvin Brown IV
V Ch: William Street
Pr: Stephane Cantin
Pr: Graham Jackson
CFO: Karen Krinock
CFO: Jane C Morreau
Ex VP: James L Bareuther
Ex VP: Matthew E Hamel
Ex VP: Mark I McCallum
Ex VP: Lawson E Whiting
Ex VP: Cynthia Williams
Sr VP: Brian P Fitzgerald
Sr VP: John Hayes
Sr VP: Philip A Lichtenfels
Sr VP: Tim Nall
Sr VP: Lisa P Steiner
VP: Jane Adam
VP: Gerry Anderson
VP: Mary Barrazotto
VP: Cheryl Beckman
Board of Directors: Michael A Todman, Joan C Lordi Amble, Martin S Brown, Stuart R Brown, Bruce L Byrnes, Patrick Bousquet-Chavanne, John D Cook, Sandra A Frazier, Augusta Brown Holland, Michael J Roney

D-U-N-S 18-273-7015
BROWNE BOTTLING CO INC
2712 Tealwood Dr, Oklahoma City, OK 73120-1705
Tel (405) 232-1158 *Founded/Ownrshp* 1987
Sales 61.8MM^E *EMP* 1,200
SIC 2086 Soft drinks: packaged in cans, bottles, etc.
Ch Bd: Stephen B Browne
VP: Stephen R Kerr
Dir IT: Joanne McCartey

D-U-N-S 00-530-2385 IMP
BROWNELLS INC (IA)
200 S Front St, Montezuma, IA 50171-1184
Tel (641) 623-5401 *Founded/Ownrshp* 1939
Sales 246.1MM^E *EMP* 241^E
SIC 5091 5941 Hunting equipment & supplies; Ammunition, sporting; Firearms, sporting; Sporting goods & bicycle shops
Ch Bd: Frank R Brownell III
**Pr:* Peter R Brownell
**Pr:* Brownell Peter R
Web Prj Mg: Parker Stoner
Sls&Mrk Ex: Elisa Bardole

D-U-N-S 00-736-6438 IMP
■ BROWNING-FERRIS INDUSTRIES INC (DE)
(*Suby of* REPUBLIC SERVICES) ★
18500 N Allied Way # 100, Phoenix, AZ 85054-3101
Tel (480) 627-2700 *Founded/Ownrshp* 1970, 1928
Sales 2.2MMM^E *EMP* 8,554^E
SIC 4953 4959 7359 Refuse systems; Garbage: collecting, destroying & processing; Rubbish collection & disposal; Sanitary landfill operation; Sanitary services; Portable toilet rental
Ch Bd: Thomas V Weelden
**Ch Bd:* Thomas Van Weelden
CFO: Robin Mota
**CFO:* Thomas W Ryan
Ofcr: Edward Evans
Ex VP: Timothy Donovan
**Sr VP:* Peter S Hathaway
VP: Chris Synek
Exec: Brent Killough
Exec: Claudia Pasek
Exec: Jennifer Ruminski

D-U-N-S 06-353-1792
■ BROWNING-FERRIS INDUSTRIES OF CALIFORNIA INC
(*Suby of* BROWNING-FERRIS INDUSTRIES INC) ★
9200 Glenoaks Blvd, Sun Valley, CA 91352-2613
Tel (818) 790-5410 *Founded/Ownrshp* 1972
Sales 255.5MM^E *EMP* 1,000
SIC 4953 Garbage: collecting, destroying & processing
Pr: Don Swierenga

D-U-N-S 03-478-6962
■ BROWNING-FERRIS INDUSTRIES OF TENNESSEE INC
ALLIED WASTE SERVICES MEMPHIS
(*Suby of* BROWNING-FERRIS INDUSTRIES INC) ★
3840 Homewood Rd, Memphis, TN 38118-6131
Tel (901) 794-3800 *Founded/Ownrshp* 1970
Sales 297.3MM^E *EMP* 900
SIC 4953 Refuse collection & disposal services
Dist Mgr: Barry Thomas

D-U-N-S 18-883-9849
BROWNS SUPER STORES INC
SHOPRITE OF ROXBOROUGH
700 Delsea Dr, Westville, NJ 08093-1229
Tel (856) 933-7000 *Founded/Ownrshp* 1988
Sales 227.7MM^E *EMP* 2,200
SIC 5411 Supermarkets, chain
Pr: Jeffrey Brown
CFO: Steve Prusienski
Board of Directors: Paul Brauer

D-U-N-S 83-104-2069
BROWNSTEIN HYATT FARBER SCHRECK LLP
410 17th St Ste 2200, Denver, CO 80202-4432
Tel (303) 223-1100 *Founded/Ownrshp* 2007
Sales 87.2MM^E *EMP* 510^E
SIC 8111 Legal services
Pt: Norman Philip Brownstein
Pt: Steve Farber
Mng Pt: Bruce James
COO: Wayne Forman
COO: Dean Nakayama
Exec: Karen Godfrey
Off Mgr: Robin Gomez
Off Mgr: Portia M Williams
Dir IT: Meg Harrington
Counsel: David P Cohen
Counsel: Nathaniel Friends

D-U-N-S 03-091-7579
BROWNSVILLE INDEPENDENT SCHOOL DISTRICT
BISD
1900 E Price Rd, Brownsville, TX 78521-2495
Tel (956) 548-8000 *Founded/Ownrshp* 1915
Sales 373.8MM^E *EMP* 7,500
Accts Pattillo Brown & Hill Llp B
SIC 8211 Public elementary & secondary schools
**CFO:* Lucio Mendoza
CFO: Miguel Salinas
Bd of Dir: Caty Presas-Garcia
Trst: Gloria Garza
VP: Delia N Rodriguez
Exec: Cassandra Abete
Exec: Christina Frausto
Exec: Sandra Saldana
Exec: Claudia Toro
Dir Sec: Oscar Garcia
Genl Mgr: Mary Garza

BROWNSVILLE PUBLIC UTILITIES B
See PUBLIC UTILITIES BOARD

D-U-N-S 18-777-8295 IMP
BROWNWOOD HOSPITAL LP
BROWNWOOD REGIONAL MEDICAL CTR
1501 Burnet Rd, Brownwood, TX 76801-8520
Tel (325) 646-8541 *Founded/Ownrshp* 1969
Sales 104.5MM *EMP* 596
SIC 8062 General medical & surgical hospitals
CEO: Claude E Camp III
Chf Rad: Henry McGowen
Dir Vol: Donna Hair
COO: Doug Garner
CFO: John Montoise
VP: Tammy Means
Exec: Jackie McClure
Dir Risk M: Cynthia Scott
Dir QC: Misty Woodard
Opers Mgr: Travis Noble
Pathlgst: Deanna D Belli

BROWNWOOD REGIONAL MEDICAL CTR
See BROWNWOOD HOSPITAL LP

D-U-N-S 07-213-4786
BROX INDUSTRIES INC (MA)
1471 Methuen St, Dracut, MA 01826-5499
Tel (978) 454-9105 *Founded/Ownrshp* 1982
Sales 233.1MM^E *EMP* 175
SIC 1442 1499 1611 1629 1794 2951 Construction sand mining; Gravel mining; Asphalt mining & bituminous stone quarrying; Highway & street paving contractor; Land clearing contractor; Excavation work; Asphalt paving mixtures & blocks
Pr: Stephen M Brox
CFO: Cecilia P Nickerson
VP: George C Brox
Div Mgr: Roy Fagan
Sfty Dirs: Victor Goulet
Board of Directors: Frank A Brox, Raymond L Brox

BROYHILL FURNITURE
See BFI WIND DOWN INC

D-U-N-S 07-634-9922 IMP/EXP
BRP US INC
(*Suby of* BOMBARDIER PRODUITS RECREATIFS INC)
10101 Science Dr, Sturtevant, WI 53177-1718
Tel (715) 842-8886 *Founded/Ownrshp* 1995
Sales 1.2MMM^E *EMP* 6,951
SIC 3732 Motorboats, inboard or outboard: building & repairing
CEO: Jos Boisjoli
Exec: Michael Galster
Rgnl Mgr: Michael Flesner
Dist Mgr: Sonny Schoffen
Opers Mgr: Kira Blaski
Ql Cn Mgr: Brandon Gauntt
Mktg Dir: Christopher Berg
Sls Dir: AVI Laub
Sls Mgr: Mark Benson
Sls Mgr: Larry Chisholm
Sls Mgr: Stefan Desfosses

D-U-N-S 94-851-9582
BRRH CORP
BOCA RATON COMMUNITY HOSPITAL
800 Meadows Rd, Boca Raton, FL 33486-2304
Tel (561) 395-7100 *Founded/Ownrshp* 1962
Sales 1.7MM *EMP* 1,400
Accts Crowe Horwath Llp Fort Lauder
SIC 8062 8082 8099 General medical & surgical hospitals; Home health care services; Blood related health services
Pr: Jerry J Fedele
**Ch Bd:* Bud Osborne
**Pr:* Randolph Pierce
**Ch:* Christine E Lynn
**Treas:* Dawn Javersack
**VP:* Susie McGibany
Ansthlgy: Burak Ilsin
Nutrtnst: Leslie Burman

D-U-N-S 07-125-5657 EXP
BRUCE OAKLEY INC
3700 Lincoln Ave, North Little Rock, AR 72114-6448
Tel (501) 945-0875 *Founded/Ownrshp* 1968
Sales 1.2MMM *EMP* 720
SIC 4449 5153 5261 5191 4213 River transportation, except on the St. Lawrence Seaway; Grains; Fertilizer; Fertilizer & fertilizer materials; Trucking, except local
Pr: Dennis B Oakley
COO: Steve Taylor
**CFO:* Tim Cummins
CFO: Paul Janoush
**VP:* David Choate
VP: Skip McGriff
VP: Bruce Oakley
**VP:* Edward S Bubba Vance
**VP:* Benny Weatherford
Genl Mgr: Anita Walker
Manager: Mark Wade

D-U-N-S 06-597-6651
BRUCE PACKING CO INC
BRUCEPAC
(*Suby of* JDB INC) ★
380 S Pacific Hwy 99e, Woodburn, OR 97071-5931
Tel (503) 874-3000 *Founded/Ownrshp* 2000
Sales 168.0MM^E *EMP* 800^E
SIC 2013 Cooked meats from purchased meat
Pr: Glen Golomski
**CFO:* Kristan Hoke
**VP:* Terry Buford
Opers Mgr: Cameron Cooper
Ql Cn Mgr: Scott Maddux
Ql Cn Mgr: Monica McLaughlin
Sls Dir: Rick Wiser

BRUCE PLUMBING SUPPLY
See BRUCE SUPPLY CORP

D-U-N-S 00-336-4239
BRUCE SEIBELS & CO (SC)
(*Suby of* BRUCE SEIBELS GROUP INC) ★
1501 Lady St, Columbia, SC 29201-3401
Tel (803) 748-2000 *Founded/Ownrshp* 1869, 1910
Sales NA *EMP* 200
SIC 6411 Insurance agents
CEO: Charles H Powers
**CFO:* Bryan D Rivers
VP: Michael A Culberton
VP: Terry E Fields
**VP:* Matthew McClure
Dir Risk M: Adrian Brown
QA Dir: Lisa Sease
QA Dir: Brandon Watts
Web Dev: Nicole Benson
Web Dev: Jeff Christowski
Opers Mgr: Mark Solazzo

D-U-N-S 09-499-4399
BRUCE SEIBELS GROUP INC
1501 Lady St, Columbia, SC 29201-3401
Tel (803) 748-2000 *Founded/Ownrshp* 1869
Sales NA *EMP* 225
SIC 6331 6321 6311 Fire, marine & casualty insurance & carriers; Accident insurance carriers; Health insurance carriers; Fraternal life insurance organizations
Ch Bd: Rex W Huggins
Pr: Michael A Culbertson
COO: John F Gibson
Treas: Bryan D Rivers
Assoc VP: Jennifer C Zuniga
VP: Nan D Brunson
VP: Stephen Harding
VP: Clarence E Lee
Dir Risk M: Adrian E Brown
Prin: John F Seibert
CIO: Helmut Tissler

D-U-N-S 04-917-8692 IMP
BRUCE SUPPLY CORP
BRUCE PLUMBING SUPPLY
8805 18th Ave, Brooklyn, NY 11214-4692
Tel (718) 259-4900 *Founded/Ownrshp* 1969
Sales 135.0MM^E *EMP* 100
SIC 5074 Plumbing fittings & supplies; Heating equipment (hydronic)
Pr: Bruce Wecksler
**VP:* Joseph Wecksler

BRUCEPAC
See BRUCE PACKING CO INC

D-U-N-S 04-720-1157
BRUCETON FARM SERVICE INC
BFS FOODS
1768 Mileground Rd, Morgantown, WV 26505-3753
Tel (304) 291-6980 *Founded/Ownrshp* 1974
Sales 120.0MM^E *EMP* 350
Accts Schneider Downs Pittsburgh P
SIC 5411 5172 5999 5983 5812 2048 Convenience stores, independent; Diesel fuel; Gasoline; Feed & farm supply; Fuel oil dealers; Eating places; Prepared feeds
CEO: Marshall Bishop
VP: Bradley J Groves
**Prin:* Carolyn Randolph

D-U-N-S 83-829-4478
BRUCKMANN ROSSER SHERRILL & CO INC
B R S
126 E 56th St Fl 29, New York, NY 10022-3691
Tel (212) 521-3700 *Founded/Ownrshp* 1995
Sales 610.8MM^E *EMP* 7,819
SIC 6726 Investment offices
VP: Paul D Kaminski
Mng Dir: Thomas J Baldwin
**Mng Dir:* Tom Baldwin
**Mng Dir:* Bruce Bruckmann
**Mng Dir:* Nicholas R Sheppard
Mng Dir: Stephen Sherrill

D-U-N-S 00-738-3904
BRUCKNER TRUCK SALES INC (TX)
9471 E Interstate 40, Amarillo, TX 79118-6960
Tel (806) 376-6273 *Founded/Ownrshp* 1932
Sales 524.0MM *EMP* 900
Accts Clifton Larson Allen Llp Dall
SIC 5511 Trucks, tractors & trailers: new & used
Pr: Brian M Bruckner
**CFO:* Wesley L Lawhorn
**Ex VP:* Chris B Bruckner
**VP:* Keith Martin
**VP:* Brian Murphy
Board of Directors: Brian M Bruckner, Chris B Bruckner, John Deason, Charles King, Wesley L Lawhorn, Keith Martin, Brian Murphy

BRUEGGER'S BAGELS
See FLOUR CITY BAGELS INC

D-U-N-S 13-695-9371
BRUEGGERS ENTERPRISES INC
12201 Merit Dr Ste 900, Dallas, TX 75251-3139
Tel (802) 660-4020 *Founded/Ownrshp* 1983
Sales 246.5MM^E *EMP* 2,400
SIC 5461 Bagels
CEO: James J Greco
**Pr:* David T Austin
**CFO:* Robert Parette
**VP:* Scott D Berkman
**VP:* Chris Cheek
VP: Mark Elsmore
**VP:* Kim A Nastri
**VP:* Donald J Ritacca
**VP:* John C Wadhams

D-U-N-S 13-450-5978 IMP
▲ BRUKER CORP
40 Manning Rd, Billerica, MA 01821-3915
Tel (978) 663-3660 *Founded/Ownrshp* 2000
Sales 1.6MMM *EMP* 6,000^E
Tkr Sym BRKR *Exch* NGS
SIC 3826 3844 Spectrometers; Mass spectrometers; X-ray apparatus & tubes
Ch Bd: Frank H Laukien
Pr: Rene Lenggenhager

Pr: Mark R Munch
Pr: Juergen Srega
CFO: Anthony L Mattacchione
VP: Joe Anacleto
VP: Michael G Knell
VP: Anthony Mattacchione
Genl Mgr: Lisa McDaniel
Genl Mgr: George Tang
CTO: Lindsey Linnell
Board of Directors: Robert Rosenthal, Stephen W Fesik, Chris Van Ingen, Cynthia M Friend, Marc A Kastner, Richard D Kniss, William A Linton, Gilles J Martin, John Ornell, Richard A Packer, Hermann Requardt

D-U-N-S 87-729-8661 IMP
■ **BRUKER DALTONICS INC**
(*Suby of* BRUKER CORP) ★
40 Manning Rd, Billerica, MA 01821-3915
Tel (978) 667-9580 *Founded/Ownrshp* 1991
Sales 185.0MM^E *EMP* 670
SIC 3826 5049 Spectrometers; Analytical instruments
CEO: Frank H Laukien
**COO:* Joerg Laukien
**CFO:* John J Hulburt CPA
**Treas:* Michael G Knell
**Treas:* David E Plunkett
VP: Hans Baum
**VP:* Ulrich Giessmann PHD
**VP:* Gary Kruppa
VP: Giessmann Ulrich
**VP:* John Wronka PHD
Mktg Dir: Deepak Sharma

D-U-N-S 04-386-5930 EXP
BRUMOS MOTOR CARS INC (FL)
10231 Atlantic Blvd, Jacksonville, FL 32225-6602
Tel (904) 724-1080 *Founded/Ownrshp* 1960, 1990
Sales 121.2MM^E *EMP* 350
SIC 5511

D-U-N-S 11-315-2011
BRUNDAGE-BONE CONCRETE PUMPING INC
6461 Downing St, Denver, CO 80229-7225
Tel (303) 289-4444 *Founded/Ownrshp* 2014
Sales 133.8MM^E *EMP* 477
SIC 1771

D-U-N-S 12-159-7462 IMP
BRUNO INDEPENDENT LIVING AIDS INC
1780 Executive Dr, Oconomowoc, WI 53066-4830
Tel (262) 953-5405 *Founded/Ownrshp* 1987
Sales 94.6MM^E *EMP* 300
SIC 3842 Technical aids for the handicapped; Orthopedic appliances
Pr: Michael Bruno II
**VP:* Beverly Bruno
Exec: Jan Gregg
DP Exec: Bob Herold
Sys Mgr: R Hildebran
Mfg Mgr: Alan Karch
Plnt Mgr: Rory Lamp
Prd Mgr: Jerry Gnabasik
Pr Dir: Jay Schroeter
Mktg Mgr: Kandi Albright
Mktg Mgr: Anne Moore

D-U-N-S 19-601-8352 IMP/EXP
BRUNSWICK BOWLING PRODUCTS LLC
(*Suby of* BBP INVESTMENT HOLDINGS, LLC)
525 W Laketon Ave, Muskegon, MI 49441-2601
Tel (231) 725-3300 *Founded/Ownrshp* 1986
Sales 108.9MM^E *EMP* 500
SIC 3949 Sporting & athletic goods; Bowling equipment & supplies; Bowling alleys & accessories
Pr: Brent Perrier
Pr: Austin Rothbard
**CFO:* Corey Dykstra
VP: Philip Hahn
IT Man: Cheyney Rushing
Mktg Mgr: Jen Waldo

D-U-N-S 00-227-0239 IMP/EXP
BRUNSWICK CELLULOSE LLC
(*Suby of* GP CELLULOSE LLC) ★
1400 9th St, Brunswick, GA 31520-3240
Tel (912) 265-5780 *Founded/Ownrshp* 2004
Sales 228.8MM^E *EMP* 700
SIC 2611 2421 2899 2631 Pulp produced from wood base; Sawmills & planing mills, general; Sodium chloride, refined; Paperboard mills
CEO: Patrick J Boushka
**Pr:* W Wesley Jones
**CFO:* Martin D Agard
Sfty Mgr: Steve Kirk

D-U-N-S 00-130-7636
▲ **BRUNSWICK CORP**
1 N Field Ct, Lake Forest, IL 60045-4811
Tel (847) 735-4700 *Founded/Ownrshp* 1845
Sales 4.1MMM *EMP* 12,692
Accts Deloitte And Touche Llp Chica
Tkr Sym BC *Exch* NYS
SIC 3519 3732 3949 7933 5091 Outboard motors; Marine engines; Boats, fiberglass: building & repairing; Motorboats, inboard or outboard: building & repairing; Sporting & athletic goods; Reels, fishing; Rods & rod parts, fishing; Bowling alleys & accessories; Bowling centers; Billiard equipment & supplies
Ch Bd: Mark D Schwabero
Pr: William J Barrington
Pr: Tzau J Chung
Pr: Andrew E Graves
Pr: William J Gress
Pr: Peter B Hamilton
Pr: Robert J Parmentier
Pr: John C Pfeifer
Pr: Nick Stickler
Pr: John E Stransky
Pr: Keri A Theophilus
Pr: Cynthia M Trudell
Pr: John W S Ward
COO: James Orcutt
COO: James Panici
COO: Stephen M Wolpert
CFO: Peter Hamilton
CFO: William L Metzger
Treas: Bill Metzger
Chf Mktg O: Anne Belec
Ofcr: Brenna Preisser

D-U-N-S 10-005-8213
BRUNSWICK COUNTY BOARD OF EDUCATION
35 Referendum Dr Ne, Bolivia, NC 28422-7578
Tel (910) 253-2900 *Founded/Ownrshp* 1880
Sales 78.9MM^E *EMP* 2,000
SIC 8211 School board
Ch: Olaf Thorsen

D-U-N-S 07-967-6497
BRUNSWICK COUNTY SCHOOLS
35 Referendum Dr Ne, Bolivia, NC 28422-7578
Tel (910) 253-2900 *Founded/Ownrshp* 2015
Sales 20.9MM^E *EMP* 1,921^E
SIC 8211 Public elementary & secondary schools
V Ch: Olaf Thorsen
Bd of Dir: John Thompson
Ofcr: John Rogers
Ex Dir: Susan Rutledge
Info Man: Heather Whiting
Pr Dir: Jessica Swencki
Teacher Pr: Jerry Oates
Instr Medi: Acacia Dixon
Psych: Sara Predieri
HC Dir: Helen Davis
Pgrm Dir: Reeda Hargrove

D-U-N-S 05-255-2288
BRUNSWICK ELECTRIC MEMBERSHIP CORP
795 Ocean Hwy W, Supply, NC 28462-4057
Tel (910) 754-4391 *Founded/Ownrshp* 1939
Sales 162.0MM *EMP* 150
SIC 4911 Distribution, electric power
CEO: Robert W Leavitt
**Pr:* Hubert Brittian
VP: Don Hughes
**VP:* Joann B Simmons
Genl Mgr: Rob Michel

D-U-N-S 06-337-4565 IMP/EXP
BRUNSWICK FAMILY BOAT CO INC
US MARINE
17825 59th Ave Ne, Arlington, WA 98223-6452
Tel (360) 435-5571 *Founded/Ownrshp* 1986
Sales NA *EMP* 1,635
SIC 3732

D-U-N-S 06-433-9769
BRUNSWICK NOVANT MEDICAL CENTER
NOVANT HEALTH BRUNSWICK MEDICA
240 Hospital Dr Ne, Bolivia, NC 28422-8346
Tel (336) 277-1120 *Founded/Ownrshp* 2011
Sales 94.2MM *EMP* 237
SIC 8011 Medical centers
Prin: Paul Genson
**Pr:* Shelbourn Stevens

D-U-N-S 00-598-2095 IMP
■ **BRUSS CO** (IL)
GOLDEN TROPHY STEAKS
(*Suby of* TYSON FRESH MEATS INC) ★
3548 N Kostner Ave, Chicago, IL 60641-3898
Tel (773) 282-2900 *Founded/Ownrshp* 1937, 1997
Sales 140.7MM^E *EMP* 230
SIC 5147 5142 2013 2011 Meats, fresh; Meat, frozen: packaged; Sausages & other prepared meats; Meat packing plants
Pr: Donnie Smith
CFO: Michael Porcoro
**VP:* Dan Bernkopf
**Prin:* Anthony Cericoa
Genl Mgr: Anthony Cericola
Sfty Mgr: Lorri Baker

D-U-N-S 02-035-4718
BRYAN CAVE LLP
1 Metropolitan Sq, Saint Louis, MO 63102-2723
Tel (314) 259-2000 *Founded/Ownrshp* 1873
Sales 435.5MM^E *EMP* 2,559
SIC 8111 General practice law office
Pt: Walter L Metcalfe Jr
Pt: Irvin V Belzer
Pt: Kathie Claret
Pt: Anthony N Fiducia
Pt: Dennis C Fleischmann
Pt: Steven M Kornblau
Pt: Jilali Maazouz
Pt: Steven H Sunshine
Pt: Frank P Wolff
Mng Pt: Constantin Achillas
Mng Pt: Vincent Alfieri
Mng Pt: Marcy J Bergman
Mng Pt: William Perry Brandt
Mng Pt: Eckart Budelmann
Mng Pt: Robin R Dubas
Mng Pt: Keith A Dunsmore
Mng Pt: Jennifer A Jackson
Mng Pt: Joseph O McCoy
Mng Pt: Lynn S McCreary
Mng Pt: Randall H Miller
Mng Pt: Ladawn Naegle

D-U-N-S 07-979-8879
BRYAN COUNTY SCHOOLS
8810 Us Highway 280 E, Black Creek, GA 31308-5615
Tel (912) 851-4000 *Founded/Ownrshp* 2015
Sales 9.8MM^E *EMP* 1,100^E
SIC 8211 Public elementary & secondary schools
HC Dir: Trey Robertson

D-U-N-S 83-032-3338
BRYAN HEALTH
1600 S 48th St, Lincoln, NE 68506-1299
Tel (402) 481-1111 *Founded/Ownrshp* 1985
Sales 6.5MM *EMP* 4,344
SIC 8062 General medical & surgical hospitals
Pr: Kimberly Russel
**Ch Bd:* Gene Brake
**V Ch:* Steven Erwin
COO: John T Woodrich
**Trst:* David Dyke MD
**Trst:* Jon Hinrichs MD
**Trst:* Andrew Hove Jr
**Trst:* Jack Huck
**Trst:* William Lester
**Trst:* Prem Paul Dvm
**Trst:* Donde Plowman PHD
**Trst:* Renee Sjulin
Top Exec: Hal Smith
Dir Rx: Jerome Wohleb
Board of Directors: R L Wilson

D-U-N-S 03-507-0317
BRYAN HEALTH WEST CAMPUS
GENERALLY YOURS GIFT SHOP
2300 S 16th St, Lincoln, NE 68502-3780
Tel (402) 475-1011 *Founded/Ownrshp* 1952
Sales 481.7MM *EMP* 4,000
SIC 8062 General medical & surgical hospitals
Pr: Kim Russel
Pr: Ken Foster
**CFO:* Jennifer Lesoing
CFO: Shirley Travis
Doctor: Sharon Harms
Doctor: Vivek Kulkarni
Pharmcst: Bill Corkle
Pharmcst: Scott Pierson
Occ Thrpy: Marilyn Viehl

D-U-N-S 07-391-9615
BRYAN INDEPENDENT SCHOOL DISTRICT
101 N Texas Ave, Bryan, TX 77803-5315
Tel (979) 209-1000 *Founded/Ownrshp* 1930
Sales 158.3MM *EMP* 2,065
Accts Pattillo Brown & Hill Llp W
SIC 8211 Public elementary & secondary schools
Off Mgr: Linda Baldwin
Pr Dir: Brandon Webb
Schl Brd P: David Stasny
Psych: Catie Bushman
Psych: Sylvia Luera
HC Dir: Karen Byers

D-U-N-S 07-291-9954
BRYAN MEDICAL CENTER
(*Suby of* BRYAN HEALTH) ★
1600 S 48th St, Lincoln, NE 68506-1283
Tel (402) 481-3190 *Founded/Ownrshp* 1926
Sales 558.8MM *EMP* 3,970
SIC 8062 General medical & surgical hospitals
CEO: Kim Russel
**Pr:* Craig Ames
**CEO:* R Lynn Wilson
**CFO:* Russell Gronewold
Trst: Edward Mlinek
Ofcr: Joe Loudon
VP: Ken Foster
VP: Cathy Parker
VP: John J Trapp
Dir Lab: Christa Engel
**Ex Dir:* Keith Miller

D-U-N-S 07-832-0455
BRYAN TEXAS UTILITIES
BTU
205 E 28th St, Bryan, TX 77803-6902
Tel (979) 821-5700 *Founded/Ownrshp* 2011
Sales 143.6MM^E *EMP* 135^E
SIC 4911 Distribution, electric power
Prin: Kean Register
V Ch: Paul Turney
Treas: David Bairrington
Dir Risk M: Lee Starr
Assoc Dir: Allen Wood
Div Mgr: Ken Lindberg
IT Man: Hugh Gannon
Mktg Mgr: Carl Benner
Snr Mgr: John Hall

D-U-N-S 18-486-2977
BRYANSTON GROUP INC
BUCKHEAD HOTEL MANAGEMENT CO
1886 State Route 52 52, Hopewell Junction, NY 12533-6656
Tel (845) 223-3603 *Founded/Ownrshp* 1992
Sales 20.3MM^E *EMP* 1,200
SIC 7011 Hotels & motels
Ch Bd: Stanley Tollman
Ex VP: Brett Tollman

D-U-N-S 05-661-3599
BRYANT & STRATTON COLLEGE INC (NY)
2410 N Forest Rd Ste 101, Getzville, NY 14068-1503
Tel (716) 250-7500 *Founded/Ownrshp* 1854
Sales 60.1MM^E *EMP* 1,800
SIC 8244 Business & secretarial schools
Pr: Francis J Felser
**Ch Bd:* Bryant H Prentice III
Exec: Victoria Hernick
CTO: Frederick Zarnowski
Dir IT: Bruce Coscia
IT Man: Utku Kanik
HC Dir: Roman Yagnitinsky

BRYANT MUNGO
See TEMPERATURE EQUIPMENT CORP

D-U-N-S 10-009-7906
BRYANT SCHOOL DISTRICT 25
200 Nw 4th St, Bryant, AR 72022-3424
Tel (501) 847-5600 *Founded/Ownrshp* 1920
Sales 84.3MM *EMP* 1,200
Accts Hudson Cisno & Co Llp Litt
SIC 8211 Public elementary & secondary schools
Comm Dir: Devin Sherrill
Pr Dir: Phyllis Stewart
Occ Thrpy: Brittany Duty

D-U-N-S 06-984-7531
BRYANT UNIVERSITY
1150 Douglas Pike, Smithfield, RI 02917-1291
Tel (401) 232-6000 *Founded/Ownrshp* 1864
Sales 189.7MM^E *EMP* 725^E
Accts Kpmg Llp Boston Ma
SIC 8221 College, except junior
Pr: Ronald Machtley
VP: Barry Morrison
VP: Chris R Morse
VP: John R Saddlemire
VP: Nicole Yong
Assoc Dir: Jennifer Fusco
Ex Dir: Mary Maroney
Prgrm Mgr: Kathryn M Cantwell
Off Mgr: Diane Ruotolo
Off Admin: Elizabeth Canesi
CIO: Stan Stowik

D-U-N-S 01-114-4867
BRYCE CO LLC
(*Suby of* BRYCE CORP) ★
4505 Old Lamar Ave, Memphis, TN 38118-7033
Tel (901) 369-4400 *Founded/Ownrshp* 1999
Sales 115.8MM^E *EMP* 600
SIC 2671 Plastic film, coated or laminated for packaging
CEO: Thomas J Bryce

D-U-N-S 05-024-1371 IMP
BRYCE CORP (TN)
4505 Old Lamar Ave, Memphis, TN 38118-7063
Tel (901) 369-4400 *Founded/Ownrshp* 1969
Sales 350.0MM *EMP* 800
SIC 6719 Investment holding companies, except banks
Ch Bd: Thomas J Bryce
CFO: Ramon Marus Jr
Ex VP: Sean Bowie
Ex VP: Steve Perkins
VP: Fraser Humphreys
VP: Chris Neely
VP: Stephen Perkins
VP: Susan Rickman
VP: Bobby Scroggins
Exec: Nancy Russell
Dir Soc: John Yeganeh

BRYLANE
See FULLBEAUTY BRANDS INC

BRYLANE HOME
See FULLBEAUTY BRANDS LP

BRYMAN SCHOOL
See HIGH-TECH INSTITUTE INC

D-U-N-S 00-790-9989
▲ **BRYN MAWR BANK CORP** (PA)
801 W Lancaster Ave, Bryn Mawr, PA 19010-3305
Tel (610) 525-1700 *Founded/Ownrshp* 1986
Sales NA *EMP* 530^E
Accts Kpmg Llp Philadelphia Pennsy
Tkr Sym BMTC *Exch* NGS
SIC 6022 State commercial banks
Pr: Francis J Leto
**Ch Bd:* Britton H Murdoch
COO: Alison Eichert
CFO: Michael W Harrington
Sr Tst Off: Lisa Piergallini
Ex VP: Harry R Madeira
Sr VP: Mike Bunn
VP: J Keefer-Hugill
VP: Lynne R Lewitt
VP: John Metz
VP: Barbara Piccotti
VP: John Roman
VP: Andrew Stump
Dir Risk M: Denise Rinear
Board of Directors: Michael J Clement, Andrea F Gilbert, Wendell F Holland, Scott M Jenkins, Jerry L Johnson, David E Lees, A John May, Lynn B McKee, Frederick C Peters II

D-U-N-S 06-739-8420
BRYN MAWR COLLEGE
101 N Merion Ave, Bryn Mawr, PA 19010-2899
Tel (610) 526-5000 *Founded/Ownrshp* 1885
Sales 225.0MM *EMP* 777
SIC 8221 College, except junior
CEO: Hannah Holborn Gray
Recvr: James Kent
Recvr: Moore Verdier
**Ch Bd:* Sally Zeckhauser
**Pr:* Nancy Vickers
**Treas:* Jerry Berenson
**Treas:* John Griffith
Top Exec: Sarah Jenness
Top Exec: Camilla Mackay
Exec: Martin Mastascusa
Assoc Dir: Elizabeth K Schwartz
Dir: Martha Dean

BRYN MAWR HOSPITAL
See MAIN LINE HOSPITALS INC

D-U-N-S 82-897-4899
BRYN MAWR HOSPITAL
130 S Bryn Mawr Ave, Bryn Mawr, PA 19010-3143
Tel (610) 526-3620 *Founded/Ownrshp* 1994
Sales 297.1MM *EMP* 1^E
SIC 8742 Hospital & health services consultant
Pr: Andrea Gilbert

D-U-N-S 60-964-6393
■ **BRYN MAWR TRUST CO**
(*Suby of* BRYN MAWR BANK CORP) ★
801 W Lancaster Ave, Bryn Mawr, PA 19010-3396
Tel (610) 581-4819 *Founded/Ownrshp* 1889
Sales NA *EMP* 358
SIC 6022 State commercial banks
CEO: Ted Peters
Mng Pt: Robert McLaughlin
**Treas:* Joseph W Rebl
Ofcr: Rande Whitham
Ofcr: Jackie Womack
**Ex VP:* Alison Gers
**Ex VP:* Joseph G Keefer
Ex VP: Robert Riccardi
**Ex VP:* Robert J Ricciardi
**Ex VP:* John G Roman
Sr VP: Chip Cobb
Sr VP: Ronald Dankanich
Sr VP: James Egan
**Sr VP:* June Falcone
**Sr VP:* Richard J Fuchs
**Sr VP:* Paul M Kisler Jr
Sr VP: Donald B Kriele
Sr VP: Lynn Mander
**Sr VP:* William R Mixon
Sr VP: Anthony T Poluch
Sr VP: Bob Sammartino

D-U-N-S 08-814-9620
BRYNWOOD PARTNERS II LIMITED PARTNERSHIP
8 Sound Shore Dr Ste 265, Greenwich, CT 06830-7264
Tel (203) 622-1790 *Founded/Ownrshp* 1988
Sales 210.6MM^E *EMP* 900
SIC 6282 4731 Investment advice; Freight forwarding
CEO: Hendrik J Hartong Jr
**Genl Pt:* John T Gray
**Genl Pt:* Joan Y Mc Cabe
Mng Pt: Dario U Margve
**Pr:* Ian B Mactaggart
**CFO:* Nicholas Dicarlo
**Chf Cred:* Guy Einav

D-U-N-S 17-220-0615
BRYNWOOD PARTNERS V LIMITED PARTNERSHIP
8 Sound Shore Dr Ste 265, Greenwich, CT 06830-7264
Tel (203) 622-1790 *Founded/Ownrshp* 2004
Sales 116.1MM^E *EMP* 725
SIC 6282 1751 3442 5031 3354 Investment advice; Window & door installation & erection; Metal doors; Metal doors, sash & trim; Aluminum extruded products
Pt: Hendrik J Hartong Jr
Pt: Ian B Mactaggart
Pt: Robert Sperry

D-U-N-S 83-289-1860
BRYNWOOD PARTNERS VII LP
8 Sound Shore Dr Ste 265, Greenwich, CT 06830-7264
Tel (203) 622-1790 *Founded/Ownrshp* 1984
Sales 348.9MM^E *EMP* 560^E
SIC 6211 Security brokers & dealers
Mng Pt: Hendrik Hartong III

D-U-N-S 14-169-7651 IMP
BS LIQUIDATING LLC
BOB'S STORES DISTRIBUTION CTR
(*Suby of* EASTERN OUTFITTERS LLC) ★
160 Corporate Ct, Meriden, CT 06450-7177
Tel (203) 235-5775 *Founded/Ownrshp* 2016
Sales 589.8MM^E *EMP* 2,700
SIC 5651 Family clothing stores
CEO: Mark Walsh
Pr: Jeff Shaffer
Sr VP: Scott Hampson
VP: Rita Bertone
VP: Kevin Campbell
VP: Ava Gaunt
VP: Paula Habershaw
VP: Tom Hassell
VP: Ava Hill-Gaunt
VP: Eric Niedmann
VP: Lisa Ramos
VP: Fritsch Tracy
VP: Thomas Williams
Exec: Kathy Raczka

D-U-N-S 07-883-3331
BSA HEALTH SYSTEM OF AMARILLO LLC (TX)
(*Suby of* AHS LEGACY OPERATIONS LLC) ★
1600 Wallace Blvd, Amarillo, TX 79106-1799
Tel (806) 212-2000 *Founded/Ownrshp* 2013
Sales 10.8MM^E *EMP* 1,004^E
SIC 8062 General medical & surgical hospitals
Prin: Bob Williams

BSC
See BORDER STATES ELECTRIC SUPPLY OF MINNESOTA INC

D-U-N-S 96-052-4445 IMP/EXP
BSH HOME APPLIANCES CORP
(*Suby of* BSH HAUSGERATE GMBH)
1901 Main St Ste 600, Irvine, CA 92614-0521
Tel (949) 440-7100 *Founded/Ownrshp* 1998
Sales 564.1MM^E *EMP* 1,500
SIC 3639 Major kitchen appliances, except refrigerators & stoves
Pr: Michael Traub
Pr: Christofer Von Nagel
CFO: Guenther Knoeckel
**CFO:* Stefan Koss
CFO: Herbert Lutzke
Genl Mgr: Marc Herzfeld
Telecom Mg: Linda Muggli
IT Man: Matt Bronowski
Tech Mgr: Alex Chau
Sls Dir: Ace Ensign
Mktg Mgr: John Jackson

BSI GROUP, THE
See BI-CON SERVICES INC

D-U-N-S 08-045-0667
BSI HOLDINGS INC
2495 Uravan St, Aurora, CO 80011-3539
Tel (303) 371-2200 *Founded/Ownrshp* 2015
Sales 500.0MM *EMP* 1,130
SIC 6719 3589 5093 3715 3823 5051 Investment holding companies, except banks; Garbage disposers & compactors, commercial; Ferrous metal scrap & waste; Semitrailers for truck tractors; Humidity instruments, industrial process type; Structural shapes, iron or steel
Pr: William Kelly
**CFO:* Michael Dorsey

BSI INSPECTORATE AMERICA
See INSPECTORATE AMERICA HOLDING INC

BSN
See BIO-ENGINEERED SUPPLEMENTS & NUTRITION INC

D-U-N-S 17-633-2310 IMP
BSN SPORTS LLC
(*Suby of* VARSITY BRANDS HOLDING CO INC) ★
1901 Diplomat Dr, Farmers Branch, TX 75234-8914
Tel (972) 484-9484 *Founded/Ownrshp* 2014
Sales 745.1MM^E *EMP* 1,040
SIC 5091 Sporting & recreation goods
CEO: Adam L Blumenfeld
**Pr:* Terrence M Babilla
**CFO:* John Pitts
**Ex VP:* Kurt Hagen
**Ex VP:* Tevis Martin
VP: Michael Caravati
VP: Phil Dickman
VP: Robert Dickman
VP: Eugene Grant
Brnch Mgr: Chris Reynolds
IT Man: Lavonna Weddington

D-U-N-S 94-931-8331
▲ BSQUARE CORP
110 110th Ave Ne Ste 300, Bellevue, WA 98004-5855
Tel (425) 519-5900 *Founded/Ownrshp* 1994
Sales 106.6MM *EMP* 191^E
Tkr Sym BSQR *Exch* NGM
SIC 7371 8711 Computer software development & applications; Engineering services
Pr: Jerry D Chase
**Ch Bd:* Andrew S G Harries
CFO: Martin L Heimbigner
VP: Scott B Caldwell
VP: Scott Mahan
VP: David Wagstaff
VP: Mark D Whiteside
VP: Mark Whiteside
Prgrm Mgr: Raylene Keating
IT Man: Todd Rostalski
Sftwr Eng: Biswajit Ghosh
Board of Directors: Robert J Chamberlain, Mary Jesse, Elliott H Jurgensen Jr, William D Savoy, Kendra A Vandermeulen

D-U-N-S 13-234-3877
■ BSWIFT LLC
(*Suby of* AETNA INC) ★
10 S Riverside Plz # 1100, Chicago, IL 60606-3708
Tel (312) 261-5750 *Founded/Ownrshp* 2014
Sales NA *EMP* 140
SIC 6371 7373 Union welfare, benefit & health funds; Systems integration services
CEO: Sanjiv Anand
Pt: Judd Wagner
**CFO:* Dave Tuttle
**Ex VP:* Raymond Seaver
Sr VP: Josh Trent
VP: Chris Brewer
VP: Nancy Brock
VP: Tracey Eisman
VP: Steffan Haithcox
VP: Charlotte Stacey
Assoc Dir: Jim Ruth

D-U-N-S 60-606-2602 IMP
BT AMERICAS INC
ACUITAS DIGITAL
8951 Cypress Waters Blvd # 200, Coppell, TX 75019-4763
Tel (877) 272-0832 *Founded/Ownrshp* 1982
Sales 548.6MM^E *EMP* 3,500
SIC 8748 Telecommunications consultant
VP: Colin Spence
**CFO:* James Malcolm Dibbo

D-U-N-S 05-271-1228
BT CONFERENCING INC
(*Suby of* BT GROUP PLC)
30 Braintree Hill Park # 301, Braintree, MA 02184-8712
Tel (617) 801-6700 *Founded/Ownrshp* 2001
Sales 321.5MM^E *EMP* 620
SIC 4813 Telephone/video communications
CEO: Aaron McCormack
**Pr:* Carlos Zamora
COO: Robert Belmar
**CFO:* Bernard Barlow
CFO: Andrew Freedman
**Treas:* Garry Wardle
VP: James McCarthy
**VP:* David Stark
Dir Bus: George Sandmann
Dir Bus: Laura Soulages
Brnch Mgr: Timothy Dees

BT INFONET
See INFONET SERVICES CORP

BT PRIME MOVER
See RAYMOND-MUSCATINE INC

BT RADIANZ
See RADIANZ AMERICAS INC

D-U-N-S 83-103-8596
BTAC ACQUISITION LLC
2550 W Tyvola Rd Ste 300, Charlotte, NC 28217-4579
Tel (704) 998-3100 *Founded/Ownrshp* 2006
Sales 182.7MM^E *EMP* 3,605
SIC 5192 7822 5065 5045 Books; Television tape distribution; Tapes, audio & video recording; Computer software
CEO: Tom Morgan

D-U-N-S 83-103-8703
BTAC HOLDING CORP
2550 W Tyvola Rd Ste 300, Charlotte, NC 28217-4579
Tel (704) 998-3100 *Founded/Ownrshp* 2006
Sales 194.5MM^E *EMP* 3,603
SIC 5192 7822 5065 5045 Books; Television tape distribution; Tapes, audio & video recording; Computer software
CEO: Tom Morgan

D-U-N-S 03-150-3196
BTC WHOLESALE DISTRIBUTORS INC
100 Airview Ln, Alabaster, AL 35007-4834
Tel (205) 324-2581 *Founded/Ownrshp* 1969
Sales 201.3MM *EMP* 95
Accts Carr Riggs & Ingram Llc Birm
SIC 5194 5145 5087 5149 5122 Tobacco & tobacco products; Candy; Chewing gum; Beauty salon & barber shop equipment & supplies; Health foods; Druggists' sundries
CEO: Frank P D'Amico III

D-U-N-S 02-361-1882 IMP
■ BTD MANUFACTURING INC
(*Suby of* OTTER TAIL CORP) ★
1111 13th Ave Se, Detroit Lakes, MN 56501-3736
Tel (218) 847-4446 *Founded/Ownrshp* 1990
Sales 1.2MMM^E *EMP* 1,026
SIC 3469 3544 Metal stampings; Special dies, tools, jigs & fixtures
CEO: Paul Gintner
COO: Robert Bradford
**Treas:* Kevin G Moug
**Ex VP:* Marty Kiebke
VP: Joseph Krall
VP: Craig Rix
**VP:* Doug Small
**VP:* Dave Welte
Dir IT: Clint Bachmann
QC Dir: Chad Berg
Opers Mgr: Chelsea Manke

D-U-N-S 02-630-8515
BTD MANUFACTURING INC
177 Six Pine Ranch Rd, Batesville, IN 47006-9248
Tel (812) 934-5616 *Founded/Ownrshp* 2000
Sales 119.0MM^E *EMP* 500
SIC 3469 3544 Metal stampings; Special dies & tools; Jigs & fixtures
Pr: Jody Fledderman
Ch Bd: Ron Fledderman
VP: Ronda Green
VP: Robert Holtel
VP: Gene Lambert
VP: James Wintz
VP Mfg: Jay Fledderman

D-U-N-S 92-947-2769
BTF/CFI INC
CRUNCH FITNESS CENTER
(*Suby of* BALLY TOTAL FITNESS HOLDING CORP) ★
144 W 38th St, New York, NY 10018-5006
Tel (212) 993-0300 *Founded/Ownrshp* 2001
Sales 134.7MM^E *EMP* 2,200
SIC 6794 7991 5621 5411 Franchises, selling or licensing; Physical fitness clubs with training equipment; Aerobic dance & exercise classes; Ready-to-wear apparel, women's; Delicatessens
Ch Bd: Michael Feder
**CEO:* Keith Worts
Sr VP: Bob Dowdy
VP Prd: Inna Shamis

D-U-N-S 12-859-7833
BTIG LLC
BAYPOINT TRADING
600 Montgomery St Fl 6, San Francisco, CA 94111-2708
Tel (415) 248-2200 *Founded/Ownrshp* 2003
Sales 129.4MM^E *EMP* 330
SIC 6211 Security brokers & dealers; Security brokers & dealers; Investment firm, general brokerage
**CFO:* Brian Endres
Ofcr: Austin Hamilton
VP: Kevin McDonald
VP: Charlton W Moore
Mng Dir: Chris Casanovas
**Mng Dir:* Kevin Chessen
Mng Dir: Phil Dauber
Mng Dir: Matthew Fitzpatrick
Mng Dir: Chris Gardner
Mng Dir: Wes Gradone
Mng Dir: Brandon Hughes
Board of Directors: Daniel Howell

D-U-N-S 13-271-7567
BTS GROUP INC
2620 Sw 27th Ave, Miami, FL 33133-3005
Tel (305) 358-5850 *Founded/Ownrshp* 2001
Sales NA *EMP* 50
SIC 6159 Finance leasing, vehicles: except automobiles & trucks
CEO: Rafael Olloqui
**Pr:* Ricardo Olloqui

BTU
See BRYAN TEXAS UTILITIES

BUBBA'S
See ROVIN INC

D-U-N-S 05-217-9470
BUC-EES LTD
327 Fm 2004 Rd, Lake Jackson, TX 77566-4980
Tel (979) 230-2930 *Founded/Ownrshp* 1982
Sales 179.4MM^E *EMP* 2,313
SIC 8741

BUCA DI BEPPO
See BUCA INC

D-U-N-S 82-464-7390
BUCA INC
BUCA DI BEPPO
(*Suby of* PLANET HOLLYWOOD INTERNATIONAL INC) ★
4700 Millenia Blvd # 400, Orlando, FL 32839-6020
Tel (407) 903-5500 *Founded/Ownrshp* 2008
Sales 190.8MM^E *EMP* 5,650^E
SIC 5812 Italian restaurant
CEO: Thomas Avallone
COO: Modesto Alcala
**CFO:* Dennis J Goetz
CFO: Kaye O'Leary
CFO: Kaye R O'Leay
Ofcr: Cynthia Rodahl
Sr VP: Anthony K Jones
Sr VP: Mickey Mills
Sr VP: Lane Schmiesing
VP: Deborah Canez
VP: Jeff Friedman
VP: Eric Haseman
VP: Jason Kieser
VP: Anthony Penn
VP: Shawn Richard
VP: Tom Sorfleet
VP: David Suddath
VP: Andy Yates

D-U-N-S 04-206-0771
BUCCANEER HOLDINGS LLC
8125 Highwoods Palm Way, Tampa, FL 33647-1776
Tel (813) 637-5000 *Founded/Ownrshp* 2011
Sales 861.4MM^E *EMP* 2,538^E
SIC 4813 4812 ; Data telephone communications; Cellular telephone services
Prin: Scott Anderson

D-U-N-S 92-976-6178
BUCCINI/POLLIN GROUP INC
BPG
322 A St Ste 300, Wilmington, DE 19801-5354
Tel (302) 691-2100 *Founded/Ownrshp* 1994
Sales 256.5MM^E *EMP* 80^E
SIC 6552 Subdividers & developers
Pr: Dave Pollin
**Pr:* Greg J Miller
CFO: Barbara Neuse
**Ch:* David B Pollin
Sr VP: Darren Anzelone
**VP:* Robert Buccini
**VP:* Brandon S Flury
**Prin:* Christopher Buccini
Genl Mgr: Cathy Larson

D-U-N-S 15-459-9922
BUCH CONSTRUCTION INC
11292 Buch Way, Laurel, MD 20723-2077
Tel (301) 369-3500 *Founded/Ownrshp* 1984
Sales 189.3MM *EMP* 100
SIC 1542

BUCHANAN HAULING & RIGGING
See BUCHANAN LOGISTICS INC

D-U-N-S 06-953-1197
BUCHANAN HAULING & RIGGING INC
4625 Industrial Rd, Fort Wayne, IN 46825-5205
Tel (260) 471-1877 *Founded/Ownrshp* 1996
Sales 89.2MM^E *EMP* 160
SIC 4212 Light haulage & cartage, local
Pr: Geary Buchanan
**CFO:* Dan Rutherford
Ex VP: Becky Buchanan
**VP:* Rebecca Buchanan
VP: Sherry Collins
VP: Mike Wardzinski
Dir Risk M: Rick Hawkins
Rgnl Mgr: Jessica Pappert
IT Man: Phil Gray
VP Opers: Gary Horton
Trfc Dir: Justin Beal

D-U-N-S 07-498-2018
BUCHANAN INGERSOLL & ROONEY PC
301 Grant St Fl 20, Pittsburgh, PA 15219-1410
Tel (412) 562-8800 *Founded/Ownrshp* 1970
Sales 235.5MM^E *EMP* 1,239
SIC 8111 General practice law office
Ch Bd: Joseph A Dougherty
**Ch Bd:* John A Barbour
**COO:* Nolan W Kurtz
**CFO:* Michael J Pauvlinch
Chf Mktg O: Mark P Trice
Exec: Jennifer Minter
**CIO:* Philip Casale
Dir IT: Daniel Duffy
IT Man: Paul Dell
Mktg Dir: Shari Boyle
Genl Couns: Sue Friedberg

BUCHANAN, JOHN L MD
See CORVALLIS CLINIC P C

D-U-N-S 60-662-3556
BUCHANAN LOGISTICS INC
BUCHANAN HAULING & RIGGING
4625 Industrial Rd, Fort Wayne, IN 46825-5205
Tel (260) 471-1877 *Founded/Ownrshp* 1996
Sales 89.5MM^E *EMP* 150
SIC 4731 Freight transportation arrangement
Pr: Geary Buchanan
**Treas:* Chad Buchanan
Genl Mgr: Dave Miller
Opers Mgr: Jaclyn Miller

D-U-N-S 08-374-0782
BUCHER AND CHRISTIAN CONSULTING INC
BCFORWARD
9777 N College Ave, Indianapolis, IN 46280-1628
Tel (317) 493-2000 *Founded/Ownrshp* 1998
Sales 73.5MM^E *EMP* 1,254
SIC 7379
Pr: Justin P Christin
**VP:* Douglas R Heath
Dir Bus: Matthew Deiter
Prgrm Mgr: Lana Gallo
Snr Sftwr: Jason Carmichael
Dir IT: Nate Dotzlaf
Snr PM: Bill Baker
Snr PM: Marty McLaughlin
Board of Directors: Jim Obermaier

D-U-N-S 94-414-7131
BUCHHEIT ENTERPRISES INC
33 Pcr 540, Perryville, MO 63775-8757
Tel (573) 547-1010 *Founded/Ownrshp* 1990
Sales 175.8MM *EMP* 600
Accts Kerber Eck & Braeckel Llp C
SIC 4213 4212 5251 4225 Trucking, except local; Local trucking, without storage; Hardware; General warehousing & storage
Pr: Tim Buchheit
**Sec:* Jon Buchheit
**VP:* Nick Buchheit
VP: Eric Hasty

BUCK BROS DIVISION
See GREAT NECK SAW MANUFACTURERS INC

D-U-N-S 03-322-7695
■ BUCK CONSULTANTS LLC
XEROX
(*Suby of* A C S HUMAN RESOURCES SOLUTIONS INC) ★
485 Lexington Ave Fl 10, New York, NY 10017-2652
Tel (212) 330-1000 *Founded/Ownrshp* 1997

Sales 183.7MM[E] *EMP* 2,000
SIC 8742 6282 2741 Compensation & benefits planning consultant; Investment advice; Technical papers: publishing only, not printed on site
CEO: Michael Roberts
Sr VP: Mike Davis
Sr VP: Jim Reid
VP: Marleen Eyssen
VP: Robert Kalman
VP: Lynch Robinson
Creative D: Allison Artnak
Dir Bus: Robert Lis
Prin: Harold Loeb
Mng Dir: Steven Maxwell
**Mng Dir:* Frank Pirrone

D-U-N-S 80-258-8843
BUCK HOLDING LP
2800 Sand Hill Rd Ste 200, Menlo Park, CA 94025-7080
Tel (615) 855-5161 *Founded/Ownrshp* 2007
Sales NA *EMP* 90,000
SIC 5331

BUCKEYE CABLE SYSTEM
See BUCKEYE CABLEVISION INC

D-U-N-S 05-416-5857
BUCKEYE CABLEVISION INC (OH)
BUCKEYE CABLE SYSTEM
(*Suby of* BCI) ★
2700 Oregon Rd, Northwood, OH 43619-1057
Tel (419) 724-9802 *Founded/Ownrshp* 1965
Sales 159.8MM[E] *EMP* 400
SIC 4841 Cable & other pay television services
Pr: David Huey
**Pr:* Chip Carstensen
**CFO:* Rick Mlcek
**Ex VP:* Bradley Mefferd
**VP:* Joseph Jensen

D-U-N-S 17-367-2312
BUCKEYE CHECK CASHING INC
FIRST VIRGINIA
(*Suby of* EASY MONEY) ★
6785 Bobcat Way Ste 200, Dublin, OH 43016-1443
Tel (614) 798-5900 *Founded/Ownrshp* 2012
Sales NA *EMP* 3,000
SIC 6099 Check cashing agencies
CEO: Ted Saunders
**Pr:* Kyle Hanson

D-U-N-S 00-419-0203
BUCKEYE CORRUGATED INC (OH)
B C I
822 Kumho Dr Ste 400, Fairlawn, OH 44333-9298
Tel (330) 576-0590 *Founded/Ownrshp* 1958
Sales 196.7MM[E] *EMP* 570
SIC 2653 Boxes, corrugated: made from purchased materials
Pr: Douglas A Bosnik
Pr: Robert Butterfield
**CFO:* Mark A Husted
Admn Mgr: Deborah Wheeler
Prd Mgr: Robert Bailey
Prd Mgr: Don Laurie
Sls Mgr: Scott Barnett

D-U-N-S 19-666-5772
■ **BUCKEYE DISCOUNT INC**
(*Suby of* SPARTANNASH CO) ★
1020 Ford St, Maumee, OH 43537-1820
Tel (419) 893-9401 *Founded/Ownrshp* 1999
Sales 70.7MM[E] *EMP* 1,850
Accts Ernst & Young Llp
SIC 5912 Drug stores
Ch Bd: Wallace D Iott
**Pr:* Richard B Iott
**Treas:* Waldo E Yeager

D-U-N-S 00-532-3214
■ **BUCKEYE ENERGY SERVICES LLC**
(*Suby of* BUCKEYE PARTNERS LP) ★
1 Greenway Plz Ste 600, Houston, TX 77046-0121
Tel (832) 615-8600 *Founded/Ownrshp* 2007
Sales 88.4MM[E] *EMP* 172[E]
SIC 8748 Energy conservation consultant
Exec: Amanda Segura

D-U-N-S 04-107-2547 IMP/EXP
BUCKEYE FIRE EQUIPMENT CO
110 Kings Rd, Kings Mountain, NC 28086-2090
Tel (704) 739-7415 *Founded/Ownrshp* 1975
Sales 106.3MM[E] *EMP* 275
SIC 3569 Firefighting apparatus
Pr: Thomas J Bower
**Sec:* William Cowley
**VP:* Kevin Bower
Plnt Mgr: Ramsey Reed

D-U-N-S 80-154-4016 IMP
BUCKEYE FLORIDA LIMITED PARTNERSHIP
1 Buckeye Dr, Perry, FL 32348-7702
Tel (850) 584-1121 *Founded/Ownrshp* 1993
Sales 228.8MM[E] *EMP* 900
SIC 2611

D-U-N-S 78-433-2475
BUCKEYE GP HOLDINGS LP
1 Greenway Plz Ste 600, Houston, TX 77046-0121
Tel (832) 615-8600 *Founded/Ownrshp* 2010
Sales 135.4MM[E] *EMP* 1,877
SIC 4789 4213 4226 4212 Pipeline terminal facilities, independently operated; Liquid petroleum transport, non-local; Petroleum & chemical bulk stations & terminals for hire; Petroleum haulage, local
CEO: Forrest E Wylie
Pr: Clark C Smith
CFO: Keith E St Clair
VP: Khalid A Muslih
VP: Joe Sauger
VP: William H Schmidt Jr

D-U-N-S 07-713-2280 IMP/EXP
BUCKEYE INTERNATIONAL INC
2700 Wagner Pl, Maryland Heights, MO 63043-3400
Tel (314) 291-1900 *Founded/Ownrshp* 1975
Sales 122.2MM[E] *EMP* 295
SIC 2842 Specialty cleaning preparations
Pr: Kristopher G Kosup
CFO: John Eharhart
**VP:* Lyndons Bleeker
**VP:* Scott M Criswell
**VP:* Michael Gabrion
VP: Robert Tibbetts
Brnch Mgr: Michael Barber
Genl Mgr: Chris Haldi
Genl Mgr: Tom Lachenmaier
Genl Mgr: Darin Rhea
Natl Sales: Ryan Stewart

D-U-N-S 11-256-9892
▲ **BUCKEYE PARTNERS LP**
1 Greenway Plz Ste 600, Houston, TX 77046-0121
Tel (832) 615-8600 *Founded/Ownrshp* 1886
Sales 3.4MMM *EMP* 1,765
Accts Deloitte & Touche Llp Housto
Tkr Sym BPL *Exch* NYS
SIC 4612 4789 4226 4213 Crude petroleum pipelines; Pipeline terminal facilities, independently operated; Petroleum & chemical bulk stations & terminals for hire; Liquid petroleum transport, non-local
Ch Bd: Clark C Smith
Genl Pt: Buckeye GP LLC
CFO: Keith E St Clair
Sr VP: Todd J Russo
Opers Mgr: Christa Hopkins
Opers Mgr: Stephen W Wing
Plnt Mgr: Dusty Lawrence
Snr PM: Clayton Carlisle
Snr Mgr: Robert Benson
Snr Mgr: Lewis Collings
Snr Mgr: Dina Conway

D-U-N-S 16-099-0842
■ **BUCKEYE PIPE LINE CO L P**
(*Suby of* BUCKEYE PARTNERS LP) ★
5002 Buckeye Rd, Emmaus, PA 18049-5347
Tel (484) 232-4000 *Founded/Ownrshp* 1986
Sales 115.0MM[E] *EMP* 504
SIC 4613 Refined petroleum pipelines; Gasoline pipelines (common carriers)
Pr: William Shea
VP: Sam J Garbis
Tech Mgr: Todd Gehiringer
Sfty Dirs: Robin Gott

D-U-N-S 05-136-4057
BUCKEYE POWER INC
OHIO RURAL ELECTRIC COOPS
6677 Busch Blvd, Columbus, OH 43229-1101
Tel (614) 781-0573 *Founded/Ownrshp* 1949
Sales 639.8MM *EMP* 300
Accts Bdo Usa Llp Chicago Illino
SIC 8611 4911 Business associations; Generation, electric power
Ch Bd: Steven Nelson
**Pr:* Anthony J Ahern
Treas: Nicholas Baker
Ofcr: Jim Palmisano
**VP:* Bobby Daniel
Comm Dir: Jeff Brehm

D-U-N-S 79-831-8028 IMP/EXP
BUCKEYE TECHNOLOGIES INC
(*Suby of* GEORGIA-PACIFIC LLC) ★
1001 Tillman St, Memphis, TN 38112-2038
Tel (901) 320-8100 *Founded/Ownrshp* 2013
Sales 461.3MM[E] *EMP* 1,270
SIC 2611 3081 Pulp produced from non-wood fiber base; Pulp produced from wood base; Film base, cellulose acetate or nitrocellulose plastic
CEO: John B Crowe
**CFO:* Steven G Dean
Treas: Daryn Abercrombie
**Ex VP:* Douglas L Dowdell
**Sr VP:* Charles S Aiken
**Sr VP:* Sheila Jordan Cunningham
Sr VP: Henry P Doggrell
Sr VP: E A Eppinger
Sr VP: William M Handel
Sr VP: Michael Scheerer
VP: Darrell Adams
VP: F Gray Carter
VP: Christian Chavassieu
VP: Horst G Ttsche-K Hn
VP: Jerry Huff
VP: Phillip C Reese
Exec: Jeff Lewis
Exec: Heinz Springborn
Exec: Crystal Townsend
Dir Risk M: Mike Nelson

D-U-N-S 07-956-2867
■ **BUCKEYE TEXAS PARTNERS HOLDINGS LLC**
(*Suby of* BUCKEYE PARTNERS LP) ★
1 Greenway Plz Ste 600, Houston, TX 77046-0121
Tel (832) 615-8600 *Founded/Ownrshp* 2014
Sales 97.3MM[E] *EMP* 1,270[E]
SIC 6719 Investment holding companies, except banks
Pr: Clark C Smith

D-U-N-S 07-958-2819
■ **BUCKEYE TEXAS PARTNERS LLC**
(*Suby of* BUCKEYE TEXAS PARTNERS HOLDINGS LLC) ★
1 Greenway Plz Ste 600, Houston, TX 77046-0121
Tel (832) 615-8600 *Founded/Ownrshp* 2014
Sales 172.4MM[E] *EMP* 1,270[E]
SIC 6719 4491 Investment holding companies, except banks; Docks, piers & terminals
CEO: Clark C Smith

D-U-N-S 36-138-4279 EXP
■ **BUCKHEAD BEEF CO**
(*Suby of* BUCKHEAD BEEF CO INC) ★
355 Progress Rd, Auburndale, FL 33823-2712
Tel (863) 508-1050 *Founded/Ownrshp* 2005
Sales 225.0MM[E] *EMP* 250[E]
SIC 2011 Beef products from beef slaughtered on site
CEO: John Foster
**Ch Bd:* Ronald G Boatwright
**Pr:* Jerry Jones
**CFO:* Clay Jordan
CFO: Andrea Ling
**Sr VP:* Corry Check
**Sr VP:* Woody Ham
**Sr VP:* Chad Steine
VP: Elaine Bennett
VP: Milo Harwell
VP: Randy Johnston

D-U-N-S 10-203-0228 IMP/EXP
■ **BUCKHEAD BEEF CO INC**
(*Suby of* SYSCO CORP) ★
4500 Wickersham Dr, College Park, GA 30337-5122
Tel (404) 355-4400 *Founded/Ownrshp* 1996
Sales 202.5MM[E] *EMP* 266[E]
SIC 5142 5146 5421

BUCKHEAD HOTEL MANAGEMENT CO
See BRYANSTON GROUP INC

D-U-N-S 00-101-2319 IMP/EXP
■ **BUCKHORN INC**
(*Suby of* MYERS INDUSTRIES INC) ★
55 W Techne Center Dr A, Milford, OH 45150-9779
Tel (513) 831-4402 *Founded/Ownrshp* 1981
Sales 145.7MM[E] *EMP* 400
SIC 3089 Plastic containers, except foam
Sr VP: Joel Grant
CFO: John McFadden
Exec: Lynn Armstrong
Ex Dir: Eric T Derflinger
Dist Mgr: Kirk Pinto
QA Dir: Bill Snyder
Dir IT: Duke Duncanson
Sls Dir: Lane Pence
Sls Mgr: Stan Dunton
Sls Mgr: Ray Kuchman
Sls Mgr: Ray McKinney

D-U-N-S 03-505-5219 IMP
▲ **BUCKLE INC** (NE)
2407 W 24th St, Kearney, NE 68845-4915
Tel (308) 236-8491 *Founded/Ownrshp* 1948
Sales 1.1MMM *EMP* 8,600
Tkr Sym BKE *Exch* NYS
SIC 5661 5632 5621 5611 Shoe stores; Apparel accessories; Women's clothing stores; Ready-to-wear apparel, women's; Teenage apparel; Dress shops; Men's & boys' clothing stores; Clothing, men's & boys': everyday, except suits & sportswear; Clothing, sportswear, men's & boys'
Pr: Dennis H Nelson
**Ch Bd:* Daniel J Hirschfeld
**CFO:* Karen B Rhoads
Treas: Thomas B Heacock
Ex VP: Kari G Smith
Sr VP: Robert M Carlberg
Sr VP: Brett P Milkie
VP: Diane L Applegate
VP: Kyle L Hanson
VP: Kelli D Molczyk
Area Mgr: Angela Fiore
Board of Directors: Robert E Campbell, Bill L Fairfield, Bruce L Hoberman, Michael E Huss, John P Peetz III, James E Shada

D-U-N-S 02-927-9213
BUCKLES-SMITH ELECTRIC CO
801 Savaker Ave, San Jose, CA 95126-3712
Tel (408) 280-7777 *Founded/Ownrshp* 1979
Sales 90.9MM[E] *EMP* 100
SIC 5084 5063 Industrial machinery & equipment; Electrical supplies
CEO: Art Cook
Treas: Matt Peterson
**VP:* Pat Berry
**VP:* Roger Stanger
CTO: Carrie Smith
Opers Mgr: Rick Evans
Sales Exec: Paul Brann
Mktg Dir: Tod Whitaker
Mktg Mgr: Thea Copeland
Sls Mgr: Thomas Page
Sales Asso: Laurie Smith

D-U-N-S 96-952-3179
BUCKLEY TRANSPORT LOGISTICS INC
197 Airport Rd, Columbia, MS 39429-9041
Tel (601) 731-6309 *Founded/Ownrshp* 2001
Sales 100.0MM *EMP* 100
SIC 4213 Trucking, except local
Pr: Stacy Buckley
**VP:* Tim Buckle

D-U-N-S 18-895-3434 IMP/EXP
BUCKMAN LABORATORIES INC
(*Suby of* BUCKMAN LABS) ★
1256 N Mclean Blvd, Memphis, TN 38108-1297
Tel (901) 278-0330 *Founded/Ownrshp* 1945
Sales 127.6MM[E] *EMP* 350
SIC 2869 2819 Industrial organic chemicals; Industrial inorganic chemicals
Ch Bd: Katherine Buckman Gibson
**Pr:* James K Doan
**CFO:* David Rosenthal
**Treas:* Charles Shaw
Treas: Willy Vanhelder
**Ex VP:* Robert Obrien
**Ex VP:* Peter C Tchouros
**VP:* Michael E Alpert
VP: Michael Alpert
VP: Michael Anstey
**VP:* Charles E Carncross
VP: Shawn Frenzel
**VP:* Katherine Davis Gibson
**VP:* Stephen C Messick
Assoc Dir: Brad Walden

BUCKMAN LABS
See BULAB HOLDINGS INC

D-U-N-S 04-357-3591 IMP
BUCKMANS INC (PA)
BUCKMAN'S SKI SHOP
105 Airport Rd, Pottstown, PA 19464-3438
Tel (610) 495-7495 *Founded/Ownrshp* 1965, 2002
Sales 135.4MM[E] *EMP* 325
SIC 5169 5941

BUCKMAN'S SKI SHOP
See BUCKMANS INC

D-U-N-S 00-303-0335
BUCKNELL UNIVERSITY (PA)
1 Dent Dr, Lewisburg, PA 17837-2029
Tel (570) 577-2000 *Founded/Ownrshp* 1846
Sales 206.3MM *EMP* 1,300[E]
Accts Kpmg Llp Harrisburg Pa
SIC 8221 University
Pr: John C Bravman
Pr: Linda Clinger
Treas: Charlotte Clegg
Treas: Michael Cover
Chf Inves: Christopher Brown
Ofcr: Michael C Griffiths
Ofcr: Nathan Kahle
Ofcr: Barbara Martin
Ofcr: Patrick Ventura
VP: Sean Coyne
VP: Anthony Gingerelli
VP: Clinton Kittrell
VP: Julie Kohn
VP: Matthew McAnear
VP: Taylor McCready
VP: Lynn Pierson
VP: Lavonne Poteet
**VP:* David Surgala
Exec: Amanda Rose
Assoc Dir: Lisa Hoover

BUCKS COUNTY COURIER TIMES
See COURIER TIMES INC

D-U-N-S 02-197-3102
BUCKS COUNTY INTERMEDIATE UNIT 22
705 N Shady Retreat Rd, Doylestown, PA 18901-2507
Tel (215) 348-2940 *Founded/Ownrshp* 2007
Sales 116.9MM *EMP* 1,755
Accts Maillie Llp Oaks Pennsylvan
SIC 8651 Political organizations
Pr: Michael Hartline
V Ch: Denise Hooper
**VP:* Stephen Corr
**Ex Dir:* Dr Mark Hoffman
IT Man: Dan Lezoche
Psych: Teresa Merrigan
Psych: Amy Thomas
Occ Thrpy: Chris Churilla
Pgrm Dir: James Coyle

D-U-N-S 07-373-5979
BUCKS COUNTY OF
OFFICE OF THE CONTROLLER
55 E Court St Fl 5, Doylestown, PA 18901-4318
Tel (215) 348-6424 *Founded/Ownrshp* 1782
Sales NA *EMP* 2,500
Accts Zelenkofske Axelrod Llc Jamis
SIC 9111 Executive offices;
**Ch Bd:* Michael G Fitzpatrick
**COO:* Leader Brian Hessenthaler
**Treas:* William R Snyder

D-U-N-S 03-510-9461
BUCKS INC
AMOCO
5001 Dodge St, Omaha, NE 68132-2919
Tel (402) 558-9860 *Founded/Ownrshp* 1983
Sales 175.5MM[E] *EMP* 400
SIC 5541 Filling stations, gasoline
Pr: Steve Buchanan
**CFO:* Keil Brumit

BUCRA
See BUTTE COUNTY RICE GROWERS ASSOCIATION INC

D-U-N-S 10-149-5885
BUDCO GROUP INC
O/B LEASING COMPANY
1100 Gest St, Cincinnati, OH 45203-1114
Tel (513) 621-6111 *Founded/Ownrshp* 1982
Sales 195.1MM *EMP* 1,800
SIC 7359 Equipment rental & leasing
Pr: Otto Budig Jr
**VP:* George J Budig

D-U-N-S 02-489-1178
BUDD GROUP INC
2325 S Stratford Rd, Winston Salem, NC 27103-6223
Tel (336) 765-9324 *Founded/Ownrshp* 1964
Sales 94.2MM *EMP* 3,500
Accts Cannon & Company Llp Winston
SIC 0781 7349 Landscape services; Building cleaning service
CEO: Joseph R Budd
**Pr:* Yasser Youssef
**COO:* John Larsen
CFO: Keith Bagby
**CFO:* R Keith Bagby
**CFO:* Gerald Chrisco
VP: Claudia Martinez
Rgnl Mgr: Stephan Miller
Area Mgr: Juan Rubio
Brnch Mgr: Michael Dickson
Brnch Mgr: Jerry Ranson

BUDD MAYER OF TAMPA
See ADVANTAGE SALES & MARKETING

BUDDY'S HOME FURNISHINGS
See BUDDYS NEWCO LLC

D-U-N-S 96-262-9940
BUDDYS NEWCO LLC
BUDDY'S HOME FURNISHINGS
6608 E Adamo Dr, Tampa, FL 33619-3416
Tel (813) 623-5461 *Founded/Ownrshp* 2012
Sales 105.5MM[E] *EMP* 400
SIC 7359 6794 Furniture rental; Home entertainment equipment rental; Television rental; Franchises, selling or licensing
Ch Bd: Brian R Kahn
**Pr:* Joseph Gazzo
**CEO:* Joseph F Gazzo III

BUDGET & CTRL BD EXEC DIRS OFF
See EXECUTIVE OFFICE OF STATE OF SOUTH CAROLINA

D-U-N-S 05-768-7824
BUDGET MAINTENANCE CONCRETE SERVICES INC
135 Walnut St, Pottstown, PA 19464-5420
Tel (610) 323-7702 *Founded/Ownrshp* 1978
Sales 91.1MM^E *EMP* 300
SIC 5087 7349 Janitors' supplies; Cleaning service, industrial or commercial
Pr: John J Allen Jr
CFO: Susan Koury
**Treas:* Gerald Allen
**Sr VP:* John A Jones
Off Mgr: Stephanie Palko
Snr PM: Bill Obrien

D-U-N-S 12-678-5133 IMP
■ BUDGET RENT A CAR SYSTEM INC
BUDGET RENT-A-CAR
(*Suby of* AVIS BUDGET GROUP INC) ★
6 Sylvan Way Ste 1, Parsippany, NJ 07054-3826
Tel (973) 496-3500 *Founded/Ownrshp* 2002
Sales 251.4MM^E *EMP* 10,580
SIC 7514 Rent-a-car service
Pr: William N Plamondon
**CFO:* David B Wyshner
**Prin:* Kevin M Sheehan
CTO: Mary Lebla
Sales Exec: Torrun La Belle
Mktg Mgr: Steve Hern

BUDGET RENT-A-CAR
See BUDGET RENT A CAR SYSTEM INC

BUDGET RENT-A-CAR
See MALCO ENTERPRISES OF NEVADA INC

BUDGET RENT-A-CAR
See BUDGET TRUCK RENTAL LLC

D-U-N-S 96-363-8838
■ BUDGET TRUCK RENTAL LLC
BUDGET RENT-A-CAR
(*Suby of* AVIS BUDGET GROUP INC) ★
6 Sylvan Way Ste 1, Parsippany, NJ 07054-3826
Tel (973) 496-3500 *Founded/Ownrshp* 2004
Sales 372.5MM^E *EMP* 21,000
SIC 7514 Rent-a-car service
Sr VP: Joe Ferraro
Sr VP: Karen Sclafani
VP: Eric Schlanger
Exec: Elaine Vitale
IT Man: Holly Hurdle

BUDS POLICE SUPPLY
See BUDSGUNSHOP.COM LLC

D-U-N-S 00-306-2136 IMP
BUDSGUNSHOP.COM LLC
BUDS POLICE SUPPLY
1105 Industry Rd, Lexington, KY 40505-3846
Tel (859) 368-0371 *Founded/Ownrshp* 2007
Sales 150.0MM *EMP* 125
SIC 5941 Firearms
**CFO:* Michael Crooker
Opers Mgr: Doug Ramsey

D-U-N-S 00-893-1412 IMP
BUEHLER FOOD MARKETS INC
BUEHLER'S
(*Suby of* E&H FAMILY GROUP INC) ★
1401 Old Mansfield Rd, Wooster, OH 44691-9050
Tel (330) 264-4355 *Founded/Ownrshp* 1947
Sales 382.1MM^E *EMP* 2,500
SIC 5411 Supermarkets, chain
Pr: Daniel Buehler
**Ch Bd:* Eugene Buehler
CFO: Mark Klingbeil
**CFO:* Ron Ocasek
**VP:* Scott Buehler
VP: Rick Lowe
Genl Mgr: Christina Melillo
IT Man: Judy Stoller
VP Mktg: Bob Buehler
Advt Dir: Deb Wilcox

D-U-N-S 01-645-7871
BUEHLER FOODS INC
IGA
(*Suby of* HOUCHENS MARKETS) ★
1100 W 12th Ave, Jasper, IN 47546-8150
Tel (812) 482-1366 *Founded/Ownrshp* 2008
Sales 206.4MM^E *EMP* 2,600
SIC 5411 Supermarkets, chain
CEO: David Buehler
**Treas:* Joe Buehler
Dist Mgr: Ken Streicher
Dir IT: Scott Brandt

BUEHLER'S
See BUEHLER FOOD MARKETS INC

BUENO FOODS
See EL ENCANTO INC

D-U-N-S 08-018-6727
BUFFALO CHECK BEER LLC
P.O. Box 9635 (98109-0635)
Tel (312) 320-3717 *Founded/Ownrshp* 2016
Sales 100.0MM *EMP* 1
SIC 2082 Beer (alcoholic beverage)

D-U-N-S 03-173-4861
BUFFALO CITY SCHOOL DISTRICT
BUFFALO PUBLIC SCHOOLS
65 Niagara Sq Rm 712, Buffalo, NY 14202-3307
Tel (716) 816-3500 *Founded/Ownrshp* 2002
Sales 889.8MM *EMP* 3,700
Accts Freedmaxick Cpas Pc Buffalo
SIC 8211 Public elementary & secondary schools
IT Man: Mike Hume
Site Mgr: Lisa Baines
Pr Dir: Elena Cala
Instr Medi: Michael Cambria
HC Dir: Assunta Ventresca

D-U-N-S 94-002-4433
BUFFALO CONSTRUCTION INC
2700 Stanley Gault Pkwy # 130, Louisville, KY 40223-5133
Tel (502) 327-4686 *Founded/Ownrshp* 1997
Sales 121.8MM *EMP* 50
Accts Strothman And Company Psc Lou
SIC 1542 Commercial & office building contractors
Pr: Scott A Gregor
**CFO:* John Hunter
Treas: John Wilkinson
**VP:* Abe Abraham
VP: Phyllis Kirwan
Dir IT: Nathan Sharp

BUFFALO CRUSHED STONE
See NEW ENTERPRISE STONE & LIME CO INC

D-U-N-S 06-840-3229
BUFFALO EXCHANGE LTD
203 E Helen St, Tucson, AZ 85705-7411
Tel (520) 622-2711 *Founded/Ownrshp* 1974
Sales 84.7MM *EMP* 700
SIC 5621

D-U-N-S 08-568-5709
BUFFALO HOSPITAL SUPPLY CO INC
B H S
4039 Genesee St Ste 100, Buffalo, NY 14225-1904
Tel (716) 626-9400 *Founded/Ownrshp* 1977
Sales 84.6MM^E *EMP* 125
SIC 5047 Medical equipment & supplies; Surgical equipment & supplies
Ch Bd: Michael J Burke
**CEO:* Gary M Skura
**COO:* Stephen Corcoran
**CFO:* Margaret King
**Ex VP:* Ryan M Burke
Sls&Mrk Ex: Morgan Lucio
Sls Mgr: Benjamin Cooley

D-U-N-S 12-620-2899
BUFFALO INVESTORS CORP
(*Suby of* STARFIRE HOLDING CORP) ★
1 Wall Street Ct Apt 980, New York, NY 10005-3404
Tel (212) 702-4363 *Founded/Ownrshp* 2000
Sales 1.4MMM^E *EMP* 3,760
SIC 3743 4741 Freight cars & equipment; Rental of railroad cars
VP: Richard T Buonato

D-U-N-S 02-079-4251
BUFFALO MARINE SERVICE INC (TX)
8201 E Erath St, Houston, TX 77012-2109
Tel (713) 923-2106 *Founded/Ownrshp* 1964, 1970
Sales 169.8MM^E *EMP* 100
SIC 5172 Engine fuels & oils
Pr: Patrick Studdert
**Sec:* Diane A Howard
**VP:* Robert G Harrison
**VP:* Charles H King Jr
**VP:* Tim Studdert

BUFFALO NIAGARA INTL ARPRT
See NIAGARA FRONTIER TRANSPORTATION AUTHORITY

D-U-N-S 14-064-6360
BUFFALO ORLANDO I LLC
570 Delaware Ave, Buffalo, NY 14202-1206
Tel (716) 886-0211 *Founded/Ownrshp* 2000
Sales 55.8MM^E *EMP* 2,000
SIC 8741 Hotel or motel management
Prin: Nathan Benderson
CFO: Brian Evers
Bd of Dir: David Baldauf

BUFFALO PUBLIC SCHOOLS
See BUFFALO CITY SCHOOL DISTRICT

D-U-N-S 00-400-9221
BUFFALO ROCK CO (AL)
PEPSICO
111 Oxmoor Rd, Birmingham, AL 35209-5967
Tel (205) 942-3435 *Founded/Ownrshp* 1901
Sales 400.8MM^E *EMP* 2,400
SIC 2086 5962 5149

BUFFALO SABRES
See NIAGARA FRONTIER HOCKEY LP

D-U-N-S 06-082-8308
BUFFALO SERVICES INC
B KWIK FOOD MART
747 S Broadway St, McComb, MS 39648-5131
Tel (601) 684-7702 *Founded/Ownrshp* 2001
Sales 100.0MM *EMP* 150
Accts Alford Holloway & Smith Pllc
SIC 5172 5411 6519 4212 Gasoline; Lubricating oils & greases; Gases, liquefied petroleum (propane); Convenience stores, independent; Real property lessors; Petroleum haulage, local
CEO: Clifton Van Cleave
**CFO:* Kyle Smith
IT Man: Stephanie Lopez

D-U-N-S 84-729-1767
BUFFALO VILLAGE ASSOC 190 CAROLINA BUF
WHITNEY REHAB APARTMENTS
190 Carolina St, Buffalo, NY 14201-2147
Tel (716) 847-6313 *Founded/Ownrshp* 2009
Sales 20.8MM^E *EMP* 3,800
SIC 6513 Apartment building operators
Sr VP: Leeann Morein

D-U-N-S 10-162-9418
▲ BUFFALO WILD WINGS INC
5500 Wayzata Blvd # 1600, Minneapolis, MN 55416-1241
Tel (952) 593-9943 *Founded/Ownrshp* 1982
Sales 1.8MMM *EMP* 44,500^E
Tkr Sym BWLD *Exch* NGS
SIC 5812 6794 Grills (eating places); Franchises, selling or licensing
Pr: Sally J Smith
Ch Bd: James M Damian
COO: James M Schmidt
Ofcr: Kathleen M Benning
Ex VP: Craig Donohue
Ex VP: Carol Meyer
Sr VP: Emil L Sanders
Sr VP: Jeffrey B Sorum
VP: Chad Anderson
VP: Emily C Decker
VP: Bob Ruhland
Board of Directors: Dale M Applequist, Cindy L Davis, Andre Fernandez, Michael P Johnson, Hal Lawton, J Oliver Maggard, Jerry R Rose

D-U-N-S 80-122-8805
BUFFALO WINGS & RINGS LLC
564 Old State Route 74 # 3, Cincinnati, OH 45244-1519
Tel (513) 831-9464 *Founded/Ownrshp* 2005
Sales 6.2MM^E *EMP* 1,000
Accts Steven Potter & Company Cpa S
SIC 5812 Chicken restaurant

BUFFALO WOOD PRODUCTS DIV
See KYANITE MINING CORP

D-U-N-S 13-720-9966
BUFFET PARTNERS LP
FURR'S FAMILY DINING
120 Chula Vis, San Antonio, TX 78232-2234
Tel (210) 403-3725 *Founded/Ownrshp* 2003
Sales 494.9M^E *EMP* 3,200
SIC 5812
Ch Bd: Ray Hemmig
Pt: Steve Barnhill
CFO: David Siebert
CFO: Monty Standifer

D-U-N-S 00-355-2358
BUFFETS HOLDINGS LLC
OLD COUNTRY BUFFET
120 Chula Vista Hollywood, San Antonio, TX 78232
Tel (210) 403-3725 *Founded/Ownrshp* 2000
Sales 566.4MM^E *EMP* 33,000
SIC 5812 Restaurant, family: chain; Buffet (eating places)
Ch Bd: Frederick J Iseman
CFO: Jim Hillman
CFO: A Keith Wall
V Ch Bd: Roe H Hatlen
Ex VP: Michael R Kirk
Ex VP: Karlin A Linhardt
Ex VP: H Thomas Mitchell
Ex VP: Kurt Nahikian
VP: Dave Wagner
VP: Don Van Der Wiel
Ex Dir: Mark Radde
Board of Directors: Robert A Ferris, Steven M Lefkowitz, David S Lobel, Robert M Rosenberg

D-U-N-S 12-117-7398
BUFFETS LLC
OLD COUNTRY BUFFET RESTAURANTS
(*Suby of* FOOD MANAGEMENT PARTNERS INC) ★
120 Chula Vis, Hollywood Park, TX 78232-2234
Tel (651) 994-8608 *Founded/Ownrshp* 2015
Sales 848.5MM^E *EMP* 18,000
SIC 5812 8741 Buffet (eating places); Restaurant, family: chain; Pizzeria, chain; Restaurant management
**Pr:* Glenn Drasher
**Pr:* Karlin Linhardt
**Pr:* Andrews Mike
**CEO:* Anthony Wedo
**CFO:* Keith Kravcik
**CIO:* Patrick Benson

D-U-N-S 07-656-3402
BUFFINGTON & ASSOCIATES INC
BUFFINGTON ASSOCIATES
5775 Las Positas Rd, Livermore, CA 94551-7819
Tel (925) 583-1600 *Founded/Ownrshp* 1973
Sales 125.0MM *EMP* 60
SIC 3423 Plumbers' hand tools
Pr: Joseph Norton
**VP Sls:* Frank Mullin

BUFFINGTON ASSOCIATES
See BUFFINGTON & ASSOCIATES INC

D-U-N-S 93-996-6362
BUFFINGTON HARBOR RIVERBOAT LLC
21 Buffington Harbor Dr, Gary, IN 46406-3000
Tel (219) 977-9999 *Founded/Ownrshp* 1995
Sales 11.6MM^E *EMP* 1,000
SIC 5812 7993 Eating places; Gambling establishments operating coin-operated machines
VP: Tara Robinson

D-U-N-S 00-210-9304 IMP/EXP
BUFKOR INC (NY)
(*Suby of* WORLD INDUSTRIAL RESOURCES CORP) ★
1801 Stonebrook Ln, Safety Harbor, FL 34695-5503
Tel (727) 572-9991 *Founded/Ownrshp* 1958
Sales 67.0MM^E *EMP* 3,950
SIC 5199 2084 Jewelry boxes; Bags, baskets & cases; Wines, brandy & brandy spirits
Pr: Paul Ditz
Ch: Henry Yarhi
VP: Reginald Martin
MIS Dir: Mar Sundell
Board of Directors: Neil Dorman, Jurg Egli, David Yarhi, Henry Yarhi

BUFORD HIGHWAY FARMERS MARKET
See ATLANTA ORIENTAL FOOD WHOLESALE CO

D-U-N-S 02-827-2482
BUFORD OIL CO INC
9925 8 3/4 Ave, Hanford, CA 93230-4716
Tel (559) 582-9028 *Founded/Ownrshp* 1931
Sales 105.6MM *EMP* 14
SIC 5172

D-U-N-S 79-805-4698
BUGABOO CREEK HOLDINGS INC
1450 Us Highway 22 Ste 4, Mountainside, NJ 07092-2619
Tel (908) 518-1800 *Founded/Ownrshp* 2007
Sales 40.4MM^E *EMP* 2,400
SIC 5812 Steak & barbecue restaurants
Pr: Russell D Anton

D-U-N-S 00-318-4108 IMP/EXP
BUHLER AEROGLIDE CORP (NC)
(*Suby of* BUHLER AG)
100 Aeroglide Dr, Cary, NC 27511-6900
Tel (919) 278-2925 *Founded/Ownrshp* 1928
Sales 89.5MM^E *EMP* 311
SIC 3556 3585 3567 Food products machinery; Refrigeration & heating equipment; Industrial furnaces & ovens
Pr: J Fredrick Kelly Jr
**Pr:* Andy Sharpe
**CFO:* Carmen Schlatter
**CFO:* Michael S Williams
Sr VP: Da A Humphreys
**VP:* Mark Paulson Pe
Ex Dir: Paul Branson
Snr Mgr: Rick Palmer

D-U-N-S 00-622-3705 IMP/EXP
BUHLER INC
(*Suby of* BUHLER HOLDING AG)
13105 12th Ave N, Plymouth, MN 55441-4509
Tel (763) 847-9900 *Founded/Ownrshp* 1957
Sales 180.8MM *EMP* 187^E
SIC 3556 3542 3535 3564 Food products machinery; Cutting, chopping, grinding, mixing & similar machinery; Die casting machines; Conveyors & conveying equipment; Pneumatic tube conveyor systems; Bulk handling conveyor systems; Dust or fume collecting equipment, industrial
CEO: Rene Steiner
**Pr:* Achim Klotz
Pr: Franz Signer
COO: Holger Feldhege
CFO: Raphael Krucker
**CFO:* Markus Nikles
Exec: Jason Pintuff
Area Mgr: Cristian Atienza
Off Admin: Romy-Monira Scholz
Dir IT: Dominik Ladner
Opers Mgr: Chris Hilt

D-U-N-S 00-327-5970 IMP
BUILD GROUP INC (CA)
457 Minna St Ste 100, San Francisco, CA 94103-2914
Tel (415) 367-9399 *Founded/Ownrshp* 2006
Sales 390.5MM *EMP* 80
Accts Dzh Phillips Llp San Francisc
SIC 1542 Commercial & office building contractors
Pr: Ross Edwards Jr
Pr: Todd C Pennington
CFO: Jason Berry
**CFO:* Stephen Nerhein
Dir Bus: John Dunsing
Dir Bus: John Santori
Info Man: Kim Zabel
QI Cn Mgr: Michael Meaney

D-U-N-S 00-857-8841
▲ BUILD-A-BEAR WORKSHOP INC
1954 Innerbelt Bus Ctr Dr, Saint Louis, MO 63114-5719
Tel (314) 423-8000 *Founded/Ownrshp* 1997
Sales 377.6MM *EMP* 4,100
Tkr Sym BBW *Exch* NYS
SIC 5945 6794 Hobby, toy & game shops; Toys & games; Franchises, selling or licensing
CEO: Sharon Price John
**Ch Bd:* Mary Lou Fiala
COO: J Christopher Hurt
CFO: Voin Todorovic
Chf Mktg O: Gina Collins
Ofcr: Eric Fencl
Ofcr: Jennifer Kretchmar
Board of Directors: Maxine Clark, James M Gould, Timothy Kilpin, Braden Leonard, Sarah Personette, Coleman Peterson, Michael Shaffer

D-U-N-S 84-717-4989 EXP
BUILD.COM INC
FAUCETDIRECT.COM
(*Suby of* WOLSELEY PLC)
402 Otterson Dr Ste 100, Chico, CA 95928-8247
Tel (800) 375-3403 *Founded/Ownrshp* 2007
Sales 221.8MM^E *EMP* 380
SIC 5074 5999 Plumbing fittings & supplies; Plumbing & heating supplies
CEO: Christian B Friedland
Pr: Erik Lukasek
**Chf Mktg O:* Danielle Porto Mohn
VP: Ryan Brewer
**VP:* Lindsay Fee
VP: Julie Gardner
VP: Devin Hout
**VP:* Brandon Proctor
QA Dir: Ed Rose
Dir IT: Thor Howe
IT Man: John Forristel

BUILDER MAGAZINE
See HW HOLDCO LLC

D-U-N-S 02-008-8633
■ BUILDER SERVICES GROUP INC
(*Suby of* TOPBUILD CORP) ★
260 Jimmy Ann Dr, Daytona Beach, FL 32114-1318
Tel (386) 304-2222 *Founded/Ownrshp* 1993
Sales 839.8MM^E *EMP* 4,156^E
SIC 1742 Acoustical & insulation work
Pr: James A Hazelwood
**CEO:* Robert Buck
**Treas:* John G Sznewajs
**VP:* Lawrence F Leaman
**VP:* Jerry W Mollien
Board of Directors: Eugene A Gargaro Jr, John R Leekley

D-U-N-S 07-345-3557
BUILDER SUPPORT SERVICES INC
FOREST MATERIAL SUPPLY
4125 Atlanta Rd Se, Smyrna, GA 30080-6577
Tel (770) 907-3400 *Founded/Ownrshp* 1974
Sales 302.4MM^E *EMP* 650
SIC 1531 6531 Operative builders; Speculative builder, single-family houses; Real estate agents & managers
CEO: John Wieland
**Pr:* Danny Fincher
**Pr:* Eric Price
**CEO:* Terry Russell

*CFO: Jt McMickle
*CFO: Shelly Pruitt
CFO: Doug Ray
*Sr VP: David Durham
VP: Phil White
VP: John H Wieland
DP Exec: Chuck King

BUILDERS FIRST SOURCE
See BUILDERS FIRSTSOURCE - ATLANTIC GROUP LLC

BUILDERS FIRSTSOURCE
See PROBUILD CO LLC

D-U-N-S 18-165-2231 IMP
■ BUILDERS FIRSTSOURCE - ATLANTIC GROUP LLC
BUILDERS FIRST SOURCE
(Suby of BUILDERS FIRSTSOURCE INC) ★
5330 Spectrum Dr Ste L, Frederick, MD 21703-7302
Tel (301) 631-2282 Founded/Ownrshp 2000
Sales 4.0MMM EMP 1,500
SIC 5031 5211 Lumber, plywood & millwork; Lumber products
CEO: Floyd Sherman
CFO: Chad Crow

D-U-N-S 03-237-9463 IMP/EXP
■ BUILDERS FIRSTSOURCE - FLORIDA LLC
(Suby of BUILDERS FIRSTSOURCE INC) ★
6550 Roosevelt Blvd, Jacksonville, FL 32244-4011
Tel (904) 772-6100 Founded/Ownrshp 1954
Sales 97.3MM^E EMP 400
SIC 5031 Lumber: rough, dressed & finished
CEO: Floyd F Sherman
CFO: M Chad Crow
Sr VP: Donald F McAleenan
Genl Mgr: Greg Birtsch
Genl Mgr: Sam Cardozo
IT Man: Travis Cogdill
Opers Mgr: Bill Renaud
Prd Mgr: Alejandro Calderaro
Sales Exec: Bob Dickson
Sls Mgr: Darin Plummer
Sales Asso: Justin Preuss

D-U-N-S 17-998-2137
▲ BUILDERS FIRSTSOURCE INC
2001 Bryan St Ste 1600, Dallas, TX 75201-3017
Tel (214) 880-3500 Founded/Ownrshp 1998
Sales 3.5MMM EMP 14,000
Tkr Sym BLDR Exch NGS
SIC 2431 2421 5211 Millwork; Doors & door parts & trim, wood; Moldings & baseboards, ornamental & trim; Staircases, stairs & railings; Building & structural materials, wood; Lumber & other building materials
CEO: Floyd F Sherman
*Ch Bd: Paul S Levy
Pr: M Chad Crow
CFO: Peter Jackson
Sr VP: Donald F McAleenan
Sr VP: Morris E Tolly
VP: Dave Snyder
Off Mgr: Sharlene Brown
IT Man: Bobby Webb
Sales Asso: Freddie Aldridge
Sales Asso: Alan Aufderhar
Board of Directors: Daniel Agroskin, David A Barr, Cleveland A Christophe, Michael Graff, Robert C Griffin, Kevin J Kuse, Brett N Milgrim, Craig A Steinke

D-U-N-S 07-806-9200 IMP/EXP
■ BUILDERS FIRSTSOURCE- SOUTHEAST GROUP LLC
(Suby of BUILDERS FIRSTSOURCE INC) ★
2451 E Highway 501, Conway, SC 29526-9508
Tel (843) 347-4224 Founded/Ownrshp 1999
Sales 333.8MM^E EMP 2,500
SIC 5211 2431 Lumber & other building materials; Millwork & lumber; Doors, storm: wood or metal; Windows, storm: wood or metal; Doors, wood
Prin: Morris E Tolly

D-U-N-S 82-677-6361
■ BUILDERS FIRSTSOURCE-TEXAS GROUP LP
(Suby of BUILDERS FIRSTSOURCE INC) ★
3403 E Abram St, Arlington, TX 76010-1415
Tel (214) 880-3500 Founded/Ownrshp 2006
Sales 133.0MM^E EMP 760
SIC 5031 5033 2439

BUILDERS INSULATION NH
See INSTALLED BUILDING PRODUCTS LLC

D-U-N-S 00-891-0523 IMP
BUILDERS SUPPLY CO INC (NE)
5701 S 72nd St, Omaha, NE 68127-3900
Tel (402) 331-4500 Founded/Ownrshp 1951
Sales 97.4MM EMP 210
SIC 5211 5031

D-U-N-S 01-939-7884 IMP
BUILDING 19 INC
319 Lincoln St, Hingham, MA 02043-1729
Tel (781) 749-6900 Founded/Ownrshp 1964
Sales 90.5MM^E EMP 1,100
SIC 5311 Department stores, discount
Ch Bd: Gerald Elovitz
*Pr: William Elovitz

D-U-N-S 08-143-0621
BUILDING CENTER INC (NC)
10201 Industrial Dr, Pineville, NC 28134-6520
Tel (704) 889-8182 Founded/Ownrshp 1977
Sales 215.0MM^E EMP 300
SIC 5031 2431 Lumber, plywood & millwork; Millwork; Doors, wood; Windows, wood
Ch Bd: Edgar L Norris Sr
*Pr: Edgar L Norris Jr
*CFO: Grant Phillip
*VP: Lawrence E Norris

BUILDING CLEANING CONTRACTORS
See DON HENRY JR & SONS

D-U-N-S 62-487-3402
BUILDING MAINTENANCE SERVICE LLC
MBSC DIV
11 Penn Plz, New York, NY 10001-2006
Tel (212) 714-0004 Founded/Ownrshp 2003
Sales 70.7MM^E EMP 2,500^E
SIC 7349 Building & office cleaning services
CEO: Michael Doherty
*CFO: Carol Gambardella
Sr VP: Sedat Osmanovic
Sr VP: Robert Tucker
*VP: Joel Birner
*VP: Juan Francisco
*VP: Michael Silvestro
VP: Brian M Snow
Dir Sec: Steven Cleary
Genl Mgr: Alicia Barron

D-U-N-S 00-922-4080 IMP
BUILDING MATERIAL DISTRIBUTORS INC
B M D
225 Elm Ave, Galt, CA 95632-1558
Tel (209) 745-3001 Founded/Ownrshp 1943
Sales 286.9MM^E EMP 318
SIC 5031 Building materials, exterior; Building materials, interior; Window frames, all materials; Door frames, all materials
Ch: Mike Garrison
*Pr: Jeff Gore
*CFO: Jim Colson
*Ch: Steven Ellinwood
Brnch Mgr: Frank Babcock

BUILDING MATERIALS & HOME CTRS
See MARVINS LLC

BUILDING MATERIALS CORP AMER
See BMCA HOLDINGS CORP

D-U-N-S 17-863-2253 IMP/EXP
BUILDING MATERIALS HOLDING CORP
BMC
720 E Park Blvd Ste 115, Boise, ID 83712-7756
Tel (208) 331-4300 Founded/Ownrshp 1997
Sales 1.9MM^E EMP 4,800
SIC 5211 5031
CEO: Peter C Alexander
COO: Wes Barker
*CFO: Michael Kestner
*Ex VP: Michael Badgley
*VP: Malini Balakrishnan
*VP: Eric R Beem
VP: Eric Beem
VP: Leroy Custer
*VP: Jim Frank
Exec: Dion Maroney
Dir Risk M: Len Baumann
Board of Directors: Marc Chasman, Dennis Downer, Jay B Hunt, Michael A Maidy, Carl R Vertuca Jr

D-U-N-S 03-475-4036 IMP
BUILDING PLASTICS INC
BPI
3263 Sharpe Ave, Memphis, TN 38111-3700
Tel (901) 744-6200 Founded/Ownrshp 2001
Sales 219.7MM EMP 403
Accts Cannon Wright Blount Pllc Mem
SIC 5023 Floor coverings
Pr: Daniel Riley
Pr: Elaine Bennett
*CFO: Wallace McAlexander
Dir IT: Brenda Sinquerfield
IT Man: Lowery Wilder
VP Opers: Sherry Nymoen
Mfg Dir: John Dale
S&M/VP: John Anderson
Mktg Dir: Detra Burleson
Mktg Dir: Michelle Harper

D-U-N-S 00-643-8139
BUILDING SERVICE (WI)
B S I
W222n630 Cheaney Rd, Waukesha, WI 53186-1697
Tel (414) 358-5080 Founded/Ownrshp 1947
Sales 95.2MM^E EMP 200^E
SIC 5021 1542 5023 Office & public building furniture; Commercial & office building contractors; Home furnishings; Carpets
Pr: Peter Kordus
CEO: Ralph Kuehn
CFO: James Kuehn
Ex VP: Roger Daniels
VP: Janet Phillips
VP: Kathy Schwab
Dir IT: Kim Liepert
Sls Mgr: Shayne Ferguson

BUILDING SERVICE DEPARTMENT
See METHODIST HOSPITAL

BUILT NY
See SURESOURCE LLC

D-U-N-S 00-702-3658 IMP/EXP
BULAB HOLDINGS INC (TN)
BUCKMAN LABS
1256 N Mclean Blvd, Memphis, TN 38108-1241
Tel (901) 278-0330 Founded/Ownrshp 1945
Sales 261.4MM^E EMP 1,500
SIC 2819 2869 Industrial inorganic chemicals; Industrial organic chemicals
Ch Bd: Katherine Buckman Gibson
*CEO: Steven B Buckman
*CFO: Michael Huthwaite
CFO: David Rosenthal
*Ch: Katherine Buckman Davis
Div/Sub He: Waldie Jooste
Mktg Dir: Lela Gerald
Mktg Mgr: Chris Rooks

BULK HANDLING SYSTEMS
See EMERGING ACQUISITIONS LLC

D-U-N-S 08-522-8377 IMP
■ BULK MOLDING COMPOUNDS INC
(Suby of CITADEL PLASTICS HOLDINGS INC) ★
1600 Powis Ct, West Chicago, IL 60185-1016
Tel (630) 377-1065 Founded/Ownrshp 2008
Sales 144.9MM^E EMP 200
SIC 3087 Custom compound purchased resins
CEO: Mike Huff
*Pr: Christopher Vaisvil
*CFO: Rick Dettman
VP: Gregory Knipp
*VP: Francis Zappitelli
*VP: Robert Zurek
Genl Mgr: Mark Bieberstein
Off Admin: Jean Beck
Opers Mgr: Michelle Creech
Ql Cn Mgr: Ron Cash
Sls Mgr: Rick Faulk

BULK WAREHOUSE
See MID SOUTH SALES INC

D-U-N-S 05-322-0711
BULKMATIC TRANSPORT CO INC
2001 N Cline Ave, Griffith, IN 46319-1008
Tel (219) 972-7630 Founded/Ownrshp 1970
Sales 326.2MM^E EMP 1,100
SIC 4213 4731 4212 Trucking, except local; Liquid petroleum transport, non-local; Freight transportation arrangement; Local trucking, without storage
Pr: Albert Y Bingham Jr
Pr: Peter Miller
Sr VP: E Larry Smith
VP: Dan Flanagan
VP: Lori Laster
VP: Larry Smith
Rgnl Mgr: Mel McKern
Genl Mgr: Leonard Ringhoff
VP Opers: Jose F Soto
Trfc Dir: Nate Morgan
Opers Mgr: Keith Brown

D-U-N-S 78-246-7666
BULL DATA SYSTEMS INC
(Suby of BULL)
285 Billerica Rd Ste 200, Chelmsford, MA 01824-4174
Tel (978) 294-6000 Founded/Ownrshp 1989
Sales 89.6MM^E EMP 2,200
SIC 3571 3577 7378 Electronic computers; Computer peripheral equipment; Computer maintenance & repair
Pr: Gervais Pellissier
*CFO: Eves Blanc
Treas: David W Bradbury
*Sec: Richard Griesbach
VP: Michael Berman
VP: Pat Mansfield
Genl Mgr: Jane Fine
Genl Mgr: Ralph Hamwey
Genl Mgr: Dianne McDaniel
Genl Mgr: James Moore
Genl Mgr: Joseph Tocci

D-U-N-S 05-180-2627 IMP
BULL HN INFORMATION SYSTEMS INC
(Suby of BULL DATA SYSTEMS INC) ★
285 Billerica Rd Ste 200, Chelmsford, MA 01824-4174
Tel (978) 294-6000 Founded/Ownrshp 1970
Sales 83.4MM^E EMP 500
SIC 5045 7373 Computer peripheral equipment; Systems integration services
Pr: David Bradbury
*Pr: Philippe Vannier
*CFO: David W Beradbury
*Treas: Steven Kuehl
VP: Luc Saint-Jeannet

D-U-N-S 06-464-6763 IMP/EXP
BULL MOOSE TUBE CO
(Suby of CAPARO INDUSTRIES PLC)
1819 Clarkson Rd Ste 100, Chesterfield, MO 63017-5040
Tel (636) 537-1249 Founded/Ownrshp 1988
Sales 258.8MM^E EMP 685
SIC 3317 Steel pipe & tubes
Pr: John J Meyer
VP: Vern Bozarth
VP: Matt Davis
VP: Mike Dustmann
VP: Rick Stillman
Genl Mgr: Jack Isles
Genl Mgr: Randy R Thompson
Prd Mgr: Matt Marcella
VP Sls: Rick Dobbs
Sls Mgr: Roy Swartz
Sales Asso: Matthew Chrum

D-U-N-S 00-281-5017
BULLEY & ANDREWS
1755 W Armitage Ave, Chicago, IL 60622-1189
Tel (773) 235-2433 Founded/Ownrshp 1891
Sales 310.4MM^E EMP 400^E
SIC 1542 1541 Commercial & office building, new construction; Industrial buildings, new construction
Ch Bd: Allan E Bulley Jr
*Pr: Allan E Bulley III
VP: Michael Sudol
VP: Wade Werth
VP Bus Dev: Patrick Healy
VP Sls: Steve Sever
Snr PM: Mike Lemmons
Snr PM: Philip Robertson
Snr PM: Tom Smith

D-U-N-S 13-878-3563
BULLEY & ANDREWS LLC
MEYNE COMPANY DIV , THE
(Suby of BULLEY & ANDREWS) ★
1755 W Armitage Ave, Chicago, IL 60622-1189
Tel (312) 207-2100 Founded/Ownrshp 1999
Sales 305.0MM EMP 350
SIC 1541 1542 Industrial buildings, new construction; Commercial & office building, new construction
CFO: Mark Evans

D-U-N-S 08-100-4616
BULLITT COUNTY PUBLIC SCHOOLS
1040 Highway 44 E, Shepherdsville, KY 40165-6122
Tel (502) 869-8000 Founded/Ownrshp 1910
Sales 93.9MM^E EMP 1,800
SIC 8211 Public elementary & secondary schools
*V Ch: Mike Robison

D-U-N-S 80-048-5208
BULLITT COUNTY PUBLIC SCHOOLS
1040 Highway 44 E, Shepherdsville, KY 40165-6122
Tel (502) 869-8000 Founded/Ownrshp 2007
Sales 46.5MM^E EMP 1,500^E
SIC 8211 Public elementary & secondary schools
*VP: Dolores Ashby
Dir Sec: Sarah Hardin
Pr Dir: John Roberts
Teacher Pr: Jennifer Wooley
HC Dir: Lesa Bodine

D-U-N-S 15-774-9425
BULLOCH COUNTY BOARD OF EDUCATION
150 Williams Rd Ste A, Statesboro, GA 30458-1398
Tel (912) 764-6201 Founded/Ownrshp 1796
Sales 121.2MM^E EMP 1,400
SIC 8211 Public senior high school
Ch Bd: Levon Wilson
IT Man: Margret Oglesby
Netwrk Eng: Robby Bragdon
Sls Mgr: Emerson Chester

D-U-N-S 07-979-8857
BULLOCH COUNTY SCHOOLS
150 Williams Rd Ste A, Statesboro, GA 30458-1398
Tel (912) 212-8500 Founded/Ownrshp 2015
Sales 19.3MM^E EMP 1,789^E
SIC 8211 Public elementary & secondary schools
V Ch: Mike Sparks
CIO: Craig Liggett
MIS Dir: Patty Webb
Netwrk Eng: Robby Bragdon
Teacher Pr: Philip Tremble
Psych: Mary B Hodgin
HC Dir: Kathy Wood

D-U-N-S 00-150-2822 IMP/EXP
BULOVA CORP (NY)
(Suby of CITIZEN WATCH CO., LTD.)
350 5th Ave Fl 29, New York, NY 10118-2900
Tel (212) 497-1875 Founded/Ownrshp 1874, 2008
Sales 108.8MM^E EMP 500
SIC 5094 Clocks, watches & parts
Int Pr: John Wille
*Pr: Jeffrey Cohen
Pr: Sian Williams
COO: Paul Sayegh
COO: Ron Spencer
Ex VP: Robert Christiano
*Ex VP: Mary Beth Trypus
VP: Herschel H Hiat
VP: Michael Kunz
VP: Ann Mercier
CIO: Lou Dubrosa

BUMBLE BEE
See BEE BUMBLE FOODS LLC

D-U-N-S 78-582-3456
BUMBLE BEE PARENT INC
280 10th Ave, San Diego, CA 92101-7406
Tel (858) 715-4000 Founded/Ownrshp 2011
Sales 133.6MM EMP 551
SIC 2013 2032 2033 Beef stew from purchased meat; Chili with or without meat: packaged in cans, jars, etc ; Vegetables & vegetable products in cans, jars, etc.
CEO: Eric Lindberg

D-U-N-S 14-435-8975 IMP/EXP
BUMBLE BEE SEAFOODS INC
280 10th Ave, San Diego, CA 92101-7406
Tel (858) 715-4068 Founded/Ownrshp 2000
Sales 308.8MM^E EMP 3,000
SIC 2091 2047

D-U-N-S 02-462-1930
BUMGARNER OIL CO INC (NC)
CUBBARD EXPRESS
2004 Highland Ave Ne, Hickory, NC 28601-4336
Tel (828) 322-4377 Founded/Ownrshp 1954
Sales 90.2MM^E EMP 115^E
SIC 5172 5983 Fuel oil; Fuel oil dealers
Pr: Glenn A Bumgarner
Treas: Glenda Henson
*VP: David Bumgarner

BUMPER TO BUMPER
See CROW-BURLIGAME CO

D-U-N-S 08-133-3403
BUNCOMBE COUNTY SCHOOL DISTRICT
175 Bingham Rd, Asheville, NC 28806-3800
Tel (828) 251-0499 Founded/Ownrshp 1897
Sales 162.4MM^E EMP 2,811
Accts Johnson Price & Sprinkle Pa A
SIC 8211 Public elementary & secondary schools
Exec: Gaylen Ehrlichman
Dir Sec: Belvin Hall
Dir IT: Janet Casey
Dir IT: Pam Smathers
Pr Dir: Donald Porter
Teacher Pr: Cynthia Lopez
HC Dir: Debby Bryant

BUNGE FOODS GROUP
See BUNGE NORTH AMERICA INC

D-U-N-S 87-643-1672 EXP
BUNGE GLOBAL MARKETS INC
(Suby of BUNGE LIMITED)
50 Main St, White Plains, NY 10606-1901
Tel (914) 684-3300 Founded/Ownrshp 2013
Sales 89.1MM^E EMP 65
SIC 5153 5159 Grains; Wheat; Corn; Barley; Oil nuts, kernels, seeds
CEO: Soren Schroder
*Pr: Archie Gwathmey
*CEO: Alberto Weisser

D-U-N-S 00-508-2862 EXP
BUNGE MILLING INC
(Suby of BUNGE FOODS GROUP) ★
11720 Borman Dr, Saint Louis, MO 63146-4129
Tel (314) 292-2000 Founded/Ownrshp 1946, 1979
Sales 162.4MM^E EMP 596
SIC 2041 2075 Flour & other grain mill products; Soybean oil mills
Pr: Todd Bastean
CEO: Carl L Hausmann

Sr VP: Fred W Luckey
Sr VP: Michael M Scharf

D-U-N-S 00-512-9432 EXP
BUNGE NORTH AMERICA FOUNDATION (MO)
(*Suby of* BUNGE FINANCE LIMITED)
11720 Borman Dr, Saint Louis, MO 63146-4129
Tel (314) 872-3030 *Founded/Ownrshp* 1934
Sales 88.0MM^E *EMP* 470
SIC 2075 2079 2048 2834 Soybean oil, cake or meal; Soybean protein concentrates & isolates; Lecithin, soybean; Soybean oil, refined: not made in soybean oil mills; Vegetable refined oils (except corn oil); Poultry feeds; Livestock feeds; Feed premixes; Feed supplements; Veterinary pharmaceutical preparations
CEO: Todd A Bastean
**CFO:* George P Allard
**Treas:* George Allard
**Sr VP:* John L Clarke
**VP:* D Wade Ellis
**VP:* Karen D Roebuck

D-U-N-S 00-698-1435 IMP/EXP
BUNGE NORTH AMERICA INC (NY)
BUNGE FOODS GROUP
(*Suby of* BUNGE LIMITED)
11720 Borman Dr, Saint Louis, MO 63146-4129
Tel (314) 292-2000 *Founded/Ownrshp* 1923, 2013
Sales 3.5MMM^E *EMP* 4,583
SIC 5153 Grains; Wheat; Corn; Barley
Pr: Todd Bastean
**Ch Bd:* Soren Schroder
**CFO:* George P Allard
**Treas:* Aaron Elliott
Bd of Dir: Kathryn Clifford
Bd of Dir: John Klein
**Ex VP:* Tim Gallagher
Ex VP: Timothy J Gallagher
**Sr VP:* David G Kabbes
**VP:* Wade Ellis
VP: Matt Gibson
VP: Fred Luckey
**VP:* John Sabourin
VP: Michael A Snow

D-U-N-S 00-766-0640
BUNKERS INTERNATIONAL CORP (FL)
1071 S Sun Dr Ste 3, Lake Mary, FL 32746-2405
Tel (407) 328-7757 *Founded/Ownrshp* 1996
Sales 850.0MM *EMP* 80
SIC 7389 5172 Brokers' services; Fuel oil
CEO: John T Canal
Pr: Paul Pappaceno
**CFO:* Alfred Canal
**Sr VP:* Maria Teresa Canal
**VP:* David Noakes
**VP:* Bill Preusch

D-U-N-S 00-507-8522 IMP/EXP
BUNN-O-MATIC CORP
5020 Ash Grove Dr, Springfield, IL 62711-6329
Tel (217) 529-6601 *Founded/Ownrshp* 1963
Sales 195.7MM^E *EMP* 600^E
SIC 3589

BUNZL DISTRIBUTION
See BUNZL INDUSTRIAL INC

BUNZL DISTRIBUTION
See BUNZL USA HOLDINGS LLC

D-U-N-S 78-501-8151 IMP/EXP
BUNZL DISTRIBUTION CALIFORNIA LLC
(*Suby of* BUNZL SHARED SERVICES) ★
1 Cityplace Dr Ste 200, Saint Louis, MO 63141-7067
Tel (888) 997-5959 *Founded/Ownrshp* 1989
Sales 205.0MM^E *EMP* 115
SIC 5113 Industrial & personal service paper; Paper & products, wrapping or coarse; Paperboard & products
CEO: Patrick L Larmon
**Genl Mgr:* Scot Gregory
IT Man: Dave Prince
Sls Mgr: Doug Saffle

D-U-N-S 80-985-9775
BUNZL DISTRIBUTION MIDCENTRAL INC
ARCH LOGISTICS
(*Suby of* BUNZL SHARED SERVICES) ★
11434 Moog Dr, Saint Louis, MO 63146-3528
Tel (314) 569-2800 *Founded/Ownrshp* 2000
Sales 1.3MMM^E *EMP* 1,212^E
SIC 5199 Packaging materials
Pr: Pat Larmon
Pr: Matthew Noel
Exec: Rick McMillen
Sls Mgr: Steve Rebecca

D-U-N-S 15-093-7431 IMP/EXP
BUNZL DISTRIBUTION USA LLC
BUNZL SHARED SERVICES
(*Suby of* BUNZL USA INC) ★
1 Cityplace Dr Ste 200, Saint Louis, MO 63141-7067
Tel (314) 997-5959 *Founded/Ownrshp* 2006
Sales 5.9MMM^E *EMP* 200
SIC 5131 Piece goods & notions
Pr: Patrick Larmon
Pr: Mark Brasher
Ex VP: Jeff Earnhart
Sr VP: Dave Riviere
VP: Mark Sementilli
VP: Thomas Zatkulak
Genl Mgr: Kyle Rostosky

D-U-N-S 62-798-5468
BUNZL INDUSTRIAL INC
BUNZL DISTRIBUTION
(*Suby of* BUNZL USA INC) ★
1 Cityplace Dr Ste 200, Saint Louis, MO 63141-7067
Tel (314) 997-5959 *Founded/Ownrshp* 1981
Sales 92.0MM^E *EMP* 475
SIC 3089 Injection molding of plastics
Pr: Paul Twidgen
**Sec:* Jane Jennewein
Ex VP: Jeff Earnhart
Ex VP: Mark Sementilli
Sr VP: Earl Engleman
Sr VP: Terry Frank
Sr VP: John Howlett
Sr VP: Daniel Lett
Sr VP: Jim Schulz
VP: Peggy Nance
Genl Mgr: Anthony Hadbcock

D-U-N-S 07-924-6913
BUNZL INTERNATIONAL SERVICES INC (VA)
(*Suby of* BUNZL SHARED SERVICES) ★
1 Cityplace Dr Ste 200, Saint Louis, MO 63141-7067
Tel (314) 997-5959 *Founded/Ownrshp* 2013
Sales 3.6MMM^E *EMP* 20
SIC 5131 Piece goods & notions
Pr: Patrick L Larmon
**Treas:* James McCool
**VP:* Earl W Engleman
**VP:* Mark Sementilli

D-U-N-S 01-154-7361 IMP
BUNZL NEW JERSEY INC
(*Suby of* BUNZL SHARED SERVICES) ★
27 Distribution Way, Monmouth Junction, NJ 08852-3001
Tel (732) 821-7000 *Founded/Ownrshp* 1953
Sales 321.8MM^E *EMP* 175^E
SIC 5113 5169 Industrial & personal service paper; Bags, paper & disposable plastic; Cups, disposable plastic & paper; Napkins, paper; Chemicals & allied products
Ch Bd: Paul G Lorenzini
**Treas:* Jeff Earnhart
**VP:* Mark Brasher
Opers Mgr: Lorraine Swanson

BUNZL SHARED SERVICES
See BUNZL DISTRIBUTION USA LLC

D-U-N-S 79-954-0588 IMP/EXP
BUNZL USA HOLDINGS LLC
BUNZL DISTRIBUTION
(*Suby of* BUNZL OVERSEAS HOLDINGS LIMITED)
1 Cityplace Dr Ste 200, Saint Louis, MO 63141-7067
Tel (314) 997-5959 *Founded/Ownrshp* 1997
Sales 6.6MMM^E *EMP* 3,685
SIC 5162 5113 Plastics products; Industrial & personal service paper
Ex Dir: Patrick Larmon
VP: Eric Hill
Mktg Mgr: Pat Oliverio

D-U-N-S 05-965-1869 IMP
BUNZL USA INC
(*Suby of* BUNZL DISTRIBUTION) ★
1 Cityplace Dr Ste 200, Saint Louis, MO 63141-7067
Tel (314) 997-5959 *Founded/Ownrshp* 1959
Sales 6.5MMM^E *EMP* 3,625
SIC 5113 5162 5085 Industrial & personal service paper; Plastics products; Packing, industrial
Pr: Patrick Larmon
Ex VP: Jeff Earnhart
Sr VP: John Howlett
**Sr VP:* Jane Jennewein
Sr VP: Jim Schulz
VP: J T Bailey
VP: Scott Blanchard
VP: Burton Farquharson
VP: Jeff Firnett
VP: John Lyday
VP: Jim McCool
VP: Tom Zatkulak

D-U-N-S 87-265-3050
BUPA INSURANCE CO
AMEDEX
(*Suby of* BRITISH UNITED PROVIDENT ASSOCIATION LIMITED(THE))
17901 Old Cutler Rd, Palmetto Bay, FL 33157-6424
Tel (305) 275-1400 *Founded/Ownrshp* 1973
Sales NA *EMP* 200^E
SIC 6321 Health insurance carriers
Pr: Michael Carricarte
Pr: Diego Fernandez
VP: John Carlson
IT Man: Maritza Rodriguez

D-U-N-S 10-340-6203
BURBANK LUTHER SAVINGS
LUTHER BURBANK SAVINGS CORP
(*Suby of* LUTHER BURBANK CORP) ★
500 3rd St, Santa Rosa, CA 95401-6321
Tel (707) 578-9216 *Founded/Ownrshp* 1982
Sales NA *EMP* 72
SIC 6036 6035 Savings & loan associations, not federally chartered; Federal savings & loan associations
Pr: John Biggs
Sr Pt: Tom Batson
**Ch Bd:* Victor S Trione
Ofcr: David Thomas
Ex VP: Susan Allison
Sr VP: Robert Armstrong
Sr VP: Tim Sorenson
VP: Joanne Bell
Snr Ntwrk: Don Claybrook
CIO: Todd Van Sickel

D-U-N-S 08-943-3791
BURBANK UNIFIED SCHOOL DISTRICT
1900 W Olive Ave, Burbank, CA 91506-2438
Tel (818) 729-4400 *Founded/Ownrshp* 1879
Sales 95.3MM^E *EMP* 1,500
SIC 8211 Public combined elementary & secondary school; Public junior high school; Public senior high school; Public adult education school
Pr: Larry Applebaum
Bd of Dir: Trish Burnett
Bd of Dir: Connie Lackey
**VP:* Dave Kemp
Off Mgr: Kelley Dickson
Dir IT: George Martinez
Teacher Pr: Anita Schackmann
Psych: Sharon Aponik
HC Dir: Lenora Aguilera
Snr PM: Mohammad Kashani-Jou

D-U-N-S 36-106-5915
BURCH MANAGEMENT CO INC
10723 Composite Dr, Dallas, TX 75220-1207
Tel (214) 358-0055 *Founded/Ownrshp* 1986
Sales 44.0MM^E *EMP* 1,450
SIC 8741 5813 5812 Business management; Night clubs; Eating places
Pr: Duncan Burch
**VP:* Steven W Craft
**VP:* Kathie K Golden
**VP:* Gene Leclaire
**VP:* Bert Stair

D-U-N-S 00-746-0025 IMP/EXP
BURD & FLETCHER CO (MO)
5151 E Geospace Dr, Independence, MO 64056-3321
Tel (816) 257-0291 *Founded/Ownrshp* 1885
Sales 93.8MM^E *EMP* 375
SIC 2657 2752 6512 Folding paperboard boxes; Commercial printing, lithographic; Commercial & industrial building operation
Ch Bd: John A Young III
Pr: Jack Knight
**COO:* Peter Young
CFO: John Gordon
VP: Kenneth Moore
CIO: Russ Leaton
Sls Mgr: Guy Ane
Board of Directors: John A Young

D-U-N-S 87-929-3116
■ **BUREAU OF ALCOHOL TOBACCO FIREARMS & EXPLOSIVES**
A T F
(*Suby of* UNITED STATES DEPARTMENT OF JUSTICE) ★
99 New York Ave Ne # 5514, Washington, DC 20002-3325
Tel (202) 648-8500 *Founded/Ownrshp* 1972
Sales NA *EMP* 4,800
SIC 9651 Alcoholic beverage control board, government;
**CFO:* David Horn
**CFO:* Vivian Michalic
CFO: Marquerite R Moccia
**CFO:* Melanie Stinnett
**CIO:* Roger Beasley

D-U-N-S 92-679-4165
■ **BUREAU OF CONSULAR AFFAIRS**
(*Suby of* UNITED STATES DEPT OF STATE) ★
2201 C St Nw Ste 6811, Washington, DC 20520-0099
Tel (202) 647-9576 *Founded/Ownrshp* 1978
Sales NA *EMP* 1,144
SIC 9721

D-U-N-S 87-982-4324
■ **BUREAU OF CUSTOMS AND BORDER PROTECTION**
(*Suby of* EXECUTVE OFC OF US GOVT) ★
1300 Pennsylvania Ave Nw, Washington, DC 20229-0002
Tel (202) 927-0529 *Founded/Ownrshp* 1927
Sales NA *EMP* 58,000
SIC 9711 National security;
Ex Dir: J Chappell H Lawson
Off Mgr: Cecilia Walker
Telecom Mg: Kristie Hunt

D-U-N-S 04-154-0563
■ **BUREAU OF ENGRAVING AND PRINTING**
B E P
(*Suby of* UNITED STATES DEPT OF TREASURY) ★
14th And C St Sw, Washington, DC 20228-0001
Tel (202) 874-2361 *Founded/Ownrshp* 1862
Sales NA *EMP* 5,000
Accts Kpmg Llp Washington Dc
SIC 9311 Taxation;
CFO: Gwen House
Assoc Dir: Robert Scherer

D-U-N-S 00-647-7533
BUREAU OF ENGRAVING INC
6465 Wayzata Blvd Ste 240, Minneapolis, MN 55426-1723
Tel (612) 788-1000 *Founded/Ownrshp* 1989
Sales 88.9MM^E *EMP* 650
SIC 2752 8249 Commercial printing, lithographic; Commercial art school
CEO: Lynne Alexander
Pr: Tom Stuart
CFO: Allan Degran
**CFO:* Arnold Stull
VP: Russ Ackerman
**VP:* John C Buckbee III
**VP:* Patrick Stuart
**Prin:* Lisa Jetland Alexander
**Prin:* Marilee A Stevens
Dir IT: John Henderson
Dir IT: Brian Lorsung
Board of Directors: Lisa Jetland Alexander, Marilee A Stevens

D-U-N-S 13-022-1646 IMP
■ **BUREAU OF IMMIGRATION & CUSTOMS ENFORCEMENT**
(*Suby of* EXECUTVE OFC OF US GOVT) ★
500 12th St Sw, Washington, DC 20536-5098
Tel (202) 732-2427 *Founded/Ownrshp* 2003
Sales NA *EMP* 16,159^E
SIC 9721 9311 Immigration services, government; Customs bureau

D-U-N-S 92-603-8407
■ **BUREAU OF INDIAN AFFAIRS**
BIA
(*Suby of* UNITED STATES DEPARTMENT OF INTERIOR) ★
1849 C St Nw, Washington, DC 20240-0001
Tel (202) 208-6123 *Founded/Ownrshp* 1824
Sales NA *EMP* 1,100
SIC 9131 Indian reservation;
Sr Cor Off: Kirk Rodgers
Exec: Leonard Wines
Ex Dir: Carla Flanagan
Admn Mgr: Sherry Matteccui
DP Dir: Archibald Wells
Opers Mgr: John Ketcher

D-U-N-S 93-273-8065
■ **BUREAU OF LABOR STATISTICS**
(*Suby of* UNITED STATES DEPARTMENT OF LABOR) ★
2 Massachusetts Ave Ne, Washington, DC 20212-0002
Tel (202) 691-5200 *Founded/Ownrshp* 1913
Sales NA *EMP* 2,544
SIC 9651 Bureaus of standards, government;
Pr: Jo-Ann Yu
Ofcr: Charles Benrubi
Admn Mgr: Robert Keller
Dir IT: Rick Kryger
IT Man: Antonio Caraballo
IT Man: Bobby Holstein
IT Man: Erivine Ll
Sftwr Eng: Yana Proudkii
Plnt Mgr: Robert Gddle
Snr Mgr: Michael Hirniak
Snr Mgr: Jacqueline Michael-Midkiff

D-U-N-S 92-603-8563
■ **BUREAU OF LAND MANAGEMENT**
WASHINGTON OFFICE
(*Suby of* UNITED STATES DEPARTMENT OF INTERIOR) ★
1849 C St Nw Rm 5665, Washington, DC 20240-0001
Tel (202) 208-3801 *Founded/Ownrshp* 1946
Sales NA *EMP* 9,000
SIC 9512 Land management agency, government;
Ofcr: Carl Trentee
Secur Mgr: Sherman Gillespie

D-U-N-S 00-324-4084
BUREAU OF NATIONAL AFFAIRS INC
BLOOMBERG BNA
(*Suby of* BLOOMBERG BUSINESSWEEK) ★
1801 S Bell St Ste Cn110, Arlington, VA 22202-4501
Tel (703) 341-3000 *Founded/Ownrshp* 1929, 2011
Sales 598.2MM^E *EMP* 1,638^E
SIC 2711 2721 Newspapers; Periodicals: publishing only
Pr: Gregory C McCaffery
**Pr:* Daniel Doctoroff
Pr: Mike Mackay
Pr: Scott Mozarsky
**COO:* Dan Fine
COO: Sue Martin
**CFO:* Robert P Ambrosini
**Treas:* Peter T Grauer
**Ex VP:* Cynthia J Bolbach
Ex VP: Joseph Breda
**Ex VP:* Eunice L Bumgardner
Ex VP: Daniel M Fine
Ex VP: Richard A Montella
Ex VP: Alan P Olschwang
VP: Alex Butler
VP: John Camp
VP: Ken Crutchfield
VP: Michael Eisenstein
VP: Baker Evans
VP: Lisa A Fitzpatrick
VP: Linda Kaufman

D-U-N-S 78-554-7035
■ **BUREAU OF RECLAMATION**
(*Suby of* UNITED STATES DEPARTMENT OF INTERIOR) ★
1849 C St Nw, Washington, DC 20240-0001
Tel (202) 513-0501 *Founded/Ownrshp* 1902
Sales NA *EMP* 5,875
SIC 9511 Air, water & solid waste management;
Sr Cor Off: Derrill Cowing
Ofcr: Rose Davis
Ofcr: Nora Jenn
Ofcr: Daniel Vinay
Adm Dir: Shenee Turner
Prgrm Mgr: Parry Brian
Area Mgr: Michael Collins
Area Mgr: Brian Person
Off Mgr: Merylin Collier
DP Exec: Denise Arbuckle
Telecom Mg: John Ricker

D-U-N-S 87-982-7566
BUREAU OF THE PUBLIC DEBT
BPD PARKERSBURG OFFICE
200 3rd St 5f, Parkersburg, WV 26106-5300
Tel (304) 480-6514 *Founded/Ownrshp* 1940
Sales NA *EMP* 1,500
SIC 9311

D-U-N-S 13-027-6004
BUREAU SERVICE CO
22069 Us Highway 34, Princeton, IL 61356-8305
Tel (815) 875-2800 *Founded/Ownrshp* 1933
Sales 115.1MM^E *EMP* 180
SIC 5191 5172 5153 5411 7542 Chemicals, agricultural; Fertilizer & fertilizer materials; Feed; Grass seed; Petroleum products; Grains; Convenience stores; Carwashes
CFO: Tony Marchand
Bd of Dir: Alan Madison
VP: Tim Green
Genl Mgr: Dave Horras
Off Mgr: Jenny Noder
IT Man: Steve Holzworth
Plnt Mgr: Dave Geiger
Plnt Mgr: Dennis Ohlson
Plnt Mgr: Dave Schulte
Pr Dir: Larry Jernas
Mktg Mgr: James Stetson

BUREAU VERITAS
See ONECIS INSURANCE CO

D-U-N-S 83-225-8433
BUREAU VERITAS HOLDINGS INC
(*Suby of* BUREAU VERITAS)
1601 Sawgrass Corporate S Ste 400, Sunrise, FL 33323
Tel (954) 835-9309 *Founded/Ownrshp* 1988
Sales 462.2MM^E *EMP* 1,660^E
SIC 7389 8748 8711 8742 Building inspection service; Business consulting; Engineering services; Management consulting services
**Pr:* Pedro Guimaraes

VP: Steven Black
VP: Laurent Clavel
VP: Philippe Donche-Gay
VP: Brett Hensley
Dir Bus: Don Wolfe
Genl Mgr: David Vigil
IT Man: Jane Potts
Opers Mgr: Patrick Field
Mktg Dir: Christy Dale
Genl Couns: Andrew Hibbert

D-U-N-S 07-841-5114
BUREAU VERITAS NORTH AMERICA INC
(*Suby of* US LABORATORIES INC) ★
1601 Sawgrs Corp Pkwy, Sunrise, FL 33323-2883
Tel (954) 236-8100 *Founded/Ownrshp* 2003
Sales 133.2MM *EMP* 1,145
SIC 7389 8748 8734 8711 8742 Inspection & testing services; Building inspection service; Environmental consultant; Testing laboratories; Soil analysis; Water testing laboratory; Engineering services; Management consulting services
Pr: Pedro Guimaraes
**CEO:* Didier Michaud
COO: Philippe Donche-Gay
**CFO:* Sami Badarani
**CFO:* Luis Damasceno
**Ex VP:* Robert W Donze
**Ex VP:* Isam Hasenin
**Ex VP:* Alexander A Hockman
**Ex VP:* Robert Hughes
**Ex VP:* Gregory F Rzonca
Sr VP: Robert Lieckfield
**VP:* Steven Black
**VP:* Heather B Bush
**VP:* William S Munoz
**VP:* Gustavo Valdivia
**VP:* Derek Wong

BURGEONING
See MAURICIO ESPINOSA

BURGER KING
See WESFAM RESTAURANTS INC

BURGER KING
See GOLDCO LLC

BURGER KING
See P D M CO INC

BURGER KING
See SCHUSTER ENTERPRISES INC

BURGER KING
See TWOTON INC

BURGER KING
See CARROLS CORP

BURGER KING
See BRAVOGRAND INC

BURGER KING
See MANCHA DEVELOPMENT CO LLC

BURGER KING
See TRI CITY FOODS OF ILLINOIS INC

BURGER KING
See GENESH INC

BURGER KING
See NORTHWIND INVESTMENTS INC

BURGER KING
See CARIBBEAN RESTAURANTS LLC

BURGER KING
See HORIZON FOOD SERVICE INC

BURGER KING
See CIMMS INC

BURGER KING
See MID AMERICA CORP

BURGER KING
See HEARTLAND HOME FOODS INC

BURGER KING
See HART RESTAURANT MANAGEMENT INC

BURGER KING
See BOSTON-WYMAN INC

BURGER KING
See DAKOTA KING INC

BURGER KING
See KING VENTURE INC

BURGER KING
See NEWCOMB ENTERPRISES INC JOHN

BURGER KING
See QUALITY DINING INC

BURGER KING
See FAMILY DINING INC

BURGER KING
See HOUSTON FOODS INC

BURGER KING
See CARROLS LLC

D-U-N-S 96-808-8364 IMP
BURGER KING CAPITAL HOLDINGS LLC
(*Suby of* BURGER KING HOLDINGS INC) ★
5505 Blue Lagoon Dr, Miami, FL 33126-2029
Tel (305) 378-3000 *Founded/Ownrshp* 2012
Sales 29.3MM[E] *EMP* 5,008[E]
SIC 5812 Fast-food restaurant, chain
CEO: Bernardo Hees

D-U-N-S 00-414-5645 IMP/EXP
BURGER KING CORP (FL)
(*Suby of* BURGER KING HOLDINGS INC) ★
5505 Blue Lagoon Dr, Miami, FL 33126-2029
Tel (305) 378-3000 *Founded/Ownrshp* 1954
Sales 594.3MM[E] *EMP* 10,870
SIC 5812 6794 Fast-food restaurant, chain; Franchises, selling or licensing
Pr: Jose Augusto Dias
Pr: John H Dasburg
Pr: Julio Ramirez
**Pr:* Peter Tan
**CEO:* John W Chidsey
**CFO:* Cedric Burgher
**CFO:* Joshua Kobza
**Treas:* Ben Wells
**Chf Cred:* Denny Post
**Ex VP:* Jonathan Fitzpatrick
Sr VP: Chris Anderson
Sr VP: Mike Kappitt
VP: Rick N Brown
VP: Brian Gies
VP: Steven F Grover
VP: Robert Perkins
Dir Surg: Hal Rossiter
Dir Surg: Sherry Ulsh

D-U-N-S 07-909-3512
BURGER KING HOLDCO LLC
JUSTICE HOLDCO
(*Suby of* BURGER KING WORLDWIDE INC) ★
5505 Blue Lagoon Dr, Miami, FL 33126-2029
Tel (305) 378-3000 *Founded/Ownrshp* 2012
Sales 810.7MM[E] *EMP* 16,041[E]
SIC 5812 Fast-food restaurant, chain
CEO: Daniel Schwartz
CFO: Joshua Kobza

D-U-N-S 62-382-7651 IMP
BURGER KING HOLDINGS INC
(*Suby of* JUSTICE HOLDCO) ★
5505 Blue Lagoon Dr, Miami, FL 33126-2029
Tel (305) 378-3000 *Founded/Ownrshp* 2012
Sales 810.7MM[E] *EMP* 34,248[E]
SIC 5812 6794 Fast-food restaurant, chain; Franchises, selling or licensing
CEO: Bernardo Hees
**Ch Bd:* Alexandre Behring
Pr: Russell B Klein
Pr: Peter Robinson
Pr: Greg Ryan
Pr: Ann Striker
Pr: Peter Tan
Pr: Steve Wiborg
Pr: Rich Wyckoff
**CFO:* Daniel S Schwartz
Ofcr: Denny Marie
Ex VP: Heitor Gon Alves
Ex VP: Felipe Athayde
**Ex VP:* Flavia Faugeres
Ex VP: Rodrigo Musiello
Ex VP: Sami Siddiqui
**Sr VP:* Jill Granat
Sr VP: John Schafulber
VP: Chris Anderson
VP: Kevin Fernandez
**VP:* Jacqueline Friesner
Board of Directors: Paul J Fribourg, Alan Parker, Carlos Alberto Sicupira, Marcel Herrmann Telles, Alexandre Van Damme

D-U-N-S 07-853-4769
BURGER KING WORLDWIDE INC
(*Suby of* RESTAURANT BRANDS INTERNATIONAL LIMITED PARTNERSHIP)
5505 Blue Lagoon Dr, Miami, FL 33126-2029
Tel (305) 378-3000 *Founded/Ownrshp* 2012, 2014
Sales 810.7MM[E] *EMP* 2,420[E]
SIC 5812 Fast-food restaurant, chain
CEO: Daniel S Schwartz
**CFO:* Joshua Kobza
**Chf Mktg O:* Axel Schwan
**Ex VP:* Heitor Goncalves

D-U-N-S 36-246-4141
BURGERBUSTERS INC
TACO BELL
2242 W Great Neck Rd, Virginia Beach, VA 23451-1555
Tel (757) 412-0112 *Founded/Ownrshp* 1986
Sales 110.5MM[E] *EMP* 3,000[E]
SIC 5812 Fast-food restaurant, chain
Pr: Tassos J Paphites
CFO: Byron Hudson
CFO: David Lajoie
**VP:* William M Dragas
Mktg Dir: Yianni Achilleos

D-U-N-S 00-631-0726
BURGERS OZARK COUNTRY CURED HAMS INC
BURGER'S SMOKE HOUSE
32819 Highway 87, California, MO 65018-3227
Tel (573) 796-3134 *Founded/Ownrshp* 1952
Sales 98.3MM[E] *EMP* 200
SIC 5147 5812 2015 2013 Meats & meat products; Eating places; Poultry slaughtering & processing; Bacon, side & sliced: from purchased meat; Ham, smoked: from purchased meat
Pr: Steven Burger
CFO: Karen Williams
**Treas:* Ted Rohrbach
VP: Chris Mouse
Exec: Sandra Ratcliff
IT Man: Matthew Williams
Sls Mgr: Randy Less

BURGER'S SMOKE HOUSE
See BURGERS OZARK COUNTRY CURED HAMS INC

BURGERVILLE USA
See HOLLAND INC

D-U-N-S 00-431-1015
BURGESS & NIPLE INC
5085 Reed Rd, Columbus, OH 43220-2513
Tel (502) 254-2344 *Founded/Ownrshp* 1952
Sales 126.0MM[E] *EMP* 693
SIC 8711 8712 Engineering services; Architectural engineering
CEO: Ronald R Schultz
**Pr:* Kenneth R Davis Jr
VP Opers: Jim Garrison
Snr Mgr: Sarah Johanssen

D-U-N-S 61-648-0575 IMP/EXP
BURGESS-NORTON MFG CO INC
(*Suby of* AMSTED INDUSTRIES INC) ★
737 Peyton St, Geneva, IL 60134-2189
Tel (630) 232-4100 *Founded/Ownrshp* 2005
Sales 145.1MM[E] *EMP* 440[E]
SIC 3399 3592 3452 Powder, metal; Pistons & piston rings; Pins
Pr: Brett E Vasseuer
Treas: James Boyes
**Treas:* G E Chamberlin
VP: Brice Barker
**VP:* M J Cook
**VP:* G M Randich
**VP:* Tom Schneider
Genl Mgr: Robert Douthat
Store Mgr: Frank Rosa
Mtls Mgr: Troy Alfter
Mtls Mgr: Bob Gill

D-U-N-S 00-895-5163
▲ BURKE & HERBERT BANK & TRUST CO INC
100 S Fairfax St, Alexandria, VA 22314-3383
Tel (703) 299-8491 *Founded/Ownrshp* 1852
Sales NA *EMP* 317
Tkr Sym BHRB *Exch* OTO
SIC 6022 State commercial banks; State trust companies accepting deposits, commercial
CEO: Charles K Collum Jr
**Pr:* E Hunt Burke
Pr: Dan Convery
Pr: Erik Darm
Pr: Brian Lawrence
**Pr:* W Scott McSween
Bd of Dir: Anne McPhillips
**Ofcr:* Charles B Lanman Jr
Ofcr: Debra Mills
Ofcr: Charles Persico
Trst Ofcr: Michael K Green Jr
Trst Ofcr: Theresa Hoyt
Ex VP: William Newell
Ex VP: Jeffrey Stryker
Sr VP: Carl E Pollard
VP: Khalil Y Abu-Ghannam
VP: Nancy Adcock
VP: Gaile Binder
VP: Leonard Clark
VP: Joseph Collum
VP: Barbara Cupp
Board of Directors: Kenneth L Wainstein

D-U-N-S 08-132-1911
BURKE COUNTY PUBLIC SCHOOLS
700 E Parker Rd, Morganton, NC 28655-6762
Tel (828) 437-4770 *Founded/Ownrshp* 1967
Sales 81.4MM[E] *EMP* 2,000
SIC 8211 Public elementary & secondary schools
Genl Mgr: Camille Welch
Dir IT: Mike Cabiness
Dir IT: Seng Xiong
Info Man: Angie Barrier
Info Man: Terri Carter
Pr Dir: Judy Lowery
Teacher Pr: Sharon Colawn
Psych: Adrian Hurst

D-U-N-S 01-918-7061 IMP
BURKE DISTRIBUTING CORP
89 Teed Dr, Randolph, MA 02368-4201
Tel (781) 767-6056 *Founded/Ownrshp* 1965
Sales 123.1MM[E] *EMP* 300
SIC 5181 Beer & other fermented malt liquors
Pr: William G Burke
**Treas:* Charles Balkam
Treas: Charlie Balkam
Sls Mgr: Sean Obrien
Sales Asso: Ryan Morell

D-U-N-S 00-911-8886 IMP/EXP
BURKE INDUSTRIES INC
(*Suby of* MANNINGTON RSILIENT FLOORS DIV) ★
2250 S 10th St, San Jose, CA 95112-4197
Tel (408) 297-3500 *Founded/Ownrshp* 2008
Sales 180.7MM[E] *EMP* 657[E]
SIC 3069 2822 2821 3061 Flooring, rubber: tile or sheet; Molded rubber products; Polyethylene, chlorosulfonated (hypalon); Silicone rubbers; Plastics materials & resins; Silicone resins; Mechanical rubber goods
Pr: Robert Pitman
**CFO:* Edward Reginelli
IT Man: John Fenster
IT Man: Bob Heathcoate
Tech Mgr: Dan Garrison
Sfty Dirs: Bob Heathcote
VP Sls: Mike Moshfegh
VP Sls: Steve Roades
Manager: Robert Murphy

D-U-N-S 19-722-2748
BURKES MECHANICAL INC
2 Industrial Rd, Brent, AL 35034-3817
Tel (205) 926-5847 *Founded/Ownrshp* 1986
Sales 123.2MM[E] *EMP* 750
SIC 1711 Mechanical contractor
VP: Herbie E Burke Jr
**VP:* Mistie D Burkes
Sfty Mgr: Debra Sullivan

D-U-N-S 80-633-6520
BURKES OUTLET STORES INC
(*Suby of* BEALLS INC) ★
1806 38th Ave E, Bradenton, FL 34208-4708
Tel (941) 747-2355 *Founded/Ownrshp* 1987
Sales 133.8MM[E] *EMP* 1,675[E]
SIC 5651 Family clothing stores
CEO: Stephen M Knopik
**Pr:* Robert Beall
**VP:* Lee Harmon

D-U-N-S 02-753-2357
BURKHART DENTAL SUPPLY CO
2502 S 78th St, Tacoma, WA 98409-9053
Tel (253) 474-7761 *Founded/Ownrshp* 1888
Sales 168.3MM[E] *EMP* 360
Accts Moss & Adams Llp Tacoma Was
SIC 5047 Medical & hospital equipment
Pr: Lori Burkhart Isbell
Pr: Paige Mead
**VP:* Greg Biersack
**VP:* Delene Losch
**VP:* Jeff Reece
Brnch Mgr: Steve Sinclair
Genl Mgr: Derek Johnson
Opers Mgr: Michael Baxter
Natl Sales: Carol Schienle
Mktg Mgr: Mark Beagley
Mktg Mgr: David Wolkenhauer

D-U-N-S 84-497-4535
BURKS COMPANIES
191 Peachtree St Ne # 800, Atlanta, GA 30303-1740
Tel (404) 589-4600 *Founded/Ownrshp* 1991
Sales 112.2MM[E] *EMP* 1,010
SIC 1752 5085 7349 4953 8999 Floor laying & floor work; Industrial supplies; Chemical cleaning services; Hazardous waste collection & disposal; Information bureau
**CFO:* Nathaniel Roberts
Ex VP: Talithacumi N Burks

D-U-N-S 01-562-9756 IMP/EXP
BURLEIGH POINT LTD
BILLABONG U S A
(*Suby of* BILLABONG INTERNATIONAL LIMITED)
117 Waterworks Way, Irvine, CA 92618-3110
Tel (949) 428-3200 *Founded/Ownrshp* 1997
Sales 123.1MM[E] *EMP* 200
SIC 2339 2331 2329 Aprons, except rubber or plastic: women's, misses', juniors'; Women's & misses' blouses & shirts; Knickers, dress (separate): men's & boys'
CEO: McNeil Seymour Fiske Jr
**Pr:* Ed Leasure
**Pr:* Paul Naude
**CEO:* Neil Fiske
**COO:* Jeff Streader
**VP:* Tom Gumpert
Dir IT: Patrick Allen

D-U-N-S 09-240-4284
BURLESON INDEPENDENT SCHOOL DISTRICT
1160 Sw Wilshire Blvd, Burleson, TX 76028-5719
Tel (817) 245-1000 *Founded/Ownrshp* 1900
Sales 111.6MM *EMP* 2,000
Accts Weaver And Tidwell Llp Fo
SIC 8211 Public elementary school; Public junior high school; Public senior high school
Pr: Michael Ancy
CFO: Paula Pucker
CFO: Karen Wiesman
Ofcr: Mark Pate
**VP:* Shawn Minor
Off Mgr: Mary E Burch
Off Mgr: Lydia Smylie
Pr Dir: Ashley Logan
Teacher Pr: Coby Kirkpatrick
Psych: Rebecca Baird
Psych: Debbie Pennington

BURLINGTON COAT FACTORY
See LUXURY LINENS OF NASHVILLE INC

D-U-N-S 62-389-2499 EXP
BURLINGTON COAT FACTORY HOLDINGS INC
(*Suby of* BAIN CAPITAL PARTNERS LLC) ★
1830 N Route 130, Burlington, NJ 08016-3020
Tel (609) 387-7800 *Founded/Ownrshp* 2006
Sales 1.3MMM[E] *EMP* 31,402
SIC 5651 5632 5719 5947 5712 Family clothing stores; Fur apparel, made to custom order; Linens; Bath accessories; Gifts & novelties; Bar fixtures, equipment & supplies
CEO: Thomas A Kingsbury
**Pr:* Joshua Bekenstein
**Ex VP:* Charles Guardiola
**Ex VP:* Fred Hand
**Ex VP:* Marc D Katz
**VP:* Jordan Hitch
**VP:* Robert Lapenta Jr

D-U-N-S 07-962-6807
■ BURLINGTON COAT FACTORY HOLDINGS LLC
(*Suby of* BURLINGTON HOLDINGS, LLC)
1830 N Route 130, Burlington, NJ 08016-3020
Tel (609) 387-7800 *Founded/Ownrshp* 2014
Sales 4.4MMM[E] *EMP* 30,095[E]
SIC 5311 Department stores

D-U-N-S 78-824-3637
■ BURLINGTON COAT FACTORY INVESTMENTS HOLDINGS INC
(*Suby of* BURLINGTON COAT FACTORY HOLDINGS LLC) ★
1830 N Route 130, Burlington, NJ 08016-3020
Tel (609) 387-7800 *Founded/Ownrshp* 2006
Sales 4.4MMM *EMP* 30,095[E]
SIC 5311 Department stores
Ch Bd: Thomas A Kingsbury
CFO: Marc Katz
Chf Mktg O: Hobart Sichel
Ex VP: Janet Dhillon
Ex VP: Joyce Manning Magrini
VP: Beth Wonski
Board of Directors: Joshua Bekenstein, Frank Cooper III, Jordan Hitch, John J Mahoney, William P McNamara, Tricia Patrick, Paul J Sullivan, Mary Ann Tocio

D-U-N-S 80-955-9073
■ BURLINGTON COAT FACTORY REALTY OF MORROW INC
(*Suby of* BURLINGTON COAT FACTORY WAREHOUSE CORP) ★
1830 N Route 130, Burlington, NJ 08016-3020
Tel (609) 387-7800 *Founded/Ownrshp* 1984
Sales 34.5MM[E] *EMP* 1,200
SIC 5651 Family clothing stores
Prin: Thomas A Kingsbury
Board of Directors: Michael Prince

D-U-N-S 07-521-5400 IMP/EXP
■ BURLINGTON COAT FACTORY WAREHOUSE CORP
(*Suby of* BURLINGTON COAT FACTORY INVESTMENTS HOLDINGS INC) ★
1830 N Route 130 # 2006, Burlington, NJ 08016-3020
Tel (609) 387-7800 *Founded/Ownrshp* 1983
Sales 142.0M *EMP* 24,065
SIC 5311 Department stores, discount

Pr: Thomas A Kingsbury
CFO: Todd Weyrich
Treas: Robert Lapenta Jr
Chf Mktg O: Joan Ahsam
Ofcr: Robert L Lapenta
Ex VP: Joyce Manning Magrini
Ex VP: Stephen E Milstein
Ex VP: Paul C Tang
Ex VP: Charles Thomas
Sr VP: John D Crimminsk
VP: Lorenzo Figureoa
VP: Hobart P Sichel
Dir Risk M: Thomas B Culotta
Dir Bus: Liza Debari
Dir Bus: Nathaniel Taylor

D-U-N-S 08-080-3232
■ BURLINGTON COAT FACTORY WAREHOUSE OF MONMOUTH INC
(*Suby of* BURLINGTON COAT FACTORY WAREHOUSE CORP) ★
1830 N Route 130, Burlington, NJ 08016-3020
Tel (609) 387-7800 *Founded/Ownrshp* 1976
Sales 97.7MM^E *EMP* 1,280
SIC 5651 Family clothing stores
VP: Henrietta Milstein

D-U-N-S 00-243-0411
BURLINGTON DRUG CO INC
91 Catamount Dr, Milton, VT 05468-3236
Tel (802) 893-5105 *Founded/Ownrshp* 1891
Sales 353.4MM^E *EMP* 235
SIC 5122 Drugs & drug proprietaries; Proprietary (patent) medicines; Pharmaceuticals; Druggists' sundries
Pr: John D Mitiguy
**Pr:* Michael J Mitiguy
**VP:* Maria M Burns
**VP:* Christopher Mitiguy
MIS Dir: Jim Towsend
Manager: Bob Peet
Sales Exec: Steven Hayes

D-U-N-S 16-060-1576 IMP/EXP
BURLINGTON INDUSTRIES LLC
(*Suby of* INTERNATIONAL TEXTILE GROUP INC) ★
804 Green Valley Rd # 300, Greensboro, NC 27408-7039
Tel (336) 379-6220 *Founded/Ownrshp* 2007
Sales 337.5MM^E *EMP* 3,000
SIC 2231 2211 2221 2273 2262 2261 Bleaching yarn & fabrics: wool or similar fibers; Upholstery fabrics, wool; Denims; Draperies & drapery fabrics, cotton; Upholstery fabrics, cotton; Tickings; Polyester broadwoven fabrics; Draperies & drapery fabrics, manmade fiber & silk; Upholstery fabrics, manmade fiber & silk; Carpets & rugs; Finishing plants, manmade fiber & silk fabrics; Finishing plants, cotton
CEO: Joe Gorga
Ex VP: Pat Palmer

BURLINGTON LINCOLN MERCURY HON
See BURLINGTON MOTORS INC

D-U-N-S 02-444-4853
BURLINGTON MOTORS INC
BURLINGTON LINCOLN MERCURY HON
660 Huffman Mill Rd, Burlington, NC 27215-5123
Tel (336) 584-1701 *Founded/Ownrshp* 1964
Sales 87.0MM *EMP* 97
SIC 5511 Automobiles, new & used
Pr: William C Ingold
VP: W D Ingol
**VP:* W Daryl Ingold

D-U-N-S 92-782-4730
■ BURLINGTON NORTHERN SANTA FE LLC
(*Suby of* BERKSHIRE HATHAWAY INC) ★
2650 Lou Menk Dr, Fort Worth, TX 76131-2830
Tel (800) 795-2673 *Founded/Ownrshp* 2010
Sales 21.9MMM *EMP* 4,800^E
SIC 4731 4011 Freight transportation arrangement; Railroads, line-haul operating
Ch Bd: Matthew K Rose
Pr: David Clark
Pr: Lance French
**Pr:* Carl R Ice
**CFO:* Julie A Piggott
Treas: Douglas Langston
Treas: Karen Lekashman
VP: Paul B Anderson
VP: David Fleenor
VP: David Freeman
VP: Terry Huddle
VP: Jon I Stevens
VP: Steven Klug
VP: Jack Schroeder
Exec: Garry Bender
Board of Directors: Stevan B Bobb, Warren E Buffett, Gregory C Fox, Marc D Hamburg, Roger Nober

D-U-N-S 19-170-7793 IMP
■ BURLINGTON RESOURCES INC
(*Suby of* CONOCOPHILLIPS) ★
600 N Dairy Ashford Rd, Houston, TX 77079-1100
Tel (281) 293-1000 *Founded/Ownrshp* 2006
Sales 249.7MM^E *EMP* 2,214
SIC 1311 5172 4922 4612 Crude petroleum production; Natural gas production; Petroleum products; Pipelines, natural gas; Crude petroleum pipelines
COO: Randy L Limbacher
**CFO:* Steven J Shapiro
Sr VP: L David Hanower
Sr VP: John A Williams

BURLINGTON SHOES
See SHOE SHOW INC

D-U-N-S 07-913-5721
▲ BURLINGTON STORES INC
2006 Route 130, Burlington, NJ 08016-9716
Tel (609) 387-7800 *Founded/Ownrshp* 1972
Sales 5.1MMM *EMP* 37,500^E
Accts Deloitte & Touche Llp Parsipp
Tkr Sym BURL *Exch* NYS
SIC 5311 5961 Department stores; Catalog & mail-order houses
Ch Bd: Thomas A Kingsbury
CFO: Marc Katz
Ex VP: Janet Dhillon
Ex VP: Janet L Dhillon
Ex VP: Charlie Guardiola
Ex VP: Fred Hand
Ex VP: Joyce Manning Magrini
Ex VP: Mike Metheny
Ex VP: Rick Seeger
Ex VP: Hobart Sichel
Ex VP: Jennifer Vecchio
VP: Melanie Grant
VP: Tony Hughes
VP: Michael Kennedy
VP: Mike Prince
VP: Paul Tang
Board of Directors: Joshua Bekenstein, Ted English, Jordan Hitch, John J Mahoney, William P McNamara, Tricia Patrick, Paul J Sullivan, Mary Ann Tocio

D-U-N-S 01-356-1626 IMP/EXP
BURMAX CO INC
BURMAX NEW YORK WAREHOUSE
28 Barretts Ave, Holtsville, NY 11742-2127
Tel (631) 447-8700 *Founded/Ownrshp* 1962
Sales 104.2MM^E *EMP* 150
SIC 5087 7231 Barber shop equipment & supplies; Beauty parlor equipment & supplies; Beauty shops
Ch Bd: Burton Scheff
**Pr:* Steven Scheff
**CFO:* Thomas Forte
Mktg Dir: Lois Zuhoski

BURMAX NEW YORK WAREHOUSE
See BURMAX CO INC

D-U-N-S 83-237-5559
■ BURNDY AMERICAS INC
(*Suby of* HUBBELL INC) ★
47 E Industrial Pk Dr, Manchester, NH 03109-5311
Tel (603) 647-5000 *Founded/Ownrshp* 1992
Sales 190.7MM^E *EMP* 1,392^E
SIC 3643 5063 Current-carrying wiring devices; Electrical apparatus & equipment
Pr: Rodd Ruland

D-U-N-S 83-239-1796 IMP/EXP
■ BURNDY LLC
(*Suby of* BURNDY AMERICAS INC) ★
47 E Industrial Park Dr, Manchester, NH 03109-5311
Tel (603) 626-3730 *Founded/Ownrshp* 2009
Sales 160.4MM *EMP* 741
SIC 3643 5063 Electric connectors; Wire & cable
Pr: Rodd Ruland
**CFO:* Kevin P Ryan
Sr Cor Off: Robert Citney
VP: Betsy Babcock
Genl Mgr: Julie Bly
Genl Mgr: Lorraine Paquette
Genl Mgr: Kathleen Robicheau
Genl Mgr: Jackie Sylvia
CTO: Taylor Boyko
Plnt Mgr: Alan Beck
Plnt Mgr: Fred Chisolm

D-U-N-S 09-248-8022
BURNETT COMPANIES CONSOLIDATED INC
CHOICE STAFFING
9800 Richmond Ave Ste 800, Houston, TX 77042-4548
Tel (713) 977-4777 *Founded/Ownrshp* 1974
Sales 69.4MM *EMP* 2,000
Accts Briggs & Veselka Co Houston
SIC 7361 8243 Employment agencies; Software training, computer
Pr: Susan Burnett
COO: Christina Gomez
**CFO:* Rusty Burnett
VP: Debbie D'Ambrosio
VP: Barbara Jax
Dir Risk M: Debbie Dambrosio
Dist Mgr: Edna Hardin
Dist Mgr: Jessica Wheeler
Opers Mgr: Maggie Dunn
Sls&Mrk Ex: Eva Newsome
Mktg Dir: Makenzie Burnett

D-U-N-S 00-603-0902 IMP/EXP
BURNETTE FOODS INC
701 S Us Highway 31, Elk Rapids, MI 49629-9525
Tel (231) 264-8116 *Founded/Ownrshp* 1972
Sales 135.0MM^E *EMP* 380
Accts Hill Shroderus And Co
SIC 2033 Fruit juices: packaged in cans, jars, etc.; Fruits: packaged in cans, jars, etc.; Vegetables: packaged in cans, jars, etc.
Pr: William R Sherman
**COO:* John Pelizzari
CFO: Jennifer Boyer
**Sec:* Theodore Sherman
**VP:* Robert Sherman

D-U-N-S 00-152-5054 IMP
BURNHAM HOLDINGS INC
1241 Harrisburg Ave, Lancaster, PA 17603-2515
Tel (717) 390-7800 *Founded/Ownrshp* 2002
Sales 190.4MM *EMP* 794
Accts Baker Tilly Virchow Krouse Ll
SIC 3433 Heating equipment, except electric; Boilers, low-pressure heating: steam or hot water; Oil burners, domestic or industrial
Pr: Douglas S Brossman
**Ch Bd:* Albert Morrison III
CFO: Dale R Bowman
Bd of Dir: Elizabeth Freimer
Bd of Dir: Elizabeth Hughes
**Ex VP:* Chris Drew
VP: John Roda
MIS Dir: Steven Beck
Board of Directors: William F Dodge II, Eleanor B Drew, George W Hodges, Thomas C Kile, John W Lyman, Elizabeth H McMullan, Robert P Newcomer, Donald A Stern

D-U-N-S 05-545-1405 IMP
BURNS & MCDONNELL ENGINEERING CO INC
(*Suby of* BURNS & MCDONNELL INC) ★
9400 Ward Pkwy, Kansas City, MO 64114-3319
Tel (816) 333-9400 *Founded/Ownrshp* 1986
Sales 1.6MMM^E *EMP* 1,800
SIC 1382 8711 Oil & gas exploration services; Mechanical engineering; Consulting engineer
CEO: Gregory M Graves Pe
CFO: Dennis Scott
Sr VP: Don Greenwood
Sr VP: John Nobles
Sr VP: Walt Womack
Snr PM: Matthew Lind

D-U-N-S 17-369-5917
BURNS & MCDONNELL INC
9400 Ward Pkwy, Kansas City, MO 64114-3319
Tel (816) 333-9400 *Founded/Ownrshp* 1985
Sales 1.6MMM^E *EMP* 2,000
SIC 8711 8741 Consulting engineer; Construction management
CEO: Gregory M Graves
Pt: Mark Nelson
**Pr:* Paul Fischer
**Pr:* Don Greenwood
**Pr:* Ray Kowalik
**Pr:* John Olander
Pr: Mellisa Wood
**Pr:* David Yeamans
CFO: Dennis W Scott
**CFO:* Denny Scott
Assoc VP: Arnold Olender
Sr VP: Ron Coker
Sr VP: Mike Fenske
Sr VP: Rick Halil
Sr VP: Bob Reymond
Sr VP: Melissa Wood
VP: Henry Aboujawdeh
VP: Ben Biller
VP: Greg Gould
VP: Benjamin Greek
VP: Stephen Kane
Board of Directors: Paul Fischer, John Olander

D-U-N-S 07-269-7378 IMP/EXP
BURNS & ROE GROUP INC
800 Kinderkamack Rd Ste 1, Oradell, NJ 07649-1563
Tel (201) 265-2000 *Founded/Ownrshp* 1932
Sales 51.7MM^E *EMP* 1,004
SIC 8711 Engineering services
Pr: K Keith Roe
**Treas:* Michael Marcopoto
**Sr VP:* Russell Smith
VP: Michael Clark
VP: Bill Gattoni
VP: Ralph Hunter
**VP:* Andrew Ratzkin
**VP:* Hollace L Roe
**VP:* Randall B Roe
Dir IT: Wayne Uffleman

BURNS & WILCOX
See AJK ENTERPRISES INC

D-U-N-S 03-963-1999
BURNS & WILCOX LTD
FLOYD WEST & COMPANY
(*Suby of* H W KAUFMAN FINANCIAL GROUP INC) ★
120 Kaufm Finan Cente 30, Farmington Hills, MI 48334
Tel (248) 932-9000 *Founded/Ownrshp* 1966
Sales NA *EMP* 1,000
SIC 6331 6411 Fire, marine & casualty insurance; Fire, marine & casualty insurance & carriers; Property damage insurance; Insurance agents & brokers
Pr: Alan Jay Kaufman
**CFO:* Daniel T Muldowney
**Ex VP:* George S Allen
Ex VP: B Dantoni
**Sr VP:* A Gary Batten
**Sr VP:* Donald R Carson
**Sr VP:* David Price
VP: Jeffrey Diefenbach
VP: Carol Dunaway
VP: James Epting
VP: Michael Maharaj
VP: Reid Wilson

D-U-N-S 00-510-9009
BURNS CONSULTING INC (AZ)
THYMES
15414 N 7th St 8122, Phoenix, AZ 85022-3519
Tel (602) 993-3070 *Founded/Ownrshp* 1991
Sales 300.0MM *EMP* 2
SIC 8742 7389 Business consultant;
Pr: Gregg Johnson
**VP:* Carol Johnson

D-U-N-S 17-002-2789
BURNS GROUP UNLIMITED LLC
BURNSGROUP PR
833 Piedmont Ave Ne Ste B, Atlanta, GA 30308-1453
Tel (404) 873-0772 *Founded/Ownrshp* 2000
Sales 90.0MM *EMP* 4
SIC 8743 Public relations services

BURNSGROUP PR
See BURNS GROUP UNLIMITED LLC

D-U-N-S 07-973-4158
BURNSVILLE EAGAN SAVAGE INDEPENDENT SCHOOL DISTRICT 191
ADMINISTRATIVE SERVICES CENTER
100 River Ridge Ct, Burnsville, MN 55337-1613
Tel (952) 707-2000 *Founded/Ownrshp* 1955
Sales 79.9MM^E *EMP* 1,300
Accts Malloy Montague Karnowski R
SIC 8211 Public elementary & secondary schools
Ex Dir: Stephanie Corbey
Dir Sec: Susan Thompson
Dir IT: Doug Johnson
Pr Dir: Ruth Dunn
Pr Dir: Gary Kubat
Pr Dir: Aldo Sicoli
Teacher Pr: Stacey Sovine
HC Dir: Dawn Willson

D-U-N-S 01-094-8813
BURNSVILLE-EAGAN-SAVAGE BOARD OF EDUCATION
100 River Ridge Ct, Burnsville, MN 55337-1613
Tel (952) 707-2000 *Founded/Ownrshp* 1958
Sales 113.8MM *EMP* 109^E
Accts Malloy Montague Karnowski R
SIC 8211 School board
Ch Bd: Bob Vandenboom
**Ex Dir:* Sue Grisom
Psych: Kelsey Parkin
Psych: Nichole Short

D-U-N-S 94-678-2877 IMP/EXP
BURPEE HOLDING CO INC
800 Roosevelt Rd Ste 216, Glen Ellyn, IL 60137-5839
Tel (215) 674-4900 *Founded/Ownrshp* 1995
Sales 117.2MM^E *EMP* 350
SIC 0181 5191 Seeds, vegetable: growing of; Seeds, flower: growing of; Farm supplies
Pr: George Ball Jr
**COO:* Chris G Romas
**CFO:* C Hans Miller

BURPEE SEEDS
See W ATLEE BURPEE CO

D-U-N-S 06-202-6208
BURRELLES INFORMATION SERVICES LLC
BURRELLESLUCE
30b Vreeland Rd, Florham Park, NJ 07932-1926
Tel (973) 992-6600 *Founded/Ownrshp* 1888, 1964
Sales 140.5MM^E *EMP* 1,500
SIC 7389
COO: Rudolf Litzlbeck
VP: James Waggoner

BURRELLESLUCE
See BURRELLES INFORMATION SERVICES LLC

D-U-N-S 07-547-9931 IMP/EXP
BURRIS LOGISTICS
BURRIS RETAIL LOGISTICS
501 Se 5th St, Milford, DE 19963-2022
Tel (302) 839-4531 *Founded/Ownrshp* 1939
Sales 3.5MMM^E *EMP* 1,600
SIC 5142 4222 4213 Packaged frozen goods; Storage, frozen or refrigerated goods; Refrigerated products transport
Prin: Maria Wittmeyer
**CFO:* Wayne Romanczuk
VP: Brian Haley
VP: Rob Hayes
VP: Karen Kappra
VP: Christopher Turk
Exec: Derrick Giuttari
Genl Mgr: Greg Cyganiewicz
Genl Mgr: Nick Falk
Genl Mgr: Allen Finley
Genl Mgr: Tim Peifley

BURRIS RETAIL LOGISTICS
See BURRIS LOGISTICS

D-U-N-S 00-791-9590
BURROUGHS & CHAPIN CO INC (SC)
8800 Marina Pkwy, Myrtle Beach, SC 29572-8101
Tel (843) 448-5123 *Founded/Ownrshp* 1895, 1990
Sales 363.7MM^E *EMP* 1,730^E
SIC 6552 6515 6519 6512 Subdividers & developers; Mobile home site operators; Real property lessors; Nonresidential building operators
CEO: James W Apple Jr
**Ch Bd:* James E Burroughs
**Pr:* Jim Rosenberg
**CFO:* J Bratton Fennell
CFO: Barry R Spivey
**Ex VP:* Terry Horak
**Ex VP:* Andy Tilmont
VP: Jane Sufka

D-U-N-S 07-861-8005
BURROUGHS INC
41100 Plymouth Rd, Plymouth, MI 48170-1892
Tel (734) 737-4000 *Founded/Ownrshp* 2010
Sales 571.6MM^E *EMP* 2,410^E
SIC 5049 Bank equipment & supplies
CEO: Larry McCarter
VP: Bruce Young
IT Man: Michael Anstess
IT Man: Paul Christensen
Sftwr Eng: Tom Bondy

D-U-N-S 83-322-8773 IMP/EXP
BURROUGHS PAYMENT SYSTEMS INC
41100 Plymouth Rd, Plymouth, MI 48170-1892
Tel (734) 737-4000 *Founded/Ownrshp* 2009
Sales 215.0MM^E *EMP* 572^E
SIC 5049 Bank equipment & supplies
Pr: Alan Howard
**CFO:* Jerry Doubler
Sr VP: Larry McCarter
VP: Alan Grote
VP: Bruce Young

D-U-N-S 96-155-1293
BURROW GLOBAL LLC
B G
6200 Savoy Dr Ste 800, Houston, TX 77036-3384
Tel (713) 963-0930 *Founded/Ownrshp* 2010
Sales 166.6MM *EMP* 550
SIC 1542 6799 Commercial & office building contractors; Investors
CEO: Michael Burrow
**COO:* Gary Knight
COO: Steve Watkins
**CFO:* Bob Raiford
CFO: Tom Williams
**Ofcr:* Nigel James
Ex VP: Tom Rutherford
Sr VP: Michael O'Keefe
Sr VP: Saji Samuel
Sr VP: Jeffrey Schiller
Sr VP: Loretta Watkins
VP: Buster Burnett
**VP:* Steve Maricelli
VP: Jim Weaver

D-U-N-S 09-519-0500
BURROW GLOBAL SERVICES LLC (TX)
(*Suby of* B G) ★
6200 Savoy Dr Ste 800, Houston, TX 77036-3384
Tel (713) 963-0930 *Founded/Ownrshp* 1978
Sales 136.7MM *EMP* 303^E

SIC 1542 1541 8711 Commercial & office building, new construction; Industrial buildings & warehouses; Construction & civil engineering; Designing: ship, boat, machine & product
**Pr:* Nigel James
**Pr:* Gary Knight
COO: Jim Spence
**CFO:* Bob Raiford
CFO: Tom Williams
**Sr VP:* John Meyer
Sfty Dirs: Richard Hart
Snr PM: John Wantuch

D-U-N-S 00-222-9920 IMP/EXP
BURROWS PAPER CORP (NY)
501 W Main St Ste 1, Little Falls, NY 13365-1899
Tel (315) 823-2300 *Founded/Ownrshp* 1919
Sales 215.6MM^E *EMP* 900
SIC 2621 2671 2611 2679

D-U-N-S 06-322-0441
BURRTEC WASTE GROUP INC
9890 Cherry Ave, Fontana, CA 92335-5202
Tel (909) 429-4200 *Founded/Ownrshp* 1999
Sales 300.3MM^E *EMP* 562
SIC 4953 Rubbish collection & disposal; Recycling, waste materials
Pr: Cole Burr

D-U-N-S 05-562-7392
BURRTEC WASTE INDUSTRIES INC (CA)
(*Suby of* BURRTEC WASTE GROUP INC) ★
9890 Cherry Ave, Fontana, CA 92335-5298
Tel (909) 429-4200 *Founded/Ownrshp* 1978
Sales 295.3MM^E *EMP* 381
SIC 4953 4212 Rubbish collection & disposal; Recycling, waste materials; Local trucking, without storage
Pr: Cole Burr
CFO: Robert Coon
VP: Eric Herbert
VP: Trevor Scrogins
Div Mgr: Bill Jones
Div Mgr: Victor Urena
Genl Mgr: Richard Crocket
Genl Mgr: Richard Nino
Genl Mgr: Tim Williams
Site Mgr: Letty Vasquez
Opers Supe: Luis Gutierrez

D-U-N-S 17-370-8645
BURRUS INVESTMENT GROUP INC
DOUBLETREE HOTEL
401 Veterans Memrl, Metairie, LA 70005-2957
Tel (504) 455-7600 *Founded/Ownrshp* 1985
Sales 73.6MM^E *EMP* 1,000
SIC 6799 Investors
Pr: George J Newton III
**Ch:* David R Burrus
**Sec:* Chris D Schott

BURRY FOODSERVICE
See QUALITY BAKERIES LLC

D-U-N-S 07-941-3413
BURTEK HOLDINGS INC
50325 Patricia St, Chesterfield, MI 48051-3803
Tel (586) 421-8000 *Founded/Ownrshp* 2012
Sales 172.4MM^E *EMP* 315^E
SIC 7371 3812 8711 Computer software development & applications; Radar systems & equipment; Defense systems & equipment; Acceleration indicators & systems components, aerospace; Engineering services; Building construction consultant
Pr: Jeff Daniel
**VP:* Gregory Gallagher

D-U-N-S 06-422-8356 IMP/EXP
BURTON CORP
D N A
80 Industrial Pkwy, Burlington, VT 05401-5434
Tel (802) 862-4500 *Founded/Ownrshp* 1978
Sales 136.9MM^E *EMP* 450
SIC 3949 Snow skiing equipment & supplies, except skis
Ch: Jake Burton Carpenter
**Pr:* John Lacy
**CEO:* Donna Carpenter
**CEO:* Mike Reesr
CFO: Mike Rees
**Sr VP:* Philippe Gouzes
VP: Josee Blake
VP: Jeff Boliba
VP: Anne M Dacyshyn
VP: Greg Dacyshyn
VP: Jennifer Mincar
VP: Matthew Ross
VP: Craig Smith
VP: Justin Wheating
Dir Soc: Ian Warda

D-U-N-S 03-535-2939
BURTON LUMBER & HARDWARE CO
1170 S 4400 W, Salt Lake City, UT 84104-4413
Tel (801) 952-3700 *Founded/Ownrshp* 1911
Sales 131.1MM *EMP* 250
Accts Haynie & Company Salt Lake Ci
SIC 5211 5251 Lumber & other building materials; Builders' hardware
Pr: Daniel S Burton
CFO: Joann Hall
**VP:* Jeff Burton
**VP:* Mark Burton
Genl Mgr: Brian Carlson
IT Man: Charlynn Ageunnorh
IT Man: Hans Noerring
Tech Mgr: Jake Hoopes
Opers Mgr: Jed Smith

D-U-N-S 61-348-0946 IMP/EXP
■ **BURTS BEES INC**
(*Suby of* CLOROX CO) ★
210 W Pettigrew St, Durham, NC 27701-3666
Tel (919) 998-5200 *Founded/Ownrshp* 2007
Sales 109.4MM^E *EMP* 530
SIC 2844 5122 5087 Cosmetic preparations; Cosmetics, perfumes & hair products; Beauty parlor equipment & supplies
CEO: John Replogle
**Ch Bd:* M Beth Springer
**Treas:* Charles R Conradi
**VP:* Daniel J Heinrich
**VP:* Angela Hilt
IT Man: Tray Vance
Mktg Mgr: Juan Arrieta
Mktg Mgr: John Feeney
Mktg Mgr: William Melendez
Snr Mgr: Lenny Leonard

BUS, THE
See OAHU TRANSIT SERVICES INC

BUSAKSHAMBAN
See TRELLEBORG SEALING SOLUTIONS US INC

D-U-N-S 01-285-0665 IMP/EXP
BUSCH AGRICULTURAL RESOURCES LLC
(*Suby of* ANHEUSER-BUSCH COMPANIES LLC) ★
3636 S Geyer Rd Fl 2, Saint Louis, MO 63127-1237
Tel (314) 577-2000 *Founded/Ownrshp* 1980
Sales 164.9MM^E *EMP* 1,100
SIC 2044 2083 0181 5153 Milled rice; Malt; Barley malt; Sod farms; Grain & field beans
Ch: Donald Kloth
**Pr:* Melvern K Anderson
**Pr:* Melvin Anderson
**VP:* Cick Emerson
Exec: Jim Feuerstein

D-U-N-S 78-749-0432 EXP
BUSCH CONSOLIDATED INC
(*Suby of* BUSCH SE)
516 Viking Dr, Virginia Beach, VA 23452-7316
Tel (757) 463-7800 *Founded/Ownrshp* 1991
Sales 106.6MM^E *EMP* 230^E
SIC 5084 3563 Pumps & pumping equipment; Vacuum pumps, except laboratory
Pr: Ing K Busch
**VP:* Ayhan Busch
VP: Paul Swank

BUSCHE ENTERPRISE DIVISION INC
See BUSCHE PERFORMANCE GROUP INC

BUSCHE PERFORMANCE GROUP
See SHIPSTON GROUP US INC

D-U-N-S 17-592-7342 IMP
BUSCHE PERFORMANCE GROUP INC
BUSCHE ENTERPRISE DIVISION INC
(*Suby of* BUSCHE PERFORMANCE GROUP) ★
1563 E State Road 8, Albion, IN 46701-9702
Tel (260) 636-7030 *Founded/Ownrshp* 2014
Sales 132.0MM^E *EMP* 800
SIC 3599 Machine shop, jobbing & repair
Pr: Nick Busche
Mng Dir: Barbara Owen
QC Dir: Tom Keller
Mtls Mgr: Cheryl Smith
Ql Cn Mgr: Bret Cooper
Ql Cn Mgr: Jeff Roberts
Mktg Dir: Mark Garrison
Sls Dir: Leann Gray

BUSCH'S FRESH FOOD MARKET
See BUSCHS INC

D-U-N-S 07-756-9846
BUSCHS INC
BUSCH'S FRESH FOOD MARKET
2240 S Main St, Ann Arbor, MI 48103-5831
Tel (734) 998-2666 *Founded/Ownrshp* 1975
Sales 155.9MM^E *EMP* 1,150
SIC 5411 Supermarkets, chain
CEO: Mike Brooks
**CFO:* Tina Scrupsky
**Sec:* Douglas Busch
VP: Doug Busch
VP: Kristina Simmons
Ex Dir: Tom Hash
Ex Dir: Tim Surma

D-U-N-S 00-693-6223
■ **BUSEY BANK**
(*Suby of* FIRST BUSEY CORP) ★
100 W University Ave # 100, Champaign, IL 61820-3910
Tel (217) 365-4500 *Founded/Ownrshp* 1868
Sales NA *EMP* 403
SIC 6022 State commercial banks
Pr: Thomas Good
**CFO:* Barb Jones
**Treas:* Ed Paine
Ofcr: Barb Kelly
Ofcr: Laurie Ohls
**Ex VP:* Susan Abbott
Ex VP: Bill Borrini
Ex VP: Susan Miller
**Ex VP:* Don Monteith
**Ex VP:* Lee O'Neill
Ex VP: Robert Plecki Jr
**Ex VP:* Donald J Schlorff
Ex VP: David R Wample
**Ex VP:* David R Wampler
Ex VP: Nancy Weimer
Sr VP: Jeffrey Bell
Sr VP: Randy C Eddy
Sr VP: Jeremy Frieburg
Sr VP: Linda Smith
VP: Aimee Aubry
VP: Stacy Cruz

D-U-N-S 00-337-7538 IMP
BUSH BROTHERS & CO
1016 E Weisgarber Rd, Knoxville, TN 37909-2669
Tel (865) 450-4130 *Founded/Ownrshp* 1908
Sales 186.6MM^E *EMP* 650
SIC 2033 2032 Hominy: packaged in cans, jars, etc.; Sauerkraut: packaged in cans, jars, etc.; Vegetables: packaged in cans, jars, etc.; Beans, baked with meat: packaged in cans, jars, etc.
CEO: James B Ethier
**CFO:* David Shapland
**Sr VP:* Ronald Dix
**Sr VP:* Tom C Rugotzke
**VP:* Tom Ferriter
**VP:* Steve Harrison
VP: Ray Kielarowski
**VP:* Phil Perkins PHD
**Div Mgr:* Craig McQuiddy
Dir IT: Drew Everett
IT Man: Jeff Austin

D-U-N-S 14-255-5536 IMP
■ **BUSH HOG INC**
(*Suby of* ALAMO GROUP INC) ★
2501 Griffin Ave, Selma, AL 36703-1918
Tel (800) 363-6096 *Founded/Ownrshp* 2009
Sales 102.6MM^E *EMP* 500
SIC 3523 Farm machinery & equipment
Pr: Richard Pummell
Pr: Ken Spear
CFO: James Bearden
**VP:* Robert H George
**VP:* Howard W May
**VP:* Matt G Mikesell
VP: Bob Moore
**VP:* Richard J Wehrle
Genl Mgr: Shirley Worrell
Dir IT: Mike Clark
**VP Sls:* Tom Taylor

D-U-N-S 80-918-2744
BUSH INDUSTRIES CORP
9850 Atlantic Blvd, Jacksonville, FL 32225-6536
Tel (904) 725-0911 *Founded/Ownrshp* 1984
Sales 169.2MM^E *EMP* 211
SIC 5511 New & used car dealers
Pr: Tom Bush Jr
**VP:* John P Bush
DP Exec: Lisa Fagin
Sales Asso: Marty Seymour

D-U-N-S 00-211-1961 IMP/EXP
BUSH INDUSTRIES INC
1 Mason Dr, Jamestown, NY 14701-9200
Tel (716) 665-2000 *Founded/Ownrshp* 1959, 2004
Sales 169.1MM^E *EMP* 316
SIC 2511 2521 Wood household furniture; Desks, office: wood; Cabinets, office: wood; Bookcases, office: wood; Panel systems & partitions (free-standing), office: wood
CEO: Jim Garde
CFO: Debbie Chudy
**CFO:* Neil A Frederick
Treas: Neil Frederick
**Ex VP:* Mike Evans
**Ex VP:* Jerry Green
**Ex VP:* Steve Phelan
**VP:* Larry Genareo
Creative D: Annet Lyth
CIO: Pamela Burgess
CTO: Paul S Bush
Board of Directors: Jim Garde

BUSH, TOM BMW
See TOM BUSH VOLKSWAGEN INC

D-U-N-S 19-347-4483
BUSHKILL GROUP INC
FERNWOOD RESORT
(*Suby of* RESORTS GROUP INC) ★
1008 Sand Hill Creek Rd, East Stroudsburg, PA 18302
Tel (570) 588-6661 *Founded/Ownrshp* 1988
Sales 58.6MM^E *EMP* 1,355
SIC 7011 Hotels; Resort hotel
Pr: W Andrew Worthington
COO: Mark Turner
VP: John Briggs
**VP:* Thomas V Casale
VP: Bruce Hagedorn
IT Man: Lisa Herman

D-U-N-S 61-187-9636 IMP/EXP
■ **BUSHNELL HOLDINGS INC**
BUSHNELL SPORTS OPTICS
(*Suby of* BUSHNELL OUTDOOR PRODUCTS) ★
9200 Cody St, Overland Park, KS 66214-1734
Tel (913) 752-3400 *Founded/Ownrshp* 1995
Sales 148.6MM^E *EMP* 462
SIC 3851 5049 5091 Ophthalmic goods; Optical goods; Sporting & recreation goods
CEO: Mark Deyoung
CFO: David Broadbent
VP: Mike Belick
Genl Mgr: Leah Wilson
CTO: Jim Edmiston
Dir IT: Larry Lucas
Natl Sales: Scott Whitehead
Mktg Mgr: Laura Pfeifer

D-U-N-S 61-691-7662 IMP
■ **BUSHNELL INC**
BUSHNELL OUTDOOR PRODUCTS
(*Suby of* VISTA OUTDOOR INC) ★
9200 Cody St, Overland Park, KS 66214-1734
Tel (913) 752-3400 *Founded/Ownrshp* 1980
Sales 218.4MM^E *EMP* 587^E
SIC 3827 Binoculars
CEO: Mark Deyoung
IT Man: Monty King
Natl Sales: Kim Hosey
Natl Sales: Randy Hudson
Pr Mgr: Paul Arnhold

BUSHNELL OUTDOOR PRODUCTS
See BUSHNELL INC

BUSHNELL SPORTS OPTICS
See BUSHNELL HOLDINGS INC

D-U-N-S 00-697-8811 IMP
■ **BUSHWICK METALS LLC**
AZCO STEEL
(*Suby of* MARMON/KEYSTONE LLC) ★
560 N Washington Ave # 2, Bridgeport, CT 06604-2900
Tel (888) 399-4070 *Founded/Ownrshp* 1999
Sales 186.3MM^E *EMP* 222
SIC 5051

D-U-N-S 80-614-0583
BUSINESS & DECISION NORTH AMERICA INC
(*Suby of* BUSINESS & DECISION)
900 W Valley Rd Ste 1000, Wayne, PA 19087-1813
Tel (610) 230-2500 *Founded/Ownrshp* 2005
Sales 124.2MM^E *EMP* 2,800
SIC 7372 Business oriented computer software
CEO: Robin Kearon
Ex VP: Todd Wilkerson
VP: Wayne Dickert
VP: Andrew Fletcher
Genl Mgr: Christian Oram
Mktg Dir: Sarah Brisbin
Snr PM: Jim Beasley

D-U-N-S 07-827-8835 IMP
■ **BUSINESS AND SUPPORT SERVICES**
NAF BUSINESS AND SUPPORT SVCS
(*Suby of* MARINE CORPS INTELLIGENCE) ★
3044 Catlin Ave, Quantico, VA 22134-5003
Tel (703) 432-0109 *Founded/Ownrshp* 1903
Sales 548.5MM^E *EMP* 12,000
SIC 7997 Membership sports & recreation clubs
VP: Jessica Bradley
Dir Soc: Gary Karr
Prin: Amanda Ayers
Admn Mgr: Sheila Dabrowski
Dept Mgr: Vendella Davis
DP Exec: Rycourt Freeman
IT Man: Kay Hewitt
Opers Mgr: Larry Cribb
Opers Mgr: Lillian Thomashoffman
Mktg Dir: Sharon Diaz
Mktg Mgr: Mary C McReynolds

D-U-N-S 96-802-6265
BUSINESS DEVELOPMENT CORP OF AMERICA
405 Park Ave Fl 15, New York, NY 10022-9406
Tel (212) 415-6500 *Founded/Ownrshp* 2011
Sales 195.8MM *EMP* 1
Accts Kpmg Llp New York New York
SIC 8748 Business consulting
Ofcr: John H Grady
CFO: Nicholas Radesca

BUSINESS INTELLHGENCER JOURNAL
See LNP MEDIA GROUP INC

BUSINESS INTERIORS BY STAPLES
See STAPLES CONTRACT & COMMERCIAL INC

D-U-N-S 80-393-1369
BUSINESS JOURNAL PUBLICATIONS INC
(*Suby of* STREET & SMITH SPORTS GROUP) ★
4350 W Cypress St Ste 800, Tampa, FL 33607-4180
Tel (813) 342-2472 *Founded/Ownrshp* 1984
Sales 113.2MM^E *EMP* 1,500
SIC 2711 Newspapers: publishing only, not printed on site
Prin: Arthur Porter

D-U-N-S 79-063-4364 IMP
BUSINESS OBJECTS INC
(*Suby of* SAP SE)
3410 Hillview Ave, Palo Alto, CA 94304-1395
Tel (650) 849-4000 *Founded/Ownrshp* 2007
Sales 316.5MM^E *EMP* 5,208
SIC 5045 Computer software
CEO: John Schwarz
CFO: Vronique D'Adhemar
CFO: Bruno Walmsley
**Ch:* Xuanloan Ho
Chf Mktg O: Jonathan Becker
**Chf Mktg O:* Marge Breya
Ex VP: Jagdish Mirani
Ex VP: Greg Wolfe
Grp VP: Tom Malone
Sr VP: Keith Budge
Sr VP: Deborah Byron
**Sr VP:* Herve Couturier
Sr VP: Mark Doll
**Sr VP:* Susan J Wolfe
**VP:* Sheri Anderson
**VP:* Scott Bajtos
VP: Neil S Mendelson
VP: Catherine Buan Peterson
VP: Janet Wood
Exec: Jesse Sims

BUSINESS OF FINANCE
See AIRPORT COMMISIONS

BUSINESS ONLINE PAYROLL
See SUREPAYROLL INC

D-U-N-S 00-693-0473
■ **BUSINESS PROPERTY LENDING INC** (DE)
(*Suby of* GENERAL ELECTRIC CAPITAL CORP) ★
500 W Monroe St, Chicago, IL 60661-3671
Tel (312) 441-7000 *Founded/Ownrshp* 1919
Sales NA *EMP* 2,695
SIC 6153 6799 6162 6159 Mercantile financing; Factoring services; Venture capital companies; Real estate investors, except property operators; Mortgage bankers; Equipment & vehicle finance leasing companies; Machinery & equipment finance leasing; Loan institutions, general & industrial; Intermediate investment banks
Ch Bd: Richard Almeida
Pr: Daniel Marszalek
Pr: James D McGrane
Pr: John Petrovski
**Pr:* Frederick E Wolfert
CFO: Lauralee E Martin
Treas: Anthony O'Beirne
**Chf Cred:* Michael J Litwin
Chf Mktg O: Stephen Ban
Ofcr: Nina B Eidell
Ofcr: Charles W Heller
Ex VP: John L Guy
Ex VP: Robert Radway
**Ex VP:* Kenichiro Tanaka
Sr VP: Jay Foster
Sr VP: Lawrence G Hund
Sr VP: Carik H Langendorfer
Sr VP: Coleen Lusian
Sr VP: Dan Murphy

BUSINESS SERVICE CENTER
See UNMC PHYSICIANS

D-U-N-S 02-279-3116
■ **BUSINESS TELECOM LLC**
(*Suby of* EARTHLINK HOLDINGS CORP) ★
4300 Six Forks Rd Ste 500, Raleigh, NC 27609-5718
Tel (919) 863-7000 *Founded/Ownrshp* 1984

Sales 500.3MM^E *EMP* 975
SIC 4813 4812 Long distance telephone communications; Paging services
Ch: Jay Braukman

D-U-N-S 06-506-4284 IMP/EXP
BUSINESS TELECOMMUNICATIONS SERVICES INC
B T S
(*Suby of* BTS GROUP INC) ★
2620 Sw 27th Ave, Miami, FL 33133-3005
Tel (305) 358-5850 *Founded/Ownrshp* 1993
Sales 280.8MM *EMP* 43^E
SIC 4813 5999 8748 Telephone communications broker; Telephone & communication equipment; Telecommunications consultant
CEO: Rafael Olloqui
**Pr:* Ricardo Olloqui
**Sec:* Andreas Proano

D-U-N-S 80-748-6865
BUSINESS TRANSPORTATION & HOUSING AGENCY STATE OF CALIFORNIA
(*Suby of* EXECUTIVE OFFICE OF STATE OF CALIFORNIA) ★
915 Capitol Mall, Sacramento, CA 95814-4801
Tel (916) 323-5400 *Founded/Ownrshp* 1970
Sales NA *EMP* 37,009
SIC 9611 9621 9531 9532 Administration of general economic programs; ; Regulation, administration of transportation; ; Housing programs; ; Urban & community development;

BUSINESS TRNSP & HSING AGCY
See CALIFORNIA DEPARTMENT OF HOUSING & COMMUNITY DEVELOPMENT

BUSTAMANTE, FRED WOOD PRODUCTS
See ABE ORLANDO BUSTAMANTE

D-U-N-S 78-107-1279 IMP
BUTH-NA-BODHAIGE INC
BODY SHOP
(*Suby of* BODY SHOP INC) ★
77 Deans Rhode Hall Rd, Monmouth Junction, NJ 08852-3019
Tel (732) 348-2152 *Founded/Ownrshp* 1988
Sales 181.5MM^E *EMP* 2,000
SIC 5999 Perfumes & colognes
CEO: Paul Kimberley
**Pr:* Carl Colquett
COO: Peter Saunders
**CFO:* Kim Mattoon
**CFO:* Robert Smith
VP: Richard Begnan
VP: Jason Feltman
**VP:* Kelly McAninch
**VP:* Todd Meyer
VP: Sierra William
Pr Mgr: Bruce Kent

D-U-N-S 07-949-9978
BUTLER AMERICA HOLDINGS INC
3820 State St Ste A, Santa Barbara, CA 93105-3182
Tel (805) 884-9538 *Founded/Ownrshp* 2014
Sales 138.5MM^E *EMP* 1,000^E
SIC 6719 Investment holding companies, except banks
Pr: Christine Ciocca
**CFO:* Rob Olson
**VP:* Edward Fabian
**VP:* Jim Heun

D-U-N-S 96-980-6368
BUTLER AMERICA LLC
(*Suby of* BUTLER AMERICA HOLDINGS INC) ★
3820 State St Ste B, Santa Barbara, CA 93105-3182
Tel (203) 926-2700 *Founded/Ownrshp* 2014
Sales 19.3MM^E *EMP* 1,000^E
SIC 8711 8748 7361 Engineering services; Telecommunications consultant; Labor contractors (employment agency)
Pr: Christine Ciocca
**CEO:* Robert Olson
**CFO:* Stephen Morrison
**VP:* Bharani K Aroll
**VP:* James Elsner
**VP:* Edward Fabian

D-U-N-S 60-374-7515 EXP
■ **BUTLER ANIMAL HEALTH HOLDING CO LLC**
BUTLER ANIMAL SUPPLY
(*Suby of* HENRY SCHEIN INC) ★
400 Metro Pl N Ste 100, Dublin, OH 43017-3340
Tel (614) 761-9095 *Founded/Ownrshp* 2005
Sales 1.3MMM^E *EMP* 856^E
SIC 5122 5149 5047 Drugs, proprietaries & sundries; Pharmaceuticals; Biologicals & allied products; Pet foods; Veterinarians' equipment & supplies
CFO: Leo McNeil
Sls Mgr: Derek Card
Sls Mgr: Gary Schmidt
Sls Mgr: Jamie Schneider
Sls Mgr: Lora Temple
Sales Asso: Kathy Holthouser

D-U-N-S 60-375-0329 IMP/EXP
■ **BUTLER ANIMAL HEALTH SUPPLY LLC**
HENRY SCHEIN ANIMAL HEALTH
(*Suby of* BUTLER ANIMAL SUPPLY) ★
400 Metro Pl N Ste 100, Dublin, OH 43017-3340
Tel (855) 724-3461 *Founded/Ownrshp* 2012
Sales 1.3MMM *EMP* 790
SIC 5122 5149 5047 Drugs, proprietaries & sundries; Biologicals & allied products; Pharmaceuticals; Veterinarians' equipment & supplies
Pr: Francis Dirksmeier
Pr: Tom Rogan
CFO: Russell Cooke
Ex VP: Anthony Johnson
VP: Fred Bravo
Ex Dir: Ken Parish
Ex Dir: Mike Powers
IT Man: Michael Kahn
IT Man: Donna Smith
IT Man: Michelle Vestey
Web Dev: Matthew Bowlin

BUTLER ANIMAL SUPPLY
See BUTLER ANIMAL HEALTH HOLDING CO LLC

D-U-N-S 01-304-6156
BUTLER CAPITAL CORP
60 Cuttermill Rd Ste 214, Great Neck, NY 11021-3104
Tel (212) 980-0606 *Founded/Ownrshp* 1981
Sales 213.7MM^E *EMP* 1,946
SIC 6211 Investment bankers
Pr: Gilbert Butler

D-U-N-S 06-170-6040
BUTLER COUNTY OF OHIO
315 High St Fl 6, Hamilton, OH 45011-6056
Tel (513) 887-3278 *Founded/Ownrshp* 1987
Sales NA *EMP* 2,500
Accts Julian & Grube Inc Westervil
SIC 9121 County commissioner;

BUTLER DIGITAL SERVICES
See LEHIGH BLUE PRINT CO INC

D-U-N-S 14-817-3651
BUTLER HEALTH SYSTEM INC
BUTLER MEMORIAL HOSPITAL
1 Hospital Way, Butler, PA 16001-4670
Tel (724) 283-6666 *Founded/Ownrshp* 1898
Sales 240.8MM *EMP* 3,000^E
SIC 8062 General medical & surgical hospitals
Pr: Ken Defurio
CFO: Ann Krebs
**CFO:* Anne Krebs
Ofcr: Paula Hooper
**VP:* Thomas A Genevro
**VP:* Paula L Hooper
VP: Thomas McGill
VP: Stephanie Roskovski
Dir Rx: Martin Shulik
**Chf Nrs Of:* Karen Allen
Ex Dir: Deborah Sinz

D-U-N-S 06-871-8253
BUTLER HEALTHCARE PROVIDERS
BUTLER MEMORIAL HOSPITAL
(*Suby of* BUTLER HEALTH SYSTEM)
1 Hospital Way, Butler, PA 16001-4670
Tel (724) 283-6666 *Founded/Ownrshp* 1983
Sales 240.5MM *EMP* 1,300
SIC 8062 General medical & surgical hospitals
Pr: Ken Defurio
Dir Rad: James W Backstrom
Off Mgr: Brenda Andreassi

D-U-N-S 15-726-1637
BUTLER INTERNATIONAL INC
3820 State St Ste A, Santa Barbara, CA 93105-3182
Tel (805) 882-2200 *Founded/Ownrshp* 1985
Sales 88.4MM^E *EMP* 3,600
SIC 7363 8742 Help supply services; Management consulting services
Ch Bd: Edward M Kopko
**CFO:* Mark Koscinski
**Sr VP:* James J Beckley
Mktg Mgr: Ren E Ward
Board of Directors: Thomas F Comeau, Walter O Lecroy, Hugh G McBreen, Frank H Murray, Louis F Petrossi, Wesley B Tyler, Ronald Uyematsu

D-U-N-S 00-892-5919 EXP
BUTLER MACHINERY CO
3401 33rd St S, Fargo, ND 58104-8822
Tel (701) 298-1700 *Founded/Ownrshp* 1969
Sales 246.2MM^E *EMP* 750
SIC 5082 7353 7699

BUTLER MEMORIAL HOSPITAL
See BUTLER HEALTHCARE PROVIDERS

BUTLER MEMORIAL HOSPITAL
See BUTLER HEALTH SYSTEM INC

D-U-N-S 07-270-1949
BUTLER SERVICE GROUP INC
(*Suby of* BUTLER INTERNATIONAL INC) ★
3820 State St Ste A, Santa Barbara, CA 93105-3182
Tel (201) 891-5312 *Founded/Ownrshp* 1987
Sales 29.1MM^E *EMP* 3,000
SIC 7363 8711 8748 3661 7538 Engineering help service; Engineering services; Communications consulting; Telephone & telegraph apparatus; General automotive repair shops
Pr: Edward M Kopko
CFO: Michael C Hellriegel
Sr VP: R Scott Silver Hill

D-U-N-S 00-385-4569
BUTLER SUPPLY INC (MO)
965 Horan Dr, Fenton, MO 63026-2401
Tel (636) 349-9000 *Founded/Ownrshp* 1941
Sales 103.4MM *EMP* 200
SIC 5063

D-U-N-S 03-093-7890
BUTLER TECHNOLOGY & CAREER DEVELOPMENT SCHOOLS
3603 Hmlton Middletown Rd, Hamilton, OH 45011-2241
Tel (513) 868-1911 *Founded/Ownrshp* 1923
Sales 48.9MM *EMP* 1,200
Accts Mary Taylor Cpa Blue Ash Oh
SIC 8211 Public combined elementary & secondary school; Public vocational/technical school
CEO: Robert Sommers
**Treas:* Randy Bertram
IT Man: Ryan Burgess
Teacher Pr: Marnie Durham

D-U-N-S 07-957-3192
BUTLER UNIVERSITY
4600 Sunset Ave, Indianapolis, IN 46208-3487
Tel (317) 940-8000 *Founded/Ownrshp* 1855
Sales 192.5MM *EMP* 805^E
Accts Bkd Llp Indianapolis Indian
SIC 8221 University
Pr: James M Danko
Treas: Bruce E Arick
Treas: Jennifer Sage
VP: Thomas Weede
Assoc Dir: Doug Howell
Assoc Dir: Jennie Jones
Assoc Dir: Keith B Magnus
Assoc Dir: Richard B Rown
Assoc Dir: Rachel Vaught
Dir Soc: Carl Heck
Ex Dir: Margy Nebesio

D-U-N-S 03-403-7141
BUTTE COUNTY OFFICE OF EDUCATION
1859 Bird St, Oroville, CA 95965-4854
Tel (530) 532-5650 *Founded/Ownrshp* 2010
Sales 23.4MM^E *EMP* 1,053^E
SIC 8211 School board
Prin: Carlos Meza
Assoc Dir: Abarca Dominguez
Ex Dir: Nathan Rose
Off Admin: Maria Cisneros
Off Admin: Erika Flores
IT Man: Kirby White
Psych: Heather Lindstrom
Occ Thrpy: Kari Tosse

D-U-N-S 00-916-7255
BUTTE COUNTY RICE GROWERS ASSOCIATION INC
BUCRA
1193 Richvale Hwy, Richvale, CA 95974
Tel (530) 345-7103 *Founded/Ownrshp* 2014
Sales 95.1MM^E *EMP* 85
Accts Matson & Isom Chico Californ
SIC 5191 0723 5261 Fertilizer & fertilizer materials; Chemicals, agricultural; Rice drying services; Fertilizer
CEO: Carl D Hoff
**CFO:* Gary Deyoung
**VP:* Steve Birdsong
**VP:* Susan Ricketts

BUTTER KERNEL
See FARIBAULT FOODS INC

D-U-N-S 00-304-5291 IMP
BUTTER KRUST BAKING CO INC
(*Suby of* BIMBO BAKERIES USA INC) ★
249 N 11th St, Sunbury, PA 17801-2433
Tel (570) 286-5845 *Founded/Ownrshp* 1920, 2011
Sales 146.9MM^E *EMP* 700
SIC 2051 Bakery: wholesale or wholesale/retail combined
Pr: James G Apple
**CFO:* Brenda Swisher
**VP:* Tim Apple
Genl Mgr: Sarah Jeffries
CIO: Ian Jones
IT Man: Todd Bordner
Sfty Dirs: Derek Hartland
Ql Cn Mgr: Wolfe Christo
Ql Cn Mgr: Chris Wolfe
Sls Mgr: Bob Dixon
Sls Mgr: Mike Hennard

BUTTER KRUST THRIFT SHOP
See FLOWERS BAKING CO OF SAN ANTONIO LLC

D-U-N-S 12-226-2280 EXP
BUTTERBALL LLC
GUSTO PACKING COMPANY
1 Butterball Ln, Garner, NC 27529-5971
Tel (919) 255-7900 *Founded/Ownrshp* 2006
Sales 1.8MMM *EMP* 2,500
SIC 2015

BUTTERKRUST BAKERIES
See SOUTHERN BAKERIES INC

D-U-N-S 02-675-1990 IMP
BUTTERY CO LLP
BUTTERY HARDWARE
201 W Main St, Llano, TX 78643-1995
Tel (325) 247-4141 *Founded/Ownrshp* 1892
Sales 93.2MM^E *EMP* 130
SIC 5072 5074 5063 5091 5211 5251 Hardware; Plumbing fittings & supplies; Electronic wire & cable; Ammunition, sporting; Lumber & other building materials; Hardware
Pt: Brenda Durst
Pt: William Bettery
Pt: John Buttery
Pt: Jean Wallace

BUTTERY HARDWARE
See BUTTERY CO LLP

D-U-N-S 03-691-0275
BUTTONWILLOW WAREHOUSE CO INC
(*Suby of* TECH AGRICULTURAL INC) ★
125 Front St, Buttonwillow, CA 93206
Tel (661) 764-5234 *Founded/Ownrshp* 1948
Sales 90.1MM^E *EMP* 75
SIC 5191 Fertilizer & fertilizer materials
Pr: Donald Houchin
**COO:* Brad Crowder
**CFO:* Scott Stanley
**VP:* Wallace Houchin

D-U-N-S 05-242-3605
BUTZ ENTERPRISES INC
840 Hamilton St, Allentown, PA 18101-2455
Tel (610) 395-6871 *Founded/Ownrshp* 1978
Sales 329.7MM *EMP* 225
SIC 8741 Construction management
CEO: Lee A Butz
**Pr:* Greg L Butz
**Treas:* Raymond Federici
Board of Directors: Lee A Butz, Mary Butz

D-U-N-S 01-097-7796 IMP/EXP
■ **BUY BEST PURCHASING LLC**
COWBOOM
(*Suby of* BEST BUY ENTERPRISE SERVICES INC) ★
7601 Penn Ave S, Richfield, MN 55423-8500
Tel (612) 291-1000 *Founded/Ownrshp* 2000
Sales 1.3MMM^E *EMP* 220^E
SIC 5065 Electronic parts & equipment
CEO: Hubert Joly
**Pr:* Bradbury Anderson
**CFO:* Sharon McCollam

D-U-N-S 92-778-3845 IMP/EXP
■ **BUY BUY BABY INC**
(*Suby of* BED BATH & BEYOND INC) ★
895 E Gate Blvd Ste 2, Garden City, NY 11530-2142
Tel (516) 507-3400 *Founded/Ownrshp* 2007
Sales 95.4MM^E *EMP* 650
SIC 5641 5999 2023 Children's & infants' wear stores; Infants' wear; Baby carriages & strollers; High chairs; Baby formulas
CEO: Steven H Temares
Area Mgr: Aj Fernandez
Dist Mgr: Mark McConnell
Dist Mgr: Barry McHale
Genl Mgr: Margareta Boyle
Store Mgr: Candice Beck
Store Mgr: Jennifer Dainer
Store Mgr: Terrie Diallo
Store Mgr: Gina Lopez
Store Mgr: Jennifer Nelson
Store Mgr: Kelly Paxton

D-U-N-S 01-772-3156 IMP
BUYERS PRODUCTS CO
9049 Tyler Blvd, Mentor, OH 44060-4800
Tel (440) 974-8888 *Founded/Ownrshp* 1965
Sales 98.5MM^E *EMP* 160
SIC 5013 3714 Truck parts & accessories; Motor vehicle parts & accessories
Pr: James Kleinman
**VP:* Mark Saltzman
IT Man: Pam Davey
Netwrk Mgr: Rick Haywood
Netwrk Mgr: Rick Haywwod
Opers Mgr: Aaron Gayheart
Plnt Mgr: Gary Kadow
Mktg Dir: Thomas Cain
Sls Mgr: Ernie Kish
Sls Mgr: Greg Labardee
Sls Mgr: Jeff Margelowsky

BUZZI UNICEM
See LONE STAR INDUSTRIES INC

BUZZI UNICEM USA
See RC LONESTAR INC

D-U-N-S 04-785-6679 IMP
BUZZI UNICEM USA INC
(*Suby of* BUZZI UNICEM USA) ★
100 Brodhead Rd Ste 230, Bethlehem, PA 18017-8935
Tel (610) 882-5000 *Founded/Ownrshp* 1988
Sales 576.5MM^E *EMP* 1,474
SIC 3241 Portland cement
Pr: Dave Nepereny
**Treas:* Dirk Beese
**VP:* Nancy L Krial
VP: Thomas Marnell
Exec: Daniel Pilgreen
Genl Mgr: Mark Kluesner
CIO: Mike Parker
MIS Dir: Chuck Bothell
Tech Mgr: Darrell F Elliot
Software D: Roger Reed
Sfty Mgr: Corena Callahan

D-U-N-S 07-979-5251
BVH INC
11401 Lamar Ave, Overland Park, KS 66211-1508
Tel (913) 458-2000 *Founded/Ownrshp* 2014
Sales 2.9MMM *EMP* 8,495
Accts Kpmg Llp Kansas City Mo
SIC 8711 8741 Consulting engineer; Construction management
Ch Bd: Steve L Edwards
CFO: Karen L Daniel
Treas: Angela L Hoffman
Ex VP: Timothy W Triplett
VP: Ralph J Dyro
VP: Jeffrey J Stamm

D-U-N-S 06-672-3990
BVU AUTHORITY
15022 Lee Hwy, Bristol, VA 24202-4256
Tel (276) 821-6100 *Founded/Ownrshp* 1951
Sales 89.1MM^E *EMP* 180^E
Accts Brown Edwards And Company Ll
SIC 4931 Electric & other services combined
Pr: Wesley R Rosenbalm
CFO: Stacy Bright
CFO: Stacy Pomrenke
VP: Robert Snodgra
VP: Robert Snodgrass

BW CONTAINER SYSTEMS
See BARRY-WEHMILLER CONTAINER SYSTEMS INC

D-U-N-S 00-223-7121 IMP
■ **BW ELLIOTT MANUFACTURING CO LLC**
(*Suby of* ACTUANT CORP) ★
11 Beckwith Ave, Binghamton, NY 13901-1726
Tel (607) 772-0404 *Founded/Ownrshp* 1999
Sales 97.4MM^E *EMP* 295
SIC 3568 3492 3531 Power transmission equipment; Shafts, flexible; Joints, swivel & universal, except aircraft & automotive; Control valves, fluid power: hydraulic & pneumatic; Construction machinery
CEO: Richard Allbritton
**Pr:* George Scherer
COO: Cyril Macinka
VP: Frank Canto
Genl Mgr: Matt Nagle
IT Man: Harriett Beams
IT Man: Sandy Falank
IT Man: Scott Stoughton
S&M/VP: David Morley
Snr Mgr: Sonia Moore
Snr Mgr: Ray Strauss

BW PAPERSYSTEMS
See BARRY-WEHMILLER PAPERSYSTEMS INC

D-U-N-S 80-999-3520 IMP/EXP
BWAY CORP
(*Suby of* STONE CANYON INDUSTRIES LLC) ★
8607 Roberts Dr Ste 250, Atlanta, GA 30350-2237
Tel (770) 645-4800 *Founded/Ownrshp* 2016
Sales 956.6MM^E *EMP* 58^E

SIC 3411 3089 Metal cans; Can lids & ends, metal; Oil cans, metal; Plastic containers, except foam; Tubs, plastic (containers)
Pr: Kenneth M Roessler
* *COO:* Tarek Maguid
* *CFO:* Donald W Pearson
* *Ex VP:* Leslie L Bradshaw
Ex VP: Elizabeth Divine
* *Ex VP:* Michael A Noel
Ex VP: Tom Sult
Sr VP: Paul Kile
VP: Robert C Coleman
VP: Darrell W Davis
VP: Bryan Hepper
VP: Richard Jakubecy
VP: Teresa Kimbrell

D-U-N-S 11-785-1449 IMP/EXP
BWAY HOLDING CO
(*Suby of* BWAY PARENT CO INC) ★
8607 Roberts Dr Ste 250, Atlanta, GA 30350-2237
Tel (770) 645-4800 *Founded/Ownrshp* 2011
Sales 776.8MM^E *EMP* 2,700^E
SIC 3411 3089 Metal cans; Can lids & ends, metal; Oil cans, metal; Plastic containers, except foam; Tubs, plastic (containers)
Pr: Kenneth M Roessler
* *CFO:* Michael Clauer
* *Treas:* Jeffrey M O'Connell
* *Ex VP:* Kevin W McNairc
* *Sr VP:* Kevin C Kern
VP: Michael G Bero
VP: Darrell W Davis
VP: Charlie R Watling
Trfc Mgr: Donnie Walton
VP Sls: Henry E Harrell
Sls Mgr: John Homan

D-U-N-S 96-801-8965
BWAY INTERMEDIATE CO INC
8607 Roberts Dr Ste 250, Atlanta, GA 30350-2237
Tel (770) 645-4800 *Founded/Ownrshp* 2010
Sales 1.4MMM^E *EMP* 2,701^E
SIC 3411 3089 Metal cans; Can lids & ends, metal; Oil cans, metal; Plastic containers, except foam; Tubs, plastic (containers)
Pr: Kenneth M Roessler
* *COO:* Tarek Maguid
* *Ex VP:* Leslie L Bradshaw
* *Ex VP:* Michael A Noel

D-U-N-S 96-887-7899
BWAY INTERMEDIATE CO INC
(*Suby of* BWAY PARENT CO INC) ★
3 First National Plz, Chicago, IL 60602-5008
Tel (312) 895-1000 *Founded/Ownrshp* 2010
Sales NA *EMP* 2,700
SIC 6719 Investment holding companies, except banks
Pr: Kenneth M Roessler

D-U-N-S 96-288-7704
BWAY PARENT CO INC
(*Suby of* BWAY INTERMEDIATE CO INC) ★
3200 S Kilbourn Ave, Chicago, IL 60623-4829
Tel (773) 890-3300 *Founded/Ownrshp* 2010
Sales 776.8MM^E *EMP* 2,700^E
SIC 3411 3089 Metal cans; Can lids & ends, metal; Oil cans, metal; Plastic containers, except foam; Tubs, plastic (containers)
CEO: Kenneth M Roessler
* *Pr:* Thomas S Souleles
* *COO:* Tarek Maguid
* *CFO:* Donald W Pearson
* *Ex VP:* Leslie L Bradshaw
* *Ex VP:* Michael A Noel

D-U-N-S 06-658-7320 IMP/EXP
BWI COMPANIES INC
1355 N Kings Hwy, Nash, TX 75569-2121
Tel (903) 838-8561 *Founded/Ownrshp* 1981
Sales 354.6MM^E *EMP* 279
SIC 5191 Farm supplies; Garden supplies
Ch: Bob Bunch
* *Pr:* James S Bunch
* *Treas:* Susan Buchanan
* *Sec:* Betty Bunch
Bd of Dir: Brian Bridges
* *Ex VP:* Michael Mize
VP Sls: Mark Fomby
Mktg Mgr: Randy Townsend
Sls Mgr: Joel Green
Sls Mgr: Cody Jackson
Sls Mgr: Jason E Platzer

D-U-N-S 78-319-7184
BWT LLC
(*Suby of* ATERIAN INVESTMENT PARTNERS LP) ★
201 Brookfield Pkwy, Greenville, SC 29607-5773
Tel (864) 990-0050 *Founded/Ownrshp* 2012
Sales 117.0MM^E *EMP* 450
SIC 3398 Metal heat treating
Pr: Jeffery Hemmer
* *Pr:* Michael Wellham
* *COO:* Ben Crawford
* *CFO:* Keith Beasley
Manager: Alejandro Grosvald

D-U-N-S 96-803-7221
▲ BWXT TECHNOLOGIES INC
BWXT
800 Main St Ste 4, Lynchburg, VA 24504-1533
Tel (980) 365-4300 *Founded/Ownrshp* 1867
Sales 1.4MMM *EMP* 5,300^E
Tkr Sym BWXT *Exch* NYS
SIC 3621 3829 Power generators; Nuclear instrument modules
Pr: P Sandy Baker
* *Ch Bd:* John A Fees
Pr: William A Fox III
Pr: Joseph G Henry
COO: Rex D Geveden
* *CFO:* David S Black
Chf Cred: James D Canafax
Sr VP: Benjamin H Bash
VP: Jason S Kerr
IT Man: Robert Hancock

BWXT
See BWX TECHNOLOGIES INC

D-U-N-S 11-124-2293 IMP
■ BWXT GOVERNMENT GROUP INC
(*Suby of* BWXT INVESTMENT CO) ★
2016 Mount Athos Rd, Lynchburg, VA 24504-5447
Tel (434) 522-6000 *Founded/Ownrshp* 2002
Sales 1.0MMM^E *EMP* 8,000^E
SIC 3443 Nuclear core structurals, metal plate
CEO: Mary Salomone
* *CFO:* David S Black
* *Treas:* Jenny Apker
* *Sr VP:* Benjamin H Bash
* *Sr VP:* James D Canafax
* *VP:* Regina W Carter
Off Mgr: David Lindsey

D-U-N-S 78-752-3976
■ BWXT INVESTMENT CO
(*Suby of* BWXT) ★
11525 N Community House, Charlotte, NC 28277-3609
Tel (704) 625-4900 *Founded/Ownrshp* 2010
Sales 2.9MMM^E *EMP* 11,000
SIC 3511 3443 3564 1629 1541 7699 Turbines & turbine generator set units, complete; Purification & dust collection equipment; Industrial plant construction; Power plant construction; Industrial buildings, new construction; Renovation, remodeling & repairs: industrial buildings; Industrial machinery & equipment repair
Pr: Peyton Baker
CFO: Anthony Colatrella
Sr VP: James D Canafax
Sr VP: Kairus Tarapore
VP: Marc A Hamer
VP: Leslie Kass
VP: Peter Waanders
IT Man: Jim Dodsworth
IT Man: Eric Richards
Tech Mgr: Tom Snyder
Opers Mgr: Greg Shikaze

D-U-N-S 82-930-7920
■ BWXT NUCLEAR OPERATIONS GROUP INC
(*Suby of* BWXT GOVERNMENT GROUP INC) ★
2016 Mount Athos Rd, Lynchburg, VA 24504-5447
Tel (434) 522-6000 *Founded/Ownrshp* 2008
Sales 587.2MM^E *EMP* 3,800^E
SIC 3443 Fabricated plate work (boiler shop)
Pr: Joseph Henry
* *Treas:* David Black
Board of Directors: David Black, James Canafax, Joseph Henry

D-U-N-S 93-835-6771
■ BWXT TECHNICAL SERVICES GROUP INC
(*Suby of* BWXT GOVERNMENT GROUP INC) ★
2016 Mount Athos Rd, Lynchburg, VA 24504-5447
Tel (434) 522-6000 *Founded/Ownrshp* 2007
Sales 246.1M^E *EMP* 8,000
SIC 8711 8731 Engineering services; Commercial physical research
Pr: E James Ferland
* *Pr:* William Fox
COO: Susan Alexander
Treas: Faith Adams
VP: Jenny L Apker
Brnch Mgr: James Barnes
Genl Mgr: Linda Bauer
Genl Mgr: Pete Goumas
Genl Mgr: Mike Sedler
Dir IT: Barry Cantor
IT Man: Greg Bailey

D-U-N-S 00-922-9808 IMP
BYER CALIFORNIA
66 Potrero Ave, San Francisco, CA 94103-4800
Tel (415) 626-7844 *Founded/Ownrshp* 1964
Sales 387.2MM^E *EMP* 1,200
Accts Comyns Smith Mccleary & Deav
SIC 2331 Women's & misses' blouses & shirts
CEO: Allan G Byer
* *COO:* Philip Byer
CFO: Ed Manberg
* *CFO:* Ed Manburg
* *Sec:* Marian Byer
Bd of Dir: Charles Frasier
* *VP:* Barbara Berling
* *VP:* Max Curry
* *VP:* Joel Feldman
VP: Mandar Ghosalkar
* *VP:* Jeff Zukerberg
Creative D: Katherine Miner

BYERS CAR RENTALS
See GEO BYERS SONS HOLDING INC

D-U-N-S 05-103-1730
BYERS ENGINEERING CO
6285 Barfield Rd Fl 4, Atlanta, GA 30328-4322
Tel (404) 843-1000 *Founded/Ownrshp* 1971
Sales 133.9MM^E *EMP* 1,000
SIC 8711 7371

D-U-N-S 04-166-1737 IMP/EXP
BYK ADDITIVES INC
(*Suby of* BYK-CHEMIE GMBH)
1212 Church St, Gonzales, TX 78629-3008
Tel (830) 672-2891 *Founded/Ownrshp* 2013
Sales 224.7MM^E *EMP* 225
SIC 1459 3295 3297 Clays (common) quarrying; Minerals, ground or treated; Minerals, ground or otherwise treated; Earths, ground or otherwise treated; Nonclay refractories
Ch: Seifi Ghasemi
* *Pr:* Andrew M Ross
* *Pr:* Vernon S Summer
* *CEO:* Frank Wright
* *CFO:* Alison Avery
* *CFO:* Robert J Zatta
* *VP:* Thomas J Riordan
Sls Mgr: Terry Pierce

D-U-N-S 05-806-3707 IMP/EXP
BYK USA INC
(*Suby of* BYK-CHEMIE GMBH)
524 S Cherry St, Wallingford, CT 06492-4453
Tel (203) 265-2086 *Founded/Ownrshp* 1963
Sales 125.3MM^E *EMP* 118
SIC 2851 Paints & paint additives
Ch Bd: Dirk Plas
* *CFO:* Nicholas J Caputi
Dir IT: Glen Giannelli

D-U-N-S 14-831-1483
BYLINE BANCORP INC
180 N La Salle St Ste 300, Chicago, IL 60601-3110
Tel (773) 843-7800 *Founded/Ownrshp* 1978
Sales NA *EMP* 600
SIC 6712 6162 Bank holding companies; Mortgage bankers & correspondents
Pr: Alberto Paracchini
* *Pr:* Peter A Fasseas
* *Ex VP:* A W Schaumleffel
Sr VP: Michael Scipione
VP: Megan B Biggam
VP: Elisa Cintron

D-U-N-S 06-249-0503
BYLINE BANK
(*Suby of* BYLINE BANCORP INC) ★
3639 N Broadway St, Chicago, IL 60613-4421
Tel (773) 244-7000 *Founded/Ownrshp* 1972
Sales NA *EMP* 260
SIC 6022 6163 6021 State commercial banks; Loan brokers; National commercial banks
CEO: Scott Yelvington
Ch Bd: Peter A Fasseas
COO: Lisa Wente
Sr VP: Bill Chioros
Sr VP: Jim Kuncl
Sr VP: Roberta Kushen
VP: Dan Delgadillo
VP: Joe Horwath
VP: John Karabis
VP: Matthew Markley
VP: Jurate O'Brien
VP: Gerald Roman
VP: Sandra Thoms
VP: Leta Walter

D-U-N-S 18-403-3348
BYRAM HEALTHCARE CENTERS INC
MEDIQ USA HOLDINGS
(*Suby of* MEDIQ INTERNATIONAL B.V.)
120 Bloomingdale Rd # 301, White Plains, NY 10605-1518
Tel (914) 286-2000 *Founded/Ownrshp* 2008
Sales 97.8MM^E *EMP* 529
SIC 5999 5047 Incontinent care products; Hospital equipment & supplies; Diagnostic equipment, medical
Ch Bd: Perry Bernocchi
Pr: Jocelyn Hirschfeld
Pr: Janet D Ruehle
Pr: David Zelaskowski
* *CFO:* Marcel Overweel
Ofcr: Michelle L Knowles
* *Ex VP:* Marianne Rose
VP: Beth Jarm
VP: Jason Miller
VP: Dione Montano
* *VP:* Renee Picard Walsh

D-U-N-S 19-564-7180
BYRIDER SALES OF INDIANA S LLC
J.D. BYRIDER
12802 Hmlton Crssing Blvd, Carmel, IN 46032-5424
Tel (317) 249-3000 *Founded/Ownrshp* 1995
Sales 126.6MM^E *EMP* 281^E
SIC 5521 Automobiles, used cars only
CEO: Steve Wedding
Mng Pt: Timothy Bullock
Mng Pt: Ben Goodman
COO: Phillip Ratkovic
* *Sec:* William Brunner
* *VP:* Todd Gunderson
* *VP:* Jeff Higgins
* *VP:* Brad Malott
* *VP:* Steve Petersen
Genl Mgr: Angela Batten
Genl Mgr: Dale Boone

D-U-N-S 01-324-6939
BYRNE DAIRY INC (NY)
2394 Us Route 11, La Fayette, NY 13084-9583
Tel (315) 475-2121 *Founded/Ownrshp* 1932, 1979
Sales 278.8MM^E *EMP* 620
SIC 2026 2024 Milk processing (pasteurizing, homogenizing, bottling); Ice cream, packaged: molded, on sticks, etc.; Ice cream, bulk
Ch Bd: Carl Byrne
CFO: Scott Matukas
VP: Mark Byrne
VP: Eric Greiner
* *Prin:* William M Byrne Jr
Rgnl Mgr: James Kehoe
Genl Mgr: Kingsley Irobunda
Genl Mgr: James Obrist
Genl Mgr: Scott Smith
Snr Ntwrk: Robert Brois
Dir IT: Eric Caballaro

D-U-N-S 96-376-4738
BZ INTERMEDIATE HOLDINGS LLC
1111 W Jefferson St, Boise, ID 83702-5383
Tel (208) 384-7000 *Founded/Ownrshp* 2010
Sales 2.5MMM *EMP* 12^E
SIC 8211 Elementary & secondary schools
CEO: Alexander Toeldte

C

D-U-N-S 13-472-3316 IMP
C & A MARKETING INC
RITZ CAMERA
114 Tived Ln E, Edison, NJ 08837-3076
Tel (201) 881-1900 *Founded/Ownrshp* 2012
Sales 262.3MM^E *EMP* 500
SIC 5065 8742 7384 5946 7359 7221 Electronic parts & equipment; Marketing consulting services; Photofinish laboratories; Camera & photographic supply stores; Photographic equipment rental; Photographic studios, portrait
Pr: Harry Klein
CFO: Abe Berkowitz
VP: Yoel Holtzman
VP: Moshe Isaacson
VP: Chaim Piekarski
Mng Dir: Michael Roth
CTO: Aaron Oppenheim
Mktg Dir: Liora Simpson

D-U-N-S 05-604-1841
C & A TOOL ENGINEERING INC
4100 N Us 33 N, Churubusco, IN 46723
Tel (260) 693-2167 *Founded/Ownrshp* 1977
Sales 133.7MM^E *EMP* 525
SIC 3544 3545 Diamond dies, metalworking; Machine tool accessories
Pr: Conrow R D
CFO: Bob Austin
VP: Rob Marr
* *VP:* Robert Marr
Genl Mgr: Ralph Bunn
Opers Mgr: Scott Leitch
Ql Cn Mgr: Chris Dunn
Ql Cn Mgr: Angela Elick
Ql Cn Mgr: Hogan Smith
Sls Mgr: Jack Green

D-U-N-S 10-209-3127
C & C HOLDING INC
2238 Pinson Valley Pkwy, Birmingham, AL 35217-2009
Tel (205) 841-6666 *Founded/Ownrshp* 1982
Sales 190.0MM^E *EMP* 300
Accts Sovereign Cpa Group Llc
SIC 5082 1629 5084 General construction machinery & equipment; Mining machinery & equipment, except petroleum; Blasting contractor, except building demolition; Industrial machinery & equipment
Ch Bd: John J Cowin
* *Pr:* James P Cowin

D-U-N-S 80-403-5504 IMP/EXP
C & C NORTH AMERICA INC
(*Suby of* COSENTINO SAU)
2245 Texas Dr Ste 600, Sugar Land, TX 77479-2190
Tel (281) 207-4461 *Founded/Ownrshp* 2009
Sales 419.0MM^E *EMP* 550^E
SIC 5032

D-U-N-S 80-334-7749
C & C PRODUCE INC
CC PRODUCE
1100 Atlantic Ave, North Kansas City, MO 64116-4139
Tel (816) 241-4425 *Founded/Ownrshp* 1982
Sales 135.5MM^E *EMP* 120
SIC 5148 Fresh fruits & vegetables
Pr: John Conforti
* *VP:* Nick Conforti
* *Prin:* Joe Cali
Opers Mgr: Michelle Nichols

D-U-N-S 79-849-9747 IMP/EXP
C & C TECHNOLOGIES INC
730 E Kaliste Saloom Rd, Lafayette, LA 70508-2547
Tel (337) 210-0000 *Founded/Ownrshp* 2015
Sales 85.1MM^E *EMP* 500
SIC 8713

D-U-N-S 00-300-4207 IMP/EXP
C & J CLARK AMERICA INC (PA)
BOSTONIAN SHOE CO
(*Suby of* CLARKS AMERICAS INC) ★
60 Tower Rd, Waltham, MA 02451-1022
Tel (617) 964-1222 *Founded/Ownrshp* 1898, 1977
Sales 944.9MM^E *EMP* 2,400
SIC 3143 5139 5661 Boots, dress or casual: men's; Shoes; Men's shoes
Pr: Gary Champion
Treas: Maureen Grady
Sr VP: Bob Miller
VP: Joe Battaglini
VP: Mark Bovckley
VP: Sharon Schuler
IT Man: Dick Scheerer
Natl Sales: Brian Alves

D-U-N-S 04-663-0323
C & K INDUSTRIAL SERVICES INC (OH)
5617 E Schaaf Rd, Independence, OH 44131-1334
Tel (216) 642-0055 *Founded/Ownrshp* 1980
Sales 113.1MM^E *EMP* 200
SIC 4959 7349 Sweeping service: road, airport, parking lot, etc.; Building maintenance services
Pr: Arthur Karas
Ex VP: Beau Barker
* *VP:* George Karas
Exec: Lynn Clark
Sfty Mgr: Daniel Mitchem

D-U-N-S 02-760-9569
C & K MARKET INC
RAY'S FOOD PLACE
850 Ohare Pkwy Ste 100, Medford, OR 97504-7720
Tel (541) 469-3113 *Founded/Ownrshp* 1956
Sales 352.6MM^E *EMP* 2,000
SIC 5411 Grocery stores
CEO: Karl Wissmann
* *CEO:* Douglas Nidiffer
* *CFO:* David D Doty
Sr Cor Off: Ben Gallego
* *VP:* Rocky Campbell
* *VP:* Jon Wissmann
CTO: Brad Wilson
Snr Mgr: Sherrill Seaward

D-U-N-S 00-310-3751
C & T A CO INC
11535 Hopewell Rd, Hagerstown, MD 21740-2178
Tel (800) 458-3835 *Founded/Ownrshp* 1959
Sales 117.1MM^E *EMP* 300
Accts Flurie Slick & Kinnett Cpas
SIC 5541 5172 7359 7699 Gasoline service stations; Petroleum products; Portable toilet rental; Septic tank cleaning service
Pr: Adna Fulton
* *Treas:* Barbara Jean Fulton
* *VP:* Brad Fulton
* *VP:* Mark Fulton
* *VP:* Steven D Fulton
VP: Charles Goodie
Exec: Gary Monn

Dist Mgr: Susan Tibbens
Site Mgr: Joy Carbaugh

D-U-N-S 11-862-0889
C & W FISH CO INC
7508 Se Autumn Ln, Hobe Sound, FL 33455-7813
Tel (772) 283-1184 *Founded/Ownrshp* 1982
Sales 2.5MM *EMP* 4,925
SIC 5199 5146 Bait, fishing; Fish, fresh
VP: J H Crane
**Pr:* Lloyd C Winstead III
**Prin:* Lydia Crane
Off Mgr: Kevin Scott

C A A
See CREATIVE ARTISTS AGENCY LLC

D-U-N-S 01-693-4721 IMP
C A MUER CORP
(*Suby of* LSRI HOLDINGS INC) ★
400 Galleria Ofc Ctr, Southfield, MI 48034-8473
Tel (248) 226-9400 *Founded/Ownrshp* 2002
Sales 41.5MM^E *EMP* 2,100
SIC 5812 Eating places
Pr: Roger Zingle
VP: Jim Blake
VP: Greg Ochoa

D-U-N-S 04-404-9088
C A RASMUSSEN INC
28548 Livingston Ave, Valencia, CA 91355-4171
Tel (661) 367-9040 *Founded/Ownrshp* 1964
Sales 87.7MM^E *EMP* 200
SIC 1629 1611 Earthmoving contractor; Grading
Pr: Charles A Rasmussen
**CFO:* D I C K Greenburg
**VP:* Tim Macdonald
**VP:* Mike Medema
**VP:* Doug Misley

C A S A ANDERSON CNTY FAX LINE
See COUNTY OF ANDERSON

D-U-N-S 60-385-1361
■ **C AND C POWER LINE INC**
(*Suby of* POWER CORP OF AMERICA) ★
12035 Palm Lake Dr, Jacksonville, FL 32218-3833
Tel (904) 751-6020 *Founded/Ownrshp* 2014
Sales 119.4MM^E *EMP* 125
Accts Bishop And Draper Cpa Jackso
SIC 4911 1731 Transmission, electric power; Distribution, electric power; Electric power systems contractors; General electrical contractor
Pr: Jesse B Colley
VP: Michael E Sprenger

C B
See COASTAL BRIDGE CO LLC

C B
See CARLTON-BATES CO

C B E
See CAPITOL BUSINESS EQUIPMENT INC

D-U-N-S 00-311-9054 EXP
C B FLEET CO INC (VA)
FLEET LABORATORIES
4615 Murray Pl, Lynchburg, VA 24502-2235
Tel (434) 528-4000 *Founded/Ownrshp* 1916, 2014
Sales 185.7MM^E *EMP* 376
SIC 2834 Pharmaceutical preparations
Pr: Jeffrey R Rowan
**Ch Bd:* Steve Lamonte
**CFO:* Robert Lemon
**Treas:* Joseph T Carroll
Treas: John Schmidtbauer
VP: R A Lemon Jr
VP: Cheryl Vernon
Rgnl Mgr: Linda Reese
IT Man: Ron Flander
Netwrk Eng: Steve Lairson
Mktg Dir: Neil Heller

C B M PROPERTY MANAGEMENT
See CBM 2012 A CALIFORNIA LIMITED PARTNERSHIP

D-U-N-S 04-552-4923 IMP
C B NICHOLS EGG RANCH
331 W Citrus St, Colton, CA 92324-1412
Tel (626) 452-9110 *Founded/Ownrshp* 1977
Sales 84.8MM^E *EMP* 80
SIC 5144 5499 Eggs; Eggs & poultry
Pr: Steven A Nichols
**Treas:* Kathleen Nichols
Off Mgr: Alma Valenzuela

C B S
See NATIONAL AMUSEMENTS INC

C B U
See CALIFORNIA BAPTIST UNIVERSITY

D-U-N-S 78-508-4067 IMP/EXP
C C 1 BEER DISTRIBUTORS INC
MEDALLA DISTRIBUTORS PR
(*Suby of* COCA-COLA) ★
107 Carr 174, Bayamon, PR 00959-1910
Tel (787) 288-6400 *Founded/Ownrshp* 1999
Sales 236.0MM *EMP* 6
Accts Rsm Puerto Rico San Juan Pue
SIC 5181 Beer & other fermented malt liquors
Pr: Carlos De La Cruz Sr
**VP:* Alberto La Cruz

D-U-N-S 94-124-2018 IMP
C C 1 LIMITED PARTNERSHIP
COCA-COLA
3201 Nw 72nd Ave, Miami, FL 33122-1317
Tel (305) 599-2337 *Founded/Ownrshp* 1995
Sales 240.3MM *EMP* 1,000
Accts Pricewaterhousecoopers Llp Ha
SIC 2086 Bottled & canned soft drinks
Pt: Carlos M Delacruz
Pt: Manuel Kadre
Pt: Aberto De La Cruz
CFO: Rogger Tovar

D-U-N-S 94-395-6326 IMP/EXP
C C 1 LIMITED PARTNERSHIP
COCA-COLA
107 Carr 174, Bayamon, PR 00959-1910
Tel (787) 288-6400 *Founded/Ownrshp* 1995
Sales 345.1MM *EMP* 816
Accts Rsm Puerto Rico San Juan Pue
SIC 2086 Bottled & canned soft drinks
Pt: Alberto De La Cruz
**Pt:* Carlos De La Cruz Sr
**Pt:* Rosa De La Cruz

C C C
See COPYRIGHT CLEARANCE CENTER INC

C C C
See CONSOLIDATED CONTAINER CO LP

C C C S D
See CENTRAL CONTRA COSTA SANITARY DISTRICT FACILITIES FINANCING AUTHORITY

D-U-N-S 00-194-5385
C C CLARK INC (MS)
501 Academy Rd, Starkville, MS 39759-4047
Tel (662) 323-4317 *Founded/Ownrshp* 1932, 1969
Sales 167.0MM *EMP* 500^E
SIC 5149 2086 Groceries & related products; Bottled & canned soft drinks
Pr: Albert C Clark
**VP:* Harold N Clark
**VP:* W Dal Clark
CTO: William D Dal Clark

D-U-N-S 00-892-3948
C C DICKSON CO
456 Lakeshore Pkwy, Rock Hill, SC 29730-4205
Tel (803) 980-8000 *Founded/Ownrshp* 1933
Sales 246.0MM^E *EMP* 500
SIC 5075 5078 5074

C C E C
See CASS COUNTY ELECTRIC COOP INC

C C I S D
See CORPUS CHRISTI INDEPENDENT SCHOOL DISTRICT

D-U-N-S 08-529-0336
C C MYERS INC
3286 Fitzgerald Rd, Rancho Cordova, CA 95742-6811
Tel (916) 635-9370 *Founded/Ownrshp* 1977
Sales 113.8MM^E *EMP* 225
SIC 1622

C C O
See COLORADO COUNTY OIL CO INC

C C O
See COMMUNITY CARE INC

D-U-N-S 93-256-7449
C CTEXAS INC
TEXAS LAND & CATTLE CO
3130 Lemmon Ave, Dallas, TX 75204-2316
Tel (214) 526-4664 *Founded/Ownrshp* 1993
Sales 36.7MM^E *EMP* 1,500
SIC 5812 Eating places
Pr: David Franklin
COO: Mark Medmansky
**VP:* Aaron Fogiel

C D C
See KINDERCARE EDUCATION LLC

D-U-N-S 02-720-7745
■ **C D HARTNETT CO**
(*Suby of* MCLANE CO INC) ★
302 N Main St, Weatherford, TX 76086-3245
Tel (817) 594-3813 *Founded/Ownrshp* 2004
Sales 300.2MM *EMP* 211
SIC 5141 5122

C D I
See CDI CONTRACTORS LLC

D-U-N-S 62-514-4340
C D LISTENING BAR INC
SUPER D PHANTOM DISTRIBUTION
17822 Gillette Ave Ste A, Irvine, CA 92614-0527
Tel (949) 225-1170 *Founded/Ownrshp* 1990
Sales 341.6MM^E *EMP* 730
SIC 5099

C D M
See CDM CONSTRUCTORS INC

C D S
See CUSTOMIZED DISTRIBUTION SERVICES INC

C E D
See CONSOLIDATED ELECTRICAL DISTRIBUTORS INC

C E E U S
See COOPERATIVE ELECTRIC ENERGY UTILITY SUPPLY INC

C E I
See COATING EXCELLENCE INTERNATIONAL LLC

C E M C
See CUMBERLAND ELECTRIC MEMBERSHIP CORP

C F G
See CONTINENTAL PAPER GRADING CO

D-U-N-S 00-238-9310 IMP/EXP
C F MARTIN & CO INC
MARTIN GUITAR COMPANY, THE
510 Sycamore St, Nazareth, PA 18064-1000
Tel (610) 759-2837 *Founded/Ownrshp* 1833
Sales 115.0MM^E *EMP* 800
SIC 3931

D-U-N-S 00-312-5416 IMP/EXP
C F SAUER CO (VA)
2000 W Broad St, Richmond, VA 23220-2000
Tel (804) 359-5786 *Founded/Ownrshp* 1887
Sales 379.9MM^E *EMP* 850
Accts Ernst & Young
SIC 2087 Flavoring extracts & syrups
Pr: Conrad F Sauer IV
**CFO:* William F Uhlik
**Treas:* Michelle T Rader
**VP:* Mark A Sauer
Board of Directors: Charles L Cabell, Roy E Cabell Jr, Mark W Claud

C G G
See CGG SERVICES (US) INC

C G I
See COLUMBIA GRAIN INC

C G I
See CGI FEDERAL INC

C G I
See CORPORATE GRAPHICS INTERNATIONAL INC

C G S
See COMPUTER GENERATED SOLUTIONS INC

D-U-N-S 00-643-9095 IMP
C G SCHMIDT INC
11777 W Lake Park Dr, Milwaukee, WI 53224-3047
Tel (414) 577-1177 *Founded/Ownrshp* 1920
Sales 88.6MM^E *EMP* 122
Accts Baker Tilly Virchow Krause Ll
SIC 1542 8741 Nonresidential construction; Construction management
Pr: Richard L Schmidt Jr
**V Ch:* Geoffrey Knudson
**COO:* Mikelis Abuls
**Sr VP:* Dan Davis
VP: Daniel Davis
**VP:* Keith Swenson
**Exec:* Timothy Just
**Prin:* James Hans
**Prin:* Greg Morelli
Telecom Ex: Eric Elfner
Sfty Dirs: Frank Slamar

C H A
See CLOUGH HARBOUR & ASSOCIATES LLP

D-U-N-S 01-449-2748 IMP/EXP
C H BRIGGS CO
2047 Kutztown Rd, Reading, PA 19605-3025
Tel (800) 355-1000 *Founded/Ownrshp* 1967
Sales 202.7MM^E *EMP* 165
SIC 5072 Builders' hardware; Furniture hardware
CEO: Julia H Klein
**Pr:* Jonathan Peters
**COO:* Donald Sthalk
**CFO:* Judith Direnzo
**Chf Mktg O:* Luis Arias
**VP:* Jill Meese
**CIO:* Scott Withers

C H C
See COMMONWEALTH HEALTH CORP INC

D-U-N-S 00-811-5099
C H GUENTHER & SON INC
PIONEER FLOUR MILLS
2201 Broadway St, San Antonio, TX 78215-1135
Tel (210) 227-1401 *Founded/Ownrshp* 1851
Sales 391.2MM^E *EMP* 750
SIC 2041 2051 2045 2052 2099 Flour mills, cereal (except rice); Bread, cake & related products; Bread, all types (white, wheat, rye, etc): fresh or frozen; Biscuits, baked: baking powder & raised; Rolls, bread type: fresh or frozen; Biscuit mixes, prepared: from purchased flour; Bakery products, dry; Food preparations
Prin: Scott Petty Jr
**CFO:* Janelle Sykes
**Sr VP:* Dennis Daniels
**VP:* Brett Alvheim
VP: Chuck Hanson
**VP:* Thomas McRae
QA Dir: Joyce Meaders
Netwrk Mgr: Eddie Clark
Sls Mgr: Carlo Baglione

C H I
See CONEMAUGH HEALTH INITIATIVES INC

D-U-N-S 80-441-7152 IMP/EXP
■ **C H I OVERHEAD DOORS INC**
(*Suby of* CHI OVERHEAD DOORS) ★
1485 Sunrise Dr, Arthur, IL 61911-1684
Tel (217) 543-2135 *Founded/Ownrshp* 1981
Sales 110.9MM^E *EMP* 500
SIC 3442 Garage doors, overhead: metal
CEO: Timothy Miller
**CFO:* Tisha L Pfeiffer

D-U-N-S 00-750-6298 IMP
C H INDUSTRIES INC
(*Suby of* II MILLENNIUM HOLDINGS CO.)
1700 Columbian Club Dr, Carrollton, TX 75006-5517
Tel (972) 416-1304 *Founded/Ownrshp* 1958
Sales 87.5MM^E *EMP* 424
SIC 2599 3444 3469 Hospital beds; Sheet metalwork; Forming machine work, sheet metal; Metal stampings
Pr: Charles E Hasty
**Sr VP:* John A Carbona
**VP:* Laurie Hasty

D-U-N-S 00-196-3396 IMP/EXP
C H POWELL CO
TANDEM GLOBAL LOGISTICS
75 Shawmut Rd, Canton, MA 02021-1408
Tel (781) 302-7300 *Founded/Ownrshp* 1919
Sales 92.9MM^E *EMP* 215
Accts Walsh Jastrem & Browne Llp
SIC 4731 Freight transportation arrangement
Pr: Charles Powell
**CFO:* Andrew Powell
**Treas:* David Powell
**VP:* Robert Powell
Brnch Mgr: Gilbert Villate

C H R
See CRESCENT HOTELS & RESORTS LLC

D-U-N-S 01-056-5182
C H R CORP (PA)
RUTTER'S FARM STORES
2295 N Susquehanna Trl C, York, PA 17404-8495
Tel (717) 848-9827 *Founded/Ownrshp* 1974
Sales 168.5MM^E *EMP* 1,500
SIC 5411 Convenience stores, chain
Pr: Scott E Hartman
**Treas:* Tim L Rutter
**VP:* Terry Hayostek
VP: George Sepic
Dir Risk M: Robert Perkins

D-U-N-S 78-369-8863 IMP/EXP
■ **C H ROBINSON INTERNATIONAL INC**
(*Suby of* CH ROBINSON WORLDWIDE INC) ★
14701 Charlson Rd, Eden Prairie, MN 55347-5076
Tel (952) 683-2800 *Founded/Ownrshp* 1989
Sales 423.1MM *EMP* 250
SIC 4731 Foreign freight forwarding
Prin: John P Wiehoff
**Pr:* Bryan D Foe
**CFO:* Chad M Lindbloom
Ch: Clark Hange
**Sr VP:* Jim Butts
Sr VP: Gregory Coven
**Sr VP:* Chad Lindbloom
**VP:* Ben Campbell
VP: Tom Mahlke
VP: Scott A Satterlee
Ex Dir: Kent Stuart

D-U-N-S 00-627-4765 IMP/EXP
C HAGER & SONS HINGE MANUFACTURING CO
HAGER HINGE COMPANY
139 Victor St, Saint Louis, MO 63104-4724
Tel (314) 772-4400 *Founded/Ownrshp* 1890
Sales 119.3MM^E *EMP* 550
SIC 3429 Manufactured hardware (general); Door locks, bolts & checks
CEO: August W Hager III
**Pr:* Charles C Hager Jr
**CEO:* August W Hager III
COO: Josh D Hager
CFO: Brian Josephson
Treas: Henry Belz III
Ex VP: Warren Hager
**VP:* Archer L Hager II
**VP:* Ralph J Hager
**VP:* Warren J Hager
VP: Ed Schlef
**VP:* Alice B Wiegand

D-U-N-S 18-328-3233
C I B C OPPENHEIMER HOLDINGS INC
CANADIAN IMPERIAL BNK COMMERCE
(*Suby of* CIBC DELAWARE HOLDINGS INC) ★
425 Lexington Ave Fl 5, New York, NY 10017-3903
Tel (212) 856-4000 *Founded/Ownrshp* 1997
Sales 614.2MM^E *EMP* 7,000^E
SIC 6211 Dealers, security
CFO: Kristin Reichardt
Dir IT: Derek Ranjitsingh

C I G
See CAMBRIDGE INFORMATION GROUP INC

D-U-N-S 78-332-2154
C J APPLE II INC
(*Suby of* APPLEBEES NGHBORHOOD GRILL BAR) ★
741 Centre View Blvd # 100, Crestview Hills, KY 41017-5435
Tel (859) 331-3900 *Founded/Ownrshp* 1997
Sales 49.4MM *EMP* 1,500
SIC 5812 Grills (eating places)
Pr: Curtis James
CFO: Lynn Hehman
**CFO:* Jeffry Kreger
**VP:* James Borke

C J SPECIALTY RENTAL TOOLS
See C&J ENERGY SERVICES INC

C L A
See CLIFTONLARSONALLEN LLP

C L M
See GRAYMONT (WI) LLC

D-U-N-S 07-765-5983
C L P CORP
MCDONALD'S
121 Summit Pkwy, Birmingham, AL 35209-4707
Tel (205) 943-0417 *Founded/Ownrshp* 1970
Sales 50.0MM *EMP* 1,626
SIC 5812 Fast-food restaurant, chain
CEO: Max Cooper
**VP:* Cheryl W Grise
Board of Directors: Cheryl W Grise

C L S
See CAPITOL LIGHT & SUPPLY CO

D-U-N-S 06-242-9816 IMP
C L SMITH CO INC
1311 S 39th St, Saint Louis, MO 63110-2591
Tel (314) 771-1202 *Founded/Ownrshp* 1975
Sales 111.5MM^E *EMP* 120
SIC 5085 Plastic bottles; Drums, new or reconditioned
CEO: CL Smith
**Pr:* Nancy Newby
CFO: Roger Archibald
**CFO:* Daniel McAteer
**VP:* Duane Pursley
**VP:* Kelly Shillito
Genl Mgr: John Wichlenski
Off Mgr: Cindy Monroe
IT Man: William Clifford
Ql Cn Mgr: Carl Garland
Sls Mgr: Leslie Licavoli

C M A CONSULTING SERVICES
See CURRIER MCCABE & ASSOCIATES INC

C M C
See CMC STEEL HOLDING CO

D-U-N-S 00-732-4924 IMP/EXP
■ C M C STEEL FABRICATORS INC (TX)
CMC RBAR SAN ANTNIO E LOCATION
(*Suby of* C M C) ★
1 Steel Mill Dr, Seguin, TX 78155-7510
Tel (830) 372-8200 *Founded/Ownrshp* 1978
Sales 526.3MM^E *EMP* 1,896
SIC 3312 3441 Structural shapes & pilings, steel; Fabricated structural metal
Pr: Tracy Porter
CFO: Kyle Craft
* *Treas:* Carey Dubois
* *Treas:* Louis A Federle
* *VP:* Murray McClean

C M P
See CENTRAL MAINE POWER CO INC

D-U-N-S 88-473-3874
C MT PARTNERS
7277 164th Ave Ne Rtc1, Redmond, WA 98052-7823
Tel (425) 580-6000 *Founded/Ownrshp* 2000
Sales 37.1MM^E *EMP* 1,266
SIC 4812 Cellular telephone services

D-U-N-S 00-336-2050
C M TUCKER LUMBER COMPANIES LLC (SC)
(*Suby of* CM TUCKER LUMBER COMPANIES LLC) ★
601 N Pearl St, Pageland, SC 29728-1628
Tel (843) 672-6135 *Founded/Ownrshp* 1946, 2002
Sales 151.5MM *EMP* 250
Accts Pricewaterhousecoopers Llp C
SIC 2491 Structural lumber & timber, treated wood
CEO: David Tucker
* *Pr:* Paul Tucker
* *VP:* Andrew Tucker

C M W
See CENTRAL MAINTENANCE AND WELDING INC

C N H
See CASE NEW HOLLAND INDUSTRIAL INC

C N I
See CNI ENTERPRISES INC

D-U-N-S 03-069-6434
C N L HOTEL DEL PARTNERS LP
1500 Orange Ave, San Diego, CA 92118-2918
Tel (619) 522-8299 *Founded/Ownrshp* 2004
Sales 9.3MM^E *EMP* 1,100
SIC 7011 Hotels & motels
Pt: Todd Shallan
CFO: David Nadeau

C N M
See CENTRAL NEW MEXICO COMMUNITY COLLEGE

C N S I
See CLIENT NETWORK SERVICES INC

C O X
See COXCOM LLC

D-U-N-S 00-883-4103
C OVERAA & CO (CA)
OVERAA CONSTRUCTION
200 Parr Blvd, Richmond, CA 94801-1191
Tel (510) 234-0926 *Founded/Ownrshp* 1907
Sales 158.5MM^E *EMP* 350
Accts Gallina Llp Novato Californi
SIC 1541 Industrial buildings, new construction
CEO: Jerry Overaa
* *Pr:* Christopher Manning
Ofcr: Roy Samuelsz
Genl Mgr: Elizabeth Brown
Off Admin: Valerie Prestella
IT Man: Erin O Disman
IT Man: Erin Dissman
IT Man: Sarah Muren
Mktg Dir: Kara Gragg

C P B
See C P BUCKNER STEEL ERECTION INC

D-U-N-S 02-446-0271 IMP
C P BUCKNER STEEL ERECTION INC
C P B
4732 S Nc Highway 54, Graham, NC 27253-9215
Tel (336) 376-8888 *Founded/Ownrshp* 1970
Sales 129.0MM^E *EMP* 451^E
SIC 1791 7353 Structural steel erection; Precast concrete structural framing or panels, placing of; Cranes & aerial lift equipment, rental or leasing
Ch Bd: Eddie Williams
* *Pr:* Douglas Williams
* *Sec:* Carol Williams
Sls Mgr: June Sparrow

C P C C
See CENTRAL PIEDMONT COMMUNITY COLLEGE

D-U-N-S 09-941-7599
C P C HOME ATTENDANT PROGRAM
40 Worth St Fl 13, New York, NY 10013-2904
Tel (212) 219-8100 *Founded/Ownrshp* 2001
Sales 91.1MM *EMP* 50
SIC 8999 Personal services

C P G
See CHURCH PENSION GROUP SERVICES CORP

C P I
See CHATSWORTH PRODUCTS INC

C P M
See CPM-US LLC

C P M P
See CLINICAL PRACTICE MANAGEMENT PLAN

C P S
See COMPLETE PROTOTYPE SERVICES INC

D-U-N-S 06-300-6738 IMP
C P SHADES INC
403 Coloma St, Sausalito, CA 94965-2827
Tel (415) 331-4581 *Founded/Ownrshp* 1973
Sales 135.3MM^E *EMP* 437
SIC 2339 5621 Women's & misses' athletic clothing & sportswear; Sportswear, women's; Women's sportswear
Pr: David Weinstein
* *Treas:* Denise Weinstein
* *VP:* Alison Pownall
Off Mgr: Cyndi Pettibone

C P W
See CRANSTON PRINT WORKS CO INC

D-U-N-S 00-697-3408 IMP
▲ C R BARD INC (NJ)
730 Central Ave, New Providence, NJ 07974-1199
Tel (908) 277-8000 *Founded/Ownrshp* 1907
Sales 3.4MMM *EMP* 14,900
Tkr Sym BCR *Exch* NYS
SIC 3841 3845 3842 Surgical & medical instruments; Blood transfusion equipment; Surgical instruments & apparatus; Electromedical equipment; Electrocardiographs; Surgical support systems: heart-lung machine, exc. iron lung; Patient monitoring apparatus; Surgical appliances & supplies; Surgical appliances & supplies; Bandages & dressings; Implants, surgical
Ch Bd: Timothy M Ring
Pr: Jim C Beasley
Pr: Timothy P Collins
Pr: John P Groetelaars
* *Pr:* John H Weiland
CFO: Christopher S Holland
Grp VP: Sharon M Luboff
Sr VP: John A Deford
Sr VP: Samrat S Khichi
VP: Sharon Alterio
VP: David Blaber
VP: Patricia G Christian
VP: Patricia Christian
VP: Mike Daly
VP: Vincent Gunari
VP: Jim Hawking
VP: Chris Holland
VP: Larry Lee
VP: Frank Lupaselli
VP: Frank Lupisella Jr
VP: Will Robinson
Board of Directors: Tony L White, David M Barrett, Marc C Breslawsky, Robert M Davis, Herbert L Henkel, John C Kelly, David F Melcher, Gail K Naughton, Tommy G Thompson, Anthony Welters

C R I
See COOPERATIVE RESOURCES INTERNATIONAL INC

D-U-N-S 00-896-1690
C R MEYER AND SONS CO
CR MEYER
895 W 20th Ave, Oshkosh, WI 54902-6766
Tel (920) 235-3350 *Founded/Ownrshp* 1888
Sales 450.1MM^E *EMP* 500
SIC 1542 1796 1541 Commercial & office building contractors; Machinery installation; Industrial buildings, new construction
* *Ch Bd:* F M Pinkerton
* *Pr:* Darren J Lett
* *CEO:* Phillip J Martini
Treas: Howard J Lee
* *Treas:* Tom Smits
* *VP:* Bill Heier
* *VP:* James E Leuthold
VP: James E Luthold
* *VP:* Brad Riutta
* *VP:* James C Schultz
* *VP:* Jerad Wilson

D-U-N-S 03-281-8809 IMP
C R P INDUSTRIES INC
35 Commerce Dr, Cranbury, NJ 08512-3503
Tel (609) 578-4100 *Founded/Ownrshp* 1944
Sales 100.0MM^E *EMP* 150
SIC 5013 5085 5063 Automotive supplies & parts; Rubber goods, mechanical; Motors, electric
CEO: Daniel Schildge
Pr: Dan Schildge
COO: Scott Shea
Ex VP: Chris Von Lenski
VP: Abe Garweg
VP: Michael Palm
Adm Dir: Sabine Gilson
Dir IT: Steve Boytis
VP Sls: Trevor Potter

C R S
See COMMERCIAL ROOFING SPECIALTIES INC

C S & P CRYOGENICS
See CS&P TECHNOLOGIES LP

C S C
See CORP SERVICE CO INC

C S C
See CONTEMPORARY SERVICES CORP

C S C
See COMMUNICATIONS SUPPLY CORP

C S D
See CONSOLIDATED SERVICE DISTRIBUTORS INC

C S D
See CAREER SYSTEMS DEVELOPMENT CORP

C S G
See CLEANING SERVICE GROUP INC

C S I
See CLOSURE SYSTEMS INTERNATIONAL INC

C S I
See COMPUTER SERVICES INC

C S I
See CSI ELECTRICAL CONTRACTORS INC

C S I
See CSI INTERNATIONAL INC

C S M
See COLUMBIA ST MARYS HOSPITAL MILWAUKEE INC

C S M
See COLLEGE OF SOUTHERN MARYLAND FOUNDATION INC

C S N
See COMPANHIA SIDERURGICA NACIONAL LLC

C S S
See CYBERNET SOFTWARE SYSTEMS INC

C S T
See CUSTOM SENSORS & TECHNOLOGIES INC

C S U
See CLEVELAND STATE UNIVERSITY

C S U
See CONNECTICUT STATE UNIVERSITY SYSTEM

C S V SALES
See NATIONAL FOOD GROUP INC

D-U-N-S 18-638-9219 IMP
C SCEC-USA INC
CHINA CONSTRUCTION AMERICA
(*Suby of* CHINA STATE CONSTRUCTION ENGINEERING CORPORATION)
525 Washington Blvd Fl 31, Jersey City, NJ 07310-1606
Tel (201) 876-2788 *Founded/Ownrshp* 1985
Sales 51.8MM^E *EMP* 1,300
SIC 8742 Site location consultant
Pr: Ning Yuan
* *Treas:* Mason Gao
VP: Art Blattner
VP: Bruce Cashon
VP: Shang Haiqing
VP: Larry Hannon
VP: John Hillock
VP: Alice Lee
VP: Manny Longobardo
Brnch Mgr: Kaj Ahlmann
CIO: Leigh Berrell

C SPIRE
See CELLULAR SOUTH INC

C. STEIN DISTRIBUTING
See STEIN DISTRIBUTING INC

D-U-N-S 18-116-1779
C STEIN INC
IDAHO DISTRIBUTING
4719 S Market St, Boise, ID 83705-5411
Tel (208) 378-0550 *Founded/Ownrshp* 1998
Sales 142.9MM *EMP* 160
SIC 5181 5182 5149 4941 5921 Beer & other fermented malt liquors; Wine; Beverages, except coffee & tea; Water supply; Beer (packaged)
CEO: Craig Stein
* *Pr:* Dennis McAuliff
* *CFO:* Rob Schneider
* *Sr VP:* David Morrison

C STORES
See DAVIS OIL CO

C T C
See CONCURRENT TECHNOLOGIES CORP

D-U-N-S 07-329-5511
C T CORP SYSTEM
WOLTERS KLUWER CORP LEGAL SVCS
(*Suby of* WOLTERS KLUWER UNITED STATES INC) ★
111 8th Ave Fl 13, New York, NY 10011-5213
Tel (212) 894-8940 *Founded/Ownrshp* 1988
Sales 318.9MM^E *EMP* 1,563
SIC 8111 Corporate, partnership & business law
CEO: Richard Flynn
* *CFO:* Joseph D'Avanzo
Chf Mktg O: Emily K Fitton
VP: Sami Hero
VP: Michael Radigan
VP: Paul Wanuga
Snr Sftwr: Anatoliy Ashkinadze
Dir IT: Trip McCue
Dir IT: Galina Vaynerman
Sales Exec: Paul Beach
VP Mktg: David King

C T I
See CHICAGO TUBE AND IRON CO

D-U-N-S 78-309-6444
C TERRY HUNT INDUSTRIES INC
5420 Perimeter Rd, Valdosta, GA 31601
Tel (229) 244-6707 *Founded/Ownrshp* 1999
Sales 144.2MM^E *EMP* 300
SIC 1629 Industrial plant construction
* *CFO:* Mary Lynn Hunt
* *VP:* Joel Hunt

C U A
See CATHOLIC UNIVERSITY OF AMERICA

C U C
See CLAREMONT MCKENNA COLLEGE FOUNDATION

C U C
See CLAREMONT GRADUATE UNIVERSITY

C U FINANCIAL GROUP
See LAKE MICHIGAN CREDIT UNION

C V E
See CACHE VALLEY ELECTRIC CO

C V G
See NATIONAL SEATING CO

C V I
See CLEAN VENTURE INC

C V S OPTICAL LAB DIV
See VISION SERVICE PLAN

D-U-N-S 08-156-5376
C V STARR & CO (CA)
(*Suby of* C V STARR & CO INC) ★
101 2nd St Ste 2500, San Francisco, CA 94105-3666
Tel (415) 216-4000 *Founded/Ownrshp* 1948
Sales NA *EMP* 433
SIC 6411 Insurance agents, brokers & service
Pr: William J Weichold
* *Sec:* Mary R Whelan
* *Ex VP:* Jeffrey M Hafter
Sr VP: John Atherton
Dir IT: Frank Tanabe

D-U-N-S 04-359-0116
C V STARR & CO INC (NV)
90 Park Ave Fl 7, New York, NY 10016-1301
Tel (212) 230-5050 *Founded/Ownrshp* 1940
Sales 125.3MM^E *EMP* 433
SIC 6719 Investment holding companies, except banks
Pr: Maurice Raymond Greenberg
* *Treas:* John Casale
Ofcr: John Moffatt
VP: Doug Bell

C V WATER DISTRICT
See COACHELLA VALLEY WATER DISTRICT

D-U-N-S 00-685-3162
C W DRIVER INC (CA)
468 N Rosemead Blvd, Pasadena, CA 91107-3010
Tel (626) 351-8800 *Founded/Ownrshp* 1919, 1981
Sales 284.9MM^E *EMP* 300
SIC 1542 Commercial & office building, new construction
Pr: Dana Roberts
CFO: Bessie Kouvara
Sr VP: John Janacek
Sr VP: Robert Maxwell
VP: Steven S Nelson
VP: John Thornton
Exec: Richard Freeark
Dir Bus: Betty L Senes
Off Mgr: Monica Marsh
Mktg Dir: Jennifer Vasquez
Snr PM: David Edwards

C W OHIO
See CASCADE OHIO INC

D-U-N-S 09-459-3589
C W ROBERTS CONTRACTING INC
3372 Capital Cir Ne, Tallahassee, FL 32308-3710
Tel (850) 385-5060 *Founded/Ownrshp* 1972
Sales 205.9MM^E *EMP* 365
SIC 1611 General contractor, highway & street construction
Pr: Robert P Flowers
* *VP:* Darryl Carpenter
* *VP:* Ned P Fleming III
* *VP:* Alan Palmer
Opers Mgr: Don Stanley

D-U-N-S 00-481-4000
C W WRIGHT CONSTRUCTION CO INC
C.W. WRIGHTS
11500 Iron Bridge Rd, Chester, VA 23831-1449
Tel (804) 768-1054 *Founded/Ownrshp* 2001
Sales 299.1MM^E *EMP* 700
SIC 1623 Electric power line construction
CEO: E J Spruill
* *Pr:* Richard K Booth
* *Pr:* Michael Walker
* *CFO:* Mason Chapman
* *Sr VP:* Jerry Hamman
* *VP:* Mark W Nunn
Div Mgr: Larry Young
Off Mgr: Susan Forest
Off Mgr: Tracey White
IT Man: Todd Whaley
IT Man: Todd Wiley

D-U-N-S 02-018-4946 IMP/EXP
C&C INDUSTRIES INC
(*Suby of* ERIKS N.V.)
10350 Clay Rd Ste 250, Houston, TX 77041-8762
Tel (713) 466-1644 *Founded/Ownrshp* 2005
Sales 98.0MM^E *EMP* 31
SIC 3999 5085 Atomizers, toiletry; Valves & fittings
Pr: Dale K Lutz
VP: Danny Dahlberg
Rgnl Mgr: Skip Manning
Genl Mgr: Steve Chin
Opers Mgr: Gerrit Dungen
Sls Dir: Lacie Purcell

C&D INTERIORS
See C&D ZODIAC INC

D-U-N-S 15-398-7490 IMP/EXP
C&D TECHNOLOGIES INC
C&D TECHNOLOGIES PWR SOLUTIONS
(*Suby of* ANGELO) ★
1400 Union Meeting Rd # 110, Blue Bell, PA 19422-1952
Tel (215) 619-7815 *Founded/Ownrshp* 2012
Sales 517.0MM^E *EMP* 1,500
SIC 3612 3691 3613 3692 3674 Transformers, except electric; Rectifier transformers; Lead acid batteries (storage batteries); Panel & distribution boards & other related apparatus; Primary batteries, dry & wet; Semiconductors & related devices
Pr: Christian Rheault
* *CFO:* Ian J Harvie
CFO: Lisa Rainwater
Treas: David Coke
Ofcr: Jay Frankhouser
VP: Mark D Amatrudo
* *VP:* David Anderson
VP: Jim Bartlet
VP: Monty Baveja
VP: Don Gerstle
VP: Leslie S Holden
VP: Justin Hu
* *VP:* Frank Izzi
* *VP:* Joe Jergl
VP: Joseph Jergl
VP: Jim Leoeonard
VP: David McKinney
VP: John J Murray Jr
VP: Bernie Radecki
VP: Pamela J Reich
VP: Chris Viola
Board of Directors: Pamela L Davies, Kevin P Dowd, David S Gee, William Harral III, Robert I Harries, George Mackenzie, Stanley W Silverman, Ellen C Wolf

C&D TECHNOLOGIES PWR SOLUTIONS
See C&D TECHNOLOGIES INC

D-U-N-S 05-799-9070 IMP
C&D ZODIAC INC
C&D INTERIORS
(*Suby of* ZODIAC AEROSYSTEMS) ★
5701 Bolsa Ave, Huntington Beach, CA 92647-2063
Tel (714) 934-0000 *Founded/Ownrshp* 2005
Sales 1.3MMM^E *EMP* 4,000
SIC 3728 Aircraft parts & equipment
CEO: Jude F Dozor
**Pr:* Clarence Au-Young
**CFO:* John Maglione
**Ex VP:* John Hargreaves
**Ex VP:* Mike McCarthy
**Ex VP:* Jean Pelchat
**VP:* Zeke Andrews
VP: Mitch Rierson
Exec: Jim Delpinto
IT Man: Chris Gebo
Netwrk Eng: Mamta Shah

D-U-N-S 01-331-0987
▲ **C&F FINANCIAL CORP**
802 Main St, West Point, VA 23181-9574
Tel (804) 843-2360 *Founded/Ownrshp* 1994
Sales NA *EMP* 598^E
Tkr Sym CFFI *Exch* NGS
SIC 6022 State commercial banks
Ch Bd: Larry G Dillon
**Pr:* Thomas F Cherry
CFO: Jason E Long

D-U-N-S 07-962-9150 IMP/EXP
C&F FOODS INC
15620 E Valley Blvd, City of Industry, CA 91744-3926
Tel (626) 723-1000 *Founded/Ownrshp* 1975
Sales 399.5MM^E *EMP* 350
SIC 5153 Grain & field beans
CEO: Manuel G Fernandez
**Pr:* Luis Faura
**CFO:* Cesar A Mejia
MIS Dir: Rose Jung
Dir IT: Werner Schlag
QI Cn Mgr: James Kauli

D-U-N-S 00-609-0500 IMP/EXP
■ **C&H DISTRIBUTORS LLC**
(*Suby of* GLOBAL INDUSTRIAL EQUIPMENT) ★
11200 W Parkland Ave, Milwaukee, WI 53224-3127
Tel (800) 607-8520 *Founded/Ownrshp* 1990, 2015
Sales 185.4MM^E *EMP* 353
SIC 5084 Industrial machinery & equipment; Safety equipment; Materials handling machinery
Pr: David E McKeon
CFO: Daniel Paruzynski
**Prin:* Michael Snapper
VP Mktg: Mike Snapper

D-U-N-S 03-557-1798
C&H INDUSTRIAL SERVICES INC
542 Penny St, Franklinville, NJ 08322-2835
Tel (856) 875-8152 *Founded/Ownrshp* 1999
Sales 8.5MMM *EMP* 25^E
SIC 7349 1542 Building maintenance services; Commercial & office building contractors
Pr: David Cross
**VP:* Harriet Cross
**VP:* Adrianne Hassinger

D-U-N-S 01-764-8016
C&J ENERGY SERVICES INC
C J SPECIALTY RENTAL TOOLS
(*Suby of* NABORS RED LION LIMITED)
3990 Rogerdale Rd, Houston, TX 77042-5142
Tel (713) 325-6000 *Founded/Ownrshp* 2010, 2015
Sales 1.9MMM^E *EMP* 3,744^E
SIC 1382 1389 Aerial geophysical exploration oil & gas; Hydraulic fracturing wells
CEO: Joshua E Comstock
**Pr:* Randy McMullen
**CEO:* Joshua Comstock
**COO:* Donald Gawick
Ofcr: Steven Carter
**Ofcr:* James H Prestidge Jr
Ex VP: Danielle Hunter
**Ex VP:* Ted Moore
VP: John Foret
Off Mgr: Lisa Harpole
Dir IT: Bill McCown
Board of Directors: Darren M Friedman, Adrianna Ma, Michael Roemer, C James Stewart III, H H Wommack III

D-U-N-S 08-837-2789
C&J SPEC-RENT SERVICES INC
C&J SPECIALTY RENTAL TOOLS
(*Suby of* C J SPECIALTY RENTAL TOOLS) ★
3990 Rogerdale Rd, Houston, TX 77042-5142
Tel (713) 260-9900 *Founded/Ownrshp* 1997
Sales 1.1MMM^E *EMP* 800
SIC 5065 Electronic parts & equipment
CEO: Joshua E Comstock
**Pr:* Larry Heidt
**CEO:* Lou Lee
**COO:* Brett Barrier
**CFO:* Randy McMullen
**Treas:* Dean Castleberry
**VP:* Mark Cashiola
**VP:* John D Foret
Sls Dir: Tommy Balez

C&J SPECIALTY RENTAL TOOLS
See C&J SPEC-RENT SERVICES INC

D-U-N-S 60-216-4910 IMP
C&J WELL SERVICES INC
NABORS
(*Suby of* NABORS RED LION LIMITED)
3990 Rogerdale Rd, Houston, TX 77042-5142
Tel (281) 874-0035 *Founded/Ownrshp* 2015
Sales 1.8MMM^E *EMP* 1,407
SIC 1389 Mud service, oil field drilling; Oil field services; Surveying wells; Servicing oil & gas wells
CEO: Randy McMullen Jr
**COO:* Don Gawick
**Ex VP:* Ted Moore
VP: Jose S Cadena
**Dir Sec:* James H Prestidge Jr
Area Supr: Jose Garnica

D-U-N-S 01-131-2548
C&M MARINE AVIATION SERVICES INC (TX)
9200 King Arthur Dr, Dallas, TX 75247-3610
Tel (214) 654-9270 *Founded/Ownrshp* 1991
Sales 230.0MM *EMP* 13
SIC 2399 Seat belts, automobile & aircraft
CEO: Sali A Barney
VP: Michael Rousey

D-U-N-S 04-488-5648 IMP
C&M TIRE INC
CROSS MIDWEST TIRE CO
401 S 42nd St, Kansas City, KS 66106-1005
Tel (913) 321-3003 *Founded/Ownrshp* 2003
Sales 160.0MM^E *EMP* 300
SIC 5531 7534 5014 3312 Automotive tires; Rebuilding & retreading tires; Tire recapping; Automobile tires & tubes; Truck tires & tubes; Wheels
Pr: Greg Trum
**VP:* Art Ensley
Store Mgr: Doug Ogden

D-U-N-S 12-761-3060
C&N ETHANOL MARKETING LLC
(*Suby of* NOBLE AMERICAS CORP) ★
8011 34th Ave S Ste 350, Minneapolis, MN 55425-1632
Tel (888) 263-8357 *Founded/Ownrshp* 2016
Sales 550.0MM *EMP* 14
SIC 8742 Marketing consulting services
Pr: Jon Bjornstad
**Sr VP:* Eric Fobes

D-U-N-S 00-184-2467 IMP/EXP
C&S WHOLESALE GROCERS INC
C&S WHOLESALE PRODUCE
7 Corporate Dr, Keene, NH 03431-5042
Tel (603) 354-7000 *Founded/Ownrshp* 1984
Sales 30.7MMM^E *EMP* 17,000
SIC 5141 5147 5143 5142 5122 5145 Groceries, general line; Meats, fresh; Dairy products, except dried or canned; Packaged frozen goods; Drugs, proprietaries & sundries; Cosmetics, perfumes & hair products; Confectionery; Candy
Pr: Richard B Cohen
**CFO:* Joseph Schena
**Treas:* Timothy D Ludlow
**Ex VP:* Scott Charlton
Ex VP: Geoff Davis
**Ex VP:* Peter Fiore
**Ex VP:* Bruce Johnson
Ex VP: Mike Newbold
Ex VP: Robert Palmer
Sr VP: Christopher Brown
Sr VP: Mitch Davis
Sr VP: Walter Pong
**Sr VP:* Jim Weidenheimer
**VP:* Alejandro Rodriguez Bas
VP: William Chamlin
VP: Scott Foster
VP: Mark Franke
VP: Keith Frosceno
VP: Tom Gemmell
VP: Andrew Goodwin
VP: Brian Granger

C&S WHOLESALE PRODUCE
See C&S WHOLESALE GROCERS INC

D-U-N-S 80-440-9489
C&S WHOLESALE SERVICES INC
(*Suby of* C&S WHOLESALE PRODUCE) ★
208 Bi Lo Blvd, Greenville, SC 29607-5346
Tel (864) 234-1999 *Founded/Ownrshp* 2005
Sales 217.4MM^E *EMP* 3,267^E
SIC 5141 Food brokers
CEO: Rick Cohen
VP: Kip Faulhaber
Exec: Tammy Outlaw
CIO: Steven Ortega

D-U-N-S 05-345-6083
C&W FACILITY SERVICES INC
C&W SERVICES
(*Suby of* CUSHMAN & WAKEFIELD HOLDINGS INC) ★
275 Grove St Ste 3-200, Auburndale, MA 02466-2274
Tel (617) 527-5222 *Founded/Ownrshp* 2015
Sales 98.4MM^E *EMP* 14,000
SIC 7349 6531 Building maintenance services; Building cleaning service; Janitorial service, contract basis; Cleaning service, industrial or commercial; Real estate agents & managers; Real estate leasing & rentals; Real estate brokers & agents
Pr: Paul Bedborough
COO: George A Keches
CFO: James Lawlor
Ex VP: Rob Cookson
Ex VP: Carole Jurkash
Sr VP: David Giamichael
VP: Bruce L Charboneau
VP: Jim Craig
VP: Walter Crow
VP: Bill Crowe
VP: George Doolin
VP: Michael Dunn
VP: Vanessa Eustace
VP: Bill Maliff
VP: Bill Romine
VP: Steve Stephens
Board of Directors: Richard Leupen, Robert Shibuya

C&W SERVICES
See C&W FACILITY SERVICES INC

C-A-L RANCH STORES
See C-A-L STORES COMPANIES INC

D-U-N-S 03-396-3422 IMP
C-A-L STORES COMPANIES INC
C-A-L RANCH STORES
665 E Anderson St, Idaho Falls, ID 83401-2020
Tel (208) 523-3359 *Founded/Ownrshp* 1989
Sales 233.2MM^E *EMP* 250
SIC 5191 Farm supplies
Pr: Howard Johnston
**CFO:* Jerry Ward
VP: Terry Bjarnson
VP: Bill Bunker
**VP:* Don Skeen
Mktg Mgr: Dustin Lee

C-BASS
See CREDIT-BASED ASSET SERVICING AND SECURITIZATION LLC

D-U-N-S 12-058-5950 IMP
C-CARE LLC
979 Corporate Blvd, Linthicum Heights, MD 21090-2211
Tel (410) 850-0035 *Founded/Ownrshp* 2000
Sales 118.7MM^E *EMP* 110
SIC 5122 Cosmetics
CFO: Kevin Kavenagh CPA
**Pr:* Ullrich Metzler
**VP:* Andy Davis
**VP:* Ron Hoch
VP Sls: Valerie Vail

C-CURE
See CUSTOM BUILDING PRODUCTS INC

D-U-N-S 61-850-9079 IMP
C-E MINERALS INC
MULCOA
(*Suby of* IMERYS)
100 Mansell Ct E Ste 615, Roswell, GA 30076-4841
Tel (770) 225-7900 *Founded/Ownrshp* 1990
Sales 354.8MM^E *EMP* 320
SIC 1099 1446 3295 6512 Aluminum ore mining; Silica mining; Silica sand mining; Minerals, ground or otherwise treated; Commercial & industrial building operation
Pr: Steven Fortier

D-U-N-S 07-838-8166
C-III CAPITAL PARTNERS LLC
5221 N O Connor Blvd, Irving, TX 75039-3714
Tel (972) 868-5300 *Founded/Ownrshp* 2010
Sales 171.5MM^E *EMP* 1,100^E
SIC 6519 6726 6361 6411 Sub-lessors of real estate; Management investment funds, closed-end; Real estate title insurance; Insurance information & consulting services
Pr: Frank M Garrison
CFO: James A Aston
Sr VP: Deborah A Bacon
Sr VP: Nancy Bown
Sr VP: Brian S Brennan
Sr VP: Tammy Cherry
Sr VP: Mitzie Crider
Sr VP: Sharon A Ezell
Sr VP: David W Koepke
Sr VP: Peter K Kofoed
Sr VP: Steve Luther
Sr VP: Scot M McLaughlin
Sr VP: Jerod Miller
Sr VP: Kathy Patterson
Sr VP: Dixon M Rich
Sr VP: Ginger A Schuette
Sr VP: Ryan Stephens
Sr VP: Russell Tuman
VP: Terri Alfred
VP: Ross T Bickel
VP: Chris Brantley

D-U-N-S 03-256-1961 IMP/EXP
C-TECH INDUSTRIES INC
KARCHER NORTH AMERICA
(*Suby of* KARCHER NORTH AMERICA INC) ★
4275 Nw Pacific Rim Blvd, Camas, WA 98607-8801
Tel (360) 833-1600 *Founded/Ownrshp* 2004
Sales 84.8MM^E *EMP* 400
SIC 3589 2841 3559 High pressure cleaning equipment; Textile soap; Recycling machinery
CEO: Hannes Subert
CEO: Andy Gale
COO: Mark Haley
CFO: Thorsten Binkert
CFO: Thorsten Dinkert
CFO: Peter Lynch
CFO: Bob Mazzacavallo
Treas: Susan Gilbert
Sr VP: Paul Linton
VP: Bill Allen
VP: Phorsten Binkert
VP: Jeff Fithian
VP: Donita Gardner
VP: Jon Mueller
VP: Bill Ott
VP: Jim Perris

C-TECH SYSTEMS DIVISION
See MEDALIST INDUSTRIES INC

D-U-N-S 03-978-3279 IMP
C-USA INC
1005 E Woodmen Rd, Colorado Springs, CO 80920-3181
Tel (719) 594-4100 *Founded/Ownrshp* 2015
Sales 149.3MM^E *EMP* 1,151
SIC 5947 5961 2771 Gift shop; Cards, mail order; Gift items, mail order; Mail order house; Greeting cards
CEO: Wendy L Huxta
**Pr:* Wendy Heck
**CFO:* Kirby Heck
VP: Nancy Hecker
Advt Mgr: Alicia Morey

C/O COURT SQ CAPITL PARTNERS
See MDI HOLDINGS LLC

C/S CORPORATE
See CONSTRUCTION SPECIALTIES INC

D-U-N-S 01-817-6234 IMP
C3/CUSTOMERCONTACTCHANNELS INC (FL)
1200 S Pine Island Rd # 200, Plantation, FL 33324-4413
Tel (954) 849-0622 *Founded/Ownrshp* 2010
Sales 291.5MM^E *EMP* 7,315^E
SIC 7389 Telephone services
CEO: Richard Mondre
**Pr:* Richard N Ferry
**CFO:* Anthony J Macaione
**Ch:* Mark Gordon
**Sr VP:* Curt Gooden
VP: Karen Dimezzo
**VP:* Kenneth Epstein
VP: Kory Laszewski
IT Man: David Ulrich
Sls Dir: Dennis Hernandez

D-U-N-S 60-569-5808
CA COURTESY DEMOS INC
85 Flagship Dr Ste C, North Andover, MA 01845-6160
Tel (978) 296-2600 *Founded/Ownrshp* 1986
Sales 96.1MM^E *EMP* 3,000
SIC 7389 Demonstration service
Pr: Claire Bishop
Genl Mgr: Tarryn Daisy

D-U-N-S 00-503-3485 IMP
CA CURTZE CO (PA)
CURTZE FOOD SERVICE
1717 E 12th St, Erie, PA 16511-1723
Tel (814) 452-2281 *Founded/Ownrshp* 1878
Sales 256.1MM^E *EMP* 255
SIC 5141 5147 5142 Groceries, general line; Meats & meat products; Fish, frozen: packaged; Meat, frozen: packaged; Poultry, frozen: packaged
Pr: C Bruce Kern II
**Pr:* Bruce Kern Jr
**CEO:* Bruce Kern Sr
COO: Randy Work
Chf Mktg O: Janet Dennan
**VP:* B Scott Kern
VP: Scott Kern
MIS Mgr: Debbie Keim
VP Sls: John Irish
Sales Asso: Christopher Mong

D-U-N-S 08-039-9256 EXP
▲ **CA INC**
520 Madison Ave Fl 22, New York, NY 10022-4327
Tel (800) 225-5224 *Founded/Ownrshp* 1976
Sales 4.0MMM *EMP* 11,600
Accts Kpmg Llp New York New York
Tkr Sym CA *Exch* NGS
SIC 7372 8742 Business oriented computer software; Application computer software; Management consulting services
CEO: Michael P Gregoire
Ch Bd: Arthur F Weinbach
CFO: Richard J Beckert
CFO: Kieran J McGrath
Chf Mktg O: Lauren P Flaherty
Ex VP: Otto Berkes
Ex VP: Michael C Bisignano
Ex VP: Jacob Lamm
VP: Dennis Brunner
VP: Brendan Doherty
VP: Dana Iacovelli
VP: Vineet Joseph
VP: Keith Larney
VP: Eric Levy
VP: David Maryles
VP: Edward Perry
VP: Bryan Reid
VP: Abdul Riyaz
VP: Kristin H Saunders
VP: Rick Schwartz
VP: Joseph Starpoli
Board of Directors: Jens Alder, Raymond J Bromark, Jeffrey G Katz, Kay Koplovitz, Christopher B Lofgren, Richard Sulpizio, Laura S Unger, Renato Zambonini

D-U-N-S 80-075-1141 IMP
CA LINDMAN INC
10401 Guilford Rd, Jessup, MD 20794-9117
Tel (410) 724-0040 *Founded/Ownrshp* 1990
Sales 131.6MM^E *EMP* 400
SIC 1542 Commercial & office buildings, renovation & repair
Pr: Robert G Pusheck
**VP:* Jeff W Procter
Brnch Mgr: Tom Ray Jr
Genl Mgr: Scott Carter
Snr PM: Mike Horne

D-U-N-S 82-639-0833
CA PERRY & SON TRANSIT INC
4033 Virginia Rd, Hobbsville, NC 27946-9508
Tel (252) 221-4463 *Founded/Ownrshp* 1990
Sales 140.0MM *EMP* 35
SIC 4213 4212 Trucking, except local; Local trucking, without storage
Pr: Sidney Perry
**VP:* Mary S Copeland

D-U-N-S 79-827-5228
CABARRUS COUNTY SCHOOL
4401 Old Airport Rd, Concord, NC 28025-7188
Tel (704) 786-6191 *Founded/Ownrshp* 1994
Sales 194.7MM^E *EMP* 3,400
Accts Anderson Smith & Wike Pllc S
SIC 8211 Public elementary school; Public junior high school; Public senior high school
Adm Dir: George Douglas
MIS Dir: Michael Stocks
HC Dir: John Bastlest

D-U-N-S 61-177-6428
CABAZON BAND OF MISSION INDIANS
84245 Indio Springs Dr, Indio, CA 92203-3405
Tel (760) 342-2593 *Founded/Ownrshp* 1989
Sales NA *EMP* 1,050
SIC 9131 Indian reservation;
Ch Bd: John James
**Sec:* Angela Roosevelt
Genl Mgr: Leilani Gomez
IT Man: Frank Lewis

D-U-N-S 03-500-0363
▲ **CABELAS INC** (DE)
1 Cabelas Dr, Sidney, NE 69162-3028
Tel (308) 254-5505 *Founded/Ownrshp* 1961
Sales 4.0MMM *EMP* 19,700
Tkr Sym CAB *Exch* NYS
SIC 5961 5941 Fishing, hunting & camping equipment & supplies: mail order; Clothing, mail order (except women's); Sporting goods & bicycle shops

CEO: Thomas L Millner
**Ch Bd:* James W Cabela
Pr: Scott K Williams
CFO: Ralph W Castner
Bd of Dir: Beth Pritchard
Ofcr: Charles Baldwin
Ex VP: Douglas R Means
VP: Cory Bergstrom
VP: Justin L Smith
CIO: Larry Popps
QA Dir: Thomas Mohs
Board of Directors: Theodore M Armstrong, John H Edmondson, Dennis Highby, Michael R McCarthy, Donna M Molrod, Beth M Pritchard, Peter S Swinburn, James R Wright

D-U-N-S 07-680-8807
CABELL COUNTY BOARD-EDUCATION
2850 5th Ave, Huntington, WV 25702-1436
Tel (304) 528-5000 *Founded/Ownrshp* 1933
Sales 55.2MM^E *EMP* 1,600
SIC 8211 Public elementary & secondary schools
VP: Mary Neely
**Prin:* Pamela Baley
**Brnch Mgr:* Pamela Silver
Board of Directors: Jeremy Baisden, Patty Pauley, Tim Stewart

D-U-N-S 10-057-2809
CABELL COUNTY SCHOOL DIST INC
2850 5th Ave, Huntington, WV 25702-1436
Tel (304) 528-5000 *Founded/Ownrshp* 1983
Sales 53.0MM^E *EMP* 1,239^E
SIC 8211 Public elementary & secondary schools; Public elementary school; Public junior high school; Public senior high school
Dir Sec: Tim Stewart
MIS Dir: Jeremy Baisden
Pr Dir: Jedd Flowers
Teacher Pr: Deborah Smith
HC Dir: Sherri Woods

CABELL HOME HEALTH SERVICES
See HUNTINGTON CABELL HOSPITAL INC

CABLCON
See QUAD ELECTRONICS INC

D-U-N-S 87-884-0594 IMP
■ CABLE NEWS NETWORK INC
CNN
(*Suby of* ADULT SWIM GAMES) ★
1 Cnn Ctr Nw 12, Atlanta, GA 30303-2762
Tel (404) 878-2276 *Founded/Ownrshp* 1979
Sales 1.0MMM^E *EMP* 5,392
SIC 4833 Television broadcasting stations
CEO: Tom Johnson
**CFO:* Wayne H Pace
Ex VP: Cindy Patrick
Ex VP: Janet Rolle
Sr VP: Deborah Cooper
VP: Matthew Drooker
VP: Nancy Duffy
VP: Richard Griffiths
VP: Will King
VP: Barry Koch
VP: Trish Lemley
VP: Nancy Leung
VP: Jeff Mattison
VP: Lorie McCarthy
VP: Cecilia Persson
VP: Priscilla Saunders
VP: Brett Weitz
VP Bus Dev: Alex Gonzalez
Creative D: Dan Brown

D-U-N-S 09-857-8669 IMP
■ CABLE NEWS NETWORK LP LLLP
CNN
(*Suby of* ADULT SWIM GAMES) ★
1 Cnn Ctr Nw, Atlanta, GA 30303-2762
Tel (404) 522-8873 *Founded/Ownrshp* 1979
Sales 180.4MM^E *EMP* 2,200
SIC 4833 Television broadcasting stations
CEO: Walter Isaacson
COO: Greg D'Alba
Ex VP: Susan M Bunda
Ex VP: Jonathan Davies
Ex VP: Susan Grant
Ex VP: Tony Maddox
Sr VP: Christopher Crommett
Sr VP: Kenneth Estenson
Sr VP: Rena Golden
Sr VP: Katherine Green
Sr VP: Nancy Lane
VP: Meredith Artley

D-U-N-S 15-595-5644
▲ CABLE ONE INC
210 E Earll Dr Fl 6, Phoenix, AZ 85012-2626
Tel (602) 364-6000 *Founded/Ownrshp* 1986
Sales 807.2MM *EMP* 1,972
Tkr Sym CABO *Exch* NYS
SIC 4813 4841 Telephone communication, except radio; ; ; Cable & other pay television services
Ch Bd: Thomas O Might
Pr: Julia M Laulis
CFO: Kevin P Coyle
Ofcr: Michael E Bowker
Sr VP: Stephen A Fox
Sr VP: Charles B McDonald
Sr VP: Alan H Silverman
VP: Kevin Coyle
Board of Directors: Naomi M Bergman, Brad D Brian, Thomas S Gayner, Deborah J Kissire, Alan G Spoon, Wallace R Weitz, Katharine B Weymouth

CABLE REP ADVERTISING
See COX MEDIA LLC

D-U-N-S 07-593-5999
■ CABLECOM LLC
(*Suby of* DYCOM INDUSTRIES INC) ★
8602 Maltby Rd, Woodinville, WA 98072-8035
Tel (360) 668-1300 *Founded/Ownrshp* 1998
Sales 87.0MM^E *EMP* 690
SIC 1623 1731 Cable television line construction; Telephone & telephone equipment installation
Pr: Paul Graves
**VP:* Michael Burt
**Prin:* Joe Joe Lemke
Dir IT: Tom Meehan
Opers Mgr: Jim Birkenheier

CABLETRON
See ENTERASYS NETWORKS INC

CABLEVISION
See CSC HOLDINGS LLC

D-U-N-S 80-003-1320
CABLEVISION LIGHTPATH INC
(*Suby of* CABLEVISION) ★
200 Jericho Quadrangle, Jericho, NY 11753-2701
Tel (516) 803-2300 *Founded/Ownrshp* 1991
Sales 708.0MM^E *EMP* 1,805
SIC 4841 Cable & other pay television services
Pr: David Pistacchio
**Ch Bd:* Charles F Dolan
**Pr:* James L Dolan
**Sr VP:* Joe Caruso
Sr VP: Jennifer Comunale
**Sr VP:* David Kniffin
Sr VP: John Macario
**Sr VP:* Julia McGrath
**Sr VP:* Christopher Rabii
Sr VP: Rangachari Sairam
**Sr VP:* Robin Silverman
VP: Sean Fassett
VP: Ernest Hoffmann
VP: Jose Lugo
VP: Tom Welsh
VP: Geoffrey Whalen

D-U-N-S 01-400-0363
CABLEVISION SYSTEMS CORP
(*Suby of* ALTICE N.V.)
1111 Stewart Ave, Bethpage, NY 11714-3581
Tel (516) 803-2300 *Founded/Ownrshp* 2016
Sales 6.5MMM *EMP* 13,556
SIC 4841 Cable television services; Direct broadcast satellite services (DBS)
CEO: James L Dolan
Pr: Kristin Dolan
**Pr:* Brian G Sweeney
**COO:* Kristin A Dolan
**Treas:* Kevin F Watson
Ex VP: Thomas C Dolan
**Ex VP:* David G Ellen
Ex VP: J Gault
Ex VP: Tom Makin
Ex VP: Robert Sullivan
Sr VP: Victoria M Mink
VP: Mark Berlinsky
VP: Cindi Buckwalter
VP: Joe Charno
VP: Mark Eberly
VP: Jamie Gorman
VP: Kate Mahajuodeen
VP: Steve Mirabile
VP: Tom Montemagno
VP: Bret Richter
VP: Charles R Schueler

D-U-N-S 80-003-1338
CABLEVISION SYSTEMS LONG ISLAND CORP
(*Suby of* CABLEVISION) ★
1111 Stewart Ave, Bethpage, NY 11714-3581
Tel (516) 803-2300 *Founded/Ownrshp* 2001
Sales 169.4MM^E *EMP* 899
SIC 4841 Cable & other pay television services
Ch Bd: Charles F Dolan
VP: Sherry Brennan

D-U-N-S 00-291-6737 IMP
CABLOFIL INC
CABLOFIL/LEGRAND
(*Suby of* LEGRAND HOLDING INC) ★
8319 State Route 4, Mascoutah, IL 62258-2824
Tel (618) 566-3230 *Founded/Ownrshp* 2005
Sales 142.1MM^E *EMP* 500
SIC 3443 Cable trays, metal plate
Pr: Timothy Place
CFO: Jim Kramer
**Treas:* James Laperriere
**VP:* Robert Julian

CABLOFIL/LEGRAND
See CABLOFIL INC

D-U-N-S 00-101-3580 IMP/EXP
▲ CABOT CORP
2 Seaport Ln Ste 1300, Boston, MA 02210-2019
Tel (617) 345-0100 *Founded/Ownrshp* 1882
Sales 2.4MMM *EMP* 4,300
Accts Deloitte & Touche Llp Boston
Tkr Sym CBT *Exch* NYS
SIC 2895 3081 3084 2819 3339 Carbon black; Polyethylene film; Plastics pipe; Silica, amorphous; Primary nonferrous metals; Tantalum refining; Columbian refining (primary); Germanium refining (primary)
Pr: Sean D Keohane
**Ch Bd:* John F O'Brien
CFO: Eduardo E Cordeiro
Ex VP: Nicholas S Cross
Sr VP: Brian A Berube
Sr VP: Hobart C Kalkstein
Sr VP: Friedrich Von Gottberg
Board of Directors: Juan Enriquez, William C Kirby, Roderick C G Macleod, John K McGillicuddy, Patrick M Prevost, Sue H Rataj, Lydia W Thomas, Matthias L Wolfgruber, Mark S Wrighton

D-U-N-S 00-176-5916
CABOT CREAMERY COOPERATIVE INC
(*Suby of* AGRI-MARK INC) ★
193 Home Farm Way, Waitsfield, VT 05673-7512
Tel (978) 552-5500 *Founded/Ownrshp* 1919
Sales 109.9MM^E *EMP* 300
SIC 2022 5143 5451 Natural cheese; Cheese; Butter; Cheese
Pr: Richard Stammer
Chf Mktg O: Roberta Macdonald
Exec: Amy Levine
Prgrm Mgr: Jen Flannigan
Dir IT: Robert Pembroke
IT Man: Dan Boutin
Netwrk Eng: Mark Frederick
Opers Mgr: Matt Hill
Plnt Mgr: Rob Hirss
Plnt Mgr: Chris Pearl
Trfc Mgr: Joe Young

D-U-N-S 61-715-5197 IMP
■ CABOT INTERNATIONAL CAPITAL CORP
(*Suby of* CABOT CORP) ★
2 Seaport Ln Ste 1300, Boston, MA 02210-2058
Tel (617) 345-0100 *Founded/Ownrshp* 1966
Sales 120.8MM^E *EMP* 150
SIC 5169 Chemicals & allied products
CEO: Kenneth Burns

D-U-N-S 12-434-3547
▲ CABOT MICROELECTRONICS CORP
870 N Commons Dr, Aurora, IL 60504-7963
Tel (630) 375-6631 *Founded/Ownrshp* 1999
Sales 430.4MM *EMP* 1,111
Accts Pricewaterhousecoopers Llp Ch
Tkr Sym CCMP *Exch* NGS
SIC 2842 Polishing preparations & related products
Pr: David H Li
**Ch Bd:* William P Noglows
CFO: William S Johnson
VP: H Carol Bernstein
VP: Yumiko Damashek
VP: Thomas F Kelly
VP: Ananth Naman
VP: Daniel Pike
VP: Daniel D Woodland
Dir Bus: Daniel McMullen
IT Man: Kris Leong
Board of Directors: Robert J Birgeneau, H Laurence Fuller, Richard S Hill, Barbara A Klein, Edward J Mooney, Susan M Whitney, Geoffrey Wild, Steven V Wilkinson

D-U-N-S 60-792-5757
▲ CABOT OIL & GAS CORP
840 Gessner Rd Ste 1400, Houston, TX 77024-4152
Tel (281) 589-4600 *Founded/Ownrshp* 1989
Sales 1.3MMM *EMP* 459^E
Tkr Sym COG *Exch* NYS
SIC 1311 Natural gas production; Crude petroleum production
Ch Bd: Dan O Dinges
CFO: Scott C Schroeder
Treas: Matthew P Kerin
Sr VP: Jeffrey W Hutton
VP: G Kevin Cunningham
VP: Todd L Liebl
VP: Steven W Lindeman
VP: Phillip L Stalnaker
Board of Directors: Dorothy M Ables, Rhys J Best, Robert S Boswell, Robert Kelley, W Matt Ralls

CABOT PUBLIC SCHOOLS
See CABOT SCHOOL DISTRICT 4 (INC)

D-U-N-S 04-061-9934
CABOT SCHOOL DISTRICT 4 (INC)
CABOT PUBLIC SCHOOLS
602 N Lincoln St, Cabot, AR 72023-2601
Tel (501) 843-3363 *Founded/Ownrshp* 1900
Sales 47.0MM^E *EMP* 1,000
SIC 8211 Public elementary & secondary schools; Public junior high school; Public senior high school
Dir Sec: Keri Jackson
Pr Dir: Amanda Elizandro
Pr Dir: Liz Massey
HC Dir: Vonda Morgan

CABRILLO COLLEGE
See CABRILLO COMMUNITY COLLEGE DISTRICT FINANCING CORP

D-U-N-S 06-910-7373
CABRILLO COMMUNITY COLLEGE DISTRICT FINANCING CORP
CABRILLO COLLEGE
6500 Soquel Dr, Aptos, CA 95003-3119
Tel (831) 479-6100 *Founded/Ownrshp* 1959
Sales 7.8MM *EMP* 1,500
Accts Vavrinek Trine Day & Co Ll
SIC 8222 7922 8221 Community college; Theatrical producers & services; Colleges universities & professional schools
Pr: Dr Laurel Jones
**Pr:* Brian King
Pr: Victoria Lewis
VP: Barbara Shingai
Exec: Joe Jordan
CIO: Lile Cruse
Pgrm Dir: Ann S Smeltzer

D-U-N-S 16-242-3545
CABS HOME ATTENDANTS SERVICE INC
44 Varet St, Brooklyn, NY 11206-4014
Tel (718) 388-0220 *Founded/Ownrshp* 1979
Sales 48.5MM *EMP* 1,680
Accts Defino & D Elia Llp Bellmore
SIC 8082 Home health care services
Ex Dir: Kenneth Block
**Pr:* William G Pernisek
**Treas:* Adolfo Alayon

D-U-N-S 11-339-3763
CACHE COUNTY SCHOOL DISTRICT
CACHE PRESCHOOL
2063 N 1200 E, North Logan, UT 84341-2099
Tel (435) 752-3925 *Founded/Ownrshp* 1998
Sales 139.4MM *EMP* 2,300
Accts Allred Jackson North Logan U
SIC 8211 Public junior high school; Public elementary school
**Pr:* Tamara Grange
Bd of Dir: Richard Knight
Exec: Lynette Riggs
Psych: Bardett Bagley
HC Dir: Karen Peterson

D-U-N-S 01-200-5186
CACHE CREEK CASINO RESORT
(*Suby of* YOCHA DEHE WINTUN NATION) ★
14455 State Highway 16, Brooks, CA 95606-9707
Tel (530) 796-3118 *Founded/Ownrshp* 2007
Sales 116.4MM^E *EMP* 2,000
SIC 7011 Casino hotel
VP: Mike Leonard
VP: Mark Longshore
VP: Joe Maloney
Exec: Anthony Harrington
Snr Ntwrk: Daniel Ogden
IT Man: Tavis Feese

D-U-N-S 07-847-4756
CACHE INC
256 W 38th St Fl 3, New York, NY 10018-9129
Tel (212) 575-3200 *Founded/Ownrshp* 1975
Sales 216.7MM *EMP* 2,652^E
SIC 5632 5621 5961 Women's accessory & specialty stores; Apparel accessories; Women's clothing stores; Women's sportswear; Dress shops; Women's apparel, mail order
Ch Bd: Jay Margolis
CFO: Anthony F Dipippa
Ex VP: Rabia Farhang
Sr VP: Lusia Moskvicheva
VP: Bart Heminover
VP: Jane Inman
VP: Tongyan T Wang
Store Mgr: Carol Hall
Board of Directors: Gene G Gage, Robert C Grayson, Charles J Hinkaty, J David Scheiner

D-U-N-S 07-861-5745
CACHE OF VIRGINIA INC
(*Suby of* CACHE INC) ★
256 W 38th St Fl 3, New York, NY 10018-9129
Tel (212) 840-4226 *Founded/Ownrshp* 2006
Sales 69.6MM^E *EMP* 2,652
SIC 5632 5621 Women's accessory & specialty stores; Apparel accessories; Women's clothing stores; Women's sportswear; Dress shops
Ch Bd: Jay Margolis

CACHE PRESCHOOL
See CACHE COUNTY SCHOOL DISTRICT

D-U-N-S 00-681-3109 IMP
CACHE VALLEY ELECTRIC CO
C V E
875 N 1000 W, Logan, UT 84321-7800
Tel (435) 752-6405 *Founded/Ownrshp* 1915
Sales 269.5MM^E *EMP* 1,000
SIC 1731 General electrical contractor
Pr: James D Laub
**CFO:* Brett Heggi
**Treas:* Mark Montgomery
**VP:* Nathan Wickizer
Telecom Ex: Jeff Grandia
Snr Ntwrk: Kyle Hambright
Dir IT: Jeremy Bud
Dir IT: Charlie Minich
Dir IT: Andrew Petersen
IT Man: Jeff Jensen
Mtls Mgr: Chris Rongastad

D-U-N-S 14-499-1051
■ CACI ENTERPRISE SOLUTIONS INC
(*Suby of* CACI INC - FEDERAL) ★
1100 N Glebe Rd Ste 200, Arlington, VA 22201-4797
Tel (703) 841-7800 *Founded/Ownrshp* 2004
Sales 92.8MM^E *EMP* 1,535^E
SIC 7373 Computer integrated systems design
Ch Bd: J P London
**Pr:* John Mengucci
**CEO:* Kenneth Asbury
**CFO:* Thomas Mutryn
**Ofcr:* Arnold Morse
VP: Judith B Kassel
VP: Gary R Madison
VP: Samuel Strickland
Exec: William J Clancy
Exec: John J Davis
Exec: Jeffrey P Elefante
Exec: Stephen L Waechter

D-U-N-S 09-410-7844
■ CACI INC - FEDERAL
(*Suby of* CACI INTERNATIONAL INC) ★
1100 N Glebe Rd Ste 200, Arlington, VA 22201-4797
Tel (703) 841-7800 *Founded/Ownrshp* 1975
Sales 1.5MMM^E *EMP* 4,074^E
SIC 7373 7372 7371 8711

D-U-N-S 04-553-4641
▲ CACI INTERNATIONAL INC
1100 N Glebe Rd Ste 200, Arlington, VA 22201-4797
Tel (703) 841-7800 *Founded/Ownrshp* 1962
Sales 3.7MMM *EMP* 15,300^E
Tkr Sym CACI *Exch* NYS
SIC 7373 4899 7371 Computer systems analysis & design; Turnkey vendors, computer systems; Data communication services; Computer software development; Computer software systems analysis & design, custom
Pr: Kenneth Asbury
**Ch Bd:* J P London
COO: Dan Mansfield
COO: John S Mengucci
CFO: Thomas A Mutryn
Sr Cor Off: Nancy Peters
Ofcr: Brian Johnson
Ex VP: Marjorie R Bailey
Ex VP: Jerry Briggs
Ex VP: Jody A Brown
Ex VP: Albert M Calland III
Ex VP: Larry Clifton
Ex VP: Deborah B Dunie
Ex VP: Donald Fulop
Ex VP: Lowell Jacoby
Ex VP: Karl Johnson
Ex VP: Joseph Kellogg
Ex VP: J W Koegel
Ex VP: Krisstie Kondrotis
Ex VP: Dale Luddeke
Ex VP: Valerie J Lyons
Board of Directors: Michael A Daniels, James S Gilmore III, William L Jews, Gregory G Johnson, James L Pavitt, Warren R Phillips, Charles P Revoile, William S Wallace

D-U-N-S 07-836-8844
■ CACI NSS INC
(*Suby of* CACI INC - FEDERAL) ★
11955 Freedom Dr Fl 2, Reston, VA 20190-5673
Tel (703) 434-4000 *Founded/Ownrshp* 2011
Sales 88.1MM[E] *EMP* 499[E]
SIC 7373 8711 Systems engineering, computer related; Systems integration services; Systems software development services; Computer systems analysis & design; Aviation &/or aeronautical engineering
Pr: Ken Asbury
Genl Mgr: Gary Shiffman

D-U-N-S 05-248-4255
■ CACI TECHNOLOGIES INC
(*Suby of* CACI INC - FEDERAL) ★
1100 N Glebe Rd Ste 200, Arlington, VA 22201-4797
Tel (703) 841-7800 *Founded/Ownrshp* 1968
Sales 227.9MM[E] *EMP* 1,512[E]
SIC 7373 8711

D-U-N-S 61-570-9800
■ CACI-ISS INC
(*Suby of* CACI INC - FEDERAL) ★
1100 N Glebe Rd Ste 200, Arlington, VA 22201-4797
Tel (703) 841-7800 *Founded/Ownrshp* 2006
Sales 54.3MM[E] *EMP* 1,070[E]
SIC 7371 Custom computer programming services
Ch Bd: J P London
**Pr:* William M Fairl
**CEO:* Paul M Confoni
**Ex VP:* Thomas A Mutryn
**Sr VP:* Arnold D Morse

CACIQUE CHEESE
See CACIQUE INC

D-U-N-S 36-413-7463
CACIQUE DISTRIBUTORS US
14923 Proctor Ave, La Puente, CA 91746-3206
Tel (626) 961-3399 *Founded/Ownrshp* 1994
Sales 188.6MM[E] *EMP* 240
SIC 5143 Dairy products, except dried or canned
CEO: Francoise Mattice
**Pr:* Gilbert L De Cardenas
CFO: Wendy Morgan
Opers Mgr: Carlos Wong
Sls Dir: Bob Cashen
Mktg Mgr: Diana Loza

D-U-N-S 07-093-6554
CACIQUE INC (CA)
CACIQUE CHEESE
14940 Proctor Ave, City of Industry, CA 91746-3219
Tel (626) 961-3399 *Founded/Ownrshp* 1976
Sales 86.3MM[E] *EMP* 242
SIC 2022 Cheese, natural & processed
CEO: Ana De Cardenas-Raptis
**CFO:* Francoise Mattice
Sr Cor Off: Gilbert Cardenas
**Ex VP:* Jennie De Cardenas
**VP:* Gilbert B De Cardenas
Area Mgr: Jose Aguilera
Genl Mgr: Christiann Arapostathis
Genl Mgr: Robert Cashen
Plnt Mgr: Vu Ngo
Mktg Dir: Enrique Botello
Mktg Dir: Margaret Tom

D-U-N-S 07-166-6614
CACTUS FEEDERS INC
2209 Sw 7th Ave Ste 200, Amarillo, TX 79106-6777
Tel (806) 373-2333 *Founded/Ownrshp* 1975
Sales 195.9MM[E] *EMP* 500
SIC 0211 Beef cattle feedlots
Ch: Michael Engler
**CFO:* Matt Forrester
**CFO:* Brad Hastings
**Ch:* Paul Engler
**Sr VP:* Paul Defoor
**Sr VP:* Mark Engler
**Sr VP:* Steve Johnson
Off Mgr: Clay Wilkins
CTO: Dave Grove
IT Man: Piper Bennett
IT Man: Corey White

D-U-N-S 08-606-2882 IMP
CACTUS HOLDINGS INC
WESTERN BEEF
4705 Metropolitan Ave, Ridgewood, NY 11385-1046
Tel (718) 417-3770 *Founded/Ownrshp* 1999
Sales 650.0MM *EMP* 3,000
SIC 5411 5147 5144 5146 5148 5143 Supermarkets; Meats & meat products; Poultry & poultry products; Fish & seafoods; Fresh fruits & vegetables; Dairy products, except dried or canned
Pr: Peter Castellana Jr
CFO: Harold Lee
**Ex VP:* Joseph Castellana
Genl Mgr: Rocky Rodriguez
CTO: Ramo Ramgopal
Dir IT: Ernest Braun
Advt Dir: Jasmin Valle

D-U-N-S 96-953-2386 IMP/EXP
CACTUS WELLHEAD LLC
1 Greenway Plz Ste 200, Houston, TX 77046-0199
Tel (713) 626-8800 *Founded/Ownrshp* 2011
Sales 181.1MM[E] *EMP* 300[E]
SIC 3533 Oil & gas drilling rigs & equipment
CEO: Scott Bender
CFO: Brian Small
Brnch Mgr: Logan McFadden
Dir IT: David Stokes
IT Man: David Gayle
Opers Mgr: Greg Babineaux
Opers Mgr: Adan Campos
Opers Mgr: Shane Guinn
Opers Mgr: Greg Richard
Mktg Dir: Eric Bender
Sales Asso: Jacob Ehlers

CADACO DIVISION
See RAPID DISPLAYS INC

D-U-N-S 07-859-8907 EXP
CADDELL CONSTRUCTION CO (DE) LLC
(*Suby of* CADDELL CONSTRUCTION CO INC) ★
2700 Lagoon Park Dr, Montgomery, AL 36109-1100
Tel (334) 272-7723 *Founded/Ownrshp* 2011
Sales 382.4MM *EMP* 1[E]
Accts Carr Riggs & Ingram Llc Mon
SIC 1542 1541 Commercial & office buildings, renovation & repair; Specialized public building contractors; Industrial buildings & warehouses
Prin: John Caddell

D-U-N-S 10-208-7285 IMP/EXP
CADDELL CONSTRUCTION CO INC
2700 Lagoon Park Dr, Montgomery, AL 36109-1100
Tel (334) 272-7723 *Founded/Ownrshp* 1983
Sales 382.4MM *EMP* 226
Accts Carr Riggs & Ingram Llc Mon
SIC 1542 1541 Commercial & office building, new construction; Industrial buildings, new construction
CEO: Eddie Stewart
Ofcr: Oearo Jones
VP: Del Buck
Exec: Terry McDaniel
Dir IT: Andrew Taylor

D-U-N-S 62-128-5589
CADDO PARISH COMMISSION
525 Marshall St, Shreveport, LA 71101-3551
Tel (318) 226-6891 *Founded/Ownrshp* 2006
Sales 91.5MM[E] *EMP* 18[E]
Accts Carr Riggs & Ingram Llc Shre
SIC 7361 Registries
Prin: Ernie Robnson

D-U-N-S 07-980-2892
CADDO PARISH PUBLIC SCHOOLS
1961 Midway St, Shreveport, LA 71108-2201
Tel (318) 603-6300 *Founded/Ownrshp* 2015
Sales 99.6MM[E] *EMP* 4,576[E]
SIC 8211 Public elementary & secondary schools
Dir Sec: Roy Murry
Pr Dir: Bill Strother
Instr Medi: Catherine Smith
HC Dir: Anthony Tisdale

D-U-N-S 04-921-4232
CADDO PARISH SCHOOL BOARD
1961 Midway St, Shreveport, LA 71108-2200
Tel (318) 636-0210 *Founded/Ownrshp* 1877
Sales 241.5MM[E] *EMP* 5,680
Accts Allen Green & Williamson Llp
SIC 8211 Public elementary & secondary schools
COO: James W Woolfolk
**COO:* James W Woolfolk
Bd of Dir: Bonita Crawford
Prin: Mary D Rounds
Tech Mgr: Sonya Webb
Board of Directors: James W Woolfolk

CADENCE AEROSPACE
See AEROSPACE PARTS HOLDINGS INC

D-U-N-S 05-456-5970
CADENCE AEROSPACE LLC
(*Suby of* CADENCE AEROSPACE) ★
610 Newport Ctr Dr Ste 950, Newport Beach, CA 92660
Tel (949) 877-3630 *Founded/Ownrshp* 2010
Sales 218.7MM[E] *EMP* 192[E]
SIC 3728 Aircraft body assemblies & parts
CEO: Ron Case
**Ch Bd:* Larry Reznick
**COO:* Mike Coburn
**CFO:* Don Devore

D-U-N-S 96-784-7729
CADENCE BANCORP LLC
2800 Post Oak Blvd # 3800, Houston, TX 77056-6100
Tel (713) 871-4000 *Founded/Ownrshp* 2009
Sales NA *EMP* 1,200[E]
SIC 6021 National commercial banks
CEO: Paul B Murphy Jr
**CFO:* Valerie C Toalson
Ex VP: Sarah Peterson
Ex VP: Jerry Powell
Ex VP: Randy Schultz
CIO: Frank D Cox Jr
CIO: Lillibett Machado

D-U-N-S 00-403-1191
CADENCE BANK NA
(*Suby of* CADENCE FINANCIAL CORP) ★
2100 3rd Ave N, Birmingham, AL 35203-3371
Tel (205) 326-2265 *Founded/Ownrshp* 1974
Sales NA *EMP* 1,200
SIC 6021 National commercial banks
Pr: Sam Tortorici
Chf Cred: Robert Booth
Ex VP: Jerry Powell
Ex VP: Thomas Prince
Sr VP: William Lovell
Sr VP: Leon Manning
Sr VP: Kacy Owsley
Sr VP: Andrew Smith
VP: WEI-Jin Dai
VP: Michael Dorosh
VP: Pradeep Fernandes
VP: Christina Houghton
VP: Felicia James
VP: Todd Joyner
VP: Gaines Livingston
VP: Dipender Saluja
VP: Lee Wenger
VP: Amy West
Exec: Fady Abushahla
Exec: Michael Dolan
Exec: Jyoti Taxali

D-U-N-S 10-406-8093
▲ CADENCE DESIGN SYSTEMS INC
2655 Seely Ave Bldg 5, San Jose, CA 95134-1931
Tel (408) 943-1234 *Founded/Ownrshp* 1988
Sales 1.7MMM *EMP* 6,700
Tkr Sym CDNS *Exch* NGS
SIC 7372 Prepackaged software; Application computer software
Pr: Lip-Bu Tan
**Ch Bd:* John B Shoven
**CFO:* Geoffrey G Ribar
**Sr VP:* Thomas P Beckley
**Sr VP:* James J Cowie
**Sr VP:* Anirudh Devgan
Sr VP: Martin N Lund
**Sr VP:* Neil Zaman
VP: Victor Berman
VP: Peter Connor
VP: Jim Cowie
VP: Lou Holt
VP: Joe Mastroianni
VP: Moshe Rubin
VP: Saugat Sen
VP: Christopher Tice
VP: Veronica Watson
Board of Directors: Mark W Adams, Susan L Bostrom, James D Plummer, George M Scalise, Roger S Siboni, Young K Sohn, Alberto Sangiovanni-Vincen

D-U-N-S 15-650-5745
CADENCE FINANCIAL CORP
(*Suby of* CADENCE BANCORP LLC) ★
301 E Main St, Starkville, MS 39759-8089
Tel (662) 323-1341 *Founded/Ownrshp* 2011
Sales NA *EMP* 1,200[E]
SIC 6021 National commercial banks
CEO: Mark A Abernathy
**CFO:* Richard T Haston
Sr Cor Off: Lewis Mallory
**Chf Cred:* Teresa Hemphill
Sr VP: Jonathan Boydstun
Sr VP: William L Gullett
VP: Donald J Bugea Jr
VP: Shelby Burkhardt
**VP:* John R Davis
VP: Clifton B Fowler
CIO: Terry Jones

D-U-N-S 01-835-3420
CADENCE MCSHANE CONSTRUCTION CO LLC
5057 Keller Springs Rd, Addison, TX 75001-6231
Tel (972) 239-2336 *Founded/Ownrshp* 2008
Sales 88.4MM[E] *EMP* 120
Accts Warady & Davis Llp Deerfield
SIC 1541 1542 Industrial buildings, new construction; Commercial & office building contractors
CEO: James A McShane P E
**Pr:* Michael Geach
**Pr:* Will Hodges
**Treas:* Melvin Meyer
Chf Inves: Molly McShane
**VP:* William L Brady
**VP:* G Dan Delforge
VP: Stephen Doyle
**VP:* John Heim Jr
VP: Srinath P Kasturi
**VP:* Craig Morris
VP: Roger Pavlovich
**VP:* Roger Pavolich
**VP:* Shawn Pyatt
**VP:* Charles H White
VP Bus Dev: Glenn Denham

CADENCE STRUCTURES DIV
See SOUTHERN PAN SERVICES CO

D-U-N-S 60-810-4238
CADET HOLDING CORP
(*Suby of* AEGON USA, INC.)
4333 Edgewood Rd Ne, Cedar Rapids, IA 52499-0001
Tel (319) 398-8511 *Founded/Ownrshp* 1988
Sales NA *EMP* 2,700
SIC 6311 Life insurance carriers
Pr: Pat Baird
Treas: Ronald F Mosher
Board of Directors: Patrick E Falconio, Virgil D Wagner

D-U-N-S 61-779-6029
CADILLAC CASTING INC
1500 4th Ave, Cadillac, MI 49601-9062
Tel (231) 779-9600 *Founded/Ownrshp* 1922
Sales 120.3MM[E] *EMP* 400
SIC 3714 Motor vehicle wheels & parts; Motor vehicle brake systems & parts
Pr: Daniel D Minor
**COO:* Mark Wightman
**CFO:* Brian Nyland
**Treas:* Todd Carlson
**VP:* Alex Boosalis

D-U-N-S 00-532-1385 IMP
CADILLAC COFFEE CO (MI)
7221 Innovation Blvd, Fort Wayne, IN 46818-1333
Tel (248) 545-2266 *Founded/Ownrshp* 1929, 1898
Sales 93.3MM[E] *EMP* 98
SIC 5149 7389 Coffee, green or roasted; Coffee service
Pr: Guy Gehlert
VP: John R Gehlert Jr
Sls Mgr: Rob Tasma

D-U-N-S 00-531-7193 IMP
CADILLAC PRODUCTS INC
HOOSIER ELECTRONICS FINCL SVCS
5800 Crooks Rd Ste 100, Troy, MI 48098-2830
Tel (248) 813-8200 *Founded/Ownrshp* 1942
Sales 182.3MM[E] *EMP* 633
SIC 3714 3081 2673 3089 Motor vehicle parts & accessories; Polyethylene film; Plastic bags: made from purchased materials; Thermoformed finished plastic products
Ch Bd: Robert J Williams Sr
**Pr:* Michael P Williams II
**Pr:* Robert J Williams Jr
CFO: Debra Osborn
**Treas:* Roger K Williams
Prgrm Mgr: Kevin Morse
IT Man: Jim Krizan
IT Man: Robert Molnar
Opers Mgr: Steve Lawrence
Plnt Mgr: Tom Cooper
Natl Sales: Oscar Meza

D-U-N-S 82-905-5594
CADILLAC PRODUCTS PACKAGING CO
5800 Crooks Rd, Troy, MI 48098-2830
Tel (248) 879-5000 *Founded/Ownrshp* 1999
Sales 101.0MM[E] *EMP* 425
SIC 3081 Packing materials, plastic sheet
CEO: Robert J Williams Jr

D-U-N-S 10-332-4161
CADLE LIMITED LIABILITY CO
(*Suby of* OCHARLEYS) ★
3900 E Market St, Warren, OH 44484-4708
Tel (330) 856-3176 *Founded/Ownrshp* 1998
Sales 15.8MM[E] *EMP* 1,198[E]
SIC 5812 Fast-food restaurant, chain

CADMAN ADMINISTRATION
See CADMAN INC

D-U-N-S 79-494-6475 IMP
CADMAN INC
CADMAN ADMINISTRATION
(*Suby of* HANSON LEHIGH INC) ★
7554 185th Ave Ne Ste 100, Redmond, WA 98052-8566
Tel (425) 867-1234 *Founded/Ownrshp* 1939
Sales 90.2MM[E] *EMP* 430
SIC 3273 Ready-mixed concrete
Pr: James Derkatch
CFO: Lori Ketterlin
**Treas:* Linda George
VP: Bill Sayer
Opers Mgr: Mike Bennett
Sls Mgr: Keith Smyth

D-U-N-S 00-311-7710
■ CADMUS JOURNAL SERVICES INC
CADMUS SPECIALTY PUBLICATION
(*Suby of* CENVEO PUBLISHER SERVICES) ★
2901 Byrdhill Rd, Richmond, VA 23228-5805
Tel (804) 264-2711 *Founded/Ownrshp* 1904, 1984
Sales 91.7MM[E] *EMP* 850
SIC 2752 Commercial printing, lithographic; Commercial printing, offset; Periodicals, lithographed
Ex VP: John H Phillips
Treas: David E Bosher
Sr VP: David G Wilson Jr

D-U-N-S 11-906-8542 IMP/EXP
■ CADMUS JOURNAL SERVICES INC
CENVEO PUBLISHER SERVICES
(*Suby of* CENVEO INC) ★
2901 Byrdhill Rd, Henrico, VA 23228-5805
Tel (804) 287-5680 *Founded/Ownrshp* 1993
Sales 787.3MM[E] *EMP* 3,300
SIC 2752 2721 2741 Commercial printing, lithographic; Promotional printing, lithographic; Magazines: publishing & printing; Miscellaneous publishing
CEO: Robert G Burton Sr
CFO: Scott Goodwin
Sr VP: Wayne B Luck
VP: Lisa S Licata
Genl Mgr: Renee Stirnaman
Snr Mgr: Benita Horton

CADMUS SPECIALTY PUBLICATION
See CADMUS JOURNAL SERVICES INC

D-U-N-S 07-103-2908
CADWALADER WICKERSHAM & TAFT LLP
CADWALADER'S
200 Liberty St, New York, NY 10281-1003
Tel (212) 504-6000 *Founded/Ownrshp* 1994
Sales 203.7MM[E] *EMP* 1,280
SIC 8111 General practice law office
Mng Pt: Robert O Links Jr
Owner: Tony V Pezzano
Owner: Bartholomew Verdirame
Pt: Jodi Avergun
Pt: Bret Campbell
Pt: Drew G L Chapman
Pt: Peter Friedman
Pt: R Ronald Hopkinson
Pt: Stewart A Kagan
Pt: Geoffrey W Levin
Pt: Brian McGovern
Pt: Gregory P Patti
Mng Pt: Robert O'Links
Ch: Jim Woolery
Ofcr: Michelle Da Costa

CADWALADER'S
See CADWALADER WICKERSHAM & TAFT LLP

D-U-N-S 08-002-2015 IMP/EXP
CAE USA INC
CAE USA PRODUCTS
(*Suby of* CAE(US) INC) ★
4908 Tampa West Blvd, Tampa, FL 33634-2411
Tel (813) 885-7481 *Founded/Ownrshp* 2001
Sales 347.4MM[E] *EMP* 800
SIC 3699 7373 8299 8249 8711 Electronic training devices; Flight simulators (training aids), electronic; Computer integrated systems design; Flying instruction; Aviation school; Engineering services
Pr: Raymond Duquette
**Treas:* John Atkinson
Ex VP: Anthony Brancato
Admn Mgr: Dorsey Kemp
Telecom Ex: Jared Stein
Snr Sftwr: Brian Register
IT Man: Kevin Lundy
Site Mgr: Tim Bush
Sales Exec: Ray Duquett
Snr Mgr: Mike Wynn

CAE USA PRODUCTS
See CAE USA INC

D-U-N-S 15-089-3097 IMP/EXP
CAE(US) INC
(*Suby of* CAE INC)
1011 Ct Rd Ste 322, Wilmington, DE 19805
Tel (813) 885-7481 *Founded/Ownrshp* 1995
Sales 371.6MM[E] *EMP* 3,000
SIC 3559 Cryogenic machinery, industrial
Pr: Stephane Lefebvre
Treas: Darrel Lane
IT Man: Elise Charlebois
IT Man: Linda Faulkenstein
IT Man: Bruno Leduc

CAESAR'S
See CAESARS WORLD INC

CAESAR'S
See CAESARS NEW JERSEY INC

CAESAR'S
See CAESARS PALACE CORP

D-U-N-S 07-920-4241
▲ CAESARS ACQUISITION CO
1 Caesars Palace Dr, Las Vegas, NV 89109-8969
Tel (702) 407-6000 *Founded/Ownrshp* 2013
Sales 29.6MM^E *EMP* 1,300
Tkr Sym CACQ *Exch* NGS
SIC 7011 Casino hotel
Pr: Mitch Garber
CFO: Craig Abrahams
Sr VP: Michael Cohen
Board of Directors: Marc Beilinson, Philip Erlanger, Don Kornstein, Karl Peterson, Marc Rowan, David Sambur

D-U-N-S 60-698-4268 IMP
▲ CAESARS ENTERTAINMENT CORP
1 Caesars Palace Dr, Las Vegas, NV 89109-8969
Tel (702) 407-6000 *Founded/Ownrshp* 1937
Sales 4.6MMM *EMP* 33,000^E
Tkr Sym CZR *Exch* NGS
SIC 7011 7999 Casino hotel; Gambling establishment
Pr: Mark Frissora
**Ch Bd:* Gary W Loveman
Pr: Tom Arasi
Pr: Don Marrandino
Pr: Tom O'Donnell
CFO: Eric Hession
Treas: Lindsay Garcia
Ex VP: Janis Jones Blackhurst
Ex VP: Richard D Broome
Ex VP: Richard Broome
Ex VP: John Burns
Ex VP: Donald Colvin
Ex VP: Timothy R Donovan
Ex VP: Max Mills
Ex VP: Les Ottolenghi
Ex VP: Mary Thomas
Sr VP: Darold Londo
VP: Nathan Armogan
VP: Diane Askwyth
VP: Jill Barrett
VP: Janet Beronio
Board of Directors: Eric Press, Jeffrey Benjamin, David Bonderman, Kelvin Davis, Mark Frissora, Fred J Kleisner, Marc Rowan, David B Sambur, Lynn C Swann, Christopher J Williams

D-U-N-S 10-731-9436 IMP
■ CAESARS ENTERTAINMENT OPERATING CO INC
HARRAH'S
(*Suby of* CAESARS ENTERTAINMENT CORP) ★
1 Caesars Palace Dr, Las Vegas, NV 89109-8969
Tel (702) 407-6000 *Founded/Ownrshp* 1995
Sales 1.9MMM^E *EMP* 30,000
SIC 7999 Gambling establishment
Pr: John Payne
CFO: Mary Elizabeth Higgins
Treas: Jonathan Halkyard
Ex VP: Steven Bell
Ex VP: John Boushy
Ex VP: Bernie Delury
Sr VP: John Baker
Sr VP: Scott E Wiegand
VP: Ken Kuick
VP: Carol Tabrizi
VP: Mary Thomas
VP: Xenia Wunderlich
Board of Directors: David Bonderman, Kelvin Davis, Marc Rowan, David Sambur, Steven Winograd

D-U-N-S 07-938-7575
■ CAESARS GROWTH PARTNERS LLC
(*Suby of* CAESARS ACQUISITION CO) ★
1 Caesars Palace Dr, Las Vegas, NV 89109-8969
Tel (702) 407-6586 *Founded/Ownrshp* 2014
Sales 2.3MM^E *EMP* 1,150
SIC 7011 Hotels & motels
Ch Bd: Gary W Loveman

D-U-N-S 62-708-3306 IMP
■ CAESARS LICENSE CO LLC
BALLYS LAS VEGAS
(*Suby of* BALLYS LAS VEGAS) ★
3645 Las Vegas Blvd S, Las Vegas, NV 89109-4321
Tel (702) 739-4111 *Founded/Ownrshp* 1968
Sales 47.3MM^E *EMP* 1,100
SIC 7999 Gambling establishment; Gambling machines, operation; Off-track betting
Pr: Marilyn Winn
**VP:* Brad McPherson
**VP:* Stephen Opdyke

D-U-N-S 09-371-5282
■ CAESARS NEW JERSEY INC
CAESAR'S
(*Suby of* HARRAHS) ★
2100 Pacific Ave, Atlantic City, NJ 08401-6612
Tel (609) 348-4411 *Founded/Ownrshp* 2005
Sales 103.7MM^E *EMP* 3,500
SIC 7011 Casino hotel
Pr: Carlos Tolosa
VP Sls: Tammy Puchliakow
Sls Mgr: Lisa Kletac

D-U-N-S 62-755-6459
■ CAESARS PALACE CORP
CAESAR'S
(*Suby of* CAESARS) ★
3570 Las Vegas Blvd S, Las Vegas, NV 89109-8933
Tel (702) 731-7110 *Founded/Ownrshp* 1964
Sales 127.2MM^E *EMP* 6,500^E
SIC 7011 Casino hotel
Pr: Gary W Loveman
Pr: Gary Selesner
IT Man: Lyle Bell

CAESARS PALACE HOTEL & CASINO
See DESERT PALACE INC

D-U-N-S 16-004-1653
■ CAESARS RIVERBOAT CASINO LLC
HORSESHOE CASINO HOTEL
(*Suby of* HARRAHS) ★
11999 Casino Center Dr Se, Elizabeth, IN 47117-7753
Tel (812) 969-6000 *Founded/Ownrshp* 2005
Sales 71.3MM^E *EMP* 2,200
SIC 7011 Casino hotel
Genl Mgr: Eileen Moore

D-U-N-S 04-118-0076 IMP
■ CAESARS WORLD INC
CAESAR'S
(*Suby of* HARRAHS) ★
3570 Las Vegas Blvd S, Las Vegas, NV 89109-8924
Tel (702) 731-7110 *Founded/Ownrshp* 2005
Sales 909.3MM *EMP* 13,000
SIC 7011 7999 5812 6552 5611 5621 Casino hotel; Resort hotel; Gambling establishment; Eating places; Subdividers & developers; Clothing, sportswear, men's & boys'; Women's clothing stores
Pr: Gary W Loveman
**Pr:* Mark Dodson
**Pr:* John Payne
**CFO:* Scott La Porta
**Ex VP:* Clive Cummis
Ex VP: Richard Mahoney
**VP:* Mark Hedley
VP: Ramesh Sadhwani
MIS Dir: Larry Lewis

D-U-N-S 60-497-4857
CAFE ENTERPRISES INC
FATZ CAFE
4324 Wade Hampton Blvd B, Taylors, SC 29687-2254
Tel (864) 322-1331 *Founded/Ownrshp* 1999
Sales 105.0MM *EMP* 2,000
SIC 5812 Eating places
CEO: Jim Balis
Mng Pt: Tom Clark
**COO:* Richie Cannon
**CFO:* Don Camacho
**CFO:* Fred Grant Jr
**VP:* Krista Albera
**VP:* Sara Anderson
**VP:* Steve Corson
VP: Eric Holman
**VP:* Stephen Loftis
VP: Jim Streicher

D-U-N-S 11-511-4209 IMP
CAFE VALLEY INC
7000 W Buckeye Rd, Phoenix, AZ 85043-4306
Tel (602) 278-2909 *Founded/Ownrshp* 1984
Sales 145.0MM^E *EMP* 250
SIC 2099 Bread crumbs, not made in bakeries
CEO: Ronald D Ogan
Pr: Grant Gasson
**CFO:* Roy Koscielniak
VP: Dan Ferguson
**VP:* Lisa Holmes
VP: Brett Morrison
VP: Ted Pilato
**VP:* Larry R Polhill
VP Sls: Gary Lochrie

D-U-N-S 15-471-3189 IMP
▲ CAFEPRESS INC
11909 Shelbyville Rd, Louisville, KY 40243-1453
Tel (502) 995-2268 *Founded/Ownrshp* 1999
Sales 104.5MM *EMP* 357^E
Tkr Sym PRSS *Exch* NGS
SIC 4813 5961 ; Catalog & mail-order houses
Ch Bd: Fred E Durham III
CFO: Garett Jackson
Chf Mktg O: Maheesh Jain
Creative D: Immanuel Kester
Web Dev: Lauren Scheier
Board of Directors: Anthony C Allen, Mary Ann Arico, Patrick J Connolly, Kenneth McBride, Nick Swinmurn

D-U-N-S 02-458-5788 IMP
CAFFEY DISTRIBUTING CO INC
8749 W Market St, Greensboro, NC 27409-9653
Tel (336) 668-0877 *Founded/Ownrshp* 1962
Sales 109.6MM^E *EMP* 260
SIC 5181 Beer & other fermented malt liquors
Pr: Christopher Caffey
**CFO:* Bill Richardson
**VP:* Rick Stell
VP Sls: Jackie Cassada
Mktg Mgr: Jeff Johnson
Sls Mgr: Scott Schaefer

D-U-N-S 09-054-5278 IMP/EXP
CAGUAS MUNICIPALITY
CENTER MNICPL OPERATIONS TRNSP
Calle Padial Final Esq, Caguas, PR 00725
Tel (787) 743-2476 *Founded/Ownrshp* 1774
Sales NA *EMP* 2,300
SIC 9111 Mayors' offices;
Prin: William Miranda

D-U-N-S 00-922-6614
CAGWIN & DORWARD
CAGWIN & DORWARD LDSCP CONTRS
1565 S Novato Blvd, Novato, CA 94947-4143
Tel (415) 892-7710 *Founded/Ownrshp* 1992
Sales 93.8MM^E *EMP* 270
SIC 0782 Landscape contractors
CEO: Steven J Glennon
**VP:* Wayne Richards
**Prin:* Hannah Diaz
**Prin:* Dennis Dougherty
**Prin:* Kristen Giomi
**Prin:* Khrysti Jones
Rgnl Mgr: Ron Macler
Rgnl Mgr: Ryan Williams
Opers Mgr: Lorrie Harter
Opers Mgr: Chris Lawrence
Mktg Mgr: Hannah Hawkins

CAGWIN & DORWARD LDSCP CONTRS
See CAGWIN & DORWARD

CAHABA GBA
See CAHABA GOVERNMENT BENEFIT ADMINISTRATORS LLC

D-U-N-S 19-601-8787
CAHABA GOVERNMENT BENEFIT ADMINISTRATORS LLC
CAHABA GBA
500 Corporate Pkwy, Birmingham, AL 35242-2932
Tel (205) 220-1900 *Founded/Ownrshp* 2005
Sales NA *EMP* 678
SIC 6324 Hospital & medical service plans
Exec: Janice Miller
Board of Directors: Ron Whitehead

D-U-N-S 02-000-2077 IMP
CAHILL CONTRACTORS INC (CA)
425 California St # 2200, San Francisco, CA 94104-2207
Tel (415) 986-0600 *Founded/Ownrshp* 1974
Sales 233.0MM *EMP* 162^E
Accts Gallina Llp Walnut Creek Cal
SIC 1542 Commercial & office building, new construction
CEO: John E Cahill Jr
**Pr:* Chuck Palley
**Sec:* Darrell Diamond
Snr PM: Kevin Dugan

CAHOKIA GRAIN
See CONSOLIDATED GRAIN & BARGE CO

D-U-N-S 01-740-6147
CAHP HEALTH BENEFITS TRUST
2030 V St, Sacramento, CA 95818-1730
Tel (916) 732-2155 *Founded/Ownrshp* 2008
Sales 153.3MM *EMP* 2
Accts Gilbert Associates Inc Sacr
SIC 6733 Trusts
CEO: Jon H Hamm

CAI
See COMPUTER AID INC

CAI
See COMBUSTION ASSOCIATES INC

CAI COMPANY
See CALIFORNIA AUTOMOBILE INSURANCE CO

D-U-N-S 60-566-2659 EXP
▲ CAI INTERNATIONAL INC
1 Market Plz Ste 900, San Francisco, CA 94105-1009
Tel (415) 788-0100 *Founded/Ownrshp* 1989
Sales 249.6MM *EMP* 128^E
Tkr Sym CAI *Exch* NYS
SIC 7359 Shipping container leasing
Pr: Victor M Garcia
Ch Bd: Hiromitsu Ogawa
CFO: Timothy B Page
Sr VP: Daniel J Hallahan
VP: Camille G Cutino
VP: Matthew Easton
VP: Steven J Garcia
Board of Directors: Marvin Dennis, William Liebeck, David G Remington, Gary M Sawka

D-U-N-S 04-281-5076 IMP
CAITO FOODS SERVICE INC
3120 N Post Rd, Indianapolis, IN 46226-6538
Tel (800) 652-8165 *Founded/Ownrshp* 1976
Sales 290.5MM^E *EMP* 500
SIC 5148 Fresh fruits & vegetables
CEO: Robert Kirch
**Ch Bd:* Philip Caito IV
**Pr:* Fred Caito
**VP:* Larry Cox
**Prin:* Joseph Caito
IT Man: Cindy Garrett
Opers Mgr: Robert Smith
Ql Cn Mgr: Gary Culver

D-U-N-S 07-337-1015
CAJON VALLEY UNION SCHOOL DISTRICT
750 E Main St, El Cajon, CA 92020-4012
Tel (619) 588-3000 *Founded/Ownrshp* 1921
Sales 144.4MM *EMP* 1,587
Accts Wilkinson Hadley King & Co L
SIC 8211 Public elementary & secondary schools
Prin: Ronald Damshen
**Pr:* Ken Jensen
**Pr:* Tamera Otero
Bd of Dir: Suzanne Mullins
**VP:* Jill D Barto
**VP:* Deanne Marko
**Prin:* Jill Barto
**Prin:* Justin Slagle
Off Admin: Melanie Barnes
CTO: Jonathon Guertin
Pr Dir: Kari Hull

D-U-N-S 06-546-9496
CAJUN CONSTRUCTORS LLC
(*Suby of* CAJUN INDUSTRIES LLC) ★
15635 Airline Hwy, Baton Rouge, LA 70817-7318
Tel (225) 753-5857 *Founded/Ownrshp* 1973
Sales 521.0MM *EMP* 1,000
Accts Hannis T Bourgeois Llp Bato
SIC 1623 4952 1541 1542 Water, sewer & utility lines; Pipeline wrapping; Sewerage systems; Industrial buildings & warehouses; Industrial buildings, new construction; Commercial & office buildings, renovation & repair
CEO: Ken Jacob
Pr: Todd W Grigsby
COO: John English
CFO: Shane Recile
Ch: L Lane Grigsby
Ex VP: Milton Graugnard
Sr VP: Michael Calabrese
Sr VP: Euclid Michel
VP: Mike Barber
VP: Jan Lass
VP: Mike Lavespere
VP: Mike Moran

D-U-N-S 80-442-2090
CAJUN DEEP FOUNDATIONS LLC
(*Suby of* CAJUN INDUSTRIES LLC) ★
15635 Airline Hwy, Baton Rouge, LA 70817-7318
Tel (225) 753-5857 *Founded/Ownrshp* 2006
Sales 85.3MM *EMP* 250
Accts Hannis T Bourgeois Llp Bato
SIC 1389 Construction, repair & dismantling services
Pr: Mike Moran
VP: Scott Callaway

D-U-N-S 80-442-2801
CAJUN INDUSTRIES LLC
15635 Airline Hwy, Baton Rouge, LA 70817-7318
Tel (225) 753-5857 *Founded/Ownrshp* 2006
Sales 559.8MM *EMP* 1,500
Accts Hannis T Bourgeois Llp Bato
SIC 1389 Construction, repair & dismantling services
CEO: Ken Jacob
**Ex VP:* Milton Graugnard
VP: Michael Bates
VP: Carlton Janise
**VP:* Donnie McDowell
CIO: Jan Lass
Site Mgr: Anthony Morris
Sfty Mgr: Beau Gibson
Sfty Mgr: Hurley Henson
Sfty Mgr: Fred Radley
Sls Dir: Tim Moore

D-U-N-S 17-510-7130
CAJUN OPERATING CO
CHURCH'S CHICKEN
980 Hammond Dr Ste 1100, Atlanta, GA 30328-8187
Tel (770) 350-3800 *Founded/Ownrshp* 2004
Sales 257.4MM^E *EMP* 4,950
Accts Dixon Hughes Pllc Atlanta G
SIC 5812 Chicken restaurant
CEO: Joseph Christina
Pr: John F Bowie
CFO: Dusty Profumo
CFO: Louis Profumo
Treas: Mitch Blocker
Bd of Dir: Harsha V Agadi
Chf Mktg O: Anthony M Lavely
Ofcr: Sharon Starks
VP: Mike Kuzminsky
VP: Debra Miller
VP: Craig Prusher

D-U-N-S 78-706-0826 IMP/EXP
CAL DIVE INTERNATIONAL INC
2500 Citywest Blvd # 2200, Houston, TX 77042-3031
Tel (713) 361-2600 *Founded/Ownrshp* 1975
Sales 516.9MM *EMP* 1,550
SIC 7389 1623 1629

CAL FIRE
See FORESTRY AND FIRE PROTECTION CALIFORNIA DEPARTMENT OF

CAL POLY
See CALIFORNIA POLYTECHNIC STATE UNIVERSITY

D-U-N-S 02-892-9438
CAL POLY POMONA FOUNDATION INC
3801 W Temple Ave Bldg 55, Pomona, CA 91768-2557
Tel (909) 869-2950 *Founded/Ownrshp* 1966
Sales 64.5MM *EMP* 2,200
Accts Davidf Prenovost Cpa Pomona
SIC 8699 Charitable organization
Ch: J Michael Ortiz
**CEO:* David Karacozoff
CFO: David Prenovost
**Sec:* Dr Whinney Dong
**Ex Dir:* Paul Storey
Dir IT: Randy Townsend

CAL STATE LA
See CALIFORNIA STATE UNIVERSITY LOS ANGELES

CAL STRS
See CALIFORNIA STATE TEACHERS RETIREMENT SYSTEM

D-U-N-S 15-526-0318 IMP/EXP
CAL-CHLOR CORP
627 Jefferson St, Lafayette, LA 70501-6907
Tel (337) 264-1449 *Founded/Ownrshp* 1987
Sales 214.6MM^E *EMP* 95
Accts Broussard Poche Lewis & Brea
SIC 5169 Calcium chloride; Industrial chemicals
Pr: Todd M Trahan
**CEO:* Mark S Hanna
**CFO:* Ken Matthews
**Sec:* James Zehnder II
Adm Dir: Jackie Wing
Plnt Mgr: Derwin Duchenois

D-U-N-S 96-799-0339 IMP
CAL-COMP ELECTRONICS (USA) CO LTD
CCSD
9877 Waples St, San Diego, CA 92121-2922
Tel (858) 587-6900 *Founded/Ownrshp* 1981
Sales 86.7MM^E *EMP* 299^E
SIC 3625 Actuators, industrial
CEO: Shyh-Yong Shen
**CFO:* Richard Lucas
VP: Joseph Donoghue
**Prin:* Jack Chang
Prgrm Mgr: Debra Amiri-Abarghoui
Prgrm Mgr: Vance Bitton
Genl Mgr: Jason Powell
Ql Cn Mgr: Cassidy Clark

D-U-N-S 10-669-7456 IMP
CAL-COMP USA (INDIANA) INC
TOTAL ELECTRONICS
(*Suby of* CAL-COMP ELECTRONICS (THAILAND) PUBLIC COMPANY LIMITED)
1 Technology Way, Logansport, IN 46947-1710
Tel (574) 739-2929 *Founded/Ownrshp* 2010
Sales 172.6MM^E *EMP* 400
SIC 3672 Circuit boards, television & radio printed
CEO: Jack Chang
COO: Tom Conrad
**COO:* John Yerger
**Treas:* Nick Ferry
VP: Ronald L Rehberger
IT Man: Ryan Buck
Opers Mgr: Scott Smith

D-U-N-S 05-064-3436
▲ CAL-MAINE FOODS INC
3320 W Woodrow Wilson Ave, Jackson, MS 39209-3409
Tel (601) 948-6813 *Founded/Ownrshp* 1957
Sales 1.9MMM *EMP* 3,072
Tkr Sym CALM *Exch* NGS
SIC 0252 Chicken eggs
Ch Bd: Adolphus B Baker
COO: Sherman L Miller
CFO: Timothy A Dawson
VP: Matt Arrowsmith
VP: Michael D Castleberry
VP: Robert L Holladay Jr
VP: Joe M Wyatt
Sales Exec: John Walton
VP Sls: Charles J Hardin
Board of Directors: Letitia C Hughes, James E Poole, Steve W Sanders

CAL/EPA
See CALIFORNIA ENVIRONMENTAL PROTECTION AGENCY

D-U-N-S 80-835-2376
CALABRIO INC
400 1st Ave N Ste 300, Minneapolis, MN 55401-1721
Tel (763) 592-4600 *Founded/Ownrshp* 2007
Sales 95.2MM^E *EMP* 155
SIC 5045 7371 Computer software; Computer software development & applications
Pr: Tom Goodmanson
**CFO:* Theresa McGlothlen
CFO: Richard Oakley
Bd of Dir: Kay Johnson
**Sr VP:* Dale Bastian
Sr VP: Charles Burnett
**Sr VP:* Tim Kraskey
VP: John Hanson
**VP:* Rebecca Martin
VP: Rohini Sackmann
VP: Brett Theisen

D-U-N-S 00-910-8028 IMP
CALAMCO
1776 W March Ln Ste 420, Stockton, CA 95207-6427
Tel (209) 982-1000 *Founded/Ownrshp* 1957
Sales 112.1MM *EMP* 35
Accts Moss Adams Llp Stockton Cali
SIC 5169 Ammonia
Pr: Robert C Brown
**VP:* Lee Gardiner
**VP:* Dan Stone
Rgnl Mgr: Natalie Foss

D-U-N-S 14-310-5752
▲ CALAMOS ASSET MANAGEMENT INC
2020 Calamos Ct Ofc, Naperville, IL 60563-2796
Tel (630) 245-7200 *Founded/Ownrshp* 2004
Sales 230.8MM *EMP* 348^E
Tkr Sym CLMS *Exch* NGS
SIC 6211 6282 Security brokers & dealers; Security brokers & dealers; Investment advice; Investment advisory service; Investment counselors; Investment research
CEO: John S Koudounis
**Ch Bd:* John P Calamos Sr
Pr: Robert F Behan
CFO: Thomas E Herman
Board of Directors: Keith M Schappert, William N Shiebler

D-U-N-S 60-309-2615
■ CALAMOS INVESTMENTS LLC
(*Suby of* CALAMOS ASSET MANAGEMENT INC) ★
2020 Calamos Ct Ofc, Naperville, IL 60563-2787
Tel (630) 245-7200 *Founded/Ownrshp* 2004
Sales 110.6MM^E *EMP* 196
SIC 6211 6282 Security brokers & dealers; Investment advice; Investment advisory service; Investment counselors; Investment research
Ofcr: Charles Pope
**Ex VP:* Gary D Black
Sr VP: Maryann Bianchini
Sr VP: Robert Bush
Sr VP: Greg Kuhl
Sr VP: John McClenahan
VP: Melissa Ahern
VP: Doug Berman
**VP:* Nimish S Bhatt
VP: Ronald Crudo
VP: Geoff Frankenthal
VP: Shannon Hay
VP: Anita Knotts
VP: Terrence Labant
VP: Yanni Sianis
VP: Ken Sorenson
VP: Todd Speed
VP: Evan Wald
VP: Matt Wendell
**VP:* Randall T Zipfel
Assoc Dir: Ian Walker

D-U-N-S 04-452-6671 IMP/EXP
▲ CALAMP CORP
15635 Alton Pkwy Ste 250, Irvine, CA 92618-7328
Tel (949) 600-5600 *Founded/Ownrshp* 1981
Sales 280.7MM *EMP* 490^E
Tkr Sym CAMP *Exch* NGS
SIC 3663 Radio & TV communications equipment; Microwave communication equipment; Amplifiers, RF power & IF
Pr: Michael Burdiek
**Ch Bd:* A J Moyer
CFO: Richard Vitelle
Sr VP: Garo Sarkissian
VP: Steve Moran
VP: Anand Rau
Off Mgr: Jimmy Armstrong
Snr Sftwr: Alexandre Dlagnekov
Sftwr Eng: Jeremy Martinez
Sales Asso: Barbara Ramirez
Board of Directors: Kimberly Alexy, Jeffery Gardner, Amal Johnson, Jorge Titinger, Larry Wolfe

D-U-N-S 00-291-0586 IMP/EXP
CALANDRA FRANK INC (PA)
JENNMAR
258 Kappa Dr, Pittsburgh, PA 15238-2818
Tel (412) 963-9071 *Founded/Ownrshp* 1922
Sales 496.8MM^E *EMP* 660
SIC 1241 Preparing shafts or tunnels, anthracite mining; Preparing shafts or tunnels, bituminous or lignite mining
Pr: John M Calandra
Ex VP: James A Ceresa
VP: Frank Calandra Jr

D-U-N-S 00-838-8373
▲ CALATLANTIC GROUP INC
CALATLANTIC HOMES
15360 Barranca Pkwy, Irvine, CA 92618-2215
Tel (949) 789-1600 *Founded/Ownrshp* 1965
Sales 3.5MMM *EMP* 2,850
Accts Ernst & Young Llp Irvine Cal
Tkr Sym CAA *Exch* NYS
SIC 1531 1521 6162 6541 Operative builders; Single-family housing construction; Mortgage brokers, using own money; Title & trust companies
Pr: Larry T Nicholson
**Ch Bd:* Scott D Stowell
COO: Peter G Skelly
CFO: Jeff J McCall
Chf Mktg O: Wendy L Marlett
Ex VP: John P Babel
VP: Brian Bencz
VP: Alan Vitug
Counsel: Paul Weckerly
Board of Directors: Bruce A Choate, Douglas C Jacobs, William L Jews, David J Matlin, Robert E Mellor, Norman J Metcalfe, Peter Schoels, Charlotte St Martin

CALATLANTIC HOMES
See CALATLANTIC GROUP INC

D-U-N-S 00-690-6655
▲ CALAVO GROWERS INC (CA)
1141 Cummings Rd Ste A, Santa Paula, CA 93060-9118
Tel (805) 525-1245 *Founded/Ownrshp* 1924
Sales 856.8MM *EMP* 2,064^E
Tkr Sym CVGW *Exch* NGS
SIC 5148 5142 5149 Fruits, fresh; Fruits, frozen; Groceries & related products
Ch Bd: Lecil E Cole
Pr: Kenneth J Catchot
CFO: B John Lindeman
VP: Alan C Ahmer
VP: Michael A Browne
VP: Alex Ramirez
Dist Mgr: Stanley Ken
Dist Mgr: Mike Nunez
Genl Mgr: Claudio Madrid
IT Man: Peter Shore
Opers Supe: Yolanda Ruiz
Board of Directors: Donald M Sanders, George H Barnes, Dorcas H Thille, Marc L Brown, Scott Van Der Kar, Egidio Carbone Jr, Michael A Digregorio, Harold Edwards, James Helin, Steven W Hollister, John M Hunt, J Link Leavens

D-U-N-S 80-429-4291 EXP
CALBEE NORTH AMERICA LLC
72600 Lewis & Clark Dr, Boardman, OR 97818
Tel (541) 481-6550 *Founded/Ownrshp* 2006
Sales 130.0MM *EMP* 325
SIC 5145 Snack foods
Pr: Gene Jensen

D-U-N-S 07-980-2441
CALCASIEU PARISH PUBLIC SCHOOLS
3310 Broad St, Lake Charles, LA 70615-3808
Tel (337) 217-4000 *Founded/Ownrshp* 2015
Sales 193.6MM^E *EMP* 4,500^E
SIC 8211 Public elementary & secondary schools
Ofcr: John Melton
Exec: Billy Chapman
Exec: Leether Johnson
Dir Risk M: Skylar Giardina
Area Supr: Francis Durr
MIS Dir: Paula Michalko
Trfc Dir: Amber Istre
Pr Dir: Kirby Smith

D-U-N-S 07-417-9144
CALCASIEU PARISH SCHOOL BOARD
3310 Broad St, Lake Charles, LA 70615-3808
Tel (337) 217-4000 *Founded/Ownrshp* 1841
Sales 247.0MM^E *EMP* 4,500^E
Accts Allen Green & Williamson Llp
SIC 8211 School board
Pr: Mack Dellafosse
CFO: Wilfred Bourne
**CFO:* Karl Bruchhaus
CFO: BJ Dyer
Ofcr: Remy Broussard
Sfty Mgr: Ron Hayes
Psych: Shelley Goldstein

D-U-N-S 79-524-5778
CALCEUS TOPCO INC
(*Suby of* CALCEUS TOPCO LP) ★
601 Lexington Ave, New York, NY 10022-4611
Tel (212) 753-6300 *Founded/Ownrshp* 2013
Sales 141.3MM^E *EMP* 3,055^E
SIC 6719 Investment holding companies, except banks
CEO: John Megrue
Prin: Alex Pellegrini

D-U-N-S 78-307-9127
CALCEUS TOPCO LP
601 Lexington Ave, New York, NY 10022-4611
Tel (212) 753-6300 *Founded/Ownrshp* 2013
Sales 304.5MM^E *EMP* 3,058^E
SIC 6719 Investment holding companies, except banks

D-U-N-S 00-690-4072 IMP/EXP
CALCOT LTD
AMERICAN COTTON COOP ASSN
1900 E Brundage Ln, Bakersfield, CA 93307-2789
Tel (661) 327-5961 *Founded/Ownrshp* 1927
Sales 172.6MM *EMP* 150
Accts Eadie And Payne Llp Redlands
SIC 5159 Cotton, raw
CEO: Jarral T Neeper
CFO: Roxanne F Wang
Treas: Miguel Mory
VP: David L Hand
VP Sls: John Burch

D-U-N-S 03-051-6843
CALDWELL COUNTY SCHOOLS
1914 Hickory Blvd Sw, Lenoir, NC 28645-6470
Tel (828) 728-8407 *Founded/Ownrshp* 1974
Sales 83.0MM^E *EMP* 2,000
SIC 8211 Public elementary & secondary schools
Ch: Darrell Pennell
Bd of Dir: Carole Jenkins
Comm Dir: Libby Brown
Psych: Liz Grose

D-U-N-S 14-779-3871
CALDWELL GROUP LLC
4000 Tower Rd, Louisville, KY 40219-1901
Tel (502) 964-3361 *Founded/Ownrshp* 1887
Sales 126.6MM^E *EMP* 490^E
SIC 3443 Tanks, standard or custom fabricated: metal plate
Pr: Bernard S Fineman

D-U-N-S 07-105-6238
CALDWELL MEMORIAL HOSPITAL INC
321 Mulberry St Sw, Lenoir, NC 28645-5716
Tel (828) 757-5577 *Founded/Ownrshp* 1945
Sales 200.0MM *EMP* 850
SIC 8062 General medical & surgical hospitals
Pr: Laura J Easton
Pr: Bill Devereux
**COO:* Rebecca Smith
**VP:* Donald F Gardner Jr
Dir Lab: Brenda Ritch
Dir Rx: Sheryl Reid
CIO: Phillip Mell
MIS Dir: Rod Christenson
Pr Dir: Kimberly Edmisten
Doctor: Crystal Dula
Doctor: Jeanette Larson MD

D-U-N-S 00-637-5141
CALDWELL TANKS INC
(*Suby of* CALDWELL GROUP LLC) ★
4000 Tower Rd, Louisville, KY 40219-1901
Tel (502) 964-3361 *Founded/Ownrshp* 1985
Sales 112.9MM^E *EMP* 400
SIC 3443 5084 3441 Tanks, standard or custom fabricated: metal plate; Tank towers, metal plate; Industrial machinery & equipment; Fabricated structural metal
Pr: Bernard S Fineman
Treas: William Lee
VP: Mitchell Burchett
VP: Ryan Harvey
VP: Rick Suel
Exec: Megan Myer
CIO: Patricia Cabezas
Sfty Mgr: Dave Ewald
Sfty Mgr: Rebecca Sabraoui
Opers Mgr: Mike Braden
Plnt Mgr: Dennis McMahan

D-U-N-S 01-676-9861
CALEDONIA FARMERS ELEVATOR CO INC (MI)
146 E Main St Se, Caledonia, MI 49316-9488
Tel (616) 891-4150 *Founded/Ownrshp* 1918
Sales 83.9MM^E *EMP* 60
Accts Balestra Harr & Scherer Cpas
SIC 5153 5169 5251 5261 Grains; Chemicals & allied products; Hardware; Nursery stock, seeds & bulbs
CEO: Dwayne Ruthig
**Pr:* Louis Waayenberg
**Treas:* Lynn Otto
**VP:* Roger Sikkema
Sls Dir: Dave Shellenbarger

D-U-N-S 14-849-7993 IMP
CALENDAR HOLDINGS LLC
6411 Burleson Rd, Austin, TX 78744-1414
Tel (512) 386-7220 *Founded/Ownrshp* 2009
Sales 118.4MM^E *EMP* 560
SIC 5943 5945 Stationery stores; Games (chess, backgammon & other durable games)
CEO: Marc Winkelman
**Pr:* Paul Hoffman
**COO:* Mary Allen
**CFO:* Jim Hull
**Ex VP:* Mike Hejny
**Ex VP:* Scott Jackson
VP: Christi Graybill
**VP:* Michelle Landrum
**VP:* Abel Mireles
**VP:* Jennifer Schubert
VP: Jason Yau

D-U-N-S 19-300-0734 IMP
■ CALENERGY OPERATING CORP
(*Suby of* MIDAMERICAN) ★
1111 S 103rd St Fl 4, Omaha, NE 68124-1072
Tel (402) 398-7200 *Founded/Ownrshp* 1987
Sales 106.6MM^E *EMP* 300
SIC 3621 Power generators
Ch Bd: David L Sokol
**Pr:* Stephen Larsen

D-U-N-S 12-182-9183
CALERA CAPITAL MANAGEMENT INC
580 California St # 2200, San Francisco, CA 94104-1000
Tel (415) 632-5200 *Founded/Ownrshp* 1996
Sales 151.4MM^E *EMP* 432
SIC 6211 Investment firm, general brokerage
Pt: Robert Jaunich II
**Pt:* J T Farrell
**Pt:* M N Williamson
CFO: Daniel Dumais
CFO: Jeremey Thatcher
Admn Mgr: Michelle Rossa
Genl Couns: Kr Baker

D-U-N-S 00-626-6787 IMP
▲ CALERES INC (NY)
8300 Maryland Ave, Saint Louis, MO 63105-3645
Tel (314) 854-4000 *Founded/Ownrshp* 1878
Sales 2.5MMM *EMP* 11,000
Accts Ernst & Young Llp St Louis
Tkr Sym CAL *Exch* NYS
SIC 5661 5139 Men's shoes; Women's shoes; Children's shoes; Footwear, athletic; Shoes
Ch Bd: Diane M Sullivan
CFO: Kenneth H Hannah
Treas: Diego Jost
Ofcr: Douglas W Koch
Ex VP: Daniel Ruderer
Sr VP: Dan Friedman
Sr VP: Jocelyn S Hebert
Sr VP: Dan Karpel
Sr VP: Michelle Kunderer
Sr VP: Tim Meyer
Sr VP: Jeffrey M Sanders
Sr VP: Mark A Schmitt
Sr VP: Jeffrey E Struve
VP: Jim Carder
VP: Geoff Green
VP: Jim Hanna
VP: Todd Hasty
VP: Clay Jenkins
VP: Daniel L Karpel
VP: Jeffrey A Kuhn
VP: Roger Lee
Board of Directors: Mario L Baeza, W Lee Capps III, Lori H Greeley, Carla Hendra, Ward M Klein, Steven W Korn, Patricia G McGinnis, W Patrick McGinnis

CALEX
See VALLEY HOSPITAL MEDICAL CENTER

D-U-N-S 84-373-8498 EXP
CALFRAC WELL SERVICES CORP
(*Suby of* CALFRAC WELL SERVICES LTD)
717 17th St Ste 1445, Denver, CO 80202-3303
Tel (303) 293-2931 *Founded/Ownrshp* 1999
Sales 596.9MM *EMP* 268
SIC 1389 Hydraulic fracturing wells
CEO: Douglas R Ramsay
**Pr:* Fernando Aguilar
**CFO:* Michael J McNulty
**Sr VP:* Tom J Medvedic
**VP:* Larry L Burleson
**Prin:* Rob Montgomery
**Prin:* Robert L Sutherland
Board of Directors: Gordon A Dibb, Ronald P Mathison

D-U-N-S 00-431-9810 IMP/EXP
▲ CALGON CARBON CORP
3000 Gsk Dr, Moon Township, PA 15108-1375
Tel (412) 787-6700 *Founded/Ownrshp* 1942
Sales 535.0MM *EMP* 1,090
Accts Deloitte & Touche Llp Pittsbu
Tkr Sym CCC *Exch* NYS
SIC 2819 7699 3589 3564 Charcoal (carbon), activated; Industrial equipment services; Water treatment equipment, industrial; Sewage treatment equipment; Air purification equipment
Ch Bd: Randall S Dearth
COO: Robert P O'Brien
CFO: Leroy M Ball Jr
CFO: Robert M Fortwangler
CFO: Robert Fortwangler
Treas: Marshall J Morris
Ex VP: Jim Coccagno
Ex VP: Stevan R Schott
Ex VP: Brent Smith
Sr VP: John S Stanik
Sr VP: Chad Whalen
VP: Jonathan H Maurer
VP: Steve Nolder
Exec: Robert Deithorn
Exec: A F Kerst
Dir Bus: Bill Aldridge
Dir Bus: Jim Farmerie
Board of Directors: J Rich Alexander, William J Lyons, Louis S Massimo, William R Newlin, John J Paro, Julie S Roberts, Timothy G Rupert, Donald C Templin

CALHOUN COUNTY BOARD EDUCATION
See CALHOUN COUNTY SCHOOL DISTRICT

D-U-N-S 09-885-5745
CALHOUN COUNTY SCHOOL DISTRICT
CALHOUN COUNTY BOARD EDUCATION
4400 Mcclellan Blvd, Anniston, AL 36206-2809
Tel (256) 741-7400 *Founded/Ownrshp* 1820
Sales 64.8MM^E *EMP* 1,100
SIC 8211 Public elementary & secondary schools; High school, junior or senior; Kindergarten
VP: Rick Carder
Prin: Andy Ward
IT Man: Jeremy Carpenter

D-U-N-S 87-483-7214
CALHOUN COUNTY SCHOOL DISTRICT
119 W Main St, Pittsboro, MS 38951-9771
Tel (662) 412-3152 *Founded/Ownrshp* 1994
Sales 85.4MM^E *EMP* 500
SIC 8211 Public elementary & secondary schools
**CFO:* Teresa Dunn

D-U-N-S 02-384-0171
CALHOUN MANAGEMENT CORP
WENDY'S
108 Elm St, Clemson, SC 29631-1013
Tel (864) 624-9962 *Founded/Ownrshp* 1996
Sales 30.8MM^E *EMP* 1,025
SIC 5812 Fast-food restaurant, chain
Pr: Pickens M Lindsay

D-U-N-S 04-130-2169
CALIBER BODYWORKS OF TEXAS INC
CALIBER COLLISION CENTERS
(Suby of CALIBER HOLDINGS CORP) ★
401 E Corp Dr Ste 150, Lewisville, TX 75057
Tel (469) 948-9500 Founded/Ownrshp 1997
Sales 7.9MM^E EMP 3,700^E
SIC 7532 Body shop, automotive
CEO: Steve Grimshaw
*COO: Mark Sanders
*CFO: Bob Gary
*Chf Mktg O: Greg Clark
*Ofcr: Ron Davis
*VP: Shawn Hezar
Off Mgr: Wayne Walker
*CIO: Janet Deberardinis

D-U-N-S 78-832-0950
CALIBER BODYWORKS PSA OF TEXAS INC
CALIBER COLLISION CENTERS
(Suby of CALIBER HOLDINGS CORP) ★
401 E Corp Dr Ste 150, Lewisville, TX 75057
Tel (469) 948-9500 Founded/Ownrshp 1991
Sales 205.4MM^E EMP 1,650
SIC 7532 Collision shops, automotive
Pr: Steve H Grimshaw
CEO: Sandy O'Brien
*COO: Mark Sanders
*CFO: J Robert Gary
*CFO: Robert Kliewe
Ofcr: Gregory M Nichols
Sr VP: Bob Gary
VP: Vanessa Davidson
VP: David Goldstein
VP: Ken Hanley
VP: Shawn Hezar

D-U-N-S 61-428-9366
CALIBER CAPITAL GROUP LLC
5900 Katella Ave Ste A101, Cypress, CA 90630-5019
Tel (714) 507-1998 Founded/Ownrshp 2005
Sales 92.3MM^E EMP 2,214
SIC 6282 8111 Investment advice; Legal services

D-U-N-S 07-888-1122
■ **CALIBER CO**
SAVAGE ARMS
(Suby of VISTA OUTDOOR INC) ★
100 Springdale Rd, Westfield, MA 01085-1624
Tel (413) 642-4260 Founded/Ownrshp 2015
Sales 101.9MM^E EMP 600^E
SIC 3484 Rifles or rifle parts, 30 mm. & below; Shotguns or shotgun parts, 30 mm. & below
CEO: Mark Deyoung

CALIBER COLLISION CENTERS
See CALIBER BODYWORKS OF TEXAS INC

CALIBER COLLISION CENTERS
See CALIBER BODYWORKS PSA OF TEXAS INC

D-U-N-S 02-286-7870
CALIBER FUNDING LLC
6031 Connection Dr # 200, Irving, TX 75039-2613
Tel (866) 373-2968 Founded/Ownrshp 2008
Sales NA EMP 900^E
SIC 6153

D-U-N-S 79-975-5061
CALIBER HOLDINGS CORP
401 E Corp Dr Ste 150, Lewisville, TX 75057
Tel (469) 948-9500 Founded/Ownrshp 2013
Sales 1.4MMM^E EMP 3,713
SIC 6719 Investment holding companies, except banks
Pr: Steve Grimshaw
*COO: Mark Sanders
*CFO: J Robert Gary
*Sr VP: Greg Clark
*CIO: Janet Deberardinis
VP Sls: Ty Gammill

D-U-N-S 61-342-5834 IMP/EXP
CALIBER HOME LOANS INC
3701 Regent Blvd, Irving, TX 75063-2312
Tel (800) 401-6587 Founded/Ownrshp 2013
Sales NA EMP 915^E
SIC 6153 Working capital financing
CEO: Sanjiv Das
Pr: John Gibson
CFO: John D Burr
*COO: Bernard Smith
COO: Russ Smith
*CFO: Stephen Smith
Chf Mktg O: Tim Kirchner
Ofcr: Kennis Bell
Ofcr: Jim Jamsay
Ofcr: Cindy Woods
Ex VP: John Bianchi
Ex VP: Donna Edwards
Ex VP: Terry McCoy
Ex VP: Phil Shoemaker
Sr VP: Michael Brown
Sr VP: Patricia Dooley
Sr VP: Jerry Jamieson
Sr VP: Judy Leto
Sr VP: Al Murad
Sr VP: John Sayre
Sr VP: Matt Schilling

CALIBER POINT
See HEXAWARE TECHNOLOGIES INC

D-U-N-S 55-549-8187
CALIBRE SYSTEMS INC
6354 Walker Ln Ste 300, Alexandria, VA 22310-3252
Tel (703) 797-8500 Founded/Ownrshp 1989
Sales 263.8MM^E EMP 682^E
Accts Argy Wiltse & Robinson Pc
SIC 7379 8748 Computer related consulting services; Systems analysis & engineering consulting services
Pr: Joseph A Martore
Pr: Jeffrey L Doerr
*Pr: W Michael Polster
*CFO: Jeffrey E Giangiuli
*CFO: John C Mutarelli
*Ex VP: Robert W Larrick Jr
*Ex VP: William Maxwell
Sr VP: Craig College
VP: Judy L Butts
VP: Michelle V Caylor
VP: Charles J Fowler
VP: Robert Gollhofer
VP: Sandra Gregory
VP: Shawn Gundrum
VP: Daniel C Myung
VP: William B Newnam
VP: Timothy O'Connor
VP: Ted S Richan
VP: Philip M Rizzi
VP: Mindy L Scott
VP: Earle A Shaw
Board of Directors: Joseph H Reynolds, R L Vanantwerp

CALICO CORNERS
See EVERFAST INC

CALIF STATE UNIVERSITY
See UNIVERSITY ENTERPRISES CORP AT CSUSB

D-U-N-S 07-463-2456
CALIFORNIA ACADEMY OF SCIENCES (CA)
55 Music Concourse Dr, San Francisco, CA 94118-4503
Tel (415) 379-8000 Founded/Ownrshp 1853
Sales 95.5MM EMP 655
Accts Lb Pricewaterhousecoopers Llp
SIC 8422 2721 8412 Aquarium; Periodicals: publishing only; Museums & art galleries
Pr: John Hafernik
COO: Scott Moran
*CFO: Alison Brown
Bd of Dir: Peter Fenton
Bd of Dir: Kris Pettersen
Ofcr: Stephanie Stone
Assoc Dir: Andrea Forker
Assoc Dir: Mindee Kashiwagi
Assoc Dir: Mortensen Meghan
Assoc Dir: Tamara Schwarz
Assoc Dir: Percy Stevens

CALIFORNIA ALMOND GROWERS EXCH
See DIAMOND BLUE GROWERS

D-U-N-S 02-846-7991
■ **CALIFORNIA AMERICAN WATER CO**
(Suby of AMERICAN WATER WORKS CO INC) ★
655 W Broadway Ste 1410, San Diego, CA 92101-8491
Tel (619) 409-7703 Founded/Ownrshp 1965
Sales 115.4MM^E EMP 327
SIC 4941 Water supply
Pr: Kent Turner
COO: Judith Almond
CFO: Christopher Buls
VP: Anthony J Cerasuolo
Board of Directors: Kevin Murray, Blanca Zarazua

D-U-N-S 79-152-3483
■ **CALIFORNIA AUTOMOBILE INSURANCE CO**
CAI COMPANY
(Suby of MERCURY GENERAL CORP) ★
555 W Imperial Hwy, Brea, CA 92821-4802
Tel (714) 232-8669 Founded/Ownrshp 1962
Sales NA EMP 800
SIC 6331 Automobile insurance
Pr: George Joseph
*CFO: Leo Lam

CALIFORNIA BANK & TRUST
See ZB NATIONAL ASSOCIATION

D-U-N-S 07-334-5365 IMP/EXP
CALIFORNIA BANK & TRUST
11622 El Camino Real # 200, San Diego, CA 92130-2051
Tel (858) 793-7400 Founded/Ownrshp 1995
Sales NA EMP 1,910
SIC 6022

D-U-N-S 05-384-5582
CALIFORNIA BAPTIST UNIVERSITY
C B U
8432 Magnolia Ave, Riverside, CA 92504-3297
Tel (951) 689-5771 Founded/Ownrshp 1950
Sales 227.1MM EMP 300
Accts Vicenti Lloyd & Stutzman Glen
SIC 8221 College, except junior
Pr: Ronald L Ellis
*CFO: Mark Howe
VP: Adam Burton
VP: Arthur Cleveland
VP: Kent Dacus
*VP: L Kent Dacus
*VP: Bruce Hitchcock
VP: Marilyn Johnson
VP: John Petty
VP: David Lane Poole
Ex Dir: Jeff McNair

CALIFORNIA BASIC
See MIAS FASHION MANUFACTURING CO INC

D-U-N-S 62-698-6009 IMP/EXP
CALIFORNIA BEES INC
AM WAX
14381 Industry Cir, La Mirada, CA 90638-5810
Tel (714) 228-1999 Founded/Ownrshp 2005
Sales 108.0MM^E EMP 7
SIC 5149 Groceries & related products
CEO: Yunlong Peng
*Pr: Jisang MA

CALIFORNIA CAFE
See TAVISTOCK RESTAURANTS LLC

D-U-N-S 07-717-9869
CALIFORNIA CAPITAL INSURANCE CO
CAPITAL INSURANCE GROUP
2300 Garden Rd, Monterey, CA 93940-5326
Tel (831) 233-5500 Founded/Ownrshp 1985
Sales NA EMP 400
SIC 6331 Fire, marine & casualty insurance & carriers; Automobile insurance
Pr: L Arnold Chatterton
*COO: Andrew Doll
*CFO: Davis Tyndall
*VP: Walter Benett
*VP: John Halberstadt
*VP: Radhakrishna Mydam
*VP: Thomas Scherff
Brnch Mgr: John Higbee
Brnch Mgr: John McLaughlin

D-U-N-S 13-127-8616
CALIFORNIA CARTAGE CO LLC
2931 Redondo Ave, Long Beach, CA 90806-2445
Tel (562) 427-1143 Founded/Ownrshp 1987
Sales 121.5MM^E EMP 220
SIC 4226 8741 8721 Storage of goods at foreign trade zones; Management services; Accounting, auditing & bookkeeping
Pr: John Amato
VP: Kent Prokop
Genl Mgr: Chris Brinson
Off Mgr: Veronica Lopez
IT Man: Jesse Jauregui
Opers Mgr: Charlene Fields
Opers Mgr: Arthur Hutton
Opers Mgr: Kevin Rivera
Sls&Mrk Ex: Jim Gill
Mktg Dir: Eric McClintick

D-U-N-S 07-611-8116
CALIFORNIA CASCADE INDUSTRIES
(Suby of CANWEL BUILDING MATERIALS GROUP LTD)
7512 14th Ave, Sacramento, CA 95820-3539
Tel (916) 736-3353 Founded/Ownrshp 2015
Sales 83.6MM^E EMP 200
SIC 2491 2421 Wood preserving; Sawmills & planing mills, general
Pr: Stuart D Heath
*CFO: Richard Rose
*Sec: Kyle Keaton
VP: Gus Prouty
Genl Mgr: Harvey Molatore
Plnt Mgr: Gary Galbraith

CALIFORNIA CASUALTY
See CALIFORNIA CASUALTY MANAGEMENT CO

D-U-N-S 00-922-6861
CALIFORNIA CASUALTY INDEMNITY EXCHANGE
1900 Almeda De Las Pulgas, San Mateo, CA 94403-1222
Tel (650) 574-4000 Founded/Ownrshp 1914
Sales NA EMP 900
SIC 6331 Workers' compensation insurance; Automobile insurance; Property damage insurance; Fire, marine & casualty insurance & carriers
Ch: Thomas R Brown
*CFO: Mike Ray
Bd of Dir: Mark Kvamme
Assoc VP: Julie Schillings
Ex VP: Thomas Weatherford
VP: Randy Bias
VP: Andy Feit
VP: Kerrigan Finn
VP: Andrew Grygiel
VP: Mike Makely
VP: David McNeil
VP: Max Schireson
VP: Ian Small
VP Bus Dev: Daniel Budiman
Exec: Michael Carey
Exec: Bill Watson

D-U-N-S 07-187-1131
CALIFORNIA CASUALTY MANAGEMENT CO
CALIFORNIA CASUALITY
1900 Almeda De Las Pulgas, San Mateo, CA 94403-1298
Tel (650) 574-4000 Founded/Ownrshp 1917
Sales NA EMP 670
SIC 6331 8741 Reciprocal interinsurance exchanges: fire, marine, casualty; Management services
Ch Bd: Carl B Brown
Pr: Joseph L Volponi
CFO: Michael Ray
Sr VP: James R Englese
VP: Judy Jao
VP: Mike McCormick
VP: Tom Richardson
Dir IT: Renato Nanez
IT Man: Arul Santiagu
Web Prj Mg: Keith Felton
Web Dev: Stephanie Graham
Board of Directors: Kenneth G Berry, Carl Brown, Thomas Brown, Peter Goldberg, James Sevey, Joseph Volponi

D-U-N-S 00-915-7876 IMP
CALIFORNIA CEDAR PRODUCTS CO
2385 Arch Airport Rd # 500, Stockton, CA 95206-4405
Tel (209) 932-5002 Founded/Ownrshp 1937
Sales 97.9MM^E EMP 575
SIC 2499 Pencil slats, wood; Logs of sawdust & wood particles, pressed
Pr: Charles Berolzheimer
Pr: Paula Sullivan
*CFO: Susan Macintyre

CALIFORNIA CENTER BANK
See BBCN BANK

CALIFORNIA CHOICE
See CHOICE ADMINISTRATORS INSURANCE SERVICES INC

D-U-N-S 07-360-4563
CALIFORNIA CITY OF SAN BERNARDINO
300 N D St, San Bernardino, CA 92418-0001
Tel (909) 384-5128 Founded/Ownrshp 1854
Sales NA EMP 1,760
Accts Rogers Anderson Malody & Sco
SIC 9111 City & town managers' offices;
Treas: Palupe losefa
*Treas: David Kennedy
Genl Mgr: Ellen Clifford
IT Man: Marcus Anderson
IT Man: Michael Eckley
Sls&Mrk Ex: Randy Kuettle

D-U-N-S 61-154-9564
■ **CALIFORNIA COMFORT SYSTEMS USA**
(Suby of COMFORT SYSTEMS USA INC) ★
7740 Kenamar Ct, San Diego, CA 92121-2425
Tel (858) 564-1100 Founded/Ownrshp 1983
Sales 95.6MM^E EMP 399
SIC 1711 Heating & air conditioning contractors
CEO: Kenneth Hoving
*Pr: Roger Well
*VP: William George
*VP: Trent McKenna
*Genl Mgr: Bo Macaraeg

D-U-N-S 10-572-1898
CALIFORNIA COMMERCE CLUB INC
COMMERCE CASINO
6131 Telegraph Rd, Commerce, CA 90040-2501
Tel (323) 721-2100 Founded/Ownrshp 1982
Sales 87.5MM^E EMP 2,600
SIC 7011 5812 Casino hotel; Eating places
CEO: Haig Papaian
*CFO: Dante Oliveto
*VP: Harvey Ross
*VP: Andrew Schneiderman
*VP: Ralph Wong
Dir Sec: Mike Sana
Dir IT: Vigen Mirzayann
IT Man: Steven Romeyn

D-U-N-S 94-915-5576
CALIFORNIA COMMUNITY COLLEGES SYSTEM
1102 Q St Fl 4, Sacramento, CA 95811-6549
Tel (916) 445-8752 Founded/Ownrshp 1994
Sales 83.5M EMP 2,651^E
Accts Pine Pedroncelli & Aguilar Inc
SIC 8221 Colleges universities & professional schools
CEO: Drummond Marshall
VP: Scott Himelstein
Genl Mgr: Walt Dimantova
Genl Mgr: Erik Skinner
IT Man: Monica Mello
Sls&Mrk Ex: Paige M Door

D-U-N-S 03-818-0378
CALIFORNIA COMMUNITY FOUNDATION
221 S Figueroa St Ste 400, Los Angeles, CA 90012-3760
Tel (213) 413-4130 Founded/Ownrshp 1915
Sales 270.2MM^E EMP 60^E
Accts Kmpg Llp Los Angeles Califor
SIC 6732 Charitable trust management
Pr: Antonia Hernandez
*Ch Bd: Tom Unterman
*CFO: Steve Cobb
CFO: Elizabeth Hernandez
Ofcr: Roy Allen
Ofcr: James Herr
Ofcr: Tamu Jones
Ofcr: Moraya A Moini
Ofcr: Peter Rivera
Sr VP: Judith Spiegel
VP: Maria Blanco
*VP: Peter Dunn
VP: Efrain Escobedo
VP: John Kobara
VP: Paul Schulz
Board of Directors: Louise Henry Bryson, Carlos R Moreno, Todd Quinn, Marie Brooks Washington

D-U-N-S 00-986-8035 IMP/EXP
CALIFORNIA DAIRIES INC (CA)
2000 N Plaza Dr, Visalia, CA 93291-9358
Tel (559) 625-2200 Founded/Ownrshp 1938, 1999
Sales 271.5MM^E EMP 755
SIC 2026 2021 2023 Fluid milk; Creamery butter; Dry, condensed, evaporated dairy products
CEO: Andrei Mikhalevsky
*Ch Bd: John Azevedo
*COO: Dave Bush
*CFO: David Camp
*Sr VP: Joe L Heffington
*VP: Eric Erba

D-U-N-S 80-833-2407
CALIFORNIA DEPARTMENT OF CONSUMER AFFAIRS
(Suby of CALIFORNIA GOVERNMENT OPERATIONS AGENCY) ★
1625 N Market Blvd # 103, Sacramento, CA 95834-2929
Tel (916) 574-7130 Founded/Ownrshp 1994
Sales NA EMP 3,600^E
SIC 9611 Consumer protection office, government;
Ex Dir: Donald Krpan
CIO: Debbie Balaam

D-U-N-S 80-851-3709
CALIFORNIA DEPARTMENT OF CORRECTIONS & REHABILITATION
(Suby of EXECUTIVE OFFICE OF STATE OF CALIFORNIA) ★
1515 S St, Sacramento, CA 95811-7243
Tel (916) 341-7066 Founded/Ownrshp 1856
Sales NA EMP 42,000
SIC 9223 Prison, government;
Ofcr: Wade Critz
Ofcr: Gail Crooms
Ofcr: Crisanto Legaspi
Ofcr: Kenneth Martin
Ofcr: Erika Meyer
Ofcr: Isaac Morales
Ofcr: Theresa Moreno
Ofcr: Minh Nguyen
Ofcr: Manuel Olivas
Ofcr: Lenard Pennisi
Ofcr: David Richardson
Ofcr: Marshall Saipher
Ofcr: Catherine Sanchez

D-U-N-S 55-654-8071
CALIFORNIA DEPARTMENT OF DEVELOPMENTAL SERVICES
PORTERVILLE DEVELOPMENTAL CTR
(Suby of CHHS) ★
1600 9th St, Sacramento, CA 95814-6414
Tel (916) 654-1690 Founded/Ownrshp 1978

Sales NA *EMP* 9,275
SIC 9431 Administration of public health programs;
Comm Dir: Nancy Lungren
Adm Dir: Barbara Eichler
Ex Dir: Pamela Meeker
Genl Mgr: Pamela Robison
Off Mgr: Gloria Rhodes
IT Man: Kevin Curtis
Opers Mgr: John Loveridge
Mktg Dir: Monica Lopez

D-U-N-S 80-748-0843
CALIFORNIA DEPARTMENT OF EDUCATION
(*Suby of* EXECUTIVE OFFICE OF STATE OF CALIFORNIA) ★
1430 N St Ste 5602, Sacramento, CA 95814-5901
Tel (916) 319-0815 *Founded/Ownrshp* 2001
Sales NA *EMP* 1,600
SIC 9411 Administration of educational programs;
Genl Mgr: Ernie Thornberg

D-U-N-S 61-421-5531
CALIFORNIA DEPARTMENT OF EMPLOYMENT DEVELOPMENT
(*Suby of* LABOR AND WORKFORCE DEVELOPMENT AGENCY, CALIFORNIA)
800 Capitol Mall 83, Sacramento, CA 95814-4807
Tel (916) 654-8210 *Founded/Ownrshp* 1970
Sales NA *EMP* 9,000
SIC 9441 Equal employment opportunity office, government;
VP: Maria Seames
Genl Mgr: Robert Nesman
Off Mgr: Thelma Snowder
Netwrk Eng: Richard Rau
Snr Mgr: Tad Allred

D-U-N-S 80-832-2358
CALIFORNIA DEPARTMENT OF FISH AND WILDLIFE
CDFW
(*Suby of* CALIFORNIA NATURAL RESOURCES AGENCY) ★
1416 9th St Fl 12, Sacramento, CA 95814-5515
Tel (916) 445-0411 *Founded/Ownrshp* 1850
Sales NA *EMP* 2,300
SIC 9512 Land, mineral & wildlife conservation;
Ofcr: Patrick Foy
Ofcr: Brian Kwake
Ofcr: Troy Swauger
Genl Mgr: Lisa Bays
Genl Mgr: Blaine Nickens
Sys Mgr: Jim Groh
Sys Mgr: Mike Haynie

D-U-N-S 96-160-6167
CALIFORNIA DEPARTMENT OF GENERAL SERVICES
(*Suby of* STATE OF CALIFORNIA) ★
707 3rd St, West Sacramento, CA 95605-2811
Tel (916) 376-5000 *Founded/Ownrshp* 1965
Sales NA *EMP* 4,000
SIC 9199 General government administration;
Rgnl Mgr: Greg Simmons
CIO: Jamie Mangreen

D-U-N-S 87-820-3967
CALIFORNIA DEPARTMENT OF HOUSING & COMMUNITY DEVELOPMENT
BUSINESS TRNSP & HSING AGCY
(*Suby of* BUSINESS TRANSPORTATION & HOUSING AGENCY STATE OF CALIFORNIA) ★
1800 3rd St Fl 1, Sacramento, CA 95811-6943
Tel (916) 445-4782 *Founded/Ownrshp* 1909
Sales NA *EMP* 3,009
SIC 9531 9532 Housing programs; ; Urban & community development;

D-U-N-S 80-748-7772
CALIFORNIA DEPARTMENT OF INDUSTRIAL RELATIONS
(*Suby of* LABOR AND WORKFORCE DEVELOPMENT AGENCY, CALIFORNIA)
455 Golden Gate Ave Fl 8, San Francisco, CA 94102-7001
Tel (415) 557-0100 *Founded/Ownrshp* 1927
Sales NA *EMP* 6,600
SIC 9651 Labor regulatory agency;
Brnch Mgr: Steve Honjio
Dist Mgr: Michael Frye
Genl Mgr: Robert Mason
IT Man: Susan De Castro

D-U-N-S 80-674-4876
CALIFORNIA DEPARTMENT OF INSURANCE
INSURANCE COMMISSIONER
(*Suby of* EXECUTIVE OFFICE OF STATE OF CALIFORNIA) ★
300 Capitol Mall Ste 1700, Sacramento, CA 95814-4313
Tel (916) 492-3500 *Founded/Ownrshp* 1850
Sales NA *EMP* 1,342
SIC 9651 Insurance commission, government;
Prin: John Garamendi
Ofcr: Rhonda Clark
Orthpdst: Lance Jensen

D-U-N-S 80-748-6691
CALIFORNIA DEPARTMENT OF JUSTICE
(*Suby of* EXECUTIVE OFFICE OF STATE OF CALIFORNIA) ★
1300 I St Ste 1142, Sacramento, CA 95814-2963
Tel (916) 324-5437 *Founded/Ownrshp* 1850
Sales NA *EMP* 3,655
SIC 9222 Attorney General's office;

D-U-N-S 80-824-3414
CALIFORNIA DEPARTMENT OF MOTOR VEHICLES
DMV BUDGET AND ANALYSIS
(*Suby of* BUSINESS TRANSPORTATION & HOUSING AGENCY STATE OF CALIFORNIA) ★
2415 1st Ave, Sacramento, CA 95818-2606
Tel (916) 657-6847 *Founded/Ownrshp* 1931
Sales NA *EMP* 4,300
SIC 9621 Motor vehicle licensing & inspection office, government
Ofcr: Dee Ngo
Ex Dir: Larry Fritz
Admn Mgr: Debra Alexander
CIO: Bernard Soriano
DP Exec: Unmi Kwak
IT Man: Robbie Crockett
IT Man: Carol Wong

D-U-N-S 17-207-0807
CALIFORNIA DEPARTMENT OF PARKS AND RECREATION
(*Suby of* CALIFORNIA NATURAL RESOURCES AGENCY) ★
1416 9th St Ste 1041, Sacramento, CA 95814-5510
Tel (800) 777-0369 *Founded/Ownrshp* 1926
Sales NA *EMP* 5,000
SIC 9512 Land, mineral & wildlife conservation;

D-U-N-S 80-832-1897
CALIFORNIA DEPARTMENT OF PESTICIDE REGULATION
(*Suby of* CAL/EPA) ★
1001 I St, Sacramento, CA 95814-2828
Tel (916) 445-4000 *Founded/Ownrshp* 1991
Sales NA *EMP* 1,267
SIC 9511 Environmental agencies;
Genl Mgr: Leslie Ford
Genl Mgr: Lu Saephanh

D-U-N-S 01-299-7563
CALIFORNIA DEPARTMENT OF PUBLIC HEALTH
(*Suby of* STATE OF CALIFORNIA) ★
1615 Capitol Ave, Sacramento, CA 95814-5015
Tel (916) 558-1700 *Founded/Ownrshp* 2010
Sales NA *EMP* 3,800
SIC 9431

D-U-N-S 80-851-3097
CALIFORNIA DEPARTMENT OF REHABILITATION
(*Suby of* CHHS) ★
721 Capitol Mall Fl 6, Sacramento, CA 95814-4702
Tel (916) 558-5683 *Founded/Ownrshp* 1963
Sales NA *EMP* 1,875
SIC 9431 Categorical health program administration, government;
Ofcr: Suzanne Chan
Ofcr: Jennifer S Lim
**Ofcr:* Erin Treadwell
Genl Mgr: Simone Dumas
Genl Mgr: Tina Watson
IT Man: Julie Sanchez

D-U-N-S 80-888-6063
CALIFORNIA DEPARTMENT OF STATE HOSPITALS
CALIFRNIA HLTH HUMN SRVCS AGCY
(*Suby of* CHHS) ★
1600 9th St Ste 120, Sacramento, CA 95814-6434
Tel (916) 654-3890 *Founded/Ownrshp* 1978
Sales NA *EMP* 8,152
SIC 9431 Mental health agency administration, government;
Psych: Susan Velasquez

D-U-N-S 07-882-7395
CALIFORNIA DEPARTMENT OF STATE HOSPITALS-ATASCADERO FIRE DEPARTMENT
10333 El Camino Real, Atascadero, CA 93422-5808
Tel (805) 468-2501 *Founded/Ownrshp* 1954
Sales 42.4MM[E] *EMP* 1,953
SIC 8063 Psychiatric hospitals
Pt: Christopher Stuiber

D-U-N-S 19-065-8153
CALIFORNIA DEPARTMENT OF VETERANS AFFAIRS
(*Suby of* EXECUTIVE OFFICE OF STATE OF CALIFORNIA) ★
1227 O St Ste 105, Sacramento, CA 95814-5891
Tel (800) 952-5626 *Founded/Ownrshp* 1921
Sales NA *EMP* 1,300
SIC 9451 Administration of veterans' affairs;
IT Man: Cindy Lindsey

D-U-N-S 17-121-4307
CALIFORNIA DEPARTMENT OF WATER RESOURCES
(*Suby of* CALIFORNIA NATURAL RESOURCES AGENCY) ★
1416 9th St, Sacramento, CA 95814-5511
Tel (916) 653-9394 *Founded/Ownrshp* 1994
Sales NA *EMP* 3,000
SIC 9511 Water control & quality agency, government
CFO: Perla Nettobrown
CIO: Tim Garza
IT Man: Jessica Chin

D-U-N-S 61-367-3185
CALIFORNIA DEPT OF SOCIAL SERVICES
(*Suby of* CHHS) ★
744 P St, Sacramento, CA 95814-6413
Tel (916) 657-2598 *Founded/Ownrshp* 1970
Sales NA *EMP* 4,200
SIC 9441 Administration of social & manpower programs;
VP: Renee Daaboul
Prgrm Mgr: Regina Mauldin
Genl Mgr: Geraldine Walker

D-U-N-S 94-900-7744
CALIFORNIA DEPT OF TRANSPORTATION
CALTRANS
(*Suby of* BUSINESS TRANSPORTATION & HOUSING AGENCY STATE OF CALIFORNIA) ★
1120 N St, Sacramento, CA 95814-5680
Tel (916) 654-5266 *Founded/Ownrshp* 1970
Sales NA *EMP* 20,600
SIC 9621 Regulation, administration of transportation;
Adm Dir: Teresa Favila
Brnch Mgr: Jon Hamaguchi
DP Exec: Will Brown
VP Opers: Sherrie Ford
Snr Mgr: Greg Larson

D-U-N-S 07-082-4099
CALIFORNIA EMERGENCY PHYSICIANS FOUNDATION
CEP AMERICA
2100 Powell St Ste 900, Emeryville, CA 94608-1844
Tel (510) 350-2700 *Founded/Ownrshp* 1975
Sales 500.0MM *EMP* 1,300
SIC 8621

D-U-N-S 96-860-0056
CALIFORNIA ENDOWMENT
1000 N Alameda St, Los Angeles, CA 90012-1804
Tel (800) 449-4149 *Founded/Ownrshp* 1996
Sales 159.6MM *EMP* 110
SIC 8399 Fund raising organization, non-fee basis
Pr: Robert K Ross
Pr: Robert Alaniz
COO: Julie Tugend
**CFO:* Dan C Deleon
Bd of Dir: Marion Standish
Chf Inves: Ren Goupillaud
Chf Inves: Reny Goupillaud
Chf Inves: Ruth Wernig
Ofcr: Cecilia Echeverr A
Ofcr: George Flores
Ofcr: Mary Fulton
Ex VP: Irene Ibarra
**Ex VP:* Martha Jimenez
VP: Anthony Iton
VP: Tony Iton
VP: Selna Leland
VP: Daniel Zingale
Exec: Michael Millman
Dir Soc: Randall Lowe
Comm Dir: Leticia Alejandrez

D-U-N-S 80-748-7327
CALIFORNIA ENVIRONMENTAL PROTECTION AGENCY
CAL/EPA
(*Suby of* EXECUTIVE OFFICE OF STATE OF CALIFORNIA) ★
1001 I St, Sacramento, CA 95814-2828
Tel (916) 323-2514 *Founded/Ownrshp* 1991
Sales NA *EMP* 3,897
SIC 9511 Air, water & solid waste management;

D-U-N-S 80-748-7459
CALIFORNIA GOVERNMENT OPERATIONS AGENCY
(*Suby of* EXECUTIVE OFFICE OF STATE OF CALIFORNIA) ★
915 Capitol Mall Ste 200, Sacramento, CA 95814-4801
Tel (916) 651-9011 *Founded/Ownrshp* 1969
Sales NA *EMP* 16,250
SIC 9611 Administration of general economic programs;
**CEO:* Janet Mammini

D-U-N-S 80-748-6923
CALIFORNIA HEALTH & HUMAN SERVCS AGENCY
CHHS
(*Suby of* EXECUTIVE OFFICE OF STATE OF CALIFORNIA) ★
1600 9th St Ste 460, Sacramento, CA 95814-6439
Tel (916) 654-3454 *Founded/Ownrshp* 1970
Sales NA *EMP* 18,750
SIC 9431 9441 Administration of public health programs; ; Administration of social & manpower programs;
Ex Dir: Jennifer Nelson
**Genl Couns:* Douglas M Press

D-U-N-S 05-387-9235 IMP
CALIFORNIA HOSPITAL MEDICAL CENTER FOUNDATION
(*Suby of* DIGNITY HEALTH) ★
1401 S Grand Ave, Los Angeles, CA 90015-3010
Tel (213) 748-2411 *Founded/Ownrshp* 1926
Sales 396.8MM *EMP* 1,500
SIC 8062 Hospital, medical school affiliated with nursing & residency
Ch Bd: Phillip C Hill
**Pr:* Nathan R Nusbaum
**Pr:* Margaret R Peterson
**COO:* Harold Newton
**CFO:* Clark Underwood
Sr VP: Jan Yergen
VP: Erlinda Bolor
**VP:* Linda Bolor
VP: Sandra Davis-Houston
**VP:* David Milovich
**VP:* Bob Quarfoot

D-U-N-S 07-528-9413
■ **CALIFORNIA HOTEL AND CASINO**
(*Suby of* BOYD GAMING CORP) ★
12 E Ogden Ave, Las Vegas, NV 89101-2992
Tel (702) 385-1222 *Founded/Ownrshp* 1988
Sales 115.8MM[E] *EMP* 4,815
SIC 7011 Casino hotel
Pr: Keith Smith

D-U-N-S 96-952-8850
CALIFORNIA INDEPENDENT SYSTEM OPERATOR CORP
CALIFORNIA ISO
250 Outcropping Way, Folsom, CA 95630-8773
Tel (916) 351-4400 *Founded/Ownrshp* 1997
Sales 213.4MM *EMP* 530
Accts Pricewaterhousecoopers Llp Wa
SIC 4911 Distribution, electric power; Transmission, electric power
Pr: Stephen Berberich
**Ch Bd:* Bob Foster
**CFO:* William J Regan
CFO: Ryan Seghesio
Treas: Philip Leiber
Treas: Philip Leiver
Bd of Dir: Andrew Ulmer
Sr VP: Joanne Serina
**VP:* Roger Collanton
**VP:* Jim Detmers
**VP:* Karen Edson
VP: Angela Glover
**VP:* Charles King
VP: Chris McIntosh
Exec: Kristina Osborne

D-U-N-S 87-830-9491
CALIFORNIA INSTITUTE OF ARTS
24700 Mcbean Pkwy, Valencia, CA 91355-2340
Tel (661) 255-1050 *Founded/Ownrshp* 1961
Sales 84.1MM *EMP* 500[E]
SIC 8221 8231 8249 Colleges universities & professional schools; Libraries; Commercial art school
CEO: Steven Lavine
Pt: Steven Kotler
**Pr:* Joan Abrahamson
**CEO:* Thomas L Lee
**Ch:* Austin M Beutner
Bd of Dir: Mona Heinze
Assoc VP: Michael Carter
**Sr VP:* James B Lovelace
Assoc Dir: Mirjana Jokovic
Comm Dir: Stuart Frolick
Opers Mgr: Roxane Chenault

D-U-N-S 00-958-4210 IMP
CALIFORNIA INSTITUTE OF TECHNOLOGY
CALTECH
1200 E California Blvd, Pasadena, CA 91125-0001
Tel (626) 395-6811 *Founded/Ownrshp* 1891
Sales 2.3MMM[E] *EMP* 3,980
Accts Pricewaterhousecoopers Llp Lo
SIC 8733 Research institute
Pr: Edward M Stolper
**Ch Bd:* Kent Kresa
Pr: Robert L O'Rourke
**Pr:* Edward M Stolper
CFO: Daniel I Meron
Treas: Sharon E Patterson
Trst: Gordon M Binder
Trst: Robert C Bonner
Trst: Brigitte M Bren
Trst: Harold Brown
Trst: John E Bryson
Trst: Milton M Chang
Trst: John S Chen
Trst: Robert B Chess
Trst: William H Davidow
Trst: Lounette M Dyer
Trst: Thomas E Everhart
Trst: Gilad I Elbaz
Trst: Arthur L Goldstein
Trst: William T Gross
Trst: Frederick J Hameetman

D-U-N-S 96-404-4122
CALIFORNIA IRONWORKERS FIELD WELFARE PLAN
131 N El Molino Ave # 330, Pasadena, CA 91101-1873
Tel (626) 792-7337 *Founded/Ownrshp* 2010
Sales 127.8MM *EMP* 3
Accts Bernard Kotkin And Company Llp
SIC 8631 Labor unions & similar labor organizations
Prin: Glen Cline

CALIFORNIA ISO
See CALIFORNIA INDEPENDENT SYSTEM OPERATOR CORP

D-U-N-S 00-968-0471
CALIFORNIA LUTHERAN UNIVERSITY
60 W Olsen Rd, Thousand Oaks, CA 91360-2700
Tel (805) 493-3135 *Founded/Ownrshp* 1959
Sales 164.0MM *EMP* 600
Accts Moss Adams Llp Stockton Ca
SIC 8221 University
CEO: Christopher W Kimball
Assoc VP: Ryan Vanommeren
**VP:* Karen Davis
**VP:* William Rosser
**VP:* R Stephen Wheatly
VP: Stephen Wheatly
Exec: Marie Cheever
Assoc Dir: Christine Paul
Assoc Dir: Harry Starn
CIO: Kenneth Pflueger
Dir IT: Michaela Reaves

D-U-N-S 17-363-7554
CALIFORNIA MARINE CLEANING INC
2049 Main St, San Diego, CA 92113-2216
Tel (619) 231-8788 *Founded/Ownrshp* 1985
Sales 86.2MM[E] *EMP* 160
SIC 4953 Hazardous waste collection & disposal
CEO: Matthew R Carr
**Pr:* Matt Carr
**CFO:* Hazel Carr
Genl Mgr: Joe Enjem

CALIFORNIA NANOSYSTEMS INST
See UNIVERSITY OF CALIFORNIA SANTA BARBARA

D-U-N-S 05-260-0251 IMP
CALIFORNIA NATURAL PRODUCTS (CA)
POWER AUTOMATION SYSTEMS
15789 Mckinley Ave, Lathrop, CA 95330-9701
Tel (209) 249-1616 *Founded/Ownrshp* 1976
Sales 112.7MM[E] *EMP* 230
SIC 2099 8731 3612 Food preparations; Syrups; Food research; Autotransformers, electric (power transformers)
CEO: Pat R Mitchell
**VP:* Rodney Tipton
Mktg Dir: Bruce Ferree
Sls Dir: Andy Hicks
Manager: Mark Houltzhouser
Genl Couns: Briana Delong
Genl Couns: Sarah Mitchell

D-U-N-S 80-748-7277
CALIFORNIA NATURAL RESOURCES AGENCY
(*Suby of* EXECUTIVE OFFICE OF STATE OF CALIFORNIA) ★
1416 9th St Ste 1311, Sacramento, CA 95814-5509
Tel (916) 653-5656 *Founded/Ownrshp* 1850

Sales NA *EMP* 6,711
SIC 9512 Land, mineral & wildlife conservation;
CEO: Mike Christman

D-U-N-S 13-455-3366
CALIFORNIA NEWSPAPER LIMITED PARTNERSHIP
(*Suby of* DIGITAL FIRST MEDIA) ★
194 Ford Rd, Ukiah, CA 95482-3469
Tel (707) 467-9111 *Founded/Ownrshp* 1999
Sales 179.1MM[E] *EMP* 3,500[E]
Accts Internal Documents
SIC 2711 Newspapers, publishing & printing
Prin: James Dsiegrist
Genl Pt: Stephens Media Group
Pt: Gerald Grilly
Pt: James Siegrist

D-U-N-S 06-537-4134
CALIFORNIA NEWSPAPERS LIMITED PARTNERSHIP
INLAND VALLEY DAILY BULLETIN
(*Suby of* DIGITAL FIRST MEDIA) ★
605 E Huntington Dr # 100, Monrovia, CA 91016-6352
Tel (626) 962-8811 *Founded/Ownrshp* 1997, 2000
Sales 178.7MM[E] *EMP* 2,900
SIC 2711 Newspapers: publishing only, not printed on site
Pr: Ron Hasse
VP: Jim Maurer
VP: Mark Welches
Ex Dir: Louis Friedman
Off Mgr: Denise Varnado
Sales Exec: Michael Moreno

CALIFORNIA PACIFIC MEDICAL CTR
See SUTTER BAY HOSPITALS

D-U-N-S 05-461-1694
CALIFORNIA PHYSICIANS SERVICE (CA)
BLUE SHIELD OF CALIFORNIA
50 Beale St Bsmt 2, San Francisco, CA 94105-1819
Tel (415) 229-5000 *Founded/Ownrshp* 1939
Sales NA *EMP* 4,500
Accts Deloitte & Touche Llp San Fra
SIC 6324 Hospital & medical service plans
Ch Bd: Bruce Bodoken
**Pr:* Paul Markovich
CEO: Karen Vigil
CFO: Heidi Field
**CFO:* Heidi Kunz
CFO: Michael Murray
**Chf Mktg O:* Eric Book
**Sr VP:* Edward Cymerys
Sr VP: Seth A Jacobs
Sr VP: David Joyner
**Sr VP:* Elinor Mackinnon
Sr VP: Michael G Mathias
Sr VP: Kathy Swenson
Sr VP: Ken Wood
Sr VP: Amy Yao
VP: David Arnold
VP: Cecily Ashmun
VP: James Elliott
VP: Stewart M Kiner
VP: Robert Martin
VP: Kristen Miranda
Board of Directors: Vanessa C L Chang

D-U-N-S 14-767-3511
CALIFORNIA PIZZA KITCHEN INC
(*Suby of* CPK HOLDINGS INC) ★
12181 Bluff Creek Dr Fl 5, Playa Vista, CA 90094-3235
Tel (310) 342-5000 *Founded/Ownrshp* 2011
Sales 544.8MM[E] *EMP* 14,000
SIC 5812 Pizza restaurants; Caterers
Pr: Gerard Johan Hart
COO: Kim Boerema
**COO:* Susan M Collyns
CFO: H G Carrington Jr
CFO: Greg Levin
CFO: Chris Morris
**Chf Cred:* Sarah Goldsmith Grover
**Sr VP:* Thomas P Beck
Sr VP: Julie Carruthers
VP: Tom Beck
VP: Kathleen Bush
VP: Ashley Ceraolo
VP: Rudy Sugueti
Board of Directors: William C Baker, Leslie E Bider, Marshall S Geller, Charles G Phillips, Alan I Rothenberg

D-U-N-S 85-884-1802
CALIFORNIA POLYTECHNIC STATE UNIVERSITY
CAL POLY
(*Suby of* CALIFORNIA STATE UNIVERSITY SYSTEM) ★
1 Grand Ave, San Luis Obispo, CA 93407-9000
Tel (805) 756-7414 *Founded/Ownrshp* 1901
Sales 207.1MM[E] *EMP* 3,000
SIC 8221 9411 University; Administration of educational programs;
Pr: Jeffrey Armstrong
Ofcr: Oliver Torres
**Sr VP:* Cynthia Villa
**VP:* Keith Humphrey
VP: Cornel N Morton
VP: Sandra Ogren
Assoc Dir: Barbara Andre
Assoc Dir: Grant Trexler
Ex Dir: Brian Dietterick
Ex Dir: Barbara Melvin
CIO: Timothy J Kearns

D-U-N-S 94-909-2795
CALIFORNIA PUBLIC EMPLOYEES RETIREMENT SYSTEM
(*Suby of* CALIFORNIA GOVERNMENT OPERATIONS AGENCY) ★
400 Q St, Sacramento, CA 95811-6201
Tel (916) 795-3000 *Founded/Ownrshp* 1932
Sales NA *EMP* 1,700
SIC 6371 9441 Pension funds; Administration of social & manpower programs;
CEO: Anne Stausboll
**Pr:* Rob Feckner
Ofcr: Mike Claybar
**Ofcr:* Ronald E Gene Reich
**Ofcr:* Kathie Vaughn
**Ofcr:* Robert D Walton
**Ofcr:* Terri Westbrook
**Ex VP:* Gloria Moore Andrews
**Ex VP:* Jarvio A Grevious
**VP:* Robert F Carlson
**Genl Couns:* Peter H Mixon

D-U-N-S 07-939-5911
▲ **CALIFORNIA RESOURCES CORP**
9200 Oakdale Ave Fl 9, Chatsworth, CA 91311-6506
Tel (888) 848-4754 *Founded/Ownrshp* 2014
Sales 2.4MMM *EMP* 1,990[E]
Tkr Sym CRC *Exch* NYS
SIC 1311 Crude petroleum & natural gas
Pr: Todd A Stevens
Ch Bd: William E Albrecht
CFO: Marshall D Smith
Ex VP: Robert A Barnes
Ex VP: Shawn M Kerns
Ex VP: Frank E Komin
Ex VP: Roy Pineci
Ex VP: Michael L Preston
Ex VP: Charles F Weiss
Ex VP: Darren Williams
Board of Directors: Justin A Gannon, Ronald L Havner, Catherine A Kehr, Harold M Korell, Richard W Moncrief, Robert V Sinnott, Timothy J Sloan

D-U-N-S 01-710-1887
■ **CALIFORNIA RESOURCES ELK HILLS LLC**
(*Suby of* CALIFORNIA RESOURCES CORP) ★
11109 River Run Blvd, Bakersfield, CA 93311-8957
Tel (661) 412-5000 *Founded/Ownrshp* 1997, 1998
Sales 104.9MM[E] *EMP* 400
SIC 2911 Oils, fuel
Genl Mgr: Shaun Kerns

D-U-N-S 62-721-3734
■ **CALIFORNIA RESOURCES PRODUCTION CORP**
VINTAGE PRODUCTION CALIFORNIA
(*Suby of* CALIFORNIA RESOURCES CORP) ★
11109 River Run Blvd, Bakersfield, CA 93311-8957
Tel (661) 869-8000 *Founded/Ownrshp* 2014
Sales 113.8MM[E] *EMP* 200
SIC 1311 1382 Crude petroleum production; Oil & gas exploration services
Prin: Todd A Stevens
**Pr:* Richard Oringderff
**CEO:* Todd Stevens

D-U-N-S 02-916-6832
CALIFORNIA SHELLFISH CO INC
818 E Broadway C, San Gabriel, CA 91776-1902
Tel (415) 923-7400 *Founded/Ownrshp* 1948
Sales 117.1MM[E] *EMP* 723
SIC 2092 Fresh or frozen packaged fish
**CFO:* Dave Zeller

D-U-N-S 10-011-9200
CALIFORNIA SQUARE LIMITED PARTNERSHIP
1600 Garland Ave, Louisville, KY 40210-2481
Tel (502) 589-9034 *Founded/Ownrshp* 1983
Sales 30.9MM[E] *EMP* 3,900
SIC 6513 Apartment building operators
Pt: Leon Gill
Sr VP: Leeann Morein

D-U-N-S 07-186-8954
CALIFORNIA STATE AUTOMOBILE ASSOCIATION INTER-INSURANCE BUREAU
TRIPLE A
(*Suby of* CSAA TRAVEL AGENCY) ★
1276 S California Blvd, Walnut Creek, CA 94596-5123
Tel (925) 287-7600 *Founded/Ownrshp* 1902
Sales NA *EMP* 2,208
SIC 6331 Automobile insurance
CEO: James R Pouliot
**Pr:* Paula Downey
QA Dir: Shed Collins
QA Dir: Samuel Pinto
IT Man: Noreen Williams

D-U-N-S 94-900-4246
CALIFORNIA STATE BOARD OF EQUALIZATION
(*Suby of* EXECUTIVE OFFICE OF STATE OF CALIFORNIA) ★
450 N St, Sacramento, CA 95814-4311
Tel (916) 445-6464 *Founded/Ownrshp* 1879
Sales NA *EMP* 4,000
SIC 9311 Finance, taxation & monetary policy;
Ex Dir: Ramon J Hirsig
Chf Cred: Brian Coty
Bd of Dir: Bill Leonard
Genl Mgr: Kevin McCarley
CIO: Brenda Fleming

D-U-N-S 80-898-4181
CALIFORNIA STATE TEACHERS RETIREMENT SYSTEM
CAL STRS
(*Suby of* CALIFORNIA GOVERNMENT OPERATIONS AGENCY) ★
100 Waterfront Pl, West Sacramento, CA 95605-2807
Tel (800) 228-5453 *Founded/Ownrshp* 1913
Sales NA *EMP* 535[E]
SIC 6371 9441 Pension, health & welfare funds; Administration of social & manpower programs;
CEO: James D Mosman
Chf Inves: Christopher Ailman
Ofcr: Ricardo Duran
Ofcr: Charles Haase
Ofcr: Richard Rose
Exec: Cassandra Lichnock
Comm Dir: Krista Noonan
Comm Man: Linda Armstrong
Comm Man: Kathy Halstead
IT Man: Michelle Mussuto
Netwrk Eng: Melanie Shimazu

D-U-N-S 01-620-8121
CALIFORNIA STATE UNIVERSITY CHICO
(*Suby of* CALIFORNIA STATE UNIVERSITY SYSTEM) ★
400 W 1st St, Chico, CA 95929-0001
Tel (530) 898-4636 *Founded/Ownrshp* 1887
Sales 157.1MM[E] *EMP* 2,000[E]
SIC 8221 9411 University; Administration of educational programs;
Pr: Paul J Zingg
Top Exec: Joseph Crotts
Assoc VP: Ron McConnell
VP: Luke Alward
VP: Ahmad Boura
VP: Christian J Burke
VP: Ethan Copitch
VP: Lorraine Hoffman
VP: Lori Miller
VP: Cassandra Saulan
VP: Peter Smits
VP: Gudrun Snyder
Assoc Dir: Lupe Jimenez
Assoc Dir: Linda Post
Assoc Dir: Rick Rees
Assoc Dir: Gloria Torbeck

D-U-N-S 60-631-9309
CALIFORNIA STATE UNIVERSITY EAST BAY
CSU EAST BAY
(*Suby of* CALIFORNIA STATE UNIVERSITY SYSTEM) ★
25800 Carlos Bee Blvd Sa, Hayward, CA 94542-3000
Tel (510) 885-3500 *Founded/Ownrshp* 1957
Sales 17.3MM *EMP* 1,600
Accts Macias Gini & O Connell Llp S
SIC 8221 9411 University; Administration of educational programs;
Pr: Leroy Morishita
CFO: David Demauro
CFO: Janna Tenenbaum
Chf Mktg O: Tom Koenigsberg
Assoc VP: Debbie Brothwell
Assoc VP: Martin Castillo
Assoc VP: Herbert Eder
VP: Kathleen Brady
VP: Debbie Chaw
VP: Tanya Hauck
VP: James Houpis
Assoc Dir: Ilana Samuels

D-U-N-S 14-193-7123
CALIFORNIA STATE UNIVERSITY LONG BEACH
(*Suby of* CALIFORNIA STATE UNIVERSITY SYSTEM) ★
1250 N Bellflower Blvd, Long Beach, CA 90840-0004
Tel (562) 985-4111 *Founded/Ownrshp* 2004
Sales 405.1MM[E] *EMP* 7,500
Accts Onisko & Scholz Llp Lonb Bea
SIC 8221 9411 University; Administration of educational programs;
Pr: F King Alexander
Pr: Soraya M Coley
Treas: Jecenia Vera
Assoc VP: Michael Losquadro
VP: Karen Salazar
Dir Risk M: Stephanie Williams
Assoc Dir: Stephanie Moreno
Adm Dir: Justine E Bllock
DP Exec: Richard Bodell
IT Man: Scott Woodyard
Opers Mgr: Larry Himmel

D-U-N-S 79-410-5598
CALIFORNIA STATE UNIVERSITY LOS ANGELES
CAL STATE LA
(*Suby of* CALIFORNIA STATE UNIVERSITY SYSTEM) ★
5151 State University Dr, Los Angeles, CA 90032-4226
Tel (323) 343-3000 *Founded/Ownrshp* 1927
Sales 199.4MM[E] *EMP* 2,201[E]
Accts Kpmg Llp Los Angeles Ca
SIC 8221 9411 University; Administration of educational programs;
Pr: William A Covino
CFO: George A Pardon
VP: Kyle C Button
VP: Susan Cash
VP: Ethan Lipton
VP: Anthony R Ross
Adm Dir: John R Feis
Adm Dir: Julissa Gutierrez
Adm Dir: James Montoya
Ex Dir: Nancy Miron
Ex Dir: Randi Moore

D-U-N-S 00-410-2153
CALIFORNIA STATE UNIVERSITY SAN BERNARDINO
CSUSB
(*Suby of* CALIFORNIA STATE UNIVERSITY SYSTEM) ★
5500 University Pkwy, San Bernardino, CA 92407-2318
Tel (909) 537-5000 *Founded/Ownrshp* 1987
Sales 117.6MM[E] *EMP* 1,200
Accts Rogers Anderson Malody & Sco
SIC 8221 9411 University; Administration of educational programs;
Pr: Albert K Karnig
VP: Rong Chen
Prgrm Mgr: Bernard Mauricia
Mtls Mgr: Joseph Liscano
Opers Mgr: Aaron Burgess

D-U-N-S 01-115-8792
CALIFORNIA STATE UNIVERSITY SAN MARCOS
(*Suby of* CALIFORNIA STATE UNIVERSITY SYSTEM) ★
333 S Twin Oaks Valley Rd, San Marcos, CA 92096-0001
Tel (760) 750-4000 *Founded/Ownrshp* 2009
Sales 44.5MM[E] *EMP* 1,680
Accts Kpmg Llp Los Angeles Ca
SIC 8221 9411 University; Administration of educational programs;
Pr: Karen Haynes
Pr: Travis Gregory
Ofcr: Christine Vaughan
Assoc VP: Scott Gross
Assoc VP: Mark Norita
Ex VP: Aaron Herrscher
VP: Berta Cuaron
VP: April Emerson
VP: Linda Hawk
VP: Christopher Morales
VP: Ebony Wiley
Assoc Dir: Domenica Pearl
Assoc Dir: Todd Snedden

D-U-N-S 94-738-1554
CALIFORNIA STATE UNIVERSITY SYSTEM
(*Suby of* EXECUTIVE OFFICE OF STATE OF CALIFORNIA) ★
401 Golden Shore, Long Beach, CA 90802-4210
Tel (562) 951-4000 *Founded/Ownrshp* 1961
Sales 2.1MMM[E] *EMP* 45,000
Accts Kpmg Llp Irvine Ca
SIC 8221 9411 University; Administration of educational programs;
Ch: Lou Monville
Pr: Edmund G Brown Jr
CFO: Robyn Pennington
CFO: Steve Relyea
Assoc VP: Debbie Brothwell
VP: Steven V Butler
Exec: Christine Miller
Exec: Hugh Pforsich
Exec: Sara Whalen
Exec: Cynthia Wyatt
Assoc Dir: Pilar Pacheco

D-U-N-S 11-835-2921 IMP
CALIFORNIA STEEL INDUSTRIES INC
SI
14000 San Bernardino Ave, Fontana, CA 92335-5259
Tel (909) 350-6300 *Founded/Ownrshp* 1984
Sales 239.8MM[E] *EMP* 872[E]
Accts Ernst & Young Llp Los Angeles
SIC 3312 3317 Slabs, steel; Plate, sheet & strip, except coated products; Pipes, wrought: welded, lock joint or heavy riveted
Pr: Marcelo Botelho
**Ch Bd:* Hiroshi Adachi
**Ch Bd:* Tadaaki Yamaguchi
COO: James Declusin
CFO: Robert Roberson
Treas: Robert McPherson
Ex VP: Harry Allin
**Ex VP:* Ricardo Bernardes
**Ex VP:* Brett Guge
Ex VP: Scott Starr
Exec: Lewis Ford
Board of Directors: Renato Almeida, Aristides Corbellini, Kazuo Fujisawa

D-U-N-S 07-187-0729
CALIFORNIA TEACHERS ASSOCIATION
1705 Murchison Dr, Burlingame, CA 94010-4583
Tel (650) 697-1400 *Founded/Ownrshp* 1907
Sales 187.1MM *EMP* 410
Accts Deloitte Tax Llp San Francisc
SIC 8621 8631 Education & teacher association; Labor unions & similar labor organizations
Ex Dir: Carolyn Doggett
Ex Dir: Mike Kress
Rgnl Mgr: Gail Holmes
Sls Dir: Rick Wathen

D-U-N-S 96-851-3239
CALIFORNIA TRUSFRAME LLC
CTF
23665 Cajalco Rd, Perris, CA 92570-8181
Tel (951) 657-7491 *Founded/Ownrshp* 2011
Sales 110.0MM *EMP* 685[E]
SIC 2439 Trusses, wooden roof
CEO: Steve Stroder
**CFO:* Susan Engquist
**Ch:* Kenneth Cloyd
IT Man: Richard Dinkler

D-U-N-S 55-547-2161
■ **CALIFORNIA UNITED BANK**
(*Suby of* CU BANCORP) ★
818 W 7th St Ste 220, Los Angeles, CA 90017-3449
Tel (213) 430-7000 *Founded/Ownrshp* 2004
Sales NA *EMP* 112[E]
SIC 6022 State commercial banks
Pr: David Rainer
**COO:* Anne A Williams
**CFO:* Robert Denin
**CFO:* Karen A Schoenbaum
Ofcr: Christine Kordik
**Ex VP:* Stephen Carpenter
Ex VP: David Kohn
**Ex VP:* Sam Kunianski
Ex VP: Stephen Pihl
Ex VP: David Plourde
**Ex VP:* William Sloan
Ex VP: Anita Wolman
Sr VP: Arthur Bergmann
Sr VP: Michael Clayton
Sr VP: Michael Clinton
Sr VP: David De Filippo
Sr VP: Kim D Defenderfer
Sr VP: Aileen Garrigues
Sr VP: Shelley Gibson
**Sr VP:* Emily Hamilton
Sr VP: Rich Hernandez

D-U-N-S 13-149-8144
CALIFORNIA UNITED MECHANICAL INC
2185 Oakland Rd, San Jose, CA 95131-1574
Tel (408) 232-9000 *Founded/Ownrshp* 2003
Sales 95.4MM[E] *EMP* 350
SIC 1711 Mechanical contractor
CEO: Tom Sosine
V Ch: Dirk Durham
**Pr:* Jon Gundersen
CFO: Jerry Patterson
**VP:* Blaine Flickner
VP: Neal Fox
IT Man: Winton Wong

Sfty Dirs: Patty Middleton
Snr PM: Ron Rusca

D-U-N-S 00-691-3578
■ CALIFORNIA WATER SERVICE CO (CA)
(*Suby of* CALIFORNIA WATER SERVICE GROUP) ★
1720 N 1st St, San Jose, CA 95112-4598
Tel (408) 367-8200 *Founded/Ownrshp* 1926
Sales 529.4MM[E] *EMP* 640
SIC 4941 Water supply
CEO: Martin A Kropelnicki
**Pr:* Michael P Ireland
**VP:* Helen Del Grosso
**VP:* Francis S Ferraro
**VP:* Robert R Guzzetta
Dir Risk M: Jim Simunovich
IT Man: Albert Quintero

D-U-N-S 00-644-8992
▲ CALIFORNIA WATER SERVICE GROUP
1720 N 1st St, San Jose, CA 95112-4598
Tel (408) 367-8200 *Founded/Ownrshp* 1999
Sales 588.3MM *EMP* 1,155[E]
Accts Deloitte & Touche Llp San Fra
Tkr Sym CWT *Exch* NYS
SIC 4941 Water supply
Pr: Martin A Kropelnicki
**Ch Bd:* Peter C Nelson
CFO: Thomas F Smegal III
VP: Shannon C Dean
VP: David B Healey
VP: Robert J Kuta
VP: Michael B Luu
VP: Lynne P McGhee
VP: Paul G Townsley
VP: Timothy D Treloar
CTO: Shannon Dean
Board of Directors: Gregory E Aliff, Terry P Bayer, Edwin A Guiles, Bonnie G Hill, Thomas M Krummel, Richard P Magnuson, Linda R Meier, Lester A Snow, George A Vera

D-U-N-S 80-961-8379
CALIFORNIAS VALUED TRUST
520 E Herndon Ave, Fresno, CA 93720-2907
Tel (559) 437-2960 *Founded/Ownrshp* 2008
Sales 687.5MM *EMP* 1
SIC 6733 Trusts
Ex Dir: Valerie Cornuelle
Ex Dir: David Vaughn

CALIFRNIA GOVT OPERATIONS AGCY
See FRANCHISE TAX BOARD CALIFORNIA

CALIFRNIA HLTH HUMN SRVCS AGCY
See CALIFORNIA DEPARTMENT OF STATE HOSPITALS

D-U-N-S 93-321-0197 IMP
■ CALIPER LIFE SCIENCES INC
(*Suby of* PERKINELMER HOLDINGS INC) ★
68 Elm St, Hopkinton, MA 01748-1668
Tel (508) 435-9500 *Founded/Ownrshp* 2011
Sales 98.9MM[E] *EMP* 400
SIC 3826
Pr: E Kevin Hrusovsky
Pr: Andrea W Cho
CFO: Peter F McAree
Sr VP: Bruce J Bal
Sr VP: Paula J Cassidy
Sr VP: Stephen E Creager
VP: Andrea W Chow PHD
VP: Joseph H Griffith IV
VP: Anne R Kopf-Sill
VP: Nicholas Mitropoulos
VP: Robert E Nagl
VP: Auro Nair PHD
VP: Mike Pento
Dir Bus: Robert Cohen

D-U-N-S 07-665-1314
CALISTA CORP
5015 Bus Pk Blvd Ste 3000, Anchorage, AK 99503
Tel (907) 279-5516 *Founded/Ownrshp* 1972
Sales 355.6MM[E] *EMP* 1,300
SIC 6512 7363 2711 Nonresidential building operators; Help supply services; Newspapers: publishing only, not printed on site
Pr: Andrew Guy
**COO:* Christine Klein
**CFO:* Sharon Weddleton
Bd of Dir: George Guy
**VP:* June McAtee
Sls Mgr: Mark John
**Genl Couns:* Marcia Davis
Genl Couns: Bonnie Paskvan
Board of Directors: Earl R Chase

D-U-N-S 11-347-2042 IMP/EXP
▲ CALIX INC
1035 N Mcdowell Blvd, Petaluma, CA 94954-1173
Tel (707) 766-3000 *Founded/Ownrshp* 1999
Sales 407.4MM *EMP* 895[E]
Tkr Sym CALX *Exch* NYS
SIC 3663 4899 4813 Radio & TV communications equipment; Data communication services; Communication signal enhancement network system; Telephone communication, except radio
Pr: Carl Russo
**Ch Bd:* Don Listwin
CFO: William Atkins
Ex VP: Michael Weening
Dir Bus: Martin Laney
Snr Sftwr: Bruce Bender
Snr Sftwr: Saurav Dasgupta
Snr Sftwr: Earl Olsen
Snr Ntwrk: Martin Guenther
Sls Dir: Joseph Haddad
Manager: Peirce Arjen
Board of Directors: Christopher Bowick, Kevin Denuccio, Michael Everett, Michael Flynn, Adam Grosser, Michael Matthews, Thomas Pardun, Kevin Peters

D-U-N-S 00-238-5441
CALKINS MEDIA INC (PA)
INTELLIGENCER/RECORD THE
333 N Broad St, Doylestown, PA 18901-3407
Tel (215) 949-4000 *Founded/Ownrshp* 1804, 1898
Sales 253.5MM[E] *EMP* 2,035
SIC 2711 Newspapers, publishing & printing
CEO: Mark G Contreras
**Pr:* Mike Jameson
**CFO:* Michael White
**Treas:* Edward J Birch
**VP:* Jeff Benninghoff
**VP:* Shirley Ellis
**VP:* Thomas J Spurgeon
**VP:* Guy Tasaka
Exec: Matthew Neder
**Genl Mgr:* Art Lanham
Genl Mgr: Karl Smith

CALLAHAN AMS MACHINE COMPANY
See OMYA INC

D-U-N-S 01-158-8027 IMP
CALLAHAN CHEMICAL CO
S Broad St & Filmore Ave, Palmyra, NJ 08065
Tel (856) 786-7900 *Founded/Ownrshp* 1958
Sales 97.3MM[E] *EMP* 72
SIC 5169 Industrial chemicals
CEO: John Callahan
**Pr:* Tim Dooling
Genl Mgr: Kathy Stanwood
Off Mgr: David Simpson
Plnt Mgr: Jim Calahan

D-U-N-S 17-471-8655
CALLAHAN INC
80 1st St, Bridgewater, MA 02324-1071
Tel (508) 279-0012 *Founded/Ownrshp* 2004
Sales 172.8MM *EMP* 130
Accts Kirkland Albrecht & Fredrickso
SIC 1542 Nonresidential construction
Pr: Patrick Callahan
COO: Doug Morrison
**CFO:* Dennis Sheehan
**VP:* Michael Callahan
Exec: Stephen Callahan
Exec: Steve Carley
Exec: Joe Roche
Off Mgr: Gail Dibona
Mktg Dir: Raj Bhangoo
Mktg Mgr: Kellie Jackson

D-U-N-S 05-702-2303 IMP
CALLANAN INDUSTRIES INC
(*Suby of* OLDCASTLE MATERIALS GROUP) ★
1245 Kings Rd Ste 1, Schenectady, NY 12303-2824
Tel (518) 374-2222 *Founded/Ownrshp* 1985
Sales 118.2MM[E] *EMP* 440
SIC 3272 2951 Concrete products, precast; Asphalt paving mixtures & blocks
Pr: Jonas Havens
Sfty Dirs: Kevin D Browne
Plnt Mgr: Bryan Francett
Plnt Mgr: Dominick Testo
Mktg Dir: Don Fane
Mktg Mgr: Darlene Brunner

D-U-N-S 07-910-8889
■ CALLAWAY GOLF BALL OPERATIONS INC
(*Suby of* CALLAWAY GOLF CO) ★
2180 Rutherford Rd, Carlsbad, CA 92008-7328
Tel (760) 931-1771 *Founded/Ownrshp* 2003
Sales 525.0M[E] *EMP* 1,700
SIC 5091 Golf equipment
CEO: Chip Brewer

D-U-N-S 05-557-1012 IMP/EXP
▲ CALLAWAY GOLF CO
2180 Rutherford Rd, Carlsbad, CA 92008-7328
Tel (760) 931-1771 *Founded/Ownrshp* 1982
Sales 843.7MM *EMP* 1,700[E]
Tkr Sym ELY *Exch* NYS
SIC 3949 2329 2339 6794 Golf equipment; Shafts, golf club; Balls: baseball, football, basketball, etc.; Bags, golf; Men's & boys' sportswear & athletic clothing; Athletic (warmup, sweat & jogging) suits: men's & boys'; Women's & misses' athletic clothing & sportswear; Athletic clothing: women's, misses' & juniors'; Women's & misses' accessories; Patent buying, licensing, leasing
Pr: Oliver G Brewer III
**Ch Bd:* Ronald S Beard
Pr: Anthony Thornley
COO: Bob Penicka
CFO: Bradley J Holiday
CFO: Robert K Julian
Chf Mktg O: Jack Oconnor
Ofcr: Leslie Hoeskstra
Sr Ex VP: Richard Helmstetter
Sr VP: Alan Hocknell
Sr VP: Donna Kaptain
Sr VP: Bill Knees
Sr VP: Mark Leposky
Sr VP: Brian Lynch
VP: Patrick Burke
VP: Sailendra Koorapati
Board of Directors: Samuel H Armacost, John C Cushman III, John F Lundgren, Richard L Rosenfield, Linda B Segre, Anthony S Thornley

D-U-N-S 07-428-4944
CALLAWAY NURSING HOME
1300 W Lindsay Ave, Sulphur, OK 73086-6650
Tel (580) 622-2416 *Founded/Ownrshp* 1956
Sales 258.9MM *EMP* 53
SIC 8059 Nursing home, except skilled & intermediate care facility
Pr: Sam Jewell

D-U-N-S 08-817-3026 IMP
▲ CALLIDUS SOFTWARE INC
CALLIDUSCLOUD
4140 Dublin Blvd Ste 400, Dublin, CA 94568-7757
Tel (925) 251-2200 *Founded/Ownrshp* 1996
Sales 173.0MM *EMP* 997[E]
Tkr Sym CALD *Exch* NGM
SIC 7371 7372 Custom computer programming services; Business oriented computer software
Pr: Leslie J Stretch
**Ch Bd:* Charles M Boesenberg
CFO: Bob L Corey
CFO: Roxanne Oulman
Sr VP: Robert C Conti
Sr VP: Jimmy Duan
Sr VP: Jimmy C Duan
Sr VP: Giles House
Sr VP: Jeffrey Saling
VP: Hesham Eassa
VP: Steven Hancock
VP: David Hunsinger
VP: Matthew Kenneally
VP: Shreesha Ramdas
Mng Ofcr: Mike Roberts
Board of Directors: Michele Vion Choka, Mark A Culhane, Kevin Klausmeyer, David B Pratt, Murray D Rode, James D White

CALLIDUSCLOUD
See CALLIDUS SOFTWARE INC

D-U-N-S 96-268-8540
CALLISON ARCHITECTURE HOLDING LLC
1420 5th Ave Ste 2400, Seattle, WA 98101-1345
Tel (206) 623-4646 *Founded/Ownrshp* 2006
Sales 119.5MM *EMP* 250
Accts Sweeney Conradps Bellevue
SIC 6719 Personal holding companies, except banks
CFO: Greg Parker

D-U-N-S 04-779-1769
CALLISONRTKL INC
(*Suby of* ARCADIS N.V.)
901 S Bond St, Baltimore, MD 21231-3339
Tel (410) 537-6000 *Founded/Ownrshp* 2007
Sales 201.9MM *EMP* 1,236
SIC 8712 Architectural services
CEO: Lance K Josal
Assoc VP: William Caldwell
Assoc VP: Damian Donati
Assoc VP: Fiona Muelken
VP: Yvonne Colacion
VP: Phillips Engelke
VP: Dan Freed
VP: Robert Stamen
VP: Alan Wilson
CIO: Ardeshir Alaiandust

D-U-N-S 03-683-7615
■ CALLON OFFSHORE PRODUCTION INC (MS)
(*Suby of* CALLON PETROLEUM CO) ★
200 N Canal St, Natchez, MS 39120-3212
Tel (601) 442-1601 *Founded/Ownrshp* 1983
Sales 96.1MM[E] *EMP* 65
SIC 1311 1382 Crude petroleum production; Natural gas production; Oil & gas exploration services
Pr: Fred Callon
**VP:* Tom Schwager

D-U-N-S 05-711-3318
▲ CALLON PETROLEUM CO
200 N Canal St, Natchez, MS 39120-3212
Tel (601) 442-1601 *Founded/Ownrshp* 1950
Sales 137.5MM *EMP* 93[E]
Accts Ernst & Young Llp New Orleans
Tkr Sym CPE *Exch* NYS
SIC 1311 Crude petroleum & natural gas; Crude petroleum & natural gas production
Ch Bd: Fred L Callon
Pr: Joseph C Gatto Jr
COO: Gary A Newberry
VP: Mitzi P Conn
VP: Michael O'Connor
VP: Jerry A Weant
Board of Directors: Matthew Regis Bob, Michael L Finch, L Richard Flury, Larry D McVay, Anthony J Nocchiero, James M Trimble, John C Wallace

D-U-N-S 93-841-0024 IMP
■ CALLON PETROLEUM OPERATING CO
CPE
(*Suby of* CALLON PETROLEUM CO) ★
200 N Canal St, Natchez, MS 39120-3212
Tel (601) 442-1601 *Founded/Ownrshp* 1950
Sales 118.2MM[E] *EMP* 80
SIC 1311 Crude petroleum production; Natural gas production
Ch Bd: Fred L Callon
**CFO:* Joseph C Gatto
**Treas:* Roger W Smith
**Sr VP:* Gary A Newbury
**VP:* Thomas E Schwager
**VP:* Kathy G Tilley
**VP:* Jerry A Weant
**VP:* Bobby F Weatherly

D-U-N-S 15-761-2292 IMP
▲ CALLOWAYS NURSERY INC
4200 Airport Fwy Ste 200, Fort Worth, TX 76117-6200
Tel (817) 222-1122 *Founded/Ownrshp* 1986
Sales 145.3MM[E] *EMP* 600
Tkr Sym CLWY *Exch* OTO
SIC 5261 Lawn & garden supplies; Christmas trees (natural); Nursery stock, seeds & bulbs
Pr: James C Estill
**CFO:* Dan Reynolds
**VP:* John Cosby
VP: John S Peter
**VP:* John Peters
**VP:* Daniel Reynolds
**VP:* Marce Ward
**VP:* Sam Weger

D-U-N-S 19-418-0246
CALM INC
MORTGAGE MASTER
(*Suby of* LOANDEPOT.COM LLC) ★
102 Elm St, Walpole, MA 02081-1933
Tel (508) 850-4100 *Founded/Ownrshp* 2015
Sales NA *EMP* 306
SIC 6163 Mortgage brokers arranging for loans, using money of others
Pr: Paul G Anastos
CFO: David Harrington
Treas: Ann C Thomsen

D-U-N-S 00-828-8342
■ CALMAT CO
VULCAN MATERIALS
(*Suby of* LEGACY VULCAN LLC) ★
500 N Brand Blvd Ste 500, Glendale, CA 91203-3319
Tel (818) 553-8821 *Founded/Ownrshp* 1929
Sales 407.5MM[E] *EMP* 2,000
SIC 2951 1442 1429 3273 6512 6552 Asphalt & asphaltic paving mixtures (not from refineries); Construction sand & gravel; Igneous rock, crushed & broken-quarrying; Ready-mixed concrete; Commercial & industrial building operation; Land subdividers & developers, residential
CEO: Tom Hill
**Pr:* James W Smack
**COO:* Danny R Shepherd
**CFO:* Daniel F Sansone
CFO: Cindy Vu
VP: Brian Ferris
VP: Paul Hughes
VP: Jim Schladen
VP: Robert Sears
VP: Ronnie Walker
VP: Scott Wilcott

D-U-N-S 00-504-8400 IMP
■ CALPHALON CORP
(*Suby of* NEWELL BRANDS INC) ★
3 Glenlake Pkwy, Atlanta, GA 30328-3447
Tel (770) 418-7100 *Founded/Ownrshp* 1942
Sales 115.6MM[E] *EMP* 350[E]
SIC 3365 3469 Cooking/kitchen utensils, cast aluminum; Metal stampings
CEO: William A Burke
CFO: Ronald L Hardnock
Creative D: Doreen Robideaux

D-U-N-S 08-722-1008 IMP
CALPINE CONTAINERS INC (CA)
6425 N Palm Ave Ste 104, Fresno, CA 93704-1084
Tel (559) 519-7199 *Founded/Ownrshp* 1895, 1848
Sales 169.7MM[E] *EMP* 228
SIC 5113 5085 2441 2448 Corrugated & solid fiber boxes; Boxes, paperboard & disposable plastic; Box shooks; Boxes, crates, etc., other than paper; Boxes, wood; Pallets, wood
CEO: Walter D Tindell
**CFO:* Kenneth A Sommers
**Prin:* E C Rathbun
Opers Mgr: Keith Oden
VP Sls: Scott R Hickman
Mktg Dir: Eva Hammond

D-U-N-S 11-271-0876 EXP
▲ CALPINE CORP
717 Texas St Ste 1000, Houston, TX 77002-2743
Tel (713) 830-2000 *Founded/Ownrshp* 1984
Sales 6.4MMM *EMP* 2,609[E]
Tkr Sym CPN *Exch* NYS
SIC 4911 Electric services; Transmission, electric power; Generation, electric power; Distribution, electric power
Pr: John B Hill III
V Ch: Keith Young
CFO: Zamir Rauf
Treas: Todd A Thornton
Chf Cred: Trey Griggs
Ex VP: Charlie Gates
Ex VP: W G Griggs III
Ex VP: W Thaddeus Miller
Ex VP: W Miller
Sr VP: Jeff Koshkin
Sr VP: Alex Makler
VP: JP Arcuri
VP: Darron Granger
VP: Bob Hayes
VP: Greg McAuley
VP: James Sandt
VP: William Taylor
Board of Directors: Frank Cassidy, Michael W Hofmann, David C Merritt, W Benjamin Moreland, Robert Mosbacher Jr, Denise M O'leary

D-U-N-S 16-966-8212
■ CALPINE ENERGY SERVICES LP
(*Suby of* CALPINE CORP) ★
717 Texas St Ste 1000, Houston, TX 77002-2743
Tel (713) 830-2000 *Founded/Ownrshp* 1999
Sales 406.3MM[E] *EMP* 1,578
SIC 4911 Electric services
Pr: Thad Hill
Pr: Loreen Tabbut
Ex VP: Thaddeus Miller
Ex VP: Zamir Rauf
Sr VP: John Adams
Sr VP: Hether Benjamin-Brown
Sr VP: Dick Keyser
VP Opers: Bill Ferguson
Opers Mgr: Ron Chasse

D-U-N-S 96-825-4276
■ CALPINE ENERGY SOLUTIONS LLC
NOBLE AMERICAS ENERGY SOLUTIONS
(*Suby of* CALPINE CORP) ★
401 W A St Ste 500, San Diego, CA 92101-7991
Tel (877) 273-6772 *Founded/Ownrshp* 2016
Sales 313.3MM[E] *EMP* 400[E]
SIC 4931 4932 Electric & other services combined; Gas & other services combined
Pr: Jim Wood
VP: Alex Fazekas-Paul
VP: Gayle McCutchan
VP: Drake Welch
Mng Dir: Michael L Mann
Sls Mgr: Teresa Acosta

D-U-N-S 03-736-9167
■ CALPINE MID-ATLANTIC ENERGY LLC
(*Suby of* CALPINE CORP) ★
717 Texas St Ste 1000, Houston, TX 77002-2743
Tel (713) 830-2000 *Founded/Ownrshp* 2010
Sales 177.6MM[E] *EMP* 1,000[E]
SIC 4932 Gas & other services combined
Treas: Anthony Kamerick

D-U-N-S 62-196-1929 IMP
CALPORTLAND CO
ARIZONA PORTLAND CEMENT
(*Suby of* TAIHEIYO CEMENT USA INC) ★
2025 E Financial Way, Glendora, CA 91741-4692
Tel (626) 852-6200 *Founded/Ownrshp* 1990
Sales 121.6MM^E *EMP* 190
SIC 3241 3273 5032 Portland cement; Ready-mixed concrete; Brick, stone & related material
Ch Bd: Michio Kimura
**Pr:* James A Repman
**CEO:* Allen Hamblen
CFO: Jeff Matthews
**CFO:* James A Wendoll
Treas: Matthew Hissong
**V Ch Bd:* Noboru Kasai
**Sr VP:* John Renninger
**Sr VP:* Robert West
**VP:* John Bennett
**VP:* J Michael Burton
VP: Tom Edwards
**VP:* Rick Patton
VP: Steven A Regis
**VP:* Craig W Starkey
VP: Steve Whitley
Exec: Aniya Powell
Board of Directors: Noboru Kasai, Michio Kimura, James A Repman

D-U-N-S 02-524-2913 IMP
CALSONICKANSEI NORTH AMERICA INC (TN)
CKNA
(*Suby of* CALSONIC KANSEI CORPORATION)
1 Calsonic Way, Shelbyville, TN 37160-2031
Tel (931) 684-4490 *Founded/Ownrshp* 1983, 2001
Sales 1.5MMM^E *EMP* 3,250^E
SIC 3585 Air conditioning, motor vehicle
CEO: Shingo Yamamoto
**Pr:* Seiichi Kakizawa
**Pr:* Kiyoto Shinohra
**COO:* Eric Huch
**COO:* Bharat Vennapusa
**Ex VP:* Toshimasa Yamane
**Sr VP:* Mike Layne
**Sr VP:* Koji Takei
**Sr VP:* Mike Turner
**VP:* Chris Bradford
**VP:* Daniel Davidson

CALTECH
See CALIFORNIA INSTITUTE OF TECHNOLOGY

D-U-N-S 96-270-1681
CALTIUS PARTNERS IV LP
11766 Wilshire Blvd # 850, Los Angeles, CA 90025-6538
Tel (310) 996-9585 *Founded/Ownrshp* 2008
Sales 102.1MM^E *EMP* 451^E
SIC 6282 Investment advice
Mng Dir: Michael Kane

CALTRAIN
See PENINSULA CORRIDOR JOINT POWERS BOARD

CALTRANS
See CALIFORNIA DEPT OF TRANSPORTATION

D-U-N-S 12-203-5918 EXP
CALTROL INC
1385 Pama Ln Ste 111, Las Vegas, NV 89119-3849
Tel (702) 966-1800 *Founded/Ownrshp* 2004
Sales 159.1MM^E *EMP* 191
SIC 5084 Controlling instruments & accessories
Pr: Joseph Taormina
COO: Eric Alexander
COO: Craig Jackson
**CFO:* Michael Threet
VP: Kevin Bornhoft
VP: Phil O'Leary
Mktg Mgr: Blake McCaffery
Manager: Brian Pitcher
Board of Directors: Dan English, John McCauley

D-U-N-S 62-049-9699 IMP/EXP
■ **CALUMET LUBRICANTS CO LIMITED PARTNERSHIP**
CALUMET SPCIALTY PDTS PARTNERS
(*Suby of* CALUMET OPERATING LLC) ★
2780 Waterfront Pkwy Ste 200 E, Indianapolis, IN 46214
Tel (317) 328-5660 *Founded/Ownrshp* 1990
Sales 259.2MM^E *EMP* 375
SIC 2992 Lubricating oils
Mng Pt: F W Grube
CFO: R P Murray II
Off Admin: Kelly Felts
IT Man: Mike Marchetti
VP Opers: Timothy Barnhart
Sfty Dirs: Grady Lee
Plnt Mgr: Jeff Lang

D-U-N-S 03-147-1133
■ **CALUMET OPERATING LLC**
(*Suby of* CALUMET SPECIALTY PRODUCTS PARTNERS LP) ★
2780 Waterfront Pkwy, Indianapolis, IN 46214
Tel (317) 328-5660 *Founded/Ownrshp* 2005
Sales 259.2MM^E *EMP* 375^E
SIC 2992 Lubricating oils

CALUMET SPCIALTY PDTS PARTNERS
See CALUMET LUBRICANTS CO LIMITED PARTNERSHIP

D-U-N-S 61-752-7713 EXP
▲ **CALUMET SPECIALTY PRODUCTS PARTNERS LP**
2780 Waterfront Pkwy Ste 200 E, Indianapolis, IN 46214
Tel (317) 328-5660 *Founded/Ownrshp* 2005
Sales 4.2MMM *EMP* 2,100^E
Tkr Sym CLMT *Exch* NGS
SIC 2911 2992 Solvents; Mineral waxes, natural; Fuel additives; Lubricating oils
CEO: Timothy Go
Genl Pt: Calumet GP
CFO: R Patrick Murray II
Treas: Dee Winchester
Ex VP: Bruce A Fleming
VP: Shane Terry
Mktg Dir: Debby Neubauer

D-U-N-S 01-696-7433
■ **CALUMET SUPERIOR LLC**
(*Suby of* CALUMET SPECIALTY PRODUCTS PARTNERS LP) ★
2407 Stinson Ave, Superior, WI 54880-4486
Tel (715) 398-3533 *Founded/Ownrshp* 2011
Sales 96.6MM^E *EMP* 49^E
SIC 2992 Lubricating oils & greases
Opers Mgr: James Kowitz

CALVARY CEMETERY
See CATHOLIC DIOCESE OF MEMPHIS

D-U-N-S 07-992-0427 IMP
CALVARY HOSPITAL INC
1740 Eastchester Rd, Bronx, NY 10461-2392
Tel (718) 518-2000 *Founded/Ownrshp* 1900
Sales 110.4MM *EMP* 900
Accts Grant Thornton Llp New York
SIC 8069 Specialty hospitals, except psychiatric; Cancer hospital
Pr: Frank A Calamari
Dir Vol: Joanne Medici
**COO:* Richard Kutilek
COO: Richard Kutliek
VP: Michael Brescia
VP: Nancy D'Agostino
VP: Steve Schoener
Dir Lab: Lawrence Berg
Dir Pat Ac: Philip Nies
CIO: Patrick Martin
Cmptr Lab: Mildred Colon

D-U-N-S 08-315-7250
■ **CALVERT CLIFFS NUCLEAR POWER PLANT INC** (MD)
CONSTELLTN ENEGY NCLEAR GRP
(*Suby of* CONSTELLATION ENERGY NUCLEAR GROUP LLC) ★
750 E Pratt St, Baltimore, MD 21202-3142
Tel (410) 495-4600 *Founded/Ownrshp* 2000
Sales 4.3MMM^E *EMP* 1,200
SIC 4911 ; Generation, electric power
Pr: Michael Jay Wallace
**Treas:* Steve Mormann
**VP:* Charles H Cruise

D-U-N-S 07-962-8765
CALVERT COUNTY PUBLIC SCHOOLS
1305 Dares Beach Rd, Prince Frederick, MD 20678-4208
Tel (410) 535-1700 *Founded/Ownrshp* 2014
Sales 34.2MM^E *EMP* 1,963^E
SIC 8211 Public elementary & secondary schools
Bd of Dir: Donald Cherry
MIS Dir: Rick Lippert
Dir IT: Tamara Horsemen
IT Man: Carrie Campbell
Pr Dir: Karen Maxey
HC Dir: Kris Knode

D-U-N-S 06-487-1122 IMP
CALVERT MEMORIAL HOSPITAL OF CALVERT COUNTY (MD)
100 Hospital Rd, Prince Frederick, MD 20678-4017
Tel (410) 535-4000 *Founded/Ownrshp* 1916
Sales 129.7MM *EMP* 1,000
SIC 8062 General medical & surgical hospitals
Pr: James J Xinis
Dir Recs: Donna Harris
**CFO:* Kirk Blandford
Bd of Dir: Diana B Doswell
Bd of Dir: Sheldon E Golldberg
**VP:* Carrie Forrest
**VP:* Barbara Polak
VP: Lynn Smith
Dir Lab: Michelle Bowen
Ex Dir: Harry Malecki
Genl Mgr: Melissa Carnes

D-U-N-S 02-902-3025 IMP
CALVEY INC
(*Suby of* ERNEST PAPER) ★
7728 Wilbur Way, Sacramento, CA 95828-5630
Tel (916) 681-4800 *Founded/Ownrshp* 1946
Sales 102.4MM^E *EMP* 60
SIC 5113 Boxes, paperboard & disposable plastic; Corrugated & solid fiber boxes
Ch: A Charles Wilson
**Pr:* Tim Wilson

D-U-N-S 01-106-2692
CALVI ELECTRIC CO
14 S California Ave Ste 1, Atlantic City, NJ 08401-6491
Tel (609) 345-0151 *Founded/Ownrshp* 1977
Sales 86.4MM^E *EMP* 500
SIC 1731 General electrical contractor
Pr: George Brestle
**Ex VP:* Charles Bauenhuber
**VP:* Michael Brestle

D-U-N-S 05-366-5980
CALVIN COLLEGE
3201 Burton St Se, Grand Rapids, MI 49546-4388
Tel (616) 526-6000 *Founded/Ownrshp* 1876
Sales 126.4MM *EMP* 3,774
Accts Plante & Moran Pllc Portage
SIC 8661 Religious organizations
Pr: Michael K Le Roy
Ofcr: Jennifer Ambrose
Ofcr: Robert Terpstra
Sr VP: David Vanhouten
**VP:* Russell Bloem
VP: Henry E Devries
**VP:* Ken Erffmeyer
**VP:* Shirley Vogelzang Hoogstra
**VP:* Sally Vander Ploeg
Exec: Lary Ramirez
Assoc Dir: Dana Hebreard
Assoc Dir: Jeanne Nienhuis
Assoc Dir: Tasha Paul

CALVIN KLEIN COLLECTION DIV
See CALVIN KLEIN INC

CALVIN KLEIN FOOTWEAR
See JIMLAR CORP

D-U-N-S 13-135-6727 IMP
■ **CALVIN KLEIN INC**
CALVIN KLEIN COLLECTION DIV
(*Suby of* PVH CORP) ★
205 W 39th St Lbby 2, New York, NY 10018-3104
Tel (212) 719-2600 *Founded/Ownrshp* 1985
Sales 113.3MM^E *EMP* 700
SIC 5651 5137 5136 5611 5621 6794 Unisex clothing stores; Women's & children's clothing; Men's & boys' clothing; Men's & boys' clothing stores; Women's clothing stores; Franchises, selling or licensing
CEO: Paul T Murry III
Ch Bd: Emanuel Chirico
Pr: Steve Shiffman
COO: Gabriella Forte
CFO: Michael Fishoff
Ofcr: Raf Simons
Ex VP: Barrie Scardina
VP: Dawn Buonocore-Atlas
VP: Jennifer Crawford
VP: Michael Delellis
VP: Richard Durant
VP: Holly Getty
VP: Betsy Hussey
VP: Deirdre Miles
VP: Dale Rozmiarek
VP: Barry Schwartz
VP: Pamela Silverstein
VP: Amy Skulnik
VP: Henry Smedley
VP: Brian Sobelman
VP: Trisha Szeli

D-U-N-S 86-125-1460
■ **CALVIN KLEIN JEANSWEAR CO**
CALVIN KLEIN KIDSWEAR
(*Suby of* WARNACO GROUP INC) ★
205 W 39th St Lbby 2, New York, NY 10018-3104
Tel (212) 292-9290 *Founded/Ownrshp* 1997
Sales 50.3MM^E *EMP* 1,160
SIC 5611 5621 Men's & boys' clothing stores; Women's clothing stores
Prin: Colleen Glew
**Pr:* Thomas Murry
VP: Tal Plaisance

CALVIN KLEIN KIDSWEAR
See CALVIN KLEIN JEANSWEAR CO

D-U-N-S 11-501-5039
CALYPSO TECHNOLOGY INC
595 Market St Ste 1800, San Francisco, CA 94105-2827
Tel (415) 817-2400 *Founded/Ownrshp* 2005
Sales 180.0MM^E *EMP* 800
Accts Ernst & Young Llp San Jose C
SIC 5734 Software, business & non-game
CEO: Kishore Bopardikar
Pr: Pieter Hamman
**Pr:* Pascal Xatart
**Ch:* Charles Marston
**Sr VP:* Kirk Inglis
**Sr VP:* Gerard Rafie
**Sr VP:* Tej Sidhu
VP: Gordon Chan
VP: Andreas Drabert
VP: Mel Gadd
VP: Denise Pierre
VP: Mark Robinson
**VP:* Talat Sadiq
VP: Jonathan D Walsh
VP: Andrei Zelentsovsky

CAM
See CONSOLIDATED AEROSPACE MANUFACTURING LLC

D-U-N-S 78-326-7669
CAM BUILDERS LLC
537 Highway 26, Hatchechubbee, AL 36858-2607
Tel (334) 667-6695 *Founded/Ownrshp* 1988
Sales 450.0MM *EMP* 8
SIC 1542 Commercial & office building contractors
Pr: Jack Mazzola Jr
Pr: Charles A Mazzola
Off Mgr: Betsy Mazzola

D-U-N-S 15-721-2861
CAMAC INTERNATIONAL CORP
1330 Post Oak Blvd Ste 22, Houston, TX 77056-3031
Tel (713) 965-5100 *Founded/Ownrshp* 2001
Sales 1.4MMM *EMP* 1,500
SIC 8711 6552 1382 8741 1389 Engineering services; Subdividers & developers; Oil & gas exploration services; Construction management; Oil consultants
Ch: Kase Lawal
**Pr:* Kamoru A Lawal
**Ex VP:* J Alex Loftus
**Ex VP:* Daniel Ogbonna
**Sr VP:* Fisoye Delano
VP: Jeana R Herrington
VP: Catalino Punzalan
VP: Karim Souidi
**Exec:* Gregory Marinho
**VP Admn:* Rose Valenzuela
Genl Mgr: Laide Olufemi

D-U-N-S 06-919-3113 IMP
CAMACO LLC
(*Suby of* CHEMICAL) ★
37000 W 12 Mile Rd, Farmington Hills, MI 48331-3032
Tel (248) 442-6800 *Founded/Ownrshp* 1998
Sales 237.7MM^E *EMP* 800
SIC 3565 3499 Packaging machinery; Automobile seat frames, metal
CEO: Arvind Pradhan
COO: John Reizian
Ofcr: Lee Spruit
Exec: Pamela Cooper
Prgrm Mgr: Joe Silvestri
Mtls Mgr: Stephanie Fox
Ql Cn Mgr: Sue Malone

D-U-N-S 04-172-7426 IMP/EXP
CAMANCHACA INC
(*Suby of* COMPANIA PESQUERA CAMANCHACA S.A.)
7200 Nw 19th St Ste 410, Miami, FL 33126-1226
Tel (305) 406-9560 *Founded/Ownrshp* 2001
Sales 160.2MM^E *EMP* 14
Accts Kaufman Rossin & Co Miami
SIC 5146 Fish & seafoods
CEO: Ricardo Garcia
**Pr:* Bert O Bachman
**Ch:* Jorge Fernandez
**Treas:* Daniel Bortnik
Ofcr: Cesar Lago
Natl Sales: Paul Struzziero
Manager: Leo Parlato

D-U-N-S 79-707-7075
■ **CAMARILLO HEALTHCARE CENTER**
(*Suby of* ENDURA HEALTHCARE) ★
205 Granada St, Camarillo, CA 93010-7715
Tel (805) 482-9805 *Founded/Ownrshp* 2007
Sales 2.2MM^E *EMP* 1,201^E
SIC 8741 Nursing & personal care facility management

D-U-N-S 16-071-5983
CAMBA INC
1720 Church Ave Ste 2, Brooklyn, NY 11226-2673
Tel (718) 287-2600 *Founded/Ownrshp* 1978
Sales 110.5MM *EMP* 1,000^E
Accts Raich Ende Malter & Co Llp Ne
SIC 8399 Community action agency
CEO: Joanne M Oplustil
**Ch:* Katherine Oneill
**Sec:* Daniel Ramm
**VP:* Christopher Zarra
Comm Dir: Beverly Cheuvront
Comm Dir: Phoebe McGinn
Dir Sec: Dante Thomas
Prgrm Mgr: Devin Chapman
Prgrm Mgr: Carlos Guevara
Prgrm Mgr: Donna Lalwani
Prgrm Mgr: Rick Rodriguez

D-U-N-S 60-957-0742
CAMBER CORP
(*Suby of* NEW MOUNTAIN CAPITAL I LLC) ★
670 Discovery Dr Nw, Huntsville, AL 35806-2802
Tel (256) 922-0200 *Founded/Ownrshp* 1990
Sales 204.9MM^E *EMP* 597
SIC 8731 7371 Commercial physical research; Computer software systems analysis & design, custom
CEO: Philip O Nolan
**Ch Bd:* Walter P Batson Jr
**Pr:* James Brabston
**CFO:* Joseph M Cormier
CFO: Joseph Cormier
CFO: Michael Whyte
Ex VP: Gregg Donley
**Ex VP:* Gene Kakalec
Ex VP: John Lord
Ex VP: Dave Ohle
Ex VP: David H Ohle
**Ex VP:* Bruce Schoemer
Sr VP: Joe Reale
**Sr VP:* Mike Whyte
Sr VP: Michael Williams
Sr VP: Mike Williams
VP: Phoebe Allen
VP: Chris Balcik
VP: Joseph D Blaquiere
VP: Tom Emsley
VP: Ken Foxton

D-U-N-S 15-177-0955
CAMBER GOVERNMENT SOLUTIONS INC
(*Suby of* CAMBER CORP) ★
12730 Fair Lakes Cir, Fairfax, VA 22033-4901
Tel (703) 653-8000 *Founded/Ownrshp* 2014
Sales 107.3MM^E *EMP* 596
SIC 7371 7379 Computer software development & applications; Computer related consulting services
Pr: John Lord
**CFO:* Mike Whyte
Ex VP: Sara Decarlo
**VP:* Michael Paige
Exec: Tracy McKay
Web Dev: Jack Okorn
Software D: John Oo
Software D: Vikas Patel
Software D: John Scarfone
Secur Mgr: William J Scharf
Board of Directors: Mary Cross

D-U-N-S 08-690-0268
CAMBIA HEALTH SOLUTIONS INC
100 Sw Market St, Portland, OR 97201-5723
Tel (503) 225-5336 *Founded/Ownrshp* 1996
Sales NA *EMP* 5,800
SIC 6321 6411 6324 Accident & health insurance; Insurance claim processing, except medical; Hospital & medical service plans
Pr: Mark B Ganz
Pr: Scott Powers
COO: Jared L Short
**CFO:* Vince Price
Ex VP: John Morgan
Ex VP: Richard Popiel
**Ex VP:* Jared L Short
**Ex VP:* Dudley Slater
Sr VP: Steven Gaspar
Sr VP: Carol Kruse
Sr VP: Laurent P Rotival
VP: Melissa Christian
VP: Donald McNees
VP: Mohan Nair
VP: John Osborn
VP: John Partin
VP: John Prassas
VP: Ang Sun
VP: Chip Terhune
VP: John Wagner
VP: Kristen Wright

D-U-N-S 83-299-7212
■ CAMBIUM LEARNING GROUP INC
(*Suby of* VSS-CAMBIUM HOLDINGS III LLC) ★
17855 Dallas Pkwy Ste 400, Dallas, TX 75287-6857
Tel (214) 932-9500 *Founded/Ownrshp* 2009
Sales 144.9MM *EMP* 585^E
Tkr Sym ABCD *Exch* NGM
SIC 8299 8211 7372 Educational services; Specialty education; Educational computer software
CEO: John Campbell
**Ch Bd:* Joe Walsh
Pr: Jeffrey A Elliott
Pr: Bob Holl
Pr: David Shuster
CFO: Barbara Benson
**Sr VP:* Carolyn Getridge
CTO: Paul Fonte
Board of Directors: David F Bainbridge, Walter G Bumphus, Clifford K Chiu, Thomas Kalinske, Harold O Levy, Jeffrey T Stevenson

D-U-N-S 14-581-7040
■ CAMBIUM LEARNING INC
VOYAGER
(*Suby of* CAMBIUM LEARNING GROUP INC) ★
17855 Dallas Pkwy Ste 400, Dallas, TX 75287-6857
Tel (214) 932-9500 *Founded/Ownrshp* 2003
Sales 99.0MM^E *EMP* 400
SIC 2731 Book publishing
CEO: John Campbelle
**CFO:* Barbara Benson
Sr VP: Carolyn Getridge
Sr VP: Rolando Rodriguez
VP: Jahnell Pereira
Ex Dir: Marty Masters
CTO: Paul Fonte

D-U-N-S 78-297-4257 IMP
■ CAMBREX CHARLES CITY INC
(*Suby of* CAMBREX CORP) ★
1205 11th St, Charles City, IA 50616-3466
Tel (641) 257-1000 *Founded/Ownrshp* 1991
Sales 101.5MM^E *EMP* 220
SIC 2834 2899 2865 2048 Pharmaceutical preparations; Chemical preparations; Cyclic crudes & intermediates; Prepared feeds
CEO: Steven M Klosk
VP: Joe L Nettleton
**VP Opers:* Joe Nettleton
Snr Mgr: Brad Morton

D-U-N-S 15-059-6716 IMP/EXP
▲ CAMBREX CORP
1 Meadowlands Plz # 1510, East Rutherford, NJ 07073-2214
Tel (201) 804-3000 *Founded/Ownrshp* 1981
Sales 433.3MM *EMP* 1,290^E
Accts Bdo Usa Llp Woodbridge Nj
Tkr Sym CBM *Exch* NYS
SIC 2834 Pharmaceutical preparations; Drugs acting on the respiratory system; Drugs acting on the gastrointestinal or genitourinary system; Drugs acting on the central nervous system & sense organs
Pr: Steven M Klosk
COO: Shawn P Cavanagh
CFO: Gregory P Sargen
VP: James G Farrell
VP: Samantha M Hanley
Area Mgr: Jonathan Herman
Mktg Mgr: Aldo Magnini
Snr Mgr: Paul Meserole
Board of Directors: Shlomo Yanai, Rosina B Dixon, Claes Glassell, Louis J Grabowsky, Bernhard Hampl, Kathryn Rudie Harrigan, Leon J Hendrix Jr, Ilan Kaufthal, William Korb, Peter G Tombros

D-U-N-S 05-882-9396 IMP/EXP
CAMBRIA CO LLC
31496 Cambria Ave, Le Sueur, MN 56058-4528
Tel (507) 665-5003 *Founded/Ownrshp* 1999
Sales 356.9MM^E *EMP* 1,000
SIC 5211 3429 Tile, ceramic; Cabinets, kitchen; Manufactured hardware (general)
Ch: Mark Davis
**Pr:* Marty Davis
**CFO:* Jim Ward
**Ex VP:* Jeff Hovanec
**Ex VP:* Peter Martin
Ex VP: Brian Scoggin
Sr VP: Tripp Parker
Sfty Mgr: Alanna Lee

D-U-N-S 03-173-8722
CAMBRIAN COAL CORP
15888 Ferrells Creek Rd, Belcher, KY 41513-8501
Tel (606) 754-9898 *Founded/Ownrshp* 2000
Sales 158.5MM^E *EMP* 903^E
SIC 1081 Metal mining services
Pr: James Booth
**Sec:* J Mark Campbell
**VP:* Joe Collier
**VP:* Ted McGinnes

D-U-N-S 09-149-2710
CAMBRIDGE ASSOCIATES LLC
125 High St Ste 1505, Boston, MA 02110-2751
Tel (617) 457-7500 *Founded/Ownrshp* 2000
Sales 458.8MM^E *EMP* 1,000
SIC 6282 Investment advisory service
Pr: David Druley
CFO: Melanie M Kinnon
Treas: Brenda Mills
Sr Cor Off: Barry Caldwell
Ofcr: Jill Bicks
VP: Michele G Ballarin
VP: Richard Bolduc
VP: Martha Campbell
VP: Rick Childs
VP: Sandy Guab
VP: Chelsea Hewitt
VP: Kevin Kendell
VP: John Kenney
VP: Varun Mehta
VP: Robert Parry
Dir Teleco: Christina Iacone
Assoc Dir: Amy Callahan
Assoc Dir: Mary M Carlson
Assoc Dir: John Hudson
Assoc Dir: Benjamin Reis
Assoc Dir: Grant Steele

D-U-N-S 85-946-6302
CAMBRIDGE COMPUTER SERVICES INC
271 Waverley Oaks Rd # 301, Waltham, MA 02452-8469
Tel (781) 250-3000 *Founded/Ownrshp* 1991
Sales 120.9MM^E *EMP* 75
SIC 5045 7373 7371 7379

D-U-N-S 15-773-2301
CAMBRIDGE FINANCIAL GROUP INC
1374 Massachusetts Ave, Cambridge, MA 02138-3822
Tel (617) 864-8700 *Founded/Ownrshp* 1998
Sales NA *EMP* 310
Accts Federal Deposit Insurance Corp
SIC 6036 Savings & loan associations, not federally chartered
Pr: Wayne F Patenaude
**Ch Bd:* James Ingram
Chf Cred: Jerry Peterson
VP: Brad Bauer
VP: Julie Morrison
VP: Lisa Sassone
Exec: Valerie Kervick
Exec: Darren Sayers
Mng Dir: Buck Newsome

CAMBRIDGE HEALTH ALLIANCE
See CAMBRIDGE PUBLIC HEALTH COMMISSION

D-U-N-S 86-913-2555
CAMBRIDGE HEALTH ALLIANCE PHYSICIANS ORGANIZATION INC
350 Main St Ste 16, Malden, MA 02148-5023
Tel (617) 498-1000 *Founded/Ownrshp* 1992
Sales 116.5MM *EMP* 370
Accts Pricewaterhousecoopers Llp Bo
SIC 8011 Primary care medical clinic; Psychiatrists & psychoanalysts
Pr: John O'Brien

D-U-N-S 17-558-2808
■ CAMBRIDGE HOME HEALTH CARE INC
(*Suby of* ALMOST FAMILY INC) ★
9510 Ormsby Station Rd # 300, Louisville, KY 40223-5016
Tel (330) 270-8661 *Founded/Ownrshp* 2011
Sales 29.3MM^E *EMP* 1,600
SIC 8082 Home health care services
Pr: Nancy Diller-Shively
**CFO:* Susan Fassoles
Ofcr: Angela Szabo
**VP:* Kirk Shively
Dir IT: Mike Arshinkoff

D-U-N-S 14-984-0444
CAMBRIDGE HOSPITAL
1493 Cambridge St, Cambridge, MA 02139-1099
Tel (617) 665-1000 *Founded/Ownrshp* 2004
Sales 66.8MM^E *EMP* 1,000
SIC 8062 General medical & surgical hospitals
CEO: Dennis Keith
Obsttrcn: Jennifer Retsinas

D-U-N-S 08-003-8244
CAMBRIDGE HOTEL MANAGEMENT LLC
(*Suby of* NEW CASTLE HOTELS LLC) ★
2 Crporate Driveshelton, Shelton, CT 06484
Tel (203) 925-8370 *Founded/Ownrshp* 2015
Sales 1.7MM^E *EMP* 2,144^E
SIC 7011 Hotel, franchised

D-U-N-S 11-920-8296
CAMBRIDGE INFORMATION GROUP INC
C I G
888 7th Ave Ste 1701, New York, NY 10106-1799
Tel (301) 961-6700 *Founded/Ownrshp* 1970
Sales 484.9MM^E *EMP* 1,600
SIC 2741 Technical manual & paper publishing
Ch: Robert Snyder
**CEO:* Andrew M Snyder
**COO:* Michael K Chung
**Sr VP:* Barbara Inkellis
**Sr VP:* Larisa Avner Trainor
**VP:* Pankaj Sharma
VP Sls: Derek Dawson
Mktg Dir: Tina Creguer
Mktg Dir: Nancy Liberman
Sls Dir: Keith Courtney
Sls Dir: David Desalvo

D-U-N-S 61-204-7787 IMP
CAMBRIDGE INTEGRATED SERVICES GROUP INC
(*Suby of* XCHANGING SOLUTIONS (SINGAPORE) PTE. LIMITED)
7369 Sheridan St Ste 301, Hollywood, FL 33024-2776
Tel (954) 966-4772 *Founded/Ownrshp* 2004
Sales 71.4MM^E *EMP* 2,200
SIC 8742 7389 Management consulting services; Industry specialist consultants; Financial services
CEO: David Andrews
**Pr:* Wesley O'Brien
**COO:* Peter Imbrogno
COO: Paul Serong
**V Ch Bd:* Satyen Patel
Ex VP: Nora M Conway
**Ex VP:* Rich Gros

D-U-N-S 08-030-6097
■ CAMBRIDGE INTERNATIONAL HOLDINGS CORP
(*Suby of* REXNORD CORP) ★
105 Goodwill Rd, Cambridge, MD 21613-2980
Tel (410) 901-4979 *Founded/Ownrshp* 2012, 2016
Sales 150.7MM^E *EMP* 500
SIC 3291 Abrasive metal & steel products
CEO: Tracy Tyler

D-U-N-S 88-471-9717 IMP/EXP
CAMBRIDGE INTERNATIONAL INC
105 Goodwill Rd, Cambridge, MD 21613-2980
Tel (410) 228-3000 *Founded/Ownrshp* 2012
Sales 154.0MM^E *EMP* 500
SIC 3496 Wire cloth & woven wire products; Conveyor belts; Mesh, made from purchased wire
VP: Jerry Gordon
CFO: Robert B Lee
CFO: Crystal Willey
Mng Dir: Douglas Klassen
Sfty Mgr: Tony Strickroth
VP Mktg: Larry Windsor

D-U-N-S 83-695-1194
CAMBRIDGE INVESTMENT RESEARCH INC
1776 Pleasant Plain Rd, Fairfield, IA 52556-8757
Tel (641) 472-5100 *Founded/Ownrshp* 1995
Sales 240.3MM^E *EMP* 600
SIC 6211 Security brokers & dealers
CEO: Eric Schwartz
Sr Pt: Holliey Brinkmeier
Pt: Matt Goodwin
COO: Ryan Reineke
CFO: Jerry Oliver
Chf Cred: Tom Anderson
Assoc VP: Julie Gebert
Assoc VP: Melissa Loner
Assoc VP: Andrea Smith
Ex VP: Carol Fischer
Ex VP: Jim Guy
Sr VP: Kyle Selberg
VP: Cris Alvarez
VP: Colleen Bell
VP: Peter Dollive
VP: Jeff Evanello
VP: Lorna Horn
VP: Chris Jenkins
VP: Bobbi Martin
VP: Seth Miller
VP: Barry Schmidt

D-U-N-S 13-222-4036
CAMBRIDGE INVESTMENTS LLC
ARBY'S
8745 Aero Dr Ste 306, San Diego, CA 92123-1763
Tel (858) 244-0419 *Founded/Ownrshp* 1998
Sales 18.2MM^E *EMP* 1,300
SIC 5812 Fast-food restaurant, chain

D-U-N-S 96-755-7732
CAMBRIDGE PETROLEUM HOLDING INC
31 S Plank Rd Unit 105, Newburgh, NY 12550-3945
Tel (516) 542-4900 *Founded/Ownrshp* 2011
Sales 96.7MM^E *EMP* 625^E
SIC 5983 5541 5984 5172 5074 Fuel oil dealers; Filling stations, gasoline; Propane gas, bottled; Fuel oil; Plumbing & hydronic heating supplies
CEO: Bjorn Aaserod

D-U-N-S 80-526-2995
CAMBRIDGE PUBLIC HEALTH COMMISSION
CAMBRIDGE HEALTH ALLIANCE
1493 Cambridge St, Cambridge, MA 02139-1047
Tel (617) 665-1000 *Founded/Ownrshp* 1891
Sales 286.8MM^E *EMP* 2,700
SIC 8062 General medical & surgical hospitals
CEO: Patrick Wardell
**CEO:* Dennis Keefe
**CFO:* Jill Batty
Bd of Dir: John Francis
**Ex VP:* Paul Allison
**Ex VP:* Allison Bayer
Ex VP: Renee Kessler
**Sr VP:* Arthur S Battle Jr
**Sr VP:* Gordon H Boudrow
**Sr VP:* Elizabeth Cadigan
**Sr VP:* Linda Chin
**Sr VP:* Joy Curtis
**Sr VP:* Judith Klickstein
Dir OR: Dorothy Kelleher
Creative D: Chris Censullo

D-U-N-S 17-907-7847
CAMBRIDGE PUBLIC SCHOOLS
159 Thorndike St, Cambridge, MA 02141-1528
Tel (617) 349-6400 *Founded/Ownrshp* 2010
Sales 41.9MM^E *EMP* 1,388^E
SIC 8211 Public elementary & secondary schools
Genl Mgr: Miranda Fasulo

D-U-N-S 83-288-1606
CAMBRIDGE-LEE HOLDINGS INC
(*Suby of* GRUPO IUSA, S.A. DE C.V.)
86 Tube Dr, Reading, PA 19605-9274
Tel (610) 926-4141 *Founded/Ownrshp* 1993
Sales 211.9MM^E *EMP* 800^E
SIC 5051 3351 5084 Steel; Copper; Aluminum bars, rods, ingots, sheets, pipes, plates, etc.; Tubing, copper & copper alloy; Machine tools & metalworking machinery

D-U-N-S 00-834-7437 IMP
CAMBRO MANUFACTURING CO INC
5801 Skylab Rd, Huntington Beach, CA 92647-2051
Tel (714) 848-1555 *Founded/Ownrshp* 1951
Sales 310.8MM^E *EMP* 782
SIC 3089 Trays, plastic; Plastic containers, except foam
CEO: Argyle Campbell
CFO: Dave Capestro
Ofcr: Sandy Contreras
VP: Chip Jarvis
Exec: Ed Berecz
Creative D: Juan Alcantar
Comm Man: Bud Chambers
Rgnl Mgr: Steve Lee
Rgnl Mgr: Paul Micallef
Rgnl Mgr: Jeff Sohn
Genl Mgr: Omer Turgay

D-U-N-S 11-912-0129
CAMC HEALTH SYSTEM INC
501 Morris St, Charleston, WV 25301-1326
Tel (304) 388-5432 *Founded/Ownrshp* 1983
Sales 725.7M *EMP* 6,000
Accts Deloitte Tax Llp Chicago Il
SIC 8062 General medical & surgical hospitals
Pr: David Ramsey
**COO:* Glen Trotty
**CFO:* Larry Hudson
**Prin:* Susan Hill-Goodman
Pathlgst: William E Mangano
Genl Couns: Marshall A McMullen Jr

D-U-N-S 04-371-2561 IMP/EXP
CAMCO MANUFACTURING INC (NC)
121 Landmark Dr, Greensboro, NC 27409-9626
Tel (336) 668-7661 *Founded/Ownrshp* 1966
Sales 162.8MM *EMP* 350
Accts Dixon Hughes Goodman Llp Win
SIC 3949 Camping equipment & supplies
CEO: Donald R Caine
**Pr:* Dwayne Moore
**CEO:* Lisa C Cook
**CFO:* Edward D Gorman
CFO: David Horton
**CFO:* Elizabeth B Tedder
Dir Bus: Martin Thorne
Off Mgr: Darlene Cloutier
Info Man: Lisa Tedder
Plnt Mgr: Chris Barnwell
Trfc Mgr: Joel Turney

D-U-N-S 05-675-8399
CAMCORP INTERESTS LTD
10410 Windamere Lakes Blvd, Houston, TX 77065-4996
Tel (281) 671-9000 *Founded/Ownrshp* 1993
Sales 236.6MM *EMP* 1
Accts Evans & Chastain Houston Tx
SIC 1521 6798 6552 New construction, single-family houses; Real estate investment trusts; Land subdividers & developers, residential
Pr: Mike Wilkinson
CFO: Tom Connally

D-U-N-S 11-494-9936
CAMDEN CITY BOARD OF EDUCATION FOUNDATION INC
201 N Front St, Camden, NJ 08102-1661
Tel (856) 966-2000 *Founded/Ownrshp* 1854
Sales 56.3M *EMP* 4,000
SIC 8211 Public elementary & secondary schools; Elementary school
IT Man: Natalie Goode
IT Man: Jamil Rivers

D-U-N-S 07-979-9121
CAMDEN CITY PUBLIC SCHOOLS
CITY OF CAMDEN
201 N Front St, Camden, NJ 08102-1661
Tel (856) 966-2000 *Founded/Ownrshp* 2015
Sales 32.2MM^E *EMP* 4,776^E
SIC 8211 Public elementary & secondary schools
Dir Sec: Anthony Bland
CTO: Robert Hersh
Teacher Pr: Emily Nielson
HC Dir: Renee Wickersty
Genl Couns: Bryant Horsley

D-U-N-S 07-498-6423
CAMDEN CLARK MEDICAL CENTER - ST JOSEPH CAMPUS
(*Suby of* CAMDEN-CLARK MEDICAL CENTER) ★
800 Garfield Ave, Parkersburg, WV 26101-5340
Tel (304) 424-4111 *Founded/Ownrshp* 2011
Sales 98.4MM^E *EMP* 652^E
SIC 8062 General medical & surgical hospitals
CEO: Michael King
**VP:* Allen Butcher
Dir Sec: Tom Joyce

D-U-N-S 08-491-0835
CAMDEN COUNTY BOARD OF EDUCATION
311 S East St, Kingsland, GA 31548-5157
Tel (912) 729-5687 *Founded/Ownrshp* 1964
Sales 24.3MM^E *EMP* 1,100
Accts Russell W Hinton Cpa Cgfm
SIC 8211 School board
Ch Bd: Herbert Rowland
**V Ch:* Daniel Simpson
CFO: Angila Easton

D-U-N-S 07-695-4254
CAMDEN COUNTY COLLEGE
200 College Dr, Blackwood, NJ 08012-3240
Tel (856) 227-7200 *Founded/Ownrshp* 1967
Sales 41.7MM^E *EMP* 1,000
SIC 8222 Community college
Ch Bd: John T Hanson
**Pr:* Raymond Yannuzzi
IT Man: Ryan Clark

D-U-N-S 80-004-5783
CAMDEN COUNTY SCHOOL DISTRICT
311 S East St, Kingsland, GA 31548-5157
Tel (912) 729-5687 *Founded/Ownrshp* 2000
Sales 55.1MM^E *EMP* 1,200
SIC 8211 Public elementary & secondary schools
Sls Mgr: Jennie Bentle

D-U-N-S 92-674-0861
CAMDEN DEVELOPMENT INC
(*Suby of* CAMDEN PROPERTY TRUST) ★
11 Greenway Plz Ste 2400, Houston, TX 77046-1124
Tel (713) 354-2500 *Founded/Ownrshp* 1993
Sales 68.1MM^E *EMP* 1,750
SIC 6531 6552 Real estate managers; Subdividers & developers
Ch Bd: Richard Campo
Pr: D Keith Oden
COO: H Malcolm Stewart
CFO: Dennis M Steen
Ex VP: Malcolm H Stewart
Sr VP: Steven Kddington
Sr VP: James M Hinton
VP: Kim Callahan
CTO: Keith Oden

CAMDEN HEALTH CENTER
See DEACONESS LONG TERM CARE OF MISSOURI INC

D-U-N-S 08-125-6497
■ CAMDEN NATIONAL BANK (INC) (ME)
(*Suby of* CAMDEN NATIONAL CORP) ★
2 Elm St, Camden, ME 04843-1947
Tel (207) 236-8821 *Founded/Ownrshp* 1875, 1975
Sales NA *EMP* 102
Accts Berry Dunn Mcneil & Parker Llc
SIC 6022 State commercial banks
Pr: Gregory Dufour

Ch Bd: Rendle Jones
Pr: Gregory A Dofour
Sr VP: Carolyn Carson-Crosby
Sr VP: Linda Gilbert
VP: Joanne Campbell
VP: Jane Mickeriz
VP: Francis J O'Hara Jr
VP: Nancy M Tracy
Genl Mgr: James Markos Jr
Board of Directors: Robert D Merrill

D-U-N-S 14-426-2888
▲ CAMDEN NATIONAL CORP
2 Elm St, Camden, ME 04843-1947
Tel (207) 236-8821 *Founded/Ownrshp* 1984
Sales NA *EMP* 652[E]
Tkr Sym CAC *Exch* NGS
SIC 6021 6733 National commercial banks; Trusts
Pr: Gregory A Dufour
**Ch Bd:* Karen W Stanley
COO: Deborah A Jordan
Ex VP: Joanne T Campbell
Ex VP: June B Parent
Board of Directors: Carl J Soderberg, Ann W Bresnahan, Lawrence J Starrs, David C Flanagan, Craig S Gunderson, John W Holmes, S Catherine Longley, David J Ott, James H Page, John M Rohman, Robin A Sawyer

D-U-N-S 80-723-0990
CAMDEN PROPERTY TRUST
11 Greenway Plz Ste 2400, Houston, TX 77046-1124
Tel (713) 354-2500 *Founded/Ownrshp* 1993
Sales 892.9MM *EMP* 1,750
SIC 6798 Real estate investment trusts
Ch Bd: Richard J Campo
**Pr:* D Keith Oden
COO: H Malcolm Stewart
CFO: Alexander J Jessett
Ofcr: Belia Martha
Ex VP: William W Sengelmann
Sr VP: Stephen R Hefner
VP: Laurie Baker
VP: Bill Sengelmann
VP: Ross Wehman
CIO: Kristy P Simonette
Board of Directors: Scott S Ingram, Lewis A Levey, William B McGuire Jr, F Gardner Parker, William F Paulsen, Frances Aldrich Sevilla-Sa, Steven A Webster, Kelvin R Westbrook

D-U-N-S 03-457-5766
■ CAMDEN TELEPHONE CO INC
TDS
(*Suby of* TDS TELECOMMUNICATIONS CORP) ★
210 W Main St, Camden, IN 46917-9631
Tel (608) 831-1000 *Founded/Ownrshp* 1995
Sales 853.0MM *EMP* 2,700
SIC 4813 Local & long distance telephone communications
Pr: David Wittwer
Treas: Noal Hutton

D-U-N-S 00-223-3997
CAMDEN WIRE CO INC
INTERNATIONAL WIRE GROUP
(*Suby of* BARE WIRE DIVISION) ★
12 Masonic Ave, Camden, NY 13316-1294
Tel (315) 245-3800 *Founded/Ownrshp* 1929, 1997
Sales 116.9MM[E] *EMP* 700
SIC 3351 3357 Wire, copper & copper alloy; Nonferrous wiredrawing & insulating
Pr: Rodney Kent
VP: Vince Donaldson
VP: Chuck Lovengoth
Genl Mgr: Charles Knapp
Dir IT: Peter Ernenwein
Plnt Mgr: Ken Suits
VP Sls: Charles H Levenguth

CAMDEN-CLARK MEDICAL CENTER
See CAMDEN-CLARK MEMORIAL HOSPITAL CORP

D-U-N-S 07-498-0095
CAMDEN-CLARK MEMORIAL HOSPITAL CORP
CAMDEN-CLARK MEDICAL CENTER
(*Suby of* WVUHS) ★
800 Garfield Ave, Parkersburg, WV 26101-5340
Tel (304) 424-2111 *Founded/Ownrshp* 1898
Sales 217.0MM *EMP* 1,600[E]
SIC 8062 General medical & surgical hospitals
Ch: Christopher Chriss
Chf Rad: Michael Hensley
**Pr:* Thomas Corder
**CFO:* Allen Buther
Chf Mktg O: Jennifer Leavitt
Ofcr: Earl Totten
VP: A V Criss III
Dir Risk M: Fred Ervin
Dir Case M: Cindy Kern
Dir Lab: Bobbi Ward
Mng Ofcr: Kimberley Couch

D-U-N-S 82-493-7759
CAMEO GLOBAL INC
STS
4695 Chabot Dr Ste 101, Pleasanton, CA 94588-2756
Tel (925) 479-7800 *Founded/Ownrshp* 1993
Sales 113.7MM[E] *EMP* 650
SIC 7373 7371 7379 7363 4813 8742 Computer integrated systems design; Systems software development services; Computer software development; Computer related consulting services; Computer hardware requirements analysis; Computer related maintenance services; Temporary help service; ; Management information systems consultant
CEO: Philippe Verhees
Pr: William Stockton
COO: Kishore Jha
CFO: Beri Kasper
Snr Ntwrk: Christophe Standaert
VP Opers: Kish Jha
Mktg Dir: Nathalie Van

CAMEO MARBLE
See LOUISVILLE TILE DISTRIBUTORS INC

CAMERA ART
See HERFF JONES LLC

D-U-N-S 07-849-4065
CAMERON CO
4646 W Sam Houston Pkwy N, Houston, TX 77041-8214
Tel (713) 513-3300 *Founded/Ownrshp* 1920
Sales 228.8MM[E] *EMP* 1,551[E]
SIC 3823 Flow instruments, industrial process type
Pr: Nannette D Easterling

D-U-N-S 92-637-3234 IMP
CAMERON DICKINSON CONSTRUCTION CO INC
6184 Innovation Way, Carlsbad, CA 92009-1728
Tel (760) 438-9114 *Founded/Ownrshp* 1996
Sales 99.6MM *EMP* 40
SIC 1542 8741 Commercial & office building, new construction; Restaurant construction; Shopping center construction; Management services; Construction management
VP: Ron Gordines
VP: Nathan Morton
Dir IT: Charles Blue

CAMERON DRILLING SYSTEMS
See CAMERON TECHNOLOGIES INC

D-U-N-S 80-204-8785
CAMERON ENTERPRISES A LIMITED PARTNERSHIP
AMERICAN FIDELITY ASSURANCE
9000 Cameron Pkwy, Oklahoma City, OK 73114-3701
Tel (405) 523-2000 *Founded/Ownrshp* 1985
Sales 1.0MMM[E] *EMP* 2,500[E]
SIC 6733 Trusts
CEO: Bill Cameron
Genl Pt: William Cameron

D-U-N-S 05-090-2907 IMP
CAMERON INC
1036 Destrehan Ave, Harvey, LA 70058-2517
Tel (504) 371-3000 *Founded/Ownrshp* 2010
Sales 94.4MM[E] *EMP* 600
SIC 1389 Oil field services; Gas field services
Pr: William C Lemmer
CFO: Mike Mayer
**VP:* H Keith Jennings
Div Mgr: Mike Moity

D-U-N-S 87-904-1309
CAMERON INTERNATIONAL CORP
(*Suby of* SCHLUMBERGER LIMITED) ★
4646 W Sam Houston Pkwy N, Houston, TX 77041-8214
Tel (713) 513-3300 *Founded/Ownrshp* 2016
Sales 8.7MMM *EMP* 23,000
Accts Ernst & Young Llp Houston Te
SIC 3533 3563 3491 Oil & gas field machinery; Oil field machinery & equipment; Gas field machinery & equipment; Air & gas compressors; Automatic regulating & control valves
Pr: R Scott Rowe
**CFO:* Charles M Sledge
**Ofcr:* Steven P Geiger
Sr VP: William C Lemmer
**VP:* Dennis S Baldwin
VP: Dennis Baldwin
VP: Celine B Gerson
VP: Hunter W Jones
VP: Steven W Roll
VP: Mark Schubert
VP: Charles Sledge
VP: Brett Smith
VP: Stephen Tomlinson
Dir Bus: Darrin Yenzer
Board of Directors: Bruce W Wilkinson, H Paulett Eberhart, Peter J Fluor, Douglas L Foshee, Rodolfo Landim, Jack B Moore, Michael E Patrick, Timothy J Probert, Jon Erik Reinhardsen, Brent J Smolik

D-U-N-S 80-973-9563 EXP
CAMERON INTERNATIONAL HOLDING CORP
(*Suby of* CAMERON INTERNATIONAL CORP) ★
4646 W Sam Houston Pkwy N, Houston, TX 77041-8214
Tel (713) 513-3300 *Founded/Ownrshp* 2004
Sales 133.6MM[E] *EMP* 118[E]
SIC 1389 Oil field services; Fishing for tools, oil & gas field; Fire fighting, oil & gas field

D-U-N-S 03-657-2170
CAMERON MITCHELL RESTAURANTS LLC (OH)
OCEAN PRIME
515 Park St, Columbus, OH 43215-2039
Tel (614) 621-3663 *Founded/Ownrshp* 1998, 1993
Sales 116.8MM[E] *EMP* 1,078
SIC 8741 5812 Restaurant management; Eating places
**Pr:* David Miller
VP: Stacey Connaughton
Sls Mgr: Abby Antonick

D-U-N-S 16-152-3055 IMP
CAMERON SOLUTIONS INC
NATCO
(*Suby of* NATCO GROUP INC) ★
11210 Equity Dr Ste 100, Houston, TX 77041-8239
Tel (713) 849-7500 *Founded/Ownrshp* 1989
Sales 432.8MM[E] *EMP* 2,100
SIC 3533 1389 3569 Gas field machinery & equipment; Oil field machinery & equipment; Oil & gas wells: building, repairing & dismantling; Separators for steam, gas, vapor or air (machinery)
Ch Bd: John U Clarke
Pr: William C Lemmer
Treas: Jaime Ledergerber
VP: Stuart Taylor
Sfty Mgr: Jim Leblanc
Board of Directors: Frank Smith

D-U-N-S 80-675-9148
CAMERON TECHNOLOGIES INC
CAMERON DRILLING SYSTEMS
(*Suby of* CAMERON INTERNATIONAL CORP) ★
4646 W Sam Houston Pkwy N, Houston, TX 77041-8214
Tel (713) 513-3300 *Founded/Ownrshp* 2003
Sales 163.3MM[E] *EMP* 400
SIC 5084 3533 Oil well machinery, equipment & supplies; Oil field machinery & equipment
Pr: Jim Wright
VP: Pat Holley

D-U-N-S 00-835-4821 IMP
CAMFIL USA INC
(*Suby of* CAMFIL AB)
1 N Corporate Dr, Riverdale, NJ 07457-1715
Tel (973) 616-7300 *Founded/Ownrshp* 1938
Sales 209.7MM[E] *EMP* 700
SIC 3564 3569 Purification & dust collection equipment; Filters, air: furnaces, air conditioning equipment, etc.; Air purification equipment; Dust or fume collecting equipment, industrial; Filters; Filters, general line: industrial
Pr: Armando Brunetti
**CFO:* Frank Shahin
**Ofcr:* Allan O'Connell
**Ofcr:* Johan Ryrberg
VP: Michael Foley
VP: Stan Jadwinski
**VP:* John Vissers
Mng Dir: Paul Cleveland
Area Mgr: Rhys Anderson
Brnch Mgr: Travis Gepson
Brnch Mgr: Jim Ward

D-U-N-S 04-941-9377
CAMINO REAL FOODS INC
CAMINO REAL KITCHENS
2638 E Vernon Ave, Vernon, CA 90058-1825
Tel (323) 585-6599 *Founded/Ownrshp* 2007
Sales 127.1MM[E] *EMP* 410
Accts Rbz Llp Los Angeles Califor
SIC 2038 Ethnic foods, frozen
Pr: Rob Cross
**CFO:* Richard Lunsford
CFO: Chris Perry
Prd Mgr: Juan Salazar

CAMINO REAL KITCHENS
See CAMINO REAL FOODS INC

CAMOPLAST CROCKER
See EXO-S US LLC

CAMOPLAST SOLIDEAL
See CAMSO USA INC

CAMP GROUP
See CAMPGROUP LLC

D-U-N-S 93-813-2115
CAMP RECOVERY CENTERS L P
6100 Tower Cir Ste 1000, Franklin, TN 37067-1509
Tel (408) 998-7260 *Founded/Ownrshp* 1995
Sales 62.3MM[E] *EMP* 5,000
SIC 8069 Substance abuse hospitals
Pt: Barry Karlin
**Pt:* Susan Del Bene
**Pt:* Daniel Newby
**Pt:* Kathy Sylvia

D-U-N-S 06-252-0093
CAMP SYSTEMS INTERNATIONAL INC
11 Continental Blvd Ste C, Merrimack, NH 03054-4341
Tel (603) 595-0030 *Founded/Ownrshp* 2000
Sales 92.9MM[E] *EMP* 552
SIC 7374

D-U-N-S 03-033-6309
CAMPBELL & CO INC
2850 Quarry Lake Dr # 302, Baltimore, MD 21209-3874
Tel (410) 413-2600 *Founded/Ownrshp* 1972
Sales 122.1MM[E] *EMP* 140
SIC 6221 Futures brokers & dealers, commodity
Ch Bd: Keith Campbell
**Ch Bd:* D Keith Campbell
**Pr:* Michael Harris
Pr: Lora Kelley
**CEO:* G William Andrews
**CFO:* Gregory Donovan
Chf Cred: Stefanie Bingham
Sr Ex VP: James Little
Sr VP: Greg Donovan
VP: Phillip Caballero
VP: John Hampton
VP: Darvin Sterner
Board of Directors: G William Andrews, Keith Campbell, Michael Harris, Thomas Lloyd

D-U-N-S 01-911-5711 IMP
CAMPBELL CONCRETE & MATERIALS LP (TX)
GULF CAOST STABILIZED MTLS
(*Suby of* HANSON LEHIGH INC) ★
16155 Park Row Ste 120, Houston, TX 77084-6971
Tel (281) 592-5201 *Founded/Ownrshp* 1998, 2011
Sales 126.4MM[E] *EMP* 500
SIC 3273 Ready-mixed concrete
Ltd Pt: Lehigh C Company
Mng Pt: Scott Ducoff

D-U-N-S 08-669-9790 IMP
CAMPBELL COUNTY HOSPITAL DISTRICT
CAMPBELL COUNTY MEMORIAL HOSP
501 S Burma Ave, Gillette, WY 82716-3426
Tel (307) 688-1551 *Founded/Ownrshp* 1975
Sales 142.8MM *EMP* 1,043[E]
Accts Cliftonlarsonallen Llp Minnea
SIC 8062 General medical & surgical hospitals
CEO: Robert Morasko
**CFO:* Andy Fitzgerald
**CFO:* Dalton Hubor
VP: Debra Tonn
Prin: Jonni Belden
Off Mgr: Vicki Henshaw
Doctor: Garry G Becker MD
Nrsg Dir: Ramona Bushor
Nrsg Dir: Amy Mastellar
Nrsg Dir: Amy Masteller

CAMPBELL COUNTY MEMORIAL HOSP
See CAMPBELL COUNTY HOSPITAL DISTRICT

D-U-N-S 09-330-3675
CAMPBELL COUNTY SCHOOL DISTRICT 1
1000 W 8th St, Gillette, WY 82716-3423
Tel (307) 682-5171 *Founded/Ownrshp* 1964
Sales 157.4MM *EMP* 1,600
Accts Bennett Weber & Hermstad Llp
SIC 8211 Public elementary school; Public junior high school; Public senior high school; Public combined elementary & secondary school
Dir Sec: Michelle Reynolds
**Off Mgr:* Larry Reznicek
MIS Dir: Amy Taylor
Pr Dir: Jeff Wasserburger
Instr Medi: Kay Daly

D-U-N-S 83-046-2821
CAMPBELL FUND TRUST
2850 Quarry Lake Dr, Baltimore, MD 21209-3874
Tel (410) 413-2600 *Founded/Ownrshp* 2009
Sales 146.1MM *EMP* 2[E]
Accts Deloitte & Touche Llp
SIC 6221 Commodity contracts brokers, dealers
Pr: Bruce Lester Cleland

CAMPBELL GROUP
See CAMPBELL HAUSFELD LLC

D-U-N-S 15-067-8886 EXP
■ CAMPBELL HAUSFELD LLC
CAMPBELL GROUP
(*Suby of* MARMON GROUP LLC) ★
100 Production Dr, Harrison, OH 45030-1477
Tel (513) 367-4811 *Founded/Ownrshp* 2015
Sales 158.3MM[E] *EMP* 309
SIC 3563 3546 3548 Air & gas compressors including vacuum pumps; Spraying outfits: metals, paints & chemicals (compressor); Power-driven handtools; Welding apparatus
Pr: Eric Tinnemeyer
**CFO:* Dave Kohlmayer
VP: Edward Andros
VP: Frank Cann
VP: Josh Davis
VP: Randy Smith
VP: Frances Ann Ziemniak
VP Inf Sys: Larry Rud
VP Sls: Tinn Meyer
Mktg Mgr: Jim Rosplock
Sls Mgr: Jeff Jackson

CAMPBELL OIL & GAS
See CAMPBELL RENTALS LLC

D-U-N-S 01-816-7460
CAMPBELL OIL CO (OH)
7977 Hills & Dales Rd Ne, Massillon, OH 44646-6798
Tel (330) 833-8555 *Founded/Ownrshp* 1939
Sales 175.5MM[E] *EMP* 447
Accts Bruner-Cox Llp Canton Oh
SIC 5171 Petroleum bulk stations & terminals
Pr: Brian D Campbell
**Owner:* Chris Campbell
**Owner:* Wesley S Campbell
**CEO:* Mac Campbell Jr
Treas: Doug Combs
IT Man: Jim Horton
VP Sls: Nino Iadanza
Mktg Mgr: Joe Kennen

D-U-N-S 02-453-5940
CAMPBELL RENTALS LLC
CAMPBELL OIL & GAS
418 Peanut Plant Rd, Elizabethtown, NC 28337
Tel (910) 862-7657 *Founded/Ownrshp* 1994
Sales 136.8MM[E] *EMP* 188
Accts Thompson Price Scott Adams
SIC 5171 5411 5541 Petroleum bulk stations & terminals; Convenience stores, independent; Filling stations, gasoline
Pr: Dallas M Campbell Jr
CFO: Jimmy Dail
**VP:* Chris Campbell

D-U-N-S 80-821-5060
CAMPBELL RESOURCES LTD
CAMPBELL TRAVEL
14800 Landmark Blvd # 155, Dallas, TX 75254-7007
Tel (972) 716-2500 *Founded/Ownrshp* 1983
Sales 84.5MM *EMP* 51
SIC 4724 Travel agencies
CEO: William B Campbell
**Ch:* Robert S Campbell
Ex VP: Steve Garrett
VP: Ashley Andries
**VP:* Sandra W Davenport
**VP:* Hilary Roberts
Dir Soc: Charlie Broyles
CTO: Steve Ewing
IT Man: Bob Channel
IT Man: Bob Channell

D-U-N-S 00-697-1881
■ CAMPBELL SALES CO (NJ)
(*Suby of* CAMPBELL SOUP CO) ★
1 Campbell Pl, Camden, NJ 08103-1701
Tel (856) 342-4800 *Founded/Ownrshp* 1923
Sales 74.7MM[E] *EMP* 2,400
SIC 8743 Sales promotion
Pr: Mike Salzberg
**Treas:* Brenda Edgerton
Ofcr: M C Johnson
**VP:* James Baldwin
**VP:* John Dieleuterio
CIO: Doreen A Wright

D-U-N-S 00-128-8042
▲ CAMPBELL SOUP CO
1 Campbell Pl, Camden, NJ 08103-1799
Tel (856) 342-4800 *Founded/Ownrshp* 1869
Sales 7.9MMM *EMP* 18,600
Tkr Sym CPB *Exch* NYS

SIC 2032 2038 2033 2052 2051 2096 Canned specialties; Soups & broths: canned, jarred, etc.; Spaghetti: packaged in cans, jars, etc.; Beans & bean sprouts, canned, jarred, etc.; Frozen specialties; Dinners, frozen & packaged; Breakfasts, frozen & packaged; Lunches, frozen & packaged; Canned fruits & specialties; Chili sauce, tomato: packaged in cans, jars, etc.; Cookies & crackers; Bread, cake & related products; Potato chips & similar snacks
Pr: Denise M Morrison
Dir Recs: Celeste Petrei
**Ch Bd:* Les C Vinney
Pr: Ed Carolan
CFO: Anthony P Disilvestro
Treas: Ashok Madhavan
Ofcr: Robert W Morrissey
Sr VP: Adam G Ciongoli
VP: Michael Paul
VP: Patricia Principato
VP: Charles Vila
VP: Roger Wilson
Board of Directors: Mary Alice D Malone, Bennett Dorrance, Randall W Larrimore, Marc B Lautenbach, Sara Mathew, Keith R McLoughlin, Charles R Perrin, Nick Shreiber, Tracey T Travis

CAMPBELL TERRACE APARTMENTS
See CT ASSOCIATES OF ILLINOIS LP

CAMPBELL TRAVEL
See CAMPBELL RESOURCES LTD

D-U-N-S 06-911-7539
CAMPBELL UNION HIGH SCHOOL DIST
3235 Union Ave, San Jose, CA 95124-2009
Tel (408) 371-0960 *Founded/Ownrshp* 1900
Sales 90.0MM *EMP* 600
SIC 8211 Public senior high school
Psych: Jeannette Medina
HC Dir: Meagan O'Neal
Board of Directors: Connie Dulany, Diane Gordon, Vickie Purser, Shawn Rafoth, Paulette Reeder, Toni Selzler, Sheryl Usry, Toni Williamson

D-U-N-S 07-558-6057
CAMPBELL UNIVERSITY INC
148 Main St, Buies Creek, NC 27506
Tel (910) 893-1240 *Founded/Ownrshp* 1934
Sales 127.1MM *EMP* 1,000
Accts Bdo Usa Llp Raleigh Nc
SIC 8221 University
Pr: Jerry M Wallace
**Treas:* James H Ellerbe
**Treas:* James O Roberts
VP: Dwaine Greene
Pharmcst: Kara Maryansky

CAMPERS WORLD APPAREL GROUP
See AUTHENTIC LIFESTYLE PRODUCTS LLC

D-U-N-S 07-667-0280
CAMPGROUP LLC
CAMP GROUP
4 New King St Ste 130, White Plains, NY 10604-1228
Tel (914) 997-2177 *Founded/Ownrshp* 1998
Sales 59.9MM[E] *EMP* 2,000
SIC 7032 Summer camp, except day & sports instructional
CEO: Andy Benerofe
Pr: Mark Benerofe
CFO: Jeffrey Bershad
VP: Jancy Dorfman
Off Mgr: Debbie Lasner

D-U-N-S 08-029-1017
▲ CAMPING WORLD HOLDINGS INC
250 Parkway Dr Ste 270, Lincolnshire, IL 60069-4346
Tel (847) 808-3000 *Founded/Ownrshp* 1966
Sales 47.4MM[E] *EMP* 7,444[E]
Tkr Sym CWH *Exch* NYS
SIC 7513 6159 7539 Truck rental & leasing, no drivers; Equipment & vehicle finance leasing companies; Finance leasing, vehicles: except automobiles & trucks; Automotive repair shops
Ch Bd: Marcus A Lemonis
Pr: Mark J Boggess
Pr: Roger L Nuttall
CFO: Thomas F Wolfe

D-U-N-S 36-130-6962 IMP
CAMPING WORLD INC
RV DEALERS MARKETPLACE
(*Suby of* GOOD SAM) ★
650 Three Springs Rd, Bowling Green, KY 42104-7561
Tel (270) 781-2718 *Founded/Ownrshp* 1991
Sales 952.6MM[E] *EMP* 1,378
SIC 5561 5961 Recreational vehicle parts & accessories; Catalog & mail-order houses
CEO: Marcus Lemonis
Ch Bd: Stephen Adams
Pr: Mark Boggess
Pr: John Sirpilla
Pr: Bruce Wright
CFO: Jim Debruzzi
Ex VP: Brent Moody
Sr VP: Don Smith
VP: Roger Anderson
VP: Derek Gigliotti
VP: Paul Inman
VP: Matt Jeppsen
VP: David McKillip
VP: Randy Rahe
VP: Mike Siemens
VP: Tj Smith
VP: Brock Whinnery
Exec: Jeff Crum

CAMPING WORLD RV SALES
See FREEDOMROADS HOLDING CO LLC

D-U-N-S 06-862-3508
CAMPUS COURSE PAKS INC
1 South Ave Fl 1, Garden City, NY 11530-4213
Tel (516) 877-3967 *Founded/Ownrshp* 1994
Sales 237.4MM *EMP* 5
SIC 2731 Books: publishing only
Pr: Wayne Piskin

D-U-N-S 96-410-0916
CAMPUS CREST COMMUNITIES INC
2100 Rexford Rd Ste 300, Charlotte, NC 28211-3484
Tel (704) 496-2500 *Founded/Ownrshp* 2010
Sales 106.7MM *EMP* 632[E]
SIC 6798 6552 6531 Real estate investment trusts; Land subdividers & developers, residential; Real estate leasing & rentals
Prin: Richard S Kahlbaugh
Pr: Aaron Halfacre
CEO: David Coles
CFO: Donnie Bobbitt
CFO: John Makuch
Genl Mgr: Deb Haley
Board of Directors: Randall H Brown, James W McCaughan, Denis McGlynn, Curtis McWilliams, Raymond Mikulich, Lauro Gonzalez-Moreno, Daniel L Simmons

D-U-N-S 05-745-8770
CAMPUS CRUSADE FOR CHRIST INC
NEW LIFE PUBLICATIONS
100 Lake Hart Dr, Orlando, FL 32832-0100
Tel (407) 826-2000 *Founded/Ownrshp* 1951
Sales 241.4MM[E] *EMP* 7,688
SIC 8661 Religious organizations
Pr: Stephen B Douglass
Bd of Dir: Mike Alverts
VP: Dela Adadevoh
VP: Kenneth Heckmann
Dir Risk M: Pete Johnson
Comm Dir: Mike Adamson
Comm Dir: Robin Muscarella
Off Mgr: Hyet Field
Dir IT: Dennis Brockman
Dir IT: Trent Schaller
Software D: Dave Baker

D-U-N-S 93-104-7229
CAMPUS MANAGEMENT CORP
TALISMA
5201 Congress Ave C220, Boca Raton, FL 33487-3600
Tel (561) 923-2500 *Founded/Ownrshp* 1988
Sales 207.2MM[E] *EMP* 800
SIC 7373 8741 Systems software development services; Systems integration services; Management services
CEO: Jim Milton
**Ch Bd:* Gregory J Dukat
Pr: Carl Fisher
**Pr:* David W Meek
CFO: Karen O Byrne
**CFO:* Anders Nessen
**Ofcr:* Mark Armstrong
Top Exec: Srivatsa T Sreenivasarao
Sr VP: Jim Brigadier
Sr VP: Timothy S Gilbert
**Sr VP:* Cynthia L Haynie
**Sr VP:* Viki Hucke-Mccright
**Sr VP:* James T Lynn
**Sr VP:* Raj Mruthyunjayappa
Sr VP: Brian H Nelson
Sr VP: Sean P Ryan
VP: Raymond Blackwood
VP: Kirk Bodick
VP: Mike Dillon
VP: Dan Frazier
VP: Brian Gilbert
Board of Directors: Thomas J Fitzpatrick

D-U-N-S 11-859-7889 IMP/EXP
CAMSO USA INC
CAMOPLAST SOLIDEAL
(*Suby of* CAMSO INC)
306 Forsyth Hall Dr, Charlotte, NC 28273-5817
Tel (704) 374-9700 *Founded/Ownrshp* 2010
Sales 231.5MM[E] *EMP* 380
SIC 5531 5014 Automotive tires; Tires & tubes
CEO: Bob Bulger
**Sec:* Charlie Nartker
VP: Benoit Bessette
VP: Rene Picard
Mktg Mgr: Richard Lane
Manager: Phillip Baird
Sls Mgr: Brian Avery

CAMUTO GROUP
See VCS GROUP LLC

D-U-N-S 78-946-6492 IMP
CAMUTO GROUP LLC
(*Suby of* CAMUTO GROUP) ★
411 W Putnam Ave Ste 210, Greenwich, CT 06830-6263
Tel (203) 413-7100 *Founded/Ownrshp* 2006
Sales 124.0MM[E] *EMP* 300[E]
SIC 5139 Footwear
Ex VP: Leah Robert
Sr VP: Phil Barousse
Sr VP: Fernando Bertollo
VP: Chris D'Elia
VP: Jessica Elliott
VP: Carol Kim
VP: Andy Lukacovic
VP: Mark Lynn
VP: Greg Morel
VP: Shawn Reed
VP: Sarah Rosen
VP: Diana Takach
VP: Kelly Wilson
Dir: Grant Campbell
Creative D: Renee Hatico

D-U-N-S 07-938-6764
CAN CAPITAL INC
414 W 14th St Fl 3, New York, NY 10014-1013
Tel (914) 725-9301 *Founded/Ownrshp* 1998
Sales NA *EMP* 409
SIC 6153 Working capital financing
CEO: Daniel Demeo
Pr: Daniel Flax
Pr: Glenn Goldman
CFO: Shiladitya Ray
CFO: Aman Verjee
Chf Mktg O: James Mendelsohn
Ofcr: Kenneth Gang
Ofcr: Ritesh Gupta
Ofcr: Chris Moloney
Ofcr: Parris Sanz
VP: Anthony Cespedes
VP: Frank Getter
VP: Jodi Leo

CANA
See PATRICK INDUSTRIES INC

D-U-N-S 00-136-6855 IMP
CANADA DRY BOTTLING CO OF NEW YORK LP
11202 15th Ave, College Point, NY 11356-1428
Tel (718) 358-2000 *Founded/Ownrshp* 1980
Sales 233.6MM[E] *EMP* 300[E]
SIC 5149 Soft drinks
Pt: Harold A Honickman

CANADA DRY OF DELAWARE VALLEY
See FOULKROD ASSOCIATES

D-U-N-S 05-338-7890 IMP
CANADA DRY POTOMAC CORP
3600 Pennsy Dr, Hyattsville, MD 20785-1611
Tel (301) 773-5500 *Founded/Ownrshp* 1970
Sales 373.0MM[E] *EMP* 575
SIC 5149 Soft drinks
Pr: Bob Brockway
**CFO:* Joe Stanley
**VP:* Marvin L Goldstein

D-U-N-S 04-737-7973 IMP
CANADIAN AMERICAN OIL CO INC
DIVISADERO TOUCHLESS CAR WASH
444 Divisadero St 100, San Francisco, CA 94117-2211
Tel (415) 621-8676 *Founded/Ownrshp* 1968
Sales 89.2MM[E] *EMP* 450
SIC 5541 6512 6552 Gasoline service stations; Commercial & industrial building operation; Subdividers & developers
Pr: Roy Shimek

CANADIAN IMPERIAL BNK COMMERCE
See C I B C OPPENHEIMER HOLDINGS INC

D-U-N-S 18-782-6557
CANADIAN IMPERIAL HOLDINGS INC
CIBC WORLD MARKETS
(*Suby of* CANADIAN IMPERIAL BANK OF COMMERCE)
425 Lexington Ave Bsmt C2, New York, NY 10017-3903
Tel (212) 856-4000 *Founded/Ownrshp* 1982
Sales NA *EMP* 4,200
SIC 6719 Investment holding companies, except banks
CEO: Gary Brown
Top Exec: Donald R Lindsay

CANADIAN NATIONAL ILL CENTL RR
See ILLINOIS CENTRAL RAILROAD CO

CANADIAN NATIONAL RAILWAY CO
See WISCONSIN CENTRAL LTD

CANADIAN PACIFIC RAILWAY
See SOO LINE RAILROAD CO

CANADIAN PACIFIC RAILWAY
See SOO LINE CORP

D-U-N-S 00-984-4846
CANAL BARGE CO INC (LA)
CANAL TERMINAL COMPANY
835 Union St Ste 300, New Orleans, LA 70112-1469
Tel (504) 581-2424 *Founded/Ownrshp* 1933
Sales 158.3MM[E] *EMP* 840
SIC 4449 4424 5171 Canal & intracoastal freight transportation; Deep sea domestic transportation of freight; Petroleum terminals
Pr: Merritt Lane
CFO: Doug Downing
**Sr VP:* David M Lane
VP: Tom Dowie
VP: Troy Remy
Genl Mgr: Whitney Brown
Genl Mgr: William Pegher
Dir IT: Harvey Wright
IT Man: Brett Hulin
Opers Mgr: Roy McManus
VP Mktg: Larry Barbish

CANAL INDEMNITY COMPANY
See CANAL INSURANCE CO

D-U-N-S 00-791-9731
CANAL INSURANCE CO (SC)
CANAL INDEMNITY COMPANY
400 E Stone Ave, Greenville, SC 29601-1618
Tel (800) 452-6911 *Founded/Ownrshp* 1939
Sales NA *EMP* 240
SIC 6331 Fire, marine & casualty insurance & carriers; Automobile insurance
CEO: John R Pollock
**CEO:* David Pauly
**CFO:* John N Diblanda
**Chf Mktg O:* Timothy Hogan
**Ofcr:* Bob Pace
Ex VP: Kirk Goeldner
Sr VP: Rick Timmons
**VP:* Joyce Dunn
VP: Christopher Greene
VP: Pat Lennon
VP: Billy Moore
**VP:* Francis Timmons
VP: Sydney Timmons
Board of Directors: Lansing Crane, Claude C Lilly, Victor L Lund, David Pauly

CANAL TERMINAL COMPANY
See CANAL BARGE CO INC

D-U-N-S 04-591-1658 EXP
CANAM STEEL CORP
(*Suby of* GROUPE CANAM INC)
4010 Clay St, Point of Rocks, MD 21777-2016
Tel (301) 874-5141 *Founded/Ownrshp* 1973
Sales 201.1MM[E] *EMP* 760
SIC 3441 5051 Building components, structural steel; Iron & steel (ferrous) products
Pr: Mary K Gordon
**VP:* Ronald W Teppe II
Genl Mgr: Ron Peppe
IT Man: Louis Bungo

D-U-N-S 00-697-6914
■ CANANDAIGUA NATIONAL BANK & TRUST CO
(*Suby of* CANANDAIGUA NATIONAL CORP) ★
72 S Main St, Canandaigua, NY 14424-1999
Tel (585) 394-4260 *Founded/Ownrshp* 1887
Sales NA *EMP* 235
SIC 6021 National commercial banks
Pr: George W Hamlin IV
**Ch Bd:* Alan J Stone
Bd of Dir: Wendy Leaney
VP: Jeffrey Barker
VP: Thomas Benner
VP: Noleen Burch
VP: Lynn Carleton
VP: Michael J Drexler
VP: Lori R Ellis
VP: Cheryl Hurd
VP: Charleen Kalocsai
VP: Adam Leszyk
VP: David Morrow
VP: Joann Nieman
VP: Sandra Roberts
VP: Stephen Rossi
VP: Mary Szabat
VP: James P Terwilliger

D-U-N-S 78-594-6120
▲ CANANDAIGUA NATIONAL CORP
72 S Main St, Canandaigua, NY 14424-1905
Tel (585) 394-4260 *Founded/Ownrshp* 1984
Sales NA *EMP* 537[E]
Tkr Sym CNND *Exch* OTO
SIC 6021 National commercial banks; National trust companies with deposits, commercial
CEO: George W Hamlin IV
**Ch Bd:* Frank H Hamlin III
Pr: Robert Simpson
**CFO:* Lawrence A Heilbronner
Ofcr: Richard H Hawks
Ofcr: Lindsay Lilly
Ofcr: Mark Mazzochetti
Ofcr: Shelly Tierson
Trst Ofcr: Kevin Kinney
**Ex VP:* Steven H Swartout
Sr VP: Robert L Lowenthal Jr
VP: Gary L Babbitt
VP: G J Blatt Jr
VP: Charleen Cordaro
VP: Gwen Crawford
VP: Joann Roberts
VP: Linda Schnitzler
VP: Bill Vandamme
VP: Vincent Yacuzzo
VP: Roz Zatyko
Board of Directors: Richard C Fox, Daniel P Fuller, Stephen D Hamlin, Richard P Miller Jr, Robert G Sheridan, Caroline C Shipley, Sue S Stewart, Alan J Stone

D-U-N-S 96-995-9944
CANARY LLC
410 17th St Ste 1320, Denver, CO 80202-4424
Tel (303) 309-1185 *Founded/Ownrshp* 2007
Sales 433.6MM[E] *EMP* 400[E]
SIC 1389 Oil field services
CEO: Dan Eberhart
**COO:* Donald Pfister
**CFO:* Curtis Leonard
**Sr VP:* Mark Tassin
Brnch Mgr: Joey Darby
Dist Mgr: Larry Nistor
VP Opers: Brian Pearson
Sls Mgr: Jeff Erickson

D-U-N-S 06-808-0621 IMP/EXP
CANBERRA CORP
3610 N Hlland Sylvania Rd, Toledo, OH 43615
Tel (419) 724-4300 *Founded/Ownrshp* 1964
Sales 92.7MM[E] *EMP* 205
SIC 2842 Specialty cleaning, polishes & sanitation goods; Specialty cleaning preparations
Pr: R Bruce Yacko
CFO: Melaine Andrews
CFO: Bill Schneck
**Ch:* James C Lower
**Sec:* William Schneck
IT Man: Jermy Weraez
Plnt Mgr: John Hunsinger
Mktg Dir: Jennifer Arbaugh
Mktg Dir: Todd Schimmoeller
Manager: Terrence Cukierski

D-U-N-S 01-759-2135 IMP
CANBERRA INDUSTRIES INC
(*Suby of* MIRION TECHNOLOGIES INC) ★
800 Research Pkwy, Meriden, CT 06450-7169
Tel (203) 238-2351 *Founded/Ownrshp* 2016
Sales 92.6MM[E] *EMP* 290[E]
SIC 3829 4813 Nuclear radiation & testing apparatus; Voice telephone communications
CEO: Jean Bernard Koehl
CFO: Fabrice Burtin
VP: Marc Morelli
VP: Thomas Pennington
VP: Bud Sielaff
Exec: Elizabeth Groeller
Genl Mgr: Donna Tippett
Snr Sftwr: Rex Battenberg
Snr Sftwr: ARI Hartstein
Dir IT: Pauline Mowry
Netwrk Mgr: Tony Dinicola

CANCER CENTER
See SOUTHWEST WASHINGTON MEDICAL CENTER

CANCER TREATMENT CENTER TULSA
See SOUTHWESTERN REGIONAL MEDICAL CENTER INC

CANCER TREATMENT CENTERS AMER
See EASTERN REGIONAL MEDICAL CENTER INC

D-U-N-S 19-603-1553
CANCER TREATMENT CENTERS OF AMERICA INC
CTCA
(Suby of TRANSLATIONAL ONCOLOGY RESEARCH INTERNATIONAL INC) ★
5900 Broken Sound Pkwy, Boca Raton, FL 33487-2797
Tel (800) 615-3055 Founded/Ownrshp 2011
Sales 169.6MM^E EMP 1,900
SIC 8069 Cancer hospital
Pr: Steve Mackin
*Ch Bd: Richard J Stephenson
Pr: Maurie Markman
CFO: Randy Cartwright
CFO: Phil Picchitti
*Treas: Craig Hollick
Sr Cor Off: Richard Stevenson
Bd of Dir: Douglas B Rath
Ofcr: Devin C Carty
Ex VP: Walt Hilker
Sr VP: Jacklynn Lesniak
VP: Herb Debarba
VP: Barry Hamp
VP: Robert Hauser
*VP: Cecilia Taylor
Exec: Chrissy Agnew
Board of Directors: Colin Low

D-U-N-S 05-346-8385 IMP
CANDELA CORP (DE)
SYNERON CANDELA
(Suby of SYNERON CANDELA) ★
530 Boston Post Rd, Wayland, MA 01778-1833
Tel (949) 716-6670 Founded/Ownrshp 1970, 1984
Sales 108.6MM^E EMP 326
SIC 3845 Laser systems & equipment, medical
Pr: Louis P Scafuri
COO: Dale Merritt
CFO: Derek Tsechrintzis
Treas: Bob Quinn
VP: George A Abe
VP: Jeff Marble
VP: Karl Meincke
VP: Iain Miller
Genl Mgr: Mike Lemarier
Genl Mgr: Vicki Wolff-Long
*CTO: James C Hsia

D-U-N-S 17-424-8773 IMP
CANDLE CORP OF AMERICA
(Suby of TLC) ★
600 Sherwood Dr, Union City, TN 38261-1800
Tel (731) 885-7836 Founded/Ownrshp 2011
Sales 109.2MM^E EMP 650
SIC 5023 5199 Decorative home furnishings & supplies; Gifts & novelties
Pr: Frederic Contino
*Ch Bd: Robert B Goergen
VP: Mark Bondurant
*VP: Treesa Hundley
Admn Mgr: Karen Carr

D-U-N-S 07-930-5441
CANDLE-LITE CO LLC
(Suby of LUMINEX HD&F CO) ★
10521 Millington Ct Ste B, Blue Ash, OH 45242-4022
Tel (513) 563-1113 Founded/Ownrshp 2014
Sales 204.3MM^E EMP 492
SIC 3999 Candles
CEO: Calvin Johnston
*VP: Gary Prampero
Snr Mgr: Russ Elias

D-U-N-S 07-972-6256
CANDLELIGHT INVESTMENT HOLDINGS INC
1980 Industrial Dr, Sterling, IL 61081-9064
Tel (815) 632-6800 Founded/Ownrshp 2012
Sales 591.3MM^E EMP 550
SIC 5199 Advertising specialties
Pr: Troy Noard
CFO: Linda Jankowski

D-U-N-S 04-295-7233
CANDLER HOSPITAL INC
5353 Reynolds St, Savannah, GA 31405-6015
Tel (912) 819-6000 Founded/Ownrshp 1985
Sales 250.5MM EMP 1,600
Accts Draffin & Tucker Llp Albany
SIC 8062 General medical & surgical hospitals
Pr: Paul P Hinchey
Pr: William Carr
Pr: Brigit Carreras
*CFO: Greg Schaack
VP: Margaret Beatty
Dir Rx: Paul Caprenter
Mktg Dir: Melissa Allen
Doctor: Brian Anderson
Doctor: Sheila Lowe
Doctor: Ericka Petty

D-U-N-S 07-911-9158
CANFOR SOUTHERN PINE LLC
3700 Claypond Rd, Myrtle Beach, SC 29579-7330
Tel (843) 236-8402 Founded/Ownrshp 2013
Sales 300.0MM EMP 25^E
SIC 5031 Lumber, plywood & millwork
Pr: Fred Stimpson
*Sr VP: Mark Feldinger
*Sr VP: Wayne Guthrie
*VP: Keith McGregor

D-U-N-S 07-148-6583
CANISIUS COLLEGE
2001 Main St, Buffalo, NY 14208-1098
Tel (716) 883-7000 Founded/Ownrshp 1870
Sales 97.2MM EMP 827^E
SIC 8221

CANNED FOODS GROCERY OUTLET
See GROCERY OUTLET INC

D-U-N-S 13-911-0618
CANNERY CASINO RESORTS LLC
9107 W Russell Rd, Las Vegas, NV 89148-1243
Tel (702) 507-5700 Founded/Ownrshp 2001
Sales 94.7MM^E EMP 1,860
SIC 7011 Casino hotel
CFO: Eric C Matejevich
VP: Ryan Paulos

D-U-N-S 04-402-1038
CANNON COCHRAN MANAGEMENT SERVICES INC
CCMSI
(Suby of CCMSI HOLDINGS INC) ★
2 E Main St Towne Ctr, Danville, IL 61832
Tel (217) 446-1089 Founded/Ownrshp 1978
Sales NA EMP 1,184
SIC 6411 Insurance claim adjusters, not employed by insurance company
CEO: G Bryan Thomas
*CFO: John Kluth
VP: Carrie Milholland
Brnch Mgr: William Gourde
Brnch Mgr: Phil Rodgers
CTO: Shelden Bretchel
IT Man: Bill Picer
Sales Exec: Liz Davis
Mktg Dir: Kristi Weaver

D-U-N-S 06-745-4850
CANNON CORP
CANNON DESIGN
2170 Whitehaven Rd, Grand Island, NY 14072-2025
Tel (716) 773-6800 Founded/Ownrshp 1950
Sales 92.3MM^E EMP 910
SIC 8712 Architectural engineering
CEO: Bradley Lukanic
*Ch Bd: John D Cannon
*Pr: Mark Mendell
*CEO: Gary R Miller
*CFO: David Carlino
Bd of Dir: Millard Berry
Assoc VP: Roberto Cruz Niemiec
VP: Patricia Beagle
VP: Mike Dlugosz
VP: Christopher T Hayes

D-U-N-S 19-567-2472 IMP/EXP
CANNON COUNTY KNITTING MILLS INC
VAL D'OR
237 Castlewood Dr Ste F, Murfreesboro, TN 37129-5166
Tel (615) 890-2938 Founded/Ownrshp 1986
Sales 37.0MM EMP 1,500
SIC 2231 Apparel & outerwear broadwoven fabrics
Ch Bd: Martin Granoff
*Pr: Stanley Kaskel
*Pr: Joe Murphy
*CEO: Brad Gibens
*CFO: Bill Perkoski
*VP: Jerry Eckstein
VP: Joseph Murphy

CANNON DESIGN
See CANNON CORP

CANNON EQUIPMENT COMPANY
See CANNON EQUIPMENT LLC

D-U-N-S 05-654-2780 IMP/EXP
■ **CANNON EQUIPMENT LLC**
CANNON EQUIPMENT COMPANY
(Suby of MARMON GROUP LLC) ★
324 Washington St W, Cannon Falls, MN 55009-1142
Tel (507) 263-6426 Founded/Ownrshp 2014
Sales 221.7MM^E EMP 200^E
SIC 5085 Industrial supplies
VP: Tina Atwell
VP: Brian Benson
VP: Kenny Ramsey
VP: Randal Vogt
Genl Mgr: Shane Beaudin
Genl Mgr: Dave Fournelle
DP Exec: Delos Fritz
IT Man: Hannorah Olson
VP Opers: Colin Leyden
Mfg Mgr: Chip Betts
Plnt Mgr: Randy Odman

D-U-N-S 05-832-3890
CANNON VALLEY COOPERATIVE
1500 Highway 3 S, Northfield, MN 55057-4429
Tel (507) 645-9556 Founded/Ownrshp 1921
Sales 87.0MM EMP 20
Accts Carlson Highland & Co Llp
SIC 5541 5171 1711 5191 5153 5211

D-U-N-S 00-602-2586 IMP
■ **CANNON-MUSKEGON CORP** (MI)
(Suby of PCC SPS FASTENER DIVISION) ★
2875 Lincoln St, Norton Shores, MI 49441-3313
Tel (231) 759-2831 Founded/Ownrshp 1952
Sales 84.0MM^E EMP 180
SIC 3313 3341 3339 3312 Alloys, additive, except copper: not made in blast furnaces; Secondary nonferrous metals; Primary nonferrous metals; Blast furnaces & steel mills
Pr: Douglas Orr
*Ch Bd: Mark Dunagan
*VP: Alva Bettis
*VP: Kenneth Harris
Genl Mgr: Erik Gentzkow

CANNONDALE SPORTS GROUP
See CYCLING SPORTS GROUP INC

D-U-N-S 78-689-8726
CANON BUSINESS PROCESS SERVICES INC
(Suby of CANON USA INC) ★
460 W 34th St Fl 6, New York, NY 10001-2320
Tel (212) 502-2100 Founded/Ownrshp 1997
Sales 436.0MM^E EMP 4,545
SIC 8741 Business management
Pr: Joseph Marciano
*Pr: Stephen Mackay
*COO: Walter Baransky
VP: Wayne Frahn
Rgnl Mgr: Ron Jackson
Area Mgr: John McPhillips
Area Mgr: Eddie Rivera
MIS Dir: John Castaldo
Netwrk Mgr: Jee L Tan
Site Mgr: Natasha Ballentine
Site Mgr: Jarvis Partman

D-U-N-S 02-197-4928
CANON FINANCIAL SERVICES INC
(Suby of CANON USA INC) ★
158 Gaither Dr Ste 200, Mount Laurel, NJ 08054-1716
Tel (856) 813-1000 Founded/Ownrshp 1990
Sales NA EMP 225
SIC 6159 7389 Finance leasing, vehicles: except automobiles & trucks; Financial services
Pr: Kris Tedo
Ofcr: Charles Profera
IT Man: Patrick Loughney
Netwrk Mgr: John Rivera
Opers Mgr: Mark Orr
Snr Mgr: Vickie Efrom
Snr Mgr: Philip Morse
Snr Mgr: Amy Pagano
Snr Mgr: Paul Prado
Snr Mgr: Susan Zitterman

D-U-N-S 62-333-8670 IMP
CANON FINANCIAL SERVICES INC
(Suby of CANON INC.)
5600 Broken Sound Blvd Nw, Boca Raton, FL 33487-3515
Tel (561) 997-3100 Founded/Ownrshp 1996
Sales 105.7MM^E EMP 700
SIC 5045 Computers, peripherals & software; Printers, computer
Pr: Marc O Gingold
Pr: H W Krause
*COO: Tom Long
VP: Dominic Caputo
*VP: Daniel P Hart
VP: Terry Howatt
VP: Timothy Moylan
VP: Joseph Vetillo

D-U-N-S 07-161-9878 IMP
CANON SOLUTIONS AMERICA INC (NY)
CANON USA - CORPORATE HDQTR
(Suby of CANON USA INC) ★
1 Canon Park, Melville, NY 11747-3036
Tel (631) 330-5000 Founded/Ownrshp 1971
Sales 1.3MMM^E EMP 6,600
SIC 7389 Advertising, promotional & trade show services
Ch Bd: Yoroku Adachi
*Pr: Toyotsugu Kuwamura
*Treas: Kunihiko Tedo
*V Ch Bd: Seymour Liebman
Sr VP: Robert Reddy
VP: Valerie Belli
Exec: Peter Lopes
Brnch Mgr: Nancy Carter
Brnch Mgr: Larry Cendejas
Genl Mgr: Jim Rosetta
Snr Ntwrk: Colin Carvey

CANON USA - CORPORATE HDQTR
See CANON SOLUTIONS AMERICA INC

D-U-N-S 04-153-0692 IMP/EXP
CANON USA INC
(Suby of CANON INC.)
1 Canon Park, Melville, NY 11747-3036
Tel (516) 328-5000 Founded/Ownrshp 1965
Sales 3.7MMM^E EMP 11,167
SIC 5044 5065 5045 3861 3577 5043 Photocopy machines; Typewriters; Duplicating machines; Calculators, electronic; Facsimile equipment; Computers & accessories, personal & home entertainment; Computer peripheral equipment; Printers, computer; Photocopy machines; Printers, computer; Photographic cameras, projectors, equipment & supplies
Ch Bd: Joe Adachi
*Pr: Yuichi Ishizuka
Pr: Toru Nishizawa
Pr: Richard P Palmieri
Treas: Toshiyuki Sanematsu
Ofcr: Seymour E Liebman
*Ex VP: Seymour Liebman
Ex VP: Tamotsu Nakamura
Ex VP: Joseph G Warren
Sr VP: Toyo Kuwamura
*Sr VP: Yoshinori Shimono
Sr VP: Kunihiko Tedo
VP: Naoki Ayata
VP: Charles Bruschi
VP: Nobuhiko Kitajima
VP: Tony Maruyana
VP: N Scott Millar
VP: Ellen Pitchford
VP: Kazuhiko Sasahara
VP: Stan Skorayko

D-U-N-S 15-324-7531 IMP/EXP
CANON VIRGINIA INC
(Suby of CANON USA INC) ★
12000 Canon Blvd, Newport News, VA 23606-4201
Tel (757) 881-6000 Founded/Ownrshp 1985
Sales 300.9MM^E EMP 1,820
SIC 3861 3577 3555 4953 Photographic equipment & supplies; Computer peripheral equipment; Printing trades machinery; Recycling, waste materials
Ch: Yoroku Adachi
*Pr: Toru Nishizawa
*Treas: Kunihiko Tedo
*Ex VP: Akira Machida
*Sr VP: John Briggs
*Sr VP: Byron Ruble
*Sr VP: Hiroki Shimizu
VP: Wesley Firman
Prgrm Mgr: Cornelia Steinert
Ql Cn Mgr: Andrew Lepak
Sales Exec: Tim McNelly
Board of Directors: Hiroshi Sasame

D-U-N-S 07-181-2843
CANRIG DRILLING TECH LTD
515 W Greens Rd Ste 1200, Houston, TX 77067-4536
Tel (281) 774-5600 Founded/Ownrshp 1994
Sales 92.4MM^E EMP 317^E
SIC 3532 Drills & drilling equipment, mining (except oil & gas)
Pr: Christopher Papouras
COO: John Sanchez
VP: Doug Campbell
VP: Brian Ellis
VP: Rob Guillory
*VP: Kevin Harsy
*VP: Gregory J Kostiuk
Snr Sftwr: Pradeep Annaiyappa
QA Dir: Anja Hunter
Opers Mgr: Thomas Cecil
Opers Mgr: Andre Perales

D-U-N-S 01-114-1033 IMP/EXP
▲ **CANTEL MEDICAL CORP**
150 Clove Rd Ste 36, Little Falls, NJ 07424-2100
Tel (973) 890-7220 Founded/Ownrshp 1963
Sales 664.7MM EMP 1,840
Accts Ernst & Young Llp New York N
Tkr Sym CMN Exch NYS
SIC 3841 3589 Surgical & medical instruments; Water purification equipment, household type
Pr: Jorgen B Hansen
Ch Bd: Charles M Diker
CFO: Peter G Clifford
V Ch Bd: George L Fotiades
Ex VP: Eric W Nodiff
Ex VP: Craig Sheldon
Ex VP: Seth M Yellin
Sr VP: Steven C Anaya

CANTERBURY TOWERS
See WORCESTER EPISCOPAL HOUSING CO LIMITED PARTNERSHIP

D-U-N-S 09-293-7309
CANTEX HEALTH CARE CENTERS LLC
BRENTWOOD PLACE
2537 Golden Bear Dr, Carrollton, TX 75006-2377
Tel (214) 954-4114 Founded/Ownrshp 1978
Sales 53.9MM^E EMP 1,200
SIC 8051 Extended care facility
CEO: Robin F Underhill
COO: Melanie A Gittiban
CFO: Mark S Voye
Ex Dir: Michael Mileski
Ex Dir: Barbara Robin
IT Man: John Martin
MIS Mgr: Faith Canright
Nrsg Dir: Meagan Myers

D-U-N-S 78-660-7606 IMP/EXP
CANTEX INC
(Suby of M I C) ★
301 Commerce St Ste 2700, Fort Worth, TX 76102-4127
Tel (817) 215-7000 Founded/Ownrshp 2012
Sales 182.9MM^E EMP 700
SIC 3084 3089 Plastics pipe; Fittings for pipe, plastic
Pr: Don Wirtanon
*Pr: Don Wirtanen
*CEO: Hisayoshi Uno
*CFO: Kevin Calcote
VP: Martin Blackburn
VP: Steve Ediger
*VP: Ray Gameson
VP: Ray Gamison
*VP: Dave Merker
*VP: Steve Tollefson
*VP: Greg Wilson

D-U-N-S 08-177-6510
CANTON CITY SCHOOL DISTRICT
305 Mckinley Ave Nw, Canton, OH 44702-1717
Tel (330) 438-2500 Founded/Ownrshp 1900
Sales 48.7MM^E EMP 1,800
Accts Dave Yost Canton Ohio
SIC 8211 Public elementary & secondary schools
*Treas: Jeff Gruber
*Treas: Jeffrey Gruber
CIO: Frederick Dawson
Schl Brd P: Lisa Gissendaner
Schl Brd P: John Rinaldi
HC Dir: Susan Ross

D-U-N-S 00-446-5142 IMP/EXP
CANTON DROP FORGE INC (OH)
(Suby of CORDIER GROUP HOLDINGS INC) ★
4575 Southway St Sw, Canton, OH 44706-1995
Tel (330) 477-4511 Founded/Ownrshp 1903, 1987
Sales 142.5MM^E EMP 300
SIC 3462 3463 3356 3312 Iron & steel forgings; Nonferrous forgings; Nonferrous rolling & drawing; Blast furnaces & steel mills
Ch: James J O'Sullivan Jr
*Pr: Brad Ahbe
CFO: Todd Gary
*VP: Dan Antos
VP: Daniel Antos
*VP: Todd Gray
*VP: Bill Maykowski
*VP: Bill Newhouse
*Prin: I H Taylor Et Al
*Prin: J B Weida
VP Mfg: Brad Abhe
Board of Directors: Dale Haase, Daniel J O'donovan, Fred H Zolinger

D-U-N-S 07-411-4562 IMP
CANTON FOOD CO INC
750 S Alameda St, Los Angeles, CA 90021-1624
Tel (213) 688-7707 Founded/Ownrshp 1999
Sales 111.3MM^E EMP 106
SIC 5141 5146 5411 5421 5149 4222 Groceries, general line; Seafoods; Grocery stores; Seafood markets; Groceries & related products; Refrigerated warehousing & storage
CEO: Shiu Lit Kwan
*Pr: Cho W Kwan
*CEO: Shui Lit Kwan
*VP: Wai Kam Kwan

D-U-N-S 14-423-4747
CANTON WIND-DOWN CO
A C I
5711 Research Dr, Canton, MI 48188-2261
Tel (734) 467-8121 Founded/Ownrshp 1984
Sales 119.5MM^E EMP 1,000
SIC 1731 Cable television installation; Voice, data & video wiring contractor
Pr: Michael A Falsetti
CFO: Kristin Gignac
*VP: Richard E Kish
*VP: Micheal Kurcz

VP: Karen L Yales
Dir IT: Gary A Ciak

D-U-N-S 07-582-1405
CANTON-POTSDAM HOSPITAL
50 Leroy St, Potsdam, NY 13676-1799
Tel (315) 265-3300 *Founded/Ownrshp* 1952
Sales 137.5MM *EMP* 480
SIC 8062 General medical & surgical hospitals
Ch: Edward Mucenski
**Ch Bd:* David Patterson
COO: Linda Summers
CFO: Joseph Demeo
**CFO:* Richard Jacobs
CFO: Tony Vavra
**Ch:* Margaret Addan
Bd of Dir: E S Howlett
VP: Susan Hodgson
VP: Deanna Page
Dir Inf Cn: Nancy Wood
Dir Rx: Jennifer Nye
Dir Rx: Jennifer Starnes

CANTOR FITZGERALD
See FITZGERALD CANTOR L P

D-U-N-S 96-519-9821
CANTOR FITZGERALD & CO INC
110 E 59th St Fl 5, New York, NY 10022-1733
Tel (212) 938-5000 *Founded/Ownrshp* 1983
Sales NA *EMP* 1,000
SIC 6211

D-U-N-S 07-105-2161
CANTOR FITZGERALD SECURITIES CORP
(*Suby of* CANTOR FITZGERALD) ★
499 Park Ave, New York, NY 10022-1240
Tel (212) 938-5000 *Founded/Ownrshp* 1972
Sales 129.3MM^E *EMP* 2,216
SIC 6211

CANUSA HERSHMAN RECYCLING CO
See CANUSA HERSHMAN RECYCLING LLC

D-U-N-S 11-855-4042 EXP
CANUSA HERSHMAN RECYCLING LLC
CANUSA HERSHMAN RECYCLING CO
45 Ne Industrial Rd # 105, Branford, CT 06405-6801
Tel (203) 488-0887 *Founded/Ownrshp* 2002
Sales 156.7MM^E *EMP* 150
SIC 4953 Refuse systems; Recycling, waste materials
CEO: Ethan Hershman
**Ch Bd:* Bruce Fleming
**Pr:* Jonathan Sloan
**CFO:* Todd Laggis
VP Admn: Michael Gajewski

D-U-N-S 07-983-2415
CANYON FUEL CO LLC
6100 Dutchmans Ln Fl 9, Louisville, KY 40205-3279
Tel (502) 584-6022 *Founded/Ownrshp* 1996
Sales 806.0MM *EMP* 1,000
SIC 1241 Coal mining exploration & test boring
Ch: John Siegel

D-U-N-S 07-080-1238
CANYON INDEPENDENT SCHOOL DISTRICT
3301 N 23rd St, Canyon, TX 79015-6166
Tel (806) 677-2600 *Founded/Ownrshp* 1900
Sales 81.9MM *EMP* 1,175
Accts Brown Graham & Company Pc
SIC 8211 Public elementary school; Public junior high school; Public senior high school
Ex Dir: Justin Richardson
CTO: Tracey Tennison
IT Man: Carla Chisum
Teacher Pr: Ken Carriere
Psych: Norman Ronda

CANYON RIM CARE CENTRE
See ZIONS MOUNTAIN VIEW HOME AND ASSOCIATES LTD

D-U-N-S 08-169-1149
CANYON STATE OIL CO INC
(*Suby of* SC FUELS) ★
2640 N 31st Ave, Phoenix, AZ 85009-1523
Tel (602) 269-7981 *Founded/Ownrshp* 2006
Sales 84.8MM^E *EMP* 210^E
SIC 5172 5531 Lubricating oils & greases; Automotive & home supply stores
VP: Todd Hernke
**Treas:* Michel Salbaing
Info Man: Keith Butler
Opers Mgr: Lauren Hutton

CANYON VISTA MEDICAL CENTER
See VISTA RCHP-SIERRA INC

CANYONS, THE
See ASC UTAH INC

D-U-N-S 82-985-6496
CANYONS SCHOOL DISTRICT
9361 S 300 E, Sandy, UT 84070-2902
Tel (801) 826-5340 *Founded/Ownrshp* 2009
Sales 297.8MM *EMP* 4,500^E
Accts Squire & Company Pc Orem Ut
SIC 8211 Public combined elementary & secondary school
Dir Sec: Kevin Ray
Dir IT: Scott McCombs
Web Dev: Tyler Toone
Pr Dir: Melinda Colton
Pr Dir: Jeff Haney
Teacher Pr: Stephen Dimond
Instr Medi: Susan Chase
Psych: Sanders Lisa
HC Dir: Tamra Baker
HC Dir: Teresa Scheidler

C.A.P.
See COLLEGE OF AMERICAN PATHOLOGISTS

D-U-N-S 15-042-0396
CAP GEMINI AMERICA INC
(*Suby of* CAPGEMINI CONSULTING) ★
623 5th Ave Fl 33, New York, NY 10022-9104
Tel (917) 934-8000 *Founded/Ownrshp* 2005
Sales 467.9MM^E *EMP* 2,500
SIC 7379

D-U-N-S 05-940-2961
CAP GROUP INC
DUNKIN' DONUTS
77 Washington St, Weymouth, MA 02188-1702
Tel (781) 335-9650 *Founded/Ownrshp* 1999
Sales 98.7MM^E *EMP* 1,499^E
SIC 5461 Doughnuts
Prin: Ed Cappola

D-U-N-S 13-448-4393
CAP-MPT
333 S Hope St Fl 8, Los Angeles, CA 90071-3001
Tel (213) 473-8600 *Founded/Ownrshp* 1977
Sales NA *EMP* 200
Accts Ernst & Young Llp Chicago I
SIC 6351 Liability insurance
CEO: Jim Weidner
**Ch Bd:* Michael Wormley MD
**CFO:* John Donaldson
**Sr VP:* Nancy Brusegaard Johnson
**VP:* Thomas Andre
VP: Ernest R Khirallah
VP: John Raleigh
Exec: Nancy Brusegaard
**Prin:* Cindy Belcher
Netwrk Mgr: Wilson Lautchang
Software D: Carole A Lambert

CAPA
See COLUMBUS ASSOCIATION FOR PERFORMING ARTS

D-U-N-S 07-837-5979 IMP/EXP
CAPACITY OF TEXAS INC (TX)
TRAILER JOCKEY
(*Suby of* COLLINS INDUSTRIES INC) ★
401 Capacity Dr, Longview, TX 75604-5341
Tel (903) 759-0610 *Founded/Ownrshp* 1975, 1984
Sales 88.8MM^E *EMP* 125
SIC 3537 Tractors, used in plants, docks, terminals, etc.: industrial
Pr: Scott Lord
Pr: Nick Miles
**Treas:* Donald Collins Jr
**VP:* Joseph Belle
**VP:* Jerry Looney
Dir Bus: Kevin Hebert

D-U-N-S 07-322-6227
CAPE CANAVERAL HOSPITAL INC
HEALTH FIRST HEALTH PLANS
(*Suby of* HEALTH FIRST HEALTH PLANS) ★
701 W Cocoa Beach Cswy, Cocoa Beach, FL 32931-5595
Tel (321) 799-7111 *Founded/Ownrshp* 1984
Sales 103.5MM *EMP* 964
SIC 8062 General medical & surgical hospitals
Pr: R Roy Wright
**CFO:* Robert C Galloway
**Ch:* Kevin B Steele
**Sec:* Thomas Hollingsworth
Dir Inf Cn: Joan Scabarozi
Dir Risk M: Cheryl Gregory
Dir Case M: Anita M Clure
Dir Rad: Thomas H Clarke
Dir Rx: Ron McGrier
Dir IT: Mark Amy
Sfty Mgr: James Kendige

D-U-N-S 00-695-4549
CAPE COD FIVE CENTS SAVINGS BANK
19 West Rd, Orleans, MA 02653-3204
Tel (508) 240-0555 *Founded/Ownrshp* 1855
Sales NA *EMP* 450
SIC 6036 State savings banks, not federally chartered
CEO: Dorothy A Savarese
Pr: William Hourihan
COO: Donna N Snow
**Treas:* Philp Wong
Ofcr: Debra Anderson
Ofcr: Michelle Donahue
Ofcr: Emmy Hamilton
Ofcr: Peter Horne
Ofcr: Dawn Johnson
Ofcr: Beth A Meehan
Ofcr: Cathy Silva
Ofcr: Helen Souza
Sr Inv Off: Rachael Aiken
Trst Ofcr: Beth Thompson
Ex VP: Joel Brickman
**Ex VP:* Bruce Hammatt Jr
**Ex VP:* Leonard Sullivan
Ex VP: Bert Talerman
VP: Kimberly Chesnut
VP: Vanessa Greene
VP: Barbara Knapp

D-U-N-S 11-561-7529
CAPE COD HEALTHCARE INC
27 Park St, Hyannis, MA 02601-5230
Tel (508) 862-5030 *Founded/Ownrshp* 1984
Sales 724.5MM *EMP* 1,850
Accts Pricewaterhousecoopers Llp Bo
SIC 8062 General medical & surgical hospitals
Pr: Michael K Lauf
**CFO:* Michael Connors
CFO: Thomas Severance
VP: Jean Butler
VP: Jeanne Fallon
VP: Mary Franco
VP: Jack D Lipomi
VP: Victor Oliveira
Dir Risk M: Joan Martinelli
Dir Risk M: Lisa Tager
Comm Dir: Robin Lord

D-U-N-S 07-172-0601
CAPE COD HOSPITAL
(*Suby of* CAPE COD HEALTHCARE INC) ★
27 Park St, Hyannis, MA 02601-5203
Tel (508) 862-7575 *Founded/Ownrshp* 1919
Sales 462.2MM *EMP* 1,700
SIC 8062 8011 8063 General medical & surgical hospitals; Primary care medical clinic; Psychiatric hospitals
CEO: Michael K Lauf
Chf Rad: Charles Diana
COO: Karin Anderson
**COO:* Arthur Mombourquette
Chf Mktg O: James Butterick
**Sr VP:* Theresa M Ahern
**Sr VP:* Michael L Connors
Sr VP: Jeff Dykens
**Sr VP:* Jeanne Fallon
VP: Mike Connors
VP: Patrick Kane
VP: Jack D Lipomi
VP: Stephanie Nadolny
Dir Lab: Cheryl Connon

D-U-N-S 00-633-4080
CAPE ELECTRICAL SUPPLY LLC
P B ELECTRICAL SUPPLY
(*Suby of* GRAYBAR ELECTRIC CO INC) ★
489 Kell Farm Dr, Cape Girardeau, MO 63701-9028
Tel (573) 431-1838 *Founded/Ownrshp* 2016
Sales 97.1MM^E *EMP* 195
SIC 3699 5063 Electrical equipment & supplies; Electrical apparatus & equipment
Pr: Kyle Thoma
CFO: Glen French
VP: Craig Jeter
Rgnl Mgr: Ed Kasten
Brnch Mgr: Jim Hughes
Brnch Mgr: John Lunini
Brnch Mgr: Bill Pickens
Brnch Mgr: Lindel Worley
Genl Mgr: Gary Messmer
Off Mgr: Sandy Kassel
Store Mgr: Stanley Taylor

D-U-N-S 14-804-0736
CAPE ENVIRONMENTAL MANAGEMENT INC
500 Pinnacle Ct Ste 100, Norcross, GA 30071-3630
Tel (770) 908-7200 *Founded/Ownrshp* 1991
Sales 287.5MM^E *EMP* 315
SIC 1542 1541 Nonresidential construction; Industrial buildings & warehouses
CEO: Fernando J Rios
**Pr:* Kurt Gates
**CFO:* Les Flynn
**CFO:* Richard Vallejo
**Sr VP:* Chris Caviness
**VP:* Monica Cooper
Off Mgr: Elaine Linnar
Snr PM: Michael Spradling

D-U-N-S 07-557-5738
CAPE FEAR COMMUNITY COLLEGE
(*Suby of* NORTH CAROLINA COMMUNITY COLLEGE SYSTEM) ★
411 N Front St, Wilmington, NC 28401-3910
Tel (910) 362-7000 *Founded/Ownrshp* 1958
Sales 2.6MM *EMP* 1,000^E
SIC 8222 9411 Community college; Administration of educational programs;
Pr: Ted Springs
VP: Carl Brown
**VP:* Dr Amanda Lee
**VP:* Cammellia Rice
Comm Man: Bret Hering
Store Mgr: Cheryl Baucom
Pgrm Dir: Dan Reid

CAPE FEAR VALLEY HEALTH SYSTEM
See CUMBERLAND COUNTY HOSPITAL SYSTEM INC

D-U-N-S 36-099-2841 IMP
CAPE FEAR VALLEY MEDICAL CENTER
1638 Owen Dr, Fayetteville, NC 28304-3424
Tel (910) 615-4000 *Founded/Ownrshp* 2005
Sales 630.0MM *EMP* 2,711
SIC 8011 Offices & clinics of medical doctors
CEO: Michael Nagowski
**CFO:* Sandra Williams
Dir Rad: David J Allison
CTO: Shawanna McKethan
Pathlgst: Charles Scott
Doctor: Ali Husain
Doctor: Niveen Iskander
Doctor: Robert Maughan
Doctor: Elizabeth Schaider
Doctor: Larry Withers

D-U-N-S 62-420-8864
CAPE HEALTH SYSTEM INC
2 Stone Harbor Blvd, Cape May Court House, NJ 08210-2138
Tel (609) 463-2000 *Founded/Ownrshp* 1988
Sales 43.4M *EMP* 1,000
SIC 8741 Hospital management; Nursing & personal care facility management
Pr: Joanne Carrocino
Pr: Michael Morley
**Ch:* Herbert Hornsby
VP: Richard Falivena
Dir Rad: Keith Babore

D-U-N-S 00-971-4101
CAPE MEMORIAL HOSPITAL INC
BRIGHT IDEAS GIFT SHOP
(*Suby of* BRIGHT IDEAS GIFT SHOP) ★
636 Del Prado Blvd S, Cape Coral, FL 33990-2668
Tel (239) 424-2000 *Founded/Ownrshp* 1996
Sales 204.6MM *EMP* 50
SIC 8062 General medical & surgical hospitals
CEO: James R Nathan
Doctor: James Borden MD
Doctor: Juan C Domingo MD
Doctor: Bharath Radhakrishna
HC Dir: Karen McKitrick

D-U-N-S 13-523-5778
CAPE REGIONAL MEDICAL CENTER INC
2 Stone Harbor Blvd, Cape May Court House, NJ 08210-2138
Tel (609) 463-2000 *Founded/Ownrshp* 1950
Sales 118.8MM *EMP* 1,200
SIC 8062 General medical & surgical hospitals
Pr: Joanne Carrocino
**CFO:* William Zeuner
VP: Richard P Falazena
Dir Rad: Keith Babore
Dir Rx: Rich Artymowicz
Dir Bus: Scott Ohntrup
**Prin:* Suketu Nanavati
Off Mgr: Karen Grimley
CIO: Rich Wheatly
QC Dir: Joyce Rieck
Prd Mgr: Bruce Bethune

D-U-N-S 83-850-4975
▲ CAPELLA EDUCATION CO
225 S 6th St Fl 9, Minneapolis, MN 55402-4319
Tel (888) 227-3552 *Founded/Ownrshp* 1991
Sales 430.2MM *EMP* 2,887^E
Tkr Sym CPLA *Exch* NGS
SIC 8221 Colleges universities & professional schools; Professional schools; Colleges & universities; University
Ch Bd: J Kevin Gilligan
CFO: Steven L Polacek
Ofcr: Peter M Ramstad
VP: Renee L Jackson
Snr Mgr: Joel Reiss
Board of Directors: Darrel R Tukua, Rita D Brogley, H James Dallas, Matthew W Ferguson, Michael A Linton, Michael L Lomax, Jody G Miller, Stephen G Shank, David W Smith, Jeffrey W Taylor

D-U-N-S 07-999-0951
CAPELLA HEALTH HOLDINGS LLC
(*Suby of* MPT OPERATING PARTNERSHIP LP) ★
1000 Urban Center Dr # 501, Vestavia, AL 35242-2532
Tel (205) 969-3455 *Founded/Ownrshp* 2015
Sales 713.4MM^E *EMP* 6,000^E
SIC 6798 8062 Real estate investment trusts; General medical & surgical hospitals
Pr: Edward Haldag

D-U-N-S 36-391-2093
CAPELLA HEALTHCARE INC
RRCH HEALTHCARE PARTNERS
(*Suby of* CAPELLA HOLDINGS INC) ★
103 Continental Pl # 200, Brentwood, TN 37027-1042
Tel (615) 764-3000 *Founded/Ownrshp* 2005
Sales 713.4MM *EMP* 6,000
SIC 8062 General medical & surgical hospitals
Ch: Daniel S Slipkovich
**Ch Bd:* James Anderson
**Pr:* Michael Wiechart
Pr: Beth Wright
COO: Nancy Locke
COO: Bill Southwick
CFO: Denise W Arren
**CFO:* Denise Warren
**Ex VP:* Neil W Kunkel
**Ex VP:* Andrew Slusser Slusser
**Sr VP:* Sam Moody
Sr VP: Erik Swensson MD
Sr VP: Lori Wooten
VP: Rick Charbonneau
VP: Holly Clark
VP: Ray Coffey
VP: Ben Ross
VP: Davis Turner
VP: Lee Yuill
Dir Lab: Dawn Parker
Dir Rad: Teresa Fletcher

D-U-N-S 03-249-5086
CAPELLA HOLDINGS INC
(*Suby of* CAPELLA HEALTH HOLDINGS LLC) ★
103 Continental Pl # 200, Brentwood, TN 37027-1042
Tel (615) 844-9800 *Founded/Ownrshp* 2015
Sales 713.4MM^E *EMP* 6,000^E
SIC 8062 6719 General medical & surgical hospitals; Investment holding companies, except banks
Pr: Michael A Wiechart
CFO: Andrew Slusser
Ex VP: Donald J Bivacca
Ex VP: Mark Medley
Sr VP: Alan Smith

D-U-N-S 03-202-0245
■ CAPELLA UNIVERSITY INC
(*Suby of* CAPELLA EDUCATION CO) ★
225 S 6th St Fl 9, Minneapolis, MN 55402-4319
Tel (612) 339-8650 *Founded/Ownrshp* 1993
Sales 180.9MM^E *EMP* 2,500^E
SIC 8221 Colleges universities & professional schools; Colleges & universities; University; Professional schools
CEO: Kevin Gilligan
Pr: Mike Buttry
**Pr:* Richard Senese
**CFO:* Louis Martin
Treas: Faeth Brian
Bd of Dir: Kimberly Spoor
**Chf Mktg O:* Mary Miller
**Sr VP:* Steven L Polacek
VP: Barbara R Beebe
VP: Leslie Bronk
VP: Deborah Bushway
VP: Diana Johnson
**VP:* Gregory W Thom

CAPELLI OF NY
See GMA ACCESSORIES INC

CAPGEMINI CONSULTING
See CAPGEMINI NORTH AMERICA INC

D-U-N-S 00-513-7810
CAPGEMINI FINANCIAL SERVICES INTERNATIONAL INC (IL)
(*Suby of* CAPGEMINI CONSULTING) ★
6400 Shafer Ct Ste 100, Rosemont, IL 60018-4916
Tel (847) 384-6100 *Founded/Ownrshp* 1989
Sales 124.6MM^E *EMP* 1,500
SIC 7371 Custom computer programming services
CEO: Raymond J Spencer
**COO:* Aiman Ezzat
**CFO:* Rakesh Malani
Treas: Shishir Ranjan
**Ofcr:* Jean A Cholka
**Ex VP:* Ken Coppins
**Ex VP:* Larry Gordon
Mng Dir: Roger Van Scoy

D-U-N-S 19-847-4686
CAPGEMINI FINANCIAL SERVICES USA INC
(*Suby of* CAPGEMINI FINANCIAL SERVICES INTERNATIONAL INC) ★
6400 Shafer Ct Ste 100, Rosemont, IL 60018-4916
Tel (847) 384-6100 *Founded/Ownrshp* 1995
Sales 124.6MM^E *EMP* 1,200
SIC 7373 Systems software development services
Pr: Thierry Delaporte

D-U-N-S 12-881-5607
CAPGEMINI NORTH AMERICA INC
CAPGEMINI CONSULTING
(*Suby of* CAP GEMINI)
623 5th Ave Fl 33, New York, NY 10022-9104
Tel (212) 314-8000 *Founded/Ownrshp* 2002
Sales 2.6MMM^E *EMP* 42,984
SIC 7379
CEO: Paul Hermelin
CEO: Dave Bonner
CEO: Lanny Cohen
CEO: Raymond Spencer
**Treas:* Richard Plessner
Chf Mktg O: Christopher K Williams
Ofcr: Vincent Shepherd
**Ofcr:* Kim Smith
VP: Alvi Abuaf
VP: Douglas Charles
VP: Randy Cousins
VP: Wayne H Harper
VP: James Pizzo
VP: Steve Rudderham
VP: Derek Shipes
VP: Jean-Claude Viollier
Assoc Dir: Annette Miiller

D-U-N-S 83-216-6750
CAPGEMINI US LLC
623 5th Ave Fl 33, New York, NY 10022-9104
Tel (917) 934-8000 *Founded/Ownrshp* 2000
Sales 363.5MM^E *EMP* 2,000
SIC 8748

D-U-N-S 03-057-7993
CAPISTRANO UNIFIED SCHOOL DISTRICT
33122 Valle Rd, San Juan Capistrano, CA 92675-4859
Tel (949) 234-9200 *Founded/Ownrshp* 1965
Sales 269.8MM^E *EMP* 4,500
SIC 8211 School board
CEO: John M Alpay
Admn Mgr: T K Frantz
Dir IT: Susan Holiday
Dir IT: Gabe Salinas
IT Man: Barbara Scholl
Pr Dir: Robert Miller
Teacher Pr: Tim Brooks
HC Dir: Mike Beekman

D-U-N-S 01-220-3696
CAPITAL AREA SERVICE CO INC
CAPITAL AREA SERVICES COMPANY
(*Suby of* CFMI) ★
200 Kanawha Blvd E, Charleston, WV 25301-2511
Tel (304) 346-3800 *Founded/Ownrshp* 1991
Sales NA *EMP* 640
SIC 6324 6321 Health maintenance organization (HMO), insurance only; Accident & health insurance
VP: Sam Tire

CAPITAL AREA SERVICES COMPANY
See CAPITAL AREA SERVICE CO INC

D-U-N-S 96-981-7931
CAPITAL AUTOMOTIVE REAL ESTATE SERVICES INC
8270 Greensboro Dr # 950, Mc Lean, VA 22102-3800
Tel (703) 288-3075 *Founded/Ownrshp* 2014
Sales 201.9MM^E *EMP* 33^E
SIC 6798 Real estate investment trusts
Pr: Jay M Ferriero
**Treas:* Erica B Powers
Sr VP: William J Beck
Sr VP: Christopher J Sokira

D-U-N-S 05-950-6076
■ **CAPITAL BANK CORP**
(*Suby of* CAPITAL BANK FINANCIAL CORP) ★
333 Fayetteville St, Raleigh, NC 27601-1747
Tel (919) 645-0868 *Founded/Ownrshp* 2011
Sales NA *EMP* 1,375
SIC 6022 State commercial banks
Pr: R Eugene Taylor
Pr: Chris McCoy
Pr: B Grant Yarber
CFO: Christopher G Marshall
Ofcr: Damon Amato
Ofcr: Mark Cox
Ofcr: Dennis Farmer
Ofcr: William Griffin
Ofcr: William Harvey
Ofcr: Stacy Jobe
Ofcr: Lee McInnis
Ofcr: David Moore
Ofcr: Raymond Morales
Ofcr: Karen Trentham
Ofcr: Scott Welch
Ofcr: Cara Whittaker
Ofcr: Sheldon Williamson
Ex VP: R Bruce Singletary
Sr VP: Kim Howren
VP: Ken Folz
VP: Patricia Hayhurst

D-U-N-S 00-253-8639
▲ **CAPITAL BANK FINANCIAL CORP**
4725 Piedmont Row Dr, Charlotte, NC 28210-4270
Tel (704) 554-5901 *Founded/Ownrshp* 2009
Sales NA *EMP* 1,389^E
Accts Crowe Horwath Llp Fort Lauder
Tkr Sym CBF *Exch* NGS
SIC 6021 National commercial banks
Ch Bd: R Eugene Taylor
CFO: Christopher G Marshall
Chf Cred: R Bruce Singletary
Ex VP: Vincent M Lichtenberger
Exec: Maria Justo
Exec: Kenneth Kavanagh

D-U-N-S 96-344-2277
■ **CAPITAL BANK NA**
(*Suby of* CAPITAL BANK FINANCIAL CORP) ★
121 Alhambra Plz Ste 1601, Coral Gables, FL 33134-4541
Tel (305) 444-1660 *Founded/Ownrshp* 2010
Sales NA *EMP* 485
SIC 6021 National commercial banks
CEO: Gene Taylor
**CFO:* Chris Marshall
Ofcr: Tim Coley
Ex VP: Vincent Lichtenberger
Sr VP: Edward Tietjen
Sr VP: Sonia Wiseman
VP: Maria Cerdeiras
VP: Keith Johnson
VP: Joe Robbins
VP: Henry Sieloff
VP: Amanda Wojoski

D-U-N-S 06-169-1689
CAPITAL BLUE CROSS (PA)
2500 Elmerton Ave, Harrisburg, PA 17177-9799
Tel (717) 541-7000 *Founded/Ownrshp* 1937, 1938
Sales NA *EMP* 1,900
SIC 6321 Disability health insurance
CEO: William Lehr Jr
**Pr:* Gary D St Hilaire
**CFO:* Michael Cleary
CFO: Robert Durante
CFO: Gary Saint Hilaire
Bd of Dir: John J Aguirre
Bd of Dir: Jeffrey S Bader
Bd of Dir: Barbara A Baylor
Bd of Dir: Ronald E Boyer
Bd of Dir: Matthew A Clemens
Bd of Dir: Thomas H Deshong
Bd of Dir: Vicki Dubuisson
Bd of Dir: Kelly L Edwards
Bd of Dir: David C Finch
Bd of Dir: Jeffrey E Fix
Bd of Dir: Dennis J Guth
Bd of Dir: Ronald J Jacobs
Bd of Dir: M J Johnston
Bd of Dir: Robert E Kessler
Bd of Dir: Paul V Kilker
Bd of Dir: Lee E Knepp

D-U-N-S 05-585-0878
CAPITAL BUILDING SERVICES GROUP INC
CBSG
540 Capital Dr Ste 100, Lake Zurich, IL 60047-6754
Tel (847) 847-3800 *Founded/Ownrshp* 2010
Sales 31.8MM^E *EMP* 1,100
SIC 7349 Janitorial service, contract basis
Pr: Rick Aiello
**Owner:* Randy Sanders
**VP:* Oscar Gallegos
**VP:* Kimberly Zacharkiewicz
Rgnl Mgr: Thomas Rawski
Area Mgr: Greg Pahl
Board of Directors: Randy Sanders

D-U-N-S 01-911-5690
CAPITAL CANDY CO INC
32 Burnham St, Barre, VT 05641-4708
Tel (802) 476-6689 *Founded/Ownrshp* 1938
Sales 99.7MM^E *EMP* 110
SIC 5145 5194 5122 5141 5149 Confectionery; Tobacco & tobacco products; Druggists' sundries; Groceries, general line; Groceries & related products
Pr: George Burnes
CFO: Kim Hewitt
**VP:* Prudence Burnes
Sales Asso: Kyle Lafountain

CAPITAL CARE RHBILITATION SVCS
See DMN MANAGEMENT SERVICES LLC

CAPITAL CARING
See CAPITAL HOSPICE

D-U-N-S 92-699-5481
■ **CAPITAL CITY BANK**
(*Suby of* CAPITAL CITY BANK GROUP INC) ★
217 N Monroe St, Tallahassee, FL 32301-7690
Tel (850) 402-7700 *Founded/Ownrshp* 1995
Sales NA *EMP* 767
SIC 6022 State commercial banks
Pr: Thomas A Barron
CFO: J Davis
Bd of Dir: Frederick Carroll III
Ex VP: Randolph Briley
Ex VP: William Colledge
**Ex VP:* Kim Davis
**Ex VP:* Mitchell R Englert
Ex VP: Bill Johnston
**Ex VP:* Marvin W Strickland
Ex VP: Edwin N West
**Sr VP:* Edward Canup
**Sr VP:* Jean Cottrell
**Sr VP:* Noel Ellis
**Sr VP:* Charles S Johnson
Sr VP: Jep Larkin
**Sr VP:* Karen Love
**Sr VP:* Robert K Mayer
Sr VP: Ross P Obley
Sr VP: William R Odigues
Sr VP: Frances Purvis
Sr VP: Donald Ruggiero
Board of Directors: William Butler

D-U-N-S 11-974-9604
▲ **CAPITAL CITY BANK GROUP INC**
217 N Monroe St, Tallahassee, FL 32301-7690
Tel (850) 402-7000 *Founded/Ownrshp* 1982
Sales NA *EMP* 894^E
Tkr Sym CCBG *Exch* NGS
SIC 6022 State commercial banks
Ch Bd: William G Smith Jr
Pr: Alicia Ronan
CFO: J Kimbrough Davis
**Treas:* Thomas A Barron
Trst Ofcr: Erica Hunter
VP: Sterling Bryant
VP: Craig Ellard
VP: Jim Scarboro
Off Mgr: Shelly Irvin
Off Mgr: Becky Magwood
Board of Directors: Allan G Bense, Frederick Carroll III, J Everitt Drew, John K Humphress, Lina S Knox, Henry Lewis III, John G Sample Jr

D-U-N-S 00-818-1273
CAPITAL CITY PRESS LLC
ADVOCATE , THE
10705 Reiger Rd, Baton Rouge, LA 70809-4520
Tel (225) 383-1111 *Founded/Ownrshp* 1906
Sales 117.3MM^E *EMP* 600
SIC 2711 2752 Newspapers, publishing & printing; Commercial printing, lithographic
Pr: David Manship
DP Exec: Barry Blanc
Opers Mgr: Susan Devillier

D-U-N-S 02-563-5747
CAPITAL DIGESTIVE CARE LLC (MD)
12510 Prosperity Dr # 200, Silver Spring, MD 20904-1663
Tel (240) 485-5203 *Founded/Ownrshp* 2007
Sales 90.0MM^E *EMP* 300
SIC 8011 Gastronomist
CEO: Arnold Levy
COO: Kevin Harlen
VP: Michael Weinstein

D-U-N-S 15-309-3120
CAPITAL DISTRIBUTING LLC
SIX POINT BEVERAGES
421 N Portland Ave, Oklahoma City, OK 73107-6109
Tel (405) 521-1511 *Founded/Ownrshp* 2001
Sales 110.9MM^E *EMP* 170
SIC 5181 Beer & ale
Genl Mgr: Gordon Green
**VP:* Rick Higginson
Mktg Mgr: Jessica Green

D-U-N-S 11-923-8806
CAPITAL DISTRICT PHYSICIANS HEALTH PLAN INC
500 Patroon Creek Blvd, Albany, NY 12206-5006
Tel (518) 641-3700 *Founded/Ownrshp* 1984
Sales 1.4MMM *EMP* 700
Accts Bonadio & Co Llp Albany Ny
SIC 8011 Health maintenance organization
Pr: John Bennett
**Pr:* William Cromie
COO: Regina Monthony
Treas: Bruce Cohen
Chf Mktg O: Brian Morrissey
Sr VP: Frederick Galt
Sr VP: Bruce D Nash
VP: Sigrid Cerio
VP: John Demers
VP: Robert Hinckley
VP: Robert Little
VP: Kevin Mowll
VP: Sheila Nelson
VP: Andy Prior
VP: Cynthia Wicks
Exec: Wayne Alger
Exec: Ellen Pierce
Exec: Lisa C Stratton
Comm Dir: Janet Flanagan

D-U-N-S 00-718-1688
■ **CAPITAL ELECTRIC CONSTRUCTION CO INC**
(*Suby of* MDU RESOURCES GROUP INC) ★
600 Broadway Blvd Ste 600, Kansas City, MO 64105-1544
Tel (816) 472-9500 *Founded/Ownrshp* 1957
Sales 168.8MM^E *EMP* 350
SIC 1731 General electrical contractor
Pr: Michael A Wells
Sr VP: Mike Martin
VP: Dennis Stowell
Sfty Dirs: Sam Smith
Snr PM: Steve Hill

D-U-N-S 07-845-3618
CAPITAL FOR MERCHANTS LLC
CFM
(*Suby of* ADVANCED PAYMENT SOLUTIONS) ★
250 Stephenson Hwy, Troy, MI 48083-1117
Tel (248) 269-6000 *Founded/Ownrshp* 2005
Sales NA *EMP* 500
SIC 6153 Working capital financing; Credit card services, central agency collection
Pr: Jeff Bankowski

D-U-N-S 05-640-0310
CAPITAL FORD INC
CAPITAL FORD RENTAL
4900 Capital Blvd, Raleigh, NC 27616-4407
Tel (919) 790-4600 *Founded/Ownrshp* 1985
Sales 272.0MM *EMP* 250
SIC 5511 Automobiles, new & used
Pr: Timothy W Michael
**Sec:* Chester Michael III
Genl Mgr: Jerry Mosley
Off Mgr: Monika Kiliti
IT Man: Ricky Apple
Sls Mgr: Mike Shane
Sales Asso: Mitchell Anderson
Sales Asso: Ed Barnes
Sales Asso: Kevin Braswell
Sales Asso: Jarvis Cheek
Sales Asso: Ron Clifton

CAPITAL FORD RENTAL
See CAPITAL FORD INC

D-U-N-S 05-476-4212 IMP
CAPITAL FOREST PRODUCTS INC (MD)
111 Gibralter Ave, Annapolis, MD 21401-3140
Tel (410) 280-6102 *Founded/Ownrshp* 1981
Sales 105.9MM *EMP* 20
Accts Kahn Berman Solomon Taibel
SIC 5031 Lumber, plywood & millwork
Pr: Mike L Tichenor
**Sec:* Barbara Tichenor

CAPITAL GROUP, THE
See CAPITAL GROUP COMPANIES INC

D-U-N-S 06-384-3387
CAPITAL GROUP COMPANIES INC
CAPITAL GROUP, THE
333 S Hope St Fl 55, Los Angeles, CA 90071-3061
Tel (213) 486-9200 *Founded/Ownrshp* 1931
Sales 2.5MMM^E *EMP* 3,180
SIC 6282 6091 6722 8741 Investment advice; Nondeposit trust facilities; Mutual fund sales, on own account; Management services
CEO: Philip De Toledo
Pr: Jennifer Butler
Pr: Cindi Grossinger
Pr: Kevin Hogan
Pr: Tim Lambert
Pr: Thomas Lavandosky
Pr: Paul Liu
Pr: Maria Lockard
Pr: Sakura Mizuno
Pr: Paula Orologas
Pr: Matthew Saak
Ofcr: Russell Lemley
Ofcr: Anthony Seiffert
Trst Ofcr: Barbara Brewer
Ex VP: Martin Romo
Sr VP: Doreen Gee
VP: Hilda Applbaum
VP: John Armour
VP: Canise Arredondo
VP: Patricia Artigas
VP: Curtis Baker

D-U-N-S 05-769-3939
CAPITAL HEALTH PLAN INC
2140 Centerville Rd, Tallahassee, FL 32308-4314
Tel (850) 383-3333 *Founded/Ownrshp* 1978
Sales 651.8MM *EMP* 423
SIC 8011

D-U-N-S 06-436-6065
CAPITAL HEALTH SYSTEM INC
750 Brunswick Ave, Trenton, NJ 08638-4143
Tel (609) 394-6000 *Founded/Ownrshp* 1997
Sales 585.5MM *EMP* 3,000^E
Accts Withumsmithbrown Pc Morristow
SIC 8062 General medical & surgical hospitals
Pr: Al Maghazehe
**Ch Bd:* Samuel J Plumeri Jr
**CFO:* Shane Fleming
**Ex VP:* Larry Disanto
Nurse Mgr: Martine Marsan
Dir IT: Ken Szeliga
Telecom Mg: Robert Vaccarino
Sls&Mrk Ex: Jayne O'Connor
Doctor: Mary Welsh
Doctor: Kristopher Young
Pharmcst: Lauren Farrell
Board of Directors: Anthony C Hooper, Michael L Somerstein, Linda Wood

D-U-N-S 09-636-4633
CAPITAL HOSPICE
CAPITAL CARING
2900 Telestar Ct, Falls Church, VA 22042-1206
Tel (703) 538-2065 *Founded/Ownrshp* 1977
Sales 85.1MM *EMP* 500
SIC 8082 8052 Home health care services; Intermediate care facilities
Pr: Malene Smith-Davis
V Ch: David M Dunning
**CFO:* David A Schwind
Treas: Frank Gomes
**Sec:* Mark Weber
VP: Diane Rigsby
Exec: Debi Benner
Dir Soc: Dee Paige
Genl Mgr: Chip Cagle
Genl Mgr: Carolyn Richar
Genl Mgr: Stefan Scholz

CAPITAL INSURANCE GROUP
See CALIFORNIA CAPITAL INSURANCE CO

D-U-N-S 07-136-8109 IMP
■ **CAPITAL IQ INC**
(*Suby of* S&P GLOBAL INC) ★
55 Water St Fl 49, New York, NY 10041-0004
Tel (212) 438-8736 *Founded/Ownrshp* 2004
Sales 83.2MM^E *EMP* 700
SIC 8742 Banking & finance consultant; Business consultant
Mng Pt: Neal D Goldman
**Mng Pt:* Steven B Turner
Assoc VP: Danielle Roski
**Sr VP:* Brendan Dolan
Sr VP: Andrew McDonnell
VP: Scott Brennan
**VP:* John Burke
VP: John Desmond
VP: Claudia Fauber
VP: Mark Fenton
VP: Traceylee Gaskin
VP: Robert Glashow
VP: Alan Katz
VP: Kevin Morrissey
VP: Michael Privitera
VP: Todd Smith
VP: Janet Sternberger
VP: Katharina R Voudouris
Dir Risk M: Eric Staffin
Assoc Dir: Limor Zahav

D-U-N-S 02-362-5098
CAPITAL LIGHTING & SUPPLY LLC
CAPITAL TRISTATE
(*Suby of* SONEPAR USA) ★
8511 Pepco Pl, Upper Marlboro, MD 20772-2500
Tel (301) 909-6500 *Founded/Ownrshp* 1958
Sales 684.7MM^E *EMP* 600
SIC 5063 Electrical apparatus & equipment
Pr: John Hardy
**COO:* Alan Rosenfeld
VP: Anthony Fleming
**VP:* Michael Hensley
Exec: Debbie Frye
Brnch Mgr: Steve Hines
Brnch Mgr: Wayne Kramer
Dir IT: Carl Price
Sls Mgr: Daniel Smyser
Sales Asso: Patrick Horine

Section I
Businesses Alphabetically

D-U-N-S 03-589-3395 EXP
CAPITAL LUMBER CO (AZ)
5110 N 40th St Ste 242, Phoenix, AZ 85018-2151
Tel (602) 381-0709 *Founded/Ownrshp* 1948
Sales 375.0MM *EMP* 286
SIC 5031 Building materials, exterior
Pr: Denny Elmer
**Pr:* Sam Sanregret
**Ch:* John E Gaskin
**VP:* Michael Darby
Div Mgr: Edward Brown
Div Mgr: Tracy Madsen
Div Mgr: Van Vanderhoff
Div Mgr: Matt Yates
Natl Sales: Lance Doalson
Merch Mgr: Carl Shelley
Sls Mgr: Bill Butner

D-U-N-S 87-671-1250
CAPITAL MEDICAL CENTER
RRCH HEALTHCARE PARTNERS
(*Suby of* RRCH HEALTHCARE PARTNERS) ★
3900 Capital Mall Dr Sw, Olympia, WA 98502-5026
Tel (360) 754-5858 *Founded/Ownrshp* 1997
Sales 114.2MM *EMP* 500
SIC 8062 8011 General medical & surgical hospitals; Offices & clinics of medical doctors
CEO: Jim Geist
Chf Mktg O: Susan Kent
Dir Lab: Kathy J Staffordbeck
Dir Rx: Charlotte Mehegan
Off Mgr: Laura Hudgins
Dir IT: Brian Felter
Mtls Dir: Patrick Atkinson
Sls&Mrk Ex: Julie Leydelmyer
Mktg Dir: Renee Crotte
Mktg Dir: Renee Crotty
Doctor: Brian Anderson

CAPITAL MERCURY APPAREL
See CAPITAL-MERCURY APPAREL LTD

D-U-N-S 13-759-6524
CAPITAL METROPOLITAN TRANSPORTATION AUTHORITY
2910 E 5th St, Austin, TX 78702-4895
Tel (512) 389-7400 *Founded/Ownrshp* 1985
Sales 28.7MM *EMP* 1,300
Accts Padgett Stratemann & Co Ll
SIC 4111 Bus line operations; Trolley operation
Prin: Gerald Robichaux Sr
Comm Man: Francine Pares
**Prin:* Leslie Browder
Snr Ntwrk: Lori Hyde
IT Man: Mark Clendennen
IT Man: Jane Schroter
MIS Mgr: Tania Kierklewski
MIS Mgr: Mark Xavier
Genl Couns: Catherine Rinaldi

CAPITAL MT
See NTHRIVE SOLUTIONS

D-U-N-S 92-837-6628
▲ CAPITAL ON DECK INC
1400 Broadway Fl 25, New York, NY 10018-5225
Tel (888) 269-4246 *Founded/Ownrshp* 2006
Sales NA *EMP* 638
Tkr Sym ONDK *Exch* NYS
SIC 6153 Working capital financing
Ch Bd: Noah Breslow
COO: James Hobson
CFO: Howard Katzenberg
Ofcr: Nick Brown
Sr VP: Gagan Kanjlia
VP: Ofer Bar-Zakai
VP: Martha Dreiling
VP: Pamela Rice
VP: Paul Rosen
Snr Sftwr: Victoria Au
Sftwr Eng: Samuel Brice
Board of Directors: David Hartwig, Daniel S Henson, Bruce P Nolop, James D Robinson III, Jane J Thompson, Ronald F Verni, Neil E Wolfson

D-U-N-S 19-671-5635
■ CAPITAL ONE AUTO FINANCE INC
(*Suby of* CAPITAL ONE FINANCIAL CORP) ★
7933 Preston Rd, Plano, TX 75024-2302
Tel (800) 946-0332 *Founded/Ownrshp* 1998
Sales NA *EMP* 2,400
SIC 6141 Automobile loans, including insurance
CEO: Sanjiv Yajnik
Pt: Brian Peterson
VP: Larry Rodriguez
Exec: Lauren Mitchell
Area Mgr: Matthew Cross
Area Mgr: Michael Darding
Area Mgr: Charlie Fratus
Area Mgr: Mal Robinson
Area Mgr: Courtney West
Snr Sftwr: Marseld Dedgjonaj
Dir IT: Fred Walker

D-U-N-S 00-592-4600
■ CAPITAL ONE BANK
(*Suby of* CAPITAL ONE FINANCIAL CORP) ★
275 Broadhollow Rd, Melville, NY 11747-4823
Tel (631) 844-1376 *Founded/Ownrshp* 2007
Sales NA *EMP* 7,146
SIC 6022 State commercial banks
CEO: Richard D Fairbank
Pr: John Adam Kanas
Pr: Michael C Slocum
CFO: Rob Anderson
CFO: Daniel M Healy
**V Ch Bd:* John Bohlsen
Ex VP: William Hynes
Ex VP: William McCahill
VP: Meg Beaufrere
VP: Laura Lowy
VP: Jane Marzoli

D-U-N-S 14-776-2764
■ CAPITAL ONE BANK
(*Suby of* CAPITAL ONE FINANCIAL CORP) ★
1680 Capital One Dr, Mc Lean, VA 22102-3407
Tel (804) 967-1000 *Founded/Ownrshp* 1994
Sales NA *EMP* 13,180
SIC 6021 National commercial banks
Ch Bd: Richard D Fairbank
Genl Pt: Shamez Kanji
**Pr:* Nigel W Morris
**Ex VP:* John G Finneran Jr
Sr VP: Kenneth Abramowitz
Sr VP: Andrew Bella
Sr VP: Kenneth Geiger
VP: Dave Jeppesen
VP: Mark Preston
VP: Toby Russell
VP: Konrad Schwarz
VP: David Steier
Dir Risk M: Theresa R Hughes

D-U-N-S 87-818-5453
▲ CAPITAL ONE FINANCIAL CORP
1680 Capital One Dr, Mc Lean, VA 22102-3407
Tel (703) 720-1000 *Founded/Ownrshp* 1994
Sales NA *EMP* 45,400[E]
Tkr Sym COF *Exch* NYS
SIC 6021 6141 National trust companies with deposits, commercial; Personal credit institutions; Automobile & consumer finance companies
Ch Bd: Richard D Fairbank
Pr: Philip Allen
Pr: Caryl Caponi
Pr: Marie Casimir
Pr: Erin Cooney
Pr: Toma Epps
Pr: Jesus Estrada
Pr: Michael Exum
Pr: Shaheen L Farah
Pr: David Ingram
Pr: Kala Kuhlthau
Pr: Amber Mortensen
Pr: Carl Pomplon
Pr: Kristie Robinson
Pr: Charlie Roch
Pr: Michael C Slocum
Pr: Hubert Sodogandji
Pr: Kim Staman
Pr: Max Valdary
Pr: Jonathan W Witter
Pr: Sanjiv Yajnik
Board of Directors: Catherine G West, Patrick W Gross, Ann Fritz Hackett, Lewis Hay III, Benjamin P Jenkins III, Peter Thomas Killalea, Pierre E Leroy, Peter E Raskind, Mayo A Shattuck III, Bradford H Warner

D-U-N-S 78-425-4547
CAPITAL ONE FSB
1680 Capital One Dr, Mc Lean, VA 22102-3407
Tel (610) 350-9074 *Founded/Ownrshp* 1996
Sales NA *EMP* 50,000
SIC 6021 National commercial banks

D-U-N-S 00-694-7543
■ CAPITAL ONE NATIONAL ASSOCIATION
(*Suby of* CAPITAL ONE FINANCIAL CORP) ★
1680 Capital One Dr, Mc Lean, VA 22102-3407
Tel (800) 655-2265 *Founded/Ownrshp* 1870, 2005
Sales NA *EMP* 6,032
SIC 6021 National commercial banks
Pr: Richard D Fairbank
**Pr:* Herb Boydstun
**CFO:* Marsha Gassan
**Ch:* E R Bo Campbell
**Sr VP:* Mary E Delaat

D-U-N-S 83-763-0326
■ CAPITAL ONE SERVICES LLC
(*Suby of* CAPITAL ONE FINANCIAL CORP) ★
1680 Capital One Dr, Mc Lean, VA 22102-3407
Tel (703) 720-1000 *Founded/Ownrshp* 1995
Sales NA *EMP* 6,669
SIC 6141 Personal credit institutions
Pr: Richard D Fairbank
CFO: Teresa Lawson
Ofcr: Mark Douce
Ofcr: Rena Friske
Ex VP: Stephen Mugford
Sr VP: Joseph Bonavita
**Sr VP:* John G Finneran
Sr VP: Yu Huang
Sr VP: Andy Ramamoorthy
Sr VP: Karl Werwath
VP: Amy Anderson
VP: Steve Braden
VP: Jared Brown
VP: Cheryl Denenea
VP: Ernie Eustis
VP: Eric Gutierrez
VP: Marlene Hulem
VP: Drew Jacobs
VP: Scott Joyce
VP: Brandon Key
VP: Ed Maino

CAPITAL PAYMENT PLAN
See IPFS CORP

D-U-N-S 09-190-3765
CAPITAL REGION BOCES
BOCES
900 Watervliet Shaker Rd # 102, Albany, NY 12205-1016
Tel (518) 862-4924 *Founded/Ownrshp* 1953
Sales 88.1MM[E] *EMP* 1,000
SIC 8211 Specialty education
Comm Man: Deborah Bush-Suflita
Ex Dir: Gene Silverman
Genl Mgr: Wendy Ashley
Teacher Pr: Robert Zordan

D-U-N-S 14-426-5550
CAPITAL REGION HEALTH CARE CORP
CONCORD HOSPITAL
250 Pleasant St, Concord, NH 03301-7539
Tel (603) 225-2711 *Founded/Ownrshp* 1944
Sales 431.3MM[E] *EMP* 3,000[E]
Accts Baker Newman & Noyes Portland
SIC 8741 8062 8051 8093 8082 Hospital management; General medical & surgical hospitals; Skilled nursing care facilities; Specialty outpatient clinics; Home health care services
CEO: Robert Stiegmeyer
Chf Path: Gary York
**Pr:* Michael Green
COO: Joe Conley
**Treas:* Bruce R Burns
Trst: Thomas D Akey
Trst: James Cook
Trst: Glenn Currie
Trst: Claudia Walker
Trst: Maura Weston
Trst: Ronald Wilbur
VP: Domenic Ciavarro
VP: Brandi Emerson
VP: David Green
VP: Louis Josephson
Board of Directors: Gary Light

D-U-N-S 07-196-4001
CAPITAL REGION MEDICAL CENTER
1125 Madison St, Jefferson City, MO 65101-5200
Tel (573) 632-5000 *Founded/Ownrshp* 1945
Sales 160.8MM *EMP* 1,200
SIC 8062 General medical & surgical hospitals
Pr: Edward F Farnsworth
Chf Rad: Denzil Hawesdavis
Bd of Dir: Jhan Hurn
Ofcr: Jim Pfautsch
VP: Jason Cecil
VP: Randall Haight
VP: Cathy Luebbert
VP: Thomas Niekamp
VP: Lynne Voskamp
**VP:* Janet Weckenborg
Dir Risk M: Jennifer Fallen
Dir Rad: Kristy Trent

D-U-N-S 04-647-0043
CAPITAL RESEARCH AND MANAGEMENT CO
(*Suby of* CAPITAL GROUP) ★
333 S Hope St Fl 55, Los Angeles, CA 90071-3061
Tel (213) 486-9200 *Founded/Ownrshp* 1944
Sales 310.7MM[E] *EMP* 700
SIC 6282 Investment research; Manager of mutual funds, contract or fee basis
Ch Bd: R Michael Shanahan
Ch Bd: James F Rothenberg
V Ch: Wally Stern
Pr: Timothy Armour
Treas: Larry C Lemmonsen
Treas: Susi Silverman
Ofcr: Bruce Meikle
Ex VP: Jonathan Knowles
Ex VP: Eva Sudol
Sr VP: Hilda Applbaum
Sr VP: David Barclay
**Sr VP:* Gordon Crawford
Sr VP: David Daigle
Sr VP: Gina Despres
Sr VP: Joyce Gordon
Sr VP: David Hoag
Sr VP: Thomas Hogh
Sr VP: Sung Lee
Sr VP: Jesper Lyckeus
Sr VP: Kelly Webb
VP: Chuck Freadhoff
Board of Directors: James E Drasdo, James K Dunton, Robert Gao'donnell, Abner D Goldstine, Catherine M Ward

CAPITAL SAFETY
See D B INDUSTRIES INC

D-U-N-S 00-179-4036 IMP/EXP
■ CAPITAL SAFETY INC
(*Suby of* 3M CO) ★
7900 Intl Dr Ste 405, Bloomington, MN 55425
Tel (612) 216-5800 *Founded/Ownrshp* 1973, 2015
Sales 142.6MM[E] *EMP* 518[E]
SIC 3842 Personal safety equipment
CEO: Stephen G Oswald
Mng Pt: Ed Plant
Pr: Kevin Coplan
VP: Michael Booke
VP: Dan Gasman
Dir Bus: Dale Bartelson
Area Mgr: Jeff Dalgleish
Area Mgr: Dominick Marchesiello
Off Mgr: Beth Trende
VP Opers: Barry White
Mtls Mgr: Wade Fick

D-U-N-S 13-839-4361 IMP/EXP
CAPITAL SALES CO
1471 E 9 Mile Rd, Hazel Park, MI 48030-1960
Tel (248) 542-4400 *Founded/Ownrshp* 2007
Sales 202.7MM *EMP* 60
Accts Stefforia Petik & Associates
SIC 5141 7311 Groceries, general line; Advertising agencies
Pr: Sam Haddad

D-U-N-S 06-008-4365
CAPITAL SCHOOL DISTRICT
198 Commerce Way, Dover, DE 19904-8210
Tel (302) 672-1500 *Founded/Ownrshp* 1929
Sales 69.0MM[E] *EMP* 1,173
SIC 8211 Public elementary school; Public junior high school; Public senior high school; School board
IT Man: Dennis Wooton
Schl Brd P: Phil Martino
Teacher Pr: Mary Cooke

D-U-N-S 62-383-1539
▲ CAPITAL SENIOR LIVING CORP
14160 Dallas Pkwy Ste 300, Dallas, TX 75254-4383
Tel (972) 770-5600 *Founded/Ownrshp* 1990
Sales 412.1MM *EMP* 7,384
Tkr Sym CSU *Exch* NYS
SIC 8051 8052 Skilled nursing care facilities; Intermediate care facilities
CEO: Lawrence A Cohen
Ch Bd: Michael W Reid
Pr: Keith N Johannessen
CFO: Carey P Hendrickson
Sr VP: David W Beathard Sr
Sr VP: David R Brickman
VP: Gregory P Boemer
VP: Gary Fernandez
VP: Joseph G Solari
Board of Directors: Philip A Brooks, Ed Grier, E Rodney Hornbake, Jill M Krueger, Kimberly S Lody, Ronald A Malone

D-U-N-S 80-287-2028
■ CAPITAL SENIOR LIVING INC
RETIREMENT LIVING COMMUNITIES
(*Suby of* CAPITAL SENIOR LIVING CORP) ★
14160 Dallas Pkwy Ste 300, Dallas, TX 75254-4383
Tel (972) 770-5600 *Founded/Ownrshp* 1997
Sales 21.4MM[E] *EMP* 2,244
SIC 6513 Residential hotel operation; Retirement hotel operation
Ch: James A Stroud
**Pr:* Keith N Johannessen
**CEO:* Lawrence A Cohen
**CFO:* Ralph Beattie
**Sr VP:* David Beathard Sr
**Sr VP:* David Brickman
**Sr VP:* Carey Hendrickson

D-U-N-S 00-541-7753 IMP
CAPITAL TIRE INC (OH)
WHOLESALE TIRE DIVISION
1001 Cherry St, Toledo, OH 43608-2995
Tel (419) 241-5111 *Founded/Ownrshp* 1920, 1962
Sales 214.0MM[E] *EMP* 170
SIC 5014 Automobile tires & tubes; Truck tires & tubes
Owner: Thomas B Geiger
Sr VP: Brian Haas
**VP:* Carl J EBY
**VP:* Robert J Scheick
Genl Mgr: Bob Hajjar

D-U-N-S 02-402-0532
CAPITAL TITLE OF TEXAS LLC (TX)
2400 Dallas Pkwy Ste 560, Plano, TX 75093-4381
Tel (972) 682-2700 *Founded/Ownrshp* 1999
Sales NA *EMP* 200
SIC 6361 Title insurance
CEO: William C Shaddock
**Pr:* Keith Hafner
Ofcr: Melanie Fey
**Ex VP:* Jason Schnell
Sr VP: Chris Mitchell
**Sr VP:* Carl Pankratz
VP: Tracy McMahon
VP: Phillip Scalise
VP: Morgan Wright
Dir Bus: Zac Bohl
Dir Bus: Vika Kuznetsova
Dir Bus: Tracy Neeper

CAPITAL TRISTATE
See CAPITAL LIGHTING & SUPPLY LLC

D-U-N-S 00-135-9942 IMP/EXP
CAPITAL-MERCURY APPAREL LTD (NY)
CAPITAL MERCURY APPAREL
1385 Broadway Rm 1800, New York, NY 10018-6001
Tel (212) 704-4800 *Founded/Ownrshp* 1956
Sales NA *EMP* 2,100
SIC 2321 2331

D-U-N-S 82-773-0735
CAPITALSOURCE BANK
130 S State College Blvd, Brea, CA 92821-5807
Tel (714) 989-4600 *Founded/Ownrshp* 2008
Sales NA *EMP* 250
SIC 6022

D-U-N-S 00-378-3425
CAPITALSOURCE INC
633 W 5th St Ste 33, Los Angeles, CA 90071-2005
Tel (213) 443-7700 *Founded/Ownrshp* 2000
Sales NA *EMP* 515[E]
SIC 6159

D-U-N-S 00-811-9422 IMP
CAPITOL AGGREGATES INC (TX)
CAPITOL CEMENT DIVISION
(*Suby of* ZACHRY CONSTRUCTION & MATERIALS INC) ★
11551 Nacogdoches Rd, San Antonio, TX 78217-2337
Tel (210) 655-3010 *Founded/Ownrshp* 1957
Sales 169.0MM[E] *EMP* 525
SIC 3241 1442 1422 2951 4011 Portland cement; Construction sand mining; Gravel mining; Limestones, ground; Asphalt & asphaltic paving mixtures (not from refineries); Railroads, line-haul operating
Pr: Greg Hale
**CEO:* David Zachry
**CFO:* Len Harral
**Treas:* Andy Stokes
**Sr VP:* Leonard R Harral
**Sr VP:* Tim Watt
**VP:* David Disbrow
**VP:* Max L Frailey
**VP:* Max Frailey
**VP:* Joel Galassini
**VP:* Warren A Stokes
Board of Directors: Max Frailey, Greg Hales, Len Harral, Tim Watt, David Zachry

D-U-N-S 36-452-2581
CAPITOL BANCORP LTD
200 N Washington Sq, Lansing, MI 48933-1320
Tel (517) 487-6555 *Founded/Ownrshp* 1982
Sales NA *EMP* 580[E]
SIC 6021 National commercial banks
Ch Bd: Joseph D Reid
Pr: Clinton D Dunn
Pr: Cristin Reid English
Pr: Thomas S Giovanelli
**Pr:* Cristin K Reid
Pr: John C Smythe
Pr: Bruce A Thomas
Pr: Bruce Thomas
Chf Cred: David D Fortune
Ofcr: Todd C Surline
Ex VP: Mike Moran
Sr VP: B A Thoms
VP: Candice G Randolph Sr
Board of Directors: James C Epolito, Gary A Falkenberg, Joel I Ferguson, Kathleen A Gaskin, Lewis D Johns, Michael L Kasten, Steven L Maas, Calvin D Meeusen, Lyle W Miller

D-U-N-S 00-320-3239
CAPITOL BROADCASTING CO INC (NC)
2619 Western Blvd, Raleigh, NC 27606-2125
Tel (919) 890-6000 *Founded/Ownrshp* 1937

Sales 184.8MM[E] *EMP* 500
SIC 4833 4832 4841 8732

D-U-N-S 61-899-0543 IMP
CAPITOL BUILDING SUPPLY INC
(*Suby of* G M S) ★
8429 Euclid Ave, Manassas Park, VA 20111-2375
Tel (703) 631-6772 *Founded/Ownrshp* 1988
Sales 107.9MM[E] *EMP* 140
SIC 5032 5039 5033 5051 Drywall materials; Ceiling systems & products; Insulation materials; Steel
CEO: Richard Mueller
**Pr:* Mike Anderson
**VP:* Brad Crist
Admn Mgr: Bill Lang
Admn Mgr: George Penn
Div Mgr: Bill Naehle
Store Mgr: Jason Martin
Opers Mgr: Dan Thomas
Sales Asso: Mike Green
Sales Asso: Andrew Heinbaugh
Sales Asso: William Hopkins

D-U-N-S 06-712-9015
CAPITOL BUSINESS EQUIPMENT INC
C B E
645 S Mcdonough St, Montgomery, AL 36104-5811
Tel (334) 265-8903 *Founded/Ownrshp* 1990
Sales 93.1MM[E] *EMP* 210
SIC 5045 5044 7699 5065 Computers, peripherals & software; Cash registers; Cash register repair; Security control equipment & systems
CEO: Loring White
**CFO:* James Anderson
**VP:* Kathy White
Dir IT: Keith Smith
Software D: Stephen Goodwin

CAPITOL CEMENT DIVISION
See CAPITOL AGGREGATES INC

D-U-N-S 06-092-9689
▲ CAPITOL FEDERAL FINANCIAL INC
700 S Kansas Ave Fl 1, Topeka, KS 66603-3809
Tel (785) 235-1341 *Founded/Ownrshp* 1999
Sales NA *EMP* 691[E]
Accts Deloitte & Touche Llp Kansas
Tkr Sym CFFN *Exch* NGS
SIC 6035 Federal savings banks
Ch Bd: John B Dicus
CFO: Kent G Townsend
Ofcr: Kathy Spain
Ex VP: Natalie G Haag
Ex VP: Natalie Haag
Ex VP: Carlton A Ricketts
Ex VP: Frank H Wright
VP: Jerry Billinger
VP: Deb Campos
VP: Mike Cast
VP: Ed Cox
VP: Rhonda Dennis
VP: Clint Devoe
VP: Wanda Espinosa
VP: Mark Hernandez
VP: Deborah Johnston
VP: Ronda Maass
VP: Rodney Martin
VP: Kevin Moore
VP: Kevin Morgison
VP: Timothy Murray
Board of Directors: Morris J Huey II, Jeffrey M Johnson, Michael T McCoy, James G Morris, Reginald L Robinson, Jeffrey R Thompson, Marilyn S Ward

D-U-N-S 07-307-2274
■ CAPITOL FEDERAL SAVINGS BANK
(*Suby of* CAPITOL FEDERAL FINANCIAL INC) ★
700 S Kansas Ave Fl 1, Topeka, KS 66603-3894
Tel (785) 235-1341 *Founded/Ownrshp* 2015
Sales NA *EMP* 691
SIC 6035 Federal savings & loan associations
Ch Bd: John B Dicus
CFO: Kent Townsend
Ex VP: R Joe Aleshire
Ex VP: Larry K Brubaker
Ex VP: Rick Jackson
VP: Jennifer Raine
IT Man: Angenette Garcia-Soza

CAPITOL GREEN
See CENTRAL TOWERS PRESERVATION LP

CAPITOL HOME HEALTH
See ADVANCED HEALTH CONCEPTS

D-U-N-S 00-643-6281
■ CAPITOL INDEMNITY CORP (WI)
(*Suby of* CAPITOL TRANSAMERICA CORP) ★
1600 Aspen Cmns Ste 400, Middleton, WI 53562-4772
Tel (608) 829-4200 *Founded/Ownrshp* 1959
Sales NA *EMP* 218
SIC 6331 6351 Property damage insurance; Fire, marine & casualty insurance: stock; Surety insurance; Fidelity insurance
CEO: David F Pauly
**Pr:* James McIntyre
**CFO:* Frederick Taransky
Board of Directors: Larry Burcalow, Michael J Larson, Reinhart H Postweiler, Kenneth P Urso

D-U-N-S 19-630-3275
CAPITOL LAKES RETIREMENT COMMUNITY
METHODIST HEALTH CENTER
(*Suby of* UNITYPOINT HEALTH-MERITER) ★
110 S Henry St, Madison, WI 53703-3172
Tel (608) 283-2000 *Founded/Ownrshp* 1982
Sales 9.8MM *EMP* 1,070[E]
SIC 6513 8051 8052 8361 Residential hotel operation; Skilled nursing care facilities; Intermediate care facilities; Residential care
Pr: Tim Conroy

D-U-N-S 00-453-2917
CAPITOL LIGHT & SUPPLY CO
C L S
270 Locust St, Hartford, CT 06114-2023
Tel (860) 549-1230 *Founded/Ownrshp* 2002
Sales 617.3M[E] *EMP* 10,001

SIC 5063 Lighting fixtures; Electrical construction materials
Pr: David Mullane
COO: Barry Wolff
CFO: Robert Canyock
Sr VP: Kevin Depatie
VP: Simon Atkinson
VP: Don Ripley
Dept Mgr: Regina Dumas
Dept Mgr: Stephen Lippert
Brnch Mgr: Dave Bevan
Brnch Mgr: David Coombs
Brnch Mgr: Vito Costantiello

CAPITOL MANUFACTURING DIVISION
See PHOENIX FORGE GROUP LLC

D-U-N-S 19-595-8280
CAPITOL MATERIALS OF SAVANNAH INC
(*Suby of* G M S) ★
305 Telfair Rd, Savannah, GA 31415-9503
Tel (912) 232-0952 *Founded/Ownrshp* 2005
Sales 128.8MM[E] *EMP* 325[E]
SIC 5082 Contractors' materials
CEO: Richard K Mueller
**Pr:* Brian Buttrey
**CFO:* Richard A Whitcomb

D-U-N-S 01-769-3339
CAPITOL PARTNERS I LP
1808 I St Nw Ste 200, Washington, DC 20006-5419
Tel (202) 955-7960 *Founded/Ownrshp* 1998
Sales 19.1MM[E] *EMP* 3,000
SIC 8082 6211 Home health care services; Security brokers & dealers
Mng Pt: T J Jubeir
Sr VP: Julie Jubeir
Sr VP: Julie Jubier

D-U-N-S 09-635-5953
■ CAPITOL POLICE US
(*Suby of* CONGRESS UNITED STATES) ★
119 D St Ne, Washington, DC 20510-0119
Tel (202) 593-3647 *Founded/Ownrshp* 1828
Sales NA *EMP* 1,207
SIC 9221 Bureau of criminal investigation, government
Pr: Carl W Hoecker
IT Man: Robert Clark

D-U-N-S 00-838-2913
CAPITOL RECORDS LLC
EMI MUSIC DISTRIBUTION
1750 Vine St, Los Angeles, CA 90028-5274
Tel (213) 462-6252 *Founded/Ownrshp* 2012
Sales 52.2MM[E] *EMP* 1,500
SIC 7389 8999 Music & broadcasting services; Music arranging & composing
CFO: Lustin Morris
Sr VP: Ron Laffitte
Sr VP: Justin Morris
VP: Jason Boyd
VP: Jim Brennan
VP: Michael Howe
VP: Kate Miller
VP: Eric Samson
VP: Matt Sawin
VP: Pat Shah
VP: Gary Spivack
VP: Aaron Striegel
VP: Paula Tuggey
VP: Lance Turner
VP: Jane Ventom

D-U-N-S 06-189-6424
CAPITOL REGION EDUCATION COUNCIL FOUNDATION INC (CT)
CREC
111 Charter Oak Ave, Hartford, CT 06106-1912
Tel (860) 524-4068 *Founded/Ownrshp* 1966
Sales 363.9MM *EMP* 1,800
Accts Blum Shapiro & Company Pc
SIC 8299 Educational services
COO: Sandy Serrano
Comm Man: Jerry Clapis
Ex Dir: Donald P Walsh
Mng Dir: David Daye
Mng Dir: James Keller
Off Admin: Rebecca Gonzalez
Off Admin: Lynne Witowski
Dir IT: David Wu
Secur Mgr: Chris Nolan
Pr Dir: Aura Alvarado
Teacher Pr: Regina Terrell

D-U-N-S 06-815-7742 IMP/EXP
CAPITOL SALES CO INC
1245 Trapp Rd Ste 130, Eagan, MN 55121-1268
Tel (651) 688-6830 *Founded/Ownrshp* 1986
Sales 85.3MM[E] *EMP* 72
SIC 5064 5065 8742 Electrical entertainment equipment; Communication equipment; Incentive or award program consultant
Pr: Curtis A Hayes
Sales Exec: Steve Konsor

D-U-N-S 06-202-7979
CAPITOL SECURITY POLICE INC
703 Calle Victor Lopez, San Juan, PR 00909-2843
Tel (787) 727-1700 *Founded/Ownrshp* 1998
Sales 38.1MM *EMP* 2,000
SIC 7381 Security guard service
Pr: Miguel Portilla
**VP:* Angel Munoz

D-U-N-S 04-467-0347
■ CAPITOL TRANSAMERICA CORP
(*Suby of* ALLEGHANY INSURANCE HOLDINGS LLC) ★
1600 Aspen Cmns Ste 400, Middleton, WI 53562-4772
Tel (608) 829-4200 *Founded/Ownrshp* 2002
Sales NA *EMP* 250
SIC 6331 6351 Property damage insurance; Fire, marine & casualty insurance: stock; Surety insurance; Fidelity insurance
Prin: Jacqueline Melonas
**COO:* James McIntyre
**CFO:* Frederick Taransky

D-U-N-S 02-507-0269 IMP
CAPITOL WHOLESALE MEATS INC
FONTANINI ITLN MEATS SAUSAGES
8751 W 50th St, Mc Cook, IL 60525-3132
Tel (708) 485-4800 *Founded/Ownrshp* 1973
Sales 146.9MM[E] *EMP* 414
SIC 2013 Frozen meats from purchased meat; Prepared pork products from purchased pork
CEO: Eugene Fontanini
**Pr:* Joanne Fontanini
CFO: Steve Fradkin
Genl Mgr: Charles L Brown
Sales Asso: Jennifer McCain

D-U-N-S 00-202-2929
CAPITOL-EMI MUSIC INC
E M D
1750b Vine St, Los Angeles, CA 90028-5209
Tel (323) 462-6252 *Founded/Ownrshp* 1996
Sales NA *EMP* 1,500
SIC 3652

D-U-N-S 14-038-6199
■ CAPLEASE INC
(*Suby of* VEREIT INC) ★
1065 Avenue Of The Americ, New York, NY 10018-0976
Tel (212) 217-6300 *Founded/Ownrshp* 2013
Sales 162.0MM *EMP* 17[E]
SIC 6798 Real estate investment trusts
Ch Bd: Paul H McDowell
**Pr:* William R Pollert
**CFO:* Shawn P Seale
**Sr VP:* Robert C Blanz
Sr VP: Michael J Naughton
**VP:* Paul C Hughes

CAPLUGS
See PROTECTIVE INDUSTRIES INC

D-U-N-S 80-043-2994
CAPMARK BANK
116 Welsh Rd, Horsham, PA 19044-2296
Tel (801) 569-4606 *Founded/Ownrshp* 2007
Sales NA *EMP* 17[E]
SIC 6022 State commercial banks
Prin: M Danny Wall

D-U-N-S 95-998-5755
CAPMARK FINANCE INC
(*Suby of* BLUESTEM GROUP INC) ★
7075 Flying Cloud Dr, Eden Prairie, MN 55344-3532
Tel (215) 328-4622 *Founded/Ownrshp* 1973
Sales NA *EMP* 979
Accts Price Waterhouse Llp New York
SIC 6162 Mortgage bankers
Pr: William C Gallagher
VP: Ronald O Verrilli

D-U-N-S 01-465-4966
CAPP INC
201 Marple Ave, Clifton Heights, PA 19018-2414
Tel (610) 394-1100 *Founded/Ownrshp* 1990
Sales 111.3MM[E] *EMP* 95
SIC 5084 3699

CAPPUCCINO COLLECTION
See SAUMIL DIAM LLC

D-U-N-S 19-535-6621
CAPRICORN INVESTORS II LP
30 E Elm St, Greenwich, CT 06830-6529
Tel (203) 861-6600 *Founded/Ownrshp* 1988
Sales 3.3MM *EMP* 6,614
SIC 2676 5461 6794 Diapers, paper (disposable): made from purchased paper; Bakeries; Patent owners & lessors
Genl Pt: Herbert Winokur Jr
Genl Pt: James M Better
Genl Pt: Nathaniel A Gregory
Genl Pt: Dudley C Mecum

D-U-N-S 87-990-4019 IMP/EXP
■ CAPROCK COMMUNICATIONS CORP
(*Suby of* HARRIS CORP) ★
4400 S Sam Houston Pkwy E, Houston, TX 77048-5902
Tel (281) 482-0289 *Founded/Ownrshp* 2010
Sales 116.1MM[E] *EMP* 440
SIC 4813 Local & long distance telephone communications
Ch Bd: Jere W Thompson Jr
**Pr:* Leo J Cyr
**Pr:* Tracey Haslam
**CFO:* Paul Rainey
**CFO:* James E Skinner
**VP:* Alan Aronowitz
VP: Ken Bonvillian
**VP:* Kenneth L Monblatt

D-U-N-S 19-489-1230
CAPROCK HOME HEALTH SERVICES INC
CAPROCK MEDICAL SUPPLY
8806 University Ave, Lubbock, TX 79423-3152
Tel (806) 748-7722 *Founded/Ownrshp* 1983
Sales 66.5MM[E] *EMP* 2,200
SIC 8082 Home health care services
Pr: Marciano Morales
**Ex VP:* Carlos Morales
**Genl Couns:* Martha Morales

CAPROCK MEDICAL SUPPLY
See CAPROCK HOME HEALTH SERVICES INC

D-U-N-S 19-013-9204
■ CAPROCK PIPELINE CO
(*Suby of* ONEOK INC) ★
100 W 5th St Ste Ll, Tulsa, OK 74103-4213
Tel (918) 588-7900 *Founded/Ownrshp* 2000
Sales 175.5MM[E] *EMP* 3,000
SIC 4922 Pipelines, natural gas
Pr: David Kyle
**VP:* Curtis Dinan
**VP:* Dan Walker

D-U-N-S 95-673-2093 IMP
CAPSONIC AUTOMOTIVE INC
460 2nd St, Elgin, IL 60123-7008
Tel (847) 888-7300 *Founded/Ownrshp* 1996

Sales 139.0MM[E] *EMP* 500
Accts Crowe Horwath Llp Oak Brook
SIC 3625 3679 3674 Motor controls & accessories; Switches, electric power; Harness assemblies for electronic use: wire or cable; Radiation sensors
Pr: Gregory G Liautaud
VP: Seth Gutkowski

D-U-N-S 00-825-0409 IMP
CAPSTAN CALIFORNIA INC
16100 S Figueroa St, Gardena, CA 90248-2617
Tel (310) 366-5999 *Founded/Ownrshp* 1959
Sales 89.3MM[E] *EMP* 500
SIC 3499 Friction material, made from powdered metal
CEO: Mark Paullin
CFO: Bonita Gonzales

D-U-N-S 17-500-9786
▲ CAPSTEAD MORTGAGE CORP
8401 N Central Expy # 800, Dallas, TX 75225-4404
Tel (214) 874-2323 *Founded/Ownrshp* 1985
Sales 216.3MM *EMP* 14[E]
Accts Ernst & Young Llp Dallas Te
Tkr Sym CMO *Exch* NYS
SIC 6798 Real estate investment trusts
Pr: Phillip A Reinsch
**Ch Bd:* Jack Biegler
Ex VP: Robert R Spears Jr
CIO: Behnam Niknam

CAPSTONE
See COUGHLAN COMPANIES INC

D-U-N-S 80-811-2804
CAPSTONE COMMODITIES LLC
1311 Chisholm Trl, Round Rock, TX 78681-2968
Tel (512) 671-6626 *Founded/Ownrshp* 2007
Sales 167.0MM *EMP* 7
SIC 5191 5999 Animal feeds; Feed & farm supply
Pr: Michael Rickert

D-U-N-S 07-877-6443
CAPSTONE DIGITAL LLC
(*Suby of* CAPSTONE) ★
1710 Roe Crest Dr, North Mankato, MN 56003-1806
Tel (507) 385-8280 *Founded/Ownrshp* 2011
Sales 93.0MM *EMP* 85
SIC 2731 Books: publishing only
Pr: Todd R Brekhus
CEO: G Thomas Ahern
COO: William R Rouse

D-U-N-S 01-503-6055
CAPSTONE LOGISTICS LLC (GA)
6525 The Corners Pkwy, Norcross, GA 30092-3344
Tel (770) 414-1929 *Founded/Ownrshp* 2011, 2014
Sales 210.9MM[E] *EMP* 701[E]
SIC 4789 Cargo loading & unloading services
CEO: Steve Taylor
Pr: Wade Castle
VP: Bryan Meister
Dir Bus: Craig Pearson

D-U-N-S 85-899-4239 IMP/EXP
▲ CAPSTONE TURBINE CORP
21211 Nordhoff St, Chatsworth, CA 91311-5844
Tel (818) 734-5300 *Founded/Ownrshp* 1988
Sales 85.2MM *EMP* 236[E]
Accts Kpmg Llp Los Angeles Califor
Tkr Sym CPST *Exch* NGM
SIC 3511 Turbines & turbine generator sets
Pr: Darren R Jamison
**Ch Bd:* Gary D Simon
CFO: Jayme L Brooks
CFO: Edward I Reich
CFO: Lonnie Schnell
Ex VP: James D Crouse
Ex VP: John C Fink
Ex VP: Fink John
Ex VP: Walter McBride
Sr VP: Paul Chancellor
Sr VP: Robert Gleason
VP: Stephen F Gillette
VP: Richard B Lewis
VP: Kevin Young
VP Bus Dev: Steve Gillette
Board of Directors: Richard J Atkinson, Noam Lotan, Gary J Mayo, Eliot G Protsch, Holly A Van Deursen, Darrell J Wilk

CAPSUGEL A DIVISION OF PFIZER
See CAPSUGEL MANUFACTURING INC

D-U-N-S 96-749-6733 IMP
CAPSUGEL INC
412 Mount Kemble Ave 200c, Morristown, NJ 07960-6674
Tel (862) 242-1700 *Founded/Ownrshp* 2011
Sales 637.9MM[E] *EMP* 2,000
SIC 2834 Antibiotics, packaged
CEO: Guido Driesen
**COO:* Fabrice Quaghebeur
**Chf Mktg O:* Philip Laut
Off Mgr: Karen Jefferson
Cmptr Lab: Sophie Keersmaeker
QA Dir: Shirley Blocker
Opers Mgr: Blaise Winch
Sls Mgr: Joachim Meier

D-U-N-S 78-739-3409 IMP
CAPSUGEL MANUFACTURING INC
CAPSUGEL A DIVISION OF PFIZER
(*Suby of* CAPSUGEL INC) ★
535 Emerald Rd N, Greenwood, SC 29646-9669
Tel (864) 223-2270 *Founded/Ownrshp* 2011
Sales 136.9MM[E] *EMP* 600[E]
SIC 2899 Gelatin capsules
Pr: Guido Driesen

D-U-N-S 00-193-6079 IMP/EXP
CAPSULE INTERNATIONAL LLC
(*Suby of* CAPSULE INTERNATIONAL HOLDINGS LLC)
1100 Northbrook Dr, Trevose, PA 19053-8403
Tel (215) 552-3700 *Founded/Ownrshp* 1927
Sales 152.3MM[E] *EMP* 1,240
SIC 3089 Plastic containers, except foam; Jars, plastic
Pr: Grant H Beard

**Ch Bd:* L White Matthews
**CFO:* J Mark Borseth

D-U-N-S 05-103-6937 IMP/EXP
CAPSULE PA INC
CONSTAR PLASTICS
1100 Northbrook Dr Fl 2, Trevose, PA 19053-8403
Tel (215) 552-3700 *Founded/Ownrshp* 2012
Sales NA *EMP* 1,238
SIC 3089 3085

CAPT
See CELINA ALUMINUM PRECISION TECHNOLOGY INC

D-U-N-S 14-014-6197
CAPTAIN DS LLC
624 Grassmere Park Ste 30, Nashville, TN 37211-3671
Tel (615) 391-5461 *Founded/Ownrshp* 2013
Sales 276.4MM[E] *EMP* 5,000
SIC 5812 Seafood restaurants
Pr: Phil Greifeld
Pr: Janet Duckham
**CFO:* Keith Davis
Ex VP: Michael Lippert
CIO: Chris Crabtree
Pr Mgr: Jennifer Legel
Mktg Mgr: Sam Brenner
Mktg Mgr: Ben Powell
Genl Couns: Mike N Folks

D-U-N-S 09-969-5210
CAPTEL INC
450 Science Dr, Madison, WI 53711-1169
Tel (608) 238-5400 *Founded/Ownrshp* 2001
Sales 115.5MM[E] *EMP* 1,000[E]
SIC 3842 Hearing aids
Pr: Robert Engelke

D-U-N-S 04-987-7319 IMP/EXP
■ CAPTIVE PLASTICS INC
(*Suby of* BERRY PLASTICS CORP) ★
101 Oakley St, Evansville, IN 47710-1237
Tel (812) 424-2904 *Founded/Ownrshp* 1969, 2008
Sales 189.8MM[E] *EMP* 1,235
SIC 3089 Plastic containers, except foam; Closures, plastic; Injection molding of plastics
COO: John Dezio
**VP:* Rick Carroll
**VP:* Rolland Strasser

D-U-N-S 09-511-4997 IMP/EXP
CAPTIVE-AIRE SYSTEMS INC (NC)
AQUA-MATIC
4641 Paragon Park Rd # 104, Raleigh, NC 27616-3407
Tel (919) 882-2410 *Founded/Ownrshp* 1978, 1981
Sales 258.7MM[E] *EMP* 600
Accts R Scott Grady Cpa Pllc Ral
SIC 3444 Restaurant sheet metalwork
Pr: Robert L Luddy
CFO: William Francis
**Treas:* William H Francis Jr
Bd of Dir: Shannon Lack
Exec: Ryan Leonard
Assoc Dir: Patrick Villella
Rgnl Mgr: Dave Christensen
Rgnl Mgr: Jesse Dobbelaere
Rgnl Mgr: Mark Profet
Rgnl Mgr: Jonathan Story
Snr Sftwr: Joe Manger

CAPUTO'S FRESH MARKETS
See CAPUTOS NEW FARM PRODUCE INC

D-U-N-S 08-906-1725 IMP
CAPUTOS NEW FARM PRODUCE INC
CAPUTO'S FRESH MARKETS
520 E North Ave, Carol Stream, IL 60188-2125
Tel (630) 620-4444 *Founded/Ownrshp* 1958
Sales 115.1MM[E] *EMP* 700
SIC 5431 5411 5148 5149 Fruit stands or markets; Vegetable stands or markets; Grocery stores; Frozen food & freezer plans, except meat; Fruits, fresh; Vegetables, fresh; Groceries & related products
CEO: Robert Presta
**Pr:* Antonella Caputo Presta
Mktg Dir: Curt Case

D-U-N-S 03-639-8589
CAR ENTERPRISES INC
1040 N Benson Ave, Upland, CA 91786-2157
Tel (909) 932-9242 *Founded/Ownrshp* 2001
Sales 154.7MM[E] *EMP* 400[E]
SIC 5541 5411 Filling stations, gasoline; Convenience stores
Pr: Sam Anabi

D-U-N-S 15-535-8112
CAR TOYS INC
VERIZON WIRELESS AUTHORIZED RET
400 Fairview Ave N # 900, Seattle, WA 98109-5371
Tel (206) 443-2726 *Founded/Ownrshp* 1987
Sales 369.1MM[E] *EMP* 2,500
SIC 5731 5999 Sound equipment, automotive; Telephone equipment & systems
Ch: Daniel Brettler
**Pr:* David Drew
**CFO:* Robert L Jensen
Rgnl Mgr: Argola Russell
Dist Mgr: Oscar Amador
Dist Mgr: Craig Bertsch
Dist Mgr: Marc Outzen
Dist Mgr: Teddy Sarno
Dist Mgr: Jason Seth
Dist Mgr: Landon Womack
Dist Mgr: Charles Zaragoza

D-U-N-S 96-311-2578
CAR WASH PARTNERS INC
MISTER CAR WASH
(*Suby of* ONEX CORPORATION)
1503 S Collins St, Plant City, FL 33563
Tel (813) 754-0777 *Founded/Ownrshp* 1996
Sales 287.5MM[E] *EMP* 5,000
SIC 7542 7549 Carwashes; Lubrication service, automotive
Ch Bd: Ron Peterson
Pr: John Lai
CFO: Lawrence Minich
VP: Dave Hail
Dir IT: Terry Hale
VP Mktg: Brad Simonis

CAR-BER TESTING SERVICES
See CARBER HOLDINGS INC

D-U-N-S 01-870-8271
CARABETTA ENTERPRISES INC
200 Pratt St Ofc, Meriden, CT 06450-4268
Tel (203) 237-7400 *Founded/Ownrshp* 1950
Sales 144.8MM[E] *EMP* 450
SIC 1522 1542 1521 6512 Apartment building construction; Commercial & office building, new construction; New construction, single-family houses; Commercial & industrial building operation
CEO: Joseph F Carabetta
**VP:* Salvatore P Carabetta
Dir IT: Diane Logobicio
Opers Mgr: Mary Liptak

D-U-N-S 08-836-5767
CARAHSOFT TECHNOLOGY CORP (MD)
1860 Michael Faraday Dr # 100, Reston, VA 20190-5328
Tel (703) 871-8500 *Founded/Ownrshp* 1999
Sales 1.0MMM *EMP* 500
SIC 5045 Computers
Pr: Craig P Abod
**CFO:* John Bukman
VP: Amira Ali
Prgrm Mgr: Chris Heibert
Off Mgr: Marianne Trigg
IT Man: Robert Zimmerman
Sls Dir: Will Jones
Sls Dir: Brian O'Donnell
Sls Dir: Michael Shrader
Mktg Mgr: Julie Dutton
Mktg Mgr: Jenna Shepard

D-U-N-S 01-684-2395
CARAMAGNO FOODS CO
14255 Dequindre St, Detroit, MI 48212-1572
Tel (313) 869-8200 *Founded/Ownrshp* 1946
Sales 212.0MM[E] *EMP* 150
SIC 5141 5142 Groceries, general line; Packaged frozen goods
Pr: Daniel Caramagno
CFO: Dave Pieper
**VP:* Joseph C Caramagno
**Prin:* Martin Caramagno

D-U-N-S 17-722-5265
CARAT FUSION INC
CARAT USA
(*Suby of* DENTSU AEGIS NETWORK USA) ★
1 South Sta 300, Boston, MA 02110-2212
Tel (617) 449-4100 *Founded/Ownrshp* 1986
Sales 47.8MM[E] *EMP* 1,699
SIC 7319 Media buying service
Pr: Daniel Belmont
**CFO:* Christopher Todisco
VP: Jennifer Berry
VP: Adam Cahill
VP: Bill Hewson
Mng Dir: Jane Deery

CARAT USA
See CARAT FUSION INC

D-U-N-S 09-860-1255
CARAT USA INC
(*Suby of* DENTSU AEGIS NETWORK USA) ★
150 E 42nd St, New York, NY 10017-5612
Tel (212) 591-9100 *Founded/Ownrshp* 2011
Sales 59.6MM[E] *EMP* 1,000
SIC 7319 Media buying service
CEO: Doug Ray
Sr VP: Laura Hernandez
Sr VP: Johann Wachs
VP: Nikola Blagg
VP: John Keanna
Assoc Dir: Zachary Graney
Mktg Mgr: Clare Elias

D-U-N-S 62-772-9023 IMP/EXP
CARAUSTAR CUSTOM PACKAGING GROUP INC
(*Suby of* TAMA PAPERBOARD) ★
5000 Austell Powder Sprin, Austell, GA 30106-2440
Tel (770) 948-3101 *Founded/Ownrshp* 1997
Sales 145.2MM[E] *EMP* 783
SIC 2657 Folding paperboard boxes
CEO: Michael Patton

D-U-N-S 00-315-5355 IMP/EXP
CARAUSTAR INDUSTRIAL AND CONSUMER PRODUCTS GROUP INC (GA)
(*Suby of* TAMA PAPERBOARD) ★
2031 Carolina Place Dr, Fort Mill, SC 29708-6947
Tel (803) 548-5100 *Founded/Ownrshp* 2007
Sales 243.0MM[E] *EMP* 1,523[E]
SIC 2655 2671 2679 Tubes, fiber or paper: made from purchased material; Packaging paper & plastics film, coated & laminated; Paper products, converted
Pr: Jimmy A Russell

D-U-N-S 03-949-7029 IMP/EXP
CARAUSTAR INDUSTRIES INC (NC)
TAMA PAPERBOARD
5000 Astell Pwdr Sprng Rd, Austell, GA 30106-2427
Tel (770) 948-3101 *Founded/Ownrshp* 1987, 2013
Sales 1.5MMM[E] *EMP* 3,800
SIC 2655 2631 2679 2656 2652 Tubes, fiber or paper: made from purchased material; Cores, fiber: made from purchased material; Paperboard mills; Folding boxboard; Paperboard products, converted; Food containers (liquid tight), including milk cartons; Setup paperboard boxes
Pr: Michael C Patton
CFO: Ronald Domanico
CFO: Michael T Murren
Treas: William A Nix
VP: Thomas C Dawson
**VP:* Scott O'Melia
IT Man: Kaci Turner

D-U-N-S 17-632-7369
CARAVAN FACILITIES MANAGEMENT LLC
CK SECURITY & SAFETY SOLUTIONS
1400 Weiss St Ste 1, Saginaw, MI 48602-5278
Tel (989) 239-2126 *Founded/Ownrshp* 1997
Sales 128.8MM *EMP* 2,145[E]
Accts Rehmann Robson Saginaw Mi
SIC 7349 Building maintenance, except repairs; Janitorial service, contract basis
Ch Bd: Brandon J Bordeaux
CFO: Dennis Argyle
Genl Mgr: Doug Landon
IT Man: Nancy Ratajczak
Sfty Dirs: Ken Zintel

D-U-N-S 00-714-6897 IMP/EXP
CARAVAN INGREDIENTS INC (GA)
CORBION-CARAVAN
(*Suby of* CORBION N.V.)
7905 Quivira Rd, Lenexa, KS 66215-2732
Tel (913) 890-5500 *Founded/Ownrshp* 1945, 1988
Sales 192.7MM[E] *EMP* 700
SIC 2099 2821 5084 2087

D-U-N-S 79-767-4553
CARBER HOLDINGS INC
CAR-BER TESTING SERVICES
(*Suby of* PLATTE RIVER VENTURES LLC) ★
12600 N Featherwood Dr # 450, Houston, TX 77034-4451
Tel (713) 797-2859 *Founded/Ownrshp* 2002
Sales 122.6MM[E] *EMP* 250
Accts Deloitte & Touche Llp
SIC 1389 7389 Testing, measuring, surveying & analysis services; Petroleum refinery inspection service
CEO: Jim Nattier
**Pr:* John Tucci
**CFO:* Hank Winfield
Genl Mgr: Roy Harrell

D-U-N-S 12-361-2264 IMP/EXP
CARBIDE INDUSTRIES LLC
4400 Bells Ln, Louisville, KY 40211-2143
Tel (502) 775-4100 *Founded/Ownrshp* 2007
Sales 100.0MM[E] *EMP* 200
SIC 2813 2819 Acetylene; Calcium carbide
Pr: Jim Carrell
CFO: Darrell Higgins
Genl Mgr: Grant Cullen
Genl Mgr: Michael Simons
CIO: Lois Bryan
IT Man: Darin Jett
Tech Mgr: Greg Brasel
Opers Mgr: Doug Robertson
Plnt Mgr: Dan Wharton
Sls Mgr: Richard Dippolito

D-U-N-S 15-155-2437
▲ CARBO CERAMICS INC
575 N Dairy Ashford Rd # 30, Houston, TX 77079-1117
Tel (281) 921-6400 *Founded/Ownrshp* 1987
Sales 279.5MM *EMP* 665[E]
Tkr Sym CRR *Exch* NYS
SIC 3291 5945 8742 7371 Abrasive products; Ceramics supplies; Management consulting services; Custom computer programming services
Pr: Gary A Kolstad
**Ch Bd:* William C Morris
CFO: Ernesto Bautista III
Chf Cred: John R Bakht
VP: Chad Cannan
VP: Ellen Smith
QA Dir: Charlie Bergeron
VP Mfg: Roger L Riffey
VP Opers: Mark L Edmunds
VP Mktg: Don P Conkle
Board of Directors: Sigmund L Cornelius, Chad C Deaton, James B Jennings, Henry E Lentz Jr, Randy L Limbacher, Robert S Rubin

D-U-N-S 00-628-2347 IMP/EXP
■ CARBOLINE CO
(*Suby of* RPM INTERNATIONAL INC) ★
2150 Schuetz Rd, Saint Louis, MO 63146-3517
Tel (314) 644-1000 *Founded/Ownrshp* 1999
Sales 248.2MM[E] *EMP* 500
SIC 2851 Lacquers, varnishes, enamels & other coatings
Pr: Randy Roth Sr
VP: Dallas Finch
VP: Douglas Moore
Genl Mgr: Paul Quinlan
Dir IT: Shawn Rice
IT Man: Mike Beckman
Ql Cn Mgr: Marikay Speckert
Mktg Mgr: Will Fultz

CARBOLOY
See SECO HOLDING CO INC

D-U-N-S 11-363-8394
CARBON BLACK INC
1100 Winter St Fl 4, Waltham, MA 02451-1473
Tel (617) 393-7400 *Founded/Ownrshp* 2002
Sales 84.5MM[E] *EMP* 535
SIC 7371 7379 Computer software writing services; ; Computer related consulting services
Pr: Patrick Morley
CFO: Gordon Pothier
Chf Mktg O: Tom Murphy
Chf Mktg O: Eric Schurr
Ex VP: Doug Cahill
Ex VP: Jim Clemens
Ex VP: Adam Liberman
VP: Tom Barsi
VP: Ed Filippine
VP: Pedro Santos
Dir Sec: Nick Levay
Board of Directors: Ron Nordin, Tony Zingale

D-U-N-S 08-202-8523
CARBON-LEHIGH INTERMEDIATE UNIT 21
4210 Independence Dr, Schnecksville, PA 18078-2580
Tel (610) 799-4111 *Founded/Ownrshp* 1971
Sales 64.6MM[E] *EMP* 1,000
SIC 8211 Specialty education
Ex Dir: Robert Keegan
Snr Ntwrk: Scott McHenry
MIS Dir: Esse Azar
IT Man: Erik Malmberg
Teacher Pr: Michele Edwards
Psych: Julie Kunkle

D-U-N-S 19-494-6757
▲ CARBONITE INC
2 Avenue De Lafayette # 2, Boston, MA 02111-1748
Tel (617) 587-1100 *Founded/Ownrshp* 2005
Sales 136.6MM *EMP* 623[E]
Tkr Sym CARB *Exch* NGM
SIC 7372 7374 Prepackaged software; Data processing & preparation
Pr: Mohamad Ali
**Ch Bd:* David Friend
**CFO:* Anthony Folger
Sr VP: Christopher Doggett
Sr VP: Norman Guadagno
Sr VP: Paul Mellinger
**Sr VP:* David Raissipour
VP: Robert Frost
**VP:* Danielle Sheer
VP: Ron Trackey
VP: Irwin Weiss
Board of Directors: Scott Daniels, Jeffry Flowers, Peter Gyenes, Charles Kane, Todd Krasnow, Stephen Munford

CARBOTROL FOODS
See WM H LEAHY ASSOCIATES INC

D-U-N-S 61-684-0513
■ CARDCONNECT LLC
(*Suby of* FTS HOLDING CORPORATION)
1000 Continental Dr # 300, King of Prussia, PA 19406-2848
Tel (484) 581-2200 *Founded/Ownrshp* 2005
Sales 458.2MM *EMP* 7[E]
SIC 7389 Credit card service
CEO: Jeffrey Shanahan
**Ch Bd:* Brian Shanahan
Pr: Mike Davis
Pr: Matthew Smith
**COO:* Patrick Shanahan
**CFO:* Chuck Bernicker
**Ofcr:* Scott Dowty
**Dir Sec:* Kevin Gainer
**CTO:* Rob Nathan

CARDELL CABINETRY
See BJT PROPERTIES INC

D-U-N-S 05-832-0011 IMP
■ CARDIAC PACEMAKERS INC
CPI
(*Suby of* BOSTON SCIENTIFIC CORP) ★
4100 Hamline Ave N, Saint Paul, MN 55112-5700
Tel (651) 638-4000 *Founded/Ownrshp* 2006
Sales 480.4MM[E] *EMP* 2,500
SIC 3845 Pacemaker, cardiac; Defibrillator
CEO: Michael F Mahoney
CFO: Jeffrey Capello
Treas: Kath Blomehafer
Prin: Ray Elliott
IT Man: Barbara Becker
IT Man: Stefani Hannah
IT Man: Monica Hayek
IT Man: Michele Peterson
IT Man: Nichole Schroepfer
IT Man: Todd Vogel
Board of Directors: Keith Brauer, James M Cornelius, Ronald W Dollens

CARDIAC SCIENCE OPERATING CO
See CS ESTATE INC

CARDIAC SURGERY BUSINESS UNIT
See SORIN GROUP USA INC

D-U-N-S 02-793-9805
■ CARDINAL BANK
(*Suby of* CARDINAL FINANCIAL CORP) ★
8270 Greensboro Dr # 100, Mc Lean, VA 22102-4908
Tel (703) 584-3400 *Founded/Ownrshp* 1998
Sales NA *EMP* 321
SIC 6021 6162 National commercial banks; Mortgage bankers
CEO: Christopher W Bergstrom
**Ch Bd:* Bernard H Clineburg
Pr: Walsh Carr
**Pr:* Kevin Reynolds
**COO:* Alice P Frazier
Ofcr: Marc J Blumenstein
Ofcr: Kathy Harbold
Ofcr: Eileen A Kennedy
Ofcr: Robert Lane
Ofcr: Jose A Rodriquez
**Ofcr:* Todd W Rowley
Ofcr: Travis R Slocum
Ofcr: Lauren M Vanduser
Assoc VP: Sokhea Ean
Assoc VP: Shalini J Kapur
Ex VP: Sushil K Clarence
**Ex VP:* Jennifer L Deacon
Ex VP: Andrew J Peden
Ex VP: Mark Wendel
Sr VP: Kelly Bell
Sr VP: Hilary J Blackburn

D-U-N-S 00-700-1878
CARDINAL CARRYOR INC (KY)
1055 Grade Ln, Louisville, KY 40213-2610
Tel (502) 363-6641 *Founded/Ownrshp* 1947, 2007
Sales 86.0MM[E] *EMP* 212
SIC 5084 7699 7359 5085 3535 Materials handling machinery; Industrial machinery & equipment repair; Equipment rental & leasing; Industrial supplies; Conveyors & conveying equipment
Pr: Bradley W Baker
**VP:* Douglas J Brumleve
Sls Mgr: Mike Kuhn

D-U-N-S 62-141-4437
CARDINAL ETHANOL LLC
1554 N County Rd 600 E, Union City, IN 47390
Tel (765) 964-3137 *Founded/Ownrshp* 2005
Sales 222.9MM *EMP* 49
Accts Boulay Pllp Minneapolis Minn
Tkr Sym CRDE *Exch* OTO

SIC 2869 2085 Ethyl alcohol, ethanol; Distillers' dried grains & solubles & alcohol
Pr: Jeff Painter
**Ch Bd:* Robert John Davis
CFO: William Dartt
Plnt Mgr: Jeremey Herlyn
Board of Directors: Dale A Schwieterman, Robert Baker, J Phillip Zicht, Ralph Brumbaugh, Thomas C Chronister, David Mathews Dersch, William Garth, Everett Leon Hart, Cyril George Lefevre, Lewis M Roch III, Curtis Allan Rosar

D-U-N-S 00-877-7661
▲ CARDINAL FINANCIAL CORP (VA)
8270 Greensboro Dr # 500, Mc Lean, VA 22102-3800
Tel (703) 584-3400 *Founded/Ownrshp* 1997
Sales NA *EMP* 851^E
Accts Kpmg Llp Mclean Virginia
Tkr Sym CFNL *Exch* NGS
SIC 6021 6211 8741 National commercial banks; Mortgages, buying & selling; Financial management for business
Pr: Christopher W Bergstrom
**Ch Bd:* Bernard H Clineburg
COO: Alice P Frazier
CFO: Mark A Wendel
Ex VP: Carl Dodson
Ex VP: Eleanor D Schmidt
Sls Mgr: Jason Barton
Board of Directors: Steven M Wiltse, B G Beck, William G Buck, Sidney O Dewberry, Michael A Garcia, J Hamilton Lambert, Barbara B Lang, William J Nassetta, William E Peterson, Alice M Starr

D-U-N-S 00-624-9015 IMP/EXP
CARDINAL GLASS INDUSTRIES INC (MN)
CARDINAL LG
775 Pririe Ctr Dr Ste 200, Eden Prairie, MN 55344
Tel (952) 229-2600 *Founded/Ownrshp* 1962, 1987
Sales 932.7MM^E *EMP* 5,500
SIC 3231 3211

D-U-N-S 07-595-7076
■ CARDINAL HEALTH 100 INC
BINDLEY WESTERN DRUG
(*Suby of* CARDINAL HEALTH INC) ★
7000 Cardinal Pl, Dublin, OH 43017-1091
Tel (614) 757-5000 *Founded/Ownrshp* 2006
Sales 181.4MM^E *EMP* 1,435
SIC 5122 5047 Drugs, proprietaries & sundries; Pharmaceuticals; Cosmetics, perfumes & hair products; Druggists' sundries; Medical & hospital equipment
Ch Bd: William E Bindley
**Treas:* Michael L Shinn
**Ex VP:* Keith W Burks
**VP:* Gregory S Beyerl
VP: Kathy Byrne
IT Man: Kelly Brown

D-U-N-S 78-663-7033 IMP
■ CARDINAL HEALTH 108 LLC
CARDINAL HLTH SPCLTY PHRM DIST
(*Suby of* CARDINAL HEALTH INC) ★
305 Tech Park Dr Ste 113, La Vergne, TN 37086-3633
Tel (615) 287-5200 *Founded/Ownrshp* 1992
Sales 224.7MM^E *EMP* 1,000
SIC 5122 5047 Pharmaceuticals; Medical & hospital equipment
Pr: Ray Perez
**VP:* David Canniff
**VP:* Neil Spence
Genl Mgr: Thomas Burke
Dir IT: Gary Davis

D-U-N-S 05-272-7484
■ CARDINAL HEALTH 109 INC
OWEN HEALTH CARE
(*Suby of* CARDINAL HEALTH INC) ★
1330 Enclave Pkwy, Houston, TX 77077-2577
Tel (281) 749-4000 *Founded/Ownrshp* 1969, 1997
Sales 85.2MM^E *EMP* 1,300
SIC 8741 Hospital management
CEO: David L Schtotterbeck
**Pr:* Dwight Winstead
**Treas:* Linda S Harty
**VP:* Jorge M Gomez

D-U-N-S 96-102-7315 IMP/EXP
■ CARDINAL HEALTH 200 LLC
(*Suby of* CARDINAL HEALTH INC) ★
3651 Birchwood Dr, Waukegan, IL 60085-8337
Tel (847) 578-9500 *Founded/Ownrshp* 1999
Sales 1.0MMM^E *EMP* 1,200
SIC 5047 Medical & hospital equipment
Pr: Steve Inacker
Dir Rx: Tim Larson

D-U-N-S 19-781-7497 IMP
■ CARDINAL HEALTH 301 LLC
PYXIS DATA SYSTEMS
(*Suby of* CARDINAL HEALTH INC) ★
7000 Cardinal Pl, Dublin, OH 43017-1091
Tel (614) 757-5000 *Founded/Ownrshp* 1996
Sales 165.6MM^E *EMP* 1,320
SIC 5047 Medical & hospital equipment; Dental equipment & supplies
CEO: R Kerry Clark
Ch Bd: Robert D Walter
Pr: Stephen S Thomas
VP: Thomas Bang
VP: Laird Broadfield
VP: James Hale
VP Mfg: Shawn Orr

D-U-N-S 78-709-4275 IMP/EXP
■ CARDINAL HEALTH 407 INC
(*Suby of* CARDINAL HEALTH INC) ★
3001 Red Lion Rd Ste Ag, Philadelphia, PA 19114-1123
Tel (215) 501-1210 *Founded/Ownrshp* 1996
Sales 50.6MM^E *EMP* 1,000
SIC 7389 3086 3089 Packaging & labeling services; Packaging & shipping materials, foamed plastic; Thermoformed finished plastic products
Ch: Robert Walter
Pr: Bill Mitchell
CFO: Steven J Magiera
VP: Donald Titus

D-U-N-S 06-941-0546 IMP
■ CARDINAL HEALTH 414 LLC (DE)
(*Suby of* CARDINAL HEALTH INC) ★
7000 Cardinal Pl, Dublin, OH 43017-1091
Tel (614) 757-5000 *Founded/Ownrshp* 1974, 2003
Sales 242.0MM^E *EMP* 2,000
SIC 2834 2835 Pharmaceutical preparations; Radioactive diagnostic substances
Pr: Lisa Ashby
CEO: George S Barrett
Ex VP: Shelley Bird
Ex VP: Mark Blake
Sr VP: Nick Augustinos
Sr VP: Jack L Coffey
Sr VP: Sheila H Coop

D-U-N-S 09-753-7435
▲ CARDINAL HEALTH INC
7000 Cardinal Pl, Dublin, OH 43017-1091
Tel (614) 757-5000 *Founded/Ownrshp* 2016
Sales 121.5MMM *EMP* 24,400
Tkr Sym CAH *Exch* NYS
SIC 5122 5047 8741 3842 Drugs, proprietaries & sundries; Pharmaceuticals; Druggists' sundries; Blood plasma; Surgical equipment & supplies; Hospital equipment & supplies; Management services; Surgical appliances & supplies
Ch Bd: George S Barrett
CEO: David Schlotterbeck
CFO: Michael C Kaufmann
Treas: Matt Kazar
Bd of Dir: David P King
Ofcr: Carole S Watkins
Ex VP: Kirk Bantz
Ex VP: Stephen T Falk
Ex VP: Steve Falk
Ex VP: Patricia B Morrison
Ex VP: Patty Morrison
Ex VP: Renard Pawlak
Ex VP: Gilberto Quintero
Sr VP: Joe Gottron
VP: David Allen
VP: Charles Aragon
VP: Elie Bahou
VP: James Barker
VP: Bill Bartelson
VP: Diane Beatty
VP: Pete Beckwith
Board of Directors: David P King, David J Anderson, Colleen F Arnold, Carrie S Cox, Calvin Darden, Bruce L Downey, Patricia A Hemingway Hall, Clayton M Jones, Gregory B Kenny, Nancy Killefer

D-U-N-S 09-004-7341 IMP/EXP
■ CARDINAL HEALTH PR 120 INC
(*Suby of* CARDINAL HEALTH INC) ★
10 Carr 165 Km24, Guaynabo, PR 00968-8034
Tel (787) 625-4100 *Founded/Ownrshp* 2008
Sales 150.4MM^E *EMP* 335
Accts Ernst & Young Llp San Juan P
SIC 5122 5047 Pharmaceuticals; Medical & hospital equipment
VP: Ismael Villarreal
**Sr VP:* Debbie Weitzman
**VP:* Carla Fernndez
**VP:* Michele Montalvo
**VP Sls:* Hari Sabnani

D-U-N-S 06-829-5174
■ CARDINAL HEALTH SYSTEMS INC (OH)
(*Suby of* CARDINAL HEALTH INC) ★
14 Schoolhouse Rd, Somerset, NJ 08873-1213
Tel (732) 537-6544 *Founded/Ownrshp* 1988, 2000
Sales 95.0MM^E *EMP* 5,000
SIC 7372 2834 Prepackaged software; Pharmaceutical preparations
Pr: Jeff Henderson
Ex VP: Carole Watkins
VP: Giolio Perillo
CTO: John Bufington

CARDINAL HLTH SPCLTY PHRM DIST
See CARDINAL HEALTH 108 LLC

CARDINAL LG
See CARDINAL GLASS INDUSTRIES INC

D-U-N-S 83-068-6684
CARDINAL LOGISTICS HOLDINGS LLC
(*Suby of* CENTERBRIDGE PARTNERS LP) ★
5333 Davidson Hwy, Concord, NC 28027-8478
Tel (972) 228-7300 *Founded/Ownrshp* 2008
Sales 1.3MMM^E *EMP* 3,040
SIC 4213 4731 Trucking, except local; Truck transportation brokers
CEO: Tom Hostetler
**Ch Bd:* Tom White
**Pr:* Jerry Bowman
**CFO:* Michael Roberts
**Ch:* Vin McLoughlin
**Ch:* Leo Suggs
**Treas:* Robert C Larose
**Ofcr:* Jeff Lester
**Sr VP:* John Hove
**VP:* Dan Curtis
**VP:* Michael Skipworth

D-U-N-S 01-347-8482
CARDINAL LOGISTICS MANAGEMENT CORP (NC)
(*Suby of* CARDINAL LOGISTICS HOLDINGS LLC) ★
5333 Davidson Hwy, Concord, NC 28027-8478
Tel (704) 786-6125 *Founded/Ownrshp* 1980, 2013
Sales 700.0MM^E *EMP* 1,500
SIC 4213 Trucking, except local
Pr: Jerry Bowman
**COO:* David Edwards
**CFO:* Michael Roberts
**Ch:* Vincent P McLoughlin
Treas: Kay Carroll
**Treas:* Thomas M Toton
**Sr VP:* Earnie Seibert
**Sr VP:* Kimmy G Whitten
VP: Ron Gillum
**VP:* Thomas Hostetler
VP: Eric Lee
VP: Travis Maxey
VP: Skip Stritzinger
VP: Nick Witte
VP Bus Dev: Gary Graven

D-U-N-S 16-002-0558 IMP
CARDINAL LOGISTICS MANAGEMENT INC
5333 Davidson Hwy, Concord, NC 28027-8478
Tel (704) 786-6125 *Founded/Ownrshp* 1997
Sales 1.8MM^E *EMP* 1,500
SIC 4212 4213 1541

D-U-N-S 00-715-3505 IMP/EXP
CARDINAL SCALE MANUFACTURING CO (MO)
DETECTO SCALE
203 E Daugherty St, Webb City, MO 64870-1929
Tel (417) 673-4631 *Founded/Ownrshp* 1950
Sales 132.4MM^E *EMP* 600
SIC 3596 Weighing machines & apparatus
Pr: David H Perry
Pr: Stephen Langford
CFO: Charlie Masters
**Treas:* Rebecca Perry
VP: Fred Cox
Creative D: Todd Williams
QA Dir: Gary Harper
Dir IT: Tim Fredrickson
IT Man: Howard Hawkins
Tech Mgr: Carl Benfield
VP Mktg: Jonathan Sabo

CARDINAL SHOWER ENCLOSURES
See HOSKIN & MUIR INC

D-U-N-S 07-115-8604
CARDINAL STRITCH UNIVERSITY INC
6801 N Yates Rd, Milwaukee, WI 53217-3945
Tel (414) 410-4000 *Founded/Ownrshp* 1937
Sales 45.3MM *EMP* 1,200
Accts Cliftonlarsonallen Llp Milwa
SIC 8221 University
Pr: James P Loftus
VP: Sushmita Acharya
VP: Marna E Boyle
VP: Michael Brauer
VP: John Glynn
Assoc Dir: Kristine Bueno
Ex Dir: Linda Plagman
Dir Sec: Andrew De Rubertis
Brnch Mgr: Jennifer Chamberlain
Off Admin: Megan Holloway
Netwrk Mgr: Steve Tracy

D-U-N-S 93-894-8379 IMP
CARDINGTON YUTAKA TECHNOLOGIES INC
(*Suby of* YUTAKA GIKEN CO., LTD.)
575 W Main St, Cardington, OH 43315-9796
Tel (419) 864-8777 *Founded/Ownrshp* 2009
Sales 213.9MM^E *EMP* 875
SIC 3714 Motor vehicle parts & accessories
Pr: Hirokazu Kawuai
**Ex VP:* Fred Razavi
CTO: Stephanie Lemaster
Plnt Mgr: Ray Welch

CARDIOLOGY DEPT
See HOWARD UNIVERSITY HOSPITAL

D-U-N-S 17-639-0318
■ CARDIONET LLC
(*Suby of* BIOTELEMETRY INC) ★
1000 Cedar Hollow Rd, Malvern, PA 19355-2300
Tel (610) 729-5060 *Founded/Ownrshp* 2013
Sales 154.8MM^E *EMP* 728^E
SIC 3845 Cardiographs
Pr: Joseph H Capper
**Ch Bd:* Kirk E Gorman
**CFO:* Heather C Getz
**Sr VP:* Andy Broadway
**Sr VP:* Fred Broadway III
**Sr VP:* Peter Ferola
Sr VP: Michael D Geldart
Sr VP: Manny Gerolamo
**Sr VP:* George Hrenko
Sr VP: Charles Taylor
**Sr VP:* Daniel Wisniewski
Board of Directors: Ronald A Ahrens, Anthony J Conti, Eric N Prystowsky, Rebecca W Rimel, Robert J Rubin

D-U-N-S 13-402-8968
CARDIOVASCULAR & THORACIC SURGICAL GROUP OF WICHITA FALLS P A
UNITED RGONAL PHYSICIANS GROUP
912 Burnett St, Wichita Falls, TX 76301-3208
Tel (940) 764-8570 *Founded/Ownrshp* 1983
Sales 271.3MM *EMP* 6
SIC 8011 Cardiologist & cardio-vascular specialist
Pr: Phyllis Cowling
Off Mgr: Dusty Rhoads

D-U-N-S 02-495-4518
▲ CARDIOVASCULAR SYSTEMS INC
CSI
1225 Old Highway 8 Nw, Saint Paul, MN 55112-6416
Tel (651) 259-1600 *Founded/Ownrshp* 2000
Sales 178.1MM *EMP* 597^E
Tkr Sym CSII *Exch* NGM
SIC 3841 Surgical & medical instruments
Ch Bd: Scott Ward
COO: Kevin Kenny
CFO: Laurence L Betterley
Sr VP: Paul Koehn
Sls Dir: Michael Tozzi
Manager: Evan Pritchard
Sls Mgr: Leonel Cantu
Sls Mgr: Brian Frazier
Sls Mgr: Brian George
Sls Mgr: Laney Gonzalez
Sls Mgr: Amy Koscielski
Board of Directors: Scott Bartos, Brent G Blackey, Edward Brown, William E Cohn, Augustine Lawlor, Leslie L Trigg

D-U-N-S 01-853-0915 IMP
CARDIS DEPARTMENT STORE INC
CARDI'S FURNITURE
1 Furniture Way, Swansea, MA 02777-3424
Tel (508) 379-7500 *Founded/Ownrshp* 1948
Sales 96.4MM^E *EMP* 400
SIC 5712 Furniture stores
Pr: Nicholas Cardi Jr
**Treas:* Peter Cardi
Sfty Mgr: Maria Pacheco
Opers Mgr: Edward Diorio
Sls Mgr: Joseph Casey
Sales Asso: Todd Paschoal

CARDI'S FURNITURE
See CARDIS DEPARTMENT STORE INC

D-U-N-S 07-839-1683
CARDNO INC
(*Suby of* CARDNO USA INC) ★
10004 Park Meadows Dr # 300, Lone Tree, CO 80124-5453
Tel (720) 257-5800 *Founded/Ownrshp* 2011
Sales 174.2MM^E *EMP* 403^E
SIC 8711 8748 8742 8741 Engineering services; Environmental consultant; Management consulting services; Planning consultant; Construction management
Ch: Richard Wankmuller
**Pr:* Mark Swatek
**Ch:* Andrew Buckley
Treas: Jeff Forbes
**Treas:* Ben Smith
**VP:* David Blankenhorn
**VP:* Steve Clay
**VP:* Robert Clemens
**VP:* Julia Guynn
**VP:* Steve Howarth
**VP:* Robert Kroeger
**VP:* Mike Lancioni
**VP:* Lance Lariscey
**VP:* Mark Pitchford
**VP:* Michael Renshaw
**VP:* William Roberts
**VP:* Keith Romstad
**VP:* Craig Snyder

D-U-N-S 96-744-8734
CARDNO USA INC
(*Suby of* CARDNO LIMITED)
10004 Park Meadows Dr # 300, Lone Tree, CO 80124-5453
Tel (720) 257-5800 *Founded/Ownrshp* 2007
Sales 454.3MM *EMP* 1,700^E
Accts Kpmg Llp Brisbane
SIC 8711 5045 8748 Engineering services; Computer software; Environmental consultant
Ch: Richard Wankmuller
**Pr:* Michael Renshaw
**Pr:* Mark Swatek
**Ch:* Andrew Buckley
**Treas:* Jeff Forbes
**Treas:* Ben Smith
**VP:* Julia Guynn

D-U-N-S 18-961-7772
CARDON & ASSOCIATES INC
2749 E Covenanter Dr, Bloomington, IN 47401-5454
Tel (812) 332-2265 *Founded/Ownrshp* 1981
Sales 159.1MM^E *EMP* 2,000
SIC 8741 6513 8742 Nursing & personal care facility management; Apartment building operators; Hospital & health services consultant
Pr: Stephen W Moore
**CFO:* Kent Rogers

D-U-N-S 04-328-0163 IMP
CARDONE INDUSTRIES INC (PA)
5501 Whitaker Ave, Philadelphia, PA 19124-1799
Tel (215) 912-3000 *Founded/Ownrshp* 1967, 1973
Sales 1.2MMM^E *EMP* 5,000
SIC 3465 3714 Body parts, automobile: stamped metal; Motor vehicle parts & accessories
CEO: Terry McCormack
**Pr:* Michael Cardone Jr
**CFO:* Kevin Bagby
**Treas:* John Brawer
Treas: John H Brawner
Sr VP: Sal Lo Dico
**Sr VP:* Marshall Hosel
Creative D: David Syers

D-U-N-S 14-458-0052
▲ CARDTRONICS INC
3250 Briarpark Dr Ste 400, Houston, TX 77042-4462
Tel (832) 308-4000 *Founded/Ownrshp* 1993
Sales 1.2MMM *EMP* 1,739
Tkr Sym CATM *Exch* NGS
SIC 7389 5049 Credit card service; Financial services; Bank equipment & supplies
CEO: Steven A Rathgaber
**Ch Bd:* Dennis F Lynch
Pr: David W Dove
COO: Edward H West
Ofcr: Gerardo Garcia
Ofcr: Jonathan Simpson-Dent
Ex VP: Jeffery B Keith
Ex VP: Rick Updyke
VP: Kurt Duhn
VP: Diana Hayes
VP: Christy Nusz
VP: Bennett Robinson
VP: Jason Sacco
VP: Jeff Ude
Exec: P Michael McCarthy
Dir Risk M: Gonzalo Jimenez

D-U-N-S 03-535-3770
CARDWELL DISTRIBUTING INC
(*Suby of* RELADYNE INC) ★
8137 S State St Bldg 1, Midvale, UT 84047-3244
Tel (801) 561-4251 *Founded/Ownrshp* 1965
Sales 259.1MM^E *EMP* 78
SIC 5171 7549 5172 5983 Petroleum bulk stations & terminals; Petroleum bulk stations; Lubrication service, automotive; Engine fuels & oils; Diesel fuel; Fuel oil; Lubricating oils & greases; Fuel oil dealers
Pr: William G Rawson
**VP:* Tom R Leiter

Genl Mgr: Trent Horrocks
Plnt Mgr: Kenny Rhodes

D-U-N-S 14-508-3023
CARDWORKS INC
(Suby of CARDWORKS LP) ★
101 Crossways Park Dr W, Woodbury, NY 11797-2020
Tel (516) 576-0404 Founded/Ownrshp 2001
Sales 688.4MM[E] EMP 800
SIC 7322 7389 Collection agency, except real estate; Credit card service
Ch Bd: Donald Berman
*Pr: David Watson
*CFO: Vincent J Caruso
Ex VP: Sharon Hill
Mng Dir: Matt Berman
*CIO: John G Strong
IT Man: Laurie Soto
Netwrk Eng: Tom McComb

D-U-N-S 18-755-7731
CARDWORKS LP
101 Crossways Park Dr W, Woodbury, NY 11797-2020
Tel (516) 576-0404 Founded/Ownrshp 1999
Sales 688.4MM[E] EMP 800
SIC 7389 Credit card service
Pt: Albert T Jaronczyk
Pt: Donald Berman
Pt: David Watson

D-U-N-S 05-961-2995
CARE
2000 Polk St, Stevens Point, WI 54481-5876
Tel (715) 345-5620 Founded/Ownrshp 2007
Sales 85.0MM EMP 100
SIC 8299 Arts & crafts schools
Prin: Connie Negaard

CARE A LOT FUND
See CARE-A-LOT FUND

D-U-N-S 07-804-7727
CARE ALLIANCE HEALTH INC
BON SECOURS
(Suby of BON SECOURS HEALTH SYSTEM INC) ★
2095 Henry Tecklenburg Dr, Charleston, SC 29414-5733
Tel (843) 402-1000 Founded/Ownrshp 1882
Sales 215.8MM EMP 1,052
SIC 8062 General medical & surgical hospitals
CEO: David Dunlap
*CEO: Allen Carroll
*CFO: Bret Johnson
*Sr VP: Mark Dickson

D-U-N-S 07-971-2751
CARE CAPITAL PROPERTIES INC
191 N Wacker Dr Ste 1200, Chicago, IL 60606-1903
Tel (312) 881-4700 Founded/Ownrshp 2015
Sales 327.9MM[E] EMP 56
Tkr Sym CCP Exch NYS
SIC 6798 Real estate investment trusts
CEO: Raymond J Lewis
COO: Timothy A Doman
CFO: Lori B Wittman
Ex VP: Kristen M Benson
Sr VP: Anna N Fitzgerald
Board of Directors: Douglas Crocker II, John S Gates Jr, Ronald G Geary, Jeffrey A Melehorn, John L Workman

D-U-N-S 07-948-0275
CARE FINDERS TOTAL CARE LLC
171 Main St Ste 2, Hackensack, NJ 07601-7118
Tel (201) 342-5122 Founded/Ownrshp 2014
Sales 7.3MM[E] EMP 3,099[E]
Accts Weisermazars Llp New York Ne
SIC 8082 Home health care services
CEO: Kevin Rogers

D-U-N-S 07-886-2458
CARE FUSION
10020 Pacific Mesa Blvd, San Diego, CA 92121-4386
Tel (858) 617-2000 Founded/Ownrshp 2013
Sales 159.2MM[E] EMP 869[E]
SIC 2834 Pharmaceutical preparations
Pr: Kieran Gallehue
Pr: Erik Barnes
Exec: Juergen Popp
Snr Sftwr: Brian Bowman
Snr Ntwrk: David Schaber
Cmptr Lab: Carla Thornton
Software D: Trevor Borden
Software D: Stephen Shelton
Sftwr Eng: Xiaodong Zhang
Ql Cn Mgr: Edgar Esquerra
VP Sls: Eric Honroth

D-U-N-S 05-289-0217
CARE GROUP LLC
ST VINCENT MEDICAL GROUP
8333 Naab Rd Ste 340, Indianapolis, IN 46260-1983
Tel (317) 338-5050 Founded/Ownrshp 1977
Sales 285.6MM EMP 1,000
SIC 8011 8093 Cardiologist & cardio-vascular specialist; Specialty outpatient clinics
CFO: Mary Hogan

D-U-N-S 60-304-2433
CARE INITIATIVES
1611 Westlakes Pkwy, West Des Moines, IA 50266-8370
Tel (515) 224-4442 Founded/Ownrshp 1988
Sales 167.8MM EMP 3,000
Accts Mcgladrey Llp Des Moines Ia
SIC 8051 8052 Skilled nursing care facilities; Intermediate care facilities
Pr: Miles King
CFO: Stephen Marlow
CFO: Mike McDaniel
*Treas: Steve Marlow
Ofcr: Lavonne Edwards
Sr VP: Mike M Daniel
Sr VP: Mike Mc Daniel
VP: Charleen Schlepp
Exec: Lori Harvey
Genl Mgr: Ryan McCoy
Off Admin: Laura Espinoza

CARE INVESTMENT TRUST
See TIPTREE OPERATING CO LLC

D-U-N-S 11-642-7907
CARE NEW ENGLAND HEALTH SYSTEM INC
45 Willard Ave, Providence, RI 02905-3218
Tel (401) 453-7900 Founded/Ownrshp 1995
Sales 1.0MMM EMP 6,500
Accts Pricewaterhousecoopers Llp Bo
SIC 8063 8062 8069 8093 8082 Psychiatric hospitals; General medical & surgical hospitals; Specialty hospitals, except psychiatric; Specialty outpatient clinics; Visiting nurse service
Pr: John Hynes
V Ch: Cynthia Patterson
V Ch: Richard P Welch
VP: Gail Costa
CTO: Jonathan Dubois
Tech Mgr: Michael Beauparlant
Web Dev: Christina Shoppell
QC Dir: Denise Henry
Sls&Mrk Ex: Joseph Dowling
Opthamlgy: Donald Fargnoli
Opthamlgy: Salvatore Loporchio

D-U-N-S 09-834-7573
CARE ONE AT HOLMDEL LLC
(Suby of CARE ONE LLC) ★
188 State Route 34, Holmdel, NJ 07733-2125
Tel (732) 946-4200 Founded/Ownrshp 2001
Sales 14.6MM EMP 2,000
SIC 8322 Rehabilitation services
CFO: Nicole Sellmeyer

D-U-N-S 14-734-9570
CARE ONE LLC
173 Bridge Plz N, Fort Lee, NJ 07024-7575
Tel (201) 242-4000 Founded/Ownrshp 1998
Sales 388.1MM[E] EMP 6,000
SIC 8051 8052 Skilled nursing care facilities; Intermediate care facilities
CEO: Daniel E Straus
Pr: Deborah Scher
CFO: Matthew Marcos
Ex VP: Alberto Lugo
Sr VP: Karen Davidson
Sr VP: Ian Oppel
VP: Seth Gribetz
VP: Maureen Powers
Mng Dir: Andre Davis
Genl Mgr: Mark Neri
Off Mgr: Yesenia Martinez

CARE PARTNERS
See COMMUNITY CAREPARTNERS INC

D-U-N-S 78-855-2453
CARE SOURCE LLC
9114 Philadelphia Rd # 214, Baltimore, MD 21237-4348
Tel (410) 391-2627 Founded/Ownrshp 1996
Sales 34.7MM[E] EMP 2,200
SIC 7361 Employment agencies

CARE USA
See COOPERATIVE FOR ASSISTANCE AND RELIEF EVERYWHERE INC

D-U-N-S 61-968-2354
CARE WISCONSIN FIRST INC
ELDER CARE HOUSE PLAN
1617 Sherman Ave, Madison, WI 53704-5930
Tel (608) 240-0020 Founded/Ownrshp 1976
Sales 184.9MM EMP 525
Accts Wipfli Llp Milwaukee Wi
SIC 8322 Adult day care center
CEO: Karen Musser
COO: Ken Eimers
Ex VP: Scott Johnson

D-U-N-S 02-555-0901
CARE-A-LOT FUND
CARE A LOT FUND
1344 W 4675 S, Ogden, UT 84405-3690
Tel (801) 627-0900 Founded/Ownrshp 1939
Sales 126.6M EMP 1,400
SIC 7389 Financial services
Pr: Rick Craid

D-U-N-S 80-625-8500
▲ CARE.COM INC
77 4th Ave Ste 5, Waltham, MA 02451-7567
Tel (781) 642-5900 Founded/Ownrshp 2006
Sales 138.6MM EMP 681[E]
Tkr Sym CRCM Exch NYS
SIC 4813
Ch Bd: Sheila Lirio Marcelo
CFO: Michael Echenberg
Off Mgr: Candace Macdonald
CTO: David Krupinski
Prd Mgr: Angela Bruso
Mktg Mgr: Michelle Manne
Sales Asso: Matt Winkler
Board of Directors: Tony Florence, Chet Kapoor, J Sanford Miller, Joanna Rees, I Duncan Robertson, Brian Swette

D-U-N-S 11-058-0433
CAREALLIANCE HEALTH SERVICES
ROPER ST FRANCIS HEALTHCARE
316 Calhoun St, Charleston, SC 29401-1113
Tel (843) 724-2000 Founded/Ownrshp 1998
Sales 827.2MM EMP 5,000[E]
Accts Deloitte & Touche Llp Charlo
SIC 8741 Hospital management
Pr: David Dunlap
Dir Vol: Mitzi Neely
Pt: Douglas Bowling
V Ch: Charles T Cole
*CFO: Bret Johnson
CFO: Richard Stephens
Treas: Edmund Puckhaber
Ofcr: Douglas Fraser
Ex VP: Sullivan John
VP: Ellen Brown
VP: Carolyn Cantey
*VP: Mark Dickson
*VP: Carolyn Donohue
*VP: Greg Edwards
VP: Terence Fleming
VP: Lisa Irvin
VP: Pennie Peralta
VP: Lisa Schafer
VP: Steven Shapiro
VP: Michael Taylor
VP: Mike Taylor

D-U-N-S 14-860-5462
CARECORE NATIONAL LLC
EVICORE HEALTHCARE
400 Buckwalter Place Blvd, Bluffton, SC 29910-5150
Tel (800) 918-8924 Founded/Ownrshp 2001
Sales 427.7MM[E] EMP 800
SIC 8011 Radiologist
CEO: John J Arlotta
*Pr: Douglas K Tardio
*CFO: William Tausig
Ex VP: Roger Cheek
Ex VP: Natalie Glover
Ex VP: Shelley Weiner
*Ex VP: Richard Weininger
VP: Karen Amato
VP: Cayce Awe
VP: Mitch Barnes
VP: Scott Bowman
VP: Adam Corona
VP: Ed Ernest
VP: Lauryssa Humm
VP: Kathleen Mercier
VP: Ken Reach
VP: Ann REA
VP: Debbie Stern
Exec: Tracey Geogerian
Dir Lab: Pamela Hines

D-U-N-S 15-553-0454
CARECRAFT INC
880 Carlsbad Village Dr # 202, Carlsbad, CA 92008-2324
Tel (949) 373-3333 Founded/Ownrshp 1986
Sales 89.0MM EMP 10
Accts Dubina & Lee Inc Cpas San D
SIC 8611 Business associations
CEO: Greg Howard
*VP: Christine Guerena

D-U-N-S 14-735-5411
CARECYCLE SOLUTIONS LLC
3406 Main St, Dallas, TX 75226-1642
Tel (214) 698-0600 Founded/Ownrshp 2003
Sales 49.5MM[E] EMP 1,100[E]
SIC 8082 Home health care services
CEO: S W Bazzle
Pr: Kristy McCorkle
*Pr: James E Sowell
COO: Cheryl Bazzle
*CFO: Joe Johnson
Sr VP: Georgia Brown
Sr VP: Jeff Whitaker
VP: Deb Richardson
VP: Sara Wriborg
Creative D: Suzanne Merrifield
*Prin: Wayne Bazzle

D-U-N-S 88-473-6273
▲ CAREER EDUCATION CORP
231 N Martingale Rd # 100, Schaumburg, IL 60173-2007
Tel (847) 781-3600 Founded/Ownrshp 1994
Sales 847.2MM EMP 6,687
Tkr Sym CECO Exch NGS
SIC 8221 8244 8299 Colleges universities & professional schools; Business & secretarial schools; Cooking school
Pr: Todd S Nelson
*Ch Bd: Thomas B Lally
CFO: Andrew J Cederoth
Sr VP: Jeffrey D Ayers
Sr VP: Jeffrey R Cooper
Sr VP: Andrew H Hurst
Sr VP: John R Kline
VP: Jeff Busam
VP: Susan Callahan
VP: Matt Charpentier
VP: Lysa Clemens
VP: Laura Fisher
VP: Ashish Ghia
VP: Dawn Kalamaras
VP: Matt Kinnich
VP: Susan Krieger
VP: Chris Labounty
VP: Gil Polanco

D-U-N-S 02-578-9231
CAREER GROUP INC (CA)
FOURTHFLOOR FASHION TALENT
10100 Santa Monica Blvd # 900, Los Angeles, CA 90067-4138
Tel (310) 277-8188 Founded/Ownrshp 1980
Sales 88.6MM[E] EMP 2,400
SIC 7361 Executive placement
CEO: Michael B Levine
*Pr: Susan Levine
*CFO: Scott H Pick

D-U-N-S 16-091-6276
CAREER NETWORK AFFILIATES INC
38 Ivanhoe Dr, Manalapan, NJ 07726-1724
Tel (732) 972-3000 Founded/Ownrshp 1989
Sales 90.0MM EMP 500
SIC 7361 Employment agencies
Pr: Dave Schnitzer
VP: William Bittenmaster
VP: Johnson Smith

D-U-N-S 01-291-9465
CAREER PARTNERS INTERNATIONAL LLC
125 Summer St Ste 1020, Boston, MA 02110-1681
Tel (919) 401-4260 Founded/Ownrshp 1987
Sales 41.1MM[E] EMP 1,600[E]
SIC 8742 General management consultant
CEO: Karen D O'Boyle
COO: Mark Hornberger
VP: Dottie Austin
VP: Brian Hedrick
VP: Terry McCloy
VP: Sue Rowley

D-U-N-S 19-502-9202
CAREER SYSTEMS DEVELOPMENT CORP
C S D
(Suby of OWL COMPANIES) ★
75 Thruway Park Dr # 100, West Henrietta, NY 14586-9793
Tel (585) 334-8080 Founded/Ownrshp 2001
Sales 102.5MM EMP 1,039
SIC 8741 8331 Management services; Job training & vocational rehabilitation services
Ch Bd: Gregory J Burden
Sr VP: John F Muto
Exec: Scott Makin
Ex Dir: Dennis Essom
Prgrm Mgr: Barb Bird
Prgrm Mgr: Cynthia Fair
IT Man: Mary Holley

D-U-N-S 09-530-1110
■ CAREERBUILDER LLC
(Suby of TEGNA INC) ★
200 N La Salle St # 1100, Chicago, IL 60601-1014
Tel (773) 527-3600 Founded/Ownrshp 2008
Sales 265.9MM[E] EMP 1,470
SIC 7361 Registries
CEO: Matthew Ferguson
*Pr: Brent Rasmussen
*CFO: Kevin Knapp
VP: Roger Fugett
*VP: Rosemary Haefner
VP: Jason Lovelace
Mng Dir: Justin Jackson
Snr Sftwr: Craig Bishop
Snr Sftwr: Jamal Hashim
Snr Sftwr: Ellen Huang
Snr Sftwr: Hai Liu

D-U-N-S 12-267-6224
CAREERS USA INC
6501 Congress Ave Ste 200, Boca Raton, FL 33487-2840
Tel (561) 995-7000 Founded/Ownrshp 1981
Sales 532.3MM[E] EMP 20,000
SIC 7361 Employment agencies; Placement agencies
CEO: Marilyn J Ounjian
*Pr: George E Ounjian
*Ex VP: Jennifer O Johnson
Ex Dir: Jon Ounjian
Ex Dir: Kori Ounjian
Brnch Mgr: Michelle Kulchinsky
Snr Ntwrk: Gabriel Kissler
VP Opers: Mandy Wilson
Mktg Dir: Julia Duval
Mktg Dir: Sharon Gardner

D-U-N-S 11-915-7089
CAREFIRST BLUECHOICE INC
(Suby of CAREFIRST BLUECROSS BLUESHIELD) ★
10455 Mill Run Cir, Owings Mills, MD 21117-4208
Tel (202) 479-8000 Founded/Ownrshp 2002
Sales NA EMP 145
Accts Ernst & Young Llp Baltimore
SIC 6321 8011 6411 Accident & health insurance; Health maintenance organization; Insurance agents, brokers & service
Pr: Eric Baugh
*CFO: G Mark Chaney
VP: Ann Gallant
VP: Ed Mallon
VP: Mike McShain
VP: Glenn Rothman
VP: Gwendolyn Skillern
VP: Maria Tildon
VP: Stephen Wiggins
VP: Winston Wong
MIS Dir: Eric Strausman

CAREFIRST BLUECROSS BLUESHIELD
See GROUP HOSPITALIZATION AND MEDICAL SERVICES INC

D-U-N-S 79-078-6578
CAREFIRST INC
GROUP HOSPITAL & MEDICAL SVC
10455 Mill Run Cir, Owings Mills, MD 21117-4208
Tel (301) 805-5005 Founded/Ownrshp 1934
Sales NA EMP 6,000
SIC 6324 Hospital & medical service plans
CEO: Chuck Burrell
Sr Cor Off: Joseph Lizza
Bd of Dir: Ron N Bowers
Ex VP: Eric Baugh
Ex VP: Chris Holt
Sr VP: Shematek Joe
Sr VP: Jon P Shematek
VP: Jennifer Baldwin
VP: Bruce M Edwards
VP: Andy Fitzsimmons
VP: Mary Heckwolf
VP: Jeanne A Kennedy
VP: Ken Sullivan
Board of Directors: Donald M Parsons Jr

D-U-N-S 10-147-7891
CAREFIRST OF MARYLAND INC
CFMI
(Suby of GROUP HOSPITAL & MEDICAL SVC) ★
10455 Mill Run Cir, Owings Mills, MD 21117-4208
Tel (410) 581-3000 Founded/Ownrshp 1984
Sales NA EMP 4,000
SIC 6324 Health maintenance organization (HMO), insurance only
CEO: Chester Burrell
CFO: Mark Chaney
Ex VP: John A Picciotto
IT Man: Ronald Evans
IT Man: Said Saidian
Board of Directors: Donald M Parsons

D-U-N-S 02-474-5942
■ CAREFREE COMMUNITIES INC
CAREFREE RV RESORT
(Suby of SUN COMMUNITIES INC) ★
6991 E Camelback Rd B310, Scottsdale, AZ 85251-2493
Tel (480) 423-5700 Founded/Ownrshp 1990
Sales 118.2MM[E] EMP 300
SIC 6515 Mobile home site operators

CEO: David A Napp
Dir IT: Ann Claudio

CAREFREE RV RESORT
See CAREFREE COMMUNITIES INC

D-U-N-S 82-882-1350 IMP/EXP
■ CAREFUSION 213 LLC
(Suby of CAREFUSION CORP) ★
3750 Torrey View Ct, San Diego, CA 92130-2622
Tel (800) 523-0502 Founded/Ownrshp 2008
Sales 195.3MM^E EMP 950
SIC 2834 Pharmaceutical preparations
CEO: David L Schlotterbeck
*COO: Dwight Windstead
*CFO: Edward Borkowski

D-U-N-S 36-062-4720 EXP
■ CAREFUSION 303 INC
ALARIS SYSTEMS
(Suby of CAREFUSION CORP) ★
10020 Pacific Mesa Blvd, San Diego, CA 92121-4386
Tel (858) 617-2000 Founded/Ownrshp 2009
Sales 524.1MM^E EMP 4,500
SIC 3841 Surgical & medical instruments
Pr: David L Schlotterbeck
*CFO: William C Bopp
*Treas: Robert F Mathews
Genl Mgr: Rusty Frantz

D-U-N-S 82-996-4563 IMP
■ CAREFUSION CORP
(Suby of BECTON DICKINSON AND CO) ★
3750 Torrey View Ct, San Diego, CA 92130-2622
Tel (858) 617-2000 Founded/Ownrshp 2015
Sales 5.4MMM^E EMP 16,000^E
SIC 3841 3845 8742 Surgical & medical instruments; Surgical instruments & apparatus; Electromedical equipment; Respiratory analysis equipment, electromedical; Hospital & health services consultant
*Ex VP: Donald Abbey
Ex VP: Cathy Cooney
Ex VP: Ron Frisbie
Ex VP: Gordon La Fortune
Ex VP: Gord Lafortune
Ex VP: Roger Marchetti
Ex VP: Mike Paolucci
Ex VP: Joan B Stafslien
Sr VP: Scott Bostick
Sr VP: Carlos M Nunez
*Sr VP: Jonathan Wygant
VP: Michael Aviotti
VP: Brion Bailey
VP: Paul Belgrove
VP: Brian Bonnell
VP: Mark Branday
VP: Robert Brown
VP: Jeff Bruno
VP: Yona Capobianco
VP: Jean-Michel Deckers
VP: Donovan Delmare

D-U-N-S 80-121-8087
■ CAREFUSION SOLUTIONS LLC
(Suby of CAREFUSION CORP) ★
3750 Torrey View Ct, San Diego, CA 92130-2622
Tel (858) 617-2100 Founded/Ownrshp 2007
Sales 273.1MM^E EMP 3,600
SIC 5047 Medical equipment & supplies
CEO: Keiran Gallahue
Pr: Tom Leonard
CFO: James Hinrichs
Ex VP: Don Abbey
Sr VP: Scott Bostick

D-U-N-S 07-172-3563
CAREGROUP INC
375 Longwood Ave Fl 7, Boston, MA 02215-5395
Tel (617) 667-1715 Founded/Ownrshp 1896
Sales 1.5MMM EMP 12,000
Accts Kpmg Llp Boston Massachusett
SIC 8741 Hospital management
Pr: John T Szum
Ofcr: Edward Grab
*VP: Joseph Appleyard
VP: Aliza L Samuels
Dir Lab: Lynne Uhl
Adm Dir: Gary Shillin
Admn Mgr: Donald Wood
Nurse Mgr: Dona Clark
CIO: Jane Moncreiff
Dir IT: Robert Todd
Dir IT: Anne Wheeler

D-U-N-S 00-796-6018
CAREINGTON INTERNATIONAL CORP (TX)
7400 Gaylord Pkwy, Frisco, TX 75034-9463
Tel (972) 335-6970 Founded/Ownrshp 1922, 1996
Sales NA EMP 130
SIC 6324 6411 Hospital & medical service plans; Insurance agents, brokers & service
CEO: Barbara Williams
*Ch Bd: Martin Rinker
*CFO: Melissa Baumann
*Sr VP: Chuck Misasi
VP: Stephen Paz
VP: Greg Rudisill
Dir IT: Neha Mehta
Mktg Dir: Ed Cline
Sls Dir: Clyde Ponder

D-U-N-S 02-766-1723
CARELINK NETWORK INC
1333 Brewery Park Blvd, Detroit, MI 48207-4544
Tel (313) 656-0000 Founded/Ownrshp 2009
Sales 137.8MM EMP 15
SIC 8099 Medical services organization
Prin: Chuck Dvorak

D-U-N-S 79-690-6410
■ CAREMARK INTERNATIONAL LLC
(Suby of CAREMARK RX INC) ★
2211 Sanders Rd, Northbrook, IL 60062-6128
Tel (847) 559-4700 Founded/Ownrshp 1992
Sales 438.4MM^E EMP 1,617^E
SIC 5961 6411 8099 8092 8093 Pharmaceuticals, mail order; Medical insurance claim processing, contract or fee basis; Blood related health services; Kidney dialysis centers; Respiratory therapy clinic
Pr: Edwin Crawford

D-U-N-S 09-688-8250 IMP
■ CAREMARK LLC (CA)
(Suby of CAREMARK INTERNATIONAL LLC) ★
2211 Sanders Rd, Northbrook, IL 60062-6128
Tel (847) 559-4700 Founded/Ownrshp 1979, 1991
Sales 438.4MM^E EMP 3,500
SIC 5961 6411 8099 8092 8093 8742 Pharmaceuticals, mail order; Medical insurance claim processing, contract or fee basis; Blood related health services; Kidney dialysis centers; Respiratory therapy clinic; Management consulting services
CEO: Howard A McLure
*Pr: Richard P Scardina
*Treas: Connie M Isley
*VP: Sara J Finley
*VP: David Golding
VP: Tom Gore
VP: Olga Matlin
VP: Yvonne Southwell
Dir Soc: Joyce Wiltse
IT Man: Chris Schlenker
Software D: Jose Deguzman

D-U-N-S 92-842-9281
■ CAREMARK PHC LLC
PHARMACARE MANAGEMENT SVCS LLC
(Suby of CVS HEALTH CORP) ★
695 George Washington Hwy, Lincoln, RI 02865-4257
Tel (401) 334-0069 Founded/Ownrshp 1994
Sales 50.3MM^E EMP 1,552
SIC 8011 5912 Internal medicine practitioners; Drug stores & proprietary stores
COO: Glen Laschober
*Pr: Greg Weishar
Ex VP: Jack Bruner
VP: Christine Kyle
Exec: Charlene Hrivnak
Exec: Kimberly Troy
Prin: Joel Ramirez
Dist Mgr: Bob Ignatowicz
Dist Mgr: Lester Klein
*CIO: John Kernaghan
Pharmcst: Gina Yun

D-U-N-S 80-441-4852
■ CAREMARK RX INC
(Suby of CVS HEALTH CORP) ★
445 Great Circle Rd, Nashville, TN 37228-1403
Tel (615) 687-7400 Founded/Ownrshp 2007
Sales 1.3MMM^E EMP 13,628
SIC 5961 Pharmaceuticals, mail order
Ch Bd: Edwin M Crawford
COO: Howard A McLure
CFO: Peter J Clemens IV
Treas: Peter Clemens IV
Ex VP: Charles C Clark
*Ex VP: Edward L Hardin Jr
Ex VP: Bradley S Karro
Ex VP: Kirk McConnell
Ex VP: Richard P Scardina
Ex VP: William R Spalding
Sr VP: Sara J Finley
Sr VP: Phil Lostus
Sr VP: Mark Proulx
VP: Jan Berger
VP: Frank Burpo
VP: Brian Correia
VP: Bob Eisendrath
VP: Nathan Frank
VP: Ryan Hall
VP: Steve Littel
VP: Glenn McRae

D-U-N-S 79-066-3090
■ CAREMARKPCS HEALTH LLC
(Suby of CAREMARK RX INC) ★
211 Commerce St Ste 800, Nashville, TN 37201-1817
Tel (615) 743-6600 Founded/Ownrshp 2004
Sales 66.3MM^E EMP 6,500
SIC 8742 Hospital & health services consultant
Ch Bd: David Halbert
*CFO: Yon Yoon Jorden
*V Ch Bd: Jon Halbert
*Chf Mktg O: Craig S Schub
*Ex VP: John H Sattler
*Sr VP: Susan S Demars
*Exec: Danny Phillips
Dir Rx: Jennifer Simmons
QA Dir: Anne Jacobs
QA Dir: Doreen Zukowski
IT Man: Apurva Doshi

D-U-N-S 07-668-6435
CAREMOUNT MEDICAL PC
MKMG
110 S Bedford Rd, Mount Kisco, NY 10549-3446
Tel (914) 241-1050 Founded/Ownrshp 1989
Sales 127.8MM^E EMP 900
SIC 8011 Physicians' office, including specialists
Ch Bd: Scott Hayworth MD
COO: Christopher Sclafani
Exec: Laura Preza
Dir Risk M: Rosemarie White
Genl Mgr: Denise Iarussi
Off Mgr: Purnima Desai
Off Mgr: Patricia Mader
CIO: Nicholas Korchinski
Cmptr Lab: Celeste Derosa
Netwrk Eng: Pedro Ubilla
Mktg Mgr: Sonia Young

CARENTERS SOUTH WEST ADM
See CARPENTERS HEALTH AND WELFARE TRUST FOR

D-U-N-S 82-969-0981
CAREOREGON INC
315 Sw 5th Ave Ste 900, Portland, OR 97204-1739
Tel (503) 416-4100 Founded/Ownrshp 1994
Sales 851.4MM EMP 140
Accts Lb Kpmg Llp Seattle Wa
SIC 8621 Health association
Pr: Chris Krenk

COO: Tracie Barcenas
CFO: Beth Dehamel
CFO: Carolyn Rankin
Ofcr: Lynne Shoemaker
VP: John Frejuk
*Ex Dir: Mylia Christensen
Dir IT: Rod Gaul
Mktg Mgr: Kevin Brooks
Snr Mgr: Barbara K Adriance
Snr Mgr: Rose Englert

D-U-N-S 07-914-7241
CAREPOINT HEALTH MANAGEMENT ASSOCIATES LLC
10 Exchange Pl Fl 15, Jersey City, NJ 07302-4934
Tel (201) 795-8554 Founded/Ownrshp 2013
Sales 567.6MM^E EMP 1^E
SIC 8062 General medical & surgical hospitals
*Ex VP: W Peter Daniels
Netwrk Eng: Scott Whitney

CAREPRO MEDICAL ONE
See ADVANTAGE HEALTH SYSTEMS INC

D-U-N-S 80-049-7836
CARESOURCE MANAGEMENT GROUP CO
230 N Main St, Dayton, OH 45402-1263
Tel (937) 224-3300 Founded/Ownrshp 1989
Sales NA EMP 900
SIC 6321 Health insurance carriers
CEO: Pamela B Morris
*COO: Bobby Jones
COO: Leslie W Naamon
*Chf Mktg O: Craig Thiele MD
Ex VP: Janet Grant
VP: Pamela Morris
VP: Jim Peters
VP: Steve Skerl
Comm Man: Lori Deaton
Ex Dir: Cathy Ponitz
Nurse Mgr: Sandy Spencer
Board of Directors: Thomas Breitenbach, Kevin R Brown, J Thomas Maultsby, Pamela B Morris

D-U-N-S 83-922-6334
CARESOUTH HEALTH SYSTEM INC
1 10th St Ste 500, Augusta, GA 30901-0103
Tel (706) 855-5533 Founded/Ownrshp 1998
Sales 127.1MM^E EMP 3,750
SIC 8099 Medical services organization
CEO: Rich Griffin
Pr: Sheri Dunn
Pr: Jason Fox
Pr: Sharon Oxford
VP: Gary Liuzzo
VP: Isabel McQuade
CTO: Jorita Sevy
Manager: Tom Rankin
Sls Mgr: Alice Meeks

D-U-N-S 94-772-6022
CARESOUTH HOME HEALTH SERVICES LLC
CARESUTH HMECARE PROFESSIONALS
(Suby of CARESOUTH HEALTH SYSTEM INC) ★
1 10th St Ste 500, Augusta, GA 30901-0103
Tel (706) 855-5533 Founded/Ownrshp 1998
Sales 124.4MM EMP 2,800
SIC 8082 Home health care services
CEO: Rick Griffin
*CFO: John Southern
Dir IT: Jennifer Johnson
IT Man: Lisa Williamson

D-U-N-S 79-316-9512 IMP/EXP
CARESTREAM HEALTH INC
(Suby of ONEX CORPORATION)
150 Verona St, Rochester, NY 14608-1733
Tel (585) 627-1800 Founded/Ownrshp 2007
Sales 1.3MMM^E EMP 7,000
SIC 8011 7374 Radiologist; Data processing service
CEO: Kevin J Hobert
Ch Bd: Robert M Le Blanc
Pr: Lisa Ashby
Pr: Jianqing Bennett
CFO: Barry Canipe
Treas: Ann Svoboda
Chf Mktg O: Norman Yung
Ofcr: Terrance P Callanan
Ofcr: Patricia Mellon
Ofcr: Sarah Obrien
Ofcr: Ralph E Olney
Ofcr: Duane Sachs
VP: Neil Bryant
VP: Jo Campbell
VP: Jane Duffy-White
VP: Peter Hunt
VP: Dawn Safford
Board of Directors: Joseph F Dooley, William A Sanger, Michael L Smith

CARESUTH HMECARE PROFESSIONALS
See CARESOUTH HOME HEALTH SERVICES LLC

D-U-N-S 15-768-9233
CAREY INTERNATIONAL INC
CAREY LIMOUSINE
4530 Wscnsin Ave Nw Ste 5, Washington, DC 20016
Tel (202) 895-1200 Founded/Ownrshp 2009
Sales 266.2MM^E EMP 700
SIC 4119 6794 Limousine rental, with driver; Local rental transportation; Franchises, selling or licensing
Pr: Gary L Kessler
Pr: Judy Barron
*COO: Sally A Snead
Ex VP: Mitchell Lahr
Sr VP: J J Millard
Sr VP: Eugene Willard
VP: Joel Barch
VP: Phillip J Gilpin
VP: Georgia Grover
VP: David Ng
VP: Sally Snead
Dir Soc: Susanna Klingler
Board of Directors: Robert W Cox, Dennis I Meyer, Nicholas J St George, Joseph V Vittoria

D-U-N-S 03-297-0097
CAREY JOHNSON OIL CO INC (OK)
EZ GO
701 Sw F Ave, Lawton, OK 73501-4542
Tel (580) 595-8300 Founded/Ownrshp 1964
Sales 105.6MM^E EMP 200
SIC 5171 Petroleum bulk stations
Pr: Karey Johnson Jr
*Ch Bd: Bedford Mitchell
*VP: Paul Korhonen
Exec: Jo Cable
Mktg Dir: Michael Fitzpatrick

CAREY LIMOUSINE
See CAREY INTERNATIONAL INC

D-U-N-S 83-276-7870
CAREY WATERMARK INVESTORS INC
50 Rockefeller Plz, New York, NY 10020-1605
Tel (212) 492-1100 Founded/Ownrshp 2008
Sales 542.1MM EMP 972^E
Accts Pricewaterhousecoopers Llp N
SIC 6798 7011 Real estate investment trusts; Hotels & motels
CEO: Michael G Medzigian
*Ch Bd: Trevor P Bond
COO: Thomas E Zacharias
CFO: Mark Decesaris
CFO: Hisham A Kader

D-U-N-S 13-564-6297 IMP/EXP
CARGILL COCOA & CHOCOLATE INC
(Suby of CARGILL INC) ★
20 N Broad St, Lititz, PA 17543-1005
Tel (717) 626-1131 Founded/Ownrshp 1992
Sales 89.8MM^E EMP 426
SIC 2066 Chocolate; Cocoa & cocoa products
Pr: Donald E Pearson
V Ch: Paul D Conway
*Sec: Jayme D Olson
VP: Hugo Der Goes
*VP: Scott M Naatjes

D-U-N-S 00-624-9189 IMP/EXP
CARGILL INC
15407 Mcginty Rd W, Wayzata, MN 55391-2399
Tel (952) 742-7575 Founded/Ownrshp 1930
Sales 107.1MMM EMP 150,000
SIC 5153 2075 2046 2048 2011 2015

D-U-N-S 13-154-9388 EXP
CARGILL KITCHEN SOLUTIONS INC
(Suby of CARGILL INC) ★
206 W 4th St, Monticello, MN 55362-8524
Tel (763) 271-5600 Founded/Ownrshp 2007
Sales 138.5MM^E EMP 700
SIC 2015 Egg processing
Pr: Michael Luker
Sec: M A Kurschner
VP: James A Guyre
Dir Opers: Dennis Darnell

D-U-N-S 07-137-4854 IMP/EXP
CARGILL MEAT SOLUTIONS CORP
(Suby of CARGILL INC) ★
151 N Main St Ste 900, Wichita, KS 67202-1410
Tel (316) 291-2500 Founded/Ownrshp 1974
Sales 673.8MM^E EMP 20,000
SIC 2011 5147 4213

D-U-N-S 82-463-4708
CARGO AIRPORT SERVICES USA LLC
CONSOLIDATED AVIATION SERVICES
(Suby of AIRLINE SERVICES) ★
Cargo Bldg 261 N Boundary, Jamaica, NY 11430
Tel (718) 244-0900 Founded/Ownrshp 2016
Sales 338.8MM^E EMP 5,000
SIC 4789 Cargo loading & unloading services
Pr: Michael A Duffy
*COO: Steve Crescenti
Prin: Liane Kelly

D-U-N-S 15-536-4594
CARGO FORCE INC
6705 Sw 57th Ave Ste 700, South Miami, FL 33143-3649
Tel (305) 740-3252 Founded/Ownrshp 2002
Sales 33.7MM EMP 1,000
Accts Brunt Sweeney Matz Pa Cp
SIC 4581 Airfreight loading & unloading services
CEO: Anthony C Romeo
Pr: Robert W Phelan
CEO: Anthony Romeo
COO: Jared Azcuy
CFO: Chuck Little
Genl Mgr: Matt Benavidez
Genl Mgr: Mildred Camacho
Genl Mgr: Marcin Trzeciak
Opers Mgr: Fabian Niebles

D-U-N-S 83-059-2577
CARGOTEC HOLDING INC
(Suby of CARGOTEC OYJ)
415 E Dundee St, Ottawa, KS 66067-1543
Tel (785) 242-2200 Founded/Ownrshp 2002
Sales 168.8MM^E EMP 550
SIC 3593 3537 Fluid power cylinders, hydraulic or pneumatic; Industrial trucks & tractors
Pr: Lennart Brelin
*Pr: Greg Hewitt
*Pr: Mike Manning
*Treas: Clay Weitzel
*Treas: Bob Wills
VP: Ingo Erhardt
Sls Mgr: Vincent Hruska

CARGOTEC SERVICES USA
See KALMAR SOLUTIONS LLC

D-U-N-S 00-537-8567 IMP/EXP
CARHARTT INC (MI)
5750 Mercury Dr, Dearborn, MI 48126-4167
Tel (313) 271-8460 Founded/Ownrshp 1889
Sales 1.4MMM^E EMP 3,000
Accts Plante & Moran Pllc Southfie

SIC 2326 2329 2325 Men's & boys' work clothing; Overalls & coveralls; Work shirts: men's, youths' & boys'; Jackets, overall & work; Men's & boys' leather, wool & down-filled outerwear; Coats (oiled fabric, leatherette, etc.): men's & boys'; Hunting coats & vests, men's; Dungarees: men's, youths' & boys'; Jeans: men's, youths' & boys'
Pr: Mark Valade
CFO: Linda P Hubbard
Trst: Peter Cook
Ex VP: Michelle Woodburn
Sr VP: Jane Niemi
VP: Tony Ambroza
VP: Glenda Arnold
VP: Eric Dodson
VP: David Lee
VP: Andi Lobdell
VP: Joe Monahan
VP: Jennifer Piscopink
VP: Tom Slone
Dir: William Hardy

CARI COMPANY
See CARI INVESTMENT CO LLC

D-U-N-S 15-748-1441
CARI INVESTMENT CO LLC
CARI COMPANY
222 N Vermont St, Covington, LA 70433-3240
Tel (985) 635-6009 *Founded/Ownrshp* 1961
Sales 104.9MM[E] *EMP* 300
SIC 6211 4424 3731 5146 Security brokers & dealers; Coastwide transportation, freight; Shipbuilding & repairing; Fish & seafoods
Pr: Christian G Vaccari
**Treas:* Richard W Cryar

D-U-N-S 07-856-9483
CARIB ENERGY (USA) LLC
(*Suby of* CROWLEY PETROLEUM SERVICES INC) ★
9487 Regency Square Blvd, Jacksonville, FL 32225-8183
Tel (904) 727-2559 *Founded/Ownrshp* 2013
Sales 56.0MM[E] *EMP* 1,130[E]
SIC 3533 Gas field machinery & equipment
Pr: Greg Buffington
Genl Mgr: Jeffrey Brunell

D-U-N-S 78-721-8387
CARIBBEAN ARCHITECTS & ENGINEERS
D14 Calle 6 Apt 1101, Guaynabo, PR 00966-1674
Tel (787) 783-5500 *Founded/Ownrshp* 1999
Sales 99.6MM *EMP* 30
Accts De Angel & Campania San Juan
SIC 8711 8712 Professional engineer; Architectural engineering
Pt: Bolivar Guzman
Pt: Rene Silva

D-U-N-S 79-442-7927
CARIBBEAN FINANCIAL GROUP INC
EL SOL
(*Suby of* IRVING PLACE CAPITAL LLC) ★
20807 Biscayne Blvd # 200, Miami, FL 33180-1410
Tel (305) 933-6601 *Founded/Ownrshp* 2006
Sales NA *EMP* 1,024
SIC 6141 Licensed loan companies, small
CEO: Oriol Segarra
**CFO:* Tomas Chadwick
**VP:* Laura Pirado

D-U-N-S 09-004-7259 IMP/EXP
CARIBBEAN PRODUCE EXCHANGE LLC
2 Carr 869, Catano, PR 00962-5840
Tel (787) 793-0750 *Founded/Ownrshp* 1960, 1979
Sales 85.5MM *EMP* 139
Accts Psv & Co Psc San Juan Puert
SIC 5148 Fruits, fresh; Vegetables, fresh
Ch: Gualberto Rodriguez II
Pr: Gualberto Rodriguez III
Genl Mgr: Jose Curras
Sls Mgr: Felix Malave
Sls Mgr: Jonia Nandis

D-U-N-S 09-023-5573 IMP/EXP
■ **CARIBBEAN REFRESCOS INC**
(*Suby of* COCA-COLA CO) ★
Carr 172 Km 13 4 Bo Monte St Ca, Cidra, PR 00739
Tel (787) 739-8452 *Founded/Ownrshp* 1968
Sales 154.6MM[E] *EMP* 406
SIC 2087 Concentrates, drink; Concentrates, flavoring (except drink)
Pr: Steven Heyer
CFO: Gary Fayard
VP: Harry Anderson
VP: William Hawkins III
VP: Fred Yochum

D-U-N-S 09-117-6875 IMP
CARIBBEAN RESTAURANTS LLC
BURGER KING
(*Suby of* BKH ACQUISITION HOLDCO I LLC) ★
Rd 5 Km 27 4 Bldg 1, Catano, PR 00962
Tel (787) 474-7777 *Founded/Ownrshp* 2007
Sales 147.0MM[E] *EMP* 6,000
SIC 5812 Fast-food restaurant, chain
Pr: Aniseto Solares
**CFO:* Carlos Garcia
Sr VP: Glen Helton
**Sr VP:* Juan Jose Jimenez
**Sr VP:* Rafael Lavin

D-U-N-S 10-575-2059
CARIBBEAN TEMPORARY SERVICES INC
1431 Ave Ponce De Leon, San Juan, PR 00907-4026
Tel (787) 724-5643 *Founded/Ownrshp* 1983
Sales 55.4MM[E] *EMP* 2,465
SIC 7363 Temporary help service
Pr: Tere Durand Manzanal
**Ex VP:* Rose M Villamil Durand
**Ex VP:* Xiomara Villamil Durand
**Ex Dir:* Angel Lacomba

CARIBE BAKERS
See HOLSUM DE PUERTO RICO INC

D-U-N-S 02-690-7332 IMP
■ **CARIBE GE INTERNATIONAL OF PUERTO RICO INC**
(*Suby of* GENERAL ELECTRIC CO) ★
980 Ave San Luis, Arecibo, PR 00612-3848
Tel (787) 878-1420 *Founded/Ownrshp* 1996
Sales 47.7MM[E] *EMP* 1,342
Accts Kpmg Peat Marwick
SIC 3613 Power circuit breakers
Pr: Paul Sledzik

CARIBINER GROUP, THE
See AUDIO VISUAL SERVICES GROUP INC

D-U-N-S 80-122-2456 IMP
CARIBOU COFFEE CO INC
(*Suby of* JAB BEECH INC) ★
3900 Lake Breeze Ave, Minneapolis, MN 55429-3921
Tel (763) 592-2200 *Founded/Ownrshp* 2013
Sales 367.3MM[E] *EMP* 6,086[E]
SIC 5812 5499 6794 Coffee shop; Coffee; Franchises, selling or licensing
CEO: Michael Tattersfield
**CFO:* Timothy J Hennessy
**Sr VP:* Dan E Lee
**Sr VP:* Alfredo V Martel
**Sr VP:* Henry J Suerth
VP: Janet Astor
VP: Ross Gilbertson
VP: Paul Turek
VP: R Paul Turek
Dist Mgr: Angela Hibbs
Store Mgr: Fran Guenther
Board of Directors: Kip R Caffey, Sarah Palisi Chapin, Wallace B Doolin, Gary A Graves, Charles H Ogburn, Philip H Sanford

D-U-N-S 07-793-3315
CARILION CLINIC
1906 Belleview Ave Se, Roanoke, VA 24014-1838
Tel (540) 981-7900 *Founded/Ownrshp* 1981
Sales 800.9MM *EMP* 9,200
SIC 8741 Hospital management
Pr: Nancy Howell Agee
**CFO:* Don Lorton
**Treas:* David Hagadorn
Bd of Dir: Thomas Mantey
Ex VP: Jeanne S Armentrout
Ex VP: Patrice Weiss
VP: Tim Auwarter
VP: Sharon Bass
VP: Larry Carter
VP: Freida Driver
VP: William Flattery
VP: Stephen A Morgan
VP: Gary Scott
**VP:* Rob Vaughan
VP: Carolyn Webster
Dir Rx: Clara A Spencer

D-U-N-S 15-338-7865 IMP
CARILION MEDICAL CENTER
CARILION ROANOKE MEMORIAL HOSP
(*Suby of* CARILION CLINIC) ★
1906 Belleview Ave Se, Roanoke, VA 24014-1838
Tel (540) 981-7000 *Founded/Ownrshp* 1982
Sales 1.0MMM *EMP* 6,390
Accts Deloitte & Touche Llp Charlot
SIC 8011 8062 Offices & clinics of medical doctors; General medical & surgical hospitals
CEO: Nancy Howell Agee
Chf OB: Dennis R Scribner Jr
V Ch: Eduardo Lara-Torre
**Pr:* Steve Arner
**CFO:* Donald E Lorton
**Treas:* George Robert Vaughan Jr
**Treas:* Rob Vaughan
Ofcr: Tonya Low
VP: Joseph Austin
VP: Carolyn Chrisman
VP: Gary Kirby

D-U-N-S 13-139-3688
CARILION NEW RIVER VALLEY MEDICAL CENTER
2900 Lamb Cir Ste 150, Christiansburg, VA 24073-6341
Tel (540) 731-2000 *Founded/Ownrshp* 1988
Sales 896.7MM *EMP* 800
SIC 8062 General medical & surgical hospitals
Pr: Donald Halliwill
**CEO:* John Piatkowski

CARILION ROANOKE MEMORIAL HOSP
See CARILION MEDICAL CENTER

D-U-N-S 07-551-3697
CARING PEOPLE ALLIANCE
8 Penn Ctr, Philadelphia, PA 19103-2125
Tel (215) 545-5230 *Founded/Ownrshp* 1934
Sales 103.1MM *EMP* 300
Accts Marcum Llp Bala Cynwyd Pa
SIC 8351 Child day care services
CEO: Arlene F Bell
CFO: Edward Ring
VP: Edward J Christie Jr
**VP:* M E Jones
Genl Mgr: Murray McPherson
Site Mgr: Desiree Crawford
Pgrm Dir: Olga Gibbs
Pgrm Dir: Marjorie Shoemaker
Pgrm Dir: Bonita Taylor
Pgrm Dir: Lisa Zulewski

D-U-N-S 01-100-2982
CARINGTON HEALTH SYSTEMS
FRANKLIN RIDGE CARE FACILITY
8200 Beckett Park Dr, Hamilton, OH 45011
Tel (513) 682-2700 *Founded/Ownrshp* 2004
Sales 78.8MM[E] *EMP* 3,000
SIC 8741 8051 Hospital management; Nursing & personal care facility management; Skilled nursing care facilities
Pr: Glyndon Powell
**VP:* Edward Byington
Nrsg Dir: Tammy Smith
HC Dir: Lisa Henderson

D-U-N-S 06-329-4540
CARIOCA CO
2601 W Dunlap Ave Ste 10, Phoenix, AZ 85021-2711
Tel (602) 395-2600 *Founded/Ownrshp* 1972
Sales 123.6MM *EMP* 300
Accts Jaffa Simmons Pllc Mesa Ari
SIC 5541 5411 Filling stations, gasoline; Convenience stores, chain
Pr: Marvin L Rose
**CFO:* Eric S Young
**Treas:* Wilford A Cardon
**Treas:* Mark Rose
**VP:* Dixon Cowley

CARITAS CHRISTI HEALTH CARE
See STEWARD HEALTH CARE SYSTEM LLC

CARITAS CHRISTI HEALTH CARE
See MORTON HOSPITAL AND MEDICAL CENTER INC

CARITAS MEDICAL GROUP
See TAS-CSEMCB INC

CARITAS NORWOOD HOSPITAL
See TAS-CNH INC

D-U-N-S 09-144-3734
■ **CARITEN INSURANCE CO**
(*Suby of* HUMANA INC) ★
2160 Lakeside Centre Way # 200, Knoxville, TN 37922-0202
Tel (865) 470-7470 *Founded/Ownrshp* 2008
Sales NA *EMP* 400
SIC 6324 Hospital & medical service plans
Pr: Lance Hunsinger
CFO: Charles Majdalani

D-U-N-S 00-282-3334
CARL BELT INC (MD)
11521 Milnor Ave, Cumberland, MD 21502-5131
Tel (240) 362-0270 *Founded/Ownrshp* 1962
Sales 94.8MM[E] *EMP* 190
SIC 1542 Commercial & office building, new construction; Commercial & office buildings, renovation & repair
Pr: Carl O Belt Jr
**Treas:* Thomas Wolf
**Sr VP:* Kevin S Hite
**VP:* Richard Blair
**VP:* Mark A Farris
**VP:* Larry Myers

D-U-N-S 00-520-4631
CARL BUDDIG AND CO
950 175th St, Homewood, IL 60430-2027
Tel (708) 798-0900 *Founded/Ownrshp* 1943
Sales 157.7MM[E] *EMP* 500
SIC 2013 2022 Smoked meats from purchased meat; Sausages from purchased meat; Natural cheese
Pr: Robert Budding
COO: Carl Buddig
Treas: Jim Gow
**Co-CEO:* Thomas Buddig
Ex VP: Roger Buddig
Ex VP: Thomas R Buddig
**VP:* Dan Wynn
Exec: Joy Anthonsen
Dir IT: Daniel Alsager
Dir IT: William Bodel
IT Man: Dan Everett

D-U-N-S 04-470-9129 IMP
CARL F EWIG INC
MARTEC INTERNATIONAL
529 Dowd Ave, Elizabeth, NJ 07201-2103
Tel (908) 248-9001 *Founded/Ownrshp* 1950
Sales 104.4MM[E] *EMP* 200
SIC 5088 Marine supplies
Ch Bd: Thomas A Ewig
**Pr:* Alex Ewig
VP: Dan Gugliotta

D-U-N-S 02-783-1361 IMP
CARL KARCHER ENTERPRISES INC
CARL'S JR.
(*Suby of* HARDEES) ★
1200 N Harbor Blvd, Anaheim, CA 92801-2493
Tel (714) 776-8054 *Founded/Ownrshp* 1994
Sales 289.8MM[E] *EMP* 11,100
SIC 5812 Fast-food restaurant, chain
Ch Bd: William P Foley II
**Pr:* Andrew F Puzder
**CFO:* Dennis Lacey
**VP:* Anne Blumenstein
VP: Michael Murphy
IT Man: David Oshiro
IT Man: Nicki Sonar

D-U-N-S 07-530-7926
CARL WARREN & CO
17862 17th St Ste 111, Tustin, CA 92780-2170
Tel (800) 572-6900 *Founded/Ownrshp* 1956
Sales NA *EMP* 180
SIC 6411 Insurance claim adjusters, not employed by insurance company
COO: Tom Boylan
**VP:* Mark Bernstein
**VP:* Allison Duncan

D-U-N-S 00-699-2523 IMP
CARL ZEISS INC
(*Suby of* CARL ZEISS AG)
1 Zeiss Dr, Thornwood, NY 10594-1996
Tel (914) 747-1800 *Founded/Ownrshp* 1969
Sales 311.1MM[E] *EMP* 500
SIC 3827 5049 3829 5084 3826 Optical instruments & apparatus; Optical goods; Measuring & controlling devices; Instruments & control equipment; Analytical instruments
Prin: Dr Michael Kaschke
Pr: Cheryl Sarli
**CFO:* James A Olivo
**VP:* Meg Donohue
VP: Scott Margolin
VP: Frank Pingaro
**VP:* John Roulat
VP: Marlene Thomson
Exec: Dorothy Brown
Dir Bus: Mark Espinet
Mng Dir: Edward Mancini

D-U-N-S 96-271-2550 IMP/EXP
CARL ZEISS INDUSTRIAL METROLOGY LLC
(*Suby of* CARL ZEISS INC) ★
6250 Sycamore Ln N, Maple Grove, MN 55369-6309
Tel (763) 533-9990 *Founded/Ownrshp* 1996
Sales 88.2MM[E] *EMP* 300
SIC 3545 3825 Machine tool accessories; Instruments to measure electricity
CEO: Michael Kaschke

D-U-N-S 36-274-7011 IMP
CARL ZEISS MEDITEC INC
(*Suby of* CARL ZEISS MEDITEC AG)
5160 Hacienda Dr, Dublin, CA 94568-7562
Tel (925) 557-4100 *Founded/Ownrshp* 2000
Sales 224.5MM[E] *EMP* 705[E]
SIC 3827 Optical instruments & lenses
Pr: Ralph Kuschnereit
Pr: Joseph Redner
COO: Laurens Steger
**CFO:* Roberto Deger
Chf Mktg O: Christine Randle
Sr VP: Angelo Rago
VP: Craig Altschuler
VP: Pepe Davis
VP: Jeff Rospert
VP: Jeffrey Schmidt
Prgrm Mgr: Elliott Hutton
Board of Directors: Christian Muller

D-U-N-S 03-837-6674
CARL ZEISS MICROSCOPY LLC
(*Suby of* CARL ZEISS INC) ★
1 Zeiss Dr, Thornwood, NY 10594-1996
Tel (914) 747-1800 *Founded/Ownrshp* 2001
Sales 112.6MM[E] *EMP* 300
SIC 5049 Optical goods
Pr: James Sharp
VP: Melissa Wilkins
Dir IT: Don Francis
IT Man: Mario Maldonado
Opers Mgr: Brian Calvary

D-U-N-S 92-902-1715 IMP
CARL ZEISS MICROSCOPY LLC
LLC, CARL ZEISS NTS
(*Suby of* CARL ZEISS INC) ★
1 Corporate Pl Ste 3, Peabody, MA 01960-3827
Tel (978) 826-1500 *Founded/Ownrshp* 2010
Sales 100.9MM[E] *EMP* 349[E]
SIC 5047 3826 Medical laboratory equipment; Microscopes, electron & proton
Pr: James Sharp
Pr: Richard Comunale
**Pr:* Daniel McGee
**VP:* Philip Gottlied
**VP:* Kenneth Patterson
IT Man: Davis Terry
Software D: Nick Fitton

D-U-N-S 80-987-5487 IMP
CARL ZEISS VISION INC
(*Suby of* CARL ZEISS VISION INTERNATIONAL GMBH)
12121 Scripps Summit Dr, San Diego, CA 92131-4608
Tel (858) 790-7700 *Founded/Ownrshp* 2005
Sales 167.3MM[E] *EMP* 878
SIC 3827 3851 Lenses, optical: all types except ophthalmic; Lenses, ophthalmic
CEO: Ulrich Krauss
**Pr:* Joseph Donahoe
CFO: Ron Dutt
CFO: Carmen Sarracco
VP: David Keane
VP: Jim Runchey
CTO: Jacci Sinclair
IT Man: David Armstrong
IT Man: Laurie Klitzke
Mktg Dir: Veneeta Eason
Mktg Mgr: Meredith Feldman
Board of Directors: Raymund Heinen, Hanspeter Muerle

D-U-N-S 07-915-1171 IMP
CARLE FOUNDATION
611 W Park St, Urbana, IL 61801-2529
Tel (217) 383-3311 *Founded/Ownrshp* 1946
Sales 249.3MM *EMP* 5,284
Accts Ernst & Young Us Llp Indianap
SIC 8062 General medical & surgical hospitals
CEO: James C Leonard MD
**Treas:* Robert Tonkinson
**Ofcr:* Michael Sutter
**Ex VP:* Matthew Gibb MD
**VP:* John Snyder
Mtls Dir: Debbie Schmidt
Doctor: Mark E Faith

D-U-N-S 10-569-9982 IMP
CARLE FOUNDATION HOSPITAL
CARLE HOSPITAL
(*Suby of* CARLE FOUNDATION) ★
611 W Park St, Urbana, IL 61801-2529
Tel (217) 326-2900 *Founded/Ownrshp* 1982
Sales 690.9MM *EMP* 2,500[E]
SIC 8062 General medical & surgical hospitals
Ch: Marty Smith
CFO: Dennis Hesh
CFO: Pat Owens
Bd of Dir: Sean Grambart
VP: Cheryl Gerow
VP: Scott Harding
VP: Carol Hovis
VP: Ashley Hummel
VP: Napoleon Knight
VP: Susan Mellendorf
VP: Megan Oxley
VP: Rick Rinehart
VP: Lauren Schmid
VP: Jennifer Schwartz
VP: Bonnie Standley
Exec: Rich Tewell
Dir Rad: Tim Sapyta
Dir Rx: Chris Howard

D-U-N-S 04-910-2873
CARLE HEALTH CARE INC
611 W Park St, Urbana, IL 61801-2529
Tel (217) 383-3206 Founded/Ownrshp 2010
Sales 255.1MM EMP 22E
Accts Ernst & Young Us Llp Indianap
SIC 8099 Health & allied services
Prin: John Snyder

D-U-N-S 07-560-6517
CARLE HOLDING CO INC
602 W University Ave, Urbana, IL 61801-2530
Tel (217) 383-3311 Founded/Ownrshp 2010
Sales 1.1MMME EMP 2,500
SIC 8011 Clinic, operated by physicians
Prin: Gregg M Wallander
*CEO: Bruce Wellman MD
Off Mgr: Allen Rinehart
Pharmcst: Frank Saracco

CARLE HOSPITAL
See CARLE FOUNDATION HOSPITAL

D-U-N-S 06-818-4449
CARLETON COLLEGE
1 N College St, Northfield, MN 55057-4044
Tel (507) 222-4000 Founded/Ownrshp 1866
Sales 139.7MM EMP 650E
Accts Cliftonlarsonallen Llp Minnea
SIC 8221 College, except junior
Pr: Steven G Poskanzer
*Pr: Fredrick A Rogers
Trst: Beth Davis
Ofcr: Leslie Vanderwood
VP: Rebecca Deland
Assoc Dir: Carol Trosset
Off Admin: Emily Perlman
Snr Sftwr: Siobhan McMahon
Info Man: Susannah Shmurak
Pgrm Dir: Erin Chamlee

D-U-N-S 13-610-8342 IMP
CARLETON LIFE SUPPORT SYSTEMS INC
COBHAM MISSION SYSTEM
(Suby of CARLETON TECHNOLOGIES INC) ★
2734 Hickory Grove Rd, Davenport, IA 52804-1203
Tel (563) 383-6000 Founded/Ownrshp 2002
Sales 212.4MME EMP 500
SIC 3679 Cryogenic cooling devices for infrared detectors, masers
Ch: John Devaney
*Pr: Gordon Abele
*CFO: Simon Nicholls
*Sec: Kevin McKeown
Genl Mgr: Katie Engels
Dir IT: Craig Armstrong
IT Man: Todd Whorton
VP Mktg: Patricia Steinbrecher
Mktg Mgr: Paul Thronson
Sls Mgr: Nigel Atkinson
Sls Mgr: Anna Lathan

D-U-N-S 17-534-4068
CARLETON TECHNOLOGIES INC
(Suby of COBHAM HOLDINGS INC) ★
10 Cobham Dr, Orchard Park, NY 14127-4195
Tel (716) 662-0006 Founded/Ownrshp 1987
Sales 235.8MME EMP 815
SIC 3728 Aircraft parts & equipment
Pr: Kelly Coffield
*Ch Bd: Kenneth Kota
*Ofcr: Timothy Sopko
*Ofcr: David Squires
*Ofcr: W Glenn Yarborough
*Ofcr: James Zigel
Genl Mgr: Nicholas Dziama
*Genl Mgr: Kenneth A Kota
Dir IT: Jim Talty
Sfty Dirs: Chuck Connelly

D-U-N-S 96-805-9209 IMP
CARLEX GLASS AMERICA LLC
CARLEX GLASS COMPANY
7200 Centennial Blvd, Nashville, TN 37209-1013
Tel (615) 350-7500 Founded/Ownrshp 2010
Sales 206.4MME EMP 700
SIC 3231 Products of purchased glass; Mirrored glass; Mirrors, truck & automobile: made from purchased glass; Windshields, glass: made from purchased glass
Pr: Jim Shepherd
Treas: Yoshi Ikeno

CARLEX GLASS COMPANY
See CARLEX GLASS AMERICA LLC

D-U-N-S 62-111-7563 IMP
CARLEX GLASS CO LLC
(Suby of CENTRAL GLASS CO., LTD.)
77 Excellence Way, Vonore, TN 37885-2123
Tel (423) 884-1105 Founded/Ownrshp 2011
Sales 220.0MME EMP 350
SIC 5013 Automobile glass
VP: Bill Long

D-U-N-S 01-771-1859 IMP
CARLEX GLASS OF INDIANA INC
(Suby of CENTRAL GLASS CO., LTD.)
1209 E Big Beaver Rd, Troy, MI 48083-1905
Tel (586) 365-4900 Founded/Ownrshp 1987
Sales 861.0MME EMP 5,884
SIC 3211 Flat glass
Pr: Jim Davis
CFO: Charles Wilson
*VP: Ralph J Gerson

D-U-N-S 01-683-4036
CARLILE BANCSHARES INC
201 Main St Ste 1320, Fort Worth, TX 76102-3117
Tel (817) 877-4440 Founded/Ownrshp 2009
Sales 141.7MME EMP 825
SIC 6719 Investment holding companies, except banks
CEO: Tom C Nichols
Pr: Don E Cosby
CFO: Mindy Hegi
Chf Cred: Max R Hefner
Ofcr: Alan D Masters
VP: Jean Rankin

D-U-N-S 12-208-1243
CARLILE TRANSPORTATION SYSTEMS INC
K&W TRANSPORTATION
(Suby of TOTE INC) ★
1800 E 1st Ave, Anchorage, AK 99501-1834
Tel (907) 276-7797 Founded/Ownrshp 2013
Sales 104.6MME EMP 500
SIC 4212 4213 4731 Local trucking, without storage; Trucking, except local; Contract haulers; Freight consolidation
Pr: Armstrong James
*CFO: Terry Smith
*Sec: Simpson Hugh
VP: John Armstrong
VP: Tom Hendrix
*VP: John Mc Donald
Sfty Mgr: Sara Perez
Opers Mgr: Tom Hubbard
Opers Mgr: Jon Vantreeck
Sales Asso: Sally Jolicoeur

D-U-N-S 00-114-9673 IMP
CARLING TECHNOLOGIES INC (CT)
CARLINGSWITCH
60 Johnson Ave, Plainville, CT 06062-1181
Tel (860) 793-9281 Founded/Ownrshp 1920
Sales 1.1MM EMP 2,600
Accts Whittlesey & Hadley Pc Hartfo
SIC 3643 3613 3612 Electric switches; Power circuit breakers; Transformers, except electric
Pr: Richard W Sorenson
*Ex VP: Jennifer Buddenhagen
Ex VP: Jennifer Buddenhagen
*Ex VP: Edward Rosenthal
*Ex VP: Richard Sorenson Jr
VP: Simon Cordner
VP: Michael A Fasano
VP: Robert W Lauben
VP: David Pippa
*VP: Paul Soucy
VP: Harold Wiegard
Exec: Gary Corde

CARLINGSWITCH
See CARLING TECHNOLOGIES INC

CARLISLE
See CARLSTAR GROUP LLC

CARLISLE BELTS
See TIMKEN SMO LLC

D-U-N-S 60-732-5136 IMP
■ **CARLISLE BRAKE & FRICTION INC**
CBF
(Suby of CARLISLE COMPANIES INC) ★
6180 Cochran Rd, Solon, OH 44139-3306
Tel (440) 528-4000 Founded/Ownrshp 2003
Sales 325.2MME EMP 2,000
SIC 3751 Brakes, friction clutch & other: bicycle
Pr: Karl T Messmer
VP: Kevin Doherty
VP: Thomas Gilbride
VP Admn: Thomas Gilbert
Genl Mgr: Debbie Butler
Dir IT: Brian Moran
Plnt Mgr: Matthew Jereb
Ql Cn Mgr: Steve Hamstra
Ql Cn Mgr: Wes Pedersen
Sls Mgr: Cathy Szall
Sales Asso: Jaymin Patel

D-U-N-S 00-300-5766 IMP/EXP
▲ **CARLISLE COMPANIES INC**
16430 N Scottsdale Rd, Scottsdale, AZ 85254-1518
Tel (704) 501-1100 Founded/Ownrshp 1917
Sales 3.5MMM EMP 12,000
Accts Ernst & Young Llp Charlotte
Tkr Sym CSL Exch NYS
SIC 2952 3714 3312 3357 3263 Roofing materials; Motor vehicle parts & accessories; Wheels, motor vehicle; Wire products, steel or iron; Fiber optic cable (insulated); Cookware, fine earthenware
Pr: D Christian Koch
Ch Bd: David A Roberts
CFO: Steven J Ford
VP: Scott C Selbach
VP: Kevin P Zdimal
Board of Directors: Robin J Adams, Robert G Bohn, Jonathan Collins, James D Frias, Terry D Growcock, Gregg A Ostrander, Corrine D Ricard, Lawrence A Sala

D-U-N-S 96-192-1806 IMP/EXP
■ **CARLISLE CONSTRUCTION MATERIALS LLC**
CARLISLE SYNTEC
(Suby of CARLISLE COMPANIES INC) ★
1285 Ritner Hwy, Carlisle, PA 17013-9381
Tel (717) 245-7000 Founded/Ownrshp 1993
Sales 606.7MME EMP 1,000
SIC 2952 3069 5031 2899 2891 Roof cement: asphalt, fibrous or plastic; Roofing, membrane rubber; Building materials, exterior; Chemical preparations; Adhesives & sealants
Pr: John Altmeyer
VP: Calgero John
VP: Orlando Lobo
VP: Mary C Ohandly
*VP: Nick Shears
Dist Mgr: Adam Lenhart
Dist Mgr: Alan Mitchell
Dist Mgr: Eric Nickler
Dist Mgr: Derek Richey
Dist Mgr: Jason Scarlette
IT Man: Stanley Rice

D-U-N-S 78-732-5208 IMP
■ **CARLISLE CORP**
CARLISLE SYNTEC SYSTEMS (DIV)
(Suby of CARLISLE COMPANIES INC) ★
11605 N Community Hse Rd, Charlotte, NC 28277-4797
Tel (704) 501-1100 Founded/Ownrshp 1968
Sales 660.8MME EMP 6,973
SIC 2952 2899 3011 2295 3089 3577 Roofing materials; Waterproofing compounds; Industrial tires, pneumatic; Tape, varnished: plastic & other coated (except magnetic); Injection molded finished plastic products; Computer peripheral equipment
Ch Bd: Stephen P Munn
*Ch Bd: David A Roberts
V Ch: Paul J Choquette Jr
*COO: Dennis J Hall
*CFO: John S Barsanti
CFO: Louis Jehl
CFO: Kirk F Vincent
*VP: Steven J Ford
Dir IT: Bob Brown

CARLISLE FOOD SERVICE
See CARLISLE FOODSERVICE PRODUCTS INC

D-U-N-S 00-508-6491 IMP/EXP
■ **CARLISLE FOODSERVICE PRODUCTS INC**
CARLISLE FOOD SERVICE
(Suby of CARLISLE COMPANIES INC) ★
4711 E Hefner Rd, Oklahoma City, OK 73131-6114
Tel (405) 528-3011 Founded/Ownrshp 1983
Sales 194.4MME EMP 800
SIC 3089 3269 Plastic containers, except foam; Plastic kitchenware, tableware & houseware; Stoneware pottery products
Pr: Trent Freiberg
VP: Jeff Fisher
VP: Todd Manor
Genl Mgr: Danielle Beauchamp
Genl Mgr: Gary Hagar
CTO: Jeffrey Bainbridge
IT Man: Monte Shawareb
Tech Mgr: Greg Unruh
Web Dev: Brad Bartlow
Web Dev: Chad Jennings
Software D: Glynn Fish

D-U-N-S 10-620-9497
■ **CARLISLE HMA INC**
CARLISLE REGIONAL MEDICAL CTR
(Suby of HMA) ★
361 Alexander Spring Rd, Carlisle, PA 17015-6940
Tel (717) 249-1212 Founded/Ownrshp 2001
Sales 92.4MME EMP 900E
SIC 8062 General medical & surgical hospitals; Hospital, AMA approved residency
CEO: Rich Newell
*Ch Bd: Kenneth Tuckey
*COO: Mark Harmon
*CFO: Mike Johnson
*Treas: Ray Wolfe
Dir Lab: Dick Chang
Dir Lab: Judi Largent
Dir Rx: Michelle Rarick
MIS Dir: Sherry Aby
IT Man: Jerry Aby
Pathlgst: Sun Kim

D-U-N-S 07-121-7004 IMP
■ **CARLISLE HMA LLC**
(Suby of HMA) ★
361 Alexander Spring Rd, Carlisle, PA 17015-6940
Tel (717) 243-1900 Founded/Ownrshp 2001
Sales 56.4MME EMP 1,280
SIC 8062 General medical & surgical hospitals
Ansthlgy: Howard L Alster

D-U-N-S 07-574-3641
CARLISLE INC
CARLISLE INTERCONNECT TECH
7911 S 188th St Ste 100, Kent, WA 98032-1099
Tel (425) 251-0700 Founded/Ownrshp 2008
Sales 132.1MME EMP 750
SIC 3643 5065 5063 Current-carrying wiring devices; Electronic parts & equipment; Wire & cable
Pr: John Berlin
Pt: James Atwood
Pt: Gordon Napier
*CFO: Amelia Murillo
*Treas: Julia Chandler
VP: Shena Barlas
VP: Brian Canann
Prin: Joseph Lipscomb
Prin: Brent Whisenant
Mng Dir: Dan Akerson
Mng Dir: Wael Badazid

CARLISLE INTERCONNECT
See TRI-STAR ELECTRONICS INTERNATIONAL INC

CARLISLE INTERCONNECT TECH
See CARLISLE INC

CARLISLE INTERCONNECT TECH
See TENSOLITE LLC

D-U-N-S 96-367-4986 IMP
■ **CARLISLE INTERCONNECT TECHNOLOGIES INC**
(Suby of CARLISLE COMPANIES INC) ★
100 Tensolite Dr, Saint Augustine, FL 32092-0590
Tel (904) 829-5600 Founded/Ownrshp 1994
Sales 463.7MME EMP 8,533E
SIC 3679 3399 3678 3357 3643 5063 Harness assemblies for electronic use: wire or cable; Metal fasteners; Electronic connectors; Communication wire; Fiber optic cable (insulated); Aircraft wire & cable, nonferrous; Current-carrying wiring devices; Electrical apparatus & equipment
Pr: John E Berlin
*Treas: Kevin Zdimal

D-U-N-S 06-616-9004
CARLISLE LLC
263 Wagner Pl, Memphis, TN 38103-3808
Tel (901) 526-5000 Founded/Ownrshp 1982
Sales 130.7MME EMP 3,500
SIC 5812 8741 6531 Fast-food restaurant, chain; Hotel or motel management; Real estate managers
Pr: Chance Carlisle
*Ch Bd: Gene D Carlisle
CFO: Marc Mullis
*Ex VP: Karen Carlisle
*VP: Don Nichols
*VP: Paul Volpe

Dist Mgr: Don Sapp
IT Man: Robbie Loyed
VP Opers: Greg Jones
Mktg Mgr: Kristin Budzak

CARLISLE REGIONAL MEDICAL CTR
See CARLISLE HMA INC

CARLISLE SYNTEC
See CARLISLE CONSTRUCTION MATERIALS LLC

CARLISLE SYNTEC SYSTEMS (DIV)
See CARLISLE CORP

CARL'S JR.
See CARL KARCHER ENTERPRISES INC

CARL'S JR.
See T W M INDUSTRIES

CARLS JUNIOR
See CLK INC

D-U-N-S 96-257-7987
■ **CARLSBAD MEDICAL CENTER LLC**
(Suby of COMMUNITY HEALTH SYSTEMS INC) ★
2430 W Pierce St, Carlsbad, NM 88220-3597
Tel (575) 887-4100 Founded/Ownrshp 1996
Sales 93.2MM EMP 600
SIC 8062 General medical & surgical hospitals
CEO: Cathy Hibbs
*CEO: Kelly Duke
Dir Case M: Kiki Weston
Dir Soc: Bryan Rayroux
QC Dir: Billie Rutledge
Doctor: Joseph Ford
Pharmcst: Joanna Yeh
Dir Health: Julie Hewitt

D-U-N-S 05-093-1867
CARLSBAD SD MICHELLE WHS
6225 El Camino Real Ste P, Carlsbad, CA 92009-1604
Tel (760) 331-5000 Founded/Ownrshp 2010
Sales 80.0MM EMP 1,000
SIC 8299 Arts & crafts schools

D-U-N-S 07-873-0926
CARLSBAD UNIFIED SCHOOL DISTRICT
6225 El Camino Real, Carlsbad, CA 92009-1604
Tel (760) 331-5000 Founded/Ownrshp 1921
Sales 130.4MM EMP 1,000
Accts Wilsinson Hadley King & Co Ll
SIC 8211 Public elementary & secondary schools
Bd of Dir: Ruthann Pearlman
Bd of Dir: Sachiko Suzuki
*Prin: Suzanne O'Connell

D-U-N-S 79-702-1201
CARLSON BROS INC
17250 New Lenox Rd B, Joliet, IL 60433-9758
Tel (815) 727-2200 Founded/Ownrshp 1988
Sales 89.4MM EMP 45
Accts Mack & Associates Morris Ill
SIC 1542 Fire station construction
Pr: Robb Carlson
*VP: Mark Carlson

D-U-N-S 78-005-3695 IMP
CARLSON CRAFT INC
EIMICKE
(Suby of TAYLOR CORP) ★
1750 Tower Blvd, North Mankato, MN 56003-1708
Tel (507) 625-5011 Founded/Ownrshp 2005
Sales 131.4MME EMP 990
SIC 2759 Commercial printing; Invitation & stationery printing & engraving; Invitations: printing; Post cards, picture: printing
CEO: Bill Rose
Pr: Kevin Svenson
Genl Mgr: Barbara Kaus
Dir IT: Richard Rotchadl
IT Man: Darcy Enter
IT Man: Tim Perrizo
VP Mktg: Stephanie Schmid

D-U-N-S 60-251-3673
CARLSON HOLDINGS INC
701 Carlson Pkwy, Minnetonka, MN 55305-5240
Tel (763) 212-5000 Founded/Ownrshp 1938
Sales 3.4MMME EMP 191,838
SIC 7011 5812 6794 7389 4724 Hotels & motels; Eating places; Patent owners & lessors; Promoters of shows & exhibitions; Travel agencies
CEO: Trudy Rautio
*Pr: Marilyn Carlson Nelson
*CEO: Douglas Anderson
CFO: Mark Herreid
*Treas: John M Diracles
*Ex VP: Jeffrey Balagna
Ex VP: Elizabeth Bastoni
*Sr VP: William Van Brunt
VP: James Baldassari
VP: Jean-Marc Busato
VP: Mary Kay Caschetta
VP: Harjit Dhillon
*VP: Robert Kleinschmidt
VP: Christer Larsson
VP: Lyle Lewis
VP: Sean Shannon
VP: Tammy Lee Stanoch
Board of Directors: Gregory R Page, Lee Chaden, Lawrence Perlman, Harald Einsmann, Barbara Carlson Gage, Edwin C Gage, Geoffrey Gage, Scott Gage, Diana L Nelson, Glen Nelson, Wendy Nelson

D-U-N-S 60-280-2746
CARLSON HOTELS LIMITED PARTNERSHIP
(Suby of CARLSON INC) ★
Carlson Parkway 701 Twr St Carlson Parkw, Minneapolis, MN 55459
Tel (763) 212-1000 Founded/Ownrshp 1988
Sales 1.4MMME EMP 20,000
SIC 6794 7011 5812 5813 Franchises, selling or licensing; Hotel, franchised; Resort hotel, franchised; Restaurant, family: chain; Bar (drinking places)
CEO: Marilyn Carlson Nelson
Pr: Curtis C Nelson
CFO: Trudy Rautio

D-U-N-S 04-815-7069
CARLSON HOTELS MANAGEMENT CORP
RADISSON INN
(*Suby of* RADISSON INN) ★
701 Tower Carlson Pkwy, Hopkins, MN 55305
Tel (763) 212-5000 *Founded/Ownrshp* 1967
Sales 617.6MM[E] *EMP* 17,000
SIC 6794 6531 6552 Franchises, selling or licensing; Real estate managers; Land subdividers & developers, commercial
VP: Frederic Deschamps
Genl Mgr: Trudy Rautio
IT Man: Michael Meyers

D-U-N-S 00-787-3433
CARLSON INC (MN)
(*Suby of* CARLSON HOLDINGS INC) ★
701 Carlson Pkwy, Minnetonka, MN 55305-5240
Tel (763) 212-5000 *Founded/Ownrshp* 1938
Sales 3.4MMM[E] *EMP* 166,718
SIC 7011 5812 6794 8742 8743 7389 Hotels; Resort hotel; Restaurant, family: chain; Franchises, selling or licensing; Training & development consultant; Marketing consulting services; Incentive or award program consultant; Sales promotion; Trading stamp promotion & redemption; Coupon redemption service
Ch Bd: Marilyn Carlson Nelson
Pr: Hubert Joly
Pr: Curtis C Nelson
CEO: Trudy A Rautio
COO: David Berg
COO: Sean Shannon
CFO: John Priem
Treas: John M Diracles
Chf Cred: Kim Olson
Ex VP: Mike Andrew
Ex VP: Bob Briggs
Ex VP: Robert Fox
Ex VP: Brad Hall
Ex VP: Gordon McKinnon
Ex VP: Cynthia Rodahl
Ex VP: Finn Schulz
Ex VP: William A Van Brunt
Ex VP: Cathy Voss
Sr VP: Mark Herreid
Sr VP: William A Van Brunt
VP: Carmen Baker

CARLSON QUALITY BRAKE
See INTERNATIONAL BRAKE INDUSTRIES INC

D-U-N-S 82-478-6370 IMP/EXP
CARLSON RESTAURANTS INC
TGI FRIDAY'S
19111 Dallas Pkwy, Dallas, TX 75287-3199
Tel (972) 662-5400 *Founded/Ownrshp* 1990
Sales 585.8MM[E] *EMP* 19,999
SIC 5812 Restaurant, family: chain
CEO: Nicholas P Shepherd
**Pr:* Kathryn M Kotel
COO: Dave Maag
**Ex VP:* Thomas Kurrikoff
**Ex VP:* Lee Sanders
Sr VP: Anne Varano
VP: Joseph Hsu
VP: Kathy Kotel
VP: Ian Saunders
VP Bus Dev: Jean Baudrand
Ex Dir: Eric Bierbrier

D-U-N-S 83-083-9549 IMP
CARLSON SYSTEMS HOLDINGS INC
SOUTHERN CARLSON
(*Suby of* SOUTHERNCARLSON) ★
10840 Harney St, Omaha, NE 68154-2638
Tel (402) 593-5300 *Founded/Ownrshp* 2015
Sales 175.8MM[E] *EMP* 332
SIC 5085 5199 Fasteners, industrial: nuts, bolts, screws, etc.; Packaging materials
Pr: Peter Todd Carlson
**Treas:* Don Munchrath
Off Mgr: Kathy Lehmann

CARLSON WAGONLIT TRAVEL
See B4 TRAVEL GROUP INC

D-U-N-S 03-910-6906
CARLSON WAGONLIT TRAVEL INC
CWT
(*Suby of* CARLSON INC) ★
701 Carlson Pkwy, Minnetonka, MN 55305-5240
Tel (763) 212-1000 *Founded/Ownrshp* 1997
Sales 2.0MMM[E] *EMP* 22,000
SIC 4724 Travel agencies; Tourist agency arranging transport, lodging & car rental
Pr: Hakan Ericsson
Bd of Dir: Tracey Wilt
Ex VP: Martine Gerow
Ex VP: Gordon McKinnon
VP: Loren Brown
VP: Brent Lonson
VP: Pat Moran
VP: Shelly Ocallaghan
VP: Judy Peplinski
VP: Paul Quirk
VP: Linda Reding
VP: Tim Webert
Exec: Joanie Miskowiec
Dir Bus: Gail Bayne

D-U-N-S 60-758-7037 IMP/EXP
CARLSTAR GROUP LLC
CARLISLE
725 Cool Springs Blvd, Franklin, TN 37067-2702
Tel (615) 503-0220 *Founded/Ownrshp* 2013
Sales 1.0MMM[E] *EMP* 2,776
SIC 3714 5014 3499 5013 2296 Wheels, motor vehicle; Tires & tubes; Wheels: wheelbarrow, stroller, etc.: disc, stamped metal; Wheels, motor vehicle; Fabric for reinforcing industrial belting
Pr: John Salvatore
Ex VP: Ashish Goel
VP: Brent Glendening
VP: Barry Littrell
VP: Max Narancich
Manager: Dane Epp
Snr Mgr: Corey McLemore

D-U-N-S 06-553-1535
CARLTON CARDS RETAIL INC
SUMMIT STATIONERS
(*Suby of* AMERICAN GREETINGS CORP) ★
1 American Rd, Cleveland, OH 44144-2398
Tel (216) 252-7300 *Founded/Ownrshp* 1973
Sales 221.2MM[E] *EMP* 3,200
SIC 5947 5943 Greeting cards; Gift shop; Stationery stores; Office forms & supplies
CEO: Pat Papesh
**Pr:* Thomas H Johnston
**Treas:* Dale A Cable
VP: Matt Stein
**VP:* Gary Weiss
MIS Dir: Robert Portman
Opers Mgr: Dick Sikorski
Mktg Dir: Gabrielle Oliff
Mktg Mgr: Radhika Balasubramaniam

D-U-N-S 00-656-2375 IMP
■ **CARLTON-BATES CO** (AR)
C B
(*Suby of* WESCO DISTRIBUTION INC) ★
3600 W 69th St, Little Rock, AR 72209-3110
Tel (501) 562-9100 *Founded/Ownrshp* 1957
Sales 315.1MM[E] *EMP* 532
SIC 5065 Electronic parts & equipment; Communication equipment; Video equipment, electronic
Pr: Stephen Van Oss
**Treas:* Brian Michael Brailer
**VP:* Daniel Ambrose Brailer
Dist Mgr: Todd Hall
Dir IT: Steve Whitley
Prd Mgr: Todd Martin
Mktg Mgr: Townsend Jennifer
Mktg Mgr: Paul Stickels
Mktg Mgr: Jennifer Townsend
Sls Mgr: Erika Adams
Sls Mgr: Sandy Haner

CARLYLE GROUP, THE
See CARLYLE INVESTMENT MANAGEMENT LLC

D-U-N-S 17-540-6842
▲ **CARLYLE GROUP L P**
1001 Pennsylvania Ave Nw 220s, Washington, DC 20004-2573
Tel (202) 729-5626 *Founded/Ownrshp* 1987
Sales 3.0MMM *EMP* 1,700
Tkr Sym CG *Exch* NGS
SIC 6726 6282 Investment offices; Investment advice
Co-CEO: William E Conway Jr
Genl Pt: Carlyle G C
Pr: Christopher Pharr
Pr: Glenn A Youngkin
CFO: Curtis L Buser
Co-CEO: David M Rubenstein
Assoc VP: Maximilian Caldwell
Assoc VP: Justin Kim
Assoc VP: Rebecca Sugarman
VP: William Allen
VP: Charlie Arsenault
VP: Seth Davis
VP: Jeffrey Gui
VP: Paul Maggiano
VP: David McCarey
VP: Patrick McCarter
VP: Karen McMonagle
VP: Alan Thompson
VP: Ward Young

D-U-N-S 94-323-8089
CARLYLE HOLDINGS INC
7911 S 188th St Ste 100, Kent, WA 98032-1099
Tel (425) 251-0700 *Founded/Ownrshp* 2013
Sales 93.3MM[E] *EMP* 1,300
SIC 3643 5065 5063 Current-carrying wiring devices; Electronic parts & equipment; Wire & cable
Ch Bd: David Roberts
**Pr:* John Berlin
**Pr:* Carol A O'Mack
**Treas:* Kevin Zdimal
**Sec:* Diane M Johansson

D-U-N-S 79-118-7656
■ **CARLYLE INVESTMENT MANAGEMENT LLC**
CARLYLE GROUP, THE
(*Suby of* CARLYLE GROUP L P) ★
1001 Pennsylvania Ave Nw, Washington, DC 20004-2505
Tel (202) 729-5385 *Founded/Ownrshp* 1996
Sales 337.7MM[E] *EMP* 20,837[E]
SIC 6282 Investment advice
Pr: Glenn A Youngkin
CFO: Curtis L Buser
VP: Siddhartha Ahluwalia
VP: R Pace Barker
VP: Aaron Benway
VP: Douglas V Brandely
VP: Jennifer Haaz
VP: Karthic Jayaraman
Prin: Jamie Adams
Mng Dir: Karen Bechtel
Mng Dir: Curt Buser

D-U-N-S 09-366-0434
■ **CARLYLE PARTNERS II LP**
(*Suby of* CARLYLE GROUP L P) ★
1001 Pennsylvania Ave Nw, Washington, DC 20004-2505
Tel (202) 347-2626 *Founded/Ownrshp* 1998
Sales 18.0MM[E] *EMP* 1,700
SIC 3612 Transformers, except electric
Pt: David Rubenstein

D-U-N-S 55-685-4649
■ **CARLYLE PARTNERS III LP**
(*Suby of* CARLYLE GROUP L P) ★
1001 Penn Ave Nw Ste 220, Washington, DC 20004-2525
Tel (202) 347-2626 *Founded/Ownrshp* 1999
Sales NA *EMP* 4,715
SIC 6719 Investment holding companies, except banks
Pt: Carolyn Weimer

D-U-N-S 80-636-7616
■ **CARLYLE PARTNERS IV LP**
(*Suby of* CARLYLE GROUP) ★
1001 Pennsylvania Ave Nw, Washington, DC 20004-2505
Tel (202) 729-5626 *Founded/Ownrshp* 2007
Sales 336.6MM[E] *EMP* 20,800[E]
SIC 8711 8069 8051 Aviation &/or aeronautical engineering; Specialty hospitals, except psychiatric; Skilled nursing care facilities
Pr: Glenn A Youngkin

D-U-N-S 02-389-0577 IMP/EXP
▲ **CARMAX INC**
12800 Tuckahoe Creek Pkwy, Richmond, VA 23238-1124
Tel (804) 747-0422 *Founded/Ownrshp* 1993
Sales 15.1MMM *EMP* 22,429
Accts Kpmg Llp Richmond Virginia
Tkr Sym KMX *Exch* NYS
SIC 5521 5511 6141 Automobiles, used cars only; Pickups & vans, used; Automobiles, new & used; Pickups, new & used; Installment sales finance, other than banks
CEO: Bill Nash
**Ch Bd:* Thomas J Folliard
**Ch Bd:* William R Tiefel
Pr: Rusty Jordan
COO: William C Wood Jr
CFO: Thomas W Reedy
Ofcr: James Lyski
Ex VP: Edwin J Hill
Sr VP: Jon G Daniels
Sr VP: Eric M Margolin
Sr VP: Shamim Mohammad
VP: Robert M Adams
VP: Diane Cafritz
VP: Patricia Gangwer
VP: Jon Geske
VP: Lynn Mussatt
Dir Risk M: Grady Dixon
Board of Directors: Ronald E Blaylock, Alan B Colberg, Jeffrey E Garten, Shira Goodman, W Robert Grafton, Edgar H Grubb, Marcella Shinder, John T Standley, Mitchell D Steenrod

D-U-N-S 04-076-0977
CARMEL CENTRAL SCHOOL DISTRICT
81 South St, Patterson, NY 12563-3111
Tel (845) 878-2094 *Founded/Ownrshp* 1900
Sales 85.2MM[E] *EMP* 2,000
Accts Raymond G Preusser Cpa Pc
SIC 8211 Public elementary & secondary schools
IT Man: Lynne Caruso
Psych: Brenda Kuech

D-U-N-S 07-203-6569
CARMEL CLAY SCHOOLS
CEF
5201 E Main St, Carmel, IN 46033-9822
Tel (317) 844-9961 *Founded/Ownrshp* 1966
Sales 113.2MM[E] *EMP* 2,000
SIC 8211 Public elementary school; Public junior high school; Public senior high school
**Pr:* Layla Spanenberg
**VP:* Andrew Klein
Trfc Dir: Valerie Meyer

D-U-N-S 14-842-1725
CARMEL PARTNERS INC
1000 Sansome St 1, San Francisco, CA 94111-1323
Tel (415) 273-2900 *Founded/Ownrshp* 2005
Sales 84.0MM[E] *EMP* 490
SIC 6531 6519 Real estate agents & managers; Real property lessors
CEO: Ron Zeff
**Mng Pt:* Quinn R Barton III
**Pr:* Michael Lahorgue
**CFO:* Dennis Markus
**Sr VP:* Richard Bennion
Sr VP: Liz Tennican
**VP:* Brian Smith
**VP:* John Williams

CARMEUSE LIME & STONE
See O-N MINERALS CO (OHIO)

D-U-N-S 07-498-6035 IMP/EXP
CARMEUSE LIME & STONE INC
(*Suby of* CARMEUSE NATURAL CHEMICALS) ★
11 Stanwix St Fl 21, Pittsburgh, PA 15222-1327
Tel (412) 995-5500 *Founded/Ownrshp* 1974
Sales 1.1MMM[E] *EMP* 2,000[E]
SIC 1422 Crushed & broken limestone
Pr: Thomas A Buck
**CFO:* Bruce Inglis
**Treas:* Mary D Colin
**VP:* Jack Fahler
**VP:* Paul Tunnicliffe
**VP:* Kevin White
CIO: Patrick Worms
QC Dir: Robert Rinker
**S&M/VP:* Bruce Routhieaux
Mktg Dir: Julian Danvers
Counsel: Jessica Holcomb

D-U-N-S 02-107-3510 IMP
CARMEUSE LIME INC
CARMEUSE NATURAL CHEMICALS
(*Suby of* CARMEUSE SA)
11 Stanwix St Fl 21, Pittsburgh, PA 15222-1327
Tel (412) 995-5500 *Founded/Ownrshp* 1997
Sales 2.4MMM[E] *EMP* 3,500
SIC 1422 3274 Crushed & broken limestone; Lime
CEO: Yves Willems
**CFO:* Bruce Inglis
**Treas:* Steve Simon
VP: Jack Fahler
VP: Guss Grimsley
**VP:* Kevin Whyte
**VP:* Kathy Wiley
Genl Mgr: Felicia Reid
Tech Mgr: George McKotch
VP Opers: Julianne McDaniel
Opers Mgr: Mark Georgiana

CARMEUSE NATURAL CHEMICALS
See CARMEUSE LIME INC

D-U-N-S 00-679-4630
▲ **CARMIKE CINEMAS INC** (GA)
1301 1st Ave, Columbus, GA 31901-2109
Tel (706) 576-3400 *Founded/Ownrshp* 1930
Sales 804.3MM *EMP* 8,500[E]
Accts Deloitte & Touche Llp Atlanta
Tkr Sym CKEC *Exch* NGM
SIC 7832 Exhibitors, itinerant: motion picture
Pr: S David Passman III
**Ch Bd:* Roland C Smith
Pr: A Dale Mayo
COO: Fred W Van Noy
CFO: Richard B Hare
Chf Mktg O: Rob Collins
Ofcr: Fred Friedel
Sr VP: Daniel E Ellis
VP: Jeffrey A Cole
VP: John A Lundin
Dist Mgr: Domenick Barone

D-U-N-S 07-281-2118
CARNEGIE HALL CORP
881 Sventh Ave At 57th St, New York, NY 10019
Tel (212) 903-9600 *Founded/Ownrshp* 1960
Sales 113.6MM *EMP* 148[E]
Accts Lb Kpmg Llp Mc Lean Va
SIC 7922 6531 Performing arts center production; Real estate managers
Ex Dir: Clive Gillinson
CFO: Patricia Long
Treas: Mike McCarthy
Assoc Dir: Kevin Groob
Assoc Dir: Jennifer Hempel
Assoc Dir: Sean Morrow
Assoc Dir: Patrick Sharpe
Genl Mgr: Anna Weber
Dir IT: Bronwen Stine
IT Man: Tak Lai
Web Dev: Michael Peppler

D-U-N-S 07-216-5699 IMP
CARNEGIE INSTITUTE
CARNEGIE MUSEUMS OF PITTSBURGH
4400 Forbes Ave, Pittsburgh, PA 15213-4007
Tel (412) 622-3131 *Founded/Ownrshp* 1895
Sales 120.2MM[E] *EMP* 1,200
SIC 8412 Museum; Art gallery, noncommercial; Arts or science center
Pr: Jo Ellen Parker
Treas: Terrence O'Hora
Act CFO: Kevin Hiles
Ofcr: Patrick McShea
VP: Ann Metzger
Dir: Patrick Moore
Off Mgr: Patricia Johnson
CIO: Amy Wilson
IT Man: Kevin Griffin
Opers Mgr: John Lyon
Pr Mgr: Jonathan Gaugler

CARNEGIE INSTITUTION FOR SCIEN
See CARNEGIE INSTITUTION OF WASHINGTON

D-U-N-S 07-264-1707
CARNEGIE INSTITUTION OF WASHINGTON
CARNEGIE INSTITUTION FOR SCIEN
1530 P St Nw, Washington, DC 20005-1910
Tel (202) 387-6400 *Founded/Ownrshp* 1902
Sales 187.0MM *EMP* 500
SIC 8733 Scientific research agency
Pr: Richard Meserve
**VP:* Gary Kowalczyk
Exec: Sharon Bassin
Dir Lab: Diane Chermak
Dir Lab: M Yee
**Prin:* John C Botts
**Prin:* John F Crawford
**Prin:* Michael A Duffy
Genl Mgr: Timothy Doyle
CIO: Gotthard Saghi-Szabo
Web Dev: Michael Kamuiru

D-U-N-S 05-218-4116 IMP
CARNEGIE MELLON UNIVERSITY
5000 Forbes Ave, Pittsburgh, PA 15213-3890
Tel (412) 268-2000 *Founded/Ownrshp* 1900
Sales 1.1MMM *EMP* 4,913
Accts Pricewaterhousecoopers Llp Pi
SIC 8221 University
Pr: Subra Suresh
V Ch: Kears E Pollock
COO: Miller Chris
COO: Janet Cohen
COO: John Leong
**CFO:* Amir Rahnamay-Azer
Trst: Alessandro Ovi
Trst: Alexander C Speyer Jr
Chf Inves: Charles A Kennedy
Ex VP: Mark S Kamlet
VP: Bonita Cersosimo
Assoc Dir: Tara Branstad
Assoc Dir: Daniel Corletti
Assoc Dir: Ann Julian
Assoc Dir: Judi Mancuso
Assoc Dir: James Spanswick

CARNEGIE MUSEUMS OF PITTSBURGH
See CARNEGIE INSTITUTE

D-U-N-S 12-159-7652 IMP
CARNES CO INC
600 College Ave, Pewaukee, WI 53072-3572
Tel (262) 691-9900 *Founded/Ownrshp* 1986
Sales 109.4MM[E] *EMP* 550
SIC 3822 3444 3585 3669 Auto controls regulating residntl & coml environmt & applncs; Ducts, sheet metal; Ventilators, sheet metal; Humidifying equipment, except portable; Metal detectors
Ch: Brian L Nahey

CARNIVAL
See AVT GROCERY INC

D-U-N-S 96-866-3323
■ **CARNIVAL CELEBRATION INC**
(*Suby of* CARNIVAL CORP) ★
3655 Nw 87th Ave, Doral, FL 33178-2418
Tel (305) 599-2600 *Founded/Ownrshp* 2000
Sales 282.1M[E] *EMP* 3,151[E]

SIC 4481 Deep sea passenger transportation, except ferry
Prin: Timothy W Strickland

D-U-N-S 05-613-4315
▲ CARNIVAL CORP
3655 Nw 87th Ave, Doral, FL 33178-2418
Tel (305) 599-2600 *Founded/Ownrshp* 1972
Sales 15.7MMM *EMP* 82,200
Tkr Sym CCL *Exch* NYS
SIC 4481 4725 7011 Deep sea passenger transportation, except ferry; Sightseeing tour companies; Hostels; Casino hotel
Pr: Arnold W Donald
**Ch Bd:* Micky Arison
COO: Alan B Buckelew
CFO: David Bernstein
VP: Mario Hrsak
VP: Carlos Orta
Dir Soc: Velma Jaghai
Dir Bus: Kelley Corbett
Dir Bus: Janet Jones
Software D: Mark Novell
Netwrk Eng: Alex Montoya
Board of Directors: Jonathon Band, Debra Kelly-Ennis, Richard J Glasier, John Parker, Stuart Subotnick, Laura Weil, Randall J Weisenburger

D-U-N-S 04-775-6366
■ CARO FOODS INC
(*Suby of* P F G) ★
2324 Bayou Blue Rd, Houma, LA 70364-4301
Tel (985) 872-1483 *Founded/Ownrshp* 1960, 1987
Sales 138.2MM[E] *EMP* 210
SIC 5141 Food brokers
Ch: Doug Steenland
**Pr:* Ralph Boudreau
**CEO:* George Holm
**Sr VP:* Bob Evans
**Sr VP:* Michael L Miller
**Sr VP:* Carol Price
**VP:* Louis Taylor

D-U-N-S 06-398-8711
CAROCO INC
SKYLINE CHILI
8635 Colerain Ave, Cincinnati, OH 45251-2915
Tel (513) 385-1244 *Founded/Ownrshp* 1973
Sales 100.0MM *EMP* 25
SIC 5812 Restaurant, family: chain
Pr: Stephen Simon

D-U-N-S 62-799-1516 IMP/EXP
CAROLE FABRICS CORP
(*Suby of* HUNTER DOUGLAS INC) ★
633 Nw Frontage Rd, Augusta, GA 30907-2406
Tel (706) 863-4742 *Founded/Ownrshp* 1990
Sales 116.6MM[E] *EMP* 506
SIC 2221 2591 5131 5949 2392 2391 Draperies & drapery fabrics, manmade fiber & silk; Bedspreads, silk & manmade fiber; Window shades; Window blinds; Piece goods & other fabrics; Fabric stores piece goods; Household furnishings; Curtains & draperies
Pr: W Geiger
**CFO:* G Khan
**VP:* Bob Johnson
**VP:* Tom Jones
**VP:* Robert Thompson

D-U-N-S 03-050-1183
CAROLINA ADVENTIST RETIREMENT SYSTEMS INC
PISGAH MANOR HEALTH CARE CTR
95 Holcombe Cove Rd, Candler, NC 28715-9450
Tel (828) 667-9851 *Founded/Ownrshp* 1975
Sales 634.7MM[E] *EMP* 200
SIC 8052 8051 8082 Intermediate care facilities; Skilled nursing care facilities; Home health care services
CEO: David Kidder
Brnch Mgr: Julia Gibson
IT Man: Angela Smith

D-U-N-S 00-321-9789 IMP/EXP
CAROLINA BIOLOGICAL SUPPLY CO (NC)
2700 York Rd, Burlington, NC 27215-3387
Tel (336) 584-0381 *Founded/Ownrshp* 1927
Sales 122.2MM[E] *EMP* 435
SIC 5049 2836 3829 3826 3821

D-U-N-S 04-755-8325 EXP
CAROLINA CANNERS INC
300 Highway 1 S, Cheraw, SC 29520-2835
Tel (843) 537-5281 *Founded/Ownrshp* 1968
Sales 101.9MM[E] *EMP* 335
SIC 2086 Carbonated beverages, nonalcoholic: bottled & canned
Pr: Brantley Burnett
**CEO:* Jeff Stevens
**Treas:* Jeff Minges
**VP:* Walter Egan
**VP:* Lee Teeter
Sales Exec: Ed Sellers
S&M/VP: Sterling Whitley

D-U-N-S 00-323-2709 IMP/EXP
CAROLINA CONTAINER CO (NC)
DIGITAL HIGH POINT
(*Suby of* NEW-INDY JV CORP.)
909 Prospect St, High Point, NC 27260-8273
Tel (336) 883-7146 *Founded/Ownrshp* 1928, 2015
Sales 162.2MM[E] *EMP* 500
SIC 5999 Packaging materials: boxes, padding, etc.
CEO: Nicholas Smith
**Pr:* Ronald T Sessions
**CFO:* Randall L Black
IT Man: Bryan Starnen

D-U-N-S 00-202-2903 IMP
CAROLINA DESIGNS LTD (NC)
BLYTH HOME SCENTS INTL
999 E Touhy Ave Ste 500, Des Plaines, IL 60018-2749
Tel (847) 294-1100 *Founded/Ownrshp* 1933
Sales NA *EMP* 1,300
SIC 3999

D-U-N-S 06-269-0326 IMP
CAROLINA EASTERN INC (SC)
1820 Savannah Hwy Ste G1, Charleston, SC 29407-6296
Tel (843) 571-0411 *Founded/Ownrshp* 1972
Sales 88.2MM[E] *EMP* 325
SIC 5261 5191 Fertilizer; Fertilizer & fertilizer materials
Ch Bd: Alton C Phillips
**Ex VP:* S A Rodgers Jr
VP: Graham Matthews
**VP:* Butch Rodgers

D-U-N-S 05-301-5640 IMP
CAROLINA FOODS INC (NC)
1807 S Tryon St, Charlotte, NC 28203-4471
Tel (704) 333-9812 *Founded/Ownrshp* 1934
Sales 137.9MM[E] *EMP* 350
SIC 2051 Pastries, e.g. danish: except frozen
Pr: Paul R Scarborough
**CFO:* Kathryn Scarborough
**VP:* Sallie Scarborough
Natl Sales: Henry Hagadorn

D-U-N-S 04-227-3276
CAROLINA HANDLING LLC
3101 Piper Ln, Charlotte, NC 28208-6499
Tel (704) 357-6273 *Founded/Ownrshp* 1989
Sales 219.2MM[E] *EMP* 356
SIC 5084 Materials handling machinery
QA Dir: Garry Parnell
Dir IT: Ed Hall
IT Man: Ron Ewing
Manager: Steve Zager

D-U-N-S 12-911-8209
CAROLINA HEALTHCARE CENTER OF CUMBERLAND LP
4600 Cumberland Rd, Fayetteville, NC 28306-2412
Tel (910) 429-1690 *Founded/Ownrshp* 2000
Sales 1.0MMM *EMP* 150
Accts Rsm Mcgladrey Charlotte Nc
SIC 8741 8051 Hospital management; Nursing & personal care facility management; Skilled nursing care facilities
Pt: W Heywood Fralin
Pt: Karen H Waldron
CFO: Joy Futrell
CFO: Melissa K Snuggs
VP: N Ronald Covington
Exec: Brenda Munn
Exec: Karon Prince

CAROLINA INSTITUTE FOR DEVELO
See UNIVERSITY OF NORTH CAROLINA AT CHAPEL HILL

D-U-N-S 78-041-0007
CAROLINA INTERNATIONAL TRUCKS INC
1619 Bluff Rd, Columbia, SC 29201-4913
Tel (803) 799-4923 *Founded/Ownrshp* 1982
Sales 129.3MM[E] *EMP* 250
SIC 5511 Trucks, tractors & trailers: new & used
Pr: Richard D Ryan
CFO: Kaye Shuler
**Prin:* Dick Ryan
Ex Dir: Mandy Harling
Off Mgr: Brenda Paschal
Manager: Larry Sickles
Sls Mgr: Carl Orfield

CAROLINA MEDICAL CENTER MERCY
See MERCY MEDICAL SERVICE INC

D-U-N-S 19-902-4097
CAROLINA MEDICAL CENTER UNION
(*Suby of* CAROLINAS HEALTHCARE SYSTEM) ★
600 Hospital Dr, Monroe, NC 28112-6000
Tel (704) 283-3100 *Founded/Ownrshp* 2005
Sales 120.1MM[E] *EMP* 2,000
SIC 8062 General medical & surgical hospitals
Pr: Michael Lutes
VP: Sandy Butler
**Prin:* John Moore
Doctor: Joy Bates

D-U-N-S 00-321-7965 IMP
CAROLINA MILLS INC (NC)
618 N Carolina Ave, Maiden, NC 28650-1170
Tel (828) 428-9911 *Founded/Ownrshp* 1928, 1947
Sales 94.4MM[E] *EMP* 600[E]
SIC 2281 2211 2221 2257 2511 2512 Knitting yarn, spun; Weaving yarn, spun; Upholstery fabrics, cotton; Canton flannels, cotton; Upholstery fabrics, manmade fiber & silk; Dyeing & finishing circular knit fabrics; Tables, household: wood; Upholstered household furniture
Ch Bd: George A Moretz
**CFO:* Bryan E Beal
VP Mfg: Steve Dobbins Jr

D-U-N-S 04-728-0136
CAROLINA MOTOR CLUB INC
AAA CAROLINAS
6600 Aaa Dr, Charlotte, NC 28212-8259
Tel (704) 377-3600 *Founded/Ownrshp* 1922
Sales 99.0MM[E] *EMP* 720
Accts Mcgladrey & Pullen Llp Charl
SIC 8699 4724 Automobile owners' association; Tourist agency arranging transport, lodging & car rental
Pr: David E Parsons
CFO: Jess Davis
VP: Kelly Howard
Rgnl Mgr: Stephen Simmons
Genl Mgr: Jeff Monroe

D-U-N-S 11-816-1504
CAROLINA MUNICIPALITY
GOBIERNO MUNICIPAL AU
Ignacio Arzuaga St, Carolina, PR 00985
Tel (787) 757-2626 *Founded/Ownrshp* 1857
Sales NA *EMP* 2,235
SIC 9111 Mayors' offices

D-U-N-S 78-013-2833
■ CAROLINA NORTH MIDLAND RAILROAD CO
(*Suby of* NORFOLK SOUTHERN RAILWAY CO) ★
3 Commercial Pl, Norfolk, VA 23510-2108
Tel (757) 629-2645 *Founded/Ownrshp* 1982
Sales 24.8MM[E] *EMP* 1,281[E]
SIC 4011 Railroads, line-haul operating
Pr: Stephen C Tobias
**Treas:* Thomas Mahoney
**Sec:* Reginald J Chaney
**Sec:* Sandra Pierce

CAROLINA PNES REGIONAL MED CTR
See HARTSVILLE LLC

D-U-N-S 00-334-5949
CAROLINA PRIDE FOODS INC (SC)
1 Packer Ave, Greenwood, SC 29646-3460
Tel (864) 229-5611 *Founded/Ownrshp* 1920
Sales 184.5MM[E] *EMP* 930[E]
SIC 2013 Luncheon meat from purchased meat; Cured meats from purchased meat; Bologna from purchased meat; Puddings, meat from purchased meat
Pr: Evans T Barnette
**Ch Bd:* William A Barnette Jr
**Pr:* Mark Litts
**VP:* Michael Cox
**VP:* Don Holton
**VP:* Thomas Jackson

D-U-N-S 62-781-6002
CAROLINA RESTAURANT GROUP INC
WENDY'S
8040 Arrowridge Blvd # 100, Charlotte, NC 28273-5604
Tel (704) 525-3434 *Founded/Ownrshp* 1969
Sales 98.1MM[E] *EMP* 2,500
SIC 5812 Fast-food restaurant, chain
Pr: Quint Graham
CFO: Gary M Iller
**CFO:* Gary M Miller
**Ofcr:* Darrell Ferguson
**Ofcr:* Cameron M Harris
**Ofcr:* H Keith Stoneman
Dist Mgr: James Gladden
Dist Mgr: Steve Halberg
Mktg Dir: Kathy Alvis
Mktg Dir: Jenny Valenti

D-U-N-S 79-702-2790
CAROLINA RHA/NORTH MR INC
1200 Rdgfeld Blvd Ste 270, Asheville, NC 28806
Tel (828) 322-4200 *Founded/Ownrshp* 1988
Sales 24.4MM[E] *EMP* 2,000
SIC 8744 Facilities support services
Pr: John West

D-U-N-S 62-247-8246 EXP
CAROLINA SKIFF LLC
3231 Fulford Rd, Waycross, GA 31503-8705
Tel (912) 287-0547 *Founded/Ownrshp* 2003
Sales 104.8MM[E] *EMP* 250
SIC 5091 3732 Boat accessories & parts; Boats, fiberglass: building & repairing
CEO: Joseph I Kirkland III
IT Man: Jim Burkhardt

D-U-N-S 12-226-3023 IMP
CAROLINA SUNROCK LLC
(*Suby of* SUNROCK GROUP HOLDINGS CORP) ★
1001 W B St, Butner, NC 27509-1821
Tel (919) 575-4502 *Founded/Ownrshp* 2000
Sales 168.5MM[E] *EMP* 150
SIC 1429 3273 2951 1411 Trap rock, crushed & broken-quarrying; Ready-mixed concrete; Asphalt paving mixtures & blocks; Dimension stone
Ex VP: Ken Randolph

D-U-N-S 00-699-7597
■ CAROLINA TELEPHONE AND TELEGRAPH CO LLC (NC)
CENTURYLINK
(*Suby of* CENTURYLINK) ★
100 Centurylink Dr, Monroe, LA 71203-2041
Tel (318) 388-9000 *Founded/Ownrshp* 1900, 2006
Sales 191.0MM[E] *EMP* 1,861[E]
SIC 4813 8721 5065 Local & long distance telephone communications; Local telephone communications; Billing & bookkeeping service; Telephone & telegraphic equipment; Telephone equipment
Pr: William E Cheek

D-U-N-S 02-446-7359 IMP/EXP
CAROLINA TRACTOR & EQUIPMENT CO INC (NC)
CATERPILLAR AUTHORIZED DEALER
9000 Statesville Rd, Charlotte, NC 28269-7680
Tel (704) 596-6700 *Founded/Ownrshp* 1926
Sales 460.1MM[E] *EMP* 665
SIC 5082 5084 5013 7353 7359 7629 General construction machinery & equipment; Materials handling machinery; Automotive engines & engine parts; Heavy construction equipment rental; Equipment rental & leasing; Electrical repair shops
CEO: Ed Weisiger Jr
**CFO:* Robert Russell
**Sr VP:* Mike Brown
Sr VP: Kevin Franklin
**VP:* Tom Bell
**VP:* Vic Morris
IT Man: Etienne Geldehuys
Sftwr Eng: Bob Wallace
Sales Exec: Billy Martin
Mktg Dir: Mike Tropsha
Manager: Woody Jones

D-U-N-S 14-318-6141 IMP/EXP
CAROLINA WHOLESALE GROUP INC
ARLINGTON INDUSTRIES
425 E Arrowhead Dr, Charlotte, NC 28213-6378
Tel (704) 598-8101 *Founded/Ownrshp* 2004
Sales 325.3MM[E] *EMP* 250
SIC 5044 Office equipment
Pr: Larry Huneycutt

**CFO:* Rob Collins
**VP:* Trey Price

CAROLINA WINE COMPANY
See MARTIGNETTI GROCERY CO INC

D-U-N-S 07-202-7931
CAROLINAEAST MEDICAL CENTER
2000 Neuse Blvd, New Bern, NC 28560-3449
Tel (252) 633-8111 *Founded/Ownrshp* 1962
Sales 320.5MM *EMP* 1,630
SIC 8062 General medical & surgical hospitals
Pr: G Raymond Leggett III
**CFO:* Tammy Sherron
VP: Lesley Hunter
**VP:* Rosanne Leahy
**VP:* Bruce Martin
**VP:* Cindy Turco
Dir Rx: Genelle Butz
Psych: Malinda L Breda

CAROLINAS HEALTHCARE
See STANLY REGIONAL MEDICAL CENTER

CAROLINAS HEALTHCARE SYSTEM
See CHARLOTTE-MECKLENBURG HOSPITAL AUTHORITY

CAROLINAS HEALTHCARE SYSTEM
See CAROLINAS MEDICAL CENTER-LINCOLN

D-U-N-S 79-106-7320
CAROLINAS MEDICAL CENTER AT HOME LLC
LEVINE CHILDREN'S HOSPITAL
(*Suby of* CAROLINAS HEALTHCARE SYSTEM) ★
1000 Blythe Blvd, Charlotte, NC 28203-5812
Tel (704) 355-3165 *Founded/Ownrshp* 2007
Sales 73.8MM[E] *EMP* 5,071[E]
SIC 8062 General medical & surgical hospitals
Prin: Dennie R Underwood
Doctor: Teresita Y Nelson MD

D-U-N-S 07-105-9489
CAROLINAS MEDICAL CENTER NORTHEAST (NC)
NORTHEAST MEDICAL CENTER
920 Church St N, Concord, NC 28025-2927
Tel (704) 783-3000 *Founded/Ownrshp* 1937
Sales 557.8MM *EMP* 4,500
SIC 8062 8221 General medical & surgical hospitals; Colleges universities & professional schools
CEO: Michael C Tarwater
**Pr:* Phyllis Wingate-Jones
COO: Bill Hubbard
VP: Kathleen F Grew
Dir Lab: Ed Smith
Ex Dir: Gale Deal
Ex Dir: Beverly Flynn
CIO: Keith Mc Neice
Dir IT: Linda Bresnahan
Dir IT: Mark Williams
Telecom Mg: Beth Webster

CAROLINAS MEDICAL CENTER UNION
See UNION MEMORIAL REGIONAL MEDICAL CENTER INC

D-U-N-S 17-603-3025 IMP
CAROLINAS MEDICAL CENTER-LINCOLN
CAROLINAS HEALTHCARE SYSTEM
433 Mcalister Rd, Lincolnton, NC 28092-4147
Tel (980) 212-2000 *Founded/Ownrshp* 1995
Sales 105.2MM *EMP* 550
SIC 8062 General medical & surgical hospitals
CEO: Michael C Tarwater
**Pr:* Joseph G Piemont
CFO: Jarrett Morris
**Ex VP:* Greg A Gombar
VP: Al Arrowood
VP: Lesley Chambless
VP: James Ramsey
Dir Lab: Mary Pound
Dir Rad: John Shelon
CIO: Morris Cornwell
QA Dir: Melissa Freeman

D-U-N-S 04-627-0869 IMP/EXP
CAROLINAS RECYCLING GROUP LLC
2061 Nazareth Church Rd, Spartanburg, SC 29301-5943
Tel (864) 439-7039 *Founded/Ownrshp* 1998
Sales 110.0MM[E] *EMP* 400
Accts Dixon Hughes Pllc Greenville
SIC 5093 Ferrous metal scrap & waste; Nonferrous metals scrap
Pr: Marvin Siegel
**CFO:* Michael E Munafo
**Ch:* Danny Rifkin
VP: Larry E Seay
VP: Paul Siegel

D-U-N-S 04-580-9316
CAROLLO ENGINEERS PC
2700 Ygnacio Valley Rd # 300, Walnut Creek, CA 94598-3466
Tel (925) 932-1710 *Founded/Ownrshp* 2010
Sales 217.6MM[E] *EMP* 625
SIC 8711 Consulting engineer
Pr: Balakrishnan Narayanan
Pt: Gary Meyerhofer
**Treas:* Rick D Wheadon
**VP:* Larry E Elliott
VP: Robb Grantham
Genl Mgr: Steve Kessler
IT Man: Jeff Manas
Snr Mgr: Gary Deis

CAROMONT HEALTH
See CAROMONT REGIONAL MEDICAL CENTER

D-U-N-S 62-205-8519
CAROMONT HEALTH INC
2525 Court Dr, Gastonia, NC 28054-2140
Tel (704) 834-2000 *Founded/Ownrshp* 1984
Sales 37.1MM *EMP* 2,400
Accts Dixon Hughes Goodman Llp Ashe
SIC 8741 8093 Nursing & personal care facility management; Hospital management; Specialty outpatient clinics

CEO: Douglas Luckett
Pr: Donetta Horseman
CEO: Randall Kelley
CFO: David O'Connor
Ex VP: Jerome Levine MD
Ex VP: Maria Long
VP: Kathleen Besson
VP: Bonnie Faust
VP: Kathleen Harwell
VP: Dave Huber
VP: Steve Rubin
Exec: Tammy Pyles

D-U-N-S 13-092-1286
CAROMONT MEDICAL GROUP INC
2525 Court Dr, Gastonia, NC 28054-2140
Tel (704) 671-7483 *Founded/Ownrshp* 1985
Sales 106.3MM *EMP* 24[E]
Accts Dixon Hughes Goodman Llp Ashe
SIC 7363 Medical help service
CEO: Douglas Luckett
**COO:* Kathleen Besson
**Prin:* Wayne Shovelin

D-U-N-S 60-280-9779
CAROMONT OCCUPATIONAL MEDICINE LLC
2525 Court Dr, Gastonia, NC 28054-2140
Tel (704) 834-2000 *Founded/Ownrshp* 2005
Sales 92.7MM *EMP* 16
SIC 8099 Health screening service
CFO: Renee Broome

D-U-N-S 07-107-1682
CAROMONT REGIONAL MEDICAL CENTER
CAROMONT HEALTH
(*Suby of* CAROMONT HEALTH INC) ★
2525 Court Dr, Gastonia, NC 28054-2140
Tel (704) 333-9033 *Founded/Ownrshp* 1984
Sales 423.9MM *EMP* 1,849[E]
Accts Dixon Hughes Goodman Llp Ashe
SIC 8062 General medical & surgical hospitals
Dir Vol: Julie Young
**COO:* Terry L Jones
**CFO:* David O Connor
VP: Jeffory Canose MD
**VP:* W Kathleen Harwell
**VP:* Robert F Henderson Jr
**VP:* Jerome Levine
VP: Andrea Serra
Nurse Mgr: Robin Lang
Doctor: Kristen Alford MD

D-U-N-S 14-451-8321
CARONDELET HEALTH
SAINT JOSEPH HEALTH CENTER
1000 Carondelet Dr, Kansas City, MO 64114-4673
Tel (816) 942-4400 *Founded/Ownrshp* 1983
Sales 39.2MM *EMP* 3,000
Accts Deloitte Tax Llp Cincinnati
SIC 8082 Home health care services
CEO: Michael Dorsey
**Pr:* Fleury Yelvington
**CFO:* Steve Cleary
Treas: R E Mac Naughton
**VP:* Deb Ohnoutka
Nurse Mgr: Candy Quillin
Secur Mgr: Mike Kruger

D-U-N-S 10-281-7624
CARONDELET HEALTH NETWORK
(*Suby of* ASCENSION HEALTH) ★
2202 N Forbes Blvd, Tucson, AZ 85745-1412
Tel (520) 872-7542 *Founded/Ownrshp* 2002
Sales 482.7MM *EMP* 5,218
SIC 8062

D-U-N-S 02-164-9816
CARONDELET PHYSICIAN SERVICES INC
(*Suby of* SAINT JOSEPH HEALTH CENTER) ★
1000 Carondelet Dr, Kansas City, MO 64114-4673
Tel (816) 943-2679 *Founded/Ownrshp* 2007
Sales 20.6MM[E] *EMP* 2,379[E]
SIC 8011 Offices & clinics of medical doctors

D-U-N-S 93-394-5750
CAROUSEL CAPITAL CO LLC
201 N Tryon St Ste 2450, Charlotte, NC 28202-1152
Tel (704) 372-2040 *Founded/Ownrshp* 1996
Sales 98.5MM[E] *EMP* 600
SIC 6211 Investment bankers
Mng Pt: Nelson Schwab III
CFO: Robert Kreidler
VP: Alan Welch Jr
Dir Soc: Mary Boswell

D-U-N-S 92-745-0510
CAROUSEL INDUSTRIES OF NORTH AMERICA INC
659 South County Trl, Exeter, RI 02822-3412
Tel (401) 667-5400 *Founded/Ownrshp* 1994
Sales 288.4MM[E] *EMP* 1,050
SIC 7389 Telephone services
CEO: Jeffrey Gardner
CFO: Richard A Proulx
Sr VP: James Marsh
VP: Alex Capo
VP: Bob Harkins
VP: Robert Harkins
VP: Michael J Vickers
Prin: Charles Mirviss
IT Man: Robert Downey
Netwrk Eng: Paul Klebaur
Netwrk Eng: Gerry McOmber

D-U-N-S 00-310-9444 IMP/EXP
CARPENTER CO (VA)
5016 Monument Ave, Richmond, VA 23230-3620
Tel (804) 359-0800 *Founded/Ownrshp* 1948, 1980
Sales 2.1MMM[E] *EMP* 5,000
SIC 3086 1311 2869 2297 2392 2821 Insulation or cushioning material, foamed plastic; Carpet & rug cushions, foamed plastic; Padding, foamed plastic; Crude petroleum & natural gas; Industrial organic chemicals; Bonded-fiber fabrics, except felt; Household furnishings; Plastics materials & resins
Ch Bd: Stanley F Pauley
**Pr:* Mike Lowery
COO: Susan Carpenter
**CFO:* Holly Powell
**Ex VP:* J A Hacker
VP: Peter Diana
VP: David Friend
VP: Arthur Hidalgo
VP: Bill Stanford
Exec: Mark Carpenter
Brnch Mgr: Kyle Shearer

CARPENTER COMPONENTS FLORIDA
See CARPENTER CONTRACTORS OF AMERICA INC

D-U-N-S 04-999-8685
CARPENTER CONTRACTORS OF AMERICA INC
CARPENTER COMPONENTS FLORIDA
3900 Ave D Nw, Winter Haven, FL 33880
Tel (863) 294-6449 *Founded/Ownrshp* 1954
Sales 203.2MM[E] *EMP* 1,000
SIC 1751 2439 2431 Carpentry work; Trusses, wooden roof; Panel work, wood
Pr: Donald L Thiel
**Sec:* Terrance B Smith
**VP:* Maria Cornelius
**VP:* Billy D Fritsch
IT Man: Ken Bellotte

D-U-N-S 02-312-0615
CARPENTER FUNDS ADMINISTRATIVE OFFICE OF NORTHERN CALIFORNIA INC
CARPENTERS HEALTH AND WELFARE
265 Hegenberger Rd # 100, Oakland, CA 94621-1443
Tel (510) 639-3996 *Founded/Ownrshp* 2009
Sales 307.3MM[E] *EMP* 2[E]
SIC 6733 Trusts
CEO: David Lee

D-U-N-S 04-474-5909
CARPENTER HOLDINGS INC
(*Suby of* CARPENTER CO) ★
5016 Monument Ave, Richmond, VA 23230-3620
Tel (804) 359-0800 *Founded/Ownrshp* 1984
Sales 305.8MM[E] *EMP* 4,000
SIC 3086 Insulation or cushioning material, foamed plastic
Ch Bd: Stanley F Pauley
**Pr:* Michael Lowery
**CFO:* Holly Powell

D-U-N-S 00-234-4315 IMP/EXP
▲ CARPENTER TECHNOLOGY CORP
2 Meridian Blvd, Wyomissing, PA 19610-3202
Tel (610) 208-2000 *Founded/Ownrshp* 1889
Sales 1.8MMM *EMP* 4,900[E]
Tkr Sym CRS *Exch* NYS
SIC 3312 3443 3255 3316 3315 Stainless steel; Bar, rod & wire products; Primary finished or semifinished shapes; Tool & die steel; Plate work for the nuclear industry; Clay refractories; Cold finishing of steel shapes; Steel wire & related products
Pr: Tony R Thene
**Ch Bd:* Gregory A Pratt
COO: Joseph E Haniford
CFO: Damon Audia
CFO: Damon J Audia
Treas: Michael Hajost
Ofcr: Tom Cramsey
Sr VP: David L Strobel
VP: Mick Cataldi
VP: James D Dee
VP: Timothy Lain
VP: Tracy Lucas
VP: Brian J Malloy
VP: Dudley Merchant
VP: Stephen A Peskosky
VP: John Rice
VP: Rich Tinsman
VP: Sunil Y Widge
VP: Andrew Ziolkowski
Board of Directors: Carl G Anderson Jr, Phillip M Anderson, I Martin Inglis, Steven E Karol, Robert R McMaster, Peter N Stephans, Kathryn C Turner, Jeffrey Wadsworth, Stephen M Ward Jr

CARPENTER'S BENEFIT FUND OF PH
See CARPENTERS HEALTH AND WELFARE FUND

D-U-N-S 01-116-7074
CARPENTERS HEALTH & WELFARE TRUST FUND OF ST LOUIS
1419 Hampton Ave, Saint Louis, MO 63139-3100
Tel (314) 644-4802 *Founded/Ownrshp* 1974
Sales 198.4MM *EMP* 61
Accts Wolfe Nilges Nahorski Pc St L
SIC 8631 Employees' association
**Prin:* Carolyn Perez

CARPENTERS HEALTH AND WELFARE
See CARPENTER FUNDS ADMINISTRATIVE OFFICE OF NORTHERN CALIFORNIA INC

D-U-N-S 08-188-7721
CARPENTERS HEALTH AND WELFARE FUND
CARPENTER'S BENEFIT FUND OF PH
1811 Spring Garden St # 1, Philadelphia, PA 19130-3998
Tel (215) 568-0430 *Founded/Ownrshp* 1960
Sales NA *EMP* 40
Accts Novak Francella Llc Bala Cynw
SIC 6371 Pension, health & welfare funds
Pr: Noel Orr
**Prin:* Edward Coryell
**Prin:* Walter P Palmer Jr

D-U-N-S 04-485-5992
CARPENTERS HEALTH AND WELFARE TRUST FOR
CARENTERS SOUTH WEST ADM
533 S Fremont Ave Ste 410, Los Angeles, CA 90071-1716
Tel (213) 386-8590 *Founded/Ownrshp* 2001
Sales 237.6MM *EMP* 1
SIC 1751 Carpentry work
Ch: Doug McCarron

D-U-N-S 10-297-2049
CARPENTERS SOUTHWEST ADMINISTRATIVE CORP
533 S Fremont Ave, Los Angeles, CA 90071-1712
Tel (213) 386-8590 *Founded/Ownrshp* 1982
Sales 41.0MM[E] *EMP* 1,461
SIC 7011 Hotels & motels
CEO: Douglas McCarron
Ofcr: Brooke Reid

D-U-N-S 11-601-0364
CARPENTERS WELFARE BENEFIT FUND OF NEW YORK CITY (INC)
NEW YORK DST CNL CPTRS BFT FD
395 Hudson St Fl 9, New York, NY 10014-7450
Tel (212) 366-7300 *Founded/Ownrshp* 1966
Sales NA *EMP* 80
SIC 6371 Pension, health & welfare funds
Ex Dir: Stuart Grabois

CARPET ONE
See FLOORS INC

D-U-N-S 82-517-4019 IMP/EXP
CARPETERIA FLOORING CENTERS LLC
42212 10th St W Ste 2a, Lancaster, CA 93534-7020
Tel (661) 951-2200 *Founded/Ownrshp* 2002
Sales 2.0MM *EMP* 2,000
SIC 5713 Carpets
Prin: Barry White
**Pt:* Jack Dandohdeman

CARQUEST
See AUTOMOTIVE PARTS HEADQUARTERS INC

CARQUEST
See GENERAL PARTS INTERNATIONAL INC

CARQUEST AUTO PARTS
See GENERAL PARTS INC

CARR AUTO GROUP
See CARR CHEVROLET INC

D-U-N-S 03-028-9185
■ CARR BUSINESS SYSTEMS INC (NY)
(*Suby of* GLOBAL IMAGING SYSTEMS INC) ★
500 Commack Rd Unit 110, Commack, NY 11725-5021
Tel (631) 249-9880 *Founded/Ownrshp* 1937, 1998
Sales 123.5MM[E] *EMP* 150
SIC 5044 7699 Copying equipment; Photocopy machine repair
Ch Bd: David Herbine
**Pr:* Mitchell Cohen

D-U-N-S 18-629-8071
CARR CHEVROLET INC
CARR AUTO GROUP
15005 Sw Tualatin Vly, Beaverton, OR 97003-5137
Tel (503) 644-2161 *Founded/Ownrshp* 1989
Sales 104.0MM[E] *EMP* 260
SIC 5511 Automobiles, new & used; Vans, new & used; Pickups, new & used
Pr: Bradley Preble
**Ch:* Wallace L Preble
**VP:* Brad Preble
Sales Exec: Jeff Carrier
Sls Mgr: Bryan Lindsay

D-U-N-S 12-751-0790
CARR RIGGS & INGRAM LLC
901 Boll Weevil Cir # 200, Enterprise, AL 36330-1314
Tel (334) 347-0088 *Founded/Ownrshp* 1997
Sales 148.3MM[E] *EMP* 772
SIC 8721 Certified public accountant
Pt: Sara Applewhite
**Pt:* Brian Barksdale
Pt: James N Bearden
Pt: Carson L Eddy
Pt: Britt Finch
Pt: Phyllis S Ingram
Pt: Stephen C Riggs
Pt: Matt Schaeffer
Pt: Scott Schumpert
Pt: Michael Scott
Pt: Richard A Weidner
Mng Pt: William H Carr

D-U-N-S 88-477-2146
■ CARRABBAS ITALIAN GRILL INC
(*Suby of* OUTBACK STEAKHOUSE) ★
2202 N West Shore Blvd # 5, Tampa, FL 33607-5747
Tel (813) 288-8286 *Founded/Ownrshp* 1995
Sales 256.5MM[E] *EMP* 10,000
SIC 5812 Italian restaurant
Pr: Steve Shalemon
**CEO:* Allen A William III
**CFO:* Montgomery Dirk A
**CFO:* Shlemon Steven T
Sr Cor Off: Deland Kolwes
**Ex VP:* Kadow Joseph J
**VP:* William Kadow J
**VP:* Andi Jacobs
**VP:* Bill Kadow
Brnch Mgr: Justin Beachut
Brnch Mgr: Dave Harvey

CARRAIGE HOUSE APARTMENTS
See CARRIAGE HOUSE PRESERVATION LP

CARRAIGE HOUSE OF COLUMBIA
See GENE B GLICK CO INC

D-U-N-S 07-547-3819
CARRAWAY METHODIST HEALTH SYSTEMS
CARRAWAY METHODIST MEDICAL CTR
1600 Carraway Blvd, Birmingham, AL 35234-1990
Tel (205) 502-4100 *Founded/Ownrshp* 1916
Sales 33.7MM[E] *EMP* 1,500
Accts Warren Averett Kimbrough & M
SIC 8069 8062 Specialty hospitals, except psychiatric; Hospital, AMA approved residency
Ch Bd: Robert P Carraway
**CEO:* Steve Blaine
COO: Shannon Winslott
COO: Joe Wolan
Dir Lab: Kurvilla George
Dir Sec: Doyle Beasley
Netwrk Mgr: Andrian Cordell
Mktg Mgr: Dave Smitherman
Surgeon: Melissa Seaman
Ansthlgy: Frederick P Judson
Ansthlgy: Ralph T Lyerly

CARRAWAY METHODIST MEDICAL CTR
See CARRAWAY METHODIST HEALTH SYSTEMS

D-U-N-S 00-210-0907 EXP
■ CARRIAGE HOUSE COMPANIES INC
(*Suby of* TREEHOUSE PRIVATE BRANDS INC) ★
196 Newton St, Fredonia, NY 14063-1332
Tel (716) 672-4321 *Founded/Ownrshp* 1986
Sales 388.4MM[E] *EMP* 1,500
SIC 2099 2033 2035 2087 Syrups; Canned fruits & specialties; Dressings, salad: raw & cooked (except dry mixes); Concentrates, drink
CEO: Kevin Hunt
**VP:* Mary Jane Knight
**VP:* Rich Koulouris
VP: Marsha Schneibwind
VP Mktg: John Sterling

D-U-N-S 83-290-1958
CARRIAGE HOUSE PRESERVATION LP
CARRAIGE HOUSE APARTMENTS
135 W Old St, Petersburg, VA 23803-3225
Tel (804) 733-6225 *Founded/Ownrshp* 2009
Sales 30.5MM[E] *EMP* 3,900
SIC 6513 Apartment building operators
Sr VP: Leeann Morein

D-U-N-S 78-212-8367
▲ CARRIAGE SERVICES INC
3040 Post Oak Blvd # 300, Houston, TX 77056-6513
Tel (713) 332-8400 *Founded/Ownrshp* 1991
Sales 242.5MM *EMP* 2,317
Tkr Sym CSV *Exch* NYS
SIC 7261 6553 Funeral service & crematories; Cemetery subdividers & developers
Ch Bd: Melvin C Payne
Pt: Mark R Bruce
Pr: Paul D Elliott
Pt: Shawn R Phillips
Pr: David J Decarlo
Treas: Carl B Brink
CIO: Jeff Parker
IT Man: Jennifer Flores
Board of Directors: Barry K Fingerhut, Bryan D Leibman, Donald D Patteson Jr, James R Schenck

D-U-N-S 03-119-4707
CARRICO IMPLEMENT CO INC
JOHN DEERE AUTHORIZED DEALER
3160 Us 24 Hwy, Beloit, KS 67420-1577
Tel (785) 738-5744 *Founded/Ownrshp* 1973
Sales 89.3MM *EMP* 62
SIC 5083 Farm implements; Lawn machinery & equipment; Garden machinery & equipment
Pr: Ronald Ellenz
**VP:* Joan Ellenz
Sls Mgr: Rodger Budke

CARRIER BRANDS FLORIDA
See CARRIER ENTERPRISE LLC

D-U-N-S 03-628-3708 IMP/EXP
■ CARRIER COMMERCIAL REFRIGERATION INC
CARRIER WORLD HEADQUARTERS
(*Suby of* UNITED TECHNOLOGIES CARRIER) ★
1 Carrier Pl, Farmington, CT 06032-2562
Tel (860) 674-3000 *Founded/Ownrshp* 2005
Sales 93.3MM[E] *EMP* 500
SIC 3585 Refrigeration & heating equipment
Pr: Robert E Galli
Pr: Thomas Hoffman
Pr: Diana Sousa
CFO: Donna Hewitt
VP: Peter Dragich
Mng Dir: Steve Holden
Genl Mgr: Gregory Alcorn
Genl Mgr: Ralph Bott
Genl Mgr: Dennis Lane
Dir IT: Dave Roth
Sfty Mgr: Rolf Dietrichson
Board of Directors: Bob Robertson

D-U-N-S 11-820-2456 IMP/EXP
■ CARRIER COMMERCIAL REFRIGERATION INC
WELLS/BLOOMFIELD INDUSTRIES
(*Suby of* UNITED TECHNOLOGIES CARRIER) ★
3 Farm Glen Blvd Ste 301, Farmington, CT 06032-1981
Tel (336) 245-6400 *Founded/Ownrshp* 1991
Sales 610.3MM[E] *EMP* 4,282
SIC 3556 3631 3585 3589 3634 Ice cream manufacturing machinery; Dairy & milk machinery; Household cooking equipment; Refrigeration equipment, complete; Beer dispensing equipment; Food warming equipment, commercial; Cooking equipment, commercial; Coffee brewing equipment; Dryers, electric: hand & face; Hair dryers, electric
**Pr:* Mark D Morelli
**Treas:* Christopher Witzky
VP: James Grob
VP: Linda Kilbryde
VP: David S Ring
VP: Torsten T Rling
VP: Dennis D Smith
Genl Mgr: Pierre Thom
S&M/VP: C W Best

D-U-N-S 00-131-7072 IMP/EXP
■ CARRIER CORP
UNITED TECHNOLOGIES CARRIER
(*Suby of* UNITED TECHNOLOGIES CORP) ★
17900 Bee Line Hwy, Jupiter, FL 33478-6414
Tel (561) 796-2000 *Founded/Ownrshp* 1978, 1979
Sales 12.1MMM[E] *EMP* 44,545
SIC 3585 Air conditioning equipment, complete; Heating equipment, complete; Room coolers, portable; Heat pumps, electric
CEO: Geraud Darnis
**Treas:* Christopher Witzky
**Sr VP:* Ted Amyuni
**VP:* Chuck Balawajder

*VP: Ted Fetterman
*VP: Robert Galli

D-U-N-S 00-135-5390 IMP
■ CARRIER ENTERPRISE LLC
CARRIER BRANDS FLORIDA
(*Suby of* WATSCO INC) ★
4300 Golf Acres Dr, Charlotte, NC 28208-5861
Tel (704) 394-7311 *Founded/Ownrshp* 2009
Sales 830.8MM^E *EMP* 1,390
SIC 5075 Warm air heating & air conditioning
Pr: David Meyers
*COO: John Bartro
*CFO: Michael Tourtelot
*CFO: Mike Tourtelot
*VP: Barry Logan
*VP: Sandy Porzucek
Mng Dir: Jim Vickers
IT Man: Kara Mack
Board of Directors: Jacques Bories, Robert Mc-Dounough, Ana Menendez

CARRIER WORLD HEADQUARTERS
See CARRIER COMMERCIAL REFRIGERATION INC

D-U-N-S 03-116-0273
CARRIX INC (WA)
(*Suby of* FRS CAPITAL CORP) ★
1131 Sw Klickitat Way, Seattle, WA 98134-1108
Tel (206) 623-0304 *Founded/Ownrshp* 1994
Sales 1.3MMM^E *EMP* 11,000^E
SIC 4491 Stevedoring
Pr: Knud Stubkjaer
*Ex VP: Daniel Flynn
*VP: Jason Davis
*VP: Kyle Lukins
*VP: Jaime Neal
Dir Sec: Kirk Vaughan
IT Man: Heath Johnson
Board of Directors: Jill Jansen

D-U-N-S 80-983-7313
▲ CARRIZO OIL & GAS INC
500 Dallas St Ste 2300, Houston, TX 77002-4724
Tel (713) 328-1000 *Founded/Ownrshp* 1993
Sales 429.2MM *EMP* 215
Tkr Sym CRZO *Exch* NGS
SIC 1311 Crude petroleum & natural gas
Pr: Sylvester P Johnson IV
*Ch Bd: Steven A Webster
COO: Brad Fisher
CFO: David L Pitts
VP: Jack Bayless
VP: Greg Conaway
VP: Gregory F Conaway
VP: Jeff Hayden
VP: Gerald A Morton
VP: Michael Reese
VP: Dick Smith
VP: Richard H Smith
Board of Directors: Thomas L Carter Jr, Robert F Fulton, F Gardner Parker, Roger A Ramsey, Frank A Wojtek

CARROL ELC MEMBERSHIP COOP
See CARROLL ELECTRIC MEMBERSHIP CORP

D-U-N-S 04-068-4086
CARROLL COUNTY BOARD OF EDUCATION
CARROLL COUNTY SCHOOL SYSTEM
164 Independence Dr, Carrollton, GA 30116-7506
Tel (770) 834-3348 *Founded/Ownrshp* 1872
Sales 107.5MM^E *EMP* 1,900
SIC 8211 Public elementary & secondary schools
Opers Mgr: Linda Cunfer
Psych: Kimberly Muniz

D-U-N-S 62-140-3757
CARROLL COUNTY HEALTH SERVICES CORP
CARROLL HOSPITAL CENTER
200 Memorial Ave, Westminster, MD 21157-5726
Tel (410) 848-3000 *Founded/Ownrshp* 1957
Sales NA *EMP* 1,650
Accts Kpmg Llp Baltimore Md
SIC 6324 Hospital & medical service plans
Ch: Stephen Bohn
*Pr: John Sernulka
IT Man: Christopher Bunty
Pathlgst: Dixon V King
Doctor: Robert P Wackmd MD

D-U-N-S 16-580-7889
CARROLL COUNTY PUBLIC SCHOOLS
125 N Court St Ste 101, Westminster, MD 21157-5192
Tel (410) 751-3128 *Founded/Ownrshp* 2004
Sales 146.5MM^E *EMP* 3,992^E
SIC 8211 Public elementary & secondary schools
Dir Sec: Duane Williams
Off Mgr: Donna Box
Pr Dir: Carey Gaddis
Instr Medi: Irene Hildebrandt

CARROLL COUNTY SCHOOL SYSTEM
See CARROLL COUNTY BOARD OF EDUCATION

D-U-N-S 07-979-8964
CARROLL COUNTY SCHOOLS
164 Independence Dr, Carrollton, GA 30116-7506
Tel (770) 832-3568 *Founded/Ownrshp* 2015
Sales 30.6MM^E *EMP* 1,959^E
SIC 8211 Public elementary & secondary schools
Pgrm Dir: Kathryn Poole

D-U-N-S 00-378-8163
CARROLL ELECTRIC COOPERATIVE CORP (AR)
920 Highway 62 Spur, Berryville, AR 72616-4527
Tel (870) 423-2161 *Founded/Ownrshp* 1937
Sales 125.2MM^E *EMP* 192
Accts Bolinger Segars Gilbert And Mo
SIC 4911 5812 Distribution, electric power; Eating places
Pr: Rob Boaz
VP: David Dykstra
DP Dir: Mitch Raney
IT Man: Dwayne Mellont

D-U-N-S 00-692-5689
CARROLL ELECTRIC MEMBERSHIP CORP (GA)
CARROL ELC MEMBERSHIP COOP
155 N Highway 113, Carrollton, GA 30117-7501
Tel (770) 832-3552 *Founded/Ownrshp* 1936
Sales 115.6MM *EMP* 134
SIC 4911 Electric services
Pr: E A Jakins III
*CFO: Clifford Thompson
Exec: Lynn Jacobs
Comm Man: Jay Gill
Rgnl Mgr: Trina W Farris
VP Opers: Tim Martin

D-U-N-S 13-782-5027
CARROLL FULMER HOLDING CORP
CARROLL FULMER LOGISTICS
8340 American Way, Groveland, FL 34736-8587
Tel (352) 429-5000 *Founded/Ownrshp* 2002
Sales 159.2MM *EMP* 497^E
Accts Bunting Tripp & Ingley Llp
SIC 4731 Truck transportation brokers
Pr: Philip Fulmer
*Pr: Cynthia F Turner
*CFO: James Gauger
*Treas: Timothy Fulmer
*Sr VP: Barbara Fulmer
*VP: Carroll A Fulmer

CARROLL FULMER LOGISTICS
See CARROLL FULMER HOLDING CORP

D-U-N-S 11-279-5534
CARROLL FULMER LOGISTICS CORP
(*Suby of* CARROLL FULMER LOGISTICS) ★
8340 American Way, Groveland, FL 34736-8587
Tel (352) 429-5000 *Founded/Ownrshp* 2002
Sales 145.6MM^E *EMP* 420
Accts Bunting Tripp & Ingley Llp
SIC 4731 Truck transportation brokers
Pr: Philip R Fulmer
*Ch Bd: Carroll Fulmer
*Pr: Tim Fulmer
Pr: Arthur Hodge
*CFO: James E Gauger
*Treas: Cynthia F Turner
*VP: Caroll A Fulmer
*VP: Timothy A Fulmer
Dir Risk M: Josh Fulmer

CARROLL HOSPITAL CENTER
See CARROLL COUNTY HEALTH SERVICES CORP

D-U-N-S 07-494-1857
CARROLL HOSPITAL CENTER INC
(*Suby of* LIFEBRIDGE HEALTH INC) ★
200 Memorial Ave, Westminster, MD 21157-5726
Tel (410) 848-3000 *Founded/Ownrshp* 2015
Sales 229.2MM *EMP* 1,100^E
Accts Dixon Hughes Goodman Llp Rock
SIC 8062 Hospital, AMA approved residency
Pr: Leslie Simmons
*CFO: Kevin Kelbly
Bd of Dir: David Salinger
*Chf Mktg O: Mark Olszyk
VP: Ellen Myers
VP: Sharon Sanders
IT Man: Christopher Bunty

D-U-N-S 00-799-5905
CARROLL INDEPENDENT FUEL LLC (MD)
2700 Loch Raven Rd, Baltimore, MD 21218-4729
Tel (410) 235-1066 *Founded/Ownrshp* 1907
Sales 964.4MM^E *EMP* 1,248
SIC 5172 5983 Fuel oil; Lubricating oils & greases; Gasoline; Fuel oil dealers
Pr: John Phelps
*Ch Bd: Richard B Phelps III
*CFO: David Shade
CFO: Paul Simon
Genl Mgr: Bonnie Mitchell
Sls Dir: Paul Leonard
Corp Couns: Michael Jennings

D-U-N-S 02-192-9187
CARROLL INDEPENDENT SCHOOL DISTRICT
3051 Dove Rd, Grapevine, TX 76051-4707
Tel (817) 949-8230 *Founded/Ownrshp* 1957
Sales 107.6MM *EMP* 950
Accts Haynes & Associates Pc Roa
SIC 8211 Public elementary school; Public junior high school; Public senior high school
Brnch Mgr: Sharon Eaves
Brnch Mgr: Kim Pool
Schl Brd P: Christopher Archer
HC Dir: Mary Johnston

CARROLL TIRE
See CARROLLS LLC

D-U-N-S 04-209-6792 EXP
CARROLLS LLC
CARROLL TIRE
(*Suby of* TBC CORP) ★
4281 Old Dixie Hwy, Atlanta, GA 30354-4011
Tel (404) 366-5476 *Founded/Ownrshp* 1998
Sales 208.8MM^E *EMP* 500
SIC 5014 5013 Automobile tires & tubes; Truck tires & tubes; Motor vehicle supplies & new parts
CEO: Erik R Olsen
*CFO: Timothy J Miller
Treas: Timothy Miller
Brnch Mgr: Nick Gandy
Genl Mgr: Don Pylant
Off Mgr: Judy Klafta
Sales Exec: Jim Schank
Mktg Dir: Brent Wolak

D-U-N-S 06-897-8048
CARROLLTON-FARMERS BRANCH INDEPENDENT SCHOOL DISTRICT
1445 N Perry Rd, Carrollton, TX 75006-6134
Tel (972) 968-6100 *Founded/Ownrshp* 1916, 1997
Sales 306.2MM *EMP* 4,020
Accts Hankins Eastup Deaton Tonn
SIC 8211 Public elementary & secondary schools; Public elementary school; Public junior high school; Public senior high school
CIO: Andy Berning
MIS Dir: Robert Welsh
Pr Dir: Pam Pena
HC Dir: Melony Bergos

D-U-N-S 04-855-2129
■ CARROLS CORP
BURGER KING
(*Suby of* CARROLS RESTAURANT GROUP INC) ★
968 James St, Syracuse, NY 13203-2596
Tel (315) 424-0513 *Founded/Ownrshp* 1968
Sales 482.5MM^E *EMP* 15,500
SIC 5812 Fast-food restaurant, chain
Ch Bd: Daniel T Accordino
*CFO: Paul R Flanders
Chf Cred: John Haywood
VP: Heatherly Bishop
VP: Michael Biviano
*VP: Timothy J Lalonde
VP: John Lukas
*VP: Joseph A Zirkman
Dist Mgr: Stephanie Lenoir
Dist Mgr: Sara Sargent
Genl Mgr: Donna Rhoades
Board of Directors: Nicholas Daraviras, Brian P Friedman, Joel M Handel, Jack A Smith, Clayton E Wilhite

D-U-N-S 96-869-2637
■ CARROLS LLC
BURGER KING
(*Suby of* BURGER KING) ★
968 James St, Syracuse, NY 13203-2503
Tel (315) 424-0513 *Founded/Ownrshp* 2008
Sales 46.4MM^E *EMP* 1,177^E
SIC 5812 Fast-food restaurant, chain
Ch Bd: Alan Vituli

D-U-N-S 15-150-1046
▲ CARROLS RESTAURANT GROUP INC
968 James St, Syracuse, NY 13203-2503
Tel (315) 424-0513 *Founded/Ownrshp* 1960
Sales 859.0MM *EMP* 20,350^E
Tkr Sym TAST *Exch* NGS
SIC 5812 6794 Fast-food restaurant, chain; Franchises, selling or licensing
Pr: Daniel T Accordino
Pr: Paul R Flanders
VP: Richard G Cross
VP: Timothy J Lalonde
VP: William E Myers

CARRS QUALITY CENTERS
See SAFEWAY SELECT GIFT SOURCE INC

D-U-N-S 15-430-5213 IMP/EXP
CARRUTH-DOGGETT INC
TOYOTA LIFT OF HOUSTON
7110 North Fwy, Houston, TX 77076-1309
Tel (713) 675-7000 *Founded/Ownrshp* 1991
Sales 221.8MM^E *EMP* 300
SIC 5084 7359 7699 Industrial machinery & equipment; Equipment rental & leasing; Industrial machinery & equipment repair
Pr: Wm Leslie Doggett
*CFO: Brian McLemore
Brnch Mgr: Jim Groome
Genl Mgr: Jim Flowers
Dir IT: James Faucett
Sls Mgr: Steve Door

CARRY TRANSIT
See SUPERIOR BULK LOGISTICS INC

D-U-N-S 94-560-3272 IMP
CARRY-ON TRAILER INC
(*Suby of* AMERICAN TRAILER WORKS INC) ★
101 Joe Harvey St, Lavonia, GA 30553-1276
Tel (706) 356-5379 *Founded/Ownrshp* 1996
Sales 243.2MM^E *EMP* 750
SIC 3799 Trailers & trailer equipment
CEO: J Pearson
CFO: Douglas Clark

D-U-N-S 02-428-5814
■ CARS.COM LLC
(*Suby of* TEGNA INC) ★
175 W Jackson Blvd Fl 8, Chicago, IL 60604-2913
Tel (312) 601-5000 *Founded/Ownrshp* 2014
Sales 144.3MM^E *EMP* 770
SIC 7313 Electronic media advertising representatives
Pr: Alex Vetter
CFO: Robert Gallagher
Sr Cor Off: Bruce Mitchell
Bd of Dir: Brent Bonnett
Chf Mktg O: Colette Laforce
Chf Mktg O: Brooke Skinner Ricketts
VP: Josh Chapman
VP: Kayne Grau
VP: Brian Hershey
VP: Gregory McGivney
VP: Stephen Page
VP: Dan Smith
Co-Founder: Mitch Golub

D-U-N-S 05-707-5285
CARSON OIL CO INC
3125 Nw 35th Ave, Portland, OR 97210-1637
Tel (503) 829-5441 *Founded/Ownrshp* 1971
Sales 173.7MM^E *EMP* 300
SIC 5172 Fuel oil; Diesel fuel; Gasoline; Lubricating oils & greases
Pr: Lance C Woodbury
*Ch Bd: John A Carson
CFO: Terry Mohr
VP: Jeff Rouse
Dir IT: Bob Rogus
IT Man: Russ Zard
Info Man: Bob Couch
Mktg Dir: Sierra R Koepfle
Manager: Karen Bennett
Genl Couns: Marti Sharp

D-U-N-S 07-611-3240
CARSON TAHOE REGIONAL HEALTHCARE
1600 Medical Pkwy, Carson City, NV 89703-4625
Tel (775) 445-8000 *Founded/Ownrshp* 2001
Sales 245.8MM *EMP* 1,500
SIC 8062 General medical & surgical hospitals
CEO: Ed Epperson
*CFO: Ann Beck
*Ch: Basil Chryssos
*Treas: Jonathan Miller
Ofcr: April Lucas
Ofcr: Kitty McKay
*VP: Cathy Dinaue
VP: Doug Self
Dir Lab: Terry Phillips
Chf Nrs Of: Kelly Wilcher
CIO: Kayleen Mahlberg

D-U-N-S 07-998-1479
CARTAMUNDI EAST LONGMEADOW LLC
(*Suby of* CARTAMUNDI NV)
443 Shaker Rd, East Longmeadow, MA 01028-3124
Tel (413) 526-2000 *Founded/Ownrshp* 2015
Sales 100.0MM^E *EMP* 400
SIC 3944 3999 Board games, puzzles & models, except electronic; Novelties, bric-a-brac & hobby kits
CEO: Jeffrey Lombard
CFO: Eric Defilipi
VP: Jill Hambley
IT Man: Allen Walski
Sls Mgr: Lindsey Williams

D-U-N-S 02-641-7709
■ CARTER & BURGESS INC
(*Suby of* JACOBS ENGINEERING GROUP INC) ★
777 Main St Ste 2500, Fort Worth, TX 76102-5307
Tel (817) 735-6000 *Founded/Ownrshp* 1967
Sales 99.3MM^E *EMP* 3,200
SIC 8711 8712 8713 Engineering services; Civil engineering; Structural engineering; Consulting engineer; Architectural engineering; Surveying services
Pr: Benjamin G Watts
*Treas: John W Prosser Jr
Ex VP: John Carter
*VP: George A Kunberger
*VP: H Thomas McDuffie Jr
*VP: Kevin J McMahon
Prgrm Mgr: Matthew Coffman
IT Man: Ryan Hooley
IT Man: Chris Smith
IT Man: Mike Wagar
Mktg Mgr: Jim Chlup

D-U-N-S 96-177-5033
CARTER BANK & TRUST
1300 Kings Mountain Rd, Martinsville, VA 24112-7268
Tel (276) 656-1776 *Founded/Ownrshp* 2006
Sales NA *EMP* 1,014^E
SIC 6022 State commercial banks
Ch Bd: Worth Harris Carter Jr
CFO: Jane Ann Davis
Sr VP: Carol Ann Bondurant
Sr VP: Robert L Dye III
Sr VP: John Gardner
Sr VP: Dianne S Hall
Sr VP: Phyllis Karavatakis
Sr VP: Bradford M Kendrick
Sr VP: Brenda A Kendrick
Sr VP: Steven M Moses
Sr VP: William E Oeters

D-U-N-S 07-316-9765
CARTER BLOODCARE
2205 Highway 121, Bedford, TX 76021-5950
Tel (817) 412-5000 *Founded/Ownrshp* 1959
Sales 119.7MM *EMP* 800
SIC 2836 Blood derivatives; Extracts; Plasmas
CEO: Merlyn Sayers
*CFO: Walter Ott
*Ex VP: Bobby Grigsby
CTO: Denise Dickens
QA Dir: Vickie Love
Dir IT: Derk Pelton
Opers Mgr: Tonna Buster
Opers Mgr: Howard Jenkins
Opers Mgr: Melonye Rodgers
Pathlgst: Jeannie Chiu

D-U-N-S 96-778-4997
CARTER BLOODCARE FDN
2205 Highway 121, Bedford, TX 76021-5950
Tel (817) 412-5121 *Founded/Ownrshp* 2011
Sales 129.3MM *EMP* 4^E
SIC 8011 General & family practice, physician/surgeon
Prin: Demia Brown

D-U-N-S 96-631-5397
CARTER CENTER COLABORATIVE INC
453 Freedom Pkwy Ne, Atlanta, GA 30307-1406
Tel (404) 420-5100 *Founded/Ownrshp* 2011
Sales 95.1MM *EMP* 42
Accts Kpmg Llp Greensboro Nc
SIC 8221 Colleges universities & professional schools
Prin: John B Hardman

D-U-N-S 15-773-8295
CARTER CENTER INC
453 Freedom Pkwy Ne, Atlanta, GA 30307-1406
Tel (404) 420-5100 *Founded/Ownrshp* 1981
Sales 101.7MM *EMP* 200
Accts Kpmg Llp Greensboro Nc
SIC 8651 8412 Political action committee; Museums & art galleries
CEO: John Hardman
Ch Bd: James E Carter
Treas: Christopher Brown
VP: Richard Nixon
VP: Phil Weiss
Dir Teleco: Angela Hale
Assoc Dir: Emily Staub
Prin: Mary Ann Peters
IT Man: Charles Kong

D-U-N-S 02-041-3696
CARTER EXPRESS INC
(*Suby of* JP HOLDING CO INC) ★
4020 W 73rd St, Anderson, IN 46011-9609
Tel (765) 778-6961 *Founded/Ownrshp* 1992
Sales 128.5MM[E] *EMP* 800[E]
SIC 4213 4212 Trucking, except local; Local trucking, without storage
Pr: John Paugh
**VP:* Philip Hammel
Sfty Dirs: Rick Wisener
Opers Mgr: Brittni Miller
Opers Mgr: Shari Mullins
**VP Sls:* Dave Wilson

D-U-N-S 07-911-0519 IMP/EXP
CARTER FUEL SYSTEMS LLC
101 E Industrial Blvd, Logansport, IN 46947-6994
Tel (800) 342-6125 *Founded/Ownrshp* 2013
Sales 142.3MM[E] *EMP* 400
SIC 3714 5989 Fuel pumps, motor vehicle; Coal

D-U-N-S 61-100-3257
CARTER LOGISTICS LLC
(*Suby of* JP HOLDING CO INC) ★
4020 W 73rd St, Anderson, IN 46011-9609
Tel (765) 778-6960 *Founded/Ownrshp* 1992
Sales 207.0MM[E] *EMP* 800
SIC 4731 Freight transportation arrangement
**COO:* Philip Hammel
CFO: Drew Huntzinger
Ex VP: Richard Deboer
Software D: Brian Buckles
Sftwr Eng: Tamara Allison
Sfty Dirs: Jim Stetnish
Site Mgr: Jason Covell

CARTER LUMBER
See CARTER-JONES COMPANIES INC

D-U-N-S 04-571-8160
CARTER LUMBER INC
(*Suby of* CARTER LUMBER) ★
601 Tallmadge Rd, Kent, OH 44240-7331
Tel (330) 673-6100 *Founded/Ownrshp* 1964
Sales 150.5MM[E] *EMP* 425
SIC 5211 Lumber & other building materials
Pr: Neil Sackett
**CFO:* Jeffrey S Donley
Sr Cor Off: Jeffrey Donley
Netwrk Mgr: Ron Ferrell

D-U-N-S 00-794-1743 IMP/EXP
CARTER MACHINERY CO INC
1330 Lynchburg Tpke, Salem, VA 24153-5416
Tel (540) 387-1111 *Founded/Ownrshp* 1984, 2011
Sales 2.4MMM[E] *EMP* 1,200
SIC 5082 3531 General construction machinery & equipment; Mining machinery & equipment, except petroleum; Construction machinery
CEO: James J Parker
**Pr:* John Betzel
**CFO:* Daniel E Strelka
**Ex VP:* Andrew Parker
Sls Mgr: James Hardy

CARTER MYERS AUTOMOTIVE
See PETERSBURG MOTOR CO INC

D-U-N-S 96-802-6349
CARTER VALIDUS MISSION CRITICAL REIT INC
4890 W Kennedy Blvd # 650, Tampa, FL 33609-1840
Tel (813) 287-0101 *Founded/Ownrshp* 2009
Sales 214.8MM *EMP* 10
SIC 6798 Real estate investment trusts
Ch Bd: John E Carter
Pr: Michael A Seton
CFO: Todd M Sakow

D-U-N-S 07-690-2691
CARTER-JONES COMPANIES INC
CARTER LUMBER
601 Tallmadge Rd, Kent, OH 44240-7331
Tel (330) 673-6100 *Founded/Ownrshp* 1934
Sales 1.1MMM *EMP* 3,225
Accts Bdo Usa Llp Akron Oh
SIC 5211 5031 6552 Lumber & other building materials; Lumber: rough, dressed & finished; Subdividers & developers
Pr: Neil Sackett
CFO: Jeffrey Donley

D-U-N-S 00-452-8212 IMP
CARTER-JONES LUMBER CO (OH)
(*Suby of* CARTER LUMBER) ★
601 Tallmadge Rd, Kent, OH 44240-7331
Tel (330) 673-6100 *Founded/Ownrshp* 1934
Sales 272.7MM[E] *EMP* 1,575
SIC 5211 5031 Lumber & other building materials; Lumber: rough, dressed & finished; Millwork; Building materials, exterior; Building materials, interior
CEO: Neil Sackett
**CFO:* Jeffrey S Donley

D-U-N-S 08-416-6404
CARTERET COUNTY BOARD OF EDUCATION (INC)
107 Safrit Dr, Beaufort, NC 28516-9017
Tel (252) 728-4583 *Founded/Ownrshp* 1920
Sales 22.7MM[E] *EMP* 1,175
SIC 8211 School board
Ch: Perry Harker

D-U-N-S 04-002-9613
CARTERET COUNTY GENERAL HOSPITAL CORP
TAYLOR EXTENDED CARE
3500 Arendell St, Morehead City, NC 28557-2901
Tel (252) 808-6000 *Founded/Ownrshp* 1967
Sales 142.5MM *EMP* 1,031
SIC 8093 8062 Specialty outpatient clinics; General medical & surgical hospitals
Ch: Pat Joyce
**Ch Bd:* John Davis
**Pr:* F A Odell III
**CEO:* Richard Brvenik
**Treas:* Doug Brady
Bd of Dir: James Loynes
**VP:* Donna Cheek
Dir Lab: Dana Shelley
Dir Rad: Ken McBride
Ex Dir: Robert Kornegay
CIO: Kyle Marek

CARTER'S FACTORY OUTLET
See WILLIAM CARTER CO

D-U-N-S 16-006-8433 IMP/EXP
▲ **CARTERS INC**
3438 Peachtree Rd Ne # 1800, Atlanta, GA 30326-1554
Tel (678) 791-1000 *Founded/Ownrshp* 1865
Sales 3.0MMM *EMP* 16,800[E]
Tkr Sym CRI *Exch* NYS
SIC 2361 2369 Dresses: girls', children's & infants'; Shirts: girls', children's & infants'; T-shirts & tops: girls', children's & infants'; Blouses: girls', children's & infants'; Girls' & children's outerwear
Ch Bd: Michael D Casey
Pr: Brian J Lynch
CFO: Richard F Westenberger
Ex VP: Kevin D Corning
Ex VP: Peter R Smith
Sr VP: Julie A D'Emilio
Sr VP: William G Foglesong
Sr VP: Jeffrey B Williams
Sr VP: Jill A Wilson
Sr VP: Michael C Wu
VP: Trevor Agard
VP: Marie Davis
VP: Julie Demilio
VP: Carlo H Hanna
VP: Christopher Prete
VP: Cathy Rens
Creative D: Vivian Mize
Board of Directors: Amy Woods Brinkley, Giuseppina Buonfantino, Vanessa J Castagna, A Bruce Cleverly, Paul Fulton, William J Montgoris, David Pulver, Thomas E Whiddon

D-U-N-S 80-958-1080
■ **CARTERS RETAIL INC**
(*Suby of* CARTERS INC) ★
3438 Peachtree Rd Ne, Atlanta, GA 30326-1554
Tel (203) 926-5000 *Founded/Ownrshp* 1999
Sales 3.0MM *EMP* 6,547
SIC 5641 Children's & infants' wear stores
CEO: Frederick Rowan
**Pr:* Joseph Pacifico
**CEO:* Michael Casey
**CFO:* Richard F Westenberger
**VP:* Michael Heider
**Ex Dir:* Michael Sykes

D-U-N-S 04-788-1607
■ **CARTERSVILLE MEDICAL CENTER LLC**
COLUMBIA HCA
(*Suby of* HOSPITAL CORPORATION OF AMERICA) ★
960 Joe Frank Harris, Cartersville, GA 30120-2129
Tel (770) 382-1530 *Founded/Ownrshp* 1998
Sales 130.2MM *EMP* 700
SIC 8361 Rehabilitation center, residential: health care incidental
Chf Nrs Of: Miriam Eide
IT Man: Zina Frazier
IT Man: Steven Spivey
Doctor: John Brunette
HC Dir: Angel Shellhorse

D-U-N-S 07-615-2578
CARTHAGE COLLEGE
2001 Alford Park Dr, Kenosha, WI 53140-1994
Tel (262) 551-8500 *Founded/Ownrshp* 1847
Sales 135.7MM *EMP* 250
Accts Baker Tilly Virchow Krause Llp
SIC 8221 College, except junior
Ch Bd: Edward Smed
**Pr:* F Gregory Campbell
Pr: Sam Jones
Pr: Todd Kelley
Pr: Ronald Luthman
CFO: William ABT
Assoc VP: Dean Clark
VP: Gene Engeldinger
IT Man: Rikka Johnson
Trfc Dir: Dennis Shaw
Opers Mgr: Isaac Smith

CARTI
See CENTRAL ARKANSAS RADIATION THERAPY INSTITUTE INC

D-U-N-S 11-202-0649
■ **CARTUS CORP**
(*Suby of* REALOGY GROUP LLC) ★
40 Apple Ridge Rd, Danbury, CT 06810-7366
Tel (203) 205-3400 *Founded/Ownrshp* 1970
Sales 644.8MM[E] *EMP* 3,200
SIC 7389 Relocation service
Pr: Kevin J Kelleher
**CFO:* Eric Barnes
**CFO:* Anthony E Hull
**Ex VP:* Marilyn J Wasser
Sr VP: Scott Becker
**Sr VP:* Bruce Perlman
**Sr VP:* Seth I Truwit
VP: Jack Craven
VP: Pat Dedonato
VP: Patrice Heinzer
VP: Michael Mancini
VP: Denise Porter
VP: Lawrence J Post
VP: Steve Slabaugh
VP: Pamela Uhl
Dir Bus: Hamilton Farias
Dir Bus: Kathy Hennessy
Dir Bus: Mike Puckett
Board of Directors: Tom Davis, Jack Hall, Michael P Monaco, Richard A Smith

D-U-N-S 07-753-1465
CARTWRIGHT SCHOOL DISTRICT NO83
5220 W Indian School Rd, Phoenix, AZ 85031-2605
Tel (623) 691-4000 *Founded/Ownrshp* 1884
Sales 88.1MM[E] *EMP* 1,901
Accts Larsonallen Llp Mesa Arizona
SIC 8211 Public elementary & secondary schools
**Pr:* Lydia Hernandez
**VP:* Rosa Cantu
Dir Sec: Claus Hanold
Pr Dir: Veronica Sanchez
Pr Dir: Joyce Yancy
Psych: Kathryn Schelbar
Psych: Darcie Smiley

D-U-N-S 07-959-7995
CARUS GROUP INC
315 5th St, Peru, IL 61354-2859
Tel (815) 223-1500 *Founded/Ownrshp* 1915
Sales 150.6MM *EMP* 350
Accts Rsm Us Llp Chicago Illinois
SIC 2819 Industrial inorganic chemicals; Potassium compounds or salts, except hydroxide or carbonate
**VP:* Gregory G Thiess
**VP:* Judy Wierman

D-U-N-S 62-555-2989
CARY OIL CO INC
(*Suby of* COC PROPERTIES INC) ★
110 Mackenan Dr Ste 300, Cary, NC 27511-7901
Tel (919) 462-1100 *Founded/Ownrshp* 1990
Sales 1.2MMM[E] *EMP* 100
Accts Batcelor Tillery & Roberts L
SIC 5172 5171 Gasoline; Petroleum bulk stations
Pr: Don Stephenson Jr
**CFO:* Jason Holt
**Treas:* Rick Stephenson
**VP:* Jim Bosworth
**VP:* Mark Maddox
**VP:* Betty Phillips
**VP:* Craig Stephenson
Board of Directors: A P Stephenson, Paul Stephenson, Avery Wagoner

D-U-N-S 08-906-9975
CARYLON CORP
2500 W Arthington St, Chicago, IL 60612-4108
Tel (312) 666-7700 *Founded/Ownrshp* 1949
Sales 149.4MM[E] *EMP* 1,025
SIC 7699 1629 7349 8748 4959

D-U-N-S 09-885-6339
■ **CAS INC**
(*Suby of* WYLE SERVICES CORP) ★
100 Quality Cir Nw, Huntsville, AL 35806-4529
Tel (256) 922-4200 *Founded/Ownrshp* 1979
Sales 103.3MM[E] *EMP* 1,100
SIC 8711 7371

D-U-N-S 96-890-7381
CAS RESIDENTIAL LLC
1201 Elm St Ste 1600, Dallas, TX 75270-2038
Tel (214) 965-6000 *Founded/Ownrshp* 2006
Sales 48.6MM[E] *EMP* 5,000[E]
SIC 6531 Real estate brokers & agents

CASA DEL SOL CENTER
See PEAK MEDICAL LAS CRUCES LLC

D-U-N-S 07-752-7489
CASA GRANDE COMMUNITY HOSPITAL
BANNER RESEARCH INSTITUTE
(*Suby of* BANNER RESEARCH INSTITUTE) ★
1800 E Florence Blvd, Casa Grande, AZ 85122-5303
Tel (520) 426-6300 *Founded/Ownrshp* 2014
Sales 99.1MM *EMP* 750
Accts Moss Adams Llp Stockton Ca
SIC 8062 General medical & surgical hospitals
CEO: Rona Curphy
**CFO:* Karen Francis
Dir Rad: Frank Mollica
Pathlgst: Morgan J Brown
Surgeon: Elias A Nalli

CASABLANCA FAN COMPANY
See HUNTER FAN CO

D-U-N-S 82-644-8052
▲ **CASCADE BANCORP**
1100 Nw Wall St, Bend, OR 97703-1935
Tel (541) 617-3500 *Founded/Ownrshp* 1990
Sales NA *EMP* 513[E]
Tkr Sym CACB *Exch* NAS
SIC 6022 State commercial banks
Pr: Terry E Zink
**Ch Bd:* Ryan R Patrick
CFO: Gregory D Newton
**V Ch Bd:* Patricia L Moss
Ofcr: Peggy Biss
Ofcr: Sandra R Gianotti
Ofcr: Daniel J Lee
Ofcr: Charles N Reeves
Ex VP: Peggy L Biss
Ex VP: Johnathan Choe
Ex VP: Julie Miller
Ex VP: Michael M Mooney
VP: Amy Berger
VP: Jamie Eichman
VP: Jeff Huhn
VP: Jodi Lopez

D-U-N-S 00-903-1378 IMP/EXP
CASCADE CORP
(*Suby of* TOYOTA INDUSTRIES CORPORATION)
2201 Ne 201st Ave, Fairview, OR 97024-9799
Tel (503) 669-6300 *Founded/Ownrshp* 1943
Sales 538.0MM[E] *EMP* 1,900[E]
SIC 3537 3531 Lift trucks, industrial: fork, platform, straddle, etc.; Construction machinery
CEO: Robert Warren
**Pr:* Richard S Anderson
COO: Warren Robert
**Treas:* John Cushing
Treas: Kurt G Wollenber
Ex VP: Nick Leontidis
Sr VP: Ron Filegan
VP: Frank R Altenhofen
VP: Frank Altenhofen
VP: Peter D Drake
VP: Robert Francis
VP: Kevin Grabski
VP: Charlie S Mitchelson
**VP:* Jeffrey K Nickoloff
VP: Jeffrey K Nicoloff
VP: Anthony F Spinelli
VP: Gary Tyson
Exec: Yvette Gray

D-U-N-S 07-662-7454 IMP
CASCADE DESIGNS INC
4000 1st Ave S, Seattle, WA 98134-2301
Tel (206) 583-0583 *Founded/Ownrshp* 1972
Sales 127.6MM[E] *EMP* 400
SIC 2515 3089 3949 8733 Mattresses & bedsprings; Air mattresses, plastic; Camping equipment & supplies; Research institute
Ch Bd: John D Burroughs
**Pr:* Joe Mc Swiney
**Treas:* David Burroughs
VP: Mona West
IT Man: Dana Wilke
Mktg Mgr: Tania Balderrama
Sls Mgr: Donald Riha
Sls Mgr: Thomas Threlkeld
Corp Couns: Eric Hobbs

D-U-N-S 06-020-0342 IMP/EXP
CASCADE ENGINEERING INC
3400 Innovation Ct Se, Grand Rapids, MI 49512-2085
Tel (616) 975-4800 *Founded/Ownrshp* 1973
Sales 358.8MM *EMP* 1,800
Accts Bdo Usa Llp Grand Rapids Mi
SIC 3089 Injection molding of plastics
Pr: Mark Miller
Pr: Christina Keller
**Ch:* Frederick P Keller
**Treas:* Joseph P Maier
**Ex VP:* Kenyatta Brame
**VP:* Judy Bland
**VP:* Jo-Anne Perkins
**VP:* Dianna L Stephens
VP: Scott Suits
**VP:* Lance Tennant
Prgrm Mgr: Ryan Cleaver
Board of Directors: Graig Hall, Derek Kaufman, Frederick Keller

D-U-N-S 10-796-4397
■ **CASCADE MICROTECH INC**
(*Suby of* FORMFACTOR INC) ★
9100 Sw Gemini Dr, Beaverton, OR 97008-7127
Tel (503) 601-1000 *Founded/Ownrshp* 2016
Sales 143.9MM *EMP* 1[E]
SIC 3825 3674 7372 Instruments to measure electricity; Test equipment for electronic & electric measurement; Semiconductors & related devices; Wafers (semiconductor devices); Application computer software
Pr: Michael D Burger
CFO: Jeff A Killian
Sr VP: Nancy Olson
VP: Claus Dietrich
VP: K R Gleason
VP: Steven L Harris
VP: Ken Smith
VP: Mark Stager
Prgrm Mgr: Liz Kennedy
Prgrm Mgr: Dave Shelley
Admn Mgr: Kimberly Eriksen

D-U-N-S 00-794-2584
■ **CASCADE NATURAL GAS CORP** (WA)
(*Suby of* MDU RESOURCES GROUP INC) ★
8113 W Grandridge Blvd, Kennewick, WA 99336-7166
Tel (509) 734-4500 *Founded/Ownrshp* 1953, 2007
Sales 180.4MM[E] *EMP* 374
SIC 4924 Natural gas distribution
Pr: David W Stevens
**Ch Bd:* Larry L Pinnt
**Pr:* Nicole A Kivisto
**Pr:* K Frank Morehouse
CFO: J D Wessling
**Sr VP:* Jon T Stoltz
VP: Linda Cies
**VP:* Scott W Madison
VP: Julie Marshall
VP: Larry C Rosek
**Prin:* Scott M Boggs
Board of Directors: Carl Burnham Jr, Thomas E Cronin, David A Ederer, Brooks G Ragen

D-U-N-S 78-440-4683 IMP
CASCADE OHIO INC
C W OHIO
1209 Maple Ave, Conneaut, OH 44030-2120
Tel (440) 593-5800 *Founded/Ownrshp* 1991
Sales 86.2MM[E] *EMP* 282
SIC 2431 3442 Windows & window parts & trim, wood; Louver windows, glass, wood frame; Windows, wood; Metal doors, sash & trim
Pr: Nicholas N Noirot
CFO: Gary Trapp
**VP:* Gary C Trapp

D-U-N-S 01-953-3595 IMP
CASCADE SCHOOL SUPPLIES INC
1 Brown St, North Adams, MA 01247-3318
Tel (413) 663-3716 *Founded/Ownrshp* 1984
Sales 110.8MM[E] *EMP* 150
SIC 5049 School supplies
Pr: Peter L Cote
**Treas:* William A Wells
**VP:* Todd Shafer

D-U-N-S 04-577-6432 IMP
■ **CASCADE STEEL ROLLING MILLS INC**
(*Suby of* SCHNITZER STEEL INDUSTRIES INC) ★
3200 Ne Highway 99w, McMinnville, OR 97128-9399
Tel (503) 472-4181 *Founded/Ownrshp* 1964
Sales 88.6MM[E] *EMP* 425
SIC 3312 Blast furnaces & steel mills; Bar, rod & wire products; Fence posts, iron & steel
Pr: Jeff Dyck
IT Man: Ron Linker

CASCADE WINDOWS
See WINDOW PRODUCTS INC

CASCADES CNTNERBOARD PACKG INC
See CASCADES CONTAINERBOARD PACKAGING INC

D-U-N-S 18-115-7769 IMP
CASCADES CONTAINERBOARD PACKAGING INC
CASCADES CNTNERBOARD PACKG INC
(*Suby of* CASCADES CANADA ULC)
4001 Packard Rd, Niagara Falls, NY 14303-2202
Tel (716) 285-3681 *Founded/Ownrshp* 1987
Sales 998.7MM[E] *EMP* 4,900[E]
SIC 2631 2653 Container board; Corrugated & solid fiber boxes
VP: Charles Malo
**Treas:* Sal Sciarrino
Bd of Dir: Eric Laflamme
**VP:* Robert Lanthier
**VP:* Jean Parent
**VP:* Maurice Plante
Genl Mgr: Jean Goulet
Genl Mgr: Mario Lacharit
Genl Mgr: Luc Langevin
Genl Couns: Lucie Lalonde

D-U-N-S 07-918-2139
CASCADES TISSUE GROUP - NEW YORK INC
(*Suby of* CASCADES INC)
148 Hudson River Rd, Wynantskill, NY 12198
Tel (518) 238-1900 *Founded/Ownrshp* 2002
Sales 120.0MM *EMP* 175
SIC 2679 Pressed fiber & molded pulp products except food products
**Ch Bd:* Alaine Lemaire
**Pr:* Jean Jobin
**VP:* Allan Hogg

D-U-N-S 05-750-5877
CASCADIA BEHAVIORAL HEALTHCARE INC
847 Ne 19th Ave Ste 100, Portland, OR 97232-2684
Tel (503) 238-0769 *Founded/Ownrshp* 1995
Sales 57.5MM *EMP* 1,000
Accts Moss-Adams Llp Portland Oreg
SIC 8322 8093 8063 8361 Individual & family services; Specialty outpatient clinics; Psychiatric hospitals; Residential care
Pr: Derald Walker PHD
**COO:* Maggie Bennington-Davis
**CFO:* Beth Barker
**VP:* Jim Hlava
Dir IT: Frank Villa
Pr Dir: Samantha Ridderbusch

D-U-N-S 78-098-5169
CASE CONSTRUCTION EQUIPMENT INC
(*Suby of* C N H) ★
700 State St, Racine, WI 53404-3343
Tel (262) 636-6011 *Founded/Ownrshp* 1999
Sales NA *EMP* 8,000
SIC 6159 3531 3523 Agricultural loan companies; Construction machinery; Farm machinery & equipment
Pr: Harold Boyanovsky
**Ch Bd:* Sergio Marchionne
**Pr:* Mario Ferla
**Pr:* Marco Mazzu
Netwrk Mgr: Mark Yurich
Mtls Mgr: John Hall
Manager: Joel Flores
Manager: Trent Hardy
Manager: Zach Hetterick
Manager: Eric Thomas
Sls Mgr: Dennis Sharp

D-U-N-S 83-783-2492
CASE FARMS LLC
CASE FOODS
385 Pilch Rd, Troutman, NC 28166-8782
Tel (704) 528-4501 *Founded/Ownrshp* 1995
Sales 295.1MM[E] *EMP* 825
SIC 2015 8731 Poultry slaughtering & processing; Commercial physical research
CFO: Michael Popowycz
Treas: Rob Johnson
VP: Greg Whisenant
Plnt Mgr: Jason Arnold

D-U-N-S 80-208-8922 IMP/EXP
CASE FARMS PROCESSING INC
(*Suby of* CASE FOODS INC) ★
385 Pilch Rd, Troutman, NC 28166-8782
Tel (704) 528-4501 *Founded/Ownrshp* 1994
Sales 228.8MM[E] *EMP* 2,747
SIC 2015 Poultry slaughtering & processing
Pr: Thomas R Shelton
**COO:* Kevin Phillips
**CFO:* Michael Popowycz
Dir IT: Greg Whisenant

CASE FOODS
See CASE FARMS LLC

D-U-N-S 18-335-8647 EXP
CASE FOODS INC
385 Pilch Rd, Troutman, NC 28166-8782
Tel (704) 528-4501 *Founded/Ownrshp* 1986
Sales 413.7MM[E] *EMP* 6,253
SIC 2015 Poultry, processed
Pr: Thomas Shelton
Pr: David Van Hoose

D-U-N-S 82-945-3992 IMP
CASE FOUNDATION CO
(*Suby of* KELLER FOUNDATIONS LLC) ★
1325 Lake St, Roselle, IL 60172-3300
Tel (630) 529-2911 *Founded/Ownrshp* 1994
Sales 149.7MM *EMP* 220
Accts Kpmg Llp Baltimore Md
SIC 1629 Caisson drilling
Pr: Daniel Bien
**CFO:* Patrick O'Neill
Top Exec: Roy Friedlander
Ex VP: Deana Frey
**Sr VP:* Jim Cahill
**VP:* Matt Klanica
VP: William Lederer
VP: Eric J Risberg
MIS Dir: Lori Ackerman
Sys Mgr: Timothy Carstens

D-U-N-S 82-989-3358 IMP
CASE NEW HOLLAND INDUSTRIAL INC
C N H
(*Suby of* CNH INDUSTRIAL N.V.)
700 State St, Racine, WI 53404-3343
Tel (262) 636-6011 *Founded/Ownrshp* 1999
Sales 3.8MMM[E] *EMP* 8,000
SIC 3523 3531 Farm machinery & equipment; Construction machinery
CEO: Sergio Marchionne

D-U-N-S 00-892-1611 EXP
CASE PAPER CO INC
500 Mamaroneck Ave Fl 2, Harrison, NY 10528-1600
Tel (914) 899-3500 *Founded/Ownrshp* 1943
Sales 473.3MM[E] *EMP* 250
SIC 5111 Printing paper
Pr: Robin Schaffer
CFO: Alan Hochstadt
Sales Exec: Eric Baacke
Sales Exec: Louis Bernstein
Sales Exec: Jean Whitsett
Mktg Dir: Mark Rubenstein

D-U-N-S 07-775-8407 IMP
CASE WESTERN RESERVE UNIVERSITY
10900 Euclid Ave, Cleveland, OH 44106-4901
Tel (216) 368-2000 *Founded/Ownrshp* 1967
Sales 926.2MM *EMP* 5,500
Accts Pricewaterhousecoopers Llp Cl
SIC 8221 University
Pr: Barbara R Snyder
COO: Damian Dwan
COO: Marlene Gambatese
CFO: Sharon McGowan
**CFO:* Hossein Sadid
CFO: John F Sideras
Treas: Robert C Brown
Trst: Caroline Kovac
Trst: George L Majoros
Chf Inves: Sally J Staley
Assoc VP: Larry Gibson
Assoc VP: Mark Henderson
Ex VP: Randy Harmatz
Ex VP: Elizabeth Novak
Ex VP: Steven Standley
Sr VP: Mike Szubski
Sr VP: John Wheeler
VP: Christine Ash
VP: James L Bildner
VP: Richard Bischoff
VP: John Campi

D-U-N-S 36-078-6631
CASEDHOLE SOLUTIONS INC
1720 N Airport Rd, Weatherford, OK 73096-3321
Tel (580) 772-8900 *Founded/Ownrshp* 2012
Sales 164.4MM[E] *EMP* 115
SIC 1389

D-U-N-S 06-053-9780
■ CASELLA WASTE MANAGEMENT INC (DE)
(*Suby of* CASELLA WASTE SYSTEMS INC) ★
25 Green Hill Ln, Rutland, VT 05701-3854
Tel (802) 775-0325 *Founded/Ownrshp* 1975
Sales 195.5MM[E] *EMP* 680
SIC 4953 4212 Rubbish collection & disposal; Liquid waste, collection & disposal; Recycling, waste materials; Local trucking, without storage
CEO: John W Casella
Pr: Douglas Casella

D-U-N-S 94-913-9281
▲ CASELLA WASTE SYSTEMS INC
25 Green Hill Ln, Rutland, VT 05701-3804
Tel (802) 775-0325 *Founded/Ownrshp* 1975
Sales 546.5MM *EMP* 1,900
Tkr Sym CWST *Exch* NGS
SIC 4953 Garbage: collecting, destroying & processing; Recycling, waste materials
Ch Bd: John W Casella
Pr: Edwin D Johnson
CFO: Edmond R Coletta
Sr VP: David L Schmitt
Board of Directors: Michael T Burke, James F Callahan Jr, Douglas R Casella, Emily Nagle Green, William P Hulligan, James E O'connor, James C Pappas, Gregory B Peters, Joseph G Doody Brett W Fra

D-U-N-S 00-698-9091
CASEPICK SYSTEMS LLC
200 Research Dr, Wilmington, MA 01887-4442
Tel (978) 284-2800 *Founded/Ownrshp* 2007
Sales 3.5MMM *EMP* 8
SIC 3549 Assembly machines, including robotic
Snr Sftwr: Marty Friedman

CASEY FAMILY SERVICES
See ANNIE E CASEY FOUNDATION INC

D-U-N-S 07-592-0348
CASEY INDUSTRIAL INC
1400 W 122nd Ave Ste 200, Westminster, CO 80234-3440
Tel (541) 926-8641 *Founded/Ownrshp* 1998
Sales 396.0MM[E] *EMP* 600
SIC 1541 8741 Industrial buildings, new construction; Construction management
VP: Kellen Walters
COO: Stephen Brague
**CFO:* Dave Albion
CFO: Jim McHose
Ofcr: Jason Sipes
**VP:* Troy Jones
**VP:* Jim Koontz
VP: Dave Leblanc
Dir Bus: Todd Lueck
CTO: Larry Williams
Sfty Mgr: Christina Mitchell

D-U-N-S 02-201-0664
▲ CASEYS GENERAL STORES INC
1 Se Convenience Blvd, Ankeny, IA 50021-9437
Tel (515) 965-6100 *Founded/Ownrshp* 1959
Sales 7.1MMM *EMP* 31,766
Tkr Sym CASY *Exch* NGS
SIC 5411 5541 Grocery stores; Convenience stores, chain; Gasoline service stations
Ch Bd: Robert J Myers
Pr: Terry W Handley
CFO: William J Walljasper
Sr VP: Sam J Billmeyer
Sr VP: Julia L Jackowski
Sr VP: John C Soupene
Site Mgr: Michelle Singleton
VP Mktg: Michael R Richardson

D-U-N-S 83-952-3636
■ CASEYS MARKETING CO
(*Suby of* CASEYS GENERAL STORES INC) ★
1 Se Convenience Blvd, Ankeny, IA 50021-9437
Tel (515) 965-6100 *Founded/Ownrshp* 1995
Sales 667.1MM[E] *EMP* 5,769[E]
SIC 5411 5172 5141 5812 Convenience stores, chain; Gasoline; Groceries, general line; Pizza restaurants
CEO: Robert J Myers
**Pr:* Michael R Richardson
**Treas:* Russell D Sukut
**Sec:* Eli Wirtz
**VP:* Cleo Kuhns

D-U-N-S 60-386-9038
■ CASEYS RETAIL CO
(*Suby of* CASEYS GENERAL STORES INC) ★
1 Se Convenience Blvd, Ankeny, IA 50021-9437
Tel (515) 965-6100 *Founded/Ownrshp* 2004
Sales 384.1MM[E] *EMP* 6,419[E]
SIC 5411 Grocery stores
CEO: Ronald Lamb

CASH AMERICA
See FRONTIER MERGER SUB LLC

D-U-N-S 04-330-5796
■ CASH AMERICA FINANCIAL SERVICES INC
(*Suby of* CASH AMERICA) ★
1600 W 7th St, Fort Worth, TX 76102-2599
Tel (817) 335-1100 *Founded/Ownrshp* 1983
Sales 89.7MM[E] *EMP* 886
Accts Pricewaterhousecoopers Llp Fo
SIC 5932 Used merchandise stores
Pr: Daniel R Feehan
**Ch:* Jack R Daugherty
Ex VP: Bill Horne
VP: Brad Lamar
VP: Guhan Raghu
VP: Timothy Rees
Exec: Gino Belmontes
Exec: Bellorin Carlos
Exec: Louis Costa
Exec: Randall Donithan
Exec: Chris Garrett
Exec: Darrell Harper
Exec: Russ Herzog
Exec: Aaron Hoffstadter
Exec: Janine Hunt
Exec: Dustin Long
Exec: Eric Molina
Exec: Eugene Pope
Exec: Mario Sanchez
Exec: David Winn
Exec: Jose Zorrilla

D-U-N-S 08-016-6987
CASH AMERICA INVESTMENTS INC
1600 W 7th St, Fort Worth, TX 76102-2599
Tel (817) 335-1100 *Founded/Ownrshp* 1989
Sales 24.9MM[E] *EMP* 5,982
SIC 5932 6099 Pawnshop; Check cashing agencies
CEO: Jack Daugherty

CASH CENTRAL
See DIRECT FINANCIAL SOLUTIONS LLC

CASH IT HERE
See CONTINENTAL CURRENCY SERVICES INC

CASH REGISTER
See DIRECT GENERAL INSURANCE CO

CASH STORE
See COTTONWOOD FINANCIAL ADMINISTRATIVE SERVICES LLC

D-U-N-S 03-505-3677
CASH-WA DISTRIBUTING CO OF KEARNEY INC
401 W 4th St, Kearney, NE 68845-7825
Tel (308) 237-3151 *Founded/Ownrshp* 1934, 1967
Sales 395.3MM *EMP* 539
SIC 5149 5046 5194 Groceries & related products; Commercial equipment; Tobacco & tobacco products
Pr: Thomas J Henning
**CFO:* Edward Bloomfield
**Treas:* Greg L Henning
CIO: Riessland Judy
Sftwr Eng: Scott Willson
Opers Mgr: Jim Schaefer
Sales Exec: Sara Grabowski
Manager: John Moritz
Manager: Joel Wilcher
Sales Asso: Sean Caligiuri

D-U-N-S 78-673-2714
CASHCALL INC
1 City Blvd W Ste 102, Orange, CA 92868-3621
Tel (949) 752-4600 *Founded/Ownrshp* 2000
Sales NA *EMP* 1,400
SIC 6141 Personal finance licensed loan companies, small
CEO: John Paul Reddam
Chf Mktg O: Ethan Taub
Dir IT: Michelle Turcios
Counsel: Alan Lindeke

CASHIERS OFFICE
See UNIVERSITY OF HAWAII SYSTEMS

D-U-N-S 61-646-6731
CASHMAN DREDGING AND MARINE CONTRACTING CO LLC
(*Suby of* JAY CASHMAN INC) ★
549 South St, Quincy, MA 02169-7318
Tel (617) 890-0600 *Founded/Ownrshp* 2003
Sales 90.0MM *EMP* 200
SIC 1629 Marine construction
CEO: Dale Pyatt
**VP:* Bill Hussin

D-U-N-S 00-959-5984 IMP/EXP
CASHMAN EQUIPMENT CO
CATERPILLAR AUTHORIZED DEALER
3300 Saint Rose Pkwy, Henderson, NV 89052-3985
Tel (702) 649-8777 *Founded/Ownrshp* 1931
Sales 382.4MM[E] *EMP* 730
SIC 5084 5063 7353 7699 Industrial machinery & equipment; Generators; Heavy construction equipment rental; Construction equipment repair
Pr: Michael C Pack
Genl Mgr: Ana L Chavez
Genl Mgr: Dave Griffin
Genl Mgr: Ana Mendez
Genl Mgr: Bruce Zupancic
Dir IT: Joel Larson
IT Man: Robert Schmiesing
Sls Mgr: Ed Hintz
Sls Mgr: Joni Tally
Sales Asso: Frank Larsen

CASINO APACHE TRAVEL CENTER
See INN OF MOUNTAIN GODS RESORT AND CASINO

CASINO AZTAR
See AZTAR INDIANA GAMING CO LLC

D-U-N-S 80-010-0802
CASINO QUEEN INC
CROWN HOTEL
200 Front St, East Saint Louis, IL 62201-1222
Tel (618) 874-5000 *Founded/Ownrshp* 1991
Sales 64.1MM[E] *EMP* 1,250[E]
SIC 7999 7011 Gambling establishment; Casino hotel
Pr: Jeffrey K Watson
**CFO:* Bob Barrows

D-U-N-S 05-185-7019 IMP/EXP
CASIO AMERICA INC
(*Suby of* CASIO HOLDINGS INC) ★
570 Mount Pleasant Ave, Dover, NJ 07801-1631
Tel (973) 361-5400 *Founded/Ownrshp* 1957
Sales 88.9MM[E] *EMP* 250
SIC 5044 5045 5094 5099 Accounting machines, excluding machine program readable type; Cash registers; Computers; Watches & parts; Musical instruments parts & accessories
CEO: Yuji Sasajina
Ex VP: John Homlish
VP: Kazuhiro Kashio
**Genl Mgr:* Robert Shapiro
Mktg Dir: Kazuo Murakami
Sls Mgr: Margaret Frei
Sales Asso: Jack White

D-U-N-S 08-114-0118 IMP/EXP
CASIO HOLDINGS INC
(*Suby of* CASIO COMPUTER CO., LTD.)
570 Mount Pleasant Ave, Dover, NJ 07801-1631
Tel (973) 361-5400 *Founded/Ownrshp* 1999
Sales 88.9MM[E] *EMP* 250
SIC 5044 Accounting machines, excluding machine program readable type; Cash registers
Ch Bd: Hideaki Terada
Web Dev: Yefim Furlender

D-U-N-S 07-336-0323
CASS CONSTRUCTION INC
1100 Wagner Dr, El Cajon, CA 92020-3047
Tel (619) 590-0929 *Founded/Ownrshp* 1974
Sales 109.2MM[E] *EMP* 350[E]
SIC 1623 1611 Underground utilities contractor; Grading
Ch Bd: Jimmie Nelson
**Pr:* Kyle P Nelson
VP: Jerry Gaeir
**VP:* Laura Nelson
VP: Angelina Parravano

D-U-N-S 00-699-8108
CASS COUNTY ELECTRIC COOP INC
C C E C
3312 42nd St S Ste 200, Fargo, ND 58104-7084
Tel (701) 356-4400 *Founded/Ownrshp* 1937
Sales 113.4MM *EMP* 95
Accts Eide Bailly Llp Fargo Nd
SIC 4911 Distribution, electric power
CEO: Scott Handy
**CFO:* Chad Sapa
Sr VP: Kevin Bunn
**Sr VP:* Brad Schmidt
VP: Marshal Albright
Ex Dir: Tim Sanden

D-U-N-S 11-903-8354
▲ CASS INFORMATION SYSTEMS INC
12444 Powerscort Dr # 550, Saint Louis, MO 63131-3612
Tel (314) 506-5500 *Founded/Ownrshp* 1982
Sales 122.0MM *EMP* 989[E]
Tkr Sym CASS *Exch* NGS
SIC 7389 7374 6029 Personal service agents, brokers & bureaus; Data processing & preparation; Computer processing services; Service bureau, computer; Commercial banks
Ch Bd: Eric H Brunngraber
Pr: Mark A Campbell
Pr: Gary B Langfitt
Pr: Robert J Mathias
CFO: P Stephen Appelbaum
Ofcr: Ray McCormick
VP: Terrence Cowee
S&M/VP: Gary Nutter
Board of Directors: Ralph W Clermont, Lawrence A Collett, Robert A Ebel, Benjamin F Edwards IV, James J Lindemann, Randall L Schilling, Franklin D Wicks Jr

D-U-N-S 00-389-6024
CASSENS TRANSPORT CO (IL)
(*Suby of* CASSENS CORP.)
145 N Kansas St, Edwardsville, IL 62025-1770
Tel (618) 656-3006 *Founded/Ownrshp* 1917, 1981
Sales 102.2MM[E] *EMP* 1,212

SIC 4213 4231

D-U-N-S 07-711-1227
CASSIDY TURLEY COMMERCIAL REAL ESTATE SERVICES INC
COLLIERS TURLEY MARTIN TUCKER
(*Suby of* CUSHMAN & WAKEFIELD INC) ★
7700 Forsyth Blvd Ste 900, Saint Louis, MO 63105-1826
Tel (314) 862-7100 *Founded/Ownrshp* 2009
Sales 195.5MM^E *EMP* 2,000
SIC 6531 Real estate agents & managers; Real estate managers; Appraiser, real estate; Real estate brokers & agents
Ch: Walter D Pinkard Jr
V Ch: Clarence Turley
**Pr:* Michael Kamm
Pr: Diane Paddison
**CEO:* Joseph Stettinius Jr
**COO:* Shelley Phibbons-Radomski
**CFO:* John J Fleury
CFO: Bill Florent
**Ex VP:* Kevin Hughes
Ex VP: Pat Lindley
**Ex VP:* Dean Mueller
Sr VP: Hegger Joseph
VP: Nick Barela
VP: Peter Buckey
VP: Julie Cubbage
VP: Dawn Grant
VP: Karen McShea
VP: Tim Monger
VP: Brent Morris
VP: Jack Pence
VP: Duane Poppe

D-U-N-S 96-333-6669
CASSIDY TURLEY INC
DTZ
2101 L St Nw Ste 700, Washington, DC 20037-1556
Tel (202) 463-2100 *Founded/Ownrshp* 2009
Sales 315.9MM^E *EMP* 3,809
SIC 6531

D-U-N-S 11-868-3820
CASSLING DIAGNOSTIC IMAGING INC
13808 F St, Omaha, NE 68137-1102
Tel (402) 334-5000 *Founded/Ownrshp* 1984
Sales 85.8MM^E *EMP* 15
SIC 5047 7699 X-ray machines & tubes; X-ray film & supplies; X-ray equipment repair; Harness repair shop
Pr: Mike Cassling
**CFO:* Steve Chambers
VP: Kyle Salem
CIO: Layne Oberto
Dir IT: Roger Hill
Sfty Mgr: Brian Eardman
Sls Dir: Jeff Chamer
Sls Dir: Jackie Foster
Sls Mgr: Chuck Bertelson
Snr PM: Dan Olson

CASTCAL IDNTIFICATION CONCEPTS
See COMPUTYPE INC

D-U-N-S 01-761-9487
CASTELLINI CO LLC
(*Suby of* CASTELLINI HOLDING CO LLC) ★
2 Plum St, Highland Heights, KY 41076-9120
Tel (800) 233-8560 *Founded/Ownrshp* 1969
Sales 213.8MM *EMP* 375
SIC 5148 4212 4213 Fruits, fresh; Vegetables, fresh; Local trucking, without storage; Contract haulers
CIO: Dan Taylor
IT Man: Melissa Brooks
Opers Mgr: Tim Bolender

D-U-N-S 07-827-6195
CASTELLINI HOLDING CO LLC
2 Plum St, Highland Heights, KY 41076-9120
Tel (859) 442-4673 *Founded/Ownrshp* 2002
Sales 606.3MM^E *EMP* 1,800
SIC 5148 Fruits, fresh; Vegetables, fresh

D-U-N-S 05-236-1588
CASTLE & COOKE MORTGAGE LLC
13751 S Wadsworth Park Dr # 101, Draper, UT 84020-2103
Tel (866) 461-7101 *Founded/Ownrshp* 2005
Sales NA *EMP* 250
SIC 6162 Mortgage bankers & correspondents
Pr: Adam Thorpe
COO: Richard H Kline
Ofcr: Damian Alexander
Ofcr: Matthias Allred
Ofcr: Tara Azaroff
Ofcr: Anne Bell
Ofcr: Linda Bertuzzi
Ofcr: Tyree Bingham
Ofcr: Colleen Bruening
Ofcr: Marcus Burton
Ofcr: Samuel Bushman
Ofcr: Val Carey
Ofcr: Jennifer Caro
Ofcr: Brian Caruso
Ofcr: Amar Chadha
Ofcr: Mike Christensen
Ofcr: Kirsten Coffelt
Ofcr: Debi Copfer
Ofcr: Steve Copus
Ofcr: Michael Cornachio
Ofcr: Julie Crow

CASTLE GROUP
See CASTLE MANAGEMENT INC

D-U-N-S 17-956-3424 IMP
CASTLE HARLAN PARTNERS III LP
MARIE CALLENDER'S PIE SHOPS
(*Suby of* HARLAN CASTLE INC) ★
150 E 58th St Fl 38, New York, NY 10155-0017
Tel (212) 644-8600 *Founded/Ownrshp* 1997
Sales 194.3MM^E *EMP* 13,450
SIC 5812 6282 6211 8732 Restaurant, family: chain; Investment advice; Security brokers & dealers; Commercial nonphysical research
Ch: John K Castle
**Pr:* Leonard M Harlan
**VP:* Thomas M Hickey
**VP:* John E Morningstar
**VP:* Sylvia F Rosen
Board of Directors: David B Pittaway

D-U-N-S 78-243-8829
CASTLE HARLAN PARTNERS IV LP
(*Suby of* HARLAN CASTLE INC) ★
150 E 58th St Fl 38, New York, NY 10155-0017
Tel (212) 644-8600 *Founded/Ownrshp* 2002
Sales 5.5MMM^E *EMP* 13,450
SIC 6799 6719 Venture capital companies; Personal holding companies, except banks
CEO: John K Castle
Pt: Leonard M Harlan

D-U-N-S 00-822-7571
CASTLE MANAGEMENT INC (FL)
CASTLE GROUP
12270 Sw 3rd St Ste 200, Plantation, FL 33325-2811
Tel (800) 337-5850 *Founded/Ownrshp* 1995
Sales 89.1MM^E *EMP* 450
SIC 6512 Nonresidential building operators
Pr: Patrick J Donnelly
**CFO:* Craig Vaughan
**VP:* Robert Donnelly
Pr Dir: Cathy Donnelly

D-U-N-S 07-251-9762
CASTLE MEDICAL CENTER
640 Ulukahiki St, Kailua, HI 96734-4498
Tel (808) 263-5500 *Founded/Ownrshp* 1963
Sales 157.2MM *EMP* 1,050
SIC 8062 Hospital, affiliated with AMA residency
Pr: Kevin Robert
CFO: Wendy Barker
VP: Alan Hs Cheung
VP: Travis Clegg
VP: Laura Westphal
Dir Lab: Thelma Morta
Dir Lab: Margaret Wasielewski
Off Mgr: Norma Livingston
CTO: Brian Ruthe
Mtls Mgr: Daryl Carter
Obsttrcn: Kirk Hirata

D-U-N-S 04-856-3483
CASTLE PARTNERS LLC
6787 Millstone St, Highlands Ranch, CO 80130-3843
Tel (303) 884-1157 *Founded/Ownrshp* 2010
Sales 100.0MM *EMP* 90
SIC 5172 5013 Gases, liquefied petroleum (propane); Pumps, oil & gas

D-U-N-S 13-062-3510
CASTLES OF WORLD INC
AFFORDABLETOURS.COM
11150 Cash Rd, Stafford, TX 77477-4313
Tel (281) 269-2600 *Founded/Ownrshp* 2002
Sales 86.0MM *EMP* 80
SIC 4724 Travel agencies
Co-Pr: Jaime Fernandez
Co-Pr: Rodrigo Fernandez
Sr VP: Quinton Harp
VP: Lucy Fernandez
Ql Cn Mgr: Lesa Caden
Mktg Mgr: George Pitiranggon

D-U-N-S 79-137-8800
CASTLETON COMMODITIES INTERNATIONAL LLC
2200 Atlantic St Ste 800, Stamford, CT 06902-6834
Tel (203) 564-8100 *Founded/Ownrshp* 2012
Sales 533.3MM^E *EMP* 300
SIC 4923 Gas transmission & distribution
Pr: William C Reed II
Pr: Craig Jarchow
Pr: Victoria Pospisil
Pr: Dean Wang
COO: Magesh Nair
CFO: Dan Hines
Ex VP: Ram P Challa
Ex VP: Michael G Dowling
Ex VP: Michael Goldstein
Ex VP: David Wallace
Sr VP: Joe Rothbauer
VP: Alex Antestenis
VP: Peter Banziger
VP: Esther Chan
VP: Lauren Haymond
VP: David Lloyd
VP: Keisa McPartland
VP: Victoria Powers
VP: Jay Reynolds
VP: Michael Rinaldi
VP: Alexandr Savchenko

D-U-N-S 79-410-3445
CASTLETON COMMODITIES TRADING GP LLC
(*Suby of* CASTLETON COMMODITIES INTERNATIONAL LLC) ★
2200 Atlantic St Ste 800, Stamford, CT 06902-6834
Tel (203) 564-8100 *Founded/Ownrshp* 2001
Sales 97.2MM^E *EMP* 300^E
SIC 4923 Gas transmission & distribution
Pr: William C Reed II
VP: Scott Harwood

D-U-N-S 60-677-5682
CASUAL RESTAURANT CONCEPTS INC
APPLEBEE'S
205 S Hoover Blvd Ste 402, Tampa, FL 33609-3591
Tel (813) 286-2006 *Founded/Ownrshp* 1989
Sales 100.3MM^E *EMP* 1,161
SIC 5813 5812

D-U-N-S 07-850-6886
■ **CAT LOGISTICS INC**
CLI
(*Suby of* CATERPILLAR INC) ★
500 N Morton Ave, Morton, IL 61550-1527
Tel (309) 675-1000 *Founded/Ownrshp* 2011
Sales 110.8MM^E *EMP* 2,075^E
SIC 4225 5045 4213 General warehousing & storage; Computers, peripherals & software; Computer software; Trucking, except local
Pr: Stephen P Larson
**CFO:* Phillip A Weingart
**Treas:* Robin D Beran
**Treas:* Bonnie J Lemke
VP: Richard R Burritt
VP: Deborah S Heidewald
VP: Barbara J Hodel
VP: Edwin E O'Neil Jr
**VP:* Laurence S Wilken

D-U-N-S 82-823-7789
▲ **CATALENT INC**
14 Schoolhouse Rd, Somerset, NJ 08873-1213
Tel (732) 537-6200 *Founded/Ownrshp* 2007
Sales 1.8MMM *EMP* 8,700^E
Tkr Sym CTLT *Exch* NYS
SIC 2834 Pharmaceutical preparations
Pr: John R Chiminski
**Ch Bd:* Chinh E Chu
Pr: Aristippos Gennadios
Pr: Scott Houlton
Pr: Barry Littlejohns
CFO: Matthew Walsh
Sr VP: William Downie
Sr VP: Steven Fasman
Sr VP: Sharon Johnson
Sr VP: Stephen Leonard
Sr VP: Lance Miyamoto
Board of Directors: Melvin D Booth, J Martin Carroll, Rolf Classon, Gregory T Lucier, E Bruce McEvoy, Donald E Morel Jr, James Quella, Jack Stahl

D-U-N-S 79-643-6181 IMP/EXP
■ **CATALENT PHARMA SOLUTIONS INC**
(*Suby of* CATALENT INC) ★
14 Schoolhouse Rd, Somerset, NJ 08873-1213
Tel (732) 537-6200 *Founded/Ownrshp* 2007
Sales 1.8MMM *EMP* 8,300
SIC 2834 3841 Pharmaceutical preparations; Medical instruments & equipment, blood & bone work
Pr: John R Chiminski
**COO:* Dan Novin
**CFO:* Matthew Walsh
**Sr VP:* Michael Del Priore
Sr VP: Christine Dolan
**Sr VP:* Stephen Leonard
Sr VP: Alessandro Maselli
**Sr VP:* Kurt Nielsen
VP: Jay Feldman
VP: Michael Jenkins
VP: Sally Langa
VP: Julien Meissonnier
VP: Joel Tobin
Exec: Steve Mezzano
Exec: Eric Norman
Board of Directors: Michael Dal Bello, Melvin D Booth, Paul Clark, Arthur J Higgins, Bruce McEvoy, James Quella

D-U-N-S 04-391-1403 IMP
■ **CATALENT PHARMA SOLUTIONS LLC**
(*Suby of* CATALENT PHARMA SOLUTIONS INC) ★
2210 Lake Shore Dr, Woodstock, IL 60098-6919
Tel (815) 338-9500 *Founded/Ownrshp* 2009
Sales 184.0MM *EMP* 500
SIC 5084 Packaging machinery & equipment
CEO: John Chiminski
**CFO:* Matthew Walsh
**Sr VP:* Harry Weininger
**CIO:* Roy Satchell

D-U-N-S 11-281-7440
CATALINA MARKETING CORP
CATALINA MARKETING NETWORK
(*Suby of* CHECKOUT HOLDING CORP) ★
200 Carillon Pkwy, Saint Petersburg, FL 33716-1242
Tel (727) 579-5000 *Founded/Ownrshp* 1992
Sales 269.2MM^E *EMP* 1,225^E
SIC 7319 Coupon distribution
CEO: Greg Delaney
Pr: Dan Colligan
Pr: Mike McClorey
Pr: Renee Selman
CFO: Michael L Barna
Ch: Tommy G Thompson
**Ofcr:* Dak Liyanearachchi
**Ofcr:* Michael Murray
**Ex VP:* Michael Barna
**Ex VP:* Michael Bernhoerster
**Ex VP:* Debbie Booth
Ex VP: Deborah A Booth
**Ex VP:* Andrea Bortner
Ex VP: Andrea R Bortner
**Ex VP:* Aira Parker
Ex VP: Ira H Parker
**Ex VP:* Steve Rubinow
**Ex VP:* Cary P Siegel
Sr VP: Gerry Groe
Sr VP: Stan Maxwell
VP: David Broscow
Board of Directors: Tod Johnson

CATALINA MARKETING NETWORK
See CATALINA MARKETING CORP

CATALINA RESTAURANT COMPANY
See CATALINA RESTAURANT GROUP INC

D-U-N-S 07-528-5262 IMP
CATALINA RESTAURANT GROUP INC
CATALINA RESTAURANT COMPANY
120 Chula Vis, Hollywood Park, TX 78232-2234
Tel (760) 804-5750 *Founded/Ownrshp* 1996, 2015
Sales 127.9MM^E *EMP* 4,000
SIC 5812 Restaurant, family: chain
Pr: Masahiro Kenmotsu
**Ex VP:* Jim Kensinger
Sr VP: Tony Barr
VP: Greg Brenneman
VP: Eliza Henry
VP: Peter Sirkin
Opers Mgr: Susan Sullizan
VP Sls: D Krehbiel
Mktg Dir: Cyndi Darlington
Mktg Dir: Karen Rogers
Sls Dir: Dan Howard

D-U-N-S 07-979-4177
CATALINA SOLAR 2 LLC
15445 Innovation Dr, San Diego, CA 92128-3432
Tel (888) 903-6926 *Founded/Ownrshp* 2011
Sales 255.7MM^E *EMP* 826
SIC 4911 Electric services
Pr: Tristan Grimbert
**VP:* Ryan Pfaff

D-U-N-S 07-937-4787
CATALINA SOLAR LESSEE LLC
(*Suby of* EDF RENEWABLE ENERGY INC) ★
11585 Willow Springs Rd, Rosamond, CA 93560
Tel (888) 903-6926 *Founded/Ownrshp* 2014
Sales 265.9MM^E *EMP* 826
SIC 4911 Electric services
Pr: Tristan Grimbert

D-U-N-S 60-817-0788
CATALYST OILFIELD SERVICES 2016 LLC
(*Suby of* CANADIAN ENERGY SERVICES & TECHNOLOGY CORP)
11999 E Us Highway 158, Gardendale, TX 79758-4341
Tel (432) 563-0727 *Founded/Ownrshp* 2016
Sales 147.3MM^E *EMP* 150^E
SIC 1389 Oil field services
Area Mgr: Wacey Moore
Area Mgr: Richard Urias
Area Mgr: Gary White
Sales Exec: Trey Womack

D-U-N-S 15-083-2574 IMP/EXP
CATALYST PAPER (USA) INC
(*Suby of* CATALYST PAPER CORPORATION)
2200 6th Ave Ste 800, Seattle, WA 98121-1827
Tel (206) 838-2070 *Founded/Ownrshp* 2016
Sales 700.0MM *EMP* 40
SIC 5111 Printing & writing paper
Pr: Matthew Stapleton
**CFO:* Brian Baarda
**Treas:* Pat Sakai
**VP:* James Bayles

D-U-N-S 07-836-9954
CATALYST PAPER HOLDINGS INC
(*Suby of* CATALYST PAPER CORPORATION)
2200 6th Ave Ste 800, Seattle, WA 98121-1827
Tel (604) 247-4018 *Founded/Ownrshp* 1993
Sales 44.5MM^E *EMP* 1,000^E
SIC 6719 Investment holding companies, except banks
Pr: Matthew Stapleton

D-U-N-S 07-977-0030
CATALYST PAPER OPERATIONS INC
(*Suby of* CATALYST PAPER HOLDINGS INC) ★
2200 6th Ave Ste 800, Seattle, WA 98121-1827
Tel (604) 247-4018 *Founded/Ownrshp* 2015
Sales 180.4MM^E *EMP* 1,000^E
SIC 2611 Pulp manufactured from waste or recycled paper
Pr: Matthew Stapleton
Treas: Pat Sakai

D-U-N-S 04-089-2510
■ **CATAMARAN CORP**
OPTUM RX
(*Suby of* PRESCRIPTION SOLUTIONS) ★
1600 Mcconnor Pkwy Fl 1, Schaumburg, IL 60173-6802
Tel (800) 282-3232 *Founded/Ownrshp* 2015
Sales 21.5MMM *EMP* 4,500^E
SIC 8742 Compensation & benefits planning consultant
CEO: Mark A Thierer
Pr: Gregory Kosater
CFO: Michael Shapiro
Chf Cred: Ellen Duffield
Chf Mktg O: Sumit Dutta
Ex VP: Jeffrey Park
Ex VP: John Romza
Ex VP: Joel Saban
Sr VP: Clifford Berman
Sr VP: Barry Davis
Sr VP: Sumit X Dutta
Sr VP: Michael Edwards
Sr VP: Mark Halloran
Sr VP: Kelly Kettlewell
Sr VP: Ellen Nelson
Sr VP: Edward Stubbers
VP: Jim Baker
VP: Donna Campagna
VP: Kirsten Hines
VP: Jon Reid

D-U-N-S 79-983-2761
■ **CATAMARAN HEALTH SOLUTIONS LLC**
(*Suby of* OPTUM RX) ★
800 King Farm Blvd # 300, Rockville, MD 20850-6697
Tel (301) 548-2900 *Founded/Ownrshp* 2012
Sales 156.8MM^E *EMP* 1,429^E
SIC 5912 6411 Drug stores & proprietary stores; Insurance agents, brokers & service
CEO: Mark Thierer
Pr: Babette Edgar
Pr: Richard Keane
CFO: Andrew Brynes
CFO: Jeff Park
Bd of Dir: Steven B Epstein
Ex VP: Rick Bates
Ex VP: Darren Sivertsen
Sr VP: Wayne Dix
Sr VP: Chris Myers
VP: Jack Haggerty

D-U-N-S 78-697-6597
■ **CATAMARAN PBM OF ILLINOIS II INC**
(*Suby of* CATAMARAN HEALTH SOLUTIONS LLC) ★
1417 Lake Cook Rd Ste 100, Deerfield, IL 60015-5238
Tel (847) 374-2640 *Founded/Ownrshp* 2011
Sales 83.8MM^E *EMP* 1,000
SIC 5961 Pharmaceuticals, mail order
Pr: Gregory D Wasson
**CFO:* Bob Zimmerman
**VP:* Jack Cantlin
**VP:* Dennis Merrifield
**VP:* Melissa Sobie
Dir Rx: Elizabeth Young

D-U-N-S 03-668-8943
CATAMOUNT CONSTRUCTORS INC
1527 Cole Blvd Ste 100, Lakewood, CO 80401-3421
Tel (303) 679-0087 *Founded/Ownrshp* 1997
Sales 287.7MM^E *EMP* 142

Accts Eks&H Lllp Denver Colorado
SIC 1542 Commercial & office building, new construction
CEO: Geoffrey G Wormer
**Pr:* Jeff Cochran
**CEO:* Geoff Wormer
COO: Harvey Cochran
CFO: Michael Plungis
**Sec:* Jeffrey Cochran
**Sr VP:* Tom Seaman
VP: Kurt T Kenchel
**VP:* Jeffrey P Sidwell
Dir Bus: Eric Voelker
**Prin:* Jeffrey L Cochran

D-U-N-S 15-229-3614
CATAPULT LEARNING LLC
2 Aquarium Dr Ste 100, Camden, NJ 08103-1085
Tel (856) 831-7909 *Founded/Ownrshp* 2003
Sales 52.0MM[E] *EMP* 4,822
SIC 8299 Educational services
Ch Bd: Stuart Udell
V Ch: William Rhodes
Pr: Marc Hoban
Pr: Steve Quattrociocchi
**Pr:* Andrea Vargas
**CEO:* Jeffrey Cohen
CFO: Sean Creamer
Trst: Irrevocable Idgt
Ofcr: David Bushnell
**Ofcr:* Sharon Haverlak
Sr VP: Kristen E Campbell
VP: Bill Backall
VP: Richard Bavaria
VP: David Compte
VP: Christopher Eden
VP: Eurmon Hervey
VP: Eurmon Hervey Jr Ed D
VP: Leah Mallon
VP: Elizabeth A Menchaca
VP: Andrew Ordover
VP: Earle Pratt

D-U-N-S 95-804-5346
CATAPULT TECHNOLOGY LTD
11 Canal Center Plz Fl 2, Alexandria, VA 22314-1595
Tel (240) 482-2100 *Founded/Ownrshp* 1998
Sales 89.8MM[E] *EMP* 700[E]
SIC 7373 8742 Systems integration services; Management consulting services
CEO: Mark E Hunker
**Pr:* Mark Hunker
**Pr:* Barry Kane
**CFO:* David Thronton
Assoc VP: Jeff McCracken
**Ex VP:* Robert B Smith
Sr VP: Kyle Mulhall
**VP:* Fred Haggard
**VP:* Dave Lyons
**VP:* John Scarcella
**VP:* Diane Whitmoyer

D-U-N-S 07-979-8918
CATAWBA COUNTY SCHOOLS
10 E 25th St, Newton, NC 28658-2763
Tel (828) 464-8333 *Founded/Ownrshp* 2015
Sales 74.4MM[E] *EMP* 2,150[E]
SIC 8211 Public elementary & secondary schools
CEO: Dan Brigman
IT Man: Mitzi Story
Pr Dir: Sally Pitofsky
HC Dir: Michael Ratchford

D-U-N-S 07-450-8557
CATAWBA VALLEY MEDICAL CENTER INC
810 Fairgrove Church Rd, Hickory, NC 28602-9617
Tel (828) 326-3000 *Founded/Ownrshp* 1967
Sales 211.8MM *EMP* 1,450
SIC 8062 General medical & surgical hospitals
Pr: Tony Rose
Chf Rad: Knox Tate
Dir Vol: Betty Long
Assoc VP: Edward Beard Jr
**VP:* David Boone
VP: Guy Guarino
Exec: Elliot Boston
Dir Lab: Ernest Dellinger
VP Admn: Lisa Hamby
Dir IT: Lori Kent
Software D: Michele McGlamery

D-U-N-S 06-233-3984
CATELLI BROS INC
CATELLI BROS VEAL & LAMB PDTS
50 Ferry Ave, Camden, NJ 08103-3006
Tel (856) 869-9293 *Founded/Ownrshp* 1980
Sales 112.1MM[E] *EMP* 350
SIC 5147 Meats & meat products
Pr: Anthony Catelli Jr
**CFO:* Norm Gunn
**Sec:* Antionette Catelli
**VP:* James Catelli
Exec: Therese Wells

CATELLI BROS VEAL & LAMB PDTS
See CATELLI BROS INC

CATEM NORTH AMERICA
See EBERSPAECHER NORTH AMERICA INC

D-U-N-S 60-955-4811
CATERAIR HOLDINGS CORP
(*Suby of* LSG SKY CHEFS USA INC) ★
524 E Lamar Blvd, Arlington, TX 76011-3929
Tel (817) 792-2100 *Founded/Ownrshp* 1996
Sales 69.3MM[E] *EMP* 6,000
SIC 5812 Caterers
CEO: Donald West
Board of Directors: George W Bush, Marc E Leland, Frederic V Malek, R Michael McCullough, John D Miller, Arthur D Miltenberger, Stephen L Norris, Charles O Rossotti

CATERPILLAR
See FOLEY EQUIPMENT CO

CATERPILLAR
See LOUISIANA MACHINERY CO LLC

CATERPILLAR
See WHEELER MACHINERY CO

CATERPILLAR
See WAGNER EQUIPMENT CO

CATERPILLAR AUTHORIZED DEALER
See FOLEY INC

CATERPILLAR AUTHORIZED DEALER
See SOUTHWORTH-MILTON INC

CATERPILLAR AUTHORIZED DEALER
See ALBAN TRACTOR CO INC

CATERPILLAR AUTHORIZED DEALER
See THOMPSON TRACTOR CO INC

CATERPILLAR AUTHORIZED DEALER
See JOHNSON MACHINERY CO

CATERPILLAR AUTHORIZED DEALER
See BLANCHARD MACHINERY CO

CATERPILLAR AUTHORIZED DEALER
See YANCEY BROS CO

CATERPILLAR AUTHORIZED DEALER
See PATTEN INDUSTRIES INC

CATERPILLAR AUTHORIZED DEALER
See ZIEGLER INC

CATERPILLAR AUTHORIZED DEALER
See GREGORY POOLE EQUIPMENT CO

CATERPILLAR AUTHORIZED DEALER
See OHIO MACHINERY CO

CATERPILLAR AUTHORIZED DEALER
See WARREN POWER & MACHINERY INC

CATERPILLAR AUTHORIZED DEALER
See CASHMAN EQUIPMENT CO

CATERPILLAR AUTHORIZED DEALER
See CAROLINA TRACTOR & EQUIPMENT CO INC

CATERPILLAR AUTHORIZED DEALER
See JOHN FABICK TRACTOR CO

CATERPILLAR AUTHORIZED DEALER
See HAWTHORNE MACHINERY CO

CATERPILLAR AUTHORIZED DEALER
See QUINN SHEPHERD MACHINERY

CATERPILLAR AUTHORIZED DEALER
See PUCKETT MACHINERY CO

CATERPILLAR AUTHORIZED DEALER
See QUINN CO

CATERPILLAR AUTHORIZED DEALER
See WARREN POWER & MACHINERY LP

CATERPILLAR AUTHORIZED DEALER
See THOMPSON MACHINERY COMMERCE CORP

CATERPILLAR AUTHORIZED DEALER
See WESTERN STATES EQUIPMENT CO

CATERPILLAR AUTHORIZED DEALER
See PANTROPIC POWER INC

CATERPILLAR AUTHORIZED DEALER
See N C MACHINERY CO

CATERPILLAR AUTHORIZED DEALER
See N C POWER SYSTEMS CO

CATERPILLAR AUTHORIZED DEALER
See TRACTOR & EQUIPMENT CO

CATERPILLAR AUTHORIZED DEALER
See HAWTHORNE PACIFIC CORP

D-U-N-S 07-911-0848 EXP
■ CATERPILLAR BRAZIL LLC
(*Suby of* CATERPILLAR INC) ★
100 Ne Adams St, Peoria, IL 61629-0002
Tel (309) 675-1000 *Founded/Ownrshp* 2006
Sales 261.1MM[E] *EMP* 5,701
SIC 3523 Farm machinery & equipment
Prin: Luiz Carlos Calil

D-U-N-S 04-941-9112 IMP/EXP
■ CATERPILLAR FINANCIAL SERVICES CORP
(*Suby of* CATERPILLAR INC) ★
2120 West End Ave, Nashville, TN 37203-5341
Tel (615) 341-1000 *Founded/Ownrshp* 1981
Sales NA *EMP* 1,767[E]
SIC 6159

D-U-N-S 04-176-6403 IMP/EXP
■ CATERPILLAR GLOBAL MINING AMERICA LLC
D B T
(*Suby of* CATERPILLAR GLOBAL MINING LLC) ★
2045 W Pike St, Houston, PA 15342-1000
Tel (724) 743-1200 *Founded/Ownrshp* 1995
Sales 273.3MM[E] *EMP* 909
SIC 3532 7629 Mining machinery; Electrical repair shops
Pr: William Tate
VP Prd: Jim Johnston

D-U-N-S 00-607-6129 IMP/EXP
■ CATERPILLAR GLOBAL MINING LLC
(*Suby of* CATERPILLAR INC) ★
1100 Milwaukee Ave, South Milwaukee, WI 53172-2013
Tel (414) 762-0376 *Founded/Ownrshp* 1880, 2011
Sales 2.7MMM[E] *EMP* 9,800
SIC 3531 3532 3599 Draglines, powered; Shovel loaders; Drills, bits & similar equipment; Drills & drilling equipment, mining (except oil & gas); Machine shop, jobbing & repair
Pr: Christopher C Curfman
**CFO:* Julie A Lagacy
Ofcr: Jim Nickolas
Sr VP: Marc L Staff
Prgrm Mgr: Joshua Sprague
MIS Dir: Richard Rohlinger
Dir IT: Mark Severns
Sfty Mgr: Marita Stannis

Ql Cn Mgr: Edward Wasrud
Sls Mgr: William Barkley

D-U-N-S 00-507-0479 IMP/EXP
▲ CATERPILLAR INC
100 Ne Adams St, Peoria, IL 61629-0002
Tel (309) 675-1000 *Founded/Ownrshp* 1925
Sales 47.0MMM *EMP* 105,700
Tkr Sym CAT *Exch* NYS
SIC 3531 3519 3511 6531 6321 6331 Construction machinery; Engines, diesel & semi-diesel or dual-fuel; Gasoline engines; Gas turbine generator set units, complete; Hydraulic turbine generator set units, complete; Fiduciary, real estate; Accident insurance carriers; Fire, marine & casualty insurance: stock
Ch Bd: Douglas R Oberhelman
Pr: Robert B Charter
Pr: Bradley M Halverson
Pr: Denise C Johnson
Pr: Thomas A Pellette
Pr: Edward J Rapp
Pr: D James Umpleby III
Ofcr: James B Buda
Sr VP: David P Bozeman
VP: Thomas J Bluth
VP: Gwenne A Henricks
Board of Directors: Susan C Schwab, David L Calhoun, Miles D White, Daniel M Dickinson, Juan Gallardo, Jesse J Greene Jr, Jon M Huntsman Jr, Dennis A Muilenburg, William A Osborn, Debra L Reed, Edward B Rust Jr

D-U-N-S 96-895-3948
■ CATERPILLAR LOGISTICS INC
(*Suby of* CATERPILLAR INC) ★
500 N Morton Ave, Morton, IL 61550-1575
Tel (309) 266-3591 *Founded/Ownrshp* 2011
Sales 91.1MM[E] *EMP* 3,000
SIC 4225 General warehousing & storage
Pr: Stephen P Larson
Genl Couns: Wes Blumenshine

D-U-N-S 00-621-0009 IMP/EXP
■ CATERPILLAR PAVING PRODUCTS INC
(*Suby of* CATERPILLAR INC) ★
9401 85th Ave N, Minneapolis, MN 55445-2199
Tel (763) 425-4100 *Founded/Ownrshp* 1985
Sales 98.7MM[E] *EMP* 625
SIC 3531 Construction machinery; Bituminous, cement & concrete related products & equipment; Scrapers, graders, rollers & similar equipment; Crushers, grinders & similar equipment
Pr: James Mc Reynolds
**Treas:* Steve Lehnhausen
Opers Mgr: Paul Malnati

D-U-N-S 12-028-6633 IMP/EXP
■ CATERPILLAR S A R L LLC
(*Suby of* CATERPILLAR INC) ★
100 Ne Adams St, Peoria, IL 61629-0002
Tel (309) 675-1000 *Founded/Ownrshp* 1960
Sales 196.5MM[E] *EMP* 450
SIC 5082 General construction machinery & equipment
CEO: Jim Owens
**Pr:* Stuart Levenick
**Pr:* Douglas Oberhelman
**Pr:* Gerard Vittecoq
**Pr:* Steve Wunning

D-U-N-S 00-715-8827 IMP
■ CATERPILLAR WORK TOOLS INC
(*Suby of* CATERPILLAR INC) ★
400 Work Tool Rd, Wamego, KS 66547-1299
Tel (904) 786-8700 *Founded/Ownrshp* 1990
Sales 85.2MM[E] *EMP* 335
SIC 3531 Construction machinery attachments
Pr: Paolo Fellin
**Treas:* Mike Guyer
VP: Robert Hunter
**VP:* Chris Langbardt
**VP:* Warren Wereaui

D-U-N-S 00-965-9483 IMP
■ CATHAY BANK
(*Suby of* CATHAY GENERAL BANCORP) ★
9650 Flair Dr, El Monte, CA 91731-3005
Tel (626) 279-3698 *Founded/Ownrshp* 1990
Sales NA *EMP* 854
SIC 6022 State commercial banks
Ch Bd: Dunson K Cheng
**CFO:* Heng W Chen
Ofcr: Dickson Chan
Ofcr: Steven Chen
Ofcr: Rose Chow
Ofcr: Corey Jenrich
Ofcr: Jason Jiang
**Ex VP:* James R Brewer
Ex VP: Donald Chow
**Ex VP:* Edward K Kim
**Ex VP:* Irwin Wong
Ex VP: Kelly Wu
Sr VP: Olha Holland
Sr VP: Chang Liu
**Sr VP:* Perry P Oei
VP: Jay Cheng
VP: Yenny Chiang
VP: Mary Donnelly
VP: Sandra Kenyon
VP: Aileen Luh
VP: Jinny Moon

D-U-N-S 62-644-5258
▲ CATHAY GENERAL BANCORP
777 N Broadway, Los Angeles, CA 90012-2819
Tel (213) 625-4700 *Founded/Ownrshp* 1990
Sales NA *EMP* 1,074
Accts Kpmg Llp Los Angeles Califor
Tkr Sym CATY *Exch* NGS
SIC 6022 State commercial banks
Pr: Pin Tai
**Ch Bd:* Dunson K Cheng
COO: Irwin Wong
CFO: Heng W Chen
**V Ch Bd:* Anthony M Tang
**V Ch Bd:* Peter Wu
Ofcr: Donald S Chow

VP: Gregory Badura
VP: Andy Hsu
VP: Jennifer Powells
VP: Veronica Tsang

CATHEDRAL SACRED HEART
See ROMAN CATHOLIC DIOCESE OF RICHMOND

D-U-N-S 62-012-4821
CATHEDRAL SQUARE PHARMACY
732 N Jackson St Ste 300, Milwaukee, WI 53202-4605
Tel (414) 277-6510 *Founded/Ownrshp* 2005
Sales 71.8MM[E] *EMP* 5,000
SIC 5912 Drug stores
Pr: Lee Brideau
**CFO:* Charles Dreaher
**VP:* William Hart
Opers Mgr: Tom Kmezich

CATHERINES
See CHARMING SHOPPES INC

D-U-N-S 15-724-0854 IMP/EXP
■ CATHERINES INC
(*Suby of* CATHERINES) ★
3750 State Rd, Bensalem, PA 19020-5903
Tel (215) 245-9100 *Founded/Ownrshp* 2000
Sales 307.5MM[E] *EMP* 2,500
SIC 5632 5621 Apparel accessories; Ready-to-wear apparel, women's
CEO: Bernard J Wein
**Pr:* Diane M Paccione
**CFO:* Ben Bull
**Treas:* David C Forell
**Ex VP:* E Glenn Irelan
**VP:* Dorothy M Dawson
**Prin:* Eric M Specter

D-U-N-S 36-230-4073 IMP
■ CATHERINES STORES CORP
(*Suby of* CATHERINES) ★
3750 State Rd, Bensalem, PA 19020-5903
Tel (551) 777-6700 *Founded/Ownrshp* 2000
Sales 71.8MM[E] *EMP* 2,535
SIC 5632 5621 Apparel accessories; Ready-to-wear apparel, women's
Pr: Diane M Paccione
**CFO:* Ben Bull
**Treas:* Dorothy M Dawson
VP: Lynn Gore
Dir IT: David Hoch
VP Mktg: Barbara Grate
Mktg Mgr: Rachel Perskie

CATHOLIC ARCHDCESE K C IN KANS
See ARCHDIOCESE OF KANSAS CITY IN KANSAS

CATHOLIC ARCHDIOCESE ATLANTA
See CATHOLIC FOUNDATION OF NORTH GEORGIA INC

D-U-N-S 93-878-6282
CATHOLIC ARCHDIOCESE OF MOBILE
356 Government St, Mobile, AL 36602-2316
Tel (251) 434-1585 *Founded/Ownrshp* 1825
Sales 10.5MM[E] *EMP* 1,069
SIC 8661 Religious organizations
**Prin:* Oscar H Lipscomb

D-U-N-S 04-424-9589 IMP
CATHOLIC BISHOP OF CHICAGO
ARCHDIOCESE OF CHICAGO
835 N Rush St, Chicago, IL 60611-2030
Tel (312) 534-8200 *Founded/Ownrshp* 1843
Sales 493.6MM[E] *EMP* 9,604
Accts Deloitte & Touche Llp Chicag
SIC 8661 Catholic Church
Prin: Francis Cardinal George
Comm Dir: Joshua Mercer
**Prin:* Most Rev Blase J Cupich
Genl Couns: Mary Hynes
Snr Mgr: Jim Bannon

CATHOLIC BOARD OF EDUCATION
See CATHOLIC DIOCESE OF CLEVELAND

CATHOLIC CENTER, THE
See CATHOLIC DIOCESE OF KANSAS CITY-ST JOSEPH

CATHOLIC CHARITIES ARCHDOCESE
See CATHOLIC CHARITIES OF ST LOUIS

CATHOLIC CHARITIES BALTIMORE
See ASSOCIATED CATHOLIC CHARITIES INC

D-U-N-S 02-056-5453
CATHOLIC CHARITIES DIOCESE OF BROOKLYN & QUEENS
CRIBBIN HOUSE
191 Joralemon St, Brooklyn, NY 11201-4306
Tel (718) 722-6000 *Founded/Ownrshp* 1899
Sales 146.0MM[E] *EMP* 4,000
Accts Reznick Group Pc Bethesda
SIC 8322 8361 Child related social services; Geriatric social service; Children's home; Home for the aged
CEO: Robert Siebel
**Pr:* Thomas Kevin Murtha
**CFO:* Alan Wolinetz
**Treas:* Joseph F Collins III
**VP:* Janice Aris
**VP:* Patricia Bowles
**VP:* Judith Kleve

D-U-N-S 05-692-6215
CATHOLIC CHARITIES NEIGHBORHOOD SERVICES INC
CATHOLIC CHRTIES BRKLYN QUEENS
191 Joralemon St, Brooklyn, NY 11201-4306
Tel (718) 722-6000 *Founded/Ownrshp* 1947
Sales 130.1MM *EMP* 2,000
Accts Kpmg Llp New York Ny
SIC 8059 8322 Home for the mentally retarded, exc. skilled or intermediate; Individual & family services
CEO: Robert Siebel
**COO:* Alan Wolinetz
**VP:* Kenneth G Haag
**Ex Dir:* Thaddeus Taberski

CATHOLIC CHARITIES NH
See NEW HAMPSHIRE CATHOLIC CHARITIES INC

D-U-N-S 06-995-8528
CATHOLIC CHARITIES OF ARCHDIOCESE OF CHICAGO
CATHOLIC CHARITIES OF CHICAGO
721 N La Salle Dr, Chicago, IL 60654-3751
Tel (312) 655-7000 *Founded/Ownrshp* 1918
Sales 175.7MM *EMP* 3,000^E
Accts Deloitte & Touche Llp Chicago
SIC 8399 Community development groups
Pr: Msgr Michael M Boland
Pr: Alice Lohman
**CFO:* Cynthia D Smetana
Assoc Dir: Anjanette Nero
Dir Soc: Jodi Hill
Comm Dir: Khristine Kappel
Ex Dir: Walter Osley
Info Man: Mary Walter
Counsel: Michele Bianchi

CATHOLIC CHARITIES OF CHICAGO
See CATHOLIC CHARITIES OF ARCHDIOCESE OF CHICAGO

D-U-N-S 14-853-6790
CATHOLIC CHARITIES OF DIOCESE OF ALBANY
40 N Main Ave Ste 1, Albany, NY 12203-1484
Tel (518) 453-6650 *Founded/Ownrshp* 1917
Sales 41.6MM *EMP* 1,100
Accts Bonadio & Co Llp Albany Ny
SIC 8322 Individual & family services; Family counseling services; First aid service; Homemakers' service
CEO: Vincent W Colonno
Ofcr: Aaron Howland

D-U-N-S 07-159-7348
CATHOLIC CHARITIES OF ROMAN CATHOLIC DIOCESE OF SYRACUSE NY
240 E Onondaga St, Syracuse, NY 13202-2608
Tel (315) 470-1450 *Founded/Ownrshp* 1925
Sales 53.0MM *EMP* 3,000
Accts Dermody Burke & Brown Cpas Llc
SIC 8661 Catholic Church
Prin: Rev Msgr J Robert Yeazel
**Prin:* Rev Timothy Elmer
Prin: Ann Keeney
Pr Dir: Danielle Cummings

D-U-N-S 12-325-0607
CATHOLIC CHARITIES OF ST LOUIS
CATHOLIC CHARITIES ARCHDOCESE
4445 Lindell Blvd, Saint Louis, MO 63108-2403
Tel (314) 367-5500 *Founded/Ownrshp* 1912
Sales 3.2MM *EMP* 1,495
Accts Kerber Eck & Braeckel Llp St
SIC 8699 8322 Charitable organization; Individual & family services
Pr: Tom Gorski

CATHOLIC CHARITIES OFFICE
See CATHOLIC DIOCESE OF ERIE

CATHOLIC CHRTIES BRKLYN QUEENS
See CATHOLIC CHARITIES NEIGHBORHOOD SERVICES INC

D-U-N-S 06-997-8724
CATHOLIC CHURCH EXTENSION SOCIETY OF UNITED STATES OF AMERICA
150 S Wacker Dr Ste 2000, Chicago, IL 60606-4214
Tel (312) 236-7240 *Founded/Ownrshp* 1905
Sales 6.3MM^E *EMP* 6,040
Accts Deloitte & Touche Llp Chicago
SIC 8661 Catholic Church
Pr: John J Wall
**COO:* Thomas Gordon
**CFO:* Kevin McGowan
**VP:* Angela D'Antonio
**VP:* Julie Turley

D-U-N-S 79-900-6341
CATHOLIC COMMUNITY SERVICES OF WESTERN WASHINGTON
100 23rd Ave S, Seattle, WA 98144-2302
Tel (206) 328-5696 *Founded/Ownrshp* 1988
Sales 123.8MM *EMP* 80^E
Accts Watson & Mcdonell Pllc Seattl
SIC 8322 Individual & family services
Pr: Michael Reichert
**Treas:* Frank Freemean
Sr Cor Off: Anissa B Frick
Ofcr: Michael Buller
**VP:* Irene Ward
Assoc Dir: Jennifer Shin
Admn Mgr: Sue Buchholz
Genl Mgr: Bill Schmidt
Pgrm Dir: Bob Fortner

CATHOLIC DIOCESE BATON ROUGE
See ROMAN CATHOLIC CHURCH OF DIOCESE OF BATON ROUGE

D-U-N-S 02-348-8778
CATHOLIC DIOCESE OF ARLINGTON
200 N Glebe Rd Ste 901, Arlington, VA 22203-3728
Tel (703) 841-2500 *Founded/Ownrshp* 1974
Sales 142.0MM^E *EMP* 4,000
SIC 8661 Catholic Church

D-U-N-S 09-140-5787
CATHOLIC DIOCESE OF BIRMINGHAM IN ALABAMA
2121 3rd Ave N, Birmingham, AL 35203-3314
Tel (205) 838-8307 *Founded/Ownrshp* 1812, 1988
Sales 53.6MM^E *EMP* 1,300
SIC 8661 Catholic Church
**CFO:* Bob Salers

D-U-N-S 00-452-9186
CATHOLIC DIOCESE OF CLEVELAND
CATHOLIC BOARD OF EDUCATION
1404 E 9th St Ste 201, Cleveland, OH 44114-1722
Tel (216) 696-6525 *Founded/Ownrshp* 1847
Sales 72.6MM^E *EMP* 2,000
SIC 8661 Catholic Church
Comm Man: Linda Corcoran
Ex Dir: Carol Anne Smith
Ex Dir: Rebecca J Tollefson
Counsel: Andrej Lah

D-U-N-S 07-214-9669
CATHOLIC DIOCESE OF ERIE
CATHOLIC CHARITIES OFFICE
429 E Grandview Blvd, Erie, PA 16504-2603
Tel (814) 824-1111 *Founded/Ownrshp* 1953
Sales 19.1MM *EMP* 8,000
Accts Bkd Llp Erie Pennsylvania
SIC 8661 Catholic Church
Prin: Stephen E Blaire
**CFO:* Dave Murphy

D-U-N-S 08-096-7664
CATHOLIC DIOCESE OF FORT WORTH
800 W Loop 820 S, Fort Worth, TX 76108-2919
Tel (817) 560-3300 *Founded/Ownrshp* 1847
Sales 17.9MM *EMP* 1,100
Accts Rylander Clay & Opitz Llp F
SIC 8661 Catholic Church
CEO: Stephen J Berg
Dir IT: Chris Kasner

D-U-N-S 07-306-9494
CATHOLIC DIOCESE OF KANSAS CITY-ST JOSEPH
CATHOLIC CENTER, THE
850 Main St, Kansas City, MO 64105-2006
Tel (816) 756-1850 *Founded/Ownrshp* 1878
Sales 63.7MM^E *EMP* 1,300
SIC 8661 8211 8351 8361 6553 Catholic Church; Catholic senior high school; Catholic elementary school; Preschool center; Children's home; Cemeteries, real estate operation
Assoc Dir: Kathleen Beyers
Comm Dir: Rebecca Summers
**Prin:* Raymond J Boland
**Prin:* Jude Huntz
Admn Mgr: Leann Lakin
Off Mgr: Jake Livingston
Advt Dir: Cid Prevost

D-U-N-S 08-479-1532
CATHOLIC DIOCESE OF MEMPHIS
CALVARY CEMETERY
5825 Shelby Oaks Dr, Memphis, TN 38134-7316
Tel (901) 373-1200 *Founded/Ownrshp* 1971
Sales 108.3MM *EMP* 1,200
Accts Watkins Uiberall Pllc Memphi
SIC 8661 Religious organizations
CFO: James Abernathy
Dir IT: Ayanna Bill
IT Man: Alie Lifsey

D-U-N-S 07-456-2810
CATHOLIC DIOCESE OF ROCKFORD
555 Colman Center Dr, Rockford, IL 61108-2705
Tel (815) 399-4300 *Founded/Ownrshp* 1908
Sales 164.0MM *EMP* 2,850
SIC 8661 8322 8361 8211 6553 Catholic Church; Social service center; Rest home, with health care incidental; Catholic senior high school; Cemetery association
Bd of Dir: Robert Sherry
Admn Mgr: Sharon Mattis
Admn Mgr: Kim Smith
Admn Mgr: Lisa Wedig
Off Mgr: Lori Kuehne
IT Man: Joe Schneider

D-U-N-S 06-920-0244
CATHOLIC DIOCESE OF SAVANNAH
2170 E Victory Dr, Savannah, GA 31404-3918
Tel (912) 201-4100 *Founded/Ownrshp* 1850
Sales 15.9MM *EMP* 1,400
Accts Daniel & Duncan Llc Savannah
SIC 8661 8211 Religious organizations; Catholic Church; Catholic elementary & secondary schools
Dir IT: Chuck Wilson

CATHOLIC DIOCESE OF TRENTON
See DIOCESE OF TRENTON

D-U-N-S 08-484-5551
CATHOLIC DIOCESE OF WICHITA INC (KS)
424 N Broadway Ave, Wichita, KS 67202-2377
Tel (316) 269-3900 *Founded/Ownrshp* 1887
Sales 42.2MM^E *EMP* 1,100
SIC 8661 8051 Catholic Church; Skilled nursing care facilities
Pr: Bishop Michael O Jackels
CFO: Bryan Coulter
**Sec:* Robert Hemberger

D-U-N-S 06-988-2959
CATHOLIC DIOCESE OF WILMINGTON INC
ROMAN CTHLIC DOCESE WILMINGTON
1925 Delaware Ave, Wilmington, DE 19806-2301
Tel (302) 573-3100 *Founded/Ownrshp* 1868
Sales 33.2MM^E *EMP* 1,400
SIC 8661 Catholic Church
Pr: W Francis Malooly
Admn Mgr: Patricia Killen

CATHOLIC DIOCESES PALM BEACH
See CON EL OF DIOCESE OF PALM BEACH INC

CATHOLIC ELDERCARE BY DAY
See CATHOLIC ELDERCARE COMMUNITY FOUNDATION INC

D-U-N-S 01-424-9044
CATHOLIC ELDERCARE COMMUNITY FOUNDATION INC
CATHOLIC ELDERCARE BY DAY
817 Main St Ne, Minneapolis, MN 55413-1931
Tel (612) 379-1370 *Founded/Ownrshp* 1980
Sales 2.3MM *EMP* 2,001
SIC 8051 Convalescent home with continuous nursing care
Pr: Mary Broderick

D-U-N-S 93-875-1229
CATHOLIC FINANCIAL SERVICES CORP
(*Suby of* CATHOLIC KNIGHTS INSURANCE SOCIETY INC) ★
1100 W Wells St Ste 1, Milwaukee, WI 53233-2316
Tel (414) 278-6550 *Founded/Ownrshp* 1994
Sales NA *EMP* 90
SIC 6311 6211 Fraternal life insurance organizations; Security brokers & dealers
Pr: William O'Toole
Bd of Dir: Richard Kremel
Ofcr: Jennifer Kienbaum
VP: Fred Muenkel
Dist Mgr: Kristin O'Connell
CTO: William Thompson

D-U-N-S 06-917-6915
CATHOLIC FOUNDATION OF NORTH GEORGIA INC
CATHOLIC ARCHDIOCESE ATLANTA
2401 Lake Park Dr Se # 100, Smyrna, GA 30080-8862
Tel (404) 920-7300 *Founded/Ownrshp* 1956
Sales 3.4MM *EMP* 2,500
SIC 8661 Catholic Church
**CFO:* Brad Wilson
Off Mgr: Rocio Zamarron
MIS Dir: Tom Pope

D-U-N-S 17-374-6918
CATHOLIC GUARDIAN SERVICES
1011 1st Ave Fl 10, New York, NY 10022-4112
Tel (212) 371-1011 *Founded/Ownrshp* 1913
Sales 84.7MM *EMP* 1,000
SIC 8322 8361 Child related social services; Group foster home; Home for the mentally handicapped
Ex Dir: Craig Longley
Genl Mgr: Thomas Smith

CATHOLIC HEALTH
See MERCY HOSPITAL OF BUFFALO

CATHOLIC HEALTH EAST
See MOUNT CARMEL HEALTH SYSTEM

CATHOLIC HEALTH EAST
See TRINITY HEALTH CORP

CATHOLIC HEALTH EAST
See ST MARYS HEALTH CARE SYSTEM INC

CATHOLIC HEALTH EAST
See HOLY CROSS HEALTH INC

CATHOLIC HEALTH EAST
See ST FRANCIS HOSPITAL INC

CATHOLIC HEALTH EAST
See SAINT ALPHONSUS REGIONAL MEDICAL CENTER INC

CATHOLIC HEALTH EAST
See OUR LADY OF LOURDES HEALTH CARE SERVICES INC

CATHOLIC HEALTH EAST
See MERCY MEDICAL CENTER FOUNDATION - NORTH IOWA

D-U-N-S 04-084-1632
CATHOLIC HEALTH EAST
CATHOLIC HEALTH SYSTEM
3805 West Chester Pike # 100, Newtown Square, PA 19073-2329
Tel (610) 355-2000 *Founded/Ownrshp* 2013
Sales NA *EMP* 50,000
SIC 8062 8051 8052 8059 8011

D-U-N-S 94-818-5459
CATHOLIC HEALTH INITIATIVES
CHI
198 Inverness Dr W, Englewood, CO 80112-3637
Tel (303) 298-9100 *Founded/Ownrshp* 1986
Sales 8.7MMM^E *EMP* 72,500^E
SIC 8062 8051 8741 General medical & surgical hospitals; Skilled nursing care facilities; Hospital management; Nursing & personal care facility management
Pr: Kevin E Lofton
Dir Recs: Brian Eichmann
Pr: Sumana Nallapati
COO: Gerald Picerno
**COO:* Michael T Rowan
CFO: John Deakyne
CFO: Lynn Ellis
Ofcr: Michael Ronning
Assoc VP: Randy Gates
Ex VP: Colleen Blye
Ex VP: Kurt Sligar
Ex VP: John Yox
Sr VP: John F Dicola
Sr VP: Ketul J Patel
VP: Sam Alfano
VP: John F Anderson
VP: Mark Bjornson
VP: Jim Bocian
VP: Jennifer Bringardner
VP: John Cicero
VP: Todd Conklin

D-U-N-S 07-347-8166
CATHOLIC HEALTH INITIATIVES - IOWA CORP
MERCY MEDICAL CTR - DES MOINES
(*Suby of* CHI) ★
1111 6th Ave, Des Moines, IA 50314-2613
Tel (515) 247-3121 *Founded/Ownrshp* 1995
Sales 733.5MM *EMP* 6,100
Accts Catholic Health Initiatives E
SIC 8062 General medical & surgical hospitals
CEO: David Vellinga
Dir OR: Kevin Tilley
Dir Rx: Abbey Pitzenberger
Dir Rx: Heather Rickertsen
Adm Dir: Keith Wachter
Dir Sec: Ron Muecke
Tech Mgr: William Hanlon
Ansthlgy: Christine Carstensen
Ansthlgy: Kenton Hall
Ansthlgy: Eric Meek
Ansthlgy: Thomas Monachino

D-U-N-S 79-113-3593
CATHOLIC HEALTH INITIATIVES COLORADO
ST ANTHONY CENTRAL HOSPITAL
198 Inverness Dr W, Englewood, CO 80112-3637
Tel (303) 290-6500 *Founded/Ownrshp* 1996
Sales 1.7MMM *EMP* 8,000^E
Accts Lb Catholic Health Initiatives
SIC 8741 8062 Hospital management; General medical & surgical hospitals
CEO: Kevin E Lofton
**Pr:* Gregory H Burfitt
COO: Jameson Smith Fache
CFO: Randy Safady
Ofcr: Sharon Pappas
Ex VP: Al Banisch
Ex VP: Edward Fchim
Ex VP: Ruthita Fike
Ex VP: Kathleen Scott
Ex VP: Grant Wicklund
Sr VP: Nancy Hoffman
VP: Bob Fling
VP: Geoffrey Lawton Pharmd
VP: Shelly Whitmore

D-U-N-S 96-496-2356
CATHOLIC HEALTH INITIATIVES COLORADO
PENROSE - ST FRANCES HLTH SVCS
2222 N Nevada Ave, Colorado Springs, CO 80907-6819
Tel (719) 776-5911 *Founded/Ownrshp* 2010
Sales 950.0M *EMP* 2,520
SIC 8699 Charitable organization
CFO: Danny Reeves

D-U-N-S 07-834-0460
CATHOLIC HEALTH INITIATIVES COLORADO FOUNDATION
CHI
(*Suby of* CHI) ★
1010 Three Springs Blvd, Durango, CO 81301-8296
Tel (970) 247-4311 *Founded/Ownrshp* 1982
Sales 172.3MM *EMP* 800
Accts Catholic Health Initiatives E
SIC 8062 General medical & surgical hospitals
Pr: Thomas D Gessel
**VP:* Nancy Hoyt
**VP:* William McConnell
**VP:* William Plauth
**VP:* Cathy Roberts
Dir Rx: Jenny O' Block
Sls&Mrk Ex: Constance Toddghanizadeh

D-U-N-S 78-562-1194
CATHOLIC HEALTH INITIATIVES WESTERN REGION
(*Suby of* CHI) ★
1149 Market St, Tacoma, WA 98402-3515
Tel (253) 552-4100 *Founded/Ownrshp* 1998
Sales 610.2MM^E *EMP* 3,270
SIC 8742 Hospital & health services consultant
Pr: Joseph Wilczek
**CFO:* Mike Fitzgerald

CATHOLIC HEALTH SYSTEM
See CATHOLIC HEALTH EAST

D-U-N-S 18-004-5155
CATHOLIC HEALTH SYSTEM INC
144 Genesee St Fl 1, Buffalo, NY 14203-1560
Tel (716) 862-2400 *Founded/Ownrshp* 1985
Sales 128.2MM *EMP* 8,400
SIC 8741 8062 5999 8051 Administrative management; Financial management for business; General medical & surgical hospitals; Medical apparatus & supplies; Skilled nursing care facilities
Pr: Joseph D McDonald
Bd of Dir: Michael Landi
Dir Lab: Rhonda Boulden
QA Dir: Pat Dean
Netwrk Eng: Mark Schmitt
Pr Dir: Joann Cavanaugh
Pathlgst: Ashok Koul
Surgeon: Bryan Butler
Surgeon: Maciej Dryjski
Ansthlgy: Amy I Alvarez Perez
Ansthlgy: George H Bancroft

D-U-N-S 01-438-8792
CATHOLIC HEALTH SYSTEM OF LONG ISLAND INC (NY)
CATHOLIC HLTH SVCS LONG ISLAND
992 N Village Ave, Rockville Centre, NY 11570-1002
Tel (516) 705-3700 *Founded/Ownrshp* 1997
Sales 35.1MM *EMP* 13,500
Accts Pricewaterhousecoopers Llp Ne
SIC 8062 General medical & surgical hospitals
Pr: Alan D Guerci MD
**COO:* Dennis Verzi
CFO: June Burke
**Act CFO:* William Armstrong
Ofcr: Bernadette Catanzaro
Ex VP: Charles Bov
**Ex VP:* David Decerbo
Ex VP: Donna M O'Brien
**Ex VP:* Patrick M Oshaughnessy
**Sr VP:* Terence M O'Brien
**Sr VP:* Anthony Pellicano
**Sr VP:* James Spencer
VP: Jim Spencer
Dir Lab: John Chumas
Dir Lab: Louanne Regensberg
Dir Lab: Kevin Richard
Dir Rx: Steven Cabble

CATHOLIC HEALTHCARE WEST
See CHANDLER REGIONAL MEDICAL CENTER

D-U-N-S 07-877-2738
CATHOLIC HEALTHCARE WEST
ST MARY'S MEDICAL CENTER
(*Suby of* DIGNITY HEALTH) ★
450 Stanyan St, San Francisco, CA 94117-1019
Tel (415) 668-1000 *Founded/Ownrshp* 1855, 1831
Sales 220.6MM *EMP* 1,100^E
SIC 8062 General medical & surgical hospitals
Pr: Ken Steele
Ofcr: Carmen Frye

Ofcr: Heather Otanez
VP: Russ Braun
VP: Mary A Brown
Dir Rx: Helena Lim
**Ex Dir:* Margine Sako
Dir IT: Mike House
Mktg Dir: Dee Mostofi
Ansthlgy: Julian D Medina
Ansthlgy: Chihying J Wang

D-U-N-S 17-926-4544
CATHOLIC HEALTHCARE WEST SOUTHERN CALIFORNIA
(*Suby of* DIGNITY HEALTH) ★
1050 Linden Ave, Long Beach, CA 90813-3321
Tel (562) 491-9000 *Founded/Ownrshp* 1997
Sales 42.8MM^E *EMP* 1,601
SIC 8062 General medical & surgical hospitals
COO: Jeff Winter
**CFO:* Gary Conner

CATHOLIC HLTH SVCS LONG ISLAND
See CATHOLIC HEALTH SYSTEM OF LONG ISLAND INC

CATHOLIC HLTH SYS LONG ISLAND
See ST FRANCIS HOSPITAL ROSLYN NEW YORK

D-U-N-S 05-529-4888
CATHOLIC KNIGHTS INSURANCE SOCIETY INC
1100 W Wells St Ste 1, Milwaukee, WI 53233-2316
Tel (414) 273-6266 *Founded/Ownrshp* 1885
Sales NA *EMP* 125
SIC 6311 6411 6211 6141 Fraternal life insurance organizations; Insurance agents, brokers & service; Security brokers & dealers; Personal credit institutions
Pr: Daniel J Steininger
**Sec:* Allan G Lorge

D-U-N-S 00-813-6608
CATHOLIC LIFE INSURANCE
1635 Ne Loop 410 Ste 300, San Antonio, TX 78209-1694
Tel (210) 828-9921 *Founded/Ownrshp* 1901
Sales NA *EMP* 102
Accts Carneiro Chumney & Co Lc San
SIC 6311 6411 Benevolent insurance associations; Insurance agents, brokers & service
Pr: J Michael Belz
Treas: Thomas Petri
VP: Kathleen K May
IT Man: Patrick Massey

D-U-N-S 82-702-1382
CATHOLIC MEDICAL CENTER
100 Mcgregor St, Manchester, NH 03102-3770
Tel (603) 663-6888 *Founded/Ownrshp* 1974
Sales 316.4MM *EMP* 1,500
Accts Baker Newman & Noyes Portland
SIC 8062 General medical & surgical hospitals
CEO: Joseph Pepe MD
Dir Recs: Jeff Butler
V Ch: Rose M Phillips
**Pr:* Alyson Pitman Giles
COO: Raymond Bonito
COO: Brian Pew
CFO: Ted Dudley
Treas: Benjamin Westbrook
VP: Mary Ann
VP: Lori Berube
VP: Daniel Bouvier
VP: Lu Mula
VP: Lu Mulla
Exec: Karen Belanger
Exec: Michael Dubois
Dir Inf Cn: Karen Kennett
Dir Rx: Barbara Case

D-U-N-S 00-957-5130
CATHOLIC MEDICAL CENTER PHYSICIAN PRACTICE ASSOCIATES
100 Mcgregor St, Manchester, NH 03102-3730
Tel (603) 668-3545 *Founded/Ownrshp* 1974
Sales 19.7MM *EMP* 1,400
SIC 8062 8011 General medical & surgical hospitals; Offices & clinics of medical doctors
Pr: Alyson Pitman Giles

CATHOLIC MEDICAL MISSION BD
See CATHOLIC MEDICAL MISSION BOARD INC

D-U-N-S 07-683-2765
CATHOLIC MEDICAL MISSION BOARD INC
CATHOLIC MEDICAL MISSION BD
100 Wall St Fl 9, New York, NY 10005-5765
Tel (212) 242-7757 *Founded/Ownrshp* 1928
Sales 290.0MM *EMP* 38
Accts Marks Paneth & Shron Llp New
SIC 8011 Offices & clinics of medical doctors
Pr: John F Galbraith
V Ch: F W Smullen III
**Pr:* Bruce Wilkinson
CFO: Michael O'Hara
Bd of Dir: Paul Maguire
Sr VP: Marivette Cannon
Rgnl Mgr: Erin Snyder
Dir IT: Joshua Freeman
Opers Mgr: Yves Edme

CATHOLIC MUTUAL GROUP
See CATHOLIC MUTUAL RELIEF SOCIETY OF AMERICA

D-U-N-S 00-696-9984
CATHOLIC MUTUAL RELIEF SOCIETY OF AMERICA (NE)
CATHOLIC MUTUAL GROUP
10843 Old Mill Rd, Omaha, NE 68154-2607
Tel (402) 551-8765 *Founded/Ownrshp* 1889
Sales NA *EMP* 225
SIC 6351 Liability insurance
Pr: Michael A Intrieri
**Pr:* Joseph T Beveridge
COO: Tina Chavez
**VP:* Ray Miller
**VP:* Rev David L Ricken
**VP:* Bishop Michael J Sheenan
Dir Risk M: Frank Ward
MIS Dir: Paul Cunningham

Web Dev: Brad Jackson
Mktg Dir: Tom Sauser
Mktg Mgr: Greg Standish

D-U-N-S 07-443-6684
CATHOLIC ORDER OF FORESTERS INC (IL)
355 Shuman Blvd, Naperville, IL 60563-8494
Tel (630) 983-4900 *Founded/Ownrshp* 1883
Sales NA *EMP* 185
SIC 6311 Fraternal life insurance organizations
Pr: David Huber
Treas: Thomas Munninghoff
**Sec:* Stuart Cuchanan
Ex VP: Gregory Temple
VP: Larry Mills
Sls Mgr: Kathy Graham

D-U-N-S 06-820-5541
CATHOLIC RELIEF SERVICES - UNITED STATES CONFERENCE OF CATHOLIC BISHOPS (DC)
CRS - USCCB
228 W Lexington St, Baltimore, MD 21201-3443
Tel (410) 625-2220 *Founded/Ownrshp* 1943
Sales 738.6MM *EMP* 5,879
Accts Rsm Us Llp Gaithersburg Mary
SIC 8322 Emergency social services; Disaster service
Pr: Carolyn Woo
**COO:* Sean Callahan
**CFO:* Mark Palmer
Ofcr: Kim Pozniak
**Ex VP:* Annemarie Reilly
**VP:* Joan Rosenhauer

CATHOLIC SCHOOLS OFFICE, THE
See DIOCESE OF STOCKTON EDUCATIONAL OFFICE

D-U-N-S 07-599-8468
CATHOLIC SOCIAL SERVICES OF DIOCESE OF SCRANTON INC (PA)
DIOCESE OF SCRANTON, THE
516 Fig St, Scranton, PA 18505-1753
Tel (570) 207-2283 *Founded/Ownrshp* 1939, 1877
Sales 57.1MM^E *EMP* 2,226
SIC 8661 2711 8211 8322 6553 Catholic Church; Newspapers: publishing only, not printed on site; Seminary; Catholic elementary & secondary schools; Youth center; Cemetery association
Prin: Joseph C Bambera
Off Mgr: Betty Miller

D-U-N-S 07-649-9961
CATHOLIC UNITED FINANCIAL
3499 Lexington Ave N, Saint Paul, MN 55126-7055
Tel (651) 490-0170 *Founded/Ownrshp* 1878
Sales 88.2MM *EMP* 50
SIC 8641 6411 Fraternal associations; Life insurance agents
Ch Bd: Michael G McGovern
**Sr VP:* Dennis Olson
Ex Dir: Susan K Albrecht
Rgnl Mgr: Gregory Gall

D-U-N-S 04-196-2788 IMP
CATHOLIC UNIVERSITY OF AMERICA
C U A
620 Michigan Ave Ne, Washington, DC 20064-0002
Tel (202) 319-5000 *Founded/Ownrshp* 1887
Sales 232.3MM *EMP* 4,239
Accts Pricewaterhousecoopers Llp Ba
SIC 8221 University
Pr: John Garvey
Pr: Rachel Battles
Pr: Tanith Corsi
Pr: Suzanne McCarthy
**Treas:* Ralph Beaudoin
VP: Julie Isha
VP: Michael Kushner
VP: Christopher Lydon
VP: Jonathan Sawyer
Assoc Dir: Joanna Bader
Assoc Dir: Kathryn Marshall

D-U-N-S 00-413-2630
■ **CATLETTSBURG REFINING LLC**
(*Suby of* MARATHON PETROLEUM CO LP) ★
11631 Us Route 23, Catlettsburg, KY 41129-8953
Tel (606) 921-3333 *Founded/Ownrshp* 1997
Sales 169.2MM^E *EMP* 1,042
SIC 2911 Petroleum refining; Gasoline blending plants; Oils, fuel; Liquefied petroleum gases, LPG
CEO: Doug Sparkman
Plnt Mgr: James E Cantrell

CATNAPPER
See CLEVELAND CHAIR CO INC

CATNAPPER
See JACKSON FURNITURE INDUSTRIES INC

D-U-N-S 02-446-7763 IMP/EXP
▲ **CATO CORP**
8100 Denmark Rd, Charlotte, NC 28273-5975
Tel (704) 554-8510 *Founded/Ownrshp* 1946
Sales 1.0MMM *EMP* 10,500
Tkr Sym CATO *Exch* NYS
SIC 5621 5632 5137 5699 5311 5641 Women's clothing stores; Ready-to-wear apparel, women's; Women's accessory & specialty stores; Women's & children's clothing; Sports apparel; Department stores; Children's & infants' wear stores; Children's wear
Ch Bd: John P D Cato
CFO: John R Howe
Treas: Bethany Garrett
Ex VP: Michael T Greer
Ex VP: Gordon Smith
Ex VP: Gordon D Smith
Sr VP: Robert Sandler
VP: Bill Coe
VP: Joe Forbidussi
VP: Steve Headley
VP: Larry Mouser
VP: Robin Paxton
VP: Randilynn Pollino
VP: Lowell Pugh
VP: Debbie Shinn
VP: Clayton Smith

Board of Directors: Thomas B Henson, Bryan F Kennedy III, Thomas E Meckley, Bailey W Patrick, D Harding Stowe, Edward I Weisiger Jr

D-U-N-S 02-266-4080
CATO INC
1004 Parsons Rd, Salisbury, MD 21801-8431
Tel (410) 546-1215 *Founded/Ownrshp* 1960
Sales 104.4MM^E *EMP* 50
SIC 5172 Gasoline; Diesel fuel; Kerosene; Lubricating oils & greases
Pr: Michael G Abercrombie Jr
**CFO:* Russell C Winters

CATOOSA COUNTY PUBLIC SCHL SYS
See CATOOSA COUNTY PUBLIC SCHOOLS

D-U-N-S 09-175-2162
CATOOSA COUNTY PUBLIC SCHOOLS
CATOOSA COUNTY PUBLIC SCHL SYS
307 Cleveland St, Ringgold, GA 30736-2057
Tel (706) 965-3977 *Founded/Ownrshp* 2005
Sales 115.0MM *EMP* 1,900
Accts Greg S Griffin-State Auditor
SIC 8211 9411 Public elementary & secondary schools; Administration of educational programs

D-U-N-S 96-751-9588
CATTERTON PARTNERS CORP
L CATTERTON
599 W Putnam Ave, Greenwich, CT 06830-6005
Tel (203) 629-4901 *Founded/Ownrshp* 1989
Sales 240.9MM^E *EMP* 1,419
SIC 6211 Investment firm, general brokerage
Pr: J Michael Chu
Sr Pt: Julian Mack
Sr Pt: Nikhil Thukral
Mng Pt: Michael Chu
Ofcr: David McPherson
Ofcr: Dan Reid
Ofcr: Kevin S Zadourian
VP: Mark Grabowski
VP: Tehmina Haider
VP: Farah Khan
Prin: Glenda Branch

D-U-N-S 00-480-9141 IMP/EXP
CAUDILL SEED AND WAREHOUSE CO INC (KY)
CAUDILL SEED CO
1402 W Main St, Louisville, KY 40203-1328
Tel (502) 583-4402 *Founded/Ownrshp* 1947
Sales 115.3MM^E *EMP* 130
SIC 5191 5261 Seeds: field, garden & flower; Nursery stock, seeds & bulbs
Pr: Pat Caudill
**COO:* Dan Caudill
**CFO:* Iris Mudd
Div Mgr: Mark Pickett
Info Man: Stan Milan

CAUDILL SEED CO
See CAUDILL SEED AND WAREHOUSE CO INC

D-U-N-S 07-950-9359
CAUSE FOR CHANGE LLC (MA)
370 Hudson Rd, Sudbury, MA 01776-1633
Tel (617) 571-6990 *Founded/Ownrshp* 2014
Sales 47.9MM^E *EMP* 2,014
SIC 5137 Women's & children's clothing

D-U-N-S 00-766-2851
■ **CAVALIER HOME BUILDERS LLC**
(*Suby of* CAVALIER HOMES INC) ★
32 Wilson Blvd 100, Addison, AL 35540
Tel (256) 747-1575 *Founded/Ownrshp* 1984
Sales 72.5MM^E *EMP* 1,000
SIC 2451 Mobile homes

D-U-N-S 11-804-6796
■ **CAVALIER HOMES INC**
(*Suby of* SOUTHERN ESTATES) ★
32 Wilson Blvd Ste 100, Addison, AL 35540
Tel (256) 747-1575 *Founded/Ownrshp* 2009
Sales 140.3MM^E *EMP* 1,012^E
SIC 2451 Mobile homes
Pr: Bobby Tesney
CFO: Michael R Murphy
CFO: Michael Murphy
Ex VP: Barry Mixon
Ex VP: John Mixon
VP: Douglas Jumper

CAVALIER MAID SERVICE
See CAVALIER MAINTENANCE SERVICES INC

D-U-N-S 08-234-6602
CAVALIER MAINTENANCE SERVICES INC
CAVALIER MAID SERVICE
2722 Merrilee Dr Ste 300, Fairfax, VA 22031-4400
Tel (703) 849-1100 *Founded/Ownrshp* 1977
Sales 55.2MM^E *EMP* 1,750
SIC 7349 Building maintenance services
CEO: Kevin S Rohan
**Pr:* William T Warnecki
**CFO:* Paul C Renick
**VP:* Deann Greene
**Prin:* Maria C Tueros
Area Mgr: Rosa Duarte
Area Mgr: Jorge Lopez
Area Mgr: Maria Miranda
Area Mgr: Yancy Umanzor

D-U-N-S 83-276-7938
■ **CAVALIER TELEPHONE CORP**
(*Suby of* PAETEC HOLDING CORP) ★
2134 W Laburnum Ave, Richmond, VA 23227-4342
Tel (804) 422-4000 *Founded/Ownrshp* 2010
Sales 144.8MM^E *EMP* 2,001^E
SIC 4813 Telephone communication, except radio
CEO: Danny Bottoms
Ex VP: Robert D Moore Jr
Sr VP: Mary K O'Connell Sr

D-U-N-S 04-900-7359
CAVALIER TELEPHONE LLC
2134 W Laburnum Ave, Richmond, VA 23227-4342
Tel (804) 422-4100 *Founded/Ownrshp* 2011
Sales 646.8MM^E *EMP* 2,000
SIC 4813 4812 Local telephone communications; Long distance telephone communications; Radio telephone communication
Ch: Brad Evans
CIO: Gregory Wood

D-U-N-S 17-530-5973
CAVALIER TELEPHONE MID-ATLANTIC LLC
(*Suby of* CAVALIER TELEPHONE LLC) ★
2134 W Laburnum Ave, Richmond, VA 23227-4342
Tel (804) 422-4100 *Founded/Ownrshp* 2005
Sales 100.0MM^E *EMP* 2,000
SIC 4813 4812 Telephone communication, except radio; Radio telephone communication
CEO: Danny Bottoms
**Pr:* Robert M Keane
**CFO:* Sarahbeth Murphy
VP: Martin W Clift Jr
VP: Greg Jones

D-U-N-S 00-445-7966
CAVALIERS HOLDINGS LLC
QUICKEN LOANS ARENA
1 Center Ct, Cleveland, OH 44115-4001
Tel (216) 420-2000 *Founded/Ownrshp* 2004
Sales 79.3MM^E *EMP* 1,300^E
SIC 7941 6512 Basketball club; Nonresidential building operators
Sr VP: Tracy Marek
VP: Gayle Bibby-Creme
VP: Antony Bonavita
VP: Kerry Bubolz
VP: Michael Conley
VP: Pat Fitzgerald
VP: Dionna Widder
Dir Soc: Bryan Ralston
Genl Mgr: Damy Farry
Dir IT: Edward Kordel
IT Man: Steve Shure

D-U-N-S 11-309-5157
CAVALIERS OPERATING CO LLC
Q, THE
(*Suby of* QUICKEN LOANS ARENA) ★
1 Center Ct, Cleveland, OH 44115-4001
Tel (216) 420-2000 *Founded/Ownrshp* 2005
Sales 60.0MM^E *EMP* 1,300
Accts Vanessa L Blevins Cpa Washing
SIC 7941 Sports clubs, managers & promoters
CEO: Len Komorski
COO: Scott Woodruff
VP: Kerry Bubolz
VP: Chris Poole
Off Admin: Leora Lugasy
Genl Couns: Jason Hillman

D-U-N-S 00-901-5264
▲ **CAVCO INDUSTRIES INC**
1001 N Central Ave # 800, Phoenix, AZ 85004-1962
Tel (602) 256-6263 *Founded/Ownrshp* 1965
Sales 712.3MM *EMP* 3,750
Tkr Sym CVCO *Exch* NGS
SIC 2451 5271 Mobile homes; Mobile homes, personal or private use; Mobile homes
Pr: Joseph H Stegmayer
CFO: Daniel L Urness
Ofcr: Mark Simon
Sr VP: Steven K Like
VP: Tim Gage
IT Man: Steven G Bunger
Board of Directors: William C Boor, Steven G Bunger, David A Greenblatt, Jack Hanna

D-U-N-S 11-336-0903 IMP
CAVENDER STORES LTD
CAVENDER'S BOOT CITY
7820 S Broadway Ave, Tyler, TX 75703-5241
Tel (903) 509-9509 *Founded/Ownrshp* 1998
Sales 173.0MM^E *EMP* 1,500
SIC 5699 5661 Western apparel; Women's boots; Men's boots; Women's shoes
Pr: Joe Cavender
CFO: James R Thompson
Chf Mktg O: Godbey Acker
VP: Mike Cavender
Exec: Steve Schofield
Info Man: Kent Gibson
Mktg Dir: Terry Cooper
Sales Asso: Stephen Edwards

CAVENDER'S BOOT CITY
See CAVENDER STORES LTD

D-U-N-S 83-871-7320 IMP
CAVENDISH FARMS INC
(*Suby of* CAVENDISH AGRI SERVICES LIMITED)
5855 3rd St Se, Jamestown, ND 58401-6800
Tel (701) 252-5222 *Founded/Ownrshp* 2001
Sales 204.4MM^E *EMP* 225
SIC 5142 2099 Packaged frozen goods; Food preparations
Pr: Robert Irving
Exec: Tamara Oliver
Sls Dir: Troy Havenga

D-U-N-S 00-738-1031
CAVINESS BEEF PACKERS LTD (TX)
CAVINESS PACKING CO
3255 Us Highway 60, Hereford, TX 79045
Tel (806) 357-2443 *Founded/Ownrshp* 1962, 2001
Sales 148.7MM^E *EMP* 750
SIC 2011

CAVINESS PACKING CO
See CAVINESS BEEF PACKERS LTD

D-U-N-S 83-009-0051
▲ **CAVIUM INC**
2315 N 1st St, San Jose, CA 95131-1010
Tel (408) 943-7100 *Founded/Ownrshp* 2000
Sales 412.7MM *EMP* 1,005^E
Tkr Sym CAVM *Exch* NGS
SIC 3674 Semiconductors & related devices
Ch Bd: Syed B Ali
COO: Muhammad Raghib Hussain
CFO: Arthur D Chadwick
Sr VP: Vincent P Pangrazio
VP: Anil Jain
Genl Mgr: Raj Singh

Snr Sftwr: Ken Bullis
Snr Sftwr: Ananth Jasty
Snr Sftwr: Michael Mascarenhas
IT Man: Glenn Sullivan
Sftwr Eng: Ashutosh Gangwar
Board of Directors: Brad W Buss, Edward H Frank, Sanjay Mehrotra, C N Reddy, Anthony S Thornley

D-U-N-S 80-782-9952
■ CAVTEL HOLDINGS LLC
(*Suby of* CAVALIER TELEPHONE CORP) ★
2134 W Laburnum Ave, Richmond, VA 23227-4342
Tel (804) 422-4107 *Founded/Ownrshp* 2006
Sales 144.8MME *EMP* 2,000E
SIC 4813 Local telephone communications
CEO: Brad Evans

D-U-N-S 11-847-8387 IMP
CAWSL ENTERPRISES INC
(*Suby of* SUPERIOR GROUP INC) ★
3411 Silverside Rd, Wilmington, DE 19810-4812
Tel (302) 478-6160 *Founded/Ownrshp* 1984
Sales 100.1MME *EMP* 2,000
SIC 6211 Investment firm, general brokerage
Pr: Thomas L Sandor
**Sec:* John A Sanders
**VP:* William G Warden III
**VP:* William G Warden IV

D-U-N-S 60-823-6667 IMP
CAYRE GROUP LTD
1407 Broadway Fl 41, New York, NY 10018-2348
Tel (212) 789-7000 *Founded/Ownrshp* 1992
Sales 130.0MM *EMP* 80
SIC 5137 Infants' wear
Ch Bd: Stanley Cayre
**Pr:* Amin Cayre
Pr: Tina Florio
CTO: Nisha Desai
VP Sls: Jack Cayre
VP Sls: John Strashun

D-U-N-S 10-774-1191
CAYUGA MEDICAL CENTER AT ITHACA INC
101 Dates Dr, Ithaca, NY 14850-1342
Tel (607) 274-4011 *Founded/Ownrshp* 2002
Sales 175.3MM *EMP* 1,055
SIC 8062 Hospital, affiliated with AMA residency
Ex Dir: D Rob Mackenzie
**CEO:* John Rudd
Bd of Dir: Julie L O'Toole
**VP:* John Collett
**VP:* Lloyd Darlow MD
**VP:* Ellen Dugan
**VP:* David Evelyn
VP: Susan Nohelty
**VP:* Alan Pederson
VP: Tony Votaw
MIS Dir: Bruce Hall

CB & I LUMMUS GLOBAL INC
See LUMMUS OVERSEAS CORP

D-U-N-S 80-687-0080
CB HOLDING CORP
1 Congress St Ste 113, Boston, MA 02114-2016
Tel (617) 720-2994 *Founded/Ownrshp* 2005
Sales NA *EMP* 6,700
SIC 6712 Bank holding companies
CEO: Russell D'Anton
**CEO:* Sam Borgese
CFO: David Dick
CFO: Ed Schwartz
Ex VP: Craig Godfrey
VP: Mark La Morticella
VP Opers: Herve Laplume
VP Opers: Steve Valentine

D-U-N-S 15-239-2291
CB NORTH LLC
480 W Beach St, Watsonville, CA 95076-4555
Tel (831) 786-1642 *Founded/Ownrshp* 2004
Sales 10.4MME *EMP* 1,000
SIC 0191 General farms, primarily crop

D-U-N-S 18-002-6619
■ CB RICHARD ELLIS MEMPHIS LLC
(*Suby of* CBRE GROUP INC) ★
2620 Thousand Oaks Blvd # 4000, Memphis, TN 38118-2461
Tel (901) 528-1000 *Founded/Ownrshp* 2015
Sales 115.5MME *EMP* 745
SIC 6531 8742 Real estate agents & managers; Real estate consultant
Ex VP: Kelly Truitt
VP: Kevin B Clarkson

D-U-N-S 01-857-4942
■ CB RICHARD ELLIS REAL ESTATE SERVICES LLC
(*Suby of* CBRE GROUP INC) ★
200 Park Ave Fl 19, New York, NY 10166-1899
Tel (212) 984-8000 *Founded/Ownrshp* 2003
Sales 930.5MME *EMP* 6,000
SIC 6531 6162 Real estate agents & managers; Mortgage bankers
Ex Dir: Andrew Hatherly

D-U-N-S 03-078-9379
CB TECHNOLOGIES INC
750 The City Dr S Ste 225, Orange, CA 92868-4976
Tel (714) 573-7733 *Founded/Ownrshp* 2001
Sales 85.7MM *EMP* 43E
Accts Starr & Walters Accountancy C
SIC 7379 7373 Computer related maintenance services; Computer integrated systems design
CEO: Kelly Ireland
**CFO:* Rachel Nelson
Sr VP: Michael Archibeque
Sr VP: Eric Bradford
Sr VP: Stan Galanski
VP: Robert Maynard

D-U-N-S 06-333-5046
CB TRAVEL CORP (UT)
CHRISTOPHERSON BUSINESS TRAVEL
5588 S Green St Ste 300, Salt Lake City, UT 84123-6965
Tel (801) 327-7700 *Founded/Ownrshp* 1953, 2005
Sales 384.0MM *EMP* 200
SIC 4724 Travel agencies
Pr: Michael Camero
**Ch:* Camille Cameron
Dir IT: Ty Cameron
IT Man: Dave McKenna

CB VATAMERICA
See VATAMERICA LP

CB&I
See CHICAGO BRIDGE & IRON CO

D-U-N-S 02-938-2525
CB&I AREVA MOX SERVICES LLC
(*Suby of* SHAW GROUP INC) ★
Savannah River Site, Aiken, SC 29801
Tel (803) 819-2000 *Founded/Ownrshp* 2002
Sales 163.0MME *EMP* 1,607
Accts Kpmg Llp Charlotte Nc
SIC 8741 Construction management
Pr: K David Stinson
**Ex VP:* Eric Chassard
**VP:* Michael Bagale
VP: Robert L Jones
**VP:* S Casey Kenney
VP: Howard Lawrence
**VP:* Gwen Nalos
**VP:* Al Sinonti
VP: Mike Zustra
**Prin:* David Stinson
CTO: Rachael Kipphut

D-U-N-S 05-967-8144 IMP
CB&I CONTRACTORS INC
(*Suby of* CHICAGO BRIDGE & IRON CO (DELAWARE)) ★
4171 Essen Ln, Baton Rouge, LA 70809-2157
Tel (225) 932-2500 *Founded/Ownrshp* 1997
Sales 567.5MME *EMP* 2,156
SIC 1541 Industrial buildings & warehouses
Pr: Ronnie Volentine
VP: Gary P Graphia
**VP:* Samuel K Robinson

D-U-N-S 10-951-5077 IMP
CB&I ENVIRONMENTAL & INFRASTRUCTURE INC
(*Suby of* CB&I GOVERNMENT SOLUTIONS INC) ★
3867 Plaza Tower Dr, Baton Rouge, LA 70816-4378
Tel (225) 932-2500 *Founded/Ownrshp* 2002
Sales 392.5MME *EMP* 5,868
SIC 8748 1794 1795 8744 8741 Environmental consultant; Excavation & grading, building construction; Wrecking & demolition work; Facilities support services; Management services
Pr: Kelly Trice
**Treas:* Bradley Lowe
**Ex VP:* Harry Dravecky
**VP:* Jeff Andrews
**VP:* Robert Bridges
**VP:* Greg Coffman
**VP:* Michael H Dillman
**VP:* Steven T Downey
**VP:* Tyson Hackenberg
**VP:* Malcolm Jarrell
**VP:* Katherine Kolibas
**VP:* William G Lamb
**VP:* Thomas P Pierro
**VP:* Tony Stempkowski
**VP:* Mick Williams
Board of Directors: Richard E Chandler Jr, Luciano Reyes, Westley S Stockton

D-U-N-S 07-961-4098
CB&I FEDERAL SERVICES LLC
2401 River Rd, Schenectady, NY 12309-1103
Tel (518) 557-2518 *Founded/Ownrshp* 2014
Sales 39.0MME *EMP* 2,500
SIC 8744

D-U-N-S 10-951-5259
CB&I FEDERAL SERVICES LLC
(*Suby of* CB&I GOVERNMENT SOLUTIONS INC) ★
1725 Duke St Ste 400, Alexandria, VA 22314-3470
Tel (202) 261-1900 *Founded/Ownrshp* 1986
Sales 727.2MME *EMP* 2,500
SIC 1521 Single-family housing construction
Pr: Robert Cochran
Genl Mgr: James Van Horn
IT Man: Mark Weaver

D-U-N-S 10-951-4559 IMP/EXP
CB&I GOVERNMENT SOLUTIONS INC
(*Suby of* SHAW GROUP INC) ★
4171 Essen Ln, Baton Rouge, LA 70809-2157
Tel (225) 932-2500 *Founded/Ownrshp* 1986
Sales 1.1MMME *EMP* 5,868
SIC 8711 8734 8748 1541 1542 1611 Pollution control engineering; Hazardous waste testing; Environmental consultant; Industrial buildings & warehouses; Commercial & office buildings, renovation & repair; General contractor, highway & street construction
Pr: George P Bevan
**COO:* Jeffrey Jenkins
**CFO:* Michael H Dillman
**Ex VP:* Vahid Ownjazayeri
**Ex VP:* William Winkler
**Sr VP:* Joe Boyer
**Sr VP:* Michael Fitzgerald
**Sr VP:* Malcolm Jarrell
**Sr VP:* Richard Lee
**Sr VP:* Alan Solow
**VP:* Shane Bellanger
**VP:* David L Bullington
**VP:* Greg Coffman
**VP:* Daniel Coover
**VP:* Robert Culbertson
**VP:* Steven Downey
**VP:* Harry Dravecky
**VP:* Larry Haser
**VP:* John Hitchings
**VP:* Katherine Lista
**VP:* Gary Locke
Board of Directors: George Bevan, Michael Dillman, Gerald Doton, William Winkler

D-U-N-S 06-401-2560 IMP/EXP
CB&I LLC
(*Suby of* CHICAGO BRIDGE & IRON COMPANY N.V.)
2103 Research Forest Dr, The Woodlands, TX 77380-2624
Tel (832) 513-1000 *Founded/Ownrshp* 1979
Sales 7.2MMME *EMP* 29,000
SIC 1791 3443 3312 Structural steel erection; Storage tanks, metal: erection; Fabricated plate work (boiler shop); Blast furnaces & steel mills
CEO: Philip K Asherman
Pr: Jeffrey J Lyash
**Pr:* Patrick K Mullen
**CFO:* Ronald A Ballschmiede
**CFO:* Michael S Taff
**Ofcr:* Richard E Chandler Jr
**Ex VP:* E Chip Ray
Ex VP: James Sabin
**Ex VP:* Luke V Scorsone
Sr VP: Patrick Jameson
**VP:* Westley S Stockton

CB&T
See SYNOVUS BANK

D-U-N-S 92-603-8654
CB&T HOLDING CORP
1100 Poydras St Ste 1800, New Orleans, LA 70163-1800
Tel (504) 525-4381 *Founded/Ownrshp* 1994
Sales NA *EMP* 153E
SIC 6022 State commercial banks
Pr: Fred B Morgan III
VP: Paul R Trapani

D-U-N-S 06-426-0409 IMP
CBA INDUSTRIES INC
669 River Dr Ste 101, Elmwood Park, NJ 07407-1361
Tel (201) 587-1717 *Founded/Ownrshp* 1970, 1991
Sales 100.2MME *EMP* 129E
SIC 5192 Newspapers
Pr: Barry Schiro
**Ch Bd:* Harold Matzner
**CFO:* Carl Casazza
Sr VP: Nicholas Passariello
**VP:* Jimmy Conaghan
Dir IT: David Schlesinger
VP Sls: Timothy Brahney

D-U-N-S 09-503-1613
CBC COMPANIES INC
250 E Broad St Fl 21, Columbus, OH 43215-3770
Tel (614) 222-4343 *Founded/Ownrshp* 1948
Sales 230.9MME *EMP* 1,400
SIC 7322

D-U-N-S 61-526-4053 EXP
CBC RESTAURANT CORP
CORNER BAKERY CAFE
(*Suby of* IL FORNAIO (AMERICA) CORP) ★
12700 Park Central Dr # 1300, Dallas, TX 75251-1523
Tel (972) 619-4100 *Founded/Ownrshp* 2005
Sales 195.7MME *EMP* 4,000
SIC 5812 6794 Cafe; Franchises, selling or licensing
CEO: Mike Hislop
**CFO:* Salil Bapat
**CFO:* Ted Croft
**CFO:* Richard Peabody
**Chf Mktg O:* Justin Lambeth
**Ofcr:* Blake Bernet
**Ofcr:* Michael J Nolan
**Sr VP:* Denise K Clemens
VP: Holland Burton
VP: Jamey Cutter
**VP:* Paul Hicks

D-U-N-S 08-296-2002
CBCINNOVIS INC (PA)
(*Suby of* CBC COMPANIES INC) ★
8 Parkway Ctr, Pittsburgh, PA 15220-3802
Tel (412) 503-9254 *Founded/Ownrshp* 1948, 1981
Sales 60.8MME *EMP* 1,000
SIC 7323 Credit bureau & agency
CEO: Jonathan H Price
**Treas:* Dirk Cantrell
**Treas:* Keith R Kotpwocz
**VP:* Pam Lahr

D-U-N-S 07-911-6558
CBE COMPANIES INC (IA)
1309 Technology Pkwy, Cedar Falls, IA 50613-6976
Tel (319) 226-5161 *Founded/Ownrshp* 2013
Sales 98.4MME *EMP* 1,000E
SIC 8742 Business planning & organizing services
CEO: Thomas R Penaluna
**Pr:* Chad W Benson
**CFO:* Robert Kahler

D-U-N-S 17-360-9025
CBE GROUP INC
(*Suby of* CBE COMPANIES INC) ★
1309 Technology Pkwy, Cedar Falls, IA 50613-6976
Tel (319) 234-6686 *Founded/Ownrshp* 1985
Sales 98.4MME *EMP* 900
SIC 7322 8742 Collection agency, except real estate; Banking & finance consultant
CEO: Thomas R Penaluna
**Pr:* Chad Benson
**CFO:* Robert Kahler
Sr VP: Michael Frost
VP: Mike Clausen
VP: Samantha Deines
VP: Stephen Ogunyemi
Exec: Mary Phillips
Exec: Kendra Richman
Prgrm Mgr: Pam Abdo
Genl Mgr: Nick Michael

D-U-N-S 87-846-4564
CBEYOND INC
(*Suby of* BIRCH COMMUNICATIONS INC) ★
320 Interstate N Pkwy 500, Atlanta, GA 30339-2205
Tel (678) 424-2400 *Founded/Ownrshp* 2014
Sales 760.3MME *EMP* 1,667
SIC 4813 7389 4899 1731 Telephone communication, except radio; ; Data telephone communications; ; Telephone services; Data communication services; Communications specialization
COO: Christopher Aversano
**CFO:* Edward James III
Software D: Dennis Fryzel
Snr Mgr: Brian Rasser

CBF
See CARLISLE BRAKE & FRICTION INC

D-U-N-S 14-835-2487
CBI SERVICES INC
(*Suby of* CHICAGO BRIDGE & IRON CO (DELAWARE)) ★
14107 S Route 59, Plainfield, IL 60544-3890
Tel (815) 439-6668 *Founded/Ownrshp* 2008
Sales 113.4MME *EMP* 300
SIC 1629 8741 Dams, waterways, docks & other marine construction; Construction management
Pr: Adam W Mohr
**Treas:* Terrence G Browne

D-U-N-S 80-807-8633
■ CBI-KANSAS INC
(*Suby of* COMMERCE BANCSHARES INC) ★
1000 Walnut St Fl 700, Kansas City, MO 64106-2158
Tel (816) 234-2000 *Founded/Ownrshp* 1977
Sales NA *EMP* 4,551
SIC 6021 National commercial banks
Pr: David W Kemper

D-U-N-S 96-573-8701
▲ CBIZ INC
6050 Oak Tree Blvd # 500, Cleveland, OH 44131-6951
Tel (216) 447-9000 *Founded/Ownrshp* 1996
Sales 750.4MM *EMP* 4,400E
Tkr Sym CBZ *Exch* NYS
SIC 8742 7389 7363 Management consulting services; Financial services; Employee leasing service
Pr: Jerome P Grisko Jr
**Ch Bd:* Steven L Gerard
Pr: Michael P Kouzelos
Pr: Chris Spurio
COO: Richard E Mills
**CFO:* Ware H Grove
**Treas:* Kelly J Marek
**V Ch Bd:* Rick L Burdick
Bd of Dir: Suzette Bull
Chf Mktg O: Mark M Waxman
Ofcr: Teresa E Bur
Ex VP: Socorro Camas
Ex VP: Robert H Garner
Sr VP: John A Fleischer
VP: Kelly Abbott
VP: Barbara Bick
VP: Cole Brown
VP: Terry Brown
VP: Teresa Bur
VP: Damian C Caracciolo
VP: Jay S Chfc
Board of Directors: Rick L Burdick, Michael H Degroote, Joseph S Dimartino, Gina D France, Sherrill W Hudson, Todd J Slotkin, Donald V Weir

D-U-N-S 80-937-3012
▲ CBL & ASSOCIATES PROPERTIES INC
2030 Hamilton Place Blvd, Chattanooga, TN 37421-6038
Tel (423) 855-0001 *Founded/Ownrshp* 1993
Sales 1.0MMM *EMP* 744
Tkr Sym CBL *Exch* NYS
SIC 6798 Real estate investment trusts
Pr: Stephen D Lebovitz
**Ch Bd:* Charles B Lebovitz
COO: Augustus N Stephas
CFO: Farzana K Mitchell
Ex VP: Ben S Landress
Ex VP: Michael I Lebovitz
Sr VP: Farzana Mitchell
VP: Tricia Cunningham
VP: Jeff Gregerson
VP: Eric Griffith
VP: Gary Roddy
VP: Ken Wittler

D-U-N-S 09-438-4252
CBM 2012 A CALIFORNIA LIMITED PARTNERSHIP
C B M PROPERTY MANAGEMENT
1010 Racquet Club Dr # 108, Auburn, CA 95603-3000
Tel (530) 823-2477 *Founded/Ownrshp* 1979
Sales 155.4MME *EMP* 220
SIC 1531 1522 6513 6531 8741 Speculative builder, single-family houses; Multi-family dwellings, new construction; Apartment building operators; Real estate agents & managers; Construction management
CEO: John P Casper
Sec: Kellie Casper
VP: Cameo Townzen

D-U-N-S 10-793-7310
CBMC CAPITAL BUILDING MAINTENANCE CORP
5018 College Ave, College Park, MD 20740-3814
Tel (301) 277-8000 *Founded/Ownrshp* 1898
Sales 29.6MME *EMP* 1,800
SIC 7349 Janitorial service, contract basis; Building maintenance, except repairs
Pr: Eric S Francis
**CEO:* Christopher Hecker
CFO: Howard S Abramon
**CFO:* Howard S Abramson
Mktg Dir: Roxanne Paul

CBMI
See ALLEGIANCE BENEFIT PLAN MANAGEMENT INC

CBNA
See COMMUNITY BANK N A

D-U-N-S 96-875-1029
■ CBOCS TEXAS LLC
(*Suby of* CRACKER BARREL OLD COUNTRY STORE INC) ★
305 S Hartmann Dr, Lebanon, TN 37087-4779
Tel (615) 235-4096 *Founded/Ownrshp* 2011

Sales 21.3MM[E] *EMP* 3,534[E]
SIC 5812 Eating places
Prin: Sandy Cochran

CBOE
See CHICAGO BOARD OPTIONS EXCHANGE INC

D-U-N-S 96-219-6064
▲ CBOE HOLDINGS INC
400 S Lasalle St, Chicago, IL 60605
Tel (312) 786-5600 *Founded/Ownrshp* 2006
Sales 634.5MM *EMP* 520[E]
Accts Deloitte & Touche Llp Chicago
Tkr Sym CBOE *Exch* NGS
SIC 6231 Security & commodity exchanges; Stock option exchanges
CEO: Edward T Tilly
**Ch Bd:* William J Brodsky
Pr: Edward L Provost
CFO: Alan J Dean
Bd of Dir: Eden R Martin
Ofcr: Alexandra Albright
Ex VP: Joanne Moffic-Silver
Ex VP: Gerald T O'Connell
VP: Luann Oshea
VP: David S Reynolds
VP: Mike Todd
Dir Bus: Michael Mollet

D-U-N-S 18-599-5750 IMP
CBOL CORP
19850 Plummer St, Chatsworth, CA 91311-5652
Tel (818) 704-8200 *Founded/Ownrshp* 1987
Sales 162.0MM[E] *EMP* 131
SIC 5065 5072 5013 5088 5084 5162 Electronic parts & equipment; Hardware; Staples; Motor vehicle supplies & new parts; Transportation equipment & supplies; Industrial machinery & equipment; Plastics materials & basic shapes
COO: Howard Nam
**CEO:* Spencer H Kim
**CFO:* Kenneth Cheung
Sr VP: Robert Jondall
Genl Mgr: Jason Koh

D-U-N-S 08-866-1418
■ CBORD GROUP INC
(*Suby of* ROPER TECHNOLOGIES INC) ★
950 Danby Rd Ste 100c, Ithaca, NY 14850-5795
Tel (607) 257-2410 *Founded/Ownrshp* 1975
Sales 120.7MM[E] *EMP* 461
SIC 7372 5045 Application computer software; Computer peripheral equipment; Computers
Pr: Max Steinhardt
**Pr:* Tim Tighe
CFO: Paul Soni
**Ex VP:* Bruce Lane
Sr VP: Randy Eckels
**Sr VP:* Karen Sammon
VP: Aric Alibrio
**VP:* Larry Delaney
VP: Shawn McCarthy
**VP:* Lucy Staley
Exec: John Russo

D-U-N-S 60-262-7940
■ CBOT HOLDINGS INC
(*Suby of* CME GROUP INC) ★
141 W Jackson Blvd, Chicago, IL 60604-2992
Tel (312) 435-3500 *Founded/Ownrshp* 2003
Sales 91.2MM[E] *EMP* 770
SIC 6231 Security & commodity exchanges; Futures exchanges, contract
Pr: Bernard W Dan
V Ch: Robert F Corvino
**CFO:* Glen M Johnson
Ofcr: Kevin Ohara
**Ex VP:* Bryan T Durkin
Sr VP: Chip Bennett
Sr VP: James G Bennett
VP: James Brady
VP: Steve Dickey
VP: Ethel Laughlin
VP: David Prosperi

D-U-N-S 00-718-2850
■ CBRE GLOBAL INVESTORS LLC
GLOBAL INNOVATION PARTNER
(*Suby of* CBRE INC) ★
515 S Flower St Ste 3100, Los Angeles, CA 90071-2233
Tel (213) 683-4200 *Founded/Ownrshp* 1995
Sales 152.8MM[E] *EMP* 1,100
SIC 8742 Real estate consultant
CEO: Ritson Ferguson
Pr: Vance G Maddocks
COO: Peter Di Corpo
COO: Stuart Savidge
**CFO:* Maurice Voskuilen
Sr VP: Matthew Yao
Mng Dir: Philip Hench
Mng Dir: Don Morse
Mng Dir: Jeremy J Plummer
CIO: Sophie Van Oosterom
Snr Mgr: Alberto Fossati

D-U-N-S 61-760-8104
▲ CBRE GROUP INC
400 S Hope St Ste 25, Los Angeles, CA 90071-2800
Tel (213) 613-3333 *Founded/Ownrshp* 1906
Sales 10.8MMM *EMP* 70,000
Tkr Sym CBG *Exch* NYS
SIC 6531 6162 8742 Real estate agent, commercial; Real estate managers; Appraiser, real estate; Mortgage bankers; Real estate consultant
Pr: Robert E Sulentic
**Ch Bd:* Ray Wirta
Pr: Calvin W Frese Jr
Pr: Michael J Lafitte
CEO: William F Concannon
CEO: T Ritson Ferguson
CFO: Gil Borok
CFO: James R Groch
Ofcr: J Christopher Kirk
Ex VP: Laurence H Midler
Board of Directors: Brandon B Boze, Curtis F Feeny, Bradford M Freeman, Christopher T Jenny, Gerardo I Lopez, Frederic V Malek, Paula R Reynolds, Laura D Tyson

D-U-N-S 05-921-1508 IMP
■ CBRE INC
(*Suby of* CBRE GROUP INC) ★
400 S Hope St Ste 25, Los Angeles, CA 90071-2800
Tel (310) 477-5876 *Founded/Ownrshp* 2004
Sales 1.9MMM[E] *EMP* 12,617
SIC 6726 6531 Investment offices; Real estate agent, commercial; Real estate managers; Appraiser, real estate
Pr: Bob Sulentic
V Ch: Robert Given
V Ch: Tracy Kennedy
V Ch: Jay Wagley
COO: Steven Swerdlow
**CFO:* Kenneth J Kay
**Treas:* Debbie Fan
Ex VP: Peter Finn
Ex VP: Jeff Glenn
Ex VP: Michael Hines
Ex VP: Lisa Konieczka
Ex VP: Andrew Majewski
Sr VP: Rod J Apodaca
Sr VP: Jim Beaty
Sr VP: Kirk Beebe
Sr VP: Chris Burdett
Sr VP: Bill Crean
Sr VP: William Cuddy
Sr VP: Ron Kastner
Sr VP: Dwight Newell
Sr VP: Richard Ridgway

D-U-N-S 00-131-7056 IMP/EXP
■ CBS BROADCASTING INC
WESTINGHOUSE
(*Suby of* WESTINGHOUSE CBS HOLDING CO INC) ★
51 W 52nd St, New York, NY 10019-6119
Tel (212) 975-4321 *Founded/Ownrshp* 1927
Sales 2.2MMM[E] *EMP* 6,400
SIC 4833 4832 7812 Television broadcasting stations; Radio broadcasting stations; Television film production
Pr: Leslie Moonves
**COO:* Joseph Ianniello
**Ch:* Sumner M Redstone
Ex VP: Darin Bassin
Ex VP: Jack Sussman
Sr VP: John Frazee
Sr VP: Josie Thomas
VP: Brelinda Brelin
VP: Bridgette Bridge
VP: Paul Friedman
Comm Dir: Lori Conrad

D-U-N-S 15-428-7825
■ CBS CORP
(*Suby of* C B S) ★
51 W 52nd St Bsmt 1, New York, NY 10019-6188
Tel (212) 975-4321 *Founded/Ownrshp* 1986
Sales 13.8MMM *EMP* 16,260
Tkr Sym CBS *Exch* NYS
SIC 4833 4832 7312 2731 Television broadcasting stations; Radio broadcasting stations; Outdoor advertising services; Books: publishing only
Ch Bd: Leslie Moonves
Pr: Tirso Navarro
COO: Joseph R Ianniello
CFO: Reid Sullivan
Treas: Georgette Morrow
V Ch Bd: Shari Redstone
Chf Cred: Gil Schwartz
Bd of Dir: Patrick Corr
Ex VP: Jonathan H Anschell
Ex VP: Harry Isaacs
Ex VP: Richard M Jones
Ex VP: Lawrence Liding
Ex VP: John Orlando
Ex VP: Rik Toulon
VP: Mark Beatty
VP: Betty E Berlamino
VP: Robin Bona
VP: Mariel Brady
VP: Allan Bressler
VP: Joe Butkovich
VP: Barry Chamberlain
Board of Directors: David R Andelman, Joseph A Califano Jr, William S Cohen, Gary L Countryman, Bruce S Gordon, Linda M Griego, Arnold Kopelson, Charles K Gifford Leonard, Doug Morris

D-U-N-S 80-853-9506
■ CBS INTERACTIVE INC
CBSI
(*Suby of* CBS CORP) ★
235 2nd St, San Francisco, CA 94105-3124
Tel (415) 344-2000 *Founded/Ownrshp* 2008
Sales 328.5MM[E] *EMP* 2,705
SIC 7319 7375 4832 Distribution of advertising material or sample services; On-line data base information retrieval; Radio broadcasting stations
Ch Bd: Jarl Mohn
Pt: Eric Foote
Pr: Barry Briggs
Pr: Jim Lanzone
Bd of Dir: Serious Pie
Ex VP: Stephen Colvin
Ex VP: Joseph Gillespie
VP: Andy Beal
VP: Chris Castro
VP: Nathan Collier
VP: Steve Comstock
VP: Dale Durrett
VP: Eric Franklin
VP: Jeff Grossman
VP: Georges Haddad
VP: Wendy Hogan
VP: Kathryn Kulik
VP: Ken Lagana
VP: Tom Lisack
VP: Shane McGilloway
VP: Fred McIntyre

CBS OUTDOOR LLC
See OUTFRONT MEDIA LLC

D-U-N-S 05-989-8486
■ CBS RADIO INC
(*Suby of* CBS CORP) ★
1271 Ave Of The Amer 44, New York, NY 10020-1401
Tel (212) 314-9200 *Founded/Ownrshp* 2001
Sales 1.2MMM[E] *EMP* 5,890
SIC 4832 7312 Radio broadcasting stations; Outdoor advertising services; Billboard advertising; Poster advertising, outdoor
Pr: Dan Mason
Pr: Ezra Kucharz
Pr: Michael Weiss
COO: Anton Guitano
CFO: Jacques Tortoroli
Ex VP: Scott Herman
Sr VP: Jo Ann Haller
VP: Alan Blum
VP: Rory Flynn
VP: Jeff Hedges
VP: Daniel P Mason
VP: John Sheehan
Exec: Erin Kapner
Exec: Simone Rowson-Green
Dir Soc: Melinda Lee
Dir Soc: Sarah Thomas

CBSG
See CAPITAL BUILDING SERVICES GROUP INC

CBSI
See CBS INTERACTIVE INC

CBT COMPANY
See BELTING CO OF CINCINNATI

CBTS
See CINCINNATI BELL TECHNOLOGY SOLUTIONS INC

D-U-N-S 83-133-9333
■ CC HOLDINGS GS V LLC
(*Suby of* CROWN CASTLE INTERNATIONAL CORP) ★
1220 Augusta Dr Ste 500, Houston, TX 77057-2263
Tel (713) 570-3000 *Founded/Ownrshp* 2009
Sales 607.2MM *EMP* 1[E]
Accts Pricewaterhousecoopers Llp Pi
SIC 4812 Cellular telephone services
CEO: W Benjamin Moreland

CC INDUSTRIES
See HENRY CROWN AND CO

D-U-N-S 04-390-3376
CC INDUSTRIES INC
(*Suby of* CC INDUSTRIES) ★
222 N La Salle St # 1000, Chicago, IL 60601-1121
Tel (312) 855-4000 *Founded/Ownrshp* 1948
Sales 407.6MM *EMP* 1,483
SIC 6552 Land subdividers & developers, commercial
CEO: William H Crown
**Ch Bd:* Lester Crown
Ex VP: William Kankler
Ex VP: William C Kunkler
**VP:* Mel Cohen
**VP:* James S Crown
**VP:* Charles H Goodman
Dir IT: Vitaly Tsinman

D-U-N-S 61-031-3025 IMP
CC METALS AND ALLOYS LLC
CCMA
(*Suby of* GAA) ★
1542 N Main St, Calvert City, KY 42029-8929
Tel (270) 395-7631 *Founded/Ownrshp* 2012
Sales 89.1MM[E] *EMP* 200
SIC 3313 3341 3295 Ferroalloys; Secondary nonferrous metals; Minerals, ground or treated
CEO: Mordechai Korf
**CFO:* Barry Nuss
VP: Douglas Lee
IT Man: Michael Boulais
IT Man: Richard Sherry

CC PRODUCE
See C & C PRODUCE INC

D-U-N-S 07-995-3868
■ CC SCN FIBER LLC
(*Suby of* CROWN CASTLE INTERNATIONAL CORP) ★
1220 Augusta Dr Ste 600, Houston, TX 77057-6801
Tel (713) 570-3000 *Founded/Ownrshp* 2015
Sales 101.2MM[E] *EMP* 4,001[E]
SIC 4899 7622 4812 Data communication services; Antenna repair & installation; Radio telephone communication
Pr: Benjamin W Moreland

D-U-N-S 03-055-6120
CC SERVICES INC
COUNTRY FINANCIAL
(*Suby of* ILLINOIS FARM BUREAU) ★
1701 Towanda Ave, Bloomington, IL 61701-2057
Tel (309) 821-3372 *Founded/Ownrshp* 1975, 1925
Sales 576.7MM[E] *EMP* 3,604
SIC 8742 6411

D-U-N-S 00-603-6649
■ CC VIII HOLDINGS LLC
(*Suby of* CHARTER COMMUNICATIONS HOLDINGS LLC) ★
12405 Powerscourt Dr, Saint Louis, MO 63131-3673
Tel (314) 543-2411 *Founded/Ownrshp* 1998
Sales 45.8MM[E] *EMP* 1,600
SIC 4841 Cable television services

D-U-N-S 80-762-5296
CC-NAPLES INC
HYATT HOTEL
(*Suby of* HYATT HOTEL) ★
704 Village Cir, Naples, FL 34110-7909
Tel (239) 596-4702 *Founded/Ownrshp* 1992
Sales 11.8MM *EMP* 1,050
SIC 8741 Nursing & personal care facility management
Pr: Penny Pritzker
CFO: Jim Sieber
IT Man: Chuck Hayes
**VP Opers:* Ben Pierce

D-U-N-S 08-023-4434
■ CC-RENO LLC
CIRCUS CIRCUS RENO HT & CASINO
(*Suby of* ELDORADO RESORTS INC) ★
500 N Sierra St, Reno, NV 89503-4717
Tel (775) 328-9469 *Founded/Ownrshp* 2015
Sales 18.2MM[E] *EMP* 2,000
SIC 7011 Casino hotel
VP: Tony Mavrides
CFO: Nancy King
Exec: Julia Portillo
Dir Soc: Diana Altura
Sls Mgr: Marie A Cruz

CCA
See COMMONWEALTH CHARTER ACADEMY

D-U-N-S 19-835-4339 IMP
CCA CIVIL INC
445 South St Ste 310, Morristown, NJ 07960-6475
Tel (862) 701-7200 *Founded/Ownrshp* 2005
Sales 104.5MM *EMP* 500
SIC 1611 Highway & street construction
Pr: Peter Will

D-U-N-S 07-915-1541
■ CCA CLUB OPERATIONS HOLDINGS LLC
(*Suby of* CLUBCORP HOLDINGS INC) ★
3030 L B Johnson Fwy # 400, Dallas, TX 75234-2786
Tel (972) 243-6191 *Founded/Ownrshp* 2010
Sales 760.2MM[E] *EMP* 13,300
SIC 7997 Membership sports & recreation clubs
Pr: Eric L Affeldt

D-U-N-S 03-089-7300
CCBC INC
1 Mi Jack Way, Homewood, IL 60430-4618
Tel (708) 206-0500 *Founded/Ownrshp* 1984
Sales 97.6M *EMP* 1,600
SIC 6719

D-U-N-S 14-297-8381
■ CCBCC OPERATIONS LLC
COCA-COLA
(*Suby of* COCA-COLA BOTTLING CO CONSOLIDATED) ★
4100 Coca Cola Plz, Charlotte, NC 28211-3588
Tel (704) 364-8728 *Founded/Ownrshp* 2004
Sales 638.9MM[E] *EMP* 4,300
SIC 2086 Bottled & canned soft drinks
CEO: J Frank Harrison III
CFO: James E Harris Jr
DP Exec: Robert Pettus
QA Dir: Kathy Burrill
IT Man: Thomas Dejuneas
Info Man: Bob Hogue
QI Cn Mgr: Rick Smith

CCBHO
See COMMUNITY CARE BEHAVIORAL HEALTH ORGANIZATION

CCC
See CONSOLIDATED CONTAINER CO LLC

D-U-N-S 03-396-6076
CCC ACQUISITION HOLDINGS INC
(*Suby of* BAIN CAPITAL PARTNERS LLC) ★
200 Clarendon St Ste 4000, Boston, MA 02116-5045
Tel (617) 516-2000 *Founded/Ownrshp* 2012
Sales 280.5MM[E] *EMP* 4,690[E]
SIC 6719 2821 Investment holding companies, except banks; Public utility holding companies; Polyvinyl chloride resins (PVC)
CEO: Seth Meisel

D-U-N-S 05-456-8845 IMP/EXP
CCC ASSOCIATES CO (AL)
THOMPSON & ELM
3601 Wetumpka Hwy, Montgomery, AL 36110-2749
Tel (334) 272-2140 *Founded/Ownrshp* 1950
Sales 87.0MM[E] *EMP* 285
SIC 5193 5992

D-U-N-S 15-181-8457 IMP/EXP
CCC GROUP INC
INDUSTRIAL MECHANICAL COMPANY
(*Suby of* GUTHRIE & HUEBNER CO INC) ★
5797 Dietrich Rd, San Antonio, TX 78219-3599
Tel (210) 661-4251 *Founded/Ownrshp* 2003
Sales 463.8MM[E] *EMP* 2,500
Accts Rinaldo J Gonzalez Pc San An
SIC 1541 1629 1542 Industrial buildings, new construction; Mine loading & discharging station construction; Commercial & office building, new construction
Pr: Arthur D Huebner
COO: Timothy J Henning
CFO: Nita Martinez
CFO: Nita B Mc Bride
Sr VP: Milton D Huebner
VP: Roger W Crider
VP: Patrick B Egger
VP: Jack R Hockey
VP: Kenneth R R Huebner
VP: John M Moran Jr
VP: Robert L Urban
Dir Bus: Daniel Gary
Board of Directors: Jack F Farris Chairman, Bruce A Jeffrey, Richard D Swarthout

D-U-N-S 11-924-2720 IMP
CCC HOLDING LLC
3332 Partridge Ln Bldg A, Baton Rouge, LA 70809-2413
Tel (225) 368-3900 *Founded/Ownrshp* 1997
Sales 194.3MM[E] *EMP* 1,000
SIC 2095 5149 5812 Roasted coffee; Coffee, green or roasted; Fast food restaurants & stands

D-U-N-S 03-900-2951
CCC INFORMATION SERVICES INC
222 Mrchds Mart Plz 900, Chicago, IL 60654
Tel (312) 222-4636 *Founded/Ownrshp* 2013
Sales 222.1MM[E] *EMP* 1,100
SIC 7371 Computer software development
Ch Bd: Githesh Ramamurthy
CFO: Andrew G Balbirer

V Ch Bd: J Laurence Costin Jr
Sr VP: David Merritt
VP: Vijay Lingineni
VP: Reza Rooholamini
Genl Mgr: Barrett Callaghan
Genl Mgr: Jim Dickens
Snr Sftwr: Jeff Boulanger
Snr Sftwr: Van Hoang
Snr Sftwr: Dariusz Kuc

D-U-N-S 17-778-7058 IMP/EXP
CCC PARTS CO
NATIONAL TRCK PARTS OF MIDWEST
(*Suby of* TRUCKPRO LLC) ★
420 S 145th East Ave, Tulsa, OK 74108-1303
Tel (918) 838-9797 *Founded/Ownrshp* 2013
Sales 115.8MM^E *EMP* 275
SIC 5531 Truck equipment & parts
Pr: Donald Hardin

CCC WHOLESALE
See CHASE CASH & CARRY INC

D-U-N-S 17-094-4149
■ **CCE HOLDINGS LLC**
(*Suby of* SOUTHERN UNION GAS) ★
1 Ugi Ctr Fl 2, Wilkes Barre, PA 18711-0600
Tel (713) 989-2000 *Founded/Ownrshp* 2008
Sales 75.4MM^E *EMP* 2,248
SIC 4922 Pipelines, natural gas
VP: George Aldrich
VP: Jennifer Cawley
VP: Susan Groce
VP: Steve Hotte
VP: Willie Johnson
VP: Robert Kerrigan

D-U-N-S 82-919-1266
CCE/DFS INC
201 Defense Hwy Ste 202, Annapolis, MD 21401-7096
Tel (410) 263-6422 *Founded/Ownrshp* 2008
Sales 85.4MM^E *EMP* 550
SIC 1542 8711 8744 Nonresidential construction; Engineering services; Facilities support services
CEO: William A Grice
**CFO:* Marc Krens
Off Mgr: Jenna Davis

D-U-N-S 83-607-0870
CCF BRANDS LLC
5211 W Village Pkwy # 101, Rogers, AR 72758-8104
Tel (479) 464-0544 *Founded/Ownrshp* 1999
Sales 732.1MM *EMP* 58
Accts Frost Pllc Little Rock Arkan
SIC 5144 5142 Eggs; Packaged frozen goods
Pr: Justin Whaley
**Ch Bd:* Ron Whaley
Pr: Scotty Roberson
**COO:* Bob Hodges
**CFO:* Doug Parker
**Sr VP:* Sean Hatch
**Sr VP:* Dennis McDowell
VP: Bill Bradley
VP: Gabrielle Chambers
VP: Tonya Horn
VP: Diana Sparks
VP: Monte Terry

D-U-N-S 07-096-8790
CCG HOLDINGS LLC
CLEARVIEW CINEMAS
(*Suby of* CABLEVISION) ★
1111 Stewart Ave, Bethpage, NY 11714-3533
Tel (516) 803-2300 *Founded/Ownrshp* 2011
Sales 3.0MM^E *EMP* 2,644^E
SIC 7832 Motion picture theaters, except drive-in
Sr VP: Victoria Mink

D-U-N-S 15-077-8376
■ **CCH II LLC**
(*Suby of* CHARTER COMMUNICATIONS INC) ★
12405 Powerscourt Dr, Saint Louis, MO 63131-3673
Tel (314) 965-0555 *Founded/Ownrshp* 2003
Sales 4.8MM *EMP* 23,800^E
SIC 4841 Cable & other pay television services
Pr: Carl E Vogel

D-U-N-S 00-509-4370 IMP
CCH INC
(*Suby of* WOLTERS KLUWER UNITED STATES INC) ★
2700 Lake Cook Rd, Riverwoods, IL 60015-3867
Tel (847) 267-7000 *Founded/Ownrshp* 1996
Sales 1.0MMM^E *EMP* 4,743
SIC 2721 2731 7389 7338 8732 7371 Statistical reports (periodicals): publishing & printing; Books: publishing & printing; Pamphlets: publishing & printing; Legal & tax services; Secretarial & typing service; Research services, except laboratory; Computer software development
CEO: Jason Marx
Pr: Christopher F Kane
COO: Ted Kubak
COO: David Lyser
CFO: Douglas Winterrose
Sec: Bruce C Lenz
Ex VP: Teresa Mackintosh
VP: Paul Gazzolo
VP: Richard J Parker
Prin: William Zale
Off Mgr: Joyce Ridley
Board of Directors: Rebecca Karnes-Hensley, Nancy McKinstry, Hugh Yarrington

CCHP
See CHINESE COMMUNITY HEALTH PLAN

CCI
See CLEVELAND CONSTRUCTION INC

CCI
See CONTAMINANT CONTROL INC

D-U-N-S 00-721-9595 IMP/EXP
CCI CORP
(*Suby of* TRUCKPRO LLC) ★
420 S 145th East Ave, Tulsa, OK 74108-1303
Tel (918) 743-6005 *Founded/Ownrshp* 1953, 2013
Sales 206.8MM^E *EMP* 1,600
SIC 5531 Truck equipment & parts
CEO: Steve Riordan
**CFO:* Steve Martin

D-U-N-S 00-780-9304
CCI MECHANICAL INC
(*Suby of* REDWOOD INDUSTRIES INC) ★
2345 S Cci Way, West Valley City, UT 84119-1250
Tel (801) 973-9000 *Founded/Ownrshp* 1961
Sales 140.8MM^E *EMP* 300
SIC 1711 Mechanical contractor
Pr: Davis Mullholand
CFO: Gary Gibson
**Treas:* Jeffrey A Tack
**VP:* Michael R Kladis
**VP:* Steven Kramer
**VP:* D Patrick Lynch
VP: Patrick Lynch
**VP:* Kevin S Tolley
Genl Mgr: Steve Campbell
Genl Mgr: David Katsanevas
Off Mgr: Kathy Bonnett

D-U-N-S 10-234-5238
CCI SYSTEMS INC
PACKERLAND BROADBAND
105 Kent St, Iron Mountain, MI 49801-1553
Tel (906) 774-6621 *Founded/Ownrshp* 1985
Sales 163.8MM *EMP* 800
SIC 5065

CCI VALUE
See CONTROL COMPONENTS INC

CCI/COAKLEYTECH
See ONETOUCHPOINT MIDWEST CORP

D-U-N-S 07-957-0452
CCJV
5001 Rogerdale Rd, Houston, TX 77072
Tel (713) 375-8051 *Founded/Ownrshp* 2013
Sales 78.6MM^E *EMP* 1,007^E
SIC 4924 Natural gas distribution

D-U-N-S 60-354-6326 IMP
CCL INDUSTRIES CORP
CCL LABEL
(*Suby of* CCL INTERNATIONAL INC)
15 Controls Dr, Shelton, CT 06484-6111
Tel (203) 926-1253 *Founded/Ownrshp* 1982
Sales 812.5MM^E *EMP* 10,400
SIC 2759 2992 3411 2819 2844 Flexographic printing; Letterpress printing; Lubricating oils & greases; Aluminum cans; Industrial inorganic chemicals; Cosmetic preparations; Lipsticks; Shampoos, rinses, conditioners: hair; Deodorants, personal
CEO: Geoffrey T Martin
**Pr:* Wayne M E McLeod
**Treas:* Steve Lancaster
VP: Al Green
IT Man: Ian Miller
Prd Mgr: Wayne Dutertre
Prd Mgr: Dave Rodriguez

CCL LABEL
See CCL INDUSTRIES CORP

D-U-N-S 01-809-4016 IMP
CCL LABEL (DELAWARE) INC
(*Suby of* SYNTEL) ★
15 Controls Dr, Shelton, CT 06484-6111
Tel (203) 926-1253 *Founded/Ownrshp* 1987
Sales 135.1MM^E *EMP* 1,000
SIC 2759 Labels & seals: printing
Pr: Serge De Paoli
**VP:* Ronald Perin
**VP:* Victor Theriault

D-U-N-S 15-416-3414 IMP/EXP
CCL LABEL INC
SYNTEL
(*Suby of* CCL INDUSTRIES INC)
161 Worcester Rd Ste 504, Framingham, MA 01701-5315
Tel (508) 872-4511 *Founded/Ownrshp* 1987
Sales 1.2MMM^E *EMP* 2,000
SIC 2759 3411 2671 Flexographic printing; Letterpress printing; Aluminum cans; Packaging paper & plastics film, coated & laminated
Pr: Geoffrey Martin
**CFO:* Victor Theriault
**Treas:* Steve Lancaster
**Treas:* Sean Washchuk
**VP:* Lalitha Vaidyanathan
Exec: Christie Bailey
Dir Bus: Cliff Brockman
QA Dir: Kimberly Huffman
QA Dir: Yvette Rodriguez
Snr Mgr: Michael Berry

CCLA
See COSCO CONTAINER LINES AMERICAS INC

CCM
See COUNTY COLLEGE OF MORRIS

CCMA
See CC METALS AND ALLOYS LLC

CCMC
See AGERO - CHECK

D-U-N-S 62-639-9281
CCMC CORP
CONNECTICUT CHILDRENS MED CTR
282 Washington St, Hartford, CT 06106-3322
Tel (860) 545-9490 *Founded/Ownrshp* 1985
Sales 310.6MM^E *EMP* 1,117
Accts Withumsmithbrown Pc Morristow
SIC 8069 7389 8299 Children's hospital; Fund raising organizations; Educational services
Ch Bd: Martin J Gavin
**Pr:* Larry Gold
**Ex VP:* Paul Dworkin MD
**Sr VP:* Andrea L Benin MD

D-U-N-S 55-592-2959
CCMP CAPITAL ADVISORS LP
277 Park Ave Fl 27, New York, NY 10172-0003
Tel (212) 600-9600 *Founded/Ownrshp* 2005
Sales 1.1MMM^E *EMP* 2,523
SIC 6726 Investment offices
Pr: Steve Murray
VP: Robert Stabile
Mng Dir: Mark McFadden

D-U-N-S 07-986-2493
CCMP CAPITAL INVESTORS III LP
245 Park Ave Fl 16, New York, NY 10167-2402
Tel (212) 600-9600 *Founded/Ownrshp* 2012
Sales 158.5M^E *EMP* 2,605
SIC 6799 Investors

CCMSI
See CANNON COCHRAN MANAGEMENT SERVICES INC

D-U-N-S 80-013-1414
CCMSI HOLDINGS INC
2 E Main St Ste 208, Danville, IL 61832-5844
Tel (217) 446-1089 *Founded/Ownrshp* 2007
Sales 750.9MM^E *EMP* 1,184^E
SIC 8748 Employee programs administration
CFO: John Kluth II

D-U-N-S 15-095-0116
■ **CCO HOLDINGS LLC**
(*Suby of* CCH II LLC) ★
12405 Powerscourt Dr, Saint Louis, MO 63131-3673
Tel (314) 965-0555 *Founded/Ownrshp* 2003
Sales 6.5MMM^E *EMP* 23,800^E
Accts Kpmg Llp St Louis Missouri
SIC 4841 4813 7389 Cable & other pay television services; ;Telephone services
Pr: Michael J Lovett
**Ex VP:* Gregory L Doody
**Ex VP:* Marwan Fawaz
**Ex VP:* Ted W Schremp
**Sr VP:* Kevin D Howard

D-U-N-S 15-106-8710
■ **CCO NR HOLDINGS LLC**
(*Suby of* CHARTER COMMUNICATIONS OPERATING LLC) ★
12405 Powerscourt Dr, Saint Louis, MO 63131-3673
Tel (314) 965-0555 *Founded/Ownrshp* 2003
Sales 665.3MM^E *EMP* 15^E
SIC 4841 Cable & other pay television services

D-U-N-S 04-447-2306
▲ **CCOM GROUP INC**
275 Wagaraw Rd, Hawthorne, NJ 07506-1451
Tel (973) 427-8224 *Founded/Ownrshp* 1964
Sales 86.1MM *EMP* 154^E
Tkr Sym CCOM *Exch* OTC
SIC 5074 5075 Plumbing & hydronic heating supplies; Heating equipment (hydronic); Plumbing fittings & supplies; Air conditioning & ventilation equipment & supplies
CEO: Pete Gasiewicz
**Ch Bd:* Michael Goldman
**CEO:* Peter Gasiewicz
**CFO:* William Salek
**Ex VP:* Melissa Goldman-Williams

CCP INDUSTRIES
See TRANZONIC COMPANIES

D-U-N-S 07-998-8648 EXP
CCP MANAGEMENT INC
3401 Phillips Hwy, Jacksonville, FL 32207-5609
Tel (904) 398-7177 *Founded/Ownrshp* 1973
Sales 84.6MM^E *EMP* 62^E
SIC 5032 5169 Concrete building products; Chemicals & allied products
CEO: Martin S Harrell
**Ch Bd:* William H Harrell
**Pr:* Frank W Allcorn IV
**COO:* David H Sheffield
**Treas:* Janice M Antico
**VP:* Judy Jones
Genl Mgr: Eddie Miranda

CCPS
See CECIL COUNTY PUBLIC SCHOOLS

CCPS
See FOUNDATION FOR PUBLIC SCHOOL CHILDREN OF CHARLES COUNTY INC

CCS
See CLARKSTON COMMUNITY SCHOOLS

CCS MEDICAL
See DEGC ENTERPRISES (US) INC

D-U-N-S 62-162-9588
CCS MEDICAL HOLDINGS INC
(*Suby of* HIGHLAND CAPITAL MANAGEMENT LP) ★
1505 L B Johnson Fwy # 600, Farmers Branch, TX 75234-6074
Tel (972) 628-2100 *Founded/Ownrshp* 2007
Sales 220.1MM^E *EMP* 1,434
Accts Ernst & Young Llp
SIC 5999 5912 5961 Convalescent equipment & supplies; Hospital equipment & supplies; Orthopedic & prosthesis applications; Drug stores; Proprietary (non-prescription medicine) stores; Pharmaceuticals, mail order
Pr: Dirk Allison
**CFO:* James Dunlop
CFO: Stephen M Saft
**CFO:* Michael A Sicuro
**Ex VP:* Michael Iskra

D-U-N-S 12-857-4923
CCS MEDICAL INC
(*Suby of* CCS MEDICAL HOLDINGS INC) ★
1505 L B Johnson Fwy # 600, Farmers Branch, TX 75234-6074
Tel (972) 628-2100 *Founded/Ownrshp* 2002
Sales 216.5MM^E *EMP* 1,400
SIC 5999 5912 5961 Convalescent equipment & supplies; Hospital equipment & supplies; Orthopedic & prosthesis applications; Drug stores; Proprietary (non-prescription medicine) stores; Pharmaceuticals, mail order
Pr: Dirk Allison
Pr: Laurie Gillam
**CEO:* Michael A Sicuro
Ofcr: Sean Browne
Ex VP: Michael Geldart
Ex VP: Zeke Zoccoli
Dir IT: Kim Dinh
VP Opers: Michael Hendrickson
Opers Mgr: Scott Smith
Sls Dir: Micah Sutton
Cert Phar: Leah Prescott

CCSD
See CHARLESTON COUNTY SCHOOL DISTRICT DEVELOPMENT CORP

CCSD
See CLARKE COUNTY SCHOOL DISTRICT

CCSD
See CAL-COMP ELECTRONICS (USA) CO LTD

C.C.S.I.
See CONTINENTAL CONCESSION SUPPLIES INC

D-U-N-S 07-930-7981
CCTM1 LLC
2000 Corporate Dr, Canonsburg, PA 15317-8564
Tel (724) 416-2000 *Founded/Ownrshp* 1999
Sales 41.0MM^E *EMP* 1,000
SIC 4813 Telephone communication, except radio
CEO: Ben Moreland
Pr: Blake Hawk

CCX
See SUMITOMO FORESTRY AMERICA INC

CD
See CENTRAL DAUPHIN SCHOOL DISTRICT AUTHORITY

D-U-N-S 00-578-1356
CD SMITH CONSTRUCTION INC (WI)
889 E Johnson St, Fond Du Lac, WI 54935-2933
Tel (920) 924-2900 *Founded/Ownrshp* 1936
Sales 203.4MM^E *EMP* 440^E
Accts Grant Thornton Llp Milwaukee
SIC 1542 1541 Commercial & office building contractors; Institutional building construction; Industrial buildings & warehouses
Ch: Thomas D Baker
**Pr:* Gary M Smith
**Treas:* Robert Baker
VP: Steve Schmitz
**VP:* Justin Smith
Exec: Judy Goldsmith
IT Man: Lawrence Foster

CD&R ROADHOUSE HOLDINGS
See STERLING GROUP PARTNERS II LP

CD-ADAPCO
See ANALYSIS & DESIGN APPLICATION CO LTD

D-U-N-S 80-152-7628 IMP
CDA INC
8500 S Tryon St, Charlotte, NC 28273-3312
Tel (704) 504-1877 *Founded/Ownrshp* 2000
Sales 144.8MM^E *EMP* 186
SIC 5099 3652 Compact discs; Pre-recorded records & tapes
Pr: Raymond B Zerrusen
**COO:* Doug Franzen
**CFO:* Marty Carter
**Ex VP:* Mike Glover
Ex VP: Kris Peavy

CDC
See CENTERS FOR DISEASE CONTROL AND PREVENTION

D-U-N-S 02-771-6034 IMP
CDC OREGON INC
COLUMBIA DISTRIBUTING
3601 Nw Yeon Ave, Portland, OR 97210-1319
Tel (503) 289-9600 *Founded/Ownrshp* 2012
Sales 817.1MM^E *EMP* 1,500
Accts Moss Adams Llp Portland Oreg
SIC 5182 5181 5149 Wine; Beer & other fermented malt liquors; Beverages, except coffee & tea
Ch: Edward Maletis
**Pr:* Gregg Christiansen
CFO: Lee Jacobson
**CFO:* Paul Meade
**Sec:* John E Von Schlegell
VP: Jeff Lyons
VP: Mike Specht
VP: Dan Taylor
VP: Todd Tobin
Dist Mgr: Steve Huber
CIO: Michael Swatman

D-U-N-S 79-101-7853
CDC SOFTWARE HOLDINGS INC
(*Suby of* CDC CORPORATION)
Two Cncourse Pkwy Ste 800, Atlanta, GA 39901-0001
Tel (770) 351-9600 *Founded/Ownrshp* 2010
Sales 124.6MM^E *EMP* 1,951
SIC 7372 7379 8243 Business oriented computer software; Computer related consulting services; Software training, computer
Ch Bd: Peter Yip
**Pr:* Bruce Cameron
**CFO:* Roy B Goodman
**V Ch Bd:* John Clough
Ofcr: Rachel L Bailey
Ofcr: Latrice Fowler
Ofcr: Richard Wang
Sr VP: Jeffrey Longoria
Exec: Sandra Deloach
Assoc Dir: Leslie McDonald
Assoc Dir: Monica A Smith
Assoc Dir: James T Wassell

D-U-N-S 79-066-0059
CDC SOFTWARE INC
APTEAN
(*Suby of* APTEAN INC) ★
4325 Alexander Dr, Alpharetta, GA 30022-3740
Tel (770) 351-9600 *Founded/Ownrshp* 2012
Sales 267.5MM^E *EMP* 1,818^E
SIC 5045 Computer software
CEO: Stephen Dexter
**Ch Bd:* John Clough
**Pr:* Bruce Cameron

*Pr: Monte Ford
COO: Anne Kohler
*CFO: Derrick D Anderson
CFO: Stephen Dexter
*CFO: Daniel Eidson
CFO: James Fitzgibbons
Ex VP: Jay Baitler
Ex VP: William Geist
Sr VP: Paul Plaia
VP: Aaron Almansa
VP: Patrick Baca
VP: Mario Baldasserini
VP: Ann Belair
VP: Gilbert Breath
VP: David Cahn
VP: Anil Dwivedi
VP: Karen Forristal
VP: Carolyn Gidyk

CDFW
See CALIFORNIA DEPARTMENT OF FISH AND WILDLIFE

D-U-N-S 02-932-5131
CDH-DELNOR HEALTH SYSTEM
CENTRAL DUPAGE HEALTH
(Suby of NORTHWESTERN MEMORIAL HEALTHCARE) ★
25 N Winfield Rd, Winfield, IL 60190
Tel (630) 933-1600 Founded/Ownrshp 1980
Sales 182.1MMM EMP 1,600
SIC 8071 8741

D-U-N-S 17-415-2447
■ CDI CONTRACTORS LLC
C D I
(Suby of DILLARDS INC) ★
3000 Cantrell Rd, Little Rock, AR 72202-2010
Tel (501) 666-4300 Founded/Ownrshp 2008
Sales 284.5MM EMP 300
Accts Kpmg Llp Dallas Tx
SIC 1542 Commercial & office building, new construction; Commercial & office buildings, renovation & repair
Pr: E Lloyd Garrison
*COO: Mark Beach
*CFO: Chris Johnson
Bd of Dir: William T Dillard II
VP: Matt Bodishbaugh
*VP: Matthew Bodishbaugh
*VP: David Day
Div Mgr: Jonathan Semans
Off Mgr: Patricia Loveland
Dir IT: Brian Smith
Opers Mgr: Dan Bowen

D-U-N-S 00-259-9934
▲ CDI CORP (PA)
1735 Market St Ste 200, Philadelphia, PA 19103-7531
Tel (215) 569-2200 Founded/Ownrshp 1950
Sales 985.4MM EMP 900
Tkr Sym CDI Exch NYS
SIC 8711 7371 7373 7376 7361 7363 Engineering services; Custom computer programming services; Computer integrated systems design; Computer facilities management; Employment agencies; Help supply services
CEO: Michael Castleman
*Ch Bd: Walter R Garrison
Pr: David Arkless
Pr: Hugo Malan
*CFO: Michael S Castleman
*Ofcr: Brian D Short
Ex VP: Rich Giannone
*Ex VP: William J Wasilewski
Sr VP: Raymond Barratt
Sr VP: Ted Collins
Sr VP: Dennis J Vito
VP: Robert Bergeron
VP: Sheldon Bruha
VP: Andy Curtis
VP: Ronald J Friedman
VP: Rebecca Gratto
VP: Cyndi Harris
VP: David R Lavis
VP: Dean Magliozzi
VP: Beth Murray
VP: Ed Pallo
Board of Directors: Joseph L Carlini, Michael J Emmi, Lawrence C Karlson, Ronald J Kozich, Anna M Seal, Albert E Smith, Barton J Winokur

D-U-N-S 19-194-8025
■ CDI CORP
(Suby of CDI CORP) ★
1735 Market St Ste 200, Philadelphia, PA 19103-7531
Tel (215) 569-2200 Founded/Ownrshp 1950
Sales 175.9MM[E] EMP 800
SIC 7363 8711 7361 6794 Temporary help service; Engineering services; Placement agencies; Franchises, selling or licensing
Pr: Roger Ballou
Pr: Michael Fatig
*CFO: James M Powers Jr
Treas: Arlington A Nagle Jr
*Ex VP: Stuart Batchelor
Ex VP: Rich Giannone
*Ex VP: Robert Larney
*Ex VP: William Wasilewski
Sr VP: Brian D Shor
*Sr VP: Brian D Short
*VP: Thomas D Dileonardo
Board of Directors: Lawrence Karlson, Timothy J Kearney, Ronald Kozich, Mark A Prygocki Sr

D-U-N-S 79-404-4099 IMP
CDI ENERGY PRODUCTS INC
FENNER ADVANCED SEALING TECH
(Suby of FAST) ★
8103 Rankin Rd, Humble, TX 77396-1484
Tel (281) 446-6662 Founded/Ownrshp 1974
Sales 126.2MM[E] EMP 370
SIC 3053 Oil seals, rubber
Pr: Leonard Casey
Pr: Brian James
CFO: Woody Haas
*Treas: Ben Ficklen
VP: Peter Bennett
VP: Anthony Griffith
QA Dir: Richard Hager
Dir IT: Dennis Bretherton
IT Man: David Foll
VP Mfg: Edwin Chavez
Prd Mgr: Alex Muraviyov

D-U-N-S 09-783-3248
■ CDI MARINE CO LLC
(Suby of CDI CORP) ★
4600 Village Ave, Norfolk, VA 23502-2060
Tel (757) 763-6666 Founded/Ownrshp 1977
Sales 97.5MM[E] EMP 800
SIC 8711 8712 3732 3731 Marine engineering; Architectural services; Boat building & repairing; Shipbuilding & repairing
Pr: Joseph Barbano
Opers Mgr: Brenda Wilson
Board of Directors: Steve Karlovic

D-U-N-S 07-952-5018
▲ CDK GLOBAL INC
1950 Hassell Rd, Hoffman Estates, IL 60169-6308
Tel (847) 397-1700 Founded/Ownrshp 2014
Sales 2.1MMM EMP 8,700
Accts Deloitte & Touche Llp Chicago
Tkr Sym CDK Exch NGS
SIC 7372 Business oriented computer software
Pr: Brian P Macdonald
Ch Bd: Leslie A Brun
Pr: Andrew Dean
Pr: Robert N Karp
CFO: Alfred A Nietzelm
Ex VP: Rajiv K Amar
Ex VP: Lee J Brunz
Ex VP: Dan Flynn
Ex VP: Scott L Mathews
Ex VP: Malcolm Thorne
VP: Dave Carson
VP: Tim Hardin
VP: Ted Moore
VP: Doran Patten
VP: Mike Sailor
VP: Jennifer Williams
Board of Directors: Willie A Deese, Amy J Hillman, Eileen J Martinson, Stephen A Miles, Robert E Radway, Stephen F Schuckenbrock, Frank S Sowinski, Robert M Tarkoff

D-U-N-S 01-241-7349
CDK PERFORATING LLC
NINE ENERGY SERVICE
(Suby of NINE ENERGY SERVICE INC) ★
6500 West Fwy Ste 600, Fort Worth, TX 76116-2118
Tel (817) 945-1051 Founded/Ownrshp 2006
Sales 136.5MM[E] EMP 265[E]
SIC 1389 Perforating well casings

D-U-N-S 80-590-7391
CDM CONSTRUCTORS INC
C D M
(Suby of CDM SMITH INC) ★
75 State St Ste 701, Boston, MA 02109-1940
Tel (617) 452-6000 Founded/Ownrshp 1992
Sales 414.0MM EMP 500
Accts Pricewaterhousecoopers Llp Bo
SIC 1541 1623 Industrial buildings & warehouses; Water, sewer & utility lines; Oil & gas line & compressor station construction; Communication line & transmission tower construction
Pr: Paul R Shea
CFO: Paul Camell
*Treas: Robert J Anton
*Treas: Eric J Hartmann
VP: Robert Cabral
*VP: John V Czapor
VP: Michael Edgar
VP: Jane Madden
VP: Julia Nault
VP: David Parry
VP: Mike Savage
VP: Michael Schmidt
VP: Larry Schwartz

D-U-N-S 16-156-3440
CDM FEDERAL PROGRAMS CORP
CDM SMITH
(Suby of CDM SMITH INC) ★
3201 Jermantown Rd # 400, Fairfax, VA 22030-2874
Tel (703) 691-6500 Founded/Ownrshp 1986
Sales 93.1MM[E] EMP 525
SIC 8711 8742 8744 8748 8999 Engineering services; Management consulting services; Facilities support services; Business consulting; Actuarial consultant
CEO: Timothy Wall
*Pr: Gwen E Baker
*Pr: Darwin L Nelson
*CFO: David A Martin
*Sr VP: Michael C Malloy
VP: Christopher Gabel
VP: Dan Rodrigo
*VP: Michael Schwan
*VP: P Michael Schwan
Exec: Gerrit Visser
IT Man: Terry Camden

D-U-N-S 02-251-2680
■ CDM RESOURCE MANAGEMENT LLC
(Suby of ENERGY TRANSFER PARTNERS LP) ★
20405 State Hwy Ste 700, Houston, TX 77070
Tel (281) 376-2980 Founded/Ownrshp 1997
Sales 758.8MM[E] EMP 316
SIC 1389 Oil field services; Pumping of oil & gas wells
Pr: Chad Lenamon
CFO: Richard W Fairchild Jr
VP: Roger Allison
VP: Trey Shaddox
Plnt Mgr: Susan Shwarts
Ql Cn Mgr: Allen Goodrum
Mktg Mgr: Deidra Turnak

CDM SMITH
See CDM FEDERAL PROGRAMS CORP

D-U-N-S 05-599-0261
CDM SMITH INC
75 State St Ste 701, Boston, MA 02109-1940
Tel (617) 452-6000 Founded/Ownrshp 1970
Sales 1.2MMM EMP 5,800
SIC 8711

D-U-N-S 07-878-0909
CDM-AECOM MULTIMEDIA JOINT VENTURE
3201 Jermantown Rd # 400, Fairfax, VA 22030-2874
Tel (703) 691-6500 Founded/Ownrshp 2013
Sales 52.8MM[E] EMP 4,300
SIC 8711 Engineering services

D-U-N-S 02-349-6267
■ CDMI LLC
(Suby of MAGELLAN PARTNERS RX INC) ★
130 Bellevue Ave Unit 201, Newport, RI 02840-4407
Tel (401) 619-5210 Founded/Ownrshp 2014
Sales NA EMP 5,022[E]
SIC 6324 Hospital & medical service plans
Pr: Susan Petrovas
COO: Robert Muszynski

CDOT INFORMATIONS SYSTEMS CTR
See COLORADO DEPARTMENT OF TRANSPORTATION

CDPHO
See COOLEY DICKINSON PHYSICIAN HOSPITAL ORGANIZATION INC

D-U-N-S 06-500-5671
CDPQ US INC
(Suby of FONDS SOCIAL DES EMPLOYES DE LA CAISSE DE DEPOT ET PLACEMENT DU QUEBEC)
1211 6th Ave Ste 3001, New York, NY 10036-8717
Tel (212) 596-6300 Founded/Ownrshp 2005
Sales 100.7MM[E] EMP 1,000
SIC 6799 Investors
Pr: Michael Sabia

D-U-N-S 03-950-6154 IMP/EXP
■ CDR MANUFACTURING INC
AYRSHIRE ELECTRONICS
(Suby of KEYTRONICEMS) ★
10200 Forest Green Blvd, Louisville, KY 40223-5165
Tel (502) 625-0760 Founded/Ownrshp 2014
Sales 148.7MM[E] EMP 500[E]
SIC 3679 3672 3699 Rheostats, for electronic end products; Printed circuit boards; Electrical equipment & supplies
CEO: Milo D Bryant
*Pr: Gary L Lehren
*COO: W Brian Porter
Sr VP: Myron Blackburn
VP: Craig Green
VP: Karen Hartz
VP: Tony Meger

CDR PIGMENTS & DISPERSIONS
See FLINT GROUP US LLC

D-U-N-S 07-935-0068
■ CDRSVM HOLDING LLC
(Suby of SERVICEMASTER GLOBAL HOLDINGS INC) ★
860 Ridge Lake Blvd, Memphis, TN 38120-9434
Tel (901) 597-1400 Founded/Ownrshp 2007
Sales 1.0MMM[E] EMP 12,000[E]
SIC 6719 Investment holding companies, except banks

CDS
See CLUB DEMONSTRATION SERVICES INC

D-U-N-S 06-277-0144
CDS GLOBAL INC (IA)
(Suby of HEARST MAGAZINES) ★
1901 Bell Ave Ste 19, Des Moines, IA 50315-1087
Tel (866) 897-7987 Founded/Ownrshp 1972
Sales 258.7MM[E] EMP 2,500[E]
SIC 7389 7375 7374 Subscription fulfillment services: magazine, newspaper, etc.; Data base information retrieval; Data processing service
Pr: Debra Janssen
*CFO: Kenneth J Barloon
*Ch: Malcolm Netburn
Ex VP: Eileen White
Sr VP: Nancy Gessman
VP: Susan K Brown
VP: Jamey Heinze
VP: Micheline Oleson
VP Bus Dev: John Goering
Exec: Courtenay Villhauer
CTO: Frank Livaudais

D-U-N-S 06-233-3851
CDS OFFICE SYSTEMS INC
CDS OFFICE TECHNOLOGIES
612 S Dirksen Pkwy, Springfield, IL 62703-2183
Tel (800) 367-1508 Founded/Ownrshp 1971
Sales 147.2MM[E] EMP 120
SIC 5044 5999 7629 7378 3861 3577 Office equipment; Copying equipment; Business machines & equipment; Facsimile equipment; Business machine repair, electric; Computer maintenance & repair; Photographic equipment & supplies; Computer peripheral equipment
Pr: Jerome L Watson
*Pr: Markham F Watson
*CFO: Randy Johnson
*VP: John Bolser
VP: Sarah Wessels
Area Mgr: Michael Andell
Genl Mgr: Dave Raman
Off Mgr: Erin Ramoska
Tech Mgr: Nolan Burkhart
VP Opers: Bob Milner
VP Sls: Dan Watson

CDS OFFICE TECHNOLOGIES
See CDS OFFICE SYSTEMS INC

D-U-N-S 80-806-8253
▲ CDW CORP
75 Tri State Intl, Lincolnshire, IL 60069-4428
Tel (847) 465-6000 Founded/Ownrshp 1984
Sales 12.9MMM EMP 8,465
Tkr Sym CDW Exch NGS
SIC 5963 5045 5734 5961 Direct selling establishments; Computers, peripherals & software; Computer software; Computers & accessories, personal & home entertainment; Computer & software stores; Personal computers; Computer software & accessories; Computer peripheral equipment; Catalog & mail-order houses; Computer software, mail order; Computers & peripheral equipment, mail order
Ch Bd: Thomas E Richards
CFO: Ann E Ziegler
Chf Mktg O: Neal J Campbell
Ex VP: James Adams
Ex VP: Bobby Henderson
Sr VP: Dennis G Berger
Sr VP: Jonathan J Stevens
VP: Gabriel Adler
VP: Jill Billhorn
VP: Chris Corley
VP: Jim Dacey
VP: Doug Eckrote
VP: Neil B Fairfield
VP: Darren Kazich
VP: James J Lillis
VP: Sari Macrie
VP: Greg Noe
VP: Andrew Peters
VP: Christina Rother
VP: Phil Sammons
VP: Brett Schmidt

CDW G
See CDW LLC

D-U-N-S 02-615-7235
■ CDW GOVERNMENT LLC
(Suby of CDW CORP) ★
230 N Milwaukee Ave, Vernon Hills, IL 60061-4304
Tel (847) 465-6000 Founded/Ownrshp 1998
Sales 325.8MM[E] EMP 1,347
SIC 5961 5065 5734 Computer software, mail order; Computers & peripheral equipment, mail order; Electronic parts & equipment; Computer & software stores
CEO: Thomas E Richards
*Pr: Christina V Rother
*CFO: Ann E Ziegler
*Treas: Robert Welyki
*Sr VP: Dennis G Berger
*Sr VP: Douglas E Eckrote
*VP: Kevin P Adams
*VP: Anne B Ireland
VP: Bob Kirby
VP: Andy Lausch
*VP: Max Peterson
*VP: Virginia L Saggerman
Board of Directors: John Howard

D-U-N-S 96-496-4246
CDW HOLDINGS LLC
3 First National Pl, Vernon Hills, IL 60061
Tel (847) 465-6000 Founded/Ownrshp 2010
Sales 143.5M[E] EMP 6,900
SIC 5963 5045 5734 5961 Direct selling establishments; Computers, peripherals & software; Computer & software stores; Catalog & mail-order houses
Pr: Benjamin D Chereskin

D-U-N-S 10-762-7952 IMP/EXP
■ CDW LLC
CDW G
(Suby of CDW CORP) ★
75 Tri State Intl, Lincolnshire, IL 60069-4428
Tel (847) 465-6000 Founded/Ownrshp 2007
Sales 5.9MMM[E] EMP 6,800[E]
SIC 5045 Computers, peripherals & software; Computer software; Computers & accessories, personal & home entertainment
Ch: Thomas E Richards
Ex VP: Harry Harczak Jr
Sr VP: Larry Kirsch
Sr VP: Paul Kozak
VP: Jill Billhorn
VP: Daniel Callen
VP: Art Friedson
VP: Don Gordon
VP: Joe Kremer
VP: Jim Lillis
VP: Frederick K Neil
*VP: Christina Rother
VP: Steve Schuldt
Board of Directors: Steven W Alesio, Barry K Allen, Benjamin D Chereskin, Glenn M Creamer, Ted T Devine, Michael J Dominguez, George A Peinado, Donna F Zarcone

CDW TECHNOLOGIES, INC.
See CDW TECHNOLOGIES LLC

D-U-N-S 80-849-5584
■ CDW TECHNOLOGIES LLC
CDW TECHNOLOGIES, INC.
(Suby of CDW G) ★
5520 Research Park Dr, Fitchburg, WI 53711-5377
Tel (608) 288-3000 Founded/Ownrshp 2005
Sales 112.7MM[E] EMP 6,800
SIC 7373 4813 Systems integration services;
Ch Bd: Thomas E Richards
*Pr: Paul S Shain
*CFO: Brett Rimkus
CFO: Ann E Ziegler
*Sr VP: Dennis G Berger
*Sr VP: Neal J Campbell
*Sr VP: Christina M Corley
*Sr VP: Douglas E Eckrote
VP: Steven M Schuldt
Exec: Dale Schuster
Rgnl Mgr: Chuck Schmitt

D-U-N-S 07-985-4905
CE CARIBE LLC
Carretera 14 Km 25 3 St Carrete, Coamo, PR 00769
Tel (787) 825-6000 Founded/Ownrshp 2015
Sales 85.0MM EMP 2
SIC 3639 5064 Major kitchen appliances, except refrigerators & stoves; Electric household appliances

D-U-N-S 18-477-9924
▲ CEB INC
1919 N Lynn St, Arlington, VA 22209-1742
Tel (571) 303-3000 *Founded/Ownrshp* 1997
Sales 928.4MM *EMP* 4,600
Tkr Sym CEB *Exch* NYS
SIC 8742 Management consulting services; Human resource consulting services; Training & development consultant
Ch Bd: Thomas L Monahan III
CFO: Andrew Judt
*CFO: Richard S Lindahl
CFO: Kim Patmore
*Ofcr: Melody L Jones
VP: Priscilla Destefano
VP: Miriam Imoberstag
VP: Laura McKenna
VP: Laura Wilson
Assoc Dir: Jennifer Allen
Assoc Dir: Wunmi Bamiduro
Assoc Dir: Emily Johnston
Assoc Dir: Brian McAlpin
Assoc Dir: Laura Merola
Assoc Dir: Emily Warkentin
Dir Soc: Alexandra Briancon
Dir Soc: Lindsay Goldsworthy
Board of Directors: Gregor S Bailar, Stephen M Carter, Gordon J Coburn, Kathleen A Corbet, L Kevin Cox, Daniel O Leemon, Stacey Rauch, Jeffrey R Tarr

D-U-N-S 13-097-4624
CEBAL AMERICAS
ALCAN PACKAGING
101 Merritt 7 Ste 2, Norwalk, CT 06851-1060
Tel (203) 845-6356 *Founded/Ownrshp* 2003
Sales 200.0MM *EMP* 1,500^E
SIC 3082 Tubes, unsupported plastic
CEO: Christel Bories

CEC
See COMMUNITY EDUCATION CENTERS INC

D-U-N-S 83-172-9509
CEC ELECTRICAL INC
14450 Trinity Blvd # 250, Fort Worth, TX 76155-2549
Tel (817) 734-0040 *Founded/Ownrshp* 2009
Sales 151.8MM^E *EMP* 450
Accts Cliftonlarsonallen Llp Dallas
SIC 1731 General electrical contractor
Pr: Karl Ray Waddell
*Pr: Ray Waddell
*CFO: Jim Bobbit
Sr VP: Wayne Vardell
*VP: Welton Freeman

D-U-N-S 03-712-1845 IMP
CEC ENTERTAINMENT INC
(*Suby of* QUESO HOLDINGS INC.)
1707 Market Pl Ste 200, Irving, TX 75063-8049
Tel (972) 258-8507 *Founded/Ownrshp* 2014
Sales 922.5MM *EMP* 20,000
Accts Deloitte & Touche Llp Dallas
SIC 5812 7993 6794 Pizzeria, chain; Coin-operated amusement devices; Franchises, selling or licensing
CEO: Thomas Leverton
Pr: J Roger Cardinale
COO: Mark Gordon
CFO: Dale Black
Ex VP: Randy G Forsythe
VP: Daniel Dickson
VP: Blake Huggins
VP: Lois Perry
VP: Mahesh Sadarangani
VP: Gary Spring
Exec: William Reynolds
Dir Soc: Cristina Hayes
Board of Directors: James Chambers, Daniel E Flesh, Lance A Milken, Allen R Weiss

D-U-N-S 07-962-8789
CECIL COUNTY PUBLIC SCHOOLS
CCPS
201 Booth St, Elkton, MD 21921-5618
Tel (410) 996-5400 *Founded/Ownrshp* 2014
Sales 36.7MM^E *EMP* 1,919^E
SIC 8211 Public elementary & secondary schools
Bd of Dir: Wendy Wintersgill
Exec: Dawn Branch
Ex Dir: Georgia Clark
MIS Dir: Wesley Zimmerman
Pr Dir: Kelly Keeton
Teacher Pr: Mae Alfree
HC Dir: Michelle Ness

D-U-N-S 87-976-8075 IMP
CECO CONCRETE CONSTRUCTION DELAWARE LLC
(*Suby of* HEICO COMPANIES L L C) ★
10100 N Ambassador Dr, Kansas City, MO 64153-1310
Tel (816) 459-7000 *Founded/Ownrshp* 2014
Sales 805.3MM^E *EMP* 2,300
Accts Deloitte & Touche
SIC 1542 1522 Institutional building construction; Residential construction; Hotel/motel & multi-family home construction; Hotel/motel, new construction
CEO: Ron Schuster
*Pr: Jim Schwammen
*CFO: Mike Moorhouse
Off Admin: Lora Mandahl
Dir IT: Stephanie Thompson
Sls Mgr: Matt Minor

D-U-N-S 61-290-7381
▲ CECO ENVIRONMENTAL CORP
4625 Red Bank Rd Ste 200, Cincinnati, OH 45227-1552
Tel (513) 458-2600 *Founded/Ownrshp* 1966
Sales 367.4MM *EMP* 1,170
Tkr Sym CECE *Exch* NGS
SIC 3564 Purification & dust collection equipment
Pr: Jeffrey Lang
Pr: Brent Becker
Pr: Gennaro D'Alterio
COO: Richard Blum
CFO: Edward J Prajzner
Sr VP: Beverly Jones
VP: Chris Brown
VP: Stephen M Fritz
VP: Steve Fritz
VP: Tracy Krumme
VP: Kelli Kyriazis
VP: Jay Shah
VP: Richard Whitford
Creative D: Kevin Bittle
Dir Bus: Monica Grainger

D-U-N-S 10-991-4676
■ CECO GROUP INC
(*Suby of* CECO ENVIRONMENTAL CORP) ★
4625 Red Bank Rd Ste 200, Cincinnati, OH 45227-1552
Tel (513) 458-2600 *Founded/Ownrshp* 1999
Sales 83.6MM^E *EMP* 436
SIC 8711 3564 8734 3443 3444 1761 Engineering services; Filters, air: furnaces, air conditioning equipment, etc.; Testing laboratories; Fabricated plate work (boiler shop); Sheet metal specialties, not stamped; Sheet metalwork
Pr: Jefferey Lang
*CFO: Benton Cook

CEDA
See COMMUNITY AND ECONOMIC DEVELOPMENT ASSOCIATION OF COOK COUNTY INC

D-U-N-S 55-648-4640
CEDA INTERNATIONAL INC
(*Suby of* CEDA INTERNATIONAL CORPORATION)
2600 S Shore Blvd Ste 300, League City, TX 77573-2944
Tel (281) 478-2600 *Founded/Ownrshp* 2005
Sales 87.4MM^E *EMP* 317^E
SIC 1389 Oil field services
Pr: Joe Kinder
*Sr VP: Roger Hearn

CEDAR BOOK & CARD SHOP
See HARRISBURG NEWS CO

D-U-N-S 96-254-1103
CEDAR CREEK CORP
(*Suby of* CEDAR CREEK HOLDINGS INC) ★
450 N Macarthur Blvd, Oklahoma City, OK 73127-6619
Tel (405) 917-8300 *Founded/Ownrshp* 2011
Sales 165.6MM^E *EMP* 400^E
SIC 5039 Air ducts, sheet metal
CEO: D Wayne Trousdale
*Ch Bd: William Adams
*CFO: David Tighe

D-U-N-S 00-545-7871 IMP
CEDAR CREEK HOLDINGS INC
(*Suby of* CHARLESBANK CAPITAL PARTNERS LLC) ★
450 N Macarthur Blvd, Oklahoma City, OK 73127-6619
Tel (405) 917-8300 *Founded/Ownrshp* 2006
Sales 450.5MM^E *EMP* 400
SIC 5031 5082 Building materials, exterior; Building materials, interior; Construction & mining machinery
Ch Bd: William Adams
*COO: D Wayne Trousdale
*CFO: David Tighe

D-U-N-S 03-792-0337
CEDAR CREEK LLC
5034 Grand Ridge Dr, West Des Moines, IA 50265-5754
Tel (405) 917-8300 *Founded/Ownrshp* 2008
Sales 199.9MM^E *EMP* 328
SIC 2431 5031 Windows, wood; Lumber: rough, dressed & finished; Building materials, exterior; Doors & windows
Pr: Ted B Roberts
*Treas: Jacquelyn Fuller

D-U-N-S 96-253-4272
CEDAR CREEK LLC
(*Suby of* CEDAR CREEK HOLDINGS INC) ★
450 N Macarthur Blvd, Oklahoma City, OK 73127-6619
Tel (405) 917-8300 *Founded/Ownrshp* 2011
Sales 284.9MM^E *EMP* 400
SIC 5031 Building materials, exterior; Building materials, interior
CEO: William Adams
COO: D Wayne Trousdale
CFO: David Tighe
Opers Mgr: Jakim Finlay
Sls Mgr: Jim Beers
Sls Mgr: Jeff Wilder
Sales Asso: Mike Kingsbury

CEDAR CREEK LUMBER
See LAKE STATES LUMBER INC

D-U-N-S 06-465-5090
CEDAR ELECTRONICS HOLDINGS CORP
5440 W Chester Rd, West Chester, OH 45069-2950
Tel (513) 870-8500 *Founded/Ownrshp* 2014
Sales 139.8MM^E *EMP* 350
SIC 3812 5088 Navigational systems & instruments; Navigation equipment & supplies
CEO: David Thornhill
*Pr: Sally Washlow

D-U-N-S 00-790-4089
▲ CEDAR FAIR LP
1 Cedar Point Dr, Sandusky, OH 44870-5259
Tel (419) 626-0830 *Founded/Ownrshp* 1987
Sales 1.2MMM *EMP* 1,900
Accts Deloitte & Touche Llp Clevela
Tkr Sym FUN *Exch* NYS
SIC 7996 Amusement parks
Pr: Matthew A Ouimet
Pr: Richard A Zimmerman
CFO: Brian C Witherow
Treas: Roger Allen
Bd of Dir: Michael D Kwiatkowski
Bd of Dir: John M Scott
Ex VP: Ray Majoy
Ex VP: Duffield E Milkie
Sr VP: David R Hoffman
VP: James Archbold
VP: Carrie Boldman
VP: Milkie Duffield
VP: Stacy Frole
VP: Mike Hasman
VP: Mary Hoerig
VP: Daryle Powers
VP: Alan Schwartz
VP: Daryl Smith
VP: Bob Wagner
VP: Frank Wilburn

D-U-N-S 05-327-1086
CEDAR FARMS CO INC
2100 Hornig Rd, Philadelphia, PA 19116-4202
Tel (215) 934-7100 *Founded/Ownrshp* 1970
Sales 142.3MM^E *EMP* 125
Accts Mcgladrey & Pullen Llp Blue
SIC 5142 5144 5143 5149 Packaged frozen goods; Poultry products; Dairy products, except dried or canned; Butter; Cheese; Groceries & related products
Pr: Gus Pahides
*Owner: Gus P Pahides
*VP: Peter Pahides
Off Mgr: Mike Essaf
Sales Asso: Chris Mountis
Genl Couns: Robert Reibstein

D-U-N-S 96-762-3018
CEDAR GATE PHASE II
2350 Kanell Blvd, Poplar Bluff, MO 63901-4036
Tel (573) 785-3443 *Founded/Ownrshp* 1976
Sales 381.9MM *EMP* 80
SIC 8051 Skilled nursing care facilities
Treas: W Hoja

D-U-N-S 78-144-3866 IMP
CEDAR GROVE COMPOSTING INC
7343 E Marginal Way S, Seattle, WA 98108-3513
Tel (206) 832-3000 *Founded/Ownrshp* 1991
Sales 298.0MM^E *EMP* 400
SIC 4953 Refuse collection & disposal services
CEO: J Banchero Jr
*Treas: Katherine B Malshuk
*Ex VP: Clue Westmoreland
*VP: John Brigham
*VP: Catherine Malshuk
*VP: Susan Thoman
Dist Mgr: Casey Funke
Dir IT: Lawrence Klein
IT Man: Julie Southworth
Opers Mgr: Clint Westmoreland

CEDAR HILL CARE CENTER
See ZANDEX HEALTH CARE CORP

D-U-N-S 80-829-9460
■ CEDAR PARK HEALTH SYSTEM LP
CEDAR PARK REGIONAL MED CTR
(*Suby of* COMMUNITY HEALTH SYSTEMS INC) ★
1401 Medical Pkwy, Cedar Park, TX 78613-7763
Tel (512) 528-7000 *Founded/Ownrshp* 2006
Sales 118.6MM *EMP* 325
SIC 8062 General medical & surgical hospitals
Pt: David Klein
Genl Pt: CP Hospital GP LLC
Dir Risk M: Michelle Durham
Dir Rad: Bill Cummins
Off Mgr: Barbara Bingham
Off Mgr: Charlotte Morris
CIO: Brad Hoar
Mktg Dir: Laura Balla
Obsttrcn: John J Thoppil
Pharmcst: Donna Fowler
Pharmcst: Monica Satasia

CEDAR PARK REGIONAL MED CTR
See CEDAR PARK HEALTH SYSTEM LP

D-U-N-S 08-015-9321
CEDAR RAPIDS COMMUNITY SCHOOL DISTRICT
2500 Edgewood Rd Nw, Cedar Rapids, IA 52405-1015
Tel (319) 558-2000 *Founded/Ownrshp* 1982
Sales 233.6MM *EMP* 2,540^E
Accts Rsm Us Llp Cedar Rapids Iowa
SIC 8211 Public elementary & secondary schools
Dir Sec: Laurel Day
Pr Dir: Marcia Hughes
Teacher Pr: Rodrick Dooley
Teacher Pr: Vanessa Rave
HC Dir: Paul Hayes

D-U-N-S 07-349-6002
CEDAR RAPIDS COMMUNITY SCHOOL DISTRICT FOUNDATION
2500 Edgewood Rd Nw, Cedar Rapids, IA 52405-1015
Tel (319) 558-2000 *Founded/Ownrshp* 1982
Sales 212.5MM *EMP* 158^E
Accts Mcgladrey Llp Cedar Rapids I
SIC 8399 Fund raising organization, non-fee basis
Ch Bd: Jen Neumann
Psych: Susan Walaska
Psych: Erin Welsh

D-U-N-S 15-114-6115
▲ CEDAR REALTY TRUST INC
44 S Bayles Ave Ste 304, Port Washington, NY 11050-3765
Tel (516) 767-6492 *Founded/Ownrshp* 1984
Sales 149.2MM *EMP* 67^E
Tkr Sym CDR *Exch* NYS
SIC 6798 Real estate investment trusts
Pr: Bruce J Schanzer
*Ch Bd: Roger M Widmann
COO: Robin McBride Zeigler
CFO: Philip R Mays
Exec: Robin Zeigler
Genl Couns: Adina Storch
Board of Directors: James J Burns, Abraham Eisenstat, Pamela N Hootkin, Paul G Kirk Jr, Steven G Rogers

CEDARAPIDS
See TEREX USA LLC

CEDARGATE, THE
See PRO-AM INC

D-U-N-S 06-425-3222 IMP
CEDARLANE NATURAL FOODS INC
1135 E Artesia Blvd, Carson, CA 90746-1602
Tel (310) 886-7720 *Founded/Ownrshp* 1981
Sales 125.3MM^E *EMP* 400^E
Accts Ehernreich Burkholder And Com
SIC 2038 Frozen specialties; Dinners, frozen & packaged; Lunches, frozen & packaged
CEO: Robert Atallah
CFO: Neil Holmes
Genl Mgr: Geoffrey Bickam
CTO: Ash Husain
Dir IT: Vaserick Karabidian
Plnt Mgr: John Haddock
VP Sls: Terry Mayo
Sls Mgr: Lee Wallace

D-U-N-S 07-997-2993
CEDARS-SINAI MEDICAL CARE FOUNDATION (CA)
200 N Robertson Blvd # 101, Beverly Hills, CA 90211-1769
Tel (310) 385-3200 *Founded/Ownrshp* 1993
Sales 216.1MM *EMP* 4
Accts Ernst & Young Us Llp Irvine
SIC 8699 Charitable organization
Ex Dir: Tom Gordeon
*Ex Dir: Tom Gordon

D-U-N-S 07-530-7785 IMP
CEDARS-SINAI MEDICAL CENTER
8700 Beverly Blvd, West Hollywood, CA 90048-1804
Tel (310) 423-3277 *Founded/Ownrshp* 1902
Sales 2.7MMM *EMP* 8,000
SIC 8062 General medical & surgical hospitals
Ch Bd: Lawrence B Platt
*Ch Bd: John C Law
V Ch: Calvin Hobel
V Ch: Lee Miller
Pr: Richard Katzman
*Pr: Thomas M Priselac
*CFO: Edward M Pronchunas
*V Ch Bd: Vera Guerin
*V Ch Bd: James A Nathan
Ex VP: Peter Bravman
*Sr VP: Peter E Braveman
Sr VP: Darren Dworkin
*Sr VP: Jeanne Flores
Sr VP: Mark R Gavens
Sr VP: Michael L Langberg
Sr VP: Shlomo Melmed
VP: Linda Burnes Bolton
VP: Richard Elbaum
VP: Patricia Kittell
VP: James Laur
Assoc Dir: Marilyn Ader

D-U-N-S 08-028-8774
CEDARVILLE UNIVERSITY (CA)
251 N Main St, Cedarville, OH 45314-8564
Tel (937) 766-7700 *Founded/Ownrshp* 2016
Sales 122.6MM *EMP* 9^E
SIC 8221 University
Pr: David Rotman
Ofcr: Ryan Gathard
Ofcr: Mark E Riggs
Assoc VP: Donald Humphreys
VP: Timothy Bosworth
VP: Thomas H Comman
Exec: Janice Supplee
Comm Dir: John Davis
Ex Dir: Brandon Waltz
Dir IT: Mike Rall
Pharmcst: Douglas Anderson

D-U-N-S 04-522-8764 EXP
CEDARWOOD-YOUNG CO
ALLAN COMPANY
14620 Joanbridge St, Baldwin Park, CA 91706-1750
Tel (626) 962-4047 *Founded/Ownrshp* 1963
Sales 297.7MM *EMP* 275
Accts Dougherty & Company Glendale
SIC 5093 Waste paper
Pr: Jason Young
*CFO: Michael Ochniak
*Ch: Stephen Young
*VP: Francisco Del Rincon
*VP: Don Rogers
*VP: Bo Yang
*VP Opers: Richard Hubbard

CEDE AND COMPANY
See DEPOSITORY TRUST & CLEARING CORP

CEF
See CARMEL CLAY SCHOOLS

D-U-N-S 87-978-3900
CEGEDIM INC
(*Suby of* CEGEDIM)
1425 Us Highway 206, Bedminster, NJ 07921-2653
Tel (908) 443-2000 *Founded/Ownrshp* 2007
Sales 104.7MM^E *EMP* 500^E
SIC 7371 7372 Computer software development & applications; Prepackaged software
Pr: Laurent Schockmel
Pr: Carl L Cohen
*Pr: Angela Miccoli
CFO: Christine Crofte
Ofcr: Ron Buzzeo
Grp VP: Robert E Parisi
Sr VP: Mark Theilken
Sr VP: Stephen Webb
VP: William Buzzeo
*VP: Christine Kroft
VP: Barbara S Lyster
VP: Ronald Pearce
VP: Anthony Simonelli
VP: Nigel Whitehead

D-U-N-S 07-954-7789
■ CEHI ACQUISITION CORP
(*Suby of* COMPASS DIVERSIFIED HOLDINGS) ★
61 Wilton Rd Ste 2, Westport, CT 06880-3121
Tel (203) 221-1703 *Founded/Ownrshp* 2014
Sales 159.3MM^E *EMP* 200^E
SIC 4959 6719 Environmental cleanup services; Investment holding companies, except banks
CEO: Alan B Offenberg

CEI
See CUPERTINO ELECTRIC INC

D-U-N-S 11-847-0343
CEI GROUP INC
INTELLICLAIM, CLAIMSLINK
(*Suby of* CSI HOLDINGS INC) ★
4850 E Street Rd Ste 200, Feasterville Trevose, PA 19053-6653
Tel (215) 364-5600 *Founded/Ownrshp* 1983

Sales NA EMP 190
Accts William J Lawrence
SIC 6411 7532 Insurance claim processing, except medical; Collision shops, automotive
Pr: Wayne G Smolda
*Pr: Vincent Brigidi
*CFO: William J Lawrence
Ex VP: Richard Brigidi
*VP: Bob Glose
*VP: Claudia B Smolda
Exec: George Major
Dept Mgr: Patricia Cawley
*CIO: Steve Enoch
MIS Dir: Robert Marriott
QA Dir: Peg Delilles

D-U-N-S 11-192-3095
■ **CEI HOLDING CO**
(Suby of CLEAN EARTH HOLDINGS INC) ★
334 S Warminster Rd, Hatboro, PA 19040-3430
Tel (215) 734-1400 Founded/Ownrshp 2005
Sales 159.3MM^E EMP 200^E
SIC 1629 Earthmoving contractor
Pr: Christopher Dods

D-U-N-S 13-019-4942 IMP
CEI HOLDINGS INC
2182 State Route 35, Holmdel, NJ 07733-1125
Tel (732) 888-7788 Founded/Ownrshp 2001
Sales 245.8MM^E EMP 1,400^E
SIC 2844 7389 4225 5122 Toilet preparations; Cosmetic kits, assembling & packaging; General warehousing & storage; Cosmetics, perfumes & hair products
Pr: John F Croddick

D-U-N-S 17-520-7422
CEI LIQUIDATION ESTATES
755 W Big Beaver Rd, Troy, MI 48084-4900
Tel (248) 614-8200 Founded/Ownrshp 1987
Sales 297.6MM^E EMP 4,100^E
SIC 2451 5271 Mobile homes; Mobile homes
Pr: William C Griffiths
Sr VP: Roger K Scholten
CIO: Edward Mitzel

CEI OF TENNESSEE
See CONSTRUCTION ENTERPRISES INC

D-U-N-S 18-890-5202
▲ **CELADON GROUP INC**
9503 E 33rd St, Indianapolis, IN 46235-4207
Tel (317) 972-7000 Founded/Ownrshp 1986
Sales 1.0MMM^E EMP 6,415^E
Tkr Sym CGI Exch NYS
SIC 4212 4225 Truck rental with drivers; General warehousing
Ch Bd: Paul A Will
Pr: Jay Frieden
Pr: William E Meek
Pr: Jonathan Russell
CFO: Bobby Peavler
VP: Kenneth Core
VP: Danny Hightshue
IT Man: Cornelius Staton
Sfty Dirs: Chase Welsh
Opers Mgr: Bryan Banta
Opers Mgr: Phil Martinez
Board of Directors: Catherine Langham, Robert Long, Michael Miller

D-U-N-S 13-138-5601
■ **CELADON TRUCKING SERVICES INC**
PANTHER TRANSPORTATION SVCS
(Suby of CELADON GROUP INC) ★
9503 E 33rd St, Indianapolis, IN 46235-4207
Tel (317) 972-7000 Founded/Ownrshp 1985
Sales 744.6MM^E EMP 3,160
SIC 4213 4212 Trucking, except local; Local trucking, without storage
CEO: Paul Will
CFO: Eric Meek
Treas: Wayne Deno
Chf Mktg O: Dan Bowersox
VP: Kenneth Core
VP: Bart Middleton
VP: Nathan Roberts
Web Dev: Dennis Wright
Opers Mgr: Juan Ramos
Opers Mgr: Rodney Schultz
Sales Exec: Robert Corbin

D-U-N-S 04-472-5419 IMP/EXP
■ **CELANESE ACETATE LLC**
(Suby of CNA HOLDINGS LLC) ★
1601 Lyndon B Johnson Fwy, Dallas, TX 75234-6034
Tel (972) 443-4000 Founded/Ownrshp 1997, 2005
Sales 130.7MM^E EMP 800
SIC 2281 Manmade & synthetic fiber yarns, spun; Acetate yarn, spun: made from purchased staple
Pr: Lou Purvis
VP: Bruce Bennett
VP: Mark Oberle
VP: Donna Wegner
Ex Dir: Linda Jensen
Ex Dir: Arlene Standley
CTO: Todd Carter
Dir IT: Tony Valencic
IT Man: Keith Laird
Netwrk Eng: Lyndon Hepworth
VP Mfg: BEK Humelsine

D-U-N-S 09-741-3462 IMP
■ **CELANESE AMERICAS LLC**
KEP AMERICAS
(Suby of CELANESE US HOLDINGS LLC) ★
222 Colinas Blvd W 900n, Irving, TX 75039-5467
Tel (972) 443-4000 Founded/Ownrshp 1972
Sales 7.0MMM^E EMP 880
SIC 2821 2819 2824 5169 Plastics materials & resins; Industrial inorganic chemicals; Organic fibers, noncellulosic; Chemicals & allied products
Pr: Christopher W Jensen
*VP: Ronnie D Berry
*VP: John W Howard
VP: David Jenkins
*VP: Chuck B Kyrish
*VP: Jan L Kyrish
VP: Joseph Prew

*VP: Thomas M Scheetz
Div/Sub He: Jean Labbe

D-U-N-S 12-374-7474 IMP/EXP
■ **CELANESE CHEMICALS INC**
(Suby of CELANESE HOLDINGS LLC) ★
1601 Lyndon B Johnson Fwy, Dallas, TX 75234-6034
Tel (972) 443-4000 Founded/Ownrshp 1995
Sales 6.8MMM EMP 199
SIC 2821 2824 2865 2869 Plastics materials & resins; Organic fibers, noncellulosic; Cyclic crudes & intermediates; Dyes & pigments; Industrial organic chemicals; Amines, acids, salts, esters
CEO: Phillip M McDivin
Ofcr: Tom Scheetz
*Sr VP: Christopher W Jensen
*Sr VP: Scott A Richardson
*VP: Ronnie D Berry
*VP: Walter Keller
VP: Doug Madden
VP: John O'Dwyer
Plng Mgr: Christopher Artuso
IT Man: Paul Noble
Plnt Mgr: Jim Savage

D-U-N-S 17-020-4486
▲ **CELANESE CORP**
222 Las Colinas Blvd W # 900, Irving, TX 75039-5467
Tel (972) 443-4000 Founded/Ownrshp 1918
Sales 5.6MMM EMP 7,081
Accts Kpmg Llp Dallas Tx
Tkr Sym CE Exch NYS
SIC 2819 2821 2869 Industrial inorganic chemicals; Polyethylene resins; Acetates: amyl, butyl & ethyl; Acetic & chloroacetic acid & metallic salts
Ch Bd: Mark C Rohr
CFO: Christopher W Jensen
Treas: Steven Jasko
Treas: Divya Kottayil
Ofcr: Lori A Johnston
Ex VP: Lyndon Cole
Ex VP: Patrick D Quarles
Ex VP: Scott M Sutton
Sr VP: Gjon N Nivica Jr
Sr VP: Jay C Townsend
VP: William Antonace
VP: John Caamano
VP: Lisa Esparza
VP: Jay Felkins
VP: Rick Hall
VP: Amy Hebert
VP: Darren Major
VP: Mark Murray
VP: Mark Oberle
VP: Steven Sterin
VP: John Wardzel
Board of Directors: Jean S Blackwell, William M Brown, Edward G Galante, Kathryn M Hill, David F Hoffmeister, Jay V Ihlenfeld, John L Wulff

D-U-N-S 12-373-7285
■ **CELANESE HOLDINGS LLC**
(Suby of CNA HOLDINGS LLC) ★
1601 Lyndon B Johnson Fwy, Dallas, TX 75234-6034
Tel (972) 443-4000 Founded/Ownrshp 2005
Sales 6.8MMM^E EMP 880^E
SIC 2821 2824 Plastics materials & resins; Organic fibers, noncellulosic

D-U-N-S 18-000-1229 IMP/EXP
■ **CELANESE INTERNATIONAL CORP**
(Suby of CELANESE CORP) ★
222 Las Colinas Blvd W, Irving, TX 75039-5421
Tel (972) 443-4000 Founded/Ownrshp 2009
Sales 705.1MM^E EMP 880^E
SIC 2819 2869 Industrial inorganic chemicals; Acetates: amyl, butyl & ethyl
CEO: Mark C Rohr
Treas: Michael E Grom
*Sr VP: Todd Elliott
*Sr VP: Christopher W Jensen
*Sr VP: Scott Richardson
*Sr VP: Jay Townsend

D-U-N-S 18-000-1856 EXP
■ **CELANESE US HOLDINGS LLC**
(Suby of CELANESE CORP) ★
1601 Lyndon B Johnson Fwy, Dallas, TX 75234-6034
Tel (972) 443-4000 Founded/Ownrshp 2004
Sales 7.0MMM^E EMP 880^E
SIC 2821 2879 2819 Plastics materials & resins; Agricultural chemicals; Industrial inorganic chemicals

CELEBRATION STATION
See WHITECO INDUSTRIES INC

D-U-N-S 12-928-0264
CELEBRATION STATION PROPERTIES INC
1000 E 80th Pl Ste 420n, Merrillville, IN 46410-5686
Tel (219) 757-3500 Founded/Ownrshp 2003
Sales 15.3MM^E EMP 1,100
SIC 7999 Miniature golf course operation; Wave pool operation; Go-cart raceway operation & rentals; Recreation center
Pr: Jeffrey Morton
*Treas: Nancy Sanchez

D-U-N-S 07-329-8523
■ **CELEBRITY CRUISES INC**
AZAMARA CRUISES
(Suby of ROYAL CARIBBEAN CRUISES LTD) ★
1050 Caribbean Way, Miami, FL 33132-2028
Tel (305) 262-6677 Founded/Ownrshp 1989
Sales 204.0MM^E EMP 3,000^E
SIC 4729 Steamship ticket offices
CEO: Richard D Fain
*Pr: Michael W Bayley
*Pr: Dan Hanrahan
CFO: Jason Liberty
*CFO: Brain J Rice
Assoc VP: Zissis Koskinas
Assoc VP: Brian Powell
Assoc VP: Evangelos Sampanidis
Sr VP: Steve Han
Sr VP: Wayne Wielgus
VP: Bert Hernandez
VP: Lisa Hill
VP: Michael Jones
VP: Gregory Purdy

VP: Bradley Stein
Exec: Deoraj Singh
Assoc Dir: Chantel Harris

CELEBRITY FOODS
See ATALANTA CORP

D-U-N-S 00-189-2397 IMP
CELEBRITY INTERNATIONAL INC (NY)
VITAMINSBABY
10 W 33rd St Rm 910, New York, NY 10001-3306
Tel (212) 279-1616 Founded/Ownrshp 1965
Sales 304.1MM^E EMP 800
SIC 5137 Infants' wear; Sportswear, women's & children's
Ch Bd: Morris D Matalon
Pr: Eli Matalon
CFO: Mona El-Raheb
Treas: Samuel Matalon
VP: Michael Matalon
Exec: Fay Liff

D-U-N-S 96-363-5177
CELERION HOLDINGS INC
621 Rose St, Lincoln, NE 68502-2040
Tel (402) 476-2811 Founded/Ownrshp 2010
Sales 152.2MM^E EMP 868^E
SIC 8731 Medical research, commercial
CEO: Susan Thornton
*CFO: Joanne Rosal
*VP: Philip Bach
*VP: Michelle Combs
*VP: David Maya
Genl Mgr: Ian Downie

D-U-N-S 96-217-0390
CELERION INC
(Suby of CELERION HOLDINGS INC) ★
621 Rose St, Lincoln, NE 68502-2040
Tel (402) 476-2811 Founded/Ownrshp 2010
Sales 152.2MM^E EMP 867
SIC 8731 Medical research, commercial
Pr: Susan Thornton
*CFO: Joanne Rosal
*Ex VP: David Maya
*VP: Philip Bach
VP: Michelle Combs
*VP: Raymond Farmen
VP: Aricia Pfaff
VP: Fred Pritchard
*VP: J Fred Pritchard
VP: Heimo Scheer
Dir Surg: Ashish Shah
Assoc Dir: Tamara Cuddy
Assoc Dir: Cathleen Morton
Assoc Dir: Christine Schiebl
Assoc Dir: Curtis Sheldon
Assoc Dir: Julia Strong
Assoc Dir: Nancy Wang
Dir Rx: Dominiqe Gerbet
Dir Bus: Rajesh Krishnan

D-U-N-S 10-051-1380
CELERITY IT LLC
8401 Greensboro Dr # 500, Mc Lean, VA 22102-5128
Tel (703) 848-1900 Founded/Ownrshp 2001
Sales 84.4MM^E EMP 483^E
SIC 7379
CEO: Michael Berkman
COO: Lewis Watersfounder
*CFO: Lewis Waters
VP: Todd Florence
VP: Jay Kissman
VP: Steve Nerheim
VP: Rob Smith
Creative D: Matthew Schleyer
Dir Bus: Rashad Howard
Off Admin: Jessica Pohoreskey
IT Man: Scott Whitehouse

D-U-N-S 82-469-8252 IMP
CELESTICA LLC
(Suby of CELESTICA INC)
11 Continental Blvd # 103, Merrimack, NH 03054-4341
Tel (603) 657-3001 Founded/Ownrshp 1997
Sales 1.0MMM^E EMP 10,000
SIC 3679

D-U-N-S 02-519-0997 IMP/EXP
CELGARD LLC
MEMBRANA - CHARLOTTE
(Suby of POLYPORE INTERNATIONAL INC) ★
13800 S Lakes Dr, Charlotte, NC 28273-6738
Tel (704) 588-5310 Founded/Ownrshp 1998, 1999
Sales 89.6MM^E EMP 360^E
SIC 2821 3081 Plastics materials & resins; Unsupported plastics film & sheet
CEO: Robert B Toth
Ch: Frank Nasisi
VP: Josef Sauer
Genl Mgr: Milo Hassloch
Genl Mgr: Beth Jarnecke

D-U-N-S 17-420-1137
▲ **CELGENE CORP**
86 Morris Ave, Summit, NJ 07901-3915
Tel (908) 673-9000 Founded/Ownrshp 1986
Sales 9.2MMM EMP 6,971
Accts Kpmg Llp Short Hills New Jer
Tkr Sym CELG Exch NGS
SIC 2834 Pharmaceutical preparations
CEO: Mark J Alles
*Ch Bd: Robert J Hugin
*Pr: Jacqualyn A Fouse
CFO: Peter N Kellogg
Ch: Thomas O Daniel
Treas: Patricia Moenaert
Bd of Dir: Simona Bortolazzi
Ex VP: Gerald F Masoudi
Ex VP: Beatriz C Mateos
Ex VP: Paul Sherrington
VP: Terrie Curran
VP: Bruce Dornseif
VP: Patrick Flanigan
VP: Joe Garbus
VP: Juanita Hawkins
VP: Robert Knight
VP: Oliver Kong
VP: Julie Mathew
VP: Robert Murdock

VP: Patricia Pallier
VP: Markus Renschler
Board of Directors: Richard W Barker, Michael W Bonney, Michael D Casey, Carrie S Cox, Michael A Friedman, Julia A Haller, James Loughlin, Ernest Mario

D-U-N-S 92-640-6695 IMP
CELINA ALUMINUM PRECISION TECHNOLOGY INC
CAPT
(Suby of HONDA FOUNDRY CO.,LTD.)
7059 Staeger Rd, Celina, OH 45822-9395
Tel (419) 586-2278 Founded/Ownrshp 1995
Sales 138.7MM^E EMP 500
SIC 3592 Pistons & piston rings
Pr: Takenori Yamaguchi
*Sr VP: Jay James
Exec: Erin Schwieterman
Sfty Dirs: Shelley Young
Prd Mgr: Siegbert Fendert

CELINA INSURANCE GROUP
See CELINA MUTUAL INSURANCE CO

D-U-N-S 00-699-8959
CELINA MUTUAL INSURANCE CO (OH)
CELINA INSURANCE GROUP
1 Insurance Sq, Celina, OH 45822-1659
Tel (419) 586-5181 Founded/Ownrshp 1919
Sales NA EMP 200
SIC 6331 Fire, marine & casualty insurance: mutual
Pr: William W Montgomery
*Ch Bd: Donald W Montgomery
CFO: Phil Fullenkemp
*Treas: Phillip Fullenkamp
VP: Philip Fullenkamp
Mng Dir: John Nall
CIO: Rob Schoenfelt
IT Man: Cory McKibben
IT Man: Jane Miller
Software D: Kevin Bair
Software D: Ryan Buening

CELLAIRIS
See GLOBAL CELLULAR INC

D-U-N-S 96-890-4698 IMP/EXP
■ **CELLCO PARTNERSHIP**
VERIZON WIRELESS
(Suby of VERIZON COMMUNICATIONS INC) ★
1 Verizon Way, Basking Ridge, NJ 07920-1025
Tel (908) 306-7000 Founded/Ownrshp 2001
Sales 60.8MMM^E EMP 85,000
SIC 4812 5999 5065 Cellular telephone services; Mobile telephones & equipment; Mobile telephone equipment
CEO: Daniel Mead
Pr: Chris Felix
Pr: Mariano Legaz
Pr: Russ Preite
*Pr: John G Stratton
*COO: Marni M Walden
*CFO: Andrew Davies
CFO: Andrew N Halford
*Ex VP: Nicola Palmer
Sr VP: Kevin Zavaglia
*VP: Shankar Arumugavelu
VP: Tricha Diaz
VP: Andrys F Irlando
VP: Jeff Mango
Assoc Dir: Beth Bailey
Assoc Dir: Jerome Cheatham
Assoc Dir: Tim Farmer
Assoc Dir: Craig Jackowski
Assoc Dir: Jay Lavalley
Assoc Dir: Parthiv Patel
Assoc Dir: Sasidhar Ravula
Board of Directors: Vittorio Colao, Andrew N Halford, Lowell C McAdam, Daniel S Mead, Stephen C Pusey, Marc C Reed, Francis J Shammo

CELLCOM
See BROWN COUNTY MSA CELLULAR LIMITED PARTNERSHIP

CELLCOM
See NEW-CELL LLC

CELLMARK CHEMICALS
See CELLMARK USA LLC

D-U-N-S 10-346-5936 IMP/EXP
CELLMARK INC
UNITED INTERNATIONAL
(Suby of CELLMARK AB)
22 Pelican Way, San Rafael, CA 94901-5545
Tel (415) 927-1700 Founded/Ownrshp 1989
Sales 108.3MM^E EMP 120
SIC 5099 5093 5111 Pulpwood; Waste paper; Fine paper
*CEO: Fredrik Anderson
*CFO: Michael J Cussen
CFO: Mitra Farr
VP: Susan Blanchard
VP: Kevin Daley
VP: Gianpaolo Tasso

D-U-N-S 00-698-8927 IMP/EXP
CELLMARK PAPER INC
(Suby of CELLMARK PULP & PAPER INC) ★
80 Washington St, Norwalk, CT 06854-3049
Tel (203) 363-7800 Founded/Ownrshp 1984
Sales 85.7MM^E EMP 40
SIC 5099 5111 Pulpwood; Printing & writing paper; Printing paper; Fine paper
Pr: Joseph Hoffman
*Ex VP: Michael McKee
VP Opers: Bill Carroll
Sls Mgr: Paul Hickey
Sales Asso: Flory Pina

D-U-N-S 17-842-0311 IMP/EXP
CELLMARK PULP & PAPER INC
(Suby of UNITED INTERNATIONAL) ★
22 Pelican Way, San Rafael, CA 94901-5545
Tel (415) 927-1700 Founded/Ownrshp 1992
Sales 90.0MM^E EMP 70
SIC 5099 5111 Pulpwood; Fine paper
Pr: Johan Rafstedt

*Treas: Dominick Merole
*VP: Andreas Ceder

D-U-N-S 05-830-2696 IMP
CELLMARK USA LLC
CELLMARK CHEMICALS
(Suby of CELLMARK AB)
2 Corporate Dr 5, Shelton, CT 06484-6238
Tel (203) 541-9000 Founded/Ownrshp 2011
Sales 391.4MM[E] EMP 635[E]
SIC 5169 5051 5084 Chemicals & allied products; Carbon black; Metals service centers & offices; Aluminum bars, rods, ingots, sheets, pipes, plates, etc.; Steel; Ferroalloys; Industrial machinery & equipment
Pr: Hugo Galletta
*Ex VP: Thomas Sliker
Sr VP: Dennis Delaney
IT Man: Edward Callanan

D-U-N-S 00-349-2873 EXP
CELLOFOAM NORTH AMERICA INC (GA)
1917 Rockdale Indstrl Blv, Conyers, GA 30012-3941
Tel (770) 929-3688 Founded/Ownrshp 1979, 1998
Sales 99.0MM[E] EMP 485
SIC 3089 2821 Plastic hardware & building products; Plastics materials & resins
Pr: Gregory R Bontrager
*CFO: Amy L Johnson
CFO: Connie Pinson
*VP: Steve H Gardner
*VP: Cliff A Hanson
*VP: Roger D Pinson

D-U-N-S 06-529-5131 IMP
CELLTRON INC
1110 W 7th St, Galena, KS 66739-1379
Tel (620) 783-1333 Founded/Ownrshp 1983
Sales 118.7MM[E] EMP 400
SIC 3679 Harness assemblies for electronic use: wire or cable
Pr: John McConnell
*Treas: Stacey L Williams
Genl Mgr: Mike Kim
Genl Mgr: Paul Visconte
CTO: Jacob Cherry
Ql Cn Mgr: Jeff Barringer
Ql Cn Mgr: Keith McCoy
Sls Dir: John Ditto
Manager: Mike Beam

D-U-N-S 10-895-5816 EXP
■ **CELLU TISSUE CORP**
(Suby of CELLU TISSUE HOLDINGS INC) ★
2 Forbes St, East Hartford, CT 06108-3727
Tel (860) 289-7496 Founded/Ownrshp 1992
Sales 118.9MM[E] EMP 570
SIC 2621 3842 2676

D-U-N-S 12-945-3663 EXP
■ **CELLU TISSUE CORP-NEENAH**
CLEARWATER PAPER-NEENAH
(Suby of CELLU TISSUE HOLDINGS INC) ★
249 N Lake St, Neenah, WI 54956-2015
Tel (920) 721-9800 Founded/Ownrshp 2002
Sales 217.6MM[E] EMP 500
SIC 2621 Tissue paper
Pr: Linda K Massman
CFO: John D Hertz
Sr VP: Thomas A Colgrove
Sr VP: Michael S Gadd
Sr VP: Danny G Johansen

D-U-N-S 92-775-7179 IMP
■ **CELLU TISSUE HOLDINGS INC**
(Suby of CLEARWATER PAPER CORP) ★
12725 Morris Road Ext # 210, Alpharetta, GA 30004-3874
Tel (678) 393-2651 Founded/Ownrshp 2010
Sales 242.9MM[E] EMP 1,245[E]
SIC 2621 Tissue paper
Pr: Gordon L Jones
*CFO: Linda K Massman
*VP: Michael S Gadd
VP: Steve Martineau

D-U-N-S 80-947-1816
CELLULAR 123 INC
18414 Colima Rd Ste O, Rowland Heights, CA 91748-2883
Tel (626) 913-6788 Founded/Ownrshp 1993
Sales 90.0MM EMP 3
SIC 5999 Telephone equipment & systems
Pr: Ben Her
*VP: Joan Yu

D-U-N-S 60-823-3300 IMP
■ **CELLULAR COMMUNICATIONS OF PUERTO RICO INC**
AT&T MOBILITY
(Suby of AT&T MOBILITY LLC) ★
103 Ave Ortegon, Guaynabo, PR 00966-2505
Tel (787) 397-1000 Founded/Ownrshp 1992
Sales 138.4MM[E] EMP 1,000
SIC 4812 5999 Cellular telephone services; Telephone & communication equipment
Pr: Jose Juan Davila
Netwrk Eng: Farhat Mir
Sls Mgr: Angel Lopez

D-U-N-S 79-312-4025 IMP
CELLULAR CONNECTION LLC
525 Congressional Blvd, Carmel, IN 46032-5647
Tel (765) 651-2001 Founded/Ownrshp 1982
Sales 814.2MM[E] EMP 1,072
SIC 5065 1731 5999 5731 Telephone & telegraphic equipment; Telephone & telephone equipment installation; Telephone & communication equipment; Antennas, satellite dish
CEO: Scott Moorehead
*Pr: Omar Khan
*Pr: Stephen Moorehead
*CFO: Chad Jensen
*Sec: Phyllis Moorehead
*VP: Kevin Windle
Creative D: Jenna Gehlhausen
Rgnl Mgr: Dan Davidson
Site Mgr: Kris Leach

VP Sls: Kelly Jackson
VP Sls: Dan Will

CELLULAR ONE
See MTPCS LLC

D-U-N-S 79-585-8935
CELLULAR SALES OF KNOXVILLE INC
VERIZON WIRELESS
9040 Executive Park Dr, Knoxville, TN 37923-4607
Tel (865) 584-7555 Founded/Ownrshp 1993
Sales 152.4MM[E] EMP 500
Accts Coulter Justus Pc Knoxville
SIC 5999 Mobile telephones & equipment
CEO: Dane Scism
COO: Jt Thome
CFO: Pam Kimball
Ex VP: Brett Patterson
Genl Mgr: Jeff Raunigk
QA Dir: Kathleen Popham
Manager: Jonathan Burke
Sales Asso: Jonathan Gann
Genl Couns: Reese Thomas

D-U-N-S 62-063-7231 IMP
CELLULAR SOUTH INC
C SPIRE
(Suby of TELAPEX INC) ★
1018 Highland Pkwy # 330, Ridgeland, MS 39157-2060
Tel (855) 277-4732 Founded/Ownrshp 1988
Sales 322.7MM[E] EMP 460
SIC 4812 Cellular telephone services
Pr: James H Creekmore
*Pr: Hu Meena
*COO: Kevin Hankins
*CFO: Larry Morrison
*Sec: Wesley Goings
Sr VP: Eric Graham
Sr VP: Suzy Hays
Sr VP: Sherry Stegall
VP: Brian Caraway
VP: Wade H Creekmore Jr
VP: Tad Hamilton
VP: David Hayes
VP: Eric H Hollingsworth
VP: Barb Miller
*VP: Benjamin Pace
VP: David Smith
Comm Dir: Jim Richmond

D-U-N-S 10-817-1885 IMP
CELLUPHONE INC
6119 E Washington Blvd, Commerce, CA 90040-2436
Tel (323) 727-9131 Founded/Ownrshp 1983
Sales 216.9MM[E] EMP 250
SIC 5065 5999 Mobile telephone equipment; Telephone equipment & systems
Pr: Mitchell Mohr
*Ch Bd: Roger Fagerholm
COO: Kevin Bowman
*Sec: Steve Hallgrinson
*VP: Earl Cohen
*VP: Drew Gibson
Mktg Dir: Shawn Gillis
Mktg Dir: Jerry Kelly
Mktg Dir: Brad Terry
Mktg Dir: Adam Waugh

D-U-N-S 96-376-2000 IMP
CELLXION LLC
(Suby of SABRE COMMUNICATIONS) ★
5031 Hazel Jones Rd, Bossier City, LA 71111-5439
Tel (318) 213-2900 Founded/Ownrshp 2007
Sales 179.1MM[E] EMP 891
SIC 4812 1623 3448 3441 Cellular telephone services; Transmitting tower (telecommunication) construction; Prefabricated metal buildings; Fabricated structural metal
CEO: James D Mack

D-U-N-S 00-509-2820
CELOTEX CORP (DE)
10301 Dr Martn L Kng Jr S, Saint Petersburg, FL 33716-3704
Tel (727) 563-5100 Founded/Ownrshp 1964
Sales 86.7MM[E] EMP 1,478
SIC 3086 3275 3296 2493 2952 Insulation or cushioning material, foamed plastic; Building board, gypsum; Acoustical board & tile, mineral wool; Fiberboard, other vegetable pulp; Roofing materials
Pr: John P Borreca
CFO: Jonathan W Oorlog
VP: A Campbell
VP: Kendall Clark
VP: D Thomas
Pr Dir: Carmen Wood

D-U-N-S 12-147-2997
■ **CELTIC GROUP INC**
(Suby of CENTENE CORP) ★
233 S Wacker Dr Ste 700, Chicago, IL 60606-6300
Tel (312) 332-5401 Founded/Ownrshp 2008
Sales NA EMP 300
SIC 6321 6311 Health insurance carriers; Life insurance carriers
Ch Bd: Frederick J Manning
*VP: Diane L Millikan

D-U-N-S 11-837-7464
■ **CELTIC INSURANCE CO**
(Suby of CELTIC GROUP INC) ★
233 S Wacker Dr Ste 700, Chicago, IL 60606-6300
Tel (312) 332-5401 Founded/Ownrshp 1980
Sales NA EMP 175
Accts Ernst & Young Llp
SIC 6311 Life insurance carriers
Ch Bd: Frederick J Manning
CFO: Lewis Marszalek
VP: Barb Basham
VP: Randall Jones
Web Dev: Hitesh Shah
Sls Mgr: Amos Hubbard
Sls Mgr: Armando Torres

D-U-N-S 82-781-9157
CEMENTATION USA INC
(Suby of CEMENTATION CANADA INC)
10150 S Centennial Pkwy # 110, Sandy, UT 84070-4274
Tel (801) 937-4120 Founded/Ownrshp 2005
Sales 222.4MM[E] EMP 400
SIC 1081 Metal mining services
Pr: Justin Oleson
*Treas: Steve Leatherwood
*VP: Richard Pope
VP: Dave Setchell
Genl Mgr: Bill Tilley
Genl Mgr: William Tilley
Snr PM: Stephen Liu
Board of Directors: Peter Adams

D-U-N-S 11-276-6332
■ **CEMETERY MANAGEMENT INC**
(Suby of STEWART ENTERPRISES INC) ★
1201 S Orlando Ave # 365, Winter Park, FL 32789-7109
Tel (407) 740-7000 Founded/Ownrshp 1982
Sales 162.6MM[E] EMP 2,400
SIC 6553 6531 Cemeteries, real estate operation; Cemetery management service
Ch Bd: Frank Stewart
*Pr: Barina Marlowe
*CEO: Joe Henican

D-U-N-S 04-908-4403 IMP/EXP
CEMEX CEMENT INC
(Suby of CEMEX INC) ★
929 Gessner Rd Ste 1900, Houston, TX 77024-2317
Tel (713) 650-6200 Founded/Ownrshp 2000
Sales 1.0MMM[E] EMP 5,000
SIC 3273 3241 Ready-mixed concrete; Portland cement
VP: Thomas Damon
Treas: Jesuslejandro De La Garza
*Sec: Thomas Edgeller
Genl Mgr: Kimberly Bradley
Genl Mgr: Adam Disbrow
Dir IT: Ed Alvarado
Telecom Mg: Armanini Jamie
IT Man: James Kent
IT Man: Maurice Starbird
Opers Mgr: Kenneth Bontrager
Plnt Mgr: Mike N Gossett

D-U-N-S 07-844-0056 IMP
CEMEX CONSTRUCTION MATERIALS ATLANTIC LLC
(Suby of CEMEX INC) ★
1501 Belvedere Rd, West Palm Beach, FL 33406-1501
Tel (561) 833-5555 Founded/Ownrshp 1988
Sales 229.0MM[E] EMP 1,359[E]
SIC 3272 Concrete products
CEO: Fernando A Gonzalez
Pr: Jaime Elizondo
Pr: Joaqun Estrada
Ex VP: Maher Al-Haffar
VP: Mauricio Doehner

D-U-N-S 10-690-5966 IMP
CEMEX CONSTRUCTION MATERIALS LP
929 Gessner Rd Ste 1900, Houston, TX 77024-2317
Tel (713) 650-6200 Founded/Ownrshp 2003
Sales 222.7MM[E] EMP 2,500
SIC 3273 Ready-mixed concrete
CEO: Clarence C Comer
CFO: Francisco Salinas
Dir IT: Dennis Vader
IT Man: Richard Wiles
Opers Mgr: Ted Beamon
Opers Mgr: Glen Ganyard
Sales Asso: Steve Coleman

D-U-N-S 07-844-0061
CEMEX CONSTRUCTION MATERIALS PACIFIC LLC
(Suby of CEMEX INC) ★
1501 Belvedere Rd, West Palm Beach, FL 33406-1501
Tel (561) 833-5555 Founded/Ownrshp 2012
Sales 412.4MM[E] EMP 2,736[E]
SIC 3272 Concrete products
Pr: Rob Cutter

D-U-N-S 06-811-4177
CEMEX CONSTRUCTION MATERIALS SOUTH LLC
(Suby of CEMEX INC) ★
2088 E 20th St, Yuma, AZ 85365-2507
Tel (928) 343-4100 Founded/Ownrshp 2008
Sales 457.4MM[E] EMP 2,332
Accts Pricewaterhousecoopers Llp
SIC 3241 Portland cement
VP: Tom Green

D-U-N-S 83-259-4456
CEMEX CONSTRUCTION MATERIALS SOUTH LLC
(Suby of CEMEX MATERIALS LLC) ★
920 Mmrial Cy Way Ste 100, Houston, TX 77024
Tel (713) 650-6200 Founded/Ownrshp 2008
Sales 150.0MM[E] EMP 2,600
SIC 3271 3273 3272 1422 Blocks, concrete or cinder: standard; Ready-mixed concrete; Pipe, concrete or lined with concrete; Crushed & broken limestone

D-U-N-S 14-837-0323
CEMEX CORP
(Suby of CEMEX INC) ★
4646 E Van Buren St # 250, Phoenix, AZ 85008-6916
Tel (602) 416-2600 Founded/Ownrshp 1988
Sales 360.2MM[E] EMP 1,500
SIC 5032 3273 Cement; Ready-mixed concrete
Pr: Ignacio Murguia
*Sec: Thomas Edgeller
Area Mgr: Cory Albano
Sfty Mgr: Eric S Schubert
Sfty Mgr: David V Shell
Plnt Mgr: Lloyd Hannon

D-U-N-S 09-032-6927 IMP/EXP
CEMEX DE PUERTO RICO INC
Km 2/7 Carr, Guaynabo, PR 00968
Tel (787) 783-3000 Founded/Ownrshp 1938, 2002
Sales 184.8MM[E] EMP 750
Accts Kpmg Llp San Juan Puerto Ric
SIC 3273 3241 Ready-mixed concrete; Portland cement
Pr: Leopoldo Navarro
*Treas: Pedro M Mena
Plng Mgr: Luisa Ospina
Plnt Mgr: Jose Dominguez

D-U-N-S 10-397-4408
CEMEX EL PASO INC
(Suby of RMC USA INC) ★
1 Mckelligon Canyon Rd, El Paso, TX 79930-2634
Tel (915) 565-4681 Founded/Ownrshp 1983
Sales 88.3MM[E] EMP 680
SIC 3273 2951 5032 1442 Ready-mixed concrete; Paving blocks; Sand, construction; Stone, crushed or broken; Construction sand & gravel
Pr: Bill Poole
Dir IT: Bill Gearhart
Prd Mgr: David Macias

D-U-N-S 18-984-0945 IMP/EXP
CEMEX INC
(Suby of CEMEX, S.A.B. DE C.V.)
929 Gessner Rd Ste 1900, Houston, TX 77024-2317
Tel (713) 650-6200 Founded/Ownrshp 1988
Sales 5.8MMM[E] EMP 12,000
SIC 3273 3271 3272 5032 Ready-mixed concrete; Concrete block & brick; Concrete products; Cement
Pr: Ignacio Madridejos
Pr: Scott Ducoff
Pr: Karl Watson
Pr: Sergio Zarate
CFO: Paul Piedad
Ex VP: Frank R Craddock
Ex VP: Robert F Craddock
Ex VP: Michael Egan
Ex VP: Juan Carlos Herrera
Ex VP: Kirk Light
Ex VP: Luis Oropeza
Ex VP: Steven A Wise
VP: Antonio Castillo
VP: Timothy Cottrell
VP: Hamid Farzam
VP: Edward A Kaplan
VP: Janet Teebagy
Dir Risk M: Ted Shrader

D-U-N-S 01-071-4616 EXP
CEMEX MATERIALS LLC
(Suby of CEMEX INC) ★
1501 Belvedere Rd, West Palm Beach, FL 33406-1501
Tel (561) 833-5555 Founded/Ownrshp 1981, 2007
Sales 1.5MMM[E] EMP 9,000
SIC 3271 3273 3272 1422 Blocks, concrete or cinder: standard; Ready-mixed concrete; Pipe, concrete or lined with concrete; Crushed & broken limestone
Pr: Karl H Watson Jr
Pr: Duncan Gage
Pr: Karl Watson
*Ex VP: Robert Cutter
VP: Rod Gamble
VP: Michael R Zern
*Exec: Bob Capasso
*Exec: Frank Craddock
VP Opers: Pat Fagan

D-U-N-S 00-645-4730
CEMSTONE PRODUCTS CO
2025 Centr Poin Blvd Ste 300, Mendota Heights, MN 55120
Tel (651) 688-9292 Founded/Ownrshp 1927
Sales 167.3MM[E] EMP 400
SIC 3273 5032 1442 Ready-mixed concrete; Sand, construction; Gravel; Aggregate; Construction sand & gravel
CEO: Hammon T Becken
*Pr: Thor W Becken
*CFO: Michael Fritz
Treas: Jeff Dingman
VP: John Dickey
Software D: Nick Byrnes
Sfty Dirs: Mike Brekken
Trfc Dir: Dave Slocum
Mtls Mgr: Dan Lindemann
Sls Mgr: Jason Fritz
Board of Directors: Claude Anderson, Steve Becken, Art Gillen

D-U-N-S 00-694-6834
CENAC MARINE SERVICES LLC
742 Highway 182, Houma, LA 70364-4704
Tel (985) 872-2413 Founded/Ownrshp 1931
Sales 91.1MM[E] EMP 458
SIC 4492 Marine towing services

D-U-N-S 10-914-7306
CENAMA INC
VPS CONVENIENCE STORE GROUP
1410 Commwl Dr Ste 202, Wilmington, NC 28403
Tel (910) 395-5300 Founded/Ownrshp 2008
Sales 163.1MM[E] EMP 1,464
SIC 5411 Supermarkets, chain
Ch Bd: Walter C Worsley Jr
Pr: Jeff W Turpin
Ex VP: William Ambrose
VP: W C Worsley III
Brnch Mgr: Bob West

CENDARE
See AVIS RENTAL CAR SYSTEMS

CENEX
See MAXYIELD COOPERATIVE

CENEX
See FARMERS UNION OIL CO OF STANLEY

CENEX
See TRI-ENERGY COOPERATIVE

CENEX
See TOWN AND COUNTRY SUPPLY ASSOCIATION

CENEX HARVEST STATE
See CHS INC

D-U-N-S 00-616-3067 IMP
CENEX INC
5500 Cenex Dr, Inver Grove Heights, MN 55077-1721
Tel (800) 232-3639 *Founded/Ownrshp* 1965
Sales 57.6MMᴱ *EMP* 2,500
SIC 1311 2911 4613 4922 4789 4213 Crude petroleum production; Natural gas production; Gasoline; Greases, lubricating; Liquefied petroleum gases, LPG; Refined petroleum pipelines; Pipelines, natural gas; Storage, natural gas; Pipeline terminal facilities, independently operated; Heavy hauling; Liquid petroleum transport, non-local
Pr: John Johnson
Ex VP: Mark Palmquist

D-U-N-S 82-602-1235
CENGAGE LEARNING HOLDINGS II INC
20 Channel Ctr St, Boston, MA 02210-3437
Tel (617) 289-7700 *Founded/Ownrshp* 1994
Sales 597.9MMᴱ *EMP* 5,000
SIC 2731 Textbooks: publishing & printing
CEO: Michael Hansen
**CFO:* Dean D Durbin
**Treas:* Brian Mulligan
Chf Mktg O: Cindy Cook
**Ofcr:* Kenneth Carson
Ex VP: Michael Eisenstein
**Ex VP:* William Rieders
VP: Greg Clayton
**VP:* Lindsay Stanley
CIO: Bill Chambers
Mktg Dir: Cheryl Costantini

D-U-N-S 86-101-6442 IMP/EXP
CENGAGE LEARNING INC
COURSE TECHNOLOGY
20 Channel Ctr St, Boston, MA 02210-3437
Tel (617) 289-7700 *Founded/Ownrshp* 2007
Sales 1.5MMMᴱ *EMP* 4,810
SIC 2731 Textbooks: publishing & printing
Pr: Michael Hansen
CFO: Dave Albrecht
**CFO:* Dean D Durbin
Treas: Dennis Beckingham
**Chf Mktg O:* Sandi Kirshner
**Chf Mktg O:* Sharon Loeb
**Ofcr:* Fernando Bleichmar
Ex VP: Jonathan Hulbert
**Ex VP:* Kevin Stone
Sr VP: Susan Aspey
Sr VP: Torsten Geers
VP: Todd Markson
VP: John McHugh
**VP:* Henry Pierz
VP: Edwin Robles
Dir Teleco: John Hundemer

D-U-N-S 80-815-9078 IMP
CENIBRA INC
335 Madison Ave Fl 23, New York, NY 10017-4634
Tel (212) 818-8242 *Founded/Ownrshp* 2007
Sales 1.0MMM *EMP* 6
SIC 2611 5159 Pulp mills; Bristles

D-U-N-S 00-935-6791
CENLAR CAPITAL CORP
425 Phillips Blvd, Ewing, NJ 08618-1430
Tel (609) 883-3900 *Founded/Ownrshp* 2001
Sales NA *EMP* 450ᴱ
SIC 6035 Federal savings & loan associations
Pr: Gregory S Tornquist
**Ch Bd:* Michael W Young
**Sr VP:* Jeanne M Bader
**Sr VP:* Stephen W Gozdan
**Sr VP:* David J Miller

D-U-N-S 02-005-8533
CENLAR FSB
(*Suby of* CENLAR CAPITAL CORP) ★
425 Phillips Blvd, Ewing, NJ 08618-1430
Tel (609) 883-3900 *Founded/Ownrshp* 1912
Sales NA *EMP* 427
SIC 6035 Federal savings & loan associations
Prin: Gregory Tounquist
Ex VP: Stephen W Gozdan
Ex VP: David J Miller
Sr VP: Michael Conway
Sr VP: Lori Pinto
VP: Fran Bryant
VP: Jane Chafatelli
VP: Judy Craven
VP: Kathleen D'Amore
VP: Patricia Day
VP: Marianne Doroba
VP: Christopher J Heise
VP: Nancy Irwin
VP: Mark Kelbaugh
VP: Steven Kravitz
VP: Greg K Kuroda
VP: Henry Lieb
VP: Kelly Lutz
VP: Michael Mancino
VP: Rob Marsico
VP: Joanne P McGrath

D-U-N-S 17-135-4488
■ CENPATICO BEHAVIORAL HEALTH LLC
(*Suby of* CENTENE CORP) ★
12515-8 Res Blvd Ste 400, Austin, TX 78759
Tel (512) 406-7200 *Founded/Ownrshp* 2000
Sales NA *EMP* 556ᴱ
SIC 6324 Hospital & medical service plans
CEO: Sam Donaldson
VP: McKensie Derocher
VP: Ryan Gregory
VP: Kimberly Lancaster
VP: Claudia Sumrall
VP: Holly Williams
Snr Mgr: Jan Van

D-U-N-S 05-784-8681 IMP/EXP
CENSEA INC
650 Dundee Rd Ste 180, Northbrook, IL 60062-2753
Tel (224) 723-5800 *Founded/Ownrshp* 1983
Sales 215.0MMᴱ *EMP* 20
SIC 5146 Seafoods
Pr: Lee N Feigon
VP: Jeff Stern
Prin: Sharon Feigon

D-U-N-S 92-995-5383
■ CENSUS BUREAU UNITED STATES
(*Suby of* US DOC) ★
4600 Silver Hill Rd, Suitland, MD 20746
Tel (301) 763-2135 *Founded/Ownrshp* 2000
Sales NA *EMP* 9,500
SIC 9611 Administration of general economic programs;
COO: Thomas L Mesenbourg Jr
**Ofcr:* John M Abowd
Assoc Dir: Thomas A Louis

D-U-N-S 07-877-3104
CENTAUR ACQUISITION LLC (IN)
INDIANA GRAND
(*Suby of* CENTAUR GAMING) ★
111 Monument Cir Ste 777, Indianapolis, IN 46204-5100
Tel (317) 656-8787 *Founded/Ownrshp* 2012, 2011
Sales 38.0MMᴱ *EMP* 1,000ᴱ
SIC 7011 7948 Casino hotel; Horses, racing
CEO: Roderick J Ratcliff
Pr: Jim Brown
CFO: Tammy Schaeffer
Ex VP: Kurt E Wilson
VP: John Keeler

CENTAUR GAMING
See NEW CENTAUR LLC

D-U-N-S 19-624-5588
CENTAUR HOLDINGS LLC
111 Monument Cir, Indianapolis, IN 46204-5100
Tel (317) 656-8787 *Founded/Ownrshp* 2011
Sales 104.1MMᴱ *EMP* 1,115ᴱ
SIC 6719 Investment holding companies, except banks
CEO: Roderick J Ratcliff
**CFO:* Kurt E Wilson

D-U-N-S 06-991-6505
CENTAUR INC
111 Monument Cir, Indianapolis, IN 46204-5100
Tel (317) 656-8787 *Founded/Ownrshp* 1993
Sales 221.2MMᴱ *EMP* 1,280
SIC 7948 Horses, racing
Ch Bd: Roderick J Ratcliff
**Pr:* James L Brown
**CFO:* Tamara Schaeffer
**CFO:* Kurt E Wilson
**VP:* John Keeler
Genl Couns: Phillip Bainbridge

D-U-N-S 12-240-0336 IMP
CENTAUR INC
HEIDTMAN STEEL PRODUCTS
2401 Front St, Toledo, OH 43605-1145
Tel (419) 469-8000 *Founded/Ownrshp* 1983
Sales 273.0MMᴱ *EMP* 1,000
SIC 3312 3316 3999 Sheet or strip, steel, hot-rolled; Strip steel, cold-rolled: from purchased hot-rolled; Atomizers, toiletry
CEO: Mark Ridenour
**Ch Bd:* John C Bates

D-U-N-S 82-977-4111
CENTAUR LLC
(*Suby of* CENTAUR INC) ★
10 W Market St Ste 200, Indianapolis, IN 46204-2984
Tel (317) 656-8787 *Founded/Ownrshp* 2002
Sales 220.0MMᴱ *EMP* 1,280
SIC 7948 Horses, racing
CEO: Roderick J Ratcliff
**COO:* James L Brown
**CFO:* Kurt E Wilson

D-U-N-S 06-101-5822
CENTEGRA HEALTH SYSTEM
385 Millennium Dr Ste A, Crystal Lake, IL 60012-3761
Tel (815) 788-5800 *Founded/Ownrshp* 1982
Sales 133.6MM *EMP* 3,700
Accts Kpmg Llc Columbus Oh
SIC 8062 General medical & surgical hospitals
Ch Bd: Charie Zanck
**Pr:* Jason Sciarro
**CEO:* Michael Eesley
COO: Lori Sullivan
**CFO:* Robert Rosenberger
**Treas:* Eric Zornow
VP: Nathan Kumar
VP: Ted Z Lorenc
VP: Bob Murphy
VP: Kumar Nathan
Exec: Don Novak
Exec: Janet Reuter

D-U-N-S 00-696-9869
■ CENTEL CORP
EMBARQ
(*Suby of* CENTURYLINK) ★
100 Centurylink Dr, Monroe, LA 71203-2041
Tel (318) 388-9000 *Founded/Ownrshp* 2006
Sales 197.8MMᴱ *EMP* 2,095ᴱ
SIC 4813 4812 Local telephone communications; Long distance telephone communications; Cellular telephone services
Pr: William E Cheek
**VP:* Claudia Toussaint

D-U-N-S 80-924-5525
▲ CENTENE CORP
7700 Forsyth Blvd Ste 800, Saint Louis, MO 63105-1849
Tel (314) 725-4477 *Founded/Ownrshp* 1984
Sales NA *EMP* 18,200
Tkr Sym CNC *Exch* NYS
SIC 6324 8011 8099 Hospital & medical service plans; Cardiologist & cardio-vascular specialist; Medical services organization
Ch Bd: Michael F Neidorff
CEO: Thomas Wise
**CFO:* Jeffrey A Schwaneke
Ex VP: Cynthia J Brinkley
Ex VP: Mark Eggert
Ex VP: Theresa Erickson
**Ex VP:* Carol E Goldman
Ex VP: Jason M Harrold
Ex VP: Jesse N Hunter
**Ex VP:* Keith H Williamson
Sr VP: Mark Brooks
Sr VP: Patricia Darnley
**Sr VP:* Christopher R Isaak
VP: Ela Alarcon-Cabrera
VP: Irene Armendariz
VP: Mark Barrett
VP: Judy Bauer
VP: Keith Bernier
VP: Michael Boone
VP: Julie Boulch
VP: Kathy Bradley-Wells
Board of Directors: Orlando Ayala, Robert K Ditmore, Frederick H Eppinger, Vicki B Escarra, Richard A Gephardt, Pamela A Joseph, John R Roberts, David L Steward, Tommy G Thompson

D-U-N-S 03-873-2371
■ CENTENNIAL BANK
(*Suby of* HOME BANCSHARES INC) ★
620 Chestnut St, Conway, AR 72032-5404
Tel (501) 328-4663 *Founded/Ownrshp* 1998
Sales NA *EMP* 603
SIC 6022 State commercial banks
Pr: Tracy M French
Pr: Davy Carter
Trst Ofcr: Lisa Whitworth
VP: Robert Bourke
VP: Bedford Davie
VP: Maureen Dennis
VP: Joseph Ganley
VP: Nathan Harbert
VP: Chris Johnson
VP: Dustin Jones
VP: Chris Kelley
**VP:* Randy Mayor
VP: Amy Pierson

D-U-N-S 04-903-9787
CENTENNIAL BEVERAGE GROUP LLC
CENTENNIAL FINE WINE & SPIRITS
4011 Commerce St, Dallas, TX 75226-1712
Tel (972) 668-7335 *Founded/Ownrshp* 1996
Sales 85.6MMᴱ *EMP* 650
SIC 5921 Liquor stores
CEO: William C Hajek
**Pr:* Gregory L Wonsmos
**COO:* Ronnie D Cockerham

D-U-N-S 78-305-4422
CENTENNIAL CONTRACTORS ENTERPRISES INC
CENTENNIAL SERVICES
(*Suby of* BILFINGER SE)
11111 Sunset Hills Rd # 350, Reston, VA 20190-5327
Tel (703) 885-4600 *Founded/Ownrshp* 2003
Sales 201.8MM *EMP* 250
Accts Ernst & Young Llp Mclean Va
SIC 1542 1541 Commercial & office building, new construction; Commercial & office buildings, renovation & repair; Industrial buildings, new construction; Renovation, remodeling & repairs: industrial buildings
CEO: Mark Bailey
**CFO:* Ralf-Rainer Fuchs
Ofcr: Beasman Charles
Ofcr: Kenny Tarmon
Genl Mgr: Corey Benner

D-U-N-S 61-691-7175
■ CENTENNIAL ENERGY HOLDINGS INC
(*Suby of* MDU RESOURCES GROUP INC) ★
Schuchart Bldg 918e, Bismarck, ND 58501
Tel (701) 222-7900 *Founded/Ownrshp* 1988
Sales 1.1MMMᴱ *EMP* 1,621
SIC 1382 8748 1221 Oil & gas exploration services; Energy conservation consultant; Bituminous coal & lignite-surface mining
Pr: Martin A White
**CFO:* Warren L Robinson
**VP:* Bill Connors

D-U-N-S 62-676-2103
■ CENTENNIAL ENERGY RESOURCES LLC
(*Suby of* CENTENNIAL ENERGY HOLDINGS INC) ★
1200 W Century Ave, Bismarck, ND 58503-0911
Tel (701) 530-1000 *Founded/Ownrshp* 2003
Sales 473.2MMᴱ *EMP* 720ᴱ
SIC 4911 Electric services
CEO: Paul Gatzemeier
CFO: Doran Schwartz
Treas: Vernon Raile
VP: Dave Goodin
Dir IT: Eric Hope
Art Dir: Paige Mattson

CENTENNIAL FINE WINE & SPIRITS
See CENTENNIAL BEVERAGE GROUP LLC

D-U-N-S 60-607-3831
CENTENNIAL HEALTHCARE CORP
(*Suby of* HILLTOPPER HOLDING CORP) ★
400 Perimeter Ctr Ter Ne, Atlanta, GA 30346-1227
Tel (770) 698-9040 *Founded/Ownrshp* 2000
Sales 257.7MMᴱ *EMP* 10,000
SIC 8051 8069 8052 8741 Skilled nursing care facilities; Specialty hospitals, except psychiatric; Intermediate care facilities; Nursing & personal care facility management
Ch Bd: J Stephen Eaton
Pr: David R Wilson
CEO: Jeffrey Jellerson
CFO: Troy Antonik
CFO: Ben Grazzini
Sr VP: Daniel F Montgomery
MIS Dir: Jimmy Allen
MIS Dir: Ashley D Ardoin
MIS Dir: Kevin Arner
MIS Dir: Mike Driskel
IT Man: Chris Spencer

D-U-N-S 13-589-4900
■ CENTENNIAL MEDICAL CENTER
(*Suby of* TENET HEALTHSYSTEM MEDICAL INC) ★
12505 Lebanon Rd, Frisco, TX 75035-8298
Tel (972) 963-3333 *Founded/Ownrshp* 2002
Sales 111.8MM *EMP* 500ᴱ
SIC 8069 Specialty hospitals, except psychiatric
CEO: Joe Thomason
**COO:* Reed Hammond
**CFO:* Blaise Bondi
**Prin:* Calee Travis
HC Dir: Michelle Stukey

D-U-N-S 95-764-5666 IMP
■ CENTENNIAL PUERTO RICO OPERATIONS CORP
(*Suby of* CENTENNIAL COMMUNICATIONS CORP)
3349 State Route 138 A, Wall Township, NJ 07719-9671
Tel (732) 556-2200 *Founded/Ownrshp* 1994
Sales 92.1MMᴱ *EMP* 1,200
SIC 4812 Cellular telephone services
Pr: Michael Small
**Treas:* Pat Kameen

D-U-N-S 07-708-7484
CENTENNIAL SCHOOL DISTRICT
CSD
433 Centennial Rd, Warminster, PA 18974-5455
Tel (215) 441-6000 *Founded/Ownrshp* 1966
Sales 67.8MMᴱ *EMP* 1,150
Accts Barbacane Thornton & Company
SIC 8211 Public elementary school; Public junior high school; Public senior high school
CFO: Deborah Potter
VP: Cynthia Mueller
Prin: Diane Guinan
Dir IT: Janice Farley
Psych: Kristi Bedford

CENTENNIAL SERVICES
See CENTENNIAL CONTRACTORS ENTERPRISES INC

D-U-N-S 07-865-4055
CENTER COLLEGE
CLASSIC FARE CATERING
600 W Walnut St, Danville, KY 40422-1394
Tel (859) 238-5369 *Founded/Ownrshp* 1999
Sales 99.5MMᴱ *EMP* 65
Accts Crowe Horwath Llp Louisville
SIC 5812 Caterers
Pr: John Roush
**Pr:* Walter Craven
Assoc VP: Jamey Leahey
VP: Randy Hays
VP: Richard Trollinger
Assoc Dir: David Frey
Assoc Dir: Laura Keown
Comm Dir: Phnomphone Sirimongrhon
CIO: Keith Fowlkes
IT Man: David Abney

CENTER FOR CHILD HEALTH RES
See AMERICAN ACADEMY OF PEDIATRICS

D-U-N-S 07-158-0955
CENTER FOR CREATIVE LEADERSHIP INC (NC)
1 Leadership Pl, Greensboro, NC 27410-9427
Tel (336) 288-7210 *Founded/Ownrshp* 1970
Sales 115.0MM *EMP* 600
Accts Mcgladrey Llp Greensboro Nor
SIC 8299 2731 Educational services; Book publishing
Pr: John R Ryan
**Pr:* Bradley E Shumaker
Bd of Dir: Eric R Calhoun
Bd of Dir: Haynes G Griffin
Bd of Dir: Jamie Gurley
Bd of Dir: Thomas K Hearn
Bd of Dir: Kathy Kram
Bd of Dir: PY Lai
Bd of Dir: Peter L Richardson
Ex VP: John Butler
Ex VP: Lilly Kelly-Radford
Sr VP: David Altman
Sr VP: David G Altman
Sr VP: Portia R Mount
VP: Marcia Avedon
VP: Raymond Burse
VP: Stan Gryskiewicz
VP: Stanley Gryskiewicz
VP: Roland Smith
Exec: Jennifer Habig
Exec: Lyndon Rego

D-U-N-S 03-737-0210
CENTER FOR DISABILITY SERVICES INC
CLOVER PATCH DAY CARE
314 S Manning Blvd, Albany, NY 12208-1708
Tel (518) 437-5506 *Founded/Ownrshp* 1942
Sales 98.7MM *EMP* 2,500
Accts Center For Disability Services
SIC 8351 8093 8361 8099 Preschool center; Rehabilitation center, outpatient treatment; Home for the physically handicapped; Medical services organization
CEO: Alan Krafchin
**CEO:* George R Hearst III
**CFO:* Greg Sorrentino
**VP:* William B Palmer
**Ex Dir:* Alan Crafchan
Prgrm Mgr: Jennifer Jones
Psych: Trinya Cichy
Psych: Maryanne Yates

D-U-N-S 09-325-3011
CENTER FOR DISCOVERY INC
641 Old Route 17, Harris, NY 12742
Tel (845) 794-1400 *Founded/Ownrshp* 1954
Sales 97.8MM *EMP* 1,350ᴱ
Accts Baker Tilly Virchow Krause Llp
SIC 8361 Rehabilitation center, residential: health care incidental
CEO: Patrick H Dollard
Pr: Richard Humleker
**Pr:* John Milligan
**CFO:* Claude D'Alessandro
**Ex VP:* Caryn Andersen
**VP:* William Evans
**VP:* Marc Floyd
Genl Mgr: Thomas Burnham
Dir IT: Dean McManus
IT Man: Joe Carraccia

CENTER FOR HEALTH
See WESPATH BENEFITS AND INVESTMENTS

CENTER FOR HEALTH CARE SVCS
See BEXAR COUNTY BOARD OF TRUSTEES FOR MENTAL HEALTH MENTAL RETARDATION

D-U-N-S 09-919-5695
CENTER FOR HUMAN DEVELOPMENT INC
332 Birnie Ave, Springfield, MA 01107-1106
Tel (413) 733-6624 *Founded/Ownrshp* 1972
Sales 87.6MM *EMP* 1,100
Accts Alexander Aronson Finning & Co
SIC 8322 Social service center
Ex Dir: James Goodwin
**Treas:* Maria Goncalves
**VP:* Hank Drapalski
VP: Henry J Drapalski Jr
**VP:* William A Dvila
VP: Anthony Hebert
Ex Dir: Elaine Pendergast
Prgrm Mgr: Kimberly Puffer
Admn Mgr: Tom McGuire
Pgrm Dir: Renee Moss
Pgrm Dir: Laura Young

CENTER FOR MIGRATN DEMOGRPHY
See UNIVERSITY OF NEVADA LAS VEGAS

D-U-N-S 01-949-5527
CENTER FOR PAIN MANAGEMENT LLC
NATIONAL SPINE AND PAIN CTRS
11921 Rockville Pike # 505, Rockville, MD 20852-2758
Tel (301) 881-7246 *Founded/Ownrshp* 2007
Sales 93.0MM[E] *EMP* 750
SIC 8011 Offices & clinics of medical doctors
**Doctor:* Mark Coleman

CENTER FOR PROFESSIONAL DEV
See ITT EDUCATIONAL SERVICES INC

D-U-N-S 86-091-2252
CENTER FOR PSYCHIATRY AT WINTER HAVEN INC
200 Avenue F Ne, Winter Haven, FL 33881-4131
Tel (863) 297-1744 *Founded/Ownrshp* 1994
Sales 83.5MM *EMP* 1
SIC 8011 Psychiatrist
Pr: Lance Anastasio

CENTER FOR RURAL HEALTH
See AVERA MCKENNAN

D-U-N-S 80-030-8707
CENTER FOR SUSTAINABLE ENERGY
9325 Sky Park Ct Ste 100, San Diego, CA 92123-4380
Tel (858) 244-1177 *Founded/Ownrshp* 2001
Sales 90.0MM *EMP* 87
Accts Rhode & Roberts San Diego Ca
SIC 8748 Business consulting
Ch: Michael Akavan
**Treas:* Fred Baranowski
Ex Dir: Len Hering
Prgrm Mgr: Benjamin Airth
Prgrm Mgr: Marlene King
Prgrm Mgr: Laura Parsons
Off Mgr: Cynthia Shegog
CTO: Gene Kogan
IT Man: Irene Stillings
Pr Mgr: Chuck Colgan
Mktg Mgr: Anna Miller

D-U-N-S 07-943-5308
CENTER FOR TRANSPORTATION SAFETY LLC
(*Suby of* PHH ARVAL) ★
5700 E 56th Ave Unit I, Commerce City, CO 80022-3905
Tel (303) 227-0131 *Founded/Ownrshp* 2010
Sales 33.4MM[E] *EMP* 1,146[E]
SIC 7513 7515 Truck rental & leasing, no drivers; Passenger car leasing
Owner: Jay Shelly

CENTER FOR VENTR PHILANTHROPY
See PENINSULA COMMUNITY FOUNDATION

CENTER HEALTH CARE
See CENTER RESIDENCE CORP

D-U-N-S 05-833-9581 IMP/EXP
CENTER MANUFACTURING INC
MEC
(*Suby of* MAYVILLE ENGINEERING CO INC) ★
990 84th St Sw, Byron Center, MI 49315-9384
Tel (616) 878-3324 *Founded/Ownrshp* 2012
Sales 106.7MM[E] *EMP* 440
SIC 3499 3441 Automobile seat frames, metal; Fabricated structural metal
Pr: Richard Nielsen
**CFO:* Chris Alford
Treas: Arthur Veltman
IT Man: Chuck Ward
Plnt Mgr: Craig King

CENTER MNICPL OPERATIONS TRNSP
See CAGUAS MUNICIPALITY

CENTER OIL COMPANY
See G P & W INC

D-U-N-S 11-235-7871 IMP
CENTER OPERATING CO LP
AMERICAN AIRLINES CENTER
2500 Victory Ave, Dallas, TX 75219-7601
Tel (214) 222-3687 *Founded/Ownrshp* 1999
Sales 105.0MM[E] *EMP* 1,625[E]
SIC 7941 Sports field or stadium operator, promoting sports events; Stadium event operator services
Pt: Brad Mayne
Pt: Craig Courson
VP: Ken Kuhl
VP: Michael Reid
VP: Paul Waugh
Dir Soc: Cameron Debose
Prgrm Mgr: Jill Pigman
Dir IT: Joe Heinlein
Info Man: Kevin Liles
Software D: Mark Teal
VP Opers: Trish Hollinrake

D-U-N-S 96-524-0682
CENTER PARTNERS INC
4401 Innovation Dr, Fort Collins, CO 80525-3404
Tel (970) 206-9000 *Founded/Ownrshp* 1996
Sales NA *EMP* 1,950
SIC 7379 8742 7363

D-U-N-S 84-938-5588
CENTER RESIDENCE CORP
CENTER HEALTH CARE
314 S Manning Blvd, Albany, NY 12208-1708
Tel (518) 437-5700 *Founded/Ownrshp* 1980
Sales 20.5MM[E] *EMP* 2,100
SIC 8322 Individual & family services
Pr: Alan Krafchin
**CFO:* Gregory Sorrentino
Prin: Eleanor Curley
Ex Dir: Patrick J Bulgaro
Ex Dir: Rose Mary Lorello

D-U-N-S 80-654-4917
CENTERBRIDGE CAPITAL PARTNERS LP
375 Park Ave Fl 12, New York, NY 10152-0002
Tel (212) 672-5000 *Founded/Ownrshp* 2006
Sales 132.0MM[E] *EMP* 2,100
SIC 6799 Venture capital companies
Genl Pt: Jeffrey Gelfand
Ofcr: Elizabeth Uhl

D-U-N-S 62-538-4818
CENTERBRIDGE PARTNERS LP
375 Park Ave Fl 13, New York, NY 10152-1300
Tel (212) 672-5000 *Founded/Ownrshp* 2006
Sales 2.9MMM[E] *EMP* 6,615[E]
SIC 6282 6211 Investment advice; Investment advisory service; Investment firm, general brokerage
Mng Dir: Kyle Cruz
Mng Dir: Vivek Melwani
Mng Dir: Jason Mozingo
Mng Dir: Sam Riter
Mng Dir: Paige Ross
Mng Dir: Kimberly Terjanian
Mng Dir: Christian Wypasek
Genl Mgr: Lauren Binkley
CTO: David Avraamides
Opers Mgr: Cynthia Fuentes
Opers Mgr: Lisa Murray

D-U-N-S 78-476-8889
CENTERLIGHT HEALTHCARE INC
1250 Waters Pl Ste 602, Bronx, NY 10461-2732
Tel (347) 640-6000 *Founded/Ownrshp* 1990
Sales 687.1MM *EMP* 4,000
Accts Loeb & Troper Llp New York N
SIC 8051 8082 8322 Skilled nursing care facilities; Home health care services; Rehabilitation services
CEO: Benjamin Duster
**COO:* Joseph M Healy Jr
**COO:* Paul Rosenfeld
**CFO:* Ira Green
**Chf Cred:* Karen Eastmond
**Chf Mktg O:* Christie Otoole
**Sr VP:* Peter Fragale
**Sr VP:* Stephen Mann
VP: Swasti Apte
VP: Raffaele Piemonte

CENTERLINE TRUCKING
See DIRECTIONAL DRILLING CO LP

CENTERPLATE
See VOLUME SERVICES INC

D-U-N-S 94-132-1325
CENTERPLATE INC
(*Suby of* CENTERPLATE ULTIMATE HOLDINGS CORP) ★
2187 Atlantic St, Stamford, CT 06902-6880
Tel (800) 698-6992 *Founded/Ownrshp* 2012
Sales 1.2MMM[E] *EMP* 29,050
SIC 5812 7999 5947 7993 Concessionaire; Concession operator; Souvenirs; Gambling establishments operating coin-operated machines
Pr: Chris Verros
Pr: Jeff Tandberg
**CFO:* Hadi K Manovar
**CFO:* Kevin F McNamara
**Ofcr:* Roy Arnold
Ofcr: Gregory J Lesperance
**Ofcr:* Bob Pascal
**Ofcr:* Keith Bw Wing
Ex VP: Greg Fender
Ex VP: Hadi K Monavar
Ex VP: Hadi Monavar
Sr VP: Keith B Wking
Sr VP: Keith B King
**Sr VP:* Gregory Lesperance
VP: Ashley Brown
VP: John Erickson
VP: Marsha Graber
VP: Richard Kahn
VP: Kyle Kandel
VP: Jason Lipscomb
VP: Scott Marshall

D-U-N-S 07-888-7287
CENTERPLATE ULTIMATE HOLDINGS CORP
2187 Atlantic St, Stamford, CT 06902-6880
Tel (800) 698-6992 *Founded/Ownrshp* 2013, 1929
Sales 1.2MMM[E] *EMP* 39,858[E]
SIC 5812 7999 5947 7993 Concessionaire; Concession operator; Souvenirs; Gambling establishments operating coin-operated machines

CENTERPOINT ENERGY
See LAKESHORE ENERGY SERVICES LLC

D-U-N-S 00-793-1728 IMP
■ **CENTERPOINT ENERGY HOUSTON ELECTRIC LLC**
(*Suby of* UTILITY HOLDING LLC) ★
1111 Louisiana St, Houston, TX 77002-5230
Tel (713) 207-1111 *Founded/Ownrshp* 2002
Sales 2.8MMM *EMP* 2,650
Accts Deloitte & Touche Llp Housto
SIC 4911 Electric services; Generation, electric power; Transmission, electric power; Distribution, electric power
Ch Bd: Scott M Prochazka
COO: Scott Prochazka
CFO: William D Rogers
Sr VP: Kristie L Colvin

D-U-N-S 10-459-0802
▲ **CENTERPOINT ENERGY INC**
1111 Louisiana St Ste 264, Houston, TX 77002-5228
Tel (713) 207-1111 *Founded/Ownrshp* 2001
Sales 7.3MMM *EMP* 7,505
Tkr Sym CNP *Exch* NYS
SIC 4931 Electric & other services combined
Pr: Scott M Prochazka
**Ch Bd:* Milton Carroll
V Ch: Jeremy Bloch
CFO: William D Rogers
Bd of Dir: Walter Ferguson
Ofcr: Sue B Ortenstone
Ex VP: Thomas Standish
Sr VP: Gary Hayes
Sr VP: Kenneth M Mercado
Sr VP: Dana C O'Brien
Sr VP: Richard A Zapalac
VP: Shamyra Buckner
VP: Scott Doyle
VP: Carol Helliker
VP: Kimberly Johnston
VP: Shane Kimzey
VP: Carla Kneipp
VP: William Kuchar III
VP: Brad Tutunjian
Board of Directors: Michael P Johnson, Scott J McLean, Theodore F Pound, Susan O Rheney, Phillip R Smith, John W Somerhalder II, Peter S Wareing

D-U-N-S 00-694-8210
■ **CENTERPOINT ENERGY RESOURCES CORP**
(*Suby of* UTILITY HOLDING LLC) ★
1111 Louisiana St, Houston, TX 77002-5230
Tel (713) 207-1111 *Founded/Ownrshp* 1996, 2002
Sales 4.5MMM *EMP* 4,581
SIC 4924 4922 Natural gas distribution; Pipelines, natural gas
Ch Bd: Scott M Prochazka
CFO: William D Rogers
Sr VP: Kristie L Colvin
Sr VP: William May
VP: Pete Kirsch
VP: Cy Zebot

D-U-N-S 83-861-1739
■ **CENTERPOINT ENERGY SERVICES INC**
(*Suby of* CENTERPOINT ENERGY RESOURCES CORP) ★
1111 Louisiana St Ste 264, Houston, TX 77002-5228
Tel (713) 207-1111 *Founded/Ownrshp* 1996
Sales 696.1MM[E] *EMP* 252
SIC 4924 Natural gas distribution
Pr: David M McClanahan
Pr: Bruce Coogler
**Pr:* Scott M Prochazka
**Ex VP:* Scott E Rozzell
**Ex VP:* Thomas R Standish
**Ex VP:* Gary L Whitlock
**Sr VP:* Gregory C Harper
Genl Mgr: George Kunkle
Genl Mgr: Tj Noland
Board of Directors: E Barnett, William Transier

D-U-N-S 07-837-2416
■ **CENTERPOINT ENERGY SERVICES RETAIL LLC**
(*Suby of* CENTERPOINT ENERGY SERVICES INC) ★
1111 La St Fl 20, Houston, TX 77002
Tel (800) 752-8036 *Founded/Ownrshp* 2011
Sales 695.7MM *EMP* 35
Accts Grant Thornton Llp Tulsa Okl
SIC 4924 Natural gas distribution
Pr: David McClanahan

D-U-N-S 78-610-0201
■ **CENTERPOINT ENERGY TRANSITION BOND CO LLC**
(*Suby of* CENTERPOINT ENERGY HOUSTON ELECTRIC LLC) ★
1111 La St Ste 4667, Houston, TX 77002
Tel (713) 207-8272 *Founded/Ownrshp* 1999
Sales 116.5MM *EMP* 3
SIC 4924
Prin: Scott M Prochazka

D-U-N-S 80-109-0775
CENTERPOINT MEDICAL CENTER OF INDEPENDENCE LLC
19600 E 39th St S, Independence, MO 64057-2301
Tel (816) 698-8846 *Founded/Ownrshp* 2003
Sales 232.6MM *EMP* 1,000[E]
SIC 8062 General medical & surgical hospitals
CEO: Carolyn Caldwell
COO: Natalie Mussi
CFO: Jim Brown
CFO: Tariq Malik
Ofcr: Leona Lee
VP: Sherry Marshall
Exec: Linda Dunaway
Dir Soc: Lori Martin

D-U-N-S 07-389-1921
CENTERRA GROUP LLC
(*Suby of* AMCP SECURITY HOLDINGS, L.P.)
7121 Fairway Dr Ste 301, Palm Beach Gardens, FL 33418-3766
Tel (561) 472-0600 *Founded/Ownrshp* 2014
Sales 765.6MM[E] *EMP* 7,000
Accts Mcgladrey Llp Fort Lauderdale
SIC 7381 8744 Security guard service; Facilities support services; Base maintenance (providing personnel on continuing basis)
Pr: Paul P Donahue
COO: Steve Hafner
**CFO:* Deborah Ricci
Ofcr: Onita Welch
VP: Jeffrey Norman
VP: Gary Sayers

CENTERRA WINE COMPANY
See CONSTELLATION BRANDS US OPERATIONS INC

D-U-N-S 01-894-4035
■ **CENTERRE HEALTHCARE CORP**
(*Suby of* KINDRED HEALTHCARE INC) ★
113 Seaboard Ln Ste 201b, Franklin, TN 37067-8284
Tel (615) 846-9500 *Founded/Ownrshp* 2015
Sales 107.8MM[E] *EMP* 1,600
SIC 8011 Offices & clinics of medical doctors
Pr: Patrick Foster
Pr: Patrick Lee
**COO:* Terry Maxhimer
**CFO:* David Canniff
VP: Cristina Huerta
VP: Bob Miller
VP: Greg Sassman
Snr Mgr: Sharon Smeltzer

D-U-N-S 07-933-1081
CENTERS FOR ADVANCED ORTHOPAEDICS LLC
SOUTHERN MARYLAND ORTHOPAEDICS
6707 Democracy Blvd # 504, Bethesda, MD 20817-1166
Tel (301) 637-8710 *Founded/Ownrshp* 2012
Sales 25.4MM[E] *EMP* 1,200
SIC 8011 Internal medicine, physician/surgeon
Ex Dir: Dennis Tritinger
Treas: Subir Jossan MD
Prin: Nicholas Grosso MD

D-U-N-S 92-764-5465 IMP
■ **CENTERS FOR DISEASE CONTROL AND PREVENTION**
CDC
(*Suby of* UNITED STATES DEPARTMENT OF HEALTH & HUMAN SERVICES) ★
1600 Clifton Rd Ne, Atlanta, GA 30329-4018
Tel (404) 639-3311 *Founded/Ownrshp* 1946
Sales NA *EMP* 13,000
Accts Ernst & Young Llp Mclean Va
SIC 9431 Administration of public health programs;
COO: Sherri Berger
COO: Carlton Duncan
CFO: Kenneth Cooper
CFO: Barbara Harris
CFO: Barbara Michalson
Ofcr: Azania Heyward-James
Ofcr: Mark Stenger
Ex VP: Tom Shinnick
Exec: Joe Odonald
Dir Risk M: Christine Sofge
Assoc Dir: Joan Cioffi
Assoc Dir: Abigail Shefer
Assoc Dir: Richard Waxweiler

D-U-N-S 92-764-5622
■ **CENTERS FOR MEDICARE AND MEDICAID SERVICES**
CMS
(*Suby of* UNITED STATES DEPARTMENT OF HEALTH & HUMAN SERVICES) ★
7500 Sec Blvd Ms C31103, Baltimore, MD 21244
Tel (410) 786-3000 *Founded/Ownrshp* 1977
Sales NA *EMP* 4,700
SIC 9431 Administration of public health programs;
COO: Marilyn B Tavenner
Ex VP: Serrick McNeill
Exec: Jill Nicolaisen
Div Mgr: Cynthia Anderson
DP Exec: Jamuar Ray
DP Exec: Ray Walmsley
Dir IT: Dennis Read
IT Man: Anita Griner
IT Man: Jamaur Ray
IT Man: Regina Shock
Sls Dir: Hien Huynh

D-U-N-S 13-068-6681
■ **CENTERSTATE BANK OF FLORIDA NATIONAL ASSOCIATION**
(*Suby of* CENTERSTATE BANKS INC) ★
7722 State Road 544, Winter Haven, FL 33881-9570
Tel (863) 422-8990 *Founded/Ownrshp* 2009
Sales NA *EMP* 75
SIC 6022 State commercial banks
VP: James Antal
**CFO:* Steve Young
Ex VP: Donald M Weaver
Dir IT: Rod Anthony
Netwrk Mgr: Craig Sexton

D-U-N-S 10-283-8575
▲ **CENTERSTATE BANKS INC**
42745 Highway 27, Davenport, FL 33837-6821
Tel (863) 419-7750 *Founded/Ownrshp* 2000
Sales NA *EMP* 784[E]
Tkr Sym CSFL *Exch* NGS
SIC 6021 National commercial banks
Pr: John C Corbett
**Ch Bd:* Ernest S Pinner
COO: Stephen D Young
CFO: Jennifer L Idell
**V Ch Bd:* Charles W McPherson
Ofcr: Daniel E Bockhorst
Ofcr: Angie Massey
Ofcr: John E Tranter
Assoc VP: Dana Townsend
VP: Jim Bigger
VP: Stacy Byrd
VP: Gerri Cook
VP: Greg Felix
VP: Jarrod Hurd
VP: Evie McCutcheon
VP: Todd Norman
VP: John Roberts
VP: John Rust
Exec: Gil Pomar
Board of Directors: Joshua A Snively, James H Bingham, G Robert Blanchard Jr, C Dennis Carlton, Michael F Ciferri, Griffin A Greene, G Tierso Nunez II, Thomas E Oakley, William Knox Pou Jr, Daniel R Richey

D-U-N-S 03-236-8163
CENTERSTONE INSURANCE AND FINANCIAL SERVICES INC
BENEFITMALL
4851 Lyndon B Johnson Fwy, Dallas, TX 75244-6004
Tel (469) 791-3300 Founded/Ownrshp 1999
Sales 157.8MM EMP 650
SIC 7389 Financial services
CEO: Bernard Difiore
Mng Pt: Michele Diianni
Mng Pt: Cathy Macomber
Mng Pt: Marianne Rinaldi
Mng Pt: Eta Tierney
*Pr: Scott Kirksey
*CFO: Stephanie Bowman
Ex VP: Fred Robertson
*Sr VP: Steve Cohen
*Sr VP: Dennis Fallon
Sr VP: ARI Friedman
*Sr VP: Michael Gomes
Sr VP: Todd Slawter
*Sr VP: Mark Strippy
*Sr VP: Chris Vaerewyck
VP: Neal Alexander
VP: Kristin Komen
VP: Jeff Lewis
VP: Barbara Maxwell
VP: Brian Rubarts
VP: Tiffany Stiller

D-U-N-S 02-283-8358
CENTERSTONE OF TENNESSEE INC
44 Vantage Way, Nashville, TN 37228-1513
Tel (615) 463-6610 Founded/Ownrshp 1997
Sales 77.9MM EMP 1,500
Accts Blue & Co Llc Indianapolis I
SIC 8093 Mental health clinic, outpatient
CEO: Robert N Vero
*CEO: David Guth
*Ch: Leeann Ingram
*Chf Cred: Mike Butler
VP: Sallie Allen
VP: April D Bragg
VP: Rona Krueger
VP: Robert Siegmann
Exec: Tonya Waller
Prgrm Mgr: Maren Sheese
Prgrm Mgr: Lindsay Vinson

D-U-N-S 05-636-0258 IMP
■ **CENTEX CORP**
(Suby of PULTEGROUP INC) ★
2728 N Harwood St Ste 200, Dallas, TX 75201-1579
Tel (214) 981-5000 Founded/Ownrshp 2009
Sales 1.0MMM[E] EMP 2,463
SIC 1531 2451 6162 1542 1541 1522 Speculative builder, single-family houses; Mobile homes; Mortgage bankers; Nonresidential construction; Commercial & office building, new construction; Hospital construction; School building construction; Industrial buildings & warehouses; Industrial buildings, new construction; Residential construction; Hotel/motel, new construction; Condominium construction
Pr: Timothy R Eller
*Pr: Richard Dugas Jr
CFO: Greg Salinas
*CFO: Catherine R Smith
CFO: John Thompson
Ex VP: Michael J Wood
*Sr VP: Joseph A Bosch
*Sr VP: Mark D Kemp
Sr VP: Rex Lewis
Sr VP: Steven L McDowell
Sr VP: Jonathan R Wheeler
*Sr VP: Brian J Woram
Sr VP: Michael J Wozney
VP: Thomas J Fischer
VP: David A Greenblatt
VP: Paul M Johnston
VP: Janice M Jones

D-U-N-S 11-031-3871
■ **CENTEX FINANCIAL SERVICES LLC**
(Suby of CENTEX CORP) ★
2728 N Harwood St, Dallas, TX 75201-1516
Tel (214) 981-5000 Founded/Ownrshp 1993
Sales NA EMP 2,463
SIC 6162 Mortgage bankers
Ch Bd: J C Heywood
*CEO: John Matthews
*Ex VP: Martin Green

D-U-N-S 96-041-9471
■ **CENTEX HOME SERVICES CO LLC**
(Suby of CENTEX CORP) ★
2728 N Harwood St Ste 200, Dallas, TX 75201-1579
Tel (214) 981-5000 Founded/Ownrshp 1995
Sales 100.0MM EMP 1,500
SIC 7342 Pest control services
Ch Bd: Robert M Swartz
COO: Robert Wazner

D-U-N-S 01-643-0030
■ **CENTEX HOMES INC**
(Suby of CENTEX REAL ESTATE CORP) ★
2728 N Harwood St, Dallas, TX 75201-1516
Tel (800) 777-8583 Founded/Ownrshp 1996
Sales 804.8MM[E] EMP 4,000
SIC 1521 New construction, single-family houses
Ch Bd: Andrew J Hannigan
*Pr: Richard Dugas Jr
CFO: Nancy Hennessey
*CFO: Cathy Smith
Ex VP: Scott Batchelor
Ex VP: John B Bertero III
Ex VP: James Ellinghausen
Ex VP: Kopel James
*Ex VP: Robert Oshaughnessey
Ex VP: Joel C Sowers
*Sr VP: Steven Cook
VP: Cindy Deprater
VP: David Harrison
VP: Craig Innes
VP: Peter Keane
VP: Jeanne Martin
VP: Jerry Morgan
VP: Shyamal Parikh
*VP: Bruce Robinson
VP: Steve Schlageter
*VP: Michael Schweninger

D-U-N-S 60-322-7000
■ **CENTEX INTERNATIONAL INC**
(Suby of CENTEX CORP) ★
2728 N Harwood St Ste 200, Dallas, TX 75201-1579
Tel (214) 981-5000 Founded/Ownrshp 1987
Sales 824.8MM[E] EMP 7,750
SIC 1521 1522 New construction, single-family houses; Multi-family dwellings, new construction
CEO: Timothy R Eller
*Treas: Galye Pet

D-U-N-S 95-800-8419 IMP
■ **CENTEX REAL ESTATE CORP**
(Suby of CENTEX INTERNATIONAL INC) ★
2728 N Harwood St Ste 800, Dallas, TX 75201-1579
Tel (972) 304-2800 Founded/Ownrshp 1995
Sales 822.4MM[E] EMP 5,600
SIC 1521 New construction, single-family houses
CEO: Andrew J Hannigan
*Pr: Robert Hillman
*CFO: Andrew Kerner
Treas: Gary Esporrin
VP: Michael Albright
*VP: Melvin Chadwick
VP: Rex Lewis
CTO: Kreg Garland
CTO: Mark Kemp

D-U-N-S 06-847-6134
CENTIER BANK
(Suby of FIRST BANCSHARES INC) ★
1500 119th St, Whiting, IN 46394-1100
Tel (219) 659-0043 Founded/Ownrshp 1979
Sales NA EMP 350
SIC 6022 State commercial banks
Ch Bd: Michael E Schrage
Pr: Jean Hershberger
CFO: Scott May
Ofcr: Kathy Behary
Ofcr: Jennifer Pack
VP: Linda Flores
VP: David Schnepp
VP: John Shemaitis
Rgnl Mgr: Nicole Alcorn
Dir IT: Will Rodriguez
Opers Supe: Rosemarie Baxter

D-U-N-S 05-552-7634 IMP/EXP
CENTIMARK CORP (PA)
12 Grandview Cir, Canonsburg, PA 15317-8533
Tel (724) 743-7777 Founded/Ownrshp 1968
Sales 605.3MM EMP 2,400
Accts Schneider Downs & Co Inc P
SIC 1761 Roof repair
Ch Bd: Edward B Dunlap
*Pr: Timothy M Dunlap
*CFO: John L Heisey
Ex VP: Mark A Cooper
*Ex VP: Steve M Ferencz
Ex VP: Steven M Ferencz
*Ex VP: Robert B Fulton
*Ex VP: Sherman Gaskins
Ex VP: Sherman L Gaskins
*Ex VP: John T Godwin Jr
Ex VP: Robert T Penney
Ex VP: John Rudzik
*Ex VP: Robert J Rudzik
Ex VP: John P Scanlon
Ex VP: Kenneth W Zmich
Sr VP: Keith Battenfield
VP: Thor Cesare
VP: Landon Connolly
VP: Thor Dicesare
VP: Joe Filtz
VP: John Liekar
Board of Directors: Edward Dunlap, Timothy Dunlap, John Heisey

CENTINELA HOSPITAL MEDICAL CTR
See PRIME HEALTHCARE CENTINELA LLC

D-U-N-S 07-853-1173
CENTO FINE FOODS INC
100 Cento Blvd, West Deptford, NJ 08086-2133
Tel (856) 853-7800 Founded/Ownrshp 1990
Sales 124.6MM[E] EMP 199[E]
SIC 5141 Groceries, general line
CEO: Rick Ciccotelli
CFO: Joseph Pogue

D-U-N-S 07-474-1034
CENTRA HEALTH INC
VIRGINIA BAPTIST HOSPITAL
1920 Atherholt Rd, Lynchburg, VA 24501-1120
Tel (434) 200-3204 Founded/Ownrshp 1962
Sales 553.3MM EMP 6,000
SIC 8062 General medical & surgical hospitals
Pr: Ew Tibbs Jr
*Pr: Walker Sydnor
*Treas: Lewis C Addison
Bd of Dir: Virginia Baptist
Ofcr: Steve Austin
Ex VP: Kathryn M Pumphrey
Sr VP: Mike Barger
VP: David D Adams
VP: Joseph Dolan
VP: John Litaker
VP: Richard Marhoover
VP: Chalmers Nunn
VP: E W Tibbs
VP: Bill Varner
VP: William Varner
Assoc Dir: William Green
Assoc Dir: Johnson Lm
Dir Rad: Shannon Knight

D-U-N-S 04-120-2672
CENTRA SOTA COOPERATIVE
805 Highway 55 E, Buffalo, MN 55313-1734
Tel (763) 682-2557 Founded/Ownrshp 1942
Sales 339.7MM[E] EMP 240
SIC 5191 2875 5171 5153 Feed; Seeds: field, garden & flower; Fertilizers, mixing only; Petroleum bulk stations; Grain elevators
CEO: Jeff Johnson
Mktg Mgr: Sean Ness

D-U-N-S 14-805-8019
CENTRA TECHNOLOGY INC
25 Burlington Mall Rd # 504, Burlington, MA 01803-4145
Tel (781) 272-7887 Founded/Ownrshp 1996
Sales 111.0MM EMP 400
Accts Mayer Hoffman Mccann Pc Bos
SIC 8748 Business consulting
Pr: Harold Rosenbaum
*COO: Jack Barry
*CFO: Scott Papineau
Ofcr: Steve Yarbrough
*Ex VP: Lee Zinser
*Sr VP: Rick Bogusky
VP: Jim Harris
Ex Dir: Thomas Behling
Off Mgr: Laurie Bertrand
Web Dev: John Roberts

D-U-N-S 19-674-9543
CENTRAARCHY RESTAURANT MANAGEMENT CO
236 Albemarle Rd, Charleston, SC 29407-7522
Tel (843) 571-0096 Founded/Ownrshp 1983
Sales 57.9MM[E] EMP 1,500
SIC 5812

D-U-N-S 17-937-2222
CENTRACARE CLINIC
CENTRACARE CLINIC RIVER CAMPUS
1200 6th Ave N, Saint Cloud, MN 56303-2736
Tel (320) 240-2829 Founded/Ownrshp 1995
Sales 154.0MM EMP 5,468
Accts Mcgladrey Llp Minneapolis Mn
SIC 8011 Medical centers
Pr: Allen E Horn
*VP: Scot W Hutton
Doctor: Warren Y Ishida MD
Doctor: Paul T Moran MD
Doctor: Peter Waldusky MD

CENTRACARE CLINIC RIVER CAMPUS
See ST CLOUD HOSPITAL

CENTRACARE CLINIC RIVER CAMPUS
See CENTRACARE CLINIC

D-U-N-S 96-184-0779
CENTRACARE HEALTH SYSTEM
1406 6th Ave N, Saint Cloud, MN 56303-1900
Tel (320) 656-7020 Founded/Ownrshp 2011
Sales 115.7MM EMP 99[E]
Accts Mcgladrey Llp Minneapolis Mn
SIC 8062 General medical & surgical hospitals
Pr: Terry Pladson
Chf Path: Steven Bologna
CFO: Eric Lohn
Ofcr: Mary Bell
VP: Jim Davis
VP: Bernard Erickson
VP: Kurt Otto MD
Exec: Richard Backes
Dir Lab: Cindy Johnson
Dir Rx: Stacy Meyer
Dir Rx: Mary Phipps

CENTRAL ADMINISTRATIVE OFFICES
See ROCHESTER CITY SCHOOL DISTRICT

D-U-N-S 00-690-1433
CENTRAL ALABAMA ELECTRIC COOPERATIVE (AL)
1802 Highway 31 N, Prattville, AL 36067-6757
Tel (334) 365-6762 Founded/Ownrshp 1938
Sales 90.4MM EMP 123
Accts Gruenloh & Associates Pc Robe
SIC 4911 Distribution, electric power
Pr: Thomas Stackhouse
*Ch Bd: Chase Riddle
V Ch: Jimmie Harrison Jr
*Sec: Ruby J Neeley
VP: Jimmy Gray
Ex Dir: Milton Johnson

D-U-N-S 07-126-5581
CENTRAL ARKANSAS RADIATION THERAPY INSTITUTE INC (AR)
CARTI
8901 Carti Way, Little Rock, AR 72205-6523
Tel (501) 906-3000 Founded/Ownrshp 1976, 1970
Sales 352.0MM EMP 175
Accts Hudson Cisne & Co Llp Little
SIC 8011 8221 Radiologist; Physicians' office, including specialists; Professional schools
Off Mgr: John Holland
IT Man: Jimmy Curtis

CENTRAL BANCOMPANY
See CENTRAL CAPITAL MARKETS

D-U-N-S 07-589-0673
CENTRAL BANCOMPANY INC
238 Madison St, Jefferson City, MO 65101-3230
Tel (573) 634-1234 Founded/Ownrshp 1970
Sales NA EMP 2,500
Accts Kpmg Llp Kansas City Missour
SIC 6712 Bank holding companies
Ch Bd: Sam B Cook
*Pr: Bryan Cook
*CFO: Michael A Ittner
Trst Ofcr: Amparo Thomas
*Ex VP: Richard R Popp
Ex VP: Charles A Weber
*Sr VP: Donald R Perdue
VP: Janet Baker
*VP: James N Crabtree
*VP: Christina L Hake
VP: Rick Hollenberg
*VP: Pete J Langston
VP: Joyce Stacer
VP: Brad Wastler

D-U-N-S 09-235-4609
CENTRAL BAND OF CHEROKEE
870 Lawrence Ave, Lawrenceburg, TN 38464-4225
Tel (931) 242-6398 Founded/Ownrshp 2000
Sales 3.8MM[E] EMP 11,000
SIC 8641 Environmental protection organization
CEO: Johnny Raven Corbin

CENTRAL BANK
See CENTRAL PACIFIC BANK

CENTRAL BANK
See CENTRAL TRUST BANK

D-U-N-S 00-694-4854
CENTRAL BANK & TRUST CO
CENTRAL BANK WEALTH MGT GROUP
(Suby of CENTRAL BANCSHARES)
300 W Vine St Ste 3, Lexington, KY 40507-1666
Tel (859) 253-6222 Founded/Ownrshp 1938
Sales NA EMP 450
SIC 6022 State commercial banks
Pr: Luther Deaton Jr
COO: Robin Michul
*CFO: Pat Price
Ofcr: Dennis Barnes
Ofcr: Vicky Foster
Ofcr: Lisa Grant
Ofcr: Barb Johnson
Ofcr: Chris McGaughey
Ofcr: Brandy Osborne
Ofcr: Amy Turner
*Ex VP: Anne Carter
*Ex VP: Steve Kelley
Sr VP: Jeanne Clayton
Sr VP: Karen Crawley
Sr VP: David Moore
Sr VP: Robin Oliver
Sr VP: Tracy K Reid
Sr VP: Robert Slider
VP: Edward Barnes
VP: Ernest Dolihite
VP: Lisa Durham

CENTRAL BANK WEALTH MGT GROUP
See CENTRAL BANK & TRUST CO

D-U-N-S 78-311-4536
CENTRAL BAPTIST HOSPITAL
1740 Nicholasville Rd, Lexington, KY 40503-1431
Tel (859) 260-6100 Founded/Ownrshp 2003
Sales 348.5M EMP 2,500
Accts Deloitte Tax Llp Cincinnati
SIC 8069 Specialty hospitals, except psychiatric
Ch: John Barton
COO: Karen S Hill
Dir Inf Cn: Dee Anderson
Dir Rx: Michael Anderson
Pathlgst: John Jensen
Doctor: Christopher Ford
HC Dir: Derrick Hord
Genl Couns: Kelly R Anderson

CENTRAL BI-PRODUCTS
See FARMERS UNION INDUSTRIES LLC

CENTRAL BLOOD BANK
See SOUTH BEND MEDICAL FOUNDATION INC

D-U-N-S 07-550-8341
CENTRAL BUCKS SCHOOL DISTRICT
20 Weldon Dr, Doylestown, PA 18901-2359
Tel (267) 893-2000 Founded/Ownrshp 1948
Sales 300.0MM EMP 2,800
SIC 8351 Child day care services
Pr: Steven Corr
*Treas: Thomas McCambridge
Prin: Alan J Bernabei
Prin: Jeanann M Kahley
Prin: Greg Nolan
Web Prj Mg: Scot Kenedy
Pr Dir: Melanie Sullivan
HC Dir: Dale Stafuro

D-U-N-S 04-472-0675
CENTRAL CAPITAL MARKETS
CENTRAL BANCOMPANY
(Suby of CENTRAL BANCOMPANY INC) ★
238 Madison St, Jefferson City, MO 65101-3230
Tel (573) 634-1330 Founded/Ownrshp 1971
Sales NA EMP 10
SIC 6022 6211 State commercial banks; Security brokers & dealers
Pr: Robert Roebucks
VP: Nik Perrigo
VP: Robert C Ramey
VP: Keith Schawo

D-U-N-S 96-465-5778 IMP
CENTRAL CARBIDE LLC
(Suby of CARBIDE INDUSTRIES LLC) ★
4400 Bells Ln, Louisville, KY 40211-2143
Tel (502) 775-4100 Founded/Ownrshp 2007
Sales 100.0MM EMP 50
SIC 2819 Calcium carbide
Pr: ARA Hacet
CFO: Darrell Higgins
*CFO: Brent McWhorcer

D-U-N-S 02-459-6512
CENTRAL CAROLINA FARM & MOWER INC
JOHN DEERE AUTHORIZED DEALER
801 E Wendover Ave, Greensboro, NC 27405-6772
Tel (336) 574-4400 Founded/Ownrshp 2003
Sales 260.0MM EMP 12
SIC 5261 5082 Lawn & garden equipment; Construction & mining machinery
Pr: Joe Idol

D-U-N-S 01-242-9247 IMP
■ **CENTRAL COCA-COLA BOTTLING CO INC**
(Suby of COCA-COLA REFRESHMENTS USA INC) ★
555 Taxter Rd Ste 550, Elmsford, NY 10523-2331
Tel (914) 789-1100 Founded/Ownrshp 1980
Sales 576.3MM[E] EMP 2,100
SIC 5149 2086 8741 Soft drinks; Soft drinks: packaged in cans, bottles, etc.; Management services
CEO: Brock John F
*Ch Bd: Betty Sams Christian
*VP: Culhane John J
VP: Michael Vanaken
*VP: Palmer Vicki
Board of Directors: Benjamin Lacy IV, Lynwood Littlefield Jr

D-U-N-S 80-014-4099
CENTRAL CONNECTICUT HEALTH ALLIANCE INC
100 Grand St, New Britain, CT 06052-2016
Tel (860) 224-5757 *Founded/Ownrshp* 1986
Sales 607.0M *EMP* 3,307
Accts Ernst & Young Llp Hartford C
SIC 8741 Hospital management
Ch Bd: Frank R Miller
**Pr:* Clarence J Silvia
**Ch:* John E Dillaway
**Treas:* David R Newton
**V Ch Bd:* John Manning
Sr VP: Clarence Slivia

D-U-N-S 12-292-8351
CENTRAL CONSOLIDATED SCHOOL DIST 22
U S Hwy 64, Shiprock, NM 87420
Tel (505) 368-4984 *Founded/Ownrshp* 1950
Sales 66.9MM^E *EMP* 1,069
SIC 8211 Public elementary & secondary schools
Pr: Matthew TSO
**VP:* Lupita White
Dir IT: Rick Nussbaum
Schl Brd P: Charlie Jones
Teacher Pr: George Schumpelt

D-U-N-S 07-656-2073
CENTRAL CONTRA COSTA SANITARY DISTRICT FACILITIES FINANCING AUTHORITY
C C C S D
5019 Imhoff Pl, Martinez, CA 94553-4316
Tel (925) 228-9500 *Founded/Ownrshp* 1946
Sales 84.5MM *EMP* 250
SIC 4952 4959

D-U-N-S 00-677-8780
CENTRAL CRUDE INC
10370 Richmond Ave # 975, Houston, TX 77042-4141
Tel (713) 783-2167 *Founded/Ownrshp* 2005
Sales 516.1MM *EMP* 80^E
Accts Mcelroy Quirk & Burch Lake C
SIC 1382

D-U-N-S 07-118-9369
CENTRAL DAUPHIN SCHOOL DISTRICT AUTHORITY
CD
600 Rutherford Rd, Harrisburg, PA 17109-5227
Tel (717) 540-4606 *Founded/Ownrshp* 1952
Sales 167.7MM *EMP* 1,423^E
SIC 8211 Public junior high school
Bd of Dir: Chris J Judd
Genl Mgr: Robert Horney
MIS Dir: Lauretta Pollock
Pr Dir: Shannon Leib
Teacher Pr: Carrie Deichman
Psych: Jeffrey Barnhart
HC Dir: Scott Kuren

CENTRAL DEFENSE SECURITY
See CENTRAL DEFENSE SERVICES LLC

D-U-N-S 55-702-9498
CENTRAL DEFENSE SERVICES LLC
CENTRAL DEFENSE SECURITY
6084 Apple Tree Dr Ste 1, Memphis, TN 38115-0305
Tel (901) 322-9554 *Founded/Ownrshp* 2005
Sales 12.0MM *EMP* 1,000^E
SIC 7381 Security guard service
COO: Larry Carroll
CFO: Sharon Lubin
Ofcr: Chassity Pointer
VP Admn: Stuart Thomas
Rgnl Mgr: Jason King
Area Mgr: Stan Bowles
IT Man: Joey Catanzaro
VP Sls: Larry Heathcott

CENTRAL DUPAGE HEALTH
See CDH-DELNOR HEALTH SYSTEM

CENTRAL DUPAGE HEALTH
See DELNOR-COMMUNITY HOSPITAL

D-U-N-S 05-665-3975 EXP
CENTRAL DUPAGE HOSPITAL ASSOCIATION
(*Suby of* CENTRAL DUPAGE HEALTH) ★
25 N Winfield Rd, Winfield, IL 60190-1295
Tel (630) 933-1600 *Founded/Ownrshp* 1958
Sales 849.0MM *EMP* 1,600
Accts O Crowe Horvath Llp Calhan
SIC 8062 General medical & surgical hospitals
Pr: Brian Lemon
Dir Recs: Debra Czink
**CFO:* James T Spear
**Treas:* Jim Marseille
**Treas:* Karen Williams
Ex VP: Dan Kinsella
VP: Deb O'Donnell
Dir OR: Maura Trilla
Dir Lab: Beth Johnson
Dir Bus: Glen Malan
Chf Nrs Of: Debra Odonnell

D-U-N-S 00-890-6588
CENTRAL ELECTRIC POWER COOPERATIVE INC
2106 Jefferson St, Jefferson City, MO 65109-2066
Tel (573) 634-2454 *Founded/Ownrshp* 1949
Sales 204.9MM *EMP* 110
SIC 4911 Distribution, electric power
CEO: Donald W Shaw
**CFO:* Randell Carrender
Sr VP: Jim Lamb
VP: Michael Smith
Dir Bus: Nancy Gibler
Genl Mgr: Tom Werdenhause
Dir IT: Stacey Dudenhoeffer
Dir IT: Amy Feldmann
IT Man: Richard Scheulen
Plnt Mgr: Tim Backes
Sales Asso: J Weber

D-U-N-S 06-268-7389
CENTRAL ELECTRIC POWER COOPERATIVE INC
20 Cooperative Way, Columbia, SC 29210-3112
Tel (803) 779-4975 *Founded/Ownrshp* 1949
Sales 1.2MMM *EMP* 44
SIC 4911 Distribution, electric power
CEO: Ronald J Calcaterra
**CFO:* John Brantley
Treas: William Fleming
Sr VP: John Boyt
**Sr VP:* Art Fusco
**Sr VP:* Jim Lamb
**Prin:* John Tiencken
Prgrm Mgr: Scott Hammond

CENTRAL EUROPEAN DIST CORP
See ROUST CORP

D-U-N-S 10-149-6370
CENTRAL FIRE PROTECTION CO INC
583 Selma Rd, Springfield, OH 45505-2071
Tel (937) 322-0713 *Founded/Ownrshp* 1983
Sales 700.0MM *EMP* 41
Accts Thorn Lewis & Duncan Inc D
SIC 7389 Fire protection service other than forestry or public
Pr: Gary Adkins
**VP:* Helen Gifford
Plnt Mgr: Karla Brown

D-U-N-S 01-265-8972
CENTRAL FLORIDA BEHAVIORAL HEALTH NETWORK INC
719 S Us Highway 301, Tampa, FL 33619-4349
Tel (813) 740-4811 *Founded/Ownrshp* 1997
Sales 158.3MM *EMP* 53
SIC 8322 Individual & family services
CEO: Linda McKinnon
**COO:* Larry Lumpee
**CFO:* Julie Patel
**VP:* Marsh Monroe
Prgrm Mgr: John Cornett
CIO: Laurence Roberts

D-U-N-S 00-469-6266
CENTRAL FLORIDA EXPRESSWAY AUTHORITY
4974 Orl Tower Rd, Orlando, FL 32807-1684
Tel (407) 690-5000 *Founded/Ownrshp* 1963, 1999
Sales 325.6MM *EMP* 50
Accts Moore Stephens Lovelace Pa O
SIC 4785 Toll road operation
Ex VP: Joseph Berenis
**CFO:* Lisa Lumbard
**Ex VP:* Laura Kelley
Exec: Armando Corominas

D-U-N-S 15-269-9690
CENTRAL FLORIDA HEALTH ALLIANCE INC
LEESBURG REGIONAL MEDICAL CTR
600 E Dixie Ave, Leesburg, FL 34748-5925
Tel (352) 323-5000 *Founded/Ownrshp* 1986
Sales 381.7M *EMP* 1,900
Accts Kpmg Llp Greensboro Nc
SIC 8741 Hospital management
CEO: Lee S Huntley
**CEO:* Henderson Donald G
Dir IT: Judy Beda
IT Man: Edward Riddle

D-U-N-S 07-759-3317
CENTRAL FLORIDA INVESTMENTS INC
WESTGATE LAKES
(*Suby of* W R) ★
5601 Windhover Dr Ofc, Orlando, FL 32819-7905
Tel (407) 354-3040 *Founded/Ownrshp* 1982
Sales 748.3MM^E *EMP* 4,000
SIC 6552 7011 6531 Subdividers & developers; Hotels; Real estate brokers & agents
Ch Bd: David Siegel
**COO:* Mark Waltrip
**CFO:* Tom Dugan
CFO: David Seigel
**Ex VP:* Barry W Siegel
**VP:* Wendy Govern
Ex Dir: Marco Torres
Genl Mgr: Michael Macgillivray
Genl Mgr: Richard Moore
Genl Mgr: Courtney Paul
QA Dir: Erik Visser

D-U-N-S 96-186-9302
■ **CENTRAL FLORIDA REGIONAL HOSPITAL INC**
COLUMBIA HCA
(*Suby of* HOSPITAL COPORATION OF AMERICA) ★
1401 W Seminole Blvd, Sanford, FL 32771-6743
Tel (407) 321-4500 *Founded/Ownrshp* 2012
Sales 172.4MM *EMP* 600
SIC 8062 General medical & surgical hospitals
Pr: Thelma Smith
VP: Fisher Keith
CTO: Jill Leone
Dir QC: Arlene Fleming
Mktg Mgr: Cathy Droke
Obsttrcn: Julie Gudger
Ansthlgy: Arturo F Espinola
Doctor: Royce Hood
Doctor: Stephane Lavoie
Doctor: Jonathan Waldbaum

D-U-N-S 06-784-9109
CENTRAL FLORIDA REGIONAL TRANSPORTATION AUTHORITY
LYNX
455 N Garland Ave, Orlando, FL 32801-1518
Tel (407) 841-2279 *Founded/Ownrshp* 1972
Sales 91.1MM^E *EMP* 1,300
SIC 4111 Bus line operations
Ch Bd: Buddy Dyer
**CEO:* John M Lewis Jr
COO: Lisa Darnall
Ofcr: Lorna Hall
Ofcr: Jenny Iacovazzi
VP: Bob Bauman
Dir: Andrea Ostrodka
Creative D: John Pantuso
Comm Man: Jose Felix
**Prin:* Frank Attkisson
**Ex Dir:* Linda Waston

D-U-N-S 07-985-5391
CENTRAL FLORIDA YOUNG MENS CHRISTIAN ASSOCIATION INC
YMCA OF CENTRAL FLORIDA
433 N Mills Ave, Orlando, FL 32803-5798
Tel (407) 896-9220 *Founded/Ownrshp* 1942
Sales 66.5MM *EMP* 1,750
Accts Mcgladrey Llp Orlando Flori
SIC 8641 Youth organizations
Pr: James W Ferber
**CFO:* Mark Russel
Bd of Dir: David Allen
Bd of Dir: Dawn Ballantyne
Bd of Dir: Ella Boll
Bd of Dir: Chuck Bosworth
Bd of Dir: Chris Broome
Bd of Dir: Art Brown
Bd of Dir: Bertina Busch
Bd of Dir: Daniel Butts
Bd of Dir: Glen Chin
Bd of Dir: Frank Clarke
Bd of Dir: Craig Clayton
Bd of Dir: Eacha Daniels
Bd of Dir: Dennis Decarlo
Bd of Dir: Cheryl Finnegan
Bd of Dir: Dan Ford
Bd of Dir: Brian Fultz
Bd of Dir: Andy Gardiner
Bd of Dir: Glenn Gullikson
Bd of Dir: Bob Hansell

D-U-N-S 07-033-2510
CENTRAL FREIGHT LINES INC
5601 W Waco Dr, Waco, TX 76710-5753
Tel (254) 772-2120 *Founded/Ownrshp* 1999, 1997
Sales 1.2MMM^E *EMP* 3,553
SIC 6719 4213 Investment holding companies, except banks; Trucking, except local
Pr: Don Orr
CFO: Vicky O'Brien
**CFO:* Vicky Obrien
**Ex VP:* Tom Botsios
Exec: Tina Lewis
Dir Bus: Mari Borowski
IT Man: James Turner
Info Man: Jerry Mattiza
Trfc Dir: Matthew Massie
Opers Mgr: Alexis Gomez
Opers Mgr: Eric Scheuneman

D-U-N-S 10-108-9068
CENTRAL FREIGHT LINES INC
(*Suby of* CENTRAL FREIGHT LINES INC) ★
5601 W Waco Dr, Waco, TX 76710-5753
Tel (254) 772-2120 *Founded/Ownrshp* 2006
Sales 401.3MM^E *EMP* 3,500
SIC 4212 Local trucking, without storage
CEO: Vicky Obrien
**CEO:* Donald A Orr
**VP:* Tom Botsios
VP: Robert E Cosner

D-U-N-S 02-278-4617
CENTRAL FREIGHT MANAGEMENT LLC
CFM LOGISTICS
(*Suby of* GSF FOUNDATION) ★
11500 Olive Blvd Ste 276, Saint Louis, MO 63141-7141
Tel (314) 428-9900 *Founded/Ownrshp* 2000
Sales 85.3MM *EMP* 34
SIC 4213 Trucking, except local
Mng Pt: Quin Brewer
Off Mgr: Marie Henson

D-U-N-S 00-943-9530
▲ **CENTRAL GARDEN & PET CO**
1340 Treat Blvd Ste 600, Walnut Creek, CA 94597-7578
Tel (925) 948-4000 *Founded/Ownrshp* 1955
Sales 1.8MMM *EMP* 3,300
Tkr Sym CENT *Exch* NGS
SIC 5199 5191 Pet supplies; Garden supplies
Pr: John R Ranelli
**Ch Bd:* William E Brown
Pr: Rodolfo Spielmann
**CFO:* David N Chichester
CFO: Mary L Sonntag
Treas: Lukas Cadil
Ex VP: Neill Hines
Ex VP: Dan Pennington
Ex VP: Michael A Reed
Ex VP: Ronnie C Stapp
Sr VP: Paul Hibbert
Sr VP: William Lynch
VP: Steve Barton
VP: John Emmons
VP: Evan Harper
VP: Joanne Hiras
VP: Henry Lam
VP: Terry Langan
VP: Marilyn Leahy
VP: Lisa Lines
VP: John W Martin
Board of Directors: John B Balousek, Thomas J Colligan, Brooks M Pennington III, Alfred A Piergallini, George C Roeth, Mary Beth Springer

CENTRAL GARDEN DISTRIBUTION
See EXCEL GARDEN PRODUCTS

D-U-N-S 00-797-7069
CENTRAL GEORGIA ELECTRIC MEMBERSHIP CORP (GA)
OGLETHORPE POWER
923 S Mulberry St, Jackson, GA 30233-2329
Tel (770) 775-7857 *Founded/Ownrshp* 1937
Sales 101.6MM *EMP* 85
SIC 4911 1711 Distribution, electric power; Plumbing, heating, air-conditioning contractors
Pr: George L Weaver
**Ch Bd:* Danny Hamil
**COO:* John Fish
**Sec:* D A Robinson III
**V Ch Bd:* Warren E Holder
VP: Herschel Arant
VP: Jeff Greeson
VP: John Harkness
VP: Ben Thomason

D-U-N-S 00-195-7745
CENTRAL GROCERS INC (IL)
CENTRELLA FOODS
2600 Haven Ave, Joliet, IL 60433-8467
Tel (815) 553-8800 *Founded/Ownrshp* 1917
Sales 3.3MMM^E *EMP* 2,300^E
SIC 5141 5147 5142 5148 5143 5122 Groceries, general line; Meats, fresh; Packaged frozen goods; Fresh fruits & vegetables; Ice cream & ices; Cosmetics, perfumes & hair products; Toiletries; Drugs & drug proprietaries
Pr: Kenneth Nementh
**Pr:* James Denges
**CFO:* Tim Kubis

D-U-N-S 08-838-6672
CENTRAL HEALTH PLAN OF CALIFORNIA INC
(*Suby of* AHMC HEALTHCARE INC) ★
1055 Park View Dr Ste 355, Covina, CA 91724-3745
Tel (626) 938-7120 *Founded/Ownrshp* 2011
Sales 20.7MM^E *EMP* 3,638^E
SIC 8082 Home health care services
Pr: Sam Kam

CENTRAL HUDSON GAS & ELECTRIC
See CH ENERGY GROUP INC

D-U-N-S 60-220-0383
CENTRAL HUDSON GAS & ELECTRIC CORP
(*Suby of* CENTRAL HUDSON GAS & ELECTRIC) ★
284 South Ave Dept 100, Poughkeepsie, NY 12601-4839
Tel (845) 452-2700 *Founded/Ownrshp* 1926
Sales 671.9MM^E *EMP* 869^E
SIC 4911 4924 4932 Electric services; Natural gas distribution; Gas & other services combined
Ch Bd: Steven V Lant
**Pr:* James P Laurito
Pr: Michael Mosher
**CFO:* Christopher M Capone
Treas: Stacey A Renner
Ex VP: Joseph J Devirgilio Jr
Ex VP: John E Gould
Sr VP: Charles A Freni
Dir Sec: Richard Nuzzo
Div Mgr: Brian N Dimisko
CTO: Robb Kinnin

D-U-N-S 02-492-9549
CENTRAL ILLINOIS AG INC
200 E Sharon St, Atlanta, IL 61723-8741
Tel (217) 648-2307 *Founded/Ownrshp* 1926
Sales 99.2MM *EMP* 81
Accts Jm Abbott & Associates Ltd
SIC 5999 7699 Farm equipment & supplies; Farm machinery repair
Pr: Steven P Schmidt
**CFO:* David G Evans
**VP:* William Marcotte

D-U-N-S 03-055-6799
CENTRAL ILLINOIS TRUCKS INC
CIT
200 W Northtown Rd, Normal, IL 61761-1060
Tel (800) 322-5017 *Founded/Ownrshp* 1975
Sales 147.4MM^E *EMP* 500
SIC 5013 7538 5012

CENTRAL INSURANCE COMPANIES
See CENTRAL MUTUAL INSURANCE CO

CENTRAL INSURANCE COMPANIES
See ALL AMERICA INSURANCE CO INC

D-U-N-S 07-584-4548
CENTRAL IOWA HOSPITAL CORP
UNITYPOINT HEALTH
(*Suby of* UNITYPOINT HEALTH) ★
1200 Pleasant St, Des Moines, IA 50309-1406
Tel (515) 241-6212 *Founded/Ownrshp* 1903
Sales 548.7MM *EMP* 3,495
SIC 8062 General medical & surgical hospitals; Hospital, medical school affiliated with nursing & residency
CEO: Eric Crowell
Pr: Jean Shelton
COO: Steve Stephenson
CFO: Joe Corfits
Bd of Dir: Larry Baker
Bd of Dir: Don Ross
VP: David Burlage
VP: Paul McLoone
VP: Deb Moyer
VP: Mark Purtle
**Ex Dir:* Kara Dunham

D-U-N-S 00-582-6110
CENTRAL IOWA POWER COOPERATIVE
CIPCO
1400 Highway 13, Cedar Rapids, IA 52403-9060
Tel (319) 366-8011 *Founded/Ownrshp* 1946
Sales 194.9MM *EMP* 117
Accts Lwbj Llp West Des Moines Ia
SIC 4911 Distribution, electric power
CEO: Dennis Murdock
**Pr:* Allan Duffe
**Pr:* Keith Wirth
**Treas:* Norman Vanzante
**Sec:* Wayne Hornocker
VP: Janel Cerwick
**VP:* Marvin Focht
VP: Paul Hofman
VP: Terry Sullivan
Exec: Kim Colberg
CIO: Don Chaon

D-U-N-S 15-285-6022
CENTRAL IOWA RENEWABLE ENERGY LLC
415 Locust St, Goldfield, IA 50542-5092
Tel (515) 825-3161 *Founded/Ownrshp* 2004
Sales 181.4MM^E *EMP* 44
SIC 8731 Energy research

CENTRAL ISLIP PUBLIC SCHOOLS
See CENTRAL ISLIP UNION FREE SCHOOL DISTRICT

D-U-N-S 06-595-3754
CENTRAL ISLIP UNION FREE SCHOOL DISTRICT
CENTRAL ISLIP PUBLIC SCHOOLS
50 Wheeler Rd, Central Islip, NY 11722-2154
Tel (631) 348-5112 *Founded/Ownrshp* 1946
Sales 47.6MM[E] *EMP* 1,000
SIC 8211 Public combined elementary & secondary school
**Prin:* Denise Lowe
**Prin:* Michael Wolpert
IT Man: William Hodrinsky
HC Dir: Lawrence Philips

D-U-N-S 10-008-0266 IMP
CENTRAL KITSAP SCHOOL DISTRICT
9210 Silverdale Way Nw, Silverdale, WA 98383-9197
Tel (360) 662-1610 *Founded/Ownrshp* 1941
Sales 124.2MM *EMP* 1,286
SIC 8211 Public elementary & secondary schools
Off Mgr: Joann Randklev
IT Man: Paul Tankovich
Instr Medi: Amber Bryant

D-U-N-S 00-891-2842 IMP/EXP
■ **CENTRAL LEWMAR LLC**
XPEDX
(*Suby of* INTERNATIONAL PAPER CO) ★
261 River Rd, Clifton, NJ 07014-1551
Tel (973) 405-2300 *Founded/Ownrshp* 1920, 2007
Sales 197.7MM[E] *EMP* 550
SIC 5111 5199 Fine paper; Packaging materials
CEO: John V Feraci
**Pr:* Thomas G Kadien
**CFO:* Walter Klein
Sr VP: David H Berkowitz
**VP:* James Connelly
VP: Kevin Woodfield

D-U-N-S 00-790-8460
CENTRAL LINCOLN PEOPLES UTILITY DISTRICT JATC INC (OR)
CENTRAL LINCOLN PUD
2129 N Coast Hwy, Newport, OR 97365-1705
Tel (541) 265-3211 *Founded/Ownrshp* 1940
Sales 136.1MM[E] *EMP* 153
Accts Kenneth Kuhns & Co Salem Or
SIC 4911 Transmission, electric power; Distribution, electric power
Pr: Brad Trommlitz
Treas: William Fleenor
Treas: Frank E Lundy
VP: Tom Tymchuk
**Genl Mgr:* Paul Davies
**Genl Mgr:* Debra Smith
IT Man: Bill Reinhart
Opers Mgr: Randy Grove

CENTRAL LINCOLN PUD
See CENTRAL LINCOLN PEOPLES UTILITY DISTRICT JATC INC

D-U-N-S 78-720-8271
CENTRAL MAINE HEALTH VENTURES INC
CENTRAL MAINE MEDICAL CENTER
(*Suby of* CENTRAL MAINE MEDICAL FAMILY) ★
300 Main St, Lewiston, ME 04240-7027
Tel (207) 795-0111 *Founded/Ownrshp* 1987
Sales 319.9MM *EMP* 275
Accts Kpmg Llp Boston Ma
SIC 8049 8052 7322 8011 Occupational therapist; Intermediate care facilities; Adjustment & collection services; Offices & clinics of medical doctors
CEO: Peter E Chalke
**Pr:* William W Young Jr
COO: Steven Chapman
**Treas:* Charles T Orne
Dir Sec: Michael Barnies
Mktg Dir: Chuck Gill

D-U-N-S 12-135-0763
CENTRAL MAINE HEALTHCARE CORP
CENTRAL MAINE MEDICAL FAMILY
300 Main St, Lewiston, ME 04240-7027
Tel (207) 795-0111 *Founded/Ownrshp* 1982
Sales 358.0MM[E] *EMP* 3,000
SIC 8062 8052 8049 General medical & surgical hospitals; Intermediate care facilities; Nurses & other medical assistants
Pr: Peter Chalke
**CFO:* Phil Morissette
**VP:* Wayne Bennet
Prac Mgr: Paul Ranucci
Prgrm Mgr: Mary Doyle
Nrsg Dir: Kathy A Dulham

CENTRAL MAINE MEDICAL CENTER
See CENTRAL MAINE HEALTH VENTURES INC

D-U-N-S 07-174-5319
CENTRAL MAINE MEDICAL CENTER INC
300 Main St, Lewiston, ME 04240-7041
Tel (207) 795-0111 *Founded/Ownrshp* 1982
Sales 328.0MM *EMP* 1,200
SIC 8062 General medical & surgical hospitals
Pr: Peter E Chalke
**Treas:* Charles T Orne
Dir Rad: Charles C Humphrey
Off Mgr: Lisa Johnson
Off Mgr: Diane Mulkey
CIO: Kevin Darnell
Ansthlgy: Cynthia L Jenson
Ansthlgy: Aaron A Tebbs
Pharmcst: Derek Nadau

CENTRAL MAINE MEDICAL FAMILY
See CENTRAL MAINE HEALTHCARE CORP

D-U-N-S 00-694-8954
■ **CENTRAL MAINE POWER CO INC** (ME)
C M P
(*Suby of* CMP GROUP INC) ★
83 Edison Dr, Augusta, ME 04336-0001
Tel (207) 623-3521 *Founded/Ownrshp* 1899, 1998
Sales 1.1MMM[E] *EMP* 1,388
Accts Pricewaterhousecoopers Llp Ph
SIC 4911 Transmission, electric power; Distribution, electric power
Pr: Sara Burns
**CEO:* Stacy Dunham
**Treas:* Eric Stinneford
**VP:* Douglas Heirling
Dir Sec: Raymond Pomerleau
Mktg Mgr: Jenna Overgaard

D-U-N-S 04-149-4576
CENTRAL MAINTENANCE AND WELDING INC
C M W
2620 E Keysville Rd, Lithia, FL 33547-1605
Tel (813) 229-0012 *Founded/Ownrshp* 1966
Sales 94.7MM[E] *EMP* 350[E]
SIC 3443 1791 7692 Heat exchangers, condensers & components; Structural steel erection; Welding repair
Pr: Conrad Varnum
**COO:* Randy Coates
**Sec:* Scott M Varnum

CENTRAL MESABI MEDICAL CENTER
See RANGE REGIONAL HEALTH SERVICES

D-U-N-S 05-477-0474
CENTRAL MICHIGAN UNIVERSITY
WCMU-TV CHANNEL
1200 S Franklin St, Mount Pleasant, MI 48859-2001
Tel (989) 774-4000 *Founded/Ownrshp* 1892
Sales 336.1MM *EMP* 2,388
Accts Plante & Moran Pllc Portage
SIC 8221 5942 4833 4832 5812 University; Book stores; Television broadcasting stations; Radio broadcasting stations; Cafeteria
Pr: George E Ross
V Ch: Marilyn F Hubbard
V Ch: Sam R Kottamasu
Pr: Timothy J Gramza
**Pr:* Michael RAO
Trst: Gail F Torreano
Assoc VP: Ashley L McClellan
Assoc VP: Kimberly C Vogel
VP: Maxine Kent
**VP:* Michael Leto
VP: Ren E Walker
Assoc Dir: D Bedford
Assoc Dir: Margaret Desormes
Assoc Dir: Mark D Stranskov
Comm Dir: Heather Polinsky
Comm Man: Levi Van Tine

D-U-N-S 14-786-1405 IMP
CENTRAL MILLS INC
FREEZE
473 Ridge Rd, Dayton, NJ 08810-1323
Tel (732) 329-0032 *Founded/Ownrshp* 1986
Sales 93.9MM[E] *EMP* 225
SIC 2329 2339 2369 2322 2341 2321 Men's & boys' sportswear & athletic clothing; Sportswear, women's; Girls' & children's outerwear; Men's & boys' underwear & nightwear; Women's & children's nightwear; Men's & boys' furnishings
Ch Bd: Charles Tebele
**Pr:* Solomon Shalam

D-U-N-S 00-784-8468
CENTRAL MISSOURI AGRISERVICE LLC (MO)
DO IT BEST
211 N Lyon Ave, Marshall, MO 65340-1725
Tel (660) 886-7880 *Founded/Ownrshp* 1999
Sales 123.9MM *EMP* 100
Accts Wilson Toellner & Associates
SIC 2875 2048 5251 Fertilizers, mixing only; Prepared feeds; Hardware
Genl Mgr: John Fletcher
VP: Randy Horman
VP: Craig Miller
Genl Mgr: Bill Horgan
Mktg Mgr: Gabe Ramsey

D-U-N-S 82-506-9958 IMP
CENTRAL MOLONEY INC
2400 W 6th Ave, Pine Bluff, AR 71601-3862
Tel (870) 534-5332 *Founded/Ownrshp* 1994
Sales 118.2MM[E] *EMP* 500
SIC 3612 Transformers, except electric
Pr: Ralph R Siever
**VP:* Chris Hart
Plnt Mgr: Randy Boyd
VP Mktg: Stan Hitt
Mktg Mgr: Luanne Hensley
Manager: Kent Gossage
Sls Mgr: Chad Stone
Board of Directors: Jon Harrison, Chris Hart, Bob McKaig, Chuck Morgan, Scott Westjohn

D-U-N-S 17-559-8267 IMP
CENTRAL MOTOR WHEEL OF AMERICA INC
CMC/CLA
(*Suby of* CENTRAL MOTOR WHEEL CO.,LTD.)
150 Wheat Dr, Paris, KY 40361-2501
Tel (859) 987-0500 *Founded/Ownrshp* 2012
Sales 175.0MM[E] *EMP* 475
SIC 3714 Wheels, motor vehicle
Ex VP: Kazuo Ishikawa
**Pr:* A Nagata
**Sec:* H Suzuki
**Ex VP:* Dennis Timmons
**VP:* J Birdsong
**VP:* Kengo Sago
IT Man: Ryaen Passage
Sales Exec: Marty Seither

D-U-N-S 00-790-4790
CENTRAL MUTUAL INSURANCE CO
CENTRAL INSURANCE COMPANIES
800 S Washington St, Van Wert, OH 45891-2357
Tel (419) 238-1010 *Founded/Ownrshp* 1876
Sales NA *EMP* 590
SIC 6331 Fire, marine & casualty insurance
Ch Bd: Francis W Purmort III
**Treas:* Thad Eikenbary
VP: Jason Brown
VP: Ben Faurote
**VP:* Jeff Hanson
VP: Cindy M Hurless
VP: Kurt Muntzinger
Area Mgr: Brandy Saritas
Dir IT: Lance Moonshower
Mktg Mgr: Claire May
Mktg Mgr: Evan Purmort

D-U-N-S 00-698-4645 IMP/EXP
CENTRAL NATIONAL GOTTESMAN INC (NY)
LINDENMEYR CENTRAL
3 Manhattanville Rd # 301, Purchase, NY 10577-2123
Tel (914) 696-9000 *Founded/Ownrshp* 1931
Sales 2.4MMM[E] *EMP* 2,500
SIC 5111 5099

D-U-N-S 08-023-7622
CENTRAL NATIONAL PULP & PAPER SALES INC
(*Suby of* LINDENMEYR CENTRAL) ★
3 Manhattanville Rd, Purchase, NY 10577-2116
Tel (914) 696-9000 *Founded/Ownrshp* 2008
Sales 69.9MM[E] *EMP* 2,500
SIC 2611 Pulp mills; Pulp mills, mechanical & recycling processing
Ch: Kenneth L Wallach

D-U-N-S 07-835-1481
CENTRAL NETWORK RETAIL GROUP LLC
3753 Tyndale Dr Ste 102, Memphis, TN 38125-8511
Tel (901) 205-9075 *Founded/Ownrshp* 2011
Sales 237.4MM[E] *EMP* 750[E]
SIC 5211 Lumber & other building materials
**CFO:* David Mills
Dir IT: Doug Dann

D-U-N-S 80-443-9040
CENTRAL NEW ENGLAND HEALTHALLIANCE INC
60 Hospital Rd, Leominster, MA 01453-2205
Tel (978) 343-5000 *Founded/Ownrshp* 1993
Sales 43.8MM[E] *EMP* 1,165
SIC 8741 Hospital management; Nursing & personal care facility management
Pr: Jonathan Robbins MD
Dir Rx: Timothy Yang

D-U-N-S 07-575-4036
CENTRAL NEW MEXICO COMMUNITY COLLEGE
C N M
525 Buena Vista Dr Se, Albuquerque, NM 87106-4023
Tel (505) 224-4511 *Founded/Ownrshp* 1965
Sales 29.9MM *EMP* 2,200
Accts Axiom Cpas And Business Adviso
SIC 8249 8222 Vocational schools; Community college
Pr: Katharine W Winograd
**VP:* Phillip Bustos
**VP:* Sydney Gumthorpe
**VP:* Kathy Ulibarri
Assoc Dir: Elliot Konetzni

CENTRAL OFFICE
See UNIVERSIDAD INTERAMERICANA DE PUERTO RICO INC

CENTRAL OFFICE
See DEPARTMENT OF CORRECTIONS MINNESOTA

CENTRAL OFFICE
See FEDERAL BUREAU OF PRISONS

D-U-N-S 85-904-9798
CENTRAL OHIO FARMERS CO-OP INC
730 Bellefontaine Ave, Marion, OH 43302-6104
Tel (740) 383-2158 *Founded/Ownrshp* 2000
Sales 134.0MM[E] *EMP* 200
SIC 5153 5261 Grains; Lawnmowers & tractors
Pr: Thomas Bostic
CFO: Andrew Ruck

D-U-N-S 03-434-0547 EXP
CENTRAL OIL & SUPPLY CORP
HARDE' MARTS
2300 Booth St, Monroe, LA 71201-8368
Tel (318) 388-2602 *Founded/Ownrshp* 1967
Sales 120.7MM[E] *EMP* 220
SIC 5171 5541 Petroleum bulk stations; Filling stations, gasoline
Pr: J Hardeman Cordell
CFO: Blair Antony
**Sec:* Kathryn Reppond
Opers Mgr: Kim Turner

D-U-N-S 00-692-6794
■ **CENTRAL PACIFIC BANK**
CENTRAL BANK
(*Suby of* CENTRAL PACIFIC FINANCIAL CORP) ★
220 S King St, Honolulu, HI 96813-4590
Tel (808) 544-0500 *Founded/Ownrshp* 1954
Sales NA *EMP* 903[E]
SIC 6022 State commercial banks
Pr: John C Dean
**Ch Bd:* Crystal K Rose
V Ch: Dean Hirata
Pr: Blenn A Fujimoto
COO: Austin Imamura
CFO: Lawrence D Rodriguez
Chf Cred: Anna Hu
Chf Cred: William Wilson
Ofcr: David Chen
Ofcr: Christopher Frost
Ofcr: Molina Gomez
Ofcr: Amy Kawakami
Ofcr: Skylar Kieschnick
Ofcr: Beverly Lau
Ofcr: Melissa Moniz
Ofcr: Kelli Myers
Ofcr: Jorge Tirona
Ofcr: Raymond W Wilson
Ex VP: Glen Blackmon
Ex VP: Lance Mizumoto
Ex VP: Lee Moriwaki
Board of Directors: Wayne Kamitaki

D-U-N-S 10-307-9539
▲ **CENTRAL PACIFIC FINANCIAL CORP**
220 S King St, Honolulu, HI 96813-4526
Tel (808) 544-0500 *Founded/Ownrshp* 1982
Sales NA *EMP* 876[E]
Tkr Sym CPF *Exch* NYS
SIC 6022 State commercial banks
Ch Bd: John C Dean
Pr: Jolene Kiyono
Pr: A Catherine Ngo
CFO: Denis K Isono
Treas: Blane Asao
Ofcr: Anna Kamakahi
Ofcr: Michael Kim
Ofcr: Lance A Mizumoto
Ofcr: Shelly Talaro
Ofcr: Joshua Thompson
Ex VP: David W Hudson
Ex VP: Lee Y Moriwaki
Ex VP: Raymond W Wilson
Sr VP: Wayne H Kirihara
Sr VP: Arnold D Martines
VP: Roland H Chang
VP: Arleen Ho
VP: Norman Hong
VP: Dayna Matsumoto
VP: Patrick R Matsumoto
VP: Thuy Nguyen-Martines

D-U-N-S 05-066-9670
■ **CENTRAL PARKING CORP**
(*Suby of* SP PLUS CORP) ★
507 Mainstream Dr, Nashville, TN 37228-1208
Tel (615) 297-4255 *Founded/Ownrshp* 2012
Sales 454.7MM[E] *EMP* 14,214
SIC 7521 Parking lots; Parking garage
Pr: James A Marcum
**CFO:* Lucinda Baier
CFO: Jeffrey V Hearin
**Ex VP:* Rick West
**Sr VP:* Benjamin F Parrish
**VP:* James H Bond
VP: David Cotham
VP: Dale Hathcock
VP: Katheryn M Millwee
Area Mgr: Dan Rachi
Genl Mgr: Daryl Homer

D-U-N-S 13-104-3846
■ **CENTRAL PARKING SYSTEM INC**
(*Suby of* CENTRAL PARKING CORP) ★
507 Mainstream Dr, Nashville, TN 37228-1208
Tel (615) 297-4255 *Founded/Ownrshp* 1967
Sales 353.3MM[E] *EMP* 13,150
SIC 7521 Automobile parking
Pr: Jim Marcum
Pr: Jerry Skillett
CFO: Marc Baumann
Ex VP: Rick West
**Sr VP:* Emanual Eads
Sr VP: Daniel Huberty
Sr VP: Robert Ostrov
VP: Christina Combs
VP: David Cotham
VP: Dale Hathcock
VP: Lisa Lines

D-U-N-S 14-540-6034
CENTRAL PENINSULA GENERAL HOSPITAL INC
CENTRAL PENINSULA HOSPITAL
250 Hospital Pl, Soldotna, AK 99669-6999
Tel (907) 262-4404 *Founded/Ownrshp* 1992
Sales 274.8MM *EMP* 611
SIC 8062 General medical & surgical hospitals
CEO: Ryan Smith
Dir Vol: Elizabeth Wilson
**Pr:* Loren Karp Weimer
**CFO:* Richard Davis
**CFO:* Jason Paret
CFO: Lance Spindler
**Treas:* Son Stogsdill
**Ofcr:* Andrea Posey
**VP:* Trena Richardson
Exec: Roy Williams
Dir Inf Cn: Dana McDonald
Dir Risk M: Alan Thye
Dir Lab: Sue Myers
Dir Rx: Phil Sanders

CENTRAL PENINSULA HOSPITAL
See CENTRAL PENINSULA GENERAL HOSPITAL INC

D-U-N-S 78-424-6857
CENTRAL PENNSYLVANIA TEAMSTERS
1055 Spring St, Reading, PA 19610-1747
Tel (610) 320-5500 *Founded/Ownrshp* 2006
Sales 103.1MM *EMP* 3
Accts Novak Francella Llc Bala Cynw
SIC 8631 Labor unions & similar labor organizations
Prin: James Stricker
VP: Jeff Strause

D-U-N-S 07-105-8259
CENTRAL PIEDMONT COMMUNITY COLLEGE
C P C C
(*Suby of* NORTH CAROLINA COMMUNITY COLLEGE SYSTEM) ★
1201 Elizabeth Ave, Charlotte, NC 28204-2240
Tel (704) 330-2722 *Founded/Ownrshp* 1963
Sales 42.1MM[E] *EMP* 1,000[E]
Accts Cherry Bekaert Llp Charlotte
SIC 8222 9411 Community college;
Pr: Dr Tony Zeiss
Assoc VP: Brenda Leonard
Assoc VP: Paul Santos
**Ex VP:* Kathy Drumm
**VP:* Marcia Conston
**VP:* Micheal Moss
**VP:* Richard Zollinger
Ex Dir: Brenda Lea
Ex Dir: Dana McDonald
Ex Dir: Kathy Rummage

CENTRAL PLAINS CEMENT COMPANY
See AUDUBON MATERIALS LLC

D-U-N-S 07-920-4672
■ **CENTRAL PLAINS CEMENT CO LLC**
(*Suby of* EAGLE MATERIALS INC) ★
15100 E Crtney Athrton Rd, Sugar Creek, MO 64058-3307
Tel (816) 257-4028 *Founded/Ownrshp* 2012
Sales 415.0MM *EMP* 250
SIC 8741 Administrative management
Pr: David Challacomb

D-U-N-S 00-384-4388
CENTRAL POWER ELECTRIC COOPERATIVE INC (ND)
525 20th Ave Sw, Minot, ND 58701-6436
Tel (701) 852-4407 *Founded/Ownrshp* 1949
Sales 149.8MM *EMP* 41
SIC 4911 Distribution, electric power
Pr: Arden Fuher
**CFO:* Michael Kossan
**Treas:* Clifford Gjellstad
**Sec:* Alvin Myers
**VP:* Ervin Mund
Genl Mgr: Thomas L Meland
IT Man: Marlene Guttormson
Opers Mgr: Mark Sherman

CENTRAL POWER SYSTEMS
See POWER DISTRIBUTORS LLC

D-U-N-S 00-724-6630 IMP
CENTRAL POWER SYSTEMS & SERVICES LLC
CPS&S
9200 Liberty Dr, Pleasant Valley, MO 64068-9396
Tel (816) 781-8070 *Founded/Ownrshp* 1954, 2015
Sales 154.0MM^E *EMP* 320
SIC 5013 7629 Motor vehicle supplies & new parts; Generator repair
Pr: Robin Roberts
**Pr:* Bill Allen
Ofcr: Harlin Mitchell
**VP:* Jon Hayes
**VP:* Bryan E Redburn
IT Man: Larry Williams
Sls Dir: Len Smith
Sls Mgr: James Gregory

D-U-N-S 05-769-7807 IMP/EXP
CENTRAL PRODUCTS LLC
CENTRAL RESTAURANT PRODUCTS
(*Suby of* TAKKT AMERICA HOLDING INC) ★
7750 Georgetown Rd, Indianapolis, IN 46268-4135
Tel (317) 634-2550 *Founded/Ownrshp* 2010
Sales 96.0MM *EMP* 132
SIC 5046 5021

D-U-N-S 12-274-6654
CENTRAL PURCHASING CORP
N & S SUPPLY
205 Old Route 9, Fishkill, NY 12524-2472
Tel (845) 896-6291 *Founded/Ownrshp* 1982
Sales 141.8MM^E *EMP* 120^E
SIC 5074 5075 Plumbing & hydronic heating supplies; Air conditioning & ventilation equipment & supplies
Pr: Wayne Nussbickel
VP: Robert Nussbickel

D-U-N-S 04-522-6701 IMP/EXP
CENTRAL PURCHASING LLC
HARBOR FREIGHT TOOLS
3491 Mission Oaks Blvd, Camarillo, CA 93012-5034
Tel (805) 388-1000 *Founded/Ownrshp* 1968
Sales 1.9MMM^E *EMP* 10,000
SIC 5085 5961 5251 Tools; Tools & hardware, mail order; Tools
CEO: Eric L Smidt
COO: Robert Rene
Treas: Patty Sinner
VP: Bruce Godfray
VP: Christopher Gurtcheff
VP: Jason Sprong
Area Mgr: Elizabeth Horne
Brnch Mgr: Tim Foreman
Dir IT: Victor Harris
Dir IT: Paul Kasinski
IT Man: Joe Constant

D-U-N-S 10-853-7346
CENTRAL REFRIGERATED SERVICE LLC
5175 W 2100 S, West Valley City, UT 84120-1252
Tel (801) 924-7000 *Founded/Ownrshp* 2002
Sales 130.3MM^E *EMP* 1,650
SIC 4213 Refrigerated products transport
CEO: Jon Isaacson
**CFO:* Robert Baer
**VP:* Tork Fulton
Secur Mgr: Tyson Jones

CENTRAL REGION
See ASH GROVE MATERIALS CORP

D-U-N-S 02-421-1882
CENTRAL REGIONAL HOSPITAL
(*Suby of* NORTH CAROLINA DEPARTMENT OF HEALTH & HUMAN SERVICES) ★
300 Veazey Dr, Butner, NC 27509-1668
Tel (919) 575-7211 *Founded/Ownrshp* 2008
Sales 101.7MM^E *EMP* 1,600
SIC 8062 9431 General medical & surgical hospitals;
CEO: Mike Hennike
COO: Cliff Hood
Ofcr: Laura Harris
Prin: James W Osberg

CENTRAL RESTAURANT PRODUCTS
See CENTRAL PRODUCTS LLC

D-U-N-S 61-826-0447 IMP
CENTRAL SEAWAY CO INC
650 Dundee Rd Ste 180, Northbrook, IL 60062-2753
Tel (224) 723-5800 *Founded/Ownrshp* 1960
Sales 295.0MM *EMP* 20
SIC 5146 Seafoods
Pr: Lee Feigon
Sls Mgr: Dave Bennett

D-U-N-S 02-354-5960
CENTRAL SECURITY GROUP INC
2448 E 81st St Ste 4300, Tulsa, OK 74137-4285
Tel (918) 491-3151 *Founded/Ownrshp* 1999
Sales 90.6MM *EMP* 485
SIC 7382 Security systems services
CEO: Richard Ginsburg
**COO:* Mike Hankins
COO: Keith Patterson
**CFO:* Harry Schenk
Dir IT: Duane Dietrich

D-U-N-S 01-010-0147
CENTRAL SERVICES OF ROMAN CATHOLIC ARCHBISHOP OF BALTIMORE (INC)
ROMAN CATHOLIC CHURCH
320 Cathedral St, Baltimore, MD 21201-4421
Tel (410) 547-5555 *Founded/Ownrshp* 1832
Sales 188.7MM^E *EMP* 5,800
SIC 8661 Catholic Church
Ex Dir: Len Strom
Prgrm Mgr: Lauron Thomas
Off Mgr: Sandra Gill
Dir IT: Bill Glover
Opers Mgr: Nolan McCoy

D-U-N-S 04-671-8456
CENTRAL SHARED SERVICES LLC (VA)
1 Park Plz, Nashville, TN 37203-6527
Tel (615) 344-5228 *Founded/Ownrshp* 2004
Sales 100.3MM^E *EMP* 651^E
SIC 7011 Resort hotel

D-U-N-S 08-049-9510
■ **CENTRAL STATE TELEPHONE CO LLC**
(*Suby of* TDS TELECOMMUNICATIONS CORP) ★
525 Junction Rd, Madison, WI 53717-2152
Tel (608) 831-1000 *Founded/Ownrshp* 1969
Sales 167.9MM^E *EMP* 3,000
SIC 4813 Local telephone communications
Pr: David A Wittwer

D-U-N-S 02-137-7254 EXP
CENTRAL STATES ENTERPRISES LLC
CSE
1275 Lake Heathrow Ln # 101, Heathrow, FL 32746-4398
Tel (407) 333-3503 *Founded/Ownrshp* 1982
Sales 167.7MM^E *EMP* 100
SIC 5153 0213 0723 Grains; Hogs; Cash grain crops market preparation services
Ch Bd: Richard C Shura
**Pr:* Robert M Nawrot
CFO: Billy Shortal
**Treas:* Mark Brickey
**Ex VP:* Kenneth Cupples
**VP:* William Shortal

D-U-N-S 18-335-0669 IMP
CENTRAL STATES MANUFACTURING INC
CENTRAL STORAGE WORKS
302 Jane Pl, Lowell, AR 72745-9119
Tel (479) 770-0188 *Founded/Ownrshp* 1981
Sales 219.5MM *EMP* 294
SIC 3353 3448 7389

CENTRAL STATES PETROLEUM
See HARMS OIL CO

CENTRAL STATES SE & SW AREAS P
See CENTRAL STATES SOUTHEAST AND SOUTHWEST AREAS PENSION FUND

D-U-N-S 06-860-0279
CENTRAL STATES SOUTHEAST & SOUTHWEST AREAS HEALTH & WELFARE FUND
9377 W Higgins Rd, Rosemont, IL 60018-4973
Tel (847) 518-9800 *Founded/Ownrshp* 1950
Sales NA *EMP* 719
SIC 6371 Union welfare, benefit & health funds
Ex Dir: Thomas Nyhan

D-U-N-S 04-929-3962
CENTRAL STATES SOUTHEAST AND SOUTHWEST AREAS PENSION FUND
CENTRAL STATES SE & SW AREAS P
9377 W Higgins Rd Fl 2, Rosemont, IL 60018-4938
Tel (847) 518-9800 *Founded/Ownrshp* 1955
Sales NA *EMP* 529
SIC 6371 Pension funds
Ex Dir: Thomas C Nyhan
**COO:* William Schaefer
**CFO:* Mark F Angerame
Div Mgr: Jeffrey Brandon
Div Mgr: Peter Priede
Tech Mgr: Tim Hupe

D-U-N-S 03-128-5984 IMP
CENTRAL STATES THERMO KING INC (KS)
CSTK
7200 W 132nd St Ste 270, Overland Park, KS 66213-1135
Tel (888) 566-5743 *Founded/Ownrshp* 1955, 1975
Sales 93.2MM^E *EMP* 287
Accts Mcgladrey & Pullen Llp Kansa
SIC 5078 7623 5084 Refrigeration units, motor vehicles; Refrigeration repair service; Engines & transportation equipment
Pr: Michael Kahn
**COO:* Allen Lane
**CFO:* Don Soetaert
IT Man: Dennis Laughlin

D-U-N-S 87-774-5943 IMP
CENTRAL STATES WHOLESALE & DISTRIBUTION INC
(*Suby of* BUCHHEIT, INC.)
33 Pcr 540, Perryville, MO 63775-8757
Tel (573) 547-4260 *Founded/Ownrshp* 1993
Sales 83.7MM *EMP* 15
SIC 5031 Lumber, plywood & millwork
Pr: Tim Buchheit

D-U-N-S 00-692-9111 IMP/EXP
▲ **CENTRAL STEEL AND WIRE CO**
3000 W 51st St, Chicago, IL 60632-2198
Tel (773) 471-3800 *Founded/Ownrshp* 1909, 1996
Sales 599.1MM *EMP* 1,075
Tkr Sym CSTW *Exch* OTO
SIC 5051 Metals service centers & offices; Steel; Copper; Aluminum bars, rods, ingots, sheets, pipes, plates, etc.
CEO: Stephen E Fuhrman
**Ch Bd:* Michael X Cronin
**Pr:* John F Calhoun
COO: John Tiernan
**CFO:* Ronald V Kazmar

**VP:* Christopher Rodgers
**VP:* Michael J Sullivan
Opers Mgr: John Crowley
VP Sls: David Palough
Manager: Neal Carolan
Manager: Nick Fedorenko

CENTRAL STORAGE WORKS
See CENTRAL STATES MANUFACTURING INC

D-U-N-S 06-807-7197
CENTRAL SUFFOLK HOSPITAL
PECONIC BAY MEDICAL CENTER
1300 Roanoke Ave, Riverhead, NY 11901-2058
Tel (631) 548-6000 *Founded/Ownrshp* 1997
Sales 156.0MM *EMP* 1,200
SIC 8062 General medical & surgical hospitals
CEO: Andrew J Mitchell
V Ch: Jesse R Goodale
VP: Sharon Tietze
VP: Gerry Zunno
Exec: Debbie Masso
Dir Rx: Beatrice Cohen
Dir Rx: Ritchie Wenzel
Chf Nrs Of: Ita Berry
Off Mgr: Joyce Mahoney
Nurse Mgr: Ann Buckley
Surgeon: Peter Sultan

CENTRAL SUPPLY
See PLUMBERS SUPPLY CO

D-U-N-S 00-693-7825
CENTRAL SUPPLY CO INC
ELEGANT BATH, THE
8900 E 30th St, Indianapolis, IN 46219-1502
Tel (317) 898-2411 *Founded/Ownrshp* 1902, 1976
Sales 105.9MM *EMP* 160
SIC 5074 5063 5085 5719 Plumbing fittings & supplies; Heating equipment (hydronic); Electrical apparatus & equipment; Industrial supplies; Bath accessories
Pr: Ted Ashcraft
**CFO:* Joe Hughes
**VP:* Keith Gilbert
**VP:* Doyle McCauley
**VP:* Randy Strong
**Prin:* Gene Burt
**Prin:* David Hughes
Genl Mgr: Gene Bert
Sales Asso: Mike Barnes
Sales Asso: Todd Benefiel
Sales Asso: Miggy Cabrera

D-U-N-S 00-696-9653
■ **CENTRAL TELEPHONE CO** (DE)
CENTURYLINK
(*Suby of* EMBARQ) ★
100 Centurylink Dr, Monroe, LA 71203-2041
Tel (318) 361-5955 *Founded/Ownrshp* 1936, 1971
Sales 195.7MM^E *EMP* 2,000^E
SIC 4813 Local telephone communications;
CEO: Glen Post
**Pr:* William E Cheek
**Treas:* Leslie H Meredith
VP: Richard D McRae
**VP:* Claudia S Toussaint

D-U-N-S 00-693-2461
CENTRAL TERRITORIAL OF SALVATION ARMY
(*Suby of* SALVATION ARMY NATIONAL CORP) ★
5550 Prairie Stone Pkwy # 130, Hoffman Estates, IL 60192-3713
Tel (847) 294-2000 *Founded/Ownrshp* 1865
Sales 503.8MM^E *EMP* 15,628
SIC 8661 8322 Christian & Reformed Church; Individual & family services; Rehabilitation services
Prin: Commissioner Paul R Seiler
**Pr:* Commissioner Carol Seiler
Ofcr: Irene Castro
Ofcr: Javier Castro
Ofcr: Stuart Risdale
Exec: Christopher McGown
IT Man: Alberto Rapley
Mktg Dir: Lora Baker

D-U-N-S 96-456-8153
CENTRAL TOWERS PRESERVATION LP
CAPITOL GREEN
400 Central Ave Ste 1, Albany, NY 12206-2243
Tel (518) 438-6834 *Founded/Ownrshp* 2010
Sales 41.9MM^E *EMP* 1,828
SIC 6513 Apartment building operators
Prin: Larry Lipton

D-U-N-S 03-977-4083 EXP
CENTRAL TRANSPORT INTERNATIONAL INC (MI)
(*Suby of* CENTURION) ★
12225 Stephens Rd, Warren, MI 48089-2070
Tel (586) 467-0100 *Founded/Ownrshp* 1995
Sales 159.7MM^E *EMP* 99
SIC 4212 4213 Local trucking, without storage; Trucking, except local
Pr: Richard Rosenthal
V Ch: Matthew Moroun
VP: Frederick Calderone
VP: Lee Curvey
VP: Peter Dwyer
VP: Kurt Kusche
VP: Agnes Moroun
VP: Hugh Thomas
Exec: Leslie Massucco
Dir Bus: Brian Downing
Dir Bus: Ronald Kata
Dir Bus: Larry Minutillo
Dir Bus: Richard Wells

D-U-N-S 00-696-5263
CENTRAL TRUST BANK
CENTRAL BANK
(*Suby of* CENTRAL BANCOMPANY INC) ★
238 Madison St, Jefferson City, MO 65101-3249
Tel (573) 634-1302 *Founded/Ownrshp* 1971
Sales NA *EMP* 525
SIC 6022 State commercial banks
Pr: Kenneth Littlefield
**Ch Bd:* Sam B Cook

Pr: Julie Glaser
COO: James Sone
**CFO:* Micheal Ittner
Sr VP: Mary Wilkerson
VP: James Crabtree
VP: Heidi Lange
VP: Pam Wilson
Opers Mgr: Tammie Corder
Opers Mgr: Dave Meyer
Board of Directors: David Harrison, C Karuse, Dr Gene Rooney, J S Sanders, B Schulte, Carl Vogel

D-U-N-S 01-207-3789
CENTRAL UNIFIED SCHOOL DISTRICT
4605 N Polk Ave, Fresno, CA 93722-5334
Tel (559) 274-4700 *Founded/Ownrshp* 1922
Sales 99.9MM^E *EMP* 1,200
SIC 8211 Public elementary school; Public junior high school; Public senior high school; Public elementary & secondary schools
Prin: Sheila Moynihan
CTO: Dale Richey
Teacher Pr: Leisha Berry
Teacher Pr: Eleseo Cuellar
Instr Medi: Janet Wyle

D-U-N-S 07-803-3313
CENTRAL UNITED LIFE INSURANCE CO INC
10777 Northwest Fwy # 100, Houston, TX 77092-7336
Tel (713) 529-0045 *Founded/Ownrshp* 1962, 1994
Sales NA *EMP* 270
SIC 6311 Life insurance carriers
Ch Bd: David W Harris
**Pr:* Dan George
CFO: Kent Lamb
Sr VP: John E McGettigan
VP: Bill Bay
VP: Ann Blakey
VP: David Parsons
Exec: Angela Jones
Dir IT: Kerry Lubin
Dir IT: Teresa Moro

D-U-N-S 03-928-3101
CENTRAL VALLEY AG COOPERATIVE NONSTOCK
415 E Highway 20, Oneill, NE 68763-2308
Tel (402) 336-1263 *Founded/Ownrshp* 1998, 1996
Sales 681.5MM^E *EMP* 300
SIC 5191 Fertilizer & fertilizer materials
Pr: Doug Dersheid
**VP:* Lisa Hedstrom

D-U-N-S 04-399-6263
CENTRAL VALLEY AUTOMOTIVE INC (CA)
CENTRAL VLY VOLKSWAGEN HYUNDAI
4460 Mchenry Ave, Modesto, CA 95356-1518
Tel (209) 526-3300 *Founded/Ownrshp* 1963, 1974
Sales 112.5MM^E *EMP* 190
SIC 5511 Automobiles, new & used
Pr: John Gardner
**Sec:* John McSherry
**VP:* Deborah Gardner
Exec: Erick Alava
Sls Mgr: Brent Gardner
Sls Mgr: Tim Tarak
Board of Directors: Brent Gardner, John Gardner, John McSherry

D-U-N-S 96-109-0891
CENTRAL VALLEY COOPERATIVE
900 30th Pl Nw, Owatonna, MN 55060-5001
Tel (507) 451-1230 *Founded/Ownrshp* 2005
Sales 278.0MM^E *EMP* 170
SIC 5191 5171 5541 Fertilizer & fertilizer materials; Petroleum bulk stations; Filling stations, gasoline
CEO: Gary Mohr
**Ch Bd:* Dave Seykora

D-U-N-S 08-037-0264
CENTRAL VALLEY GAS STORAGE LLC
10 Peachtree Pl Ne, Atlanta, GA 30309-4497
Tel (404) 584-3733 *Founded/Ownrshp* 2008
Sales 1.2MMM^E *EMP* 33,000
SIC 4924 Natural gas distribution
VP: Steve Wassell

D-U-N-S 80-031-7638
CENTRAL VALLEY GENERAL HOSPITAL
ADVENTIST HEALTH
(*Suby of* ADVENTIST HEALTH SYSTEM/WEST) ★
1025 N Douty St, Hanford, CA 93230-3722
Tel (559) 583-2100 *Founded/Ownrshp* 1998
Sales 109.0MM *EMP* 410
SIC 8062 General medical & surgical hospitals
CEO: Wayne Ferch
Chf OB: Thomas Enloe
**COO:* Douglas Lafferty
CFO: Eric Martisen
CFO: Michele Waldrin
**VP:* Kirby McKague
Ansthlgy: Stephen F Ayers
Ansthlgy: James H Lundy
Ansthlgy: Michael Ohara
Ansthlgy: Ahmed Raza
Ansthlgy: Jonathan C Weeks

CENTRAL VALLEY INSULATION
See CENTRAL VALLEY SPECIALTIES INC

D-U-N-S 02-831-9932
CENTRAL VALLEY MORTGAGE SERVICE INC
1987 W Orange Ave, Porterville, CA 93257-6703
Tel (559) 782-8011 *Founded/Ownrshp* 2001
Sales NA *EMP* 49
SIC 6162 Mortgage bankers & correspondents
Pr: Megan Taggard
**VP:* Kevin Taggard

D-U-N-S 10-067-4506 IMP
CENTRAL VALLEY SCHOOL DISTRICT
19307 E Cataldo Ave, Spokane Valley, WA 99016-9404
Tel (509) 228-5404 *Founded/Ownrshp* 1890
Sales 91.6MM^E *EMP* 1,800
SIC 8211 Public elementary & secondary schools
**Pr:* Keith Clark
CFO: Janice Hutton

Bd of Dir: Tom Dingus
Bd of Dir: Amy Mason
Bd of Dir: Cynthia McMullen
VP: Debra Long
MIS Dir: Jeff Psliger
Pr Dir: Melanie Rose
Psych: Shelly Bajadali
Psych: Mary Naccarato
Psych: Danielle Stroe

D-U-N-S 12-205-3903
■ CENTRAL VALLEY SPECIALTIES INC
CENTRAL VALLEY INSULATION
(*Suby of* TRUTEAM LLC) ★
3846 E Winslow Ave, Phoenix, AZ 85040-1651
Tel (602) 437-2046 *Founded/Ownrshp* 1985
Sales 156.2MM[E] *EMP* 4,772
SIC 1742 1721 Insulation, buildings; Drywall; Residential painting; Commercial painting
Genl Mgr: Mike Henson

CENTRAL VERMONT HOSPITAL
See CENTRAL VERMONT MEDICAL CENTER INC

D-U-N-S 06-991-2442
CENTRAL VERMONT MEDICAL CENTER INC
CENTRAL VERMONT HOSPITAL
130 Fisher Rd Unit 1, Berlin, VT 05602-9000
Tel (802) 371-4100 *Founded/Ownrshp* 1984
Sales 165.1MM *EMP* 1,200[E]
SIC 8062 General medical & surgical hospitals
Ch Bd: John Nichols
Pr: Judith Tartaglia
COO: Nancy Lothian
CFO: Cheyenne Folland
CFO: Cheyenne Holland
VP: Phil Brown
VP: Susan Kruthers
VP: Helen Spring
Exec: Debbie Willis
Dir Teleco: Steve Trepanier
Dir Rad: Dixie Mercier
Dir Rx: Frank Foti

D-U-N-S 00-483-0279
CENTRAL VIRGINIA ELECTRIC COOPERATIVE INC (VA)
800 Cooperative Way, Arrington, VA 22922-3300
Tel (434) 263-8336 *Founded/Ownrshp* 1937
Sales 84.6MM *EMP* 115
SIC 4911

D-U-N-S 03-428-4499
CENTRAL VIRGINIA TRAINING CENTER
521 Colony Rd, Madison Heights, VA 24572-2105
Tel (804) 947-6313 *Founded/Ownrshp* 2010
Sales 29.1MM[E] *EMP* 1,300
SIC 8299 Educational services
Prin: Judy Dudney
Dir Inf Cn: Diana Pitre
Genl Mgr: Derrick Smith

CENTRAL VLY VOLKSWAGEN HYUNDAI
See CENTRAL VALLEY AUTOMOTIVE INC

D-U-N-S 02-023-1296
CENTRAL WASHINGTON HEALTH SERVICES ASSOCIATION (WA)
CENTRAL WASHINGTON HOSPITAL
1201 S Miller St, Wenatchee, WA 98801-3201
Tel (509) 662-1511 *Founded/Ownrshp* 1962, 1990
Sales 259.9MM *EMP* 1,100[E]
Accts Moss Adams Llp Everett Washi
SIC 8062 General medical & surgical hospitals
CEO: Peter Rutherford MD
CFO: Steve Jacobs
Treas: Kristine Loomis
V Ch Bd: Mark Heminger
Ex VP: John Hamilton
VP: Darlington Mary
Exec: Jim Wood
Dir Risk M: Marcy Vixie
Dir Rx: Craig Pedersen
Dir Pat Ac: Helen Hanson
Genl Mgr: Mindi Stuart

CENTRAL WASHINGTON HOSPITAL
See CENTRAL WASHINGTON HEALTH SERVICES ASSOCIATION

D-U-N-S 05-548-4950
CENTRAL WASHINGTON UNIVERSITY INC
400 E University Way, Ellensburg, WA 98926-7500
Tel (509) 963-1111 *Founded/Ownrshp* 1891
Sales 121.2MM[E] *EMP* 1,424[E]
SIC 8221

D-U-N-S 04-900-2090 IMP
CENTRAL WHOLESALERS INC
13401 Konterra Dr, Laurel, MD 20707-6504
Tel (800) 935-2947 *Founded/Ownrshp* 1981
Sales 267.4MM[E] *EMP* 500
SIC 5074 5063 5087 5072 5211 1799 Plumbing fittings & supplies; Heating equipment (hydronic); Electrical supplies; Janitors' supplies; Hardware; Lumber & other building materials; Cabinets, kitchen; Bathtub refinishing
Pr: Douglas Sherman
VP: Richard Barron
Dir IT: Milton Chiz
Opers Mgr: Donna Bourcier
VP Sls: Todd Johnson
Manager: Carlton Prince
Sales Asso: Monty Browning
Sales Asso: Justin Butler
Sales Asso: James McIlwain
Sales Asso: Wesley Pride
Sales Asso: Rick Smoak

D-U-N-S 61-530-9770 IMP
CENTRASTATE HEALTHCARE SYSTEM INC
901 W Main St, Freehold, NJ 07728-2537
Tel (732) 431-2000 *Founded/Ownrshp* 1988
Sales 313.1MM *EMP* 2,527
Accts Ernst & Young Llp Iselin Nj
SIC 8099 8741 Medical services organization; Hospital management; Nursing & personal care facility management
Pr: John T Gribbin
Dir Vol: Joan Nealon
Pr: Barry Asch
Pr: Robert Nyman
COO: Deborah J Teasley
CFO: John A Dellocono
Treas: James W Palmer
Bd of Dir: Robert Kayser
Trst: Patricia S Medley
Ofcr: Joseph R Iantosca
Sr VP: David A De Simone
Sr VP: Alice Guttler
VP: Linda Geisler
VP: Eugene W Grochala
VP: Ellen Gutter
VP: Kim A Kelly
VP: Michael Sordo
VP: Benjamin Weinstein
VP: Susan Wood
Exec: Howard Cohen
Dir Teleco: Barbara Aellis

D-U-N-S 06-870-8544
CENTRASTATE MEDICAL CENTER INC
901 W Main St, Freehold, NJ 07728-2549
Tel (732) 431-2000 *Founded/Ownrshp* 1964
Sales 263.2MM *EMP* 1,510
Accts Ernst & Young Llp Iselin Nj
SIC 8062 General medical & surgical hospitals
Pr: John Gribbin
COO: Dan Messina
CFO: John A Dellocono
CFO: Roger Klein
CFO: Steve Sanfilippo
Assoc VP: Carl B Ausfahl
Sr VP: Benjamin Weinstein
VP: Patricia Griffin
Exec: Barbara Corso
Dir Teleco: Barbara Aellis
Dir Rad: Jeffrey Friedenberg
Dir Rad: Mandy Sporacio
Dir Rx: John Dimatteo

D-U-N-S 07-786-7604 IMP
CENTRE COLLEGE OF KENTUCKY
600 W Walnut St, Danville, KY 40422-1394
Tel (859) 238-5200 *Founded/Ownrshp* 1819
Sales 86.6MM *EMP* 340[E]
Accts Crowe Horwath Llp Louisville
SIC 8221 College, except junior
Pr: John A Roush
CFO: Robert Keasler
Treas: John E Cuny
Assoc Dir: Gary Bugg
CIO: Keith Fowlkes
Psych: Joel Klepac
Psych: Michael Spears

D-U-N-S 96-849-5536
CENTRE LANE PARTNERS LLC
60 E 42nd St Ste 1250, New York, NY 10165-1299
Tel (646) 843-0710 *Founded/Ownrshp* 2010
Sales 185.0MM[E] *EMP* 569[E]
SIC 6799 Investors

D-U-N-S 78-831-9580
CENTRE PARTNERS MANAGEMENT LLC
825 3rd Ave Fl 40, New York, NY 10022-7592
Tel (212) 332-5800 *Founded/Ownrshp* 1986
Sales 886.0MM[E] *EMP* 2,691
SIC 6726 5112 Management investment funds, closed-end; Stationery & office supplies
Ch: Lester Pollack
Mng Pt: Bruce Pollack
COO: William Tomai
Mng Dir: Jeffrey Bartoli
Mng Dir: Nishad Chande

CENTRELLA FOODS
See CENTRAL GROCERS INC

D-U-N-S 03-972-5783 IMP/EXP
CENTREX PRECISION PLASTICS
FLEXMEDICAL DISPOSABLES
7700 Bent Dr Ste 100, Irving, TX 75063
Tel (972) 929-4804 *Founded/Ownrshp* 2008
Sales 394.0MM[E] *EMP* 3,200
SIC 3842

D-U-N-S 00-433-4843 IMP/EXP
■ CENTRIA INC
(*Suby of* NCI BUILDING SYSTEMS INC) ★
1005 Beaver Grade Rd # 2, Coraopolis, PA 15108-2964
Tel (412) 299-8000 *Founded/Ownrshp* 1993, 2015
Sales 384.3MM[E] *EMP* 679
SIC 3444 1761 3564 3449 Metal flooring & siding; Metal roofing & roof drainage equipment; Roofing, siding & sheet metal work; Blowers & fans; Miscellaneous metalwork
Pr: Raymond Caudill
Treas: Robert R Leighton
Treas: Eston C Owens
VP: James G Belardi
VP: Joseph Urso
CIO: Rafael Barreto
IT Man: Jason Bailey
IT Man: Steven Brown
Mktg Mgr: Rich Mowery
Sls Mgr: Bill Cheeley
Sls Mgr: Fred Fischer

D-U-N-S 94-881-7486
CENTRIC FINANCIAL GROUP LLC
4016 Townsfair Way # 202, Columbus, OH 43219-6083
Tel (614) 824-6100 *Founded/Ownrshp* 2009
Sales NA *EMP* 11
SIC 6311 6282 6321 Life insurance; Investment advisory service; Disability health insurance
Pr: Cheryl Evans

D-U-N-S 79-062-0384
CENTRICSIT LLC
3140 Northwoods Pkwy, Peachtree Corners, GA 30071-5711
Tel (678) 495-4732 *Founded/Ownrshp* 2007
Sales 128.2MM[E] *EMP* 100[E]
SIC 5045 Computer peripheral equipment
Pr: Derik Odegard
CFO: Richard Hans

VP: Patrick Keuller
Netwrk Eng: Chris Ginn

D-U-N-S 07-333-3221
CENTRO DE SALUD DE LA COMUNIDAD DE SAN YSIDRO INC
SAN YSIDRO HEALTH CENTER
4004 Beyer Blvd, San Ysidro, CA 92173-2007
Tel (619) 428-4463 *Founded/Ownrshp* 1969
Sales 87.1MM *EMP* 240
Accts Tca Partners Llp Fresno Ca
SIC 8093 8011 Specialty outpatient clinics; Offices & clinics of medical doctors
CEO: Kevin Mattson
Pr: M Gutierrez
VP: Matthew Weeks
Prin: Ed Martinez
CIO: Ed Estrada
Dir IT: Catia Daoud
IT Man: George Navarro
Doctor: Ferdinand Barbadillo
Doctor: Edward M Goldstein MD
Doctor: Jorge Mata
Doctor: Roman Szkopiec

D-U-N-S 05-246-4377 IMP
CENTRO INC
950 N Bend Dr, North Liberty, IA 52317-9300
Tel (319) 626-3200 *Founded/Ownrshp* 1970
Sales 235.0MM[E] *EMP* 896
SIC 3089 Molding primary plastic
Pr: Brian Olesen
Ch: Gary Rozek
Sr VP: Raju Malhotra
QA Dir: Lance Mayhew
MIS Mgr: Mitch Conant
VP Opers: Tripp Traicoff
Sfty Dirs: Brian McNeal
Opers Mgr: Kevin McMichael
Prd Mgr: Jim Lewis
QI Cn Mgr: Tony Berger
QI Cn Mgr: Eric Robinson

D-U-N-S 36-114-1935
CENTRO INTERNACIONAL DE AGRICULTURA TROPICAL
CIAT-MIAMI
7343 Nw 79th Ter, Medley, FL 33166-2211
Tel (305) 863-9127 *Founded/Ownrshp* 1977
Sales 114.2MM *EMP* 3
SIC 8731 Agricultural research
CEO: Alvin Hushner
Pr: Ruben Echeverria
CFO: Jose Hilberto Rodriguez

D-U-N-S 11-816-2379 IMP/EXP
CENTRO MEDICO DEL TURABO INC
HOSPITAL INTERAMERICANO
100 Ave Luis Munoz Marin, Caguas, PR 00725-6184
Tel (787) 653-3434 *Founded/Ownrshp* 1988
Sales 436.2MM *EMP* 1,400
SIC 8741 Management services
Pr: Joaqu N Rodr Guez Sr JD
Ch Bd: Joaquin Rodriguez Sr
Pr: Carlos M Pl Eiro
CFO: Francisco Nedina
Ex VP: Armando Rodraguez
VP: Armando Rodr Guez
VP: Lcda Heidi L Rodr Guez
VP: Jaime Rivera Due O

D-U-N-S 04-141-1484 EXP
▲ CENTRUS ENERGY CORP
6901 Rockledge Dr Ste 800, Bethesda, MD 20817-1867
Tel (301) 564-3200 *Founded/Ownrshp* 1940
Sales 418.2MM *EMP* 446
Tkr Sym LEU *Exch* ASE
SIC 1094 Uranium ore mining
Pr: Daniel B Poneman
Ch Bd: Mikel H Williams
CFO: Stephen S Greene
Sr VP: Kevin Alldred
Sr VP: Elmer W Dyke
VP: Philip G Sewell
Exec: Marian K Davis
Exec: Rose Hunter
Mfg Mgr: Ben Jordan
VP Sls: John MA Donelson
Board of Directors: Theodore J Dalheim Jr, Michael Diament, Osbert Hood, W Thomas Jagodinski, Patricia J Jamieson, William J Madia, Michael P Morrell, Hiroshi Sakamoto

D-U-N-S 07-576-2237
CENTURA HEALTH CORP
PENROSE ST FRANCIS HEALTH SVCS
188 Inverness Dr W # 500, Englewood, CO 80112-5204
Tel (303) 290-6500 *Founded/Ownrshp* 1987
Sales 257.8MM *EMP* 3,500
SIC 8069

D-U-N-S 08-677-5691
CENTURI CONSTRUCTION GROUP INC
2355 W Utopia Rd, Phoenix, AZ 85027-4167
Tel (623) 582-1235 *Founded/Ownrshp* 2014
Sales 89.6MM[E] *EMP* 180[E]
SIC 4923 Gas transmission & distribution
Pr: James P Kane

D-U-N-S 06-559-1463
CENTURION
12225 Stephens Rd, Warren, MI 48089-2010
Tel (586) 939-7000 *Founded/Ownrshp* 1970
Sales 62.0M *EMP* 4,000
SIC 4213 4212 4581 Trucking, except local; Local trucking, without storage; Air freight handling at airports
Pr: Manuel J Moroun
CFO: Terry Freund
Treas: Norm E Harned
Sr VP: Martin Deise
VP: Peter Dwyer
VP: John Locke
Dir Bus: Kevin Stutzman
Genl Mgr: John Moore
Mktg Dir: Jeff Cackowski

D-U-N-S 80-718-0398
CENTURION AIR CARGO INC
CENTURION CARGO
4500 Nw 36th St Bldg 916, Miami Springs, FL 33166-6121
Tel (305) 871-0130 *Founded/Ownrshp* 1985
Sales 500.0MM *EMP* 657[E]
SIC 4581 4522 Air freight handling at airports; Air transportation, nonscheduled
CEO: Johnny Millon
Owner: Alfonzo Rey
Pr: Ian Morgan
CFO: Marcos Montesano
Treas: Iraq Pacheco
Ofcr: Rolando Martinez
VP: Irma Barba
QC Dir: Doug Eccles
Sales Exec: Liz Figueroa
Sales Exec: Pilar Piccini

CENTURION CARGO
See CENTURION AIR CARGO INC

D-U-N-S 07-938-3011
CENTURION DISCOVERY INC
518 17th St Ste 925, Denver, CO 80202-4131
Tel (303) 645-4555 *Founded/Ownrshp* 2010
Sales 500.0MM *EMP* 5[E]
SIC 8111 Legal services
Pr: Valmir Zymeri

D-U-N-S 06-399-2168
CENTURION INDUSTRIES INC
TFC CANOPY
1107 N Taylor Rd, Garrett, IN 46738-1880
Tel (260) 357-6665 *Founded/Ownrshp* 1975
Sales 162.4MM *EMP* 900
SIC 3444 1796 Canopies, sheet metal; Millwright
Ch Bd: Kenneth L Tharp
Pr: Bradley S Parish
VP: Thomas Patterson
VP: Randy Shinkle
Genl Mgr: Brenda Foster
Genl Mgr: Thomas Galanis
Off Mgr: Mindy Boyster
Opers Mgr: Trae Berry
Opers Mgr: Gary Whipple
Plnt Mgr: Don Hulen
Plnt Mgr: Keith Moughler

D-U-N-S 01-724-6562 IMP/EXP
CENTURION MEDICAL PRODUCTS CORP
100 Centurion Way, Williamston, MI 48895-9086
Tel (517) 546-5400 *Founded/Ownrshp* 1964
Sales 155.3MM[E] *EMP* 700
SIC 3842 2759 2671

D-U-N-S 14-588-0485
■ CENTURION PIPELINE LP
(*Suby of* OCCIDENTAL PETROLEUM CORP) ★
5 Greenway Plz Ste 110, Houston, TX 77046-0521
Tel (713) 215-7000 *Founded/Ownrshp* 2003
Sales 132.8MM[E] *EMP* 120
SIC 1311 Crude petroleum & natural gas
Pr: Bryan D Humphries
Pr: David Favaloro
VP: David B Favaloro

D-U-N-S 01-195-2652 IMP
CENTURY 21 DEPARTMENT STORES LLC
(*Suby of* CENTURY 21 INC) ★
22 Cortland St, New York, NY 10007
Tel (212) 227-9092 *Founded/Ownrshp* 2000
Sales 499.0MM[E] *EMP* 2,105
Accts Berdon Accountants And Advisor
SIC 5311 Department stores, discount
Ch Bd: Raymond Gindi
CEO: Abraham Gindi
CEO: Issac A Gindi
CFO: Ezra Sultan
Ex VP: Ezra Gindi
Ex VP: Isaac S Gindi
VP: Sarah McCollum
Ex Dir: Gilbert Monge
Rgnl Mgr: Maite Tamayo
Dir IT: Ronaldo Breinsking
Dir IT: Bernado Dicarlo

D-U-N-S 02-267-1270
CENTURY 21 INC
21 Cortlandt St, New York, NY 10007-3103
Tel (212) 227-9092 *Founded/Ownrshp* 1984
Sales 499.0MM[E] *EMP* 3,000
Accts Deloitte & Touche Llp New Yor
SIC 6531 Real estate agent, residential
CEO: Raymond Gindi
Ch Bd: Abraham Gindi
CEO: Issac A Gindi
CFO: Ezra Sultan
Ex VP: Ezra Gindi

D-U-N-S 94-226-8202 IMP
▲ CENTURY ALUMINUM CO
1 S Wacker Dr Ste 1000, Chicago, IL 60606-4616
Tel (312) 696-3101 *Founded/Ownrshp* 1981
Sales 1.9MMM *EMP* 2,400
Tkr Sym CENX *Exch* NGS
SIC 3334 Primary aluminum
Pr: Michael A Bless
CFO: Rick T Dillon
Treas: Michelle M Harrison
Treas: Michelle Harrison
Ex VP: Lawrence Frost
Ex VP: Jesse E Gary
Ex VP: Wayne R Hale
VP: Jack E Gates
VP: John E Hoerner
VP: Ronald Thompson
Comm Dir: Michael Dildine
Board of Directors: Errol Glasser, Daniel Goldberg, Terence A Wilkinson

D-U-N-S 10-563-2702 IMP
■ CENTURY ALUMINUM OF KENTUCKY LLC
(*Suby of* CENTURY ALUMINUM CO) ★
1627 State Rte 271 N, Hawesville, KY 42348
Tel (270) 685-2493 *Founded/Ownrshp* 2001
Sales 228.8MM[E] *EMP* 775

SIC 3354 Aluminum extruded products
CEO: Michael A Bless
VP Opers: David Kjos

D-U-N-S 07-966-7089
■ CENTURY ALUMINUM OF SOUTH CAROLINA INC
(Suby of CENTURY ALUMINUM CO) ★
3575 U S Hwy 52, Goose Creek, SC 29445
Tel (843) 572-3700 Founded/Ownrshp 1978
Sales 174.4MM^E EMP 550
SIC 3341 Aluminum smelting & refining (secondary)
Genl Mgr: Dennis Gregory

D-U-N-S 07-911-2021 IMP
■ CENTURY ALUMINUM SEBREE LLC
(Suby of CENTURY ALUMINUM CO) ★
9404 State Route 2096, Robards, KY 42452-9735
Tel (270) 521-7811 Founded/Ownrshp 2013
Sales 147.2MM^E EMP 490
SIC 3334 Primary aluminum
Pr: Jesse Gary
*Ex VP: Jesse E Gary
*Sr VP: Shelly Harrison
*VP: John E Hoerner

D-U-N-S 82-790-0163
CENTURY ASPHALT LTD
5303 Navigation Blvd, Houston, TX 77011-1025
Tel (713) 292-2868 Founded/Ownrshp 2004
Sales 343.5MM^E EMP 200
SIC 5032 Asphalt mixture
Pr: Greg Angel
VP: Derek Angel
VP: Richard Greer

D-U-N-S 09-587-7916
▲ CENTURY BANCORP INC (MA)
400 Mystic Ave, Medford, MA 02155-6316
Tel (781) 393-4160 Founded/Ownrshp 1972
Sales NA EMP 440
Tkr Sym CNBKA Exch NGM
SIC 6022 State commercial banks; State trust companies accepting deposits, commercial
Pr: Barry R Sloane
*Ch Bd: Marshall M Sloane
CFO: William P Hornby
Trst Ofcr: Gerald S Algere
Trst Ofcr: Michele English
Trst Ofcr: Paul A Evangelista
Trst Ofcr: Brian J Feeney
Trst Ofcr: James M Flynn
Trst Ofcr: William J Gambon
Trst Ofcr: Timothy L Glynn
Trst Ofcr: Linda Sloane Kay
Trst Ofcr: Jason J Melius
Trst Ofcr: Deborah R Rush
Trst Ofcr: David B Woonton
Sr VP: Richard L Biig
VP: Bradford J Buckley
VP: Susan B Delahunt
VP: Gregory P Dormitzer
VP: Shipley C Mason
VP: Paul A Sughrue
Board of Directors: Joseph J Senna, George R Baldwin, Jo Ann Simons, Stephen R Delinsky, George F Swansburg, Marshall I Goldman, Jon Westling, Louis J Grossman, Russell B Higley, Linda Sloane Kay, Fraser Lemley, Joseph P Mercurio, Jackie Jenkins-Scott

D-U-N-S 04-707-0750
■ CENTURY BANK AND TRUST CO
OPERATIONS CENTER
(Suby of CENTURY BANCORP INC) ★
400 Mystic Ave, Medford, MA 02155-6316
Tel (781) 393-4677 Founded/Ownrshp 1972
Sales NA EMP 327
SIC 6022 State commercial banks
Ch Bd: Marshall M Sloane
*Pr: Jonathan G Sloane
*CEO: Barry R Sloane
CFO: Judy Sinclair
*Treas: William P Hornby
Ofcr: Marissa Fitzgerald
Ofcr: Brian Kelly
Ofcr: Brandon Letellier
Ofcr: Scott Rembis
Ofcr: Olga Sudakova
Top Exec: David Waryas
Trst Ofcr: Barbara Cunningham
*Ex VP: Paul A Evangelista
*Ex VP: Brian J Feeney
*Ex VP: Linda Sloane Kay
*Ex VP: David B Woonton
*Sr VP: Janice A Brandano
*Sr VP: Gregory P Dormitzer
*Sr VP: James M Flynn
*Sr VP: Philip M Gannon
*Sr VP: James J Gennaro

D-U-N-S 80-864-5340
■ CENTURY BANK AND TRUST CO
(Suby of CENTURY BANCORP INC) ★
102 Fellsway W, Somerville, MA 02145-2007
Tel (617) 629-0929 Founded/Ownrshp 2007
Sales NA EMP 46^E
SIC 6029 Commercial banks
CFO: William Hornby

D-U-N-S 36-116-9139
CENTURY CARE OF AMERICA INC
AUSTIN NURSING CENTER
14800 Saint Marys Ln # 175, Houston, TX 77079-2935
Tel (832) 448-3700 Founded/Ownrshp 1987
Sales 24.5MM^E EMP 1,000
SIC 8051 Skilled nursing care facilities
Pr: Paul Gray
*Sec: Paul Hanlon

D-U-N-S 85-903-8168
▲ CENTURY CASINOS INC
455 E Pikes Peak Ave # 210, Colorado Springs, CO 80903-3673
Tel (719) 527-8300 Founded/Ownrshp 1992
Sales 134.4MM EMP 1,638
Tkr Sym CNTY Exch NAS
SIC 7011 7929 7999 Casino hotel; Entertainment service; Gambling establishment
Ch Bd: Erwin Haitzmann
*V Ch: Peter Hoetzinger
CFO: Margaret Stapleton
VP: Andreas Terler
Board of Directors: Dinah Corbaci, Robert S Eichberg, Gottfried Schellmann

CENTURY CASUALTY COMPANY
See SOUTHERN INSURANCE UNDERWRITERS INC

D-U-N-S 80-719-7199
CENTURY COLLEGE
(Suby of GOVERNORS OFFICE) ★
3300 Century Ave N, Saint Paul, MN 55110-1253
Tel (651) 779-3300 Founded/Ownrshp 1967
Sales 94.1MM^E EMP 750
SIC 8222 9199 Community college;
Pr: Ronald Anderson
Act CFO: Bernardine Bryant
VP: Nucgaek Berbdt
VP: Pat Opatz
Off Admin: Glynae Deschene
Psych: Charlotte Nordstrom

D-U-N-S 00-771-0952
▲ CENTURY COMMUNITIES INC
8390 E Crescent Pkwy # 650, Greenwood Village, CO 80111-2940
Tel (303) 770-8300 Founded/Ownrshp 2002
Sales 734.4MM EMP 510
Tkr Sym CCS Exch NYS
SIC 1521 New construction, single-family houses; Townhouse construction
Ch Bd: Dale Francescon
Pr: Robert J Francescon
CFO: David L Messenger
VP: Todd Amberry
VP: Eric Dome
VP: Tricia Ghosh
VP: Jeremy Paddock
Dir IT: Eric Smidt
Sales Asso: Steve Becht
Sales Asso: Tyler Conroy
Sales Asso: Deanna Forsyth

D-U-N-S 05-099-1504
CENTURY CONCRETE INC
1364 Air Rail Ave, Virginia Beach, VA 23455-3318
Tel (757) 460-5366 Founded/Ownrshp 1970
Sales 84.0MM^E EMP 250
SIC 1622 1611 1771 Bridge, tunnel & elevated highway; Highway & street construction; Concrete work
Pr: Preston M White
*Pr: Michael J Hauser
*CFO: Kenneth M Bowab
*VP: Gary J Manning
*VP: A McGlauhin
*VP: A Patrick McLaughlin
Exec: Lois Arnold
*Prin: James Woodard
VP Opers: Michael Carpenter
Sfty Mgr: Swanson Ferguson

D-U-N-S 08-685-9725
CENTURY CONTRACTORS INC
CENTURY INDUSTRIAL CONTRACTORS
5100 Smith Farm Rd, Matthews, NC 28104-8132
Tel (704) 821-8050 Founded/Ownrshp 1991
Sales 108.3MM^E EMP 300
SIC 1541 Industrial buildings, new construction; Renovation, remodeling & repairs: industrial buildings
CEO: Douglas Armstrong
*Pr: Howard Smith
*CFO: Vicki Klutz
*Ch: J D Armstrong

D-U-N-S 03-879-9953
CENTURY DISTRIBUTORS INC
15710 Crabbs Branch Way, Rockville, MD 20855-2620
Tel (301) 212-9100 Founded/Ownrshp 1976
Sales 254.1MM^E EMP 180^E
SIC 5194 5145 5149 5113 Tobacco & tobacco products; Candy; Fountain supplies; Snack foods; Groceries & related products; Industrial & personal service paper
Pr: Debra Robins
*COO: David Sadugor
*CFO: James Mullen
*VP: Lori Rodman
Mktg Dir: Darren Pulvirenti

D-U-N-S 08-016-5057
CENTURY FIBER OPTICS
79 Lowland St, Holliston, MA 01746-2030
Tel (508) 429-2342 Founded/Ownrshp 1990
Sales 650.0MM EMP 58
SIC 1731 Fiber optic cable installation
Owner: Saith Tiberio

D-U-N-S 78-488-5550 EXP
■ CENTURY FOODS INTERNATIONAL LLC
(Suby of HORMEL FOODS CORP) ★
400 Century Ct, Sparta, WI 54656-2468
Tel (608) 269-1900 Founded/Ownrshp 1991
Sales 89.2MM^E EMP 500
SIC 2023 Dry, condensed, evaporated dairy products
Pr: Thomas Miskowski
CFO: Robert J Starrett
VP: Pam Benzing
VP: Wade Nolte
VP: Gene Quast
Exec: Mary Cattle
Exec: Roland Hoffman
QA Dir: Heather Cleveland
IT Man: Dennis Vosen
VP Opers: Pawel Noland
Opers Mgr: Rudy Rott

CENTURY FURNITURE INDUSTRIES
See CV INDUSTRIES INC

D-U-N-S 00-322-1868 IMP/EXP
CENTURY FURNITURE LLC (NC)
HIGHLAND HOUSE
(Suby of RHF INVESTMENTS INC) ★
401 11th St Nw, Hickory, NC 28601-4750
Tel (828) 267-8739 Founded/Ownrshp 1946, 2016
Sales 95.0MM EMP 850
SIC 2511 2512

D-U-N-S 17-854-5120
CENTURY GOLF PARTNERS MANAGEMENT LP
5430 L B Johnson Fwy 14 Ste 1400, Dallas, TX 75240
Tel (972) 419-1400 Founded/Ownrshp 2004
Sales 44.9MM^E EMP 1,061^E
SIC 7999 Golf services & professionals
CEO: Jim Hinckley
Pt: Greg Adair
Pt: Ken Story
Pt: Peter Ueberroth
Pr: Josh Smith
CFO: Brenda Gray
VP: Tom Ahern
VP: Monty Becton
VP: Gene Miller
VP: Richard Sudduth
VP: Kim Tarpley
Exec: Rafael Yoc

D-U-N-S 15-780-0723
CENTURY HEALTH ALLIANCE JOINT VENTURE
DCH REGIONAL MEDICAL CENTER
809 University Blvd E, Tuscaloosa, AL 35401-2029
Tel (205) 759-7111 Founded/Ownrshp 1995
Sales 450.5MM EMP 1
SIC 8062 8741 General medical & surgical hospitals; Nursing & personal care facility management
Ex VP: Bill Cassels
Exec: Lindy Noland
Dir Rad: John Files
Ansthlgy: Leisa Devenny
Pgrm Dir: Kimberly Logan

D-U-N-S 61-738-7535 IMP/EXP
■ CENTURY HOLDINGS INC
MILLER INDUSTRY
(Suby of MILLER INDUSTRIES INC) ★
8503 Hilltop Dr, Ooltewah, TN 37363-6841
Tel (423) 238-4171 Founded/Ownrshp 1990
Sales 128.7MM^E EMP 425
SIC 3713 Automobile wrecker truck bodies
Pr: Jeffrey I Badgley
*CFO: J Vincent Mish

D-U-N-S 61-619-6705
CENTURY INDEMNITY CO
(Suby of BRANDYWINE HOLDINGS CORP)
1601 Chestnut St, Philadelphia, PA 19192-0003
Tel (215) 761-1000 Founded/Ownrshp 1991
Sales NA EMP 300
SIC 6321 6331 6351 Accident & health insurance; Fire, marine & casualty insurance; Surety insurance
Pr: James D Engel
*Treas: Kenneth R Garrett
*VP: Paul Bergsteinsson
*VP: Michael J Daly
*VP: Joseph Rocco Liuzzi
*VP: Joseph Stagliano

CENTURY INDUSTRIAL CONTRACTORS
See CENTURY CONTRACTORS INC

D-U-N-S 07-910-7792
CENTURY INTERMEDIATE HOLDING CO
1 American Rd, Cleveland, OH 44144-2301
Tel (216) 252-7300 Founded/Ownrshp 2013
Sales 2.2MMM^E EMP 29,300^E
SIC 2771 2679 2656 2678 Greeting cards; Gift wrap, paper: made from purchased material; Cups, paper: made from purchased material; Stationery: made from purchased materials
CEO: Zev Weiss
*Pr: Jeffrey Weiss

D-U-N-S 80-011-5891 IMP/EXP
CENTURY LLC
CENTURY MARTIAL ART SUPPLY
1000 Century Blvd, Oklahoma City, OK 73110-7961
Tel (405) 732-2226 Founded/Ownrshp 1992
Sales 102.6MM^E EMP 300^E
SIC 5091 3949 Sporting & recreation goods; Sporting & athletic goods
Prin: John R Bates

CENTURY MARTIAL ART SUPPLY
See CENTURY LLC

CENTURY MEDICAL
See HEALTH CARE UNLIMITED INC

D-U-N-S 09-166-8509 IMP
CENTURY MOLD CO INC (NY)
25 Vantage Point Dr, Rochester, NY 14624-1142
Tel (585) 352-8600 Founded/Ownrshp 1978
Sales 227.0MM^E EMP 650
SIC 3089 3544 Injection molding of plastics; Industrial molds
CEO: Ron Ricotta
CFO: James Martin
*Ex VP: David F Dick
Ex VP: David Dick
*Ex VP: Terry Hodge
*VP: Meg Collins
Prgrm Mgr: Jorge Gutierrez
Prgrm Mgr: Dave Lyons
CTO: Gary Wicks
IT Man: Greg Pike
Plnt Mgr: John Buckley

CENTURY NATIONAL
See KRAMER-WILSON CO INC

CENTURY PRODUCTS
See GRACO CHILDRENS PRODUCTS INC

CENTURY SALES AND SERVICE
See TIMBERLAKE & DICKSON INC

D-U-N-S 05-037-0733
■ CENTURY THEATRES INC (CA)
(Suby of CINEMARK USA INC) ★
3900 Dallas Pkwy Ste 500, Plano, TX 75093-7871
Tel (972) 665-1000 Founded/Ownrshp 1942, 2006
Sales 205.0MM^E EMP 8,500
SIC 7833 Drive-in motion picture theaters
Pr: David Shesgreen
*Genl Pt: Syufy Century Corporation
*CEO: Alan W Stock
*COO: Victor Castillo
*CFO: Michael Dittman
*Ch: Raymond W Syufy
*Sr VP: Pat Hager
Genl Couns: Andrew McCullough

CENTURY TRADING
See ORLEANS INTERNATIONAL INC

CENTURY WHEEL & RIM
See QUALITY TRAILER PRODUCTS LP

D-U-N-S 07-529-3498
■ CENTURY-NATIONAL INSURANCE CO
(Suby of NATIONAL GENERAL HOLDINGS CORP) ★
16650 Sherman Way, Van Nuys, CA 91406-3782
Tel (818) 760-0880 Founded/Ownrshp 2016
Sales NA EMP 320
SIC 6311 Life insurance carriers
CEO: Weldon Wilson
CFO: Judy Osborn
Treas: Judith Osborn
CIO: Lou Balicki
Dir IT: Chris Stolp

CENTURYLINK
See CENTURYTEL OF IDAHO INC

CENTURYLINK
See EMBARQ FLORIDA INC

CENTURYLINK
See CENTRAL TELEPHONE CO

CENTURYLINK
See CAROLINA TELEPHONE AND TELEGRAPH CO LLC

CENTURYLINK
See CENTURYTEL OF MISSOURI LLC

CENTURYLINK
See EMBARQ MANAGEMENT CO

CENTURYLINK
See EMBARQ CORP

D-U-N-S 05-091-1668
▲ CENTURYLINK INC
100 Centurylink Dr, Monroe, LA 71203-2041
Tel (318) 388-9000 Founded/Ownrshp 1968
Sales 17.9MMM EMP 43,000
Tkr Sym CTL Exch NYS
SIC 4813 4812 Telephone communication, except radio; Local & long distance telephone communications; Local telephone communications; Long distance telephone communications; Cellular telephone services
Pr: Glen F Post III
*Ch Bd: William A Owens
Pr: Dean J Douglas
Pr: Girish K Varma
CFO: R Stewart Ewing Jr
Treas: Carol Ott
Treas: Bob Reedy
Bd of Dir: Timothy Midgett
Bd of Dir: Andy Olson
Ex VP: David D Cole
Ex VP: Daniel Davis
Ex VP: Stacey W Goff
Ex VP: Aamir Hussain
Ex VP: Maxine L Moreau
Ex VP: Scott A Trezise
Sr VP: William E Bradley
VP: Alan Alford
VP: Wyman Brent
VP: Lisa Bruch
VP: Allen Cindy
VP: Avinash Gupta
Board of Directors: Martha H Bejar, Virginia Boulet, Peter C Brown, W Bruce Hanks, Mary L Landrieu, Gregory J McCray, Michael J Roberts, Laurie A Siegel

CENTURYLINK QGS
See QWEST GOVERNMENT SERVICES INC

CENTURYLINK TECH SOLUTIONS
See SAVVIS INC

CENTURYLINK TECH SOLUTIONS
See CENTURYTEL SERVICE GROUP LLC

CENTURYLINK TS
See SAVVIS COMMUNICATIONS CORP

CENTURYLINK TS
See SAVVIS FEDERAL SYSTEMS INC

D-U-N-S 11-338-6689
■ CENTURYTEL HOLDINGS INC
(Suby of CENTURYLINK INC) ★
100 Centurylink Dr, Monroe, LA 71203-2041
Tel (318) 388-9000 Founded/Ownrshp 1998
Sales 360.8MM^E EMP 813^E
SIC 4813 Telephone communication, except radio
Pr: Glen F Post III
CFO: Stewart R Ewing

D-U-N-S 83-101-5859
■ CENTURYTEL HOLDINGS MISSOURI INC
(Suby of CENTURYTEL HOLDINGS INC) ★
100 Centurylink Dr, Monroe, LA 71203-2041
Tel (318) 388-9000 Founded/Ownrshp 2002
Sales 150.1MM^E EMP 790^E
SIC 4812 Cellular telephone services
Pr: Glen F Post III

D-U-N-S 19-666-9894
CENTURYTEL INC
519 Main St, La Jara, CO 81140
Tel (719) 274-4437 Founded/Ownrshp 2006
Sales 242.5M^E EMP 8,000^E
SIC 4813
CEO: Glenn Post

D-U-N-S 00-188-8036
■ CENTURYTEL OF IDAHO INC
CENTURYLINK
(*Suby of* CENTURYLINK INC) ★
290 N Main St, Kalispell, MT 59901-3946
Tel (703) 363-8774 *Founded/Ownrshp* 1913, 1981
Sales 256.7MM *EMP* 4
SIC 4813 Local & long distance telephone communications; Local telephone communications; Long distance telephone communications
VP: Glen Post

D-U-N-S 11-557-7160
■ CENTURYTEL OF MISSOURI LLC
CENTURYLINK
(*Suby of* CENTURYTEL HOLDINGS MISSOURI INC) ★
1151 Century Tel Dr, Wentzville, MO 63385-1955
Tel (636) 332-3011 *Founded/Ownrshp* 2001
Sales 150.1MM[E] *EMP* 787[E]
SIC 4813 Telephone communication, except radio
VP: Terry Beeler
VP: Phil Adams
Opers Mgr: Mike Polman

D-U-N-S 83-100-1628
■ CENTURYTEL OF NORTHWEST INC
(*Suby of* CENTURYTEL HOLDINGS INC) ★
100 Centurylink Dr, Monroe, LA 71203-2041
Tel (318) 388-9000 *Founded/Ownrshp* 1955
Sales 173.7MM[E] *EMP* 800[E]
SIC 4813 4812 Local & long distance telephone communications; Local telephone communications; Long distance telephone communications; Cellular telephone services
Pr: Glen F Post III
Ex VP: Scott Trezise
VP: Pat Glavin
VP: Stacey Goff
Dir IT: Michael Ditlefsen
Dir IT: Andy Hicks
Dir IT: Wayne Wier
IT Man: Shun-Li Huang
IT Man: Cindy Shivers
Netwrk Mgr: John Luoma
Netwrk Eng: Keith Barrett

D-U-N-S 06-973-7914
■ CENTURYTEL SERVICE GROUP LLC
CENTURYLINK TECH SOLUTIONS
(*Suby of* CENTURYLINK INC) ★
100 Centurylink Dr, Monroe, LA 71203-2041
Tel (318) 388-9500 *Founded/Ownrshp* 1964
Sales 86.1MM[E] *EMP* 589
SIC 8721 Billing & bookkeeping service; Payroll accounting service
Pr: Glen F Post III
**Ex VP:* Stacey W Goff
Tech Mgr: Bill Bradley

D-U-N-S 06-686-2269
■ CENTURYTEL.COM LLC
(*Suby of* CENTURYLINK INC) ★
100 Centurylink Dr, Monroe, LA 71203-2041
Tel (318) 388-9500 *Founded/Ownrshp* 1989
Sales 2.9MMM[E] *EMP* 20,300
SIC 4813 Local telephone communications
Bd of Dir: Karen Puckett
Sr VP: Maxine Moreau
VP: Emmett McDaniel
VP: Tom Singletary
Exec: Ryan Martin
Prgrm Mgr: Chris Brenneman
DP Dir: Kevin McBride
Software D: Jheramy Smith
Sls Dir: Karrie Connors
Manager: Joe Herron

D-U-N-S 00-705-9488
■ CENVEO CORP
(*Suby of* CENVEO INC) ★
200 First Stamford Pl # 200, Stamford, CT 06902-6753
Tel (303) 790-8023 *Founded/Ownrshp* 1993
Sales 1.5MMM[E] *EMP* 6,380
SIC 2677 2752 2759 Envelopes; Commercial printing, lithographic; Labels & seals: printing
Pr: James R Malone
**CFO:* Michel Salbaing
Bd of Dir: Paul Kocourek
**VP:* William W Huffman
**VP:* Keith Pratt
**VP:* Mark L Zoeller

D-U-N-S 87-864-2560
▲ CENVEO INC
200 First Stamford Pl # 200, Stamford, CT 06902-6753
Tel (203) 595-3000 *Founded/Ownrshp* 1994
Sales 1.7MMM *EMP* 7,300
Tkr Sym CVO *Exch* NYS
SIC 2677 2679 Envelopes; Tags & labels, paper
Ch Bd: Robert G Burton Jr
Pr: Dean E Cherry
Pr: Michael W Harris
Pr: Sean S Sullivan
COO: Michael G Burton
CFO: Scott J Goodwin
CFO: Karen Snyder
Ex VP: Andrew Johnson
Sr VP: Ray Hartman
Sr VP: Robert Muma
Sr VP: Tony Paul
Sr VP: Ian Scheinmann
Sr VP: Alex Vasquez
VP: Bill Beem
VP: Jane Bullis
VP: Mike Burton
VP: Kathy Caminiti
VP: Colin Christ
VP: Craig Condry
VP: Henry Decramer
VP: Rick A Delaney
Board of Directors: Gerald S Armstrong, Mark J Griffin, Susan Herbst

CENVEO PUBLISHER SERVICES
See CADMUS JOURNAL SERVICES INC

CEO
See CONSOLIDATED EXECUTIVE OFFICE

CEP AMERICA
See CALIFORNIA EMERGENCY PHYSICIANS FOUNDATION

D-U-N-S 18-323-6314 IMP
CEPHALON INC
(*Suby of* TEVA PHARMACEUTICAL INDUSTRIES LIMITED)
41 Moores Rd, Malvern, PA 19355-1113
Tel (610) 344-0200 *Founded/Ownrshp* 2011
Sales 444.9MM[E] *EMP* 3,726
SIC 2834 Pharmaceutical preparations; Drugs acting on the central nervous system & sense organs
CEO: J Kevin Buchi
Pr: William Marth
COO: Pam Cassidy
COO: Susan Ditrolio
COO: Charles Loshnowsky
COO: John Russell
COO: Feng Xie
CFO: Wilco Groenhuysen
Treas: John Aberant
Treas: Jason Yip
Ex VP: Peter E Grebow
Ex VP: Gerald J Pappert
Ex VP: Carl A Savini
Ex VP: Jeffry L Vaught
VP: Anne Brooks
VP: Peter Brown
VP: Deborah Griffin
VP: Craig Heacock
VP: Joe Turi
Exec: Dennis Winger
Assoc Dir: Brian Brown

D-U-N-S 95-671-1444
■ CEPHEID
(*Suby of* DANAHER CORP) ★
904 E Caribbean Dr, Sunnyvale, CA 94089-1189
Tel (408) 541-4191 *Founded/Ownrshp* 2016
Sales 538.5MM *EMP* 1,700[E]
SIC 3826 3841 Analytical instruments; Surgical & medical instruments
Pr: Warren Kocmond
CFO: Daniel E Madden
Ex VP: Nicolaas Arnold
Ex VP: Peter Farrell
Ex VP: Michael Fitzgerald
Ex VP: Kerry J Flom
Ex VP: Marc Haugen
Ex VP: David H Persing
Ex VP: James Post
VP: Michael Bates
VP: Thomas Herbst
VP: Birger Jansson
VP: Glynn Perry
VP: Leonard Phillips
VP: Vincent Powers

D-U-N-S 07-835-7012
CEQUEL COMMUNICATIONS HOLDINGS LLC
SUDDENLINK COMMUNICATIONS
(*Suby of* ALTICE N.V.)
520 Maryville Centre Dr, Saint Louis, MO 63141-5820
Tel (314) 965-0500 *Founded/Ownrshp* 2015
Sales 2.4MM *EMP* 6,400[E]
SIC 4841 Cable & other pay television services
CEO: Dexter Goei
**Pr:* Hakim Boubazine
**Pr:* Charles F Stewart
Ofcr: Jerry A Dow
**Sr VP:* Terry Cordova
**Sr VP:* Jerry Dow
VP: Gordon Bourne
VP: Jeff Bryant
VP: Justin Freesmeier
VP: John Fuhler
VP: John Fulher
VP: Marsha Gee
VP: Randy Goad
VP: Gregg Grigaitis
VP: Reggie Jaramillo
VP: Fuhler John
VP: Gibbs Jones
VP: Rodney Lanham
VP: Rich Lockard
VP: Christopher C McLennan
VP: John Menendez

D-U-N-S 15-128-6601
CEQUEL COMMUNICATIONS LLC
SUDDENLINK COMMUNICATIONS
(*Suby of* SUDDENLINK COMMUNICATIONS) ★
520 Maryville Centre Dr # 300, Saint Louis, MO 63141-5820
Tel (314) 965-2020 *Founded/Ownrshp* 2005
Sales 194.9MM[E] *EMP* 6,400
SIC 4813 4841 Telephone communication, except radio; Cable & other pay television services
CEO: Jerry Kent
COO: Thomas P McMillin
CFO: Mary Meduski
Ofcr: James B Fox
Ex VP: Wendy Knudsen
Sr VP: John Fuhler
Sr VP: Tyler Nau
Sr VP: Douglas Wiley
VP: Chris Arft
VP: Christopher Arft
VP: Justin Freesmeier
VP: Jason Gebhart
VP: Pamela Hermann
VP: Karen Sharkey
VP: Mike Shelton
VP: Michael Zarrilli
Comm Dir: Gene Regan

D-U-N-S 07-925-1558
CEQUEL CORP
520 Maryville Centre Dr # 300, Saint Louis, MO 63141-5820
Tel (314) 315-9400 *Founded/Ownrshp* 2012
Sales 823.6MM[E] *EMP* 6,400
SIC 4841 4813 Cable & other pay television services; Telephone communication, except radio
CEO: Jerry Kent
**COO:* Thomas P McMillin
**CFO:* Mary Meduski
**Ofcr:* James B Fox

D-U-N-S 07-829-3640
CEQUEL DATA CENTERS LP
520 Maryville Centre Dr # 300, Saint Louis, MO 63141-5820
Tel (314) 965-2020 *Founded/Ownrshp* 2010
Sales 165.9MM[E] *EMP* 865
SIC 7374 Data processing service
Ch: Jerry Kent
**COO:* Tom McMillin
**CFO:* Mary Meduski

D-U-N-S 00-423-0793 IMP/EXP
■ CEQUENT CONSUMER PRODUCTS INC
(*Suby of* HORIZON GLOBAL CORP) ★
29000 Aurora Rd Ste 2, Solon, OH 44139-7202
Tel (440) 498-0001 *Founded/Ownrshp* 1997
Sales 170.0MM *EMP* 85[E]
SIC 5531 3714 Automotive accessories; Motor vehicle parts & accessories
Pr: John Aleva
**VP:* Francis Bernart
**VP:* Abe Newman
Genl Mgr: Dale Derby
Genl Mgr: Vicki Swearingen
Dir IT: Dave Young
Mktg Dir: Eric Yukich

CEQUENT PERFORMANCE GROUP
See CEQUENT PERFORMANCE PRODUCTS INC

D-U-N-S 62-393-4502 IMP
■ CEQUENT PERFORMANCE PRODUCTS INC
CEQUENT PERFORMANCE GROUP
(*Suby of* HORIZON GLOBAL CORP) ★
47912 Halyard Dr Ste 100, Plymouth, MI 48170-2454
Tel (734) 656-3000 *Founded/Ownrshp* 1990
Sales 210.2MM[E] *EMP* 1,400
SIC 3799 3714 Trailer hitches; Trailer hitches, motor vehicle
Pr: Tom Benson
**VP:* Tom Aepelbacher
**VP:* Marcie Albright
**VP:* Paul Caruso
**VP:* Mike Finos
**VP:* Mark Gage
**VP:* John Walsh
**VP:* Todd Walstrom
**VP:* David Watza
IT Man: Jim Mezza
Sls Dir: Mike Orles

D-U-N-S 08-015-3535
■ CEQUENT UK LTD
(*Suby of* HORIZON GLOBAL CORP) ★
123 Town Square Pl, Jersey City, NJ 07310-1756
Tel (734) 656-3078 *Founded/Ownrshp* 2016
Sales 176.0MM[E] *EMP* 1,172[E]
SIC 4789 3714 5531 Cargo loading & unloading services; Trailer hitches, motor vehicle; Automobile & truck equipment & parts

D-U-N-S 05-079-1177 IMP/EXP
■ CERADYNE INC
(*Suby of* 3M CO) ★
1922 Barranca Pkwy, Irvine, CA 92606-4826
Tel (714) 549-0421 *Founded/Ownrshp* 2012
Sales 505.8MM[E] *EMP* 2,112[E]
SIC 3299 3671 Ceramic fiber; Cathode ray tubes, including rebuilt
CEO: Joel P Moskowitz
Pr: Mike Lipscombe
CFO: Jerry Pelezon
**CFO:* Jerrold J Pellizzon
Sr Cor Off: Jerry Palazon
**VP:* Thomas A Cole
VP: Earl Donald
**VP:* Peter Hartl
VP: Matthew Karmel
**VP:* Marc King
VP: Michael A Kraft
VP: Robert M Miller
**VP:* David P Reed
VP: Allen Thomas
**VP:* Jeff Waldal

CERALOX DIVISION
See SASOL CHEMICALS (USA) LLC

D-U-N-S 80-824-5489
■ CERBERUS ABP INVESTOR LLC
(*Suby of* CERBERUS CAPITAL MANAGEMENT LP) ★
299 Park Ave, New York, NY 10171-0002
Tel (212) 891-2100 *Founded/Ownrshp* 2004
Sales 1.9MMM[E] *EMP* 3,370
SIC 5031 5211 Lumber, plywood & millwork; Lumber & other building materials
COO: Mark Newport

D-U-N-S 01-478-4388 IMP/EXP
▲ CERBERUS CAPITAL MANAGEMENT LP
875 3rd Ave, New York, NY 10022-6225
Tel (212) 891-2100 *Founded/Ownrshp* 1992
Sales 40.0MMM[E] *EMP* 143,502
SIC 6722 6726 5031 5211

D-U-N-S 05-574-1459
■ CERBERUS LP LLC
(*Suby of* CERBERUS CAPITAL MANAGEMENT LP) ★
875 3rd Ave Fl 11, New York, NY 10022-7223
Tel (212) 891-2100 *Founded/Ownrshp* 2012
Sales 172.5MM[E] *EMP* 7,250[E]
SIC 7389 7374 Telephone directory distribution, contract or fee basis; Computer graphics service

D-U-N-S 80-997-4504
■ CERBERUS PARTNERS LP
(*Suby of* CERBERUS CAPITAL MANAGEMENT LP) ★
450 Park Ave Fl 28, New York, NY 10022-2740
Tel (212) 421-2600 *Founded/Ownrshp* 1992
Sales 487.7MM[E] *EMP* 8,557
SIC 6726 Investment offices
Mng Pt: Steven Feinberg
Pt: Mark Neporent
Pt: William Richter

CEREBRAL PALSY ASSOC NY STATE
See UNITED CEREBRAL PALSY ASSOCIATIONS OF NEW YORK STATE INC

D-U-N-S 11-423-0683
CEREBRAL PALSY OF MASSACHUSETTS INC
OPTIONS FOR INDEPENDENT
600 Technology Center Dr, Stoughton, MA 02072-4708
Tel (800) 924-7570 *Founded/Ownrshp* 1952
Sales 258.8MM[E] *EMP* 65
Accts Oconnor & Drew Pc Braintree
SIC 8093 Rehabilitation center, outpatient treatment
Ex Dir: Tom Zukauskas
VP: Joseph Curran
VP: Joseph K Curran Jr
VP: Janice Walsh

D-U-N-S 00-586-8641
CERES SOLUTIONS
2600 S 13th St, Terre Haute, IN 47802-3206
Tel (812) 235-8123 *Founded/Ownrshp* 1927, 1987
Sales 232.6MM[E] *EMP* 125
SIC 5153 5172 5191 Grains; Fuel oil; Farm supplies; Animal feeds; Seeds & bulbs
Pr: Del Shan Unger

D-U-N-S 00-693-6678
CERES SOLUTIONS LLP (IN)
2112 Indianapolis Rd, Crawfordsville, IN 47933-3137
Tel (765) 362-6108 *Founded/Ownrshp* 1927
Sales 299.7MM *EMP* 125
Accts Blue & Co Llc Seymour In
SIC 5191 Feed; Seeds: field, garden & flower; Fertilizer & fertilizer materials; Chemicals, agricultural
CEO: Jeff Troike
Pt: Allan Clauser Jr
Pt: Alan H McDonald
Pt: Jeffery Moore
Pt: Howard Rippey Jr
Pt: Daryl Warren
Dir Risk M: Phillip Pirtle
Brnch Mgr: Stan Mason
Brnch Mgr: Dennis Ritter
Dir IT: Erica Manns
Sls Mgr: John Parish

D-U-N-S 09-798-8307
CERES UNIFIED SCHOOL DISTRICT
2503 Lawrence St, Ceres, CA 95307-3301
Tel (209) 556-1500 *Founded/Ownrshp* 1965
Sales 79.5MM[E] *EMP* 1,054
SIC 8211 Public elementary & secondary schools
Pr: Walt L Hanline
Dir IT: Chris Higle
Dir IT: Paula Loehr
Schl Brd P: Valli Wight
Teacher Pr: David Viss
Psych: Tomas Ayala
Psych: Amy Jat
HC Dir: Kristy Britton
Snr Mgr: Elizabeth Flores

D-U-N-S 84-865-1030
CERIDIAN BENEFITS SERVICES
(*Suby of* CERIDIAN LLC) ★
3201 34th St S, Saint Petersburg, FL 33711-3828
Tel (800) 689-7893 *Founded/Ownrshp* 1996
Sales 95.5MM[E] *EMP* 1,216
SIC 8742 Compensation & benefits planning consultant
Pr: James Corcoran
**Pr:* Steve Stevenson
**CEO:* Stuart C Harvey Jr
**CEO:* David Ossip
**VP:* Webster Hill
**VP:* Alan Jones
VP: Suzanne Macdougald
**VP:* Lois M Martin
Dir Bus: Joseph Cotton
Sftwr Eng: Scott Sloan
Sftwr Eng: Tim Tobias
Board of Directors: Thomas F Costello, Mark M Goldman, Peter A Sullivan

D-U-N-S 07-916-8841
CERIDIAN HCM HOLDING INC
(*Suby of* CERIDIAN LLC) ★
3311 E Old Shakopee Rd, Minneapolis, MN 55425-1640
Tel (952) 853-8100 *Founded/Ownrshp* 2013
Sales 99.3MM[E] *EMP* 259[E]
SIC 6719 7374 Investment holding companies, except banks; Data processing & preparation; Computer processing services
CEO: David Ossip
**Pr:* Paul Elliot
**Pr:* David Mackay
**Ch:* Stuart C Harvey Jr
**Ex VP:* Lois Martin

D-U-N-S 00-625-5996
CERIDIAN LLC
(*Suby of* FOUNDATION HOLDINGS INC) ★
3311 E Old Shakopee Rd, Minneapolis, MN 55425-1640
Tel (952) 853-8100 *Founded/Ownrshp* 2007
Sales 498.8MM[E] *EMP* 350[E]
SIC 8721 Payroll accounting service
Ch Bd: Stuart Harvey
Pr: Dave Mackay
Pr: Steve Stevenson
COO: Paul Elliott
COO: Mark Merrick
COO: Michael F Shea
CFO: Mike Blackmore
CFO: Gregory J Macfarlane
CFO: Lois M Martin
Chf Mktg O: Alan Rottenberg
Ofcr: John Cardella
Ofcr: Nick Laird
Ofcr: Jennifer Stacey
Ex VP: Cande Dandel
Ex VP: Suzy Hester
Ex VP: Scott Kitching
Ex VP: Ralph Rolen
Ex VP: Michael W Sheridan
Ex VP: Kairus Tarapore

Ex VP: Bart K Valdez
Ex VP: Ceridian Ziglar

D-U-N-S 04-241-0688

▲ CERNER CORP
2800 Rock Creek Pkwy, Kansas City, MO 64117-2521
Tel (816) 201-1024 *Founded/Ownrshp* 1980
Sales 4.4MMM *EMP* 22,200ᴱ
Tkr Sym CERN *Exch* NGS
SIC 7373 Computer integrated systems design
Ch Bd: Neal L Patterson
Pr: Zane M Burke
COO: Michael R Nill
CFO: Marc G Naughton
**V Ch Bd:* Clifford W Illig
Ofcr: Julia M Wilson
Ex VP: Jeffrey A Townsend
Sr VP: Douglas S McNair
VP: Tim Kostner
VP: Donald D Trigg
VP: Debbie Yantis
Exec: Andrea Mirzaian
Board of Directors: Gerald E Bisbee Jr, Denis A Cortese, John C Danforth, Mitchell E Daniels Jr, Linda M Dillman, William B Neaves, William D Zollars

D-U-N-S 80-188-8769

■ CERNER DHT INC
(*Suby of* CERNER CORP) ★
2800 Rock Creek Pkwy, Kansas City, MO 64117-2521
Tel (816) 221-1024 *Founded/Ownrshp* 2001
Sales 58.4MMᴱ *EMP* 7,300ᴱ
SIC 8742 7372 7371 Hospital & health services consultant; Application computer software; Business oriented computer software; Custom computer programming services
Ch Bd: Neal L Patterson
Pr: Earl H Devanny III

D-U-N-S 07-952-9912

CERNX MN LLC
2355 Highway 36 W Ste 400, Roseville, MN 55113-3905
Tel (320) 372-7400 *Founded/Ownrshp* 2014
Sales 16.0MM *EMP* 1,500
SIC 4212 7389 4731 4222 Local trucking, without storage; Courier or messenger service; Freight forwarding; Warehousing, cold storage or refrigerated

CERRITOS COLLEGE
See CERRITOS COMMUNITY COLLEGE DISTRICT

D-U-N-S 07-189-6773

CERRITOS COMMUNITY COLLEGE DISTRICT
CERRITOS COLLEGE
(*Suby of* CALIFORNIA COMMUNITY COLLEGES SYSTEM) ★
11110 Alondra Blvd, Norwalk, CA 90650-6203
Tel (562) 860-2451 *Founded/Ownrshp* 1955
Sales 157.6MMᴱ *EMP* 2,005ᴱ
Accts Vavrinek Trine Day & Co Ll
SIC 8221 8222 Colleges universities & professional schools; Community college
**Pr:* Dr Linda L Lacy
VP: James Albanese
VP: William C Farmer
VP: Don Garriott
VP: Angela Hoppe-Nagao
VP: Joanna Schilling
Exec: Nicholas J Kremer
Ex Dir: Kim Holland
Psych: Gloria Bridges
Psych: Evelyn I Ryozaki
Psych: Phillip Salazar

CERRO COSO COMM COLLEGE
See KERN COMMUNITY COLLEGE DISTRICT

D-U-N-S 09-429-5045 IMP

■ CERRO FLOW PRODUCTS LLC
(*Suby of* MARMON HOLDINGS INC) ★
3000 Mississippi Ave, Sauget, IL 62206-1057
Tel (618) 337-6000 *Founded/Ownrshp* 1977, 1908
Sales 201.0MMᴱ *EMP* 1,000
SIC 3351 3331 3498 3585 5051 Tubing, copper & copper alloy; Primary copper; Fabricated pipe & fittings; Refrigeration & heating equipment; Metals service centers & offices; Copper sheets, plates, bars, rods, pipes, etc.; Tubing, metal
Pr: Gary Ewing
Pr: Michael Duggan
**Treas:* Robert C Gluth
VP: Bart Ardnt
**VP:* Eric Pilas
VP: Michael Slade
VP: Steve Swartzenberg
Rgnl Mgr: Nick Bogen
Rgnl Mgr: Jeff Reimer
Genl Mgr: John Gerfen
Genl Mgr: John Sundstrom

D-U-N-S 14-671-0702 IMP

■ CERRO WIRE LLC
CERROWIRE
(*Suby of* MARMON HOLDINGS INC) ★
1099 Thompson Rd Se, Hartselle, AL 35640-8471
Tel (256) 773-2522 *Founded/Ownrshp* 2005
Sales 437.1MMᴱ *EMP* 460
SIC 3351 Wire, copper & copper alloy
Genl Mgr: Shawn Dennison
Treas: Robert Gluth
VP: Mike Ashworth
**VP:* Richard C Bast
**VP:* Rick McDonald
Exec: Pam Colwell
Dir IT: Kimberly Harmeyer
IT Man: Herbert S Statham
VP Mfg: Myron Bernard
Plnt Mgr: Dave Hadley
Manager: Barry Schonebaum

CERROWIRE
See CERRO WIRE LLC

D-U-N-S 00-235-8265 IMP/EXP

CERTAINTEED CORP (DE)
SAINT-GOBAIN
(*Suby of* SAINT-GOBAIN DELAWARE CORP) ★
20 Moores Rd, Malvern, PA 19355-1114
Tel (610) 893-5000 *Founded/Ownrshp* 1904, 1976
Sales 2.6MMMᴱ *EMP* 6,000
SIC 3221 3292 3259 3084 3089 3432 Glass containers; Roofing, asbestos felt roll; Roofing tile, clay; Plastics pipe; Plastic hardware & building products; Plastic plumbing fixture fittings, assembly
Pr: John Crowe
**CFO:* Robert J Panaro
**Ch:* Frank Cahouet
**Treas:* John J Sweeney III
VP: Joseph Juran
VP: Kurt Pontz
VP: Michael Vanaken
Exec: Harry Bach
Exec: Scott Johnson
Div/Sub He: Luke Clarry
Comm Dir: Walt Hoyt

D-U-N-S 80-505-7994 IMP/EXP

CERTAINTEED GYPSUM INC
750 E Swedesford Rd, Wayne, PA 19087-1633
Tel (813) 286-3900 *Founded/Ownrshp* 2002
Sales 474.1MMᴱ *EMP* 1,500
SIC 3275 Gypsum products
Pr: David Engelhardt
**CFO:* Keith C Campbell
**Treas:* John Sweeney III
**VP:* Kim Biltfell
**VP:* Stephen Hawkins
**VP:* Peter Meyer
**VP:* Robert J Morrow
**VP:* Dennis Stuckey
**VP:* Darell Williams
**VP Mktg:* Neil Shaw
Board of Directors: Grant Snowden

D-U-N-S 02-648-0678

■ CERTANCE LLC
QUANTUM CORPORATION
(*Suby of* QUANTUM CORP) ★
141 Innovation Dr, Irvine, CA 92617-3211
Tel (949) 856-7800 *Founded/Ownrshp* 2005
Sales 67.2MMᴱ *EMP* 1,000
SIC 3572 Computer tape drives & components
Pr: Howard L Matthews
**Ch:* Donald L Waite
Mng Dir: Martin Vine
CIO: Tina Haines
IT Man: Helen Duckett
IT Man: Euclene Walter
Web Dev: Quang Nguyen
Sftwr Eng: CHI Lin
Pr Dir: Debra Redmond
Sales Asso: Winston Chin

CERTCO FOOD DISTRIBUTION CTR
See CERTCO INC

D-U-N-S 00-281-2899 IMP

CERTCO INC
CERTCO FOOD DISTRIBUTION CTR
5321 Verona Rd, Fitchburg, WI 53711-6050
Tel (608) 271-4500 *Founded/Ownrshp* 1975
Sales 672.6MM *EMP* 325
Accts Sattell Johnson Appel & Co
SIC 5141 Groceries, general line
Pr: Randy Simon
CFO: Pete Baus
**CFO:* Amy Niemetscheck
**VP:* Dave Ryman
Genl Mgr: Lisa Porter
**Dir IT:* Joe Dempich
Dir IT: Todd Phipps
IT Man: Robert Collins
Software D: Travis Archer
Opers Mgr: Steve Kurz
Opers Mgr: Alan Newell

D-U-N-S 02-481-1928 IMP

CERTECH INC
MORGAN TECHNICAL CERAMICS
(*Suby of* MORGANITE INDUSTRIES INC) ★
1 Park Pl W, Wood Ridge, NJ 07075-2498
Tel (201) 842-6800 *Founded/Ownrshp* 1998
Sales 110.1MMᴱ *EMP* 500ᴱ
SIC 3364 Nonferrous die-castings except aluminum
CEO: John Stang
**Pr:* James McRickard
VP: Rob Felsch
**VP:* Ross Johnson
Exec: Ron Delaney
Genl Mgr: Christopher Donovan
Sales Exec: Evan Reed

D-U-N-S 15-248-2464 IMP/EXP

CERTEX USA INC
1721 W Culver St, Phoenix, AZ 85007-1807
Tel (602) 271-9048 *Founded/Ownrshp* 2004
Sales 150.4MMᴱ *EMP* 270
SIC 5084 Hoists
Prin: Glenn M Evans
**Owner:* Glenn Evans
**CFO:* Dee Schweigert

CERTIFIED CRANES-HOIST
See ACE INDUSTRIES INC

D-U-N-S 01-063-6017

CERTIFIED LUMBER CORP
Isack Rosenberg 470 Kent, Brooklyn, NY 11211
Tel (718) 387-1233 *Founded/Ownrshp* 1974
Sales 88.2MMᴱ *EMP* 100
SIC 5031 5211 Lumber, plywood & millwork; Lumber products
Pr: Isack Rosenberg
**VP:* Abraham Rosenberg

D-U-N-S 16-829-4056

CERTIFIED PERSONNEL SERVICE AGENCY INC
CPS - CONSTRUCTION PRODUCT SUP
10201 N Mcalister Rd, La Grande, OR 97850-8703
Tel (541) 963-6678 *Founded/Ownrshp* 1992
Sales 17.7MMᴱ *EMP* 1,316
SIC 7361 Employment agencies
Pr: Beverly Lousignont
**Sec:* John Lousignont
**VP:* Karisa Lousignont

D-U-N-S 05-833-8286 IMP/EXP

CERTIFIED POWER INC
COMPONENT TECHNOLOGY
970 Campus Dr, Mundelein, IL 60060-3803
Tel (847) 573-3800 *Founded/Ownrshp* 1986
Sales 133.0MMᴱ *EMP* 536ᴱ
SIC 3714 7539 5013

CERTIS CU
See CERTIS USA LLC

D-U-N-S 94-534-9959 IMP

CERTIS USA LLC
CERTIS CU
(*Suby of* MITSUI & CO., LTD.)
9145 Guilford Rd Ste 175, Columbia, MD 21046-1952
Tel (301) 604-7340 *Founded/Ownrshp* 2001
Sales 147.7MMᴱ *EMP* 125
SIC 5191 2879 Pesticides; Pesticides, agricultural or household
Pr: Dennis Banasiak
Treas: Takuji Fukaya
Ex VP: Tim Damico
Ex VP: Shinji Takeuchi
Prin: William Piontek
Rgnl Mgr: Judy Collier
Rgnl Mgr: Joe Craig
Rgnl Mgr: Tommy Escalante
Rgnl Mgr: Richard Kelly
Rgnl Mgr: Joe Lebow
Rgnl Mgr: Remi Wright

D-U-N-S 96-679-4617

■ CERTUSBANK NATIONAL ASSOCIATION
(*Suby of* BLUE RIDGE HOLDINGS INC) ★
935 S Main St, Greenville, SC 29601-3314
Tel (864) 306-2540 *Founded/Ownrshp* 2010
Sales NA *EMP* 768ᴱ
SIC 6021 National commercial banks
CEO: Len Davenport
**CEO:* Charles M Williams
**Co-CEO:* Walter L Davis
Ex VP: Angela K Webb
Sr VP: Joe Albright
Sr VP: Kimberly Kirk
VP: Brent Williams
Exec: Leann Guarnaecia
VP Opers: Crystal Alexander

D-U-N-S 82-953-7427

■ CERTUSHOLDINGS INC
BLUE RIDGE HOLDINGS, INC.
(*Suby of* BANKUNITED INC) ★
1170 Peachtree St Nw 2400, Atlanta, GA 30309
Tel (704) 973-3917 *Founded/Ownrshp* 2015
Sales NA *EMP* 772ᴱ
SIC 6022 State commercial banks
CEO: Milton H Jones Jr
Pr: K Angela Webb

D-U-N-S 82-764-1114

■ CERULEAN COMPANIES INC
(*Suby of* ANTHEM HOLDING CORP) ★
120 Monument Cir Ste 200, Indianapolis, IN 46204-4902
Tel (317) 488-6000 *Founded/Ownrshp* 2008
Sales NA *EMP* 8
SIC 6321 Health insurance carriers
CEO: Morgan Kendrick Charles

D-U-N-S 08-026-4624

■ CES RETAIL ENERGY SUPPLY LLC
(*Suby of* CONSOLIDATED EDISON SOLUTIONS INC) ★
100 Summit Lake Dr # 410, Valhalla, NY 10595-1339
Tel (914) 286-7000 *Founded/Ownrshp* 2016
Sales 500.0MM *EMP* 100
SIC 4924 Natural gas distribution
VP: Richard Rathvon
VP: James Mueller

D-U-N-S 09-004-3761 IMP/EXP

CESAR CASTILLO INC
DROGUERIA CASTILLO
Km 21 1 Pr 1 Rr 1, Guaynabo, PR 00971
Tel (787) 999-1616 *Founded/Ownrshp* 1942, 1990
Sales 310.4MMᴱ *EMP* 500
Accts Bdo Puerto Rico Psc San Juan
SIC 5122 6552 Pharmaceuticals; Cosmetics, perfumes & hair products; Land subdividers & developers, commercial
Pr: Jos L Castillo
CFO: Maria Sanchez Bras
Treas: Jose R Castillo
VP: Cesar E Castillo

CESCO
See CRESCENT ELECTRIC SUPPLY CO

CESCO
See CRAWFORD ELECTRIC SUPPLY CO HOUSTON LTD

CESCO USA
See CITY ELECTRIC SUPPLY CO

D-U-N-S 02-236-9913

■ CESI CHEMICAL INC
(*Suby of* FLOTEK INDUSTRIES INC) ★
1004 S Plainsman Rd, Marlow, OK 73055-8600
Tel (580) 658-6608 *Founded/Ownrshp* 2001
Sales 100.4MMᴱ *EMP* 487
SIC 2087 Flavoring extracts & syrups
Pr: Jerry Dumas

D-U-N-S 00-723-3596 IMP

■ CESSNA AIRCRAFT CO
TEXTRON AVIATION
(*Suby of* TEXTRON AVIATION INC) ★
1 Cessna Blvd, Wichita, KS 67215-1424
Tel (316) 517-6000 *Founded/Ownrshp* 1927
Sales 2.4MMMᴱ *EMP* 8,600
SIC 3721 Airplanes, fixed or rotary wing
Pr: Scott Ernest

CFO: Eric Salander
Ofcr: Kimberly Anderson
Sr VP: David Brant
Sr VP: Michael Thacker
Sr VP: Brad Thress
Sr VP: Ben Westerman
VP: Ray Girardo
VP: Shortt Kriya
VP: Brian Smith
Exec: Debra Hankins

CETAC TECHNOLOGIES
See TELEDYNE INSTRUMENTS INC

CETCO
See COLLOID ENVIRONMENTAL TECHNOLOGIES CO LLC

D-U-N-S 78-447-3183 EXP

■ CETCO ENERGY SERVICES CO LLC
CETCO OIL FIELD SERVICES
(*Suby of* CETCO) ★
1001 Ochsner Blvd Ste 425, Covington, LA 70433-8152
Tel (985) 871-4700 *Founded/Ownrshp* 1992
Sales 271.2MMᴱ *EMP* 258
SIC 1389 2869 3533 Oil field services; Industrial organic chemicals; Oil field machinery & equipment
CEO: Larry Washo
**Pr:* Michael Johnson
VP: Greg Norman
Off Mgr: Shannon Maturin
Snr PM: Pmp Eldred

CETCO OIL FIELD SERVICES
See CETCO ENERGY SERVICES CO LLC

D-U-N-S 96-155-2341

CETERA FINANCIAL GROUP INC
(*Suby of* ARETEC GROUP INC) ★
200 N Sepulveda Blvd # 1200, El Segundo, CA 90245-5605
Tel (800) 879-8100 *Founded/Ownrshp* 2014
Sales 280.6MMᴱ *EMP* 700ᴱ
SIC 7389 6282 Financial services; Investment advisory service
CEO: R Lawrence Roth
**Pr:* Adam Antoniades
**CFO:* Jon C Frojen
Ex VP: David Ballard
**Ex VP:* Steve Dunlap
Ex VP: Brett Harrison
Sr VP: Cynthia A Hamel
VP: Ken Bell
VP: Becky Furnival
VP: Anthony L Notermann
Exec: Jason Mullens

D-U-N-S 80-913-5010

■ CEVA FREIGHT LLC
CEVA OCEAN LINE
(*Suby of* EAGLE) ★
15350 Vickery Dr, Houston, TX 77032-2530
Tel (281) 618-3100 *Founded/Ownrshp* 2004
Sales 862.6MMᴱ *EMP* 5,000ᴱ
Accts Carbis Walker Llp
SIC 4214 4225 4412 4512 4522 4731 Local trucking with storage; General warehousing & storage; Deep sea foreign transportation of freight; Air transportation, scheduled; Air transportation, nonscheduled; Freight transportation arrangement
CEO: Marvin O Schlanger
VP: Luis Fernando De Avila

D-U-N-S 05-458-8876

■ CEVA FREIGHT MANAGEMENT INTERNATIONAL GROUP INC
(*Suby of* EAGLE) ★
15350 Vickery Dr, Houston, TX 77032-2530
Tel (281) 618-3100 *Founded/Ownrshp* 1897, 2000
Sales 72.8MMᴱ *EMP* 1,200
SIC 4731 Domestic freight forwarding; Foreign freight forwarding; Freight consolidation; Customhouse brokers
Pr: Matthew J Ryan
COO: Paul H Graham
**Treas:* Sheila Taylor
Ex VP: Anthony G Hooey
Ex VP: Stephen J Russell
Sr VP: G Michael Lancaster
Sr VP: James Tanchon
VP: Philippe R Gilbert
VP: Rosalie Ben Joseph
**VP:* Debra Leary
VP: Les Luithle
VP: Pat Morrison
VP: Randy Sinker

D-U-N-S 15-322-8585

■ CEVA GROUND US LP
(*Suby of* EAGLE) ★
15390 Vickery Dr, Houston, TX 77032-2530
Tel (281) 227-5000 *Founded/Ownrshp* 2003
Sales 131.0MMᴱ *EMP* 475
SIC 4212 4213 Local trucking, without storage; Trucking, except local
CEO: John Pattulo
**Pr:* Joe Bento
COO: Greg Weigel
Sr VP: David French
**Sr VP:* Randy Modello
**VP:* Dave French
VP: Kathi Laughman
VP: Frank Llacqua
VP: Ron Long

D-U-N-S 11-299-8638

■ CEVA LOGISTICS LLC
EAGLE
(*Suby of* CEVA LOGISTICS US HOLDINGS INC) ★
15350 Vickery Dr, Houston, TX 77032-2530
Tel (281) 618-3100 *Founded/Ownrshp* 1984
Sales 3.4MMMᴱ *EMP* 11,500
SIC 4731 Domestic freight forwarding; Foreign freight forwarding
Pr: Ronald Talley
Sr VP: Chris Monica
Sr VP: Scott Steindorf
Dir Risk M: Maria Guerrero

Genl Mgr: Gary Wilson
IT Man: Dan Digregorio
IT Man: Vinay Sharma
Opers Mgr: Mike Knapp
Opers Mgr: Adam Miller
Opers Mgr: Dale Olbrych
Opers Mgr: Doug Peterson

D-U-N-S 80-693-8259
■ CEVA LOGISTICS US GROUP INC
(*Suby of* CEVA LOGISTICS US HOLDINGS INC) ★
10751 Deerwood Park Blvd, Jacksonville, FL 32256-4834
Tel (904) 928-1400 *Founded/Ownrshp* 2006
Sales 661.4MM[E] *EMP* 1,365
SIC 4213 4226 Automobiles, transport & delivery; Automobile dead storage
Pr: David Siler

D-U-N-S 80-692-2014
■ CEVA LOGISTICS US HOLDINGS INC
(*Suby of* CEVA LIMITED)
10751 Deerwood Park Blvd # 201, Jacksonville, FL 32256-4836
Tel (904) 928-1400 *Founded/Ownrshp* 2006
Sales 4.1MMM[E] *EMP* 11,500
SIC 4213 4226 Automobiles, transport & delivery; Automobile dead storage
Pr: Matthew Ryan
**CFO:* Rubin J McDougal
**Treas:* David P Souza

D-U-N-S 04-265-5852
■ CEVA LOGISTICS US INC
(*Suby of* CEVA LOGISTICS US GROUP INC) ★
15350 Vickery Dr, Houston, TX 77032-2530
Tel (281) 618-3100 *Founded/Ownrshp* 1980
Sales 661.4MM[E] *EMP* 1,300
SIC 4731 Freight transportation arrangement
CEO: Xavier Urbain

CEVA OCEAN LINE
See CEVA FREIGHT LLC

CF
See CONSOLIDATED FABRICATORS CORP

D-U-N-S 60-280-0380
▲ CF INDUSTRIES HOLDINGS INC
4 Parkway N Ste 400, Deerfield, IL 60015-2590
Tel (847) 405-2400 *Founded/Ownrshp* 1946
Sales 4.3MMM *EMP* 2,900[E]
Tkr Sym CF *Exch* NYS
SIC 2873 2874 Nitrogenous fertilizers; Fertilizers: natural (organic), except compost; Phosphatic fertilizers
Pr: W Anthony Will
**Ch Bd:* Stephen A Furbacher
CFO: Dennis P Kelleher
Treas: Charles Sebastyan
Ex VP: Bert A Frost
Sr VP: Douglas C Barnard
Sr VP: Christopher D Bohn
Sr VP: Wendy S Jablow
VP: Richard A Hoker
VP: Richard Hoker
VP: Eugene McCluskey
VP: Tony Will
Board of Directors: Robert C Arzbaecher, William Davisson, Stephen J Hagge, John D Johnson, Robert G Kuhbach, Anne P Noonan, Edward A Schmitt, Theresa E Wagler

D-U-N-S 00-896-6632 IMP/EXP
■ CF INDUSTRIES INC
(*Suby of* CF INDUSTRIES HOLDINGS INC) ★
4 Parkway N Ste 400, Deerfield, IL 60015-2590
Tel (847) 405-2400 *Founded/Ownrshp* 2005
Sales 4.7MMM[E] *EMP* 3,194[E]
SIC 2873 2874 Anhydrous ammonia; Urea; Phosphoric acid; Superphosphates, ammoniated or not ammoniated; Diammonium phosphate; Calcium meta-phosphate
CEO: Tony Will
**Pr:* Steve Wilson
**Sr VP:* Bert Frost
**Sr VP:* Dennis Kelleher
**VP:* Doug Barnard
**VP:* Richard Hoker

D-U-N-S 00-749-3851
■ CF INDUSTRIES NITROGEN LLC
(*Suby of* TERRA CAPITAL INC)
4 Parkway N Ste 400, Deerfield, IL 60015-2590
Tel (847) 405-2400 *Founded/Ownrshp* 1965
Sales 222.3MM[E] *EMP* 871
SIC 2875 2873 Fertilizers, mixing only; Nitrogenous fertilizers
V Ch Bd: Burton M Joyce
VP: Lee Wyatt
Tech Mgr: Jeanie Peterson
Sls Dir: Jeff Bald
Sls Dir: Dick Miller
Sls Dir: Jim Standfield

D-U-N-S 60-967-6598
■ CF INDUSTRIES SALES LLC
(*Suby of* CF INDUSTRIES HOLDINGS INC) ★
4 Parkway N Ste 400, Deerfield, IL 60015-2590
Tel (847) 405-2400 *Founded/Ownrshp* 2013
Sales 674.3MM[E] *EMP* 360
SIC 2873 Nitrogenous fertilizers
CEO: Tony Will

D-U-N-S 19-770-1030
CF MERCED LA SIERRA LLC
COUNTRY VILLA LA SIERRA
(*Suby of* COUNTRY VILLA HEALTH SERVICES) ★
2424 M St, Merced, CA 95340-2808
Tel (209) 723-4224 *Founded/Ownrshp* 1966
Sales 36.0MM[E] *EMP* 1,200
SIC 8051 Skilled nursing care facilities
Pr: Arden Bennett
**CFO:* Joel Saltzburg
**Treas:* Mathilde Albers
**VP:* Emil Damia
**VP:* William Gamboa

D-U-N-S 80-542-5675 EXP
CF&I STEEL LP
EVRAZ ROCKY MOUNTAIN STL MILLS
(*Suby of* EVRAZ OREGON STEEL) ★
1612 E Abriendo Ave, Pueblo, CO 81004-3406
Tel (719) 561-6000 *Founded/Ownrshp* 2001
Sales 172.6MM[E] *EMP* 700
SIC 3441 3317 3312 Fabricated structural metal; Steel pipe & tubes; Blast furnaces & steel mills
CEO: Conrad Winkler
**Pr:* Michael T Rehwinkel
**Ex VP:* Tigran Atayan
**Ex VP:* Kim Fields
**Ex VP:* Jerry Reed
**Ex VP:* John Zanieski
**Sr VP:* Glenda Minor
QC Dir: Mark Erspamer
Sls Mgr: Joe Kasten

D-U-N-S 61-545-4428
CFA INSTITUTE
ASSOCIATION FOR INVESTMENT
915 E High St, Charlottesville, VA 22902-4868
Tel (434) 951-5499 *Founded/Ownrshp* 1990
Sales 272.4MM *EMP* 450
Accts Pricewaterhousecoopers Llp Wa
SIC 8621 6282 8221 Professional membership organizations; Investment advice; University
Pr: Paul Smith
CFO: Timothy McLaughlin
Treas: Kim Maynard
Bd of Dir: Stanley Erwin
Top Exec: Lee Buttles
Top Exec: Bob Dannhauser
Top Exec: Rebecca Fender
Top Exec: Todd Jankowski
Sr VP: Moira J Coleman
Sr VP: Patricia D Walters
VP: Bernard Asselin
VP: Bob Beamer
VP: Denise Lambert
**VP:* Inese Romanovska
**VP:* Kari Vatanen
**VP:* Tony Watts
VP: Guy Williams
Exec: Raymond Deangelo
Dir Soc: Corbin Ailer

D-U-N-S 96-966-8321
CFA INSTITUTE RESEARCH FOUNDATION
915 E High St, Charlottesville, VA 22902-4868
Tel (434) 951-5499 *Founded/Ownrshp* 1965
Sales 231.2MM *EMP* 3
SIC 8641 Civic social & fraternal associations
Pr: John Rogers
**Treas:* Kim Maynard

D-U-N-S 80-434-3531 IMP
CFAN CO
(*Suby of* GEAE HOLDINGS II INC & FAN BLADE ASSOCIATES INC)
1000 Technology Way, San Marcos, TX 78666-8500
Tel (512) 754-3005 *Founded/Ownrshp* 1991
Sales 206.4MM[E] *EMP* 650
SIC 3724 Aircraft engines & engine parts
Pr: Benoit Cloutier
VP: Jean P Sainty
CTO: Laura Buske
Dir IT: Guy Bowen

CFBNJ
See COMMUNITY FOOD BANK OF NEW JERSEY INC

CFC
See NATIONAL RURAL UTILITIES COOPERATIVE FINANCE CORP

CFCL
See CHICAGO FREIGHT CAR LEASING CO

D-U-N-S 61-440-3579
CFHS HOLDINGS INC
MARINA DEL REY HOSPITAL
4650 Lincoln Blvd, Marina Del Rey, CA 90292-6306
Tel (310) 823-8911 *Founded/Ownrshp* 1969
Sales 99.3MM *EMP* 2,800[E]
SIC 8062 8093 8011 General medical & surgical hospitals; Weight loss clinic, with medical staff; Orthopedic physician; Sports medicine specialist, physician; Surgeon
CEO: Stacy Sean Fowler
Chf Path: James Keefe
Chf Path: Willard Worthen
**Pr:* Michael A Rembis
CFO: Frank Bryan
CFO: Kermit Newman
Ofcr: Fred Hunter
VP: David Benjamin
Dir Inf Cn: Carla Higbee
Dir Risk M: Jonathan Thornsen
Dir Lab: Margaret Kwan
Dir Bus: Mark Miller

CFI
See CONTRACT FREIGHTERS INC

D-U-N-S 94-250-3087
CFI RESORTS MANAGEMENT INC
W R
5601 Windhover Dr, Orlando, FL 32819-7914
Tel (407) 351-3350 *Founded/Ownrshp* 1995
Sales 775.8MM[E] *EMP* 5,403
SIC 8741 Management services
Pr: David A Siegel
**COO:* Mark Waltrip
**CFO:* Tom Dugan
**Ex VP:* Jim Gissy
**Ex VP:* Barry W Siegel

D-U-N-S 62-340-4449
CFJ PROPERTIES LLC
FLYING J TRAVEL PLAZA
5508 Lonas Dr, Knoxville, TN 37909-3221
Tel (801) 624-1000 *Founded/Ownrshp* 1991
Sales 947.5MM[E] *EMP* 6,250
Accts Kpmg Llp Salt Lake City Utah
SIC 5541 5812 5411 Truck stops; American restaurant; Delicatessen (eating places); Convenience stores, independent

Ch Bd: Crystal Call Maggelet

CFM
See CAPITAL FOR MERCHANTS LLC

CFM LOGISTICS
See CENTRAL FREIGHT MANAGEMENT LLC

CFMI
See CAREFIRST OF MARYLAND INC

D-U-N-S 04-208-0940
■ CFO ACCOUNTING CENTER
(*Suby of* H U D) ★
451 7th St Sw, Washington, DC 20410-0001
Tel (202) 708-0950 *Founded/Ownrshp* 1998
Sales NA *EMP* 9,000
SIC 9531 Housing agency, government;

D-U-N-S 82-939-8564
CFO CONSULTANTS INC
829 E Francis Dr, Palm Springs, CA 92262-2213
Tel (760) 899-1919 *Founded/Ownrshp* 2009
Sales 91.7MM *EMP* 1[E]
SIC 8742 Management consulting services
COO: Guohua Zheng
CFO: Ken Tsang

CFP FIRE PROTECTION
See COSCO FIRE PROTECTION INC

D-U-N-S 12-994-4633 IMP
CFP GROUP INC
1117 W Olympic Blvd, Montebello, CA 90640-5123
Tel (323) 727-0900 *Founded/Ownrshp* 1993
Sales 211.2MM *EMP* 2
SIC 3556 Food products machinery
CEO: Eric W Ek

D-U-N-S 13-334-0286
CFPB HOLDINGS LLC
CREEKSTONE FARMS PREMIUM BEEF
604 Goff Industrial Pk Rd, Arkansas City, KS 67005-8880
Tel (620) 741-3100 *Founded/Ownrshp* 2003
Sales 145.8MM[E] *EMP* 700
SIC 8731 Biological research
CIO: Tom Minton
QA Dir: Don Morrow
Dir IT: Scott Smythe
IT Man: Chad Lampson
Manager: Neil Smith
Sls Mgr: Michael Pratt
Genl Couns: Douglas Mackay

D-U-N-S 00-617-2829 IMP
CG BRETTING MANUFACTURING CO INC (WI)
3401 Lake Park Rd, Ashland, WI 54806-4967
Tel (715) 682-5231 *Founded/Ownrshp* 1890, 1999
Sales 98.9MM[E] *EMP* 450[E]
SIC 3554 3599 3565 3555 Paper industries machinery; Folding machines, paper; Machine shop, jobbing & repair; Packaging machinery; Printing trades machinery
Pr: David Bretting
**COO:* Paul Bretting
COO: Mike Willis
**CFO:* Tom Murphy
**Sec:* David M Pocernich
**VP:* Scott L Bretting

D-U-N-S 11-621-0527 EXP
CG ENTERPRISES INC
12001 Guilford Rd Ste 1, Annapolis Junction, MD 20701-1205
Tel (301) 953-3366 *Founded/Ownrshp* 1920
Sales 180.2MM[E] *EMP* 400
SIC 1611 1623 Highway & street paving contractor; General contractor, highway & street construction; Underground utilities contractor
Pr: Arthur C Cox Jr
**VP:* William G Cox
Off Mgr: Barbara Hobbie
CIO: Liz Cox

D-U-N-S 14-735-1456 IMP
CG LIQUIDATION INC
2111 Walter P Reuther Dr, Warren, MI 48091-6108
Tel (586) 575-9800 *Founded/Ownrshp* 1985
Sales 89.4MM[E] *EMP* 425
SIC 3479 3471 Painting of metal products; Plating & polishing
CEO: William P Baer
**Pr:* Frank Knoth
Pr: Ken Stallons
**CFO:* Brian Ghesquiere
Treas: Harvey Carney
VP: Robert Nesler

D-U-N-S 10-322-1354 IMP/EXP
CG POWER SYSTEMS USA INC
(*Suby of* CG POWER USA INC) ★
1 Pauwels Dr, Washington, MO 63090-1134
Tel (636) 239-6783 *Founded/Ownrshp* 1988
Sales 185.3MM[E] *EMP* 175
SIC 3612 Electronic meter transformers
**Pr:* Marc Schilledeeckx
**Sec:* Stacy Schiermeier
**Genl Mgr:* J P Davis

D-U-N-S 15-847-5363
CG POWER USA INC
(*Suby of* CG INTERNATIONAL B.V.)
7 Century Hill Dr, Latham, NY 12110-2113
Tel (518) 452-7718 *Founded/Ownrshp* 2008
Sales 185.3MM[E] *EMP* 175
SIC 8711 Consulting engineer
Ch: Marc Schillebeeckx
**CEO:* David M Klein
**CEO:* Mark Scher
Ex VP: Ravi Rajagopal
VP: Edward Calder

D-U-N-S 61-395-4916 IMP
CG ROXANE LLC
CRYSTAL GEYSER
1210 State Hwy 395, Olancha, CA 93549
Tel (760) 764-2885 *Founded/Ownrshp* 1990
Sales 121.7MM[E] *EMP* 300
SIC 2086 Water, pasteurized: packaged in cans, bottles, etc.
**CEO:* Patrice Marquet
Sls Dir: Steve Weller

D-U-N-S 05-919-9237
CGB DIVERSIFIED SERVICES INC (LA)
(*Suby of* CGB ENTERPRISES INC) ★
1608b W Lafayette Ave, Jacksonville, IL 62650-3633
Tel (217) 245-4599 *Founded/Ownrshp* 1998
Sales 160.2MM *EMP* 48
Accts Kpmg Llp New Orleans Louisia
SIC 5153 Grains
Pr: Rodney Clark
Mktg Mgr: Douglas Emery

D-U-N-S 80-677-2513
CGB ENTERPRISES INC
1127 Hwy 190 E Service Rd, Covington, LA 70433-4929
Tel (985) 867-3500 *Founded/Ownrshp* 1993
Sales 5.9MMM *EMP* 1,250
Accts Kpmg Llp New Orleans La
SIC 4221 5191 4491 Grain elevator, storage only; Bean elevator; Fertilizer & fertilizer materials; Marine cargo handling
Pr: Kevin D Adams
Mng Pt: Scott Mickey
**CFO:* Richard S Pemberton
**VP:* Gregory A Beck
**VP:* Rodney L Clark
**VP:* G Scott Leininger
VP: Scott Leininger
**VP:* Michael T Merkel
VP: Michael Smith
VP: Osamu Yako
Exec: Tim Kothe
Board of Directors: Kevin D Adams, Hiroyuki Kawasaki, Eric J Laptook, Richard S Pemberton, John D Williams

D-U-N-S 04-784-3008 IMP/EXP
CGG SERVICES (US) INC
C G G
(*Suby of* CGG)
10300 Town Park Dr, Houston, TX 77072-5236
Tel (832) 351-8300 *Founded/Ownrshp* 2007
Sales 1.7MMM[E] *EMP* 2,800
SIC 1382 Seismograph surveys; Geophysical exploration, oil & gas field
Pr: Colin Murdoch
Pr: Alice Chapman
Pr: Vincent M Thielen
**CEO:* Jean Georges Malcor
COO: Thierry Le
**CFO:* Stephane Paul Frydman
CFO: Stephane Frydman
Ex VP: Kamil Beffa
**Ex VP:* David Dragone
**Ex VP:* Eva Rudin
**Sr VP:* Batrice Place Faget
Sr VP: WEI Yang

D-U-N-S 06-496-3254 IMP/EXP
CGGVERITAS LAND (US) INC
(*Suby of* CGG)
10300 Town Park Dr, Houston, TX 77072-5236
Tel (832) 351-8300 *Founded/Ownrshp* 1931
Sales 66.1MM[E] *EMP* 1,000[E]
SIC 7699 Geophysical equipment repair
CEO: Jean-Georges Malcor
**CFO:* Stephane Paul Frydman
Ex VP: Jonathan Miller
Ex VP: Pascal Rosset
Ex VP: Thierry Roux
Sr VP: Hovey Cox
**Sr VP:* Batrice Place Faget
Sr VP: Ted Mariner
**VP:* David Dragone
VP: Gilles Elvezi
VP: Jacques Micaelli
VP: Jean-Francois Roudaut
**VP:* Eva Rudin
Exec: Dave Heather
Dir Risk M: Kenneth Nixon

D-U-N-S 06-323-7440
CGH MEDICAL CENTER
100 E Le Fevre Rd, Sterling, IL 61081-1279
Tel (815) 625-0400 *Founded/Ownrshp* 1980
Sales 199.8MM *EMP* 1,400
SIC 8062 General medical & surgical hospitals
CEO: Paul Steinke
**CEO:* Ed Andersen
**COO:* Norm Deets
**Ch:* Ronald Smeltzer
**V Ch Bd:* Bill Burke
Bd of Dir: William Burke
Ofcr: Susie Kennedy
Ofcr: Shirley Wolford
VP: Randy Davis
VP: Ben Schaab
VP: Paul G Steinke
Dir Inf Cn: Sandra Westbo
Dir Lab: Susey McDonald
Dir Rad: Eugene W Brown
Dir Rad: Gina Grennan

D-U-N-S 15-648-5823
CGI AMS
75 Livingston Ave Ste 202, Roseland, NJ 07068-3738
Tel (972) 788-0400 *Founded/Ownrshp* 1999
Sales 54.0MM[E] *EMP* 4,400
SIC 7379 8748 7374 7371 Computer related consulting services; Business consulting; Data processing & preparation; Computer software systems analysis & design, custom
Pr: Thomas A Gordon
**CEO:* Ronald Brisebois

D-U-N-S 16-233-7872
CGI FEDERAL INC
C G I
(*Suby of* CGI TECHNOLOGIES AND SOLUTIONS INC) ★
12601 Fair Lakes Cir, Fairfax, VA 22033-4920
Tel (703) 227-6000 *Founded/Ownrshp* 2004
Sales 1.2MMM[E] *EMP* 6,500

SIC 7379 7389 8999 Computer related consulting services; Financial services; Actuarial consultant
Pr: Timothy Hurlebus
Ex VP: George Schindler
Sr VP: Mark Boyajian
VP: Chrystal Davis
VP: John P Heneghan
VP: John Loonsk
VP: Gregg Mossburg
VP: Keith Quigley
VP: David Ralston
VP: George Schinder
VP: Gary Singer
VP: Paula Wells
Exec: Vera Ashworth
Exec: Sridhar Dabbeeru
Exec: Patricia Healy
Exec: Renee Kearney
Exec: William Whitney

D-U-N-S 11-884-7540
CGI INFORMATION SYSTEMS & MANAGEMENT CONSULTANTS INC
(*Suby of* CONSEILLERS EN GESTION ET INFORMATIQUE CGI INC)
600 Federal St, Andover, MA 01810-1064
Tel (978) 946-3000 *Founded/Ownrshp* 1997
Sales 76.0MM[E] *EMP* 1,254
SIC 7374 3577 7373 Data processing service; Data conversion equipment, media-to-media: computer; Computer integrated systems design
Ch Bd: Serge Godin
**CEO:* Michael E Roach
**CFO:* David Anderson

CGI NORTH AMERICA
See DG3 GROUP AMERICA INC

D-U-N-S 06-927-8570 IMP
CGITECHNOLOGIES AND SOLUTIONS INC
(*Suby of* GROUPE CGI INC)
11325 Random Hills Rd, Fairfax, VA 22030-6051
Tel (703) 267-8000 *Founded/Ownrshp* 2004
Sales 1.7MMM[E] *EMP* 9,385
SIC 7379 7373 7372 7389 Computer related consulting services; Systems integration services; Application computer software; Personal service agents, brokers & bureaus
Ch Bd: Serge Godin
Pt: Trey Kirby
**Pr:* David Henderson
**Pr:* Michael E Roach
**V Ch Bd:* Andre Imbeau
**VP:* Benoit Dube
Exec: Deborah Dewalt
Exec: Jill Kathman
Exec: Chris Wheatley
Snr Ntwrk: Christopher Day
QA Dir: Kazi Hossain

D-U-N-S 19-766-1312
CGS ADMINISTRATORS LLC
(*Suby of* BLUE CROSS BLUE SHIELD OF SOUTH CAROLINA) ★
2 Vantage Way, Nashville, TN 37228-1504
Tel (615) 244-5600 *Founded/Ownrshp* 2004
Sales NA *EMP* 1,200
SIC 6411 Medical insurance claim processing, contract or fee basis
Pr: Steve Smith
**CFO:* Mike Logan
Ofcr: Linda Martin
**VP:* Jim Doane
VP: Robert J Stansell
Genl Mgr: John Kimball
Genl Mgr: Melissa Kirchenbauer
IT Man: Scott Boyd

D-U-N-S 00-699-3695
CH ENERGY GROUP INC
CENTRAL HUDSON GAS & ELECTRIC
(*Suby of* FORTIS INC)
284 South Ave, Poughkeepsie, NY 12601-4838
Tel (845) 452-2000 *Founded/Ownrshp* 2013
Sales 1.1MMM[E] *EMP* 1,235[E]
SIC 4911 4924 Electric services; Distribution, electric power; Natural gas distribution
Ch Bd: Steven V Lant
**CFO:* Christopher M Capone
Treas: Diance Seitz
Ex VP: Joseph J Devirgilio
**Ex VP:* John E Gould
**Ex VP:* James P Laurito
VP: Joseph Devirgilio
**VP:* Margarita K Dilley
VP: Mark Holtermann
Dir IT: Rick McGowan
IT Man: Roy Lokys
Board of Directors: Margarita K Dilley, Steven M Fetter, Stanley J Grubel, Manuel J Iraola, E Michel Kruse, Edward T Tokar, Jeffrey D Tranen, Ernest R Verebelyi

D-U-N-S 07-117-6429 IMP
CH HOLDINGS USA INC
ENCLOSE
2770 Blue Waters Rd # 100, Eagan, MN 55121-1671
Tel (651) 796-6100 *Founded/Ownrshp* 1999
Sales 172.6MM[E] *EMP* 550
SIC 1791 Building front installation metal; Exterior wall system installation
Ch Bd: Greg C Sage
**Pr:* Bruce Bormhurst
**CFO:* David Coleman
IT Man: Rick Hamlin

D-U-N-S 80-673-7383
■ **CH ROBINSON CO INC**
(*Suby of* CH ROBINSON WORLDWIDE INC) ★
14701 Charlson Rd, Eden Prairie, MN 55347-5076
Tel (952) 937-7896 *Founded/Ownrshp* 2000
Sales 4.5MMM[E] *EMP* 1,020
SIC 4731 Freight transportation arrangement; Freight forwarding; Brokers, shipping
Pr: John P Wiehoff
Pr: Mike Short
**CFO:* Chad M Lindbloom
**Treas:* Troy A Renner
Sr VP: Gregory D Goven
**VP:* Ben Campbell
VP: Molly Dubois
VP: Molly M Dubois
**VP:* Jim Lemke
VP: Joseph J Mulvevill
VP: Paul A Radunz
**VP:* Scott Satterlee
**VP:* Mark Walker
Exec: Lynn Wood
Board of Directors: Ben Campbell, Chad Lindbloom, John Wiehoff

D-U-N-S 09-897-7176 IMP/EXP
■ **CH ROBINSON FREIGHT SERVICES LTD**
(*Suby of* CH ROBINSON WORLDWIDE INC) ★
1501 N Mittel Blvd Ste A, Wood Dale, IL 60191-1055
Tel (630) 766-4445 *Founded/Ownrshp* 2012
Sales 271.3MM[E] *EMP* 1,800
SIC 4731 4225

D-U-N-S 02-293-5894 IMP/EXP
▲ **CH ROBINSON WORLDWIDE INC**
14701 Charlson Rd, Eden Prairie, MN 55347-5076
Tel (952) 937-8500 *Founded/Ownrshp* 1905
Sales 13.4MMM *EMP* 13,159
Tkr Sym CHRW *Exch* NGS
SIC 4731 Freight forwarding
Ch Bd: John P Wiehoff
CFO: Andrew C Clarke
Chf Cred: Christopher J O'Brien
Ofcr: Angela K Freeman
CIO: Chad M Lindbloom
Board of Directors: Scott P Anderson, Robert Ezrilov, Wayne M Fortun, Mary J Steele Guilfoile, Jodee Kozlak, Brian P Short, James B Stake

D-U-N-S 96-939-9364
CH WILKINSON PHYSICIAN NETWORK
CHRISTUS PROVIDER NETWORK
919 Hidden Rdg, Irving, TX 75038-3813
Tel (469) 282-2000 *Founded/Ownrshp* 1993
Sales 83.9MM[E] *EMP* 24[E]
Accts Ernst & Young Us Llp Houston
SIC 8011 General & family practice, physician/surgeon
Pr: Donna Mikulecky
Treas: Grady Mullins

D-U-N-S 07-945-7694
CH2M HILL - DYNETICS SYNERGY ALLIANCE LLC
(*Suby of* CH2M HILL CONSTRUCTORS INC) ★
1515 Poydras St Ste 1550, New Orleans, LA 70112-4524
Tel (504) 593-9421 *Founded/Ownrshp* 2014
Sales 150.0MM *EMP* 1,100
SIC 8744 Facilities support services
VP: Kenneth J Melchiorre
Prin: Dave King
Prin: Gene Lupia
Prin: Ken Melchiorre
Prin: Jeff Mervin

D-U-N-S 06-336-9789
CH2M HILL ALASKA INC
(*Suby of* VECO CORP) ★
949 E 36th Ave Ste 500, Anchorage, AK 99508-4370
Tel (907) 762-1500 *Founded/Ownrshp* 1970
Sales 365.9MM[E] *EMP* 1,500
SIC 1389 Oil field services
Pr: Mark A Lasswell
**Treas:* Steven Mathews
**VP:* Bauer Martinez John
**VP:* Mathews Steven
Exec: Linda Croft
Mktg Mgr: Elizabeth Ridley

D-U-N-S 02-762-0574
CH2M HILL COMPANIES LTD
9191 S Jamaica St, Englewood, CO 80112-5946
Tel (303) 771-0900 *Founded/Ownrshp* 1946
Sales 5.4MMM *EMP* 22,000[E]
SIC 8711 Engineering services; Industrial engineers; Construction & civil engineering; Consulting engineer
Ch Bd: Jacqueline C Hinman
Pr: Mark D Fallon
CFO: Gary L McArthur
Ofcr: Shelette M Gustafson
Ex VP: Gail Chamberlain
**Ex VP:* Lisa Glatch
Ex VP: Frank C Gross Jr
Ex VP: Iosefa Matagi
Ex VP: Thomas M McCoy
Ex VP: Howard Thomas
Sr VP: Jennifer Price
Sr VP: Elisa M Speranza
VP: Joseph Arnold
VP: David Bechler
VP: Ryan L Beckman
VP: Bill Bellamy
VP: Randy Bender
VP: Doug Bitterman
VP: Vicki Bogenberger
VP: Mark Callahan
VP: Leofwin Clark
Board of Directors: Barry L Williams, Malcolm Brinded, Mark D Fallon, Charles O Holliday Jr, Scott Kleinman, Gregory T McIntyre, Antoine G Munfakh, Georgia R Nelson, Thomas L Pennella, Terry A Ruhl

D-U-N-S 80-442-7656 IMP
CH2M HILL CONSTRUCTORS INC
(*Suby of* CH2M HILL COMPANIES LTD) ★
9189 S Jamaica St, Englewood, CO 80112-5946
Tel (720) 286-2000 *Founded/Ownrshp* 1993
Sales 392.4MM[E] *EMP* 1,645
SIC 8711 Engineering services
CEO: Jacque Hinman
**Pr:* Dr James J Ferris
COO: Ronald A Campbell
CFO: Robert C Hinds
Sr VP: Joseph A Ahearn
Sr VP: Jeff Akers
Sr VP: Robert W Bailey
Sr VP: Christine M Bisio
Sr VP: Philip A Crannell
Sr VP: Thomas Dames
**Sr VP:* Don S Evans
Sr VP: Donald L Goddeau
Sr VP: Philip G Hall
Sr VP: Mark A Lasswell
Sr VP: George N Lemmon
Sr VP: Katherine M Lombardo
Sr VP: Eugene A Lupia
Sr VP: Liliana Maldonado
Sr VP: Jeffrey R Mather
Sr VP: Gregory T McIntyre
Sr VP: Thomas L Peters

D-U-N-S 14-822-7890
CH2M HILL ENGINEERS INC
(*Suby of* CH2M HILL COMPANIES LTD) ★
1500 International Dr, Spartanburg, SC 29303-6745
Tel (864) 578-2000 *Founded/Ownrshp* 2003
Sales 240.2MM[E] *EMP* 2,500
SIC 8711 8742 1629 Engineering services; Management consulting services; Industrial plant construction; Power plant construction
Pr: Fred M Brune
**Treas:* Bobby Hinds
**VP:* Donald R Zabilansky

D-U-N-S 06-324-8207
CH2M HILL INC
(*Suby of* CH2M HILL COMPANIES LTD) ★
9191 S Jamaica St, Englewood, CO 80112-5946
Tel (303) 771-0900 *Founded/Ownrshp* 1978
Sales 2.1MMM[E] *EMP* 5,346
SIC 8711 Consulting engineer
Pr: Jacqueline C Hinman
Pr: Rob Berra
Pr: Dennis Ferrera
COO: Brian Robertson
CFO: John A Madia
**Treas:* Steven Mathews
Treas: Brenda Wickham
**Sr VP:* Robert W Bailey
Sr VP: David Larter
**VP:* John Bauer-Martinez
VP: George Garcia
**VP:* Terry A Ruhl
Board of Directors: S Wyatt McCallie, Ralph R Peterson

D-U-N-S 15-402-1679
CH2M HILL INDUSTRIAL DESIGN & CONSTRUCTION INC
(*Suby of* CH2M HILL COMPANIES LTD) ★
2020 Sw 4th Ave Fl 3, Portland, OR 97201-4953
Tel (503) 224-6040 *Founded/Ownrshp* 1984
Sales 76.1MM[E] *EMP* 1,200
SIC 8711 8712 8741 7699

D-U-N-S 05-864-7470
CHA CONSULTING INC
(*Suby of* CHA HOLDINGS INC) ★
3 Winners Cir Ste 301, Albany, NY 12205-1161
Tel (518) 453-4500 *Founded/Ownrshp* 1927
Sales 160.5MM[E] *EMP* 650
SIC 8711 Consulting engineer
Pr: Raymond L Kinley
**Ch Bd:* Michael E Hollowood
**CEO:* Ray Rudolph Jr
**CFO:* Dom Bernardo
Treas: Jeff D Crosby
VP: John Hickok
VP: Brian McKenna
Off Mgr: Lisa Allen
IT Man: James Napier
Mktg Mgr: Deborah Leo
Mktg Mgr: Donna Monshower

D-U-N-S 61-540-1564
CHA HEALTH SYSTEMS INC
CHA RENETATIVE MEDICINE
3731 Wilshire Blvd # 850, Los Angeles, CA 90010-2851
Tel (213) 487-3211 *Founded/Ownrshp* 2001
Sales 281.2MM[E] *EMP* 2,500[E]
SIC 8011 Clinic, operated by physicians
CEO: Dr K Cha
**COO:* Jean Yi

D-U-N-S 96-669-1458
CHA HOLDINGS INC
3 Winners Cir, Albany, NY 12205-1161
Tel (518) 453-4500 *Founded/Ownrshp* 2008
Sales 145.9MM[E] *EMP* 650
SIC 8711 Consulting engineer
CEO: Raymond Kinley Jr

D-U-N-S 07-412-5881 IMP
CHA HOLLYWOOD MEDICAL CENTER LP
HOLLYWOOD PRESBYTERIAN MED CTR
1300 N Vermont Ave, Los Angeles, CA 90027-6098
Tel (213) 413-3000 *Founded/Ownrshp* 2004
Sales 260.5MM *EMP* 1,500[E]
SIC 8062 8351 General medical & surgical hospitals; Child day care services
CEO: Jeff A Nelson
**CFO:* Galen Gorman
Dir Rx: Sofia Gezalyan
CTO: Destina Hopkins
Dir IT: Carrie Robert

CHA RENETATIVE MEDICINE
See CHA HEALTH SYSTEMS INC

CHABOT COLLEGE
See CHABOT-LAS POSITAS COMMUNITY COLLEGE DISTRICT FINANCING CORP

D-U-N-S 07-168-0961
CHABOT-LAS POSITAS COMMUNITY COLLEGE DISTRICT FINANCING CORP
CHABOT COLLEGE
7600 Dublin Blvd Ste 102, Dublin, CA 94568-2944
Tel (925) 485-5201 *Founded/Ownrshp* 1961
Sales 55.7MM[E] *EMP* 1,714
Accts Matson And Isom Redding Ca
SIC 8222 Community college
CFO: Roy V Stutzman

D-U-N-S 07-525-5687
CHADBOURNE & PARKE LLP
1301 Ave Of The Americas, New York, NY 10019-6022
Tel (212) 408-5100 *Founded/Ownrshp* 1937
Sales 136.3MM[E] *EMP* 1,100
SIC 8111 General practice law office
Mng Pt: Andrew A Giaccia
Pt: Alan I Raylesberg
Pt: Allison M Alcasabas
Pt: Todd Alexander
Pt: Scott S Balber
Pt: Marian E Baldwin
Pt: Robin D Ball
Pt: Sohail Barkatali
Pt: Joseph A Calvaruso
Pt: Lynne Gedanken
Pt: Charez Golvala
Pt: Walter G Hanchuk
Pt: John M Hintz
Pt: Gareth Kendall
Pt: Scott A Kislin
Pt: Agnieszka Klich
Pt: Marek Krol
Pt: Tracy Laws
Pt: Sey-Hyo Lee
Pt: Mary A Lopatto
Pt: Gregory Loss

D-U-N-S 80-144-5680 IMP/EXP
CHADWELL SUPPLY INC
4907 Joanne Kearney Blvd, Tampa, FL 33619-8603
Tel (888) 341-2423 *Founded/Ownrshp* 2007
Sales 100.0MM[E] *EMP* 350
SIC 5031 1752 Building materials, exterior; Building materials, interior; Wood floor installation & refinishing
Pr: James M Chadwell
**Sec:* David Chadwell
Brnch Mgr: Chip Behmke
Brnch Mgr: John Drennen
Brnch Mgr: Scott Kellum
Genl Mgr: Allison Brandstetter
Natl Sales: James Batterton
Natl Sales: Bert Wray
VP Sls: John Daniell
Manager: Shawn Barney
Sls Mgr: Chad Bischof

CHAFFEY COLLEGE BOOKSTORE
See CHAFFEY COMMUNITY COLLEGE DISTRICT (INC)

D-U-N-S 07-608-4326
CHAFFEY COMMUNITY COLLEGE DISTRICT (INC)
CHAFFEY COLLEGE BOOKSTORE
5885 Haven Ave, Rancho Cucamonga, CA 91737-3002
Tel (909) 652-6560 *Founded/Ownrshp* 1883
Sales 48.8MM[E] *EMP* 1,400
SIC 8222 8221 Community college; Colleges universities & professional schools
Pr: Henry D Shannon
**VP:* Kathleen Brugger
VP: Michael Edwards
VP: Melanie Siddiqi
VP: Jerry Young
Telecom Mg: Margaret Gonzalez
Psych: Karina Jabalera
Psych: Katherine Wilson

D-U-N-S 08-414-9210
CHAFFEY JOINT UNION HIGH SCHOOL DISTRICT
211 W 5th St, Ontario, CA 91762-1653
Tel (909) 988-8511 *Founded/Ownrshp* 1958
Sales 123.3MM[E] *EMP* 2,000
SIC 8211 Public senior high school; High school, junior or senior
Dir IT: Thomas Vonderharr
Psych: Inez Orozco

D-U-N-S 87-788-4809
CHAI BAGEL CORP
CHOMPIES DELI REST & BKY
14431 N 73rd St, Scottsdale, AZ 85260-3131
Tel (480) 860-0475 *Founded/Ownrshp* 1995
Sales 105.7MM[E] *EMP* 261
SIC 5149 5461 5812 2052 2051 Bakery products; Bakeries; Eating places; Delicatessen (eating places); Cookies & crackers; Bread, cake & related products
Pr: Louis P Borenstein
**Treas:* Neal Borenstein
**VP:* Mark Borenstein
**VP:* Wendy Malach

D-U-N-S 00-785-0746
CHAIN ELECTRIC CO (MS)
1308 1/2 W Pine St, Hattiesburg, MS 39401-6338
Tel (601) 545-3800 *Founded/Ownrshp* 1955
Sales 136.1MM[E] *EMP* 400
SIC 1731 General electrical contractor
Pr: Bobby L Chain
**Ex VP:* John W Chain

CHAIN STORES AGE
See LEBHAR-FRIEDMAN INC

D-U-N-S 02-383-2853
CHALK MOUNTAIN SERVICES OF TEXAS LLC
2828 Chambers St, Venus, TX 76084-3320
Tel (817) 473-1931 *Founded/Ownrshp* 2006
Sales 232.3MM[E] *EMP* 600[E]
SIC 1389 Gas field services

D-U-N-S 08-584-9834 EXP
CHALLENGE DAIRY PRODUCTS INC
(*Suby of* CALIFORNIA DAIRIES INC) ★
6701 Donlon Way, Dublin, CA 94568-2850
Tel (925) 828-6160 *Founded/Ownrshp* 1976
Sales 200.0MM[E] *EMP* 221
Accts Deloitte & Touche Llp
SIC 5143 5149 Butter; Milk, canned or dried
Pr: Irvin Holmes
Pr: Jason Morris
**CFO:* Stanford Alan Maag
VP: Tom Ditto
VP: David Treiber
MIS Dir: Geoffrey Uy
Dir IT: Michael Jenkins
Sls Mgr: Brian Beebe
Sls Mgr: Jerry McCulloch
Snr Mgr: Geoffrey Wheaton

D-U-N-S 05-015-0481 IMP
CHALLENGE MFG CO
3200 Fruit Ridge Ave Nw, Grand Rapids, MI 49544-9707
Tel (616) 735-6500 *Founded/Ownrshp* 1981
Sales 801.7MM^E *EMP* 2,000
SIC 3465 Automotive stampings
Pr: Bruce Vor Broker
**Treas:* Andrew Washburn
**VP:* Douglas N Bradley
**VP:* Boyd Vor Broker
**VP:* Leonard J Rinke Jr
Ql Cn Mgr: Todd Macdoniels

D-U-N-S 12-270-1584
CHALLENGER INDUSTRIES INC
2005 N Kavaney Dr Ste A, Bismarck, ND 58501-1749
Tel (701) 255-1665 *Founded/Ownrshp* 2015
Sales 180.8MM^E *EMP* 160
SIC 5085

D-U-N-S 07-298-7464
CHALLENGER SCHOOLS
9424 S 300 W, Sandy, UT 84070-2628
Tel (801) 569-2700 *Founded/Ownrshp* 1960
Sales 109.8MM *EMP* 1,100
SIC 8351 8211

D-U-N-S 79-996-3616 IMP
■ **CHALMETTE REFINING LLC**
(*Suby of* PBF HOLDING CO LLC) ★
500 W Saint Bernard Hwy, Chalmette, LA 70043-4821
Tel (504) 281-1212 *Founded/Ownrshp* 2015
Sales 225.2MM^E *EMP* 600
SIC 2911 Petroleum refining
CEO: Thomas J Nimbley

D-U-N-S 08-438-3041 IMP
CHAMBERLAIN GROUP INC
LIFTMASTER
(*Suby of* CHAMBERLAIN MANUFACTURING CORP) ★
845 N Larch Ave, Elmhurst, IL 60126-1114
Tel (630) 279-3600 *Founded/Ownrshp* 1986
Sales 1.3MMM^E *EMP* 4,100
SIC 3699 Door opening & closing devices, electrical
CEO: Joanna Sohovich
**Ch Bd:* Craig J Duchossois
Pr: Rob Keller
**Pr:* Robert I Baker
**Pr:* James J Roberts
**CFO:* Brendan Gilboy
Ex VP: Betsy Morton
Ex VP: Brad Opel
**VP:* Kenneth Clay
**VP:* Michael E Flannery
VP: N Williams

D-U-N-S 00-528-4864 IMP/EXP
CHAMBERLAIN MANUFACTURING CORP
(*Suby of* DUCHOSSOIS GROUP INC) ★
845 N Larch Ave, Elmhurst, IL 60126-1196
Tel (630) 279-3600 *Founded/Ownrshp* 1977
Sales 1.3MMM^E *EMP* 5,665
SIC 3651 3625 3699 Household audio & video equipment; Relays & industrial controls; Door opening & closing devices, electrical
Ch: Richard L Duchossois
CFO: Lee E Johnson
**VP:* Craig J Duchossois
VP: Alex Parsadayan
**Prin:* Merton L Townsend
Mktg Dir: Tom Brookbank

D-U-N-S 14-717-1102
CHAMBERLIN WATERPROOFING & ROOFING SYSTEMS INC
7510 Langtry St, Houston, TX 77040-6629
Tel (713) 880-1432 *Founded/Ownrshp* 1897
Sales 92.0MM^E *EMP* 355
SIC 1799 1761 Waterproofing; Roofing contractor
Pr: John M Kafka
**Genl Pt:* Art Canales
**VP:* David Neal
**VP:* Marty Stroud
IT Man: Shawn Buzek
Sfty Dirs: Jeremy Waldorf
Mktg Dir: Monica Keels
Snr PM: Shane Hubbard

D-U-N-S 00-281-2873
CHAMBERS & OWEN INC (WI)
CHAMBERS & OWEN WHOLESALE
1733 Morse St, Janesville, WI 53545-0206
Tel (608) 752-7865 *Founded/Ownrshp* 1891
Sales 131.1MM^E *EMP* 275
SIC 5194 5145 5113 5141

CHAMBERS & OWEN WHOLESALE
See CHAMBERS & OWEN INC

D-U-N-S 07-217-3305
■ **CHAMBERS DEVELOPMENT CO INC**
(*Suby of* WM) ★
1001 Fannin St Ste 400, Houston, TX 77002-6759
Tel (713) 877-8793 *Founded/Ownrshp* 1995
Sales 625.6MM^E *EMP* 2,000
SIC 4953 Refuse systems; Dumps, operation of; Sanitary landfill operation; Sludge disposal sites
CEO: John Drury
Ch Bd: Alexander W Rangos Sr
**Pr:* Rodney R Proto
CFO: Earl E De Frates
Treas: Ronald H Jones
**V Ch Bd:* Kosti Shirvanian
Sr VP: Susan J Piller
Sr VP: William A Rothrock
VP: Gregory T Sangalis
VP: Bruce E Snyder

D-U-N-S 80-377-6244
CHAMBERS EXPRESS TRUCKING INC
2132 Bluebonnet Ln, Matthews, NC 28104-8558
Tel (704) 292-2916 *Founded/Ownrshp* 1985
Sales 500.0MM *EMP* 50
SIC 4212 Local trucking, without storage
Pr: Marvin Chambers

CHAMBERS MOTOR CARS OF BOSTON
See HERB CHAMBERS I-93 INC

D-U-N-S 07-119-7503 IMP
CHAMBERSBURG HOSPITAL
(*Suby of* SUMMIT HEALTH) ★
112 N 7th St, Chambersburg, PA 17201-1700
Tel (717) 267-3000 *Founded/Ownrshp* 1994
Sales 317.4MM *EMP* 1,729
Accts Smith Elliott Kearns & Company
SIC 8062 General medical & surgical hospitals
**Ch Bd:* Nancy Meyers
Pr: Sam Satzer
**CEO:* Patrick O Donnell
**Treas:* Dennis Wilson
Ofcr: Patrick O'Donnell
VP: David Carlson
VP: Michele Zeigler
Dir Rad: Glenn Wingert
QA Dir: Nancy Probst
Dir IT: John Lucabaugh
Pr Dir: Sheran White

D-U-N-S 06-087-2322
CHAMPAIGN COMMUNITY UNIT SCHOOL DISTRICT 4 (INC)
703 S New St, Champaign, IL 61820-5818
Tel (217) 351-3800 *Founded/Ownrshp* 1860
Sales 157.5MM *EMP* 1,300
Accts Baker Tilly Virchow Krause Ll
SIC 8211 8351 Public elementary & secondary schools; Preschool center
COO: John Staab
**Ex Dir:* Matthew Foster
**Ex Dir:* Kenneth Kleber
Dir IT: Sandra Duckworth
IT Man: Michele Johnson
Teacher Pr: Ken Kleber

D-U-N-S 09-972-9840
CHAMPAIGN RESIDENTIAL SERVICES INC
1150 Scioto St Ste 201, Urbana, OH 43078-2292
Tel (937) 653-1320 *Founded/Ownrshp* 1976
Sales 38.6MM *EMP* 1,200
Accts Brady Ware & Schoenfeld Inc C
SIC 8361 Home for the mentally retarded
CEO: Than Johnson
COO: Martin Fagans
CFO: Scott Delong
**Ch:* Ed Corwin
**Treas:* Jeff McCulla
Trst: Phil Edwards
Mtls Mgr: Richard Anderson
Sfty Mgr: Cindy Marks
Pr Dir: Linda Smith

CHAMPIGN CNTY RGIONAL PLG COMM
See COUNTY OF CHAMPAIGN

D-U-N-S 06-589-7688 IMP
CHAMPION BRANDS INC
5571 Fl Min Blvd S, Jacksonville, FL 32257-3682
Tel (660) 885-8151 *Founded/Ownrshp* 1985
Sales 93.1MM^E *EMP* 245^E
SIC 5181 Beer & other fermented malt liquors
Pr: Alvin E Benton Jr
**VP:* F Neal Runnels
IT Man: Becky Edenfield

D-U-N-S 04-088-1062
CHAMPION CONTAINER CORP
1455 N Michael Dr, Wood Dale, IL 60191-1015
Tel (630) 279-4600 *Founded/Ownrshp* 1975
Sales 187.9MM^E *EMP* 153^E
SIC 5113 Corrugated & solid fiber boxes
Prin: Charles S Wollensak
Genl Mgr: Dave Reich
Sales Asso: Chris Borzello

D-U-N-S 82-696-1018 EXP
CHAMPION ENERGY HOLDINGS LLC
1500 Rankin Rd Ste 200, Houston, TX 77073-4807
Tel (281) 653-5090 *Founded/Ownrshp* 2008
Sales 372.0MM^E *EMP* 470
SIC 4911 Electric services
CEO: David Tudor
**CFO:* Michael D Slaughter
**Ch:* James Crane
VP: Brenda Crockett
Sls Mgr: Jeremy Gonser

D-U-N-S 82-696-1042 IMP
■ **CHAMPION ENERGY MARKETING LLC**
(*Suby of* CALPINE CORP) ★
1500 Rankin Rd Ste 200, Houston, TX 77073-4807
Tel (281) 653-5090 *Founded/Ownrshp* 2015
Sales 328.6MM^E *EMP* 284
SIC 4911 Distribution, electric power
**Pr:* David Tudor
**CFO:* Michael Slaughter
Sr VP: Brian Tamplen
VP: David Coffman
VP: Brenda Corckett
VP: Alon Erlichman
VP: Jason Fox
VP: Jeffrey S Young

D-U-N-S 78-881-8008
■ **CHAMPION ENERGY SERVICES LLC**
(*Suby of* CHAMPION ENERGY MARKETING LLC) ★
1500 Rankin Rd Ste 200, Houston, TX 77073-4807
Tel (281) 653-5090 *Founded/Ownrshp* 2005
Sales 328.4MM^E *EMP* 200
SIC 4911 Distribution, electric power
Pr: David J Tudor
**COO:* Michael Sullivan
**CFO:* Michael Slaughter
VP: David Coffman
VP: Brenda Crockett
VP: Jeff Young
Dir Bus: Jim F Fluet
Prgrm Mgr: Bill B Blackwood
IT Man: Alon Erlichman
IT Man: Berenice Garcia
IT Man: Lamar Pagnotta

D-U-N-S 96-256-5607
CHAMPION ENTERPRISES HOLDINGS LLC
755 W Big Beaver Rd, Troy, MI 48084-4900
Tel (248) 614-8200 *Founded/Ownrshp* 2010
Sales 1.2MMM^E *EMP* 4,100^E
SIC 1521 Single-family housing construction
CEO: John N Lawless III
**CFO:* Phyllis A Knight
CFO: Sharon Sisk
Genl Mgr: Kevin Bouvia
IT Man: Tony Hubble
IT Man: Bozana Miladinovich
IT Man: Eleanor T Walk
VP Opers: Bobby Williams
Sls Mgr: Jeff Mooring
Sls Mgr: Paul Robertson

D-U-N-S 00-531-8746
CHAMPION HOME BUILDERS INC
(*Suby of* CHAMPION ENTERPRISES HOLDINGS LLC) ★
755 W Big Beaver Rd # 1000, Troy, MI 48084-4908
Tel (248) 614-8200 *Founded/Ownrshp* 1953, 2010
Sales 1.1MMM^E *EMP* 2,504
SIC 1521 2451 Single-family housing construction; Mobile homes, except recreational
Pr: Phyllis Knight
**CEO:* John N Lawless
**CFO:* Mark J Yost
VP: William H Stamer
VP Mfg: David French

D-U-N-S 00-484-4163 IMP
CHAMPION INC (MI)
180 Traders Mine Rd, Iron Mountain, MI 49801-1447
Tel (906) 779-2300 *Founded/Ownrshp* 1921
Sales 87.5MM^E *EMP* 500
SIC 8741 1542 5063 5082 3273 3272

D-U-N-S 00-818-0200
CHAMPION INDUSTRIES INC
(*Suby of* CHAMPION INDUSTRIES, INC.)
10848 Airline Hwy, Baton Rouge, LA 70816-4234
Tel (225) 291-9090 *Founded/Ownrshp* 1948
Sales 131.3MM^E *EMP* 700
SIC 2542 2759 2791 2789 2752 Showcases (not refrigerated): except wood; Maps: printing; Typesetting; Bookbinding & related work; Commercial printing, lithographic
Pr: Marshall Reynolds
Div/Sub He: Marc Kitchen
Div Mgr: Todd Ross

D-U-N-S 00-614-7342 IMP/EXP
CHAMPION LABORATORIES INC
(*Suby of* UCI) ★
200 S 4th St, Albion, IL 62806-1313
Tel (618) 445-6011 *Founded/Ownrshp* 1929, 2003
Sales 1.0MMM^E *EMP* 2,993
SIC 3714 Filters: oil, fuel & air, motor vehicle
Pr: Greg Noethlich
**Pr:* Wolfgang Winder
**CFO:* Michael Gibbons
Ofcr: Joyce Leigh
VP: Teresa Schnautz
**VP:* Keith A Zar
IT Man: Trish Berry
Plnt Mgr: David Cullison

D-U-N-S 00-425-6095 IMP
CHAMPION OPCO LLC (OH)
CHAMPION WINDOWS MANUFACTURING
12121 Champion Way, Cincinnati, OH 45241-6419
Tel (513) 924-4858 *Founded/Ownrshp* 1953
Sales 572.7MM^E *EMP* 2,000
SIC 3089 1761 3442 Window frames & sash, plastic; Siding contractor; Storm doors or windows, metal
CEO: Jim Mishler
**Pr:* Donald R Jones
**CFO:* Joe Faisant
VP: Mitch Spring
Exec: Kathy G Crawley
VP Admn: Martin Hiedet

D-U-N-S 04-423-5513
CHAMPION PACKAGING & DISTRIBUTION INC
1840 Internationale Pkwy, Woodridge, IL 60517-4944
Tel (630) 755-4220 *Founded/Ownrshp* 1989
Sales 85.2MM^E *EMP* 160
SIC 2842 2812 Ammonia, household; Chlorine, compressed or liquefied
CEO: Thomas J Pecora

CHAMPION POLYMERS RECYCLING
See INFILTRATOR WATER TECHNOLOGIES LLC

D-U-N-S 15-084-1703 IMP
CHAMPION POWER EQUIPMENT INC
12039 Smith Ave, Santa Fe Springs, CA 90670-3256
Tel (877) 338-0999 *Founded/Ownrshp* 2003
Sales 94.7MM^E *EMP* 36
SIC 5084

D-U-N-S 11-862-1275
CHAMPION SOLUTIONS GROUP INC
791 Park Of Commerce Blvd, Boca Raton, FL 33487-3632
Tel (800) 771-7000 *Founded/Ownrshp* 1983
Sales 221.4MM^E *EMP* 130
SIC 5045 5734 Computer peripheral equipment; Computer peripheral equipment
Ch: Michael Baker
**Pr:* Chris Pyle
**CFO:* Mike Priceman
VP: Joyce Schachter
Snr Sftwr: Jason Milgram
Dir IT: Batrice Vener
Opers Mgr: Candice Hardy

D-U-N-S 07-415-6910
CHAMPION WINDOW INC
(*Suby of* ATRIUM WINDOWS AND DOORS INC) ★
12427 Duncan Rd, Houston, TX 77066-2109
Tel (281) 440-7000 *Founded/Ownrshp* 2006
Sales 64.2MM^E *EMP* 1,100
SIC 3442 Storm doors or windows, metal
CEO: Ralph Zuckerberg
**CFO:* Patrick Cahill
Treas: Patrick Coffee
**VP:* J Michael Byrd
**VP:* Christopher Kiley
VP: John Sehn
Exec: Susan Forrester
Dir IT: John Thrash
IT Man: Lee Lehmann
Sfty Mgr: Bill Cordova

CHAMPION WINDOWS MANUFACTURING
See CHAMPION OPCO LLC

D-U-N-S 79-318-1764
CHAMPIONS CINCO PIPE & SUPPLY LLC
CINCO V PIPE & SUPPLY
(*Suby of* MITSUI & CO (USA) INC) ★
4 Greenspoint Mall # 16945, Houston, TX 77060-1825
Tel (713) 468-6555 *Founded/Ownrshp* 2012
Sales 300.0MM *EMP* 41
SIC 5051 Pipe & tubing, steel
CEO: Yoshikazu Miyajima
**COO:* Jesse Pearson
**CFO:* Nobuhiro Shinozaki
Sys Mgr: Errol Demirsu
Sales Asso: Andrew Luchak

D-U-N-S 06-052-5094
CHAMPLAIN COLLEGE INC
246 S Willard St, Burlington, VT 05401-3919
Tel (802) 860-2700 *Founded/Ownrshp* 1878
Sales 106.5MM *EMP* 250^E
Accts Kpmg Llp Colchester Vt
SIC 8222 Junior college
Pr: David F Finney
Pt: Nicole Ravlin
**Treas:* Daniel Mahoney
Treas: Shelley Navari
Ofcr: Patrick Kennedy
Assoc VP: Mary M Lee
**Sr VP:* David Provost
Assoc Dir: Patricia Boera
Assoc Dir: Ryan Bongard
Assoc Dir: Jennifer Jang
Dir Bus: Tom Myers

D-U-N-S 07-721-9590
CHAMPLAIN OIL CO INC
45 San Remo Dr, South Burlington, VT 05403-6348
Tel (802) 864-5380 *Founded/Ownrshp* 1963
Sales 96.6MM^E *EMP* 83
SIC 5172 5984 Petroleum products; Liquefied petroleum gas dealers
Pr: Charles A Cairns
Genl Mgr: Brian Cairns
Genl Mgr: Dwight Lafountain
Off Mgr: Scott Willard
Dir IT: Tim Peirce
Sfty Mgr: Steve Halibozek
Sls Mgr: Annette Couillard

D-U-N-S 01-114-0741
CHAMPLAIN VALLEY PHYSICIANS HOSPITAL
CVPH MEDICAL CENTER
75 Beekman St, Plattsburgh, NY 12901-1438
Tel (518) 561-2000 *Founded/Ownrshp* 1926
Sales 289.2MM *EMP* 2,000
SIC 8062 General medical & surgical hospitals
Pr: Stephens Mundy
Chf Path: Eric Gorman
**COO:* Debra Donahue
**CFO:* Joyce Rafferty
Bd of Dir: William Owens
Ofcr: Kirsten Pope
Assoc VP: Julie Brunell
Assoc VP: Bill King
Sr VP: Dana Jewerler
VP: Noreen Brady
VP: Donna Dalton
**VP:* Michelle Lebeauv
**VP:* Wouter Rietsema MD
Dir Risk M: Deborah Stewart
Dir Rad: Gary King
Dir Rx: Thomas Gosrich

D-U-N-S 15-978-1327
CHAMPPS OPERATING CORP
(*Suby of* F & H ACQUISITION CORP) ★
151 S Whittier St Ofc, Wichita, KS 67207-1095
Tel (800) 229-2118 *Founded/Ownrshp* 2007
Sales 54.2MM^E *EMP* 1,029
SIC 5812 5813 American restaurant; Bar (drinking places)
CEO: James K Zielke
Pt: Donny Feinberg
Pt: Brian James
Pt: Tim Klunk
Pt: Tom McCabe
Pt: Kevin O'Hare
Pt: James Rennie
Mng Pt: Amy Adams
**CEO:* Michael P O'Donnell
**CFO:* David D Womack
**VP:* Donna L Depoian
**VP:* J David Miller

CHAMPS
See ROBBYS SPORTING GOODS INC

CHAMPS SPORTS
See FOOT LOCKER SPECIALTY INC

D-U-N-S 17-425-3695
CHANCELIGHT INC
EDUCATIONAL SERVICES AMERICA
1321 Murfreesboro Pike, Nashville, TN 37217-2626
Tel (615) 361-4000 *Founded/Ownrshp* 1994
Sales 103.0MM^E *EMP* 2,600
SIC 8299 Educational services
CEO: Mark Claypool
Pr: Finn McLaughlin
**Pr:* Allison O Neill
**Pr:* Allison O'Neill
**CEO:* Mark K Claypool
COO: Gail Henderson
**COO:* Ann Eldridge Kolb
Ex VP: Cate Lewandowski
**Ex VP:* John M McLaughlin
Ex VP: John McLaughlin
Ex VP: Bryan Skelton

Ex VP: Brad J Wieck
**Sr VP:* Melissa Harrell
Sr VP: Stephanie Martin
VP: Karen Lefever
VP: Alan Watson
VP Bus Dev: Carmen Rivera-Jara
VP Bus Dev: Tim Ulmer

CHANCELLOR SURGERY CENTER
See SAINT ELIZABETH MEDICAL CENTER INC

CHANCELLOR'S OFFICE
See UNIVERSITY OF WISCONSIN-MADISON

D-U-N-S 55-590-9621
CHANDLER CONCRETE INC
1006 S Church St, Burlington, NC 27215-5046
Tel (336) 272-6127 *Founded/Ownrshp* 2010
Sales 125.8MM[E] *EMP* 354
SIC 3273 Ready-mixed concrete
Pr: Ted Chandler
VP: Bob Chandler
**VP:* Robert Chandler
VP: Jeff Hinkle
Off Mgr: Pat James
Dir IT: Dennis Woody
IT Man: Rich Gabrielli
IT Man: James J Woody
IT Man: Joyce Yates
Site Mgr: Randy Bryant
Ql Cn Mgr: John Weeks

D-U-N-S 11-386-8991
CHANDLER EARNHARDTS MAZDA
7300 W Orchid Ln, Chandler, AZ 85226-1000
Tel (480) 893-0000 *Founded/Ownrshp* 2004
Sales 71.8MM[E] *EMP* 1,800
SIC 5511 Automobiles, new & used
Pr: Tex Earhardt

D-U-N-S 07-445-3556
CHANDLER REGIONAL MEDICAL CENTER
CATHOLIC HEALTHCARE WEST
(*Suby of* DIGNITY HEALTH) ★
1955 W Frye Rd, Chandler, AZ 85224-6282
Tel (480) 728-3000 *Founded/Ownrshp* 1995
Sales 438.4MM *EMP* 1,900
SIC 8062 General medical & surgical hospitals
Pr: Tim Bricker
CFO: Mark Kem
VP: Marty Breeden
Dir Case M: Jean Maslan
Dir Sec: Dave Lambert
Sfty Dirs: Brian Evans
Surgeon: Kaye Prost
Obsttrcn: David Kells
Obsttrcn: Clinton Leonard
Snr PM: Kevin Blackman

D-U-N-S 00-290-1486
CHANDLER UNIFIED SCHOOL DISTRICT
1525 W Frye Rd, Chandler, AZ 85224-6112
Tel (480) 812-7000 *Founded/Ownrshp* 1934
Sales 243.9MM[E] *EMP* 4,500
SIC 8211 Public elementary & secondary schools
VP: Karin Delacroix
VP: Rose Devine
Exec: Joel Wirth
Dir IT: Steve Ydarra
IT Man: Marylou Hagerty
IT Man: Diane West
Teacher Pr: Jeff Filloon

D-U-N-S 07-874-2500
CHANDLER UNIFIED SCHOOL DISTRICT 80-HHS AFJROTC
3700 S Arizona Ave, Chandler, AZ 85248-4500
Tel (480) 883-5000 *Founded/Ownrshp* 1920
Sales 10.0MM[E] *EMP* 4,600
SIC 8211 Elementary & secondary schools

D-U-N-S 00-193-0254 IMP
CHANEL INC (NY)
(*Suby of* CHANEL)
9 W 57th St Fl 44, New York, NY 10019-2790
Tel (212) 688-5055 *Founded/Ownrshp* 1956
Sales 249.1MM[E] *EMP* 1,450
SIC 5632 2844 5122 5944 5961 5999 Apparel accessories; Cosmetic preparations; Perfumes & colognes; Perfumes; Jewelry stores; Watches; Jewelry, mail order; Perfumes & colognes
Ch Bd: Alain W Wertheimer
Pr: Christine Dagousset
Pr: Veronica Hrdy
Treas: Kenneth Ellmer
**Ex VP:* Michael Rena
Sr VP: Susan Clatworthy
Sr VP: Ava Huang
Sr VP: Adina Kagan
**Sr VP:* Michael Murphy
Sr VP: Jean Hoehn Zimmerman
VP: Christine Esteban
VP: Barbara Garjian
VP: Cecile Gaume
VP: Elizabeth Mankin
**VP:* Gary Mesnick
VP: Kate Shone
VP: Scott Widro
VP: Renette Zimmerly
Assoc Dir: Arianne Gold
Assoc Dir: Matthew Jadro

D-U-N-S 16-742-3045 IMP
CHANEY ENTERPRISES LIMITED PARTNERSHIP
2410 Evergreen Rd Ste 201, Gambrills, MD 21054-1979
Tel (410) 451-0197 *Founded/Ownrshp* 1990
Sales 141.6MM[E] *EMP* 365
SIC 3273 1442 5032 3429 Ready-mixed concrete; Construction sand & gravel; Stone, crushed or broken; Builders' hardware
Ch Bd: Francis H Chaney II
Pt: Donna C Bunn
CEO: William F Childs IV
CFO: Tom Flynn
VP: Christopher R Bunn
VP: Francis Chaney III

D-U-N-S 83-942-8976 IMP
CHANG INTERNATIONAL INC
1611 Market St, Kirkland, WA 98033-4963
Tel (206) 283-9098 *Founded/Ownrshp* 1994
Sales 84.9MM[E] *EMP* 6
SIC 5146 Seafoods
Pr: Jiangrong Jerry Chang
Treas: Amy Brecht
Ex VP: Stone Wong

D-U-N-S 04-742-1003
CHANGE HEALTHCARE HOLDINGS INC
(*Suby of* BEAGLE PARENT CORP) ★
3055 Lebanon Pike # 1000, Nashville, TN 37214-2230
Tel (615) 932-3000 *Founded/Ownrshp* 2011
Sales 1.4MMM *EMP* 3,300[E]
SIC 7374 Data processing service
Pr: Neil De Crescenzo
**CFO:* Randy Giles
**CFO:* Bob A Newport Jr
Bd of Dir: Carrie Johnson
Ofcr: Thomas W McEnery
Ofcr: Linda Whitley-Taylor
Ex VP: Alex Choy
Ex VP: Jason Erdell
Ex VP: Randy P Giles
Ex VP: Kris Joshi
**Ex VP:* Sajid Khan
Ex VP: Kevin Mahoney
Ex VP: Chris Olson
Ex VP: Greg Stevens
**Ex VP:* Gregory T Stevens
**Ex VP:* Gary D Stuart
Sr VP: Miriam J Paramore
**VP:* Kevin C Barrett
VP: Richard Brook
VP: Andrew Fischer
VP: Raymond Jebsen
Board of Directors: Michael Dal Bello, Howard L Lance, Philip M Pead, Pamela J Pure, Neil P Simpkins, Allen R Thorpe

D-U-N-S 96-244-2567
CHANGE HEALTHCARE OPERATIONS LLC
(*Suby of* MEDIFAX-EDI LLC) ★
3055 Lebanon Pike # 1000, Nashville, TN 37214-2230
Tel (615) 932-3000 *Founded/Ownrshp* 2010
Sales 306.6MM[E] *EMP* 2,200[E]
SIC 7374 8741 8099 Data processing & preparation; Management services; Childbirth preparation clinic
Pr: Neil De Crescenzo
Pr: Ben Cortright
CFO: Randy Giles
Sr VP: Jeff Kerley
Sr VP: Tommy Lewis
Sr VP: Dave Libardi
VP: Kelly Butler
Ex Dir: Leonard Williamson
DP Exec: Pramod Panasa
VP Sls: Mark Jakubik
VP Sls: Debra Stall

D-U-N-S 83-185-1113
CHANGEIS INC
1530 Wilson Blvd Ste 340, Arlington, VA 22209-2447
Tel (301) 237-1622 *Founded/Ownrshp* 2008
Sales 180.0MM *EMP* 15
SIC 8742 Management consulting services
Pr: Urvashi Malhotra

CHANGING LANES TRNSP BRKS
See ALLIED TRANSPORTATION SERVICES INC

D-U-N-S 04-020-1365
CHANNEL 1 CORP
15 River Rd Ste 210, Wilton, CT 06897-4064
Tel (203) 523-5500 *Founded/Ownrshp* 1997
Sales 23.8MM[E] *EMP* 2,000[E]
Accts Politi & Magnifico Llc
SIC 8742 Marketing consulting services
Pr: Edward Sherman
Genl Mgr: Dane Risley

CHANNEL 2
See WGBH EDUCATIONAL FOUNDATION

CHANNEL 56 KDOC
See ELLIS COMMUNICATIONS KDOC LLC

CHANNEL 7
See WHDH-TV INC

CHANNEL ALLOLY
See PRIMROSE ALLOYS INC

D-U-N-S 55-692-7572 IMP/EXP
CHANNEL CONTROL MERCHANTS LLC
6892 U S Highway 49, Hattiesburg, MS 39402-9135
Tel (601) 268-7555 *Founded/Ownrshp* 1991
Sales 160.6MM[E] *EMP* 750
SIC 5331 Variety stores
Pr: Bill C Hudson Jr
**COO:* Wynn Stevenson
**CFO:* Rick Preusch
**Sr VP:* Rick Shadix
**VP:* Ben Hudson
**Prin:* Robert T Jackson Sr
IT Man: Richard Blackledge
VP Mktg: Sue Blackmer

D-U-N-S 07-873-8300
CHANNEL POINT HOSPITALITY LLC
(*Suby of* AIMBRIDGE HOSPITALITY LLC) ★
5851 Legacy Cir Ste 400, Plano, TX 75024-5979
Tel (972) 952-0200 *Founded/Ownrshp* 2012
Sales 36.9MM[E] *EMP* 1,070
SIC 8741 Hotel or motel management
COO: Robert Burg
CFO: Judy Hendrick
Genl Mgr: Scott Gibson
IT Man: Michael Grant
VP Opers: Tony Maness

D-U-N-S 16-729-6628 IMP/EXP
CHANNEL PRIME ALLIANCE LLC
(*Suby of* RAVAGO SA)
1803 Hull Ave, Des Moines, IA 50313-4738
Tel (515) 264-4110 *Founded/Ownrshp* 2004
Sales 88.0MM[E] *EMP* 50[E]
SIC 5169 Resins, synthetic rubber
Genl Mgr: Joe Muhs
Opers Mgr: Dwight Grasmick

D-U-N-S 83-308-9621
CHANNEL TECHNOLOGIES GROUP LLC
CTG
879 Ward Dr, Santa Barbara, CA 93111-2920
Tel (805) 967-0171 *Founded/Ownrshp* 2012
Sales 60.0MM *EMP* 1,356
SIC 3812 Search & navigation equipment
CEO: Christopher E Holmes
VP: Randy Copperman
VP Opers: Art Campbell

D-U-N-S 02-788-6667
▲ **CHANNELADVISOR CORP**
3025 Carringtn Ml Blvd # 500, Morrisville, NC 27560-5440
Tel (919) 228-4700 *Founded/Ownrshp* 2001
Sales 100.5MM *EMP* 601
Tkr Sym ECOM *Exch* NYS
SIC 7372 Prepackaged software; Application computer software; Business oriented computer software
CEO: David J Spitz
**Ch Bd:* M Scot Wingo
CFO: Mark E Cook
Ofcr: Ryan C Walsh
VP: Diana S Allen
**CTO:* Aris A Buinevicius
Sales Exec: Ryan Bernthal
Sales Exec: Andrea Noel
Sales Exec: Jeff Rosefsky
Board of Directors: Timothy J Buckley, Joseph L Cowan, Janet R Cowell, Marc E Huffman, Timothy V Williams

D-U-N-S 00-414-9951 EXP
■ **CHAPARRAL BOATS INC** (GA)
(*Suby of* MARINE PRODUCTS CORP) ★
300 Industrial Park Blvd, Nashville, GA 31639-1817
Tel (229) 686-7481 *Founded/Ownrshp* 1967
Sales 123.4MM[E] *EMP* 300
SIC 3732 Boats, fiberglass: building & repairing
CEO: James A Lane Jr
**CFO:* Jeffrey M Smith
**VP:* William S Pegg
Sfty Mgr: Randy Wilson
Mktg Dir: Bill Mudgett
Board of Directors: Gary W Rollins, R Randall Rollins

D-U-N-S 62-360-4217
CHAPARRAL ENERGY INC
701 Cedar Lake Blvd, Oklahoma City, OK 73114-7806
Tel (405) 478-8770 *Founded/Ownrshp* 1988
Sales 324.3MM *EMP* 366[E]
SIC 1311 1382 Crude petroleum production; Natural gas production; Oil & gas exploration services
Ch Bd: Mark A Fischer
**Pr:* K Earl Reynolds
COO: Kevin Davis
CFO: Joseph O Evans
Sr VP: James M Miller
VP: Richard Parma
Mng Dir: Christopher Behrens
Snr Sftwr: Michael Akin
CIO: Scott Hunter
Sftwr Eng: Odessa Jones
Genl Couns: Robert Kelly
Board of Directors: Christopher Behrens, Charles A Fischer Jr, Will Jaudes

D-U-N-S 19-605-5222
CHAPARRAL ENERGY LLC
(*Suby of* CHAPARRAL ENERGY INC) ★
701 Cedar Lake Blvd, Oklahoma City, OK 73114-7806
Tel (405) 478-8770 *Founded/Ownrshp* 1988
Sales 284.1MM[E] *EMP* 300
SIC 1311 1382 Crude petroleum production; Natural gas production; Oil & gas exploration services
**Pr:* Earl Reynolds
**CEO:* Mark Fischer
**CFO:* Joseph O Evans
**Sr VP:* Don Culpepper Jr
Sr VP: John D Wehrle
Sr VP: David R Winchester
VP: Jeanette Coker
**VP:* Reggie Cook
Board of Directors: Christopher C Behrens, Karl F Kurz, Aubrey K McClendon

CHAPEL HILL COMMUNITY
See UNITED CHURCH HOMES INC

D-U-N-S 10-914-3768
CHAPEL HILL-CARRBORO CITY SCHOOL SYSTEM
CHAPEL HLL-CARRBORO CY SCHOOLS
750 S Merritt Mill Rd, Chapel Hill, NC 27516-2878
Tel (919) 967-8211 *Founded/Ownrshp* 1900
Sales 137.5MM *EMP* 2,000
Accts Anderson Smith & Wike Pllc Ro
SIC 8211 Public combined elementary & secondary school
Dir IT: Marnita Morrow
IT Man: Hunter Pendleton
Pr Dir: Jeff Nash
Mktg Mgr: Darian Harris
Schl Brd P: Janezetta Bedford
Teacher Pr: Arasi Adkins
Teacher Pr: Arasi Atkins
Teacher Pr: Erika Newkirk

CHAPEL HLL-CARRBORO CY SCHOOLS
See CHAPEL HILL-CARRBORO CITY SCHOOL SYSTEM

CHAPEL OF CHIMES
See SKYLAWN

D-U-N-S 06-740-0093 IMP/EXP
■ **CHAPEL STEEL CORP**
(*Suby of* RELIANCE STEEL & ALUMINUM CO) ★
590 N Bethlehem Pike, Ambler, PA 19002-2641
Tel (215) 793-0899 *Founded/Ownrshp* 2005
Sales 89.5MM[E] *EMP* 105
SIC 5051 Steel
Pr: Stanley Altman
**CFO:* Karla Lewis
**Treas:* G Patrick Jones
**VP:* Matt Tocci

D-U-N-S 07-327-2866
CHAPIN SCHOOL
100 E End Ave, New York, NY 10028-7498
Tel (212) 744-2335 *Founded/Ownrshp* 1901
Sales 84.0MM *EMP* 150
Accts Eisneramper Llp New York Ny
SIC 8211 Elementary school; Secondary school
CTO: Thomas Palermo
Prd Mgr: Luc Hotaling
Mktg Dir: Anneli Ballard
Psych: Shanna France

D-U-N-S 07-440-7107
CHAPMAN AND CUTLER LLP
111 W Monroe St Ste 1700, Chicago, IL 60603-4080
Tel (312) 845-3000 *Founded/Ownrshp* 2009
Sales 91.1MM[E] *EMP* 475
SIC 8111 General practice law office; Securities law; Corporate, partnership & business law; Real estate law
Pt: Richard A Cosgrove
Pt: Craig Fishman
Pt: Rachel G George
Pt: Felicia B Graham
Pt: Daniel L Johnson
Pt: Douglas L Madsen
Pt: Michael H Mitchell
Pt: Mark R Riccardi
Pt: Suzanne L Shier
Mng Pt: Marc Franson
Off Mgr: Barbara Norton

D-U-N-S 00-434-6821
CHAPMAN CORP (PA)
331 S Main St, Washington, PA 15301-6367
Tel (724) 228-1900 *Founded/Ownrshp* 1946
Sales 153.6MM[E] *EMP* 300[E]
SIC 1541 1542

D-U-N-S 07-252-8433
CHAPMAN UNIVERSITY
1 University Dr, Orange, CA 92866-1005
Tel (714) 997-6815 *Founded/Ownrshp* 1861
Sales 424.8MM *EMP* 3,300
Accts Kpmg Llp Irvine Ca
SIC 8221 College, except junior
Pr: James Doti
Pr: Mike Price
**COO:* Harold Hewitt
Ofcr: Joe Franklin
Ofcr: Eduardo A Monge
**Ex VP:* Harold W Hewitt Jr
Ex VP: Hamid Shirvani
VP: Brenton Burke
VP: Janine P Dumontelle
VP: Carrie Ferrando
VP: Kris E Olsen
VP: Jesse Richards
VP: Ben Smith
VP: Ernest Wang
VP: Parham H Williams
VP: Mark Woodland
Dir: Carol Bonner
Creative D: Jeff Brouwer

D-U-N-S 11-263-4154
CHAPMAN UNIVERSITY
SCHOOL OF FILM AND TELEVISION
(*Suby of* CHAPMAN UNIVERSITY) ★
283 N Cypress St, Orange, CA 92866-1311
Tel (714) 997-6765 *Founded/Ownrshp* 1992
Sales 369.4MM *EMP* 40
Accts Kpmg Llp Los Angeles Ca
SIC 8221 University

D-U-N-S 07-095-8327
CHAPPAQUA CENTRAL SCHOOL DISTRICT INC
HORACE GREELEY HIGH SCHOOL
70 Roaring Brook Rd, Chappaqua, NY 10514-1710
Tel (914) 238-7200 *Founded/Ownrshp* 1900
Sales 117.2MM *EMP* 515
Accts O Connor Davies Llp Harrison
SIC 8211 Public senior high school
VP: Alyson Kiesel
Adm Dir: Pamela Tow
Schl Brd P: Warren Messner

CHAPPARAL DRILLING FLUIDS
See LARIAT SERVICES INC

D-U-N-S 87-737-3290 IMP
CHARAH INC
12601 Plantside Dr, Louisville, KY 40299-6386
Tel (502) 245-1353 *Founded/Ownrshp* 1986
Sales 1.1MMM[E] *EMP* 450[E]
Accts York Neel & Co Madisonville
SIC 1081 4953 Metal mining exploration & development services; Recycling, waste materials
Prin: Charles Price
Pr: Nathan Boone
**COO:* Scott Sewell
Ex VP: Peter Dequattro
**Ex VP:* Danny Gray
**VP:* Janet Price
VP: Scott Ziegler
Rgnl Mgr: Ray Bell
Rgnl Mgr: Walter Fox
Rgnl Mgr: Bobby Raia
Genl Mgr: Keith Bolen

CHARIOT TRAVELWARE
See DAMAO LUGGAGE INTERNATIONAL INC

D-U-N-S 00-886-4865
CHARITIES AID FOUNDATION AMERICA
1800 Diagonal Rd Ste 150, Alexandria, VA 22314-2840
Tel (703) 549-8931 *Founded/Ownrshp* 1992
Sales 107.7MM *EMP* 12
SIC 8399 Fund raising organization, non-fee basis
CEO: Susan Saxon-Harrold
**Pr:* Janet Boyd
Comm Dir: Ron Crognale
Ex Dir: John Alexander
Ex Dir: Susan Saxon
Snr Mgr: John Low

CHARITY HOSPITAL
See MEDICAL CENTER OF LOUISIANA AT NEW ORLEANS

D-U-N-S 03-038-7427 IMP/EXP
CHARKIT CHEMICAL CORP
32 Haviland St Unit 1, Norwalk, CT 06854-3005
Tel (203) 299-3220 Founded/Ownrshp 1982
Sales 85.5MM^E EMP 55
SIC 5169

D-U-N-S 96-687-5135
CHARLES AND MARGERY BARANCIK FOUNDATION
520 Lake Cook Rd, Deerfield, IL 60015-5611
Tel (847) 948-9340 Founded/Ownrshp 2011
Sales 101.6MM EMP 2
SIC 8699 Charitable organization
Prin: Charles Barancik

D-U-N-S 03-488-3488
CHARLES BLALOCK & SONS INC
409 Robert Henderson Rd, Sevierville, TN 37862-1866
Tel (865) 429-5902 Founded/Ownrshp 1952
Sales 117.1MM^E EMP 250
SIC 1611 7353 3271 3255 2951 General contractor, highway & street construction; Heavy construction equipment rental; Concrete block & brick; Clay refractories; Asphalt paving mixtures & blocks
CEO: Sidney A Blalock
*Pr: James D Blalock
VP: Allen Blalock
Exec: Scott Ward
Admn Mgr: Julie Hardin
CIO: Dail Ogle
Opers Mgr: Wesley Blalock
Sls Dir: Doug Blalock

CHARLES C. PARKS CO.
See CHARLES C PARKS CO INC

D-U-N-S 03-464-0425
CHARLES C PARKS CO INC
CHARLES C. PARKS CO.
500 N Belvedere Dr, Gallatin, TN 37066-5408
Tel (615) 452-2406 Founded/Ownrshp 1935
Sales 86.2MM EMP 145
Accts Lattimore Black Morgan And Cai
SIC 5149 Groceries & related products
Pr: Crockett Parks
*COO: James R Lanier
*CFO: Tom Cripps
Sr Cor Off: Tammy Sadler
*Sr VP: Gary Pickett

D-U-N-S 07-994-1084
CHARLES COLE MEMORIAL HOSPITAL
1001 E 2nd St, Coudersport, PA 16915-8179
Tel (814) 274-9300 Founded/Ownrshp 1910
Sales 83.2MM EMP 563
Accts Bkd Llp Springfield Missouri
SIC 7352 8069 8051 Medical equipment rental; Geriatric hospital; Skilled nursing care facilities
Pr: Edward Ptchford
Dir Risk M: Lucy Lajcsak
Comm Dir: Dawn Snyder
Ex Dir: Dennis Geitner
Ex Dir: Janice Walters
Off Mgr: Theresa Long
Off Admin: Terri Duffee
Off Admin: Nadine Shade
Telecom Ex: Kim Chitester
IT Man: Patty Wilson
Pharmcst: June Caldwell

D-U-N-S 02-146-9101
CHARLES COUNTY BOARD OF EDUCATION
5980 Radio Station Rd, La Plata, MD 20646-3337
Tel (301) 934-7224 Founded/Ownrshp 1870
Sales 391.4MM EMP 3,300
SIC 8211 School board
Ch Bd: Roberta Wise
*Ch Bd: Virginia McGraw
Opers Mgr: Mike Clarry

D-U-N-S 08-057-0500
CHARLES COUNTY GOVERNMENT
COUNTY COMMISSIONERS OF CHARLE
200 Baltimore St, La Plata, MD 20646-3580
Tel (301) 645-0550 Founded/Ownrshp 1650
Sales NA EMP 1,382
Accts Sb & Company Llc Hunt Valley
SIC 9111 County supervisors' & executives' offices;
Ofcr: Joane Gulvas
Plng Mgr: Reed Faasen

D-U-N-S 07-722-7858
CHARLES DREW UNIVERSITY OF MEDICINE AND SCIENCE
1731 E 120th St, Los Angeles, CA 90059-3051
Tel (323) 563-4800 Founded/Ownrshp 1966
Sales 61.1MM EMP 1,500
Accts Haskell & White Llp Irvine C
SIC 8221 Colleges universities & professional schools
Pr: Kieth Norris
Off Mgr: Lavonne Gordon
Nurse Mgr: O Pitts

CHARLES EAST LIFE COMMUNITY
See HEBREW HOME OF GREATER WASHINGTON

CHARLES F KETTERING MEM HOSP
See KETTERING MEDICAL CENTER

CHARLES F KETTERING MEMORIAL H
See FORT HAMILTON HOSPITAL

D-U-N-S 01-173-8901
CHARLES G KOCH CHARITABLE FOUNDATION
1515 N Courthouse Rd # 200, Arlington, VA 22201-2909
Tel (703) 875-1600 Founded/Ownrshp 2008
Sales 170.2MM EMP 2
SIC 8699 Charitable organization
Prin: Marshall Berkey

D-U-N-S 04-790-8322 IMP/EXP
CHARLES INDUSTRIES LTD
5600 Apollo Dr, Rolling Meadows, IL 60008-4049
Tel (847) 806-6300 Founded/Ownrshp 1968
Sales 131.6MM^E EMP 450
SIC 3661 3629 3677 Telephones & telephone apparatus; Electronic generation equipment; Electronic transformers
Pr: Joseph T Charles
*Pr: Robert Novak
VP: Mark Hubbard
VP: G Wes Kimes
VP: Mark Rahmel
*VP: John Sieber
VP: AVI Vaidya
*VP: Doug Wible
Netwrk Mgr: Rita Jones
Natl Sales: Fred Kolacki
Mktg Dir: Grant Erwin

D-U-N-S 00-135-5411 IMP
CHARLES KOMAR & SONS INC (NY)
KOMAR COMPANY, THE
16 E 34th St Fl 10, Jersey City, NJ 07308
Tel (212) 725-1500 Founded/Ownrshp 1908
Sales 159.3MM^E EMP 371
SIC 2341 2384 5137 Women's & children's nightwear; Nightgowns & negligees: women's & children's; Robes & dressing gowns; Nightwear: women's, children's & infants'
CEO: Charles E Komar
COO: Jay Harris
CFO: Harry Gaffney
CFO: Marine Taibbi
Co-Ch Bd: Harold Komar
Treas: David L Komar
VP: Donna Nadeau

D-U-N-S 07-711-1599
CHARLES L CRANE AGENCY CO
GMAC INSURANCE
100 N Broadway Ste 900, Saint Louis, MO 63102-2736
Tel (314) 241-8700 Founded/Ownrshp 1937
Sales NA EMP 250
SIC 6411 Insurance agents, brokers & service
Pr: Michael T Reedy
*Ch Bd: R Christopher Imbs
*COO: Jerry Burnett
*Treas: William Purcell
*Sr VP: Thomas J Berra
VP: David Arm
VP: Frank Rebholz
VP: Cary Wilson

D-U-N-S 00-724-0088 IMP
CHARLES MACHINE WORKS INC
1959 W Fir St, Perry, OK 73077-5803
Tel (580) 572-3344 Founded/Ownrshp 1959
Sales 571.1MM^E EMP 1,831
SIC 3531 3541 3829 3546 Construction machinery; Drilling & boring machines; Measuring & controlling devices; Power-driven handtools
CEO: Tiffany Sewell-Howard
*Pr: Edwin Malzahn
*COO: Rick Johnson
*CFO: Angela Drake
Exec: Wayne Pagel
Dir Soc: Leslie Layne-Weaver
*Prin: Bertha D Malzahn
QA Dir: Jeff Groom
Sftwr Eng: Ed Sutton
Opers Mgr: Robert Stone
Mktg Dir: David Pierce

D-U-N-S 01-956-8208
CHARLES PANKOW BUILDERS LTD A CALIFORNIA LIMITED PARTNERSHIP
199 S Los Robles Ave # 300, Pasadena, CA 91101-2452
Tel (626) 304-1190 Founded/Ownrshp 2004
Sales 208.4MM^E EMP 500
SIC 1542 Commercial & office building contractors
Ch Bd: Rik Kunnath
Pt: Kim Lum
COO: Dick Walterhouse
CFO: Kim Petersen

D-U-N-S 06-936-6300
CHARLES REGIONAL MEDICAL CENTER FOUNDATION INC (MD)
CHARLES RGNAL MED CTR FNDATION
5 Garrett Ave, La Plata, MD 20646-5960
Tel (301) 609-4000 Founded/Ownrshp 1985
Sales 85.6MM^E EMP 668
SIC 8062 General medical & surgical hospitals
Pr: Noel Cervino
VP: Margaret Fisher
IT Man: Les Queen

CHARLES RGNAL MED CTR FNDATION
See CHARLES REGIONAL MEDICAL CENTER FOUNDATION INC

CHARLES RIVER ASSOCIATES
See CRA INTERNATIONAL INC

D-U-N-S 96-519-5477
CHARLES RIVER DEVELOPMENT INC
(Suby of CHARLES RIVER SYSTEMS INC) ★
700 District Ave Ste 400, Burlington, MA 01803-5049
Tel (781) 238-0099 Founded/Ownrshp 2007
Sales 86.9MM^E EMP 625
SIC 7371 Computer software development
Pr: Peter K Lambertus
*CFO: David Weber
*VP: Chris Aronis
*VP: Brad Hamlin
Dir Bus: Ian Hoenisch
Mng Dir: Tom Driscoll
Mng Dir: Stephen Schardin
Genl Mgr: John Reardon
Snr Sftwr: Bruce Bigelow
Snr Sftwr: Dmitry Goryayinov
Snr Sftwr: Serhiy Kovbasa

D-U-N-S 78-952-0553
■ **CHARLES RIVER LABORATORIES ASHLAND LLC**
(Suby of CHARLES RIVER LABORATORIES SA USA INC) ★
1407 George Rd, Ashland, OH 44805-8946
Tel (419) 282-8700 Founded/Ownrshp 2016
Sales 115.0MM^E EMP 670^E
SIC 8733 Research institute
CEO: David Spaight
*CFO: John Maxwell
Dir Lab: Carol Kopp
Assoc Dir: Linda Allais
*CIO: Howard Moody

D-U-N-S 01-971-6729
■ **CHARLES RIVER LABORATORIES INC**
(Suby of CHARLES RIVER LABORATORIES INTERNATIONAL INC) ★
251 Ballardvale St, Wilmington, MA 01887-1096
Tel (978) 658-6000 Founded/Ownrshp 1996
Sales 804.4MM^E EMP 2,200
SIC 8742 8734 8731 0279 Industry specialist consultants; Testing laboratories; Biological research; Laboratory animal farm
Ex VP: Davide Molho
Pr: Christopher Perkin
CFO: David Smith
Trst: Charles River
Ex VP: Thomas Ackerman
Sr VP: Jorg Geller
VP: J RG M Geller
Dir Risk M: Dean Marchetti
Assoc Dir: Julie Nack
Assoc Dir: Courtney Rodriguez
Rgnl Mgr: Tim O'Bryan
Board of Directors: Henry Wendt III, Robert Bertolini, Robert Cawthorn, Stephen D Chubb, Thompson Dean, Stephen C McCluski, Reid S Perper, Samuel O Thier, Richard Wallman, William Waltrip

D-U-N-S 11-037-6014
▲ **CHARLES RIVER LABORATORIES INTERNATIONAL INC**
251 Ballardvale St, Wilmington, MA 01887-1096
Tel (781) 222-6000 Founded/Ownrshp 1947
Sales 1.3MMM EMP 8,600^E
Tkr Sym CRL Exch NYS
SIC 8731 Commercial physical research; Biological research; Biotechnical research, commercial
Ch Bd: James C Foster
CFO: David R Smith
Ex VP: Nancy A Gillett
Ex VP: David P Johst
Ex VP: Davide Molho
Ex VP: Real Renaud
Sr VP: William D Barbo
Sr VP: John J Crowley
Sr VP: Colin Dunn
Sr VP: J RG M Geller
Sr VP: John C Ho
Sr VP: Arthur C Hubbs
Sr VP: Foster Jordan
VP: Matthew Daniel
VP: Caroline Dunnell
VP: Andre Merza
VP: Shannon Parisotto
Assoc Dir: Allen Chin
Board of Directors: Robert J Bertolini, Stephen D Chubb, Deborah T Kochevar, George E Massaro, George M Milne Jr, C Richard Reese, Craig B Thompson, Richard R Wallman

D-U-N-S 01-283-0991
■ **CHARLES RIVER LABORATORIES SA USA INC**
(Suby of CRL SAFETY ASSESSMENT INC) ★
30 Two Bridges Rd Ste 200, Fairfield, NJ 07004-1555
Tel (919) 245-3114 Founded/Ownrshp 2004
Sales 126.0MM^E EMP 733^E
SIC 8731 Commercial physical research
CEO: David Spaight
Chf Cred: Alan Findlater
CIO: Howard Moody

D-U-N-S 15-174-7060
CHARLES RIVER SYSTEMS INC
700 District Ave Ste 400, Burlington, MA 01803-5049
Tel (781) 238-0099 Founded/Ownrshp 1992
Sales 86.9MM^E EMP 625
SIC 7371 Computer software development
*CFO: David Weber
*VP: Chris Aronis
*VP: Brad Hamlin
*VP: John Zimmer
Mng Dir: Stephen Butcher

CHARLES SCHWAB
See SCHWAB HOLDINGS INC

D-U-N-S 06-302-0804
■ **CHARLES SCHWAB & CO INC**
(Suby of CHARLES SCHWAB CORP) ★
211 Main St Fl 17, San Francisco, CA 94105-1901
Tel (415) 636-7000 Founded/Ownrshp 1987
Sales 2.7MMM^E EMP 5,000^E
Accts Deloitte & Touche Llp San Fra
SIC 6211 Brokers, security; Dealers, security; Investment firm, general brokerage
CEO: Walt Bettinger
*Sr Ex VP: Tom D Seip
Ex VP: Beth Devin
Ex VP: Andrew G Gill
*Ex VP: Dawn G Lepore
*Ex VP: Elizabeth G Sawi
Sr VP: Andy Gill
*Sr VP: Geoffrey C Gradler
Sr VP: Vincent Phillips
Sr VP: Max Ruston
Sr VP: Andrew Schofield
Sr VP: Pearson William
VP: David Allison
VP: Michael Canady
VP: Sue Heldman
VP: Jake King
VP: Mike Marsh
VP: Glen Mathison
VP: Michael Moran

D-U-N-S 78-426-1252
■ **CHARLES SCHWAB BANK NATIONAL ASSOCIATION**
(Suby of CHARLES SCHWAB CORP) ★
5190 Neil Rd Ste 100, Reno, NV 89502-8532
Tel (775) 689-6800 Founded/Ownrshp 2005
Sales NA EMP 196^E
SIC 6021 National commercial banks
Pr: Moor Menei
VP: Teresa Joyce
VP: Patricia Kenny
VP: Scott Rhoades
Ex Dir: Rachel Shay
Mng Dir: Alicia Reebenacker
VP Mktg: Richard Musci

D-U-N-S 00-130-7974
▲ **CHARLES SCHWAB CORP**
211 Main St Fl 17, San Francisco, CA 94105-1901
Tel (415) 667-7000 Founded/Ownrshp 1986
Sales 6.3MMM EMP 15,300^E
Accts Deloitte & Touche Llp San Fra
Tkr Sym SCHW Exch NYS
SIC 6211 6091 6282 7389 Brokers, security; Investment bankers; Investment firm, general brokerage; Nondeposit trust facilities; Investment advice; Investment advisory service; Financial services
Pr: Walter W Bettinger II
*Ch Bd: Charles R Schwab
CFO: Joseph R Martinetto
Bd of Dir: Barbara Glass-Quintana
Ex VP: Steven H Anderson
Ex VP: Bernard J Clark
Ex VP: David R Garfield
Ex VP: Dennis Howard
Ex VP: Terri R Kallsen
Ex VP: Jim McGuire
Ex VP: Nigel J Murtagh
Ex VP: Leonard V Short III
Sr VP: Selwyn Notelovitz
Sr VP: David Thelander
VP: Brendon Anderson
VP: Cory Archibald
VP: Christopher Armstrong
VP: Viola Ashmawee
VP: Don Bakhaus
VP: Illya Bermant
VP: Jackie Bevill
Board of Directors: Arun Sarin, John K Adams Jr, Paula A Sneed, Nancy H Bechtle, Roger O Walther, C Preston Butcher, Robert N Wilson, Christopher V Dodds, Stephen A Ellis, Mark A Goldfarb, William S Haraf, Frank C Herringer, Stephen T McLin

D-U-N-S 06-658-7478
CHARLES STARK DRAPER LABORATORY INC
555 Technology Sq, Cambridge, MA 02139-3539
Tel (617) 258-1000 Founded/Ownrshp 1972
Sales 656.0MM EMP 1,134^E
Accts Pricewaterhousecoopers Llp Bo
SIC 8734 Testing laboratories
Pr: James D Shields
*VP: Jeffrey M Bentley
VP: David V Burke Jr
VP: Steve Ditullio
*VP: Steven J Ditullio
*VP: John R Dowdle
VP: Allison Looney
*VP: Elizabeth Mora
VP: Len Polizzotto
VP: Ted Rye
VP: Darryl G Sargent
VP: Joseph M Wolfe
Assoc Dir: Milton Adams
Assoc Dir: Roy Setterlund

D-U-N-S 00-152-7089
CHARLES WALKER NORTH AMERICA
9400 W 55th St, Shawnee Mission, KS 66203-2042
Tel (913) 236-9233 Founded/Ownrshp 2004
Sales 120.0MM EMP 125
SIC 5085 Industrial supplies
Pr: Mike Nechek
*CEO: Steven R Cloud
*VP: Ron Aupperley
Store Mgr: John Hughes
VP Opers: Larry Brand

D-U-N-S 13-413-7996
CHARLESBANK CAPITAL PARTNERS LLC
200 Clarendon St Fl 54, Boston, MA 02116-5021
Tel (617) 619-5400 Founded/Ownrshp 1998
Sales 1.6MMM^E EMP 2,627
SIC 6211 Investment bankers
Pr: Maura Turner
*COO: John Vander Vort
*CFO: Kevin Brown
*Sr VP: Tami Nason
VP: Samuel Bartlett
*VP: Joshua N Beer
VP: Michael Braver
VP: Scott Entwistle
VP: Joshua Klevens
*Mng Dir: Ryan Carroll
Mng Dir: Michael Choe

D-U-N-S 07-266-8940
CHARLESTON AREA MEDICAL CENTER INC (WV)
(Suby of CAMC HEALTH SYSTEM INC) ★
501 Morris St, Charleston, WV 25301-1326
Tel (304) 348-5432 Founded/Ownrshp 1905, 1971
Sales 932.5MM EMP 4,000
SIC 8062 Hospital, medical school affiliated with nursing & residency
Pr: David L Ramsey
V Ch: Mark James
*Treas: Larry Hudson
Bd of Dir: Gail Pitchford
VP: Steve Bell
*VP: Glenn Crotty Jr
*VP: Glenn Crotty
*VP: Elizabeth Keightley
VP: Elizabeth Spangler
Exec: John Pennington
Assoc Dir: Amy Smith
Dir Rad: John J Anton
Dir Rx: Clyde Spence

CHARLESTON COUNTY GOVERNMENT
See COUNTY OF CHARLESTON

D-U-N-S 03-010-3014
CHARLESTON COUNTY SCHOOL DISTRICT DEVELOPMENT CORP
CCSD
75 Calhoun St, Charleston, SC 29401-3538
Tel (843) 937-6300 *Founded/Ownrshp* 1993
Sales 318.8MM[E] *EMP* 5,000
Accts Greene Finney & Horton Mauldi
SIC 8211 Public elementary & secondary schools
Ofcr: Chris Metivier
**Prin:* Kristen Brittingham
**Prin:* Emily Elliott
**Prin:* Tim Tanner
Dir Sec: Michael Reidenbach
Dir IT: Donnie Spellman
IT Man: Rebecca Lebron
IT Man: Jarmalar Logan
IT Man: Karen Reed
IT Man: Carmen Sheppard
Prd Mgr: Todd Shaffer

D-U-N-S 06-813-1960
CHARLESTON HOSPITAL INC
ST FRANCIS HOSPITAL
(*Suby of* ST FRANCIS HOSPITAL OF CHARLE) ★
333 Laidley St, Charleston, WV 25301-1614
Tel (304) 347-6500 *Founded/Ownrshp* 2007
Sales 99.7MM *EMP* 570
SIC 8062 General medical & surgical hospitals
Pr: Dan Lauffer
CFO: Brad Owens
VP: Rebecca Brannon
VP: Ann Cella
**VP:* Renee Cross

D-U-N-S 07-371-4289
CHARLESTON SOUTHERN UNIVERSITY
9200 University Blvd, North Charleston, SC 29406-9121
Tel (843) 863-7000 *Founded/Ownrshp* 1960
Sales 84.7MM *EMP* 350[E]
Accts Capin Crouse Llp Lawrencevill
SIC 8221 University
Ch: Dr Tim Spurling
**Pr:* Mr Oswaldo Hurtado
Ofcr: Steve Hucks
VP: Luke Blackmon
VP: James Colman
**Prin:* Jairy C Hunter Jr
**Prin:* Jerry Williams
Ex Dir: Doug Hunter
Ex Dir: William Ward
CIO: Buddy Gray

CHARLESTON WATER SYSTEM
See COMMISSIONERS OF PUBLIC WORKS

D-U-N-S 07-329-7236
CHARLESTOWN COMMUNITY INC
CHARLESTOWN RETIREMENT CMNTY
719 Maiden Choice Ln, Baltimore, MD 21228-6138
Tel (410) 737-8830 *Founded/Ownrshp* 1982
Sales 93.7MM *EMP* 1,500
Accts Rsm Us Llp Baltimore Md
SIC 6513 8051 Retirement hotel operation; Extended care facility
Ex Dir: Michael Conord
Netwrk Eng: John Tokasz
Mktg Mgr: Dawn Grove

CHARLESTOWN RETIREMENT CMNTY
See CHARLESTOWN COMMUNITY INC

D-U-N-S 17-956-4349
CHARLIE BROWNS ACQUISITION CORP
CHARLIE BROWN'S STEAKHOUSE
(*Suby of* TRIMARAN FUND MANAGEMENT LLC) ★
1 Congress St Ste 113, Boston, MA 02114-2016
Tel (201) 842-3612 *Founded/Ownrshp* 2005
Sales 63.1MM[E] *EMP* 2,402
SIC 5812 Steak restaurant
Pr: Sam Borgesa
**CFO:* Ed Schwartz
Ofcr: Russell Danton

CHARLIE BROWN'S STEAKHOUSE
See CHARLIE BROWNS ACQUISITION CORP

D-U-N-S 07-985-1073
CHARLIE CHARMING HOLDINGS INC
CHARMING CHARLIE
5999 Savoy Dr, Houston, TX 77036-3307
Tel (713) 579-1936 *Founded/Ownrshp* 2008
Sales 708.6MM[E] *EMP* 3,500
SIC 5632 Women's accessory & specialty stores
CEO: Charlie Chanaratsopon
**CFO:* Thomas J Fitzgerald
**Ex VP:* Judi Langley
**Sr VP:* Scott Woods
**VP:* Melissa Whitehead

D-U-N-S 02-818-1311
CHARLIES ENTERPRISES
OK PRODUCE
1888 S East Ave, Fresno, CA 93721-3231
Tel (559) 445-8600 *Founded/Ownrshp* 1941
Sales 164.7MM[E] *EMP* 200
SIC 5148 Fruits, fresh; Vegetables, fresh
Pr: Matty Matoian
Pt: Angel Burnett
Genl Mgr: Chris Castro

CHARLIE'S PRODUCE
See TRIPLE "B" CORP

D-U-N-S 79-896-7654
CHARLOTTE CATH HIGH
(*Suby of* PASTORAL CENTER) ★
7702 Pneville Matthews Rd, Charlotte, NC 28226-3934
Tel (704) 543-1127 *Founded/Ownrshp* 2007
Sales 105.0M *EMP* 1,059[E]
SIC 8211 Catholic senior high school
Prin: Angela Montague
Treas: Mike Crotty
Prin: Randy Belk
Prin: Steve Carpenter
Prin: Jerry Healy

D-U-N-S 07-989-4927
CHARLOTTE COUNTY PUBLIC SCHOOLS
1445 Education Way, Port Charlotte, FL 33948-1052
Tel (941) 255-0808 *Founded/Ownrshp* 1888
Sales 165.5MM[E] *EMP* 1,153[E]
SIC 8211 Public elementary & secondary schools
V Ch: Ian Vincent
Dir Sec: David Leupenti
MIS Dir: Christopher Bress

D-U-N-S 01-017-3482
CHARLOTTE HUNGERFORD HOSPITAL
540 Litchfield St, Torrington, CT 06790-6600
Tel (860) 496-6666 *Founded/Ownrshp* 1916
Sales 117.7MM *EMP* 800
SIC 8062 General medical & surgical hospitals
Pr: Daniel J McIntyre
Chf Rad: Mandell Neal
VP: Jim Elliott
Dir Lab: Marilyn Spafford
Dir QC: Donna Feinstien
Orthpdst: Brian McCarthy
Opthamlgy: Ronald Berger
Doctor: Derrick A Bailey

D-U-N-S 00-315-5280
■ **CHARLOTTE OBSERVER PUBLISHING CO** (DE)
(*Suby of* MCCLATCHY CO) ★
550 S Caldwell St, Charlotte, NC 28202-2633
Tel (704) 358-5000 *Founded/Ownrshp* 1955, 2006
Sales 150.9MM[E] *EMP* 800
SIC 2711 4813 Newspapers, publishing & printing;
Pr: Ann Coulkins
**CFO:* Victor Fields
VP: Bob Burns
**VP:* Jim Lamm
**VP:* Kelly Mirt
**VP:* Ken Riddick
**VP:* Richard Rinehart
**VP:* Rick Thames
Off Mgr: Christine Vasar
Sales Asso: Paul Atkins
Snr Mgr: Randall Bratton

D-U-N-S 00-316-2013 IMP/EXP
CHARLOTTE PIPE AND FOUNDRY CO
2109 Randolph Rd, Charlotte, NC 28207-1521
Tel (704) 372-5030 *Founded/Ownrshp* 1901
Sales 644.0MM[E] *EMP* 1,300
Accts Pricewaterhousecoopers Llp
SIC 3084 3089 3321 Plastics pipe; Fittings for pipe, plastic; Soil pipe & fittings: cast iron
CEO: W Frank Dowd IV
**Pr:* Roddey Dowd Jr
**CFO:* William R Hutaff III
**Ch:* Roddey Dowd Sr
**Ch:* W Frank Dowd Jr
**Ex VP:* J Alan Biggers
**Ex VP:* E Hooper Hardison Jr
**Sr VP:* Charles E Cobb
**Sr VP:* Marshall Coble
**VP:* Mark E Black
**VP:* Astor Brown Jr
**VP:* Cameron Faison Jr
VP: Jeff Greene
VP: Chad Griffin
**VP:* C Leon Salter Jr
**VP:* Gregory L Simmons

D-U-N-S 83-236-8604
CHARLOTTE RUSSE ENTERPRISE INC
(*Suby of* ADVENT INTERNATIONAL CORP) ★
75 State St, Boston, MA 02109-1827
Tel (617) 951-9400 *Founded/Ownrshp* 2009
Sales 1.4MMM[E] *EMP* 9,460[E]
SIC 5621 Ready-to-wear apparel, women's
Pr: Andrew W Crawford
Mktg Mgr: Gohar Jadali

D-U-N-S 95-936-9240 IMP
CHARLOTTE RUSSE HOLDING INC
(*Suby of* CHARLOTTE RUSSE ENTERPRISE INC) ★
5910 Pcf Ctr Blvd Ste 120, San Diego, CA 92121
Tel (858) 587-1500 *Founded/Ownrshp* 2009
Sales 1.4MMM[E] *EMP* 9,454
SIC 5621 Teenage apparel
Ex VP: Frederick G Silny
Bd of Dir: Bernie Zeichner
**Ex VP:* Sandra Tillett
Sr VP: Jay Lepsalter
VP: Graham P Luck
Rgnl Mgr: Pam Huerta
Brnch Mgr: Karen Laporte
Brnch Mgr: Garrett Robinson
Brnch Mgr: Lisa Rosario
Brnch Mgr: John Smith
Brnch Mgr: Mark Wadges

D-U-N-S 07-874-2269 IMP
CHARLOTTE RUSSE INC
(*Suby of* CHARLOTTE RUSSE HOLDING INC) ★
5910 Pcf Ctr Blvd Ste 120, San Diego, CA 92121
Tel (858) 587-1500 *Founded/Ownrshp* 1975
Sales 1.4MMM[E] *EMP* 8,961
SIC 5621 Ready-to-wear apparel, women's
CEO: Jenny Ming
**CFO:* Patty Johnson
VP: Daniel Carter
Admn Mgr: Hope Fields
Admn Mgr: Diane Vanasdall
Dist Mgr: Valerie White
Store Mgr: Amanda Eldridge
Store Mgr: Chantel Graham
Store Mgr: Clara Rodriguez
IT Man: Tina Cammarello
Opers Mgr: Robin Papa

D-U-N-S 07-452-4513
CHARLOTTE-MECKLENBURG HOSPITAL AUTHORITY
CAROLINAS HEALTHCARE SYSTEM
1000 Blythe Blvd, Charlotte, NC 28203-5812
Tel (704) 355-2000 *Founded/Ownrshp* 1943
Sales 5.4MMM *EMP* 62,000
Accts Kpmg Llp Charlotte Nc
SIC 8062 8069 8063 8051 8011 General medical & surgical hospitals; Specialty hospitals, except psychiatric; Alcoholism rehabilitation hospital; Drug addiction rehabilitation hospital; Psychiatric hospitals; Skilled nursing care facilities; Offices & clinics of medical doctors
CEO: Eugene A Woods
Chf Path: John N Gentry
**Pr:* Greg A Gombar
Ex VP: Eugene Deladdy
Sr VP: Eugene A Deladdy Jr
VP: Jerry L Bryson
**VP:* Paul S Franz
VP: Mary Ann Rouse
Dir Rx: Don Weis
Comm Man: Scott White
Chf Nrs Of: Kate Grew

D-U-N-S 07-907-1155
CHARLOTTE-MECKLENBURG SCHOOL DISTRICT
600 E 4th St, Charlotte, NC 28202-2816
Tel (980) 343-6372 *Founded/Ownrshp* 1960
Sales 575.4MM[E] *EMP* 11,893
Accts Dixon Hughes Goodman Llp Wins
SIC 8211 Elementary & secondary schools
**Ch Bd:* Mary T McCray
Pr: Gerry Gyuire
Bd of Dir: George Dunlap
**Prin:* Timothy S Morgan
Schl Brd P: Mary McCary

D-U-N-S 06-985-2218
CHARLTON MEMORIAL HOSPITAL INC
363 Highland Ave, Fall River, MA 02720-3700
Tel (508) 679-3131 *Founded/Ownrshp* 1900
Sales 129.7MM *EMP* 1,794
SIC 8062 General medical & surgical hospitals
Pr: Ronald Goodspeed
**Treas:* William Heaney

D-U-N-S 00-169-4991 IMP
CHARMER INDUSTRIES INC (NY)
(*Suby of* BREAKTHRU BEVERAGE GROUP) ★
1950 48th St, Astoria, NY 11105-1232
Tel (718) 726-2500 *Founded/Ownrshp* 1912, 1960
Sales 126.1MM[E] *EMP* 1,000
SIC 5182 Wine; Liquor
Ch Bd: Herman I Merinoff
**Pr:* Steven Drucker
Pr: Rob Sirota
**CEO:* Charles Merinoff
**CFO:* Terence Arlotta
Treas: Gertude Merinoff
VP: Greg Baird
VP: Don Kiwor
Dir IT: Paul Fipps

CHARMERS SUNBELT
See PREMIER BEVERAGE CO LLC

CHARMING CHARLIE
See CHARLIE CHARMING HOLDINGS INC

D-U-N-S 16-669-1399 IMP
CHARMING CHARLIE LLC
(*Suby of* CHARMING CHARLIE) ★
5999 Savoy Dr, Houston, TX 77036-3307
Tel (713) 579-1936 *Founded/Ownrshp* 1992
Sales 708.6MM[E] *EMP* 3,500
SIC 5632 Women's accessory & specialty stores
CEO: Charles Chanaratsopon
Pr: Thomas J Fitzgerald
COO: Steve Lovell
Ex VP: Judi Langley
Sr VP: Melissa Whitehead
VP: Carol Brubaker
Comm Man: Steve Picklar
Dist Mgr: Barbara Van Hamme
Dir IT: Tony Mickle

D-U-N-S 05-474-4677 IMP/EXP
■ **CHARMING SHOPPES INC** (PA)
CATHERINES
(*Suby of* ASCENA RETAIL GROUP INC) ★
3750 State Rd, Bensalem, PA 19020-5989
Tel (215) 245-9100 *Founded/Ownrshp* 1969, 2012
Sales 4.2MMM[E] *EMP* 23,000
SIC 5961 5632 5621 Women's apparel, mail order; Women's accessory & specialty stores; Ready-to-wear apparel, women's
Pr: Anthony M Romano
Pr: Marla C Anderson
Pr: Bryan Q Eshelman
Pr: Jay H Levitt
Pr: Luann Via
Pr: Carol L Williams
CFO: Eric M Specter
Treas: Dottie Weston
Ex VP: Laura Johnson
Ex VP: Fredrick Lamster
Ex VP: Colin D Stern
Sr VP: Debbie Martin
Sr VP: Jeffrey A Warzel
VP: Alan Bobman
VP: Tony Camoratto
VP: Denise Davis
VP: Donna Desilets
VP: Johnathan Gambino
VP: Ashley Giles
VP: John Lee
VP: Jeffrey H Liss

D-U-N-S 01-465-8553 IMP/EXP
■ **CHARMING SHOPPES OF DELAWARE INC**
FASHION BUG
(*Suby of* CATHERINES) ★
3750 State Rd, Bensalem, PA 19020-5989
Tel (215) 245-9100 *Founded/Ownrshp* 1961
Sales 2.5MMM[E] *EMP* 7
SIC 5621 8741 Women's clothing stores; Administrative management
Pr: Alan Rosskimm
**CFO:* Eric M Specter
Treas: Dottie Weston
Genl Mgr: Anthony A Desabato
Snr Mgr: Tracy Johnson

D-U-N-S 07-886-1920
CHARMING TRIM & PACKAGING INC
28 Brookside Ct, Novato, CA 94947-3847
Tel (415) 302-7021 *Founded/Ownrshp* 2011
Sales 59.5MM[E] *EMP* 1,000
SIC 5131 3111 Trimmings, apparel; Garment leather
Pr: Richard Ringeisen
**Ex Dir:* Barry Chan

D-U-N-S 14-466-1238 IMP/EXP
■ **CHART ENERGY & CHEMICALS INC**
ENERGY AND CHEMICALS GROUP
(*Suby of* CHART INC) ★
8665 New Trils Dr Ste 100, The Woodlands, TX 77381
Tel (281) 364-8700 *Founded/Ownrshp* 1993
Sales 85.6MM[E] *EMP* 586
SIC 3443

D-U-N-S 10-227-9817 IMP/EXP
■ **CHART INC**
(*Suby of* CHART INDUSTRIES INC) ★
407 7th St Nw, New Prague, MN 56071-1010
Tel (952) 758-4484 *Founded/Ownrshp* 1999
Sales 403.2MM[E] *EMP* 2,500
SIC 3443 3842 Cryogenic tanks, for liquids & gases; Vessels, process or storage (from boiler shops): metal plate; Spheres, for liquids or gas: metal plate; Respirators
CEO: Samuel F Thomas
**CFO:* Michael F Biehl
VP: Dave Barr
**VP:* Mark Ludwig
Off Mgr: Pam Cowell

D-U-N-S 79-609-3458
▲ **CHART INDUSTRIES INC**
1 Infinity Corp Ctr Dr # 300, Cleveland, OH 44125-5370
Tel (440) 753-1490 *Founded/Ownrshp* 1992
Sales 1.0MMM *EMP* 4,266
Tkr Sym GTLS *Exch* NGS
SIC 3559 3569 3443 Cryogenic machinery, industrial; Gas producers, generators & other gas related equipment; Generators: steam, liquid oxygen or nitrogen; Heat exchangers, condensers & components; Cryogenic tanks, for liquids & gases
Ch Bd: Samuel F Thomas
Pr: Tom Smith
CFO: Michael F Biehl
Ex VP: Michael Biehl
VP: Doug Ducote
VP: Lawrence Hughes
VP: Matthew J Klaben
VP: Chris Schmoeckel
VP: Wanda Schollian
VP: Kenneth J Webster
Genl Mgr: Peter Murray

D-U-N-S 82-900-5003
■ **CHARTER COMMUNICATIONS ENTERTAINMENT II LLC**
(*Suby of* CHARTER COMMUNICATIONS HOLDINGS LLC) ★
12405 Powerscourt Dr, Saint Louis, MO 63131-3673
Tel (314) 965-0555 *Founded/Ownrshp* 2008
Sales 192.8M[E] *EMP* 4,258[E]
SIC 4841 Cable & other pay television services
Prin: David Barry

D-U-N-S 79-981-2131
■ **CHARTER COMMUNICATIONS HOLDING CO LLC**
(*Suby of* CCO HOLDINGS LLC) ★
12405 Powerscourt Dr, Saint Louis, MO 63131-3673
Tel (314) 965-0555 *Founded/Ownrshp* 2016
Sales 5.4MMM[E] *EMP* 16,700[E]
SIC 4841 Cable television services
**Pr:* Michael Lovett

D-U-N-S 82-507-9619
■ **CHARTER COMMUNICATIONS HOLDINGS LLC**
(*Suby of* CHARTER COMMUNICATIONS HOLDING CO LLC) ★
12405 Powerscourt Dr, Saint Louis, MO 63131-3673
Tel (314) 543-2480 *Founded/Ownrshp* 1999
Sales 5.4MMM[E] *EMP* 16,700[E]
SIC 4841 4813 Cable television services; Data telephone communications; Local telephone communications; Long distance telephone communications
VP: Kevin D Howard
VP: Thom Anema
VP: Natt Dardeyn
VP: Thomas Degnan
VP: Craig Lalumandier
VP: Glenn Leech
VP: Jill Stark
Prgrm Mgr: Shannon Gavornik
CTO: Connie Kovach
Dir IT: Julie Maune
IT Man: Scott Bartels
Board of Directors: Paul G Allen, W Lance Conn, Robert P May, David C Merritt, Jo Allen Patton, John H Tory, Larry W Wangberg

D-U-N-S 08-210-6332
CHARTER COMMUNICATIONS INC
400 Atlantic St Fl 10, Stamford, CT 06901-3512
Tel (203) 905-7801 *Founded/Ownrshp* 2009
Sales 9.7MMM *EMP* 23,800
SIC 4841 4813

D-U-N-S 15-077-6503
▲ **CHARTER COMMUNICATIONS INC**
400 Atlantic St, Stamford, CT 06901-3512
Tel (203) 905-7801 *Founded/Ownrshp* 1999
Sales 9.7MMM *EMP* 23,800[E]
Tkr Sym CHTR *Exch* NGS
SIC 4841 4813 Cable & other pay television services; Cable television services; Telephone communication, except radio;
Ch Bd: Thomas M Rutledge
Pr: John Bickham
CFO: Christopher L Winfrey
Chf Mktg O: Jonathan Hargis
Ex VP: Richard R Dykhouse
Sr VP: Kevin D Howard

D-U-N-S 13-062-7388
■ CHARTER COMMUNICATIONS LLC
(*Suby of* CCO HOLDINGS LLC) ★
12405 Powerscourt Dr, Saint Louis, MO 63131-3673
Tel (314) 288-3478 *Founded/Ownrshp* 2016
Sales 98.4MM^E *EMP* 23,000
SIC 8748 Telecommunications consultant
Pr: Michael J Lovett

D-U-N-S 15-106-8009
■ CHARTER COMMUNICATIONS OPERATING LLC
(*Suby of* CCO HOLDINGS LLC) ★
12405 Powerscourt Dr, Saint Louis, MO 63131-3673
Tel (314) 965-0555 *Founded/Ownrshp* 1999
Sales 930.6MM^E *EMP* 1,800
SIC 4841 Cable & other pay television services
CEO: Michael J Lovett
Treas: Michael Rose

D-U-N-S 10-334-6557
CHARTER CONSTRUCTION INC
980 S Harney St, Seattle, WA 98108-2744
Tel (206) 382-1900 *Founded/Ownrshp* 1982
Sales 102.2MM^E *EMP* 210^E
SIC 1542 Commercial & office buildings, renovation & repair; Commercial & office building, new construction
Pr: Peter Saladino
**CFO:* Dawn Stephens
**VP:* Patrick Cosentino
**VP:* Jim Donahoe
**VP:* Eric Jackson
**VP:* Brian Johnson

D-U-N-S 01-609-6815
CHARTER FOODS INC (TN)
TACO BELL
5139 Old Highway 11e, Morristown, TN 37814-1003
Tel (423) 587-0690 *Founded/Ownrshp* 1998
Sales 68.3MM^E *EMP* 1,800
SIC 5812 Fast-food restaurant, chain
Pr: Robert Jenkins

D-U-N-S 94-116-6654
CHARTER GLOBAL INC
7000 Central Pkwy # 1100, Atlanta, GA 30328-4592
Tel (888) 326-9933 *Founded/Ownrshp* 1994
Sales 90.4MM^E *EMP* 630
SIC 7371 Computer software systems analysis & design, custom
Pr: Murli Reddy
Sr VP: Ken Reaves
**VP:* Deven Reddy
Snr Sftwr: Ravi Shanker
CTO: Charles Philippin
Sftwr Eng: Agyeya Gupta

D-U-N-S 07-509-4086
■ CHARTER INDEMNITY CO
UNITRIN DATA SYSTEMS SPECIALTY
(*Suby of* KEMPER CORP) ★
8360 Lyndon B Johnson Fwy # 400, Dallas, TX 75243-1134
Tel (972) 690-5500 *Founded/Ownrshp* 2002
Sales NA *EMP* 325
SIC 6411 Insurance agents; Insurance brokers
Pr: Timothy D Bruns
VP: Kent Haston
Dir Risk M: Jerry Goodman
Admn Mgr: Calvin Nash
CIO: Kent Ashton
Sls Mgr: Doris Wheatley

D-U-N-S 05-161-8056 IMP
CHARTER MANUFACTURING CO INC
CHARTER STEEL DIVISION
1212 W Glen Oaks Ln, Mequon, WI 53092-3357
Tel (262) 243-4700 *Founded/Ownrshp* 1946
Sales 761.5MM^E *EMP* 2,000
Accts Deloitte & Touche Llp Milwau
SIC 3312 3496 Billets, steel; Miscellaneous fabricated wire products
Pr: Thomas Glaister
CFO: Todd Endres
VP: Samantha Inks
Genl Mgr: Robert Elliott
IT Man: Joel Multerer
Netwrk Eng: Joe Neuber
Snr Mgr: Chelsea Abanathie
Snr Mgr: Brad Clarkson
Snr Mgr: Austin Dostalek
Snr Mgr: Bernie Klamecki
Snr Mgr: Carli Parsons

D-U-N-S 96-351-3648
CHARTER NEX HOLDING CO
(*Suby of* MASON WELLS INC) ★
1264 E High St, Milton, WI 53563-8682
Tel (608) 531-1405 *Founded/Ownrshp* 2010
Sales 138.3MM^E *EMP* 180
SIC 3081 Polyethylene film
Pr: Kathy Bolhous

D-U-N-S 00-691-7041
■ CHARTER OAK FIRE INSURANCE CO (CT)
TRAVELERS INSURANCE
(*Suby of* TRAVELERS INSURANCE) ★
1 Tower Sq, Hartford, CT 06183-0001
Tel (860) 277-0111 *Founded/Ownrshp* 1935
Sales NA *EMP* 40
SIC 6351 6331 Liability insurance; Fire, marine & casualty insurance
Pr: Robert Lipp
V Ch: Charles J Clarke
V Ch: Michael Malvinni

D-U-N-S 00-445-3957 IMP
■ CHARTER ONE BANK NATIONAL ASSOCIATION
(*Suby of* CITIZENS BANK) ★
1215 Superior Ave E # 245, Cleveland, OH 44114-3299
Tel (216) 277-5326 *Founded/Ownrshp* 2004
Sales NA *EMP* 5,537
SIC 6021 National commercial banks
Ch Bd: Charles John Koch
V Ch: David Bowerman
V Ch: Brad L Conner
V Ch: Robert D Matthews
**CFO:* Richard Neu
Bd of Dir: John H Morison
**Ex VP:* Mark D Grossi
Ex VP: Evelyn Tressitt
Sr VP: Brad Artery
**Sr VP:* Greg Daniels
Sr VP: Jayne Diedrich
**Sr VP:* Tom Kennedy
**Sr VP:* Dominic J Salomone
Sr VP: Kevin M Walsh
VP: Frank J Grueter
**VP:* Linda Mills
VP: Brittany O'Connor
VP: Michael Otter

D-U-N-S 00-742-8274
CHARTER SCHOOLS USA INC
CSUSA
800 Corporate Dr Ste 124, Fort Lauderdale, FL 33334-3618
Tel (954) 202-3500 *Founded/Ownrshp* 1997
Sales 130.4MM^E *EMP* 755
SIC 8211
Pr: Dan Rishavy
**Pr:* Charter Schools USA
**CEO:* Jonathan Hage
CFO: Richard Garcia
Ex VP: Maia Sharpley
**VP:* Dr Edwin Friedie
**VP:* Tom Geismar
**VP:* Tom Rogers
VP: Nicole Teal
Off Mgr: Dottie Rodriguez
Dir IT: David Morgan

CHARTER STEEL DIVISION
See CHARTER MANUFACTURING CO INC

D-U-N-S 09-964-7943 IMP
CHARTER SUPPLY CO
8100 Ambssdor Cffery Pkwy, Broussard, LA 70518-5900
Tel (337) 837-2724 *Founded/Ownrshp* 1980
Sales 83.8MM^E *EMP* 88
SIC 5084 Oil well machinery, equipment & supplies
Pr: Jesse Moore
**Sec:* Linda Moore
Exec: Stephanie Picard
IT Man: Timotny Overell
Sales Asso: Jude Durousseau
Sales Asso: Mary Flores
Sales Asso: Amy Morris
Sales Asso: Jacque Rowe

CHARTERCARE HEALTH PARTNERS
See PROSPECT CHARTERCARE LLC

CHARTERHOUSE EQUITY PARTNERS
See CHARTERHOUSE GROUP INC

D-U-N-S 06-493-2130
CHARTERHOUSE GROUP INC
CHARTERHOUSE EQUITY PARTNERS
535 Madison Ave Fl 28, New York, NY 10022-4253
Tel (212) 584-3200 *Founded/Ownrshp* 1973
Sales 87.4MM^E *EMP* 2,711
SIC 8741 6799 6282 Management services; Investors; Investment advisory service
Ch Bd: Merril M Halpern
**CEO:* Thomas Dircks
**CFO:* Cheri Lieberman

D-U-N-S 80-801-3051
■ CHARTERX INC
(*Suby of* AVINODE AB)
18 W Piper Ave, Trenton, NJ 08628-1307
Tel (800) 579-1694 *Founded/Ownrshp* 2010
Sales 87.4MM^E *EMP* 6,000
SIC 4512 Air passenger carrier, scheduled
CEO: Jim Betlyon
**COO:* Bonney A Pelley
**CTO:* Doug Rank

CHARTIS INSURANCE
See AUDUBON INSURANCE CO

CHARTIS INSURANCE
See AIG PROPERTY CASUALTY INC

D-U-N-S 62-278-8230
■ CHARTIS US INC
(*Suby of* CHARTIS INSURANCE) ★
1 Executive Park Dr, Bedford, NH 03110-6913
Tel (603) 645-7000 *Founded/Ownrshp* 2009
Sales NA *EMP* 1,279
SIC 6331 Property damage insurance; Fire, marine & casualty insurance & carriers

D-U-N-S 00-138-3491
CHARTWELL COMMUNITY SERVICES INC (TX)
CHARTWELL HOME CARE
(*Suby of* JORDAN HEALTH SERVICES) ★
14295 Midway Rd Ste 400, Addison, TX 75001-3678
Tel (972) 713-3400 *Founded/Ownrshp* 2000, 2007
Sales 29.2MM^E *EMP* 3,000^E
SIC 8082 Home health care services
Pr: David N Ochoa
Treas: Paul Halpern
VP: Judy Rooney

CHARTWELL HOME CARE
See CHARTWELL COMMUNITY SERVICES INC

D-U-N-S 03-301-4643
CHARTWELLS CATERING
(*Suby of* EUREST DINING SERVICES) ★
Cumberland Col Dining, Williamsburg, KY 40769
Tel (606) 539-4358 *Founded/Ownrshp* 2002
Sales 13.7MM^E *EMP* 2,505^E
SIC 5812 Caterers
CEO: Gary Green

CHARTWELLS UNIVERSITY OF
See UNIVERSITY OF WISCONSIN STEVENS POINT

D-U-N-S 00-693-1059
CHAS LEVY CIRCULATING CO
1930 George St Ste 4, Melrose Park, IL 60160-1501
Tel (708) 356-3600 *Founded/Ownrshp* 1979
Sales 117.2MM^E *EMP* 3,245
SIC 4213 4214 5192 Trucking, except local; Local trucking with storage; Books; Magazines; Periodicals
Pr: Barbara Levy Kipper
**V Ch:* James Levy
**Pr:* Carol Kloster
VP: James Bunning
VP: Elizabeth Corvino
VP: Judith Cotton
VP: James Crawford

CHAS S LEWIS & CO
See ENVIROTECH PUMPSYSTEMS INC

D-U-N-S 08-247-2747
CHASCO CONSTRUCTORS LTD LLP (TX)
2801 E Old Settlers Blvd, Round Rock, TX 78665-2460
Tel (512) 244-0600 *Founded/Ownrshp* 1979
Sales 89.7MM *EMP* 340
SIC 1542 1771 1794 1623 Nonresidential construction; Concrete work; Excavation & grading, building construction; Underground utilities contractor
Pr: Chuck Glace
Pt: Anthony Glace
Pt: Chuk Glace
VP: Scott Badgett
VP: Charles King
Sfty Dirs: Jonathan Escalante

D-U-N-S 12-354-2870
■ CHASE BANK USA NATIONAL ASSOCIATION
(*Suby of* CBC HOLDING INC)
200 White Clay Center Dr, Newark, DE 19711-5466
Tel (302) 634-1000 *Founded/Ownrshp* 1983
Sales NA *EMP* 8,660
SIC 6022 State commercial banks
Pr: Richard J Nolan Jr
VP: David J Clark
VP: Michael P Handago
VP: Christopher Marini
VP: William A Telkowski
VP: Deb Walden
Board of Directors: Glenn S Havlicek, Thomas Jacob, Richard J Matteis, Edward Nelson, Richard J Nolan Jr, Michael J Pasiecki, Joseph L Sclafani

D-U-N-S 87-458-4857
■ CHASE BANKCARD SERVICES INC
(*Suby of* JPMORGAN CHASE BANK NATIONAL ASSOCIATION) ★
100 W University Dr, Tempe, AZ 85281-3725
Tel (480) 902-6000 *Founded/Ownrshp* 1992
Sales NA *EMP* 2,300
SIC 6021 6022 National commercial banks; State commercial banks
**Sr VP:* William V Dobbins
Mktg Dir: Desiree Lancaster

D-U-N-S 61-858-3173 IMP/EXP
■ CHASE BRASS AND COPPER CO LLC
(*Suby of* GLOBAL BRASS AND COPPER INC) ★
14212 Selwyn Dr, Montpelier, OH 43543-9595
Tel (419) 485-3193 *Founded/Ownrshp* 2007
Sales 91.5MM^E *EMP* 311
SIC 3351 Brass rolling & drawing
Pr: Devin Denner
Pr: Daniel Goehler
Pr: James Palmour
VP: Peter Santoro
Sfty Mgr: Mark Greathouse
Manager: Ryan Baird

CHASE CANCER CENTER
See AMERICAN ONCOLOGIC HOSPITAL INC

D-U-N-S 13-679-0404
CHASE CASH & CARRY INC
CCC WHOLESALE
6661 Chase Rd, Dearborn, MI 48126-1746
Tel (313) 582-1200 *Founded/Ownrshp* 2002
Sales 100.0MM *EMP* 20
SIC 5199 General merchandise, non-durable
Pr: Kamal Turfah

D-U-N-S 00-135-9769
▲ CHASE CORP (MA)
26 Summer St, Bridgewater, MA 02324-2626
Tel (508) 819-4200 *Founded/Ownrshp* 1946
Sales 238.0MM *EMP* 671
Tkr Sym CCF *Exch* ASE
SIC 3644 3479 3672 Insulators & insulation materials, electrical; Coating electrodes; Coating of metals with plastic or resins; Printed circuit boards
Pr: Adam P Chase
Ch Bd: Peter R Chase
CFO: Kenneth J Feroldi
Ofcr: Janice Crock
Ofcr: Chris Monteiro
Ofcr: Carol Stoddard
Ofcr: Mike Vandevelde
VP: Carolyn Ashby
VP: Nicole Jacks
VP: Christopher Vaughn
Ex Dir: Anthony McNease

CHASE DOORS
See CHASE INDUSTRIES INC

D-U-N-S 00-423-8499 IMP/EXP
CHASE INDUSTRIES INC (OH)
CHASE DOORS
10021 Commerce Park Dr, West Chester, OH 45246-1333
Tel (513) 860-5565 *Founded/Ownrshp* 1996, 2014
Sales 194.4MM^E *EMP* 400
SIC 3442 Metal doors, sash & trim
CEO: Jeffrey Stark
**CFO:* Drew Bachman
**Sec:* Alan D Baker
**Ex VP:* Todd Ray
VP: Sandy Ball
VP: Fred McMillan
Rgnl Mgr: Rich Noechel
Genl Mgr: Mike Hegner
IT Man: Doug Bennett
IT Man: Josh Fromholt
VP Mfg: Todd Eppert

D-U-N-S 06-870-6175
■ CHASE MANHATTAN MORTGAGE CORP
(*Suby of* JPMORGAN CHASE BANK NATIONAL ASSOCIATION) ★
343 Thornall St Ste 7, Edison, NJ 08837-2209
Tel (732) 205-0600 *Founded/Ownrshp* 1994
Sales NA *EMP* 9,000
Accts Pricewaterhousecoopers Llp N
SIC 6162 Mortgage bankers
Pr: Stephen J Rotella
**Ch Bd:* Thomas Jacob
**CFO:* Glenn Mouridy

D-U-N-S 96-376-7587
■ CHASE PAYMENTECH SOLUTIONS LLC
(*Suby of* JPMORGAN CHASE & CO) ★
14221 Dallas Pkwy Bldg 2, Dallas, TX 75254-2942
Tel (214) 849-3000 *Founded/Ownrshp* 2005
Sales NA *EMP* 2,101
SIC 6153 7389

D-U-N-S 07-108-7852 IMP
■ CHASE SCIENTIFIC GLASS INC (WI)
KIMBLE CHASE
(*Suby of* FISHER SCIENTIFIC INTERNATIONAL LLC) ★
234 Cardiff Valley Rd, Rockwood, TN 37854-4126
Tel (865) 354-4206 *Founded/Ownrshp* 1935, 2006
Sales 90.2MM^E *EMP* 450
SIC 3231 Laboratory glassware
Pr: Wes Lollar
**CFO:* Doug Ehnen
Exec: Sandy Crossett

D-U-N-S 07-882-4082
CHASSIX INC
(*Suby of* UC HOLDINGS INC) ★
300 Galleria Officentre, Southfield, MI 48034-4700
Tel (248) 728-8642 *Founded/Ownrshp* 2012
Sales 1.1MMM^E *EMP* 200^E
SIC 3714 Motor vehicle parts & accessories
CEO: Douglas Delgrosso
**CFO:* Michael Beyer
**VP:* Iwona Niec Villaire

D-U-N-S 17-897-7963
CHASTANG ENTERPRISES INC
CHASTANG FORD
6200 North Loop E, Houston, TX 77026-1936
Tel (713) 678-5000 *Founded/Ownrshp* 1994
Sales 142.0MM *EMP* 100
SIC 5511 Automobiles, new & used
Pr: Joseph Chastang
**VP:* Patrick Chastang
VP: Dan Miller
IT Man: Yanira Chavez
VP Opers: Walter Brown
Sls Mgr: Jesse Alvarez
Sls Mgr: Mike Norris
Sales Asso: Cody Delaney

CHASTANG FORD
See CHASTANG ENTERPRISES INC

CHATEAU ELAN GOLF
See FOUNTAINHEAD DEVELOPMENT LLC

D-U-N-S 07-247-7607
CHATHAM COUNTY BOARD OF EDUCATION (GA)
SAVANNAH-CHATHAM CNTY SCHL SYS
208 Bull St, Savannah, GA 31401-3997
Tel (912) 395-1000 *Founded/Ownrshp* 1866
Sales 423.4MM *EMP* 4,800^E
Accts Robinson Grimes & Company P
SIC 8211 School board; High school, junior or senior
COO: Frank Hendrix
**CFO:* Rebecca McClain
Ex Dir: Dotti Overstreet
Ex Dir: Ramon Ray
Admn Mgr: Richard Hunt
Brnch Mgr: Diane White

D-U-N-S 83-829-5665
CHATHAM FINANCIAL CORP
235 Whitehorse Ln Frnt, Kennett Square, PA 19348-2498
Tel (610) 925-3120 *Founded/Ownrshp* 1991
Sales 125.0MM *EMP* 430^E
SIC 8742 Financial consultant
CEO: Michael Bontrager
COO: Clark Maxwell
VP: Matthew Kephart
Exec: Scott Klein
Assoc Dir: Alexandra Goin
Info Man: Shelley Consiglio
Software D: Andrew Briening
Software D: Kevin Buckley
Software D: Chris Funck
Software D: Ross Schoessler
Sftwr Eng: Timothy Savery

D-U-N-S 96-217-6892
▲ CHATHAM LODGING TRUST
222 Lakeview Ave Ste 200, West Palm Beach, FL 33401-6146
Tel (561) 802-4477 *Founded/Ownrshp* 2009
Sales 276.9MM *EMP* 47
Tkr Sym CLDT *Exch* NYS
SIC 6798 Real estate investment trusts
Ch Bd: Jeffrey H Fisher
COO: Dennis M Craven
COO: Jeremy Wegner
Ex VP: Peter Willis

D-U-N-S 00-331-8383 IMP
■ CHATHAM STEEL CORP
(*Suby of* RELIANCE STEEL & ALUMINUM CO) ★
501 W Boundary St, Savannah, GA 31401-3105
Tel (912) 233-4182 *Founded/Ownrshp* 1915, 1998
Sales 123.1MM^E *EMP* 300
SIC 5051 3317

D-U-N-S 62-801-3021 IMP/EXP
CHATSWORTH PRODUCTS INC
C P I
29899 Agoura Rd Ste 120, Agoura Hills, CA 91301-2493
Tel (818) 735-6100 *Founded/Ownrshp* 1990
Sales 115.5MM^E *EMP* 460
SIC 3499 2542 Machine bases, metal; Partitions & fixtures, except wood
Pr: Larry Renaud
**Pr:* Michael Custer
**CFO:* Tom Jorgenson
**Sec:* Larry Varblow
**Ex VP:* Ted Behrens
IT Man: Li Xu
Netwrk Eng: Alan Eng
Mtls Mgr: Jay Doran
Opers Mgr: Bill Crockett
Sls Dir: Garry Yan
Manager: Casey N Scott

D-U-N-S 06-508-0066
CHATTAHOOCHEE OIL CO INC
1405 Lee Road 270, Cusseta, AL 36852-3122
Tel (706) 566-6561 *Founded/Ownrshp* 2006
Sales 200.0MM *EMP* 15
Accts Abbott Jordan & Koon Llc La
SIC 5172 Petroleum products
Ch: Mashud Reza
**Pr:* Loring F Perez

D-U-N-S 00-333-6013 IMP/EXP
CHATTEM INC
CHATTEM INTERNATIONAL
(*Suby of* SANOFI-AVENTIS US LLC) ★
1715 W 38th St, Chattanooga, TN 37409-1259
Tel (423) 821-4571 *Founded/Ownrshp* 2010
Sales 238.7MM^E *EMP* 536^E
SIC 2834 2844 2023 5963 Pharmaceutical preparations; Analgesics; Dermatologicals; Shampoos, rinses, conditioners: hair; Toilet preparations; Dietary supplements, dairy & non-dairy based; Direct sales, telemarketing
CEO: Zan Guerry
**Pr:* Robert E Bosworth
**Pr:* Robert B Long
**Chf Cred:* John Stroud
VP: Andrea Crouch
**VP:* B Derrill Pitts
**VP:* Theodore K Whitfield Jr
Assoc Dir: Mary Dragan
**Prin:* Dolly Day
Sfty Mgr: Susan Williams
Natl Sales: Judy Hoskins

CHATTEM INTERNATIONAL
See CHATTEM INC

CHAUTAUQUA
See EMERY AIR INC

D-U-N-S 07-148-8936
CHAUTAUQUA AIRLINES INC
US AIRWAYS EXPRESS
8909 Purdue Rd Ste 300, Indianapolis, IN 46268-3152
Tel (317) 484-6000 *Founded/Ownrshp* 1998
Sales 73.0MM^E *EMP* 1,589
SIC 4512 4522

CHC COMPANIES
See CORRECTIONAL HEALTHCARE COMPANIES INC

CHC KANSAS
See COVENTRY HEALTH CARE OF KANSAS INC

D-U-N-S 92-658-1018
■ **CHCA CLEAR LAKE LP**
(*Suby of* HCA HOLDINGS INC) ★
500 W Medical Center Blvd, Webster, TX 77598-4220
Tel (281) 332-2511 *Founded/Ownrshp* 1997
Sales 463.9MM *EMP* 1,904
SIC 8062 General medical & surgical hospitals
CEO: Stephen Jones Jr
Chf Rad: Kenneth W Lutschg
CFO: Jeff Fliwinski
Dir Lab: Sherry Mitchell
VP Mktg: Louis Perrin
VP Mktg: Carla Reed
HC Dir: Anne Steinbach

D-U-N-S 15-957-2846
■ **CHCA CONROE LP**
CONROE REGIONAL MEDICAL CENTER
(*Suby of* HOSPITAL COPORATION OF AMERICA) ★
504 Medical Center Blvd, Conroe, TX 77304-2808
Tel (936) 539-1111 *Founded/Ownrshp* 1995
Sales 233.7MM *EMP* 1,200
SIC 8062 General medical & surgical hospitals
CEO: Matt Davis
Pt: Tom Holt
Ex VP: Diane Henry
Dir IT: Susan O'Connell
Mtls Mgr: Lynda Shaw

D-U-N-S 07-844-7315 IMP
■ **CHCA WOMANS HOSPITAL LP**
WOMAN'S HOSPITAL OF TEXAS
(*Suby of* TRISTAR HEALTH SYSTEMS) ★
7600 Fannin St, Houston, TX 77054-1906
Tel (713) 791-7534 *Founded/Ownrshp* 1976
Sales 286.1MM^E *EMP* 1,300
SIC 8062 General medical & surgical hospitals
CEO: Linda Russell
Pt: Scott Pendley
Dir IT: Emily Lee
IT Man: Randy Lobrano
HC Dir: Robin R Brown

CHEAPOAIR
See FAREPORTAL INC

CHEATHAM COUNTY BOARD EDUCATN
See CHEATHAM COUNTY SCHOOL DISTRICT (INC)

D-U-N-S 10-007-2602
CHEATHAM COUNTY SCHOOL DISTRICT (INC)
CHEATHAM COUNTY BOARD EDUCATN
102 Elizabeth St, Ashland City, TN 37015-1101
Tel (615) 792-5664 *Founded/Ownrshp* 1909
Sales 51.7MM *EMP* 1,000
SIC 8211 Public elementary & secondary schools
Ofcr: Debi Perry
Psych: Deidrah Edwards
Psych: Linda Gray
Psych: Donna Jacobs
Psych: Melissa Looney
Psych: Melanie Spicer

D-U-N-S 96-681-8247
CHECK INTO CASH INC
201 Keith St Sw Ste 80, Cleveland, TN 37311-5867
Tel (423) 479-2400 *Founded/Ownrshp* 1993
Sales NA *EMP* 2,979
SIC 6099 Check cashing agencies
CEO: W Allan Jones Jr
**Pr:* Steve Scoggins
CFO: Bill Lane
**CFO:* William S Lane
Sr Cor Off: Laura Keepfer
VP: Chuck Floyd
VP: Mike Steimel
Prgrm Mgr: Mark Hall
Brnch Mgr: Shelia Ball
Brnch Mgr: Patrica Beal
Brnch Mgr: Kathy Bonhomme

CHECK N GO
See CNG FINANCIAL CORP

D-U-N-S 83-915-4788 IMP
CHECK POINT SOFTWARE TECHNOLOGIES INC
(*Suby of* CHECK POINT SOFTWARE TECHNOLOGIES LTD.)
959 Skyway Rd Ste 300, San Carlos, CA 94070-2723
Tel (800) 429-4391 *Founded/Ownrshp* 1996
Sales 292.4MM^E *EMP* 787
SIC 7372 Operating systems computer software
CEO: John Slavitt
**Ch Bd:* Marius Nacht
Pr: Rafael Alegre
**Pr:* Jerry Ungerman
**CFO:* Eyal Desheh
Sr Cor Off: Ken Fitzpatrick
Sr Cor Off: Kevin Piper
**Chf Mktg O:* Julie Parrish
Ex VP: Cedric Chan
Ex VP: Shlomo Kramer
VP: Asheem Chandna
VP: Eyal Deshesh
VP: Michelle Fridgen
**VP:* Neil McNamara
VP: Robert Okeefe
VP: Tony Reed
**VP:* Carol Stone
Exec: Lilliam Castellanos
Comm Man: Molly Ford

CHECKER AUTO PARTS
See CSK AUTO INC

CHECKER DISTRIBUTORS
See CHECKER NOTIONS CO INC

D-U-N-S 01-835-4589 IMP
CHECKER NOTIONS CO INC
CHECKER DISTRIBUTORS
400 W Dussel Dr Ste B, Maumee, OH 43537-1636
Tel (419) 893-3636 *Founded/Ownrshp* 1948
Sales 111.3MM^E *EMP* 125^E
SIC 5131 5092 Piece goods & other fabrics; Notions; Arts & crafts equipment & supplies
Pr: J Robert Krieger III
Mng Pt: Lisa Frantz
**VP:* Bradley Krieger
Snr Ntwrk: CAM Kilman
IT Man: Nick Edens
Opers Mgr: Jim McDonald

D-U-N-S 02-383-3429
CHECKERED FLAG MOTOR CAR CO INC
CHECKERED FLAG TOYOTA
5225 Virginia Beach Blvd, Virginia Beach, VA 23462-1899
Tel (757) 490-1111 *Founded/Ownrshp* 1964
Sales 253.4MM^E *EMP* 700
SIC 5511 7532 New & used car dealers; Top & body repair & paint shops
Pr: Stephen M Snyder
CFO: Fred Kirschbaum
**VP:* Jean M Snyder

CHECKERED FLAG TOYOTA
See CHECKERED FLAG MOTOR CAR CO INC

D-U-N-S 14-786-7907
CHECKERS DRIVE-IN RESTAURANTS INC
RALLY'S HAMBURGERS
(*Suby of* TAXI HOLDINGS CORP) ★
4300 W Cypress St Ste 600, Tampa, FL 33607-4157
Tel (813) 283-7000 *Founded/Ownrshp* 1991
Sales 160.9MM^E *EMP* 4,000
SIC 5812 6794 Drive-in restaurant; Fast-food restaurant, chain; Franchises, selling or licensing
Pr: Enrique Silva
CFO: Todd Lindsey
Sr Cor Off: Shuh Mike
Ex VP: Brian Doxser
Ex VP: Adam Noyes
Ex VP: Terri Snyder
Sr VP: Brian Doster
Sr VP: Annette Shehan
Dist Mgr: Kendra Conover
Genl Mgr: Alain Almeida
Genl Mgr: Wendy Beck

CHECKERS INDUS SAFETY PDTS
See CHECKERS INDUSTRIAL PRODUCTS LLC

D-U-N-S 18-208-0580 IMP/EXP
CHECKERS INDUSTRIAL PRODUCTS LLC
CHECKERS INDUS SAFETY PDTS
(*Suby of* AUDAX GROUP LP) ★
620 Compton St, Broomfield, CO 80020-1615
Tel (720) 890-1187 *Founded/Ownrshp* 2014
Sales 96.5MM^E *EMP* 218
SIC 3714 3965 Sanders, motor vehicle safety; Safety pins
Pr: Ray Torres

D-U-N-S 04-033-7243
■ **CHECKFREE CORP**
FISERV
(*Suby of* FISERV INC) ★
2900 Westside Pkwy, Alpharetta, GA 30004-7429
Tel (678) 375-3000 *Founded/Ownrshp* 2007
Sales 537.6MM^E *EMP* 4,300
SIC 7389 Brokers' services; Balloons, novelty & toy
CEO: Peter J Kight
Pr: David Hadesty
**Pr:* Jeffery W Yabuki
**COO:* Stephen E Olsen
CFO: Dan Alf
CFO: James Douglass
**CFO:* Thomas Hirsch
CFO: Allen M Shuman
Sr Cor Off: Phil Hall
Ex VP: Lynn D Busing
Ex VP: Tacio Caraviko
**Ex VP:* James W Cox
Ex VP: James S Douglass
**Ex VP:* Mark A Ernst
**Ex VP:* Michael P Gianoni
Ex VP: Matthew S Lewi
Ex VP: Matthew S Lewis
Ex VP: Alexander R Marasco
Ex VP: Randall McCoy
Ex VP: Terrie Ohanlon
Sr VP: Allen Shulman

D-U-N-S 79-544-9011
■ **CHECKFREE INVESTMENT CORP**
(*Suby of* FISERV) ★
4411 E Jones Bridge Rd, Norcross, GA 30092-1615
Tel (678) 375-3000 *Founded/Ownrshp* 2007
Sales 5.6MM^E *EMP* 1,099^E
SIC 7374 Data processing & preparation
Ch: Mark Johnson
VP: Art D'Angelo
VP: Gary Wirth
Dir Soc: Kimberly Schwalb
Snr Sftwr: Gabriel Beeslaar
Sls Mgr: Mary Eikenberg

D-U-N-S 14-721-2724
■ **CHECKFREE SERVICES CORP**
FISERV
(*Suby of* FISERV INC) ★
2900 Westside Pkwy, Alpharetta, GA 30004-7429
Tel (678) 375-3000 *Founded/Ownrshp* 2007
Sales 154.4MM^E *EMP* 2,925
SIC 7374 Computer processing services; Data processing service
CEO: Jardon T Bouska
Pr: Brad Perkins
CFO: Thomas J Hirsch
CFO: David E Mangum
Chf Mktg O: Donald J Macdonald
Ex VP: James W Cox
Ex VP: Mark A Ernst
Ex VP: Clifford Skelton
Sr VP: Shawn Donovan
Sr VP: Larry Green
VP: Scott Hess
VP: Stephen Lefkowitz
Exec: Gregg Kaplan

D-U-N-S 80-791-1180
CHECKOUT HOLDING CORP
1 Maritime Plz Ste 1200, San Francisco, CA 94111-3502
Tel (415) 788-5111 *Founded/Ownrshp* 2007
Sales 269.2MM^E *EMP* 1,233^E
SIC 7319 Coupon distribution
Pr: C Andrew Ballard

D-U-N-S 06-184-4015 IMP/EXP
CHECKPOINT SYSTEMS INC
(*Suby of* CCL INDUSTRIES INC)
101 Wolf Dr, West Deptford, NJ 08086-2243
Tel (856) 848-1800 *Founded/Ownrshp* 2016
Sales 587.1MM *EMP* 4,894
SIC 3699 3812 3663 Security control equipment & systems; Detection apparatus: electronic/magnetic field, light/heat; Television closed circuit equipment
Pr: George Babich Jr
CFO: James M Lucania
Ofcr: Carol P Roy
Ofcr: Robert Wiley
Ex VP: Bernard Gremillet
Ex VP: Janice McCourt
Sr VP: Carol Roy
Sr VP: John R Zile
VP: Kai Beilenhoff
VP: Jim Brodzik
VP: Arthur Ciabattoni
VP: Joseph Driscoll
VP: Lukas Geiges
VP: Steven Kovach
VP: Neil Matthews
VP: Carlos Perez
VP: Dan Reynolds
VP: Bryan T R Rowland
VP: Carl Rysdon
VP: Byron Yeung
VP: John Zile
Board of Directors: William S Antle III, Harald Einsmann, R Keith Elliott, Julie S England, Marc T Giles, Daniel R Maurer, Jack W Partridge

D-U-N-S 12-372-1180
CHECKS IN MOTION
11071 Minneapolis Dr, Hollywood, FL 33026-4940
Tel (954) 433-8080 *Founded/Ownrshp* 1985
Sales 23.1MM^E *EMP* 1,000
SIC 8721 Payroll accounting service
Pr: Pamela Lipschitz

D-U-N-S 96-689-6289
CHECKSMART FINANCIAL CO
(*Suby of* CHECKSMART FINANCIAL HOLDINGS CORP.)
6785 Bobcat Way Ste 200, Dublin, OH 43016-1443
Tel (614) 798-5900 *Founded/Ownrshp* 2012
Sales NA *EMP* 33^E
SIC 6099 Check cashing agencies
Prin: Rob Grieser

D-U-N-S 09-544-6670
CHEDDARS CASUAL CAFE INC
2900 Ranch Trl, Irving, TX 75063-7355
Tel (214) 596-6700 *Founded/Ownrshp* 2006
Sales 114.7MM^E *EMP* 3,000
SIC 5812 American restaurant
Pr: Douglas H Rogers
Mng Pt: Lisa Marsh
COO: Greg Good
Chf Mktg O: Claudia Schaefer
Ex VP: Lynne Bartusek
Ex VP: Peter Gaudreau
Sr VP: Rick Payne
Genl Mgr: Beau Billedeaux
Genl Mgr: James Philips
MIS Dir: Shelley White
Dir IT: Christopher Carroll

CHEESE AMERICA
See WISCONSIN CHEESE GROUP LLC

D-U-N-S 00-960-4443 IMP
CHEESE MERCHANTS OF AMERICA LLC
1301 Schiferl Rd, Bartlett, IL 60103-1701
Tel (630) 221-0580 *Founded/Ownrshp* 1998
Sales 106.0MM^E *EMP* 90
SIC 5143 2022 Cheese; Cheese, natural & processed
Pr: Robert Greco
**CFO:* Brian Barrett
**Ex VP:* Jim Smart
Rgnl Mgr: John Perazzo
Dir IT: Gene Yekelchik

CHEESECAKE FACTORY, THE
See CHEESECAKE FACTORY INC

D-U-N-S 79-435-1783 IHP
▲ **CHEESECAKE FACTORY INC**
CHEESECAKE FACTORY, THE
26901 Malibu Hills Rd, Calabasas Hills, CA 91301-5354
Tel (818) 871-3000 *Founded/Ownrshp* 1972
Sales 2.1MMM *EMP* 37,600
Tkr Sym CAKE *Exch* NGS
SIC 5812 2051 Eating places; Cakes, bakery: except frozen
Ch Bd: David Overton
Pr: David M Gordon
CFO: W Douglas Benn
Ex VP: Debby R Zurzolo
Sr VP: Cheryl M Slomann
QA Dir: Santiago E Rivas
Snr Mgr: Amy Lorber
Board of Directors: Edie A Ames, Alexander L Cappello, Jerome I Kransdorf, Laurence B Mindel, David B Pittaway, Herbert Simon

D-U-N-S 09-337-4650 IMP
■ **CHEESECAKE FACTORY RESTAURANTS INC**
(*Suby of* CHEESECAKE FACTORY) ★
26901 Malibu Hills Rd, Calabasas, CA 91301-5354
Tel (818) 871-3000 *Founded/Ownrshp* 1992
Sales 584.8MM^E *EMP* 24,000
SIC 5812 American restaurant
Pr: David Overton

CHEF EARL'S
See GOOD FOODS GROUP LLC

D-U-N-S 18-247-6742
CHEF SOLUTIONS HOLDINGS LLC
20 N Martingale Rd # 600, Schaumburg, IL 60173-2412
Tel (847) 762-8500 *Founded/Ownrshp* 2004
Sales NA *EMP* 6,797
SIC 2099

CHEF'S WAREHOUSE
See HOCKENBERGS EQUIPMENT AND SUPPLY CO INC

CHEFS' WAREHOUSE, THE
See DAIRYLAND USA CORP

D-U-N-S 83-070-3323
▲ **CHEFS WAREHOUSE INC**
100 E Ridge Rd, Ridgefield, CT 06877-4623
Tel (203) 894-1345 *Founded/Ownrshp* 1985
Sales 1.0MMM *EMP* 1,693^E
Tkr Sym CHEF *Exch* NGS
SIC 5141 Groceries, general line; Food brokers
Ch Bd: Christopher Pappas
CFO: John Austin
**V Ch Bd:* John Pappas
Ofcr: Patricia Lecouras
Ex VP: Gerry Egan
Ex VP: John Scott
CIO: Frank O'Dowd
Opers Mgr: Rick Donovan
Sales Exec: Judy Plesko
Sales Asso: Seth Eldridge
Sales Asso: Christelle Escamilla
Board of Directors: Dominick Cerbone, John A Couri, Joseph Cugine, John Debenedetti, Steven F Goldstone, Alan Guarino, Stephen Hanson, Katherine Oliver

CHEFZONE
See Y HATA & CO LIMITED

D-U-N-S 79-178-0294 IMP
▲ **CHEGG INC**
3990 Freedom Cir, Santa Clara, CA 95054-1204
Tel (408) 855-5700 *Founded/Ownrshp* 2005
Sales 301.3MM *EMP* 672^E
Tkr Sym CHGG *Exch* NYS
SIC 5942 Book stores; College book stores
Ch Bd: Dan Rosensweig
CFO: Andrew Brown

Chf Mktg O: Esther Lem
Ofcr: Michael Osier
Ofcr: Nathan Schultz
Sr VP: Robert Chesnut
Sftwr Eng: Yashwanth Chanamolu
Board of Directors: Renee Budig, Jeffrey Housenbold, Marne Levine, Richard Sarnoff, Ted Schlein, John York

D-U-N-S 06-022-1558
CHEHALEM HEALTH & REHAB CENTER
1900 Fulton St, Newberg, OR 97132-1806
Tel (503) 538-2108 *Founded/Ownrshp* 2001
Sales 564.6MM[E] *EMP* 3[E]
SIC 8099 Health & allied services
Prin: Donald Veverka

CHELAN FRUIT COOPERATIVE
See TROUT-BLUE CHELAN-MAGI INC

CHELAN HYDRO
See PUBLIC UTILITY DISTRICT NO 1 OF CHELAN COUNTY

CHELCO
See CHOCTAWHATCHEE ELECTRIC COOPERATIVE INC

D-U-N-S 04-834-1796
CHELSEA INDUSTRIES INC (MA)
(*Suby of* CI HOLDINGS CORP.)
46a Glen Ave, Newton, MA 02459-2066
Tel (617) 232-6060 *Founded/Ownrshp* 1926, 1989
Sales 85.7MM[E] *EMP* 740
SIC 6552 Land subdividers & developers, commercial
Ch Bd: Ronald G Casty
CFO: Ken Smaha
Treas: Emil S Bernstein
MIS Mgr: Dennis Kosydar
MIS Mgr: Bob Maiorisi
VP Sls: Arnold Shainker

D-U-N-S 08-023-5816
CHELSEA PETROLEUM PRODUCTS HOLDINGS LLC
200 Clarendon St Fl 55, Boston, MA 02116-5021
Tel (617) 531-6300 *Founded/Ownrshp* 2015
Sales NA *EMP* 334[E]
SIC 6141 Automobile loans, including insurance
Pt: Daniel Revers
Sr Pt: Robb Turner

D-U-N-S 16-726-7173 IMP
CHELSEY DIRECT LLC
110 E 59th St, New York, NY 10022-1304
Tel (201) 863-7300 *Founded/Ownrshp* 2003
Sales 525.7MM[E] *EMP* 2,350
SIC 5961 5947 5611 Catalog & mail-order houses; Furniture & furnishings, mail order; Women's apparel, mail order; General merchandise, mail order; Gifts & novelties; Men's & boys' clothing stores
CFO: George Hackett
Exec: Helen Petulla

D-U-N-S 01-907-9925 IMP/EXP
CHELTON AVIONICS INC
COBHAM AROSPC COMMUNICATIONS
(*Suby of* COBHAM HOLDINGS INC) ★
6400 Wilkinson Dr, Prescott, AZ 86301-6164
Tel (928) 708-1500 *Founded/Ownrshp* 1997
Sales 95.1MM[E] *EMP* 200[E]
SIC 3812 Search & navigation equipment
Pr: Eiji Kawaishi
**VP:* John Payne

D-U-N-S 04-999-7836
CHEM GRO OF HOUGHTON INC
504 Main St, Houghton, IA 52631
Tel (319) 469-2611 *Founded/Ownrshp* 1954
Sales 93.0MM *EMP* 35
Accts Cliftonlarsonallen Llp Dixon
SIC 5153 5191 Grains; Fertilizer & fertilizer materials
Pr: Harold H Dyer
**CFO:* Tami Arbogast
**Treas:* Greg J Dyer

D-U-N-S 07-346-0545 IMP
CHEM-NUT INC
800 Business Park Dr, Leesburg, GA 31763-5641
Tel (229) 883-7050 *Founded/Ownrshp* 1974
Sales 129.8MM[E] *EMP* 46
Accts Draffin & Tucker Llp Albany
SIC 5191 8611 Chemicals, agricultural; Fertilizer & fertilizer materials; Seeds: field, garden & flower; Business associations
CEO: Chris Payne
Ch Bd: Brinson Lanier
CFO: Jamie Carter
CFO: Keith Thomas
VP: Greg Fowler
VP: H L Smith
Manager: Jimmy Champion
Manager: Sanford Clark

CHEM-TRONICS INC. FACSIMILE
See GKN AEROSPACE CHEM-TRONICS INC

D-U-N-S 05-510-9912
▲ **CHEMED CORP**
255 E 5th St Ste 2600, Cincinnati, OH 45202-4138
Tel (513) 762-6690 *Founded/Ownrshp* 1970
Sales 1.5MMM *EMP* 14,406[E]
Tkr Sym CHE *Exch* NYS
SIC 8082 1711 7699 Home health care services; Visiting nurse service; Plumbing, heating, air-conditioning contractors; Plumbing contractors; Sewer cleaning & rodding
Pr: Kevin J McNamara
**Ch Bd:* George J Walsh III
CFO: David P Williams
Ex VP: Spencer S Lee
Ex VP: Nicholas M Westfall
VP: Arthur V Tucker Jr
Board of Directors: Joel F Gemunder, Patrick P Grace, Thomas C Hutton, Walter L Krebs, Andrea R Lindell, Thomas P Rice, Donald E Saunders, Frank E Wood

CHEMETALL AMERICAS
See CHEMETALL US INC

D-U-N-S 55-612-1200 EXP
■ **CHEMETALL US INC**
CHEMETALL AMERICAS
(*Suby of* ROCKWOOD HOLDINGS INC) ★
675 Central Ave, New Providence, NJ 07974-1560
Tel (908) 464-6900 *Founded/Ownrshp* 2004
Sales 99.5MM[E] *EMP* 340
SIC 2842 2899 2851 Specialty cleaning, polishes & sanitation goods; Sanitation preparations, disinfectants & deodorants; Metal treating compounds; Rust resisting compounds; Water treating compounds; Paints & allied products; Paint removers
Pr: Ronald Felber
**Pr:* Mark Bruner
**CFO:* Kevin Filipski
VP: Donald Lebart
**VP:* Gregory V Poff

D-U-N-S 07-918-3014
CHEMGROUP INC
2600 Thunderhawk Ct, Dayton, OH 45414-3463
Tel (937) 898-5566 *Founded/Ownrshp* 2006
Sales 116.3MM[E] *EMP* 125
SIC 5169 Industrial chemicals
Pr: Marty Wehr
**Sec:* Sue Wiford

CHEMICAL
See P & C GROUP I INC

CHEMICAL AND MATERIALS ENGRG
See UNIVERSITY OF KENTUCKY

D-U-N-S 07-422-4858
■ **CHEMICAL BANK AND TRUST CO**
(*Suby of* CHEMICAL FINANCIAL CORP) ★
333 E Main St, Midland, MI 48640-5178
Tel (989) 631-9200 *Founded/Ownrshp* 1974
Sales NA *EMP* 200
SIC 6022 State commercial banks
CEO: David B Ramaker
Pr: Richard Devries
Pr: Lynn Kerber
CFO: Laurie Gwizdala
Ofcr: Christine Lawson
Ofcr: Vicki Popke
Ofcr: Howard Rose
Ex VP: William Dixon
Ex VP: Kenneth Johnson
Ex VP: William Lauderbach
Ex VP: Joel Rahn
Sr VP: Pavel Konecny
Sr VP: Gary Richardson
VP: Carl Ahearn
VP: William Bruinsma
VP: Steve Buerger
VP: Marc Cesere
VP: Delbert Denkins
VP: Andy Dominowski
VP: Kirk Fisher
VP: Lori Gwizdala

D-U-N-S 07-635-0529
▲ **CHEMICAL FINANCIAL CORP**
235 E Main St, Midland, MI 48640-5137
Tel (989) 839-5350 *Founded/Ownrshp* 1973
Sales NA *EMP* 2,100[E]
Tkr Sym CHFC *Exch* NGS
SIC 6022 State commercial banks
Ch Bd: David B Ramaker
V Ch: Thomas W Kohn
Pr: Scott Harris
Pr: Jim Hubinger
Pr: Thomas Kohn
Pr: Anita Merchant II
Pr: Larry Morrow
COO: Leonardo Amat
COO: Robert S Rathbun
CFO: Lori A Gwizdala
Chf Mktg O: John Hatfield
Ofcr: Pavel Konecny
Ofcr: Sue Moody
Top Exec: Brian Bealow
Ex VP: William C Collins
Ex VP: William Collins
Ex VP: Lynn Kerber
Ex VP: James Milroy
Sr VP: Greg Meidt
VP: James Blanchard
VP: Robert O Burgess

CHEMICAL OR VEGOIL TRANSPORTAT
See UNI-CHARTERING USA LLC

D-U-N-S 93-886-9583 IMP/EXP
CHEMICAL RESOURCES INC
CHEMRES
103 Carnegie Ctr Ste 100, Princeton, NJ 08540-6235
Tel (609) 520-0000 *Founded/Ownrshp* 1955
Sales 110.2MM[E] *EMP* 70
Accts Cohn Reznick Eatontown Nj
SIC 5162 5169 2865 Plastics materials & basic shapes; Chemicals & allied products; Cyclic crudes & intermediates
Owner: Paul Keimig
**VP:* Jim Couture
**VP:* Bob Hamilton

D-U-N-S 05-293-7885 IMP
CHEMICAL SOLVENTS INC (OH)
3751 Jennings Rd, Cleveland, OH 44109-2889
Tel (216) 741-9310 *Founded/Ownrshp* 1970
Sales 112.5MM[E] *EMP* 110
SIC 5169 7349 3471 2992 Detergents & soaps, except specialty cleaning; Specialty cleaning & sanitation preparations; Chemical cleaning services; Cleaning & descaling metal products; Oils & greases, blending & compounding
Ch Bd: Edward Pavlish
**Sec:* Patricia Pavlish
**VP:* Blaine Davidson
VP: Ron Forster
**VP:* Gerald J Schill
**Prin:* Thos A Mason
**Prin:* E H Pavlish

D-U-N-S 09-920-2681
■ **CHEMICAL WASTE MANAGEMENT INC**
COMMODITY MARKET CENTER
(*Suby of* WASTE MANAGEMENT HOLDINGS INC) ★
1001 Fannin St Ste 4000, Houston, TX 77002-6711
Tel (713) 512-6200 *Founded/Ownrshp* 1975
Sales 110.0MM[E] *EMP* 562[E]
SIC 4953 4959 Hazardous waste collection & disposal; Chemical detoxification; Acid waste, collection & disposal; Radioactive waste materials, disposal; Toxic or hazardous waste cleanup
Pr: Joseph Holston
CFO: Greg A Robertson
Treas: Cherie C Rice
VP: Robert G Henry
VP: Larry Metter
VP: David M Myhan
VP: Edward R Schauble

D-U-N-S 02-803-5137 IMP/EXP
■ **CHEMICAL WASTE MANAGEMENT OF NORTHWEST INC**
(*Suby of* WASTE MANAGEMENT HOLDINGS INC) ★
17629 Cedar Springs Ln, Arlington, OR 97812-6570
Tel (541) 454-2030 *Founded/Ownrshp* 1995
Sales 86.7MM[E] *EMP* 147
SIC 4953 Hazardous waste collection & disposal
Genl Mgr: Pearlie Simpson
Genl Mgr: Will Spears

D-U-N-S 10-251-8144 IMP/EXP
CHEMIUM INTERNATIONAL CORP
1455 West Loop S Ste 550, Houston, TX 77027-9528
Tel (713) 622-7766 *Founded/Ownrshp* 2001
Sales 2.0MMM *EMP* 24
Accts Blieden Foerster & Company H
SIC 5172 Petroleum brokers
Pr: Ofer Levy
**VP:* Thomas Holzmann
Software D: Nicolas Folgado

D-U-N-S 06-169-7470 IMP/EXP
CHEMOIL CORP
(*Suby of* GLENCORE LTD) ★
101 N Lathrop Ave, Savannah, GA 31415-1054
Tel (912) 236-1331 *Founded/Ownrshp* 2006
Sales 158.7MM[E] *EMP* 45
SIC 5172 Fuel oil
Ch: Mark Jonathan Catton
**CEO:* Robert V Chandran
**CFO:* Fred Bendle
**Sr VP:* Sanjay Anand

D-U-N-S 86-771-4768 IMP/EXP
CHEMONICS INTERNATIONAL INC
1717 H St Nw, Washington, DC 20006-3900
Tel (202) 955-3300 *Founded/Ownrshp* 1999
Sales 370.4MM[E] *EMP* 3,500[E]
Accts Pricewaterhousecoopers Llp Mc
SIC 8742 8748 Management consulting services; Agricultural consultant
Pr: Susanna Mudge
**Ch Bd:* Eyk Van Otterloo
**CFO:* Eric Huwell
CFO: Ghaan F Nakad
Treas: Anthony Latta
**Ex VP:* Jamey Butcher
**Ex VP:* Eric Reading
**Sr VP:* Elizabeth Bassan
**Sr VP:* Tim Beans
Sr VP: Peter Bittner
Sr VP: Michelle Gardner
Sr VP: Rhett Gurian
Sr VP: Eric Howell
Sr VP: Terri Kristalsky
Sr VP: Andrew Lewis
**Sr VP:* Melissa Logan
Sr VP: Gita Maitra
Sr VP: Emet Mohr
Sr VP: Heather Peck
**Sr VP:* Richard Prather
**Sr VP:* Christopher Smith
Board of Directors: Jean Spangler, David Vaughn

D-U-N-S 07-947-9503
▲ **CHEMOURS CO**
1007 Market St, Wilmington, DE 19898-1100
Tel (302) 773-1000 *Founded/Ownrshp* 2014
Sales 5.7MMM *EMP* 8,100[E]
Tkr Sym CC *Exch* NYS
SIC 2879 Agricultural chemicals
Pr: Mark P Vergnano
Ch Bd: Richard H Brown
Pr: Christian W Siemer
CFO: Mark E Newman
Sr VP: Beth Albright
Sr VP: David C Shelton
VP: Erich Parker
Board of Directors: Curtis V Anastasio, Bradley J Bell, Mary B Cranston, Curtis J Crawford, Dawn L Farrell, Stephen D Newlin

D-U-N-S 07-955-0093
■ **CHEMOURS CO FC LLC**
(*Suby of* CHEMOURS CO) ★
1007 Market St, Wilmington, DE 19898-1100
Tel (302) 774-1000 *Founded/Ownrshp* 2014
Sales 844.5MM[E] *EMP* 1,706[E]
SIC 2879 2816 Agricultural chemicals; Titanium dioxide, anatase or rutile (pigments)
Pr: Deana J Dicosimo

D-U-N-S 12-293-2978 IMP/EXP
■ **CHEMPOINT.COM INC**
(*Suby of* UNIVAR INC) ★
411 108th Ave Ne Ste 1050, Bellevue, WA 98004-8402
Tel (425) 378-8600 *Founded/Ownrshp* 2007
Sales 236.4MM[E] *EMP* 166[E]
SIC 5169 Industrial chemicals
Pr: Greg Vas Nunes
VP: Kelly A O'Hanlon
Software D: Khris Downey
Board of Directors: Stephen N Landsman, Jeffrey H Siegel

CHEMPROBE COATING SYSTEMS
See TNEMEC CO INC

CHEMRES
See CHEMICAL RESOURCES INC

CHEMSEARCH DIVISION
See NCH CORP

CHEMSICO
See UNITED INDUSTRIES CORP

CHEMSTAR DIVISION
See AMERICAN CHEMISTRY COUNCIL INC

D-U-N-S 04-546-9160 IMP
CHEMTALL INC
(*Suby of* S N F) ★
1 Chemical Plant Rd, Riceboro, GA 31323
Tel (912) 884-3366 *Founded/Ownrshp* 1986
Sales 150.1MM[E] *EMP* 1,400
SIC 2869 Industrial organic chemicals
CEO: Peter W Nichols
CFO: Mark Schlag
VP: Jim Carlson
VP: David Kaye

D-U-N-S 61-033-2298 IMP/EXP
CHEMTEX INTERNATIONAL INC
(*Suby of* MOSSI & GHISOLFI SPA)
1979 Eastwood Rd, Wilmington, NC 28403-7214
Tel (910) 509-4400 *Founded/Ownrshp* 2009
Sales 235.5MM[E] *EMP* 800
SIC 8711 8731 Engineering services; Engineering laboratory, except testing
Pr: Pedro Losa
**Ex VP:* Dennis Leong
VP: Jose Bautista
VP: Kevin Gray
VP: Pete Howe
CTO: Thomas Mc Gannon

D-U-N-S 00-555-3011 IMP/EXP
■ **CHEMTOOL INC**
METALCOTE
(*Suby of* LUBRICANT ADDITIVES) ★
801 W Rockton Rd, Rockton, IL 61072-1647
Tel (815) 957-4140 *Founded/Ownrshp* 1963, 2013
Sales 150.6MM[E] *EMP* 500
SIC 2992 2899 2842 2841 Lubricating oils & greases; Cutting oils, blending: made from purchased materials; Rust arresting compounds, animal or vegetable oil base; Rust resisting compounds; Water treating compounds; Specialty cleaning, polishes & sanitation goods; Soap & other detergents
Pr: Tom Rajewski
Ofcr: George Bliss
Sls Mgr: Tim Little

D-U-N-S 15-427-9434 IMP/EXP
CHEMTRADE CHEMICALS CORP
GENERAL PERFORMANCE PRODUCTS
(*Suby of* CHEMTRADE GCC HOLDING CO) ★
90 E Halsey Rd Ste 301, Parsippany, NJ 07054-3709
Tel (973) 515-0900 *Founded/Ownrshp* 2014
Sales 220.7MM[E] *EMP* 500
SIC 2819 Industrial inorganic chemicals
CEO: William E Redmond Jr
**CFO:* Thomas B Testa
**VP:* Greg Gilbert
**VP:* Douglas J Grierson
**VP:* James Imbriaco
**VP:* Douglas Mc Farland
**VP:* Vincent J Opalewski

D-U-N-S 79-002-4736
CHEMTRADE CHEMICALS US LLC
GENERAL CHEMICAL
(*Suby of* GENERAL PERFORMANCE PRODUCTS) ★
90 E Halsey Rd, Parsippany, NJ 07054-3713
Tel (973) 515-0900 *Founded/Ownrshp* 2003
Sales 229.7MM[E] *EMP* 500
SIC 2812 Soda ash, sodium carbonate (anhydrous)
CEO: William E Redmond Jr
VP: Jeff Green
Exec: Robert Novo
Sls Mgr: Robert Brandau
Snr Mgr: Steve Fenske
Snr Mgr: Anabela Rocha

D-U-N-S 07-853-7886
CHEMTRADE GCC HOLDING CO
(*Suby of* CHEMTRADE WATER CHEMICAL INC.)
90 E Halsey Rd, Parsippany, NJ 07054-3713
Tel (973) 515-0900 *Founded/Ownrshp* 2009
Sales 94.3MM[E] *EMP* 502
SIC 6719 2819 Investment holding companies, except banks; Industrial inorganic chemicals
Pr: William E Redmond Jr
**VP:* Douglas Mc Farland

D-U-N-S 79-476-3867 IMP
CHEMTRADE SOLUTIONS LLC
(*Suby of* GENERAL CHEMICAL) ★
90 E Halsey Rd, Parsippany, NJ 07054-3713
Tel (973) 515-0900 *Founded/Ownrshp* 1993
Sales 206.4MM[E] *EMP* 400
SIC 5169 2819 Chemicals & allied products; Aluminum sulfate

D-U-N-S 06-538-6906 IMP/EXP
■ **CHEMTREAT INC** (VA)
(*Suby of* DANAHER CORP) ★
5640 Cox Rd Ste 300, Glen Allen, VA 23060-9297
Tel (804) 935-2000 *Founded/Ownrshp* 1968, 2007
Sales 323.9MM[E] *EMP* 750
SIC 2899 3589 Water treating compounds; Water treatment equipment, industrial
Pr: Steven A Hire
**Ex VP:* Randall L Azzarello
VP: Leo Basola
**VP:* Robert S Lutz
**VP:* Frank T McFaden
**VP:* Charles A Schwertner
VP: Anthony Yoo
Dir Bus: Paul Guidotti
Area Mgr: Dean Dilonarado
Area Mgr: Paul Fisher
Area Mgr: Ian Gaffney

D-U-N-S 08-840-0325 IMP/EXP
▲ CHEMTURA CORP
1818 Market St Ste 3700, Philadelphia, PA 19103-3640
Tel (215) 446-3911 *Founded/Ownrshp* 1954
Sales 1.7MMM *EMP* 2,500
Tkr Sym CHMT *Exch* NYS
SIC 2869 2843 2821 2911 2899 2842 Industrial organic chemicals; Surface active agents; Plastics materials & resins; Polystyrene resins; Residues; Petrolatums, nonmedicinal; Fire retardant chemicals; Oxidizers, inorganic; Water treating compounds; Sanitation preparations, disinfectants & deodorants; Degreasing solvent
Ch Bd: Craig A Rogerson
Pr: Greg McDaniel
Pr: Anne P Noonan
CFO: Stephen C Forsyth
Treas: Dalip Puri
Ex VP: James J Conway
Ex VP: Chet H Cross
Ex VP: Billie S Flaherty
Ex VP: Simon D Medley
Ex VP: Alan M Swiech
Ex VP: Robert B Weiner
VP: William Adams
VP: Laurence M Orton

D-U-N-S 60-709-5569 IMP/EXP
■ CHEMTURA USA CORP
(*Suby of* CHEMTURA CORP) ★
199 Benson Rd, Middlebury, CT 06762-3218
Tel (203) 573-2000 *Founded/Ownrshp* 1996
Sales 635.0MM^E *EMP* 2,700
SIC 2879 2869 2822 Insecticides, agricultural or household; Fungicides, herbicides; Industrial organic chemicals; Antioxidants, rubber processing: cyclic or acyclic; Accelerators, rubber processing: cyclic or acyclic; Synthetic rubber; Ethylene-propylene rubbers, EPDM polymers
Ch: Vincent A Calarco
**Treas:* John R Jepsen
**Ex VP:* Alfred F Ingulli
VP: Michael Amalfitano
**VP:* Arthur Fullerton
**VP:* Laurence Orton
VP: Charles Shambelan
Mfg Dir: Nilson Fernandes
Sfty Mgr: Robert Franko
Sfty Mgr: Michael Gagermeier
Plnt Mgr: Mike Goldberg

D-U-N-S 62-269-2994
CHENEGA CORP
3000 C St Ste 301, Anchorage, AK 99503-3975
Tel (907) 277-5706 *Founded/Ownrshp* 2006
Sales 881.6MM *EMP* 4,500
SIC 8744 7379 7376 3629 8742 Facilities support services; Computer related consulting services; Computer facilities management; Electronic generation equipment; Business planning & organizing services
Pr: Charles Totemoff
**COO:* Jeff Hueners
CFO: Patricia Ismael
Ofcr: Aubrey Marek
Sr VP: Robb A Milne
VP: Lloyd Kompkoff
VP: Kathy Kowals
VP: Deb Pomerantz
VP: Tom Reed
Dir Bus: Debra Gregory
Prgrm Mgr: Michelle Brauer

D-U-N-S 17-767-4665
CHENEGA INTEGRATED SYSTEMS LLC
(*Suby of* CHENEGA CORP) ★
14295 Pk Madow Dr Ste 400, Chantilly, VA 20151
Tel (571) 291-8500 *Founded/Ownrshp* 1998
Sales 1.8MM *EMP* 1,325
Accts Mcgladrey & Pullen Llp Frede
SIC 7381 7382 8331 Security guard service; Security systems services; Job training & vocational rehabilitation services
Genl Mgr: Tim Lamb

D-U-N-S 03-283-1471 IMP/EXP
CHENEY BROS INC
CHENEY BROTHERS
1 Cheney Way, Riviera Beach, FL 33404-7000
Tel (561) 845-4700 *Founded/Ownrshp* 1925
Sales 1.9MMM^E *EMP* 1,350
SIC 5141 5087 5113 5169 5149 Groceries, general line; Janitors' supplies; Cups, disposable plastic & paper; Dishes, disposable plastic & paper; Eating utensils, disposable plastic; Chemicals & allied products; Groceries & related products
CEO: Byron Russell
**Pr:* Bill Foley
**Pr:* Foley William
**CFO:* Michael Sullivan
**Sec:* Patti M Bell
**Sec:* Patti B Mann
**VP:* Phillip E Schwab
Dir Rx: Robert Cassel
Trfc Dir: Diane Noa
Mktg Dir: Kinna Denowitz
Sls Mgr: Charles Betts

CHENEY BROTHERS
See CHENEY BROS INC

D-U-N-S 00-860-1684
▲ CHENIERE ENERGY INC
700 Milam St Ste 1900, Houston, TX 77002-2835
Tel (713) 375-5000 *Founded/Ownrshp* 1983
Sales 270.8MM *EMP* 888
Accts Kpmg Llp Houston Texas
Tkr Sym LNG *Exch* ASE
SIC 1321 4925 4922 Liquefied petroleum gases (natural) production; Liquefied petroleum gas, distribution through mains; Pipelines, natural gas
Pr: Jack A Fusco
**Ch Bd:* G Andrea Botta
CFO: Michael J Wortley
Ofcr: Anatol Feygin
Ex VP: Tom Bullis
Ex VP: Meg A Gentle
Ex VP: R Keith Teague
Sr VP: Jean Abiteboul
Sr VP: Corey Grindal
Sr VP: Ed Lehotsky
Sr VP: Katie Pipkin
Sr VP: Greg W Rayford
Sr VP: Doug Shanda
Sr VP: Chad Zamarin
Board of Directors: Vicky A Bailey, Jonathan Christodoro, David I Foley, David B Kilpatrick, Samuel Merksamer, Donald F Robillard Jr, Heather R Zichal

D-U-N-S 07-848-4899
■ CHENIERE ENERGY INVESTMENTS LLC
(*Suby of* CHENIERE ENERGY PARTNERS LP) ★
700 Louisiana St Ste 1900, Houston, TX 77002-2767
Tel (713) 375-5000 *Founded/Ownrshp* 2006
Sales 523.0MM^E *EMP* 642^E
SIC 4922 Natural gas transmission

D-U-N-S 79-631-4271
■ CHENIERE ENERGY PARTNERS LP
(*Suby of* CHENIERE ENERGY PARTNERS LP HOLDINGS, LLC)
700 Milam St Ste 1900, Houston, TX 77002-2835
Tel (713) 375-5000 *Founded/Ownrshp* 2006
Sales 270.0MM *EMP* 888^E
Tkr Sym CQP *Exch* ASE
SIC 4924 4922 Natural gas distribution; Pipelines, natural gas
Ch Bd: Jack Fusco
Genl Pt: Cheniere E GP
Pr: R Keith Teague
Treas: Lisa Cohen
Bd of Dir: John Deutch
VP: Scott Abshire
VP: Ankit Desai
VP: Gavin Garcia
VP: Meg Gentle
VP: John Gross
VP: Drew Lynch
VP: Patricia Outtrim
VP: Len Travis

D-U-N-S 14-752-7212
CHEP (USA) INC
(*Suby of* BRAMBLES INDUSTRIES LIMITED)
5897 Windward Pkwy, Alpharetta, GA 30005-2044
Tel (770) 379-6900 *Founded/Ownrshp* 1980
Sales 540.5MM^E *EMP* 925^E
SIC 7359 Pallet rental services
Pr: Kim Rumph
CFO: Scott Spivey
Sec: Andrew Clawson
Sr VP: Melissa Schmidt
VP: Roni Garnet
Sls Mgr: Cindy Bailey
Sls Mgr: Rhonda Heuple
Genl Couns: James Frye Jr

D-U-N-S 15-014-6269
CHEP RECYCLED PALLET SOLUTIONS LLC
(*Suby of* CHEP (USA) INC) ★
8517 Suthpark Cir Ste 140, Orlando, FL 32819
Tel (713) 332-6145 *Founded/Ownrshp* 1999
Sales 517.3MM^E *EMP* 925^E
SIC 2448 0831 Pallets, wood; Forest products
Rgnl Mgr: Charles Norwood
Off Mgr: Derek Anthony
Software D: Karthik Patel
Opers Mgr: Casey Sears
Sls Mgr: Paul Prezelski
Snr Mgr: Marc Cougle
Snr Mgr: Stephen Wetter

D-U-N-S 02-288-3128
CHERNE CONTRACTING CORP
(*Suby of* KIEWIT CORP) ★
9855 W 78th St Ste 400, Eden Prairie, MN 55344-8028
Tel (952) 944-4300 *Founded/Ownrshp* 2010
Sales 111.6MM^E *EMP* 300^E
SIC 1629

CHEROKEE COUNTY BOARD OF COMMI
See COUNTY OF CHEROKEE

D-U-N-S 07-344-1677
CHEROKEE COUNTY BOARD OF EDUCATION
110 Academy St, Canton, GA 30114-3003
Tel (770) 479-1871 *Founded/Ownrshp* 1925
Sales 122.9MM^E *EMP* 2,000
SIC 8211 School board
Ch Bd: Kyla Cromer
**Ch Bd:* Mike Chapman

D-U-N-S 96-849-3606
CHEROKEE COUNTY SCHOOL DISTRICT
110 Academy St, Canton, GA 30114-3003
Tel (770) 479-1871 *Founded/Ownrshp* 2011
Sales 204.7MM^E *EMP* 3,518^E
SIC 8211 Public elementary & secondary schools
Dir Sec: Mark Kissel
Pr Dir: Barbara Jacoby

D-U-N-S 07-799-0661
CHEROKEE COUNTY SCHOOL DISTRICT 1
141 Twin Lake Rd, Gaffney, SC 29341-2526
Tel (864) 902-3500 *Founded/Ownrshp* 1897
Sales 75.1MM^E *EMP* 1,300
Accts Cline Brandt Kochenower & Co
SIC 8211 Public elementary & secondary schools
Prin: Mark Bunch
Prin: Janice Ford
Prin: Thomas Goforth
Prin: Angela L Hinton
Prin: Janice Keller
Prin: Jim Tourchberry
Prin: Rick Wilkins
Prin: Charles Wright
MIS Dir: Todd Hughes
Teacher Pr: Carl Carpenter
HC Dir: Evelyn Nelson

D-U-N-S 82-540-2886
CHEROKEE COUNTY WATER & SEWERAGE AUTHORITY
391 W Main St, Canton, GA 30114-2748
Tel (770) 591-7156 *Founded/Ownrshp* 1955
Sales 85.6MM^E *EMP* 175^E
SIC 4941 4952 Water supply; Sewerage systems
Ch: Nancy Martin
Treas: Robert Morrison
Exec: Ryan Sarks
**Genl Mgr:* Thomas Heard
DP Exec: Sharon Clark
Plnt Mgr: Clint Blackwell

D-U-N-S 03-469-2780 IMP
CHEROKEE DISTRIBUTING CO INC
200 Miller Main Cir, Knoxville, TN 37919-6017
Tel (865) 588-7641 *Founded/Ownrshp* 1982
Sales 116.7MM^E *EMP* 360^E
SIC 5181 Beer & other fermented malt liquors
CEO: George W Sampson
**Pr:* George B Sampson
**CFO:* Herbert Ogle
**Treas:* Mary S Brewington
**Ex VP:* Nell L Sampson
VP: Herb Ogle
Exec: Teresa Beason
Dir Bus: Shane Sloan

D-U-N-S 07-734-5494
CHEROKEE NATION
17675 S Muskogee Ave, Tahlequah, OK 74464-5492
Tel (918) 453-5000 *Founded/Ownrshp* 1839
Sales NA *EMP* 5,500
Accts Bkd Llp Tulsa Oklahoma
SIC 9131 Indian reservation
COO: Janet Smith
CFO: Enrique Bernal
Comm Man: Amanda Clinton
Adm Dir: Kamichia Goodman
Adm Dir: Linda Johnson
Adm Dir: Lillian Pratt
Adm Dir: Mitchell Thornbrugh
Ex Dir: Connie C Davis
Dir Sec: Mickey Spears
Off Mgr: Ernestine Pumpkin
Dir IT: Randy Alberty

D-U-N-S 14-218-2901
CHEROKEE NATION BUSINESSES LLC
CNB
(*Suby of* CHEROKEE NATION) ★
777 W Cherokee St Bldg 2, Catoosa, OK 74015-3235
Tel (918) 384-7474 *Founded/Ownrshp* 2004
Sales 925.4MM *EMP* 3,117
Accts Bkd Llp Tulsa Oklahoma
SIC 3728 5085 5088 Aircraft parts & equipment; Fasteners, industrial: nuts, bolts, screws, etc.; Transportation equipment & supplies
CEO: Shawn Slaton
**Ch Bd:* Harold Sam Ray Hart
Pr: Scott Edwards
Pr: David Mullen
Pr: Ryan Wasmus
**CFO:* Doug Evans
**Ch:* Gary Cooper
VP: John Filippe
Exec: Russell Claybrook
Dir Bus: Barry Brown
Comm Man: Amanda Clinton
Comm Man: Travis Noland

D-U-N-S 80-955-0601
CHEROKEE NATION ENTERTAINMENT LLC
(*Suby of* CHEROKEE NATION) ★
777 W Cherokee St, Catoosa, OK 74015-3235
Tel (918) 458-1696 *Founded/Ownrshp* 2013
Sales 188.7MM^E *EMP* 3,100
SIC 7999 7011 7948 5541 5993 Gambling establishment; Golf driving range; Hotels; Horse race track operation; Truck stops; Tobacco stores & stands
CEO: David Stewart
CFO: Diane Wood
**Prin:* Shawn Slaton
Genl Mgr: Travis Owens
IT Man: Wayne Johnson
Secur Mgr: Bil Caraway
Mktg Mgr: Ben Elder

D-U-N-S 01-373-2542 IMP/EXP
■ CHEROKEE PHARMACEUTICALS LLC
(*Suby of* MERCK & CO INC) ★
100 Ave C, Riverside, PA 17868
Tel (570) 271-4195 *Founded/Ownrshp* 2010
Sales 221.8MM^E *EMP* 425
SIC 5122 Pharmaceuticals
Dir Lab: Dan McClain
Dir Bus: Patrick Oates
Mfg Dir: Michael Kovach

CHEROKEE UNIFORM
See STRATEGIC PARTNERS INC

D-U-N-S 07-202-5604
CHERRY BEKAERT LLP
200 S 10th St Ste 900, Richmond, VA 23219-4064
Tel (804) 673-5700 *Founded/Ownrshp* 1963
Sales 123.6MM *EMP* 850
SIC 8721 Accounting, auditing & bookkeeping
Mng Pt: Howard Kies
**Pt:* Ronald W Lamberth
**CFO:* Ray Christopher
Ofcr: Paul Fedorkowicz
CIO: John Paul
Mktg Mgr: Sarah Holland
Snr Mgr: Greg L Akers
Snr Mgr: Laurie Carroll
Snr Mgr: Linda Suggs
Snr Mgr: Michael Valerio

D-U-N-S 06-222-0934 IMP/EXP
CHERRY CENTRAL COOPERATIVE INC
1771 N Us Highway 31 S, Traverse City, MI 49685-8748
Tel (231) 946-1860 *Founded/Ownrshp* 1973
Sales 150.6MM *EMP* 115
Accts Dennis Gartland & Niergarth
SIC 2033 Canned fruits & specialties
Pr: Steve Eiseler
**Sec:* George Wright
Ex Dir: Wendy Judson
Dir IT: Craig Johnson
IT Man: Laura Reed
Trfc Dir: Cathy Bouwkamp
Opers Mgr: Shawn Walter
Plnt Mgr: Denny Spear
Sls&Mrk Ex: Doyle Fenner
Sls Mgr: Mark Becker
Sls Mgr: Bill Trudeau
Board of Directors: Robert McMullin, V Chm

CHERRY CITY ELECTRIC
See MORROW-MEADOWS CORP

D-U-N-S 16-089-2618
CHERRY CREEK MORTGAGE CO INC
PREMIER MORTGAGE COMPANY
7600 E Orchard Rd 250n, Greenwood Village, CO 80111-2518
Tel (303) 320-4040 *Founded/Ownrshp* 1986
Sales NA *EMP* 550
SIC 6162 Mortgage companies, urban
Pr: Jeffrey S May
**CFO:* Janice Zapapas
**Ch:* Wil L Armstrong III
Ofcr: Toney Sebra
**Sr VP:* Stacey Harding
Sr VP: Jerry Kaplan
**VP:* Marco Begovich
VP: Peter Garvin
**VP:* Michael E Hole
VP: Scott Issel
VP: Thomas R Kelly
**VP:* Gary Windfield
**VP:* Jan Zapapas
VP: Kelly Zitlow
Exec: Melody Walker

D-U-N-S 18-762-5202
CHERRY CREEK RADIO LLC
7400 E Orchard Rd # 2800, Greenwood Village, CO 80111-2560
Tel (303) 468-6500 *Founded/Ownrshp* 2003
Sales 101.7MM^E *EMP* 386
SIC 4832 Radio broadcasting stations
CTO: John Hiatt
Opers Mgr: Michael McDonnal
Sls Mgr: Tyler Hill
Sls Mgr: Darla Key
Sls Mgr: Rene Wimberley

D-U-N-S 07-340-3073 IMP
CHERRY CREEK SCHOOL DISTRICT 5
4700 S Yosemite St # 223, Greenwood Village, CO 80111-1307
Tel (303) 773-1184 *Founded/Ownrshp* 1950
Sales 556.3MM *EMP* 5,707
Accts Cliftonlarsonallen Greenwood
SIC 8211 Public elementary & secondary schools; Public junior high school; Public senior high school; Public special education school
COO: Scott Schleich
CFO: Guy G Bellville
Treas: Paul Hanley
Treas: Bee Kirk
Bd of Dir: Rachael Rosales
VP: Kay Fair
Dir Sec: Karyn Fast
Off Mgr: Susan Claxon
Off Mgr: Barb Jersa
Off Mgr: Sherri Kononov
Off Mgr: Mary Polakowski

D-U-N-S 96-968-6393
CHERRY CRUSHED CONCRETE INC
6131 Selinsky Rd, Houston, TX 77048-2006
Tel (713) 987-0000 *Founded/Ownrshp* 1998
Sales 104.3MM *EMP* 78
Accts Carr Riggs & Ingram Llc Hous
SIC 5032 Concrete building products
Pr: Leonard Cherry
Pr: Joe Rizzo
**VP:* Ricky Cherry

D-U-N-S 02-262-1759
■ CHERRY HILL CONSTRUCTION INC
(*Suby of* TUTOR PERINI CORP) ★
8211 Washington Blvd, Jessup, MD 20794-9424
Tel (410) 799-3577 *Founded/Ownrshp* 2005
Sales 127.2MM *EMP* 800
Accts Deloitte & Touche Llp Los Ang
SIC 1611 1622 Highway & street construction; Highway construction, elevated; Bridge construction
Pr: Ali Catik
Treas: Dan Bell
**Sec:* William B Sparks
Bd of Dir: Robert Band
**Ex VP:* Kevin Woods
**VP:* Gregory Andricos
**VP:* Henry Cheung
VP: Anthony Wadsworth
VP: Robin Walton
Exec: Darlene Armstrong
Dir IT: Margo Hampton

D-U-N-S 80-054-0358
CHERRY HILL PUBLIC SCHOOL DISTRICT
JOHN A. CARUSI MIDDLE SCHOOL
315 Roosevelt Dr, Cherry Hill, NJ 08002-1512
Tel (856) 667-1220 *Founded/Ownrshp* 2007
Sales 5.0MM^E *EMP* 1,736^E
SIC 8211 Public junior high school
Prin: John Cafagna

D-U-N-S 82-637-8197
CHERWELL SOFTWARE LLC
10125 Federal Dr Ste 100, Colorado Springs, CO 80908-4513
Tel (719) 386-7000 *Founded/Ownrshp* 2004
Sales 85.6MM^E *EMP* 200^E
SIC 7372 Prepackaged software
CEO: Craig Harper
Ch Bd: Vance Brown
CFO: Elizabeth Salomon
VP: Timothy Pfeifer
VP: Andrew White
Dir Sec: Rob Carson
Prgrm Mgr: Sunil Salve
Genl Mgr: Doug Lingenfelter
Snr Sftwr: Mitch Blake
CTO: Arlen Feldman
QA Dir: Smitha Patil
Board of Directors: Richard Wells

D-U-N-S 00-124-0522 IMP
■ CHERYL & CO (OH)
(*Suby of* 1-800-FLOWERS.COM INC) ★
646 Mccorkle Blvd, Westerville, OH 43082-8778
Tel (614) 776-1500 *Founded/Ownrshp* 1981, 2005
Sales 86.0MM[E] *EMP* 300
SIC 2052 Cookies
Pr: Cheryl L Krueger
CFO: Dennis R Hicks
VP: Charles Fraas
VP: Lisa Henry
VP: James W Krueger
VP: William Shea
Genl Mgr: Bob Happle
Plng Mgr: Scott Miller
Prd Mgr: Jill Edwards
VP Mktg: Sheila Howell
Mktg Mgr: Dan Kaiser
Board of Directors: David T Kollat

CHESAPEAKE BEVERAGE
See MITCHELL BEVERAGE OF MARYLAND LLC

CHESAPEAKE CONFERENCE CENTER
See CITY OF CHESAPEAKE

D-U-N-S 04-944-2739
CHESAPEAKE EMPLOYERS INSURANCE CO
IWIF
8722 Loch Raven Blvd, Towson, MD 21286-2226
Tel (410) 494-2000 *Founded/Ownrshp* 1914
Sales NA *EMP* 370[E]
Accts Lb Johnson Lambert Llp Raleig
SIC 6321 Assessment associations, accident & health insurance
CEO: Thomas J Phelan
CFO: Paige Black
**Treas:* Boston Frank
Bd of Dir: Paul Gill
Ofcr: Timothy K Michels
VP: Robert Marshall
**Prin:* Maria Tildon
Off Mgr: Samson Okosagah
Snr Mgr: Stephen Fisher
Board of Directors: Maria Tildon

D-U-N-S 80-009-0045
▲ CHESAPEAKE ENERGY CORP
6100 N Western Ave, Oklahoma City, OK 73118-1044
Tel (405) 848-8000 *Founded/Ownrshp* 1989
Sales 12.7MMM *EMP* 4,400
Tkr Sym CHK *Exch* NYS
SIC 1311 Crude petroleum production; Natural gas production
Pr: Robert D Lawler
**Ch Bd:* R Brad Martin
CFO: Domenic J Dell'osso Jr
Treas: Jennifer Grigsby
Ex VP: M Christopher Doyle
Ex VP: Dana Newman
Ex VP: Frank Patterson
Ex VP: Mikell J Pigott
Ex VP: James R Webb
Sr VP: Michael A Johnson
Sr VP: Cathlyn L Tompkins
VP: Steve Evans
VP: Cathy Tompkins
Board of Directors: Gloria R Boyland, Archie W Dunham, Merrill A Miller Jr, Thomas L Ryan

D-U-N-S 07-792-3761
CHESAPEAKE HOSPITAL AUTHORITY
COMFORTCARE HOME HEALTH SVCS
736 Battlefield Blvd N, Chesapeake, VA 23320-4941
Tel (757) 312-8121 *Founded/Ownrshp* 1966
Sales 448.4MM[E] *EMP* 2,500
SIC 8062 General medical & surgical hospitals
CEO: Peter F Bastone
**COO:* Robert F Guanci
CFO: R W Cromwell
CFO: Robert Culpepper
**Treas:* David Stockmeier
Ofcr: Susan Hawley
**VP:* Kenneth R Deans Jr
**VP:* Angela McPike
VP: Carol Turnage
Dir Lab: Cheryl Paige
Off Mgr: Kathleen Malloy

D-U-N-S 07-837-6458
CHESAPEAKE HOSPITALITY LLC
6404 Ivy Ln Ste 800, Greenbelt, MD 20770-1408
Tel (301) 474-3307 *Founded/Ownrshp* 2010
Sales 11.0MM *EMP* 1,800
SIC 7011 Hotels & motels
Prin: Jeanette Sims

D-U-N-S 96-163-2689
▲ CHESAPEAKE LODGING TRUST
1997 Annapolis Exch Pkwy, Annapolis, MD 21401-3271
Tel (410) 972-4140 *Founded/Ownrshp* 2009
Sales 582.6MM *EMP* 193
Tkr Sym CHSP *Exch* NYS
SIC 6798 Real estate investment trusts
Pr: James L Francis
**Ch Bd:* Thomas A Natelli
COO: D Rick Adams
**CFO:* Douglas W Vicari
Treas: Nishil Patel
Sr VP: Graham J Wootten

D-U-N-S 10-670-1100
CHESAPEAKE MANAGEMENT SERVICES INC
CMS
1629 K St Nw Ste 300, Washington, DC 20006-1631
Tel (202) 600-7678 *Founded/Ownrshp* 1995
Sales 75.0MM *EMP* 1,400
SIC 7373 Systems integration services
Pr: Nancy Urbanski
Sr VP: Ryan James
CTO: John Backert

D-U-N-S 60-128-5422
■ CHESAPEAKE OPERATING LLC
(*Suby of* CHESAPEAKE ENERGY CORP) ★
6100 N Western Ave, Oklahoma City, OK 73118-1044
Tel (405) 848-8000 *Founded/Ownrshp* 1993
Sales 5.8MMM[E] *EMP* 4,400
SIC 1311 1389 4212 Crude petroleum production; Natural gas production; Building oil & gas well foundations on site; Mud service, oil field drilling; Local trucking, without storage
CEO: Robert Doug Lawler
**COO:* Steven C Dixon
**CFO:* Marcus C Rowland
**Treas:* Jennifer M Grigsby

CHESAPEAKE PUBLIC SCHOOLS
See CHESAPEAKE SCHOOL DISTRICT

D-U-N-S 19-307-5736
CHESAPEAKE SCHOOL DISTRICT
CHESAPEAKE PUBLIC SCHOOLS
312 Cedar Rd, Chesapeake, VA 23322-5514
Tel (757) 547-0153 *Founded/Ownrshp* 1963
Sales 322.7MM[E] *EMP* 6,000
SIC 8211 Public elementary & secondary schools
Bd of Dir: Herb Harlow
Dir Sec: Aundray Darden
Pr Dir: Kellie Goral
Psych: Lauren Gipson
HC Dir: Star A Wilson

D-U-N-S 04-195-2581
▲ CHESAPEAKE UTILITIES CORP
909 Silver Lake Blvd, Dover, DE 19904-2472
Tel (302) 734-6799 *Founded/Ownrshp* 1859
Sales 459.2MM *EMP* 832[E]
Tkr Sym CPK *Exch* NYS
SIC 4924 4911 Natural gas distribution; Distribution, electric power
Pr: Michael P McMasters
**Ch Bd:* John R Schimkaitis
CFO: Beth W Cooper
Sr VP: Elaine B Bittner
Sr VP: Stephen C Thompson
VP: James F Moriarty
VP: Sheri Richard
Genl Couns: Bill O'Brien
Board of Directors: Eugene H Bayard, Thomas J Bresnan, Ronald G Forsythe Jr, Thomas P Hill Jr, Dennis S Hudson III, Paul L Maddock Jr, Calvert A Morgan Jr, Dianna F Morgan

D-U-N-S 07-397-0238
CHESHIRE MEDICAL CENTER
DARTMOUTH-HITCHCOCK KEENE
580 Court St, Keene, NH 03431-1729
Tel (603) 354-5400 *Founded/Ownrshp* 1883
Sales 148.7MM *EMP* 1,000[E]
SIC 8062 General medical & surgical hospitals
Pr: Arthur W Nichols
V Ch: James Putnam
CFO: Jill I Batty
Trst: Mary Caffrey
Ex VP: Michael Newbold
VP: David Quigley
MIS Dir: Michael House
MIS Dir: Mary J Kamps
Mtls Mgr: Grace Brolin
Prd Mgr: David Martineau
Psych: Richard High

D-U-N-S 36-245-2042
CHESMAR HOMES LTD
450 Gears Rd Ste 400, Houston, TX 77067-4513
Tel (832) 253-0100 *Founded/Ownrshp* 2005
Sales 113.3MM[E] *EMP* 220[E]
SIC 1521 Single-family housing construction
Pt: Donal Klein
VP: Bill Clark
VP: Chris Hoover
VP: Eric Smith
VP Opers: Doug Mann
S&M/VP: Scott Merovich
Sales Asso: Nancy Cobb

D-U-N-S 02-977-9584
CHESTER BROSS CONSTRUCTION CO
6739 County Road 423, Palmyra, MO 63461-3615
Tel (573) 221-5958 *Founded/Ownrshp* 1966
Sales 107.0MM[E] *EMP* 250
Accts Gresham Smith Llc St Louis
SIC 1611 1629 Resurfacing contractor; Earthmoving contractor
Pr: Chester Bross
**Sec:* Mark Bross
**VP:* Jeff Bross
VP: Blaine Holverson
Genl Mgr: Marsha Moss

D-U-N-S 02-929-4873 EXP
CHESTER C LEHMANN CO INC
ELECTRICAL DISTRIBUTORS CO
1135 Auzerais Ave, San Jose, CA 95126-3402
Tel (408) 293-5818 *Founded/Ownrshp* 1948
Sales 166.9MM[E] *EMP* 110
SIC 5063 Electrical apparatus & equipment
CEO: Chester C Lehmann III
**Pr:* Scott Lehmann
Mktg Mgr: Darlene McEvoy
Sales Asso: Juan Pineda
Genl Couns: Gleb Finkelman

D-U-N-S 07-553-7464 IMP
CHESTER COUNTY HOSPITAL
(*Suby of* CHESTER COUNTY HOSPITAL AND HEALTH SYSTEM) ★
701 E Marshall St, West Chester, PA 19380-4421
Tel (610) 431-5000 *Founded/Ownrshp* 1892
Sales 298.0MM *EMP* 2,000
Accts Pricewaterhousecoopers Llp Ph
SIC 8062 Hospital, AMA approved residency
Pr: Michael Duncan
Dir Vol: Kathy Stocker
**Pr:* H L Perry Pepper
**COO:* Patricia Rayburn
CFO: Steve Bray
CFO: Thomas Shedlock
Treas: George Trajtenberg
Bd of Dir: Antelo Devereux
Bd of Dir: Carol Gates
Bd of Dir: Margaret Nagy
VP: Carl Adkins
**VP:* Michael Barber
**VP:* Kenneth E Flickinger
VP: Wat Hughes
VP: Mary Ost
**VP:* Paul Vanore
Exec: Chris Guattery
Dir Inf Cn: Charleen Faucette
Dir Lab: Diane Skinter
Comm Dir: Margaret D'Annunzio
Dir Rad: Michael Bleshman
Board of Directors: L L Lathrop, Richard Armstrong Jr, William Lee, J H Benner IV MD, George C Mason, David Davis III, R Marshall Phillips, A Deveraux Jr, T S Swett, R S Gawthrop Jr Esq, Robert Thompson, Hon J B Hannum, W S Wood II, M Hoberman MD, D J Kanauer, M H Lamb Esq

D-U-N-S 96-957-5096
CHESTER COUNTY HOSPITAL AND HEALTH SYSTEM
(*Suby of* CLINICAL PRACTICES OFT) ★
701 E Marshall St, West Chester, PA 19380-4421
Tel (610) 431-5000 *Founded/Ownrshp* 2013
Sales 3.3MM *EMP* 2,100[E]
SIC 8062 General medical & surgical hospitals
Pr: Michael J Duncan
COO: Michael D Barber
Treas: Kenneth E Flickinger
Sr VP: Angela R Coladonato
Sr VP: Richard Donze
Sr VP: Paul F Huberty

D-U-N-S 07-361-0859
CHESTER COUNTY INTERMEDIATE UNIT 24 (INC)
CHILD & CAREER DEVELPOMENT CTR
1525 E Lincoln Hwy, Coatesville, PA 19320-2447
Tel (610) 383-7400 *Founded/Ownrshp* 1972
Sales 99.4MM[E] *EMP* 1,300
Accts Stanley N Booz & Co
SIC 8211 Public special education school
Pr: Bonnie J Wolff
**Prin:* Susan Mateka
DP Exec: John Million
Teacher Pr: Iain Strachan
Instr Medi: Mary Curley
Psych: Joseph Dagney
Psych: Colleen Katzenmoyer
Psych: Anuja Mukherjee

D-U-N-S 78-730-9579
■ CHESTER DOWNS AND MARINA LLC
HARRAH'S CHESTER CASINO
(*Suby of* CAESARS ENTERTAINMENT CORP) ★
777 Harrahs Blvd, Chester, PA 19013-4505
Tel (484) 490-1800 *Founded/Ownrshp* 2002
Sales 129.2MM[E] *EMP* 1[E]
SIC 7011 Casino hotel
Pr: Gary W Loveman
**Treas:* Jonathan S Halkyard

D-U-N-S 00-791-0219
CHESTER WATER AUTHORITY
415 Welsh St, Chester, PA 19013-4595
Tel (610) 876-8181 *Founded/Ownrshp* 1939
Sales 103.9MM[E] *EMP* 160
SIC 4941 Water supply
Ch: Donald F Tonge

D-U-N-S 09-390-4167 IMP
CHESTER WEST HOLDINGS INC
WEST CHESTER PROTECTIVE GEAR
(*Suby of* WCM HOLDINGS INC) ★
11500 Canal Rd, Sharonville, OH 45241-1862
Tel (800) 647-1900 *Founded/Ownrshp* 1978
Sales 123.9MM[E] *EMP* 110
SIC 3842 5136 5099 5137 2381 Clothing, fire resistant & protective; Men's & boys' clothing; Safety equipment & supplies; Women's & children's clothing; Gloves, work: woven or knit, made from purchased materials
CEO: Tim Fogarty
Pr: Mark J Jahnke
Pr: Ken Meyer
Sec: Robert W Fisher
Ex VP: Jim Wilson
VP: David Fisher
VP: Roy Gifford
CIO: Mike Derge
Netwrk Eng: Glenn Strafford
Trfc Mgr: Randy Reigelsperger
Natl Sales: David Dorlack

D-U-N-S 96-972-3514
CHESTER WEST MEDICAL CENTER
WEST CHESTER HOSPITAL
(*Suby of* UC HEALTH LLC) ★
7700 University Dr, West Chester, OH 45069-2505
Tel (513) 298-3000 *Founded/Ownrshp* 2009
Sales 31.2MM[E] *EMP* 1,200
Accts Deloitte Tax Llp Cincinnati
SIC 8062 General medical & surgical hospitals
Sr VP: Kevin Joseph
Ansthlgy: Nervane M Domloj
Ansthlgy: Randy C Richter

D-U-N-S 12-413-7217
CHESTERFIELD COUNTY PUBLIC SCHOOLS
CHESTERFIELD COUNTY SCHOOL DST
9900 Krause Rd, Chesterfield, VA 23832-6535
Tel (804) 748-1405 *Founded/Ownrshp* 1970
Sales 314.7MM[E] *EMP* 6,700
SIC 8211 Public elementary school; Public junior high school; Public senior high school; Public vocational/technical school
Ch: James R Schroeder Dd
Prin: Jamie Accashian
Prin: Jeffrey Beatman
Prin: Teressa Clary
Prin: Shirley Diggs
Prin: Jeffrey Ellick
Prin: Deborah Hinton
Prin: Judith Johnston
Prin: David Joyner
Prin: Peter M Koste
Prin: Joyce Lanier

CHESTERFIELD COUNTY SCHOOL DST
See CHESTERFIELD COUNTY PUBLIC SCHOOLS

D-U-N-S 07-212-8515
CHESTERFIELDS LTD
APPLE REHAB
132 Main St, Chester, CT 06412-1340
Tel (860) 526-5363 *Founded/Ownrshp* 1993
Sales 39.0MM[E] *EMP* 2,200
SIC 8051 Skilled nursing care facilities
Pr: Brian Foley
Exec: Joann Bosworth

D-U-N-S 00-725-8163 IMP
CHESTERMAN CO
COCA-COLA
4700 S Lewis Blvd, Sioux City, IA 51106-9516
Tel (712) 252-2653 *Founded/Ownrshp* 1872
Sales 324.9MM[E] *EMP* 900
SIC 2086 Bottled & canned soft drinks
Ch Bd: Cy W Chesterman
**Pr:* Cy Chesterman Jr
Treas: Susan Bergeson
**Treas:* Karen Chesterman
**VP:* Jay Chesterman

CHESTNUT HILL FARMS
See BOUNTY FRESH LLC

CHESTNUT HILL HOSPITAL
See CHHS HOSPITAL CO LLC

CHESTNUT HILL HOSPITAL
See CHHC TRANSITION CO

D-U-N-S 92-792-4811 IMP
CHESTNUT HOLDINGS INC
670 W Market St, Akron, OH 44303-1448
Tel (330) 849-6503 *Founded/Ownrshp* 1995
Sales 148.9MM[E] *EMP* 152
SIC 3053 5014 5013 3714 Gaskets, all materials; Tires & tubes; Wheels, motor vehicle; Mufflers (exhaust), motor vehicle; Exhaust systems & parts, motor vehicle
Ch Bd: James P McCready

D-U-N-S 10-719-7733 IMP/EXP
CHET MORRISON CONTRACTORS LLC
9 Bayou Dularge Rd, Houma, LA 70363-7510
Tel (985) 868-1950 *Founded/Ownrshp* 1983
Sales 276.9MM[E] *EMP* 650
SIC 1623 3498 1629 1389 Water, sewer & utility lines; Fabricated pipe & fittings; Industrial plant construction; Oil field services
**COO:* Chet Morrison
**CFO:* Leroy Guidry
VP: Steve Becnel
VP: Craig Guidry
**VP:* Jeffrey Lee
VP: Bobby Lott
**VP:* Phil Thibodeaux
Genl Mgr: Doug Bass
IT Man: Royce Pellegrin
Sfty Mgr: Jerome Shaw
VP Mktg: Derick Bourg

D-U-N-S 14-564-1101
CHETU INC
10167 W Sunrise Blvd # 200, Plantation, FL 33322-7619
Tel (954) 342-5676 *Founded/Ownrshp* 2000
Sales 84.4MM[E] *EMP* 1,000
SIC 7379 Computer related consulting services; Computer related maintenance services
Pr: Atal Bansal
Tech Mgr: Rajat Khattar
Sftwr Eng: Mayur Saxena
Natl Sales: Bryan Van Norman
Sls Mgr: Marilyn Imparato

D-U-N-S 83-736-5162
CHEVRON AE RESOURCES LLC
1000 Commerce Dr Fl 4, Pittsburgh, PA 15275-1011
Tel (800) 251-0171 *Founded/Ownrshp* 2011
Sales 573.3MM[E] *EMP* 872[E]
SIC 4922 1311 4924

D-U-N-S 82-784-2746 IMP/EXP
■ CHEVRON CAPTAIN CO LLC
CHEVRON PRODUCTS COMPANY
(*Suby of* CHEVRON CORP) ★
6001 Bollinger Canyon Rd, San Ramon, CA 94583-5737
Tel (925) 842-1000 *Founded/Ownrshp* 1964
Sales 1.2MMM[E] *EMP* 5,000
SIC 2911 Petroleum refining
Ch Bd: John S Watson

D-U-N-S 00-138-2555
▲ CHEVRON CORP
6001 Bollinger Canyon Rd, San Ramon, CA 94583-5737
Tel (925) 842-1000 *Founded/Ownrshp* 1926
Sales 138.4MMM *EMP* 61,500
Tkr Sym CVX *Exch* NYS
SIC 2911 1311 1382 1321 5541 Petroleum refining; Crude petroleum production; Oil & gas exploration services; Natural gas liquids; Filling stations, gasoline
Ch Bd: John S Watson
CFO: Patricia E Yarrington
Treas: Ravinder Bhumbla
Bd of Dir: Kelley Mobley
Bd of Dir: Eric Upchurch
Ex VP: Joseph C Geagea
Ex VP: James W Johnson
Ex VP: George Kirkland
Ex VP: Michael K Wirth
Ex VP: Patricia Woertz
VP: Nadine Barroca
VP: Barb Burger
VP: Larry Buster
VP: Desmond Cecil
VP: Sean Connors
VP: Wendy Daboval
VP: Davey Dixon
VP: Brent Faulk
VP: Maud Faulmann

VP: Charles Hall
VP: Mark A Humphrey
Board of Directors: Robert E Deham, Linnet F Deily, Alice P Gast, Enrique Hernandez Jr, Jon M Huntsman Jr, Charles W Moorman IV, Ronald D Sugar, Inge G Thulin

D-U-N-S 07-875-5980
CHEVRON FEDERAL CREDIT UNION
500 12th St Ste 200, Oakland, CA 94607-4084
Tel (888) 884-4630 *Founded/Ownrshp* 1935
Sales 85.7MM *EMP* 185
SIC 5541 Filling stations, gasoline
Pr: James Mooney
**CFO:* Janet Lee
Chf Mktg O: Christine Smith
Ofcr: Anastasia Luu
Ex VP: John Canavan
VP: Patricia Chapman
IT Man: Mike Brill
IT Man: MEI Pang
VP Mktg: Neil Sawyer

D-U-N-S 00-698-1526
■ **CHEVRON GLOBAL ENERGY INC**
CHEVRON GLOBAL LUBRICANTS
(*Suby of* CHEVRON CORP) ★
6001 Bollinger Canyon Rd, San Ramon, CA 94583-5737
Tel (925) 842-1000 *Founded/Ownrshp* 1936
Sales 1.0MMM[E] *EMP* 7,900
SIC 2911 4731 5172 Petroleum refining; Freight transportation arrangement; Petroleum products
Ch Bd: Jock D McKenzie
Ch Bd: John S Watson
CFO: Richard J Guiltinan
**Treas:* Malcolm J McAuley
Ex VP: Pierre R Breber
Ex VP: Joseph C Geagea
Ex VP: James W Johnson
Ex VP: Michael K Wirth
VP: Richard Fernie
Genl Mgr: Barry A Chafitz
Genl Couns: F P Banning
Board of Directors: Am Caccamo, Guy J Camarata, Lloyd E Elkins, Patrick Lynch

CHEVRON GLOBAL LUBRICANTS
See CHEVRON GLOBAL ENERGY INC

D-U-N-S 04-738-7584
■ **CHEVRON INVESTOR INC**
(*Suby of* CHEVRON CORP) ★
6001 Bollinger Canyon Rd, San Ramon, CA 94583-5737
Tel (925) 842-1000 *Founded/Ownrshp* 1944
Sales 94.8MM[E] *EMP* 1,114
SIC 6799 Investors
CEO: Howard Sheppard
**CEO:* John S Watson

D-U-N-S 01-767-6961 IMP/EXP
■ **CHEVRON MARINE PRODUCTS LLC**
(*Suby of* CHEVRON CORP) ★
1500 Louisiana St, Houston, TX 77002-7308
Tel (832) 854-2767 *Founded/Ownrshp* 2008
Sales 892.5MM[E] *EMP* 300
SIC 5172 2992 2869 Engine fuels & oils; Lubricating oils & greases; Lubricating oils & greases; Industrial organic chemicals
Pr: C Michael Bandy
**CFO:* Peter M Meade

D-U-N-S 00-696-6188 IMP/EXP
■ **CHEVRON MINING INC**
(*Suby of* CHEVRON CORP) ★
116 Invrneco Dr E Ste 207, Englewood, CO 80112
Tel (303) 930-3600 *Founded/Ownrshp* 1984
Sales 324.4MM[E] *EMP* 1,400
SIC 1221 Surface mining, bituminous
Pr: Mark Smith
**VP:* John Burba
VP: M W Dix
VP: D F Gottron
**VP:* Fritz Gottron

D-U-N-S 61-284-1812 IMP/EXP
■ **CHEVRON ORONITE CO LLC**
(*Suby of* CHEVRON USA INC) ★
6001 Bollinger Canyon Rd, San Ramon, CA 94583-5737
Tel (713) 432-2500 *Founded/Ownrshp* 2000
Sales 387.0MM[E] *EMP* 1,000
SIC 2821 2899 2869 1311 Plastics materials & resins; Polystyrene resins; Chemical preparations; Industrial organic chemicals; Crude petroleum & natural gas
Pr: Desmond King
CFO: Rich Conway
S&M/VP: Jirong Xiao
Corp Couns: Mark Cervenka
Corp Couns: Marsha Penn
Corp Couns: Peggy Perser
Corp Couns: David Ream

D-U-N-S 03-891-2866 IMP/EXP
CHEVRON PHILLIPS CHEMICAL CO LLC
10001 Six Pines Dr, The Woodlands, TX 77380-1498
Tel (832) 813-4100 *Founded/Ownrshp* 2000
Sales 9.8MMM *EMP* 5,000
Accts Ernst & Young Llp Houston Te
SIC 2821 Plastics materials & resins
Pr: Peter L Cella
**Pr:* Ron Corn
**CFO:* Tim D Leveille
**CFO:* Greg G Maxwell
**Treas:* Joe M McKee
**Treas:* Trevor Roberts
**Ex VP:* Mark Lashier
**Sr VP:* Dan Coombs
**Sr VP:* Craig B Glidden
**Sr VP:* Tim Hill
Sr VP: Scott A Meyer
Sr VP: J Mike Parker
Sr VP: Tim G Taylor
VP: Dennis A Hmmond
VP: Ken Hope
VP Bus Dev: John Lupe

Board of Directors: Philip L Frederickson, John E Lowe, Patricia E Yarrington, Gary C Yesavage

D-U-N-S 15-297-5665 IMP
CHEVRON PHILLIPS CHEMICAL CO LP
CPCHEM
(*Suby of* CHEVRON PHILLIPS CHEMICAL CO LLC) ★
10001 Six Pines Dr, The Woodlands, TX 77380-1498
Tel (832) 813-4100 *Founded/Ownrshp* 2000
Sales 7.9MMM *EMP* 5,000
Accts Ernst & Young Llp Houston Te
SIC 5169 3292 3089 3084 3432 2911 Chemicals & allied products; Tubing & piping, asbestos & asbestos cement; Plastic hardware & building products; Plastics pipe; Plumbing fixture fittings & trim; Aromatic chemical products
Pr: Peter L Cella
COO: Tim G Taylor
CFO: G G Maxwell
Treas: Trevor R Roberts
Ex VP: Mark A Haney
Ex VP: Mark E Lashier
Sr VP: Ron Corn
Sr VP: Tim Hill
Sr VP: Tim Leveille
Sr VP: Rick L Roberts
VP: Mitch Eichelberger
VP: Don F Kremer
VP: Scott Meyer

D-U-N-S 79-830-9407 EXP
■ **CHEVRON PIPE LINE CO**
(*Suby of* CHEVRON CORP) ★
4800 Fournace Pl, Bellaire, TX 77401-2324
Tel (877) 596-2800 *Founded/Ownrshp* 1985
Sales 209.4MM[E] *EMP* 715
SIC 5541 Filling stations, gasoline
**Pr:* Al Williams
Ofcr: Kimberle Jones
VP: Richard Cain
Exec: Daniel Johnson
IT Man: Terry Bourland
IT Man: Robert Morgan
IT Man: Sapphie Nguyen
IT Man: Stephen White
IT Man: Curt Wiggins
Snr Mgr: Ken Bowman
Snr Mgr: Mike Didier

CHEVRON PRODUCTS COMPANY
See CHEVRON CAPTAIN CO LLC

D-U-N-S 09-998-7059 IMP
■ **CHEVRON STATIONS INC**
(*Suby of* CHEVRON USA INC) ★
6001 Bollinger Canyon Rd, San Ramon, CA 94583-5737
Tel (925) 842-1000 *Founded/Ownrshp* 1965
Sales 858.8MM[E] *EMP* 5,000
SIC 5541 5411 Filling stations, gasoline; Convenience stores
Ch: John S Watson
**Pr:* Colleen Cervantez
**CEO:* M R Kutten
**Treas:* Paul V Bennett
VP: Isaac Arowolo
**VP:* Glenn Johnson
VP: Alan Kleier

D-U-N-S 00-914-0559 IMP/EXP
■ **CHEVRON USA INC** (PA)
(*Suby of* CHEVRON CORP) ★
6001 Bollinger Canyon Rd D1248, San Ramon, CA 94583-5737
Tel (925) 842-1000 *Founded/Ownrshp* 1922
Sales 7.8MMM[E] *EMP* 17,718
SIC 5541 5511 2911 5171 Filling stations, gasoline; Automobiles, new & used; Gasoline blending plants; Petroleum bulk stations
CEO: John S Watson
**Pr:* W J Price
CFO: Patricia E Yarrington
**Ch:* D J O'Reilly
**Treas:* A D Cornwell
**Treas:* D P Smay
Ex VP: David Reeves
**Ex VP:* P J Robertson
**VP:* W E Crain
**VP:* B J Koc
**VP:* D M Krattebol
VP: Paul Spindler
Dir Bus: Bryant Korn

D-U-N-S 07-780-0266
■ **CHEVY CHASE BANK FSB**
(*Suby of* CAPITAL ONE FINANCIAL CORP) ★
7501 Wisconsin Ave Fl 11, Bethesda, MD 20814-6524
Tel (240) 497-4101 *Founded/Ownrshp* 2009
Sales NA *EMP* 3,700
SIC 6035 6411 6211 6519 6552 6719 Federal savings & loan associations; Insurance agents, brokers & service; Investment bankers; Real property lessors; Subdividers & developers; Investment holding companies, except banks
Ch Bd: B Francis Saul II
**V Ch Bd:* Alexander Rm Boyle
Ofcr: Yvette Lassiter
Ex VP: Scott W McSween
VP: Steve Brand
VP: Latrenda Hall
VP: Mark Holles
VP: Terri Martinez
VP: Joe Pearson
Prin: Philip Bronner
Adm Dir: Rose Bole

CHEVYS FRESH MEX
See CHEVYS INC

CHEVYS FRESH MEX RESTAURANT
See CHEVYS RESTAURANTS LLC

D-U-N-S 17-772-9506
CHEVYS INC
CHEVYS FRESH MEX
(*Suby of* JW CHILDS ASSOCIATES LP) ★
31100 Courthouse Dr, Union City, CA 94587-1759
Tel (510) 675-9620 *Founded/Ownrshp* 1997
Sales 123.9MM[E] *EMP* 8,000

Accts Kpmg Peat Marwick Llp San Fra
SIC 5812 5813 Mexican restaurant; Drinking places
Pr: Ronald P Mac Carone
**CFO:* Teresa Robinson
VP: Bruce Macdiarmid
**VP:* Jack O To Ole

D-U-N-S 18-000-3159
CHEVYS RESTAURANTS LLC
CHEVYS FRESH MEX RESTAURANT
(*Suby of* EL TORITO MEXICAN RESTAURANT) ★
2000 Powell St Ste 200, Emeryville, CA 94608-1779
Tel (510) 768-1400 *Founded/Ownrshp* 2004
Sales 62.2MM[E] *EMP* 3,000
SIC 5812 Mexican restaurant

D-U-N-S 02-134-6416 IMP/EXP
CHEYENNE INDUSTRIES LLC
FF INTERNATIONAL
5512 W Walsh Ln Ste 201, Rogers, AR 72758-9015
Tel (501) 812-6590 *Founded/Ownrshp* 1980
Sales 83.5MM *EMP* 45
SIC 5063 Lighting fixtures
Owner: Eric Scott
CFO: David Jeffers
VP: Chris Fletcher
Exec: Dawn Bell

D-U-N-S 07-333-0680
CHEYENNE LODGE INC
CHEYENNE LODGE NURSING HOME
716 Cedar St, Jamestown, KS 66948-3007
Tel (785) 439-6211 *Founded/Ownrshp* 1993
Sales 102.7MM *EMP* 45
SIC 8052 Intermediate care facilities
Pr: Harold L Hiedrick

CHEYENNE LODGE NURSING HOME
See CHEYENNE LODGE INC

CHEYENNE REGIONAL MEDICAL CTR
See MEMORIAL HOSPITAL OF LARAMIE COUNTY

D-U-N-S 10-111-1045 IMP
CHF INDUSTRIES INC
1 Park Ave Fl 9, New York, NY 10016-5803
Tel (212) 951-7800 *Founded/Ownrshp* 2002
Sales 129.1MM[E] *EMP* 500
SIC 5023 2221 Window covering parts & accessories; Linens & towels; Bedding, manmade or silk fabric
Pr: Frank Foley
**CFO:* Don Harwood
**VP:* Spencer Foley
VP: Jerry Pittman

D-U-N-S 05-410-2343
CHG FOUNDATION
740 Bay Blvd, Chula Vista, CA 91910-5254
Tel (619) 422-0422 *Founded/Ownrshp* 2001
Sales 622.4MM *EMP* 1
Accts Moss Adams Llp San Francisco
SIC 8699 Charitable organization

D-U-N-S 87-444-4284
CHG GROUP INC
(*Suby of* CHEMRING GROUP PLC)
23031 Ladbrook Dr, Dulles, VA 20166-2067
Tel (703) 661-0283 *Founded/Ownrshp* 1993
Sales 154.6MM[E] *EMP* 6
SIC 8741 Business management
Pr: Juan Navarro
**VP:* Michael Quensenberry
**VP:* James Williams
**Prin:* Joshua Golden
**Prin:* Michael Hubbard
**Prin:* Frederick Lewis
**Prin:* Gary Luck
**Prin:* Thomas McInerney

D-U-N-S 12-818-3345
CHG HEALTHCARE SERVICES INC
6440 S Millrock Dr # 175, Salt Lake City, UT 84121-5589
Tel (801) 930-3000 *Founded/Ownrshp* 1998
Sales 214.8MM[E] *EMP* 2,695
SIC 7363 Help supply services
CEO: Scott Beck
Ch Bd: Michael Weinholtz
COO: Mark Law
CFO: Sean Dailey
Sr VP: Kevin Ricklefs
VP: James Marshall
VP: Leslie Snavely
VP: Doug Warrick
Comm Dir: Michael Waterman
Snr Sftwr: Gahlen Fridley
Snr Sftwr: Kevin Gwynn

D-U-N-S 19-371-5463
CHG-MERIDIAN US HOLDING INC
EL CAMINO RESOURCES
(*Suby of* CHG-MERIDIAN AG)
21800 Oxnard St Ste 400, Woodland Hills, CA 91367-7532
Tel (818) 702-1800 *Founded/Ownrshp* 1986
Sales 114.9MM[E] *EMP* 718
Accts Weil & Company Llp Los Angele
SIC 7377 6159 5045 7378 Computer rental & leasing; Finance leasing, vehicles: except automobiles & trucks; Computers, peripherals & software; Computer maintenance & repair
CEO: Mathias Wagner
**Pr:* Jurgen Mossakowski
**Ex VP:* Dirk Matura
**Ex VP:* John P Sandoval
Board of Directors: Peter McCord

D-U-N-S 09-901-2726
CHG-MERIDIAN USA CORP
(*Suby of* EL CAMINO RESOURCES) ★
21800 Oxnard St Ste 400, Woodland Hills, CA 91367-7532
Tel (818) 702-1800 *Founded/Ownrshp* 1979
Sales 114.9MM *EMP* 50
Accts Kpmg Llp Los Angeles Ca
SIC 7373 Computer integrated systems design
Pr: Mathias Wagner
**CFO:* Vahe Aroyan

D-U-N-S 19-850-2205
CHH LIQUIDATING CO
8835 Germantown Ave, Philadelphia, PA 19118-2718
Tel (215) 248-8200 *Founded/Ownrshp* 2005
Sales 131.1MM[E] *EMP* 1,000
SIC 8062

D-U-N-S 13-920-7435
CHHC TRANSITION CO
CHESTNUT HILL HOSPITAL
8835 Germantown Ave, Philadelphia, PA 19118-2718
Tel (215) 248-8200 *Founded/Ownrshp* 1984
Sales 53.7MM[E] *EMP* 1,000
SIC 8062

CHHS
See CALIFORNIA HEALTH & HUMAN SERVCS AGENCY

D-U-N-S 01-696-3420
■ **CHHS HOSPITAL CO LLC**
CHESTNUT HILL HOSPITAL
(*Suby of* COMMUNITY HEALTH SYSTEMS INC) ★
8835 Germantown Ave, Philadelphia, PA 19118-2718
Tel (215) 248-8200 *Founded/Ownrshp* 2005
Sales 128.7MM *EMP* 1[E]
SIC 8062 General medical & surgical hospitals
CEO: John Cacciamani Jr
Pathlgst: Roberta Smith

CHI
See MEMORIAL HEALTH CARE SYSTEM INC

CHI
See SAINT ALPHONSUS MEDICAL CENTER - NAMPA HEALTH FOUNDATION INC

CHI
See ST CATHERINE HOSPITAL

CHI
See SAINT FRANCIS MEDICAL CENTER INC

CHI
See CATHOLIC HEALTH INITIATIVES COLORADO FOUNDATION

CHI
See MERCY HEALTH NETWORK INC

CHI
See GOOD SAMARITAN HOSPITAL OF CINCINNATI

CHI
See ALEGENT HEALTH- BERGAN MERCY HEALTH SYSTEM

CHI
See MERCY HEALTH SYSTEM OF SOUTHEASTERN PENNSYLVANIA

CHI
See CATHOLIC HEALTH INITIATIVES

D-U-N-S 17-589-7946 EXP
■ **CHI DOORS HOLDINGS INC**
CHI OVERHEAD DOORS
(*Suby of* KOHLBERG KRAVIS ROBERTS & CO LP) ★
1485 Sunrise Dr, Arthur, IL 61911-1684
Tel (217) 543-2135 *Founded/Ownrshp* 2015
Sales 127.0MM[E] *EMP* 750
SIC 3442 Metal doors, sash & trim
Pr: Jim Overholt
**CFO:* Pat Knoll
Dir IT: Roman Bulkiewicz
IT Man: Jason Mills
Prd Mgr: Marvin Otto
Sls Mgr: Dan Beckley

CHI HEALTH
See CREIGHTON ALEGENT HEALTH

D-U-N-S 84-799-0892
CHI HEALTH AT HOME
(*Suby of* TRIHEALTH HOSPITAL) ★
1700 Edison Dr Ste 300, Milford, OH 45150-2729
Tel (513) 576-0262 *Founded/Ownrshp* 1993
Sales 97.0MM[E] *EMP* 5,100
SIC 7363 8093 Help supply services; Specialty outpatient clinics
Pr: Dan Dietz
**Pr:* L T Wilburn Jr
**Prin:* Rich Smith
IT Man: Whitney Mikesell

CHI MEMORIAL HOSPITAL
See MEMORIAL HEALTH CARE SYSTEM FOUNDATION INC

D-U-N-S 79-168-4830
CHI NEBRASKA
555 S 70th St, Lincoln, NE 68510-2462
Tel (402) 219-8000 *Founded/Ownrshp* 1889
Sales 60.5MM *EMP* 1,150
Accts Catholic Health Initiatives W
SIC 8741 Hospital management
Pr: Robert J Lanik

CHI OVERHEAD DOORS
See CHI DOORS HOLDINGS INC

CHI ST. ALEXIUS HEALTH
See ST ALEXIUS MEDICAL CENTER

CHI ST. LUKE'S HEALTH
See ST LUKES HEALTH SYSTEM CORP

D-U-N-S 07-417-9060
CHI ST LUKES HEALTH BAYLOR COLLEGE OF MEDICINE MEDICAL CENTER
6624 Fannin St Ste 1100, Houston, TX 77030-2323
Tel (832) 355-1000 *Founded/Ownrshp* 1947
Sales 15.4MM *EMP* 6,000
SIC 8062 General medical & surgical hospitals
Pr: Debra Lee-Eddie
Chf OB: Dale Brown
**CEO:* David J Fine
COO: Paul M Allison
COO: Angela Shippy
Ex VP: Kelty Bake
Sr VP: T Pinckney P McIlwain
VP: Spencer Berthelsen

VP: Mark McPhee
VP: Stewart Scott
Dir Teleco: Melanie Beltram
Dir Risk M: Ann Thielke
Dir Case M: Kaye Pendarvis

CHI ST. LUKE'S HEALTH MEMORIAL
See MEMORIAL HEALTH SYSTEM OF EAST TEXAS

D-U-N-S 08-023-6344
CHIC AND SIMPLE LLC
573 Lancaster Ave, Berwyn, PA 19312-1665
Tel (610) 636-0686 *Founded/Ownrshp* 2010
Sales 120.0MM *EMP* 15
SIC 5932 Homefurnishings & appliances, second-hand
Owner: Diane Wulk

D-U-N-S 13-677-9894 EXP
CHICAGO & ILLINOIS RIVER MARKETING LLC
(*Suby of* NIDERA US LLC) ★
141 W Jackson Blvd Ste 2800, Chicago, IL 60604-2992
Tel (312) 341-3174 *Founded/Ownrshp* 1999
Sales 126.6MM *EMP* 44
Accts Ernst & Young Llp New York
SIC 5153 Grains
VP: Thomas Coyle

D-U-N-S 11-303-1231
CHICAGO 29 INC
FAMOUS HAIR
7328 Pine Valley St, Bradenton, FL 34202-4071
Tel (419) 621-9002 *Founded/Ownrshp* 1979
Sales 2.6MM^E *EMP* 1,007
SIC 7231 Unisex hair salons
Pr: Roger Hartzell

CHICAGO AREA GROUP
See CHICAGO OFFICE TECHNOLOGY GROUP INC

D-U-N-S 00-507-5635 IMP/EXP
CHICAGO BLOWER CORP
1675 Glen Ellyn Rd, Glendale Heights, IL 60139-2596
Tel (630) 858-2600 *Founded/Ownrshp* 1947
Sales 88.3MM^E *EMP* 200
SIC 3564 1711

D-U-N-S 06-951-0519
■ **CHICAGO BOARD OPTIONS EXCHANGE INC**
CBOE
(*Suby of* CBOE HOLDINGS INC) ★
400 S La Salle St Fl 1, Chicago, IL 60605-1023
Tel (312) 786-5600 *Founded/Ownrshp* 1972
Sales 276.2MM^E *EMP* 520^E
SIC 6211 6231 Security brokers & dealers; Security exchanges
Ch Bd: William Brodsky
Pr: Thomas Koestler
**Pr:* Edward Provost
**Pr:* Edward T Tilly
**CFO:* Alan J Dean
Treas: Susan Slocum
**Chf Mktg O:* Stephanie Klein
Top Exec: Greg Albin
**Ex VP:* Richard G Du Four
VP: Larry Bresnahan
VP: Eric Frait
VP: Matt Moran
VP: Jordan Naylor
VP: Debra Peters
VP: James Roche
VP: Brad Samuels
VP: Curt Schumacher
VP: Steve Sinclair
VP: Paul Stephens
VP: Michael Todorofsky
Dir Teleco: Peggy Rash

D-U-N-S 00-516-2300 IMP
CHICAGO BRIDGE & IRON CO (IL)
CB&I
(*Suby of* CHICAGO BRIDGE & IRON COMPANY N.V.)
2103 Research Forest Dr, The Woodlands, TX 77380-2624
Tel (832) 513-1000 *Founded/Ownrshp* 1889, 1967
Sales 345.4MM^E *EMP* 2,154
SIC 1791 Structural steel erection; Storage tanks, metal: erection
Pr: Philip K Asherman
**CFO:* Michael S Taff
Treas: Terry Browne
**Ex VP:* Patrick K Mullen
**Ex VP:* E Chip Ray
**Ex VP:* Luke V Scorsone
VP: Timothy J Wiggins
IT Man: Thomas Murtha
Mtls Mgr: Russ Daniels

D-U-N-S 10-538-8214
CHICAGO BRIDGE & IRON CO
128 S Tryon St Ste 400, Charlotte, NC 28202-5006
Tel (704) 331-6200 *Founded/Ownrshp* 1941
Sales 43.6MM^E *EMP* 1,100
SIC 8731 Energy research
CEO: Richard S Gill
**Pr:* Jim Hicks
**Treas:* Robert Belk
**Ex VP:* Gary P Graphia
**VP:* Malcolm H Niven
**VP:* Mansour Pourcyrous
**VP:* Clifton S Rankin

D-U-N-S 96-819-1072
CHICAGO BRIDGE & IRON CO
(*Suby of* CHICAGO BRIDGE & IRON COMPANY N.V.)
2103 Research Forest Dr, The Woodlands, TX 77380-2624
Tel (832) 513-1000 *Founded/Ownrshp* 1996
Sales 885.1MM^E *EMP* 11,000
SIC 8711 Engineering services; Industrial engineers; Mechanical engineering; Structural engineering
Pr: Philip K Asherman
**COO:* Lasse Petterson
**CFO:* Ronald A Ballschmiede
**Ofcr:* David A Delman
**Ex VP:* Beth A Bailey
**Ex VP:* Ronald E Blum
**Ex VP:* James E Bollweg
**Ex VP:* Daniel M McCarthy
Ex VP: E Chip Ray
**Ex VP:* Edgar C Ray
**Ex VP:* John W Redmon
**VP:* David P Bordages

D-U-N-S 05-216-9310
CHICAGO BRIDGE & IRON CO (DELAWARE)
(*Suby of* CHICAGO BRIDGE & IRON COMPANY N.V.)
2103 Research Forest Dr, The Woodlands, TX 77380-2624
Tel (832) 513-1000 *Founded/Ownrshp* 1979
Sales 5.2MMM^E *EMP* 29,083
SIC 8711 3325 3462 Engineering services; Industrial engineers; Mechanical engineering; Structural engineering; Steel foundries; Iron & steel forgings
Pr: Philip Asherman
**CFO:* Ronald A Ballschmiede
**Treas:* Luciano Reyes
**Ofcr:* David A Delman
**Sr VP:* Rick L Gorder

CHICAGO BROTHERS
See OVERHILL FARMS INC

D-U-N-S 06-202-0438
CHICAGO CHARTER SCHOOL FOUNDATION
11 E Adams St Ste 600, Chicago, IL 60603-6330
Tel (312) 455-7890 *Founded/Ownrshp* 1997
Sales 96.6MM *EMP* 18^E
SIC 7389 Fund raising organizations
Ex Dir: Elizabeth D Purvis
Comm Dir: Kate Proto
**Off Mgr:* Marisol Duerr

D-U-N-S 02-004-8419
CHICAGO COMMUNITY TRUST
225 N Michigan Ave # 2200, Chicago, IL 60601-7672
Tel (312) 616-8000 *Founded/Ownrshp* 1915
Sales 363.2MM *EMP* 66
Accts D Usa Llp Chicago Il
SIC 8641 Civic associations
Pr: Terry Mazany
Chf Mktg O: Daniel Ash
Mktg Dir: Eva Penar

CHICAGO CONVEYOR
See UNITED CONVEYOR CORP

D-U-N-S 78-328-0142
CHICAGO DAIRY CORP
27820 Irma Lee Cir # 200, Lake Forest, IL 60045-5132
Tel (847) 680-0300 *Founded/Ownrshp* 1991
Sales 123.0MM *EMP* 10
SIC 5143

D-U-N-S 00-510-5572 IMP
CHICAGO FAUCET CO
(*Suby of* GEBERIT AG)
2100 Clearwater Dr, Des Plaines, IL 60018-5904
Tel (847) 803-5000 *Founded/Ownrshp* 2002
Sales 105.3MM^E *EMP* 400
SIC 3432 Plumbers' brass goods: drain cocks, faucets, spigots, etc.
CEO: Andreas Nowak
VP: Eric Franklin
VP: Charles Lynch
VP: Manfred Wolpert
Genl Mgr: Thomas Schlaefer
MIS Dir: Al Silverstein
Plnt Mgr: Steve Kalisz

D-U-N-S 00-542-4775
CHICAGO FREIGHT CAR LEASING CO
CFCL
425 N Martingale Rd Fl 6, Schaumburg, IL 60173-2301
Tel (847) 318-8000 *Founded/Ownrshp* 1947
Sales 85.4MM^E *EMP* 500^E
SIC 4741 3643 Rental of railroad cars; Electric switches
Pr: Paul Deasy
**CEO:* Fred Sasser
**COO:* Shad Peterson
**CFO:* Luke Lukens
VP: John Cooney
VP: Todd Kahnm
VP: Connie Sumara
**VP:* Jay Wilensky
**VP:* Rhonda Zielinski
CTO: Cary Costello
S&M/VP: Robert Cleator

CHICAGO GOURMET STEAKS
See LINCOLN PROVISION INC

D-U-N-S 96-555-9318
CHICAGO GROWTH PARTNERS II LP
222 Merchandise Mart Plz # 1871, Chicago, IL 60654-1476
Tel (312) 698-6300 *Founded/Ownrshp* 2007
Sales 85.3MM^E *EMP* 4,384^E
SIC 6799 Investors
Pt: David Chandler

CHICAGO HEIGHTS STEEL
See CHS ACQUISITION CORP

D-U-N-S 07-231-1335
CHICAGO HOUSING AUTHORITY
60 E Van Buren St Fl 10, Chicago, IL 60605-1240
Tel (312) 791-8500 *Founded/Ownrshp* 1934
Sales NA *EMP* 2,400
SIC 9531 Housing authority, non-operating: government
CEO: Terry Peterson
Mng Pt: Keith Clincy
COO: Shirley Brown
**CFO:* Todd Gomez
VP: Marilyn Jefferson
Exec: Lisa L Roberson
Prgrm Mgr: Dorian Figgers
IT Man: Sheldon Hondras
Site Mgr: Rose M Allen
Genl Couns: Larue Little
Counsel: Edward Robles

CHICAGO INTERNATIONAL TRUCKS
See CIT INC

D-U-N-S 60-810-2950
CHICAGO MEAT AUTHORITY INC
1120 W 47th Pl, Chicago, IL 60609-4302
Tel (773) 254-3811 *Founded/Ownrshp* 1990
Sales 128.9MM^E *EMP* 330
SIC 2011 Meat packing plants
Pr: Jordan Dorfman
CFO: Dan Wang
Dir Bus: Charlie Kiolbasa
Dir IT: Wayne Bartosiak
IT Man: Margarito Alvarez
VP Opers: Scott Hardiman
Mktg Mgr: Alana Heber

D-U-N-S 05-664-8199
■ **CHICAGO MERCANTILE EXCHANGE INC** (IL)
CME
(*Suby of* CME GROUP INC) ★
20 S Wacker Dr, Chicago, IL 60606-7431
Tel (312) 930-1000 *Founded/Ownrshp* 1898, 2001
Sales 150.8MM^E *EMP* 1,250
SIC 6231

D-U-N-S 07-918-9636 IMP/EXP
CHICAGO METALLIC CO LLC
ROCKFON
(*Suby of* ROCKWOOL INTERNATIONAL A/S)
4849 S Austin Ave, Chicago, IL 60638-1400
Tel (708) 563-4600 *Founded/Ownrshp* 2013
Sales 280.1MM^E *EMP* 1,112^E
SIC 3446 5033 Architectural metalwork; Acoustical suspension systems, metal; Roofing, asphalt & sheet metal
Pr: Sandra Wilson
**Ex VP:* Loren A Jahn
**Ex VP:* Martin D Jahn
**Ex VP:* Reinhardt H Jahn
VP: Peter Jahn
Exec: Brooks Williams
Genl Mgr: Gary Madaras
Opers Mgr: Dave Neseman
Sls Mgr: John Erquiaga

D-U-N-S 00-507-0073 IMP/EXP
CHICAGO METALLIC CORP (IL)
INTERFINISH
4849 S Austin Ave, Chicago, IL 60638-1492
Tel (708) 563-4600 *Founded/Ownrshp* 1893
Sales NA *EMP* 1,112^E
SIC 3446 5033

CHICAGO MINIATURE OPTOELECTRON
See CHICL LLC

D-U-N-S 06-703-1658
■ **CHICAGO OFFICE TECHNOLOGY GROUP INC**
CHICAGO AREA GROUP
(*Suby of* GLOBAL IMAGING SYSTEMS INC) ★
3 Territorial Ct, Bolingbrook, IL 60440-4659
Tel (630) 378-9339 *Founded/Ownrshp* 1982
Sales 251.5MM^E *EMP* 250
SIC 5044 5112 Office equipment; Office supplies
Pr: Terry Dixon
VP: Cheryl Beckman
IT Man: Raymond Farias
Opers Mgr: Anthony Smith

D-U-N-S 06-619-4358
CHICAGO PARK DISTRICT
541 N Fairbanks Ct # 300, Chicago, IL 60611-3319
Tel (312) 742-7529 *Founded/Ownrshp* 1934
Sales 177.4MM^E *EMP* 3,100
SIC 7999 Recreation services
CEO: Michael P Kelly
**Pr:* Mona Castillo
COO: Patrick Levar
CFO: Stephen Hughes
**Treas:* Melinda Molloy
Ofcr: Luetha Aytch
Comm Dir: Jessica Maxey-Faulkner
Rgnl Mgr: Sean Hart
Area Mgr: Jackie Payne
CIO: Steve Maris
CTO: Shannon Carpenter

D-U-N-S 02-486-8374
CHICAGO PASTRY INC (IL)
6501 Roosevelt Rd, Berwyn, IL 60402-1100
Tel (708) 788-5320 *Founded/Ownrshp* 1981
Sales 124.2MM^E *EMP* 610
SIC 5149 5461 Bakery products; Cakes; Cookies; Bread
Pr: Renato Turano
Opers Mgr: George Poulos

CHICAGO PUBLIC SCHOOL
See BOARD OF EDUCATION OF CITY OF CHICAGO

CHICAGO PUBLIC SCHOOLS
See BOARD OF EDUCATION OF CITY OF CHICAGO

D-U-N-S 82-931-4975
CHICAGO PUBLIC SCHOOLS
CPS
42 W Madison St, Chicago, IL 60602-4309
Tel (773) 553-1000 *Founded/Ownrshp* 1883
Sales 48.7MM^E *EMP* 45,024
SIC 8211 Public elementary & secondary schools
CEO: Jesse Ruiz
Ofcr: Octavio Rivas
Dir Sec: Jadine Chou
Pr Dir: Emily Bittner
Pr Dir: Hayley Meadvin
Teacher Pr: Alicia Winckler
Instr Medi: Lisa Perez

D-U-N-S 06-618-7212 IMP
CHICAGO REVIEW PRESS INC
INDEPENDENT PUBLISHERS GROUP
814 N Franklin St Ste 100, Chicago, IL 60610-3813
Tel (312) 337-0747 *Founded/Ownrshp* 1973
Sales 85.0MM^E *EMP* 188
SIC 5192 2731 Books; Books: publishing only
CEO: Curtis Matthews Jr
**Pr:* Mark Suchomel
CFO: Cara Sample
VP: Linda Lee
VP: Clark Matthews
Sls Dir: Jason Reasoner
Mktg Mgr: Mallory Gevaert

CHICAGO SALT SERVICE
See MORTON SALT INC

CHICAGO SCHOOL, THE
See CHICAGO SCHOOL OF PROFESSIONAL PSYCHOLOGY

D-U-N-S 09-898-4081
CHICAGO SCHOOL OF PROFESSIONAL PSYCHOLOGY
CHICAGO SCHOOL, THE
325 N Wells St Fl 4, Chicago, IL 60654-7023
Tel (312) 379-1699 *Founded/Ownrshp* 1979
Sales 39.2MM *EMP* 1,300
Accts Rsm Us Llp Chicago Il
SIC 8221 Professional schools
Pr: Patricia Arredond
Assoc VP: David Iwane
VP: James Campbell
VP: Jennifer Demay
Assoc Dir: Beth Tinkham
Dept Mgr: Sabrina Pippin
Dir IT: David Rahn
Web Dev: Brandon Adamson
Opers Supe: Michael Pines
Sls&Mrk Ex: Ton Chirathivat
Psych: Rachel Klaus

D-U-N-S 10-810-9182
CHICAGO STATE UNIVERSITY
9501 S King Dr, Chicago, IL 60628-1598
Tel (773) 995-2000 *Founded/Ownrshp* 1869
Sales 154.8MM^E *EMP* 1,270^E
Accts Borschnack Pelletier & Co
SIC 8221 University
Pr: Wayne D Watson
V Ch: Randall Hampton
Pr: Sudie Davis
COO: Debbie King
**Ch:* Maurice Grant
Ofcr: Kathleen Fleming
Ofcr: Kevin Morris
Ex VP: Sylvius Moore
VP: Leroy Jones
VP: Dean Justmann
VP: Marquis Miller
VP: Sandra Westbrooks
Dir Teleco: Curticine Doyle

D-U-N-S 10-900-2576
CHICAGO SUN-TIMES FEATURES INC
(*Suby of* CNLC-STC INC) ★
350 N Orleans St Fl 10, Chicago, IL 60654-1700
Tel (312) 321-3000 *Founded/Ownrshp* 1994
Sales 66.4MM^E *EMP* 1,500
SIC 2711 2752 Newspapers, publishing & printing; Commercial printing, lithographic
Pr: David Radler
**CEO:* Tim Knight
CFO: William Barker
Opers Mgr: Maria Mareno

D-U-N-S 00-692-9319
■ **CHICAGO TITLE AND TRUST CO**
(*Suby of* FIDELITY NATIONAL FINANCIAL INC) ★
10 S La Salle St Ste 3100, Chicago, IL 60603-1028
Tel (312) 223-2000 *Founded/Ownrshp* 2000
Sales NA *EMP* 7,145^E
SIC 6361 Title insurance
Pr: John Rau
**Pr:* Raymond R Quirk
**CFO:* Al Stinson
**Ex VP:* Peter G Leemputte
**Ex VP:* Paul Sands
Sr VP: Brian Hershkowitz
VP: Miriam Golden
**Exec:* Alan N Prince
CTO: Renee Nixon
CTO: George Vanderivennett
CTO: Dennis Winter
Board of Directors: Margaret P Mac Kimm, Norman Bobbins, Landan Neal, John J Burns Jr, Peter H Dailey, Robert M Hart, Phillip Heasley, Alan P Kirby Jr, M Leanne Lachman, William K Lavin, Lawrence F Levy

D-U-N-S 05-663-5758
■ **CHICAGO TITLE INSURANCE CO**
(*Suby of* CHICAGO TITLE AND TRUST CO) ★
10 S Lasalle St Ste 2850, Chicago, IL 60603
Tel (312) 223-2402 *Founded/Ownrshp* 1985
Sales NA *EMP* 5,135
SIC 6411 6361 Insurance agents, brokers & service; Title insurance
CEO: George Scanlon
**CEO:* Raymond Quirk
**CFO:* Anthony Park
**Sr VP:* Ed Burton
**VP:* Madeline Lovejoybarewald
VP: Sean Murphy
Genl Couns: Peter Sadowski

D-U-N-S 84-968-3479
■ **CHICAGO TITLE INSURANCE CO**
(*Suby of* FIDELITY NATIONAL FINANCIAL INC) ★
4050 Calle Real, Santa Barbara, CA 93110-3413
Tel (805) 565-6900 *Founded/Ownrshp* 2006
Sales NA *EMP* 2,400
SIC 6361 Title insurance; Real estate title insurance
CEO: Raymond R Quirk
**Pr:* William Halvorsen Jr
**Treas:* A Larry Sisk
**VP:* Peter G Leemputte

D-U-N-S 92-672-7892
■ **CHICAGO TITLE INSURANCE CO**
(*Suby of* CHICAGO TITLE AND TRUST CO) ★
601 Riverside Ave, Jacksonville, FL 32204-2946
Tel (904) 854-8100 *Founded/Ownrshp* 1963
Sales NA *EMP* 5,000
SIC 6361 Title insurance
Pr: Raymond Randall Quirk
**CFO:* Anthony J Park
**Sr VP:* Michael Gravelle
VP: Neal Herman
VP: Kris Owens

VP: Christopher Reyes
VP: Michael Rich
VP: Andi Stroud
IT Man: Stas Anastasiou
IT Man: Bill Edwards
IT Man: Hoa Ly

D-U-N-S 00-553-2205
CHICAGO TRANSIT AUTHORITY (IL)
CTA
567 W Lake St Ste Cta, Chicago, IL 60661-1465
Tel (312) 664-7200 *Founded/Ownrshp* 1945
Sales 661.1MM[E] *EMP* 12,000
Accts Crowe Horwath Llp Chicago Il
SIC 4111 4789 Bus transportation; Passenger train services
Ch Bd: Terry Peterson
**Pr:* Dorval Carter Jr
COO: Peter Ousley
CFO: Karen Walker
Bd of Dir: John Bouman
Bd of Dir: Jacquelyne Grimshaw
Bd of Dir: Kevin Irvine
VP: Joe Iacobucci
VP: Jeanette Martin
Genl Mgr: Don Gismondi
Genl Mgr: Bernard Jackson

D-U-N-S 04-530-4367 IMP
■ **CHICAGO TRIBUNE CO**
(*Suby of* TRONC INC) ★
435 N Michigan Ave # 200, Chicago, IL 60611-4024
Tel (312) 222-3232 *Founded/Ownrshp* 2014
Sales 709.9MM[E] *EMP* 3,070
SIC 2711 7383 7389 7331 Newspapers, publishing & printing; News feature syndicate; Switchboard operation, private branch exchanges; Mailing service
Pr: David Hiller
COO: Kimberly Pierce-Boggs
**Sr VP:* Ken Depaola
**Sr VP:* Richard Malone
VP: Rebecca Brubaker
VP: Vincent Casanova
VP: Jeff Dorsey
VP: Bob Fleck
VP: Ira Goldstone
VP: Kenneth Harding
VP: Timothy Knight
VP: Ann Marie Lipinski
VP: Jeanette McKnight
**VP:* Alison Scholly
VP: Doug Thomas
VP: Owen Youngman

D-U-N-S 80-888-8978
■ **CHICAGO TRIBUNE NEWSPAPERS INC**
(*Suby of* CHICAGO TRIBUNE CO) ★
435 N Michigan Ave # 200, Chicago, IL 60611-4024
Tel (312) 222-3232 *Founded/Ownrshp* 1963
Sales 62.3MM[E] *EMP* 2,800[E]
SIC 7313 Newspaper advertising representative
Pr: Scott Smith
VP: Barbara Healy
Dir Rx: Matthew Brown
Snr Sftwr: Joshua Buermann
Snr Sftwr: Dan Krecichwost
Dir IT: Beverly Jackson

D-U-N-S 00-896-5485 IMP/EXP
■ **CHICAGO TUBE AND IRON CO**
CTI
(*Suby of* OLYMPIC STEEL INC) ★
1 Chicago Tube Dr, Romeoville, IL 60446-2402
Tel (815) 834-2500 *Founded/Ownrshp* 2011
Sales 250.0MM *EMP* 410
SIC 5051 3441

D-U-N-S 03-373-6273
CHICK-FIL-A INC
5200 Buffington Rd, Atlanta, GA 30349-2945
Tel (404) 765-8038 *Founded/Ownrshp* 1967
Sales 6.0MMM[E] *EMP* 6,152
SIC 5812 8741

D-U-N-S 03-722-3435
CHICKASAW DISTRIBUTORS INC
800 Bering Dr Ste 330, Houston, TX 77057-2184
Tel (713) 974-2905 *Founded/Ownrshp* 1979
Sales 136.4MM *EMP* 13
SIC 5051 Pipe & tubing, steel
CEO: Bradford Baker
**Pr:* Brian Blair
**VP:* Deborah Hebert

D-U-N-S 78-136-1639
CHICKASAW HOLDING CO
124 W Vinita Ave, Sulphur, OK 73086-3821
Tel (580) 622-2111 *Founded/Ownrshp* 1989
Sales 106.8MM *EMP* 600
Accts Eide Bailly Llp Tulsa Oklaho
SIC 4813 7371 5065 Telephone communication, except radio; Computer software development; Telephone equipment; Mobile telephone equipment; Paging & signaling equipment
CEO: RE Gauntt
**Ch Bd:* John D Evans
**Pr:* J B Bright
**COO:* Tom Riley
**Treas:* Larry Jones
**VP:* Jack Hester

D-U-N-S 07-084-8361
CHICKASAW NATION
520 Arlington St, Ada, OK 74820-2204
Tel (580) 436-2603 *Founded/Ownrshp* 1837
Sales NA *EMP* 11,500
SIC 9131 Executive & legislative combined
CFO: Jenny Trett
Bd of Dir: Paula Beene
Ofcr: Jon Evans
Sr VP: Chip Martin
Sr VP: Michael Mitchell
VP: Danny Hilliard
VP: Bill Lewis
Exec: Rebecca Chandler
Prgrm Mgr: Greg Cothran
Admn Mgr: Greg Straughn
Genl Mgr: Maggie Hart

D-U-N-S 04-075-6830
CHICKASAW NATION HEADQUARTERS ADMINISTRATION
520 Arlington St, Ada, OK 74820-2204
Tel (580) 310-6403 *Founded/Ownrshp* 1995
Sales NA *EMP* 1,007
SIC 9131 Indian reservation
Pr: Debbie Stephens

D-U-N-S 07-034-7435
CHICKASAW NATION INDUSTRIES INC
CNI
(*Suby of* CHICKASAW NATION) ★
2600 John Saxon Blvd # 100, Norman, OK 73071-1167
Tel (405) 253-8200 *Founded/Ownrshp* 1996
Sales 595.6MM[E] *EMP* 1,850
SIC 6719 Investment holding companies, except banks
CEO: David Nimmo
**COO:* Mike Mitchell
**COO:* Robert Wood
**CFO:* Mike Freeman
**Ofcr:* Rhonda Sutton
VP: Sandra Schreiner
Prgrm Mgr: Eric Robinson
Site Mgr: Michael Hawbaker
**Genl Couns:* Kirk Johnson

CHICKEN OF SEA FROZEN FOODS
See TRI-UNION FROZEN PRODUCTS INC

CHICKEN OF SEA INTERNATIONAL
See TRI-UNION SEAFOODS LLC

D-U-N-S 04-353-9667
CHICKS SPORTING GOODS LLC (CA)
979 S Village Oaks Dr, Covina, CA 91724-3617
Tel (626) 915-1685 *Founded/Ownrshp* 2007
Sales NA *EMP* 1,200
SIC 5941

D-U-N-S 03-410-3718 IMP
CHICL LLC
CHICAGO MINIATURE OPTOELECTRON
(*Suby of* REVSTONE INDUSTRIES LLC) ★
1708 Northwood Dr, Troy, MI 48084-5521
Tel (859) 294-5590 *Founded/Ownrshp* 2000, 2009
Sales 158.0MM[E] *EMP* 1,399
SIC 3641 Electric lamps
CEO: Steve Imgham
**CFO:* William Drexles
VP: Frank Robertazzi

D-U-N-S 61-217-7162
CHICO CSU RESEARCH FOUNDATION
Csuc Bldg 25 Ste 203, Chico, CA 95929-0001
Tel (530) 898-6811 *Founded/Ownrshp* 1996
Sales 41.0MM *EMP* 2,000
SIC 7389 Fund raising organizations
Ex Dir: Richard Jackson

D-U-N-S 05-935-9752
CHICO UNIFIED SCHOOL DISTRICT
1163 E 7th St, Chico, CA 95928-5999
Tel (530) 891-3000 *Founded/Ownrshp* 1965
Sales 90.9MM[E] *EMP* 1,425
SIC 8211 Public elementary & secondary schools; Public elementary school; Public junior high school; Public senior high school
**Pr:* Elizabeth Griffin
**VP:* Eileen Robinson
Off Mgr: Betsy Hobbs
DP Dir: Mike Tilton
IT Man: Jaclyn Kruger
Psych: Jennifer Carey
HC Dir: Eric Snedeker

D-U-N-S 88-425-1539 IMP/EXP
■ **CHICOPEE INC**
PGI NONWOVENS
(*Suby of* AVINTIV SPECIALTY MATERIALS INC) ★
9335 Harr Corn Pkwy Ste 3, Charlotte, NC 28269
Tel (704) 697-5100 *Founded/Ownrshp* 1995
Sales 172.8MM *EMP* 700
SIC 2297 Spunbonded fabrics
CEO: Veronica M Hagen
**COO:* Michael W Hale
**CFO:* Robert Kocourek
CFO: Willis C Moore
Mktg Mgr: Thomas Seamon

D-U-N-S 11-433-2232 IMP
▲ **CHICOS FAS INC**
11215 Metro Pkwy, Fort Myers, FL 33966-1206
Tel (239) 277-6200 *Founded/Ownrshp* 1983
Sales 2.6MMM *EMP* 22,700
Accts Ernst & Young Llp Tampa Flo
Tkr Sym CHS *Exch* NYS
SIC 5621 Ready-to-wear apparel, women's
Pr: Shelley Broader
**Ch Bd:* Ross E Roeder
Pr: Sheryl Clark
Pr: Donna M Colaco
Pr: Cynthia S Murray
Pr: Laurie J Van Brunt
COO: Jeffrey Jones
CFO: Todd E Vogensen
**V Ch Bd:* David F Dyer
Bd of Dir: Verna Gibson
Chf Mktg O: Michelle R Berardelli
Ofcr: Sara K Stensrud
Ex VP: Lee Eisenberg
Ex VP: Ann E Joyce
Ex VP: Susan Lanigan
Ex VP: Susan S Lanigan
Ex VP: Kristin L Oliver
Ex VP: Lori Shaffer
Ex VP: Eric R Singleton
Ex VP: Sara Stensrud
VP: Jennifer Adkins
Board of Directors: Janice L Fields, Verna K Gibson, John J Mahoney, Stephen E Watson, Andrea M Weiss

D-U-N-S 07-934-5747
■ **CHICOS PRODUCTION SERVICES INC** (FL)
(*Suby of* CHICOS FAS INC) ★
11215 Metro Pkwy, Fort Myers, FL 33966-1206
Tel (239) 277-6200 *Founded/Ownrshp* 2009
Sales 16.6MM[E] *EMP* 3,246[E]
SIC 5621 Ready-to-wear apparel, women's
Prin: Kent A Kleeberger

CHIEF
See MILESTONE AV TECHNOLOGIES LLC

CHIEF ADIMINISTRATIVE OFFICE
See COUNTY OF SAN DIEGO

CHIEF AUTOMOTIVE TECHNOLOGIES
See VEHICLE SERVICE GROUP LLC

CHIEF FEED MILL
See MURPHY FARMS LLC

D-U-N-S 00-749-7852 IMP/EXP
CHIEF INDUSTRIES INC
3942 W Old Highway 30, Grand Island, NE 68803-5051
Tel (308) 389-7200 *Founded/Ownrshp* 1954
Sales 493.0MM[E] *EMP* 1,645
SIC 3448 2451 3523 2869 3442 Buildings, portable: prefabricated metal; Mobile homes, except recreational; Crop storage bins; Driers (farm): grain, hay & seed; Ethyl alcohol, ethanol; Fuels; Metal doors; Sash, door or window: metal
Pr: Dj Eihusen
**CFO:* David Ostdiek
Dist Mgr: Randy Mittelstaedt
Mktg Mgr: Brian Shelton
Sls Mgr: Chad Micek
Sls Mgr: Erin Sullivan
Snr PM: Scott Baldwin
Board of Directors: Tim Wojcik

D-U-N-S 02-025-1393
CHIEF SEATTLE COUNCIL BOY SCOUTS OF AMERICA (WA)
3120 Rainier Ave S, Seattle, WA 98144-6015
Tel (206) 725-5200 *Founded/Ownrshp* 1916, 2000
Sales 8.2MM *EMP* 7,785
Accts Clark Nuber Ps Bellevue Wa
SIC 8641 Boy Scout organization
**Pr:* Robert McKenna
**CEO:* Michael Quirk
**Treas:* Michael Gibbs
VP: Lyle Hall

D-U-N-S 00-554-1461
CHIEF SUPER MARKET INC (OH)
705 Deatrick St, Defiance, OH 43512-2785
Tel (419) 782-0950 *Founded/Ownrshp* 1950
Sales 120.8MM[E] *EMP* 850
SIC 5411 Grocery stores, independent
Ch Bd: Eric C Hench
**CEO:* Todd R Taylor
**Prin:* Mark A Hench
IT Man: Mark Diller
Mktg Dir: Annette Hoeffel

CHIEFTAIN CONTRACT SERVICES
See E L HOLLINGSWORTH & CO

CHILD & CAREER DEVELPOMENT CTR
See CHESTER COUNTY INTERMEDIATE UNIT 24 (INC)

D-U-N-S 05-501-5333
CHILD CARE RESOURCE CENTER INC
20001 Prairie St, Chatsworth, CA 91311-6508
Tel (818) 717-1000 *Founded/Ownrshp* 1976
Sales 111.3MM *EMP* 750
Accts Singerlewak Llp Los Angeles
SIC 8322 Child related social services
CEO: Michael Olenick
**CFO:* Casey Quinn
**CFO:* Denise Trinh
**VP:* Ellen Cervantes
**VP:* Rick Robertss
**Ex Dir:* Lorraine Schrag
Snr Mgr: Charity Katz

CHILD DEVELOPMENT CENTER
See HEALTHSHARE INC

CHILD DEVELOPMENT CENTERS
See CHILD DEVELOPMENT INC

D-U-N-S 01-471-7785
CHILD DEVELOPMENT INC
CHILD DEVELOPMENT CENTERS
20 Great Oaks Blvd # 200, San Jose, CA 95119-1399
Tel (408) 556-7300 *Founded/Ownrshp* 1969
Sales 28.0MM *EMP* 1,500
Accts Randolph Scott & Company Cpas
SIC 8351 Child day care services
CEO: Vernon A Plaskett
Sales Exec: Jennifer Stone

D-U-N-S 80-433-6972
CHILD DEVELOPMENT SCHOOLS INC
CHILDCARE NETWORK
6053 Veterans Pkwy # 300, Columbus, GA 31909-4663
Tel (706) 562-8600 *Founded/Ownrshp* 2002
Sales 127.2MM[E] *EMP* 2,500
SIC 8351 Child day care services
CEO: Jerry Scott Cotter
**CFO:* Chris Smith
**VP:* Robert Moffett
Exec: Cassandra Baxley
Ex Dir: Angela Humphrey
Ex Dir: Sebrina Porter
Ex Dir: Priscilla Stephens
Genl Mgr: Leah Bowman
Genl Mgr: Alex Hinton

CHILD GUIDANCE CLINIC OF SPRIN
See BEHAVIORAL HEALTH NETWORK INC

D-U-N-S 08-948-3304
CHILDBIRTH EDUCATION
FINLEY HOSPITAL
350 N Grandview Ave, Dubuque, IA 52001-6388
Tel (563) 589-2406 *Founded/Ownrshp* 1970
Sales 92.7MM *EMP* 10
SIC 8062 General medical & surgical hospitals
Ex Dir: Patrica Killian

D-U-N-S 07-911-4390
CHILDCARE CAREERS LLC (CA)
1700 S El Camino Real # 201, San Mateo, CA 94402-3065
Tel (650) 372-0211 *Founded/Ownrshp* 2010, 2007
Sales 5.2MM[E] *EMP* 1,000
SIC 7363 7361 Temporary help service; Teachers' agency

CHILDCARE NETWORK
See CHILD DEVELOPMENT SCHOOLS INC

D-U-N-S 02-420-3663
CHILDERS OIL CO (KY)
DOUBLE KWIK MARKET
51 Highway 2034, Whitesburg, KY 41858-7686
Tel (606) 633-2525 *Founded/Ownrshp* 1976
Sales 565.3MM[E] *EMP* 800
SIC 5171 Petroleum bulk stations
CEO: W D Childers
**Pr:* INA Matthews
**CFO:* Charles Matthew
**Sec:* Donna Childers

D-U-N-S 06-602-6261
CHILDFUND INTERNATIONAL USA
2821 Emerywood Pkwy, Richmond, VA 23294-3726
Tel (804) 756-2700 *Founded/Ownrshp* 1938
Sales 232.1MM *EMP* 160
Accts Rsm Us Llp Mc Lean Va
SIC 8399 United Fund councils
Pr: Anne Lynam Goddard
**V Ch:* A Hugh Ewing III
**CFO:* James Tuite
Ofcr: Sarah Okot
**VP:* Marilyn Grist
IT Man: Krista Jennings
Mktg Mgr: Cindy Morgan

D-U-N-S 13-972-7221
CHILDNET INC
1100 W Mcnab Rd, Fort Lauderdale, FL 33309-1116
Tel (954) 414-6000 *Founded/Ownrshp* 2001
Sales 119.6MM *EMP* 360
Accts Cherry Bekaert Llp Fort Laude
SIC 8322 Child related social services
CEO: Emilio Benitez
**Ch Bd:* Joseph Rogers
**CFO:* Ainsworth Geddes
**CFO:* Dipak Parekh
**Treas:* Melida Akiti
**Treas:* Robert Haeffner

CHILDREACH
See PLAN INTERNATIONAL USA INC

CHILDREN ADULT AND FAMILY
See OREGON DIVISION OF ADULT & FAMILY SERVICES

D-U-N-S 92-764-5705 IMP
■ **CHILDREN AND FAMILIES ADMINISTRATION FOR**
(*Suby of* UNITED STATES DEPARTMENT OF HEALTH & HUMAN SERVICES) ★
330 C St Sw, Washington, DC 20201-0001
Tel (202) 401-1822 *Founded/Ownrshp* 1991
Sales NA *EMP* 1,400
SIC 9441 Administration of social & manpower programs;

CHILDREN HOSPITAL
See CHILDRENS FAMILY SUPPORT CENTER

D-U-N-S 00-718-1969
CHILDREN INTERNATIONAL (MO)
2000 E Red Bridge Rd, Kansas City, MO 64131-3694
Tel (816) 943-3722 *Founded/Ownrshp* 1936
Sales 188.2MM *EMP* 216[E]
Accts Bkd Llp Kansas City Missouri
SIC 8322 Individual & family services
CEO: Susana Eshleman
**VP:* Claire Bishop
**VP:* Bill Brewster
**VP:* Matt Gerard
**VP:* Carol Hall
**VP:* Jack McCanna
**VP:* Eric McCullough
**VP:* Danielle Mitchell
**VP:* Andrea Waters
Dir IT: Melanie Kidder
Netwrk Mgr: Connie Keyser
Board of Directors: Gordon Bailey, David Cacioppo, Susana Eshleman, Larry Lee, Dean Oskvig, Mike Reilly

CHILDREN OF ALABAMA
See CHILDRENS HOSPITAL OF ALABAMA

D-U-N-S 83-004-5980
CHILDREN OF AMERICA INC
5300 W Atl Ave Ste 700, Delray Beach, FL 33484
Tel (561) 999-0710 *Founded/Ownrshp* 1998
Sales 70.8MM *EMP* 1,700
SIC 8351

D-U-N-S 07-523-1977
CHILDRENS AID SOCIETY
711 3rd Ave Rm 700, New York, NY 10017-9210
Tel (212) 949-4800 *Founded/Ownrshp* 1853
Sales 117.1MM *EMP* 1,800
Accts Marks Paneth Llp New York Ny
SIC 8322 Child related social services
Pr: Phoebe Boyer
Bd of Dir: Judith K Dimon
Trst: Kevin Watson
Sr VP: Diana Marrero
VP: Drema Brown
VP: Beverly Colon
VP: Valerie Lebrew
Exec: Sandra Ramirez
Assoc Dir: Lisa Jewett
**Ex Dir:* Cwarren Moses
Off Mgr: Elizabeth Merle

D-U-N-S 79-733-3127
CHILDRENS AND PRESBYTERIAN HEALTH CARE CENTER OF NORTH TEXAS
(*Suby of* TEXAS HEALTH RESOURCES) ★
6200 W Parker Rd Ofc, Plano, TX 75093-8135
Tel (972) 981-8000 *Founded/Ownrshp* 1994
Sales 18.9MM[E] *EMP* 1,500
SIC 8062 General medical & surgical hospitals
Pr: Phil Wentworth
* *VP:* Mike Evans
CIO: Susan Anderson

D-U-N-S 14-763-2582
■ **CHILDRENS COMPREHENSIVE SERVICES INC**
(*Suby of* UNIVERSAL HEALTH SERVICES INC) ★
3401 West End Ave Ste 400, Nashville, TN 37203-6847
Tel (615) 250-0000 *Founded/Ownrshp* 2006
Sales 35.4MM[E] *EMP* 2,387
SIC 8322 Child related social services
Pr: Michael G Lindley
* *CFO:* Rodney Cawood
* *Sec:* John Edmunds
* *Ex VP:* Al Smith

D-U-N-S 60-712-2926 IMP
CHILDRENS COURTYARD INC
(*Suby of* LEARNING CARE GROUP INC) ★
21333 Haggerty Rd Ste 300, Novi, MI 48375-5537
Tel (248) 697-9000 *Founded/Ownrshp* 1992
Sales 62.0MM *EMP* 1,600
SIC 8351 Child day care services
Pr: Barbra Beck

D-U-N-S 93-302-2295
CHILDRENS CREATIVE LEARNING CENTER INC
794 E Duane Ave, Sunnyvale, CA 94085-3359
Tel (408) 732-2500 *Founded/Ownrshp* 1992
Sales 120.0MM *EMP* 3,100
SIC 8351 Child day care services
Pr: Ty Durekas
* *COO:* Dennis Vicars
Ex Dir: Joseph Dimino
Brnch Mgr: Frank Difede

D-U-N-S 02-033-8728
CHILDRENS CREATIVE LEARNING CENTERS LLC
650 Ne Holladay St # 1400, Portland, OR 97232-2045
Tel (503) 872-1300 *Founded/Ownrshp* 2008
Sales 21.0MM[E] *EMP* 2,400
SIC 8351 Child day care services
Prin: Thomas Pinnau
* *CFO:* Kelly Knox
CTO: Farina Baporia

D-U-N-S 12-404-5043
CHILDRENS FAMILY SUPPORT CENTER
CHILDREN HOSPITAL
8200 Dodge St, Omaha, NE 68114-4113
Tel (402) 955-8117 *Founded/Ownrshp* 1996
Sales 286.8MM *EMP* 10
SIC 8069 Children's hospital

D-U-N-S 14-732-4743
CHILDRENS HEALTH CARE ASSOCIATES INC
100 N 20th St Ste 301, Philadelphia, PA 19103-1454
Tel (215) 567-2422 *Founded/Ownrshp* 1986
Sales 223.0MM *EMP* 75
Accts Pricewaterhousecoopers Llp Ph
SIC 8621 Medical field-related associations
Pr: Steven Altschuler
Treas: Steve Altschuler

D-U-N-S 62-421-0498
CHILDRENS HEALTH SYSTEM INC
CHILDRENS HOSP OF KNGS DGHTERS
601 Childrens Ln, Norfolk, VA 23507-1910
Tel (757) 622-2134 *Founded/Ownrshp* 1984
Sales 13.9MM[E] *EMP* 1,905
Accts Kpmg Llp Mc Lean Va
SIC 8741 Hospital management
Pr: Jim Dahling
* *VP:* Beth Duke
Exec: Brooke Blessing

D-U-N-S 14-817-0616
CHILDRENS HEALTH SYSTEM OF TEXAS
1935 Medical District Dr, Dallas, TX 75235-7701
Tel (844) 424-4537 *Founded/Ownrshp* 1985
Sales 712.6MM[E] *EMP* 7,359
Accts Kpmg Peat Marwick Dallas Tx
SIC 8069 Children's hospital
CEO: Christopher J Durovich
* *Ex VP:* Michele Chulick

D-U-N-S 07-347-2136
CHILDRENS HEALTHCARE OF ATLANTA FOUNDATION INC
EGLESTON CHILDRENS HEALTH CTR
1405 Clifton Rd Ne, Atlanta, GA 30322-1060
Tel (404) 785-7300 *Founded/Ownrshp* 1928
Sales 88.8MM[E] *EMP* 4,500
SIC 8069 Children's hospital
CEO: Eugene A Hayes III
* *Pr:* James E Talley PHD
COO: Pradeen Chopra
* *CFO:* Ruth Fowler
VP Mktg: Klarita Wildhaber

D-U-N-S 93-865-3458
CHILDRENS HEALTHCARE OF ATLANTA INC
1600 Tullie Cir Ne, Atlanta, GA 30329-2303
Tel (404) 785-7000 *Founded/Ownrshp* 1998
Sales 334.6MM[E] *EMP* 4,000
SIC 8069 Children's hospital
CEO: Donna W Hyland
* *Pr:* Eugena A Hayes III
* *COO:* Rex Adams
* *CFO:* Ruth Fowler
* *Exec:* Susan Williams
Prac Mgr: Jody Levenstiem
Secur Mgr: Tony Davis
Opthamlgy: Leon Charkoudian
Opthamlgy: Victoria Hsu
Opthamlgy: Bryan Lusk
Opthamlgy: Yuri McKee

D-U-N-S 79-602-4966
CHILDRENS HEALTHCARE OF CALIFORNIA
1201 W La Veta Ave, Orange, CA 92868-4203
Tel (714) 997-3000 *Founded/Ownrshp* 1964
Sales 548.7MM *EMP* 1,800
Accts Kpmg Llp Los Angeles Ca
SIC 8069 Children's hospital
Pr: Kimberly C Cripe
* *COO:* Thomas Brotherton
* *CFO:* Kerri Ruppert
Ofcr: Ali Edgcomb
* *VP:* Maria Minon MD
Exec: Cheryl Arnold
Genl Mgr: Phuong Dao
Mtls Dir: Kay McLarney
Doctor: Dimitry Goufman
Snr Mgr: Vinh Lam
Snr Mgr: Allie Reynolds

CHILDREN'S HOME HEALTHCARE
See CHILDRENS HOSPITAL MEDICAL CENTER

D-U-N-S 02-071-7959
CHILDRENS HOME HEALTHCARE INC
901 Waterfall Way Ste 105, Richardson, TX 75080-6753
Tel (972) 661-3737 *Founded/Ownrshp* 2009
Sales 349.0M[E] *EMP* 4,500
SIC 8082 Home health care services
* *CFO:* Jennifer Adams

D-U-N-S 08-418-8895
CHILDRENS HOME SOCIETY OF FLORIDA (FL)
1485 S Semoran Blvd, Winter Park, FL 32792-5533
Tel (407) 657-2197 *Founded/Ownrshp* 1902
Sales 116.4MM *EMP* 2,300
Accts Mcgladrey Llp Melbourne Fl
SIC 8322 8361 Child related social services; Residential care
Ch: Robert Moser
* *Pr:* David A Bundy
* *COO:* James E Patrick
CFO: Doug Weinberg
* *CFO:* Robert J Wydra
VP: Amy Thomas
VP Admn: Susann Prochnow
Ex Dir: Andry Sweet
Pgrm Dir: Mildred Lugo

CHILDRENS HOSP OF KNGS DGHTERS
See CHILDRENS HEALTH SYSTEM INC

CHILDRENS HOSP OF PA FNDTN
See CHILDRENS HOSPITAL OF PHILADELPHIA

CHILDREN'S HOSPITAL
See LOUISIANA CHILDRENS MEDICAL CENTER INC

D-U-N-S 06-952-3405
CHILDRENS HOSPITAL
200 Henry Clay Ave, New Orleans, LA 70118-5798
Tel (504) 899-9511 *Founded/Ownrshp* 1949
Sales 196.9MM *EMP* 1,700
SIC 8069 Children's hospital
Pr: Mary Perrin
* *Pr:* Sandra L Fenwick
* *CEO:* Steve Worley
* *COO:* Justin Olsen
* *CFO:* Courtney Garrett
* *Sr VP:* Diane Michel
* *VP:* Natasha Haynes
Dir Rad: Jeanette Rossi
Dir Env Sv: Glenn Cobb
Prin: John Wallin
IT Man: Ryan Callahan

D-U-N-S 07-484-5504
CHILDRENS HOSPITAL
111 Michigan Ave Nw, Washington, DC 20010-2916
Tel (202) 232-0521 *Founded/Ownrshp* 1870
Sales 983.5MM *EMP* 6,000
Accts Grant Thornton Llp Mc Lean V
SIC 8062 General medical & surgical hospitals
Pr: Kurt Newman
VP: Brian Jessogne

D-U-N-S 96-960-2395
CHILDRENS HOSPITAL
1917 C St Ne, Washington, DC 20002-6753
Tel (202) 476-5000 *Founded/Ownrshp* 2011
Sales 970.0MM *EMP* 41[E]
Accts Grant Thornton Llp Mc Lean V
SIC 8062 General medical & surgical hospitals
Prin: Kurt Newman
MIS Dir: Gary Manion
Ql Cn Mgr: Lorna Riach
Doctor: Ashley D Hill MD

D-U-N-S 06-867-5719
CHILDRENS HOSPITAL & MEDICAL CENTER
8200 Dodge St, Omaha, NE 68114-4113
Tel (402) 955-5400 *Founded/Ownrshp* 1948
Sales 327.5MM *EMP* 1,400
SIC 8069 Children's hospital
Pr: Gary A Perkins
Sr VP: David Chistensen
VP: Debra Arnow
VP: Amy S Bones
VP: Justin Bradshaw
VP: Steve Burnham
VP: Beverly Geer
VP: Scott Kaminski
VP: Dan Mann
VP: Darla Qassem
VP: John Williams
VP: Janis Yergan
Dir OR: Barbara Schwarz

D-U-N-S 07-653-6184
CHILDRENS HOSPITAL & RESEARCH CENTER AT OAKLAND
UCSF BENIOFF CHLD HOSP OAKLAND
747 52nd St, Oakland, CA 94609-1809
Tel (510) 428-3000 *Founded/Ownrshp* 1912
Sales 178.6MM *EMP* 2,000
SIC 8062 Hospital, AMA approved residency
Pr: Bertram Lubin
Dir Recs: Kenneth Henderson
* *Ch Bd:* Harold Davis
COO: David Bertauski
* *CFO:* Kathleen Cain
* *CFO:* Rina Smith
* *Sr VP:* Betsy Biern
VP: Brad Barber
VP: Cynthia Chiarappa
VP: Carolyn Dossa
VP: Marva Furmidge
VP: Alexander Lucas
VP: Andre Piquet
VP: Rajnesh Prasad
VP: Nancy Shibata
VP: Patricia Taggart
Assoc Dir: Robert Haining

D-U-N-S 15-731-4618
CHILDRENS HOSPITAL AND HEALTH SYSTEM INC
8915 W Connell Ave, Milwaukee, WI 53226-3067
Tel (414) 266-2000 *Founded/Ownrshp* 1985
Sales 121.2MM *EMP* 3,000
Accts Sikich Llp Brookfield Wi
SIC 8069 8082 7389 7322 Children's hospital; Home health care services; Fund raising organizations; Collection agency, except real estate
Pr: Jon Vice
COO: Pat Radoszewski
* *CFO:* Tim Birkenstock
Bd of Dir: Karen Jackson
Ofcr: Mike Bolmes
Ofcr: Robert Sanders
* *Ex VP:* Cindy Christensen
* *VP:* Mike Jones
VP: Juliet Kersten
Assoc Dir: Michael Mitchell
Dir Rad: Erin Yale

CHILDRENS HOSPITAL BOSTON
See CHILDRENS HOSPITAL CORP

D-U-N-S 03-959-2594
CHILDRENS HOSPITAL CENTRAL CA
9300 Valley Childrens Pl, Madera, CA 93636-8761
Tel (559) 353-6900 *Founded/Ownrshp* 2010
Sales 435.1MM *EMP* 21[E]
SIC 8069 Children's hospital
Prin: David Meagher

D-U-N-S 02-943-8357
CHILDRENS HOSPITAL COLORADO
3123 E 16th Ave, Aurora, CO 80045
Tel (720) 777-1234 *Founded/Ownrshp* 2011
Sales 853.3MM *EMP* 35[E]
SIC 8062 General medical & surgical hospitals
Prin: Patricia Peterson
Sr VP: Jennifer Darling
Dir Rx: Paul Limberis
Psych: Michael W Kirkwood

D-U-N-S 07-644-3316
CHILDRENS HOSPITAL COLORADO
13123 E 16th Ave, Aurora, CO 80045-7106
Tel (720) 777-1234 *Founded/Ownrshp* 1908
Sales 908.1MM *EMP* 2,200
SIC 8069 Children's hospital
CEO: James Shmerling
CFO: Jeff Harrington
Ofcr: Frederick J Suchy
Sr VP: Kelly M Johnson
Sr VP: Mary Anne Leach
VP: Peggy Warner
Dir Lab: Robert Carpenter
Ex Dir: Stephanie Wasserman
Nurse Mgr: Bruce Kennedy
VP Opers: Jerrod Milton
Psych: Heather B Carroll
Board of Directors: Nancy Gary, Jules Amer MD, Jacinto Hernandez MD, Nancy P Anschutz, Michael L Kurtz MD, Marcy H Benson, Angela M Rayne, Wayne Berger, Richard L Robinson, Doris Biester, Millie Rock, Sheila Bugdanowitz, Luis D Rovira, Betsy Considine, James H Shore MD, Peter Culshaw, James A, Peter L Durante

D-U-N-S 07-659-3722 IMP
CHILDRENS HOSPITAL CORP
CHILDRENS HOSPITAL BOSTON
300 Longwood Ave, Boston, MA 02115-5737
Tel (617) 355-6000 *Founded/Ownrshp* 1800
Sales 1.0MMM *EMP* 8,000
SIC 8069 Children's hospital
CEO: James Mandell
Dir Vol: Barbara Blundell
* *Pr:* Sandra Fenwick
* *Pr:* David S Weiner
CFO: David Kirshner
Bd of Dir: Michelina Cassella
Trst: William L Boyan
Trst: Steven Fishman
Trst: George W Phillips
Chf Mktg O: Larry Benowitz
Chf Mktg O: Van M Linda
Ofcr: Mary Beckman
Ex VP: Eric M Kobren
Ex VP: Andrea A Pettinato
Dir OR: Anne Micheli
Dir Inf Cn: Gail Potter-Bynoe
Assoc Dir: Laurie Beckelman
Assoc Dir: Andrew L Frelinger
Assoc Dir: Christopher Troyanos
Dir Rx: Al J Patterson

D-U-N-S 05-227-7936 IMP
CHILDRENS HOSPITAL LOS ANGELES
4650 W Sunset Blvd, Los Angeles, CA 90027-6062
Tel (323) 660-2450 *Founded/Ownrshp* 1901
Sales 891.3MM *EMP* 3,000[E]
SIC 8069 8062 Children's hospital; General medical & surgical hospitals
Pr: Richard Cordova
* *CFO:* Lannie Tonnu
Trst: Robert Adler
Trst: Otis Booth
Trst: Thomas E Larkin
Trst: Elizabeth Lowe
Trst: Russell K Snow
Ofcr: Owen Lei
Ofcr: Mike Robbin
Trst Ofcr: Alexandra Simpson
Assoc VP: Anna Weiser
* *VP:* Steven R Garske
VP: Mary D Hacker
VP: Carolyn D Kendrick
VP: Lara Khouri
VP: Gail L Margolis
VP: Marty W Miller
VP: Kenneth J Wildes
Dir Rad: Lundblad Brian
Dir Rad: Vicente Gilsanz
Dir Env Sv: Dario Carrero

D-U-N-S 13-052-4127
CHILDRENS HOSPITAL LOS ANGELES MEDICAL GROUP INC
6430 W Sunset Blvd # 600, Los Angeles, CA 90028-7909
Tel (323) 361-2336 *Founded/Ownrshp* 2007
Sales 140.0MM *EMP* 100
Accts Kieckhafer Schiffer & Company
SIC 8011 Pediatrician
Pr: Robert Adler
COO: Phoebe Dinsmore
Mng Dir: Thomas Keens
Board of Directors: Kathy Anderson MD, James Atkinson MD, Robert Baehner MD, Ross Miller MD, Linn Murphree MD, Christopher Newph MD, Vernon Tolo MD

D-U-N-S 07-128-4913
CHILDRENS HOSPITAL MEDICAL CENTER
CHILDREN'S HOME HEALTHCARE
3333 Burnet Ave, Cincinnati, OH 45229-3039
Tel (513) 636-4200 *Founded/Ownrshp* 1883
Sales 1.5MMM *EMP* 7,700
SIC 8733 8011 8069 8731 Medical research; Clinic, operated by physicians; Children's hospital; Biotechnical research, commercial
Pr: Michael Fisher
* *CFO:* Teresa Bowling
Bd of Dir: Robert Frenck
Trst: Sharry Addison
Trst: Robert D Anning
Trst: Carol Armstrong
Trst: Lynwood Battle
Trst: Michael S Cambron
Trst: Willie F Carden Jr
Trst: Lee A Carter
Trst: Katharine Dewitt
Trst: Todd M Duncan
Trst: Barbara Fitch
Trst: Vallie C Geier
Trst: Louis D George
Trst: Camille Graham
Trst: Deborah Henretta
Trst: Michael Hirschfeld
Trst: Joyce J Keeshin
Trst: Nancy Krieger-Eddy
Trst: Denise Kuprionis

D-U-N-S 07-778-5525
CHILDRENS HOSPITAL MEDICAL CENTER OF AKRON
AKRON CHILDREN'S HOSPITAL
1 Perkins Sq, Akron, OH 44308-1063
Tel (330) 543-1000 *Founded/Ownrshp* 1891
Sales 747.4MM *EMP* 4,763
Accts Ernst & Young Llp Cleveland
SIC 8069 Children's hospital
CEO: William Considine
Chf Rad: Michael Rubin
COO: Grace Wakulchik
CFO: John P Stoner
CFO: Michael Trainer
Trst: William Hopkins
Trst: Daniel McMahon
Chf Mktg O: Mark Jacobstein
VP: Lisa Aurilio
VP: Michael Bird
VP: Cindy Dormo
VP: Mary Link
VP: Craig McGhee
VP: Chris McLean
VP: Theresa Moore
VP: Karen Richter
* *VP:* Walt Schwoeble
VP: Meridith Slosberg
VP: John Zoilo
Dir Lab: Donna Galehouse
Dir: Joann Stock

D-U-N-S 07-210-6867
CHILDRENS HOSPITAL OF ALABAMA
CHILDREN OF ALABAMA
1600 7th Ave S, Birmingham, AL 35233-1711
Tel (205) 939-9100 *Founded/Ownrshp* 1911
Sales 698.6MM *EMP* 3,329
Accts Warren Averett Llc Birmingham
SIC 8069 Children's hospital
CFO: Mike Burgess
* *Treas:* W Charles Mayer
Dir OR: Blanche Lowery
Dir Rad: Lynn Hamer
Dir Sec: Dennis Blass
Brnch Mgr: Ann Slattery
Genl Mgr: Kermilia Whitehead
CIO: Mike McDibett
CIO: Madison Mock
CIO: Heidi Thomas
* *Doctor:* Carolyn Ashworth

D-U-N-S 12-147-4100
CHILDRENS HOSPITAL OF CHICAGO MEDICAL CENTER
CHILDREN'S MEMORIAL HOSPITAL
225 E Chicago Ave, Chicago, IL 60611-2991
Tel (312) 227-4000 *Founded/Ownrshp* 1989
Sales 23.7MM *EMP* 2,420
Accts Ernst & Young Us Llp Chicago
SIC 8062 8733 Hospital, AMA approved residency; Research institute
Pr: Mary J C Hendrix
V Ch: William Schnaper
CFO: Paula M Noble
CFO: Michele Waldron

*Sr VP: Philip V Spina
CTO: Stan Krok
MIS Dir: Jennifer Stropie
Dir IT: Bob Blanchard
Netwrk Eng: Michael Bichl
Mtls Mgr: Michelle McNutt
Pathlgst: Veena Rajaram

D-U-N-S 07-475-8350
CHILDRENS HOSPITAL OF KINGS DAUGHTERS INC
CHKD
601 Childrens Ln, Norfolk, VA 23507-1910
Tel (757) 668-7000 Founded/Ownrshp 1961
Sales 332.2MM EMP 1,211
SIC 8069 8011 Children's hospital; Pediatrician
Pr: James D Dahling
*VP: Kathy Abshire
*VP: Deborah Barnes
*VP: David G Bowers
VP: David Bowers
*VP: Jo-Ann Burke
*VP: Beth M Duke
VP: Debbie McCrickard
Dir Rx: James Dice
Brnch Mgr: Beth Bowling
Nurse Mgr: Nicole Guns

CHILDREN'S HOSPITAL OF NEW JER
See NEWARK BETH ISRAEL MEDICAL CENTER INC

D-U-N-S 06-615-8494
CHILDRENS HOSPITAL OF ORANGE COUNTY
CHOC
1201 W La Veta Ave, Orange, CA 92868-4203
Tel (714) 997-3000 Founded/Ownrshp 1950
Sales 518.8MM EMP 3,200E
Accts Kpmg Llp Los Angeles Ca
SIC 8069 Children's hospital
Pr: Kimberly Cripe
*Ch Bd: L Kenneth Heuler DDS
Pr: Patricia Faiman
Pr: Sally Gallagher
COO: Debra M Mathias
CFO: Kerri Schiller
Ofcr: Cathy Mc Donnell
Sr VP: James Fabella
Sr VP: Kerri Ruppert
Sr VP: Leigh Volker
VP: Susan Burrows
VP: Waldo Romero
VP: Barbara Sanchez
Dir Rx: Grace Magedman

D-U-N-S 07-375-7627 EXP
CHILDRENS HOSPITAL OF PHILADELPHIA
CHILDRENS HOSP OF PA FNDTN
(Suby of CHOP FOUNDATION) ★
3401 Civic Center Blvd, Philadelphia, PA 19104-4319
Tel (215) 590-1000 Founded/Ownrshp 1863
Sales 68.5MME EMP 3,722E
SIC 8069 Children's hospital
Pr: Steven M Altschuler
*Ch Bd: Kim Buckley
*Pr: Madeline Bell
COO: Denise R Bowman
COO: Douglas G Hock
*CFO: Thomas Todorow
CFO: Thomas J Todorow
Trst: Alan Cohen
Chf Mktg O: George Reynolds
Ofcr: Raymond Colliton
*Ofcr: Nicholas Procyk
Ex VP: Matthew Cook
*Ex VP: Margaret M Jones
*Ex VP: Jeffrey D Kahn
Ex VP: Stuart P Sullivan
*Ex VP: Bryan Wolf
Ex VP: Bryan A Wolf
*Sr VP: Paula Agosto
Sr VP: Robert Croner
*Sr VP: K Chavanu Gorman
*Sr VP: Philip R Johnson Jr

D-U-N-S 93-329-6568
CHILDRENS HOSPITAL OF PHILADELPHIA FOUNDATION
CHOP FOUNDATION
3401 Civic Center Blvd, Philadelphia, PA 19104-4319
Tel (215) 590-1000 Founded/Ownrshp 1855
Sales 195.2MM EMP 10,000
Accts Pricewaterhousecoopers Llp Ph
SIC 8741 8399 Administrative management; Fund raising organization, non-fee basis
Ch: Richard M Armstrong Jr
Dir Recs: Gilbert Davis
*Pr: Steven Altschuler MD
VP: Peter M Grollman
Dir Soc: Elana Ten Huisen
Off Mgr: Kathy Carr
Snr Ntwrk: Carol Botte
Dir IT: Svetlana Ostapenko
Dir IT: John Pedicone
Dir IT: Mark Ramos
IT Man: Julie Ammons

D-U-N-S 04-430-4145
CHILDRENS HOSPITAL OF PITTSBURGH
(Suby of UPMC HEALTH BENEFITS) ★
1 Childrens Hospital Dr, Pittsburgh, PA 15224-1529
Tel (412) 692-5437 Founded/Ownrshp 1887
Sales 412.1MME EMP 2,500
SIC 8062 General medical & surgical hospitals
Ch Bd: Mary Joe Divoli
CFO: Mark J Giaquinto
VP: Jacqueline A Dailey
VP: Jodi Hurs
Ex Dir: Kathy Guatteri
Nurse Mgr: Elaine Lander
Doctor: David H Perlmutter

D-U-N-S 07-384-7261
CHILDRENS HOSPITAL OF WISCONSIN INC
(Suby of CHILDRENS HOSPITAL AND HEALTH SYSTEM INC) ★
9000 W Wscnsin Ave Stop 1, Milwaukee, WI 53226
Tel (414) 266-2000 Founded/Ownrshp 1894
Sales 545.6MM EMP 2,045
SIC 8069 Children's hospital
Pr: Cindy Christensen
Pr: Andrea Kusch
*Treas: Timothy L Birkenstock
VP: Tricia Geraghty
*VP: Michael Jones
*VP: Marge Nienen
VP: Monica Ricca
Exec: Lisa Steinberg
Opers Mgr: Tammy Star
Pr Mgr: Jackie Gauger
Orthpdst: Channing J Taone

D-U-N-S 96-227-1735
CHILDRENS HOSPITAL PEDIATRIC ASSOCIATES INC
20 Overland St Ste 2, Boston, MA 02215-3337
Tel (617) 919-2822 Founded/Ownrshp 2010
Sales 246.4MM EMP 4E
Accts Baker Newman & Noyes Llc Port
SIC 8011 Pediatrician
Prin: William Tarvainen

CHILDRENS HOSPITAL SAN ANTONIO
See CHRISTUS SANTA ROSA HEALTH CARE CORP

D-U-N-S 07-868-9619 IMP
CHILDRENS HOSPITALS AND CLINICS OF MINNESOTA
2525 Chicago Ave, Minneapolis, MN 55404-4518
Tel (612) 813-6000 Founded/Ownrshp 1994
Sales 284.0MME EMP 4,285
Accts Deloitte Tax Llp Minneapolis
SIC 8069 Children's hospital
CEO: Alan L Goldbloom
*Ch Bd: Russell Becker
Pr: Dave Overman
CFO: K Alec Mahmood
CFO: Todd Ostendorf
Treas: Jonathan Wood
*V Ch Bd: J Hayes Batson
Ofcr: Carol Koenecke-Grant
Ofcr: Mark C Robinson
Ofcr: Trevor W Sawallish
Ofcr: Christa Steene-Lyons
VP: David Cook
VP: Bjorn Gunnerud
VP: Jerry Massman
VP: Jerry Massmann
Comm Dir: Jan Jachimowicz
Dir Rx: Diane Alexander
Dir Rx: Greg Zarambo
Dir Env Sv: Laramie White
Board of Directors: Thomas Tefft, Pamela Alexander, Jonathan Wood, Martin Bassett, Bill Jeatran, Mary Jeffries, Cyndi Lesher, Matt Majka, Paul Marvin, Richard Murphy, Bruce Shay

CHILDREN'S MEDICAL CENTER
See DAYTON CHILDRENS HOSPITAL

D-U-N-S 07-935-8529 IMP
CHILDRENS MEDICAL CENTER OF DALLAS
(Suby of CHILDRENS HEALTH SYSTEM OF TEXAS) ★
1935 Medical District Dr, Dallas, TX 75235-7701
Tel (214) 456-7000 Founded/Ownrshp 1913
Sales 712.6MM EMP 5,318
SIC 8069 Children's hospital
Pr: Christopher Durovich
*CFO: Ray Dziesinski
*Sr VP: Doug Hock
VP: Pete Kline
Pharmcst: Patricia McLeroy

D-U-N-S 13-061-0368
CHILDRENS MEDICAL CENTER TOLEDO
DAYTON CHILDREN
1 Childrens Plz, Dayton, OH 45404-1873
Tel (937) 641-3000 Founded/Ownrshp 2003
Sales 34.2MME EMP 1,500
SIC 8069 Children's hospital
CEO: David Kensaul
*VP: Bonnie Summerville

CHILDREN'S MEMORIAL HOSPITAL
See CHILDRENS HOSPITAL OF CHICAGO MEDICAL CENTER

D-U-N-S 96-593-4610
CHILDRENS MERCY HOSPITAL FOUNDATION
2401 Gillham Rd, Kansas City, MO 64108-4619
Tel (816) 234-3000 Founded/Ownrshp 2010
Sales 1.0MMM EMP 46E
Accts Kpmg Llp Omaha Ne
SIC 8641 Civic social & fraternal associations
*COO: Karen Cox
*COO: Jo Stueve
*CFO: Sandra Aj Lawrence
*Ex VP: Charles C Roberts
IT Man: Linda Jones
Ansthlgy: Melinda Brown
Ansthlgy: Carrie Clarke
Ansthlgy: Barbara Furgason
Ansthlgy: Adam Schow
Ansthlgy: Jennifer Weiford
Doctor: Ahmed T Abdelmoiy MD

D-U-N-S 06-011-4253 IMP/EXP
CHILDRENS MIRACLE NETWORK (UT)
CMN
205 W 700 S, Salt Lake City, UT 84101-2715
Tel (801) 214-7400 Founded/Ownrshp 1982
Sales 233.9MME EMP 180
SIC 8399 Fund raising organization, non-fee basis
Pr: John R Lauck
*COO: John Hartman
*Treas: John Bozard
Ofcr: Jenni Debartolo
VP: Robert Banner
VP: Nate Graham
VP: Nick Ward
Mng Dir: Stuart Moffitt
Rgnl Mgr: Jenny Grifenhagen

D-U-N-S 60-697-7783
CHILDRENS NATIONAL MEDICAL CENTER
111 Michigan Ave Nw, Washington, DC 20010-2916
Tel (202) 476-5000 Founded/Ownrshp 1869
Sales 902.9MME EMP 6,000
SIC 8062 General medical & surgical hospitals
Pr: Kurt Newman
V Ch: Mary Ottolini
COO: Kathleen E Chavanu Gorman
CFO: Douglas T Myers
*Ch: Billie Lou Short
*Chf Mktg O: Peter Holbrook
Ofcr: Raymond S Sczudlo
Ofcr: Mendel Tuchman
Ofcr: Darryl Varnado
*Ex VP: Mark Batshaw
Ex VP: Denice Cora-Bramble
Ex VP: Elizabeth Flury
Ex VP: Pam K Sams
Ex VP: David Wessel
Sr VP: Gerard R Martin
Sr VP: Roger J Packer
Sr VP: Anthony Sandler
Sr VP: Joseph Wright
VP: Julie Butler
VP: Kathleen Coppedge
VP: Debbie Freiburg

D-U-N-S 19-909-6728 IMP/EXP
▲ CHILDRENS PLACE INC
500 Plaza Dr Ste 400, Secaucus, NJ 07094-3668
Tel (201) 558-2400 Founded/Ownrshp 1969
Sales 1.7MMM EMP 15,300
Accts Bdo Usa Llp New York Ny
Tkr Sym PLCE Exch NGS
SIC 5641 5651 Children's & infants' wear stores; Family clothing stores
Pr: Jane T Elfers
*Ch Bd: Norman Matthews
COO: June Andujar
COO: Michael Scarpa
CFO: Anurup Pruthi
Sr VP: Bradley Cost
Sr VP: Adrienne Gernand
Sr VP: Kevin Low
Sr VP: Gregory Poole
VP: Kristin Clifford
VP: Brett Flanz
VP: Carrie Gennuso
VP: Joe Monahan
VP: Caroline Morrison
Board of Directors: Joseph Alutto, John E Bachman, Marla Malcolm Beck, Susan Patricia Griffith, Joseph Gromek, Robert L Mettler, Kenneth Reiss, Stanley W Reynolds, Susan Sobbott

D-U-N-S 07-863-7576
CHILDRENS SPECIALIZED HOSPITAL INC
150 New Providence Rd # 1, Mountainside, NJ 07092-2590
Tel (888) 244-5373 Founded/Ownrshp 1891
Sales 64.3MME EMP 1,200
Accts Parentebeard Llc Clark New J
SIC 8069 8093 Specialty hospitals, except psychiatric; Rehabilitation center, outpatient treatment
CEO: Amy Mansue
*Ofcr: Christopher Haines
*Ex VP: Warren Moore
Genl Mgr: Roy Henricksen
Off Admin: Mercedes Ferreira
Off Admin: Loraine Landisi
Site Mgr: Kajsa Cappello
Psych: Rachel Hendel
Psych: Richard Leit
Cert Phar: Sandhya Balachandar

D-U-N-S 03-919-1557
CHILDRENS SPECIALTY GROUP INC
999 N 92nd St Ste C740, Milwaukee, WI 53226-4875
Tel (414) 292-7858 Founded/Ownrshp 2010
Sales 218.6MM EMP 4
Accts Pricewaterhousecoopers Llp Bo
SIC 8011

D-U-N-S 14-840-9535 IMP/EXP
CHILDRENS SURGICAL ASSOCIATES LTD
3400 Civic Center Blvd # 5, Philadelphia, PA 19104-5127
Tel (215) 590-2700 Founded/Ownrshp 1974
Sales 106.4MM EMP 130
SIC 8011 Offices & clinics of medical doctors
Ex Dir: Linda Parris
*Ex Dir: Linda Flocco
Off Mgr: Nancy Harriz
Surgeon: John Dormans
Doctor: Lisa Elden

D-U-N-S 86-147-6112
CHILDRENS TRUST
3150 Sw 3rd Ave Fl 8, Miami, FL 33129-2707
Tel (305) 571-5700 Founded/Ownrshp 2003
Sales 104.5MM EMP 95
Accts Rachlin Llp Miami Florida
SIC 6732 Charitable trust management
Pr: Modesto E Abety
Ex Dir: K Lori Hanson
IT Man: Alvaro Cabrera

D-U-N-S 19-567-4981
CHILDRESS KLEIN PROPERTIES INC
301 S College St Ste 2800, Charlotte, NC 28202-6033
Tel (704) 342-9000 Founded/Ownrshp 1988
Sales 193.8MME EMP 358
SIC 6552 6512 6531 Land subdividers & developers, commercial; Commercial & industrial building operation; Real estate agents & managers
Mng Pt: J Donald Childress
*Mng Pt: Frederick W Klein
*CFO: Harry Clements
*VP: Christine M Chase
*VP: Thomas C G Coyle Jr
*VP: John R Decker
*VP: R David Haggart
Dir Sec: William Dowdcpp
Dir Sec: James Pool
IT Man: Nelson Hendrix
Opers Mgr: Sheri Gorbey

D-U-N-S 07-258-8254
CHILDTIME CHILDCARE INC
CHILDTIME LEARNING CTRS MICH
(Suby of LEARNING CARE GROUP INC) ★
21333 Haggerty Rd Ste 300, Novi, MI 48375-5537
Tel (248) 697-9000 Founded/Ownrshp 1967
Sales 123.1MME EMP 5,500
SIC 8351 Child day care services
Pr: William D Davis
Board of Directors: Benjamin Jacobson

CHILDTIME LEARNING CTRS MICH
See CHILDTIME CHILDCARE INC

CHILI'S
See PEPPER DINING HOLDING CORP

CHILI'S
See GRAYLING CORP

CHILI'S
See MARYLAND FOODS INC

CHILI'S
See PEPPER DINING INC

CHILI'S
See INTERNATIONAL RESTAURANT SERVICES INC

D-U-N-S 88-490-3535
■ CHILIS INC
(Suby of BRINKER INTERNATIONAL INC) ★
6820 Lbj Fwy, Dallas, TX 75240-6511
Tel (972) 980-9917 Founded/Ownrshp 1991
Sales 827.8MME EMP 13,000
SIC 5812 Restaurant, family: chain
CEO: Douglas H Brooks
Mng Pt: Tricia Barton
Mng Pt: Bob Blessing
Mng Pt: Scott Burrows
Mng Pt: Andrew Catalano
Mng Pt: August Chitwood
Mng Pt: Gary Cox
Mng Pt: Raymond Fuentes
Mng Pt: Tina Gaby
Mng Pt: Jamison Matt
Mng Pt: Lindsey Moser
Mng Pt: Brian Parkinson
Mng Pt: Ryan Trueblood
Mng Pt: Kashana Warner
*Pr: Kelli Valade
VP: Doug Comings

D-U-N-S 80-964-7915
CHILL HOLDINGS INC
(Suby of DAIKIN INDUSTRIES, LTD.)
5151 San Felipe St # 500, Houston, TX 77056-3607
Tel (713) 861-2500 Founded/Ownrshp 2007
Sales 2.5MMME EMP 13,632
SIC 3585 Heating & air conditioning combination units
CEO: Takeshi Ebisu
*CEO: David L Swift
*CFO: Lawrence M Blackburn
*Treas: Mark Dolan
*Sr VP: James L Mishler
*Sr VP: William L Topper
*VP: Ardee Toppe

D-U-N-S 17-491-7336
CHILLICOTHE LONG TERM CARE INC
WESTMORELAND PLACE
7265 Kenwood Rd Ste 300, Cincinnati, OH 45236-4414
Tel (513) 793-8804 Founded/Ownrshp 1986
Sales 970.6MM EMP 220
SIC 8051 Skilled nursing care facilities
Pr: James Farley
*Ex VP: Michael Scharfenberger

D-U-N-S 06-582-1191
CHILTON HOSPITAL
97 W Parkway, Pompton Plains, NJ 07444-1647
Tel (973) 831-5000 Founded/Ownrshp 1954
Sales 184.1MM EMP 1,188
SIC 8062 General medical & surgical hospitals
Pr: Deborah K Zastocki
*Pr: Beverley Wilen
*COO: Patrick Gavin
CFO: Chris Fhalen
*Ch: Eliot H Chodosh MD
*Treas: Michael Debernardi
Ex VP: Mary Abed
VP: Richard Andrews
VP: John M Browne
*VP: James J Doyle
VP: Julia McGovern
VP: Roger Snyder
Exec: Daniel Kous
Dir Rad: Stewart Moses

D-U-N-S 80-172-4365
▲ CHIMERA INVESTMENT CORP
520 Madison Ave Rm 3200, New York, NY 10022-4324
Tel (646) 454-3759 Founded/Ownrshp 2007
Sales 872.7MM EMP 5E
Accts Ernst & Young Llp New York N
Tkr Sym CIM Exch NYS
SIC 6798 Real estate investment trusts; Mortgage investment trusts
Pr: Matthew Lambiase
COO: Choudhary Yarlagadda
CFO: Robert Colligan
CIO: Mohit Marria
Genl Couns: Phillip J Kardis II

CHIMES DC
See CHIMES DISTRICT OF COLUMBIA INC

D-U-N-S 82-583-0961
CHIMES DISTRICT OF COLUMBIA INC
CHIMES DC
4815 Seton Dr, Baltimore, MD 21215-3234
Tel (410) 358-5193 Founded/Ownrshp 1991
Sales 74.1MM EMP 1,954
SIC 8331 Vocational training agency
Ch Bd: Douglas Schimedt
*Pr: Martin Lampner
*CFO: Shawna Gottlied
*Ex VP: Albert Bussone

CHIMNEYS CRDLE ROCK APARTMENTS
See OXFORD-COLUMBIA ASSOCIATES A MARYLAND LIMITED PARTNERSHIP

D-U-N-S 18-871-5023
CHIN LEEANN INC
LEEANN CHIN RESTAURANT
3600 American Blvd W # 52, Bloomington, MN 55431-1079
Tel (952) 896-3606 *Founded/Ownrshp* 2007
Sales 28.5MM[E] *EMP* 1,000
SIC 5812 Chinese restaurant; Caterers
CEO: Lorne Goldberg
**Pr:* Greg Creathen
**CEO:* Steve Finn
Dir IT: Dan Bjorback

D-U-N-S 82-889-4076
CHINA AUTOMOTIVE SYSTEMS INC
2546 Elliott Dr, Troy, MI 48083-4604
Tel (248) 577-0353 *Founded/Ownrshp* 1999
Sales 47.9MM[E] *EMP* 3,617
SIC 5812 Chinese restaurant
Pr: Hanlin Chen

CHINA CONSTRUCTION AMERICA
See C SCEC-USA INC

D-U-N-S 55-631-9247
CHINA ENERGY CORP
6130 Elton Ave, Las Vegas, NV 89107-2538
Tel (702) 998-8146 *Founded/Ownrshp* 2005
Sales 246.0MM *EMP* 2[E]
SIC 7011 Casino hotel
Pr: Wenxiang Ding

D-U-N-S 87-665-6364
■ **CHINA FW INC**
LINCOLN NATIONAL CHINA INC
(*Suby of* LNC) ★
1300 S Clinton St, Fort Wayne, IN 46802-3506
Tel (260) 455-2000 *Founded/Ownrshp* 1994
Sales NA *EMP* 2,000
SIC 6311 Life insurance
CEO: Dennis Glass
VP: Kristi J Harkenrider
VP: Don Mockler
VP: Rick Nelson

D-U-N-S 96-747-1884
CHINA INDUSTRIAL STEEL INC
110 Wall St Fl 11, New York, NY 10005-3834
Tel (646) 328-1502 *Founded/Ownrshp* 2011
Sales 649.3MM *EMP* 2
SIC 3312 Blast furnaces & steel mills
Prin: Shenghong Liu

D-U-N-S 00-232-5082
CHINA LENOX INC
1414 Radcliffe St, Bristol, PA 19007-5413
Tel (267) 525-7800 *Founded/Ownrshp* 2007
Sales 79.7MM[E] *EMP* 1,500
SIC 3263 Semivitreous table & kitchenware

D-U-N-S 03-361-5563 IMP
CHINA MANUFACTURERS ALLIANCE LLC
CMA
406 E Huntington Dr # 200, Monrovia, CA 91016-3638
Tel (626) 301-9575 *Founded/Ownrshp* 1997
Sales 246.1MM *EMP* 45
SIC 5014 Tires & tubes
Pr: Zhiming Yang
CEO: Mike Yang
VP: Aron Murphy
VP: Walter Weller
Sales Exec: Joe Cochran
Manager: Valentino Faraone
Sls Mgr: Sid Parr

D-U-N-S 80-805-4758
CHINA NORTH EAST PETROLEUM HOLDINGS LIMITED
445 Park Ave Ste 900, New York, NY 10022-8632
Tel (212) 307-3568 *Founded/Ownrshp* 1999
Sales 99.5MM *EMP* 715
SIC 1311 Crude petroleum production
CEO: Jingfu Ll
CFO: Shaohui Chen
Board of Directors: John Nicholls

D-U-N-S 11-049-4783 IMP
CHINA SUTONG TIRE RESOURCES INC
SCTR
33402 Highway 290 A, Hockley, TX 77447-7885
Tel (713) 690-5500 *Founded/Ownrshp* 2000
Sales 125.3MM[E] *EMP* 100[E]
Accts Ata Cpa Group Llc Edison New
SIC 5014 Tires & tubes
CEO: Zhiu Yang
**COO:* Dan Hunter
VP: Nancy Jhao

D-U-N-S 12-889-6755 IMP
CHINA TELECOM (AMERICAS) CORP
(*Suby of* CHINA TELECOMMUNICATIONS CORPORATION)
607 Herndon Pkwy Ste 201, Herndon, VA 20170-5481
Tel (703) 787-0088 *Founded/Ownrshp* 2001
Sales 254.3MM *EMP* 131[E]
Accts Deloitte Touche Tohmatsu Certi
SIC 4813 Data telephone communications
CEO: Zhuo Han
Pr: Yijun Tan
VP: Lingping Kong
Dir Bus: Christopher Bennett
Sls Dir: Emily Chen
Manager: Sami Muslija
Sls Mgr: Jason Qiu

D-U-N-S 05-361-8450
CHINDEX INTERNATIONAL INC
4340 East West Hwy # 1100, Bethesda, MD 20814-4411
Tel (301) 215-7777 *Founded/Ownrshp* 2014
Sales 179.3MM *EMP* 1,749[E]
SIC 5047 8062

D-U-N-S 02-876-4849
CHINESE AMERICAN PLANNING
1 York St Fl 2, New York, NY 10013-2123
Tel (212) 219-8100 *Founded/Ownrshp* 2010
Sales 91.2MM *EMP* 2
SIC 8322 Adult day care center

D-U-N-S 78-107-6617
CHINESE COMMUNITY HEALTH CARE ASSOCIATION
445 Grant Ave Ste 700, San Francisco, CA 94108-3250
Tel (415) 955-8800 *Founded/Ownrshp* 1982
Sales 117.9MM *EMP* 7[E]
Accts Le Ho & Company Llp Daly City
SIC 8621 Health association
Ex Dir: Edward Chow

D-U-N-S 82-473-5963
CHINESE COMMUNITY HEALTH PLAN
CCHP
(*Suby of* CHINESE HOSPITAL ASSOCIATION) ★
445 Grant Ave Ste 700, San Francisco, CA 94108-3250
Tel (415) 955-8800 *Founded/Ownrshp* 1986
Sales 96.3MM *EMP* 40
Accts Kpmg Llp San Francisco Ca
SIC 8011 Health maintenance organization
Dir Case M: Dana Samples
Doctor: Everett Ai
Doctor: David Bonovich
Doctor: John Meyer
Doctor: Raymond Wong

D-U-N-S 07-877-2852
CHINESE HOSPITAL ASSOCIATION
845 Jackson St, San Francisco, CA 94133-4899
Tel (415) 982-2400 *Founded/Ownrshp* 1923
Sales 130.5MM *EMP* 285
Accts Kpmg Llp Santa Clara Ca
SIC 8621 Professional membership organizations
CEO: Brenda Yee
**COO:* Linda Schumacher
**CFO:* Thomas Bolger
Dir Risk M: Stuart Fong
Chf Nrs Of: Peggy Cmiel
Sys Mgr: Helen Lee

CHINO VALLEY LEARNING ACADEMY
See CHINO VALLEY UNIFIED SCHOOL DISTRICT

CHINO VALLEY MEDICAL CENTER
See VERITAS HEALTH SERVICES INC

D-U-N-S 07-360-7459
CHINO VALLEY UNIFIED SCHOOL DISTRICT
CHINO VALLEY LEARNING ACADEMY
5130 Riverside Dr, Chino, CA 91710-4130
Tel (909) 628-1201 *Founded/Ownrshp* 1920
Sales 95.3MM[E] *EMP* 1,960
SIC 8211

D-U-N-S 96-770-8467
CHINOS HOLDINGS INC
770 Broadway, New York, NY 10003-9522
Tel (212) 209-2500 *Founded/Ownrshp* 2010
Sales 2.5MMM[E] *EMP* 18,800[E]
SIC 5961 5621 5611 5632 6794 Women's apparel, mail order; Clothing, mail order (except women's); Mail order house; Women's clothing stores; Men's & boys' clothing stores; Apparel accessories; Franchises, selling or licensing
VP: Ronald Cami

D-U-N-S 96-800-4460
CHINOS INTERMEDIATE HOLDINGS B INC
(*Suby of* CHINOS HOLDINGS INC) ★
770 Broadway, New York, NY 10003-9522
Tel (212) 209-2500 *Founded/Ownrshp* 2011
Sales 2.5MMM[E] *EMP* 18,800[E]
SIC 5961 5621 5611 5632 6794 Catalog & mail-order houses; Women's apparel, mail order; Clothing, mail order (except women's); Mail order house; Women's clothing stores; Men's & boys' clothing stores; Apparel accessories; Franchises, selling or licensing
Ch Bd: Millard Drexler

D-U-N-S 80-605-8632
▲ **CHIPOTLE MEXICAN GRILL INC**
1401 Wynkoop St Ste 500, Denver, CO 80202-1729
Tel (303) 595-4000 *Founded/Ownrshp* 1993
Sales 4.5MMM *EMP* 59,330
Accts Ernst & Young Llp Denver Col
Tkr Sym CMG *Exch* NYS
SIC 5812 5813 Mexican restaurant; Grills (eating places); Drinking places
Ch Bd: Steve Ells
CFO: John R Hartung
**Co-CEO:* Montgomery F Moran
Chf Cred: Mark Crumpacker
Bd of Dir: John Charlesworth
VP: Karin Alexander
VP: Elvir Ibrahimpasic
Area Mgr: Tony Dibartolo
Genl Mgr: Jose Aros
Genl Mgr: Adnan Bajramaliu
Genl Mgr: Sidney Carroll
Board of Directors: Matthew Paull, Albert S Baldocchi, Paul T Cappuccio, John S Charlesworth, Neil W Flanzraich, Patrick J Flynn, Darlene J Friedman, Stephen Gillett, Robin S Hickenlooper, Ali Namvar

D-U-N-S 96-003-8917
■ **CHIPPENHAM & JOHNSTON-WILLIS HOSPITALS INC**
CJW MEDICAL CENTER
(*Suby of* HOSPITAL COPORATION OF AMERICA) ★
7101 Jahnke Rd, Richmond, VA 23225-4017
Tel (804) 327-4046 *Founded/Ownrshp* 1995
Sales 190.5MM[E] *EMP* 2,400
SIC 8062 General medical & surgical hospitals
Pr: Peter Marmerstein
**COO:* Dia Nichols
VP: Elizabeth Taliaffero
Dir Lab: Julie Stevenson
Anesthlgy: Thomas W Bohannon
Anesthlgy: Alan M Bolash
Anesthlgy: Rudolf B Wenleder
Opthamlgy: Evan J Leslie

D-U-N-S 07-474-5126
■ **CHIPPENHAM HOSPITAL INC**
CHIPPENHAM MEDICAL CENTER
(*Suby of* HCA-HOSPITAL CORP OF AMERICA) ★
7101 Jahnke Rd, Richmond, VA 23225-4044
Tel (804) 320-3911 *Founded/Ownrshp* 2007
Sales 191.0MM[E] *EMP* 3,000
SIC 8062 General medical & surgical hospitals
CEO: Peter Marmerstein
**Pr:* John L Thornton
**Treas:* Rodney H Smith MD
**VP:* Campbell G Stalker

CHIPPENHAM MEDICAL CENTER
See CHIPPENHAM HOSPITAL INC

D-U-N-S 07-478-7144
CHIPPEWA COUNTY WAR MEMORIAL HOSPITAL INC
500 Osborn Blvd, Sault Sainte Marie, MI 49783-1822
Tel (906) 635-4460 *Founded/Ownrshp* 1913
Sales 90.3MM *EMP* 500
SIC 8062 8051 General medical & surgical hospitals; Skilled nursing care facilities
VP: Susan Clow
**CFO:* Kevin Kalchik
Treas: Grant Elliott
VP: Jim Haglund
VP: Sue Tettzlaff
VP: Susan Tetzlaff
Dir Rad: Nicole Matcavitch
QA Dir: Mitch Zaborowski
Mtls Dir: Carla Cryderman
Ansthlgy: William E Goode
HC Dir: Ginger Morgan

D-U-N-S 01-086-4320
CHIPPEWA VALLEY SCHOOLS (INC)
19120 Cass Ave, Clinton Township, MI 48038-2301
Tel (586) 723-2000 *Founded/Ownrshp* 1959
Sales 188.4MM *EMP* 1,324
Accts Plante & Moran Pllc Auburn H
SIC 8211 Public elementary school; Public junior high school; Public senior high school; Public vocational/technical school
Teacher Pr: Dawn Leone

D-U-N-S 13-819-1549
CHIPPEWA VALLEY TECHNICAL COLLEGE FOUNDATION INC
620 W Clairemont Ave, Eau Claire, WI 54701-6120
Tel (715) 833-6200 *Founded/Ownrshp* 1968
Sales 32.4MM *EMP* 1,303
Accts Wipfli Llp Eau Claire Wi
SIC 8222 Technical institute
Pr: Bruce Barker
**VP:* Tom Huffcutt

D-U-N-S 02-046-8906
CHIPTON-ROSS INC (WISCONSIN)
343 Main St, El Segundo, CA 90245-3814
Tel (310) 414-7800 *Founded/Ownrshp* 1979
Sales 103.1MM *EMP* 450
SIC 7361 Executive placement
Pr: Sharon King
Board of Directors: Sharon King

D-U-N-S 05-154-1597 IMP/EXP
CHIQUITA BRANDS INTERNATIONAL INC
(*Suby of* CHIQUITA HOLDINGS LIMITED)
2051 Se 35th St, Fort Lauderdale, FL 33316-4019
Tel (954) 453-1201 *Founded/Ownrshp* 2015
Sales 3.0MMM *EMP* 20,000
SIC 0179 0174 0161 0175 2033 Banana grove; Kiwi farm; Mango grove; Pineapple farm; Citrus fruits; Grapefruit grove; Vegetables & melons; Tomato farm; Lettuce farm; Celery farm; Deciduous tree fruits; Apple orchard; Peach orchard; Pear orchard; Fruit juices: packaged in cans, jars, etc.; Vegetable juices: packaged in cans, jars, etc.
CEO: Brian Kocher
CFO: Rick P Frier
Ex VP: Manuel Rodriguez
Ex VP: James E Thompson
Sr VP: Stephen Coale
Sr VP: Chris Dugan
Sr VP: Mario Pacheco
Sr VP: Courtney Parker
Sr VP: Paolo Prudenziati
Sr VP: Helge Sparso
Sr VP: Andries Weber
VP: Joseph B Johnson
Board of Directors: Carlos Bertaco Bomfim, Michael Rubinoff, Philip Warner

D-U-N-S 19-482-2193 IMP/EXP
CHIQUITA BRANDS LLC
(*Suby of* CHIQUITA BRANDS INTERNATIONAL INC) ★
2051 Se 35th St, Fort Lauderdale, FL 33316-4019
Tel (954) 453-1201 *Founded/Ownrshp* 1986
Sales 168.2MM[E] *EMP* 260
SIC 0175 0174 0179 0161 5148 7389 Deciduous tree fruits; Citrus fruits; Banana grove; Vegetables & melons; Melon farms; Fruits, fresh; Vegetables, fresh; Purchasing service
Pr: Andrew Biles
VP: Manjit Singh

D-U-N-S 04-591-7457
CHIRO INC
MR CLEAN MAINTENANCE SYSTEMS
2260 S Vista Ave, Bloomington, CA 92316-2908
Tel (909) 879-1160 *Founded/Ownrshp* 1980
Sales 87.5MM[E] *EMP* 450[E]
SIC 5087 7349 5169 Cleaning & maintenance equipment & supplies; Cleaning service, industrial or commercial; Chemicals & allied products
Pr: Arthur Rose
**VP:* Timothy Russell
Sls Mgr: Tom Munro

D-U-N-S 82-533-4555
CHIRON CORP
(*Suby of* NOVARTIS VACCINES AND DIAGNOSTICS INC) ★
4560 Horton St, Emeryville, CA 94608-2916
Tel (510) 655-8730 *Founded/Ownrshp* 1981
Sales 108.1MM[E] *EMP* 1[E]
SIC 8099 Blood related health services
Pr: Edward E Penhoet
Sr VP: William Green
VP: Dale Johnson
VP: Gregory Schwemer
Ex Dir: Paul Dennehy

D-U-N-S 07-955-9384
CHIRON GUERNSEY HOLDINGS LP INC
12930 W Interstate 10, San Antonio, TX 78249-2248
Tel (210) 524-9000 *Founded/Ownrshp* 2011
Sales 1.8MMM[E] *EMP* 5,800[E]
SIC 3841 Surgical & medical instruments

D-U-N-S 07-830-3827
CHIRON HOLDINGS INC
(*Suby of* ACELITY LP INC) ★
12930 W Interstate 10, San Antonio, TX 78249-2248
Tel (210) 524-9000 *Founded/Ownrshp* 2005
Sales 1.9MMM[E] *EMP* 5,500[E]
SIC 2599 7352 Hospital beds; Medical equipment rental

D-U-N-S 93-359-2925
CHITIMACHA TRIBE OF LOUISIANA
155 Chitimacha Loop, Charenton, LA 70523
Tel (337) 923-4973 *Founded/Ownrshp* 1915
Sales NA *EMP* 1,160
SIC 9131 Executive & legislative combined
Ch Bd: Lony Martin
**Ch Bd:* John Paul Darden
**Treas:* Charles S Johnson
Dir: Patty Leblanc

D-U-N-S 60-366-2599 IMP
CHIYODA USA CORP
(*Suby of* CHIYODA MANUFACTURING CORPORATION)
2200 E State Road 240, Greencastle, IN 46135-7451
Tel (765) 653-2993 *Founded/Ownrshp* 2005
Sales 138.2MM[E] *EMP* 180
SIC 5013 Automotive supplies & parts
Pr: Michihiro Oe
COO: Koji Okamoto
**Ex VP:* Yoshio Ozawa
QA Dir: Homero Serapio
IT Man: Ryan Shepherd
IT Man: Ryan Sheppherd

CHKD
See CHILDRENS HOSPITAL OF KINGS DAUGHTERS INC

D-U-N-S 60-401-5420
CHOATE CONSTRUCTION CO
8200 Roberts Dr Ste 600, Atlanta, GA 30350-4148
Tel (678) 892-1200 *Founded/Ownrshp* 1989
Sales 308.3MM[E] *EMP* 350
SIC 1522 1531 1542 Residential construction; Operative builders; Nonresidential construction
Pr: William Millard Choate
**COO:* Mike Hampton
**CFO:* David A Page
Ex VP: Joe Bratcher
VP: Joe Lain
VP: Leo Villalobos
Dir Risk M: Max Joksch
Div Mgr: Croswell Brim
Genl Mgr: Christine Biggs
Off Mgr: Lisa Wolfe
IT Man: Nick Pagliaro

D-U-N-S 79-042-8754 IMP
CHOBANI LLC
147 State Highway 320, Norwich, NY 13815-3561
Tel (607) 337-1246 *Founded/Ownrshp* 2004
Sales 854.0MM[E] *EMP* 2,527
SIC 2026 Yogurt
CEO: Hamdi Ulukaya
Pr: Michael Gonda
**CFO:* Dipak Golechha
VP: Grace Simmons
CIO: Ash Mehra
QA Dir: Sean Bower
Sfty Mgr: James Kandora
Prd Mgr: Joseph Gannon
Sls Dir: Sean Blackmore
Mktg Mgr: Kathryn Becht
Mktg Mgr: Jodi Genshaft

CHOC
See CHILDRENS HOSPITAL OF ORANGE COUNTY

D-U-N-S 03-042-1332 IMP/EXP
CHOCOLAT FREY USA LTD
(*Suby of* CHOCOLAT FREY AG)
3500 Genesee St, Buffalo, NY 14225-5015
Tel (716) 340-0880 *Founded/Ownrshp* 2014
Sales 106.0MM[E] *EMP* 500
SIC 5145 Candy
Pr: Christoph Schmassmann
Ch Bd: Hans-Ruedi Christen

D-U-N-S 12-889-6870
CHOCTAW ARCHIVING ENTERPRISE
(*Suby of* CHOCTAW NATION OF OKLAHOMA) ★
2101 W Arkansas St, Durant, OK 74701-5643
Tel (580) 920-1501 *Founded/Ownrshp* 2004
Sales 24.6MM *EMP* 1,050
SIC 8711 4226 Engineering services; Document & office records storage
Mng Ofcr: Nate Cox
Mng Ofcr: Gregg Robinson

D-U-N-S 08-315-5007
CHOCTAW MANAGEMENT SERVICES ENTERPRISE
CMSE
2101 W Arkansas St, Durant, OK 74701-5643
Tel (580) 924-8280 *Founded/Ownrshp* 1996
Sales 89.0MM *EMP* 30
Accts Dennis And Company Llc Tulsa

SIC 8099 8011 8031 Blood related health services; Offices & clinics of medical doctors; Offices & clinics of osteopathic physicians
CEO: Gregg Robinson

D-U-N-S 08-073-5806
CHOCTAW NATION OF OKLAHOMA
529 N 16th Ave, Durant, OK 74701-3610
Tel (580) 924-8280 *Founded/Ownrshp* 1906
Sales NA *EMP* 7,000
SIC 9131 Indian reservation;
Prin: Gregory E Pyle
Exec: Ryan Garner
**Prin:* Kelly Elliott
Ex Dir: Jerry Tomlinson
Dir IT: Dustin Skiles
Dir IT: Dustin Stark
IT Man: Robert Shults
Surgeon: Amanda Chisum-Price
Occ Thrpy: Dave Wright
Assoc Ed: Lisa Reed

CHOCTAW RESORT DEV ENTPS
See CHOCTAW RESORT DEVELOPMENT ENTERPRISE

D-U-N-S 12-305-3600
CHOCTAW RESORT DEVELOPMENT ENTERPRISE
CHOCTAW RESORT DEV ENTPS
(*Suby of* MISSISSIPPI BAND OF CHOCTAW INDIANS) ★
Highway 16 W, Philadelphia, MS 39350
Tel (866) 447-3275 *Founded/Ownrshp* 2003
Sales 163.3MM[E] *EMP* 4,000[E]
SIC 7011 Casino hotel
Pr: Holly Gagnon
**CFO:* Lawrence Kovach
VP: Jason A Stump
**Ex Dir:* Dewitt Caillavet
Pr Mgr: Ryan Griffin

D-U-N-S 00-482-6889
CHOCTAWHATCHEE ELECTRIC COOPERATIVE INC (FL)
CHELCO
1350 Baldwin Ave, Defuniak Springs, FL 32435-2310
Tel (850) 892-2111 *Founded/Ownrshp* 1940
Sales 92.8MM *EMP* 135
Accts Tipton Marler Garner & Chastai
SIC 4911 Distribution, electric power
Pr: Ronald C Jones
Pr: Chris Eddy
**CEO:* James E Smith
CFO: Wayne Thompson
**VP:* Gerald Edmondson
VP: Steve Wolfrom
**Prin:* Burt E Cosson
**Prin:* Gayle G Hughes
**Prin:* Don A McKnight
Telecom Ex: Mike Richards
DP Exec: Ken Green

D-U-N-S 15-860-1257
CHOICE ADMINISTRATORS INSURANCE SERVICES INC
CALIFORNIA CHOICE
721 S Parker St Ste 200, Orange, CA 92868-4772
Tel (714) 542-4200 *Founded/Ownrshp* 2001
Sales NA *EMP* 500
SIC 6411 Insurance agents, brokers & service
Pr: Ron Goldstein
Pr: Kevin J Counihan
Sr VP: Tamra Reise
**Sr VP:* Brenda Scott
**VP:* Raymond D Godeke
VP: Steve Van Wart
**VP:* John M Word
VP Mktg: Michael Payton
Manager: Sue Coppin
Manager: David McClintock
Manager: Drew Miller

D-U-N-S 19-739-7854
CHOICE HOMES INC
1600 E Lamar Blvd Ste 400, Arlington, TX 76011-4724
Tel (817) 652-5100 *Founded/Ownrshp* 1987
Sales 98.2MM[E] *EMP* 500
Accts Pricewaterhousecoopers Llp Da
SIC 1521 New construction, single-family houses
Ch Bd: Bill Bowerman
**Pr:* Dan Couture
**CEO:* Bob Ladd
**CFO:* Steve Garza

D-U-N-S 36-420-0360
▲ CHOICE HOTELS INTERNATIONAL INC
1 Choice Hotels Cir, Rockville, MD 20850-5140
Tel (301) 592-5000 *Founded/Ownrshp* 1997
Sales 859.8MM *EMP* 1,462
Tkr Sym CHH *Exch* NYS
SIC 7011 7373 Hotels; Hotel, franchised; Computer integrated systems design
CEO: Stephen P Joyce
**Ch Bd:* Stewart W Bainum Jr
Pr: Patrick S Pacious
Ofcr: Patrick J Cimerola
Ex VP: Patti Goodrich
Sr VP: Scott E Oaksmith
Sr VP: Simone Wu
VP: Jeff Lobb
Board of Directors: Barbara T Alexander, William L Jews, Monte J M Koch, Liza K Landsman, Scott A Renschler, Ervin R Shames, Gordon A Smith, John P Tague

D-U-N-S 07-523-3015
CHOICE LOGISTICS INC (NY)
1 Whitehall St Fl 12, New York, NY 10004-2138
Tel (917) 344-4000 *Founded/Ownrshp* 1964
Sales 100.0MM *EMP* 200
SIC 4731

D-U-N-S 80-829-9879 IMP
CHOICE PRODUCTS USA LLC
CLUB'S CHOICE FUNDRAISING
3421 Truax Ct, Eau Claire, WI 54703-6925
Tel (715) 833-8761 *Founded/Ownrshp* 1991
Sales 102.5MM[E] *EMP* 165
SIC 5199 7389 2041 Advertising specialties; Fund raising organizations; Pizza mixes

CHOICE STAFFING
See BURNETT COMPANIES CONSOLIDATED INC

CHOICEPOINT
See LEXISNEXIS RISK ASSETS INC

CHOMPIES DELI REST & BKY
See CHAI BAGEL CORP

CHOP FOUNDATION
See CHILDRENS HOSPITAL OF PHILADELPHIA FOUNDATION

D-U-N-S 00-695-0828
CHOPTANK ELECTRIC COOPERATIVE INC
24820 Meeting House Rd, Denton, MD 21629-1919
Tel (410) 479-0420 *Founded/Ownrshp* 1938
Sales 139.2MM *EMP* 160
Accts Adams Jenkins And Cheatham R
SIC 4911 1731 Distribution, electric power; Electrical work
Pr: Michael Wheatley Sr
**Ch:* Carl R Widdowson
Bd of Dir: John J Burke Jr
Bd of Dir: Francis A Callahan Jr
**Sr VP:* Michael Wheatley
Opers Mgr: Jackie Butler

D-U-N-S 02-233-0042
CHOPTANK TRANSPORT INC
3601 Choptank Rd, Preston, MD 21655-1220
Tel (410) 673-2240 *Founded/Ownrshp* 1998
Sales 180.1MM *EMP* 175[E]
Accts Tgm Group Llc
SIC 4731 Brokers, shipping
Pr: Geoffrey A Turner
COO: Pam Hutchinson
Genl Mgr: Paul Ayers
Genl Mgr: Brian Carr
Genl Mgr: Charlene Keller
Genl Mgr: Grant Lehman
Genl Mgr: Danis Muzzy
Natl Sales: Keith Ludwig
Sls Mgr: Crystal Tanner
Sls Mgr: Lloyd Thomas
Snr Mgr: Julie White

CHORE-TIME PLTY PROD SYSTEMS
See CTB INC

D-U-N-S 01-376-3894
CHP OF WASHINGTON
720 Olive Way Ste 300, Seattle, WA 98101-1830
Tel (206) 521-8833 *Founded/Ownrshp* 2010
Sales NA *EMP* 2
SIC 6411 Insurance information & consulting services
Prin: Stacy Kessel

D-U-N-S 00-160-4164 IMP/EXP
CHR HANSEN (WI)
(*Suby of* CHR. HANSEN HOLDING A/S)
9015 W Maple St, Milwaukee, WI 53214-4213
Tel (414) 607-5700 *Founded/Ownrshp* 1878, 1994
Sales 400.0MM *EMP* 320
SIC 2099 Food preparations
Pr: David Carpenter
Ex VP: Henrik Jacobi
Sr VP: Kurt Seagrist
**VP:* Robert Brill
Exec: Carol Voight
Sfty Dirs: Rick Tourillott
Opers Mgr: Brett Ball
Sls Dir: Sune Schmoelker
Board of Directors: Ole Andersen, Didier Debrosse, Sven Laulund, Jorgen Nielsen, Henrik Poulsen, Martin Gerhard Seidel, Frederic Stevenin, Mark Wilson

D-U-N-S 08-862-7559
CHRIS CAM CORP
HEARTLAND PAPER
808 W Cherokee St, Sioux Falls, SD 57104-0341
Tel (605) 336-1190 *Founded/Ownrshp* 1908
Sales 90.8MM[E] *EMP* 149[E]
SIC 5113 5169 5111 Industrial & personal service paper; Industrial chemicals; Fine paper
Prin: Sandra Christenson
Sales Asso: Dennis Pressley

CHRIS J. YAHNIS
See YAHNIS CO

D-U-N-S 06-656-5003
CHRISP CO
43650 Osgood Rd, Fremont, CA 94539-5631
Tel (510) 656-2840 *Founded/Ownrshp* 1979
Sales 85.5MM[E] *EMP* 180[E]
SIC 1611 Highway signs & guardrails
CEO: Robert P Chrisp
**VP:* David Morris
**VP:* Roger Weisbrod

CHRIST HOSPITAL
See HUDSON HOSPITAL OPCO LLC

D-U-N-S 04-610-5360
CHRIST HOSPITAL
CHRIST HOSPITAL HEALTH SERVICES
(*Suby of* CAREPOINT HEALTH MANAGEMENT ASSOCIATES LLC) ★
176 Palisade Ave, Jersey City, NJ 07306-1196
Tel (201) 795-8200 *Founded/Ownrshp* 2010
Sales 202.2MM *EMP* 1[E]
SIC 8062 General medical & surgical hospitals
Ex Dir: Herb Caillouet
CTO: Lupo Vaccarella
IT Man: Mike Starrett
Netwrk Mgr: Tom Kwapniewski
Pathlgst: Antonio Cabreros
Nrsg Dir: Mary Cardoso
Snr Mgr: Patrick Ryan

D-U-N-S 17-493-3374
CHRIST HOSPITAL
2139 Auburn Ave, Cincinnati, OH 45219-2989
Tel (513) 585-2000 *Founded/Ownrshp* 1891
Sales 647.3MM *EMP* 4,000
Accts Ernst & Young Us Llp Columbus
SIC 8062 Hospital, medical school affiliated with nursing & residency
CEO: Jack Cook
Pr: Allan Jones
**Pr:* Mike Keating
COO: Mike Schwebler
**CFO:* Chris Bergman
CFO: George Popco
CFO: George Popko
CFO: Fred Sanders
Ofcr: Deborah Hayes
Ofcr: Joanne Murphy
**VP:* Heather Adkins
VP: Victor Dipilla
VP: Jennifer Garcia
**VP:* Berc Gawne
**VP:* Paul Gelter
**VP:* Peter Greis
**VP:* Elizabeth Johnson
VP: Thomas Kereiakes

CHRIST HOSPITAL HEALTH SERVICES
See CHRIST HOSPITAL

D-U-N-S 14-445-7983
CHRIST HOSPITAL HEALTH SERVICES CORP
176 Palisade Ave, Jersey City, NJ 07306-1196
Tel (201) 795-8200 *Founded/Ownrshp* 1980
Sales 101.5MM *EMP* 1,200
Accts Ernst & Young Llp
SIC 6719 Investment holding companies, except banks
Pr: John Shea
**Pr:* Robert Chaloner

D-U-N-S 80-858-7380 IMP
CHRISTENSEN ENTERPRISES INC
GATOR TIRE
333 Thorpe Rd, Orlando, FL 32824-8136
Tel (407) 830-6401 *Founded/Ownrshp* 1964
Sales 95.8MM[E] *EMP* 247
SIC 5531 7538 7532 Automotive tires; General automotive repair shops; Top & body repair & paint shops
Pr: Frederick Christensen
Store Mgr: Tom Reed

CHRISTENSEN FAMILY FARMS
See CHRISTENSEN FARMS & FEEDLOTS INC

D-U-N-S 87-713-3033
CHRISTENSEN FARMS & FEEDLOTS INC
CHRISTENSEN FAMILY FARMS
23971 County Road 10, Sleepy Eye, MN 56085-4701
Tel (507) 794-5310 *Founded/Ownrshp* 1991
Sales 445.0MM[E] *EMP* 1,000
SIC 0213 Hog feedlot
CEO: Glenn Stolt
**VP:* Glen Christensen
Adv Bd Mbr: Randall Stoecker
Dir IT: Amy Nlw
IT Man: Jan Tollefson
Mktg Dir: Ron Schoo

D-U-N-S 11-374-2670
CHRISTENSEN FUND
487 Bryant St, San Francisco, CA 94107-1316
Tel (415) 644-0135 *Founded/Ownrshp* 1957
Sales 151.5MM *EMP* 11
SIC 8699 Charitable organization
Pr: C Diane Christensen
VP: Carmen Christensen
VP: Karen Christensen
**Ex Dir:* Kenith Wilson

D-U-N-S 11-302-4954 EXP
CHRISTIAN AID MINISTRIES
GOOD SAMARITAN, THE
4464 State Route 39, Millersburg, OH 44654-9677
Tel (330) 893-2428 *Founded/Ownrshp* 1981
Sales 106.4MM *EMP* 228
Accts Lb Payne White And Schmutz Cpa
SIC 8322 5999 Individual & family services; Disaster service; Religious goods
Pr: David N Troyer
**Prin:* Paul Weaver

D-U-N-S 87-475-7362
CHRISTIAN AID MINISTRIES
(*Suby of* GOOD SAMARITAN) ★
4464 State Rte 39 E, Berlin, OH 44610
Tel (330) 893-2428 *Founded/Ownrshp* 1986
Sales 156.6MM *EMP* 25
Accts Byerley & Payne Cpa S
SIC 8661 5999 5947 Religious organizations; Religious goods; Gift baskets

D-U-N-S 04-817-5442
CHRISTIAN AND MISSIONARY ALLIANCE FOUNDATION INC
SHELL POINT VILLAGE
15101 Shell Point Blvd, Fort Myers, FL 33908-1694
Tel (239) 466-1111 *Founded/Ownrshp* 1967
Sales 103.0MM *EMP* 750
Accts Bkd Llp Fort Myers Fl
SIC 6513 8051 8059 Retirement hotel operation; Skilled nursing care facilities; Personal care home, with health care
Ch: Mark T Ofarrell
**Pr:* Peter Dys
**Treas:* John W Davidson
Sfty Mgr: Monica Lindewirth

D-U-N-S 05-583-1457
CHRISTIAN APPALACHIAN PROJECT INC
6550 S Ky Route 321, Hagerhill, KY 41222-8613
Tel (606) 789-9791 *Founded/Ownrshp* 1964
Sales 84.7MM *EMP* 185
Accts Dean Dorton Allen Ford Pllc L
SIC 8322 Individual & family services
Pr: Guy Adams
**Treas:* Greg Mink

D-U-N-S 79-040-6334
CHRISTIAN BLIND MISSION INTERNATIONAL INC
228 Adley Way, Greenville, SC 29607-6511
Tel (864) 239-0065 *Founded/Ownrshp* 1976
Sales 146.5MM *EMP* 8
Accts Martin Smith & Company Cpas Pa
SIC 8661 Religious organizations
CEO: Caryl Garcia

D-U-N-S 00-377-2563
CHRISTIAN BROADCASTING NETWORK INC
700 CLUB
977 Centerville Tpke, Virginia Beach, VA 23463-1001
Tel (757) 226-3030 *Founded/Ownrshp* 1960
Sales 293.8MM *EMP* 941
Accts Lb Kpmg Llp Mc Lean Va
SIC 8661 4833 4832 5999 4724 Religious organizations; Television broadcasting stations; Religious; Religious goods; Travel agencies
Ch: Pat Robertson
**CEO:* Gordon Robertson
VP: Barbara Ritter
VP: Michael Stonecypher
IT Man: Edwin Arcceo
Netwrk Eng: Michael Hoke
Opers Mgr: Sheryl Ford
Opers Mgr: Mark Nowak
VP Mktg: John Turver
Board of Directors: Harald Bredesen, Paul A Holcombe Jr, William L McConkey, Joel D Tucciarone

D-U-N-S 96-649-2634
CHRISTIAN BROTHERS EMPLOYEE BENEFIT TRUST
1205 Windham Pkwy, Romeoville, IL 60446-1672
Tel (630) 378-2900 *Founded/Ownrshp* 2011
Sales NA *EMP* 2
Accts Plante & Moran Pllc Chicago
SIC 6411 Insurance agents, brokers & service
CEO: Michael Quirk

D-U-N-S 17-787-8097
CHRISTIAN BROTHERS INVESTMENT SERVICES INC
RELIGIOUS COMMUNITIES TRUST
20 N Wacker Dr Ste 2000, Chicago, IL 60606-3002
Tel (312) 526-3343 *Founded/Ownrshp* 1981
Sales 272.1MM *EMP* 45
SIC 6282 Investment advisory service
Pr: Michael W O'Hern
**Pr:* Brother O'Hearn
**Chf Inves:* John W Geissinger
VP: James R Grant Jr
VP: Frank Haines
Mktg Dir: Robert Stelben

CHRISTIAN COUNTY PUB SCHOOLS
See CHRISTIAN COUNTY SCHOOL DISTRICT FINANCE CORP

D-U-N-S 07-967-4529
CHRISTIAN COUNTY SCHOOL DISTRICT FINANCE CORP (KY)
CHRISTIAN COUNTY PUB SCHOOLS
200 Glass Ave, Hopkinsville, KY 42240-2471
Tel (270) 887-7000 *Founded/Ownrshp* 1989, 1930
Sales 75.5MM[E] *EMP* 1,600
SIC 8211 Public elementary & secondary schools
**Pr:* Barry Cornelius
**Treas:* Rim Watson
**VP:* Sheila Cottrell
MIS Dir: Tracey Pelletier
Pr Dir: Heather Lancaster
HC Dir: Brad Hawkins

D-U-N-S 00-441-4983 IMP/EXP
■ CHRISTIAN HARPERCOLLINS PUBLISHING INC (TN)
(*Suby of* WILLIAM MORROW PUBLISHING) ★
501 Nelson Pl, Nashville, TN 37214-3600
Tel (615) 889-9000 *Founded/Ownrshp* 1961, 2012
Sales 133.4MM[E] *EMP* 493
SIC 2731 Books: publishing only
Pr: Mark Schoenwald
**CFO:* Stuart Bitting
VP: Pamela Clements
VP: Brian Hampton
IT Man: Scott Gibbs
**Genl Couns:* Frank Wentworth

D-U-N-S 78-570-8751
CHRISTIAN HEALTHCARE MINISTRIES INC
127 Hazelwood Ave, Barberton, OH 44203-1316
Tel (330) 848-1511 *Founded/Ownrshp* 1961
Sales 85.1MM *EMP* 40
Accts Bruner Cox Llp Akron Oh
SIC 8011 Offices & clinics of medical doctors
Ex Dir: Howard Russell
**CFO:* Roger Kittelson

D-U-N-S 96-527-1872
CHRISTIAN HEALTHCARE MINISTRIES INC
127 Hazelwood Ave, Barberton, OH 44203-1316
Tel (800) 791-6225 *Founded/Ownrshp* 2010
Sales 85.1MM *EMP* 1[E]
Accts Bruner-Cox Llp Akron Ohio
SIC 8661 Religious organizations
Pr: Howard S Russell

D-U-N-S 12-148-5820
CHRISTIAN HEALTHCARE OF MISSOURI INC
CORNERSTONE HEALTH CARE
5305 W Village Pkwy # 12, Rogers, AR 72758-8102
Tel (479) 464-0200 *Founded/Ownrshp* 1999
Sales 44.1MM[E] *EMP* 1,358
SIC 8059 Nursing home, except skilled & intermediate care facility
Pr: Alan Kilgore

D-U-N-S 07-561-2697
CHRISTIAN HOMES INC
CHRISTIAN VILLAGE
200 N Postville Dr, Lincoln, IL 62656-1978
Tel (217) 732-9651 *Founded/Ownrshp* 1962

Sales 118.7MM^E *EMP* 2,200
SIC 8052 8051 Intermediate care facilities; Skilled nursing care facilities
Pr: Timothy Phillippe
**Ch Bd:* Robert Crosby
**V Ch:* Dick Hart
CFO: Susan McGee
Bd of Dir: Randy Clark
Bd of Dir: Amy Hanson
VP: Linda Biondo
**VP:* Jeff Hill
VP: Jeff Hills
**VP:* Susan McGhee
Exec: Debby Chaligoj
Exec: Richard Hart
Exec: Jane Ingram
Exec: Larry Kuester

D-U-N-S 06-855-3163
CHRISTIAN HOSPITAL NORTHEAST - NORTHWEST (MO)
11133 Dunn Rd, Saint Louis, MO 63136-6163
Tel (314) 355-2300 *Founded/Ownrshp* 1903
Sales 239.2MM *EMP* 2,493
SIC 8062 8322 General medical & surgical hospitals; Individual & family services
Pr: Ronald McMullen
**Pr:* Paul Macek
**VP:* Jennifer Cortia
**VP:* Bryan Hartwick
**VP:* Sebastian Rueckert
Dir Rx: Nancy Konieczny
Dir Pat Ac: Mary Cody
Doctor: Carol Hemker

D-U-N-S 15-044-3133
CHRISTIAN HOSPITAL NORTHEAST SURGERY CENTER
(*Suby of* BJC HEALTHCARE) ★
11133 Dunn Rd, Saint Louis, MO 63136-6163
Tel (314) 355-2300 *Founded/Ownrshp* 2000
Sales 78.4MM^E *EMP* 2,500
SIC 8742 8049 5912 Hospital & health services consultant; Food & beverage consultant; Occupational therapist; Drug stores
Pr: Paul Macek
**CFO:* John Katsianis
CIO: Dianne Tattitch

CHRISTIAN J KNOX & ASSOCIATES
See KNOX & ASSOCIATES LLC

CHRISTIAN VILLAGE
See CHRISTIAN HOMES INC

D-U-N-S 07-706-9243
CHRISTIANA CARE HEALTH SERVICES INC
CHRISTIANA HOSPITAL
501 W 14th St, Wilmington, DE 19801-1013
Tel (302) 733-1000 *Founded/Ownrshp* 1985
Sales 1.2MMM^E *EMP* 8,800
SIC 8062 General medical & surgical hospitals
Pr: Robert Laskowski
**Pr:* Janice Nevins
**Sec:* Howard Cohen
**Ex VP:* Gary Ferguson
**Sr VP:* Sharon Anderson
**Sr VP:* Rosa M Colon-Kolacko
**Sr VP:* Thomas L Corrigan
**Sr VP:* Alan S Greenglass
**VP:* Richard Ellis
VP: Michelle Shiavoni
VP: Donna Swain

D-U-N-S 18-121-2226
CHRISTIANA CARE HEALTH SYSTEM INC
CHRISTIANA HOSPITAL
(*Suby of* CHRISTIANA HOSPITAL) ★
200 Hygeia Dr, Newark, DE 19713-2049
Tel (302) 733-1000 *Founded/Ownrshp* 1998
Sales 526.0MM^E *EMP* 8,500
SIC 8741 Hospital management
Pr: Robert Laskowski MD
**Chf Mktg O:* Janice E Nevin
**Sr VP:* Buddy Elmore
Sr VP: James Newman
VP: Rosa Colon-Kolacko
VP: Janice Nevin
Mng Dir: Alfred A Fletcher
Genl Mgr: John Lednum
CIO: Randy Gaboriault
Obsttrcn: Richard Derman
Doctor: Damian Andrisani

CHRISTIANA HOSPITAL
See CHRISTIANA CARE HEALTH SERVICES INC

CHRISTIANA HOSPITAL
See CHRISTIANA CARE HEALTH SYSTEM INC

D-U-N-S 02-500-8558
CHRISTIE CLINIC LLC (IL)
101 W University Ave, Champaign, IL 61820-3981
Tel (217) 366-1200 *Founded/Ownrshp* 1929
Sales 110.8MM^E *EMP* 860
SIC 8011 Clinic, operated by physicians
CEO: Alan Gleghorn
Ex Dir: Gary Wackerlin
Ex Dir: Mark Wiener
Off Mgr: Sarah Winger
MIS Dir: Bill Lane
Nutrtnst: Jane Valentine
Doctor: Samuel Feinberg
Doctor: Dolores Fernandez
Doctor: Shawn Love
Doctor: Chris Schmidt
Doctor: Salman Sheikh

D-U-N-S 13-845-8125
CHRISTIE DIGITAL SYSTEMS INC
(*Suby of* USHIO INC.)
10550 Camden Dr, Cypress, CA 90630-4600
Tel (714) 236-8610 *Founded/Ownrshp* 1999
Sales 136.4MM^E *EMP* 210^E
SIC 3861 6719 Projectors, still or motion picture, silent or sound; Investment holding companies, except banks
Pr: Rex Balz
Exec: Anna Escudero
IT Man: Josh Kolbeck
Sfty Mgr: Pam Lothman
VP Sls: Craig Shoulder
Sls Dir: Simon Smith
Manager: Sean Hoey
Manager: Mark Ouwerkerk
Sls Mgr: Matt Curry
Snr Mgr: Lewis Sorensen

D-U-N-S 12-712-9380 IMP/EXP
CHRISTIE DIGITAL SYSTEMS USA INC
(*Suby of* CHRISTIE DIGITAL SYSTEMS INC) ★
10550 Camden Dr, Cypress, CA 90630-4600
Tel (714) 527-7056 *Founded/Ownrshp* 2007
Sales 136.4MM^E *EMP* 210^E
SIC 5043 Projection apparatus, motion picture & slide
Pr: Jack Kline
Ex VP: Clark Williams
VP: Susie Beiersdorf
VP: Kathryn Cress
VP: Pam Preston
Software D: Stuart Macdonald
Software D: Steve McFadden
Software D: Jason Parachoniak

D-U-N-S 08-521-2348
CHRISTIES INC
(*Suby of* CHRISTIE'S INTERNATIONAL PLC)
20 Rockefeller Plz, New York, NY 10020
Tel (212) 636-2000 *Founded/Ownrshp* 1997
Sales 144.2MM^E *EMP* 651
SIC 7389

D-U-N-S 10-381-0891
CHRISTINA SCHOOL DISTRICT
600 N Lombard St, Wilmington, DE 19801-4429
Tel (302) 552-2600 *Founded/Ownrshp* 1981
Sales 147.5MM^E *EMP* 2,416
SIC 8211 Elementary & secondary schools
**Pr:* David Resler
**VP:* Frederick Polaski
Genl Mgr: Robert Silber
Genl Mgr: Cindy Wallace

D-U-N-S 00-696-0041
CHRISTMAN CO (MI)
208 N Capitol Ave Fl 4, Lansing, MI 48933-1357
Tel (517) 482-1488 *Founded/Ownrshp* 1894, 1933
Sales 140.1MM^E *EMP* 400
SIC 8741 1542 1541 1629 Construction management; School building construction; Hospital construction; Industrial buildings & warehouses; Waste water & sewage treatment plant construction
Pr: Steven F Roznowski
Ex VP: John O'Toole
**Ex VP:* Jay H Smith
**Sr VP:* James M Cash
**Sr VP:* Steven J Frederickson
**VP:* John A Holmstrom
**VP:* Scott J Jones
VP: Ken Norton
**VP:* John M O'Toole
**VP:* Ronald D Staley
Exec: Tom Whitmore
Dir Bus: Amy Baumer

CHRISTMAS MOUNTAIN VILLAGE
See DELLONA ENTERPRISES INC

D-U-N-S 05-346-3998 IMP
■ **CHRISTMAS TREE SHOPS INC** (MA)
(*Suby of* BED BATH & BEYOND INC) ★
650 Liberty Ave, Union, NJ 07083-8107
Tel (908) 688-0888 *Founded/Ownrshp* 1961, 2003
Sales 512.1MM^E *EMP* 3,200
SIC 5331 Variety stores
Pr: Charles G Bilezikian
Pr: Danny Courtier
**Pr:* Todd Johnson
**Treas:* Doreen Bilezikian
**Treas:* Eugene A Castagna
VP: Erik Dervalk
VP: Mike Honeynan
**VP:* Ed Kopil
Store Mgr: Christopher Gall
CIO: Richard Fagan
DP Dir: Richard Brown

D-U-N-S 15-758-5878 IMP/EXP
▲ **CHRISTOPHER & BANKS CORP**
2400 Xenium Ln N, Plymouth, MN 55441-8777
Tel (763) 551-5000 *Founded/Ownrshp* 1956
Sales 383.8MM *EMP* 4,355
Tkr Sym CBK *Exch* NYS
SIC 5621 5632 5961 Ready-to-wear apparel, women's; Apparel accessories; Women's apparel, mail order
Pr: Luann Via
**Ch Bd:* Lisa W Wardell
COO: Peter G Michielutti
Sr VP: Monica L Dahl
Sr VP: Luke R Komarek
Sr VP: Michelle L Rice
Sr VP: Cindy J Stemper
VP: Cindy Stemper
VP: Marc A Ungerman
Site Mgr: Michelle Barbrie
Site Mgr: Amy Dewey
Board of Directors: Jonathan Duskin, Seth R Johnson, Kent A Kleeberger, William F Sharpe III, Laura A Weil

D-U-N-S 02-287-9167 IMP
■ **CHRISTOPHER & BANKS INC**
(*Suby of* CHRISTOPHER & BANKS CORP) ★
2400 Xenium Ln N, Plymouth, MN 55441-8777
Tel (763) 551-5000 *Founded/Ownrshp* 1992
Sales 564.0MM^E *EMP* 6,400
SIC 5621 Ready-to-wear apparel, women's
CEO: Luann Via
Pr: Paul Wente
**COO:* Peter G Michielutti
**CFO:* Rodney Carter
**Chf Cred:* Luke Komarek
**Chf Mktg O:* Susan Connell
**Sr VP:* Monica Dahl
**Sr VP:* Gary Thompson
VP: Brooke Asher
VP: Kim Decker
VP: Nancy C Sott
VP: Barb Spilane

D-U-N-S 87-933-0801
CHRISTOPHER NEWPORT UNIVERSITY
(*Suby of* STATE COUNCIL OF HIGHER EDUCATION FOR VIRGINIA) ★
1 Avenue Of The Arts, Newport News, VA 23606-3072
Tel (757) 594-7000 *Founded/Ownrshp* 1977
Sales 111.6MM^E *EMP* 767
SIC 8221 Colleges universities & professional schools
Pr: Paul S Trible
Ofcr: Lourdes Roach
**VP:* William Brauer
**VP:* Cynthia Perry
VP: Adelia P Thompson
Exec: Nannette Bouknight
Comm Dir: Bruce Bronstein
Off Mgr: Kim Carson
Off Mgr: Laila Shishineh

D-U-N-S 05-563-5940 IMP
CHRISTOPHER RANCH LLC
305 Bloomfield Ave, Gilroy, CA 95020-9565
Tel (408) 847-1100 *Founded/Ownrshp* 1953
Sales 114.0MM^E *EMP* 200
SIC 0139 0175 Herb or spice farm; Cherry orchard
CIO: Corey Tennant

CHRISTOPHERSON BUSINESS TRAVEL
See CB TRAVEL CORP

D-U-N-S 07-136-7887
CHRISTUS HEALTH (TX)
919 Hidden Rdg, Irving, TX 75038-3813
Tel (469) 282-2000 *Founded/Ownrshp* 1998
Sales 673.4MM *EMP* 25,000
Accts Ernst & Young Us Llp Fort Wor
SIC 8062 8051 General medical & surgical hospitals; Skilled nursing care facilities
CEO: Ernie Sadau
**Ch Bd:* Catherine Dulle
COO: Ernie Sadau
CFO: Jay Harron
CFO: Jay Herrin
**CFO:* Jay Herron
**Ch:* Richard L Clarke
Bd of Dir: Mark Greenway
Chf Mktg O: Shanna Clark
Ofcr: Janet Dubois
**Sr VP:* George Conklin
**Sr VP:* Mary T Lynch
**Sr VP:* Peter Maddox
**Sr VP:* Linda McClung
**Sr VP:* Ernie W Sadau
VP: David Boggan
VP: Karen Bonner
VP: Michael Davis
VP: Gerard F Heeley
VP: Harveyanne Leimbrook
VP: Jeff Puckett

D-U-N-S 07-908-7007
CHRISTUS HEALTH
U.S. FAMILY HEALTH PLAN
(*Suby of* CHRISTUS HEALTH) ★
919 Hidden Rdg, Irving, TX 75038-3813
Tel (281) 936-6000 *Founded/Ownrshp* 1998
Sales 129.3MM^E *EMP* 1^E
SIC 8062 General medical & surgical hospitals
CEO: Ernie Sadau
VP: Marty Margetts
Ex Dir: Marshall Bolyard
Prgrm Mgr: Steve Calvo
Admn Mgr: Karen Morris
CTO: Robert Fox
VP Opers: Joseph Barcie

D-U-N-S 11-886-9036
CHRISTUS HEALTH ARK-LA-TEX
CHRISTUS SAINT MICHAEL HEALTH SYSTEM
(*Suby of* CHRISTUS HEALTH) ★
2600 Saint Michael Dr, Texarkana, TX 75503-5220
Tel (903) 614-1000 *Founded/Ownrshp* 1994
Sales 259.5MM *EMP* 1,800
Accts Ernst & Young Us Llp Indianap
SIC 8062 General medical & surgical hospitals
Pr: Chris Karam
**Treas:* Shawn Barnett
**VP:* Glen Boles
**VP:* John Graham
**VP:* Pam Kennedy
**VP:* Jason Rounds

D-U-N-S 04-342-9182
CHRISTUS HEALTH CENTRAL LOUISIANA (LA)
CHRISTUS ST FRNCES CBRINI HOSP
3330 Masonic Dr, Alexandria, LA 71301-3841
Tel (318) 487-1122 *Founded/Ownrshp* 1950
Sales 236.9MM *EMP* 2,000^E
SIC 8062 General medical & surgical hospitals
CEO: Stephen Wright
COO: Gene Woods
CFO: Deborah White
Off Mgr: Candace Wesley
IT Man: Pragnesh Patel
Pathlgst: Irene I Manlapaz
Obsttrcn: Barry Bieber
Obsttrcn: Gordon Bowers
Obsttrcn: Amanda Ingalls
Obsttrcn: Jaime Middleton
Obsttrcn: Edan Moran

D-U-N-S 13-390-4057
CHRISTUS HEALTH GULF COAST
CHRISTUS ST JOHN HOSPITAL
18300 Saint John Dr, Houston, TX 77058-6302
Tel (281) 333-5503 *Founded/Ownrshp* 1991
Sales 112.2MM *EMP* 754^E
SIC 8062 General medical & surgical hospitals
Pr: Tom Royer
**CEO:* Ernie Sadau
**CEO:* Nancy Tittman
**CFO:* David Witt
Dir Lab: Rebecca Simon
Dir Rx: Thournam Tren
Off Mgr: Linda Wickam
QA Dir: Janet Dubois
Dir IT: Pat Hale
IT Man: Steve Martin
Psych: Jose Ballesteros

D-U-N-S 16-839-8704
CHRISTUS HEALTH GULF COAST
CHRISTUS SAINT CATHERINE HOSPITAL
(*Suby of* CHRISTUS HEALTH) ★
919 Hidden Rdg, Irving, TX 75038-3813
Tel (281) 599-5700 *Founded/Ownrshp* 2003
Sales 148.4MM *EMP* 2,800
SIC 8062 General medical & surgical hospitals
CEO: Ernie Sadau
**CFO:* Buddy Whiddon
Admn Mgr: Karen Morris
Phys Thrpy: Kim Granhaug

D-U-N-S 14-004-7007
CHRISTUS HEALTH NORTHERN LOUISIANA
CHRISTUS SCHUMPER HEALTH SYSTE
1 Saint Mary Pl, Shreveport, LA 71101-4343
Tel (318) 681-4500 *Founded/Ownrshp* 1975
Sales 195.2MM *EMP* 1,900
Accts Ernst & Young Us Llp Houston
SIC 8069 Eye, ear, nose & throat hospital
Pr: Stephen F Wright
CFO: Russell Touchet
**Treas:* Scott Merryman
MIS Dir: Jose Gonzalez
Sls&Mrk Ex: Nancy Dugas
Doctor: Jim Goodman
Pharmcst: Laura Dial
Pharmcst: Gary Folks

D-U-N-S 04-280-5056
CHRISTUS HEALTH SOUTHEAST TEXAS
CHRISTUS HOSPITAL ST MARY
(*Suby of* CHRISTUS HEALTH) ★
3600 Gates Blvd, Port Arthur, TX 77642-3858
Tel (409) 985-7431 *Founded/Ownrshp* 1984
Sales 11.3MM^E *EMP* 1,100
SIC 8062 General medical & surgical hospitals
CEO: Ellen Jones
COO: Kevin Harmon
**CFO:* Bill Hecht
VP: Betty Chenevert
VP: Tim Wilson
Mktg Mgr: Shana Briggs
Opthamlgy: Asad S Abba
Opthamlgy: Joann Hensel
Opthamlgy: Jerry S Lehmann
Opthamlgy: Richard A Levcy
Opthamlgy: John W Miller

D-U-N-S 07-844-8313
CHRISTUS HEALTH SOUTHEAST TEXAS
CHRISTUS ST. ELIZABETH
(*Suby of* CHRISTUS HEALTH) ★
2830 Calder St, Beaumont, TX 77702-1809
Tel (409) 892-7171 *Founded/Ownrshp* 1896
Sales 25.7MM^E *EMP* 2,500^E
SIC 8062 General medical & surgical hospitals
CEO: Ellen Jones
Chf Rad: Daniel Roubein
Chf Rad: Daniel Roubin
COO: Mike Pierce
Dir Rad: Elizabeth Blanchette
Mng Dir: Daniel Karnicki
Genl Mgr: Bene Rutman
Dir IT: Anita Johnson
Sls&Mrk Ex: Heather Bowler
Mktg Mgr: Mary Edwards
Psych: Dia Abochamh

D-U-N-S 07-711-5897
CHRISTUS HEALTH SOUTHWESTERN LOUISIANA
CHRISTUS ST PATRICK HOSPITAL
524 Dctor Mchael Dbkey Dr, Lake Charles, LA 70601-5725
Tel (337) 436-2511 *Founded/Ownrshp* 1921
Sales 132.4MM *EMP* 1,018^E
Accts Ernst & Young Us Llp Fort Wor
SIC 8062 General medical & surgical hospitals
Pr: Stephen F Wright
**Pr:* Ellen Jones
COO: Mike McEachern
**Treas:* Scott Merryman
Chf Mktg O: Mary Rohnke
Dir Lab: Dan Fruge
Dir Rad: David Boudreaux
Dir Sec: Kevin Semien
Sls&Mrk Ex: Karen Stubblefield
Pathlgst: Paula Eapen
HC Dir: Lake Charles

CHRISTUS HOSPITAL ST MARY
See CHRISTUS HEALTH SOUTHEAST TEXAS

CHRISTUS PROVIDER NETWORK
See CH WILKINSON PHYSICIAN NETWORK

CHRISTUS SAINT CATHERINE HOSPITAL
See CHRISTUS HEALTH GULF COAST

CHRISTUS SAINT MICHAEL HEALTH SYSTEM
See CHRISTUS HEALTH ARK-LA-TEX

CHRISTUS SAINT VINCENT
See ST VINCENT HOSPITAL

CHRISTUS SANTA ROSA HEALTH
See CHRISTUS SANTA ROSA HOME CARE

D-U-N-S 13-377-2277
CHRISTUS SANTA ROSA HEALTH CARE CORP
CHILDRENS HOSPITAL SAN ANTONIO
333 N Santa Rosa St, San Antonio, TX 78207-3108
Tel (210) 704-2011 *Founded/Ownrshp* 1980
Sales 635.5MM *EMP* 3,700
Accts Ernst & Young Us Llp Indianap
SIC 8063 8069 Psychiatric hospitals; Specialty hospitals, except psychiatric
Pr: Don Beeler
**Pr:* Patrick B Carrier
**COO:* Renato Baciarelli
**CFO:* Kenneth Kolb

Ex Dir: James Houser
CIO: John Amos
Psych: Robert Duran
Psych: Debra Vasquez
Psych: Kenneth W Washburn
Pathlgst: David N Hekes
Pathlgst: William W Hinchey

D-U-N-S 07-692-7743
CHRISTUS SANTA ROSA HOME CARE
CHRISTUS SANTA ROSA HEALTH
(*Suby of* CHILDRENS HOSPITAL SAN ANTONIO) ★
4241 Woodcock Dr Ste A100, San Antonio, TX 78228-1337
Tel (210) 704-2011 *Founded/Ownrshp* 1998
Sales 87.6MM *EMP* 50
SIC 7389 Personal service agents, brokers & bureaus
COO: Dave Bertauski

CHRISTUS SCHUMPER HEALTH SYSTE
See CHRISTUS HEALTH NORTHERN LOUISIANA

D-U-N-S 05-511-8137
CHRISTUS SPOHN HEALTH SYSTEM CORP
SPOHN MEMORIAL HOSPITAL
(*Suby of* CHRISTUS HEALTH) ★
1702 Santa Fe St, Corpus Christi, TX 78404-1857
Tel (361) 881-3000 *Founded/Ownrshp* 1965
Sales 17.3MM^E *EMP* 1,689^E
SIC 8062 Hospital, AMA approved residency
Pr: Bruce Holestwene
Chf Rad: Chandra S Katragadda
COO: Tony Heep
CFO: Ferdinand Gaenzel
**CFO:* Sandra Williams
VP: Linda Cadigan
Secur Mgr: Christins Hassen
Psych: Crystal Campos
Psych: Gerald Kizerian
Psych: Jerome A Leesang
Psych: Anthony Montez

CHRISTUS ST. ELIZABETH
See CHRISTUS HEALTH SOUTHEAST TEXAS

CHRISTUS ST FRNCES CBRINI HOSP
See CHRISTUS HEALTH CENTRAL LOUISIANA

CHRISTUS ST JOHN HOSPITAL
See CHRISTUS HEALTH GULF COAST

CHRISTUS ST PATRICK HOSPITAL
See CHRISTUS HEALTH SOUTHWESTERN LOUISIANA

D-U-N-S 80-138-9698
CHRISTUS TRINITY MOTHER FRANCES HEALTH SYSTEM
TRINI MOTH FRAN HOSP AND CLIN
800 E Dawson St, Tyler, TX 75701-2036
Tel (903) 593-8441 *Founded/Ownrshp* 2007
Sales 752.1MM *EMP* 4,000^E
Accts Bkd Llp Dallas Texas
SIC 8062 Hospital, affiliated with AMA residency
Pr: Jay Lindsay Bradley
Dir Vol: Annette Rios
Ch Bd: Daryl Pritchard
CFO: Bill Bellefant
CFO: William Bellenfant
Sr VP: Tom Wilken
VP: Jeffrey Hyde
Chf Nrs Of: Jean Coleman
**Prin:* Brandon E Crim
**Prin:* Beth Moore
**Prin:* Randy Tucker Murff

D-U-N-S 19-382-3408 IMP
■ **CHROMALLOY COMPONENT SERVICES INC**
(*Suby of* GEMOCO DIVISION) ★
303 Industrial Park Rd, San Antonio, TX 78226-1838
Tel (210) 331-2300 *Founded/Ownrshp* 2012
Sales 153.7MM^E *EMP* 1,300
SIC 7699 3724 Industrial equipment services; Engine repair & replacement, non-automotive; Aircraft engines & engine parts
Ch Bd: Martin Weinstein
**Pr:* Greg Baladjanian
**COO:* Chris Richardson
**CFO:* Kenneth Binder
CFO: Robert Brown
VP: James Faris
Genl Mgr: Traci Johnson
Sls Dir: Franco Amendola

D-U-N-S 01-195-7438 IMP
■ **CHROMALLOY GAS TURBINE LLC**
GEMOCO DIVISION
(*Suby of* KOLLSMAN INSTRUMENT DIVISION) ★
3999 Rca Blvd, Palm Beach Gardens, FL 33410-4219
Tel (561) 935-3571 *Founded/Ownrshp* 1986
Sales 579.1MM^E *EMP* 1,300
SIC 3724 7699 4581 3764 3769 3533 Aircraft engines & engine parts; Engine mount parts, aircraft; Engine repair & replacement, non-automotive; Aircraft servicing & repairing; Guided missile & space vehicle propulsion unit parts; Propulsion units for guided missiles & space vehicles; Guided missile & space vehicle parts & auxiliary equipment; Guided missile & space vehicle parts & aux eqpt, rsch & dev; Oil & gas field machinery
VP: Andrea Colombo
VP: James Thibodeau
Prgrm Mgr: Ivelisse Boerenko
Prgrm Mgr: James Whitton
Genl Mgr: Bob Francis
Genl Mgr: Mike Harris
Genl Mgr: Jeff Johnson
Genl Mgr: Mike Kieky
QA Dir: Matthew Emmons
IT Man: Harvey Freeman
QC Dir: Keith Kolomichuk

D-U-N-S 10-067-3115 IMP/EXP
CHROMALOX INC
OGDEN
(*Suby of* IRVING PLACE CAPITAL LLC) ★
103 Gamma Dr Ste 2, Pittsburgh, PA 15238-2981
Tel (412) 967-3800 *Founded/Ownrshp* 1915
Sales 394.5MM^E *EMP* 1,250
SIC 3567 Heating units & devices, industrial: electric
CEO: Scott Dysert
**Pr:* Tony Castor
**CFO:* Edward Cumberledge
**Ch:* Steve Brian
Treas: Joe Mangieri
**VP:* Robert Mihalco
Plnt Mgr: Felix Garza
VP Mktg: Bill Kennedy
VP Mktg: Mike Schulz
VP Sls: Karen Judkins
VP Sls: William Kennedy

D-U-N-S 01-408-5616
CHRONIC DISEASE FUND
6900 Dallas Pkwy Ste 200, Plano, TX 75024-7126
Tel (972) 608-7175 *Founded/Ownrshp* 2011
Sales 250.2MM *EMP* 24^E
SIC 7363 Medical help service
Prin: Michael Banigan

D-U-N-S 93-122-4153
CHRYSALIS PACKAGING AND ASSEMBLY CORP
CHRYSPAC
130 W Edger Avenu Sut, Milwaukee, WI 53207
Tel (414) 744-8550 *Founded/Ownrshp* 1999
Sales 79.1MM^E *EMP* 1,540
SIC 7389 Packaging & labeling services
Pr: William P Beckett
**Treas:* Kenneth A Mackenzie
**VP:* Donna Firman
**VP:* Dave Schrader
Admn Mgr: Robyn Brenson

CHRYSLER JEEP DDGE CY MCKINNEY
See MCKINNEY DODGE INC

CHRYSPAC
See CHRYSALIS PACKAGING AND ASSEMBLY CORP

CHS
See EASTERN FARMERS COOPERATIVE

D-U-N-S 14-835-7759 EXP
CHS ACQUISITION CORP
CHICAGO HEIGHTS STEEL
211 E Main St, Chicago Heights, IL 60411-4270
Tel (708) 756-5648 *Founded/Ownrshp* 1985
Sales 87.4MM^E *EMP* 250
SIC 3312 Fence posts, iron & steel; Structural shapes & pilings, steel
Pr: Bradley R Corral
**Sec:* Richard R Gollner

CHS CAPITAL
See CHS PRIVATE EQUITY V LP

D-U-N-S 60-400-6692 IMP/EXP
CHS CAPITAL LLC
300 N La Salle Dr # 4925, Chicago, IL 60654-3485
Tel (312) 876-1840 *Founded/Ownrshp* 1997
Sales 94.7MM^E *EMP* 539
SIC 5084 Hydraulic systems equipment & supplies
**Pt:* Andrew W Code
**Pt:* Thomas J Formolo
**Pt:* Marcus J George
**Pt:* Peter Gotsch
**Pt:* Daniel J Hennessy
**Pt:* Richard A Lobo
VP: Kevin Bochenek
**VP:* Traci G Breen
**VP:* Ronelle Deshazer
VP: Krista Hatcher
VP: Cameron Smith

D-U-N-S 79-436-2251
CHS COOPERATIVES
TEMCO
5500 Cenex Dr Ste 1, Inver Grove Heights, MN 55077-1721
Tel (651) 355-6000 *Founded/Ownrshp* 1992
Sales 132.6MM^E *EMP* 1,000
SIC 5211 Insulation & energy conservation products
CEO: Carl Casale
**CFO:* John Schmidt
**Ex VP:* Shirley Cunningham
**Ex VP:* Jay Debertin
Board of Directors: David Bielenberg

D-U-N-S 00-614-7177
▲ **CHS INC**
5500 Cenex Dr, Inver Grove Heights, MN 55077-1721
Tel (651) 355-6000 *Founded/Ownrshp* 1930
Sales 30.3MMM *EMP* 12,536
Tkr Sym CHSCO *Exch* NGS
SIC 5153 5191 2075 1311 2911 4613 Grains; Soybeans; Corn; Wheat; Fertilizers & agricultural chemicals; Soybean oil mills; Soybean flour & grits; Soybean oil, cake or meal; Crude petroleum production; Natural gas production; Gasoline; Greases, lubricating; Liquefied petroleum gases, LPG; Refined petroleum pipelines
Pr: Carl Casale
**Ch Bd:* David Bielenberg
Pr: Keith Illa
COO: Shirley Cunningham
COO: Jay Debertin
COO: Jay D Debertin
**CFO:* Timothy Skidmore
Sr Cor Off: Rodney Farley
**V Ch Bd:* Curt Eischens
**V Ch Bd:* Steve Fritel
**Ex VP:* Lynden Johnson
**Ex VP:* James Zappa
**Ex VP:* Lisa Zell
Sr VP: Jean Briand
VP: G M Bargefreight
VP: Manuel San Miguel
VP: Curtis Slykhuis
Board of Directors: Greg Kruger, Donald Anthony, Edward Malesich, Clinton J Blew, Perry Meyer, Dennis Carlson, Steve Riegel, Jon Erickson, Daniel Schurr, Mark Farrell, Alan Holm, David Johnsrud, David Kayser, Randy Knecht

D-U-N-S 02-430-2317
CHS INC
CENEX HARVEST STATE
3645 98th Ave Sw, Taylor, ND 58656-9761
Tel (701) 483-6781 *Founded/Ownrshp* 1947
Sales 247.5MM^E *EMP* 125
SIC 5153 5191 Grain elevators; Farm supplies
CEO: Robert S Ryan
**Genl Mgr:* Delane Thom

D-U-N-S 00-714-5956
■ **CHS MCPHERSON REFINERY INC**
N C R A
(*Suby of* CHS INC) ★
2000 S Main St, McPherson, KS 67460-9402
Tel (620) 241-2340 *Founded/Ownrshp* 1943
Sales 4.0MMM *EMP* 700
Accts Pricewaterhousecoopers Llp Mi
SIC 2911 4612 4213 Petroleum refining; Gasoline; Diesel fuels; Oils, fuel; Crude petroleum pipelines; Liquid petroleum transport, non-local
Pr: Carl Casale
**COO:* Shirley Cunningham
**COO:* Jay Debertin
**CFO:* Timothy Skidmore
**Ex VP:* Lisa Zell
VP: Galen Menard
VP: Ronald Schaumburg
Genl Mgr: Judy Lenherr
IT Man: Jason Beckman
Sfty Dirs: Jeff Dees
Opers Mgr: Les Larson

D-U-N-S 78-765-6219
CHS PRIVATE EQUITY V LP
CHS CAPITAL
300 N La Salle Dr # 4925, Chicago, IL 60654-3485
Tel (312) 876-1840 *Founded/Ownrshp* 2006
Sales 641.2MM^E *EMP* 1,150^E
SIC 5085 Glass bottles
Mng Pt: Brian Psimmons
Pt: Thomas J Formolo
Pt: Marcus J George
Pt: David O Hawkins
Pt: Daniel J Hennessy
Pt: Code Hennessy Simmons LLC
VP: Krista Hatcher
VP: Laura L Lester
VP: Jocelyn R Stanley

CHS PROFESSIONAL SERVICES
See CHSPSC

D-U-N-S 96-379-2200
CHS SERVICES INC
992 N Village Ave, Rockville Centre, NY 11570-1002
Tel (516) 705-1935 *Founded/Ownrshp* 2011
Sales 147.1MM *EMP* 1
Accts Pricewaterhousecoopers Llp Ne
SIC 8741 Management services
Prin: Marcy Dunn

D-U-N-S 96-246-8497
■ **CHSPSC**
CHS PROFESSIONAL SERVICES
(*Suby of* COMMUNITY HEALTH SYSTEMS INC) ★
4000 Meridian Blvd, Franklin, TN 37067-6325
Tel (615) 465-7000 *Founded/Ownrshp* 1991
Sales 106.7MM^E *EMP* 718^E
SIC 8062 6321 General medical & surgical hospitals; Health insurance carriers

CHUBB
See FEDERAL INSURANCE CO

CHUBB
See WESTCHESTER FIRE INSURANCE CO INC

CHUBB
See ESIS INC

D-U-N-S 00-167-1411
CHUBB & SON INC
(*Suby of* INA CHUBB HOLDINGS INC) ★
15 Mountainview Rd, Warren, NJ 07059-6795
Tel (908) 903-2000 *Founded/Ownrshp* 2016
Sales NA *EMP* 225
SIC 6399 Deposit insurance
CEO: John D Finnegan
**Pr:* John J Degnan
Pr: Yelena Zeltser
**CFO:* Richard G Spiro
**Treas:* Juliette Amerman
**Treas:* Douglas A Nordstrom
**Treas:* Philip J Sempier
**Ex VP:* Paul J Krump
**Sr VP:* Henry G Gulick
**Sr VP:* John F Kirby Jr
**Sr VP:* Glenn A Montgomery
**VP:* Dino E Robusto
Exec: Ieva Rozgaite

D-U-N-S 80-382-8136
CHUBB AMERICA SERVICE CORP
(*Suby of* LINCOLN FINANCIAL SPORTS INC) ★
1 Granite Pl, Concord, NH 03301-3258
Tel (603) 224-7741 *Founded/Ownrshp* 2008
Sales 56.4MM^E *EMP* 2,314^E
SIC 8741 Management services
Pr: David Stonecipher
Sr VP: Warren L Reynolds

D-U-N-S 80-382-9092
CHUBB CAPITAL CORP
(*Suby of* INA CHUBB HOLDINGS INC) ★
15 Mountainview Rd, Warren, NJ 07059-6795
Tel (908) 903-2000 *Founded/Ownrshp* 2016
Sales NA *EMP* 2,000
SIC 6321 Health insurance carriers
CEO: John Finnegan
**Prin:* John Degman
**Prin:* Tom Motamed

D-U-N-S 04-416-8144
CHUBB CORP (NJ)
15 Mountainview Rd, Warren, NJ 07059-6795
Tel (908) 903-2000 *Founded/Ownrshp* 1967
Sales NA *EMP* 10,200
SIC 6331

D-U-N-S 83-443-6487
CHUBB EXECUTIVE RISK INC
(*Suby of* INA CHUBB HOLDINGS INC) ★
82 Hopmeadow St, Simsbury, CT 06070
Tel (860) 408-2000 *Founded/Ownrshp* 2016
Sales NA *EMP* 481
SIC 6411 Insurance agents, brokers & service
Pr: Stephen J Sills
**Pr:* Robert V Deutsch
COO: John J Degnan
Sr VP: Michele Fincher
VP: Kenneth Goldstein
VP: Louise Van Dyck
Mktg Mgr: Maureen Peruta

D-U-N-S 79-101-8505
CHUBB GROUP HOLDINGS INC
(*Suby of* CHUBB LIMITED)
1133 Ave Of The Americas, New York, NY 10036-6710
Tel (212) 827-4400 *Founded/Ownrshp* 1999
Sales NA *EMP* 7,700^E
SIC 6411 Insurance agents, brokers & service
CEO: Evan G Greenberg
**Treas:* Kenneth Koreyva
**VP:* Brian E Dowd
VP: Stephen M Haney

D-U-N-S 80-912-9294
CHUBB GROUP OF INSURANCE COMPANIES
(*Suby of* INA CHUBB HOLDINGS INC) ★
15 Mountainview Rd, Warren, NJ 07059-6795
Tel (908) 903-2000 *Founded/Ownrshp* 2016
Sales NA *EMP* 216^E
SIC 6331 Fire, marine & casualty insurance
CEO: John D Finnegan
CEO: Jalil Rehman
COO: Greg Arms
Ofcr: William Dornhecker
Ofcr: Rochelle Feine
Ofcr: Ross Grubin
Sr VP: Michael Reicher
VP: Christina Anderson
VP: Debbie Mullikin
QA Dir: Veronica Bolden
IT Man: Glen Horsewood

D-U-N-S 82-989-5171
CHUBB US HOLDING INC
ACE US HOLDINGS, INC.
(*Suby of* ACE LIMITED)
1601 Chestnut St, Philadelphia, PA 19192-0003
Tel (215) 640-1000 *Founded/Ownrshp* 1999
Sales NA *EMP* 4,000
SIC 6411 6331 Insurance agents, brokers & service; Fire, marine & casualty insurance & carriers
CEO: Dominic J Frederico
**CFO:* Robert Jefferson
Ex VP: Ace Snapshot
Sr VP: Bryan Tedford
VP: Patricia Barrett
VP: Patricia Bens
VP: Cynthia Bentley
VP: Paul Cunney
VP: Brian Flynn
VP: Kristi Janicek
VP: Domingos Lopes
VP: Rich Luca
VP: Lori Marino
VP: Joseph McCole
VP: Jon Peeples
VP: Michael Piccolino
VP: Gregg Rentko
VP: Tony Rivera
VP: Michael Schmidt
VP: Brad Sensibar
VP: Stefan Szulc

D-U-N-S 06-768-6147
CHUCK HUTTON CHEVROLET CO (TN)
2471 Mount Moriah Rd, Memphis, TN 38115-1594
Tel (901) 365-9700 *Founded/Ownrshp* 1950, 1973
Sales 100.2MM^E *EMP* 337^E
SIC 5511

D-U-N-S 60-321-1277 IMP
CHUCK LATHAM ASSOCIATES INC
18403 Longs Way Unit 102, Parker, CO 80134-9006
Tel (303) 699-2905 *Founded/Ownrshp* 1989
Sales 229.7MM^E *EMP* 1,000
SIC 5199 Pet supplies
CEO: Chuck Latham
**CFO:* Jeffry Kahler
**VP:* Kathryn Latham

CHUCKY'S COUNTRY STORE
See ALDIN ASSOCIATES LIMITED PARTNERSHIP

CHUGACH
See WOLF CREEK FEDERAL SERVICES INC

D-U-N-S 07-184-4021 IMP
CHUGACH ALASKA CORP
3800 Cntrpint Dr Ste 1200, Anchorage, AK 99503
Tel (907) 563-8866 *Founded/Ownrshp* 1972
Sales 758.4MM *EMP* 4,822
SIC 8744 4959 7361 0851 7373 Base maintenance (providing personnel on continuing basis); Oil spill cleanup; Employment agencies; Forestry services; Value-added resellers, computer systems
CEO: Gabriel Kompkoff
V Ch: Gary P Kompkoff
Ofcr: Melanie Osborne
**Ex VP:* Angela Astle
Dir Risk M: Debbie Conklin
Prgrm Mgr: Phil Demarco
Prgrm Mgr: Chauncey Klingensmith
Prgrm Mgr: David Melvin
Prgrm Mgr: Richard Tessenear
Netwrk Eng: Scott Burgin
Netwrk Eng: John Christian

D-U-N-S 06-093-9349
CHUGACH ELECTRIC
5601 Electron Dr, Anchorage, AK 99518-1081
Tel (907) 563-7494 *Founded/Ownrshp* 2011
Sales 312.5MM *EMP* 90^E
Accts Kpmg Llp Anchorage Ak
SIC 1731 Electrical work

Pr: Bruce Davidson
Opers Mgr: Scott Sanner

D-U-N-S 00-389-9341
CHUGACH ELECTRIC ASSOCIATION INC
5601 Electron Dr, Anchorage, AK 99518-1081
Tel (907) 563-7494 *Founded/Ownrshp* 1948
Sales 216.4MM *EMP* 291
SIC 4911 Electric services
CEO: Bradley W Evans
**Ch Bd:* Janet Reiser
CFO: Sherri Highers
**V Ch Bd:* Susan Reeves
Sr VP: Paul R Risse
Sr VP: Lee D Thibert
VP: Tyler E Andrews
VP: William J Bernier
VP: Lee Thibert
VP: Ronald Vecera
Trfc Dir: Jonathan Skinner
Board of Directors: Sisi Cooper, Harry T Crawford Jr, Bruce Dougherty, James Henderson

D-U-N-S 82-903-0365
CHUGACH FEDERAL SOLUTIONS INC
(*Suby of* CHUGACH GOVERNMENT SOLUTIONS LLC) ★
3800 Cntrpint Dr Ste 1200, Anchorage, AK 99503
Tel (907) 563-8866 *Founded/Ownrshp* 2008
Sales 220.5MM *EMP* 1,153
SIC 1542 Nonresidential construction
CEO: Gabriel Kompkoff
**Pr:* Mel Lynch
**Ex VP:* Angela Astle
**Ex VP:* Gail Forrest
**Ex VP:* Melanie Osborne

D-U-N-S 55-663-7366
CHUGACH GOVERNMENT SERVICES INC
(*Suby of* CHUGACH GOVERNMENT SOLUTIONS LLC) ★
3800 Cntrpint Dr Ste 1200, Anchorage, AK 99503
Tel (907) 563-8866 *Founded/Ownrshp* 2005
Sales 86.7MM *EMP* 1,146
SIC 1542 Nonresidential construction
Pr: Mel Lynch
**Ch Bd:* Sheri D Buretta
**CEO:* Chris Viramontes
VP: Dale Tolleson
Dir IT: Randy Reed
IT Man: Michael Anselmi
IT Man: Angelina Bryant
IT Man: Bev Hansen
IT Man: Brandon Newpher

D-U-N-S 07-882-3398
CHUGACH GOVERNMENT SOLUTIONS LLC
(*Suby of* CHUGACH ALASKA CORP) ★
3800 Cntrpint Dr Ste 1200, Anchorage, AK 99503
Tel (907) 563-8866 *Founded/Ownrshp* 2013
Sales 687.8MM *EMP* 4,300
SIC 6719 Investment holding companies, except banks

D-U-N-S 02-124-1694
CHUKCHANSI GOLD RESORT & CASINO
711 Lucky Ln, Coarsegold, CA 93614-8206
Tel (866) 794-6946 *Founded/Ownrshp* 2010
Sales 46.1MM^E *EMP* 1,400
SIC 7011 Casino hotel
Owner: Richard Williams
CFO: Larry King
Ofcr: Chanel Wright
Genl Mgr: Matt Olin

D-U-N-S 14-863-0176
CHUKCHANSI INDIAN HOUSING AUTHORITY
8080 N Palm Ave Ste 207, Fresno, CA 93711-5797
Tel (559) 370-4141 *Founded/Ownrshp* 1997
Sales NA *EMP* 1,359^E
SIC 9531 Housing authority, non-operating: government
Ex Dir: Reggie Lewis

D-U-N-S 06-615-6274
CHULA VISTA ELEM SCHOOL DISTRICT
84 E J St, Chula Vista, CA 91910-6115
Tel (619) 425-9600 *Founded/Ownrshp* 1892
Sales 145.6MM^E *EMP* 2,500
SIC 8211 Public elementary & secondary schools; Public elementary school; Kindergarten; School board
**Pr:* Larry Cunningham
**CFO:* Susan Fahle
**VP:* Glendora Tremper
IT Man: Ismael Zepeda
Pr Dir: Anthony Millican
Instr Medi: Gloria Ciriza

D-U-N-S 83-613-6721
CHUMASH CASINO RESORT
3400 E Highway 246, Santa Ynez, CA 93460-9405
Tel (805) 686-0855 *Founded/Ownrshp* 1994
Sales 84.0MM^E *EMP* 890^E
SIC 7999 7011 Gambling establishment; Resort hotel
CFO: Carol Clearwater
Exec: John Featherstone
Genl Mgr: Jonathan Gregory
**Genl Mgr:* William Peters
Dir IT: Ed Jara
Dir IT: John Ormond
Dir IT: Peter Succullo
IT Man: Dante Dacanay
IT Man: Kris Rosson
Prd Mgr: Eddie Estave
Mktg Dir: John Blair

CHUNG'S GOURMET FOODS
See CHUNGS PRODUCTS LP

D-U-N-S 61-778-9008 IMP
CHUNGS PRODUCTS LP
CHUNG'S GOURMET FOODS
3907 Dennis St, Houston, TX 77004-2520
Tel (713) 741-2118 *Founded/Ownrshp* 2005
Sales 88.0MM^E *EMP* 130
SIC 5142 2038 Packaged frozen goods; Frozen specialties

D-U-N-S 00-121-1952 IMP/EXP
▲ CHURCH & DWIGHT CO INC
500 Charles Ewing Blvd, Ewing, NJ 08628-3448
Tel (609) 806-1200 *Founded/Ownrshp* 1846
Sales 3.3MMM *EMP* 4,400
Accts Deloitte & Touche Llp Parsip
Tkr Sym CHD *Exch* NYS
SIC 2841 2812 2842 2844 2819 Detergents, synthetic organic or inorganic alkaline; Sodium bicarbonate; Bleaches, household: dry or liquid; Fabric softeners; Deodorants, nonpersonal; Toothpastes or powders, dentifrices; Ammonium compounds, except fertilizers
Pr: Matthew T Farrell
COO: Michael Huston
CFO: Richard A Dierker
Ex VP: Britta B Bomhard
Ex VP: Mark G Conish
Ex VP: Patrick D De Maynadier
Ex VP: Paul A Siracusa
Ex VP: Louis H Tursi Jr
VP: Kenneth S Colbert
VP: Robert Coleman
VP: Zvi Eiref
VP: Steven J Katz
VP: Nowell Lionel
Board of Directors: T Rosie Albright, Bradley C Irwin, Robert D Leblanc, Robert K Shearer, Janet S Vergis, Arthur B Winkleblack

D-U-N-S 00-614-5379
CHURCH MUTUAL INSURANCE CO
3000 Schuster Ln, Merrill, WI 54452-3863
Tel (715) 536-5577 *Founded/Ownrshp* 1897
Sales NA *EMP* 750
Accts Kpmg Llp Milwaukee Wi
SIC 6411 Insurance agents, brokers & service
Pr: Richard V Poirier
COO: Rich Poirier
CFO: Daniel T Vander Heiden
CFO: Jeffrey Steffen
Treas: Herman Vanderberg
Bd of Dir: Robert Buckley
Ex VP: Thomas B Morgan
Sr VP: Randy Brandner
Sr VP: Kevin Root
VP: Christopher Graham
VP: Timothy Householder
VP: Laura Hughes
VP: Richard Huseby
VP: Karen Karow
VP: Patrick Moreland
VP: Timothy J O'Leary
VP: David Springborn

D-U-N-S 00-333-5338
CHURCH OF GOD
2490 Keith St Nw, Cleveland, TN 37311-1317
Tel (423) 472-3361 *Founded/Ownrshp* 1884
Sales 51.6MM *EMP* 1,140
Accts Arnett Kirskey Kimsey Sulli
SIC 8661 Church of God
CEO: Dan Gayet
**Pr:* Al Taylor
**COO:* Scot T Carter
Counsel: Dennis Watkins

CHURCH OF JSUS CHRST OF LD STS
See CORP OF PRESIDENT OF CHURCH OF JESUS CHRIST OF LATTER-DAY SAINTS

CHURCH OF JSUS CHRST OF LD STS
See DESERET MANAGEMENT CORP

D-U-N-S 10-438-2148 IMP
CHURCH OF SCIENTOLOGY FLAG SERVICE ORGANIZATION INC
(*Suby of* IAS ADMINISTRATION) ★
210 S Fort Harrison Ave, Clearwater, FL 33756-5109
Tel (727) 461-1282 *Founded/Ownrshp* 1981
Sales 26.4MM^E *EMP* 1,200
SIC 8661

D-U-N-S 17-829-6778 IMP
CHURCH OF SCIENTOLOGY INTERNATIONAL
IAS ADMINISTRATION
6331 Hollywood Blvd # 801, Los Angeles, CA 90028-4698
Tel (323) 960-3500 *Founded/Ownrshp* 1981
Sales 95.8MM^E *EMP* 1,400
SIC 8661 Religious organizations
CEO: Heber C Jentzsch
**Treas:* Ellen Reynolds
Prgrm Mgr: Jamie Royce
Software D: Daniel Woodard

D-U-N-S 04-469-5963
CHURCH PENSION GROUP SERVICES CORP
C P G
19 E 34th St Fl 3, New York, NY 10016-4367
Tel (212) 592-1800 *Founded/Ownrshp* 1914
Sales NA *EMP* 385
SIC 6371 6321 6311 6331 2731 Pension funds; Health insurance carriers; Life insurance carriers; Fire, marine & casualty insurance: stock; Books: publishing only
Pr: T Period D Sullivan
**COO:* Patricia Coller
**CFO:* Daniel Kasle
**Sr VP:* William Pye
Sr VP: Curt Ritter
VP: Joe Carella
**Prin:* Mary Kate Wold
Off Mgr: Debra St Bernard
Web Dev: Julian McDermott
Netwrk Eng: Andrew Poon

D-U-N-S 07-476-1099
CHURCH SCHOOLS IN DIOCESE OF VIRGINIA
8727 River Rd, Richmond, VA 23229-8303
Tel (804) 288-6045 *Founded/Ownrshp* 1920
Sales 111.4MM *EMP* 650
SIC 8211 Catholic elementary & secondary schools
Pr: David H Charlton

**Ch Bd:* T Justin Morrell
**Treas:* Jack H Broadway Jr

CHURCH SEAT CO
See BEMIS MANUFACTURING CO INC

D-U-N-S 03-609-2716 IMP
CHURCHILL COMPANIES
333 S 7th St Ste 3100, Minneapolis, MN 55402-2442
Tel (612) 673-6700 *Founded/Ownrshp* 1982
Sales 358.0MM^E *EMP* 1,625^E
SIC 3211 3824 5083 Structural glass; Counters, revolution; Farm equipment parts & supplies
Pr: John Fauth
**CFO:* Steven Larson
Ofcr: Alastair Merrick
**VP:* Joseph Kohler
VP: Andrew Leonard

D-U-N-S 00-935-2212 IMP
CHURCHILL CORPORATE SERVICES INC
CHURCHILL LIVING
56 Utter Ave, Hawthorne, NJ 07506-2117
Tel (973) 636-9400 *Founded/Ownrshp* 1996
Sales 90.2MM^E *EMP* 247
SIC 6513 7389 Apartment building operators; Relocation service
CEO: Yudel Kahan
Pr: Julio Morales
Chf Mktg O: Raymond Ko
VP: Yukiko Inoue
**VP:* Mordecai Inzlicht
VP: Mark Pooley
Exec: Rob Dougherty
Assoc Dir: Raizy Friedman
Web Dev: Chana Wachsman
Natl Sales: Eric Fleming
Sls Mgr: Jennifer Hammond

D-U-N-S 00-694-5182
▲ CHURCHILL DOWNS INC
600 N Hurstbourne Pkwy, Louisville, KY 40222-5385
Tel (502) 636-4400 *Founded/Ownrshp* 1928
Sales 1.2MMM *EMP* 4,530^E
Tkr Sym CHDN *Exch* NGS
SIC 7948 7993 3578 Race track operation; Thoroughbred horse racing; Gambling machines, coin-operated; Betting machines, pari-mutuel
CEO: William C Carstanjen
**Ch Bd:* Robert L Evans
Pr: William E Mudd
CFO: Marcia A Dall
Ex VP: Alan K TSE
Sr VP: Ben Murr
VP: John Asher
VP: Erik Furlan
VP: Kristine Stabler
VP: Patrick Troutman
Dir Soc: Nick Bennett
Board of Directors: Ulysses L Bridgeman Jr, Craig J Duchossois, Richard L Duchossois, Robert L Fealy, Aditi J Gokhale, Daniel P Harrington, G Watts Humphrey Jr, R Alex Rankin

D-U-N-S 07-909-3965
CHURCHILL INSURANCE ASSOCIATES INC (KY)
1700 Eastpoint Pkwy, Louisville, KY 40223-4140
Tel (502) 244-1343 *Founded/Ownrshp* 2008
Sales NA *EMP* 300^E
SIC 6411 Insurance agents, brokers & service
Pr: Bruce W Ferguson
**Treas:* James K Johnson
**VP:* Scott C Ferguson
**VP:* Jack D Stewart

CHURCHILL LIVING
See CHURCHILL CORPORATE SERVICES INC

CHURCH'S CHICKEN
See FALCON HOLDINGS LLC

CHURCH'S CHICKEN
See CAJUN OPERATING CO

D-U-N-S 07-830-4733
▲ CHUYS HOLDINGS INC
1623 Toomey Rd, Austin, TX 78704-1098
Tel (512) 473-2783 *Founded/Ownrshp* 1982
Sales 287.0MM *EMP* 7,295
Tkr Sym CHUY *Exch* NGS
SIC 5812 Eating places; Mexican restaurant
Pr: Steve Hislop
**Ch Bd:* Michael Young
**Ch Bd:* John Zapp
CFO: Jon Howie
Ofcr: Sharon Russell
VP: Michael Hatcher
Board of Directors: Randall M Dewitt, Doug Schmick, Ira Zecher

D-U-N-S 05-385-3714
■ CHUYS ON HWY 183 INC
(*Suby of* CHUYS HOLDINGS INC) ★
1623 Toomey Rd, Austin, TX 78704-1098
Tel (512) 473-2783 *Founded/Ownrshp* 2001
Sales 180.9M^E *EMP* 2,373^E
SIC 5812 Family restaurants
Pr: Michael R Young

D-U-N-S 93-109-9071
CHUYS OPCO INC
CHUY'S RESTAURANT
1623 Toomey Rd, Austin, TX 78704-1098
Tel (512) 473-2783 *Founded/Ownrshp* 1993
Sales 144.4MM^E *EMP* 5,000
SIC 5812

CHUY'S RESTAURANT
See CHUYS OPCO INC

D-U-N-S 17-079-4775
CI (TRANSPLACE) HOLDINGS LLC
TRANSPLACE INTERNATIONAL
(*Suby of* TRANSPLACE TEXAS LP) ★
3010 Gaylord Pkwy Ste 200, Frisco, TX 75034-8679
Tel (972) 731-4500 *Founded/Ownrshp* 2000
Sales 83.6MM^E *EMP* 600
SIC 4731 Freight transportation arrangement
CEO: Thomas K Sanderson

Ch Bd: Jun-Sheng Li
Pr: Frank McGuigan
COO: George Abernathy
CFO: Steven Crowther
Ex VP: Robert Brescia
Sr VP: Steve Robinson
VP: Vincent Chiodo

D-U-N-S 78-648-1718
CI CAPITAL PARTNERS LLC
500 Park Ave Fl 8, New York, NY 10022-1606
Tel (212) 752-1850 *Founded/Ownrshp* 2006
Sales 99.3MM^E *EMP* 660
SIC 6726 Investment offices
CEO: Frederick J Iseman
Mng Pt: Frederick Iseman
Pr: Steven M Lefkowitz
COO: John Forbes
VP: Robert M Kopera
VP: Robert Kopera
VP: Andrew Pardo
VP: Evan J Weinstein
VP: Evan Weinstein

D-U-N-S 02-242-7435
CI&T INC
(*Suby of* CI&T SOFTWARE S/A)
630 Freedom Bus Ctr Dr # 300, King of Prussia, PA 19406-0201
Tel (610) 482-4810 *Founded/Ownrshp* 2006
Sales 73.2MM^E *EMP* 1,600
SIC 7371 Computer software development
Pr: Cesar Nivaldogon
**VP:* Leonardo Mattiazzi

CIA
See CULINARY INSTITUTE OF AMERICA

CIA
See CUSTARD INSURANCE ADJUSTERS INC

D-U-N-S 10-913-2519
CIANBRO COMPANIES
1 Hunnewell Ave, Pittsfield, ME 04967-1241
Tel (207) 487-3311 *Founded/Ownrshp* 2001
Sales 630.6MM *EMP* 2,314
Accts Berry Dunn Mcneil & Parker Ll
SIC 1629 1622 1542 1541 8742 Marine construction; Power plant construction; Bridge construction; Commercial & office building, new construction; Industrial buildings, new construction; Construction project management consultant
Ch Bd: Peter G Vigue
**CFO:* Kyle K Holmstrom
**Ofcr:* Michael W Bennett
**Ex VP:* Thomas E Stone

D-U-N-S 00-685-4210 IMP
CIANBRO CORP
(*Suby of* CIANBRO COMPANIES) ★
101 Cianbro Sq, Pittsfield, ME 04967-6301
Tel (207) 487-3311 *Founded/Ownrshp* 2002
Sales 464.8MM *EMP* 1,639
Accts Berry Dunn Mcneil & Parker Ll
SIC 1622 1629 1542 1541 8742 Bridge construction; Marine construction; Power plant construction; Commercial & office building, new construction; Industrial buildings, new construction; Construction project management consultant
CEO: Peter G Vigue
V Ch: Robert J Desardins
**Pr:* Peter A Vigue
**CFO:* Kyle K Holmstrom
CFO: Aldo Servello
**Ofcr:* Michael W Bennett
Ofcr: Alan R Burton
**Sr VP:* Earle A Cianchette
Sr VP: Earle Cianchette
**Sr VP:* Malcolm Cianchette
**VP:* Richard S Brescia
**VP:* Charles B Cianchette
VP: Charlie Cianchette
**VP:* Peter E Cianchette
**VP:* Joseph D Cote
VP: Linc Denison
**VP:* Thomas E Stone
**VP:* Frank J Susi
Exec: Lew Gatcomb
Board of Directors: Kenneth L Cianchette, Malcolm C Cianchette, Frederick H Hauck, Elias M Karter, James G Vamvakias, James D A Van Hoften, Peter G Vigue

D-U-N-S 00-396-4584
CIAT
7343 Nw 79th Ter, Medley, FL 33166-2211
Tel (305) 863-9126 *Founded/Ownrshp* 2008
Sales 133.1MM *EMP* 4^E
SIC 5099 Durable goods

CIAT-MIAMI
See CENTRO INTERNACIONAL DE AGRICULTURA TROPICAL

D-U-N-S 02-596-8909 IMP
CIBA VISION CORP
ALCON
6201 South Fwy, Fort Worth, TX 76134-2001
Tel (817) 551-6881 *Founded/Ownrshp* 2011
Sales 228.8MM^E *EMP* 966^E
SIC 3851 Contact lenses
Prin: Tom Steiner
VP: Stephen Wilson
Assoc Dir: David Flores
Assoc Dir: Mike Lockwood
Assoc Dir: Dana Sager
CIO: Anjana Harve
IT Man: Kwan-Young Lee
Mtls Mgr: Luke Bakken
VP Sls: Kate Benedict
Manager: Jeff Willemsen
Snr PM: Anna Waygand

D-U-N-S 83-872-5976
CIBA VISION INC
(*Suby of* ALCON LABORATORIES INC) ★
333 Howard Ave, Des Plaines, IL 60018-1907
Tel (847) 294-3000 *Founded/Ownrshp* 1990
Sales 210.9MM^E *EMP* 2,820
SIC 3851 Contact lenses

Genl Mgr: Bernie Bartlette
VP Sls: Tom Steiner

D-U-N-S 05-822-1495
CIBC DELAWARE HOLDINGS INC
(*Suby of* CANADIAN IMPERIAL BANK OF COMMERCE)
300 Madison Ave Bsmt C2, New York, NY 10017-6213
Tel (212) 856-4000 *Founded/Ownrshp* 1998
Sales 688.5MM[E] *EMP* 10,020[E]
SIC 6211 Dealers, security
Assoc VP: Ernie Knoblauch
VP: Tomasz Krzyzanowski
Ex Dir: Jeff Appleby
Ex Dir: Bernard Garra
Ex Dir: Andrew Gongaware
Ex Dir: Mark A Kennedy
Ex Dir: Anamika Samanta
Ex Dir: Jeff Wilson
Mng Dir: Chris Bell
Mng Dir: Jay Elkins
Mng Dir: Richard Griffis

CIBC WORLD MARKETS
See CANADIAN IMPERIAL HOLDINGS INC

D-U-N-S 07-279-5917
CIBC WORLD MARKETS CORP
(*Suby of* CANADIAN IMPERIAL BANK OF COMMERCE)
425 Lexington Ave Bsmt C2, New York, NY 10017-3903
Tel (212) 667-7000 *Founded/Ownrshp* 1975
Sales 561.9MM[E] *EMP* 3,000
SIC 6211 6311 6531 Dealers, security; Investment bankers; Life insurance; Real estate brokers & agents
CEO: Gary W Brown
* *Pr:* Gerald McCouthey
CFO: Daniel Brown
Sr VP: Chuck Gerber
* *VP:* Richard Nesbitt
VP: Achilles Perry
Ex Dir: David Alessio
Ex Dir: Chris Atkin
Ex Dir: Michelle Gottlieb
Ex Dir: Ted Levine
Mng Dir: Alex Mainero

D-U-N-S 07-278-1511
▲ CIBER INC
6312 S Fiddlers Green Cir 320n, Greenwood Village, CO 80111-4946
Tel (303) 220-0100 *Founded/Ownrshp* 1974
Sales 786.9MM *EMP* 6,000
Tkr Sym CBR *Exch* NYS
SIC 7373 7379 Computer integrated systems design; Computer related consulting services; Data processing consultant
Pr: Michael Boustridge
* *Ch Bd:* Mark A Floyd
Pr: Vivek K Marla
CFO: Christian M Mezger
Sr VP: Chris Batson
Sr VP: Michael Casullo
Sr VP: Jim Miller
Sr VP: Andy Nicholson
Sr VP: M Sean Radcliffe
Sr VP: Dave Siebert
IT Man: Kenn Bowens
Board of Directors: Richard K Coleman Jr, H Paulett Eberhart, Mark Lewis, Bobby G Stevenson

D-U-N-S 13-241-3142
CIC GROUP INC
530 Maryville Centre Dr, Saint Louis, MO 63141-5825
Tel (314) 682-2900 *Founded/Ownrshp* 2002
Sales 837.9MM[E] *EMP* 1,500
SIC 7692 3542 8741 Welding repair; Machine tools, metal forming type; Management services
Pr: Donald H Lange
* *Treas:* Derek J Falb
* *Ex VP:* Jimmy L Nelson
VP: Francesco Lagutaine
Off Mgr: Jennifer Rossomanno

D-U-N-S 06-117-9719
■ CICA LIFE INSURANCE CO OF AMERICA
(*Suby of* CITIZENS INC) ★
400 E Anderson Ln, Austin, TX 78752-1224
Tel (512) 836-9730 *Founded/Ownrshp* 1968
Sales NA *EMP* 100
SIC 6311 Life insurance carriers
CEO: Rick Riley
* *CFO:* Thomas Kopetic
* *Ex VP:* Larry Welch

D-U-N-S 10-001-6443
CICERO PUBLIC SCHOOL DISTRICT 99
5110 W 24th St, Cicero, IL 60804-2948
Tel (708) 863-4856 *Founded/Ownrshp* 1890
Sales 93.2MM[E] *EMP* 1,700
SIC 8211 Public elementary & secondary schools; School board
Dir Sec: Fernando Rurv
MIS Dir: Brad Randmark
IT Man: Roxann Bartik
Teacher Pr: Rita Tarullo

D-U-N-S 86-867-9267
■ CICH INC
(*Suby of* CNO FINANCIAL GROUP INC) ★
11825 N Pennsylvania St, Carmel, IN 46032-4555
Tel (317) 817-6100 *Founded/Ownrshp* 1987
Sales NA *EMP* 500
SIC 6311 Life insurance
Pr: Mark A Ferucci
* *Treas:* Kim E Lutthans
Ofcr: James Adams
* *VP:* William T Devanney Jr
* *VP:* David A Hill
Creative D: Michael Garber

D-U-N-S 80-666-9768 IMP
▲ CIENA CORP
7035 Ridge Rd, Hanover, MD 21076-1426
Tel (410) 694-5700 *Founded/Ownrshp* 1992
Sales 2.4MMM *EMP* 5,345
Accts Pricewaterhousecoopers Llp Ba
Tkr Sym CIEN *Exch* NYS
SIC 3661 7373 Fiber optics communications equipment; Computer integrated systems design; Systems software development services
Pr: Gary B Smith
* *Ch Bd:* Patrick H Nettles
Pr: Henry Kim
COO: Francois Locoh-Donou
CFO: James E Moylan Jr
Treas: Beth Dolce
Treas: Gregory Sikon
Ofcr: Dennis Morgen
Ex VP: Ted Horan
Sr VP: David M Rothenstein
Sr VP: Marcus H Starke
VP: James Adams
VP: Robert M Auci
VP: Scotty Benda
VP: Charles C CHI
VP: Eric Danielson
VP: James Dodd
VP: James Frodsham
VP: Mark Gorman
VP: Randall Harris
VP: Ronald Jones
Board of Directors: Harvey B Cash, Bruce L Claflin, Lawton W Fitt, Patrick T Gallagher, T Michael Nevens, Judith M O'brien, Michael J Rowny

D-U-N-S 17-504-2076
CIESCO INC
(*Suby of* NOVINGER GROUP INC) ★
109 Miller Ln, Harrisburg, PA 17110-1728
Tel (717) 232-5825 *Founded/Ownrshp* 1987
Sales 105.3MM[E] *EMP* 90
SIC 5032 5033 5169 5039 Drywall materials; Insulation, thermal; Adhesives, chemical; Ceiling systems & products
Pr: Frank J Kruse Jr
* *CFO:* Patrick Hospodavis
* *Treas:* James D Novinger
* *Sec:* Jeffrey G Depew
* *VP:* Timothy G Kephart

D-U-N-S 03-122-4448
■ CIFC CORP
(*Suby of* CIFC LLC) ★
250 Park Ave Ste 400, New York, NY 10177-0502
Tel (212) 624-1200 *Founded/Ownrshp* 2004
Sales 122.5MM *EMP* 82[E]
Accts Deloitte & Touche Llp New Yor
SIC 6722 Management investment, open-end
Pr: Stephen J Vaccaro
* *Ch Bd:* Jeffrey S Serota
Pr: Oliver Wriedt
CFO: Rahul Agarwal
* *V Ch Bd:* Peter Gleysteen
Chf Cred: Julian Weldon

D-U-N-S 03-749-3994
■ CIFC LLC
(*Suby of* FAB HOLDINGS I LP) ★
250 Park Ave Ste 400, New York, NY 10177-0502
Tel (212) 624-1200 *Founded/Ownrshp* 2016
Sales 122.5MM *EMP* 82
Tkr Sym CIFC *Exch* NAS
SIC 6722 Management investment, open-end
Pr: Stephen J Vaccaro
* *Pr:* Oliver Wriedt
CFO: Rahul Agarwal
Chf Cred: Julian Weldon

CIGIE
See COUNCIL OF INSPECTORS GENERAL ON INTEGRITY AND EFFICIENCY

CIGNA
See CONNECTICUT GENERAL LIFE INSURANCE CO

CIGNA
See CONNECTICUT GENERAL CORP

D-U-N-S 61-686-1845
■ CIGNA BEHAVIORAL HEALTH INC
(*Suby of* CIGNA) ★
11095 Viking Dr Ste 350, Eden Prairie, MN 55344-7234
Tel (952) 996-2000 *Founded/Ownrshp* 1997
Sales NA *EMP* 1,118
SIC 6324 Hospital & medical service plans
CEO: Jodi Aronson Prohofsky
* *COO:* Karen K Cierzan
* *CFO:* Dave Bourdon
* *Ex VP:* Ann McClanathan
Sr VP: Rhonda R Beale
VP: Timothy Burton
VP: Christa Hyland
VP: Jeff Rubin
Snr Ntwrk: Paul Sigsworth
DP Exec: Dave Patterson
Dir IT: Michelle Leet

D-U-N-S 02-905-3964
▲ CIGNA CORP
900 Cottage Grove Rd, Bloomfield, CT 06002-2920
Tel (860) 226-6000 *Founded/Ownrshp* 1792
Sales NA *EMP* 39,300
Tkr Sym CI *Exch* NYS
SIC 6324 6311 6351 6321 Group hospitalization plans; Dental insurance; Health maintenance organization (HMO), insurance only; Life insurance carriers; Surety insurance; Disability health insurance; Accident insurance carriers
Pr: David M Cordani
* *Ch Bd:* Isaiah Harris Jr
Pr: Herbert A Fritch
Pr: Rich Hoeckh
Pr: Ralph Holmes
Pr: Tom Lonergan
Pr: Matthew G Manders
Pr: Jason D Sadler
CFO: Thomas A McCarthy
Chf Mktg O: Lisa R Bacus
Ex VP: Mark L Boxer
Ex VP: Nicole S Jones
Ex VP: John M Murabito
VP: Matt Alberico
VP: Michael Conrad
VP: Brian Cuddeback
VP: Gary Edwards
VP: Paul Fruhwirth
VP: William Gagnon
VP: John Godsill
VP: Tom Golias
Board of Directors: Eric J Foss, Michelle D Gass, Jane E Henney, Roman Martinez IV, John M Partridge, James E Rogers, Eric C Wiseman, Donna F Zarcone, William D Zollars

D-U-N-S 13-061-4985
■ CIGNA DENTAL HEALTH INC
(*Suby of* CIGNA) ★
300 Nw 82nd Ave Ste 700, Plantation, FL 33324-7807
Tel (954) 514-6600 *Founded/Ownrshp* 1984
Sales NA *EMP* 460[E]
SIC 6324 Dental insurance
Pr: Karen S Rohan
* *VP:* Gail Garcia
Cert Phar: Anuthida Piercy

D-U-N-S 13-624-7017
■ CIGNA GLOBAL HOLDINGS INC
(*Suby of* CIGNA HOLDINGS INC) ★
590 Naamans Rd, Claymont, DE 19703-2308
Tel (302) 797-3469 *Founded/Ownrshp* 2003
Sales NA *EMP* 242
SIC 6311 6512 6411 Life insurance; Nonresidential building operators; Property & casualty insurance agent
Pr: Joanne Dorak
* *Ch Bd:* Paul B Lukens

D-U-N-S 83-174-4102
■ CIGNA HEALTH AND LIFE INSURANCE CO
(*Suby of* CIGNA) ★
900 Cottage Grove Rd, Bloomfield, CT 06002-2920
Tel (860) 226-6000 *Founded/Ownrshp* 2008
Sales NA *EMP* 484[E]
SIC 6311 Life insurance
CEO: David Cordani
* *Ex VP:* Lisa Bacus

D-U-N-S 61-685-9310
■ CIGNA HEALTH CORP
(*Suby of* CIGNA) ★
900 Cottage Grove Rd, Bloomfield, CT 06002-2920
Tel (860) 226-6000 *Founded/Ownrshp* 1987
Sales NA *EMP* 7,600
SIC 6324 Health maintenance organization (HMO), insurance only
CEO: David Cordani
* *Ex VP:* Mark Boxer
Sr VP: Kelly Dill
VP: Ed Stacey
* *VP:* Raymond R Zielger

D-U-N-S 06-987-7074
■ CIGNA HEALTH MANAGEMENT INC
INTERNTNAL RHBLTTION ASSOC INC
(*Suby of* CIGNA) ★
900 Cottage Grove Rd, Bloomfield, CT 06002-2920
Tel (860) 226-0533 *Founded/Ownrshp* 1997
Sales 98.4MM[E] *EMP* 3,624
SIC 8742 Hospital & health services consultant
Pr: David M Cordani
Ex VP: Robert Zito
VP: Michael Showalter

D-U-N-S 08-545-9964
■ CIGNA HEALTHCARE OF ARIZONA INC
(*Suby of* HEALTHSOURCE INC) ★
25500 N Norterra Dr, Phoenix, AZ 85085-8200
Tel (623) 587-4402 *Founded/Ownrshp* 1997
Sales NA *EMP* 2,541
SIC 6324 Health maintenance organization (HMO), insurance only
Pr: Edward S Kim
Pr: Brian Dickerson
COO: Bob Carroll
CFO: Bryan McGroarty
* *Treas:* Scott R Lambert
* *Chf Mktg O:* Dave Seeley
VP: Bryan Barber
VP: Maggie Braje
* *VP:* Gilbert M Burkel
VP: Mary Hahn
VP: Michael Slice
VP: Mark Verre

D-U-N-S 02-853-9211
■ CIGNA HEALTHCARE OF CALIFORNIA INC
(*Suby of* HEALTHSOURCE INC) ★
400 N Brand Blvd Ste 400, Glendale, CA 91203-2357
Tel (818) 500-6262 *Founded/Ownrshp* 2003
Sales NA *EMP* 600
Accts Pricewaterhousecoopers Llp
SIC 6324 Health maintenance organization (HMO), insurance only
Pr: Leroy Volberding
VP: Barry Ford
VP: Randy Mathews
VP: Sandy Mayer
VP: Eugene Rapisardi
Dir Rx: Nancy Ho
IT Man: Cynthia Jonescampbell
Snr Mgr: Ann Haines

D-U-N-S 61-685-2638
■ CIGNA HEALTHCARE OF COLORADO INC
(*Suby of* HEALTHSOURCE INC) ★
8525 E Orchard Rd, Greenwood Village, CO 80111-5002
Tel (303) 305-1000 *Founded/Ownrshp* 1997
Sales NA *EMP* 150
SIC 6324 Health maintenance organization (HMO), insurance only
Pr: Darryl Edmonds
VP: Tracy Hudson
VP: R Jones
IT Man: Kristy Seidenstricker
IT Man: Pete Winslow
Software D: Kevin Malmgren
Opers Mgr: Russel Quan
Snr Mgr: Doug Radtke

D-U-N-S 15-143-6045
■ CIGNA HEALTHCARE OF CONNECTICUT INC
(*Suby of* HEALTHSOURCE INC) ★
900 Cottage Grove Rd, Bloomfield, CT 06002-2920
Tel (860) 226-2300 *Founded/Ownrshp* 1997
Sales NA *EMP* 60
SIC 6324 Hospital & medical service plans
CEO: David Cordani
Pr: Eric Elliott
Pr: Scott Evelyn
Pr: Sue Podbielski
Pr: Dennis Wilson
* *CFO:* Jn Rubin
Sr VP: Brett Browchuk
* *Sr VP:* John Coyle
* *Sr VP:* Donald Grossman MD
Sr VP: Steve Parham
Sr VP: Ken Sperling
VP: Michael Muchnicki

D-U-N-S 10-894-4554
■ CIGNA HEALTHCARE OF FLORIDA INC
(*Suby of* HEALTHSOURCE INC) ★
2701 N Rocky Point Dr # 178, Rocky Point, FL 33607-5917
Tel (215) 761-1000 *Founded/Ownrshp* 1997
Sales NA *EMP* 774
Accts Price Waterhouse Llp
SIC 6324 Health maintenance organization (HMO), insurance only
Pr: Betty Kimmel
Pr: Susan Knapp Pinnas
* *Treas:* Stephen Chester Stachele
VP: Wilkosz Diane
Ex Dir: Stephen Harris
* *Ex Dir:* Michael Subasic
Div Mgr: Bradley Arms
* *Med Dir:* Peter Dandalides MD

D-U-N-S 15-516-5137
■ CIGNA HEALTHCARE OF ILLINOIS INC
(*Suby of* HEALTHSOURCE INC) ★
525 W Monroe St Ste 1800, Chicago, IL 60661-3722
Tel (312) 496-5340 *Founded/Ownrshp* 1997
Sales NA *EMP* 320
SIC 6324 Health maintenance organization (HMO), insurance only
Pr: Patrick Boughey
VP: Matthew Alberico
VP: Thomas Golias
* *VP:* Sherry Husa
VP: Kathleen Seebert
Off Mgr: Dawn Ferrara
VP Sls: Robert Fry
Sls Mgr: Mark Gaunya
* *Med Dir:* Aslam Kham MD JD

D-U-N-S 60-939-1198
■ CIGNA HEALTHCARE OF SOUTH CAROLINA INC
(*Suby of* HEALTHSOURCE INC) ★
146 Fairchild St Ste 100, Daniel Island, SC 29492-7506
Tel (800) 949-0325 *Founded/Ownrshp* 1986
Sales NA *EMP* 120
SIC 6324 Health maintenance organization (HMO), insurance only
Pr: Steve White
Div Mgr: Nancy Bergland

D-U-N-S 11-846-9428
■ CIGNA HOLDINGS INC
(*Suby of* CIGNA CORP) ★
590 Naamans Rd, Claymont, DE 19703-2308
Tel (215) 761-1000 *Founded/Ownrshp* 1982
Sales NA *EMP* 24,642
SIC 6311 6321 6331 6512 6514 6282 Life insurance; Health insurance carriers; Fire, marine & casualty insurance; Commercial & industrial building operation; Residential building, four or fewer units: operation; Investment advice
Ch Bd: Paul B Lukens
* *Pr:* William C Hartman
* *Treas:* Maureen H Ryan
* *VP:* Samuel E Larosa

D-U-N-S 07-524-4319
■ CIGNA LIFE INSURANCE CO OF NEW YORK
(*Suby of* CIGNA) ★
Two Liberty Place, Philadelphia, PA 19192-0001
Tel (215) 761-2355 *Founded/Ownrshp* 1965
Sales NA *EMP* 74
SIC 6321 6311 Health insurance carriers; Life insurance carriers
Pr: Robert Brickweg
Pr: Henri Cournand
Pr: Cerise Johnson
Pr: Kathy Overbye
Treas: Barry McHale
Ex VP: Robert Stone
Sr VP: Steve Disch
Sr VP: Mark Marsters
VP: Marcy F Blender
VP: Mark J Boggess
VP: Antoinette Bonacci
VP: Christopher Coloian
VP: David Dupree
VP: Nancy Goldstein
VP: Karen King
VP: Gidget La Peddie
VP: Ed Laclair
VP: Scott R Lambert
VP: Curtis Mathews
VP: Gerald Meyn
VP: Brian Sweeney
Board of Directors: J S Breckinridge, B A Buge, E T Elliot, D G Heth, Carl E Horton, Patrick Kane, Arthur C Reeds, C H Symington, Jeffrey Drain

D-U-N-S 13-767-8710
■ CIGNA RE CORP
(*Suby of* CIGNA) ★
900 Cottage Grove Rd, Hartford, CT 06152-0001
Tel (860) 726-6000 *Founded/Ownrshp* 2012
Sales NA *EMP* 189[E]

SIC 6311 6321 Life insurance; Accident & health insurance
Ofcr: Patrick M Jones
VP: Dietrich Krauland
VP: Scott D Schneider
Dir IT: David Anderson
Tech Mgr: Anthony White
VP Sls: Kim Shepard
Sls Dir: Karen Pike
Snr Mgr: Doug Radtke

CIGNA TEL-DRUG
See TEL-DRUG INC

D-U-N-S 96-950-8774
CII / OCI JOINT VENTURE
6862 Elm St Ste 500, Mc Lean, VA 22101-3838
Tel (703) 358-8800 Founded/Ownrshp 2011
Sales 30.0M EMP 1,679
SIC 1542 Specialized public building contractors
Prin: Wahid Hakki
Prin: Osama Bishai
Prin: Joe Romagnoli

D-U-N-S 14-432-7343
■ CILCORP INC
AES
(Suby of AMEREN CORP) ★
300 Liberty St, Peoria, IL 61602-1404
Tel (309) 677-5271 Founded/Ownrshp 1985
Sales 1.1MMM EMP 1,366
SIC 4911 4924 Generation, electric power; Transmission, electric power; Distribution, electric power; Natural gas distribution
Ch Bd: Gary L Rainwater
CFO: Warner L Baxter
Treas: Jerre E Birdsong
VP: Martin J Lyons
VP: Robert J Sprowls
VP: Steven R Sullivan
Board of Directors: Daniel F Cole, Patrick T Stokes, Thomas R Voss

D-U-N-S 82-969-1195
CIM COMMERCIAL TRUST CORP
(Suby of URBAN PARTNERS II LLC)
17950 Preston Rd Ste 600, Dallas, TX 75252-5656
Tel (972) 349-3200 Founded/Ownrshp 2014
Sales 268.4MM EMP 33E
Accts Bdo Usa Llp Los Angeles Ca
SIC 6798 Real estate investment trusts
CEO: Charles E Garner II
*Ch Bd: Richard Ressler
Pr: Jan F Salit
CFO: David Thompson
Ofcr: Amy Shusterman
Software D: Scott Thompson
Board of Directors: Douglas Bech, Robert Cresci, Kelly Eppich, Frank Golay, Shaul Kuba, Avraham Shemesh

D-U-N-S 10-995-1504
CIM TRUCKING INC
(Suby of SIMS METAL MANAGEMENT) ★
2232 S Blue Island Ave, Chicago, IL 60608-4412
Tel (773) 927-6611 Founded/Ownrshp 1995
Sales 23.7MME EMP 1,142E
SIC 4212 Local trucking, without storage
VP: David A Carpenter

D-U-N-S 94-560-1599
CIMA ENERGY LTD
100 Waugh Dr Ste 500, Houston, TX 77007-4600
Tel (713) 209-1112 Founded/Ownrshp 1996
Sales 136.1MME EMP 65
Accts Deloitte & Touche Llp Houston
SIC 1311 Crude petroleum & natural gas
CEO: Charles M Oglesby
Pr: Thomas K Edwards
CFO: Michael D Rupe

D-U-N-S 12-080-9749
▲ CIMAREX ENERGY CO
1700 N Lincoln St # 3700, Denver, CO 80203-4553
Tel (303) 295-3995 Founded/Ownrshp 2002
Sales 1.4MMM EMP 991E
Tkr Sym XEC Exch NYS
SIC 1311 Crude petroleum & natural gas production
Ch Bd: Thomas E Jorden
*COO: Joseph R Albi
CFO: Paul Korus
Sr VP: Francis B Barron
Sr VP: Stephen Bell
VP: Francis Barron
VP: Roger Burau
VP: Charles Hinson
VP: Mitch Lehn
VP: Thomas A Richardson
VP: Thomas Richardson
VP: James H Shonsey
Exec: John Lambuth
Board of Directors: Hans Helmerich, David A Hentschel, Harold R Logan Jr, Floyd R Price, Monroe W Robertson, Lisa A Stewart, Michael J Sullivan, L Paul Teague

D-U-N-S 00-696-5479 IMP
CIMARRON LUMBER AND SUPPLY CO
SUTHERLANDS LUMBER COMPANY
4000 Main St, Kansas City, MO 64111-2313
Tel (816) 756-3000 Founded/Ownrshp 1947
Sales 133.6MME EMP 130
SIC 5031 Lumber: rough, dressed & finished; Building materials, interior; Building materials, exterior
CEO: Dilip R Vellodi
CFO: Steve Scott
Dir IT: Bill Bryan

D-U-N-S 06-926-5445
CIMARRON UNDERGROUND INC (KS)
8375 Melrose Dr, Lenexa, KS 66214-1629
Tel (913) 438-2981 Founded/Ownrshp 1977
Sales 108.0MME EMP 200
Accts Boan & Connealy Overland Park
SIC 1623 1731 Underground utilities contractor; Pipeline construction; Communication line & transmission tower construction; Fiber optic cable installation

CEO: Michelle Lowe
Pr: Kurt Gowdy
CFO: Ray Linden
VP: Fred Harrah
Exec: Gary Gowdy

D-U-N-S 96-244-1502 IMP
CIMC USA INC
289 Water Tower Dr, Monon, IN 47959-8160
Tel (219) 253-2054 Founded/Ownrshp 2002
Sales 241.2MME EMP 3
SIC 1541 Food products manufacturing or packing plant construction
Pr: Guiping LI
*VP: Liu Yanjia

D-U-N-S 05-538-4866
CIMCO RESOURCES INC
1616 Windsor Rd, Loves Park, IL 61111-4252
Tel (815) 986-7211 Founded/Ownrshp 2001
Sales 200.0MM EMP 125
SIC 5093 7389 Metal scrap & waste materials; Brokers' services
Pr: John E Gralewski
*CFO: Scott Anderson
*Treas: Danial Pecora
*Prin: Sam Jacob

D-U-N-S 92-793-0052 IMP
■ CIMCOOL INDUSTRIAL PRODUCTS LLC
(Suby of MILACRON LLC) ★
3000 Disney St, Cincinnati, OH 45209-5028
Tel (888) 246-2665 Founded/Ownrshp 2009
Sales 155.1MME EMP 380E
SIC 5169 Chemicals & allied products
CEO: Tom Goeke
*Pr: Robert McKee
*CFO: John Francy
*VP: David Lawrence
VP: Gina Marek
Dist Mgr: Steve F Barnes
Dist Mgr: Curtis Jones
Dist Mgr: Greg Myers
Sftwr Eng: Andrei Bialevich
Sls Mgr: Kenneth Hough
Sls Mgr: Mike Skora

D-U-N-S 11-503-4993
CIMMS INC
BURGER KING
3061 Riverside Dr, Los Angeles, CA 90039-2060
Tel (323) 674-0203 Founded/Ownrshp 1978
Sales 76.5MME EMP 2,500
SIC 5812 Fast-food restaurant, chain
Pr: Ralph Cimmarusti
CFO: Howard Schwartz
*VP: Lawrence Cimmarusti

D-U-N-S 10-914-6170 EXP
CIMPRESS USA INC
(Suby of VISTAPRINT B.V.)
275 Wyman St Ste 100, Waltham, MA 02451-1218
Tel (866) 614-8002 Founded/Ownrshp 1999
Sales 92.5MME EMP 190
SIC 2752 Commercial printing, lithographic
Pr: Robert Keane
*Pr: Wendy Cebula
*Pr: Janet Holian
*COO: Don Nelson
CFO: Mike Giannetto
*CFO: Ernst Teunissen
*Sr VP: Jim Cutler
*Sr VP: Lawrence Gold
VP: Keith Davis
VP: Jon Habeski
VP: Tim Martin
VP: Cindy Starr
Exec: Kristin E Bergeron

D-U-N-S 93-326-2768 IMP
■ CINCH CONNECTIVITY SOLUTIONS INC
(Suby of BEL FUSE INC) ★
1700 S Finley Rd, Lombard, IL 60148-4884
Tel (847) 739-0300 Founded/Ownrshp 2014
Sales 800.0MM EMP 700
SIC 3678 3679 Electronic connectors; Harness assemblies for electronic use: wire or cable
Pr: Pete Bittner
*CFO: Robert Leppert
VP: Steve Armstrong
VP: Dennis Delcampo
VP: Rick Vanderah
Genl Mgr: Matt Meares
Opers Mgr: Kent Schultz

D-U-N-S 02-161-8694
■ CINCH CONNECTORS INC
(Suby of BEL FUSE INC) ★
1700 S Finley Rd, Lombard, IL 60148-4890
Tel (630) 705-6001 Founded/Ownrshp 2010
Sales 156.7MME EMP 1,000
SIC 3643 3678 Connectors & terminals for electrical devices; Electronic connectors
Pr: Michael Murray
*VP: Bob Cwynar
Dir Rx: Mark Falkingham
Genl Mgr: Larry Stanley
Opers Mgr: Dave Bell
Sls Mgr: Nick Radojkovic

D-U-N-S 10-149-6735 IMP/EXP
▲ CINCINNATI BELL INC
221 E 4th St Ste 700, Cincinnati, OH 45202-4118
Tel (513) 397-9900 Founded/Ownrshp 1873
Sales 1.1MMM EMP 3,250
Tkr Sym CBB Exch NYS
SIC 4813 7373 7374 7379 Telephone communication, except radio; Local & long distance telephone communications; Local telephone communications; ; Systems software development services; Data processing service; Computer related consulting services;
Pr: Theodore H Torbeck
Mng Pt: Jennifer W Christensen
*Ch Bd: Phillip R Cox
COO: Leigh R Fox
CFO: Renita Clark
CFO: Andrew R Kaiser
Bd of Dir: Lesley Bayer

Bd of Dir: Neal Marksberry
Assoc VP: Anne Howard
Ex VP: Andrew Howell
VP: Joshua T Duckworth
VP: Jason Praeter
VP: Anthony Schulte
VP: Christopher J Wilson
Board of Directors: John W Eck, Craig F Maier, Russel P Mayer, Lynn A Wentworth, Martin J Yudkovitz, John M Zrno

D-U-N-S 83-568-4853
■ CINCINNATI BELL TECHNOLOGY SOLUTIONS INC
CBTS
(Suby of CINCINNATI BELL INC) ★
4600 Montgomery Rd # 400, Cincinnati, OH 45212-2600
Tel (513) 841-2287 Founded/Ownrshp 1994
Sales 196.7MME EMP 502
SIC 7379 5734 Computer related consulting services; Computer peripheral equipment
CEO: Theodore H Torbeck
*Pr: John Burns
*CFO: Leigh R Fox
Sr VP: Tony Bradds
VP: Jeff Betteker
*VP: Leigh Fox
*VP: Scott Seger
*VP: Don Verdon
*VP: Christopher J Wilson
Exec: Debbie Casazza
Exec: Shelby Neely

D-U-N-S 00-699-9239
■ CINCINNATI BELL TELEPHONE CO
(Suby of CINCINNATI BELL INC) ★
209 W 7th St Fl 1, Cincinnati, OH 45202-2373
Tel (513) 565-9402 Founded/Ownrshp 1873, 2010
Sales 813.4MME EMP 2,150E
SIC 4813 Telephone communication, except radio; Local telephone communications; Long distance telephone communications; Data telephone communications
CFO: Brian A Ross
*COO: Rodney D Dir
CFO: Gary J Wotaszek
*Treas: Mark Peterson
Sr VP: Mary E McCann
IT Man: Kim Williams
Opers Mgr: David Stahl

CINCINNATI DIV
See SUMCO USA SALES CORP

D-U-N-S 05-129-0153
▲ CINCINNATI FINANCIAL CORP
6200 S Gilmore Rd, Fairfield, OH 45014-5141
Tel (513) 870-2000 Founded/Ownrshp 1968
Sales NA EMP 4,493
Tkr Sym CINF Exch NGS
SIC 6311 6411 Life insurance carriers; Property & casualty insurance agent
Pr: Steven J Johnston
Ch Bd: Kenneth W Stecher
Pr: Michael Barron
CFO: Michael J Sewell
Bd of Dir: Julie Caplinger
Sr VP: Lisa A Love
VP: Thomas Hogan
VP: Tom Kelly
VP: Chris Kendall
VP: Ronald Klimkowski
VP: Gary J Kline
VP: Eric N Mathews
VP Bus Dev: Phil Howard
Board of Directors: Thomas R Schiff, William F Bahl, Douglas S Skidmore, Gregory T Bier, John F Steele Jr, Dirk J Debbink, Larry R Webb, Linda W Clement-Holmes, Kenneth C Lichtendahl, W Rodney McMullen, David P Osborn, Gretchen W Price, John J Schiff Jr

D-U-N-S 00-425-3878
CINCINNATI INC (OH)
7420 Kilby Rd, Harrison, OH 45030-8915
Tel (513) 367-7100 Founded/Ownrshp 1898
Sales 87.6MME EMP 325E
SIC 3549

D-U-N-S 78-221-0223
■ CINCINNATI INDEMINTY CO
(Suby of CINCINNATI INSURANCE CO) ★
6200 S Gilmore Rd, Fairfield, OH 45014-5141
Tel (513) 870-2000 Founded/Ownrshp 1988
Sales NA EMP 600
SIC 6331 Fire, marine & casualty insurance & carriers
Pr: John Schiff
COO: Michael Sewell
*V Ch Bd: James E Benoski
*Sr VP: T F Elchynski
Sr VP: Ken Stecher
VP: Anthony Henn
CTO: Todd Pendery
IT Man: Craig Forrester

D-U-N-S 00-699-9197
■ CINCINNATI INSURANCE CO
(Suby of CINCINNATI FINANCIAL CORP) ★
6200 S Gilmore Rd, Fairfield, OH 45014-5141
Tel (513) 870-2000 Founded/Ownrshp 1950
Sales NA EMP 4,000
SIC 6311 6331 6321 6211

D-U-N-S 19-989-6739
■ CINCINNATI LIFE INSURANCE CO
(Suby of CINCINNATI INSURANCE CO) ★
6200 S Gilmore Rd, Fairfield, OH 45014-5141
Tel (513) 870-2000 Founded/Ownrshp 1988
Sales NA EMP 950
SIC 6311 Life insurance
Pr: David M Popplewell
*Treas: Kenneth W Stecher
Sr VP: Eric N Mathews
VP: Brad E Behringer
VP: Douglas Bogenreif
VP: David Burbrink

VP: Theresa A Hoffer
Counsel: Teresa L Cracas
Counsel: Stephen C Roach

D-U-N-S 07-288-9959
CINCINNATI PUBLIC SCHOOLS
2651 Burnet Ave, Cincinnati, OH 45219-2551
Tel (513) 363-0000 Founded/Ownrshp 1829
Sales 654.4MM EMP 7,070
Accts Caudill & Associates Cpa Por
SIC 8211 Public elementary school; Public junior high school; Public senior high school
*CFO: Jonathan Boid
CFO: Jonathan Boyd
Comm Dir: Janet Walsh
Genl Mgr: Rebecca Vogler
IT Man: Rebecca Ruckel
Schl Brd P: Eve Bolton
Teacher Pr: Paul McDole
Psych: Jim Ayers
Psych: William J Demeo
Snr Mgr: Adrienne Maka

D-U-N-S 07-286-9308
CINCINNATI STATE TECHNICAL AND COMMUNITY COLLEGE
3520 Central Pkwy, Cincinnati, OH 45223-2612
Tel (513) 569-1500 Founded/Ownrshp 1966
Sales 46.6MM EMP 1,000
SIC 8222

CINCO V PIPE & SUPPLY
See CHAMPIONS CINCO PIPE & SUPPLY LLC

D-U-N-S 05-648-7531
CINCOM SYSTEMS INC
55 Merchant St Ste 100, Cincinnati, OH 45246-3761
Tel (513) 612-2300 Founded/Ownrshp 1968
Sales 121.0MME EMP 500
SIC 7373 Computer integrated systems design
Ch Bd: Thomas M Nies
CFO: Dan Vogel
*Treas: Gerald Shawhan
VP: Greg Mills
VP: Gillis West
Snr Sftwr: Kevin Ansberry
Snr Sftwr: Frederick Borden
Snr Sftwr: Jean-Yves Gobeil
Snr Sftwr: Kevin Greek
Snr Sftwr: Mark Grinnell
Snr Sftwr: Tom Robinson
Board of Directors: Victoria S Nies-Dowling, Jennifer M Nies-Mckeever, Eric L Nies, Thomas M Nies Jr, Tina Nies

D-U-N-S 00-136-4749
▲ CINEDIGM CORP
902 Broadway Fl 9, New York, NY 10010-6036
Tel (212) 206-8600 Founded/Ownrshp 2000
Sales 104.4MM EMP 126E
Tkr Sym CIDM Exch NGM
SIC 7384 7389 7371 Film developing services; Home movies, developing & processing; Music & broadcasting services; Music distribution systems; Computer software development
Ch Bd: Christopher J McGurk
Pr: William S Sondheim
CFO: Jeffrey S Edell
Ex VP: Gary S Loffredo
Board of Directors: Peter C Brown, Ronald L Chez, Patrick W O'brien, Zvi M Rhine

D-U-N-S 79-892-9365
▲ CINEMARK HOLDINGS INC
3900 Dallas Pkwy Ste 500, Plano, TX 75093-7871
Tel (972) 665-1000 Founded/Ownrshp 2006
Sales 2.8MMM EMP 28,300E
Tkr Sym CNK Exch NYS
SIC 6531 Real estate agent, residential
CEO: Mark Zoradi
*Ch Bd: Lee Roy Mitchell
Pr: Valmir Fernandes
CFO: Sean Gamble
Ex VP: Michael Cavalier
Ex VP: Tom Owens
CIO: Doug Fey
Info Man: Scott Bauer
Board of Directors: Darcy Antonellis, Benjamin D Chereskin, Steven P Rosenberg, Enrique F Senior, Carlos M Sepulveda, Donald G Soderquist, Raymond W Syufy, Nina G Vaca

D-U-N-S 11-121-3232 IMP
■ CINEMARK INC
(Suby of CINEMARK HOLDINGS INC) ★
3900 Dallas Pkwy Ste 500, Plano, TX 75093-7871
Tel (800) 246-3627 Founded/Ownrshp 2006
Sales 316.4MME EMP 12,900E
SIC 7832 Motion picture theaters, except drive-in
Ch Bd: Lee Roy Mitchell
CFO: Robert Copple
VP: James Meredith
VP: Steve Zuehlke
MIS Dir: Philip Wood
VP Mktg: Charlotte Allen
Board of Directors: Benjamin D Chereskin, Peter R Ezersky, Steven P Rosenberg, Enrique F Senior, Carlos M Sepulveda, Donald G Soderquist, Roger T Staubach, Raymond W Syufy

D-U-N-S 36-183-2041 IMP
■ CINEMARK USA INC
(Suby of CINEMARK HOLDINGS INC) ★
3900 Dallas Pkwy Ste 500, Plano, TX 75093-7865
Tel (972) 665-1000 Founded/Ownrshp 1984
Sales 2.8MMM EMP 16,500
SIC 7832 Motion picture theaters, except drive-in
CEO: Mark Zoradi
*Ch Bd: Lee Roy Mitchell
Pr: Robert Copple
CFO: Sean Gamble
*V Ch Bd: Timothy Warner
Ex VP: Michael Cavalier
VP: Walter Hebert
VP: John Lundin
VP: Margaret E Richards
VP Mktg: Charlie Street
Board of Directors: Darcy Antonellis, Benjamin D Chereskin, Steven P Rosenberg, Enrique F Senior,

Carlos M Sepulveda, Donald G Soderquist, Raymond W Syufy, Nina B Vaca

CINEPOLIS USA
See USA CINEMA INVESTMENT HOLDINGS INC

D-U-N-S 03-970-1113
■ CINER ENTERPRISES INC
(Suby of AKKAN ENERJI VE MADENCILIK ANONIM SIRKETI)
5 Concourse Pkwy Ste 2500, Atlanta, GA 30328-7108
Tel (770) 375-2300 Founded/Ownrshp 2015
Sales 615.4MM^E EMP 884^E
SIC 1474 2812 Soda ash (natural) mining; Soda ash, sodium carbonate (anhydrous)
CEO: Kirk Milling
*CFO: Kevin Kremke
*VP: Nicole C Daniel
*VP: Jim Dass

D-U-N-S 93-367-6462 IMP/EXP
■ CINER RESOURCES CORP
(Suby of CINER ENTERPRISES INC) ★
5 Concourse Pkwy, Atlanta, GA 30328-5350
Tel (770) 375-2300 Founded/Ownrshp 2015
Sales 615.4MM^E EMP 506
SIC 1474 2812 Soda ash (natural) mining; Alkalies & chlorine
CEO: Kirk Milling
CFO: Paul Francese
*CFO: Charles Kim
*CFO: Kevin Kremke
*Ch: SOOY Lee
*VP: Brent Bailey
*VP: Nicole C Daniel

D-U-N-S 07-910-4769
■ CINER RESOURCES LP
(Suby of CINER WYOMING HOLDING CO) ★
5 Concourse Pkwy Ste 2500, Atlanta, GA 30328-7108
Tel (770) 375-2300 Founded/Ownrshp 2013, 2015
Sales 486.4MM EMP 476^E
Tkr Sym CINR Exch NYS
SIC 1474 Soda ash (natural) mining
Ch Bd: Kirk H Milling
Genl Pt: Ciner R LLC
CFO: Kevin L Kremke

D-U-N-S 82-648-9788
■ CINER WYOMING HOLDING CO
(Suby of CINER RESOURCES CORP) ★
5 Concourse Pkwy, Atlanta, GA 30328-5350
Tel (770) 375-2300 Founded/Ownrshp 1991
Sales 486.5MM^E EMP 480^E
SIC 1474 2812 Soda ash (natural) mining; Soda ash, sodium carbonate (anhydrous)
CEO: Tugay Ciner

D-U-N-S 62-114-2884 IMP
■ CINER WYOMING LLC
(Suby of CINER RESOURCES LP) ★
254 County Rd 4/6, Green River, WY 82935
Tel (307) 875-2600 Founded/Ownrshp 2015
Sales 143.7MM^E EMP 378
SIC 2812 Soda ash, sodium carbonate (anhydrous)
CEO: Kirk H Milling
*CFO: Kevin Kremke
*VP: Jim Dass

D-U-N-S 80-978-8672 IMP
■ CINERGY CORP
(Suby of DUKE ENERGY CAROLINAS LLC) ★
139 E 4th St, Cincinnati, OH 45202-4003
Tel (513) 421-9500 Founded/Ownrshp 2006
Sales 2.1MMM^E EMP 7,842
SIC 4911 4924 Distribution, electric power; Generation, electric power; Transmission, electric power; Natural gas distribution
Pr: David L Hauser
Pr: John Campbell
CFO: Steven Schrader
*CFO: Steven K Young
Treas: Stephen Demay
Ex VP: M Harkness
VP: Jaim De La Espriella
Exec: Jennifer Weber
VP Mktg: Scott Laidlaw
Mktg Mgr: Janine Lutz

D-U-N-S 08-499-1814
■ CINERGY POWER GENERATION SERVICES LLC
(Suby of CINERGY CORP) ★
139 E 4th St, Cincinnati, OH 45202-4003
Tel (513) 421-9500 Founded/Ownrshp 1997
Sales 1.6MMM^E EMP 1,699^E
SIC 4911 Transmission, electric power

CINGULAR WIRELESS
See SOUTHWESTERN BELL MOBILE SYSTEMS LLC

D-U-N-S 78-337-1255 IMP
■ CINMAR LLC
FRONTGATE CATALOG
(Suby of HSN INC) ★
5566 W Chester Rd, West Chester, OH 45069-2914
Tel (513) 603-1000 Founded/Ownrshp 1995
Sales 89.7MM^E EMP 200^E
SIC 5961 5023 5712 Catalog sales; Rugs; Bedding & bedsprings
VP: Andrew Daniel
Dir: Gina Wingett
Genl Mgr: Bill Daly
CIO: Schaefer John
QA Dir: Guy Galinsky
Dir IT: Bob Young
VP Mktg: Andrew Franzoni
Art Dir: Kelly Popejoy

CINNABON
See FOCUS BRANDS INC

D-U-N-S 61-898-1711 IMP
CINRAM GROUP INC
437 New Sanford Rd, La Vergne, TN 37086-4184
Tel (615) 287-3800 Founded/Ownrshp 2015
Sales 557.1MM^E EMP 1,300
SIC 3695 Magnetic disks & drums
CEO: Steve Brown
*CFO: John Bell
*Ex VP: David Ashton
*Ex VP: Neil Ballantine
*Ex Dir: Fred Rudolph
IT Man: Joan Duncan

D-U-N-S 62-006-2752 IMP/EXP
CINRAM INC
1600 Rich Rd, Richmond, IN 47374-1435
Tel (416) 298-8190 Founded/Ownrshp 1990
Sales 228.8MM^E EMP 5,400
SIC 3652 3695

D-U-N-S 09-536-3057 IMP
CINRAM MANUFACTURING INC
1400 E Lackawanna St, Olyphant, PA 18448-0999
Tel (570) 383-3291 Founded/Ownrshp 2003
Sales 228.8MM^E EMP 7,595
SIC 3652 Phonograph record blanks; Magnetic tape (audio): prerecorded; Compact laser discs, prerecorded
Pr: Dave Rubenstein
Ex VP: Frank Apostolico

D-U-N-S 05-648-1716 IMP/EXP
▲ CINTAS CORP
6800 Cintas Blvd, Cincinnati, OH 45262
Tel (513) 459-1200 Founded/Ownrshp 1968
Sales 4.9MMM EMP 32,000
Tkr Sym CTAS Exch NGS
SIC 7218 2337 2326 5084 Industrial uniform supply; Uniforms, except athletic: women's, misses' & juniors'; Work uniforms; Safety equipment
CEO: Scott D Farmer
*Ch Bd: Robert J Kohlhepp
Pr: J Phillip Holloman
CFO: J Michael Hansen
Bd of Dir: Lynn Burton
Ex VP: Karyn Hidalgo
Sr VP: Thomas E Frooman
VP: Dave Bingham
VP: Greg Birkenhauer
VP: Jay Bruscato
VP: James Critchfield
VP: Greg Eling
VP: Larry L Fultz
VP: Michelle Goret
VP: Mark Greiner
VP: Glenn Larsen
VP: Pamela Lowe
VP: John W Milligan
VP: Dave Pollack
VP: Jim Rozakis
Exec: Michele Thoren
Board of Directors: Gerald S Adolph, John F Barrett, Melanie W Barstad, Robert E Coletti, Richard T Farmer, James J Johnson, Joseph Scaminace, Ronald W Tysoe

D-U-N-S 78-479-6849
■ CINTAS CORP NO 1
(Suby of CINTAS CORP) ★
6800 Cintas Blvd, Mason, OH 45040-9151
Tel (513) 459-1200 Founded/Ownrshp 1987
Sales 244.2MM^E EMP 27,000
SIC 7213 5136 5137 7549 Uniform supply; Uniforms, men's & boys'; Uniforms, women's & children's; Automotive maintenance services
Ch Bd: Richard T Farmer
*CFO: William C Gale
Treas: Michael L Thompson
*V Ch Bd: Robert Kohlhepp
*VP: Karen L Carnahan
*VP: Michael Thompson
IT Man: Josh Jodrey

D-U-N-S 96-216-2983 IMP
■ CINTAS CORP NO 2
CINTAS FIRST AID & SAFETY
(Suby of CINTAS CORP) ★
6800 Cintas Blvd, Mason, OH 45040-9151
Tel (513) 459-1200 Founded/Ownrshp 2000
Sales 2.8MMM^E EMP 20,000
SIC 5084 Safety equipment
CEO: Scott D Farmer
*Treas: Mike L Thompson
*Ex VP: Thomas E Frooman
*Ex VP: Robert J Kohlhepp

D-U-N-S 96-216-2603
■ CINTAS CORP NO 3
(Suby of CINTAS CORP) ★
6800 Cintas Blvd, Mason, OH 45040-9151
Tel (513) 459-1200 Founded/Ownrshp 1995
Sales 95.5MM^E EMP 3,098^E
SIC 7218 Industrial uniform supply; Wiping towel supply; Treated equipment supply: mats, rugs, mops, cloths, etc.
CEO: Scott D Farmer
*Pr: J Philipp Holloman
*Treas: Michael Thompson

CINTAS FIRST AID & SAFETY
See CINTAS CORP NO 2

D-U-N-S 55-707-3863
■ CINTAS R US INC
(Suby of CINTAS CORP) ★
6800 Cintas Blvd, Cincinnati, OH 45262
Tel (513) 459-1200 Founded/Ownrshp 1991
Sales 9.5MM^E EMP 1,500
SIC 7218 Industrial uniform supply
CEO: Scott Farmer
*Pr: Richard T Farmer

D-U-N-S 96-216-3114
■ CINTAS-RUS LP
(Suby of CINTAS CORP) ★
6800 Cintas Blvd, Mason, OH 45040-9151
Tel (513) 459-1200 Founded/Ownrshp 2000
Sales 32.4MM^E EMP 2,422^E
SIC 7218 Industrial uniform supply
CEO: Scott D Farmer

D-U-N-S 02-107-4307
CIOX HEALTH LLC
HEALTHPORT
(Suby of NEW MOUNTAIN CAPITAL LLC) ★
925 North Point Pkwy # 350, Alpharetta, GA 30005-5210
Tel (800) 367-1500 Founded/Ownrshp 2014
Sales 442.0MM EMP 7,500
SIC 7375 Information retrieval services
CEO: Edward Coleman
*CFO: Paul Parrish

CIPCO
See CENTRAL IOWA POWER COOPERATIVE

D-U-N-S 18-505-2776
CIRAULO BROTHERS BUILDING CO
SQUARE DEAL BUILDING SUPPLY
7670 19 Mile Rd, Sterling Heights, MI 48314-3221
Tel (586) 731-3670 Founded/Ownrshp 1984
Sales 158.3MM^E EMP 60
SIC 5031 5211 1761 Building materials, exterior; Building materials, interior; Door & window products; Gutter & downspout contractor
Pr: Vincenzo Ciraulo
*Prin: Larry Ranke

D-U-N-S 10-853-9045
CIRCLE B ENTERPRISES HOLDING CO INC
731 N Main St Ste 106, Sikeston, MO 63801-2151
Tel (573) 471-1276 Founded/Ownrshp 1991
Sales 39.6MM^E EMP 2,800
SIC 8059 Nursing home, except skilled & intermediate care facility
Pr: Brad Bedell
*Treas: Lonnie Hasty

D-U-N-S 00-105-6063 IMP
CIRCLE GRAPHICS INC
120 9th Ave Ste B, Longmont, CO 80501-4798
Tel (303) 532-2370 Founded/Ownrshp 2005
Sales 133.9MM^E EMP 600^E
SIC 2759 7374 Commercial printing; Computer graphics service
CEO: Andrew Cousin
*Pr: Hank Ridless
*Chf Mktg O: Judy Toran Cousin
Sr VP: Bruce Neeld
VP: Mary Prisco
Dir Bus: Brian Miller
Genl Mgr: Paul Stals
IT Man: Jonathan Burke
IT Man: Seth Northausen
IT Man: Doug Ouellette
Prd Mgr: Dave Bridges

D-U-N-S 00-966-8054
■ CIRCLE INTERNATIONAL INC
HARPER GROUP
(Suby of CEVA FREIGHT MANAGEMENT INTERNATIONAL GROUP INC) ★
15350 Vickery Dr, Houston, TX 77032-2530
Tel (281) 618-3100 Founded/Ownrshp 1989
Sales 61.4MM^E EMP 1,000
SIC 4731 Freight forwarding; Customhouse brokers
Ch: James R Crane
*Pr: E Joseph Bento
COO: Greg Weigel
*Treas: Douglas Seckel
Ex VP: John Wertheimer
*VP: Rae Fawcett
VP: Leighton T Henderson

CIRCLE K
See MAGNESS OIL CO

CIRCLE K
See MACS CONVENIENCE STORES LLC

CIRCLE K
See STRIPES LLC

D-U-N-S 10-545-7662 IMP
CIRCLE K STORES INC
(Suby of ALIMENTATION COUCHE-TARD INC)
1130 W Warner Rd, Tempe, AZ 85284-2816
Tel (602) 728-8000 Founded/Ownrshp 2003
Sales 3.0MMM^E EMP 14,000
SIC 5411 5541 Convenience stores, chain; Gasoline service stations
Pr: Brian Hannasch
*VP: Joe Chiovera
*VP: Kathy Cunnington
*VP: Darrell Davis
VP: Bruce Landini
*VP: David Morgan
Genl Mgr: Bruce Allen
Genl Mgr: Robert Brown
Genl Mgr: Jane Johnson
Genl Mgr: Daniel Morton
Software D: Gloria Abril

D-U-N-S 60-321-4318 IMP
CIRCLE PEAK CAPITAL MANAGEMENT LLC
1325 Ave Of The Americas, New York, NY 10019-6026
Tel (646) 230-8812 Founded/Ownrshp 2002
Sales 816.7MM^E EMP 4,775
SIC 2053 6799 Pies, bakery: frozen; Venture capital companies
CEO: R Adam Smith
Bd of Dir: Joseph S Rhodes
*Prin: James H Clippard
*Prin: Holbrook M Forusz

CIRCLE PORSCHE
See ALANT CORP

D-U-N-S 10-462-4221 IMP/EXP
▲ CIRCOR INTERNATIONAL INC
30 Corporate Dr Ste 200, Burlington, MA 01803-4252
Tel (781) 270-1200 Founded/Ownrshp 1999
Sales 656.2MM EMP 2,500^E
Tkr Sym CIR Exch NYS
SIC 3492 Fluid power valves & hose fittings; Control valves, fluid power: hydraulic & pneumatic
Pr: Scott A Buckhout
*Ch Bd: David F Dietz
Pr: Vincent Sandoval
Pr: Erik Wiik
CFO: Rajeev Bhalla
Treas: Tanya Dawkins
Ofcr: Andrew Farnsworth
VP: Clayton B Billey
VP: Frederic Burditt
VP: Sumit Mehrotra
VP: David F Mullen
VP: Arjun Sharma
VP: Mike Terrell
VP: Prabhu Thomas
VP Bus Dev: Steve Cartolano
Board of Directors: Douglas M Hayes, Norman E Johnson, Helmuth Ludwig, John A O'donnell, Peter M Wilver

D-U-N-S 88-308-3024
■ CIRCUS AND ELDORADO JOINT VENTURE LLC
SILVER LEGACY RESORT CASINO
(Suby of ELDORADO RESORTS INC) ★
407 N Virginia St, Reno, NV 89501-1138
Tel (777) 329-4777 Founded/Ownrshp 2015
Sales 113.2MM^E EMP 1,800^E
SIC 7011 Casino hotel; Resort hotel
CEO: Gary L Carano
*CFO: Stephanie D Lepori
IT Man: Michael Brown
Info Man: Dusty Durkee
Natl Sales: Carol Creekman

D-U-N-S 79-294-5586
■ CIRCUS CIRCUS CASINOS INC
CIRCUS CIRCUS HOTEL & CASINO
(Suby of MANDALAY BAY RESORT AND CASINO) ★
2880 Las Vegas Blvd S, Las Vegas, NV 89109-1138
Tel (702) 734-0410 Founded/Ownrshp 1983
Sales 137.5MM^E EMP 2,800^E
SIC 7011 Casino hotel
Pr: Donald Thrasher
Treas: Daniel J D'Arrigo
Exec: Bob Obrien
Secur Mgr: Marlon Beals
Natl Sales: Laurie Digrandi
Mktg Dir: Tom Malloy
Snr Mgr: Timothy Cole

CIRCUS CIRCUS HOTEL & CASINO
See CIRCUS CIRCUS CASINOS INC

CIRCUS CIRCUS RENO HT & CASINO
See CC-RENO LLC

CIRI
See COOK INLET REGION INC

D-U-N-S 79-465-5589
CIRI - STROUP INC
MILE HI VALET SERVICE
1 Park Pl Ste 200, Annapolis, MD 21401-3581
Tel (410) 267-6111 Founded/Ownrshp 1984
Sales 10.3MM^E EMP 1,000
SIC 7299 Valet parking
Pr: Rob Stroup
*VP: Joe Ciri

D-U-N-S 82-804-8277
CIRI DEVELOPMENT CORP
NORTH WIND GROUP
(Suby of CIRI) ★
1425 Higham St, Idaho Falls, ID 83402-1513
Tel (208) 528-8718 Founded/Ownrshp 2009
Sales 92.9MM EMP 86
Accts Cooper Norman Pocatello Idah
SIC 6519 6552 Real property lessors; Subdividers & developers
CEO: Margaret L Brown
COO: Sophie R Minich
CFO: Patrick W Duke
VP: Gregory P Razo
Genl Mgr: Jade Dye

D-U-N-S 11-010-9048
CIRKS CONSTRUCTION INC
KDC CONSTRUCTION
2570 E Cerritos Ave, Anaheim, CA 92806-5636
Tel (714) 632-6717 Founded/Ownrshp 1995
Sales 93.5MM EMP 270
Accts John R Bates Cpa Santa Ana
SIC 1542 Nonresidential construction
CEO: Kenneth Dean Cirks
COO: Mike Dunne
*CFO: Kathleen Cirks
Genl Mgr: Carrie Castle
Genl Mgr: Christopher Sanders
Sales Exec: Paul Spiekerman
Snr PM: Curt Walters

D-U-N-S 13-109-1659 IMP/EXP
CIRQUE DU SOLEIL AMERICA INC
(Suby of CIRQUE DU SOLEIL INC)
980 Kelly Johnson Dr 2nd, Las Vegas, NV 89119-3768
Tel (702) 352-0200 Founded/Ownrshp 1995
Sales 155.3MM^E EMP 1,500^E
SIC 7929 Entertainers & entertainment groups
Pr: Guy Laliberte
*Pr: Daniel Lamarre
*Treas: Robert Blain
Off Mgr: Amy Reams
Pr Mgr: Anita Nelving

CIRRUS AIRCRAFT
See CIRRUS DESIGN CORP

D-U-N-S 60-590-1982 IMP
CIRRUS DESIGN CORP
CIRRUS AIRCRAFT
(Suby of CIRRUS INDUSTRIES INC) ★
4515 Taylor Cir, Hermantown, MN 55811-1548
Tel (218) 727-2737 Founded/Ownrshp 1996
Sales 235.0MM EMP 800
SIC 3721 Aircraft
Ch Bd: Dale Klapmeier
*Pr: Patrick Waddick
Sr VP: David Glorius
VP: Ian Bentley
VP: Gregory Bowles
VP: Paul Brey
VP: Jon Dauplaise
VP: Curtis Landherr
*VP: Todd Simmons

Dir Risk M: Daniel Desanto
Ex Dir: Paul Fiduccia

D-U-N-S 03-391-9510
CIRRUS INDUSTRIES INC
4515 Taylor Cir, Hermantown, MN 55811-1548
Tel (218) 727-2737 *Founded/Ownrshp* 1984
Sales 235.0MM[E] *EMP* 800
SIC 3721 Aircraft
**Pr:* Alan Klapmeier
**Pr:* Pat Wadick
**CFO:* Owen Gohlke
**Prin:* Brent Wouters

D-U-N-S 11-330-3614
▲ CIRRUS LOGIC INC
800 W 6th St, Austin, TX 78701-2722
Tel (512) 851-4000 *Founded/Ownrshp* 1984
Sales 1.1MMM *EMP* 1,104[E]
Accts Ernst & Young Llp Austin Te
Tkr Sym CRUS *Exch* NGS
SIC 3674 Microcircuits, integrated (semiconductor)
Pr: Jason P Rhode
**Ch Bd:* Alan R Schuele
CFO: Thurman K Case
Chf Cred: Jo-Dee M Benson
Div VP: Eric C Smith
VP: Dee M Benson
VP: Jo Benson
VP: Andrew Brennan
VP: Gregory Scott Thomas
VP: Bruce Tull
VP: Stan Victor
Board of Directors: John C Carter, Alexander M Davern, Timothy R Dehne, Christine King, William D Sherman, David J Tupman

D-U-N-S 15-380-4570 EXP
▲ CISCO SYSTEMS INC
170 W Tasman Dr, San Jose, CA 95134-1706
Tel (408) 526-4000 *Founded/Ownrshp* 1984
Sales 49.2MMM *EMP* 71,833
Tkr Sym CSCO *Exch* NGS
SIC 3577 7379 Computer peripheral equipment; Data conversion equipment, media-to-media: computer;
CEO: Charles H Robbins
**Ch Bd:* John T Chambers
CFO: Kelly A Kramer
Chf Cred: Mark Chandler
Bd of Dir: Mary Cirillo
Bd of Dir: David Draper
Bd of Dir: Antoinette Eckersley
Bd of Dir: Kevin Hughes
Bd of Dir: Richard Kovacevich
Bd of Dir: Brad Pavelec
Ex VP: Chris Dedicoat
Ex VP: Pankaj Patel
Ex VP: Pankaj S Patel
Sr VP: Jesper Andersen
Sr VP: Guillermo Diaz Jr
Sr VP: Rebecca J Jacoby
Sr VP: Bryan Palma
Sr VP: Karen Walker
VP: Georges Antoun
VP: Debbie Bernard
VP: Andy Blackburn
Board of Directors: Steven M West, Carol A Bartz, M Michele Burns, Michael D Capellas, Amy L Chang, Brian L Halla, John L Hennessy, Kristina M Johnson, Roderick C McGeary, Arun Sarin

CISCO SYSTEMS INTERNATIONAL
See SCIENTIFIC-ATLANTA LLC

D-U-N-S 05-927-3941
■ CISCO WEBEX LLC
WEBEX.COM
(*Suby of* CISCO SYSTEMS INC) ★
170 W Tasman Dr, San Jose, CA 95134-1706
Tel (408) 435-7000 *Founded/Ownrshp* 1995
Sales 186.0MM[E] *EMP* 2,411
SIC 7389 4813 Teleconferencing services; Data telephone communications; Voice telephone communications
Ex VP: Yugantar Saikia
VP: Hesham Eassa
VP: Morris Porter
VP: Mitch Tarica
Exec: Christopher Dereux
Exec: Ashish Gupta
Exec: Barbara Harvey
Exec: Minh Tran
Dir Surg: John Bow
Dir Surg: Patrick Moran
Ex Dir: Sagarika Mohapatra

D-U-N-S 00-519-1895
CISION US INC
130 E Randolph St Fl 7, Chicago, IL 60601-6164
Tel (312) 922-2400 *Founded/Ownrshp* 1892
Sales 177.4MM[E] *EMP* 1,310[E]
SIC 7389 2741 7331 Press clipping service; Miscellaneous publishing; Mailing service
CEO: Kevin Akeroyd
**Pr:* Jason Edelboim
Chf Mktg O: Mark Thabit
**Ex VP:* Jack Pearlstein
VP: K Brown
VP: Venessa Bugasch
VP: Karey Hoffman
VP: Kevin Hoppenrath
VP: Ryan Rohaley
Dir Soc: Mary-Morgan Limperis
Comm Dir: Breeanna Straessle
Dir Bus: Jay Krall
Dir Bus: Beth Roed

CIT
See CENTRAL ILLINOIS TRUCKS INC

D-U-N-S 13-677-3608
CIT BANK
2150 S 1300 E Ste 400, Salt Lake City, UT 84106-4336
Tel (801) 412-6800 *Founded/Ownrshp* 2000
Sales NA *EMP* 21[E]
SIC 6036

D-U-N-S 82-999-9486
■ CIT BANK NA
(*Suby of* CIT GROUP INC) ★
75 N Fair Oaks Ave, Pasadena, CA 91103-3651
Tel (626) 535-4300 *Founded/Ownrshp* 2009
Sales NA *EMP* 850[E]
SIC 6021 National commercial banks
Prin: Joseph Otting
**Ch Bd:* Ellen R Alemany
Pr: James P Broom
Pr: James L Hudak
Pr: C Jeffrey Knittel
Pr: Steven Solk
**Treas:* Kenneth A Brause
Chf Cred: Kris Gagnon
Chf Cred: Kevin Young
Ofcr: Robert C Rowe
Ex VP: Grant Kevin Ahearn
Ex VP: Bryan D Allen
Ex VP: Matthew Galligan
**Ex VP:* Stacey Goodman
**Ex VP:* Carol Hayles
Ex VP: Ken Horner
**Ex VP:* Robert J Ingato
Ex VP: Kurt Johnson
Ex VP: Jay Jones
Ex VP: Jay Sanders
Ex VP: Jeff Shular
Board of Directors: Dorene C Dominguez, Michael J Embler, Alan L Frank, Steven T Mnuchin, David M Moffett, R Brad Oates, Marianne Miller Parrs, Gerald Rosenfeld, Sheila A Stamps

D-U-N-S 96-972-3050
■ CIT FINANCE LLC
(*Suby of* CIT BANK NA) ★
1 Cit Dr, Livingston, NJ 07039-5703
Tel (973) 740-5000 *Founded/Ownrshp* 2011
Sales NA *EMP* 107[E]
SIC 6159 Machinery & equipment finance leasing
Pr: Dan Riggs

D-U-N-S 86-844-4696
■ CIT FINANCIAL USA INC
(*Suby of* CIT GROUP INC) ★
1 Cit Dr, Livingston, NJ 07039-5703
Tel (973) 740-5000 *Founded/Ownrshp* 1994
Sales NA *EMP* 500
SIC 6159 Equipment & vehicle finance leasing companies
Pr: Bradley Nullmeyer
CFO: Kenneth Brause
CFO: Kenneth D Reynolds
CFO: Robert Schenker
Sr VP: Timothy J White
VP: Charles J Day
VP: Robert J Ingato
VP: Frank Madeira
VP: Cynthia Mazzetta
VP: Kathleen A Nassaney
VP: William L Schumm
VP: Linda M Seufert

D-U-N-S 00-698-1492
■ CIT GROUP (NJ) LLC
(*Suby of* CIT GROUP INC) ★
1 Cit Dr, Livingston, NJ 07039-5703
Tel (973) 740-5000 *Founded/Ownrshp* 1908
Sales 187.2MM[E] *EMP* 690
SIC 8741 Administrative management; Financial management for business
CEO: John A Thain
**V Ch Bd:* Joseph A Pollicino
**Ex VP:* Thomas L Abbate
**Ex VP:* William Baronoff
VP: Carolyn Menz

D-U-N-S 15-536-1595 IMP/EXP
▲ CIT GROUP INC
11 W 42nd St Fl 7, New York, NY 10036-8012
Tel (212) 461-5200 *Founded/Ownrshp* 1908
Sales NA *EMP* 4,900
Tkr Sym CIT *Exch* NYS
SIC 6022 6162 6159 6141 State commercial banks; Mortgage bankers; Equipment & vehicle finance leasing companies; Machinery & equipment finance leasing; Consumer finance companies
Ch Bd: Ellen R Alemany
Pr: Matthew Galligan
Pr: James L Hudak
Pr: Joy Kelly
Pr: C Jeffrey Knittel
Pr: Joyce Mason-Fingal
Pr: Terry McCreery
Pr: Maria Recasino
Pr: Steve Solk
Pr: Steven Solk
COO: Stacey Goodman
CFO: E Carol Hayles
Chf Cred: Marisa J Harney
Ofcr: Bryan D Allen
Ofcr: Raymond D Matsumoto
Ofcr: Kelley Morrell
Ofcr: Robert C Rowe
Ex VP: Stuart Alderoty
Ex VP: Andrew T Brandman
Ex VP: James J Duffy
Ex VP: Robert J Ingato
Board of Directors: Peter J Tobin, Michael Brosnan, Laura S Unger, Michael A Carpenter, Alan Frank, William M Freeman, R Brad Oates, Marianne Miller Parrs, Gerald Rosenfeld, John R Ryan, Sheila A Stamps

D-U-N-S 05-666-8270
■ CIT GROUP/COMMERCIAL SERVICES INC
(*Suby of* CIT GROUP INC) ★
11 W 42nd St Fl 11, New York, NY 10036-8002
Tel (212) 461-5200 *Founded/Ownrshp* 2012
Sales NA *EMP* 850
SIC 6153 Purchasers of accounts receivable & commercial paper
Ch Bd: Jonathan A Lucas
Ch: John F Daly
Sr VP: Charles R Powell

D-U-N-S 05-848-4569
CIT INC
CHICAGO INTERNATIONAL TRUCKS
103 S Larkin Ave, Joliet, IL 60436-1230
Tel (815) 741-7500 *Founded/Ownrshp* 2004
Sales 126.5MM[E] *EMP* 350
SIC 5511 Trucks, tractors & trailers: new & used
Pr: Gerald G Beals
**Sec:* Shelby Howard
**VP:* Ken Yacobozzi

D-U-N-S 92-609-4384
■ CIT SMALL BUSINESS LENDING CORP
(*Suby of* CIT GROUP INC) ★
1 Cit Dr, Livingston, NJ 07039-5703
Tel (973) 740-5000 *Founded/Ownrshp* 1991
Sales NA *EMP* 1,000
SIC 6036 Savings & loan associations, not federally chartered
Prin: Ellen R Alemany
Sr VP: William Hopf
VP: Edward Burns
VP: Richard Clark
VP: Gary J Gardiner
VP: Chris Hardwick
VP: William Odrady
Mng Dir: Jason Meek
Manager: Wade Phelps

D-U-N-S 17-760-4626
CITADEL BROADCASTING CO
7201 W Lake Mead Blvd # 400, Las Vegas, NV 89128-8366
Tel (702) 804-5200 *Founded/Ownrshp* 1993
Sales NA *EMP* 3,500
SIC 4832

D-U-N-S 78-042-9841
■ CITADEL BROADCASTING CORP
(*Suby of* CUMULUS MEDIA INC) ★
3280 Peachtree Rd Ne # 2300, Atlanta, GA 30305-2430
Tel (404) 949-0700 *Founded/Ownrshp* 1993
Sales 437.5MM[E] *EMP* 4,100
SIC 4832 Radio broadcasting stations
Pr: Lewis W Dickey Jr
**CFO:* Randy L Taylor

D-U-N-S 10-853-3399
CITADEL FEDERAL CREDIT UNION INC
520 Eagleview Blvd, Exton, PA 19341-1119
Tel (610) 380-6000 *Founded/Ownrshp* 1937
Sales NA *EMP* 310
SIC 6061 Federal credit unions
V Ch: Glenn Saltis
**Pr:* Jeff March
**CFO:* Maria Stafy
VP: Lisa Allison
VP: Michael Haldeman
VP: Pamela Krupansky
VP: Jim McCrudden
VP: Eric Skinner
Exec: Margolit Hillsberg
Exec: Charles Retif
Exec: Theresa Stringer

D-U-N-S 01-570-7898
■ CITADEL INTERMEDIATE HOLDINGS LLC
(*Suby of* CITADEL PLASTICS HOLDINGS INC) ★
3637 Ridgewood Rd, Fairlawn, OH 44333-3123
Tel (330) 666-3751 *Founded/Ownrshp* 2008
Sales 195.6MM[E] *EMP* 456[E]
SIC 5162 Plastics resins
CEO: Bernard Rzepka

D-U-N-S 05-233-4117
CITADEL LAND INC
WASHINGTON HOMES
1802 Brightseat Rd # 600, Landover, MD 20785-4232
Tel (301) 683-6498 *Founded/Ownrshp* 1992
Sales 700.0MM *EMP* 500
SIC 6552 Subdividers & developers
Pr: Geaton Decesaris Jr

D-U-N-S 84-789-9226
CITADEL LLC
131 S Dearborn St Ste 200, Chicago, IL 60603-5563
Tel (312) 395-2100 *Founded/Ownrshp* 1990
Sales 721.2MM[E] *EMP* 1,000[E]
SIC 6211 Traders, security
CEO: Kenneth Cordele Griffin
COO: Gerald Albert Beeson
COO: Chris Martin
Ofcr: Lauren Butkus
Top Exec: Derek Kaufman
Top Exec: Jaine Mehring
Top Exec: Mark Stainton
VP: David Dillon
VP: William Halabi
VP: Laurie Haning
VP: Jennifer Hong
VP: Jing Jan
VP: Karen Jones
VP: Chuck Lugay
VP: Brad Mann
Exec: Matthew McCann
Assoc Dir: Larry Troksa

D-U-N-S 06-957-5331
■ CITADEL PLASTICS HOLDINGS INC
(*Suby of* HGGC CITADEL PLASTICS INTERMEDIATE HOLDINGS, INC.)
3637 Ridgewood Rd, Fairlawn, OH 44333-3123
Tel (330) 666-3751 *Founded/Ownrshp* 2015
Sales 208.5MM[E] *EMP* 430[E]
SIC 6719 Investment holding companies, except banks
CEO: Bernard Rzepka
Sr VP: Dwayne Dillahay
Off Admin: Bryan Farmer
Sfty Dirs: Greg Gray

D-U-N-S 83-170-6689
■ CITADEL PLASTICS HOLDINGS INC
(*Suby of* A SCHULMAN INC) ★
150 N Radnor Chester Rd, Wayne, PA 19087-5252
Tel (484) 844-0231 *Founded/Ownrshp* 2015
Sales 472.7MM *EMP* 550
SIC 5162 Plastics resins

CEO: Mike Huff
VP: Hector Diaz-Stringel

CITARELLA
See GREENWICH VILLAGE FISH CO INC

D-U-N-S 17-832-6633
CITATION CRUDE MARKETING INC
(*Suby of* CITATION OIL & GAS CORP) ★
14077 Cutten Rd, Houston, TX 77069-2212
Tel (281) 891-1000 *Founded/Ownrshp* 1997
Sales 710.0MM *EMP* 12[E]
SIC 5172 Crude oil
Pr: Forrest E Harrell Jr
**VP:* Jerry Martin

D-U-N-S 18-809-3199
CITATION INSURANCE CO
(*Suby of* MAPFRE USA CORP) ★
211 Main St, Webster, MA 01570-2249
Tel (508) 943-9000 *Founded/Ownrshp* 1981
Sales NA *EMP* 5
SIC 6411 Property & casualty insurance agent
Pr: Arthur J Remillard Jr
**Treas:* Gerald Fels
CTO: Richard Rapacki

D-U-N-S 05-877-8853
CITATION OIL & GAS CORP
14077 Cutten Rd, Houston, TX 77069-2212
Tel (281) 891-1000 *Founded/Ownrshp* 1985
Sales 273.7MM *EMP* 507
SIC 1311 1382 Crude petroleum production; Natural gas production; Oil & gas exploration services
Ch Bd: Forrest E Harrell
**Pr:* C F Harrell
**COO:* Curtis Harrell
**CFO:* Chris Phelps
**Sr VP:* Steve Anna
**VP:* Curtis Carver
VP: Craig Townsend
VP: Wayne Wiesen

CITGO
See J D STREETT & CO INC

CITGO
See GALATI YACHT SALES LLC

D-U-N-S 85-870-6773 IMP/EXP
CITGO HOLDING INC
(*Suby of* PDV HOLDING INC) ★
1293 Eldridge Pkwy, Houston, TX 77077-1670
Tel (281) 531-0004 *Founded/Ownrshp* 1986
Sales 2.7MMM[E] *EMP* 5,000
SIC 2911 2992 5171 4213 Petroleum refining; Gasoline; Diesel fuels; Jet fuels; Lubricating oils & greases; Petroleum bulk stations & terminals; Trucking, except local
Ch Bd: Claus Graf
**Pr:* Alonso Velasco
CFO: Luis Vierma
**VP:* Angel Olmeta

D-U-N-S 94-241-4244 IMP
CITGO INVESTMENT CO
(*Suby of* CITGO PETROLEUM CORP) ★
6100 S Yale Ave Ste 1200, Tulsa, OK 74136-1905
Tel (918) 254-6062 *Founded/Ownrshp* 1996
Sales 221.8MM[E] *EMP* 1,400[E]
SIC 2911 Petroleum refining
Pr: Jerry E Thompson
**CEO:* Phoenix Rodiriguez
**VP:* Peer L Anderson

D-U-N-S 10-241-7268 IMP/EXP
CITGO PETROLEUM CORP
(*Suby of* CITGO HOLDING INC) ★
1293 Eldridge Pkwy, Houston, TX 77077-1670
Tel (832) 486-4000 *Founded/Ownrshp* 1983
Sales 2.5MMM[E] *EMP* 4,000
SIC 2911 5171 4213 4612 Petroleum refining; Gasoline; Diesel fuels; Jet fuels; Petroleum bulk stations & terminals; Trucking, except local; Crude petroleum pipelines
CEO: Nelson P Martinez
Treas: Maritza Villanueva
**VP:* Eduardo Assef
**VP:* Jim Cristman
VP: Dar O Merch N
**VP:* Jose Pereira
VP: Gustavo Vel Squez
**VP:* Fernando Valera
VP: Gustavo Velasquez
Dir Risk M: Pete Colarelli
Prin: Rafael Gomez Abreu
Board of Directors: Nelson Martinez, William Padron, Luis Vierma

CITGO REFINERY
See PDV MIDWEST REFINING LLC

D-U-N-S 00-694-9655
■ CITI ASSURANCE SERVICES INC
AMERICAN HEALTH & LF INSUR CO
(*Suby of* CITIFINANCIAL CREDIT CO) ★
3001 Meacham Blvd Ste 100, Fort Worth, TX 76137-4615
Tel (817) 348-7500 *Founded/Ownrshp* 1954
Sales NA *EMP* 400
SIC 6321 6411 Health insurance carriers; Life insurance agents
Pr: Peter B Dahlberg
CFO: Micah Bueheler
CFO: Robert Healy
VP: Candace Richter
CTO: Darrell Gambero
MIS Dir: Janna Sappenfield

D-U-N-S 06-975-9579
■ CITI FINANCIAL AUTO
(*Suby of* CITIGROUP INC) ★
250 E John Carpenter Fwy, Irving, TX 75062-2806
Tel (972) 652-4000 *Founded/Ownrshp* 1969, 2001
Sales NA *EMP* 4,500
SIC 6141 Consumer finance companies
Pr: Thomas R Slone
Treas: John F Hughes
VP: Joe Flores

D-U-N-S 78-771-6331
■ CITI INVESTOR SERVICES INC
(*Suby of* CITIBANK NA) ★
105 Eisenhower Pkwy Ste 2, Roseland, NJ 07068-1640
Tel (973) 461-2500 *Founded/Ownrshp* 2007
Sales NA *EMP* 5,000
SIC 6411 7374 Pension & retirement plan consultants; Data processing service
Pr: Robert Wallace
Pr: Eric Anderson
Pr: James L Fox
Pr: Fred Naddaff
Chf Mktg O: Frederick Schmidt
Ofcr: Gary Boccio
**Ex VP:* J Robert Jones Jr
**Ex VP:* William W Neville
Sr VP: Armando Ramirez
Sr VP: Gerald Roth
VP: Michelle Juarbe
Exec: Ivelis Reyes

D-U-N-S 05-900-2977
▲ CITI TRENDS INC
104 Coleman Blvd, Savannah, GA 31408-9565
Tel (912) 236-1561 *Founded/Ownrshp* 1946
Sales 683.7MM *EMP* 5,500
Accts Kpmg Llp Jacksonville Florid
Tkr Sym CTRN *Exch* NGS
SIC 5611 5621 5641 5632 Men's & boys' clothing stores; Women's clothing stores; Dress shops; Women's sportswear; Children's & infants' wear stores; Children's wear; Infants' wear; Lingerie (outerwear); Handbags; Costume jewelry; Apparel accessories
Ch Bd: R Edward Anderson
Pr: Jason T Mazzola
COO: Bruce D Smith
Chf Cred: Ivy D Council
Sr VP: Charles D Crowell
Sr VP: James A Dunn
VP: Elizabeth Burrows
VP: Victor Cheng
VP: Yuriy Kushnir
VP: Melissa Mercado
VP: Chuck Strickland

D-U-N-S 00-698-3704 IMP
■ CITIBANK NA
(*Suby of* CITIGROUP INC) ★
399 Park Ave Bsmt 1, New York, NY 10022-4699
Tel (212) 559-1000 *Founded/Ownrshp* 1998
Sales NA *EMP* 118,240
SIC 6021 6153 6091 6099 6162 National commercial banks; Mercantile financing; Nondeposit trust facilities; Travelers' checks issuance; Mortgage bankers; Loan correspondents
CEO: Barbara J Desoer
Pr: Thierry Jenar
Pr: Timothy Robless
Pr: John Welch
CEO: Michael Corbat
COO: Michael R Dunn
CFO: Max Lucas
V Ch Bd: Onno H Ruding
Ofcr: Gary Fisher
Ofcr: Joani Van Wyk
Ex VP: Rick Kapur
Ex VP: Karen Shechtman
Sr VP: Elizabeth Craig
Sr VP: Raleigh V John
VP: Igor Aminov
VP: Robert Ball
VP: Nor Basir
VP: Sumit Basu
VP: Michael Black
VP: Stacey Bowen
VP: Deanna Bump
Board of Directors: D Wayne Calloway, John M Deutch, Duncan P Hennes, Reuben Mark, Richard D Parsons, Rozanne L Ridgway, Robert B Shapiro, Frank A Shrontz, Franklin A Thomas

D-U-N-S 05-435-3644
■ CITIBANK NATIONAL ASSOCIATION
(*Suby of* CITIGROUP INC) ★
701 E 60th St N, Sioux Falls, SD 57104-0493
Tel (605) 331-2626 *Founded/Ownrshp* 1981, 2009
Sales NA *EMP* 9,123
SIC 6021 National commercial banks
Pr: Ken Stork
**VP:* Dennis Lee
**VP:* Kari Logan
**Mng Dir:* Reginald Chen
**Mng Dir:* Usama Mikdashi
CIO: Gary Hoberman
Web Dev: Betty Schack
Doctor: Shrikant Bhat

D-U-N-S 15-458-1771
■ CITICORP BANKING CORP
(*Suby of* CITIGROUP INC) ★
1 Penns Way, New Castle, DE 19721-2300
Tel (302) 323-3140 *Founded/Ownrshp* 1979
Sales NA *EMP* 19,100
SIC 6162 Mortgage bankers & correspondents
Pr: Richard Collins
Mng Dir: Kent Lorentzen

D-U-N-S 13-148-8397
■ CITICORP CREDIT SERVICES INC
(*Suby of* CITIGROUP INC) ★
One Court Square 25th Flr, Long Island City, NY 11120-0001
Tel (718) 248-3192 *Founded/Ownrshp* 1969
Sales 593.2MM^E *EMP* 18,634
SIC 7389

D-U-N-S 15-179-2389
■ CITICORP CREDIT SERVICES INC
(*Suby of* ASSOCIATES FIRST CAPITAL CORP) ★
50 Northwest Point Blvd, Elk Grove Village, IL 60007-1032
Tel (847) 597-3000 *Founded/Ownrshp* 1985
Sales 87.7MM^E *EMP* 2,720^E
SIC 7374 7389 7379 6141 Data processing service; Credit card service; Computer related consulting services; Personal credit institutions

VP: Larry H Myatt

D-U-N-S 79-617-0553
■ CITICORP DEL-LEASE INC
(*Suby of* CITIBANK NATIONAL ASSOCIATION) ★
1 Penns Way, New Castle, DE 19721-2300
Tel (302) 323-3801 *Founded/Ownrshp* 2006
Sales NA *EMP* 1,000
SIC 6022 6311 6321 State commercial banks; Life insurance; Disability health insurance
Pr: William Silver
Treas: Nick Lamour
VP: Timothy Cormany
VP: Gregory Taylor
Dir IT: Mark Maxwell
Board of Directors: Robert Delfoe, J Marius Leap

D-U-N-S 00-698-2896
■ CITICORP DINERS CLUB INC
CITIGROUP
(*Suby of* CITIBANK NATIONAL ASSOCIATION) ★
50 Northwest Point Blvd, Elk Grove Village, IL 60007-1032
Tel (847) 472-6041 *Founded/Ownrshp* 1949, 1981
Sales NA *EMP* 9,123
SIC 6021 National commercial banks
Pr: Brenda Gaines
**CFO:* Jerry Wolff
Sr VP: Jon Zuspann
VP: Pat Heyne
VP: Elsa Krokos
VP: Sue Perkinson
Dir Risk M: Shailesh Dhiman
Snr Mgr: Kimberly Meyer

D-U-N-S 05-523-2656
CITICORP NORTH AMERICA INC
450 Mamaroneck Ave Ste A, Harrison, NY 10528-2402
Tel (914) 899-7000 *Founded/Ownrshp* 1987
Sales NA *EMP* 4,067
SIC 6153 6159

D-U-N-S 78-630-3040
■ CITICORP SELECT INVESTMENTS INC
(*Suby of* CITIBANK NA) ★
1 Court Sq Fl 24, Long Island City, NY 11101
Tel (212) 559-1000 *Founded/Ownrshp* 1989
Sales 169.5MM^E *EMP* 750
SIC 6282 Investment advisory service
Ch Bd: Steven J Freiberg
**Ch Bd:* William J Maguire
Treas: Nancy Baroutas
Sr VP: Denise Arbesu
Sr VP: David Valcic
VP: Jill Maitland
VP: Bernadette Tripaldi
Dir Risk M: Carl Cho
Mng Dir: Christopher Abbate
Mng Dir: Sumanta Panigrahi
**CIO:* John Schwartzman

D-U-N-S 00-694-9929
■ CITIFINANCIAL CREDIT CO
(*Suby of* CITICORP BANKING CORP) ★
300 Saint Paul St Fl 3, Baltimore, MD 21202-2120
Tel (410) 332-3000 *Founded/Ownrshp* 1912, 1999
Sales NA *EMP* 19,000
SIC 6141 6162 7389 6331 6159 6022 Consumer finance companies; Installment sales finance, other than banks; Mortgage bankers; Credit card service; Fire, marine & casualty insurance; Property damage insurance; Fire, marine & casualty insurance: stock; Automobile insurance; Machinery & equipment finance leasing; State commercial banks
Ch Bd: Robert B Willumstad
Pr: Dave Gamache
**Pr:* Marjorie Magner
Pr: Carlton Matthews
CFO: David Keaves
CFO: David Neades
**CFO:* David Neaves
**Ex VP:* Linda S Davis
VP: Joan Cronin
VP: D Decarlosandro
VP: Gary B Hopkins
Dir Risk M: Debasmit Mohanty

CITIGROUP
See CITICORP DINERS CLUB INC

D-U-N-S 01-845-7739
■ CITIGROUP FINANCIAL PRODUCTS INC
(*Suby of* CITIGROUP GLOBAL MARKETS HOLDINGS INC) ★
388 Greenwich St, New York, NY 10013-2375
Tel (212) 816-6000 *Founded/Ownrshp* 1999
Sales 892.4MM^E *EMP* 6,900
SIC 6211 Dealers, security
Ch Bd: Deryck C Maughan
Treas: Eric Aboaf
**Treas:* Thomas Jasper
**Treas:* Mark I Kleinman
VP: Margaret Ammirati
**Exec:* Jay Mandelbaum
Mng Dir: Richard Banziger
Mng Dir: Robert Chesley
Mng Dir: Sunita Koshy
Mng Dir: Jason Wortendyke
Software D: Sharad Kumar

D-U-N-S 00-214-1281
■ CITIGROUP GLOBAL MARKETS HOLDINGS INC (NY)
(*Suby of* CITIGROUP INC) ★
388 Greenwich St, New York, NY 10013-2375
Tel (212) 816-6000 *Founded/Ownrshp* 1874, 1997
Sales 6.1MMM *EMP* 39,000
SIC 6211 Investment bankers; Distributors, security; Traders, security; Securities flotation companies
Ch Bd: James Forese
VP: David Pustylnik
Mng Dir: Nicholas Letica
Tech Mgr: Vitaliy Dubinskiy
Software D: Andrea Dicaprio

D-U-N-S 00-699-0428
■ CITIGROUP GLOBAL MARKETS INC
(*Suby of* CITIGROUP GLOBAL MARKETS HOLDINGS INC) ★
388 Greenwich St Fl 18, New York, NY 10013-2375
Tel (212) 816-6000 *Founded/Ownrshp* 1997
Sales 4.7MMM^E *EMP* 28,000
SIC 6211 6221 6282 Security brokers & dealers; Brokers, security; Dealers, security; Investment bankers; Commodity brokers, contracts; Investment advisory service; Investment research
Ch Bd: James Forese
**CEO:* Robert Druskin
COO: Alan S Macdonald
**CFO:* Hans Marth
Treas: Eric W Aboaf
Sr VP: Basil Darwish
Sr VP: Nareg Dermanuelian
Sr VP: Ruby Leung
VP: Spencer Goodman
VP: Damian Oberding
VP: Keith Pinniger
VP: Christo Realov
**VP:* Danielle Romero Sr
VP: Richard Saybolt
VP: Courtney Storz

D-U-N-S 19-732-9691 IMP/EXP
▲ CITIGROUP INC
399 Park Ave, New York, NY 10022-4699
Tel (212) 559-1000 *Founded/Ownrshp* 1988
Sales NA *EMP* 231,000
Tkr Sym C *Exch* NYS
SIC 6021 6141 6331 6311 6321 National commercial banks; Consumer finance companies; Installment sales finance, other than banks; Property damage insurance; Fire, marine & casualty insurance: stock; Automobile insurance; Workers' compensation insurance; Life insurance carriers; Life reinsurance; Accident insurance carriers; Health insurance carriers; Indemnity plans health insurance, except medical service
CEO: Michael L Corbat
Ch Bd: Michael E O'Neill
Pr: James A Forese
CEO: Francisco Aristeguieta
CEO: Stephen Bird
CEO: James C Cowles
CEO: Barbara Desoer
CEO: Jane Fraser
CEO: William J Mills
CFO: John C Gerspach
Ofcr: Bradford Hu
Board of Directors: Anthony M Santomero, Ellen M Costello, Joan E Spero, Ernesto Zedillo Ponce De L, Diana L Taylor, Duncan P Hennes, William S Thompson Jr, Peter B Henry, James S Turley, Franz B Humer, Renee J James, Eugene M McQuade, Gary M Reiner, Judith Rodin

D-U-N-S 19-973-3374
■ CITIGROUP VENTURE CAPITAL INTERNATIONAL DE CORP
(*Suby of* CITIGROUP INC) ★
731 Lexington Ave Fl 21, New York, NY 10022-1344
Tel (212) 559-5099 *Founded/Ownrshp* 2005
Sales 367.2MM^E *EMP* 2,010
SIC 6799 Venture capital companies
Prin: Bob Khanna
Pr: Michael Black
Sr VP: Viqar Ali
Sr VP: Paul Army
Sr VP: Wanda Bell
Sr VP: Gregory M Eisel
Sr VP: Fred Hess
Sr VP: Gisela Sucre
Sr VP: Virginia Volpe
VP: Michael Botek
VP: Steve Brennan
VP: Joseph Caiati
VP: Kevin S Chen
VP: Lev Feldman
VP: Luis Fontanilla
VP: Mark Gilder
VP: Steven Goodfriend
VP: John Harrington
VP: Brian Huffman
VP: Doris McLaughlin
VP: Andre Mol

D-U-N-S 15-511-5819
CITIHOPE INTERNATIONAL INC
629 Main St Ste 2, Margaretville, NY 12455-8019
Tel (845) 586-6202 *Founded/Ownrshp* 1985
Sales 93.1MM *EMP* 10
Accts Davidson Fox & Company Llp Bi
SIC 8322 Individual & family services
COO: Paul Moore II
**Treas:* Jessica Moore

D-U-N-S 09-794-2163
■ CITIMORTGAGE INC
(*Suby of* CITICORP BANKING CORP) ★
1000 Technology Dr, O Fallon, MO 63368-2240
Tel (636) 261-2484 *Founded/Ownrshp* 1987
Sales NA *EMP* 4,900
SIC 6162 Mortgage bankers
**Ch Bd:* Carl E Levinson
**COO:* David Lowman

D-U-N-S 05-343-5525
CITIZEN POTAWATOMI NATION
TRIBAL GOVERNMENT
1601 Gordon Cooper Dr, Shawnee, OK 74801-9002
Tel (405) 275-3121 *Founded/Ownrshp* 1935
Sales 69.5MM^E *EMP* 2,300
Accts Bkd Llp Tulsa Ok
SIC 7992 5411 7011 8412 Public golf courses; Convenience stores; Casino hotel; Museum
Ch: John A Rocky' Barrett
V Ch: John Barrett
**CFO:* Susan Blair
**Treas:* D Wayne Trousdale
Ofcr: Christie Gilmore
Ofcr: Rodney Kitchen
Genl Mgr: Kasie Nichols
CIO: Starsha Seamon
Dir IT: Jt Summerlin

Software D: Anthony Arington
Software D: Justin Dunsworth

D-U-N-S 07-882-2863 IMP
CITIZEN WATCH CO OF AMERICA INC
(*Suby of* CITIZEN WATCH CO., LTD.)
1000 W 190th St, Torrance, CA 90502-1040
Tel (310) 532-8463 *Founded/Ownrshp* 2007
Sales 107.3MM^E *EMP* 300
SIC 5094 3829

D-U-N-S 05-448-6048
■ CITIZENS AND FARMERS BANK
(*Suby of* C&F FINANCIAL CORP) ★
802 Main St, West Point, VA 23181-9574
Tel (804) 843-2360 *Founded/Ownrshp* 1927
Sales NA *EMP* 250
SIC 6022 State commercial banks
CEO: Larry Dillon
**Pr:* Thomas Cherry
Pr: Gail Letts
CFO: Jason Long
VP: Ellen Howard
VP: Teresa Weaver
Brnch Mgr: Don Hillbish
VP Sls: Maria Campbell
Board of Directors: Julie Richardson Agnew

CITIZENS BANK
See CITIZENS FINANCIAL GROUP INC

D-U-N-S 00-695-9290
CITIZENS BANK
328 S Saginaw St Lbby, Flint, MI 48502-1926
Tel (810) 766-7500 *Founded/Ownrshp* 2011
Sales NA *EMP* 1,970^E
SIC 6022 6159 6162

D-U-N-S 00-791-8469 IMP/EXP
■ CITIZENS BANK NATIONAL ASSOCIATION
(*Suby of* CITIZENS BANK) ★
1 Citizens Plz Ste 1, Providence, RI 02903-1339
Tel (401) 282-7000 *Founded/Ownrshp* 1828, 2005
Sales NA *EMP* 14,772
SIC 6021 National commercial banks
Ch Bd: Bruce Van Saun
Pr: Chris Nard
Pr: Chris Ward
**CFO:* Eric W Aboaf
Sr VP: Richard Davis
Sr VP: Matthew M Egan
Sr VP: Michael R Goulet
VP: Ilda S Amado
VP: Mary Gendreau
VP: William R Gray Jr
VP: Stephan Joe
VP: Brenda L Lapierre
VP: Shelbey Lukowicz-Allen
VP: Scott McCaughey
VP: Shawn M Wilks
VP: Lori Williams
VP: Noreen Ann Winderlick

D-U-N-S 00-695-4184
■ CITIZENS BANK OF MASSACHUSETTS
(*Suby of* CITIZENS BANK) ★
28 State St Fl 13, Boston, MA 02109-1774
Tel (617) 725-5900 *Founded/Ownrshp* 1832
Sales NA *EMP* 1,645
SIC 6021 National commercial banks
Pr: Lawrence K Fish
Sr Pt: Gregory C Foy
CFO: Lori Evans
**CFO:* Kathleen Guilfoyle
**Ex VP:* Robert Crowley
Sr VP: Peter Galligan
**Sr VP:* William Granchelli
Sr VP: Mary Lenz
**VP:* Arlene Fortunato
VP Admn: Mike Dasaro

D-U-N-S 08-945-2101
■ CITIZENS BANK OF PENNSYLVANIA
(*Suby of* CITIZENS BANK) ★
130 N 18th St, Philadelphia, PA 19103-2757
Tel (267) 671-1000 *Founded/Ownrshp* 2001
Sales NA *EMP* 4,880
SIC 6022 6021 State commercial banks; National commercial banks
Pr: Daniel K Fitzpatrick
Ex VP: Karen A Bohn
Ex VP: Christophe P Terlizzi
Sr VP: Irene H Annan
Sr VP: Irene Horstmann Hannan
VP: Deborah J Khan
CIO: William Wray
Board of Directors: Stanley A Lowe

D-U-N-S 06-613-9155
■ CITIZENS BUSINESS BANK
(*Suby of* CVB FINANCIAL CORP) ★
701 N Haven Ave Ste 350, Ontario, CA 91764-4920
Tel (909) 980-4030 *Founded/Ownrshp* 1973
Sales NA *EMP* 784
SIC 6022 State commercial banks
Pr: Christopher D Myers
**Ch Bd:* D Linn Wiley
**CFO:* Edward J Biebrich Jr
**CFO:* Richard Thomas
**V Ch Bd:* George A Borba Jr
**V Ch Bd:* Raymond V Obrien III
**Chf Cred:* James F Dowd
Ex VP: Jay Coleman
**Ex VP:* David C Harvey
Sr VP: Paul Blankenship
Sr VP: Jeffrey S Boyer
Sr VP: Hector Gutierrez
Sr VP: Eric B Lucero
Sr VP: Paul F Rodeno
Sr VP: Ana Speer
Sr VP: Paul Stanislaw
VP: Deborah Andreotti
VP: Albert Chan
VP: Tammy Cornwell
VP: Kim Elias
VP: David Escalante
Board of Directors: Anna Kan, Ronald O Kruse, Raymond Vincent Obrien III

CITIZENS COMMUNICATIONS-CABS
See FRONTIER COMMUNICATIONS CORP

D-U-N-S 00-696-6790
CITIZENS ELECTRIC CORP
1500 Rand Ave, Perryville, MO 63775-1039
Tel (877) 876-3511 *Founded/Ownrshp* 1947
Sales 123.2MM *EMP* 90
SIC 4911 Distribution, electric power
CEO: Anthony Campbell
**Pr:* John Lottes
**CFO:* Van Robinson
Treas: Richard Dewilde
**Treas:* Herbert Fallert
**Treas:* Karl Klaus
**VP:* Alvin Franke
Brnch Mgr: John Rauh
VP Opers: Ron Klein

D-U-N-S 00-642-1481
CITIZENS ENERGY GROUP
CITIZENS GAS
2020 N Meridian St, Indianapolis, IN 46202-1306
Tel (317) 924-3341 *Founded/Ownrshp* 1935
Sales 711.4MM *EMP* 1,100
SIC 4925 Gas: mixed, natural & manufactured
Pr: Carey B Lykins
Treas: Lawrence O'Connor
Treas: Larry Oconnor
Bd of Dir: Daniel F Evans Jr
Bd of Dir: James Wade
Ofcr: Latona Prentice
**Sr VP:* Martin C Dusel
**Sr VP:* M Jean Richcreek
VP: Mark C Jacob
VP: John Lucas
Exec: Brenda Wade
Board of Directors: David Appel, Dennis Brady, Robert A Clark, David Goodrich, Mary Anne Mills, Andrew J Paine, James A Wade, Frank D Walker

D-U-N-S 93-350-5083
CITIZENS ENERGY SERVICES CO LLC
(*Suby of* CITIZENS GAS) ★
2020 N Meridian St, Indianapolis, IN 46202-1306
Tel (317) 927-6110 *Founded/Ownrshp* 1993
Sales 314.8MM[E] *EMP* 550
SIC 4924 Natural gas distribution
Pr: Carey Lykins
**CFO:* Jeffrey Harrison
**VP:* Aaron Johnson

D-U-N-S 03-054-7699
CITIZENS EQUITY FIRST CREDIT UNION
5401 W Everett M Dirksen, Peoria, IL 61607-1188
Tel (309) 633-3603 *Founded/Ownrshp* 1937
Sales NA *EMP* 730
SIC 6062 State credit unions
Pr: Mark Spenny
**COO:* Matt Mamer
**CFO:* Charles E Walker
Sr VP: Keith Reynolds
**VP:* Mary E Conrady
**VP:* Marianne A Moll
Off Mgr: Nicole Perry
CTO: Tim Dunton
Netwrk Eng: Mike Wise
VP Mktg: Sue Portscheller

D-U-N-S 79-740-5875
CITIZENS FINANCIAL CORP
BANKPLUS
202 E Jackson St, Belzoni, MS 39038-3524
Tel (662) 746-6811 *Founded/Ownrshp* 1981
Sales NA *EMP* 206
SIC 6022 6021 6141 State trust companies accepting deposits, commercial; National commercial banks; Financing: automobiles, furniture, etc., not a deposit bank
Pr: William A Ray
Ch Bd: Thomas G Peaster
CFO: Eloise S Patridge
VP: John Greenlee

D-U-N-S 13-175-8724 IMP/EXP
▲ CITIZENS FINANCIAL GROUP INC
CITIZENS BANK
1 Citizens Plz Ste 1, Providence, RI 02903-1345
Tel (401) 456-7000 *Founded/Ownrshp* 2015
Sales NA *EMP* 17,700
Tkr Sym CFG *Exch* NYS
SIC 6022 State commercial banks
Ch Bd: Bruce Van Saun
**CFO:* Eric W Aboaf
V Ch Bd: David Bowerman
V Ch Bd: Brad L Conner
V Ch Bd: Donald H McCree III
Ofcr: Brenda Watson
**Ex VP:* Malcolm Griggs
VP: Jason Briglia
VP: Timothy Burrill
VP: Isabel De Almeida
VP: Erik Johnson
VP: Leanne Kearney
VP: Steven Lionberger
VP: Paul Moriarty
VP: Kevin Murphy
VP: Frank Quaratiello
VP: Mandeep Singh
VP: Kelley Walker

D-U-N-S 03-584-3119
CITIZENS FIRST BANK (WI)
101 S Main St, Viroqua, WI 54665-1647
Tel (608) 637-3133 *Founded/Ownrshp* 1912, 2016
Sales NA *EMP* 50
SIC 6022

CITIZENS GAS
See CITIZENS ENERGY GROUP

D-U-N-S 60-180-8637
▲ CITIZENS INC
400 E Anderson Ln Ste 600, Austin, TX 78752-1223
Tel (512) 837-7100 *Founded/Ownrshp* 1969
Sales NA *EMP* 122[E]
Accts Ernst & Young Llp San Antonio
Tkr Sym CIA *Exch* NYS
SIC 6311 6321 Life insurance; Life insurance carriers; Accident & health insurance
CEO: Geoffrey M Kolander
Ch Bd: Robert Sloan Jr
CFO: David S Jorgensen
Ofcr: Kay E Osbourn
Board of Directors: E Dean Gage, Terry Maness, Steven F Shelton

D-U-N-S 00-695-9761
■ CITIZENS INSURANCE CO OF AMERICA
(*Suby of* HANOVER INSURANCE CO) ★
808 N Highlander Way, Howell, MI 48843-1076
Tel (517) 546-2160 *Founded/Ownrshp* 1993
Sales NA *EMP* 743
SIC 6331 Automobile insurance; Workers' compensation insurance; Fire, marine & casualty insurance & carriers
Pr: Paul Mueller
Treas: Joseph O Marker
VP: Patrick J Coffey
VP: Roger E Powlison

D-U-N-S 80-459-6760
■ CITIZENS INSURANCE CO OF MIDWEST
(*Suby of* HANOVER INSURANCE CO) ★
808 N Highlander Way, Howell, MI 48843-1076
Tel (517) 546-2160 *Founded/Ownrshp* 1995
Sales NA *EMP* 1[E]
SIC 6331 Fire, marine & casualty insurance
Pr: Marita Zuraitis
VP: Todd Bavery
VP: Matthew Mitchell
IT Man: Richard Luger

D-U-N-S 01-743-0273
CITIZENS LLC
870 S Main St, Vermontville, MI 49096-9468
Tel (517) 726-0514 *Founded/Ownrshp* 1988
Sales 91.2MM *EMP* 40
SIC 5191 5153 5999 2041

D-U-N-S 06-945-8024
CITIZENS MEDICAL CENTER
2701 Hospital Dr, Victoria, TX 77901-5749
Tel (361) 573-9181 *Founded/Ownrshp* 1956
Sales 28.6MM *EMP* 1,200
Accts Bkd Llp Houston Tx
SIC 8062 General medical & surgical hospitals
CEO: David P Brown
Chf Path: Leonard P Gietz
Chf OB: Tanya E Seiler
Chf Rad: Stephen W Tibbitts
**CFO:* Phil Hacker
CFO: Nancy Richardson
CFO: Stephen Thames
Bd of Dir: Omar Rachid
Ofcr: Cherie Brzozowski
Ofcr: Robert Kirk
VP: John B Jones
Dir Inf Cn: Bonnie Petti
Dir Lab: Sammie Sue Hendrix
Dir Bus: Keith Holland
Dir Env Sv: Rick Collie

D-U-N-S 13-958-3426
CITIZENS MEMORIAL HOSPITAL DISTRICT
1500 N Oakland Ave, Bolivar, MO 65613-3011
Tel (417) 326-6000 *Founded/Ownrshp* 1983
Sales 123.0MM *EMP* 122[E]
SIC 8011 Specialized medical practitioners, except internal
CEO: Donald Babb
CFO: Gary Fulbright
Ofcr: Kim Tilley
CIO: Denni McColm
Doctor: David B Rogers MD
Diag Rad: Jana B Horner

D-U-N-S 05-391-9650
CITIZENS MEMORIAL HOSPITAL DISTRICT OF POLK COUNTY
CMH
1500 N Oakland Ave, Bolivar, MO 65613-3011
Tel (417) 326-6000 *Founded/Ownrshp* 1982
Sales 78.2MM[E] *EMP* 1,400
SIC 8062 8011 8082 General medical & surgical hospitals; Medical centers; Home health care services
Pr: Donald Babb
**COO:* Jeff Miller M S
**CFO:* Gary Fulbright
Prgrm Mgr: Charles Gangluff
IT Man: Adam Carney

D-U-N-S 12-998-0616 IMP
CITIZENS OF HUMANITY LLC
GOLDSIGN
5715 Bickett St, Huntington Park, CA 90255-2624
Tel (323) 923-1240 *Founded/Ownrshp* 2002
Sales 86.7MM[E] *EMP* 180[E]
SIC 2339 Jeans: women's, misses' & juniors'
CEO: Jerome Dahan
**Pr:* Amy Williams
VP: Shelley Barham
CTO: Jared Freedman
Sls Dir: Suzanne Jones

D-U-N-S 80-405-1456
CITIZENS PROPERTY INSURANCE CORP
2101 Maryland Cir, Tallahassee, FL 32303-1001
Tel (888) 685-1555 *Founded/Ownrshp* 2002
Sales NA *EMP* 1,050
SIC 6311 Life insurance funds, savings bank
Pr: Barry Gilway
COO: Jennifer Montero
**CFO:* Sharon Binnun
**Ex VP:* Susanne Murphy
VP: Billye Murphy-Elpers
VP: Robert Sellers
Sys Admin: Alan Young
IT Man: William Joy
Opers Mgr: Gary Bryant

D-U-N-S 07-883-8512
CITIZENS RX LLC
1144 Lake St Ste 401, Oak Park, IL 60301-1043
Tel (888) 545-1120 *Founded/Ownrshp* 2010
Sales 500.0MM *EMP* 125
SIC 8742 Management consulting services
Ofcr: Jonathan Lichterman
VP: Sue Mellin
CIO: Jim Brady

D-U-N-S 83-238-9683
CITIZENS STATE BANK
1709 N Grant St, Roma, TX 78584-5407
Tel (956) 849-2311 *Founded/Ownrshp* 1978
Sales NA *EMP* 40
SIC 6022 State commercial banks
Pr: Salinas Roberto
**Sr VP:* Angie S Canales
**VP:* Clarissa B Alvarez
**VP:* Raul P Moreno Jr
**Exec:* Lucio E Gonzalez Jr

D-U-N-S 00-691-8304
■ CITIZENS TELECOMMUNICATIONS CO OF CALIFORNIA INC
FRONTIER
(*Suby of* FRONTIER COMMUNICATIONS CORP) ★
9260 E Stockton Blvd, Elk Grove, CA 95624-1456
Tel (916) 686-3000 *Founded/Ownrshp* 1946
Sales 111.2MM[E] *EMP* 383[E]
Accts Kpmg Llp New York Ny
SIC 4813 Local telephone communications; Long distance telephone communications
Ch Bd: Mary Agnes Wilderotter
Treas: Donald Armour V-P
VP: Livingston E Ross

D-U-N-S 84-849-6105
■ CITIZENS TELECOMMUNICATIONS CO OF NEW YORK INC
FRONTIER
(*Suby of* FRONTIER COMMUNICATIONS CORP) ★
137 Harrison St, Gloversville, NY 12078-4803
Tel (518) 773-6466 *Founded/Ownrshp* 1993
Sales 118.4MM[E] *EMP* 408
SIC 4813 Local & long distance telephone communications
Ch Bd: Mary Agnes Wilderotter

D-U-N-S 14-769-7796
■ CITIZENS TELECOMMUNICATIONS CO OF TENNESSEE LLC
FRONTIER
(*Suby of* FRONTIER COMMUNICATIONS CORP) ★
250 S Franklin Ave, Cookeville, TN 38501-3167
Tel (931) 528-0501 *Founded/Ownrshp* 1995
Sales 87.1MM[E] *EMP* 300
SIC 4813 Telephone communication, except radio
Ch Bd: Mary Agnes Wilderotter

D-U-N-S 00-693-8351 IMP
CITIZENS WATER
(*Suby of* CITIZENS GAS) ★
2020 N Meridian St, Indianapolis, IN 46202-1306
Tel (317) 631-1431 *Founded/Ownrshp* 1881, 2008
Sales 257.6MM[E] *EMP* 450
SIC 4941 Water supply
Pr: David Gadis
Pr: Donna Dunn
COO: Tim Bedgood
CFO: Jacqueline Groth
Sr VP: Jim Keifner
**VP:* Lou Ann Baker
VP: Lou Baker
**VP:* Kathy Baumes
**VP:* Paul Dicken
VP: Steven Hopper
VP: Lee Lundberg
Dir Bus: Michael Froom

D-U-N-S 87-859-3623
■ CITIZENSHIP & IMMIGRATION SERVICES US
USCIS
(*Suby of* EXECUTVE OFC OF US GOVT) ★
20 Ma Ave Nw Rm 3000, Washington, DC 20529-2090
Tel (202) 272-1000 *Founded/Ownrshp* 1891
Sales NA *EMP* 31,000
SIC 9721 Immigration services, government;
Exec: Amanda Clark

D-U-N-S 60-459-6346
▲ CITRIX SYSTEMS INC
851 W Cypress Creek Rd, Fort Lauderdale, FL 33309-2040
Tel (954) 267-3000 *Founded/Ownrshp* 1989
Sales 3.2MMM *EMP* 9,500
Tkr Sym CTXS *Exch* NGS
SIC 7372 Prepackaged software
Pr: Kirill Tatarinov
Pt: Craig Stilwell
Ch Bd: Robert M Calderoni
COO: David J Henshall
Chf Mktg O: Timothy A Minahan
Sr VP: Christopher S Hylen
Sr VP: Klaus Oestermann
Sr VP: Carlos E Sartorius
VP: Diana Askin
VP: Bill Burley
VP: William L Burley
VP: Brian Carter
VP: Andrew Cohen
VP: Michael Cristinziano
VP: Samm Distasio
VP: Chris Fleck
VP: Tony Gomes
VP: Saul Gurdus
VP: Faisal Hanafi
VP: Kim Haniger
VP: Kim Hibler
Board of Directors: Nanci E Caldwell, Jesse A Cohn, Robert D Daleo, Murray J Demo, Peter J Sacripanti, Graham V Smith, Godfrey R Sullivan

CITRUS COLLEGE
See CITRUS COMMUNITY COLLEGE DISTRICT

D-U-N-S 07-624-6321
CITRUS COMMUNITY COLLEGE DISTRICT
CITRUS COLLEGE
(*Suby of* CALIFORNIA COMMUNITY COLLEGES SYSTEM) ★
1000 W Foothill Blvd, Glendora, CA 91741-1899
Tel (626) 963-0323 *Founded/Ownrshp* 1961
Sales 1.0MM[E] *EMP* 1,414
Accts Vicenti Lloyd & Stutzman Llp
SIC 8222 Community college
Pr: Geraldine Perry
CFO: Steve Avalos
Treas: Gerhard Peters
Trst: Joanne Montgomery
Trst: Edward Ortell
VP: Carol R Horton
VP: Irene Malmgren
VP: Arvid Spor
Off Mgr: Michael Viera
Store Mgr: Eric Magallon
DP Exec: Bill McCusker

D-U-N-S 16-168-1606
CITRUS CORP
1400 Smith St Ste 3902, Houston, TX 77002-7327
Tel (713) 853-6161 *Founded/Ownrshp* 1980
Sales 382.9MM[E] *EMP* 500
SIC 4923 Gas transmission & distribution
CEO: Stanley C Horton
**CFO:* Roderick Hayslett
**Sr VP:* Drew Fossum

D-U-N-S 92-653-4702
CITRUS COUNTY SCHOOL BOARD LEASING CORP
CITRUS COUNTY SCHOOLS
1007 W Main St, Inverness, FL 34450-4625
Tel (352) 726-1931 *Founded/Ownrshp* 2009
Sales 62.1MM[E] *EMP* 2,126
Accts David W Martin Cpa Tallahas
SIC 8211 Public elementary & secondary schools
Ch Bd: Thomas Kennedy
MIS Dir: Steve Chamblin
Teacher Pr: Suzanne Swain

CITRUS COUNTY SCHOOLS
See CITRUS COUNTY SCHOOL BOARD LEASING CORP

D-U-N-S 07-979-8966
CITRUS COUNTY SCHOOLS
1007 W Main St, Inverness, FL 34450-4625
Tel (352) 726-1931 *Founded/Ownrshp* 2009
Sales 16.8MM[E] *EMP* 2,195[E]
SIC 8211 Public elementary & secondary schools

D-U-N-S 16-711-6289
CITRUS HEALTH CARE INC
(*Suby of* CEF HOLDINGS INC)
101 S Hoover Blvd Ste 100, Tampa, FL 33609-5400
Tel (813) 490-7931 *Founded/Ownrshp* 2003
Sales NA *EMP* 260
SIC 6324 Health maintenance organization (HMO), insurance only
Pr: Bruce Carpenter
**CFO:* Craig Depart
IT Man: Kevin Buckley

D-U-N-S 09-271-3965
■ CITRUS HMA INC
(*Suby of* HMA) ★
6201 N Suncoast Blvd, Crystal River, FL 34428-6712
Tel (352) 563-5488 *Founded/Ownrshp* 2003
Sales 94.7MM *EMP* 500
SIC 8062 General medical & surgical hospitals
**VP:* Stephen L Midkiff
Dir Lab: Richard Munsell
Off Mgr: Cheryl Williams
Mktg Mgr: Dorothy Pernu
Pathlgst: Joana Fabe
Occ Thrpy: Bradley H Ruben

CITRUS MEMORIAL HEALTH SYSTEM
See FOUNDATION RESOLUTION CORP

CITRUS OLEO
See J TECH SALES LLC

D-U-N-S 78-128-5788
CITRUS VALLEY HEALTH PARTNERS INC
INTER COMMUNITY HOSPITAL
210 W San Bernardino Rd, Covina, CA 91723-1515
Tel (626) 331-7331 *Founded/Ownrshp* 1983
Sales 58.1MM *EMP* 2,800
Accts Ernst & Young Llp Los Angeles
SIC 8741 Administrative management
CEO: Robert Curry
**Pr:* James Yoshioka
**COO:* Alvia Polk
**CFO:* Lois Conyers
**Chf Mktg O:* Paveljit Bindra
Sr VP: Lisa Faust
Sr VP: David McCobb
VP: David Kessler
Dir Risk M: Marilyn Griffin
IT Man: Linda Waddell

D-U-N-S 04-647-1330
CITRUS VALLEY MEDICAL CENTER INC (CA)
1115 S Sunset Ave, West Covina, CA 91790-3940
Tel (626) 962-4011 *Founded/Ownrshp* 1959
Sales 397.2MM *EMP* 3,500
Accts Ernst & Young Llp Los Angele
SIC 8062 General medical & surgical hospitals
Pr: Robert Curry
**COO:* Elvia Foulke
**CFO:* Roger Sharma
Dir Risk M: Jill Jacobs
Opers Mgr: John Bell

D-U-N-S 00-409-1732 IMP/EXP
CITRUS WORLD INC
FLORIDA'S NATURAL GROWERS
20205 Hwy 27, Lake Wales, FL 33853-3080
Tel (863) 676-1411 *Founded/Ownrshp* 1934
Sales 224.6MM[E] *EMP* 800
SIC 2037 Fruit juice concentrates, frozen
CEO: Stephen M Caruso
**Ch Bd:* Joe L Davis Jr
**Pr:* Dennis Broadaway
**CFO:* William Hendry
**VP:* David Crumbley
VP: Gary Dewitt
VP: Fred D Fulks
**VP:* Frank M Hunt III

*VP: Charles Matthews
VP: Bill Watson
Rgnl Mgr: Robert Weaver

D-U-N-S 07-819-7944
CITY & BOROUGH OF JUNEAU
155 S Seward St, Juneau, AK 99801-1397
Tel (907) 789-0819 Founded/Ownrshp 1900
Sales NA EMP 1,171
Accts Elgee Rehfeld Mertz Llc June
SIC 9111 City & town managers' offices;
Ofcr: Doug Liermann
Ofcr: Renee Loree
Ofcr: Ronald Schramm
Off Mgr: Sam Sanbei

D-U-N-S 07-313-2409
CITY & COUNTY OF DENVER
CITY MAYORS OFFICE
1437 Bannock St Rm 350, Denver, CO 80202-5390
Tel (720) 865-9000 Founded/Ownrshp 1861
Sales NA EMP 9,053
SIC 9111

D-U-N-S 07-770-1647
CITY & COUNTY OF HONOLULU
530 S King St Rm 208, Honolulu, HI 96813-3018
Tel (808) 523-4141 Founded/Ownrshp 1907
Sales NA EMP 8,000
Accts Kmh Llp Honolulu Hawaii
SIC 9111 City & town managers' offices;
Ex Dir: Debra Morakawa
*Mng Dir: Ember Shinn
Genl Mgr: Lorraine Oyabu
MIS Mgr: Jian WEI Huang
Mktg Dir: Michael Pang
Counsel: David Z Arakawa

D-U-N-S 04-600-4081 IMP
CITY & COUNTY OF SAN FRANCISCO
1 Dr Carlton B Goodlett P, San Francisco, CA 94102-4604
Tel (415) 554-7500 Founded/Ownrshp 1850
Sales NA EMP 30,000
Accts Macias Gini O Connell Llp Wal
SIC 9111 Executive offices;
*Treas: Susan Leal
Bd of Dir: Niki Solis
Ofcr: Samuel Nwigwe
Ofcr: Paul Ospital
Ofcr: Mary G Starkweather
Assoc Dir: Renee Hayes
*Prin: Tomio Takeshita
Ex Dir: Cynthia Goldstein
Ex Dir: Miguel A Gamia O Jr
Genl Mgr: Craig Dziedzic
Snr Mgr: Jeff Myers

CITY 1ST
See CITY FIRST MORTGAGE SERVICES LLC

CITY ADMINISTRATION
See BOULDER CITY OF (INC)

CITY ATTY OFFICE
See CITY OF HOLLYWOOD

D-U-N-S 00-738-3391
CITY BANK (TX)
(Suby of SOUTH PLAINS FINANCIAL INC) ★
5219 City Bank Pkwy Fl 1, Lubbock, TX 79407-3590
Tel (806) 792-7101 Founded/Ownrshp 1963, 1993
Sales NA EMP 300
SIC 6022 State commercial banks
Pr: Cory Newsom
*COO: Paul Ehlers
*CFO: Sandra Wallace
*Ch: Curtis Griffith

D-U-N-S 03-632-5488
CITY BANK
(Suby of SOUTH PLAINS FINANCIAL INC) ★
500 Main St, Silverton, TX 79257
Tel (806) 823-2426 Founded/Ownrshp 1946
Sales NA EMP 8
SIC 6022 State commercial banks
Pr: Kyle Fuston

D-U-N-S 03-260-9265 IMP
CITY BEVERAGES LLC
10928 Florida Crown Dr, Orlando, FL 32824-7031
Tel (407) 851-7100 Founded/Ownrshp 1997
Sales 129.5MM[E] EMP 220
SIC 5181 Beer & other fermented malt liquors
Pt: Ford W Kiene
IT Man: Joel Velez
IT Man: Jill Wisth
Sls&Mrk Ex: Luis Estep
Sls Dir: Colby Kiene

D-U-N-S 19-688-9963 IMP
CITY BREWING CO LLC
BLUES CITY BREWERY
925 3rd St S, La Crosse, WI 54601-4411
Tel (608) 785-4200 Founded/Ownrshp 2000
Sales 225.3MM[E] EMP 400[E]
SIC 2082 Malt beverage products
CEO: George Parke III
CFO: Gregory Inda
*CFO: Gregory INA
VP: Connie Michaels
QA Dir: Monica Dunigan
QA Dir: Nickolas Pappert
Info Man: Thomas Pofi
Sftwr Eng: Kenneth Ganster
QC Dir: Jeff Goulet
Opers Supe: Ellis Oliver
Sfty Mgr: Jim Jacobson

D-U-N-S 03-038-8781
CITY CENTER HOLDINGS LLC
3950 Las Vegas Blvd S, Las Vegas, NV 89119-1005
Tel (702) 632-9800 Founded/Ownrshp 2010
Sales 1.1MMM EMP 0[E]
Accts Deloitte & Touche Llp Las Ve
SIC 6719 Holding companies

CITY COLLEGE
See MONTANA STATE UNIVERSITY-BILLINGS

D-U-N-S 07-464-5284
CITY COLLEGE OF SAN FRANCISCO
50 Phelan Ave, San Francisco, CA 94112-1898
Tel (415) 239-3000 Founded/Ownrshp 1970
Sales 216.8MM[E] EMP 3,097
SIC 8221 8222 Colleges universities & professional schools; Community college
Pr: John Rizzo
CFO: John Bilmont
Ofcr: Phuoc S Dang
Ofcr: Gwynne Leong
*VP: Anita Grier
VP: Melanie Ortanez
Off Admin: San Ly
CTO: Denise McCarthy
Dir IT: W Hong
IT Man: Rebeca Chavez
IT Man: Susan Quan

CITY COLLEGES OF CHICAGO
See BOARD OF TRUSTEES OF COMMUNITY COLLEGE DISTRICT 508 (INC)

CITY COUNCIL
See CITY OF WORCESTER

D-U-N-S 19-516-9248
CITY COUNTY INSURANCE SERVICES
1212 Court St Ne, Salem, OR 97301-4181
Tel (503) 763-3800 Founded/Ownrshp 1981
Sales NA EMP 16
SIC 6411 8111 Insurance agents, brokers & service; Legal services
Ex Dir: Lynn McNamara

D-U-N-S 00-225-3979
CITY ELECTRIC CO INC (NY)
501 W Genesee St, Syracuse, NY 13204-2301
Tel (315) 474-7841 Founded/Ownrshp 1919, 1992
Sales 116.1MM[E] EMP 90
SIC 5063 5085 Electrical construction materials; Industrial supplies
CEO: Sandra Rosecrans
Ex VP: William McBride
*VP: Andrew Esce
IT Man: Edward Schlueter
Oper/Mgr: Redonna Geelan
Sls Mgr: Vinnie Degennaro
Sls Mgr: Hilton Shattuck
Sls Mgr: Leonard Sheitz
Sales Asso: Dave Ames
Sales Asso: Brian Goetz
Sales Asso: Michael Timmons

D-U-N-S 10-185-3273 IMP/EXP
CITY ELECTRIC SUPPLY CO
CESCO USA
400 S Record St Ste 100, Dallas, TX 75202-4806
Tel (214) 123-1234 Founded/Ownrshp 1983
Sales 638.7MM[E] EMP 2,500
SIC 5063 Electrical supplies
Pr: Thomas A Hartland Mackie
VP: Smith Gary
VP: Len Grafstrom
VP: John Gray
VP: Jim Lawson
VP: Russell J Swanson
Brnch Mgr: Steve Baker
Brnch Mgr: Jerry Burkett
Brnch Mgr: Jeff Cole
Brnch Mgr: Mike Ford
Brnch Mgr: Mark A Fralick

D-U-N-S 03-543-2421
CITY FIRST MORTGAGE SERVICES LLC
CITY 1ST
750 S Main St Ste 104, Bountiful, UT 84010-6371
Tel (801) 299-1770 Founded/Ownrshp 1993
Sales NA EMP 120[E]
SIC 6162 Mortgage bankers & correspondents
CEO: Gerret Van Wagoner
Ofcr: Nathan Scott
Brnch Mgr: Daren Crockett
Brnch Mgr: Suzanne Hudson
Brnch Mgr: Chris Smith
Brnch Mgr: David Stanley
Ql Cn Mgr: Matt McGuire
Mktg Dir: Scott Cannon
Genl Couns: Brian T Hunt

D-U-N-S 06-567-5746 IMP/EXP
CITY FURNITURE INC
6701 Hiatus Rd, Tamarac, FL 33321-6406
Tel (954) 597-2200 Founded/Ownrshp 1971
Sales 333.0MM[E] EMP 1,050
SIC 5712 Waterbeds & accessories
Pr: Keith Koenig
CFO: Steven Wilder
VP: Diego Terzano
VP: J Stephen Wilder
Dir Risk M: Gislaine Sosa
Genl Mgr: Jeff Amann
Genl Mgr: Joanne Doty
Genl Mgr: Crystal Mills
Snr Sftwr: Francisko Paternoster
Site Mgr: Paul Baublitz
Manager: Rhonda Socol

CITY HALL
See CITY OF LANSING

CITY HALL
See CITY OF HIGH POINT

CITY HALL
See CITY OF BRIDGEPORT

CITY HALL
See CITY OF NORTHAMPTON

D-U-N-S 18-304-2050
CITY HARVEST INC
6 E 32nd St Fl 5, New York, NY 10016-5422
Tel (646) 412-0600 Founded/Ownrshp 1982
Sales 115.1MM EMP 140
Accts Grant Thornton Llp New York
SIC 8322 Individual & family services
Ex Dir: Jilly Stephens
VP: Kevin Duffy
VP: Mary Beth Henson
Assoc Dir: Rebecca Fontes

Dir IT: Vincent Spinella
Snr Mgr: Meg Davidson

D-U-N-S 14-730-4091
▲ **CITY HOLDING CO**
25 Gatewater Rd, Charleston, WV 25313-1408
Tel (304) 769-1100 Founded/Ownrshp 1981
Sales NA EMP 853[E]
Tkr Sym CHCO Exch NGS
SIC 6021 National commercial banks
Pr: Charles R Hageboeck
*Ch Bd: C Dallas Kayser
CFO: David L Bumgarner
Ofcr: Jeffrey D Legge
Ex VP: John A Derito
Ex VP: Craig G Stilwell
Board of Directors: James L Rossi, John R Elliot, Sharon H Rowe, Charles W Fairchilds, William H File III, Robert D Fisher, Jay C Goldman, Patrick C Graney III, David W Hambrick, Tracy W Hylton II, J Thomas Jones

D-U-N-S 07-745-6606
CITY HOSPITAL INC
UNIVERSITY HEALTHCARE BERKLEY
2500 Hospital Dr, Martinsburg, WV 25401-3402
Tel (304) 264-1000 Founded/Ownrshp 1984
Sales 111.3MM[E] EMP 822[E]
SIC 8062 General medical & surgical hospitals
VP: Christopher Knight
VP Mktg: Teresa McCabe

D-U-N-S 83-300-7136
CITY HOSPITAL INC
BERKELEY MEDICAL CENTER
2000 Foundation Way # 2310, Martinsburg, WV 25401-9197
Tel (304) 264-1244 Founded/Ownrshp 1939
Sales 171.7MM EMP 2,000
SIC 8062 General medical & surgical hospitals
Pr: Anthony Zelenka
Doctor: Robert E Bowen MD

D-U-N-S 86-764-2886
CITY LINE APTS
155a Mytilene Dr, Newport News, VA 23605-1852
Tel (757) 838-5553 Founded/Ownrshp 1977
Sales 45.1MM[E] EMP 3,900
SIC 6513 Apartment building operators
Sr VP: Leeann Morein

D-U-N-S 01-882-7675
CITY LINE DISTRIBUTORS INC
CITY LINE FOODS
20 Industry Dr, West Haven, CT 06516-1442
Tel (203) 931-3707 Founded/Ownrshp 1985
Sales 177.5MM EMP 200
SIC 5141 5142 5147 5113

CITY LINE FOODS
See CITY LINE DISTRIBUTORS INC

CITY MANAGER'S OFFICE
See CITY OF FORT LAUDERDALE

CITY MAYORS OFFICE
See CITY & COUNTY OF DENVER

D-U-N-S 00-911-6153 IMP
CITY MILL CO LIMITED (HI)
DO IT BEST
660 N Nimitz Hwy, Honolulu, HI 96817-5032
Tel (808) 533-3811 Founded/Ownrshp 1899
Sales 83.0MM[E] EMP 450
SIC 5211

D-U-N-S 00-690-4395 IMP
CITY NATIONAL BANK
(Suby of RBC USA HOLDCO CORP) ★
555 S Flower St Ste 2500, Los Angeles, CA 90071-2326
Tel (310) 888-6000 Founded/Ownrshp 1968
Sales NA EMP 3,000
SIC 6021 6022 National commercial banks; State commercial banks
Ch Bd: Russell Goldsmith
Pr: Gina Calipes
*Pr: Christopher J Warmuth
Pr: John Zhang
*CFO: Christopher J Carey
Ofcr: Charles Gilbert
Ofcr: Bobbie Larkin
Trst Ofcr: Paula Laliberte
*Ex VP: Michael B Cahill
Ex VP: Marianne Lamutt
*Ex VP: Michael Pagano
*Ex VP: Richard Shier
*Ex VP: Michael R Walker
Sr VP: Edwin Aquino
Sr VP: Robin Balding
Sr VP: Kevin Conroy
Sr VP: Raymond J Deriggi
Sr VP: Jim Ellaboudy
Sr VP: Kevin Fitze
*Sr VP: Gregory T Glover
Sr VP: Karen Gmunder
Board of Directors: Mohamad Ali, Alison Davis

D-U-N-S 07-388-3712
CITY NATIONAL BANK
CITY NATIONAL BANK OF FLORIDA
(Suby of BANCO DE CREDITO E INVERSIONES)
25 W Flagler St Fl 3, Miami, FL 33130-1785
Tel (305) 577-7333 Founded/Ownrshp 2014
Sales NA EMP 440
SIC 6021 National commercial banks
Pr: Jorge Gonzalez
Chf Cred: Hugo Loynaz
Ofcr: Nicole Chin
Ofcr: Orlando Marquez
Ofcr: Ivonne Noda
Ofcr: Eduardo Santamaria
Ex VP: Mara Suarez
Sr VP: Mario Carballo
Sr VP: Mike Dowling
Sr VP: Ricardo Garbati
Sr VP: Orlando Gonzalez
Sr VP: David Lukes
Sr VP: Jeff Watts
VP: Jorge Aguirre

VP: Edward D Barber
VP: Brett Bigenho
VP: Reginald Breton
VP: Suzy Day
VP: Yolanda Duarte
VP: Carol Fine
VP: Marc K Gagnon

CITY NATIONAL BANK OF FLORIDA
See CITY NATIONAL BANK

D-U-N-S 00-895-8779
■ **CITY NATIONAL BANK OF WEST VIRGINIA**
(Suby of CITY HOLDING CO) ★
3601 Maccorkle Ave Se, Charleston, WV 25304-1498
Tel (304) 926-3301 Founded/Ownrshp 1982
Sales NA EMP 750
Accts Ernst & Young Llp Charleston
SIC 6021 National trust companies with deposits, commercial
Pr: Skip Hageboeck
CFO: David Bungarner
*Ex VP: Terry Childers
*Ex VP: Craig Stilwell
VP: Bobby Pauley
VP: Aileen Takio
MIS Dir: Jeff Legge
Sls&Mrk Ex: Christy Hastings

D-U-N-S 96-369-0917
CITY NATIONAL BANK OF WEST VIRGINIA
25 Gatewater Rd, Cross Lanes, WV 25313-1408
Tel (304) 769-1189 Founded/Ownrshp 1957
Sales NA EMP 6[E]
SIC 6021 National commercial banks

CITY O AGAWAM
See TOWN OF AGAWAM

D-U-N-S 08-107-8891
CITY OF ABILENE
555 Walnut St, Abilene, TX 79601-5254
Tel (325) 676-6200 Founded/Ownrshp 1882
Sales NA EMP 1,177
Accts Davis Kinard & Co Pc Abile
SIC 9111 City & town managers' offices;
Ofcr: Eric Eder
Ex Dir: Rodney Taylor
IT Man: Sheryl Fillmon
Opers Mgr: William Brock

D-U-N-S 07-674-2329
CITY OF AKRON
166 S High St Rm 502, Akron, OH 44308-1622
Tel (330) 375-2720 Founded/Ownrshp 1825
Sales NA EMP 2,866
Accts Dave Yost Auditor Of State C
SIC 9111 Mayors' offices;
Treas: John Tomei
Bd of Dir: Pat McMillan
Ofcr: Pierre Irvine
Ofcr: Rick Oldaker
Ofcr: Michael Shaeffer
Ofcr: Howard Vaughn
Ofcr: Eric Wagner
VP: John Otterman
Exec: Rick Edwards
Mng Dir: Jeff Bronowski
IT Man: William Fatica

D-U-N-S 07-392-8111
CITY OF ALAMEDA
2263 Santa Clara Ave, Alameda, CA 94501-4477
Tel (510) 747-7400 Founded/Ownrshp 1854
Sales NA EMP 2,650
Accts Maze & Associates Pleasant Hi
SIC 9111 City & town managers' offices;
CFO: Glenda Jay

D-U-N-S 06-054-3808
CITY OF ALBANY
24 Eagle St Rm 102, Albany, NY 12207-1913
Tel (518) 434-5100 Founded/Ownrshp 1686
Sales NA EMP 2,000
SIC 9111 City & town managers' offices;
Treas: Kathy Sheehan
*Pr: Hon Carolyn McLaughlin
Treas: Darius Shahinfar
Genl Mgr: Ron Vogel
IT Man: Andrew Sterling
Genl Couns: Gary Stglmeier

D-U-N-S 06-760-2169
CITY OF ALBANY
222 Pine Ave Ste 560, Albany, GA 31701-2531
Tel (229) 883-6955 Founded/Ownrshp 1838
Sales NA EMP 1,000
Accts Mauldin & Jenkins Llc Macon
SIC 9121 City council;
Dir IT: Jorge Salinas
Opers Supe: Kenneth Parker

D-U-N-S 00-711-1891
CITY OF ALBUQUERQUE
400 Marquette Ave Nw, Albuquerque, NM 87102-2117
Tel (505) 768-3000 Founded/Ownrshp 1706
Sales NA EMP 6,500
Accts Moss Adams Llp Albuquerque N
SIC 9111 City & town managers' offices;
Treas: Cilia Aglialoro
Ofcr: Greg Stricklin
Off Admin: Theresa Valencia
Dir IT: Chike Nwagbo
IT Man: Stephanie Romero
Mktg Mgr: Desiree Cawley
Mktg Mgr: Dave Mathews

D-U-N-S 07-485-3250 IMP/EXP
CITY OF ALEXANDRIA
301 King St, Alexandria, VA 22314-3211
Tel (703) 746-4000 Founded/Ownrshp 1749
Sales NA EMP 2,375
Accts Cliftonlarsonallen Llp Arling
SIC 9111 Mayors' offices

D-U-N-S 06-856-9656
CITY OF ALLENTOWN
MAYOR'S OFFICE
435 Hamilton St, Allentown, PA 18101-1603
Tel (610) 437-7546 *Founded/Ownrshp* 1762
Sales NA *EMP* 3,513
Accts Maher Duessel Harrisburg Due
SIC 9111 City & town managers' offices;
Treas: Joe McDonald
Ex Dir: Jerome Frank
MIS Dir: Sharon Deiberth
Board of Directors: David Bausch, David Howells, Marty Velazquez

D-U-N-S 06-503-2807
CITY OF AMARILLO
509 Se 7th Ave Rm 303, Amarillo, TX 79101-2539
Tel (806) 378-3000 *Founded/Ownrshp* 1887
Sales NA *EMP* 2,000
Accts Connor Mcmillon Mitchell S
SIC 9111 City & town managers' offices
Ofcr: Adrian Hernandez
Prgrm Mgr: Laci Scott
Dir IT: Jeff Konishi
IT Man: Lupe Quinonez
Netwrk Mgr: John Grist

D-U-N-S 06-132-0917
CITY OF AMES
515 Clark Ave, Ames, IA 50010-6187
Tel (515) 239-5140 *Founded/Ownrshp* 1870
Sales NA *EMP* 1,705
Accts Eidebailly Llp Dubuque Iowa
SIC 9111 City & town managers' offices;
Treas: Chris Betts
**Treas:* Roger Wisecup
Ofcr: Jamie Miller
Ofcr: Edward Morton
Ofcr: Duane Pitcher
Ex Dir: Nancy Carroll
IT Man: Alan Young
Trfc Dir: Pamela Dodd
Sls&Mrk Ex: Susan Gwiasda

D-U-N-S 04-432-9993 IMP
CITY OF ANAHEIM
200 S Anaheim Blvd, Anaheim, CA 92805-3820
Tel (714) 765-5162 *Founded/Ownrshp* 1857
Sales NA *EMP* 3,100[E]
Accts Kpmg Llp Irvine Ca
SIC 9121 City council
Dir Soc: Matthew Trout

D-U-N-S 06-837-8231 IMP/EXP
CITY OF ARLINGTON (TX)
101 W Abram St, Arlington, TX 76010-7102
Tel (817) 275-3271 *Founded/Ownrshp* 1876
Sales NA *EMP* 2,477
Accts Grant Thornton Llp Dallas Te
SIC 9111 Executive offices;
CFO: Anna Mosqueda
Ofcr: Jason Banks
Ofcr: Sheila Griffith
Ofcr: Ben Lopez
Ofcr: Trenecia Williams
Exec: Jay Warren
Dir: Jim Parajon
Ex Dir: Carolyn Mentesana
CIO: Dennis John
Web Dev: Nancy Le

D-U-N-S 06-537-2500
CITY OF ATLANTA (GA)
55 Trinity Ave Sw # 3900, Atlanta, GA 30303-3543
Tel (404) 330-6100 *Founded/Ownrshp* 1837
Sales NA *EMP* 8,885
Accts Kpmg Llp Atlanta Ga
SIC 9111 Mayors' offices;
**Pr:* Lisa Borders
COO: Luz Borrero
**CFO:* J Anthony Beard
Treas: Susan Joyce
**Ofcr:* Stephanie Stuckey Benfield
Ofcr: Knut Hauer
Ofcr: Yolonda Paschall
Ofcr: Thomas Sutton
Ofcr: Albert Taylor
Ofcr: Daniel Titus
Ofcr: Antwoin D Williams
Exec: Lisa Bond
Exec: Ashley Stukes
Dir Lab: Thomas Bourne
Comm Dir: Brenda Ross

D-U-N-S 07-705-9376
CITY OF ATLANTIC CITY (INC)
1301 Bacharach Blvd, Atlantic City, NJ 08401-4600
Tel (609) 347-5300 *Founded/Ownrshp* 1854
Sales NA *EMP* 1,550
Accts Ford - Scott & Associates Llc
SIC 9111 Mayors' offices;
Comm Man: Amy Menzel
Genl Mgr: Tom Monaghan
MIS Dir: Sheila Johnson

D-U-N-S 07-571-0475
CITY OF ATTLEBORO
77 Park St Ste 1, Attleboro, MA 02703-2353
Tel (508) 223-2222 *Founded/Ownrshp* 1914
Sales NA *EMP* 1,350
Accts Hague Sahady & Co Pc Fal
SIC 9111 Executive offices, state & local;
Treas: Ethel Sandbach
Exec: Heather Porreca
MIS Dir: William Lennox

D-U-N-S 07-458-2131
CITY OF AURORA
44 E Downer Pl, Aurora, IL 60505-3302
Tel (630) 892-8811 *Founded/Ownrshp* 1837
Sales NA *EMP* 1,200
Accts Sikich Naperville Illinois
SIC 9111 Mayors' offices;
Ofcr: Mike Milewski
Ofcr: Connie Perez
Ofcr: John Sefton
Ofcr: Jeff Zimmerman
Exec: Mark Anderson
Dir IT: Linda Read
IT Man: Marty Wolding

D-U-N-S 07-576-9703
CITY OF AURORA
15151 E Alameda Pkwy, Aurora, CO 80012-1555
Tel (303) 739-7056 *Founded/Ownrshp* 1891
Sales NA *EMP* 2,671
Accts Bkd Llp Denver Co
SIC 9111 9511 Executive offices; City & town managers' offices; County supervisors' & executives' offices; Mayors' offices;
Ofcr: Robert Freil
Ex VP: Mike Brown
CTO: Bobby Johnson
Board of Directors: George Noe,michelle Wolfe,

D-U-N-S 06-643-2683 IMP
CITY OF AUSTIN
301 W 2nd St, Austin, TX 78701-4652
Tel (512) 974-2000 *Founded/Ownrshp* 1839
Sales NA *EMP* 10,922
Accts Deloitte & Touche Llp Austin
SIC 9111 City & town managers' offices;
Ofcr: Jerome Bauzon
Ofcr: Enrique Colorado
Ofcr: Isabella Rizer
Ofcr: Jennifer Walls
VP: Gordon Derr
Dir Risk M: Leslie Milvo
Div Mgr: Charles Vaclavik
Genl Mgr: Russell Meyer
CIO: Pete Collins
CIO: Stephen Elkins
IT Man: Ken Whelan

D-U-N-S 06-381-0972
CITY OF BAKERSFIELD
1600 Truxtun Ave Fl 5th, Bakersfield, CA 93301-5140
Tel (661) 326-3000 *Founded/Ownrshp* 1898
Sales NA *EMP* 1,570
Accts Brown Armstrong Accountancy Co
SIC 9111 City & town managers' offices;
Ofcr: Tim Berchtold
Dir: Jacqui Kitchen

D-U-N-S 05-234-0973
CITY OF BALTIMORE
100 Holliday St Ste 250, Baltimore, MD 21202-3459
Tel (410) 396-3835 *Founded/Ownrshp* 1797
Sales NA *EMP* 26,400
Accts Kpmg Llp Washington Dc
SIC 9111
V Ch: Nicholas D'Adamo Jr
V Ch: Brandon Scott
V Ch: Carl Stokes
Ofcr: Reginald Coates
VP: Edward Reisinger
IT Man: David Brown
IT Man: George Nilson
IT Man: Reginald Scriber
Sls&Mrk Ex: Sue Ziegler
VP Mktg: Peggy Schultz
Mktg Dir: Otis Rolley

D-U-N-S 07-194-8301
CITY OF BATON ROUGE
PARISH OF EAST BATON ROUGE
222 Saint Louis St Rm 301, Baton Rouge, LA 70802-5832
Tel (225) 389-3061 *Founded/Ownrshp* 1817
Sales NA *EMP* 4,400
Accts Postlethwaite & Netterville B
SIC 9111 City & town managers' offices;
Telecom Ex: Ray Starns

D-U-N-S 09-185-7037
CITY OF BAYONNE
630 Avenue C, Bayonne, NJ 07002-3878
Tel (201) 858-6046 *Founded/Ownrshp* 1861
Sales NA *EMP* 1,627
SIC 9111 Executive offices
IT Man: Janet Convery

D-U-N-S 07-390-1118
CITY OF BEAUMONT
801 Main St, Beaumont, TX 77701-3548
Tel (409) 880-3716 *Founded/Ownrshp* 1838
Sales NA *EMP* 1,200
Accts Whitley Penn Llp Houston Te
SIC 9111 City & town managers' offices;
Treas: Kandy Daniel
Ofcr: Paul D Hulsey Jr
Sfty Dirs: Joel Sistrunk
Sls Dir: Freddie Willard

D-U-N-S 07-184-2611
CITY OF BELLEVUE
450 110th Ave Ne, Bellevue, WA 98004-5514
Tel (425) 452-6800 *Founded/Ownrshp* 1953
Sales NA *EMP* 1,175
Accts Brian Sontagg Cgfm Olympia
SIC 9111 City & town managers' offices;
Ofcr: Vittorio Mangione
Ofcr: Rob Wood
VP: Chelo Picardal
Exec: Nancy Kartes
Prgrm Mgr: Julie Vanwallendael
Off Mgr: Teri Robinson
Snr PM: Susan Harper

D-U-N-S 07-652-9924
CITY OF BERKELEY
2120 Milvia St, Berkeley, CA 94704-1113
Tel (510) 981-7300 *Founded/Ownrshp* 1878
Sales NA *EMP* 1,520
Accts Badawi & Associates Oakland
SIC 9121 City council;
VP: Brian Evans
Ex Dir: Tia Ingram
Dir IT: Marcus Bell
IT Man: Ivan Lapidus
Software D: Beth Thorman

D-U-N-S 07-951-5219
CITY OF BEVERLY
191 Cabot St Rm 1, Beverly, MA 01915-5849
Tel (978) 922-2500 *Founded/Ownrshp* 1668
Sales NA *EMP* 1,600
SIC 9121 City council;
Ofcr: Steve Frederickson
Dir: Aaron Clausen
IT Man: Paul Cohen

D-U-N-S 07-210-3559 IMP
CITY OF BIRMINGHAM
710 20th St N Ste 600, Birmingham, AL 35203-2281
Tel (205) 254-2000 *Founded/Ownrshp* 1871
Sales NA *EMP* 4,300
Accts Banks Finley White & Co Bi
SIC 9111 Mayors' offices;
**Pr.* Johnathan Austin
CIO: Srikanth Karra
IT Man: Aaron Saxton

D-U-N-S 07-224-2811
CITY OF BOCA RATON
201 W Palmetto Park Rd, Boca Raton, FL 33432-3730
Tel (561) 393-7896 *Founded/Ownrshp* 1925
Sales NA *EMP* 1,326
Accts Marcum Llp West Palm Beach
SIC 9111 City & town managers' offices;
COO: Rex McClun
**Ch:* Scott Singer
Ofcr: Nicholas Hanooman
Ofcr: John Harbilas
Ofcr: Mary Mullen
Exec: Pamela Gardner
Exec: Gail Medina
Exec: Constance Scott
Comm Man: Cerina Anderson
Dir IT: Walter Scrivens
Dir IT: Sandy Stevens

D-U-N-S 07-001-7017
CITY OF BOISE (ID)
150 N Capitol Blvd, Boise, ID 83702-5920
Tel (208) 384-4422 *Founded/Ownrshp* 1834, 1866
Sales NA *EMP* 1,400
Accts Eide Bailly Llp Boise Idaho
SIC 9111 Mayors' offices;
Treas: Richard Downen
Ofcr: Eric Arthur
Ofcr: Olivia Aulbach
Ofcr: Guy Bourgeau
Ofcr: Courtney Chamberlain
Ofcr: Mark Dalpiaz
Ofcr: Dena Gambrel
Ofcr: Michael Garner
Ofcr: Casey Hancuff
Ofcr: Michael Miraglia
Ofcr: Brett Quilter
Ofcr: Jason Rose
Ofcr: Jim Schiffler
Ofcr: Wade Spain
Ofcr: Michael K Walker
Ofcr: Jeff Wudarcki

D-U-N-S 07-381-2083 IMP
CITY OF BOSTON
1 City Hall Sq Ste 242, Boston, MA 02201-1020
Tel (617) 635-4545 *Founded/Ownrshp* 1630
Sales NA *EMP* 18,760
Accts Kpmg Llp Boston Ma
SIC 9111
Comm Man: Shirley Billings
Ex Dir: John Dunlap
Ex Dir: Theresa Lynn
Ex Dir: Victoria Williams

D-U-N-S 07-540-4137
CITY OF BRIDGEPORT
CITY HALL
999 Broad St Ste 2, Bridgeport, CT 06604-4320
Tel (203) 576-3964 *Founded/Ownrshp* 1836
Sales NA *EMP* 3,646
Accts Blum Shapiro & Company Pc
SIC 9111 Mayors' offices;
**Treas:* Sharon D Lemdon
Ofcr: Neil Bonney
Ofcr: Dennis Buckley
Ofcr: Erin McDonough
Ofcr: Andrew Nunn
Comm Dir: Elaine Ficarra
Secur Mgr: Vaughn Sims

D-U-N-S 06-066-5783
CITY OF BRISTOL
111 N Main St Ste 17, Bristol, CT 06010-8184
Tel (860) 584-6100 *Founded/Ownrshp* 1785
Sales NA *EMP* 1,000
Accts Rsm Us Llp New Haven Connect
SIC 9111
MIS Dir: Scott Smith

D-U-N-S 07-658-1008
CITY OF BROCKTON
45 School St, Brockton, MA 02301-4063
Tel (508) 580-7123 *Founded/Ownrshp* 1700
Sales NA *EMP* 30,000
Accts Cliftonlarsonallen Llp Boston
SIC 9111 City & town managers' offices;
Ofcr: Shane Bpd
Ex Dir: John McGarry
Dir IT: Don Fongeallaz
Dir IT: Bill Santos
IT Man: Bethany Couture
Psych: Elana Bowers

D-U-N-S 07-461-5097
CITY OF BROWNSVILLE
1001 E Elizabeth St # 234, Brownsville, TX 78520-5156
Tel (956) 542-2064 *Founded/Ownrshp* 1853
Sales NA *EMP* 1,162
Accts Long Chilton Llp Cpas Brown
SIC 9111 Executive offices;
Exec: Patty Gonzales

D-U-N-S 07-148-2491
CITY OF BUFFALO
65 Niagara Sq Rm 201, Buffalo, NY 14202-3392
Tel (716) 851-4200 *Founded/Ownrshp* 1832
Sales NA *EMP* 3,426
Accts Drescher & Malecki Llp Cheek
SIC 9111 City & town managers' offices;
Ex Dir: Brendan Mehaffy
Ex Dir: Crystal Rodriguez
Snr Mgr: Dinash Lal

D-U-N-S 07-190-6432
CITY OF BURBANK
275 E Olive Ave, Burbank, CA 91502-1232
Tel (818) 238-5800 *Founded/Ownrshp* 1911
Sales NA *EMP* 1,400[E]
Accts White Nelsn Diehl Evans Llp I
SIC 9111 Mayors' offices

D-U-N-S 07-156-5170
CITY OF BURLINGTON
425 S Lexington Ave, Burlington, NC 27215-4200
Tel (336) 222-5060 *Founded/Ownrshp* 1866
Sales NA *EMP* 1,612
SIC 9111

D-U-N-S 07-658-4341
CITY OF CAMBRIDGE
795 Massachusetts Ave, Cambridge, MA 02139-3219
Tel (617) 349-4260 *Founded/Ownrshp* 2007
Sales NA *EMP* 2,000
Accts Kpmg Llp Boston Ma
SIC 9111 City & town managers' offices;

CITY OF CAMDEN
See CAMDEN CITY PUBLIC SCHOOLS

D-U-N-S 07-706-9581
CITY OF CAMDEN
520 Marke St City Hall 4t, Camden, NJ 08101
Tel (856) 757-7200 *Founded/Ownrshp* 1823
Sales NA *EMP* 1,312
SIC 9111 City & town managers' offices;
Pr: Francisco Moran
VP: Curtis Jenkins
Site Mgr: Rose A Holland
Board of Directors: Michael H C Devlin, Gwendolyn Faison, Angel Fuentes, James R Mathis Jr, Israel Nieves, Benjamin C Walters

D-U-N-S 06-041-0289
CITY OF CANTON
218 Cleveland Ave Sw, Canton, OH 44702-1906
Tel (330) 438-4300 *Founded/Ownrshp* 1822
Sales NA *EMP* 1,100
Accts Dave Yost Canton Ohio
SIC 9111
Ofcr: Andrew Moore
Ex Dir: Samuel Sliman
Pr Dir: Lisa Miller

D-U-N-S 07-939-2854
CITY OF CAPE CORAL
1015 Cultural Park Blvd, Cape Coral, FL 33990-1216
Tel (239) 242-3410 *Founded/Ownrshp* 2014
Sales NA *EMP* 1,505
SIC 9111
Sls Mgr: Dawn Andrews

D-U-N-S 08-263-6440
CITY OF CAPE CORAL
1015 Cultural Park Blvd, Cape Coral, FL 33990-1216
Tel (239) 574-0401 *Founded/Ownrshp* 1970
Sales NA *EMP* 1,100
Accts Cliftonlarsonallen Llp Fort
SIC 9111 City & town managers' offices;
Ofcr: Jamie Bungard
Ofcr: Carlos Mena
Genl Mgr: Stephen Pohlman
Sales Asso: Douglas Sayers
Snr Mgr: Bart Connelly

D-U-N-S 06-520-5148
CITY OF CEDAR RAPIDS
101 1st St Se, Cedar Rapids, IA 52401-1205
Tel (319) 286-5080 *Founded/Ownrshp* 1849
Sales NA *EMP* 1,400
Accts Rsm Llp Davenport Iowa
SIC 9111 Mayors' offices;
CIO: Julie Macauley
IT Man: Titof Aquice

D-U-N-S 07-752-4981
CITY OF CHANDLER
175 S Arizona Ave, Chandler, AZ 85225-7526
Tel (480) 782-2000 *Founded/Ownrshp* 1920
Sales NA *EMP* 1,000
Accts Heinfeld Meech & Co Pc T
SIC 9111 City & town managers' offices;
Admn Mgr: Sherry Kiyler
CTO: Bob Graffius
Sales Exec: Doug Ballard

D-U-N-S 07-799-0786 IMP
CITY OF CHARLESTON
116 Meeting St, Charleston, SC 29401-2216
Tel (843) 795-7543 *Founded/Ownrshp* 1670
Sales NA *EMP* 1,250
Accts Mauldin & Jenkins Llc Macon
SIC 9111 Executive offices;
Ofcr: Matthew T Wojslawowicz

D-U-N-S 07-106-4166 IMP
CITY OF CHARLOTTE
600 E 4th St, Charlotte, NC 28202-2816
Tel (704) 336-7600 *Founded/Ownrshp* 1768
Sales NA *EMP* 5,011
Accts Cherry Bekaert Llp Raleigh N
SIC 9111 City & town managers' offices;
Ofcr: John Gombar
VP: Charles Jones
VP: Ben Russell
Dir Lab: Roger Thompson
Dir IT: Grey Drum
Board of Directors: Danny Diehl, Greg C Gaskins, Greg C Gaskins, Timothy Mayes, Kim McMillan, Jerry Pinkard, Curt Walton

D-U-N-S 04-311-2341
CITY OF CHATTANOOGA
101 E 11th St Ste G13, Chattanooga, TN 37402-4247
Tel (423) 425-3700 *Founded/Ownrshp* 1838
Sales NA *EMP* 2,500
Accts Henderson Hutcherson & Mccullo
SIC 9111 Mayors' offices;
**CFO:* Daisy W Madison
**Treas:* Barry Teague
Ofcr: Terry Barnes
Ofcr: Justin Brumbaugh

Ofcr: Jonathan Parker
Ofcr: KristofferTinney
Comm Dir: Lacie Stone
Genl Mgr: Natalie Dickey

D-U-N-S 07-382-3387
CITY OF CHELSEA
OFFICE OF THE TREASURER
500 Broadway Ste 1, Chelsea, MA 02150-2900
Tel (617) 466-4240 *Founded/Ownrshp* 1637
Sales NA *EMP* 1,000
SIC 9111 City & town managers' offices;
Treas: Richard Boulrice
Ofcr: Ricky King
Dir IT: John Cowhig

D-U-N-S 06-341-4759
CITY OF CHESAPEAKE
CHESAPEAKE CONFERENCE CENTER
306 Cedar Rd, Chesapeake, VA 23322-5597
Tel (757) 382-6586 *Founded/Ownrshp* 1963
Sales NA *EMP* 2,893
Accts Cherry Bekaert Llp Virginia B
SIC 9111 City & town managers' offices;
**Treas:* Barbara O Carraway
Treas: Kevin Cooke
Ofcr: Paul Gorski
Ofcr: Jeffrey Smith
VP: Susie Lee
VP: Alvin Pimienta
**Prin:* John DeTriquet
Off Mgr: Lucia Rocca
QA Dir: Robin Spellman
Dir IT: MMC D Moore
IT Man: Wendy Hu
Board of Directors: Council Members, Dr Rebecca C W Adams, John E Allen, Dr John M DeTriquet, Arthur L Dwyer, Dalton S Edge, Dr Alan P Krasnoft, Dwight M Parker, S Z Ritter, Patricia P Willis

D-U-N-S 00-174-9605
CITY OF CHICAGO
MAYOR'S OFFICE
121 N La Salle St, Chicago, IL 60602-1202
Tel (312) 744-5000 *Founded/Ownrshp* 1837
Sales NA *EMP* 40,000
Accts Deloitte & Touche Llp Chicag
SIC 9111 City & town managers' offices;
Ofcr: George Coleman
Ofcr: Donna Long
Ofcr: Jamie L Rhee
Dir IT: Rob Hague
Dir IT: Zachary Williams
IT Man: Norbert Diaz
IT Man: Latoya Vaughn

D-U-N-S 06-698-1218
CITY OF CHICOPEE
274 Front St, Chicopee, MA 01013-2899
Tel (413) 594-1490 *Founded/Ownrshp* 1659
Sales NA *EMP* 2,000
SIC 9111 Mayors' offices;
**Treas:* Ernest Laflamme Jr
Off Mgr: Joann Gagnon

D-U-N-S 04-332-5158
CITY OF CINCINNATI
801 Plum St Rm 246, Cincinnati, OH 45202-5704
Tel (513) 352-3221 *Founded/Ownrshp* 1788
Sales NA *EMP* 5,964
Accts Clark Schaefer Hackett & Co
SIC 9111 City & town managers' offices;
**Pr:* Wendell Young
Ofcr: George Engleman
Ofcr: Amy Moore
**Prin:* Roxanne Qualls
Genl Mgr: Karen Alder
Genl Mgr: Nicole Lee
Sys Mgr: Tony Lewellyn
Snr Mgr: Terrance Nestor

D-U-N-S 08-145-6428 IMP
CITY OF CLARKSVILLE
1 Public Sq Ste 4, Clarksville, TN 37040-3463
Tel (931) 648-6106 *Founded/Ownrshp* 1784
Sales NA *EMP* 1,000
Accts Crosslin & Associates Nashvil
SIC 9111 Mayors' offices;
COO: Deanna McLaughlin
**CFO:* Ben Griffin
CFO: Laurie Matta
Exec: Pamela Cooper
Exec: Jack Frazier
Exec: Joel Wallace
IT Man: Debbie Smith

D-U-N-S 07-830-7303
CITY OF CLEARWATER
MYCLEARWATER
Clearwater Cy Hl Fl 3, Clearwater, FL 33756
Tel (727) 562-4567 *Founded/Ownrshp* 1897
Sales NA *EMP* 1,700
Accts Mayer Hoffman Mccann Pc Cle
SIC 9111 City & town managers' offices;
Dir IT: Dan Mayer
Opers Mgr: Gordon Wills
Mktg Dir: Joelle Castelli

D-U-N-S 07-675-5081
CITY OF CLEVELAND
601 Lakeside Ave E Rm 210, Cleveland, OH 44114-1015
Tel (216) 664-2000 *Founded/Ownrshp* 1836
Sales NA *EMP* 8,073
Accts Clark Schaefer Hackett & Co
SIC 9111 City & town managers' offices;
CFO: Shameka Jones
**Treas:* Algernon Walker
Ofcr: George Dedek
Pr Dir: Michael O'Malley

D-U-N-S 96-318-6288
CITY OF CLOVIS BOARD OF EDUCATION SCHOOL DISTRICT 1
1009 N Main St, Clovis, NM 88101-5932
Tel (575) 769-4300 *Founded/Ownrshp* 2010
Sales 10.9MM[E] *EMP* 1,200
SIC 8211 Elementary & secondary schools
Pr: Paul Cordova

D-U-N-S 04-270-5052
CITY OF COLORADO SPRINGS
ADMINISTRATIVE BUILDING
107 N Nevada Ave Ste 300, Colorado Springs, CO 80903-1305
Tel (719) 385-2489 *Founded/Ownrshp* 2012
Sales 279.0MM *EMP* 123[E]
Accts Rubinbrown Llp Denver Co
SIC 5085 Springs

CITY OF COLUMBIA
See COLUMBIA CITY OF (INC)

D-U-N-S 07-370-7366
CITY OF COLUMBIA
1737 Main St, Columbia, SC 29201-2819
Tel (803) 545-3075 *Founded/Ownrshp* 1854
Sales NA *EMP* 1,800
Accts Webster Rogers Llp Columbia
SIC 9111 Mayors' offices;
Ex Dir: Leshia Gray
Pr Dir: Leshia Utsey

D-U-N-S 05-136-9916
CITY OF COLUMBUS
MAYOR'S OFFICE
90 W Broad St Rm B33, Columbus, OH 43215-9061
Tel (614) 645-7671 *Founded/Ownrshp* 1834
Sales NA *EMP* 8,385
Accts Clark Schaefer Hackett & Co
SIC 9111 Mayors' offices;
Treas: Thomas Isaacs
Ofcr: David Sawyer
Comm Man: Melanie Crabill
Comm Man: Alesia Howard
Genl Mgr: Philip Carter
Off Mgr: Cathy Smith
CIO: Gary R Cavin
CTO: Craig Seeds
Pr Dir: Robin Davis
Snr Mgr: Greg Davies

D-U-N-S 06-945-7786
CITY OF CORPUS CHRISTI
MAYOR'S OFFICE
1201 Leopard St, Corpus Christi, TX 78401-2120
Tel (361) 880-3000 *Founded/Ownrshp* 1852
Sales NA *EMP* 3,518
Accts Collier Johnson & Woods Pc
SIC 9111 City & town managers' offices;
Ex Dir: Katherine Conoly
Admn Mgr: Diana Garza
Admn Mgr: Regina Lee

D-U-N-S 06-042-2763
CITY OF CUYAHOGA FALLS
CUYAHOGA FALLS NATATORIUM
2310 2nd St, Cuyahoga Falls, OH 44221-2583
Tel (330) 971-8230 *Founded/Ownrshp* 1868
Sales NA *EMP* 1,049
Accts Ciuni & Panichi Inc Clevela
SIC 9111 Mayors' offices;

D-U-N-S 04-463-4483
CITY OF DALLAS
DALLAS CITY HALL
1500 Marilla St, Dallas, TX 75201-6390
Tel (214) 670-3146 *Founded/Ownrshp* 1856
Sales NA *EMP* 13,000
Accts Grant Thornton Llp Dallas T
SIC 9111 City & town managers' offices;
Ofcr: Robert Beltran
Ofcr: Monica Contreras
Ofcr: Eloisa Mariscal
Ofcr: Scott McAvoy
Ofcr: Shawn Mosley
Ofcr: Eric Pierce
Ofcr: Johnny Ramos
Ofcr: Jose Ruiz
Snr Mgr: Charlotta Riley

D-U-N-S 06-600-8251
CITY OF DANVILLE
427 Patton St, Danville, VA 24541-1215
Tel (434) 799-5100 *Founded/Ownrshp* 1728
Sales NA *EMP* 1,200
Accts Dixon Hughes Goodman Llp Newp
SIC 9111 City & town managers' offices;

D-U-N-S 00-447-8194
CITY OF DAYTON
101 W 3rd St, Dayton, OH 45402-1859
Tel (937) 333-3333 *Founded/Ownrshp* 1796
Sales NA *EMP* 2,000
Accts Plattenburg & Associates Inc
SIC 9111 City & town managers' offices;
CEO: Warren Price
**CEO:* Jacquelyn Y Powell
**Treas:* Annette Brown
Ofcr: Mike Galbraith
Exec: Matt Joseph
Ex Dir: Lois Greene
Div Mgr: Kathy Emery
Dir IT: Amanda Mundy
IT Man: Doug Baltes
IT Man: Robert Lyons
IT Man: Ariel Walker

D-U-N-S 07-138-0190
CITY OF DENTON
CITY OF DENTON TEXAS
215 E Mckinney St, Denton, TX 76201-4299
Tel (940) 349-8200 *Founded/Ownrshp* 1866
Sales NA *EMP* 1,000
Accts Weaver And Tidwell Llp Da
SIC 9111 City & town managers' offices;
CFO: Bryan Lingly
Ofcr: Cleopatra Birckbichler
Ofcr: Ryan Grelle
Ofcr: Karon Terry
Brnch Mgr: Terri Gibbs
Brnch Mgr: Terri Sharp
Off Admin: Juanita Clarke
Off Admin: Bell Elizabeth
CTO: Trevena Royal
Tech Mgr: Jennifer Reaves
Mktg Mgr: Maria Denison

CITY OF DENTON TEXAS
See CITY OF DENTON

D-U-N-S 07-349-8909
CITY OF DES MOINES
400 Robert D Ray Dr Ste B, Des Moines, IA 50309-1813
Tel (515) 283-4500 *Founded/Ownrshp* 1851
Sales NA *EMP* 1,668
Accts Mcgladrey Llp Des Moines Iow
SIC 9111 City & town managers' offices;
Ofcr: Amelia Morris
Brnch Mgr: Bonnie Grant
Genl Mgr: Heide Green
IT Man: John Newman
Opers Mgr: Royce Hammitt

D-U-N-S 00-653-0661
CITY OF DETROIT (MI)
MAYOR'S OFFICE
2 Woodward Ave Rm 1126, Detroit, MI 48226-3443
Tel (313) 224-3400 *Founded/Ownrshp* 1701
Sales NA *EMP* 17,416
Accts Kpmg Llp Detroit Michigan
SIC 9111 City & town managers' offices;
CFO: Sean Werdlow
Assoc Dir: Kylee Mitchell
Genl Mgr: Anita Berry
CIO: Dave Rayford
Web Dev: Goran Bankovic
Sales Exec: Russell Griffore
Counsel: John E Johnson
Board of Directors: Clyde Cleveland, Kenneth V Cockrel Jr, Sheila M Cockrel, Kay Everett, Nicholas Hood III, Maryann Mahaffey, Brenda M Scott, Alberta Tinsley-Talabi, Council Members

D-U-N-S 07-556-6695
CITY OF DURHAM
101 City Hall Plz, Durham, NC 27701-3328
Tel (919) 560-4333 *Founded/Ownrshp* 1869
Sales NA *EMP* 2,200
Accts Cherry Bekaert & Holland Ll
SIC 9111 Mayors' offices
Board of Directors: Paul Miller, Cynthia D Brown, Isaac A Robinson, Howard Clement, Diane Wright, Tyrone Cox, Council Members, Virginia Engelhard, Kimball Griffin, Frank Hyman, Angela Langley, Erick W Larson, Floyd B McKissick Jr

D-U-N-S 07-117-3637
CITY OF EAST ORANGE
44 City Hall Plz, East Orange, NJ 07018-4502
Tel (973) 266-5140 *Founded/Ownrshp* 1863
Sales NA *EMP* 1,100
SIC 9111 Mayors' offices;
CFO: William Senande
**CFO:* Victoria Walker
Ofcr: Rochelle Evans

D-U-N-S 07-571-4501
CITY OF EAST PROVIDENCE
145 Taunton Ave, East Providence, RI 02914-4505
Tel (401) 435-7521 *Founded/Ownrshp* 1862
Sales NA *EMP* 1,516
Accts Bacon & Company Llc Warwick
SIC 9111 City & town managers' offices
Genl Mgr: Gerald Leach
CIO: Kelly Ahrens
Instr Medi: Rebekah Gendron
Board of Directors: Joseph La Risa, Gerald Lynch, Norman Miranda, Robert Sullivan, Council Members

D-U-N-S 05-887-3019
CITY OF EL PASO
1 Civic Center Plz, El Paso, TX 79901-1153
Tel (915) 541-4000 *Founded/Ownrshp* 1871
Sales NA *EMP* 5,500
Accts Bkd Llp Dallas Texas
SIC 9111 City & town managers' offices;
CFO: Mark Sutter
Genl Mgr: Nancy Melendez-Forbes
IT Man: Patricia Degman
Opers Mgr: Bryan Crowe

D-U-N-S 06-080-3152
CITY OF ELIZABETH
50 Winfield Scott Plz, Elizabeth, NJ 07201-2408
Tel (908) 820-4111 *Founded/Ownrshp* 1855
Sales NA *EMP* 1,200
Accts Louis C Mai Cpa & Associates
SIC 9111 Mayors' offices;
**Prin:* Richard Huston

D-U-N-S 05-496-8045
CITY OF EUGENE
99 W 10th Ave Ste 310, Eugene, OR 97401-3024
Tel (541) 682-5010 *Founded/Ownrshp* 1862
Sales NA *EMP* 1,440
Accts Isler Cpa Eugene Oregon
SIC 9111 City & town managers' offices;
Ofcr: Sherryl Lockhart
Ofcr: Doana Nowakowski
Prgrm Mgr: Ethan Nelson
Dir IT: Sarah Medary
Trfc Dir: Marie Longworth
Pr Mgr: Brian Richardson

D-U-N-S 05-427-6688
CITY OF EVANSVILLE (IN)
EVANSVILLE CIVIC CTR COMPLEX
1 Nw Martin Luther, Evansville, IN 47708
Tel (812) 436-4994 *Founded/Ownrshp* 1819
Sales NA *EMP* 1,400
Accts State Board Of Accounts India
SIC 9121 City council;
**Pr:* H Dan Adams
**Pr:* Steve Bagbey
Treas: Rick Davis
Ex Dir: Joseph Ballard
Genl Mgr: Jane Reel

D-U-N-S 05-730-7456
CITY OF EVERETT
2930 Wetmore Ave Ste 100, Everett, WA 98201-4044
Tel (425) 257-8700 *Founded/Ownrshp* 1893
Sales NA *EMP* 1,183
Accts Jan M Jutte Cpa Cgfm Olymp
SIC 9111 City & town managers' offices;
**CFO:* Debra Bryant
**Treas:* Suzy Haugen
Dir Risk M: Christi Muth-Schulz
Pr Dir: Kate Reardon

D-U-N-S 10-028-1526
CITY OF EVERETT
484 Broadway Rm 14, Everett, MA 02149-3694
Tel (617) 394-2270 *Founded/Ownrshp* 1892
Sales NA *EMP* 1,200
SIC 9111 City & town managers' offices;
**Treas:* Domenico D'Angelo

D-U-N-S 04-001-0019
CITY OF FAIRFIELD
1000 Webster St, Fairfield, CA 94533-4883
Tel (707) 428-7569 *Founded/Ownrshp* 1859
Sales NA *EMP* 1,646
Accts Vavrinek Trine Day & Co Ll
SIC 9111 City & town managers' offices;
CIO: James Perez

D-U-N-S 07-571-6456
CITY OF FALL RIVER
1 Government Ctr, Fall River, MA 02722-7700
Tel (508) 324-2000 *Founded/Ownrshp* 1803
Sales NA *EMP* 2,302
SIC 9111 City & town managers' offices;

D-U-N-S 04-003-1700
CITY OF FAYETTEVILLE
433 Hay St, Fayetteville, NC 28301-0007
Tel (910) 433-1990 *Founded/Ownrshp* 1750
Sales NA *EMP* 1,443
Accts Cherry Bekaert Llp Fayettevil
SIC 9111 City & town managers' offices;
**CFO:* Lisa Smith
Ofcr: Sharien Molina
Genl Mgr: Kelly Nicot

D-U-N-S 07-534-8052
CITY OF FITCHBURG
166 Boulder Dr Ste 108, Fitchburg, MA 01420-3168
Tel (978) 345-9567 *Founded/Ownrshp* 1764
Sales NA *EMP* 1,250
Accts Melanson Heath & Company Pc
SIC 9111 Mayors' offices;
Ex Dir: Dan Curley

D-U-N-S 00-494-9475
CITY OF FOLSOM (CA)
50 Natoma St, Folsom, CA 95630-2614
Tel (916) 355-7200 *Founded/Ownrshp* 1946
Sales NA *EMP* 1,324
Accts Vavrinek Trine Day & Co Ll
SIC 9111 Mayors' offices;
Ofcr: Bill Bradshaw
Ofcr: Jeana Stover
Ex Dir: Robert Goss

D-U-N-S 00-494-9541
CITY OF FONTANA
8353 Sierra Ave, Fontana, CA 92335-3598
Tel (909) 350-7605 *Founded/Ownrshp* 1952
Sales NA *EMP* 1,300
Accts Lance Soll & Lunghard Llp Br
SIC 9111 City & town managers' offices;
CFO: Ulric Jones
Ofcr: Andrew Vestey
Dir IT: Dennis Vlasich
IT Man: Anita Lakhani

D-U-N-S 07-836-2597
CITY OF FORT COLLINS
215 N Mason St, Fort Collins, CO 80524-4402
Tel (970) 221-6770 *Founded/Ownrshp* 1873
Sales NA *EMP* 1,400
Accts Mcgladrey Llp Denver Colorad
SIC 9111 City & town managers' offices;
Ofcr: Todd Hopkins
Genl Mgr: Lisa Alexander

D-U-N-S 07-221-9595
CITY OF FORT LAUDERDALE
CITY MANAGER'S OFFICE
100 N Andrews Ave, Fort Lauderdale, FL 33301-1016
Tel (954) 828-5013 *Founded/Ownrshp* 1911
Sales NA *EMP* 2,396
Accts Ernst & Young Llp Boca Raton
SIC 9111 City & town managers' offices;
Treas: Clyde J Cole
Ofcr: Chaz Adams
Ofcr: Juan Cabrera
Ofcr: Salvatore Viscusi
Div Mgr: Mark Blanco
Genl Mgr: Barbara Smith
Tech Mgr: Jay Stacy
Secur Mgr: Gary Gray

D-U-N-S 06-470-2616
CITY OF FORT WAYNE
200 E Berry St, Fort Wayne, IN 46802-2731
Tel (260) 427-1111 *Founded/Ownrshp* 1829
Sales NA *EMP* 1,910
Accts State Of Indiana Paul D Joyc
SIC 9111 Mayors' offices;
Ofcr: Rick Schlup
Exec: Rachel Blakeman
Exec: Larry Campbell
Exec: Frank Suarez
Dir Risk M: Nancy McAfee
Genl Mgr: Mark Knepper
Genl Mgr: Mary Nelson-Janisse
CTO: James Scott
IT Man: Betty Clark
IT Man: Rich Laudeman

D-U-N-S 07-317-0458 IMP/EXP
CITY OF FORT WORTH
1000 Throckmorton St, Fort Worth, TX 76102-6311
Tel (817) 392-6118 *Founded/Ownrshp* 1842
Sales NA *EMP* 5,698
SIC 9111

D-U-N-S 07-884-4992
CITY OF FRANKFORT
1200 Kentucky Ave, Frankfort, KY 40601-1185
Tel (502) 875-8500 *Founded/Ownrshp* 2013
Sales 3.0MMM *EMP* 269
SIC 7389

D-U-N-S 07-654-9104
CITY OF FREMONT
3300 Capitol Ave, Fremont, CA 94538-1514
Tel (510) 284-4000 *Founded/Ownrshp* 1956
Sales NA *EMP* 1,000
Accts Macias Gini & O Connell Llp W
SIC 9111 Mayors' offices;
Ofcr: Mark Dang
Dir Risk M: Steven Schwarz
Genl Mgr: Tricia Fan
Opers Mgr: Mike Sung

D-U-N-S 11-463-1018
CITY OF FREMONT
3300 Capitol Ave, Fremont, CA 94538-1514
Tel (510) 574-2050 *Founded/Ownrshp* 1994
Sales NA *EMP* 2,000
SIC 9121 City council
Ofcr: Teresa Hebebrand

D-U-N-S 07-188-7855
CITY OF FRESNO
2600 Fresno St, Fresno, CA 93721-3620
Tel (559) 621-7001 *Founded/Ownrshp* 1885
Sales NA *EMP* 2,600
Accts Macias Gini & O Connell Llp
SIC 9111 Mayors' offices;
Ofcr: Ruben Barrios
Ofcr: Lloyd Flores
Ofcr: Lisa Harwood
Exec: Matt Otstot
Mktg Dir: Nick P Yovino

D-U-N-S 01-052-2159
CITY OF GAINESVILLE
GAINESVILLE REGIONAL UTILITIES
200 E University Ave, Gainesville, FL 32601-3400
Tel (352) 334-5010 *Founded/Ownrshp* 1854
Sales NA *EMP* 2,400
SIC 9111 City & town managers' offices;
**Genl Mgr:* Michael Kurtz
IT Man: Kelly Ferrel

D-U-N-S 05-868-2162
CITY OF GARLAND
200 N 5th St, Garland, TX 75040-6314
Tel (972) 205-2000 *Founded/Ownrshp* 1891
Sales NA *EMP* 2,000
Accts Deloitte & Touche Llp Dallas
SIC 9111 City & town managers' offices;
Ofcr: Alexis Crockett
Dir: Rick Vasquez
Off Mgr: Cindy Smith

D-U-N-S 06-746-9437
CITY OF GARY
401 Broadway Ste 100, Gary, IN 46402-1236
Tel (219) 881-1301 *Founded/Ownrshp* 1906
Sales NA *EMP* 1,500
Accts State Of Indiana Indianapolis
SIC 9121
Dir: Christopher Meyers
Ex Dir: Shirley Hawkins

D-U-N-S 03-038-4325
CITY OF GLENDALE
141 N Glendale Ave Fl 2, Glendale, CA 91206-4975
Tel (818) 548-2085 *Founded/Ownrshp* 1906
Sales NA *EMP* 2,000
Accts Vavrinek Trine Day & Co Ll
SIC 9111 City & town managers' offices;
Bd of Dir: Zinda Jimenez
Genl Mgr: Shu-Jun Li

D-U-N-S 07-752-3579
CITY OF GLENDALE
5850 W Glendale Ave Fl 4, Glendale, AZ 85301-2599
Tel (623) 930-2000 *Founded/Ownrshp* 1910
Sales NA *EMP* 1,000E
Accts Cliftonlarsonallen Llp Phoen
SIC 9111 City & town managers' offices;
Pr: Jim Cummings
Ofcr: Mike Michelsen
Exec: Michael Young
Comm Man: Sue Breding
Sys Mgr: Joe Trasancos
Natl Sales: Danielle Dutsch
Snr Mgr: Chuck Montgomery

D-U-N-S 96-345-7374
CITY OF GLENDALE MUNICIPAL PROPERTY CORP
5850 W Glendale Ave, Glendale, AZ 85301-2563
Tel (623) 930-2820 *Founded/Ownrshp* 2010
Sales 165.0MM *EMP* 1
Accts Heinfeld Meech & Co Pc Phoeni
SIC 7389 Personal service agents, brokers & bureaus
Prin: Leland Peterson

D-U-N-S 06-222-2997
CITY OF GRAND RAPIDS
300 Monroe Ave Nw Unit 1, Grand Rapids, MI 49503-2281
Tel (616) 456-3000 *Founded/Ownrshp* 1850
Sales NA *EMP* 1,830
SIC 9111

D-U-N-S 07-157-2374
CITY OF GREENSBORO
300 W Washington St, Greensboro, NC 27401-2624
Tel (336) 373-2002 *Founded/Ownrshp* 1808
Sales NA *EMP* 2,650
Accts Cherry Bekaert Llp Raleigh N
SIC 9111
Ofcr: Gregory Bailey
Ofcr: Barry Levine
Ofcr: Shawn Roscoe
Ofcr: James Schwochow
Ofcr: Ecolia Watkins
Telecom Mg: Gerrad Biffle
Opers Mgr: Melanie Neal
Opers Mgr: Denise Seals

D-U-N-S 06-747-9923
CITY OF HAMMOND
5925 Calumet Ave, Hammond, IN 46320-2556
Tel (219) 853-6301 *Founded/Ownrshp* 1884
Sales NA *EMP* 1,289
SIC 9111 Mayors' offices
**Pr:* Dannial Repay
Ofcr: Antwian Windmon

D-U-N-S 06-601-9902
CITY OF HAMPTON
22 Lincoln St, Hampton, VA 23669-3522
Tel (757) 728-5177 *Founded/Ownrshp* 1610
Sales NA *EMP* 1,875
Accts Cherry Bekaert Llp Virginia B
SIC 9111 City & town managers' offices;
**Treas:* Molly Ward Jr
Ex Dir: Bill Greeves

D-U-N-S 00-453-4707
CITY OF HARTFORD
HARTFORD CITY HALL
550 Main St Ste 1, Hartford, CT 06103-2913
Tel (860) 757-9311 *Founded/Ownrshp* 1784
Sales NA *EMP* 10,000
Accts Rsm Us Llp New Haven Connect
SIC 9111 City & town managers' offices;
COO: David Panagore
**Treas:* Kathleen Plam
Opers Mgr: Edison Silva
Psych: Rosemarie Gupton
Snr PM: Lionel Rigler
Snr Mgr: John Bazzano

D-U-N-S 07-659-6204
CITY OF HAVERHILL
City Hl Rm 100, Haverhill, MA 01830
Tel (978) 374-2300 *Founded/Ownrshp* 1641
Sales NA *EMP* 1,200
Accts Giusti Hingston And Company
SIC 9111 Mayors' offices;
Ofcr: Orlando Pacheco

D-U-N-S 07-623-0267 IMP
CITY OF HENDERSON
240 S Water St, Henderson, NV 89015-7227
Tel (702) 267-2323 *Founded/Ownrshp* 1953
Sales NA *EMP* 3,775
Accts Piercy Bowler Taylor & Kern L
SIC 9111 City & town managers' offices;
Ofcr: Michael Cluff
Ofcr: Brian Estep
Ofcr: Michelle French
Ofcr: Robert Honea
Ofcr: Jeff Leake
Ofcr: Monica Manig
Ofcr: Marc Smith
Ofcr: Cody Walker
Ofcr: Michael Webster
Dir Risk M: Robert Osip
**Prin:* Jacob Snow

D-U-N-S 07-847-6975
CITY OF HIALEAH
501 Palm Ave, Hialeah, FL 33010-4719
Tel (305) 883-8075 *Founded/Ownrshp* 1925
Sales NA *EMP* 1,800
Accts Alberni Caballero & Company Ll
SIC 9111 City & town managers' offices;
**Pr:* Luis Gonzalez
COO: Ray Perez
Ofcr: Oscar Amago
Ofcr: Maureen Carulo
Ofcr: Dominick Fradera
Ofcr: Nicholas Lopez
Ofcr: Rosemary Novo
Ofcr: Oscar Oliveros
Off Admin: Laura Ramsay
Telecom Mg: Antonio Arce
Sales Exec: Raul Martinez

D-U-N-S 07-158-1938
CITY OF HIGH POINT
CITY HALL
211 S Hamilton St, High Point, NC 27260-5397
Tel (336) 883-3289 *Founded/Ownrshp* 1806
Sales NA *EMP* 1,200
Accts Mcgladrey Llp Greensboro Nor
SIC 9111 City & town managers' offices;
Ofcr: Geanine Pregel
Ofcr: Roy Watts
IT Man: Susan Patterson

D-U-N-S 78-722-7847
CITY OF HOLLYWOOD
CITY ATTY OFFICE
2600 Hollywood Blvd Ste B, Hollywood, FL 33020-4800
Tel (954) 921-3435 *Founded/Ownrshp* 2006
Sales NA *EMP* 1,300
SIC 9222 Legal counsel office, government
Genl Mgr: Cathy Swanson
Dir IT: John Barletta
Mktg Dir: Manuel Pila

D-U-N-S 06-698-1572
CITY OF HOLYOKE
536 Dwight St, Holyoke, MA 01040-5086
Tel (413) 322-5510 *Founded/Ownrshp* 1850
Sales NA *EMP* 3,068
Accts Melanson Heath & Company Pc
SIC 9111 Mayors' offices;
Off Mgr: Debbie Reardon
HC Dir: Marcus Gabrieli

D-U-N-S 06-669-2369
CITY OF HOPE
1500 E Duarte Blvd, Duarte, CA 91010
Tel (626) 256-4673 *Founded/Ownrshp* 1929
Sales 1.4MMM *EMP* 2,400
SIC 8741 8399

D-U-N-S 60-309-0247
CITY OF HOPE
1500 Duarte Rd Fl 4, Duarte, CA 91010-3012
Tel (626) 256-4673 *Founded/Ownrshp* 1980
Sales 1.4MMM *EMP* 1E
SIC 8069 Cancer hospital

D-U-N-S 07-865-1958
CITY OF HOPE MEDICAL FOUNDATION (CA)
1500 Duarte Rd, Duarte, CA 91010-3012
Tel (626) 256-4673 *Founded/Ownrshp* 2012
Sales 142.2MM *EMP* 1
Accts Ernst & Young Us Llp Irvine
SIC 8733 Noncommercial research organizations
Prin: Robert W Stone

D-U-N-S 80-763-5982
CITY OF HOPE NATIONAL MEDICAL CENTER
1500 Duarte Rd, Duarte, CA 91010-3012
Tel (626) 256-4673 *Founded/Ownrshp* 1948
Sales 860.5MM *EMP* 1,900
SIC 8062 General medical & surgical hospitals
CEO: Michael A Friedman
**CEO:* Robert Stone
Bd of Dir: Jill Olausson
Assoc VP: William Davis
Exec: Cynthia Garcia
Dir Lab: Dayson Moreira
Dir Rad: Lawrence E Williams
Adm Dir: Leonard Chen
Prgrm Mgr: Kim Lu
CIO: Paul Conocenti
VP Inf Sys: Michael J Sauk

D-U-N-S 04-576-1095 IMP
CITY OF HOUSTON
901 Bagby St, Houston, TX 77002-2049
Tel (713) 837-0311 *Founded/Ownrshp* 1836
Sales NA *EMP* 23,235
Accts Deloitte & Touche Llp Houston
SIC 9111 Executive offices;
Trst: Jorge Cruz-Aedo
Ofcr: Pamela Berger
Ofcr: George Edwards
Ofcr: Anthony Hall
Ofcr: Luis Hernandez
Ofcr: Lavearn Newsome
Ofcr: Rafael A Pantoja
VP: Kirk Drummond
Exec: Alvin Wright
Dir Soc: Melissa Tatum
Comm Dir: Janice Evans

D-U-N-S 07-814-3948
CITY OF HUNTINGTON BEACH
2000 Main St, Huntington Beach, CA 92648-2763
Tel (714) 536-5202 *Founded/Ownrshp* 1909
Sales NA *EMP* 1,659
SIC 9199 ;
**Treas:* Alisa Chupchen
Ofcr: M Hogan-Garcia
IT Man: Cheri Bauman

D-U-N-S 07-209-3727
CITY OF HUNTSVILLE
308 Fountain Cir Sw Fl 8, Huntsville, AL 35801-4240
Tel (256) 427-5080 *Founded/Ownrshp* 1811
Sales NA *EMP* 2,400
Accts Beason & Nalley Inc Huntsvi
SIC 9111 City & town managers' offices;
**Pr:* Will Culver
Ofcr: Billy Clardy
Ofcr: Julian Johnson
Ofcr: Saundra Simmons
Ofcr: Greg Spruell
DP Exec: Thomas McDonough
Snr Mgr: Mike Keel

D-U-N-S 60-822-8565
CITY OF HUNTSVILLE ELECTRIC SYSTEMS
HUNTSVILLE UTILITIES
112 Spragins St Nw, Huntsville, AL 35801-4902
Tel (256) 535-1200 *Founded/Ownrshp* 1805
Sales 517.9MME *EMP* 634
SIC 4911 Electric services
Pr: William C Pippin
Ofcr: Jimmie Butler
VP: John Olshefski
Board of Directors: Rod McLeroy

D-U-N-S 07-625-9456
CITY OF INDEPENDENCE
INDEPENDENCE CITY HALL
111 E Maple Ave, Independence, MO 64050-3066
Tel (816) 325-7000 *Founded/Ownrshp* 1827
Sales NA *EMP* 1,100
SIC 9111 City & town managers' offices;
Ex VP: Amanda Wadington

D-U-N-S 06-789-0848
CITY OF INDIANAPOLIS
200 E Washington St # 2501, Indianapolis, IN 46204-3333
Tel (317) 327-3601 *Founded/Ownrshp* 1832
Sales NA *EMP* 3,850
Accts Bkd Llp Indianapolis Indiana
SIC 9111 Mayors' offices;
Dir Lab: Michael Medler
Counsel: Chris Cotterill
Snr PM: Michelle Winfield
Snr Mgr: Ken Clark
Snr Mgr: Beth Howen

D-U-N-S 07-411-8456
CITY OF INGLEWOOD
1 W Manchester Blvd, Inglewood, CA 90301-1764
Tel (310) 412-5301 *Founded/Ownrshp* 1908
Sales NA *EMP* 1,100
Accts Mayer Hoffman Mccann Pc Irv
SIC 9111 Mayors' offices;
Ofcr: David Ramirez
Telecom Mg: Jane Lindsay
IT Man: Matthew Chambers
Sftwr Eng: Thomas Lee

D-U-N-S 07-251-1363
CITY OF IRVINE (CA)
1 Civic Center Plz, Irvine, CA 92606-5208
Tel (949) 724-6000 *Founded/Ownrshp* 1971
Sales NA *EMP* 1,340E
Accts Lance Soll & Lunghard Llp B
SIC 9121 9111 City council; City & town managers' offices
Ofcr: Kayla Wiebe
Ex Dir: Doug Williford
Snr Mgr: Jeff Noble

D-U-N-S 06-414-2888
CITY OF IRVING
825 W Irving Blvd, Irving, TX 75060-2860
Tel (972) 721-2600 *Founded/Ownrshp* 1914
Sales NA *EMP* 1,635
Accts Grant Thornton Llp Dallas T
SIC 9111 City & town managers' offices;
Dir Vol: Carla Morgan
Trst: James Donovan
Ofcr: Rodney Bergeron
Ofcr: Lukas Kratochvil
Ofcr: Rawley Miller
Ofcr: Naya Pope
Ofcr: Kim Vanderveen
Exec: Steven Reed
Ex Dir: Richard Huff
Off Admin: Cheryl Miles
Sales Exec: Ed Barry

D-U-N-S 02-086-4955
CITY OF JACKSON
219 S President St, Jackson, MS 39201-2361
Tel (601) 960-1111 *Founded/Ownrshp* 1822
Sales NA *EMP* 2,100
Accts Bank Finley White & Co Jac
SIC 9111 City & town managers' offices;
**Treas:* Felicia Young
VP: Frank Bluntson
Board of Directors: A Seven Member City Counci

D-U-N-S 00-407-6998 IMP
CITY OF JACKSONVILLE
117 W Duval St Fl Mess, Jacksonville, FL 32202-3737
Tel (904) 630-1776 *Founded/Ownrshp* 1832
Sales NA *EMP* 7,908
Accts Mcgladrey Llp Jacksonville F
SIC 9111 Mayors' offices;
CFO: Mike Weinstein
Chf Inves: Joey Greive
Ofcr: Donna Campbell
Ofcr: Christy L Conn
Ofcr: Daniel T Delgado
Ofcr: Coxen Jerryg
Ofcr: Sam Mousa
Ofcr: Jerry R Stickland
Exec: Dan Macdonald
Dir Soc: Brent Fine
Prgrm Mgr: Chardae Hancock

D-U-N-S 07-879-9982
CITY OF JACKSONVILLE
JACKSONVILLE SHERIFFS OFFICE
501 E Bay St, Jacksonville, FL 32202-2927
Tel (904) 630-0500 *Founded/Ownrshp* 1832
Sales NA *EMP* 3,000
SIC 9221 Police protection
Ofcr: Nuria Archbold
Ofcr: Wally Banks
Ofcr: Scott Bartleson
Ofcr: Mark P Bialkoski
Ofcr: Paul Bouda
Ofcr: Joseph Bruce
Ofcr: Bryan Burnett
Ofcr: Jimmie Collins
Ofcr: Robert Coyle
Ofcr: Justin Cross
Ofcr: Corey Debolt
Ofcr: Thomas Edwards
Ofcr: Brad Emerson
Ofcr: Karen Goodin
Ofcr: Trent Helms
Ofcr: Frank Holtsman
Ofcr: Marie Horton
Ofcr: Douglas Howell
Ofcr: Deon Johnson
Ofcr: Brandi Keune
Ofcr: Lance Liggett

D-U-N-S 06-750-1403
CITY OF JERSEY CITY
280 Grove St, Jersey City, NJ 07302-3610
Tel (201) 547-5000 *Founded/Ownrshp* 1820
Sales NA *EMP* 3,171
Accts Donahue Gironda & Doria By Fa
SIC 9111 Mayors' offices;
CFO: Donna Mauer
Ofcr: Ed Coleman
Genl Mgr: Lorraine Cecchini
IT Man: Elizabeth Castillo

D-U-N-S 07-901-8230
CITY OF JOHNSON CITY
601 E Main St, Johnson City, TN 37601-4880
Tel (423) 434-6000 *Founded/Ownrshp* 1869
Sales NA *EMP* 1,600
Accts Blackburn Childers & Steagall
SIC 9111 City & town managers' offices;
**Prin:* Denis Peterson
Admn Mgr: Susan Reed
Off Mgr: Michael Peterson
Netwrk Eng: Robert McClain
Pr Dir: Becky Hilbert
Snr Mgr: John Lowry

D-U-N-S 07-928-3214
CITY OF KALAMAZOO
241 W South St, Kalamazoo, MI 49007-4796
Tel (269) 337-8047 *Founded/Ownrshp* 1884
Sales NA *EMP* 1,056
Accts Abraham & Gaffney Pc East
SIC 9111 City & town managers' offices;
Opers Supe: Lorraine Brown
Opers Supe: Yvonne Thrash

D-U-N-S 06-898-0739
CITY OF KILLEEN
101 College St, Killeen, TX 76541-6105
Tel (254) 501-7895 *Founded/Ownrshp* 1892
Sales NA *EMP* 1,000
Accts Weaver And Tidwell Llp Da
SIC 9111
IT Man: Brian Supak

D-U-N-S 04-245-3530
CITY OF KNOXVILLE
400 W Main St Rm L108, Knoxville, TN 37902-2494
Tel (865) 215-2040 Founded/Ownrshp 1791
Sales NA EMP 1,608
SIC 9111

D-U-N-S 07-867-3670
CITY OF LA CROSSE
400 La Crosse St, La Crosse, WI 54601-3374
Tel (608) 784-8477 Founded/Ownrshp 1856
Sales NA EMP 1,500
Accts Hawkins Ash Cpas Llp La Cros
SIC 9111 City & town managers' offices;
Ofcr: Eric Christianson
Ofcr: Aaron Erdmann
Ofcr: Todd Fischer
Ofcr: Tom Hansen
Ofcr: Philip Martin
Ofcr: Joel Miller
Sales Asso: Stephanie Churchill

D-U-N-S 02-147-8573
CITY OF LAKE CHARLES
326 Pujo St, Lake Charles, LA 70601-4269
Tel (337) 491-1201 Founded/Ownrshp 1867
Sales NA EMP 1,093
Accts Mcelroy Quirk & Burch Lake C
SIC 9111 Mayors' offices;
Ofcr: Lecia McCullough
MIS Dir: Ray Abedie
MIS Dir: Susan Augustine
IT Man: Sheila Nunez
Snr Mgr: Rick Reppond

D-U-N-S 02-099-7912
CITY OF LAKELAND
228 S Massachusetts Ave, Lakeland, FL 33801-5012
Tel (863) 834-6000 Founded/Ownrshp 1885
Sales NA EMP 2,400
Accts Crowe Horwath Llp Lakeland
SIC 9111
COO: Tara Walls
Exec: Elizabeth Bass
Exec: Scott Lewis
Exec: Steve Wagner
Off Mgr: Sylvia Harris

D-U-N-S 06-983-5882
CITY OF LANSING
CITY HALL
124 W Michigan Ave Fl 5, Lansing, MI 48933-1670
Tel (517) 483-4433 Founded/Ownrshp 1859
Sales NA EMP 1,250
Accts Rehmann Robson Llc Grand Rapi
SIC 9111 City & town managers' offices
IT Man: Chad Gamble

D-U-N-S 06-946-3594
CITY OF LAREDO
LAREDO WATERWORKS SYSTEM
1110 Houston St, Laredo, TX 78040-8019
Tel (956) 791-7308 Founded/Ownrshp 1755
Sales NA EMP 2,100
Accts Canales Garza & Baum Pllc L
SIC 9111 Mayors' offices
Comm Man: San Rangel

D-U-N-S 07-921-0803
CITY OF LARGO
201 Highland Ave N, Largo, FL 33770-2512
Tel (727) 587-6700 Founded/Ownrshp 1905
Sales NA EMP 1,100
Accts Carr Riggs & Ingram Llc C
SIC 9111 Mayors' offices;
Ofcr: Tracy Brown
Ex Dir: Kimball Adams
CIO: Michael Pearlman
CIO: Harold Schomaker
CTO: Jill Sassone
IT Man: David Barber
Snr Mgr: Eileen Crowell
Board of Directors: Patricia Burke, Harriet K Crozier, Patricia Gerard, Jean M Halvorsen, Charlie Harper, Martin Shelby

D-U-N-S 07-760-9279
CITY OF LAS CRUCES
700 N Main St, Las Cruces, NM 88001-1120
Tel (575) 541-2000 Founded/Ownrshp 1908
Sales NA EMP 1,396
Accts Moss Adams Llp Albuquerque N
SIC 9111 City & town managers' offices;
COO: Daniel Avila
Treas: Mark Sutter
Ofcr: Luis Balderrama
Ofcr: Chris Carrillo
Ofcr: Dick Gephardt
Ofcr: Lisa Larocque
Ofcr: Lucy Lucero
Ofcr: Tom Murphy
Ofcr: Michael Roach
Ofcr: Jason Sauceda
Ofcr: Mark Winson
Exec: Tony Parra
Dir Risk M: Mark Castillo
Dir Soc: Monte Rout

D-U-N-S 03-038-1610
CITY OF LAS VEGAS (NV)
495 S Main St, Las Vegas, NV 89101-2986
Tel (702) 229-6321 Founded/Ownrshp 1911
Sales NA EMP 2,500
Accts Piercy Bowler Taylor & Kern L
SIC 9111 Executive offices, state & local;
Sr Cor Off: Michelle Thackston
Ofcr: Richard Atkins
Ofcr: Shani J Coleman
Ofcr: Tracy Ford
Adm Dir: Sharon Segerblom
Genl Mgr: Patty Braganza
IT Man: Scott Waber
Snr Mgr: Jonathan Foster

D-U-N-S 07-952-3171
CITY OF LAWRENCE
200 Common St, Lawrence, MA 01840-1517
Tel (978) 620-3010 Founded/Ownrshp 1847
Sales NA EMP 2,700
Accts Powers & Sullivan Llc Wakefi
SIC 9111 Mayors' offices;
Ofcr: Laiza Onge
VP: Nilka A Rodriquez
*Prin: Theresa Park
*Prin: Abel Vargas
Off Mgr: Karen Anderson
MIS Dir: Rob Harhen

D-U-N-S 07-536-4216
CITY OF LEOMINSTER
25 West St Ste 5, Leominster, MA 01453-5647
Tel (978) 534-7500 Founded/Ownrshp 1740
Sales NA EMP 1,143
SIC 9111 Mayors' offices
*Treas: David Laplant

D-U-N-S 05-125-9786
CITY OF LINCOLN
555 S 10th St Rm B115, Lincoln, NE 68508-2803
Tel (402) 441-7511 Founded/Ownrshp 1867
Sales NA EMP 2,000
Accts Bkd Llp Lincoln Ne
SIC 9111 City & town managers' offices
Ofcr: Nancy Brienzo
Ofcr: Michael Mandery
Ofcr: Ralph Martin
Ofcr: Pat Ribeiro
Genl Mgr: Barb Baier
Off Mgr: Kathleen Chadwick
Off Admin: Terri Storer
IT Man: Rod Johnson
IT Man: Kimberley Taylor-Riley

D-U-N-S 06-530-3794
CITY OF LITTLE ROCK
500 W Markham St, Little Rock, AR 72201-1415
Tel (501) 371-4510 Founded/Ownrshp 1835
Sales NA EMP 2,200
Accts Bkd Llp Little Rock Ar
SIC 9199 Supply agency, government
Bd of Dir: Brad Cazort
Bd of Dir: Erma Hendrix
Ofcr: Laurie Baehr
Ex Dir: Stephan McAteer
Genl Mgr: Brian Jones
Off Admin: Dora Fulks
Off Admin: Christian Zeigler
Sales Exec: Terri Branson
Pr Mgr: Meg Matthews

D-U-N-S 07-529-5832 IMP
CITY OF LONG BEACH
333 W Ocean Blvd Fl 10, Long Beach, CA 90802-4664
Tel (562) 570-6450 Founded/Ownrshp 1897
Sales NA EMP 5,028
Accts Kpmg Llp Los Angeles Ca
SIC 9111 City & town managers' offices
*Treas: David Nakamoto
Snr Ntwrk: Racy Pel
IT Man: Steven Ditmars
IT Man: Daniel Payne
IT Man: Sereivuth Prak

D-U-N-S 06-992-8349
CITY OF LOS ANGELES
200 N Spring St Ste 303, Los Angeles, CA 90012-3239
Tel (213) 978-0600 Founded/Ownrshp 1781
Sales NA EMP 41,000
Accts Macias Gini & O Connell Llp L
SIC 9111 Mayors' offices
Ofcr: John Egan
*Prin: Jinny Pak
Div Mgr: Maryam Abbassi
Pr Dir: Jackie David
Snr Mgr: Matt Szabo

D-U-N-S 05-821-3893
CITY OF LUBBOCK
1625 13th St, Lubbock, TX 79401-3830
Tel (806) 775-2016 Founded/Ownrshp 1909
Sales NA EMP 2,700
Accts Bkd Llp Dallas Tx
SIC 9111 Mayors' offices
CFO: Lee A Dunbuld
Bd of Dir: Garett Nelson
Ofcr: Kia Riemath
Exec: Barbara Blake
Exec: Gilbert Quant
Genl Mgr: Maurice Pearl
Dir IT: David McGaughey

D-U-N-S 01-003-8073
CITY OF LYNCHBURG
900 Church St Ste 102, Lynchburg, VA 24504-1620
Tel (434) 455-3990 Founded/Ownrshp 1850
Sales NA EMP 1,340E
Accts Brown Edwards & Company Ll
SIC 9111 Mayors' offices
*Prin: Bonnie Svrcek
Dir IT: Mike Goetz
IT Man: Kenneth Glover

D-U-N-S 06-917-4449
CITY OF MACON
700 Poplar St, Macon, GA 31201-2097
Tel (478) 751-7258 Founded/Ownrshp 1823
Sales NA EMP 1,420
Accts Mauldin & Jenkins Llc Macon
SIC 9111 Mayors' offices;

D-U-N-S 07-614-7909
CITY OF MADISON
210 Martin Luther, Madison, WI 53703
Tel (608) 266-4671 Founded/Ownrshp 1856
Sales NA EMP 2,918
Accts Baker Tilly Virchow Krause Ll
SIC 9111 City & town managers' offices;
Prin: Katharine Kuritz
Snr Mgr: Timothy Mrowiec
Snr Mgr: Johnny Winston

D-U-N-S 04-500-9073
CITY OF MANCHESTER
FINANCE DEPARTMENT
1 City Hall Plz, Manchester, NH 03101-2025
Tel (603) 624-6460 Founded/Ownrshp 1735
Sales NA EMP 1,351E
Accts Mcgladrey & Pullen New Haven
SIC 9111 Executive offices, state & local
*Treas: Sharon Wickens
Ofcr: Kyle Daly
Ofcr: Neil Penttinen
*Ofcr: William Sanders
Ofcr: James Tierney
IT Man: Michelle Bogardus
IT Man: Karrie Gaulin

D-U-N-S 07-810-4403
CITY OF MARIETTA
205 Lawrence St Ne, Marietta, GA 30060-1738
Tel (770) 794-5507 Founded/Ownrshp 1834
Sales NA EMP 1,071
Accts Crace Galvis Mcgrath Llc Ken
SIC 9111 City & town managers' offices;
Ofcr: Vikki Randolph
MIS Dir: Gene Estensen
MIS Dir: Dezerine Gordon
Software D: Rick Steffes

D-U-N-S 04-563-3484
CITY OF MARLBOROUGH
140 Main St Ofc 4, Marlborough, MA 01752-3812
Tel (508) 460-3775 Founded/Ownrshp 1890
Sales NA EMP 1,109
SIC 9111 City & town managers' offices;

D-U-N-S 06-672-3842
CITY OF MARYVILLE
404 W Broadway Ave, Maryville, TN 37801-4710
Tel (865) 273-3401 Founded/Ownrshp 1795
Sales NA EMP 1,156
Accts Ingram Overholt & Bean Pc A
SIC 9121 City council;
Dir Risk M: Leland C Blackwood

D-U-N-S 08-395-5245
CITY OF MC ALLEN
1300 W Houston Ave, McAllen, TX 78501-5002
Tel (956) 681-1000 Founded/Ownrshp 1911
Sales NA EMP 1,694
Accts Grants Thornton Llp Houston
SIC 9111 City & town managers' offices
Ofcr: Nancy Cuellar
Pgrm Dir: Piedad Martinez

D-U-N-S 07-661-7547
CITY OF MEDFORD
85 George P Hassett Dr, Medford, MA 02155-3299
Tel (781) 396-5500 Founded/Ownrshp 1892
Sales NA EMP 1,400
SIC 9111 Executive offices
*Treas: Alfred P Pompeo Jr

D-U-N-S 05-138-6258
CITY OF MEMPHIS
125 N Main St Ste 468, Memphis, TN 38103-2030
Tel (901) 576-6657 Founded/Ownrshp 1826
Sales NA EMP 6,000
Accts Banks Finley White & Co Me
SIC 9111 Mayors' offices;
Ofcr: Wain Gaskins
Genl Mgr: Dewanna Smith
CIO: Darryl D Adderson
CIO: Joseph Sanders
Snr Mgr: Michael Jones

D-U-N-S 08-831-6351
CITY OF MERIDEN
142 E Main St Rm 218, Meriden, CT 06450-5605
Tel (203) 630-4124 Founded/Ownrshp 1806
Sales NA EMP 1,690
Accts Blum Shapiro West Hartford C
SIC 9111 City & town managers' offices;

D-U-N-S 02-014-1404 IMP
CITY OF MESA
20 E Main St, Mesa, AZ 85201-7425
Tel (480) 644-2011 Founded/Ownrshp 1878
Sales NA EMP 4,068
Accts Cliftonlarsonallen Phoenix A
SIC 9111 Mayors' offices
Dir Vol: Michelle Alvis-White
Ofcr: Ryan Gallaugher
Ofcr: Melissa Gill
Ofcr: Sam Jeppsen
Ofcr: Carol Karcher
Ofcr: Nate Peterson
Ofcr: Shauna Robinson
Ofcr: Cecilia Sagers
VP: Bracha Etgar
Exec: Brett McGee
Prin: Randy Booze

D-U-N-S 06-898-6181
CITY OF MESQUITE
1515 N Galloway Ave, Mesquite, TX 75149-2300
Tel (972) 216-6218 Founded/Ownrshp 1903
Sales NA EMP 1,000
Accts Grant Thornton Llp Dallas T
SIC 9111 City & town managers' offices;
CIO: Zack Lajoie
CTO: Michele Brand
Sales Exec: Michelle Brand

D-U-N-S 07-662-4162
CITY OF METHUEN
41 Pleasant St, Methuen, MA 01844-3179
Tel (978) 983-8505 Founded/Ownrshp 1725
Sales NA EMP 1,159
Accts Melanson Heath Andover Ma
SIC 9111 County supervisors' & executives' offices;
Genl Mgr: Lauri Antonacci
Genl Mgr: Patricia Antoon
Genl Mgr: Kim Fone
IT Man: Peter Stone
IT Man: Christina Touma-Conway

D-U-N-S 07-222-0791
CITY OF MIAMI
MAYOR'S OFFICE
3500 Pan American Dr Fl 2, Miami, FL 33133-5595
Tel (305) 250-5300 Founded/Ownrshp 1896
Sales NA EMP 3,000
Accts Ernst & Young Llp Miami Fl
SIC 9111 City & town managers' offices;
COO: Elsa Jaramillo
Ofcr: Yvette Smith
Exec: John Greco
Brnch Mgr: Alejandro Vilarello
Snr PM: Maria M Pineda

D-U-N-S 02-054-6289 IMP/EXP
CITY OF MIAMI BEACH
MIAMI BEACH CONVENTION CENTER
1700 Convention Center Dr # 3, Miami Beach, FL 33139-1824
Tel (305) 673-7000 Founded/Ownrshp 1915
Sales NA EMP 1,700
Accts Mcgladrey Llp Miami Florida
SIC 9111 Mayors' offices;
COO: Jorge M Gonzalez
Ofcr: Yolanda Cintado-Seiglie
Ofcr: Silvia Escobar
Ofcr: Alberto Martinez
Exec: Vivian Thayer
Dir Risk M: Andrew Bejel
Dir Soc: Paulina Rgg
Comm Man: Clarise Ferguson
Comm Man: Jennifer Jenkins
Ex Dir: Richard Rivera
Genl Mgr: John Shumaker

D-U-N-S 00-643-4211
CITY OF MILWAUKEE
OFFICE OF MAYOR
200 E Wells St, Milwaukee, WI 53202-3515
Tel (414) 286-3321 Founded/Ownrshp 1846
Sales NA EMP 8,427E
SIC 9111

D-U-N-S 06-653-0411
CITY OF MINNEAPOLIS
350 S 5th St Ste 325m, Minneapolis, MN 55415-1315
Tel (612) 673-3000 Founded/Ownrshp 1867
Sales NA EMP 5,000
Accts State Of Minnesota-Officer Of
SIC 9111 City & town managers' offices;
Genl Mgr: Terri Spencer

D-U-N-S 01-039-6687
CITY OF MOBILE (AL)
205 Government St, Mobile, AL 36602-0001
Tel (251) 208-7395 Founded/Ownrshp 1702
Sales NA EMP 2,300
Accts Smith Dukes & Buckalew Llp M
SIC 9111 Mayors' offices;
COO: Michael Barton
*Prin: Ben Brooks
Ex Dir: Barbara Malkove
Snr Mgr: James Barber
Snr Mgr: Lester Hargrove

D-U-N-S 07-315-1961
CITY OF MONROE (LA)
700 Washington St, Monroe, LA 71201-6826
Tel (318) 329-2310 Founded/Ownrshp 1820
Sales NA EMP 1,200E
Accts Luffey Huffman Ragsdale & So
SIC 9111 Mayors' offices;
Genl Mgr: Marc Keenan
Genl Mgr: Christopher Phelps
MIS Dir: Anita Eppinette

D-U-N-S 07-896-1885
CITY OF MONTGOMERY
103 N Perry St, Montgomery, AL 36104-3728
Tel (334) 625-2025 Founded/Ownrshp 1847
Sales NA EMP 2,895
Accts Jackson Thornton & Co Pc Mon
SIC 9111 City & town managers' offices;
Adm Dir: Linda Reynolds
Netwrk Eng: Al Davis
Opers Mgr: Clevy Gibson

D-U-N-S 08-955-3861
CITY OF MURFREESBORO
111 W Vine St, Murfreesboro, TN 37130-3573
Tel (615) 849-2629 Founded/Ownrshp 1817
Sales NA EMP 1,094E
Accts Jobe Hastings & Associates M
SIC 9111 Executive offices, state & local;

D-U-N-S 03-014-9813
CITY OF MUSKOGEE FOUNDATION
120 N 3rd St, Muskogee, OK 74401-6603
Tel (918) 577-6562 Founded/Ownrshp 2010
Sales 83.7MM EMP 3
SIC 8641 Civic social & fraternal associations
Prin: Frank W Merrick
Ex Dir: Kim Lynch
Ex Dir: Frank Merrick

D-U-N-S 07-000-0815
CITY OF NAPERVILLE
400 S Eagle St, Naperville, IL 60540-5278
Tel (630) 420-6111 Founded/Ownrshp 1831
Sales NA EMP 1,000
Accts Sikich Llp Naperville Illino
SIC 9111 City & town managers' offices
Ofcr: Bill Boyle
Ofcr: Nick Liberio
Ofcr: Mike McLean
Off Mgr: Mary Kay Biernacki
Opers Mgr: John Schaub
Opers Mgr: Christine Schwartzhoff

D-U-N-S 05-906-2406
CITY OF NEW BRITAIN
27 W Main St, New Britain, CT 06051-2283
Tel (860) 826-3415 Founded/Ownrshp 1754
Sales NA EMP 1,037
Accts Blum Shapiro & Company Pc
SIC 9111 City & town managers' offices;
*Prin: Rebecca Samalerni
Dir IT: Adam Pokorski

D-U-N-S 07-539-6754
CITY OF NEW HAVEN
165 Church St Fl 2, New Haven, CT 06510-2010
Tel (203) 946-8200 Founded/Ownrshp 1633
Sales NA EMP 4,500
Accts Mcgladrey Llp New Haven Conn
SIC 9111 Mayors' offices;

D-U-N-S 00-820-5338
CITY OF NEW ORLEANS (LA)
MAYOR'S OFFICE
1300 Perdido St Bsmt Fl2, New Orleans, LA 70112-2128
Tel (504) 658-4900 *Founded/Ownrshp* 1718
Sales NA *EMP* 6,658
Accts Postlethwaite & Netterville N
SIC 9111 Executive offices;
CFO: Reginald Zeno
Ofcr: Kenneth Marchese
VP: Tyra Brown
Exec: Keith Lampkin
Comm Dir: Clarence Williams
Prin: Mosanda Mvula
Genl Mgr: Jonthan Wisbey
IT Man: Kati Bambrick
Mktg Dir: Sally Forman
Pr Dir: Hilary Irvin

D-U-N-S 07-329-9026
CITY OF NEW YORK
City Hl, New York, NY 10007
Tel (212) 788-3000 *Founded/Ownrshp* 1625
Sales NA *EMP* 310,000
SIC 9111 Executive offices;
Ex Dir: Diane Dalessandro
Ex Dir: Desir E Kim

D-U-N-S 06-429-2980
CITY OF NEWARK NEW JERSEY
920 Broad St, Newark, NJ 07102-2660
Tel (973) 733-3934 *Founded/Ownrshp* 1693
Sales NA *EMP* 4,000
SIC 9111 City & town managers' offices;
Ofcr: David Lippman
Board of Directors: Augusto Amador, Mildred Crump, Carlos Gonzalez, John James, Gayle Chaneyfield-Jenkins, Joseph McAllum, Edward Osborne, Luis Quintana, Anibal Ramos Jr

D-U-N-S 06-602-1627
CITY OF NEWPORT NEWS
2400 Washington Ave Main, Newport News, VA 23607-4300
Tel (757) 926-8411 *Founded/Ownrshp* 1896
Sales NA *EMP* 5,000
Accts Cherry Bekaert Llp Richmond
SIC 9111 City & town managers' offices;
Sr VP: Tammie L Clark
VP: Summer A Deming
Exec: Ane Brinkman
* *Prin:* James M Bourey
Mng Dir: Patricia K Cline
Brnch Mgr: Jay McCormick
Off Admin: Crystal R Bell
Off Admin: Everette M Seay
Mktg Dir: Chevone Blackman

D-U-N-S 07-657-6826
CITY OF NEWTON
1000 Cmmwl Ave Newton Ctr, Newton, MA 02459
Tel (617) 796-1200 *Founded/Ownrshp* 1688
Sales NA *EMP* 3,000
Accts Cliftonlarsonallen Llp Boston
SIC 9111 City & town managers' offices;

D-U-N-S 07-993-5268
CITY OF NIAGARA FALLS
MAYOR'S OFFICE
745 Main St, Niagara Falls, NY 14301-1703
Tel (716) 286-4310 *Founded/Ownrshp* 1892
Sales NA *EMP* 1,415
Accts Bonadio & Co Llp Pittsford
SIC 9111 Mayors' offices;
Genl Mgr: George Amendola

D-U-N-S 03-011-5281
CITY OF NORTH CHARLESTON
2500 City Hall Ln, North Charleston, SC 29406-6538
Tel (843) 554-5700 *Founded/Ownrshp* 1994
Sales NA *EMP* 1,000
Accts Greene Finney & Horton Llp M
SIC 9121 City council;
Dir Risk M: Leslie Mitchum
Ex Dir: Paul Wieters
Off Mgr: Sarah Boyce
Pgrm Dir: Tammie Emanuel

D-U-N-S 07-528-8985
CITY OF NORTH LAS VEGAS
2250 Las Vegas Blvd N # 100, North Las Vegas, NV 89030-5872
Tel (702) 633-1007 *Founded/Ownrshp* 1946
Sales NA *EMP* 2,200
Accts Piercy Bowler Taylor & Kern L
SIC 9111 City & town managers' offices; ; Mayors' offices
Pr: Heather McAlister
Ofcr: Terry Graham
Ofcr: Mark Hoyt
Ofcr: Tom Martens
Ofcr: Jeff Pollard
Ofcr: Leonard Taylor
Exec: Brenda Johnson
Exec: Bernie Lucido
Comm Dir: Mitch Fox
Ex Dir: Eric Dabney
Brnch Mgr: Eddie Avirso
Board of Directors: Shari Buck, William E Robinson, Council Persons Stephanie

D-U-N-S 07-921-7444
CITY OF NORTHAMPTON
CITY HALL
210 Main St Rm 4, Northampton, MA 01060-3110
Tel (413) 587-1249 *Founded/Ownrshp* 1654
Sales NA *EMP* 1,203
SIC 9111

D-U-N-S 07-541-0415
CITY OF NORWALK
125 East Ave, Norwalk, CT 06851-5702
Tel (203) 854-7900 *Founded/Ownrshp* 1649
Sales NA *EMP* 1,927
Accts Mcgladrey Llp New Haven Conn
SIC 9111 City & town managers' offices;
Treas: Clinton Egerton

Creative D: Robert Sodaro
MIS Dir: Nancy Joyce
Dir IT: Karen Vecchio

D-U-N-S 05-067-2427
CITY OF OAKLAND (CA)
150 Frank H Ogawa Plz # 3332, Oakland, CA 94612-2021
Tel (510) 238-3280 *Founded/Ownrshp* 1852
Sales NA *EMP* 4,000
Accts Macias Gini & O Connell Llp O
SIC 9111 City & town managers' offices;
VP: Carla Rivers
Dir Risk M: Deborah Cornwell
Dir: Rachel Flynn
Ex Dir: Daniel Purnell
IT Man: Rebecca Dowdakin
Software D: Stephen Weeks
Pgrm Dir: Preston Pinkney
Pgrm Dir: Megan Seccombe

D-U-N-S 05-594-7428
CITY OF OCALA
110 Se Watula Ave, Ocala, FL 34471-2180
Tel (352) 401-3914 *Founded/Ownrshp* 1880
Sales NA *EMP* 1,100
Accts Purvis Gray & Company Llp Oc
SIC 9111 City & town managers' offices
Genl Mgr: Tammi Haslam

D-U-N-S 07-337-0678
CITY OF OCEANSIDE
300 N Coast Hwy, Oceanside, CA 92054-2859
Tel (760) 435-3830 *Founded/Ownrshp* 1888
Sales NA *EMP* 1,000
Accts Lance Soll & Lunghard Llp B
SIC 9111 City & town managers' offices;
IT Man: Renee Bojorquez
IT Man: Dave Riha

D-U-N-S 07-313-1542
CITY OF OKLAHOMA CITY
100 N Walker Ave, Oklahoma City, OK 73102-2230
Tel (405) 297-2506 *Founded/Ownrshp* 1889
Sales NA *EMP* 4,500
Accts Bkd Llp Oklahoma City Oklaho
SIC 9111 City & town managers' offices;

D-U-N-S 07-698-1265
CITY OF OMAHA
1819 Farnam St Rm 300, Omaha, NE 68183-1000
Tel (402) 444-5000 *Founded/Ownrshp* 1857
Sales NA *EMP* 2,800
Accts Bkd Llp Omaha Nebraska
SIC 9111 City & town managers' offices;
Treas: Donna Waller
Ofcr: Allen Straub
Ofcr: Scott Sungy
Ofcr: Marcus Taylor
Ofcr: Scott Zymball
Exec: Darci Tierney
Dir: James Thele
Genl Mgr: Renee Biglow
Opers Mgr: Tom Aeschliman
Snr Mgr: Eric White

D-U-N-S 07-813-6223
CITY OF ONTARIO
303 E B St, Ontario, CA 91764-4196
Tel (909) 395-2012 *Founded/Ownrshp* 1891
Sales NA *EMP* 1,053
Accts Lance Soll & Lunghard Llp B
SIC 9111 City & town managers' offices;
Ofcr: Floyd Clark

D-U-N-S 05-151-4222
CITY OF ORANGE TOWNSHIP
29 N Day St, Orange, NJ 07050-3608
Tel (973) 266-4000 *Founded/Ownrshp* 1872
Sales NA *EMP* 1,000
Accts Mcenerney Brady & Company Ll
SIC 9111 City & town managers' offices;
* *CFO:* Jack Kelly
CFO: Joy Lascari
Ofcr: Joseph Alston
Ofcr: Harold Anderson
Ofcr: Sabriya Baker
Ofcr: Jean Barbosa
Ofcr: Leo Barsanti
Ofcr: Tangela Brown
Ofcr: Peter Cassidy
Ofcr: Robert Cherry
Ofcr: Eric Davis
Ofcr: Troy Deberry
Ofcr: Lia Dickens
Ofcr: Charles Eaddy
Ofcr: Christopher Garey
Ofcr: Betty Hill
Ofcr: Edward Hunter
Ofcr: Michele Jackson
Ofcr: Joegy Jacob
Ofcr: Washington James
Ofcr: John Lopez

D-U-N-S 05-594-7485
CITY OF ORLANDO (FL)
1 City Cmmns 400 S Orange, Orlando, FL 32801
Tel (407) 246-2121 *Founded/Ownrshp* 1875
Sales NA *EMP* 3,000
Accts Moore Stephens Lovelace Pa
SIC 9111 City & town managers' offices;
CFO: Raymond Elwell
Treas: Bruce C Harter
Ofcr: Hilary Bledsoe
Ofcr: Dana Johnston
Ofcr: Michael Lemmerman
Ofcr: Jose Varela
Exec: Michelle Guido
Exec: Cassandra Lafser
Comm Man: April Michael
Sys/Mgr: Mark Hoover
Trfc Dir: Vicki Maldonado

D-U-N-S 08-179-0214 IMP
CITY OF OXNARD
OXNARD CITY HALL
300 W 3rd St Uppr Fl4, Oxnard, CA 93030-5729
Tel (805) 385-7803 *Founded/Ownrshp* 1903
Sales NA *EMP* 1,100

Accts White Nelson Diehl Evans Llp
SIC 9111 Mayors' offices;
Treas: Danielle Navas
Genl Mgr: Tanya Williams

D-U-N-S 05-052-0782
CITY OF PALO ALTO
250 Hamilton Ave, Palo Alto, CA 94301-2593
Tel (650) 329-2571 *Founded/Ownrshp* 1894
Sales NA *EMP* 1,000
SIC 9111

D-U-N-S 02-890-0439
CITY OF PASADENA
100 N Garfield Ave, Pasadena, CA 91101-1726
Tel (626) 744-4386 *Founded/Ownrshp* 1886
Sales NA *EMP* 1,800
Accts Brown Armstrong Accountancy Co
SIC 9111 City & town managers' offices;
Ofcr: Ann Erdman
Ofcr: Ruth Guitron
Ofcr: Shannon Reece
Ofcr: Andre Temurian
Ex Dir: Serfin Espinoza
Ex Dir: Don Repella
Prgrm Mgr: Joy De Castro
Div Mgr: Rachel Estuar
Dir IT: Chuck Braun
Telecom Mg: Kevin Hughes
IT Man: Ali Ardekani

D-U-N-S 06-215-8563
CITY OF PEABODY
24 Lowell St, Peabody, MA 01960-5446
Tel (978) 532-3000 *Founded/Ownrshp* 1650
Sales NA *EMP* 1,500[E]
Accts Powers & Sullivan Wakefield
SIC 9111 Mayors' offices;

D-U-N-S 02-448-5310
CITY OF PEMBROKE PINES (FL)
10100 Pines Blvd Fl 5, Pembroke Pines, FL 33026-6042
Tel (954) 431-4330 *Founded/Ownrshp* 1961
Sales NA *EMP* 1,943[E]
SIC 9111
Treas: Gloria Glasser
Bd of Dir: Michelle Reyes
Ofcr: Kris Gulliver
Ofcr: Scott Krajewski
Ofcr: George Velez
Ofcr: Steve Wetterer
VP: James Cherof
IT Man: James Gallo
Snr Mgr: Dave Smith

D-U-N-S 00-249-4128
CITY OF PEORIA
8401 W Monroe St, Peoria, AZ 85345-6560
Tel (623) 773-7148 *Founded/Ownrshp* 1957
Sales NA *EMP* 1,600
Accts Heinfeld Meech & Co Pc P
SIC 9111
Ofcr: Cynthia Garcia
Ofcr: Michael Griffin
Ofcr: Lisa Hale
Ofcr: Matthew Lebaron
Ofcr: Mark Newman
Ofcr: Stephen Parks
Ofcr: English Quals
Ofcr: Scott Young
Dir IT: Mark Bsachofner
IT Man: Teresa Corless
Sls Mgr: Dean Rawson

D-U-N-S 00-232-3145
CITY OF PHILADELPHIA
215 City Hall, Philadelphia, PA 19107-3214
Tel (215) 686-2181 *Founded/Ownrshp* 1682
Sales NA *EMP* 29,862
Accts Gerald V Micciulla Cpa Phil
SIC 9111
Ofcr: Stanley Brown
Rgnl Mgr: Janet Stevenson
DP Exec: Inez Crocker
DP Exec: Patricia Gilberti
Snr Mgr: Irvin Anglin
Snr Mgr: Richard Bossert
Snr Mgr: Darryl Gilbert
Snr Mgr: Clinton Johnson
Snr Mgr: Matthew Myers

D-U-N-S 07-898-4358 IMP
CITY OF PHOENIX
200 W Washington St Fl 11, Phoenix, AZ 85003-1611
Tel (602) 262-7111 *Founded/Ownrshp* 1881
Sales NA *EMP* 14,000
Accts Grant Thornton Llp Phoenix A
SIC 9111 Mayors' offices
Genl Mgr: Mike Blea
Genl Mgr: Robyn Sahid
CIO: Charles T Thompson
DP Exec: Philip McNeely
DP Exec: Matt Robinson
Sls&Mrk Ex: Lexie Van Haren

D-U-N-S 06-873-9689
CITY OF PITTSBURGH
414 Grant St, Pittsburgh, PA 15219-2409
Tel (412) 255-2640 *Founded/Ownrshp* 1816
Sales NA *EMP* 3,500
Accts Maher Duessel Pittsburgh Pen
SIC 9111 Mayors' offices;
Ofcr: Andrew Baker
Ofcr: Glenn Bogert
Ofcr: Ed Cunningham
Ofcr: Jeffrey Dean
Ofcr: Melissa Delval
Ofcr: Eric Engelhardt
Ofcr: Cynthia Ferretti
Ofcr: James Gahr
Ofcr: Rufus Jones
Ofcr: Christopher Jordan
Ofcr: Christopher Mosesso
VP: John Gardell
Comm Man: Timothy McNulty

D-U-N-S 07-485-3573
CITY OF PLANO
1520 Ave K, Plano, TX 75074
Tel (972) 941-7121 *Founded/Ownrshp* 1879
Sales NA *EMP* 2,000
Accts Kpmg Llp Dallas Tx
SIC 9111 City & town managers' offices;
Dir Risk M: Darrell Edwards

D-U-N-S 05-497-1197
CITY OF PORTLAND
1221 Sw 4th Ave Rm 340, Portland, OR 97204-1900
Tel (503) 823-4120 *Founded/Ownrshp* 1850
Sales NA *EMP* 5,684
Accts Moss Adams Llp Eugene Oregon
SIC 9111 City & town managers' offices;
Ofcr: Amalia Alarcon
Ofcr: Brian Hughes
Ofcr: Darren Posey
Dir Risk M: Kate Wood
Div Mgr: Jody Yates
IT Man: Carolyn Glass
IT Man: Paul Rothi
Opers Mgr: Celia Heron
Sls Mgr: Joseph Wahl

D-U-N-S 07-174-7802
CITY OF PORTLAND
389 Congress St Rm 110, Portland, ME 04101-3568
Tel (207) 874-8665 *Founded/Ownrshp* 1786
Sales NA *EMP* 2,500
Accts Runyon Kersteen Ouellette Sou
SIC 9111 City & town managers' offices;
Genl Mgr: Karen Marston

D-U-N-S 01-005-2488
CITY OF PORTSMOUTH (VA)
801 Crawford St Fl 5, Portsmouth, VA 23704-3867
Tel (757) 393-8000 *Founded/Ownrshp* 1752
Sales NA *EMP* 2,000
Accts Cherry Bekaert Llp Virginia B
SIC 9111 City & town managers' offices;
CEO: Kenneth I Wright
Ofcr: Kelton Millhouse
Genl Mgr: Diane Culpepper

D-U-N-S 06-985-3752
CITY OF PROVIDENCE
MAYOR'S OFFICE
25 Dorrance St Unit 1, Providence, RI 02903-1738
Tel (401) 421-7740 *Founded/Ownrshp* 1636
Sales NA *EMP* 2,800
Accts Marcum Llp Providence Rhode
SIC 9111 City & town managers' offices;

D-U-N-S 07-953-2107
CITY OF QUINCY
QUINCY CITY HALL
1305 Hancock St, Quincy, MA 02169-5119
Tel (617) 376-1000 *Founded/Ownrshp* 1995
Sales NA *EMP* 2,300
Accts Powers & Sullivan Llc Wakefi
SIC 9111 City & town managers' offices;
V Ch: Kevin Coughlin
V Ch: Doug Gutro
* *Pr:* George White
* *CFO:* Warren Sproul
Treas: James Chiccino
* *Treas:* Deborah Coughlin
* *Treas:* Michael McFarland
Ofcr: Richard Bryan
Ofcr: Danny Church
Ofcr: Brian Coen
Ofcr: Dwayne Goldman
Ofcr: Ken Wood
Board of Directors: Bill Harding

D-U-N-S 02-047-2601
CITY OF RACINE
730 Washington Ave, Racine, WI 53403-1146
Tel (262) 636-9101 *Founded/Ownrshp* 1830
Sales NA *EMP* 1,000
Accts Baker Tilly Virchow Krause Ll
SIC 9111 City & town managers' offices;
Ofcr: Jennifer Ball
Ofcr: Marcia Fernholz
Ofcr: Justin Koepnick
Ofcr: Amy Matsen
Exec: Sarah Clemons
Exec: Mike Kosterman
Exec: Martin Pavilonis
Ex Dir: Doug Stansil
Genl Mgr: Kathleen Fischer
Genl Mgr: Willie McDonald
HC Dir: Dottie-Kay Bowersox

D-U-N-S 04-437-9568
CITY OF RALEIGH
222 W Hargett St, Raleigh, NC 27601-1316
Tel (919) 996-3000 *Founded/Ownrshp* 1792
Sales NA *EMP* 4,000
Accts Cherry Bekaert Llp Raleigh N
SIC 9111 Mayors' offices;
Dir Vol: Cindy Trumbower
CFO: Perry E James
Sr Cor Off: Chad Warren
Sr Cor Off: Joseph Wilkins
Ofcr: Casey Clark
Ofcr: Joseph Montemurro
Ofcr: Ervin Pete
Ofcr: Stephen Snowden
Ofcr: Doug Taylor
VP Bus Dev: Chris Palumbo
Prgrm Mgr: Valerie Malloy

D-U-N-S 07-612-1904
CITY OF RENO
1 E 1st St Fl 1, Reno, NV 89501-1609
Tel (775) 334-2020 *Founded/Ownrshp* 1903
Sales NA *EMP* 1,600
Accts Piercy Bowler Taylor & Kern L
SIC 9111 City & town managers' offices;
Ofcr: Shelley Berto
Ofcr: Kenneth Deberg
Ofcr: Jason Stallcop
Sr VP: Tabitha Whitlock
Ex Dir: Susan Parker
Ex Dir: Roger Van Valkenburg
Ex Dir: Steve Varela

Genl Mgr: Michele Hobbs
Genl Mgr: Jill Olsen
Off Admin: Cindy Leslie
Off Admin: Theresa Tavernier

D-U-N-S 00-313-3840
CITY OF RICHMOND
900 E Broad St Ste 201, Richmond, VA 23219-1907
Tel (804) 646-7970 *Founded/Ownrshp* 1737
Sales NA *EMP* 5,315
Accts Cherry Bekaert & Holland Llp
SIC 9111 City & town managers' offices;
Pr: Ketisha Bullard
Ofcr: Christopher Cirino
*Ofcr: Selena Cuffee-Glenn
Ofcr: Tasharnda Gainey
Ofcr: Melanie Givens
Ofcr: Mary Greene
Ofcr: Robert Gregory
Ofcr: Clifton Jackson Jr
Ofcr: Graham Lang
Ofcr: Claude Picard
Ofcr: Anthony Richio
Ofcr: Iteka Smith
Ofcr: Gladys Walker
Ofcr: Alla Winfrey
VP: Sheila Shepperson

D-U-N-S 08-877-0706
CITY OF RICHMOND
450 Civic Center Plaza, Richmond, CA 94804-1661
Tel (510) 620-6727 *Founded/Ownrshp* 1938
Sales NA *EMP* 1,158
Accts Maze & Associates Pleasant Hi
SIC 9111 County supervisors' & executives' offices;
Ex Dir: Robin Poindexter
Genl Mgr: Lashonda White
Off Mgr: Noni Thomas

D-U-N-S 04-050-2114
CITY OF RIVERSIDE
HOUSING AUTHORITY OF THE CITY
3900 Main St Fl 7, Riverside, CA 92522-0002
Tel (951) 826-5311 *Founded/Ownrshp* 1883
Sales NA *EMP* 2,700
Accts Macias Gini & O Connell Llp N
SIC 9111 City & town managers' offices;
*CFO: Paul Sundeen

D-U-N-S 06-235-1739
CITY OF ROANOKE
215 Church Ave Sw Ste 461, Roanoke, VA 24011-1521
Tel (540) 853-2333 *Founded/Ownrshp* 1884
Sales NA *EMP* 1,600
Accts Cherry Bekaert Llp Roanoke V
SIC 9111 City & town managers' offices;
*Treas: Evelyn Powers
Genl Mgr: Robyn Schon
Mktg Dir: Viki Arias
Snr Mgr: Robert Durant

D-U-N-S 00-246-5805
CITY OF ROCHESTER
400 Dewey Ave, Rochester, NY 14613-2513
Tel (585) 428-6755 *Founded/Ownrshp* 1834
Sales NA *EMP* 3,200
Accts Freed Maxick Cpas Pc Roche
SIC 9111 City & town managers' offices;
VP: Elaine Spaull
Exec: Pam Bialaszewski
Dir IT: Tony Sutera
IT Man: Charles Benincasa
IT Man: Steve Mickle

D-U-N-S 07-456-5755
CITY OF ROCKFORD
425 E State St, Rockford, IL 61104-1068
Tel (779) 348-7300 *Founded/Ownrshp* 1851
Sales NA *EMP* 1,300
Accts Lauterbach & Amen Llp Warren
SIC 9111 Mayors' offices;
Ofcr: Brenda Stromquist
Assoc VP: Matthew Phillips
Ex Dir: Patrick Hayes
Genl Mgr: Sandi Leombruni
Off Mgr: Chris Washington
Off Admin: Susan Diehl
Dir IT: Glenn Trommels

D-U-N-S 07-611-9643 IMP
CITY OF ROSEVILLE
311 Vernon St, Roseville, CA 95678-2649
Tel (916) 774-5200 *Founded/Ownrshp* 1909
Sales NA *EMP* 1,001
Accts Maze & Associates Pleasant Hi
SIC 9111 City & town managers' offices;

D-U-N-S 07-379-5957 IMP
CITY OF SACRAMENTO
915 I St Fl 5, Sacramento, CA 95814-2613
Tel (916) 808-5300 *Founded/Ownrshp* 1849
Sales NA *EMP* 4,500
Accts Macias Gini & O Connell Llp
SIC 9111 City & town managers' offices;
Comm Dir: Isabelle Gaillard
Prgrm Mgr: Tina Lee-Vogt
IT Man: Katy Nguyen
VP Mktg: Sonya Bradley
Snr Mgr: Faith Recio

CITY OF SAINT GEORGE
See ST GEORGE CITY GOVERNMENT (INC)

D-U-N-S 00-622-2343
CITY OF SAINT PAUL (MN)
15 Kellogg Blvd W Ste 390, Saint Paul, MN 55102-1615
Tel (651) 266-8500 *Founded/Ownrshp* 1838
Sales NA *EMP* 3,358
Accts Rebecca Otto/Greg Hierlinger
SIC 9111 City & town managers' offices;
Ofcr: Jason Brubaker
Ofcr: Alta Schaffer
Ofcr: Siobhan Tolar
Dir Soc: Peg Fuller
Comm Dir: Joseph Campbell
CIO: Tarek Tomes
Mktg Dir: Joe Ellickson
Snr Mgr: Dino Guerin

D-U-N-S 07-319-4920
CITY OF SAINT PETERSBURG
175 5th St N, Saint Petersburg, FL 33701-3708
Tel (727) 893-7111 *Founded/Ownrshp* 1892
Sales NA *EMP* 2,800
Accts Mayer Hoffman Mccann Pc Clea
SIC 9111 City & town managers' offices;
CFO: John Green
Dir Risk M: Cathryn Bernoskie
Dir IT: Donna Mattick

D-U-N-S 06-599-8536
CITY OF SALEM
114 N Broad St, Salem, VA 24153-3734
Tel (540) 375-4112 *Founded/Ownrshp* 1802
Sales NA *EMP* 1,307
Accts Brown Edwards Roanoke Virgin
SIC 9111 Mayors' offices;
Treas: David Crescenzi

D-U-N-S 07-382-0813
CITY OF SALEM
93 Washington St, Salem, MA 01970-3528
Tel (978) 745-9595 *Founded/Ownrshp* 1626
Sales NA *EMP* 1,200
Accts Powers & Sullivan Llc Wakefi
SIC 9111 City & town managers' offices;
Genl Mgr: Edward O'Sullivan
DP Dir: Joanne Rust
IT Man: Jane Guy

D-U-N-S 07-997-7534
CITY OF SALEM
555 Liberty St Se Rm 230, Salem, OR 97301-3513
Tel (503) 588-6255 *Founded/Ownrshp* 1857
Sales NA *EMP* 1,022
SIC 9111 9224 9221 City & town managers' offices; ; Fire protection; Police protection
COO: Brent Dehart
Ofcr: Brent Hedrick
Ofcr: Patrick Long
Ofcr: Nelson Morales
Ofcr: Suzanne Nelson
Ofcr: Dave Sellers
Ofcr: Pat Tewell
Ofcr: Stephanie Wile
Ofcr: Pao Xiong
Exec: Tracy Divers
Ex Dir: Tim Gerling

D-U-N-S 07-295-7822
CITY OF SALT LAKE CITY
MAYOR'S OFFICE
451 S State St Rm 145, Salt Lake City, UT 84111-3102
Tel (801) 535-7704 *Founded/Ownrshp* 1851
Sales NA *EMP* 3,200
Accts Eide Bailly Llp Salt Lake Ci
SIC 9111 City & town managers' offices;
Pr: Kevin Staples
COO: Karen Denton
Ofcr: Bryan Hemsley
Dir Soc: Christina Judd
Adm Dir: Kevin Bergstrom
Plng Mgr: Nick Norris
Plng Mgr: Michaela Oktay
Netwrk Mgr: Chad Korb
Sfty Dirs: Rick Graham
Prd Mgr: Jesse Schaefer
Pgrm Dir: David Terry

D-U-N-S 06-642-8400
CITY OF SAN ANTONIO
City Hall 100 Military Plz, San Antonio, TX 78205
Tel (210) 207-6000 *Founded/Ownrshp* 1718
Sales NA *EMP* 12,000
Accts Grant Thornton Llp Houston T
SIC 9199 Supply agency, government; Civil rights commission, government;
CFO: Ben Gorzell
Ofcr: Jason Bratton
Ofcr: Juan Cortez
Ofcr: Victoria Garcia
Ofcr: Juan Hernandez
Ofcr: Jorge Patino
Ofcr: Christopher Redman
Ofcr: Dee Smith
Ofcr: Anastacio Torres
Assoc VP: Mario Vazquez
Exec: Erik Gomez
Exec: Florencio Pea
Exec: Carl Wedige

D-U-N-S 00-958-1208
CITY OF SAN DIEGO (CA)
202 C St, San Diego, CA 92101-3860
Tel (619) 236-6330 *Founded/Ownrshp* 1850
Sales NA *EMP* 11,200[E]
Accts Macias Gini & O Connell Llp S
SIC 9111 City & town managers' offices;
VP Opers: Luther Bobis
Snr Mgr: Paz Gomez

D-U-N-S 06-354-1874
CITY OF SAN JOSE
200 E Santa Clara St, San Jose, CA 95113-1905
Tel (408) 535-3500 *Founded/Ownrshp* 1846
Sales NA *EMP* 7,500
Accts Macias Gini & O Connell Llp
SIC 9111 Mayors' offices
COO: Cecelia Aguilar
CFO: Marianne Bourgeois
Ofcr: Liane McMahon
VP: Arian Collen
VP: Kevin Maung
Ex Dir: Ralph Qualif
Mng Dir: Fran McVey
Admn Mgr: Nancy Price
Brnch Mgr: Patricia O Hearn
Genl Mgr: Grace Martinez
Sls Dir: Mark McMinn

D-U-N-S 08-315-3247
CITY OF SANTA ANA
20 Civic Center Plz Fl 8, Santa Ana, CA 92701-4058
Tel (714) 647-5400 *Founded/Ownrshp* 1869
Sales NA *EMP* 2,044[E]
Accts Macias Gini & O Connell Llp N
SIC 9111 City & town managers' offices;
Dir Vol: Cheryl Eberly

VP: John Franks
Off Admin: Evie Martinez
Dir IT: Gregg Wiles
Board of Directors: Bruce Dunams

D-U-N-S 06-207-6765
CITY OF SANTA BARBARA
735 Anacapa St, Santa Barbara, CA 93101-2203
Tel (805) 564-5334 *Founded/Ownrshp* 1850
Sales NA *EMP* 1,500
SIC 9111

D-U-N-S 07-631-6676
CITY OF SANTA CLARA
1500 Warburton Ave, Santa Clara, CA 95050-3796
Tel (408) 615-2200 *Founded/Ownrshp* 1852
Sales NA *EMP* 1,200
SIC 9111

D-U-N-S 06-942-0818
CITY OF SANTA FE (NM)
200 Lincoln Ave, Santa Fe, NM 87501-1904
Tel (505) 955-6532 *Founded/Ownrshp* 1610
Sales NA *EMP* 1,700
Accts Accounting & Consulting Group
SIC 9111 Mayors' offices;
Treas: Janet Davis
*Prin: Javier Gonzales
Genl Mgr: Kathryn Ravling
Genl Mgr: Francisco Rivera
Plng Mgr: Sandra Aguilar

D-U-N-S 07-415-2596
CITY OF SANTA MONICA
1685 Main St, Santa Monica, CA 90401-3248
Tel (310) 458-8411 *Founded/Ownrshp* 1886
Sales NA *EMP* 2,100
Accts Macias Gini & O Connell Llp
SIC 9111 City & town managers' offices
Ofcr: K D Hicks
Ofcr: Jerry Tucker
Prin: Rod Gould
Web Dev: Kevin Hobson

D-U-N-S 06-919-1039
CITY OF SAVANNAH (GA)
2 E Bay St, Savannah, GA 31401-1225
Tel (912) 651-6415 *Founded/Ownrshp* 1753
Sales NA *EMP* 2,000
Accts Krt Cpas Pc Savannah Georgi
SIC 9111 City & town managers' offices;

D-U-N-S 07-446-5238
CITY OF SCOTTSDALE MUNICIPAL PROPERTY CORP (AZ)
SCOTTSDALE, CITY OF
7447 E Indian School Rd R, Scottsdale, AZ 85251-3922
Tel (480) 312-7859 *Founded/Ownrshp* 1967
Sales NA *EMP* 25,000
Accts Cliftonlarsonallen Llp Phoen
SIC 9111 City & town managers' offices;
Pr: Larry G Aungst
*CFO: Craig Clifford
*Treas: Jan Dolan
*Treas: Kenneth R Harder
Ofcr: Nicole Engstrom
*VP: William P Schrader
IT Man: Cherise Moss

D-U-N-S 00-948-3561
CITY OF SEATTLE
SEATTLE HUMAN SERVICES
700 5th Ave Ste 4350, Seattle, WA 98104-5008
Tel (206) 684-0702 *Founded/Ownrshp* 1851
Sales NA *EMP* 10,000
Accts Jan M Jutte Cpa Cgfm Olymp
SIC 9111 Executive offices;
Comm Man: Lori Patrick
Genl Mgr: Michael Mociulski
Dir IT: Robert Johnson
IT Man: Bruce Hills
Software D: Neil Berry
Trfc Dir: Ayanna White
Snr PM: Mark Schiller

D-U-N-S 00-948-3629
CITY OF SEATTLE-CITY LIGHT DEPARTMENT
(*Suby of* SEATTLE HUMAN SERVICES) ★
700 5th Ave Ste 3200, Seattle, WA 98104-5065
Tel (206) 684-3200 *Founded/Ownrshp* 1902
Sales 931.0MM[E] *EMP* 1,600
Accts Baker Tilly Virchow Krauze Llp
SIC 4911 Distribution, electric power
CEO: Jorge Carrasco
*CFO: Brian Brunfield
Exec: David Foster
Ex Dir: Mary Effertz
Ex Dir: Jennifer Greenlee
QA Dir: Lenny Yap
IT Man: Glenn Amy
IT Man: Ian Smith
Netwrk Eng: Kelly Walker
Secur Mgr: Doug Williams

D-U-N-S 07-541-4151
CITY OF SHELTON
54 Hill St, Shelton, CT 06484-3267
Tel (203) 924-1555 *Founded/Ownrshp* 1789
Sales NA *EMP* 1,000
Accts Levitsky & Berney Woodbridge
SIC 9111 City & town managers' offices;

D-U-N-S 06-974-1908
CITY OF SHREVEPORT
DOWNTOWN MUNICIPAL AIRPORT
505 Travis St Ste 600, Shreveport, LA 71101-3028
Tel (318) 673-7900 *Founded/Ownrshp* 1898
Sales NA *EMP* 3,000
Accts Bkd Llp Dallas Texas
SIC 9111 Mayors' offices;
*Ofcr: Ken Antee
Dir Risk M: Tom Cody
Prgrm Mgr: Tracey Graham
Genl Mgr: Sharon Pilkinton

D-U-N-S 07-803-4683
CITY OF SIOUX FALLS
224 W 9th St, Sioux Falls, SD 57104-6407
Tel (605) 367-8000 *Founded/Ownrshp* 1838
Sales NA *EMP* 1,400
Accts Eide Bailly Llp Sioux Falls
SIC 9121 City council;
*Prin: Marsha Kumlien
Ex Dir: Mike Hall
Sys Mgr: John Klemme
Genl Couns: Gary Colwill

D-U-N-S 07-662-1572
CITY OF SOMERVILLE
93 Highland Ave, Somerville, MA 02143-1740
Tel (617) 666-3311 *Founded/Ownrshp* 1842
Sales NA *EMP* 1,000
Accts Powers & Sullivan Llc Wakedfi
SIC 9111 Mayors' offices;
*Treas: Shelia Tracy
Ofcr: Mike Wyatt
CIO: Jim Halloran

D-U-N-S 10-003-3265
CITY OF SOMERVILLE
42 Cross St, Somerville, MA 02145-3246
Tel (617) 625-6600 *Founded/Ownrshp* 1992
Sales NA *EMP* 1,000[E]
SIC 9111 City & town managers' offices;
*Prin: Anthony Pierantozzi

D-U-N-S 07-432-7123
CITY OF SOUTH BEND
227 W Jefferson Blvd, South Bend, IN 46601-1830
Tel (574) 235-9216 *Founded/Ownrshp* 1865
Sales NA *EMP* 1,214
Accts Paul D Joyce Cpa Indianapol
SIC 9111 City & town managers' offices;

D-U-N-S 05-753-1253
CITY OF SPOKANE
PARK & RECREATION DEPT
808 W Spokane Falls Blvd, Spokane, WA 99201-3333
Tel (509) 625-6200 *Founded/Ownrshp* 1881
Sales NA *EMP* 2,000
Accts Troy Kelley
SIC 9111 City & town managers' offices;
Ofcr: Larry Bowman
Ofcr: Michael Carr
Ofcr: Brian Cestnik
Ofcr: Rex Olson
Ofcr: Melora Sharts
Sr VP: Sandy Scott
Off Mgr: Tia Tauscher
Plng Mgr: Jay Cousins
Dir IT: Michael Sloon
IT Man: Bill Myers
IT Man: Paul Trautman

D-U-N-S 00-685-2255
CITY OF SPRINGFIELD
840 N Boonville Ave, Springfield, MO 65802-3832
Tel (417) 864-1000 *Founded/Ownrshp* 1838
Sales NA *EMP* 1,800
Accts Bkd Llp Springfield Missour
SIC 9111
COO: Don Kliment
Ofcr: Luke Dorrell
Exec: Linda Williams
Genl Mgr: Justin Dement
Genl Mgr: Jody Vernon
Dir IT: Sharon Pitts

D-U-N-S 06-524-6050
CITY OF SPRINGFIELD
800 E Monroe St Ste 300, Springfield, IL 62701-1699
Tel (217) 789-2200 *Founded/Ownrshp* 1832
Sales NA *EMP* 1,800
Accts Sikich Llp Springfield Illin
SIC 9111 City & town managers' offices;
Genl Mgr: Timothy Davlin
IT Man: Debbie Malwick
IT Man: Patrick Schweitzer

D-U-N-S 05-397-1214
CITY OF ST LOUIS
ST LOUIS CITY HALL
1200 Market St Rm 212, Saint Louis, MO 63103-2805
Tel (314) 622-3201 *Founded/Ownrshp* 1809
Sales NA *EMP* 4,500
Accts Kpmg Llp St Louis Missouri
SIC 9121 Town council
Treas: Larry C Williams
Ofcr: Cathy Smentkowski
VP: Lyda Krewson
IT Man: Walter Davis
Snr Mgr: Ted Elfrink

D-U-N-S 07-212-1601
CITY OF STAMFORD
888 Washington Blvd, Stamford, CT 06901-2902
Tel (203) 977-4150 *Founded/Ownrshp* 1893
Sales NA *EMP* 2,878
Accts O Connor Davies Llp Stamford
SIC 9111 Mayors' offices;
Bd of Dir: David Martin
Bd of Dir: Marion McGarry
Bd of Dir: Elaine Mitchell
Bd of Dir: Annie Summerville
Ofcr: Sean Boeger
Ofcr: Paul Deriu
VP: Rosanne McManus
Snr Mgr: Gloria Depina

D-U-N-S 06-887-2274
CITY OF STOCKTON
425 N El Dorado St, Stockton, CA 95202-1997
Tel (209) 937-8212 *Founded/Ownrshp* 1849
Sales NA *EMP* 2,200
Accts Mgo Llp Sacramento Californ
SIC 9111 City & town managers' offices;
Prgrm Mgr: Ariana Ayala
IT Man: Erie Luces

D-U-N-S 06-694-8704
CITY OF SUNRISE
10770 W Oakland Park Blvd, Sunrise, FL 33351-6899
Tel (954) 746-3297 *Founded/Ownrshp* 1961

Sales NA *EMP* 1,200
Accts Marcum Llp Fort Lauderdale F
SIC 9111 City & town managers' offices
Treas: Jack Lazarowitz

D-U-N-S 07-160-7675
CITY OF SYRACUSE
MAYOR'S OFFICE
233 E Wshngtn St Ste 231, Syracuse, NY 13202-1423
Tel (315) 448-8005 *Founded/Ownrshp* 1848
Sales NA *EMP* 6,456
Accts Testone Marshall & Discenza
SIC 9111 Mayors' offices;

D-U-N-S 07-313-5535
CITY OF TACOMA
AMERICA'S 1 WIRED CITY
747 Market St, Tacoma, WA 98402-3726
Tel (253) 591-5088 *Founded/Ownrshp* 1880
Sales NA *EMP* 2,500
Accts Brian Sonntag Cgfm Olympia
SIC 9111 City & town managers' offices;
* *Treas:* Teresa Sedmak
Ofcr: Jessie Adkins
Ofcr: Dylan Harrison
Ofcr: Scott Stanley
VP: Tess Colby
Genl Mgr: Michael San Soucie
Off Mgr: Stephanie Audas
Off Admin: Jennifer Joyce
Off Admin: Julie Knudson
Off Admin: Cecilia Moullet
Off Admin: Kathy Palmer

D-U-N-S 03-278-5466
CITY OF TACOMA DEPARTMENT OF PUBLIC UTILITIES
CLICK NETWORK
3628 S 35th St, Tacoma, WA 98409-3115
Tel (253) 502-8900 *Founded/Ownrshp* 1880
Sales 414.4MM *EMP* 1,407
Accts Moss Adams Llp Tacoma Washin
SIC 4911 4941 4899 4013 4841 Electric services; Water supply; Data communication services; Switching & terminal services; Cable & other pay television services
CEO: Bill Gaines
CFO: Dave Rosholm
Ofcr: Gloria Fletcher
Ofcr: Dylan Harrison
Ofcr: Erika Tucci
VP: David Lacaille
Genl Mgr: Maria Kossan
Off Admin: Kathy Manno
Dir IT: Anthony Kendall
Dir IT: Mary Morrison
Dir IT: Blair Williams

D-U-N-S 05-907-1860
CITY OF TAMPA
306 E Jackson St Fl 7, Tampa, FL 33602-5223
Tel (813) 274-8211 *Founded/Ownrshp* 1857
Sales NA *EMP* 4,500
Accts Crowe Horwath Llp Tampa Flo
SIC 9111 Executive offices, national;
Ofcr: Michael Peterson
Plng Mgr: Randy Goers
Netwrk Eng: Debra Mueller
Board of Directors: James Buckner, Shannon Edge, Adrienne Kernaghan, Liana Lopez, Bonnie Wise

CITY OF TAUNTON
See TAUNTON MUNICIPAL LIGHTING PLANT

D-U-N-S 04-009-5333
CITY OF TAUNTON
141 Oak St, Taunton, MA 02780-4431
Tel (508) 821-1000 *Founded/Ownrshp* 1890
Sales NA *EMP* 1,700
SIC 9111 City & town managers' offices;
Board of Directors: Gill Enos

D-U-N-S 07-446-6814
CITY OF TEMPE
31 E 5th St, Tempe, AZ 85281-3680
Tel (480) 350-8355 *Founded/Ownrshp* 1893
Sales NA *EMP* 1,813
Accts Heinfeld Meech & Co Pc
SIC 9111 City & town managers' offices;
Ofcr: Renee Page
Ofcr: John Southard

D-U-N-S 05-939-7653
CITY OF TOLEDO
1 Government Ctr Ste 2050, Toledo, OH 43604-2281
Tel (419) 245-1050 *Founded/Ownrshp* 1837
Sales NA *EMP* 3,000
Accts Clark Schaefer Hackett & Co T
SIC 9111 Mayors' offices;
CEO: Paula Hicks-Hudson
Ofcr: Thomas Davis
Adm Dir: Robert Summersett
IT Man: Gloria Dawson

D-U-N-S 10-860-4976
CITY OF TOPEKA EMPLOYEES FRIENDSHIP FUND
620 Se Madison St Ste 203, Topeka, KS 66607-1118
Tel (785) 368-3749 *Founded/Ownrshp* 1857
Sales NA *EMP* 1,500
Accts Wendling Noe Nelson & Johnson
SIC 9199 General government administration
COO: Kevin Rooney
Exec: Mishelle Wilcox
Genl Mgr: Simon Martinez
Pr Dir: Aly Van Dyke

D-U-N-S 06-667-4169
CITY OF TORRANCE
3031 Torrance Blvd, Torrance, CA 90503-5059
Tel (310) 328-5310 *Founded/Ownrshp* 1921
Sales NA *EMP* 1,656
Accts Mayer Hoffman Mccann Pc Irvin
SIC 9111 City & town managers' offices;
* *Treas:* Dana Cortez
Exec: Steven Jenkinson
Dir IT: Eric Ngo
Dir IT: Rick Shigaki

Software D: James Toomey
Opers Mgr: Steven Cooper
Sls Mgr: Kent Sentinella
Snr Mgr: Brian Clune

D-U-N-S 07-949-8796
CITY OF TRENTON
319 E State St, Trenton, NJ 08608-1809
Tel (609) 989-3030 *Founded/Ownrshp* 1792
Sales NA *EMP* 13,000
Accts Warren A Broudy Cpa Cgfm P
SIC 9111 City & town managers' offices;
CFO: Janet Schoenhaar

D-U-N-S 07-245-0869
CITY OF TUCSON
TUCSON PAYROLL DEPT
255 W Alameda St, Tucson, AZ 85701-1362
Tel (520) 791-4561 *Founded/Ownrshp* 1877
Sales NA *EMP* 5,900
Accts Cliftonlarsonallen Llp Tucson
SIC 9111 City & town managers' offices;
Exec: Michael Graham
Exec: Cristina Polsgrove
Dir Risk M: Allie Matthews
Comm Man: David Frye

D-U-N-S 07-866-2251
CITY OF TULSA (OK)
175 E 2nd St Ste 15129, Tulsa, OK 74103-3201
Tel (918) 596-2100 *Founded/Ownrshp* 1898
Sales NA *EMP* 3,897
Accts Mcgladrey Llp Kansas City Mi
SIC 9111 Executive offices;
Ofcr: Michelle Allen
Ofcr: Warren Bigelow
Ofcr: Don Deramus
Ofcr: Merlin Griffin
Ofcr: Pam Listar
Ofcr: Paula Maker
Ofcr: Jason Muse
Ofcr: Kofi Wallace
Div/Sub He: Rod Hummel
Admn Mgr: Carol Jones
Off Admin: Tammie Osborne

D-U-N-S 11-264-9736
CITY OF TUSCALOOSA
2201 University Blvd, Tuscaloosa, AL 35401-1541
Tel (205) 349-2010 *Founded/Ownrshp* 2005
Sales NA *EMP* 1,300
Accts Jamisonmoney Farmer Pc Tuscal
SIC 9111 City & town managers' offices;
Ofcr: Tim Bailey
Ofcr: Jimmy Smith
Sfty Dirs: Willie Simpson

D-U-N-S 01-073-4663
CITY OF VANCOUVER
415 W 6th St, Vancouver, WA 98660-3375
Tel (360) 619-1068 *Founded/Ownrshp* 1825
Sales NA *EMP* 1,100[E]
Accts Brian Sonntag Cgfm Olympia
SIC 9121
Ofcr: Jeffrey Anaya
Ofcr: Matthew Bachelder
Ofcr: Julie Ballou
Ofcr: Jason Beach
Ofcr: Mark Brinski
Ofcr: Scott Burnette
Ofcr: Jason Calhoun
Ofcr: David Chamblee
Ofcr: Mike Day
Ofcr: Roger Evans
Ofcr: Leonard Gabriel
Ofcr: Robert Givens
Ofcr: Frank Gomez
Ofcr: Gerardo Gutierrez
Ofcr: Shane Hall
Ofcr: Spencer Harris
Ofcr: John Janisch
Ofcr: Erik Jennings
Ofcr: David Jensen
Ofcr: Edward Letarte
Ofcr: Don Magarian
Board of Directors: Jack Berkman, Jeannine Harris, Pat Jollota, Jim Moeller, Dan Tonkovich, Council Members

D-U-N-S 07-473-6299
CITY OF VIRGINIA BEACH
2401 Courthouse Dr, Virginia Beach, VA 23456-9120
Tel (757) 385-4508 *Founded/Ownrshp* 1963
Sales NA *EMP* 16,000
Accts Cherry Bekaert & Holland Llp
SIC 9111 City & town managers' offices;
Ofcr: James Bauder

D-U-N-S 07-509-0779
CITY OF WACO
300 Austin Ave, Waco, TX 76701-2209
Tel (254) 750-5600 *Founded/Ownrshp* 1913
Sales NA *EMP* 1,516
Accts Jaynes Reitmeier Boyd & Therre
SIC 9111 City & town managers' offices;
COO: Richard Howell
Prgrm Mgr: Laurel Churchman
Genl Mgr: Joyce Southwood
Netwrk Mgr: Ron Holland
Info Man: Adam Scruggs
Opers Supe: Steve Miller
Opers Supe: Graeme Seibel
Mktg Dir: Stacy Maness
Sls Mgr: Sandi L Lane

D-U-N-S 07-661-9014
CITY OF WALTHAM
610 Main St Fl 2, Waltham, MA 02452-5580
Tel (781) 314-3000 *Founded/Ownrshp* 1630
Sales NA *EMP* 1,400
Accts Sullivan Rogers & Company Ll
SIC 9111 City & town managers' offices;
* *Treas:* Thomas Magno
Ofcr: June Conway
* *Ofcr:* Joe Juppe
* *Ofcr:* Joe Pedtula

D-U-N-S 07-840-9653
CITY OF WARREN
1 City Sq Ste 215, Warren, MI 48093-5290
Tel (586) 574-4500 *Founded/Ownrshp* 1957
Sales NA *EMP* 1,179
Accts Plante & Moran Pllc Detroit
SIC 9111 City & town managers' offices;
* *Pr:* Mary Camp
* *Pr:* Scott Stevens
Treas: Marilyn Marrocco
* *Treas:* Cherelin Moceri
Bd of Dir: John Kupiec
Bd of Dir: Dolores Thomas
Bd of Dir: Steven Watripont

D-U-N-S 07-539-9949
CITY OF WATERBURY
236 Grand St, Waterbury, CT 06702-1933
Tel (203) 574-6712 *Founded/Ownrshp* 1674
Sales NA *EMP* 3,200[E]
Accts Blum Shapiro & Company Pc
SIC 9111 Mayors' offices;
V Ch: Antoinette Spinelli
Ofcr: Elizabeth Sanderson

D-U-N-S 03-076-9376
CITY OF WEST PALM BEACH
401 Clematis St, West Palm Beach, FL 33401-5319
Tel (561) 822-1200 *Founded/Ownrshp* 1894
Sales NA *EMP* 1,600
Accts Marcum Llp West Palm Beach F
SIC 9111 City & town managers' offices;
Ofcr: Aaron Sam
Exec: Patrick Cooney
Ex Dir: Neil Melick
Genl Mgr: Mary Pinak
DP Exec: William Swisher
Dir IT: Darlene Snowball

D-U-N-S 06-698-5037
CITY OF WESTFIELD
59 Court St Ste 1, Westfield, MA 01085-3528
Tel (413) 572-6200 *Founded/Ownrshp* 1920
Sales NA *EMP* 1,770
SIC 9111 Mayors' offices
* *Treas:* Gregory Kallfa
Treas: Meghan Kane
* *Treas:* Meghan Miller
Ofcr: Jeffrey Baillargeon
Ofcr: Joe Mitchell
Brnch Mgr: Ron Skroczky
IT Man: Michael McCabe
Pr Dir: Lawrence Smith

D-U-N-S 05-946-3133
CITY OF WICHITA FALLS
1300 7th St, Wichita Falls, TX 76301-2305
Tel (940) 761-7462 *Founded/Ownrshp* 1889
Sales NA *EMP* 1,400
Accts Edgin Parkman Fleming & Flem
SIC 9111 City & town managers' offices
Dir IT: Blake Jurecek
Netwrk Mgr: Neal Howard

D-U-N-S 06-739-3900
CITY OF WILMINGTON
DELAWARE DIVISION OF REVENUE
800 N French St Fl 5, Wilmington, DE 19801-3590
Tel (302) 576-2415 *Founded/Ownrshp* 1739
Sales NA *EMP* 1,000
Accts Bdo Usa Llp Wilmington De
SIC 9111 Executive offices; Mayors' offices
* *Treas:* Henry W Supinski
Dir Lab: Mattew Miller
Ex Dir: Peter Besecker
Dir IT: James Lewis
Snr Mgr: Tanya Washington

D-U-N-S 07-200-7875
CITY OF WILMINGTON
305 Chestnut St, Wilmington, NC 28401-4019
Tel (910) 341-7800 *Founded/Ownrshp* 1739
Sales NA *EMP* 1,000
Accts Mcgladrey Llp Wilmington Nor
SIC 9111 Mayors' offices;
Ofcr: John Barham

D-U-N-S 07-158-2712
CITY OF WINSTON-SALEM
101 N Main St, Winston Salem, NC 27101-4033
Tel (336) 727-8000 *Founded/Ownrshp* 1753
Sales NA *EMP* 2,400
Accts Cherry Bekaert Llp Raleigh N
SIC 9111 Mayors' offices;
COO: Dorrell Brown
Brnch Mgr: Derwick Paige
Dir IT: Chris Roy

D-U-N-S 07-381-1812
CITY OF WOBURN
10 Common St Ste 12, Woburn, MA 01801-6724
Tel (781) 932-4400 *Founded/Ownrshp* 1889
Sales NA *EMP* 1,250
SIC 9111 City & town managers' offices;
Ofcr: Dana Gately

D-U-N-S 06-230-8804
CITY OF WOONSOCKET (RI)
169 Main St, Woonsocket, RI 02895-4330
Tel (401) 762-6400 *Founded/Ownrshp* 1888
Sales NA *EMP* 1,500
Accts Cohnreznick Llp Woonsocket R
SIC 9111 Mayors' offices;
Ofcr: Glen Thuot

D-U-N-S 07-674-4325
CITY OF WOOSTER
538 N Market St, Wooster, OH 44691-3406
Tel (330) 263-5200 *Founded/Ownrshp* 1796
Sales NA *EMP* 1,000
Accts Rea & Associates Inc
SIC 9111 Executive offices;
CFO: Scott Boyes
Nurse Mgr: Karen Steiner
IT Man: James Dodd
IT Man: Bob Eshelman
Mktg Dir: David Rhoad

D-U-N-S 06-578-2575
CITY OF WORCESTER
CITY COUNCIL
455 Main St Rm 112, Worcester, MA 01608-1805
Tel (508) 799-1049 *Founded/Ownrshp* 1684
Sales NA *EMP* 5,637
Accts Cliftonlarsonallen Llp Boston
SIC 9111 Executive offices;
CTO: Dori Vecchio
Mktg Dir: John Hill

D-U-N-S 07-272-2903
CITY OF YONKERS
40 S Broadway Ste 1, Yonkers, NY 10701-3715
Tel (914) 377-6000 *Founded/Ownrshp* 1646
Sales NA *EMP* 2,500
Accts O Connor Davies Llp Harriso
SIC 9111 Mayors' offices;
Assoc Dir: Edward Dodge
Comm Dir: Christina Gilmartin
Ex Dir: Patricia D McDow
Ex Dir: Edward Sheeran
Genl Mgr: Stephen Radziminsky
Netwrk Mgr: Bill Murphy

D-U-N-S 07-899-8184
CITY OF YUMA
1 City Plz, Yuma, AZ 85364-1436
Tel (928) 373-5187 *Founded/Ownrshp* 1854
Sales NA *EMP* 1,200
Accts Heinfeld Meech & Co Pc P
SIC 9111 Mayors' offices
* *CFO:* Donald Wicks
Dir Risk M: Micheal Little
Ex Dir: Jack Dodd
Admn Mgr: Kay Eldridge
IT Man: Steven Holland
IT Man: Richard Nichols
Netwrk Eng: Christopher Wood

CITY PAPER OF BALTIMORE
See SCRANTON TIMES L P

D-U-N-S 02-688-8362
CITY PIPE AND SUPPLY CORP
2101 W 2nd St, Odessa, TX 79763-4411
Tel (432) 332-1541 *Founded/Ownrshp* 1942
Sales 96.4MM *EMP* 98
SIC 5051 5085 Pipe & tubing, steel; Valves & fittings
Pr: Brett Lossin
* *VP:* Leslie Jones
* *VP:* Charles Justice
Mktg Mgr: Kit Dennis

D-U-N-S 00-701-6919
CITY POINT REALTY LLC
1275 N Clybourn Ave, Chicago, IL 60610-8752
Tel (312) 255-1500 *Founded/Ownrshp* 2007
Sales 250.0MM *EMP* 7
SIC 6531 Real estate brokers & agents

CITY PROVISION
See GERRITYS SUPER MARKET INC

D-U-N-S 00-793-6073 IMP
CITY PUBLIC SERVICES OF SAN ANTONIO
CPS ENERGY
145 Navarro St, San Antonio, TX 78205-2986
Tel (210) 353-2222 *Founded/Ownrshp* 1942
Sales 2.6MMM[E] *EMP* 3,743
Accts Garza Preis & Co Llc/Baker
SIC 4931 4932 Electric & other services combined; Gas & other services combined
CEO: Doyle Benedy
Pt: Deborah Gunn
* *Ch Bd:* Steve Hennigan
* *CFO:* Richard Williamson
CFO: Richard E Williamson
Trst: Julian Castro
Trst: Arthur Kocian
Ofcr: Jelynne Leblanc
Ex VP: Michael K Otara
Ex VP: Carolyn E Shellman
Sr VP: Kenneth Emery
Sr VP: Gary Shaub
VP: Justin Locke
VP: Eugene Montreuil
VP: Jesse Orta
VP: Judy Palmieri
VP: Richard Pena
VP: Tammy Preiss
VP: Jim Pruske
VP: Hubert Smith
VP: Jeffrey M Tuttle

D-U-N-S 10-037-8942
CITY SCHOOL DISTRICT KINGSTON NY
KINGSTON CITY SCHOOLS CNSLD
61 Crown St, Kingston, NY 12401-3833
Tel (845) 339-3000 *Founded/Ownrshp* 1800
Sales 56.6MM[E] *EMP* 1,117
SIC 8211 Public combined elementary & secondary school
Pr: Matthew McCoy
Bd of Dir: Maureen Bowers
Trst: Christopher Farrell
Sr VP: Carol Kennedy
* *VP:* Nora Scherer
Dir Sec: Lashawn Parker
MIS Dir: Gary Thomcheck Jr
Dir IT: Judy Eckhardt
IT Man: Nellere Donovan
IT Man: Carla Habernig
Teacher Pr: John Voerg

D-U-N-S 08-075-4054
CITY SCHOOL DISTRICT OF CITY OF ELMIRA NY (NY)
ELMIRA CITY SCHOOL DISTRICT
951 Hoffman St, Elmira, NY 14905-1715
Tel (607) 735-3000 *Founded/Ownrshp* 1957
Sales 116.6MM *EMP* 1,500
SIC 8211 Public elementary & secondary schools
VP: Mary Lamont
Ex Dir: James Mirando
Genl Mgr: Melissa Mendolera
CTO: Tom Hara
IT Man: Johna Arikian
Pr Dir: Kristine Butler

Schl Brd P: Dan Hurley
HC Dir: Thomas Morrell

D-U-N-S 07-401-2857
CITY SCHOOL DISTRICT OF CITY OF NIAGARA FALLS (NY)
NIAGARA FALLS BOARD OF EDUCATI
630 66th St, Niagara Falls, NY 14304-2212
Tel (716) 286-4211 *Founded/Ownrshp* 1900
Sales 146.4MM *EMP* 1,200E
Accts Drescher & Malecki Llp Cheek
SIC 8211 Public elementary & secondary schools
**Pr:* Robert Keveangin
VP: Kevin Dobbs
Prin: Diane Coty
Teacher Pr: Maria Massaro

D-U-N-S 09-619-2109
CITY SCHOOL DISTRICT OF NEW ROCHELLE (INC)
515 North Ave, New Rochelle, NY 10801-3405
Tel (914) 576-4243 *Founded/Ownrshp* 1930
Sales 80.5MME *EMP* 2,000
SIC 8211 Public elementary & secondary schools
**Pr:* Jerome Smith
VP: Lianne Merchant
Ex Dir: Kelly Johnson
Off Mgr: Carol Mazzola
Off Mgr: Sally Moss
Off Mgr: Kathy Umbro
CIO: Susan Yom
MIS Dir: Liz Damico
Teacher Pr: Joseph Williams
Psych: Maria Nunez

D-U-N-S 10-790-2520 IMP
CITY SPORTS INC
77 N Washington St # 500, Boston, MA 02114-1908
Tel (617) 391-9100 *Founded/Ownrshp* 1983
Sales 143.8MME *EMP* 720
SIC 5699 Sports apparel
Pr: Edward Albertian
COO: Sean Scales
CFO: Jim Kessler
Chf Mktg O: Ted Manning
Ex VP: Michael Mosca
Sr VP: Andrew Almquist
VP: Michael Kennedy

D-U-N-S 07-326-8849
CITY UNIVERSITY OF NEW YORK
AFFIRMATIVE ACTION/EEO DEPT
230 W 41st St Fl 10, New York, NY 10036-7207
Tel (212) 397-5600 *Founded/Ownrshp* 1847
Sales 1.8MMME *EMP* 33,642
SIC 8221

D-U-N-S 01-312-0931
CITY UTILITIES OF SPRINGFIELD MO
301 E Central St, Springfield, MO 65802-3858
Tel (417) 863-9000 *Founded/Ownrshp* 1945
Sales 698.6MME *EMP* 980
Accts Bkd Llp Springfield Missour
SIC 4924 4941 Natural gas distribution; Water supply
Genl Mgr: Scott Miller
Dir Teleco: Lori Capps
Off Admin: Sherri Baxter
CTO: Pam Armstrong
Snr Mgr: Pamela Armstrong

D-U-N-S 07-353-1774
CITY WATER & LIGHT PLANT OF CITY OF JONESBORO
400 E Monroe Ave, Jonesboro, AR 72401-2924
Tel (870) 935-5581 *Founded/Ownrshp* 1906
Sales 101.3MM *EMP* 190
SIC 4931

D-U-N-S 03-150-6934
CITY WHOLESALE GROCERY CO INC
300 Industrial Dr, Birmingham, AL 35211-4456
Tel (205) 795-4533 *Founded/Ownrshp* 1926
Sales 103.9MME *EMP* 165
SIC 5194 5141 5145 5122 Tobacco & tobacco products; Groceries, general line; Candy; Cosmetics, perfumes & hair products
Pr: Peter N Dichiara
**Treas:* James M Carra
**VP:* Jerry A Dichiara
Exec: Alesia Snead

D-U-N-S 13-072-0717
CITY WIDE HOLDING CO INC
15447 W 100th Ter, Lenexa, KS 66219-1289
Tel (913) 888-5700 *Founded/Ownrshp* 1980
Sales 87.5MME *EMP* 300E
SIC 1542 1522 5087 7349 Commercial & office building, new construction; Multi-family dwelling construction; Janitors' supplies; Janitorial service, contract basis
Pr: Elizabeth A Oddo
**Treas:* Brad Oddo
**VP:* Rick Oddo
Sales Exec: Mike Sawicki

D-U-N-S 05-082-5066
CITY WIDE INSULATION OF MADISON INC (WI)
ALPINE INSULATION
4501 Triangle St, Mc Farland, WI 53558-9440
Tel (608) 838-4141 *Founded/Ownrshp* 1969
Sales 94.6MME *EMP* 500
SIC 1742 Insulation, buildings
Pr: Mark Murphy
**Ch Bd:* George Murphy
**Sec:* Brian Murphy
**VP:* John Murphy

D-U-N-S 62-237-4122
CITY YEAR INC
287 Columbus Ave Ste 1, Boston, MA 02116-6805
Tel (617) 927-2500 *Founded/Ownrshp* 1988
Sales 140.7MM *EMP* 572
Accts Kpmg Llp Boston Ma
SIC 8299 Educational services
Pr: Michael Brown
Pt: Felicia Jones
Pt: Richard Klawiter
Pt: David Page
**Pr:* Jim Balfanz
COO: James Balfanz
COO: Kathy Calvin
**COO:* Sean Holleran
**CFO:* Evelyn Barnes
Bd of Dir: James N Perry
Chf Mktg O: Jennie Johnson
**Ex VP:* Annmaura Connolly
Sr VP: Robert L Gordon III
Sr VP: Jeff Jablow
VP: Lisa Cunningham
VP: David Gallacher
VP: Mike Kogelis
VP: Vangie Maynard
VP: Robin Mink
VP: Frank Mood
VP: Kristen Ritchie

D-U-N-S 05-303-9293
CITYSERVICEVALCON LLC
640 W Montana St, Kalispell, MT 59901-3834
Tel (406) 755-4321 *Founded/Ownrshp* 2003
Sales 179.0MM *EMP* 150
SIC 5172 5983 Fuel oil; Fuel oil dealers
**Prin:* Benjamen M Binger

D-U-N-S 88-371-8322
CITYWIDE FINANCIAL INC
13731 E Mississippi Ave, Aurora, CO 80012-3628
Tel (303) 365-4050 *Founded/Ownrshp* 1985
Sales NA *EMP* 26
SIC 6162 Mortgage bankers
VP: Toni Brock
**Ch Bd:* Vincent Schmitz
**Pr:* Jeff Schmitz
**Treas:* Beverly Freng

D-U-N-S 80-026-6376
CIVC PARTNERS LP
191 N Wacker Dr Ste 1100, Chicago, IL 60606-1904
Tel (312) 521-2000 *Founded/Ownrshp* 2002
Sales 311.0MME *EMP* 1,110
SIC 8742 6799 Management consulting services; Investors
VP: Doug Potters
Pt: Micheal Miller
VP: Dan Helle

D-U-N-S 07-993-2735
▲ CIVEO CORP
333 Clay St Ste 4980, Houston, TX 77002-4101
Tel (713) 510-2400 *Founded/Ownrshp* 1977
Sales 517.9MME *EMP* 1,900E
Tkr Sym CVEO *Exch* NYS
SIC 7011 Hotels & motels; Hotels
Pr: Bradley J Dodson
**Ch Bd:* Douglas E Swanson
CFO: Frank C Steininger
Sr VP: Peter L McCann
Sr VP: Allan D Schoening

D-U-N-S 07-923-9397
■ CIVEO US HOLDINGS LLC
(*Suby of* CIVEO CORP) ★
333 Clay St Ste 4980, Houston, TX 77002-4101
Tel (713) 510-2400 *Founded/Ownrshp* 2015
Sales 517.9MME *EMP* 1,900E
SIC 7011 Hotels & motels; Hotels
Pr: Bradley J Dodson
**Ch Bd:* Douglas E Swanson
CFO: Frank C Steininger
Sr VP: Peter L McCann
VP: Carolyn J Stone
Board of Directors: C Ronald Blankenship, Martin A Lambert, Constance B Moore, Richard A Navarre, Gary L Rosenthal, Charles Szalkowski

D-U-N-S 04-654-5398
CIVES CORP (DE)
CIVES STEEL COMPANY
3700 Mansell Rd Ste 500, Alpharetta, GA 30022-1505
Tel (770) 993-4424 *Founded/Ownrshp* 1952
Sales 453.1MM *EMP* 1,103
SIC 3441 3713 3443

CIVES STEEL COMPANY
See CIVES CORP

D-U-N-S 02-276-5045 EXP
CIVICSOLAR INC
426 17th St Ste 600, Oakland, CA 94612-2849
Tel (800) 409-2257 *Founded/Ownrshp* 2009
Sales 95.1MME *EMP* 75
SIC 5074 5211 Heating equipment & panels, solar; Solar heating equipment
CEO: Stewart Rentz
CFO: Tom Wong
**VP:* Kerim Baran
VP: Michael Jeffrey Goldberg
**VP:* Michael Palar
Tech Mgr: Eric Lorenz
Sales Exec: Tom Bone
VP Sls: Thomas Bone

D-U-N-S 93-209-4345
CIVIGENICS INC
(*Suby of* CEC) ★
290 Donald Lynch Blvd # 301, Marlborough, MA 01752-4705
Tel (508) 486-9300 *Founded/Ownrshp* 2007
Sales 24.6MME *EMP* 1,600
SIC 8741 Management services
Pr: Roy Ross
**CFO:* Donald Leef
**VP:* Steve Afeman
IT Man: Peter Dodt

D-U-N-S 36-160-9878
CIVIL & ENVIRONMENTAL CONSULTANTS INC
333 Baldwin Rd Ste 1, Pittsburgh, PA 15205-1751
Tel (412) 429-2324 *Founded/Ownrshp* 1989
Sales 119.9MM *EMP* 615
Accts Schneider Downs & Co Inc P
SIC 8711 0781 Engineering services; Civil engineering; Landscape architects
CEO: Kenneth R Miller
**COO:* Daniel F Szwed
**CFO:* Harry J Soose
Chf Mktg O: Gordon Bottomley
**Sr VP:* James P Nairn
VP: Randy Bodnar
VP: Scott Brown
VP: Stephen Dixon
VP: Chris Forsha
VP: Aaron Hurt
VP: Steve Menoff
VP: Dennis Miller
**VP:* David N Olson
VP: Jonathan Pachter
VP: Cynthia C Sphr
VP: Paul Tomiczek
Comm Man: Tara Kirkman

D-U-N-S 07-545-8935 IMP
CIVIL AIR PATROL INC
NATIONAL HEADQUARTERS
105 S Hansell St Bldg 714, Maxwell Afb, AL 36112-5937
Tel (334) 953-7748 *Founded/Ownrshp* 1941
Sales NA *EMP* 10,500
SIC 9711 Civil Defense
CEO: Joseph Vazquez
Ofcr: Steven Solomon
Board of Directors: Don Rowland

D-U-N-S 06-683-1603 IMP
CIVIL SERVICE EMPLOYEES ASSOCIATION INC
CSEA
143 Washington Ave, Albany, NY 12210-2303
Tel (518) 257-1000 *Founded/Ownrshp* 1910
Sales 132.1MM *EMP* 350
Accts Pricewaterhousecoopers Llp Ha
SIC 8631 Labor union
Pr: Daniel Donohue
**Treas:* Joseph McMullen
VP: Sean Ledwith
**VP:* Mary E Sullivan
Off Mgr: Rhonda Cafarelli
Off Mgr: Christine Meehan
Opers Mgr: Willia M McMullen

D-U-N-S 02-283-5103
CIVISTA MEDICAL CENTER INC
UMMS
(*Suby of* UMMS) ★
5 Garrett Ave, La Plata, MD 20646-5960
Tel (301) 609-4000 *Founded/Ownrshp* 1938
Sales 124.4MM *EMP* 37E
Accts Grant Thornton Llp Philadelph
SIC 8062 General medical & surgical hospitals
Ch Bd: Louis Jenkins Jr
VP: Paul Blackwood
VP: Bill Grimes
Dir Lab: Kausha Patel
QA Dir: Dana Johnson
Dir IT: Kathy Peters
IT Man: Leslie Queen
HC Dir: Madelyn Deutschman

D-U-N-S 07-888-0605
CIVITAS MEDIA LLC
130 Harbour Place Dr # 300, Davidson, NC 28036-7441
Tel (704) 897-6020 *Founded/Ownrshp* 2012
Sales 1.4MMME *EMP* 8,847E
SIC 2711 Newspapers, publishing & printing
COO: Scott Champion
CFO: Jeff Sherman
VP: Jim Lawitz

D-U-N-S 07-941-7880
▲ CIVITAS SOLUTIONS INC
313 Congress St Fl 6, Boston, MA 02210-1218
Tel (617) 790-4800 *Founded/Ownrshp* 1980
Sales 1.4MMM *EMP* 22,300E
Tkr Sym CIVI *Exch* NYS
SIC 8082 Home health care services
Pr: Bruce F Nardella
**Ch Bd:* Edward M Murphy
COO: Brett I Cohen
CFO: Denis M Holler
CIO: Jeffrey M Cohen

D-U-N-S 06-300-6006
CIW ENTERPRISES INC
24 Elmwood Ave, Mountain Top, PA 18707-2100
Tel (800) 233-8366 *Founded/Ownrshp* 1998
Sales 157.0MME *EMP* 351E
SIC 3442 3446 2431 Rolling doors for industrial buildings or warehouses, metal; Open flooring & grating for construction; Millwork; Doors, wood
Pr: Andrew Cornell
**Treas:* David Connell
**VP:* G Bruce Burwell
**VP:* Steven Gallagher
**VP:* Joseph Heller
**VP:* Lauretta O'Hara
**VP:* Paul Sugarman

D-U-N-S 07-989-3402
CJ HOLDING CO
(*Suby of* NABORS RED LION LIMITED)
3990 Rogerdale Rd, Houston, TX 77042-5142
Tel (713) 325-6086 *Founded/Ownrshp* 2014
Sales NA *EMP* 2,609
SIC 6719 Investment holding companies, except banks
CEO: Joshua Comstock

D-U-N-S 07-525-6081 IMP/EXP
CJ KOREA EXPRESS USA CORP
UNITED AIRFREIGHT SERVICES
(*Suby of* CJ KOREA EXPRESS CORPORATION)
18805 S Laurel Park Rd, Rancho Dominguez, CA 90220-6004
Tel (714) 994-1200 *Founded/Ownrshp* 1974
Sales 95.1MM *EMP* 146
Accts Yeil Accounting America Llp L
SIC 4731 4783 4225 Agents, shipping; Foreign freight forwarding; Freight consolidation; Packing & crating; General warehousing
Pr: Byung Uk Lee
**Treas:* Young Jun Choi

CJP
See COMBINED JEWISH PHILANTHROPIES OF GREATER BOSTON INC

CJW MEDICAL CENTER
See CHIPPENHAM & JOHNSTON-WILLIS HOSPITALS INC

CK POWER
See WESTERN DIESEL SERVICES INC

CK SECURITY & SAFETY SOLUTIONS
See CARAVAN FACILITIES MANAGEMENT LLC

D-U-N-S 04-102-0863 IMP
CK TECHNOLOGIES LLC
(*Suby of* CASCADE ENGINEERING INC) ★
1701 Magda Dr, Montpelier, OH 43543-9368
Tel (419) 485-1110 *Founded/Ownrshp* 2002
Sales 156.2MME *EMP* 350
SIC 3089 3999 Plastic containers, except foam; Injection molding of plastics; Atomizers, toiletry
CEO: Mark Miller
Exec: Carrie Arnold
Prgrm Mgr: Kerry Fisher
Prgrm Mgr: Holly Sims
IT Man: Mike Ellerman
Mtls Mgr: Kip Baird
Plnt Mgr: Eric Martz
Ql Cn Mgr: Fausto Paz
Ql Cn Mgr: Ron Schoettley
Mktg Mgr: Jack ARB

D-U-N-S 87-672-0715 IMP
CKE RESTAURANTS HOLDINGS INC
HARDEE'S
6307 Carpinteria Ave A, Carpinteria, CA 93013-2908
Tel (805) 745-7500 *Founded/Ownrshp* 2013
Sales 999.1MME *EMP* 23,000
SIC 5812 6794 Fast-food restaurant, chain; Franchises, selling or licensing
CEO: Andrew F Puzder
COO: Amir Siddiqi
**COO:* Eric Williams
**CFO:* Theodore Abajian
**Ofcr:* E Michael Murphy
Ex VP: Richard E Fortman
**Ex VP:* Noah J Griggs Jr
Ex VP: E Murphy
Ex VP: Robert Starke
Ex VP: Jim Sullivan
Sr VP: Steve Evans
Sr VP: Carol L O'Neill
Sr VP: Charles A Seigel
VP: John Beisler
VP: Anne Blumenstein
VP: Karen Eadon
VP: Michael Woida
Board of Directors: Daniel E Ponder Jr, Jerold H Rubinstein, C Thomas Thompson

D-U-N-S 08-369-1881 IMP
CKL CORP
IMPERIAL BEVERAGE
3825 Emerald Dr, Kalamazoo, MI 49001-7919
Tel (269) 382-4200 *Founded/Ownrshp* 1933
Sales 91.3MME *EMP* 215
SIC 5181 5182 5149

CKNA
See CALSONICKANSEI NORTH AMERICA INC

CKS PACKAGING
See CKS PACKAGING INC

D-U-N-S 14-815-3265 IMP/EXP
CKS PACKAGING INC
CKS PACKAGING
350 Great Sw Pkwy Sw, Atlanta, GA 30336-2333
Tel (404) 691-8900 *Founded/Ownrshp* 1985
Sales 540.4MME *EMP* 1,250
SIC 3089 Plastic containers, except foam
CEO: John R Sewell
**Pr:* William A Pace
**COO:* Scott K Sewell
**CFO:* Dan Fischer
**Ch:* Charles K Sewell
Ofcr: Patty Johnson
**Ex VP:* Dewayne Phillips
VP: Paul Ford
VP: Marshall Henderson
**VP:* Drew Sewell
Brnch Mgr: Mike Trafficano

D-U-N-S 08-023-4484
CKT SERVICES INC
412 N Main St Ste 100, Buffalo, WY 82834-1761
Tel (713) 581-0819 *Founded/Ownrshp* 2015
Sales 100.0MM *EMP* 6E
SIC 5172 7699 Crude oil; Agricultural equipment repair services
CEO: Scott E Frickman
**VP:* David Socol

D-U-N-S 17-790-4141
CL THOMAS INC
9701 Us Highway 59 N, Victoria, TX 77905-5567
Tel (361) 573-7662 *Founded/Ownrshp* 1980
Sales 314.3MME *EMP* 2,015
SIC 5411 5541 Convenience stores; Gasoline service stations
CEO: Cliff Thomas
**Pr:* Jeff Johanson
CFO: Bonnie Reeves
**VP:* Carlton L Labeff
**VP:* Bill Russell
**VP:* Clifton L Thomas Jr
Store Mgr: Susie Martinez
Dir IT: Kit Mitchell
VP Opers: Mark Gresham
Sls Mgr: Ty Koenning
Genl Couns: William Russell

CL&P
See CONNECTICUT LIGHT AND POWER CO

CLA ESTATE SERVICES
See CLA USA INC

D-U-N-S 00-341-0045
CLA USA INC (MO)
CLA ESTATE SERVICES
9300 Wade Blvd Ste 100, Frisco, TX 75035-2175
Tel (214) 472-5000 *Founded/Ownrshp* 1998
Sales NA *EMP* 450
SIC 6411 Insurance agents, brokers & service
Pr: Charles A Loper III
**VP:* Steven Morgan
Off Mgr: Teresa Beesinger
Sls Dir: Chris Garrett

CLA-VAL CO
See GRISWOLD INDUSTRIES

D-U-N-S 00-607-4413 IMP/EXP
CLACK CORP (WI)
CLACK MFG
4462 Duraform Ln, Windsor, WI 53598-9716
Tel (608) 846-3010 *Founded/Ownrshp* 1939
Sales 153.9MM *EMP* 260
Accts Kiesling & Associates
SIC 3589 3089 Sewage & water treatment equipment; Blow molded finished plastic products; Injection molding of plastics
Ch Bd: Richard Clack
**Pr:* Pete Chermak
**VP:* Robert A Clack
CTO: Dennis Thompson
Sftwr Eng: David Peters
Sfty Dirs: Kirk Moldenhauer
Trfc Dir: Dennis Davidson
Opers Mgr: Steven R Kelliher
Plnt Mgr: Chuck Oyer
Plnt Mgr: Brent Starry
Manager: Bob Curtis

CLACK MFG
See CLACK CORP

D-U-N-S 05-596-8135
CLACKAMAS COMMUNITY COLLEGE FOUNDATION
19600 Molalla Ave, Oregon City, OR 97045-8980
Tel (503) 594-6100 *Founded/Ownrshp* 1966
Sales 2.4MM *EMP* 1,620
SIC 8222 Community college
CEO: Joan Truesdall
**Pr:* Pam Bloom
**VP:* Elizabeth Lunday
Exec: Tim Pantages

D-U-N-S 09-472-2816 IMP
CLAIM JUMPER RESTAURANTS LLC
1510 West Loop S, Houston, TX 77027-9505
Tel (949) 756-9001 *Founded/Ownrshp* 1977
Sales 104.6MM[E] *EMP* 3,600
SIC 5812 American restaurant
Pr: Kilman Fertitta
VP: Michael Brady
VP: Dan Smith
**Prin:* Craig Nickoloff
Rgnl Mgr: Wendy Howard
Genl Mgr: Dan Engleken
IT Man: Jeff Miller
Sls&Mrk Ex: Kris Guthrie

D-U-N-S 12-653-7141
■ **CLAIMS ADMINISTRATION CORP**
(*Suby of* FIRST HEALTH GROUP CORP) ★
15400 Calhoun Dr Ste 300, Rockville, MD 20855-2756
Tel (301) 762-5806 *Founded/Ownrshp* 2002
Sales NA *EMP* 1,100
SIC 6411 Insurance claim adjusters, not employed by insurance company
Pr: Thomas Deyulia
CFO: Tom Kirkpatrick
**VP:* Cindy Henderson
IT Man: Ronald Hess

CLAIMS CENTER
See ISLAND INSURANCE CO LIMITED

CLAIMS CONFERENCE
See CONFERENCE ON JEWISH MATERIAL CLAIMS AGAINST GERMANY INC

D-U-N-S 78-425-9405
CLAIMS SERVICES GROUP LLC
(*Suby of* SOLERA HOLDINGS INC) ★
6111 Bollinger Canyon Rd, San Ramon, CA 94583-5186
Tel (925) 866-1100 *Founded/Ownrshp* 1980
Sales NA *EMP* 1,105[E]
SIC 6411 Medical insurance claim processing, contract or fee basis
Pr: Tony Aquila

D-U-N-S 05-843-2303 IMP/EXP
CLAIRES BOUTIQUES INC
(*Suby of* CLAIRES STORES INC) ★
11401 Pines Blvd, Pembroke Pines, FL 33026-4117
Tel (954) 438-0433 *Founded/Ownrshp* 1994
Sales 1.1MMM[E] *EMP* 15,000
SIC 5632 5699 5999 5943 5947 Costume jewelry; Apparel accessories; Handbags; T-shirts, custom printed; Posters; Stationery stores; Gifts & novelties
Ch Bd: Rowland Schaefer
**Treas:* Ira D Kaplan
**Sr VP:* Marla L Schaefer
Dist Mgr: Camille Head
Store Mgr: Taylor Borek
Store Mgr: Amanda Hansen
Sls Mgr: Aydala Barba-Carabez

D-U-N-S 80-034-5873 IMP
CLAIRES INC
2400 W Central Rd, Hoffman Estates, IL 60192-1930
Tel (847) 765-1100 *Founded/Ownrshp* 2007
Sales 1.8MMM[E] *EMP* 18,900[E]
SIC 5632 5947 Women's accessory & specialty stores; Gift, novelty & souvenir shop
CEO: Beatrice Lafon
Pr: Peter P Copses
Sr VP: Michael R Basler
Sr VP: Holly Cohen
Sr VP: Peter Collyer
Sr VP: David Devany
VP: J Per Brodin
VP: Colleen Collins
VP: Ron Douglass
VP: Greg Hackman
VP: Bill Hoeller
VP: Jihi Kim
VP: Tina Peroni
VP: Jean Ponder
VP: Maryann Porter
VP: Deborah Winkleblack

D-U-N-S 00-412-4731 IMP
CLAIRES STORES INC (FL)
(*Suby of* CLAIRES INC) ★
3 Sw 129th Ave, Pembroke Pines, FL 33027-1775
Tel (954) 433-3900 *Founded/Ownrshp* 1961, 2007
Sales 1.4MMM *EMP* 18,900
SIC 5632 Women's accessory & specialty stores; Apparel accessories; Costume jewelry
CEO: Beatrice Lafon
CFO: J Per Brodin
CFO: Scott Huckins
VP: Colleen Collins
VP: Blaine Robinson
Dist Mgr: Heidi Barker
MIS Dir: Benjie Sabalvaro
Board of Directors: Peter P Copses, Robert J Dinicola, George G Golleher, Ron Marshall, Lance A Milken

D-U-N-S 07-666-3889
CLALLAM COUNTY PUBLIC HOSPITAL DISTRICT 2
OLYMPIC MEDICAL CENTER
939 Caroline St, Port Angeles, WA 98362-3909
Tel (360) 417-7000 *Founded/Ownrshp* 1940
Sales 155.5MM *EMP* 1,000
SIC 8062 General medical & surgical hospitals
CEO: Eric Lewis
Dir Vol: Kathy Coombes
**CFO:* Julie Roxter
CFO: Julie Ruukstad
Bd of Dir: Angie Graff
Ofcr: Mic Sager
Dir Risk M: Donna Davison
Dir Rx: Karen Brath
Dir Rx: Karen Bright
Genl Mgr: Julie Rukstad
Sfty Dirs: Julie Sell

D-U-N-S 15-534-2553
CLAMPETT INDUSTRIES LLC
EMG
10461 Mill Run Cir # 1100, Owings Mills, MD 21117-4206
Tel (410) 785-6200 *Founded/Ownrshp* 2003
Sales 130.3MM[E] *EMP* 450
SIC 8748 6531 Environmental consultant; Real estate managers
CEO: Claude Limoges
**Pr:* Nestor Benavides
**COO:* Robin Cook
COO: Aliza Stern
**Ex VP:* Timothy Mains
Ex VP: Mark R Ohde
Ex VP: Ronald Stupi
Sr VP: Debra Andrews
Sr VP: Matthew Munter
VP: William Ciancaglini
Prgrm Mgr: Matt Anderson

D-U-N-S 00-894-6485 IMP
CLAMPITT PAPER CO OF DALLAS GP LLC
FASCLAMPITT DIVISIONS
9207 Ambassador Row, Dallas, TX 75247-4587
Tel (214) 638-3300 *Founded/Ownrshp* 1951
Sales 125.3MM[E] *EMP* 205
SIC 5111

D-U-N-S 02-474-8063
CLANCY & THEYS CONSTRUCTION CO INC (NC)
516 W Cabarrus St, Raleigh, NC 27603-1912
Tel (919) 834-3601 *Founded/Ownrshp* 1949
Sales 255.8MM[E] *EMP* 320
SIC 1542 1541 Commercial & office building, new construction; Industrial buildings, new construction
Pr: David T Clancy
COO: Harry Stallings
**CFO:* Andrew L Oakley
**Ex VP:* Joel Clancy
**Ex VP:* Tick Clancy
VP: Dean Conklin
**VP:* Thomas Glasgow
IT Man: Zachary Cromer
Mktg Dir: Kenneth Morris
Snr PM: David Farrar
Snr PM: Bill Macdonald

CLARA CITY FARMERS ELEVATOR
See PRINSBURG FARMERS CO-OP

D-U-N-S 07-515-3882
CLARA MAASS MEDICAL CENTER (INC) (NJ)
1 Clara Maass Dr, Belleville, NJ 07109-3550
Tel (973) 450-2000 *Founded/Ownrshp* 1982
Sales 271.8MM *EMP* 1,649[E]
SIC 8062 General medical & surgical hospitals
CEO: Mary Ellen Clyne
V Ch: Robert Gaccione Jr
**CFO:* Terri Cologie
**Ex VP:* Thomas A Biga
VP: Jane N Kessler
Exec: Maureen Freundlich
Ex Dir: Thomas A Big
**CIO:* Don Lutz
Ansthlgy: Jagdip Desai
Ansthlgy: Jennifer Marcus
Doctor: Joe Dib

D-U-N-S 00-651-2669 IMP/EXP
■ **CLARCOR AIR FILTRATION PRODUCTS INC** (KY)
(*Suby of* CLARCOR INC) ★
100 River Ridge Cir, Jeffersonville, IN 47130-8974
Tel (502) 969-2304 *Founded/Ownrshp* 1964
Sales 265.3MM[E] *EMP* 1,100
SIC 3564 Air cleaning systems
CEO: Chris Conway
Pr: Douglas Griffin
Ofcr: Paul Maple
VP: Jon Gallisdorfer
VP: Joseph Hovekamp
VP: Jim Snoddy
Prin: Kevin Bush
Brnch Mgr: Ken Irwin
Brnch Mgr: Joann Rodriguez
MIS Dir: Harvey Goble
IT Man: Theresa Milliner
Board of Directors: Norman E Johnson

D-U-N-S 00-516-2417
▲ **CLARCOR INC**
840 Crescent Centre Dr # 600, Franklin, TN 37067-4687
Tel (615) 771-3100 *Founded/Ownrshp* 1904
Sales 1.4MMM *EMP* 6,093
Tkr Sym CLC *Exch* NYS
SIC 3714 3599 3564 3569 3411 3089 Filters: oil, fuel & air, motor vehicle; Oil filters, internal combustion engine, except automotive; Gasoline filters, internal combustion engine, except auto; Air intake filters, internal combustion engine, except auto; Purification & dust collection equipment; Filters, air: furnaces, air conditioning equipment, etc.; Filter elements, fluid, hydraulic line; Metal cans; Food containers, metal; Plastic containers, except foam; Closures, plastic
Ch Bd: Christopher L Conway
Pr: Jacob Thomas
Pr: Keith White
CFO: David J Fallon
Ofcr: David J Lindsay
VP: Sudhir Nair
VP: Stefan Polywka
VP: Todd Rumsey
VP: Christopher White
VP: Richard M Wolfson
Exec: Patrick Clark
Board of Directors: James L Packard, James W Bradford Jr, Robert J Burgstahler, Wesley M Clark, Nelda J Connors, Paul Donovan, Mark A Emkes, Thomas W Giacomini, Robert H Jenkins, Phillip R Lochner Jr

CLARCOR INDUSTRIAL AIR
See BHA ALTAIR LLC

CLARE ROSE BEVERAGE
See CLARE ROSE INC

D-U-N-S 01-302-1910 IMP/EXP
CLARE ROSE INC (NY)
CLARE ROSE BEVERAGE
100 Rose Executive Blvd, East Yaphank, NY 11967-1524
Tel (631) 475-2337 *Founded/Ownrshp* 1936, 1964
Sales 199.9MM *EMP* 267
SIC 5181 Beer & other fermented malt liquors
Ch Bd: Sean Rose
**CFO:* Monica Ray
**CFO:* Monica Wray
VP: Matt Holthaus
**VP:* Matthew Holthaus
**VP:* Gary Neumen
**VP:* Lisa Rose
**VP:* Darwin Thomas
Snr Sftwr: Dan Koliadko

D-U-N-S 07-618-3789
CLAREMONT GRADUATE UNIVERSITY
CUC
(*Suby of* CLAREMONT UNIVERSITY CONSORTIUM)
150 E 10th St, Claremont, CA 91711-5909
Tel (909) 607-8632 *Founded/Ownrshp* 1925
Sales 89.9MM *EMP* 250[E]
Accts Moss Adams Llp Stockton Ca
SIC 8221 University
CEO: Deborah Freund
**Pr:* Robert Kiltgaard
Ofcr: Sara Hollar
Snr Mgr: Carl Cohn
Assoc Ed: Carol Wilson

D-U-N-S 00-966-1893
CLAREMONT MCKENNA COLLEGE FOUNDATION
CUC
(*Suby of* CLAREMONT UNIVERSITY CONSORTIUM)
500 E 9th St, Claremont, CA 91711-5929
Tel (909) 621-8088 *Founded/Ownrshp* 1947
Sales 155.1MM *EMP* 370
Accts Moss Adams Llp Los Angeles C
SIC 8221 College, except junior
Pr: Erin Watkins
**Ch Bd:* Harry T McMahon
**Pr:* Hiram E Chodosh
Pr: Michael Denny
Pr: Marcie Gardner
Pr: Melissa Schild
CFO: Melissa Barnes
CFO: Jim Duncalman
CFO: Denise Leyk
CFO: Sylvia Pinon-Gomez
CFO: Shelly Zahrt-Egbert
**Treas:* Robin J Aspinall
Treas: Federick Weis
Chf Inves: James Floyd
VP: Max Benavidez
VP: Peter Uvin
VP: Michael Watchorn
VP: Rebecca L Zimberlin
**VP:* Matthew G Bibbens '92
Assoc Dir: Jose Huezo

D-U-N-S 12-048-5730
CLAREMONT RESTAURANT GROUP LLC
WESTERN STEER
129 Fast Ln, Mooresville, NC 28117-6421
Tel (704) 660-5939 *Founded/Ownrshp* 1975
Sales 76.0MM[E] *EMP* 1,800
SIC 5812 Steak restaurant
MIS Dir: Ken Stone

D-U-N-S 17-726-1757
CLARENDON NATIONAL INSURANCE CO (MD CORP)
(*Suby of* ENSTAR GROUP LIMITED)
411 5th Ave Fl 5, New York, NY 10016-2221
Tel (212) 790-9700 *Founded/Ownrshp* 2011
Sales NA *EMP* 80
SIC 6321 1542 1541 7011 Reinsurance carriers, accident & health; Commercial & office building contractors; Industrial buildings, new construction; Hotels
CEO: Betlef Steiner
**Pr:* Robert Ferguson
**CFO:* Anders Larsson
VP: Matt Mascia

D-U-N-S 10-870-6425 IMP/EXP
CLARIANT CORP
(*Suby of* CLARIANT AG)
4000 Monroe Rd, Charlotte, NC 28205-7782
Tel (704) 331-7000 *Founded/Ownrshp* 1886
Sales 677.1MM[E] *EMP* 1,540[E]
SIC 2869 2819 Industrial organic chemicals; Industrial inorganic chemicals
Pr: Kenneth L Golder
CFO: Patrick Jany
Treas: Walter B Fowlkes IV
Treas: Walter Fowlkes
**Treas:* Jennifer Morningstar
**Ex VP:* Daniel McCarthy
VP: Matthias Brommer
VP: Aldo Donnarumma
VP: Dragos Gavriluta
**VP:* David Jarrett
Exec: Tod Waldrop
Board of Directors: Christopher S Barnard-Sec, Kenneth L Golder, Andreas Walde

D-U-N-S 07-996-1089
CLARIANT PLASTICS & COATINGS USA INC
(*Suby of* CLARIANT CORP) ★
4000 Monroe Rd, Charlotte, NC 28205-7782
Tel (704) 331-7000 *Founded/Ownrshp* 2015
Sales 193.8MM[E] *EMP* 721[E]
SIC 2869 2819 Industrial organic chemicals; Industrial inorganic chemicals
Pr: Kelly Sperr
**Pr:* Kenneth L Golder
**Treas:* Jennifer Morningstar

D-U-N-S 00-633-8099 EXP
CLARIDGE PRODUCTS AND EQUIPMENT INC (IL)
601 Highway 62 65 S, Harrison, AR 72601-6148
Tel (870) 743-2200 *Founded/Ownrshp* 1947
Sales 93.3MM[E] *EMP* 418
SIC 2531 3354 2541 2542

D-U-N-S 17-194-8839
CLARIENT DIAGNOSTIC SERVICES INC
(*Suby of* NEOGENOMICS LABORATORIES INC) ★
31 Columbia, Aliso Viejo, CA 92656-1460
Tel (949) 425-5700 *Founded/Ownrshp* 2015
Sales 99.8MM *EMP* 400[E]
Accts Crowe Horwath Llp Tampa Flor
SIC 3841 3826 8071 Diagnostic apparatus, medical; Magnetic resonance imaging apparatus; Medical laboratories; Testing laboratories
Ch Bd: Douglas M Vanoort
**Pr:* Steven C Jones
**Pr:* Michael J Pellini MD
**CEO:* Cynthia Collins
**COO:* Nina Green
**CFO:* George A Cardoza
**CFO:* Michael R Rodriguez
**CFO:* Renika Seghal
CFO: Renika Sehgal
Ofcr: Kenneth J Bloom MD
Ofcr: Douglas T Ross PHD
**Sr VP:* David J Daly
Sr VP: Karen K Garza
**VP:* Jennifer Balliet
VP: David Daly
**VP:* Mark Machulcz
VP: Irwin Scher

CLARINS FRAGRANCE GROUP DIV
See CLARINS USA INC

D-U-N-S 03-959-4114 EXP
CLARINS USA INC
CLARINS FRAGRANCE GROUP DIV
(*Suby of* CLARINS FRANCE)
1 Park Ave Fl 19, New York, NY 10016-5802
Tel (212) 223-2956 *Founded/Ownrshp* 1980
Sales 173.7MM[E] *EMP* 150
SIC 5122 Cosmetics, perfumes & hair products
Pr: Jonathan Zrihen
**Ch Bd:* Marc S Rosenblum
VP: Gary Green
VP: Jamie Manchester
VP: Marc Rosenblum
VP: Lionel Uzan
Advt Dir: Maria Pefinas
Mktg Mgr: Stacey Bradie
Mktg Mgr: Leslie Derderian
Mktg Mgr: Benoit Guerin
Mktg Mgr: Han Paik

D-U-N-S 12-131-1935
CLARION CAPITAL PARTNERS LLC
527 Madison Ave Fl 10, New York, NY 10022-4349
Tel (212) 821-0111 *Founded/Ownrshp* 2016
Sales 150.0MM[E] *EMP* 1,098
SIC 6799 Venture capital companies
Mng Pt: Marc Utay
CFO: Peter Zappulla
Sr VP: Christopher Roscoe
VP: Janice W Chan
Mng Dir: Jeffrey Johnson

D-U-N-S 04-849-9651 IMP/EXP
CLARION CORP OF AMERICA (CA)
(*Suby of* CLARION CO., LTD.)
6200 Gateway Dr, Cypress, CA 90630-4842
Tel (310) 327-9100 *Founded/Ownrshp* 1964
Sales 470.7MM *EMP* 213
SIC 5064 Radios, motor vehicle
Pr: Tsuneo Hayashi
**Pr:* Tatsuhiko Izumi
**Ex VP:* Chris Honma
Sr VP: Calvin Nichols

CLARION HOTEL
See COMFORT CALIFORNIA INC

D-U-N-S 07-834-3419
■ CLARION PARTNERS LLC
(*Suby of* LEGG MASON INC) ★
230 Park Ave Fl 12, New York, NY 10169-0009
Tel (212) 883-2500 *Founded/Ownrshp* 1995, 2016
Sales 237.4MM^E *EMP* 99
SIC 6722 Management investment, open-end
CEO: Stephen J Furnary
Pr: David Gilbert
Pr: John Wanamaker
CFO: Patrick J Tully Jr
Sr VP: Theresa M Buscher
Sr VP: Denise Garcia
Sr VP: Charles Kemp
Sr VP: Dan Reid
Sr VP: Paula Schaefer
Sr VP: Joseph Steblay
VP: Colleen Corwell
VP: David Dipaolo
VP: Teresa Fitzpatrick
VP: Matthew Gittleman
VP: April Matthews
VP: Debra Murphy
VP: Frank Ortiz
VP: Christopher Ponig

D-U-N-S 11-960-5744
CLARITY INDUSTRIES LLC
9265 Hunterboro Dr, Brentwood, TN 37027-6118
Tel (330) 528-3400 *Founded/Ownrshp* 1996
Sales 114.1MM^E *EMP* 500
SIC 3089 Plastic hardware & building products

D-U-N-S 04-502-4320 IMP
CLARK - PACIFIC CORP
CLARK PACIFIC
1980 S River Rd, West Sacramento, CA 95691-2817
Tel (916) 371-0305 *Founded/Ownrshp* 1966
Sales 135.8MM^E *EMP* 500
SIC 3272 5032 Concrete products, precast; Brick, stone & related material
Pr: Robert Clark
Treas: Sharron Clark
**Prin:* Bob Clark
Genl Mgr: James Clark
CIO: Rick Short
Netwrk Mgr: Spencer Burroughs
Sys Mgr: Rick Riggs
Info Man: Michael Ito
Mtls Dir: Annika Chase
Sfty Mgr: Chris Cann
Opers Mgr: Kevin Frulan

D-U-N-S 05-414-6402 IMP
CLARK ASSOCIATES INC
CLARK FOOD SERVICE EQUIPMENT
2205 Old Philadelphia Pike, Lancaster, PA 17602-3400
Tel (717) 392-7550 *Founded/Ownrshp* 1971
Sales 103.0MM *EMP* 394
SIC 5046 7623

D-U-N-S 17-529-0894
CLARK BRANDS LLC
4200 Commerce Ct Ste 350, Lisle, IL 60532-0923
Tel (630) 355-8918 *Founded/Ownrshp* 2003
Sales 249.3MM^E *EMP* 3,151
SIC 6794 7389 5541 5812 Franchises, selling or licensing; Credit card service; Gasoline service stations; Eating places
Pr: Stephen Ruch
VP: Corey Frank
Web Dev: Eric Chelmecki

CLARK COLOR LABS
See DISTRICT PHOTO INC

D-U-N-S 06-676-7021 IMP
CLARK CONSTRUCTION GROUP LLC
(*Suby of* CLARK CONSTRUCTION LLC) ★
7500 Old Georgetown Rd # 15, Bethesda, MD 20814-6812
Tel (301) 272-8100 *Founded/Ownrshp* 2016
Sales 3.7MMM^E *EMP* 3,000
SIC 1542 1611 1522 Commercial & office building, new construction; General contractor, highway & street construction; Residential construction
Pr: Robert D Moser Jr
**COO:* Harold K Roach Jr
CFO: Timothy R Yost
**Ex VP:* Susan Williamson Ross
Sr VP: James A Hooff
Sr VP: Gary Schalmo
VP: Hani Alawneh
VP: Jim Ansari
VP: John Barotti
VP: Tom Benton
VP: Kenneth Carlson
VP: Mark Chandler
VP: Joe Conover
VP: Keith Couch
VP: Steve Dell
VP: Jim Douglas
VP: Jeff Jasnoff
VP: Lincoln Lawrence
VP: Randy Sibold
VP: Al Sylvester
VP: David Trolian

D-U-N-S 08-020-6726
CLARK CONSTRUCTION LLC (MD)
7500 Old Georgetown Rd # 1500, Bethesda, MD 20814-6815
Tel (301) 272-8337 *Founded/Ownrshp* 2015
Sales 3.7MMM^E *EMP* 3,000^E
SIC 1542 Commercial & office building, new construction
Pr: Robert D Moser Jr
Sr VP: Tim Bohrer

D-U-N-S 00-672-6619
CLARK CONTRACTORS LLC
ARKANSAS CLARK CONTRACTORS
15825 Cantrell Rd, Little Rock, AR 72223-4249
Tel (501) 868-3133 *Founded/Ownrshp* 2009
Sales 116.0MM *EMP* 79
SIC 1542 Commercial & office building contractors
CFO: Keith Jacks
VP: Danny Bennett
VP: Tucker O'Neal

CLARK COUNTY BD COMMISSIONERS
See COUNTY OF CLARK

D-U-N-S 00-280-9287
CLARK COUNTY SCHOOL DIST
5101 Obannon Dr Apt 233, Las Vegas, NV 89146-3459
Tel (702) 799-1042 *Founded/Ownrshp* 2011
Sales 2.9MMM *EMP* 11^E
SIC 8211 Public elementary & secondary schools
Prin: Ken Ivey

D-U-N-S 07-794-9238
CLARK COUNTY SCHOOL DISTRICT
5100 W Sahara Ave, Las Vegas, NV 89146-3406
Tel (702) 799-5000 *Founded/Ownrshp* 1956
Sales 3.0MMM^E *EMP* 37,361^E
Accts Eide Bailly Llp Las Vegas Ne
SIC 8211 Public elementary & secondary schools
CFO: Jeff Weiller
Bd of Dir: Jacqueline Brown
Dir Sec: Jeff Levering
Off Mgr: Danielle Caruso
Off Mgr: Karen Steik
Off Mgr: Sandi Webb
Off Admin: Janette Scott
DP Exec: Peter Locatelli
MIS Dir: Dan Wray
IT Man: Pamela Hamilton
Netwrk Mgr: Jim Beckett

D-U-N-S 04-823-4975 IMP
CLARK DISTRIBUTING CO INC
300 Oakland Flatrock Rd, Oakland, KY 42159-9766
Tel (270) 563-4735 *Founded/Ownrshp* 1969
Sales 100.0MM *EMP* 183
SIC 5149 5181 Groceries & related products; Beer & ale
CEO: W Dal Clark Jr
**Pr:* George P Clark
**VP:* Albert Clark
VP: Harold Clark
Genl Mgr: Jeff Brasher

D-U-N-S 06-486-2345
CLARK ENTERPRISES INC (MD)
7500 Old Georgetown Rd # 7, Bethesda, MD 20814-6195
Tel (301) 657-7100 *Founded/Ownrshp* 1972
Sales 2.4MMM^E *EMP* 4,200
SIC 6552 4832 7359 1521 1542 6726 Land subdividers & developers, commercial; Radio broadcasting stations; Industrial truck rental; Single-family housing construction; Nonresidential construction; Investment offices
Ch Bd: A James Clark
**Pr:* Lawrence C Nussdorf
CFO: James J Brinkman
**Ex VP:* Robert J Flanagan
**Sr VP:* Terri D Klatzkin
**Sr VP:* Rebecca L Owen
IT Man: Kerry Sarkkinen

D-U-N-S 00-121-1697 EXP
CLARK EQUIPMENT CO
BOBCAT COMPANY
(*Suby of* DOOSAN BOBCAT INC.)
250 E Beaton Dr, West Fargo, ND 58078-2656
Tel (701) 241-8700 *Founded/Ownrshp* 1920, 2012
Sales 2.5MMM *EMP* 5,000
Accts Deloitte & Touche Llp Atlanta
SIC 3599 3531 Air intake filters, internal combustion engine, except auto; Construction machinery
Pr: Richard Goldsbury
VP: Jim Adkins
VP: Bruce Collins
VP: Joel Honeyman
VP: Gary Hornbacher
Dist Mgr: Shane Christensen
Genl Mgr: Micah Smith
IT Man: Crystal Stram
Plnt Mgr: Tom Dallman
Sales Exec: Dirk Pettit
VP Sls: Scott Nelson

D-U-N-S 18-818-7884 IMP/EXP
■ CLARK FILTER INC
(*Suby of* CLARCOR INC) ★
3649 Hempland Rd, Lancaster, PA 17601-1323
Tel (717) 285-5941 *Founded/Ownrshp* 1943
Sales 844.4MM^E *EMP* 3,500
SIC 3564 3714 Blowers & fans; Motor vehicle parts & accessories
Ch Bd: Norm Johnson
COO: Kathy Horn
Treas: Bruce Klein
VP: Peter Nangle
IT Man: Scott Nemeth
VP Opers: Richard Kurcina
VP Opers: Richard Kurina
Sales Exec: Patricia A Manno
VP Mktg: John Musone

CLARK FOOD SERVICE EQUIPMENT
See CLARK ASSOCIATES INC

D-U-N-S 07-861-6240
CLARK FOUNDATION
1 Rockefeller Plz Fl 31, New York, NY 10020-2011
Tel (212) 977-6900 *Founded/Ownrshp* 1931
Sales 87.9MM *EMP* 69
SIC 6732 Charitable trust management
Pr: Jane Forbes Clark
**Treas:* Kevin Moore
**VP:* Alexander Treadwell
Ex Dir: Doug Bauer
Off Mgr: Kathy Cathler
CTO: Tim Chizak
IT Man: Joe Sellitto

CLARK LABORATORIES
See TRINITY BIOTECH INC

CLARK MEM OUTPATIENT SURGERY
See CLARK MEMORIAL HOSPITAL

D-U-N-S 05-869-4142
CLARK MEMORIAL HOSPITAL
CLARK MEM OUTPATIENT SURGERY
1220 Missouri Ave, Jeffersonville, IN 47130-3743
Tel (812) 282-6631 *Founded/Ownrshp* 1919
Sales 162.1MM *EMP* 1,500
SIC 8062 8063

D-U-N-S 04-775-5335
CLARK OIL CO INC
720 Station St, Waynesboro, MS 39367-2733
Tel (601) 735-4847 *Founded/Ownrshp* 1962
Sales 111.1MM^E *EMP* 260
SIC 5541 5172 Gasoline service stations; Service station supplies, petroleum
Pr: Jon F Clark
**Treas:* Robert Clark

CLARK PACIFIC
See CLARK - PACIFIC CORP

D-U-N-S 04-741-7589
CLARK PEST CONTROL OF STOCKTON INC
555 N Guild Ave, Lodi, CA 95240-0809
Tel (209) 368-7152 *Founded/Ownrshp* 1946
Sales 108.2MM *EMP* 1,000
Accts Gatto Pope & Walwick Llp Sa
SIC 7342 Exterminating & fumigating; Pest control in structures; Termite control
CEO: Joseph Clark
VP: Jeffrey Clark
VP: Terry Clark
Brnch Mgr: Bryan Alger
Snr Ntwrk: Mike East
Dir IT: Mike Butchko
IT Man: Fred Speer
Software D: Parthasarathy Vasudevan
Sls Mgr: Travis Mickel

CLARK PUBLIC UTILITIES
See PUBLIC UTILITY DISTRICT 1 OF CLARK COUNTY

D-U-N-S 12-486-4880
CLARK REALTY CAPITAL LLC
(*Suby of* CLARK ENTERPRISES INC) ★
4401 Wilson Blvd Ste 600, Arlington, VA 22203-4195
Tel (703) 294-4500 *Founded/Ownrshp* 1993
Sales 46.1MM^E *EMP* 2,091^E
SIC 1522 1531 1542 Residential construction; Operative builders; Nonresidential construction
VP: Tom Sedeski

D-U-N-S 61-537-0330
CLARK RESOURCES INC
321 N Front St, Harrisburg, PA 17101-1225
Tel (717) 230-8861 *Founded/Ownrshp* 2002
Sales 404.0MM *EMP* 157^E
SIC 8741 Management services
Pr: Fredrick A Clark

D-U-N-S 16-083-1723
CLARK RICHARDSON AND BISKUP CONSULTING ENGINEERS INC
CRB
1251 Nw Briarcliff Pkwy # 500, Kansas City, MO 64116-1795
Tel (816) 880-9800 *Founded/Ownrshp* 1984
Sales 123.1MM^E *EMP* 365
SIC 8711 Mechanical engineering; Electrical or electronic engineering; Consulting engineer
Pr: Doyle Clark
**CEO:* Jeff Biskup
**VP:* Jeffery Biskup
IT Man: Jason Schaeffer

D-U-N-S 02-287-4348
CLARK THEDA MEDICAL CENTER
5320 W Michaels Dr, Appleton, WI 54913-8446
Tel (920) 735-7650 *Founded/Ownrshp* 2009
Sales 179.4MM *EMP* 3
SIC 8011 Medical centers
Prin: Pat Hawley

D-U-N-S 82-938-5777
CLARK-NEXSEN/CH2M HILL
9191 S Jamaica St, Englewood, CO 80112-5946
Tel (303) 771-0900 *Founded/Ownrshp* 2015
Sales 280.8M^E *EMP* 1,200
SIC 8711 Engineering services
**Owner:* Clark Nexsen
**Pt:* Ch2m Hill

D-U-N-S 09-373-2329 IMP
CLARKE AMERICAN CHECKS INC
(*Suby of* M & F WORLDWIDE CORP) ★
15955 La Cantera Pkwy, San Antonio, TX 78256-2589
Tel (210) 694-1492 *Founded/Ownrshp* 1991
Sales 889.0MM^E *EMP* 4,100
SIC 2782 2759 2752 Checkbooks; Business forms: printing; Commercial printing, lithographic
Pr: Charles T Dawson
Pr: Louis Sanchez
Pr: Dan Singleton
COO: Brad Wheeless
CFO: Peter A Fera Jr
Treas: Robert Sosa
Ofcr: Steven L Reynolds
Ex VP: Rick Ebrey
Ex VP: Mike Fay
Sr VP: Don Dolan
Sr VP: Steve Moyer

D-U-N-S 61-139-9783
CLARKE COUNTY SCHOOL DISTRICT
CCSD
240 Mitchell Bridge Rd, Athens, GA 30606-2043
Tel (706) 546-7721 *Founded/Ownrshp* 1801
Sales 106.2MM^E *EMP* 1,878
Accts Greg S Griffin Atlanta Geor
SIC 8211 Public elementary & secondary schools
Pr Dir: Anisa Sullivan-Moore
Teacher Pr: Sherrie Freeman
HC Dir: Amy Roark

D-U-N-S 01-762-1749 IMP
CLARKE POWER SERVICES INC
3133 E Kemper Rd, Cincinnati, OH 45241-1516
Tel (513) 771-2200 *Founded/Ownrshp* 2004
Sales 277.1MM *EMP* 600
Accts Ernst & Young Llp
SIC 5084 Industrial machinery & equipment; Engines & parts, diesel
CEO: Mark Andreae
**Pr:* Kirk Andreae
**CFO:* Paul Loebig
**VP:* Riley Asher
**VP:* Don Bixler
**VP:* Randy Keach
**VP:* Dane Petrie
Brnch Mgr: Billy Erwin
Opers Mgr: Michael Ledford

D-U-N-S 61-346-7901 IMP/EXP
CLARKS AMERICAS INC
(*Suby of* C. & J. CLARK (HOLDINGS) LIMITED)
60 Tower Rd, Waltham, MA 02451-1022
Tel (617) 796-5000 *Founded/Ownrshp* 1983
Sales 945.1MM^E *EMP* 2,800
SIC 5661 5139 Shoe stores; Footwear
Pr: Gary Champion
Pr: Michael Katscrbis
Sr VP: Bob Miller
Sr VP: Sharon Schuler
Mng Dir: Jennifer Ryan
Plng Mgr: Kevin Hess
VP Mktg: Lisa Vagge
VP Sls: Frank Annunziata
Sls Mgr: Lance Steinberg

D-U-N-S 00-785-6099
CLARKSON CONSTRUCTION CO INC (MO)
4133 Gardner Ave, Kansas City, MO 64120-1833
Tel (816) 483-5444 *Founded/Ownrshp* 1947
Sales 217.3MM^E *EMP* 400
SIC 1611 Concrete construction: roads, highways, sidewalks, etc.
Pr: William E Clarkson
CFO: Eldon Eikenbary
**VP:* William Clarkson Jr
Exec: Bob Fry
IT Man: Rodney Tatum

D-U-N-S 04-159-0993
CLARKSON UNIVERSITY
8 Clarkson Ave, Potsdam, NY 13676-1402
Tel (315) 268-6400 *Founded/Ownrshp* 1896
Sales 118.7MM *EMP* 700
Accts Kpmg Llp Colchester Vt
SIC 8733 Research institute
Pr: Anthony G Collins
Pr: Warren Anderson
**CFO:* James Fish
Ofcr: Kimberly Klatt
VP: Laurene Burton
VP: Andrew Dorr
VP: Tim Jones
VP: Brad Kelsey
Assoc Dir: Suzanne Davis
Off Mgr: Annette B Green
CIO: Joshua Fiske

D-U-N-S 04-057-8882
CLARKSTON COMMUNITY SCHOOLS
CCS
6389 Clarkston Rd, Clarkston, MI 48346-1613
Tel (248) 623-5400 *Founded/Ownrshp* 1898
Sales 81.3MM^E *EMP* 1,313
Accts Hungerford Aldrin Nichols &
SIC 8211 Public elementary & secondary schools; Public junior high school; Public senior high school; Preparatory school
Pr: Steve Hyer
Trst: Gregory Need
VP: Elizabeth Egan
Ex Dir: Mary Beth Rogers

CLARKSVILLE MEMORIAL HOSPITAL
See CLARKSVILLE VOLUNTEER HEALTH INC

D-U-N-S 07-546-1004
CLARKSVILLE VOLUNTEER HEALTH INC
CLARKSVILLE MEMORIAL HOSPITAL
651 Dunlop Ln, Clarksville, TN 37040-5015
Tel (931) 220-2532 *Founded/Ownrshp* 1954
Sales 153.1MM *EMP* 1,100
SIC 8062 8621 General medical & surgical hospitals; Professional membership organizations
Pr: Kim Puthoff
**Ch Bd:* Walton Smith Jr
**Ch Bd:* William H Wyatt
**CFO:* Lynn Lambert
Dir Inf Cn: Dana Sandefur
CIO: Stefan Hopper
Dir IT: Greene Scott
Mtls Dir: Kevin Rau
Pathlgst: Scott McCullough
Doctor: William J Pedigo MD
Pharmcst: Christine Dennis

D-U-N-S 06-074-2376
CLARKSVILLE-MONTGOMERY COUNTY SCHOOL SYS
621 Gracey Ave, Clarksville, TN 37040-4012
Tel (931) 648-5600 *Founded/Ownrshp* 1819, 1964
Sales 313.2MM *EMP* 4,700
Accts Page Accounting & Tax Service
SIC 8211 Public elementary & secondary schools
V Ch: Charles Foust Jr
Prin: Yvonne C Hackney
Prin: Judy L Morgan
Prin: Frank Myers
Prin: Judith A Sinks
Teacher Pr: Jeanine Johnson
Teacher Pr: Carol Joiner
HC Dir: Thomas Butler

D-U-N-S 96-774-7135 EXP
CLARKWESTERN DIETRICH BUILDING SYSTEMS LLC
(*Suby of* MISA) ★
9100 Centre Pointe Dr # 210, West Chester, OH 45069-4847
Tel (513) 870-1100 *Founded/Ownrshp* 2011
Sales 216.6MM^E *EMP* 683^E
SIC 3444 8711 3081 Studs & joists, sheet metal; Engineering services; Vinyl film & sheet
CEO: Bill Courtney
Genl Mgr: Andrea Siler-Goodrich
Plnt Mgr: Nathan Jacobs
Plnt Mgr: Brody Mautz
Manager: Jason Hodges

Sls Mgr: Brian Brentzel
Sls Mgr: Troy Kehr
Sls Mgr: Greg Sech
Sls Mgr: Chuck Webb
Sales Asso: Michelle Killingsworth
Sales Asso: Krista King

D-U-N-S 16-846-0371
CLASS PRODUCE GROUP LLC
CPG
8477 Dorsey Run Rd, Jessup, MD 20794-9304
Tel (410) 799-5700 *Founded/Ownrshp* 2004
Sales 97.3MM[E] *EMP* 190
SIC 5148 Vegetables

CLASSIC
See I C CLASS COMPONENTS CORP

CLASSIC ACURA
See SOUTHEAST TEXAS CLASSIC AUTOMOTIVE INC

D-U-N-S 02-410-9431
■ **CLASSIC AUTO GROUP INC** (NJ)
CLASSIC CHEVROLET
(*Suby of* PENSKE AUTOMOTIVE GROUP INC) ★
Black Horse Pike Rr 555, Blackwood, NJ 08012
Tel (856) 629-1900 *Founded/Ownrshp* 1991, 1998
Sales 108.5MM[E] *EMP* 520
SIC 5511 Automobiles, new & used
Pr: Roger S Penske
MIS Dir: Bill Quinn

CLASSIC BAKERY PRODUCTS
See STEVEN-ROBERT ORIGINALS LLC

CLASSIC CHEVROLET
See CLASSIC AUTO GROUP INC

D-U-N-S 02-644-4356
CLASSIC CHEVROLET LTD
1101 W State Highway 114, Grapevine, TX 76051-3991
Tel (817) 421-1200 *Founded/Ownrshp* 1988
Sales 440.0MM *EMP* 330
SIC 5511 Automobiles, new & used
Pr: Tom Durant
**CFO:* Mark Escamilla
Genl Mgr: Denny Bowen
Store Mgr: David Osburn
Sls Mgr: Mike Hicks

D-U-N-S 09-270-5482 IMP
CLASSIC DISTRIBUTING AND BEVERAGE GROUP INC
120 Puente Ave, City of Industry, CA 91746-2301
Tel (626) 330-8231 *Founded/Ownrshp* 1986
Sales 138.9MM *EMP* 261
Accts Rsm Us Llp Irvine California
SIC 5181 Beer & other fermented malt liquors
CEO: Joseph Sanchez III
**Pr:* Victor Fiss
**CFO:* John Thomas
VP Sls: Carlos Sanchez

CLASSIC FARE CATERING
See CENTER COLLEGE

CLASSIC FLAME
See TWIN-STAR INTERNATIONAL INC

D-U-N-S 10-178-1300 IMP
CLASSIC GRAPHICS LLC
(*Suby of* IMAGINE PRINT SOLUTIONS INC) ★
8335 Classic Dr, Charlotte, NC 28262-4551
Tel (704) 597-9015 *Founded/Ownrshp* 1983
Sales 87.9MM[E] *EMP* 334
SIC 2752 Commercial printing, offset
Pr: David C Pitts
Pr: Darryl Furr
Pr: Ed Warren
VP: Rick Craushaar
Prgrm Mgr: Jenn Hopper
Telecom Ex: John Whitley
CTO: Bryan Stalcup
Dir IT: Eric Smith
Software D: Scott Deeter
Software D: Bayo Fodeke
VP Opers: Rick Kraushaar

CLASSIC PARTY RENTALS
See CP OPCO LLC

CLASSIC PARTY RENTALS
See AFTER-PARTY6 INC

D-U-N-S 36-288-1711 IMP
CLASSIC PARTY RENTALS INC
901 W Hillcrest Blvd, Inglewood, CA 90301-2100
Tel (310) 966-4900 *Founded/Ownrshp* 2005
Sales NA *EMP* 2,500
SIC 7359

D-U-N-S 60-537-8793
CLASSIC RIVERDALE INC
HYATT HOTEL
200 W Madison St Ste 3700, Chicago, IL 60606-3465
Tel (312) 803-8800 *Founded/Ownrshp* 1986
Sales 67.3MM[E] *EMP* 1,300
SIC 7011 Hotels & motels
CEO: Penny Pritzker
COO: William S Sciortino
**VP:* Randal J Richardson

D-U-N-S 86-108-9027 IMP
CLASSIC SOFTTRIM INC
4516 Seton Center Pkwy # 135, Austin, TX 78759-5375
Tel (512) 873-7770 *Founded/Ownrshp* 1969
Sales 144.2MM[E] *EMP* 543
SIC 5199 Leather goods, except footwear, gloves, luggage, belting
Pr: Dwight K Forrister
CFO: Paul Simar
**Treas:* Dave Gienapp
Genl Mgr: Steve Smith
Opers Mgr: Gilbert Herrera
Opers Mgr: Kyle Penot
Sales Exec: Patti Cheeseman

D-U-N-S 00-321-6210
CLASSIC STAR GROUP LP (TX)
6324 Eden Dr, Haltom City, TX 76117-6129
Tel (817) 834-2868 *Founded/Ownrshp* 1999
Sales 404.8MM *EMP* 17
Accts Mwh Group Pc Wichita Falls
SIC 5172 Fuel oil
Genl Pt: Michael Ali
Pt: Gulamali Barwani

CLASSIC WINES OF CALIFORNIA
See BRONCO WINE CO

D-U-N-S 96-754-0498
CLAXTON MEDICAL PC
214 King St, Ogdensburg, NY 13669-1142
Tel (315) 393-1559 *Founded/Ownrshp* 2011
Sales 93.7MM *EMP* 4[E]
Accts Fust Charles Chambers Llp Syr
SIC 8011 Pediatrician
Prin: Adam D Jarrett

CLAXTON POULTRY FARMS
See NORMAN W FRIES INC

D-U-N-S 07-537-6228
CLAY COUNTY MANOR INC
CLAY COUNTY NURSING HOME
(*Suby of* A H C) ★
120 Pitcock Ln, Celina, TN 38551-4058
Tel (931) 243-3139 *Founded/Ownrshp* 1985
Sales 393.4MM *EMP* 65
SIC 8051 Skilled nursing care facilities
Pr: Jerry Ivey
**Sec:* Preston Shaw

CLAY COUNTY NURSING HOME
See CLAY COUNTY MANOR INC

D-U-N-S 00-692-1936
CLAY ELECTRIC COOPERATIVE INC
225 W Walker Dr, Keystone Heights, FL 32656-7617
Tel (352) 473-8000 *Founded/Ownrshp* 1937
Sales 362.3MM *EMP* 444
Accts Jackson Thornton & Co Pc Mo
SIC 4911 Distribution, electric power
CEO: Richard K Davis
Dir Risk M: Dennis Lendzion
Dist Mgr: Dale Furlong
Genl Mgr: Clinton Boone
Off Mgr: Bryan Gunter
Netwrk Mgr: Robert Hickenlooper
Tech Mgr: Don Herring
Netwrk Eng: Alain Espinosa
Snr Mgr: Stephen Sims

D-U-N-S 01-532-4748
CLAY FARMS
85 Cypress Ln, Yazoo City, MS 39194-3512
Tel (662) 836-7629 *Founded/Ownrshp* 2012
Sales 1.8MMM *EMP* 4
SIC 0191 General farms, primarily crop
Owner: Nathan Thomas Clay III

CLAYCO CONSTRUCTION COMPANY
See CLAYCO INC

D-U-N-S 11-904-3008
CLAYCO INC
CLAYCO CONSTRUCTION COMPANY
35 E Wacker Dr Ste 1300, Chicago, IL 60601-2110
Tel (312) 658-0747 *Founded/Ownrshp* 1984
Sales 466.1MM *EMP* 500
Accts Dglf Cpas & Business Advisors
SIC 1541 Industrial buildings, new construction; Renovation, remodeling & repairs: industrial buildings; Warehouse construction
CEO: Bob Clark
**Pt:* Kevin McKenna
**Pt:* Dave Moses
Pt: Tom Sieckhaus
COO: Steven R Sieckhaus
**CFO:* Tony Schofield
**Ex VP:* Kirk Warden
**Sr VP:* Paul Barrath
VP: Lance Cage
VP: Paul Giacoletto
VP: Kurt Jaeger
VP: Carmen H Lonstein
VP: Sandra Marks
VP: Henningfeld Reene
Dir Bus: Garth Price

CLAYTON COUNTY BOARD EDUCATION
See CLAYTON COUNTY SCHOOL DISTRICT

CLAYTON COUNTY BOARD OF COMMIS
See COUNTY OF CLAYTON

D-U-N-S 01-010-6797
CLAYTON COUNTY BOARD OF EDUCATION (GA)
CLAYTON COUNTY PUBLIC SCHOOLS
1058 5th Ave, Jonesboro, GA 30236-3299
Tel (770) 473-2700 *Founded/Ownrshp* 1923
Sales 198.9MM[E] *EMP* 5,131
Accts Mauldin & Jenkins Llc Macon
SIC 8211 Public elementary & secondary schools; High school, junior or senior

CLAYTON COUNTY PUBLIC SCHOOLS
See CLAYTON COUNTY BOARD OF EDUCATION

D-U-N-S 07-868-5258
CLAYTON COUNTY PUBLIC SCHOOLS
1058 5th Ave, Jonesboro, GA 30236-3299
Tel (678) 817-3076 *Founded/Ownrshp* 1841
Sales 8.6MM[E] *EMP* 6,800
SIC 8211 Elementary & secondary schools
CEO: Yulonda Beauford
Dir Sec: Thomas Trawick
Pr Dir: Jada Dawcan
Teacher Pr: Douglas Hendricks

D-U-N-S 96-330-1366
CLAYTON COUNTY SCHOOL DISTRICT
CLAYTON COUNTY BOARD EDUCATION
1058 5th Ave, Jonesboro, GA 30236-3299
Tel (770) 473-2700 *Founded/Ownrshp* 2010
Sales 483.5MM *EMP* 6,000
SIC 8211 Elementary & secondary schools

D-U-N-S 02-752-9684
CLAYTON COUNTY WATER AUTHORITY
1600 Battle Creek Rd, Morrow, GA 30260-4302
Tel (770) 961-2130 *Founded/Ownrshp* 1955
Sales 103.0MM *EMP* 370
Accts Mauldin & Jenkins Macon Geor
SIC 4941 4952 Water supply; Sewerage systems
CFO: Emory McHugh
Exec: Cary Santoyo
Genl Mgr: Karen Riser
IT Man: Dan Holverson
Board of Directors: Lloyd Joiner All Appointe, Marie Barber, Wes Green, Joe T Lane, Pete McQueen, Lindy Rogers, Don Whitman

CLAYTON, DUBILIER & RICE
See STERLING GROUP L P

D-U-N-S 01-718-3612 IMP
CLAYTON DUBILIER & RICE FUND V LIMITED PARTNERSHIP
375 Park Ave Fl 18, New York, NY 10152-0144
Tel (212) 407-5200 *Founded/Ownrshp* 1985
Sales 3.1MM *EMP* 4,973
SIC 3825 3661 3812 3577 3575 7372 Test equipment for electronic & electric measurement; Digital test equipment, electronic & electrical circuits; Telephone & telegraph apparatus; Switching equipment, telephone; Headsets, telephone; Search & navigation equipment; Computer peripheral equipment; Computer terminals; Prepackaged software
Ch Bd: Joseph L Rice III
**Pr:* Donald J Gogel
VP: Joanne Alves

D-U-N-S 08-040-5368
CLAYTON DUBILIER & RICE INC
375 Park Ave Fl 18, New York, NY 10152-0144
Tel (212) 407-5200 *Founded/Ownrshp* 1978
Sales 7.5MMM[E] *EMP* 33,045
SIC 6799 3589 5812 Investors; Water purification equipment, household type; Water filters & softeners, household type; Water treatment equipment, industrial; Contract food services
Pr: Donald J Gogel
Genl Pt: Bruno Deschamps
Genl Pt: Mike Ebeling
Genl Pt: Kenneth N Giuriceo
Genl Pt: Gr Gory La
Genl Pt: Enrique Lax Ba On
Genl Pt: Richard Schnall
Genl Pt: David H Wasserman
Genl Pt: Jesse Watson
Pt: Fred Kindle
Pt: Jack Welch
COO: Jillian Griffiths
Ch: Joseph L Rice III
VP: Theresa Gore
VP: Florence Terdeman
Exec: Philip W Knisely

D-U-N-S 96-154-6657
CLAYTON DUBILIER & RICE LLC
(*Suby of* CLAYTON DUBILIER & RICE INC) ★
375 Park Ave Fl 18, New York, NY 10152-0144
Tel (212) 407-5200 *Founded/Ownrshp* 2010
Sales 2.4MMM[E] *EMP* 26,620[E]
SIC 6719 6726 6211 Investment holding companies, except banks; Investment offices; Investment firm, general brokerage

D-U-N-S 19-924-1485
■ **CLAYTON HOLDINGS LLC**
(*Suby of* RADIAN GROUP INC) ★
100 Beard Sawmill Rd # 200, Shelton, CT 06484-6156
Tel (203) 926-5600 *Founded/Ownrshp* 2014
Sales 102.0MM[E] *EMP* 629[E]
SIC 8741 7389 6531 Management services; Financial management for business; Business management; Financial services; Telemarketing services; Real estate leasing & rentals
CEO: Paul T Bossidy
Pr: Robert F Bladek
**CFO:* Peter Kushel
**Ofcr:* Andy Pollock
**Ex VP:* Tom Donatacci
Ex VP: Lorenz Schwarz
Sr VP: Evan Guttman
Sr VP: Jonathan T McGrain
VP: Gregory Kaether
VP: Brent Taggart
**Int Pr:* Jeff Tennyson

D-U-N-S 04-736-0227 EXP
■ **CLAYTON HOMES INC**
OAKWOOD HOMES
(*Suby of* BERKSHIRE HATHAWAY INC) ★
5000 Clayton Rd, Maryville, TN 37804-5550
Tel (865) 380-3000 *Founded/Ownrshp* 2003
Sales 3.4MMM[E] *EMP* 14,000
SIC 2451 5271 6141 6351 6331 Mobile homes; Mobile homes; Installment sales finance, other than banks; Credit & other financial responsibility insurance; Property damage insurance
Pr: Kevin T Clayton
**Pr:* David M Booth
**Pr:* Paul Nichols
**CFO:* John J Kalec
Bd of Dir: John Phillips
VP: Mitchell Berry
VP: Victor Bourdeau
VP: Mike Buchko
VP: Damon Dickson
VP: David R Jordan
VP: Allan Morgan
VP: Chuck Morgan
VP: Dave Slagle
VP: Hugh Stash
VP: Danny Xanders
Exec: Roger McCarter
Exec: Josh Morrison

CLAYTON INDUSTRIES
See CLAYTON MANUFACTURING CO

D-U-N-S 00-823-6911 IMP
CLAYTON MANUFACTURING CO (CA)
CLAYTON INDUSTRIES
17477 Hurley St, City of Industry, CA 91744-5106
Tel (626) 443-9381 *Founded/Ownrshp* 1930
Sales 130.1MM[E] *EMP* 500
SIC 3569 3829 3511 Generators: steam, liquid oxygen or nitrogen; Dynamometer instruments; Turbines & turbine generator sets
Pr: John Clayton
**CFO:* Alexander Smirnoff
**Sr VP:* Boyd A Calvin
**VP:* Allen L Cluer
**VP:* Phyllis Nielson
**Prin:* Lance Baroldi
**Prin:* Jolyn Henson
**Prin:* Kandi Ono
**Prin:* Jeff Sandridge
Board of Directors: Harry W Colmery Jr, Stephen F Keller, I Andrew Rader

D-U-N-S 05-887-0445
▲ **CLAYTON WILLIAMS ENERGY INC**
6 Desta Dr Ste 6500, Midland, TX 79705-5519
Tel (432) 682-6324 *Founded/Ownrshp* 1991
Sales 232.3MM *EMP* 264[E]
Tkr Sym CWEI *Exch* NYS
SIC 1311 Crude petroleum & natural gas
Ch Bd: Clayton W Williams Jr
**Pr:* Mel G Riggs
Pr: Mark T Tisdale
CFO: Michael L Pollard
Bd of Dir: George Harris
VP: John F Kennedy
VP: Robert C Lyon
VP: Patrick C Reesby
VP: Boring Rick
VP: Mark Tisdale
VP: T Mark Tisdale
VP: Gregory S Welborn
Exec: Samuel L Lyssy Jr
Board of Directors: Davis L Ford, Ted Gray Jr, P Scott Martin, Ronald D Scott, Jordan R Smith, Nathan W Walton

D-U-N-S 00-785-4005 IMP
CLC ENTERPRISES INC (FL)
CLC MIAMI
11231 Nw 20th St Unit 133, Miami, FL 33172-1858
Tel (305) 640-1803 *Founded/Ownrshp* 2000
Sales 84.0MM *EMP* 51
Accts Avesta Inc Coral Springs F
SIC 5065 Mobile telephone equipment
CEO: Syed Hussain
**Pr:* Heather Hussain
**CFO:* Yami Nunez

CLC MIAMI
See CLC ENTERPRISES INC

D-U-N-S 13-738-9664
CLC OF BILOXI LLC
REHABILITATION STATION
(*Suby of* COMMUNITY ELDERCARE SERVICES LLC) ★
2279 Atkinson Rd, Biloxi, MS 39531-2209
Tel (228) 388-1805 *Founded/Ownrshp* 2000
Sales 1.1MMM *EMP* 1[E]
SIC 8051 Skilled nursing care facilities
CEO: Douglas Wright

D-U-N-S 15-443-3705
CLC OF LAUREL LLC
LAURELWOOD CLC
1036 West Dr, Laurel, MS 39440-4706
Tel (601) 425-3191 *Founded/Ownrshp* 2000
Sales 436.3MM *EMP* 29[E]
SIC 8051 Skilled nursing care facilities

D-U-N-S 60-330-4804
■ **CLEAN EARTH HOLDINGS INC**
(*Suby of* CEHI ACQUISITION CORP) ★
334 S Warminster Rd, Hatboro, PA 19040-3430
Tel (215) 734-1400 *Founded/Ownrshp* 2005
Sales 159.3MM[E] *EMP* 200[E]
SIC 4959 Environmental cleanup services
CEO: Chris Dods
**Ex VP:* Steven C Sands
Sr VP: Michael B Goebner

D-U-N-S 85-858-1903
■ **CLEAN EARTH INC**
(*Suby of* CEI HOLDING CO) ★
334 S Warminster Rd, Hatboro, PA 19040-3430
Tel (215) 734-1400 *Founded/Ownrshp* 1990
Sales 159.3MM[E] *EMP* 195[E]
Accts Kpmg Albany Ny
SIC 4959 Environmental cleanup services
CEO: Chris Dods
CFO: Bernard Guerin
Ex VP: Steven C Sands
Sr VP: Michael B Goebner
Sr VP: Michael B Goener
VP: James F Hull
VP: James Hull
VP: Averil Rance
Rgnl Mgr: Rich Crawford
Genl Mgr: Steve Donovan
Genl Mgr: John Eshelman

D-U-N-S 96-830-1320
■ **CLEAN ENERGY**
(*Suby of* CLEAN ENERGY FUELS CORP) ★
4675 Macarthur Ct Ste 800, Newport Beach, CA 92660-1895
Tel (949) 437-1000 *Founded/Ownrshp* 1996
Sales 354.5MM[E] *EMP* 1,000
SIC 4924 Natural gas distribution
Pr: Andrew Littlefair
**COO:* Mitchell Pratt
**CFO:* Robert Vreeland

D-U-N-S 04-375-7348 IMP
▲ **CLEAN ENERGY FUELS CORP**
4675 Macarthur Ct Ste 800, Newport Beach, CA 92660-1895
Tel (949) 437-1000 *Founded/Ownrshp* 2001
Sales 384.3MM *EMP* 1,084[E]

Tkr Sym CLNE *Exch* NGS
SIC 4924 4922 Natural gas distribution; Natural gas transmission
Pr: Andrew J Littlefair
**Ch Bd:* Warren I Mitchell
**COO:* Mitchell W Pratt
**CFO:* Robert M Vreeland
Chf Mktg O: James Harger
**Sr VP:* Barclay F Corbus
**Sr VP:* Peter J Grace
VP: Patrick Deville
VP: Dennis C Ding
VP: Howard Harris
VP: Marc Klein
VP: Brett Lindsay
VP: Steve McCarthy
VP: Arnie Nance
VP: Ken Nicholson
VP: Brian Powers
VP: Richard Remillard
VP: Stephen Smith
Board of Directors: John S Herrington, James C Miller III, James E O'connor, Boone Pickens, Stephen A Scully, Kenneth M Socha, Vincent C Taormina

D-U-N-S 03-932-2250 IMP/EXP
■ CLEAN HARBORS ENVIRONMENTAL SERVICES INC
(*Suby of* CLEAN HARBORS INC) ★
42 Longwater Dr, Norwell, MA 02061-1612
Tel (781) 792-5000 *Founded/Ownrshp* 1980
Sales 759.2MM^E *EMP* 3,001
SIC 4953 Hazardous waste collection & disposal
CEO: Alan S McKim
Pr: Mark Mooney
**Pr:* James M Rutledge
Sr VP: Kent Bartley
Sr VP: William Connors
VP: Paul Bratti
VP: Jim Buckley
VP: Bill Conner
Dir IT: Jack Iarusso
IT Man: Joseph McNally

D-U-N-S 15-779-3639 IMP
▲ CLEAN HARBORS INC
42 Longwater Dr, Norwell, MA 02061-1612
Tel (781) 792-5000 *Founded/Ownrshp* 1980
Sales 3.2MMM *EMP* 12,900
Tkr Sym CLH *Exch* NYS
SIC 4953 Hazardous waste collection & disposal; Refuse collection & disposal services; Garbage: collecting, destroying & processing; Recycling, waste materials
Ch Bd: Alan S McKim
V Ch: James M Rutledge
COO: Eric W Gerstenberg
CFO: Michael Battles
Treas: Mike Foley
Ofcr: Ken Shackleton
Ex VP: Christopher Catarella
Ex VP: George Curtis
Ex VP: Dave Eckelbarger
Ex VP: Cookson Eugene
Ex VP: Eric A Kraus
Ex VP: Eric Lindgren
Ex VP: Michael J Twohig
Ex VP: Brian P Weber
Sr VP: Jim Buckley
Sr VP: John Lawton
VP: Herve Bailey
VP: Josh Baker
VP: John Beals
VP: Victor Belenchia
VP: Anthony Cellucci
Board of Directors: Lauren C States, Eugene Banucci, John P Devillars, Edward G Galante, Rod Marlin, Daniel J McCarthy, John T Preston, Andrea Robertson, Thomas J Shields, John R Welch

D-U-N-S 00-723-6375 IMP
CLEAN HARBORS WICHITA LLC
UNIVERSAL LUBRICANTS, LLC
(*Suby of* UNIVERSAL COMPANIES INC) ★
2824 N Ohio St, Wichita, KS 67219-4319
Tel (316) 832-0151 *Founded/Ownrshp* 1966
Sales 123.8MM^E *EMP* 220
SIC 2992 5169 5172 Oils & greases, blending & compounding; Anti-freeze compounds; Lubricating oils & greases
VP: Ron Brazell
VP: Ned Murray

D-U-N-S 06-350-7933
CLEAN POWER LLC
(*Suby of* MARSDEN HOLDING LLC) ★
124 N 121st St, Milwaukee, WI 53226-3802
Tel (414) 302-3000 *Founded/Ownrshp* 2002
Sales 60.0MM^E *EMP* 2,200
SIC 7349 7217 Janitorial service, contract basis; Carpet & upholstery cleaning on customer premises
Pr: Jeffrey Packee
**Sr VP:* Barb Whitstone
VP: Rick Harrington
VP: Mike Stollenwerk
Dir Bus: Patty Hendrickson
Brnch Mgr: Dave Gollata

D-U-N-S 08-563-4335 IMP/EXP
CLEAN VENTURE INC
C V I
201 S 1st St, Elizabeth, NJ 07206-1502
Tel (908) 355-5800 *Founded/Ownrshp* 2015
Sales 109.8MM^E *EMP* 400
SIC 4225 4212 4953 8748 General warehousing & storage; Hazardous waste transport; Non-hazardous waste disposal sites; Environmental consultant
Pr: Michael Persico
COO: Debbie Scerbo
Genl Mgr: Steve Ganley
Opers Mgr: Mike Connolly

D-U-N-S 07-574-1181
CLEAN WATER SERVICES
2550 Sw Hillsboro Hwy, Hillsboro, OR 97123-9379
Tel (503) 681-3600 *Founded/Ownrshp* 1970
Sales 231.9MM^E *EMP* 285
SIC 4952 Sewerage systems
Genl Mgr: Bill Gaffi

COO: Brad Malatesta
VP: Mike McGough
Prgrm Mgr: Rich Hunter
Genl Mgr: Kathleen Leader
Genl Mgr: Geoff Reece
IT Man: Dave Cebula
IT Man: Marc Franck

D-U-N-S 92-665-1308
CLEANING SERVICE GROUP INC
C S G
230 North St, Danvers, MA 01923-1279
Tel (978) 750-8900 *Founded/Ownrshp* 1992
Sales 82.8MM^E *EMP* 3,000
SIC 7349 Building maintenance services
CEO: Rochelle O'Brien
**Pr:* Dennis O'Brien
VP Opers: Tom Rhodes

CLEANWISE
See NETWORK ASSOCIATES INC

CLEAR CHANNEL
See JACOR BROADCASTING OF COLORADO INC

D-U-N-S 60-940-2339
■ CLEAR CHANNEL OUTDOOR HOLDINGS INC
(*Suby of* IHEARTCOMMUNICATIONS INC) ★
200 E Basse Rd Ste 100, San Antonio, TX 78209-4490
Tel (210) 832-3700 *Founded/Ownrshp* 2005
Sales 2.8MMM *EMP* 6,000^E
Tkr Sym CCO *Exch* NYS
SIC 7312 7999 Outdoor advertising services; Bicycle rental
Ch Bd: Robert W Pittman
CEO: C William Eccleshare
CEO: Scott R Wells
CFO: Richard J Bressler
Ex VP: Christian Aaselund
Ex VP: Robert H Walls Jr
Sr VP: Scott D Hamilton
Sr VP: Steven J Macri
VP: Michael Barbaro
VP: John Callari
VP: Greg Foster
VP: Michael Overbo
VP: John Peake
VP: Tony Sawyer
Board of Directors: Blair E Hendrix, Douglas L Jacobs, Daniel G Jones, Vicente Piedrahita, Olivia Sabine, Thomas R Shepherd, Christopher M Temple, Dale W Tremblay

D-U-N-S 94-549-4359
■ CLEAR CHANNEL OUTDOOR INC
CLEAR CHANNEL OUTDOOR N AMER
(*Suby of* IHEARTCOMMUNICATIONS INC) ★
2325 E Camelback Rd # 400, Phoenix, AZ 85016-3514
Tel (602) 381-5700 *Founded/Ownrshp* 1997
Sales 10.1MM^E *EMP* 1,232
SIC 7312 Outdoor advertising services; Billboard advertising
CEO: William Eccleshare
**Pr:* Suzanne Grimes
**CFO:* Renee Krug
Chf Mktg O: Dan Levi
**Ex VP:* Christian Aaselund
**Ex VP:* Sara Lee Keller
Ex VP: Toby Sturek
Sr VP: Herbert W Hill
Sr VP: Orlando Ortiz
VP: Sean McCaffrey
Mng Dir: Greg Forster

CLEAR CHANNEL OUTDOOR N AMER
See CLEAR CHANNEL OUTDOOR INC

CLEAR CHOICE
See MARS 2000 INC

D-U-N-S 08-836-6125
CLEAR CREEK INDEPENDENT SCHOOL DISTRICT
CLEAR CREEK INTERMEDIATE SCHL
2425 E Main St, League City, TX 77573-2743
Tel (281) 284-0000 *Founded/Ownrshp* 1948
Sales 202.5MM^E *EMP* 3,250
Accts Null-Lairson Pc Texas City
SIC 8211 Public junior high school
Pr: Lauren M Tragni
Bd of Dir: Dee Scott
VP: Ken Baliker
VP: Ann Hammond
VP: Candis Price
Dir Sec: Erich Kreiter
Rgnl Mgr: Felicia Sharp
Store Mgr: Stefani Toungate
Manager: Carol Neuszer
Schl Brd P: Win Weber
Instr Medi: Sue Ferrell

CLEAR CREEK INTERMEDIATE SCHL
See CLEAR CREEK INDEPENDENT SCHOOL DISTRICT

D-U-N-S 07-885-2888
CLEAR GROUP LLC
FIREHOUSE SUBS OF CONYERS
90 Summer Walk Ct, Covington, GA 30016-8828
Tel (404) 403-0274 *Founded/Ownrshp* 2013
Sales 85.0MM *EMP* 25
SIC 5812 Sandwiches & submarines shop

D-U-N-S 79-084-7636
■ CLEAR LAKE REGIONAL MEDICAL CENTER INC
(*Suby of* HCA HOLDINGS INC) ★
500 W Medical Center Blvd, Webster, TX 77598-4220
Tel (713) 371-5000 *Founded/Ownrshp* 1994
Sales 469.3MM *EMP* 720^E
SIC 8062 General medical & surgical hospitals
CEO: Michael Roussos
MIS Dir: Ley Sampson
Telecom Mg: Chris Iguess
Surgeon: Richard P Cochran
Ansthlgy: Chung Y Kim
Diag Rad: John Hyun

D-U-N-S 04-895-0216 IMP
CLEAR LAM PACKAGING INC
1950 Pratt Blvd, Elk Grove Village, IL 60007-5993
Tel (847) 439-8570 *Founded/Ownrshp* 1969
Sales 167.9MM^E *EMP* 400^E
SIC 2671 Packaging paper & plastics film, coated & laminated
Pr: James Sanfilippo
Pr: Eileen Williams
**CFO:* Thomas Caulfield
VP: Louis Belmont
Software D: Hina Patel
Sls Dir: John Oviatt
Sls Mgr: John Mahr

CLEAR MTN NATURAL SPRING WTR
See MOUNTAIN VALLEY SPRING CO LLC

D-U-N-S 04-283-4200 IMP
CLEAR SPRINGS FOODS INC
4424 N 1500 E, Buhl, ID 83316-5247
Tel (208) 543-4316 *Founded/Ownrshp* 1966
Sales 117.2MM^E *EMP* 350
SIC 0273 2048 Trout farm; Prepared feeds
Pr: Larry Cope
**CFO:* Keith Quigley
**VP:* Cally Grindstaff
IT Man: Mavis Easterday
IT Man: Ryan Jund
**S&M/VP:* Don Riffle
Mktg Dir: Jessica Henry

D-U-N-S 83-035-0851 EXP
■ CLEAR WIRELESS LLC
(*Suby of* CLEARWIRE CORP) ★
1475 120th Ave Ne, Bellevue, WA 98005-2127
Tel (425) 216-7974 *Founded/Ownrshp* 2009
Sales 115.3MM^E *EMP* 900
SIC 4813 Telephone communication, except radio
Sr VP: Hope Cochran
**CFO:* David Sach

D-U-N-S 15-719-2803
CLEARCAPITAL.COM INC
REO NETWORK
300 E 2nd St Ste 1405, Reno, NV 89501-1508
Tel (775) 470-5656 *Founded/Ownrshp* 2001
Sales 143.5MM^E *EMP* 400
SIC 6531 Appraiser, real estate
CEO: Duane Andrews
**Pr:* Kevin Marshall
**CFO:* Gabe Nacht
Ex VP: Mike Ousley
VP: Shane Brentham
VP: Richard Clements

D-U-N-S 01-475-9873
CLEARESULT CONSULTING INC
(*Suby of* CRCI HOLDINGS INC) ★
4301 Westbank Dr Ste A250, Austin, TX 78746-4499
Tel (512) 327-9200 *Founded/Ownrshp* 2003
Sales 363.8MM^E *EMP* 962
SIC 8748 Business consulting
Pr: Aziz Virani
**COO:* Gino Torazzo
**CFO:* Benjamin Loranger
CFO: David Mehok
**Sec:* Billy E Garland
VP: Lisa Wojcicki
Board of Directors: Michael Chesser

CLEARING HOUSE, THE
See CLEARING HOUSE PAYMENTS CO L L C

D-U-N-S 07-771-4244
CLEARING HOUSE PAYMENTS CO L L C
CLEARING HOUSE, THE
1114 Avenue Of The Americ, New York, NY 10036-7772
Tel (212) 612-9200 *Founded/Ownrshp* 1853, 2008
Sales NA *EMP* 200
SIC 6099 Clearinghouse associations, bank or check
Pr: Erica Hurtt
Ex VP: Russell Fitzgibbons
Sr VP: Sujit Chakravorti
Sr VP: Jill Hershey
Sr VP: Sean Oblack
Sr VP: Parthiv Shah
Sr VP: Darrell Walsh
Sr VP: Henry Wysocki
VP: Rodney Abele
VP: Hilary Arden
VP: Maddy Fiorillo
VP: Mark Fitlin
VP: Jeffrey Joyce
VP: Susan Long
VP: Jim McDade
VP: Daniel Pokidaylo
VP: Arthur Rosenberg
VP: Jason Tornow
Dir Risk M: Alex Romeo

D-U-N-S 96-614-4961
CLEARLAKE CAPITAL GROUP LP
233 Wilshire Blvd Ste 800, Santa Monica, CA 90401-1207
Tel (310) 400-8800 *Founded/Ownrshp* 2007
Sales 776.1MM^E *EMP* 3,408
SIC 6799 Investors
Pt: Behdad Eghbali
Pt: Jose Feliciano
VP: James Pade
Genl Couns: Gretchen Arensdorf
Genl Couns: Fred Ebrahemi

D-U-N-S 79-115-2411 IMP
CLEARPATH SOLUTIONS GROUP LLC
12100 Sunset Hills Rd # 610, Reston, VA 20190-3295
Tel (703) 673-9370 *Founded/Ownrshp* 2006
Sales 123.4MM^E *EMP* 48
SIC 5045 Computers
Pr: Gary Vaughan
**Ex VP:* Nathan Reynolds
VP: Matt Smith
Snr Ntwrk: Bill Thompson
Sls Dir: Reggie Gaither
Sls Dir: Michael Nagao
Sls Dir: Dave Westervelt

D-U-N-S 08-044-4419
CLEARPEO LLC
2080 Cabot Blvd W Ste 202, Langhorne, PA 19047-1813
Tel (215) 701-9400 *Founded/Ownrshp* 2015
Sales 6.8MM^E *EMP* 1,700
SIC 7363 Employee leasing service
Prin: Joe Carfagno
CFO: Art Felderstein
VP Opers: Jim Hahl

CLEARSPAN
See ENGINEERING SERVICES & PRODUCTS CO

D-U-N-S 01-395-5914
CLEARSTAFF INC (IL)
7501 Lemont Rd Ste 220, Woodridge, IL 60517-2679
Tel (630) 985-0100 *Founded/Ownrshp* 1997
Sales 103.8MM^E *EMP* 11,500
SIC 7363 Temporary help service
Pr: Richard C Seeman

D-U-N-S 03-657-4320
CLEARVIEW CAPITAL LLC
1010 Washington Blvd # 1, Stamford, CT 06901-2208
Tel (203) 698-2777 *Founded/Ownrshp* 1999
Sales 204.4MM^E *EMP* 1,870
SIC 6799 Venture capital companies
Mng Pt: James G Andersen
**Pt:* Paul M Caliento
**Pt:* William F Case Jr
**Pt:* H F Doolittle
Pt: Harold F Doolittle
**Mng Pt:* Calvin A Neider

D-U-N-S 92-949-7303
CLEARVIEW CINEMA GROUP INC
CLEARVIEW CINEMAS
(*Suby of* CABLEVISION) ★
97 Main St Ste A, Chatham, NJ 07928-2429
Tel (973) 377-4646 *Founded/Ownrshp* 1998
Sales 35.7MM^E *EMP* 1,000
SIC 7832 Motion picture theaters, except drive-in
Pr: Chuck Goldwater

CLEARVIEW CINEMAS
See CCG HOLDINGS LLC

CLEARVIEW CINEMAS
See CLEARVIEW CINEMA GROUP INC

D-U-N-S 09-542-1959
CLEARWATER ENTERPRISES LLC
5637 N Classen Blvd, Oklahoma City, OK 73118-4015
Tel (405) 842-9200 *Founded/Ownrshp* 1999
Sales 198.9MM *EMP* 17
Accts Hogan Taylor Llp Oklahoma Ci
SIC 4924 Natural gas distribution
COO: Lisa Owens
VP: Koray Bakir

D-U-N-S 78-243-7318 IMP/EXP
▲ CLEARWATER PAPER CORP
601 W Riverside Ave # 1100, Spokane, WA 99201-0644
Tel (509) 344-5900 *Founded/Ownrshp* 2005
Sales 1.7MMM *EMP* 3,300^E
Tkr Sym CLW *Exch* NYS
SIC 2621 2631 Paper mills; Paperboard mills
Pr: Linda K Massman
**Ch Bd:* Boh A Dickey
Pr: Patrick T Burke
Pr: Thomas A Colgrove
CFO: John D Hertz
Treas: Douglas D Speddon
Sr VP: Michael S Gadd
Sr VP: Kari G Moyes
VP: Jason Roggenbauer
CIO: David Edwards
Sfty Mgr: Paul Scheel
Board of Directors: Fredric W Corrigan, Beth E Ford, Kevin J Hunt, William D Larsson, John P O'donnell, Alexander Toeldte

CLEARWATER PAPER-NEENAH
See CELLUTISSUE CORP-NEENAH

CLEARWAY AUTO PARTS
See PARTS AUTHORITY INC

D-U-N-S 14-451-3400 IMP
■ CLEARWIRE CORP
(*Suby of* SPRINT COMMUNICATIONS INC) ★
6200 Sprint Pkwy, Overland Park, KS 66251-6117
Tel (425) 216-7600 *Founded/Ownrshp* 2013
Sales 214.6MM^E *EMP* 952
SIC 4813
Ch Bd: John W Stanton
Pr: Teresa Elder
Pr: Erik E Prusch
CFO: Hope F Cochran
Sr VP: Broady R Hodder
Sr VP: John C B Saw
Prgrm Mgr: Gail Allen
Genl Mgr: Jake McCabe
CTO: Rob Mechaley
Sys Mgr: Jeffrey Kelly
Mktg Mgr: Jeff Hall

D-U-N-S 83-289-7099
CLEARWIRE INC
1490 Holly Dr, Tracy, CA 95376-3157
Tel (408) 794-8220 *Founded/Ownrshp* 2009
Sales 300.0MM *EMP* 10
SIC 8999 Actuarial consultant
Pr: Luis O Franco

D-U-N-S 08-669-4056
CLEARY BUILDING CORP
190 Paoli St, Verona, WI 53593-1809
Tel (608) 845-9700 *Founded/Ownrshp* 1978
Sales 131.7MM *EMP* 900
Accts Baker Tilly Cpas
SIC 1541 3448 Prefabricated building erection, industrial; Prefabricated metal buildings; Farm & utility buildings
Pr: Sean Cleary
**Ch Bd:* Thomas J Cleary
VP: Roger Solberg
Brnch Mgr: Brandon Abel
Brnch Mgr: Chris Baker

Brnch Mgr: Gary Durell
Brnch Mgr: Randy George
Brnch Mgr: Terry Hansen
Brnch Mgr: Nic Herron
Brnch Mgr: Travis Leeser
IT Man: Charlie Hillebrand

D-U-N-S 07-101-3270
CLEARY GOTTLIEB STEEN & HAMILTON LLP
ONE LIBERTY PLAZA
1 Liberty Plz Fl 43, New York, NY 10006-1414
Tel (212) 225-2000 *Founded/Ownrshp* 1946
Sales 427.5MM^E *EMP* 2,200
SIC 8111 General practice law office
Mng Pt: Mark Leddy
Pt: William B McGurn
CFO: Ren E M Lercher
CFO: Renee M Lercher
Ex Dir: Kelly Stevens
CIO: Michael Lechner
Dir IT: Benet Oreilly
Dir IT: Michael Volkovitsch
Telecom Mg: Naj-Lah Toussaint
IT Man: Martin Gunter
IT Man: Diane Oropallo

CLEAVER-BROOKS DIV
See CLEAVER-BROOKS INC

D-U-N-S 00-608-3927 IMP/EXP
CLEAVER-BROOKS INC (GA)
CLEAVER-BROOKS DIV
(*Suby of* HARBOUR GROUP LTD) ★
221 Law St, Thomasville, GA 31792-5962
Tel (229) 226-3024 *Founded/Ownrshp* 1931, 2012
Sales 555.7MM^E *EMP* 1,400
SIC 3589 3569 3561 3433 3443 Water treatment equipment, industrial; Generators: steam, liquid oxygen or nitrogen; Pumps & pumping equipment; Gas-oil burners, combination; Boilers: industrial, power, or marine
Pr: Bart A Aitken
**Pr:* Earle Pfefferkorn
**Pr:* Mike Valentino
**CFO:* John C Oakley
Sr VP: Paul M Anderson
Sr VP: Jim Lowell
VP: Mike Donahue
VP: Robert St-Denis
MIS Dir: Valerie Moskovich
Mfg Mgr: Craig Schlemmer
Plnt Mgr: Brad Shiell
Board of Directors: John Oakley

D-U-N-S 00-734-3809
CLEAVER-BROOKS SALES AND SERVICE INC
BOILER TUBES OF TEXAS
(*Suby of* CLEAVER-BROOKS DIV) ★
1956 Singleton Blvd, Dallas, TX 75212-3827
Tel (214) 637-0020 *Founded/Ownrshp* 2014
Sales 149.7MM^E *EMP* 180
SIC 5074 7699 1711 Boilers, power (industrial); Boiler & heating repair services; Boiler maintenance contractor; Boiler setting contractor
Pr: John M Marrinucci
Genl Mgr: John Adams
Genl Mgr: Demarcus Moore
Genl Mgr: Gary Persichini
IT Man: Karen Rivera
Sfty Dirs: Javier Casas

D-U-N-S 00-694-8178 IMP
CLECO CORPORATE HOLDINGS LLC (LA)
2030 Donahue Ferry Rd, Pineville, LA 71360-5226
Tel (318) 484-7400 *Founded/Ownrshp* 1998, 2016
Sales 1.2MMM *EMP* 1,207^E
Accts Deloitte & Touche Llp New Orl
SIC 4911 Generation, electric power; Transmission, electric power; Distribution, electric power
CEO: Darren J Olagues
Pr: George Bausewine
COO: Samuel H Charlton
CFO: Terry L Taylor
Bd of Dir: Michael Madison
Sr VP: Julia E Callis
Sr VP: Keith D Crump
Sr VP: William G Fontenot
VP: Keith Johnson
Prgrm Mgr: Bud Frederick
Dist Mgr: Danny Schaus

D-U-N-S 08-024-0892
CLECO PARTNERS LP
2030 Donahue Ferry Rd, Pineville, LA 71360-5226
Tel (318) 484-7400 *Founded/Ownrshp* 2014
Sales 111.9MM^E *EMP* 1,207
SIC 4911 Generation, electric power; Transmission, electric power; Distribution, electric power

D-U-N-S 03-955-8619 IMP
CLECO POWER LLC
(*Suby of* CLECO CORPORATE HOLDINGS LLC) ★
2030 Donahue Ferry Rd, Pineville, LA 71360-5226
Tel (318) 484-7400 *Founded/Ownrshp* 1935
Sales 1.2MMM *EMP* 1,208^E
SIC 4911 Distribution, electric power; Generation, electric power; Transmission, electric power
CEO: Bruce A Williamson
CFO: Thomas R Miller
IT Man: Micah Burnette

D-U-N-S 11-899-6037 EXP
CLEMENS FAMILY CORP
2700 Clemens Rd, Hatfield, PA 19440-4202
Tel (800) 523-5291 *Founded/Ownrshp* 1895
Sales 784.1MM^E *EMP* 2,100
SIC 0213 2011 4222 8661 Hogs; Meat packing plants; Warehousing, cold storage or refrigerated; Religious organizations
CEO: Douglas C Clemens
CFO: Craig Edsill
**Prin:* David W Budnick
**Prin:* Philip E Keeler
**Prin:* James B Wood
Ex Dir: George Wean
Mktg Mgr: Thomas Ryan

D-U-N-S 00-235-6632 IMP/EXP
CLEMENS FOOD GROUP LLC (PA)
(*Suby of* CLEMENS FAMILY CORP) ★
2700 Clemens Rd, Hatfield, PA 19440-4202
Tel (215) 368-2500 *Founded/Ownrshp* 1895, 1946
Sales 397.5MM^E *EMP* 1,800
SIC 2011 2013 Pork products from pork slaughtered on site; Sausages & other prepared meats
Ch Bd: Philip A Clemens
**Pr:* Craig H Edsill
**CEO:* Douglas Clemens
**CFO:* David W Budnick
Bd of Dir: James S Herr
Sr VP: David Koleskey
Sr VP: Bob Ruth
**VP:* Kevin Kratz
VP: Tim Martin
Exec: Michelle Alldred
Exec: Wilma Keller
Board of Directors: Rodney Brenneman, James M Herr, Donald Hunt, Frederick W Mc Brien III, Merrill S Moyer, Anthony Schiano, Dr Charles Zimmerman

D-U-N-S 04-262-9816 IMP
CLEMSON UNIVERSITY (SC)
201 Sikes Ave, Clemson, SC 29631-2177
Tel (864) 656-6182 *Founded/Ownrshp* 1893
Sales 700.8MM *EMP* 4,735
SIC 8221

CLERK'S OFFICE
See COUNTY OF SUFFOLK

CLERMONT MERCY HOSPITAL
See SISTERS OF MERCY OF CLERMONT COUNTY OHIO INC

D-U-N-S 07-908-4803
CLERMONT MOTOR SALES LLC (FL)
TOYOTA OF CLERMONT
16851 State Road 50, Clermont, FL 34711-5963
Tel (352) 404-7006 *Founded/Ownrshp* 2005
Sales 150.0MM *EMP* 165
SIC 7549 Automotive maintenance services
CEO: Joseph A Siviglia
Pr: Gregory J Michelsen
Treas: Franklin W Wilson
VP: Jordan A Siviglia

D-U-N-S 00-791-1191 IMP/EXP
CLEVELAND BROTHERS EQUIPMENT CO INC
(*Suby of* CLEVELAND BROTHERS HOLDINGS INC) ★
4565 William Penn Hwy, Murrysville, PA 15668-2003
Tel (724) 325-9421 *Founded/Ownrshp* 1948
Sales 683.1MM^E *EMP* 1,300
SIC 5082 Construction & mining machinery; Tractors, construction; Graders, motor; Excavating machinery & equipment
Pr: Jay W Cleveland Jr
COO: Tom Kirchhoff Jr
**COO:* W Thomas T Kirchhoff Jr
**CFO:* Joseph J Lundy
Treas: William T Kirchhoff Jr
**VP:* Bob Fredrickson
Dir IT: Tony Dills
MIS Mgr: Barbara Lavelle

D-U-N-S 60-937-7036
CLEVELAND BROTHERS HOLDINGS INC
5300 Paxton St, Harrisburg, PA 17111-2525
Tel (717) 564-2121 *Founded/Ownrshp* 2005
Sales 925.1MM^E *EMP* 1,501^E
SIC 7353 5082 5084 7629 Heavy construction equipment rental; Front end loaders; Road construction & maintenance machinery; Tractors, construction; Excavating machinery & equipment; Industrial machinery & equipment; Electrical repair shops
CEO: Jay Cleveland Jr
COO: Tom Kirchhoff Jr
**COO:* Thomas Kirchhoss
VP: Patricia Hays

D-U-N-S 00-333-6872 IMP
CLEVELAND CHAIR CO INC
CATNAPPER
370 9th St Se, Cleveland, TN 37311-2750
Tel (423) 476-8544 *Founded/Ownrshp* 1914
Sales 76.2MM^E *EMP* 1,200
SIC 2512 Chairs: upholstered on wood frames; Rockers: upholstered on wood frames; Recliners: upholstered on wood frames; Living room furniture: upholstered on wood frames
Ch Bd: William R Jackson
DP Dir: Anthony Bartolo

D-U-N-S 18-791-6804
CLEVELAND CLINIC FLORIDA FOUNDATION
3100 Weston Rd, Weston, FL 33331-3602
Tel (954) 689-5000 *Founded/Ownrshp* 1990
Sales 112.6MM^E *EMP* 1,185
SIC 8062 General medical & surgical hospitals
CEO: Bernardo Fernandez
COO: Chantel L Conte
**COO:* Chantel Le Conte
**CFO:* David Pettit
Dir Sec: Annette Gadus
Opthamlgy: David G Hardy

D-U-N-S 01-773-0458 IMP
CLEVELAND CLINIC FOUNDATION
CLEVELAND CLINIC HEALTH SYSTEM
9500 Euclid Ave, Cleveland, OH 44195-0002
Tel (216) 636-8335 *Founded/Ownrshp* 1921
Sales 4.2MMM *EMP* 44,000
SIC 8062 8011 8741 General medical & surgical hospitals; Medical centers; Management services
CEO: Delos M Cosgrove
COO: Williams Peacock
CFO: Steve Glass
CFO: Steven C Glass
CFO: Jennifer Lasher
Ofcr: David W Rowan
VP: Bob Frye
VP: William Riebel
VP: Brian Tilow
Dir Surg: Jason Hergenroder
Dir Rad: Abraham Levitin

CLEVELAND CLINIC HEALTH SYSTEM
See CLEVELAND CLINIC FOUNDATION

CLEVELAND CLINIC HEALTH SYSTEM
See EUCLID HOSPITAL

CLEVELAND CLINIC HEALTH SYSTEM
See FAIRVIEW HOSPITAL

CLEVELAND CLINIC HEALTH SYSTEM
See LAKEWOOD HOSPITAL ASSOCIATION

D-U-N-S 15-134-0759
CLEVELAND CLINIC HEALTH SYSTEM-WESTERN REGION
(*Suby of* CLEVELAND CLINIC HEALTH SYSTEM) ★
18101 Lorain Ave, Cleveland, OH 44111-5612
Tel (216) 476-7000 *Founded/Ownrshp* 1983
Sales 90.6MM^E *EMP* 3,500
SIC 8741 Hospital management
CEO: Fred M Degrandis
Nurse Mgr: Donna Rittenberger
Sys Mgr: Scot Linton

D-U-N-S 03-537-8520 IMP
CLEVELAND CONSTRUCTION INC
CCI
8620 Tyler Blvd, Mentor, OH 44060-4348
Tel (513) 398-8900 *Founded/Ownrshp* 1980
Sales 517.3MM^E *EMP* 800
Accts Skoda Minoti Mayfield Village
SIC 1542 1742 1752 Commercial & office building contractors; Commercial & office building, new construction; Commercial & office buildings, renovation & repair; Specialized public building contractors; Plastering, plain or ornamental; Drywall; Insulation, buildings; Acoustical & ceiling work; Floor laying & floor work
Pr: Jon Small
**CFO:* Mark T Small
VP: Meghan Bracken
VP: George Gaharan
VP: Neal Keller
VP: Dave Kurilko
VP: Jack Quinif
VP: David Sawicki
**VP:* James Small
VP: Rhett Stayer
**VP:* Keith Ziegler

D-U-N-S 07-106-3994 IMP
CLEVELAND COUNTY HEALTHCARE SYSTEM
CLEVELAND REGIONAL MEDICAL CEN
201 E Grover St, Shelby, NC 28150-3917
Tel (900) 487-3000 *Founded/Ownrshp* 1929
Sales 173.5MM *EMP* 1,200
SIC 8062 8051 General medical & surgical hospitals; Skilled nursing care facilities
CEO: Bryan Gwyn
V Ch: Edward J Brown III
V Ch: William C Cannon Jr
V Ch: Malcolm E Everett III
**CFO:* Rose Coyne
**VP:* Sam Cooper
**VP:* Sherri Deshazo
VP: Angela Orsky
**VP:* Veronica Poole-Adams
**VP:* Daniel Sweat
IT Man: Teresa Bridges

D-U-N-S 06-952-6981
CLEVELAND COUNTY SCHOOLS
400 W Marion St, Shelby, NC 28150-5338
Tel (704) 476-8000 *Founded/Ownrshp* 1911
Sales 145.8MM *EMP* 2,600
Accts Dixon Hughes Goodman Llp Win
SIC 8211 Public elementary & secondary schools
Ofcr: Peggy Johnson
Ex Dir: Patti Norman
Genl Mgr: David Lee
MIS Dir: Mark Sothard
MIS Dir: Tim Wease
Dir IT: Robert McDaniel
VP Sls: Anecia Allen
Teacher Pr: Eric Lamanna
Psych: Stephanie Greene
Phys Thrpy: Sara Grant
HC Dir: Brian Hunnell

CLEVELAND ELECTRIC
See CLEVELAND GROUP INC

D-U-N-S 00-331-6403
CLEVELAND ELECTRIC CO INC (GA)
CLEVELAND MECHANICAL SERVICES
(*Suby of* CLEVELAND ELECTRIC) ★
1281 Fulton Indus Blvd Nw, Atlanta, GA 30336-1527
Tel (404) 696-4550 *Founded/Ownrshp* 1962
Sales 177.9MM *EMP* 1,000
Accts Windham Brannon Pc Atlanta
SIC 1731 1711 1796 General electrical contractor; Mechanical contractor; Installing building equipment
Pr: John R Cleveland
**CEO:* James R Cleveland Jr
**CFO:* Kenneth D Harbour
**VP:* Vann H Cleveland

D-U-N-S 00-790-0293
■ **CLEVELAND ELECTRIC ILLUMINATING CO** (OH)
(*Suby of* FIRSTENERGY CORP) ★
76 S Main St, Akron, OH 44308-1812
Tel (800) 589-3101 *Founded/Ownrshp* 1892
Sales 542.4MM^E *EMP* 897^E
Accts Pricewaterhousecoopers Llp Cl
SIC 4911 Generation, electric power; Transmission, electric power
Pr: John E Skory
CFO: Mark T Clark
Treas: J F Pearson
Ex VP: L L Vespoli
Ex VP: Leila Vespoli
VP: Harvey L Wagner
Board of Directors: Anthony J Alexander

D-U-N-S 07-778-0336
CLEVELAND FOUNDATION
1422 Euclid Ave Ste 1300, Cleveland, OH 44115-2063
Tel (216) 861-3810 *Founded/Ownrshp* 1914
Sales 87.1MM *EMP* 75
Accts Lb Ernst & Young Us Llp India
SIC 6732 Charitable trust management; Educational trust management
CEO: Ronald B Richard
COO: Sue Krey
**Ch:* Charles P Bolton
Ofcr: Brenda Cummins
**Ex VP:* Robert E Eckardt
Ex VP: Robert Eckardt
**Sr VP:* Kate A Asbeck
**Sr VP:* Kaye Ridolfi
VP: James E Bennett III
VP: Caprice Bragg
**VP:* Leslie A Dunford
Exec: Scott Tennant

D-U-N-S 03-351-6659 EXP
CLEVELAND GROUP INC
CLEVELAND ELECTRIC
1281 Fulton Indus Blvd Nw, Atlanta, GA 30336-1527
Tel (404) 696-4550 *Founded/Ownrshp* 1965
Sales 186.6MM *EMP* 1,000
Accts Windham Brannon Pc Atlanta
SIC 1731 8741 1711 Electrical work; Construction management; Mechanical contractor; Warm air heating & air conditioning contractor; Plumbing contractors
Pr: James R Cleveland Jr
**Treas:* Kenneth D Harbour
Bd of Dir: John R Cleveland
Bd of Dir: Louie W Cleveland Jr
**Bd of Dir:* Vann H Cleveland
Bd of Dir: Sidney Kirschner
Bd of Dir: Dennis M Love
Bd of Dir: Stephen E Raville
**VP:* John Cleveland
Exec: David Cleveland
IT Man: Rob Bullion

D-U-N-S 01-287-7747
CLEVELAND HEIGHTS BOARD OF EDUCATION
2155 Miramar Blvd, University Heights, OH 44118-3301
Tel (216) 371-7171 *Founded/Ownrshp* 2001
Sales 75.0MM *EMP* 1,200
SIC 8299 Educational services
CTO: Christine Fowler

D-U-N-S 07-691-1130
CLEVELAND HEIGHTS UNIVERSITY HEIGHTS CITY SCHOOLS
2155 Miramar Blvd, University Heights, OH 44118-3301
Tel (216) 371-7171 *Founded/Ownrshp* 1902
Sales 70.2MM^E *EMP* 1,200
SIC 8211 Public senior high school; Public junior high school; Public elementary school; Public special education school
CFO: Scott Gainer
Dir IT: Donald Phillips
Sfty Dirs: Bryan Loretz
Schl Brd P: Ronald Register
Psych: Cheryl Zawacki

D-U-N-S 96-798-0181
CLEVELAND INTEGRITY SERVICES INC ★
(*Suby of* APPLIED-CLEVELAND HOLDINGS INC) ★
370669 E Old Highway 64, Cleveland, OK 74020-5702
Tel (918) 358-5735 *Founded/Ownrshp* 2010
Sales 91.9MM^E *EMP* 1,400
SIC 7389 Pipeline & power line inspection service
Pr: Randy Byers
**CFO:* Michael Frye
**Sr VP:* Jae Song
**VP:* Matt Kesmer
Off Mgr: Thomas Dawson

CLEVELAND MECHANICAL SERVICES
See CLEVELAND ELECTRIC CO INC

CLEVELAND METRO SCHL DST
See CLEVELAND MUNICIPAL SCHOOL DISTRICT

D-U-N-S 07-313-2045
CLEVELAND MUNICIPAL SCHOOL DISTRICT (OH)
CLEVELAND METRO SCHL DST
1111 Superior Ave E # 1800, Cleveland, OH 44114-2500
Tel (216) 838-0000 *Founded/Ownrshp* 2012
Sales 636.1MM^E *EMP* 9,500
Accts Dave Yost-Auditor Of State Cl
SIC 8211 8399 Public elementary & secondary schools; Advocacy group
CEO: Eric Gordon
**Ch Bd:* Denise W Link
**COO:* Patrick Zohn
**CFO:* John Scanlan
Ex Dir: Victoria Brian
Ex Dir: Lisa Durkin
**Ex Dir:* Megan Obryan
Ex Dir: Leo Serrano
Ex Dir: Joseph Vaughn
Prgrm Mgr: Timothy Glover
Off Mgr: Marcia Zashin

CLEVELAND REGIONAL MEDICAL CEN
See CLEVELAND COUNTY HEALTHCARE SYSTEM

D-U-N-S 01-084-1617
CLEVELAND STATE UNIVERSITY
C S U
2121 Euclid Ave, Cleveland, OH 44115-2226
Tel (216) 687-2000 *Founded/Ownrshp* 1965
Sales 251.1MM^E *EMP* 2,600
Accts Plante & Moran Pllc Toledo
SIC 8221 University
CEO: Lee Fisher
Pr: Shannon G Milliken
**CEO:* Ronald Berkman
Trst: Imaan Benmerzouga
Trst: Sally Florkiewicz
Trst: Marvin A McMickle

Trst: Samuel H Miller
Trst: Heidi Vielhabe
Trst: Ernest L Wilkerson Jr
Ofcr: Leigh Archibald
Ofcr: Thomas Lear
VP: John Boyle
VP: Patrick Sweeney
VP: Byron White
Assoc Dir: Bonnie Kalnasy
Assoc Dir: Alice J Khol
Assoc Dir: Thomas L Tontimonia

D-U-N-S 00-452-5499 IMP/EXP
CLEVELAND STEEL CONTAINER CORP (OH)
30310 Emerald Valley Pkwy, Solon, OH 44139-4394
Tel (440) 349-8000 *Founded/Ownrshp* 1964
Sales 163.0MM[E] *EMP* 389
SIC 3412

D-U-N-S 79-912-7204
■ CLEVELAND SYSCO INC
(*Suby of* SYSCO CORP) ★
4747 Grayton Rd, Cleveland, OH 44135-2300
Tel (216) 201-3000 *Founded/Ownrshp* 1990
Sales 283.1MM[E] *EMP* 650
SIC 5149 Groceries & related products
CEO: Bill Delaney
Ex VP: Bill Day
**Sr VP:* Chuck Staes
VP: Rick Harper
Genl Mgr: Paul Zentner
IT Man: Angel L Gonzalez
Software D: Jeff Moore
S&M/VP: Mark Kleiman
Mktg Dir: Kevin McCardle

D-U-N-S 07-951-3262
■ CLEVELAND TENNESSEE HOSPITAL CO LLC
TENNOVA HEALTHCARE-CLEVELAND
(*Suby of* TENNOVA HEALTHCARE) ★
2305 Chambliss Ave Nw, Cleveland, TN 37311-3847
Tel (423) 559-6000 *Founded/Ownrshp* 2009
Sales 466.5M[E] *EMP* 2,500
SIC 8062 General medical & surgical hospitals
CEO: Coleman Foss
Netwrk Mgr: Dale Pruitt

D-U-N-S 07-160-8728
CLEVELAND WATER DEPARTMENT
5953 Deering Ave, Cleveland, OH 44130-2306
Tel (216) 664-3168 *Founded/Ownrshp* 2011
Sales 85.2MM[E] *EMP* 1,200
SIC 4941 Water supply
Prin: Dick Kmetz

CLH GROUP, THE
See APPAREL CONCEPTS INTERNATIONAL INC

CLI
See CAT LOGISTICS INC

D-U-N-S 96-509-4279
CLI HOLDINGS INC
3950 S 700 E Ste 301, Salt Lake City, UT 84107-1303
Tel (801) 262-3942 *Founded/Ownrshp* 1989
Sales 221.2MM[E] *EMP* 380
SIC 1411 Limestone, dimension-quarrying
Pr: William E Dodge

CLICK
See KRESS STORES OF PUERTO RICO INC

CLICK BANK
See CLICK SALES INC

CLICK NETWORK
See CITY OF TACOMA DEPARTMENT OF PUBLIC UTILITIES

D-U-N-S 16-315-2676
CLICK SALES INC
CLICK BANK
917 S Lusk St Ste 200, Boise, ID 83706-5444
Tel (208) 472-9400 *Founded/Ownrshp* 2004
Sales 250.0MM *EMP* 85
SIC 5734 Computer software & accessories
CEO: Ray Morris
**COO:* Tricia Phillips
**CFO:* Glenn Michael
**VP:* Corey Davis
**VP:* Jennifer Johannsen
**VP:* Jeffrey Leget
**Prin:* Brad Wiskirchen
Sftwr Eng: Robert Gonzales

D-U-N-S 86-885-0215
CLIENT NETWORK SERVICES INC
C N S I
2277 Research Blvd, Rockville, MD 20850-3224
Tel (301) 634-4600 *Founded/Ownrshp* 1994
Sales 160.2MM *EMP* 1,000
SIC 7371 7373 7379 Computer software development; Value-added resellers, computer systems; Computer related consulting services
CEO: Biswajeet Chatterjee
**Pr:* Adnan Ahmed
**COO:* Jaytee Kanwal
**CFO:* Lawrence Sinnott
Sr VP: Bruce Adams
VP: John H Cousins
VP: Shailesh Patel
VP Bus Dev: Chuck Hall
Snr Sftwr: Damodara Gottipalli
Snr Sftwr: Vinoth Sivaperumal
Snr Sftwr: Deo Swaroop

D-U-N-S 79-509-1289 IMP
CLIF BAR & CO
1451 66th St, Emeryville, CA 94608-1004
Tel (510) 596-6300 *Founded/Ownrshp* 1986
Sales 286.0MM[E] *EMP* 300[E]
SIC 2052 5149 Organic & diet foods
CEO: Kevin Cleary
CFO: Julie Sheu
**Co-Ch Bd:* Kit Crawford
Sr VP: Michelle Ferguson
VP: Brian Braden
CTO: Jennifer Herman
QA Dir: Connie Bell

Dir IT: Gary Hensly
IT Man: Sarah Wallace
Prd Mgr: Tom Venegas
Natl Sales: Patrick Kelly

D-U-N-S 07-130-3317 IMP/EXP
CLIFF BERRY INC (FL)
851 Eller Dr, Fort Lauderdale, FL 33316-3065
Tel (954) 763-3390 *Founded/Ownrshp* 1971
Sales 96.3MM[E] *EMP* 175
SIC 4953 4959 4212 2992 4491 Liquid waste, collection & disposal; Oil spill cleanup; Environmental cleanup services; Local trucking, without storage; Lubricating oils & greases; Marine cargo handling
Ch Bd: Cliff L Berry Sr
**Pr:* Cliff L Berry II
**VP:* Larry A Doyle

D-U-N-S 07-522-8056
CLIFFORD CHANCE US LLP
(*Suby of* CLIFFORD CHANCE LLP)
31 W 52nd St Fl 3, New York, NY 10019-6127
Tel (212) 878-8000 *Founded/Ownrshp* 1930
Sales 472.5MM[E] *EMP* 6,700
SIC 8111 General practice attorney, lawyer
Mng Pt: Craig Medwick
Sr Pt: Stuart Popham
Pt: Peter Avery
Pt: Manfred Benkert
Pt: William Blumenthal
Pt: David Dibari
Pt: Huw Jenkins
Pt: Tim Page
Pt: William E Wallace III
Mng Pt: Leiv Blad
Mng Pt: Daniel Harris
Mng Pt: Matthew Layton
Pr: Pilar Riera
Exec: Ignacio Ojanguren
Comm Dir: Allan Whitescarver
Dir Bus: Geraint Hughes

D-U-N-S 13-170-2490 IMP/EXP
CLIFFORD PAPER INC
MEDIA SOLUTIONS GROUP
600 E Crescent Ave # 301, Upper Saddle River, NJ 07458-1855
Tel (201) 934-5115 *Founded/Ownrshp* 1985
Sales 385.0MM *EMP* 75
SIC 5111 Fine paper
Pr: John Clifford
CFO: Brian O Sullivan
Ex VP: Craig Clifford
VP: Paul Clifford

CLIFFS
See NORTHSHORE MINING CO

D-U-N-S 05-271-9226
CLIFFS DRILLING CO (DE)
(*Suby of* TODCO) ★
14701 Saint Marys Ln, Houston, TX 77079-2921
Tel (281) 749-1000 *Founded/Ownrshp* 1978, 2001
Sales 25.8MM[E] *EMP* 1,572
SIC 1381 Directional drilling oil & gas wells
Ch Bd: Paul Loyd Jr
**Pr:* Andrew Bakoni
**VP:* Tim Nagle

D-U-N-S 14-796-4571
▲ CLIFFS NATURAL RESOURCES INC
200 Public Sq Ste 3300, Cleveland, OH 44114-2315
Tel (216) 694-5700 *Founded/Ownrshp* 1847
Sales 2.0MMM *EMP* 5,386
Tkr Sym CLF *Exch* NYS
SIC 1011 Iron ore mining; Iron ore pelletizing
Ch Bd: C Lourenco Goncalves
Ch Bd: Brian Baird
CFO: P Kelly Tompkins
Ex VP: Terry G Fedor
Ex VP: Maurice D Harapiak
Ex VP: Terrence R Mee
Ex VP: Clifford T Smith
VP: Dana Byrne
VP: Timothy K Flanagan
Genl Mgr: Kristy Dubitsky
CIO: Mike Moscarino
Board of Directors: John T Baldwin, Robert P Fisher Jr, Susan M Green, Joseph A Rutkowski Jr, Eric M Rychel, James S Sawyer, Michael D Siegal, Gabriel Stoliar, Douglas C Taylor

CLIFFS NORTH AMERICAN COAL LLC
See SENECA NORTH AMERICAN COAL LLC

D-U-N-S 00-954-9994 IMP/EXP
CLIFFSTAR LLC
COTT BEVERAGES
(*Suby of* COTT CORPORATION)
1 Cliffstar Dr, Dunkirk, NY 14048-2800
Tel (716) 366-6100 *Founded/Ownrshp* 2010
Sales 427.3MM[E] *EMP* 1,300
SIC 2033 2086 Fruit juices: fresh; Bottled & canned soft drinks; Pasteurized & mineral waters, bottled & canned
**CFO:* Chris Cronje
**Ex VP:* Monica Consonery
**Ex VP:* Kevin Sanvidge
**Ex VP:* Richard Star
VP: Mark Obrien
Exec: Jason Cockrane
**VP Admn:* Kevin M Sanvidge
CTO: William Henry
Dir IT: William Fedick
Mktg Dir: Becky Ostrye

D-U-N-S 06-079-8949
CLIFTON BOARD OF EDUCATION INC
745 Clifton Ave, Clifton, NJ 07013-1838
Tel (973) 470-2300 *Founded/Ownrshp* 1946
Sales 76.5MM[E] *EMP* 1,200
SIC 8211 8741 Public elementary & secondary schools; Management services
Pr: Gary Passenti
HC Dir: Carol Prawetz

CLIFTON SUPPLY COMPANY
See HOWARD SUPPLY CO LLC

D-U-N-S 07-763-3311
CLIFTONLARSONALLEN LLP
C L A
220 S 6th St Ste 300, Minneapolis, MN 55402-1418
Tel (612) 376-4620 *Founded/Ownrshp* 1953
Sales 598.7MM *EMP* 4,466
SIC 8742 7371 8721 Sales (including sales management) consultant; Planning consultant; Corporate objectives & policies consultant; Computer software development & applications; Certified public accountant
CEO: Dennis M Schleper
Mng Pt: Steve Debruyn
Mng Pt: Anita Ford
COO: Scott Engelbrecht
CFO: Heidi Hillman
Exec: Larry Keen
Mng Dir: Ed Morris
Dir Sec: John Richter
IT Man: Chad Kunze
Snr Mgr: Derek Floyd
Snr Mgr: Bethany Hearn

D-U-N-S 18-289-1523
■ CLIMATE MASTER INC
(*Suby of* LSB INDUSTRIES INC) ★
7300 Sw 44th St, Oklahoma City, OK 73179-4307
Tel (405) 745-6000 *Founded/Ownrshp* 1985
Sales 228.8MM[E] *EMP* 550
SIC 3585 Refrigeration & heating equipment; Heat pumps, electric
Pr: Dan Ellis
VP Opers: Mark Ellis
VP Sls: John Bailey

CLIMATEC BUILDING TECH GROUP
See CLIMATEC LLC

D-U-N-S 05-089-5015
CLIMATEC LLC
CLIMATEC BUILDING TECH GROUP
(*Suby of* AUTOMOTIVE GROUP) ★
2851 W Kathleen Rd, Phoenix, AZ 85053-4053
Tel (602) 944-3330 *Founded/Ownrshp* 2015
Sales 193.1MM[E] *EMP* 500[E]
SIC 1731 7373 Environmental system control installation; Energy management controls; Safety & security specialization; Office computer automation systems integration
Pr: Terry Keenen
Ofcr: Laura Papenhagen
Dir Bus: Ashley Cascio
Opers Mgr: Vince Scalise

D-U-N-S 82-948-6807
CLIMATEWORKS FOUNDATION
235 Montgomery St # 1300, San Francisco, CA 94104-2902
Tel (415) 433-0500 *Founded/Ownrshp* 2008
Sales 170.3MM *EMP* 1
Accts Grant Thornton Llp San Franci
SIC 8748 Energy conservation consultant
CEO: Julie Blunden
VP: Charles McElwee
Assoc Dir: Casey Cronin
Assoc Dir: Catherine Rondinaro
Pgrm Dir: Stephen Linaweaver

D-U-N-S 00-336-8123
CLIMATIC CORP (SC)
CLIMATIC HOME PRODUCTS
1074 Pinnacle Point Dr, Columbia, SC 29223-5735
Tel (803) 765-2595 *Founded/Ownrshp* 1956
Sales 183.9MM[E] *EMP* 140
SIC 5075 Warm air heating & air conditioning
CEO: John H Bailey
**Pr:* Willis G Bailey
Ofcr: Lynn Sprinkle
**Ex VP:* Cindee Bailey
Info Man: Robert Harden
S&M/VP: Craig Ellis
Sls Mgr: Doug Allen
Sls Mgr: Rusty Nix

CLIMATIC HOME PRODUCTS
See CLIMATIC CORP

D-U-N-S 18-403-8511 IMP/EXP
■ CLIMAX MOLYBDENUM MARKETING CORP
(*Suby of* FREEPORT MCMORAN) ★
333 N Central Ave Ste 100, Phoenix, AZ 85004-2100
Tel (602) 366-8100 *Founded/Ownrshp* 2000
Sales 426.1MM[E] *EMP* 1,000
SIC 1061 3313 Molybdenum ores mining; Molybdenum silicon, not made in blast furnaces
Pr: David H Thornton
**Pr:* Richard C Adkerson
**CEO:* Robert A Day
**CEO:* James R Moffett
Treas: Barbara Buck
**VP:* Barbara J Buck
**VP:* Fred J Menzer

D-U-N-S 09-592-9592
■ CLINCH VALLEY MEDICAL CENTER INC
(*Suby of* LIFEPOINT HEALTH INC) ★
6801 Gov Gc Peery Hwy, Richlands, VA 24641-2194
Tel (276) 596-6000 *Founded/Ownrshp* 1977
Sales 85.7MM *EMP* 715[E]
SIC 8062 General medical & surgical hospitals
CEO: Peter Mulkey
Ofcr: Tim Harclerod
QA Dir: Beth Stiltner
Sfty Dirs: Jeanna Lambert
Plnt Mgr: Robert Morrow
Obsttrcn: Tim A Presnell

D-U-N-S 02-376-2859
CLINE ENERGY INC
1890 S Main St, Harrisonburg, VA 22801-5723
Tel (540) 434-7344 *Founded/Ownrshp* 1987
Sales 85.0MM *EMP* 106
Accts Brown Edwards & Company Llp
SIC 5172 5541 1521 Petroleum products; Truck stops; New construction, single-family houses
Pr: Mike Davis

**Ex VP:* Rudy Propst
**VP:* Vernon Propst

D-U-N-S 07-528-6914
CLINICA SIERRA VISTA (CA)
LAMONT COMMUNITY HEALTH CENTER
1430 Truxtun Ave Ste 400, Bakersfield, CA 93301-5220
Tel (661) 635-3050 *Founded/Ownrshp* 1971
Sales 119.8MM *EMP* 910
Accts Oscar G Armijo Palm Desert
SIC 8011 Clinic, operated by physicians
Ch Bd: Matthew Clark
**CEO:* Stephen W Schilling
**COO:* Christine Goltz
**CFO:* Consuelo E Cantu
CFO: Consuelo Contu
CFO: Sybel Waiyaki
**Treas:* Roberto Rivera
CIO: Evelyn Evely
Dir IT: Ed Gordon
IT Man: Mary Dearkland
IT Man: Robert Tapia
Board of Directors: Matthew Clark

CLINICAL ASSESSMENT
See HARCOURT ASSESSMENT INC

D-U-N-S 84-899-8084
CLINICAL CARE ASSOCIATES OF UNIVERSITY OF PENNSYLVANIA HEALTH SYSTEM
2200 Renaissance Blvd # 320, King of Prussia, PA 19406-2755
Tel (800) 789-7366 *Founded/Ownrshp* 1994
Sales 55.2MM[E] *EMP* 1,125
SIC 8011 General & family practice, physician/surgeon
Ex Dir: Kevin B Mahoney
CFO: Joe Henney

D-U-N-S 78-874-4209 IMP
CLINICAL PATHOLOGY LABORATORIES INC
(*Suby of* SONIC HEALTHCARE USA INC) ★
9200 Wall St, Austin, TX 78754-4534
Tel (512) 339-1275 *Founded/Ownrshp* 2008
Sales 155.7MM[E] *EMP* 1,500
SIC 8071 Pathological laboratory; Blood analysis laboratory; Urinalysis laboratory
Ch Bd: Robert Connor MD
**Pr:* David Schultz
**Pr:* Stephen R Shumpert
**Ch:* Paul W Miller
**VP:* David W Bryant
VP: Tony Jones
**VP:* Barbara Nelson
Rgnl Mgr: Beverly Hood
Rgnl Mgr: Chris Hybart
Rgnl Mgr: Anthony Michael
Rgnl Mgr: Leah Nickell

D-U-N-S 12-477-8358
CLINICAL PRACTICE MANAGEMENT PLAN
C P M P
Suny At Stony Brk Hsc, Stony Brook, NY 11790
Tel (631) 444-2055 *Founded/Ownrshp* 1978
Sales 141.0MM *EMP* 970
SIC 8741 Management services
Ex Dir: Ellen Dank Cohen
**CFO:* Laurie Norwick
Top Exec: Mary C Chimato
Exec: Ajmal Farooq
Assoc Dir: Andrew White
Ex Dir: Ellen Cowen
CTO: Michael Kimmel
Web Dev: Paul Focazio
Secur Mgr: Philip Siebert

CLINICAL PRACTICES OF T
See TRUSTEES OF UNIVERSITY OF PENNSYLVANIA

D-U-N-S 78-634-7286
CLINICAL RESEARCH ADVANTAGE INC
COMPREHENSIVE CLINICAL DEV
2141 E Broadway Rd # 120, Tempe, AZ 85282-1895
Tel (480) 820-5656 *Founded/Ownrshp* 1989
Sales 123.8MM[E] *EMP* 652[E]
SIC 8731 Medical research, commercial
CEO: Mark Hanley
**Pr:* David Bruggeman
**CFO:* Craig J Smith
**VP:* Joanne Mashburn
CTO: Eric Levie

D-U-N-S 03-873-7201
CLINICAS DEL CAMINO REAL INC
200 S Wells Rd Ste 200, Ventura, CA 93004-1377
Tel (805) 647-6322 *Founded/Ownrshp* 1975
Sales 104.8MM *EMP* 230
Accts Oscar G Armijo Cpa Palm Des
SIC 8093 Specialty outpatient clinics
CEO: Roberto S Juarez
CFO: Chris Velasco

D-U-N-S 96-882-9601
CLINIGEN CTS INC
(*Suby of* CLINIGEN CTS LIMITED)
790 Township Line Rd # 120, Yardley, PA 19067-4265
Tel (215) 558-7001 *Founded/Ownrshp* 2008
Sales 83.8MM *EMP* 6
SIC 5122 Pharmaceuticals
CEO: Peter George
**Sr VP:* Steve Glass

D-U-N-S 19-306-9655
CLINT INDEPENDENT SCHOOL DISTRICT
14521 Horizon Blvd, El Paso, TX 79928-8564
Tel (915) 926-4000 *Founded/Ownrshp* 1929
Sales 110.1MM[E] *EMP* 1,030
Accts Gibson Ruddock Patterson Llc
SIC 8211 9411 Public elementary & secondary schools; Administration of educational programs
Prin: Mark Ayala
VP: Jessica Garcia
Prin: Holly Fields
Prin: Pamela Howard
Prin: Richard Lopez
Prin: Michael Mackeben

Prin: Paul Pearson
Prin: Ray Saenz

CLINTON
See FARMLAND DAIRIES LLC

CLINTON ALUM & STAINLESS STL
See CLINTON ALUMINUM ACQUISITION LLC

D-U-N-S 79-138-3891
CLINTON ALUMINUM ACQUISITION LLC
CLINTON ALUM & STAINLESS STL
6270 Van Buren Rd, New Franklin, OH 44216-9743
Tel (330) 882-6743 *Founded/Ownrshp* 2007
Sales 151.8MM^E *EMP* 300^E
SIC 5051

D-U-N-S 96-182-9384
CLINTON HEALTH ACCESS INITIATIVE INC
383 Dorchester Ave # 400, Boston, MA 02127-2422
Tel (617) 774-0110 *Founded/Ownrshp* 2010
Sales 117.4MM *EMP* 99
SIC 6732 Charitable trust management
Ch Bd: William J Clinton
**CEO:* Ed Wood
**CFO:* Julie B Feder
**V Ch Bd:* Ira C Magaziner

CLINTON MANOR APARTMENTS
See RELATED CLINTON MANOR LLC

CLINTON MEMORIAL HOSPITAL INPA
See RCHP - WILMINGTON LLC

D-U-N-S 06-672-0582
CLINTON UTILITIES BOARD
1001 Chrles G Sivers Blvd, Clinton, TN 37716-3926
Tel (865) 457-9232 *Founded/Ownrshp* 1939
Sales 113.3MM^E *EMP* 110
SIC 4911

D-U-N-S 07-054-7450 IMP/EXP
CLIPPER OIL
CLIPPER OIL COMPANY
2040 Harbor Island Dr # 203, San Diego, CA 92101-1018
Tel (619) 692-9701 *Founded/Ownrshp* 1985
Sales 200.0MM *EMP* 20
SIC 5172 2873 5169 Diesel fuel; Lubricating oils & greases; Anhydrous ammonia; Salts, industrial
Founder: Kenny Alameda
**VP:* Kevin Alameda

CLIPPER OIL COMPANY
See CLIPPER OIL

D-U-N-S 18-203-7804
CLK INC
CARLS JUNIOR
72295 Manufacturing Rd, Thousand Palms, CA 92276-6615
Tel (760) 341-2992 *Founded/Ownrshp* 1985
Sales 44.8MM^E *EMP* 1,000
SIC 5812 Fast-food restaurant, chain
Pr: Carl L Karcher
CFO: Ed Lovelock
Mktg Dir: Paula Karcher

CLOFINE DAIRY & FOOD PRODUCTS
See CLOFINE DAIRY PRODUCTS INC

D-U-N-S 01-106-3211 IMP
CLOFINE DAIRY PRODUCTS INC
CLOFINE DAIRY & FOOD PRODUCTS
1407 New Rd, Linwood, NJ 08221-1199
Tel (609) 653-1000 *Founded/Ownrshp* 1969
Sales 200.0MM *EMP* 17
SIC 5143 5149 Cheese; Milk; Groceries & related products
Pr: Frederick Smith Jr
**Ch Bd:* Lawrence Clofine
VP: Harold Harmon

D-U-N-S 78-067-4797
CLONDALKIN GROUP
(*Suby of* CLONDALKIN GROUP HOLDINGS B.V.)
2000 Market St Ste 2810, Philadelphia, PA 19103-3207
Tel (215) 440-0570 *Founded/Ownrshp* 1989
Sales 224.7MM *EMP* 1,005
SIC 2657 Folding paperboard boxes
CEO: Norbert McDermott

D-U-N-S 62-112-1516 IMP/EXP
CLONDALKIN HOLDINGS INC
Crtis Centre Ste, Philadelphia, PA 19106
Tel (215) 440-0570 *Founded/Ownrshp* 1985
Sales 86.0MM^E *EMP* 1,191
SIC 2673 2621 2752 8741

D-U-N-S 00-595-0988
CLONDALKIN PHARMA & HEALTHCARE LLC (DE)
ESSENTRA MOORESTOWN
(*Suby of* ESSENTRA PLC)
1224 N Church St, Moorestown, NJ 08057-1102
Tel (856) 439-1700 *Founded/Ownrshp* 2010, 2015
Sales 165.5MM^E *EMP* 33^E
SIC 5122 8361 Pharmaceuticals; Rehabilitation center, residential: health care incidental
CEO: David Lennon

D-U-N-S 96-506-3378
■ **CLOPAY AMES TRUE TEMPER HOLDING CORP**
(*Suby of* GRIFFON CORP) ★
100 Jericho Quadrangle # 224, Jericho, NY 11753-2708
Tel (516) 938-5544 *Founded/Ownrshp* 2010
Sales 359.5MM^E *EMP* 1,691^E
SIC 3423 3799 3524 Garden & farm tools, including shovels; Shovels, spades (hand tools); Wheelbarrows; Lawn & garden equipment
CEO: Ronald J Kramer

D-U-N-S 82-612-0412 IMP/EXP
■ **CLOPAY BUILDING PRODUCTS CO INC**
IDEAL DOOR
(*Suby of* CLOPAY CORP) ★
8585 Duke Blvd, Mason, OH 45040-3100
Tel (513) 770-4800 *Founded/Ownrshp* 1859
Sales 214.4MM^E *EMP* 525
SIC 2431 3442 2436 Garage doors, overhead: wood; Garage doors, overhead: metal; Plywood, softwood
Pr: Gene Colleran
Pr: Alan Leist
Treas: Thomas D Gibbons
**VP:* Dan Beckley
VP: Daniel F Beckley
VP: Alan R Leist
**VP:* Mr Pat Lohse
VP: Steven M Lynch
VP: Edward Shin
VP: Victor Weldon
Sales Asso: John Kinsella

D-U-N-S 00-423-3243 IMP/EXP
■ **CLOPAY CORP**
(*Suby of* GRIFFON CORP) ★
8585 Duke Blvd, Mason, OH 45040-3100
Tel (800) 282-2260 *Founded/Ownrshp* 1986
Sales 984.8MM^E *EMP* 4,100
SIC 3081 3442 2431 1796 Plastic film & sheet; Garage doors, overhead: metal; Garage doors, overhead: wood; Doors, wood; Power generating equipment installation
CFO: Franklin Smith Jr
Pr: Gary Abyad
CFO: Carolyn Hauger
Sr VP: Eugene Colleran
Sr VP: Ellen Shoemaker
VP: John Palazzolo
VP: Jim Quinan
VP: Franklin H Smith
VP: Mike Taylor
VP: Sudhakar Vinod
Dir Lab: Lindy Young

D-U-N-S 82-612-0420 IMP/EXP
■ **CLOPAY PLASTIC PRODUCTS CO INC**
(*Suby of* CLOPAY CORP) ★
8585 Duke Blvd, Mason, OH 45040-3100
Tel (513) 770-4800 *Founded/Ownrshp* 1992
Sales 96.0MM^E *EMP* 452
SIC 3081 Plastic film & sheet
Pr: Alan H Koblin
**Treas:* Tom Givens

D-U-N-S 00-913-8033 EXP
▲ **CLOROX CO**
1221 Broadway Ste 1300, Oakland, CA 94612-1871
Tel (510) 271-7000 *Founded/Ownrshp* 1913
Sales 5.7MMM *EMP* 7,700^E
Tkr Sym CLX *Exch* NYS
SIC 2842 2673 2035 2844 2879 Laundry cleaning preparations; Polishing preparations & related products; Food storage & frozen food bags, plastic; Seasonings & sauces, except tomato & dry; Dressings, salad: raw & cooked (except dry mixes); Seasonings, meat sauces (except tomato & dry); Cosmetic preparations; Insecticides & pesticides
CEO: Benno Dorer
COO: Nikolaos Vlahos
COO: Dawn Willoughby
CFO: Stephen M Robb
Treas: Angela Hilt
Chf Cred: Matthew Laszlo
Chf Mktg O: Eric Reynolds
Ex VP: James Foster
Ex VP: Laura Stein
Ex VP: Frank A Tataseo
Sr VP: Jon Balousek
Sr VP: Michael J Costello
Sr VP: Denise Garner
Sr VP: Anne Hickey
VP: Jean Johnson
Board of Directors: Rogelio Rebolledo, Amy Banse, Carolyn M Ticknor, Richard H Carmona, Christopher J Williams, Spencer C Fleischer, Pamela Thomas-Graham, Pamela Thomas-Graham, Esther Lee, Allan D Mackay, Robert W Matschullat, Jeffrey Noddle

D-U-N-S 78-135-5847 EXP
■ **CLOROX INTERNATIONAL CO**
(*Suby of* CLOROX CO) ★
1221 Broadway Ste 13, Oakland, CA 94612-1837
Tel (510) 271-7000 *Founded/Ownrshp* 1972
Sales 352.1MM^E *EMP* 1,360
SIC 2842 2879 Specialty cleaning, polishes & sanitation goods; Bleaches, household: dry or liquid; Insecticides, agricultural or household
Prin: Benno Dorer
Pr: Warwick Every-Burns
CEO: Larry Peirof
Treas: Richard Mack
Sr VP: J P Kane
VP: William F Ausfahl
VP: William Lynch
MIS Dir: Ken Tandowsky
Netwrk Mgr: Jim McGowan

D-U-N-S 94-877-4013 IMP/EXP
■ **CLOROX PRODUCTS MANUFACTURING CO**
(*Suby of* CLOROX CO) ★
1221 Broadway Ste 51, Oakland, CA 94612-1837
Tel (510) 271-7000 *Founded/Ownrshp* 1996
Sales 209.8MM^E *EMP* 1,240
SIC 2842 Specialty cleaning, polishes & sanitation goods
CEO: T E Bailey
**Treas:* Karen M Rose
**VP:* Suzanne Thompson

D-U-N-S 83-940-0975 EXP
■ **CLOROX SALES CO**
(*Suby of* CLOROX CO) ★
1221 Broadway Ste 13, Oakland, CA 94612-1837
Tel (510) 271-7000 *Founded/Ownrshp* 1981
Sales 246.8MM^E *EMP* 400
SIC 5087 Cleaning & maintenance equipment & supplies

Prin: Nikolaos A Vlahos
**Pr:* Frank A Tataseo
**CEO:* Donald R Knauss

D-U-N-S 03-022-0292 IMP
■ **CLOSEOUT DISTRIBUTION INC**
(*Suby of* BIG LOTS INC) ★
300 Phillipi Rd, Columbus, OH 43228-1310
Tel (614) 278-6800 *Founded/Ownrshp* 1999
Sales 265.9MM^E *EMP* 1,200
SIC 5092 Toys & games
CEO: Michael J Potter
**Treas:* Jared A Poff

CLOSEOUT SURPLUS & SAVINGS
See CSS INC

D-U-N-S 78-825-1486 IMP/EXP
CLOSET WORLD INC
3860 Capitol Ave, City of Industry, CA 90601-1733
Tel (562) 699-9945 *Founded/Ownrshp* 1990
Sales 105.0MM^E *EMP* 650
SIC 1751 5211 Cabinet building & installation; Closets, interiors & accessories
Pr: Frank Melkonian
Pr: Sandra Sinatra
VP: Alex Jivalagian
Snr Mgr: Artinian Carl

D-U-N-S 05-825-7569 IMP/EXP
■ **CLOSETMAID CORP**
(*Suby of* EMERSON ELECTRIC CO) ★
650 Sw 27th Ave, Ocala, FL 34471-2034
Tel (352) 401-6000 *Founded/Ownrshp* 1997
Sales 347.9MM^E *EMP* 1,300
SIC 2511 Storage chests, household: wood
Pr: Robert J Clements Jr
**Treas:* David J Rabe
**VP:* Catherine Beal
**VP:* Debra M Charles
VP: William Marcy
**VP:* Craig Moeller
VP: Wally Watts
Dir IT: Stu Shaub
IT Man: Jeff Stafford
Mktg Mgr: Deidre Bauer
Mktg Mgr: Rose Cohen

D-U-N-S 80-729-8380
CLOSURE SYSTEMS INTERNATIONAL HOLDINGS INC
(*Suby of* REYNOLDS GROUP HOLDINGS LIMITED)
7702 Woodland Dr Ste 200, Indianapolis, IN 46278-2709
Tel (317) 876-0173 *Founded/Ownrshp* 2008
Sales 297.9MM^E *EMP* 800^E
SIC 7389 Packaging & labeling services
Pr: Thomas Degnan
**Treas:* Michael Graham
**VP:* Charles Cox
**VP:* Robert Smith
Natl Sales: Nancy Moll

D-U-N-S 00-603-7857 IMP/EXP
CLOSURE SYSTEMS INTERNATIONAL INC
C S I
(*Suby of* CLOSURE SYSTEMS INTERNATIONAL HOLDINGS INC) ★
7702 Woodland Dr Ste 200, Indianapolis, IN 46278-2709
Tel (317) 390-5000 *Founded/Ownrshp* 1932
Sales 271.1MM^E *EMP* 586
SIC 3334 3565 Primary aluminum; Bottling machinery: filling, capping, labeling
Pr: Malcolm P Bundey
Pr: Thomas Degnan
Ex VP: Lawrence R Purtell
VP: Tim Carr
VP: Ronald D Dickel
VP: Barringto Owens
VP: Anthony Smith
VP: Gene Troggio
VP: Marshall K White
Div/Sub He: Ronald Glah
Dir IT: Tom Blazek
Board of Directors: Kathryn S Fuller, V L Mitchell

D-U-N-S 96-547-2173
CLOTHESLINE HOLDINGS INC
399 Park Ave Fl 15, New York, NY 10022-4614
Tel (212) 607-8450 *Founded/Ownrshp* 2008
Sales 663.5MM^E *EMP* 6,400^E
SIC 6719 Investment holding companies, except banks
Pr: Daniel James

D-U-N-S 83-208-6412
▲ **CLOUD PEAK ENERGY INC**
505 S Gillette Ave, Gillette, WY 82716-4203
Tel (307) 687-6000 *Founded/Ownrshp* 1993
Sales 1.1MMM *EMP* 1,500^E
Tkr Sym CLD *Exch* NYS
SIC 1221 Bituminous coal & lignite-surface mining
Pr: Colin Marshall
**Ch Bd:* Keith Bailey
COO: Gary Rivenes
COO: Gary S Rivenes
CFO: Heath Hill
Ex VP: Bryan Pechersky
Sr VP: Bruce Jones
Sr VP: Cary Martin
Sr VP: Todd Myers
VP: Kendall Carbone
Corp Couns: Eric Pearson
Board of Directors: Patrick Condon, William T Fox III, Jeane Hull, Steven Nance, William Owens, Robert Skaggs

D-U-N-S 83-285-8349
■ **CLOUD PEAK ENERGY RESOURCES LLC**
(*Suby of* CLOUD PEAK ENERGY INC) ★
505 S Gillette Ave, Gillette, WY 82716-4203
Tel (303) 956-7596 *Founded/Ownrshp* 2008
Sales 1.4MMM *EMP* 1,200^E
Accts Pricewaterhousecoopers Llp De
SIC 1221 Bituminous coal & lignite-surface mining
CEO: Colin Marshall
**Treas:* Oscar Martinez
**Ex VP:* Michael Barrett

**Ex VP:* Gary Rivenes
**Sr VP:* Bruce Jones
**Sr VP:* Cary W Martin

D-U-N-S 80-813-5255
■ **CLOUD PEAK ENERGY SERVICES CO**
(*Suby of* CLOUD PEAK ENERGY INC) ★
505 S Gillette Ave, Gillette, WY 82716-4203
Tel (307) 687-6000 *Founded/Ownrshp* 1873
Sales 159.1MM^E *EMP* 1,633
SIC 1221 Bituminous coal surface mining
Ch: Jan Du Plessis
**CFO:* Guy Elliott
CFO: Jo-Ann Goh
**Treas:* T R Myatt

D-U-N-S 01-563-8256
CLOUD SHERPAS INC
(*Suby of* ACCENTURE PUBLIC LIMITED COMPANY)
3525 Piedmont Rd Ne 8-710, Atlanta, GA 30305-1578
Tel (404) 665-3556 *Founded/Ownrshp* 2015
Sales 100.1MM^E *EMP* 270^E
SIC 7371 Computer software development & applications
CEO: David Northington
**Pr:* Gary Diorio
**Pr:* Douglas Shepard
**Pr:* Jason Wojahn
**CFO:* Chris Arroyo
Sr VP: Mark McGrath
VP: Matt Blocha
VP: Karl Lamberth
VP: Geoff Merrick
VP: Colin Robinson
VP: Gabriel Romero
VP: Michael Thomas

D-U-N-S 95-642-7186
■ **CLOUDBLUE TECHNOLOGIES INC**
(*Suby of* INGRAM MICRO INC) ★
501 Airtech Pkwy, Plainfield, IN 46168-7408
Tel (866) 437-4258 *Founded/Ownrshp* 2007
Sales 101.4MM^E *EMP* 350
SIC 7379 Computer related maintenance services
Pr: Thomas Luther
**CFO:* Doug Guess
Sr VP: Todd Zegers
VP: Ken Corrigan
VP: Mina Izadi
QI Cn Mgr: Will Tate
Sls Dir: Jeff Mangigian
Snr Mgr: Patrick Paulin
Snr Mgr: Wendy Zapien

D-U-N-S 02-767-4371
CLOUDERA INC
1001 Page Mill Rd Bldg 3, Palo Alto, CA 94304-1009
Tel (650) 644-3900 *Founded/Ownrshp* 2008
Sales 259.9MM^E *EMP* 1,300^E
SIC 7371 5734 8331 Custom computer programming services; Software, business & non-game; Skill training center
Pr: Tom Reilly
Pr: Peter C Ellis
**CFO:* Jim Frankola
**Chf Mktg O:* Mick Hollison
VP: Patrick Ball
VP: Paul Beduhn
VP: Peter Cooper-Ellis
VP: Joe Nicholson
VP: Lars Nilsson
VP: Yoland Smyth
VP: Tim Stevens
VP: Daniel Sturman
VP: Omer Trajman
Board of Directors: Martin I Cole, Scott Dietzen, Ping Li, Steve Sordello, Kimberly Stevenson, Dick Williams

D-U-N-S 05-701-9994
CLOUGH HARBOUR & ASSOCIATES LLP
C H A
(*Suby of* CHA CONSULTING INC) ★
3 Winners Cir Ste 100, Albany, NY 12205-1161
Tel (518) 453-4500 *Founded/Ownrshp* 1952
Sales 115.4MM^E *EMP* 650
SIC 8711 Engineering services; Civil engineering; Structural engineering; Electrical or electronic engineering
CEO: Raymond J Kinley
**CEO:* Ray Rudolph Jr
COO: Bill Lucarelli
CFO: David Wahrlich
Sr VP: Gregory Corso
Sr VP: Michael Devoy
Sr VP: Jim Howe
Sr VP: Margaret M Rudzinski
VP: Rich Amadon
VP: Karen Clark
VP: William Evans
VP: John Hickok
VP: Frank Lavardera
VP: William S Lucarelli
VP: Michael Miller
VP: Ed O'Hara
VP: Tony Stellato

D-U-N-S 00-828-7534
■ **CLOUGHERTY PACKING LLC**
FARMER JOHN BRAND
(*Suby of* HORMEL FOODS CORP) ★
3049 E Vernon Ave, Vernon, CA 90058-1800
Tel (323) 583-4621 *Founded/Ownrshp* 1937
Sales 236.8MM^E *EMP* 1,300
SIC 2011 2013 Meat packing plants; Sausages & other prepared meats
Pr: Steven G Binder
VP: Tim Sinskey
IT Man: John Borgerding
Opers Mgr: Peter Auer
Opers Mgr: Sean Benson
Opers Mgr: Bob Delmore
Opers Mgr: Andrew Humphrey
QI Cn Mgr: Jim Choe
Secur Mgr: Jerome Cooper
VP Mktg: Steve Kolodin
Mktg Dir: Jon Amidel

CLOVER GLOBAL
See 4L TECHNOLOGIES INC

CLOVER PATCH DAY CARE
See CENTER FOR DISABILITY SERVICES INC

D-U-N-S 95-902-4001 IMP/EXP
CLOVER TECHNOLOGIES GROUP LLC
DEPOT INTERNATIONAL
(*Suby of* CLOVER GLOBAL) ★
4200 Columbus St, Ottawa, IL 61350-9538
Tel (815) 431-8100 *Founded/Ownrshp* 2000
Sales 253.4MM^E *EMP* 1,200
Accts Fgmk Llc Bannockburn Illino
SIC 5943 3861 Office forms & supplies; Printing equipment, photographic
Ex VP: Ino Landa
VP: Jim Ross
VP: Tanya Ware
Prd Mgr: Roger Kaufman
Mktg Mgr: Mark Richards

D-U-N-S 06-144-5813 EXP
CLOVERDALE FOODS CO
CLOVERDALE MEATS
3015 34th St Nw, Mandan, ND 58554-1312
Tel (701) 663-9511 *Founded/Ownrshp* 1972
Sales 96.2MM^E *EMP* 250
SIC 2013 5147 Sausages & other prepared meats; Meats, fresh
QA Dir: Sandy Banton
Dir IT: Luke Schafer
IT Man: Joseph Goeman
Sfty Mgr: Roxsann Chick
Opers Mgr: Duane Helbling
Plnt Mgr: Willie Mihoff
Manager: Craig Benson

CLOVERDALE MEATS
See CLOVERDALE FOODS CO

D-U-N-S 92-878-6078
CLOVERLAND DAIRY LIMITED PARTNERSHIP
2701 Loch Raven Rd, Baltimore, MD 21218-4730
Tel (410) 235-4477 *Founded/Ownrshp* 1995
Sales 99.6MM^E *EMP* 450
SIC 2026 Milk processing (pasteurizing, homogenizing, bottling)
Mng Pt: Ralph Kemp
Pt: John M Kemp
Exec: Joseph Lawrence
Dept Mgr: Dennis Lam
Genl Mgr: James Cella
VP Mktg: Al Shewbridge

D-U-N-S 00-280-5653
CLOVERLAND ELECTRIC COOPERATIVE INC (MI)
2916 W M 28, Dafter, MI 49724-9761
Tel (906) 635-6800 *Founded/Ownrshp* 1938
Sales 83.2MM *EMP* 48^E
Accts Harris Group Cpa S Traverse C
SIC 4911 Generation, electric power
Pr: Daniel Dasho
**Pr:* Carl Eagle
**CEO:* Donald D Wozniak
**CFO:* Eugene Kanikovsky
**CFO:* Bob Malaski
**VP:* Robert Schallip
**Prin:* Lois Kennedy

CLOVERLEAF PARTNERS
See CLP HEALTHCARE SERVICES INC

CLOVIS COMMUNITY COLLEGE CTR
See STATE CENTER COMMUNITY COLLEGE DISTRICT

D-U-N-S 08-025-0966
CLOVIS MUNICIPAL SCHOOL DISTRICT
1009 N Main St, Clovis, NM 88101-5932
Tel (575) 769-4300 *Founded/Ownrshp* 2016
Sales 8.6MM^E *EMP* 1,100^E
SIC 8211 Public elementary & secondary schools
Teacher Pr: Kerry Parker
HC Dir: Rhonda Sparks

D-U-N-S 07-186-7766
CLOVIS UNIFIED SCHOOL DISTRICT
1450 Herndon Ave, Clovis, CA 93611-0599
Tel (559) 327-9000 *Founded/Ownrshp* 1961
Sales NA *EMP* 6,000
Accts Jeanette L Garcia & Associate
SIC 8211 Public combined elementary & secondary school; Public junior high school; Public senior high school; Public adult education school
Bd of Dir: Sandy Bengel
Bd of Dir: Brian Heryford
Bd of Dir: Jim Van Volkinburg
VP: Brian D Heryford
Exec: Aprille Cervantes
CTO: Dan Rescinti
Teacher Pr: Roxanne Braswell
HC Dir: Rick Watson

D-U-N-S 82-694-3420
CLP HEALTHCARE SERVICES INC
CLOVERLEAF PARTNERS
10 Cadillac Dr Ste 400, Brentwood, TN 37027-1001
Tel (615) 224-8028 *Founded/Ownrshp* 2006
Sales 124.9MM^E *EMP* 3,000^E
SIC 8051 Skilled nursing care facilities
Pr: James Deal
CFO: David Andrews
CFO: Anthony D James
Sr VP: Russ Adkins
**VP:* Kerry Massey
Dir Rx: Chris Dale
Dir Bus: Mark McDonald
Ex Dir: Glenda Sinclair
Off Mgr: Kristi Waeltz
Sls Dir: Char Kirk
Sales Asso: David Banning

D-U-N-S 06-832-3117
■ **CLP HOLDINGS CORP** (NV)
(*Suby of* TRUEBLUE INC) ★
10539 Prof Cir St 200, Reno, NV 89521
Tel (775) 321-8000 *Founded/Ownrshp* 1987, 2005
Sales 150.0MM^E *EMP* 2,000
SIC 7363 7361 Temporary help service; Employment agencies
CEO: Noel Wheeler
**Pr:* Dan Cradler
**Pr:* Tres Huber
**Pr:* Bud Little
**Pr:* Ed Nubel
**Pr:* Kim Proffitt
Treas: Pauline Howe
Ex VP: Selby F Little III
VP: James E Defebaugh IV
VP: Harold W Huber III
Rgnl Mgr: James Loag

D-U-N-S 06-078-7376 IMP/EXP
CLP PB LLC
PERSEUS BOOKS GROUP
250 W 57th St Fl 15, New York, NY 10107-1307
Tel (212) 340-8100 *Founded/Ownrshp* 1996
Sales 229.8MM^E *EMP* 550
SIC 2721 Comic books: publishing only, not printed on site
**COO:* Joe Mangan
**CFO:* Charles Gallagher
VP: Chitra Bopardikar
VP: Allison Devlin
VP: Dave Diroma
VP: Bill Newlin
VP: John Quinn
VP: Carolyn Savarese
VP: Kim Wylie
Exec: Jason Brontley
Dir IT: Jack McKeown

D-U-N-S 60-555-6620
■ **CLP RESOURCES INC**
PROJECTTRADE SOLUTIONS
(*Suby of* CLP HOLDINGS CORP) ★
1015 A St, Tacoma, WA 98402-5122
Tel (775) 321-8000 *Founded/Ownrshp* 1987
Sales 150.0MM *EMP* 1,900
SIC 8742 Personnel management consultant
Pr: Noel Wheeler
CFO: Bud Little
Mktg Dir: Dottie Gallagher

CLP ST INC.
See VEXOS INC

D-U-N-S 04-193-9315
■ **CLPTOWNE INC**
(*Suby of* FORWARD AIR INC) ★
24805 Us Highway 20, South Bend, IN 46628-5911
Tel (574) 233-3183 *Founded/Ownrshp* 2015
Sales 201.0MM *EMP* 900
SIC 4731 Freight transportation arrangement
Pr: Tom Downey
**CFO:* Joseph Dooley
Ex VP: Mike Topa
Dist Mgr: Craig Billheimer
Sales Exec: Josh Grimsbo
Sales Exec: Justin Hogan
Sales Exec: Edward Murphy
Sales Exec: Lori Solomon
Sales Exec: Jim Such
Sales Exec: Vick Tiwari
Sales Exec: Vicente Vera

D-U-N-S 60-623-3919 IMP
CLUB ASSIST US LLC
BATTERY ASSIST
(*Suby of* CLUB ASSIST NORTH AMERICA INC.)
888 W 6th St Ste 300, Los Angeles, CA 90017-2729
Tel (213) 388-4333 *Founded/Ownrshp* 2001
Sales 104.0MM^E *EMP* 230
SIC 5013 Automotive batteries
VP: John Tutt
**CEO:* Stuart Davies
**Ch:* Brett Davies
**VP:* Darshan Tarikh

CLUB CAL-NEVA
See SIERRA DEVELOPMENT CO

D-U-N-S 08-860-5787 IMP
CLUB CAR LLC
(*Suby of* INGERSOLL-RAND CO) ★
4125 Washington Rd, Evans, GA 30809-3067
Tel (706) 863-3000 *Founded/Ownrshp* 1995
Sales 459.0MM^E *EMP* 1,200
SIC 3799 Cars, off-highway: electric; Golf carts, powered
Pr: Marc Dufour
**CFO:* Matthew O'Donnell
VP: Frank Borovsky
DP Exec: Patrick Crabbe
Sls Mgr: Bud Roberts

D-U-N-S 01-767-3047 IMP
CLUB CHEF LLC
(*Suby of* CASTELLINI HOLDING CO LLC) ★
3776 Lake Park Dr Unit 1, Covington, KY 41017-8171
Tel (859) 578-3100 *Founded/Ownrshp* 2002
Sales 201.9MM^E *EMP* 350
SIC 5148 Fruits, fresh; Vegetables, fresh
Pr: William Schuler
**Treas:* Christopher Fister
**Ex VP:* Jeff Klare
**VP:* Filindo Colace

D-U-N-S 36-127-7791
CLUB DEMONSTRATION SERVICES INC
CDS
(*Suby of* DAYMON WORLDWIDE INC) ★
9555 Chesapeake Dr # 100, San Diego, CA 92123-6301
Tel (858) 581-8700 *Founded/Ownrshp* 1987
Sales 195.3MM^E *EMP* 6,000
SIC 7389

D-U-N-S 01-610-1938
CLUB EXCHANGE CORP
AUTOMOBILE CLB INTR-NSRNCE EXCH
12901 N 40 Dr, Saint Louis, MO 63141-8634
Tel (314) 523-6976 *Founded/Ownrshp* 1927
Sales NA *EMP* 1,224
Accts Pricewaterhousecoopers Llp St
SIC 6331 Automobile insurance
Pr: Arthur W Johnson
**Treas:* Carl D Kraft
VP: David M Mattingly
VP: Edward F Owen
VP: Michael J Right
VP: Robert Sbhreiber

D-U-N-S 13-020-0819 IMP/EXP
CLUB MED INC (A CAYMAN ISLANDS CORP)
(*Suby of* EASY CLUB MED CLUB AQUARIUS CLUB)
75 Valencia Ave Fl 12, Coral Gables, FL 33134-6135
Tel (305) 925-9000 *Founded/Ownrshp* 1966
Sales 126.7M^E *EMP* 1,773
SIC 7011 Resort hotel
Pr: Philipe Bourguignon
**CFO:* Alan Postic
VP: Olivier Horps
Genl Mgr: Kenny Lim
Ql Cn Mgr: M C Cristini

D-U-N-S 06-120-6710
CLUB MED SALES INC (DE)
(*Suby of* EASY CLUB MED CLUB AQUARIUS CLUB)
6505 Blue Lagoon Dr # 225, Miami, FL 33126-6011
Tel (305) 925-9000 *Founded/Ownrshp* 1971, 1984
Sales 129.3MM^E *EMP* 1,289
SIC 4724 4725 7011 8741 Travel agencies; Tour operators; Resort hotel; Management services
CEO: Xavier Mufraggi
**Pr:* Howard Tanenbaun
CFO: Jerome Ferrie
VP: Sabrina Cendral
VP: Carolyne Doyon
Sls&Mrk Ex: Romy Briers
Mktg Mgr: Claire Quidor

CLUB ONE FITNESS
See CLUB ONE INC

D-U-N-S 62-164-0853
CLUB ONE INC
CLUB ONE FITNESS
555 Market St Fl 13, San Francisco, CA 94105-2860
Tel (415) 477-3000 *Founded/Ownrshp* 1999
Sales NA *EMP* 2,000
SIC 7991

D-U-N-S 78-672-0482
CLUB WORLDMARK
9805 Willows Rd Ne, Redmond, WA 98052-2540
Tel (425) 498-2500 *Founded/Ownrshp* 1992
Sales 21.2MM^E *EMP* 1,500
SIC 6531 Time-sharing real estate sales, leasing & rentals
Pr: David Herrick
Ex VP: Kim Rimmasch
VP: Dave Akins
VP: Scott Grey
CTO: Todd Logan

D-U-N-S 96-689-4672
■ **CLUBCORP CLUB OPERATIONS INC**
(*Suby of* CLUBCORP HOLDINGS INC) ★
3030 Lbj Fwy Ste 600, Dallas, TX 75234-7744
Tel (972) 243-6191 *Founded/Ownrshp* 2010
Sales 760.2MM^E *EMP* 13,300
Accts Deloitte & Touche Llp Dallas
SIC 7997 Membership sports & recreation clubs
Pr: Eric L Affeldt
**Ch Bd:* John A Beckert
COO: Mark A Burnett
CFO: Curtis D McClellan
Ex VP: Ingrid J Keiser
Ex VP: Daniel T Tilley
Ex VP: James K Walters
VP: Frank Molina
VP: April Urbine
Board of Directors: Douglas H Brooks, Janet E Grove, Martin J Newburger, Eric C Resnick, Michael S Shannon, Steven S Siegel, William E Sullivan, Bryan J Traficanti

D-U-N-S 07-910-6073
▲ **CLUBCORP HOLDINGS INC** (NV)
3030 Lbj Fwy Ste 600, Dallas, TX 75234-7744
Tel (972) 243-6191 *Founded/Ownrshp* 1967
Sales 1.0MMM *EMP* 17,800
Tkr Sym MYCC *Exch* NYS
SIC 7997 Membership sports & recreation clubs
CEO: Eric L Affeldt
**Ch Bd:* John A Beckert
Pr: Mark A Burnett
CFO: Curt D McClellan
CFO: Curtis D McClellan
Ex VP: Ingrid J Keiser
Board of Directors: Douglas H Brooks, Louis J Grabowsky, Janet E Grove, Arthur Jefferson Lamb III, Margaret M Spellings, William E Sullivan

D-U-N-S 18-417-3797
■ **CLUBCORP USA INC**
(*Suby of* CLUBCORP HOLDINGS INC) ★
3030 Lyndon B Johnson Fwy, Dallas, TX 75234-7781
Tel (972) 243-6191 *Founded/Ownrshp* 1986
Sales 564.3MM^E *EMP* 9,872
SIC 7011 7997 Resort hotel; Membership sports & recreation clubs
Pr: Eric Affeldt
**CFO:* Curt McClellan
Ex VP: Richard N Beckert
**Ex VP:* Mark Burnett
Ex VP: Douglas T Howe
Ex VP: Murray S Siegel
Sr VP: Lisa H Kislak
Sr VP: Dave C Largent
Sr VP: John H Longstreet
Sr VP: Jack C Lupton
Sr VP: James P McTeigue
Sr VP: Angela A Stephens
Sr VP: William T Walden
Sr VP: David B Woodyard
Board of Directors: Nancy McMillan Dedman, Patricia Dedman Deitz, James L Singleton

CLUB'S CHOICE FUNDRAISING
See CHOICE PRODUCTS USA LLC

CLUBSPORT OF PLEASANTON
See LEISURE SPORTS INC

D-U-N-S 18-140-9293
CLUNE CONSTRUCTION CO LP
10 S Riverside Plz # 2200, Chicago, IL 60606-3700
Tel (312) 609-3635 *Founded/Ownrshp* 1979
Sales 341.6MM^E *EMP* 250
Accts Kpmg
SIC 1542 Commercial & office building contractors
CEO: Bill Abromitis
Sr Pt: Mike Metzger
**Pt:* John Clune
**Pr:* Bob Dahlstorm
**CFO:* Emmett Glynn
**Ch:* Michael T Clune
**Sr VP:* Nancy Chin
**Sr VP:* Pat Kinsella
Sr VP: Karen Mari
Sr VP: Leina Zimmerman
VP: Peter Bahruth
VP: Adam Beck
**VP:* Denise Moy Duffy
VP: Chris Franz
VP: Patrick Kinsella
VP: Jeff Liska
**VP:* Shane Murphy
**VP:* Mike Spence
**VP:* Joe Trungale

D-U-N-S 06-356-0986
CLYDE COMPANIES INC
730 N 1500 W, Orem, UT 84057-2826
Tel (801) 802-6900 *Founded/Ownrshp* 1961
Sales 1.0MMM^E *EMP* 2,000
SIC 1611 5031 6411 Highway & street construction; Lumber, plywood & millwork; Insurance agents, brokers & service
Pr: Wilford W Clyde
VP: Daniel C Walker

D-U-N-S 02-422-6193
CLYDE INC (DC)
CLYDE'S
3236 M St Nw, Washington, DC 20007-3615
Tel (202) 333-9180 *Founded/Ownrshp* 1963
Sales 47.5MM^E *EMP* 1,076
SIC 5812 5813 American restaurant; Bar (drinking places)
Pr: John Laytham
**Ch Bd:* Sally Davidson
**CFO:* Jeffrey Owens
Bd of Dir: Robert Parson
Ofcr: Ginger Laytham
**Ex VP:* Tom Meyer
Exec: Jeff Eng
Exec: Derrick Jackson
Exec: Adam Newton
Dir Soc: Megan Kilby
Genl Mgr: David Delbene

CLYDE'S
See CLYDE INC

CM
See CONTINENTAL MILLS INC

CM
See CONSTRUCTION MATERIALS INC

D-U-N-S 06-599-6670
CM LIFE INSURANCE CO INC
(*Suby of* MASSMUTUAL) ★
140 Garden St, Hartford, CT 06105-1488
Tel (860) 987-2676 *Founded/Ownrshp* 1996
Sales NA *EMP* 5
Accts Deloitte & Touche Llp Hartfor
SIC 6311 Life insurance
Pr: Lawrence V Burkett
Treas: Edward Kline
VP: Paul D Adornato
VP: Ronald Baker
VP: Anne Melissa Dowling
VP: Maureen R Ford
VP: Isadore Jermyn
VP: John Miller
VP: Richard A Peck
**VP:* Stuart H Reese
VP: Mary E Wilson
VP: Mathew Winter

D-U-N-S 78-513-3757 IMP
CM MANUFACTURING INC
(*Suby of* STION CORP) ★
6321 San Ignacio Ave, San Jose, CA 95119-1202
Tel (408) 284-7200 *Founded/Ownrshp* 2006
Sales 104.5MM^E *EMP* 318^E
SIC 3674 Semiconductors & related devices
CEO: Chet Farris
**COO:* Vineet Dharmadhikari
**VP:* Howard Lee

D-U-N-S 12-776-3162 IMP
CM TUCKER LUMBER COMPANIES LLC
601 N Pearl St, Pageland, SC 29728-1628
Tel (843) 672-6135 *Founded/Ownrshp* 1920
Sales 166.7MM *EMP* 280^E
Accts Pricewaterhousecoopers Llp C
SIC 2491 Structural lumber & timber, treated wood

CM&B
See CONSTRUCTION MANAGEMENT & BUILDERS INC

CMA
See CHINA MANUFACTURERS ALLIANCE LLC

D-U-N-S 00-592-1358 IMP
CMA CGM (AMERICA) LLC
(*Suby of* CMA-CGM AGENCIES WORLDWIDE)
5701 Lake Wright Dr, Norfolk, VA 23502-1868
Tel (757) 961-2100 *Founded/Ownrshp* 1980, 1994
Sales 215.0MM^E *EMP* 700
SIC 4731

D-U-N-S 78-430-1681
CMC AMERICAS INC
(*Suby of* TATA CONSULTANCY SERVICES LIMITED)
4354 S Shrwd Forst Bl 175, Baton Rouge, LA 70816-4483
Tel (225) 296-8440 *Founded/Ownrshp* 1991
Sales 244.6MM *EMP* 210

SIC 7374 7379 Data processing service; Data processing consultant
CFO: Sandra Shuford
**COO:* Madhu Onteeru
Ex VP: Ravi Narayanan
Exec: Linda Cupit
Exec: Jaspal Yadav
IT Man: Nitendra Panwar

D-U-N-S 07-175-4477 IMP
CMC MISSOULA INC
COMMUNITY PHYSICIAN GROUP
2827 Fort Missoula Rd, Missoula, MT 59804-7408
Tel (406) 728-4100 *Founded/Ownrshp* 1947
Sales 188.9MM^E *EMP* 1,250^E
Accts Larson Allen Llp Minneapolis
SIC 8062 8361 General medical & surgical hospitals; Rehabilitation center, residential: health care incidental
CEO: Steve Carlson
Dir Recs: Patty Reisinger
**Pr:* Scott Hacker
CFO: Barry Kinfield
CFO: Tom Percello
CFO: Dave Richhart
Chf Mktg O: Jonathan Weisul
VP: Michael Bush
VP: Barbara Klein
**VP:* Stan Moser
VP: Jan Perry
VP: Kimberly Toms
Dir Lab: Naomi Matten

CMC RBAR SAN ANTNIO E LOCATION
See C M C STEEL FABRICATORS INC

CMC STEEL ALABAMA
See SMI STEEL LLC

D-U-N-S 19-771-7242 IMP/EXP
■ **CMC STEEL HOLDING CO**
C M C
(*Suby of* COMMERCIAL METALS CO) ★
802 N West St Ste 302, Wilmington, DE 19801-1526
Tel (302) 691-6200 *Founded/Ownrshp* 1988
Sales 645.2MM^E *EMP* 3,027
SIC 3441 3312

CMC STEEL TEXAS
See STRUCTURAL METALS INC

CMC/CLA
See CENTRAL MOTOR WHEEL OF AMERICA INC

D-U-N-S 07-884-1477
CMD SALES LLC
ELEPHANT STRUCTURES
355 Industrial Park Dr, Boone, NC 28607-3978
Tel (828) 355-7121 *Founded/Ownrshp* 2013
Sales 400.0MM *EMP* 30
SIC 1791 Building front installation metal
CEO: Robert Thomas Sofield
CFO: Kenneth Deam
Genl Mgr: Noha Habib

CME
See CHICAGO MERCANTILE EXCHANGE INC

D-U-N-S 09-190-7985
▲ **CME GROUP INC**
20 S Wacker Dr, Chicago, IL 60606-7431
Tel (312) 930-1000 *Founded/Ownrshp* 2002
Sales 3.3MMM *EMP* 2,530^E
Tkr Sym CME *Exch* NGS
SIC 6231 Security & commodity exchanges; Futures exchanges, contract
CEO: Phupinder Gill
Mng Pt: Ronald Burton
**Ch Bd:* Terrence A Duffy
V Ch: James Oliff
Pr: Kim Taylor
**CEO:* Phupinder S Gill
COO: Julie Holzrichter
CTO: John W Pietrowicz
**V Ch Bd:* Charles P Carey
Bd of Dir: William G Salatich Jr
Ofcr: Bryan T Durkin
VP: Ran An
VP: Peter Barker
VP: Richard McDonald
VP: Carla Seales-Penn
Assoc Dir: Roman Benko
Assoc Dir: Dave Bixby
Assoc Dir: Ellyn Burnett
Assoc Dir: Michelle Eure
Assoc Dir: Kevin Fortcamp
Assoc Dir: Jay Fought
Board of Directors: Patrick W Maloney, Howard J Siegel, Jeffrey M Bernacchi, Leo Melamed, Dennis A Suskind, Timothy S Bitsberger, William P Miller II, David J Wescott, Dennis H Chookaszian, James E Oliff, Steven E Wollack, Elizabeth A Cook, Ronald A Pankau, James J Zellinger, Ana Dutra, Jeremy J Perlow, Martin J Gepsman, Alex J Pollock, Larry G Gerdes, John F Sandner, Daniel R Glickman, Terry L Savage, William W Hobert, William R Shepard

CMEEC
See CONNECTICUT MUNICIPAL ELECTRIC ENERGY COOPERATIVE

D-U-N-S 07-385-1040
CMFG LIFE INSURANCE CO
CUNA MUTUAL GROUP
5910 Mineral Point Rd, Madison, WI 53705-4456
Tel (800) 356-2644 *Founded/Ownrshp* 1935
Sales NA *EMP* 4,000
Accts Deloitte & Touche Llp Chicag
SIC 6321 6311 Accident & health insurance; Mutual accident & health associations; Mutual association life insurance
CEO: Jeff Post
**Pr:* Michael B Kitchen
**COO:* Robert Trunzo
**CFO:* Jeffrey Holley
CFO: Thomas Merfeld
CFO: Gerald Pavelich
**CFO:* Alastair Shore
Ex VP: David G Brown
Ex VP: Brad Buss
Ex VP: Judith Cooper
Ex VP: Theressa Drabenstadt
Ex VP: Doug Hedlund
Ex VP: Faye Patzner
Ex VP: Scott Waite
Sr VP: Kevin Belgrade
Sr VP: Larry H Blancard
**Sr VP:* Larry Blanchard
Sr VP: Jeff Bosco
Sr VP: Michael Briggs
Sr VP: Paul Chong
Sr VP: Michaeal Defnet
Board of Directors: David Marks, Jeff Post, Alastair Shore, Robert Trunzo

CMG CONTMID GROUP
See CONTINENTAL/MIDLAND LLC

D-U-N-S 01-470-3636
■ **CMGRP INC** (NY)
WEBER SHANDWICK WORLDWIDE
(*Suby of* INTERPUBLIC GROUP OF COMPANIES INC) ★
909 3rd Ave, New York, NY 10022-4731
Tel (212) 445-8000 *Founded/Ownrshp* 1986
Sales 238.3MM^E *EMP* 686
SIC 8743 7311 7319 8742 Public relations services; Advertising agencies; Transit advertising services; Management consulting services
Ch: Jack Leslie
Ch Bd: Bradford Williams
Pr: Rob Baskin
Pr: Sara Gavin
Pr: Susan Howe
Pr: Heidi Sinclair
CEO: Andy Polansky
COO: Frank Okunak
CFO: Martin P Franken
Chf Cred: Cathy Calhoun
Ofcr: Gail Heimann
Ex VP: Cindy Drucker
Ex VP: Eddie Garrett
Ex VP: Neil Nowlin
Sr VP: Jonathan Carroll
Sr VP: Heather Gallegos
Sr VP: Joshua Kaufman
Sr VP: Tim Moore
Sr VP: Michael Presson
VP: Pete Campisi
VP: Curt Doty
Board of Directors: Andrew Bonzani, Jack Leslie

CMH
See CITIZENS MEMORIAL HOSPITAL DISTRICT OF POLK COUNTY

D-U-N-S 78-588-1087
■ **CMH CAPITAL INC**
(*Suby of* OAKWOOD HOMES) ★
1105 N Market St Ste 1300, Wilmington, DE 19801-1241
Tel (302) 651-7947 *Founded/Ownrshp* 1989
Sales 718.3MM *EMP* 11,000
SIC 6719 2451 6515 6311 Investment holding companies, except banks; Mobile homes, except recreational; Mobile home site operators; Life insurance
Pr: Kevin Clayton

D-U-N-S 14-760-8848
■ **CMH HOMES INC**
(*Suby of* CMH CAPITAL INC) ★
5000 Clayton Rd, Maryville, TN 37804-5550
Tel (865) 380-3000 *Founded/Ownrshp* 2012
Sales 238.9MM^E *EMP* 1,300
SIC 5271 Mobile homes
Pr: Kevin T Clayton
CFO: John Kalec
VP: Amber Krupacs
Brnch Mgr: Tupper Baker

D-U-N-S 11-811-9528
■ **CMH MANUFACTURING INC**
(*Suby of* CMH CAPITAL INC) ★
5000 Clayton Rd, Maryville, TN 37804-5550
Tel (865) 380-3000 *Founded/Ownrshp* 2012
Sales 1.6MMM^E *EMP* 7,700
SIC 2451 Mobile homes, except recreational
Ch: Kevin Clayton
**Pr:* Rick Strachan
**CEO:* James L Clayton
**Treas:* Steve Cook
Brnch Mgr: Doug Cox
CTO: Damon Dickson
Manager: John Weldy

D-U-N-S 80-199-1402
■ **CMH SERVICES INC**
(*Suby of* OAKWOOD HOMES) ★
5000 Clayton Rd, Maryville, TN 37804-5550
Tel (865) 380-3000 *Founded/Ownrshp* 1996
Sales 349.1MM^E *EMP* 3,343
SIC 7389 Personal service agents, brokers & bureaus
Pr: Kevin Clayton
**CFO:* David Jordan

CMHA
See CUYAHOGA METROPOLITAN HOUSING AUTHORITY

CMI
See CRITCHFIELD MECHANICAL INC

D-U-N-S 01-430-4448
CMI HOLDING CORP
1555 Bustard Rd, Kulpsville, PA 19443
Tel (215) 361-9000 *Founded/Ownrshp* 1954
Sales 175.9MM^E *EMP* 2,600
SIC 5411 6512 Supermarkets, independent; Property operation, retail establishment
Pr: James S Clemens Jr
Sr VP: Roy R Kipp
CTO: S Jack
Plnt Mgr: Craig Crosby
Plnt Mgr: Tresa Van Gorder

D-U-N-S 00-720-6105 IMP/EXP
■ **CMI TEREX CORP** (OK)
TEREX ROADBUILDING
(*Suby of* TEREX CORP) ★
9528 W I 40 Service Rd, Oklahoma City, OK 73128-7108
Tel (405) 787-6020 *Founded/Ownrshp* 1926, 2001
Sales 218.0MM^E *EMP* 1,891
SIC 3531 3715 3596 3541 3444 2951 Construction machinery; Asphalt plant, including gravel-mix type; Pavers; Graders, road (construction machinery); Truck trailers; Scales & balances, except laboratory; Truck (motor vehicle) scales; Industrial scales; Machine tools, metal cutting type; Sheet metalwork; Asphalt paving mixtures & blocks
VP: Thane A Swisher
**VP:* Bill Swisher III
**Prin:* Robert L Curtis
**Prin:* Earl G Morris
**Prin:* J S Wylie Jr
VP Mfg: George Ellis

CMN
See CHILDRENS MIRACLE NETWORK

D-U-N-S 04-291-0260
■ **CMP GROUP INC**
(*Suby of* AVANGRID INC) ★
83 Edison Dr, Augusta, ME 04336-0002
Tel (207) 623-3521 *Founded/Ownrshp* 2000
Sales 1.1MMM^E *EMP* 1,400
SIC 4911 Generation, electric power; Transmission, electric power; Distribution, electric power
Pr: Sarah Burns
Treas: Scott Mahoney
VP: Steven R Adams
VP: Kathleen A Case
VP: Thorn Dickinson
VP: Gene Jensen
VP: Stephen G Robinson
VP Opers: Douglas A Herling

D-U-N-S 07-972-5042
CMP I OWNER-T LLC
399 Park Ave Fl 18, New York, NY 10022-4968
Tel (212) 547-2609 *Founded/Ownrshp* 2014
Sales 54.4MM^E *EMP* 1,348^E
SIC 7011 Hotels & motels
VP: Laura Benner

D-U-N-S 09-686-2672 IMP
CMPC USA INC
(*Suby of* CMPC MADERAS S.A.)
1040 Crown Pointe Pkwy # 800, Atlanta, GA 30338-6908
Tel (770) 551-2640 *Founded/Ownrshp* 2002
Sales 178.2MM *EMP* 13
SIC 5099 Wood & wood by-products
CEO: Hernan Fournies
**Pr:* Pablo Sufan
Genl Mgr: Manuel Opavo

D-U-N-S 11-893-5902 IMP
■ **CMRG APPAREL LLC**
(*Suby of* DESTINATION XL GROUP INC) ★
555 Turnpike St, Canton, MA 02021-2724
Tel (781) 828-9300 *Founded/Ownrshp* 2002
Sales 68.5MM^E *EMP* 2,000
SIC 5699 2389 Designers, apparel; Men's miscellaneous accessories

CMS
See CHESAPEAKE MANAGEMENT SERVICES INC

CMS
See CENTERS FOR MEDICARE AND MEDICAID SERVICES

D-U-N-S 17-520-6614
▲ **CMS ENERGY CORP**
1 Energy Plaza Dr, Jackson, MI 49201-2357
Tel (517) 788-0550 *Founded/Ownrshp* 1987
Sales 6.4MMM *EMP* 15,120
Tkr Sym CMS *Exch* NYS
SIC 4931 4911 4924 4922 Electric & other services combined; Generation, electric power; Transmission, electric power; Distribution, electric power; Natural gas distribution; Natural gas transmission; Storage, natural gas
Pr: John G Russell
Ch Bd: David W Joos
CFO: Thomas J Webb
Sr VP: Daniel J Malone
Sr VP: Catherine M Reynolds
Sr VP: Brian F Rich
VP: Glenn P Barba
VP: Jean-Francois Brossoit
VP: Jackson Hanson
VP: Carol Isles
VP: David G Mengebier
VP: Brian Rich
VP: Jon Robinson
VP: Garrick J Rochow
VP: Michael Shore
Assoc Dir: Rob Pedrotte
Board of Directors: Laura H Wright, Jon E Barfield, Deborah H Butler, Kurt L Darrow, Stephen E Ewing, Richard M Gabrys, William D Harvey, Philip R Lochner Jr, Myrna M Soto, John G Sznewajs

D-U-N-S 18-118-7006 EXP
■ **CMS ENTERPRISES CO**
(*Suby of* CMS ENERGY CORP) ★
1 Energy Plaza Dr, Jackson, MI 49201-2357
Tel (517) 788-0550 *Founded/Ownrshp* 1987
Sales 107.4MM^E *EMP* 385
SIC 1382 4911 Oil & gas exploration services; Geophysical exploration, oil & gas field; Generation, electric power
Pr: Thomas W Elward
Treas: Jim Lowen
VP: Glenn Barba
**VP:* Carol A Isles
VP: Clifford Lawrenso
**VP:* M Clifford Lawrenso
VP: David Mengebier
**VP:* William H Stephens
**VP:* Joseph P Tomasik
Opers Mgr: Joe Eckert
Opers Mgr: Debbie Mick

CMSE
See CHOCTAW MANAGEMENT SERVICES ENTERPRISE

D-U-N-S 02-775-4642
CMT HOLDINGS INC
590 Laurelwood Rd, Santa Clara, CA 95054-2420
Tel (408) 734-3339 *Founded/Ownrshp* 1997
Sales 118.4MM^E *EMP* 80
SIC 5045 Computers, peripherals & software
CEO: Kurt M Klein
**Pr:* Mark Klein

D-U-N-S 78-722-4245
CMU & ASSOCIATES INC
HILO FISH COMPANY
55 Holomua St, Hilo, HI 96720-5142
Tel (808) 961-0877 *Founded/Ownrshp* 1988
Sales 100.0MM *EMP* 200
SIC 5146 5148 5142 Seafoods; Vegetables, fresh; Packaged frozen goods
Pr: Charles Umamoto
VP: Darcy Umamoto

D-U-N-S 07-982-8324
CMW HOLDCO INC
20000 Horizon Way Ste 600, Mount Laurel, NJ 08054-4321
Tel (267) 443-2547 *Founded/Ownrshp* 2008
Sales 274.4MM *EMP* 175
Accts Ernst & Young Llp Philadelphi
SIC 7313 Radio, television, publisher representatives
CFO: Jonathan Batt

CN
See GRAND TRUNK WESTERN RAILROAD CO

D-U-N-S 04-146-0361 IMP
CN BROWN CO
A. W. WALKER LAWN & GRDN CTRS
1 C N Brown Way, South Paris, ME 04281-1600
Tel (207) 743-9212 *Founded/Ownrshp* 1948
Sales 177.6MM^E *EMP* 1,000
SIC 5411 5541 5983 Grocery stores; Convenience stores; Convenience stores, chain; Convenience stores, independent; Gasoline service stations; Filling stations, gasoline; Fuel oil dealers
Ch Bd: Harold D Jones
**Pr:* Jinger Duryea
**Treas:* Kurt Jones
**Sr VP:* Grant A Jones
Off Mgr: Vicki Merrill
Opers Mgr: Russell Cloutier
Advt Dir: Linda McDonald
Sls Mgr: John Wheeler

D-U-N-S 62-205-1969
CNA CORP
3003 Washington Blvd, Arlington, VA 22201-2194
Tel (703) 824-2000 *Founded/Ownrshp* 1942
Sales 112.7MM *EMP* 600
SIC 8732 Business analysis
Pr: Katherine McGrady
Pr: Robert J Murray
CFO: Marijo Alhgrimm
CFO: Debuck Mr Donald G
Ex VP: Mark Lewis
Sr VP: Donald G Debuck
Sr VP: Michael Flory
Sr VP: Sherri Goodman
VP: Tim Beres
VP: Jay Bloedorn
VP: Stephen Broyhill
VP: Lewis Cabe
VP: Keith M Costa
VP: Constance A Custer
VP: Constance Custer
VP: Donald Cymrot
VP: Mark Lewellyn
VP: Jeffrey Nick
VP: George Theologus
VP: Eric V Thompson
VP: David W Vordick

D-U-N-S 04-206-4808
■ **CNA FINANCIAL CORP**
CNA INSURANCE
(*Suby of* LOEWS CORP) ★
333 S Wabash Ave Ste 300, Chicago, IL 60604-4153
Tel (312) 822-5000 *Founded/Ownrshp* 1967
Sales NA *EMP* 6,900
Tkr Sym CNA *Exch* NYS
SIC 6411 6331 6311 Insurance agents, brokers & service; Fire, marine & casualty insurance; Fire, marine & casualty insurance: stock; Life insurance; Mutual association life insurance; Life insurance carriers
Ch Bd: Thomas F Motamed
CFO: D Craig Mense
Ofcr: Liz Aguinaga
Ofcr: John Kaas
Ex VP: Jonathan D Kantor
VP: Song Kim
Board of Directors: Jose O Montemayor, Don M Randel, Joseph Rosenberg, Andrew H Tisch, James S Tisch, Marvin Zonis

D-U-N-S 05-522-2079
■ **CNA FOUNDATION**
(*Suby of* CNA INSURANCE) ★
333 S Wabash Ave Fl 1, Chicago, IL 60604-4250
Tel (312) 822-5000 *Founded/Ownrshp* 1999
Sales NA *EMP* 7,500
SIC 6331 Fire, marine & casualty insurance
Ch Bd: Stephen W Lilienthal
**CFO:* Craig Mense
CFO: D C Mense
**Sr VP:* Jonathan Kantor
VP: Thomas Pontarelli

D-U-N-S 55-671-5063
CNA HOLDING CORP
COVERALL CLEANING CONCEPTS
350 Sw 12th Ave, Deerfield Beach, FL 33442-3106
Tel (561) 922-2500 *Founded/Ownrshp* 2005
Sales 192.3MM^E *EMP* 501

SIC 7349 6794 Building maintenance services; Franchises, selling or licensing
CEO: Rick Ascolese
**COO:* Jim Congrove
CFO: Marielynn Felos
**CFO:* Marilyn Felos
**Treas:* William Mulligan
VP: Shirley Klein
VP: Joe Smid
Creative D: Cristina Hortget
Ex Dir: Laura Bach
CIO: Ibn Sofa
IT Man: Russ Douglas

D-U-N-S 00-132-6073 IMP/EXP
■ CNA HOLDINGS LLC
(*Suby of* KEP AMERICAS) ★
222 Las Colinas Blvd W, Irving, TX 75039-5421
Tel (972) 443-4000 *Founded/Ownrshp* 1918
Sales 6.9MMM^E *EMP* 880^E
SIC 2823 2821 2819 5169 8731 Acetate fibers, triacetate fibers; Rayon fibers, straw, strips & yarn; Plastics materials & resins; Polyesters; Vinyl resins; Nylon resins; Industrial inorganic chemicals; Manmade fibers; Commercial physical research
Pr: Edward Collins

D-U-N-S 08-007-8157 IMP
CNA INC
CNA INSURANCE
(*Suby of* CKNA) ★
1 Calsonic Way, Shelbyville, TN 37160-2031
Tel (931) 684-4490 *Founded/Ownrshp* 1992, 2001
Sales 510.1MM^E *EMP* 1,435
SIC 3585 Air conditioning, motor vehicle
CEO: Bunsei Kure
**Pr:* Kiyoto Shinohara
**CFO:* Tomohiko Htori

CNA INSURANCE
See CONTINENTAL CASUALTY CO INC

CNA INSURANCE
See FIDELITY & CASUALTY CO OF NEW YORK

CNA INSURANCE
See CNA FINANCIAL CORP

CNA INSURANCE
See AMERICAN CASUALTY CO OF READING PENNSYLVANIA INC

CNA INSURANCE
See CNA INC

D-U-N-S 85-955-8645 IMP/EXP
CNA INTERNATIONAL INC
DAEWOO ELECTRONICS MARKETING
940 N Central Ave, Wood Dale, IL 60191-1216
Tel (630) 238-9800 *Founded/Ownrshp* 1992
Sales 167.3MM^E *EMP* 55
SIC 5063 5064

D-U-N-S 17-955-8770
■ CNA SURETY CORP
(*Suby of* CNA INSURANCE) ★
333 S Wabash Ave Ste 41s, Chicago, IL 60604-4389
Tel (312) 822-5000 *Founded/Ownrshp* 1998
Sales NA *EMP* 719^E
SIC 6411 Insurance agents, brokers & service
Pr: John Welch
Pr: Loraine Gardner
Pr: Michael Gross
Pr: Wayne Ottoway
**CFO:* John F Corcoran
**Sr VP:* Michael A Dougherty
Sr VP: Douglas W Hinkle
Sr VP: Sarah Pang
**Sr VP:* Rosemary Quinn
VP: Michael Dougherty
VP: Walter Kubalanza
VP: Robert Peterson
VP: Thomas Pontarelli
VP: Terry Reckamp
Assoc Dir: Gerald Shapiro

CNB
See CHEROKEE NATION BUSINESSES LLC

D-U-N-S 00-791-0326
■ CNB BANK
(*Suby of* CNB FINANCIAL CORP) ★
1 S 2nd St, Clearfield, PA 16830-2355
Tel (814) 765-4577 *Founded/Ownrshp* 1934
Sales NA *EMP* 240^E
SIC 6022 State commercial banks
Pr: Joseph B Bower
COO: Richard L Greslick Jr
CFO: Charles R Guarino
CFO: Brian W Wingard
Ofcr: Donna Collins
Ex VP: Mark Breakey
Sr VP: Steve Shilling
VP: Mary Conaway
VP: Mike Haines
VP: David Ogden
VP: Karin Pfingstler
VP: Edward Proud
VP: Michael C Sutika
VP: Calvin Thomas
Board of Directors: Richard L Greslick Jr, Joel E Peterson, Nick Scott Jr

D-U-N-S 11-343-1092
▲ CNB FINANCIAL CORP
1 S 2nd St, Clearfield, PA 16830-2355
Tel (814) 765-9621 *Founded/Ownrshp* 1983
Sales NA *EMP* 395^E
Accts Crowe Horwath Llp Cleveland
Tkr Sym CCNE *Exch* NGS
SIC 6022 State commercial banks
Ch Bd: Dennis L Merrey
Pr: Vickie Baker
Pr: Joseph B Bower Jr
Pr: Gregory Dixon
COO: Richard L Greslick Jr
CFO: Brian W Wingard
Ofcr: Mark D Breakey
Ofcr: Andrew Franson
Ofcr: Cory Johnston
Ofcr: Richard Sloppy
Ofcr: Brenda Terry
Ex VP: Joseph E Dell Jr
VP: Robin Hay
VP: Andrew Roman
VP: Vincent C Turiano
VP: Joseph Yaros

D-U-N-S 01-475-4860
CNG FINANCIAL CORP (OH)
CHECK N GO
7755 Montgomery Rd # 400, Cincinnati, OH 45236-4197
Tel (513) 336-7735 *Founded/Ownrshp* 1994, 1996
Sales NA *EMP* 3,000
SIC 6099 Check cashing agencies
Pr: Jared A Davis
**Ex VP:* David Davis
VP: David Mitchell
VP: Billy Smiddy
VP: Chris Swartz
**Prin:* Robert M Beck Jr
CTO: Suzann McElhaney
Netwrk Eng: Eric Koenig

D-U-N-S 95-978-8238
CNG FINANCIAL CORP
7755 Montgomery Rd # 400, Cincinnati, OH 45236-4197
Tel (513) 336-7735 *Founded/Ownrshp* 2010
Sales 332.7M^E *EMP* 3,000
SIC 6282 Investment advice
Pr: David Davis

D-U-N-S 02-338-7062
CNG HOLDINGS INC
7755 Montgomery Rd # 400, Cincinnati, OH 45236-4197
Tel (513) 336-7735 *Founded/Ownrshp* 2006
Sales NA *EMP* 3,000
SIC 6719 Investment holding companies, except banks
Pr: A David Davis
**COO:* Douglas D Clark
CFO: Roger Dean
**Ex VP:* Jared A Davis

D-U-N-S 07-492-9634 EXP
CNH INC
(*Suby of* NEW HOLLAND NORTH AMERICA INC) ★
500 Diller Ave, New Holland, PA 17557-9301
Tel (717) 355-1121 *Founded/Ownrshp* 2001
Sales 135.1MM^E *EMP* 1^E
SIC 3523 Farm machinery & equipment
Pr: Richard Buckman
IT Man: David Kohler

D-U-N-S 00-131-5019 IMP/EXP
CNH INDUSTRIAL AMERICA LLC
(*Suby of* C N H) ★
700 St St, Racine, WI 53404
Tel (262) 636-6011 *Founded/Ownrshp* 1994
Sales 2.8MMM^E *EMP* 8,000
SIC 3523 3531 6159 Farm machinery & equipment; Tractors, farm; Combines (harvester-threshers); Cotton pickers & strippers; Construction machinery; Tractors, construction; Bulldozers (construction machinery); Loaders, shovel: self-propelled; Agricultural loan companies; Machinery & equipment finance leasing
Ch: Sergio Marchionne
CFO: Robert Wenger
Ofcr: Umberto Quadrino
Sr VP: Gerard Roullot
VP: John E Evard Jr
Dir Surg: Daniel F Nekich
Dir Risk M: Matt Reid
Dir Risk M: Robert Samuels
CTO: Keith Hanson
CTO: Peggy Hart
Dir IT: Clarence Fredrick

D-U-N-S 07-947-5019
CNH INDUSTRIAL CAPITAL LLC
5729 Washington Ave, Mount Pleasant, WI 53406-4017
Tel (262) 636-6011 *Founded/Ownrshp* 2014
Sales NA *EMP* 470
SIC 6159 Agricultural credit institutions
Pr: Steven C Bierman
CFO: Douglas S Macleod

CNI
See CHICKASAW NATION INDUSTRIES INC

D-U-N-S 11-824-9846 IMP
CNI ENTERPRISES INC
C N I
(*Suby of* FUTURIS GLOBAL HOLDINGS LLC) ★
1451 E Lincoln Ave, Madison Heights, MI 48071-4136
Tel (248) 586-3300 *Founded/Ownrshp* 2015
Sales 306.6MM^E *EMP* 1,300
SIC 2396 Automotive trimmings, fabric
Pr: Jorge Morales
COO: Ray Bomya
CFO: William K Peterson

CNI/UTI
See UNIVERSAL TRIM INC

D-U-N-S 08-068-8963
CNL FINANCIAL GROUP INC (FL)
(*Suby of* CNL HOLDINGS LLC) ★
450 S Orange Ave Ste 300, Orlando, FL 32801-3394
Tel (407) 650-1000 *Founded/Ownrshp* 1980, 2000
Sales NA *EMP* 600^E
SIC 6141 6719 Personal credit institutions; Investment holding companies, except banks
Ch Bd: James M Seneff Jr
Pr: Neil Menard
**Pr:* Timothy J Seneff
**CEO:* Thomas K Sittema
COO: Steve Shackelford
**CFO:* Lynn E Rose
**CFO:* Tracy G Schmidt
**V Ch Bd:* Robert A Bourne
VP: Donna Bass
VP: Scott Belval
VP: Steve Clover
VP: Duane Comprosky
VP: Erin Gray
VP: Campbell B Henry
VP: Sean Hickham
VP: Grant Markgraf
VP: Matt Ragsdale
VP: Kaki Rawls
VP: Gary Rosmarin
VP: Lisa Smith
VP: Gordon Wilhite

D-U-N-S 96-871-5545
CNL HEALTHCARE PROPERTIES INC
450 S Orange Ave, Orlando, FL 32801-3383
Tel (407) 650-1000 *Founded/Ownrshp* 2010
Sales 300.5MM *EMP* 2
SIC 6798 Real estate investment trusts
Ch Bd: James M Seneff
**Pr:* Stephen H Mauldin
COO: Phillip Anderson
**COO:* Kevin R Maddron
**V Ch Bd:* Thomas K Sittema
**Sr VP:* Ixchell C Duate
**Sr VP:* Holly J Greer
**Sr VP:* Joseph T Johnson
**Sr VP:* Kay S Redlich
**Sr VP:* Stephen K Rice
**Sr VP:* Sharon A Yester
**VP:* Ashley Peeper
**VP:* Joshua J Taube

D-U-N-S 13-738-3662
CNL HOLDINGS LLC
430 W 7th St Ste 219001, Kansas City, MO 64105-1407
Tel (407) 650-1000 *Founded/Ownrshp* 2000
Sales 164.0MM^E *EMP* 640^E
SIC 6519 Real property lessors
Sr VP: Mark E Patten
VP: Lauren Harris

CNL HOSPITALITY PROPERTIES
See MSR HOTELS & RESORTS INC

D-U-N-S 61-470-4109
CNL HOSPITALITY PROPERTIES II INC
1 Post Office Sq Ste 3100, Boston, MA 02109-2108
Tel (617) 964-8389 *Founded/Ownrshp* 2004
Sales 158.5MM^E *EMP* 8,000
SIC 6798 Real estate investment trusts
CEO: Thomas J Hutchison III

D-U-N-S 82-843-3529
CNL LIFESTYLE PROPERTIES INC
450 S Orange Ave, Orlando, FL 32801-3383
Tel (407) 650-1000 *Founded/Ownrshp* 2003
Sales 337.6MM *EMP* 819
Accts Pricewaterhousecoopers Llp O
SIC 6798 Real estate investment trusts
Pr: Stephen H Mauldin
**Ch Bd:* James M Seneff Jr
CFO: Tracy Schmidt
CFO: Tammy J Tipton
**V Ch Bd:* Thomas K Sittema
Sr VP: Ixchell C Duarte
Sr VP: Holly J Greer
Sr VP: Mark E Patten
VP: Curt Caffey
VP: Stephen Rice
Exec: Carolyn Gosselin
Exec: Deanna Mayer
Exec: Mark Pattn
Exec: Lynn Rose
Exec: Lorri Shaban
Exec: Carlos Valdez

D-U-N-S 14-831-1590
CNLC-STC INC
(*Suby of* SUN-TIMES MEDIA GROUP INC) ★
350 N Orleans St, Chicago, IL 60654-1975
Tel (312) 321-3000 *Founded/Ownrshp* 1994
Sales 89.3MM^E *EMP* 2,100
SIC 2711 Newspapers, publishing & printing
COO: John Cruickshank
**CFO:* J David Dodd
VP: Frederic R Lebolt
Exec: Trevor Mikus
Dir IT: Larry Kelly

CNN
See CABLE NEWS NETWORK LP LLLP

CNN
See CABLE NEWS NETWORK INC

D-U-N-S 05-236-0161
▲ CNO FINANCIAL GROUP INC
11825 N Pennsylvania St, Carmel, IN 46032-4555
Tel (317) 817-6100 *Founded/Ownrshp* 1982
Sales NA *EMP* 3,500^E
Tkr Sym CNO *Exch* NYS
SIC 6311 6321 6331 Life insurance carriers; Accident insurance carriers; Health insurance carriers; Property damage insurance; Fire, marine & casualty insurance: stock
CEO: Edward J Bonach
**Ch Bd:* Neal C Schneider
Pr: Gary C Bhojwani
CFO: Erik M Helding
Chf Inves: Eric R Johnson
Ofcr: Scott R Perry
Ex VP: Bruce Baude
Ex VP: Susan L Menzel
Ex VP: Chris Nickele
Ex VP: Christopher J Nickele
Ex VP: Matthew J Zimpfer
Sr VP: John R Kline
VP: Timothy Bischof
VP: Adiza Caldwell
VP: Vishal Mahajan
VP: Gregory Turner
Board of Directors: Ellyn L Brown, Robert C Greving, Mary R Henderson, Charles J Jacklin, Daniel R Maurer, Frederick J Sievert, Michael T Tokarz

D-U-N-S 94-797-1156
■ CNO SERVICES LLC
CONSECO
(*Suby of* CNO FINANCIAL GROUP INC) ★
11825 N Pennsylvania St, Carmel, IN 46032-4555
Tel (317) 817-6100 *Founded/Ownrshp* 1995
Sales NA *EMP* 500
SIC 6411 Insurance agents, brokers & service
Pr: James Prieur
**Pr:* Edward J Bonach
CFO: Ed Bonach
Treas: Todd Hacker
VP: Andrew Ouimet
Genl Couns: Kelly Heindl

D-U-N-S 04-661-6595
CNS CORP
500 E 9th St, Kansas City, MO 64106-2627
Tel (816) 842-6300 *Founded/Ownrshp* 1982
Sales 113.3MM^E *EMP* 255
SIC 6211 6311 4724 Mutual funds, selling by independent salesperson; Life insurance; Travel agencies
Ch Bd: Charles N Sharpe

CNSLTD ELCTRCL DSTRIBUTOR
See GDT PROPERTIES INC

D-U-N-S 07-956-1674
■ CNT ACQUISITION CORP
(*Suby of* MICROSEMI CORP) ★
1 Enterprise, Aliso Viejo, CA 92656-2606
Tel (949) 380-6100 *Founded/Ownrshp* 2014
Sales 117.0MM^E *EMP* 3,100^E
SIC 3674 Rectifiers, solid state; Zener diodes; Diodes, solid state (germanium, silicon, etc.)
CEO: James J Peterson

D-U-N-S 07-978-7936
CNX COAL RESOURCES LP
1000 Consol Energy Dr, Canonsburg, PA 15317-6506
Tel (724) 485-4009 *Founded/Ownrshp* 2015
Sales 261.6MM *EMP* 8^E
Tkr Sym CNXC *Exch* NYS
SIC 1241 Coal mining services

D-U-N-S 61-032-9273
■ CNX GAS CORP
(*Suby of* CONSOL ENERGY INC) ★
1000 Consol Energy Dr, Canonsburg, PA 15317-6506
Tel (724) 485-4000 *Founded/Ownrshp* 2010
Sales 251.2MM^E *EMP* 174^E
SIC 1311 Natural gas production
Pr: Nicholas J Deiuliis
**CFO:* William J Lyons
**Treas:* John M Reilly
**Ex VP:* Robert P King
Sr VP: J Michael Onifer
VP: Robert M Belesky
VP: Charles Hardoby
**VP:* Ronald I Campanelli
VP: Richard L Toothman
VP: Daniel Zajdel
VP Opers: Claude D Morgan
Board of Directors: Philip W Baxter, Raj K Gupta, John R Pipski

D-U-N-S 13-100-2821 IMP/EXP
CO-ALLIANCE LLP
5250 E Us Hwy 3, Avon, IN 46123
Tel (317) 745-4491 *Founded/Ownrshp* 1920
Sales 531.4MM^E *EMP* 320
SIC 5191 5171 5153 2875 Feed; Seeds: field, garden & flower; Fertilizer & fertilizer materials; Petroleum bulk stations & terminals; Grains; Fertilizers, mixing only
Pt: Kevin Still
**Pt:* John Gram
Exec: Shawn Lambert
Plnt Mgr: John Rice
Mktg Mgr: John Brammeier

CO-ENERGY A CONNELL OIL INC CO
See CONNELL OIL INC

CO-OP COMFORT CREDIT
See HOOSIER ENERGY RURAL ELECTRIC COOPERATIVE INC

D-U-N-S 17-441-9739
CO-OP COUNTRY FARMERS ELEVATOR
340 Dupont Ave Ne, Renville, MN 56284
Tel (320) 329-8377 *Founded/Ownrshp* 1986
Sales 150.5MM *EMP* 50
Accts Carlson Highland & Co Llp
SIC 5153 5191 Grains; Feed; Fertilizer & fertilizer materials; Chemicals, agricultural; Seeds: field, garden & flower
Ch Bd: Calvin Aaron
**Pr:* Craig Hebrink
**Sec:* Michael Johnson
**V Ch Bd:* Dave Kadlec
Admn Mgr: Carrie Ashburn
Off Mgr: Carla Hamre

CO-OP NETWORK
See CU COOPERATIVE SYSTEMS INC

D-U-N-S 09-945-4977 IMP
COA INC
COASTER COMPANY OF AMERICA
12928 Sandoval St, Santa Fe Springs, CA 90670-4061
Tel (562) 944-7899 *Founded/Ownrshp* 1979
Sales 235.1MM^E *EMP* 700
Accts Moss Adams Llp Irvine Califo
SIC 5021 Household furniture; Dining room furniture; Beds & bedding; Shelving
CEO: Michael Yeh
VP: Matthew Chen
VP: Al Grossman
**VP:* Lisa KAO
Dir IT: Wesley Jacobsen
Info Man: John Lee

D-U-N-S 13-921-1275
COACH AMERICA GROUP INC
8150 N Central Expy # 1000, Dallas, TX 75206-1830
Tel (972) 354-3500 *Founded/Ownrshp* 2007
Sales NA *EMP* 5,500
SIC 4141

COACH HOUSE GIFTS
See GENERAL NOVELTY LTD

D-U-N-S 62-302-6353 IMP/EXP
▲ COACH INC
10 Hudson Yards, New York, NY 10001-2157
Tel (212) 594-1850 *Founded/Ownrshp* 1941

Sales 4.4MMM *EMP* 15,100[E]
Accts Deloitte & Touche Llp New Yor
Tkr Sym COH *Exch* NYS
SIC 3171 3172 2387 3143 3144 Women's handbags & purses; Handbags, women's; Purses, women's; Personal leather goods; Apparel belts; Men's footwear, except athletic; Women's footwear, except athletic
CEO: Victor Luis
**Ch Bd:* Jide Zeitlin
Pr: Ian Bickley
Pr: Andre Cohen
CFO: Andrea Shaw Resnick
Ofcr: Sarah Dunn
Ofcr: Todd Kahn
VP: Geoffrey Bain
VP: Lisel Donaldson
VP: Adrianne Kirszner
VP: Rob McClellan
VP: David Mollon
VP: Melinda Paraie
VP: Jamie Park
Board of Directors: David Denton, Andrea Guerra, Susan Kropf, Annabelle Yu Long, Ivan Menezes, William Nuti, Stephanie Tilenius

COACH LEATHERWARE COMPANY
See COACH STORES INC

D-U-N-S 62-110-8091 IMP
COACH STORES INC
COACH LEATHERWARE COMPANY
516 W 34th St Bsmt 5, New York, NY 10001-1394
Tel (212) 643-9727 *Founded/Ownrshp* 1985
Sales 203.3MM[E] *EMP* 3,000
SIC 3171 3161 3172 2387 5137 5099 Handbags, women's; Briefcases; Personal leather goods; Apparel belts; Handbags; Apparel belts, women's & children's; Cases, carrying
CEO: Lewis Frankfort

D-U-N-S 93-823-8870
COACH USA INC
SHORTLINE BUS SYSTEMS
(*Suby of* STAGECOACH GROUP PLC)
160 S Route 17 N, Paramus, NJ 07652
Tel (201) 225-7500 *Founded/Ownrshp* 1999
Sales 554.3MM[E] *EMP* 5,000
SIC 4725 4111 4121 Arrangement of travel tour packages, wholesale; Sightseeing tour companies; Bus transportation; Taxicabs
CEO: Martin Griffiths
CFO: Linda King
CFO: Susan Stellato
**Ch:* Brian Souter
VP: Kim Rogoff
Genl Mgr: Jon Nguyen
MIS Dir: Carl Newton
Sales Exec: Kim Bratton
Sales Exec: Lisa Finigan

D-U-N-S 07-955-2626
COACHELLA VALLEY UNIFIED SCHDIST
COACHELLA VALLEY USD
87225 Church St, Thermal, CA 92274-8901
Tel (760) 399-5137 *Founded/Ownrshp* 1973
Sales 1.3MM[E] *EMP* 1,189
Accts Vavrinektrineday & Co Llp Ran
SIC 8211 Public special education school; Public elementary school
Ex Dir: Michelle Murphy
IT Man: Gabriel Gutierrez
HC Dir: Alex Gonzalez

COACHELLA VALLEY USD
See COACHELLA VALLEY UNIFIED SCHDIST

D-U-N-S 04-133-0739 IMP
COACHELLA VALLEY WATER DISTRICT
C V WATER DISTRICT
85995 Avenue 52, Coachella, CA 92236-2568
Tel (760) 398-2651 *Founded/Ownrshp* 1918
Sales 150.2MM *EMP* 515
Accts Lance Soll & Lunghard Llp B
SIC 4941 4971 4952 7389 Water supply; Water distribution or supply systems for irrigation; Sewerage systems; Water softener service
Genl Mgr: Steve Robbins
CFO: Rick Dickhaut
**Genl Mgr:* Jim Barrett
**Genl Mgr:* Robert Cheng

D-U-N-S 18-658-7523
COAKLEY & WILLIAMS CONSTRUCTION INC
7475 Wisconsin Ave # 900, Bethesda, MD 20814-3499
Tel (301) 963-5000 *Founded/Ownrshp* 1987
Sales 137.8MM[E] *EMP* 210[E]
SIC 1542 Commercial & office building, new construction; Commercial & office buildings, renovation & repair
Ch Bd: Terrance Coakley
**Pr:* Patrick J Caulfield
VP: Victoria Swope
IT Man: Aboubacar Haidara
Snr PM: Joe Illig

D-U-N-S 55-649-1934 IMP
COAST ALUMINUM AND ARCHITECTURAL INC
10628 Fulton Wells Ave, Santa Fe Springs, CA 90670-3740
Tel (562) 946-6061 *Founded/Ownrshp* 1991
Sales 168.3MM[E] *EMP* 315
SIC 5051 Miscellaneous nonferrous products; Nonferrous metal sheets, bars, rods, etc.
Pr: Thomas C Clark
COO: Julio Marrero
Genl Mgr: Karen Smith
Sls Mgr: Ricardo Sosa
Sales Asso: Monica Reyes

D-U-N-S 02-910-7109 IMP/EXP
COAST CITRUS DISTRIBUTORS
7597 Bristow Ct, San Diego, CA 92154-7419
Tel (619) 661-7950 *Founded/Ownrshp* 2003
Sales 311.5MM *EMP* 389
SIC 5148 Fresh fruits & vegetables
Ch Bd: James M Alvarez
COO: Nick Alvarez
**V Ch Bd:* Margarita Alvarez
VP: Stanley Alvarez
VP: Mica Simpson
Exec: Sara Salinas
Opers Mgr: Miguel Lara

D-U-N-S 06-760-7770
COAST COMMUNITY COLLEGE DISTRICT ENTERPRISE INC
1370 Adams Ave, Costa Mesa, CA 92626-5429
Tel (714) 438-4600 *Founded/Ownrshp* 1948
Sales 158.8MM *EMP* 4,409
Accts Vicenti Lloyd & Stutzman Llp
SIC 8222 8221 Community college; Colleges universities & professional schools
CEO: Richard T Pagel
COO: Jim Farley
Treas: Michael Bare
Trst: Jim Moreno
Trst: Jerry Patterson
**VP:* Janet Houlihan
Exec: Erin Curtis
Adm Dir: Jorge Sanchez
Ex Dir: Douglas Bennett
Off Admin: Sheena Phan
CTO: Jacqueline Fretto

D-U-N-S 19-411-8246 IMP/EXP
COAST COMPOSITES LLC
AIP AEROSPACE HOLDINGS
(*Suby of* AIP AEROSPACE) ★
1395 S Lyon St, Santa Ana, CA 92705-4608
Tel (949) 455-0665 *Founded/Ownrshp* 2012
Sales 90.7MM[E] *EMP* 300[E]
SIC 3599 Machine shop, jobbing & repair
Pr: Paul Walsh
**CFO:* Steven Littauer
Ex VP: Raphael Flores
**VP:* James Masters
Dir Bus: Tim Shumate
Genl Mgr: Kelly Muto
Genl Mgr: Jeff Patchett
CIO: Tom Delisle
VP Opers: Haik Byurat
Sls Dir: Rick Choi

D-U-N-S 87-647-1822
COAST DENTAL SERVICES INC
4010 W Boy Scout Blvd # 1100, Tampa, FL 33607-5796
Tel (813) 288-1999 *Founded/Ownrshp* 1992
Sales 139.0MM[E] *EMP* 1,700
SIC 8021 Offices & clinics of dentists
Ch Bd: Terek Diasti Dvm
Pr: Adam Diasti
CFO: Michael Branca
CFO: Timothy G Merrick
VP: Patricia Huie
VP: Kathy Marlin
Assoc Dir: Doug Brown
Off Mgr: Leo Rodriguez
IT Man: Linda Branstetter
IT Man: David Morgan
IT Man: Charisse Simpson

D-U-N-S 09-261-8651 IMP
■ **COAST DISTRIBUTION SYSTEM INC**
(*Suby of* KEYSTONE AUTOMOTIVE OPERATIONS INC) ★
350 Woodview Ave Ste 100, Morgan Hill, CA 95037-8105
Tel (408) 782-6686 *Founded/Ownrshp* 1977, 2015
Sales 118.8MM *EMP* 280
SIC 5013 Motor vehicle supplies & new parts; Trailer parts & accessories
CEO: James Musbach
CFO: Sandra A Knell
Ex VP: David A Berger
Ex VP: Dennis A Castagnola
Ex VP: Dennis Castagnola
VP: Bruce Boucher
Brnch Mgr: Ryan Albright
Manager: Lonnie Anhorn
Manager: Scott Laidlaw
Manager: Dee Wright
Sls Mgr: Daniel Begin

D-U-N-S 00-696-3847
COAST ELECTRIC POWER ASSOCIATION (MS)
18020 Highway 603, Kiln, MS 39556-8487
Tel (228) 363-7000 *Founded/Ownrshp* 1937, 1938
Sales 202.8MM *EMP* 238
Accts Jackson Thornton & Co Pc Mo
SIC 4911 Distribution, electric power
Pr: Robert J Occhi
**CFO:* John Holston
Bd of Dir: April Lollar
VP: Louis Lee
Trfc Dir: Steve Pitzer

D-U-N-S 18-405-2454
COAST FORK NURSING CENTER INC
PRESTIGE CARE INC
(*Suby of* PRESTIGE CARE INC) ★
515 Grant Ave, Cottage Grove, OR 97424-2967
Tel (541) 942-5528 *Founded/Ownrshp* 1986
Sales 577.0MM *EMP* 60
SIC 8051 Convalescent home with continuous nursing care; Extended care facility
Pr: Harold Delamarter
**Pr:* Phillip C Fogg
**CFO:* Steve Fogg

D-U-N-S 01-722-3996 EXP
■ **COAST GUARD EXCHANGE SYSTEM**
(*Suby of* USCG) ★
510 Independence Pkwy # 500, Chesapeake, VA 23320-5191
Tel (757) 420-2480 *Founded/Ownrshp* 1951
Sales 141.5MM[E] *EMP* 1,200
SIC 5399 5311 Army-Navy goods; Department stores, discount
CFO: John Best
CFO: Jim Sether
Genl Mgr: John Madjecki
Store Mgr: Brenda Schepici
Merch Mgr: Scott Poteet

D-U-N-S 93-879-0417
■ **COAST HOTELS & CASINOS INC**
(*Suby of* ORLEANS HOTEL AND CASINO) ★
4500 W Tropicana Ave, Las Vegas, NV 89103-5420
Tel (702) 367-7111 *Founded/Ownrshp* 1995
Sales 24.5MM[E] *EMP* 7,700
SIC 7011 Casino hotel
Ch Bd: Michael Gaughan
**Pr:* Harlan Braaten
**Pr:* Keith Smith
**CFO:* Gage Parrish
**Treas:* Paul J Chakmak
VP: Haroan Dorates
Genl Mgr: Mike Growney
CTO: Brenda McArthur
VP Mktg: Jimmy Bruer
VP Mktg: Pam S Dreyer
VP Mktg: Lynne R Tokoph
Board of Directors: Joseph A Blasco, F Michael Corrigan, Thomas V Girardi, Charles Silverman, Peter M Thomas, Clyde T Turner

D-U-N-S 93-895-0680
■ **COAST HOTELS AND CASINOS INC**
ORLEANS HOTEL AND CASINO, THE
(*Suby of* BOYD GAMING CORP) ★
4500 W Tropicana Ave, Las Vegas, NV 89103-5420
Tel (702) 365-7111 *Founded/Ownrshp* 1995
Sales 254.9MM[E] *EMP* 7,700
SIC 7011 Casino hotel
Pr: Keith E Smith
**Ch Bd:* Michael Gaughan
**Pr:* David Ross
**CFO:* Gage Parrish
**VP:* Brian A Larson
VP: Horst Ziura
IT Man: Nona Politano

D-U-N-S 18-672-7657
COAST PERSONNEL SERVICES INC
2295 De La Cruz Blvd, Santa Clara, CA 95050-3020
Tel (408) 653-2100 *Founded/Ownrshp* 1987
Sales 58.0MM[E] *EMP* 1,900
SIC 7363 Temporary help service
CEO: Larry K Bunker
VP: Michael Avidano
**VP:* Larry Broun
VP: Janet Marchel

D-U-N-S 08-264-3875 IMP/EXP
COAST PUMP & SUPPLY CO INC
COAST PUMP WATER TECHNOLOGIES
610 Groveland Ave, Venice, FL 34285-4613
Tel (352) 258-2291 *Founded/Ownrshp* 1980
Sales 98.1MM[E] *EMP* 90
SIC 0721 Irrigation system operation, not providing water
Ex VP: Matthew Phillips
**Pr:* Gordon W Phillips
**VP:* Mark Phillips

COAST PUMP WATER TECHNOLOGIES
See COAST PUMP & SUPPLY CO INC

D-U-N-S 15-143-3380 EXP
COAST-TO-COAST PRODUCE CO LLC
125 Commerce Ct Ste 2, Cheshire, CT 06410-1243
Tel (203) 271-2006 *Founded/Ownrshp* 1985
Sales 92.5MM *EMP* 20
Accts Cohnreznick Llp Hartford Con
SIC 5148 Fresh fruits & vegetables
**Sec:* Beverly Grove

D-U-N-S 00-318-6178 EXP
COASTAL AGROBUSINESS INC (NC)
3702 Evans St, Greenville, NC 27834-5408
Tel (252) 756-1126 *Founded/Ownrshp* 1953
Sales 162.3MM[E] *EMP* 180
SIC 5191 3523 Chemicals, agricultural; Sprayers & spraying machines, agricultural
Pr: James C Whitehurst III
Ch Bd: James C Whitehurst Jr
Sec: Ann H Whitehurst
VP: Mike Seymour
Tech Mgr: Tom McKemie
Site Mgr: Larry Waddell
Sfty Mgr: Tandy Dunn
Manager: Josh Allen

D-U-N-S 00-671-6557
COASTAL AUTO TRANSPORT LLC
4928 Us Highway 301 S, Hope Mills, NC 28348-2631
Tel (910) 429-9902 *Founded/Ownrshp* 2008
Sales 97.2MM *EMP* 4
SIC 4212 Truck rental with drivers

D-U-N-S 02-486-5115 IMP
COASTAL BEVERAGE CO INC (NC)
301 Harley Dr, Wilmington, NC 28405-3635
Tel (910) 799-3011 *Founded/Ownrshp* 1952
Sales 84.5MM[E] *EMP* 246
SIC 5181

D-U-N-S 00-284-0056
COASTAL BRIDGE CO LLC
C B
4825 Jamestown Ave, Baton Rouge, LA 70808-3225
Tel (225) 766-0244 *Founded/Ownrshp* 1952
Sales 101.6MM[E] *EMP* 200
SIC 1622 Bridge construction; Highway construction, elevated
Pr: Robert C Overall Jr
**Sec:* Gerald Tregre
**VP:* C E Milner Jr
VP: Ed Milner
IT Man: Robert Irving
Pgrm Dir: Jerry Tregre

D-U-N-S 08-048-3859
COASTAL CAROLINA UNIVERSITY
103 Tom Trout Dr, Conway, SC 29526-1000
Tel (843) 347-3161 *Founded/Ownrshp* 1954
Sales 210.0MM *EMP* 1,582
SIC 8221 Colleges universities & professional schools
Pr: David A Decenzo

D-U-N-S 96-648-6045
COASTAL CAROLINA UNIVERSITY
(*Suby of* COASTAL CAROLINA UNIVERSITY) ★
642 Century Cir, Conway, SC 29526-8279
Tel (843) 347-3161 *Founded/Ownrshp* 1954
Sales 147.3MM *EMP* 900
Accts Cline Brandt Kochenower & Co
SIC 8221 Colleges universities & professional schools
Pr: David A Decenzo
V Ch: Daniel W Moore
V Ch: Samuel J Swad
**Ch:* Edgar L Dyer
Treas: Tommy M Stringer
Trst: William S Biggs
Trst: Samuel L Frink
Trst: William L Lyles
Trst: Daniel Moore
Trst: Mark Sanford
Trst: Oran P Smith
Trst: Eugene C Spivey
Trst: Robert G Templeton
Ofcr: Lonnie Fleming
Ex VP: Sally Horner
**Sr VP:* J Ralph Byington
Sr VP: Wilbur L Garland
**VP:* Stacie A Bowie
**VP:* Deborah K Conner
VP: Haven L Hart
VP: Marvin Marozas

D-U-N-S 18-328-8778 IMP/EXP
COASTAL CHEMICAL CO LLC
(*Suby of* BRENNTAG SOUTHEAST) ★
3520 Veterans Memorial Dr, Abbeville, LA 70510-5708
Tel (337) 898-0001 *Founded/Ownrshp* 1997
Sales 736.2MM *EMP* 750
SIC 5172 5169 Lubricating oils & greases; Chemicals, industrial & heavy
Pr: Randy King
**Pr:* Jim Doyle

D-U-N-S 10-816-5176
COASTAL DEVELOPMENTAL SERVICES FOUNDATION
WESTSIDE REGIONAL CENTER
5901 Green Valley Cir # 320, Culver City, CA 90230-6938
Tel (310) 258-4000 *Founded/Ownrshp* 1982
Sales 169.7MM *EMP* 2
Accts Windes & Mcclaughry Acct Corp
SIC 8322 Individual & family services
Ex Dir: Michael Danneker
Bd of Dir: Cecilia Fabulich
Ex Dir: Denise Fernald
Prgrm Mgr: Hillary Kessler
Prgrm Mgr: Martha Thompson
Pr Dir: Mary-Lou Stusser
Phys Thrpy: Gail Smith

COASTAL ELEVATOR SERVICE
See OTIS ELEVATOR CO

COASTAL FARM & RANCH
See COASTAL FARM HOLDINGS INC

D-U-N-S 61-292-7137 IMP
COASTAL FARM HOLDINGS INC
COASTAL FARM & RANCH
1355 Goldfish Farm Rd Se, Albany, OR 97322-5154
Tel (541) 967-3450 *Founded/Ownrshp* 2008
Sales 108.6MM[E] *EMP* 428
SIC 5999 Feed & farm supply; Farm equipment & supplies
Pr: Bruce G Wheeler
**CFO:* Wendy Phelps
Sales Exec: Roy Quador

D-U-N-S 04-978-4010
COASTAL FEDERAL CREDIT UNION
1000 Saint Albans Dr, Raleigh, NC 27609-7347
Tel (919) 420-8000 *Founded/Ownrshp* 1967
Sales NA *EMP* 400
SIC 6061 Federal credit unions
Ch Bd: Joan Nelson
**Ch Bd:* Richard S Bloom
Pr: Tj Wyman
**COO:* Kris Kovacs
**CFO:* Brad Miller
**Sec:* William F Smith
Ofcr: Cindy Berger
Ofcr: Desiree Bolibaugh
Ofcr: Louis Cipriani
Ofcr: Tom Gervase
**Ofcr:* Brenda Hooks
Ofcr: Kristin Little
Ofcr: Eric K Ruch
Ofcr: Katie Sanders
Ofcr: Wil Spears
Ofcr: Brian Terwilliger
**Ex VP:* Chuck Purvis
VP: Kathleen Hassell
VP: Carlton Howard
VP: David Jacobs
VP: Marvin Jones

D-U-N-S 00-319-1079 EXP
COASTAL FOREST RESOURCES CO
COASTAL TIMBERLANDS
8007 Florida Georgia Hwy, Havana, FL 32333
Tel (850) 539-6432 *Founded/Ownrshp* 1980
Sales 121.8MM[E] *EMP* 400
SIC 2436 2491 0811 0851 Plywood, softwood; Structural lumber & timber, treated wood; Timber tracts; Forestry services
Pr: J Travis Bryant
**Ch:* Paul Barringer II
**VP:* Thomas Evans
**VP:* Kevin Luzak
Area Mgr: Don Merritt

D-U-N-S 60-304-5063
COASTAL HOTEL GROUP INC
15375 Se 30th Pl Ste 290, Bellevue, WA 98007-6500
Tel (206) 388-0400 *Founded/Ownrshp* 2000
Sales 48.3MM[E] *EMP* 1,500
SIC 7011 Hotels & motels
Pr: Yogi Hugsen
**CFO:* Peter Lafemina
Sls Dir: Roger Becker

D-U-N-S 78-650-9109
COASTAL INTERNATIONAL SECURITY INC
(*Suby of* AKAL SECURITY INC) ★
6101 Fallard Dr, Upper Marlboro, MD 20772-3878
Tel (703) 339-0233 *Founded/Ownrshp* 2001
Sales 127.1MM *EMP* 5,003
Accts Pulaskos Cpas Pc Albuquerque
SIC 7381 Security guard service
Pr: Anthony Shepherd
**CFO:* Sukhwinder Singh
**VP:* Eric Pohland

D-U-N-S 15-510-4938 IMP/EXP
COASTAL PACIFIC FOOD DISTRIBUTORS INC
1015 Performance Dr, Stockton, CA 95206-4925
Tel (909) 947-2066 *Founded/Ownrshp* 1986
Sales 1.2MMM *EMP* 459
Accts Dixon Hughes Goodman Llp Norf
SIC 5141 4225 7519 4222 Groceries, general line; General warehousing & storage; Trailer rental; Refrigerated warehousing & storage
CEO: Terrence Wood
**COO:* Jeff King
CFO: Monica Bertkey
**CFO:* Matthew Payne
**Treas:* John Payne
**VP:* Edmond Jared
Genl Mgr: Peter Hawkes

D-U-N-S 86-746-3408
COASTAL REHABILITATION HOSPITAL
NEW HANOVER REGIONAL MED CTR
2131 S 17th St, Wilmington, NC 28401-7407
Tel (910) 343-7845 *Founded/Ownrshp* 1994
Sales 727.1MM *EMP* 30[E]
SIC 8093 Rehabilitation center, outpatient treatment
Chf Path: John Turner
VP: Lori Feezor
Dir Risk M: Laura Phares
Ex Dir: Aline Lasseter
Nurse Mgr: Brandy Garris
Dir QC: Barbara Geiger
IT Man: Bert Singletary
Netwrk Mgr: Jay Brinkley
VP Opers: Kevin McDonnell
Mktg Mgr: Jennifer Windley
Doctor: ROC McCarthy

D-U-N-S 14-158-3455
COASTAL RESTAURANTS GP LLC
COZYMEL'S
6340 Intl Pkwy Ste 300, Plano, TX 75093
Tel (214) 443-1920 *Founded/Ownrshp* 2003
Sales 40.7MM[E] *EMP* 1,250
SIC 5812 Family restaurants
CFO: Wyatt Truscheit

D-U-N-S 79-204-0433
COASTAL SUNBELT INC
COASTAL SUNBELT PRODUCE
9001 Whiskey Bottom Rd, Laurel, MD 20723-1356
Tel (410) 799-8000 *Founded/Ownrshp* 2006
Sales 557.5MM[E] *EMP* 900[E]
SIC 5148 4214 0723 2099 Fresh fruits & vegetables; Local trucking with storage; Vegetable crops market preparation services; Food preparations
Pr: John Corso
COO: Dawn Morton
**CFO:* Bob Lahmann
CFO: Robert Lahmann
Exec: Krista Brown
Genl Mgr: Erica Wright
Dir IT: Richard Kreuzburg
IT Man: Ryan Lowme
Netwrk Eng: Alex Puleo
Sales Asso: Michael Crowder
Sales Asso: Mustafa Ibrahim

COASTAL SUNBELT PRODUCE
See COASTAL SUNBELT INC

COASTAL TIMBERLANDS
See COASTAL FOREST RESOURCES CO

D-U-N-S 00-478-0896
COASTAL TRANSPORT CO INC (TX)
1603 Ackerman Rd, San Antonio, TX 78219-3518
Tel (210) 661-4287 *Founded/Ownrshp* 1948, 1958
Sales 90.0MM *EMP* 650
Accts Padgett Stratemann & Co Llp
SIC 4212 4213 Liquid haulage, local; Liquid petroleum transport, non-local
CEO: Richard A Atwell
**VP:* Thomas R Braaten

COASTER COMPANY OF AMERICA
See COA INC

D-U-N-S 07-375-2156
■ **COATESVILLE HOSPITAL CORP**
BRANDYWINE HOSPITAL
(*Suby of* COMMUNITY HEALTH SYSTEMS INC) ★
201 Reeceville Rd, Coatesville, PA 19320-1542
Tel (610) 383-8000 *Founded/Ownrshp* 2001
Sales 120.5MM *EMP* 950
SIC 8062 General medical & surgical hospitals
CFO: Don Bevers
Chf Path: Kimberly A Levin
**CEO:* Jean Botkin
**CEO:* Bryan Burklow
CFO: Don Beavers
Dir OR: Justine Murphy
Dir Soc: Kathy Gillan
Comm Dir: Sherry Ryder
Dir Rx: Jeffrey Gladstone
Dir Env Sv: Adelia Daniels
Chf Nrs Of: Tammy Torres

D-U-N-S 00-672-4462 IMP/EXP
COATING EXCELLENCE INTERNATIONAL LLC
C E I
(*Suby of* CEI BLOCKER CORP)
975 Brdwy St, Wrightstown, WI 54180
Tel (920) 996-1900 *Founded/Ownrshp* 2016
Sales 228.6MM[E] *EMP* 475
SIC 2671 Plastic film, coated or laminated for packaging
CEO: Greg Tucker
Pr: Rita Cox
CFO: Julie Piton
VP: Art Bucci
VP: George Landes Jr
VP: Lynda Swenson
VP: Mike Van Abel
Area Mgr: Jason Sieg
Genl Mgr: Paul Welhouse
VP Mfg: Louann Mueller
Ql Cn Mgr: Donna Jones

D-U-N-S 00-148-2975 IMP/EXP
COATS & CLARK INC
COATS NORTH AMERICA D
(*Suby of* COATS NORTH AMERICA DE REPUBLICA DOMINICANA INC) ★
3430 Toringdon Way # 301, Charlotte, NC 28277-2446
Tel (704) 329-5800 *Founded/Ownrshp* 1995
Sales 106.9MM[E] *EMP* 3,868
SIC 2284 2281 3364 3089 2241 3965 Cotton thread; Thread from manmade fibers; Cotton yarn, spun; Manmade staple fiber yarn, spun; Zinc & zinc-base alloy die-castings; Molding primary plastic; Narrow fabric mills; Fabric tapes; Trimmings, textile; Needles, hand or machine; Hooks, crochet; Eyelets, metal: clothing, fabrics, boots or shoes
Pr: G Maxwell Perks
**VP:* Donna L Armstrong
Mng Dir: Ginta Vaidere
Mng Dir: Ruta Voveryte
Genl Mgr: Anudeep Nagalia
Off Mgr: Grace Hou
Tech Mgr: Ramkumar Thiyagarajan
Natl Sales: Fayyaz Dangra
Sls&Mrk Ex: Dennis Yellen
Sls Dir: Jeayong Kim
Sls Dir: Taina Rautapuro

D-U-N-S 00-133-9373 IMP
COATS AMERICAN INC (NJ)
COATS NORTH AMERICA
(*Suby of* COATS NORTH AMERICA D) ★
3430 Toringdon Way # 301, Charlotte, NC 28277-2446
Tel (704) 329-5800 *Founded/Ownrshp* 1898
Sales 98.3MM[E] *EMP* 1,100
SIC 2284 Cotton thread; Thread from manmade fibers; Sewing thread
CEO: Steven Baune
**Pr:* Johan Depraeter
CFO: Richard Howes
**Ch:* Mike Clasper
**Ch:* William Ostmann
**Ex VP:* Roger L Cothran
**VP:* Donna Armstrong
**VP:* Ronald V Budnick
VP: Tomothy D Cogswell
VP: Johan De Praeter
VP: Russell Karr
VP: Rex Stuckey
VP: Dennis Yelen

COATS NORTH AMERICA
See COATS AMERICAN INC

COATS NORTH AMERICA D
See COATS & CLARK INC

D-U-N-S 10-912-9437 IMP
COATS NORTH AMERICA DE REPUBLICA DOMINICANA INC
(*Suby of* COATS HOLDINGS LTD)
3430 Toringdon Way # 301, Charlotte, NC 28277-2576
Tel (800) 242-8095 *Founded/Ownrshp* 1981
Sales 139.8MM[E] *EMP* 4,225
SIC 2284 2281 3364 3089 2241 3965 Cotton thread; Thread from manmade fibers; Cotton yarn, spun; Manmade staple fiber yarn, spun; Zinc & zinc-base alloy die-castings; Molding primary plastic; Narrow fabric mills; Fabric tapes; Trimmings, textile; Needles, hand or machine; Hooks, crochet; Eyelets, metal: clothing, fabrics, boots or shoes
CEO: Johan Depraeter
**VP:* Donna Armstrong

D-U-N-S 04-674-4629 EXP
COBALT BOATS LLC
1715 N 8th St, Neodesha, KS 66757-1283
Tel (620) 325-2653 *Founded/Ownrshp* 2008
Sales 132.4MM *EMP* 620
SIC 3732 Boats, fiberglass: building & repairing
CEO: Paxson St Clair
**Pr:* Sean Callan
**CFO:* Bill Wallisch
**Sr VP:* Gary Schultz
MIS Mgr: Gene Ewert
VP Sls: Peter Delorne
Manager: Jeff Morales

D-U-N-S 92-891-3540
■ **COBALT GROUP INC**
NATIONAL INTERAD
(*Suby of* ADP) ★
605 5th Ave S Ste 800, Seattle, WA 98104-3888
Tel (206) 269-6363 *Founded/Ownrshp* 2010
Sales 95.8MM[E] *EMP* 653
SIC 7372 Business oriented computer software
CEO: John Holt
**COO:* Scott Mathews
**CFO:* Jim Beach
**Chf Mktg O:* Chris Reed
Ex VP: William Eager
Sr VP: Greg Meyer
VP: Douglas J Beighle
VP: Lee Brunz
VP: Mark Dunn
VP: Howard Gardner
VP: Julia Pizzi
VP: Chuck Russo

D-U-N-S 07-939-0853
COBALT HOLDINGS INC
101 Waukegan Rd Ste 990, Lake Bluff, IL 60044-1687
Tel (773) 230-3219 *Founded/Ownrshp* 1988
Sales 110.0MM *EMP* 15[E]
SIC 4812 4813 Cellular telephone services; Telephone communication, except radio
CEO: Paul A Moore
**Pr:* Lawrence Malone
**VP:* William Cooper
**VP:* Colin Markey

D-U-N-S 08-858-1561
COBALT MORTGAGE INC
11241 Slater Ave Ne # 110, Kirkland, WA 98033-8825
Tel (425) 605-3100 *Founded/Ownrshp* 2001
Sales NA *EMP* 1,000
SIC 6163

D-U-N-S 07-577-0271
COBANK ACB
6340 S Fiddlers Green Cir, Greenwood Village, CO 80111-4951
Tel (303) 740-6527 *Founded/Ownrshp* 1933
Sales NA *EMP* 500
SIC 6111 7359 6159 Banks for cooperatives; Equipment rental & leasing; Machinery & equipment finance leasing; Truck finance leasing; Automobile finance leasing
Pr: Robert B Engel
**Pr:* Mary E McBride
COO: Ann Trakimas
**CFO:* David P Burlage
Chf Cred: Daniel Key
Ofcr: Thomas Halverson
Ofcr: Lori L O'Flaherty
Ex VP: Antony M Bahr
Ex VP: Amy H Gales
Ex VP: Jonathan B Logan
Ex VP: Mary McBride
Ex VP: Joe Savage
Ex VP: Douglas E Wilhlm
**Sr VP:* James R Bernsten
Sr VP: Nivin Elgohary
Sr VP: Gary Fitzgerald
Sr VP: Robert F West
VP: Will Baildon
VP: Josh Batchelder
VP: Chris Clayton
VP: John Cole
Board of Directors: Stephanie Herseth Sandlin

COBB COUNTY BOARD OF COMMISSIO
See COUNTY OF COBB

D-U-N-S 10-001-3499
COBB COUNTY BOARD OF EDUCATION
514 Glover St Se, Marietta, GA 30060-2750
Tel (770) 426-3300 *Founded/Ownrshp* 1881
Sales 1.1MMM *EMP* 591[E]
Accts Mauldin & Jenkins Llc Atlant
SIC 8211 School board
Ch Bd: Randy Scamihorn
**CFO:* Cathy Adams
MIS Mgr: Becky Robinson
Psych: Janet Callahan
Psych: Alice Smith
HC Dir: Melanie Bales

D-U-N-S 96-493-5055
COBB COUNTY PUBLIC SCHOOLS
514 Glover St Se, Marietta, GA 30060-2706
Tel (770) 426-3300 *Founded/Ownrshp* 1881
Sales 1.1MMM *EMP* 10,000
Accts Ross Lane & Company Llc Atlan
SIC 8211 Public elementary & secondary schools
Treas: An Goh

D-U-N-S 03-379-0494
COBB ELECTRIC MEMBERSHIP CORP
COBB EMC
1000 Emc Pkwy Ne, Marietta, GA 30060-7908
Tel (770) 429-2100 *Founded/Ownrshp* 1938
Sales 424.5MM *EMP* 548[E]
Accts Mcnair Mclemore Middlebrooks &
SIC 4911 Distribution, electric power
CEO: WT Chip Nelson III
Pr: Glynda Thor
CFO: Peggy Ledford
**CFO:* Robert Steele
**Sec:* Cheryl G Meadows
Bd of Dir: Edward Crowell
Chf Mktg O: Mark Goddard
**VP:* Kevan Espy
VP: Sam Kelly
VP: Jay Kenyon
VP: Keith Kirkus
VP: Lil W Lasseter
VP: Steve Paolucci
VP: Tim Sosebee
Exec: Sheila Bryant

COBB EMC
See COBB ELECTRIC MEMBERSHIP CORP

COBB HOSPITAL AND MEDICAL CENTER
See COBB HOSPITAL INC

D-U-N-S 06-646-6673
COBB HOSPITAL INC
COBB HOSPITAL AND MEDICAL CENTER
(*Suby of* WELLSTAR HEALTH SYSTEM INC) ★
3950 Austell Rd, Austell, GA 30106-1121
Tel (770) 792-7600 *Founded/Ownrshp* 1986
Sales 287.5MM *EMP* 2,500[E]
SIC 8062 General medical & surgical hospitals
CEO: Reynold J Jennings
**Pr:* Kem Mullen
CFO: Jim Badinski
**CFO:* A James Budzinski
CFO: Marsha Burke
Dir Lab: Susan Woodhall
Dir Rad: Lynn Hanks
CTO: Leth Cook
IT Man: Robert Mandler
Doctor: Frank Demarino
Doctor: Daksh Joshi

COBB THEATRES
See THEATRES COBB III LLC

D-U-N-S 14-472-5280
■ **COBB-VANTRESS INC**
(*Suby of* TYSON FOODS INC) ★
4703 Highway 412 E, Siloam Springs, AR 72761-8906
Tel (479) 524-3166 *Founded/Ownrshp* 1986
Sales 354.3MM[E] *EMP* 1,740
SIC 0751 Livestock services, except veterinary
Pr: Jerry Moye
Pr: Chester Hobart
**Treas:* Jimmy Burns
VP: Mitchell Abrahamsen
VP: John Hardiman
VP: Randy Vardeman
Exec: Lorie West
Dir Lab: Joseph Schultz
Dir: Steve Iseler
**Prin:* James Bell
Genl Mgr: Aldo Rossi

COBBER BOOKSTORE
See CONCORDIA COLLEGE CORP

COBHAM
See REMEC DEFENSE & SPACE INC

D-U-N-S 80-958-0439
COBHAM ADVANCED ELECTRONIC SOLUTIONS INC
(*Suby of* COBHAM AES HOLDINGS INC) ★
305 Richardson Rd, Lansdale, PA 19446-1495
Tel (215) 996-2000 *Founded/Ownrshp* 1934
Sales 498.4MM[E] *EMP* 3,200[E]
SIC 3812 Acceleration indicators & systems components, aerospace
Pr: Jill Kale
**Treas:* Brian Drzewiecki
Prgrm Mgr: Marc Holloway
Genl Mgr: Rebecca Hettel
IT Man: Samuel Negron

D-U-N-S 82-688-8880
COBHAM AES HOLDINGS INC
(*Suby of* COBHAM HOLDINGS INC) ★
2121 Crystal Dr Ste 625, Arlington, VA 22202-3797
Tel (703) 414-5300 *Founded/Ownrshp* 2008
Sales 1.0MMM[E] *EMP* 3,600[E]
SIC 3679 3812 Microwave components; Acceleration indicators & systems components, aerospace
CEO: Jill Kale

COBHAM ANTENNA SYSTEMS MICROWA
See CONTINENTAL MICROWAVE AND TOOL CO INC

COBHAM AROSPC COMMUNICATIONS
See CHELTON AVIONICS INC

COBHAM AVCOMM
See AEROFLEX WICHITA INC

D-U-N-S 87-637-1998
COBHAM DEFENSE ELECTRONIC SYSTEMS CORP
1001 Pawtucket Blvd, Lowell, MA 01854-1040
Tel (978) 779-7000 *Founded/Ownrshp* 1994
Sales 315.8MM[E] *EMP* 2,650
SIC 3812

COBHAM DEFENSE ELECTRONICS
See COBHAM ELECTRONIC SYSTEMS INC

D-U-N-S 82-992-4591
COBHAM ELECTRONIC SYSTEMS INC
COBHAM DEFENSE ELECTRONICS
1001 Pawtucket Blvd, Lowell, MA 01854-1040
Tel (978) 442-4700 *Founded/Ownrshp* 2008
Sales NA *EMP* 1,150
SIC 3812

D-U-N-S 07-962-1666
COBHAM HOLDINGS (US) INC
(*Suby of* LOCKMAN INVESTMENTS LIMITED)
10 Cobham Dr, Orchard Park, NY 14127-4121
Tel (716) 662-0006 *Founded/Ownrshp* 2008
Sales 228.8MM[E] *EMP* 3,700
SIC 3679 3812 Microwave components; Acceleration indicators & systems components, aerospace
**Pr:* Betty Bible
Sftwr Eng: Bob Smith

D-U-N-S 00-474-0126
COBHAM HOLDINGS INC
(*Suby of* LOCKWASH US LIMITED)
10 Orchard Park Dr, Orchard Park, NY 14127
Tel (716) 662-0006 *Founded/Ownrshp* 1981
Sales 2.1MMM[E] *EMP* 3,700[E]
SIC 3679 3812 Microwave components; Acceleration indicators & systems components, aerospace
CEO: Bob Murphy
IT Man: Terry Lang

D-U-N-S 16-088-5976 IMP/EXP
COBHAM MANAGEMENT SERVICES INC
COBHAM MISSION SYSTEMS DIV
(*Suby of* COBHAM HOLDINGS INC) ★
10 Cobham Dr, Orchard Park, NY 14127-4121
Tel (716) 662-0006 *Founded/Ownrshp* 1981
Sales 228.8MM[E] *EMP* 2,650
SIC 3568 Couplings, shaft: rigid, flexible, universal joint, etc.
Pr: Warren Tucker
**Treas:* Betty Bible
Snr Sftwr: Rick Hamilton
Dir IT: Jerry Birk
Opers Mgr: Adreanne Lippa
Opers Mgr: Tim Thommen

COBHAM MISSION SYSTEM
See CARLETON LIFE SUPPORT SYSTEMS INC

COBHAM MISSION SYSTEMS DIV
See COBHAM MANAGEMENT SERVICES INC

COBHAM SATCOM
See SEATEL INC

COBHAM SEMICONDUCTOR SOLUTIONS
See AEROFLEX COLORADO SPRINGS INC

D-U-N-S 09-191-1297
■ **COBIZ BANK**
COBIZ BANK NATIONAL ASSN
(*Suby of* COBIZ FINANCIAL INC) ★
821 17th St Ste 800, Denver, CO 80202-3022
Tel (303) 293-2265 *Founded/Ownrshp* 1995
Sales NA *EMP* 260
SIC 6021 National trust companies with deposits, commercial

Ch Bd: Steve Bangert
**CEO:* Jon Lorenz
**CFO:* Lynn Andrich
**Sr VP:* Bob Ostertag
Sr VP: Tim Stack
VP: Marie Reid
Ex Dir: Aaron Bachik

COBIZ BANK NATIONAL ASSN
See COBIZ BANK

D-U-N-S 10-256-4572
▲ COBIZ FINANCIAL INC
821 17th St, Denver, CO 80202-3040
Tel (303) 312-3400 *Founded/Ownrshp* 1980
Sales NA *EMP* 532[E]
Accts Crowe Horwath Llp Sherman Oak
Tkr Sym COBZ *Exch* NGS
SIC 6021 National commercial banks
Ch Bd: Steven Bangert
Pr: Stacy Willams
COO: Richard J Dalton
CFO: Lyne B Andrich
Ex VP: Margaret Battiste
Ex VP: David E Pass Jr
Sr VP: Troy R Dumlao
Sr VP: T J Kern
Sr VP: David Pass
VP: Dale Algrim
VP: Tyrone Gant
VP: Sharon May
VP: Greg McCann
VP: Lisa Proctor
VP: Cole Wilson

D-U-N-S 10-710-7245
COBLENTZ DISTRIBUTING INC
WALNUT CREEK FOODS
3850 State Route 39, Millersburg, OH 44654-9683
Tel (800) 543-6848 *Founded/Ownrshp* 1977
Sales 95.2MM[E] *EMP* 210
SIC 5143 5451

D-U-N-S 01-347-1883
COBLESKILL STONE PRODUCTS INC (NY)
112 Rock Rd, Cobleskill, NY 12043-5738
Tel (518) 234-0221 *Founded/Ownrshp* 1954
Sales 115.2MM[E] *EMP* 185
Accts Haslun Cobleskill Ny
SIC 1422 Crushed & broken limestone
Ch: Emil Galasso
**VP:* Michael Galasso
**VP:* Daniel Kleeschulte
**VP:* Michael Moore

D-U-N-S 02-306-8539
COBORNS INC
OTHER STYLES-SEE OPERATION
1921 Coborn Blvd, Saint Cloud, MN 56301-2100
Tel (320) 252-4222 *Founded/Ownrshp* 1958
Sales 1.3MMM *EMP* 7,200
Accts Mcgladrey Llp Minneapolis Mi
SIC 5411 5541 5921 Grocery stores, chain; Filling stations, gasoline; Liquor stores
Ch Bd: Daniel Coborn
**CEO:* Chris M Coborn
**CFO:* Tom Velin
**Ex VP:* Greg Sandeno
Sr VP: Andrew Knoblauch
**VP:* Rebecca Estby
**VP:* Dale Monson
Board of Directors: Christopher Coborn, Daniel Coborn, Mark Coborn, William Drake, Robert Thueringer, Donald Wetter

D-U-N-S 00-506-8986 IMP
COBRA ELECTRONICS CORP
(*Suby of* CEDAR ELECTRONICS HOLDINGS CORP) ★
6500 W Cortland St, Chicago, IL 60707-4013
Tel (773) 889-8870 *Founded/Ownrshp* 1961, 2014
Sales 100.0MM *EMP* 156
SIC 5999 Telephone & communication equipment
Pr: Sally A Washlow
**CFO:* Marc Carr
VP: Celeste Boucher-Krickl
VP: Sandra Maxey
VP: James Miranda
Opers Mgr: Wendy Hung
Opers Mgr: Charlene Nutty
Mktg Mgr: Mark Pierre

COBRAPRO
See WORD & BROWN INSURANCE ADMINISTRATORS INC

D-U-N-S 00-894-5222
COBURN SUPPLY CO INC
390 Park St Ste 100, Beaumont, TX 77701-2996
Tel (409) 838-6363 *Founded/Ownrshp* 1934
Sales 542.6MM[E] *EMP* 750
SIC 5063 5064 5072 5074 5075 5078 Electrical apparatus & equipment; Electrical appliances, television & radio; Hardware; Plumbing & hydronic heating supplies; Warm air heating & air conditioning; Refrigeration equipment & supplies
Pr: Don Maloney
**Ex VP:* A J Maloney Jr
**VP:* Jim Fuller
VP: Paul Lee
Exec: Melissa Winn
Brnch Mgr: Bridget Thibodeaux
Brnch Mgr: Randy Weaver
Off Mgr: Anita Henderson
Off Mgr: Rita Herrington
Dir IT: David Granger
Opers Mgr: Bill Phillips

D-U-N-S 02-445-7111
COC PROPERTIES INC
110 Mackenan Dr Ste 300, Cary, NC 27511-7901
Tel (919) 462-1100 *Founded/Ownrshp* 1959
Sales 1.2MMM *EMP* 100
Accts Batchelor Tillery & Roberts
SIC 6512 5541 5411 Commercial & industrial building operation; Filling stations, gasoline; Convenience stores, independent
Ch Bd: Harry D Stephenson
**Pr:* Don Stephenson
**VP:* Jim Bosworth
**VP:* Mark Maddox
**VP:* Betty Phillips

D-U-N-S 00-905-1947
COCA COLA BOTTLING CO (INC)
COCA-COLA
155 Avery St, Walla Walla, WA 99362-1669
Tel (509) 529-0753 *Founded/Ownrshp* 1960
Sales 8.5MM *EMP* 6,530
SIC 2086 Bottled & canned soft drinks
Pr: Richard R Pelo
**VP:* John E Pelo

COCA-COLA
See ROCHESTER COCA COLA BOTTLING CORP

COCA-COLA
See BIG SPRINGS INC

COCA-COLA
See ATLANTIC BOTTLING CO

COCA-COLA
See CHESTERMAN CO

COCA-COLA
See COCA COLA BOTTLING CO (INC)

COCA-COLA
See SWIRE PACIFIC HOLDINGS INC

COCA-COLA
See REFRESHMENT PRODUCT SERVICES INC

COCA-COLA
See ODOM CORP

COCA-COLA
See GREAT PLAINS COCA COLA BOTTLING CO

COCA-COLA
See CCBCC OPERATIONS LLC

COCA-COLA
See C C 1 LIMITED PARTNERSHIP

COCA-COLA
See C C 1 LIMITED PARTNERSHIP

D-U-N-S 07-968-8478
■ COCA-COLA BEVERAGES FLORIDA LLC
(*Suby of* COCA-COLA REFRESHMENTS USA INC) ★
10117 Princess Plm Ave # 400, Tampa, FL 33610-8302
Tel (813) 327-7294 *Founded/Ownrshp* 2015
Sales 70.9MM[E] *EMP* 1,000
SIC 2086 Bottled & canned soft drinks

D-U-N-S 05-793-1230
▲ COCA-COLA BOTTLING CO CONSOLIDATED
4100 Coca Cola Plz # 100, Charlotte, NC 28211-3481
Tel (704) 557-4400 *Founded/Ownrshp* 1902
Sales 2.3MMM *EMP* 9,500
Tkr Sym COKE *Exch* NGS
SIC 2086 Bottled & canned soft drinks; Carbonated soft drinks, bottled & canned; Carbonated beverages, nonalcoholic: bottled & canned; Soft drinks: packaged in cans, bottles, etc.
Ch Bd: J Frank Harrison III
**Pr:* Henry W Flint
CFO: Clifford M Deal III
CFO: James E Harris
**V Ch Bd:* Umesh M Kasbekar
Ex VP: Robert G Chambless
Sr VP: Umesh Kasbekar
Sr VP: Kimberly A Kuo
Sr VP: Lauren C Steele
Sr VP: Michael A Strong
VP: William J Billiard
VP: Morgan H Everett
VP: David M Katz
Board of Directors: Alexander B Cummings Jr, Sharon A Decker, Morgan H Everett, Deborah H Everhart, James R Helvey III, William H Jones, James H Morgan, John W Murrey III, Dennis A Wicker

D-U-N-S 00-727-2800
COCA-COLA BOTTLING CO HIGH COUNTRY (SD)
2150 Coca Cola Ln, Rapid City, SD 57702-9358
Tel (605) 342-8222 *Founded/Ownrshp* 1936, 1956
Sales 106.6MM[E] *EMP* 200
SIC 2086 Bottled & canned soft drinks
Ch: Michael Messinger
**Pr:* M Trevor Messinger
CFO: Cary Griswald
Chf Mktg O: Michele Evans
Exec: Dean Cook
Genl Mgr: Jeff Mihm
Genl Mgr: Mike Neuman
Genl Mgr: Mike Ritter
Dir IT: Jeremy Ladson
IT Man: Amanda Jackson
Sls Mgr: Jared Schultz

D-U-N-S 08-858-5062 IMP
COCA-COLA BOTTLING CO OF NORTHERN NEW ENGLAND INC
(*Suby of* KIRIN HOLDINGS COMPANY, LIMITED)
1 Executive Park Dr # 330, Bedford, NH 03110-6977
Tel (603) 627-7871 *Founded/Ownrshp* 1978
Sales 121.6MM[E] *EMP* 950
SIC 2086

D-U-N-S 07-210-8103
COCA-COLA BOTTLING CO UNITED INC
4600 E Lake Blvd, Birmingham, AL 35217-4000
Tel (205) 238-3300 *Founded/Ownrshp* 1975
Sales 1.4MMM[E] *EMP* 2,800
SIC 2086 5962 Carbonated soft drinks, bottled & canned; Merchandising machine operators
Pr: Claude Nielsen
CFO: Hafi Chandiwala
CFO: Hafiz Chandiwala
Ex VP: M Williams Goodwyn Jr
VP: Stanley C Ellington
VP: Paul Favaron
VP: Mike Suco
Software D: Jeff Wood
Prd Mgr: Derrick Tolbert

D-U-N-S 08-033-2582
COCA-COLA BOTTLING OF HAWAII LLC
(*Suby of* COCA-COLA) ★
11400 Se 8th St Ste 300, Bellevue, WA 98004-6409
Tel (800) 767-6366 *Founded/Ownrshp* 2016
Sales 100.0MM *EMP* 528
SIC 5149 Soft drinks
Pr: John Odom
CFO: Randy Halter
Ex VP: William L Odom
VP: Jerry Dexter
VP: Jim Odom
Dir Risk M: Adam Hilpert

D-U-N-S 00-329-6175 IMP/EXP
▲ COCA-COLA CO
1 Coca Cola Plz Nw, Atlanta, GA 30313-2499
Tel (404) 676-2121 *Founded/Ownrshp* 1886
Sales 44.2MMM *EMP* 123,200
Accts Ernst & Young Llp Atlanta Ge
Tkr Sym KO *Exch* NYS
SIC 2087 2086 2033 2037 Concentrates, drink; Syrups, drink; Soft drinks: packaged in cans, bottles, etc.; Fruit drinks (less than 100% juice): packaged in cans, etc.; Fruit juices: fresh; Fruit juice concentrates, frozen
Ch Bd: Muhtar Kent
Pr: J Alexander M Douglas Jr
Pr: Irial Finan
Pr: Nathan Kalumbu
Pr: James Quincey
Pr: Atul Singh
Pr: Brian Smith
CFO: Kathy N Waller
Chf Mktg O: Marcos De Quinto
Ofcr: Alan Boehme
Sr VP: Bernhard Goepelt
Sr VP: Julie Hamilton
Sr VP: Brent Hastie
Sr VP: Ed Hays
Sr VP: Clyde C Tuggle
VP: Rhonda Applebaum
VP: Ish Arebalos
VP: Thomas Boyle
VP: Kathleen Ciaramello
VP: Wendy Clark
VP: John Farrell
Board of Directors: Robert A Kotick, Herbert A Allen, Maria Elena Lagomasino, Ronald W Allen, Sam Nunn, Marc Bolland, David B Weinberg, Ana Botin, Howard G Buffett, Richard M Daley, Barry Diller, Helene D Gayle, Alexis M Herman

D-U-N-S 96-519-3472
COCA-COLA ENTERPRISES INC
2500 Windy Ridge Pkwy Se # 700, Atlanta, GA 30339-8429
Tel (678) 260-3000 *Founded/Ownrshp* 2010
Sales 7.0MMM *EMP* 11,500
SIC 2086

D-U-N-S 06-755-5086 IMP/EXP
■ COCA-COLA EXPORT CORP
(*Suby of* COCA-COLA CO) ★
1 Coca Cola Plz Nw, Atlanta, GA 30313-2499
Tel (404) 676-2121 *Founded/Ownrshp* 2006
Sales 178.9MM[E] *EMP* 300
SIC 5149 Soft drinks
CEO: M Douglas Ivester
CFO: Gary P Fayard
**VP:* Steve Whaley

D-U-N-S 15-192-1954 IMP
■ COCA-COLA INTERAMERICAN CORP
(*Suby of* COCA-COLA CO) ★
1 Coca Cola Plz Nw, Atlanta, GA 30313-2499
Tel (404) 676-2121 *Founded/Ownrshp* 1960
Sales 113.8MM[E] *EMP* 524[E]
SIC 2086 Bottled & canned soft drinks
CEO: Muhtar Kent
VP: Rick Frazier
VP Sls: Rob Gehring
Mktg Dir: Garret Seevers

D-U-N-S 11-826-7624 IMP/EXP
■ COCA-COLA REFRESHMENTS USA INC
(*Suby of* COCA-COLA CO) ★
2500 Windy Ridge Pkwy Se, Atlanta, GA 30339-5677
Tel (770) 989-3000 *Founded/Ownrshp* 2010
Sales 5.3MMM[E] *EMP* 10,999[E]
SIC 2086 2087 Carbonated beverages, nonalcoholic: bottled & canned; Soft drinks: packaged in cans, bottles, etc.; Fruit drinks (less than 100% juice): packaged in cans, etc.; Syrups, drink; Concentrates, drink
CEO: John F Brock
Pr: Shaun Higgins
Pr: William A Holl
Pr: Terrance M Marks
**CFO:* William W Douglas III
**Ex VP:* Steven A Cahillane
**Sr VP:* John R Parker Jr
VP: E Bishop
VP: Michael P Coghlan
VP: David Cross
VP: Roy Jackson
VP: Timothy Johnson
VP: Gary McCalley
**VP:* Suzanne D Patterson
VP: Julius Pryor
VP: Edward L Sutter
VP: Lori Taylor
VP: Guy R Thomas

COCC
See CONNECTICUT ON-LINE COMPUTER CENTER INC

D-U-N-S 13-086-6817 IMP
COCHLEAR AMERICAS CORP
(*Suby of* COCHLEAR LIMITED)
13059 E Peakview Ave, Centennial, CO 80111-6511
Tel (303) 790-9010 *Founded/Ownrshp* 1985
Sales 97.0MM[E] *EMP* 115
SIC 5047 Hearing aids
CEO: Chris Smith
VP: Mike Evans
VP: Brenda Miller
VP: Steve Staller

D-U-N-S 00-283-7144 IMP
COCHRAN INC (WA)
BROADWAY ELECTRIC
12500 Aurora Ave N Main, Seattle, WA 98133-1518
Tel (206) 367-1900 *Founded/Ownrshp* 1955
Sales 186.4MM *EMP* 600
SIC 1731 7382 General electrical contractor; Security systems services
CEO: Leeann Cochran
**Pr:* Bill Doran
CFO: Tom Griffin
**Ch:* Gordon W Cochran
**VP:* Michael Heywood-Cochran
Exec: Jerod Gummer
Dept Mgr: Ron Maccario
Genl Mgr: Deborah Holt
Off Admin: Amanda Privitt
Telecom Ex: Brad Morton
Sfty Dirs: Cody Adams

D-U-N-S 06-683-8749
COCHRAN OLDSMOBILE INC
1 COCHRAN AUTOMOTIVE
4520 William Penn Hwy, Monroeville, PA 15146-2814
Tel (412) 373-3333 *Founded/Ownrshp* 1973
Sales 117.0MM[E] *EMP* 395
SIC 5511 Automobiles, new & used
Pr: Robert E Cochran
**Sr VP:* Margaret E Cochran

COCO'S
See JOJOS CALIFORNIA

COCOWEB.COM, LLC
See ECLINICAL WORKS LLC

D-U-N-S 07-844-9323 IMP
COD INTERMEDIATE LLC
(*Suby of* MACQUARIE INFRASTRUCTURE PARTNERS II INTERNATIONAL LP) ★
1330 Post Oak Blvd, Houston, TX 77056-3031
Tel (713) 292-2400 *Founded/Ownrshp* 2011
Sales 761.8MM[E] *EMP* 1,058[E]
SIC 4953 Refuse collection & disposal services; Rubbish collection & disposal; Sanitary landfill operation; Recycling, waste materials

D-U-N-S 07-308-0160 IMP
CODALE ELECTRIC SUPPLY INC
(*Suby of* SONEPAR USA) ★
5225 W 2400 S England Ct, Salt Lake City, UT 84120
Tel (801) 975-7300 *Founded/Ownrshp* 2011
Sales 366.2MM[E] *EMP* 230
SIC 5063 Electrical apparatus & equipment
Pr: Jon Mitchell
**Treas:* Andy Waring
VP: Nick Holt
VP: George Tadei
Brnch Mgr: Doug Chadwick
Brnch Mgr: Mike Mecham
Genl Mgr: Tyler Mitchell
Off Mgr: Theresa Hutchinson
Netwrk Mgr: Glen Brown
Sales Asso: Zach Andrus
Sales Asso: Danny Banks

D-U-N-S 88-449-7611 IMP
CODE 3 INC
CODE3PSE
(*Suby of* PUBLIC SAFETY EQUIPMENT INC) ★
10986 N Warson Rd, Saint Louis, MO 63114-2029
Tel (314) 996-2721 *Founded/Ownrshp* 1990
Sales 107.9MM[E] *EMP* 150
SIC 3669 3648 Emergency alarms; Lighting equipment
CFO: John Sterrenberg
**Genl Mgr:* Greg Scott

CODE3PSE
See CODE 3 INC

D-U-N-S 19-143-9603
CODINA PARTNERS LLC
135 San Lorenzo Ave # 750, Coral Gables, FL 33146-1524
Tel (305) 529-1300 *Founded/Ownrshp* 2009
Sales 98.8MM[E] *EMP* 705
SIC 6552 6531 1521 8742 Subdividers & developers; Real estate managers; Real estate brokers & agents; New construction, single-family houses; Management consulting services
Ch Bd: Armando Codina
CFO: Henry Beteler

D-U-N-S 08-518-8761
COEUR D ALENE SCHOOL DISTRICT 271
SD 271
1400 N Northwood Ctr Ct, Coeur D Alene, ID 83814-2657
Tel (208) 664-8241 *Founded/Ownrshp* 1920
Sales 69.9MM[E] *EMP* 1,200
Accts Magnuson Mchugh & Company Pa
SIC 8211 Public elementary school; Public junior high school; Public senior high school; Public special education school
Ex Dir: Hazel Bauman
V Ch: Casey Morrisroe
**Treas:* Julie Day
MIS Dir: Seth Deniston
Dir IT: Jean Bengfort
Schl Brd P: Christa Hazel

COEUR D ALENE TRIBAL BINGO
See SCOTT KRAMER

D-U-N-S 05-465-3340
COEUR DALENE TRIBE
850 A St, Plummer, ID 83851-7000
Tel (208) 686-1800 *Founded/Ownrshp* 1873
Sales NA *EMP* 1,200
SIC 9131 Indian reservation
CEO: Dave Matthison
**Ch:* Chief J Allan
Adm Dir: John Abraham

D-U-N-S 04-843-9806
▲ COEUR MINING INC
104 S Michigan Ave # 900, Chicago, IL 60603-5906
Tel (312) 489-5800 *Founded/Ownrshp* 1928

Sales 646.0MM *EMP* 2,005
Tkr Sym CDE *Exch* NYS
SIC 1041 1044 Gold ores mining; Gold ores processing; Silver ores mining; Silver ores processing
Pr: Mitchell J Krebs
COO: Frank L Hanagarne Jr
CFO: Peter C Mitchell
Sr VP: Casey M Nault
Board of Directors: Linda L Adamany, Kevin S Crutchfield, Sebastian Edwards, Randolph E Gress, Robert E Mellor, John H Robinson, J Kenneth Thompson

D-U-N-S 15-168-5427
■ COEUR-ROCHESTER INC
(*Suby of* COEUR MINING INC) ★
505 E Front Ave, Coeur D Alene, ID 83814-2755
Tel (312) 489-5800 *Founded/Ownrshp* 1985
Sales 247.9MM^E *EMP* 311
SIC 1044 Placer silver mining
VP: Casey Nault

COEXTRUDED PLASTICS TECHNOLOGY
See CPT INC

D-U-N-S 00-403-2269
COFACE NORTH AMERICA HOLDING CO
(*Suby of* CIE FCAISE ASSURANCES COMMERCE E)
1350 Broadway Rm 615, New York, NY 10018-0959
Tel (212) 389-6500 *Founded/Ownrshp* 1996
Sales NA *EMP* 450
SIC 6331 Fire, marine & casualty insurance
CEO: Michael J Ferrante
**CFO:* Pierre Fournel
**Ex VP:* Kerstin C Braun
**Ex VP:* Kenneth Moyle
Sls Dir: Michele Milone-Scherer

D-U-N-S 01-561-7905
COFACE NORTH AMERICA INC
(*Suby of* COFACE NORTH AMERICA HOLDING CO) ★
Suite 3 Bldg 100, Hightstown, NJ 08520
Tel (609) 469-0400 *Founded/Ownrshp* 1996
Sales NA *EMP* 250
SIC 6411 Insurance agents, brokers & service
Pr: Fredrik Murer
**CFO:* Pierre Fournel
**Ex VP:* Kerstin C Braun
**Sr VP:* Kenneth Moyle
**VP:* Zulfikar Bhura
**VP:* Dora Gonczy
**VP:* Christopher J Short
**Prin:* Juan Saborido

D-U-N-S 10-111-0302
COFCO (USA) INC
(*Suby of* COFCO CORPORATION)
910 Sylvan Ave Fl 1, Englewood Cliffs, NJ 07632-3306
Tel (201) 568-6788 *Founded/Ownrshp* 1982
Sales 260.5MM^E *EMP* 9
Accts Wei Wei Co Llp Flushing Ny
SIC 5153 Wheat
Pr: Mengze Liu

D-U-N-S 96-882-3034
COFCO AMERICAS RESOURCES CORP
COFCO-AGRI COFFEE COTTON GRAIN
4 Stamford Plz, Stamford, CT 06902-3834
Tel (203) 658-2820 *Founded/Ownrshp* 2011
Sales 106.4MM^E *EMP* 280^E
SIC 6221 5153 5149 2099 Commodity dealers, contracts; Grain & field beans; Cocoa; Sugar
Pr: William J Cronin
**Treas:* Christina Reynolds
**Treas:* Eric Twombly
**Ex VP:* David E Behrends
VP: Michael Davis
VP: Sohaib Iqbal
VP: James T Scholes
Exec: Sharon Brooker
Exec: Abhay Khobre

COFCO-AGRI COFFEE COTTON GRAIN
See COFCO AMERICAS RESOURCES CORP

COFFEE BEAN & TEA LEAF, THE
See INTERNATIONAL COFFEE & TEA LLC

D-U-N-S 08-597-4871 IMP/EXP
■ COFFEE BEAN INTERNATIONAL INC
(*Suby of* FARMER BROTHERS) ★
9120 Ne Alderwood Rd, Portland, OR 97220-1366
Tel (503) 227-4490 *Founded/Ownrshp* 1978
Sales 184.0MM^E *EMP* 308^E
SIC 5149 Coffee, green or roasted; Tea; Cocoa
Pr: Patrick Criteser
**Pr:* Michael Keown
**CFO:* Andy Kunkler
Prd Mgr: Terry Helsing
Prd Mgr: Arthur Klassen
Ql Cn Mgr: Daniel Schmelzle
Manager: Angela Farruggia

D-U-N-S 83-201-0842
COFFEE COUNTY SCHOOL DISTRICT
1311 Peterson Ave S, Douglas, GA 31533-4401
Tel (912) 384-2086 *Founded/Ownrshp* 2009
Sales 4.9MM^E *EMP* 1,200^E
SIC 8211 Public elementary & secondary schools

COFFEE HEALTH GROUP
See HEALTH CARE AUTHORITY OF LAUDERDALE COUNTY AND CITY OF FLORENCE

D-U-N-S 05-738-3762 IMP/EXP
▲ COFFEE HOLDING CO INC
3475 Victory Blvd Ste 4, Staten Island, NY 10314-6785
Tel (718) 832-0800 *Founded/Ownrshp* 1971
Sales 118.1MM *EMP* 69^E
Accts Marcum Llp New York Ny
Tkr Sym JVA *Exch* NAS
SIC 2095 5149 5499 Roasted coffee; Coffee, green or roasted; Coffee
Pr: Andrew Gordon
Ex VP: David Gordon

D-U-N-S 96-000-3697
■ COFFEE PARTNERS HAWAII
(*Suby of* STARBUCKS CORP) ★
210 Ward Ave Ste 105, Honolulu, HI 96814-4000
Tel (808) 545-1149 *Founded/Ownrshp* 2006
Sales 33.9MM^E *EMP* 1,300
SIC 8742 Financial consultant
Pt: Cafe Hawaii

D-U-N-S 07-585-9371
COFFEE REGIONAL MEDICAL CENTER INC
1101 Ocilla Rd, Douglas, GA 31533-2207
Tel (912) 384-1900 *Founded/Ownrshp* 1995
Sales 95.0MM *EMP* 562
SIC 8062 General medical & surgical hospitals
CEO: George L Heck III
**CFO:* Donald C Lewis Jr
CFO: Winston Tanner
Ofcr: Marian Tanner
**VP:* Sherry Thomas
Dir Lab: Teresa Chaney
Dir Rx: Peggy Kirkland
IT Man: Martha Clark
Mtls Dir: Tina Edge
Obsttrcn: Steve Diamond
Doctor: Mark T Brulte

D-U-N-S 14-240-5666 IMP
■ COFFEYVILLE RESOURCES LLC
(*Suby of* CVR ENERGY INC) ★
2277 Plaza Dr Ste 500, Sugar Land, TX 77479-6602
Tel (281) 207-3200 *Founded/Ownrshp* 2004
Sales 5.4MMM^E *EMP* 428
SIC 2911 Gasoline
Pr: Jack Lipinski
Pr: Edmund Gross
COO: Stanley A Riemann
**CFO:* Susan M Ball
**Chf Mktg O:* Martin J Power
**Ex VP:* Robert W Haugen
Ex VP: Wyatt E Jernigan
Ex VP: Kevan A Vick
Sr VP: Daniel J Daly
Sr VP: Edmund S Gross
**Sr VP:* John R Walter
VP: Steven M Eames
VP: Stirling D Pack

D-U-N-S 82-794-3445
■ COFFEYVILLE RESOURCES LLC
(*Suby of* CVR ENERGY INC) ★
10 E Cambridge Circle Dr, Kansas City, KS 66103-1334
Tel (913) 982-0500 *Founded/Ownrshp* 2008
Sales 3.4MMM^E *EMP* 1,448^E
SIC 1623 Water, sewer & utility lines
VP: Edmund Gross
CTO: Philip Rinaldi

D-U-N-S 14-426-6660
■ COFFEYVILLE RESOURCES REFINING & MARKETING LLC
(*Suby of* CVR REFINING LLC) ★
2277 Plaza Dr Ste 500, Sugar Land, TX 77479-6602
Tel (281) 207-3200 *Founded/Ownrshp* 2003
Sales 87.0MM^E *EMP* 257
SIC 2911 Petroleum refining
Pr: Jack Lipinski
**Pr:* David L Landreth
**Pr:* Patrick J Quinn
**Pr:* John R Walter
**CFO:* Susan M Ball
**Chf Cred:* Martin J Power
**Ex VP:* Edmund S Gross
**Ex VP:* Robert W Haugen

D-U-N-S 16-742-3123
■ COG OPERATING LLC
(*Suby of* CONCHO RESOURCES INC) ★
600 W Illinois Ave, Midland, TX 79701-4882
Tel (432) 685-0727 *Founded/Ownrshp* 2006
Sales 1.1MMM^E *EMP* 500^E
SIC 1382 Oil & gas exploration services
CEO: Timothy A Leach
**CFO:* Darin G Holderness

D-U-N-S 03-409-2713
■ COGENT COMMUNICATIONS GROUP INC
(*Suby of* COGENT COMMUNICATIONS HOLDINGS INC) ★
2450 N St Nw, Washington, DC 20037-3052
Tel (202) 295-4200 *Founded/Ownrshp* 2000
Sales 404.2MM *EMP* 772^E
SIC 8999 Artists & artists' studios
Ch Bd: David Schaeffer
**CFO:* Thaddeus G Weed
VP: Eric Blitz
VP: Jeffrey Karnes
**VP:* R Brad Kummer
VP: R Kummer
VP: Steven McLernon
VP: Timothy Oneill
**Exec:* Ernest Ortega
Dir IT: Travis Low
IT Man: Hipolito Chaves
Board of Directors: D Blake Bath, Steven D Brooks, Richard T Liebhaber, Marc Montagner, Timothy Weingarten

D-U-N-S 07-940-5339
▲ COGENT COMMUNICATIONS HOLDINGS INC
2450 N St Nw, Washington, DC 20037-3052
Tel (202) 295-4200 *Founded/Ownrshp* 1999
Sales 380.0MM *EMP* 772^E
Tkr Sym CCOI *Exch* NGS
SIC 4813 7372 ; ; Prepackaged software
Ch Bd: Dave Schaeffer
CFO: Thaddeus G Weed
VP: James Bubeck
VP: R Brad Kummer

D-U-N-S 10-553-2134
■ COGENT COMMUNICATIONS INC
(*Suby of* COGENT COMMUNICATIONS GROUP INC) ★
2450 N St Nw, Washington, DC 20037-3052
Tel (202) 295-4200 *Founded/Ownrshp* 2000
Sales 224.6MM^E *EMP* 475
SIC 4813 7375 ; Information retrieval services
CEO: Dave Schaeffer
**CFO:* Thaddeus Weed
**VP:* Robert Beury
Manager: Michael Russo

COGENT HEALTHCARE INC.
See COGENT MEDICAL CARE PC

D-U-N-S 00-717-1366
COGENT INC (MO)
VANDEVANTER ENGINEERNG
318 Brdwy St, Kansas City, MO 64105
Tel (816) 221-0650 *Founded/Ownrshp* 1954
Sales 98.6MM^E *EMP* 135
SIC 5084 5082 7359

D-U-N-S 05-002-5662
COGENT MEDICAL CARE PC
COGENT HEALTHCARE INC.
(*Suby of* COGENT-HMG) ★
5410 Maryland Way Ste 300, Brentwood, TN 37027-5339
Tel (615) 377-5600 *Founded/Ownrshp* 2014
Sales 89.4MM^E *EMP* 400
SIC 8062 General medical & surgical hospitals
Pr: Robert Bessler
COO: Rachel George
Board of Directors: Gene Fleming

COGENT-HMG
See HOSPITALISTS MANAGEMENT GROUP LLC

D-U-N-S 96-666-5812
■ COGENTRIX DELAWARE HOLDINGS INC
(*Suby of* COGENTRIX ENERGY POWER MANAGEMENT LLC) ★
1105 N Market St Ste 1108, Wilmington, DE 19801-1216
Tel (847) 908-2800 *Founded/Ownrshp* 1993
Sales 407.1MM^E *EMP* 513
SIC 4911 Electric services
Pr: Bruce Mc Millen
**Treas:* Tom Schwartz

D-U-N-S 13-141-1837
■ COGENTRIX ENERGY POWER MANAGEMENT LLC
(*Suby of* CARLYLE GROUP L P) ★
9405 Arrowpoint Blvd, Charlotte, NC 28273-8110
Tel (704) 525-3800 *Founded/Ownrshp* 2012
Sales 580.3MM^E *EMP* 578
SIC 4911 Electric services
Pr: Douglas L Miller
**CFO:* S Mark Rudolph
Ex VP: Bill Felts
**Sr VP:* Gary M Carraux
VP: Gary Carraux
VP: John Collins
VP: Dev Desai
VP: Robert Dowd
VP: Cliff Evans
VP: Jef Freeman
VP: John Gasborro
VP: Edward Smith

D-U-N-S 18-486-2365 EXP
■ COGGIN AUTOMOTIVE CORP
COGGIN CHEVROLET
(*Suby of* ASBURY AUTOMOTIVE GROUP INC) ★
7245 Blanding Blvd, Jacksonville, FL 32244-4503
Tel (904) 779-8030 *Founded/Ownrshp* 1970
Sales 100.4MM^E *EMP* 350
SIC 5511 Automobiles, new & used
Pr: Michael S Kearney
**Pr:* Luther W Coggin
**Treas:* Linda Marlette
Genl Mgr: Joe Umbriano
Genl Mgr: Wayne Watkins
Sls Mgr: Alex Fischer

COGGIN CHEVROLET
See COGGIN AUTOMOTIVE CORP

D-U-N-S 18-377-3332
COGHLIN COMPANIES INC
COLUMBIA TECH
27 Otis St Ste 300, Westborough, MA 01581-3373
Tel (508) 753-2354 *Founded/Ownrshp* 1986
Sales 160.0MM *EMP* 250
SIC 3613 Panel & distribution boards & other related apparatus
CEO: James W Coghlin Sr
**Pr:* Christopher J Coghlin
**Pr:* Randy Ziffer
**COO:* Madison Finlay
**CFO:* Christopher Palermo
Sr VP: Mark Baker
VP: Scott Johnson
VP: Bill Laursen
Prgrm Mgr: Susan Beinor
Dir IT: Mike Barry
Mfg Dir: Paul Marks

D-U-N-S 00-158-2027
COGHLIN CONSTRUCTION SERVICES INC (MA)
COGHLIN ELECTRICAL CONTRCTORS
100 Prescott St Ste 3, Worcester, MA 01605-1713
Tel (508) 793-0300 *Founded/Ownrshp* 2000
Sales 94.7MM *EMP* 251
Accts Bollus Lynch Llp Worcester
SIC 1731 Electrical work
Pr: Susan M Mailman

D-U-N-S 00-980-8866
COGHLIN ELECTRICAL CONTRACTORS INC
(*Suby of* COGHLIN ELECTRICAL CONTRCTORS) ★
100 Prescott St, Worcester, MA 01605-1713
Tel (508) 793-0300 *Founded/Ownrshp* 2000
Sales 91.8MM^E *EMP* 230
Accts Bollus Lynch Llp Worcester
SIC 1731 General electrical contractor; Safety & security specialization
Pr: Susan M Mailman
**CFO:* Stephen Wentzell
**Treas:* Edwin B Coghlin Jr
VP: Dave Bernard
VP: Leo McCaffrey
Snr Ntwrk: Colum Oconnor
CIO: Cristine Kelly
IT Man: Michael Gilbert

COGHLIN ELECTRICAL CONTRCTORS
See COGHLIN CONSTRUCTION SERVICES INC

D-U-N-S 05-055-9491
▲ COGNEX CORP
1 Vision Dr, Natick, MA 01760-2077
Tel (508) 650-3000 *Founded/Ownrshp* 1981
Sales 450.5MM *EMP* 1,305^E
Accts Grant Thornton Llp Boston Ma
Tkr Sym CGNX *Exch* NGS
SIC 3823 Industrial instrmnts msrmnt display/control process variable; Computer interface equipment for industrial process control
Pr: Robert J Willett
Pr: Makoto Inoue
CFO: Richard A Morin
Ofcr: Robert J Shillman
Ex VP: Richard A Marrion
Sr VP: Kris Nelson
VP: Tej Anand
VP: Patrice Denizard
VP: Carl Gerst
VP: John E McGarry
VP: Jim Peck
VP: Jim Quinlivan
VP: Dirk Rathsack
VP: Rocco Volpe
Board of Directors: Patrick A Alias, Eugene Banucci, Gene Banucci, Theodor Krantz, Jeffrey B Miller, J Bruce Robinson, Anthony Sun

D-U-N-S 79-990-1301
▲ COGNIZANT TECHNOLOGY SOLUTIONS CORP
500 Frank W Burr Blvd, Teaneck, NJ 07666-6804
Tel (201) 801-0233 *Founded/Ownrshp* 1988
Sales 12.4MMM *EMP* 221,700
Accts Pricewaterhousecoopers Llp Ne
Tkr Sym CTSH *Exch* NGS
SIC 7371 7379 7372 Computer software development & applications; Computer related consulting services; Business oriented computer software
CEO: Francisco D'Souza
**Ch Bd:* John E Klein
Pr: Rajeev Mehta
COO: Sridhar Thiruvengadam
CFO: Karen McLoughlin
**V Ch Bd:* Lakshmi Narayanan
Board of Directors: Jonathan Chadwick, Maureen Breakiron-Evans, John N Fox Jr, Michael Patsalos-Fox, Leo S Mackay Jr, Robert E Weissman, Thomas M Wendel

D-U-N-S 82-697-4789
COGNOSANTE HOLDINGS LLC
8200 Greensboro Dr # 1200, Mc Lean, VA 22102-4923
Tel (703) 206-6000 *Founded/Ownrshp* 2008
Sales 193.1MM *EMP* 1,400
Accts Grant Thornton Mc Lean Va
SIC 7389 Personal service agents, brokers & bureaus
CEO: Y Michele Kang
COO: Aaron Daniels
Ofcr: Thomas Hohman CPA
Sr VP: Len Discenza
Sr VP: Jean Marc Edier
Sr VP: Davis Foster
Sr VP: Sean M Gallagher
Sr VP: Jim Joyce
VP: Sean Bauer
VP: Vicky Bowen
VP: Dennis A Dworman
VP: Davis Foste
VP: Stephen Gantz
VP: Kevin Mostek
VP: Tom Rabung
VP: Corey Stevenson
VP: Phil Surine
Board of Directors: Thomas Daschle, Susan Fox, Bill Frist, Michele Kang

D-U-N-S 62-428-7306
COGNOSANTE LLC
(*Suby of* COGNOSANTE HOLDINGS LLC) ★
8200 Greensboro Dr # 1200, Mc Lean, VA 22102-4923
Tel (703) 206-6000 *Founded/Ownrshp* 2011
Sales 193.1MM *EMP* 293
Accts Grant Thornton Mc Lean Va
SIC 7379 8748 Computer related maintenance services; Testing services
CEO: Y Michele Kang
**Pr:* Davis Foster
**CFO:* Aaron Daniels
Ofcr: Thomas C Hohman
Sr VP: Robert Norcross
**Sr VP:* Corey Stevenson
**VP:* Julie Boughn
**VP:* Len Discenza
VP: Kenneth Dybevik
**VP:* Anita Griner
**VP:* Jim Joyce
**VP:* Erick Peters
Board of Directors: Y Michele Kang

D-U-N-S 13-020-1965
COGR INC
CORTEC GROUP
200 Park Ave Fl 20, New York, NY 10166-0005
Tel (212) 370-5600 *Founded/Ownrshp* 1986
Sales 117.7MM^E *EMP* 1,200
SIC 8742 Management consulting services
Ch Bd: Gerald Rosenberg
Mng Pt: Scott Schafler
Mng Dir: Jeff Lipsitz
CIO: Richard Schafler

D-U-N-S 14-578-7946
▲ COHEN & STEERS INC
280 Park Ave Fl 10w, New York, NY 10017-1306
Tel (212) 832-3232 *Founded/Ownrshp* 1986
Sales 328.6MM *EMP* 275^E
Tkr Sym CNS *Exch* NYS
SIC 6282 Investment advice; Investment advisory service; Manager of mutual funds, contract or fee basis

CEO: Robert H Steers
**Ch Bd:* Martin Cohen
Pr: Joseph M Harvey
COO: Adam M Derechin
CFO: Matthew S Stadler
Bd of Dir: Richard Norman
Bd of Dir: Frank Ross
Ex VP: Thomas Bohjalian
Ex VP: Todd Glickson
Ex VP: Francis C Poli
VP: Andy Humble
VP: Christopher Rhine
VP: Ed Rieger
Board of Directors: Frank T Connor, Peter L Rhein, Richard P Simon, Edmond D Villani

D-U-N-S 00-447-9119
COHEN BROTHERS INC (OH)
1723 Woodlawn Ave, Middletown, OH 45044-4348
Tel (513) 422-3696 *Founded/Ownrshp* 1924
Sales 104.3MM^E *EMP* 115
SIC 5093 3441 3341 3312 Ferrous metal scrap & waste; Nonferrous metals scrap; Fabricated structural metal; Secondary nonferrous metals; Blast furnaces & steel mills
Ch Bd: Wilbur Cohen
**Pr:* Kenneth Cohen
**Treas:* Neil Cohen
Sr VP: Adam Dumes
**Sr VP:* Donald Zulanch
**Prin:* Mose Cohen
Genl Mgr: Kyle Dean
IT Man: Jo Beck
IT Man: Joann Beck
Trfc Dir: Steve Helton
Trfc Dir: John Hess

D-U-N-S 04-371-9210
▲ COHERENT INC
5100 Patrick Henry Dr, Santa Clara, CA 95054-1112
Tel (408) 764-4000 *Founded/Ownrshp* 1966
Sales 857.3MM *EMP* 2,586
Tkr Sym COHR *Exch* NGS
SIC 3826 3845 3699 Laser scientific & engineering instruments; Laser systems & equipment, medical; Laser systems & equipment
Pr: John R Ambroseo
Ch Bd: Garry W Rogerson
CFO: Kevin Palatnik
Ex VP: Bret M Dimarco
Ex VP: Paul Sechrist
Ex VP: Helene Simonet
Ex VP: Mark Sobey
Ex VP: Luis Spinelli
VP: Lynne Reinke
IT Man: Kevin Salotti
Software D: John Thomas
Board of Directors: Jay T Flatley, Susan M James, L William Krause, Steve Skaggs

D-U-N-S 06-751-0214
COHNREZNICK LLP
1301 Ave Of The Americas, New York, NY 10019-6022
Tel (212) 297-0400 *Founded/Ownrshp* 1996
Sales 526.6MM^E *EMP* 2,000
SIC 8721 Certified public accountant
CEO: Frank Longobardi
Pt: Carolyn Danna
Mng Pt: Kenneth J Kanter
Mng Pt: George Klenovich
Mng Dir: Steve Mayer
IT Man: Anthony C Reidler
Mktg Mgr: Bruce Van Vreede
Genl Couns: Michelle Fleishman
Snr Mgr: Walter M Curry
Snr Mgr: Tara Delgavio
Snr Mgr: Jim Guild

D-U-N-S 00-345-2624 IMP
COHO DISTRIBUTING LLC
6840 N Cutter Cir, Portland, OR 97217-3943
Tel (503) 289-9600 *Founded/Ownrshp* 2008
Sales NA *EMP* 2,600
SIC 5182 Liquor
CEO: Gregg Christiansen

COHORT ENERGY COMPANY
See J-W OPERATING CO

D-U-N-S 00-838-1758 IMP
▲ COHU INC
12367 Crosthwaite Cir, Poway, CA 92064-6817
Tel (858) 848-8100 *Founded/Ownrshp* 1947
Sales 269.6MM *EMP* 1,600^E
Accts Ernst & Young Llp San Diego
Tkr Sym COHU *Exch* NGS
SIC 3825 3663 3699 Semiconductor test equipment; Microwave communication equipment; Security devices
Pr: Luis A Muller
**Ch Bd:* James A Donahue
CFO: Jeffrey D Jones
VP: John H Allen
VP: Hock W Chiang
Exec: John Allen
Tech Mgr: Travis Becker
VP Opers: Mark Bruno
Board of Directors: William E Bendush, Steven J Bilodeau, Andrew M Caggia, Robert L Ciardella, Karl H Funke

COI GRAPHICS
See SMURFIT KAPPA NORTH AMERICA LLC

COIL COATERS OF AMERICA
See FIRST AMERICAN RESOURCES CO LLC

D-U-N-S 60-939-1800 IMP
COILPLUS INC
(*Suby of* METAL ONE HOLDINGS AMERICA INC) ★
6250 N River Rd Ste 6050, Rosemont, IL 60018-4209
Tel (847) 384-3000 *Founded/Ownrshp* 2009
Sales 263.8MM^E *EMP* 415
SIC 5051 Steel
Pr: Kurt Horikiri
**CFO:* Christopher Urgo
Mtls Mgr: Brian Bauer
Sales Asso: Rhonda Ramsey

D-U-N-S 00-628-6124 IMP/EXP
COIN ACCEPTORS INC
COINCO
300 Hunter Ave, Saint Louis, MO 63124-2081
Tel (314) 725-0100 *Founded/Ownrshp* 1958
Sales 226.9MM^E *EMP* 1,200
SIC 3581

COINCO
See COIN ACCEPTORS INC

D-U-N-S 00-193-6228
COINMACH CORP
(*Suby of* COINMACH LAUNDRY CORP) ★
303 Sunnyside Blvd # 70, Plainview, NY 11803-1598
Tel (516) 349-8555 *Founded/Ownrshp* 1948, 1995
Sales 147.5MM^E *EMP* 2,000
SIC 7215 7359 5087 5064 7211 8741 Coin-operated laundries & cleaning; Laundry, coin-operated; Coin-operated machine rental services; Laundry equipment & supplies; Washing machines; Power laundries, family & commercial; Administrative management
Ch Bd: Stephen R Kerrigan
**Pr:* Mitchell Blatt
Pr: Jack Cahill
Pr: Tom Hunt
Pr: Jim Rutzick
CFO: Gary Dailey
**Sr VP:* Robert M Doyle
**VP:* John E Denson
VP: Ken Gebhardt
VP: Ed Greene
VP: Raymond Loser
VP: Hal Savzmann
VP: Tony Valli
Exec: Whitney Area
Exec: Carlos Barraza
Exec: Tim Cogdill
Exec: Dan Collins
Exec: Jose Garcia
Exec: Micheal Keller
Exec: Dan Knudsen
Exec: Sandra Lowery

D-U-N-S 16-766-5772
COINMACH HOLDINGS LLC
(*Suby of* CSC SERVICEWORKS HOLDINGS INC) ★
1017 E Morehead St # 100, Charlotte, NC 28204-2869
Tel (704) 375-1947 *Founded/Ownrshp* 2002
Sales 165.1MM^E *EMP* 6^E
SIC 7215 Laundry, coin-operated
CEO: Robert Doyle
**Sr VP:* John E Denson
Opers Mgr: Michael Torres

D-U-N-S 93-864-9050
COINMACH LAUNDRY CORP
(*Suby of* COINMACH HOLDINGS LLC) ★
1017 E Morehead St # 100, Charlotte, NC 28204-2865
Tel (704) 375-1947 *Founded/Ownrshp* 2002
Sales 165.1MM^E *EMP* 1,851^E
Accts Ernst & Young Llp
SIC 7215 Laundry, coin-operated
CEO: Robert M Doyle
**COO:* Michael E Stanky

D-U-N-S 17-030-1696
COINMACH SERVICE CORP
(*Suby of* SPIN HOLDCO INC) ★
303 Sunnyside Blvd # 70, Plainview, NY 11803-1598
Tel (516) 349-8555 *Founded/Ownrshp* 2003
Sales 129.5MM^E *EMP* 805
SIC 3633 5087 Household laundry equipment; Laundry equipment & supplies
Ch Bd: Robert M Doyle
Pr: Carol A Siebuhr
Pr: Adrian Verquer
VP: NC Charlotte
VP: MI Detroit
VP: James P McDonnell
VP: FL Orlando
Rgnl Mgr: VA Richmond

D-U-N-S 79-144-7691
■ COINSTAR LLC
OUTERWALL
(*Suby of* APOLLO GLOBAL MANAGEMENT LLC) ★
1800 114th Ave Se, Bellevue, WA 98004-6946
Tel (425) 943-8000 *Founded/Ownrshp* 2016
Sales 2.1MMM *EMP* 2,670^E
SIC 7299 7841 Coin-operated service machines: scales, shoe shine, etc.; Video disk/tape rental to the general public
CEO: Erik E Prusch
Pr: Michael J Skinner
CFO: Galen C Smith
Sr VP: Alex Camara
VP: David Asch
VP: John Beane
VP: Megan Hansen
VP: Sonia Jain
VP: Randy S Overturf
VP: Walter Paulsen
VP: Frederick Stein
VP: Sara L White
Board of Directors: Nelson C Chan, Nora M Denzel, David M Eskenazy, Ross G Landsbaum, Robert D Sznewajs, Ronald B Woodard

D-U-N-S 12-764-0931 IMP/EXP
COKEM INTERNATIONAL LTD
3880 4th Ave E, Shakopee, MN 55379-1773
Tel (952) 358-6000 *Founded/Ownrshp* 2000
Sales 125.2MM^E *EMP* 80
SIC 5092 Video games
**Ch Bd:* Paul Eibeler
**CFO:* Julianne M Turk
VP: Chris Armstrong
VP: John Homlish
**VP:* Joe Rehak
VP: Mike Thielman
IT Man: Ron Kyostia
Software D: Gordon Lindsay
Opers Mgr: Jim Halvorson
Prd Mgr: Timothy Strangis
QI Cn Mgr: Nick Roske

COKINOS ENERGY
See COKINOS NATURAL GAS CO INC

D-U-N-S 00-680-1588
COKINOS ENERGY CORP (TX)
5718 Westheimer Rd # 900, Houston, TX 77057-5757
Tel (713) 974-0101 *Founded/Ownrshp* 1997
Sales 1.0MMM^E *EMP* 11
SIC 4924 1623 Natural gas distribution; Oil & gas pipeline construction
Pr: Michael Evan Cokinos
**CFO:* Argo Georgandis
**VP:* Kevin Cokinos

D-U-N-S 10-265-8226
COKINOS NATURAL GAS CO INC
COKINOS ENERGY
(*Suby of* COKINOS ENERGY CORP) ★
5718 Westheimer Rd # 900, Houston, TX 77057-5745
Tel (713) 974-0101 *Founded/Ownrshp* 1982
Sales 1.0MMM *EMP* 11
SIC 4924 1623 Natural gas distribution; Oil & gas pipeline construction
Pr: Michael Evan Cokinos
**VP:* Christopher M Cokinos

D-U-N-S 60-610-3737 IMP
COLAS INC
(*Suby of* COLASCANADA INC)
163 Madison Ave Ste 500, Morristown, NJ 07960-7324
Tel (973) 290-9082 *Founded/Ownrshp* 1989
Sales 1.3MMM^E *EMP* 4,500
SIC 1611 1622 2951 Highway & street construction; Bridge construction; Road materials, bituminous (not from refineries)
Ch Bd: Louis R Gabanna
**COO:* Jean Vidal
**CFO:* Jean-Luc Begasse De Dhaem
**Sr VP:* James E Weeks
**VP:* Gordon R Crawley
**VP:* Anthony L Martino II
**VP:* Michel Roure
Counsel: Dan Lafrance

D-U-N-S 07-174-1268
COLBY COLLEGE
4000 Mayflower Hl, Waterville, ME 04901-8840
Tel (207) 859-4000 *Founded/Ownrshp* 1813
Sales 120.6MM *EMP* 580
Accts Mayer Hoffman Mccann Pc Bost
SIC 8221 College, except junior
Ch Bd: James B Crawford
**Pr:* William D Adams
**V Ch Bd:* Paula Crane Lunder
VP: Richard Ammons
VP: Terry Cowdrey
VP: Lori Kletzer
VP: Daniel Lugo
VP: Andy McGadney
**VP:* C Andrew McGadney
VP: Matt Proto
VP: Earl Smith
**VP:* Arnold Yasinski
Assoc Dir: Lisa Fairbanks
Assoc Dir: Buffy Higgins
Assoc Dir: Ann Hurlburt
Assoc Dir: Juliette Monet
Assoc Dir: Sandra Sohne-Johnston
Assoc Dir: Denise Walden
Comm Dir: Stephen Collins

D-U-N-S 00-532-0304 IMP/EXP
COLD HEADING CO (MI)
BEACHLAWN MORTGAGE COMPANY
(*Suby of* BEACHLAWN INC.)
21777 Hoover Rd, Warren, MI 48089-2544
Tel (586) 497-7000 *Founded/Ownrshp* 1912
Sales 105.0MM^E *EMP* 322
SIC 3452 8711 Bolts, metal; Engineering services
Ch Bd: Derek J Stevens
**Pr:* James R Joliet
COO: Jason Taffar
**CFO:* Daniel L Morrell
**VP:* William Buban
**VP:* Thomas Dharte
**VP:* Drayke Dondero
**VP:* David Goss
**VP:* Peter Kuo
VP: Greg Wronkowicz
Genl Mgr: Brigid Loffeda
Board of Directors: Michael Vanden Bussche, James Carpenter, Elmer Cecil, Edward Miller, Derek Stevens

D-U-N-S 00-615-9008 IMP
COLD SPRING GRANITE CO INC
GRANIT-BRONZ DIV
17482 Granite West Rd, Cold Spring, MN 56320-4578
Tel (320) 685-3621 *Founded/Ownrshp* 1898
Sales 299.1MM^E *EMP* 1,275
SIC 3281 1741 3366 Dimension stone for buildings; Monuments, cut stone (not finishing or lettering only); Tombstones, cut stone (not finishing or lettering only); Stone, quarrying & processing of own stone products; Masonry & other stonework; Bronze foundry
CEO: Patrick D Alexander
Pr: John Mattke
CFO: George J Schnepf
VP: Greg Flint
VP: Dan REA
Genl Mgr: Rick Barber
Genl Mgr: Kelly Kiffmeyer
Genl Mgr: Pam Overland
Sfty Mgr: Bruce Mathis
Sls Dir: Amy Thielen
Manager: Deb Bell

D-U-N-S 06-596-8786
COLD SPRING HARBOR LABORATORY ASSOCIATION INC
1 Bungtown Rd, Cold Spring Harbor, NY 11724-2209
Tel (516) 367-8446 *Founded/Ownrshp* 1963
Sales 138.1MM *EMP* 1,200
Accts Kpmg Llp Melville Ny
SIC 8733 2731 2741 8249 Noncommercial biological research organization; Educational research agency; Books: publishing only; Technical manuals: publishing only, not printed on site; Vocational apprentice training
Pr: Bruce W Stillman
Pr: Charles Prizzi
**COO:* W Dillaway Ayres Jr
**CFO:* Lari Russo
Treas: Lola Grace
Bd of Dir: Sydney Gary
Trst: James Stone
Sr VP: Bill Keen
**Sr VP:* Charles S Ryan
VP: Art Brings
VP: Phil Lembo
VP: Doreen Ware
VP: Teri F Willey
VP: Dagnia Zeidlickis
Exec: Katie Rastery

D-U-N-S 11-516-8338 IMP
COLDWATER CREEK INC
17000 Ventura Blvd # 300, Encino, CA 91316-4112
Tel (208) 263-2266 *Founded/Ownrshp* 1984
Sales 742.4MM *EMP* 6,600
SIC 5621 5961

D-U-N-S 02-987-8597
COLDWATER CREEK OUTLET STORES INC
(*Suby of* COLDWATER CREEK INC) ★
17000 Ventura Blvd # 300, Encino, CA 91316-4109
Tel (208) 265-3468 *Founded/Ownrshp* 1983
Sales 55.0MM^E *EMP* 2,500
SIC 5399

COLDWELL BANKER
See HEDGES ASSOCIATES INC

COLDWELL BANKER
See NRT COMMERCIAL UTAH LLC

D-U-N-S 04-014-0345
■ COLDWELL BANKER GUNDAKER REAL ESTATE SCHOOL
GUNDAKER REALTORS BETTER HOMES
(*Suby of* COLDWELL BANKER RESIDENTIAL BROKERAGE CO) ★
2458 Old Dorsett Rd, Maryland Heights, MO 63043-2423
Tel (314) 298-5000 *Founded/Ownrshp* 2001
Sales 45.0MM^E *EMP* 2,555
SIC 6531 Real estate agent, residential; Real estate agent, commercial
Pr: James Dohr
VP: Joe Allison
VP: Carol McCabe
Mktg Dir: Glenn Vatterott
Sales Asso: Maureen Hornberger
Sales Asso: Bert Kaslin
Sales Asso: Susan Morrow

D-U-N-S 78-960-5201
■ COLDWELL BANKER RESIDENTIAL BROKERAGE CO
(*Suby of* COLDWELL BANKER) ★
27271 Las Ramblas, Mission Viejo, CA 92691-6392
Tel (949) 367-1800 *Founded/Ownrshp* 1977
Sales NA *EMP* 2,555
SIC 6531 Real estate agent, residential
CEO: Robert Le Fever
**Pr:* Jill Morrow

D-U-N-S 06-073-4746
■ COLDWELL BANKER RESIDENTIAL REAL ESTATE
(*Suby of* COLDWELL BANKER) ★
27271 Las Ramblas, Mission Viejo, CA 92691-6392
Tel (949) 367-1800 *Founded/Ownrshp* 1998
Sales 107.3MM^E *EMP* 8,000
SIC 6531 Real estate agent, residential
Pr: Robert Becker

D-U-N-S 09-773-2887 IMP
COLE HAAN LLC
150 Ocean Rd, Greenland, NH 03840-2408
Tel (207) 846-2500 *Founded/Ownrshp* 2013
Sales 341.4MM^E *EMP* 2,152
SIC 5651 5632 Family clothing stores; Women's accessory & specialty stores; Apparel accessories
CEO: Jack A Boys
**CFO:* Lisa Kempa
Ex VP: Ron Fox
VP: Bruce Anderson
VP: Doug Ritchie
Dir Soc: Sherry Johnson
VP Mktg: Bill Zeitz
VP Sls: Jim Clopton
VP Sls: Karen Haskell
Sls Dir: Debbie Kozlowski
Merch Mgr: Brian Landman

D-U-N-S 00-622-1444 IMP
COLE PAPERS INC
COLE WHOLESALE FLOORING
1300 38th St N, Fargo, ND 58102-2802
Tel (800) 800-8090 *Founded/Ownrshp* 1918
Sales 102.2MM^E *EMP* 161
SIC 5113 5111 5169 5023 5112 5049 Industrial & personal service paper; Sanitary food containers; Disposable plates, cups, napkins & eating utensils; Bags, paper & disposable plastic; Printing paper; Detergents & soaps, except specialty cleaning; Specialty cleaning & sanitation preparations; Floor coverings; Office supplies; School supplies
Ch Bd: Robert Perkins
**CEO:* Chuck Perkins
**CFO:* Brian Haugen
**Sr VP:* Mike Hubbard
VP: Larry Seim
VP: Travis Zeck
IT Man: Tammy Bernier
VP Mktg: Gregory Hanson
VP Sls: Eric Laufenberg
Sls Mgr: Kevin Kopka
Sls Mgr: Ryan Townsend

COLE PARMER INSTRUMENT COMPANY
See COLE-PARMER INSTRUMENT CO LLC

D-U-N-S 00-798-4016
COLE TAYLOR BANK
9550 W Higgins Rd Fl 5, Rosemont, IL 60018-4907
Tel (847) 653-7000 *Founded/Ownrshp* 1997
Sales NA *EMP* 200
SIC 6022

COLE WHOLESALE FLOORING
See COLE PAPERS INC

D-U-N-S 00-885-2253 IMP
COLE-PARMER INSTRUMENT CO LLC (IL)
COLE PARMER INSTRUMENT COMPANY
(*Suby of* CPI BUYER LLC) ★
625 Bunker Ct, Vernon Hills, IL 60061-1830
Tel (847) 549-7600 *Founded/Ownrshp* 1957, 2014
Sales 249.8MM[E] *EMP* 400[E]
SIC 5049 Laboratory equipment, except medical or dental
CEO: Bernd Brust
**Pr:* Seth H Hoogasian
COO: Wilma Baker
**VP:* Amit Agarwal
Dir Bus: Jim Kaigh
Ex Dir: David Smith
Genl Mgr: Paulette Speciale
VP Mktg: Mark Graves
Mktg Dir: Brian Barnett
Sls Mgr: Craig Pfefferman
Snr Mgr: Terry Barber

D-U-N-S 82-475-6795
COLEEN M MCCORMICK
BRAZIL IRRIGATION SYSTEMS
415 Center St Dakota Pl, Ulysses, NE 68669
Tel (402) 549-2778 *Founded/Ownrshp* 1984
Sales 150.0MM *EMP* 15
SIC 8748 6799 Agricultural consultant; Investors
Owner: Coleen McCormick
Owner: Matthew J Dantas Justice

COLEGIO SAN JUSTO
See IGLESIA EPISCOPAL PUERTORRIQUENA INC

D-U-N-S 04-451-9098 IMP/EXP
COLEMAN CABLE LLC
SOUTHWIRE COLEMAN
(*Suby of* SOUTHWIRE CO LLC) ★
1530 S Shields Dr, Waukegan, IL 60085-8317
Tel (847) 672-2300 *Founded/Ownrshp* 2014
Sales 730.0MM[E] *EMP* 1,726
SIC 3661 3357 3643 Telephone cords, jacks, adapters, etc.; Nonferrous wiredrawing & insulating; Power line cable
Pr: G Gary Yetman
**CFO:* Alan C Bergschneider
**Ex VP:* Richard Carr
**Ex VP:* Michael A Frigo
**Ex VP:* Kathy Jo Van
VP: David Oriatti
Exec: Blaine Ballard
Exec: Sarah Moore

D-U-N-S 78-744-9438 IMP/EXP
■ **COLEMAN CO INC**
(*Suby of* NEWELL BRANDS) ★
1767 Denver West Blvd # 200, Golden, CO 80401-3195
Tel (316) 832-2653 *Founded/Ownrshp* 1992
Sales 1.8MMM[E] *EMP* 3,690
SIC 3086 5941 Ice chests or coolers (portable), foamed plastic; Sporting goods & bicycle shops
CEO: Robert Marcovitch
Pr: Bruno Cercley
**CFO:* Dan Hogan
Ofcr: John Shenk
VP: Terri Brooks
VP: Tim Daniel
VP: Ken Hankins
VP Opers: Jay Schroeder
Sls Dir: Matt Clark

D-U-N-S 02-508-5747
■ **COLEMAN FLOOR LLC**
(*Suby of* BMC EAST LLC) ★
1331 Davis Rd, Elgin, IL 60123-1319
Tel (847) 907-3109 *Founded/Ownrshp* 2006
Sales 100.0MM *EMP* 450
SIC 1752 Carpet laying; Ceramic floor tile installation; Vinyl floor tile & sheet installation; Resilient floor laying
Treas: James F Major
**VP:* Thomas D Coleman Jr
Div Mgr: Wayne Martin

D-U-N-S 12-820-4414
COLEMAN NATURAL FOODS LLC
1767 Denver West Blvd # 200, Golden, CO 80401-3195
Tel (303) 468-2500 *Founded/Ownrshp* 2011
Sales NA *EMP* 2,300
SIC 2011 5147 0251

D-U-N-S 88-493-2443
COLEMAN TECHNOLOGIES LLC
5337 Millenia Lakes Blvd, Orlando, FL 32839-6300
Tel (407) 481-8600 *Founded/Ownrshp* 2011
Sales NA *EMP* 1,192
SIC 4813

D-U-N-S 96-996-5255
COLEMAN WORLD GROUP LLC
1 Eagle Ridge Dr, Midland City, AL 36350
Tel (334) 803-8888 *Founded/Ownrshp* 1997
Sales 235.0MM *EMP* 2,100
SIC 4214 Local trucking with storage; Household goods moving & storage, local
CEO: Jeffrey F Coleman
CFO: Joyce Farish
Sr VP: Keith Turner

D-U-N-S 11-225-5927
COLER GOLDWATER SPECIALTY HOSPITAL & NURSING FACILITY
(*Suby of* NEW YORK CITY HLTH & HOSPITALS) ★
900 Main St, New York, NY 10044-0066
Tel (212) 848-6000 *Founded/Ownrshp* 1999
Sales 176.0MM[E] *EMP* 3,000
SIC 8069 8051 Specialty hospitals, except psychiatric; Skilled nursing care facilities
Ex Dir: Robert K Hughes
Prd Mgr: Kristin Dichiara
Prd Mgr: Madhuri Sharma
Doctor: Mohanambal Gounder

D-U-N-S 10-711-3516
COLES ENERGY INC
MICKY MART
3619 St Rt 113 E, Milan, OH 44846-9428
Tel (419) 499-1120 *Founded/Ownrshp* 1982
Sales 101.5MM[E] *EMP* 300
SIC 5172 5411 5541 Petroleum products; Convenience stores, independent; Filling stations, gasoline
Pr: Edwin M Coles
**VP:* Danny Coles
Dir IT: Rick Rinella
Mktg Mgr: Amy Coles

D-U-N-S 15-978-8926
▲ **COLFAX CORP**
420 Natl Bus Pkwy Fl 5, Annapolis Junction, MD 20701-1079
Tel (301) 323-9000 *Founded/Ownrshp* 1995
Sales 3.9MMM *EMP* 13,800
Tkr Sym CFX *Exch* NYS
SIC 3561 3829 3625 Pumps & pumping equipment; Aircraft & motor vehicle measurement equipment; Pressure transducers; Relays & industrial controls
Pr: Matthew L Trerotola
**Ch Bd:* Mitchell P Rales
CFO: C Scott Brannan
CFO: Christopher M Hix
Ex VP: Daniel A Pryor
Sr VP: Lynn Clark
Sr VP: Kevin Olsen
Sr VP: A Lynne Puckett
Sr VP: Stephen J Wittig
Sr VP: Steve Wittig
VP: Bryan Hitz
VP: Shawn Pecor
VP: Bill Roller
VP: Tom Spock
Board of Directors: Patrick W Allender, Thomas S Gayner, Rhonda L Jordan, A Clayton Perfall, Sharon Wienbar

COLFAX FLUID HANDLING
See IMO INDUSTRIES INC

D-U-N-S 07-887-6002
COLFIN JIH AHI OPCO LLC
BAYMONT INN & SUITES
109 Enterprise Ct, Greenwood, SC 29649-1666
Tel (864) 942-0002 *Founded/Ownrshp* 2012
Sales 8.1MM[E] *EMP* 1,500
SIC 7011 Inns
VP: Mark Hedstrom
Off Mgr: Cheree Goodall
IT Man: Howard Green

D-U-N-S 95-802-8581 IMP
■ **COLFOR MANUFACTURING INC**
(*Suby of* AAMCOTRANSMISSIONS) ★
3255 Alliance Rd Nw, Malvern, OH 44644-9756
Tel (330) 863-0404 *Founded/Ownrshp* 1996
Sales 135.0MM[E] *EMP* 691
SIC 3462 3599 3463 Iron & steel forgings; Machine shop, jobbing & repair; Nonferrous forgings
Ch: David C Dauch
COO: Thomas J Szymanski
CFO: Robert Krause
Ex VP: Richard F Dauch
**Ex VP:* Michael K Simonte
**Sr VP:* Alberto Satine
VP: Yogendra N Rahangdale
Plnt Mgr: Tom Fry
Ql Cn Mgr: Jason Worley
Sales Exec: Joe Wayne
Sls&Mrk Ex: Steve Bush

D-U-N-S 09-051-7327 IMP/EXP
■ **COLGATE PALMOLIVE CO DISTRIBUTORS** (DE)
COLGATE-PALMOLIVE
(*Suby of* COLGATE-PALMOLIVE CO) ★
1 St Lot 8colgate, Guaynabo, PR 00968
Tel (787) 273-5000 *Founded/Ownrshp* 1923
Sales 105.9MM[E] *EMP* 550
SIC 5122 Toiletries
Ch Bd: Reuben Mark
**VP:* Bernal Saborio
**VP:* Bill Shanahan

D-U-N-S 00-225-3615
COLGATE UNIVERSITY
13 Oak Dr, Hamilton, NY 13346-1386
Tel (315) 228-1000 *Founded/Ownrshp* 1819
Sales 189.5MM *EMP* 1,014[E]
Accts Kpmg Llp Albany Ny
SIC 8221 University
Pr: Brian Casey
Pr: Annie Angueira
**Pr:* Jeffrey Herbst
**Treas:* David B Hale
**Treas:* Brian Hutzley
Assoc VP: Mari Assaid
Assoc VP: Timothy Mansfield
VP: Alexis Benoit
VP: Scott Brown
**VP:* Murray Decock
VP: Jim Dodge
**VP:* Suzy M Nelson
VP: Adam S Weinberg
Assoc Dir: Vera Chapman
Assoc Dir: Kathryn Hollerbush
Assoc Dir: Kris Hopkins
Assoc Dir: Dawn Lafrance

COLGATE-PALMOLIVE
See COLGATE PALMOLIVE CO DISTRIBUTORS

D-U-N-S 00-134-4381
▲ **COLGATE-PALMOLIVE CO**
300 Park Ave Fl 5, New York, NY 10022-7499
Tel (212) 310-2000 *Founded/Ownrshp* 1806
Sales 16.0MMM *EMP* 37,900
Tkr Sym CL *Exch* NYS
SIC 2844 3991 2841 2842 2047 Toothpastes or powders, dentifrices; Mouthwashes; Deodorants, personal; Shaving preparations; Toothbrushes, except electric; Soap & other detergents; Detergents, synthetic organic or inorganic alkaline; Dishwashing compounds; Soap: granulated, liquid, cake, flaked or chip; Specialty cleaning, polishes & sanitation goods; Fabric softeners; Bleaches, household: dry or liquid; Dog & cat food
Ch Bd: Ian Cook
Pr: Franck Moison
COO: Fabian T Garcia
COO: Tom Obrien
COO: P Justin Skala
COO: Michael Tangney
COO: Noel R Wallace
CFO: Dennis J Hickey
CFO: Stephen C Patrik
Treas: Brian J Heidtke
Chf Mktg O: Mukul Deoras
Ofcr: Javier G Teruel
Sr VP: Andrew D Hendry
Sr VP: Daniel B Marsili
Sr VP: Bina H Thompson
VP: Issam Bachaalani
VP: Vicky Chaparro
VP: Rich Cuprys
VP: David J Deev
VP: William Devizio
VP: Victoria L Dolan
Board of Directors: Stephen I Sadove, John P Bilbrey, John T Cahill, Helene D Gayle, Ellen M Hancock, C Martin Harris, Richard J Kogan, Delano E Lewis, Lorrie M Norrington, Michael B Polk

D-U-N-S 83-019-8102
COLINX LLC
1 Independence Pt Ste 210, Greenville, SC 29615-4536
Tel (864) 607-9431 *Founded/Ownrshp* 1996
Sales 83.8MM *EMP* 1,200
Accts Elliott Davis Decosimo Llc G
SIC 4731 Freight transportation arrangement
**Pr:* Donavan A Louis
**CFO:* Eric Lynch
VP: Jeff Taube
Sftwr Eng: Andrew Kenney

D-U-N-S 09-738-9779
■ **COLISEUM PARK HOSPITAL INC**
COLUMBIA HCA
(*Suby of* HOSPITAL COPORATION OF AMERICA) ★
350 Hospital Dr, Macon, GA 31217-3838
Tel (478) 765-7000 *Founded/Ownrshp* 1994
Sales 178.3MM *EMP* 850[E]
SIC 8062 General medical & surgical hospitals
CEO: Samuel N Hazen
CFO: David G Anderson
CFO: Curtis Herrin
CFO: Roger Simmons
VP: Wade Self
Dir OR: Ben Walker
Dir Rx: Gary Cunningham
IT Man: Janelle Hollowman
Orthpdst: Gregory P Lee
Orthpdst: Derrick D Phillips
Pathlgst: Gary Walker

D-U-N-S 78-740-1496
COLLABERA INC
G C I
25 Airport Rd, Morristown, NJ 07960-4624
Tel (973) 889-5200 *Founded/Ownrshp* 1991
Sales 1.1MMM[E] *EMP* 7,000
SIC 7371 Computer software development & applications
CEO: Hiten Patel
Pr: Mike Dunphy
**Pr:* Mohan Sekhar
**CFO:* Sham Patel
**Sr VP:* Ashwin RAO Arnie
Sr VP: Ashwin RAO
VP: Len Baker
VP: Peter Holmes
VP: Joy Kundu
VP: Mohit Malkani
VP: SAI Narayan
VP: Kekin Shah
VP Bus Dev: Dawn Serpe
Dir Bus: Deepesh Patel
Dir Bus: Aaron Paul
Dir Bus: Saloni Sheth
Dir Bus: Sebastian Simoes

D-U-N-S 08-028-7503
COLLABERA TECHNOLOGIES
25 Airport Rd, Morristown, NJ 07960-4624
Tel (973) 889-5200 *Founded/Ownrshp* 2015
Sales 63.3MM[E] *EMP* 12,000
SIC 7371 Software programming applications
Exec: Sonali Modak
Opers Mgr: Sumeet Pankajakshan

D-U-N-S 07-948-6953
■ **COLLABORATIVE CARE HOLDINGS LLC**
(*Suby of* OPTUM HEALTH) ★
9900 Bren Rd E, Hopkins, MN 55343-9664
Tel (952) 936-1300 *Founded/Ownrshp* 2010
Sales NA *EMP* 156[E]
SIC 6324 Health maintenance organization (HMO), insurance only

D-U-N-S 83-010-7140
COLLECTION & CONSULTING FINANCIAL SERVICES INC
2948 Reed St Ste 100, Philadelphia, PA 19146-3519
Tel (215) 463-3477 *Founded/Ownrshp* 1996
Sales 1.8MM *EMP* 1,415
SIC 7322 Collection agency, except real estate
Pr: Anthony D Archer
**CFO:* Robert Scott

D-U-N-S 78-331-4909 IMP/EXP
COLLECTION INC
200 Bird Rd, Coral Gables, FL 33146-1403
Tel (305) 444-5555 *Founded/Ownrshp* 2009
Sales 122.6MM[E] *EMP* 280
SIC 5511

D-U-N-S 07-300-1646 IMP
COLLECTION XIIX LTD
1370 Broadway Fl 17, New York, NY 10018-7764
Tel (212) 686-8990 *Founded/Ownrshp* 1982
Sales 122.0MM[E] *EMP* 150
SIC 2339 Women's & misses' accessories
Pr: Andrew Pizzo
CFO: Mitchell Grossman
Ex VP: Sean Rimler
Sr VP: Ron D'Angelo
Sr VP: Ron Dangelo
VP: Suzan Kressel

COLLECTIONS ETC
See WINSTON BRANDS INC

COLLEGE BOARD, THE
See COLLEGE ENTRANCE EXAMINATION BOARD

D-U-N-S 07-280-5831
COLLEGE ENTRANCE EXAMINATION BOARD
COLLEGE BOARD, THE
250 Vesey St, New York, NY 10281-1052
Tel (212) 713-8000 *Founded/Ownrshp* 1990
Sales 840.6MM *EMP* 1,259
Accts Pricewaterhousecoo Ers Lp Was
SIC 8299 8221 2732 Educational services; Colleges & universities; Book printing
Pr: David Coleman
**Ch Bd:* Paul W Sechrist
V Ch: Youlonda Copeland-Morgan
V Ch: Maghan Keita
**Pr:* Gaston Caperton
Pr: Richard Weingarten
**COO:* Herb Elish
**COO:* Jeremy Singer
**CFO:* Tho Higgins
CFO: Thomas Higgins
**Treas:* Steve Titan
Trst: Peggy Cain
Trst: Madeleine E Rhyneer
**Sr VP:* Frank Ashley
**Sr VP:* Jack Buckley
**Sr VP:* Frederick H Dietrich
**Sr VP:* Hal Higginbotham
**Sr VP:* Todd Huston
Sr VP: Neil Lane
Sr VP: Andrea Mainelli
Sr VP: Andrea Mainellition

COLLEGE FUND/UNCF
See UNITED NEGRO COLLEGE FUND INC

COLLEGE HOSPITAL CERRITOS
See COLLEGE HOSPITAL COSTA MESA MSO INC

D-U-N-S 11-350-2645
COLLEGE HOSPITAL COSTA MESA MSO INC
COLLEGE HOSPITAL CERRITOS
(*Suby of* COLLEGE HOSPITAL, INC.)
301 Victoria St, Costa Mesa, CA 92627-1995
Tel (949) 642-2734 *Founded/Ownrshp* 1987
Sales 86.2MM *EMP* 225
SIC 8062

D-U-N-S 08-102-6197
COLLEGE OF AMERICAN PATHOLOGISTS (IL)
C.A.P.
325 Waukegan Rd, Northfield, IL 60093-2750
Tel (800) 323-4040 *Founded/Ownrshp* 1947
Sales 186.3MM *EMP* 565
Accts Ernst & Young Llp Chicago Il
SIC 8621 Professional membership organizations
Pr: Gene N Herbek
CFO: Stephen Myers
VP: Jill Addis
VP: Lee Breman
VP: George K Fiedler
VP: Sandy Grear
VP: John Scott
Exec: Patrick Kearns
Exec: Keith Pierson
Ex Dir: Diana Kelker
Ex Dir: Marion Malone

COLLEGE OF THE CANYONS
See SANTA CLARITA COMMUNITY COLLEGE DISTRICT

D-U-N-S 07-372-3322
COLLEGE OF CHARLESTON
UNIVERSITY CHARLESTON SC
66 George St, Charleston, SC 29424-0001
Tel (843) 953-5570 *Founded/Ownrshp* 1970
Sales 216.3MM *EMP* 1,500[E]
Accts Elliott Davis Llc Greenville
SIC 8221 College, except junior; University
Pr: Glenn McConnell
Pr: David S Battey
Trst: Donald H Belk
Trst: John H Busch
Trst: Demetria N Clemons
Trst: Frank M Gadsden
Trst: James F Hightower
Trst: William D Johnson
Trst: Lawrence R Miller
Trst: Annaliza O Moorhead
Trst: Gregory D Padgett
Trst: Sam Stafford III
Trst: Joseph F Thompson Jr
Trst: John B Wood Jr
Ex VP: George P Watt
Sr VP: George Haborak
VP: Elizabeth Kaebaum
VP: Tom Trimboli
Exec: Saundra Purvis
Assoc Dir: Kathryn A Banks

COLLEGE OF DUPAGE
See COMMUNITY COLLEGE DISTRICT 502

D-U-N-S 04-150-9506 IMP
COLLEGE OF HOLY CROSS
1 College St, Worcester, MA 01610-2395
Tel (508) 793-2011 *Founded/Ownrshp* 1843
Sales 169.6MM *EMP* 949
Accts Kpmg Llp Boston Ma
SIC 8221 College, except junior

Pr: Rev Philip L Boroughs Sj
Trst: Steven Florio
Trst: Jeremiah O'Connor
Chf Inves: Timothy M Jarry
Ofcr: Ryan Arsenault
Ofcr: Phil Gibson
**Sr VP:* Frank Vellaccio
VP: Tracy Barlok
VP: Michael J Lochhead
VP: William Ohalloran
VP: Jacqueline D Peterson
VP: Claudia Ross
Assoc Dir: Amanda Beaver
Assoc Dir: Susan Cunningham
Assoc Dir: Liz Gribbons
Assoc Dir: Debra Konicki
Assoc Dir: Christene Riendeau

D-U-N-S 06-800-1908
COLLEGE OF LAKE COUNTY
19351 W Washington St, Grayslake, IL 60030-1198
Tel (847) 543-2000 *Founded/Ownrshp* 1969
Sales 35.2MM *EMP* 1,318
Accts Rsm Us Llp Chicago Illinois
SIC 8222 Community college
Pr: Girard W Weber
V Ch: Barbara D Oilschlager
Pr: Lyla Chandy
Ex VP: Karen Senase
VP: Darl E Drummond
VP: Richard J Haney
VP: James Rock
CIO: Kamlesh Sanghvi
Web Dev: Carmen Lowry
Mktg Dir: Mitch Bienvenue
Psych: Kristen Dahl

COLLEGE OF MARIN
See MARIN COMMUNITY COLLEGE DISTRICT

D-U-N-S 03-031-5980
COLLEGE OF NEW JERSEY
2000 Pennington Rd, Ewing, NJ 08618-1100
Tel (609) 771-2495 *Founded/Ownrshp* 1855
Sales 157.2MM *EMP* 1,075
Accts Kpmg Llp Short Hills Nj
SIC 8221 College, except junior
Pr: Barbara Gittenstein
CFO: Barbara Wineberg
**Treas:* Lloyd Ricketts
**VP:* John P Donohue
**VP:* Amy Hecht
**VP:* Gregory Pogue
Assoc Dir: Andrew Stutzman
DP Exec: Luz Morales
DP Exec: Barbara Nyzio
DP Exec: Audrey Russell
DP Exec: Haneefah Shakir

COLLEGE OF THE OZARKS
See SCHOOL OF OZARKS

D-U-N-S 08-045-7955
COLLEGE OF SAINT ROSE (NY)
432 Western Ave, Albany, NY 12203-1490
Tel (518) 454-5111 *Founded/Ownrshp* 1920
Sales 85.0MM *EMP* 525
Accts Uhy Llp Albany New York
SIC 8221 College, except junior
Pr: R Mark Sullivan
Bd of Dir: Drey Martone
VP: Mary Grondahl
VP: Dennis McDonald
VP: Matthew Scherr
**VP:* Kathleen Sineo
Assoc Dir: Jorge R Osorio
Mng Dir: Mike D'Attilio
Off Mgr: Amy Zonca
Psych: Andrew Shanock

COLLEGE OF SAN MATEO
See SAN MATEO COUNTY COMMUNITY COLLEGE DISTRICT

D-U-N-S 07-493-4233
COLLEGE OF SOUTHERN MARYLAND FOUNDATION INC
C S M
8730 Mitchell Rd, La Plata, MD 20646-2867
Tel (301) 934-2251 *Founded/Ownrshp* 1958
Sales 1.2MM *EMP* 1,200
Accts Cliftonlarsonallen Llp Luther
SIC 8351 Child day care services
Pr: Bradley Gottfreid
VP: Richard Fleming
VP: Tracy Harris
VP: Tony Jernigan
VP: Daniel Mosser
Assoc Dir: Eugene Kirscht
Assoc Dir: Gene Kirscht
Ex Dir: Denise Clark
Store Mgr: Marcy Gannon
IT Man: Joel Kinison
IT Man: Parry Taylor

D-U-N-S 79-409-9619
COLLEGE OF SOUTHERN NEVADA FOUNDATION INC
3200 E Cheyenne Ave, North Las Vegas, NV 89030-4228
Tel (702) 651-4000 *Founded/Ownrshp* 1971
Sales 95.5MM^E^ *EMP* 2,900
Accts Houldsworth Russo & Company
SIC 8222 Community college
Pr: Peter O'Neill
**Treas:* Jeffrey Cooper
Ofcr: Stuart Susag
VP: Mary K Bailey
VP: Hyla Winters
Ex Dir: Jackie Matthews

D-U-N-S 05-846-3291
COLLEGE OF WESTERN IDAHO
CWI
6056 Birch Ln, Nampa, ID 83687-5192
Tel (208) 562-3200 *Founded/Ownrshp* 2010
Sales 2.0MM^E^ *EMP* 1,000
SIC 8299 Educational services
Pr: Bert Glandon

D-U-N-S 07-476-2238
COLLEGE OF WILLIAM & MARY
261 Richmond Rd, Williamsburg, VA 23185-3534
Tel (757) 221-3966 *Founded/Ownrshp* 1693
Sales 300.0MM^E^ *EMP* 3,500
SIC 8221 9411 College, except junior; Administration of educational programs;
Pr: W Taylor Reveley III
Pr: Bill Copan
Chf Inves: Brian Hiestand
Ex VP: Karen R Cottell
Ex VP: Karen Cottrell
VP: Frances Bradford
**VP:* Samuel E Jones
VP: Anna B Martin
Exec: John Falin
Exec: Maryse Fauvel
Exec: Kevin Gilliam
Exec: Howard Harris
Exec: Manuel Lacerda
Exec: Pam Sardeson
Exec: Stephen Sechrist
Exec: Casey Van Veen
Exec: Robert Vold
Board of Directors: David Williard, Francis Bradsord, Michael Connolly, Edward P Irish, Peter C Kellogg, Bernadette M Kenney, Suzanne Seurattan,jane Lop, Eugene A Roche, Glenda E White, Brian Whitson

COLLEGE PARK CAMPUS
See UNIVERSITY OF MARYLAND COLLEGE PARK

D-U-N-S 96-260-4781
■ **COLLEGE STATION HOSPITAL LP**
COLLEGE STATION MEDICAL CENTER
(*Suby of* COMMUNITY HEALTH SYSTEMS INC) ★
1604 Rock Prairie Rd, College Station, TX 77845-8345
Tel (979) 764-5100 *Founded/Ownrshp* 2007
Sales 143.8MM *EMP* 600
SIC 8062 General medical & surgical hospitals
CEO: Bud Wethington
Pt: Tom Jackson
CFO: Ken Pannell
CFO: Kenneth D Pannell
Dir Rx: Kim Feese
Cmptr Lab: Barbara Moore
Dir QC: Natalie Zamuliski
Psych: Henry Bohne

D-U-N-S 01-078-6218
COLLEGE STATION INDEPENDENT SCHOOL DISTRICT
1812 Welsh Ave, College Station, TX 77840-4800
Tel (979) 764-5400 *Founded/Ownrshp* 1948
Sales 138.9MM *EMP* 785
Accts Hereford Lynch Sellars & Kir
SIC 8211 Public elementary & secondary schools
Pr Dir: Chuck Glenewinkel

COLLEGE STATION MEDICAL CENTER
See COLLEGE STATION HOSPITAL LP

COLLEGE WORKS PAINTING
See NATIONAL SERVICES GROUP INC

D-U-N-S 78-582-2334
COLLEGIATE HOUSING FOUNDA
409 Johnson Ave, Fairhope, AL 36532-2142
Tel (251) 928-9340 *Founded/Ownrshp* 2006
Sales 93.1MM *EMP* 2
SIC 7021 Dormitory, commercially operated
Prin: Leeman H Covey

D-U-N-S 02-614-7772
COLLEGIATE HOUSING FOUNDATION
409 Johnson Ave, Fairhope, AL 36532-2142
Tel (251) 304-0055 *Founded/Ownrshp* 1996
Sales 124.4MM *EMP* 6^E^
Accts Wilkins Miller Hieronymus Llc
SIC 7299 Personal financial services
Pr: Lee Covey
**Treas:* Dr John Brooks Slaughter
**Bd of Dir:* Jack Edwards
**VP:* John Hicks

D-U-N-S 10-060-6722
COLLETON COUNTY SCHOOL DISTRICT
213 N Jefferies Blvd, Walterboro, SC 29488-2907
Tel (843) 549-5715 *Founded/Ownrshp* 1940
Sales 167.6M *EMP* 1,087
Accts Elliot Davis Llc Columbia S
SIC 8211 Public elementary & secondary schools
Dir Sec: Terry Dingle
Teacher Pr: Cliff Warren

D-U-N-S 10-001-2699
COLLIER COUNTY PUBLIC SCHOOLS
5775 Osceola Trl, Naples, FL 34109-0919
Tel (239) 377-0001 *Founded/Ownrshp* 1926
Sales 397.6MM^E^ *EMP* 6,000
Accts Cherry Bekaert & Holland Ll
SIC 8211 Public elementary & secondary schools
Ex Dir: Debbie Terry
Dir Sec: Tim Kutz
**Genl Mgr:* Nancy Sirko
Off Mgr: Amy Mullens
Off Mgr: Janie Ramirez
IT Man: Cindy Reinertsen
Pr Dir: Greg Turchetta
Teacher Pr: Ian Dean
Teacher Pr: Shari Huene-Johnson

D-U-N-S 61-453-6290
COLLIERS INTERNATIONAL PROPERTY CONSULTANTS INC
(*Suby of* COLLIERS MACAULAY NICOLLS INC)
601 Union St Ste 3320, Seattle, WA 98101-4004
Tel (206) 695-4200 *Founded/Ownrshp* 1980
Sales 104.4MM^E^ *EMP* 183
SIC 6531 Real estate brokers & agents; Real estate managers
CEO: Douglas Frye
Pr: Warren Dahlstrom
Pr: Cynthia Foster
**Pr:* Dwight Hotchkiss
**Pr:* Scott Nelson
Pr: Brian Ward
**Pr:* Karen Whitt
COO: Allen Ioshi
**COO:* Dylan E Taylor
COO: Dylan Taylor
COO: Karen J Whitt
**Treas:* Curtis Akey
**Chf Mktg O:* Christine Schultz
Ex VP: William Kaye
**Ex VP:* Jonathan Kingsley
**Ex VP:* Stephen Rutchik
Sr VP: John Johannson
Sr VP: Nick Ousman
Sr VP: Haas Reynolds
VP: Guy Preston
**VP:* Daniel L Spiegel

D-U-N-S 96-539-2264
COLLIERS INTERNATIONAL WA LLC
(*Suby of* COLLIERS MACAULAY NICOLLS INC)
601 Union St Ste 3320, Seattle, WA 98101-4004
Tel (206) 223-0866 *Founded/Ownrshp* 1978
Sales 180.0MM *EMP* 151
SIC 6531 Real estate brokers & agents
**Ch:* Douglas P Frye
**Treas:* Peter Humphries
VP: Scott Nelson
IT Man: Ted Topacio

COLLIERS TURLEY MARTIN TUCKER
See CASSIDY TURLEY COMMERCIAL REAL ESTATE SERVICES INC

D-U-N-S 14-815-8751
COLLIN COUNTY COMMUNITY COLLEGE DISTRICT
3452 Spur 399, Mckinney, TX 75069-8742
Tel (972) 758-3100 *Founded/Ownrshp* 1985
Sales 40.6MM *EMP* 2,650
Accts Grant Thornton Llp Dallas Te
SIC 8222 Community college
Pr: Neil Matkin Ed D
**Pr:* Sherry Schumann PH D
**Pr:* Dr Brenda Kihl
**Pr:* Ken Lynn
**Pr:* Dr Mary McRae
VP: Norma L Allen
VP: Julie M Bradley
VP: Barbara Money
Genl Mgr: Susan Cannon

D-U-N-S 14-747-0975 IMP/EXP
COLLINS BUS CORP
(*Suby of* COLLINS INDUSTRIES INC) ★
415 W 6th Ave, Hutchinson, KS 67505-1323
Tel (620) 662-9000 *Founded/Ownrshp* 1986
Sales 120.0MM *EMP* 290^E^
SIC 3711 Motor buses, except trackless trollies, assembly of
Ch Bd: John Becker
COO: Randall Swift
CFO: Tim Davis
**Treas:* Tom Heinsen
**VP:* Dino Cusuano
**VP:* John Doswell
QC Dir: Rachelle Ecklund
Plnt Mgr: Bryce Pfister
Sales Asso: Robin Morrell

COLLINS COMPANIES, THE
See COLLINS PINE CO

D-U-N-S 05-893-3946 IMP/EXP
COLLINS INDUSTRIES INC
(*Suby of* ASV) ★
15 Compound Dr, Hutchinson, KS 67502-4349
Tel (620) 663-5551 *Founded/Ownrshp* 1971
Sales 367.4MM^E^ *EMP* 1,148^E^
SIC 4522 Ambulance services, air
Ch Bd: Kenneth Dabrowski
**CFO:* Hans Heinsen
**VP:* John Dreasher
**VP:* Ron Sorenson

D-U-N-S 00-903-0222 EXP
COLLINS PINE CO
COLLINS COMPANIES, THE
29190 Sw Town Center Loop, Wilsonville, OR 97070-9411
Tel (503) 227-1219 *Founded/Ownrshp* 1931
Sales 138.9MM^E^ *EMP* 395
SIC 2421 2426 5211 4911 4013 Cut stock, softwood; Furniture dimension stock, hardwood; Lumber & other building materials; Generation, electric power; Switching & terminal services
Ch Bd: Cherida Collins Smith
**Pr:* Eric Schooler
**Treas:* Timothy R Bishop
**Ex VP:* R Wade Mosby
Opers Supe: Paul Eastman

D-U-N-S 95-694-5067 IMP
COLLINS TIMBER CO LLC
29100 Sw Town Ctr Loop W, Wilsonville, OR 97070-9315
Tel (503) 227-1219 *Founded/Ownrshp* 1996
Sales 102.6MM^E^ *EMP* 620
SIC 2493 Particleboard products
Ex VP: Eric Schooler
**CFO:* Marlyn Hendricks

D-U-N-S 82-868-3198 IMP/EXP
■ **COLLOID ENVIRONMENTAL TECHNOLOGIES CO LLC**
CETCO
(*Suby of* AMCOL INTERNATIONAL CORP) ★
2870 Forbs Ave, Hoffman Estates, IL 60192-3702
Tel (847) 851-1500 *Founded/Ownrshp* 1990
Sales 271.2MM^E^ *EMP* 300^E^
SIC 3259 2899 Liner brick or plates for sewer/tank lining, vitrified clay; Concrete curing & hardening compounds
Pr: Ryan F McKendrick
VP: Patrick Carpenter
Genl Mgr: Pedro Abad
IT Man: Murali Venkatraman
Mktg Mgr: Ray McLarty
Sls Mgr: Allen Bullock
Sls Mgr: Richard Heskett
Sls Mgr: Jeanette Smith

COLOMER USA
See ROUX LABORATORIES INC

COLONIAL BANK
See BB&T

D-U-N-S 05-898-5367
COLONIAL ELECTRIC SUPPLY CO
BRIGHT LIGHTS
201 W Church Rd Ste 100, King of Prussia, PA 19406-3247
Tel (610) 312-8100 *Founded/Ownrshp* 1972
Sales 152.4MM^E^ *EMP* 200
SIC 5065

COLONIAL FORD
See GREATER RICHMOND BUSINESS INC

D-U-N-S 02-112-1348 IMP/EXP
COLONIAL GROCERS INC
PAYLESS CASH & CARRY CLUB
4001 E Lake Ave, Tampa, FL 33610-8032
Tel (813) 621-8880 *Founded/Ownrshp* 1998
Sales 90.1MM *EMP* 85
Accts Warren Averett Llc Tampa Fl
SIC 0132 5141 Tobacco; Groceries, general line
Pr: Yasin Saad

D-U-N-S 80-837-6735 IMP/EXP
COLONIAL GROUP INC
101 N Lathrop Ave, Savannah, GA 31415-1054
Tel (800) 944-3835 *Founded/Ownrshp* 1993
Sales 825.7MM^E^ *EMP* 900
SIC 5171 5169 5172 4924 4492 4226 Petroleum bulk stations & terminals; Chemicals, industrial & heavy; Gasoline; Lubricating oils & greases; Natural gas distribution; Tugboat service; Liquid storage
Pr: Robert H Demere Jr
Pr: Clay Cheshire
**CFO:* Francis A Brown
Bd of Dir: Barry Deal
Ex VP: Rick Wigger
VP: Pratt Summers
VP Bus Dev: Ryan Chandler
CTO: Bob May
MIS Dir: James Mercer
**VP Opers:* William A Baker Jr
Opers Mgr: Ken Sellers
Board of Directors: Robert H Demere Jr

D-U-N-S 07-916-5411
COLONIAL INTERMEDIATE UNIT 20
6 Danforth Dr, Easton, PA 18045-7899
Tel (610) 252-5550 *Founded/Ownrshp* 1971
Sales 77.6MM^E^ *EMP* 1,100^E^
Accts Palmer And Company Easton Pe
SIC 8211 Public elementary & secondary schools
Ex Dir: Charlene M Brennan
**Ex Dir:* Jacqueline Walsh
Genl Mgr: Jon Wallitsch
IT Man: Thomas Kalinoski
Psych: Gretchen Bisher
Psych: Kathleen Dariano
Psych: Katryn Goodman
Psych: Diane Lazar
Psych: Denise Mazar
Psych: Shane Nauss
Psych: Michelle Primerano

D-U-N-S 00-791-9376
■ **COLONIAL LIFE & ACCIDENT INSURANCE CO INC** (SC)
(*Suby of* UNUM GROUP) ★
1200 Colonial Life Blvd W, Columbia, SC 29210-7670
Tel (803) 798-7000 *Founded/Ownrshp* 1939
Sales NA *EMP* 1,300
SIC 6321 6311 Accident insurance carriers; Health insurance carriers; Life insurance carriers
Pr: Tim Arnold
Pr: Randall C Horn
CFO: Josh Nelson
Sr VP: Thomas Gilligan
Sr VP: Daniel Hughey
Sr VP: Annaclair Kiger
Sr VP: Kennedy Boggs Lloyd
Sr VP: David Parker
Sr VP: Henry Price
Sr VP: Rich Williams
VP: Kyle Addy
Exec: Tracey Harris
Dir Risk M: Wayne Hamilton

COLONIAL MARBLE & GRANITE
See NTP MARBLE INC

COLONIAL NATIONAL MORTAGE
See COLONIAL SAVINGS FA

D-U-N-S 00-692-6430 IMP/EXP
COLONIAL OIL INDUSTRIES INC
(*Suby of* COLONIAL GROUP INC) ★
101 N Lathrop Ave, Savannah, GA 31415-1054
Tel (904) 396-1388 *Founded/Ownrshp* 1993
Sales 600.4MM^E^ *EMP* 186
SIC 5171 5541 Petroleum bulk stations & terminals; Filling stations, gasoline
CEO: Robert H Demere Jr
**CFO:* Francis A Brown
**VP:* William A Baker Jr
**VP:* Steven M McNear

D-U-N-S 07-263-4389
COLONIAL PARKING INC
(*Suby of* FORGE CO) ★
1050 Thms Jfrsn St Nw 100, Washington, DC 20007
Tel (202) 965-3096 *Founded/Ownrshp* 1974
Sales 60.8MM^E^ *EMP* 1,100
SIC 7521 Parking garage; Parking lots
Ch Bd: Russell C Lindner
**Pr:* Andrew C Blair
Pr: Sharon Wills
COO: Randy Boatwright
**CFO:* Richard Peterson
**CFO:* David C Souders
Treas: Sergius Gambal
**Sr VP:* Jim Proctor
VP: Gary Lindner
**VP:* James D Villa
Ex Dir: Seth Gunn

D-U-N-S 05-712-3671
■ COLONIAL PENN LIFE INSURANCE CO
(*Suby of* CNO FINANCIAL GROUP INC) ★
399 Market St, Philadelphia, PA 19181-0001
Tel (215) 928-8000 *Founded/Ownrshp* 1957
Sales NA *EMP* 350
SIC 6321 6311 Health insurance carriers; Life insurance carriers
Pr: Gregg Brestead
Treas: Daniel J Murphy
VP: William T Devanney
VP: Gaetano Fiordimondo
VP: Theresa Harvey
QA Dir: Tamesha Munson
QA Dir: Denise Shamro
QA Dir: Johnny Weatherbe
Prd Mgr: Estelle Strully
Mktg Mgr: Susan Bunting
Mktg Mgr: Patrick Burlingame

D-U-N-S 00-388-7478
COLONIAL PIPELINE CO
1185 Sanctuary Pkwy # 100, Alpharetta, GA 30009-4765
Tel (678) 762-2200 *Founded/Ownrshp* 1961
Sales 326.4MM^E^ *EMP* 700
SIC 4613 4612 4226 1389 5171 Refined petroleum pipelines; Crude petroleum pipelines; Petroleum & chemical bulk stations & terminals for hire; Pumping of oil & gas wells; Petroleum terminals
Pr: Tim Felt
VP: Rob Barbeauld
VP: Eve Brooks
VP: Barton Brown
**VP:* Kalin Jones
Exec: Michelle McIntosh
Area Mgr: Robert Daniel
Brnch Mgr: Doug Scott
Genl Mgr: Tom Guzikowski
Snr Sftwr: Kevin Balent
CTO: Michael Dubois

D-U-N-S 07-545-7606 IMP
COLONIAL PROPERTIES TRUST
2101 6th Ave N Ste 750, Birmingham, AL 35203-2775
Tel (205) 250-8700 *Founded/Ownrshp* 1993
Sales 393.5MM *EMP* 911[E]
SIC 6798 6552 6531 6513

D-U-N-S 07-485-6691
COLONIAL SAVINGS FA
COLONIAL NATIONAL MORTAGE
2600 West Fwy, Fort Worth, TX 76102-7109
Tel (817) 390-2000 *Founded/Ownrshp* 1991
Sales NA *EMP* 650
SIC 6162 6035 Mortgage bankers & correspondents; Federal savings & loan associations
Pr: David Motley
**Ch Bd:* James S Du Bose
Pr: Brent Davis
**CFO:* Ben Dempsey
Sr VP: Jack Plonien
VP: Vickie Bourassa
Mng Dir: Scott Taylor
Brnch Mgr: Berry Roberson
Dir IT: Robert Botzer
Dir IT: Richard Emerson
Sftwr Eng: David Fritz
Board of Directors: Donna Dempsey, James Dubose, William Head, George Ogle

D-U-N-S 11-549-7711
COLONIAL SCHOOL DISTRICT
318 E Basin Rd, New Castle, DE 19720-4200
Tel (302) 323-2700 *Founded/Ownrshp* 1981
Sales 51.8MM[E] *EMP* 1,300
SIC 8211

D-U-N-S 83-640-5191
COLONIAL WILLIAMSBURG CO
A CONTINUUM OF WELLNESS, THE
(*Suby of* COLONIAL WILLIAMSBURG FOUNDATION) ★
101 Visitor Center Dr, Williamsburg, VA 23185-4565
Tel (888) 965-7254 *Founded/Ownrshp* 1983
Sales 88.7MM[E] *EMP* 1,685
SIC 8741 Hospital management
Pr: Colin Campbell
Pr: Eliza Eversole
Sr VP: Michael Rierson
**VP:* John Hallowell
VP: Jim Horn
Comm Dir: Penelope Young
CTO: Sarah Houghland
DP Dir: Pete Watson
IT Man: Rick Gunther
Software D: Anthony Conyers
Sls Dir: Tom Spong

D-U-N-S 00-794-2014 IMP
COLONIAL WILLIAMSBURG FOUNDATION (VA)
427 Franklin St Rm 212, Williamsburg, VA 23185-4304
Tel (757) 229-1000 *Founded/Ownrshp* 1928
Sales 148.7MM *EMP* 3,100
SIC 5947 8412 5812 7011 Gift shop; Souvenirs; Museum; Eating places; Hotels & motels
Pr: Mitchell B Reiss
Trst: Amos B Hostetter
Sr VP: Robert Taylor
VP: Bob Jeremiah
Genl Couns: Gail Waddell

D-U-N-S 05-890-4319
■ COLONIALWEBB CONTRACTORS CO
COMFORT SYSTEMS USA CAROLINAS
(*Suby of* COMFORT SYSTEMS USA INC) ★
2820 Ackley Ave, Richmond, VA 23228-2146
Tel (804) 916-1400 *Founded/Ownrshp* 2010
Sales 213.6MM[E] *EMP* 1,100
SIC 1711 7623

D-U-N-S 00-608-8751 IMP
COLONY BRANDS INC (WI)
1112 7th Ave, Monroe, WI 53566-1364
Tel (608) 328-8400 *Founded/Ownrshp* 1925
Sales 263.7MM[E] *EMP* 1,000
SIC 5961 5143 2051 Cheese, mail order; Gift items, mail order; Cheese; Bakery: wholesale or wholesale/retail combined
Ch Bd: Raymond R Kubly Jr
**Pr:* John D Baumann
CFO: Don Hughes
**Sr VP:* Michael C Kubly
**VP:* Donald R Hughes
Ex Dir: Randall Iverson
Ex Dir: Todd Valeria
CIO: Steve Cretney
Dir IT: Mary Richardson
IT Man: Ken Hill
IT Man: Shawn Lewis

D-U-N-S 83-178-1617
▲ COLONY CAPITAL INC
515 S Flower St Fl 44, Los Angeles, CA 90071-2201
Tel (310) 282-8820 *Founded/Ownrshp* 1991
Sales 841.9MM *EMP* 347[E]
Tkr Sym CLNY *Exch* NYS
SIC 6798 Real estate investment trusts
Pr: Richard B Saltzman
**Ch Bd:* Thomas J Barrack Jr
COO: Mark M Hedstrom
CFO: Darren J Tangen
Ex Dir: Jonathan H Grunzweig
Ex Dir: Kevin P Traenkle
Board of Directors: Nancy A Curtin, George G C Parker, John A Somers, John L Steffens

D-U-N-S 80-108-3338
COLONY CAPITAL LLC
COLONY MANAGEMENT
2450 Broadway Ste 600, Santa Monica, CA 90404-3591
Tel (310) 282-8820 *Founded/Ownrshp* 1992
Sales 1.0MMM[E] *EMP* 2,263[E]
SIC 6799 7999 7011 5813 5812 Real estate investors, except property operators; Gambling & lottery services; Hotels & motels; Drinking places; Eating places
Ch: Thomas J Barrack Jr
COO: Kevin L Davis
Ex VP: Jeffrey Moore
Sr VP: Brent Elkins
Sr VP: Stefan Jaeger
Sr VP: Bryan Morland
Sr VP: Richard Welch
VP: James Herbert
VP: Sonia Kim
VP: Ryan McManus
VP: Andrea Nicholas
VP: Varun Pathria
VP: Gregory Thomas
Exec: Katrina Clarkson

D-U-N-S 01-235-6218
COLONY INSURANCE CO
(*Suby of* ARGO GROUP INTERNATIONAL HOLDINGS, LTD.)
8720 Stony Point Pkwy # 400, Richmond, VA 23235-1988
Tel (804) 560-2000 *Founded/Ownrshp* 1981, 1984
Sales NA *EMP* 200
SIC 6351 Liability insurance
CEO: Dale Pilkington
**Pr:* Mike Warfield
CFO: Matthew R Pollak
**CFO:* Scott Wilson
VP: Kevin Price

COLONY MANAGEMENT
See COLONY CAPITAL LLC

D-U-N-S 19-401-7331
COLONY RESORTS LVH ACQUISITIONS LLC
LVH-LAS VEGAS HOTEL & CASINO
3000 Paradise Rd, Las Vegas, NV 89109-1287
Tel (702) 732-5111 *Founded/Ownrshp* 1982
Sales 105.2MM[E] *EMP* 1,880
SIC 7011 Hotels & motels
CFO: Stephanie Heredia
Bd of Dir: John Ermi
**VP:* Lou Dorn
**VP:* Jay Kornegay
Exec: George Bedich
Exec: Eric Pascual
Exec: Joseph Reda
Sls Dir: Cynthia Mason
Sls Dir: Doug Wangsmo

D-U-N-S 07-941-3856
COLONY STARWOOD HOMES
8665 E Hartford Dr # 200, Scottsdale, AZ 85255-7807
Tel (480) 362-9760 *Founded/Ownrshp* 2012
Sales 271.8MM *EMP* 836[E]
SIC 6798 Real estate investment trusts
CEO: Frederick C Tuomi
**Ch Bd:* Thomas J Barrack Jr
**Ch Bd:* Barry S Sternlicht
COO: Charles D Young
CFO: Arik Prawer
Chf Mktg O: Lucas Haldeman
Ex VP: Ryan A Berry
Ex VP: Justin M Iannacone
Sr VP: Joshua Swift

D-U-N-S 84-743-6391 IMP/EXP
COLOPLAST CORP
(*Suby of* COLOPLAST A/S)
1601 W River Rd, Minneapolis, MN 55411-3431
Tel (612) 337-7800 *Founded/Ownrshp* 2011
Sales 101.9MM[E] *EMP* 500[E]
SIC 3842 2844 5047 Cosmetic restorations; Cosmetic preparations; Shaving preparations; Shampoos, rinses, conditioners: hair; Medical & hospital equipment
Pr: Lars Rasmussen
**Pr:* Claus Bjerre
Pr: Kimberly Herman
**Pr:* Steffen Hovard
**Treas:* Philip H Eickhoff
**Ex VP:* Lene Skole
**VP:* Eric Halvorson
Genl Mgr: Mary Holmstrom
Dir IT: Gerdi Jansen
IT Man: Klaus Feldam
IT Man: Don Richards
Board of Directors: Lars Einar Hansen, Lars Rasmussen, Peter Volkers

COLOR
See ALLIED CONSTRUCTION SERVICES INC

D-U-N-S 83-511-5650
COLOR ART INTEGRATED INTERIORS LLC
1325 N Warson Rd, Saint Louis, MO 63132-1807
Tel (314) 432-3000 *Founded/Ownrshp* 1995
Sales 159.0MM[E] *EMP* 200[E]
SIC 5021 7641 5999 5712 5099 2521 Office furniture; Office furniture repair & maintenance; Reupholstery; Art dealers; Office furniture; Video & audio equipment; Wood office furniture
CEO: Gary Mindel
**Ch Bd:* Joe Steiner
Pr: Jim Schnefke
**Ex VP:* David Coleman
Ex VP: Wheaton Danaher
VP: Katy Morris
Exec: Barbara A Ross
CTO: Mike Zoia
MIS Mgr: Chris Meyer
Sales Exec: Linda Taylor

D-U-N-S 05-943-3888 EXP
COLOR COMMUNICATIONS INC
4000 W Fillmore St, Chicago, IL 60624-3905
Tel (773) 638-1400 *Founded/Ownrshp* 1972
Sales 135.8MM[E] *EMP* 350[E]
SIC 2752 3993 Cards, lithographed; Advertising artwork
CEO: Stanley Lerner
**Pr:* Steven Winter
**CFO:* Thomas Connerty
VP: Harry Lerner
VP Sls: Ted Bockweg

D-U-N-S 79-825-8513 IMP/EXP
COLOR IMAGE APPAREL INC
BELLACANVAS
6670 Flotilla St, Commerce, CA 90040-1816
Tel (855) 793-3100 *Founded/Ownrshp* 1992
Sales 181.5MM[E] *EMP* 100
SIC 5137 5136 Women's & children's clothing; Men's & boys' clothing
CEO: Daniel Harris
**VP:* Marco De George

COLOR KINETICS
See PHILIPS LIGHTING NORTH AMERICA CORP

D-U-N-S 07-945-6573
COLOR SPOT HOLDINGS INC
COLOR SPOT NURSERIES
27368 Via Industria Ste 2, Temecula, CA 92590-4855
Tel (760) 695-1430 *Founded/Ownrshp* 2007
Sales 5.4MMM[E] *EMP* 3,000[E]
Accts Kpmg Llp San Diego Ca
SIC 0181 Bedding plants, growing of
CEO: Jerry Halamuda
**COO:* Chip Mello
**COO:* Oscar Truyol
**CFO:* Rodney Omps

COLOR SPOT NURSERIES
See COLOR SPOT HOLDINGS INC

D-U-N-S 92-763-2356 IMP
COLOR SPOT NURSERIES INC
(*Suby of* COLOR SPOT NURSERIES) ★
27368 Via Ste 201, Temecula, CA 92590
Tel (760) 695-1430 *Founded/Ownrshp* 1995
Sales 5.4MMM[E] *EMP* 3,000
SIC 0181

D-U-N-S 13-151-6101
COLOR-BOX LLC
GEORGIA-PACIFIC
(*Suby of* GEORGIA-PACIFIC LLC) ★
623 S G St, Richmond, IN 47374-6134
Tel (765) 966-7588 *Founded/Ownrshp* 2001
Sales 193.3MM[E] *EMP* 1,100
SIC 2653 Corrugated & solid fiber boxes
CEO: James Hannan
**Ex VP:* Christian Fischer
**Sr VP:* Michael E Adams
**Sr VP:* Julie Brehm
**Sr VP:* Tye Darland
Opers Mgr: Darrin Coates
Prd Mgr: Amy Zetzl
Mktg Dir: Chet Garner

COLORADO BANK, THE
See PINNACLE BANCORP INC

COLORADO BANK, THE
See BANK OF COLORADO

COLORADO BELL AND CASINO
See MARNELL GAMING LLC

D-U-N-S 02-097-8680 EXP
COLORADO BOXED BEEF CO
302 Progress Rd, Auburndale, FL 33823-2727
Tel (863) 967-0636 *Founded/Ownrshp* 1975
Sales 669.3MM[E] *EMP* 600
SIC 5142 5147 Meat, frozen: packaged; Meats, fresh
Pr: John Rattigan
**Ch:* Bryan N Saterbo
VP: John Saterbo
**VP:* James Woelfel
Off Mgr: Yuli Ocasio
Sls Dir: Keith Mosley
Board of Directors: Sandy Schuler

D-U-N-S 06-969-0451
COLORADO CHRISTIAN UNIVERSITY INC
8787 W Alameda Ave, Lakewood, CO 80226-2824
Tel (303) 963-3000 *Founded/Ownrshp* 1914
Sales 90.8MM *EMP* 533
Accts Capin Crouse Llp Colorado Spr
SIC 8221 Colleges universities & professional schools
Ch: William Armstrong
**Pr:* Bill Armstrong
**Pr:* Paul Eldridge
VP: Maxine Boyd
VP: Roger Chandler
**VP:* Dan Cohrs
**VP:* Shannon Dreyfuss
VP: Jim McCormick
**VP:* Glen Nelson
**VP:* Cherri Parks
**VP:* Don Stahl
Exec: Rick Garris
Assoc Dir: Valerie Stanton

D-U-N-S 05-656-1707
COLORADO COLLEGE
14 E Cache La Poudre St, Colorado Springs, CO 80903-3243
Tel (719) 389-6000 *Founded/Ownrshp* 1874
Sales 142.9MM *EMP* 800
Accts Clifton Larson Allen Llp Gree
SIC 8221 College, except junior
Pr: Jill Tiefenthaler
Pr: Paul Buckley
Ofcr: Laura Rosendo
VP: Randy Stiles
Genl Mgr: Sarah Hintz
Netwrk Eng: David Ziemba
Sls Mgr: Joan Taylor

COLORADO COMM ON HGHER EDUCATN
See COLORADO DEPARTMENT OF HIGHER EDUCATION

COLORADO COMMUNITY COLLEGE SYS
See STATE BOARD FOR COMMUNITY COLLEGES AND OCCUPATIONAL EDUCATIONAL SYSTEM

D-U-N-S 03-967-2449
COLORADO COUNTY OIL CO INC (TX)
C C O
(*Suby of* J AND L HOLDING CO INC) ★
1348 Business 71, Columbus, TX 78934-5026
Tel (979) 732-6870 *Founded/Ownrshp* 1979
Sales 138.6MM *EMP* 38
SIC 5171 Petroleum bulk stations
Pr: L L Leach III
**Treas:* Carolyn Foster
**VP:* Andrew Leach

D-U-N-S 07-647-1572
COLORADO DENTAL SERVICE INC
DELTA DENTAL OF COLORADO
4582 S Ulster St Ste 800, Denver, CO 80237-2567
Tel (303) 741-9300 *Founded/Ownrshp* 1958
Sales NA *EMP* 100
Accts Mcgladrey Llp Minneapolis Mn
SIC 6324 Dental insurance
Pr: Kathryn Paul
**VP:* Linda Arneson
**VP:* David Beal
VP Admn: Barbara Springer
Board of Directors: Cynthia Evans

D-U-N-S 87-820-7760
COLORADO DEPARTMENT OF CORRECTIONS
(*Suby of* GOVERNORS OFFICE) ★
2862 S Circle Dr, Colorado Springs, CO 80906-4101
Tel (719) 579-9580 *Founded/Ownrshp* 1876
Sales NA *EMP* 6,000
SIC 9223 Correctional institutions;
Ex Dir: Rick Raemisch
Ofcr: Richard Casias
Ofcr: David Cornella
Ofcr: Todd Mason
Ofcr: Jim Meisner
Ofcr: David Peterson
**Prin:* Roger Werholtz
Sls Mgr: Richard Curry

D-U-N-S 87-855-8519
COLORADO DEPARTMENT OF HIGHER EDUCATION
COLORADO COMM ON HGHER EDUCATN
(*Suby of* GOVERNORS OFFICE) ★
1560 Broadway Ste 1600, Denver, CO 80202-5160
Tel (303) 866-2723 *Founded/Ownrshp* 1965
Sales NA *EMP* 1,874
SIC 9411 Administration of educational programs;
Ex Dir: Tim Foster
Ex Dir: Scott Mendelsberg

D-U-N-S 01-925-9053
COLORADO DEPARTMENT OF HUMAN SERVICE
(*Suby of* STATE OF COLORADO) ★
1575 N Sherman St, Denver, CO 80203-1702
Tel (303) 866-5948 *Founded/Ownrshp* 1876
Sales NA *EMP* 5,036[E]
SIC 9441 Administration of social & manpower programs;
CFO: Ted Martin
Software D: Vanessa Trindade

D-U-N-S 87-814-7602
COLORADO DEPARTMENT OF HUMAN SERVICES
(*Suby of* GOVERNORS OFFICE) ★
1575 N Sherman St Fl 8, Denver, CO 80203-1702
Tel (303) 866-5700 *Founded/Ownrshp* 1994
Sales NA *EMP* 4,778
SIC 9441 Administration of social & manpower programs;
Ex Dir: Reggie Bicha
IT Man: Clint Woodruff

D-U-N-S 87-820-9295
COLORADO DEPARTMENT OF LABOR & EMPLOYMENT
(*Suby of* GOVERNORS OFFICE) ★
633 17th St Ste 1100, Denver, CO 80202-3611
Tel (303) 620-4700 *Founded/Ownrshp* 1950
Sales NA *EMP* 1,200
SIC 9651 9441 Inspection for labor standards & safety, government; ; Public welfare administration: non-operating, government;
Ex Dir: Ellen Golombek

D-U-N-S 87-855-9871
COLORADO DEPARTMENT OF MILITARY AND VETERANS AFFAIRS
(*Suby of* GOVERNORS OFFICE) ★
6848 S Revere Pkwy, Centennial, CO 80112-3904
Tel (720) 250-1530 *Founded/Ownrshp* 1876
Sales NA *EMP* 1,090
SIC 9711 National security;
IT Man: Insook Bhushan

D-U-N-S 87-901-5899
COLORADO DEPARTMENT OF NATURAL RESOURCES
EXECUTIVE DIRECTOR'S OFFICE
(*Suby of* GOVERNORS OFFICE) ★
1313 N Sherman St Ste 718, Denver, CO 80203-2239
Tel (303) 866-3311 *Founded/Ownrshp* 1876
Sales NA *EMP* 1,404
SIC 9512 Land, mineral & wildlife conservation;
Ex Dir: Bob Randall
**Prin:* James B Martin
Genl Mgr: Lei Zhu
IT Man: Bob Broscheid
Board of Directors: Greg Walsher

D-U-N-S 87-820-8826
COLORADO DEPARTMENT OF PUBLIC HEALTH AND ENVIRONMENT
(*Suby of* GOVERNORS OFFICE) ★
4300 E Cherry Creek S Dr, Denver, CO 80246-1523
Tel (303) 692-2000 *Founded/Ownrshp* 1994
Sales NA *EMP* 1,200
SIC 9431 9511 Administration of public health programs; ; Air, water & solid waste management;
Ex Dir: James Martin
Ex Dir: Douglas Benevanto
**Ex Dir:* Chris Urbina

D-U-N-S 87-804-6747
COLORADO DEPARTMENT OF PUBLIC SAFETY
(*Suby of* GOVERNORS OFFICE) ★
700 Kipling St Ste 1000, Lakewood, CO 80215-5897
Tel (303) 239-4400 *Founded/Ownrshp* 1876
Sales NA *EMP* 1,514E
SIC 9229
Ex Dir: Stan Hilkey
Genl Mgr: Terri Anderle
IT Man: Tamara Russ

D-U-N-S 87-798-5077
COLORADO DEPARTMENT OF TRANSPORTATION
CDOT INFORMATIONS SYSTEMS CTR
(*Suby of* GOVERNORS OFFICE) ★
4201 E Arkansas Ave, Denver, CO 80222-3406
Tel (303) 757-9557 *Founded/Ownrshp* 1994
Sales NA *EMP* 11,889E
SIC 9621 Transportation department: government, non-operating;
**CFO:* Heather Copp
Ofcr: Don C Kirkpatrick
Brnch Mgr: Vicki L Armstrong
Brnch Mgr: Maria Sobota
Brnch Mgr: Herman Stockinger
Genl Mgr: David Scheib
Software D: Greg Ostravich

D-U-N-S 01-119-8926 IMP
COLORADO FOOD PRODUCTS INC
3600 S Yosemite St # 800, Denver, CO 80237-1830
Tel (303) 409-8400 *Founded/Ownrshp* 1978
Sales 121.0MM *EMP* 18
SIC 5147

D-U-N-S 00-691-4865
■ **COLORADO INTERSTATE GAS CO LLC**
(*Suby of* KINDER MORGAN ENERGY PARTNERS LP) ★
1001 La St Ste 1000, Houston, TX 77002
Tel (713) 369-9000 *Founded/Ownrshp* 2015
Sales 404.0MM *EMP* 4E
Accts Pricewaterhousecoopers Llp Ho
SIC 4922 Pipelines, natural gas; Storage, natural gas
Pr: Mark A Kissel
CFO: David P Michels
**Ex VP:* Steven J Kean
**VP:* David R Deveau

COLORADO JUDICIAL DEPARTMENT
See JUDICIARY COURTS OF STATE OF COLORADO

D-U-N-S 05-037-5698
COLORADO KENWORTH INC
(*Suby of* MURPHY-HOFFMAN CO) ★
11120 Tomahawk Creek Pkwy, Leawood, KS 66211-2695
Tel (720) 941-0833 *Founded/Ownrshp* 1965
Sales 90.7MME *EMP* 564E
SIC 5511 New & used car dealers
Pr: Charles Keller
**CFO:* Jeffrey Johnson

COLORADO MATERIALS
See HUNTER INDUSTRIES LTD

D-U-N-S 07-575-9837
COLORADO MESA UNIVERSITY
1100 North Ave, Grand Junction, CO 81501-3122
Tel (970) 248-1020 *Founded/Ownrshp* 1925
Sales 101.3MM *EMP* 850
SIC 8221 College, except junior
Pr: Tim Foster
Pr: Steven Werman
VP: Patrick Doyle
VP: Carol Futhey
VP: Johnny Snyder
Assoc Dir: Jonathan Hinkle
Comm Man: Adam Cochran
Ex Dir: Jeremy Brown
Ex Dir: Jean Gauley
Genl Mgr: Tracy Brodrick
Store Mgr: Tyler Liff

COLORADO PREMIUM FOOD
See K2D INC

D-U-N-S 04-046-3705
COLORADO PRIME OF PENNSYLVANIA INC
1 Michael Ave, Farmingdale, NY 11735-3948
Tel (631) 694-1111 *Founded/Ownrshp* 1976
Sales 100.0MM *EMP* 65
SIC 5421 5722 Freezer provisioners, meat; Household appliance stores
Pr: John Masciandaro
**CFO:* Daniel Benjamin

D-U-N-S 78-246-5579 IMP
COLORADO ROCKIES BASEBALL CLUB LTD
2001 Blake St, Denver, CO 80205-2060
Tel (303) 292-0200 *Founded/Ownrshp* 1991
Sales 399.8M *EMP* 1,000
Accts Dunn Henritze Maline Llp Fort
SIC 7941 Baseball club, professional & semi-professional
CEO: Charles K Monfort
**V Ch:* Richard L Monfort
**Pr:* Keli S McGregor
**CFO:* Harold R Roth
Ex VP: Daniel J O'Dowd
Sr VP: Harold R Oth
IT Man: Luella Ozawa
VP Mktg: Albert Valdes
Mktg Dir: Kari Anderson
Mktg Dir: Scott Donaldson
Assoc Ed: Julian Valentin

D-U-N-S 00-743-1760
COLORADO SEMINARY
UNIVERSITY OF DENVER
2199 S Univ Blvd, Denver, CO 80210-4711
Tel (303) 871-2000 *Founded/Ownrshp* 1864
Sales 458.7MM *EMP* 2,770E
Accts Cliftonlarsonallen Llp Green
SIC 8221 University
**Ch:* Joy Burns
Ofcr: Jennifer Paar
Ex VP: Curtis Burch
VP: Armin Afshi
VP: Michael G Housman
Assoc Dir: Michele McCandless
Dir Soc: Lauri A Mlinar
Dir Soc: Diane L Roth
Ex Dir: Cathryne C Johnson
Ex Dir: Stephen Seifert
Ex Dir: Judith S White

D-U-N-S 07-834-7481
COLORADO SPRINGS CITY GOVERNMENT
COLORADO SPRINGS DEPT OF PARKS
107 N Nevada Ave, Colorado Springs, CO 80903-1305
Tel (719) 385-5900 *Founded/Ownrshp* 1872
Sales NA *EMP* 7,000
Accts Bkd Llp Colorado Spring Col
SIC 9199
Prin: Jon Saultz

COLORADO SPRINGS DEPT OF PARKS
See COLORADO SPRINGS CITY GOVERNMENT

D-U-N-S 01-062-0441
COLORADO SPRINGS SCHOOL DISTRICT 11
D11 SCHOOL
1115 N El Paso St, Colorado Springs, CO 80903-2519
Tel (719) 520-2000 *Founded/Ownrshp* 1872
Sales 272.9MM *EMP* 2,000
Accts Mcgladrey Llp Denver Colorad
SIC 8211 Public elementary & secondary schools; Public junior high school; Public senior high school
VP: David Schenkel
Exec: Rebecca Kluck
Ex Dir: John R Dethloff
Ex Dir: Beverly Johnson
Dir Sec: Nicky Soto
Admn Mgr: Libby Bailey
Admn Mgr: Julie Foster
Admn Mgr: Rusty Moomey
MIS Dir: D Shultz
IT Man: Mike Barentine
IT Man: Lisa Joseph

D-U-N-S 12-771-1760 IMP/EXP
COLORADO SPRINGS UTILITIES
121 S Tejon St Ste 200, Colorado Springs, CO 80903-2187
Tel (719) 448-4800 *Founded/Ownrshp* 1925
Sales 830.8MM *EMP* 1,800
SIC 4939 Combination utilities
CEO: Phillip H Tollefson
V Ch: Prince Dunn II
**Ofcr:* Dick Comerford
Ofcr: Sherri Newell
VP: Sharon Finstrom
Exec: Jack Wood
Pr Mgr: Susan Presti

D-U-N-S 06-971-2792
COLORADO STATE UNIVERSITY
(*Suby of* ADMINISTRATIVE OFFICE) ★
6003 Campus Delivery, Fort Collins, CO 80523-6003
Tel (970) 491-1372 *Founded/Ownrshp* 1877
Sales 11.4MM *EMP* 6,701
Accts Eide Bailly Llp Fort Collins
SIC 8221 University
Pr: Tony Frank
Pr: Becky Takeda
Bd of Dir: Jeffrey Miller
VP: Linda Kuk
Exec: Karl Bendix
Exec: Thomas Sanders
Assoc Dir: Josie Plaut
Assoc Dir: Nik Shea
Off Mgr: Joanne Divico
MIS Dir: Don Albrecht
IT Man: Jordan Fritts
Board of Directors: Larry L Curran II

D-U-N-S 94-890-5492
COLORADO STATE UNIVERSITY SYSTEM
ADMINISTRATIVE OFFICE
475 17th St Ste 1550, Denver, CO 80202-4012
Tel (303) 534-6290 *Founded/Ownrshp* 1877
Sales 1.0MMM *EMP* 6,701
Accts Bkd Llp Denver Co
SIC 8221 University
Pr: Becky Takeda
Genl Couns: Johnna Doyle
Genl Couns: Jason Johnson
Genl Couns: Michael Nolser

D-U-N-S 05-749-0187
COLORADO STATE UNIVERSITY-PUEBLO
(*Suby of* ADMINISTRATIVE OFFICE) ★
2200 Bonforte Blvd, Pueblo, CO 81001-4901
Tel (719) 549-2100 *Founded/Ownrshp* 1933
Sales 73.2MME *EMP* 1,534
Accts Mcpherson Breyfogle Daveline &
SIC 8221 University
Pr: Lesley Di Mare
Ofcr: Kevin Anderson
VP: Craig Cason
VP: Alan Rudolph
VP: Lou Swanson
Prgrm Mgr: Angela Healy
Prgrm Mgr: Beverly Marquart
Prgrm Mgr: John Staffeld
Off Mgr: Jonathon R Valdez
CTO: Rene Drabier
IT Man: Richard Thibault

D-U-N-S 14-864-2002 IMP/EXP
COLORCON INC
(*Suby of* BERWIND CORP) ★
420 Moyer Blvd, West Point, PA 19486
Tel (215) 699-7733 *Founded/Ownrshp* 1983
Sales 562.8MME *EMP* 1,191
SIC 2834 Pharmaceutical preparations
CEO: Marti Hedman
Pr: John J Byrne Jr
Pr: Luciana Paganini
CFO: John Ryan
Sec: William R Motzer
VP: Thomas Boehning
VP: David Cavacini
VP: Steve Zenuh
Exec: Bhawna Prabhakar
Dir Lab: George Reyes
Site Mgr: Jamison Bell

COLORGRAPHICS
See MADISON/GRAHAM COLOR GRAPHICS INC

D-U-N-S 19-361-1451
COLORGRAPHX INC
BECK GRAPHICS
4721 110th Ave N, Clearwater, FL 33762-4912
Tel (727) 572-6364 *Founded/Ownrshp* 2004
Sales 375.0MM *EMP* 30
SIC 2711 Commercial printing & newspaper publishing combined
Pr: George R Stulpin
**Pr:* George Stulpin

COLORPAK
See POLY-PAK INDUSTRIES INC

D-U-N-S 83-837-0484 IMP
COLORTECH INC
(*Suby of* POLYPLAST MULLER GMBH)
5712 Commerce Blvd, Morristown, TN 37814-1049
Tel (423) 587-0837 *Founded/Ownrshp* 2000
Sales 99.4MM *EMP* 195
SIC 3087 2816 Custom compound purchased resins; Color pigments
Ch: Hans Mueller
**Pr:* Alex Rom Roginski
VP: Tim Coley
**VP:* Ken Conklin
QA Dir: Anthony Hubbard
Opers Mgr: Adam Rankin
Plnt Mgr: Felix Calidonio
Snr Mgr: Edward Richard
Board of Directors: Hans Mueller

D-U-N-S 15-671-2747
COLOURS INC
233 S Washington St, Wilkes Barre, PA 18701-2802
Tel (570) 655-9510 *Founded/Ownrshp* 1972
Sales 93.0MME *EMP* 205
SIC 5198 5085 5088 Paints; Abrasives & adhesives; Abrasives; Aircraft equipment & supplies
Pr: Tim Evans
**Sec:* Linda Evans
Ex Dir: Dorena Kearney
CTO: Todd Castallucci
CTO: Shawn Shadle
CTO: Ed Webb
Mktg Dir: Joe Driesse
Mktg Dir: Bob Krupski

D-U-N-S 10-001-3515
COLQUITT COUNTY BOARD OF EDUCATION
710 28th Ave Se, Moultrie, GA 31768-7759
Tel (229) 985-1550 *Founded/Ownrshp* 1868
Sales 87.1MME *EMP* 1,200
Accts Greg S Griffin Atlanta Georg
SIC 8211 School board
Ch: Mary Beth Watson

D-U-N-S 07-979-8994
COLQUITT COUNTY SCHOOLS
710 28th Ave Se, Moultrie, GA 31768-7759
Tel (229) 890-6200 *Founded/Ownrshp* 2015
Sales 20.7MME *EMP* 1,236E
SIC 8211 Public elementary & secondary schools
MIS Dir: Emily Nichols
Pr Dir: Lou A Lardy
Instr Medi: Beau Sherman
Psych: Denise Pope

D-U-N-S 00-692-6265 IMP
COLQUITT ELECTRIC MEMBERSHIP CORP (GA)
15 Rowland Dr, Moultrie, GA 31768-4169
Tel (229) 985-3620 *Founded/Ownrshp* 1936
Sales 135.5MM *EMP* 164
SIC 4911 Distribution, electric power
Pr: Huey Hiers
**Sec:* Jimmy Griner
**VP:* Bobby Griner
**Genl Mgr:* Rick L Gaston
Opers Mgr: Sidney Zipperer

D-U-N-S 07-916-1882
COLQUITT REGIONAL MEDICAL CENTER
3131 S Main St, Moultrie, GA 31768-6925
Tel (229) 985-3420 *Founded/Ownrshp* 2014
Sales 59.5MM *EMP* 1,000
SIC 8011 Medical centers
CEO: James L Matney
**CFO:* Shamb Purohit

COLQUITT REGIONAL MEDICAL CTR
See HOSPITAL AUTHORITY OF COLQUITT COUNTY

D-U-N-S 10-206-7378
COLSA CORP
6728 Odyssey Dr Nw, Huntsville, AL 35806-3305
Tel (256) 964-5361 *Founded/Ownrshp* 2005
Sales 191.6MM *EMP* 1,100
SIC 8731 7373 8744 8711 Computer (hardware) development; Computer systems analysis & design; Systems engineering, computer related; Base maintenance (providing personnel on continuing basis); Engineering services
CEO: Francisco J Collazo
**Pr:* Richard Amos
COO: Roy Ota
Ex VP: Tony Dirienzo
VP: Penny Chilton
VP: Joe Collazo
VP: Phil Hodges
Prgrm Mgr: Lauren Dirienzo
Prgrm Mgr: Joseph Kress
Prgrm Mgr: Robert Nieves
Prgrm Mgr: James Puckett

D-U-N-S 80-743-2737
COLSON & COLSON GENERAL CONTRACTOR INC
2260 Mcgilchrist St Se # 100, Salem, OR 97302-1168
Tel (503) 586-7401 *Founded/Ownrshp* 1988
Sales 85.8MM *EMP* 50E
Accts Grove Mueller & Swank Pc Sa
SIC 1522 1542 Residential construction; Apartment building construction; Commercial & office building contractors
Pr: Norman L Brenden
**Treas:* Gregory Tibbot
Off Mgr: Teresa Hammett

D-U-N-S 11-294-5733
COLSON ASSOCIATES INC
1 N Franklin St Ste 2420, Chicago, IL 60606-3435
Tel (312) 980-1100 *Founded/Ownrshp* 2003
Sales 206.4MME *EMP* 369
SIC 8748 Business consulting
Pr: Louhon Tucker
**Pr:* Robert Pritzker
VP: Luohn Tucker

D-U-N-S 00-510-5705 IMP/EXP
COLSON GROUP INC (DE)
1 N Franklin St Ste 2420, Chicago, IL 60606-3435
Tel (312) 980-1100 *Founded/Ownrshp* 1953
Sales NA *EMP* 1,900
SIC 3429

COLT DEFENSE HOLDING
See COLT DEFENSE LLC

D-U-N-S 60-339-5794
COLT DEFENSE HOLDING LLC
547 New Park Ave, West Hartford, CT 06110-1336
Tel (860) 232-4489 *Founded/Ownrshp* 2003
Sales 287.9MME *EMP* 470
SIC 3484 Machine guns or machine gun parts, 30 mm. & below

D-U-N-S 12-139-6217
COLT DEFENSE LLC
COLT DEFENSE HOLDING
(*Suby of* COLT DEFENSE HOLDING LLC) ★
547 New Park Ave, West Hartford, CT 06110-1336
Tel (860) 232-4489 *Founded/Ownrshp* 2002
Sales 277.9MM *EMP* 470
SIC 3484 Machine guns or machine gun parts, 30 mm. & below; Carbines, 30 mm. & below
CEO: Dennis Veilleux
**CFO:* Richard Harris
Sr VP: Kenneth Juergens
Sr VP: Paul Spitale
VP: Joyce Rubino
Dir IT: Scott Daniels
Sls Mgr: Ben Grainger

D-U-N-S 05-803-6505
■ **COLT INTERNATIONAL LLC**
(*Suby of* WORLD FUEL SERVICES CORP) ★
300 Flint Ridge Rd, Webster, TX 77598-4315
Tel (281) 280-2100 *Founded/Ownrshp* 2014
Sales NA *EMP* 150E
SIC 6411 5172 Property & casualty insurance agent; Aircraft fueling services
CEO: Joel Purdom
**Pr:* Malcolm Hawkins
**CEO:* Joel C Purdom
**CFO:* Hardy Fairbanks
VP: Don Fortner
VP: Rich Harper
Exec: Amanda Goss
Dir Risk M: John E Springrose
Mng Dir: Daniel Coetzer
QA Dir: Murry Yates
Software D: Stan Matzke

D-U-N-S 00-896-2920 IMP
■ **COLTEC INDUSTRIES INC**
GARLOCK BEARINGS
(*Suby of* ENPRO INDUSTRIES INC) ★
5605 Carnegie Blvd # 500, Charlotte, NC 28209-4642
Tel (704) 731-1500 *Founded/Ownrshp* 2002
Sales 292.8MME *EMP* 1,700
SIC 3053 3519 3089 Gaskets & sealing devices; Engines, diesel & semi-diesel or dual-fuel; Marine engines; Gasoline engines; Plastic containers, except foam
Pr: Ernest F Schaub
**CFO:* William Dries
**Treas:* Robert Rehley

*VP: Richard L Magee
Mktg Mgr: Jim Palmer

D-U-N-S 61-827-2038 IMP/EXP
■ **COLTEC INDUSTRIES INC**
FAIRBANKS MORSE ENGINE
(Suby of ENPRO INDUSTRIES INC) ★
701 White Ave, Beloit, WI 53511-5447
Tel (608) 364-4411 Founded/Ownrshp 1976
Sales 149.2MM[E] EMP 428
SIC 3519 Engines, diesel & semi-diesel or dual-fuel
Pr: Stephen E Macadam
Pr: Greg Gutofki
*Treas: David S Burnett
VP: Jared Barefield
*VP: John M Childress
VP: John Vollmer
Exec: Pat Bussie
CIO: Dana Wallace
Dir IT: Dave Sievers
Sls Mgr: Chuck Anderson

D-U-N-S 01-374-5518
COLTON JOINT UNIFIED SCHOOL DISTRICT
1212 Valencia Dr, Colton, CA 92324-1798
Tel (909) 580-5000 Founded/Ownrshp 1966
Sales 119.5MM[E] EMP 1,800
SIC 8211 Public combined elementary & secondary school
Pr Dir: Katie Orloff

COLUMBIA - ST MARY'S
See COLUMBIA HOSPITAL INC

D-U-N-S 07-740-4515
COLUMBIA ASSOCIATION INC
6310 Hillside Ct Ste 100, Columbia, MD 21046-1070
Tel (410) 715-3000 Founded/Ownrshp 1965
Sales 67.2MM EMP 1,200
Accts Cohnreznick Llp Baltimore Ma
SIC 8641 Community membership club
Pr: Milton Matthews
*CFO: Susan Krabbe
CFO: Rafia P Siddiqui
Sls Mgr: Debbie Thompson

COLUMBIA AURORA MIDWIVES
See HEALTHNOTES LLC

D-U-N-S 18-407-9846
COLUMBIA BANCORP
7168 Columbia Gateway Dr, Columbia, MD 21046-3254
Tel (410) 872-9165 Founded/Ownrshp 1987
Sales NA EMP 362
SIC 6029 Commercial banks
Ch Bd: John M Bond Jr
*Pr: John A Scaldara Jr
CFO: James P Radick
CFO: Gary Schminkey
*V Ch Bd: Winfield M Kelly Jr
*V Ch Bd: James R Moxley Jr
Brnch Mgr: Margaret Hill
Board of Directors: Harry L Lundy Jr, Anand S Bhasin, Kenneth H Michael, Robert R Bowie Jr, James R Moxley III, Garnett Y Clark Jr, Dr Vincent D Palumbo, Hugh F Z Cole Jr, Mary S Scrivener, William L Hermann, Lawrence A Shulman, Charles C Holman, Maurice M Simpkins, Herschel L Langenthal, Robert N Smelkinson, Raymond G Laplaca, Theodore G Venetoulis, Morris A Little, James J Winn Jr

D-U-N-S 07-668-8605
COLUMBIA BANK
19-01 State Rt 208, Fair Lawn, NJ 07410-2832
Tel (201) 796-3600 Founded/Ownrshp 1926
Sales NA EMP 500
SIC 6035 Federal savings banks
Pr: Thomas J Kemly
COO: Alex Grinewicz
CFO: E Thomas Allen
Ofcr: Richard Abbate
Ofcr: Diane K Brett
Ofcr: Michael A Campbell
Ofcr: Alex Cirocco
Ofcr: Robert Cleveland
Ofcr: Mary A Constantine
Ofcr: Frank Kabrel
Ofcr: Geri M Kelly
Ofcr: Adriana Linder
Ofcr: Steven Long
Ofcr: Todd Malkin
Ofcr: Edward P McNally
Ofcr: John R Pietrowitz
Ofcr: Muhammad Riaz
Ofcr: Donna Rivera
Ofcr: Philip Sohn
Ofcr: Liz Spear
Ofcr: Jane Walsh
Board of Directors: Garret J Vermaas

D-U-N-S 03-146-5958
▲ **COLUMBIA BANKING SYSTEM INC**
1301 A St, Tacoma, WA 98402-4200
Tel (253) 305-1900 Founded/Ownrshp 1988
Sales NA EMP 1,868[E]
Accts Deloitte & Touche Llp Seattle
Tkr Sym COLB Exch NGS
SIC 6022 State commercial banks; State trust companies accepting deposits, commercial
Pr: Melanie J Dressel
*Ch Bd: William T Weyerhaeuser
COO: Hadley S Robbins
CFO: Clint E Stein
CFO: David C Lawson
Ex VP: Kumi Y Baruffi
Ex VP: Andrew L McDonald
Board of Directors: David A Dietzler, Craig D Eerkes, Ford Elsaesser, Mark A Finkelstein, John P Folsom, Thomas M Hulbert, Michelle M Lantow, S Mae Fujita Numata, Elizabeth W Seaton

COLUMBIA BASIN BLENDS
See WESTON LAMB SALES INC

COLUMBIA CAROLINA DIVISION
See COLUMBIA PLYWOOD CORP

D-U-N-S 07-198-9024
COLUMBIA CITY OF (INC)
CITY OF COLUMBIA
701 E Broadway, Columbia, MO 65201-4472
Tel (573) 874-7457 Founded/Ownrshp 1820
Sales NA EMP 1,300[E]
Accts Mcgladrey Llp Kansas City M
SIC 9111 Mayors' offices;
*CFO: John Blattel
Ofcr: Laura Peveler
Ofcr: Latisha Stroer
Genl Mgr: Michele Nix

COLUMBIA COL/MODESTO JR COLL
See YOSEMITE COMMUNITY COLLEGE DISTRICT

D-U-N-S 07-712-2315
COLUMBIA COLLEGE
1001 Rogers St, Columbia, MO 65216-0001
Tel (573) 875-8700 Founded/Ownrshp 1851
Sales 87.4MM EMP 1,600
Accts Bkd Llp Springfield Missour
SIC 8221 College, except junior
Pr: Scott Dalrymple
COO: Eric Ross
*CFO: Bruce Boyer
VP: Mike Randerson
*VP: Terry Smith
Comm Dir: Krista Turnbaugh
Ex Dir: Bob Hutton
Off Mgr: Ivy Leach
Off Mgr: Angi Pauley
CIO: Kevin Palmer
Web Dev: Beth Hastings

D-U-N-S 06-849-7411
COLUMBIA COLLEGE CHICAGO
600 S Michigan Ave Fl 5, Chicago, IL 60605-1996
Tel (312) 663-1600 Founded/Ownrshp 1928
Sales 261.5MM EMP 1,000
SIC 8221 College, except junior
Pr: Kwang-Wu Kim
V Ch: Warren K Chapman
Chf Mktg O: Mark Lloyd
Sr VP: Michael Davis
VP: Timothy Bauhs
VP: Patricia Bergeson
VP: Jeffrey Meece
VP: Ellen Ryan
Assoc Dir: Theresa Kerr
Assoc Dir: Carol Loverde
Dir Soc: Diana Cazares
Dir Soc: Craig Sorensen

COLUMBIA COUNTY BOARD OF EDUCA
See COLUMBIA COUNTY SCHOOL DISTRICT

D-U-N-S 04-564-5715
COLUMBIA COUNTY SCHOOL BOARD
372 W Duval St, Lake City, FL 32055-3990
Tel (386) 755-8010 Founded/Ownrshp 1900
Sales 81.5M EMP 1,500
SIC 8211 Public elementary & secondary schools
V Ch: Steve Nelson

D-U-N-S 10-064-6041
COLUMBIA COUNTY SCHOOL DISTRICT
COLUMBIA COUNTY BOARD OF EDUCA
4781 Hereford Farm Rd, Evans, GA 30809-6037
Tel (706) 541-0650 Founded/Ownrshp 1900
Sales 251.1MM EMP 3,240
Accts Serotta Maddocks Evans & Co
SIC 8211 Public elementary & secondary schools
HC Dir: Lisa Whitlock

D-U-N-S 19-577-1357
COLUMBIA COUNTY SCHOOL DISTRICT
372 W Duval St, Lake City, FL 32055-3990
Tel (386) 755-8000 Founded/Ownrshp 1882
Sales 63.0MM[E] EMP 1,400
SIC 8211 9411 Public elementary & secondary schools; Administration of educational programs
V Ch: Dana Brady
MIS Dir: Sherry Williams
IT Man: Becky Wise
Pr Dir: Brandi Keen
Schl Brd P: Keith Hudson
Schl Brd P: Linard Johnson
Teacher Pr: Frank Moore
Psych: Lorraine Zeller

COLUMBIA DISTRIBUTING
See CDC OREGON INC

D-U-N-S 03-998-9223 IMP
COLUMBIA DISTRIBUTING OF SEATTLE LLC
20301 59th Pl S, Kent, WA 98032-2144
Tel (425) 251-9300 Founded/Ownrshp 1998
Sales 108.8MM[E] EMP 650
SIC 5182 Wine

D-U-N-S 82-562-5742
COLUMBIA ELECTRICAL CONTRACTORS INC
COLUMBIA TECH
(Suby of COLUMBIA TECH) ★
27 Otis St Ste 300, Westborough, MA 01581-3373
Tel (508) 366-8297 Founded/Ownrshp 1991
Sales 138.0MM EMP 240
SIC 3613 Panel & distribution boards & other related apparatus
Pr: Christopher J Coghlin
*CFO: Christopher J Palermo
*Treas: James W Coghlin Sr
Sr VP: Laura Deming
Board of Directors: Richard J Noonan, Stephen F Wentzell

D-U-N-S 00-698-2151
■ **COLUMBIA ENERGY GROUP**
(Suby of NISOURCE INC) ★
200 Civic Center Dr, Columbus, OH 43215-4138
Tel (614) 460-4683 Founded/Ownrshp 2015
Sales 1.0MMM[E] EMP 2,100[E]
SIC 4922 1311 1731 Natural gas transmission; Crude petroleum production; Electric power systems contractors
Pr: Robert Skaggs Jr
*Pr: Robert Skaggs
*VP: Gary W Pottorff

D-U-N-S 05-228-4072
COLUMBIA FARMS INC
(Suby of NASH JOHNSON & SONS FARMS INC) ★
125 N Lee St, Leesville, SC 29070-8099
Tel (803) 532-4488 Founded/Ownrshp 1982
Sales 300.0MM[E] EMP 1,800
SIC 2015 Poultry, processed: fresh
CEO: Robert C Johsnon
CFO: James A Robison
*VP: Dennis Beasley

D-U-N-S 02-368-3279 IMP/EXP
COLUMBIA FOREST PRODUCTS CORP
(Suby of COLUMBIA FOREST PRODUCTS INC) ★
222 Sw Columbia St # 610, Portland, OR 97201-6600
Tel (503) 224-5300 Founded/Ownrshp 1997
Sales 146.4MM[E] EMP 1,200
SIC 2435 Panels, hardwood plywood
Pr: Bradley L Thompson
*VP: Clifford D Barry
*VP: John W Tritch
VP: Ed Woods
Dir IT: Steve Pung

D-U-N-S 08-197-8389 IMP/EXP
COLUMBIA FOREST PRODUCTS INC
7900 Triad Center Dr # 200, Greensboro, NC 27409-9075
Tel (336) 605-0429 Founded/Ownrshp 1976
Sales 681.9MM[E] EMP 2,500
SIC 2435 Veneer stock, hardwood; Plywood, hardwood or hardwood faced
Pr: Bradley L Thompson
*CFO: Ron Jordee
Treas: Ron Mullenburg
Ex VP: Clifford Barry
CIO: Ron Jorde
Plnt Mgr: Clay Kirkland
Plnt Mgr: Christian Noel

D-U-N-S 02-533-6004
COLUMBIA FRUIT LLC
2530 Dike Rd, Woodland, WA 98674-9522
Tel (360) 225-9575 Founded/Ownrshp 2004
Sales 83.0MM[E] EMP 170[E]
SIC 5142 5411

D-U-N-S 00-477-3586
■ **COLUMBIA GAS OF OHIO INC** (OH)
(Suby of NISOURCE INC) ★
290 W Nationwide Blvd # 114, Columbus, OH 43215-4157
Tel (614) 460-6000 Founded/Ownrshp 1951
Sales 872.1MM EMP 2,500
SIC 4924 Natural gas distribution
Pr: Jack Partridge
Pr: Dick James
*Treas: Devit Vajda
VP: George Usner

D-U-N-S 00-878-1668
■ **COLUMBIA GAS OF PENNSYLVANIA INC**
(Suby of NISOURCE INC) ★
121 Champion Way Ste 100, Canonsburg, PA 15317-5817
Tel (724) 416-6300 Founded/Ownrshp 1993
Sales 431.2MM[E] EMP 880
SIC 4924 Natural gas distribution
CEO: Robert C Skaggs Jr
*Pr: Joe Hamrock
*Pr: Mark Kempic
*Treas: David I Vajda
*Treas: Roger D Vari
*VP: William J Lavelle
*VP: Terrence J Murphy
*VP: Melanie K Popovich
VP: Ed Santry
*VP: Lawrence B Smore
*VP: Jon D Veurink
Exec: Erica Coleman

D-U-N-S 00-794-0976
■ **COLUMBIA GAS OF VIRGINIA INC** (VA)
(Suby of NISOURCE INC) ★
1809 Coyote Dr, Chester, VA 23836-2400
Tel (800) 543-8911 Founded/Ownrshp 1854
Sales 134.7MM[E] EMP 275
SIC 4924 Natural gas distribution
CEO: Robert C Skaggs
*Pr: Brent Archer
*COO: Peggy Landini
*Treas: Dennis W Mc Farland
*VP: Philip Iracane
*VP: Lawrence Smore

D-U-N-S 05-474-8041
■ **COLUMBIA GAS TRANSMISSION LLC**
(Suby of COLUMBIA PIPELINE GROUP INC) ★
200 Cizzic Ctr Dr, Columbus, OH 43216
Tel (614) 460-6000 Founded/Ownrshp 1969, 2015
Sales 880.0MM[E] EMP 1,300
SIC 4922 Pipelines, natural gas; Storage, natural gas
Pr: Glen L Kettering
Treas: David J Vajda
VP: Jeffrey W Grossman

D-U-N-S 87-265-1625 IMP/EXP
COLUMBIA GEAR CORP
(Suby of INDUSTRIAL MANUFACTURING CO LLC) ★
530 County Road 50, Avon, MN 56310-8662
Tel (440) 838-4700 Founded/Ownrshp 1981
Sales 144.8MM[E] EMP 386
SIC 3566 3462 Gears, power transmission, except automotive; Iron & steel forgings
Pr: Dana C Lynch
CFO: Gloria Notch
CIO: Fred Eggert
Sls Mgr: David Puhl
Sales Asso: Mary Gunn

D-U-N-S 09-229-5419 EXP
COLUMBIA GRAIN INC
C G I
(Suby of MARUBENI CORPORATION)
1300 Sw 5th Ave Ste 2929, Portland, OR 97201-5636
Tel (503) 224-8624 Founded/Ownrshp 1978
Sales 218.4MM[E] EMP 160
SIC 5153 Grains
CEO: Mike Wong
*Pr: James M Wong
*CFO: Steve Wright
*Sec: Matt Kenton
*Sr VP: Kurt Haarmann
*VP: Amer Badawi
*VP: Kip Callahan
VP: Randy Cartmill
VP: Bob McDonald
VP: Dan Treinen
VP: Jeff Vanpevenage

D-U-N-S 00-785-4581
■ **COLUMBIA GULF TRANSMISSION LLC**
(Suby of COLUMBIA PIPELINE GROUP INC) ★
5151 San Felipe St # 2500, Houston, TX 77056-3607
Tel (713) 386-3701 Founded/Ownrshp 1958, 2000
Sales 880.0MM[E] EMP 1,300
SIC 4922 Pipelines, natural gas
CEO: Glen Kettering
CFO: Rene Dartez
*VP: James R Downs

COLUMBIA HCA
See SPOTSYLVANIA MEDICAL CENTER INC

COLUMBIA HCA
See TIMPANOGOS REGIONAL HOSPITAL

COLUMBIA HCA
See FAWCETT MEMORIAL HOSPITAL INC

COLUMBIA HCA
See MARION COMMUNITY HOSPITAL INC

COLUMBIA HCA
See ATLANTIC MEDICAL CENTER

COLUMBIA HCA
See CARTERSVILLE MEDICAL CENTER LLC

COLUMBIA HCA
See ST DAVIDS SOUTH AUSTIN MEDICAL CENTER

COLUMBIA HCA
See HCA HOSPITAL SERVICES OF SAN DIEGO

COLUMBIA HCA
See HTI MEMORIAL HOSPITAL CORP

COLUMBIA HCA
See HCA HEALTH SERVICES OF FLORIDA INC

COLUMBIA HCA
See HCA HEALTH SERVICES OF NEW HAMPSHIRE INC

COLUMBIA HCA
See COLISEUM PARK HOSPITAL INC

COLUMBIA HCA
See GALENCARE INC

COLUMBIA HCA
See MONTGOMERY REGIONAL HOSPITAL INC

COLUMBIA HCA
See HCA HEALTH SERVICES OF TENNESSEE INC

COLUMBIA HCA
See LOS ROBLES HOSPITAL & MEDICAL CENTER

COLUMBIA HCA
See HCA HEALTH SERVICES OF FLORIDA INC

COLUMBIA HCA
See COLUMBIA HOSPITAL CORP OF SOUTH BROWARD

COLUMBIA HCA
See RESTON HOSPITAL CENTER LLC

COLUMBIA HCA
See COLUMBIA RIO GRANDE HEALTHCARE LP

COLUMBIA HCA
See CENTRAL FLORIDA REGIONAL HOSPITAL INC

COLUMBIA HCA
See COLUMBIA HOSPITAL CORP OF BAY AREA

D-U-N-S 00-967-3609 IMP
COLUMBIA HELICOPTERS INC
14452 Arndt Rd Ne, Aurora, OR 97002-9525
Tel (503) 678-7510 Founded/Ownrshp 1957
Sales 97.6MM[E] EMP 800
SIC 7699 2411 4522 Aircraft & heavy equipment repair services; Logging camps & contractors; Air cargo carriers, nonscheduled; Helicopter carriers, nonscheduled
Ch Bd: Nancy Lematta
Pr: Santiago Crespo
*Pr: Michael Fahey
Bd of Dir: David McCullam
VP: Mike Brunner
VP: Kurt Koehnke
VP: Pete Lance
*VP: Stanley Y Wilson
QA Dir: Cesar Giron
Dir IT: Tom Briody
Dir IT: Gary Trobaugh

D-U-N-S 96-482-1482
■ **COLUMBIA HOSPITAL AT MEDICAL CITY DALLAS SUBSIDIARY LP**
MEDICAL CITY DALLAS HOSPITAL
(Suby of HOSPITAL COPORATION OF AMERICA) ★
7777 Forest Ln Ste C840, Dallas, TX 75230-6868
Tel (972) 566-7000 Founded/Ownrshp 1997
Sales 176.0MM[E] EMP 2,300
SIC 8062 Hospital, medical school affiliated with residency
Pr: Britt Berrett
Chf Rad: Marcie Coben
CEO: Troy Villarreal
CFO: Mark Atchley
CFO: Kathryn Engstrom

Sr VP: Carol Gregory
VP: Samantha Collier
CIO: Chuck Laughlin
QA Dir: Kathy Shumaker

D-U-N-S 96-299-8688
■ COLUMBIA HOSPITAL CORP OF BAY AREA
COLUMBIA HCA
(*Suby of* HOSPITAL COPORATION OF AMERICA) ★
7101 S Padre Island Dr, Corpus Christi, TX 78412-4913
Tel (361) 761-1200 *Founded/Ownrshp* 1993
Sales 292.2MM *EMP* 600
SIC 8062 General medical & surgical hospitals
CEO: Jay Woodall
CTO: Sharon Torton
Info Man: Erma Carrillo
Mktg Dir: Lisa Robertson
Doctor: Miguel Berastain
Dir Health: Linda Petrus
HC Dir: Tricia O'Brien

D-U-N-S 92-647-5948
■ COLUMBIA HOSPITAL CORP OF SOUTH BROWARD
COLUMBIA HCA
(*Suby of* HOSPITAL COPORATION OF AMERICA) ★
8201 W Broward Blvd, Plantation, FL 33324-2701
Tel (954) 473-6600 *Founded/Ownrshp* 1993
Sales 138.4MM[E] *EMP* 900
SIC 8062 General medical & surgical hospitals
Chf Rad: Evelio Alvarez
COO: Scott Sihak
CFO: Oscar Vicinte
Dir IT: Andre Blanco
VP Opers: Tracy Yuddel
Doctor: Murry Drescher MD
Doctor: Fernando Moya
Doctor: Neil Tytler
HC Dir: Judith Oliver
HC Dir: Ulises Perez

D-U-N-S 05-410-5374
COLUMBIA HOSPITAL INC
COLUMBIA - ST MARY'S
4425 N Pt Wshngton Rd 1 1 Stop, Milwaukee, WI 53212
Tel (414) 961-3300 *Founded/Ownrshp* 1909
Sales 67.0MM[E] *EMP* 1,472
SIC 8062 General medical & surgical hospitals
Pr: Leo Brideau
**COO:* Therese Pandel
VP: Connie Bradley
VP: Robert D Lyon
VP: David Shapiro
Dir Rad: Kenneth E Clark
Dir Rad: Eric Dorn
Dir Rad: Apichai Jarenwattananon
Dir Rad: Patrick J McWey
Dir Rad: Anne M Reddy
Dir Rad: John P Tomashek
Dir Rx: Paul Pisarzewicz

D-U-N-S 10-546-2852
COLUMBIA HOUSING/PNC INSTITUTIONAL FUND XX LIMITED PARTNERSHIP
PNC MULTIFAMILY CAPITAL
121 Sw Morrison St # 1300, Portland, OR 97204-3117
Tel (503) 808-1300 *Founded/Ownrshp* 2000
Sales NA *EMP* 80
SIC 6099 Tax certificate sale & redemption agencies
Pt: Don Giffen
Pt: Katie Such
VP: Todd J Crow

D-U-N-S 07-802-0146
■ COLUMBIA INSURANCE CO
(*Suby of* NATIONAL INDEMNITY CO (INC)) ★
3024 Harney St, Omaha, NE 68131-9942
Tel (402) 536-3000 *Founded/Ownrshp* 1970
Sales NA *EMP* 494[E]
SIC 6331 Fire, marine & casualty insurance
Pr: Donald Wurster
**Treas:* Marc D Hamburg
**Sr VP:* Forrest N Krutter
**Sr VP:* Phillip M Wolf
**VP:* Leslie J Baller
**VP:* Dale Geistmaster
**VP:* Tracy Gulden
**VP:* Karen Rainwater
**VP:* Walter Strain

COLUMBIA INSURANCE GROUP
See COLUMBIA MUTUAL INSURANCE CO INC

D-U-N-S 96-343-3193
COLUMBIA LAKE ACQUISITION HOLDINGS INC
9 W 57th St Fl 43, New York, NY 10019-2700
Tel (212) 515-3450 *Founded/Ownrshp* 2010
Sales NA *EMP* 23,000
SIC 6719 Investment holding companies, except banks

D-U-N-S 04-595-7453 IMP
■ COLUMBIA LIGHTING INC
(*Suby of* HUBBELL INC) ★
101 Corporate Dr Ste L, Spartanburg, SC 29303-5043
Tel (864) 678-1000 *Founded/Ownrshp* 1981, 2002
Sales 89.7MM[E] *EMP* 650
SIC 3646 Commercial indusl & institutional electric lighting fixtures; Fluorescent lighting fixtures, commercial
Pr: Timothy H Powers
Treas: James Biggart
VP: Richard Davies
**VP:* Robert Ingram
Exec: Randy Lewis
Opers Mgr: Ken Parker
Snr Mgr: Lisa Grabowski

D-U-N-S 04-980-5328
COLUMBIA LUTHERAN CHARITIES
COLUMBIA MEMORIAL HOSPITAL
2111 Exchange St, Astoria, OR 97103-3329
Tel (503) 325-4321 *Founded/Ownrshp* 1927
Sales 94.2MM *EMP* 450[E]
SIC 8062

D-U-N-S 96-239-7436
■ COLUMBIA MEDICAL CENTER OF ARLINGTON SUBSIDIARY LP
(*Suby of* HOSPITAL COPORATION OF AMERICA) ★
13455 Noel Rd, Dallas, TX 75240-6620
Tel (817) 465-3241 *Founded/Ownrshp* 1975
Sales 228.2MM *EMP* 1,100
SIC 8062 General medical & surgical hospitals
CFO: Jeff Ardemagni
Dir Recs: Amber Dandridge
Pt: Patrick Brilliant
Pt: Marck Strode
VP: Cindy Plonieu
Dir Inf Cn: Sharon Kurtz
CIO: Jim Lee
Mktg Dir: Abbi Miller
Anesthlgy: Joel Ciarochi
Doctor: Kifle Admassu
Doctor: Karel A Dicke

D-U-N-S 84-949-2959
■ COLUMBIA MEDICAL CENTER OF PLANO SUBSIDIARY LP
MEDICAL CENTER PLANO
(*Suby of* HOSPITAL COPORATION OF AMERICA) ★
3901 W 15th St, Plano, TX 75075-7738
Tel (972) 596-6800 *Founded/Ownrshp* 2006
Sales 315.5MM *EMP* 1,300
SIC 8062 General medical & surgical hospitals
Genl Pt: Troy Villarreal
COO: Winston Borland
VP: Valerie Anderson
VP: Pat Edens
Dir Rx: Michael Epstein
Anesthlgy: William Adcock
Anesthlgy: Vijay Arvind
Anesthlgy: Lillian Boehler
Anesthlgy: Bertrand J Brown
Anesthlgy: John D Cao
Anesthlgy: Tu X Dao

COLUMBIA MEDICAL CONSULTANTS
See MCMC LLC

COLUMBIA MEMORIAL HOSPITAL
See COLUMBIA LUTHERAN CHARITIES

D-U-N-S 08-048-1708
COLUMBIA MEMORIAL HOSPITAL
71 Prospect Ave, Hudson, NY 12534-2907
Tel (518) 828-7601 *Founded/Ownrshp* 1989
Sales 151.6MM *EMP* 818
SIC 8062 8051 General medical & surgical hospitals; Extended care facility
COO: Jay Cahalan
**CFO:* Vincent Dingman III
Treas: Stephen K D
Dir Rad: Ronda Makoske
Dir Rx: Shanda Steenburn
Adm Dir: Barbara Brady
Dir Pat Ac: Carol Siedsma
Nurse Mgr: Brian Stewart
CIO: Cathleen Crowley
Cmptr Lab: Maryellen Holdridge
Cmptr Lab: Ronda Rainy
Board of Directors: Norman Chapin, Betsy Gramkow, Rhonda Makoswke, Dennis Pappalardi

COLUMBIA MERCY MEDICAL CENTER
See COLUMBIA-CSA/HS GREATER CANTON AREA HEALTHCARE SYSTEMS LP

D-U-N-S 60-895-6348
COLUMBIA MUTUAL INSURANCE CO INC
COLUMBIA INSURANCE GROUP
2102 Whitegate Dr, Columbia, MO 65202-2335
Tel (573) 474-6193 *Founded/Ownrshp* 1941
Sales NA *EMP* 575
SIC 6331 Fire, marine & casualty insurance: mutual
Pr: Robert J Wagner
Ch Bd: Marvin E Wright
**Treas:* Roger Ballard

D-U-N-S 15-134-5485
COLUMBIA NATIONAL GROUP INC
6600 Grant Ave, Cleveland, OH 44105-5624
Tel (216) 883-4972 *Founded/Ownrshp* 1984
Sales 107.5MM[E] *EMP* 200
SIC 5051 5093 1542 Steel; Metal scrap & waste materials; Commercial & office building contractors
Pr: David Miller
**CFO:* Stephen Ruscher

D-U-N-S 18-117-0457
■ COLUMBIA OGDEN MEDICAL CENTER INC
OGDEN REGIONAL MEDICAL CENTER
(*Suby of* HOSPITAL COPORATION OF AMERICA) ★
5475 S 500 E, Ogden, UT 84405-6905
Tel (801) 479-2111 *Founded/Ownrshp* 1996
Sales 101.7MM[E] *EMP* 950[E]
SIC 8062 8099 Hospital, affiliated with AMA residency; Blood related health services
CEO: Mark Adams
**Pr:* Samuel N Hazen
COO: Dana Oaks
**CFO:* Judd Taylor
**Treas:* David G Anderson
**VP:* John M Franck II
Dir Lab: Scott Smith
Dir Rad: John J Diemel
Dir Rx: Jennifer Calvey
CIO: Curtis Watkins
IT Man: Jeremy Hall

D-U-N-S 00-698-2177
COLUMBIA PICTURES INDUSTRIES INC
(*Suby of* SONY PICTURES STUDIOS) ★
10202 Washington Blvd, Culver City, CA 90232-3119
Tel (310) 244-4000 *Founded/Ownrshp* 1987
Sales 86.6MM[E] *EMP* 1,500
SIC 7812 Motion picture production & distribution
CEO: Michael Lynton
Pr: Doug Belgrad
Pr: Andrew Gumpert
Pr: Hannah Minghella
Pr: Matt Tolmach
CFO: Edgar Howells

Ex VP: Ronald Jacobi
Sr VP: Peter Wilkes

D-U-N-S 00-692-9467 IMP
COLUMBIA PIPE & SUPPLY CO (IL)
CP
1120 W Pershing Rd, Chicago, IL 60609-1428
Tel (773) 927-6600 *Founded/Ownrshp* 1935, 1973
Sales 143.6MM[E] *EMP* 350
SIC 5051 5085 5074

D-U-N-S 07-978-2051
■ COLUMBIA PIPELINE GROUP INC
(*Suby of* TRANSCANADA CORPORATION)
5151 San Felipe St, Houston, TX 77056-3607
Tel (713) 386-3701 *Founded/Ownrshp* 2016
Sales 1.3MMM *EMP* 1,968[E]
SIC 4922 Pipelines, natural gas
CEO: Russ Girling
VP: Bob Smith

D-U-N-S 07-957-0244
■ COLUMBIA PIPELINE PARTNERS LP
(*Suby of* COLUMBIA PIPELINE GROUP INC) ★
5151 San Felipe St # 2500, Houston, TX 77056-3607
Tel (713) 386-3701 *Founded/Ownrshp* 2007
Sales 943.6MM[E] *EMP* 1,394
Tkr Sym CPPL *Exch* NYS
SIC 4922 Natural gas transmission; Pipelines, natural gas; Storage, natural gas
CEO: Robert C Skaggs Jr
Genl Pt: Cpp GP LLC
Pr: Glen L Kettering

D-U-N-S 02-033-5907
■ COLUMBIA PLAZA MEDICAL CENTER OF FORT WORTH SUBSIDIARY LP (TX)
PLAZA CHMOTHERAPY INFUSION CTR
(*Suby of* HOSPITAL COPORATION OF AMERICA) ★
900 8th Ave, Fort Worth, TX 76104-3902
Tel (817) 336-2100 *Founded/Ownrshp* 1974, 1997
Sales 129.1MM[E] *EMP* 1,600
SIC 8062 General medical & surgical hospitals
CEO: Clay Franklin
Chf Path: Richard J J Hare
**COO:* Court Lemaistre
**CFO:* Elia Stokes
Sr VP: Thomas Frazier
VP: Edward Davidson
VP: Lisa Gore
VP: Cheryl Harrison
VP: Pamela Scott
Doctor: Richard Hare
Dir Health: Emily Herald

D-U-N-S 10-579-9613
COLUMBIA PLYWOOD CORP
COLUMBIA CAROLINA DIVISION
(*Suby of* COLUMBIA FOREST PRODUCTS INC) ★
222 Sw Columbia St # 1575, Portland, OR 97201-6600
Tel (503) 224-5300 *Founded/Ownrshp* 1982
Sales 90.2MM[E] *EMP* 897
SIC 2435 Plywood, hardwood or hardwood faced
Pr: Harry L Demorest
Pr: Bradley L Thompson
CFO: Clifford D Barry

D-U-N-S 07-879-1669
COLUMBIA PROPERTY TRUST INC
1 Glenlake Pkwy Ste 1200, Atlanta, GA 30328-7267
Tel (404) 465-2200 *Founded/Ownrshp* 2004
Sales 566.0MM *EMP* 99[E]
Accts Deloitte & Touche Llp Atlanta
SIC 6798 Real estate investment trusts
Pr: E Nelson Mills
CFO: James A Fleming
Sr VP: Brian D Berry
Sr VP: Wendy W Gill
Sr VP: Kevin A Hoover
Board of Directors: Charles R Brown, Richard W Carpenter, John L Dixon, Murray J McCabe, Michael S Robb, George W Sands, Thomas G Wattles

D-U-N-S 09-234-8788
COLUMBIA PUBLIC SCHOOLS
1818 W Worley St, Columbia, MO 65203-1038
Tel (573) 214-3400 *Founded/Ownrshp* 1872
Sales 145.4MM[E] *EMP* 2,700
SIC 8211 Public elementary & secondary schools
Ex Dir: Andrea M Follett
Pr Dir: Michelle Baumstark
Schl Brd P: James Whitt
Teacher Pr: Melinda Adams
Board of Directors: David Ballenger, Lenann Baumgardner, Kerry Crist, Elton Fay, Chuck Headley, Don Schoengarth, Russ Still

D-U-N-S 05-329-3676 EXP
COLUMBIA RECYCLING CORP
1001 Chattanooga Ave, Dalton, GA 30720-8371
Tel (706) 278-4701 *Founded/Ownrshp* 1970
Sales 111.4MM[E] *EMP* 440
SIC 2299 Textile mill waste & remnant processing
CEO: Robert G Goldberg
**CFO:* Alan Rocky Ponders
**VP:* Rocky Ponders

D-U-N-S 92-840-9127
■ COLUMBIA RIO GRANDE HEALTHCARE LP
COLUMBIA HCA
(*Suby of* HOSPITAL COPORATION OF AMERICA) ★
101 E Ridge Rd, McAllen, TX 78503-1847
Tel (956) 632-6000 *Founded/Ownrshp* 1995
Sales 188.6MM *EMP* 1,000[E]
SIC 8011 8062

D-U-N-S 00-232-5723 IMP
COLUMBIA RIVER PROCESSING INC (OR)
(*Suby of* TILLAMOOK CHEESE) ★
79588 Rippee Rd, Boardman, OR 97818-9698
Tel (541) 481-3770 *Founded/Ownrshp* 1999
Sales 84.2MM[E] *EMP* 420
SIC 2022 Cheese, natural & processed
Pr: James McMullen
**Prin:* Patrick Criteser

D-U-N-S 82-460-3013
COLUMBIA SOUTHERN EDUCATION GROUP INC
COLUMBIA SUTHERN EDUCATN GROUP
21982 University Ln, Orange Beach, AL 36561-9000
Tel (251) 943-2273 *Founded/Ownrshp* 1993
Sales 153.2MM[E] *EMP* 5,000
SIC 6719 Investment holding companies, except banks
Pr: Robert Mayes Jr
Pr: Tommy Cooley
Treas: Kerri Burgner
VP: Robert Cheek
**VP:* Chantell Cooley
VP: Elwin Jones
VP: Jessica McBride
VP: Joe Wilkins
Exec: Cynthia Ryder
Snr Sftwr: Joe Luebker
CIO: Ken Styron

D-U-N-S 00-942-0159 IMP/EXP
▲ COLUMBIA SPORTSWEAR CO (OR)
14375 Nw Science Park Dr, Portland, OR 97229-5418
Tel (503) 985-4000 *Founded/Ownrshp* 1938
Sales 2.3MMM *EMP* 5,978
Tkr Sym COLM *Exch* NGS
SIC 2329 2339 3021 2353 3949 Men's & boys' sportswear & athletic clothing; Sportswear, women's; Shoes, rubber or plastic molded to fabric; Hats, caps & millinery; Sporting & athletic goods
CEO: Timothy P Boyle
**Ch Bd:* Gertrude Boyle
Pr: Massimo Lazzari
Pr: Bryan L Timm
CFO: Thomas B Cusick
Ofcr: Peter J Bragdon
Ofcr: Richelle T Luther
Sr VP: Joseph P Boyle
Sr VP: Franco Fogliato
Sr VP: David Lawner
Sr VP: Stuart B Redsun
Sr VP: Stephen P Woodside
VP: Michael W Blackford
VP: Francois Boulot
VP: Joe Craig
VP: Brittany Frazier
VP: Patricia E Higgins
VP: Michael Hirt
VP: Stephanie Lowe
VP: Kyle Story
VP: Steve Woodside
Board of Directors: Murrey R Albers, Stephen E Babson, Sarah A Bany, Andy D Bryant, Edward S George, Walter T Klenz, Ronald E Nelson, John W Stanton, Malia H Wasson

D-U-N-S 13-944-3183
■ COLUMBIA SPORTSWEAR USA CORP
(*Suby of* COLUMBIA SPORTSWEAR CO) ★
14375 Nw Science Park Dr, Portland, OR 97229-5418
Tel (503) 985-4000 *Founded/Ownrshp* 2003
Sales 265.1MM[E] *EMP* 2,700
SIC 5137 5136 2329 2339 3021 2353 Women's & children's clothing; Women's & children's outerwear; Women's & children's sportswear & swimsuits; Women's & children's accessories; Men's & boys' clothing; Men's & boys' hats, scarves & gloves; Men's & boys' furnishings; Men's & boys' sportswear & work clothing; Men's & boys' sportswear & athletic clothing; Men's & boys' leather, wool & down-filled outerwear; Women's & misses' outerwear; Sportswear, women's; Shoes, rubber or plastic molded to fabric; Hats, caps & millinery
Pr: Timothy P Boyle
COO: Patrick D Anderson
CFO: Bryan Timm
Ch: Gertrude Boyle
Sr VP: Robert G Masin
VP: Peter Bragdon
Manager: Trent Marting

COLUMBIA ST DAVIDS DIV OFF
See ST DAVIDS HEALTHCARE PARTNERSHIP LP LLP

D-U-N-S 07-116-1129
COLUMBIA ST MARYS HOSPITAL MILWAUKEE INC
C S M
2301 N Lake Dr, Milwaukee, WI 53211-4508
Tel (414) 291-1000 *Founded/Ownrshp* 1859
Sales 447.0MM *EMP* 2,100
SIC 8062 General medical & surgical hospitals
Pr: Travis Andersen
**Pr:* Leo Burdeau
**COO:* Treasie Pandl
VP: Gerri Staffileno
Dir Rad: Michael A Braun
Dir Rad: Susan Josko
Dir Rad: Anne M Reddy
Mktg Mgr: Yvonne Szatkowski
Doctor: Anil Dogra
Doctor: Nancy Kuelz
Doctor: Anita Thakur

D-U-N-S 07-615-0473
COLUMBIA ST MARYS HOSPITAL OZAUKEE INC
COLUMBIA ST. MARY'S HUIRAS CENTER
(*Suby of* COLUMBIA ST MARYS INC) ★
13111 N Port Wash Rd, Mequon, WI 53097-2416
Tel (262) 243-7300 *Founded/Ownrshp* 2001
Sales 166.1MM *EMP* 825
SIC 8062 General medical & surgical hospitals
Pr: Edwin Montgomery
Dir Rad: Susan Sweeney
Off Mgr: Carey Krebs
Pathlgst: James A Puerner
HC Dir: Mary K Plesser

D-U-N-S 96-934-4808
COLUMBIA ST MARYS HOSPITAL OZAUKEE INC
4425 N Port Washington Rd, Glendale, WI 53212-1082
Tel (414) 326-2230 *Founded/Ownrshp* 2011
Sales 169.4MM *EMP* 9[E]
Accts Deloitte Tax Lp Milwaukee Wi

SIC 8062 General medical & surgical hospitals
Prin: Leo P Brideau

COLUMBIA ST. MARY'S HUIRAS CENTER
See COLUMBIA ST MARYS HOSPITAL OZAUKEE INC

D-U-N-S 12-898-9147
COLUMBIA ST MARYS INC
4425 N Port Washington Rd, Milwaukee, WI 53212-1082
Tel (414) 326-2495 *Founded/Ownrshp* 2001
Sales 151.2MM *EMP* 5,000
Accts Deloitte Tax Lp Milwaukee Wi
SIC 8062 General medical & surgical hospitals
Pr: Leo Burdeau
**CFO:* Charles Dreher
VP: Steven Kaplan
Dir Lab: Judy Valentino
Dir Bus: John Pernice
Doctor: Sophie Kramer

D-U-N-S 94-506-3915
■ **COLUMBIA STATE BANK**
(*Suby of* COLUMBIA BANKING SYSTEM INC) ★
1301 A St Ste 800, Tacoma, WA 98402-4205
Tel (253) 305-1900 *Founded/Ownrshp* 1988
Sales NA *EMP* 1,000
SIC 6022 State commercial banks
Pr: Melanie J Dressel
COO: Mark W Nelson
CFO: Gary R Schminkey
Ofcr: Kristine Crawford
Ofcr: Catherine Jensen-Varnadore
Ofcr: Jerri Pavitt
Assoc VP: Donna Sayre
Ex VP: Kumi Yamamoto Baruffi
Ex VP: H R Russell
Ex VP: Evans Q Whitney
Sr VP: Barbara Cooch
Sr VP: Matt Duffy
VP: Jennifer Abbatiello
VP: Rhonda Arnett
VP: Thomas Kalmbach
VP: Michelle Laborde
VP: Susan Larson
VP: Dave Lawson
VP: William Q Marshall Jr
VP: Ryan Palmquest
VP: Dean A Piotrowski

D-U-N-S 00-902-2708 IMP/EXP
COLUMBIA STEEL CASTING CO INC (OR)
10425 N Bloss Ave, Portland, OR 97203-6143
Tel (503) 286-0685 *Founded/Ownrshp* 1901
Sales 133.0MM[E] *EMP* 350
SIC 3325 Alloy steel castings, except investment
Pr: Martha B Cox
**Pr:* Don Falk
CFO: Mark Roeter
Opers Mgr: Jeffrey Marksthaler

D-U-N-S 05-910-9280
COLUMBIA SUSSEX CORP
740 Centre View Blvd, Crestview Hills, KY 41017-2750
Tel (859) 331-0091 *Founded/Ownrshp* 1972
Sales 527.4MM *EMP* 10,000
SIC 7011 5812 Hotels & motels; Eating places
Pr: William J Yung
CFO: Chris Ballad
VP: J Stanley Clayton
VP: Derek Haught
VP: Derek J Haught
VP: Theodore R Mitchel
VP: Bruce Rathje
Exec: Hilton Beach
Genl Mgr: Dallas L Colinas
Genl Mgr: Steve Eberhart
Genl Mgr: Eric Kiddle

COLUMBIA SUTHERN EDUCATN GROUP
See COLUMBIA SOUTHERN EDUCATION GROUP INC

COLUMBIA TECH
See COGHLIN COMPANIES INC

COLUMBIA TECH
See COLUMBIA ELECTRICAL CONTRACTORS INC

COLUMBIA TLLAHASSEE CMNTY HOSP
See TALLAHASSEE MEDICAL CENTER INC

D-U-N-S 96-467-2018
COLUMBIA UNITED PROVIDERS INC
MEMORIAL CAMPUS
(*Suby of* MEDICAL CENTER CAMPUS) ★
19120 Se 34th St Ste 201, Vancouver, WA 98683-1430
Tel (360) 891-1520 *Founded/Ownrshp* 1993
Sales NA *EMP* 68
Accts Kpmg Llp
SIC 6324 Hospital & medical service plans
CEO: Ann K Wheelock
**CEO:* Karen Lee

COLUMBIA VICKSBURG MEDICAL CTR
See RIVER REGION BEHAVIORAL HEALTH

COLUMBIA WOOL SCOURING MILLS
See PENDLETON WOOLEN MILLS INC

D-U-N-S 07-777-4081
COLUMBIA-CSA/HS GREATER CANTON AREA HEALTHCARE SYSTEMS LP
COLUMBIA MERCY MEDICAL CENTER
1320 Mercy Dr Nw 30, Canton, OH 44708-2614
Tel (330) 489-1000 *Founded/Ownrshp* 1995
Sales 15.9MM[E] *EMP* 2,185
SIC 8062 General medical & surgical hospitals
CEO: Jack Topoleski
**Genl Pt:* Csa Health Network
**Ltd Pt:* Columbia HCA Healthcare Corp
**CFO:* Michael Rieger

D-U-N-S 18-054-4702 IMP/EXP
COLUMBIAN CHEMICALS CO
BIRLA CARBON
(*Suby of* ADITYA BIRLA MANAGEMENT CORPORATION PRIVATE LIMITED)
1800 W Oak Commons Ct, Marietta, GA 30062-2231
Tel (770) 792-9400 *Founded/Ownrshp* 2011
Sales 332.4MM[E] *EMP* 1,300
SIC 2895 Carbon black
CEO: Kevin Boyle
Pt: Tracy Bailey
Pr: Rikki Lamba
Pr: John Loudermilk
COO: Kim Martin
CFO: Surendra Goyal
Treas: Brian English
Sr Cor Off: Roberto Martins
Bd of Dir: David Han
Ofcr: Dale Clark
Ofcr: Timothy Fedrigon
VP: Michael Blair
VP: Luciano Difeliciantonio
VP: Eric Mobelstein
VP: Gail Rinks
VP: JAS Sandhu
VP: David Young
Dir Risk M: Bill White
Dir Lab: Charles Herd

COLUMBIAN FINANCIAL GROUP
See COLUMBIAN MUTUAL LIFE INSURANCE CO INC

D-U-N-S 78-365-1995
COLUMBIAN INTERNATIONAL CHEMICALS CORP
(*Suby of* BIRLA CARBON) ★
1800 W Oak Commons Ct, Marietta, GA 30062-2231
Tel (770) 792-9400 *Founded/Ownrshp* 1975
Sales 81.5MM[E] *EMP* 1,300
SIC 6719 Personal holding companies, except banks
Pr: Manuel Iraola
**CFO:* Gabor Mezei
VP: John Loudermilk

D-U-N-S 07-159-5904
COLUMBIAN MUTUAL LIFE INSURANCE CO INC
COLUMBIAN FINANCIAL GROUP
4704 Vestal Pkwy E, Binghamton, NY 13902
Tel (607) 724-2472 *Founded/Ownrshp* 1883
Sales NA *EMP* 315
SIC 6411 Insurance agents
CEO: Thomas E Rattmann
Ex VP: Frank Crisafulli
**Sr VP:* Daniel J Fischer
**Sr VP:* Michael C S Fosbury
**Sr VP:* John Gately
Sr VP: John J Gately
**Sr VP:* Amy Colleen Purdy Godleski
**Sr VP:* Stuart W Smith
VP: Christine Cawley
VP: Jeanne Clarke
VP: Greg Nilles
VP: Paul Zurawel

COLUMBIAN TECTANK
See CST INDUSTRIES INC

D-U-N-S 10-568-8386 IMP
COLUMBUS ASSOCIATION FOR PERFORMING ARTS
CAPA
55 E State St, Columbus, OH 43215-4203
Tel (614) 469-1045 *Founded/Ownrshp* 1969
Sales 5.9MM *EMP* 1,065
Accts John Gerlach & Company Llp Co
SIC 6512 Theater building, ownership & operation
Pr: William B Conner Jr
V Ch: Michael Petrecca
**Treas:* Stephanie E Green
Bd of Dir: Carl Henn
Bd of Dir: Bonnie Milenthal
Top Exec: Greg Bryan
VP: Chris Tewell
Exec: Shubert Fisher
Pr Dir: Anthony Lupinacci
Pr Mgr: Luke Russell

COLUMBUS CASTINGS
See COLUMBUS STEEL CASTINGS CO

COLUMBUS CITY SCHOOLS
See COLUMBUS PUBLIC SCHOOL DISTRICT

D-U-N-S 10-066-4499
COLUMBUS COUNTY BOARD OF EDUCATION
817 Washington St, Whiteville, NC 28472-3046
Tel (910) 642-5168 *Founded/Ownrshp* 1800
Sales 25.9MM[E] *EMP* 1,000
SIC 8211 Public elementary & secondary schools
Ex Dir: Ronald Gore

COLUMBUS DISPATCH THE
See DISPATCH PRINTING CO

D-U-N-S 01-788-4503 IMP
COLUMBUS DISTRIBUTING CO
DELMAR DISTRIBUTING
4949 Freeway Dr E, Columbus, OH 43229-5479
Tel (614) 846-1000 *Founded/Ownrshp* 1933
Sales 94.8MM[E] *EMP* 275
SIC 5181 Beer & other fermented malt liquors
Pr: Paul Jenkins Jr
**Ch Bd:* Paul A Jenkins Jr
CFO: Jim Stahl
**V Ch Bd:* Barbara Jenkins
VP: Debbie Smith
IT Man: Kevin Loring

D-U-N-S 00-986-3051 EXP
COLUMBUS EQUIPMENT CO
KUBOTA AUTHORIZED DEALER
2323 Performance Way, Columbus, OH 43207-2473
Tel (614) 437-0352 *Founded/Ownrshp* 1951
Sales 93.6MM[E] *EMP* 195
SIC 5082 7353 General construction machinery & equipment; Heavy construction equipment rental
Pr: Josh Stivison
COO: Chris Taylor
**CFO:* Michael Sarrey
**VP:* Tim Albright
**VP:* Ernie Potter
Admn Mgr: Thomas Brasser
Brnch Mgr: Chester Gowen
Brnch Mgr: Dan Minnis
Brnch Mgr: Jeff Richards
Genl Mgr: Ray Frase
Dir IT: David Brasser

D-U-N-S 04-373-4490
COLUMBUS FAIR AUTO AUCTION INC
WEDNESDAY AUTO AUCTION
4700 Groveport Rd, Obetz, OH 43207-5217
Tel (614) 497-2000 *Founded/Ownrshp* 1984
Sales 208.2MM[E] *EMP* 620
SIC 5012 5521 Automobile auction; Used car dealers
CEO: Keith Whann
**CFO:* Bill Stackhouse
VP: Jeff Baerga
Genl Mgr: Harold Varvel
Web Dev: Brandon Moore
Opers Mgr: Chuck Dearing
Mktg Dir: Christopher Feick

D-U-N-S 00-916-9533 IMP
COLUMBUS FOODS LLC
30977 San Antonio St, Hayward, CA 94544-7109
Tel (510) 921-3400 *Founded/Ownrshp* 2006
Sales 86.5MM[E] *EMP* 345
SIC 2011 5143 5147 Luncheon meat from meat slaughtered on site; Cheese; Meats & meat products
CEO: Ralph Denisco
**Ch Bd:* John Piccetti
**CFO:* Adam Ferrif
Sr VP: Michael Fox
IT Man: Kevin Loring

COLUMBUS FOUNDRY
See DMI COLUMBUS LLC

D-U-N-S 02-692-1338
COLUMBUS GEORGIA CONSOLIDATED GOVERNMENT
MUSCOGEE COUNTY
100 10th St, Columbus, GA 31901-2736
Tel (706) 653-4000 *Founded/Ownrshp* 1971
Sales NA *EMP* 2,400[E]
Accts Albright Fortenberry & Ninas
SIC 9111 Mayors' offices

D-U-N-S 00-430-5264 IMP/EXP
COLUMBUS INDUSTRIES INC (OH)
2938 State Route 752, Ashville, OH 43103-9543
Tel (740) 983-2552 *Founded/Ownrshp* 1965
Sales 207.7MM[E] *EMP* 900
SIC 3569 Filters
Ch Bd: Harold T Pontius
**Pr:* Jeffrey Pontius
CFO: Steve Randall
**Ex VP:* Wayne Vickers
VP: Marvin Lampi
VP: Thad Ptak
**VP:* Debbie Vickers
Rgnl Mgr: Gary Francis
Dir IT: Scott Weaver
IT Man: Sharon Sims
Plnt Mgr: Fred Palm

D-U-N-S 00-210-5534 IMP/EXP
▲ **COLUMBUS MCKINNON CORP** (GA)
205 Crosspoint Pkwy, Getzville, NY 14068-1605
Tel (716) 689-5400 *Founded/Ownrshp* 1875
Sales 597.1MM *EMP* 2,896
Tkr Sym CMCO *Exch* NGS
SIC 3536 3496 3535 3537 Hoists; Cranes, industrial plant; Cranes, overhead traveling; Chain, welded; Conveyor belts; Conveyors & conveying equipment; Tables, lift: hydraulic
Pr: Timothy T Tevens
**Ch Bd:* Ernest R Verebelyi
COO: David Carmack
CFO: Gregory P Rustowicz
Treas: Jon Adams
Ex VP: Richard A Steinberg
VP: Gene P Buer
VP: Ivo Celi
VP: Richard Knoffloch
VP: Alan S Korman
VP: Charlene Miraglia
VP: Mark Paradowski
VP: Kurt F Wozniak
Exec: Andrew Gates
Board of Directors: Richard H Fleming, Linda A Goodspeed, Liam G McCarthy, Heath A Mitts, Nicholas T Pinchuk, Stephen Rabinowitz, R Scott Trumbull

D-U-N-S 04-964-9239
COLUMBUS PUBLIC SCHOOL DISTRICT
COLUMBUS CITY SCHOOLS
270 E State St Fl 3, Columbus, OH 43215-4312
Tel (614) 365-5000 *Founded/Ownrshp* 1845
Sales 498.1MM[E] *EMP* 10,000
Accts Dave Yost Columbus Ohio
SIC 8211 8299 Public elementary & secondary schools; School for physically handicapped; Educational services
**Treas:* Mike Kinneer
**VP:* Terry Boyd
Ex Dir: Machelle Kline
Dir Sec: Chris Ward
Genl Mgr: Maurice Oldham
CIO: Stephen Tankovich
IT Man: Stanley Bahorek
Pr Dir: Scott Varner

D-U-N-S 78-688-1524
COLUMBUS REGIONAL AIRPORT AUTHORITY
PORT COLUMBUS INTERNATIONAL AI
4600 Intl Gtwy Ste 2, Columbus, OH 43219
Tel (614) 239-4015 *Founded/Ownrshp* 1929
Sales 88.1MM *EMP* 383
Accts Plante & Moran Pllc Cincinna
SIC 4581 Airport
Pr: Elaine Roberts
CFO: John Byrum
VP: Torrance Richardson
VP: Brian Sarkis
Ex Dir: Dan Ricciardi
CIO: Jim Logan
IT Man: Jim Bodi
Opers Supe: Christopher Pollock
Opers Mgr: Michael Taylor
Snr Mgr: Jane Early
Snr Mgr: Floria Washington

D-U-N-S 04-004-6385
COLUMBUS REGIONAL HEALTHCARE SYSTEM (NC)
500 Jefferson St, Whiteville, NC 28472-3634
Tel (910) 642-8011 *Founded/Ownrshp* 1935
Sales 89.2MM *EMP* 625
SIC 8062 General medical & surgical hospitals
CEO: Carla Hollis
Chf Rad: Jeffrey Kotzan
CFO: Carl Barber
CFO: Carl Biber
CFO: George Harms
Ofcr: Sharon Tyler
Dir Risk M: Penny King
Dir Rx: George Floyd
Doctor: Mett Ausley
Phys Thrpy: Joe Hansen

D-U-N-S 17-813-3880 IMP
COLUMBUS REGIONAL HEALTHCARE SYSTEM INC
707 Center St Ste 300, Columbus, GA 31901-1576
Tel (706) 571-1495 *Founded/Ownrshp* 1986
Sales 39.9MM *EMP* 2,400
Accts Dixon Hughes Goodman Llp Char
SIC 8062 General medical & surgical hospitals
Pr: Scott Hill
Mng Pt: Gregory Kesler
Sr VP: Douglas Colburn
Sr VP: Andrew Morley
Sr VP: Roland L Thacker
VP: Bonnie Franco
VP: D Joiner
VP: Joseph T Wood
Dir Risk M: Suzanne Langroth
Dir Rx: Brunis Breland
Off Mgr: Debra Tarno

D-U-N-S 08-425-8789
COLUMBUS REGIONAL HOSPITAL
2400 17th St, Columbus, IN 47201-5351
Tel (812) 379-4441 *Founded/Ownrshp* 1917
Sales 249.9MM *EMP* 5[E]
SIC 8062 General medical & surgical hospitals
Pr: Jim Bickel
**CEO:* Julia C Abedian
**Ch:* Marsha L Hunt
**VP:* Diana Boyer
**VP:* Kurt Ellis
**VP:* Pam Missi
**VP:* Christina Raaf
Telecom Ex: Steve Baker
Dir IT: Gary N Folkman
Plnt Mgr: David Lenart
Opthamlgy: Lawrence Schoch

D-U-N-S 79-110-1152
COLUMBUS REGIONAL HOSPITAL
2400 17th St, Columbus, IN 47201-5351
Tel (812) 379-4441 *Founded/Ownrshp* 2007
Sales 254.2MM *EMP* 9[E]
SIC 8062 General medical & surgical hospitals
Prin: Thomas Sonderman

D-U-N-S 00-790-1739
■ **COLUMBUS SOUTHERN POWER CO**
(*Suby of* AEP) ★
1 Riverside Plz, Columbus, OH 43215-2355
Tel (614) 716-1000 *Founded/Ownrshp* 1937
Sales 2.1MMM *EMP* 1,082[E]
SIC 4911 Electric services; Distribution, electric power; Generation, electric power; Transmission, electric power
Ch Bd: Michael G Morris
Pr: Joseph Hamrock
**CFO:* Brian X Tierney
Board of Directors: Nicholas K Akins, Carl L English, D Michael Miller, Robert P Powers, Susan Tomasky

D-U-N-S 07-502-1741
COLUMBUS STATE COMMUNITY COLLEGE (OH)
CSCC
550 E Spring St, Columbus, OH 43215-1722
Tel (614) 287-2400 *Founded/Ownrshp* 1963
Sales 82.8MM *EMP* 1,400
Accts Parms & Company Llc Columbus
SIC 8222 8221 Community college; Colleges universities & professional schools
Pr: David Harrison
Sr VP: Theresa Gehr
VP: Thomas Carol
DP Exec: Eric Barsotti
DP Exec: Jameson Beall
DP Exec: Kathleen Christensen
DP Exec: Devin Jackson
DP Exec: Corey Lawson
DP Exec: Maryvonne Olama
DP Exec: Jarad Regan
DP Exec: Mitchell Shelton

D-U-N-S 12-888-3266 IMP
COLUMBUS STEEL CASTINGS CO
COLUMBUS CASTINGS
(*Suby of* COLUMBUS HOLDINGS INC)
2211 Parsons Ave, Columbus, OH 43207-2448
Tel (614) 444-2121 *Founded/Ownrshp* 2003
Sales 228.8MM[E] *EMP* 750
SIC 3325 Steel foundries
Pr: Rick Mavrakis
**CFO:* Charles B Eing
**Ch:* Ernie Pierce
**Ch:* Jack Thomas
VP: Robert Cover
**VP:* John Downes
VP: Rick Gillis
**VP:* Mike Jewell
**VP:* Steve Kachur
**VP:* Bruce Milligan
**VP:* Randy Parish

D-U-N-S 05-883-9929 IMP/EXP
COLUMBUS WEST-WARD INC
(*Suby of* EUROHEALTH (USA) INC) ★
1809 Wilson Rd, Columbus, OH 43228-9579
Tel (614) 276-4000 *Founded/Ownrshp* 2016

Sales 55.0MM^E *EMP* 1,100
SIC 2834

D-U-N-S 00-677-3261
COLUSA ELEVATOR CO (IA)
(*Suby of* CAHOKIA GRAIN) ★
13 Broadway, Nauvoo, IL 62354
Tel (217) 453-2216 *Founded/Ownrshp* 1926, 2012
Sales 122.4MM *EMP* 18
SIC 5153 Grain elevators
Pr: Dale Griffiths
**Treas:* Carol A Griffiths

D-U-N-S 62-683-9039
COLUSA INDIAN COMMUNITY COUNCIL
3730 State Highway 45 B, Colusa, CA 95932-4022
Tel (530) 458-8231 *Founded/Ownrshp* 1941
Sales NA *EMP* 1,237
SIC 9131 Indian reservation;
Ch: Wayne R Mitchum Sr

D-U-N-S 06-958-3029
COLVILLE CONFEDERATED TRIBES INC
COLVILLE TRIBAL ENTERPRISES
44 School Loop Rd, Nespelem, WA 99155
Tel (509) 634-2200 *Founded/Ownrshp* 1938
Sales NA *EMP* 1,300
SIC 9199 General government administration
**Ex Dir:* Gene Nicholson
IT Man: Frank Andrews

COLVILLE TRIBAL ENTERPRISES
See COLVILLE CONFEDERATED TRIBES INC

D-U-N-S 06-469-9010 IMP
COLWELL INC
(*Suby of* COLWELL INDUSTRIES INC) ★
2605 Marion Dr, Kendallville, IN 46755-3273
Tel (260) 347-1981 *Founded/Ownrshp* 1973
Sales 110.2MM^E *EMP* 400
SIC 2752 Cards, lithographed; Color lithography
CEO: William V Byars
**Pr:* Donovan Freeland
**Pr:* Patrick Van Arnam
**CFO:* John Olson
**Treas:* Daniel Nicklay
**Sr VP:* Kevin C Gurney
CIO: Tom Colwell

D-U-N-S 00-625-7414
COLWELL INDUSTRIES INC (MN)
1611 County Road B W # 315, Saint Paul, MN 55113-4053
Tel (612) 340-0365 *Founded/Ownrshp* 1893, 1951
Sales 128.5MM^E *EMP* 400
SIC 2752 Commercial printing, lithographic
Pr: Donovan J Freeland
Ch Bd: Thomas G Colwell
CFO: Daniel C Nicklay
V Ch Bd: Felton Tad Colwell
Plnt Mgr: Rajesh Sharma
Sales Exec: Cindy Gapter

COLWEN HOTELS
See COLWEN MANAGEMENT INC

D-U-N-S 94-752-5614
COLWEN MANAGEMENT INC
COLWEN HOTELS
230 Commerce Way Ste 200, Portsmouth, NH 03801-3274
Tel (603) 897-6100 *Founded/Ownrshp* 2001
Sales 86.2MM^E *EMP* 750^E
SIC 8742 7389 Management consulting services; Interior design services
Pr: Mark R Stebbins
**Pr:* Wendell Butcher
**Ch:* Colin Nadeau
**Prin:* Mark Schleicher
VP Opers: Jean Smith
Sls Dir: Amy Amirault

D-U-N-S 60-338-1690
■ **COMAIR HOLDINGS LLC**
(*Suby of* DELTA AIRLINES) ★
82 Comair Blvd, Erlanger, KY 41018-1212
Tel (859) 767-2550 *Founded/Ownrshp* 1999
Sales 168.6MM^E *EMP* 7,200
SIC 4512 Air passenger carrier, scheduled; Air cargo carrier, scheduled
Pr: John Bendoraitis
CFO: Dan Dixon
VP: Jack Wilson
IT Man: Randy Vieth

D-U-N-S 01-054-1498
COMAL INDEPENDENT SCHOOL DISTRICT
1404 N Interstate 35, New Braunfels, TX 78130-2817
Tel (830) 221-2000 *Founded/Ownrshp* 1956
Sales 220.6MM^E *EMP* 2,400
Accts Padgett Stratemann & Co Llp S
SIC 8611 8211 Business associations; Public elementary & secondary schools
CFO: David Andersen
**CFO:* Abel Campos
Ofcr: Jana Gomez
Prin: Jo B Jimerson
Ex Dir: Mandy Epley
IT Man: Cheryl Lucas
Tech Mgr: Brenda Sendejo
Pr Dir: Steve Stanford

D-U-N-S 07-429-4075
COMANCHE COUNTY HOSPITAL AUTHORITY
COMANCHE COUNTY MEMORIAL HOSPI
3401 W Gore Blvd, Lawton, OK 73505-6300
Tel (580) 355-8620 *Founded/Ownrshp* 1948
Sales 233.6MM *EMP* 1,800
SIC 8062 General medical & surgical hospitals
Ch: Buddy Green
**CEO:* Randy Segler
**CFO:* Brent Smith
**VP:* Pat Henry
Nurse Mgr: Lorene Anderson
CIO: Sharon Dudley
Dir IT: James Porter
Web Dev: Crystal Paschal
Pr Mgr: Connie Holcomb
Obsttrcn: Janice Lepp
Anesthlgy: John M Navarro

COMANCHE COUNTY MEMORIAL HOSPI
See COMANCHE COUNTY HOSPITAL AUTHORITY

D-U-N-S 00-640-5906 IMP/EXP
COMAU LLC
COMAU PICO
(*Suby of* COMAU SPA)
21000 Telegraph Rd, Southfield, MI 48033-4280
Tel (248) 353-8888 *Founded/Ownrshp* 1980
Sales 702.6MM^E *EMP* 1,300
SIC 3548 3829 3545 Resistance welders, electric; Testing equipment: abrasion, shearing strength, etc.; Gauges (machine tool accessories); Tools & accessories for machine tools
CEO: Riccardo Tarantini
Pr: Mark Taber
**COO:* Mauro Fenzi
CFO: Mauro Giorda
**CFO:* Joseph Shelata
Sr VP: Michael Dugas
Prgrm Mgr: Kenneth Macmillan
Prgrm Mgr: Ben McClelland
Prgrm Mgr: Todd Nowaczyk
Prgrm Mgr: Brian Rogus
Genl Mgr: Timothy Veeser

COMAU PICO
See COMAU LLC

D-U-N-S 00-240-6502 EXP
COMBE INC (DE)
1101 Westchester Ave, White Plains, NY 10604-3503
Tel (914) 694-5454 *Founded/Ownrshp* 1949
Sales 140.0MM^E *EMP* 600
SIC 2841 2834 Soap & other detergents; Soap: granulated, liquid, cake, flaked or chip; Pharmaceutical preparations
Prin: Christopher B Combe
**Pr:* Richard G Powers
**CFO:* Joseph P Gusmano
**Treas:* Jeffrey P Hochdorf
**Sr VP:* Jerome S Darby
**Sr VP:* Dominic P Demain
VP: Roberto Guil
VP: Rona Oberman
VP: Tony Santini
VP: Keech Shetty
Creative D: Enza Mullen

D-U-N-S 00-692-9475
COMBINED INSURANCE CO OF AMERICA
(*Suby of* INA CHUBB HOLDINGS INC) ★
200 E Randolph St Lbby 10, Chicago, IL 60601-6445
Tel (800) 225-4500 *Founded/Ownrshp* 1922, 2008
Sales NA *EMP* 3,200
SIC 6321 6311 Accident insurance carriers; Health insurance carriers; Life reinsurance
CEO: Richard Ravin
Pr: Chris Martin
**CFO:* Jim Hom
Sr VP: Clive Robinson
**VP:* Koorosh Beigian
VP: Art Kandarian
Exec: Robert Dinicola
MIS Dir: Noralen Long
VP Mktg: Vicente Lugo

D-U-N-S 06-216-2763
COMBINED JEWISH PHILANTHROPIES OF GREATER BOSTON INC
CJP
126 High St Fl 2, Boston, MA 02110-2707
Tel (617) 457-8500 *Founded/Ownrshp* 1895
Sales 329.8MM *EMP* 135
SIC 8399 Fund raising organization, non-fee basis
Ch: Robert J Small
**Ch Bd:* Sari Anne Rapkin
**Pr:* Barry Shrage
CFO: David Strong
**Treas:* Neil A Wallack
Ofcr: Harris Rollinger
Ofcr: Rachel L Sagaser
Assoc VP: Karyn C Leviton
VP: Gil Preuss
Assoc Dir: Samantha Harris
Assoc Dir: Caryn Lazaroff

D-U-N-S 07-109-3439
COMBINED LIFE INSURANCE CO OF NEW YORK INC (NY)
(*Suby of* COMBINED INSURANCE CO OF AMERICA) ★
11 British American Blvd # 2, Latham, NY 12110-1464
Tel (518) 220-9333 *Founded/Ownrshp* 1964
Sales NA *EMP* 700
SIC 6321 6311 Accident insurance carriers; Health insurance carriers; Life insurance carriers
Ch Bd: Richard Ravin
**VP:* Mike Hurd
**VP:* Ronald D Markovits

D-U-N-S 78-513-1293 EXP
COMBUSTION ASSOCIATES INC
CAI
555 Monica Cir, Corona, CA 92880-5447
Tel (951) 272-6999 *Founded/Ownrshp* 1991
Sales 94.8MM^E *EMP* 50
SIC 4911 3443 ; Boiler & boiler shop work
Pr: Mukund Kavia
**VP:* Kusum Kavia

D-U-N-S 04-246-7142 IMP
COMCAR INDUSTRIES INC
502 E Bridgers Ave, Auburndale, FL 33823-3721
Tel (863) 967-1101 *Founded/Ownrshp* 1963
Sales 1.3MMM^E *EMP* 5,400
SIC 4213 5521 5013 4212

D-U-N-S 78-767-2310
■ **COMCAST CABLE COMMUNICATIONS LLC**
(*Suby of* COMCAST CORP) ★
1701 John Fk Blvd, Philadelphia, PA 19103
Tel (215) 665-1700 *Founded/Ownrshp* 1985
Sales 4.8MMM^E *EMP* 15,000
SIC 4841 Cable television services
Pr: Neil Smit
**Ch Bd:* Ralph Roberts
V Ch: Julian Brodsky
V Ch: James Finnegan
Pr: Brian Roberts
COO: David N Watson
CFO: Catherine Avgiris
CFO: C S Backstrom
Treas: John Alchin
Treas: Robert Patterson
Bd of Dir: Dennis Maron
Bd of Dir: M'Kay McGrath
Bd of Dir: Kyle Peters
Bd of Dir: Kenneth Styduhar
Bd of Dir: Matthew Uren
Bd of Dir: Les Wadleigh
Ofcr: Peter Kiriacoulacos
Ofcr: Chris Satchell
Ex VP: Sree Kotay
Ex VP: Lawrence Smith
Ex VP: Matthew Strauss

D-U-N-S 86-739-8794 IMP
■ **COMCAST CABLE HOLDINGS LLC**
(*Suby of* COMCAST CORP) ★
1500 Market St Ste Lmw 3, Philadelphia, PA 19102-2110
Tel (215) 665-1700 *Founded/Ownrshp* 2002
Sales 5.5MMM^E *EMP* 41,000
SIC 4841 7922 5961 Cable television services; Satellite master antenna systems services (SMATV); Television program, including commercial producers; Television, home shopping
Sr VP: Kathy Kelly-Brown
Sr VP: Inder M Singh
VP: Raul Valentin

D-U-N-S 11-313-8424
■ **COMCAST CABLEVISION**
(*Suby of* COMCAST CORP) ★
8031 Corporate Dr, Baltimore, MD 21236-4986
Tel (410) 931-4600 *Founded/Ownrshp* 1994
Sales 4.7MMM^E *EMP* 30,000
SIC 4841 Cable television services
Pt: Brian L Roberts
Pt: Daniel Aaron
Pt: Julian A Brodsky
Pt: Allan H Reuben
Sr VP: Mary McLaughlin
VP: Susan Hoffman
IT Man: Paul Waldman
Prd Mgr: Derek Seibert

D-U-N-S 09-998-6077
■ **COMCAST CABLEVISION OF MERCER COUNTY INC**
(*Suby of* COMCAST CORP) ★
1500 Market St, Philadelphia, PA 19102-2100
Tel (215) 665-1700 *Founded/Ownrshp* 1979
Sales 386.4MM^E *EMP* 1,000
SIC 4841 Cable television services
Pr: Michael Doyle
**Pr:* Kevin Kelly
Pr: Garrett P Smith
COO: Franklyn Athias
**Ch:* Bryan Roberts
Co-CFO: Michael J Angelakis
Ofcr: Peter Kiriacoulacos
Ex VP: John Alchin
Ex VP: David L Cohen
Sr VP: Art Block
Sr VP: Greg Butz
Sr VP: Mark A Coblitz
Sr VP: Cynthia K Hook
Sr VP: David Juliano
Sr VP: Melissa Maxfield
Sr VP: Ernie Pighini
Sr VP: Larry Salva
Sr VP: Robert S Victor
VP: Amy Banse
VP: Karen D Buchholz
VP: Abigail Caspar

D-U-N-S 06-428-7006
■ **COMCAST CABLEVISION OF NEW JERSEY INC**
(*Suby of* COMCAST CORP) ★
800 Rahway Ave, Union, NJ 07083-6652
Tel (908) 206-8640 *Founded/Ownrshp* 1994
Sales 116.3MM^E *EMP* 400
SIC 4841 1731 7375 Cable television services; Cable television installation; Information retrieval services
Pr: Buck Dopp
COO: Anderson Reggie
**VP:* Frank De Joy
VP: David Johnson
CIO: Tim Maloy

D-U-N-S 05-715-6663 IMP
▲ **COMCAST CORP**
1701 Jfk Blvd, Philadelphia, PA 19103-2838
Tel (215) 286-1700 *Founded/Ownrshp* 1963
Sales 74.5MMM *EMP* 153,016
Tkr Sym CMCSA *Exch* NGS
SIC 4841 4813 7812 7996 Cable television services; Subscription television services; Telephone communication, except radio; ; ; ;Television film production; Theme park, amusement
Ch Bd: Brian L Roberts
Pr: Amy Banse
Pr: Jon Litner
**Pr:* Neil Smit
COO: David N Watson
**CFO:* Michael J Cavanagh
CFO: Erin Lummer
Ch: Jack Williams
Bd of Dir: Robert Peronto
Assoc VP: Jim Peelman
Div VP: Dave Kowolenko
Ex VP: Barbara Allen
**Ex VP:* Arthur R Block
Ex VP: Greg Butz
Ex VP: Alexander D Evans
Ex VP: Marcien Jenckes
Ex VP: D'Arcy F Rudnay
**Ex VP:* Lawrence J Salva
Ex VP: Samuel H Schwartz
Sr VP: Jason S Armstrong
Sr VP: Amy L Banse

D-U-N-S 60-439-6796
■ **COMCAST HOLDINGS CORP**
(*Suby of* COMCAST CORP) ★
1701 John F Kennedy Blvd C100, Philadelphia, PA 19103-2899
Tel (215) 665-1700 *Founded/Ownrshp* 1990
Sales 4.3MMM^E *EMP* 31,000
SIC 4841 Cable & other pay television services
Ex VP: Lawrence S Smith
Treas: John R Alchin
**Ex VP:* David L Cohen
**Sr VP:* Arthur R Block
Sr VP: Lawrence J Salva
Ex Dir: Bruce Hertzfeld
Genl Mgr: Mike Daves
Prd Mgr: Brian Curran
Pr Mgr: Brad Palazzo
Snr Mgr: William Jones
Snr Mgr: Laura Minegar

D-U-N-S 78-424-3110
■ **COMCAST INTERACTIVE CAPITAL LP**
(*Suby of* COMCAST HOLDINGS CORP) ★
1701 John F Kennedy Blvd, Philadelphia, PA 19103-2838
Tel (215) 981-8450 *Founded/Ownrshp* 2006
Sales 283.4MM^E *EMP* 2,682^E
SIC 6799 Venture capital companies
CFO: Adam Black
VP: Myrna Soto
Mng Dir: Samuel Schwartz

D-U-N-S 36-141-1627
■ **COMCAST OF FLORIDA/GEORGIA/ILLINOIS/MICHIGAN LLC**
(*Suby of* COMCAST CORP) ★
4600 Touchton Rd E # 2200, Jacksonville, FL 32246-8299
Tel (904) 374-8000 *Founded/Ownrshp* 1971
Sales 295.9MM^E *EMP* 1,600
SIC 4813 4841 Telephone communication, except radio; Cable & other pay television services
Pr: Doug McMillan
Pr: Sonya Nelson
Exec: SE Team

D-U-N-S 12-868-3799
■ **COMCAST OF ILLINOIS III INC**
(*Suby of* COMCAST CABLE COMMUNICATIONS LLC) ★
1585 S Waukegan Rd, Waukegan, IL 60085-6727
Tel (847) 856-5239 *Founded/Ownrshp* 2002
Sales 228.3MM^E *EMP* 34^E
SIC 4841 Cable & other pay television services; Cable television services
Genl Mgr: Gail Spatafore

COMCAST OF MARYLAND, INC
See COMCAST OF MARYLAND LLC

D-U-N-S 08-318-0377
■ **COMCAST OF MARYLAND LLC**
COMCAST OF MARYLAND, INC
(*Suby of* COMCAST CORP) ★
9609 Annapolis Rd, Lanham, MD 20706-2005
Tel (301) 306-5774 *Founded/Ownrshp* 2000
Sales 171.0MM^E *EMP* 125
SIC 4841 Cable & other pay television services
VP: Sanford Ames
**Pr:* Kurt Pendleton
Opers Mgr: Erik Smith
Sls Mgr: Sandra Bryan

D-U-N-S 09-370-8568
■ **COMCAST OF SOUTHEAST PENNSYLVANIA LLC**
(*Suby of* COMCAST CORP) ★
200 Cresson Blvd, Oaks, PA 19456
Tel (610) 650-1000 *Founded/Ownrshp* 2001
Sales 99.9MM^E *EMP* 400
SIC 4841 Cable television services
Pr: Steve Burke
Pr: Beth Bacha
**VP:* Harry Brooks
Comm Man: Mary B Casey

D-U-N-S 07-549-2157
■ **COMCAST SPECTACOR INC**
(*Suby of* COMCAST CORP) ★
3601 S Broad St Ste 2, Philadelphia, PA 19148-5250
Tel (215) 875-5202 *Founded/Ownrshp* 1996
Sales 401.4MM^E *EMP* 1,500
SIC 8742 Management consulting services
Ch Bd: Fred Shabel
**Pr:* Richard Ruben
**Ch:* Edward Snider
**Ex VP:* Sanford Lipstein
VP: Daniel Clemmens

D-U-N-S 14-559-7782
■ **COMCAST SPOTLIGHT**
(*Suby of* COMCAST CORP) ★
5 Times Sq, New York, NY 10036-6527
Tel (212) 278-8156 *Founded/Ownrshp* 2002
Sales 197.8MM^E *EMP* 3,275
SIC 7311 Advertising agencies
Pr: Charlie Thurston
Bd of Dir: Dana Runnells
Sr VP: Maria Weaver
VP: John Drain
VP: Ed Dunbar
VP: Justin Evans
VP: Steve Feingold
VP: Bill Haase
VP: Peter Heisinger
VP: Dave Kelly
VP: Teresa Lucido
**VP:* Hank Oster
VP: Kevin Smith
VP: Rick Stanley
VP: Jeff Stone
VP: Page Thompson
VP: John Tierney
VP: Paul D Woidke
Exec: Kevin Cooney
Exec: Ken Eder
Exec: Mitchell Pink

D-U-N-S 00-414-4569
■ **COMCAST TELEPHONY COMMUNICATIONS LLC**
(*Suby of* COMCAST CORP) ★
1701 Jfk Blvd, Philadelphia, PA 19103-2838
Tel (215) 665-1700 *Founded/Ownrshp* 1994
Sales 371.8MM[E] *EMP* 1,131
SIC 4812 Cellular telephone services
Ch Bd: Ralph J Roberts
**CEO:* Brian L Roberts
**CFO:* Michael J Angelakis
**Treas:* John R Alchin
**Ex VP:* David L Cohen
**Ex VP:* Neil Smit
**Ex VP:* Lawrence S Smith
**Sr VP:* Stephen B Burke
Sr VP: Doug Gaston
Sr VP: Charlie Herrin
**VP:* Julian A Brodsky
VP: Alicia Daugherty
VP: Mike Maloney
VP: Bill Revell

D-U-N-S 18-311-0931
COMDATA HOLDINGS CORP
(*Suby of* CERIDIAN LLC) ★
5301 Maryland Way, Brentwood, TN 37027-5028
Tel (615) 370-7000 *Founded/Ownrshp* 1995
Sales 49.6MM[E] *EMP* 2,070
SIC 7374 7389 7375 Data processing service; Check validation service; Information retrieval services
Pr: Tony Holcombe
**Ex VP:* Scott Armstrong
**Ex VP:* Gary Krow
**Ex VP:* Don Leyrer
Sr VP: Henry P Cincere
Sr VP: Russ Follis
Sr VP: Charles Harris
Sr VP: L Glynn Riddle
Sr VP: David Wolverton
VP: Michael Sheridan
Board of Directors: Michael Sheridan

D-U-N-S 05-066-7112
COMDATA NETWORK INC
5301 Maryland Way, Brentwood, TN 37027-5028
Tel (615) 370-7405 *Founded/Ownrshp* 1998
Sales NA *EMP* 1,241
SIC 7374

COMEDY CENTRAL
See COMEDY PARTNERS

D-U-N-S 78-210-2693
■ **COMEDY PARTNERS**
COMEDY CENTRAL
(*Suby of* VIACOM INC) ★
345 Hudson St Fl 9, New York, NY 10014-4502
Tel (212) 767-8600 *Founded/Ownrshp* 2003
Sales 92.2MM[E] *EMP* 209
SIC 4841 Cable & other pay television services
CEO: Doug Herzog
Pr: Michele Ganeless
Treas: Richard Gay
Ex VP: Mitch Fried
Ex VP: Walter Levitt
Sr VP: Steve Albani
Sr VP: Gary S Mann
Sr VP: Cathy Tankosic
VP: Maria Arianas
VP: Gineen Finch
VP: Dennis Oleary
VP: Megan Ring
VP: John Sanborne
VP: Mitchell Semel
Exec: Seth Cohen

D-U-N-S 60-795-0763
■ **COMENITY BANK**
(*Suby of* ALLIANCE DATA SYSTEMS CORP) ★
1 Righter Pkwy Ste 100, Wilmington, DE 19803-1533
Tel (614) 729-4000 *Founded/Ownrshp* 1996
Sales NA *EMP* 200[E]
SIC 6022 State commercial banks
Pr: Timothy King

D-U-N-S 14-349-3992
■ **COMENITY CAPITAL BANK**
(*Suby of* ALLIANCE DATA SYSTEMS CORP) ★
2795 E Cottonwood Pkwy # 100, Salt Lake City, UT 84121-7090
Tel (801) 527-2272 *Founded/Ownrshp* 2003
Sales NA *EMP* 7,392
SIC 6022 State commercial banks
Ch: David Kratoville
**Pr:* Ronald J Ostler
CFO: Justin P Crowley

D-U-N-S 00-695-7856 IMP/EXP
■ **COMERICA BANK** (MI)
(*Suby of* COMERICA INC) ★
1717 Main St Ste 2100, Dallas, TX 75201-7384
Tel (214) 462-4000 *Founded/Ownrshp* 1849, 1973
Sales NA *EMP* 9,000
SIC 6021 National commercial banks
CEO: Ralph W Babb Jr
**V Ch:* Lars C Anderson
V Ch: Carol Molnar
**V Ch:* Karen L Parkhill
Pr: Rhonda K Calvert
**Pr:* Curtis C Farmer
Pr: Jeff Hasselman
Pr: Donald P Hellman
Pr: Annette G Musa
Pr: Michael A Silva
Pr: Joseph P Yurosek
COO: Albert Black
CFO: Charles Kim
Bd of Dir: John Beran
Assoc VP: Shamim Ali
Ex VP: Jon W Bilstrom
Ex VP: Nicholas Cilfone
Ex VP: Dana A Drago
Ex VP: John Killian
Ex VP: Michael H Michalak
Sr VP: James A Beaubie

D-U-N-S 00-792-6561
■ **COMERICA BANK-TEXAS**
(*Suby of* COMERICA INC) ★
1601 Elm St, Dallas, TX 75201-4701
Tel (214) 462-6831 *Founded/Ownrshp* 1927, 1988
Sales NA *EMP* 70
SIC 6021 National commercial banks
Pr: Charles Gummer
Ex VP: Melinda Chausse
Ex VP: Bridgit Chayt
**Ex VP:* Pat Faubion Sr
**Ex VP:* James Gwisdala
**Ex VP:* John Killian
**Ex VP:* Gary Orr
Sr VP: Mike Lawson
Sr VP: Michael Wilson
Sr VP: Andrew Wong
VP: David Ferree
VP: Loretta Smith

D-U-N-S 07-635-2947
▲ **COMERICA INC**
1717 Main St Mc6404, Dallas, TX 75201-4612
Tel (214) 462-6831 *Founded/Ownrshp* 1973
Sales NA *EMP* 9,103
Tkr Sym CMA *Exch* NYS
SIC 6021 6022 6091 6082 6099 6141 National commercial banks; State commercial banks; Nondeposit trust facilities; Foreign trade & international banking institutions; Automated teller machine (ATM) network; Personal credit institutions
Ch Bd: Ralph W Babb Jr
Pr: Laura Dutkowski
Pr: Curtis C Farmer
CFO: David E Duprey
Chf Cred: Peter W Guilfoile
Bd of Dir: Alex Ramirez
Ofcr: Megan D Burkhart
Ofcr: Dyana Carney
Ofcr: Janet H Stephens
Ex VP: John D Buchanan
Ex VP: Muneera S Carr
Ex VP: J Patrick Faubion
Ex VP: Judith S Love
Ex VP: Michael H Michalak
Ex VP: Paul R Obermeyer
Ex VP: Michael T Ritchie
Ex VP: Peter L Sefzik
Sr VP: Kym Hudson
VP: Roseann Beally
VP: Jennifer Bohr
VP: David G Braun

D-U-N-S 08-394-5209
■ **COMERICA INSURANCE SERVICES INC**
(*Suby of* COMERICA BANK) ★
20700 Civic Center Dr # 290, Southfield, MI 48076-4140
Tel (248) 603-3600 *Founded/Ownrshp* 1996
Sales NA *EMP* 25
SIC 6021 National commercial banks
CEO: Michael W Malone
**Pr:* Mike Doyle
**Sr VP:* Ross Rogers
VP: Steven Turtz

COMEX GROUP
See COMEX NORTH AMERICA INC

D-U-N-S 84-407-9769 IMP/EXP
■ **COMEX NORTH AMERICA INC**
COMEX GROUP
(*Suby of* SHERWIN-WILLIAMS CO) ★
101 W Prospect Ave # 1020, Cleveland, OH 44115-1093
Tel (303) 307-2100 *Founded/Ownrshp* 2013
Sales 280.5MM[E] *EMP* 2,500
SIC 2851 8742 5198 5231 Paints & paint additives; Paints, waterproof; Paints: oil or alkyd vehicle or water thinned; Corporation organizing; Paints; Paint brushes, rollers, sprayers; Wallcoverings; Paint; Paint brushes, rollers, sprayers & other supplies; Wallcoverings
Pr: Leon Cohen
**CEO:* Christopher Connor

D-U-N-S 96-830-1890
COMFORCE TELECOM INC
(*Suby of* PRO CORP) ★
999 Stewart Ave, Bethpage, NY 11714-3633
Tel (516) 437-3300 *Founded/Ownrshp* 2011
Sales 1.3MM[E] *EMP* 1,815[E]
SIC 7363 Help supply services
CEO: Andrew Schultz

D-U-N-S 61-357-5380
COMFORT CALIFORNIA INC
CLARION HOTEL
(*Suby of* SUNBURST HOSPITALITY CORP) ★
10750 Columbia Pike # 300, Silver Spring, MD 20901-4453
Tel (301) 592-3800 *Founded/Ownrshp* 1988
Sales 100.0MM[E] *EMP* 300
SIC 7011 Hotels & motels
CEO: Kevin Hanley
Off Mgr: Paul Kim

COMFORT FURNITURE
See UNITED FURNITURE INDUSTRIES INC

COMFORT INN
See TMI HOSPITALITY LP

COMFORT KEEPERS
See NEXT PHASE INC

D-U-N-S 09-667-7471
■ **COMFORT SYSTEMS USA (ARKANSAS) INC**
(*Suby of* COMFORT SYSTEMS USA INC) ★
4806 Rixie Rd, North Little Rock, AR 72117-1537
Tel (501) 834-3320 *Founded/Ownrshp* 1998
Sales 1.5MMM *EMP* 102[E]
Accts Ernst & Young Llp Houston Te
SIC 1711 Mechanical contractor
Pr: Clyde A Jester
**VP:* Trent McKenna
Sys Mgr: Eric Harbor
Sfty Dirs: Keith Daniels

D-U-N-S 00-478-1837
■ **COMFORT SYSTEMS USA (SOUTHWEST) INC** (AZ)
(*Suby of* COMFORT SYSTEMS USA INC) ★
6875 W Galveston St, Chandler, AZ 85226-2516
Tel (480) 940-8400 *Founded/Ownrshp* 1962
Sales 110.6MM[E] *EMP* 490
SIC 1711 Warm air heating & air conditioning contractor; Mechanical contractor; Plumbing contractors
Pr: Joseph Nichter Jr
**VP:* William Fourt
VP: Mike Stanfield
MIS Mgr: Jamey Hunsaker

COMFORT SYSTEMS USA CAROLINAS
See COLONIALWEBB CONTRACTORS CO

D-U-N-S 01-584-1703
▲ **COMFORT SYSTEMS USA INC**
675 Bering Dr Ste 400, Houston, TX 77057-2268
Tel (713) 830-9600 *Founded/Ownrshp* 1996
Sales 1.5MMM *EMP* 7,301
Tkr Sym FIX *Exch* NYS
SIC 1711 1731 Plumbing, heating, air-conditioning contractors; Electrical work
Pr: Brian E Lane
**Ch Bd:* Franklin Myers
CFO: William George
Ex VP: Chad Deyoung
Sr VP: Trent T McKenna
Sr VP: James Mylett
Sr VP: Julie S Shaeff
VP: Melissa Frazier
VP: Jon-Paul Weiss

COMFORTCARE HOME HEALTH SVCS
See CHESAPEAKE HOSPITAL AUTHORITY

D-U-N-S 78-749-1307 IMP/EXP
COMILOG US INC
(*Suby of* ERAMET & COMILOG CHEMICALS SPRL)
610 Pittman Rd, Baltimore, MD 21226-1792
Tel (410) 789-8800 *Founded/Ownrshp* 1987
Sales 99.0MM *EMP* 247
SIC 2819 3313 3356 Magnesium compounds or salts, inorganic; Manganese metal, not made in blast furnaces; Nonferrous rolling & drawing
Pr: Herve Montegue
CFO: Terri Abdis
**CFO:* Marc Blanquart

D-U-N-S 96-154-3027
COMLUX AMERICA LLC
COMLUX AVIATION SERVICES
(*Suby of* COMLUX MANAGEMENT AG)
2910 S High School Rd, Indianapolis, IN 46241-4924
Tel (317) 472-7370 *Founded/Ownrshp* 2009
Sales 84.8MM[E] *EMP* 300
SIC 1799 Renovation of aircraft interiors
CEO: James Soleo
**Pr:* Ettore Rodaro
**CEO:* David Edinger
Sr VP: Christophe Pelet
Genl Mgr: Mamdooh Ahmed

COMLUX AVIATION SERVICES
See COMLUX AMERICA LLC

COMM SOLUTIONS COMPANY
See COMMUNICATION CABLE CO

D-U-N-S 08-277-7657
COMMACK UNION FREE SCHOOL DISTRICT 10
480 Clay Pitts Rd, East Northport, NY 11731-3828
Tel (631) 912-2000 *Founded/Ownrshp* 1906
Sales 77.5MM[E] *EMP* 1,500
Accts Coughlin Foundotos Cullen & Da
SIC 8211 Public elementary & secondary schools
**Treas:* Kerry Reinhardt
VP: Christine Kramer
VP: Jennifer Lombardo
Genl Mgr: Andrea Petraglia
Pr Dir: Debbie Virga

D-U-N-S 08-206-1201
COMMAND ALKON INC
1800 Intl Pk Dr Ste 400, Birmingham, AL 35243
Tel (205) 879-3282 *Founded/Ownrshp* 2005
Sales 102.7MM[E] *EMP* 330
SIC 7371 5045 Computer software development & applications; Computers, peripherals & software
CEO: Phil Ramsey
**Pr:* Kenneth G Robinson
**CFO:* Betty Todd
CFO: Dick Yoakum
**Sr VP:* John Cromeans
VP: John W Cromeans
VP: Scott Killough
QA Dir: Rodney Avery
QA Dir: Delene Beck
QA Dir: Daniel Milligan
Dir IT: Shawn Flanagan

D-U-N-S 02-080-5961
▲ **COMMAND CENTER INC** (WA)
3609 S Wadsworth Blvd # 250, Lakewood, CO 80235-2197
Tel (866) 464-5844 *Founded/Ownrshp* 2003
Sales 88.5MM *EMP* 210
Tkr Sym CCNI *Exch* OTO
SIC 7361 Employment agencies
Pr: Frederick J Sandford
**Ch Bd:* John Stewart
CFO: Colette C Pieper
Ex VP: Ronald L Junck
Board of Directors: Steven M Bathgate, Richard Finlay, R Rimmy Malhotra, John Schneller, J D Smith

COMMAND GUARD SERVICES
See RESOURCE COLLECTION INC

COMMAND PACKAGING
See GRAND PACKAGING INC

D-U-N-S 05-298-5876 IMP/EXP
▲ **COMMAND SECURITY CORP** (NY)
512 Herndon Pkwy Ste A, Herndon, VA 20170-5244
Tel (703) 464-4735 *Founded/Ownrshp* 1980
Sales 133.1MM *EMP* 4,300[E]
Tkr Sym MOC *Exch* ASE
SIC 7381 Security guard service
CEO: Craig P Coy
**Ch Bd:* Thomas P Kikis
CFO: N Paul Brost
Ex VP: Scott Landry
Board of Directors: James P Heffernan, Janet L Steinmayer, Mark Sullivan

D-U-N-S 01-759-3778
■ **COMMAND TRANSPORTATION LLC**
(*Suby of* ECHO GLOBAL LOGISTICS INC) ★
600 W Chicago Ave Ste 725, Chicago, IL 60654-2522
Tel (847) 213-2200 *Founded/Ownrshp* 2015
Sales 328.7MM[E] *EMP* 550
SIC 4731 Truck transportation brokers
CEO: Paul Loeb
**Pr:* Daniel Zamost
**COO:* Jhon Cameli
**CFO:* Brian Rudich
Bd of Dir: Andy Boltz
Bd of Dir: Lewis Dowell
Sr VP: Dave Ardell
VP: Brad Bengtson
VP: Michael Boylen
VP: Dean Patterson
VP: Connie Pool
Dir Risk M: Scott Fisher

D-U-N-S 00-130-8360
COMMAND WEB OFFSET CO INC (MO)
100 Castle Rd, Secaucus, NJ 07094-1602
Tel (201) 863-8100 *Founded/Ownrshp* 1946, 1961
Sales 111.3MM[E] *EMP* 650[E]
SIC 2752 2732 Lithographing on metal; Books: printing only
Ch Bd: Andrew Merson
Chf Mktg O: Robert Rumphrey
Ex VP: Paul Frontczak
**Ex VP:* Charles B Gardner
**VP:* Steven Merson
**VP:* Alan Meyson
Genl Mgr: Michael Aiello
CIO: Robert Loganchuk
Dir IT: Robert Loganchuck
Info Man: Tajammul Awan
Prd Mgr: Louis Bottone

COMMANDER GREAT LAKES
See POWER SOLUTIONS INC

D-U-N-S 03-632-7661
COMMCARE CORP
950 W Causeway Approach C, Mandeville, LA 70471-3082
Tel (504) 324-8950 *Founded/Ownrshp* 1984
Sales 971.7MM[E] *EMP* 4,750
Accts Postlethwaite & Netterville M
SIC 8059 Personal care home, with health care
**Ch Bd:* John A Stassi II
**Sec:* Henry L Masson
**Ex VP:* L Ren Goux
VP: Jolie E Harris

D-U-N-S 82-756-2492
COMMCARE CORP
(*Suby of* COMMCARE CORP) ★
2755 Pan American Lf Ctr, New Orleans, LA 70130
Tel (504) 324-8950 *Founded/Ownrshp* 1984
Sales 965.7MM[E] *EMP* 1,500
SIC 8093 Rehabilitation center, outpatient treatment
Pr: John A Stassi II
**Treas:* Henry L Masson

D-U-N-S 78-033-7973
COMMCARE LOUISIANA
(*Suby of* COMMCARE CORP) ★
601 Poydras St, New Orleans, LA 70130-6029
Tel (504) 324-8950 *Founded/Ownrshp* 2002
Sales 3.6MM *EMP* 1,500
SIC 8093 Rehabilitation center, outpatient treatment
Pr: Landry Rene Goux
**Treas:* Henry Masson

D-U-N-S 06-642-9374 IMP/EXP
COMMEMORATIVE BRANDS INC
ARTCARVED
(*Suby of* AAC) ★
7211 Circle S Rd, Austin, TX 78745-6603
Tel (512) 444-0571 *Founded/Ownrshp* 1996
Sales 264.6MM[E] *EMP* 1,599
SIC 3911 5944 3961 Rings, finger: precious metal; Jewelry, precious stones & precious metals; Costume jewelry
CFO: Sherice P Bench
Sr VP: Parke Davis
Sr VP: Joe Trueblood
VP: Janice Dolder
VP: Norm Smith
VP: Norman Smith
Exec: Theresa Broome
Genl Mgr: Matt Gase
CTO: Gary Gerritsen
MIS Dir: Jeff Peeples
IT Man: Rebecca Clark
Board of Directors: John K Castle, David G Fiore, David A Pittaway, Zane Tankel, Edward O Vetter

D-U-N-S 17-972-2090
COMMERCE & ECONOMIC GROWTH COMMISSION NEW JERSEY
(*Suby of* EXECUTIVE OFFICE OF STATE OF NEW JERSEY) ★
20 W State St, Trenton, NJ 08608-1206
Tel (609) 292-1800 *Founded/Ownrshp* 2002
Sales NA *EMP* 1,428[E]
SIC 9611 Administration of general economic programs;
Pr: William D Watley

D-U-N-S 04-114-2522
▲ **COMMERCE BANCSHARES INC**
1000 Walnut St, Kansas City, MO 64106-2145
Tel (816) 234-2000 *Founded/Ownrshp* 1966
Sales NA *EMP* 4,859[E]
Tkr Sym CBSH *Exch* NGS
SIC 6022 6311 6162 State commercial banks; Life insurance; Mortgage bankers & correspondents
Ch Bd: David W Kemper

Pr: Stacey Goodwin
Pr: John W Kemper
Pr: Kaz Verwers
Pr: Tom Whooley
Pr: Susan Wilborn
CFO: Charles G Kim
**V Ch Bd:* Jonathan M Kemper
Chf Cred: Daniel D Callahan
Ex VP: S Foster
Sr VP: Robert J Rauscher
VP: Bruce Bienhoff
VP: Clement Buschman
VP: Susan Doyle
VP: Marla Freeman
VP: Tulio Gasperini
VP: Betty Maes
VP: Joe Morris
VP: Gordon Roewe
VP: Mossie Schallon
Board of Directors: Terry D Bassham, John R Capps, Earl H Devanny III, W Thomas Grant II, James B Hebenstreit, Benjamin F Rassieur III, Todd R Schnuck, Andrew C Taylor, Kimberly G Walker

D-U-N-S 00-696-5511 IMP
■ COMMERCE BANK
COMMERCE BANK N.A.
(*Suby of* CBI-KANSAS INC) ★
1000 Walnut St Fl 700, Kansas City, MO 64106-2158
Tel (816) 234-2000 *Founded/Ownrshp* 2011
Sales NA *EMP* 4,550
SIC 6022 State commercial banks
Ch Bd: David W Kemper
Pr: Jon Benson
Pr: Bruce Bienhoff
Pr: James G Smith
Treas: Michael Bude
**V Ch Bd:* Jonathan M Kemper
**V Ch Bd:* Seth M Leadbeater
Ofcr: Kathy Foster
Ofcr: Amy Hoehne
Ofcr: Lynn Tankesley
**Ex VP:* Kevin G Barth
**Ex VP:* Charles G Kim
**Ex VP:* Robert C Matthews Jr
**Ex VP:* Edward J Reardon II
Ex VP: Valerie Shaw
Ex VP: Eric Steinhouse
Sr VP: Sara Foster
Sr VP: Karen Grekstas
Sr VP: Whitney Morrow
Sr VP: Gregory Nickle
Sr VP: Robert J Rauscher

D-U-N-S 00-696-8838
■ COMMERCE BANK (MO) (MO)
(*Suby of* COMMERCE BANCSHARES INC) ★
1345 E Battlefield St, Springfield, MO 65804-3603
Tel (417) 869-5411 *Founded/Ownrshp* 1968
Sales NA *EMP* 412
SIC 6021 National commercial banks
Prin: Bob Hammersmith
Brnch Mgr: Nichole Goddard
IT Man: Mike Gilbert

COMMERCE BANK N.A.
See COMMERCE BANK

COMMERCE CASINO
See CALIFORNIA COMMERCE CLUB INC

D-U-N-S 80-662-3133
COMMERCE CONNECT MEDIA INC
CYGNUS BUSINESS MEDIA
(*Suby of* ABRY PARTNERS INC) ★
830 Post Rd E Fl 2, Westport, CT 06880-5222
Tel (800) 547-7377 *Founded/Ownrshp* 2000
Sales 79.6MM^E *EMP* 2,188
SIC 2721 Magazines: publishing & printing
CEO: Paul Mackler

D-U-N-S 07-534-8359
COMMERCE INSURANCE CO
(*Suby of* MAPFRE USA CORP) ★
211 Main St, Webster, MA 01570-2273
Tel (508) 943-9000 *Founded/Ownrshp* 2008
Sales NA *EMP* 1,495
SIC 6331 Property damage insurance
Pr: Jaime Tamayo
**Pr:* Arthur J Remillard Jr
**CFO:* Randal V Becker
**CFO:* Gerald Fels
Sr VP: Patrick McDonald
CIO: Angelos Spetseris
MIS Dir: Ross Whittier
Dir IT: Lisa Kontoes
IT Man: Lori Ciccarelli
Netwrk Mgr: Greg Nickerson
Tech Mgr: Joffre Levesque

D-U-N-S 02-242-2364 IMP
COMMERCE LLC
GOOD TIDINGS
7603 Energy Pkwy, Baltimore, MD 21226-1793
Tel (410) 255-3500 *Founded/Ownrshp* 1997
Sales 135.6MM^E *EMP* 310
SIC 5191 5072 5199 Garden supplies; Insecticides; Pesticides; Fertilizer & fertilizer materials; Hardware; Christmas novelties
CEO: Richard J Lessans
**CFO:* Dennis Koerner
**VP:* Gregg Cote
**VP:* Ralph Rottenberg
CIO: Jeff Appelbaum

D-U-N-S 07-652-9544
COMMERCE WEST INSURANCE CO
(*Suby of* COMMERCE INSURANCE CO) ★
6130 Stoneridge Mall Rd # 400, Pleasanton, CA 94588-3287
Tel (925) 730-6400 *Founded/Ownrshp* 1995
Sales NA *EMP* 60
SIC 6141 Automobile & consumer finance companies
Pr: Jerald Fels
CFO: Michael Vrban
VP: Albert Harris

D-U-N-S 08-034-3442
▲ COMMERCEHUB INC
201 Fuller Rd Fl 6, Albany, NY 12203-3621
Tel (518) 810-0700 *Founded/Ownrshp* 1997
Sales 87.6MM *EMP* 331^E
Tkr Sym CHUBA *Exch* NGM
SIC 7372 Prepackaged software
Pr: Francis Poore
**Ch Bd:* Richard N Baer
CFO: Mark Greenquist
Ofcr: John Hinkle
Ex VP: Richard Jones
Ex VP: Bill Kong
Sftwr Eng: David Carr

D-U-N-S 60-082-8748
COMMERCIAL BARGE LINE CO
(*Suby of* AMERICAN BARGE LINE CO) ★
1701 E Market St, Jeffersonville, IN 47130-4755
Tel (812) 288-0100 *Founded/Ownrshp* 1975
Sales 855.2MM^E *EMP* 2,245^E
SIC 3731 4449 4491 Barges, building & repairing; Canal barge operations; Marine terminals
Pr: Mark K Knoy
**COO:* Paul Tobin
**CFO:* David J Huls
**Sr VP:* Robert M Blocker
**Sr VP:* Dawn R Landry

D-U-N-S 00-979-1807
COMMERCIAL CARRIER CORP
(*Suby of* COMCAR INDUSTRIES INC) ★
502 E Brdgs Ave, Auburndale, FL 33823
Tel (863) 967-1101 *Founded/Ownrshp* 1983
Sales 57.4MM^E *EMP* 1,450
SIC 4213 Heavy hauling
Pr: Bud Coleman
**Ch Bd:* Guy Bostick
**Pr:* Tip Fowler
**Pr:* Frank Power
**Treas:* Robert Fox
**Ex VP:* Mark Bostick
VP: Thomas Heath
VP: Robert Turkett
Genl Mgr: Shawn Evans

D-U-N-S 04-330-0565
COMMERCIAL CARRIERS INSURANCE AGENCY INC (CA)
(*Suby of* MEADOWBROOK CLAIMS SERVICE) ★
12641 166th St, Cerritos, CA 90703-2135
Tel (562) 404-4900 *Founded/Ownrshp* 1979, 1983
Sales NA *EMP* 220^E
SIC 6331 Fire, marine & casualty insurance
Pr: Charles J Escalante
**Ch Bd:* Henry H Escalante
COO: Tim Hanst
**Treas:* Shannon S Walker

D-U-N-S 00-653-2105
COMMERCIAL CONTRACTING CORP (MI)
(*Suby of* COMMERCIAL CONTRACTING GROUP INC) ★
4260 N Atlantic Blvd, Auburn Hills, MI 48326-1578
Tel (248) 209-0500 *Founded/Ownrshp* 1946
Sales 209.0MM *EMP* 300
SIC 1541 1796 Industrial buildings, new construction; Machinery installation
CEO: Stephen Fragnoli
**CFO:* Steven P Teper
**Ch:* William H Pettibone
Ex VP: Timothy Crawforth
**Ex VP:* Bradford Kimmel
Ex VP: Dan Sternberg
VP: John Grix
VP: David Klann
**VP:* Joel Lewandowski
VP: Arthur Pulte
VP: Paulette Salkowski

D-U-N-S 18-377-6814
COMMERCIAL CONTRACTING GROUP INC
4260 N Atlantic Blvd, Auburn Hills, MI 48326-1578
Tel (248) 209-0500 *Founded/Ownrshp* 1987
Sales 281.8MM *EMP* 300
SIC 1796 Installing building equipment
Ch: William H Pettibone Jr
**Pr:* Stephen Fragnoli
**CFO:* Steven Teper
**Ex VP:* Bradford Kimmel
**VP:* Michael Hayes
Opers Mgr: Cesar Gonzalez

D-U-N-S 00-203-0690
■ COMMERCIAL ENVELOPE MANUFACTURING CO INC (NY)
(*Suby of* CENVEO INC) ★
900 Grand Blvd, Deer Park, NY 11729-5745
Tel (631) 242-2500 *Founded/Ownrshp* 1926, 2007
Sales 167.0MM^E *EMP* 700
SIC 2677 5112

D-U-N-S 00-532-8786 EXP
COMMERCIAL GROUP INC (MI)
COMMERCIAL GROUP LIFTING PDTS
12801 Universal Dr, Taylor, MI 48180-6844
Tel (313) 931-6100 *Founded/Ownrshp* 1956
Sales 83.6MM^E *EMP* 125
SIC 5085 5051 3496 3537 3534 Industrial supplies; Rope, wire (not insulated); Cable, wire; Cable, uninsulated wire: made from purchased wire; Wire chain; Industrial trucks & tractors; Elevators & moving stairways
Pr: Garland Knight
**CFO:* Jim Karshina
Sls Mgr: Veato Pizzo

COMMERCIAL GROUP LIFTING PDTS
See COMMERCIAL GROUP INC

D-U-N-S 00-958-1331
COMMERCIAL LUMBER & PALLET CO INC
135 Long Ln, City of Industry, CA 91746-2633
Tel (626) 968-0631 *Founded/Ownrshp* 1941
Sales 87.2MM^E *EMP* 308
SIC 2448 5031 Pallets, wood; Lumber: rough, dressed & finished
Pr: Raymond Gutierrez
Exec: Carlos Casas
Prd Mgr: Temo Escobedo

D-U-N-S 00-792-5845 IMP/EXP
▲ COMMERCIAL METALS CO
6565 N Mcarthr Blvd # 800, Irving, TX 75039-6283
Tel (214) 689-4300 *Founded/Ownrshp* 1915
Sales 4.6MMM *EMP* 9,126
Tkr Sym CMC *Exch* NYS
SIC 3312 3441 5051 5093 Blast furnaces & steel mills; Bars & bar shapes, steel, hot-rolled; Structural shapes & pilings, steel; Fabricated structural metal; Metals service centers & offices; Steel; Aluminum bars, rods, ingots, sheets, pipes, plates, etc.; Scrap & waste materials
Ch Bd: Joseph Alvarado
COO: Barbara R Smith
CFO: Robert Acevski
CFO: Mary A Lindsey
Treas: Carey J Dubois
Bd of Dir: Robert L Guido
Ex VP: Robert Cundiff
Ex VP: Phil Seidenberger
Ex VP: Robert Unfried
Ex VP: Hanns Zoellner
VP: Terry P Hatten
VP: Adam R Hickey
VP: Paul K Kirkpatrick
VP: Tom Sfikas
Board of Directors: Joseph C Winkler, Vicki L Avril, Rhys J Best, Robert L Guido, Richard B Kelson, Anthony A Massaro, Rick J Mills, Sarah E Raiss, J David Smith, Charles L Szews

D-U-N-S 62-714-2222
COMMERCIAL PRINT GROUP INC
(*Suby of* TAYLOR CORP) ★
1750 Northway Dr, North Mankato, MN 56003-2700
Tel (507) 625-2828 *Founded/Ownrshp* 2005
Sales 270.1MM^E *EMP* 582
SIC 7313 Printed media advertising representatives
CFO: Darik Aho
**Pr:* Joe Keenan

D-U-N-S 04-656-1353
COMMERCIAL ROOFING SPECIALTIES INC (GA)
C R S
2703 Peachtree Sq, Atlanta, GA 30360-2634
Tel (770) 458-0539 *Founded/Ownrshp* 1981
Sales 131.0MM^E *EMP* 100
Accts Faucett Taylor & Associates
SIC 5033 Roofing, siding & insulation
Pr: Larry Burns
**Sec:* Warren R Teague
**VP:* Chip Martin

D-U-N-S 04-611-2934 IMP
COMMERCIAL TIRE INC (ID)
2095 E Commercial St, Meridian, ID 83642-5967
Tel (208) 888-8800 *Founded/Ownrshp* 1968
Sales 203.1MM^E *EMP* 400
SIC 5531 5014 Automotive tires; Tires & tubes
Pr: J R Schwenkfelder
**Sec:* Bonnie Schwenkfelder
VP: Trudy Costes
**VP:* Trent Schwenkfelder
**Prin:* Michael Hampton
Dir IT: Nancy Mittleider
IT Man: David Campbell
Sfty Mgr: Chris Brown
S&M/VP: George Hammon
Manager: Chase Cavanaugh

COMMERCIAL UNION/ ONEBEACON
See ONEBEACON INSURANCE GROUP LLC

D-U-N-S 15-014-6855 EXP
▲ COMMERCIAL VEHICLE GROUP INC
CVG
7800 Walton Pkwy, New Albany, OH 43054-8233
Tel (614) 289-5360 *Founded/Ownrshp* 2000
Sales 825.3MM *EMP* 6,700
Tkr Sym CVGI *Exch* NGS
SIC 3714 3231 Motor vehicle parts & accessories; Windshield wiper systems, motor vehicle; Motor vehicle body components & frame; Wipers, windshield, motor vehicle; Mirrors, truck & automobile: made from purchased glass
Pr: Patrick E Miller
**Ch Bd:* Richard A Snell
Pr: Joseph Saoud
CFO: C Timothy Trenary
Prgrm Mgr: Gary Hamberg
Board of Directors: Scott C Arves, Harold C Bevis, David R Bovee, Roger L Fix, Robert C Griffin, Wayne M Rancourt

D-U-N-S 96-868-4741
COMMERZBANK AG
(*Suby of* COMMERZBANK AG)
225 Liberty St Fl 31, New York, NY 10281-1050
Tel (212) 266-7200 *Founded/Ownrshp* 2011
Sales NA *EMP* 179^E
SIC 6029 Commercial banks
VP: Daniel Weissfeld
Pr: Junis Damar
CFO: Mark Downey
Ex VP: Richard Arenaro
Ex VP: Joachim Dopp
Ex VP: Anthony Tuffy
**Sr VP:* Thomas Carney
Sr VP: Michael Leibrock
VP: Pete Basi
VP: Edward Casparius
VP: Benedict Fargione
VP: Dimitri Gavrishenko
VP: Katherine Guest
VP: Laurie Knell
VP: Gilbert Michel
VP: Moritz Mielke
VP: Stephen Ng
VP: Luzia Nicosia
VP: Laura Paradiso
VP: Rossano Rossi
VP: Michael Santoro

COMMISSIONER DEPT
See COUNTY OF MADISON

D-U-N-S 07-494-1790
COMMISSIONERS OF CARROLL COUNTY
225 N Center St, Westminster, MD 21157-5108
Tel (410) 386-2400 *Founded/Ownrshp* 1837
Sales NA *EMP* 1,045
Accts Clifton Larson Allen Llp Balt
SIC 9111 County supervisors' & executives' offices;
Pr: John Douglas Howard
**VP:* Dean Minnich
**Ex Dir:* Steve Powell
Genl Mgr: Deborah Standiford

COMMISSIONERS OF ESCAMBIA COUN
See COUNTY OF ESCAMBIA

D-U-N-S 06-701-3771
COMMISSIONERS OF PUBLIC WORKS
CHARLESTON WATER SYSTEM
103 Saint Philip St, Charleston, SC 29403-6131
Tel (843) 727-6800 *Founded/Ownrshp* 1917
Sales 128.0MM *EMP* 430
Accts Mauldin & Jenkins Llc Macon
SIC 4941 Water supply
CEO: Kin Hill
V Ch: William Koopman Jr
**COO:* Andy Fairey
**CFO:* Wesley Ropp
**Ch:* Thomas Pritchard
MIS Dir: Katherine Rigsby
IT Man: Wendy Ray
Pr Mgr: Jenny Craft

COMMODITY MARKET CENTER
See CHEMICAL WASTE MANAGEMENT INC

D-U-N-S 80-441-3011 EXP
COMMODITY SPECIALISTS CO
920 2nd Ave S Ste 850, Minneapolis, MN 55402-4002
Tel (612) 330-9889 *Founded/Ownrshp* 1993
Sales 99.6MM^E *EMP* 100
SIC 5191 Animal feeds
Ch: O William Mikkelson
**Pr:* Philip J Lindau
**Pr:* Bill Mikkelson
COO: Curt Gasper
VP: Ross Brainard
**VP:* Lawrence J Dellwo
Opers Mgr: Ryan Schultz
VP Mktg: Dan Slye

D-U-N-S 13-240-9611
COMMODORE CONSTRUCTION CORP
602 S 3rd Ave, Mount Vernon, NY 10550-4915
Tel (914) 663-4394 *Founded/Ownrshp* 2001
Sales 129.4MM^E *EMP* 300^E
SIC 1542 Commercial & office building contractors
Pr: Eilish Loughran
**CFO:* Don Cutler
VP: Alan Haines
Exec: Raymond Speckman
Genl Mgr: Tamara Stewart

D-U-N-S 00-725-9039
COMMODORE CORP
MANORWOOD HOMES
1423 Lincolnway E, Goshen, IN 46526-4657
Tel (574) 533-7100 *Founded/Ownrshp* 1990
Sales 122.6MM^E *EMP* 750
SIC 2452

COMMOMWEALTH FINANCIAL NETWORK
See COMMONWEALTH EQUITY SERVICES LLP

COMMON CENTS STORES
See MOYLE PETROLEUM CO

D-U-N-S 07-886-7504
COMMON FUND FOR NONPROFIT ORGANIZATIONS
15 Old Danbury Rd Ste 200, Wilton, CT 06897-2531
Tel (203) 563-5000 *Founded/Ownrshp* 1969
Sales 97.2MM^E *EMP* 220
Accts Pricewaterhousecoopers Llp Ne
SIC 6282 Investment advisory service
Pr: Verne O Sedlacek
**COO:* E Lyndon Tefft
Exec: Laurance R Hoagland Jr
Mng Dir: Andreas Calianos
Mng Dir: Alyssa Kraft
Mng Dir: Keith Luke
Mng Dir: Paul Von Steenburg
Counsel: Seth Thomson

COMMON PLEAS JUVENILE DIVISION
See COUNTY OF SUMMIT

D-U-N-S 07-839-8102 IMP
COMMONWEALTH - ALTADIS INC
(*Suby of* ALTADIS USA INC) ★
5900 N Andrews Ave # 1100, Fort Lauderdale, FL 33309-2354
Tel (954) 772-9000 *Founded/Ownrshp* 1991
Sales 148.1MM^E *EMP* 900
SIC 5194 Cigars
VP: Ray Soliday
**Pr:* John F Kenned

D-U-N-S 79-302-2109
COMMONWEALTH ANNUITY & LIFE INSURANCE
(*Suby of* GLOBAL ATLANTIC FINANCIAL GROUP LIMITED)
132 Turnpike Rd Ste 210, Southborough, MA 01772-2132
Tel (508) 460-2400 *Founded/Ownrshp* 2002
Sales NA *EMP* 1,442
SIC 6311 Life insurance
Pr: Michael A Reardon
**CFO:* Michael A Pirrello
**Treas:* Amol S Naik
VP: Paula Dell
IT Man: Bryan Hall

D-U-N-S 12-135-6369
COMMONWEALTH ASSISTED LIVING LLC
534 E Main St Ste B, Charlottesville, VA 22902-5395
Tel (434) 220-1055 *Founded/Ownrshp* 2009
Sales 75.0MM^E *EMP* 1,000^E
SIC 8741 Management services
**COO:* Earl Parker

*CFO: Vicky Morris
*Sr VP: Kevin Willis
VP: Robert Barrett
*VP: Tommy Comer
VP: Donna Hunt
VP: Ashley Showalter
Ex Dir: Leslie Jones
Off Mgr: Cheryl Brunk
Off Mgr: Ashley Napier
VP Sls: Delores Jacobson

D-U-N-S 14-315-3927
COMMONWEALTH CARE ALLIANCE INC
30 Winter St Fl 12, Boston, MA 02108-4743
Tel (617) 426-0600 Founded/Ownrshp 2003
Sales 297.6MM EMP 30E
Accts Mcgladrey Llp Charlestown Ma
SIC 8099 8011 Health screening service; Primary care medical clinic; Medical insurance associations
CEO: Christopher D Palmieri
*Pr: Lola Simon
*Treas: Eugene Wallace
Sr VP: Larry Gottlieb
Sr VP: Bill Perez
VP: Carol Tobias
Exec: Brenda Madden
CIO: Jefferson Lett
CTO: Hudson Hardy
Mktg Mgr: Robert Katzman
Genl Couns: Lisa Fleming

D-U-N-S 16-548-5926
COMMONWEALTH CHARTER ACADEMY
CCA
4050 Crums Mill Rd # 303, Harrisburg, PA 17112-2827
Tel (717) 651-7200 Founded/Ownrshp 2002
Sales 108.1MM EMP 300E
Accts Sd Associates Pc Elkins Park
SIC 8211

D-U-N-S 00-692-9509
■ **COMMONWEALTH EDISON CO** (IL)
(Suby of EXELON CORP) ★
440 S La Salle St, Chicago, IL 60605-1028
Tel (312) 394-4321 Founded/Ownrshp 1913, 2000
Sales 4.9MMM EMP 5,895E
SIC 4911 Generation, electric power; Transmission, electric power; Distribution, electric power
Pr: Anne R Pramaggiore
*Ch Bd: Christopher M Crane
COO: Terence R Donnelly
COO: Terrence R Donnelly
CFO: Joseph R Trpik Jr
Sr VP: Tyler Anthony
Sr VP: Fidel Marquez Jr
Sr VP: Thomas S O'Neill
VP: Mark Browning
VP: James Conway
VP: Ronald Donovan
VP: Gerald J Kozel
VP: Michael McMahan
VP: Laura Novy
VP: Carl L Segneri Jr
VP: Kevin J Waden
Board of Directors: James W Compton, A Steven Crown, Nicholas Debenedictis, Peter V Fazio Jr, Michael Moskow, Denis P O'brien

D-U-N-S 18-542-2433
COMMONWEALTH ELECTRIC CO OF MIDWEST
1901 Y St Ste 100, Lincoln, NE 68503-2497
Tel (402) 473-2214 Founded/Ownrshp 1987
Sales 121.0MM EMP 700
SIC 1731

D-U-N-S 02-172-8423
COMMONWEALTH EQUITY SERVICES LLP
COMMOMWEALTH FINANCIAL NETWORK
29 Sawyer Rd Ste 2, Waltham, MA 02453-3483
Tel (781) 398-0401 Founded/Ownrshp 1979
Sales 214.9MME EMP 430
Accts Brown & Brown Llp Cpa S Bost
SIC 6211 6282 6221 Brokers, security; Investment advice; Commodity contracts brokers, dealers
Pt: Joseph S Deitch
*Pt: Peter Wheeler
*Pr: Richard Hunter
*CEO: Wayne Bloom
Chf Mktg O: Todd H Estabrook
Ofcr: Paul Tolley
Ex VP: David Phillips
VP: Jon Bohs
VP: Jim Hommeyer
VP: Paul Scannell
VP: Everett Sutherland

D-U-N-S 05-077-3498
COMMONWEALTH GENERAL CORP
(Suby of AEGON USA, INC.)
4333 Edgewood Rd Ne, Cedar Rapids, IA 52499-3830
Tel (502) 560-2000 Founded/Ownrshp 1997
Sales NA EMP 600
SIC 6311 Life insurance carriers
Pr: William Gernert

D-U-N-S 12-178-1595
COMMONWEALTH HEALTH CORP INC
CHC
800 Park St, Bowling Green, KY 42101-2356
Tel (270) 745-1500 Founded/Ownrshp 1984
Sales 68.6MM EMP 2,700
Accts Blue & Co Llc Indianapolis I
SIC 8062 6513 General medical & surgical hospitals; Apartment building operators
Pr: Connie Smith
CFO: Roy F Boyd
Bd of Dir: John Chaney
Ofcr: Vince Willingham
*Ex VP: Jean Cherry
*Ex VP: Betsy Kullman
*Ex VP: Sarah Moore
*Ex VP: Ron Sowell
*Ex VP: Wade Stone
VP: Betsy Fache
VP: Frederick G Fache
VP: Sandy Feria
VP: Eric Hagan
VP: Melinda Joyce
VP: Doris C Thomas
VP: Doris Thomas
VP: Larry Vaughn

COMMONWEALTH HEALTH PLAN
See VIRGINIA PREMIER HEALTH PLAN INC

D-U-N-S 36-076-5754
COMMONWEALTH HOTELS LLC
100 E Rivercenter Blvd # 1050, Covington, KY 41011-1548
Tel (859) 392-2264 Founded/Ownrshp 1986
Sales 95.2MME EMP 1,000
SIC 7011 8741 Hotels & motels; Hotel or motel management; Restaurant management
Ch Bd: William P Butler
*Pr: Dan Fay
*VP: Brian Fry
*VP: Gordon L Snyder
*VP: Paul Stanton
Brnch Mgr: Jim McFarland
Genl Mgr: James Seitz
Oper/Mgr: Courtney Henry
Sls Dir: Candace Sutherland

D-U-N-S 00-791-3403
■ **COMMONWEALTH LAND TITLE INSURANCE CO**
(Suby of FIDELITY NATIONAL FINANCIAL INC) ★
201 Cncourse Blvd Ste 200, Glen Allen, VA 23059
Tel (904) 854-8100 Founded/Ownrshp 1876, 2008
Sales NA EMP 11,000
SIC 6361 Real estate title insurance
CEO: Robert J Hauser Jr
*Pr: Tedd Chambler
*Treas: Ronald Burgess Ramos
*Treas: Jeffrey A Tischler
Ofcr: Sue Orrino
*VP: Christopher L Rosati

D-U-N-S 00-696-8275
■ **COMMONWEALTH MUTUAL**
(Suby of KEMPER CORP) ★
12115 Lackland Rd, Saint Louis, MO 63146-4025
Tel (314) 644-1255 Founded/Ownrshp 1912
Sales NA EMP 1,500
SIC 6411 Insurance agents, brokers & service
Pr: Don M Royster
*Treas: Steven Mc Ginley
*Ex VP: Richard Miller
*Sr VP: Judy M Hecker
*VP: Gary Bleitner

D-U-N-S 00-700-2959
COMMONWEALTH OF KENTUCKY
700 Capital Ave Ste 100, Frankfort, KY 40601-3410
Tel (502) 564-2611 Founded/Ownrshp 1792
Sales NA EMP 34,000E
Accts Adam H Edelen Auditor Of Pub
SIC 9111 Executive offices
Ofcr: Amanda Greer
Exec: Jennifer Doom
Assoc Dir: Bill Slone
Comm Dir: Terry Sebastian
Prgrm Mgr: Nila Meeks
Off Mgr: Mae Girkey
Off Mgr: Heather Quinn
CTO: Stuart Hamling
IT Man: Joanna Alderson
Info Man: Sara Hines
Sls Mgr: David Gauss

D-U-N-S 07-313-0932
COMMONWEALTH OF MASSACHUSETTS
1 Ashburton Pl Fl 9, Boston, MA 02108-1518
Tel (617) 727-5000 Founded/Ownrshp 1788
Sales NA EMP 59,253
Accts Kpmg Llp Boston Ma
SIC 9111 Executive offices
CFO: Paul McCarthy
Genl Mgr: Daniel Cooper

D-U-N-S 87-824-8806
COMMONWEALTH OF MASSACHUSETTS DEPARTMENT OF CORRECTION
(Suby of MASSACHUSETTS DEPARTMENT OF PUBLIC SAFETY) ★
50 Maple St Ste 3, Milford, MA 01757-3680
Tel (508) 233-6530 Founded/Ownrshp 1950
Sales NA EMP 5,000
Accts Kpmg Llp Boston Ma
SIC 9121
Ofcr: Nuwanda Evans
Ofcr: Thomas Kelley
Ofcr: David Simas
Ex VP: Lon Povich
VP: Carolyn Blanks
VP: Lisa Zankman
Ex Dir: Joan Cirillo
Ex Dir: Ali Noorani
Genl Mgr: Collette Blais
Dir IT: Robert Garon
Counsel: Colin Owyang
Board of Directors: Karen Hetherson

D-U-N-S 00-302-7539 IMP/EXP
COMMONWEALTH OF PENNSYLVANIA
238 Main Capitol Building, Harrisburg, PA 17120-0022
Tel (717) 787-5962 Founded/Ownrshp 1787
Sales NA EMP 89,207
Accts Cliftonlarsonallen Llp Baltim
SIC 9111 Executive offices;
V Ch: Mike Folmer
Ofcr: Carl Reitz
Adm Dir: Lisa S Henry
Adm Dir: Idalys Villafane
Ex Dir: Brenda Esopi
CTO: Stephen Larue
IT Man: Andy Bishop
IT Man: William Mumaw
Mktg Dir: Howard Pollman
Mktg Mgr: Bruce Beardsley
Snr Mgr: Daniel Fleagle

D-U-N-S 79-656-7584
COMMONWEALTH OF PENNSYLVANIA DEPARTMENT OF CORRECTIONS
(Suby of GOVERNORS OFFICE) ★
1920 Technology Pkwy, Mechanicsburg, PA 17050-8507
Tel (717) 728-2573 Founded/Ownrshp 1984
Sales NA EMP 16,000
SIC 9223

D-U-N-S 11-816-2700
COMMONWEALTH OF PUERTO RICO
63 Calle De La Fortaleza, San Juan, PR 00901-1501
Tel (787) 721-7000 Founded/Ownrshp 1952
Sales NA EMP 17,500
Accts Deloitte & Touche Llp San Jua
SIC 9111 Governors' offices

D-U-N-S 00-313-3790
COMMONWEALTH OF VIRGINIA
101 N 14st James Monroe St, Richmond, VA 23219
Tel (804) 225-3131 Founded/Ownrshp 1788
Sales NA EMP 100,000
Accts Martha S Mavredes Cpa Audito
SIC 9111 Governors' offices;
Treas: Lee Andes
Treas: Manju Ganeriwala
Ex Dir: Diana Cantor

D-U-N-S 00-791-0441
■ **COMMONWEALTH TELEPHONE CO LLC** (PA)
FRONTIER COMMUNICATIONS
(Suby of COMMONWEALTH TELEPHONE ENTERPRISES INC) ★
100 Cte Dr Ste 2, Dallas, PA 18612-9774
Tel (570) 631-4555 Founded/Ownrshp 1897
Sales 223.6MME EMP 879E
SIC 4813 Telephone communication, except radio; Local telephone communications; Long distance telephone communications
Pr: Daniel I McCarthy
COO: Eileen M O'Neill Odu
Treas: Alan Kelsey
VP: Donald R Shassian
Genl Mgr: Stephen Euton
Genl Mgr: Ben Fauver

D-U-N-S 02-145-2255
■ **COMMONWEALTH TELEPHONE ENTERPRISES INC**
(Suby of FRONTIER COMMUNICATIONS CORP) ★
100 Cte Dr Ste 2, Dallas, PA 18612-9774
Tel (570) 631-2700 Founded/Ownrshp 1979, 2007
Sales 322.3MME EMP 1,110
Accts Pricewaterhousecoopers Llp Ph
SIC 4813 Telephone communication, except radio; Local telephone communications; Long distance telephone communications
Pr: Michael J Mahoney
*Ch Bd: Walter Scott Jr
COO: Eileen O'Neill Odum
Ex VP: Donald P Cawley
VP: Stuart Kirkwood

D-U-N-S 79-625-6261 IMP
COMMONWEALTH-ALTADIS INC
(Suby of IMPERIAL BRANDS PLC)
5900 N Andrews Ave # 1100, Fort Lauderdale, FL 33309-2354
Tel (800) 481-5814 Founded/Ownrshp 1991
Sales 112.2MME EMP 400
SIC 2111 2621 2131 Cigarettes; Paper mills; Smoking tobacco
Pr: Kevin Freudenthal
Pr: Russ Mantuso
*CFO: John Mercer
CFO: Julie Simmons
*VP: Ulric Engles
*VP: William Wilkey
Comm Man: Clayton Dickson
*Prin: Rob Wilkey
Mktg Mgr: Jorge Figueroa
Sls Mgr: Vicki Hutchinson
Sls Mgr: Renae Laroche

D-U-N-S 06-892-7893
■ **COMMSCOPE CONNECTIVITY LLC**
(Suby of COMMSCOPE HOLDING CO INC) ★
1100 Commscope Pl Se, Hickory, NC 28602-3619
Tel (828) 324-2200 Founded/Ownrshp 2015
Sales 1.4MMME EMP 9,000
SIC 4899 Communication signal enhancement network system
CEO: Marvin S Edwards Jr
*Pr: Michael D Coppin

D-U-N-S 00-624-9312 IMP
■ **COMMSCOPE CONNECTIVITY SOLUTIONS LLC** (MN)
TE CONNECTIVITY
(Suby of COMMSCOPE INC OF NORTH CAROLINA) ★
1100 Commscope Pl Se, Hickory, NC 28602-3619
Tel (828) 324-2200 Founded/Ownrshp 1953, 2015
Sales 2.0MMME EMP 9,000
SIC 3661 3357 3643 8999 Telephones & telephone apparatus; Telephone cords, jacks, adapters, etc.; Fiber optics communications equipment; Communication wire; Fiber optic cable (insulated); Connectors & terminals for electrical devices; Communication services
CEO: Marvin S Edwards Jr
Pr: Jo Anne Anderson
Pr: Hilton Nicholson
Pr: Richard B Parran Jr
Treas: Mark Borman
VP: Kimberly Hartwell
IT Man: Bob Gadbois
IT Man: Bob Wiley
Tech Mgr: Peter Meijer
Manager: Scott Dearent
Sls Mgr: Randy Dunagan

D-U-N-S 96-722-5314 IMP/EXP
▲ **COMMSCOPE HOLDING CO INC**
1100 Commscope Pl Se, Hickory, NC 28602-3619
Tel (828) 324-2200 Founded/Ownrshp 1976
Sales 3.8MMM EMP 23,000E
Tkr Sym COMM Exch NGS
SIC 3663 4899 Radio & TV communications equipment; Communication signal enhancement network system
Pr: Marvin S Edwards Jr
*Ch Bd: Frank M Drendel
COO: Randall W Crenshaw
CFO: Mark A Olson
Sr VP: Philip M Armstrong Jr
Sr VP: Michael Cross
Sr VP: Robert W Granow
Sr VP: Peter U Karlsson
Sr VP: Morgan Kurk
Sr VP: Fiona Nolan
Sr VP: Joanne L Townsend
Sr VP: Frank B Wyatt II
Board of Directors: Austin A Adams, Campbell R Dyer, Stephen C Gray, L William Krause, Joanne M Maguire, Thomas J Manning, Claudius E Watts IV, Timothy T Yates

D-U-N-S 07-062-6247 IMP/EXP
■ **COMMSCOPE INC OF NORTH CAROLINA**
(Suby of COMMSCOPE HOLDING CO INC) ★
1100 Commscope Pl Se, Hickory, NC 28602-3619
Tel (828) 324-2200 Founded/Ownrshp 2011
Sales 4.6MMME EMP 9,000E
SIC 3663 3357 3679 3812 3699 Microwave communication equipment; Antennas, transmitting & communications; Television antennas (transmitting) & ground equipment; Receiver-transmitter units (transceiver); Communication wire; Coaxial cable, nonferrous; Waveguides & fittings; Search & navigation equipment; Radar systems & equipment; Electrical equipment & supplies
Pr: Marvin S Edwards Jr
Pr: Kap Kim
COO: Randall W Crenshaw
CFO: Gerald Leonhartt
CFO: Mark A Olson
Ex VP: Julie Nielson
Ex VP: Eugene Swithenbank
Ex VP: Gene Swithenbank
Sr VP: Philip M Armstrong Jr
Sr VP: Suzan Campbell
Sr VP: Peter U Karlsson
Sr VP: Mike Kelley
Sr VP: Anne Marie Kenneally
Sr VP: Morgan Kurk
Sr VP: Mark Manning
Sr VP: Robyn T Mingle
Sr VP: Fiona Nolan
Sr VP: Kevin St Cyr
Sr VP: Chris Story
Sr VP: Robert C Suffern
Sr VP: Frank B Wyatt II

D-U-N-S 00-517-7084 IMP/EXP
■ **COMMSCOPE TECHNOLOGIES LLC**
(Suby of COMMSCOPE INC OF NORTH CAROLINA) ★
4 Westbrook Corporate Ctr, Westchester, IL 60154-5752
Tel (708) 236-6000 Founded/Ownrshp 1986
Sales 2.5MMME EMP 11,500
Accts Ernst & Young Llp Chicago Il
SIC 3663 3357 3679 3812 3699 Microwave communication equipment; Antennas, transmitting & communications; Television antennas (transmitting) & ground equipment; Receiver-transmitter units (transceiver); Communication wire; Coaxial cable, nonferrous; Waveguides & fittings; Search & navigation equipment; Radar systems & equipment; Electrical equipment & supplies
Pr: Eddie Edwards
Pr: Tom Gravely
COO: Patrick Andrew
*CFO: Marty R Kittrell
Treas: Blair McCaleb
*Sr VP: Justin C Choi
*Sr VP: John R D Dickson
VP: Ray Butler
*VP: Mark A Olson
VP: Carol Scholler
Dir Bus: Vijay Chopra

D-U-N-S 04-881-7266
COMMUNICATION CABLE CO (PA)
COMM SOLUTIONS COMPANY
140 Quaker Ln, Malvern, PA 19355-2479
Tel (610) 644-5155 Founded/Ownrshp 1974, 1998
Sales 97.2MME EMP 55
SIC 5045 7379 Computers, peripherals & software; Computer peripheral equipment; Computer related consulting services
Pr: Paul S Black
Treas: William T Black Jr
*Sec: John T Black
*VP: William F Buckalew
VP: William Buckalew
Snr Ntwrk: Christopher Gaspar
Snr Ntwrk: Vince Vevea
Netwrk Eng: Michael Haring
VP Sls: Marc Allen
VP Sls: Craig Tarnoski
Manager: Todd Koehler

D-U-N-S 79-181-9410
COMMUNICATION TECHNOLOGY SERVICES LLC
CTS
33 Locke Dr Ste 201, Marlborough, MA 01752-1168
Tel (508) 382-2700 Founded/Ownrshp 1991
Sales 84.5MME EMP 400
SIC 1731 Voice, data & video wiring contractor; Fiber optic cable installation; Telephone & telephone equipment installation
CEO: John J Tegan III
*Pr: John J Tegan Jr
CFO: Jim Russo
Exec: Brian Casto
Rgnl Mgr: Keith Wanser
Genl Mgr: Scott Macdonald

Snr Ntwrk: Christian Bryant
Opers Mgr: Brett Murphy

D-U-N-S 92-641-6934 IMP/EXP
COMMUNICATIONS & POWER INDUSTRIES LLC
CPI
(*Suby of* CPI INTERNATIONAL INC) ★
607 Hansen Way, Palo Alto, CA 94304-1015
Tel (650) 846-2900 *Founded/Ownrshp* 2010
Sales 405.7MM[E] *EMP* 1,600
SIC 3671 3679 3699 3663 Vacuum tubes; Microwave components; Power supplies, all types: static; Electrical equipment & supplies; Radio & TV communications equipment
CEO: O Joseph Caldarelli
**Pr:* Robert A Fickett
**CFO:* Joel A Littman
**VP:* John Beighley
**VP:* Don C Coleman
**Prin:* Andrew Tafler
Genl Mgr: Leeann Bautista
Genl Mgr: Thomas Cox
Info Man: Dave Morin
Mktg Mgr: Robin Stewart
Sales Asso: Tony Johns

D-U-N-S 83-555-3181
COMMUNICATIONS CORP OF AMERICA
KVEO TV
700 John St Ste 300, Lafayette, LA 70501
Tel (337) 237-1142 *Founded/Ownrshp* 1995
Sales 104.4MM[E] *EMP* 345
SIC 4832 4833 Television broadcasting stations
CEO: Thomas R Galloway
**VP:* D Wayne Elmore
VP: Tim Lynch
VP: Clark White

D-U-N-S 09-361-0905 EXP
■ **COMMUNICATIONS SUPPLY CORP**
C S C
(*Suby of* WESCO DISTRIBUTION INC) ★
200 E Lies Rd, Carol Stream, IL 60188-9418
Tel (630) 221-6400 *Founded/Ownrshp* 2006
Sales 423.3MM[E] *EMP* 900[E]
SIC 4899 Data communication services
Pr: David Bemoras
**Treas:* Brian Begg
**Treas:* Samantha O'Donoghue
Ofcr: Nick Hall
**VP:* Daniel Brailer
VP: Paul Kopera
VP: Frank Laplante
Exec: Jodi Huber
Genl Mgr: John Donaldson
Genl Mgr: Matt Hartman
Off Mgr: Rebecca Moya

COMMUNICATIONS SYSTEM WEST
See L-3 COMMUNICATIONS CORP

D-U-N-S 05-273-3714 IMP
▲ **COMMUNICATIONS SYSTEMS INC** (MN)
CSI
10900 Red Circle Dr, Minnetonka, MN 55343-9106
Tel (952) 996-1674 *Founded/Ownrshp* 1969
Sales 107.6MM *EMP* 674[E]
Tkr Sym JCS *Exch* NGM
SIC 3661 3577 3663 8748 Telephones & telephone apparatus; Telephone station equipment & parts, wire; Telephone cords, jacks, adapters, etc.; Data conversion equipment, media-to-media: computer; Receiver-transmitter units (transceiver); Telecommunications consultant
CEO: Roger H D Lacey
**Ch Bd:* Curtis A Sampson
Pr: Scott Fluegge
Pr: Scott Otis
CFO: Mark D Fandrich
CFO: Mark Fandrich
Treas: Edwin C Freeman
Sr VP: George Wakileh
Board of Directors: Luella G Goldberg, Gerald D Pint, Richard A Primuth, Randall D Sampson

D-U-N-S 08-187-7326 IMP
COMMUNICATIONS TEST DESIGN INC
CTDI
1373 Enterprise Dr, West Chester, PA 19380-5959
Tel (610) 436-5203 *Founded/Ownrshp* 1975
Sales 634.9MM[E] *EMP* 3,750
SIC 7629 7378 5065 5999 Telecommunication equipment repair (except telephones); Computer maintenance & repair; Electronic parts & equipment; Telephone & communication equipment
CEO: Jerry Parsons
Ch Bd: Gerald J Parsons
Pr: Leo Parsons
CFO: Lawrence E Morgan
VP: G Joseph Bendinelli
VP: David W Burt
VP: W Paul Cardell
VP: Keith Kibler
VP: Diana Morgan
VP: Barry Young
Prgrm Mgr: Bill Anderson

D-U-N-S 06-927-3498
COMMUNICATIONS WORKERS OF AMERICA AFL-CIO CLC
CWA
501 3rd St Nw, Washington, DC 20001-2760
Tel (202) 434-1100 *Founded/Ownrshp* 1938
Sales 150.3MM *EMP* 510
Accts Calibre Cpa Group Pllc Bethes
SIC 8631 Labor union
Pr: Christopher Schelton
Pr: Asplen Lauren
**Sec:* Annie Hill
VP: Irene Robles
Exec: Timothy Schick
Adm Dir: Susan Baxter-Fleming
IT Man: Rohit Debidin
Sales Exec: Morton Bahr

D-U-N-S 13-352-5308 IMP
■ **COMMUNISPACE CORP**
(*Suby of* DIVERSIFIED AGENCY SERVICES) ★
290 Congress St Fl 7, Boston, MA 02210-1005
Tel (617) 316-4000 *Founded/Ownrshp* 2011
Sales 125.3MM[E] *EMP* 400
SIC 4813
Pr: Diane Hessan
**CEO:* Charles Trevail
**CFO:* Gary Arena
**Ofcr:* Franco Bonadio
Ex VP: James Fieger
Sr VP: Cameron Logan
Sr VP: Julie Wittes
VP: Don Bell
VP: Tom Finocchio
VP: Tamara Glass
VP: Polly Macisaac
VP: Bob Preble
VP: Jonathan Stinnett
VP: Jessica Vlieger
Assoc Dir: Laura Chauncey
Assoc Dir: Ashley Wade
Assoc Dir: Shikha Warnick

D-U-N-S 07-671-3874
COMMUNITIES FOUNDATION OF TEXAS
5500 Caruth Haven Ln, Dallas, TX 75225-8146
Tel (214) 378-4500 *Founded/Ownrshp* 1953
Sales 133.5MM *EMP* 70
Accts Mcgladrey Llp Oklahoma City
SIC 8399 Fund raising organization, non-fee basis
Pr: Brent E Christopher
**COO:* George Tang
Bd of Dir: David Washburn
Trst: Charles J Wyly
Ofcr: Kim Fossey
**Sr VP:* Elizabeth W Bull
**VP:* J Michael Redfearn
**VP:* Kris Thomas
Comm Dir: Sylvia Martinez
**Ex Dir:* Jeverley R Cook
**Ex Dir:* John Fitzpatrick

D-U-N-S 96-209-2412
COMMUNITY & SOUTHERN BANK
3333 Rvrwood Pkwy Se # 350, Atlanta, GA 30339-3304
Tel (770) 832-3557 *Founded/Ownrshp* 2010
Sales NA *EMP* 600[E]
SIC 6022

D-U-N-S 07-688-6282
COMMUNITY AND ECONOMIC DEVELOPMENT ASSOCIATION OF COOK COUNTY INC
CEDA
567 W Lake St Ste 1200, Chicago, IL 60661-1405
Tel (312) 795-8844 *Founded/Ownrshp* 1966
Sales 134.3MM[E] *EMP* 500
Accts Crowe Horwath Llp Chicago Il
SIC 8748 Urban planning & consulting services; Economic consultant
Pr: Patricia Wilder
**COO:* Mark Enenbach
CFO: Joe Diamond
CFO: Glen Ofenloch
Treas: Ray Martino
Bd of Dir: Martha S Martinez
IT Man: John Nance
Pr Mgr: Kikanza Harris

D-U-N-S 05-521-7699 EXP
COMMUNITY ASPHALT CORP
9675 Nw 117th Ave Ste 108, Medley, FL 33178-1244
Tel (305) 884-9444 *Founded/Ownrshp* 2006
Sales 208.7MM *EMP* 640
Accts Deloitte & Touche Llp Miami
SIC 1611 2951 Highway & street paving contractor; Airport runway construction; Concrete, asphaltic (not from refineries)
CEO: Jose L Fernandez
**Pr:* John Morris
**CFO:* Agustin Arellano Jr
CFO: Martin Saitzyk
VP: Susana Herrera
VP: Vivian Marimon
Genl Mgr: Manny Aguiar
Off Mgr: Sandra Elizondo
Dir IT: Tina Laws
IT Man: Felipe Fernandez

D-U-N-S 60-769-4155
COMMUNITY BANCSHARES OF MISSISSIPPI INC
1255 W Government St, Brandon, MS 39042-3048
Tel (601) 825-4323 *Founded/Ownrshp* 1978
Sales NA *EMP* 400
SIC 6712 Bank holding companies
Ch Bd: Thomas W Colbert
V Ch: Nicholson Charles
V Ch: Wyman Jones
V Ch: Charles W Nicholson
**Pr:* Freddie Bagley
**CFO:* Tim Gray
**V Ch Bd:* George W Taylor Jr
Sr VP: Marshall Eleuterius
Sr VP: Honey Harris
**Sr VP:* William F Lehr
VP: Mike Cooper
VP: Steve Gibson

D-U-N-S 00-958-1273
COMMUNITY BANK (CA)
460 Serra Madre Villa Ave, Pasadena, CA 91107-2967
Tel (626) 577-1700 *Founded/Ownrshp* 1945
Sales NA *EMP* 300
SIC 6022 6029 State commercial banks; Commercial banks
CEO: David R Misch
**Ch Bd:* Alan Johnson
Ch Bd: Marshall V Laitsch
Pr: Alan Buckle
Pr: Enrique De Anda
Pr: Jeanna Threadgill
CFO: Nancy L Karlson
CFO: J Duncan Smith
Ofcr: Edda Bernal
Ofcr: Dely Briones
Ofcr: John McDiffett
Ex VP: Linda Betts
Ex VP: Robert Cassidy
Ex VP: John Getzelman
Ex VP: Debby Hart
Ex VP: Paul F Rodeno
Ex VP: Charles Rosen
Ex VP: Kent W Stevens
Sr VP: Jeff Boyer
Sr VP: Sean Foley
Sr VP: Mike Helmuth
Board of Directors: Matthew Denmark, Lyle Knight, Robert J Kushner, Craig H Stewart

D-U-N-S 00-697-6922
■ **COMMUNITY BANK N A**
CBNA
(*Suby of* COMMUNITY BANK SYSTEM INC) ★
5790 Widewaters Pkwy # 1, Syracuse, NY 13214-1850
Tel (315) 445-2282 *Founded/Ownrshp* 1984
Sales NA *EMP* 1,233
SIC 6021 National trust companies with deposits, commercial
COO: Mark E Tryniski
Pr: Deborah Desereaux
Pr: Gail Ramey
Ofcr: Vicki Weller
Trst Ofcr: John Jones
Ex VP: Brain Donahue
Sr VP: Bernadette R Barber
Sr VP: Richard Heidrick
Sr VP: Theresa Kalil-Lennon
Sr VP: Mary Turley
Sr VP: Paul Ward
Sr VP: Cindy Williams
Sr VP: Michael J Wilson
VP: Mark Ackerly
VP: Susan Fox
VP: Catherine Koebelin
VP: John Lanahan
VP: Joseph F Serbun
VP: James E Snook
VP: Barbara Snyder
VP: Craig Stevens

D-U-N-S 10-740-1044
▲ **COMMUNITY BANK SYSTEM INC**
5790 Widewaters Pkwy # 1, De Witt, NY 13214-1850
Tel (315) 445-2282 *Founded/Ownrshp* 1983
Sales NA *EMP* 2,340[E]
Tkr Sym CBU *Exch* NYS
SIC 6021 National commercial banks
Pr: Mark E Tryniski
**Ch Bd:* Nicholas A Dicerbo
Pr: Lorie Semmel
COO: Nancy Aiello
CFO: Scott Kingsley
Ch: Bernadette Barber
Ofcr: Brian D Donahue
Ofcr: Joseph Serbun
Ex VP: Barbara Call
Ex VP: Debra Davis
Ex VP: George J Getman
Sr VP: Timothy J Baker
VP: George J Burke
VP: Matthew Dougherty
VP: Charles Ertel
VP: Robert Frost
VP: Cindy Lefko
VP: Allison Mosher
VP: Joe Tomko
VP: Hal Wentworth
Exec: Debra Cormier
Board of Directors: Eric E Stickels, Brian R Ace, John F Whipple Jr, Mark J Bolus, Neil E Fesette, James A Gabriel, James W Gibson Jr, Michael R Kallet, Edward S Mucenski, John Parente, Sally A Steele

D-U-N-S 10-863-5970
COMMUNITY BANKSHARES INC
400 N Main St, Cornelia, GA 30531-2121
Tel (706) 778-3900 *Founded/Ownrshp* 1981
Sales NA *EMP* 574
SIC 6712 Bank holding companies
Pr: Edwin B Burr
**CFO:* Wesley A Dodd Jr
Ex VP: David H Gould Jr
**VP:* Jennifer Stapleton

D-U-N-S 94-917-6515
COMMUNITY BEHAVIORAL HEALTH
DBHIDS
801 Market St Ste 7000, Philadelphia, PA 19107-3158
Tel (215) 413-3100 *Founded/Ownrshp* 1994
Sales 802.8MM *EMP* 270
Accts Mitchell & Titus Llp Philadel
SIC 8322 Individual & family services
COO: Peter Bezrucik
CIO: Larry Finkel

COMMUNITY BLOOD CENTERS FLA
See ONEBLOOD INC

D-U-N-S 01-117-2157
COMMUNITY CARE BEHAVIORAL HEALTH ORGANIZATION
CCBHO
339 6th Ave Ste 1300, Pittsburgh, PA 15222-2507
Tel (412) 454-2120 *Founded/Ownrshp* 1996
Sales NA *EMP* 230
SIC 6324 Health maintenance organization (HMO), insurance only
CEO: James Gavin
IT Man: Gene Cecchetti

COMMUNITY CARE CENTER
See ALLIANCE COMMUNITY HOSPITAL

D-U-N-S 14-397-0205
COMMUNITY CARE CENTER OF GRENADA LLC
GRENADA LIVING CENTER
(*Suby of* COMMCARE CORP) ★
1950 Grandview Dr, Grenada, MS 38901-5066
Tel (662) 226-9554 *Founded/Ownrshp* 2004
Sales 603.4MM[E] *EMP* 4
SIC 8051 Skilled nursing care facilities
Exec: Bobbie Methvn

D-U-N-S 82-762-4623
COMMUNITY CARE CENTER OF WESTWOOD LLC
WESTWOOD MANOR NURSING AND REHABILITATION CENTER
(*Suby of* COMMCARE LOUISIANA) ★
1 Westwood Circel, Shreveport, LA 71109
Tel (318) 635-4444 *Founded/Ownrshp* 2008
Sales 422.9MM *EMP* 84[E]
SIC 8051 Skilled nursing care facilities

D-U-N-S 19-995-6269
COMMUNITY CARE CENTERS INC
312 Solley Dr Rear, Ballwin, MO 63021-5248
Tel (636) 394-3000 *Founded/Ownrshp* 1977
Sales 2.9MM *EMP* 1,000
SIC 8051 Skilled nursing care facilities
Pr: James Giardina
VP: Marilyn McDaniel

D-U-N-S 86-870-8223
COMMUNITY CARE HMO INC
218 W 6th St Ste 700, Tulsa, OK 74119-1014
Tel (918) 594-5200 *Founded/Ownrshp* 1993
Sales NA *EMP* 430
SIC 6324 Health maintenance organization (HMO), insurance only
Pr: Richard Todd
**Sr VP:* Earle Rice
VP: Jim Cage
VP: John Thomas
CIO: Valerie Hecht
QI Cn Mgr: Mary Brosseau
Psych: Steve Stewart

D-U-N-S 12-159-0152
COMMUNITY CARE INC
C C O
205 Bishops Way Ofc, Brookfield, WI 53005-6272
Tel (414) 385-6600 *Founded/Ownrshp* 1977
Sales 381.3MM *EMP* 1,100
Accts Mcgladrey Llp Madison Wi
SIC 8322 Social service center; Old age assistance
CEO: Kenneth Munson
V Ch: Robert Speer
Pr: Kirby Shoaf
COO: Alicia Modjeska
CFO: Lawrence Paplham
Ofcr: Edward Kohl
Assoc Dir: Rob McCommons
Prgrm Mgr: Karen Buono
Software D: Peter Devine
Software D: Rustem Sabitov

D-U-N-S 80-398-9800
COMMUNITY CARE ORGANIZATION
3220 W Vliet St, Milwaukee, WI 53208-2453
Tel (414) 231-4000 *Founded/Ownrshp* 2007
Sales 333.9MM *EMP* 9[E]
SIC 8011 Primary care medical clinic
Prin: Gloria Dohearty

D-U-N-S 17-433-5802
COMMUNITY CARE PHYSICIANS PC
711 Troy Schenectady Rd # 201, Latham, NY 12110-2482
Tel (518) 783-3110 *Founded/Ownrshp* 1984
Sales 80.4MM[E] *EMP* 1,000
SIC 8011 Offices & clinics of medical doctors
Pr: Shirish J Parikh
VP: Dr Rafael Verdile
Assoc Dir: Steven Schiher
IT Man: Mohammed Shahin
Mktg Mgr: Alexis Musto
Surgeon: Robert C Brasch
Surgeon: Peter E Fisk
Podiatrist: Aaron J Siebeneck
Doctor: Kyounghee Kim
Diag Rad: Lawrence Keating

D-U-N-S 10-928-3879
COMMUNITY CARE SYSTEMS INC
405 N Macarthur Blvd, Springfield, IL 62702-2312
Tel (217) 698-0200 *Founded/Ownrshp* 1980
Sales 54.7MM[E] *EMP* 2,400
SIC 8082 Visiting nurse service
Pr: William M Vala
**Pr:* Frank J Vala

D-U-N-S 17-650-1971 IMP
COMMUNITY CAREPARTNERS INC
CARE PARTNERS
68 Sweeten Creek Rd, Asheville, NC 28803-2318
Tel (828) 274-2400 *Founded/Ownrshp* 1996
Sales 37.8MM[E] *EMP* 1,200
SIC 8322 8093 Rehabilitation services; Specialty outpatient clinics
CEO: Tracy Buchanan
COO: Gary Bowers
CFO: Diann Bolick

D-U-N-S 96-862-8151
COMMUNITY CHOICE FINANCIAL INC
EASY MONEY
6785 Bobcat Way, Dublin, OH 43016-1408
Tel (614) 798-5900 *Founded/Ownrshp* 2011
Sales 527.3MM *EMP* 3,200[E]
Accts Rsm Us Llp Raleigh North Car
SIC 6799 Investors
CEO: William E Saunders Jr
Pr: Kyle Hanson
Ofcr: Lisa Vittorini
VP: Eric Austin
VP: Rob Grieser
Prin: Ted Saunders

COMMUNITY CLLEGE BLTIMORE CNTY
See COMMUNITY COLLEGE OF BALTIMORE COUNTY

COMMUNITY CNSLD SCHL DST 65
See EVANSTON CONSOLIDATED COMMUNITY SCHOOL DISTRICT 65

D-U-N-S 00-819-3575 IMP
COMMUNITY COFFEE CO LLC
(*Suby of* CCC HOLDING LLC) ★
3332 Partridge Ln Bldg A, Baton Rouge, LA 70809-2413
Tel (800) 688-0990 *Founded/Ownrshp* 1919
Sales 194.3MM[E] *EMP* 650
SIC 2095 Roasted coffee
CEO: David G Belanger
**CFO:* Antoinette Vaccaro
**Ch:* Mathew Saurage
**VP:* Michael Bourgeois
**VP:* Stephen Frantz
**VP:* Daniel Hebert
**VP:* Carl Leonard
Area Mgr: Timothy Berry
Area Mgr: Carlo Gioia
Area Mgr: Jeffery Mull
Area Mgr: Brian Smith
Board of Directors: William D Albers, Donald E Brunson, Michael A Flick, Francis I Mullin III

D-U-N-S 06-620-9610 IMP
COMMUNITY COLLEGE DISTRICT 502
COLLEGE OF DUPAGE
425 Fawell Blvd, Glen Ellyn, IL 60137-6708
Tel (630) 942-2800 *Founded/Ownrshp* 1967
Sales 118.1MM[E] *EMP* 2,470
SIC 8222 Community college
Pr: Robert L Breuder
**VP:* Thomas Glaser
VP: Jocelyn Harney
**VP:* Lynn Sapyta
Exec: Teri Jones

D-U-N-S 61-641-3332
COMMUNITY COLLEGE DISTRICT OF CENTRAL SW MO
OZARKS TECHNICAL CMNTY COLLEGE
1001 E Chestnut Expy, Springfield, MO 65802-3625
Tel (417) 447-7500 *Founded/Ownrshp* 1990
Sales 99.7MM *EMP* 900
Accts Kpm Cpas Pc Springfield Mis
SIC 8222 8221 Community college; Colleges universities & professional schools
Pr: Hall L Higdon
Bd of Dir: Rona Butrick
VP: Shirley Lawler
Store Mgr: David Hoffman
Pgrm Dir: Janet Sell

COMMUNITY COLLEGE DST 524
See MORAINE VALLEY COMMUNITY COLLEGE

COMMUNITY COLLEGE DST 528
See MCHENRY COUNTY COLLEGE

D-U-N-S 18-116-9400
COMMUNITY COLLEGE FOUNDATION
1901 Royal Oaks Dr # 100, Sacramento, CA 95815-4235
Tel (916) 418-5100 *Founded/Ownrshp* 1983
Sales 8.3MM *EMP* 1,287
Accts Grant Bennett Associates Sacr
SIC 8299 8748 Educational services; Business consulting
Pr: Richard Fowler
CFO: Rebecca Dirk
CFO: CA Sacramento
Bd of Dir: Marvin Williams
VP: Ira Ayers
Prin: Beck Edwards
**Prin:* Kirk Turner
Prgrm Mgr: Jamie Stedman
CIO: Gordon Dorff
Dir IT: James Roper

D-U-N-S 08-551-8686
COMMUNITY COLLEGE OF ALLEGHENY COUNTY
808 Ridge Ave, Pittsburgh, PA 15212-6003
Tel (412) 323-2323 *Founded/Ownrshp* 1966
Sales 43.4MM *EMP* 3,200
Accts Schneider Downs & Co Inc P
SIC 8222 Community college
Pr: Quintin B Bullock
Prgrm Mgr: Linda Raimondi
CTO: Elizabeth Zellmann
IT Man: Randy Lentz
HC Dir: Rhena McCaskill

D-U-N-S 96-556-5260
COMMUNITY COLLEGE OF BALTIMORE COUNTY
COMMUNITY CLLEGE BLTIMORE CNTY
7200 Sollers Point Rd, Baltimore, MD 21222-4649
Tel (443) 840-3620 *Founded/Ownrshp* 1998
Sales 71.8MM *EMP* 4,200[E]
Accts Clifton Larson Allen Llp Balt
SIC 8222 Community college
Pr: Sandra L Kurtinitis
VP: Christopher Herman
**VP:* Mellissa Hopp
**VP:* Robert G Kraft
**VP:* Rich Lilley
**VP:* Mark McColloch
**VP:* Kenneth Westary
Snr Ntwrk: Russell Rekoski
CTO: Ronald Hinkel
Dir IT: Susan Moylan
Info Man: Shawn Crosby

D-U-N-S 07-709-8770
COMMUNITY COLLEGE OF PHILADELPHIA FOUNDATION
1700 Spring Garden St, Philadelphia, PA 19130-3936
Tel (215) 751-8010 *Founded/Ownrshp* 1965
Sales 33.9MM *EMP* 1,500
Accts Grant Thornton Llp Philadelph
SIC 8221 College, except junior
Pr: Stephen M Curtis PHD
**VP:* Thomas R Hawk PHD
Comm Dir: Linda Wallace
Ex Dir: Matthew Bergheiser
Dir IT: Thomas Faucher

D-U-N-S 80-859-1200
COMMUNITY COLLEGE SYSTEM OF NEW HAMPSHIRE
26 College Dr, Concord, NH 03301-7407
Tel (603) 230-3500 *Founded/Ownrshp* 2007
Sales 46.9MM[E] *EMP* 1,800
SIC 8222 Community college; Technical institute
CEO: Kristyn Van Ostern
**CFO:* Kelly Chapman
CFO: David Lee
Ofcr: Julia Dower
Assoc VP: Larissa Baia
VP: Bruce Baker
VP: Alan Punches
Comm Dir: Shannon Reid
Dir IT: William Beyer
Netwrk Mgr: Keith Anderson

D-U-N-S 07-023-6195
COMMUNITY CONSOLIDATED SCHOOL DISTRICT 15 COOK COUNTY
PALATINE SCHOOL DISTRICT 15
580 N 1st Bank Dr, Palatine, IL 60067-8110
Tel (847) 963-3000 *Founded/Ownrshp* 1947
Sales 178.7MM *EMP* 2,080
Accts Miller Cooper & Co Ltd Dee
SIC 8211 Public elementary school; Public junior high school
MIS Dir: Tim Noomert
Dir IT: Amy Berry
Teacher Pr: Lisa Nuss
HC Dir: Susan Arndt

D-U-N-S 06-996-5127
COMMUNITY CONSOLIDATED SCHOOL DISTRICT 21
WHEELING SCHOOL DISTRICT 21
999 W Dundee Rd, Wheeling, IL 60090-3986
Tel (847) 520-2700 *Founded/Ownrshp* 1930
Sales 109.4MM *EMP* 1,000
Accts Evoy Kamschulte Jacobs & Co
SIC 8211 Public elementary & secondary schools
MIS Dir: Adam Denenberg
Pr Dir: Jason Klien
Teacher Pr: Denise Wheeler

D-U-N-S 01-029-5830
COMMUNITY CONSOLIDATED SCHOOL DISTRICT 59
2123 S Arlington Hts Rd, Arlington Heights, IL 60005-4105
Tel (847) 593-4300 *Founded/Ownrshp* 1900
Sales 108.6MM *EMP* 850
Accts Crowe Horwath Llp Oak Brook
SIC 8211 Public elementary & secondary schools; Public elementary school
VP: Janice Krinsky
Dir IT: Susan Ejma
Psych: Katie Grote

D-U-N-S 07-254-5882
COMMUNITY COORDINATED CARE FOR CHILDREN INC
3500 W Colonial Dr, Orlando, FL 32808-7902
Tel (407) 522-2252 *Founded/Ownrshp* 1973
Sales 90.3MM *EMP* 256
Accts Mcgladrey Llp Melbourne Fl
SIC 8322 Child guidance agency; Children's aid society
Ch: Jeremy Sloane
**Pr:* Colleen Gallagher
**Ch:* Scott Wall
**Treas:* Joseph Macau
**VP:* Patricia E Frank
**Prin:* Patrice Zahry

D-U-N-S 05-534-6837
COMMUNITY DAY CARE CENTER OF LAWRENCE INC
190 Hampshire St Ste 2, Lawrence, MA 01840-1251
Tel (978) 682-6628 *Founded/Ownrshp* 1970
Sales 87.0MM *EMP* 40[E]
Accts Alexander Aronson Finning & Co
SIC 8351 Group day care center
Pr: Sharon Thompson

D-U-N-S 18-376-1720
COMMUNITY DEVELOPMENT INSTITUTE HEAD START
10065 E Harvard Ave # 700, Denver, CO 80231-5915
Tel (720) 747-5100 *Founded/Ownrshp* 2000
Sales 150.5MM *EMP* 3,276[E]
Accts Harrington Group San Francisc
SIC 8351 Head start center, except in conjunction with school
Ex Dir: Mark Elliott
**CFO:* Trish Hershfeldt-Perry
**VP:* Janice Moore

D-U-N-S 00-868-1215
COMMUNITY EDUCATION CENTERS INC
CEC
35 Fairfield Pl, West Caldwell, NJ 07006-6206
Tel (973) 226-2900 *Founded/Ownrshp* 1996
Sales 339.6MM[E] *EMP* 3,234
SIC 8744 Correctional facility
CEO: James E Hyman
CFO: Kirsten Desilva
**CFO:* Michael Hellriegel
**Sr VP:* Michael L Caltabiano
**Sr VP:* Robert Mackey

D-U-N-S 19-837-7736
COMMUNITY ELDERCARE SERVICES LLC
2844 Traceland Dr, Tupelo, MS 38801-4200
Tel (662) 680-7300 *Founded/Ownrshp* 2000
Sales 1.1MMM[E] *EMP* 549
SIC 8741 Management services

D-U-N-S 05-056-0655
COMMUNITY FIRST MEDICAL CENTER
(*Suby of* RESURRECTION MEDICAL CENTER) ★
5645 W Addison St, Chicago, IL 60634-4403
Tel (773) 282-7000 *Founded/Ownrshp* 2013
Sales 99.7MM *EMP* 1,907[E]
SIC 8062 General medical & surgical hospitals
CEO: Sandra Bruce
CFO: Donna Diblik
Dir OR: Sherry Chillis
Pathlgst: Vickie K Rezai
Nrsg Dir: Emerita Burgess

D-U-N-S 12-357-7082 IMP
COMMUNITY FOOD BANK OF NEW JERSEY INC
CFBNJ
31 Evans Terminal, Hillside, NJ 07205-2406
Tel (908) 355-3663 *Founded/Ownrshp* 1982
Sales 96.9MM *EMP* 180
Accts Withum Smith & Brown Pc New
SIC 8322 Individual & family services
CEO: Kathleen Dichiara
Dir Vol: Maria Bocelle
**Ch Bd:* Richard Brody
**CFO:* Robert Barry
**Ch:* Alan C Levitan
**Treas:* Josh Weinreich
VP: Phyllis Dunlop
IT Man: Peter Burgdorff
Mktg Dir: Richard Uniacke
Pr Dir: Julia Kathan

D-U-N-S 06-066-0289
COMMUNITY FOUNDATION FOR GREATER ATLANTA INC
191 Peachtree St Ne # 1000, Atlanta, GA 30303-1741
Tel (404) 688-5525 *Founded/Ownrshp* 1951
Sales 122.8MM *EMP* 33
SIC 6732 Charitable trust management
Pr: Alicia Philipp
Mng Dir: Edward S Croft III

D-U-N-S 12-231-3133
COMMUNITY FOUNDATION FOR NATIONAL CAPITAL REGION
1201 15th St Nw Ste 420, Washington, DC 20005-2899
Tel (202) 263-4799 *Founded/Ownrshp* 1973
Sales 113.4MM *EMP* 30[E]
Accts Bdo Usa Llp Washington Dc
SIC 8699 Charitable organization
Pr: Terri Freeman
**CFO:* Mark Hansen

D-U-N-S 86-937-2904
COMMUNITY FOUNDATION OF GREATER MEMPHIS INC
1900 Union Ave, Memphis, TN 38104-4029
Tel (901) 728-4600 *Founded/Ownrshp* 1986
Sales 193.8MM *EMP* 15
Accts Rhea & Ivy Plc Memphis Tn
SIC 8399 Community action agency
Pr: Robert Fockler
CFO: Mack McCaul Jr
Ofcr: Susan Cooley
Ofcr: Ashley Harper
VP: Sutton Hayes
**VP:* Patti Smith
Mktg Dir: Julia McDonald

D-U-N-S 15-060-0849
COMMUNITY FOUNDATION OF NORTHWEST INDIANA INC
905 Ridge Rd, Munster, IN 46321-1773
Tel (219) 836-0130 *Founded/Ownrshp* 1985
Sales 108.8MM *EMP* 2,000[E]
SIC 8741 8062 Hospital management; General medical & surgical hospitals
Pr: Frankie Fesko
**Treas:* David E Wickland
Pharmcst: Bhavik Nana

D-U-N-S 03-306-3426
COMMUNITY FOUNDATION OF WYANDOTTE COUNTY (KS)
GREATER KANSAS CITY COMMUNITY
1055 Broadway Blvd # 150, Kansas City, MO 64105-1575
Tel (816) 842-0944 *Founded/Ownrshp* 2006
Sales 244.0MM *EMP* 2
SIC 8699 Personal interest organization
Ex Dir: Laura McKnight
COO: Patti Glass
Bd of Dir: Robert Pearson
Ofcr: Michele Gray
Sr VP: Katie Gray
Sr VP: Bill Marden
VP: George Bittner
VP: Gale Hoffman
VP: Janet Michealree
Ex Dir: Mayra Aguirre
Ex Dir: Robert Aschentrop

D-U-N-S 06-858-6432
COMMUNITY FUND OF UNITED JEWISH (CA)
JEWISH COMMUNITY FOUNDATION
4950 Murphy Canyon Rd # 100, San Diego, CA 92123-4900
Tel (858) 279-2740 *Founded/Ownrshp* 1999
Sales 113.3MM *EMP* 12
SIC 8699 8733 Charitable organization; Noncommercial research organizations
Ex Dir: Marjory Kaplan
**CFO:* Jeremy Pearl
Trst: Jeffrey Levine
Ofcr: Susan Knopman
Ofcr: Darren Schwartz
Ofcr: Kimberly Stahl
Assoc Dir: Melanie Gorelick

D-U-N-S 04-006-8405
COMMUNITY FUNDS INC
NEW YORK COMMUNITY TRUST
2 Park Ave Fl 24, New York, NY 10016-9301
Tel (212) 686-0010 *Founded/Ownrshp* 1955
Sales 284.1MM *EMP* 47
Accts Kpmg Llp
SIC 6732 Trusts: educational, religious, etc.
Ch Bd: Anne Sidamon Eristoff
**Pr:* Loria Slucsky
Ofcr: Shawn Morehead
**VP:* Joyce M Bove
VP: Carroll Wainwright Jr

D-U-N-S 11-185-5222
COMMUNITY HEALTH CHOICE INC
2636 S Loop W Ste 700, Houston, TX 77054-5630
Tel (713) 295-2200 *Founded/Ownrshp* 1996
Sales 721.0MM *EMP* 85
Accts Kpmg Llp Oklahoma City Ok
SIC 8062 General medical & surgical hospitals
CEO: Glenn Johnson
Sr VP: Ernest Mendez
VP: Fred Buckwold
VP: Alfonso Gang
VP: Mark Kline
VP: John Petrosino
VP: Alfonso Rubio
Off Mgr: Gabby Perez
Software D: Becky Cantu
QI Cn Mgr: June Liu
VP Mktg: Daisy Morales

D-U-N-S 15-450-7032
COMMUNITY HEALTH NETWORK FOUNDATION INC
7321 Shadeland Sta # 100, Indianapolis, IN 46256-3976
Tel (317) 621-1282 *Founded/Ownrshp* 1975
Sales 6.0MM *EMP* 1,649
Accts Caskey & Daily Pc Indianapoli
SIC 7389 Fund raising organizations
Pr: Joyce Irwin
**VP:* Barbara Coury
CIO: Ronald J Strachan
Sls&Mrk Ex: Pete Turner

D-U-N-S 07-206-8141
COMMUNITY HEALTH NETWORK INC
1500 N Ritter Ave, Indianapolis, IN 46219-3027
Tel (317) 355-1411 *Founded/Ownrshp* 1952
Sales 2.0MMM *EMP* 5,000
Accts Pricewaterhousecoopers Llp I
SIC 8062 General medical & surgical hospitals
Pr: Bryan Mills
Chf Path: Matthew D Carr
Chf OB: Kristina M Box
COO: Tony Javorka
**CFO:* Thomas Fischer
CFO: Joe Kessler
Bd of Dir: Karen Waninger
Ofcr: Jackie Smith
Ex VP: Suzanne Clifford
VP: Glenn Bingle
VP: Paige Dooley
VP: William Fisher
VP: Jack Frank
VP: Amy Glover
VP: Pamela Hunt
VP: Terry Layman
VP: Randall Lee
VP: Karen Lloyd
VP: Pam London
VP: Charles Meadows
VP: Anne Murphy

D-U-N-S 83-302-8561
COMMUNITY HEALTH NETWORK OF WASHINGTON
720 Olive Way Ste 300, Seattle, WA 98101-1830
Tel (206) 521-8833 *Founded/Ownrshp* 2009
Sales NA *EMP* 99
Accts Ernst & Young Us Llp Rosevill
SIC 6324 Hospital & medical service plans
CFO: Alan Lederman

D-U-N-S 03-011-6748
COMMUNITY HEALTH PARTNERS REGIONAL FOUNDATION
(*Suby of* MERCY HEALTH) ★
3700 Kolbe Rd, Lorain, OH 44053-1611
Tel (440) 960-4000 *Founded/Ownrshp* 2001
Sales 4.4MM *EMP* 1,600
SIC 8062 General medical & surgical hospitals
Pr: Brian Lockwood
Chf Rad: Francis Kearney
Dir Case M: Lynn Beres
**Prin:* Heather Nickum
**Prin:* Everett Taylor

D-U-N-S 83-054-2192
COMMUNITY HEALTH PARTNERS REGIONAL HEALTH SYSTEM
3700 Kolbe Rd, Lorain, OH 44053-1611
Tel (440) 960-4000 *Founded/Ownrshp* 2008
Sales 31.6MM *EMP* 2,000
SIC 8062

D-U-N-S 96-447-3297
COMMUNITY HEALTH PARTNERS REGIONAL MEDICAL CENTER
(*Suby of* MERCY HEALTH) ★
3700 Kolbe Rd, Lorain, OH 44053-1611
Tel (440) 960-4000 *Founded/Ownrshp* 2010
Sales 197.5MM *EMP* 2,200[E]
Accts Bkd Llp Cincinnati Oh
SIC 8011 Medical centers
Pr: Edwin M Oley
**CFO:* Cindy Dennison

D-U-N-S 92-701-5925
COMMUNITY HEALTH PLAN OF WASHINGTON
720 Olive Way Ste 300, Seattle, WA 98101-1830
Tel (206) 521-8833 *Founded/Ownrshp* 1996
Sales NA *EMP* 250
SIC 6324 Health maintenance organization (HMO), insurance only
CEO: Lance Hunsinger
COO: Mike Evans
CFO: Tim Frazier
**CFO:* Alan Leatheman
**Ch:* Peg Hopkins
**Treas:* Sheila Chilson
Sr VP: Christopher Ward
VP: Abie Castillo
VP: Alan Lederman
VP: Marilee McGuire
VP: Willem Tilstra
**VP:* Tom Trompeter
Exec: Deb Greer
Exec: Denise Page

Exec: Lindsay Scarey
Dir Rx: Rachel Koh
Dir Rx: Yusuf Rashid

COMMUNITY HEALTH SYSTEM
See COMMUNITY MEDICAL CENTER

COMMUNITY HEALTH SYSTEMS
See SPRINGS MEMORIAL HOSPITAL

D-U-N-S 13-757-2269
▲ COMMUNITY HEALTH SYSTEMS INC
4000 Meridian Blvd, Franklin, TN 37067-6325
Tel (615) 465-7000 *Founded/Ownrshp* 1985
Sales 22.5MMM *EMP* 137,000
Tkr Sym CYH *Exch* NYS
SIC 8062 8742 General medical & surgical hospitals; Hospital & health services consultant
Ch Bd: Wayne T Smith
Pr: John W McClellan
Pr: David L Miller
Pr: Lynn T Simon
CFO: W Larry Cash
Div Pres: Martin J Bonick
Div Pres: Robert O Horrar
Div Pres: Thomas D Miller
Div Pres: Michael T Portacci
Div Pres: P Paul Smith
Bd of Dir: Margaret Bass
Ofcr: Pamela T Rudisill
Ex VP: Tim L Hingtgen
Ex VP: Martin G Schweinhart
Ex VP: Rachel A Seifert
Sr VP: Kevin J Hammons
Sr VP: Manish Shah
VP: Dan Adkins
VP: Jai Agaram
VP: Jeff Aspacher
VP: Mark Barnhart
Board of Directors: John A Clerico, James S Ely III, John A Fry, William Norris Jennings, Julia B North, H Mitchell Watson Jr, H James Williams

D-U-N-S 02-921-2305
COMMUNITY HIGH SCHOOL DISTRICT 99
6301 Springside Ave, Downers Grove, IL 60516-2488
Tel (630) 795-7100 *Founded/Ownrshp* 1920
Sales 116.5MM *EMP* 545
Accts Miller Cooper & Co Ltd De
SIC 8211 Public elementary & secondary schools
CTO: David Jakes

COMMUNITY HOSP AT DOBBS FERRY
See ST JOHNS RIVERSIDE HOSPITAL DOBBS FERRY PAVILION

COMMUNITY HOSPICE N E FLORIDA
See HOSPICE TREASURE CHEST

D-U-N-S 17-111-9449
COMMUNITY HOSPICE OF NORTHEAST FLORIDA INC
4266 Sunbeam Rd Ste 100, Jacksonville, FL 32257-2426
Tel (904) 268-5200 *Founded/Ownrshp* 1978
Sales 95.2MM *EMP* 700^E
SIC 8082 8051 Home health care services; Skilled nursing care facilities
Pr: Susan P Stansel
Sr VP: Sherry Hogan
Sr VP: John Lyerly
VP Bus Dev: John McIlvaine
Prgrm Mgr: Sue Bisesi
CIO: William Bickford
IT Man: Terri Turner

COMMUNITY HOSPITAL
See MUNSTER MEDICAL RESEARCH FOUNDATION INC

COMMUNITY HOSPITAL
See NEW PORT RICHEY HOSPITAL INC

D-U-N-S 06-439-4869
COMMUNITY HOSPITAL
901 Macarthur Blvd, Munster, IN 46321-2959
Tel (219) 836-1600 *Founded/Ownrshp* 1973
Sales 131.0M *EMP* 2,000^E
Accts Mcmahon & Associates Cpas Pc
SIC 8062 General medical & surgical hospitals
Pr: Daisy Merich
Ofcr: Nancy Lund
**VP:* Gayle Parr

COMMUNITY HOSPITAL ANDERSON
See COMMUNITY HOSPITAL OF ANDERSON AND MADISON COUNTY INC

D-U-N-S 12-137-7139
COMMUNITY HOSPITAL FOUNDATION INC
23625 Holman Hwy, Monterey, CA 93940-5902
Tel (831) 625-4830 *Founded/Ownrshp* 1955
Sales 200.0MM *EMP* 2,003
Accts Moss Adams Llp San Francisco
SIC 8741 Hospital management
Pr: Steven Packer MD
Chf OB: William C Vogelpohl
**VP:* Terril Lowe
**VP:* Tim Nylen
**VP:* Cynthia Peck
**VP:* Laura Zehm
Dir Lab: Seth Bothwell
Orthpdst: Peter G Erbino
Pathlgst: Hugh E Wilson
Surgeon: David Morwood
Doctor: George H Penn MD

D-U-N-S 06-867-8721
COMMUNITY HOSPITAL GROUP INC
JFK MEDICAL CENTER
(*Suby of* JFK MEDICAL CENTER) ★
98 James St Ste 400, Edison, NJ 08820-3902
Tel (732) 321-7000 *Founded/Ownrshp* 1997
Sales 467.9MM *EMP* 3,000
Accts Baker Tilly
SIC 8062 8069 General medical & surgical hospitals; Specialty hospitals, except psychiatric
Pr: John P McGee
**Treas:* Robert J Mc Kenna
**Ex VP:* Louis P Amato
VP: Shirley Higgins
Dir Risk M: Norma Bustos
Board of Directors: Steven Weiss

D-U-N-S 05-429-0577
COMMUNITY HOSPITAL LLC (OK)
3100 Sw 89th St, Oklahoma City, OK 73159-7900
Tel (405) 602-8100 *Founded/Ownrshp* 1999
Sales 100.8MM *EMP* 500^E
SIC 8062 General medical & surgical hospitals
CEO: Brian Clenens
**COO:* Debbie Kearns Rn
**CFO:* Steve Taylor
Doctor: Dennis Foster

D-U-N-S 05-520-5298
COMMUNITY HOSPITAL OF ANDERSON AND MADISON COUNTY INC
COMMUNITY HOSPITAL ANDERSON
(*Suby of* COMMUNITY HEALTH NETWORK INC) ★
1515 N Madison Ave, Anderson, IN 46011-3453
Tel (765) 298-4242 *Founded/Ownrshp* 1961
Sales 167.5MM *EMP* 1,250
SIC 8062 8011 General medical & surgical hospitals; Offices & clinics of medical doctors
CEO: Beth Tharp
Chf Rad: Roger E Brockman
**Pr:* Dennis Carroll
**VP:* Dana Stuart
Doctor: Andrew Archual
Pgrm Dir: Meryem Cole
Pgrm Dir: Cindy Swisher

D-U-N-S 07-629-8371
COMMUNITY HOSPITAL OF MONTEREY PENINSULA
(*Suby of* COMMUNITY HOSPITAL FOUNDATION INC) ★
23625 Holman Hwy, Monterey, CA 93940-5902
Tel (831) 624-5311 *Founded/Ownrshp* 1928
Sales 560.7MM *EMP* 1,947
SIC 8069 8011 Geriatric hospital; Hematologist
Pr: Steven J Packer
**CFO:* Laura Zehm
Treas: George W Couch
Ofcr: Ronald Gaasch
**VP:* Steven X Cabrales
**VP:* Terrill Lowe
**VP:* Tim Nylen
**VP:* Cynthia Peck
Admn Mgr: Mary Chapman
Sls Mgr: Susan Ulrich
Opthamlgy: Asit S Pruthi

D-U-N-S 03-797-3760
COMMUNITY HOSPITAL OF NEW PORT RICHEY
5637 Marine Pkwy, New Port Richey, FL 34652-4316
Tel (727) 845-9127 *Founded/Ownrshp* 1997
Sales 129.7MM *EMP* 8
SIC 8062 General medical & surgical hospitals
Sr VP: John M Steele

D-U-N-S 07-360-8713
COMMUNITY HOSPITAL OF SAN BERNARDINO
(*Suby of* DIGNITY HEALTH) ★
1805 Medical Center Dr, San Bernardino, CA 92411-1217
Tel (909) 887-6333 *Founded/Ownrshp* 1976
Sales 185.4MM *EMP* 1,400
Accts Kpmg Llp San Francisco Ca
SIC 8062 Hospital, affiliated with AMA residency
Pr: June Collisone
**CFO:* Ed Sorenson
VP: Kimiko Ford
Exec: Dave Evans
Exec: Denice Findlay
IT Man: Sharon Kerns
IT Man: Redden Robert

D-U-N-S 96-187-9520
COMMUNITY HOSPITALS OF CENTRAL CALIFORNIA
COMMUNITY REGIONAL MEDICAL CEN
2823 Fresno St, Fresno, CA 93721-1324
Tel (559) 459-6000 *Founded/Ownrshp* 1982
Sales 127.4MM *EMP* 6,000
SIC 8069 Specialty hospitals, except psychiatric
Pr: Tim Joslin
IT Man: Sarah Rowe
Doctor: Dalpinder Sandhu
Nrsg Dir: Richard Brescione

D-U-N-S 06-203-4323
COMMUNITY INTERVENTION SERVICES INC
500 Boylston St Ste 1350, Boston, MA 02116-3791
Tel (617) 262-8455 *Founded/Ownrshp* 2012
Sales 104.1MM^E *EMP* 3,003^E
SIC 6719 Investment holding companies, except banks
CEO: Kevin Sheehan
CFO: Russell Allen
Chf Cred: Ed Neuhaus

D-U-N-S 06-850-9111
COMMUNITY LIVING ALLIANCE INC
1414 Macarthur Rd, Madison, WI 53714-1318
Tel (608) 242-8335 *Founded/Ownrshp* 1995
Sales 15.2MM *EMP* 1,000
Accts Rsm Mcgladrey Inc Madison
SIC 8322 Social services for the handicapped
CFO: Owen McCusker
**COO:* Todd Costello
**CFO:* Linda Daldowin
CFO: Jo Treslley

D-U-N-S 80-792-8122
COMMUNITY LIVING SERVICES INC
35425 W Michigan Ave # 1, Wayne, MI 48184-1600
Tel (734) 467-7600 *Founded/Ownrshp* 1992
Sales 132.6MM *EMP* 240
Accts Hungerford & Co Southgate M
SIC 8322 Social services for the handicapped
Pr: James Dehem
**COO:* Paul Newman
**CFO:* William Yordy
**Ch:* Dohn Hoyle
Ex Dir: Jill Halevan

D-U-N-S 86-762-9446
COMMUNITY LOANS OF AMERICA INC
8601 Dunwoody Pl Ste 406, Atlanta, GA 30350-2550
Tel (770) 587-1901 *Founded/Ownrshp* 1994
Sales 265.0MM^E *EMP* 1,800
SIC 8741 Management services; Administrative management
Pr: Robert I Reich
**CFO:* Terry E Fields
VP: John Hannah
CIO: James Strickland
DP Exec: Robert Bowes
MIS Dir: Jim Flynn
IT Man: Paul Bryant

D-U-N-S 96-786-7917
COMMUNITY MEDICAL ASSOCIATES INC
224 E Broadway Fl 5, Louisville, KY 40202-2025
Tel (502) 588-9490 *Founded/Ownrshp* 2011
Sales 283.9MM *EMP* 4
Accts Crowe Horwath Llp Louisville
SIC 8011 Offices & clinics of medical doctors
Prin: Rita Flanagan

D-U-N-S 07-467-6560
COMMUNITY MEDICAL CENTER
COMMUNITY HEALTH SYSTEM
2823 Fresno St, Fresno, CA 93721-1324
Tel (559) 459-6000 *Founded/Ownrshp* 1945
Sales 1.4MMM^E *EMP* 6,200
SIC 8062 8011 8051 General medical & surgical hospitals; Ambulatory surgical center; Clinic, operated by physicians; Extended care facility
CEO: Tim A Joslin
Chf Rad: Terril Efird
V Ch: Gordon Webster Jr
COO: Jan Coon
COO: Mike McGinnis
COO: Patrick Rafferty
COO: Craig Wagoneer
CFO: Chris Castro
CFO: Tracy Kiritani
CFO: Joe Nowicki
CFO: Stephen Walter
Trst: Ralph P Garcia
Trst: Gene Kallsen
Trst: Michael Peterson
Trst: Laurie Primavera
Ofcr: Mary Contreras
Ofcr: Jamie Franklin
Ofcr: Debra Muscio
Sr VP: Ginny R Burdick
Sr VP: Jenny Burdick
Sr VP: Craig S Castro

D-U-N-S 07-755-4921
COMMUNITY MEDICAL CENTER INC
(*Suby of* SAINT BARNABAS HEALTH CARE SYS) ★
99 Route 37 W, Toms River, NJ 08755-6423
Tel (732) 557-8000 *Founded/Ownrshp* 1952
Sales 360.8MM *EMP* 2,500
SIC 8062 Hospital, affiliated with AMA residency
CFO: Mark Ostrander
Sys Mgr: Ryan Grim

COMMUNITY MEM HEALTHCENTER
See COMMUNITY MEMORIAL HEALTH CENTER PHYSICIAN-HOSPITAL ORGANIZATION LLC

D-U-N-S 07-474-1406
COMMUNITY MEMORIAL HEALTH CENTER PHYSICIAN-HOSPITAL ORGANIZATION LLC
COMMUNITY MEM HEALTHCENTER
125 Buena Vista Cir, South Hill, VA 23970-1431
Tel (434) 447-3151 *Founded/Ownrshp* 1950
Sales 86.0MM^E *EMP* 750^E
SIC 8062 8051

D-U-N-S 07-532-8450 IMP
COMMUNITY MEMORIAL HEALTH SYSTEM
COMMUNITY MEMORIAL HOSPITAL
147 N Brent St, Ventura, CA 93003-2809
Tel (805) 652-5011 *Founded/Ownrshp* 1933
Sales 353.7MM *EMP* 2,200
Accts Ernst & Young Us Llp Irvine
SIC 5912 Drug stores
Pr: Gary Wilde
Dir Recs: Mary Jane Greene
Dir Recs: Mary Greene
Dir Recs: Teresa Kohn
Pr: Steve Caryer
**COO:* Adam Thunell
CFO: Kimberly Ellison
CFO: Sharon McGowon
Bd of Dir: Fritz Huntsinger
Bd of Dir: Kathryne Weldon
Chf Mktg O: Denise Drury
VP: Cynthia Demotte
**VP:* David Glyar
Dir OR: Marilyn Harris
Dir Risk M: Sally Yungtum
Dir Rx: Gene Day
Dir Rx: Frank Dunst
Dir Rx: Gary Metelak

COMMUNITY MEMORIAL HOSPITAL
See COMMUNITY MEMORIAL HEALTH SYSTEM

D-U-N-S 05-410-3577
COMMUNITY MEMORIAL HOSPITAL OF MENOMONEE FALLS INC
W180n8085 Town Hall Rd, Menomonee Falls, WI 53051-3518
Tel (262) 251-1000 *Founded/Ownrshp* 1962
Sales 181.9MM *EMP* 1,500
Accts Kpmg Llp Columbus Oh
SIC 8062 General medical & surgical hospitals
CEO: Catherine A Jacobson
**Pr:* William Bester
CFO: Lisa Krause
**Treas:* Scott R Hawig
VP: Michael Unger
Dir OR: Bobbie Sanders
Telecom Ex: Robert Degrand
QA Dir: Kim Urbain
Mktg Dir: Kerry Freiberg
Obsttrcn: Gary R Valestin
Doctor: Michael Anderson

D-U-N-S 95-787-7459 IMP
COMMUNITY MEMORIAL HOSPITAL SAN BUENAVENTURA INC
PURCHASING DEPARTMENT
147 N Brent St, Ventura, CA 93003-2809
Tel (805) 652-5072 *Founded/Ownrshp* 1927
Sales 285.0MM *EMP* 99
SIC 8062 General medical & surgical hospitals
VP: David Glyar
VP: Adam Thunell
Ex Dir: Michael Bakst

D-U-N-S 93-269-5380
COMMUNITY MERCY FOUNDATION
(*Suby of* MERCY HEALTH) ★
1 S Limestone St Ste 700, Springfield, OH 45502-1249
Tel (937) 328-7000 *Founded/Ownrshp* 1950
Sales 3.2MM *EMP* 2,270
SIC 8641 Civic social & fraternal associations
Ch: James Roediger
**Pr:* Paul Hiltz Interim
**COO:* Gary A Hagens
Ofcr: Dr Don Johnson
**VP:* John Dempsey
**Ex Dir:* Kristy McCready

D-U-N-S 83-199-2636
COMMUNITY MERCY HEALTH PARTNERS
SPRINGFIELD REGIONAL MEDICAL C
100 Medical Center Dr, Springfield, OH 45504-2687
Tel (937) 523-6670 *Founded/Ownrshp* 1969
Sales 223.8MM *EMP* 1,600^E
SIC 8062 General medical & surgical hospitals
CEO: Paul Hiltz
COO: Gary A Hagens
CFO: John Dempsey
VP: Terry Boys
VP: Ron Connovich
VP: Katrina English
VP: Sherry Nelson
VP: Marianne Potina
VP: Terry Weinburger

COMMUNITY NEWSPAPER
See GATEHOUSE MEDIA MASSACHUSETTS I INC

D-U-N-S 96-852-9610 IMP
COMMUNITY NEWSPAPER HOLDINGS INC
445 Dexter Ave Ste 7000, Montgomery, AL 36104-3892
Tel (334) 293-5800 *Founded/Ownrshp* 1997
Sales 941.6MM^E *EMP* 5,686
SIC 2711 4833 Newspapers; Television broadcasting stations
Pr: Donna Barrett
**COO:* Keith Blevins
**CFO:* Lynn Pearson
Sr Cor Off: Dee Dennis
Ofcr: Judy Harris
**Ex VP:* Steve McPhaul
**Sr VP:* Jennifer Pustaver
VP: Brad Dennison
VP: William Ketter
VP: Amy Lee
Admn Mgr: Brett Wallace

D-U-N-S 08-864-2004
COMMUNITY NEWSPAPERS INC
2365 Prince Ave A, Athens, GA 30606-6003
Tel (706) 548-0010 *Founded/Ownrshp* 1989
Sales 88.8MM^E *EMP* 500
SIC 2752 Commercial printing, lithographic
Pr: Dink Nesmith
Pr: Eric Nesmith
**Ch:* Tom Wood
MIS Dir: Michelle Anderson
Dir IT: Michael McCarroll

D-U-N-S 80-602-8122
COMMUNITY OPTIONS INC
COMMUNITY OPTIONS OF NEW JERSE
16 Farber Rd, Princeton, NJ 08540-5913
Tel (609) 951-9900 *Founded/Ownrshp* 1989
Sales 92.1MM *EMP* 1,200
Accts Withum Smith Brown Pc Philade
SIC 8322 Social services for the handicapped
Pr: Robert P Stack
Ex Dir: Richard Brownlow
Ex Dir: Marilee Waterman
Prgrm Mgr: Kasatra Evans
Prgrm Mgr: Amanda Franklin
Dir IT: Aaron Gold
Web Dev: Reeta Hart

COMMUNITY OPTIONS OF NEW JERSE
See COMMUNITY OPTIONS INC

COMMUNITY PARTNERSHIP CENTER
See HOPE NETWORK

D-U-N-S 62-291-4422
COMMUNITY PARTNERSHIP FOR PREVENTION OF HOMELESSNESS INC
801 Pennsylvania Ave Se # 31, Washington, DC 20003-2167
Tel (202) 543-5298 *Founded/Ownrshp* 1989
Sales 96.3MM *EMP* 15
Accts Deleon & Stang Cpa S Gaithers
SIC 8322 Individual & family services
Ex Dir: Sue Marshall
Ex Dir: Vincent Keane

D-U-N-S 17-997-0660
COMMUNITY PHARMACY SERVICES
1822 Mulberry St, Scranton, PA 18510-2369
Tel (570) 969-8000 *Founded/Ownrshp* 1996
Sales 34.8MM^E *EMP* 1,800
SIC 8741 Hospital management
Pr: C R Hartman MD
VP: Barbara Bossi
VP: Joseph Fisne
VP: Dr Edward Margules

COMMUNITY PHYSICIAN GROUP
See CMC MISSOULA INC

D-U-N-S 78-746-2238
COMMUNITY PHYSICIANS OF INDIANA INC
7240 Shadeland Sta # 300, Indianapolis, IN 46256-3944
Tel (317) 621-7455 *Founded/Ownrshp* 2006
Sales 238.3MM *EMP* 28^E
Accts Caskey & Daily Pc Indianap
SIC 8011 Offices & clinics of medical doctors
Pr: Dave Shapiro

COMMUNITY PLYTHINGS RIFTON EQP
See COMMUNITY PRODUCTS LLC

D-U-N-S 01-644-8412 IMP
COMMUNITY PRODUCTS LLC
COMMUNITY PLYTHINGS RIFTON EQP
2032 Route 213 St, Rifton, NY 12471-7700
Tel (845) 658-8799 *Founded/Ownrshp* 1998
Sales 88.5MM *EMP* 250^E
SIC 3842 2511 3844 Orthopedic appliances; Children's wood furniture; Therapeutic X-ray apparatus & tubes
CEO: John Rhodes

D-U-N-S 14-903-2237
COMMUNITY PROVIDER OF ENRICHMENT SERVICES INC
CPES
4825 N Sabino Canyon Rd, Tucson, AZ 85750-6427
Tel (480) 516-0298 *Founded/Ownrshp* 1980
Sales 61.2MM^E *EMP* 1,500
SIC 8322 Social services for the handicapped; Child related social services
Pr: Roger Deshaias
**CFO:* Arnold Enoki
**VP:* Robert Bennetti
Assoc Dir: Cindy Gallon
Assoc Dir: Joyce Gatson
Assoc Dir: Beatrice Ortiz

D-U-N-S 60-857-4695
COMMUNITY PROVIDERS INC
75 Beekman St, Plattsburgh, NY 12901-1438
Tel (518) 561-2000 *Founded/Ownrshp* 1984
Sales 1.7M *EMP* 1,650
Accts Kpmg Llp
SIC 8062 8741 6512 General medical & surgical hospitals; Hospital management; Nursing & personal care facility management; Commercial & industrial building operation
Pr: Stephens Mundy
Ex Dir: David Chafetz
Doctor: Susan Brodeur

COMMUNITY REGIONAL MEDICAL CEN
See COMMUNITY HOSPITALS OF CENTRAL CALIFORNIA

COMMUNITY REXALL PHARMACY
See COMMUNITY SURGICAL SUPPLY OF TOMS RIVER INC

D-U-N-S 01-058-6111
COMMUNITY SERVICE OFFICE
WILKES UNIVERSITY
84 W South St, Wilkes Barre, PA 18766-0997
Tel (570) 408-5905 *Founded/Ownrshp* 2010
Sales 106.1MM *EMP* 1
Accts Kpmg Llp Mclean Va
SIC 8999 Services
Pr: Eugene S Farley

D-U-N-S 09-944-1420
COMMUNITY SERVICES GROUP INC
320 Highland Dr, Mountville, PA 17554-1232
Tel (717) 285-7121 *Founded/Ownrshp* 1972
Sales 80.7MM^E *EMP* 2,000
SIC 8093 8059 Mental health clinic, outpatient; Home for the mentally retarded, exc. skilled or intermediate
Pr: Susan C Blue
**CFO:* Jennifer Steigelman
**Treas:* William J McCuen
Doctor: Brian Condron
Pgrm Dir: Lisa Basci
Pgrm Dir: Leah Gillespie
Pgrm Dir: James Martin
Board of Directors: Dana Henning, Janice Lovegrove, Marilyn Olds

D-U-N-S 01-177-1664
COMMUNITY SURGICAL SUPPLY OF TOMS RIVER INC
COMMUNITY REXALL PHARMACY
1390 Rte 37 W, Toms River, NJ 08755-4924
Tel (732) 349-2990 *Founded/Ownrshp* 1962
Sales 185.4MM^E *EMP* 300
Accts Withum Smith & Brown Pc Red
SIC 5047 7352 5912 Surgical equipment & supplies; Medical equipment rental; Drug stores
Pr: Michael Fried
**Pr:* Jerrold Fried
**VP:* Howard Fried
**VP:* Joann Fried
IT Man: Gary Natter

D-U-N-S 10-382-8471
▲ COMMUNITY TRUST BANCORP INC
346 N Mayo Trl, Pikeville, KY 41501-1847
Tel (606) 432-1414 *Founded/Ownrshp* 1980
Sales NA *EMP* 984^E
Tkr Sym CTBI *Exch* NGS
SIC 6022 State commercial banks; State trust companies accepting deposits, commercial
Ch Bd: Jean R Hale
CFO: Kevin J Stumbo
Ex VP: James B Draughn
Ex VP: James J Gartner
Ex VP: Mark A Gooch
Ex VP: C Wayne Hancock
Ex VP: Steven E Jameson
Ex VP: D Andrew Jones
Ex VP: Larry W Jones
Ex VP: Richard W Newsom
Ex VP: Ricky D Sparkman
Ex VP: Andy D Waters
Board of Directors: Charles J Baird, Nick Carter, James E McGhee II, M Lynn Parrish, James R Ramsey, Anthony W St Charles

D-U-N-S 03-582-2535
■ COMMUNITY TRUST BANK
(*Suby of* COMMUNITY TRUST BANK INC) ★
155 Main St, Whitesburg, KY 41858-7314
Tel (606) 633-0161 *Founded/Ownrshp* 1947, 1987
Sales NA *EMP* 36
SIC 6022 6021 State trust companies accepting deposits, commercial; National commercial banks
CEO: Reed Caudill
Pr: Mark Gooch
Ofcr: Rick Stamper
Ex VP: Cary Davis
**VP:* James M Caudill Jr
Prin: Barry Caudill
Prin: Sheila Meade
Board of Directors: Herbert Caudill, Bill Joe Collier, Hoover Dawahare, Dexter Dixon

D-U-N-S 00-694-6156 IMP
■ COMMUNITY TRUST BANK INC
(*Suby of* COMMUNITY TRUST BANCORP INC) ★
346 N Mayo Trl, Pikeville, KY 41501-1847
Tel (606) 432-1414 *Founded/Ownrshp* 1903
Sales NA *EMP* 1,000
SIC 6021 National trust companies with deposits, commercial
Ch Bd: Jean Hale
COO: Jill Williams
Ex VP: James J Gartner
Ex VP: Kevin Stumbo
Sr VP: Steve Belcher
Sr VP: Roger Davis
Sr VP: Sandra Payne
**Sr VP:* Gary Young
VP: Terry L Spears
Board of Directors: J Mark Campbell

D-U-N-S 83-938-6299
COMMUNITY TRUST FINANCIAL CORP
1511 N Trenton St, Ruston, LA 71270-2327
Tel (318) 255-2222 *Founded/Ownrshp* 1991
Sales NA *EMP* 511
SIC 6712 Bank holding companies
Ch: John F Emory
**Pr:* Drake Mills
VP: James Jones

D-U-N-S 04-418-7656
COMMUNITY UNIT SCHOOL DISTRICT 200
CUSD 200
130 W Park Ave, Wheaton, IL 60189-6460
Tel (630) 682-2000 *Founded/Ownrshp* 1972
Sales 219.5MM *EMP* 1,600
Accts Miller Cooper & Co Ltd Dee
SIC 8211 Public elementary school; Public junior high school; Public senior high school
Treas: Maureen Zuburt
MIS Dir: Ed Ferry
MIS Dir: Rodney Mack

D-U-N-S 11-583-3840
COMMUNITY UNIT SCHOOL DISTRICT 205
BOARD OF EDUCATION
932 Harrison St, Galesburg, IL 61401-3057
Tel (309) 343-3623 *Founded/Ownrshp* 1946
Sales 34.7MM *EMP* 1,245
SIC 8211 8741 Public elementary school; Public junior high school; Public senior high school; Public special education school; Management services
**Treas:* Chris Brown
Dir IT: Rick Lawsha

D-U-N-S 07-459-1058
COMMUNITY UNIT SCHOOL DISTRICT 300
D300
2550 Harnish Dr, Carpentersville, IL 60110
Tel (847) 426-1300 *Founded/Ownrshp* 1948
Sales 133.2MM^E *EMP* 2,200
Accts Baker Tilly Virchow Krause Llp
SIC 8211 Public elementary & secondary schools; Public junior high school; Public senior high school
**Pr:* Anne Miller
**CFO:* Susan Harkin
Prin: Tammy Poole
Adm Dir: Scott Zeigler
Site Mgr: Ken Cameron
Schl Brd P: John Court

D-U-N-S 02-140-8435
COMMUNITY UNIT SCHOOL DISTRICT 303
201 S 7th St, Saint Charles, IL 60174-2664
Tel (630) 513-3030 *Founded/Ownrshp* 2001
Sales 213.3MM *EMP* 2,000
SIC 8211 Public elementary & secondary schools
Assoc Dir: Barbara Beyer
Comm Dir: John Lyday
Genl Mgr: Wendy Sedwick
DP Exec: Kim Van Sickle
Dir IT: Mark Poi
IT Man: Michelle Gupta
IT Man: George Limberis
IT Man: Kathy Pelinski
IT Man: John Reichling
Trfc Dir: Michelle Cook
Pr Dir: Jim Blaney

D-U-N-S 01-023-6727
COMMUNITY UNIT SCHOOL DISTRICT 95
LAKE ZURICH SCHOOL DISTRICT 95
400 S Old Rand Rd, Lake Zurich, IL 60047-2459
Tel (847) 438-2831 *Founded/Ownrshp* 1903
Sales 91.3MM *EMP* 800
Accts Eder Casella & Co Mchenry
SIC 8211 Public elementary school; Public junior high school; Public senior high school
Exec: Julia Becich
Prin: Dave Gardner
Prin: Mark Kuzniewski
Prin: Susan Zissman

D-U-N-S 05-500-1382
COMMUNITY UNITED METHODIST HOSPITAL INC
UNION COUNTY HOSPITAL
1305 N Elm St, Henderson, KY 42420-2783
Tel (270) 827-7700 *Founded/Ownrshp* 1948
Sales 161.3MM *EMP* 1,300
Accts Mcelroy Mitchell & Associates
SIC 8062 General medical & surgical hospitals
CEO: Bruce D Begley
Chf Rad: Anthony Perkins
Pr: Debbie Willett
CFO: David Massengale
VP: Ann Heavrin
Dir Lab: Rayanna Riley
CIO: Jamie Reid
CTO: Stephanie Jenkins
QA Dir: Marie White
Dir IT: Rich Johnson
Opers Mgr: Fahmi Ramin

D-U-N-S 07-713-6695 IMP
COMMUNITY WHOLESALE TIRE DIS INC
9124 Pershall Rd, Hazelwood, MO 63042-2821
Tel (314) 241-3737 *Founded/Ownrshp* 1964
Sales 90.9MM^E *EMP* 150
SIC 5014

D-U-N-S 03-069-3337
COMMUNITYAMERICA CREDIT UNION
YELLOW FINANCIAL CREDIT UNION
9777 Ridge Dr, Lenexa, KS 66219-9746
Tel (913) 905-7000 *Founded/Ownrshp* 1940
Sales NA *EMP* 370
SIC 6062 6163 State credit unions, not federally chartered; Loan brokers
CEO: Lisa Ginter
CFO: Dennis Baumgartner
Ofcr: Diane Steele
Ofcr: Pat Yokley
Sr VP: Carrie O'Connor
VP: Jennifer Boren
**Prin:* Katie Douglass
**Prin:* Todd Karnatz
**Prin:* Guy Russo
Brnch Mgr: Dana Gering
Brnch Mgr: Kat Hnatyshyn

D-U-N-S 19-661-0104
COMMUNITYBANK OF TEXAS NATIONAL ASSOCIATION
5999 Delaware St, Beaumont, TX 77706-7607
Tel (409) 861-7200 *Founded/Ownrshp* 2012
Sales NA *EMP* 60^E
SIC 6163 6029 6022 6021 Loan agents; Commercial banks; State commercial banks; National commercial banks
Prin: George Casseb
**CFO:* Donna Dillon
Sr Ex VP: Robert Pigott
Ex VP: George Simonton
Sr VP: Mike Mulloy
VP: Walter Wilkerson
Adm Dir: Heather Guidry

D-U-N-S 04-878-7886
COMMUNITYCARE MANAGED HEALTHCARE PLANS OF OKLAHOMA INC
218 W 6th St, Tulsa, OK 74119-1004
Tel (918) 594-5200 *Founded/Ownrshp* 1998
Sales NA *EMP* 423
SIC 6324 Health maintenance organization (HMO), insurance only
Pr: Richard Todd
COO: Keith Harvey
**CFO:* Earle Rice
**Ex VP:* Nancy Horstmann
VP: Jason Cuaderes
VP: Alexis Higginbotham
CIO: Lorenzo Marquez

D-U-N-S 84-923-9223
COMMUNITYONE BANCORP
1017 E Morehead St # 200, Charlotte, NC 28204-2865
Tel (336) 626-8300 *Founded/Ownrshp* 1984
Sales NA *EMP* 571^E
SIC 6021

D-U-N-S 00-892-3781
■ COMMUNITYONE BANK NATIONAL ASSOCIATION
(*Suby of* CAPITAL BANK CORP) ★
101 Sunset Ave, Asheboro, NC 27203-5607
Tel (336) 625-4012 *Founded/Ownrshp* 2016
Sales NA *EMP* 67^E
SIC 6712 6021 Bank holding companies; National commercial banks
Mng Dir: Joe Diggs
COO: Maggie Norris
CFO: David Neilsen
Chf Cred: Neil Machovec
Ofcr: Tanji Bradley
Ofcr: Roger Cleveland
Ofcr: Brad Day
Ofcr: Sue Hackney
Ofcr: Zeta Pittman
Ex VP: Debbie Auman
Ex VP: Terry Coffelt
Ex VP: Beth Desimone
Ex VP: Pam Frey
Ex VP: Greg Heaton
Ex VP: Rmark Hensley
Sr VP: Jim Derrickson
Sr VP: Kim Graham
Sr VP: Gaines Legare
Sr VP: Chuck Wingo
VP: David Barrows
VP: Myra Birt

D-U-N-S 94-378-8265
▲ COMMVAULT SYSTEMS INC
1 Commvault Way, Tinton Falls, NJ 07724-3096
Tel (732) 870-4000 *Founded/Ownrshp* 1988
Sales 595.1MM *EMP* 2,379
Tkr Sym CVLT *Exch* NGS
SIC 7373 7372 7376 Computer integrated systems design; Prepackaged software; Computer facilities management
Ch Bd: N Robert Hammer
**COO:* Alan G Bunte
CFO: Brian Carolan
Sr VP: Ron Miiller
VP: Robert Kaloustian
VP: Kevin Orr
CTO: Brian Brockway
Sys Mgr: Bheemesh Dwarampudi
Sales Exec: Jon Rahmani
Sls Dir: Tony Degeorge
Sls Dir: Todd Sommers
Board of Directors: Joseph F Eazor, Frank J Fanzilli Jr, Armando Geday, Keith Geeslin, F Robert Kurimsky, Daniel Pulver, Gary B Smith, David F Walker

COMP MED
See COMPREHENSIVE MEDICAL CARE AFFILIATES INC

D-U-N-S 17-486-3571
COMP-VIEW INC
COMPVIEW
10035 Sw Arctic Dr, Beaverton, OR 97005-4181
Tel (503) 641-8439 *Founded/Ownrshp* 1987
Sales 123.9MM^E *EMP* 129
SIC 5043 Projection apparatus, motion picture & slide
Pr: Scott Birdsall
Bd of Dir: Paul White
Chf Mktg O: Tami Zeidlhack
**Ex VP:* Mark Madison
Genl Mgr: Dave Ewing
Genl Mgr: Deb Foley
Genl Mgr: Denise Landcaster
Dir IT: Dennis Zeidlhack
QC Dir: Judy Carlson
Sales Asso: Kelli Hobson

D-U-N-S 03-247-1687 IMP
COMPANHIA SIDERURGICA NACIONAL LLC
C S N
(*Suby of* COMPANHIA SIDERURGICA NACIONAL.)
455 W Industrial Dr, Terre Haute, IN 47802-9266
Tel (812) 299-4157 *Founded/Ownrshp* 2001
Sales 121.7MM^E *EMP* 200
SIC 3316 3312 Cold-rolled strip or wire; Iron & steel: galvanized, pipes, plates, sheets, etc.
VP: Eneas Diniz
IT Man: Dennis Cooper
Sales Asso: Jeff Sommers

D-U-N-S 00-698-2292
COMPANION LIFE INSURANCE CO (NY)
(*Suby of* UNITED OF OMAHA LIFE INSURANCE CO) ★
888 Veterans Hwy Ste 515, Hauppauge, NY 11788-2934
Tel (866) 371-8905 *Founded/Ownrshp* 1949
Sales NA *EMP* 16
SIC 6311 Life insurance carriers
Ch Bd: Dan Neary
**Treas:* Fred C Boddy
**Sec:* Michael Huss

D-U-N-S 13-144-7294 IMP
■ COMPAQ COMPUTER CARIBBEAN INC
(*Suby of* HEWLETT PACKARD ENTERPRISE CO) ★
1 Calle Sonata 3, Guaynabo, PR 00969-3708
Tel (787) 781-0505 *Founded/Ownrshp* 2015
Sales 100.0MM^E *EMP* 60
SIC 5045 7378 Computers, peripherals & software; Computer & data processing equipment repair/maintenance
Pr: Abelardo Ruiz
Pr: Fernando Lopez Brito
Treas: Serafin Massol

D-U-N-S 07-875-9520
COMPAREX USA INC
COMPAXTON
(*Suby of* COMPAREX AG)
600 N Pearl St Ste 1960, Dallas, TX 75201-2868
Tel (972) 734-5223 *Founded/Ownrshp* 2012
Sales 98.4MM^E *EMP* 170
SIC 5045 7371 Computers, peripherals & software; Computer software; Software programming applications
CEO: John Havlick
**Dir Surg:* Bruce Altmann

COMPASS BANK
See BBVA COMPASS BANCSHARES INC

D-U-N-S 07-896-3279 IMP
COMPASS BANK
(*Suby of* BANCO BILBAO VIZCAYA ARGENTARIA SOCIEDAD ANONIMA)
15 20th St S Ste 100, Birmingham, AL 35233-2011
Tel (205) 297-1986 *Founded/Ownrshp* 2007
Sales NA *EMP* 10,851
SIC 6021 National commercial banks
Pr: D Paul Jones Jr
Pr: Kamal Ali
Pr: Harold Shults Jr
COO: Jeff David
COO: Cecilia Rodriguez
**CFO:* Garrett R Hegel
Bd of Dir: Eduardo Aguirre
Bd of Dir: Laurie C Cannon
Bd of Dir: Richard D Danford
Bd of Dir: Andrew F Giesen
Bd of Dir: W G Johnston
Bd of Dir: John C Myers
Bd of Dir: Sam H Nay
Bd of Dir: Leonard O Turner
Ofcr: Jose Luis Blanco
Ofcr: Javier Hern Ndez
Ofcr: Sue Ann Sansoucy
Ex VP: Joan R Baraba
Ex VP: James D Barri
Ex VP: George M Boltwood
Ex VP: Sandra E Cown

COMPASS CEMENTING SERVICES
See COMPASS WELL SERVICES LLC

D-U-N-S 82-885-3650 IMP/EXP
COMPASS CHEMICAL INTERNATIONAL LLC
(Suby of ITALMATCH CHEMICALS SPA)
5544 Oakdale Rd Se, Smyrna, GA 30082-5238
Tel (404) 696-6711 Founded/Ownrshp 2016
Sales 100.6MM^E EMP 62^E
SIC 5169 3589 Chemicals & allied products; Water treatment equipment, industrial
Pr: Daniel McCaul
Off Mgr: Arthur Dutton
Plnt Mgr: Jerry Putnam
Natl Sales: Daniel K McCaul
Sls Mgr: Ted Perez

D-U-N-S 79-429-2297
▲ **COMPASS DIVERSIFIED HOLDINGS**
61 Wilton Rd Ste 2, Westport, CT 06880-3121
Tel (203) 221-1703 Founded/Ownrshp 2005
Sales 805.3MM EMP 2,728^E
Tkr Sym CODI Exch NYS
SIC 6211 Investment firm, general brokerage
CEO: Alan B Offenberg
Ch Bd: C Sean Day
CFO: Ryan J Faulkingham
VP: Ryan Faulkingham
VP: Zach Sawtelle

D-U-N-S 82-517-0843
■ **COMPASS GROUP DIVERSIFIED HOLDINGS LLC**
(Suby of COMPASS DIVERSIFIED HOLDINGS) ★
60 One Wilton Rd Fl 2, Westport, CT 06880
Tel (203) 221-1703 Founded/Ownrshp 2005
Sales 738.0MM^E EMP 2,728
SIC 6726 Unit investment trusts
CEO: Alan B Offenberg
*Ch Bd: C Sean Day
*CFO: James J Bottiglieri
Board of Directors: Gordon M Burns, Harold S Edwards, D Eugene Ewing, Mark H Lazarus

D-U-N-S 16-916-3065
COMPASS GROUP INTERNATIONAL LLC
61 Wilton Rd Ste 2, Westport, CT 06880-3121
Tel (203) 221-1703 Founded/Ownrshp 1998
Sales 27.8MM^E EMP 1,950
SIC 7361 7363 Placement agencies; Labor resource services
Mng Pt: I Joseph Massoud

D-U-N-S 61-170-1327 IMP
COMPASS GROUP USA INC
EUREST DINING SERVICES
(Suby of COMPASS GROUP USA INVESTMENTS LLP) ★
2400 Yorkmont Rd, Charlotte, NC 28217-4511
Tel (704) 329-4000 Founded/Ownrshp 1929
Sales 5.1MMM^E EMP 140,000
SIC 5812 Contract food services
CEO: Tony McDonald
COO: Karl G Behrens
*CFO: George Mboya
CFO: Adrian Meredith
*Treas: Gary Z Zauf
Bd of Dir: Glenn Davenport
Ex VP: Barbara Johnston
Ex VP: Kurt Kimball
Ex VP: Amy Knepp
Sr VP: Bernard Brewster
Sr VP: Chris Kowalewski
VP: Palmer Brown
VP: Mike Deley
VP: Roland Falcon
VP: Ron Gastin
VP: Patti Girardi
VP: Doug Hensler
VP: Robert Kovacs
VP: Mark O'Callaghan
VP: Brett Warcola
Exec: Ruby Vera

D-U-N-S 13-303-6264 IMP/EXP
COMPASS GROUP USA INVESTMENTS LLP
(Suby of COMPASS GROUP HOLDINGS PUBLIC LIMITED COMPANY)
2400 Yorkmont Rd, Charlotte, NC 28217-4511
Tel (704) 328-4000 Founded/Ownrshp 1997
Sales 31.4MMM^E EMP 360,000
SIC 6726 Investment offices
COO: Gary Green
Pr: Tod Nissle
*CFO: Tom Androf
*Treas: Gary Zauf
Sr Cor Off: Vincent Berkeley
VP: Daniel Teeters
IT Man: Craig Ward
VP Mktg: Charles Halliburton

D-U-N-S 82-722-1698 IMP/EXP
COMPASS HEALTH BRANDS CORP
ROSCOE MEDICAL
6753 Engle Rd Ste A, Middleburg Heights, OH 44130-7935
Tel (800) 947-1728 Founded/Ownrshp 2014
Sales 87.0MM^E EMP 220
SIC 5047 Medical equipment & supplies
Pr: Paul Guth
*COO: Henry Lin
*CFO: Jim Hileman
VP: Mike Giesken
*VP: Tony West
*VP Mktg: Jeff Swain
*VP Sls: Ryan Moore

D-U-N-S 11-319-4211
COMPASS HEALTH INC
PATHWAYS CMNTY BHVRAL HLTHCARE
1800 Community, Clinton, MO 64735-8804
Tel (660) 885-8131 Founded/Ownrshp 1974
Sales 128.3MM EMP 550
Accts Bkd Llp Kansas City Missour
SIC 8011 8069 8093 8361 Psychiatric clinic; Substance abuse hospitals; Substance abuse clinics (outpatient); Residential care
Pr: Linda Grgurich
Dir Recs: Lisa M Webb
*CEO: Tim Swinfard
*CFO: Dave Turner
VP: Gloria Miller
Dir: Brian Martin
Off Mgr: Cindy Hill
CTO: Richard Colvert
Dir QC: Connie S Chappelle
VP Mktg: Shawn Schmidli
Doctor: Mehrunissa Ali

D-U-N-S 94-534-1097 IMP
COMPASS HEALTH INC
MISSION VIEW HEALTH CENTER
200 S 13th St Ste 208, Grover Beach, CA 93433-2263
Tel (805) 474-7010 Founded/Ownrshp 1986
Sales 20.0MM EMP 1,100
SIC 8059 Nursing home, except skilled & intermediate care facility
CEO: Darren Smith
*Pr: Mark Woolpert
CFO: Bill Gerish
IT Man: Scott Alexander
VP Opers: Angela Hopkins

D-U-N-S 86-109-1833
COMPASS HOLDINGS INC
(Suby of COMPASS GROUP USA INVESTMENTS LLP) ★
2400 Yorkmont Rd, Charlotte, NC 28217-4511
Tel (704) 328-4000 Founded/Ownrshp 1999
Sales 71.8MM^E EMP 117,000^E
SIC 5812 5962 Contract food services; Lunchrooms & cafeterias; Merchandising machine operators
Pr: Gary Green
CEO: Dennis Hogan
*Ex VP: Kurt Kimball
*Sr VP: Palmer Brown
VP: Adam Freed
*Co-Founder: Fedele Bauccio

D-U-N-S 11-894-0279 IMP/EXP
■ **COMPASS MINERALS AMERICA INC**
(Suby of COMPASS MINERALS INTERNATIONAL INC) ★
9900 W 109th St Ste 600, Overland Park, KS 66210-1436
Tel (913) 344-9100 Founded/Ownrshp 2001
Sales 146.0MM^E EMP 1,200
SIC 2899 1479 Salt; Rock salt mining
CEO: Angelo C Brisimitzakis
Treas: Carol Wood
Ofcr: Jerry Smith
*VP: Keith Clark
VP: Lloyd Davis
VP: Cherie Zielger
Exec: Cindy Collins
Mng Dir: Mike Runyon
IT Man: Lonnie Porter
Tech Mgr: Jim Blake
Plnt Mgr: Mike Adanis

D-U-N-S 84-920-7956 IMP/EXP
■ **COMPASS MINERALS GROUP INC**
(Suby of COMPASS MINERALS INTERNATIONAL INC) ★
9900 W 109th St Ste 600, Overland Park, KS 66210-1436
Tel (913) 344-9100 Founded/Ownrshp 2003
Sales 857.3MM EMP 180
SIC 2819 2899 Sodium compounds or salts, inorg., ex. refined sod. chloride; Salt
Pr: Angelo C Brisimitzakis
CFO: Rodney Underdown
Treas: Carol Wood
Bd of Dir: Robert Boyle
Sr VP: Steve Berger
Sr VP: Jack Leunig
Sr VP: Robert Miller
VP: Dennis Bergeson
VP: Ron Bryan
VP: David Goadby
VP: Victoria Heider
VP: Kevin Thimmesch
VP: Michael Zinke
Comm Man: Tara Hart

D-U-N-S 13-346-8996 IMP/EXP
▲ **COMPASS MINERALS INTERNATIONAL INC**
9900 W 109th St Ste 100, Overland Park, KS 66210-1436
Tel (913) 344-9200 Founded/Ownrshp 1993
Sales 1.1MMM EMP 1,984^E
Tkr Sym CMP Exch NYS
SIC 1474 2899 2819 Potash, soda & borate minerals; Salt; Potassium compounds or salts, except hydroxide or carbonate; Sodium compounds or salts, inorg., ex. refined sod. chloride; Sodium sulfate, glauber's salt, salt cake
Pr: Francis J Malecha
CFO: Matthew J Foulston
Treas: Carol Wood
Sr VP: Steven N Berger
Sr VP: David J Goadby
Sr VP: Jack C Leunig
Sr VP: Robert D Miller
Sr VP: Diana C Toman
Plnt Mgr: Dan Loebach
Ql Cn Mgr: Cameron Vincent
Sls Dir: Todd Kipper

D-U-N-S 12-372-0638
COMPASS WATER SOLUTIONS INC
15542 Mosher Ave, Tustin, CA 92780-6425
Tel (949) 222-5777 Founded/Ownrshp 2010
Sales 100.0MM EMP 80
SIC 3589 Water treatment equipment, industrial
CEO: Thomas Farshler
*CFO: Bill Tidmore

D-U-N-S 05-233-6755
COMPASS WELL SERVICES LLC
COMPASS CEMENTING SERVICES
4100 Intl Plz Ste 500, Fort Worth, TX 76109
Tel (817) 244-2555 Founded/Ownrshp 2010
Sales 193.7MM^E EMP 240^E
SIC 1389 1382 Cementing oil & gas well casings; Oil & gas exploration services
Ch: Colin F Raymond
*CFO: Tina Castillo
Snr Mgr: James Popham

D-U-N-S 07-443-6841
COMPASSION INTERNATIONAL INC
12290 Voyager Pkwy, Colorado Springs, CO 80921-3694
Tel (719) 487-7000 Founded/Ownrshp 1952
Sales 768.3MM EMP 2,002
Accts Kpmg Llp Denver Colorado
SIC 8399 Advocacy group
Pr: Santiago Mellado
Ch: Karen Wesolowski
Genl Mgr: Kenneth Morgan
IT Man: Andrew Wright
Software D: Roman Hammes
Snr Mgr: Robert Lane

D-U-N-S 14-188-3319
COMPASSIONATE CARE HOSPICE OF CENTRAL NEW JERSEY LLC
261 Connecticut Dr Ste 1, Burlington, NJ 08016-4177
Tel (609) 267-1178 Founded/Ownrshp 2005
Sales 67.0MM^E EMP 1,112^E
SIC 8082 Home health care services
CEO: Milton Heching
Dir Vol: James Chew
Dir Vol: Kim Urquhart
Pgrm Dir: Stacey Rowse

COMPAXTON
See COMPAREX USA INC

D-U-N-S 05-825-1703
COMPDENT OF GEORGIA INC
100 Mansell Ct E Ste 400, Roswell, GA 30076-4859
Tel (770) 998-8936 Founded/Ownrshp 1999
Sales NA EMP 1,000
SIC 6324 6311 Hospital & medical service plans; Dental insurance; Life insurance
Ch: David Klock
*Ch Bd: David R Klock
*CEO: Kirk Rothrock
*CFO: George Dunaway
*VP: Bruce A Mitchell
IT Man: Mark Owens

D-U-N-S 13-128-5335
■ **COMPELLENT TECHNOLOGIES INC**
DELL COMPELLENT
(Suby of DELL COMPUTER) ★
12982 Valley View Rd, Eden Prairie, MN 55344-3657
Tel (952) 294-3300 Founded/Ownrshp 2011
Sales 135.1MM^E EMP 387
SIC 3571 3695 Electronic computers; Computer software tape & disks: blank, rigid & floppy
CEO: Michael S Dell
*COO: John P Guider
COO: Andy Wigart
*CFO: John R Judd
Bd of Dir: David N Short
VP: Michael Beach
*VP: Brian P Bell
VP: Jack Rahner
Exec: Brad Spratt
Mng Dir: Craig N Stockdale
Snr Sftwr: Brian Forney
Board of Directors: Charles Beeler, Sherman L Black, Kevin L Roberg, R David Spreng, Sven A Wehrwein

D-U-N-S 80-958-6311
COMPETITOR GROUP INC
COMPETITOR MAGAZINE
(Suby of CALERA CAPITAL MANAGEMENT INC) ★
9477 Waples St Ste 150, San Diego, CA 92121-2937
Tel (858) 450-6510 Founded/Ownrshp 2012
Sales 105.9MM^E EMP 230^E
SIC 2721 7941 Magazines: publishing & printing; Sports promotion
CEO: David Abeles
*Pr: Scott Dickey
*COO: Steve Gintowt
*CFO: Barrett Garrison
*Chf Mktg O: Keith Kendrick
Sr VP: Tracy Sundlun

COMPETITOR MAGAZINE
See COMPETITOR GROUP INC

D-U-N-S 13-603-5537
COMPEX LEGAL SERVICES INC
325 Maple Ave, Torrance, CA 90503-2602
Tel (310) 782-1801 Founded/Ownrshp 1974
Sales 92.3MM^E EMP 400
SIC 8111 7338 7334 Specialized legal services; Secretarial & court reporting; Photocopying & duplicating services
CEO: Arvind Korde
*Ch: Nitin Mehta
*Sr VP: Anthony Bazurto
*VP: Humildad Pasimio
*VP: Rajesh Rangaswamy
Brnch Mgr: Charles Utz
Genl Mgr: Kimberly Martinez
Genl Mgr: Salvador H Zamora
IT Man: Merlyn Balingit
Software D: Sebastian Zites
Sftwr Eng: Jaspal S Sahdev

D-U-N-S 14-384-4673 IMP
■ **COMPLETE ENERGY SERVICES INC**
(Suby of COMPLETE PRODUCTION SERVICES INC) ★
1001 La St Ste 2900, Houston, TX 77002
Tel (713) 654-2200 Founded/Ownrshp 2003
Sales 212.5MM^E EMP 800
SIC 1382 Oil & gas exploration services
Pr: John D Schmitz
CFO: Mike Nippo
Area Mgr: Melvin Clay

D-U-N-S 04-932-0778 IMP
COMPLETE MILLWORK SERVICES INC
4909 Goni Rd Ste A, Carson City, NV 89706-0351
Tel (775) 246-0485 Founded/Ownrshp 1998
Sales 91.2MM^E EMP 200
SIC 5031 Millwork
CEO: John L Robertson
*Pr: David R Becher
*Treas: Tracy L Brantingham
Area Mgr: Danka Chappell
Snr PM: Joe Becher

D-U-N-S 03-293-1417 IMP/EXP
■ **COMPLETE PRODUCTION SERVICES INC**
(Suby of SUPERIOR ENERGY SERVICES INC) ★
1001 Louisiana St, Houston, TX 77002-5089
Tel (281) 372-2300 Founded/Ownrshp 2001, 2011
Sales 2.2MMM^E EMP 6,572
SIC 1389 1381 Oil field services; Drilling oil & gas wells
Pr: Joseph C Winkler
*Pr: Brian K Moore
*CFO: Jose A Bayardo
*VP: Ronald L Boyd
VP: Mary Jones
*VP: Jeff Kaufmann
*VP: James F Maroney
VP: Kenneth L Nibling
VP: Mark A Songer
*VP: Robert S Taylor
IT Man: Michael Roth

D-U-N-S 93-868-3927
COMPLETE PROTOTYPE SERVICES INC
C P S
44783 Morley Dr, Clinton Township, MI 48036-1357
Tel (586) 690-8897 Founded/Ownrshp 1995
Sales 92.2MM^E EMP 280
SIC 3543 3714 Industrial patterns; Motor vehicle body components & frame
Pr: Chris Michayluk
Ex Dir: Brian Davert
Prgrm Mgr: Ken Borkowski
Genl Mgr: Aaron Malinowski
Manager: Jay N Nelson

D-U-N-S 05-287-6401
COMPLETERX LTD
3100 S Gessner Rd Ste 640, Houston, TX 77063-3796
Tel (713) 355-1196 Founded/Ownrshp 1998
Sales 84.9MM EMP 380
Accts Bkd Llp Houston Tx
SIC 8742 Hospital & health services consultant
Genl Pt: Terry Andrus
Pt: Mark Stubbs
COO: Rick Burnett
Ofcr: Suzan Kucukarslan
Exec: Cristy Hall
Exec: Vickie Hatch
Sls Dir: Andy Emery
Sls Dir: Peter Snell
Mktg Mgr: Lauren Haire
Pharmcst: Kim Echols
Pharmcst: Shawn Mercer
Board of Directors: Desiree Halgreen

COMPLIANCEONLINE
See METRICSTREAM INC

D-U-N-S 13-188-6871
COMPMANAGEMENT INC
(Suby of SEDGWICK CMS HOLDINGS INC) ★
6377 Emerald Pkwy, Dublin, OH 43016-3272
Tel (614) 376-5300 Founded/Ownrshp 2006
Sales NA EMP 611
SIC 6411 Insurance agents, brokers & service
CEO: Stephen Brown
Pr: Cheryl Powers
*Pr: Jonathan Wagner
*Ex VP: Richard Kurth
*Sr VP: Daniel Sullivan
VP: Nicolas Principe
Rgnl Mgr: Nancy McDonald
Off Admin: Julie Eckenrode
Netwrk Eng: Stephen Elliott

D-U-N-S 01-295-0804
COMPONENT ASSEMBLY SYSTEMS INC
620 Fifth Ave Ste 1, Pelham, NY 10803-1240
Tel (212) 567-5737 Founded/Ownrshp 1964
Sales 166.2MM^E EMP 750
SIC 1751 1742 Carpentry work; Drywall; Acoustical & ceiling work
Ch Bd: H Lewis Rapaport
*Pr: Arthur Doerner
*CFO: Les Napach
*VP: John Marone
*VP: Fred Merrill
*VP: Paul Palowski
Genl Mgr: V Wyker
IT Man: Derrick Smith
Opers Mgr: Maryanne Carey

COMPONENT TECHNOLOGY
See CERTIFIED POWER INC

COMPORIUM COMMUNICATIONS
See COMPORIUM INC

D-U-N-S 00-986-2665
COMPORIUM INC (SC)
COMPORIUM COMMUNICATIONS
330 E Black St, Rock Hill, SC 29730-5377
Tel (803) 326-6011 Founded/Ownrshp 1894, 1912
Sales 232.0MM^E EMP 536
SIC 4813 Local telephone communications
CEO: Bryant G Barnes
*CFO: Kevin Cage
Ex VP: John Barnes
IT Man: Cathy Billingsley

COMPOSITE GROUP, THE
See HPC HOLDINGS LLC

COMPOSITES ONE
See GLS COMPOSITES DISTIBUTION CORP

D-U-N-S 07-154-8171 IMP/EXP
COMPOSITES ONE LLC
(Suby of COMPOSITES ONE) ★
85 W Algonquin Rd Ste 600, Arlington Heights, IL 60005-4421
Tel (847) 437-0200 Founded/Ownrshp 2012
Sales 514.7MM^E EMP 371
SIC 5162 Plastics materials & basic shapes
VP: Walt Beaver
VP: Dick Holland
VP: Judith Webster
Genl Mgr: Dwight Baker
Genl Mgr: Dave Forner

Genl Mgr: Joe Johnston
Sftwr Eng: Lisa Catalano
Opers Mgr: Damin Hall
Opers Mgr: Casey Solomon
Manager: Lisa Ewald
Manager: Sam Swenson

D-U-N-S 80-735-1403
COMPOSTELA FUND OF ROMAN CATHOLIC DIOCESE OF BROOKLYN NEW YORK
(*Suby of* ROMAN CATHOLIC DIOCESE OF BROOKLYN) ★
75 Greene Ave, Brooklyn, NY 11238-1003
Tel (718) 623-5231 *Founded/Ownrshp* 2008
Sales 122.6MM^E *EMP* 2,800^E
SIC 6722 Management investment, open-end
Prin: Neil Cawley
Ex Dir: Thomas F Flood

COMPREHENSIVE CLINICAL DEV
See CLINICAL RESEARCH ADVANTAGE INC

D-U-N-S 18-890-7240
COMPREHENSIVE HEALTH CARE OF OHIO INC
EMH REGIONAL HEALTHCARE SYSTEM
630 E River St, Elyria, OH 44035-5902
Tel (440) 329-7500 *Founded/Ownrshp* 1985
Sales 18.2MM *EMP* 1,712
Accts Ernst & Young Us Llp Pittsbur
SIC 8741 Hospital management
Pr: Donald Sheldon
VP: Jill Cooksey
VP: Fran Gardner
Dir Case M: Lori Dickson
Nurse Mgr: Anita Keathley
DP Exec: Jim Wilson
Tech Mgr: John Schneider
VP Opers: Don Miller
Ansthlgy: Kalva Reddy
Doctor: Ademola Abiose
Doctor: Richard Hausrod

D-U-N-S 07-841-1793
COMPREHENSIVE HEALTH HOLDINGS INC
8810 Astronaut Blvd, Cape Canaveral, FL 32920-4239
Tel (321) 783-2720 *Founded/Ownrshp* 2011
Sales 142.2MM *EMP* 1,400
SIC 8011 Occupational & industrial specialist, physician/surgeon
CEO: Morill M Hall Jr
* *Treas:* Jack Gray
* *VP:* Ned Cooper
* *VP:* Todd Hall
* *VP:* Gary Palmer
* *VP:* Stuart Clark Stu

D-U-N-S 62-128-8930
■ **COMPREHENSIVE HEALTH MANAGEMENT INC**
(*Suby of* WELLCARE HEALTH PLANS INC) ★
8735 Henderson Rd, Tampa, FL 33634-1143
Tel (813) 206-1033 *Founded/Ownrshp* 1998
Sales 98.4MM^E *EMP* 1,600
SIC 8741 Hospital management
Pr: Heath Schiesser
Pr: Tina McIntosh
* *CFO:* Andrew L Asher
Ex VP: Stuart Clark
VP: Todd Hall
Dir Bus: Tom Ryan
Snr Sftwr: David Stidham
Dir IT: Eileen Peitsch
Snr Mgr: Jared McKee

D-U-N-S 93-252-3962
COMPREHENSIVE LOGISTICS CO INC
4944 Belmont Ave Ste 202, Youngstown, OH 44505-1055
Tel (800) 734-0372 *Founded/Ownrshp* 1995
Sales 104.2MM *EMP* 700
Accts Cohen & Company Cpas Youngst
SIC 4225 4731 General warehousing; Customs clearance of freight
Ch Bd: Don Constantini
Chf Mktg O: Donald Rendulic
* *Ex VP:* Brad Constantini
VP: Rick Diefenderfer
VP: Steve Olender
Genl Mgr: Brian Hume
QC Dir: Jeff Peters
Site Mgr: Shawn Cowie
Opers Mgr: Carol Leversen
Ql Cn Mgr: Lisa Modispaugh

D-U-N-S 10-726-6660
COMPREHENSIVE MEDICAL CARE AFFILIATES INC
COMP MED
218 W 6th St 704, Tulsa, OK 74119-1004
Tel (918) 594-5202 *Founded/Ownrshp* 1982
Sales NA *EMP* 400
SIC 6324 Hospital & medical service plans
Pr: Richard Todd
* *Treas:* Earle Rice

D-U-N-S 01-093-1397
COMPREHENSIVE PHARMACY SERVICES LLC
(*Suby of* PPS HOLDINGS INC) ★
6409 N Quail Hollow Rd, Memphis, TN 38120-1414
Tel (901) 748-0470 *Founded/Ownrshp* 2000
Sales 88.9MM^E *EMP* 668
SIC 8742 8741 Management consulting services; Management services
CEO: Don Nickleson
Pr: Dave Bono
Pr: Melissa Cox
Pr: Mike Densmore
Pr: Glenn Etow
Pr: Marcia Gutfeld
Pr: Reid Toda
Pr: Marney Wilkerson
CFO: Sam Daniel
CFO: Brian Johnson
Ex VP: Gentry Hughes
Sr VP: Mark Miller
Sr VP: Jeffrey Quinlan
VP: Tracy Becker
VP: Larry Bridger
VP: Sherry O Dell
VP: Marvin Finnefrock
VP: Boscoe Godfrey
VP: Jeff Lackman
VP: Sherry Odell
VP: Rod Recor

D-U-N-S 01-032-5012 IMP
■ **COMPRESSCO INC**
(*Suby of* TETRA TECHNOLOGIES INC) ★
1313 Se 25th St, Oklahoma City, OK 73129-6433
Tel (405) 677-0221 *Founded/Ownrshp* 1993
Sales 86.2MM^E *EMP* 420^E
SIC 3533 Gas field machinery & equipment
Pr: Ronald Foster
COO: Larry Deutsch
* *CFO:* James Rounsavall
CFO: Ammie Winter
VP: L Affeld
* *VP:* Kevin Book
VP: Mark Corlee
* *VP:* Ted Garner
VP: Kenny Sylvester
* *VP:* Sheri Vanhooser
IT Man: Steve Everhart

D-U-N-S 05-946-8694
■ **COMPRESSOR SYSTEMS INC**
CSI
(*Suby of* CSI COMPRESSCO LP) ★
3809 S Fm 1788, Midland, TX 79706-2662
Tel (432) 563-1170 *Founded/Ownrshp* 2014
Sales 111.8MM^E *EMP* 518
SIC 7359 7699 3563 Propane equipment rental; Industrial equipment services; Air & gas compressors
CEO: Richard Folger
* *Pr:* Roy P Jacobs
* *Pr:* Timothy A Knox
* *Pr:* David Murdock
Treas: Craig Conder
VP: Mary Dunlap
VP: Murray D Hambrick
VP: Erich Hardaway
VP: Tim Knox
VP: Lloyd V Roberts
VP: Henry R Sheeran

COMPSEC
See COMPUTER SECURITY SOLUTIONS LLC

D-U-N-S 83-100-5848
COMPSERVICES INC
INDEPNDNCE HOSP INDEMNITY PLAN
(*Suby of* BLUE CROSS) ★
1717 Arch St Fl 45, Philadelphia, PA 19103-2835
Tel (215) 587-1829 *Founded/Ownrshp* 1997
Sales NA *EMP* 161
SIC 6321 Accident & health insurance
Pr: Donald J Liskay
* *VP:* Lee Herzer
* *VP:* Joseph Santore
Opers Mgr: Mark Morse

D-U-N-S 61-537-3128
COMPSOURCE MUTUAL INSURANCE CO
1901 N Walnut Ave, Oklahoma City, OK 73105-3295
Tel (405) 232-7663 *Founded/Ownrshp* 2006
Sales NA *EMP* 350^E
SIC 6331 Workers' compensation insurance
Pr: Jason Clark
CFO: Steve Hardin
Chf Inves: Donna Romberg
VP: Victor Carneiro
VP: Christa Elmore
VP: Mark Gruber
Software D: Kenny Rajiah
Sftwr Eng: Bob Hibbert
Snr Mgr: Stan Anderson
Board of Directors: Glen Clark, Jason Clark, Steve Compton, Linda Morgan, Debbie Willingham

D-U-N-S 77-993-5295
COMPSYCH EMPLOYEE ASSISTANCE PROGRAMS INC
455 N Ctyfrnt Plz Dr # 1300, Chicago, IL 60611-5377
Tel (312) 595-4000 *Founded/Ownrshp* 1990
Sales 98.4MM^E *EMP* 2,000
SIC 8742 Personnel management consultant
Ch Bd: Richard A Chaifetz
* *CFO:* Robert Jacobson
IT Exec: Matt Wood
CIO: Wendy Kiest
CIO: Julie Lemke

D-U-N-S 02-076-1227
COMPTON UNIFIED SCHOOL DISTRICT
501 S Santa Fe Ave, Compton, CA 90221-3814
Tel (310) 604-6508 *Founded/Ownrshp* 1970
Sales 138.0MM^E *EMP* 3,800
SIC 8211 Public elementary & secondary schools; High school, junior or senior; Public adult education school
Dir Sec: William Wu
Schl Brd P: Micah Ali
Teacher Pr: Bryon Syphion
HC Dir: Jacquelyn Arion

D-U-N-S 96-647-5055
COMPTROLLER OF MARYLAND OFFICE OF
(*Suby of* EXECUTIVE OFFICE OF STATE OF MARYLAND) ★
80 Calvert St L1, Annapolis, MD 21401-1907
Tel (410) 260-7801 *Founded/Ownrshp* 1966
Sales NA *EMP* 1,258
SIC 9311 Controllers' office, government;
Prin: Peter Franchot
* *Prin:* Linda Tanton

D-U-N-S 80-830-2327
COMPTROLLER OF PUBLIC ACCOUNTS TEXAS
(*Suby of* EXECUTIVE OFFICE OF STATE OF TEXAS) ★
111 E 17th St Rm 138, Austin, TX 78701
Tel (512) 763-8550 *Founded/Ownrshp* 1845
Sales NA *EMP* 31,000
Accts John Keel Cpa State Auditor
SIC 9311 Controllers' office, government;
Prin: Leonard Higgins
Genl Couns: Eva G Brooks
Genl Couns: Marcia Moore
Genl Couns: Sandra Sciarra

COMPTROLLER OF THE STATE OF NY
See NEW YORK STATE OFFICE OF STATE COMPTROLLER

COMPTROLLER'S OFFICE
See BOARD OF TRUSTEES OF ILLINOIS STATE UNIVERSITY

D-U-N-S 11-046-2835 IMP
COMPUCASE CORP
ORION TECH
16720 Chestnut St Ste C, City of Industry, CA 91748-1038
Tel (626) 336-6588 *Founded/Ownrshp* 1995
Sales 161.1MM^E *EMP* 1,500
SIC 3572 Computer storage devices
Pr: Doung Fu Hsu
* *Genl Mgr:* Aaron Tao

D-U-N-S 80-799-0333
COMPUCOM SYSTEMS HOLDING LLC
(*Suby of* THOMAS H LEE ADVISORS II LP) ★
7171 Forest Ln, Dallas, TX 75230-2306
Tel (972) 856-3600 *Founded/Ownrshp* 2013
Sales 3.3MMM^E *EMP* 11,005^E
SIC 7373 5045 7378 8748 Local area network (LAN) systems integrator; Computers, peripherals & software; Computers & accessories, personal & home entertainment; Computer software; Computer peripheral equipment; Computer maintenance & repair; Business consulting
COO: Jeffery E Frick
CFO: Michael W Simpson
Ch: James W Dixon
Treas: John Massey
Sr VP: William D Barry
Sr VP: David Hall
Sr VP: Richard Jorgensen
Sr VP: Michael Nolan
Sr VP: Kevin Shank
Sr VP: Timothy Shea
VP: Tiffany Brown
VP: Rick McDonough
VP: Diana Meacham
VP: Scott Ward
Dir Soc: Sandra Demler
Dir Soc: Melissa Ward

D-U-N-S 07-549-5903
COMPUCOM SYSTEMS INC
(*Suby of* COMPUCOM SYSTEMS HOLDING LLC) ★
8383 Dominion Pkwy, Plano, TX 75024-8512
Tel (972) 856-3600 *Founded/Ownrshp* 1981, 2013
Sales 3.3MMM^E *EMP* 11,000^E
SIC 7373 5045 7378 8748 Local area network (LAN) systems integrator; Computers, peripherals & software; Computers & accessories, personal & home entertainment; Computer software; Computer peripheral equipment; Computer maintenance & repair; Business consulting
CEO: Dan Stone
* *Pr:* James W Dixon
* *CEO:* Anthony Doye
CFO: Noah Asher
* *CFO:* Michael Simpson
Treas: Robert Joubran
Chf Mktg O: Jonathan K James
Sr VP: Jill Welch
VP: Dave Borgese
VP: Tiffany Brown
VP: Jim Carey
VP: Bill D'Onofrio
VP: Jason Davis
VP: Lisa Dewar
VP: Bridget Karlin
VP: John Laufenberg
VP: Mark Loder
VP: Matthew Olson
VP: Romolo Pallini
VP: Dean Parsons
VP: Shawn Reddington
Board of Directors: Don Doctor

D-U-N-S 10-263-1199
COMPUDATA PRODUCTS INC
CPI OFFICE PRODUCTS
1301 Ridgeview Ste 100, Lewisville, TX 75057-6018
Tel (972) 280-0922 *Founded/Ownrshp* 1972
Sales 183.8MM^E *EMP* 165
SIC 5112 Data processing supplies; Business forms
CEO: Kenneth W Smith Sr
* *CFO:* Stephen Richman
* *Treas:* Wayne L Smith
Area Mgr: James Hightower

D-U-N-S 08-040-6202
COMPUGEN SYSTEMS INC
5847 San Felipe St # 1700, Houston, TX 77057-3000
Tel (713) 821-1739 *Founded/Ownrshp* 2014
Sales 600.0MM *EMP* 1,800
SIC 7379 Computer related consulting services
Pr: Harry Zarek

D-U-N-S 04-046-3739
COMPULINK CORP
1205 Gandy Blvd N, Saint Petersburg, FL 33702-2428
Tel (727) 579-1065 *Founded/Ownrshp* 1984
Sales 167.1MM^E *EMP* 591
SIC 3679 Electronic loads & power supplies
Pr: Stephen Shevlin
VP: Brian Mahoney
VP: Jeff V Van Horn Rcdd
* *VP:* Robert T Wilkin
Exec: Mary Bourque
MIS Dir: Greg Payne
IT Man: Marta McFeeture
VP Opers: Doug Franzese
Ql Cn Mgr: Brenda Hodges
Ql Cn Mgr: Phil Raymond
Natl Sales: Richard Goodridge

D-U-N-S 78-754-0269
COMPUNNEL SOFTWARE GROUP INC
103 Morgan Ln Ste 102, Plainsboro, NJ 08536-3300
Tel (609) 606-9010 *Founded/Ownrshp* 2007
Sales 108.1MM *EMP* 900^E
Accts Atul Malhotra & Co Llc Holm
SIC 7371 Computer software development & applications
CEO: Amit Gaur
* *Pr:* Sriraj Mallick
CFO: Himanshu Kumar
* *CFO:* Rakesh Shah
Ex VP: Karthik Natarajan
* *Ex VP:* Arun Prakash
Prgrm Mgr: Cara Black
VP Sls: Milind Naik
Sls Mgr: Nishant Sachdeva
Snr Mgr: Jovy Dias
Snr Mgr: Ashish Handa

D-U-N-S 07-942-0278
COMPUPAY HOLDINGS CORP
3450 Lakeside Dr Ste 400, Miramar, FL 33027-3273
Tel (469) 791-3300 *Founded/Ownrshp* 2003
Sales 93.0MM^E *EMP* 650^E
SIC 6719 Investment holding companies, except banks
CEO: Bernard Difiore

D-U-N-S 12-142-8098 EXP
■ **COMPUSA INC**
COMPUSA MANAGEMENT
(*Suby of* SYSTEMAX INC) ★
14951 Dallas Pkwy, Dallas, TX 75254-7892
Tel (972) 982-4000 *Founded/Ownrshp* 2008
Sales 95.2MM^E *EMP* 1,000
SIC 5734 5045 5961 Computer & software stores; Computer peripheral equipment; Computer software & accessories; Computers, peripherals & software; Computer peripheral equipment; Computer software; Computers & accessories, personal & home entertainment; Computers & peripheral equipment, mail order; Computer software, mail order
Int Pr: Bill Weinstein
COO: Peter Hanelt
VP: Richard Levine
VP: Hans Reller
VP: Robert Seay
Genl Mgr: Philip Benton
Genl Mgr: Randy Sergeant
Store Mgr: Rodolfo Bottinelli
Store Mgr: Vincent Cabral
Store Mgr: Jason McEwen
Store Mgr: Howard Orloff

COMPUSA MANAGEMENT
See COMPUSA INC

D-U-N-S 13-027-2206
■ **COMPUTATIONAL SYSTEMS INC**
(*Suby of* EMERSON ELECTRIC CO) ★
8000 W Florissant Ave, Saint Louis, MO 63136-1414
Tel (314) 553-2000 *Founded/Ownrshp* 1997
Sales 280.6MM^E *EMP* 1,200
SIC 3829 Vibration meters, analyzers & calibrators; Stress, strain & flaw detecting/measuring equipment
Mng Pt: Brian Humes
* *Pt:* John Berra
Chf Mktg O: Don Marshall
VP: Augustine Digiovanni
VP: Robert Walker
Sls Mgr: Rob Holdenried

D-U-N-S 07-372-7919
COMPUTER AID INC
CAI
1390 Ridgeview Dr Ste 300, Allentown, PA 18104-9065
Tel (610) 530-5000 *Founded/Ownrshp* 1981
Sales 449.9MM^E *EMP* 1,340
SIC 7371 Custom computer programming services
CEO: Anthony J Salvaggio
* *Pr:* Thomas Salvaggio
* *CFO:* Andrew McIntyre
Admn Mgr: Eugne Clater
Brnch Mgr: Kevin Kuros
Genl Mgr: David F Broderick
Genl Mgr: Jim Phillips
IT Man: Fran Lesusky
Mktg Mgr: Paul Smith
Sls Mgr: Raed Alsarhan
Sls Mgr: Tom Berry

COMPUTER COMPANY, THE
See MAGELLAN MEDICAID ADMINISTRATION INC

D-U-N-S 18-116-2546
COMPUTER CONSULTING OPERATIONS SPECIALISTS INC
600 Corporate Pointe # 1010, Culver City, CA 90230-7677
Tel (310) 568-5000 *Founded/Ownrshp* 1985
Sales 183.4MM^E *EMP* 2,000
SIC 4813 4899 5045 7378 Telephone communication, except radio; Data communication services; Computers, peripherals & software; Computer maintenance & repair
Pr: Brian Hardy
* *VP:* Shirley Franklin

D-U-N-S 13-134-4673
COMPUTER GENERATED SOLUTIONS INC
C G S
200 Vesey St Fl 27, New York, NY 10281-1017
Tel (212) 408-3800 *Founded/Ownrshp* 1984
Sales 478.8MM^E *EMP* 5,000
Accts Mcgladrey New York Ny
SIC 7373 7379 7371 8243 Computer integrated systems design; Systems software development services; Systems integration services; Value-added resellers, computer systems; Computer related consulting services; Computer software development; Software training, computer
Pr: Phil Friedman
* *Pr:* Paul Magel
* *CFO:* Edward Galati
Sr VP: Nicolas Kokaly
Sr VP: Micheal Millis
* *Sr VP:* John Samuel
Sr VP: Dough Stephen
VP: Jim Falino
VP: Peter Kalotschke

VP: Kelly Stacey
VP: Jeffrey White

D-U-N-S 05-355-4382
COMPUTER HORIZONS CORP
2001 Us Highway 46 # 310, Parsippany, NJ 07054-1315
Tel (973) 257-5030 *Founded/Ownrshp* 1969
Sales 146.2MM^E *EMP* 1,474
SIC 7373 Computer integrated systems design
Pr: Dennis J Conroy
**Ch Bd:* Eric Rosenfeld
CFO: Barbara Rodriguez
VP: Charles McCourt
VP: Dan Scrone

D-U-N-S 04-635-3892
COMPUTER MERCHANT LTD
TCM
95 Longwater Cir, Norwell, MA 02061-1635
Tel (781) 878-1070 *Founded/Ownrshp* 1979
Sales 107.0MM *EMP* 1,500
Accts Jameson & Company Llc Bedfor
SIC 7379 7371 Computer related consulting services; Computer software development & applications
Pr: John R Danieli
COO: William Allen
**Sec:* Cheryl Danieli
Ex VP: Edward Gregory
VP: Cheryle A Brady
VP: John Prestidge
Exec: Jarrod Desjardin
Mng Dir: Richard Kohler
Genl Mgr: Robert Retalic
CIO: Rusty Bruns
Mktg Mgr: Daniel Donovan

D-U-N-S 03-826-5989
▲ COMPUTER PROGRAMS AND SYSTEMS INC
CPSI
6600 Wall St, Mobile, AL 36695-4512
Tel (251) 639-8100 *Founded/Ownrshp* 1979
Sales 182.1MM *EMP* 1,960^E
Tkr Sym CPSI *Exch* NGS
SIC 7373 7371 Turnkey vendors, computer systems; Custom computer programming services
Pr: J Boyd Douglas
**Ch Bd:* David A Dye
CFO: Matt J Chambless
Ex VP: Victor S Schneider
Sr VP: Robert D Hinckle
Sr VP: Troy D Rosser
Sftwr Eng: Ildar Sadykov
Sls Dir: Richard Jones
Sls Mgr: Laura Grandquest
Board of Directors: Charles P Huffman, John C Johnson, W Austin Mulherin III, A Robert Outlaw Jr, William R Seifert II

COMPUTER SCIENCE
See UNIVERSITY OF GEORGIA

D-U-N-S 00-958-1091
▲ COMPUTER SCIENCES CORP
CSC
1775 Tysons Blvd, Tysons, VA 22102-4284
Tel (703) 245-9675 *Founded/Ownrshp* 1959
Sales 7.1MMM *EMP* 66,000^E
Accts Deloitte & Touche Llp Mclean
Tkr Sym CSC *Exch* NYS
SIC 7376 7374 7379 7373 7323 Computer facilities management; Data processing & preparation; Computer processing services; Computer related consulting services; Systems integration services; Credit reporting services
Ch Bd: J Michael Lawrie
COO: Mike Madden
CFO: Paul N Saleh
Treas: Hc Charles Diao
Treas: Marc A Kirsch
Bd of Dir: Linda Campbell
Ex VP: William L Deckelman Jr
Ex VP: Stephen Hilton
Ex VP: James R Smith
VP: Daniel Brown
VP: John Dickson
VP: Dan Hushon
VP: Gawie M Nienaber
VP: Pat Reidy
VP: Diane Rohleder
VP: Fran Selby
VP: James Taylor
VP: Steve Van Horn
Board of Directors: Herman E Bulls, Bruce B Churchill, Mark Foster, Brian Patrick Macdonald, Peter Rutland, Robert F Woods, Lizabeth H Zlatkus

D-U-N-S 96-859-4101 IMP
COMPUTER SECURITY SOLUTIONS LLC
COMPSEC
11 Canal Center Plz Fl 2, Alexandria, VA 22314-1595
Tel (703) 956-5700 *Founded/Ownrshp* 2012
Sales 125.1MM *EMP* 14
SIC 5045 Computers, peripherals & software
CEO: Chad Wagner
**VP:* Cabot Davis

D-U-N-S 06-296-8664
COMPUTER SERVICES INC
C S I
3901 Technology Dr, Paducah, KY 42001-5201
Tel (800) 545-4274 *Founded/Ownrshp* 1965
Sales 308.9MM^E *EMP* 968
SIC 7374 Data processing service
CEO: Steven A Powless
**Pr:* R Stanley Eckenburg
**CFO:* David L Simon
Bd of Dir: Linda Vitale
**Chf Mktg O:* Kedran H Whitten
**Ofcr:* George McGourty
Ex VP: John Reynolds
VP: Zaid Akhter
VP: Andy Burkett
VP: Mark Buse
VP: Stanley R Eckenberg
VP: Bob Ezell
VP: Cheryl L Harris
VP: Matthew Hasson
VP: David Hyberger
VP: Keith Koester
VP: Phillip Lunsford
VP: Giovanni Mastronardi
VP: Keith Monson
VP: Larry Moore
VP: Jeanette Murphy
Board of Directors: Richard A Anderson, Constantine Curris, Basil N Drossos, Bruce R Gall, Terrance Haas, David R Perry, Steven A Powless, Linda Johnson Vitale, John A Williams

D-U-N-S 06-364-0072
▲ COMPUTER TASK GROUP INC
CTG
800 Delaware Ave, Buffalo, NY 14209-2094
Tel (716) 882-8000 *Founded/Ownrshp* 1966
Sales 369.4MM *EMP* 3,600^E
Tkr Sym CTG *Exch* NGS
SIC 7371 7379 7361 Custom computer programming services; Computer related consulting services; Employment agencies
Pr: Arthur W Crumlish
**Ch Bd:* Daniel J Sullivan
CFO: Brendan M Harrington
Sr VP: Arthur V Crumlish
Sr VP: Filip J Gyd
Sr VP: Filip J L Gyde
Sr VP: Peter P Radetich
VP: Robert Barras
VP: Alfred A Hamilton
VP: Angela Rivera
VP: Rick Sullivan
Exec: Jim Campbell
Board of Directors: James R Helvey III, David H Klein, William D McGuire, Valerie Rahmani

D-U-N-S 92-978-7356
COMPUTERSHARE INC
(*Suby of* COMPUTERSHARE LIMITED)
250 Royall St, Canton, MA 02021-1011
Tel (781) 575-2000 *Founded/Ownrshp* 2000
Sales 1.0MMM^E *EMP* 2,200
SIC 6289 6211 Stock transfer agents; Security brokers & dealers
CEO: Donald Kenney
Pr: Michael Lapolla
**Pr:* Steven Rothbloom
COO: Mort Comer
**CFO:* John Morgan
Treas: Thomas Spataro
Top Exec: Laurie E McDonald
VP: Marc Aronson
VP: Ladislav Capik
VP: Michael Duncan
VP: Brian Goslin
VP: Vincent Graffeo
VP: Brian Heffernan
VP: Don Hirsch
VP: Shirley Nessralla
VP: Gary Obermiller
VP: Charlie Rossi
VP: Mike Smart

D-U-N-S 13-404-1834
COMPUTERSHARE INVESTOR SERVICES LLC
(*Suby of* COMPUTERSHARE LIMITED)
1290 Ave Of The Americas, New York, NY 10104-0101
Tel (312) 588-4700 *Founded/Ownrshp* 2000
Sales 267.5MM^E *EMP* 1,508
SIC 6289 6211 6282 Security transfer agents; Security brokers & dealers; Investment advice
Pr: Steve Rothbloom
CFO: Tom Honan
VP: Chris Morris
VP: Sharon Tulloh

D-U-N-S 09-193-9319
COMPUTERSHARE LLC
(*Suby of* COMPUTERSHARE INC) ★
2 N La Salle St Ste 200, Chicago, IL 60602-3704
Tel (312) 588-4992 *Founded/Ownrshp* 2000
Sales 239.2MM^E *EMP* 900
SIC 6289 Stock transfer agents
VP: Mark Jacobs
Admn Mgr: Anar Alibhai
IT Man: Geoff Edwards
Sales Exec: Tom Coons

D-U-N-S 01-035-3910
COMPUTYPE INC
CASTCAL IDNTIFICATION CONCEPTS
2285 County Road C W, Saint Paul, MN 55113-2567
Tel (651) 633-0633 *Founded/Ownrshp* 1966
Sales 93.3MM^E *EMP* 250
SIC 2759 2672 2679 3565 3577 2671 Commercial printing; Poster & decal printing & engraving; Adhesive papers, labels or tapes: from purchased material; Tags & labels, paper; Labeling machines, industrial; Computer peripheral equipment; Packaging paper & plastics film, coated & laminated
CEO: William E Roach
Pr: Gloria Engfer
CFO: Sarah Richardson
**VP:* Peter Baker
**VP:* John Newton
**VP:* Steve Treichel
Exec: Cindy Roberts
IT Man: W Mayhew
IT Man: Erik Payeur
IT Man: Dave Petersen
IT Man: Suzanne Wessels

D-U-N-S 07-277-3849 IMP
COMPUWARE CORP
ABEND-AID MARKETING COMPANY
(*Suby of* COMPUWARE HOLDINGS LLC) ★
1 Campus Martius Fl 4, Detroit, MI 48226-5099
Tel (313) 227-7300 *Founded/Ownrshp* 2014
Sales 720.0MM *EMP* 500^E
SIC 7372 7371 Prepackaged software; Computer software development; Software programming applications
Pr: Chris O'Malley
Pr: Ken Baldwin
Pr: Christopher Omalley
Pr: Tommi White
COO: Joseph Domizio
CFO: Joe Aho
CFO: Joseph Angileri
Chf Mktg O: Tom Stevenson
Ex VP: Paul Czarnik
Ex VP: Sucharita Mulpuru
Ex VP: Denise A Starr
Sr VP: Lisa Elkin
Sr VP: Pete Harteveld
VP: John Bellow
VP: Erick Clauson
VP: Mitzi Hunter
VP: Danielle Lee
VP: Nicolas Robbe
VP: Rose Rowe
VP: Mike Zinda
Assoc Dir: John Kriegel

D-U-N-S 00-532-9374
COMPUWARE HOLDINGS LLC
(*Suby of* THOMA BRAVO LLC) ★
1 Campus Martius, Detroit, MI 48226-5099
Tel (313) 227-7300 *Founded/Ownrshp* 2014
Sales 720.0MM^E *EMP* 2,534^E
SIC 7371 Computer software systems analysis & design, custom
Pt: Seth Boro
Pt: Marcel Bernard
Pt: Orlando Bravo
Pt: Holden Spaht
Pt: Carl Thoma
CFO: Amy Coleman Redenbaugh

COMPVIEW
See COMP-VIEW INC

D-U-N-S 80-763-9901
■ COMPX INTERNATIONAL INC
(*Suby of* N L INDUSTRIES INC) ★
5430 Lbj Fwy Ste 1700, Dallas, TX 75240-2620
Tel (972) 448-1400 *Founded/Ownrshp* 1993
Sales 108.9MM *EMP* 512^E
Tkr Sym CIX *Exch* ASE
SIC 3699 3714 Security devices; Mufflers (exhaust), motor vehicle
CEO: David A Bowers
**Ch Bd:* Bobby D O'Brien
Pr: Scott C James
CFO: James W Brown
Treas: John A St Wrba
Ex VP: Kelly D Luttmer
Ex VP: Gregory M Swalwell
VP: Steven S Eaton
VP: A Andrew R Louis
VP: Andrew B Nace
Sls Mgr: Tim Peters
Board of Directors: Thomas E Barry, Loretta J Feehan, Elisabeth C Fisher, Robert D Graham, Ann Manix, Cecil H Moore Jr, Mary A Tidlund

COMPX NATIONAL
See COMPX SECURITY PRODUCTS INC

D-U-N-S 16-652-3600 IMP
■ COMPX SECURITY PRODUCTS INC
COMPX NATIONAL
(*Suby of* COMPX INTERNATIONAL INC) ★
26 Old Mill Rd, Greenville, SC 29607-5312
Tel (864) 286-1122 *Founded/Ownrshp* 2002
Sales 99.2MM^E *EMP* 466
SIC 3429 Locks or lock sets
Pr: Scott C James
**VP:* Jay A Fine
**VP:* Darryl R Halbert
VP: Raymond Staton
**VP:* Gregg W Walla
**VP:* Steven Watson
Genl Mgr: Robert Vale

D-U-N-S 10-672-4599
▲ COMSCORE INC
11950 Democracy Dr # 600, Reston, VA 20190-5653
Tel (703) 438-2000 *Founded/Ownrshp* 1999
Sales 329.1MM *EMP* 1,043
Tkr Sym SCOR *Exch* NGS
SIC 7372 Prepackaged software; Application computer software; Business oriented computer software
CEO: Gian Fulgoni
V Ch: William P Livek
**V Ch:* Serge Matta
**COO:* Cameron Meierhoefer
**CFO:* David Chemerow
Ex VP: Linda Abraham
Ex VP: Manish Bhatia
**Ex VP:* Christiana L Lin
Sr VP: Aaron Fetters
VP: Umar Arshad
VP: Walter Burgman
VP: Paul Davis
VP: Anne Hunter
VP: James Lindsay
VP: Shara Mitchell
VP: Graham Mudd
VP: Vince O'Neill
VP: Mike Pilcher
VP: Joe Quinn
VP: Sandy Viteri
VP: Samantha Voisin
Board of Directors: Russell Fradin, William J Henderson, William Katz, Ronald J Korn, Joan M Lewis

COMSTOCK MORTGAGE
See GUILD MORTGAGE CO

D-U-N-S 05-481-4132
▲ COMSTOCK RESOURCES INC (NV)
5300 Town And Country Blv, Frisco, TX 75034-6892
Tel (972) 668-8800 *Founded/Ownrshp* 1919
Sales 252.4MM *EMP* 125^E
Tkr Sym CRK *Exch* NYS
SIC 1311 Crude petroleum production; Natural gas production
Ch Bd: M Jay Allison
**Pr:* Roland O Burns
COO: Mack D Good
Treas: Daniel K Presley
VP: D Dale Gillette
VP: Russell W Romoser
VP: Larae L Sanders
VP: Richard D Singer
VP: Blaine M Stribling
VP Mktg: Michael D McBurney
Board of Directors: Elizabeth B Davis, David K Lockett, Cecil E Martin, Frederic D Sewell, David W Sledge, Jim L Turner

COMSTOR
See WESTCON GROUP INC

D-U-N-S 01-641-0789
■ COMSYS INFORMATION TECHNOLOGY SERVICES LLC
(*Suby of* EXPERIS US INC) ★
2050 E Asu Cir Ste 120, Tempe, AZ 85284-1839
Tel (877) 626-6797 *Founded/Ownrshp* 2011
Sales 102.3MM^E *EMP* 832
SIC 7371 7374 Software programming applications; Computer software systems analysis & design, custom; Computer software development; Data processing service
Pr: Larry L Enterline
Sr VP: Ken R Bramlett Jr
Ex Dir: Patrick Dillon
Mng Dir: Karla Meador
Mng Dir: Eric Mele
Software D: Jeff Jappinga

D-U-N-S 04-186-8365 IMP/EXP
▲ COMTECH TELECOMMUNICATIONS CORP
68 S Service Rd Ste 230, Melville, NY 11747-2350
Tel (631) 962-7000 *Founded/Ownrshp* 1967
Sales 411.0MM *EMP* 978^E
Tkr Sym CMTL *Exch* NGS
SIC 3663 Microwave communication equipment; Amplifiers, RF power & IF; Mobile communication equipment
Pr: Fred Kornberg
COO: Michael Galletti
CFO: Michael D Porcelain
Sr VP: Richard L Burt
Board of Directors: Edwin Kantor, Ira S Kaplan, Robert G Paul, Lawrence J Waldman

D-U-N-S 79-945-2883
COMVERGE INC
(*Suby of* PEAK HOLDING CORP.)
5390 Triangle Pkwy # 300, Norcross, GA 30092-8001
Tel (678) 802-8011 *Founded/Ownrshp* 2012
Sales 131.8MM^E *EMP* 562^E
SIC 3822 Auto controls regulating residntl & coml environmt & applncs
Pr: Gregory J Dukat
Pt: Robert Warden
Ex VP: David Mathieson
Sr VP: D John Gagnon
Sr VP: David Neal
VP: Shane Fay
**Prin:* Fraser Preston
**Prin:* Joseph Zulli
Prgrm Mgr: Katie Papadimitriu
Genl Mgr: Brian Sullivan
Off Admin: Valerie Haro

D-U-N-S 07-868-7784
COMVERSE INC
810 7th Ave Fl 32, New York, NY 10019-5868
Tel (212) 739-1060 *Founded/Ownrshp* 1984
Sales 93.7MM^E *EMP* 2,700
SIC 7371 Computer software development
CEO: Philippe Tartavull
Sr VP: Eric Singh

D-U-N-S 13-020-5297
COMVERSE TECHNOLOGY INC
810 7th Ave, New York, NY 10019-5818
Tel (212) 739-1000 *Founded/Ownrshp* 2013
Sales 147.5MM^E *EMP* 3,200
SIC 7372 7371

COMVEST GROUP
See COMVEST INVESTMENT PARTNERS III LP

D-U-N-S 78-057-5499
COMVEST INVESTMENT PARTNERS III LP
COMVEST GROUP
525 Okeechobee Blvd # 1050, West Palm Beach, FL 33401-6349
Tel (561) 727-2000 *Founded/Ownrshp* 2003
Sales 830.1MM^E *EMP* 3,100^E
SIC 4731 5912 5999 3652 8742 1731 Transportation agents & brokers; Drug stores & proprietary stores; Medical apparatus & supplies; Pre-recorded records & tapes; Management consulting services; Electrical work
Ch: Michael Falk
**Pt:* Geoffrey D Alexander
VP: Jared Grigg
VP: Leo Koo

D-U-N-S 83-143-0637
COMVEST NATIONSHEALTH HOLDINGS LLC
(*Suby of* COMVEST GROUP) ★
525 Okeechobee Blvd # 1050, West Palm Beach, FL 33401-6349
Tel (561) 727-2000 *Founded/Ownrshp* 2009
Sales 262.4MM^E *EMP* 1,400
SIC 5912 5999 Drug stores & proprietary stores; Medical apparatus & supplies
CEO: Michael S Falk

D-U-N-S 07-917-2633
COMVEST PARTNERS
525 Okeechobee Blvd # 1050, West Palm Beach, FL 33401-6351
Tel (561) 727-2000 *Founded/Ownrshp* 2014
Sales 326.2M^E *EMP* 1,450
SIC 6799 Investors
Pt: Michael S Falk
Pt: John Caple
Pt: Micheal S Falk
Pt: Roger Marrero
VP: Adam Bentkover
VP: Michael Niegsch

D-U-N-S 83-272-8708
COMVEST VELOCITY ACQUISITION I LLC
(*Suby of* COMVEST GROUP) ★
525 Okeechobee Blvd # 1050, West Palm Beach, FL 33401-6349
Tel (561) 727-2000 *Founded/Ownrshp* 2009
Sales 93.4MM^E *EMP* 1,060^E
SIC 6719 Investment holding companies, except banks
Pr: Jose Gordo

D-U-N-S 80-132-5895
CON EL OF DIOCESE OF PALM BEACH INC
CATHOLIC DIOCESES PALM BEACH
9995 N Military Trl, Palm Beach Gardens, FL 33410-5460
Tel (561) 775-9500 *Founded/Ownrshp* 1984
Sales 5.6MM *EMP* 1,085
SIC 8661 Catholic Church
**Treas:* Basil J Zaloom
**Prin:* Charles N Bartola

CON WASTE
See CONSOLIDATED WASTE SERVICES CORP

CON-WAY ENTERPRISE SVCS INC
See XPO ENTERPRISE SERVICES INC

D-U-N-S 00-725-8908 IMP/EXP
▲ CONAGRA BRANDS INC
CONAGRA FOODS
222 Merchandise Mart Plz, Chicago, IL 60654-1103
Tel (312) 549-5000 *Founded/Ownrshp* 1919
Sales 11.6MMM *EMP* 20,900
Accts Kpmg Llp Omaha Nebraska
Tkr Sym CAG *Exch* NYS
SIC 2099 2038 2013 Food preparations; Dessert mixes & fillings; Seasonings & spices; Ready-to-eat meals, salads & sandwiches; Frozen specialties; Dinners, frozen & packaged; Lunches, frozen & packaged; Sausages & other prepared meats
Pr: Sean M Connolly
Ch Bd: Steven F Goldstone
Pr: Thomas M McGough
Pr: Thomas P Werner
CFO: David S Marberger
Ofcr: Charisse Brock
Ofcr: Darren C Serrao
Ex VP: Colleen R Batcheler
Ex VP: Dave Biegger
Ex VP: David B Biegger
Sr VP: Robert G Wise
Board of Directors: Craig P Omtvedt, Bradley A Alford, Thomas K Brown, Stephen G Butler, Thomas Dickson, Joie A Gregor, William G Jurgensen, Richard H Lenny, Ruth Ann Marshall, Timothy R McLevish

D-U-N-S 10-829-2624 IMP/EXP
■ CONAGRA DAIRY FOODS CO INC
(*Suby of* CONAGRA FOODS) ★
222 Merchandise Mart Plz, Chicago, IL 60654-1103
Tel (630) 848-0975 *Founded/Ownrshp* 1986
Sales 172.4MM^E *EMP* 1,564
SIC 2022 Natural cheese; Processed cheese
Pr: Richard G Scalise
COO: Tim Harris

CONAGRA FOODS
See CONAGRA BRANDS INC

CONAGRA FOODS LAMB WESTON INC
See WESTON LAMB INC

D-U-N-S 04-240-3188 IMP/EXP
■ CONAGRA GROCERY PRODUCTS CO LLC
HUNT FOODS COMPANY
(*Suby of* CONAGRA FOODS) ★
11 Conagra Dr, Omaha, NE 68102-5011
Tel (630) 857-1000 *Founded/Ownrshp* 2000
Sales 104.3MM^E *EMP* 484
SIC 2033 2079 2099 2032 2066 5149 Tomato products: packaged in cans, jars, etc.; Tomato sauce: packaged in cans, jars, etc.; Tomato paste: packaged in cans, jars, etc.; Catsup: packaged in cans, jars, etc.; Cooking oils, except corn: vegetable refined; Salad oils, except corn: vegetable refined; Popcorn, packaged: except already popped; Peanut butter; Puddings, except meat: packaged in cans, jars, etc.; Ethnic foods: canned, jarred, etc.; Beans, baked without meat: packaged in cans, jars, etc.; Chili with or without meat: packaged in cans, jars, etc.; Instant cocoa; Groceries & related products
VP Opers: Jay Duffy

CONAIR
See IPEG INC

D-U-N-S 00-166-1222 IMP/EXP
CONAIR CORP
PERSONAL CARE APPLIANCES DIV
1 Cummings Point Rd, Stamford, CT 06902-7901
Tel (203) 351-9000 *Founded/Ownrshp* 1959, 2002
Sales 2.2MMM *EMP* 3,478
SIC 3634 3631 3639 3999 Electric housewares & fans; Hair dryers, electric; Curling irons, electric; Hair curlers, electric; Household cooking equipment; Major kitchen appliances, except refrigerators & stoves; Barber & beauty shop equipment
Pr: Ronald T Diamond
COO: Yvette Walker
**CFO:* Eric Herman
**Treas:* John A Vele
Bd of Dir: Nicholas A Cioffi
Bd of Dir: Matilda Raffa Cuomo
Bd of Dir: James M Dubin
Bd of Dir: William Duncan
Bd of Dir: Denis Rizzuto
Bd of Dir: Henry J Singer
Bd of Dir: Stuart Subotnick
Bd of Dir: Uzi Zucker
**Ofcr:* Kathleen Fong
**Sr VP:* John J Mayorek
Sr VP: Pat Yannotta
**VP:* Michael Baldino
VP: Tom Focone
VP: Richard Margulies
VP: Thomas Perko
VP: Elizabeth Pettit
VP: Suzanne Piehl

D-U-N-S 00-315-1735 IMP/EXP
CONBRACO INDUSTRIES INC
APOLLO VALVES
(*Suby of* AALBERTS INDUSTRIES N.V.)
701 Matthews Mint Hill Rd, Matthews, NC 28105-1706
Tel (704) 841-6000 *Founded/Ownrshp* 2010
Sales 175.9MM^E *EMP* 1,235
SIC 3625 3494

D-U-N-S 79-863-5736
■ CONCENTRA HEALTH SERVICES INC
CONCENTRA MEDICAL CENTERS
(*Suby of* CONCENTRA OPERATING CORP) ★
5080 Spectrum Dr Ste 400w, Addison, TX 75001-6443
Tel (972) 364-8000 *Founded/Ownrshp* 1997
Sales 351.7MM^E *EMP* 5,900
SIC 8093 8011 Specialty outpatient clinics; Clinic, operated by physicians
Ch: Daniel Thomas
**Pr:* Bruce Broussard
**Pr:* Keith Newton
**CEO:* Jim Greenwood
**Treas:* James Bloem
**Treas:* Rusty Foster
Assoc VP: Mary Kelley
Ex VP: Ken Cancienne
**Ex VP:* John Delorimier
Ex VP: Tom Fogarty
**Ex VP:* W Tom Fogarty
**Ex VP:* Thomas E Kiraly
**Ex VP:* Mark Solls
**Sr VP:* John Anderson
Sr VP: John R Anderson
**Sr VP:* Greg Gilbert
Sr VP: Gregory M Gilbert
Sr VP: John Levene
Sr VP: William R Lewis
Sr VP: Daryl Risinger
VP: Stephen Gilhooly

D-U-N-S 09-919-0548
■ CONCENTRA INC
CONCENTRIX HOSP NETWRK ADDISON
(*Suby of* SELECT MEDICAL HOLDINGS CORP) ★
5080 Spectrum Dr Ste 400w, Addison, TX 75001-6443
Tel (972) 364-8000 *Founded/Ownrshp* 2015
Sales 389.4MM^E *EMP* 11,342^E
SIC 8011

CONCENTRA MEDICAL CENTERS
See CONCENTRA HEALTH SERVICES INC

D-U-N-S 08-545-1172
■ CONCENTRA OPERATING CORP
(*Suby of* CONCENTRIX HOSP NETWRK ADDISON) ★
5080 Spectrum Dr Ste 400w, Addison, TX 75001-6443
Tel (972) 364-8000 *Founded/Ownrshp* 1997
Sales 389.2MM^E *EMP* 11,316^E
SIC 8093 Specialty outpatient clinics
CEO: James M Greenwood
**Ch Bd:* Norman C Payson
Pr: Bob Ratini
**Pr:* Daniel J Thomas
Pr: Jeff Wainstein
**CFO:* Thomas E Kiraly
Assoc VP: Rebecca Tomlinson
**Ex VP:* Richard A Parr II
VP: John R Anderson
VP: Dan Brien
VP: Ken Cancienne
VP: Geneva Giang
Exec: Kathy D Orourke
Board of Directors: John K Carlyle, Carlos A Ferrer, David A George, D Scott Mackesy, Steven E Nelson, Paul B Queally, Richard J Sabolik, William H Wilcox

D-U-N-S 55-607-1041
■ CONCENTRIX CORP
(*Suby of* SYNNEX CORP) ★
3750 Monroe Ave, Pittsford, NY 14534-1302
Tel (585) 218-5300 *Founded/Ownrshp* 2006
Sales 120.0MM^E *EMP* 475
SIC 7379 7331 7311 Computer related maintenance services; Direct mail advertising services; Advertising agencies
Pr: Chris Caldwell
**Ch Bd:* Kevin M Murai
**COO:* Dennis Polk
VP: Jyllene Miller
**VP:* Dick Rapach
VP: John Witek
Creative D: Jennifer Wagner
Prgrm Mgr: Mark Padernal
CIO: Johnson Yeung
Dir IT: Robert Fardette
Dir IT: Michael Hagan

CONCENTRIX HOSP NETWRK ADDISON
See CONCENTRA INC

D-U-N-S 07-850-8032
▲ CONCEPT DEVELOPMENT PARTNERS LLC
500 Crescent Ct Ste 250, Dallas, TX 75201-6995
Tel (214) 871-6819 *Founded/Ownrshp* 2010
Sales 232.0MM^E *EMP* 3,236^E
SIC 6726 5812 5813 Investment offices; Eating places; Drinking places

D-U-N-S 05-472-8106
CONCEPT GREEN ENERGY SOLUTIONS INC (CA)
13824 Yorba Ave, Chino, CA 91710-5518
Tel (855) 459-6535 *Founded/Ownrshp* 2010
Sales 98.4MM^E *EMP* 4,000
SIC 7389 5211 Design services; Energy conservation products
Pr: Liang Gao
**Prin:* Henry F Hsieh

CONCEPT PACKAGING GROUP
See SOUTHLAND CONTAINER CORP

D-U-N-S 09-779-3186
CONCESSIONS INTERNATIONAL LLC
566 Wells St Sw, Atlanta, GA 30312-2426
Tel (404) 681-0300 *Founded/Ownrshp* 1979
Sales 94.0MM^E *EMP* 2,000
SIC 5812 5963 5947 Concessionaire; Newspapers, home delivery, not by printers or publishers; Gift shop
CEO: Donata Russell Major
Sr VP: Denise Kevil
VP: Basil Banko
VP: Milton Castillo
Genl Mgr: Leonard Crayton
Off Mgr: Dorothy Watford
Mktg Dir: Sheila Jones

D-U-N-S 80-676-5900
▲ CONCHO RESOURCES INC
600 W Illinois Ave, Midland, TX 79701-4882
Tel (432) 683-7443 *Founded/Ownrshp* 2006
Sales 1.8MMM *EMP* 1,121
Tkr Sym CXO *Exch* NYS
SIC 1311 Crude petroleum & natural gas; Crude petroleum & natural gas production
Ch Bd: Timothy A Leach
COO: E Joseph Wright
CFO: Jack F Harper
Chf Cred: C William Giraud
Sr VP: J Steve Guthrie
Sr VP: Matthew G Hyde
VP: Keith Corbett
VP: Larry Gates
Secur Mgr: Bill Vanderland
Counsel: Carol Leach
Board of Directors: Steven L Beal, Tucker S Bridwell, William H Easter III, Gary A Merriman, Ray M Poage, Mark B Puckett, John P Surma

CONCO CEMENT COMPANY
See GONSALVES & SANTUCCI INC

CONCO FOOD SERVICES
See CONSOLIDATED COMPANIES INC

D-U-N-S 02-249-0242 IMP
■ CONCORD BUYING GROUP INC
A.J. WRIGHT
(*Suby of* TJ MAXX) ★
770 Cochituate Rd, Framingham, MA 01701-4666
Tel (508) 390-4000 *Founded/Ownrshp* 1998
Sales 119.5MM^E *EMP* 2,000
SIC 5651 Family clothing stores
Pr: George Iacono
**Treas:* Mary Reynolds
Treas: Leanne Small
**Sec:* Ann McCauley
**Sr VP:* Robert Arnold
**VP:* Tom Francis
VP: Angela Mastrangelo

D-U-N-S 79-694-1946
■ CONCORD CORPORATE SERVICES INC
(*Suby of* CONCORD EFS NATIONAL BANK) ★
1100 Carr Rd, Wilmington, DE 19809-1610
Tel (302) 791-8200 *Founded/Ownrshp* 1999
Sales NA *EMP* 1,040
SIC 6099 Electronic funds transfer network, including switching
Pr: Edward T Haslam

D-U-N-S 05-177-9072
■ CONCORD EFS INC
CONCORD EFS NATIONAL BANK
(*Suby of* FIRST DATA CORP) ★
7000 Goodlett Farms Pkwy # 300, Cordova, TN 38016-4916
Tel (901) 371-8000 *Founded/Ownrshp* 2004
Sales NA *EMP* 2,640
SIC 6099 7389 6091 5044 Electronic funds transfer network, including switching; Charge account service; Check validation service; Nondeposit trust facilities; Bank automatic teller machines
CEO: Charles T Fote
Ex VP: Michael Whealy
Sr VP: John Brown
VP: Vicki Birdsong
VP: Thomas Dowling
VP: Joyce Kelso
VP: Don Kesner
VP: Donald Kesner
VP: Melinda Mercurio
VP: Ryan Ramey

CONCORD EFS NATIONAL BANK
See CONCORD EFS INC

D-U-N-S 09-998-8524
CONCORD ELECTRIC SUPPLY LIMITED
(*Suby of* CITY ELECTRICAL FACTORS LIMITED)
2701 Boston Rd Ste 100, Wilbraham, MA 01095-1800
Tel (413) 599-1750 *Founded/Ownrshp* 2000
Sales 346.1MM^E *EMP* 2,500
SIC 5063 Electrical apparatus & equipment
Pr: Martina Varela
**Treas:* James Henderson
**VP:* John Gray
**Prin:* David Rosso

D-U-N-S 04-481-2055 IMP/EXP
CONCORD FOODS INC
RED-E-MADE
10 Minuteman Way, Brockton, MA 02301-7508
Tel (508) 580-1700 *Founded/Ownrshp* 1968
Sales 95.2MM^E *EMP* 218
Accts O Connor & Drew Pc Braintre
SIC 2099 2045 Food preparations; Dessert mixes & fillings; Prepared flour mixes & doughs
Ch: R Geoffrey Neville
**Pr:* Paul E Neville
Ql Cn Mgr: Justina Aspinwall
Natl Sales: Cosmo Dinitto
Sls Mgr: Roland Laurent
Snr Mgr: Gabriel Alves

D-U-N-S 12-229-6015
CONCORD FOODS INC
4601 E Guasti Rd, Ontario, CA 91761-8105
Tel (909) 975-2000 *Founded/Ownrshp* 1985
Sales 124.2MM^E *EMP* 100^E

SIC 5141 Groceries, general line
Pr: Nick J Sciortino Jr
**CFO:* Roy Sciortino
**VP:* John Sciortino
Manager: Dennis Parker

D-U-N-S 04-352-0998
CONCORD GENERAL MUTUAL INSURANCE CO
CONCORD GROUP INSURANCE CO
4 Bouton St, Concord, NH 03301-5023
Tel (603) 224-4086 *Founded/Ownrshp* 1928
Sales NA *EMP* 204
SIC 6331 Fire, marine & casualty insurance: mutual
COO: Linda J Day
**Treas:* Daniel Rodgers
Treas: Jaslath Slattery
Ofcr: Kevin Migliozzi
Sr VP: McLean Warren
VP: Ann Mahar
**VP:* Thomas J McConnell
VP: Thomas McConnell
VP: Warren C McLean
VP: Michael P Nolin Jr
VP: Paul Rocheford
VP: McConnell Thomas
VP: Richard Welch

CONCORD GROUP INSURANCE CO
See CONCORD GENERAL MUTUAL INSURANCE CO

CONCORD HOSPITAL
See CAPITAL REGION HEALTH CARE CORP

D-U-N-S 07-397-7399 IMP
CONCORD HOSPITAL INC
(*Suby of* CONCORD HOSPITAL) ★
250 Pleasant St, Concord, NH 03301-2598
Tel (603) 227-7000 *Founded/Ownrshp* 1985
Sales 396.3MM *EMP* 2,000^E
SIC 8062 General medical & surgical hospitals
CEO: Robert Steigmeyer
Chf Rad: James Fuller
**COO:* Joseph Conley
COO: Douglas Connor
CFO: Janice Buerger
CFO: Bruce R Buns
**CFO:* Bruce R Burns
Treas: Michael Schuman
Trst: D Akey
Trst: Thomas D Akey
Trst: Mary Boucher
Trst: Tom C Brown
Trst: David Stevenson
Trst: William Stone
Ofcr: Fina Yatco
**Sr VP:* David Green
**VP:* Diane Allen
VP: Kevin Call
VP: Mark Carwell
VP: Domenic Ciavarro
VP: Jean Tenhaken

D-U-N-S 80-096-1674
CONCORD HOSPITALITY ENTERPRISES CO
11410 Common Oaks Dr, Raleigh, NC 27614-7002
Tel (919) 455-2900 *Founded/Ownrshp* 1988
Sales 177.6MM^E *EMP* 1,500
SIC 7011 Hotels & motels
Pr: Mark Laport
Pr: Andy Burch
Pr: Timothy E Osiecki
Ex VP: Nick Kellock
Sr VP: Heather Mallard
Sr VP: Kevin McAteer
Sr VP: Matt McClelland
Sr VP: Ken Polo
Sr VP: Grant L Sabroff
VP: Richard Branca
VP: Brian Cornell
VP: Scott Ness
VP: Kenneth R Polo
Dir Risk M: Rabon M Mayes
Dir Risk M: Judy Santell

D-U-N-S 62-049-5242
CONCORD HOSPITALITY INC
VILLAGE INN RESTAURANT
1701 Windhoek Dr, Lincoln, NE 68512-1273
Tel (402) 421-2551 *Founded/Ownrshp* 1987
Sales 159.7MM^E *EMP* 5,000
SIC 5812 7011 7311 Restaurant, family: chain; Hotels; Advertising agencies
Pr: Lawrence S Bird
**Sec:* Nancy Bird
VP: Edward Jones
VP: Greg Osinof
**Prin:* Margaret Stine
Sls Dir: Joe Laporta
Board of Directors: Lawrence S Bird, Ryan Bird, Frank Slater

D-U-N-S 94-333-0530
CONCORD INTERNATIONAL INC
(*Suby of* CHASSIX INC) ★
300 Galleria Officentre # 501, Southfield, MI 48034-8460
Tel (248) 728-8642 *Founded/Ownrshp* 2013
Sales 137.2MM^E *EMP* 150
SIC 3465 Body parts, automobile: stamped metal
CEO: Douglas Delgrosso

D-U-N-S 80-947-4554
CONCORD MANAGEMENT CO INC
1551 Sandspur Rd, Maitland, FL 32751-6138
Tel (407) 741-8600 *Founded/Ownrshp* 1990
Sales 71.7MM^E *EMP* 1,200
SIC 6513 Apartment building operators
Pr: Paul M Missigman
CFO: Douglas Celin
**VP:* Tricia Doody
Opers Mgr: Tammi Romero
Board of Directors: Jeffery S Ginsburg, Ronald M Ginsburg

D-U-N-S 36-425-2890
CONCORD MANAGEMENT LTD
1551 Sandspur Rd, Maitland, FL 32751-6138
Tel (407) 741-8600 *Founded/Ownrshp* 1995

Sales 51.7MM^E *EMP* 1,200
SIC 6531 Real estate agents & managers
Pr: Ed Kleiman
Pr: Andrew Frye
Pr: Wayne McDaniel
* *Pr:* Ed Wood
* *CFO:* Doug Selin
Ex VP: Robin Robuck
VP: Karen Brandell
VP: Sharon Ivey
VP: Brenda McCarthy
Rgnl Mgr: Megan Davidson
Dist Mgr: Melanie Caglioni

D-U-N-S 80-955-5675
CONCORD NEIGHBORHOOD CORP
APPLEBEES NGHBURHOOD GRILL BAR
(*Suby of* VILLAGE INN RESTAURANT) ★
1701 Windhoek Dr, Lincoln, NE 68512-1273
Tel (402) 421-2551 *Founded/Ownrshp* 1994
Sales 76.2MM^E *EMP* 2,900
SIC 5812 Restaurant, family: chain
Pr: Larry Bird
* *Ex VP:* Nancy Bird
* *VP:* John Gabel
* *VP:* Margaret Stine
Off Mgr: Lou Slosson

D-U-N-S 08-022-0245
CONCORDANCE HEALTHCARE SOLUTIONS LLC
SENECA MEDICAL
85 Shaffer Park Dr, Tiffin, OH 44883-9290
Tel (419) 455-2153 *Founded/Ownrshp* 2015
Sales 789.5MM^E *EMP* 1,109
SIC 5047 Medical & hospital equipment
Co-Pr: Roger Benz
COO: Jaysen Stevenson
CFO: Todd Howell
Co-Pr: Tom Harris

D-U-N-S 07-136-4293
CONCORDIA COLLEGE CORP
COBBER BOOKSTORE
901 8th St S, Moorhead, MN 56562-0001
Tel (218) 299-4000 *Founded/Ownrshp* 1891
Sales 83.5MM *EMP* 830
Accts Baker Tilly Virchow Krause Llp
SIC 8299 Religious school
Pr: William J Craft
Assoc VP: Bruce Wieweg
Dir Risk M: Roger Olson
Assoc Dir: Annette Kirchner
Assoc Dir: Karen Lee
Assoc Dir: Denise Phillippe
Ex Dir: Stewart W Herman
CTO: Dan Anderson
IT Man: Gordon Moe
Netwrk Mgr: Dennis Duncan
Mktg Mgr: John Dana

D-U-N-S 93-200-4211
CONCORDIA HEALTH PLAN
1333 S Kirkwood Rd, Saint Louis, MO 63122-7226
Tel (314) 965-9917 *Founded/Ownrshp* 2001
Sales NA *EMP* 1
SIC 6411 Insurance agents, brokers & service
Ex Dir: Dan Leeman
VP: Michael Berkley

D-U-N-S 07-955-1066
CONCORDIA HEALTHCARE USA INC
(*Suby of* CONCORDIA INTERNATIONAL CORP)
4950 Brambleton Ave Ste F, Roanoke, VA 24018-4120
Tel (434) 980-8146 *Founded/Ownrshp* 2013
Sales 120.0MM^E *EMP* 115
SIC 5122 Pharmaceuticals
CEO: Aaron Hullett

D-U-N-S 09-632-8109
CONCORDIA LUTHERAN MINISTRIES
CONCORDIA VISITING NURSES
134 Marwood Rd, Cabot, PA 16023-2245
Tel (724) 352-1571 *Founded/Ownrshp* 1882
Sales 11.6MM *EMP* 1,500
SIC 8051 Extended care facility
CEO: Keith E Frndak
* *CFO:* Paul Brand
IT Man: Jennifer Tano
Pr Dir: Tariogh Crawford
Nrsg Dir: Wendy Moore

D-U-N-S 07-608-4946 IMP
CONCORDIA UNIVERSITY
1530 Concordia, Irvine, CA 92612-3203
Tel (949) 854-8002 *Founded/Ownrshp* 1972
Sales 92.5MM *EMP* 185
Accts Baker Tilly Virchow Krause Llp
SIC 8221 University
Pr: Dr Jacob A O Preus
CFO: Carolyn Chesebrough
CFO: Kevin Tilden
Ofcr: Sean Mellott
Ex VP: Dean Vieselmeyer
VP: Kurt Krueger
VP: Allen Rudy
VP: Hal Whelphy
Exec: Roger Philips
Assoc Dir: Nancy Jessup
Ex Dir: Dan Waite

D-U-N-S 05-716-3396
CONCORDIA UNIVERSITY WISCONSIN INC
CUW
12800 N Lake Shore Dr, Mequon, WI 53097-2418
Tel (262) 243-5700 *Founded/Ownrshp* 1881
Sales 149.4MM *EMP* 350
SIC 8221 University
Pr: Patrick T Ferry
Pr: Thomas Phillip
* *COO:* Allen Prochnow
* *Sr VP:* Duane H Hilgendorf
VP: Ken Gaschk
Exec: Jeff Bandurski
Assoc Dir: Stacey Brunner
Netwrk Mgr: Mark Newhouse
Board of Directors: Ned Sisney

CONCORDIA VISITING NURSES
See CONCORDIA LUTHERAN MINISTRIES

D-U-N-S 19-644-4512
CONCRETE CO
1030 1st Ave, Columbus, GA 31901-2402
Tel (706) 256-5700 *Founded/Ownrshp* 1956
Sales 209.7MM^E *EMP* 286
SIC 1442 3272 Construction sand & gravel; Concrete products
Ch Bd: Frank D Foley III
VP: Tracy Nissen
VP: Eric Nix

CONCRETE DEMOLITION
See PENHALL INTERNATIONAL CORP

CONCRETE NOR'WEST DIVISION
See MILES SAND & GRAVEL CO

D-U-N-S 07-862-5281
CONCRETE PIPE & PRECAST LLC
11352 Virginia Precast Rd, Ashland, VA 23005-7920
Tel (804) 798-6068 *Founded/Ownrshp* 2012
Sales 222.7MM^E *EMP* 618^E
SIC 3272 Sewer pipe, concrete; Concrete products used to facilitate drainage
Pr: Bill Tichacek

CONCRETE REINFORCING PRODUCTS
See AGROYCE METAL MARKETING LLC

D-U-N-S 80-808-6834
CONCRETE STRATEGIES LLC
(*Suby of* CLAYCO CONSTRUCTION CO) ★
2199 Innerbelt Bus Ctr Dr, Saint Louis, MO 63114-5721
Tel (314) 595-6300 *Founded/Ownrshp* 2006
Sales 83.8MM *EMP* 250
Accts Dglf Nashville Tennessee
SIC 1791 1799 Precast concrete structural framing or panels, placing of; Erection & dismantling of forms for poured concrete
Pr: Joseph C Vitale
* *CEO:* Robert G Clark
* *COO:* Pat Moriarity
CFO: Judy Alexander
CFO: Michael P Murphy
Ex VP: John Diciurcio
Ex VP: Kenneth Leach
Sr VP: Paul Giacoletto
Sr VP: Ralph Johnson
Sr VP: Paul Little
Sr VP: Edward McNeill
VP: Larry Chapman
VP: Tim Gallagher
* *VP:* Barclay Gebel
VP: C D Moses
VP: Bill Mueller
VP: Steve Sieckhaus
Dir Bus: Bruce Wolferding

D-U-N-S 02-446-9637
CONCRETE SUPPLY HOLDINGS INC
3823 Raleigh St, Charlotte, NC 28206-2042
Tel (704) 372-2930 *Founded/Ownrshp* 1958
Sales 92.9MM^E *EMP* 384
SIC 3273

D-U-N-S 86-726-2263
CONCUR TECHNOLOGIES INC
(*Suby of* SAP AMERICA INC) ★
601 108th Ave Ne Ste 1000, Bellevue, WA 98004-4750
Tel (425) 702-8808 *Founded/Ownrshp* 2014
Sales 352.8MM^E *EMP* 4,900^E
Accts Grant Thornton Llp Seattle W
SIC 7372 7371 Business oriented computer software; Custom computer programming services
Pr: Mike Eberhard
CFO: Frank Pelzer
Bd of Dir: Mike Odom
* *Ofcr:* Barry Padgett
Ofcr: Kyle Sugamele
Ex VP: Robert Cavanaugh
Ex VP: Tom Depasquale
Ex VP: Michael L Eberhard
Ex VP: Robson Grieve
Ex VP: Michael W Hilton
Ex VP: Michael T Koetting
* *Ex VP:* Bob Robinson
Ex VP: Bob Robison
Ex VP: John Torrey
* *Sr VP:* Jim Lucier
VP: Sanjay Almeida
VP: Neil Charney
VP: John Dietz
VP: Dan Gerrity
VP: Donna E Hilty
VP: Darren Koch

D-U-N-S 83-271-5606
CONCURRENT PARTNERS LLLP
800 Cncrse Pkwy S Ste 200, Maitland, FL 32751
Tel (407) 571-1550 *Founded/Ownrshp* 2006
Sales 498.4MM^E *EMP* 9,100
SIC 8051 Skilled nursing care facilities

D-U-N-S 18-973-7810
CONCURRENT TECHNOLOGIES CORP
C T C
100 Ctc Dr, Johnstown, PA 15904-1935
Tel (814) 266-2874 *Founded/Ownrshp* 1994
Sales 139.1MM *EMP* 800
SIC 8711 Consulting engineer
Pr: Edward J Sheehan Jr
Treas: Karl M Kushner
Sr VP: David H Artman
Sr VP: Margaret Divirgilio
VP: George W Appley
VP: Vicki Barbur
VP: Michael Nash
VP: Jerry Rhudson
Exec: Diane Costlow
Ex Dir: Greg Holt
Brnch Mgr: Mark Kipps

COND NAST'S
See CONDE NAST INTERNATIONAL INC

D-U-N-S 78-481-0488
CONDE NAST INTERNATIONAL INC
COND NAST'S
1 World Trade Ctr, New York, NY 10007-0089
Tel (212) 286-2860 *Founded/Ownrshp* 2006
Sales 302.1MM^E *EMP* 1,331^E
SIC 2721 Magazines: publishing & printing
CEO: Charles H Townsend
* *Pr:* Edward Menicheschi
Pr: Gina Sanders
* *CEO:* Robert A Sauerberg Jr
* *CFO:* John Bellando
* *CFO:* David Geithner
* *Ex VP:* Fred Santarpia
Art Dir: Noah Dreier

CONDE NAST PUBLICATIONS
See ADVANCE MAGAZINE PUBLISHERS INC

D-U-N-S 02-352-9522
CONDON OIL CO
126 E Jackson St, Ripon, WI 54971-1378
Tel (920) 748-3186 *Founded/Ownrshp* 1980
Sales 203.8MM^E *EMP* 600
SIC 5541 Filling stations, gasoline
Pr: B Kent Bauman
* *VP:* Robert Reiser
VP Opers: Thomas Reinsch
Mktg Dir: Tom Arps

D-U-N-S 10-596-6167
CONDOR 3 CORP
(*Suby of* TOWER GROUP INTERNATIONAL LTD)
120 Broadway Ste 31, New York, NY 10271-3100
Tel (212) 655-2000 *Founded/Ownrshp* 2012
Sales NA *EMP* 1,800
SIC 6331 Property damage insurance
CEO: Michael Lee
* *CFO:* William Hitselberger

D-U-N-S 18-414-1497 IMP
CONDOTTE AMERICA INC
(*Suby of* SOCIETA' ITALIANA PER CONDOTTE D'ACQUA SPA)
10790 Nw 127th St, Medley, FL 33178-3197
Tel (305) 670-7585 *Founded/Ownrshp* 1987
Sales 100.8MM *EMP* 220
Accts Cherry Bekaert Llp Coral Gabl
SIC 1611 1622 1542 Highway & street paving contractor; Bridge construction; Tunnel construction; Nonresidential construction
Pr: Enrique I Espino
VP: Danny Garcia
VP: Luciano Giudice
VP: Ernesto Guerrieri
* *VP:* Luciano Logiudice
* *VP:* Andres G Mendoza
VP: Andres Mendoza
VP: Keyvan Sangelaji
VP Opers: Brian Quinlan

D-U-N-S 17-525-9738
CONDUMEX INC
(*Suby of* GRUPO CONDUMEX, S.A. DE C.V.)
900 Avenue S, Grand Prairie, TX 75050-1133
Tel (800) 925-9473 *Founded/Ownrshp* 1987
Sales 440.8MM *EMP* 85
Accts Pricewaterhousecoopers Llp D
SIC 7389 5063 Purchasing service; Telephone & telegraph wire & cable
Pr: Alejandro Sanchez
VP: Jose Equis
* *VP:* Humberto Gutierrez-Olvera
* *VP:* Jose Luis Lisea
VP: Humberto G Olvera
* *VP Sls:* Jose Perez Equis
VP Sls: Jose Perez

D-U-N-S 16-037-1485 IMP/EXP
CONE DENIM LLC
CONE DENIM MILLS
(*Suby of* INTERNATIONAL TEXTILE GROUP INC) ★
804 Green Valley Rd # 300, Greensboro, NC 27408-7013
Tel (336) 379-6220 *Founded/Ownrshp* 2007
Sales 360.0MM^E *EMP* 3,200
SIC 2211 Denims
Prin: John Bakane
Comm Dir: Delores Sides

CONE DENIM MILLS
See CONE DENIM LLC

CONE HEALTH
See MOSES H CONE MEMORIAL HOSPITAL OPERATING CORP

CONE HEALTH FOUNDATION
See MOSES CONE-WESLEY LONG COMMUNITY HEALTH FOUNDATION INC

D-U-N-S 07-952-5704
CONE MIDSTREAM PARTNERS LP
1000 Consol Energy Dr, Canonsburg, PA 15317-6506
Tel (724) 485-4000 *Founded/Ownrshp* 2014
Sales 203.4MM *EMP* 5
Accts Ernst & Young Llp Pittsburgh
Tkr Sym CNNX *Exch* NYS
SIC 4922 Natural gas transmission
Ch Bd: John T Lewis
Genl Pt: Cone Midstream GP LLC
COO: Joseph M Fink
CFO: David M Khani
Mktg Dir: Steve Malyuk

D-U-N-S 00-942-0485
■ **CONECTIV LLC**
(*Suby of* EXELON) ★
800 N King St Ste 400, Wilmington, DE 19801-3543
Tel (202) 872-2680 *Founded/Ownrshp* 1998
Sales 2.9MMM^E *EMP* 5,000
SIC 4911 4924 1731 5172 Generation, electric power; Transmission, electric power; Distribution, electric power; Natural gas distribution; Electrical work; Crude oil
CEO: John M Derrick Jr
Pr: Dennis R Wraase
Ex VP: Byron Elson
Prin: Gary Stockbritge
Board of Directors: Thomas S Shaw, William T Torgerson, Dennis R Wraase

D-U-N-S 08-109-5945
CONEJO VALLEY UNIFIED SCHOOL DISTRICT
1400 E Janss Rd, Thousand Oaks, CA 91362-2198
Tel (805) 497-9511 *Founded/Ownrshp* 1974
Sales 190.6MM *EMP* 3,000
Accts Vavrinek Trine Day & Co Ll
SIC 8211 Public elementary & secondary schools
* *Treas:* Randi Dennen
* *VP:* Sue Wells
Off Mgr: Beate Kunze
Off Mgr: Denise Valentino
Pr Dir: Elle Welch
Schl Brd P: Peggy Buckles
Teacher Pr: Marina Mihalevsky
Psych: Kim Charnofsky
Psych: Rik Napora
HC Dir: Juan Santos
HC Dir: Kari Taketa

D-U-N-S 96-091-3978
■ **CONEMAUGH HEALTH INITIATIVES INC**
C H I
(*Suby of* CONEMAUGH HEALTH SYSTEM INC) ★
1020 Franklin St, Johnstown, PA 15905-4109
Tel (814) 534-9000 *Founded/Ownrshp* 1994
Sales 84.6MM *EMP* 348
Accts Bkd Llp Louisville Ky
SIC 8741 8721 Hospital management; Nursing & personal care facility management; Billing & bookkeeping service
Pr: Elaine Lambert

D-U-N-S 05-105-7447
CONEMAUGH HEALTH SYSTEM
CONEMAUGH PHYSICIAN GROUP
4186 Cortland Dr, New Paris, PA 15554-7706
Tel (814) 839-4108 *Founded/Ownrshp* 2010
Sales 84.6MM *EMP* 2
Accts Bkd Llp Louisville Ky
SIC 8099 Health & allied services
Prin: Henry Schoenthal

D-U-N-S 96-160-1028
■ **CONEMAUGH HEALTH SYSTEM INC**
(*Suby of* DUKE LIFEPOINT HEALTHCARE) ★
1086 Franklin St, Johnstown, PA 15905-4305
Tel (814) 534-9000 *Founded/Ownrshp* 2014
Sales 509.5MM *EMP* 3,500
SIC 8062 8741 General medical & surgical hospitals; Management services; Nursing & personal care facility management
CEO: Scott Becker
Pr: Beth Sandak
* *CFO:* Edward Depasquale
Treas: Barbara Godish
Bd of Dir: Louise Pugliese
VP: Joan M Roscoe
Exec: Susan Benya
Dir Inf Cn: Jean Rearick
Ex Dir: Alan Drew
CIO: Joseph Dado
VP Opers: Nmoryken Joh

CONEMAUGH PHYSICIAN GROUP
See CONEMAUGH HEALTH SYSTEM

D-U-N-S 04-752-0234 IMP/EXP
CONESTOGA WOOD SPECIALTIES CORP
245 Reading Rd, East Earl, PA 17519-9549
Tel (717) 445-6701 *Founded/Ownrshp* 1964
Sales 270.4MM^E *EMP* 1,175
SIC 2431 2521 2434 Doors, wood; Trim, wood; Moldings, wood: unfinished & prefinished; Wood office furniture; Cabinets, office: wood; Wood kitchen cabinets
Pr: Anthony Hahn
COO: Keith Weber
* *Ch:* Norman Hahn
Exec: Joe Ford
CTO: Jamie Simmers
CTO: Alex Wallace
Software D: Aaron Sears
Ql Cn Mgr: Arnaldo Gomez
Ql Cn Mgr: Terry Renninger
S&M/VP: Steve Holcomb
Snr Mgr: Pauline Dietrich

D-U-N-S 14-318-0417
CONEXIS BENEFIT ADMINISTRATORS LP
(*Suby of* COBRAPRO) ★
721 S Parker St Ste 300, Orange, CA 92868-4732
Tel (714) 835-5006 *Founded/Ownrshp* 2003
Sales NA *EMP* 357
SIC 6411 Insurance information & consulting services
Pr: Michael Close
VP: Brad Inghram

D-U-N-S 07-140-9460
CONFEDERATED SALISH & KOOTENAI TRIBES INC
42487 Complex Blvd, Pablo, MT 59855
Tel (406) 675-2700 *Founded/Ownrshp* 1855
Sales 87.8MM^E *EMP* 1,100
Accts Redw Llc Albuquerque New Mex
SIC 7011 Hotels & motels
Ch: Joe Durglo
* *Treas:* Ron Trahan
Ofcr: Marshall Pablo
Div Mgr: Bill Foust

D-U-N-S 14-240-3760
CONFEDERATED TRIBES OF COLVILLE RESERVATION
TRIBAL EMPLOYMENT RIGHTS OFF
1 Colville St, Nespelem, WA 99155
Tel (509) 634-2857 *Founded/Ownrshp* 1872
Sales NA *EMP* 1,200
SIC 9131 Indian reservation;
Ex Dir: Carlien Anderson
* *Ex Dir:* Ms Mary Hall
Netwrk Mgr: Anne Marchand

D-U-N-S 04-126-6073 IMP
CONFEDERATED TRIBES OF WARM SPRINGS RESERVATION OF OREGON
WARM SPRINGS COMPOSITE PDTS
1233 Veterans St, Warm Springs, OR 97761
Tel (541) 553-1161 *Founded/Ownrshp* 1855
Sales 9.9MM *EMP* 1,150
SIC 7011 4832 0811 Hotels & motels; Radio broadcasting stations; Timber tracts
Treas: Bonnie Langeliers
CFO: Charles Currier
Treas: Michael Collins
**Sec:* Charles Calica
Ex Dir: Scott Moses
Plnt Mgr: Jim Mehlberg
Prd Mgr: Shawn Harry

D-U-N-S 02-162-4874
CONFERENCE ON JEWISH MATERIAL CLAIMS AGAINST GERMANY INC
CLAIMS CONFERENCE
1359 Broadway Rm 2000, New York, NY 10018-7841
Tel (646) 536-9100 *Founded/Ownrshp* 1952
Sales 643.7MM *EMP* 15
SIC 8699 Charitable organization
Ex VP: Gideon Taylor
**Pr:* Israel Singer
**Ch:* Julius Berman
CTO: James Rios
Web Dev: Kara Kovacev

D-U-N-S 02-822-4712
CONFIE SEGUROS HOLDING CO
7711 Center Ave Ste 200, Huntington Beach, CA 92647-9124
Tel (714) 252-2649 *Founded/Ownrshp* 2007
Sales NA *EMP* 25[E]
SIC 6411 Insurance agents, brokers & service
CEO: Joseph Waked
**Pr:* Mordy Rothberg

D-U-N-S 82-768-5392
CONFIE SEGUROS INC
FREEWAY INSURANCE
(*Suby of* CONFIE SEGUROS HOLDING CO) ★
7711 Center Ave Ste 200, Huntington Beach, CA 92647-9124
Tel (714) 252-2500 *Founded/Ownrshp* 2007
Sales NA *EMP* 2,010[E]
SIC 6411 Insurance brokers
CEO: Joseph Waked
**Pr:* Mordy Rothberg
**COO:* Valeria Rico
**CFO:* Robert Trebing

D-U-N-S 07-871-9310
CONFLUENCE HEALTH (WA)
820 N Chelan Ave, Wenatchee, WA 98801-2028
Tel (509) 663-8711 *Founded/Ownrshp* 2012
Sales 97.4MM *EMP* 600
Accts Moss Adams Llp Everett Wa
SIC 8011 Medical centers
CEO: Peter Rutherford MD
**CFO:* John Doyle

CONFORM AUTOMOTIVE
See FORMED FIBER TECHNOLOGIES INC

CONFORM GROUP
See DETROIT TECHNOLOGIES INC

D-U-N-S 15-081-0166
CONFORTI PLUMBING INC
6080 Pleasant Valley Rd C, El Dorado, CA 95623-4257
Tel (530) 622-0202 *Founded/Ownrshp* 1977
Sales 65.8MM[E] *EMP* 1,020
SIC 1711 Plumbing contractors
Pr: Marvin Collins
**CFO:* Jan Zygalinski

D-U-N-S 09-100-8615 IMP
CONGAR INTERNATIONAL CORP
(*Suby of* ALTADIS USA INC) ★
Km 72 Hm 2 Rr 14, Cayey, PR 00736
Tel (787) 738-2106 *Founded/Ownrshp* 2001
Sales 109.9MM *EMP* 650[E]
Accts Pricewaterhousecoopers Llp Sa
SIC 2121 Cigars
Pr: Kevin Sreudenthal
**VP:* Carmelo Jiminez

D-U-N-S 79-337-7151 IMP/EXP
CONGLOBAL INDUSTRIES LLC
(*Suby of* ITS TECHNOLOGIES & LOGISTICS LLC) ★
8200 185th St Ste A, Tinley Park, IL 60487-9244
Tel (925) 543-0977 *Founded/Ownrshp* 2013
Sales 117.9MM[E] *EMP* 800
SIC 3743 4213 4231 1799 7699

D-U-N-S 15-428-1158 IMP/EXP
CONGOLEUM CORP
3500 Quakerbridge Rd, Trenton, NJ 08619-1206
Tel (609) 584-3000 *Founded/Ownrshp* 1986
Sales 186.7MM[E] *EMP* 523
SIC 3081 5713 8741 Floor or wall covering, unsupported plastic; Tile, unsupported plastic; Floor covering stores; Management services
CEO: Robert Moran
CFO: Howard N Feist III
CFO: Chris O'Connor
Sr VP: Dennis P Jarosz
Sr VP: John L Russ III
VP: Keith Anderson
VP: Mark Kulling
Dir Lab: Ray Allenbach
MIS Dir: Carmella Pagano
QA Dir: Bill Hoffman
Mktg Mgr: Meghan Malone
Board of Directors: Jeffrey H Coats, Mark N Kaplan, William M Marcus, Mark S Newman, Adam H Slutsky, C Barnwell Straut

D-U-N-S 16-190-6011
■ **CONGRESS UNITED STATES**
(*Suby of* U S GOVERNMENT) ★
U S Capitol Senate Office, Washington, DC 20510-0001
Tel (202) 225-3121 *Founded/Ownrshp* 1787
Sales NA *EMP* 19,500[E]
SIC 9121 Congress;
VP: Joseph Biden
**Pr:* Ted Stevens

D-U-N-S 02-389-9795
■ **CONIFER HEALTH SOLUTIONS LLC**
(*Suby of* TENET HEALTHCARE CORP) ★
3560 Dallas Pkwy, Frisco, TX 75034-8635
Tel (469) 803-3000 *Founded/Ownrshp* 2008
Sales 521.0MM[E] *EMP* 11,000[E]
SIC 8082 Home health care services
CEO: Stephen M Mooney
**Pr:* Megan North
**Pr:* Dorothy Rubio
Pr: Craig Schaffer
**CFO:* Daniel M Karnuta
Chf Cred: Lea Fourkiller
**Chf Cred:* Allen Hobbs
Chf Mktg O: Thomas E Lynn
**Ofcr:* James F Brashear
**Ofcr:* Mecole Brown
**Ofcr:* Lisa Hodges
Sr VP: Matt Michaels
**Sr VP:* Janie Patterson
**Sr VP:* Norma Zeringue
VP: Dawn Castro
VP: Scott Lockwood
**VP:* Bridget McKenzie
VP: Roger Rydell
VP: David Schmidt
VP: Barry Schochet
Dir Bus: Deborah Green

D-U-N-S 19-803-4022
CONIFER REALTY LLC
1000 University Ave # 500, Rochester, NY 14607-1286
Tel (585) 324-0500 *Founded/Ownrshp* 2000
Sales 94.3MM[E] *EMP* 500
SIC 6531 Real estate agents & managers
CEO: Timothy D Fournier
Ch: Richard J Crossed
Ex VP: Andrew I Crossed
Ex VP: Joan F Hoover
Ex VP: Thomas Johnson
VP: Sandra Gorie
Opers Mgr: Maria Santana

D-U-N-S 94-387-5435
CONKLIN CARS SALINA LLC
1400 E 11th Ave, Hutchinson, KS 67501-2712
Tel (785) 825-8271 *Founded/Ownrshp* 1996
Sales 91.6MM[E] *EMP* 300
SIC 5511 Automobiles, new & used
Genl Mgr: Myron Sasse
Genl Mgr: Randy White
Mktg Mgr: Tony Hoover
**Sls Mgr:* Scott Conklin
Sls Mgr: Todd Hopkins
Sls Mgr: Steve Swartz

D-U-N-S 19-244-3745
CONKLIN FANGMAN INVESTMENT CO INC
1400 E 11th Ave, Hutchinson, KS 67501-2712
Tel (620) 662-4467 *Founded/Ownrshp* 1974
Sales 120.0MM *EMP* 148
SIC 7515 5511 7538 5521 Passenger car leasing; New & used car dealers; General automotive repair shops; Used car dealers
Pr: Stuart Conklin Jr
Treas: Mary A Conklin
**VP:* Scott D Conklin
**VP:* Stuart Conklin III
**VP:* Joseph P Fangman

D-U-N-S 18-548-1058
CONLAN CO
1800 Parkway Pl Se # 1010, Marietta, GA 30067-8293
Tel (770) 423-8000 *Founded/Ownrshp* 1987
Sales 589.8MM *EMP* 352
Accts Smith Adcock And Company Llp
SIC 1542 1541 Commercial & office building, new construction; Commercial & office buildings, renovation & repair; Industrial buildings & warehouses
CEO: Gary D Condron
**CFO:* Bill Hayne
**VP:* B Austin Sr
**VP:* David Staley Exec
**VP:* Stuart Price Exec
**VP:* Tom Lutz
**VP:* Ryan Triesenberg

D-U-N-S 00-596-8177
CONLON CONSTRUCTION CO OF IOWA (IA)
1100 Rockdale Rd, Dubuque, IA 52003-7875
Tel (563) 583-1724 *Founded/Ownrshp* 1935
Sales 88.9MM[E] *EMP* 200
SIC 1542 8741 1541 Commercial & office building, new construction; Commercial & office buildings, renovation & repair; Construction management; Industrial buildings, new construction; Renovation, remodeling & repairs: industrial buildings
Pr: Stephen D Conlon
**Treas:* Michael J Conlon
VP: Tim Conlon
Exec: Keefe Gaherty

D-U-N-S 80-467-8092
CONMAC INVESTMENTS INC
2301 Mclain St, Newport, AR 72112-3655
Tel (870) 523-6576 *Founded/Ownrshp* 1977
Sales 121.4MM[E] *EMP* 350
SIC 5511 Automobiles, new & used; Trucks, tractors & trailers: new & used; Vans, new & used
Pr: John Conner Jr

D-U-N-S 07-159-5540 IMP/EXP
▲ **CONMED CORP**
525 French Rd Ste 3, Utica, NY 13502-5994
Tel (315) 797-8375 *Founded/Ownrshp* 1970
Sales 719.1MM *EMP* 3,400[E]
Tkr Sym CNMD *Exch* NGS
SIC 3845 3841 Electromedical apparatus; Electrocardiographs; Patient monitoring apparatus; Surgical instruments & apparatus; Trocars; Suction therapy apparatus; Probes, surgical
Pr: Curt Hartman
**Ch Bd:* Mark E Tryniski
**Pr:* Curt R Hartman
CFO: Luke A Pomilio
CFO: Robert D Shallish
Ex VP: Heather L Cohen
Ex VP: Joseph G Darling
Ex VP: Daniel S Jonas
Ex VP: Mark D Snyder
Ex VP: Don Tosby
VP: Terence M Berge
VP: Chip Jones
VP: Ken Pelerossi
VP: Neill Quinn
VP: Terry Sheppard
Board of Directors: Martha Goldberg Aronson, David Bronson, Brian P Concannon, Charles M Farkas, Jo Ann Golden, Dirk M Kuyper, Jerome J Lande, John L Workman

D-U-N-S 79-141-7160
CONMED HEALTHCARE MANAGEMENT INC
(*Suby of* CORRECT CARE SOLUTIONS LLC) ★
7250 Parkway Dr Ste 400, Hanover, MD 21076-3400
Tel (410) 712-4760 *Founded/Ownrshp* 2012
Sales 75.1MM[E] *EMP* 1,931
SIC 8062 General medical & surgical hospitals
Ch Bd: Richard W Turner PHD
CFO: Thomas W Fry
Ex VP: Heather Cohen
Ex VP: Stephen B Goldberg
Ex VP: Ronald H Grubman
Board of Directors: Edward B Berger, John W Colloton, Charles Crocker, John Pappajohn, Jeffrey W Runge

D-U-N-S 62-126-4225
CONMED INC
(*Suby of* CONMED HEALTHCARE MANAGEMENT INC) ★
7250 Parkway Dr Ste 400, Hanover, MD 21076-3400
Tel (410) 567-5520 *Founded/Ownrshp* 2007
Sales 39.7MM[E] *EMP* 1,300
SIC 8011 Offices & clinics of medical doctors; Medical centers
Pr: Richard Turner
**CFO:* Thomas W Fry
Treas: Richard Olson
**Chf Mktg O:* Steven Boldberg

CONMED LINVATEC
See LINVATEC CORP

CONMET
See CONSOLIDATED METCO INC

D-U-N-S 02-605-0195 IMP
■ **CONN APPLIANCES INC**
(*Suby of* CONNS INC) ★
4055 Technology Frst, The Woodlands, TX 77381-2007
Tel (409) 832-1696 *Founded/Ownrshp* 1998
Sales 349.2MM[E] *EMP* 1,793[E]
SIC 5722 5731 7629 6141 7359

D-U-N-S 06-873-5048 IMP
CONN-SELMER INC
SELMER PARIS
(*Suby of* STEINWAY MUSICAL INSTRUMENTS INC) ★
600 Industrial Pkwy, Elkhart, IN 46516-5414
Tel (574) 522-1675 *Founded/Ownrshp* 1993
Sales 170.9MM[E] *EMP* 1,200
SIC 3931 5736 Musical instruments; Pianos, all types: vertical, grand, spinet, player, etc.; Brass instruments & parts; Woodwind instruments & parts; Pianos
Pr: John Stonner
**CFO:* Judy Minik
Top Exec: Scott Anderson
Dist Mgr: Rick Hanby
Dist Mgr: Todd Rodrigue
Dist Mgr: Frank Rosso
Dist Mgr: Rich Wetzel
Genl Mgr: Scott Gervais
Software D: James Scheibelhut
Mfg Mgr: Kathy Sopnicar
Plnt Mgr: Doug White

D-U-N-S 00-827-5224 IMP
CONNAUGHT GROUP LTD
423 W 55th St Fl 3, New York, NY 10019-4460
Tel (212) 315-4486 *Founded/Ownrshp* 1981
Sales 83.7MM[E] *EMP* 450
SIC 5137 Sportswear, women's & children's
Pr: Caroline Bowen
**Ch Bd:* William Rondina
**COO:* Larry Klein
**VP:* Eileen Balaban-Eisenberg
VP: Dennis Gulla
Rgnl Mgr: Lori Cronican
Snr Mgr: Nancy Beasley

D-U-N-S 14-606-6894
CONNECT AMERICA.COM LLC
WWW.MEDICALALARM.COM
1 Belmont Ave Fl 9, Bala Cynwyd, PA 19004-1611
Tel (610) 356-3307 *Founded/Ownrshp* 2004
Sales 98.6MM[E] *EMP* 250[E]
SIC 5065 5999

CONNECT COMPUTERS
See GENERAL PROCUREMENT INC

D-U-N-S 82-680-2675
CONNECTICARE INC
(*Suby of* EMBLEMHEALTH INC) ★
175 Scott Swamp Rd, Farmington, CT 06032-3342
Tel (860) 674-5700 *Founded/Ownrshp* 1996
Sales NA *EMP* 415[E]
SIC 6324 Hospital & medical service plans
Pr: Michael R Wise
**Treas:* Omas L Tran
Sr VP: Paul Philpott
VP: Mary Bannon
VP: Ed Fennell
VP: Heidi Sirota
VP: Nancy Tiberio
VP: Mark Verre
Dir QC: Robin Clarke
Dir IT: Kevin McCarthy
Dir IT: Jerry Queen

CONNECTICUT CHILDRENS MED CTR
See CCMC CORP

D-U-N-S 07-731-4268
CONNECTICUT CHILDRENS MEDICAL CENTER
(*Suby of* CONNECTICUT CHILDRENS MED CTR) ★
282 Washington St, Hartford, CT 06106-3322
Tel (860) 545-9000 *Founded/Ownrshp* 1985
Sales 293.8MM *EMP* 1,117
SIC 8069 Children's hospital
Pr: Martin J Gavin
**Ch Bd:* Thomas Barnes
Pr: Greg Latz
**COO:* Theresa Hendricksen
**CFO:* Gerald J Boisvert
**CFO:* Patrick Garvey
**V Ch Bd:* Mark Luvinberg
**Ex VP:* Paul Dworkin MD
**Sr VP:* Andrea L Benin MD
**VP:* Alison Auciello
**VP:* Leonard Banco
Exec: Rachel Cunningham
Exec: Lawrence Milan
Assoc Dir: Terry Dehnel
Dir Rad: Timothy Brown

D-U-N-S 06-925-6162
CONNECTICUT COLLEGE (CT)
270 Mohegan Ave, New London, CT 06320-4150
Tel (860) 447-1911 *Founded/Ownrshp* 1911
Sales 162.7MM *EMP* 1,017[E]
Accts Kpmg Llp Hartford Ct
SIC 8221 College, except junior
Pr: Leo I Higdon Jr
**Pr:* Katherine Bergeron
Ofcr: Alison Darrell
Ofcr: Brian Walsh
VP: Patricia Carey
VP: Frances Foley
VP: Ann Goodwin
VP: Lee Hisle
**VP:* Paul L Maroni
VP: Martha Merrill
VP: Tracee Reiser
VP: Claire Von Loesecke
Assoc Dir: Joshua Edmed
Assoc Dir: Eva Kovach
Assoc Dir: Jennifer Stein

D-U-N-S 00-118-3748 IMP/EXP
CONNECTICUT CONTAINER CORP (CT)
UNICORR GROUP
455 Sackett Point Rd, North Haven, CT 06473-3199
Tel (203) 248-2161 *Founded/Ownrshp* 1946
Sales 154.5MM[E] *EMP* 290
SIC 2653 3993 3412 2631 Corrugated boxes, partitions, display items, sheets & pad; Signs & advertising specialties; Metal barrels, drums & pails; Paperboard mills
Pr: Harry A Perkins
CFO: Allan Campbell
CFO: Gerry Earnshaw
CFO: Jim Ferrera
**VP:* Louis Ceruzzi
VP: Thomas Laird
Plnt Mgr: Berry Besen
Plnt Mgr: John Gregland

D-U-N-S 80-785-0417
CONNECTICUT DEPARTMENT OF ADMINISTRATIVE SERVICES
(*Suby of* GOVERNORS OFFICE STATE OF CONNECTICUT) ★
165 Capitol Ave Ste 7, Hartford, CT 06106-1632
Tel (860) 713-5100 *Founded/Ownrshp* 1995
Sales NA *EMP* 1,806
SIC 9199 General government administration;
Ofcr: Jim McKenna

D-U-N-S 80-785-0730
CONNECTICUT DEPARTMENT OF CHILDREN AND FAMILIES
(*Suby of* GOVERNORS OFFICE STATE OF CONNECTICUT) ★
505 Hudson St, Hartford, CT 06106-7107
Tel (860) 566-2700 *Founded/Ownrshp* 1993
Sales NA *EMP* 15,000
SIC 9441 Administration of social & manpower programs;
CFO: Gregory Messner
Comm Dir: Gary Kleeblatt
Genl Mgr: Deborah Ennis
Genl Mgr: Rick Rome
IT Man: Skip Burnham

D-U-N-S 80-785-0938
CONNECTICUT DEPARTMENT OF CORRECTION
(*Suby of* GOVERNORS OFFICE STATE OF CONNECTICUT) ★
24 Wolcott Hill Rd, Wethersfield, CT 06109-1152
Tel (860) 692-7481 *Founded/Ownrshp* 1968
Sales NA *EMP* 6,000
SIC 9223 House of correction, government

D-U-N-S 80-785-2694
CONNECTICUT DEPARTMENT OF DEVELOPMENTAL SERVICES
STATE OF CONNECTICUT DMR
(*Suby of* GOVERNORS OFFICE STATE OF CONNECTICUT) ★
460 Capitol Ave, Hartford, CT 06106-1308
Tel (860) 424-3000 *Founded/Ownrshp* 1975
Sales NA *EMP* 4,700
SIC 9431 Mental health agency administration, government;
**CFO:* Vincent O'Connell
Genl Mgr: Crescentino Secchiaroli
Off Admin: Galitza Martinez
Pr Dir: Robert Prentice

D-U-N-S 17-188-0859
CONNECTICUT DEPARTMENT OF EMERGENCY SERVICES & PUBLIC PROTECTION
(*Suby of* CONNECTICUT DEPARTMENT OF PUBLIC SAFETY) ★
1111 Country Club Rd, Middletown, CT 06457-2389
Tel (860) 685-8000 *Founded/Ownrshp* 1903
Sales NA *EMP* 1,600
SIC 9221 State police;

D-U-N-S 80-785-1225
CONNECTICUT DEPARTMENT OF ENERGY & ENVIRONMENTAL PROTECTION
(*Suby of* GOVERNORS OFFICE STATE OF CONNECTICUT) ★
79 Elm St Fl 3, Hartford, CT 06106-1650
Tel (860) 424-4100 *Founded/Ownrshp* 1995
Sales NA *EMP* 1,000
SIC 9511 Environmental protection agency, government;
Ofcr: Paul Vance
Ofcr: Lisa Zaccagnino
Prgrm Mgr: Stephanie P Marino
Snr Mgr: Min T Huang
Snr Mgr: Terry J Obey

D-U-N-S 80-785-2538
CONNECTICUT DEPARTMENT OF MENTAL HEALTH AND ADDICTION SERVICES
(*Suby of* GOVERNORS OFFICE STATE OF CONNECTICUT) ★
410 Capitol Ave Fl 4, Hartford, CT 06106-1367
Tel (860) 418-7000 *Founded/Ownrshp* 2003
Sales NA *EMP* 3,600
SIC 9431 Mental health agency administration, government

D-U-N-S 80-785-3197
CONNECTICUT DEPARTMENT OF PUBLIC SAFETY
(*Suby of* GOVERNORS OFFICE STATE OF CONNECTICUT) ★
1111 Country Club Rd, Middletown, CT 06457-2389
Tel (860) 685-8000 *Founded/Ownrshp* 1995
Sales NA *EMP* 1,600
SIC 9221 9229 State police; ; Public order & safety statistics centers;

D-U-N-S 02-728-1976
CONNECTICUT DEPARTMENT OF PUBLIC WORKS
(*Suby of* GOVERNORS OFFICE STATE OF CONNECTICUT) ★
165 Capitol Ave Ste 6, Hartford, CT 06106-1630
Tel (860) 713-5790 *Founded/Ownrshp* 2005
Sales NA *EMP* 1,411ᴱ
SIC 9511 Waste management program administration, government;

D-U-N-S 80-785-4294
CONNECTICUT DEPARTMENT OF REVENUE SERVICES
(*Suby of* GOVERNORS OFFICE STATE OF CONNECTICUT) ★
450 Columbus Blvd Ste 1, Hartford, CT 06103-1837
Tel (860) 297-5962 *Founded/Ownrshp* 1995
Sales NA *EMP* 1,497
SIC 9311 Finance, taxation & monetary policy;

D-U-N-S 80-785-4435
CONNECTICUT DEPARTMENT OF SOCIAL SERVICES
(*Suby of* GOVERNORS OFFICE STATE OF CONNECTICUT) ★
55 Farmington Ave Fl 1, Hartford, CT 06105-3730
Tel (860) 424-4908 *Founded/Ownrshp* 1993
Sales NA *EMP* 1,432
SIC 9441 Administration of social & manpower programs;
IT Man: Erin Guilmette
Doctor: Robert Zavoski

D-U-N-S 80-785-4583
CONNECTICUT DEPARTMENT OF TRANSPORTATION
(*Suby of* GOVERNORS OFFICE STATE OF CONNECTICUT) ★
2800 Berlin Tpke, Newington, CT 06111-4113
Tel (860) 594-3000 *Founded/Ownrshp* 1895
Sales NA *EMP* 3,200
SIC 9621 Regulation, administration of transportation;
CFO: Robert C Ard
**CFO:* Robert C Card
VP: Robert Fairbanks
Div Mgr: Frank J Busch

D-U-N-S 80-785-4724
CONNECTICUT DEPARTMENT OF VETERANS AFFAIRS
(*Suby of* GOVERNORS OFFICE STATE OF CONNECTICUT) ★
287 West St, Rocky Hill, CT 06067-3501
Tel (860) 721-5891 *Founded/Ownrshp* 1987
Sales NA *EMP* 15,970ᴱ
SIC 9451 Administration of veterans' affairs;
IT Man: Vatsal Desai
IT Man: David Weathers

D-U-N-S 00-691-6597 IMP
CONNECTICUT DISTRIBUTORS INC (CT)
333 Lordship Blvd, Stratford, CT 06615-7100
Tel (203) 377-1440 *Founded/Ownrshp* 1933
Sales 149.3MMᴱ *EMP* 241
SIC 5182 Liquor; Wine
Pr: Brian Albenze
**Pr:* Andrew Hillman
**CFO:* Edgar Garcia
Mktg Mgr: Joe Palisi
Sls Mgr: Peter Apotrias
Sls Mgr: Jay Kanji

D-U-N-S 09-722-1246
■ **CONNECTICUT ENERGY CORP**
(*Suby of* UIL HOLDINGS CORP) ★
60 Marsh Hill Rd, Orange, CT 06477-3663
Tel (203) 382-8111 *Founded/Ownrshp* 2014
Sales 152.7MMᴱ *EMP* 450
SIC 4911 4932 Distribution, electric power; Gas & other services combined
Pr: J R Crespo
**VP:* Vincent L Ammann Jr

CONNECTICUT GALVANIZING
See HIGHWAY SAFETY CORP

D-U-N-S 14-492-6839
■ **CONNECTICUT GENERAL CORP**
CIGNA
(*Suby of* CIGNA HOLDINGS INC) ★
900 Cottage Grove Rd, Bloomfield, CT 06002-2920
Tel (860) 226-6000 *Founded/Ownrshp* 1982
Sales NA *EMP* 24,260
SIC 6311 6321 Life insurance carriers; Accident insurance carriers
CEO: David Cordani
**CEO:* H Edward Hanway
**Ex VP:* Lisa Bacus
**Ex VP:* Mark Boxer
Ex VP: Carole Hodsdon
**Ex VP:* Nicole Jones
Exec: Barbara Alex
Exec: Decorti R Tonge
Ex Dir: Douglas Stewart

D-U-N-S 00-691-7082
■ **CONNECTICUT GENERAL LIFE INSURANCE CO**
CIGNA
(*Suby of* CIGNA) ★
900 Cottage Grove Rd, Bloomfield, CT 06002-2920
Tel (860) 226-6000 *Founded/Ownrshp* 1865
Sales NA *EMP* 1,055
SIC 6311 6321 Life insurance carriers; Accident insurance carriers; Health insurance carriers
Pr: David Cordani
**Treas:* Stephen Stachelek
**Ex VP:* Lisa Bacus
**Ex VP:* Mark Boxer
**Ex VP:* Nicole Jones
Sr VP: Joseph Michael Fitzgerald
**Prin:* Thomas C Jones
**Prin:* Matt Manders

D-U-N-S 09-810-8962
CONNECTICUT INSTITUTE FOR BLIND INC
OAK HILL SCHOOL
120 Holcomb St, Hartford, CT 06112-1529
Tel (860) 242-2274 *Founded/Ownrshp* 1893
Sales 78.1MM *EMP* 1,200
Accts Blum Shapiro & Company Pc
SIC 8211 8361 School for physically handicapped; School for the retarded; Home for the deaf & blind; Home for the mentally handicapped; Home for the physically handicapped
Pr: Patrick J Johnson
**VP:* James T Jones
**VP:* Stanley Soby
**VP:* Kjell T Tollefsen
Board of Directors: Theodore M Maltbie, Peter Birrell, John F Reynolds III, Carolyn Harris-Burney, Michael V Sack, Mary Louise Casey, Joseph A Sims, John J Dwyer, Patricia M Williams, Louise Fisher, Ned E Wentworth V Chb, Thomas J Gallagher, Alan C Keiller Are All Dir, Carolyn S Guiney, Jerald D Hassett, Thomas C Lee Jr

D-U-N-S 00-691-7090 IMP
■ **CONNECTICUT LIGHT AND POWER CO**
CL&P
(*Suby of* EVERSOURCE ENERGY) ★
107 Selden St, Berlin, CT 06037-1616
Tel (860) 665-5000 *Founded/Ownrshp* 1927
Sales 2.8MMM *EMP* 1,240ᴱ
Accts Deloitte & Touche Llp Hartfor
SIC 4911 Electric services; Distribution, electric power; Generation, electric power; Transmission, electric power
Pr: Werner J Schweiger
**Ch Bd:* Thomas J May
**CFO:* James J Judge
CFO: James Judge
**Sr VP:* Gregory B Butler
VP: Jay S Buth
IT Man: John Nachilly

D-U-N-S 09-207-8351
CONNECTICUT MUNICIPAL ELECTRIC ENERGY COOPERATIVE
CMEEC
30 Stott Ave, Norwich, CT 06360-1508
Tel (860) 889-4088 *Founded/Ownrshp* 1976
Sales 176.0MM *EMP* 34
SIC 4911 Distribution, electric power
CEO: Drew Rankin
**Pr:* Julio Leandri
**VP:* Joseph Dudek
IT Man: Ellen Kachmar

D-U-N-S 00-113-9294
■ **CONNECTICUT NATURAL GAS CORP**
(*Suby of* UIL HOLDINGS CORP) ★
77 Hartland St Ste 405, East Hartford, CT 06108-3259
Tel (860) 727-3000 *Founded/Ownrshp* 2010
Sales 223.2MMᴱ *EMP* 350
SIC 4924 Natural gas distribution
Pr: Robert M Allessio
VP: Wayne Jones
VP: H Kraiza
VP: Russ Leavitt

D-U-N-S 06-926-0610
CONNECTICUT ON-LINE COMPUTER CENTER INC (CT)
COCC
100 Executive Blvd Ste 1, Southington, CT 06489-1040
Tel (860) 678-0444 *Founded/Ownrshp* 1967
Sales 126.9MMᴱ *EMP* 372
SIC 7374

D-U-N-S 08-505-9467
CONNECTICUT PIE INC
DIANA'S BAKERY
35 Pearl St, Enfield, CT 06082-3504
Tel (860) 741-3781 *Founded/Ownrshp* 1975
Sales 147.0MMᴱ *EMP* 150
SIC 5149 5461 Bakery products; Doughnuts; Pastries; Pies; Cakes
Pr: Patrick Macari
**Ch:* Diana Macari
**VP:* Gerald R Macari

CONNECTICUT SPRING & STAMPING
See CONNECTICUT SPRING AND STAMPING CORP

D-U-N-S 00-114-3007 IMP
CONNECTICUT SPRING AND STAMPING CORP (CT)
CONNECTICUT SPRING & STAMPING
48 Spring Ln, Farmington, CT 06032-3140
Tel (860) 677-1341 *Founded/Ownrshp* 1939
Sales 124.9MMᴱ *EMP* 500
SIC 3469 3495 3493 Stamping metal for the trade; Machine parts, stamped or pressed metal; Wire springs; Precision springs; Steel springs, except wire
Pr: William Stevenson
Chf Mktg O: Debbie A Tine
**VP:* Chuck Thomas
Ex Dir: Harry Lindroth
Genl Mgr: Gerald Godburn
IT Man: Kathleen McIntyre
**VP Sls:* Steve Dicke
Mktg Mgr: Caroline Domijan

D-U-N-S 07-953-9708
CONNECTICUT STATE COLLEGES & UNIVERSITIES BOARD OF REGENTS FOR HIGHER EDUCATION
CSCU
61 Woodland St, Hartford, CT 06105-2345
Tel (860) 723-0000 *Founded/Ownrshp* 2012
Sales 1.2MMM *EMP* 160
SIC 8221 Colleges & universities
Ch Bd: Nicholas Donofrio
**CFO:* Chris Forster
**Prin:* Erin A Fitzgerald
**Prin:* Michael Kozlowski

D-U-N-S 02-045-2210
CONNECTICUT STATE UNIVERSITY SYSTEM
C S U
61 Woodland St, Hartford, CT 06105-2345
Tel (860) 493-0000 *Founded/Ownrshp* 1983
Sales 202.3MMᴱ *EMP* 2,800
Accts Pricewaterhousecoopers Llp Ha
SIC 8221 Colleges universities & professional schools
Pr: Gregory W Gray
**Ch Bd:* Lawrence D McHugh
**CFO:* Pamela J Kedderis
CFO: Pam Kidderis
CFO: Erika Steiner
**V Ch Bd:* Karl J Krapek
Ofcr: Susan Grant
Ofcr: Alessandra Lundberg
Ofcr: Lutishia Pershad
VP: Elaine Clark
VP: Laurie Dunn
VP: David Levinson
VP: Steve Weinberger
Assoc Dir: Eric Lessne
Dir: Corby Coperthwaite
Comm Dir: Maribel Luz

D-U-N-S 08-963-3150
CONNECTICUT VNA INC
(*Suby of* MASONICARE CORP) ★
33 N Plains Industrial Rd, Wallingford, CT 06492-5841
Tel (203) 679-5300 *Founded/Ownrshp* 1997
Sales 39.7MM *EMP* 2,000
SIC 8082 8741 Visiting nurse service; Management services
Pr: Donna Galluzzo
IT Man: David Molusis

D-U-N-S 04-412-0822
▲ **CONNECTICUT WATER SERVICE INC**
93 W Main St, Clinton, CT 06413-1645
Tel (860) 669-8636 *Founded/Ownrshp* 1956
Sales 96.0MM *EMP* 266ᴱ
Tkr Sym CTWS *Exch* NGS
SIC 4941 6531 1623 Water supply; Real estate agents & managers; Water main construction
Ch Bd: Eric W Thornburg
CFO: David C Benoit
VP: Craig J Patla
VP: Maureen P Westbrook
Genl Mgr: Robert Doffek
Board of Directors: Richard H Forde, Mary Ann Hanley, Heather Hunt, Bradford A Hunter, Lisa J Thibdaue, Carol P Wallace, Ellen C Wolf

CONNECTION, THE
See DATA LISTING SERVICES LLC

CONNECTION
See MOREDIRECT INC

D-U-N-S 83-177-6344
CONNECTION EDUCATION INC
(*Suby of* PEARSON INC) ★
1001 Fleet St Fl 5, Baltimore, MD 21202-4351
Tel (443) 529-1000 *Founded/Ownrshp* 2011
Sales 345.9MMᴱ *EMP* 2,820
SIC 6719 Investment holding companies, except banks
Ofcr: Steven Guttentag
**CFO:* Theodore R Ochs
Treas: Jim Flanagan
Bd of Dir: Petra Jauregui
Bd of Dir: Grace Magley
Bd of Dir: Laura Sanders
Bd of Dir: John Tidwell
Sr VP: Linda Leftrict
VP: Matt Buckleman
VP: Jean Kenney
VP: Martha Revenaugh
VP: Bob Sullivan

D-U-N-S 78-842-5643
CONNECTIONS COMMUNITY SUPPORT PROGRAMS INC
3821 Lancaster Pike, Wilmington, DE 19805-1512
Tel (302) 984-2302 *Founded/Ownrshp* 1985
Sales 85.1MM *EMP* 700
Accts Whisman Giordano & Associates
SIC 8322 8361 8049 Rehabilitation services; General counseling services; Substance abuse counseling; Home for the mentally handicapped; Geriatric residential care; Home for destitute men & women; Rehabilitation center, residential: health care incidental; Psychiatric social worker
CEO: Catherine Devaney McKay
COO: Chris De Vaney
**COO:* Chris Devaney
Exec: Adam Taylor
Opers Supe: Adrienne Evans
Doctor: Gerald Mehalick
Pgrm Dir: Eric Robinson

D-U-N-S 12-731-4743
CONNECTIONS EDUCATION LLC
(*Suby of* CONNECTION EDUCATION INC) ★
1001 Fleet St Fl 5, Baltimore, MD 21202-4351
Tel (443) 529-1000 *Founded/Ownrshp* 2001
Sales 57.7MMᴱ *EMP* 1,000
SIC 8299 Educational services
Pr: Steven Guttentag
**COO:* Ted Ochs
Treas: Jamin Brown
Bd of Dir: Aaron Coe
Bd of Dir: Charlotte Collins
Bd of Dir: Marisa Delgado
Bd of Dir: Stewart Elkin
Bd of Dir: Elaine Pavlich
Bd of Dir: Amy Phillips
Bd of Dir: Bonnie Smith
**Sr VP:* Susan Fancher
Sr VP: Pat Laystrom
VP: Armando Colombo
VP: Jill Hamilton
VP: Donna Hutchison
VP: Randall Zylstra

D-U-N-S 11-307-1906
▲ **CONNECTONE BANCORP INC**
301 Sylvan Ave, Englewood Cliffs, NJ 07632-2539
Tel (201) 816-8900 *Founded/Ownrshp* 1983
Sales NA *EMP* 166ᴱ
Tkr Sym CNOB *Exch* NGS
SIC 6022 State commercial banks
Ch Bd: Frank Sorrentino III
CFO: William S Burns
Chf Cred: Laura Criscione
Chf Cred: Michael McGrover

D-U-N-S 18-691-6792
■ **CONNECTONE BANK**
(*Suby of* CONNECTONE BANCORP INC) ★
301 Sylvan Ave Ste 1, Englewood, NJ 07632-2539
Tel (201) 816-8900 *Founded/Ownrshp* 2005
Sales NA *EMP* 29ᴱ
SIC 6022 State commercial banks
Pr: Paul E Fitzgerald
Pr: Alejandra Pazmino
CFO: Frank W Baier
CFO: William Burns
Chf Cred: Louis Manderino
Chf Cred: Mark Santasieri
Ofcr: Laura Criscione
Ofcr: Aditya Kishore
Ex VP: Elizabeth Magennis
Sr VP: Mark Cardone
Sr VP: Maria Gendelman
Sr VP: Michael McGrover
VP: Syed W Ameen
VP: Francis J Conover
VP: Tom Cosentino
VP: Thomas D Demedici
VP: Lee Ehudin
VP: Susan Fetner
VP: Chris Licata
VP: Christopher Linteris
VP: Carleen Lombardi

D-U-N-S 10-551-2623
▲ **CONNECTURE INC**
18500 W Corp Dr Ste 250, Brookfield, WI 53045
Tel (262) 432-8282 *Founded/Ownrshp* 1999
Sales 95.8MM *EMP* 427
Tkr Sym CNXR *Exch* NGM
SIC 7371 Computer software development & applications
Pr: Jeffery Surges
**Ch Bd:* David A Jones Jr
COO: Mary Guerrero
CFO: James P Purko
Chf Mktg O: Stephanie Meyer
Ex VP: David Sockel
Ex VP: William A Spehr
Sr VP: Mark Granville
Sr VP: Peter Urbain
VP: Tim Allaway
VP: Chris Bean
VP: Aaron Downend
VP: Ryan Howells
VP: Travis Potts
Board of Directors: A John Ansay, Vickie L Capps, Brett S Carlson, Paul Kusserow, Robert Douglas Schneider, Russell S Thomas, Alan J Ying

D-U-N-S 00-697-5049
CONNELL CO
CONNELL RICE & SUGAR CO
200 Connell Dr Ste 4100, Berkeley Heights, NJ 07922-2899
Tel (908) 673-3700 *Founded/Ownrshp* 1926
Sales 543.4MMᴱ *EMP* 620
Accts Cohn Reznick Llp Eatontown N
SIC 6552 6512 7359 5082 Land subdividers & developers, residential; Commercial & industrial building operation; Equipment rental & leasing; Construction & mining machinery
Pr: Grover Connell

*CFO: Terry Connell
*Ex VP: Duane Connell
Sr VP: David Freidin
Sr VP: Ron Giaier
*VP: Richard Bartok
VP: Richard E Bartok
*VP: Carlton Blake
*VP: Shane Connell
*VP: Mark R Decker
VP: Paul King
VP: Kenneth O'Neill
VP: Richard Ringler

D-U-N-S 17-436-3044 IMP/EXP
CONNELL LIMITED PARTNERSHIP
DANLY IEM
1 International Pl Fl 31, Boston, MA 02110-2602
Tel (617) 737-2700 Founded/Ownrshp 1987
Sales 500.0MM EMP 3,160
SIC 3443 3444 3341 3544 6719 Heat exchangers, condensers & components; Sheet metalwork; Aluminum smelting & refining (secondary); Die sets for metal stamping (presses); Investment holding companies, except banks
Pt: Margot C Connell
Pt: Frank A Doyle
Pt: Catherine R Gallagher
Pt: Kurt Keady
VP: Carlton Blake
CIO: Curt Kadey

D-U-N-S 10-338-0333
CONNELL OIL INC
CO-ENERGY A CONNELL OIL INC CO
1015 N Oregon Ave, Pasco, WA 99301-5986
Tel (509) 547-3326 Founded/Ownrshp 1987
Sales 120.1MM EMP 70
Accts Northwest Cpa Group Llc Richl
SIC 5171 Petroleum bulk stations & terminals
Owner: Bradley C Bell
Off Mgr: Danielle Smith
Sls Mgr: Jeffrey Garoutte

CONNELL RICE & SUGAR CO
See CONNELL CO

D-U-N-S 02-642-0505 IMP
CONNER INDUSTRIES INC
3800 Sandshell Dr Ste 235, Fort Worth, TX 76137-2429
Tel (817) 847-0361 Founded/Ownrshp 1981
Sales 140.0MM EMP 495
SIC 5211 5031 Lumber & other building materials; Lumber: rough, dressed & finished
CEO: Joseph McCormick
Ch Bd: Kurien Jacob
Pr: Mike Hans
Pr: Thomas R Rice
CFO: David Denton
Treas: Stephen L Fowler
Sls Mgr: Robert Payne

D-U-N-S 12-919-6598
CONNER STRONG & BUCKELEW COMPANIES INC
401 Route 73 N Ste 300, Marlton, NJ 08053-3426
Tel (877) 861-3220 Founded/Ownrshp 2007
Sales NA EMP 290
SIC 6411

D-U-N-S 07-751-3570
CONNETQUOT CENTRAL SCHOOL DISTRICT OF ISLIP
780 Ocean Ave, Bohemia, NY 11716-3631
Tel (631) 244-2203 Founded/Ownrshp 1961
Sales 56.9MM[E] EMP 1,126[E]
SIC 8211 Public elementary & secondary schools

D-U-N-S 83-985-3223
CONNEXITY INC
SHOPZILLA.COM
(Suby of SYMPHONY TECHNOLOGY GROUP LLC) ★
12200 W Olympic Blvd # 300, Los Angeles, CA 90064-1041
Tel (310) 571-1235 Founded/Ownrshp 2011
Sales 125.0MM[E] EMP 325
SIC 4813 7383 ; News syndicates
CEO: William Glass
COO: Scott Macon
CFO: Brad Kates
Ex VP: Bob Michaelian
Sr VP: David Bixler
Sr VP: Blythe Holden
Sr VP: Lonna Bell Rimestad
VP: Burzin Engineer
VP: Daniel Sheehy
Snr Sftwr: Pete Chudykowski
Snr Sftwr: Victor Igumnov

CONNEXTIONS HEALTH
See CONNEXTIONS INC

D-U-N-S 02-062-0311 IMP
■ **CONNEXTIONS INC**
CONNEXTIONS HEALTH
(Suby of UNITEDHEALTH GROUP INC) ★
9395 S John Young Pkwy, Orlando, FL 32819-8612
Tel (407) 926-2411 Founded/Ownrshp 2001
Sales 257.7MM[E] EMP 2,810
SIC 7379 7331 Computer related consulting services; Direct mail advertising services
CEO: Jack Lefort
*Pr: Steven G Auerbach
COO: Todd Baxter
*CFO: Michael Cooper
CFO: Steve E Russell
*Ex VP: Bill Hohns
*Ex VP: Robert Panepinto
Sr VP: Paul Perleberg
*Sr VP: Tom Young
VP: Natasha Clyburn
VP: Darius Denmark
VP: Jaclyn Hill
VP: Letha Lewis
VP: Jalisa Maxwell
VP: Kalana Rowell
VP: Elena Webb
VP: Candice Wesley
VP: Janet Ziomek

D-U-N-S 00-779-0884
CONNEXUS ENERGY
UTILITY TRUCK SERVICES
14601 Ramsey Blvd Nw, Ramsey, MN 55303-6775
Tel (763) 323-2600 Founded/Ownrshp 2008
Sales 270.0MM EMP 250
Accts Eide Bailly Llp Sioux Falls
SIC 4911 Distribution, electric power
CEO: Mike Rajala
*CFO: Michael Bash
*Ch: Peter Wojciechowski
*VP: John Gasal
*VP: Don Haller
*VP: Pete Miller
*VP: Matt Yseth
Snr Mgr: Brian Simonson

D-U-N-S 05-419-1143
CONNING & CO
(Suby of AQUILINE CAPITAL PARTNERS LLC) ★
1 Financial Plz Fl 13, Hartford, CT 06103-2627
Tel (860) 299-2100 Founded/Ownrshp 2009
Sales 92.3MM[E] EMP 295
SIC 6722 Management investment, open-end
Pr: Linwood Bradford
Pr: William M Bourque
Pr: Heather Depaolo
Pr: Stephen Puglisi
*CFO: Jung Lee
*CFO: Fred M Schpero
Ofcr: Robert Pearce
*Ex VP: Donald L McDonald
*Ex VP: Thomas D Sargent
*Sr VP: Seth C Miller
*Sr VP: Steven F Piaker
*Sr VP: Stephen R Pivacek
*Sr VP: Gary K Ransom
*Sr VP: David N Reid
*Sr VP: William C Shenton
VP: Bill Allen
VP: Dmitri Artemiev
VP: Cfa Battistini
VP: Terry Bonini
VP: Mary P Campbell
VP: Bhalendu Deshpande

CONNOLLY
See COTIVITI LLC

CONNOLLY IHEALTH
See COTIVITI USA LLC

D-U-N-S 00-798-2960
CONNOR CO (IL)
2800 Ne Adams St, Peoria, IL 61603-2806
Tel (309) 693-7229 Founded/Ownrshp 1936
Sales 154.3MM[E] EMP 230
Accts Clifton Gunderson Llp Peoria
SIC 5074 5075 Plumbing & hydronic heating supplies; Furnaces, except electric & warm air; Pipes & fittings, plastic; Water heaters, except electric; Air conditioning equipment, except room units
Pr: Susan Collins
*Pr: Stan Collins
Exec: Julie Driscoll
Brnch Mgr: Michelle Pemberton
Brnch Mgr: Todd Ross
Brnch Mgr: Gary Scott
Mktg Mgr: Nick Lavin
Sls Mgr: Wes Grim
Sales Asso: Tara Boyer
Sales Asso: Scott Kochuyt
Sales Asso: Scott Laird

D-U-N-S 13-920-9279 IMP
▲ **CONNS INC**
4055 Technology Frst, The Woodlands, TX 77381-2007
Tel (936) 230-5899 Founded/Ownrshp 1890
Sales 1.6MMM EMP 4,600[E]
Accts Ernst & Young Llp Houston T
Tkr Sym CONN Exch NGS
SIC 5722 5731 5261 5712 Household appliance stores; Gas household appliances; Electric household appliances; Kitchens, complete (sinks, cabinets, etc.); Radio, television & electronic stores; Lawn & garden equipment; Mattresses
Pr: Norman Miller
*Ch Bd: Norman L Miller
Pr: Michael J Poppe
Pr: David W Trahan
CFO: Thomas R Moran
CFO: Lee Wright
Treas: Melissa Allen
Chf Cred: John Davis
Ofcr: George Bchara
Ofcr: Brian A Daly
VP: Robert F Bell
VP: Clint Harwood
VP: Jamie L Pierce
VP: Todd F Renaud
VP: Donald A Welch
Board of Directors: James H Haworth, Kelly M Malson, Bob L Martin, Douglas H Martin, William E Saunders Jr, William Schofman

CONOCO
See KAYO OIL CO

D-U-N-S 11-881-9478 IMP/EXP
▲ **CONOCOPHILLIPS**
600 N Dairy Ashford Rd, Houston, TX 77079-1100
Tel (281) 293-1000 Founded/Ownrshp 2001
Sales 30.9MMM EMP 15,900
Accts Ernst & Young Llp Houston Te
Tkr Sym COP Exch NYS
SIC 1311 1382 Crude petroleum & natural gas; Oil & gas exploration services
Ch Bd: Ryan M Lance
Pr: Willie Chiang
Pr: Bob Hassler
Pr: Larry Ziemba
CFO: Jeff W Sheets
Ex VP: Matt J Fox
Ex VP: Matthew J Fox
Ex VP: Alan J Hirshberg
Ex VP: Donald E Wallette Jr
Sr VP: Larry E Archibald
Sr VP: Janet L Carrig
Sr VP: Ryan Lance
Sr VP: Andrew Lundquist
VP: Glenda M Schwarz
Board of Directors: Richard L Armitage, Richard H Auchinleck, Charles E Bunch, James E Copeland Jr, Gay Huey Evans, John V Faraci, Jody Freeman, Robert A Niblock, Herald J Norvik

D-U-N-S 00-842-7692 IMP
■ **CONOCOPHILLIPS HOLDING CO**
(Suby of CONOCOPHILLIPS) ★
600 N Dairy Ashford Rd, Houston, TX 77079-1100
Tel (281) 293-1000 Founded/Ownrshp 2002
Sales 874.1MM[E] EMP 16,900
SIC 2911 5171 5541 Petroleum refining; Gasoline; Liquefied petroleum gases, LPG; Greases, lubricating; Petroleum bulk stations & terminals; Gasoline service stations
Pr: J J Mulva
*CFO: J A Carrig
Ex VP: John Lowe
VP: Rob McKee
Genl Couns: Ralph Burch
Genl Couns: Stephen F Gates
Board of Directors: T C Knudson, J E Lowe

D-U-N-S 00-137-5088 IMP/EXP
CONOPCO INC (NY)
UNILEVER FOODS DRY
(Suby of UNILEVER UNITED STATES INC) ★
700 Sylvan Ave, Englewood Cliffs, NJ 07632-3113
Tel (201) 894-2727 Founded/Ownrshp 1880, 1986
Sales 482.2MM[E] EMP 4,800
SIC 2035 2038 2086 2024 2844 2841

D-U-N-S 03-396-3646
CONRAD & BISCHOFF INC
PHILLIPS 66
2251 N Holmes Ave, Idaho Falls, ID 83401-1520
Tel (208) 522-8174 Founded/Ownrshp 1941
Sales 91.5MM[E] EMP 160
SIC 5171 5411 5541 Petroleum bulk stations; Convenience stores; Filling stations, gasoline
Pr: James Hansen
*CFO: Jeff Waldon
*VP: Kirkland Hansen

D-U-N-S 00-143-5270 IMP/EXP
CONRAD FAFARD INC
770 Silver St, Agawam, MA 01001-2907
Tel (413) 786-4343 Founded/Ownrshp 2006
Sales NA EMP 1,000
SIC 5191 2875

D-U-N-S 00-817-2785 IMP
▲ **CONRAD INDUSTRIES INC** (DE)
1100 Brashear Ave Ste 200, Morgan City, LA 70380-1930
Tel (985) 702-0195 Founded/Ownrshp 1948
Sales 175.9MM[E] EMP 520
Accts Darnall Sikes Gardes & Frede
Tkr Sym CNRD Exch OTO
SIC 3731 Shipbuilding & repairing
Ch Bd: John P Conrad Jr
Ch Bd: J Parker Conrad
COO: Terry T Frickey
COO: Scott J Theriot
CFO: Cecil Hernandez
VP: Tom Dehart
VP: Carl Hebert
VP: Rene J Leonard
VP: Brett Wolbrink
Genl Mgr: Karen Longmire
Genl Mgr: Jim McElroy
Board of Directors: Michael J Harris

D-U-N-S 03-223-8560
CONRAD YELVINGTON DISTRIBUTORS INC
CYDI
2328 Bellevue Ave, Daytona Beach, FL 32114-5614
Tel (386) 257-5504 Founded/Ownrshp 1960
Sales 136.0MM[E] EMP 250
SIC 5032 5261 Sand, construction; Gravel; Aggregate; Sod
Ch: Conrad F Yelvington
*Pr: Gary C Yelvington
*CFO: Mark Klebe
*Treas: Charlie Brown
*Treas: Susan Yelvington
*VP: Margaret Yelvington
Sls&Mrk Ex: Trish Herndon

D-U-N-S 80-695-1364
CONRAIL INC
(Suby of GREEN ACQUISITION CORP) ★
1717 Arch St Ste 1310, Philadelphia, PA 19103-2844
Tel (215) 209-5027 Founded/Ownrshp 1999
Sales 239.0MM[E] EMP 7,404
SIC 4011 Railroads, line-haul operating
Pr: D R Goode
*Treas: Joseph Rogers
*VP: James A Hixon
Mng Dir: Kim C Small
Pr Dir: Jocelyn Hill

D-U-N-S 04-033-5119
CONROE INDEPENDENT SCHOOL DISTRICT
3205 W Davis St, Conroe, TX 77304-2039
Tel (936) 709-7751 Founded/Ownrshp 1924
Sales 552.1MM EMP 6,223
SIC 8211 Public elementary & secondary schools; Public junior high school; Public senior high school; Public vocational/technical school
Pr Dir: Sarah Wood
Schl Brd P: Ray Sanders
Instr Medi: Jarod Lambert

CONROE REGIONAL MEDICAL CENTER
See CHCA CONROE LP

CONSECO
See WILCO LIFE INSURANCE CO

CONSECO
See CNO SERVICES LLC

D-U-N-S 05-437-5902
CONSECO VARIABLE INSURANCE CO (TX)
(Suby of INVIVA INC) ★
11825 N Pennsylvania St, Carmel, IN 46032-4604
Tel (317) 817-6100 Founded/Ownrshp 1935, 1994
Sales NA EMP 3,500
SIC 6311 Life insurance carriers
CEO: Stephen C Hilbert
*CFO: Rollin M Dick
*Ex VP: Jon Sabl
*Sr VP: Lynn C Tyson
Mktg Mgr: Karen Bissonette

D-U-N-S 00-798-1434
CONSERV FS INC
1110 Mcconnell Rd, Woodstock, IL 60098-7310
Tel (815) 334-5950 Founded/Ownrshp 1928
Sales 197.7MM EMP 140
Accts Cliftonlarsonallen Llp Norma
SIC 5171 5191 Petroleum bulk stations; Chemicals, agricultural; Fertilizer & fertilizer materials; Seeds: field, garden & flower; Garden supplies
Genl Mgr: Dave Mottet
*CFO: Chuck Woods
Bd of Dir: Dale Cox
VP: Gary Bormet
VP: Jim Coens
VP: Craig Zuidema
Exec: Tom Diehl
Exec: John Henning
IT Man: Dan Serum
IT Man: Dan Serun
Opers Mgr: Douglas Hild

D-U-N-S 18-970-7011
CONSERVATION FUND A NONPROFIT CORP
1655 Fort Myer Dr # 1300, Arlington, VA 22209-3199
Tel (703) 525-6300 Founded/Ownrshp 2001
Sales 242.6MM EMP 95
Accts Cbiz Mhm Llc Bethesda Md
SIC 8422 Arboretum
Pr: Larry Selzer
VP: Rex Boner
VP: David K Phillips
Assoc Dir: Kathleen Marks
Assoc Dir: Wendy Taylor
Prgrm Mgr: Jennifer Griffin
Genl Mgr: Christine Fisher
Off Mgr: Holly Newberger
Off Mgr: Geoff Wittreich
CIO: Wendy Richardson
Opers Mgr: Carrie Gombos

D-U-N-S 07-959-3305
CONSERVATION INTERNATIONAL FOUNDATION
2011 Crystal Dr Ste 500, Arlington, VA 22202-3787
Tel (703) 341-2400 Founded/Ownrshp 1987
Sales 152.4MM EMP 166[E]
Accts Mcgladrey & Pullen Llp Gaithe
SIC 8748 Environmental consultant
Pr: Gary Edson
Ofcr: Kristin Bergantz
Ofcr: Philip Bowles
Ofcr: Marcelo Tognelli
Sr VP: Cynthia McKee
Sr VP: Amelia Smith
Sr VP: Greg Stone
Sr VP: Will Turner
VP: Lisa Famolare
VP: Celia Harvey
VP: Daniela Raik
VP: Lilian Spijkerman
VP: Kristen Walker

D-U-N-S 17-519-1923
CONSERVATION INTERNATIONAL FOUNDATION
1003 K St Nw Ste 404, Washington, DC 20001-4424
Tel (703) 341-2400 Founded/Ownrshp 1987
Sales 96.8MM EMP 950
SIC 8641 Environmental protection organization
Ch Bd: Peter N Seligman
*Pr: Russell Mittermeier
*COO: Niels Crone
*CFO: Barbara Dipietro
Ex VP: Jennifer Morris
Sr VP: David Emmett
Sr VP: Albert Mwangi
Sr VP: Fabio Scarano
*Sr VP: Amelia Smith
VP: Jos M Da Silva
VP: L On Rajaobelina
VP: Katherine Sierra

D-U-N-S 61-943-9284
CONSERVATION SERVICES GROUP INC
50 Washington St Ste 3000, Westborough, MA 01581-1013
Tel (508) 836-9500 Founded/Ownrshp 1984
Sales 112.2MM EMP 300
Accts Cbiz Tofias Boston Ma
SIC 8748 Energy conservation consultant
CEO: Stephen L Cowell
*Pr: Tina M Bennett
*Pr: Larry Brown
Pr: Lisa Ludwig
Pr: Vanessa Richter
*CFO: Wanda Reindorf
*Treas: Bradley Steele
Ex VP: Alexander Crosett
*Sr VP: Mark Dyen
*VP: Paul Cimino
*VP: Lex Crosett
VP: Bob Eckel
VP: Andrew Fisk
VP: Rick Giles
VP: Kathryn Orfino
VP: Eric Roberts
*VP: Patricia Stanton
*VP: Mary Eddy Stewart
Dir Bus: Brian Draczynski
Board of Directors: Lynn Stein

D-U-N-S 96-344-3499
CONSIGLI BUILDING GROUP INC
72 Sumner St, Milford, MA 01757-1663
Tel (508) 473-2580 Founded/Ownrshp 2009

Sales 368.4MM^E *EMP* 550^E
SIC 1542 Nonresidential construction
Pr: Anthony M Consigli

D-U-N-S 00-144-1724 IMP
CONSIGLI CONSTRUCTION CO INC (MA)
(*Suby of* CONSIGLI BUILDING GROUP INC) ★
72 Sumner St, Milford, MA 01757-1663
Tel (508) 473-2580 *Founded/Ownrshp* 1905, 1959
Sales 252.8MM^E *EMP* 390
SIC 1541 1542 Industrial buildings, new construction; Renovation, remodeling & repairs: industrial buildings; Commercial & office building, new construction
Pr: Anthony M Consigli
**CFO:* J Scott Lerner
CFO: Scott Lerner
Treas: Henry Consigli Jr
**VP:* Matthew D Consigli
Pr Mgr: Helen Novak

D-U-N-S 79-171-8307
CONSIGLI CONSTRUCTION NY LLC
KIRCHHFF-CNSIGLI CNSTR MGT LLC
(*Suby of* CONSIGLI BUILDING GROUP INC) ★
199 West Rd Ste 100, Pleasant Valley, NY 12569-7975
Tel (845) 635-1121 *Founded/Ownrshp* 2009
Sales 87.5MM^E *EMP* 160
SIC 1542 Nonresidential construction
CEO: Joe Kirchhoff
**Pr:* Greg Burns
Exec: Paul McCoy
Genl Mgr: Mike Winters

D-U-N-S 78-700-8408
▲ CONSOL ENERGY INC
1000 Consol Energy Dr, Canonsburg, PA 15317-6506
Tel (724) 485-4000 *Founded/Ownrshp* 1864
Sales 3.1MMM *EMP* 3,114
Tkr Sym CNX *Exch* NYS
SIC 1221 1222 1311 Bituminous coal & lignite-surface mining; Bituminous coal-underground mining; Natural gas production
Pr: Nicholas J Deiuliis
**Ch Bd:* William N Thorndike Jr
CFO: David M Khani
Ofcr: Stephen W Johnson
VP: Joe Fink
VP: Stephanie L Gill
VP: C Kristopher Hagedorn
Comm Dir: Brian Aiello
Dir IT: Kevin Freyvogel
Sfty Dirs: John Heffelfinger
VP Sls: Dennis Duffy
Board of Directors: Alvin R Carpenter, William E Davis, Maureen E Lally-Green, Gregory A Lanham, Bernard Lanigan Jr, John T Mills, Joseph Platt, William P Powell, Edwin S Roberson

D-U-N-S 80-389-6828 EXP
■ CONSOL ENERGY SALES CO
(*Suby of* CONSOL ENERGY INC) ★
1000 Consol Energy Dr, Canonsburg, PA 15317-6506
Tel (724) 485-4000 *Founded/Ownrshp* 1991
Sales 221.8MM^E *EMP* 450
SIC 5052 Coal
Pr: B Pusateri
**CEO:* Brett Harvey
COO: Bart Hyita
**CFO:* B Lyon
**Treas:* J Reily
VP: D Auch
VP: Ronald Florjancic
**VP:* J Grech
VP: Vj Lyons
**VP:* D Orr
VP: John Reilly
**VP:* W Rieland

D-U-N-S 80-389-6752
■ CONSOL PENNSYLVANIA COAL CO LLC
(*Suby of* CONSOL ENERGY INC) ★
1000 Consol Energy Dr, Canonsburg, PA 15317-6506
Tel (724) 485-4000 *Founded/Ownrshp* 1992
Sales NA *EMP* 1,200
SIC 1311 1222 Natural gas production; Bituminous coal-underground mining
Pr: Peter B Lilly
**Pr:* James Brock
**Treas:* J M Reilly

CONSOLDTED CMMNCTIONS HOLDINGS
See CONSOLIDATED COMMUNICATIONS INC

D-U-N-S 07-928-5203
CONSOLIDATED AEROSPACE MANUFACTURING LLC
CAM
1425 S Acacia Ave, Fullerton, CA 92831-5317
Tel (714) 521-5060 *Founded/Ownrshp* 2012
Sales 83.5MM^E *EMP* 152^E
SIC 3812 Search & navigation equipment
CEO: Dave Werner

CONSOLIDATED AVIATION SERVICES
See CARGO AIRPORT SERVICES USA LLC

D-U-N-S 03-794-8056 IMP
CONSOLIDATED CASTING CORP (TX)
1501 S Interstate 45, Hutchins, TX 75141
Tel (972) 225-7305 *Founded/Ownrshp* 1966, 1996
Sales 99.5MM^E *EMP* 200
SIC 3324 3369 Commercial investment castings, ferrous; Nonferrous foundries
Ch Bd: Richard Grant
COO: Krueger Roger

D-U-N-S 78-287-1230 IMP
CONSOLIDATED CATFISH COMPANIES LLC
COUNTRY SELECT CATFISH
299 South St, Isola, MS 38754-9405
Tel (662) 962-3101 *Founded/Ownrshp* 2001
Sales 123.1MM^E *EMP* 400
SIC 2092 Fish, fresh: prepared
**CFO:* David Gray
**VP:* Frank Davis
VP: Debbie Fraley
**VP:* Jack Perkins

D-U-N-S 94-577-0840 IMP/EXP
CONSOLIDATED CIGAR HOLDINGS INC
(*Suby of* ALTADIS HOLDINGS USA INC) ★
5900 N Andrews Ave # 1100, Fort Lauderdale, FL 33309-2367
Tel (954) 772-9000 *Founded/Ownrshp* 2001
Sales 258.1MM^E *EMP* 1,410
SIC 2121 Cigars; Cigarillos
Pr: Gary R Ellis
**CFO:* James M Parnofiello

CONSOLIDATED COMFORT GROUP
See BAKER DISTRIBUTING CO LLC

CONSOLIDATED COMMUNICATIONS
See ENVENTIS TELECOM INC

D-U-N-S 00-693-4590
▲ CONSOLIDATED COMMUNICATIONS HOLDINGS INC
121 S 17th St, Mattoon, IL 61938-3987
Tel (217) 235-3311 *Founded/Ownrshp* 1894
Sales 775.7MM *EMP* 1,783^E
Tkr Sym CNSL *Exch* NGS
SIC 4813 Local telephone communications; Long distance telephone communications
Ch Bd: Robert J Currey
**Pr:* C Robert Udell Jr
**CFO:* Steven L Childers
**Sr VP:* Steven J Shirar
VP: Dawn Frost
IT Man: John Polston

D-U-N-S 11-747-8529
■ CONSOLIDATED COMMUNICATIONS INC
CONSOLDTED CMMNCTIONS HOLDINGS
(*Suby of* CONSOLIDATED COMMUNICATIONS HOLDINGS INC) ★
121 S 17th St, Mattoon, IL 61938-3915
Tel (217) 235-3311 *Founded/Ownrshp* 2008
Sales 418.9MM^E *EMP* 963^E
SIC 4813 Telephone communication, except radio;
CEO: Robert J Currey
Pr: Steve Shirar
COO: Bob Ochs
CFO: Steve Childers
Ch: Richard A Lumpkin
VP: Penny Miller
Mng Dir: Dominic Giangrasso
CIO: Bob Udell
CIO: Chris Young
Netwrk Eng: Gary Castle

D-U-N-S 13-309-9338
■ CONSOLIDATED COMMUNICATIONS OF ILLINOIS CO
ILLINOIS CONSOLIDATED TELE CO
(*Suby of* CONSOLIDATED COMMUNICATIONS HOLDINGS INC) ★
121 S 17th St, Mattoon, IL 61938-3915
Tel (217) 235-3311 *Founded/Ownrshp* 1924
Sales 134.4MM^E *EMP* 309
SIC 4813 Local & long distance telephone communications;
Pr: Richard Lumpkin
**Pr:* Robert J Currey
DP Dir: Jeff Ritke

D-U-N-S 00-577-7164
■ CONSOLIDATED COMMUNICATIONS SERVICES CO
(*Suby of* CONSOLIDATED COMMUNICATIONS HOLDINGS INC) ★
350 S Loop 336 W, Conroe, TX 77304-3308
Tel (936) 756-0611 *Founded/Ownrshp* 2004
Sales 188.3MM^E *EMP* 433
SIC 4813 Telephone communication, except radio
Pr: Robert J Currey
**Ch Bd:* Richard A Lumpkin
**VP:* Stephen Childers
CTO: Donna Jordan
**VP Sls:* Joe Dively
Mktg Mgr: Lisa Brooks

D-U-N-S 00-694-7410
CONSOLIDATED COMPANIES INC (LA)
CONCO FOOD SERVICES
918 Edwards Ave, New Orleans, LA 70123-3125
Tel (318) 869-3061 *Founded/Ownrshp* 1918, 1992
Sales 128.2MM^E *EMP* 504
SIC 5141 Groceries, general line
Pr: Winslow J Chadwick Jr
**VP:* Victor J Kurzweg III

CONSOLIDATED CONTAINER COMPANY
See CONSOLIDATED CONTAINER HOLDINGS LLC

D-U-N-S 07-583-0005 IMP
CONSOLIDATED CONTAINER CO LLC
CCC
(*Suby of* CONSOLIDATED CONTAINER INTERMEDIARY LLC) ★
3101 Towercreek Pkwy Se, Atlanta, GA 30339-3256
Tel (678) 742-4600 *Founded/Ownrshp* 2012
Sales 857.0MM *EMP* 2,700
SIC 3089 Plastic containers, except foam
CEO: Sean Fallmann
**CFO:* Richard P Sehring
**Sr VP:* Louis Lettes

D-U-N-S 10-132-7229 IMP
CONSOLIDATED CONTAINER CO LP
C C C
(*Suby of* CONSOLIDATED CONTAINER CO) ★
3101 Towercreek Pkwy Se, Atlanta, GA 30339-3256
Tel (678) 742-4600 *Founded/Ownrshp* 1999
Sales 809.3MM^E *EMP* 3,000
SIC 3089 3999 Plastic containers, except foam; Atomizers, toiletry
CEO: Sean Fallmann
CFO: Richard Sehring
Sr VP: Robert K Brower
VP: Greg Wall
Mng Dir: Bob Henry
Off Mgr: Cindy Jones
Off Admin: Elaine Nichols
Software D: Snehal Murudkar
Netwrk Eng: Mike Miller

VP Mfg: Dan Murphy
VP Opers: Suzanne Neville

D-U-N-S 07-980-4543 IMP/EXP
CONSOLIDATED CONTAINER HOLDINGS LLC
CONSOLIDATED CONTAINER COMPANY
(*Suby of* CCC ACQUISITION HOLDINGS INC) ★
3101 Towercreek Pkwy Se P, Atlanta, GA 30339-3256
Tel (678) 742-4600 *Founded/Ownrshp* 2012
Sales 2.3MMM^E *EMP* 4,675
SIC 2671 7389 5113 Plastic film, coated or laminated for packaging; Packaging & labeling services; Boxes & containers
CEO: Sean R Fallmann
**CFO:* Richard P Sehring

D-U-N-S 01-952-8023
CONSOLIDATED CONTAINER INTERMEDIARY LLC
(*Suby of* CONSOLIDATED CONTAINER CO) ★
3101 Towercreek Pkwy Se, Atlanta, GA 30339-3256
Tel (678) 742-4600 *Founded/Ownrshp* 2012
Sales 857.0MM^E *EMP* 3,500^E
SIC 5113 2671 Boxes & containers; Plastic film, coated or laminated for packaging
CEO: Sean R Fallmann
**CFO:* Richard Sehring

D-U-N-S 05-646-3573 IMP/EXP
■ CONSOLIDATED DIESEL INC
(*Suby of* CUMMINS INC) ★
9377 N Us Highway 301, Whitakers, NC 27891-8621
Tel (252) 437-6611 *Founded/Ownrshp* 1981
Sales 16.0MM^E *EMP* 1,400
SIC 3519

D-U-N-S 06-383-0988
■ CONSOLIDATED DISPOSAL SERVICE LLC
BRIGGEMAN DISPOSAL SERVICE
(*Suby of* REPUBLIC SERVICES INC) ★
12949 Telegraph Rd, Santa Fe Springs, CA 90670-4049
Tel (562) 347-2100 *Founded/Ownrshp* 1998
Sales 98.1MM^E *EMP* 200
SIC 4953 Rubbish collection & disposal
Pr: Tom Vogt

D-U-N-S 00-698-2359 IMP
■ CONSOLIDATED EDISON CO OF NEW YORK INC
(*Suby of* CONSOLIDATED EDISON INC) ★
4 Irving Pl, New York, NY 10003-3502
Tel (212) 460-4600 *Founded/Ownrshp* 1884
Sales 10.3MMM *EMP* 13,200^E
Accts Pricewaterhousecoopers Llp Ne
SIC 4911 4924 4961 Generation, electric power; Transmission, electric power; Distribution, electric power; Natural gas distribution; Steam heating systems (suppliers of heat)
CEO: John McAvoy
**Ch Bd:* Kevin Burke
Pr: Craig S Ivey
CFO: Robert N Hoglund
Treas: Scott Sanders
Ex VP: Mary McCartney
Sr VP: John F Miksad
Sr VP: Elizabeth D Moore
Sr VP: Claude Trahan
Sr VP: Horace Webb
CTO: Bob Headlund
Board of Directors: L Frederick Sutherland, Vincent A Calarco, George Campbell Jr, Michael J Del Giudice, Ellen V Futter, John F Killian, Armando J Olivera, Sally H Pinero, Michael W Ranger, Linda S Sanford

D-U-N-S 00-294-4531 IMP
▲ CONSOLIDATED EDISON INC (NY)
4 Irving Pl, New York, NY 10003-3502
Tel (212) 460-4600 *Founded/Ownrshp* 1884
Sales 12.5MMM *EMP* 14,806
Accts Pricewaterhousecoopers Llp Ne
Tkr Sym ED *Exch* NYS
SIC 4931 Electric & other services combined
Ch Bd: John McAvoy
CFO: Robert Hoglund
Treas: Scott Sanders
Sr VP: Elizabeth D Moore
VP: Robert Muccilo
Board of Directors: Vincent A Calarco, George Campbell Jr, Michael J Del Giudice, Ellen V Futter, John F Killian, Armando J Olivera, Michael W Ranger, Linda S Sanford, L Frederick Sutherland

D-U-N-S 96-449-3246
CONSOLIDATED EDISON MASTER RETIREE HEALTH VEBA TRUST FOR WEEKLY EES
P.O. Box 5100 (02206-5100)
Tel (617) 664-9564 *Founded/Ownrshp* 2010
Sales 149.6MM *EMP* 2^E
Accts Buckconsultants Secaucus Nj
SIC 6733 Trusts

D-U-N-S 80-988-7904
■ CONSOLIDATED EDISON SOLUTIONS INC
(*Suby of* CONSOLIDATED EDISON INC) ★
100 Summit Lake Dr # 410, Valhalla, NY 10595-1339
Tel (914) 286-7000 *Founded/Ownrshp* 1993
Sales 500.0MM^E *EMP* 203
SIC 4924 4911 8748 Natural gas distribution; Electric services; Energy conservation consultant
Pr: Jorge Lopez
VP: Michael W Gibson
VP: Mark S Glucksman
VP: Paul F Mapelli
VP: James Mueller
Prin: Mary Hamby
CIO: Jack Barsky
Sftwr Eng: Kalyana Vadala
Snr Mgr: Ray Saracino

D-U-N-S 00-887-3804 EXP
CONSOLIDATED ELECTRICAL DISTRIBUTORS INC
C E D
1920 Westridge Dr Ste 107, Irving, TX 75038-2901
Tel (972) 582-5300 *Founded/Ownrshp* 2000
Sales 10.0MMM^E *EMP* 13,356
SIC 5063 5211

D-U-N-S 04-981-3181 IMP
CONSOLIDATED ENTERPRISES INC
WORTZ BEVERAGE MINNESOTA
(*Suby of* WIRTZ CORP) ★
680 N Lake Shore Dr Fl 19, Chicago, IL 60611-4548
Tel (312) 943-7000 *Founded/Ownrshp* 1935
Sales 85.9MM^E *EMP* 500
SIC 5182 Liquor
Pr: W Rockwell Wirtz
**CFO:* Max Mohler

D-U-N-S 13-576-8708
■ CONSOLIDATED EXECUTIVE OFFICE
CEO
(*Suby of* OFFICES, BOARDS & DIVISIONS)
950 Pennsylvania Ave Nw, Washington, DC 20530-0009
Tel (202) 616-6788 *Founded/Ownrshp* 2003
Sales NA *EMP* 1,999^E
SIC 9222 United States attorneys' offices;
Prin: Lee Lufthos

D-U-N-S 15-059-9033 IMP
CONSOLIDATED FABRICATION AND CONSTRUCTORS INC
3851 Ellsworth St, Gary, IN 46408-2030
Tel (219) 884-6150 *Founded/Ownrshp* 1985
Sales 83.2MM^E *EMP* 300^E
SIC 1623 Oil & gas pipeline construction
Pr: Ronald D Spork
**Sec:* Richard Spork
Div Mgr: Mark Ekaitis
IT Man: Jim Kish
Mtls Mgr: Tom Zager
Mktg Dir: Tony Schackmuth
Sls Mgr: Sol Sasoon

D-U-N-S 09-306-5811 IMP
CONSOLIDATED FABRICATORS CORP (CA)
CF
14620 Arminta St, Van Nuys, CA 91402-5902
Tel (818) 901-1005 *Founded/Ownrshp* 1974
Sales 109.9MM *EMP* 373
Accts Squar Milner Llp Los Angeles
SIC 3443 5051 3444 Dumpsters, garbage; Steel; Studs & joists, sheet metal
CEO: Michael J Melideo
**Pr:* Jeff Lombardi
Mng Dir: Brian A Atwater
Genl Mgr: Brandon Jones
Sls&Mrk Ex: Kim Gibbons
Sales Asso: Jennifer Capote

D-U-N-S 16-284-9264
CONSOLIDATED FIRE PROTECTION LLC
(*Suby of* MX HOLDINGS US) ★
153 Technology Dr Ste 200, Irvine, CA 92618-2461
Tel (949) 727-3277 *Founded/Ownrshp* 1999
Sales 110.4MM^E *EMP* 1,440
SIC 7389 Fire protection service other than forestry or public
CEO: Rob Salek
**Pr:* Keith Fielding
Exec: Maddy Malin
Dir IT: Jeff Murtari
IT Man: Michael Holtorf

CONSOLIDATED FLORAL SOLUTIONS
See USA BOUQUET LLC

D-U-N-S 09-845-4184 IMP/EXP
CONSOLIDATED GLASS & MIRROR CORP
GUARDIAN INDUSTRIES
(*Suby of* GUARDIAN INDUSTRIES CORP) ★
110 Jack Guynn Dr, Galax, VA 24333-2534
Tel (276) 236-5196 *Founded/Ownrshp* 1992
Sales 1.1MMM^E *EMP* 19,000
SIC 3231 Products of purchased glass; Mirrored glass
Pr: Scott Thompson
**Treas:* Doug Girdler
VP: Mike Sizemore
Opers Mgr: Jason Criner
Plnt Mgr: Dennis Carroll

D-U-N-S 07-868-4827
CONSOLIDATED GLASS HOLDINGS INC
500 Grant Ave Ste 201, East Butler, PA 16029-2111
Tel (866) 412-6977 *Founded/Ownrshp* 2011
Sales 114.3MM^E *EMP* 150^E
SIC 5039 3211 6719 1793 Glass construction materials; Flat glass; Investment holding companies, except banks; Glass & glazing work
Pr: Paul Cody

D-U-N-S 13-452-9742
CONSOLIDATED GOVERMENT OF GA INC
METRA COLUMBUS TRANSIT SYS
814 Linwood Blvd, Columbus, GA 31901-1962
Tel (706) 653-4410 *Founded/Ownrshp* 1972
Sales 229.2MM *EMP* 85
Accts Albright Fortenberry & Ninas
SIC 4111 Local & suburban transit
Pt: Isaiah Hugley

D-U-N-S 05-022-3296
CONSOLIDATED GRAIN & BARGE CO
CAHOKIA GRAIN
(*Suby of* CGB ENTERPRISES INC) ★
Washington & Water St, Wayne City, IL 62895
Tel (618) 895-2181 *Founded/Ownrshp* 1993
Sales 5.7MMM *EMP* 650
Accts Kpmg Llp New Orleans Louisia
SIC 4221 5153 4449 4491 Grain elevator, storage only; Grain & field beans; Canal barge operations; Marine cargo handling
IT Man: John Volichko

D-U-N-S 00-969-4719 EXP
CONSOLIDATED GRAIN & BARGE INC
(*Suby of* CAHOKIA GRAIN) ★
1001 Highway 190 E Svc Rd, Covington, LA 70433
Tel (985) 867-3500 *Founded/Ownrshp* 1977
Sales 5.7MMM *EMP* 550
SIC 5153 Grains
Pr: Kevin D Adams
**Ex VP:* Richard S Pemberton
**VP:* G Scott Leininger

D-U-N-S 17-494-0270 IMP/EXP
■ **CONSOLIDATED GRAPHICS INC**
(*Suby of* RR DONNELLEY) ★
5858 Westheimer Rd # 200, Houston, TX 77057-5643
Tel (713) 787-0977 *Founded/Ownrshp* 2014
Sales 1.7MMM^E *EMP* 5,288
SIC 2752 Commercial printing, lithographic
CEO: Joe R Davis
**CFO:* Jon C Biro
Ofcr: Contact Michael
Ex VP: John Green
VP: Paul Castain
VP: Dan Furry
VP: Condy Smith
VP: Trate Sue
Exec: Bob Broberg
Exec: Chris Coville
Genl Mgr: Kurt Johnson

D-U-N-S 02-096-3526
CONSOLIDATED HIGH SCHOOL DISTRICT NO 230 NOT FOR PRO
VICTOR J ANDREW HIGH SCHOOL
15100 S 94th Ave Uppr, Orland Park, IL 60462-3239
Tel (708) 349-5759 *Founded/Ownrshp* 1980
Sales 169.7MM *EMP* 900
Accts Wermer Rogers Doran & Ruzon
SIC 8211 Public senior high school
Dir IT: John Connolly
Pr Dir: Carla Erdey

D-U-N-S 06-794-4538
CONSOLIDATED LIBRARY DISTRICT NO 3
MIDCONTINENT PUBLIC LIBRARY
15616 E Us Highway 24, Independence, MO 64050-2057
Tel (816) 836-8175 *Founded/Ownrshp* 1965
Sales 41.1MM *EMP* 1,050
Accts Cochran Head Vick & Co Pc
SIC 8231 Public library
Ex Dir: Dick Wilding
Bd of Dir: Teresa Johnson
Exec: Marlene Boggs
Brnch Mgr: Cindy S Grant
Brnch Mgr: Tammy Parrott
Genl Mgr: Kirsten Grubbs
IT Man: Brian Gash

D-U-N-S 00-905-6037 IMP/EXP
CONSOLIDATED METCO INC
CONMET
5701 Se Columbia Way, Vancouver, WA 98661-5963
Tel (360) 828-2599 *Founded/Ownrshp* 1999
Sales 739.6MM^E *EMP* 2,000
SIC 3365 3363 3089 3714 3443 3312 Aluminum & aluminum-based alloy castings; Aluminum die-castings; Injection molded finished plastic products; Fuel systems & parts, motor vehicle; Fabricated plate work (boiler shop); Hot-rolled iron & steel products
Pr: Edward J Oeltjen
**Treas:* Glenn Chamberlin
**VP:* John E Waters
VP Bus Dev: Larry Sanford
Exec: Lina Krisciokaityte
Dir IT: Jill Molyneaux
IT Man: Fausto Murillo
IT Man: Kelly Talarico
Mfg Mgr: Doug Pomphrey
Opers Mgr: Richard Tracy
Ql Cn Mgr: Phillip Briggs

D-U-N-S 00-698-2383
■ **CONSOLIDATED NATURAL GAS CO** (DE)
(*Suby of* DOMINION RESOURCES INC) ★
120 Tredegar St, Richmond, VA 23219-4306
Tel (804) 819-2000 *Founded/Ownrshp* 1999
Sales 565.9MM^E *EMP* 4,700
SIC 1311 4922 4924 Natural gas production; Natural gas transmission; Natural gas distribution
Pr: Thomas F Farrell II
CFO: Thomas N Chewning
Assoc VP: Daniel Madden
VP: Steven A Rogers
Natl Sales: Shannon Venable

D-U-N-S 01-569-3703
■ **CONSOLIDATED NUCLEAR SECURITY LLC**
BABCOCK WLCOX TECH SVCS PANTEX
(*Suby of* BWXT) ★
2373 Farm To Market Rd, Amarillo, TX 79120
Tel (806) 477-3000 *Founded/Ownrshp* 2012
Sales 881.3MM^E *EMP* 3,300
SIC 7382 Security systems services
Pr: Morgan Smith
**CEO:* James Haynes
CFO: Ragan Rodgers
Ofcr: Chris Neumann
**VP:* Brian Reilly
Exec: Lonnie Flake
**Prin:* K K Clegg
**Prin:* Scott Kennedy
**Prin:* Damian Thomas
Prgrm Mgr: Dennis Penza
IT Man: Joshua Compton

D-U-N-S 07-839-0708
CONSOLIDATED NUCLEAR SECURITY LLC
Y-12 NATIONAL SECURITY COMPLEX
301 Bear Creek Rd, Oak Ridge, TN 37830-2504
Tel (865) 576-3456 *Founded/Ownrshp* 2012
Sales NA *EMP* 8,000
SIC 9229 Public safety bureau, government
Pr: Morgan Smith
Sls Dir: Barry Totten

D-U-N-S 00-384-6839
CONSOLIDATED OIL WELL SERVICES LLC
CONSOLIDATED OIL WELL SVCS LLC
(*Suby of* Q CONSOLIDATED OIL WELL SERVICES LLC) ★
1322 S Grant Ave, Chanute, KS 66720-2854
Tel (620) 431-9210 *Founded/Ownrshp* 1956
Sales 90.7MM^E *EMP* 140^E
SIC 1389 Oil field services; Cementing oil & gas well casings; Acidizing wells
Pr: S D Stanfield
**Pr:* Stephen D Stanfield
VP: Josh Bentsen

CONSOLIDATED OIL WELL SVCS LLC
See CONSOLIDATED OIL WELL SERVICES LLC

CONSOLIDATED PAPER COMPANY
See PAPER ENTERPRISES INC

D-U-N-S 03-150-7445
CONSOLIDATED PIPE & SUPPLY CO INC
VULCAN PLASTICS
1205 Hilltop Pkwy, Birmingham, AL 35204-5002
Tel (205) 323-7261 *Founded/Ownrshp* 1960
Sales 575.7MM *EMP* 700
Accts Warren Averett Llc Birmingha
SIC 3494 Valves & pipe fittings
Pr: Howard J Kerr
Sec: Barry Howton
Ex VP: Bob Kerr
Ex VP: Robert W Kerr
Brnch Mgr: Craig Brown
Brnch Mgr: Tommy Hallmark
Brnch Mgr: David Keck
Brnch Mgr: Allen Lepine
Genl Mgr: Bill Adcox
Genl Mgr: Mark Mathias
Sls Mgr: Danny Dunn

CONSOLIDATED PRECISION PDTS
See HITCHCOCK INDUSTRIES INC

D-U-N-S 04-936-3229 IMP
CONSOLIDATED PRECISION PRODUCTS CORP
CPP POMONA
(*Suby of* WARBURG PINCUS LLC) ★
1621 Euclid Ave Ste 1850, Cleveland, OH 44115-2126
Tel (909) 595-2252 *Founded/Ownrshp* 1999
Sales 598.7MM^E *EMP* 1,500
SIC 3365 3324 Aluminum foundries; Steel investment foundries
CEO: James V Stewart
**Pr:* Steve Clodfelter
**CFO:* Ron Hamilton
CFO: Buck McNichols
**VP:* Debbie Comstock
**VP:* Ali Ghavami
VP: Benjamin Mahr
VP: Gowri Shankar
**VP Mktg:* Dan Steele
**VP Sls:* Mel Crosier

D-U-N-S 03-029-8400 EXP
CONSOLIDATED RAIL CORP
(*Suby of* CONRAIL INC) ★
1717 Arch St Ste 1310, Philadelphia, PA 19103-2844
Tel (800) 456-7509 *Founded/Ownrshp* 1976
Sales 135.3MM^E *EMP* 1,500
SIC 4011 Railroads, line-haul operating
Pr: Timothy T O'Toole
**Pr:* Ronald L Batory
**Sr VP:* John A Mc Kelvey
VP: Robert Wagner
**Prin:* Donald Nelson

CONSOLIDATED REHABILITATION CO
See CONSOLIDATED SERVICES GROUP INC

D-U-N-S 04-852-6482 IMP
CONSOLIDATED RESTAURANT COMPANIES INC (DE)
EL CHICO RESTAURANT
12200 N Stemmons Fwy, Dallas, TX 75234-5888
Tel (972) 241-5500 *Founded/Ownrshp* 1998
Sales 302.2MM^E *EMP* 7,980
SIC 5812 6794 Eating places; Franchises, selling or licensing
V Ch: John D Harkey
**Treas:* Paul Hargett
**VP:* Bill Watson

D-U-N-S 05-976-8143
CONSOLIDATED RESTAURANT OPERATIONS INC
SPAGHETTI WAREHOUSE ITLN GRILL
(*Suby of* EL CHICO RESTAURANT) ★
12200 N Stemmons Fwy, Dallas, TX 75234-5888
Tel (972) 241-5500 *Founded/Ownrshp* 1999
Sales 170.3MM^E *EMP* 3,480
SIC 5812 6794 Italian restaurant; Franchises, selling or licensing
Pr: John R W Cracken
Pr: Joette Cox
COO: Mark Lamm
CFO: Paul Hargett
Treas: James Snell
VP: Mark Czaus
VP: Toby Hartman
VP: Rocky Vanover
VP: Rob Weaver
Exec: Reuben Lozano
**Prin:* John D Harkey Jr

D-U-N-S 04-704-3096
CONSOLIDATED SCHOOL DISTRICT 158
650 Academic Dr, Algonquin, IL 60102-4423
Tel (847) 659-6158 *Founded/Ownrshp* 1934
Sales 83.1MM^E *EMP* 1,400
Accts Evans Marshall & Pease Pc
SIC 8211 8741 Public elementary & secondary schools; Public elementary school; Public junior high school; Public senior high school; Management services
Bd of Dir: Paul Troy
Ofcr: Dan Armstrong
Genl Mgr: Mark Altmayer
Genl Mgr: Debra Salm
Dir IT: Chris Budzynski
Netwrk Mgr: Greg Conrad
Pr Mgr: Kimieth Rutherford
Instr Medi: Mary Olsen
Psych: Sue Banjavcic
Psych: Toni Klein
Snr Mgr: Linda Stoka

D-U-N-S 15-095-2505
CONSOLIDATED SCHOOL DISTRICT 2 (INC)
RAYTOWN QUALITY SCHOOLS
6608 Raytown Rd, Raytown, MO 64133-5240
Tel (816) 268-7000 *Founded/Ownrshp* 1930
Sales 134.0MM *EMP* 1,389
Accts Marr And Adams Pc Kansas C
SIC 8211 Public elementary school; Public junior high school; Public senior high school; Public special education school
Assoc Dir: Michael Deen
Trfc Dir: Robin Stuart
Pr Dir: Danielle Nixon
Teacher Pr: Marlene Devilbis
Psych: Eileen Fratzke
Psych: Rob Ukleya

D-U-N-S 10-001-1832
CONSOLIDATED SCHOOL DISTRICT OF NEW BRITAIN
272 Main St, New Britain, CT 06051-2203
Tel (860) 827-2200 *Founded/Ownrshp* 1873
Sales 55.1MM^E *EMP* 1,340
SIC 8211 Elementary & secondary schools
**Prin:* Ronald Jakubowski
**Prin:* Gene Pianka
Schl Brd P: Sharon B Saavebra

CONSOLIDATED SCHOOL DST 6
See FOX C-6 SCHOOL DISTRICT

D-U-N-S 01-152-7009 IMP
CONSOLIDATED SERVICE DISTRIBUTORS INC
C S D
905 Murray Rd, East Hanover, NJ 07936-2200
Tel (908) 687-5800 *Founded/Ownrshp* 1937
Sales 101.9MM^E *EMP* 85
SIC 5145 5194 Confectionery; Tobacco & tobacco products
Pr: Steven Simon
**Pr:* Kenneth Simon
**CFO:* Bill German
**Ch:* Herbert Lefkowitz
**Sec:* Mark Leskowitz
Mktg Mgr: Marie Rodriguez

D-U-N-S 16-941-5924
CONSOLIDATED SERVICES GROUP INC
CONSOLIDATED REHABILITATION CO
1555 Bustard Rd Ste 100, Lansdale, PA 19446-5700
Tel (215) 661-0500 *Founded/Ownrshp* 1980
Sales NA *EMP* 400
SIC 6411 Loss prevention services, insurance
Pr: Michael A Morrone
Pr: Missy Pudimott
Pr: Kevin Rawlins
CFO: Marianne Nagy
**Ex VP:* Craig Goldstein
**Sr VP:* Lee Ann Iannelli
**Sr VP:* John Miller
**Sr VP:* Stan Tomasevich
VP: Jennifer Goldstein
VP: Lee Iannelli
VP: Maria Longworth
VP: Greg Olsten

D-U-N-S 00-790-8585
CONSOLIDATED SUPPLY CO (OR)
FIXTURE GALLERY, THE
7337 Sw Kable Ln, Tigard, OR 97224-7986
Tel (503) 620-7050 *Founded/Ownrshp* 1928, 1978
Sales 176.1MM^E *EMP* 300^E
SIC 5074 5085 Plumbing & hydronic heating supplies; Plumbing fittings & supplies; Pipes & fittings, plastic; Industrial supplies
Ch: Karolyn J Neupert
**CEO:* Karolyn Neupert Hockley
**CFO:* Robert Bruce
**Treas:* Kevin R Neupert
Exec: Pauline Mueller
Brnch Mgr: Todd Coleman
Brnch Mgr: Pat Danforth
Brnch Mgr: Mitch Davis
Brnch Mgr: Casey Doyle
Brnch Mgr: Greg Jackson
Brnch Mgr: Steve Jordan

D-U-N-S 04-755-5453 IMP/EXP
CONSOLIDATED SYSTEMS INC
METAL DEK GROUP
650 Rosewood Dr, Columbia, SC 29201-4604
Tel (803) 771-7920 *Founded/Ownrshp* 1968
Sales 166.8MM^E *EMP* 400
SIC 3444 3479 4213

D-U-N-S 07-105-7251
■ **CONSOLIDATED THEATRES INC**
(*Suby of* REGAL ENTERTAINMENT GROUP) ★
5970 Fairview Rd Ste 600, Charlotte, NC 28210-2111
Tel (704) 554-1695 *Founded/Ownrshp* 1990, 2008
Sales 20.6MM^E *EMP* 1,200
SIC 7832 5441 Motion picture theaters, except drive-in; Confectionery produced for direct sale on the premises
Pr: Herman A Stone

D-U-N-S 15-288-7295 IMP
CONSOLIDATED VISION GROUP INC
AMERICAS BEST CNTCTS EYGLASSES
(*Suby of* NATIONAL VISION INC) ★
296 Grayson Hwy, Lawrenceville, GA 30046-5737
Tel (770) 822-3600 *Founded/Ownrshp* 1998
Sales 177.4MM^E *EMP* 1,525
SIC 5995 Optical goods stores
Ch Bd: Gregory L Segall
**Pr:* Barry Feinberg

D-U-N-S 15-235-7245
CONSOLIDATED WASTE SERVICES CORP
CON WASTE
Km 9 Rr 189, Gurabo, PR 00778
Tel (787) 273-7649 *Founded/Ownrshp* 2003
Sales 87.3MM^E *EMP* 1,200
SIC 4212 Garbage collection & transport, no disposal
Pr: Carlos Contreras
Off Mgr: Juanu Contreras

D-U-N-S 00-791-5523 IMP
CONSOLIDATION COAL CO INC
(*Suby of* MURRAY ENERGY CORP) ★
1000 Consol Energy Dr, Canonsburg, PA 15317-6506
Tel (740) 338-3100 *Founded/Ownrshp* 1965, 2013
Sales 2.3MMM^E *EMP* 2,667
SIC 1221 Bituminous coal surface mining
Pr: Bart I Hyita
**Treas:* John Reilly
**VP:* Loius Barlettai Jr

D-U-N-S 92-792-3250
CONSORTIUM FOR ELECTIONS & POLITICAL PROCESS STRENGTHENING
1225 I St Nw Ste 700, Washington, DC 20005-5962
Tel (202) 408-9450 *Founded/Ownrshp* 1995
Sales 108.2MM *EMP* 1
Accts Rsm Mcgladrey Inc Vienna Va
SIC 8651 Political organizations

D-U-N-S 06-576-7717
CONSPEC MARKETING AND MFG CO
(*Suby of* DAYTON SUPERIOR CORP) ★
636 S 66th Ter, Kansas City, KS 66111-2344
Tel (913) 287-1700 *Founded/Ownrshp* 2000
Sales 76.6MM^E *EMP* 1,000
SIC 2819 Industrial inorganic chemicals
Prin: Elizabeth Maday

D-U-N-S 80-666-2508
CONSTANCE FOOD GROUP INC
NORRIS FOOD SERVICES
545 Johnson Ave Ste 10, Bohemia, NY 11716-2698
Tel (631) 582-1144 *Founded/Ownrshp* 1992
Sales 124.1MM^E *EMP* 300
Accts Albrecht Viggiano Zureck & C
SIC 5149 5141 Sandwiches; Bakery products; Groceries, general line
Ch Bd: William J Norris
**Pr:* Michael Norris
**VP:* Jeanette Norris
VP: Darlene Picariello

D-U-N-S 06-194-5858
■ **CONSTANT CONTACT INC**
(*Suby of* ENDURANCE INTERNATIONAL GROUP HOLDINGS INC) ★
1601 Trapelo Rd Ste 329, Waltham, MA 02451-7357
Tel (781) 472-8100 *Founded/Ownrshp* 2015
Sales 331.6MM *EMP* 1,400
SIC 7373 4813 7331 Computer integrated systems design; Systems software development services; ; Direct mail advertising services
Pr: Hari Ravichandran
CFO: Marc Montagner
Treas: Steve Fritsch
Bd of Dir: Sam Silberman
Sr VP: Thomas C Howd
Sr VP: Joel A Hughes
Sr VP: Christopher M Litster
VP: Wiley Cerilli
VP: David Gilbertson
VP: Joel Hughes
VP: Catherine Kniker
VP: Bob Nault
VP: Raymond E Nault
VP: Daniel A Richards
VP: Piyum Samaraweera
VP: Stephen Shipley
VP: Alec Stern
VP Bus Dev: Matt Lee

CONSTAR PLASTICS
See CAPSULE PA INC

D-U-N-S 15-278-7461
■ **CONSTELLA GROUP LLC**
SRA INTERNATIONAL
(*Suby of* S R A) ★
2605 Meridian Pkwy # 200, Durham, NC 27713-5254
Tel (919) 544-8500 *Founded/Ownrshp* 1983
Sales 80.0MM^E *EMP* 1,200
SIC 7371 8742 7375 8748 8731 8071 Custom computer programming services; Business planning & organizing services; On-line data base information retrieval; Data base information retrieval; Test development & evaluation service; Commercial physical research; Medical laboratories
Prin: Stephen Hughes
COO: Jeffrey N Jordan
CFO: James J Scheuer
Ex VP: Deborah H Alderson
Sr VP: Stephen Tolbert
VP: Susan Acker-Walsh
VP: Kym Denny
VP: Tony Mitchell
VP: Timothy M Schur
IT Man: Mark Cochran
IT Man: Jon Kelly

D-U-N-S 05-965-1117 IMP/EXP
▲ **CONSTELLATION BRANDS INC**
207 High Point Dr # 100, Victor, NY 14564-1061
Tel (585) 678-7100 *Founded/Ownrshp* 1945
Sales 6.5MMM *EMP* 7,200
Accts Kpmg Llp Rochester New York
Tkr Sym STZ *Exch* NYS
SIC 2084 5182 5181 2082 2085 2087 Wines, brandy & brandy spirits; Wine & distilled beverages; Wine; Neutral spirits; Beer & other fermented malt liquors; Beer (alcoholic beverage); Distilled & blended liquors; Concentrates, drink
Pr: Robert Sands
Ch Bd: Richard Sands
Pr: F Paul Hetterich
Pr: John A Wright
CFO: David Klein
Ch: William F Hackett

Ofcr: Thomas M Kane
Ex VP: Tom Kane
Ex VP: Thomas J Mullin
Ex VP: William A Newlands
Sr VP: Erica Crawford
Sr VP: Jared Fix
Sr VP: Georgia Lamb
VP: Fred Berrios
VP: Peter Bruno
VP: K K Carey
VP: Elizabeth Choate
VP: John Clemens
VP: Sandy Dominach
VP: Mark Elder
VP: Paula Fitzgerald
Board of Directors: Frederic Cumenal, Jerry Fowden, Barry A Fromberg, Robert L Hanson, Ernesto M Hernandez, James A Locke III, Daniel J McCarthy, Judy A Schmeling, Keith E Wandell

D-U-N-S 16-010-4709 IMP/EXP
■ CONSTELLATION BRANDS US OPERATIONS INC
CENTERRA WINE COMPANY
(*Suby of* CONSTELLATION BRANDS INC) ★
235 N Bloomfield Rd, Canandaigua, NY 14424-1059
Tel (585) 396-7600 *Founded/Ownrshp* 1994
Sales 495.7MM^E *EMP* 1,790^E
SIC 2084 Wines
CEO: John Wright
Pr: William F Hackett
COO: Jim Debonis
CFO: Christopher Stenzel
Chf Mktg O: Christopher Lynch
Sr VP: Kocoloski Jim
VP: Dawn Deperrior
VP: Marc Donati
VP: Greg Gessner
VP: Evan Goldstein
VP: Georgia Lamb
VP: Andrea Smalling
VP Bus Dev: Lou Applebaum

CONSTELLATION ENERGY
See EXELON GENERATION CO LLC

D-U-N-S 06-250-0678 IMP
CONSTELLATION ENERGY GROUP INC
100 Constellation Way, Baltimore, MD 21202-6302
Tel (410) 470-2800 *Founded/Ownrshp* 1995
Sales NA *EMP* 7,800^E
SIC 4911 4924 1711

D-U-N-S 08-317-1657
■ CONSTELLATION ENERGY NUCLEAR GROUP LLC (MD)
(*Suby of* EXELON CORP) ★
100 Constellation Way 200c, Baltimore, MD 21202-6302
Tel (410) 783-2800 *Founded/Ownrshp* 1999, 2012
Sales 4.9MMM^E *EMP* 2,300
SIC 4911 Generation, electric power
Pr: Henry B Barron
Ch Bd: Charles Pardee
COO: Maria G Korsnick
CFO: Bernard Minvielle
Ofcr: John Heffley
VP: Bridget W Horner
Snr Sftwr: Jeremy Hanson
IT Man: Joseph Butler
IT Man: Christopher Kelley
Board of Directors: Charles Berardesco, J Bradley Fewell, Michael Pacilio, Carol Peterson, Jeffrey Williams

D-U-N-S 96-890-1137
■ CONSTELLATION ENERGY RESOURCES LLC
(*Suby of* EXELON CORP) ★
750 E Pratt St, Baltimore, MD 21202-3142
Tel (410) 470-2800 *Founded/Ownrshp* 2012
Sales 1.0MMM^E *EMP* 2,000^E
SIC 4911 4924 Generation, electric power; Natural gas distribution
CEO: Joseph Nigro
**COO:* David Ellsworth
**Sr VP:* Kathleen L Barrn
**Sr VP:* Paul R Bonney
**Sr VP:* Gary Fromer
Dir IT: Cathy Stryjewski
IT Man: Christopher Brown

D-U-N-S 84-173-9824
■ CONSTELLATION ENERGY SERVICES INC
(*Suby of* CONSTELLATION ENERGY RESOURCES LLC) ★
1716 Lawrence Dr, De Pere, WI 54115-9108
Tel (920) 617-6100 *Founded/Ownrshp* 2014
Sales 246.6MM^E *EMP* 268
SIC 4911 Distribution, electric power
Pr: Mark P Huston
VP: Jody Spaeth
VP: Ruqaiyah Stanley-Lolles
Sales Exec: Patrick Bowland
Sls&Mrk Ex: Jenny Short

D-U-N-S 14-109-2333
■ CONSTELLATION NEWENERGY - GAS DIVISION LLC
(*Suby of* CONSTELLATION ENERGY RESOURCES LLC) ★
9960 Corporate Campus Dr, Louisville, KY 40223-4098
Tel (502) 426-4500 *Founded/Ownrshp* 2012
Sales 165.5MM^E *EMP* 330
SIC 4924 Natural gas distribution
Ofcr: Bret Feller
VP: Brian Baumgardner
**VP:* Bryan Robinson

D-U-N-S 87-972-3468
■ CONSTELLATION NEWENERGY INC
NEW ENERGY
(*Suby of* CONSTELLATION ENERGY RESOURCES LLC) ★
1310 Point St Fl 9, Baltimore, MD 21231-3380
Tel (410) 783-2800 *Founded/Ownrshp* 2002
Sales 441.8MM^E *EMP* 280
SIC 4911 8748 Electric services; Energy conservation consultant
Pr: Michael Kagan
Treas: Coleen Hanna
Bd of Dir: Mayo A Shattuck
VP: Martha A Duggn
VP: Andrew L Good
VP: Carrie Hitt
VP: David L Rehn
**Mng Dir:* Mark P Huston
Genl Mgr: Keith Black
Opers Mgr: Gary Sperier
Mktg Dir: Charles Welsh

D-U-N-S 13-855-9559
■ CONSTELLATION NUCLEAR SERVICES L L C
(*Suby of* CONSTELLATION ENERGY NUCLEAR GROUP LLC) ★
39 W Lexington St, Baltimore, MD 21201-3910
Tel (410) 234-7950 *Founded/Ownrshp* 2001
Sales 504.8MM^E *EMP* 586^E
SIC 4911 Electric services
Pr: Boone Kenneth
**Pr:* Robert S Walker

D-U-N-S 14-594-6674 IMP
■ CONSTELLATION PUMPS CORP
(*Suby of* CLFX LLC)
10571 Telg Rd Ste 201, Glen Allen, VA 23059
Tel (804) 327-5664 *Founded/Ownrshp* 2000
Sales 78.5MM^E *EMP* 1,159^E
SIC 3561 Pumps & pumping equipment
CFO: G S Faison

D-U-N-S 83-246-5673
CONSTELLATIONS ENTERPRISE LLC
1775 Logan Ave, Youngstown, OH 44505-2622
Tel (330) 740-8208 *Founded/Ownrshp* 2007
Sales 392.0MM^E *EMP* 1,317
SIC 8741 Management services

D-U-N-S 96-613-3477
CONSTELLIS HOLDINGS LLC
850 Puddin Ridge Rd, Moyock, NC 27958-8679
Tel (252) 435-2488 *Founded/Ownrshp* 2016
Sales 248.3MM^E *EMP* 1,000
SIC 6719 Investment holding companies, except banks
CEO: Jason Deyonker
Pr: Dean Bosacki
CFO: Rosalind Kadasi
Ofcr: Gearoid Moore
Prgrm Mgr: Jeff Johnson

D-U-N-S 08-040-4415 IMP
CONSTELLIUM METAL PROCUREMENT LLC
2415 Rosedale St Ste H, Muscle Shoals, AL 35661-6427
Tel (256) 443-7435 *Founded/Ownrshp* 2016
Sales 373.0MM *EMP* 14
SIC 7389 Brokers' services
Sr VP: Andrew Logsdon

D-U-N-S 09-057-0149 IMP/EXP
■ CONSTELLIUM ROLLED PRODUCTS RAVENSWOOD LLC
(*Suby of* APOLLO GLOBAL MANAGEMENT LLC) ★
859 Century Rd, Ravenswood, WV 26164
Tel (304) 273-7000 *Founded/Ownrshp* 2011
Sales 228.8MM^E *EMP* 839
SIC 3353 Aluminum sheet & strip

CONSTELLTN ENEGY NCLEAR GRP
See CALVERT CLIFFS NUCLEAR POWER PLANT INC

D-U-N-S 09-568-3595
CONSTRUCTION ENTERPRISES INC
CEI OF TENNESSEE
2179 Edward Curd Ln # 100, Franklin, TN 37067-5789
Tel (615) 332-8880 *Founded/Ownrshp* 1994
Sales 116.2MM^E *EMP* 50
Accts Lewis Smith & Associates Pc
SIC 1522 1542 Multi-family dwellings, new construction; Institutional building construction
CEO: Bill Landers
**CFO:* Tom Ford
**Ex VP:* Giny Knudsen
**VP:* Horace Brown
**VP:* Gary Myers
VP: John Sakich
**VP:* Teresa Sands
**Prin:* John W Landers
Board of Directors: Bill Landers, John Blankenship, Thomas Ford, John Landers

D-U-N-S 80-077-8078
CONSTRUCTION MANAGEMENT & BUILDERS INC
CM&B
75 Sylvan St Ste C103, Danvers, MA 01923-2765
Tel (781) 246-9400 *Founded/Ownrshp* 1992
Sales 150.0MM *EMP* 80
SIC 8741 Construction management
CEO: Kevin G Puopolo
**Pr:* Sean Fahy
**CFO:* Steve Krauss
CFO: Pam Thomas
**Treas:* Margaret A Puopolo

D-U-N-S 14-820-3193
CONSTRUCTION MANAGEMENT SERVICES INC
3600 Silverside Rd, Wilmington, DE 19810-5100
Tel (302) 478-4200 *Founded/Ownrshp* 1984
Sales 223.0MM *EMP* 1,300
Accts Horty & Horty Pa Wilmington
SIC 1731 8741 General electrical contractor; Construction management
Pr: William A Goeller
**Treas:* Gerard J Herr
**VP:* Michael C Goeller
**VP Admn:* Regina M Camponelli

D-U-N-S 04-647-6537 EXP
CONSTRUCTION MATERIALS INC
CM
4350 Northern Blvd, Montgomery, AL 36110-3020
Tel (334) 272-8200 *Founded/Ownrshp* 1968
Sales 163.8MM^E *EMP* 250
SIC 5031 5051 Lumber, plywood & millwork; Metals service centers & offices
Ch Bd: Thomas C Crews
**Pr:* John G Crews
**CFO:* Micheal Elmore
**Sec:* Elsie Crews
**VP:* Gregory S Crews
VP: West Crews
**VP:* Ann Crews West
Genl Mgr: John Crews
Opers Mgr: Lance Whitworth
Sales Exec: Kit Agee
Sales Asso: Steve Cargill

D-U-N-S 00-528-4906 IMP
CONSTRUCTION PRODUCTS INC (IA)
(*Suby of* EFCO) ★
1800 Ne 46th Ave, Des Moines, IA 50313-2655
Tel (515) 313-4253 *Founded/Ownrshp* 1955
Sales 122.9MM^E *EMP* 300
SIC 3536 3544 Hoists; Industrial molds
CEO: K Eichmann
**Pr:* Brian West
**Treas:* B Hansell
Sfty Dirs: Kevin Maitland

D-U-N-S 62-247-1050
CONSTRUCTION PROTECTIVE SERVICES INC
CPS MATERIALS
436 W Walnut St, Gardena, CA 90248-3137
Tel (800) 257-5512 *Founded/Ownrshp* 1992
Sales 60.7MM^E *EMP* 1,000
SIC 7381 7382

D-U-N-S 00-219-4280 IMP/EXP
CONSTRUCTION SPECIALTIES INC
C/S CORPORATE
3 Werner Way Ste 100, Lebanon, NJ 08833-2230
Tel (908) 236-0800 *Founded/Ownrshp* 1948
Sales 375.7MM^E *EMP* 1,159
SIC 3446 3354 3443 3272 3585 Railings, prefabricated metal; Railings, bannisters, guards, etc.: made from metal pipe; Guards, made from pipe; Aluminum extruded products; Columns (fractioning, etc.): metal plate; Floor slabs & tiles, precast concrete; Air conditioning units, complete: domestic or industrial
Pr: Ronald F Dadd
**CFO:* Edward Altieri
Treas: Amelia Snyder
Bd of Dir: Lori Neitz
VP: Gene Beierle
**VP:* R Gordon Stewart
VP: Charles Van Koten
VP Mfg: Michael Creamer
VP Mktg: Paul R Moulton
VP Sls: Ken Major
Manager: Bill Philips
Board of Directors: James W Blaney, Ellen Hallock-Hakes, Dr Thomas B Hakes, J Bradford Hallock

CONSTRUCTIVE PLAYTHINGS
See U STOY CO INC

CONSULATE HEALTH CARE CHESWICK
See TANDEM HEALTH CARE OF CHESWICK INC

D-U-N-S 83-253-8701
CONSULATE HEALTH CARE LLC
(*Suby of* CONCURRENT PARTNERS LLLP) ★
800 Concourse Pkwy S, Maitland, FL 32751-6152
Tel (407) 571-1550 *Founded/Ownrshp* 2006
Sales 487.7MM^E *EMP* 9,100
SIC 8051 Skilled nursing care facilities
CEO: Bill Mathies
COO: Chris Bryson
CFO: Russell D Ragland
Ofcr: Veronique K Keller
Sr VP: Johnathan Silliter
VP: Michael Laughrun
VP: Lisa Murphy
VP: Kurt Rodriguez
VP: Jennifer Trapp
VP: Jared Van Doorn
VP: Sandy Wheeler
Exec: Nancy Plyler

D-U-N-S 01-515-9549
CONSULATE MANAGEMENT CO LLC
EDGEWOOD MANOR OF WESTERVILLE
800 Concourse Pkwy S, Maitland, FL 32751-6152
Tel (407) 571-1550 *Founded/Ownrshp* 2006
Sales 679.6MM^E *EMP* 12,000
SIC 8051 8059 8071 8093 Skilled nursing care facilities; Nursing home, except skilled & intermediate care facility; Personal care home, with health care; Rest home, with health care; X-ray laboratory, including dental; Rehabilitation center, outpatient treatment
**CEO:* Joseph D Conte
**Ex VP:* Jeff Jellerson
**Sr VP:* Troy Antonik
VP: Dan Davies
VP: Joseph Lesntrino
VP: Frank F Phillips Jr
CIO: Myron Brown

D-U-N-S 05-574-0336 IMP
CONSUMER AUTO PARTS INC
75 Fortune Blvd, Milford, MA 01757-1746
Tel (508) 634-0600 *Founded/Ownrshp* 2007
Sales 88.6MM^E *EMP* 400
SIC 5531 5013

D-U-N-S 94-176-0217 IMP
CONSUMER CELLULAR INC
12447 Sw 69th Ave, Portland, OR 97223-8517
Tel (503) 675-8988 *Founded/Ownrshp* 1995
Sales 124.2MM^E *EMP* 800
SIC 4812 Cellular telephone services; Paging services
Pr: John S Marick
Genl Mgr: Greg Pryor
Site Mgr: Tiffany Smith

CONSUMER DIRECT SERVICES
See NIGHTINGALE NURSING SERVICE INC

D-U-N-S 11-319-9348
CONSUMER DIRECTIONS INC
425 E Saint Germain St # 200, Saint Cloud, MN 56304-0728
Tel (320) 420-3423 *Founded/Ownrshp* 2001
Sales 19.7MM *EMP* 2,000
Accts Schlenner Wenner & Co St Cl
SIC 7361 8721 Employment agencies; Payroll accounting service
CEO: Lisa Kampfer
**CFO:* Shantel Jaszcak

CONSUMER GUIDE
See PUBLICATIONS INTERNATIONAL LTD

D-U-N-S 18-403-9832
CONSUMER HOME MORTGAGE INC
115 Broadhollow Rd, Melville, NY 11747-4992
Tel (631) 547-6840 *Founded/Ownrshp* 1986
Sales NA *EMP* 180
SIC 6163 Mortgage brokers arranging for loans, using money of others
Pr: Robert Standfast

D-U-N-S 82-812-1389
CONSUMER LOAN SERVICES LLC
811 Monitor St, La Crosse, WI 54603-3188
Tel (877) 791-1257 *Founded/Ownrshp* 2010
Sales NA *EMP* 47
SIC 6162 Mortgage bankers
Pr: Jay Garten

D-U-N-S 78-132-8026
▲ CONSUMER PORTFOLIO SERVICES INC
3800 Howard Hughes Pkwy, Las Vegas, NV 89169-0925
Tel (949) 753-6800 *Founded/Ownrshp* 1991
Sales NA *EMP* 935^E
Accts Crowe Horwath Llp Sherman Oak
Tkr Sym CPSS *Exch* NGM
SIC 6141 Financing: automobiles, furniture, etc., not a deposit bank; Installment sales finance, other than banks
Ch Bd: Charles E Bradley Jr
CFO: Jeffrey P Fritz
Sr VP: Mark A Creatura
Sr VP: John P Harton
Board of Directors: Chris A Adams, Brian J Rayhill, William B Roberts, Gregory S Washer, Daniel S Wood

D-U-N-S 16-185-3338
CONSUMER PRODUCT DISTRIBUTORS INC
J. POLEP DISTRIBUTION SERVICES
705 Meadow St, Chicopee, MA 01013-4820
Tel (413) 592-4141 *Founded/Ownrshp* 1986
Sales 968.9MM *EMP* 400
Accts Meyers Brothers Kalicka Pc
SIC 5194 5141 7389 5145 Smoking tobacco; Groceries, general line; Coffee service; Candy
Pr: Jeff Polep
**CFO:* Bill Fitzsimmons
**CFO:* William Fitzsimmons
**Ex VP:* Kenneth Morris
**VP:* Stephen J Martin
VP: Steve Peterson
VP: Lori Polep
**VP:* Lori Polep Saffer
Dir Sec: Benjamin Omerovic
Genl Mgr: Alan Plotkin
Dir IT: Dan Herington

CONSUMER REPORTS
See CONSUMERS UNION OF UNITED STATES INC

D-U-N-S 60-689-4095
CONSUMER SOURCE INC
PRIMEDIA
(*Suby of* PRIMEDIA) ★
3585 Engrg Dr Ste 100, Norcross, GA 30092
Tel (678) 421-3000 *Founded/Ownrshp* 1994
Sales 164.1MM^E *EMP* 800
SIC 2741 Guides: publishing only, not printed on site
COO: Gary Austin
VP: Scott Asher
VP: Mark Brooks
VP: Michael Herman
VP: James Moon
VP: Michael Shaw
Exec: Bruce Merrill
Brnch Mgr: Rodney Barton
Genl Mgr: Nathan Addesa
CIO: Jes Caplan
CTO: Mike Child

D-U-N-S 12-204-0053
CONSUMER TECHNOLOGY ASSOCIATION
CTA
1919 S Eads St Ste Ll, Arlington, VA 22202-3028
Tel (703) 907-7600 *Founded/Ownrshp* 1999
Sales 90.8MM *EMP* 150^E
Accts Lb Bdo Usa Llp Mc Lean Va
SIC 8611 Trade associations
Pr: Gary J Shapiro
Ch Bd: Randy Fry
Ch Bd: Jay McLellan
COO: Glenda Macmullin
Bd of Dir: Eric Davidson
Bd of Dir: Miguel Gil
VP: Karen Chupka
VP: Kara Dickerson
VP: Brian Markwalter
VP: Denise Medved
VP: Ellen Savage
VP: Gary Shapiro
VP: Tyler Suiters
Exec: Henry Muyshondt
Board of Directors: Michael Fasulo, Henry Juszkiewicz, Mike Mohan, Eliott Peck, John Penney, Sally Washlow

D-U-N-S 01-716-9186
CONSUMERS CONCRETE CORP
CONSUMERS SAND & GRAVEL CO
3508 S Sprinkle Rd, Kalamazoo, MI 49001-0813
Tel (269) 342-0136 *Founded/Ownrshp* 1933
Sales 107.1MM^E *EMP* 460
SIC 3273 3271 5032 Ready-mixed concrete; Blocks, concrete or cinder: standard; Gravel; Sand, construction
Ch: Tom W Thomas
**Pr:* Stephen A Thomas
**CFO:* Bruce Stanley
**VP:* Donald B Thomas Jr
**VP:* Gregory A Thomas
VP: Gregory A Thoms

D-U-N-S 00-896-0023
CONSUMERS COOPERATIVE ASSOCIATION OF EAU CLAIRE
MEGAFOODS
1201 S Hastings Way, Eau Claire, WI 54701-4459
Tel (715) 836-8700 *Founded/Ownrshp* 1935
Sales 91.8MM^E *EMP* 800
SIC 5411 5541 Grocery stores, independent; Convenience stores, independent; Filling stations, gasoline
Pr: Margarette Melrose

D-U-N-S 00-695-9803 IMP
■ CONSUMERS ENERGY CO
(*Suby of* CMS ENERGY CORP) ★
1 Energy Plaza Dr, Jackson, MI 49201-2357
Tel (517) 788-0550 *Founded/Ownrshp* 1886
Sales 6.1MMM *EMP* 7,394
SIC 4931 4911 4924 Electric & other services combined; Electric services; Distribution, electric power; Generation, electric power; Transmission, electric power; Natural gas distribution
Pr: John G Russell
CFO: Thomas J Webb
Sr VP: John M Butler
Sr VP: Daniel J Malone
Sr VP: Catherine M Reynolds
Sr VP: Brian F Rich
VP: Glenn P Barba
VP: Guy Packard
Snr Mgr: Mark Maida
Board of Directors: Myrna M Soto, Jon E Barfield, John G Sznewajs, Deborah H Butler, Laura H Wright, Kurt L Darrow, Stephen Ewing, Richard M Gabrys, William D Harvey, David W Joos, Philip R Lochner Jr, John G Russell

CONSUMERS LIFE INSURANCE CO
See MEDICAL MUTUAL OF OHIO

CONSUMERS SAND & GRAVEL CO
See CONSUMERS CONCRETE CORP

CONSUMERS SUPPLY DISTRIBUTING
See CSD INC

D-U-N-S 07-839-7131
CONSUMERS SUPPLY DISTRIBUTING LLC
718 N Derby Ln, North Sioux City, SD 57049-3020
Tel (712) 255-6927 *Founded/Ownrshp* 2011
Sales 166.2MM^E *EMP* 170^E
SIC 5122 Vitamins & minerals
**Pr:* David Patee
CFO: Glen Boehmer
**VP:* Dan Patee

D-U-N-S 00-159-9539
CONSUMERS UNION OF UNITED STATES INC (NY)
CONSUMER REPORTS
101 Truman Ave, Yonkers, NY 10703-1057
Tel (914) 378-2000 *Founded/Ownrshp* 1936, 1986
Sales 263.0MM *EMP* 480
Accts Kpmg Llp New York Ny
SIC 2741 2721 7389 Miscellaneous publishing; Magazines: publishing only, not printed on site; Fund raising organizations
Ch Bd: Diane Archer
**Ch Bd:* Walter D Bristol
V Ch: Thomas A Wathen
**Pr:* James Guest
**Pr:* Marta Tellado
COO: Laurence Bunin
CFO: Richard Gannon
**Treas:* Debra Cowan
**Treas:* Steven R Hill
Sr Ex VP: Erin Gudeux
Ex VP: Joel Gurin
VP: Jessie Becker
VP: Lisa Cribari
VP: Jason Fox
VP: Eileen Hershenov
VP: Chris Meyer
VP: John Sateja
VP: Shar Taylor
Assoc Dir: Nancy Crowfoot
Assoc Dir: Carol Lappin
Comm Dir: David Butler
Board of Directors: Joaquin Alvarado, R Anthony Benten

D-U-N-S 07-949-0206
■ CONTACT SOLUTIONS LLC
(*Suby of* VERINT SYSTEMS INC) ★
11950 Democracy Dr # 250, Reston, VA 20190-6284
Tel (703) 480-1620 *Founded/Ownrshp* 2016
Sales 41.7MM^E *EMP* 1,000
SIC 7379 7371 7389 ; Computer software development & applications; Telephone answering service
CEO: Michael Southworth
COO: Vete Clements
CTO: Randy Holl

D-U-N-S 05-301-2001
CONTAINER CO OF CAROLINA (DE)
ALLIED WASTE SVCS FORT MILL
3358 Highway 51, Fort Mill, SC 29715-8348
Tel (704) 377-0161 *Founded/Ownrshp* 2008
Sales 249.4MM^E *EMP* 500
SIC 4953

D-U-N-S 02-186-2984
■ CONTAINER LIFE CYCLE MANAGEMENT LLC
(*Suby of* GREIF USA LLC) ★
425 Winter Rd, Delaware, OH 43015-8903
Tel (740) 549-6087 *Founded/Ownrshp* 2010
Sales 266.9MM^E *EMP* 434
SIC 5093 Barrels & drums
**Pr:* Randy Stacy

D-U-N-S 07-908-9424 IMP
▲ CONTAINER STORE GROUP INC
500 Freeport Pkwy, Coppell, TX 75019-7420
Tel (972) 538-6000 *Founded/Ownrshp* 1978
Sales 794.6MM *EMP* 5,300^E
Tkr Sym TCS *Exch* NYS
SIC 5719 Closet organizers & shelving units; Kitchenware; Bath accessories
Ch Bd: William A Tindell III
**Pr:* Melissa Reiff
CFO: Jodi Taylor
CFO: Jodi L Taylor
**Ofcr:* Sharon Tindell
Ex VP: John Thrailkill
VP: Peter A Lodwick

D-U-N-S 09-241-2758 IMP
■ CONTAINER STORE INC
(*Suby of* CONTAINER STORE GROUP INC) ★
500 Freeport Pkwy Ste 100, Coppell, TX 75019-3998
Tel (972) 538-6000 *Founded/Ownrshp* 1978
Sales 599.7MM^E *EMP* 4,000
SIC 5719 Closet organizers & shelving units
CEO: William A Kip Tindell III
**Pr:* Melissa Reiff
**CFO:* Natalie Levy
VP: Barbara Anderson
VP: Peggy Doughty
VP: Eva Gordon
VP: Melissa Reif
VP: Audrey Robertson
VP: Casey Shilling
**VP:* Sharon Tindell
VP: Joe Wilkinson
Board of Directors: Caryl M Stern

D-U-N-S 06-603-9223 IMP
CONTAINERPORT GROUP INC
(*Suby of* WORLD SHIPPING INC) ★
1340 Depot St Ste 103, Cleveland, OH 44116-1741
Tel (440) 333-2009 *Founded/Ownrshp* 1971
Sales 105.0MM^E *EMP* 350
SIC 3715 Truck trailers
CEO: Frederick Hunger
**Pr:* Richard C Coleman
**Pr:* Russell A Graef
**Sr VP:* Glenn A Fehribach
**Sr VP:* James R Kramer
Sr VP: James Kramer
Sr VP: Bob Leef
**Sr VP:* David N Messer
**VP:* Robert L Lee
VP: Fred Marsicano
Dir Risk M: Dan Davis

D-U-N-S 61-512-1035
CONTAMINANT CONTROL INC
CCI
3434 Black And Decker Rd, Hope Mills, NC 28348-9331
Tel (910) 484-6841 *Founded/Ownrshp* 1989
Sales 105.1MM^E *EMP* 163
SIC 4959 Environmental cleanup services
CEO: Mark F Vestal
**Pr:* William G Taylor
CFO: Debra Tallon
**VP:* Al Bustin
IT Man: John Johnson

D-U-N-S 16-004-6322 IMP/EXP
CONTANDA LLC
WESTWAY GROUP, LLC
(*Suby of* BISHOP INFRASTRUCTURE II ACQUISITION COMPANY, INC.)
365 Canal St Ste 2900, New Orleans, LA 70130-6522
Tel (504) 525-9741 *Founded/Ownrshp* 2013
Sales 85.4MM^E *EMP* 271^E
SIC 4226 2048 Liquid storage; Feed supplements
CEO: Gene McClain
**CFO:* Thomas A Masilla Jr
Sr VP: Robert H Lewis
VP: Enin Falshaw
VP: Arthur Huguley IV
VP: Marie O'Donnell
**VP:* Chad Saltzman

D-U-N-S 82-550-4843
▲ CONTANGO OIL & GAS CO
717 Texas St Ste 2900, Houston, TX 77002-2836
Tel (713) 236-7400 *Founded/Ownrshp* 1986
Sales 116.5MM *EMP* 73^E
Tkr Sym MCF *Exch* ASE
SIC 1311 Crude petroleum & natural gas
Pr: Allan D Keel
**Ch Bd:* Joseph J Romano
CFO: E Joseph Grady
Sr VP: Thomas H Atkins
Sr VP: A Carl Isaac
Sr VP: Jay S Mengle
VP: John A Thomas

D-U-N-S 08-574-7376 IMP/EXP
CONTEC LLC
1011 State St, Schenectady, NY 12307-1500
Tel (518) 382-8150 *Founded/Ownrshp* 2008
Sales 871.2MM^E *EMP* 2,500
SIC 5065 7629 Television parts & accessories; Electrical equipment repair services; Telecommunication equipment repair (except telephones)
CEO: Hari Pillai
COO: Carroll Foreman
CFO: Jochen Vogt
VP: Richard Kielb
Exec: Darby Racey
Opers Mgr: Chris Birball
Sales Asso: Patrick Crowley

D-U-N-S 08-026-8088
CONTECH ENGINEERED SOLUTIONS INC
9025 Centre Pointe Dr # 400, West Chester, OH 45069-9700
Tel (513) 645-7000 *Founded/Ownrshp* 2012
Sales 175.6MM^E *EMP* 1,300
SIC 3444 3084 3317 3441 3443 Sheet metalwork; Culverts, sheet metal; Plastics pipe; Steel pipe & tubes; Fabricated structural metal; Fabricated plate work (boiler shop)
Pr: Michael Rafi
**CFO:* Jim Waters
**VP:* J Paul Allen
VP: Michael Carfagno
VP: Timothy Keilty
Area Mgr: Clayton Fawcett
Dist Mgr: Doug Maxwell
Dir IT: Mike Haskell
IT Man: Tom Jaeger
Netwrk Eng: Tob Fowler
Plnt Mgr: Chris Hajek

D-U-N-S 15-529-4440 IMP/EXP
CONTECH ENGINEERED SOLUTIONS LLC
(*Suby of* QUIKRETE HOLDINGS INC) ★
9025 Ctr Pinte Dr Ste 400, West Chester, OH 45069
Tel (513) 645-7000 *Founded/Ownrshp* 2016
Sales 563.1MM^E *EMP* 1,247
SIC 3444 3084 3317 3441 3443 Sheet metalwork; Culverts, sheet metal; Plastics pipe; Steel pipe & tubes; Fabricated structural metal; Fabricated plate work (boiler shop)
Pr: Mike Rafi
Pr: Vernon B Cameron
Pr: MO Heshmati
Pr: Thomas P Slabe
Pr: Steve R Spanagel
CFO: Jeffrey S Lee
CFO: James P Waters
Treas: Steve Skerl
Sr VP: William H Cordes
Sr VP: Richard G Stepien
VP: Paul Allen
VP: Jeff Beechan
VP: Robert Berry
VP: Frank Birney
VP: Michael Carfagno
VP: Jeff Collins
VP: Mark Nickel

D-U-N-S 11-468-5548
■ CONTEL FEDERAL SYSTEMS INC
(*Suby of* GTE CORP) ★
600 Hidden Rdg, Irving, TX 75038-3809
Tel (972) 718-5600 *Founded/Ownrshp* 1976
Sales 112.5MM^E *EMP* 1,500
SIC 3661 4813 Telephone & telegraph apparatus; Telephone communication, except radio
Pr: William M Edwards III
VP: Thomas W Muldoon
Board of Directors: Marianne Drost

D-U-N-S 06-892-1071
CONTEMPORARY SERVICES CORP
C S C
17101 Superior St, Northridge, CA 91325-1961
Tel (818) 885-5150 *Founded/Ownrshp* 1973
Sales 273.8MM^E *EMP* 5,000^E
SIC 7361 Employment agencies
CEO: Damon Zumwalt
**Pr:* Jim Granger
COO: Jonathan Fleming
VP: Mark Camillo
Exec: Malik Jones
Dir Soc: Mike Anderson
Dir Soc: Stephanie Bray
Dir Soc: Darold Gray
Dir Soc: Daryl Laughbaum
Dir Soc: Rachelle Lemoine
Dir Soc: Casey McNulty
Dir Soc: Ryan Schneider
Board of Directors: Stephen Mirabile

D-U-N-S 06-285-5714
CONTENT CRITICAL SOLUTIONS INC
(*Suby of* MAINTECH ACQUISITION) ★
121 Moonachie Ave, Moonachie, NJ 07074-1802
Tel (201) 528-2777 *Founded/Ownrshp* 2013
Sales 98.4MM^E *EMP* 1,356^E
SIC 7379
CEO: Frederick Van Alstyne
Pr: Sean Heffernan
**COO:* Walt Huryk
CTO: John Slaney
VP Opers: Carl Sattaur
Sls Mgr: Fabian Garcia

D-U-N-S 14-862-8436
■ CONTENT EPLUS SERVICES INC
(*Suby of* EPLUS INC) ★
13595 Dulles Tech Dr, Herndon, VA 20171-3413
Tel (703) 984-8400 *Founded/Ownrshp* 2001
Sales 224.2MM^E *EMP* 200^E
SIC 7371 Computer software development
Ch Bd: Phillip G Norton
**Pr:* Bruce Bower
**CFO:* Steven Mencarini
**Treas:* Kleyton Parkhurst
VP: Ken Farber

D-U-N-S 96-262-1335
CONTENT INGRAM GROUP INC
(*Suby of* INGRAM INDUSTRIES INC) ★
1 Ingram Blvd, La Vergne, TN 37086-3629
Tel (615) 793-5000 *Founded/Ownrshp* 2009
Sales 87.4MM^E *EMP* 102^E
SIC 5192 Books
Pr: Shawn Morin
**Ch Bd:* John R Ingram
**CFO:* Brian Dauphin
VP: Karen Cross
VP: Jeff McCall
VP: Rob Montgomery
VP: David Shealy
VP: Adam Sigler
VP: George Tattersfield
VP: Ross Womack
VP: Marcus Woodburn
VP: Ana Zaragoza

Exec: Wayne Keegan
Dir Teleco: Phil Watson

D-U-N-S 04-718-7448
CONTI CORP
CONTI ELECTRIC
6417 Center Dr Ste 120, Sterling Heights, MI 48312-2600
Tel (586) 274-4800 *Founded/Ownrshp* 1969
Sales 656.8MM^E *EMP* 2,500
SIC 1731 1711 Electrical work; General electrical contractor; Plumbing, heating, air-conditioning contractors; Mechanical contractor; Fire sprinkler system installation
Pr: Paul Duhaime
**Treas:* Andrew Conti
VP: John Spavale
Opers Mgr: Steve Freebury
Snr PM: Victor Calleja
Snr PM: Patrick McIntyre
Board of Directors: John A Conti

CONTI ELECTRIC
See CONTI CORP

D-U-N-S 62-612-4804
CONTI ENTERPRISES INC
CONTI GROUP, THE
2045 Lincoln Hwy, Edison, NJ 08817-3334
Tel (732) 520-5000 *Founded/Ownrshp* 1989
Sales 199.0MM^E *EMP* 500
Accts Cohn Reznick Llp Eatontown N
SIC 1611 1622 1623 General contractor, highway & street construction; Highway construction, elevated; Sewer line construction; Water main construction
CEO: Kurt G Conti
**COO:* Patrick Hogan
**COO:* William Picken
**CFO:* Dominic Mustillo
Ofcr: Cullin Wible
VP: Anthony Labato
VP: Matthew Skidmore
VP: Vincent Ugenti
VP: Jeanine Wright
Mtls Mgr: Sean Ridgway
Corp Couns: Steve Hedges

CONTI GROUP, THE
See CONTI ENTERPRISES INC

D-U-N-S 18-683-1624 IMP/EXP
CONTINENTAL AGENCY INC
1768 W 2nd St, Pomona, CA 91766-1206
Tel (909) 595-8884 *Founded/Ownrshp* 1987
Sales 150.6MM^E *EMP* 64
Accts Huang & Huang Walnut Califor
SIC 4731 Customhouse brokers
CEO: Jimmy Jaing
**Pr:* Beverly Jiang

D-U-N-S 08-201-2238 IMP/EXP
■ CONTINENTAL ALLOYS & SERVICES INC
(*Suby of* RELIANCE STEEL & ALUMINUM CO) ★
18334 Stuebner Airline Rd, Spring, TX 77379-5466
Tel (281) 376-9600 *Founded/Ownrshp* 2006
Sales 89.9MM^E *EMP* 153
SIC 5051 Pipe & tubing, steel
CEO: James D Hoffman
Pr: David Sapunjis
Pr: Randy Zajicek
CFO: Thomas M Urban
VP: Karla Lewis
VP: Silva Yeghyayan
Sales Asso: Shawn Weidemann

D-U-N-S 09-771-3663 IMP/EXP
CONTINENTAL AMERICAN CORP
PIONEER BALLOON CO
5000 E 29th St N, Wichita, KS 67220-2113
Tel (316) 685-2266 *Founded/Ownrshp* 1979
Sales 172.4MM^E *EMP* 900
SIC 2759 3069

D-U-N-S 10-911-6988
■ CONTINENTAL AMERICAN INSURANCE CO
AFLAC GROUP INSURANCE
(*Suby of* AFLAC INC) ★
1600 Williams St, Columbia, SC 29201-2220
Tel (803) 256-6265 *Founded/Ownrshp* 2009
Sales NA *EMP* 180^E
SIC 6411 Insurance agents, brokers & service
CEO: D Christian Goodall
**Ch:* Leon S Goodall
Ex VP: Chuck Shields
Ex VP: Newton Walker
**VP:* James Hennessy
Dir IT: Christian Goodall
Mktg Mgr: Emily Carter
Mktg Mgr: Laquita McFadden

D-U-N-S 00-692-9574
CONTINENTAL ASSURANCE CO
(*Suby of* WILTON RE US HOLDINGS INC) ★
333 S Wabash Ave Fl 43, Chicago, IL 60604-4107
Tel (312) 822-5000 *Founded/Ownrshp* 1956, 2014
Sales NA *EMP* 199
SIC 6411 6371 6321 Insurance agents, brokers & service; Pensions; Accident & health insurance
CEO: Thomas F Motamed
**CFO:* D Craig Mense
S&M/VP: Paula Hays

D-U-N-S 78-276-6633 IMP
CONTINENTAL AUTOMOTIVE INC
CONTINENTAL TIRE
(*Suby of* CONTINENTAL CAOUTCHOUC-EXPORT-GMBH)
1830 Macmillan Park Dr, Fort Mill, SC 29707-7712
Tel (704) 583-3900 *Founded/Ownrshp* 2006
Sales 3.4MMM^E *EMP* 8,250
SIC 3011 8711
Pr: Jochen Etzel
Pr: Martin Delouw
**Pr:* Bernd Frangenberg
Sfty Mgr: Teresa McIlrath
Mktg Dir: Clif Armstrong
Mktg Mgr: Barbara Desantis
Mktg Mgr: Thomas B Roydhouse

Sls Mgr: Travis Despain
Counsel: Daryl Hollnagel

D-U-N-S 05-917-7100 IMP/EXP
CONTINENTAL AUTOMOTIVE SYSTEMS INC
TEMIC AUTOMOTIVE NORTH AMERICA
(*Suby of* CONTINENTAL TIRE) ★
1 Continental Dr, Auburn Hills, MI 48326-1581
Tel (248) 393-5300 *Founded/Ownrshp* 1998
Sales 988.0MM[E] *EMP* 2,063
SIC 3714 Motor vehicle brake systems & parts
CEO: John Sanderson
**Pr:* Kathryn Blackwell
**Pr:* David Stout
CFO: Christop Kohlhaussen
**VP:* Rocky Istavan
VP: Jennifer Wahnschaff
Dir Lab: Joe Mackey
Dir Bus: Allan Losey
Mng Dir: Nick Randell
Prgrm Mgr: Dave Frankfurth
Prgrm Mgr: Dirk Matthijs

D-U-N-S 07-908-3344
▲ CONTINENTAL BUILDING PRODUCTS INC
12950 Worldgate Dr # 700, Herndon, VA 20170-6041
Tel (703) 480-3800 *Founded/Ownrshp* 2013
Sales 421.6MM *EMP* 546[E]
Tkr Sym CBPX *Exch* NYS
SIC 3275 Gypsum products; Gypsum board; Wallboard, gypsum
Pr: James Bachmann
CFO: Dennis Schemm
Sr VP: David Obergefell
Sr VP: Timothy Power
Sr VP: Dennis Romps
Board of Directors: J Barner, Edward Bosowski, Michael O Moore, Chadwick S Suss, Jack Sweeny

D-U-N-S 00-807-6697 IMP
CONTINENTAL CARBON CO
(*Suby of* CSRC USA CORP.)
16850 Park Row, Houston, TX 77084-5023
Tel (281) 647-3700 *Founded/Ownrshp* 1936
Sales 102.4MM[E] *EMP* 280
SIC 2895 3624 Carbon black; Carbon & graphite products
Ch Bd: Leslie C Y Koo
**Pr:* Dennis Hetu
COO: Steve Brown
**CFO:* Edward Carroll
CFO: Tom Carroll
Dir IT: Carlton Jim
VP Mktg: Thomas Moccia

D-U-N-S 07-069-4989
CONTINENTAL CARBONIC PRODUCTS INC
(*Suby of* MATHESON TRI-GAS INC) ★
3985 E Harrison Ave, Decatur, IL 62526-5534
Tel (217) 428-2068 *Founded/Ownrshp* 2014
Sales 273.8MM[E] *EMP* 700
SIC 2813 Carbon dioxide; Dry ice, carbon dioxide (solid)
Pr: John W Funk
CFO: John Ewers
**VP:* Mark D Hatton
VP: Jason Taulbee
Area Mgr: Nathan Carl
Area Mgr: Kyle Smith
Brnch Mgr: Bryan Andrews
Brnch Mgr: Viany Cartagena
Brnch Mgr: Jim Ferragamo
Brnch Mgr: Bob Grewe
Brnch Mgr: John Higgins

D-U-N-S 00-692-9582
■ CONTINENTAL CASUALTY CO INC
CNA INSURANCE
(*Suby of* CNA INSURANCE) ★
333 S Wabash Ave Ste 300, Chicago, IL 60604-4107
Tel (312) 822-5000 *Founded/Ownrshp* 1897
Sales NA *EMP* 6,900
SIC 6331 Fire, marine & casualty insurance & carriers; Property damage insurance
Ch Bd: Thomas F Motamed
CEO: Claudia Kleyweg
CFO: John Corcoran
CFO: Robert Deutsch
CFO: Peter E Jokil
**CFO:* D Craig Mense
VP: Richard Dubberke
**VP:* Marie Hotza
**VP:* Craig L Meadors
VP: Laurie Munson
CIO: Larry Bowlin

D-U-N-S 00-860-4878 IMP/EXP
■ CONTINENTAL CEMENT CO LLC
(*Suby of* SUMMIT MATERIALS INC) ★
16100 Swingley Ridge Rd, Chesterfield, MO 63017-1786
Tel (636) 532-7440 *Founded/Ownrshp* 2015
Sales 110.0MM *EMP* 262
SIC 3241 4953 Portland cement; Recycling, waste materials

D-U-N-S 07-607-5423 IMP/EXP
CONTINENTAL CONCESSION SUPPLIES INC
C.C.S.I.
575 Jericho Tpke Ste 300, Jericho, NY 11753-1847
Tel (516) 739-8777 *Founded/Ownrshp* 1993
Sales 291.7MM[E] *EMP* 207
SIC 5145 Popcorn & supplies; Candy
Ch Bd: Aaron Slonim
**CFO:* Kevin Fitzpatrick
Rgnl Mgr: Scott Murgatroyd
Sls Mgr: Marty Leiske
Sls Mgr: David Reling
Sales Asso: Walter Schwartz

D-U-N-S 04-361-4023 IMP
■ CONTINENTAL CORP
(*Suby of* CNA INSURANCE) ★
111 8th Ave, New York, NY 10011-5201
Tel (212) 440-3000 *Founded/Ownrshp* 1995
Sales NA *EMP* 1,813
SIC 6331 6351 6321 6159 8741 6411 Property damage insurance; Fire, marine & casualty insurance: stock; Automobile insurance; Workers' compensation insurance; Fidelity insurance; Surety insurance bonding; Credit & other financial responsibility insurance; Accident insurance carriers; Health insurance carriers; Loan institutions, general & industrial; Management services; Insurance adjusters
Ch Bd: Thomas F Motamed
Ch Bd: Dennis Chookaszian
Pr: Philip L Engel
CFO: J Heath Fitzsimmons
VP: Peter E Jokiel
VP: Donald M Lowry
VP: Donald C Rycroft
VP: William H Sharkey
S&M/VP: Christophe D Introno
Sls Mgr: Scott Pall

D-U-N-S 09-142-4960
CONTINENTAL CURRENCY SERVICES INC (CA)
CASH IT HERE
1108 E 17th St, Santa Ana, CA 92701-2600
Tel (714) 569-0300 *Founded/Ownrshp* 1977
Sales NA *EMP* 575
SIC 6099 Check cashing agencies; Electronic funds transfer network, including switching; Money order issuance
Pr: Fred Kunik
**Ch Bd:* Irving Barr
**COO:* David Wilder
CFO: William J Nolan
Ofcr: Helen Cho
Ofcr: Rebecca Wischkaemper
Dist Mgr: Jerry Chavez
Dist Mgr: Doris Murphy
Dist Mgr: Douglas Sanford
Genl Mgr: Alan Harris
IT Man: Em Castillo

CONTINENTAL DATA GRAPHICS
See CONTINENTAL GRAPHICS CORP

D-U-N-S 00-718-5556 IMP
CONTINENTAL DISC CORP (MO)
(*Suby of* R F H) ★
3160 W Heartland Dr, Liberty, MO 64068-3385
Tel (816) 792-1500 *Founded/Ownrshp* 1965
Sales 86.8MM[E] *EMP* 367
SIC 3491 3498 7699 3494 Pressure valves & regulators, industrial; Process control regulator valves; Pipe fittings, fabricated from purchased pipe; Valve repair, industrial; Valves & pipe fittings
Pr: David Brown
Pr: Evan Scheier
IT Man: Stacy Brinton
QC Dir: Shane Bacon
Manager: Dylan Marksman

D-U-N-S 96-271-8953
CONTINENTAL DISTRIBUTORS INC
CONTINENTAL SERVICES
35710 Mound Rd, Sterling Heights, MI 48310-4726
Tel (586) 268-3835 *Founded/Ownrshp* 1997
Sales 113.3MM[E] *EMP* 500
SIC 5962 5812 Food vending machines; Caterers
Pr: Jim Bardy
**Ex VP:* Mitch Kusiak
VP: Kathryn Blackwell
IT Man: Kristin Scott
Sls Mgr: Mary Peralta

D-U-N-S 83-045-4489
CONTINENTAL ENERGY SYSTEMS LLC
SEMCO ENERGY
1411 3rd St Ste A, Port Huron, MI 48060-5480
Tel (800) 624-2019 *Founded/Ownrshp* 2008
Sales 722.8MM[E] *EMP* 1,370
SIC 4924 Natural gas distribution
Ch Bd: J Russell Triedman
**Pr:* Arthur Pendleton
**Pr:* George A Schreiber Jr
**CFO:* Michael V Palmeri
**Ex VP:* Peter F Clark
**Sr VP:* Lance S Smotherman
Dir Risk M: Richard W Straney
Off Mgr: Deb Johnson

D-U-N-S 61-158-8703
■ CONTINENTAL EXCHANGE SOLUTIONS INC
RIA FINANCIAL SERVICE
(*Suby of* EURONET WORLDWIDE INC) ★
7001 Village Dr Ste 200, Buena Park, CA 90621-2232
Tel (562) 345-2100 *Founded/Ownrshp* 2007
Sales NA *EMP* 1,543[E]
SIC 6099 Electronic funds transfer network, including switching
CEO: Juan C Bianchi
COO: Timothy A Fanning
CFO: Shawn D Fielder
Sr VP: Anthony Grandidge
VP: Cindy Ashcraft
VP: Ray Butner
VP: Rosario Escarpita
VP: David Munger
VP: Randy Reategui
VP: Christopher Toumajian
VP: Alonzo Venegas
VP: Jessica Yee

CONTINENTAL FLORAL GREEN
See CONTINENTAL WHOLESALE FLORISTS INC

D-U-N-S 12-976-0880
■ CONTINENTAL GLOBAL GROUP INC
(*Suby of* MINING JOY MACHINERY) ★
438 Industrial Dr, Winfield, AL 35594-4503
Tel (205) 487-6492 *Founded/Ownrshp* 1997
Sales 355.2MM *EMP* 1,430
SIC 3535 Conveyors & conveying equipment
Pr: Ronald W Kaplan
**CFO:* Jeffrey A Behrendt
**VP:* James L Smothers

D-U-N-S 00-698-2409 IMP/EXP
CONTINENTAL GRAIN CO
767 5th Ave Fl 15, New York, NY 10153-0015
Tel (212) 207-5930 *Founded/Ownrshp* 1926
Sales 2.5MMM[E] *EMP* 14,200
SIC 2015 2041

D-U-N-S 15-158-9009
■ CONTINENTAL GRAPHICS CORP
CONTINENTAL DATA GRAPHICS
(*Suby of* BOEING CO) ★
4060 N Lakewood Blvd, Long Beach, CA 90808-1700
Tel (714) 503-4200 *Founded/Ownrshp* 2000
Sales 175.5MM[E] *EMP* 1,200
SIC 3724 7371 7372 7374 Aircraft engines & engine parts; Computer software development; Application computer software; Computer graphics service
CEO: David Malmo
CFO: Fenton Markevich
**CFO:* James Mills
**Ex VP:* Michael Parven
VP: Kelly Moyes
VP: Thomas Spangler
Comm Man: Zeyad Maasarani
Mktg Dir: Mona Rice
Snr Mgr: Robert Coronel

D-U-N-S 82-514-5097
CONTINENTAL LABOR RESOURCES INC
900 Mohawk St Ste 120, Bakersfield, CA 93309-7441
Tel (661) 635-0335 *Founded/Ownrshp* 1993
Sales 57.2MM[E] *EMP* 2,885
SIC 7363 Temporary help service
Pr: Gloria Hernandez
**Sec:* Karen Cain

D-U-N-S 00-692-9624
▲ CONTINENTAL MATERIALS CORP
440 S La Salle St # 3100, Chicago, IL 60605-5020
Tel (312) 541-7200 *Founded/Ownrshp* 1954
Sales 136.8MM *EMP* 563
Accts Bkd Llp Indianapolis Indian
Tkr Sym CUO *Exch* ASE
SIC 3585 3273 5031 Refrigeration & heating equipment; Ready-mixed concrete; Building materials, exterior; Doors
Ch Bd: James G Gidwitz
CFO: Mark S Nichter

D-U-N-S 03-524-3609
CONTINENTAL MICROWAVE AND TOOL CO INC
COBHAM ANTENNA SYSTEMS MICROWA
(*Suby of* COBHAM AES HOLDINGS INC) ★
11 Continental Dr, Exeter, NH 03833-4564
Tel (603) 775-5200 *Founded/Ownrshp* 1996
Sales 135.1MM[E] *EMP* 454
SIC 3679 Microwave components
CEO: John McNulla
**Pr:* Rick Pierson
**CFO:* Richard Gregorio

D-U-N-S 00-924-1167 IMP/EXP
CONTINENTAL MILLS INC (WA)
CM
18100 Andover Park W, Tukwila, WA 98188-4703
Tel (253) 872-8400 *Founded/Ownrshp* 1932, 1967
Sales 262.6MM[E] *EMP* 575
SIC 2045 2038 Flours & flour mixes, from purchased flour; Breakfasts, frozen & packaged
Ch Bd: John M Heily
**COO:* Ronald W Wise
**CFO:* Michael D Castle
Treas: Peter Hughes
**Sr VP:* Charles Berry
**Sr VP:* Mark Harris
**Sr VP:* James M Hershberger
**Sr VP:* Michael Meredith
**Sr VP:* Clyde Walker
**VP:* Patrick Baraya
VP: Kraig Bergmann
**VP:* Douglas Deeth
VP: Andy Heily
**VP:* Robert Higbee
**VP:* Marc Kropack
Dir Bus: Jeff Shuman

D-U-N-S 17-078-3117 IMP
CONTINENTAL MOTORS INC
CONTINENTAL MOTORS SERVICES
(*Suby of* TECHNIFY MOTOR (USA) INC) ★
2039 S Broad St, Mobile, AL 36615-1286
Tel (251) 438-3411 *Founded/Ownrshp* 2011
Sales 108.1MM[E] *EMP* 400[E]
SIC 3724 Aircraft engines & engine parts
Pr: Rhett C Ross
**CFO:* William Read
**Sr VP:* Stephen Ginger
**Sr VP:* Ken Suda
**Sr VP:* Shan Tian
**VP:* Susan Ames

CONTINENTAL MOTORS SERVICES
See CONTINENTAL MOTORS INC

D-U-N-S 00-196-4170 IMP/EXP
CONTINENTAL OFFICE FURNITURE CORP (OH)
CONTINNTAL OFFICE ENVIRONMENTS
2601 Silver Dr, Columbus, OH 43211-1056
Tel (614) 262-5010 *Founded/Ownrshp* 1941
Sales 110.0MM *EMP* 190
Accts Gbq Partners Llc Columbus Oh
SIC 5021 1752 Office furniture; Wood floor installation & refinishing
CEO: Ira Sharfin
**Ch Bd:* Franklin Kass
**Ch Bd:* John Lucks Jr
Pr: Vicki Commeans
**Pr:* Kyle Johnson
COO: Tom Onstott
Ex VP: Nick Magoto
VP: Kent Beightler
VP: Joe Canup
VP: Joe Hitschler
VP: Rob Owens
VP: Rene Phipps
VP: Lisa Welch
Exec: Pam Blair
Exec: Sharon Oaks

D-U-N-S 02-508-9160 IMP/EXP
CONTINENTAL PAPER GRADING CO
C F G
1623 S Lumber St, Chicago, IL 60616-1192
Tel (312) 226-2010 *Founded/Ownrshp* 2002
Sales 162.0MM *EMP* 70
Accts Morrison & Morrison Ltd Chic
SIC 5093 Waste paper
CEO: William D Harrow
Pr: Mark St Cyr
Sec: Tony Aukett
VP: Gary Schultz
Off Mgr: Shana Jones
Plnt Mgr: Troy Yerger
VP Sls: Jay Raemisch

CONTINENTAL PRODUCTS
See MEXICO PLASTIC CO

D-U-N-S 02-262-6956
CONTINENTAL REAL ESTATE COMPANIES
150 E Broad St Ste 200, Columbus, OH 43215-3644
Tel (614) 221-1800 *Founded/Ownrshp* 1979
Sales 105.8MM[E] *EMP* 200
SIC 1542 1541 Commercial & office building, new construction; Industrial buildings & warehouses
Ch Bd: Franklin Kass
**CFO:* James Conway
**VP:* John Lucks Jr
VP: Brett Robinson

CONTINENTAL RENTALS
See CONTINENTAL RESOURCES INC

D-U-N-S 00-142-2583
CONTINENTAL RESOURCES INC (MA)
CONTINENTAL RENTALS
175 Middlesex Tpke Ste 1, Bedford, MA 01730-1469
Tel (781) 275-0850 *Founded/Ownrshp* 1962
Sales 479.0MM *EMP* 300
Accts Gt Reilly & Company Milton
SIC 5045 5065 7377 7359 7378 7629 Computer peripheral equipment; Computer software; Electronic parts & equipment; Computer peripheral equipment rental & leasing; Electronic equipment rental, except computers; Computer peripheral equipment repair & maintenance; Electrical measuring instrument repair & calibration
CEO: Mary Nardella
**Pr:* James F McCann Jr
**COO:* Kevin E McCann
**CFO:* James M Bunt
**VP:* James D Keady
Dir Bus: Mitch Lapin
Mng Dir: Wayne Molle
Snr Ntwrk: Lino Vega
CIO: Sam Schoelen
Sales Asso: Ryan Carey
Sales Asso: Gina Drogowski
Board of Directors: Elizabeth Busiek, Ann Dempsey, Pat Kirchner, Ann F McCann, Cathy Shattuck

D-U-N-S 07-429-2095
▲ CONTINENTAL RESOURCES INC
20 N Broadway, Oklahoma City, OK 73102-9213
Tel (405) 234-9000 *Founded/Ownrshp* 1967
Sales 2.6MMM *EMP* 1,143
Tkr Sym CLR *Exch* NYS
SIC 1311 Crude petroleum production; Natural gas production
Ch Bd: Harold G Hamm
Pr: Jack H Stark
CFO: John D Hart
Sr VP: Pat Bent
Sr VP: Glen Brown
Sr VP: Eric S Eissenstat
Sr VP: Gary E Gould
Sr VP: Steven K Owen
Sr VP: Ramiro F Rangel
Snr Mgr: Darin Pendleton
Board of Directors: William B Berry, David L Boren, Ellis L McCain, John T McNabb II, Mark E Monroe

CONTINENTAL SERVICES
See CONTINENTAL DISTRIBUTORS INC

D-U-N-S 05-403-7997
CONTINENTAL STRUCTURAL PLASTICS HOLDINGS CORP
255 Rex Blvd, Auburn Hills, MI 48326-2954
Tel (248) 237-7800 *Founded/Ownrshp* 2005
Sales 798.6MM[E] *EMP* 2,700
SIC 3089 Plastic processing
CEO: Frank Macher
**Pr:* Steve Rooney
**CFO:* Jon Smith
**VP:* Probir Guha
**VP:* Frank Silvagi

D-U-N-S 00-531-9959 IMP
CONTINENTAL STRUCTURAL PLASTICS INC
(*Suby of* CSP HOLDING CORP) ★
255 Rex Blvd, Auburn Hills, MI 48326-2954
Tel (248) 237-7800 *Founded/Ownrshp* 1998
Sales 798.6MM[E] *EMP* 2,300
SIC 3089 Plastic processing
CEO: Frank Macher
**CFO:* Jon Smith
VP: Phil Kusky
Prgrm Mgr: Janice Recchia
Prgrm Mgr: Christal Schmideberg
Prgrm Mgr: Ron Tomaszewski
IT Man: Anthony Sexton
Mtls Mgr: Joe Huggins
Mfg Mgr: Brent Cagala
Plnt Mgr: Tracy Gray
Ql Cn Mgr: Dwight Bowman

D-U-N-S 03-197-5191 IMP
CONTINENTAL TEVES INC
1 Continental Dr, Auburn Hills, MI 48326-1581
Tel (248) 393-5300 *Founded/Ownrshp* 1998
Sales 232.6MM[E] *EMP* 1,877
SIC 3714

CONTINENTAL TIRE
See CONTINENTAL AUTOMOTIVE INC

D-U-N-S 12-179-3137 IMP/EXP
CONTINENTAL TIRE AMERICAS LLC
CONTINENTAL TIRES
(*Suby of* CONTINENTAL TIRE HOLDING US LLC) ★
1830 Macmillan Park Dr, Fort Mill, SC 29707-7712
Tel (800) 450-3187 *Founded/Ownrshp* 2010
Sales 1.6MMM[E] *EMP* 3,075
SIC 3011 Tires & inner tubes
CEO: Jochen Etzel
Pr: Matthias Schonberg
CFO: Narendra M Pathipati
Treas: Todd Currier
VP: Paul Williams
Exec: Stephani Canty
Sfty Dirs: Ken Miller
Plnt Mgr: Terry Graham
Ql Cn Mgr: Rick Morris

D-U-N-S 96-548-2743 IMP
CONTINENTAL TIRE HOLDING US LLC
(*Suby of* CONTINENTAL GLOBAL HOLDING NETHERLANDS B.V.)
1830 Macmillan Park Dr, Fort Mill, SC 29707-7712
Tel (704) 588-5895 *Founded/Ownrshp* 2010
Sales 1.5MMM[E] *EMP* 6,196[E]
SIC 3011 Tires & inner tubes

CONTINENTAL TIRES
See CONTINENTAL TIRE AMERICAS LLC

CONTINENTAL WESTERN GROUP
See CONTINENTAL WESTERN INSURANCE CO

D-U-N-S 05-918-5041
■ CONTINENTAL WESTERN INSURANCE CO
CONTINENTAL WESTERN GROUP
(*Suby of* BERKLEY REGIONAL INSURANCE CO) ★
11201 Douglas Ave, Urbandale, IA 50322-3780
Tel (515) 473-3000 *Founded/Ownrshp* 1986
Sales NA *EMP* 390
Accts Kpmg Llp Des Moines Ia
SIC 6331 Fire, marine & casualty insurance
Pr: Michael Garrett Connor
**Ch Bd:* William R Berkley
**Treas:* Robert F Buehler
**Treas:* Ann M Collins
VP: Tom Boots
VP: Steven Freebom
VP: Linsdy Oster
VP: Robert Shepard
VP: Walter Stradley
**VP:* John F Thelen
VP: Jeff West

D-U-N-S 02-701-9033 IMP
CONTINENTAL WHOLESALE FLORISTS INC
CONTINENTAL FLORAL GREEN
1777 Ne Loop 410, San Antonio, TX 78217-5209
Tel (210) 654-6543 *Founded/Ownrshp* 1954
Sales 83.7MM[E] *EMP* 150
SIC 5193 Nursery stock
Pr: Larson G Everett
CFO: Arthur McNamee
**Sec:* Nuria Everett
**VP:* Jerome Everett

D-U-N-S 06-514-8389
CONTINENTAL WINGATE CO INC
1 Charles River Pl, Needham, MA 02494-2750
Tel (781) 707-9000 *Founded/Ownrshp* 1971
Sales 178.6MM[E] *EMP* 2,500
SIC 6513 8051 Apartment building operators; Skilled nursing care facilities
CEO: Gerald Schuster
**Treas:* Brian Callahan
**VP:* Mark Schuster

D-U-N-S 14-363-1294
CONTINENTAL/MIDLAND LLC
CMG CONTMID GROUP
(*Suby of* CONTMID HOLDINGS, INC.)
24000 S Western Ave, Park Forest, IL 60466-3428
Tel (708) 747-1200 *Founded/Ownrshp* 2014
Sales 225.1MM[E] *EMP* 593
SIC 3452 Bolts, nuts, rivets & washers
CEO: Philip Johnson
**CFO:* Charles Beto
CFO: Julie Oleary
VP: Joe Ballarini
Ql Cn Mgr: Ricardo Aspiras
Ql Cn Mgr: Mark Rowbotham
VP Sls: Robert Kaminski
Sls Mgr: David Krause

D-U-N-S 11-883-8593
CONTINGENT NETWORK SERVICES LLC
4400 Port Union Rd, West Chester, OH 45011-9714
Tel (513) 616-5773 *Founded/Ownrshp* 2002
Sales 112.7MM[E] *EMP* 228[E]
SIC 7379 7373

CONTINNTAL OFFICE ENVIRONMENTS
See CONTINENTAL OFFICE FURNITURE CORP

D-U-N-S 02-633-1139
CONTINUCARE HEALTHSERVICES INC
(*Suby of* ERLANGER HEALTH SYSTEM) ★
1501 Riverside Dr Ste 350, Chattanooga, TN 37406-4329
Tel (423) 386-1000 *Founded/Ownrshp* 2008
Sales 4.5MM[E] *EMP* 1,033[E]
SIC 8099 Health & allied services

D-U-N-S 00-967-7104
CONTINUUM ENERGY LLC
1323 E 71st St Ste 300, Tulsa, OK 74136-5068
Tel (918) 492-2840 *Founded/Ownrshp* 2014
Sales 3.2MMM *EMP* 275[E]
Accts Grant Thornton Co
SIC 4923 Gas transmission & distribution
Pr: Jason Few
**CEO:* David House
**CFO:* Sherrie Barnes
**Ex VP:* Alex Goldberg
Sr VP: Christy Spraggs

D-U-N-S 02-511-2181
CONTINUUM ENERGY SERVICES LLC
(*Suby of* CONTINUUM ENERGY LLC) ★
1323 E 71st St Ste 300, Tulsa, OK 74136-5068
Tel (918) 492-2840 *Founded/Ownrshp* 1998
Sales 1.9MMM[E] *EMP* 159
Accts Grant Thornton Llp Tulsa Okl
SIC 4923 Gas transmission & distribution
CFO: Dan Hawk
Ex VP: Pat Giroir
Genl Mgr: John Pettus
Pgrm Dir: Rick Pemberton

D-U-N-S 08-674-7735
CONTINUUM MIDSTREAM LLC
SEMINOLE ENERGY SERVICES
(*Suby of* CONTINUUM ENERGY LLC) ★
1323 E 71st St Ste 300, Tulsa, OK 74136-5068
Tel (918) 492-2840 *Founded/Ownrshp* 1999
Sales 1.1MMM *EMP* 75[E]
Accts Grant Thornton Llp Tulsa Okl
SIC 4922 Pipelines, natural gas
VP: Uday RAO
IT Man: Nijas Kolothody

CONTINUUMHR
See PAYROLL MADE EASY INC

CONTOUR NEXT
See ASCENSIA DIABETES CARE US INC

D-U-N-S 07-654-7421
CONTRA COSTA COMMUNITY COLLEGE DISTRICT
500 Court St Fl 1, Martinez, CA 94553-1200
Tel (925) 229-1000 *Founded/Ownrshp* 1948
Sales 54.3MM[E] *EMP* 1,680
SIC 8222 Community college
CEO: Elmer Bugg
**CFO:* Doug Roberts
IT Man: Helen Benjamin

D-U-N-S 02-898-0803
■ CONTRA COSTA ELECTRIC INC
(*Suby of* DYN SPECIALTY CONTRACTING INC) ★
825 Howe Rd, Martinez, CA 94553-3441
Tel (925) 229-4250 *Founded/Ownrshp* 1946
Sales 97.6MM[E] *EMP* 400
SIC 1731 Electrical work
Pr: Michael Dias
CFO: Dave Galli
VP: Charlie Hadsell
VP: Joey Ramirez
VP: Tom Tatro
Board of Directors: Frank T Macinnis

D-U-N-S 00-921-2747
CONTRA COSTA NEWSPAPERS INC
CONTRA COSTA TIMES
(*Suby of* DIGITAL FIRST MEDIA) ★
175 Lennon Ln Ste 100, Walnut Creek, CA 94598-2466
Tel (925) 935-2525 *Founded/Ownrshp* 2006
Sales 134.2MM[E] *EMP* 1,146
SIC 2711 Newspapers, publishing & printing
CEO: George Riggs
**Pr:* John Armstrong
VP: Michael Noble
CTO: Victor Carniglia
Dir IT: Chris Boisvert
Prd Mgr: Roger Williams

CONTRA COSTA TIMES
See CONTRA COSTA NEWSPAPERS INC

D-U-N-S 07-655-6588 IMP
CONTRA COSTA WATER DISTRICT INC
1331 Concord Ave, Concord, CA 94520-4907
Tel (925) 688-8000 *Founded/Ownrshp* 1936
Sales 107.6MM *EMP* 335
Accts Maze & Associates Pleasant Hi
SIC 4941 Water supply
Pr: Joseph L Campbell
Bd of Dir: Peter Colby
Bd of Dir: Mary Neher
Bd of Dir: Leah Orloff
VP: Chris Dundon
Exec: Michele Bautista
Exec: Margaret Ramirez
IT Man: Steven Bow
IT Man: Ralph Peterson

D-U-N-S 15-459-1549 IMP/EXP
CONTRACK WATTS INC
(*Suby of* CONTRACK (CYPRUS) LIMITED)
6862 Elm St Fl 5, Mc Lean, VA 22101-3897
Tel (703) 358-8800 *Founded/Ownrshp* 1985
Sales 372.6MM[E] *EMP* 3,000
Accts Kpmg Llp Mclean Virginia
SIC 1541 Dry cleaning plant construction
Pr: Wahid Hakki
COO: Christine McGuire
**COO:* Christine McGuire-Ingersoll
**CFO:* Joseph Romagnoli
**VP:* Osama Bishai
Exec: Frank McConnell
IT Man: Heather Dorner

CONTRACT
See EMERALD EXPOSITIONS LLC

D-U-N-S 96-075-6476
CONTRACT ENVIRONMENTAL SERVICES INC
636 Powdersville Rd, Easley, SC 29642-1961
Tel (864) 306-7785 *Founded/Ownrshp* 1996
Sales 43.6MM[E] *EMP* 1,200
SIC 8748 Environmental consultant
Pr: Ed Massey

D-U-N-S 05-638-5438
CONTRACT FREIGHTERS INC
CFI
(*Suby of* TRANSFORCE INC)
4701 E 32nd St, Joplin, MO 64804-3482
Tel (417) 623-5229 *Founded/Ownrshp* 1951
Sales 306.4MM[E] *EMP* 453[E]
SIC 4213 Automobiles, transport & delivery
CEO: Timothy Staroba

D-U-N-S 05-779-5122 IMP/EXP
CONTRACT PHARMACAL CORP
135 Adams Ave, Hauppauge, NY 11788-3633
Tel (631) 231-4610 *Founded/Ownrshp* 1974
Sales 282.2MM[E] *EMP* 950
SIC 2834

CONTRACTING & MATERIAL COMPANY
See MEADE ELECTRIC CO INC

D-U-N-S 00-385-3280
CONTRACTING & MATERIAL CO (IL)
(*Suby of* MEADE ELECTRIC CO) ★
9550 W 55th St Ste A, Countryside, IL 60525-3641
Tel (708) 588-6000 *Founded/Ownrshp* 1913, 1983
Sales 171.3MM[E] *EMP* 450
SIC 4922 1623 4612 1731 Natural gas transmission; Oil & gas pipeline construction; Crude petroleum pipelines; Electrical work
Ch Bd: Joseph Lizzadro
Pr: Frank J Lizzadro
Sec: John S Lizzadro

D-U-N-S 00-652-7949 IMP
CONTRACTORS STEEL CO
36555 Amrhein Rd, Livonia, MI 48150-1182
Tel (734) 464-4000 *Founded/Ownrshp* 1962
Sales 101.2MM *EMP* 380
Accts Robinson Pietras Kalisky & C
SIC 5051 Metals service centers & offices
Pr: Donald R Simon
**VP:* Ralph Hartsoe
**VP:* Esther Simon
IT Man: Michelle Veneziano
Sales Asso: Eric Wagner

D-U-N-S 96-877-9061
CONTRADO BBH HOLDINGS LLC
(*Suby of* VERSA CAPITAL MANAGEMENT LLC) ★
2929 Arch St Fl 27, Philadelphia, PA 19104-2857
Tel (215) 609-3400 *Founded/Ownrshp* 2011
Sales 341.5MM[E] *EMP* 1,500[E]
SIC 3579 Envelope stuffing, sealing & addressing machines; Mailing machines; Address labeling machines; Voting machines
Prin: R Emrich

D-U-N-S 05-031-2008
▲ CONTRAN CORP
5430 Lyndon B Johnson Fwy, Dallas, TX 75240-2601
Tel (972) 233-1700 *Founded/Ownrshp* 1979
Sales 1.8MMM[E] *EMP* 7,175
SIC 2816 Titanium dioxide, anatase or rutile (pigments)
V Ch Bd: Glenn R Simmons
**Pr:* Steve Watson
**CEO:* Harold C Simmons
CFO: Bobby O'Brien
CFO: Bobby D Obrien
**VP:* E K Anderson
Genl Mgr: Robert Gross
Mktg Dir: Dain Rakestraw

CONTRIBUTIONSHIP COMPANIES
See PHILADELPHIA CONTRIBUTIONSHIP FOR INSURANCE OF HOUSES FROM LOSS BY FIRE

D-U-N-S 09-472-2568
CONTROL AIR CONDITIONING CORP (CA)
5200 E La Palma Ave, Anaheim, CA 92807-2019
Tel (714) 777-8600 *Founded/Ownrshp* 1978
Sales 102.9MM[E] *EMP* 360
SIC 1711 Warm air heating & air conditioning contractor
Pr: Kendrick Ellis
**Sec:* Eileen Ellis
**VP:* Stan Ellis
VP: Mike Pence
Sales Exec: Gerry Morones
Sls&Mrk Ex: John Martinez
Mktg Dir: Glenn Shimoda
Snr Mgr: Leticia Amador
Board of Directors: Kendrick Ellis, Stanley Ellis

D-U-N-S 08-298-0715
CONTROL BUILDING SERVICES INC
CONTROL CLEANING SERVICES
333 Meadowlands Pkwy Fl 1, Secaucus, NJ 07094-1814
Tel (201) 864-1900 *Founded/Ownrshp* 1975
Sales 143.9MM[E] *EMP* 6,500
SIC 7349 0782 Janitorial service, contract basis; Landscape contractors
Ch Bd: Edward Turen
**VP:* Neal Turen

CONTROL CLEANING SERVICES
See CONTROL BUILDING SERVICES INC

D-U-N-S 01-859-7310 IMP
CONTROL COMPONENTS INC
CCI VALUE
(*Suby of* IMI AMERICAS INC) ★
22591 Avenida Empresa, Rcho STA Marg, CA 92688-2012
Tel (949) 858-1877 *Founded/Ownrshp* 1981
Sales 173.3MM[E] *EMP* 900
SIC 3491 Process control regulator valves
Ch Bd: Martin Lamb
**Pr:* Mike Senens-Slanagan
**CFO:* Scott Krzywicki
Ex VP: Paul Cosgrove
Sr VP: Jay Faramarzi
Sr VP: Sergio Sartanio
**VP:* Dean Capper
VP: Charles Fernald
**Ex Dir:* Ian Whiting
VP Sls: Sergio Sartoni
Manager: James Niles

D-U-N-S 15-432-3059
CONTROL ENVIRONMENTAL SERVICES INC
737 New Durham Rd Ste 1, Edison, NJ 08817-2849
Tel (732) 548-5272 *Founded/Ownrshp* 1985
Sales 264.0MM *EMP* 50
SIC 0782 Landscape contractors
CEO: Edward Turen
**VP:* Neal Turen
Sls Mgr: Jeff Wood

D-U-N-S 04-581-8549
CONTROL SOUTHERN INC
3850 Lakefield Dr, Suwanee, GA 30024-1241
Tel (770) 495-3100 *Founded/Ownrshp* 1990
Sales 132.7MM[E] *EMP* 65
SIC 5084 Industrial machinery & equipment
Pr: Doug Turner
**CFO:* Ciss Welch

D-U-N-S 14-260-6370
▲ CONTROL4 CORP
11734 S Election Rd, Draper, UT 84020-6877
Tel (801) 523-3100 *Founded/Ownrshp* 2003
Sales 163.1MM *EMP* 519[E]
Tkr Sym CTRL *Exch* NGS
SIC 3679 7372 Electronic circuits; Electronic loads & power supplies; Electronic switches; Operating systems computer software
Ch Bd: Martin Plaehn
CFO: Mark Novakovich
Chf Cred: Greg Bishop
Sr VP: Eric Anderson
Sr VP: James B Arnold
Sr VP: Susan Cashen
Sr VP: Jeff Dungan
VP: Alexander Danoyan
Exec: Leana Nitzen
Area Mgr: Coleman Radford
Snr Sftwr: David Fay
Board of Directors: Rob Born, James Caudill, David C Habiger, Jeremy Jaech, Mark Jensen, Phil Molyneux

D-U-N-S 02-823-1165 IMP
CONTROLLED MOTION SOLUTIONS INC
MOBILE HOSE AND HYDRAULIC SUP
911 N Poinsettia St, Santa Ana, CA 92701-3827
Tel (661) 324-2260 *Founded/Ownrshp* 1961
Sales 90.6MM[E] *EMP* 100
SIC 5085 Seals, industrial; Valves & fittings; Hose, belting & packing
Pr: Mark Law
**CEO:* Mark Force
CIO: Phil Vice
CTO: Jeff Geyer
Mktg Dir: Sylvia Rand
Mktg Mgr: Eddie Malone
Sls Mgr: Joe Gonzalez
Sales Asso: Graciela Rios

D-U-N-S 09-068-1610
CONTROLLER CALIFORNIA STATE
(*Suby of* EXECUTIVE OFFICE OF STATE OF CALIFORNIA) ★
300 Capitol Mall Ste 1850, Sacramento, CA 95814-4345
Tel (916) 445-2636 *Founded/Ownrshp* 1850
Sales NA *EMP* 1,500
SIC 9311 Controllers' office, government;

CONTROLLERS OF THE CURRENCY
See OCC NATIONAL BANK EXAMINERS

D-U-N-S 08-033-7402
CONTURA COAL SALES LLC
1 Alpha Pl, Bristol, VA 24209
Tel (276) 619-4451 *Founded/Ownrshp* 2016
Sales 1.4MMM[E] *EMP* 10
SIC 5052 Coal

D-U-N-S 07-125-8438
CONVACARE MANAGEMENT INC
2908 Hawkins Dr, Searcy, AR 72143-4802
Tel (501) 305-3153 *Founded/Ownrshp* 1999
Sales 24.3MM[E] *EMP* 1,000
SIC 8051 Skilled nursing care facilities
CEO: Joey Wiggins

CONVATEC HEALTHCARE A, S.A.R.
See CONVATEC INC

D-U-N-S 94-798-9757 IMP
CONVATEC INC
CONVATEC HEALTHCARE A, S.A.R.
(*Suby of* NORDIC CAPITAL SVENSKA AB)
1160 Rte 22 Ste 201, Bridgewater, NJ 08807-2931
Tel (908) 904-2500 *Founded/Ownrshp* 2008
Sales 2.8MMM[E] *EMP* 8,000[E]
SIC 3841 Surgical & medical instruments
CEO: Paul Moraviec
**Pr:* Dave Johnson
**CFO:* John Cannon
**Sr VP:* Adrienne McNally
VP: Adam Deutsch
Exec: Andrea Beugnon
Exec: Kathryn Soper
Exec: Marrilee Summers
Rgnl Mgr: Lee Haney
Rgnl Mgr: Mark Woerner
IT Man: Michael Mandarano

CONVENIENCE VALET
See MECHANICAL SERVANTS LLC

CONVERGE
See PCG TRADING LLC

CONVERGE
See PCG PARENT CORP

D-U-N-S 03-407-6054
CONVERGENCE MARKETING INC
7361 Coca Cola Dr Ste A, Hanover, MD 21076-1950
Tel (443) 888-5100 *Founded/Ownrshp* 2001
Sales 35.8MM *EMP* 2,500[E]
SIC 8742 Marketing consulting services
Pr: Christian Miller
**CFO:* Bob Bender
**Sr VP:* Tom Robinson
**VP:* Patti Morehouse

CONVERGENCE TECHNOLOGIES
See GHSP INC

D-U-N-S 17-510-0903
CONVERGENCE TECHNOLOGIES INC
CONVERGENCE TECHNOLOGIES NY
80 State St, Albany, NY 12207-2541
Tel (914) 697-7669 *Founded/Ownrshp* 2004
Sales 158.9MM[E] *EMP* 350
SIC 7373 Systems integration services
Ch Bd: Leonard Fassler

CONVERGENCE TECHNOLOGIES NY
See CONVERGENCE TECHNOLOGIES INC

D-U-N-S 96-276-1768
CONVERGENT RESOURCES HOLDINGS LLC
(*Suby of* ACCOUNT CONTROL TECHNOLOGY HOLDINGS INC) ★
555 N Point Ctr E Ste 175, Alpharetta, GA 30022-1528
Tel (866) 867-0179 *Founded/Ownrshp* 2014
Sales 151.6MM[E] *EMP* 3,579[E]
SIC 8741 Management services
COO: Greg Rassier
Pr: Derek A Pickell
**CEO:* Mike Meyer
CTO: Derek Whitaker

D-U-N-S 07-351-4593
CONVERGENT RESOURCES INC
(*Suby of* CONVERGENT RESOURCES HOLDINGS LLC) ★
555 N Point Ctr E Ste 175, Alpharetta, GA 30022-1528
Tel (770) 512-3670 *Founded/Ownrshp* 1998
Sales 151.6MM[E] *EMP* 2,600
SIC 7322 Collection agency, except real estate
CEO: Michael Micek
**Pr:* Casey Kostecka
**CFO:* Jacob Lewis
**CFO:* Kevin Shiotelis
**Ex VP:* Jeff Hunter
VP: Adam Bury
VP: Mark Friedrich
**VP:* Richard Sterman
Ex Dir: Paul Morino
Telecom Mg: Bob Savery

D-U-N-S 79-251-9063
CONVERGEONE HOLDINGS CORP
3344 Highway 149, Eagan, MN 55121-2316
Tel (651) 994-6800 *Founded/Ownrshp* 2014
Sales 654.7MM[E] *EMP* 982
SIC 4813 5999 1731 Telephone communication, except radio; Telephone equipment & systems; Telephone & telephone equipment installation
CEO: John A McKenna Jr
**Pr:* John Lyons
**Pr:* Paul Maier
**CFO:* Jeffrey E Nachbor
**CTO:* Mark Langanki

D-U-N-S 82-541-0319
CONVERGEONE INC
(*Suby of* CONVERGEONE HOLDINGS CORP) ★
3344 Highway 149, Eagan, MN 55121-2316
Tel (651) 994-6800 *Founded/Ownrshp* 1993
Sales 496.2MM[E] *EMP* 710
SIC 4813 5999 1731 Telephone communication, except radio; Telephone equipment & systems; Telephone & telephone equipment installation
CEO: John Lyon
**Ch Bd:* John McKenna
**CFO:* Jeff Nachbor
VP: Jim Felicetti
Software D: Jeremy Western
Natl Sales: Jim Bird
Natl Sales: Bridget Brown
Natl Sales: Jeffrey Miller
Natl Sales: Carrie Tish
VP Mktg: Scott Sund
VP Sls: Pete Anderson

D-U-N-S 78-530-7260
CONVERGEX GROUP LLC
1633 Broadway Ste 1300, New York, NY 10019-6708
Tel (212) 468-7500 *Founded/Ownrshp* 2006
Sales 334.3MM[E] *EMP* 657
SIC 6211 Security brokers & dealers
CEO: Eric W Noll
Ch Bd: Joseph Velli
Pr: Muhammad Aleem
Pr: Robert Harrison
CEO: Joseph N Cangemi
CEO: Greg Voetsch
COO: William Murphy
COO: Charles E Rappold
CFO: Fredrick Arnold
CFO: Conor McCarthy
CFO: Christopher Springer
Chf Mktg O: Eric Soderberg
Ofcr: Kelli Annequin
Sr VP: Hassan Chaudry
Sr VP: Brian Elliott
Sr VP: Joseph Emanuelli
VP: Mohsin Ali
VP: Michael Balice
VP: Ada Braylovskaya
VP: Delroy Bromfield
VP: Graham Brown

D-U-N-S 02-964-0740
CONVERGINT TECHNOLOGIES LLC
1 Commerce Dr, Schaumburg, IL 60173-5302
Tel (847) 620-5000 *Founded/Ownrshp* 2001
Sales 469.1MM *EMP* 2,147
Accts Plante & Moran Pllc Chicago
SIC 7382 Burglar alarm maintenance & monitoring
Ch Bd: Dan Moceri
**CEO:* Ken Lochiatto
**CFO:* Wally Winkel
Sr VP: Sean Flint
VP: Michael Duncan
VP: Greg Kubacki
VP: Richard Norman
VP: Tony Varco
VP: Barry Yatzor
VP Bus Dev: Mike Kuhn
Genl Mgr: Doug Lyle

D-U-N-S 02-575-0394
▲ CONVERGYS CORP (OH)
201 E 4th St, Cincinnati, OH 45202-4206
Tel (513) 723-7000 *Founded/Ownrshp* 1996
Sales 2.9MMM *EMP* 130,000
Tkr Sym CVG *Exch* NYS
SIC 7374 7373 Data processing service; Computer integrated systems design
Pr: Andrea J Ayers
**Ch Bd:* Jeffrey H Fox
COO: Marjorie M Connelly
CFO: Craig Holmes
CFO: Andre S Valentine
Ofcr: Jarrod B Pontius
VP: Vivek Goel
VP: Christine Lee
VP: Joel Lewis
VP: Patty Lillge
VP: Ed Margulies
Board of Directors: Cheryl K Beebe, Richard R Devenuti, Joseph E Gibbs, Joan E Herman, Thomas L Monahan III, Ronald L Nelson, Richard F Wallman

D-U-N-S 02-997-8434 EXP
■ CONVERGYS CUSTOMER MANAGEMENT GROUP INC
(*Suby of* CONVERGYS CORP) ★
201 E 4th St Bsmt, Cincinnati, OH 45202-4206
Tel (513) 723-6104 *Founded/Ownrshp* 1998
Sales 394.4MM[E] *EMP* 20,250
SIC 7389 8732 Telemarketing services; Market analysis or research
Pr: David F Dougherty
**COO:* Ronald E Schultz
**CFO:* Andre S Valentine
Mktg Dir: Michael Bockelman
Board of Directors: Richard Findlay, Steven G Rolls

D-U-N-S 03-928-8605
■ CONVERSANT LLC
(*Suby of* ALLIANCE DATA SYSTEMS CORP) ★
30699 Russell Ranch Rd # 250, Westlake Village, CA 91362-7319
Tel (818) 575-4500 *Founded/Ownrshp* 2014
Sales 573.1MM *EMP* 1,143
SIC 7375 4813 On-line data base information retrieval;
Pr: John Giuliani
Pr: Oded Benyo
COO: David Yovanno
**CFO:* John Pitstick
**Chf Mktg O:* Scott Eagle
Ofcr: Jim Rund
Sr VP: Matthew Boyd
Sr VP: Raju Malhotra
Sr VP: Bill Todd
**VP:* Scott P Barlow
VP: Valueclick Carl
VP: Lynn D'Alessandro
VP: Robert Sherry
VP: Dean Swinson
VP: Tony Winders
Board of Directors: David S Buzby, James A Crouthamel, James R Peters, Jeffrey F Rayport, Brian A Smith

D-U-N-S 60-439-0054
CONVERSE AND CO INC
314 S Pine St Ste 200, Spartanburg, SC 29302-2677
Tel (864) 542-2301 *Founded/Ownrshp* 1987
Sales 114.5MM *EMP* 4
SIC 5052 Coal
Ch: Justin Converse

D-U-N-S 01-810-5341 IMP
■ CONVERSE INC
(*Suby of* NIKE INC) ★
1 Love Joy Wharf, Boston, MA 02114-2114
Tel (978) 983-3300 *Founded/Ownrshp* 2001
Sales 243.4MM[E] *EMP* 261
SIC 5139 5661 Footwear, athletic; Footwear, athletic
CEO: Jack A Boys
**Pr:* James A Cahoun
**CFO:* Lisa Kempa
**Ch:* Marsden Cason
**Treas:* Robert W Woodruff
Sr VP: Ned Frederick
VP: Richard Copcutt
VP: Bob Dimke
VP: Sarah Hoffmann
VP: John R Hoke III
VP: James Jellison
**VP:* David Maddocks
VP: Joe Rogers
VP: Stuart Spiegel
Exec: Susan Walsh
Exec: Angela White
Comm Man: Kelly Murnaghan

CONVERTEAM
See GE ENERGY POWER CONVERSION USA INC

D-U-N-S 10-117-5529 IMP/EXP
CONVERTIBLE CASTLE INC
BERNIE & PHYL'S FURNITURE
308 E Main St, Norton, MA 02766-2520
Tel (800) 244-9350 *Founded/Ownrshp* 1983
Sales 97.1MM[E] *EMP* 400
SIC 5712 Furniture stores
Merch Mgr: Robert Pironti

D-U-N-S 14-940-5271
CONVEY HEALTH SOLUTIONS INC
1 Financial Plz Fl 14, Fort Lauderdale, FL 33394-0052
Tel (954) 903-5000 *Founded/Ownrshp* 2016
Sales 288.6MM[E] *EMP* 1,400
SIC 5912 5999 Drug stores & proprietary stores; Medical apparatus & supplies
CEO: Stephen Farrell
COO: Timothy Fairbanks
Chf Cred: Joanne Thompson
Ofcr: Chc N Bailey
Ex VP: Tracy M Schmidt
Ex VP: Jonathan Starr
VP: Nicole Bailey
VP: Yvonne Daugherty
VP: Alan Smith
VP: Scott E Tracey
CTO: Giray Akar

D-U-N-S 01-501-3431 EXP
CONVOY OF HOPE
330 S Patterson Ave # 100, Springfield, MO 65802-2278
Tel (417) 823-8998 *Founded/Ownrshp* 1994
Sales 130.9MM *EMP* 125
Accts Bkd Llp Springfield Mo
SIC 8322 Disaster service; Outreach program
Pr: Hal Donaldson
**Pr:* Jim Batten
CFO: Matt Metzger
**Sr VP:* Keith Boucher
Sr VP: Kary Kingsland
**VP:* Erick Meier
Dir Surg: Jeff Nene
**VP Admn:* Randy Rich
Dir IT: Tim Kotras

D-U-N-S 00-796-2178
CONWAY CORP (AR)
1307 Prairie St, Conway, AR 72034-5344
Tel (501) 450-6000 *Founded/Ownrshp* 1929
Sales 108.5MM *EMP* 250
SIC 4911 4941 4841

D-U-N-S 07-373-1242
CONWAY HOSPITAL AUXILIARY
CONWAY MEDICAL CENTER
300 Singleton Ridge Rd, Conway, SC 29526-9142
Tel (843) 347-7111 *Founded/Ownrshp* 1928
Sales 75.5M *EMP* 1,100
Accts Smith Sapp Myrtle Beach Sc
SIC 8062 General medical & surgical hospitals
Pr: Philip Clayton
**CFO:* Bret Barr
Bd of Dir: James Adamson
Bd of Dir: Greg Gough
VP: Tony Minshew
Dir Lab: Luann Skipper
Dir Rx: Robert Gajewski
Off Mgr: Pat Marshall
CIO: Micky Waters
Info Man: Brian Feske
Mktg Dir: Julie Snowden

D-U-N-S 13-060-9584
CONWAY HOSPITAL INC
CONWAY MEDICAL CENTER
300 Singleton Ridge Rd, Conway, SC 29526-9142
Tel (843) 347-7111 *Founded/Ownrshp* 1928
Sales 191.7MM *EMP* 1,200
SIC 8062 General medical & surgical hospitals
CEO: Philip A Clayton
**CFO:* Bret Barr
CFO: Shelley Marsh
Bd of Dir: Greg Gough
Chf Mktg O: Russell Derrick
VP: Blair Hanger
**VP:* J Craig Hyman
Ex Dir: Bernard Berns
Off Mgr: Judy Squires
Doctor: Christo Courban
Doctor: Daniel Gordon

CONWAY MEDICAL CENTER
See CONWAY HOSPITAL AUXILIARY

CONWAY MEDICAL CENTER
See CONWAY HOSPITAL INC

CONWAY OFFICE SOLUTIONS
See CONWAY TECHNOLOGY GROUP LLC

CONWAY OIL COMPANY
See NEBRASKA-IOWA SUPPLY CO INC

CONWAY REGIONAL HEALTH SYSTEMS
See CONWAY REGIONAL MEDICAL CENTER INC

D-U-N-S 07-566-5695
CONWAY REGIONAL MEDICAL CENTER INC
CONWAY REGIONAL HEALTH SYSTEMS
2302 College Ave, Conway, AR 72034-6297
Tel (501) 329-3831 *Founded/Ownrshp* 1938
Sales 132.5MM *EMP* 1,200
Accts Bkd Llp Little Rock Ar
SIC 8062 General medical & surgical hospitals
**Pr:* James M Lambert
**CFO:* Steven Rose
Assoc Dir: DOT Welch
Dir Rx: James Reed
Dir Env Sv: Gary Qualls
MIS Dir: Bob Hambuchen
Dir IT: Bob Himbuchen
Opers Mgr: Luann Stiefvater
Orthpdst: Jeff Marotte
Obsttrcn: Josh Ward
Doctor: Richard Bronfman

D-U-N-S 04-025-4641
■ CONWAY TECHNOLOGY GROUP LLC
CONWAY OFFICE SOLUTIONS
(*Suby of* GLOBAL IMAGING SYSTEMS INC) ★
10 Capitol St, Nashua, NH 03063-1007
Tel (603) 889-1665 *Founded/Ownrshp* 1995
Sales 112.0MM[E] *EMP* 156
SIC 5044 5065 7699 7359 Office equipment; Photocopy machines; Mailing machines; Facsimile equipment; Office equipment & accessory customizing; Business machine & electronic equipment rental services
Ch Bd: Tom Johnson
Pr: Paul Mosley
Pr: Carl Tourigny
Treas: Ray Schilling
V Ch Bd: James B Conway
VP: Steve Barrett
VP: Ann Maynard
VP: Michael McKenna
Sls Mgr: Paul Donehue

D-U-N-S 00-482-9555 IMP
■ CONWED PLASTICS LLC
(*Suby of* LEUCADIA NATIONAL CORP) ★
2810 Weeks Ave Se, Minneapolis, MN 55414-2835
Tel (612) 623-1700 *Founded/Ownrshp* 2005
Sales 146.2MM[E] *EMP* 430[E]
SIC 3089 Netting, plastic
Pr: Chris Hatzenbuhler
CEO: Linda Wiens
CFO: Craig McKeen
IT Man: Tom Dippold
Mktg Dir: Scott Eliason
Sls Mgr: Jonathan Kunz

D-U-N-S 07-910-3421
COOK & BOARDMAN GROUP LLC
3916 Westpoint Blvd, Winston Salem, NC 27103-6719
Tel (336) 768-8872 *Founded/Ownrshp* 2014
Sales 181.3MM[E] *EMP* 565[E]
SIC 2431 Door frames, wood; Doors & door parts & trim, wood; Doors, combination screen-storm, wood; Doors, wood
CEO: Chuck Hummel

D-U-N-S 79-189-3782
COOK CHILDRENS HEALTH CARE SYSTEM
801 7th Ave, Fort Worth, TX 76104-2733
Tel (682) 885-4555 *Founded/Ownrshp* 1996
Sales 133.0MM *EMP* 2,000[E]
Accts Bkd Llp Houston Tx
SIC 8069 Specialty hospitals, except psychiatric
CEO: Russell Tolman
**Pr:* Rick W Merrill
**CFO:* Stephen W Kimmel
Treas: Rafael Garza
Trst: Michael J Deitchman
Trst: Susan L Hess
Trst: James Miller
Trst: Wilfred Raine
Trst: Jason V Terk
Trst: Paul Thornton
Ofcr: Jody Hawkins
**Sr VP:* Linda S Chappell
**Sr VP:* John W McNey
**Sr VP:* Larry L Tubb
VP: William Craig
VP: Stanley Davis
VP: Julie Hunter
VP: David Lancaster
VP: Angie McCrary
**VP:* George B Montague
VP: Frank Rossi

D-U-N-S 60-133-6626
COOK CHILDRENS HEALTH PLAN
(*Suby of* COOK CHILDRENS HEALTH CARE SYSTEM) ★
801 7th Ave, Fort Worth, TX 76104-2733
Tel (817) 334-2247 *Founded/Ownrshp* 1998
Sales 284.2MM *EMP* 27
Accts Bkd Llp Houston Tx
SIC 8082 Home health care services
Pr: Doris Hunt
Ofcr: Melanie Corcoran

D-U-N-S 07-854-4194
COOK CHILDRENS MEDICAL CENTER
(*Suby of* COOK CHILDRENS HEALTH CARE SYSTEM) ★
801 7th Ave, Fort Worth, TX 76104-2796
Tel (682) 885-4000 *Founded/Ownrshp* 1918
Sales 753.8MM *EMP* 2,000
SIC 8069 Children's hospital
Pr: Rick W Merrill
Dir Vol: Jill Koss
COO: Aaron M Kimberly
Trst: Michael J Deitchman
Trst: Jeffrey Moreland
Trst: Joann Sanders
Trst: Jason Terk
Ofcr: Joanne Sanders
Ex VP: Lakami Bryant
VP: Diane Crane
VP: Paula Webb
Dir Inf Cn: Lisa La Rue
Dir Soc: Margie O'Donnell
Dir: Grant Harris
Dir Rx: Mark Thomas

D-U-N-S 83-650-3888
COOK CHILDRENS PHYSICIAN NETWORK
(*Suby of* COOK CHILDRENS HEALTH CARE SYSTEM) ★
801 7th Ave, Fort Worth, TX 76104-2733
Tel (682) 885-6800 *Founded/Ownrshp* 1992
Sales 230.4MM *EMP* 801
SIC 8011 Offices & clinics of medical doctors
Pr: W B Nelson MD
**CFO:* Ted Matthews
**Ch:* Howard Kelfer MD
**Treas:* Clive Daniels MD
**VP:* Ryan Champlin
Doctor: Christopher Mann

COOK CHOCOLATE COMPANY
See WORLDS FINEST CHOCOLATE INC

D-U-N-S 96-083-2855
COOK COUNTY BUREAU OF HEALTH SERVICES
1900 W Polk St Ste 220, Chicago, IL 60612-3723
Tel (312) 864-7571 *Founded/Ownrshp* 1996
Sales NA *EMP* 8,114
SIC 9431
**CFO:* Alvin Holly

COOK ENDOSCOPY
See COOK INC

D-U-N-S 08-703-7362
COOK GROUP INC
750 N Daniels Way, Bloomington, IN 47404-9120
Tel (812) 339-2235 *Founded/Ownrshp* 1963
Sales 765.2MM[E] *EMP* 1,790
SIC 3841 3821 3845 6411 6512 6211 Surgical instruments & apparatus; Catheters; Holders, surgical needle; Hypodermic needles & syringes; Pipettes, hemocytometer; Pacemaker, cardiac; Insurance agents; Commercial & industrial building operation; Stock brokers & dealers
Ch Bd: William A Cook
**Pr:* Kem Hawkins
Pr: Barry Slowey
**CEO:* Stephen L Ferguson
**Treas:* John Kamstra
Ofcr: Jim Gardner
Div VP: Andy Hoffa
Sr VP: April Lavender

VP: David Breedlove
VP: Andy Cron
**VP:* Chuck Franz
VP: Allison Giles
VP: Bruce Gingles
VP: Gretchen Gutman
VP: Jim Heckman
**VP:* Robert K Irie
VP: Connie Jackson
VP: Cynthia Kretz
VP: David Reed
VP: Thomas Roberts
VP: Francine Small

D-U-N-S 04-282-3948 IMP
COOK INC
COOK ENDOSCOPY
(*Suby of* COOK GROUP INC) ★
750 N Daniels Way, Bloomington, IN 47404-9120
Tel (812) 339-2235 *Founded/Ownrshp* 1963
Sales 442.1MM^E *EMP* 1,790
SIC 3841 Catheters
Pr: M Kem Hawkins
**Pr:* Phyllis McCullough
COO: Scott Eells
**Ch:* Steve Ferguson
**Treas:* Thomas Osborne
VP: Christina Ann
VP: Christina Annt
**VP:* Brian Bates
VP: Phil Nowell
Dist Mgr: Gregory Bowen
Dist Mgr: Mauricio Carrillo

D-U-N-S 07-663-0334
COOK INLET REGION INC
CIRI
725 E Fireweed Ln Ste 800, Anchorage, AK 99503-2245
Tel (907) 274-8638 *Founded/Ownrshp* 1972
Sales 125.9MM^E *EMP* 86
SIC 6552 1382 1389 6519 4832 4833 Subdividers & developers; Oil & gas exploration services; Oil field services; Real property lessors; Radio broadcasting stations; Television translator station
Pr: Sophie R Minich
**CFO:* Stig Colberg
Bd of Dir: Robert Harris
Bd of Dir: Katrina Jacuk
**Sr VP:* Barbara Donatelli
**Sr VP:* Ethan Schutt
**VP:* Bruce Anders
**VP:* Chad Nugent
VP: Dave Pfeifer
**VP:* Gregory Razo
Comm Dir: Jim Jager

D-U-N-S 07-577-6369
COOK MARAN & ASSOCIATES INC
(*Suby of* PRIME RISK PARTNERS INC) ★
461 Pantigo Rd, East Hampton, NY 11937-2647
Tel (631) 324-1440 *Founded/Ownrshp* 2015
Sales NA *EMP* 131
SIC 6321 Accident & health insurance carriers
Pr: Leonard Scioscia
CFO: Marc J Fishstein
VP: Peggy Eichhorn
VP: Tom Niland
VP: Tim O'Brien
Admn Mgr: Patricia Matheson
Opers Mgr: Jess Leach
VP Sls: Brian Finnell
VP Sls: Mark Fitzgerald

D-U-N-S 07-437-5825
COOK-ILLINOIS CORP (IL)
2100 Clearwater Dr # 250, Oak Brook, IL 60523-2077
Tel (708) 560-9840 *Founded/Ownrshp* 1970
Sales 219.5MM^E *EMP* 1,400
SIC 4151 School buses
Pr: John Benish
**CFO:* Greg Fischer
**VP:* John Knoelke
VP: Marco Marino

D-U-N-S 07-994-0262
COOKE SEAFOOD USA INC
(*Suby of* COOKE AQUACULTURE INC)
2000 Nrthgate Cmmrce Pkwy, Suffolk, VA 23435-2142
Tel (757) 673-4500 *Founded/Ownrshp* 2015
Sales 320.5MM^E *EMP* 1,160
SIC 2092 Fresh or frozen packaged fish
CEO: Glenn Cooke

COOKEVILLE REGIONAL CANCER CTR
See COOKEVILLE REGIONAL MEDICAL CENTER

D-U-N-S 06-909-8267
COOKEVILLE REGIONAL MEDICAL CENTER (TN)
COOKEVILLE REGIONAL CANCER CTR
1 Medical Center Blvd, Cookeville, TN 38501-4294
Tel (931) 528-2541 *Founded/Ownrshp* 1950
Sales 258.0MM *EMP* 2,300
SIC 8062 General medical & surgical hospitals
CEO: Paul Korth
**Ch Bd:* David Hatcher
**COO:* Scott Williams
Dir Lab: Marilyn Key
Dir Sec: Joe Lwanyszyn
Dir Sec: Jim Nevins
Doctor: Glenn Hall
Doctor: Marc Paul
Doctor: Melvin Rapelyea

COOKS HAM
See FARMLAND FOODS INC

D-U-N-S 03-156-5690
COOKS PEST CONTROL INC
1741 5th Ave Se Ste A, Decatur, AL 35601-5923
Tel (256) 355-3285 *Founded/Ownrshp* 1950
Sales 141.2MM *EMP* 1,380
Accts Barnes Blackwell & Co Pc
SIC 7342 Pest control services
Ch: John Cook Jr
**Pr:* James M Aycock
**COO:* Joseph K Harris
**CFO:* Sam Alfano
**Sec:* Eleanor Cook

**Sr VP:* George White
Genl Mgr: Jonathan Davis
VP Sls: Jerry Baker
Mktg Mgr: Jay Isom

D-U-N-S 93-751-4784 IMP
■ **COOKTEK INDUCTION SYSTEM LLC**
(*Suby of* MIDDLEBY CORP) ★
2801 Trade Ctr, Carrollton, TX 75007-4630
Tel (312) 563-9600 *Founded/Ownrshp* 2009
Sales 219.8MM^E *EMP* 2,060
SIC 5046 Commercial cooking & food service equipment
Pr: Warren Graber

COOL SURGE
See UNIVERSAL COMMERCE LLC

D-U-N-S 19-961-6954
COOLEY DICKINSON HEALTH CARE CORP
COOLEY DICKINSON HOSPITAL
30 Locust St, Northampton, MA 01060-2052
Tel (413) 582-2000 *Founded/Ownrshp* 1885
Sales 151.1MM *EMP* 1,079^E
SIC 8062 General medical & surgical hospitals
Treas: Charles Staelin
Chf Path: Lisa Glantz
Chf Rad: James Donnelly
Pr: Paul Higgins
Bd of Dir: William Gorth
Bd of Dir: Nancy Reeves
Trst: Peter Siersma
Chf Mktg O: Mark Novotny
Ofcr: Jennifer Margolis
Ofcr: Linda Medeiros
Exec: Gary H Weiss
Dir: Diane Dukette
Dir Rx: Michael Paquette

COOLEY DICKINSON HOSPITAL
See COOLEY DICKINSON HEALTH CARE CORP

D-U-N-S 06-699-1605
COOLEY DICKINSON HOSPITAL INC
(*Suby of* COOLEY DICKINSON HOSPITAL) ★
30 Locust St, Northampton, MA 01060-2093
Tel (413) 582-2000 *Founded/Ownrshp* 1984
Sales 151.1MM *EMP* 1,075
SIC 8062 8063 8069 General medical & surgical hospitals; Psychiatric hospitals; Substance abuse hospitals
Ch Bd: Matthew Pitoniak
**Pr:* Sanford Belden
**Pr:* Craig N Melin
**Pr:* Craig Melin
**Treas:* Charles Staelin

D-U-N-S 78-937-8366
COOLEY DICKINSON PHYSICIAN HOSPITAL ORGANIZATION INC
CDPHO
30 Locust St, Northampton, MA 01060-2093
Tel (413) 582-2343 *Founded/Ownrshp* 2006
Sales 152.2MM *EMP* 18^E
SIC 8062 General medical & surgical hospitals
Prin: Diane Quinn
Treas: Karen Hogan

D-U-N-S 02-532-8365 IMP/EXP
COOLEY GROUP HOLDINGS INC
50 Esten Ave, Pawtucket, RI 02860-4840
Tel (401) 724-0510 *Founded/Ownrshp* 1926
Sales 120.0MM^E *EMP* 200
SIC 5211 3069 Roofing material; Roofing, membrane rubber
Ch Bd: P R Siener
**Pr:* Jeffrey Flath
**CEO:* Daniel Dwight
**COO:* David Pettey
**CFO:* Ronald Markovsky
**Ch:* P Robert Siener Jr
VP: Sandy Bodell
DP Dir: Richard Vieira

D-U-N-S 00-119-9728 IMP/EXP
COOLEY INC
(*Suby of* COOLEY GROUP HOLDINGS INC) ★
50 Esten Ave, Pawtucket, RI 02860-4840
Tel (401) 724-9000 *Founded/Ownrshp* 2001
Sales 120.0MM^E *EMP* 200
SIC 2295 3069 2262 Coated fabrics, not rubberized; Roofing, membrane rubber; Screen printing: man-made fiber & silk broadwoven fabrics
CEO: Daniel Dwight
Ch Bd: P R Siener
Pr: Jeffrey Flath
CFO: Ronald Markovsky
VP: Bryan Rose
VP: Stephen Siener
Exec: Ryan Cooley
CTO: Christopher Ragosta
IT Man: Sandy Bodells
Tech Mgr: Justin Silvia
Natl Sales: Pat O'Rourke

D-U-N-S 06-013-6504
COOLEY LLP
3175 Hanover St, Palo Alto, CA 94304-1130
Tel (650) 843-5000 *Founded/Ownrshp* 1935
Sales 192.2MM^E *EMP* 1,400
SIC 8111 Specialized law offices, attorneys; Corporate, partnership & business law
Pt: Tom Reicher -
**Pt:* Kenneth J Adelson
Pt: Mike Attanasio
Pt: Andrew Basile
Pt: David Bresnick
**Pt:* Janet L Callum
**Pt:* Craig Dauchy
Pt: Craig E Dauchy
Pt: Richard Frank
Pt: Wendy C Goldstein
Pt: Danish Hamid
Pt: Tami J Howie
Pt: Eric C Jensen
Pt: Margaret H Kavalaris
Pt: Christopher Kearns
Pt: Barbara Kosacz
Pt: Michael X Marinelli
Pt: Frederick T Muto

**Pt:* Fredrick Muto
**Pt:* Ross Nadel
**Pt:* Stephen Neal

D-U-N-S 00-165-6318
COONEY CONVALESCENT HOME
2555 E Broadway St, Helena, MT 59601-4991
Tel (406) 447-1651 *Founded/Ownrshp* 1930
Sales 455.1MM *EMP* 90
SIC 8059 8051 Convalescent home; Skilled nursing care facilities

D-U-N-S 03-515-6702
COOP HUSKER
2468 33rd Ave, Columbus, NE 68601-2310
Tel (402) 564-2704 *Founded/Ownrshp* 1921
Sales 169.3MM *EMP* 85
Accts Gardiner Thomsen Cpas Lincol
SIC 5153 5191 Grains; Fertilizer & fertilizer materials; Feed
Pr: Dwight Loeske

D-U-N-S 02-310-8483
COOP WHEATON-DUMONT ELEVATOR INC
6587 Us Highway 75, Wheaton, MN 56296-5441
Tel (320) 563-8152 *Founded/Ownrshp* 1926
Sales 303.2MM *EMP* 120
Accts Carlson Highland & Co Llp N
SIC 5153 5191 Grains; Fertilizer & fertilizer materials; Chemicals, agricultural; Feed
CEO: Philip Deal
**VP:* Ronald Sanasack
Sfty Mgr: Sonya Frisch
Plnt Mgr: Hank Frisch
Plnt Mgr: Brian Montonye
Plnt Mgr: Jeremy Ostby

D-U-N-S 01-762-3422 IMP
COOPER & CO INC
10179 Commerce Park Dr, West Chester, OH 45246-1335
Tel (513) 671-6067 *Founded/Ownrshp* 1945
Sales 86.0MM^E *EMP* 675
SIC 5944 Watches
Co-Pr: David S Cooper
Treas: Dave Griffith
**Treas:* David Griffiths
**Co-Pr:* Martin Cooper
**VP:* Cindy George
Exec: Patty Hattfield
Dir IT: Randall Grandstaff
Sales Exec: Linda Pikins
Sales Exec: Carol Wilson
Mktg Dir: Lori Biller
Mktg Dir: Mary Pauken

D-U-N-S 05-396-9408 IMP/EXP
COOPER B-LINE INC
EATON
(*Suby of* EATON ELECTRIC HOLDINGS LLC) ★
509 W Monroe St, Highland, IL 62249-1331
Tel (618) 654-2184 *Founded/Ownrshp* 1971, 2007
Sales 340.6MM^E *EMP* 1,200
SIC 3441 3443 3452 3444 3429 3356 Fabricated structural metal; Cable trays, metal plate; Bolts, nuts, rivets & washers; Sheet metalwork; Manufactured hardware (general); Nonferrous rolling & drawing
Pr: Richard H Fearon
Sr VP: Todd Davis
VP: Thomas McCarron
VP: Jimmy L Tipton Jr
Prin: Kevin C Kissling
Genl Mgr: Ken Walma
IT Man: Eric Augustin
IT Man: Nick Duncan
Opers Mgr: John Mulhall
Manager: Greg Jeckstadt
Board of Directors: Dr Carl T Cori, Dr David R Harvey

D-U-N-S 06-994-3079 IMP/EXP
COOPER BUSSMANN LLC
(*Suby of* EATON ELECTRIC HOLDINGS LLC) ★
114 Old State Rd, Ellisville, MO 63021-5915
Tel (636) 527-1324 *Founded/Ownrshp* 2008
Sales 594.8MM^E *EMP* 3,217
SIC 3613 3699 3643 Fuses, electric; Electrical equipment & supplies; Current-carrying wiring devices
Pr: Ivo Jurek
VP: Karl Markus
Opers Mgr: Rich Helgeson
Manager: Kamil Daouk
Manager: Michael Pille
Sls Mgr: Mitchell Barrineau
Sls Mgr: Pam Benzion
Sales Asso: Mary Frazier
Sales Asso: Matt Moss

D-U-N-S 03-544-1997 IMP
COOPER COMMUNITIES INC
COOPER HOMES
903 N 47th St, Rogers, AR 72756-9622
Tel (479) 246-6500 *Founded/Ownrshp* 1985
Sales 84.1MM^E *EMP* 400
Accts Hogan Taylor Llp Fayettevill
SIC 5251 Hardware
Pr: John A Cooper Jr
Pr: Randy Brucker
Pr: Daniel W Cooper
**Pr:* John A Cooper III
Pr: Dewitt Smith
Pr: Tommy L Spencer
**CFO:* M Kent Burger
**Treas:* Brian P Wood
**Sr VP:* J Neff Basore Jr
**Sr VP:* William H Kennedy III
Sr VP: Lyle N Shelor

D-U-N-S 02-418-7130
▲ **COOPER COMPANIES INC**
6140 Stoneridge Mall Rd # 590, Pleasanton, CA 94588-3772
Tel (925) 460-3600 *Founded/Ownrshp* 1980
Sales 1.8MMM *EMP* 10,200^E
Accts Kpmg Llp San Francisco Calif
Tkr Sym COO *Exch* NYS
SIC 3851 3842 Contact lenses; Surgical appliances & supplies; Gynecological supplies & appliances
Pr: Robert S Weiss
**Ch Bd:* A Thomas Bender

COO: Daniel G McBride
CFO: Gregory W Matz
Treas: Albert G White III
**V Ch Bd:* Allan E Rubenstein
Ofcr: Carol R Kaufman
VP: B Norris Battin
VP: Randal L Golden
Exec: Charlene Ogilby
Dir IT: Steven Lim
Board of Directors: Colleen E Jay, Michael H Kalkstein, William A Kozy, Jody H Lindell, Gary S Petersmeyer, Steven Rosenberg, Allan E Rubenstein, Stanley Zinberg

COOPER CROUSE HINDS ELEC PDTS
See COOPER CROUSE-HINDS LLC

D-U-N-S 06-529-3870 IMP/EXP
COOPER CROUSE- HINDS LLC
MOLDED PRODUCTS DIVISION
(*Suby of* EATON CORP) ★
4758 Washington St, La Grange, NC 28551-8150
Tel (252) 566-3014 *Founded/Ownrshp* 2004
Sales 279.6MM^E *EMP* 2,954
SIC 3069 3643 Hard rubber & molded rubber products; Current-carrying wiring devices
Sls Mgr: Asim Saeed

D-U-N-S 15-677-5947 IMP
COOPER CROUSE-HINDS LLC
COOPER CROUSE HINDS ELEC PDTS
(*Suby of* EATON CORP) ★
1201 Wolf St, Syracuse, NY 13208-1376
Tel (315) 477-7000 *Founded/Ownrshp* 2012
Sales 123.0MM^E *EMP* 1,300
SIC 3699 Fire control or bombing equipment, electronic
CEO: Alexander M Cutler
**Pr:* Grant L Gawronski
VP: John Dinger
VP: Hugh Goodridge
VP: Barbara Hapner
VP: Amy Hartzer
VP: Rick Johnson
Sales Asso: Patrick Kane

COOPER FARMS
See COOPER HATCHERY INC

COOPER FOODS
See V H COOPER & CO INC

D-U-N-S 00-541-6698
COOPER HATCHERY INC (OH)
COOPER FARMS
22348 Road 140, Oakwood, OH 45873-9303
Tel (419) 594-3325 *Founded/Ownrshp* 1934
Sales 256.7MM^E *EMP* 1,400
SIC 0254 0253 2015 5153 2048 Poultry hatcheries; Turkey farm; Turkey, processed; Grains; Prepared feeds
Pr: James R Cooper
**COO:* Gary A Cooper
**CFO:* Janice Fiely
**Treas:* Anada E Cooper
**VP:* Neil Diller
Exec: Athena Brown
Prgrm Mgr: Morgan Kacy
IT Man: Mike Wapplehorst

D-U-N-S 13-920-2717
COOPER HEALTH CARE
1 Cooper Plz Ste 504, Camden, NJ 08103-1461
Tel (856) 342-2000 *Founded/Ownrshp* 1985
Sales 97.0MM^E *EMP* 4,500
SIC 8741 Hospital management; Nursing & personal care facility management
Pr: Drchristopher Olivia
**CFO:* John Gates
**Ex VP:* Gary Young
Psych: Dina Silverman

D-U-N-S 06-989-6165 IMP
COOPER HEALTH SYSTEM
COOPER UNIVERSITY HOSPITAL
1 Cooper Plz, Camden, NJ 08103-1461
Tel (856) 342-2000 *Founded/Ownrshp* 1875
Sales 1.0MMM *EMP* 4,900
Accts Ernst & Young Llp Iselin Nj
SIC 8062 General medical & surgical hospitals
CEO: John P Sheridan Jr
COO: Ralph P Dean
COO: Adrienne Kirby
**COO:* George J Weinroth
CFO: Dennis R Poeme
CFO: Dennis Roemer
CFO: Douglas Shirley
**Ch:* George E Norcross III
Treas: William Smith
Trst: Mary Gayman
Trst: Raymond Meillier
Trst: Duane Myers
Top Exec: Gary E Stahl
Sr VP: Maureen P Barnes
VP: Peggy Leone
VP: Simon Samantha
Assoc Dir: Kimberly Allenbach

COOPER HOMES
See COOPER COMMUNITIES INC

D-U-N-S 00-333-8936 IMP
COOPER HOSIERY MILLS INC (AL)
4005 Gault Ave N, Fort Payne, AL 35967-8120
Tel (256) 845-1491 *Founded/Ownrshp* 1980
Sales 100.0MM^E *EMP* 950
SIC 2252 Men's, boys' & girls' hosiery
Pr: Mack Cooper
VP: Danny M Hughes

D-U-N-S 18-148-2378 IMP/EXP
COOPER INDUSTRIES LLC
(*Suby of* EATON CORP) ★
600 Travis St Ste 5400, Houston, TX 77002-3013
Tel (713) 209-8400 *Founded/Ownrshp* 2012
Sales 2.5MMM^E *EMP* 26,860
Accts Ernst & Young Llp Houston Te

SIC 3646 3612 3613 3644 3546 3423 Commercial indusl & institutional electric lighting fixtures; Ceiling systems, luminous; Fluorescent lighting fixtures, commercial; Transformers, except electric; Power & distribution transformers; Power transformers, electric; Voltage regulators, transmission & distribution; Panel & distribution boards & other related apparatus; Power circuit breakers; Switches, electric power except snap, push button, etc.; Fuses & fuse equipment; Noncurrent-carrying wiring services; Electric outlet, switch & fuse boxes; Electric conduits & fittings; Power-driven handtools; Drills & drilling tools; Hand & edge tools; Wrenches, hand tools; Hammers (hand tools); Soldering tools
Pr: Stephen Duke Cooper
Treas: Ben Wallace
**VP:* Dawn Cooper
VP: Grant L Gawronski
VP: Mary L Glowacki
VP: Tim Russell
VP: Vince Saporita
Dir Lab: John Kucera
Assoc Dir: Dan Woodham
Snr Ntwrk: Mark Toby
CIO: Diane Bulgrin

D-U-N-S 01-032-2555 IMP/EXP
COOPER LIGHTING LLC
EATON COOPER LIGHTING
(*Suby of* EATON ELECTRIC HOLDINGS LLC) ★
1121 Highway 74 S, Peachtree City, GA 30269-3019
Tel (770) 486-4800 *Founded/Ownrshp* 1997
Sales 1.5MMM[E] *EMP* 6,739
SIC 3648 3646 Lighting equipment; Commercial indusl & institutional electric lighting fixtures
Pr: Neal Schrimsher
CEO: Alexander M Cutler
CFO: Craig Arnold
CFO: Heather Robinson
Sr VP: William W Blausey Jr
VP: Kevin Arthur
VP: Daniel Castillo
VP: Seth Hall
VP: Hugo Milan
VP: Melissa Scheppele
Assoc Dir: Joseph Canale

D-U-N-S 09-257-9627
COOPER MARINE & TIMBERLANDS CORP
(*Suby of* SMITH COOPER/T CORP) ★
118 N Royal St, Mobile, AL 36602-3603
Tel (251) 434-5000 *Founded/Ownrshp* 1999
Sales 322.4MM[E] *EMP* 700[E]
SIC 5199 2421 Sawdust; Wood chips, produced at mill
Pr: George Brown
VP: Theodore A Erickson Jr
**Prin:* Johnson Michael G
Mng Dir: Tim Mire

D-U-N-S 00-611-7444 IMP/EXP
COOPER POWER SYSTEMS LLC
(*Suby of* EATON CORPORATION PUBLIC LIMITED COMPANY)
2300 Badger Dr, Waukesha, WI 53188-5951
Tel (262) 524-4227 *Founded/Ownrshp* 2007
Sales 1.8MMM[E] *EMP* 4,300
SIC 3612 3613 3644 3643 3629 3679 Power transformers, electric; Distribution transformers, electric; Switchgear & switchgear accessories; Fuses, electric; Insulators & insulation materials, electrical; Electric switches; Connectors & terminals for electrical devices; Capacitors, a.c., for motors or fluorescent lamp ballasts; Power supplies, all types: static
Pr: Michael A Stoessl
Pr: Tim Erickson
**Pr:* Diane K Schumacher
**Treas:* Alan J Hill
VP: Randall B Ammerman
VP: James A Chokey
VP: Larry Coble
VP: Margi Herriot
VP: Donald P Ingols
VP: Eddie E Scott
VP: Laurence K Wendahl
VP: Jerry Yakel
Exec: Sharon Berner

D-U-N-S 00-503-7601 IMP/EXP
▲ **COOPER TIRE & RUBBER CO INC**
701 Lima Ave, Findlay, OH 45840-2388
Tel (419) 423-1321 *Founded/Ownrshp* 1914
Sales 2.9MMM *EMP* 9,119
Tkr Sym CTB *Exch* NYS
SIC 3011 Automobile tires, pneumatic; Truck or bus tires, pneumatic; Motorcycle tires, pneumatic; Retreading materials, tire
CEO: Bradley E Hughes
Ch Bd: Thomas P Capo
CFO: Ginger M Jones
Ofcr: Brenda S Harmon
Sr VP: Allen Tsaur
Sr VP: Stephen Zamansky
VP: Dave Craig
VP: James Kline
VP: Chuck Yurkovich
Comm Dir: Cathy Huffman
VP Mfg: Scott Jamieson
Board of Directors: Steven M Chapman, Susan F Davis, John J Holland, John F Meier, Gary S Michel, John H Shuey, Robert D Welding

D-U-N-S 12-254-3783 IMP
COOPER TOOLS INC
(*Suby of* EATON ELECTRIC HOLDINGS LLC) ★
670 Industrial Dr, Lexington, SC 29072-3763
Tel (803) 359-1200 *Founded/Ownrshp* 2007
Sales 190.2MM[E] *EMP* 1,500
SIC 3546 Power-driven handtools
Pr: Laura K Ulz

COOPER UNIVERSITY HOSPITAL
See COOPER HEALTH SYSTEM

D-U-N-S 00-128-7986 IMP/EXP
COOPER WIRING DEVICES INC
(*Suby of* EATON ELECTRIC HOLDINGS LLC) ★
203 Cooper Cir, Peachtree City, GA 30269-3075
Tel (770) 631-2100 *Founded/Ownrshp* 1920, 2007
Sales 202.2MM[E] *EMP* 1,000
SIC 3643 3613 Plugs, electric; Caps & plugs, electric: attachment; Sockets, electric; Lamp sockets & receptacles (electric wiring devices); Fuses, electric
CEO: David Pawl
Pr: Darron Lacey
**Pr:* Jeffrey M Roberts
**CFO:* Tyler W Johnson
Ex VP: George Katsarakes
**Ex VP:* Neal W Kluger
Ex VP: W Taylor
VP: James Knapik
Dist Mgr: Michael Hurd
IT Man: James Burgreen
VP Opers: Ed Russman

D-U-N-S 05-051-1724
COOPER-BOOTH WHOLESALE CO LP
200 Lincoln West Dr, Mountville, PA 17554-1543
Tel (717) 285-8000 *Founded/Ownrshp* 2002
Sales 167.9MM[E] *EMP* 170
SIC 5194 5145 5122 5141 Tobacco & tobacco products; Cigarettes; Cigars; Candy; Druggists' sundries; Groceries, general line
Pr: Barry Margolis
Recvr: Damian Colon
Pr: Lori Homsher
Pr: Drew Schenk
VP: Greg Reichardt
Rgnl Mgr: Brett Dunhoft
Sales Asso: Dennis Kline

D-U-N-S 00-418-3273 IMP
■ **COOPER-STANDARD AUTOMOTIVE INC** (OH)
(*Suby of* COOPER-STANDARD HOLDINGS INC) ★
39550 Orchard Hill Pl, Novi, MI 48375-5329
Tel (248) 596-5900 *Founded/Ownrshp* 1936, 2004
Sales 3.5MMM *EMP* 27,000
SIC 3714 Motor vehicle parts & accessories
Ch Bd: Jeffrey S Edwards
Pr: Julie Hess
**Pr:* Bill Pumphrey
**COO:* Keith D Stephenson
**CFO:* Matthew W Hardt
**Ofcr:* Larry E Ott
**Sr VP:* Aleksandra A Miziolek
VP: Robert Johnson
Prgrm Mgr: Michael Camerella
Prgrm Mgr: Norma Medina
IT Man: Paul Diller

D-U-N-S 36-129-3918
▲ **COOPER-STANDARD HOLDINGS INC**
39550 Orchard Hill Pl, Novi, MI 48375-5329
Tel (248) 596-5900 *Founded/Ownrshp* 2004
Sales 3.3MMM *EMP* 29,000
Tkr Sym CPS *Exch* NYS
SIC 3714 Motor vehicle parts & accessories
Ch Bd: Jeffrey S Edwards
Pr: Song Min Lee
Pr: Juan Fernando De Miguel Posada
Pr: D William Pumphrey Jr
COO: Keith D Stephenson
CFO: Matthew W Hardt
Ofcr: Larry E Ott
Sr VP: Aleksandra A Miziolek
VP: Jonathan P Banas
VP: Brian Griffin
Dir Risk M: Guy Todd

D-U-N-S 04-449-7501
COOPER/T SMITH STEVEDORING CO INC
(*Suby of* SMITH COOPER/T CORP) ★
118 N Royal St Ste 1100, Mobile, AL 36602-3600
Tel (251) 431-6100 *Founded/Ownrshp* 1911
Sales 148.4MM[E] *EMP* 900
SIC 4491 Stevedoring; Unloading vessels
Pr: David J Cooper
**Treas:* Jamie K Davidson
**Ex VP:* Richard Murray III
Sr VP: George Brown

D-U-N-S 09-003-6344
COOPERATIVA DE SEGUROS MULTIPLES DE PUERTO RICO
Expreso Ls America Y Mira, San Juan, PR 00927
Tel (787) 758-8585 *Founded/Ownrshp* 1965
Sales NA *EMP* 517
SIC 6331 6351 Fire, marine & casualty insurance; Surety insurance
Pr: Rene A Campos Carbonell
**VP:* Hugo Serrano Arroyo
**VP:* Jose E Burgos
**VP:* Jose M Martinez
**VP Mktg:* Zulma Delgado Pol

D-U-N-S 07-805-4681
COOPERATIVE ELECTRIC ENERGY UTILITY SUPPLY INC
C E E U S
101 Enterprise Pkwy, West Columbia, SC 29170-2249
Tel (800) 922-3590 *Founded/Ownrshp* 1974
Sales 89.0MM *EMP* 100
Accts Mcnair Mclemore Middlebrooks
SIC 5063 Electrical apparatus & equipment
Ch: Wayne Furtick
Pr: Scott Bryant
**CEO:* Donald E McCord
Chf Mktg O: Bill Barna
**Prin:* David Felkel

D-U-N-S 00-890-2835 EXP
COOPERATIVE ELEVATOR CO
7211 E Michigan Ave, Pigeon, MI 48755-5202
Tel (989) 453-4500 *Founded/Ownrshp* 1915
Sales 209.9MM *EMP* 136
Accts Cliftonlarsonallen Llp Middle
SIC 5172 5191 5541 5261 5153 Petroleum products; Seeds: field, garden & flower; Filling stations, gasoline; Fertilizer; Beans, dry: bulk
Ch Bd: Kurt Ewald
**V Ch Bd:* David Houghpaling

D-U-N-S 07-789-3378
COOPERATIVE ENERGY A MISSISSIPPI ELECTRIC COOPERATIVE
SOUTH MISSISSIPPI ELECTRIC PWR
7037 U S Highway 49, Hattiesburg, MS 39402-9128
Tel (601) 579-0215 *Founded/Ownrshp* 1941
Sales 917.6MM *EMP* 238
SIC 4911 Generation, electric power; Transmission, electric power
Pr: Henry C Waterer Jr
**VP:* Billy Harden
**VP:* Harlan Rogers
**Genl Mgr:* James M Compton
Plnt Mgr: Jerry Hudson

D-U-N-S 00-749-1871
COOPERATIVE FARMERS ELEVATOR
1219 Main St, Rock Valley, IA 51247-1301
Tel (712) 476-5321 *Founded/Ownrshp* 1899
Sales 178.4MM[E] *EMP* 140
SIC 5153 5191 Grain elevators; Feed
Pr: Keith Boer
Off Mgr: Kristi Klingenberg

D-U-N-S 00-179-3082
COOPERATIVE FOR ASSISTANCE AND RELIEF EVERYWHERE INC (GA)
CARE USA
151 Ellis St Ne, Atlanta, GA 30303-2420
Tel (404) 681-2552 *Founded/Ownrshp* 1946
Sales 492.0MM[E] *EMP* 10,000
Accts Ernst & Young Us Llp Atlanta
SIC 8641 8322 Civic social & fraternal associations; Individual & family services
CEO: Helene Gayle
**CFO:* Vickie J Barrow-Klien
Ofcr: Clark Efaw
Ofcr: Elizabeth Noznesky
Sr VP: Ted Jastrzebski
VP: Phil Mazzara
Exec: Mary Rumbley
Exec: Margaret Schnitzler
Ex Dir: Karen Bailes
Genl Mgr: Ana Gerio
CTO: Rolando Siles

D-U-N-S 85-875-3536
COOPERATIVE HEALTH SERVICES INC
(*Suby of* OWENSBORO HEALTH INC) ★
811 E Parrish Ave, Owensboro, KY 42303-3258
Tel (270) 688-3075 *Founded/Ownrshp* 1992
Sales 111.1MM[E] *EMP* 3,200
Accts Ernst & Young Us Llp Indianap
SIC 8071 Medical laboratories
CFO: John Hackbarth
**COO:* Greg Stahan
**Chf Mktg O:* Scott E Gaines

D-U-N-S 04-885-5415 IMP
COOPERATIVE HOUSING FOUNDATION CORP
GLOBAL COMMUNITIES
8601 Georgia Ave Ste 300, Silver Spring, MD 20910-3438
Tel (301) 587-4700 *Founded/Ownrshp* 1952
Sales 169.6MM *EMP* 1,300
Accts Gelman Rosenberg & Freedman
SIC 8732 Commercial nonphysical research
Pr: David A Weiss
V Ch: Lauri Fitz-Pegado
V Ch: Robert A Mosbacher Jr
**CFO:* Abhishek Bhasin
Ofcr: Moctar Toumbou
**Ex VP:* Michel Holsten
Sr VP: Judith A Hermnson
**VP:* Guillermo Birmingham
VP: Christine V Emery
VP: Robyn McGuckin
VP: Ann Nicocelli
VP: Bill Simpson
VP: William Simpson
Exec: Janie Payne

D-U-N-S 03-518-9836 IMP
COOPERATIVE PRODUCERS INC
MID NEBRASKA LUBRICANTS
265 N Showboat Blvd, Hastings, NE 68901-7002
Tel (402) 463-5148 *Founded/Ownrshp* 1915
Sales 206.9MM[E] *EMP* 550
Accts Pawling Finn & Torrell Cpas
SIC 2048 5153 Cereal-, grain-, & seed-based feeds; Grain & field beans; Grains
CEO: Steve Domm
**COO:* Dan Olson
**CFO:* Rich Adam
**CFO:* Mark Thieszen
**CFO:* Charles Trutna
**VP:* Jim Dell
**VP:* Phil Ramsel
**VP:* Lyle Weitzel
**Prin:* Phil J Askey
**Prin:* Larry Harrenstein
**Prin:* Brad Quadhamer
Board of Directors: Phil J Askey, Larry Harrenstein, Joel Nuss, Gail Ortegren, Brad Quadhamer, Kevin Rainforth, Brent Woodman

D-U-N-S 85-948-1152 EXP
COOPERATIVE REGIONS OF ORGANIC PRODUCER POOLS
ORGANIC VALLEY
1 Organic Way, La Farge, WI 54639-6604
Tel (608) 625-2602 *Founded/Ownrshp* 1988
Sales 946.9MM *EMP* 764
Accts Baker Tilly Virchow Krause Ll
SIC 5148 5143 Vegetables; Dairy products, except dried or canned
CEO: George Siemon
**COO:* Louise Hemstead
**CFO:* Michael Bedessem
VP: Jerry McGeorge
Ex Dir: Lewis Goldstein
Genl Mgr: Beth Petrillo
Genl Mgr: Helen J Zitzmann
Dir IT: George Neill
IT Man: Heather Christianson
IT Man: Cindy Schmitz
Opers Mgr: Ryan McKittrick

D-U-N-S 80-935-7486
COOPERATIVE RESOURCES INTERNATIONAL INC
C R I
117 E Green Bay St, Shawano, WI 54166-2443
Tel (715) 526-2141 *Founded/Ownrshp* 1993
Sales 202.1MM *EMP* 1,500
Accts Wipfli Llp Appleton Wi
SIC 0751 5159 0762 8731 Artificial insemination services, livestock; Dairy herd improvement association services; Milk testing services; Semen, bovine; Farm management services; Agricultural research
CEO: R D Wilson
**Treas:* Lawrence J Romuald
VP: David Koepke
VP: Huub Plate
Opers Mgr: Ron Visser
Manager: Erin Berger
Sls Mgr: James Bayne
Sls Mgr: Larry Swartz

D-U-N-S 01-538-7364
COOPERS HAWK INTERMEDIATE HOLDING LLC
COOPERS HAWK WINERY & REST
5325 9th Ave, Countryside, IL 60525-3602
Tel (708) 839-2920 *Founded/Ownrshp* 2007
Sales 304.7MM[E] *EMP* 1,407[E]
SIC 8741 2084 5182 5812 Restaurant management; Wines; Wine; Eating places
VP: Ben Hummer
VP: Tara Snyder
Exec: Randall Sabado

COOPERS HAWK WINERY & REST
See COOPERS HAWK INTERMEDIATE HOLDING LLC

D-U-N-S 03-488-6218
COOPERS STEEL FABRICATORS INC ()
503 N Hillcrest Dr, Shelbyville, TN 37160-3617
Tel (931) 684-7962 *Founded/Ownrshp* 1960
Sales 103.5MM *EMP* 110
Accts Winnett Associates Pllc Shel
SIC 3441 1791 Fabricated structural metal; Structural steel erection
Pr: Gary Cooper
**Treas:* Barry Cooper
VP Mktg: Jim Patterson

D-U-N-S 80-189-5244 IMP/EXP
■ **COOPERSURGICAL INC**
(*Suby of* COOPER COMPANIES INC) ★
95 Corporate Dr, Trumbull, CT 06611-1350
Tel (203) 601-5200 *Founded/Ownrshp* 1990
Sales 191.4MM[E] *EMP* 426
SIC 5047 3842 3841 3845 Medical equipment & supplies; Gynecological supplies & appliances; Surgical & medical instruments; Electromedical equipment
Pr: Paul Remmell
**CFO:* Alan T Tucker
**Ex VP:* Robert D Auerbach
**VP:* Kerry Blair
**VP:* Cheryl H Bogardus
VP: Mark Curtis
VP: Richard Fox
VP: Erik Halstenrud
Genl Mgr: Pam Holler
Genl Mgr: Gregory Russo
Snr Sftwr: Earl F Glynn

D-U-N-S 78-931-4010 IMP
■ **COOPERVISION INC**
OCULAR SCIENCES A COOPERVISION
(*Suby of* COOPER COMPANIES INC) ★
209 High Point Dr, Victor, NY 14564-1061
Tel (585) 385-6810 *Founded/Ownrshp* 1980
Sales 329.5MM *EMP* 660
SIC 3851 Contact lenses
Ch Bd: Thomas Bender
Genl Pt: Moses Marx
**Pr:* Bob Ferrigno
**Pr:* Andrew Sedweg
**CFO:* John Calcagno
CFO: Matz Greg
Treas: Albert G White
Bd of Dir: A Bender
Bd of Dir: Rodney E Folden
Ex VP: Daniel McBride
Ex VP: Steven M Neil
VP: Juan C Aragon
VP: B N Battin
VP: James Gardner
VP: Randy Golden
VP: Aaron Green
VP: J C Marmo
VP: Joan Martt
VP: Greg Matz
VP: Daniel G McBride
VP: Eugene J Midlock

D-U-N-S 07-564-7925
COORDINATED SERVICES MANAGEMENT INC
3333 Peters Creek Rd Nw, Roanoke, VA 24019-2719
Tel (540) 366-0622 *Founded/Ownrshp* 1981
Sales 74.9MM[E] *EMP* 1,200
SIC 8741 Nursing & personal care facility management
Pr: Robert M Mc Nichols
Ex VP: Mary E McNichols
**VP:* Mary Elyn Lauth

D-U-N-S 62-240-6635 EXP
■ **COORS BREWING CO**
(*Suby of* MOLSON COORS BREWING CO) ★
17735 W 32nd Ave, Golden, CO 80401-1217
Tel (303) 279-6565 *Founded/Ownrshp* 1990
Sales 555.7MM[E] *EMP* 2,000
SIC 2082 Malt beverages; Beer (alcoholic beverage); Ale (alcoholic beverage); Near beer
Pr: Peter Swinbur
**Ch Bd:* Peter H Coors
CFO: Stewart Glendinning
CFO: Susan Meyers
Treas: Katherine L Macwilliams
Sr VP: L Don Brown

Sr VP: M Caroline Turner
VP: Alvin C Babb
VP: Robert W Ehret Sr
VP: Robert W Joanis
VP: Marvin D Johnson
VP: Hugo Patino
VP: John A Schallenkamp
VP: Larry W Seymour
VP: Al Timothy
Exec: Bob Dee
Exec: Clinton Edenfield
Exec: Dean Garnas
Exec: Ron George
Exec: Karl Liebl
Exec: Bill Maddock
Board of Directors: Charles M Herington, Franklin W Hobbs, Randall Oliphant

D-U-N-S 05-873-1969 IMP
■ COORS DISTRIBUTING CO
(*Suby of* COORS BREWING CO) ★
5400 Pecos St, Denver, CO 80221-6404
Tel (303) 433-6541 *Founded/Ownrshp* 1971
Sales 119.5MM^E *EMP* 400
SIC 5181 4212 Beer & ale; Local trucking, without storage
CEO: Scott Whitley
Off Mgr: Linda Whitmarsh
Mktg Dir: Jennifer Degraff
Sls Mgr: Andrea German

D-U-N-S 02-642-0919 IMP
COORS DISTRIBUTING CO OF FORT WORTH
2550 Mcmillian Pkwy, Fort Worth, TX 76137-5001
Tel (817) 838-1600 *Founded/Ownrshp* 1959
Sales 85.9MM^E *EMP* 280
SIC 5181 Beer & other fermented malt liquors
Pr: Larry R Antin
**CFO:* George H Shotwell
**VP:* Timmy W Anfin

D-U-N-S 07-048-6204 IMP
COORS OF AUSTIN LP (TX)
10300 Metropolitan Dr, Austin, TX 78758-4947
Tel (512) 837-6550 *Founded/Ownrshp* 1975, 2002
Sales 110.2MM^E *EMP* 220
SIC 5181 Beer & other fermented malt liquors
Pt: Ann Butler
CFO: Matt Harris
Genl Mgr: Deli Boothe

COORSTEK AMAZING SOLUTIONS
See COORSTEK INC

D-U-N-S 00-705-7334 IMP/EXP
COORSTEK INC
COORSTEK AMAZING SOLUTIONS
(*Suby of* COORSTEK LLC) ★
14143 Denver West Pkwy # 400, Lakewood, CO 80401-3266
Tel (303) 271-7000 *Founded/Ownrshp* 1999
Sales 919.1MM^E *EMP* 2,900
SIC 3545 Machine tool attachments & accessories
CEO: John K Coors
Ex VP: Bill Wells
**VP:* Richard A Bilancia
**VP:* Janet D Comerford
**VP:* Megan McGinley
**VP:* James P Sufka
Prgrm Mgr: Scott Woods
Genl Mgr: Harry Hodgson
Genl Mgr: Karl Pfaffenbach
Genl Mgr: Patience Ramsey
IT Man: Scott Huntley

D-U-N-S 07-934-7091
COORSTEK LLC
(*Suby of* KEYSTONE HOLDINGS LLC) ★
16000 Table Mountain Pkwy, Golden, CO 80403-1640
Tel (303) 271-7000 *Founded/Ownrshp* 2013
Sales 919.1MM^E *EMP* 2,900
SIC 3264 3053 3081 3082 3545 Porcelain electrical supplies; Gaskets, packing & sealing devices; Unsupported plastics film & sheet; Unsupported plastics profile shapes; Machine tool accessories
Genl Mgr: Glen Griffin

D-U-N-S 14-162-1768
COP CONSTRUCTION LLC
242 S 64th St W, Billings, MT 59106-2740
Tel (406) 656-4632 *Founded/Ownrshp* 2003
Sales 89.4MM *EMP* 225
SIC 1622 1629 Bridge construction; Waste water & sewage treatment plant construction
Pr: Edward W Bedell
**CFO:* Richard J Morrison
IT Man: Kathy Thorson

D-U-N-S 15-998-9248
■ COPANO ENERGY LLC
(*Suby of* KINDER MORGAN ENERGY PARTNERS LP) ★
1001 La St Ste 1000, Houston, TX 77002
Tel (713) 621-9547 *Founded/Ownrshp* 2001
Sales 326.9MM^E *EMP* 394^E
SIC 4922 4925 Pipelines, natural gas; Gas production and/or distribution
Pr: Steven J Kean
COO: James Wade
Sr VP: John N Goodpasture
VP: Kimberly A Dang
VP: Tom Glover
VP: Jordan Mintz
VP: Rob Schaefer
Dir Risk M: Ding Yuan
Area Mgr: Robert Ellis
IT Man: Ryan Hulett
VP Opers: James Doss

D-U-N-S 02-957-2047
▲ COPART INC
14185 Dallas Pkwy Ste 300, Dallas, TX 75254-1327
Tel (972) 391-5000 *Founded/Ownrshp* 1982
Sales 1.2MMM *EMP* 4,267
Tkr Sym CPRT *Exch* NGS
SIC 5012 Automobile auction
CEO: A Jayson Adair
**Ch Bd:* Willis J Johnson
**Pr:* Vincent W Mitz
COO: Sean Eldridge
CFO: William E Franklin
Ofcr: Robert H Vannuccini
Sr VP: Vikrant Bhatia
Sr VP: John Lindle
Sr VP: Paul A Styer
VP: Brett Adair
VP: Bruce Bishop
VP: Vinay Kudithipudi
VP: Jerry Sullivan
VP: Diane Yassa
Board of Directors: Matt Blunt, Steven D Cohan, Daniel J Englander, James E Meeks, Thomas N Tryforos

D-U-N-S 00-626-9872
COPE PLASTICS INC (IL)
4441 Indl Dr, Alton, IL 62002
Tel (618) 466-0221 *Founded/Ownrshp* 1946
Sales 217.6MM^E *EMP* 372
SIC 5162 3599 Plastics sheets & rods; Resins, synthetic; Plastics products; Machine & other job shop work
CEO: Jane Saale
**Pr:* P Jane Saale
**COO:* Jeff Maynard
**CFO:* John F Theen
**VP:* Gene A Appal
**VP:* James P McCormick
Rgnl Mgr: Dean Bryson
Brnch Mgr: Theresa Byford
Brnch Mgr: Taylor Fondren
Brnch Mgr: Mike Russell
Brnch Mgr: Steve Van Pelt

D-U-N-S 11-277-9137
COPELANDS OF NEW ORLEANS INC
POPEYES CHICKEN & BISCUITS
2601 Severn Ave, Metairie, LA 70002-5934
Tel (504) 830-1000 *Founded/Ownrshp* 1983
Sales 71.2MM^E *EMP* 2,500
SIC 5812 5813 Cajun restaurant; Cocktail lounge
Pr: Alvin C Copeland
CFO: Darius Gilanfar
Off Mgr: Deana Englert
IT Man: Linda Carver
MIS Mgr: Bill Jones
MIS Mgr: Richard Talluto

D-U-N-S 12-344-5210
COPIAH COMMUNITY CARE CENTER LLC
COPIAH LIVING CENTER
(*Suby of* COMMCARE CORP) ★
806 W Georgetown St, Crystal Springs, MS 39059-9453
Tel (601) 892-1880 *Founded/Ownrshp* 2002
Sales 318.2MM *EMP* 75
SIC 8051 Skilled nursing care facilities

COPIAH LIVING CENTER
See COPIAH COMMUNITY CARE CENTER LLC

COPLEY MEMORIAL HOSPITAL
See RUSH-COPLEY MEDICAL CENTER INC

D-U-N-S 07-458-4749
COPLEY MEMORIAL HOSPITAL INC
(*Suby of* COPLEY MEMORIAL HOSPITAL) ★
2000 Ogden Ave, Aurora, IL 60504-7222
Tel (630) 978-6200 *Founded/Ownrshp* 1886
Sales 311.3MM *EMP* 1,100
Accts Deloitte Tax Llp Chicago Il
SIC 8062 General medical & surgical hospitals
Pr: Barry Finn
**CFO:* Brenda Banwyhe
Netwrk Eng: Jack Weiner
Plnt Mgr: Rodney Horton
Doctor: Robert J Edwards MD
Doctor: David Vik

COPLEY NEWSPAPERS
See COPLEY PRESS INC

D-U-N-S 00-826-9052
COPLEY PRESS INC
COPLEY NEWSPAPERS
7776 Ivanhoe Ave, La Jolla, CA 92037-4572
Tel (858) 454-0411 *Founded/Ownrshp* 1928
Sales 92.6MM^E *EMP* 4,170
SIC 7383 2711 7011

D-U-N-S 78-968-7803 IMP
COPPEL CORP
(*Suby of* COPPEL, S.A. DE C.V.)
503 Scaroni Ave, Calexico, CA 92231-9791
Tel (760) 357-3707 *Founded/Ownrshp* 1991
Sales 335.8MM *EMP* 80
Accts Jp Caliman Corporation Cpa
SIC 5021 5137 5136 Household furniture; Women's & children's clothing; Men's & boys' clothing
CEO: Hermann Gerzabek
Pr: Ruben Coppel
CFO: Enrique Coppel

D-U-N-S 00-602-1224
COPPELL INDEPENDENT SCHOOL DISTRICT
200 S Denton Tap Rd, Coppell, TX 75019-3205
Tel (214) 496-6000 *Founded/Ownrshp* 1959
Sales 131.1MM *EMP* 900
Accts Rutherford Taylor & Company
SIC 8211 Public elementary school; Public junior high school; Public senior high school
MIS Dir: Kathy Creek
Teacher Pr: Kristen Streeter
HC Dir: Regina Owens

COPPER AND COPPER TUBE
See GD COPPER (USA) INC

D-U-N-S 07-491-2791
COPPER CELLAR CORP
COPPER CELLAR RESTAURANT
3001 Industrial Pkwy E, Knoxville, TN 37921-1711
Tel (865) 673-3400 *Founded/Ownrshp* 1975
Sales 37.0MM^E *EMP* 1,100
SIC 5812 5813 American restaurant; Seafood restaurants; Barbecue restaurant; Drinking places
Pr: Michael D Chase
Genl Mgr: Tammy Perkins
Mktg Dir: Kelsey Chase

COPPER CELLAR RESTAURANT
See COPPER CELLAR CORP

D-U-N-S 01-520-7152 IMP/EXP
COPPER RIVER SEAFOODS INC
1118 E 5th Ave, Anchorage, AK 99501-2759
Tel (907) 424-3721 *Founded/Ownrshp* 1996
Sales 259.6MM^E *EMP* 850
SIC 2091 5146 Canned & cured fish & seafoods; Fish & seafoods
Pr: Scott Blake
COO: Mark Hansen
CFO: Dan Case
**Sec:* Philip Fillingham
**VP:* William A Bailey III
Dir IT: Jason Christy

D-U-N-S 05-790-6059 IMP/EXP
COPPER STATE BOLT & NUT CO INC (AZ)
COPPER STATE PHX
3602 N 35th Ave, Phoenix, AZ 85017-4408
Tel (602) 272-2384 *Founded/Ownrshp* 1972
Sales 154.3MM^E *EMP* 360
Accts Eide Bailly
SIC 5072 3452 Miscellaneous fasteners; Bolts, nuts, rivets & washers
CEO: Robert Calfee III
COO: Brad Brown
COO: Jason Moon
**VP:* Virginia Calfee
**VP:* Brian Cates
**VP:* Carl Spackman
**VP:* Paul Tiffany
**Mng Dir:* Sarah Shannon
Dir IT: Kurt Hinkforth
Opers Mgr: Christopher Lukesh
Sls Mgr: Bryan Rosser
Board of Directors: Margaret Calfee, Robert M Calfee III, Virginia Calfee, Peter Calihan, Yates Hudson, Sarah Shannon

COPPER STATE PHX
See COPPER STATE BOLT & NUT CO INC

D-U-N-S 00-442-7886
COPPERAS COVE INDEPENDENT SCHOOL DISTRICT
703 W Avenue D, Copperas Cove, TX 76522-2000
Tel (254) 547-1227 *Founded/Ownrshp* 1885
Sales 78.6MM^E *EMP* 1,172
Accts Lott Vernon & Company Pc
SIC 8211 Public elementary & secondary schools
Pr: Joan Manning
Bd of Dir: Robert D Cook
**Bd of Dir:* Jim Copeland
**VP:* Inez Faison
**Ex Dir:* Rose Cameron
Genl Mgr: Graham Glenn
Off Mgr: Jutta Salser
Dir IT: Lenann Welter
IT Man: Brenda Essenburg
Netwrk Mgr: Henry Blair
Pr Dir: Wendy Sledd

D-U-N-S 80-517-0685
COPPERPOINT MUTUAL INSURANCE CO
SCF ARIZONA
3030 N 3rd St Ste 110, Phoenix, AZ 85012-3089
Tel (602) 631-2300 *Founded/Ownrshp* 1969
Sales NA *EMP* 453
SIC 6331 Workers' compensation insurance
Pr: Don Smith
**Ch Bd:* Bruce Thoeny
**Pr:* Jerry N Le Compte
**Ex VP:* Rick Degraw
**Ex VP:* Brent Nelson
**VP:* Jon Allen
**VP:* Christopher E Kamper
**VP:* Harvey Taulton
QA Dir: Melissa Butler
QA Dir: Roxanna Lopez
IT Man: Marvin Jones

COPYING CONCEPTS
See SUMNER GROUP INC

D-U-N-S 09-296-2869
COPYRIGHT CLEARANCE CENTER INC (NY)
C C C
222 Rosewood Dr Fl 10, Danvers, MA 01923-4599
Tel (978) 750-8400 *Founded/Ownrshp* 1977
Sales 145.7MM^E *EMP* 344
SIC 6794 7375 Patent owners & lessors; Data base information retrieval
Pr: Tracey L Armstrong
**Pr:* Joseph S Alen
**CFO:* Richard A Ruf
**Sr VP:* Theodore O Buchholz
Sr VP: Gretchen Gasser-Ellis
**Sr VP:* Roberty S Weiner
**VP:* John Deaver
**VP:* Bruce Funkhouser
**VP:* Gretchen L Gasser-Ellis
**VP:* Fredrick Haber
**VP:* Woody Johnson
**VP:* Haralambos Marmanis
**VP:* Betsy P Nietsch
VP: Michele Nivens
**VP:* Kathleen N Smith
**VP:* Lisa M Stapleton
Exec: Marianne Bright
Exec: Jim Colbert
Exec: Emily Sheahan

D-U-N-S 04-610-5948
CORAL REEF CAPITAL GROUP LLC
757 3rd Ave, New York, NY 10017-2013
Tel (646) 599-9680 *Founded/Ownrshp* 2008
Sales 124.5MM^E *EMP* 600^E
SIC 6799 1081 Investors; Metal mining exploration & development services
Pt: Marceau Schlumberger

CORAM CVS/SPCLTY INFUSION SVCS
See CORAM LLC

D-U-N-S 83-108-8864
■ CORAM LLC
CORAM CVS/SPCLTY INFUSION SVCS
(*Suby of* CVS HEALTH CORP) ★
555 17th St Ste 1500, Denver, CO 80202-3900
Tel (303) 292-4973 *Founded/Ownrshp* 2014
Sales 128.6MM^E *EMP* 4,600
SIC 8082 Home health care services
Pr: Alberto Garcia
Exec: Dawn Foley
Dir Rx: Linda Lewis
Dir IT: Ashwini Hassija
Manager: Jami Braudrick
Manager: Steve Calvery
Manager: Jennifer McCormick
Manager: Jim Miles
Manager: Andrew Monroe
Manager: Michele Moucatel
Snr Mgr: Sean Blosser

D-U-N-S 00-823-3275 IMP
CORBAN ENERGY GROUP CORP
418 Falmouth Ave, Elmwood Park, NJ 07407-3305
Tel (201) 509-8555 *Founded/Ownrshp* 2012
Sales 150.0MM *EMP* 20
SIC 1623 3443 5085 Natural gas compressor station construction; Cryogenic tanks, for liquids & gases; Tanks, pressurized
Pr: Daniel Chung
**Genl Mgr:* Howard Adams

CORBIN RUSSWIN ARCH HDWR
See CORBIN RUSSWIN INC

D-U-N-S 82-520-9042 IMP
CORBIN RUSSWIN INC
CORBIN RUSSWIN ARCH HDWR
(*Suby of* ASSA ABLOY AB)
225 Episcopal Rd, Berlin, CT 06037-1524
Tel (860) 225-7411 *Founded/Ownrshp* 1994
Sales 111.5MM^E *EMP* 500
SIC 3429 Door locks, bolts & checks; Locks or lock sets
Pr: Martin Huddart
COO: Kimberly Cummins
**Treas:* John C Davenport
**Prin:* John R Carlson
**Prin:* Mike Mortillaro

D-U-N-S 78-212-2147 IMP/EXP
CORBION AMERICA HOLDINGS INC
CSM AMERICA INC.
(*Suby of* CORBION N.V.)
7905 Quivira Rd, Lenexa, KS 66215-2732
Tel (913) 890-5500 *Founded/Ownrshp* 1983
Sales 258.0MM^E *EMP* 5,615
SIC 2819 2869 2041 2023 Industrial inorganic chemicals; Industrial organic chemicals; Flour mixes; Ice cream mix, unfrozen: liquid or dry
CEO: Tjerk De Ruiter
CFO: Eddy Van Rhede Van Der Kloot
CFO: Sven Thormahlen

CORBION-CARAVAN
See CARAVAN INGREDIENTS INC

CORBION-PURAC
See PURAC AMERICA INC

D-U-N-S 00-664-9615
CORBRO LLC (CA)
STEVENS CREEK VOLKSWAGEN
4490 Stevens Creek Blvd, San Jose, CA 95129-1104
Tel (408) 260-9300 *Founded/Ownrshp* 2000
Sales 85.0MM *EMP* 130
SIC 5511 New & used car dealers
Pr: Steven Cornelius

D-U-N-S 07-329-4303
CORBUS LLC
(*Suby of* SOIN INTERNATIONAL LLC) ★
1129 Miamisbrg Cntrvle Rd Ste, Dayton, OH 45449
Tel (937) 226-7724 *Founded/Ownrshp* 1998
Sales 88.5MM^E *EMP* 700^E
SIC 8741 7373 Business management; Systems software development services
Ch Bd: Rajesh K Soin
**COO:* Joseph A Basalla
**VP:* Kevin Robie
**Prin:* Steve Catanzarita

D-U-N-S 14-355-2862
CORCENTRIC COLLECTIVE BUSINESS SYSTEM CORP
(*Suby of* NATIONALEASE) ★
7927 Jones Branch Dr # 3200, Mc Lean, VA 22102-3322
Tel (703) 790-7272 *Founded/Ownrshp* 2002
Sales 535.9MM *EMP* 117
SIC 7372 Prepackaged software
Pr: Douglas W Clark
COO: Matt Clark
CFO: Mark Joyce
Sr VP: Dave Lindeen
VP: Rob Devincent
VP: Jeff Grygiel
VP: Clint Johnston
Snr Sftwr: Deepak Halale
Software D: Jeff Folinus
Software D: Michael Selector
VP Mktg: Kate Freer

D-U-N-S 12-156-1997
■ CORCORAN GROUP INC
(*Suby of* COLDWELL BANKER) ★
660 Madison Ave Fl 11, New York, NY 10065-8447
Tel (212) 355-3550 *Founded/Ownrshp* 2001
Sales 543.8MM^E *EMP* 9,000
SIC 6531 Real estate agent, residential
CEO: Pamela Liebman
COO: Susan Zabatta
**CFO:* David Fite
CFO: Segler Scott
Ex VP: Bill Cunningham
Ex VP: Tresa Hall
Ex VP: Deirdre Jowers
Sr VP: Joan Hegner
Sr VP: Carol A Kelly
Sr VP: Frank Percesepe

Sr VP: Bill Yahn
VP: Nicholas Athanail
VP: Kenny Blumstein
VP: Dan Brady
VP: Cee Brown
VP: Leighton Candler
VP: James Crow
VP: Nina De Rovira
VP: Heide Dechter
VP: Gary Depersia
VP: Christine Dugan

CORD FINANCIAL SERVICES
See FIKES WHOLESALE INC

D-U-N-S 07-647-0525 IMP
CORDEN PHARMA COLORADO INC
(*Suby of* INTERNATIONAL CHEMICAL INVESTORS II SA)
2075 55th St, Boulder, CO 80301-2803
Tel (303) 442-1926 *Founded/Ownrshp* 2011
Sales 100.0MM *EMP* 350
SIC 2833 8748 2834 Organic medicinal chemicals: bulk, uncompounded; Business consulting; Pharmaceutical preparations
Pr: Jean Lund
VP: Christian Ewers
* *VP:* Don Fitzgerald
VP: James Wilson
Assoc Dir: Celia Alexander
Assoc Dir: Alan Benson
Assoc Dir: Brian Case
Assoc Dir: Jane Meyer
Assoc Dir: Frieder Mitzel
Assoc Dir: Peter Rosyk
Assoc Dir: Torsten Woehr

D-U-N-S 15-133-5346
CORDIER GROUP HOLDINGS INC
4575 Southway St Sw, Canton, OH 44706-1933
Tel (330) 477-4511 *Founded/Ownrshp* 1985
Sales 142.5MM[E] *EMP* 301
SIC 3462 Iron & steel forgings
Ch: James J O'Sullivan Jr
VP: John Motsay

D-U-N-S 79-092-4054
CORDILLERA COMMUNICATIONS LLC
POST AND CAREER, THE
(*Suby of* POST & COURIER) ★
134 Columbus St, Charleston, SC 29403-4809
Tel (843) 577-7111 *Founded/Ownrshp* 1986
Sales 89.2MM[E] *EMP* 670
SIC 2711 3663 Newspapers, publishing & printing; Television broadcasting & communications equipment
* *Pr:* Travis Rockey
* *Treas:* John Barnwell

D-U-N-S 00-412-1059 IMP/EXP
■ **CORDIS CORP** (FL)
(*Suby of* CARDINAL HEALTH INC) ★
6500 Paseo Padre Pkwy, Fremont, CA 94555-3658
Tel (510) 248-2500 *Founded/Ownrshp* 1959, 2015
Sales 353.6MM[E] *EMP* 2,079
SIC 3841 3842 Surgical & medical instruments; Catheters; Surgical appliances & supplies; Implants, surgical
Pr: Celine Martin
Ch Bd: Robert W Croce
VP: James J Barr
VP: Ronald C Dadino
VP: Harman A Grossman
VP: Christian M Spaulding
VP: Carl J St Bernard
Genl Mgr: David Gildea
CIO: Steve Wilson
MIS Dir: Jorge Arango

D-U-N-S 03-446-6474
■ **CORDIS INTERNATIONAL CORP**
(*Suby of* JOHNSON & JOHNSON) ★
14201 Nw 60th Ave, Miami Lakes, FL 33014-2802
Tel (305) 824-2000 *Founded/Ownrshp* 1968
Sales 120.2MM[E] *EMP* 1,000[E]
SIC 2834 Pharmaceutical preparations
Pr: Donald O'Dwer
* *Pr:* Jesse Pin
* *Treas:* Wayne C Casebolt
* *Sec:* Daniel G Hall

D-U-N-S 07-621-8163 IMP
CORDOVA BOLT INC
5601 Dolly Ave, Buena Park, CA 90621-1831
Tel (714) 739-7500 *Founded/Ownrshp* 1975
Sales 103.5MM[E] *EMP* 25
SIC 5072 Nuts (hardware); Bolts; Miscellaneous fasteners
Pr: Mark A Cordova
* *VP:* Matthew J Cordova
Sls Mgr: Terry Swihart

D-U-N-S 02-198-2822
CORDOVA FOLSOM UNIFIED SCHOOL DISTRICT
1965 Birkmont Dr, Rancho Cordova, CA 95742-6407
Tel (916) 294-9000 *Founded/Ownrshp* 1949
Sales 97.7MM[E] *EMP* 2,000
SIC 8211 Public elementary & secondary schools
Pr: Ed Short
* *Pr:* Zak Ford
* *CFO:* Deborah Bettencourt

D-U-N-S 87-906-8765
■ **CORE AUTOMOTIVE TECHNOLOGIES LLC**
(*Suby of* CORE MOLDING TECHNOLOGIES INC) ★
800 Manor Park Dr, Columbus, OH 43228-9762
Tel (614) 870-5000 *Founded/Ownrshp* 2004
Sales 130.5MM *EMP* 70
SIC 3714 5521 Motor vehicle body components & frame; Used car dealers

D-U-N-S 14-601-1643
CORE BTS INC
(*Suby of* CONVERGENCE TECHNOLOGIES NY) ★
10201 N Illinois St # 240, Indianapolis, IN 46290-1114
Tel (317) 566-6200 *Founded/Ownrshp* 2006
Sales 158.9MM *EMP* 350
SIC 7373 Systems integration services
Pr: Frank Albi
* *CFO:* Barry P Lewis
* *Ch:* John D White
Treas: Jamie McGouin
Ofcr: Lawrence Strickling
VP: Tony Defeciani
VP: Tom Distefano
VP: Marcus Dolce
VP: Daniel Gallagher
VP: Lisa Lyons-Cassidy
VP: John Samz
Exec: Greg Litynski
Board of Directors: Teri Bruns, Walter Cook II

D-U-N-S 07-936-4436
CORE CONSTRUCTION GROUP LTD (IL)
866 N Main St, Morton, IL 61550-1602
Tel (309) 263-0808 *Founded/Ownrshp* 1979
Sales 782.7MM *EMP* 450
Accts Source By E Mail On January 7
SIC 8741 Construction management
Pr: Mark A Steffen
* *Treas:* Michael J Thomas
* *Ex VP:* Dennis Barber

D-U-N-S 02-622-0772
CORE CONSTRUCTION INC
3036 E Greenway Rd, Phoenix, AZ 85032-4414
Tel (602) 494-0800 *Founded/Ownrshp* 1982
Sales 175.9MM *EMP* 60
SIC 1542 1541 Commercial & office building, new construction; Specialized public building contractors; Industrial buildings, new construction
Pr: Jim K Jacobs
COO: Mark Stefferi
* *Treas:* John Verhoff
Ofcr: Shafiq Mohammad
* *Ex VP:* Dennis Barber
Ex VP: Brad Roberts
Off Mgr: Terrie Wilcoxon
IT Man: Bryan Barstow
Mktg Dir: Jessica Bateman
Snr PM: Don Frank

D-U-N-S 96-434-2948
CORE CONSTRUCTION SERVICES LLC
3131 N I 10 Service Rd E # 401, Metairie, LA 70002-6054
Tel (504) 733-2212 *Founded/Ownrshp* 2010
Sales 120.1MM[E] *EMP* 345
SIC 1542 Commercial & office buildings, renovation & repair
CFO: Michael Thomas
Genl Mgr: Tom Budde

CORE DIGITAL MEDIA
See CPL HOLDINGS LLC

D-U-N-S 06-380-8536
CORE HEALTH & FITNESS LLC
STAR TRAC
4400 Ne 77th Ave Ste 300, Vancouver, WA 98662-6857
Tel (360) 326-4090 *Founded/Ownrshp* 2011
Sales 384.2MM[E] *EMP* 300
SIC 5091 Fitness equipment & supplies

D-U-N-S 14-867-9140
CORE INC
1201 New York Ave Nw # 420, Washington, DC 20005-3917
Tel (202) 332-0063 *Founded/Ownrshp* 2004
Sales 188.1MM *EMP* 22
SIC 8733 Medical research
Pr: Richad West

D-U-N-S 00-406-5765 IMP
CORE INDUSTRIES LLC
STAR TRAC
(*Suby of* STAR TRAC) ★
4400 Ne 77th Ave Ste 300, Vancouver, WA 98662-6857
Tel (360) 326-4090 *Founded/Ownrshp* 1997
Sales 330.0MM[E] *EMP* 300[E]
SIC 5091 Fitness equipment & supplies
COO: Dustin Grosz
* *Prin:* Jim Davis

D-U-N-S 87-820-3033 IMP
CORE LABORATORIES LP
(*Suby of* CORE LABORATORIES N.V.)
6316 Windfern Rd, Houston, TX 77040-4950
Tel (713) 328-2673 *Founded/Ownrshp* 2001
Sales 797.5MM *EMP* 5,000
Accts Pricewaterhousecoopers Llp Ho
SIC 1389 Oil field services; Gas field services
Pr: David M Demshur
Pr: Elizabeth Blanchard
COO: Monty Davis
CFO: Richard Bergmark
Bd of Dir: John D Denson
VP: Mark Elvig
VP: Mike Flecker
VP: Jim U Gresham
VP: Ted Griffin
VP: Evelyn Medvin
VP: Greg Salter
VP: Tommy D Williams
VP: Jie Zhou
Dir Lab: Nada Bardaghji
Dir Lab: Senya Kleynman
Dir Lab: Robert Simmons
Board of Directors: Joseph R Perna

D-U-N-S 19-650-6336
CORE METALS GROUP LLC
TENNESSEE ALLOYS COMPANY
(*Suby of* GLOBE SPECIALTY METALS INC) ★
324 1/2 Penco Rd, Weirton, WV 26062-3813
Tel (304) 914-4360 *Founded/Ownrshp* 2010
Sales 139.8MM[E] *EMP* 150
SIC 5051 Metals service centers & offices

D-U-N-S 96-550-7312
▲ **CORE MOLDING TECHNOLOGIES INC**
800 Manor Park Dr, Columbus, OH 43228-9762
Tel (614) 870-5000 *Founded/Ownrshp* 1988
Sales 199.0MM *EMP* 1,525
Tkr Sym CMT *Exch* ASE
SIC 3089 Molding primary plastic
Pr: Kevin L Barnett
* *Ch Bd:* James L Simonton
CFO: John P Zimmer
VP: Terrence J O'Donovan
VP: William R Ringling
VP Opers: Robert P Price
Opers Mgr: Tim Harper
VP Sls: Terry Donovan
Board of Directors: Thomas R Cellitti, James F Crowley, Ralph O Hellmold, Matthew E Jauchius, Andrew O Smith

D-U-N-S 82-709-7960
CORE PHYSICIANS LLC
7 Holland Way Fl 1, Exeter, NH 03833-2997
Tel (603) 580-7939 *Founded/Ownrshp* 2007
Sales 96.8MM[E] *EMP* 1,950[E]
SIC 8062 General medical & surgical hospitals

D-U-N-S 62-099-2412
CORE STAFFING SERVICES INC
40 Wall St Ste 1600, New York, NY 10005-1328
Tel (212) 766-1222 *Founded/Ownrshp* 1988
Sales 83.6MM[E] *EMP* 2,000
SIC 7361 Employment agencies
Pr: Mitchell Heine

D-U-N-S 13-355-1643
CORE TECHNOLOGY SOLUTIONS LIMITED LIABILITY CO
CTS
80 S Jefferson Rd, Whippany, NJ 07981-1049
Tel (973) 588-4533 *Founded/Ownrshp* 2003
Sales 98.4MM[E] *EMP* 1,500
SIC 7379 7373 Computer related consulting services; Systems integration services
CEO: Gary Dedoussis
* *CFO:* James J Inzalaco
* *Bd of Dir:* Brian Swenson
* *Prin:* Eugene Skopal
CIO: Sol Rozenburg
Sls Mgr: Abdul Motiwala

D-U-N-S 04-970-5064
■ **CORE-MARK DISTRIBUTORS INC**
ADEL GROCERY
(*Suby of* CORE-MARK INTERNATIONAL INC) ★
4820 N Church Ln, Smyrna, GA 30080
Tel (404) 792-2000 *Founded/Ownrshp* 2004
Sales 212.1MM[E] *EMP* 370[E]
SIC 5194 5141 5145 5113 Tobacco & tobacco products; Groceries, general line; Confectionery; Snack foods; Industrial & personal service paper
CEO: Thomas Perkins
* *CFO:* Stacy Loretz

D-U-N-S 16-778-6461
▲ **CORE-MARK HOLDING CO INC**
395 Oyster Point Blvd # 415, South San Francisco, CA 94080-1932
Tel (650) 589-9445 *Founded/Ownrshp* 1888
Sales 11.0MMM *EMP* 6,655[E]
Tkr Sym CORE *Exch* NGS
SIC 5141 5194 5145 5122 5199 5149 Groceries, general line; Tobacco & tobacco products; Cigarettes; Confectionery; Druggists' sundries; General merchandise, non-durable; Groceries & related products
Pr: Thomas B Perkins
Ch Bd: Randolph I Thornton
Pr: Eric J Rolheiser
CFO: Christopher M Miller
Sr VP: Christopher K Hobson
Sr VP: Scott E McPherson
Sr VP: William G Stein
Sr VP: Christopher L Walsh

CORE-MARK INTERNATIONAL
See CORE-MARK MIDCONTINENT INC

D-U-N-S 10-387-9391
■ **CORE-MARK INTERNATIONAL INC**
(*Suby of* CORE-MARK HOLDING CO INC) ★
395 Oyster Point Blvd # 415, South San Francisco, CA 94080-1955
Tel (650) 589-9445 *Founded/Ownrshp* 1995
Sales 3.4MMM[E] *EMP* 4,030
SIC 5141 5194 Groceries, general line; Cigarettes
CEO: Thomas Perkins
* *Pr:* Eric Rolheiser
CFO: Tom Barry
* *CFO:* Stacy Loretz
CFO: Stacy Loretz-Congdon
CFO: Stacey Lorez-Congdon
* *Sr VP:* Scott McPherson
Sr VP: Todd L Stevens
VP: Gerald J Bolduc
VP: John Somers
VP: William Stein
VP: Chris Walsh

D-U-N-S 10-299-4928
■ **CORE-MARK INTERRELATED COMPANIES INC**
ALLIED MERCHANDISING INDUSTRY
(*Suby of* CORE-MARK INTERNATIONAL INC) ★
311 Reed Cir, Corona, CA 92879-1349
Tel (951) 272-4790 *Founded/Ownrshp* 1989
Sales 154.0MM[E] *EMP* 96[E]
SIC 5199 5122 5087 General merchandise, non-durable; Druggists' sundries; Service establishment equipment
CEO: Thomas Perkins
* *Pr:* Mike Dunn
* *CEO:* J Michael Walsh
Off Mgr: Laura Castro
CIO: Gerald Buldoc
Opers Mgr: Bill Murray
Sls Mgr: Chris Hobson

D-U-N-S 15-105-2214
■ **CORE-MARK MIDCONTINENT INC**
CORE-MARK INTERNATIONAL
(*Suby of* CORE-MARK INTERNATIONAL INC) ★
395 Oyster Point Blvd # 415, South San Francisco, CA 94080-1932
Tel (650) 589-9445 *Founded/Ownrshp* 1981
Sales 289.9MM[E] *EMP* 472[E]
SIC 5194 5141 Tobacco & tobacco products; Groceries, general line
CEO: J M Walsh
* *Pr:* Thomas Perkins
* *Sec:* Gregory P Antholzner
* *VP:* Stacy Loretz Congdon

D-U-N-S 07-950-6489
CORE-MARK OHIO
30300 Emerald Valley Pkwy, Solon, OH 44139-4394
Tel (650) 589-9445 *Founded/Ownrshp* 2014, 1888
Sales 111.8MM[E] *EMP* 150
SIC 5194 Cigarettes
CEO: Tom Perkins

D-U-N-S 15-973-4151
▲ **CORECIVIC INC**
10 Burton Hills Blvd, Nashville, TN 37215-6105
Tel (615) 263-3000 *Founded/Ownrshp* 1983
Sales 1.7MMM *EMP* 14,055
Tkr Sym CXW *Exch* NYS
SIC 6798 8744 8361 8299 Real estate investment trusts; Facilities support services; Jails, privately operated; Rehabilitation center, residential: health care incidental; Educational services
Pr: Damon T Hininger
* *Ch Bd:* Mark A Emkes
Pr: Jean Shuttleworth
Pr: Jimmy Turner
CFO: David M Garfinkle
Chf Cred: Harley G Lappin
Ex VP: Anthony L Grande
Ex VP: Tony Grande
Ex VP: Steve Groom
Ex VP: Scott Irwin
Ex VP: Lucibeth Mayberry
VP: Michael Nalley
VP: John Pfeiffer
VP: Mike Quinlan
VP: Susie Simmons
Board of Directors: Donna M Alvarado, Robert J Dennis, Stacia A Hylton, C Michael Jacobi, Anne L Mariucci, Thurgood Marshall Jr, Charles L Overby, John R Prann Jr

D-U-N-S 15-686-3011
▲ **CORELOGIC INC**
40 Pacifica Ste 900, Irvine, CA 92618-7487
Tel (949) 214-1000 *Founded/Ownrshp* 1894
Sales 1.5MMM *EMP* 6,500
Tkr Sym CLGX *Exch* NYS
SIC 7323 7299 8742 8732

D-U-N-S 01-614-1470
■ **CORELOGIC SOLUTIONS LLC**
(*Suby of* CORELOGIC INC) ★
40 Pacifica Ste 900, Irvine, CA 92618-7487
Tel (949) 214-1000 *Founded/Ownrshp* 1997
Sales 323.5MM[E] *EMP* 4,800
SIC 7375 Information retrieval services
CEO: Anad Nallathambi
CFO: Jennifer McElderry
CFO: Margaret Yankovich
VP: Gayle Jennings
VP: Cheryl Larson
VP: Max O Valdes

D-U-N-S 03-119-2276 IMP
COREPHARMA LLC
(*Suby of* ROUNDTABLE HEALTHCARE PARTNERS LP) ★
215 Wood Ave, Middlesex, NJ 08846-2554
Tel (732) 356-0318 *Founded/Ownrshp* 2005
Sales 103.7MM[E] *EMP* 221
SIC 2834 Pills, pharmaceutical
CEO: Stephen White
* *Pr:* Grace Breen
* *Sr VP:* Don Allen
* *Sr VP:* James Mastakas
* *VP:* Vishal Gupta

D-U-N-S 02-203-2869
COREPOWER YOGA MANAGEMENT LLC
3001 Brighton Blvd # 269, Denver, CO 80216-5089
Tel (303) 813-9020 *Founded/Ownrshp* 2007
Sales 78.4MM[E] *EMP* 1,873[E]
SIC 8741 Management services
CEO: Amy Shecter
Pr: Chad Kilpatrick
COO: Kari Ament

D-U-N-S 01-990-2802
■ **CORESITE LLC**
(*Suby of* CORESITE REALTY CORP) ★
1001 17th St Ste 500, Denver, CO 80202-2461
Tel (866) 777-2673 *Founded/Ownrshp* 2010
Sales 265.7MM[E] *EMP* 350[E]
SIC 6798 Real estate investment trusts
Pr: Thomas Ray
* *Sr VP:* Derek McCandless
Sr VP: Steven Smith
VP: Billie Haggard
VP: Jonathan Litvany
VP: Mark Norton
VP: Erik Salazar
VP: Mike Sitter
Off Mgr: Anet Epperson
Opers Mgr: Jeron Bryant
Opers Mgr: Lee McDaniel

D-U-N-S 96-362-9253
▲ **CORESITE REALTY CORP**
1001 17th St Ste 500, Denver, CO 80202-2461
Tel (866) 777-2673 *Founded/Ownrshp* 2010
Sales 333.2MM *EMP* 391[E]
Tkr Sym COR *Exch* NYS
SIC 6798 Real estate investment trusts
Pr: Paul E Szurek
* *Ch Bd:* Robert G Stuckey
CFO: Jeffrey S Finnin
Sr VP: Derek S McCandless
Sr VP: Steven J Smith
Sr VP: Dominic M Tobin
Sr VP: Brian P Warren
Dir Soc: Danielle Hagel
Genl Mgr: Neil Giles
Opers Mgr: James Hofnagle
Opers Mgr: Chuck Short
Board of Directors: James A Attwood Jr, Michael R

Koehler, J David Thompson, David A Wilson

D-U-N-S 82-504-1890
CORESLAB STRUCTURES (ATLANTA) INC
(*Suby of* CORESLAB HOLDINGS U S INC)
1655 Noahs Ark Rd, Jonesboro, GA 30236-6143
Tel (770) 471-1150 *Founded/Ownrshp* 1993
Sales 228.8MM^E *EMP* 7,571
SIC 3272 1771 Concrete products; Concrete work
Pr: Mario Franciosa
**CFO:* Sidney Spiegel
**VP:* John Slaats
Exec: Joe Adamson
Exec: James Lane
IT Man: Tommy Lancater
Plnt Mgr: David Lee
Sales Exec: Keith Stepp

D-U-N-S 62-696-9430
CORESOURCE INC
(*Suby of* TRUSTMARK COMPANIES) ★
400 N Field Dr, Lake Forest, IL 60045-4809
Tel (847) 615-1500 *Founded/Ownrshp* 1997
Sales NA *EMP* 1,887
SIC 6324 6411 Hospital & medical service plans; Medical insurance claim processing, contract or fee basis
Pr: Mark Schmidt
Pr: Doug Reilly
**CFO:* Clare Smith
VP: Bob Bridwell
VP: David Earle
VP: Nancy Eckrich
VP: Lee Rufty
Reg Pr: Bob Wolfkiel
Dir IT: Troy Bowman
VP Opers: Lloyd Sarrel

D-U-N-S 00-692-9665 IMP
COREY STEEL CO
(*Suby of* OPTIMA SPECIALTY STEEL INC) ★
2800 S 61st Ct, Cicero, IL 60804-3091
Tel (800) 323-2750 *Founded/Ownrshp* 1947
Sales 136.1MM^E *EMP* 200
Accts Selden Fox Ltd Oak Brook I
SIC 3316 5051 Bars, steel, cold finished, from purchased hot-rolled; Aluminum bars, rods, ingots, sheets, pipes, plates, etc.
CEO: Mordechai Korf
Treas: Andrew F Praxmarer
VP: John M Decker
VP: John W Kenefick
VP: Kevin A Lavery
Board of Directors: Ronald C Kamp, Thomas E Ladky, Mark E Macdonald, Otto H Maurer, Richard J Perkins, William D Perkins, Thomas E Swaney

D-U-N-S 04-783-5889
CORGAN ASSOCIATES INC
401 N Houston St, Dallas, TX 75202-3354
Tel (214) 748-2000 *Founded/Ownrshp* 1979
Sales 90.8MM^E *EMP* 324
SIC 8712 7389 Architectural services; Interior designer
CEO: Robert K Morris
V Ch: Jeff Groth
CEO: Bob Morris
COO: Jon D Holzheimer
VP: Bob Emery
VP: Kyle Hester
VP: Tina Larsen
VP: David Lind
VP: Jonathan Massey
VP: Mitch Paradise
VP: Dav Rice
VP: James Rojas
VP: Staci Seyer
VP: John Trupiano
VP: Lindsay Wilson
VP: David Zatopek
Dir Bus: Mark Ruttner

D-U-N-S 12-780-7589 IMP
CORHART REFRACTORIES CORP
(*Suby of* SAINT-GOBAIN CRYSTALS) ★
10300 Ormsby Park Pl # 450, Louisville, KY 40223-6168
Tel (502) 423-6324 *Founded/Ownrshp* 1980
Sales 93.0MM^E *EMP* 1^E
SIC 3255 3297 Clay refractories; Nonclay refractories
Pr: Thomas J Larkin
**Genl Mgr:* Kyle Greene
Sls&Mrk Ex: Peter Scott

D-U-N-S 18-940-5954 IMP
CORIANT INTERNATIONAL INC
TELLABS
(*Suby of* CORIANT OPERATIONS INC) ★
1415 W Diehl Rd, Naperville, IL 60563-2349
Tel (630) 798-8800 *Founded/Ownrshp* 1987
Sales 790.6MM^E *EMP* 2,370
SIC 4813 Local telephone communications
CEO: Shaygan Kheradpir
**Pr:* Herbert Merz
**Pr:* Robert Pulland
**Ch:* Michael J Birck
IT Man: Tyrone Griggs
IT Man: Roberto Perez
Sftwr Eng: Dan Gilleland
Mktg Dir: Robert Shore
Sls Dir: Dave Ringquist
Snr Mgr: Greg Degnan

D-U-N-S 62-387-3879
CORIANT NORTH AMERICA LLC
(*Suby of* MARLIN EQUITY PARTNERS LLC) ★
1415 W Diehl Rd, Naperville, IL 60563-2349
Tel (630) 798-4238 *Founded/Ownrshp* 2013
Sales 1.0MMM *EMP* 2,500
SIC 5065 Telephone equipment
Ch Bd: Shaygan Kheradpir

D-U-N-S 79-825-1633 IMP
CORIANT OPERATIONS INC
1415 W Diehl Rd, Naperville, IL 60563-2349
Tel (847) 382-8817 *Founded/Ownrshp* 1992
Sales 790.6MM^E *EMP* 2,525
SIC 3661 Telephone & telegraph apparatus
Pr: Pat Dipietro
**CEO:* Shaygan Kheradpir
**CFO:* Gary Spitz
**Ex VP:* Ken Craft
**Ex VP:* Tarcisio Ribeiro
Sr VP: Thomas Cooke
VP: Carl A Dewilde
**VP:* Patrick Dipietro
VP: Daniel P Kelly
VP: K K Matthews
VP: Thomas Minichiello
VP: Scott Morgan
VP: Richard Schroder

D-U-N-S 60-372-2419
CORINTHIAN CAPITAL GROUP LLC
601 Lexington Ave Rm 5901, New York, NY 10022-4622
Tel (212) 920-2300 *Founded/Ownrshp* 2005
Sales 374.8MM^E *EMP* 1,040
SIC 6211 Investment firm, general brokerage
CEO: Peter Van Raalte
**Ch:* Steven J Kumbel
VP: Adam Fitzner
Mng Dir: Tony Pucillo

D-U-N-S 55-722-1397 IMP/EXP
CORINTHIAN INC
STATUS LEATHER
41 Henson Rd, Corinth, MS 38834-1423
Tel (662) 287-7835 *Founded/Ownrshp* 1993
Sales 120.0MM *EMP* 600
SIC 2512 Upholstered household furniture
Pr: Vick L Etheridge
**Prin:* Billy J Caperton
Sls Mgr: Jason Etheridge

D-U-N-S 13-676-9978
CORINTHIAN SCHOOLS INC
(*Suby of* CORINTHIAN COLLEGES, INC.)
124 Washington St Ste 101, Foxboro, MA 02035-1368
Tel (714) 427-3001 *Founded/Ownrshp* 1995
Sales 153.9MM^E *EMP* 15,200
SIC 8249 Vocational schools
CEO: Jack D Massimino
**Pr:* David G Moore
**CFO:* Maureen Findley
CFO: Richard Lokey
Snr Sftwr: Roya Mehrfar
Snr Sftwr: Yu Yuan
Dir IT: Tim Graham
Dir IT: Lara Moser
IT Man: Shannon Hagedorn
Software D: Scott Roach
Netwrk Eng: Bob Kavanagh

D-U-N-S 15-937-4029
CORIX UTILITIES (US) INC
CORIX WATER PRODUCTS
(*Suby of* CORIX UTILITIES INC)
11020 W Plank Ct Ste 100, Wauwatosa, WI 53226-3279
Tel (414) 203-8700 *Founded/Ownrshp* 2004
Sales 171.0MM^E *EMP* 900^E
SIC 1731 7389 Computerized controls installation; Meter readers, remote
Pr: Brett Hodson
COO: John Hoy
VP: Rhonda Dyce
**VP:* Kevin G Meagher
VP: John Stover
Area Mgr: Jefffrey Watson
Genl Mgr: Ed Yanoshita
IT Man: Erik Bjerkelund
Opers Mgr: Chris Burr
Sales Asso: Jerry Anderson
Sales Asso: Rick Rodriguez

CORIX WATER PRODUCTS
See CORIX UTILITIES (US) INC

D-U-N-S 01-155-3920
CORIXA CORP
GLAXOSMITHKLINE BIO N AMER
(*Suby of* G S K) ★
325 N Bridge St, Marietta, PA 17547-1134
Tel (717) 426-6557 *Founded/Ownrshp* 1994
Sales 94.2MM^E *EMP* 1^E
SIC 5122 Drugs, proprietaries & sundries
Pr: John Picken
**Prin:* Ed Everett

D-U-N-S 09-908-9963
CORIZON HEALTH INC
103 Powell Ct, Brentwood, TN 37027-7046
Tel (800) 729-0069 *Founded/Ownrshp* 1978
Sales 386.3MM^E *EMP* 2,881
SIC 8011 Offices & clinics of medical doctors
CEO: Woodrow A Myers Jr
**Pr:* Scott A Bowers
**COO:* Jim Donovan
**CFO:* Douglas Thompson
**Chf Mktg O:* Calvin B Johnson PHD
**Ofcr:* Scot Ward
Ex VP: Michael Taylor
Sr VP: Jim Courtney
Sr VP: Andrew Schwarcz
VP: Cindy Black
VP: Clair Cochran
VP: Joanna B Garcia
VP: Scott Hoffman
VP: Fred Hutchison
VP: Scotty Lee
VP: Khristine Olguin
VP: Rebecca Pinney
VP: Bill Steiger
VP: George Vaughan
VP: Gaylan Williams
Board of Directors: Richard Hallworth Stuart C

D-U-N-S 60-608-4705
CORIZON LLC
(*Suby of* CORIZON HEALTH INC) ★
12647 Olive Blvd Ste 400, Saint Louis, MO 63141-6345
Tel (314) 919-8501 *Founded/Ownrshp* 1982
Sales NA *EMP* 2,880
SIC 8011 Offices & clinics of medical doctors
CEO: Woodrow A Myers Jr
**Pr:* Scott A Bowers
CFO: Janet Wilson
**Chf Mktg O:* Calvin B Johnson PHD
Sr VP: Steve Hernandez
VP: Rhonda Alamanza III
VP: Georgia Perdue
VP: Todd Sparlin
VP: Jay Wendy
Dir Bus: Martha Harbin
Chf Nrs Of: Becky Pinney

CORKEN GOOD SERVICE
See CORKEN STEEL PRODUCTS CO

D-U-N-S 00-885-6494
CORKEN STEEL PRODUCTS CO (KY)
CORKEN GOOD SERVICE
7920 Kentucky Dr, Florence, KY 41042-2915
Tel (859) 291-4664 *Founded/Ownrshp* 1955
Sales 93.4MM^E *EMP* 135
SIC 5075 3444 5051 8742 6411 Furnaces, warm air; Air conditioning equipment, except room units; Sheet metalwork; Sheets, metal; Management consulting services; Insurance agents, brokers & service
**Treas:* Donald Corken Jr

D-U-N-S 07-091-5582
CORMAN CONSTRUCTION INC
(*Suby of* CG ENTERPRISES INC) ★
12001 Guilford Rd, Annapolis Junction, MD 20701-1201
Tel (301) 953-0900 *Founded/Ownrshp* 1983
Sales 166.3MM^E *EMP* 350^E
SIC 1611 1622 1623 General contractor, highway & street construction; Bridge construction; Underground utilities contractor; Pipe laying construction; Sewer line construction; Water main construction
Pr: William G Cox
**VP:* Arthur C Cox Jr
**VP:* Jo Ellen Sines
Snr PM: Tucker Waite

D-U-N-S 00-692-7982
CORN BELT ENERGY CORP (IL)
1 Energy Way, Bloomington, IL 61705-6356
Tel (309) 661-1004 *Founded/Ownrshp* 1938
Sales 85.9MM *EMP* 83
Accts Kerber Eck & Braeckel Llp Car
SIC 4911 4924 Distribution, electric power; Natural gas distribution
**VP:* Steve Hancock
**VP:* Michael Volker

D-U-N-S 00-479-6462
CORN BELT POWER COOPERATIVE
1300 13th St N, Humboldt, IA 50548-1163
Tel (515) 332-7700 *Founded/Ownrshp* 1947, 1986
Sales 130.0MM *EMP* 98
Accts Kpmg Llp Omaha Nebraska
SIC 4911 Generation, electric power
Pr: Feldman Donald
Pr: Kevin Bornhoft
**Treas:* David Onken
**Sr VP:* Karen Berte
VP: Kathy Taylor
VP: Michael Thatcher
VP: James Vermeer
Comm Man: Lynn Miller
Mktg Dir: Jim Sayers

D-U-N-S 94-792-8292
CORN LP
(*Suby of* CENTRAL IOWA RENEWABLE ENERGY LLC) ★
1303 Highway 3 E, Goldfield, IA 50542-5090
Tel (515) 825-3161 *Founded/Ownrshp* 2005
Sales 181.4MM *EMP* 35
SIC 2869 Ethyl alcohol, ethanol
Pr: John Gazaway
**VP:* Paul Rasmussen
Genl Mgr: Brad Davis
Plnt Mgr: Andy Miller
Prd Mgr: Judd Forth

D-U-N-S 01-788-5732 IMP
CORNA KOKOSING CONSTRUCTION CO (OH)
6235 Westerville Rd, Westerville, OH 43081-4041
Tel (614) 901-8844 *Founded/Ownrshp* 1995
Sales 112.3MM^E *EMP* 200
Accts Plante & Moran Pllc Southfie
SIC 1541 1542 8741 Industrial buildings & warehouses; Nonresidential construction
Pr: Mark Corna
**Treas:* James Graves
**Ex VP:* Jim Negron
**Sr VP:* Josh Corna

D-U-N-S 00-747-9132
CORNEJO & SONS LLC
(*Suby of* SUMMIT MATERIALS LLC) ★
2060 E Tulsa St, Wichita, KS 67216-2440
Tel (316) 522-5100 *Founded/Ownrshp* 2010
Sales 85.8MM^E *EMP* 250^E
SIC 1542 1794 1795 1611 Commercial & office building, new construction; Excavation & grading, building construction; Demolition, buildings & other structures; Surfacing & paving
CEO: Ronald Cornejo
**Pr:* Marty Cornejo
**VP:* Richard Cornejo
**VP:* Kirk Howie
Genl Mgr: Georges Ausseil
Genl Mgr: Tim Zynda
CIO: Michele Reynolds
IT Man: Levi Hobart
Mtls Mgr: Jose Beltran
Ql Cn Mgr: Randy Roths
Sls Mgr: Chris Blasdel

D-U-N-S 00-614-7086 EXP
■ **CORNELIUS INC** (MN)
(*Suby of* MARMON GROUP LLC) ★
101 Regency Dr, Glendale Heights, IL 60139-2206
Tel (630) 539-6850 *Founded/Ownrshp* 1935, 2014
Sales 225.0MM *EMP* 350
SIC 3585 3556 3586 Soda fountain & beverage dispensing equipment & parts; Food products machinery; Measuring & dispensing pumps
CEO: Tim Hubbard
Pr: Alen Duncan
VP: Craig Heetland

D-U-N-S 00-782-9344 IMP
CORNELL & CO INC
224 Cornell Ln, Westville, NJ 08093
Tel (856) 742-1900 *Founded/Ownrshp* 1900
Sales 141.5MM^E *EMP* 350^E
SIC 1542 1541 Commercial & office building, new construction; Industrial buildings, new construction
Pr: Delor Cornell
**CFO:* Kevin Brockway
**Sr VP:* Charlie Dougherty
**VP:* Larry Morris
**VP:* Otto Schatz

D-U-N-S 07-403-7177
CORNELL ABRAXAS GROUP INC
ABRAXAS YOUTH & FAMILY SVCS
(*Suby of* GEO REENTRY INC) ★
2840 Liberty Ave Ste 300, Pittsburgh, PA 15222-4776
Tel (412) 361-0695 *Founded/Ownrshp* 1997
Sales 29.4MM^E *EMP* 1,100
SIC 8399 Social change association
Pr: Arlene Lissner
**COO:* Tom Jenkins
**VP:* Jack Godlesky
Psych: John Lay
Psych: Michael Likens

D-U-N-S 05-358-4629 IMP
CORNELL TRADING INC
APRIL CORNELL
131 Battery St, Burlington, VT 05401-5208
Tel (802) 879-1271 *Founded/Ownrshp* 1981
Sales 135.1MM^E *EMP* 650
SIC 5023 5137 5719 5621 Linens & towels; Women's & children's clothing; Bedding (sheets, blankets, spreads & pillows); Linens; Ready-to-wear apparel, women's
Pr: Chris Cornell
COO: Basil Stetson
**CFO:* Mark Davitt
**VP:* April Cornell
Sales Exec: Cheri Blazek

D-U-N-S 00-225-4837 IMP
CORNELL UNIVERSITY
308 Duffield Hall, Ithaca, NY 14853-2700
Tel (607) 254-4636 *Founded/Ownrshp* 1987
Sales 2.1MMM^E *EMP* 12,207^E
SIC 8221 8011 University; Offices & clinics of medical doctors
Pr: Elizabeth Garrett
Pr: Paul Streeter
COO: Adel Hussein
**CFO:* Joanne M Destefano
Treas: Don Allen
Bd of Dir: Alexander Gaeta
Trst: Cheryl Francis
VP: Donald Bilderback
VP: Frank Disalvo
VP: Monica Geber
VP: Steven Henkind
VP: Dan Huttenlocher
VP: Mikhail Kostin
**VP:* Joel M Malina
VP: Joel Malina
VP: Michele Moody-Adams
VP: George Opperman
VP: Brian Smith
VP: Eva Tardos
VP: Tracey Thompson
VP: Linda K Tripp

D-U-N-S 00-214-8989 IMP
CORNELL-DUBILIER ELECTRONICS INC
140 Technology Pl, Liberty, SC 29657-3300
Tel (864) 843-2277 *Founded/Ownrshp* 1936, 1983
Sales 109.7MM^E *EMP* 450
SIC 3675 3677 Electronic capacitors; Electronic coils, transformers & other inductors
Pr: James P Kaplan
VP: E Brino
VP: Michele Gaeta
**VP:* Michael Kaplan
Genl Mgr: Michael Selvaggi
CTO: Randy Lesley
Sls Mgr: Dick Donohue
Sales Asso: Rene Halstead

D-U-N-S 00-134-4944 IMP/EXP
CORNELLCOOKSON INC
(*Suby of* CIW ENTERPRISES INC) ★
24 Elmwood Ave, Mountain Top, PA 18707-2100
Tel (570) 474-6773 *Founded/Ownrshp* 1828, 2015
Sales 114.2MM^E *EMP* 350
SIC 3442 Rolling doors for industrial buildings or warehouses, metal
Pr: Andrew Cornell
**CFO:* Paul Sugarman
Ch: M Cornell
**VP:* G Bruce Burnwell
**VP:* Thomas Druby
VP: Joe Heller
**VP:* Joseph Heller
VP: Roger Martin
**VP:* Lauretta O'Hara
**VP:* Sean Smith
Prgrm Mgr: Steve Grimes

CORNER BAKERY CAFE
See CBC RESTAURANT CORP

D-U-N-S 04-845-9179
CORNERSTONE ADVISORS
2711 Stewart Ave, Wausau, WI 54401-4140
Tel (715) 849-3697 *Founded/Ownrshp* 2013
Sales 120.0MM *EMP* 4
SIC 6211 Investment bankers
Owner: Edward Fox
Mktg Dir: Mona Fox

D-U-N-S 17-955-6795
CORNERSTONE AFFILIATES INC
6120 Stoneridge, Pleasanton, CA 94588
Tel (925) 924-7100 *Founded/Ownrshp* 2005
Sales 207.0MM *EMP* 2,000
Accts Moss-Adams Llp San Francisco
SIC 8322 Old age assistance

Pr: David B Ferguson
**VP:* Andrew McDonald

D-U-N-S 01-614-5489 IMP
CORNERSTONE APPAREL INC
PAPAYA CLOTHING
5807 Smithway St, Commerce, CA 90040-1605
Tel (323) 724-3600 *Founded/Ownrshp* 1999
Sales 160.0MM^E *EMP* 1,700
SIC 5621 Women's clothing stores
Ch Bd: Kuk Hwan Choi
**CEO:* Kenneth Choi
**VP:* Rachael Choi
**VP:* Tae Yi

D-U-N-S 03-198-5679 IMP/EXP
■ **CORNERSTONE BRANDS INC**
(*Suby of* HSN INC) ★
5568 W Chester Rd, West Chester, OH 45069-2914
Tel (513) 603-1000 *Founded/Ownrshp* 1998
Sales 344.3MM^E *EMP* 2,000
SIC 5961 Catalog & mail-order houses
CFO: Jim Pekarek
VP: Lisa Barnes
VP: Bill Johnson
VP: Cindy Proctor
VP: Matthew Smith
VP: Patrick Vonderhaar
VP: Kenneth Walker
VP: Paul Wolf
Ex Dir: Micah McFadden
Genl Mgr: Bill Daly
Snr Sftwr: Tracy Schuhwerk

D-U-N-S 96-751-2810 IMP/EXP
CORNERSTONE CHEMICAL CO
10800 River Rd, Westwego, LA 70094-2040
Tel (504) 431-9511 *Founded/Ownrshp* 2011
Sales 193.1MM^E *EMP* 450^E
SIC 2822 2821 Butadiene-acrylonitrile, nitrile rubbers, NBR; Melamine resins, melamine-formaldehyde
CEO: Greg Zoglio
**COO:* Paul Mikesell
**CFO:* Eifion Jones

D-U-N-S 01-426-6832
CORNERSTONE DETENTION PRODUCTS INC (AL)
14000 Al Highway 20, Madison, AL 35756-4426
Tel (256) 355-2396 *Founded/Ownrshp* 1998
Sales 166.7MM^E *EMP* 240^E
Accts Truitt Tingle & Paramore Llc
SIC 1542 Nonresidential construction
CEO: C Mitch Claborn
**Ex VP:* Shannon Claborn
**Ex VP:* David Watts
**Ex VP:* Kerrick Whisenant
**VP:* Joe Hargrove
**VP:* Jeff Lee
**VP:* Mike Root
Exec: Brian Day
Manager: Andrea Ward
Board of Directors: Sam Banks

CORNERSTONE HEALTH CARE
See CHRISTIAN HEALTHCARE OF MISSOURI INC

D-U-N-S 83-922-1967
CORNERSTONE HEALTH CARE PA
1701 Westchester Dr # 850, High Point, NC 27262-7008
Tel (336) 802-2700 *Founded/Ownrshp* 1995
Sales 290.7MM^E *EMP* 1,878
SIC 8741 8099 Hospital management; Blood related health services
Pr: Grace Terrell
**CFO:* Paul Miller
**Treas:* Michael Draelos MD
Chf Mktg O: Eric Neuville
**VP:* Dr James Anderson
Exec: Kim Fisher
Surgeon: Gary L Biesecker
Opthamlgy: Robert J Davanzo
Phys Thrpy: Mark Clepper

D-U-N-S 62-485-7157
CORNERSTONE HOME LENDING INC
1177 West Loop S Ste 200, Houston, TX 77027-9083
Tel (713) 599-2895 *Founded/Ownrshp* 1986
Sales NA *EMP* 850
SIC 6162 Mortgage bankers & correspondents
CEO: Marc Laird
Ofcr: Derek Bolls
**Ex VP:* Julie Pietho
**Sr VP:* Cindy Annis
Sr VP: Nancy Newhard-Belcher
Sr VP: Cmb J Piepho
VP: Patricia Ahmad
**VP:* Judith Belanger
VP: Bertha Casas
**VP:* Sandy Coffman
**VP:* Gordon Gilbert Jr

D-U-N-S 12-866-7701
▲ **CORNERSTONE ONDEMAND INC**
1601 Cloverfield Blvd 620s, Santa Monica, CA 90404-4178
Tel (310) 752-0200 *Founded/Ownrshp* 1999
Sales 339.6MM *EMP* 1,361^E
Tkr Sym CSOD *Exch* NGS
SIC 7372 Prepackaged software
Pr: Adam L Miller
COO: Kirsten Helvey
CFO: Brian Swartz
Ex VP: Steven D Seymour
Sr VP: Adam Weiss
VP: Mike Erlin
VP: John Geraci
VP: Tara Neumann
Dir Sec: David J Carter
Snr Sftwr: Tony Abell
Snr Sftwr: Yonatan Meiri
Board of Directors: R C Mark Baker, Harold W Burlingame, Robert Cavanaugh, James McGeever, Joseph P Payne, Kristina Salen

D-U-N-S 82-531-9767 IMP/EXP
CORNERSTONE RESEARCH & DEVELOPMENT INC
CORNERSTONE US
900 S Depot Dr, Ogden, UT 84404-1300
Tel (801) 337-9400 *Founded/Ownrshp* 1992
Sales 134.9MM^E *EMP* 400^E
SIC 2834 Vitamin, nutrient & hematinic preparations for human use
CEO: Partha Kundu
Pr: Mike Beardall
Pr: Steve Hatchett
COO: Jared Leishman
Sr VP: Mark Pedersen
VP: Terry Keller
VP: Scott Murrin
Exec: Richard Williams
QA Dir: Isabel Tovar

D-U-N-S 36-165-4643
CORNERSTONE RESEARCH INC
1000 El Camino Real # 250, Menlo Park, CA 94025-4315
Tel (650) 853-1660 *Founded/Ownrshp* 1989
Sales 99.2MM^E *EMP* 600
SIC 8748 7389 Economic consultant; Financial services
Ch: Cynthia Zollinger
**Pr:* Michael E Burton
CFO: Lee Reamy
**Sr VP:* Catherine Galley
**Sr VP:* Michael Keeley
**Sr VP:* Allan Kleidon
VP: Victoria Lazear
VP: Stewart Mayhew
**VP:* Christine Nelson
**VP:* Andrew H Roper
**VP:* Grace Zales

CORNERSTONE STAFFING
See SMITH TEMPORARIES INC

D-U-N-S 13-201-7125
CORNERSTONE STAFFING SOLUTIONS INC
7020 Koll Center Pkwy, Pleasanton, CA 94566-3103
Tel (925) 426-6900 *Founded/Ownrshp* 2003
Sales 107.0MM^E *EMP* 2,200
SIC 7361 Employment agencies
CEO: Steve Trexel
**Ex VP:* John Dias
Area Mgr: Deborah Martin
Brnch Mgr: Selina Paniagua
Brnch Mgr: Kimberly Winklepleck
Off Mgr: Lisa Guerrero
Dir IT: Andrew Lin
Sls Mgr: Jessica Mc Donald
Snr Mgr: Mario Gatan

CORNERSTONE US
See CORNERSTONE RESEARCH & DEVELOPMENT INC

D-U-N-S 60-681-4770
CORNET TECHNOLOGY INC
CTI
6800 Versar Ctr, Springfield, VA 22151-4174
Tel (703) 658-3400 *Founded/Ownrshp* 1989
Sales 119.9MM^E *EMP* 140
Accts Argy Wiltse & Robinson Oc
SIC 5065 3669 3577 Communication equipment; Intercommunication systems, electric; Computer peripheral equipment
Pr: Natarajan Kumar
**CFO:* Paravin Dand
VP: Pierre Bretault
Dir Bus: John Alexander
Dir Bus: Tim Kokinda
Prgrm Mgr: Donald Hammell
Snr Sftwr: Owen Lyon
CIO: Max Salas
IT Man: Susan McKinney
Sftwr Eng: Srinivasan Ramaswamy
Ql Cn Mgr: Donna Tregear

D-U-N-S 06-961-8465
CORNETT HOSPITALITY LLC
HOOTERS
2120 Staples Mill Rd, Richmond, VA 23230-2917
Tel (804) 678-9000 *Founded/Ownrshp* 2000
Sales NA *EMP* 1,000
SIC 8741

D-U-N-S 79-284-7469
CORNETT MANAGEMENT CO INC
2120 Staples Mill Rd # 300, Richmond, VA 23230-2917
Tel (804) 678-9000 *Founded/Ownrshp* 1992
Sales 26.7MM^E *EMP* 1,000
SIC 5812 American restaurant
Pr: James Cornett III
**Sec:* Ronald H Clark

CORNHUSKER PRESS
See DUTTON-LAINSON CO

CORNING CONSUMER PRODUCTS CO
See CORNING VITRO CORP

D-U-N-S 07-368-3799 IMP
CORNING HOSPITAL
HEALTHWRKS WELLNESS FITNES CTR
(*Suby of* GUTHRIE CLINIC) ★
1 Guthrie Dr, Corning, NY 14830-2899
Tel (607) 937-7200 *Founded/Ownrshp* 1900
Sales 97.1MM *EMP* 621
SIC 8062 Hospital, professional nursing school
Pr: Shirley Magana
**CFO:* Fran Macafee
VP: David Austin

D-U-N-S 00-130-7735 IMP/EXP
▲ **CORNING INC** (NY)
1 Riverfront Plz, Corning, NY 14831-0002
Tel (607) 974-9000 *Founded/Ownrshp* 1851
Sales 9.1MMM *EMP* 35,700
Accts Pricewaterhousecoopers Llp Ne
Tkr Sym GLW *Exch* NYS
SIC 3229 3357 3661 3674 Glass fiber products; Glass tubes & tubing; TV tube blanks, glass; Fiber optic cable (insulated); Telephone & telegraph apparatus; Semiconductors & related devices
Ch Bd: Wendell P Weeks
V Ch: Lawrence D McRae
Pr: Mark A Beck
Pr: James P Clappin
Pr: John Geniviva
CFO: R Tony Tripeny
Treas: Mark S Rogus
Bd of Dir: Lisa Emel
Ofcr: Jeffrey W Evenson
Ofcr: Lisa Ferrero
Ex VP: Martin J Curran
Ex VP: Clark S Kinlin
Ex VP: David L Morse
Sr VP: Thomas R Hinman
Sr VP: Christine M Pambianchi
Sr VP: Lewis A Steverson
VP: David Bassett
VP: Adriane Brown
VP: Cheryl Capps
VP: Joe Dunning
VP: Jeffrey Evenson
Board of Directors: Deborah D Rieman, Donald W Blair, Hansel E Tookes II, Stephanie A Burns, Mark S Wrighton, John A Canning Jr, Richard T Clark, Robert F Cummings Jr, Deborah A Henretta, Daniel P Huttenlocher, Kurt M Landgraf, Kevin J Martin

D-U-N-S 07-368-3773 EXP
■ **CORNING INTERNATIONAL CORP**
(*Suby of* CORNING INC) ★
1 Riverfront Plz, Corning, NY 14831-0002
Tel (607) 974-9000 *Founded/Ownrshp* 1856
Sales 731.6MM^E *EMP* 3,500
SIC 3229 5945 Pressed & blown glass; Ceramics supplies
Ch Bd: John W Loose
**Pr:* James W Wheat
**CEO:* Wendell P Weeks
**CFO:* James B Flaws
**VP:* Kirk P Gregg
**VP:* Kenneth C KAO
**VP:* Clark N Liscomb
**VP:* Lawrence D McRae
**VP:* Dr David L Morse
**VP:* Augusto Saperira

D-U-N-S 08-898-1543
■ **CORNING NETOPTIX**
(*Suby of* CORNING INC) ★
69 Island St Ste T, Keene, NH 03431-3507
Tel (603) 357-7662 *Founded/Ownrshp* 2006
Sales 57.0MM^E *EMP* 10,000
SIC 3827 3851 3826

D-U-N-S 08-133-1142 IMP
■ **CORNING OPTICAL COMMUNICATIONS LLC**
(*Suby of* CORNING INC) ★
800 17th St Nw, Hickory, NC 28601-3336
Tel (828) 901-5000 *Founded/Ownrshp* 1977
Sales 747.8MM^E *EMP* 4,000
SIC 3661 Fiber optics communications equipment
CEO: Clark Kinlin
Ofcr: Martin J Curran
Ofcr: Joseph A Miller
Ex VP: Eric Musser
Sr VP: Malcolm Barnett
Sr VP: John R Sicotte
VP: Steven Karaffa
VP: Holly Paeper
Off Mgr: Darren Schmidt
Dir IT: John Holt
Dir IT: Eric Michaels

D-U-N-S 08-027-7949
■ **CORNING RESEARCH & DEVELOPMENT CORP**
(*Suby of* CORNING INC) ★
1 Riverfront Plz, Corning, NY 14831-0002
Tel (607) 974-9000 *Founded/Ownrshp* 2016
Sales 81.0MM *EMP* 1,500
SIC 8731 Commercial physical research
Pr: Wendell P Weeks
Pr: Lawrence D McRae
Ofcr: Yvonne Maurice Fierro
Prin: David L Morse

D-U-N-S 78-959-5063 IMP/EXP
■ **CORNING VITRO CORP**
CORNING CONSUMER PRODUCTS CO
(*Suby of* CORNING INC) ★
1 Riverfront Plz, Corning, NY 14830-2556
Tel (607) 974-8605 *Founded/Ownrshp* 1992
Sales 228.8MM^E *EMP* 7,000
Accts Price Waterhouse
SIC 3229 3469 Pressed & blown glass; Household cooking & kitchen utensils, metal
Pr: Peter Campanella
Pr: John W Loose
**CFO:* Pamela C Schneider
**Sr VP:* Hayward R Gipson
**VP:* Thomas E Blumer
VP: Dawn M Cross
VP: David G Rauscher
Board of Directors: Roger G Ackerman, Van C Campbell

D-U-N-S 00-446-8385 IMP
CORNWELL QUALITY TOOLS CO (OH)
667 Seville Rd, Wadsworth, OH 44281-1077
Tel (330) 336-3506 *Founded/Ownrshp* 1919
Sales 124.8MM *EMP* 170
SIC 5085 3423 6794

CORONA REGIONAL MED CTR HOSP
See UHS-CORONA INC

D-U-N-S 19-359-9099
CORP FOR PUBLIC BROADCASTING
401 9th St Nw Ste 200, Washington, DC 20004-2129
Tel (202) 879-9600 *Founded/Ownrshp* 2007
Sales 463.6MM *EMP* 99^E
SIC 7812 Motion picture & video production
Pr: Patricia Harrison
**V Ch:* Patricia Cahill
CFO: William P Tayman
CFO: William Tayman
**Ch:* Bruce Ramer
VP: Anne Brachman
VP: Letitia King
VP: Jennifer Lawson
VP: Jackie Livesay
VP: Richard Loutsch
VP: Debra Sanchez
VP: Greg Schnirring
VP: Westwood Smithers
Exec: Connie Jiang
Exec: Camille Morgan

D-U-N-S 07-827-2006
CORP FOR TRAVEL PROMOTION
BRAND USA, THE
1725 I St Nw Ste 800, Washington, DC 20006-2408
Tel (202) 536-2060 *Founded/Ownrshp* 2010
Sales 137.6MM *EMP* 20
Accts Moss Adams Llp Stockton Ca
SIC 7389 Advertising, promotional & trade show services
Pr: Christopher L Thompson
Pt: Tom Garzilli
Ch Bd: Tom Klein
CFO: Donald Richardson
Chf Mktg O: Yvonne La Penotiere
Counsel: Jake Conte

D-U-N-S 07-663-0177
CORP OF CATHOLIC ARCHBISHOP OF SEATTLE
ARCHDIOCESE OF SEATTLE
910 Marion St, Seattle, WA 98104-1274
Tel (206) 382-4884 *Founded/Ownrshp* 1861
Sales 62.7MM^E *EMP* 3,000
SIC 8661

D-U-N-S 07-926-5732
CORP OF GONZAGA UNIVERSITY
502 E Boone Ave, Spokane, WA 99258-1774
Tel (509) 328-4220 *Founded/Ownrshp* 1886
Sales 214.6MM *EMP* 1,200^E
Accts Moss Adams Llp Spokane Washi
SIC 8221 University
Pr: Thayne M McCulloh
Pr: James Voiss
**Treas:* Charles Murphy
Trst: T J Greenan
Trst: Shannon McCambridge
VP: Marissa Alcorn
VP: Danny Costello
**VP:* Patricia O'Connell Killen
VP: Joe Smith
VP: Margot Stanfield
Assoc Dir: Shelly Radtke

D-U-N-S 00-250-2615
CORP OF HAVERFORD COLLEGE
370 Lancaster Ave, Haverford, PA 19041-1336
Tel (610) 896-1000 *Founded/Ownrshp* 1833
Sales 90.3MM *EMP* 600^E
Accts Cliftonlarsonallen Llp Plymo
SIC 8221 University
Pr: Kimberly W Benston
**VP:* G Richard Wynn
Assoc Dir: Emily Cronin
**Prin:* Stephen Emmerson

D-U-N-S 06-536-5041
CORP OF MERCER UNIVERSITY
1400 Coleman Ave, Macon, GA 31207-0001
Tel (478) 301-2700 *Founded/Ownrshp* 1833
Sales 341.0MM *EMP* 1,658
Accts Kpmg Llp Greensboro Nc
SIC 8221 University
Pr: William D Underwood
**Ch Bd:* David Hudson
**Pr:* William Underwood
Assoc VP: Kenneth Quattlebaum
Sr VP: Thomas G Estes
**VP:* G Lynwood Donald
Exec: Brian Dalton
Exec: Allen London
Exec: James Netherton
Dir Lab: Richard Amoss
Dir Soc: Claude Marriotini

CORPORATION OF PRES OF THE
See BRIGHAM YOUNG UNIVERSITY

D-U-N-S 00-194-0170
CORP OF PRESIDENT OF CHURCH OF JESUS CHRIST OF LATTER-DAY SAINTS (UT)
CHURCH OF JSUS CHRST OF LD STS
50 W North Temple, Salt Lake City, UT 84150-9709
Tel (801) 240-1000 *Founded/Ownrshp* 1923
Sales 2.4MMM^E *EMP* 16,000
SIC 8661 8221 Church of Jesus Christ of Latter-Day Saints (Mormon Church); Colleges universities & professional schools
Pr: Thomas S Monson
Ofcr: Roger Christensen
Admn Mgr: Amy Stratford
DP Exec: Lamar White
IT Man: Rodney Hyde
IT Man: Craig Wilson
Sls&Mrk Ex: Kimberly Holst

D-U-N-S 07-300-7411
CORP OF PRESIDING BISHOP OF CHURCH OF JESUS CHRIST OF LATTER-DAY SAINTS
BEEHIVE CLOTHING
(*Suby of* CHURCH OF JSUS CHRST OF LD STS) ★
50 E North Temple, Salt Lake City, UT 84150-9001
Tel (801) 240-1000 *Founded/Ownrshp* 1967
Sales 626.9MM^E *EMP* 11,827
SIC 8661 Church of Jesus Christ of Latter-Day Saints (Mormon Church)
Pr: Thomas S Monson

D-U-N-S 04-451-9650 IMP
CORP SERVICE CO INC
C S C
2711 Centerville Rd # 400, Wilmington, DE 19808-1646
Tel (302) 636-5400 *Founded/Ownrshp* 1975

Sales 537.1MM^E *EMP* 1,120
SIC 7389 Financial services; Legal & tax services
CEO: Rodman Ward III
Pr: Thomas Porth
**Chf Cred:* Ian McConnel
VP: Ej Dealy
VP: Steve Gades
VP: Alan Halpern
VP: Andrew Panaccione
Dir Soc: Melissa Davis
Dir IT: Chris Daly
IT Man: Phil Heizer
IT Man: Jeff Kirk

D-U-N-S 80-940-5343 IMP/EXP
CORPAC STEEL PRODUCTS CORP
20803 Biscayne Blvd # 502, Aventura, FL 33180-1432
Tel (305) 933-8599 *Founded/Ownrshp* 1992
Sales 178.4MM *EMP* 90
Accts Crowe Horwath Llp Fort Lauder
SIC 5051 Iron & steel (ferrous) products
Pr: Jorge Woldenberg
**CFO:* Edgardo Vargas
VP: Bruce Spencer
**VP:* Idel Woldenberger
Genl Mgr: Guillermo Selva
Sales Asso: Tyler Hout

D-U-N-S 09-038-1336
CORPORACION DEL FONDO DEL SEGURO DEL ESTADO
STATE INSURANCE FUND
Urb La Riviera Se 1024, Rio Piedras, PR 00921
Tel (787) 793-5959 *Founded/Ownrshp* 1935
Sales NA *EMP* 4,000
SIC 9441 Workmen's compensation office, government
MIS Mgr: Manuel Lanza
MIS Mgr: Oscar Ramos

D-U-N-S 03-922-4540
CORPORATE CAPITAL TRUST INC
450 S Orange Ave, Orlando, FL 32801-3383
Tel (866) 933-1960 *Founded/Ownrshp* 2010
Sales 311.1MM *EMP* 2
SIC 6733 Trusts
Pr: Steve Shackelford

D-U-N-S 09-393-9510
CORPORATE CLEANING SYSTEMS INC
3370 Turfway Rd Ste 190, Erlanger, KY 41018-3167
Tel (859) 371-5252 *Founded/Ownrshp* 1962
Sales 28.9MM^E *EMP* 1,200
SIC 7349 Janitorial service, contract basis
Pr: Benjamin Alper
**Ch:* Tony Alper
Dir Bus: Gus Sevastianos

D-U-N-S 02-331-7063
CORPORATE CONSULTING GROUP INC
133 Boston Post Rd 15, Weston, MA 02493-2525
Tel (978) 461-8000 *Founded/Ownrshp* 2001
Sales NA *EMP* 4,000
SIC 7371

D-U-N-S 16-487-1878 IMP/EXP
■ **CORPORATE EXPRESS US FINANCE INC**
(*Suby of* STAPLES INC) ★
1 Environmental Way, Broomfield, CO 80021-3416
Tel (303) 664-2000 *Founded/Ownrshp* 2008
Sales 738.6MM^E *EMP* 8,717
SIC 5943 Office forms & supplies
Ch Bd: Frans Koffrie
**Pr:* Jay L Mutschler
CFO: Gary M Jacobs
**CFO:* Robert T Vanhees
VP: Barbara W Burton
VP: Emily Demasi
VP: Chris Knudson
VP: Jeff Lasher
VP: Cathy Schuster
Exec: Tom Flavin
Exec: C D Macaulay
Exec: Deb Malmstrom
Exec: Mary Nobles

D-U-N-S 17-806-2048 IMP
■ **CORPORATE EXPRESS US INC**
(*Suby of* CORPORATE EXPRESS US FINANCE INC) ★
1 Environmental Way, Broomfield, CO 80021-3416
Tel (303) 664-2000 *Founded/Ownrshp* 1985
Sales 738.6MM^E *EMP* 8,000
SIC 5943 Office forms & supplies
Pr: Jay Mutschler
Pr: John Acampora
Pr: Maria Ayres
Pr: Ed Carr
Pr: Dave Grove
Pr: John Howe
Pr: Bill Jones
Pr: Greg McLeod
Pr: John Nixon
Pr: Rick Toppin
**CFO:* Robert Vanhees
VP: Peter Herbert
VP: Dan Perry
VP: Brian Rindels
VP: Scott Zinn

D-U-N-S 18-169-7913
CORPORATE FINANCE ASSOCIATES OF COLUMBUS INC
671 Camden Yard Ct, Columbus, OH 43235-3492
Tel (614) 457-9219 *Founded/Ownrshp* 1987
Sales 100.0MM *EMP* 100
SIC 8742 7389 6211 Business consultant; Brokers, business: buying & selling business enterprises; Security brokers & dealers
Pr: Charles E Washbush

D-U-N-S 08-003-9145
CORPORATE FOOD SERVICES INC
(*Suby of* SODEXO INC & AFFILIATES) ★
9801 Washington Blvd, Gaithersburg, MD 20878
Tel (301) 987-4000 *Founded/Ownrshp* 1989
Sales 25.9MM^E *EMP* 5,008^E
SIC 8741 Management services

D-U-N-S 60-661-2406
CORPORATE GRAPHICS INTERNATIONAL INC
C G I
(*Suby of* TAYLOR CORP) ★
1885 Northway Dr, North Mankato, MN 56003-2756
Tel (507) 625-4400 *Founded/Ownrshp* 2006
Sales 197.3MM^E *EMP* 450
SIC 2752 Offset & photolithographic printing
Pr: Nate Mullikin
**CFO:* Tom Johnson
Treas: Albert Fallenstein
VP: Nathan Mullikin
Genl Mgr: Bob Gonynor
VP Opers: Rich Inman
Prd Mgr: Grant Davis
VP Mktg: Lawrence Wagner
VP Sls: Dino Scalia
Mktg Dir: Steve Lawrence
Mktg Mgr: Todd Miller

D-U-N-S 79-649-9002
CORPORATE GROUP INC
7123 W Calumet Rd, Milwaukee, WI 53223-4007
Tel (414) 355-7740 *Founded/Ownrshp* 1985
Sales 104.3MM^E *EMP* 300
SIC 8711 1731 Engineering services; General electrical contractor
Pr: Richard D Gebhardt
**VP:* James E Pike
Mktg Mgr: Shelley McGrew

CORPORATE INTERIORS DELAWARE
See CORPORATE INTERIORS INC

D-U-N-S 92-955-7387 IMP
CORPORATE INTERIORS INC
CORPORATE INTERIORS DELAWARE
223 Lisa Dr, New Castle, DE 19720-4193
Tel (302) 322-1008 *Founded/Ownrshp* 1985
Sales 86.3MM^E *EMP* 115
SIC 5021 2521 Office & public building furniture; Wood office furniture
Pr: Janice K Leone
CFO: Mark Maderro
**VP:* Neil Marshall
**VP:* Patricia Tobin
IT Man: Lois Goodchild
IT Man: Patricia Rauch
Snr PM: Steven Didonato

CORPORATE OFFICE
See NORTHGATE GONZALEZ INC

D-U-N-S 93-162-2500
CORPORATE OFFICE PROPERTIES TRUST
6711 Columbia Gateway Dr, Columbia, MD 21046-2294
Tel (443) 285-5400 *Founded/Ownrshp* 1998
Sales 625.4MM *EMP* 383
Accts Pricewaterhousecoopers Llp Ba
SIC 6798 Real estate investment trusts
Pr: Stephen E Budorick
**Ch Bd:* Thomas F Brady
CFO: Anthony Mifsud
Ex VP: Wayne Lingafelter
Sr VP: Karen M Singer
Sr VP: Jud Williams
VP: Holly Edington
VP: David Finch
VP: Kathleen Geil
VP: Randall M Griffin
VP: Lee Murray
VP: Scott Robuck
VP: Gregory Thor
VP: Frank Ziegler
Board of Directors: Robert L Denton, Philip L Hawkins, Elizabeth A Hight, David M Jacobstein, Steven D Kesler, C Taylor Pickett

D-U-N-S 60-780-1495
CORPORATE PERSONNEL NETWORK INC
PREFERRED PERSONNEL CALIFORNIA
3552 Green Ave Ste 200, La Habra, CA 90631
Tel (562) 493-1503 *Founded/Ownrshp* 1992
Sales 63.3MM^E *EMP* 5,000
SIC 7363 Temporary help service
Pr: Joann Idleman
**Pr:* Teresa Garcia
**CEO:* Charles K Idleman
VP: Hubert Idleman
VP Sls: Craig Mask

D-U-N-S 10-330-6564
■ **CORPORATE PROPERTY ASSOCIATES 15 INC**
(*Suby of* W P CAREY INC) ★
50 Rockefeller Plz, New York, NY 10020-1605
Tel (212) 492-1100 *Founded/Ownrshp* 2001
Sales 249.8MM *EMP* 5^E
SIC 6798 Real estate investment trusts
Pr: Jason E Fox
**COO:* Thomas E Zacharias
**Mng Dir:* John D Miller

D-U-N-S 80-197-4713
CORPORATE PROPERTY ASSOCIATES 16 - GLOBAL INC
50 Rockefeller Plz Fl 2, New York, NY 10020-1607
Tel (212) 492-1100 *Founded/Ownrshp* 2003
Sales 323.1MM *EMP* 5^E
SIC 6798

D-U-N-S 96-250-7914
CORPORATE PROPERTY ASSOCIATES 17 - GLOBAL INC
CPA:17
50 Rockefeller Plz Fl 2, New York, NY 10020-1607
Tel (212) 492-1100 *Founded/Ownrshp* 2007
Sales 327.1MM *EMP* 4
Accts Pricewaterhousecoopers Llp Ne
SIC 6798 Real estate investment trusts
CEO: Trevor P Bond
COO: Thomas E Zacharias
CFO: Catherine D Rice
CIO: John D Miller
Netwrk Mgr: Virginia Lentino

D-U-N-S 07-328-6031
CORPORATE PROPERTY INVESTORS
305 E 47th St, New York, NY 10017-2303
Tel (212) 421-8200 *Founded/Ownrshp* 1971
Sales 128.4MM *EMP* 200
SIC 6798 Real estate investment trusts
Pr: Hans C Mautner
Pr: Mark S Ticotin
CFO: Michael L Johnson
Ch: Disque D Deane
Treas: Robert Lowenfish
Sr VP: G Martin Fell
Sr VP: J Michael Maloney
VP: William Blintzer
VP: Daniel J Cohen
VP: Jane Fortenberry
VP: William J Lyons
VP: Harold Rolfe
VP: Robert J Ross
VP: James M Selonick
VP: Bruce S Tobin
VP: Lois Weiss
VP: Thomas Zacharias
Board of Directors: Robert E Angelica, Dirk Van Den Bos, Gilbert Butler, David P Feldman, Andrea Geisser, Damon Mezzacappa, S Lawrence Prendergast, Daniel Rose, Jan Hwr Van Der Vlist

D-U-N-S 01-419-7246
CORPORATE RESOURCE SERVICES INC
160 Broadway Rm 1300, New York, NY 10038-4240
Tel (646) 443-2380 *Founded/Ownrshp* 1994
Sales 663.9MM^E *EMP* 800^E
SIC 7363 8742 Help supply services; Management consulting services
Ch Bd: John P Messina Sr
Pr: Mark S Levine
Pr: Frank Vaccaro
Ex VP: Adrian Hobbs
Board of Directors: Joseph Cassera, James Foley

D-U-N-S 08-028-5945
CORPORATE RISK HOLDINGS III INC
HIRERIGHT
3349 Michelson Dr Ste 150, Irvine, CA 92612-8881
Tel (949) 428-5839 *Founded/Ownrshp* 2015
Sales 11.3MM^E *EMP* 1,700
SIC 7389 Personal investigation service
CEO: John Fennelley
Pr: Stefano Malnati
CFO: Thomas Spaeth
Ofcr: Jim Weber
VP: Steven Spencer
Exec: Karla E Astronomo
Exec: Dawn Hirsch
QA Dir: Jennifer Deyo
Sales Exec: Sheila Williams

D-U-N-S 94-723-6667
CORPORATE RISK HOLDINGS LLC
600 3rd Ave Fl 4, New York, NY 10016-1919
Tel (212) 896-2001 *Founded/Ownrshp* 1996
Sales 111.9MM^E *EMP* 407
SIC 6719 8748 7375 7389 Investment holding companies, except banks; Business consulting; Information retrieval services; Personal investigation service
CEO: David R Fontaine
**Treas:* Joseph S Dubow
**Ofcr:* Jeffrey S Campbell
**Sr VP:* Andrew Grimmig
**Sr VP:* Brett D Weinblatt

D-U-N-S 94-697-1488
CORPORATE SECURITY SOLUTIONS INC
CSS
8066 Fulton St E, Ada, MI 49301-9100
Tel (616) 248-3372 *Founded/Ownrshp* 2005
Sales 23.0MM^E *EMP* 1,000
SIC 7382 Protective devices, security
Pr: Chris Frain
**Ex VP:* Andrew Shaffer

D-U-N-S 10-565-8806
CORPORATE SERVICES GROUP HOLDINGS INC
(*Suby of* IMPELLAM HOLDINGS LIMITED)
10740 N Gessner Rd # 400, Houston, TX 77064-1240
Tel (713) 438-1411 *Founded/Ownrshp* 1998
Sales 162.5MM^E *EMP* 14,000
SIC 7363 Temporary help service
Pr: Jennifer Beck
**CFO:* John Vlha
**Treas:* Geoffrey I Brailey
**VP:* Roger C Eden

D-U-N-S 04-457-3330
CORPORATE TRADE INC
CTI THE LARGEST IN THE WORLD
51 John F Kennedy Pkwy, Short Hills, NJ 07078-2704
Tel (973) 218-2551 *Founded/Ownrshp* 2001
Sales 206.0MM *EMP* 211
SIC 7389 Solvents recovery service
Pr: Brian Egan
**CFO:* Bill Green

D-U-N-S 02-094-8030
CORPORATE TRAVEL CONSULTANTS INC (IL)
CORPTRAV MANAGEMENT GROUP
450 E 22nd St Ste 100, Lombard, IL 60148-6175
Tel (630) 691-9100 *Founded/Ownrshp* 1976
Sales 222.4MM *EMP* 120
SIC 4724 Travel agencies
Pr: Linda Jane Batio
VP: Ms Barb Lea-Maijala

CORPOREX CAPITAL
See CORPOREX REALTY & INVESTMENT LLC

D-U-N-S 03-974-5336
CORPOREX COMPANIES LLC
100 E Rivercntr Blvd 11 Ste 1100, Covington, KY 41011
Tel (859) 292-5500 *Founded/Ownrshp* 1977
Sales 241.2MM^E *EMP* 3,000
SIC 6798 Realty investment trusts

D-U-N-S 78-785-8661
CORPOREX REALTY & INVESTMENT LLC
CORPOREX CAPITAL
100 E Rivercntr Ste 1100, Covington, KY 41011
Tel (859) 292-5500 *Founded/Ownrshp* 1990
Sales 216.5MM^E *EMP* 750
SIC 1542 6531 6552 8741 6512 Commercial & office building, new construction; Commercial & office buildings, renovation & repair; Design & erection, combined: non-residential; Real estate managers; Subdividers & developers; Construction management; Commercial & industrial building operation
Prin: William P Butler
**Ex VP:* Mark R Arstingstall
**Ex VP:* J William Blackham III
**Ex VP:* Thomas Deere
**VP:* Dan Daniele

D-U-N-S 78-408-3359
CORPSOURCE HOLDINGS LLC
(*Suby of* SOURCEHOV LLC) ★
2701 E Grauwyler Rd, Irving, TX 75061-3414
Tel (866) 321-5854 *Founded/Ownrshp* 2013
Sales 340.3MM^E *EMP* 4,518^E
SIC 7375 7334 7374 Information retrieval services; Photocopying & duplicating services; Data processing service
CEO: Ron Cogburn

CORPTRAV MANAGEMENT GROUP
See CORPORATE TRAVEL CONSULTANTS INC

D-U-N-S 05-512-3988
CORPUS CHRISTI INDEPENDENT SCHOOL DISTRICT
C C I S D
801 Leopard St, Corpus Christi, TX 78401-2421
Tel (361) 886-9200 *Founded/Ownrshp* 1909
Sales 357.4MM^E *EMP* 5,920
Accts Collier Johnson & Woods Pc
SIC 8211 Public elementary & secondary schools
Bd of Dir: Lisa O Hair
Bd of Dir: Toni Moynihan-Mccoy
Ofcr: John Moffett
Ex Dir: David Ramos
Ex Dir: Gloria Taylor
Dir Sec: Kirby Warnke
Genl Mgr: Donna Hohn
Genl Mgr: Scott Outlaw
DP Exec: James Gold
IT Man: Minerva Flores
Netwrk Mgr: Juan Huerta

CORPUS CHRISTI SHIP CHANNEL
See TRAFIGURA TERMINALS LLC

D-U-N-S 14-498-3348
CORRECT CARE SOLUTIONS LLC
1283 Murfreesboro Pike # 500, Nashville, TN 37217-2421
Tel (800) 592-2974 *Founded/Ownrshp* 2004
Sales 507.3MM^E *EMP* 4,000
SIC 8011 Dispensery, operated by physicians
Pr: Jerry Boyle
Pr: John E Newby
Assoc VP: Guy Smith
**Ex VP:* Jon Bosch
**Ex VP:* Chris Bove
**Ex VP:* Patrick Cummiskey
Ex VP: Stephen Goldberg
Ex VP: Jorene Kerns
**Ex VP:* Cary McClure
Sr VP: Andrew Walter
VP: Connie Carrillo
VP: Susan Gritton
VP: Joel Jensen
Dir Risk M: John McCauley
Dir Bus: Kim Christie

D-U-N-S 01-070-4430
CORRECT RX PHARMACY SERVICES INC
1352 Charwood Rd Ste C, Hanover, MD 21076-3125
Tel (800) 636-0501 *Founded/Ownrshp* 2003
Sales 95.8MM *EMP* 94
Accts Dixon Hughes Goodman Llp Tyso
SIC 5122 Pharmaceuticals
Pr: Ellen H Yankellow
**Treas:* Jim Tristani
VP: Sandra Osteen

CORRECTIONAL HEALTH CARE
See CORRECTIONAL MEDICAL CARE INC

D-U-N-S 80-221-1230
CORRECTIONAL HEALTHCARE COMPANIES INC
CHC COMPANIES
7388 S Revere Pkwy # 707, Centennial, CO 80112-3942
Tel (615) 312-7286 *Founded/Ownrshp* 2006
Sales 98.3MM^E *EMP* 2,500
SIC 8011 8744 Medical centers; Correctional facility
CEO: R Dirk Allison
Pr: Dale B Wolf
COO: Don Houston
CFO: Bruce McDaniel
Chf Mktg O: Dr Raymond Herr
Ex VP: Brad Bickham
Sr VP: Wendy Dunegan
VP: Jim Anderson
VP: Elizabeth Falcon
VP: Eddie Samalio
VP Inf Sys: Al Armijo

D-U-N-S 10-223-9683
CORRECTIONAL MEDICAL CARE INC
CORRECTIONAL HEALTH CARE
980 Harvest Dr Ste 202, Blue Bell, PA 19422-1955
Tel (215) 542-5800 *Founded/Ownrshp* 2001
Sales NA *EMP* 315
SIC 6324 8742 Health maintenance organization (HMO), insurance only; Hospital & health services consultant
CEO: Maria Carpio
Pr: Brad Ebel
**Pr:* Emre Umar
Mktg Dir: Bradford Ebelas

D-U-N-S 82-562-2251
CORRECTIONAL SERVICES CORP LLC
(*Suby of* GEO GROUP INC) ★
621 Nw 53rd St Ste 700, Boca Raton, FL 33487-8242
Tel (561) 893-0101 *Founded/Ownrshp* 2005
Sales 60.1MM[E] *EMP* 1,075[E]
SIC 8744 Correctional facility
Pr: George C Zoley
**Pr:* Wayne Calabrese
**CFO:* John O'Rourke
**Treas:* David Watson
**Sr VP:* John Bulfin
**VP:* John M Hurley
**VP:* Maier Marcel
**VP:* Shayn C March

D-U-N-S 80-856-1799
CORRECTIONS DEPARTMENT NEW MEXICO
(*Suby of* GOVERNORS OFFICE NEW MEXICO) ★
4337 State Highway 14, Santa Fe, NM 87508-1530
Tel (505) 827-8793 *Founded/Ownrshp* 1912
Sales NA *EMP* 2,300
SIC 9223 Detention center, government;
**CFO:* Jolene M Gonzalez

D-U-N-S 08-002-0050
CORRIGAN BROTHERS INC (MO)
LYON SHEET METAL WORKS DIV
3545 Gratiot St, Saint Louis, MO 63103-2921
Tel (314) 771-6200 *Founded/Ownrshp* 1975
Sales 90.0MM[E] *EMP* 273
SIC 1711 1761 1623 Warm air heating & air conditioning contractor; Sheet metalwork; Pipeline construction
Pr: Dennis Corrigan
**Treas:* Timothy E Corrigan
VP: Jeff Hoerner
IT Man: Dan Cihon
Sfty Dirs: Adam Spiroff

D-U-N-S 10-863-1649 IMP/EXP
■ **CORRPRO COMPANIES INC**
(*Suby of* INSITUFORM TECHNOLOGIES LLC) ★
1055 W Smith Rd, Medina, OH 44256-2444
Tel (330) 723-5082 *Founded/Ownrshp* 2009
Sales 169.4MM[E] *EMP* 716
SIC 3699 8711 Electrical equipment & supplies; Engineering services
Pr: David H Kroon
**CFO:* Marcus Alexander
CFO: Marilyn A Eisele
Ex VP: Gehring George
**Ex VP:* Dorwin Hawn
Ex VP: Grady Joiner
Ex VP: Barry W Schadeck
**Sr VP:* David Martin
**Sr VP:* David Morris
VP: David Hickey
**VP:* Holly Sharp
VP: Gerry Williams
VP: Stanley P Zupan
Exec: Irwin Joubert
Exec: James McWright

D-U-N-S 01-938-5155
CORRUGADOS DE BAJA CALIFORNIA
2475 Paseo De Las A, San Diego, CA 92154
Tel (619) 662-8672 *Founded/Ownrshp* 2012
Sales 228.8MM[E] *EMP* 900
SIC 2653 Corrugated & solid fiber boxes
Pr: Smurfit Kappa

CORRUGATING DIVISION
See JET CORR INC

D-U-N-S 08-387-4677 IMP/EXP
CORSICANA BEDDING LLC
3001 S Us Highway 287, Corsicana, TX 75109-9381
Tel (903) 872-2591 *Founded/Ownrshp* 1971
Sales 289.4MM[E] *EMP* 550
SIC 2515 Mattresses, innerspring or box spring; Box springs, assembled
CEO: Mark Kuchenrither
**Ch Bd:* Caroll Moran
CFO: Kim Cobb
Dir IT: Ted Trepinski

D-U-N-S 07-107-8786 IMP
■ **CORT BUSINESS SERVICES CORP**
CORT FURNITURE
(*Suby of* WESCO FINANCIAL CORP) ★
15000 Conference Ste 440, Chantilly, VA 20151
Tel (703) 968-8500 *Founded/Ownrshp* 2000
Sales 561.8MM[E] *EMP* 2,100
SIC 7359 5712 5932 Furniture rental; Furniture stores; Furniture, secondhand
Pr: Jeffery D Pederson
COO: Lloyd Lenson
CFO: Deborah Lansford
Ex VP: Richard Ritter
Ex VP: Martin Walcher
VP: George Bertrand
VP: John L Brack Jr
VP: Bob Buzzell
VP: Lauren Castle
**VP:* Michael G Conners
VP: Michael G Connors
VP: David Davis
VP: Chuck Edmonds
VP: Paula Green
VP: Jon Hile
**VP:* Deborah K Lansford
VP: Tom Petersen
VP: Johnathan Roby
VP: Jeff Rowe
**VP:* Victoria Stiles
VP: Lisa Woodworth

CORT FURNITURE
See CORT BUSINESS SERVICES CORP

CORTEC GROUP
See COGR INC

D-U-N-S 08-047-8364
CORTES NP ACQUISITION CORP
(*Suby of* PLATINUM EQUITY PARTNERS LLC) ★
1050 Dearborn Dr, Columbus, OH 43085-1544
Tel (614) 888-0246 *Founded/Ownrshp* 2016
Sales 1.7MMM[E] *EMP* 6,479
SIC 3679 3585 Power supplies, all types: static; Air conditioning units, complete: domestic or industrial
Pr: Rob Johnson
**CFO:* Frank P Simpkins
**Treas:* Mary Ann Sigler
**Grp VP:* Stephen H Liang
**VP:* Matthew S Dean
**VP:* Eva M Kalawski
**VP:* Gary Niederpruem
**VP:* Stephen T Zollo

D-U-N-S 07-977-3723
CORTLAND IMPROVEMENTS LLC
3424 Peachtree Rd Ne # 300, Atlanta, GA 30326-1118
Tel (404) 965-3988 *Founded/Ownrshp* 2013
Sales 85.0MM *EMP* 96
SIC 6531 Real estate agents & managers
CEO: Steven Defrancis
COO: Clyde Stutts
CFO: Ned Stiker
Treas: David Lawson
Ofcr: Brad Brown
Ofcr: Amy McCullough
Ofcr: Amy Yoakum
Ex VP: Mike Altman

CORTLAND REGIONAL MEDICAL CENT
See P C CORTLAND PATHOLOGY

D-U-N-S 79-059-2682
CORVAC COMPOSITES LLC
(*Suby of* HUMPHREY COMPANIES LLC) ★
4450 36th St Se, Kentwood, MI 49512-1917
Tel (616) 281-4026 *Founded/Ownrshp* 2001
Sales 108.5MM[E] *EMP* 500
SIC 3559 Automotive related machinery
Pr: James Fitzell
VP: James Green

D-U-N-S 78-174-8863
CORVAL GROUP INC
1633 Eustis St, Saint Paul, MN 55108-1219
Tel (651) 645-0451 *Founded/Ownrshp* 2006
Sales 189.2MM[E] *EMP* 500[E]
SIC 8742 Management consulting services
Pr: Paul Jordan
**COO:* James Simon
**CFO:* Neil Kennedy
Ex VP: Jim Andrie
Ql Cn Mgr: Steve Worner
Mktg Dir: Donna Marsh

D-U-N-S 02-151-9199
CORVALLIS CLINIC P C
BUCHANAN, JOHN L MD
3680 Nw Samaritan Dr, Corvallis, OR 97330-3737
Tel (541) 754-1150 *Founded/Ownrshp* 1996
Sales 58.6MM[E] *EMP* 1,000
SIC 8011 5912 Clinic, operated by physicians; Drug stores
Pr: William R Ferguson
**Pr:* Markhame S Giblin
**CEO:* Andrew Perry
**COO:* Rod Aust
**CFO:* Douglas Bourdo

D-U-N-S 62-036-6708
▲ **CORVEL CORP**
2010 Main St Ste 600, Irvine, CA 92614-7272
Tel (949) 851-1473 *Founded/Ownrshp* 1987
Sales 503.5MM *EMP* 3,508[E]
Accts Haskell & White Llp Irvine C
Tkr Sym CRVL *Exch* NGS
SIC 8741 8011 Nursing & personal care facility management; Internal medicine practitioners; Medical insurance associations
Ch Bd: V Gordon Clemons
CFO: Richard J Schweppe
Treas: Shari Muniz
Sr VP: Diane J Blaha
VP: Greg Dorn
Brnch Mgr: Amanda Cadwallader
Brnch Mgr: Elizabeth Lowry
Dist Mgr: Laura Schumacher
CIO: Michael G Combs
Ql Cn Mgr: Tara Kerz
Board of Directors: Steven J Hamerslag, Alan R Hoops, R Judd Jessup, Jean H Macino, Jeffrey J Michael

D-U-N-S 05-718-3828
CORVIAS GROUP LLC
1405 S County Trl, East Greenwich, RI 02818-5081
Tel (401) 228-2800 *Founded/Ownrshp* 2013
Sales 325.8MM[E] *EMP* 99
SIC 7389
CEO: John G Picerne
Pr: Richard Giusti
**Pr:* Michael De La Rosa
Pr: Ronald Phillips
Ex VP: Robert Lewis
Sr VP: Dennis Blanchette
**Sr VP:* Laura Calenda
**Sr VP:* Kerrie Iemma
Sr VP: Gary Kalinofski
**Sr VP:* Donna Sinnery
VP: Greg Cannito
VP: Mark Dewey
VP: Geoff Eisenacher
VP: Jennifer Sousa

D-U-N-S 03-405-1271
CORVIAS MILITARY LIVING LLC
(*Suby of* CORVIAS GROUP LLC) ★
1405 S County Trl Ste 510, East Greenwich, RI 02818-5097
Tel (401) 228-2800 *Founded/Ownrshp* 1998
Sales 325.6MM[E] *EMP* 99[E]
SIC 1522 Residential construction
COO: Michael Delarosa
**COO:* Randall Ell
Ex VP: Maria Montalvo
Sr VP: Donna Sinnery
VP: John Hood
VP: Robert Lewis
VP: Lazz McKenzie
VP: Paul Naughton

D-U-N-S 02-763-4307
CORY JOSEPH HOLDING LLC
JOSEPH CORY COMPANIES
150 Mdwlands Pkwy Fl 3, Secaucus, NJ 07094-2304
Tel (201) 795-1000 *Founded/Ownrshp* 1934
Sales 85.1MM[E] *EMP* 300
Accts Rothstein Kass & Company Pc
SIC 4212 Local trucking, without storage
**Pr:* Marin Dragojevic
COO: Robert Alter
CFO: Odeh Ahmad
VP: Patrick Cory
Rgnl Mgr: Mike Lesczynski
Genl Mgr: Matthew Massoud
IT Man: Joseph Disbrow

D-U-N-S 04-040-1135
CORYELL COUNTY MEMORIAL HOSPITAL AUTHORITY
CORYELL MEMORIAL HOSPITAL
1507 W Main St, Gatesville, TX 76528-1024
Tel (254) 248-6247 *Founded/Ownrshp* 1975
Sales 115.8MM *EMP* 300
SIC 8062 General medical & surgical hospitals
CEO: David K Byrom

CORYELL MEMORIAL HOSPITAL
See CORYELL COUNTY MEMORIAL HOSPITAL AUTHORITY

D-U-N-S 05-291-2511
CORYELL STEEL INC (TX)
2005 N Main St 136, Gatesville, TX 76528
Tel (254) 223-3987 *Founded/Ownrshp* 1985
Sales 100.0MM *EMP* 4
SIC 5051 Iron or steel semifinished products
Pr: April Nowlain

D-U-N-S 18-556-3611
COSATECH INC
1415 W 22nd St Towe Flr, Oak Brook, IL 60523-2074
Tel (630) 684-2331 *Founded/Ownrshp* 2003
Sales 43.8MM[E] *EMP* 2,479[E]
SIC 7373 Computer integrated systems design
Pr: Hieu Le
**VP:* Ann Le

D-U-N-S 14-577-2380
COSCO CONTAINER LINES AMERICAS INC
CCLA
(*Suby of* CHINA OCEAN SHIPPING (GROUP) COMPANY)
100 Lighting Way Fl 3, Secaucus, NJ 07094-3681
Tel (201) 422-0500 *Founded/Ownrshp* 2005
Sales 139.6MM[E] *EMP* 591
SIC 4731 Agents, shipping
Pr: Liu Hanbo
Pr: Jia Yu
CFO: Jin Huang
**Ex VP:* Zhu Jiandong
**Ex VP:* Zhang Xiaolan
**Ex VP:* Lu Zemin
Ex VP: Jiandong Zhu
Exec: Apostolos Ahalkias
Exec: Marwa Elwaraa
Exec: Chong Lang
Mng Dir: Ali Ghandour

D-U-N-S 62-527-8767
COSCO FIRE PROTECTION INC
CFP FIRE PROTECTION
(*Suby of* MX HOLDINGS US) ★
29222 Rancho Viejo Rd # 205, San Juan Capistrano, CA 92675-1045
Tel (714) 974-8770 *Founded/Ownrshp* 1989
Sales 155.6MM *EMP* 601
Accts Pricewaterhousecoopers Llp I
SIC 1711 1731 5999 Fire sprinkler system installation; Fire detection & burglar alarm systems specialization; Fire extinguishers
CEO: Keith R Fielding
Treas: Roger Jump
VP: Barry Fielding
VP: Theodore Hanson
VP: Alexander Hernandez
VP: Al Smith
Off Mgr: Lisa Dean
Off Mgr: Penny Wilson
Off Admin: Catherine Fernando
CIO: Adam Tousley
CTO: Roberto Mireles

COSCO HOME & OFFICE PDTS DIV
See DOREL JUVENILE GROUP INC

D-U-N-S 00-641-5087
COSCO INC
(*Suby of* DOREL JUVENILE GROUP) ★
2525 State St, Columbus, IN 47201-7443
Tel (812) 372-0141 *Founded/Ownrshp* 1935, 1992
Sales 380.0MM *EMP* 1,000
SIC 3944 2511 2514 Strollers, baby (vehicle); Child restraint seats, automotive; Walkers, baby (vehicle); High chairs, children's: wood; Cribs: wood; Cribs: metal; Stools, household, padded or plain: metal; Serving carts & tea wagons: metal; Tables, household: metal
Pr: Nick Costides
Pr: Richard W Holdeman
Ex VP: Jon Reynolds
VP: Ron Campbell
VP: Richard Donnelly
MIS Dir: Richard Murray
VP Mfg: Jeff Hale
VP Mfg: Jerry Smith
Plnt Mgr: Scott Wagner
Ql Cn Mgr: Peter Avens
Art Dir: Adonna Combs

COSCO INDUSTRIES
See NAVITOR INC

D-U-N-S 03-711-9930
COSENTINO ENTERPRISES INC
PRICE CHOPPER GROCERY STORE
8700 E 63rd St, Kansas City, MO 64133-4726
Tel (913) 749-1500 *Founded/Ownrshp* 1979
Sales 180.1MM[E] *EMP* 1,500
SIC 5411

D-U-N-S 83-810-9023
COSENTINO GROUP II INC
COSENTINO PRICE CHOPPER
8700 E 63rd St, Kansas City, MO 64133-4726
Tel (816) 358-2270 *Founded/Ownrshp* 1948
Sales 146.2MM[E] *EMP* 2,000[E]
SIC 5411 Supermarkets
Pr: David G Cosentino
CTO: Dennis Reilly

COSENTINO PRICE CHOPPER
See COSENTINO GROUP II INC

COSERV ELECTRIC
See DENTON COUNTY ELECTRIC COOPERATIVE INC

D-U-N-S 10-252-2583
COSERV UTILITY HOLDINGS LP
7701 S Stemmons Fwy, Corinth, TX 76210-1842
Tel (940) 321-4640 *Founded/Ownrshp* 2001
Sales 96.8MM[E] *EMP* 270
SIC 4911 Distribution, electric power
Pt: Michael Dreystring
Treas: Donnie Clary

D-U-N-S 79-774-5796
COSI INC
294 Washington St Ste 510, Boston, MA 02108-4612
Tel (857) 415-5000 *Founded/Ownrshp* 1998
Sales 89.8MM *EMP* 1,725[E]
SIC 5812 6794 Eating places; Franchises, selling or licensing
Pr: Patrick Bennett
**Ch Bd:* Mark Demilio
CFO: Miguel Rossy-Donovan
Ofcr: Randy Kominsky
VP: James Lux
VP: Willy Nicolini
Board of Directors: Jean Birch, Michael Collins, David Lloyd

D-U-N-S 14-715-4517 IMP
COSMA AMERICA HOLDINGS INC
MAGNA
(*Suby of* MAGNA INTERNATIONAL INC)
750 Tower Dr, Troy, MI 48098-2863
Tel (248) 524-5300 *Founded/Ownrshp* 1995
Sales 466.3MM *EMP* 4,253
SIC 3714 Motor vehicle parts & accessories
CEO: Donald J Walker
VP: Don Maahs
VP: Tom More
Prgrm Mgr: Mike Hernden
Prgrm Mgr: Brien Jones
Prgrm Mgr: Dorothy Marsh
Prgrm Mgr: Jason Pawloski
Prgrm Mgr: Jay Turner
Ql Cn Mgr: Kevin Cousino
Ql Cn Mgr: Matthew Mroz
Ql Cn Mgr: Scott Schulte

COSMA ENGINEERING
See COSMA INTERNATIONAL OF AMERICA INC

D-U-N-S 18-183-9679 IMP
COSMA INTERNATIONAL OF AMERICA INC
COSMA ENGINEERING
(*Suby of* MAGNA) ★
750 Tower Dr, Troy, MI 48098-2863
Tel (248) 631-1100 *Founded/Ownrshp* 1978
Sales 433.8MM[E] *EMP* 1,864
SIC 3714 Motor vehicle parts & accessories
CEO: Don Walker
**VP:* Elizabeth Maccabe
Genl Mgr: Sean Doyle
Dir IT: Dave Truchan
Sls Dir: Dan Kenny

D-U-N-S 00-591-7047 IMP
COSMETIC ESSENCE LLC
(*Suby of* CEI HOLDINGS INC) ★
2182 Hwy 35, Holmdel, NJ 07733-1125
Tel (732) 888-7788 *Founded/Ownrshp* 1952, 2004
Sales 245.8MM[E] *EMP* 696
SIC 2844 7389 4225 Toilet preparations; Cosmetic kits, assembling & packaging; General warehousing & storage
CEO: Peter G Martin
CFO: Joan Soden
**Prin:* Tina Caputo
MIS Dir: Rick Hopkins

COSMOLAB, INC.
See SCHWAN COSMETICS USA INC

COSMOPOLITAN OF LAS VEGAS, THE
See NEVADA PROPERTY 1 LLC

COSMOPROF
See BEAUTY SYSTEMS GROUP LLC

COST CUTTERS
See MARKETS LLC

D-U-N-S 02-917-4612 IMP/EXP
■ **COST PLUS INC**
COST PLUS WORLD MARKET
(*Suby of* BED BATH & BEYOND INC) ★
1201 Marina Village Pkwy # 100, Alameda, CA 94501-1143
Tel (510) 893-7300 *Founded/Ownrshp* 1946
Sales 656.1MM[E] *EMP* 390
SIC 5712 5713 5719 5947 5499 5921 Furniture stores; Rugs; Beddings & linens; Window furnishings; Wicker, rattan or reed home furnishings; Kitchenware; Gifts & novelties; Artcraft & carvings; Gourmet food stores; Beverage stores; Wine & beer
CEO: Barry J Feld
**Pr:* Jane L Baughman
**COO:* Jeffrey A Turner
**CFO:* Eugene A Castagna
CFO: John Lattrell
CFO: Clay Selland
Treas: Malcolm R Carden
Ex VP: Theresa A Strickland
VP: Michael S Adams
VP: Chris Cooper
VP: Allan J Gardner
**VP:* Charles Miltner

VP: Laura Reynolds
VP: Judith A Soares
Exec: Esther Ong

COST PLUS WORLD MARKET
See COST PLUS INC

COSTA DEL MAR
See COSTA INC

D-U-N-S 04-402-5609 IMP/EXP
COSTA FARMS LLC
21800 Sw 162nd Ave, Miami, FL 33170-2004
Tel (305) 247-3248 *Founded/Ownrshp* 1961
Sales 235.7MM^E *EMP* 2,700
SIC 0181 Nursery stock, growing of; Plants, potted: growing of; Shrubberies grown in field nurseries
**CFO:* Mary Sanchez
Genl Mgr: Chauncy Jordan
Software D: Nury Avila
Software D: Jose Hernandez
Opers Mgr: Jack Leard
Sls Mgr: Greg Hawkins

D-U-N-S 00-196-7173 IMP/EXP
COSTA FRUIT & PRODUCE CO (MA)
18 Bunker Hill Indus Park, Boston, MA 02129-1621
Tel (617) 241-8007 *Founded/Ownrshp* 1949
Sales 178.3MM^E *EMP* 195^E
SIC 5148 5143 5142 5141 Fresh fruits & vegetables; Vegetables, fresh; Cheese; Yogurt; Packaged frozen goods; Groceries, general line
Pr: Manuel R Costa
CFO: Kevin Linnehan
Treas: Anna Costa
VP Opers: Brad Woodgate
Sales Asso: Jennifer Withrow

D-U-N-S 00-120-1508 IMP/EXP
COSTA INC (RI)
COSTA DEL MAR
(*Suby of* ESSILOR INTERNATIONAL)
2361 Mason Ave Ste 100, Daytona Beach, FL 32117-5163
Tel (386) 274-4000 *Founded/Ownrshp* 1916, 2014
Sales 176.2MM^E *EMP* 1,030^E
SIC 3851 Glasses, sun or glare
CEO: Chas Macdonald
**Pr:* Eric Thoreux
**CFO:* Anthony Dipaola
**Ex VP:* Jeffrey J Giguere
VP: Peter J Canole
VP: Gail Compagnone
VP: Charles Macdonald
VP: Charles S Mellen
Dir IT: Bonnie McDonald
Software D: Edward Honauer
Mktg Mgr: Nicole Ralston

D-U-N-S 18-890-8909
▲ COSTAR GROUP INC
1331 L St Nw Ste 2, Washington, DC 20005-4361
Tel (202) 346-6500 *Founded/Ownrshp* 1987
Sales 711.7MM *EMP* 2,631^E
Tkr Sym CSGP *Exch* NGS
SIC 7375 Information retrieval services; On-line data base information retrieval; Remote data base information retrieval
Pr: Andrew C Florance
**Ch Bd:* Michael R Klein
Pr: Frederick G Saint
Pr: Cameron C Stewart
CFO: Scott T Wheeler
Ofcr: Rebecca Carr
Ofcr: Frank A Simuro
Ex VP: Francis A Carchedi
Ex VP: Matthew F W Linnington
Sr VP: Lisa C Ruggles
VP: Jason Butler
VP: Susan Jeffress
Board of Directors: Michael J Glosserman, Warren H Haber, John W Hill, Laura Cox Kaplan, Christopher J Nassetta, David J Steinberg

COSTCO WHOLESALE
See PRICE CO

D-U-N-S 62-418-3773
COSTCO WHOLESALE CANADA LTD
999 Lake Dr Ste 200, Issaquah, WA 98027-5367
Tel (425) 313-8100 *Founded/Ownrshp* 1998
Sales 110.0MMM *EMP* 4,000
SIC 5141

D-U-N-S 10-339-1843
▲ COSTCO WHOLESALE CORP
999 Lake Dr Ste 200, Issaquah, WA 98027-5367
Tel (425) 313-8100 *Founded/Ownrshp* 1983
Sales 118.7MMM *EMP* 218,000
Accts Kpmg Llp Seattle Washington
Tkr Sym COST *Exch* NGS
SIC 5399 Warehouse club stores
Pr: W Craig Jelinek
**Ch Bd:* Jeffrey H Brotman
COO: James P Murphy
COO: Joseph P Portera
COO: Ron M Vachris
COO: Dennis R Zook
**CFO:* Richard A Galanti
Ex VP: Franz E Lazarus
Ex VP: John D McKay
Ex VP: Paul G Moulton
Ex VP: Timothy L Rose
Board of Directors: Maggie A Wilderotter, Susan L Decker, Daniel J Evans, Hamilton E James, Richard M Libenson, John W Meisenbach, Charles T Munger, Jeffrey S Raikes, James D Sinegal, John W Stanton

D-U-N-S 06-040-5933 IMP
■ COTEAU PROPERTIES CO (OH)
FREEDOM MINE
(*Suby of* NORTH AMERICAN COAL CORP) ★
204 County Road 15, Beulah, ND 58523
Tel (701) 873-2281 *Founded/Ownrshp* 1972, 1957
Sales 211.3MM *EMP* 400
Accts Earnst & Young Llp Richmond
SIC 1221 Surface mining, lignite

D-U-N-S 07-975-0384
COTIVITI CORP
50 Danbury Rd, Wilton, CT 06897-4448
Tel (203) 642-0727 *Founded/Ownrshp* 2012
Sales 101.9MM^E *EMP* 2,500
SIC 8721 Accounting, auditing & bookkeeping
Pr: Douglas Williams
**CFO:* Steven Senneff
Prin: Regina Slockett
**Genl Couns:* Jonathan Olefson

D-U-N-S 08-024-8851
▲ COTIVITI HOLDINGS INC
115 Prmter Ctr Pl Ste 700, Atlanta, GA 30346-1280
Tel (770) 379-2800 *Founded/Ownrshp* 2012
Sales 541.3MM *EMP* 2,830^E
Tkr Sym COTV *Exch* NYS
SIC 8721 Accounting, auditing & bookkeeping
CEO: J Douglas Williams
**Ch Bd:* David Swift
COO: David Beaulieu
CFO: Steve Senneff
Ex VP: Richard Pozen
Sr VP: Damien Creavin
Sr VP: Jonathan Olefson
VP: James Day
Pgrm Dir: Kenneth Turturro

D-U-N-S 06-759-2733
COTIVITI LLC
CONNOLLY
50 Danbury Rd, Wilton, CT 06897-4448
Tel (203) 529-2000 *Founded/Ownrshp* 1979
Sales 98.4MM^E *EMP* 3,000
SIC 8721 Accounting, auditing & bookkeeping
CEO: Douglas Williams
**Treas:* Steven Senneff
Sr VP: James H Riehl
**VP:* Adrienne Calderone
VP: Kevin Clark
VP: Robert Donohue
VP: Skip Proctor
VP: Kenneth Turturro
Mng Dir: John Heighway
Prgrm Mgr: Simar Raina
Snr Sftwr: Robert Lysik

D-U-N-S 07-966-5408
COTIVITI USA LLC
CONNOLLY IHEALTH
(*Suby of* COTIVITI CORP) ★
50 Danbury Rd, Wilton, CT 06897-4448
Tel (203) 529-2000 *Founded/Ownrshp* 2014
Sales 98.4MM^E *EMP* 2,500
SIC 7389 Financial services
CEO: J Douglas Williams
**CFO:* Steven Senneff
VP: Steve Palma
**Prin:* Regina Slockett

COTO TECHNOLOGY
See KEARNEY-NATIONAL INC

COTT BEVERAGES
See CLIFFSTAR LLC

D-U-N-S 55-704-9475 IMP
COTT BEVERAGES INC
(*Suby of* COTT CORPORATION)
5519 W Idlewild Ave, Tampa, FL 33634-8016
Tel (813) 313-1800 *Founded/Ownrshp* 1991
Sales 887.7MM^E *EMP* 2,600
SIC 2086 Carbonated beverages, nonalcoholic: bottled & canned
CEO: Jerry Fowden
Pr: Jon Carter
Pr: Aaron Gold
**CFO:* Neal Cravens
Treas: Micheal Zimmerman
Bd of Dir: Gregory Monahan
Ex VP: Robert J Flaherty
VP: Michael Creamer
Dir Bus: Jamie Holt
Genl Mgr: Frank Cosenza
Genl Mgr: Randy Malmstrom

D-U-N-S 83-116-7973
COTT CORP
5519 W Idlewild Ave, Tampa, FL 33634-8016
Tel (813) 313-1800 *Founded/Ownrshp* 1955
Sales 2.2MMM *EMP* 3,945^E
SIC 2086

D-U-N-S 02-839-3205 IMP/EXP
■ COTTAGE BAKERY INC
FROZEN BAKERY
(*Suby of* TREEHOUSE FOODS INC) ★
1831 S Stockton St, Lodi, CA 95240-6302
Tel (209) 334-3616 *Founded/Ownrshp* 2014
Sales 217.5MM^E *EMP* 400
SIC 5149 2051 2053

D-U-N-S 03-644-9267
COTTAGE HEALTH
SANTA BARBARA COTTAGE HOSPITAL
400 W Pueblo St, Santa Barbara, CA 93105-4353
Tel (805) 682-7111 *Founded/Ownrshp* 1996
Sales 594.1MM *EMP* 2,422
SIC 8399 8062 Health systems agency; General medical & surgical hospitals
Pr: Ronald C Werft
Chf Rad: James Benzian
Bd of Dir: J K Beckmen
Bd of Dir: Chris Flynn
Bd of Dir: Donna Kell
**Ex VP:* Steven Fellows
**Sr VP:* Joan Bricher
**VP:* Ronald Biscaro
**VP:* Wende Cappetta
**VP:* Karen L Jones
VP: Karen Jones
VP: Sharon Lutz
VP: Tiana Riskowski
VP: Melinda Staveley
VP: Edmund Wrobleski
VP: Ed Wroblewski MD

COTTAGE HOSPITAL CHILDRENS CTR
See SANTA BARBARA COTTAGE HOSPITAL

D-U-N-S 04-059-3121
COTTINGHAM & BUTLER INC
800 Main St, Dubuque, IA 52001-6807
Tel (800) 793-5235 *Founded/Ownrshp* 1957
Sales NA *EMP* 320
SIC 6411

COTTON EXCHANGE, THE
See MJ SOFFE LLC

D-U-N-S 08-035-9129
COTTON PARENT INC
370 Knollwood St, Winston Salem, NC 27103-1835
Tel (336) 726-8876 *Founded/Ownrshp* 2016
Sales 518.7MM^E *EMP* 4,610^E
SIC 5461 Doughnuts
Pr: Tony Thompson

D-U-N-S 60-358-0606
COTTON PATCH CAF LLC
(*Suby of* ALTAMONT CAPITAL PARTNERS LLC) ★
600 E Dallas Rd Ste 300, Grapevine, TX 76051-4191
Tel (817) 865-6500 *Founded/Ownrshp* 2015
Sales 65.3MM^E *EMP* 1,600
SIC 5812 Restaurant, family: independent; Cafe
CEO: Kathy Nelson
**CFO:* Kevin Barnes

COTTON SURVEYING COMPANY
See JONES & CARTER INC

D-U-N-S 11-122-3939
COTTONWOOD FINANCIAL ADMINISTRATIVE SERVICES LLC
CASH STORE
1901 Gateway Dr Ste 200, Irving, TX 75038-2425
Tel (972) 753-0822 *Founded/Ownrshp* 1996
Sales NA *EMP* 220
SIC 6141 Consumer finance companies
VP Opers: Travis Crooks
CFO: Keith Schatzle
Ofcr: Izabella Mendez
Ex VP: Mike McMillin
VP: Matthew Baulier
VP: Matt Schwab
Dir Risk M: Joe Waters
Area Mgr: Carolyn Bowling
Dept Mgr: Amberlee McCarty
Opers Mgr: Amber L Miller
Mktg Mgr: Charlene Nyhart

D-U-N-S 06-647-7142 EXP
■ COTTRELL INC
(*Suby of* MARKEL VENTURES INC) ★
2125 Candler Rd, Gainesville, GA 30507-8402
Tel (770) 532-7251 *Founded/Ownrshp* 2014
Sales 165.2MM^E *EMP* 450
SIC 3713 Car carrier bodies
CEO: Danny Zink
**Pr:* Leland Bull
**CFO:* Mike Klukaszewski
**Ex VP:* Elwood Feldman
Sr VP: John Omullane
**VP:* Steve Katona
VP: James Prater
Exec: Sean Blair
**Exec:* Mark Wright
MIS Dir: Mike Klu
Manager: Stephen Brown

D-U-N-S 95-866-2223 IMP/EXP
■ COTY INC
(*Suby of* JAB HOLDINGS B.V.)
350 5th Ave Ste 2700, New York, NY 10118-2700
Tel (212) 389-7300 *Founded/Ownrshp* 1904
Sales 4.3MMM *EMP* 10,060
Tkr Sym COTY *Exch* NYS
SIC 2844 Toilet preparations; Perfumes & colognes; Cosmetic preparations
CEO: Camillo Pane
**Ch Bd:* Lambertus J H Becht
Pr: Edgar Huber
CFO: Patrice De Talhouet
Treas: Kevin Monaco
Ex VP: Mario Reis
Sr VP: Ralph Macchio
Sr VP: Ayesha Zafar

D-U-N-S 78-957-3201 IMP
■ COTY US LLC
PRIVATE PORTFOLIO
(*Suby of* COTY INC) ★
350 5th Ave Fl C1700, New York, NY 10118-0110
Tel (212) 389-7000 *Founded/Ownrshp* 1996
Sales 428.4MM^E *EMP* 713
SIC 2844 Perfumes & colognes; Cosmetic preparations
CEO: Bart Becht
Ex VP: Patrice De Talhout
Ex VP: Camillo Pane
Ex VP: Mario Reis
Sr VP: Jules Kaufman
Secur Mgr: Miguel Gonzalez
Plas Surg: David Russell

D-U-N-S 07-991-9571
COUCHE-TARD US INC
(*Suby of* ALIMENTATION COUCHE-TARD INC)
4080 W Jnathan Moore Pike, Columbus, IN 47201-8667
Tel (812) 379-9227 *Founded/Ownrshp* 2011
Sales 4.6MMM^E *EMP* 15,226
SIC 5411 Convenience stores, chain
CEO: Brian Hannasch

D-U-N-S 02-713-3453
COUFAL-PRATER EQUIPMENT LLC
3110 W Highway 21, Bryan, TX 77803-1241
Tel (979) 822-7684 *Founded/Ownrshp* 2004
Sales 85.2MM^E *EMP* 160
SIC 5999 7699 5082 Farm equipment & supplies; Flags; Agricultural equipment repair services; Farm machinery repair; Tractor repair; Construction & mining machinery
**Pr:* Philip Hitchcock
Genl Mgr: Gilbert Rezendiz
Store Mgr: Travis Meyer
IT Man: Jamie Schatz
Board of Directors: Kirk Fernandez

D-U-N-S 05-863-5616 IMP
COUGAR OIL INC
SOUTHERN ENERGY DIVISION
1411 Water Ave, Selma, AL 36703-3806
Tel (334) 875-2023 *Founded/Ownrshp* 1971
Sales 90.8MM *EMP* 60
Accts Stapp And Stapp Pc Selma
SIC 5171 5983 5172 Petroleum bulk stations; Fuel oil dealers; Petroleum products
Pr: J Larry Jones
**Sec:* Rex M Jones
**VP:* William L Jones Jr
Genl Mgr: Jim Sims
Trfc Mgr: Norman Dunkin

D-U-N-S 05-962-7492 IMP
COUGHLAN COMPANIES INC
CAPSTONE
1710 Roe Crest Dr, North Mankato, MN 56003-1806
Tel (507) 345-8100 *Founded/Ownrshp* 1992
Sales 124.5MM^E *EMP* 500
SIC 7361 1741 Employment agencies; Masonry & other stonework
CEO: G Thomas Ahern
**Pr:* James P Coughlan
VP: Gary Hachfeld
**Prin:* Thomas Ahern

COUGHLIN AUTOMOTIVE GROUP
See COUGHLIN CHEVROLET INC

D-U-N-S 09-973-2968
COUGHLIN CHEVROLET INC
COUGHLIN AUTOMOTIVE GROUP
9000 Broad St Sw, Pataskala, OH 43062-7879
Tel (740) 964-9191 *Founded/Ownrshp* 1989
Sales 86.4MM^E *EMP* 250
SIC 5511 5012 7538 7532 5531 Automobiles, new & used; Pickups, new & used; Automobiles & other motor vehicles; General automotive repair shops; Top & body repair & paint shops; Automotive & home supply stores
Pr: Al Coughlin
**VP:* Michael Coughlin
**Prin:* Frederick J Simon
Genl Mgr: Dan Turner
Sls Mgr: Joe Westbrook

D-U-N-S 04-614-3053
COULSON OIL CO INC
1434 Pike Ave 38, North Little Rock, AR 72114-4077
Tel (501) 376-4222 *Founded/Ownrshp* 1969
Sales 159.2MM^E *EMP* 250
SIC 5172 5541 5411 6512 Gasoline; Filling stations, gasoline; Convenience stores, independent; Property operation, retail establishment
Ch Bd: JW White
**Pr:* Mike Coulson
**CFO:* R H Gladden
**VP:* Mary Ann Dawkins
VP Sls: Dave Zakrzewski

D-U-N-S 61-856-0221
COULTER COMPANIES INC
4700 N Sterling Ave Ste 2, Peoria, IL 61615-3665
Tel (309) 686-8033 *Founded/Ownrshp* 1985
Sales 815.2MM^E *EMP* 527
SIC 4953 8711 Hazardous waste collection & disposal; Refuse collection & disposal services; Pollution control engineering
Pr: Royal Coulter
**Sec:* Steve Davison
VP: Jeff Coulter
VP: Erin Fuller

D-U-N-S 08-021-7433
COUNCIL BLUFFS COMMUNITY SCHOOL DISTRICT (IA)
300 W Broadway Ste 1600, Council Bluffs, IA 51503-9054
Tel (712) 328-6419 *Founded/Ownrshp* 1846
Sales 64.0MM^E *EMP* 1,200
Accts Schroer And Associates Pc C
SIC 8211 Public elementary & secondary schools
**CFO:* Dean Wilson
Bd of Dir: Deb Mohling
Bd of Dir: Dwain Pedersen
Prin: Franklin Staff
Ex Dir: Tim Hamilton
MIS Dir: David Fringer
IT Man: Matt Haan
IT Man: Mary Newman
Sftwr Eng: Nina Reedy
Pr Dir: Diane Ostrowski

D-U-N-S 96-685-0682
COUNCIL INTERNATIONAL STUDY PROGRAMS INC (ISP)
300 Fore St Fl 2, Portland, ME 04101-4236
Tel (207) 553-4000 *Founded/Ownrshp* 1998
Sales 120.9MM *EMP* 32^E
SIC 8211 High school, junior or senior
Prin: Robert E Fallon

D-U-N-S 07-831-4763
■ COUNCIL OF INSPECTORS GENERAL ON INTEGRITY AND EFFICIENCY
CIGIE
(*Suby of* G S A) ★
1717 H St Nw Ste 825, Washington, DC 20006-3920
Tel (202) 292-2604 *Founded/Ownrshp* 2011
Sales NA *EMP* 1,200
SIC 9199 General government administration;
Ofcr: Brett Wilson
Ex Dir: Mark D Jones

D-U-N-S 03-767-2003
COUNCIL ROCK SCHOOL DISTRICT
30 N Chancellor St, Newtown, PA 18940-2202
Tel (215) 944-1000 *Founded/Ownrshp* 1966
Sales 215.7MM *EMP* 1,700
Accts Bbd Llp
SIC 8211 Public elementary & secondary schools
Treas: Robert Riegel
Adm Dir: Charlie Rehm
MIS Dir: Matt Fredericksor
Schl Brd P: Andrew Block
Teacher Pr: Christine Trioli

D-U-N-S 14-429-3636
COUNTERTRADE PRODUCTS INC
7585 W 66th Ave, Arvada, CO 80003-3969
Tel (303) 424-7015 Founded/Ownrshp 1985
Sales 160.6MM^E EMP 161^E
SIC 5045 Computers, peripherals & software
CEO: Marlene R Calabria
*Pr: Joseph M Calabria
Dir IT: Jared Griego
VP Opers: Dan Hays

D-U-N-S 12-436-3730
COUNTRY CLUB CARE
1904 N Hwy 81, Duncan, OK 73533-1429
Tel (580) 255-4600 Founded/Ownrshp 1965
Sales 408.6MM EMP 90
SIC 8059 Nursing home, except skilled & intermediate care facility
Pr: Lynn Gregston
*VP: Jerry L Gregston

COUNTRY CURTAINS
See FITZPATRICK COMPANIES INC

D-U-N-S 01-965-4342 IMP/EXP
COUNTRY CURTAINS INC
(Suby of COUNTRY CURTAINS) ★
705 Pleasant St, Stockbridge, MA 01262
Tel (413) 243-1474 Founded/Ownrshp 1996
Sales 86.8MM^E EMP 450
SIC 2391 Curtains & draperies
Pr: Philip J McAvoy
*Ch Bd: Joann Brown
*Ch Bd: Jane P Fitzpatrick
*CEO: William H Booth
CFO: Don Frank
*Treas: Paula S Beck
Ex VP: Sandra Dignard
VP: Brian Pratt
Exec: Paula Murray
Dir Risk M: Marilyn Hansen
Dir Risk M: Marilyn Hanson
Dir Bus: Leslie Parsenios

D-U-N-S 01-407-9636
COUNTRY FAIR INC
(Suby of UNITED REFINING CO) ★
2251 E 30th St, Erie, PA 16510-2590
Tel (814) 898-1111 Founded/Ownrshp 2001
Sales 191.0MM^E EMP 1,350
SIC 5411 5541 Convenience stores, chain; Filling stations, gasoline
Pr: Myron Turfitt
*Treas: Douglas I Scalise
*Treas: James E Murphy
*VP: Paul Levis
*VP: Paul C Rankin
Rgnl Mgr: Dave Dankert
Dir IT: Sandy Palmer
Site Mgr: Elias Kassab
Site Mgr: Jacque Shoup
Site Mgr: Fred Zdarko
Opers Mgr: Kevin Beichner

COUNTRY FINANCIAL
See CC SERVICES INC

D-U-N-S 00-586-9078
■ **COUNTRY FRESH LLC**
COUNTRY FRESH WESLEY
(Suby of DEAN FOODS CO) ★
2555 Buchanan Ave Sw, Grand Rapids, MI 49548-1006
Tel (616) 243-0173 Founded/Ownrshp 1946, 1999
Sales 201.4MM^E EMP 820
SIC 2026 2024 2097 Milk processing (pasteurizing, homogenizing, bottling); Cottage cheese; Dips, sour cream based; Yogurt; Ice cream & frozen desserts; Ice cream & ice milk; Manufactured ice
Genl Mgr: Kevin Begin
Sr VP: Joe Risdon
*VP: Rob Hollandsworth

COUNTRY FRESH WESLEY
See COUNTRY FRESH LLC

COUNTRY HEARTH
See PAN-O-GOLD BAKING CO

COUNTRY INSURANCE & FINCL SVCS
See COUNTRY LIFE INSURANCE CO

COUNTRY KITCHEN
See LEPAGE BAKERIES INC

D-U-N-S 00-692-7990
COUNTRY LIFE INSURANCE CO
COUNTRY INSURANCE & FINCL SVCS
(Suby of ILLINOIS AGRICULTURAL HOLDING CO)
1701 Towanda Ave, Bloomington, IL 61701-2057
Tel (309) 557-3000 Founded/Ownrshp 1928
Sales NA EMP 520
SIC 6311 6321

COUNTRY MEADOWS
See GEORGE M LEADER FAMILY CORP

D-U-N-S 61-791-9717
COUNTRY MEADOWS ASSOCIATES
COUNTRY MEADOWS AT HOME
(Suby of COUNTRY MEADOWS) ★
830 Cherry Dr, Hershey, PA 17033-3402
Tel (717) 533-2474 Founded/Ownrshp 1985
Sales 68.2MM^E EMP 1,500
SIC 8051 8059 8741 Skilled nursing care facilities; Personal care home, with health care; Management services
Pt: G Michael Leader III
Genl Pt: George M Leader Family Corp
COO: David Leader

COUNTRY MEADOWS AT HOME
See COUNTRY MEADOWS ASSOCIATES

D-U-N-S 00-692-8006
COUNTRY MUTUAL INSURANCE CO INC (IL)
COUNTRYFINANCIAL
(Suby of ILLINOIS FARM BUREAU) ★
1701 Towanda Ave, Bloomington, IL 61701-2057
Tel (309) 821-3000 Founded/Ownrshp 1925
Sales NA EMP 5,000
SIC 6411 Insurance agents, brokers & service
CEO: John D Blackburn
*COO: Barbara Bauer
Ex VP: Steve Denault
Sr VP: Gabriel Carrillo
Sr VP: Kelvin Schill
Sr VP: Doyle Williams
VP: Shelly Prehoda
CIO: Brad Hildestad
Dir IT: Betty Cupach
Dir IT: Brian Scottberg
IT Man: Joe Morrow

D-U-N-S 02-439-6442
COUNTRY PRIDE COOPERATIVE INC (SD)
DO IT BEST
648 W 2nd St, Winner, SD 57580-1230
Tel (605) 842-2711 Founded/Ownrshp 1940
Sales 141.6MM^E EMP 200
Accts Gardiner Thomsen Pc Sioux
SIC 5153 5172 5191 5411 5211 Grains; Diesel fuel; Fuel oil; Gasoline; Lubricating oils & greases; Fertilizers & agricultural chemicals; Feed; Convenience stores, independent; Lumber & other building materials
CEO: Mike Trosen
*CFO: Marsha Whetham
*Treas: Marsha Lowrey
VP: David Hartley
*VP: Linda Husher
Sfty Dirs: Chad Hanson

D-U-N-S 88-422-6002 IMP/EXP
COUNTRY PURE FOODS INC
(Suby of SAPPORO INTERNATIONAL INC.)
681 W Waterloo Rd, Akron, OH 44314-1547
Tel (330) 753-2293 Founded/Ownrshp 2015
Sales 267.9MM^E EMP 450
SIC 2033 2037 2086 Fruit juices: fresh; Fruit juice concentrates, frozen; Fruit drinks (less than 100% juice): packaged in cans, etc.
CEO: Raymond Lee
CFO: Tom Kolb
Co-CEO: Kenny Sadai
Sr VP: Paul Sukalich
VP: Andy Major
VP: Donna Souza
VP: Liz Wilson
QA Dir: Shetal Patel
Ql Cn Mgr: Bobby Hartfield
Ql Cn Mgr: Matthew Hudkins
Ql Cn Mgr: Alejandro Marquez

COUNTRY ROADS
See IRWIN SEATING CO

COUNTRY SELECT CATFISH
See CONSOLIDATED CATFISH COMPANIES LLC

D-U-N-S 61-909-2732
COUNTRY STONE INC
6300 75th Ave Ste A, Milan, IL 61264-3267
Tel (309) 787-1744 Founded/Ownrshp 2000
Sales 164.4MM^E EMP 390
SIC 2499 2875 3273 3281 Mulch, wood & bark; Potting soil, mixed; Ready-mixed concrete; Cut stone & stone products
Owner: Ronald D Bjustrom
Off Mgr: Jane Kenny

D-U-N-S 01-668-9569
COUNTRY VIEW FAMILY FARMS INC
(Suby of CLEMENS FAMILY CORP) ★
1301 Fulling Mill Rd # 3000, Middletown, PA 17057-5990
Tel (267) 663-0100 Founded/Ownrshp 1998
Sales 89.5MM EMP 5
SIC 0213 0191 Hogs; General farms, primarily crop
CEO: Philip A Clemens
*Pr: Robert M Ruth
*CFO: Dave Budnick

COUNTRY VILLA HEALTH SERVICES
See COUNTRY VILLA SERVICE CORP

COUNTRY VILLA LA SIERRA
See CF MERCED LA SIERRA LLC

D-U-N-S 07-412-7994
COUNTRY VILLA SERVICE CORP (CA)
COUNTRY VILLA HEALTH SERVICES
2400 E Katella Ave # 800, Anaheim, CA 92806-5955
Tel (310) 574-3733 Founded/Ownrshp 1972
Sales 154.7MM^E EMP 1,800
SIC 8741 Nursing & personal care facility management; Hospital management
CEO: Stephen Reissman
*Ex VP: Diane Reissman
*VP: Cheryl Petterson
Ex Dir: Andy Levin
Dietician: Tracy Zoleta

D-U-N-S 10-171-3584
COUNTRY VINTNER INC
(Suby of WINEBOW GROUP LLC) ★
12305 N Lakeridge Pkwy, Ashland, VA 23005-8181
Tel (804) 752-3670 Founded/Ownrshp 2008
Sales 206.5MM^E EMP 375
SIC 5182 Wine
CEO: David B Townsend
*CFO: Dean Ferrell
Ofcr: Matthew Tucker
*VP: Michael Collier
VP: Laura Depasquale
*VP: Richard Gliot
*VP: Michael Shepherd
Dir Rx: Mark Longsworth
Dir Bus: Patrick Taylor
Dist Mgr: Pat Dudding
Dist Mgr: Lucas Rosin

D-U-N-S 07-425-6629
COUNTRY-WIDE INSURANCE CO
40 Wall St Fl 13, New York, NY 10005-1399
Tel (212) 514-7000 Founded/Ownrshp 1963
Sales NA EMP 200
SIC 6411 Insurance agents, brokers & service
Pr: Michael D Jaffe
*Pr: Raymond Cheven
COO: Nick Filacouris
*CFO: Myles Saposnick
Bd of Dir: Gerald Schlissel
VP: Adam Cheven
*VP: Barbara Ann Cheven
*VP: Walter Convery
VP: Lavina Laungani
*VP: Martin Lyev
*VP: Walter Schlie

COUNTRYFINANCIAL
See COUNTRY MUTUAL INSURANCE CO INC

D-U-N-S 00-790-2869
COUNTRYMARK COOPERATIVE HOLDING CORP
225 S East St Ste 144, Indianapolis, IN 46202-4059
Tel (800) 808-3170 Founded/Ownrshp 1938
Sales 483.4MM^E EMP 425
SIC 5172 2911 1382 1311 6719 Petroleum products; Petroleum refining; Aerial geophysical exploration oil & gas; Crude petroleum & natural gas production; Investment holding companies, except banks
Pr: Charles Smith
*VP: John Deaton
VP: Rick Sumner
VP: Pat Ward
VP Mktg: Jon Lantz
Sls Mgr: Steve Thomas

D-U-N-S 03-061-1396
COUNTRYSIDE ESTATES INC
WARNER NURSING HOME
Hwy 64 E, Warner, OK 74469
Tel (918) 463-5143 Founded/Ownrshp 1976
Sales 392.5MM EMP 60
SIC 8052 Intermediate care facilities
Pr: Scott Rogers
*Treas: Roy Jenkins
*VP: Dusty Rogers
Dir Soc: Stephanie Williamson

D-U-N-S 01-799-4542
COUNTRYSIDE FOODS LLC
I & K DISTRIBUTORS
(Suby of LIPARI FOODS OPERATING CO LLC) ★
26661 Bunert Rd, Warren, MI 48089-3650
Tel (586) 447-3500 Founded/Ownrshp 2007
Sales 147.4MM^E EMP 689
SIC 5141 2099 Groceries, general line; Salads, fresh or refrigerated; Pizza, refrigerated: except frozen; Noodles, uncooked: packaged with other ingredients
Pr: Robert Fishbein
CFO: Carl Warschausky
Treas: John Barry
VP: Raymond Feldmeier
VP: Jeff Racheter
Dir Surg: Janie Minkin
Opers Mgr: Dave Klausing

D-U-N-S 04-768-9971
■ **COUNTRYWIDE FINANCIAL CORP**
(Suby of BANK OF AMERICA CORP) ★
4500 Park Granada, Calabasas, CA 91302-1613
Tel (818) 225-3000 Founded/Ownrshp 2008
Sales NA EMP 50,600
SIC 6162 6211 6361 6411 6163 6799 Mortgage bankers; Brokers, security; Dealers, security; Title insurance; Life insurance agents; Loan brokers; Real estate investors, except property operators
Ch Bd: Angelo R Mozilo
*Pr: David Sambol
COO: Jack W Schakett
CFO: Eric P Sieracki
Ex VP: Christian Ingerslev
Ex VP: David Kuhn
VP: Eric Donato
VP: Stephen Douglas
VP: Robert V James
VP: Dale Ledbetter
VP: Stas Melnikov
VP: Pete Presland-Byrne
VP: Paul Runyun
VP: Steve Tannehill
VP: Al Tappe
VP: Joseph Velazquez

D-U-N-S 06-206-5099
■ **COUNTRYWIDE HOME LOANS INC** (NY)
(Suby of COUNTRYWIDE FINANCIAL CORP) ★
225 W Hillcrest Dr, Thousand Oaks, CA 91360-7883
Tel (818) 225-3000 Founded/Ownrshp 1969
Sales NA EMP 9,700
SIC 6162 Mortgage bankers
Ch Bd: Michael Schloessmann
*Ch Bd: Angelo R Mozilo
*Pr: David Sambol
*COO: Carlos M Garcia
*CFO: Thomas K McLaughlin
Treas: Shiley Sandefur
*Ofcr: Jeremy V Gross
*Ofcr: Richard S Lewis
Ex VP: Joe D Anderson
Ex VP: E Cameron King
Ex VP: David Walker
VP: David Cassan
VP: Mike Crocker
VP: Donald Gallien
VP: Kim Givens
VP: Robert Huntly
VP: Tisa Jackson
VP: Michael Kascsak
VP: Rick Loritsch
VP: Jennifer Norman
VP: Prasad Pedireddi

D-U-N-S 04-044-2445
COUNTRYWIDE HR
(Suby of WORLDWIDE STAFFING RESOURCES INC.)
135 Fox Rd Ste F, Knoxville, TN 37922-3410
Tel (877) 257-6662 Founded/Ownrshp 2013

Sales 98.4MM^E EMP 8,000
SIC 8721 7361 Payroll accounting service; Employment agencies; Placement agencies

COUNTY ADMINISTRATOR'S OFFICE
See COUNTY OF SONOMA

D-U-N-S 19-135-4773
COUNTY BROADCASTING CO LLC
30 How St, Haverhill, MA 01830-6131
Tel (603) 668-6400 Founded/Ownrshp 2005
Sales 270.0MM EMP 20
SIC 4832 Radio broadcasting stations

COUNTY CLERK OFFICE
See COUNTY OF SHAWNEE

D-U-N-S 04-075-4012
COUNTY COLLEGE OF MORRIS
CCM
214 Center Grove Rd, Randolph, NJ 07869-2086
Tel (973) 328-5000 Founded/Ownrshp 1968
Sales 41.7MM^E EMP 1,000^E
Accts Larson Allen Llp Blue Bell P
SIC 8222 Community college
Pr: Edward J Yaw
*Ch: Jeffrey M Advokat
*Treas: Thomas A Pepe
*VP: Dwight Smith
Assoc Dir: Jenny Denaro
Sls Mgr: Bob Lipka

COUNTY COMMISSIONERS
See COUNTY OF LANCASTER

COUNTY COMMISSIONERS OF CHARLE
See CHARLES COUNTY GOVERNMENT

COUNTY EXECUTIVE OFFICE
See COUNTY OF ORANGE

COUNTY EXECUTIVE OFFICE
See COUNTY OF ROCKLAND

D-U-N-S 87-889-7073
COUNTY FORD NORTH INC
450 W Vista Way, Vista, CA 92083-5829
Tel (760) 945-9900 Founded/Ownrshp 1992
Sales 96.7MM^E EMP 225
SIC 5511 5521 7538 7515 5531 Automobiles, new & used; Used car dealers; General automotive repair shops; Passenger car leasing; Automotive parts
Pr: James E Crowley
CFO: Wayne Meyer
Sr VP: Alex Perez
Sr VP: Mike Schwab
*VP: Scott Crowley
*VP: Jeffrey Friestedt
*VP: Joseph Weir
Off Mgr: Cindy Saunders
Sls Mgr: Todd Nielsen

COUNTY LINE DIVISION
See BEST CHAIRS INC

COUNTY MANAGER OFFICE
See GASTON COUNTY

COUNTY MARKET
See MINERS INC

COUNTY MARKET
See NIEMANN FOODS FOUNDATION

COUNTY MARKET
See TIDYMANS MANAGEMENT SERVICES INC

D-U-N-S 00-613-9257 IMP
COUNTY MATERIALS CORP (WI)
WISCONSIN BRICK & BLOCK
205 North St, Marathon, WI 54448-9647
Tel (715) 443-2434 Founded/Ownrshp 1947
Sales 384.0MM^E EMP 1,400
SIC 3271 5211 3273 3272 1442 Blocks, concrete or cinder: standard; Lumber & other building materials; Masonry materials & supplies; Ready-mixed concrete; Concrete products; Construction sand & gravel
Pr: Tim Sonnentag
*VP: William Sonnentag
Off Mgr: Minerva Garner
IT Man: Andy Dupree
Mtls Mgr: Tony Pelczarski
Opers Mgr: Scott McVicker
Sls Mgr: Ryan Castle
Sls Mgr: Nathan Mitchell
Sales Asso: Paul Casanova

D-U-N-S 09-203-1459
COUNTY OF ADA (ID)
200 W Front St, Boise, ID 83702-7300
Tel (208) 287-7080 Founded/Ownrshp 1890
Sales NA EMP 1,250
Accts Eide Bailly Llp Boise Idaho
SIC 9121 County commissioner;
Ch Bd: Roger Simmons
V Ch: Sherry Morgan
Ex Dir: Doug Heikkila
Dir IT: Serio Atonio
IT Man: Rich Eveland
IT Man: Kathleen Graves

D-U-N-S 07-647-6373
COUNTY OF ADAMS
4430 S Adams County Pkwy W5000a, Brighton, CO 80601-8222
Tel (720) 523-6100 Founded/Ownrshp 1902
Sales NA EMP 1,740
Accts Cliftonlarsonallen Llp Green
SIC 9532 County planning & development agency, government
Treas: Brigitte Grimm
Ex Dir: Pat Myers

D-U-N-S 01-050-8711
COUNTY OF ALACHUA
12 Se 1st St 2, Gainesville, FL 32601-6826
Tel (352) 374-3605 Founded/Ownrshp 1834
Sales NA EMP 2,029
Accts Carr Riggs & Ingram Gainesvi
SIC 9111 Executive offices;
V Ch: Robert Hutchinson
Exec: Rhonda Baxter

D-U-N-S 07-157-2986
COUNTY OF ALAMANCE
RECREATION AND PARKS
124 W Elm St, Graham, NC 27253-2802
Tel (336) 228-1312 *Founded/Ownrshp* 1849
Sales NA *EMP* 3,117
Accts Martin Starnes & Associates C
SIC 9111
Ofcr: Tammy Crawford
Dir Rx: Suzanne Walker
CIO: Ginger Graves
IT Man: Susan Roberts
HC Dir: Barry Bass

D-U-N-S 06-416-5053
COUNTY OF ALAMEDA
1221 Oak St Ste 555, Oakland, CA 94612-4224
Tel (510) 272-6691 *Founded/Ownrshp* 1853
Sales NA *EMP* 8,000
Accts Macias Gini & O Connell Llp
SIC 9111 Executive offices;
**Ch Bd:* Keith Carson
Ofcr: Linda K Moore
Admn Mgr: Kai Mander
Off Mgr: Juan Matta
Telecom Ex: Don Bliss
CTO: Tim Dupuis
Dir IT: Mark Deluca
Dir IT: Dave Macdonald
Dir IT: Tedros Tecle
Sys/Dir: David McDonald
IT Man: Sriram Gurumurthy

D-U-N-S 06-053-6653
COUNTY OF ALBANY
112 State St Rm 900, Albany, NY 12207-2020
Tel (518) 447-7130 *Founded/Ownrshp* 1800
Sales NA *EMP* 3,300
SIC 9111 Executive offices;
Ex Dir: Daniel P McCoy
Ofcr: Erica Anderson
Exec: John Curran
Genl Mgr: David Reilly
CIO: Joseph Paratore
Dir IT: Perry Blanchard
IT Man: Matthew Cross
HC Dir: Jennifer Travis

D-U-N-S 06-602-2047
COUNTY OF ALBEMARLE
401 Mcintire Rd Rm 149, Charlottesville, VA 22902-4579
Tel (434) 296-5855 *Founded/Ownrshp* 1744
Sales NA *EMP* 3,280
Accts Robinson Farmer Cox Associat
SIC 9111 Executive offices;
Exec: Thomas C Foley
CIO: Vincent Scheivert
IT Man: Stephen Taylor
Psych: Karen Ferrer
Psych: Chris Melnik

D-U-N-S 00-190-5736
COUNTY OF ALLEGHENY (PA)
436 Grant St Ste 104, Pittsburgh, PA 15219-2403
Tel (412) 350-5300 *Founded/Ownrshp* 1778
Sales NA *EMP* 7,013
Accts Zelenkofske Axelrod Llc Pitts
SIC 9111 Governors' offices;
Ofcr: Anthony Gray

D-U-N-S 07-756-6644
COUNTY OF ALLEN
301 N Main St, Lima, OH 45801-4434
Tel (419) 228-3700 *Founded/Ownrshp* 1831
Sales NA *EMP* 1,200
Accts Dave Yost Columbus Ohio
SIC 9111 Executive offices;
CFO: Ben Diepenbrock
**Treas:* Rachael Gilroy
Genl Mgr: Joe Covay
Genl Mgr: Michelle Halsell

D-U-N-S 07-892-0717
COUNTY OF ALLEN (IN)
Courthouse Rm 201, Fort Wayne, IN 46802
Tel (260) 449-7245 *Founded/Ownrshp* 1816
Sales NA *EMP* 2,800
Accts State Board Of Accounts India
SIC 9111 Executive offices;
Pr: Edwin J Rousseau

D-U-N-S 07-490-1612
COUNTY OF ANDERSON
C A S A ANDERSON CNTY FAX LINE
100 N Main St Rm 115, Clinton, TN 37716-3616
Tel (865) 457-6200 *Founded/Ownrshp* 1801
Sales NA *EMP* 2,300[E]
Accts Justin P Wilson Nashville Te
SIC 9111 Executive offices;
Genl Mgr: Terry Frank
Ofcr: Kari Hancock
Ofcr: Brian Porter
Brnch Mgr: Barry E Pelizzari

D-U-N-S 06-487-5974
COUNTY OF ANNE ARUNDEL
ANNAPOLIS AREA LIBRARY
44 Calvert St Ste 1, Annapolis, MD 21401-1930
Tel (410) 222-1166 *Founded/Ownrshp* 1650
Sales NA *EMP* 4,600
Accts Cliftonlarsonallen Llp Baltim
SIC 9111 County supervisors' & executives' offices
Ex Dir: Laura Numan
V Ch: Daniel E Klostrman
**Exec:* John Hammond
**Exec:* Steven Schuh
Comm Dir: David Abrams
Ex Dir: Frank Marzucco
Prgrm Mgr: Karen H Henry
QA Dir: Carol Lorenz
Pgrm Dir: Doreen E McGill
Snr Mgr: Dennis Ward

D-U-N-S 07-177-1083
COUNTY OF ANOKA
2100 3rd Ave, Anoka, MN 55303-2235
Tel (763) 421-4760 *Founded/Ownrshp* 1857
Sales NA *EMP* 1,800
SIC 9111

D-U-N-S 07-341-0680
COUNTY OF ARAPAHOE
ARAPAHOE COUNTY
5334 S Prince St, Littleton, CO 80120-1136
Tel (303) 795-4620 *Founded/Ownrshp* 1907
Sales NA *EMP* 1,880
Accts Clifton Larson Allen Llp Gree
SIC 9111 Executive offices;
Ch Bd: Susan Beckman
Genl Mgr: Theresa Chappell

D-U-N-S 05-628-5042
COUNTY OF ARLINGTON
2100 Clarendon Blvd # 500, Arlington, VA 22201-5447
Tel (703) 228-3130 *Founded/Ownrshp* 1920
Sales NA *EMP* 4,000
Accts Cliftonlarsonallen Llp Arlin
SIC 9111 County supervisors' & executives' offices;
Genl Mgr: Barbara Donnellan
COO: Bob Mace
Treas: Paul Derby
Treas: Peter Olivere
Bd of Dir: Katie Cristol
Ofcr: Sean Carrig
Ofcr: Alan Lowrey
Ofcr: Igor Scherbakov
VP: Stefanie Pryor
Exec: Jesse Boeding
Exec: Suzanne Sundburg

D-U-N-S 92-603-8696
COUNTY OF ASHTABULA
25 W Jefferson St, Jefferson, OH 44047-1027
Tel (440) 576-3783 *Founded/Ownrshp* 1811
Sales NA *EMP* 1,200
Accts Dave Yost Columbus Ohio
SIC 9111 Executive offices;
Treas: Dawn Cragon
Ofcr: Bryan Rose
Genl Mgr: Dawn Gates
IT Man: Mickey Mihalick

D-U-N-S 07-949-7897
COUNTY OF ATLANTIC
ATLANTIC COUNTY GOVERNMENT
1333 Atlantic Ave, Atlantic City, NJ 08401-7212
Tel (609) 345-6700 *Founded/Ownrshp* 1837
Sales NA *EMP* 1,700
Accts Hutchins Farrell Meyer & All
SIC 9111 County supervisors' & executives' offices;
Exec: Dennis Levinson
COO: John Lamey
Board of Directors: James A Carney, Kirk W Conover, James Curio, Dennis Levinson, Rev Lawton Nelson Jr, Joseph A Nickels III, John Risley, Thomas Russo, Joseph F Silipena

D-U-N-S 07-343-8418
COUNTY OF AUGUSTA-RICHMOND
535 Telfair St, Augusta, GA 30901-2371
Tel (706) 821-2429 *Founded/Ownrshp* 1789
Sales NA *EMP* 2,700
Accts Mauldin & Jenkins Llc Macon
SIC 9111
Comm Man: Lauren Smith
**Ex Dir:* Sharon Broady
Opers Mgr: Sam Smith

D-U-N-S 06-487-5644
COUNTY OF BALTIMORE
400 Washington Ave Rm 100, Baltimore, MD 21204-4610
Tel (410) 887-2008 *Founded/Ownrshp* 1659
Sales NA *EMP* 7,683
Accts Cliftonlarsonallen Llp Baltim
SIC 9111 Executive offices;
Exec: Kevin Kamenetz
Ofcr: George Blevins
Ofcr: John Dawson
Ofcr: Josh Harding
Ofcr: Michele Herget
Ofcr: Carlos Selvi
Ofcr: Matthew Weatherly
Ofcr: Robert Wright
Creative D: Lauren Watley
Off Admin: Daisy Brunner
Off Admin: Jennifer Palmere

D-U-N-S 07-278-1412
COUNTY OF BAY
515 Center Ave Ste 401, Bay City, MI 48708-5941
Tel (989) 895-4130 *Founded/Ownrshp* 1857
Sales NA *EMP* 1,300
Accts Rehman Robson Saginaw Mi
SIC 9111 Executive offices;
Exec: Thomas L Hickner
**Treas:* Rick Brzezinski
Ofcr: Michael Regulski
Ex Dir: Joseph Rivert

D-U-N-S 08-077-5331
COUNTY OF BEAUFORT
100 Ribaut Rd, Beaufort, SC 29902-4453
Tel (843) 255-7151 *Founded/Ownrshp* 1800
Sales NA *EMP* 1,100
Accts Cherry Bekaert Llp Augusta G
SIC 9111 Executive offices;
VP: Leith Webb
IT Man: Heather Spaeth

D-U-N-S 06-875-4019
COUNTY OF BEAVER
810 3rd St, Beaver, PA 15009-2139
Tel (724) 728-5700 *Founded/Ownrshp* 1800
Sales NA *EMP* 1,500
Accts The Binkley Kanavy Group Llc
SIC 9111
Ch Bd: Joe Spanik
**Treas:* Charles Gibbons
**Treas:* Connie Javens
Ofcr: Sean Bunney
Ofcr: John Davis
Dept Mgr: Joseph West
Opers Mgr: William Pasquale

D-U-N-S 07-668-7284
COUNTY OF BERGEN
1 Bergen County Plz Ste 1, Hackensack, NJ 07601-7075
Tel (201) 336-6000 *Founded/Ownrshp* 1683
Sales NA *EMP* 2,347
SIC 9111 Executive offices;
Exec: James Tedesco

D-U-N-S 04-325-1883
COUNTY OF BERKS
BERKS COUNTY CLERK OF COURTS
633 Court St, Reading, PA 19601-4302
Tel (610) 478-6640 *Founded/Ownrshp* 1752
Sales NA *EMP* 2,500
Accts Reinsel Kuntz Lesher Llp Wyom
SIC 9111 Executive offices;
**Treas:* Nelson Long

D-U-N-S 06-942-4356
COUNTY OF BERNALILLO
1 Civic Plz Nw Fl 10, Albuquerque, NM 87102-2111
Tel (505) 468-7240 *Founded/Ownrshp* 1912
Sales NA *EMP* 2,000
Accts Moss Adams Llp Albuquerque N
SIC 9111
Ofcr: Veronica Espinosa
**Prin:* Destry Hunt
Ex Dir: Mary Herrera
IT Man: Terry Groves
Ql Cn Mgr: Carolina Fernandez
Pr Dir: Tia Bland

D-U-N-S 07-048-7020
COUNTY OF BEXAR
101 W Nueva Ste 1019, San Antonio, TX 78205-3482
Tel (210) 335-2626 *Founded/Ownrshp* 1837
Sales NA *EMP* 4,200
Accts Garza/Gonzalez & Associates S
SIC 9111 Executive offices;

D-U-N-S 07-491-6206
COUNTY OF BLOUNT
341 Court St, Maryville, TN 37804-5906
Tel (865) 273-5700 *Founded/Ownrshp* 1796
Sales NA *EMP* 1,800
Accts Justin P Wilson Nashville T
SIC 9111 Executive offices;

D-U-N-S 07-575-5199
COUNTY OF BOULDER
BOULDER COUNTY
2020 13th St, Boulder, CO 80302
Tel (303) 441-3500 *Founded/Ownrshp* 1926
Sales NA *EMP* 1,400
SIC 9111

D-U-N-S 07-151-4434
COUNTY OF BRADLEY
155 Broad St Nw Ste H, Cleveland, TN 37311-5000
Tel (423) 728-7141 *Founded/Ownrshp* 1835
Sales NA *EMP* 1,800
Accts Justin P Wilson Nashville T
SIC 9111 Executive offices;
Ex Dir: Judy Calliway

D-U-N-S 04-034-1430
COUNTY OF BRAZORIA
111 E Locust St Ste 303, Angleton, TX 77515-4664
Tel (979) 864-1275 *Founded/Ownrshp* 1837
Sales NA *EMP* 1,040
Accts Kennemer Masters & Lunsford
SIC 9111 Executive offices;
Off Mgr: Debra Peltier
Genl Couns: Jeri Yenne

D-U-N-S 06-693-8358
COUNTY OF BROWARD
BOARD OF COUNTY COMMISSIONERS
115 S Andrews Ave Ste 409, Fort Lauderdale, FL 33301-1817
Tel (954) 357-7050 *Founded/Ownrshp* 1915
Sales NA *EMP* 40,500
Accts Crowe Horwath Llp Fort Lauder
SIC 9111 Executive offices;
CFO: Ken Jenne
CFO: Robert Miracle
Sr VP: Carlos Molinet
Dir Risk M: John Burkholder
Genl Mgr: Alan Tiano
Netwrk Mgr: Alan Saranga
Opers Mgr: John Kay
Mktg Mgr: Stephen Grubb
Psych: Ladez Watkins
Board of Directors: Josephus Eggelletion

D-U-N-S 06-832-0811
COUNTY OF BROWN
BROWN COUNTY
2077 Airport Dr Ste 18, Green Bay, WI 54313-5596
Tel (920) 448-4035 *Founded/Ownrshp* 1818
Sales NA *EMP* 1,705
Accts Schenck Sc Green Bay Wiscons
SIC 9111 Executive offices;
Exec: Carol Kelso
Genl Mgr: Sue Bertrand

D-U-N-S 87-920-3560
COUNTY OF BUNCOMBE
200 College St Ste 300, Asheville, NC 28801-3040
Tel (828) 250-4100 *Founded/Ownrshp* 1791
Sales NA *EMP* 2,028
Accts Gould Killian Cpa Group Pa
SIC 9111 Executive offices;
Prin: Wanda Greene
V Ch: Janet Burhoe-Jones
Nurse Mgr: Nelle Gregory

D-U-N-S 07-948-4036
COUNTY OF BURLINGTON
49 Rancocas Rd, Mount Holly, NJ 08060-1317
Tel (609) 265-5000 *Founded/Ownrshp* 1681
Sales NA *EMP* 3,000
Accts Bowman & Company Llp Woodbur
SIC 9199 Supply agency, government
**CFO:* Kurt Brock
**Treas:* Christine Nociti
Ofcr: Todd M Viereck
Ex Dir: George Nyikita
IT Man: Mike Patton

D-U-N-S 07-612-4395
COUNTY OF BUTTE
TREASURES OFFICE
25 County Center Dr # 110, Oroville, CA 95965-3366
Tel (530) 538-7701 *Founded/Ownrshp* 1850
Sales NA *EMP* 2,000
Accts Gallina Llp Roseville Calif
SIC 9311 Finance, taxation & monetary policy;
CFO: Greg Iturria
**Treas:* C Linda Barnes
**Bd of Dir:* Jane Dolan
Ofcr: John Blacklock
Ofcr: John Gulserian
Ofcr: Paul J Hahn
VP: Eva Puciata
CTO: Kim Yamaguchi
Counsel: Bruce Alpert

D-U-N-S 08-686-1630
COUNTY OF CABARRUS
65 Church St S, Concord, NC 28025-3549
Tel (704) 920-2107 *Founded/Ownrshp* 1793
Sales NA *EMP* 1,000
Accts Martin Starnes & Associates C
SIC 9111 Executive offices;
Prin: Michael K Downs
Ex Dir: Coleman Keeter
Prgrm Mgr: Jane Cauthen
Off Mgr: Monica Bayha
Netwrk Eng: Greg Keller

D-U-N-S 03-772-2758
COUNTY OF CALVERT
BOARD OF CTY COMM CALVERT CNTY
175 Main St, Prince Frederick, MD 20678-3337
Tel (410) 535-1600 *Founded/Ownrshp* 1954
Sales NA *EMP* 1,189
Accts Sb & Company Llc Hunt Valley
SIC 9111 County supervisors' & executives' offices;
**Pr:* Jerry Clark
**Pr:* Patt Mutter
Treas: Novalea Tracysoper
**VP:* Steve Weem
Ex Dir: Kevin Atticks
Genl Mgr: Roberta Baker
Genl Mgr: Rachel Griffith
Dir IT: Joe Klausner
Snr Mgr: Paul Meadows
Snr Mgr: Yvette Myers

D-U-N-S 07-553-4412
COUNTY OF CAMDEN
520 Market St Fl 11, Camden, NJ 08102-1300
Tel (856) 225-5000 *Founded/Ownrshp* 1844
Sales NA *EMP* 2,100
Accts Bowman & Company Llp
SIC 9111 Executive offices;
Brnch Mgr: Edward Borden
Psych: Inocencia Gutierrez
Psych: Jyi Peterson

D-U-N-S 01-054-6679
COUNTY OF CAMERON
JUDGE'S OFFICE
1100 E Monroe St, Brownsville, TX 78520-5883
Tel (956) 544-0823 *Founded/Ownrshp* 1843
Sales NA *EMP* 1,400
Accts Long Chilton Llp Brownsville
SIC 9111 Executive offices;
Prin: Gilberto Hinojosa
Treas: David Bentancourt
Off Mgr: Jaime Buentello
CTO: Juan Saldana
Counsel: Angela De Garza

D-U-N-S 07-475-0308
COUNTY OF CAMPBELL
47 Court House Ln, Rustburg, VA 24588-9701
Tel (434) 332-9667 *Founded/Ownrshp* 1781
Sales NA *EMP* 2,926
Accts Robinson Farmer Cox Associat
SIC 9111 Executive offices;
Dir IT: Ann Blair
IT Man: Minna Lombardi

D-U-N-S 07-552-5899
COUNTY OF CAPE MAY
4 Moore Rd, Cape May Court House, NJ 08210-1654
Tel (609) 465-1125 *Founded/Ownrshp* 1690
Sales NA *EMP* 1,057
Accts Ford Scott & Associates Llc-
SIC 9111 Executive offices;
Treas: Francine Springer

D-U-N-S 08-367-7138
COUNTY OF CATAWBA
100 Southwest Blvd Bldg A, Newton, NC 28658-3901
Tel (828) 465-8200 *Founded/Ownrshp* 1842
Sales NA *EMP* 1,174
Accts Martin Starnes & Associates
SIC 9111 Executive offices;
Ofcr: Cindy Travis
**Prin:* Tom Lundy
CIO: Terry Bledsoe

D-U-N-S 07-404-3944
COUNTY OF CATTARAUGUS
303 Court St, Little Valley, NY 14755-1028
Tel (716) 938-9111 *Founded/Ownrshp* 1808
Sales NA *EMP* 1,400
Accts Drescher & Malecki Llp Cheek
SIC 9111 Executive offices;
Ch: Norm Marsh
**Treas:* Joseph Keller
Treas: Kelly Reed
Pr Dir: Dawn Miller

D-U-N-S 09-732-2861
COUNTY OF CHAMPAIGN
CHAMPIGN CNTY RGIONAL PLG COMM
1776 E Washington St Ofc, Urbana, IL 61802-4581
Tel (217) 384-3772 *Founded/Ownrshp* 2000
Sales NA *EMP* 1,000
Accts Cliftonlarsonallen Llp Champa

SIC 9199
CEO: Debra Busey
Ch Bd: Patricia Avery
Treas: Daniel Welch
IT Man: Timothy Breen

D-U-N-S 07-372-8248
COUNTY OF CHARLESTON
CHARLESTON COUNTY GOVERNMENT
4045 Bridge View Dr, Charleston, SC 29405-7464
Tel (843) 958-4000 Founded/Ownrshp 1949
Sales NA EMP 2,200
Accts Scott And Company Llc Columbi
SIC 9111 Executive offices;
CFO: Keith Bustraan
Exec: Jennie Davis
Ex Dir: Dan L Chandler
Genl Mgr: James Neal
Genl Mgr: Chuck Wiggins
Sftwr Eng: Johnna Murray
Counsel: Joseph Dawson

D-U-N-S 04-022-3463
COUNTY OF CHARLOTTE
18500 Murdock Cir Ste 423, Port Charlotte, FL 33948-1068
Tel (941) 637-2199 Founded/Ownrshp 1921
Sales NA EMP 3,000
Accts Cherry Bekaert Llp Orlando F
SIC 9111 Executive offices;
*CFO: Tommy White
Genl Mgr: Pamela Kirchner
Genl Mgr: Kelly Studenwalt
Dir IT: Steve Churchill
IT Man: Christine Lee
IT Man: Jerry Livingston

D-U-N-S 07-403-5726
COUNTY OF CHAUTAUQUA
3 N Erie St, Mayville, NY 14757-1007
Tel (716) 753-7111 Founded/Ownrshp 1808
Sales NA EMP 1,500
Accts Drescher & Malecki Llp Cheek
SIC 9121
Exec: Vincent Horrigan
Exec: Paul Abram
*Exec: Gregory Edwards
Exec: Norman Green

D-U-N-S 07-968-5707
COUNTY OF CHEMUNG (NY)
320 E Market St, Elmira, NY 14901-3004
Tel (607) 737-2925 Founded/Ownrshp 1836
Sales NA EMP 1,000
Accts Efp Rotenberg Llp Rochester
SIC 9111 Executive offices;
Ch: Donna Draxler
*Treas: Joseph Sartori
*Exec: Thomas Santulli
*Prin: Andrea P Fairchild
*Prin: Cornellius Millikan

D-U-N-S 07-343-3807
COUNTY OF CHEROKEE
CHEROKEE COUNTY BOARD OF COMMI
1130 Bluffs Pkwy, Canton, GA 30114-5632
Tel (678) 493-6000 Founded/Ownrshp 1831
Sales NA EMP 1,443
Accts Mauldin & Jenkins Llc Atlant
SIC 9111 Executive offices
Ch: Lb Ahrens
CFO: Amy J Davis
CFO: Janelle Funk
IT Man: Ariana Freimuth
Board of Directors: J J Biello, Bobby Hawthorn, Jimmy Long, Rebecca Ray MD

D-U-N-S 07-312-8647
COUNTY OF CHESTER
313 W Market St, West Chester, PA 19382-2804
Tel (610) 344-6000 Founded/Ownrshp 1682
Sales NA EMP 2,800
Accts Zelenkofske Axelrod Llc Jamis
SIC 9111
Ch: Terence Farrell
V Ch: David Snyder
Ofcr: Mark Rupsis

D-U-N-S 07-474-6942
COUNTY OF CHESTERFIELD
9901 Lori Rd, Chesterfield, VA 23832-6626
Tel (804) 748-1000 Founded/Ownrshp 1749
Sales NA EMP 4,618
Accts Kpmg Llp Richmond Va
SIC 9111 Executive offices;
Ofcr: Bill Calliott
Ofcr: Martin Franciscus
Ofcr: Kimberly Mitchell
Ofcr: Jack Reid
*Prin: Steve Elswick
Ex Dir: Debbie Burcham
Trfc Dir: Phyllis Steedley
Snr Mgr: Paul L Newton

D-U-N-S 09-699-2656
COUNTY OF CLACKAMAS
2051 Kaen Rd, Oregon City, OR 97045-4035
Tel (503) 655-8459 Founded/Ownrshp 1843
Sales NA EMP 2,000
Accts Moss Adams Llp Eugene Orego
SIC 9199
*Treas: Shari A Anderson
Ofcr: John Krummenacker
Off Mgr: Brandi Pelham
Opers Supe: Brandy Ritter
Pr Mgr: Timothy Heider
Pr Mgr: Gary Schmidt

D-U-N-S 03-078-3757
COUNTY OF CLARK
CLARK COUNTY BD COMMISSIONERS
1300 Franklin St, Vancouver, WA 98660-2865
Tel (360) 397-2232 Founded/Ownrshp 1850
Sales NA EMP 1,700
Accts Brian Sonntag Cgfm Olympia
SIC 9111 Executive offices;
Top Exec: Ali Safayi
Snr Sftwr: Steve Cox
Dir IT: Glenn Olson
Board of Directors: Judie Stanton Are Commissi, Betty Sue Morris, Craig Pridemore

D-U-N-S 07-500-0166
COUNTY OF CLARK
50 E Columbia St Fl 5, Springfield, OH 45502-1133
Tel (937) 521-2005 Founded/Ownrshp 1818
Sales NA EMP 1,200
SIC 9111 County supervisors' & executives' offices;
Pr: Richard Lones

D-U-N-S 08-378-2953 IMP
COUNTY OF CLARK
500 S Grand Central Pkwy # 6, Las Vegas, NV 89155-4502
Tel (702) 455-3530 Founded/Ownrshp 1909
Sales NA EMP 8,528
Accts Kafoury Armstrong & Co Cpas
SIC 9111 County supervisors' & executives' offices
V Ch: Larry Brown
*CFO: Yolanda King
Treas: Laura Fitzpatrick
Bd of Dir: Kathleen Staite
Bd of Dir: Lawrence Weekly
Ofcr: Linda Sisson
VP: Steve Smith
Exec: Dan Kulin
Brnch Mgr: Ted Droessler
Genl Mgr: Anna Danchik
Genl Mgr: Mark Gamett
Board of Directors: Mary Beth Scow, Yvonne Atkinson, Steve Sisolak, Susan Brager, Lawrence Weekly, Larry Brown, Myrna Williams, Tom Collins, Bruce Woodbury, Chris Giunchigliani, Lorraine Hunt, Erin Kenny, Mary Kinkaid, Lance Malone

D-U-N-S 07-254-0040
COUNTY OF CLAY (FL)
BOARD OF COUNTY COMMISSIONERS
477 Houston St, Green Cove Springs, FL 32043-2438
Tel (904) 269-6376 Founded/Ownrshp 1858, 1859
Sales NA EMP 1,200
Accts Mcgladrey Llp Jacksonville F
SIC 9111 Executive offices;
*CFO: Elise Gann
CFO: Sharonda Johnson
Off Mgr: Linda Hoover

D-U-N-S 06-922-7536
COUNTY OF CLAYTON
CLAYTON COUNTY BOARD OF COMMIS
112 Smith St, Jonesboro, GA 30236-3539
Tel (770) 477-3208 Founded/Ownrshp 1858
Sales NA EMP 2,400
Accts Mauldin & Jenkins Llc Macon
SIC 9111 Mayors' offices
Ch: Eldrin Bell
COO: Anthony Brister
CFO: Ramona Thurman
Ofcr: Marc Jordan
Ofcr: Tom Reimers
Ofcr: James Walker
Genl Mgr: Marcus Ingram
Dir IT: Robert Phinney
Dir IT: Tim Watrous
VP Mktg: Deborah Nichols
Mktg Dir: Katherine Dodson

D-U-N-S 07-743-5543
COUNTY OF CLERMONT
177 E Main St, Batavia, OH 45103-2902
Tel (513) 732-7980 Founded/Ownrshp 1800
Sales NA EMP 1,350
Accts Dave Yost Columbus Ohio
SIC 9111 Executive offices;
Prin: David Spinney
Ofcr: Debby Bailey
Genl Mgr: Sherri Cmar
Genl Mgr: Jennifer Hartley
Dir IT: Steve Rabolt

D-U-N-S 07-593-1576
COUNTY OF COBB
COBB COUNTY BOARD OF COMMISSIO
100 Cherokee St Ste 400, Marietta, GA 30090-7004
Tel (770) 528-3300 Founded/Ownrshp 1832
Sales NA EMP 5,000
Accts Moore & Cubbedge Llp Mariett
SIC 9512 Land, mineral & wildlife conservation
Ch Bd: Tim Lee
Ofcr: Daryl Gray
Ofcr: Miranda Louis
Ofcr: Tami Nichelson
Ofcr: Jessica Parrott
Ofcr: Daniel Spiker
Ofcr: Kenneth Veal
IT Man: Curtis Tesar

D-U-N-S 02-012-6041
COUNTY OF COCHISE
LOCAL GOVERNMENT
1415 W Melody Ln Bldg G, Bisbee, AZ 85603-3027
Tel (520) 432-9200 Founded/Ownrshp 1880
Sales NA EMP 1,200
Accts Debbie Davenport Auditor Gene
SIC 9111 Executive offices;
Dir IT: Randy Streeter

D-U-N-S 07-444-4506
COUNTY OF COCONINO
219 E Cherry Ave, Flagstaff, AZ 86001-4634
Tel (928) 679-7120 Founded/Ownrshp 1891
Sales NA EMP 1,307
Accts Debbie Davenport Phoenix Ari
SIC 9111 Executive offices;
Board of Directors: Liz Archuleta, Matt Ryan, Carl Taylor

D-U-N-S 07-699-7790
COUNTY OF COLLIER
3299 Tamiami Trl E # 700, Naples, FL 34112-5746
Tel (239) 252-8999 Founded/Ownrshp 1923
Sales NA EMP 2,000
Accts Cliftonlarsonallen Llp Naples
SIC 9111 Executive offices;
COO: Paul Mattausch
Exec: Kristi Lester
Dir Teleco: John Daly
CIO: Shirley Watral
IT Man: Michael Barrios
IT Man: Mark Fowski
Sfty Mgr: Michael T Dock
Mktg Dir: Marie Francois
Mktg Mgr: Mary Paz
Snr PM: Julio Ordonez
Snr Mgr: Jonathan Warford

D-U-N-S 07-487-3449
COUNTY OF COLLIN
2300 Bloomdale Rd, McKinney, TX 75071-8517
Tel (972) 424-1460 Founded/Ownrshp 1846
Sales NA EMP 1,400
Accts Pattillo Brown & Hill Llp
SIC 9111
Pr: Lara Jaramillo
Ofcr: Cecilia Avogaro
Ofcr: Amy Campi
Ofcr: Doritha Cunningham
Ofcr: Jana Dickey
Ofcr: Edgar Espinoza
Ofcr: Alan Frazier
Ofcr: Gary Jackson
Ofcr: Zach Migura
Ofcr: Molly Norton
*Prin: Janna Benson-Caponera

D-U-N-S 05-034-5883
COUNTY OF CONTRA COSTA
625 Court St Ste 100, Martinez, CA 94553-1231
Tel (925) 957-5280 Founded/Ownrshp 1850
Sales NA EMP 7,193
Accts Macias Gini & O Connell Llp W
SIC 9111 Executive offices;
Prin: David Twa
*CFO: Robert Campbell
Treas: Russell V Watts

D-U-N-S 00-552-5829
COUNTY OF COOK (IL)
118 N Clark St, Chicago, IL 60602-1304
Tel (312) 603-5500 Founded/Ownrshp 1831
Sales NA EMP 26,500
Accts Rsm Us Llp Chicago Illinois
SIC 9111 Executive offices;
Pr: Toni Preckwinkle
Ofcr: Donna L Dunnings
Board of Directors: Ted Lechowicz, Jerry Butler, Mary Mc Donald, Allan Carr, Maria Pappas, John Daley, Herbert Schumann, Frank A Damato, Richard Siebel, Danny Davis, Bobbie Steele, Marco Domico, John Stroger, Robert Gooley, Carl R Hansen, Irene C Hernandez

D-U-N-S 08-261-1971
COUNTY OF CULPEPER
302 N Main St, Culpeper, VA 22701-2622
Tel (540) 727-3427 Founded/Ownrshp 1749
Sales NA EMP 1,500
Accts Robinson Farmer Cox Associat
SIC 9111 Executive offices;
Pr: Frank Bossio

D-U-N-S 07-489-1482
COUNTY OF CUMBERLAND
2 N Main St Ste 303, Crossville, TN 38555-4583
Tel (931) 484-5730 Founded/Ownrshp 1856
Sales NA EMP 1,200
Accts Justin P Wilson Nashville T
SIC 9111 Executive offices;
IT Man: Beth Richards

D-U-N-S 08-857-1690
COUNTY OF CUMBERLAND
117 Dick St, Fayetteville, NC 28301-5763
Tel (910) 678-7740 Founded/Ownrshp 1800
Sales NA EMP 2,200
Accts Cherry Bekaert Llp Fayettevi
SIC 9111 Executive offices;
Ex Dir: James Silman
Genl Mgr: Kelly Autry
Dir IT: Betty Clark

D-U-N-S 06-604-7804
COUNTY OF CUYAHOGA
BOARD OF COUNTY COMMISSIONERS
1215 W 3rd St, Cleveland, OH 44113-1532
Tel (216) 443-7022 Founded/Ownrshp 1810
Sales NA EMP 9,800
Accts Deloitte & Touche Llp Clevela
SIC 9121 County commissioner;
*CEO: Bob Reid
Treas: Richard Sensenbrenner
Ofcr: Yvonne Gibson
Exec: Koula Celebrezze
Brnch Mgr: Gerald McFaul
IT Man: Patrick J Coyne

D-U-N-S 08-237-6658
COUNTY OF DAKOTA
DAKOTA COUNTY COURTHOUSE
1590 Highway 55, Hastings, MN 55033-2343
Tel (651) 437-3191 Founded/Ownrshp 1849
Sales NA EMP 1,870
Accts Rebecca Otto Saint Paul Mn
SIC 9111 Executive offices;
Ch Bd: Michael Turner
*Ch Bd: Kathleen A Gaylord
*Treas: Thomas Novak
Exec: Tim Mozey
Dir IT: Dan Cater
IT Man: Tim Auld
Board of Directors: Patrice Bataglia, Joseph Harris, Paul Krause, Donald Maher, Nancy Schouweil

D-U-N-S 07-312-8597
COUNTY OF DALLAS
509 Main St Fl 6, Dallas, TX 75202-3521
Tel (214) 653-6472 Founded/Ownrshp 1846
Sales NA EMP 6,600
SIC 9111 Executive offices;
Treas: Pauline Medrano
IT Man: Tracy Hines
Software D: Ping Huangfu
Netwrk Eng: Jim Wiggins

D-U-N-S 07-614-8766
COUNTY OF DANE
DANE COUNTY CITY HALL
210 M Lthr Kng Jr Blv 425, Madison, WI 53703
Tel (608) 266-4114 Founded/Ownrshp 1836
Sales NA EMP 1,568
Accts Baker Tilly Virchow Krause Ll
SIC 9121
Exec: Kathleen Falk
Sr Cor Off: Bruce Willett
Dir Risk M: Dan Lowndes
Sfty Dirs: Scott Teuscher
Opers Mgr: David Caes

D-U-N-S 07-120-7955
COUNTY OF DAUPHIN
Market & Front Sts, Harrisburg, PA 17101
Tel (717) 780-6300 Founded/Ownrshp 1785
Sales NA EMP 1,500
Accts Zelenkofske Axelrod Llc Harri
SIC 9111 County supervisors' & executives' offices
Ch: Jeffrey T Haste
*VP: Mike Pries

D-U-N-S 06-142-0535
COUNTY OF DEKALB
BOARD OF COMMISSIONERS
1300 Commerce Dr, Decatur, GA 30030-3222
Tel (404) 371-2881 Founded/Ownrshp 1922
Sales NA EMP 7,300
Accts Kpmg Llp Atlanta Ga
SIC 9532
CEO: Vernon Jones
*CEO: Lee May
Ofcr: Kelvin Walton
Ofcr: Felton Williams
Snr Mgr: Luz Borrero

D-U-N-S 07-164-3472
COUNTY OF DELAWARE
101 N Sandusky St, Delaware, OH 43015-1732
Tel (740) 368-1800 Founded/Ownrshp 1808
Sales NA EMP 1,150
Accts Dave Yost Columbus Ohio
SIC 9111 Executive offices;

D-U-N-S 07-486-3127
COUNTY OF DENTON
110 W Hickory St, Denton, TX 76201-4116
Tel (940) 349-3100 Founded/Ownrshp 1846
Sales NA EMP 1,150
Accts Pattio Brown & Hill Llp
SIC 9111 Executive offices;
*Treas: Cindy Brown
Ofcr: Matthew Goldfarb
Exec: Sandi Brackeen
Snr Mgr: Bill Schultz

D-U-N-S 08-583-9728
COUNTY OF DICKSON
Court House Sq, Charlotte, TN 37036
Tel (615) 789-5093 Founded/Ownrshp 1900
Sales NA EMP 1,100
Accts John G Morgan Nashville Ten
SIC 9111 Executive offices;
Ofcr: Troy Martin

D-U-N-S 06-947-6133
COUNTY OF DU PAGE (IL)
421 N County Farm Rd, Wheaton, IL 60187-3978
Tel (630) 407-6000 Founded/Ownrshp 1839
Sales NA EMP 2,998
Accts Baker Tilly Virchow Krause Ll
SIC 9111 Executive offices;
Ch Bd: Daniel J Cronin
V Ch: Rose Fitzpatrick
*CFO: Fred Backfield
CFO: Paul Rafac
Treas: Jeremy Dotson
Dir IT: Ray Rehberg
IT Man: John Loper
Web Dev: Gerry Renner
Sls Mgr: Stefan Hanus

D-U-N-S 08-856-4075
COUNTY OF DURHAM
200 E Main St Ste 235, Durham, NC 27701-3649
Tel (919) 560-0035 Founded/Ownrshp 1881
Sales NA EMP 1,800
Accts Cherry Bekaert Llp Raleigh
SIC 9111 Executive offices;
Adm Dir: Joycelyn Dennis
Div Mgr: Ryan Eaves
Snr Ntwrk: Brian Owen
MIS Dir: Beth Wanner
MIS Dir: Elizabeth Wanner
Software D: Joe Perez
Opers Mgr: Shawn Davis
Secur Mgr: Ed Miller

D-U-N-S 07-154-3201
COUNTY OF EL DORADO
330 Fair Ln, Placerville, CA 95667-4103
Tel (530) 621-5830 Founded/Ownrshp 1917
Sales NA EMP 1,500
Accts Gallina Llp Roseville Calif
SIC 9111

D-U-N-S 07-644-4017
COUNTY OF EL PASO
200 S Cascade Ave Ste 100, Colorado Springs, CO 80903-2202
Tel (719) 520-7276 Founded/Ownrshp 1861
Sales NA EMP 2,000
Accts Rubinbrown Llp Denver Co
SIC 9111 Executive offices;
VP: Debbie White
Sys/Dir: Dale Marriott
IT Man: Nikki Simmons
Software D: Luke Ward
Mktg Dir: Greg Ruben

D-U-N-S 09-897-0403
COUNTY OF EL PASO
500 E San Antonio Ave # 314, El Paso, TX 79901-2419
Tel (915) 546-2000 Founded/Ownrshp 1849
Sales NA EMP 2,771
Accts Gibson Ruddock Patterson Llc

SIC 9111 County supervisors' & executives' offices;
CIO: Oscar Gonzalez
Telecom Mg: Rudy Luna
IT Man: Tom Leclare
Netwrk Mgr: David Gracia

D-U-N-S 01-046-8023
COUNTY OF ERIE
ERIE COUNTY COURTHOUSE
140 W 6th St Erie, Erie, PA 16501
Tel (814) 451-6000 *Founded/Ownrshp* 1826
Sales NA *EMP* 1,826
Accts Zelenkofske Axelrod Llc Pitts
SIC 9111
Ofcr: Corey Murphy
Genl Mgr: Sueellen Pasquale
Telecom Mg: Fran Skellie

D-U-N-S 07-147-9059 IMP
COUNTY OF ERIE
ERIE COUNTY
95 Franklin St Rm 1603, Buffalo, NY 14202-3914
Tel (716) 858-8500 *Founded/Ownrshp* 1821
Sales NA *EMP* 10,200
Accts Erie County Comptroller Buffa
SIC 9111 County supervisors' & executives' offices;
Exec: Mark Poloncarz
Exec: Gregory Gach
Genl Mgr: Kenneth Schlosser
Snr Mgr: Maria Whyte

D-U-N-S 07-507-9673
COUNTY OF ESCAMBIA
COMMISSIONERS OF ESCAMBIA COUN
221 Palafox Pl Ste 200, Pensacola, FL 32502-5835
Tel (850) 595-3000 *Founded/Ownrshp* 1821
Sales NA *EMP* 1,898
Accts Warren Averett Llc Pensacola
SIC 9111 Executive offices;
**Prin:* Robert McLaughlin
IT Man: Sharon Harrell

D-U-N-S 01-089-9284
COUNTY OF ESSEX
ESSEX COUNTY HOSPITAL CENTER
465 Martn L King Jr Blvd, Newark, NJ 07102
Tel (973) 621-4454 *Founded/Ownrshp* 1798
Sales NA *EMP* 5,300
Accts Samuel Klein And Company-Josep
SIC 9111 Executive offices;
Prin: Joseph N Divincenzo
**Treas:* Ron Weitz
Board of Directors: Dolores Battle, Sarah Bost, James Cavanaugh, Arthur Clay, Michael Delahunty, Joseph Di Vincenzo, Leroy Jones, Monroe Jay Lustbader, Joseph Parlavecchio

D-U-N-S 92-992-3266
COUNTY OF FAUQUIER
FAUQUIER COUNTY OFFICE OF ADULT COURT SERVICES
(*Suby of* COUNTY OF FAUQUIER)
70 Culpeper St, Warrenton, VA 20186-3218
Tel (540) 422-8080 *Founded/Ownrshp* 1996
Sales 160.5MM *EMP* 10
SIC 8322 Individual & family services

D-U-N-S 07-032-7549
COUNTY OF FORSYTH
110 E Main St Ste 210, Cumming, GA 30040-2474
Tel (770) 781-2101 *Founded/Ownrshp* 1854
Sales NA *EMP* 1,200
Accts Mauldin & Jenkins Llc Atlant
SIC 9111 Executive offices;
CFO: Dave Gruen
Dir IT: John Rusk

D-U-N-S 07-156-9586
COUNTY OF FORSYTH
44 FINANCE DEPARTMENT
201 N Chestnut St, Winston Salem, NC 27101-4120
Tel (336) 703-2050 *Founded/Ownrshp* 1849
Sales NA *EMP* 1,938
Accts Cherry Bekaert Llp Raleigh
SIC 9111 Executive offices;
IT Man: Glenn Peddle

D-U-N-S 08-149-7075
COUNTY OF FORT BEND
301 Jackson St Ste 719, Richmond, TX 77469-3108
Tel (281) 342-3411 *Founded/Ownrshp* 1837
Sales NA *EMP* 1,800
Accts Sandersen Knox & Co Llp Sug
SIC 9111 Executive offices;
Ofcr: Marshia Cox
Ofcr: Norma Garza
Ofcr: Yadira Rodriguez
Ofcr: Kelly Walger
Dir Risk M: Wyatt Scott
Brnch Mgr: Larry Wagenbach
Genl Mgr: Joyce Wendel
IT Man: Sandy Janzaik
Opers Mgr: Bob Clarkson
Snr Mgr: Brian Petrilla
Snr Mgr: Graig Temple

D-U-N-S 07-475-8202
COUNTY OF FRANKLIN
1255 Franklin St Ste 106, Rocky Mount, VA 24151-1289
Tel (540) 483-3030 *Founded/Ownrshp* 1786
Sales NA *EMP* 1,235
Accts Robinson Farmer Cox Associat
SIC 9111 Executive offices;
Ch: Jody D Brown
V Ch: Charles Wagner
Treas: Lynda F Messenger
Snr Mgr: Billy F Nremtp

D-U-N-S 06-319-9665
COUNTY OF FREDERICK
355 Montevue Ln 101, Frederick, MD 21702-8213
Tel (301) 600-9000 *Founded/Ownrshp* 1712
Sales NA *EMP* 1,800
Accts S B & Company Llc Hunt Valle
SIC 9111 County supervisors' & executives' offices;
**Pr:* Bud Otis
Treas: Mary Jackman
**Ofcr:* Paul Dial
Ofcr: Renee Kane
Ofcr: Chris Welte
Ex Dir: Marie Keegin
Pr Dir: Theresa Benner
Mktg Mgr: Shawn Dennison
Snr Mgr: Michael Dmuchowski

D-U-N-S 06-646-5071
COUNTY OF FULTON
141 Pryor St Sw, Atlanta, GA 30303-3444
Tel (404) 612-4000 *Founded/Ownrshp* 1853
Sales NA *EMP* 6,000
Accts Pjc Group Llc Atlanta Georg
SIC 9111
Ofcr: Anna Henry
Ofcr: Rhapsody Little
Ofcr: Ricardo Rucker
Ofcr: Lakeshia Thomas
Ofcr: Sean Wade
**Prin:* Patrick O'Conner
Prgrm Mgr: Renee Ferguson
Off Admin: Maxine Harper
Off Admin: Adeline Johnson
Dir IT: Ryan Fernandez

D-U-N-S 08-150-7709
COUNTY OF GALVESTON
722 21st St Fl 1, Galveston, TX 77550-2318
Tel (409) 795-2100 *Founded/Ownrshp* 1848
Sales NA *EMP* 1,036
Accts Null-Lairson Pc Texas City
SIC 9111 Executive offices;
Genl Mgr: Connie Nicholson
IT Man: Troy Stringer

D-U-N-S 07-840-4738
COUNTY OF GENESEE (MI)
GENESEE ROAD COMMISSION
1101 Beach St Fl 3, Flint, MI 48502-1428
Tel (810) 257-3040 *Founded/Ownrshp* 1835
Sales NA *EMP* 1,015
Accts Plante Moran Pllc Southfield
SIC 9111 Executive offices;
CFO: McShane Paul
**Treas:* Daniel Kildee
Ofcr: Charlene Sierakowski
Board of Directors: Floyd Cleck, Randy Ensley, John Gleason, Richard Hammel, Tim Herman, Bob Myers, John Northrup, Fred Schaltz

D-U-N-S 08-583-9611
COUNTY OF GILES
222 W Madison St, Pulaski, TN 38478-3223
Tel (931) 424-4001 *Founded/Ownrshp* 1800
Sales NA *EMP* 1,033[E]
SIC 9111
Ex Dir: Janet Vanzandt
IT Man: Beth Moore

D-U-N-S 07-904-2545
COUNTY OF GREENE
204 N Cutler St Ste 206, Greeneville, TN 37745-3847
Tel (423) 798-1703 *Founded/Ownrshp* 1794
Sales NA *EMP* 1,876
Accts Justin Wilson Nashville Tenn
SIC 9111
**Trst:* Dan Walker

D-U-N-S 07-799-1206
COUNTY OF GREENVILLE
301 University Rdg # 2400, Greenville, SC 29601-3636
Tel (864) 467-7105 *Founded/Ownrshp* 1786
Sales NA *EMP* 1,750
Accts Elliott Davis Llc Greenville
SIC 9111
VP: Phyllis Martin
Genl Mgr: Lisa Shealy
Software D: Anna Henderson
Counsel: Wanda Adams
Counsel: H D Campbell
Counsel: Jonathan Gregory
Counsel: Bryna Seay
Pgrm Dir: Judy Steadman

D-U-N-S 07-156-3613
COUNTY OF GUILFORD
ADMINISTRATION OFFICE
301 W Market St, Greensboro, NC 27401-2514
Tel (336) 641-3836 *Founded/Ownrshp* 1771
Sales NA *EMP* 2,700
Accts Cherry Bekaert & Holland Llp
SIC 9111

D-U-N-S 06-894-9296
COUNTY OF HAMILTON
OFFICE OF COUNTY ADMINISTRATOR
138 E Court St Rm 607, Cincinnati, OH 45202-1226
Tel (513) 946-4400 *Founded/Ownrshp* 1790
Sales NA *EMP* 6,000
SIC 9111 Executive offices;
**Treas:* Robert A Goering
Treas: John Murphy
VP: David Sellers
Brnch Mgr: Dan Dormis

D-U-N-S 07-491-1298
COUNTY OF HAMILTON
MAYOR'S OFFICE
208 Courths 625 Ga Av 201, Chattanooga, TN 37402
Tel (423) 209-6100 *Founded/Ownrshp* 1819
Sales NA *EMP* 1,800
Accts Mauldin & Jenkins Chattanooga
SIC 9111 Executive offices;
Bd of Dir: Rhonda Thurman

D-U-N-S 06-600-0480
COUNTY OF HANOVER
7497 County Complex Rd, Hanover, VA 23069-1529
Tel (804) 365-6000 *Founded/Ownrshp* 1850
Sales NA *EMP* 1,404
Accts Kpmg Llp Richmond Va
SIC 9111 Executive offices;
**Ofcr:* Kimberly Ludwig

D-U-N-S 06-940-2428
COUNTY OF HARFORD
HARFORD CNTY GOVERNMENT TRSRY
220 S Main St, Bel Air, MD 21014-3820
Tel (410) 638-3314 *Founded/Ownrshp* 1972
Sales NA *EMP* 1,400
Accts Sb & Company Llc Hunt Valley
SIC 9111 Executive offices
Exec: David Craig
**Pr:* William Boniface
**Treas:* Kathryn Hewitt
Treas: Rick Pernas
Bd of Dir: Debbie Braam
Genl Mgr: Marybeth Cooley
CIO: Jeff Griffith

D-U-N-S 07-220-6378
COUNTY OF HARRIS
ADMINISTRATIVE OFFICES
201 Caroline St Ste 800, Houston, TX 77002-1961
Tel (713) 755-6411 *Founded/Ownrshp* 1836
Sales NA *EMP* 14,000
Accts Deloitte & Touche Llp Housto
SIC 9111 County supervisors' & executives' offices
IT Man: Eric Cadow

D-U-N-S 09-463-6073
COUNTY OF HAWAII
25 Aupuni St Ste 107, Hilo, HI 96720-4245
Tel (808) 961-8211 *Founded/Ownrshp* 1909
Sales NA *EMP* 2,000
Accts N&K Cpas Inc Honolulu Hawai
SIC 9111 Executive offices;
Dir IT: Burt Tsuchiya
Sfty Dirs: Charmaine Kamaka

D-U-N-S 07-473-5515
COUNTY OF HENRICO
PUBLIC UTILITIES, DEPARTMENT O
4301 E Parham Rd, Henrico, VA 23228-2745
Tel (804) 501-4000 *Founded/Ownrshp* 1611
Sales NA *EMP* 9,178
Accts Kpmg Llp Richmond Va
SIC 9111 9511 Executive offices; ; Air, water & solid waste management;
Ex Dir: Frederick Agostino
Off Mgr: Pirich Mary
Off Admin: Elizabeth Patacca
Web Dev: Kevin Dykes
Pr Mgr: Gary Boyd
Snr Mgr: Mike Cox

D-U-N-S 05-704-7581
COUNTY OF HENRY
140 Henry Pkwy, McDonough, GA 30253-6696
Tel (770) 288-6000 *Founded/Ownrshp* 1821
Sales NA *EMP* 1,700
Accts Mauldin & Jenkins Llc Macon
SIC 9111
CFO: Mike Bush
**Ch Bd:* Elizabeth Mathis

D-U-N-S 07-321-2920
COUNTY OF HERNANDO
20 N Main St, Brooksville, FL 34601-2817
Tel (352) 754-4201 *Founded/Ownrshp* 1835
Sales NA *EMP* 1,300
Accts Purvis Gray & Company Sarasot
SIC 9111 Executive offices;
Ofcr: Chris Erickson
Ex Dir: Teresa Hill

D-U-N-S 07-461-7804
COUNTY OF HIDALGO
HIDALGO COUNTY WELFARE DEPT
100 N Closner Blvd # 303, Edinburg, TX 78539-3563
Tel (956) 289-7850 *Founded/Ownrshp* 1852
Sales NA *EMP* 1,400
SIC 9111 Executive offices;
Sys Admin: Renato Cuellar
Sys Admin: Pj Rivera

D-U-N-S 06-967-2137
COUNTY OF HILLSBOROUGH
ADMINISTRATION
601 E Kennedy Blvd Fl 23, Tampa, FL 33602-4932
Tel (813) 276-2720 *Founded/Ownrshp* 1834
Sales NA *EMP* 10,000
Accts Cherry Bekaert Llp Tampa Fl
SIC 9111 Executive offices;
V Ch: Jim Norman
Ofcr: Heidi Basgall
Ex Dir: Dara Chenevert
Ex Dir: Ronald Gardner
Genl Mgr: Robert Dicecco
Genl Mgr: Lavonne Nelson
CTO: Sal Luongo
CTO: Julie Roberts
Dir IT: Idania Alfonso
IT Man: Scott Cutler
IT Man: Sharon Valentine

D-U-N-S 09-387-6811
COUNTY OF HORRY
1301 2nd Ave, Conway, SC 29526-5209
Tel (843) 915-5000 *Founded/Ownrshp* 1801
Sales NA *EMP* 2,100
SIC 9111

D-U-N-S 10-122-5787
COUNTY OF HUDSON
HUDSON COUNTY CORRECTIONAL CTR
567 Pavonia Ave Fl 4, Jersey City, NJ 07306-1803
Tel (201) 795-6000 *Founded/Ownrshp* 1840
Sales NA *EMP* 2,800
SIC 9111 9223 Executive offices; ; Jail, government
Ch Bd: Silverio A Vega
Trst: Neil Carroll
Exec: Thomas A Degise

D-U-N-S 08-156-2514
COUNTY OF HUMBOLDT
825 5th St, Eureka, CA 95501-1107
Tel (707) 268-2543 *Founded/Ownrshp* 1853
Sales NA *EMP* 1,900
Accts Gallina Llp Roseville Calif
SIC 9111 Executive offices
Ofcr: Nikki Slater
Dir Risk M: Amy Nilsen
**Prin:* Kathy Hayes
**Prin:* Phillip Smith-Hanes
Genl Mgr: Rachelle Davis
Board of Directors: Stan Dixon, Paul Kirk, Bonnie Neely, Roger Rodoni, John Woolley

D-U-N-S 07-335-4573
COUNTY OF IMPERIAL
940 W Main St Ste 208, El Centro, CA 92243-2879
Tel (760) 482-4556 *Founded/Ownrshp* 1907
Sales NA *EMP* 1,800
Accts Hutchinson And Bloodgood Llp
SIC 9121 County commissioner;
CEO: Ralph Cordova Jr
**CEO:* Joe Picazo Jr

D-U-N-S 04-057-4592
COUNTY OF INGHAM
Ingham County Court House, Mason, MI 48854
Tel (517) 676-7206 *Founded/Ownrshp* 1839
Sales NA *EMP* 1,200
Accts Plante & Moran Pllc Detroit
SIC 9111 Executive offices;

D-U-N-S 01-073-3509
COUNTY OF JACKSON
10 S Oakdale Ave, Medford, OR 97501-2902
Tel (541) 774-6001 *Founded/Ownrshp* 1852
Sales NA *EMP* 1,001
Accts James Lanzarotta Partner For
SIC 9111 Mayors' offices
Ofcr: Jim Boeckl
Ofcr: Karey Casebier
Ofcr: Dana Cline
Ofcr: Michael Elkinton
Ofcr: Cindi Girard
Ofcr: Bryan Hescock
Ofcr: Jeremy Hubbard
Ofcr: Daniel Lupes
Ofcr: Debbie Moss
Ofcr: Jason Zanni
Div Mgr: Rick Hammel

D-U-N-S 07-194-6313
COUNTY OF JACKSON
2902c Shortcut Rd, Pascagoula, MS 39567-1842
Tel (228) 769-3258 *Founded/Ownrshp* 1900
Sales NA *EMP* 3,000
SIC 9111 Executive offices;

D-U-N-S 01-080-7535
COUNTY OF JEFFERSON
JEFFERSON COUNTY
1149 Pearl St Ste 301, Beaumont, TX 77701-3631
Tel (409) 835-8466 *Founded/Ownrshp* 1836
Sales NA *EMP* 1,200
Accts Pattillo Brown & Hill Llp C
SIC 9111 Executive offices;

D-U-N-S 07-577-2376
COUNTY OF JEFFERSON
100 Jefferson County Pkwy, Golden, CO 80401-6000
Tel (303) 271-8585 *Founded/Ownrshp* 2005
Sales NA *EMP* 3,000
Accts Eide Bailly Llp Golden Color
SIC 9111 Executive offices;
CEO: Jim Moore
Ofcr: Allen Boivert
Ofcr: Mark Hubbard
Ex Dir: Shelley Walton
Off Admin: Erica Opp
CIO: Jim Smith
IT Man: Bernadette Berger
IT Man: Dean Davis
IT Man: Sue Mundy

D-U-N-S 07-730-8039
COUNTY OF JEFFERSON
175 Arsenal St Rm 2, Watertown, NY 13601-2549
Tel (315) 785-3055 *Founded/Ownrshp* 1864
Sales NA *EMP* 1,000
Accts Dreschoer & Malecki Llp Cheek
SIC 9111 Executive offices;
Ch Bd: Caroline Fitzpatrick
Treas: Nancy D Brown
Treas: Dorena Kimball
Ex Dir: Paul Warneck

D-U-N-S 96-402-4843
COUNTY OF JEFFERSON
VINTAGE RESERVE METRO DST
(*Suby of* COUNTY OF JEFFERSON) ★
100 Jefferson County Pkwy, Golden, CO 80419-0001
Tel (303) 216-2987 *Founded/Ownrshp* 2010
Sales 214.5MM[E] *EMP* 1[E]
SIC 4941 Water supply
Prin: Jim Everson
Ofcr: Merle Slusser
Off Admin: Kelly Prewitt
CTO: Cynthia Shaw
IT Man: Dean Davis
Opers Mgr: Mike Secary
Snr Mgr: Jolene Bracy
Snr Mgr: Patricia Mundell
Snr Mgr: James Smith

D-U-N-S 07-302-2857
COUNTY OF JOHNSON
111 S Cherry St Ste 1200, Olathe, KS 66061-3451
Tel (913) 715-0435 *Founded/Ownrshp* 1851
Sales NA *EMP* 2,242
Accts Allen Gibbs & Houlik Lc Wic
SIC 9111 Executive offices;
Prin: Michael B Press
COO: Joe Waters
Ofcr: Pj Born
Ofcr: Laura Brewer
Ofcr: Robert A Ford
Ofcr: Hannes Zacharias
Exec: Gerald Hay
Admn Mgr: Greg Baldwin
Admn Mgr: Paul Stewart
CIO: Paul Haugan
IT Man: Scott Caldwell
Board of Directors: Geroge R Gross, Johnna Lingle, Annabeth Surbaugh, Douglas E Wood

D-U-N-S 09-759-9104
COUNTY OF JOHNSTON
JOHNSTON CNTY BD COMMISSIONERS
207 E Johnston St, Smithfield, NC 27577-3938
Tel (919) 989-5100 *Founded/Ownrshp* 1746
Sales NA *EMP* 1,100
Accts Thompson Price Scott Adams
SIC 9111 County supervisors' & executives' offices;
Ch Bd: Tony Braswell

D-U-N-S 02-090-6988
COUNTY OF KALAMAZOO
201 W Kalamazoo Ave # 101, Kalamazoo, MI 49007-3726
Tel (269) 384-8305 *Founded/Ownrshp* 1830
Sales NA *EMP* 1,000
Accts Bdo Usa Llp Kalamazoo Mi
SIC 9111 Executive offices;
Prin: Duane Triemstra
VP: Minna Gorsalitz
**Prin:* Lee Adams
**Prin:* Lotte Jarnefelt
Genl Mgr: Rachael Grover
CIO: Tammy Woodhams
Dir IT: Cindy Lowe

D-U-N-S 01-022-1786
COUNTY OF KANE
719 S Batavia Ave, Geneva, IL 60134-3077
Tel (630) 232-3400 *Founded/Ownrshp* 1830
Sales NA *EMP* 1,200
Accts Wermer Rogers Doran & Ruzon
SIC 9111 Executive offices;
**Ch Bd:* Michael McCoy
CFO: Bill Lake
**Treas:* David Rickert
Dir IT: Roger Fahnestock
Dir IT: Mitzi Strike

D-U-N-S 11-321-8945
COUNTY OF KAUAI
4444 Rice St Ste 150, Lihue, HI 96766-1340
Tel (808) 241-4200 *Founded/Ownrshp* 1906
Sales NA *EMP* 1,010
Accts N&K Cpas Inc Honolulu Hawa
SIC 9111
Ofcr: Matthew Beadle
Ofcr: Richard Brown
Ofcr: Paddy Ramson
Ofcr: Aaron Relacion
Ofcr: Elton Ushio
Ofcr: Scott Williamson

D-U-N-S 08-048-7838
COUNTY OF KENOSHA
1010 56th St, Kenosha, WI 53140-3738
Tel (262) 653-2552 *Founded/Ownrshp* 1860
Sales NA *EMP* 1,000
Accts Virchow Krause & Company Llp
SIC 9111 Executive offices;
Ch Bd: Dennis Elverman
**Exec:* Allan K Kehl
Ex Dir: Dave Knoerr
Ex Dir: Sharon Timmons

D-U-N-S 06-381-1350
COUNTY OF KERN
1115 Truxtun Ave Rm 505, Bakersfield, CA 93301-4630
Tel (661) 868-3690 *Founded/Ownrshp* 1866
Sales NA *EMP* 8,000
Accts Brown Armstrong Ac Bakersfie
SIC 9111 Executive offices;
Bd of Dir: Antanette Reed
VP: Carol Cox
**Prin:* Laura Akey
Genl Mgr: Alex Alva

D-U-N-S 07-574-7667
COUNTY OF KING
401 5th Ave Ste 3, Seattle, WA 98104-1818
Tel (206) 296-4040 *Founded/Ownrshp* 1853
Sales NA *EMP* 13,300
Accts Jan M Jutte Cpa Cgfm Acting
SIC 9111 County supervisors' & executives' offices;
Exec: Dow Constantine
Ofcr: Marlin Blizinsky
Ofcr: Scott Miller
Exec: Lorene Moore
Snr Ntwrk: Jeff Kass

D-U-N-S 07-467-5075
COUNTY OF KINGS
1400 W Lacey Blvd, Hanford, CA 93230-5997
Tel (559) 582-0326 *Founded/Ownrshp* 1893
Sales NA *EMP* 1,184
Accts Brown Armstrong Bakersfield
SIC 9111 Executive offices;
Treas: Vj Brann
Ofcr: Marc Cerda
Ofcr: Darrin Ellis
Ex Dir: Lydia Rees
Snr Mgr: Rick Smith
Board of Directors: Tony Barba, Joe Neves, Tony Oliveira, Jon Rachford, Alene Taylor

D-U-N-S 07-185-5191
COUNTY OF KITSAP
619 Division St, Port Orchard, WA 98366-4614
Tel (360) 337-7164 *Founded/Ownrshp* 1857
Sales NA *EMP* 1,579
SIC 9111

D-U-N-S 07-489-3033
COUNTY OF KNOX
400 W Main St Rm 615, Knoxville, TN 37902-2424
Tel (865) 215-2005 *Founded/Ownrshp* 1792
Sales NA *EMP* 2,500
Accts Pugh & Company Pc Knoxvill
SIC 9111 Executive offices;
Dir IT: Dick Moran

D-U-N-S 07-650-4885
COUNTY OF LA CROSSE
400 4th St N, La Crosse, WI 54601-3227
Tel (608) 785-9581 *Founded/Ownrshp* 1836
Sales NA *EMP* 1,350
Accts Cliftonlarsonallen Llp Minnea
SIC 9111

Ch: Steve Doyle
Ex Dir: Noreen Kuroski
Genl Mgr: Jim Becker
Genl Mgr: Bryan Jostad
Dir IT: Cliff Gosney
Dir IT: John Parshall
IT Man: Jonathan Edwards
Counsel: Bill Shepherd

D-U-N-S 07-112-5090
COUNTY OF LAKE
LAKE COUNTY ADMINISTRATION CEN
8 N State St Ste 215, Painesville, OH 44077-3955
Tel (440) 350-2500 *Founded/Ownrshp* 1832
Sales NA *EMP* 2,000
Accts Mary Taylor Cpa Cleveland O
SIC 9111 Executive offices;
Prin: Mildred M Teuscher
**Treas:* John Crocker
Ofcr: Jackie George
Dir: Jason Boyd
Dir IT: Jason Webster

D-U-N-S 07-459-1652
COUNTY OF LAKE
18 N County St Fl 8, Waukegan, IL 60085-4304
Tel (847) 377-2373 *Founded/Ownrshp* 1839
Sales NA *EMP* 2,800
Accts Baker Tilly Virchow Krause Ll
SIC 9111 Executive offices;
Ch Bd: Suzi Schmidt
Pr: Rochelle M Jakaitis
Bd of Dir: Carol Calabresa
Bd of Dir: Brent Paxton
Ofcr: Michelle McPherson
Ex Dir: Robert Zastany
CTO: Dan Horan
Dir IT: Phil Balke
IT Man: Anita Patel
Psych: Charissa Simon

D-U-N-S 07-921-4136
COUNTY OF LAKE (FL)
LAKE COUNTY BOCC
315 W Main St, Tavares, FL 32778-3813
Tel (352) 343-9808 *Founded/Ownrshp* 1887
Sales NA *EMP* 1,772
Accts Moore Stephens Lovelace Pa
SIC 9111 Executive offices;
Ofcr: Kevin McDonald
IT Man: Niki Booth

D-U-N-S 06-867-6535
COUNTY OF LANCASTER
COUNTY COMMISSIONERS
555 S 10th St Rm 110, Lincoln, NE 68508-2803
Tel (402) 441-4944 *Founded/Ownrshp* 1865
Sales NA *EMP* 1,000
Accts Allen Gibbs & Houlik Lc Wic
SIC 9111 Executive offices;
Treas: Candace Meredith
IT Man: Rhonda Ryan

D-U-N-S 07-119-3551
COUNTY OF LANCASTER
150 N Queen St Ste 712, Lancaster, PA 17603-3562
Tel (717) 299-8262 *Founded/Ownrshp* 1729
Sales NA *EMP* 1,900
Accts S B & Company Llc Hunt Valle
SIC 9111 County supervisors' & executives' offices; ; Governors' offices
Sls Mgr: Elizabeth Guthridge

D-U-N-S 03-078-6248
COUNTY OF LANE (OR)
125 E 8th Ave, Eugene, OR 97401-2926
Tel (541) 682-4203 *Founded/Ownrshp* 1851
Sales NA *EMP* 1,405
Accts Moss Adams Llp Eugene Oregon
SIC 9111 County supervisors' & executives' offices;
Genl Mgr: Jeanne Sun
Opers Supe: Corey Buller
Psych: Melissa Arnone
Psych: C Baskerville
Snr PM: Janet Labonte

D-U-N-S 03-044-6819
COUNTY OF LARIMER
200 W Oak St Ste 4000, Fort Collins, CO 80521-2713
Tel (970) 498-5930 *Founded/Ownrshp* 1876
Sales NA *EMP* 1,200
SIC 9111

D-U-N-S 01-346-1611
COUNTY OF LEE
2115 2nd St, Fort Myers, FL 33901-3012
Tel (239) 533-2737 *Founded/Ownrshp* 1907
Sales NA *EMP* 3,000
Accts Cherry Bekaert Llp Tampa Fl
SIC 9111 Executive offices;
Prin: Roger Desjarlais
**Ex Dir:* Jeff Mulder

D-U-N-S 07-361-8605
COUNTY OF LEHIGH
17 S 7th St, Allentown, PA 18101-2401
Tel (610) 782-3000 *Founded/Ownrshp* 1820
Sales NA *EMP* 3,500
Accts Reinsel Kuntz Lesher Llp Lanc
SIC 9111 Executive offices;
CEO: Thomas Muller
Ofcr: Lauren Berke
Ofcr: Sally Bortz
Ofcr: Timothy Salgado
Ofcr: Joseph Vazquez
Comm Man: Dennis Steckel
**Prin:* George Samuelson
Adm Dir: Catherine Squires
Ex Dir: Maureen McManus
Brnch Mgr: James Martin
CTO: Troy Stone

D-U-N-S 03-011-5885
COUNTY OF LEXINGTON
212 S Lake Dr, Lexington, SC 29072-3410
Tel (803) 785-8100 *Founded/Ownrshp* 1804
Sales NA *EMP* 1,240
Accts Brittingham Brown Prince & H
SIC 9111 Executive offices;

CFO: Randolph Poston
**Ch:* Todd Cullum
Dir: Charles Compton
Comm Man: Richard Dolan
Comm Man: Michael Moore
Admn Mgr: Tim Oswald
Admn Mgr: Michael Stacey
Tech Mgr: Larry Oates
Snr PM: Chuck Whipple

D-U-N-S 03-752-4790
COUNTY OF LICKING
LICKING COUNTY COMMISSIONERS
20 S 2nd St, Newark, OH 43055-5602
Tel (740) 670-5040 *Founded/Ownrshp* 1803
Sales NA *EMP* 1,293
SIC 9111
**Treas:* Scott Ryan

D-U-N-S 07-980-2542
COUNTY OF LORAIN
LORAIN COUNTY TREASURER
226 Middle Ave, Elyria, OH 44035-5629
Tel (440) 329-5201 *Founded/Ownrshp* 1900
Sales NA *EMP* 2,000
SIC 9111

D-U-N-S 05-223-8763 IMP
COUNTY OF LOS ANGELES
LOS ANGELES COUNTY TAX COLLECT
500 W Temple St Ste 375, Los Angeles, CA 90012-3550
Tel (213) 974-1101 *Founded/Ownrshp* 1850
Sales NA *EMP* 100,000
Accts Macias Gini & O Connell Llp L
SIC 9111 Mayors' offices
CEO: Sachi A Hamai
Ofcr: Robert Osborne
Ex Dir: Laura Zucker
Genl Mgr: Craig Hirakawa
Genl Mgr: Al Tizani
CIO: David Hamamoto
IT Man: Jonathan Arfin
IT Man: Anne Bartolotti
IT Man: Jeremy Ll
IT Man: Alvia Shaw
IT Man: Cheri Thomas

D-U-N-S 06-810-4322
COUNTY OF LUCAS
AUDITOR OFFICE
1 Government Ctr Ste 600, Toledo, OH 43604-2255
Tel (419) 213-4406 *Founded/Ownrshp* 1835
Sales NA *EMP* 3,500
Accts Spilman Hills & Heidebrink L
SIC 9111 Executive offices;
**Prin:* Anita Lopez
Genl Mgr: Laura Lloyd-Jenkins

D-U-N-S 07-425-0242
COUNTY OF MACOMB
120 N Main St, Mount Clemens, MI 48043-5605
Tel (586) 469-5260 *Founded/Ownrshp* 1923
Sales NA *EMP* 2,200
Accts Plante & Moran Pllc Clinton
SIC 9111 Executive offices;
Prin: David Flynn
**V Ch:* Peter Lund
**Treas:* Ted Wahby
Prgrm Mgr: Mark Gregor
Genl Mgr: Thomas Gaeschke

D-U-N-S 00-493-9377
COUNTY OF MADERA
AUDITOR CONTROLLER
209 W Yosemite Ave, Madera, CA 93637-3534
Tel (559) 675-7726 *Founded/Ownrshp* 1893
Sales NA *EMP* 1,000
SIC 9111 Executive offices;
Treas: Robert Dewall
**Prin:* Michael Keitz

D-U-N-S 00-107-0903
COUNTY OF MADISON
COMMISSIONER DEPT
100 Northside Sq, Huntsville, AL 35801-8815
Tel (256) 532-3492 *Founded/Ownrshp* 1808
Sales NA *EMP* 1,095
SIC 9111 Executive offices;
Ch Bd: Mike Gillespie
Dir IT: Larry Tisdale

D-U-N-S 04-014-0154
COUNTY OF MADISON
157 N Main St Rm 382, Edwardsville, IL 62025-1965
Tel (618) 692-7040 *Founded/Ownrshp* 1812
Sales NA *EMP* 1,064
Accts Scheffel Boyle Edwardsville
SIC 9111 Executive offices;
**Ch:* Alan Dunstan
Genl Mgr: Joe Parente

D-U-N-S 07-759-4810
COUNTY OF MANATEE
MANATEE COUNTY GOVERNMENT
1112 Manatee Ave W, Bradenton, FL 34205-7804
Tel (941) 748-4501 *Founded/Ownrshp* 1855
Sales NA *EMP* 1,600[E]
SIC 9121

D-U-N-S 07-753-5144
COUNTY OF MARICOPA
301 W Jefferson St # 960, Phoenix, AZ 85003-2143
Tel (602) 506-3011 *Founded/Ownrshp* 1871
Sales NA *EMP* 15,751
Accts State Of Arizona Office Of The
SIC 9111 Executive offices;
CFO: Shelby Scharbach
Ofcr: Rosie Rodriguez
Ofcr: Rebecca Sunenshine
VP: Patricia Edgar
Assoc Dir: Robert Bill
Genl Mgr: Robert Harwood
CIO: David L Stevens
Dir IT: Jeff Abbott
Dir IT: Phillip Vankley
IT Man: Karl Gosch
IT Man: Claudia Ramirez

Board of Directors: A Five Member Board of Sup

D-U-N-S 07-878-7744
COUNTY OF MARIN (CA)
1600 Los Gamos Dr Ste 200, San Rafael, CA 94903-1807
Tel (415) 473-6358 *Founded/Ownrshp* 1850
Sales NA *EMP* 2,122
Accts Gallina Llp Roseville Califo
SIC 9111 Executive offices
Adm Dir: Matthew Hymel
Genl Mgr: Mina Martinovich
IT Man: Auna Harris
Snr Mgr: Rwena Holaday

D-U-N-S 05-097-3718
COUNTY OF MARION
FINANCIAL SERVICES
451 Division St Ne Ste 1, Salem, OR 97301-2569
Tel (503) 588-5212 *Founded/Ownrshp* 1843
Sales NA *EMP* 1,400
Accts Grove Mueller & Swank Pc
SIC 9121

D-U-N-S 60-576-8886
COUNTY OF MARION
MARION COUNTY AUDITOR OFFICE
200 E Washington St # 801, Indianapolis, IN 46204-3307
Tel (317) 327-3001 *Founded/Ownrshp* 1822
Sales NA *EMP* 3,175[E]
SIC 9111 County supervisors' & executives' offices;
CFO: Aaron Hood
Genl Mgr: Julie Voorhies
Netwrk Eng: Michael Higdon

D-U-N-S 07-768-0155
COUNTY OF MAUI
200 S High St, Wailuku, HI 96793-2155
Tel (808) 270-7855 *Founded/Ownrshp* 1904
Sales NA *EMP* 2,000
Accts N&K Cpas Inc Honolulu Hawa
SIC 9111 Executive offices;
V Ch: Robert Carroll
Ofcr: Ernest Grace
Genl Mgr: Linda Tokuoka
CIO: Jacob Verkerke

D-U-N-S 07-823-9845
COUNTY OF MAURY
5 Public Sq, Columbia, TN 38401-3306
Tel (931) 381-3690 *Founded/Ownrshp* 1807
Sales NA *EMP* 1,650
Accts Justin P Wilson Comptroller
SIC 9111 Executive offices
Exec: James L Bailey Jr
Ex Dir: Erin Jaggers
Dir IT: Jim Dooley
Dir IT: Bill Wells

D-U-N-S 07-449-8353
COUNTY OF MECKLENBURG
600 E 4th St, Charlotte, NC 28202-2816
Tel (704) 336-2108 *Founded/Ownrshp* 1762
Sales NA *EMP* 4,800
Accts Cherry Bekaert Llp Raleigh N
SIC 9111 Executive offices;
IT Man: Tyane Johnson

D-U-N-S 01-083-6047
COUNTY OF MEDINA (OH)
144 N Brdwy St Rm 201, Medina, OH 44256
Tel (330) 722-9208 *Founded/Ownrshp* 1818
Sales NA *EMP* 1,184
Accts Dave Yost Columbus Ohio
SIC 9111 Executive offices;
CEO: Christopher Jakab
Treas: John Burke
Genl Mgr: Laura Labak
Board of Directors: Ferris W Brown

D-U-N-S 07-877-0880
COUNTY OF MENDOCINO
501 Low Gap Rd Rm 1010, Ukiah, CA 95482-3734
Tel (707) 463-4441 *Founded/Ownrshp* 1850
Sales NA *EMP* 1,100
Accts Gallina Llp Roseville Califo
SIC 9111 Executive offices;
CEO: Tom Mitchell
**Treas:* Shari Schapmire
IT Man: Glen Capobianco
Snr Mgr: Jill Martin

D-U-N-S 07-876-7951
COUNTY OF MERCED (CA)
2222 M St, Merced, CA 95340-3729
Tel (209) 385-7511 *Founded/Ownrshp* 1855
Sales NA *EMP* 2,700
Accts Brown Armstrong Bakersfield
SIC 9111 Executive offices;
Ofcr: Deborah Mason
CIO: Mark Nauss

D-U-N-S 05-417-7662
COUNTY OF MERCER
ADMINISTRATION OFFICE
640 S Broad St, Trenton, NJ 08611-1822
Tel (609) 989-6502 *Founded/Ownrshp* 1838
Sales NA *EMP* 1,682
Accts Eugene J Elias Cpa - Mercadi
SIC 9111 Executive offices;
V Ch: William S Agress
V Ch: Alan Hershey
V Ch: Steve Jany
**Treas:* David Miller
**Ex Dir:* Brian Hughes

D-U-N-S 06-894-4164
COUNTY OF MIAMI
201 W Main St, Troy, OH 45373-3239
Tel (937) 440-5900 *Founded/Ownrshp* 1807
Sales 98.9MM *EMP* 850
Accts Dave Yost Dayton Ohio
SIC 9111 County supervisors' & executives' offices
Pr: Richard L Cultice
**Pr:* John F Evans
**Treas:* Pat Quillen

D-U-N-S 00-414-8292 IMP/EXP
COUNTY OF MIAMI-DADE
111 Nw 1st St Ste 2550, Miami, FL 33128-1933
Tel (305) 375-5147 *Founded/Ownrshp* 1906
Sales NA *EMP* 30,000E
SIC 9111 County supervisors' & executives' offices;
**Pr:* Roberto Pelaez
Sys Eng: Donald Sofronsky

D-U-N-S 07-660-1863
COUNTY OF MIDDLESEX
MIDDLESEX COUNTY TREASURER
40 Thorndike St, Cambridge, MA 02141-1715
Tel (617) 494-4113 *Founded/Ownrshp* 1643
Sales NA *EMP* 1,100
SIC 9111 Executive offices;
**Treas:* James E Fahey Jr
Dir IT: Alex Leone

D-U-N-S 04-067-1521
COUNTY OF MOBILE
205 Government St, Mobile, AL 36644-0001
Tel (251) 574-5077 *Founded/Ownrshp* 1812
Sales NA *EMP* 1,500
Accts Ronald L Jones Chief Examine
SIC 9111 County supervisors' & executives' offices;
Mktg Dir: Nancy Johnson

D-U-N-S 07-753-1937
COUNTY OF MOHAVE
700 W Beale St, Kingman, AZ 86401-5711
Tel (928) 753-0729 *Founded/Ownrshp* 1864
Sales NA *EMP* 1,086
Accts Debbie Davenport Cpa Phoenix
SIC 9111 Executive offices;
Ch Bd: Gary Watson
Treas: Katheryn Greenawalt
Off Admin: Terri Chavez
Off Admin: Tiffany Mitchell
Off Admin: Patricia Osullivan
IT Man: Terri Bryant
IT Man: Brenda Dehaan
Sfty Dirs: Warren Twitchell

D-U-N-S 06-870-4485
COUNTY OF MONMOUTH
MONMOUTH COUNTY
1 E Main St, Freehold, NJ 07728-2273
Tel (732) 431-7000 *Founded/Ownrshp* 1675
Sales NA *EMP* 3,800
Accts Holman Frenia Allison Pc F
SIC 9111 County supervisors' & executives' offices;
V Ch: William Potter III
Board of Directors: Thomas Arnone, John Curley, Craig Marshall, Teri O'connor

D-U-N-S 07-967-8249
COUNTY OF MONROE
39 W Main St Ste 110, Rochester, NY 14614-1408
Tel (585) 428-5301 *Founded/Ownrshp* 1821
Sales NA *EMP* 4,800
Accts Kpmg Llp Rochester Ny
SIC 9111 Executive offices;
Ex Dir: Maggie Brooks
CIO: Nelson Rivera

D-U-N-S 07-629-8439
COUNTY OF MONTEREY
168 W Alisal St Fl 3, Salinas, CA 93901-2487
Tel (831) 755-5040 *Founded/Ownrshp* 1850
Sales NA *EMP* 4,600
SIC 9111

D-U-N-S 02-605-1276
COUNTY OF MONTGOMERY
501 N Thompson St, Conroe, TX 77301-2500
Tel (936) 539-7885 *Founded/Ownrshp* 1837
Sales NA *EMP* 1,300
Accts Pattillo Brown & Hill Llp
SIC 9111 Executive offices;
CIO: Marshall Shirley
IT Man: Phyllis Martin

D-U-N-S 04-226-0711 IMP
COUNTY OF MONTGOMERY
530 Port Indian Rd, Norristown, PA 19403-3502
Tel (610) 278-3072 *Founded/Ownrshp* 1784
Sales NA *EMP* 3,278
Accts Maillie Llp Oaks Pennsylvani
SIC 9111 Executive offices;
Ch Bd: Josh Shapiro
**COO:* Lauren M Lambrugo
**CFO:* Uri Z Monson
**Prin:* Leslie Richards
Ex Dir: Gerald Birkelbach
Dir IT: Dave Connelley
Software D: Charles Brant

D-U-N-S 06-201-4378
COUNTY OF MONTGOMERY
101 Monroe St Fl 15, Rockville, MD 20850-2503
Tel (240) 777-8220 *Founded/Ownrshp* 1776
Sales NA *EMP* 7,400
Accts Cliftonlarsonallen Llp Balti
SIC 9111 Mayors' offices
Ex Dir: Linda Herman
Ofcr: Michael Prather
Exec: Michael Dorsey
Prin: Iskah Legett
Prin: Amy Moskowitz
Prgrm Mgr: Jessica Jones
Genl Mgr: Lenny Moore

D-U-N-S 07-127-7115
COUNTY OF MONTGOMERY
451 W 3rd St Fl 4, Dayton, OH 45422-0001
Tel (937) 225-4000 *Founded/Ownrshp* 1788
Sales NA *EMP* 5,000
Accts Plattenburg & Associates Inc
SIC 9111 Executive offices;
Dir IT: James Alford
IT Man: Janet Holman

D-U-N-S 60-585-2854
COUNTY OF MONTGOMERY
755 Roanoke St Ste 2e, Christiansburg, VA 24073-3169
Tel (540) 382-5700 *Founded/Ownrshp* 1776
Sales NA *EMP* 1,700
Accts Brown Edwards & Company Ll
SIC 9111 Executive offices;
Bd of Dir: Todd Murray
Ofcr: Christopher Lucas
Ofcr: Mavin Ogle
**Ex Dir:* Donna Brown
Off Admin: Teresa Mullen
Dir IT: Phil Martin

D-U-N-S 08-061-1700
COUNTY OF MORRIS
Court St, Morristown, NJ 07960
Tel (973) 285-6010 *Founded/Ownrshp* 1739
Sales NA *EMP* 2,250
Accts Nisivoccia Llp Mount Arlingto
SIC 9111 Executive offices;
**Treas:* Glenn Roe
Ex Dir: Christopher Marra
Genl Mgr: Jacqueline Connelly

D-U-N-S 03-078-4888
COUNTY OF MULTNOMAH
MULTNOMAH COUNTY
501 Se Hawthorne Blvd # 100, Portland, OR 97214-3587
Tel (503) 988-3511 *Founded/Ownrshp* 1854
Sales NA *EMP* 5,000
Accts James C Lanzarotta Partner
SIC 9111 Executive offices;
Ch Bd: Jeff Cogen
Ofcr: Nicole Cleary
Ofcr: Javelin Hardy
Ofcr: Jessica Morkert-Shibley
Ofcr: Leticia Navarro
Ex Dir: Abbey Stamp
Prgrm Mgr: Tina Birch
Prgrm Mgr: Patty Doyle
Prgrm Mgr: Irma Jimenez
Prgrm Mgr: John Lindenthal
IT Man: Rodney Chin

D-U-N-S 07-259-6349
COUNTY OF MUSKEGON
ADMINISTRATION OFFICE
990 Terrace St, Muskegon, MI 49442-3395
Tel (231) 724-6520 *Founded/Ownrshp* 1859
Sales NA *EMP* 1,200
Accts Rehmann Robson Muskegon Mi
SIC 9111 Executive offices;
Ch: Terry Sabo
Ex Dir: Tim Burgess

D-U-N-S 07-168-8188
COUNTY OF NAPA
1195 Third St Ste 310, NAPA, CA 94559-3035
Tel (707) 253-4421 *Founded/Ownrshp* 1850
Sales NA *EMP* 1,300
SIC 9111

D-U-N-S 00-241-4696
COUNTY OF NASSAU
1550 Franklin Ave, Mineola, NY 11501-4801
Tel (516) 571-3131 *Founded/Ownrshp* 1899
Sales NA *EMP* 14,500
Accts Deloitte & Touche Llp Jericho
SIC 9111 County supervisors' & executives' offices;
Exec: Edward P Mangano
**Treas:* Steven Conkling

D-U-N-S 01-097-9029
COUNTY OF NEVADA
950 Maidu Ave, Nevada City, CA 95959-8600
Tel (530) 265-1480 *Founded/Ownrshp* 1854
Sales NA *EMP* 1,025
Accts Gallina Llp Roseville Ca
SIC 9111 Executive offices;
CEO: Richard Haffy
Genl Mgr: Ryan Gruver

D-U-N-S 07-709-5057
COUNTY OF NEW CASTLE
87 Reads Way, New Castle, DE 19720-1648
Tel (302) 395-5555 *Founded/Ownrshp* 1673
Sales NA *EMP* 1,200
Accts Cliftonlarsonallen Llp Baltim
SIC 9111 Executive offices;
Exec: Christopher Coons
CFO: Ronald A Morris
Ofcr: David Del Grande
Ofcr: Yvette Price
VP: James McElhinney
**Exec:* Thomas Gordon
Exec: Penrose Hollins
Comm Dir: Antonio Prado
Genl Mgr: Sophia Hanson

D-U-N-S 04-002-9563
COUNTY OF NEW HANOVER
230 Govt Ctr Dr 125, Wilmington, NC 28403
Tel (910) 798-7187 *Founded/Ownrshp* 1729
Sales NA *EMP* 1,200
Accts Martin Starnes & Associates C
SIC 9111 Executive offices;
V Ch: Jonathan Barfield
Ofcr: Mark Boyer
Ofcr: Ellis Pinder
Sr VP: Tracy Ash
IT Man: Teresa Hewett
Plnt Mgr: Al Canady
Board of Directors: William A Caster, Ted Davis Jr Elected Every, Robert G Greer

D-U-N-S 06-752-3886
COUNTY OF NIAGARA
175 Hawley St, Lockport, NY 14094-2740
Tel (716) 439-7085 *Founded/Ownrshp* 1825
Sales NA *EMP* 1,700
Accts Toski & Co Cpas Pc Willi
SIC 9111 Executive offices;
Prin: Michael J Violante
**Ch:* Sean O Connor

D-U-N-S 07-365-6647
COUNTY OF NORTHAMPTON
669 Washington St, Easton, PA 18042-7401
Tel (610) 559-3000 *Founded/Ownrshp* 1752
Sales NA *EMP* 1,673
Accts Cliftonlarsonallen Llp Plymou
SIC 9111 Executive offices;
Ofcr: Tabatha Gartner
Comm Dir: Robert Mateff
Off Mgr: Denise Kobrin
Info Man: David Hill
Netwrk Eng: Bob Mace

D-U-N-S 07-849-5025
COUNTY OF NUECES
901 Leopard St Rm 304, Corpus Christi, TX 78401-3602
Tel (361) 888-0556 *Founded/Ownrshp* 1846
Sales NA *EMP* 1,100
Accts Ernest R Garza & Company Pc
SIC 9111 Executive offices, national;
Genl Mgr: Maria Bedia
Genl Mgr: Roxana Sandoval

D-U-N-S 00-491-2929
COUNTY OF OAKLAND
1200 N Telegraph Rd Ste 1, Pontiac, MI 48341-1043
Tel (248) 858-1000 *Founded/Ownrshp* 1820
Sales NA *EMP* 4,229
Accts Plante & Moran Plc Southfield
SIC 9111 Executive offices;
Exec: L Brooks Patterson
**Treas:* Patrick M Dohany
Bd of Dir: Jacy Garrison
VP: Kavin Bertram
Dist Mgr: Velvet Savage
Off Admin: Lynn Hernandez
CIO: Phil Bertolini
Sfty Dirs: Dean Schultz
Opers Mgr: James Henry
Opers Mgr: Debbie Thompson
Sales Exec: Kim Soncrainte

D-U-N-S 08-404-6192
COUNTY OF OCEAN
101 Hooper Ave, Toms River, NJ 08753-7605
Tel (732) 929-2101 *Founded/Ownrshp* 1850
Sales NA *EMP* 1,600
Accts William E Antonides Cpa Wall
SIC 9111 Executive offices;
Prin: Joseph H Vicari
Comm Dir: Richard Middleton
Snr Mgr: Robert Sarino

D-U-N-S 06-543-0530
COUNTY OF OKLAHOMA
320 Robert S Kerr Ave # 505, Oklahoma City, OK 73102-3412
Tel (405) 270-0082 *Founded/Ownrshp* 1907
Sales NA *EMP* 1,949
Accts Gary A Jones Cpa Cfe Oklah
SIC 9111 Executive offices;
Chf Inves: Mark Seikel

D-U-N-S 07-763-4210
COUNTY OF OLMSTED
OLMSTED COUNTY HEALTH DEPT
151 4th St Se Ste 11, Rochester, MN 55904-3710
Tel (507) 328-6001 *Founded/Ownrshp* 1855
Sales NA *EMP* 1,552
Accts Rebecca Otto/Greg Hierlinger
SIC 9111 Executive offices;
Ofcr: Jeremy Ernste
Ofcr: Erin Johnson
Ofcr: Dennis Karp
Ofcr: Nathan Pike
**Ofcr:* Joe Zogel
Dir Risk M: Joan Till-Born
Assoc Dir: Dale Ignatius
Prgrm Mgr: Holly Busby
Telecom Mg: David Nault
IT Man: Mike Brown
Sls&Mrk Ex: Nicole Jensson

D-U-N-S 07-581-4186
COUNTY OF ONEIDA
800 Park Ave Ste 5, Utica, NY 13501-2939
Tel (315) 798-5780 *Founded/Ownrshp* 1846
Sales NA *EMP* 1,700
Accts Drescher & Malecki Llp Cheekt
SIC 9111 Executive offices;
Ex Dir: Anthony Pecente
**CFO:* Joseph Timpano
Exec: Deborah Joanis
Adv Bd Mbr: Dan Sullivan
Ex Dir: Joseph Griffo

D-U-N-S 07-729-0492
COUNTY OF ONONDAGA
1000 Erie Blvd W, Syracuse, NY 13204-2748
Tel (315) 435-8683 *Founded/Ownrshp* 1795
Sales NA *EMP* 4,500
Accts Testone Marshall Discenza Llp
SIC 9111 Executive offices;
Prin: Joanne M Mahoney
Ofcr: Laura Collins
Ofcr: Bonnie Karasinski
Ofcr: Melissa Wenham
Ofcr: Tanya Wickline
Exec: Cynthia Clift
**Exec:* Nicholas J Pirro
Ex Dir: Brian McKee
Ex Dir: Holly Rosenthal
Ex Dir: Kevin Zimmerman
Brnch Mgr: Samuel Barber

D-U-N-S 07-201-0689
COUNTY OF ONSLOW
4024 Richlands Hwy, Jacksonville, NC 28540-8872
Tel (910) 455-1750 *Founded/Ownrshp* 1754
Sales NA *EMP* 1,164
Accts Carr Riggs & Ingram Llc La G
SIC 9111 Executive offices;
Ofcr: Ellen McMillan

D-U-N-S 07-968-6838
COUNTY OF ONTARIO
20 Ontario St, Canandaigua, NY 14424-1802
Tel (585) 396-4400 *Founded/Ownrshp* 1780
Sales NA *EMP* 1,220
Accts Toski & Co Pc Williamsville
SIC 9111
Ch: John F Marren
**Ch:* Theodore M Fafinski
Ofcr: Kimberly Huber
Ofcr: Karl Nelson
Ofcr: Tina Schneider
Dir: Tom Harvey
IT Man: Hans Finke

D-U-N-S 00-965-7602
COUNTY OF ORANGE
COUNTY EXECUTIVE OFFICE
333 W Santa Ana Blvd 3f, Santa Ana, CA 92701-4084
Tel (714) 834-6200 *Founded/Ownrshp* 1889
Sales NA *EMP* 21,000
Accts Macias Gini & O Connell Llp N
SIC 9431
CEO: Frank Kim
CEO: Michael Gincola
CFO: Bob Franz
CFO: Bob Franze
Prin: Mary Chin
CTO: Lori White
IT Man: Joshua Wallingford

D-U-N-S 01-298-1593
COUNTY OF ORANGE
265 Main St, Goshen, NY 10924-1619
Tel (845) 291-2480 *Founded/Ownrshp* 1683
Sales NA *EMP* 2,700
SIC 9121
Exec: Edward A Diana
Exec: Kenneth Kohol
Genl Mgr: Kathlee Derose

D-U-N-S 06-479-7251 IMP
COUNTY OF ORANGE
BOARD OF COUNTY COMMISSIONERS
201 S Rosalind Ave Fl 5, Orlando, FL 32801-3527
Tel (407) 836-7390 *Founded/Ownrshp* 1824
Sales NA *EMP* 7,315
Accts Cherry Bekaert Llp Orlando F
SIC 9111 Executive offices;

D-U-N-S 07-253-7657
COUNTY OF OSCEOLA
1 Courthouse Sq, Kissimmee, FL 34741-5440
Tel (407) 742-2000 *Founded/Ownrshp* 1887
Sales NA *EMP* 1,600
Accts Moore Stephens Lovelace Pa O
SIC 9111 Executive offices;
Ch: Frank Attkinson
V Ch: Nancy Smith
Bd of Dir: Kevin Brown
Ex Dir: John McCue
Off Mgr: Vickyjo Brozovic

D-U-N-S 07-582-4532
COUNTY OF OSWEGO
46 E Bridge St, Oswego, NY 13126-2118
Tel (315) 349-8393 *Founded/Ownrshp* 1816
Sales NA *EMP* 1,100
Accts Ciaschi Dietershagen Little
SIC 9111 Executive offices;
**Treas:* John W Kruk
Ofcr: Doug Rice
Ofcr: Mark Smith
Exec: Kara Alheim
Exec: Kelly Jordal
Genl Mgr: Daniel Stevens

D-U-N-S 07-476-9340
COUNTY OF OUTAGAMIE
OUTAGAMIE COUNTY
410 S Walnut St, Appleton, WI 54911-5920
Tel (920) 832-1684 *Founded/Ownrshp* 1914
Sales NA *EMP* 1,200
Accts Schenck Sc Green Bay Wiscon
SIC 9111 Executive offices;
**Ch Bd:* Cliff Sanderfoot
**Treas:* Dina Mumford
**Exec:* Robert Toby Paltzer
MIS Dir: Tom Pynaker
Genl Couns: Joseph Guidote

D-U-N-S 07-847-0481
COUNTY OF PALM BEACH
MILITARY PARK FIRE DISTRICT
301 N Olive Ave Frnt, West Palm Beach, FL 33401-4703
Tel (561) 355-2959 *Founded/Ownrshp* 1912
Sales NA *EMP* 5,500
Accts Rsm Us Llp West Palm Beach F
SIC 9111 County supervisors' & executives' offices;
Dir Vol: Lisa Combs
Treas: Bob Jenks
Ex Dir: Linda Bullard
Ex Dir: Regina Goldenberg
Ex Dir: Kevin Reagan
Ex Dir: Lorraine Szyms
Prgrm Mgr: Charles Spalding
Brnch Mgr: Mike Cloran
Brnch Mgr: Anne Gannon
Off Mgr: Je'riise Hansen
CTO: Les Davis

D-U-N-S 06-967-7953
COUNTY OF PASCO
8731 Citizens Dr, New Port Richey, FL 34654-5572
Tel (727) 847-2411 *Founded/Ownrshp* 1887
Sales NA *EMP* 1,540
Accts Kpmg Llp Tampa Fl
SIC 9111 Executive offices;
Ofcr: Carol Whitehead
Exec: Douglas Tobin
Dir Risk M: Steve Whitaker
Brnch Mgr: Marc Salton
MIS Dir: Bill Compton
IT Man: Pat Broz
Snr Mgr: Katie M Millen

D-U-N-S 06-314-8811
COUNTY OF PASSAIC
ADMINISTRATION
401 Grand St Ste 1, Paterson, NJ 07505-2023
Tel (973) 881-4405 *Founded/Ownrshp* 1837
Sales NA *EMP* 2,500
Accts Lerch Vinci & Higgins Llp Fa
SIC 9111 County supervisors' & executives' offices;
CFO: Daniel Gonzales
CFO: Tim Roberts
Treas: Margaret S Cherone

Dir: Carol Ryle
Comm Dir: Keith Kazmark
Dir Bus: Debbie Hoffman
Genl Mgr: Flavio Rivera
Off Mgr: Dorothy Gilmore
Dir IT: Walter Charles
HC Dir: Joseph Surowiec

D-U-N-S 07-143-6208
COUNTY OF PEORIA
324 Main St, Peoria, IL 61602-2302
Tel (309) 672-6056 *Founded/Ownrshp* 1825
Sales NA *EMP* 1,000
Accts Baker Tilly Virchow Krause
SIC 9111 Executive offices
Ch: Thomas O'Neill III
* *Treas:* Edward O Connor III
Bd of Dir: G A Mayer
Bd of Dir: Charles G Roth
Bd of Dir: Craig S Young
Doctor: Susan B Bishop

D-U-N-S 07-185-0887
COUNTY OF PIERCE
615 S 9th St Ste 100, Tacoma, WA 98405-4680
Tel (253) 798-7285 *Founded/Ownrshp* 1852
Sales NA *EMP* 2,270
Accts Troy Kelley Olympia Washingt
SIC 9111 Executive offices;
CEO: Patricia McCarthy
Exec: Pat Tobin
CTO: Jack Rusler
IT Man: Michele Quinones

D-U-N-S 07-444-7095
COUNTY OF PINAL
31 N Pinal St, Florence, AZ 85132
Tel (520) 866-6000 *Founded/Ownrshp* 1875
Sales NA *EMP* 2,700
Accts Walker & Armstrong Llp Phoeni
SIC 9111 Executive offices;
CFO: Maureen Arnold
* *CFO:* Victoria Prins
Ofcr: Brian Hillman
Genl Mgr: Randon Riffey
IT Man: Sandra Hernandez
Plnt Mgr: Steve Abraham

D-U-N-S 05-520-0216
COUNTY OF PINELLAS
BOARD OF COUNTY COMMISSIONERS
315 Court St Rm 300, Clearwater, FL 33756-5165
Tel (727) 464-3485 *Founded/Ownrshp* 1911
Sales NA *EMP* 6,800
Accts Crowe Horwath Llp Tampa Flor
SIC 9121 County commissioner
Prin: Katherine Burbridge
V Ch: David Slonena
Bd of Dir: Hector Collazo
Ofcr: Christopher Short
IT Man: Charles Greene

D-U-N-S 07-154-9588
COUNTY OF PLACER (CA)
2968 Richardson Dr, Auburn, CA 95603-2640
Tel (530) 889-4200 *Founded/Ownrshp* 1851
Sales NA *EMP* 3,024
Accts Vavrinek Trine Day & Co Ll
SIC 9111 Executive offices;
CEO: Andrew Health
Off Mgr: Shannon Selland
MIS Mgr: Clark Moots
Board of Directors: Rex Bloomfield, Ed Bonner, Bill Santucci, Harriett White, Jim Williams

D-U-N-S 18-319-3770
COUNTY OF POLK
111 Court Ave Ste 390, Des Moines, IA 50309-2255
Tel (515) 286-3200 *Founded/Ownrshp* 1846
Sales NA *EMP* 1,500
Accts Cliftonlarsonallen Llp West D
SIC 9111 Executive offices;
IT Man: Jo E Bigelow
Netwrk Eng: Scott Horman

D-U-N-S 07-777-4495
COUNTY OF PORTAGE
449 S Meridian St Fl 7, Ravenna, OH 44266-2914
Tel (330) 297-3561 *Founded/Ownrshp* 1807
Sales NA *EMP* 1,300
Accts James G Zupka Cpa Inc
SIC 9111 County supervisors' & executives' offices
Pr: Maureen Frederick
* *VP:* Kathleen Chandler
CIO: Brian Kelley
Sfty Dirs: Michelle Ripley
Board of Directors: Kathleen Chandler, Charles Keiper II, Christopher Smeiles

D-U-N-S 05-859-2189
COUNTY OF PRINCE GEORGES
PRINCE GEORGE'S COUNTY GOV
14741 Gvrnor Oden Bwie Dr, Upper Marlboro, MD 20772-3043
Tel (301) 952-6000 *Founded/Ownrshp* 1769
Sales NA *EMP* 12,000
Accts Cliftonlarsonallen Llp Baltim
SIC 9111 Executive offices;
Exec: Jack Johnson

D-U-N-S 00-309-6740 IMP/EXP
COUNTY OF PRINCE WILLIAM (VA)
PRINCE WILLIAM COUNTY, VIRGINI
1 County Complex Ct, Woodbridge, VA 22192-9202
Tel (703) 792-4640 *Founded/Ownrshp* 1731
Sales NA *EMP* 2,700
Accts Cherry Bekaert Llp Tysons Cor
SIC 9111
Exec: Melissa S Peacor
Ch Bd: Durward Grubbs
Ofcr: Jonathan Perok
VP: Scott Donaldson
Genl Mgr: Corey Stewart
Off Mgr: Penny Whitney
CTO: Jan Kleindl
IT Man: Marie Snyder
Sales Exec: Phillis Aggrey
Snr Mgr: Michelle Attreed

D-U-N-S 06-592-4177
COUNTY OF PUTNAM
2509 Crill Ave Ste 900, Palatka, FL 32177-4267
Tel (386) 329-0205 *Founded/Ownrshp* 1848
Sales NA *EMP* 1,000
Accts Carr Riggs & Ingram Llc Pa
SIC 9111 Executive offices;

D-U-N-S 01-035-4488
COUNTY OF RAMSEY (MN)
15 Kellogg Blvd W Ste 270, Saint Paul, MN 55102-1659
Tel (651) 266-8044 *Founded/Ownrshp* 1849
Sales NA *EMP* 4,000
Accts Office Of State Auditor St Pa
SIC 9111 Executive offices;
CEO: Julie Kleinschmidt
* *CFO:* Lee Mehrkens
* *Ofcr:* Matt Bostrom

D-U-N-S 07-370-9883
COUNTY OF RICHLAND
2020 Hampton St, Columbia, SC 29204-1002
Tel (803) 576-2600 *Founded/Ownrshp* 1799
Sales NA *EMP* 1,400
Accts Elliot Davis Llc Columbia So
SIC 9111 Executive offices;
Ofcr: Willette Brown
Ofcr: Milton Pope
Ex Dir: Neil Ardoline
Genl Mgr: Paul Alcantar
Genl Mgr: Natashia Dozier
CIO: Janet Claggett
MIS Dir: Barbara Scott
Pr Dir: Stephany Snowden
Counsel: Dolly Garfield
Counsel: Elizabeth McLean
Counsel: Larry Smith

D-U-N-S 07-690-4812
COUNTY OF RICHLAND
50 Park Ave E Ste 3, Mansfield, OH 44902-1863
Tel (419) 774-5501 *Founded/Ownrshp* 1803
Sales NA *EMP* 1,100
Accts Dave Yost Auditor Of State C
SIC 9111 Executive offices;
* *Treas:* W Hamilton

D-U-N-S 07-251-4789
COUNTY OF RIVERSIDE (CA)
CREST PROJECT
4080 Lemon St Fl 11, Riverside, CA 92501-3609
Tel (951) 955-1110 *Founded/Ownrshp* 1893
Sales NA *EMP* 20,000
Accts Brown Armstrong Accountancy Co
SIC 9111 County supervisors' & executives' offices
Ofcr: Ivan Chand
Exec: Ray Smith
Netwrk Mgr: Eduardo Laborde
Sls&Mrk Ex: Ron Kirk

D-U-N-S 06-235-3610
COUNTY OF ROANOKE
5204 Bernard Dr, Roanoke, VA 24018-4345
Tel (540) 772-2004 *Founded/Ownrshp* 1838
Sales NA *EMP* 2,938
Accts Cherry Bekaert Llp Roanoke V
SIC 9111 Executive offices;
* *CFO:* Diane Hyatt
* *Treas:* Kevin Hutchins
Dir: Philip Thompson
Ex Dir: Billy Driver
CTO: Elaine Carver

D-U-N-S 07-537-5113
COUNTY OF ROBERTSON
108 Crthuse 501 S Main St, Springfield, TN 37172
Tel (615) 384-2476 *Founded/Ownrshp* 1796
Sales NA *EMP* 1,200
Accts Justin P Wilson Nashville T
SIC 9111 Executive offices;

D-U-N-S 07-384-5968
COUNTY OF ROCK
51 S Main St, Janesville, WI 53545-3951
Tel (608) 757-5660 *Founded/Ownrshp* 1836
Sales NA *EMP* 1,100
Accts Baker Tilly Virchow Krause Ll
SIC 9111 Executive offices;
Ch Bd: Richard K Ott
Treas: Vicki Brown
Genl Mgr: Colin Byrnes

D-U-N-S 07-543-7848
COUNTY OF ROCKLAND
COUNTY EXECUTIVE OFFICE
11 New Hempstead Rd # 100, New City, NY 10956-3664
Tel (845) 638-5122 *Founded/Ownrshp* 1796
Sales NA *EMP* 3,100
Accts O Connor Davies Munns & Dobbin
SIC 9111
Exec: Edwin Day
V Ch: William Darden
Ex Dir: David Farrison
MIS Dir: Laurie Sarter

D-U-N-S 07-449-4014
COUNTY OF ROWAN
130 W Innes St Ste 120, Salisbury, NC 28144-4365
Tel (704) 636-0361 *Founded/Ownrshp* 1753
Sales NA *EMP* 3,000
Accts Martin Starnes & Associates C
SIC 9111 Executive offices

D-U-N-S 06-436-7980 IMP
COUNTY OF RUTHERFORD
1 Public Sq Ste 101, Murfreesboro, TN 37130-3629
Tel (615) 898-7745 *Founded/Ownrshp* 1900
Sales NA *EMP* 3,000
Accts Justin P Wilson Nashville T
SIC 9199 9111 ; Executive offices

D-U-N-S 07-155-0800
COUNTY OF SACRAMENTO
700 H St Ste 7650, Sacramento, CA 95814-1280
Tel (916) 874-5544 *Founded/Ownrshp* 1850
Sales NA *EMP* 10,968
Accts Vavrinek Trine Day & Co Ll
SIC 9111 Executive offices;
Prin: Nav Gill
Ofcr: Adrian Brown
VP: Kent Craney
Exec: Laurie Slothower
* *Prin:* Patrick Kennedy
* *Prin:* Susan Peters
* *Prin:* Phils Serna
Prgrm Mgr: Shannon Alley
Prgrm Mgr: Surinder Singh
CIO: David Villanueva
IT Man: Brian Honeycutt

D-U-N-S 07-313-3894 IMP/EXP
COUNTY OF SALT LAKE
MAYOR'S OFFICE
2001 S State St S2-200, Salt Lake City, UT 84190-0001
Tel (801) 468-3225 *Founded/Ownrshp* 1850
Sales NA *EMP* 4,200
Accts Squire & Company Pc Orem
SIC 9111 Executive offices;
Pr: Janyce Syndergaard
Treas: Anna Gallagher
Ofcr: Doug Willmore
Sr VP: Jun Li
Assoc Dir: Rory Payne
Dir Soc: Mindy Nielsen
Comm Dir: Patrick Leary
Prgrm Mgr: Kathy Garrett
Prgrm Mgr: Staci Hemingway
Genl Mgr: Carrie Hackworth
Genl Mgr: Marian Hubbard

D-U-N-S 07-359-0812
COUNTY OF SAN BERNARDINO
385 N Arrowhead Ave, San Bernardino, CA 92415-0103
Tel (909) 387-3841 *Founded/Ownrshp* 1853
Sales NA *EMP* 6,094
Accts Vavrinek Trine Day & Co Ll
SIC 9111 Executive offices;
Ch: Janice Rutherford
* *Prin:* Wally Hill
Genl Mgr: William Crafter
Genl Mgr: Terry Thompson
DP Dir: Jeff Carter
DP Dir: Gilbert Vanegas
IT Man: Alex Canizalez
IT Man: Darrell Harris
Software D: Jose Echevarria

D-U-N-S 00-958-1646
COUNTY OF SAN DIEGO (CA)
CHIEF ADIMINISTRATIVE OFFICE
1600 Pacific Hwy Ste 209, San Diego, CA 92101-2422
Tel (619) 531-5880 *Founded/Ownrshp* 1850
Sales NA *EMP* 17,000
Accts Vavrinek Trine Day & Co Ll
SIC 9111 Executive offices;
Genl Mgr: Dale Fleming
Genl Mgr: Andrew Pease
Genl Mgr: Charo Tilaro
Doctor: Jill Yonemura

D-U-N-S 08-722-6056
COUNTY OF SAN JOAQUIN
44 N San Joaquin St # 640, Stockton, CA 95202-2924
Tel (209) 468-3203 *Founded/Ownrshp* 1850
Sales NA *EMP* 6,498[E]
Accts Brown Armstrong Accountancy Co
SIC 9111 Executive offices;
Off Admin: Tonya Arevalos
Off Admin: Nicole Devencenzi
Off Admin: Kameisha Nalls
Off Admin: Rachael Ruiz
Off Admin: Donna Strange
Off Admin: Esperanza Valenzuela

D-U-N-S 05-922-7611
COUNTY OF SAN LUIS OBISPO
Government Center Rm. 300, San Luis Obispo, CA 93408-0001
Tel (805) 781-5040 *Founded/Ownrshp* 1860
Sales NA *EMP* 3,500
Accts Gallina Llp Roseville Calif
SIC 9111
Admn Mgr: Helen McCann
IT Man: Ron Kester
IT Man: Roberta Mangini

D-U-N-S 07-313-2177 IMP
COUNTY OF SAN MATEO
400 County Ctr, Redwood City, CA 94063-1662
Tel (650) 363-4123 *Founded/Ownrshp* 1856
Sales NA *EMP* 4,558
Accts Macias Gini & O Connell Llp
SIC 9111 Executive offices;
V Ch: Mike Aratow
COO: David Cherniss
CFO: Gina Wilson
Ofcr: Hannah Kahn
Ex VP: Lisa Mancini
Ex Dir: Peggy Thompson
Brnch Mgr: Carole Groom
Cmptr Lab: Sumaya Wallace
Dir IT: Anita Booker
IT Man: Tim Benton
IT Man: Dennis Ryan

D-U-N-S 01-071-8658
COUNTY OF SANTA BARBARA (CA)
105 E Anapamu St Rm 406, Santa Barbara, CA 93101-2065
Tel (805) 568-3400 *Founded/Ownrshp* 1850
Sales NA *EMP* 4,582
Accts Brown Armstrong Bakersfield
SIC 9111 County supervisors' & executives' offices;
Ch Bd: Brooks Firestone
* *Ch Bd:* Joseph Centeno
Prin: Ken Masuda
Prin: Shirley Moore

D-U-N-S 06-911-8289
COUNTY OF SANTA CLARA
3180 Newberry Dr Ste 150, San Jose, CA 95118-1566
Tel (408) 299-5105 *Founded/Ownrshp* 1850
Sales NA *EMP* 14,500
Accts Macias Gini & O Connell Llp W
SIC 9199 Supply agency, government
Exec: Jeffrey V Smith
COO: George Kennedy
Div Mgr: Bev Sumcad
Dir IT: Bruce Overoye
IT Man: Vincent Hikida
IT Man: Gabe Jones
IT Man: Jimmy Liang
Netwrk Eng: Alan Whitlow
Snr PM: Abha Gupta

D-U-N-S 06-911-7208
COUNTY OF SANTA CRUZ
701 Ocean St Rm 520, Santa Cruz, CA 95060-4015
Tel (831) 454-2100 *Founded/Ownrshp* 1850
Sales NA *EMP* 1,654
Accts Brown Armstrong Accountancy Co
SIC 9111 Executive offices;
Owner: Marianne Ellis
* *Ch Bd:* Mardi Wormoudt
Brnch Mgr: Tom Bolich

D-U-N-S 02-085-9039
COUNTY OF SANTA ROSA BOARD OF PUBLIC INSTRUCTION
5086 Canal St, Milton, FL 32570-2257
Tel (850) 983-5000 *Founded/Ownrshp* 1900
Sales 88.1MM[E] *EMP* 2,200
SIC 8211 School board
Ch Bd: Hugh Winkles

D-U-N-S 07-319-2924
COUNTY OF SARASOTA
1660 Ringling Blvd, Sarasota, FL 34236-6808
Tel (941) 861-5165 *Founded/Ownrshp* 1921
Sales NA *EMP* 3,600
SIC 9111 Executive offices;
Bd of Dir: Bill Kocur
Ofcr: Dave Tuck
Dir: Thomas C Polk
Dir IT: Kenneth Watson

D-U-N-S 02-066-2086
COUNTY OF SARATOGA
25 W High St, Ballston Spa, NY 12020-1963
Tel (518) 884-4742 *Founded/Ownrshp* 1792
Sales NA *EMP* 1,500
SIC 9111 Executive offices;
Treas: Andrew Jarosh
* *Treas:* Samuel J Pitcheralle
* *Prin:* William Hyde
CTO: Bill Warmp

D-U-N-S 05-637-5637
COUNTY OF SCHENECTADY
620 State St, Schenectady, NY 12305-2112
Tel (518) 285-8435 *Founded/Ownrshp* 1809
Sales NA *EMP* 1,400
Accts Uhy Llp Albany New York
SIC 9111 Executive offices;
Ofcr: David Leffingwell

D-U-N-S 05-657-7166
COUNTY OF SEDGWICK
525 N Main St Ste 823, Wichita, KS 67203-3728
Tel (316) 660-9000 *Founded/Ownrshp* 1870
Sales NA *EMP* 2,500
Accts Allen Gibbs & Houlik Lc C
SIC 9111 Executive offices;
CFO: Chris Chronis
Ofcr: Brad Brush
Ofcr: George Donaldson
Ofcr: Kate Flavin
Ofcr: Greg Friedman
Ofcr: Roderick Gray
Ofcr: Ginnette Gunnels
Ofcr: Mark Irvine
Ofcr: Norvett Jacques
Ofcr: Pedro E Juarez
Ofcr: Bryan E Ronk
Ofcr: Regina Vitale
Ofcr: Connie J Wells
Exec: Rebecca Page
Exec: Mike Pepoon

D-U-N-S 06-783-4358
COUNTY OF SEMINOLE
1101 E 1st St, Sanford, FL 32771-1468
Tel (407) 665-7664 *Founded/Ownrshp* 1913
Sales NA *EMP* 2,234
Accts Moore Stephens Lovelace Pc
SIC 9111 Executive offices;
* *Ch Bd:* Carlton Henley
* *Ch Bd:* Daryl McLain
Prgrm Mgr: Sandy Neminski
IT Man: Angela Singleton

D-U-N-S 07-612-4536
COUNTY OF SHASTA
ADMINISTRATION OFFICE
1450 Court St Ste 308a, Redding, CA 96001-1680
Tel (530) 225-5561 *Founded/Ownrshp* 1850
Sales NA *EMP* 2,000
SIC 9199 Supply agency, government
* *Prin:* Larry Lees
IT Man: Mallory Larson
IT Man: Thomas Schreiber

D-U-N-S 03-066-0864
COUNTY OF SHAWNEE
COUNTY CLERK OFFICE
200 Se 7th St, Topeka, KS 66603-3922
Tel (785) 233-8200 *Founded/Ownrshp* 1855
Sales NA *EMP* 1,000
Accts Cochran Head Vick & Co Pa
SIC 9111 Executive offices;
* *Ch:* Vic Miller
Ex Dir: John Kabus
Snr Mgr: Barbara Heston

D-U-N-S 07-385-1842
COUNTY OF SHEBOYGAN
508 New York Ave, Sheboygan, WI 53081-4126
Tel (920) 459-3000 *Founded/Ownrshp* 1858
Sales NA *EMP* 1,300
Accts Schenck Sl Green Bay Wiscon
SIC 9111 Executive offices;
Ch: William Goehring
CFO: Timothy Finch

Genl Mgr: Wendy Charnon
IT Man: Josh McDermott

D-U-N-S 04-117-4889
COUNTY OF SHELBY
SHELBY COUNTY BD COMMISSIONERS
160 N Main St Fl 4, Memphis, TN 38103-1866
Tel (901) 222-2050 *Founded/Ownrshp* 1819
Sales 1.0MMM *EMP* 7,990
Accts Watkins Uiberall Pllc/Banks
SIC 5511 Automobiles, new & used
Comm Dir: Shawn Pachucki
Off Mgr: Anna Whalley

D-U-N-S 07-924-7979
COUNTY OF SNOHOMISH
3000 Rockefeller Ave Ms508, Everett, WA 98201-4046
Tel (425) 388-3460 *Founded/Ownrshp* 1861
Sales NA *EMP* 2,500
Accts Brian Sonntag Cgfm Olympia
SIC 9111 Executive offices;
Prin: Tam T Bui
Ofcr: Tom Barnett
**Exec:* Aaron Reardon
**Prin:* Gompf Robert
Ex Dir: Peter Camp
Div Mgr: Cammy Hart-Anderson
IT Man: Carl Detert
Netwrk Eng: Kirk Copple
Pgrm Dir: Jessica Gurley

D-U-N-S 07-655-3148
COUNTY OF SOLANO
675 Texas St Ste 2600, Fairfield, CA 94533-6338
Tel (707) 784-6706 *Founded/Ownrshp* 1850
Sales NA *EMP* 2,600
Accts Macias Gini & O Connell Llp S
SIC 9111 Executive offices;
Ofcr: Pearla Cuerdo
Ofcr: James Leland
Ofcr: Glenn Myer
Ofcr: Patrick Neely
Ofcr: William Reardon
Exec: Christine Castillo
Exec: Anjoli Ferguson
Exec: Mike Yankovich
Prgrm Mgr: Chris Shipman
CIO: Ira Rosenthal
IT Man: Carol S Cain

D-U-N-S 07-824-6147
COUNTY OF SOMERSET
20 Grove St, Somerville, NJ 08876-2306
Tel (908) 231-7000 *Founded/Ownrshp* 1688
Sales NA *EMP* 1,200[E]
Accts Suplee Clooney & Company Wes
SIC 9111 Executive offices;
VP: Lynn Weckworth
MIS Dir: Robert Klingel
Software D: Diane Mari

D-U-N-S 08-012-6444
COUNTY OF SONOMA
COUNTY ADMINISTRATOR'S OFFICE
585 Fiscal Dr 100, Santa Rosa, CA 95403-2824
Tel (707) 565-2431 *Founded/Ownrshp* 1850
Sales NA *EMP* 5,260
Accts Vavrinek Trine Day & Co Ll
SIC 9111 Executive offices;
CFO: Gail Goring
**Ch:* Margaret Killian
**Treas:* Rodney Dole
Dir Risk M: Marcia Chadbourne
Genl Mgr: Cathy Patton
Off Admin: Joanne Atkerson
Off Admin: Erica Chavez
Off Admin: Jamie Shinn
IT Man: Kishore Jayaswal
IT Man: Bobbi Rivera
IT Man: Dana Shern

D-U-N-S 07-371-7688
COUNTY OF SPARTANBURG
SPARTANBURG COUNTY COUNCIL
Main Level Ste 1000 366 N, Spartanburg, SC 29303
Tel (864) 596-2509 *Founded/Ownrshp* 1785
Sales NA *EMP* 1,449
Accts Mcabee Schwartz Halliday & C
SIC 9121 County commissioner;
Ch: Jeffrey A Horton
Genl Mgr: Sharon West
Dir IT: Kim Danner

D-U-N-S 01-020-5078
COUNTY OF SPOKANE
1116 W Broadway Ave, Spokane, WA 99260-2052
Tel (509) 477-2265 *Founded/Ownrshp* 1878
Sales NA *EMP* 1,850
Accts Brian Sonntag Cgfm
SIC 9121 County commissioner;
Pr: Cindy Beachell
Pr: Sara Coup
Pr: Sherry Fleck
Pr: Denice Graf
Pr: Jennifer Hess
Pr: Dawn Pitts
**CEO:* Marshall Farnell
Ofcr: Cameron Kurowski
Ofcr: Jonathan McGovern
Ofcr: Lanny Minuto
Ofcr: Tori Peterson
Ofcr: Rebecca Phifer
Ofcr: Jill Proctor
Ofcr: Diana Salinas
Ofcr: Patti Spilker
Ofcr: Lori Zaagman-Bacon

D-U-N-S 07-323-6739
COUNTY OF ST JOHNS
500 San Sebastian Vw, Saint Augustine, FL 32084-8686
Tel (904) 209-0300 *Founded/Ownrshp* 1821
Sales NA *EMP* 1,200
Accts Carr Riggs & Ingram Llc Gaine
SIC 9111 Executive offices;
Ex Dir: Glenn Hestings

D-U-N-S 07-591-3061
COUNTY OF ST LOUIS
EXECUTIVE OFFCE
41 S Central Ave, Saint Louis, MO 63105-1719
Tel (314) 615-7016 *Founded/Ownrshp* 1812
Sales NA *EMP* 4,100
Accts Rebecca Otto Saint Paul Mn
SIC 9111 Executive offices;
Exec: Charles Dooley
Dir Vol: Richard Bruenderman
Ofcr: Kevin Funston
Ofcr: Don Jacquin
Ofcr: Kathy Kelly
CIO: Michael Duncan
IT Man: Barbara Sommer
Board of Directors: Kathleen Burkett, John Campisi, Hazel Erby, Barbara Fraser, Michael O'mara, Gregory F Quinn, Colleen Wasinger, Council Members

D-U-N-S 07-313-6772
COUNTY OF STANISLAUS
1010 10th St Ste 5100, Modesto, CA 95354-0872
Tel (209) 525-6398 *Founded/Ownrshp* 1854
Sales NA *EMP* 4,972
Accts Brown Armstrong Accountancy Co
SIC 9111 Executive offices;

D-U-N-S 07-980-0751
COUNTY OF STARK
POLICE DEPARTMENT
110 Central Plz S Ste 240, Canton, OH 44702-1410
Tel (330) 451-7371 *Founded/Ownrshp* 1808
Sales NA *EMP* 2,630
Accts Dave Yost-Auditor Of State Co
SIC 9111 Executive offices;
Treas: Gary Zeigler
Genl Mgr: Rota Cutter
Snr Mgr: Ross A Rhodes

D-U-N-S 83-077-3128
COUNTY OF STARK
BOARD OF COMMISSIONERS
110 Central Plz S Ste 240, Canton, OH 44702-1410
Tel (330) 451-7999 *Founded/Ownrshp* 2009
Sales NA *EMP* 2,400
SIC 9199
Pr: Todd Bosley

D-U-N-S 06-594-9190
COUNTY OF SUFFOLK
100 Veterans Hwy, Hauppauge, NY 11788-5402
Tel (631) 853-4000 *Founded/Ownrshp* 1683
Sales NA *EMP* 12,814
Accts Deloitte & Touche Llp Jerich
SIC 9111 County supervisors' & executives' offices
Exec: Steve Levy
**Treas:* Angie Carpenter
Treas: Angie M Carpenter
Ofcr: Phyllis Seidman
VP: Tom Muratore
**Prin:* Steven Bellone
Dist Mgr: Paul Tenyenhuis
Snr Mgr: Scott Coyne
Snr Mgr: Karl Klug

D-U-N-S 15-593-9960
COUNTY OF SUFFOLK
CLERK'S OFFICE
1 City Hall Sq Ste 550, Boston, MA 02201-1070
Tel (617) 635-4000 *Founded/Ownrshp* 1628
Sales NA *EMP* 1,195
SIC 9111 Executive offices;
Off Mgr: Jay Chung
CIO: Sally Glora

D-U-N-S 03-066-5103
COUNTY OF SULLIVAN
SULLIVAN COUNTY HIGHWAY DEPT
3411 Highway 126 Ste 201, Blountville, TN 37617-4564
Tel (423) 323-6400 *Founded/Ownrshp* 1890
Sales NA *EMP* 2,385
Accts Justin P Wilson Nashville T
SIC 9111 Executive offices;
Ex Dir: Richard Venable
Exec: Gayvern Moore
Brnch Mgr: Ambre Torbett

D-U-N-S 14-748-3465
COUNTY OF SUMMIT
COMMON PLEAS JUVENILE DIVISION
650 Dan St, Akron, OH 44310-3909
Tel (330) 643-2500 *Founded/Ownrshp* 1840
Sales NA *EMP* 3,354
Accts Dave Yost Columbus Ohio
SIC 9111
Prin: Russell M Pry
**Ex Dir:* Jim McCarthy
Genl Mgr: Mary Spaugy
IT Man: Todd Schauffler

D-U-N-S 09-566-6020
COUNTY OF SUMNER
355 N Belvedere Dr Rm 302, Gallatin, TN 37066-5410
Tel (615) 452-3604 *Founded/Ownrshp* 1852
Sales NA *EMP* 2,654
SIC 9111 Executive offices;
Exec: Hank Thompson

D-U-N-S 07-183-7728
COUNTY OF THURSTON
2000 Lakeridge Dr Sw, Olympia, WA 98502-6001
Tel (360) 754-3800 *Founded/Ownrshp* 1889
Sales NA *EMP* 1,122
Accts Troy Kelley State Auditor Ol
SIC 9111 Executive offices;
**Prin:* C Moore
Genl Mgr: Heidi Prihoda
IT Man: Diana Benson
IT Man: Gail Gosney

D-U-N-S 09-918-2131
COUNTY OF TIPTON
100 Court Sq E, Covington, TN 38019-2506
Tel (901) 476-0219 *Founded/Ownrshp* 1823
Sales NA *EMP* 2,000
Accts Justin P Wilson Nashville T
SIC 9111 Executive offices;

Ex Dir: Lee Johnston
**Ex Dir:* William J Huffman

D-U-N-S 03-090-8842
COUNTY OF TRAVIS
AUDITORS OFFICE
700 Lavaca St Fl 11, Austin, TX 78701-3101
Tel (512) 854-9125 *Founded/Ownrshp* 1839
Sales NA *EMP* 3,900[E]
Accts Atchley & Associates Llp Aust
SIC 9111 Executive offices;
**Treas:* Dolores Ortega-Carter
Ofcr: Lorena Escobar
Ofcr: Olie L Pope
VP: Mary Villalpando
VP: Barbara Wilson
Exec: Roger Wade
Dir Risk M: Bill Paterson
Prgrm Mgr: Stacy Landry
CIO: Tanya Acevedo
CIO: Dolores Carter
Dir IT: Rod Brown

D-U-N-S 07-075-7943
COUNTY OF TRUMBULL
TRUMBULL COUNTY AUDITOR'S OFFI
160 High St Nw, Warren, OH 44481-1061
Tel (330) 675-2420 *Founded/Ownrshp* 1800
Sales NA *EMP* 1,390
Accts Dave Yost Youngstown Ohio
SIC 9111 Executive offices;
Exec: Leslie Stredney

D-U-N-S 07-186-1884
COUNTY OF TULARE
ADMINISTRATIVE OFFICE
2800 W Burrel Ave, Visalia, CA 93291-4541
Tel (559) 636-5005 *Founded/Ownrshp* 1852
Sales NA *EMP* 4,485
Accts Brown Armstrong Ac Bakersfiel
SIC 9111 Executive offices;
Ofcr: Jean M Rousseau
Div Mgr: Jay Jones

D-U-N-S 06-455-3571
COUNTY OF TULSA
500 S Denver Ave, Tulsa, OK 74103-3838
Tel (918) 596-5000 *Founded/Ownrshp* 1907
Sales NA *EMP* 2,227
Accts Gary A Jones Cpa Cfe Oklah
SIC 9111 County supervisors' & executives' offices
Sr Cor Off: Steven Kormondy
Ofcr: Tom R Gerard
Ofcr: Taressa Maybee
Ofcr: Erin McKelvey
Ofcr: Lisa Moore
**Prin:* Robert Dick
Dir IT: Jeff Martin
IT Man: Justin Brown
IT Man: Doris Emery
IT Man: Sean Farver
Netwrk Eng: Garrett Guthrie

D-U-N-S 07-876-8967
COUNTY OF TUOLUMNE
2 S Green St, Sonora, CA 95370-4618
Tel (209) 533-5521 *Founded/Ownrshp* 1850
Sales NA *EMP* 1,100
Accts Macias Gini & O Connell Llp S
SIC 9111 County supervisors' & executives' offices;
**Ch Bd:* Mark Thornton
Ofcr: Bill Sandman
Ofcr: Todd Stolp
Prgrm Mgr: Lisa Domser
Prgrm Mgr: Cinnamon Lampi
IT Man: Robert Chapman
IT Man: Michelle Ronning

D-U-N-S 07-720-9740
COUNTY OF ULSTER
244 Fair St, Kingston, NY 12401-3806
Tel (845) 340-3000 *Founded/Ownrshp* 1683
Sales NA *EMP* 1,300
SIC 9111
Prin: Mike Hein
**Ch:* Terry Bernardo
**Prin:* Burton Gulnic Jr

D-U-N-S 07-755-2842
COUNTY OF UNION
10 Elizabeth Ave, Elizabeth, NJ 07206
Tel (908) 659-7407 *Founded/Ownrshp* 1857
Sales NA *EMP* 2,700
SIC 9111 County supervisors' & executives' offices;
Ex Dir: George W Devanney
**Prin:* Angel G Estrada
**Prin:* Deborah P Scanlon
**Prin:* Carolyn Sullivan
**Ex Dir:* Alfred Faella
Brnch Mgr: John Tuit
Genl Mgr: Alfred J Faella
CTO: Chris Meehan
Dir IT: Matt Odonald

D-U-N-S 06-669-1122
COUNTY OF VENTURA
800 S Victoria Ave, Ventura, CA 93009-0003
Tel (805) 654-2551 *Founded/Ownrshp* 1873
Sales NA *EMP* 7,433
Accts Vavrinek Trine Day & Co Ll
SIC 9111 Executive offices;
Ofcr: Marty Robinson
Ofcr: Liz Cameron
Ofcr: Jerry Noble
Ofcr: Paula Oberst
Dir Risk M: Susan Klein
Comm Man: Bill Nash
Admn Mgr: Derrick Wilson
Genl Mgr: Sue Hughes
Off Mgr: Benjamin Martinez
IT Man: David Hersog
IT Man: Michael Sanders

D-U-N-S 06-784-9901
COUNTY OF VOLUSIA
123 W Indiana Ave Ste A, Deland, FL 32720-4615
Tel (386) 736-2700 *Founded/Ownrshp* 1854
Sales NA *EMP* 11,000
Accts James Moore & Co Pl Dayto

SIC 9111 Executive offices;
Ex Dir: Renee Tallevast
Genl Mgr: Trudy Tyler
Dir IT: Scott Bowen
Opers Mgr: Tara Boujoulian

D-U-N-S 01-962-5961
COUNTY OF WAKE
300 S Salisbury St # 4800, Raleigh, NC 27601-1751
Tel (919) 856-6160 *Founded/Ownrshp* 1771
Sales NA *EMP* 3,700
Accts Elliott Davis Decosimo Pllc
SIC 9111 County supervisors' & executives' offices
**V Ch:* Phil Matthews
**Ch:* Joe Bryan
Ofcr: Seth Komansky
Ofcr: Cody Martin
Dir Risk M: Kate George
IT Man: Jeanne Flynn
Tech Mgr: John Higgins

D-U-N-S 07-087-5125
COUNTY OF WALTON
571 E Nelson Ave Ste 301, Defuniak Springs, FL 32433-1342
Tel (850) 892-8115 *Founded/Ownrshp* 1880
Sales NA *EMP* 1,150
Accts Carr Riggs & Ingram Llc
SIC 9111 Executive offices;
Ofcr: Jason Fox

D-U-N-S 07-115-1526
COUNTY OF WALWORTH
100 W Walworth St Ste 116, Elkhorn, WI 53121-1769
Tel (262) 741-4241 *Founded/Ownrshp* 1839
Sales NA *EMP* 1,020
Accts Baker Tilly Virchow Krause Ll
SIC 9111 Executive offices;
Ch: Nancy Russell
**Treas:* James Goetz
Bd of Dir: John Ennis
Phys Thrpy: Peggy Schneider

D-U-N-S 07-365-4105
COUNTY OF WARREN (NJ)
165 County Road 519 Ste 1, Belvidere, NJ 07823-1927
Tel (908) 475-6500 *Founded/Ownrshp* 1924
Sales NA *EMP* 1,000
Accts Nisivoccia Llp-Davis H Evans
SIC 9111 Executive offices;
Treas: Charles Houck
Sales Exec: Terence Lee

D-U-N-S 08-337-5402
COUNTY OF WARREN
406 Justice Dr Rm 323, Lebanon, OH 45036-2523
Tel (513) 695-1242 *Founded/Ownrshp* 1803
Sales NA *EMP* 1,348
Accts Dave Yost-Auditor Of State Co
SIC 9111 Executive offices;
Treas: James Aumann
Ofcr: Roger Barnes
QA Dir: Tracy Heimbach

D-U-N-S 06-058-8563
COUNTY OF WASHINGTON
WASHINGTON COUNTY
155 N 1st Ave Ste 300, Hillsboro, OR 97124-3001
Tel (503) 846-8685 *Founded/Ownrshp* 1843
Sales NA *EMP* 1,800
Accts Talbot Korvola & Warwick Llp
SIC 9111
CFO: Wayne Lowry
Genl Mgr: Linden Chin
Genl Mgr: Dawn Smith

D-U-N-S 07-378-6998
COUNTY OF WASHOE
1001 E 9th St Bldg A, Reno, NV 89512-2845
Tel (775) 328-2552 *Founded/Ownrshp* 1861
Sales NA *EMP* 2,800
Accts Kafoury Armstrong & Co Reno
SIC 9311
Ch: Matt Smith
**Ch Bd:* Robert Larkin
Ch: Ted Short
Bd of Dir: Holly McGee
Ofcr: Kelly Mullin
VP: Don Ensminger
Assoc Dir: Arnie Maurins
Prgrm Mgr: Richard Sanchez
Genl Mgr: Pam Rasmussen
Snr Ntwrk: Brad Bachman
Dir IT: Donald Cavallo

D-U-N-S 02-011-1969
COUNTY OF WASHTENAW
220 N Main St, Ann Arbor, MI 48104-1413
Tel (734) 222-4357 *Founded/Ownrshp* 1826
Sales NA *EMP* 1,600
Accts Rehmann Robson Jackson Mi
SIC 9111 Executive offices;

D-U-N-S 07-383-7338
COUNTY OF WAUKESHA
515 W Mrland Blvd Ste G72, Waukesha, WI 53188
Tel (262) 548-7902 *Founded/Ownrshp* 1846
Sales NA *EMP* 1,433[E]
Accts Baker Tilly Virchow Krause Ll
SIC 9111 Executive offices, state & local
Prin: Daniel Finley
**Ch Bd:* James Dwyer
**Pr:* Richard Manke
**Treas:* Pamela Reeves
Off Mgr: Dani Danielski
IT Man: Nancy Mojica

D-U-N-S 07-313-4884
COUNTY OF WAYNE
WAYNE COUNTY
500 Griswold St Fl 31, Detroit, MI 48226-3480
Tel (313) 224-5952 *Founded/Ownrshp* 1796
Sales NA *EMP* 4,856
SIC 9111

D-U-N-S 07-367-1067
COUNTY OF WAYNE
9 Pearl St Rm 1, Lyons, NY 14489-1138
Tel (315) 946-5400 Founded/Ownrshp 1823
Sales NA EMP 1,000
Accts Raymond F Wager Cpa Pc Henr
SIC 9111 Executive offices;
Ch: Eileen Dehart
*Ch Bd: James Hoffman
*Treas: Frederick Hoffman
*Treas: Thomas Warnick

D-U-N-S 07-076-4279
COUNTY OF WEAKLEY
8319 Highway 22 Ste B, Dresden, TN 38225-2415
Tel (731) 364-5413 Founded/Ownrshp 1900
Sales NA EMP 1,048
Accts John G Morgan Nashville Ten
SIC 9111 Executive offices;
Exec: Ron Gifford
Brnch Mgr: Deanna Chappell

D-U-N-S 06-944-6219
COUNTY OF WEBB
JUVENILE DETENTION CENTER
1000 Houston St, Laredo, TX 78040-8017
Tel (956) 523-4600 Founded/Ownrshp 1848
Sales NA EMP 1,200
Accts Garza/Gonzalez & Associates S
SIC 9111 Executive offices;
Prin: Tano E Tijerina

D-U-N-S 07-575-7955
COUNTY OF WELD
1150 O St, Greeley, CO 80631-9596
Tel (970) 356-4000 Founded/Ownrshp 1865
Sales NA EMP 1,500
Accts Mcgee Hearne & Paiz Llp Che
SIC 9111 County supervisors' & executives' offices
Ch Bd: Barbara Kirkmeyer
Exec: Jennifer Finch
Ex Dir: Mark E Wallace
CIO: Ryan Rose
IT Man: Sherri Carmin

D-U-N-S 07-270-5213
COUNTY OF WESTCHESTER
148 Martine Ave, White Plains, NY 10601-3311
Tel (914) 995-2000 Founded/Ownrshp 1683
Sales NA EMP 5,927
SIC 9111 Executive offices;
Ex Dir: Kevin J Plunkett
V Ch: Lyndon Williams
Bd of Dir: Joseph Gibney
Ofcr: Rob Giordano
Ofcr: Carol McDaniel
Ofcr: Donald Smith
VP: Robert Funicello
VP: Lukas Herbert
Dir Risk M: Anthony Dibono
Ex Dir: David Jackson
Prgrm Mgr: Chris Andritsopoulos

D-U-N-S 07-693-0049
COUNTY OF WILLIAMSON
710 S Main St Ste 303, Georgetown, TX 78626-5701
Tel (512) 943-1550 Founded/Ownrshp 1848
Sales NA EMP 1,300
Accts Weaver And Tidwell Llp Housto
SIC 9111 Executive offices;
Ofcr: Lori Laws
Ex Dir: Bobby Seiferman
Brnch Mgr: Grant Strohman
CIO: Cathy Atkinson
IT Man: Julie Kiley
Genl Couns: Brent Webster

D-U-N-S 01-024-3822
COUNTY OF WINNEBAGO
404 Elm St Ste 104, Rockford, IL 61101-1244
Tel (815) 319-4444 Founded/Ownrshp 1844
Sales NA EMP 1,350^E
Accts Sikich Llp Rockford Illinois
SIC 9111 Executive offices;
Ch Bd: Kris Cohn
*Ch: Scott Christiansen
Treas: Susan Goral
Ofcr: Donna Apgar
Comm Dir: Todd Hughes
Ex Dir: Kim A Ponder
Pgrm Dir: Taryn Marko

D-U-N-S 07-616-9242
COUNTY OF WINNEBAGO
112 Otter Ave, Oshkosh, WI 54901-5008
Tel (920) 236-4800 Founded/Ownrshp 1840
Sales NA EMP 1,110
Accts Schenck Sc Green Bay Wiscons
SIC 9131
Exec: Jane Van De Hey
*Ch Bd: David Albrecht

D-U-N-S 01-020-3644
COUNTY OF YAKIMA
128 N 2nd St Rm 408, Yakima, WA 98901-2639
Tel (509) 574-1500 Founded/Ownrshp 1865
Sales NA EMP 1,200
Accts Brian Sonntag Cgfm Olympia
SIC 9111 Executive offices;
CFO: Craig Warner

D-U-N-S 07-447-2796
COUNTY OF YAVAPAI
1015 Fair St, Prescott, AZ 86305-1807
Tel (928) 771-3200 Founded/Ownrshp 1864
Sales NA EMP 1,250
Accts Debbie Davenport Phoenix Ari
SIC 9111 Executive offices;
Ch Bd: Rowle P Simmons
Ch Bd: Carol Springers
COO: Michael Holmes
Genl Mgr: Tina Brown
Genl Mgr: Mary Doren
IT Man: Jim Argyle
Netwrk Eng: Jason Deka

D-U-N-S 07-377-0646
COUNTY OF YOLO
625 Court St Ste 102, Woodland, CA 95695-3490
Tel (530) 666-8114 Founded/Ownrshp 1850
Sales NA EMP 1,200
SIC 9111
Ex Dir: Sharon Jensen
Ofcr: Terri Chadwick
Ofcr: Christine Crawford
Ofcr: Teri Huerta
Ex Dir: Patrick Blacklock
IT Man: Tom Bates
IT Man: Joe Fischer
Info Man: Jeremy Levish
Software D: Kyle Gohn

D-U-N-S 03-854-6552
COUNTY OF YORK
6 S Congress St, York, SC 29745-1835
Tel (803) 684-8511 Founded/Ownrshp 1785
Sales NA EMP 1,000
SIC 9111 Executive offices;
Ofcr: Ricky Lemmons
Ofcr: Matthew Tavella
Genl Mgr: Nancy Montrayfeild

D-U-N-S 08-161-3564
COUNTY OF YORK (PA)
28 E Market St Rm 216, York, PA 17401-1587
Tel (717) 771-9964 Founded/Ownrshp 1749
Sales NA EMP 2,600
Accts Zelenkofske Axelrod Llc Harri
SIC 9111 Executive offices;
Pr: Steven Chronister
*VP: Doug Hoke
Brnch Mgr: Vanessa Shive

D-U-N-S 04-049-9964
COUNTY OF YUBA
YUBA COUNTY BOARD SUPERVISORS
915 8th St Ste 109, Marysville, CA 95901-5273
Tel (530) 749-7575 Founded/Ownrshp 1858
Sales NA EMP 1,000
Accts Gallina Llp Roseville Califo
SIC 9111 Executive offices;
Dir: Wendy Hartman
Div Mgr: Jeremy Strang
CIO: Paul Lavalley
Dir IT: Doug McCoy

D-U-N-S 07-446-3811
COUNTY OF YUMA
YUMA COUNTY
198 S Main St, Yuma, AZ 85364-1424
Tel (928) 373-1010 Founded/Ownrshp 1864
Sales NA EMP 1,050
Accts Fester & Chapman Pc Phoenix
SIC 9111 Executive offices;
Ofcr: Brenda Mendez
Dir IT: Ed Jin

D-U-N-S 79-057-7006
▲ **COUPA SOFTWARE INC**
1855 S Grant St Fl 4, San Mateo, CA 94402-7034
Tel (650) 931-3200 Founded/Ownrshp 2006
Sales 83.6MM EMP 590^E
Tkr Sym COUP Exch NGS
SIC 7372 Prepackaged software; Business oriented computer software
Ch Bd: Robert Bernshteyn
CFO: Todd Ford
Ex VP: Tom Aitchison
Ex VP: Ray Martinelli
Sr VP: Ravi Thakur
VP: Roger Goulart
VP: Raja Hammoud
VP: Jonathan Stueve
VP: Kevin Turner
VP: David Williams
Dir Risk M: Steven Winter
Board of Directors: Charles Beeler, Leslie Campbell, Roger Siboni, Scott Thompson, Frank Van Veenendaal

D-U-N-S 80-782-8780 EXP
COUPLED PRODUCTS LLC
2651 S 600 E, Columbia City, IN 46725-9097
Tel (260) 248-3200 Founded/Ownrshp 2008
Sales 111.1MM^E EMP 650
SIC 3714 Motor vehicle parts & accessories
Pr: Joseph Kochan
*Ex VP: Jonathan Drew
*VP: Dawn Brazwell
Plnt Mgr: Tina Johnson
QI Cn Mgr: Joe Straub

D-U-N-S 06-216-3183
COURIER CORP
15 Wellman Ave, North Chelmsford, MA 01863-1315
Tel (978) 251-6000 Founded/Ownrshp 1824
Sales 283.2MM EMP 1,576^E
SIC 2732 2731

D-U-N-S 78-407-5905 IMP
■ **COURIER KENDALLVILLE INC**
(Suby of RAVEN VENTURES LLC) ★
2500 Marion Dr, Kendallville, IN 46755-3270
Tel (260) 347-3044 Founded/Ownrshp 2015
Sales 91.4MM^E EMP 480^E
SIC 2732 Book printing
Pr: James F Conway III
*CFO: Peter M Folger
*Sr VP: Rajeev Balakrishna
Mfg Dir: Sharon Dobias
Plnt Mgr: Kenneth Lapka

D-U-N-S 00-235-8349
COURIER TIMES INC
BUCKS COUNTY COURIER TIMES
(Suby of INTELLIGENCER/RECORD) ★
8400 Bristol Pike, Levittown, PA 19057-5117
Tel (215) 949-4011 Founded/Ownrshp 1954
Sales 132.9MM^E EMP 1,275
SIC 2711 Newspapers, publishing & printing
Pr: Mike Jameson
*Pr: Gary K Shorts
*Treas: Edward Birch
*Treas: Michael White
*VP: Jeff J Benninghoff
*VP: Shirley C Ellis
*VP: Charles Smith
Dir Bus: Myra Cortado
Genl Mgr: Jake Volcsko

COURIER-JOURNAL, THE
See COURIER-JOURNAL INC

D-U-N-S 00-636-7049
■ **COURIER-JOURNAL INC**
COURIER-JOURNAL, THE
(Suby of TEGNA INC) ★
525 W Broadway, Louisville, KY 40202-2137
Tel (502) 582-4011 Founded/Ownrshp 2006
Sales 83.7MM^E EMP 1,201
SIC 2711 Newspapers, publishing & printing
Pr: Arnold H Garson
*Pr: Wesley Jackson
*Ch: Denise Ivey
*VP: Mike Huot
*VP: Bennie Ivory
*VP: Gracia C Martore
VP: Tom Travis
Prin: Ken Hodge

COURSE TECHNOLOGY
See CENGAGE LEARNING INC

D-U-N-S 92-849-6744
COURSECO INC
1670 Corp Cir Ste 201, Petaluma, CA 94954
Tel (707) 763-0335 Founded/Ownrshp 1989
Sales 33.9MM^E EMP 1,025
SIC 7992 Public golf courses
Pr: Thomas B Isaak
*Pr: Tom Bugbee
*CFO: Craig Hazel
VP: Russ Erickson
VP: Scott Wackowski
VP Sls: Lance Merrihew

COURT APPEALS, MARYLAND STATE
See COURT OF APPEALS MARYLAND STATE

D-U-N-S 00-760-8854
COURT OF APPEALS MARYLAND STATE
COURT APPEALS, MARYLAND STATE
(Suby of STATE OF MARYLAND) ★
580 Taylor Ave, Annapolis, MD 21401-2352
Tel (410) 260-1500 Founded/Ownrshp 1997, 1998
Sales NA EMP 2,000
SIC 9211 State courts;
Ex Dir: Allen Clark
Ex Dir: Diane Pawlowicz
Dir IT: Barbara Hansman

D-U-N-S 36-070-9216
COURT OF APPEALS OF DISTRICT OF COLUMBIA
(Suby of OFFICE OF CONTRACTING AND PROC) ★
500 Indiana Ave Nw, Washington, DC 20001-2131
Tel (202) 879-2700 Founded/Ownrshp 1978
Sales NA EMP 1,250
SIC 9211 State courts;
Prin: Annice Wagner
IT Man: Fran Segall

D-U-N-S 03-299-9828
■ **COURT OF APPEALS UNITED STATES**
(Suby of SUPREME COURT UNITED STATES) ★
1 Columbus Cir Ne, Washington, DC 20544-0003
Tel (202) 879-1010 Founded/Ownrshp 1871, 1891
Sales NA EMP 5,500^E
SIC 9211 Federal courts;
*CFO: Dana Frendz

D-U-N-S 86-745-8499
COURT SQUARE CAPITAL LIMITED
55 E 52nd St Rm 3400, New York, NY 10055-0006
Tel (212) 752-6110 Founded/Ownrshp 1972
Sales 190.5MM^E EMP 8,443^E
SIC 8743 6162 Sales promotion; Mortgage bankers & correspondents
Ch Bd: Philip Dunne
*Mng Pt: William Comfort
*Mng Pt: Anthony P Mirra
*Mng Pt: David T Nguyen
*Mng Pt: John P Overbay
*Mng Pt: Jeffrey F Vogel
VP: Jeffrey Abramoff
VP: Steve Lamb
VP: Jeffrey Vogel
Mng Dir: Richard E Mayberry
Off Mgr: Diane Jackman

D-U-N-S 61-053-7735 IMP
COURT SQUARE CAPITAL PARTNERS LP
55 E 52nd St Rm 3400, New York, NY 10055-0006
Tel (212) 752-6110 Founded/Ownrshp 2006
Sales 884.3MM^E EMP 5,802^E
SIC 6799 2731 2721 Venture capital companies; Book publishing; Periodicals
Pt: Anthony P Mirra
Genl Pt: Walter Wilkerson
Pt: John Kim
Mng Pt: Albert A Holman
Mng Pt: Thomas F McWilliams
VP: Richard E Mayberry

D-U-N-S 00-796-1659
COURTESY CHEVROLET (AZ)
1233 E Camelback Rd, Phoenix, AZ 85014-3381
Tel (602) 279-3232 Founded/Ownrshp 1955
Sales 132.5MM^E EMP 254^E
SIC 5511 5013 7538 Automobiles, new & used; Automotive supplies & parts; General automotive repair shops
Pr: Mildred M Fitzgerald
*Sec: K Michelle Hegg
*VP: William R Gruwell
Genl Mgr: Rolland Schreiber
Sls Dir: Scott Gruwell
Sls Mgr: Antoine Tenman

D-U-N-S 02-329-3954
COURTESY CORP
2700 National Dr Ste 100, Onalaska, WI 54650-6709
Tel (608) 781-8080 Founded/Ownrshp 1968
Sales 90.9MM^E EMP 3,000
SIC 5812 Fast-food restaurant, chain
Pr: Richard Lommen
Mktg Mgr: Evan Newman

COURTHOUSE
See GLOUCESTER COUNTY NEW JERSEY (INC)

COURTYARD BY MARRIOTT
See COURTYARD MANAGEMENT CORP

COURTYARD BY MRROTT SPRNGFIELD
See HAMMONS INC

D-U-N-S 82-504-4779
■ **COURTYARD MANAGEMENT CORP**
COURTYARD BY MARRIOTT
(Suby of MARRIOTT INTERNATIONAL INC) ★
10400 Fernwood Rd, Bethesda, MD 20817-1102
Tel (301) 380-3000 Founded/Ownrshp 1987
Sales 80.1MM^E EMP 1,000
SIC 7011 Hotels & motels
Prin: David Grissen

COUSHATA ALLIANCE
See COUSHATTA ALLIANCE

D-U-N-S 61-837-6719
COUSHATTA ALLIANCE
COUSHATA ALLIANCE
1940 C C Bel Rd, Elton, LA 70532-5317
Tel (337) 584-1401 Founded/Ownrshp 1972
Sales NA EMP 3,223
SIC 9131 Indian reservation
Ch: Lovelin Poncho
Ofcr: Leatrus Miller
Ofcr: Michael Tarpley
VP: Michelle Litteral
Off Mgr: Darla Thompson

D-U-N-S 00-331-6718
▲ **COUSINS PROPERTIES INC**
191 Peachtree St Ne # 500, Atlanta, GA 30303-1740
Tel (404) 407-1000 Founded/Ownrshp 1962
Sales 381.6MM EMP 257^E
Tkr Sym CUZ Exch NYS
SIC 6798 Real estate investment trusts
Pr: Lawrence L Gellerstedt III
V Ch: Thomas D Bell
COO: M Colin Connolly
CFO: Gregg D Adzema
Treas: Mary Caneer
Treas: John D Harris Jr
Chf Inves: Colin Connolly
Ex VP: William Bassett
Ex VP: John S McColl
Ex VP: Michael I Cohn
Sr VP: Darryl D Bonner
Sr VP: Mark Dickenson
Sr VP: Walter L Fish
Sr VP: Pamela F Roper
VP: Leeann Attanucci
VP: Thad Ellis
VP: Randy Faltys
VP: David Nelson
VP: Josh Pirtle
Board of Directors: Robert M Chapman, Tom G Charlesworth, Lillian C Giornelli, S Taylor Glover, James H Hance Jr, Donna W Hyland, R Dary Stone

D-U-N-S 06-173-9967
COUSINS SUBMARINES INC
COUSINS SUBS
N83w13400 Leon Rd, Menomonee Falls, WI 53051-3306
Tel (262) 253-7700 Founded/Ownrshp 1972
Sales 138.0MM^E EMP 4,000
SIC 5812 Sandwiches & submarines shop
CEO: William Specht
*Pr: Christine A Specht
CFO: Jason Westhoff
Genl Mgr: Crystal Johnson
Dir IT: Scott Lewis
Opers Mgr: Shelly Hurzler

COUSINS SUBS
See COUSINS SUBMARINES INC

COVALENCE COATED PRODUCTS
See COVALENCE SPECIALTY COATINGS LLC

D-U-N-S 80-040-2807 EXP
■ **COVALENCE SPECIALTY ADHESIVES LLC**
(Suby of BERRY PLASTICS CORP) ★
101 Oakley St, Evansville, IN 47710-1237
Tel (812) 424-2904 Founded/Ownrshp 2006
Sales 220.8MM^E EMP 1,150
SIC 2891 Adhesives & sealants
Pr: Thomas Salmon
VP: John Rice

D-U-N-S 80-566-4666 IMP
■ **COVALENCE SPECIALTY COATINGS LLC**
COVALENCE COATED PRODUCTS
(Suby of BERRY PLASTICS CORP) ★
101 Oakley St, Evansville, IN 47710-1237
Tel (812) 424-2904 Founded/Ownrshp 2006
Sales 99.8MM^E EMP 1,000
SIC 2672 Coated paper, except photographic, carbon or abrasive
Pr: Jeffrey D Thompson
Bd of Dir: Steven C Graham
Ex VP: David Graziosi
VP: Gail Lehman
VP: Gary Powell

D-U-N-S 93-753-3768 IMP
■ **COVANCE INC**
(Suby of LABORATORY CORP OF AMERICA HOLDINGS) ★
210 Carnegie Ctr Ste 106, Princeton, NJ 08540-6233
Tel (609) 452-4440 Founded/Ownrshp 2015
Sales 1.7MMM^E EMP 12,501^E
SIC 8731 8734 8733 8732 Biological research; Biotechnical research, commercial; Medical research, commercial; Commercial physical research; Testing laboratories; Noncommercial research organizations; Research institute; Commercial nonphysical research
CEO: Joseph L Herring
CFO: Alison A Cornell

Chf Cred: John Watson
Ex VP: Rick Cimino
Ex VP: Deborah Keller
Sr VP: Mark Eisenach
Sr VP: James Lovett
Sr VP: Lisa Uthgenannt
VP: Christine Baker
VP: Honggang Bi
VP: Nigel Brown
VP: Pam Druhan
VP: Kate Hillson
VP: Jeffrey Hurwitz
VP: Jerry Maggio
VP: Ben Quartley
VP: Nicole Roeves
VP: John Spegele
VP: Chris Springall
VP: Steve Street
VP: Paul Surdez
Board of Directors: Robert Barchi, Gary E Costley, Sandra L Helton, John McCartney, Joseph C Scodari, Bradley T Sheares

D-U-N-S 04-748-1528
■ COVANCE LABORATORIES INC
(*Suby of* COVANCE INC) ★
3301 Kinsman Blvd, Madison, WI 53704-2523
Tel (608) 241-4471 *Founded/Ownrshp* 1990
Sales 180.6MM[E] *EMP* 1,800
SIC 8734 Testing laboratories
CEO: Joseph Herring
Sr Pt: Shelley Osborn
COO: Shana Dalton
VP: Pam Druhan
VP: Margaret Mordin
VP: Caroline Schaefer
VP: Catherine Veum
Assoc Dir: Deborah Glick
Assoc Dir: Mike Koch
Dir IT: Matt Coutts

D-U-N-S 10-392-7463
■ COVANCE RESEARCH PRODUCTS INC
(*Suby of* COVANCE INC) ★
310 Swamp Bridge Rd, Denver, PA 17517-8723
Tel (717) 336-4921 *Founded/Ownrshp* 2002
Sales 350.2MM[E] *EMP* 380
SIC 0279 2836 2834

D-U-N-S 13-023-5161 IMP
■ COVANTA ARC LLC
(*Suby of* COVANTA ENERGY LLC) ★
445 South St, Morristown, NJ 07960-6475
Tel (862) 345-5000 *Founded/Ownrshp* 1984
Sales 219.3MM[E] *EMP* 656
SIC 4953 Refuse collection & disposal services
CEO: Anthony J Orlando

D-U-N-S 12-227-6124 IMP
■ COVANTA ENERGY GROUP INC
(*Suby of* COVANTA ENERGY LLC) ★
445 South St, Morristown, NJ 07960-6475
Tel (862) 345-5000 *Founded/Ownrshp* 1984
Sales 232.2MM[E] *EMP* 355
SIC 1541 1629 4953 4931 Industrial buildings & warehouses; Waste disposal plant construction; Incinerator operation;
CEO: Anthony J Orlando
COO: Bruce W Stone
Sr VP: Jeffrey R Horowitz
Sr VP: John M Klett
Board of Directors: Jeffrey F Friedman, Robert E Smith

D-U-N-S 00-132-8053 IMP
■ COVANTA ENERGY LLC
(*Suby of* COVANTA HOLDING CORP) ★
445 South St Ste 400, Morristown, NJ 07960-6475
Tel (862) 345-5000 *Founded/Ownrshp* 1939, 1987
Sales 1.2MMM[E] *EMP* 3,000
SIC 4953 4911 Recycling, waste materials; Distribution, electric power
Pr: Anthony J Orlando
V Ch: Abraham Zaleznik
Pr: Tom Lyons
Pr: Allard M Nooy
**COO:* Seth Myones
COO: Bruce Stone
CFO: Vincent Dugan
**CFO:* Sanjiv Khattri
CFO: Robert Shapard
Treas: Louis Walters
Ex VP: Joseph J Burgess
Ex VP: Joseph Burgess
Ex VP: Gary Crane
**Ex VP:* John Klett
Ex VP: John M Klett
Ex VP: John Macaniff
**Ex VP:* Timothy J Simpson
Sr VP: Marc Strassler
VP: Brian Bahor
VP: Vincent Bolognini
VP: Thomas Bucks

COVANTA HAVER ASSOCIATES
See COVANTA HAVERHILL INC

D-U-N-S 10-217-6393 IMP/EXP
■ COVANTA HAVERHILL INC
COVANTA HAVER ASSOCIATES
(*Suby of* COVANTA ENERGY LLC) ★
100 Recovery Way, Haverhill, MA 01835-3516
Tel (978) 372-6288 *Founded/Ownrshp* 1986
Sales 178.8MM[E] *EMP* 165
SIC 4953 1629 4931 Recycling, waste materials; Waste disposal plant construction; Electric & other services combined
Pr: Stephen J Jones
**CEO:* Anthony J Orlando
**Ex VP:* Michael J De Castro
**Ex VP:* Brad Helgeson
**Ex VP:* Derek W Veenhof

D-U-N-S 00-195-0773
▲ COVANTA HOLDING CORP
445 South St, Morristown, NJ 07960-6475
Tel (862) 345-5000 *Founded/Ownrshp* 1992
Sales 1.6MMM *EMP* 3,800
Tkr Sym CVA *Exch* NYS
SIC 4953 4911 Recycling, waste materials; Distribution, electric power
Pr: Stephen J Jones
**Ch Bd:* Samuel Zell
CFO: Bradford J Helgeson
Ofcr: Michael A Wright
Ex VP: Michael J De Castro
Ex VP: Seth Myones
Ex VP: Timothy J Simpson
Ex VP: Bruce Stone
Ex VP: Derek W Veenhof
Sr VP: Matthew R Mulcahy
VP: Beth Hurley
VP: Neil C Zieselman

D-U-N-S 14-453-7602
■ COVANTA HONOLULU RESOURCE RECOVERY VENTURE
H R R V
(*Suby of* COVANTA HAVER ASSOCIATES) ★
91-174 Hanua St, Kapolei, HI 96707-1735
Tel (808) 682-2099 *Founded/Ownrshp* 1983
Sales 178.8MM[E] *EMP* 147
SIC 4911 Generation, electric power
CEO: Anthony J Orlando
Pt: Covanta Projects of Hawaii
COO: Seth Myones
CFO: Sanjiv Khattri
Genl Mgr: Robert Webster

D-U-N-S 61-986-6866
■ COVANTA SYSTEMS INC
(*Suby of* COVANTA ENERGY GROUP INC) ★
445 South St, Morristown, NJ 07960-6475
Tel (862) 345-5000 *Founded/Ownrshp* 1984
Sales 193.6MM[E] *EMP* 175
SIC 4953 Refuse systems; Recycling, waste materials
Pr: Steven Jones

COVE SHOE COMPANY DIVISION
See HH BROWN SHOE CO INC

D-U-N-S 02-484-9226
COVELLI ENTERPRISES INC (OH)
O'CHARLEYS
3900 E Market St Ste 1, Warren, OH 44484-4787
Tel (330) 856-3176 *Founded/Ownrshp* 1978
Sales 404.4MM[E] *EMP* 8,000
SIC 5812 Restaurant, family: chain
CEO: Julie Ault
**Pr:* Sam Covelli
**VP:* Robert Fiorino
Exec: Dean Rucker
Off Mgr: Ann Cunningham
Dir IT: Anthony Biegacki
Dir IT: Dave Cirillo
Dir IT: Dave Sutphin
VP Opers: Bryan Kachmer
Mktg Dir: Liz Fiorino
Mktg Dir: Ashlee Mauti

D-U-N-S 12-617-4635
COVENANT AVIATION SECURITY LLC
(*Suby of* COVENANT SERVICES WORLDWIDE LLC) ★
400 Quadrangle Dr Ste A, Bolingbrook, IL 60440-3457
Tel (630) 771-0800 *Founded/Ownrshp* 2002
Sales 32.0MM[E] *EMP* 1,300
SIC 7381 Security guard service
VP: Christine Mueller
Ex VP: Michael Bolles
IT Man: Martin Maziarz
Opers Mgr: Lisa Thompson
Secur Mgr: James McFadden

D-U-N-S 83-791-2302
COVENANT CARE CALIFORNIA LLC
(*Suby of* COVENANT CARE LLC) ★
27071 Aliso Creek Rd # 100, Aliso Viejo, CA 92656-5325
Tel (949) 349-1200 *Founded/Ownrshp* 1994
Sales 187.4MM[E] *EMP* 4,500
SIC 8051 Skilled nursing care facilities
Pr: Robert Levin
**COO:* Mary A Evans
COO: Mary Evans
**CFO:* Christine Sims
**VP:* Judy Elmore
**VP:* Debbie Nix
VP: Tambria Turco
Dir Soc: Sandra Raab
Dir Soc: Sharon Thompson
Off Mgr: Donna Durkin
Off Mgr: Misty Fitch

D-U-N-S 87-623-1200
COVENANT CARE LLC
27071 Aliso Creek Rd # 100, Aliso Viejo, CA 92656-5325
Tel (949) 349-1200 *Founded/Ownrshp* 1994
Sales 206.9MM[E] *EMP* 5,000[E]
SIC 8051

D-U-N-S 18-681-6989
COVENANT HEALTH
100 Fort Sanders W Blvd, Knoxville, TN 37922-3353
Tel (865) 531-5555 *Founded/Ownrshp* 1996
Sales 883.9MM[E] *EMP* 2,469
SIC 8062 General medical & surgical hospitals
CEO: Anthony L Spezia
**Pr:* Larry Martin
**CFO:* John Geppi
CFO: Gregory Sommers
**Ex VP:* Larry Kleinman
**Ex VP:* Jim Vandersteeg
**VP:* Joseph D Mc Donald

D-U-N-S 18-835-0367
COVENANT HEALTH CARE SYSTEM INC
WHEATON FRANCISCAN HEALTHCARE
1126 S 70th St Ste S306, Milwaukee, WI 53214-3151
Tel (414) 456-3000 *Founded/Ownrshp* 1980
Sales 549.8MM[E] *EMP* 1,746
SIC 8062 General medical & surgical hospitals
Ch Bd: W F Loebig
**Pr:* Paul Dell Uomo
Opers Mgr: Bud Mettille

D-U-N-S 93-934-2390
COVENANT HEALTH SYSTEM
(*Suby of* ST JOSEPH HEALTH SYSTEM) ★
3615 19th St, Lubbock, TX 79410-1209
Tel (806) 725-1011 *Founded/Ownrshp* 1998
Sales 570.4MM *EMP* 5,700
Accts Ernst & Young Us Llp Austin
SIC 8062 General medical & surgical hospitals
CEO: Richard Parks
**COO:* Troy Thibodeaux
**CFO:* John Grigson
**CFO:* Denise Saenz
Ofcr: Adam Nguyen
VP: Steve Beck
VP: Bill Bopp
VP: Clarke Cochran
VP: Lindy Lauderdale
VP: Sharon Prather
Dir Rx: Angela Howard
Dir Rx: Bill Welch

D-U-N-S 10-232-8812
COVENANT HEALTH SYSTEM INC
3421 W 9th St, Waterloo, IA 50702-5401
Tel (319) 236-4111 *Founded/Ownrshp* 1988
Sales 274.5MM *EMP* 2,291
SIC 8062 General medical & surgical hospitals
Pr: Davod A Ferreli
**Pr:* Jack Busentery

COVENANT HEALTHCARE
See COVENANT MEDICAL CENTER INC

D-U-N-S 08-097-6327
COVENANT HEALTHCARE INC (TN)
PENINSULA OUTPATIENT CENTER
1451 Bowell Springs Blvd, Knoxville, TN 37909
Tel (865) 970-9800 *Founded/Ownrshp* 1974
Sales 119.0MM *EMP* 330
Accts Mc Williams & Company Cpas
SIC 8093 Mental health clinic, outpatient
Pr: Barbara Blevins
Board of Directors: Peter Alliman, Bill Busing, Allen Edwards, Dawn Ford, Gerald Harriss DDS, Marcia Hathcock, Ron Justus, Bobbie Oats Rancher, Wayne Roach

D-U-N-S 07-520-9411
COVENANT HOUSE
5 Penn Plz Ste 201, New York, NY 10001-1841
Tel (212) 727-4000 *Founded/Ownrshp* 1969
Sales 66.7MM *EMP* 1,860
Accts Grant Thornton Llp New York
SIC 8322 8361 Emergency shelters; Children's home
CEO: Kevin Ryan
Dir Vol: Sheila Walton
COO: Carlette S Mack
**Treas:* Daniel Mc Carthy
VP: Meredith Fabian
VP: Arlene Lozano
VP: Tom Manning
Ex Dir: Sof A A Argumedo
Off Mgr: Anne Bruce
CTO: Alice Steigerwald
IT Man: Anthony Depalma

D-U-N-S 07-205-1936
COVENANT MANAGEMENT SYSTEMS LP
4515 Seton Center Pkwy # 220, Austin, TX 78759-5290
Tel (512) 338-8388 *Founded/Ownrshp* 1998
Sales 101.4MM[E] *EMP* 1,400
SIC 8011 Clinic, operated by physicians
Pt: Norman Chenven
CFO: Jack Foster
Software D: Jonathan Knapek

D-U-N-S 02-302-1319
COVENANT MEDICAL CENTER INC
COVENANT HEALTHCARE
1447 N Harrison St, Saginaw, MI 48602-4727
Tel (989) 583-0000 *Founded/Ownrshp* 1998
Sales 535.9MM *EMP* 4,000[E]
SIC 8062 General medical & surgical hospitals
CEO: Edward Bruff
**Pr:* Spencer T Maidlow
COO: Mark W Knight
**CFO:* Mark Gronda
VP: Dave Nall
VP: Joe Ruth
VP: Michael Schultz
VP: Gwen Stafford
Dir Rx: Terry Wernette
CIO: Connie Hendrick
Dir IT: Keith Grantham

D-U-N-S 13-979-0257
COVENANT MEDICAL CENTER INC
WHEATON FRANCISCAN HEALTHCARE
3421 W 9th St, Waterloo, IA 50702-5401
Tel (319) 272-7296 *Founded/Ownrshp* 2003
Sales 279.9MM *EMP* 2,300[E]
SIC 8062 General medical & surgical hospitals
Pr: Jack Dusenbery
CFO: Michelle Panicucci
**CFO:* Shelli Panicucci
VP: Jeff Halverson
Ex Dir: James Peterson
Off Mgr: Nancy Schaefer
Dir QC: Dee Fox
Surgeon: Gary Knudson
Doctor: Frank Barby
Doctor: Randall Bremner
Doctor: Matthew Targoff

D-U-N-S 13-718-5869
COVENANT MEDICAL GROUP
(*Suby of* ST JOSEPH HEALTH SYSTEM) ★
3506 21st St Ste 506, Lubbock, TX 79410-1233
Tel (806) 725-4130 *Founded/Ownrshp* 2003
Sales 105.1MM *EMP* 33[E]
Accts Ernst & Young Llp Irvine Ca
SIC 8011 Internal medicine, physician/surgeon
Prin: Steven Combs MD
Doctor: Cathy Malouf
Doctor: Kaiser R Tarafdar MD

D-U-N-S 60-277-9642
COVENANT MEDICAL GROUP
524 E 40th St Unit B, Lubbock, TX 79404-2807
Tel (806) 725-9800 *Founded/Ownrshp* 1997
Sales 120.9MM *EMP* 80[E]
SIC 8011 Offices & clinics of medical doctors
Prin: Robert J Salem
COO: Kristen Kothmann

D-U-N-S 62-210-9833
COVENANT RETIREMENT COMMUNITIES INC
COVENANT SOLUTIONS
5700 Old Orchard Rd, Skokie, IL 60077-1036
Tel (773) 878-2294 *Founded/Ownrshp* 1886
Sales 3.3MM *EMP* 3,016[E]
SIC 8741

D-U-N-S 80-006-7233
COVENANT SECURITY SERVICES LTD
400 Quadrangle Dr Ste A, Bolingbrook, IL 60440-3457
Tel (630) 771-0800 *Founded/Ownrshp* 1997
Sales 50.0MM[E] *EMP* 1,500
SIC 7381 Security guard service
Pr: Gregory Iannuzzi
Sr VP: William E Holden Sr
**VP:* Melinda Lazar
Exec: Joyce Arcuri
Sales Exec: Teri La Paso

D-U-N-S 14-099-3309
COVENANT SERVICES WORLDWIDE LLC
400 Quadrangle Dr Ste A, Bolingbrook, IL 60440-3457
Tel (630) 771-0800 *Founded/Ownrshp* 2003
Sales 39.4MM[E] *EMP* 1,348[E]
SIC 7381 Security guard service
Ch: Mindy Jacobson
CEO: Michael P Murray
CFO: Jerry Park
VP: Michael Kochan

COVENANT SOLUTIONS
See COVENANT RETIREMENT COMMUNITIES INC

D-U-N-S 14-760-7360
■ COVENANT TRANSPORT INC
(*Suby of* COVENANT TRANSPORTATION GROUP INC) ★
400 Birmingham Hwy, Chattanooga, TN 37419-2346
Tel (423) 821-1212 *Founded/Ownrshp* 1985
Sales 486.0MM[E] *EMP* 4,202
SIC 4213 Trucking, except local
Ch Bd: David R Parker
**COO:* Joey Hogan
**Treas:* M David Hughes
Bd of Dir: Niel Nielson
**Ex VP:* R H Lovin Jr
Sr VP: Richard Cribbs
VP: John Daniel
Dir: Michael Holbrook
Brnch Mgr: Gene Naukanm
IT Man: David Ray
Sales Exec: Richard Holdridge
Board of Directors: Jeffery Acuff, James Brower, Richard Cribbs, Charles Eddy, Jeffrey Paulsen, Robert Stephens, Jeffrey Taylor, Richard Towe

D-U-N-S 87-653-3548
▲ COVENANT TRANSPORTATION GROUP INC
400 Birmingham Hwy, Chattanooga, TN 37419-2346
Tel (423) 821-1212 *Founded/Ownrshp* 1986
Sales 724.2MM *EMP* 4,400[E]
Tkr Sym CVTI *Exch* NGS
SIC 4213 Trucking, except local
Ch Bd: David R Parker
Pr: Joey B Hogan
COO: Samuel F Hough
COO: Paul Newbourne
CFO: Richard B Cribbs
Treas: M Paul Bunn
Ex VP: R H Lovin Jr
Board of Directors: William T Alt, Robert E Bosworth, Bradley A Moline, Herbert J Schmidt

D-U-N-S 13-139-6900
COVENTRY FIRST LLC
(*Suby of* COVENTRY GROUP INC) ★
7111 Valley Green Rd, Fort Washington, PA 19034-2207
Tel (877) 836-8300 *Founded/Ownrshp* 1999
Sales NA *EMP* 200[E]
SIC 6311 Life insurance
Pr: Marybeth Baxter
CFO: Antonio Iz
**Ofcr:* Nat Shapo
**Ex VP:* Reid Buerger
VP: Michael Freedman
VP: Kevin Kline
Creative D: Wayne Thompson
Sftwr Eng: Robert Rivera
VP Mktg: David Cherkas
Mktg Dir: Sheylea Graybill
Counsel: Josh May

D-U-N-S 13-920-9258
COVENTRY GROUP INC
(*Suby of* MONTGOMERY CAPITAL INC) ★
7111 Valley Green Rd # 320, Fort Washington, PA 19034-2298
Tel (215) 233-5100 *Founded/Ownrshp* 2016
Sales NA *EMP* 295
SIC 6311 Life insurance
Ch Bd: Alan H Buerger
Pr: Ryan Brusca
**Pr:* Constance M Buerger
CFO: Antonio Muriiz
Ex VP: Thomas Zielinski
Sr VP: Claudia Bjere
Sr VP: David Cherkas
Sr VP: David Finkel
Sr VP: Michael Freedman
Sr VP: Davina Lane
Sr VP: Amy Welsh
VP: Rob Aronchick
VP: Andrew Asher
VP: Peter Clay
VP: Joshua Funt
VP: Francine Johnson

VP: Gary Kuchera
VP: Beverley Messenger
VP: Daniel Odonnell

D-U-N-S 17-518-1999
■ COVENTRY HEALTH CARE INC
(*Suby of* AETNA INC) ★
6720 Rockledge Dr 700b, Bethesda, MD 20817-1883
Tel (301) 581-0600 *Founded/Ownrshp* 2013
Sales NA *EMP* 14,400
SIC 6324 Health maintenance organization (HMO), insurance only
Pr: Karen S Rohan
Pr: Brian Carpenter
**CFO:* Randy Giles
**Treas:* Elaine R Cofrancesco
Bd of Dir: David Drury
Bd of Dir: Thomas Graf
Ofcr: Debra Nuckols
Ex VP: Harv Demovick
Ex VP: Michael Kasper
**Sr VP:* John J Ruhlmann
**Sr VP:* Shirley R Smith
VP: David Baer
**VP:* Jerry J Bellizzi
VP: Peter Clay
VP: Ron Cordova
VP: Harry Creasey
VP: Matthew D Eyles
VP: Valerie Keller
VP: Armando Luna Jr
VP: Karen Snyder
VP: Les Sowa

D-U-N-S 92-949-2239
■ COVENTRY HEALTH CARE OF CAROLINAS INC
(*Suby of* COVENTRY HEALTH CARE INC) ★
2801 Slater Rd Ste 200, Morrisville, NC 27560-8477
Tel (919) 337-1800 *Founded/Ownrshp* 1995
Sales NA *EMP* 160
SIC 6324 Health maintenance organization (HMO), insurance only
CEO: Tracy Baker
**COO:* Peter Chauncey
**CFO:* William Dewey
VP: Robert Talbot
Genl Mgr: Megan Toomey-Mickle
VP Sls: James Fricchione

D-U-N-S 60-250-9697
■ COVENTRY HEALTH CARE OF KANSAS INC
CHC KANSAS
(*Suby of* COVENTRY HEALTH CARE INC) ★
9401 Indian Creek Pkwy # 1300, Overland Park, KS 66210-2021
Tel (800) 969-3343 *Founded/Ownrshp* 2002
Sales NA *EMP* 990
SIC 6324 8011 Health maintenance organization (HMO), insurance only; Pediatrician
Ex Dir: George Wheeler
**Pr:* Allan Wise

D-U-N-S 15-093-3141
■ COVENTRY HEALTH CARE OF MISSOURI INC
(*Suby of* COVENTRY HEALTH CARE INC) ★
550 Maryville Centre Dr # 300, Saint Louis, MO 63141-5818
Tel (314) 506-1700 *Founded/Ownrshp* 1990
Sales NA *EMP* 335
SIC 6324 Group hospitalization plans; Dental insurance
Pr: Roman Kulich
COO: Claudia Bjerre

D-U-N-S 80-841-4176
■ COVENTRY HEALTH CARE WORKERS COMPENSATION INC
(*Suby of* COVENTRY HEALTH CARE INC) ★
3200 Highland Ave, Downers Grove, IL 60515-1223
Tel (630) 737-7900 *Founded/Ownrshp* 2007
Sales 257.1MM[E] *EMP* 4,000[E]
SIC 5047 Medical & hospital equipment
Pr: James E McGarry
**VP:* John Stelben

D-U-N-S 62-525-1913
■ COVENTRY HEALTH PLAN OF FLORIDA INC
FHS ACT 1 TECHNICAL SERVICES
(*Suby of* COVENTRY HEALTH CARE INC) ★
1340 Concord Ter, Sunrise, FL 33323-2830
Tel (954) 858-3000 *Founded/Ownrshp* 2007
Sales NA *EMP* 450
SIC 6324 Health maintenance organization (HMO), insurance only
Pr: Joseph R Berding
**CFO:* Tom Wyss
Ofcr: Marc Scott
**VP:* Ken Edwards
Trfc Mgr: Jennifer Eaton

COVER TO COVER
See DAKOTA NEWS INC

COVERALL CLEANING CONCEPTS
See COVERALL NORTH AMERICA INC

COVERALL CLEANING CONCEPTS
See CNA HOLDING CORP

D-U-N-S 15-308-5865
COVERALL NORTH AMERICA INC
COVERALL CLEANING CONCEPTS
(*Suby of* COVERALL CLEANING CONCEPTS) ★
350 Sw 12th Ave, Deerfield Beach, FL 33442-3106
Tel (561) 922-2500 *Founded/Ownrshp* 2005
Sales 192.3MM[E] *EMP* 476
SIC 6794 7349 Franchises, selling or licensing; Building maintenance services
CFO: Marilyn Felos
COO: Jim Congrove
CFO: Mike Elkin
**Rgnl VP:* Laura Bach
**Rgnl VP:* Jay Harper
**Rgnl VP:* Michelle Teague

VP: Edward Cruz
VP: Valerie Dennis
**VP Admn:* Shirley Klein
Genl Mgr: Audrey Holmes
Genl Mgr: Mark Smith
Board of Directors: David Kreilein

D-U-N-S 02-440-8705 IMP/EXP
COVERIS FLEXIBLES US LLC
(*Suby of* EXOPACK HOLDING) ★
50 International Dr # 100, Greenville, SC 29615-4832
Tel (773) 877-3300 *Founded/Ownrshp* 2001, 2014
Sales 1.1MMM[E] *EMP* 2,265
SIC 2673 Bags: plastic, laminated & coated
CEO: Gary Masse
**Pr:* Tom Vale
**CFO:* Mike Alger
CFO: Miles McHugh
**Treas:* Dwayne Owens
**Treas:* John Thomas
Plnt Mgr: Wayne Mashe

COVERIS HOLDING
See COVERIS KEY HOLDINGS LLC

D-U-N-S 62-278-0588
COVERIS HOLDING CORP
EXOPACK HOLDING
(*Suby of* COVERIS HOLDING) ★
8600 W Bryn Mawr Ave, Chicago, IL 60631-3579
Tel (773) 877-3300 *Founded/Ownrshp* 2001
Sales 1.0MMM[E] *EMP* 2,899[E]
SIC 6719 2673 2631 Investment holding companies, except banks; Bags: plastic, laminated & coated; Container, packaging & boxboard
CEO: Gary Masse
**COO:* Steve Mullins
**CFO:* Michael Alger
**Treas:* Duane Owens
Tech Mgr: Rod Reeves

D-U-N-S 83-168-6840
COVERIS KEY HOLDINGS LLC
COVERIS HOLDING
(*Suby of* COVERIS HOLDINGS SA)
345 Cedar Springs Ave, Spartanburg, SC 29302-2926
Tel (864) 596-7300 *Founded/Ownrshp* 2005
Sales 1.0MMM[E] *EMP* 2,900[E]
SIC 2673 2631 6719 Bags: plastic, laminated & coated; Container, packaging & boxboard; Investment holding companies, except banks
CEO: Gary Masse
**CFO:* Michael Alger
**Treas:* Duane Owens
VP: Thomas Costigan
VP: Kathleen McJohn

D-U-N-S 00-449-6600 IMP/EXP
COVERIS RIGID NA INC (DE)
(*Suby of* EXOPACK HOLDING) ★
50 International Dr # 100, Greenville, SC 29615-4832
Tel (864) 225-9750 *Founded/Ownrshp* 1969, 2014
Sales 153.5MM[E] *EMP* 500
SIC 2671 3089 Plastic film, coated or laminated for packaging; Injection molding of plastics
CEO: Gary Masse
**CFO:* Mike Alger

D-U-N-S 02-601-4928
COVERT BUICK INC
SATURN
11750 Research Blvd Ste D, Austin, TX 78759-2446
Tel (512) 583-3000 *Founded/Ownrshp* 1979
Sales 86.4MM[E] *EMP* 186
SIC 5511 7532 Automobiles, new & used; Body shop, automotive
Pr: Duke Covert
CFO: Janet Sopronyi
**Sec:* Philip Robinson
**VP:* Rox Covert
**VP:* Bradford W Elliott
Genl Mgr: Cory Covert
Genl Mgr: Brad Elliot
Genl Mgr: Bart Gunkel
Sls Mgr: Jason Bruce
Sales Asso: Tom Barnett
Sales Asso: Kenneth Ruiz

COVERYS
See PROMUTUAL GROUP INC

COVES EDGE
See MILES HEALTH CARE INC

D-U-N-S 11-211-6117 IMP/EXP
COVESTRO LLC
(*Suby of* COVESTRO DEUTSCHLAND AG)
1 Covestro Cir, Pittsburgh, PA 15205-9723
Tel (412) 413-2000 *Founded/Ownrshp* 2015
Sales 5.0MMM *EMP* 2,500
SIC 2891 2821 Adhesives & sealants; Polyurethane resins; Elastomers, nonvulcanizable (plastics); Polycarbonate resins
Pr: Jerry Maccleary
CFO: John Lemmex
Genl Mgr: Kylee Fink
Genl Mgr: Michael Gallagher
CTO: John Jacobs
Dir IT: Paul Lapierre
IT Man: Joe Dregallo
Mfg Mgr: Dominique Green
Opers Mgr: Herman Campbell
Prd Mgr: Arlene Smith
Mktg Mgr: Jeanne Liu

D-U-N-S 08-032-9810
COVEY PARK II LLC
8401 N Central Expy # 700, Dallas, TX 75225-4402
Tel (214) 548-6000 *Founded/Ownrshp* 2016
Sales 200.0MM *EMP* 104
SIC 1311 Natural gas production
Co-CEO: John D Jacobi
Co-CEO: Alan Levande

COVIDIEN
See MEDTRONIC

COVIDIEN
See EV3 ENDOVASCULAR INC

COVIDIEN HEALTHCARE
See COVIDIEN HOLDING INC

D-U-N-S 80-577-0828 IMP/EXP
COVIDIEN HOLDING INC
COVIDIEN HEALTHCARE
(*Suby of* MEDTRONIC INC) ★
710 Medtronic Pkwy, Minneapolis, MN 55432-5603
Tel (508) 261-8000 *Founded/Ownrshp* 1998
Sales 954.9MM[E] *EMP* 2,470
SIC 3842 Surgical appliances & supplies
Sr VP: John H Masterson
Pr: Andy Ray
COO: Ron Harding
CFO: Steve Amelio
**Treas:* Martina Hund-Mejean
Bd of Dir: John M Connors
VP: Lisa Britt
**VP:* J William McArthur
VP: Sandra McNeill
VP: Keizo Sahashi
Dir Bus: Roberta Guthery
Dir Bus: Daniel Naimey

D-U-N-S 05-861-4483 IMP/EXP
COVIDIEN LP
(*Suby of* MEDTRONIC PUBLIC LIMITED COMPANY)
15 Hampshire St, Mansfield, MA 02048-1113
Tel (508) 261-8000 *Founded/Ownrshp* 2015
Sales 5.6MMM[E] *EMP* 20,300
SIC 3842 3841 3845 5122 Surgical appliances & supplies; Surgical & medical instruments; Needles, suture; Respiratory analysis equipment, electromedical; Magnetic resonance imaging device, nuclear; Drugs, proprietaries & sundries
Pr: Bryan C Hanson
Pr: Ed Kalous
Pr: Timothy R Wright
**Treas:* Gregory Andrulonis
VP: Charlie Bland
VP: Joel Brandon
VP: Richard G Brown
VP: Eric C Green
VP: John M Griffin
VP: Vince Kaiman
VP: Paul McAvoy
VP: Stacy Enxing Seng
VP: Mike Spears
VP: Peter Sturtevant
VP: Peter L Wehrly
Exec: Susan T Rigo
Dir Surg: Michael Gunning
Dir Surg: Marco Polizzi
Dir Bus: Caron Salkin

D-U-N-S 07-783-3051
COVILLE INC
8065 N Point Blvd Ste O, Winston Salem, NC 27106-3287
Tel (336) 759-0115 *Founded/Ownrshp* 1975
Sales 115.6MM[E] *EMP* 113
SIC 5131 Piece goods & other fabrics
Pr: Don Trexler
CFO: Henry Jordan
**VP:* Laurie Trexler

COVINA VALLEY USD
See COVINA-VALLEY UNIFIED SCHOOL DISTRICT FACILITIES FINANCE CORP

D-U-N-S 07-020-3732
COVINA-VALLEY UNIFIED SCHOOL DISTRICT FACILITIES FINANCE CORP
COVINA VALLEY USD
519 E Badillo St, Covina, CA 91723-2803
Tel (626) 974-7000 *Founded/Ownrshp* 1896
Sales 143.9MM[E] *EMP* 2,636
SIC 8211 Public combined elementary & secondary school
CEO: Jennifer Root
Genl Mgr: Richard Sheehan
Sys Mgr: Rob Fitzgerald

D-U-N-S 07-264-6524
COVINGTON & BURLING LLP
1 Citycenter 850 Tenth, Washington, DC 20001
Tel (202) 662-6000 *Founded/Ownrshp* 1919
Sales 303.4MM[E] *EMP* 1,600
SIC 8111 General practice law office
Genl Pt: Timothy C Hester
Pt: Jonathan S Blake
Pt: Roger Enock
Pt: Haywood S Gilliam Jr
Pt: Charles Miller
Pt: Linda L Thompson
Mng Pt: Peter W Bogaert
Mng Pt: Donald W Brown
Mng Pt: Nelson W Cunningham
V Ch: Lanny A Breuer
Ex Dir: John B Waters

D-U-N-S 03-290-4729
COVINGTON BOARD OF EDUCATION
25 E 7th St, Covington, KY 41011-2401
Tel (859) 292-5800 *Founded/Ownrshp* 1900
Sales 46.0MM *EMP* 1,000
SIC 8211 Public elementary & secondary schools

D-U-N-S 14-498-7674
COW CREEK BAND OF UMPQUA TRIBE OF INDIANS
COW CREEK GMING RGULATORY COMM
2371 Ne Stephens St, Roseburg, OR 97470-1399
Tel (541) 957-8945 *Founded/Ownrshp* 1981
Sales NA *EMP* 1,000
SIC 9131 6321 7999 Indian reservation; Fraternal accident & health insurance organizations; Gambling & lottery services; Bingo hall
Ex Dir: Carl Salter
Ex Dir: Justin Mathison

COW CREEK GMING RGULATORY COMM
See COW CREEK BAND OF UMPQUA TRIBE OF INDIANS

COWAN LOGISTICS
See COWAN SYSTEMS LLC

D-U-N-S 82-483-7249 IMP
COWAN SYSTEMS LLC
COWAN LOGISTICS
4555 Hollins Ferry Rd, Baltimore, MD 21227-4610
Tel (410) 247-0800 *Founded/Ownrshp* 1994
Sales 435.0MM *EMP* 1,800
SIC 4213 Trucking, except local
Pr: Dennis Morgan
CFO: Joe Scheiner
Sr VP: Richard Warner
VP: Richard Cichon
VP: Steven Wells
VP: Wayne Zdenek
Dir Bus: Salvatore Dani
Genl Mgr: Chris Aversa
Snr Ntwrk: Tariq Qureshi
CTO: Sal Randazzo
VP Opers: Jim Mechlinski

COWBOOM
See BUY BEST PURCHASING LLC

D-U-N-S 09-949-3322
■ COWEN AND CO LLC
(*Suby of* COWEN HOLDINGS INC) ★
599 Lexington Ave Fl 19, New York, NY 10022-7773
Tel (646) 562-1000 *Founded/Ownrshp* 1940
Sales 108.1MM[E] *EMP* 300
SIC 6211 Brokers, security; Dealers, security
CEO: Jeffrey Solomon
**Pr:* Kim Fennebresque
Pr: Ken Hagan
CFO: Alyson I Goldfarb
**CFO:* Thomas Conner
CFO: Steve Lasota
Bd of Dir: Mark E Kaplan
Ofcr: John Fiorello
Ofcr: John Holmes
Sr VP: Andrea Black
VP: Sharon Andrews
VP: Kris Blohm
VP: John Kernan
VP: Owen Littman
VP: Denis Molloy
VP: Kyle Rasbach
VP: Carolyne Rumah
VP: Aubrey Smith
VP: Rob Weir
VP: Peggy Winslow
VP: Dave Yeung

D-U-N-S 83-314-4004
▲ COWEN GROUP INC
599 Lexington Ave, New York, NY 10022-6030
Tel (212) 845-7900 *Founded/Ownrshp* 1994
Sales 464.5MM *EMP* 769[E]
Tkr Sym COWN *Exch* NGS
SIC 6211 6722 Security brokers & dealers; Mutual funds, selling by independent salesperson; Management investment, open-end; Mutual fund sales, on own account
Ch Bd: Peter A Cohen
Pr: Michael Singer
Pr: Jeffrey M Solomon
COO: John Holmes
CFO: Stephen A Lasota
Board of Directors: Katherine E Dietze, Steven Kotler, Jerome S Markowitz, Jack H Nusbaum, Douglas A Rediker, Joseph R Wright

D-U-N-S 78-059-0563
■ COWEN HOLDINGS INC
(*Suby of* COWEN GROUP INC) ★
599 Lexington Ave Fl 26, New York, NY 10022-7650
Tel (212) 562-1000 *Founded/Ownrshp* 2009
Sales 233.8MM *EMP* 449[E]
Accts Pricewaterhousecoopers Llp Ne
SIC 6211 6159 Security brokers & dealers; Intermediate investment banks
CFO: Thomas K Conner
Pr: Farah Naz
COO: Ren Kraenzlin
Ofcr: Mark A Egert
VP: Matthew Reber
VP: Christopher A White
Div/Sub He: Stuart Gould
Prin: Nicholas Desin
Ex Dir: Jack Nussbaum
Ex Dir: C Richards
Mng Dir: Todd Ackerman

D-U-N-S 07-979-8809
COWETA COUNTY SCHOOL SYSTEM
237 Jackson St, Newnan, GA 30263-1154
Tel (770) 254-2800 *Founded/Ownrshp* 2015
Sales 220.0MM *EMP* 2,950[E]
SIC 8211 Public elementary & secondary schools
CFO: Cathe Nixon
Trst: Lisa Skinner
Comm Dir: Dean Jackson

D-U-N-S 13-314-3438
COWETA COUNTY SCHOOL SYSTEM BOARD OF EDUCATION
237 Jackson St, Newnan, GA 30263-1154
Tel (770) 254-2801 *Founded/Ownrshp* 1969
Sales 209.0MM[E] *EMP* 3,000
Accts Greg S Griffin Atlanta Geor
SIC 8211 School board
Ch: Frank Farmer
**V Ch:* Larry Robertson

D-U-N-S 00-402-6654 EXP
COWIN EQUIPMENT CO INC (AL)
(*Suby of* C & C HOLDING INC) ★
2238 Pinson Valley Pkwy, Birmingham, AL 35217-2009
Tel (205) 841-6666 *Founded/Ownrshp* 1940, 1982
Sales 150.0MM *EMP* 205
SIC 5082 General construction machinery & equipment
Pr: James P Cowin
COO: Dan Searcy
Sec: George Tickle
VP: John J Cowin
VP: Rod Drake
VP: Tim Gann
VP: Dennis McPoland
VP: P Virnich

D-U-N-S 00-906-6879
COWLES PUBLISHING CO (WA)
JOURNAL OF BUSINESS
999 W Riverside Ave, Spokane, WA 99201-1006
Tel (509) 459-5000 *Founded/Ownrshp* 1882, 1883
Sales 154.0MMᴱ *EMP* 850
SIC 2711 2611 2621 4833 Newspapers, publishing & printing; Pulp produced from wood base; Newsprint paper; Television broadcasting stations
Pr: William Stacey Cowles
Prd Mgr: Laurie Lunzer
Assoc Ed: Rebecca Nappi

COWLITZ COUNTY PUD
See PUBLIC UTILITY DISTRICT NO 1 OF COWLITZ COUNTY

D-U-N-S 06-073-5404
COWORX STAFFING SERVICES LLC
1375 Plainfield Ave Ste 1, Watchung, NJ 07069-5482
Tel (908) 757-5300 *Founded/Ownrshp* 2000
Sales 1.0MMMᴱ *EMP* 50,000
SIC 7361 8721 Employment agencies; Payroll accounting service
Assoc VP: Henry Kielbasa
Ex VP: Ken Sudnikovich
Ex Dir: Tara Perroty
Area Mgr: Bonnie Cavallo
Brnch Mgr: Gia Page
Brnch Mgr: Ursula Sowinski
Site Mgr: Jessica Brower
Opers Mgr: Meredith Adragna

D-U-N-S 00-901-7252
COX ARIZONA TELCOM LLC
(*Suby of* COX COMMUNICATIONS ARIZONA LLC) ★
1400 Lake Hearn Dr Ne, Brookhaven, GA 30319-1464
Tel (404) 843-5000 *Founded/Ownrshp* 1956, 2013
Sales 2.7MMMᴱ *EMP* 22,000ᴱ
SIC 4841 Cable television services
Prin: Jim Robbins
**Pr:* Patrick J Esser
**CFO:* Mark F Bowser
**Ex VP:* Jill Campbell
**Ex VP:* Barry R Elson
**Ex VP:* Kevin Hart
**Ex VP:* Rhonda Taylor
**Sr VP:* Ajit M Dalvi
**Sr VP:* Jimmy W Hayes
**Sr VP:* David Woodrow
VP: Steve Rivley

D-U-N-S 78-766-3421
COX AUTO TRADER PUBLICATIONS INC
(*Suby of* COX ENTERPRISES INC) ★
100 W Plume St, Norfolk, VA 23510-1618
Tel (757) 531-7000 *Founded/Ownrshp* 2006
Sales 227.7MMᴱ *EMP* 5,000
SIC 2721 Periodicals: publishing only
Pr: Sandy Schwartz
**CFO:* Willie Dorsey
Manager: Kristen Oliver

COX AUTOMOTIVE
See AUTOTRADER.COM INC

D-U-N-S 14-976-3104 IMP/EXP
COX AUTOMOTIVE INC
(*Suby of* COX ENTERPRISES INC) ★
3003 Summit Blvd Fl 200, Brookhaven, GA 30319-1469
Tel (404) 843-5000 *Founded/Ownrshp* 1988
Sales 7.1MMMᴱ *EMP* 37,500
SIC 5012

D-U-N-S 10-066-7026
COX BUSINESS SERVICES LLC
(*Suby of* C O X) ★
1400 Lake Hearn Dr Ne, Brookhaven, GA 30319-1464
Tel (404) 843-5000 *Founded/Ownrshp* 2013
Sales 660.0MM *EMP* 140
SIC 4813 Telephone communication, except radio
Mktg Dir: Jonathon Cobb

COX CASTLE
See COX CASTLE & NICHOLSON LLP

D-U-N-S 06-670-2515
COX CASTLE & NICHOLSON LLP
COX CASTLE
2029 Cntury Nicholson Llp, Los Angeles, CA 90067
Tel (310) 284-2200 *Founded/Ownrshp* 1968
Sales 98.0MM *EMP* 235
SIC 8111 General practice attorney, lawyer
Pt: Gary A Glick
Pt: Lindsey H Barr
Pt: Robin L Bennett
Pt: Kenneth B Bley
Pt: Erica A Bose
Pt: Margo N Bradish
Pt: Preston W Brooks
Pt: Marlene Goodfried
Pt: Edward F Quigley
Pt: David W Wensley
Pt: Mathew A Wyman
Pt: Amanda Arnall
Pr: Eugenie Coloma-Smith
Pr: Negar Nourmohamadi
COO: Janet Kasabian

D-U-N-S 07-921-9169
COX COMMUNICATIONS ARIZONA LLC
(*Suby of* C O X) ★
6305 Pchtree Dunwoody Rd, Atlanta, GA 30328-4535
Tel (404) 843-5000 *Founded/Ownrshp* 2001, 2013
Sales 2.7MMMᴱ *EMP* 764ᴱ
SIC 4841 Cable television services

D-U-N-S 04-365-8160
COX COMMUNICATIONS CALIFORNIA LLC
(*Suby of* C O X) ★
6205 Pachtree Dunwoody Rd, Atlanta, GA 30328-4524
Tel (404) 843-5000 *Founded/Ownrshp* 2013
Sales 83.7MMᴱ *EMP* 1,646ᴱ
SIC 4841 Cable television services
Prin: Patrick J Esser
Snr Mgr: Tom Dlugolecki
Board of Directors: Mark Bowser, Patrick Esser, Jennifer Hightower

D-U-N-S 01-088-6542
COX COMMUNICATIONS INC
(*Suby of* COX ENTERPRISES INC) ★
1550 W Deer Valley Rd, Phoenix, AZ 85027-2121
Tel (404) 269-6736 *Founded/Ownrshp* 1994
Sales 8.6MMM *EMP* 21,323
SIC 4841 Cable & other pay television services
Pr: Tony Setchel
Prin: Heather Housen

D-U-N-S 78-911-1374 IMP
COX COMMUNICATIONS INC
(*Suby of* COX ENTERPRISES INC) ★
6205 B Pchtree Dunwody Ne, Atlanta, GA 30328-4524
Tel (404) 843-5000 *Founded/Ownrshp* 1994
Sales 6.0MMMᴱ *EMP* 22,405
SIC 4841 4813 Cable television services; Local & long distance telephone communications
Pr: Patrick J Esser
Pr: John Bell
**COO:* Jill Campbell
**CFO:* Mark F Bowser
Treas: Susan W Coker
Bd of Dir: Bryan McIntyre
Bd of Dir: John Price
**Ofcr:* Mark Greatrex
Ex VP: Len Barlik
**Ex VP:* Kevin Hart
Ex VP: Steve Necessary
**Ex VP:* Asheesh Saksena
Sr VP: Jay Allbaugh
Sr VP: Sam Attisha
Sr VP: David A Bialis
Sr VP: David Blau
**Sr VP:* Christopher J Bowick
Sr VP: Marilyn Burrows
**Sr VP:* James A Hatcher
Sr VP: Mark A Kaish
Sr VP: Percy J Kirk
Board of Directors: John M Dyer, Patrick J Esser, Jimmy W Hayes

D-U-N-S 04-291-6895
COX COMMUNICATIONS LAS VEGAS INC
(*Suby of* COX COMMUNICATIONS INC) ★
6205 Pachtree Dunwoody Rd, Atlanta, GA 30328-4524
Tel (404) 269-7898 *Founded/Ownrshp* 1998
Sales 584.4MMᴱ *EMP* 2,700
SIC 4841 Cable & other pay television services
Pr: Pat Esser
**CFO:* Mark Bowser
**Treas:* Maria Friedman
Ex VP: Jill Campbell
VP: Joe Luppino
VP: Belinda Patterson
**VP:* Steve Rowley
Ex Dir: Troy Broussard
Ex Dir: Beth Dunning
Ex Dir: Troy Meyers
Prgrm Mgr: Clay Robbins

D-U-N-S 04-690-1799 IMP/EXP
COX ENTERPRISES INC
6205 Pachtree Dunwoody Rd, Atlanta, GA 30328-4524
Tel (678) 645-0000 *Founded/Ownrshp* 1968
Sales 33.7MMMᴱ *EMP* 60,000
SIC 4841 4813 2711 4833 7389 4832 Cable & other pay television services; Telephone communication, except radio; Commercial printing & newspaper publishing combined; Television broadcasting stations; Auctioneers, fee basis; Radio broadcasting stations
Ch: James Kennedy
Pr: Mark Dawson
Pr: Jon Gamble
**Pr:* S Taylor Glover
Pr: George Markley
Pr: Betsy Vencius
**CEO:* John M Dyer
**CEO:* Christopher Williams
**COO:* Alex Taylor
**CFO:* Dallas Clement
CFO: Dallas S Clement
Treas: Richard Jacobson
Ex VP: Brian Cooper
**Ex VP:* Marybeth N Leamer
Ex VP: Alexander C Taylor
VP: Mark Beck
VP: Lance Beitler
VP: Brett Blattman
VP: Robert Cahn
VP: Anthony Dacong
VP: Maria Friedman
Board of Directors: Henry Parry-Okeden

COX HEALTH
See LESTER E COX MEDICAL CENTER

D-U-N-S 62-674-5736
COX HOLDINGS INC
(*Suby of* COX ENTERPRISES INC) ★
1400 Lake Hearn Dr Ne, Brookhaven, GA 30319-1464
Tel (404) 843-5000 *Founded/Ownrshp* 1985
Sales 4.3MMMᴱ *EMP* 22,530
SIC 4841 4813 Cable & other pay television services; Telephone communication, except radio
VP: Preston Barnett

D-U-N-S 00-334-7150 EXP
COX INDUSTRIES INC (SC)
860 Cannon Bridge Rd, Orangeburg, SC 29115-7284
Tel (803) 534-7467 *Founded/Ownrshp* 1952
Sales 205.5MMᴱ *EMP* 400
SIC 2411 2491 Wooden bolts, hewn; Poles, posts & pilings: untreated wood; Structural lumber & timber, treated wood
CEO: R Michael Johnson
**COO:* Greg Campbell
CFO: Phil Tetterton
VP: Joe Passadore
IT Man: Linda McDaniel
Opers Mgr: John Harrell
Sls Mgr: James Norton

D-U-N-S 09-327-4868
COX INTERIOR INC (KY)
1751 Old Columbia Rd, Campbellsville, KY 42718-9011
Tel (270) 789-3129 *Founded/Ownrshp* 1978
Sales 206.9MMᴱ *EMP* 790
SIC 2431 Moldings, wood: unfinished & prefinished; Trim, wood; Staircases, stairs & railings; Doors & door parts & trim, wood
Pr: Barry G Cox
CFO: Lillian Lawhorn Smith
Sec: Kay Cox Legg
VP: Lanny Cox
Dir IT: Gary Bell
Sales Asso: Randy Huntzinger

COX MEDIA GROUP
See NEW MANHEIM AUTO AUCTIONS LIMITED (INC)

D-U-N-S 80-920-2294
COX MEDIA GROUP LLC
(*Suby of* COX ENTERPRISES INC) ★
6205 Pachtree Dunwoody Rd, Atlanta, GA 30328-4524
Tel (678) 645-0000 *Founded/Ownrshp* 1993
Sales 1.7MMM *EMP* 18,967
SIC 4833 4832 7922 7313 Television broadcasting stations; Radio broadcasting stations; Television program, including commercial producers; Television & radio time sales
Pr: Bill Hoffman
CFO: Brett Fennell
CFO: Charles Odom
Treas: Susan Coker
Bd of Dir: Jamie Kennedy
Ofcr: Laurissa Phillips
Rgnl VP: Marc W Morgan
Ex VP: John M Dyer
Ex VP: Andrew S Fisher
Ex VP: Kim Guthrie
Ex VP: Kevin Hart
Ex VP: Bill Hendrich
Ex VP: Neil Johnston
Ex VP: Michael J Joseph
Ex VP: Robert S Neil
Ex VP: Kevin T O'Brien
Ex VP: Marian Pittman
Ex VP: Alex Taylor
Sr VP: Harry Delaney
Sr VP: Richard A Reis
Sr VP: John J Rouse Jr

D-U-N-S 00-424-3077
COX MEDIA GROUP OHIO INC
(*Suby of* ATLANTA JOURNAL & CONSTITUTION) ★
1611 S Main St, Dayton, OH 45409-2547
Tel (937) 225-2000 *Founded/Ownrshp* 1993
Sales 128.3MMᴱ *EMP* 1,000
SIC 2711 Newspapers, publishing & printing
VP: Julia Wallace
CFO: Robert Zikias
VP: Mark Beck
VP: Phonda Gamble
DP Exec: Julie Campbell
Dir IT: Dennis Behm
IT Man: Ken Canfield
VP Opers: Joe McKinnon
Sales Exec: Pat Jones
Mktg Dir: Lynn Hulsey
Mktg Mgr: Barbara Kedziora

D-U-N-S 61-573-5115
COX MEDIA LLC
CABLE REP ADVERTISING
(*Suby of* C O X) ★
1400 Lake Hearn Dr Ne, Brookhaven, GA 30319-1464
Tel (404) 843-5000 *Founded/Ownrshp* 2013
Sales 319.2MMᴱ *EMP* 1,649ᴱ
SIC 4841 7313 Cable television services; Radio, television, publisher representatives
Pr: James O Robbins
**Treas:* Jimmy Hayes
Sr VP: Bill Fitzimmons
VP: Jennifer Chinn
**VP:* Ajit Dalvi
VP: Michael Latino
VP: Mark McGuire
VP: Kevin Moran
VP: Shelli Osborn
VP: James Renkin
VP: Stephen Rowley
VP: Scott Wise

D-U-N-S 13-336-9772
COX NEVADA TELCOM LLC
(*Suby of* COX COMMUNICATIONS LAS VEGAS INC) ★
1400 Lake Hearn Dr Ne, Brookhaven, GA 30319-1464
Tel (404) 269-7898 *Founded/Ownrshp* 2003
Sales 64.8MMᴱ *EMP* 1,380
SIC 4841 Cable & other pay television services
Pr: Patrick Esser
CFO: Mark Bowser
Treas: Katherine Decker
VP: Steve Rowley

D-U-N-S 88-460-0545 IMP
COX NEWSPAPERS INC
ATLANTA JOURNAL & CONSTITUTION
(*Suby of* COX MEDIA GROUP LLC) ★
6205 Peachtree Dunwoody, Atlanta, GA 30328-4524
Tel (678) 645-0000 *Founded/Ownrshp* 1993
Sales 1.3MMMᴱ *EMP* 15,000
SIC 2711 Newspapers
Pr: Sanford Schwartz
**Ex VP:* Michael Joseph
VP: Jami Buck-Swann
VP: Christopher Capelli
**VP:* Cathy Coffey
**VP:* Stan Richmond
VP: Bob Willoughby
VP Bus Dev: Lacey Lewis
Snr Sftwr: Edward Serzo
Dir IT: Dan Leonard
IT Man: Greg Ciul

D-U-N-S 05-487-2130
COX OIL CO INC
MAVERICK QUICK SHOPS
623 Perkins St, Union City, TN 38261-3949
Tel (731) 885-6444 *Founded/Ownrshp* 1970
Sales 143.6MMᴱ *EMP* 435
Accts Alexander Thompson Arnold Pllc
SIC 5541 5411 Filling stations, gasoline; Convenience stores
CEO: Mark McBride
**Ch Bd:* Michael E Cox
**Pr:* Barry James
**Treas:* Jacqueline Richardson
Exec: Lori Jackson

D-U-N-S 95-957-1399
COX RADIO INC
(*Suby of* COX MEDIA GROUP LLC) ★
6205 Pachtree Dunwoody Rd, Atlanta, GA 30328-4524
Tel (678) 645-0000 *Founded/Ownrshp* 2009
Sales 182.2MMᴱ *EMP* 2,033
SIC 4832 Radio broadcasting stations
Pr: Bill Hoffman
**COO:* Marc W Morgan
**CFO:* Neil O Johnston
Bd of Dir: W Nick
VP: Rob Babin
VP: Mark Beck
VP: Perkins Faith
VP: Joe George
**VP:* Richard A Reis
VP: Nick Roberts
VP: Deborah Thomas

D-U-N-S 78-214-4661
COX SOUTHWEST HOLDINGS LP
(*Suby of* COX COMMUNICATIONS INC) ★
3015 S Southeast Loop 323, Tyler, TX 75701-7320
Tel (903) 595-3701 *Founded/Ownrshp* 1999
Sales 41.5MMᴱ *EMP* 1,200
SIC 4841 Cable television services
Pr: James O Robins
**VP:* Janet Bernard

COX TARGET MEDIA
See VALPAK DIRECT MARKETING SYSTEMS INC

D-U-N-S 36-427-4126
COX TARGET MEDIA INC
VALPAK DIRECT MKTG SYSTEMS
(*Suby of* COX ENTERPRISES INC) ★
1 Valpak Ave N, Saint Petersburg, FL 33716-4102
Tel (727) 399-3000 *Founded/Ownrshp* 1968
Sales 81.8MMᴱ *EMP* 1,245
SIC 7331 8741 8742 2759 Direct mail advertising services; Administrative management; Management consulting services; Commercial printing
Pr: Michael Vivio
**Treas:* Katherine K Decker
**Treas:* Buddy Solimon
Ex VP: Joe Bourdow
Ex VP: Mike Collette
Ex VP: Robert Oswaks
**Ex VP:* Jim Sampey
**Sr VP:* Melissa L Fisher
VP: Tom Bates
VP: Ann Boeker
VP: Dale Campbell
VP: Brian Cooper
**VP:* Maria Friedman
VP: Steve Gracie
VP: Jon Harms
VP: Jeff Hausman
VP: Amy King
VP: Sullivan Lisa
VP: Rick McElwain
VP: Phil Mettra
VP: Carol Osborne

D-U-N-S 16-192-2286 IMP
COX TEXAS NEWSPAPERS LP
AUSTIN AMERICAN STATESMAN
(*Suby of* LUFKIN DAILY NEWS) ★
305 S Congress Ave, Austin, TX 78704-1200
Tel (512) 445-3500 *Founded/Ownrshp* 1985
Sales 116.4MMᴱ *EMP* 1,500
SIC 2711 Newspapers
VP: Steve Dorsey
Exec: Lennell Duggan
Prin: Susie Ellwood
Opers Mgr: Jason Jarrett
Sls Dir: Sylvia Rodriguez
Mktg Mgr: Susanne Harm
Snr Mgr: Brian Gaar

D-U-N-S 55-671-5696
COX TEXAS PUBLICATIONS INC
LUFKIN DAILY NEWS
(*Suby of* ATLANTA JOURNAL & CONSTITUTION) ★
6205 Pachtree Dunwoody Rd, Atlanta, GA 30328-4524
Tel (404) 843-5000 *Founded/Ownrshp* 1985
Sales 503.8MMᴱ *EMP* 15,000
SIC 2711 Newspapers
Pr: Jay Smith
**Treas:* Charles B Solmon
**VP:* Sandy Schwartz

D-U-N-S 07-309-6666 EXP
COX WOOD PRESERVING CO
(*Suby of* COX INDUSTRIES INC) ★
860 Cannon Bridge Rd, Orangeburg, SC 29115-7284
Tel (803) 534-7467 *Founded/Ownrshp* 1998
Sales 88.1MMᴱ *EMP* 200
SIC 2491 Wood preserving
CEO: Michael Johnson
**Pr:* Brian Hayson
**COO:* Greg Campbell
IT Man: Hailey Kizer

D-U-N-S 07-117-2589
COXCOM LLC
COX
(*Suby of* COX ENTERPRISES INC) ★
1400 Lake Hearn Dr Ne, Brookhaven, GA 30319-1464
Tel (404) 843-5000 *Founded/Ownrshp* 1996
Sales 4.0MMMᴱ *EMP* 1,000
SIC 4841 4813 Cable television services; Local & long distance telephone communications
CEO: Pat Esserr
**Treas:* Coker Susan W
**Ex VP:* Mark F Bowser
**Ex VP:* Jill Campbell
**Sr VP:* Billy Farina
**VP:* Nicole Buie
**VP:* Sarah Knott
VP: Robert Latvis
**VP:* Garry McCollum
VP: Jim Ruel
VP: Toni Stubbs

COXHEALTH
See LESTER E COX MEDICAL CENTERS

D-U-N-S 06-510-1842
COXS FOODARAMA INC (TX)
10810 S Post Oak Rd, Houston, TX 77035-3102
Tel (713) 723-8683 Founded/Ownrshp 1973
Sales 87.2MM^E EMP 600
SIC 5411 Grocery stores, independent
Pr: Carrol Cox
*Sec: Kim Alepa
*VP: Gary Fisher
*VP: Patricia Smith

D-U-N-S 02-095-6764
COYANOSA GAS SERVICES CORP
10214 Walkerton Ln, Oakton, VA 22124-3031
Tel (703) 938-7984 Founded/Ownrshp 2001
Sales 95.3MM EMP 2
Accts Rmd Financial Inc Rockville
SIC 4924 Natural gas distribution
Pr: Jerry V Curry

D-U-N-S 04-761-6958
COYNE INTERNATIONAL ENTERPRISES CORP
COYNE TEXTILE SERVICES
140 Cortland Ave, Syracuse, NY 13202-3411
Tel (315) 475-1626 Founded/Ownrshp 1929
Sales 84.5MM^E EMP 745
SIC 7218

COYNE TEXTILE SERVICES
See COYNE INTERNATIONAL ENTERPRISES CORP

D-U-N-S 82-846-7923
■ **COYOTE LOGISTICS LLC**
(Suby of UPS) ★
2545 W Diversey Ave Fl 3, Chicago, IL 60647-7172
Tel (877) 626-9683 Founded/Ownrshp 2015
Sales 624.4MM^E EMP 2,000
SIC 4731 Freight transportation arrangement
CEO: Jeff Silver
Pr: James Jacobs
*COO: Jim Sharman
*CFO: Jonathan Sisler
*Ofcr: Chris Pickett
VP: Dennis Hedlund
VP: Kris Kovacs
VP: Jodi Navta
VP: Jason Rice
*VP: Joson Rice
Genl Mgr: David Herbert

D-U-N-S 08-477-1682
COZEN OCONNOR
1650 Market St Ste 2800, Philadelphia, PA 19103-7325
Tel (215) 665-2053 Founded/Ownrshp 1970
Sales 236.8MM^E EMP 1,100
SIC 8111 General practice attorney, lawyer; Taxation law; Real estate law; Corporate, partnership & business law
CEO: Michael J Heller
Mng Pt: Vincent R McGuinness Jr
Mng Pt: Thomas McKay
V Ch: Warren F Jacoby
*Pr: Thomas A Decker
Pr: Cindy Mooney
COO: David W Ellman
*CFO: Cyndi Stains
CFO: Hank Windmoeller
Ofcr: Elise Spata
VP: Lanny Schwartz

COZYMEL'S
See COASTAL RESTAURANTS GP LLC

CP
See COLUMBIA PIPE & SUPPLY CO

D-U-N-S 07-852-2024
CP DENTAL LLC
2727 Skyway Dr, Santa Maria, CA 93455-1413
Tel (800) 433-6628 Founded/Ownrshp 2011
Sales 151.7MM^E EMP 710^E
SIC 3843 Dental equipment

D-U-N-S 02-318-9418
CP FEEDS LLC
16322 W Washington St, Valders, WI 54245-9761
Tel (920) 775-9600 Founded/Ownrshp 2000
Sales 125.6MM EMP 40
Accts Erickson & Associates Sc A
SIC 5153 5191 Grains; Feed
Genl Mgr: Jim Loefer
Sales Asso: Michelle Klemme

D-U-N-S 00-101-7545 IMP/EXP
CP KELCO US INC (GA)
(Suby of JM HUBER CORP) ★
3100 Cumberland Blvd Se # 600, Atlanta, GA 30339-5940
Tel (678) 247-7300 Founded/Ownrshp 2000
Sales 679.5MM^E EMP 2,500
SIC 2899 Sizes
Pr: Donald Rubright
Pr: Maureen Bellantoni
*CFO: Phillip Patterson
Bd of Dir: David D Fry
VP: Brian Bender
VP: E C Bowman
VP: Rodney Canada
VP: Bart Edward
VP: Martin Sapone
VP: John Tayler
VP: Didier Viala
Dir Risk M: David Gault
*Dir Risk M: John Taylor

D-U-N-S 07-944-3673
CP OPCO LLC
CLASSIC PARTY RENTALS
(Suby of CP HOLDING)
901 W Hillcrest Blvd, Inglewood, CA 90301-2100
Tel (310) 966-4900 Founded/Ownrshp 2014
Sales 250.0MM^E EMP 2,300
SIC 7299 Facility rental & party planning services
Pr: Brent Mumford
*CFO: Charles Brown

D-U-N-S 07-917-7087
CPA 17 LIMITED PARTNERSHIP
W. P. CAREY FOUNDATION
50 Rockefeller Plz, New York, NY 10020-1605
Tel (212) 492-1100 Founded/Ownrshp 2007
Sales 365.8MM EMP 1
SIC 8742 Financial consultant
CEO: Trevor P Bond

CPA:17
See CORPORATE PROPERTY ASSOCIATES 17 - GLOBAL INC

D-U-N-S 01-965-5588
CPC LOGISTICS INC (MO)
14528 South Outer 40 Rd # 210, Chesterfield, MO 63017-5743
Tel (314) 542-2266 Founded/Ownrshp 1973
Sales 299.8MM^E EMP 3,700
SIC 4731 Freight transportation arrangement
CEO: Doug Crowell
CFO: Duane Trower
Ex VP: Robert Boyich
Ex VP: Larry Foltz
Ex VP: Butch Wallis
VP: John Bickel Jr
VP: Jeff Hart
VP: Bill Steimel
Rgnl Mgr: Al Potter
Div Mgr: Ken Pruitt
Opers Supe: Jim Ponder
Board of Directors: John Bickel, John Dowell, Daniel Legear

CPCHEM
See CHEVRON PHILLIPS CHEMICAL CO LP

D-U-N-S 07-840-4207
CPD ALASKA LLC
(Suby of CROWLEY MARITIME CORP) ★
201 Arctic Slope Ave, Anchorage, AK 99518-3033
Tel (907) 777-5505 Founded/Ownrshp 2011
Sales 615.9MM^E EMP 270^E
SIC 5171 Petroleum bulk stations & terminals

CPE
See CALLON PETROLEUM OPERATING CO

CPES
See COMMUNITY PROVIDER OF ENRICHMENT SERVICES INC

D-U-N-S 00-137-4123 IMP/EXP
■ **CPFILMS INC**
SOLUTIAS PERFORMANCE FILMS DIV
(Suby of SOLUTIA INC) ★
4210 The Great Rd, Fieldale, VA 24089-3531
Tel (276) 627-3000 Founded/Ownrshp 1932
Sales 173.2MM^E EMP 700
SIC 3081 Plastic film & sheet
Pr: Jeff Quinn
*Prin: Allen Izey

CPG
See CLASS PRODUCE GROUP LLC

CPG INTERNATIONAL
See CPG INTERNATIONAL INC

D-U-N-S 10-620-5172
■ **CPG INTERNATIONAL INC**
CPG INTERNATIONAL
(Suby of ARES MANAGEMENT LLC) ★
888 N Keyser Ave, Scranton, PA 18504-9723
Tel (570) 558-8000 Founded/Ownrshp 2013
Sales 250.4MM^E EMP 692^E
SIC 3089 3272 Plastic hardware & building products; Prefabricated plastic buildings; Building materials, except block or brick: concrete
CEO: Eric K Jungbluth
Pr: Jason Grommon
Sr VP: Ken Buck
VP: Jim Gross
VP: Don Wharton
Exec: Sandy Jones
S&M/VP: Bruce Merklinghaus

D-U-N-S 02-978-6477
CPH MONARCH HOTEL LLC
ST REGIS RESORT MONARCH BEACH
(Suby of WASHINGTON HOLDINGS) ★
1 Monarch Beach Resort, Dana Point, CA 92629-4085
Tel (949) 234-3200 Founded/Ownrshp 2014
Sales 62.4MM^E EMP 1,100
SIC 7011 Resort hotel
Pr: Paul Makarechian
Sls Mgr: Denise McConnell
Board of Directors: Mark Rob

CPI
See CARDIAC PACEMAKERS INC

CPI
See COMMUNICATIONS & POWER INDUSTRIES LLC

D-U-N-S 05-484-0228
CPI AEROSTRUCTURES INC (NY)
91 Heartland Blvd, Edgewood, NY 11717-8330
Tel (631) 586-5200 Founded/Ownrshp 1980
Sales 100.2MM EMP 280
Tkr Sym CVU Exch ASE
SIC 3728 Aircraft parts & equipment
Pr: Douglas McCrosson
*Ch Bd: Eric S Rosenfeld
CFO: Vincent Palazzolo
VP: Barry Fratello
Prgrm Mgr: Jessica Hill
Board of Directors: Harvey J Bazaar, Carey E Bond, Michael Faber, Kenneth McSweeney, Walter Paulick, Terry Stinson

D-U-N-S 07-975-1255
CPI BUYER LLC
(Suby of GTCR LLC) ★
300 N La Salle Dr # 5600, Chicago, IL 60654-3406
Tel (312) 382-2200 Founded/Ownrshp 2014
Sales 252.9MM^E EMP 353^E
SIC 5049 Laboratory equipment, except medical or dental
Pr: Bernd Brust
*CFO: Rajesh Asarpota

D-U-N-S 03-066-7182 EXP
CPI CARD GROUP - COLORADO INC
(Suby of CPI HOLDING CO) ★
10368 W Centennial Rd A, Littleton, CO 80127-4296
Tel (303) 973-9311 Founded/Ownrshp 1995
Sales 83.8MM^E EMP 350^E
SIC 3089 Identification cards, plastic
Pr: Steve Montross
CFO: David Brush
CFO: Scott Heck
Ofcr: Lisa Jacoba
VP: Antonio Accornero
VP: Diane Jackson
VP: Russ McGrane
VP: Docia Myer
Dir Bus: Guillaume Grincourt
Board of Directors: Janice Platzer

D-U-N-S 08-000-3365
CPI CARD GROUP INC
10368 W Centennial Rd A, Littleton, CO 80127-4296
Tel (303) 973-9311 Founded/Ownrshp 2007, 1982
Sales NA EMP 1,386
Tkr Sym PMTS Exch NGS
SIC 6153 Short-term business credit
Pr: Steven Montross
*Ch Bd: Bradley Seaman
CFO: David Brush
Ofcr: Lisa Jacoba
Ex VP: William Dinker
Sr VP: Jason Bohrer
Board of Directors: Diane Fulton, Douglas Pearce, Robert Pearce, Nicholas Peters David Rown, Silvio Tavares

D-U-N-S 36-391-1046 IMP
CPI HOLDING CO
10368 W Centennial Rd, Littleton, CO 80127-4295
Tel (303) 973-9311 Founded/Ownrshp 1995
Sales 111.2MM^E EMP 350
SIC 2821 Plastics materials & resins
Pr: Steve Montross
*Treas: Russell Mc Grane
*Prin: Antonio Accornero

D-U-N-S 96-820-2353
CPI INTERNATIONAL HOLDING CORP
811 Hansen Way, Palo Alto, CA 94304-1031
Tel (650) 846-2900 Founded/Ownrshp 2011
Sales 494.6MM EMP 5^E
SIC 3679 Electronic circuits
CEO: O Joe Caldarelli
*Pr: Robert A Fickett
CFO: Joel Littman
*VP: John R Beighley
*VP: John Overstreet
*VP: Andrew E Tafler

D-U-N-S 60-609-6639
CPI INTERNATIONAL INC
(Suby of VERITAS CAPITAL MANAGEMENT LLC) ★
811 Hansen Way, Palo Alto, CA 94304-1031
Tel (650) 846-2801 Founded/Ownrshp 2011
Sales 446.3MM^E EMP 1,600
SIC 3671 3679 3699 3825 Traveling wave tubes; Vacuum tubes; Microwave components; Power supplies, all types: static; Electrical equipment & supplies; Radio frequency measuring equipment
CEO: O Joe Caldarelli
*Pr: Robert A Fickett
COO: Peter Kolda
*CFO: Joel A Littman
Treas: Veronica Tsui
Ofcr: Robert Reardon
*VP: John R Beighley
*VP: Don C Coleman
VP: Andrew Tafler
VP: Sean Villa-Lovoz
Snr Sftwr: Howard Gantz

CPI OFFICE PRODUCTS
See COMPUDATA PRODUCTS INC

D-U-N-S 07-830-8623
CPK HOLDINGS INC
Embarcadero Ctr, San Francisco, CA 94111
Tel (415) 983-2700 Founded/Ownrshp 2011
Sales 544.8MM^E EMP 14,610^E
SIC 5812 6794 Pizza restaurants; Franchises, selling or licensing
CEO: David Dominik
Pt: Neale Attenborough

D-U-N-S 06-691-3980
CPL HOLDINGS LLC
CORE DIGITAL MEDIA
12181 Bluff Creek Dr # 250, Playa Vista, CA 90094-3236
Tel (310) 348-6800 Founded/Ownrshp 2012
Sales 200.0MM EMP 200^E
SIC 5331 6719 5961 Variety stores; Investment holding companies, except banks;
CFO: Patrick Gregory
*CEO: Stephen Krenzer
VP: Yvette Garcia
VP: Jonathan Ripper
VP: Jay Roberts
Snr Mgr: Corinne Abeyta

D-U-N-S 80-818-5040
CPL INDUSTRIES INC
1111 Cedar Creek Rd, Grafton, WI 53024-9403
Tel (262) 377-2210 Founded/Ownrshp 1968
Sales NA EMP 2
SIC 6712 Bank holding companies
CEO: Charles P La Bahn
*Pr: Robert J Nowakowski
*CFO: Ridge Braunschweig

D-U-N-S 04-243-3800 IMP
CPM ACQUISITION CORP
CROWN ACQUISITION
(Suby of CPM HOLDINGS INC) ★
2975 Airline Cir, Waterloo, IA 50703-9631
Tel (319) 232-8444 Founded/Ownrshp 2001
Sales 179.1MM^E EMP 600^E
SIC 3523 Cabs, tractors & agricultural machinery
*CFO: Doug Ostrich
Prgrm Mgr: Mike Shaffer
Mtls Mgr: Reva Potter
Sls Mgr: Scott Anderson

D-U-N-S 14-723-5030
CPM DEVELOPMENT CORP
PRE-MIX
(Suby of OLDCASTLE MATERIALS GROUP) ★
5111 E Broadway Ave, Spokane Valley, WA 99212-0928
Tel (509) 534-6221 Founded/Ownrshp 1984
Sales 288.5MM^E EMP 1,100
SIC 3273 1771 3272 Ready-mixed concrete; Blacktop (asphalt) work; Concrete products
Pr: John Shogren
*CFO: Paul Salisbury
*Treas: Charles Brown
Ofcr: Gayle Langley
Ofcr: Eloisa Llata
*VP: Susan Lewis-Devaney
Genl Mgr: Barb Dougherty
Genl Mgr: John Madden
Genl Mgr: Bill Ohlsen

D-U-N-S 18-190-8216 IMP
CPM HOLDINGS INC
(Suby of GILBERT GLOBAL EQUITY CAPITAL LLC) ★
2975 Airline Cir, Waterloo, IA 50703-9631
Tel (336) 248-5181 Founded/Ownrshp 1996
Sales 265.1MM^E EMP 600^E
SIC 5084 Processing & packaging equipment
Pr: Ted Waitman
*CFO: Doug Ostrich
IT Man: Terry Beek
IT Man: Mark Heimann
IT Man: Phil Wellhausen
Genl Couns: Emily Chase

D-U-N-S 08-600-2078
CPM LTD INC
MANPOWER
1855 1st Ave Ste 300, San Diego, CA 92101-2668
Tel (619) 237-9900 Founded/Ownrshp 1977
Sales 49.5MM^E EMP 1,400
SIC 7363 Manpower pools
Pr: Philip Blair
*CFO: Tony Evenson
*Treas: Catherine Blair
VP: Debbie Dunn
*VP: Linda Katz
*VP: Mel Katz
VP: Allan W McKisson

D-U-N-S 87-930-8542
■ **CPM-US LLC**
C P M
(Suby of OMNICOM GROUP INC) ★
1999 Bryan St Ste 3200, Dallas, TX 75201-6813
Tel (800) 648-0722 Founded/Ownrshp 1994
Sales 38.7MM^E EMP 3,000
SIC 7311 Advertising agencies
CEO: Chuck Sombor
COO: Philip Sirley
CFO: Richard Jones
VP: Frank A Napolitano
VP: Craig Tieman
VP: Craig Tiernan
*VP: Carolyn Wright
VP: Andrea Young
VP Sls: Pat Lockrid

D-U-N-S 14-667-2964 EXP
■ **CPO COMMERCE LLC**
(Suby of MICROUNITED DIVISION) ★
120 W Bellevue Dr Ste 300, Pasadena, CA 91105-2579
Tel (626) 585-3600 Founded/Ownrshp 2014
Sales 121.1MM^E EMP 81
SIC 5072 Power tools & accessories
Pr: Robert H Tolleson
*COO: Girisha Chandraraj
*CFO: Todd A Shelton
*Treas: Robert J Kelderhouse
*Sr VP: Eric A Blanchard
*VP: Kenneth M Nickel
Dir IT: Greg Reynaert
Sftwr Eng: David Ferril
VP Opers: Alan Lenertz
Mktg Dir: Ryan Cosme
Mktg Mgr: Ed Leddy

CPP POMONA
See CONSOLIDATED PRECISION PRODUCTS CORP

D-U-N-S 00-222-7080
CPP-SYRACUSE INC
(Suby of CPP POMONA) ★
901 E Genesee St, Chittenango, NY 13037-1325
Tel (315) 687-0014 Founded/Ownrshp 1987
Sales 101.9MM^E EMP 350
SIC 3324 3369 3356 Aerospace investment castings, ferrous; Nonferrous foundries; Nonferrous rolling & drawing
CEO: James Stewart
Exec: Paul H Smith
CIO: Tim Wayfield
Mfg Dir: Tom Cacace
Opers Mgr: Barry Weary
Sls Mgr: John Derosia

CPS
See CHICAGO PUBLIC SCHOOLS

CPS - CONSTRUCTION PRODUCT SUP
See CERTIFIED PERSONNEL SERVICE AGENCY INC

D-U-N-S 18-672-5560
CPS 1 REALTY LP
PLAZA HOTEL
768 5th Ave, New York, NY 10019-1685
Tel (212) 759-3000 Founded/Ownrshp 2004
Sales 60.8MM^E EMP 1,200
SIC 7011 7299 5812 Resort hotel; Banquet hall facilities; Eating places
Genl Pt: Miki Naftali
Pr: Gary Schweikert

CPS ENERGY
See CITY PUBLIC SERVICES OF SAN ANTONIO

CPS MATERIALS
See CONSTRUCTION PROTECTIVE SERVICES INC

D-U-N-S 83-012-7341
CPS SECURITY SOLUTIONS INC
436 W Walnut St, Gardena, CA 90248-3137
Tel (310) 818-1030 Founded/Ownrshp 2007
Sales 53.2MM[E] EMP 1,200[E]
SIC 7381 Security guard service
Pr: Chris Coffey
*CFO: William Babcock
*Ex VP: Scott R Barnes
Area Mgr: Charlie Nelson

CPS&S
See CENTRAL POWER SYSTEMS & SERVICES LLC

CPSI
See COMPUTER PROGRAMS AND SYSTEMS INC

D-U-N-S 16-485-9840
CPT INC
COEXTRUDED PLASTICS TECHNOLOGY
3706 Enterprise Dr, Janesville, WI 53546-8737
Tel (608) 314-2020 Founded/Ownrshp 1991
Sales 800.0MM EMP 25
SIC 3089 5162 Trays, plastic; Plastics products
Pr: Linda Bracha

D-U-N-S 01-837-7486 IMP/EXP
CPW AMERICA CO
(Suby of CORINTH PIPEWORKS HOLDING COMPANY S.A.)
750 Town And Country Blvd # 920, Houston, TX 77024-3980
Tel (281) 752-7300 Founded/Ownrshp 2000
Sales 150.0MM EMP 7
Accts Briggs & Veselka
SIC 5051 Pipe & tubing, steel
CEO: Dianne Burger
*CFO: Ioannis Stavropoulos
*VP: Mark Soloninka

D-U-N-S 60-919-6670 IMP
CPX INC
410 E Kent St, Kentland, IN 47951-8625
Tel (219) 474-5280 Founded/Ownrshp 1989
Sales 105.3MM[E] EMP 350
SIC 3089 3694 Molding primary plastic; Harness wiring sets, internal combustion engines
Pr: Michael Sanders
*Treas: Douglas K Miller
Ql Cn Mgr: Brianne Carroll

D-U-N-S 83-227-8290
CPX INTERACTIVE HOLDINGS LLC
CPXI
1441 Broadway Fl 18, New York, NY 10018-1905
Tel (646) 863-8309 Founded/Ownrshp 2007
Sales 111.0MM[E] EMP 175
SIC 7313 Electronic media advertising representatives
CEO: Michael Seiman
COO: Michael Zacharski
CFO: Michael Fleischman
Chf Mktg O: Jeffrey Hirsch
Ex VP: Tiffany Coletti Kaiser
Ex VP: Mark Papia
Sr VP: Joseph Gallagher
Sr VP: Chris Monteleone
Sr VP: Gil Resh
VP: James Faherty
VP: Matt Friedman

CPXI
See CPX INTERACTIVE HOLDINGS LLC

D-U-N-S 00-942-8988
CR ENGLAND INC
4701 W 2100 S, Salt Lake City, UT 84120-1223
Tel (800) 421-9004 Founded/Ownrshp 1946
Sales 1.4MMM[E] EMP 6,500
Accts Tanner Llc Salt Lake City Ut
SIC 4213 Refrigerated products transport; Contract haulers
Ch Bd: Daniel E England
Pr: Tracy Brown
*Pr: Josh England
Pr: Sam Scott
*CEO: Chad England
*COO: Zach England
*COO: Brandon Harrison
*CFO: Tj McGeean
*Co-Ch Bd: Dean England
*Ex VP: Corey England
Ex VP: Corey D England
*Ex VP: Todd England
Ex VP: Todd D England
Ex VP: David A Kramer
*Sr VP: Michael L Bunnell
VP: Mike Bunnell
VP: Dustin England
*VP: Tj England
VP: Nelson Hayes
VP: Ryan Holm
VP: Doug Kading

CR LAURENCE
See CR LAURENCE CO INC

D-U-N-S 02-854-1415 IMP/EXP
CR LAURENCE CO INC
CR LAURENCE
(Suby of CRH PUBLIC LIMITED COMPANY)
2503 E Vernon Ave, Vernon, CA 90058-1826
Tel (323) 588-1281 Founded/Ownrshp 2015
Sales 582.3MM[E] EMP 1,600
SIC 3714 5072 5039 Sun roofs, motor vehicle; Hand tools; Glass construction materials
CEO: Donald E Friese
Ql Cn Mgr: Farnoosh Fazlollahi
Mktg Mgr: Chris Hanstad
Mktg Mgr: Dave Nelson
Sls Mgr: Paul Kennedy

CR MEYER
See C R MEYER AND SONS CO

D-U-N-S 05-478-7882
CR&R INC (CA)
11292 Western Ave, Stanton, CA 90680-2912
Tel (714) 826-9049 Founded/Ownrshp 1950, 1963
Sales 110.0MM[E] EMP 1,300
SIC 4953 4212 7359

D-U-N-S 07-952-5325
▲ CRA INTERNATIONAL INC (MA)
CHARLES RIVER ASSOCIATES
200 Clarendon St, Boston, MA 02116-5092
Tel (617) 425-3000 Founded/Ownrshp 1965
Sales 303.5MM EMP 3[E]
Tkr Sym CRAI Exch NGS
SIC 8742 Management consulting services; Financial consultant
Pr: Paul Maleh
Ch Bd: Rowland Moriarty
CFO: Chad Holmes
Ex VP: Arnold Lowenstein
VP: Justus Dehnen
VP: Bill Hardin
VP: Ron Langford
VP: Anthony Rose
VP: G S Solomon
VP: Kristofer Swanson
VP: Lars Wiethaus

D-U-N-S 78-364-5633
CRA LLC
8901 E Pima Center Pkwy # 230, Scottsdale, AZ 85258-4618
Tel (480) 889-9900 Founded/Ownrshp 1991
Sales 127.0MM EMP 8
SIC 8742 Management consulting services
*Pt: Phil De Angelis
Sls&Mrk Ex: Todd Vesledahl

CRA SERVICES
See GHD SERVICES INC

CRABAR/GBF INC.
See CRABAR/GBF INC

D-U-N-S 09-192-0301
■ CRABAR/GBF INC
CRABAR/GBF INC.
(Suby of ENNIS INC) ★
68 Vine St, Leipsic, OH 45856-1488
Tel (419) 943-2141 Founded/Ownrshp 2003
Sales 127.4MM[E] EMP 51[E]
SIC 2752 Business form & card printing, lithographic
CEO: Keith Walters
CFO: Marshall Griffen

D-U-N-S 05-888-0378 IMP/EXP
CRABTREE & EVELYN LTD
(Suby of KHUAN CHOO INTERNATIONAL LIMITED)
102 Peake Brook Rd, Woodstock, CT 06281-3429
Tel (800) 272-2873 Founded/Ownrshp 2012
Sales 451.2MM[E] EMP 667
SIC 5122 5149 2844 Toilet soap; Toiletries; Pickles, preserves, jellies & jams; Specialty food items; Toilet preparations
Pr: Kevin J Coen
*Treas: Koh Han Seow
Dist Mgr: Dawn Cole
Dist Mgr: Davis McClarren
Dist Mgr: Celeste Southard
Dist Mgr: Anna Tipton
Plng Mgr: Jessie Brady
Store Mgr: Kevin Sanchez
MIS Dir: John Richmond
Dir IT: S R Bauer
IT Man: Robert Lincoln

D-U-N-S 05-067-1296
▲ CRACKER BARREL OLD COUNTRY STORE INC (TN)
305 S Hartmann Dr, Lebanon, TN 37087-4779
Tel (615) 444-5533 Founded/Ownrshp 1969
Sales 2.9MMM EMP 73,000
Accts Deloitte & Touche Llp Nashvil
Tkr Sym CBRL Exch NGS
SIC 5812 5947 Restaurant, family: chain; Gift, novelty & souvenir shop; Gift shop; Novelties
Pr: Sandra B Cochran
*Ch Bd: James W Bradford
CFO: Jill M Golder
VP: Jeffrey M Wilson
VP: Michael J Zylstra
Board of Directors: Thomas H Barr, Glenn A Davenport, Richard J Dobkin, Norman E Johnson, William W McCarten, Coleman H Peterson, Andrea M Weiss

D-U-N-S 05-864-2096
CRACKER BOX LLC
110 Cracker Box Ln, Hot Springs, AR 71913-5418
Tel (501) 455-4909 Founded/Ownrshp 1997
Sales 85.6MM EMP 150
Accts Searcy & Associates Llc Mont
SIC 5411 Convenience stores

CRADER DISTRIBUTING
See CRADER EQUIPMENT CO

D-U-N-S 00-648-4893
CRADER EQUIPMENT CO
CRADER DISTRIBUTING
(Suby of KAISER MIDWEST INC) ★
808 Highway 34 W, Marble Hill, MO 63764-4302
Tel (573) 238-2675 Founded/Ownrshp 1943
Sales 152.0MM EMP 40
Accts Van De Ven Llc Cape Girardea
SIC 5083 5084 Lawn machinery & equipment; Chainsaws
CEO: Donald D Crader
*Pr: Stanley Crader
COO: Stan Beel
*Sec: Val Crader
*VP: Rebecca Hurst

D-U-N-S 08-446-5145 IMP/EXP
CRAFCO INC (AZ)
(Suby of ERGON INC) ★
6165 W Detroit St, Chandler, AZ 85226-2633
Tel (480) 505-8030 Founded/Ownrshp 1976
Sales 121.9MM[E] EMP 300
SIC 2951 3531 Asphalt & asphaltic paving mixtures (not from refineries); Pavers
Pr: Donald M Brooks
*VP: Jim Chehovits
*VP: Mark Manning
Exec: Jan Fager
Area Mgr: Tim Morris
Area Mgr: Jason Raya
Mtls Mgr: Shelly Erickson
Sls Mgr: N Kelly
Sls Mgr: Tom Kelly
Sls Mgr: Ed Misajet

D-U-N-S 01-146-9848 IMP/EXP
▲ CRAFT BREW ALLIANCE INC
929 N Russell St, Portland, OR 97227-1733
Tel (503) 331-7270 Founded/Ownrshp 1981
Sales 204.1MM EMP 820
Tkr Sym BREW Exch NGM
SIC 2082 Ale (alcoholic beverage); Beer (alcoholic beverage)
CEO: Andrew J Thomas
*Ch Bd: David R Lord
COO: J Scott Mennen
CFO: Joseph K Vanderstelt
Ofcr: Kenneth C Kunze
VP: John W Glick
Sls Dir: Lee Shanahan
Mktg Mgr: Steven Hallstone
Manager: Chris Squier
Board of Directors: Timothy P Boyle, Marc J Cramer, Paul D Davis, Kevin R Kelly, Thomas D Larson, John D Rogers Jr

D-U-N-S 00-791-8592 IMP/EXP
CRAFTMADE INTERNATIONAL INC
JEREMIAH
(Suby of LITEX INDUSTRIES LIMITED) ★
650 S Royal Ln Ste 100, Coppell, TX 75019-3836
Tel (972) 393-3800 Founded/Ownrshp 1985, 2011
Sales 112.0MM[E] EMP 255
SIC 5064 5063 Fans, household: electric; Lighting fixtures
CEO: Jean Liu
Pr: Brad Dale Heimann
Sls Mgr: Dave Rauschuber

D-U-N-S 05-792-7451 IMP/EXP
CRAFTMASTER FURNITURE INC
(Suby of UNIVERSAL FURNITURE INTL) ★
221 Craftmaster Rd, Hiddenite, NC 28636-9309
Tel (828) 632-9786 Founded/Ownrshp 2006
Sales 87.6MM[E] EMP 450
Accts Capps Foster & Company Hick
SIC 2512 Upholstered household furniture; Couches, sofas & davenports: upholstered on wood frames; Chairs: upholstered on wood frames; Rockers: upholstered on wood frames
CEO: Roy Calcagne
*CFO: Anderson Shih
Bd of Dir: Steve Lackey
VP: Kevin Mann
VP: Greg Rogers
Exec: Larry Chapman
Dir IT: Dewey Poteat
IT Man: James Thomson
VP Sls: Lance Foster

D-U-N-S 16-952-1304
CRAFTWORKS RESTAURANTS & BREWERIES GROUP INC
(Suby of CRAFTWORKS RESTAURANTS & BREWERIES LLC) ★
8001 Arista Pl Unit 500, Broomfield, CO 80021-4135
Tel (623) 878-8822 Founded/Ownrshp 2016
Sales 666.3MM[E] EMP 6,500[E]
SIC 6719 Personal holding companies, except banks
CEO: Frank Day
Pr: Rob Jakoby
Treas: Alan Guthals

D-U-N-S 96-556-9549
CRAFTWORKS RESTAURANTS & BREWERIES INC
8001 Arista Pl Unit 500, Broomfield, CO 80021-4135
Tel (303) 664-4000 Founded/Ownrshp 2010
Sales 442.5MM EMP 12,000
SIC 5812 Eating places
CEO: Srinivas Kumar
*CFO: Brian Morrow
VP: Mark Belanger
VP: Scott Curry
VP: Tom Dargen
*VP: Mike Mrlik II
VP: Aaron Ruben
*Genl Couns: Rebecca Fischer

D-U-N-S 07-923-2317
CRAFTWORKS RESTAURANTS & BREWERIES LLC
(Suby of CRAFTWORKS RESTAURANTS & BREWERIES INC) ★
201 W Main St Ste 301, Chattanooga, TN 37408-1174
Tel (423) 424-2000 Founded/Ownrshp 2013
Sales 666.3MM[E] EMP 15,646[E]
SIC 5812 Eating places
Pr: Allen Corey
VP: Rob Stickley

D-U-N-S 09-931-3991
CRAIG F SORENSEN CONSTRUCTION INC
SCI
918 S 2000 W, Syracuse, UT 84075-6926
Tel (801) 773-4390 Founded/Ownrshp 1977
Sales 128.8MM[E] EMP 400
SIC 1623 1731

D-U-N-S 07-645-3174
CRAIG HOSPITAL
3425 S Clarkson St, Englewood, CO 80113-2899
Tel (303) 789-8000 Founded/Ownrshp 1907
Sales 87.4MM EMP 700
SIC 8069 Specialty hospitals, except psychiatric
CEO: Mike Fordyce
*CFO: Julie Keegan
Sr VP: Dana Polonsky
Dir Risk M: Darlene Poplawski
Dir: Barbara Page
Comm Man: Jordan Ames
CTO: Jill Stelley
QA Dir: Cindy Braden
QC Dir: Cindy Dahlberg
Doctor: Frederick Coville
Doctor: Robert Kruse

CRAIG REALTY GROUP
See EUREKA REALTY PARTNERS INC

D-U-N-S 01-638-4674
CRAIN AUTOMOTIVE HOLDINGS LLC
CRAIN KIA
5890 Warden Rd, Sherwood, AR 72120-6000
Tel (501) 542-5000 Founded/Ownrshp 1999
Sales 500.0MM EMP 600
SIC 5511 Automobiles, new & used
Sls Mgr: Mike Mayabb
Sls Mgr: Ramona Riddle
Sls Mgr: Tim Walls
Sales Asso: Terence Harshaw
Sales Asso: Mike Osburn

D-U-N-S 00-506-5891
CRAIN COMMUNICATIONS INC (IL)
1155 Gratiot Ave, Detroit, MI 48207-2732
Tel (313) 446-6000 Founded/Ownrshp 1916
Sales 225.0MM EMP 1,045
SIC 2721 2711 Magazines: publishing only, not printed on site; Newspapers, publishing & printing
Ch Bd: Keith E Crain
*Pr: Rance E Crain
*CFO: Bob Recchia
CFO: Tom Stevens
*Treas: Mary Kay Crain
Ofcr: Gavin Souter
Ex VP: Christopher Crain
*Ex VP: William A Morrow
Sr VP: David S Klein
VP: Robert C Adams
VP: Allison Arden
VP: Christopher Battaglia
VP: David Blake
VP: Peter Brown
*VP: Kc Crain
VP: Robert Felsenthal
VP: Todd Johnson
VP: Mary L Kramer
*VP: Brennan Lafferty
*VP: Thomas M Marantette
VP: Joyce McGarvy

CRAIN KIA
See CRAIN AUTOMOTIVE HOLDINGS LLC

D-U-N-S 00-206-7155 IMP/EXP
CRANE & CO INC
CRANE CURRENCY
30 South St, Dalton, MA 01226-1797
Tel (617) 648-3714 Founded/Ownrshp 1801
Sales 443.4MM[E] EMP 1,378
SIC 2621 5943 Paper mills; Bank note paper; Securites paper; Writing paper; Stationery stores
CEO: Stephen P Defalco
*CFO: Douglas Prince
Board of Directors: Ivan Montoya

CRANE AEROSPACE & ELECTRONICS
See ELDEC CORP

D-U-N-S 96-539-5192
■ CRANE AEROSPACE INC
(Suby of CRANE INTERNATIONAL HOLDINGS INC) ★
100 Stamford Pl, Stamford, CT 06902-6740
Tel (203) 363-7300 Founded/Ownrshp 2002
Sales 319.2MM[E] EMP 1,730[E]
SIC 3492 Control valves, fluid power: hydraulic & pneumatic

CRANE CHEMPHARMA
See MCC HOLDINGS INC

D-U-N-S 00-128-0726
▲ CRANE CO
100 1st Stamford Pl # 300, Stamford, CT 06902-6784
Tel (203) 363-7300 Founded/Ownrshp 1855
Sales 2.7MMM EMP 11,300
Tkr Sym CR Exch NYS
SIC 3492 3494 3594 3589 3728 5031 Control valves, fluid power: hydraulic & pneumatic; Pipe fittings; Pumps, hydraulic power transfer; Pumps, hydraulic, aircraft; Water treatment equipment, industrial; Aircraft parts & equipment; Brakes, aircraft; Aircraft assemblies, subassemblies & parts; Military aircraft equipment & armament; Lumber, plywood & millwork; Doors & windows; Building materials, exterior; Building materials, interior
Pr: Max H Mitchell
Pr: Thomas J Craney
Pr: Brendan J Curran
CFO: Richard A Maue
Treas: Tazewell S Rowe
Sr VP: Bradley L Ellis
Sr VP: Louis V Pinkham
VP: Augustus I Dupont
VP: Curtis A Baron Jr
VP: Anthony D Pantaleoni
VP: Diana Quach
VP: Edward S Switter
VP Bus Dev: Kris Salovaara
Comm Man: Christopher Lawrence
Board of Directors: Peter O Scannell, Martin R Benante, James L L Tullis, E Thayer Bigelow, Donald G Cook, Robert S Evans, Richard S Forte, Ronald C Lindsay, Philip R Lochner Jr, Ellen McClain, Jennifer M Pollino

CRANE CURRENCY
See CRANE & CO INC

D-U-N-S 07-838-8451 IMP
■ CRANE ELECTRONICS INC
INTERPOINT
(Suby of CRANE INTERNATIONAL HOLDINGS INC) ★
10301 Willows Rd Ne, Redmond, WA 98052-2529
Tel (425) 882-3100 Founded/Ownrshp 2003
Sales 102.8MM[E] EMP 545
SIC 3679 Electronic loads & power supplies; Oscillators
CEO: George E Lombard

*Pr: Robert Tavares
*Treas: Andrew Krawitt
*VP: Ed Fuhr
Ex Dir: Simon Abel
Prgrm Mgr: Tj Baradari
Prgrm Mgr: Bruce Finley
Prgrm Mgr: Adrian Gavrilescu
Prgrm Mgr: Abraham Hsu
Prgrm Mgr: Kweon Peter
Prgrm Mgr: Michael Rohona

D-U-N-S 02-313-3374
CRANE ENGINEERING SALES INC
707 Ford St, Kimberly, WI 54136-2210
Tel (920) 733-4425 Founded/Ownrshp 1968
Sales 221.8MM^E EMP 82
SIC 5084 5085 5074 Industrial machinery & equipment; Pumps & pumping equipment; Filters, industrial; Water purification equipment
CEO: Lance Crane
CFO: Ed Voet
Dir IT: Mary Warnke
IT Man: Renee Sweere
Sls Dir: Mike Baxter

D-U-N-S 83-278-1228
CRANE GROUP CO
330 W Spring St Ste 200, Columbus, OH 43215-2389
Tel (614) 754-3000 Founded/Ownrshp 2002
Sales 150.2MM^E EMP 1,292^E
SIC 8741 Management services
CEO: Tanny Crane
*Pr: Mike Crane
Genl Couns: Timothy T Miller

D-U-N-S 00-428-9989
CRANE GROUP COMPANIES LIMITED
(Suby of CRANE GROUP CO) ★
2141 Fairwood Ave, Columbus, OH 43207-1753
Tel (614) 443-4891 Founded/Ownrshp 1947, 2001
Sales 138.2MM^E EMP 1,100
SIC 3089

D-U-N-S 96-536-1582
■ **CRANE INTERNATIONAL HOLDINGS INC**
(Suby of CRANE CO) ★
100 Stamford Pl, Stamford, CT 06902-6740
Tel (203) 363-7300 Founded/Ownrshp 1997
Sales 943.0MM^E EMP 650^E
SIC 3492 Control valves, fluid power: hydraulic & pneumatic
CEO: Max H Mitchell
*Pr: Brendan Curran
*Pr: Louis V Pinkham
*Pr: Robert E Tavares

D-U-N-S 05-962-8557 IMP/EXP
■ **CRANE MERCHANDISING SYSTEMS INC**
CRANE NATIONAL VENDERS
(Suby of CRANE CO) ★
2043 Wdlnd Pkwy Ste 102, Saint Louis, MO 63146
Tel (314) 298-3500 Founded/Ownrshp 1993
Sales 239.6MM^E EMP 1,132^E
SIC 3589 5087 Coffee brewing equipment; Vending machines & supplies
Pr: Bradley Ellis
VP: Ignacio Cruz
VP: Steve Turner
Snr Sftwr: Joe Reed
Dir IT: Douglas Davisson
IT Man: Rich Smith
Sftwr Eng: Jeremy Vacek
Mfg Dir: Daniel J Schmucker
Opers Mgr: Cavell Watson
VP Sls: Thomas Freas
Sls Dir: Mike Poth

D-U-N-S 07-841-8851 IMP
■ **CRANE MERCHANDISING SYSTEMS INC**
(Suby of CRANE CO) ★
3330 Crane Way, Williston, SC 29853
Tel (803) 266-5000 Founded/Ownrshp 1993
Sales 125.7MM^E EMP 570^E
SIC 3581 3531 Automatic vending machines; Cranes
Pr: Bradley Ellis
VP: Stephen Garwood
*Prin: Doug Huffer

CRANE NATIONAL VENDERS
See CRANE MERCHANDISING SYSTEMS INC

D-U-N-S 79-452-4686 IMP/EXP
■ **CRANE PAYMENT INNOVATIONS INC**
M E I
(Suby of CRANE CO) ★
3222 Phoenixville Pike # 200, Malvern, PA 19355-9615
Tel (610) 430-2700 Founded/Ownrshp 1998
Sales 166.0MM^E EMP 500^E
SIC 3578 Change making machines
Pr: Kurt Gallo
Telecom Ex: Jim McGonigle
Tech Mgr: Stephen Marsh
VP Mfg: Miguel Aguilar
VP Mktg: Mary Rampe
Mktg Dir: Chuck Reed
Mktg Dir: Andy Reichlin

D-U-N-S 11-537-3227 IMP/EXP
CRANE PLUMBING LLC
41 Cairns Rd, Mansfield, OH 44903-8992
Tel (419) 522-4211 Founded/Ownrshp 1984
Sales 124.4MM^E EMP 1,300
SIC 3261 3431 3088 Bathroom accessories/fittings, vitreous china or earthenware; Metal sanitary ware; Bathtubs: enameled iron, cast iron or pressed metal; Shower stalls, metal; Sinks: enameled iron, cast iron or pressed metal; Shower stalls, fiberglass & plastic
CEO: Kevin Oak
Sls Mgr: Ken Sapp

D-U-N-S 07-934-2366 IMP/EXP
■ **CRANE PUMPS & SYSTEMS INC**
(Suby of CRANE CHEMPHARMA) ★
420 3rd St, Piqua, OH 45356-3918
Tel (937) 773-2442 Founded/Ownrshp 1946
Sales 156.2MM^E EMP 811
SIC 3561 Pumps & pumping equipment
Pr: Jim Lavish

CFO: Dan Crowe
VP: Patrick Rienks
VP: Lynn White
VP Opers: Glen Ziegler
Manager: Kathy Ketcham
Snr Mgr: Robert Wooton

D-U-N-S 07-934-2552
CRANE STATIONARY
1466 Curran Hwy, North Adams, MA 01247-3964
Tel (413) 664-2527 Founded/Ownrshp 2014
Sales 61.5MM^E EMP 2,000
SIC 2621 Stationery, envelope & tablet papers
Prin: Charlene Gero

D-U-N-S 82-836-1613
CRANE WORLDWIDE LOGISTICS LLC
1500 Rankin Rd, Houston, TX 77073-4800
Tel (281) 443-2777 Founded/Ownrshp 2008
Sales 787.8MM^E EMP 2,700
SIC 4731 Freight forwarding
Ch: Jim Crane
*Pr: John Magee
*COO: Keith Winters
Ofcr: Tracey Abram
VP: Kelli Klanderud
*VP: Christina Ptasinski
*VP: Tim Zubradt
Mng Dir: Andrew Barnes
Brnch Mgr: Brent Thomas
Snr Sftwr: Chad Smutny
IT Man: Derek Miller

CRANEL IMAGING
See CRANEL INC

D-U-N-S 14-863-2466
CRANEL INC
CRANEL IMAGING
8999 Gemini Pkwy Ste A, Columbus, OH 43240-2250
Tel (614) 431-8000 Founded/Ownrshp 1985
Sales 91.9MM^E EMP 100
SIC 5045 Computers, peripherals & software; Computer peripheral equipment
Pr: Craig Wallace
*CFO: Michael Tracy
*Ch: James Wallace
Ofcr: Michael T Cush
*VP: Leslie Duff
*VP: Joseph Jackson
*VP: Scott Slack
Dist Mgr: Dennis Fields
CTO: Michael C Cush
Sftwr Eng: Ewan Todd
Sls Dir: Laura Bova

D-U-N-S 04-378-4396
CRANES PERSONAL DESIGN SERVICES
(Suby of CRANE CURRENCY) ★
1466 Curran Hwy, North Adams, MA 01247-3964
Tel (413) 664-4321 Founded/Ownrshp 1967
Sales 26.9MM^E EMP 1,378
SIC 7389 2796 2759 Engraving service; Platemaking services; Commercial printing
Pr: John Schultze
*Treas: David Crane
*VP: Micheal Cummings
*VP: Edward Czarnecki
Genl Mgr: Steve Nelson
DP Mgr: Monte Shepard

D-U-N-S 00-143-8480 IMP
CRANSTON PRINT WORKS CO INC
C P W
1381 Cranston St, Cranston, RI 02920-6789
Tel (401) 943-4800 Founded/Ownrshp 1934
Sales 149.9MM^E EMP 147
Accts Sansiveri Kimball & Mcnamee
SIC 2261 2262 2899 Bleaching cotton broadwoven fabrics; Dyeing cotton broadwoven fabrics; Printing of cotton broadwoven fabrics; Bleaching: manmade fiber & silk broadwoven fabrics; Chemical preparations
Pr: Frederic Rockefeller Jr
*Prin: James Thorpe
Mktg Dir: Cyndi Hershey
Manager: Debra Coffman

D-U-N-S 04-378-8041
CRANSTON PUBLIC SCHOOLS
845 Park Ave, Cranston, RI 02910-2790
Tel (401) 270-8000 Founded/Ownrshp 1994
Sales 66.1MM^E EMP 1,200
SIC 8211 Public elementary & secondary schools
CFO: Joseph Balducci
Prin: Susan Bryan
MIS Dir: John Campellone
MIS Dir: Richard Fratantwano
Dir IT: Donna-Marie Frappier
Schl Brd P: Janice Ruggieri
Teacher Pr: Raymond Votto

CRATE & BARREL
See EUROMARKET DESIGNS INC

D-U-N-S 07-105-0819
CRAVATH SWAINE & MOORE LLP
825 8th Ave Lbby L, New York, NY 10019-7475
Tel (212) 474-1000 Founded/Ownrshp 2007
Sales 98.4MM^E EMP 1,450
SIC 8111 General practice law office
Ch: Evan R Chesler
Pt: C Allen Parker
CFO: Guy Mirabello
Sr Cor Off: Marisol Davila
VP: Benjamin Diessel
VP: Kris Heinzelman
Exec: Jennifer Nolino
Assoc Dir: Lisa Kalen
Comm Man: Robin Shanzer
Ex Dir: Steven D Spiess
Telecom Ex: Yesenia Montilla

D-U-N-S 10-066-4507
CRAVEN COUNTY SCHOOL DISTRICT
3600 Trent Rd, New Bern, NC 28562-2224
Tel (252) 514-6300 Founded/Ownrshp 1981
Sales 67.6MM^E EMP 1,700
Accts Pittard Perry & Crone Inc Go
SIC 8211 Public elementary & secondary schools

Ch: Carroll G Ipock II
Ofcr: Denise Altman
Ex Dir: Jason Jones
Psych: Angela McCoy-Speight
HC Dir: Debbie Hodges
Board of Directors: Betty Blythe

CRAWDADDY'S
See SPECIALTY RESTAURANTS CORP

D-U-N-S 04-100-7717
CRAWFORD & CO
1001 Summit Blvd Ste 500, Brookhaven, GA 30319-6410
Tel (404) 300-1000 Founded/Ownrshp 1941
Sales NA EMP 8,941
Accts Ernst & Young Llp Atlanta Ge
SIC 6411 8111 8099 6331 Insurance agents, brokers & service; Insurance adjusters; Insurance claim adjusters, not employed by insurance company; Insurance claim processing, except medical; Specialized legal services; Medical services organization; Workers' compensation insurance; Automobile insurance; Fire, marine & casualty insurance & carriers; Property damage insurance
CEO: Harsha V Agadi
*Ch Bd: Charles H Ogburn
Pr: Danielle M Lisenbey
CEO: Kenneth A Cutshaw
CEO: Ian V Muress
CEO: Larry C Thomas
CFO: W Bruce Swain Jr
Ofcr: Bonnie C Sawdey
Ex VP: Brian S Flynn
Ex VP: Ken M Fraser
Ex VP: Allen W Nelson
Sr VP: Dalerick M Carden
Sr VP: Michael F Reeves
Board of Directors: P George Benson, Jesse C Crawford, Jesse C Crawford Jr, Roger A S Day, James D Edwards, Joia M Johnson, D Richard Williams

D-U-N-S 80-382-9985
CRAWFORD & CO HEALTHCARE MANAGEMENT INC
(Suby of CRAWFORD & CO) ★
1001 Summit Blvd, Brookhaven, GA 30319-6408
Tel (404) 256-0830 Founded/Ownrshp 1977
Sales NA EMP 856
SIC 6411 Insurance agents, brokers & service
CEO: Tom Crawford
Ex VP: Joe Caporaso
Ex VP: Kevin B Frawley
Sr VP: Jeanne C Finegan
Sr VP: Timothy A O'Neill
VP: John P Lennon
Genl Mgr: Howard Rogers
IT Man: John Lennon
IT Man: Heidi Wood

D-U-N-S 78-253-1888
CRAWFORD CR CONSTRUCTION LLC
1102 S Happy Hollow Rd, Fayetteville, AR 72701-7249
Tel (479) 251-1161 Founded/Ownrshp 2006
Sales 126.0MM EMP 28
Accts James E Childress Cpa Pa S
SIC 1542 Commercial & office building contractors

D-U-N-S 08-550-8955
CRAWFORD ELECTRIC SUPPLY CO HOUSTON LTD
CESCO
(Suby of SONEPAR USA) ★
7390 Northcourt Rd, Houston, TX 77040-4379
Tel (281) 501-4440 Founded/Ownrshp 1990
Sales 702.4MM^E EMP 780
SIC 5063 Electrical apparatus & equipment
Pr: Jeff Metzler
Pr: David Jackson
Genl Mgr: Michael Font
IT Man: David Watkins
Mktg Dir: Jenny Conway
Sales Asso: Debbie Clark
Sales Asso: Clint Counts

D-U-N-S 15-760-2715 IMP/EXP
CRAWFORD ELECTRIC SUPPLY CO INC
(Suby of SONEPAR USA) ★
7390 Northcourt Rd, Houston, TX 77040-4379
Tel (713) 476-0788 Founded/Ownrshp 2006
Sales 106.0MM^E EMP 54
SIC 5063 Electrical apparatus & equipment
Pr: Tim Horny
*CEO: Jeff Metzler
*Treas: Kathy Rusko
*VP: Neil Clay
VP: Kelly Johns
VP: Jeremy Lawrence
*VP: Jim Schmidt
*Prin: Bryan Brennan
*Prin: Albert Daugherty
*Prin: Rodney Nolen
Brnch Mgr: Lucas Horan

D-U-N-S 10-802-3003 IMP/EXP
CRAWFORD GROUP INC
600 Corporate Park Dr, Saint Louis, MO 63105-4204
Tel (314) 512-5000 Founded/Ownrshp 1990
Sales 6.0MMM^E EMP 68,993
SIC 7514 7515 Rent-a-car service; Passenger car leasing
Pr: Pamela Nicholson
*CFO: William W Snyder
VP: Steven Bloom
VP: Jo Ann Kindle
VP: Christine B Taylor
Board of Directors: Priscilla Hill-Ardoin, David W Kemper, Craig S Kennedy, Donald L Ross, Harold Lee Scott Jr, Diane M Sullivan, Byron D Trott

D-U-N-S 01-059-6336 IMP
CRAWFORD SUPPLY GROUP INC
BATH & KITCHEN BY CRAWFORD
8150 Lehigh Ave Ste A, Morton Grove, IL 60053-2600
Tel (847) 967-0550 Founded/Ownrshp 2003
Sales 130.0MM^E EMP 183
SIC 5074 Plumbing & hydronic heating supplies; Water softeners

Pr: Sig Feiger
*VP: Steve Feiger
Opers Mgr: Janet Borst
Opers Mgr: Greg Digles

D-U-N-S 19-369-4577
▲ **CRAY INC**
901 5th Ave Ste 1000, Seattle, WA 98164-2058
Tel (206) 701-2000 Founded/Ownrshp 1987
Sales 724.6MM EMP 1,282
Accts Peterson Sullivan Llp Seattle
Tkr Sym CRAY Exch NGS
SIC 3571 7379 Electronic computers; Computer related maintenance services
Pr: Peter J Ungaro
Pr: Mamoru Nakano
CFO: Brian C Henry
Chf Mktg O: Fred Kohout
Sr VP: Daniel G Kim
Sr VP: Ian W Miller
Sr VP: Ly-Huong T Pham
Sr VP: Steven L Scott
VP: Charles D Fairchild
VP: Nick Gorga
VP: Larry Hoelzeman
VP: John Howarth
VP: John Josephakis
VP: Catalin Morosanu
VP: Charles A Morreale
VP: Michael C Piraino
VP: Stehpen Scott
VP: Eddie Smith
VP: Margaret Williams
VP: Andrew Wyatt
Board of Directors: Martin Homlish, Stephen C Kiely, Sally G Narodick, Daniel C Regis, Max Schireson, Brian V Turner

CRAYOLA EXPERIENCE, THE
See CRAYOLA LLC

D-U-N-S 00-137-4909 IMP/EXP
CRAYOLA LLC
CRAYOLA EXPERIENCE, THE
(Suby of MIX HOLDINGS INC) ★
1100 Church Ln, Easton, PA 18040-5999
Tel (610) 253-6271 Founded/Ownrshp 1864, 1984
Sales 620.6MM^E EMP 1,650
SIC 3952 3951 3295 3944 Lead pencils & art goods; Crayons: chalk, gypsum, charcoal, fusains, pastel, wax, etc.; Chalk: carpenters', blackboard, marking, tailors', etc.; Paints, except gold & bronze: artists'; Markers, soft tip (felt, fabric, plastic, etc.); Clay, ground or otherwise treated; Games, toys & children's vehicles; Craft & hobby kits & sets
Pr: Smith Holland
*CFO: Dona Fisher
*Ex VP: Chuck Linden
*Ex VP: Michelle Powers
*Ex VP: Peter S Ruggiero
VP: Nancy Conrad
VP: Dennis Gormley
VP: Vicky Lozano
VP: Rob Mack
Exec: Nicole Nix
Genl Mgr: Paul Zadorsky

CRB
See CLARK RICHARDSON AND BISKUP CONSULTING ENGINEERS INC

D-U-N-S 03-865-4211
■ **CRC HEALTH CORP**
(Suby of CRC HEALTH GROUP INC) ★
20400 Stevens Creek Blvd, Cupertino, CA 95014-2296
Tel (877) 272-8668 Founded/Ownrshp 2006
Sales 452.2MM EMP 4,019
SIC 8069 8099 8322 8093 Drug addiction rehabilitation hospital; Medical services organization; General counseling services; Substance abuse clinics (outpatient)
CEO: Jerome E Rhodes
*Ch Bd: R Andrew Eckert
CFO: Leanne M Stewart
Ofcr: Philip L Herschman
Sr VP: Pamela B Burke
Sr VP: David Duerst
Dir IT: Caroline Hsieh
Board of Directors: Steven Barnes, Chris Gordon, Barry R McCaffrey, Scott Wells

D-U-N-S 13-634-6215
■ **CRC HEALTH CORPORATE**
WILLAMETTE VALLEY TRTMNT CTR
(Suby of CRC HEALTH CORP) ★
20400 Stevens, Cupertino, CA 95014
Tel (408) 367-0044 Founded/Ownrshp 2002
Sales 56.9MM^E EMP 4,019
SIC 8093 Substance abuse clinics (outpatient)
CEO: R Andrew Eckert
CFO: Kevin Hogge
Treas: Sandra J Tullis
Chf Mktg O: Gary Fisher
VP: Pamela B Burke
VP: James Hudak
VP Opers: John Peloquin
VP Mktg: Jonathan Ciampi
Board of Directors: Steven Barnes, John Connaughton, Chris Gordon, Barry R McCaffrey, Elliot Sainer

D-U-N-S 61-948-1661 IMP
■ **CRC HEALTH GROUP INC**
(Suby of ACADIA HEALTHCARE CO INC) ★
20400 Stev Creek Blvd 6, Cupertino, CA 95014
Tel (877) 272-8668 Founded/Ownrshp 2015
Sales 452.2MM^E EMP 5,420^E
SIC 8099 Medical services organization
CEO: Jerome E Rhodes
*CFO: Leanne M Stewart
*Ofcr: Philip L Herschman
Ex VP: Kathleen Sylvia
Sr VP: Ann Miller
VP: Debra Halladay
VP: Teri Rodman
Exec: Jesse Aguilar
Rgnl Mgr: Casey Jones
Off Mgr: Eileen Arnold
Opers Supe: Andrea Harvey

D-U-N-S 06-988-0029 EXP
CRC INDUSTRIES INC
(*Suby of* BERWIND INDUSTRIES INC) ★
885 Louis Dr, Warminster, PA 18974-2869
Tel (215) 674-4300 *Founded/Ownrshp* 1981
Sales 97.7MM^E *EMP* 205
SIC 2992 3471 2899 2842 Lubricating oils & greases; Plating & polishing; Chemical preparations; Specialty cleaning, polishes & sanitation goods
Pr: Dennis Conlon
**Pr:* Scott Gray
**Treas:* Van Billet
Exec: Patricia Christian
Exec: Joe Windish
Rgnl Mgr: Scott Flynn
Sls Mgr: Jay Silverman

D-U-N-S 10-207-4176
■ CRC INSURANCE SERVICES INC
(*Suby of* BB&T CORP) ★
1 Metroplex Dr Ste 400, Birmingham, AL 35209-6895
Tel (205) 870-7790 *Founded/Ownrshp* 2002
Sales NA *EMP* 1,700
SIC 6411 Insurance brokers
**Pr:* Ron Helveston
Pr: Diane Iervolino
**COO:* Charles Wood
Ex VP: Alda Joffe
**Ex VP:* Mike Johnston
**Ex VP:* West McAdams
VP: Brent Belman
VP: Allyson Benda
VP: Gino Grieco
VP: Cindy Randolph
VP: Melissa Raspino
VP: Daniel Rossen
VP: Jason Schmahl
VP: Natalie Sienkiewicz
VP: Lora Sisson
VP: JC Sparling
VP: Matthew Whitelaw

D-U-N-S 06-840-9797
CRCI HOLDINGS INC
4301 Westbank Dr A-250, Austin, TX 78746-6568
Tel (512) 327-9200 *Founded/Ownrshp* 2010
Sales 255.8MM^E *EMP* 962
SIC 6719 Investment holding companies, except banks
CEO: Glenn Garland

D-U-N-S 03-649-4420
CRDENTIA CORP
1964 Howell Branch Rd # 103, Winter Park, FL 32792-1042
Tel (520) 327-2651 *Founded/Ownrshp* 1997
Sales 21.9MM^E *EMP* 1,437^E
SIC 7363 Medical help service
CEO: John B Kaiser
**Ch Bd:* C Fred Toney
**COO:* Jean Stewart
**CFO:* James J Terbeest
Sr VP: Matt Cahillane
Sr VP: Mike Emery
Sr VP: Dan Ross
**Sr VP:* Randall Turnbull
VP: Penny Kirsch
VP Opers: Tim Jones
VP Mktg: Christina Hogan

CREAM-O-LAND DAIRIES
See CREAM-O-LAND DAIRY INC

D-U-N-S 80-975-0925
CREAM-O-LAND DAIRIES LLC
529 Cedar Ln, Florence, NJ 08518-2511
Tel (609) 499-3601 *Founded/Ownrshp* 1943
Sales 91.2MM^E *EMP* 260
SIC 5143 Dairy products, except dried or canned
CFO: Lisa Schneier

D-U-N-S 01-154-3220 IMP
CREAM-O-LAND DAIRY INC
CREAM-O-LAND DAIRIES
529 Cedar Ln, Florence, NJ 08518-2511
Tel (609) 499-3601 *Founded/Ownrshp* 1946
Sales 213.3MM^E *EMP* 260
SIC 5143 5149 Dairy products, except dried or canned; Milk; Dairy depot; Juices; Soft drinks
Pr: Jay Schneier
**Ch Bd:* Arthur Schneier
CFO: Lisa M Schneier
CFO: Carl Swick
**Treas:* Phyllis Schneier
**VP:* Robert Schneier

D-U-N-S 00-429-9038
CREAMER METAL PRODUCTS INC (OH)
77 S Madison Rd, London, OH 43140-1444
Tel (740) 852-1752 *Founded/Ownrshp* 1945, 1982
Sales 1.0MMM *EMP* 30^E
SIC 3523 Farm machinery & equipment
Pr: Karen C Peters
**VP:* Robert Snyder

CREAMLAND DAIRIES
See DEAN DAIRY HOLDINGS LLC

CREATION TCHNOLOGIES-LEXINGTON
See CREATION TECHNOLOGIES KENTUCKY INC

D-U-N-S 83-190-8731 IMP
CREATION TECHNOLOGIES KENTUCKY INC
CREATION TCHNOLOGIES-LEXINGTON
(*Suby of* CREATION TECHNOLOGIES INC)
1001 Klein Rd Ste 100, Plano, TX 75074-3750
Tel (859) 253-3066 *Founded/Ownrshp* 1994
Sales 83.7MM^E *EMP* 325
SIC 3679 3672 Electronic circuits; Printed circuit boards
Pr: Arthur R Tymos
Ex VP: John Zurborg
**VP:* Craig Schuster
Genl Mgr: Greg Howard

D-U-N-S 18-198-9203 IMP
CREATION TECHNOLOGIES WISCONSIN INC
(*Suby of* CREATION TECHNOLOGIES INC)
2250 W South Branch Blvd, Oak Creek, WI 53154-4907
Tel (414) 761-0400 *Founded/Ownrshp* 2002
Sales 141.5MM^E *EMP* 350
SIC 3672 Printed circuit boards
Genl Mgr: Brian Johnson
**Ex VP:* Douglas Besse
Genl Mgr: Dan Dery

D-U-N-S 08-269-1601
CREATIVE ARTISTS AGENCY LLC
C A A
2000 Avenue Of The Stars # 100, Los Angeles, CA 90067-4705
Tel (424) 288-2000 *Founded/Ownrshp* 1995
Sales 107.1MM^E *EMP* 1,200
SIC 7922 Agent or manager for entertainers
Ch: Rick Nicita
Pt: Kevin Gelbard
Mng Pt: Steve Lafferty
CFO: Bob Goldman
VP: Adam Eisen
VP: Bruce King
VP: Rick Marroquin
VP: David Zedeck
Exec: Christy Marburger
Exec: Victoria O'Seni
Exec: Darnell Strom
Exec: Nick Styne
Exec: Mario Tirado

D-U-N-S 80-788-7484
CREATIVE CHOICE HOMES INC
CREATIVE CHOICE MANAGEMENT
8895 N Military Trl 206e, West Palm Beach, FL 33410-6291
Tel (561) 627-7988 *Founded/Ownrshp* 1984
Sales 322.1MM *EMP* 1,500
SIC 6552 4813 Subdividers & developers; Telephone communication, except radio
Pr: Dilip Barot
**Pr:* Yashpal Kakkar
CFO: Gopi Barot
Trst: Dinesh Pandya
VP: Avraham Alfasi
VP: Richard Jerez
VP: Jason Larson
VP: Gustavo Ramirez

CREATIVE CHOICE MANAGEMENT
See CREATIVE CHOICE HOMES INC

D-U-N-S 05-062-0442 IMP
CREATIVE FOAM CORP
S P P D
300 N Alloy Dr, Fenton, MI 48430-2649
Tel (574) 546-4238 *Founded/Ownrshp* 1969
Sales 198.2MM^E *EMP* 600
SIC 3061 3089 3053 3086 3069 Mechanical rubber goods; Injection molded finished plastic products; Gaskets, packing & sealing devices; Plastics foam products; Foam rubber
Ch Bd: Roger Morgan
Pr: Wayne Blessing
V Ch Bd: Peter Swallow
Ex VP: Bruce Graham
Plnt Mgr: Joe Pinerio

D-U-N-S 83-195-0972
CREATIVE HAIRDRESSERS INC
1577 Spring Hill Rd # 600, Vienna, VA 22182-2284
Tel (703) 269-5400 *Founded/Ownrshp* 1974
Sales 1.2MMM^E *EMP* 10,000
SIC 5999 7231 Hair care products; Hairdressers; Unisex hair salons
Pr: Dennis F Ratner
Pr: Lisa Rieve
**CFO:* Ben Teicher
VP: Rich Gatti
**VP:* Susan Gustafson
**VP:* Lester D Mardiks
**VP:* Gary Ratner
VP: Warren Ratner

D-U-N-S 79-210-6999 IMP/EXP
CREATIVE HOLDINGS INC
(*Suby of* CREATIVE TECHNOLOGY LTD.)
1901 Mccarthy Blvd, Milpitas, CA 95035-7427
Tel (408) 428-6600 *Founded/Ownrshp* 1992
Sales 111.2MM^E *EMP* 900
SIC 5045 3577 3931 3674 8711 3651 Computers; Data conversion equipment, media-to-media: computer; Musical instruments; Keyboards, piano or organ; Synthesizers, music; Integrated circuits, semiconductor networks, etc.; Engineering services; Speaker systems
Pr: Sim Wong Hoo
**Pr:* Craig McCugh
Dir Surg: Phil So' Shaughnessy

D-U-N-S 19-542-8123 IMP
CREATIVE LABS INC
(*Suby of* CREATIVE HOLDINGS INC) ★
1901 Mccarthy Blvd, Milpitas, CA 95035-7427
Tel (408) 428-6600 *Founded/Ownrshp* 1988
Sales 109.8MM^E *EMP* 600
SIC 5045 5734 3577 Computer peripheral equipment; Computer & software stores; Computer peripheral equipment
CEO: Keh Long Ng
**Pr:* Craig McHugh
Prgrm Mgr: Robert Gilsdorf
Genl Mgr: Jeff Stoen
IT Man: David Cassel
IT Man: Brad Devoross
IT Man: Tony Lim
IT Man: Xiaobo Luo
Mktg Mgr: Eric Loong

D-U-N-S 02-723-6058
CREATIVE MANAGEMENT SERVICES LLC
MC SQUARE
3 Alpine Ct, Chestnut Ridge, NY 10977-5647
Tel (845) 578-1651 *Founded/Ownrshp* 1999
Sales 95.3MM^E *EMP* 323
SIC 7389 Advertising, promotional & trade show services
CFO: William Medve
Pr: Vickie Stafford
VP: Bernie Massett
VP: Todd Simon
Comm Dir: Caroline Meyers

D-U-N-S 92-731-4443 IMP
CREATIVE OFFICE ENVIRONMENTS
EYEWAY
11798 N Lakeridge Pkwy, Ashland, VA 23005-8152
Tel (804) 329-0400 *Founded/Ownrshp* 1995
Sales 130.3MM^E *EMP* 160
SIC 5021 Office furniture
CEO: Robert P Delille
**Pr:* Richard Carr
COO: Valerie Carboni
CFO: Lawrence Gumprich
VP: Jim Hopkins

D-U-N-S 19-707-7779
CREATIVE OFFICE INTERIORS INC
CREATIVE OFFICE PAVILION
1 Design Center Pl # 734, Boston, MA 02210-2313
Tel (617) 956-4100 *Founded/Ownrshp* 1988
Sales 242.0MM^E *EMP* 280
SIC 5021 Office furniture
Pr: Joe Gardner
CFO: Angelo Benedictis
**Treas:* Sam Scialabba
VP: Michael Clancy
VP: Derek Macdonald
VP: Barb Mokler
VP: Scott Peckham
**Genl Mgr:* Greg Bertovich
**Genl Mgr:* Jerry Weber
IT Man: Robert Delvecchio

CREATIVE OFFICE PAVILION
See CREATIVE OFFICE INTERIORS INC

D-U-N-S 14-799-4206
CREATIVE ORTHOTICS & PROSTHETICS INC
1300 College Ave Ste 1, Elmira, NY 14901-1154
Tel (607) 734-7215 *Founded/Ownrshp* 2014
Sales 51.9MM^E *EMP* 1,050^E
SIC 3842 5999 5047 Limbs, artificial; Artificial limbs; Hospital equipment & furniture
Pr: John Renz

D-U-N-S 61-149-4402 IMP
CREATIVE SOLUTIONS GROUP INC
DIAM INTERNATIONAL
555 Tuckahoe Rd, Yonkers, NY 10710-5709
Tel (914) 771-4200 *Founded/Ownrshp* 1999
Sales 93.9MM^E *EMP* 1,212
SIC 3993 Displays & cutouts, window & lobby
CEO: Edward Winder
**Ch Bd:* William I Ecker

D-U-N-S 18-295-0105
CREATIVE SURFACES INC
OLDCASTLE SURFACES
1400 W Marietta St Nw, Atlanta, GA 30318-4976
Tel (205) 988-3246 *Founded/Ownrshp* 1987
Sales 2.0MM *EMP* 35,000
SIC 2541 1799

D-U-N-S 96-211-9462
CREATIVE TESTING SOLUTIONS
CTS
2424 W Erie Dr, Tempe, AZ 85282-3113
Tel (602) 343-7000 *Founded/Ownrshp* 2009
Sales 218.4MM *EMP* 425
Accts Ernst & Young Us Llp Phoenix
SIC 8099 Blood related health services
Pr: Sally Caglioti
Pr: Marc Pearce
**CFO:* Susan Barnes
**VP:* Eugene Robertson
VP: Phillip Williamson
Tech Mgr: Ted Montagot
**Med Dir:* German Leparc MD
Board of Directors: Gary K Wilde, Roy Berke, J Daniel Connor, James Covert, Donald Doddridge, William G Green, Tim O'brien, Melvyn C Rothman, Ronald Waekerlan, Rick Walsh

CREC
See CAPITOL REGION EDUCATION COUNCIL FOUNDATION INC

D-U-N-S 08-774-3530
▲ CREDIT ACCEPTANCE CORP
25505 W 12 Mile Rd # 2300, Southfield, MI 48034-8316
Tel (248) 353-2700 *Founded/Ownrshp* 1972
Sales NA *EMP* 1,425^E
Tkr Sym CACC *Exch* NGS
SIC 6141 Financing: automobiles, furniture, etc., not a deposit bank
CEO: Brett A Roberts
**Ch Bd:* Donald A Foss
Pr: Steven M Jones
CFO: Kenneth S Booth
Treas: Douglas W Busk
Ofcr: Arthur L Smith
Ofcr: Daniel A Ulatowski
VP: Jonathan Lum
VP: Wayne Mancini
CIO: John S Soave
Sls Dir: Ali Akyuz
Board of Directors: Glenda J Flanagan, Thomas N Tryforos, Scott J Vassalluzzo

D-U-N-S 14-776-2871
CREDIT AGRICOLE AMERICA SERVICES INC
CREDIT AGRICOLE CORP & INV BNK
(*Suby of* CREDIT AGRICOLE GLOBALPARTNERS INC) ★
1301 Ave Of The Americas, New York, NY 10019-6022
Tel (212) 261-7000 *Founded/Ownrshp* 2004
Sales NA *EMP* 100
SIC 6159 Intermediate investment banks
**COO:* George Levitt
Chf Mktg O: Christine Cremel
Ofcr: Nicolas Boulay
Assoc VP: Benny Azaraev
Assoc VP: Darlene Caulford
Assoc VP: Joe Centrone
Assoc VP: Emanuel Reznic
VP: Joseph Agoglia
VP: Chris Boyce-Valentine
VP: Lilly Lin
VP: Jonathan Rick
VP: Amar Shapiro
Board of Directors: Edmond Alphandery, Frank E Dangeard, Marc Deschamps

CREDIT AGRICOLE CORP & INV BNK
See CREDIT AGRICOLE AMERICA SERVICES INC

D-U-N-S 85-849-9825
CREDIT AGRICOLE GLOBALPARTNERS INC
(*Suby of* CREDIT LYONNAIS)
1301 Ave Of The Americas, New York, NY 10019-6022
Tel (212) 261-7000 *Founded/Ownrshp* 1968
Sales 155.2MM^E *EMP* 372
SIC 6211 Brokers, security; Dealers, security; Investment bankers
Prin: Jacques Busquet

CREDIT BUREAU OF BEAUMONT
See CSC CREDIT SERVICES INC

D-U-N-S 80-945-4358
CREDIT CARD PROCESSING USA INC
MSI MERCHANT SERVICES
2202 N Irving St, Allentown, PA 18109-9554
Tel (908) 790-1777 *Founded/Ownrshp* 1993
Sales 85.1MM *EMP* 44
Accts Withum Smith + Brown Pc Some
SIC 7389 Credit card service
Pr: George Mayo
**Sec:* Mario Parisi
**VP:* Andrew Czujko

D-U-N-S 11-293-6331
CREDIT ONE BANK NATIONAL ASSOCIATION
(*Suby of* CREDIT ONE FINANCIAL) ★
585 Pilot Rd, Las Vegas, NV 89119-3619
Tel (702) 269-3900 *Founded/Ownrshp* 1984
Sales NA *EMP* 400
SIC 6021 National commercial banks
Pr: Robert Dejong
**CFO:* George Hughes
Sr Ex VP: Berkman Hong
Ex VP: Sam Dommer
Sr VP: Don Blackhurst
Sr VP: Bill Bostwick
Sr VP: Michael Coleman
Sr VP: Mamta Kapoor
VP: Mike Brown
VP: Gary Harwood
VP: Mike Imhof
VP: Helen Lanham
VP: Amelia Nieman
VP: Deena Rancier
VP: Jim Shaughnessy
VP: Lisa Sturm
VP: Drew Verts
Dir Risk M: John Andross

D-U-N-S 11-292-3545
CREDIT ONE FINANCIAL
585 Pilot Rd, Las Vegas, NV 89119-3619
Tel (702) 269-1000 *Founded/Ownrshp* 1993
Sales NA *EMP* 400^E
SIC 6021 National commercial banks
Pr: Robert Dejong
VP: Jody Ciuffetelli
VP Mktg: Jody Ciussetelli

D-U-N-S 00-698-2995
CREDIT SUISSE (USA) INC (DE)
(*Suby of* CREDIT SUISSE FIRST BOSTON) ★
11 Madison Ave Frnt 1, New York, NY 10010-3680
Tel (212) 325-2000 *Founded/Ownrshp* 1959
Sales 4.1MMM^E *EMP* 10,899
Accts Kpmg Llp New York New York
SIC 6211 6282 6799 Investment bankers; Security brokers & dealers; Investment advisory service; Investment research; Venture capital companies
Pr: Brady W Dougan
CFO: David C Fisher
Treas: Peter J Feeney
Mng Dir: Stephen Dunne
Mng Dir: Neil Moskowitz
Mng Dir: D Neil Radey
**Mng Dir:* Lewis H Wirshba
VP Sls: Sarah Blondin
Mktg Mgr: Debra Darville
Doctor: Alan Alperin MD
Doctor: Jamie Nicholson MD

D-U-N-S 82-831-5205
CREDIT SUISSE ASSET MANAGEMENT LLC
(*Suby of* CREDIT SUISSE (USA) INC) ★
11 Madison Ave Bsmt 1b, New York, NY 10010-3629
Tel (212) 325-2000 *Founded/Ownrshp* 1999
Sales 399.2MM^E *EMP* 193^E
SIC 6211 Security brokers & dealers
V Ch: Leandro S Galban
CFO: Paul Wirth
VP: Ryan Bott
VP: Zev Kindler
VP: Raj Sakthi
Mng Dir: Peter Aliprantis
Mng Dir: Paul Arango
Mng Dir: Michael Baldinger
Mng Dir: Joe Friedman
Mng Dir: Neil Harvey
Mng Dir: Jeff Kiely

CREDIT SUISSE FIRST BOSTON
See CREDIT SUISSE HOLDINGS (USA) INC

D-U-N-S 04-046-3556
CREDIT SUISSE HOLDINGS (USA) INC
CREDIT SUISSE FIRST BOSTON
(*Suby of* CREDIT SUISSE GROUP AG)
11 Madison Ave Bsmt 1b, New York, NY 10010-3629
Tel (646) 935-0299 *Founded/Ownrshp* 1997
Sales NA *EMP* 28,162

SIC 6712 Bank holding companies
Pr: Brady W Dougan
Pt: Derek Jones
Pt: Arnaud Lipkowicz
V Ch: David Mulford
Pr: Mark Katz
Pr: Francesca Krist
Pr: Ben Weetman
COO: Alastair Cairns
**Treas:* Galina Guale
Sr Cor Off: George Jamgochian
Ofcr: Joanne Foster
Ex VP: Andrew Smith
VP: Fabien Antignac
VP: David Bach
VP: George Ching
VP: Eugene Choe
VP: Kim Cuozzo
VP: Kevin Dempsey
VP: Vaishali Javeri
VP: Tammy Jelinek
VP: Oliver Jenni
Board of Directors: Thomas W Bechtler, Gerald Clark, Walter B Kielholz, Peter Brabeck-Letmathe, Joe L Roby, Daniel L Vasella

D-U-N-S 00-698-3688
CREDIT SUISSE SECURITIES (USA) LLC
(*Suby of* CREDIT SUISSE FIRST BOSTON) ★
11 Madison Ave Bsmt 1b, New York, NY 10010-3698
Tel (212) 325-2000 *Founded/Ownrshp* 1918, 1988
Sales 4.3MMM^E^ *EMP* 4,683
SIC 6211 Dealers, security; Investment bankers
Pr: Brady W Dougan
**V Ch:* Gary G Lynch
Pr: Francesca Krist
COO: Philippe Clemencon
CFO: Renato Fassbind
**CFO:* David Mathers
Treas: Galina Guale
**Treas:* Lewis H Wirsba
Ofcr: Roger Machlis
Assoc VP: Edwin Gomez
VP: Paul Aliprandi
VP: Michael Chaisanguanthum
VP: Brandon Chin
VP: Kevin Dempsey
VP: Alison Gavin
VP: Terry Hebert
VP: Navrooz Irani
VP: Ali Khan
**VP:* Zev Kindler
VP: Peter Kueng
VP: Reinhard Lindner

D-U-N-S 01-563-3720
CREDIT-BASED ASSET SERVICING AND SECURITIZATION LLC
C-BASS
333 Thornall St Ste 602, Edison, NJ 08837-2220
Tel (212) 850-7700 *Founded/Ownrshp* 1996
Sales 89.2MM^E^ *EMP* 1,200
Accts Deloitte & Touche Llp
SIC 8732 Business economic service
CEO: Bruce Williams
**COO:* Saul Sanders
Chf Cred: Lisa Brzezinski
Sr VP: Shane Ross
**Sr VP:* Robert L Weinstein
VP: Peter Berkey
VP: Lynne Rapapport
VP: Eric Silver
VP: Diane Westerback
VP: Rick Williams
Mng Dir: Peter Cerevin

D-U-N-S 09-021-2866
CREDO 180 CAPITAL PARTNERS
5405 Alton Pkwy 5a, Irvine, CA 92604-3717
Tel (949) 274-4405 *Founded/Ownrshp* 1988
Sales 300.0MM *EMP* 11
SIC 6282 7373 Investment advisory service; Value-added resellers, computer systems
**Pt:* Rob Winkelmann
Sr VP: Kirstin L Gooldy
VP: Brad Abbott
VP: Allan Karsh
VP Opers: David Kramer

D-U-N-S 18-325-2501 IMP
▲ CREE INC
4600 Silicon Dr, Durham, NC 27703-8475
Tel (919) 407-5300 *Founded/Ownrshp* 1987
Sales 1.6MMM *EMP* 6,237
Tkr Sym CREE *Exch* NGS
SIC 3674 3672 Semiconductors & related devices; Light emitting diodes; Microcircuits, integrated (semiconductor); Printed circuit boards
Pr: Charles M Swoboda
CFO: Michael E McDevitt
Ex VP: Franco Plastina
Board of Directors: Clyde R Hosein, Robert A Ingram, Darren R Jackson, C Howard Nye, John B Replogle, Thomas H Werner, Anne C Whitaker

CREEKSTONE FARMS PREMIUM BEEF
See CFPB HOLDINGS LLC

D-U-N-S 12-908-8196 IMP/EXP
CREEKSTONE FARMS PREMIUM BEEF LLC
(*Suby of* CREEKSTONE FARMS PREMIUM BEEF) ★
604 Goff Industrial Pk Rd, Arkansas City, KS 67005-8880
Tel (620) 741-3100 *Founded/Ownrshp* 2003
Sales 145.8MM^E^ *EMP* 700
SIC 2011 Beef products from beef slaughtered on site
CEO: Dennis Buhlke
**CFO:* Leon Trautwein
VP: Ron Fickler

D-U-N-S 06-209-3521 IMP
CREEL PRINTING & PUBLISHING CO INC (NV)
CREEL PRINTING COMPANY
6330 W Sunset Rd, Las Vegas, NV 89118-3318
Tel (702) 735-8161 *Founded/Ownrshp* 1953, 1972
Sales 152.0MM^E^ *EMP* 350^E^
SIC 2752 Commercial printing, lithographic
CEO: Allan H Creel
**CFO:* Deborah J Creel
CFO: Heidi Creel
Ex VP: Micah Armijo
VP: Chris Evans
**VP:* Gary Kasufkin
Netwrk Mgr: Mike Stegner
Sales Exec: Steve Tedio
Mktg Dir: Skip Mitchell
Sls Dir: Steve Berry

CREEL PRINTING COMPANY
See CREEL PRINTING & PUBLISHING CO INC

D-U-N-S 09-276-0040
CREGGER CO INC (SC)
637 N 12th St, West Columbia, SC 29169-6418
Tel (803) 217-0710 *Founded/Ownrshp* 1978
Sales 130.7MM^E^ *EMP* 110
SIC 5074 5064 Plumbing & hydronic heating supplies; Pipes & fittings, plastic; Sanitary ware, china or enameled iron; Plumbing & heating valves; Washing machines; Refrigerators & freezers; Clothes dryers, electric & gas; Microwave ovens, non-commercial
Pr: Morris Cregger
**Sec:* Sheila Cregger

D-U-N-S 07-917-2742
CREIGHTON ALEGENT CLINIC
12809 W Dodge Rd, Omaha, NE 68154-2155
Tel (402) 343-4343 *Founded/Ownrshp* 2013
Sales 244.4MM *EMP* 5
Accts Catholic Health Initiatives O
SIC 8062 Hospital, affiliated with AMA residency
Prin: Richard Hachten II
**Prin:* Cindy Johnson
Genl Couns: Chuck Sederstrom

D-U-N-S 79-557-2205
■ CREIGHTON ALEGENT HEALTH
CREIGHTON UNIV MED CTR-ST JO
(*Suby of* TENET HEALTHCARE CORP) ★
601 N 30th St, Omaha, NE 68131-2128
Tel (402) 449-4000 *Founded/Ownrshp* 1984
Sales 158.1MM^E^ *EMP* 2,000
SIC 8062 General medical & surgical hospitals
CEO: Cliff A Robertson
**Pr:* Leslie R Andersen
CFO: Timothy Meier
**Prin:* Kevin J Nokels
CIO: Rick Sweeney
Pathlgst: Edward Adickes
Pathlgst: Richard Baltaro
Pathlgst: Hina J Naushad
Doctor: Murray Casey
Doctor: Michael McGuire
Pharmcst: Megan Peters

D-U-N-S 80-935-6504
CREIGHTON ALEGENT HEALTH
CHI HEALTH
(*Suby of* CHI) ★
12809 W Dodge Rd, Omaha, NE 68154-2155
Tel (402) 343-4300 *Founded/Ownrshp* 2012
Sales 516.4MM *EMP* 8,600
Accts Lb Catholic Health Initiatives
SIC 5912 Drug stores
Pr: Cliff Robertson MD
Pr: Richard Rolston MD
**COO:* Joan Neuhaus
CFO: Tim Meier
**CFO:* Jeanette Wojtalewicz
Treas: Cindy Johnson
**Sr VP:* Bonnie Burnett
**Sr VP:* Nancy Wallace
VP: Leigh Bertholf
VP: Ann Schumacher
VP: Charles Sederteron
VP: Jason Yungtum

D-U-N-S 01-895-7894
CREIGHTON SCHOOL DISTRICT
2702 E Flower St, Phoenix, AZ 85016-7498
Tel (602) 381-6000 *Founded/Ownrshp* 1884
Sales 46.7MM^E^ *EMP* 1,000
SIC 8211 Public junior high school; Public elementary school
CTO: Barbara Murphy
Dir IT: Ed Stolze
IT Man: James Stolze
Schl Brd P: Matthew Jewett
Teacher Pr: Susan Lugo
Psych: Winona Considine

CREIGHTON UNIV MED CTR-ST JO
See CREIGHTON ALEGENT HEALTH

D-U-N-S 05-330-9332 IMP/EXP
CREIGHTON UNIVERSITY
2500 California Plz, Omaha, NE 68178-0002
Tel (402) 280-2900 *Founded/Ownrshp* 1878
Sales 531.1MM *EMP* 5,000
SIC 8221 University
Pr: Timothy R Lannon
CFO: Robert Glow
Assoc VP: Deb Fortina
VP: John C Erneh
Assoc Dir: Bette Poutre
Ex Dir: Thomas Baechle
Ex Dir: Cherie Sempek
Off Mgr: Sheryl Oviatt
IT Man: Arvind Jagannathan
Sales Exec: Jim Corr
Sales Exec: Liz Flaherty

D-U-N-S 10-357-0289 IMP
CRENLO CAB PRODUCTS INC
(*Suby of* IES) ★
1600 4th Ave Nw, Rochester, MN 55901-2573
Tel (507) 289-3371 *Founded/Ownrshp* 2011
Sales 162.0MM^E^ *EMP* 698
SIC 2522 3531 2542 3713 3469 3444 Office furniture, except wood; Cabs, for construction machinery; Cabinets: show, display or storage: except wood; Truck & bus bodies; Metal stampings; Sheet metalwork
Pr: David Kilburn
CFO: Gene Astolfi
VP: Charles Goulding
VP: Keith Thompson

Web Prj Mg: Matt Krichbaum
Manager: Sean Radler

D-U-N-S 17-520-4010
CREO CAPITAL PARTNERS LLC
12400 Walsh Ave Ste 1100, Los Angeles, CA 90066-6608
Tel (310) 230-8600 *Founded/Ownrshp* 2004
Sales 102.8MM^E^ *EMP* 262^E^
SIC 6726 Investment offices
CFO: Brent Shapiro
Mng Dir: Joe Bratter
Mng Dir: Joshua Fox

D-U-N-S 83-147-1920
CRESA PARTNERS LLC
200 State St Ste 13a, Boston, MA 02109-2684
Tel (617) 758-6000 *Founded/Ownrshp* 1998
Sales 194.7MM^E^ *EMP* 855
SIC 8742 6531 Management consulting services; Real estate agent, commercial
CEO: James Underhill
CFO: Edward Fothergill
Assoc VP: Brandon Leitner
Assoc VP: Ryan Orton
Ex VP: Jim Dezell
Sr VP: Bob McGriff
Sr VP: Roger O'Neal
VP: Carol Adey
VP: Rollie Andre
VP: Paul Andrews
VP: Krista Bailey
VP: Ralph Benzakein
VP: Chad Bermingham
VP: Scott Bumpas
VP: Deborah Cox
VP: Paul Delaney
VP: Peg Ellefson
VP: Greg Fischer
VP: Charlie Floberg
VP: Jeff Gagnon
VP: Dan Gallup

D-U-N-S 84-935-5151
CRESCENT BANK & TRUST
(*Suby of* CB&T HOLDING CORP) ★
1100 Poydras St Ste 100, New Orleans, LA 70163-0100
Tel (504) 556-5950 *Founded/Ownrshp* 1991
Sales NA *EMP* 120
SIC 6021 National commercial banks
Pr: Fred B Morgan III
**COO:* Ed Bourgeois
**CFO:* Barry Bleakley
Treas: Leon K Poche
Ofcr: Deborah Goodenough
Sr Ex VP: Donald Howie

D-U-N-S 01-408-0977 IMP
CRESCENT CROWN DISTRIBUTING LLC
5900 Almonaster Ave, New Orleans, LA 70126-7138
Tel (504) 240-5900 *Founded/Ownrshp* 2001
Sales 535.7MM^E^ *EMP* 1,158
SIC 5181 Beer & ale
CEO: James R Moffett Jr
**CFO:* Joseph M Dempsey
Ex VP: Rich Marchant
VP: Christopher Bourg
VP: Don Dorand
VP: Terry Morrison
Dist Mgr: Ryan Saladino
Genl Mgr: William Pananos
Off Mgr: Josh Gregory
Off Mgr: Kimberly Guidry
Off Mgr: Clair Lee

D-U-N-S 15-097-6103
CRESCENT DIRECTIONAL DRILLING LP
2040 Aldine Western Rd, Houston, TX 77038-1208
Tel (281) 668-9500 *Founded/Ownrshp* 2003
Sales 283.9MM^E^ *EMP* 330^E^
SIC 1381 Directional drilling oil & gas wells
CEO: George Moody
Genl Pt: Martin Lyons
Pt: Leon Hopson
Pt: Buckner Roane
Pt: Mike Torres
Ch Bd: Carol McFadden
CFO: Jesse Perez
VP: Danny Jatzlau
Exec: Kayley Halquist
Sfty Dirs: Dennis Rome
Opers Mgr: Roger Bailey

D-U-N-S 05-100-1576
CRESCENT ELECTRIC SUPPLY CO
CESCO
7750 Timmerman Dr, East Dubuque, IL 61025-1357
Tel (815) 747-3145 *Founded/Ownrshp* 1919
Sales 1.5MMM^E^ *EMP* 1,500
SIC 5063 Electrical apparatus & equipment
Pr: Martin Burbridge
COO: Darrin Anderson
CFO: Jim Etheredge
Treas: Carol Hoffman
Sr VP: Dennis E Desousa
Sr VP: Dick Schmid
VP: Dick Hoffman
Dist Mgr: Carl Otterness
Sls&Mrk Ex: Jim Clark

D-U-N-S 60-289-7683
CRESCENT HOTELS & RESORTS LLC
C H R
10306 Eaton Pl Ste 430, Fairfax, VA 22030-2201
Tel (703) 279-7820 *Founded/Ownrshp* 2002
Sales 172.0MM^E^ *EMP* 2,700^E^
SIC 7011 Hotels & motels
CEO: Michael George
Pr: Lou Esposito
Ch: E Robert Roskind
Ex VP: Evan Studer
Sr VP: Lovell Casiero
Sr VP: Anthony Tony Cohen
Sr VP: Michael Metcalf
Sr VP: Shawn Stuckey
Sr VP: Phil Wolf
VP: William F Driscoll
VP: George Schweitzer

D-U-N-S 11-916-1719
CRESCENT PACKING CORP
1970 New Hwy, Farmingdale, NY 11735-1102
Tel (631) 253-0700 *Founded/Ownrshp* 1984
Sales 100.0MM *EMP* 25
SIC 5147 Meats, fresh
**CEO:* Larry Cornelia
Plnt Mgr: Charlie Fetter
Sls Mgr: Kevin Connelly

D-U-N-S 00-632-7340
CRESCENT PARTS & EQUIPMENT CO INC (MO)
JOHNSON CONTRLS AUTHORIZED DLR
5121 Manchester Ave, Saint Louis, MO 63110-2013
Tel (314) 647-5511 *Founded/Ownrshp* 1944, 1990
Sales 83.1MM^E^ *EMP* 95
SIC 5075 Warm air heating & air conditioning; Air conditioning equipment, except room units; Compressors, air conditioning; Condensing units, air conditioning
Pr: George C Giudici
**CFO:* Mark Lammert
**VP:* Guy Giudici
Brnch Mgr: Ray Meyer
Mktg Dir: Paul Diraimondo
Sls Dir: Ken Perotta
Sls Mgr: Mark Conley
Sls Mgr: Micah Mudd
Sales Asso: Steven Crook

D-U-N-S 87-898-1406
CRESCENT REAL ESTATE EQUITIES CO
(*Suby of* CRESCENT REAL ESTATE HOLDINGS LLC) ★
777 Main St Ste 2260, Fort Worth, TX 76102-5309
Tel (817) 321-2100 *Founded/Ownrshp* 2009
Sales 386.9MM^E^ *EMP* 748
SIC 6798 Real estate investment trusts
Owner: John C Goff
COO: Jason E Anderson
Sr VP: John L Zogg
VP: Bruce M Basham
VP: Anthony B Click
VP: Michael Lewis
VP: Joseph F Pitchford
VP: Joseph Pitchford
VP: Tom Shaw
VP: Jeffrey Stevens
VP: Brenna Wadleigh

D-U-N-S 96-750-8081
CRESCENT REAL ESTATE HOLDINGS LLC
(*Suby of* BARCLAYS CAPITAL INC) ★
777 Main St Ste 2260, Fort Worth, TX 76102-5309
Tel (817) 321-2100 *Founded/Ownrshp* 2009
Sales 386.9MM^E^ *EMP* 748^E^
SIC 6798 Real estate investment trusts

D-U-N-S 07-105-7319
CRESCENT RESOURCES LLC
227 W Trade St Ste 1000, Charlotte, NC 28202-1664
Tel (980) 321-6000 *Founded/Ownrshp* 1969, 2007
Sales 106.5MM^E^ *EMP* 180
SIC 6552 Subdividers & developers
Pr: Todd Mansfield
Pr: Andrew Carmody
Pr: Brian Natwick
CFO: Kevin H Lambert
CFO: Wayne Mc Gee
Sr VP: Fred A Byers
Sr VP: Patrick Henry
Sr VP: Margaret Jennesse
Sr VP: James M Short Jr
Sr VP: Stephen Yetts
VP: Jim Atkinson
VP: John Bell
VP: John Classe Jr
VP: Brenda M Lenaburg
VP: Scott Munday
VP: Tyler Niess
VP: Dean Norton
VP: Jay Page
VP: Thomas Webb
VP: Tom Webb
VP: Denon Williams

D-U-N-S 01-301-7734
CRESCENT SERVICES LLC (WV)
5721 Nw 132nd St, Oklahoma City, OK 73142-4437
Tel (405) 603-1200 *Founded/Ownrshp* 2006
Sales 1.2MMM^E^ *EMP* 700
SIC 1389 Oil field services
CFO: Nick Hughes
COO: Nick Andrews
VP: Shawn Priddy
VP: Ryan Stover
Opers Mgr: Derrick Bennett

D-U-N-S 04-824-2259 IMP
CRESLINE PLASTIC PIPE CO INC
600 N Cross Pointe Blvd, Evansville, IN 47715-9119
Tel (812) 428-9300 *Founded/Ownrshp* 1966
Sales 142.3MM^E^ *EMP* 350
SIC 3084 Plastics pipe
Ch Bd: John H Schroeder
**Pr:* Richard A Schroeder
**VP:* Gary Richmond
VP Mfg: Bruce Abbott
VP Mfg: Mike Hatley
**VP Sls:* Tom Walker
Sls Mgr: Jeff Algaier
Board of Directors: John C Schroeder

D-U-N-S 07-657-5646
CRESSON SECURE TREATMENT UNIT
160 Gould St Ste 300, Needham, MA 02494-2300
Tel (781) 559-4900 *Founded/Ownrshp* 1979
Sales 148.7MM *EMP* 1,600
Accts Alexander Aronson Finning & Co
SIC 8361 Residential care for the handicapped; Juvenile correctional facilities
Pr: Andy Pond
**CFO:* Joel Kershner
Treas: Stephen Webster
Sr VP: Gregory Canfield
**VP:* Robert Guttentag
Pgrm Dir: Donna Grisi

D-U-N-S 01-046-9922
CREST CADILLAC INC
CREST INFINITY
2701 Northcrest Dr, Plano, TX 75075-8103
Tel (972) 423-7700 *Founded/Ownrshp* 1987
Sales 139.4MM^E *EMP* 400^E
SIC 5511 Automobiles, new & used
Pr: Larry Van Tuyl
**Treas:* Robert J Holcomb
**Treas:* John Morford
**VP:* Michael A Brosin
Exec: Karen Mounts
IT Man: Al Clifford
Info Man: Laura Reeves
Sls Dir: Darin Partin
Sales Asso: Brian Weaver

D-U-N-S 03-301-8904
CREST DISCOUNT FOODS INC (OK)
CREST FOODS
2200 W 15th And Santa Fe, Edmond, OK 73013
Tel (405) 733-2330 *Founded/Ownrshp* 1946
Sales 173.1MM^E *EMP* 1,000
SIC 5411 Supermarkets, independent
Pr: Bruce Harroz
**VP:* Kevin Ergenbright
Brnch Mgr: Kevin Quick

CREST FOODS
See CREST DISCOUNT FOODS INC

D-U-N-S 00-507-2905
CREST FOODS CO INC (IL)
905 Main St, Ashton, IL 61006-9259
Tel (800) 435-6972 *Founded/Ownrshp* 1946, 1957
Sales 97.0MM^E *EMP* 546
SIC 2023 7336

D-U-N-S 05-352-4336 IMP
CREST FURNITURE INC
VALUE CITY
30 Tower Rd, Dayton, NJ 08810-1571
Tel (732) 355-9200 *Founded/Ownrshp* 1970
Sales 113.0MM *EMP* 350
SIC 5712 Furniture stores
Pr: Simon E Kaplan
**Pr:* Sidney Rechtman
Mktg Dir: Mitchell Keller

D-U-N-S 06-547-7630
CREST INDUSTRIES
4725 Highway 28 E, Pineville, LA 71360-4730
Tel (318) 767-5530 *Founded/Ownrshp* 1973
Sales 259.6MM *EMP* 415^E
Accts Lester Miller & Wells Alexan
SIC 3699 3612 3441 5063 2439 Electrical equipment & supplies; Transformers, except electric; Fabricated structural metal; Electrical apparatus & equipment; Structural wood members
Pr: Kenneth L Robison
CFO: Robert L Brinkerhoff
VP: John Doggett
IT Man: Donald Stewart

CREST INFINITY
See CREST CADILLAC INC

D-U-N-S 82-567-3189
CREST OPERATIONS LLC
(*Suby of* CREST INDUSTRIES) ★
4725 Highway 28 E, Pineville, LA 71360-4730
Tel (318) 448-0274 *Founded/Ownrshp* 1977
Sales 255.4MM *EMP* 300^E
Accts Lester Miller & Wells Alexan
SIC 3441 2439 3699 5063 3612 Fabricated structural metal; Structural wood members; Electrical equipment & supplies; Electrical apparatus & equipment; Transformers, except electric
VP: John Doggett
Off Mgr: Tracy Blalock
Dir IT: Scott Robison

CREST PROJECT
See COUNTY OF RIVERSIDE

D-U-N-S 01-433-7095
CREST PUMPING TECHNOLOGIES LLC
(*Suby of* NINE ENERGY SERVICE INC) ★
6500 West Fwy Ste 601, Fort Worth, TX 76116-2181
Tel (817) 484-5100 *Founded/Ownrshp* 2014
Sales 140.7MM^E *EMP* 300
SIC 1389 Pumping of oil & gas wells
Pr: David Crombie
**CFO:* Kevin Palma

D-U-N-S 02-965-6543 IMP
■ **CREST STEEL CORP**
(*Suby of* RELIANCE STEEL & ALUMINUM CO) ★
6580 General Rd, Riverside, CA 92509-0103
Tel (310) 830-2651 *Founded/Ownrshp* 1964
Sales 115.4MM^E *EMP* 90
SIC 5051 Steel
CEO: James D Hoffman
**Pr:* Kris Farris
**CFO:* David Vercuche
**CFO:* Dave Zertuche
Off Mgr: Sue Michaels
Prd Mgr: Chris Baumgarten
Trfc Mgr: Hector Guzman
Trfc Mgr: Chris Semanu
VP Sls: Steve Hale

D-U-N-S 95-845-3581
CRESTMARK BANK
(*Suby of* CRESTMARK BANCORP, INC.)
5480 Corporate Dr, Troy, MI 48098-2641
Tel (248) 641-5100 *Founded/Ownrshp* 1996
Sales NA *EMP* 78
SIC 6022 State commercial banks
CEO: W David Tull
Pr: Elizabeth Costa
**Pr:* Mick Goik
Pr: Heath Holdbrooks
Sr VP: Bryan Alsobrooks
**Sr VP:* Martin F Blake
**Sr VP:* Dominick L Debello
**Sr VP:* Gus Mattia
VP: John Gullman
VP: Dombrowsky Kelly
VP: Jerry Tidd
Board of Directors: Patricia E Mooradian

D-U-N-S 04-919-0469
CRESTONE PEAK RESOURCES LLC
370 17th St Ste 2170, Denver, CO 80202-5612
Tel (720) 410-8500 *Founded/Ownrshp* 2015
Sales 90.0MM *EMP* 122
SIC 1381 Drilling oil & gas wells
CEO: Tony Buchanon
Treas: Jonathan Saunders
Board of Directors: Roger Huang

D-U-N-S 06-929-8214 IMP/EXP
CRESTRON ELECTRONICS INC
15 Volvo Dr, Rockleigh, NJ 07647-2507
Tel (201) 767-3400 *Founded/Ownrshp* 1971
Sales 615.8MM^E *EMP* 2,000
SIC 3571 3651 1731 3663 3499 3669 Minicomputers; Household audio & video equipment; Electrical work; Radio & TV communications equipment; Fire- or burglary-resistive products; Intercommunication systems, electric
Pr: Randy Klein
**COO:* Dan Feldstein
CFO: David Hakula
VP: Brian Daley
Rgnl Mgr: Paul Riley
Rgnl Mgr: Scott Smith
Brnch Mgr: Steve Alexander
Brnch Mgr: Brian Lewis
Snr Sftwr: Belal Ahmed
Snr Sftwr: Colm Coady
CTO: Fred Bargetzi

CRESTVIEW CENTER
See CRESTVIEW NORTH INC

D-U-N-S 94-350-0785
■ **CRESTVIEW CONVALESCENT HOME INC**
HILLCREST CENTER
(*Suby of* GENESIS HEALTHCARE CORP) ★
1245 Church Rd, Wyncote, PA 19095-1800
Tel (215) 884-9990 *Founded/Ownrshp* 1998
Sales 1.6MMM *EMP* 180
SIC 8051 Skilled nursing care facilities
Dir Soc: Jerri Johnson

D-U-N-S 18-791-8024
■ **CRESTVIEW HOSPITAL CORP**
NORTH OKALOOSA MEDICAL CENTER
(*Suby of* COMMUNITY HEALTH SYSTEMS INC) ★
151 E Redstone Ave, Crestview, FL 32539-5352
Tel (850) 423-1000 *Founded/Ownrshp* 1993
Sales 950.0MM *EMP* 605
SIC 8062 General medical & surgical hospitals
CEO: David Fuller
**Pr:* Martin G Schweinhart
**CFO:* Jim Andrews
**CFO:* Larry W Cash
**VP:* James W Doucette
**VP:* Kevin J Hammons
Exec: Laura Frye
Dir IT: Jenny Zietler
Mktg Dir: Rachel Neighbors
Doctor: Patricia S Hambley MD
Nrsg Dir: Pam Bates

D-U-N-S 94-324-7809
■ **CRESTVIEW NORTH INC**
CRESTVIEW CENTER
(*Suby of* GENESIS HEALTHCARE CORP) ★
262 Tollgate Rd, Langhorne, PA 19047-1377
Tel (215) 968-4650 *Founded/Ownrshp* 1997
Sales 1.5MMM^E *EMP* 167
SIC 8051 Skilled nursing care facilities
Pr: George L Chapman
**VP:* Scott A Estes
Exec: Terri Lazer
Mng Dir: Barry Volpert

D-U-N-S 80-675-8178
CRESTVIEW PARTNERS LP
667 Madison Ave Fl 10, New York, NY 10065-8029
Tel (212) 906-0700 *Founded/Ownrshp* 2007
Sales 2.4MMM^E *EMP* 10,237
SIC 6211 Investment firm, general brokerage
Pt: Brian Cassidy
**Pt:* Quentin Chu
**Pt:* Bob Delaney
**Pt:* Rich Demartini
**Pt:* Bob Hurst
**Pt:* Jeff Marcus
**Pt:* Tom Murphy
**Pt:* Barry Volpert
CFO: Evelyn Pellicone
VP: Alex Binderow
VP: Caroline Bliss
VP: Cindy Cheung
VP: Alexander Rose

D-U-N-S 04-365-0675
CRESTWOOD BEHAVIORAL HEALTH INC
101 CORPORATE-SACRAMENTO
520 Capitol Mall Ste 800, Sacramento, CA 95814-4716
Tel (510) 651-1244 *Founded/Ownrshp* 1997
Sales 148.0MM *EMP* 1,746
Accts Moss Adams Llp Stockton Cal
SIC 8063 Psychiatric hospitals
Pr: George Lytal
**VP:* Patricia Blum
Genl Mgr: Margaretta Rosero

D-U-N-S 03-994-9222 IMP
▲ **CRESTWOOD EQUITY PARTNERS LP**
700 Louisiana St Ste 2550, Houston, TX 77002-2756
Tel (832) 519-2200 *Founded/Ownrshp* 2001
Sales 2.6MMM *EMP* 1,300
Tkr Sym CEQP *Exch* NYS
SIC 5984 5172 Liquefied petroleum gas dealers; Propane gas, bottled; Petroleum products; Gases, liquefied petroleum (propane)
Ch Bd: Robert G Phillips
Genl Pt: Crestwood Equity GP
CFO: Michael J Campbell
CFO: Robert Halpin
Sr VP: Steven M Dougherty
Sr VP: Joel C Lambert
Sr VP: William H Moore
VP: John Black

D-U-N-S 07-937-0251
CRESTWOOD EQUITY PARTNERS LP
2 Brush Creek Blvd Ste 20, Kansas City, MO 64112-1712
Tel (816) 842-8181 *Founded/Ownrshp* 2001
Sales 192.1MM^E *EMP* 140^E
SIC 5172 Gases, liquefied petroleum (propane)
CEO: Robert G Phillips
Pr: Heath Deneke
Pr: Bill Gautreaux
Pr: Russ Kovin
CFO: Mike Campbell
Sr VP: Steven Dougherty

D-U-N-S 18-778-3337
CRESTWOOD HEALTHCARE LP
CRESTWOOD MEDICAL CENTER
1 Hospital Dr Sw, Huntsville, AL 35801-6455
Tel (256) 429-4000 *Founded/Ownrshp* 1996
Sales 142.8MM^E *EMP* 1,100
SIC 8062 General medical & surgical hospitals
Pt: Pam Hudson
CFO: Terry L Brown
CFO: Sherry Jones
Chf Nrs Of: Connie Watson
Ex Dir: Karen Hill
DP Dir: Deidra Williams
Opers Mgr: Lynn Moody
Pathlgst: Stephanie Jackson
Obsttrcn: Karen Raiford
Ansthlgy: Murali K Gadde
Opthamlgy: Heather Estopinal

CRESTWOOD MEDICAL CENTER
See CRESTWOOD HEALTHCARE LP

D-U-N-S 78-767-1309
■ **CRESTWOOD MIDSTREAM PARTNERS LP**
(*Suby of* CRESTWOOD EQUITY PARTNERS LP) ★
700 Louisiana St Ste 2550, Houston, TX 77002-2756
Tel (832) 519-2200 *Founded/Ownrshp* 2015
Sales 2.6MMM *EMP* 1,300^E
SIC 4922 Natural gas transmission
Pr: Robert G Phillips
Genl Pt: Crestwood Midstream GP LLC
CFO: Robert T Halpin
Snr PM: Darrin Barnes

D-U-N-S 80-704-1954
CRESTWOOD MIDSTREAM PARTNERS LP
700 Louisiana St Ste 2550, Houston, TX 77002-2756
Tel (832) 519-2200 *Founded/Ownrshp* 2004
Sales 213.9MM *EMP* 5^E
SIC 4922

D-U-N-S 00-729-6403
CRETE CARRIER CORP
400 Nw 56th St, Lincoln, NE 68528-8843
Tel (402) 475-9521 *Founded/Ownrshp* 1966
Sales 1.0MMM *EMP* 6,000
SIC 4213 4212 6512 Trucking, except local; Refrigerated products transport; Contract haulers; Truck rental with drivers; Nonresidential building operators
Pr: Tonn Ostergard
**COO:* Dean Troester
**VP:* Jeremie Kerkman
**VP:* Cindy Turman
**Exec:* Timothy Aschoff
Comm Dir: Andy Brabec
Sales Exec: Holly Ostgard
Natl Sales: Tim Stakolich
Mktg Dir: Todd Sanning
Sls Mgr: Christopher Grosc
Genl Couns: Curtis Ruwe

D-U-N-S 01-028-8132
CRETE-MONEE SCHOOL DISTRICT NO 201-U
1500 S Sangamon St, Crete, IL 60417-2831
Tel (708) 367-8300 *Founded/Ownrshp* 1948
Sales 84.6MM *EMP* 569
Accts Rsm Us Llp Chicago Illinois
SIC 8211 Public combined elementary & secondary school
Pr Dir: Natalie Nash

D-U-N-S 00-617-3900
CRETEX COMPANIES INC (MN)
311 Lowell Ave Nw, Elk River, MN 55330-2597
Tel (763) 441-2121 *Founded/Ownrshp* 1917
Sales 385.1MM^E *EMP* 1,700
SIC 3272 3089 3841 Concrete products; Concrete products used to facilitate drainage; Injection molding of plastics; Surgical & medical instruments; Surgical lasers
Pr: Lynn P Schuler
CFO: Lynn Schuler
**Ch:* Charles R Watson
Ex VP: Don Schumacher
**VP:* Steven Ragaller
**VP:* Jeff Wollerman
Dir IT: John Klinkenborg
IT Man: Archie Olson
Mktg Mgr: Scott Olson

CREVENNA OAKS APARTMENTS
See CREVENNA OAKS PRESERVATION LP

D-U-N-S 01-107-2860
CREVENNA OAKS PRESERVATION LP
CREVENNA OAKS APARTMENTS
11550 Oak Bluff Ct, Burke, VA 22015
Tel (703) 323-7964 *Founded/Ownrshp* 1978
Sales 878.0M *EMP* 3,900
SIC 6513 7389 Apartment building operators;
Mng Pt: Leeann Morein

D-U-N-S 14-717-6523 IMP
CRH AMERICA INC
(*Suby of* OLDCASTLE INC) ★
900 Ashwood Pkwy Ste 600, Atlanta, GA 30338-7501
Tel (770) 804-3363 *Founded/Ownrshp* 1978
Sales 824.1MM^E *EMP* 3,500
SIC 3272 Concrete products
Ch Bd: Liam O'Mahony
**CFO:* Michael O'Driscoll
**Sr VP:* Michael D Lynch
**VP:* Joseph Mc Cullough
VP Mktg: John Kemp

CRIBBIN HOUSE
See CATHOLIC CHARITIES DIOCESE OF BROOKLYN & QUEENS

D-U-N-S 11-981-3439
■ **CRICKET COMMUNICATIONS LLC**
CRICKET WIRELESS
(*Suby of* LCW WIRELESS) ★
7337 Trade St, San Diego, CA 92121-2423
Tel (858) 882-6000 *Founded/Ownrshp* 1999
Sales 555.3MM^E *EMP* 750
SIC 4812 Radio telephone communication
CEO: S Douglas Hutcheson
Pr: Nitu Arora
Pr: David Davis
Pr: Glen Flowers
Pr: Annette Jacobs
Pr: Tim Ostrowski
CFO: Amin I Khalifa
Ex VP: Al Moschner
VP: Aaron Maddox
VP: Tony Muscato
VP: Philip Risken
VP: Cathy Shackleford
Exec: Tiffany Gould

CRICKET STX
See STX WIRELESS OPERATIONS LLC

CRICKET WIRELESS
See CRICKET COMMUNICATIONS LLC

D-U-N-S 10-199-0703 IMP/EXP
CRIDER INC
1 Plant Ave, Stillmore, GA 30464
Tel (912) 562-4435 *Founded/Ownrshp* 1983
Sales 197.9MM^E *EMP* 401
SIC 2099 Food preparations
CEO: W A Crider Jr
VP: Gary Clay
**VP:* Max Harrell
QA Dir: Jason Stansel
Dir IT: Ron Sasser
Sfty Mgr: Douglas Sikes
Manager: Firas Hamdan
Snr Mgr: Bill Crider

D-U-N-S 04-199-9389
CRIMSON CAPITAL SILICON VALLEY
CRIMSON INVESTMENTS
1000 Marina Blvd Ste 105, Brisbane, CA 94005-1839
Tel (650) 325-8673 *Founded/Ownrshp* 1998
Sales 385.1MM^E *EMP* 1,377
SIC 6799 3429 Venture capital companies; Manufactured hardware (general)
Mng Dir: John Paul Ho

CRIMSON INVESTMENTS
See CRIMSON CAPITAL SILICON VALLEY

D-U-N-S 03-789-7329 IMP/EXP
CRISP INDUSTRIES INC
323 Energy Way, Bridgeport, TX 76426
Tel (940) 683-4070 *Founded/Ownrshp* 1977
Sales 85.3MM^E *EMP* 135^E
SIC 5032 Aggregate
Pr: John I Crisp
Genl Mgr: Doug Swoveland
Off Mgr: Terry Holland

D-U-N-S 80-870-6795
■ **CRISPIN PORTER & BOGUSKY LLC**
(*Suby of* MDC PARTNERS INC) ★
6450 Gunpark Dr, Boulder, CO 80301-3309
Tel (303) 628-5100 *Founded/Ownrshp* 2007
Sales 98.4MM^E *EMP* 840
SIC 7311 Advertising agencies
Owner: Anthony Picciano
VP: Lauren Barger
Exec: Benny Thomas
Creative D: Benjamin Carey
Creative D: Henrik Delehag
Creative D: Mona Hasan
Creative D: Graham McCann
Creative D: Sesh Moodley
Prin: Roy Petersen
QA Dir: Tracy Wynkoop
Snr PM: Samantha Calvert

D-U-N-S 00-950-2014
CRISTA MINISTRIES
CRISTWOOD PARK
19303 Fremont Ave N, Shoreline, WA 98133-3800
Tel (206) 546-7200 *Founded/Ownrshp* 1948
Sales 105.4MM *EMP* 1,200
Accts Clark Nuber Ps Bellevue Wa
SIC 8322 8051 8211 Individual & family services; Skilled nursing care facilities; Private combined elementary & secondary school
Pr: Robert Lonac
**Owner:* Craig Campbell
**Pr:* Dale Cowles
**Pr:* Brad Decker
**Pr:* Bob Lonac
**CFO:* Brad Kirkpatrick
**Ch:* David Ederer
**Treas:* Kevin Gabelein
Ex VP: John Welch
VP: Nancy Christel
VP: Mark Crozet
**VP:* John Jordan
**VP:* Kirsten Miller
Dir Rx: Wentina Hurtado

D-U-N-S 36-151-8582 IMP/EXP
CRISTAL
CRISTAL GLOBAL
(*Suby of* THE NATIONAL TITANIUM DIOXIDE CO. LTD (CRISTAL))
20 Wight Ave Ste 100, Hunt Valley, MD 21030-2060
Tel (410) 229-4440 *Founded/Ownrshp* 2011
Sales 83.4MM^E *EMP* 117^E

SIC 1241 3531 2816 2869 1321 3631 Coal mining services; Construction machinery; Titanium dioxide, anatase or rutile (pigments); Industrial organic chemicals; Propane (natural) production; Household cooking equipment
Pr: William M Landuyt
*Pr: Neal Gallagher
*CFO: John E Lushefski
CFO: D Seibel
*Treas: Bill Scott
Sr VP: Kamal A Balawi
Sr VP: Timothy E Dowdl
Sr VP: Art Seibel
VP: Omar Najjar
VP: Fadi Trabzuni
VP: Thomas Van Valkenburgh

CRISTAL GLOBAL
See CRISTAL

D-U-N-S 96-499-9820
CRISTAL INORGANIC CHEMICALS US INC
(Suby of MILLENNIUM) ★
20 Wight Ave Ste 150, Cockeysville, MD 21030-2062
Tel (410) 229-4400 Founded/Ownrshp 2007
Sales 27.0MM^E EMP 4,000
SIC 2819 Catalysts, chemical
CEO: Talal Al-Shair
*Ex VP: Thomas Van Valkenburgh
*VP: Adel Abdulhadi
*VP: Emad Al-Junaidi
*VP: Fadi Trabzuni

D-U-N-S 01-984-9275 EXP
CRISTAL METALS INC
(Suby of THE NATIONAL TITANIUM DIOXIDE CO. LTD (CRISTAL))
20 Wight Ave Ste 100, Hunt Valley, MD 21030-2060
Tel (410) 229-4400 Founded/Ownrshp 2008
Sales 1.6MMM^E EMP 4,000
SIC 5051 Metals service centers & offices
Pr: Jamal Nahas
*CEO: Talal Al-Shair
*Sr VP: Abdalla Ibrahim
*VP: Robert Daniel
*VP: Sam Livingston
*VP: Omar Najjar
Admn Mgr: Tracy Huber
Snr Mgr: Selwin Gray

D-U-N-S 19-602-2230 IMP/EXP
CRISTAL USA INC
MILLENNIUM
(Suby of CRISTAL INORGANIC CHEMICALS SCHWEIZ AG)
20 Wight Ave Ste 150, Hunt Valley, MD 21030-2062
Tel (410) 229-4441 Founded/Ownrshp 1985
Sales 807.5MM^E EMP 4,000
SIC 2816 Titanium dioxide, anatase or rutile (pigments)
*Pr: Jamal Nahas
CFO: Arthur Seibel
Ex VP: Samuel Alexander
Sr VP: John Hall
Sr VP: Peter P Hanik
Sr VP: Abdalla Ibrahim
VP: Robert J Daniels
VP: Sam Livingston
VP: Thomas Van Valkenburgh
Dir IT: Lashawn Lawrence
Sls&Mrk Ex: Mario Richardson

CRISTWOOD PARK
See CRISTA MINISTRIES

D-U-N-S 08-876-4972 IMP
CRITCHFIELD MECHANICAL INC
CMI
1901 Junction Ave, San Jose, CA 95131-2103
Tel (408) 437-7000 Founded/Ownrshp 1977
Sales 222.1MM EMP 500
SIC 1711

D-U-N-S 18-628-3909 IMP/EXP
CRITERION CATALYSTS & TECHNOLOGIES LP
(Suby of ROYAL DUTCH SHELL PLC)
910 Louisiana St Ste 2900, Houston, TX 77002-4911
Tel (713) 241-3000 Founded/Ownrshp 1988
Sales 101.5MM^E EMP 400
SIC 2819 2869 Catalysts, chemical; Industrial organic chemicals
Genl Pt: Richard H Stade

D-U-N-S 78-640-5423
CRITICAL CARE SYSTEMS INC
(Suby of CCSI HOLDING 3, LLC)
108 Wilmot Rd, Deerfield, IL 60015-5145
Tel (847) 914-2500 Founded/Ownrshp 2013
Sales 29.8MM^E EMP 1,000
SIC 8082 Home health care services
CEO: Paul McConnell

D-U-N-S 80-910-3422
■ **CRITICAL HOMECARE SOLUTIONS HOLDINGS INC**
(Suby of BIOSCRIP INC) ★
2 Tower Brg 2 Tower Bridge, Conshohocken, PA 19428
Tel (610) 825-2061 Founded/Ownrshp 2010
Sales 11.5MM^E EMP 1,931
SIC 8082 Home health care services; Visiting nurse service
Pr: Robert A Cucuel
CFO: Mary Jane Graves
Sr VP: Colleen Lederer
Sr VP: Nitin Patel
Sr VP: Joey Ryan
VP: Jeff Outcalt

D-U-N-S 79-153-0558
■ **CRITICAL HOMECARE SOLUTIONS INC**
(Suby of BIOSCRIP INC) ★
1 Fayette St, Conshohocken, PA 19428-2064
Tel (720) 697-5200 Founded/Ownrshp 2016
Sales 21.5MM^E EMP 1,900
SIC 8082 Home health care services
Pr: Robert A Cucuel
*Treas: Mary Graves
*VP: Colleen Lederer

CRITICS' CHOICE VIDEO & DVD
See INFINITY RESOURCES INC

D-U-N-S 83-242-2567
CRITIGEN LLC
(Suby of TRANSOM CAPITAL GROUP LLC) ★
7604 Tech Way Ste 300, Denver, CO 80237
Tel (303) 706-0990 Founded/Ownrshp 2016
Sales 98.3MM^E EMP 600
SIC 8748 Business consulting
CEO: Jeff Haight
CFO: Mark Kelly
*Ofcr: Ed Riegelmann
Sr VP: Alan Dillsaver
Prgrm Mgr: Charlie Hopkins
Software D: Nam Nguyen
Software D: Colin Sullivan

D-U-N-S 01-086-9790
CRITTENTON HOSPITAL MEDICAL CENTER
(Suby of ASCENSION HEALTH) ★
1101 W University Dr, Rochester, MI 48307-1863
Tel (248) 652-5000 Founded/Ownrshp 1983
Sales 188.3MM EMP 1,515
Accts Plante & Moran Pllc Southfiel
SIC 8062 8011 Hospital, professional nursing school; Offices & clinics of medical doctors
CEO: Terry Hamilton
Chf Rad: Rene Loredo
*CEO: Lynn C Orfgen
*CFO: Donna Kopinski
*Ch: Robert J Lenihan II
*Treas: Dale Green
*Trst: James Holmes
Trst: Kenneth Johnson
Trst: Frederick Maibauer
VP: Diane Ferguson
Exec: Samer Kazziha
Dir Lab: Bill Corby
Dir Rx: Susan Wilson
Board of Directors: Walter Borland, Donald Buchanan, Charles Crissman, Carol Ehle, Bruce Kresge, William Mitzelfeld, Terrence J O'connor

D-U-N-S 79-282-7768
CRITTENTON HOSPITAL MEDICAL CENTER FOUNDATION
1101 W University Dr, Rochester, MI 48307-1863
Tel (248) 652-5000 Founded/Ownrshp 1983
Sales 1.2MM EMP 1,690
Accts Ernst & Young Us Llp Indian
SIC 8741 8062 Hospital management; General medical & surgical hospitals
Pr: Lynn Cofgen
V Ch: Robert J Lenihan II
COO: Howard Bosworth
Dir Lab: Steve Smithson
Pharmcst: Ed Margiewicz
Pharmcst: Paul Morrell

D-U-N-S 07-920-7686
CRIUS ENERGY LLC
(Suby of CRIUS ENERGY TRUST)
535 Connecticut Ave # 400, Norwalk, CT 06854-1713
Tel (203) 663-5089 Founded/Ownrshp 2016
Sales 137.6MM^E EMP 266^E
SIC 6719 1731 Investment holding companies, except banks; Energy management controls
CEO: Michael Fallquist
COO: Chaitu Parikh
CFO: Roop Bhullar
Ofcr: Cami Boehme
Ofcr: Barbara Clay
Ex VP: Rob Cantrell
Ex VP: Christian McArthur
Ex VP: Pat McCamley
Sr VP: Seth Zuckerman
VP: Scott Berman
VP: Kasey Cline
VP: Ben Esposito
VP: Vjollca Jusufi
VP: Martin Phillips
VP: John Smith
VP: Pradeep Tiwari

D-U-N-S 05-038-3223
CRJKK INC
450 Acorn Ln, Downingtown, PA 19335-3040
Tel (610) 518-4000 Founded/Ownrshp 1982
Sales 268.4MM^E EMP 201^E
SIC 5045 Computer software; Computer peripheral equipment
Pr: Guy Cicconi
COO: James W Cook
CFO: Eric C Schneider
VP: Renny Fidlon
VP: Frank Harms
VP: Rosemarie Miller
Genl Mgr: Kathy Brown
Snr Sftwr: Chad Cimo
CIO: Danny Curca
Sftwr Eng: Dave Metz
Sftwr Eng: Lawrence Povlow

D-U-N-S 08-033-0779
■ **CRL SAFETY ASSESSMENT INC**
(Suby of CHARLES RIVER LABORATORIES INC) ★
1407 George Rd, Ashland, OH 44805-8946
Tel (419) 952-0553 Founded/Ownrshp 2007
Sales 126.0MM^E EMP 735^E
SIC 8734 Testing laboratories

CROCKETT GARBAGE SERVICE
See RICHMOND SANITARY SERVICE INC

D-U-N-S 06-398-8120 IMP/EXP
▲ **CROCS INC**
7477 Dry Creek Pkwy, Niwot, CO 80503-8021
Tel (303) 848-7000 Founded/Ownrshp 1999
Sales 1.2MMM EMP 5,400
Tkr Sym CROX Exch NGS
SIC 3021 5139 3069 5661 2389 Shoes, rubber or rubber soled fabric uppers; Footwear; Kneeling pads, rubber; Pillows, sponge rubber; Shoe stores; Children's shoes; Men's shoes; Women's shoes; Footlets
CEO: Gregg S Ribatt
Mng Pt: Ben Morrison
*Ch Bd: Thomas J Smach
Pr: Andrew Rees

CFO: Carrie W Teffner
Sr VP: Peter Case
VP: Harvey Bierman
VP: Mike Debell
VP: Donna Flood
VP: Greg Sullivan
Creative D: Patrick O'Boyle
Creative D: Vidya Radhakrishnan

D-U-N-S 00-583-9832 EXP
CROM CORP
250 Sw 36th Ter, Gainesville, FL 32607-2889
Tel (352) 372-3436 Founded/Ownrshp 1930, 2014
Sales 250.4MM^E EMP 560
SIC 1629 Industrial plant construction
Pr: James D Copley Jr
*CFO: Walter Carlton
*Treas: James A Neff
*Sr VP: Lars J Balck
*Sr VP: Gerald J Bevis
Sr VP: Bob Puder
*Sr VP: H E Puder
VP: Bobby Oyenarte
Area Mgr: Jim Wornick
Off Mgr: Karen Howard
IT Man: Alex Barrio

D-U-N-S 17-623-1595 IMP
CRONIMET CORP
(Suby of CRONIMET FERROLEG. GMBH)
1 Pilarsky Way, Aliquippa, PA 15001-5421
Tel (724) 375-5004 Founded/Ownrshp 1997
Sales 126.0MM^E EMP 90
SIC 5093 5051 3312 Metal scrap & waste materials; Iron & steel (ferrous) products; Blast furnaces & steel mills
Pr: Frank Santoro
*Ch Bd: Guenter Pilersky
*Pr: Juergen Mross
*VP: David Porco
*VP: Robert Santoro
Genl Mgr: Brian Beaudrie
Off Mgr: Rosie Vega
Sales Exec: Santoro Frank

D-U-N-S 10-241-2244 IMP/EXP
CROP PRODUCTION SERVICES INC
(Suby of AGRIUM INC)
3005 Rocky Mountain Ave, Loveland, CO 80538-9001
Tel (970) 685-3300 Founded/Ownrshp 1982
Sales 3.8MMM^E EMP 2,900
SIC 5191 Fertilizer & fertilizer materials; Chemicals, agricultural; Herbicides; Insecticides
Pr: Steve Dyer
*VP: Tony Engel
*VP: Brent Smith
*VP: Dave Tretter
Div Mgr: Tony Anderson
Div Mgr: Bill Coleman
Div Mgr: Spencer Harris
Div Mgr: Jim Killingsworth
Div Mgr: Bob Mercer
Div Mgr: Scott Pate
Div Mgr: Duane Petersen

D-U-N-S 11-509-3189 IMP/EXP
CROSBY GROUP LLC
NATIONAL SWAGE
2801 Dawson Rd, Tulsa, OK 74110-5040
Tel (918) 834-4611 Founded/Ownrshp 2010
Sales 252.3MM^E EMP 685
SIC 3462 3429 Iron & steel forgings; Manufactured hardware (general)
Pr: Jason Struthers
*CFO: David Dixon
VP: Paul Boeckman
VP Sls: Tom Hudgins
VP Sls: Ed Richter
Manager: Jeff Ferchen
Sls Mgr: Rick Nyles

D-U-N-S 09-490-5270
CROSBY TUGS LLC
17771 Highway 3235, Galliano, LA 70354-3578
Tel (985) 632-7575 Founded/Ownrshp 1978
Sales 89.6MM^E EMP 450
SIC 4492 Tugboat service
Pr: Vinton Crosby
*CEO: Kurt Crosby
*CFO: Farrel Trosclair

D-U-N-S 07-955-5077
CROSBY US ACQUISITION CORP
(Suby of CROSBY WORLDWIDE LIMITED)
2801 Dawson Rd, Tulsa, OK 74110-5042
Tel (918) 834-4611 Founded/Ownrshp 2015
Sales 408.6MM^E EMP 5,637^E
SIC 3629 Current collector wheels, for trolley rigging
Pr: Jason Struthers

D-U-N-S 82-931-3050 IMP
CROSCILL HOME LLC
(Suby of PATRIARCH PARTNERS LLC) ★
1500 N Carolina St, Goldsboro, NC 27530-1210
Tel (919) 735-7111 Founded/Ownrshp 2008
Sales 162.0MM^E EMP 805
SIC 5023 3431 Decorative home furnishings & supplies; Bathroom fixtures, including sinks
CEO: Joe Granger
CFO: William Austin

CROSS COMPANY
See CROSS TECHNOLOGIES INC

CROSS COUNTRY GROUP
See AGERO INC

D-U-N-S 08-242-3377
▲ **CROSS COUNTRY HEALTHCARE INC**
6551 Pk Of Cmmrce Blvd Nw, Boca Raton, FL 33487-8218
Tel (561) 998-2232 Founded/Ownrshp 1996
Sales 767.4MM EMP 6,624
Tkr Sym CCRN Exch NGS
SIC 7361 7363 Nurses' registry; Medical help service
Pr: William J Grubbs
*Ch Bd: Thomas C Dircks
Pr: Vickie L Anenberg
Pr: Dennis Ducham
Pr: Timothy Fischer

CFO: William J Burns
Sr VP: Patrick Ahern
Sr VP: Deborah Dean
Sr VP: Buffy Stultz White
VP: Jerry Chico
VP: Wendi Dusseault
VP: Kimberly White
Board of Directors: W Larry Cash, Gale Fitzgerald, Richard M Mastaler, Mark Perlberg, Joseph A Trunfio

D-U-N-S 08-001-6446
CROSS COUNTRY HOME HOLDINGS INC (FL)
1625 Nw 136th Ave Ste 200, Sunrise, FL 33323-2842
Tel (954) 835-1900 Founded/Ownrshp 1996
Sales NA EMP 558^E
SIC 6351 Warranty insurance, home
CEO: Steven E Upshaw

D-U-N-S 19-601-2975
CROSS COUNTRY HOME SERVICES INC
(Suby of CROSS COUNTRY HOME HOLDINGS INC) ★
1625 Nw 136th Ave Ste 200, Sunrise, FL 33323-2842
Tel (954) 835-1900 Founded/Ownrshp 1998
Sales NA EMP 558
SIC 6351 Warranty insurance, home
CEO: Steve Upshaw
*COO: Chris Askew
*CFO: Richard Outram
*Ex VP: Doug Stein
Sr VP: Ori Lapidot
Sr VP: Mike Politz
VP: Shausta Merrill
VP: Alfred Venditti
Prgrm Mgr: Hilda Fagan
Dir IT: Darren Spurgeon
Mktg Mgr: Patty Collins

D-U-N-S 86-955-7004
CROSS FINANCIAL CORP
CROSS INSURANCE
491 Main St, Bangor, ME 04401-6296
Tel (207) 947-7345 Founded/Ownrshp 1996
Sales NA EMP 566
SIC 6411 Insurance agents & brokers
Ch Bd: Woodrow W Cross
*CEO: Royce Cross
CFO: Alice Dyer
*VP: Brent Cross
VP: Wayne Infinger
VP: Dennis Lundgren
VP: Allen L Robbins
Exec: Brandon Haney
Dir Soc: Jake Berkowitz
Dir Soc: Stesha Cano
Dir Soc: Chad Kelley

CROSS INSURANCE
See CROSS FINANCIAL CORP

D-U-N-S 01-291-0464
CROSS INTERNATIONAL INC (FL)
600 Sw 3rd St Ste 2201, Pompano Beach, FL 33060-6936
Tel (954) 657-9000 Founded/Ownrshp 2001
Sales 91.8MM EMP 70^E
Accts Batts Morrison Wales & Lee P
SIC 8322 Emergency social services
Pr: James J Cavnar
Ofcr: Ricardo Lujan
Ofcr: Claudio Merisio
Ofcr: Marie White
*VP: Brian Schutt
Comm Dir: Robyn Lees
IT Man: Chuck Scoville

D-U-N-S 93-831-8995 IMP/EXP
CROSS MATCH TECHNOLOGIES INC
(Suby of FRANCISCO PARTNERS MANAGEMENT LP) ★
3950 Rca Blvd Ste 5001, Palm Beach Gardens, FL 33410-4227
Tel (561) 622-1650 Founded/Ownrshp 2012
Sales 84.7MM^E EMP 345
SIC 3999 Fingerprint equipment
CEO: Richard Agostinelli
*Ch Bd: Donald E Nickelson
*Pr: David Buckley
*COO: Denis W Auli
*COO: Milton Dean
CFO: Michael Brewer
*CFO: Jerry Cahill
*CFO: Joseph W Kuhn
*CFO: Martin K Weinbaum
Treas: Richard Brewer
Sr Cor Off: Adrian Grundy
*Ex VP: Jack F Carver
*Sr VP: Vance Bjorn
*Sr VP: Elaine Bliss
*Sr VP: Jeff Boyce
*Sr VP: Tom Buss
Sr VP: John B Hinmon
*Sr VP: William A Smith II
*Sr VP: Eric Vermillion
VP: John Atkinson
VP: Robert Calamia

CROSS MIDWEST TIRE CO
See C&M TIRE INC

D-U-N-S 08-024-4307
CROSS OVER LLC (IA)
621 Alta Vista Dr, Carroll, IA 51401-1801
Tel (712) 790-4549 Founded/Ownrshp 2015
Sales 90.0MM^E EMP 2
SIC 8733 7389 Safety research, noncommercial;
Pr: Kim Baker
*VP: Jerry Janson

CROSS PNTE PAPER-FLAMBEAU MILL
See FLAMBEAU RIVER PAPER CORP

D-U-N-S 02-182-7581
CROSS POINT NW LLC
6803 Se Jhnson Creek Blvd, Portland, OR 97206-9457
Tel (503) 594-2800 Founded/Ownrshp 2008
Sales 155.0MM EMP 65
SIC 5012 Automobile auction
Owner: William Hardy

D-U-N-S 00-347-1539
CROSS TECHNOLOGIES INC (NC)
CROSS COMPANY
4400 Piedmont Pkwy, Greensboro, NC 27410-8121
Tel (336) 856-6000 *Founded/Ownrshp* 1954
Sales 190.8MM[E] *EMP* 180
SIC 5084 3492 Industrial machinery & equipment; Industrial machine parts; Hose & tube fittings & assemblies, hydraulic/pneumatic
CEO: Steve Earley
**CFO:* Jerry Bohnsack
Treas: Ashley James Jr
**VP:* Rock Able
Opers Mgr: Eddie George
Sls Mgr: David Baumgardner
Sls Mgr: Jeff Morton
Sls Mgr: Wade Wright
Snr PM: Randy Jones

CROSS TIMBERS OPERATING CO
See RINGWOOD GATHERING CO

D-U-N-S 15-155-0084
■ **CROSS TIMBERS OPERATING CO**
(*Suby of* CROSS TIMBERS OPERATING CO) ★
810 Houston St Ste 2000, Fort Worth, TX 76102-6223
Tel (817) 870-2800 *Founded/Ownrshp* 2000
Sales 297.4MM[E] *EMP* 226
SIC 1311 Crude petroleum production; Natural gas production
Ch Bd: Bob R Simpson
**Pr:* Steffen E Palko
**CFO:* Louis Baldwin
**Sr VP:* Larry B McDonald
**Sr VP:* Timothy L Petrus
**VP:* Nick Dungey
**VP:* Robert C Myers
**VP:* Terry L Schultz

D-U-N-S 07-856-3839
▲ **CROSSAMERICA PARTNERS LP**
515 Hamilton St Ste 200, Allentown, PA 18101-1537
Tel (610) 625-8000 *Founded/Ownrshp* 2011
Sales 2.2MMM *EMP* 1,052
Tkr Sym CAPL *Exch* NYS
SIC 5172 Petroleum products
Ch Bd: Kimberly S Lubel
Genl Pt: Crossamerica GP
Pr: Jeremy L Bergeron

D-U-N-S 92-652-7300
CROSSET CO LLC
(*Suby of* CASTELLINI HOLDING CO LLC) ★
10295 Toebben Dr, Independence, KY 41051-9615
Tel (859) 283-5830 *Founded/Ownrshp* 1993
Sales 138.3MM[E] *EMP* 260
SIC 5148 Fruits, fresh; Vegetables, fresh
Ch Bd: Robert Castellini
**Pr:* William Schuler
**Treas:* Christopher Fister
**Ex VP:* Daniel Pardekooper
**VP:* Timothy Slaughter
Exec: Joe Williams

D-U-N-S 13-301-7470
CROSSFIRE LLC
820 Airport Rd, Durango, CO 81303-8854
Tel (970) 884-4869 *Founded/Ownrshp* 2002
Sales 176.0MM *EMP* 390
SIC 1389 Oil & gas wells: building, repairing & dismantling
**Pr:* Ezra E Lee
Area Mgr: Charles Carter
Area Mgr: Chris Lummus
IT Man: Debbi Michal
Sfty Dirs: Shane Utley
Sls Mgr: Brian Pennington

D-U-N-S 61-247-9779 IMP
■ **CROSSING AUTOMATION INC**
(*Suby of* BROOKS AUTOMATION INC) ★
46702 Bayside Pkwy, Fremont, CA 94538-6582
Tel (510) 661-5000 *Founded/Ownrshp* 2004
Sales 61.1MM[E] *EMP* 1,037[E]
SIC 3559 Semiconductor manufacturing machinery
Pr: Robert B Macknight Kkk
**Pr:* Mark D Morelli
**CEO:* Stephen S Schwartz
**Ex VP:* Lindon G Robertson
**Sr VP:* David C Gray
VP: Randy Clegg
**VP:* Gerald F Connolly
VP: Gerald Ll
VP: John O'Brien
VP: Rob Woodward
Netwrk Eng: Yamin Azim

D-U-N-S 08-777-2984
CROSSLAND CONSTRUCTION CO INC
833 S East Ave, Columbus, KS 66725-2307
Tel (620) 429-1414 *Founded/Ownrshp* 1978
Sales 783.0MM[E] *EMP* 715
Accts Mayer Hoffman Mccann Pc Tope
SIC 1542 Commercial & office building, new construction
CEO: Ivan E Crossland Jr
**Pr:* Bennie L Crossland
**Ex VP:* Chris Crossland
**Ex VP:* Mike Crossland
VP: Christopher Crossland
**VP:* Mark C Crossland
VP: Danny Langerot
VP: Brad Wilson
Off Mgr: Travis Sill
Off Admin: Courtney Smith
Mtls Mgr: Colby Mitchell

D-U-N-S 07-952-2263
CROSSMARK CONSUMER ENGAGEMENTS LLC
5100 Legacy Dr, Plano, TX 75024-3104
Tel (469) 814-1000 *Founded/Ownrshp* 2013
Sales 50.4MM[E] *EMP* 3,000[E]
SIC 8742 Marketing consulting services
CEO: Ben Fisher
Pr: Jim Norred

D-U-N-S 78-512-0247 IMP
CROSSMARK INC
FOOD TRADE
5100 Legacy Dr, Plano, TX 75024-3104
Tel (469) 814-1000 *Founded/Ownrshp* 1997
Sales 3.1MMM[E] *EMP* 10,000
SIC 5141 5912 7299 Groceries, general line; Drug stores & proprietary stores; Home improvement & renovation contractor agency
CEO: Steve Schuckenbrock
**Ch Bd:* Ben Fischer
**COO:* Ken Drish
**CFO:* Don Martin
CFO: Kelly Parsons
Ex VP: Lance Andersen
Ex VP: Jim Norred
Ex VP: Johnette Oden-Brunson
Ex VP: Collin Thompson
Sr VP: Holly Meloy
VP: Shahlan Aldabagh
VP: Mike Anderson
**VP:* Cyndi Dunn
**VP:* Ken Gomez
VP: Ahmed Kamel
**VP:* Tom Koch
VP: Larry Lemieur
VP: Charlie Orndorff
VP: Chris Osborne
VP: Kevin Salmon
VP: Raj Tanna
Board of Directors: John Compton, Duncan Mac Naughton

D-U-N-S 82-645-7152
CROSSROADS AG LLC
N6055 State Road 40, Elk Mound, WI 54739-9295
Tel (715) 879-5454 *Founded/Ownrshp* 2000
Sales 86.0MM[E] *EMP* 60
SIC 5191 5171 Feed; Seeds: field, garden & flower; Fertilizer & fertilizer materials; Petroleum bulk stations & terminals

D-U-N-S 84-706-9887
CROSSROADS ARENA LLC
HSBC ARENA
(*Suby of* BUFFALO SABRES) ★
1 Seymour H Knox Iii Plz, Buffalo, NY 14203-3007
Tel (716) 855-4100 *Founded/Ownrshp* 1994
Sales 50.1MM[E] *EMP* 1,403
SIC 7389 Convention & show services

D-U-N-S 92-640-2488
CROSSROADS HOSPITALITY CO LLC
HAMPTON INN
(*Suby of* HAMPTON INN) ★
6430 Rockland Dr, Bethesda, MD 20817
Tel (301) 581-5900 *Founded/Ownrshp* 2006
Sales 27.2MM[E] *EMP* 1,100
SIC 7011 Hotels & motels
Ch Bd: Milton Fine
Pr: W Thomas Parrington Jr
Ofcr: John R Siegel
Ex VP: Robert L Froman
Ex VP: J William Richardson
Sr VP: Marvin I Droz

D-U-N-S 78-046-5618
■ **CROSSROADS RV INC**
(*Suby of* THOR INDUSTRIES INC) ★
305 Hawpatch Dr, Topeka, IN 46571
Tel (260) 593-3850 *Founded/Ownrshp* 1996
Sales 185.2MM[E] *EMP* 600
SIC 3711 Motor vehicles & car bodies
Pr: Freeman Helmuth
VP: Matt Thompson
**Prin:* Andy Cripe
IT Man: Alicia Dunafin

CROSSTEX ENERGY GP
See ENLINK MIDSTREAM GP LLC

CROSSTOWN SQUARE
See GENESIS HEALTH SYSTEMS

D-U-N-S 13-140-8148 IMP
CROSSVILLE INC
CVL LOGISTICS
(*Suby of* CURRAN GROUP INC) ★
346 Sweeney Dr, Crossville, TN 38555-5459
Tel (931) 484-2110 *Founded/Ownrshp* 1985
Sales 155.0MM[E] *EMP* 640
SIC 3253 Ceramic wall & floor tile
CEO: John E Smith
Ch: Michael Jcurran
Treas: Jordan Wolf
VP: Frank Douglas
VP: Christian Gudet
VP: Michael Thacker
Rgnl Mgr: Roy Irwin
Brnch Mgr: Enith Dosal
Brnch Mgr: Ray Hans
Genl Mgr: Donna Kerley
Dir IT: Noah Chitty

D-U-N-S 03-975-6585
CROTHALL HEALTHCARE INC
(*Suby of* CROTHALL SERVICES GROUP) ★
1500 Liberty Ridge Dr # 210, Chesterbrook, PA 19087-5583
Tel (610) 576-5100 *Founded/Ownrshp* 1991
Sales 620.7MM[E] *EMP* 8,000
SIC 8742 Management consulting services; Hospital & health services consultant
CEO: Bobby Kutteh
Pr: Chris A Spanos
**CEO:* Robert Kutteh
CFO: Frank Arcos
**CFO:* Daniel E Gatti
Ex VP: Joe Kirk
**Sr VP:* Michael Bailey
**Sr VP:* Chris Coin
**Sr VP:* Rich Menzcek
**Sr VP:* Tom Racobaldo
VP: Thomas Deringer
VP: Ted Hoffman
VP: Paul Killion
VP: Joe Longinotti
VP: Glen McQuien
VP: Bill Rothgery
VP: Larry Stebelsky
Dir Bus: Jan Jones
Dir Bus: Marti Lawson

D-U-N-S 62-302-6333
CROTHALL SERVICES GROUP
(*Suby of* COMPASS GROUP USA INVESTMENTS LLP) ★
1500 Liberty Ridge Dr # 210, Chesterbrook, PA 19087-5583
Tel (610) 576-5100 *Founded/Ownrshp* 2001
Sales 978.9MM[E] *EMP* 19,000
SIC 7349 Building maintenance services
Pr: Bobby Kutteh
VP: Thomas Racobaldo
Off Mgr: Heather Hayes

D-U-N-S 07-875-9776
CROUSE AND ASSOCIATES INSURANCE BROKERS INC (CA)
100 Pine St Ste 2500, San Francisco, CA 94111-5211
Tel (415) 982-3870 *Founded/Ownrshp* 1975
Sales NA *EMP* 45
SIC 6411 Insurance brokers
CEO: William Crouse
**Pr:* Gregory Crouse
**CFO:* Mike Grazioli
**Sr VP:* Pam Crouse
VP: Pam Quilici
Exec: Lennaine Moran
Off Mgr: David Digirolamo

D-U-N-S 96-409-2642
CROUSE HEALTH HOSPITAL INC
736 Irving Ave, Syracuse, NY 13210-1687
Tel (315) 470-7111 *Founded/Ownrshp* 2010
Sales 397.6MM *EMP* 26[E]
Accts Freed Maxick Cpas Pc Buffalo
SIC 8062 General medical & surgical hospitals
CEO: Kimberly Boynton
VP: Paul Kronenberg
Ex Dir: Carrie Berse
IT Man: Jason J Bunger

D-U-N-S 05-276-7829
CROUSE HEALTH SYSTEM INC (NY)
CROUSE IRVING MEM HOSP
736 Irving Ave, Syracuse, NY 13210-1687
Tel (315) 470-7521 *Founded/Ownrshp* 1893
Sales 391.3MM *EMP* 2,700
SIC 8062 General medical & surgical hospitals
CEO: Kimberly Boynton
VP: James Mills
Exec: Zair Carella
Dir Case M: Barbara Drapola
Comm Dir: Bob Allen
Nurse Mgr: Linda Vincent
IT Man: Pam Connelly
IT Man: Matt Mahoney
Netwrk Eng: Ernie Dewolf
Netwrk Eng: Greg Ellison
Netwrk Eng: Brad Nott

D-U-N-S 01-185-2105
CROUSE HOSPITAL AUXILIARY INC (NY)
736 Irving Ave, Syracuse, NY 13210-1690
Tel (315) 470-7111 *Founded/Ownrshp* 1917
Sales 271.0M *EMP* 2,631[E]
Accts Richard A Romer Cpa Llc Tonaw
SIC 8062 General medical & surgical hospitals
CEO: Kimberly Boynton
**Pr:* Carrie Berse
**Pr:* Paul Cronenberg
**VP:* Bob Allen
**VP:* Chris Farnum
VP: Eugene Lozner
Dir Rx: Koth Cassavaugh
Netwrk Eng: Greg Ellison
Orthpdst: Timothy Izant
Opthamlgy: Allan I Kanter
Opthamlgy: Anthony F Devincentis

CROUSE IRVING MEM HOSP
See CROUSE HEALTH SYSTEM INC

D-U-N-S 06-373-0261
CROW TRIBE OF INDIANS
Hwy 212 & 87, Crow Agency, MT 59022
Tel (406) 638-3700 *Founded/Ownrshp* 1851
Sales NA *EMP* 1,000
SIC 9131 Indian reservation;
Ch: Carl E Venne
IT Man: Karla Maccatherine CPA
IT Man: Clinton Sowden
Board of Directors: Kayle Howe, Joseph Pickett, Marvin Stewart

D-U-N-S 00-690-3363
CROW-BURLIGAME CO (AR)
BUMPER TO BUMPER
(*Suby of* CROW-BURLINGAME) ★
1901 E Roosevelt Rd, Little Rock, AR 72206-2533
Tel (501) 375-1215 *Founded/Ownrshp* 1919
Sales 107.2MM[E] *EMP* 694
SIC 5013 Automotive supplies & parts; Tools & equipment, automotive
Ch Bd: E Fletcher Lord Jr
**Treas:* Jennifer Rainwarter
**VP:* Crow Burlingame
**VP:* Bill Schlatterer
Mktg Dir: Vicki Wallace

CROW-BURLINGAME
See REPLACEMENT PARTS INC

CROWD MANAGEMENT SERVICES
See STARPLEX CORP

D-U-N-S 00-677-9896
CROWDER CONSTRUCTION CO INC
(*Suby of* CROWDER CONSTRUCTORS INC) ★
6425 Brookshire Blvd, Charlotte, NC 28216-0301
Tel (800) 849-2966 *Founded/Ownrshp* 1947
Sales 179.4MM *EMP* 900
Accts Greerwalker Llp Charlotte Nc
SIC 1622 1629 1623 Bridge construction; Waste water & sewage treatment plant construction; Industrial plant construction; Blasting contractor, except building demolition; Water & sewer line construction
Pr: Otis A Crowder
CFO: James Baldwin
**VP:* William T Crowder Jr
VP: Claudia Dodgen
Exec: Carla Doedtman
Mtls Mgr: Barry Fletcher
VP Sls: Edward Tart
Snr PM: Donald Anderson
Board of Directors: Bernard Burns, William R Holland, Paul R Leonard Jr

D-U-N-S 08-032-6797
CROWDER CONSTRUCTORS INC
6425 Brookshire Blvd, Charlotte, NC 28216-0301
Tel (704) 372-3541 *Founded/Ownrshp* 2016
Sales 179.6MM[E] *EMP* 900[E]
SIC 1623 Water & sewer line construction
CTO: Patty Jackson
Snr PM: Rocky Hollingsworth

D-U-N-S 06-156-7608
CROWE HORWATH LLP
225 W Wacker Dr Ste 2600, Chicago, IL 60606-1228
Tel (312) 899-7000 *Founded/Ownrshp* 2008
Sales 745.1MM *EMP* 2,830
Accts Crowe Horwath
SIC 8721 Certified public accountant
CEO: James Powers
Pr: Fred J Bauters
Pt: Todd Welu
COO: Joseph P Santucci Jr
Chf Mktg O: Ann Lathrop
Ofcr: Julie Wood
VP: Janice Gray
Exec: Christopher Sifter
Dir Risk M: Crystal Jareske
Assoc Dir: Dave Johnson
Brnch Mgr: Marilee Hopkins
Board of Directors: Jennifer McMahon, Alan Abel, Ken Ruiz, Lisa Brooks, Steve Schumacher, Eric Durham, Mark Strawmyer, Brent Felten, Josh Teeple, Greg Gallaway, Bret Updegraff, Dennis Hild, Sandy Hofmann, Brian Kerby, Daphne Maingot

CROWELL & MORING INTERNATIONAL
See CROWELL & MORING LLP

D-U-N-S 09-868-7445 IMP
CROWELL & MORING LLP
CROWELL & MORING INTERNATIONAL
1001 Penn Ave Nw Fl 10, Washington, DC 20004-2595
Tel (202) 624-2500 *Founded/Ownrshp* 1979
Sales 174.1MM[E] *EMP* 997
SIC 8111 Specialized law offices, attorneys
Ch Bd: Kent A Gardiner
Sr Pt: John A McLeod
Pt: Ellen Dwyer
Pt: Viva Hammer
Pt: Kevin C Mayer
Pt: Wm Randolph Smith
Pt: Kathleen Taylor Sooy
Pt: James R Stuart III
Pt: Scott Winkelman
Mng Pt: Ellen M Dwyer
Mng Pt: Emmanuel Gybels
Pr: Teresa Stanek REA
CFO: John Oliverio
Ofcr: Alyson Guthrie

D-U-N-S 09-934-8674
CROWLEY AMERICAN TRANSPORT INC
(*Suby of* CROWLEY MARITIME CORP) ★
9487 Regency Square Blvd, Jacksonville, FL 32225-8183
Tel (904) 727-2200 *Founded/Ownrshp* 1954
Sales 196.8MM[E] *EMP* 1,300
SIC 4424 Coastwide transportation, freight
VP: John Douglas
**Pr:* T B Crowley
**Treas:* Albert M Marucco
**Ex VP:* J B Rettig
**VP:* Rich Oster

D-U-N-S 00-222-9532 EXP
CROWLEY FOODS INC
(*Suby of* HP HOOD LLC) ★
93 Pennsylvania Ave, Binghamton, NY 13903-1645
Tel (800) 637-0019 *Founded/Ownrshp* 1904
Sales 214.3MM[E] *EMP* 3,000
SIC 2026 2024 Fluid milk; Fermented & cultured milk products; Yogurt; Cottage cheese; Ice cream & frozen desserts
Pr: John Kaned

D-U-N-S 83-166-7329
CROWLEY HOLDINGS INC
9487 Regency Square Blvd # 101, Jacksonville, FL 32225-7800
Tel (904) 727-2200 *Founded/Ownrshp* 2008
Sales 2.1MMM *EMP* 4,500
Accts Deloitte & Touche Llp Jackson
SIC 4412 4424 5171 5172 5541 4492 Deep sea foreign transportation of freight; Deep sea domestic transportation of freight; Coastwide transportation, freight; Intercoastal transportation, freight; Water transportation to noncontiguous territories, freight; Petroleum bulk stations & terminals; Petroleum products; Marine service station; Towing & tugboat service; Tugboat service
Ch Bd: Thomas B Crowley Jr
**Treas:* Daniel L Warner
**V Ch Bd:* William A Pennella
Ofcr: Colin Quick
**Sr VP:* John C Calvin
**Sr VP:* Carl Fox
**Sr VP:* Arthur F Mead III
**Sr VP:* Susan L Rodgers
**Sr VP:* Dan Warner
Dir Bus: Erjon Miruku
Dir Bus: Kenly Silencieux
Board of Directors: Philip E Bowles, Molly Murphy Crowley, Gary L Depolo, Earl T Kivett, Leland S Prussia, William P Vernon, Cameron W Wolfe Jr

D-U-N-S 02-842-8191
CROWLEY INDEPENDENT SCHOOL DISTRICT 912
ADMINSTRATION BLDG
512 Peach St, Crowley, TX 76036-3119
Tel (817) 297-5800 *Founded/Ownrshp* 1950
Sales 117.9MM^E *EMP* 1,737
Accts Hankins Eastup Deaton Tonn
SIC 8211 Public elementary school; Public senior high school
Dir Sec: Pat Panek
Teacher Pr: Theresa Kohler

D-U-N-S 06-915-6214
CROWLEY LINER SERVICES INC
(*Suby of* CROWLEY MARITIME CORP) ★
9487 Regency Square Blvd # 101, Jacksonville, FL 32225-7800
Tel (904) 727-2200 *Founded/Ownrshp* 1954
Sales 172.8MM^E *EMP* 1,200
SIC 4424 Coastwide transportation, freight
Ch Bd: Thomas B Crowley Jr
**Ex VP:* William A Pennella
**Sr VP:* John Calvin
**Sr VP:* John Douglass
**Sr VP:* John P Hourihan
Sr VP: John Hourihan
Sr VP: Rinus Schepen

D-U-N-S 79-513-4667
CROWLEY MARINE SERVICES INC
(*Suby of* CROWLEY MARITIME CORP) ★
1102 Sw Massachusetts St, Seattle, WA 98134-1030
Tel (206) 332-8000 *Founded/Ownrshp* 1992
Sales 476.9MM^E *EMP* 3,500
SIC 4499 Boat & ship rental & leasing, except pleasure
Ch: Thomas B Crowley Jr
**Ex VP:* William A Pennella
**Sr VP:* John Calvin
**Sr VP:* Carl Fox
**Sr VP:* Michael Roberts
**Sr VP:* Rocky Smith
**Sr VP:* Daniel Warner

D-U-N-S 06-610-9513 IMP/EXP
CROWLEY MARITIME CORP
(*Suby of* CROWLEY HOLDINGS INC) ★
9487 Regency Square Blvd, Jacksonville, FL 32225-8183
Tel (904) 727-2200 *Founded/Ownrshp* 1892
Sales 1.7MMM^E *EMP* 4,329
SIC 4412 4424 5171 5172 5541 4492 Deep sea foreign transportation of freight; Deep sea domestic transportation of freight; Coastwide transportation, freight; Intercoastal transportation, freight; Water transportation to noncontiguous territories, freight; Petroleum bulk stations & terminals; Petroleum products; Marine service station; Towing & tugboat service; Tugboat service
Ch Bd: Thomas Crowley Jr
V Ch: William A Pennella
**Treas:* Daniel Warner
Treas: Daniel L Warner
**V Ch Bd:* William Pennella
Ex VP: Kelly Conaty
Sr VP: Todd Busch
**Sr VP:* John Calvin
Sr VP: Robert B Grune
Sr VP: John P Hourihan Jr
**Sr VP:* Arthur Mead III
**Sr VP:* Michael Roberts
**Sr VP:* Susan Rodgers
Sr VP: Rinus Schepen
Sr VP: Scott G Skillman
Sr VP: Rockwell E Smith
VP: Jay Brickman
VP: Steve Collar
VP: Steve Demeroutis
VP: Greg Detiveaux
VP: Fortunato Ed
Board of Directors: Philip Bowles, Molly Murphy Crowley, Gary Depolo, Earl Kivett, Leland Prussia, William Vernon, Cameron Wolfe Jr

D-U-N-S 79-882-7874 IMP
CROWLEY PETROLEUM DIST INC
(*Suby of* CROWLEY MARINE SERVICES INC) ★
201 Arctic Slope Ave, Anchorage, AK 99518-3033
Tel (907) 822-3375 *Founded/Ownrshp* 2007
Sales 476.9MM *EMP* 100
Accts Deloitte & Touche Llp Jackson
SIC 5171 Petroleum bulk stations
Pr: Rockwell Smith
**Treas:* Daniel Warner
**VP:* Bob Cox
**VP:* Alex Sweeney

D-U-N-S 04-470-9004
CROWLEY PETROLEUM SERVICES INC (DE)
(*Suby of* CROWLEY MARITIME CORP) ★
9487 Regency Square Blvd, Jacksonville, FL 32225-8183
Tel (904) 727-2200 *Founded/Ownrshp* 2007, 2001
Sales 159.9MM^E *EMP* 2,200
SIC 4412 4424 Deep sea foreign transportation of freight; Deep sea domestic transportation of freight
VP: Rockwell E Smith
Treas: John Morton
Treas: Daniel Warner
Sr VP: John Calvin
Sr VP: Art Mead
VP: William Hogg
VP: Jeffrey Miller
VP: Nicholas Orfanidis
VP: William Osmer
VP: Kenneth Rogers
VP: Thomas Scott
VP: Stavros Skopelitis
Board of Directors: Thomas B Crowley Jr, William A Pennella, Rockwell E Smith, Richard L Swinton, William P Verdon

CROWN ACQUISITION
See CPM ACQUISITION CORP

D-U-N-S 08-555-7192
CROWN ATLANTIC CO LLC
200 Corporate Dr, Canonsburg, PA 15317
Tel (724) 416-2000 *Founded/Ownrshp* 2000
Sales 43.8MM^E *EMP* 1,000
SIC 1623 Transmitting tower (telecommunication) construction

D-U-N-S 04-710-5002
CROWN AUTO DEALERSHIPS INC
6001 34th St N, Saint Petersburg, FL 33714-1251
Tel (727) 525-4990 *Founded/Ownrshp* 1969
Sales 125.2MM^E *EMP* 325
SIC 5511 Automobiles, new & used
Pr: Dwayne Hawkins
**Pr:* Jim Myers
**CFO:* Thomas Schmidt
**Treas:* Terry Hawkins
**Sec:* James Myers
VP: Joe Lanphier
**VP:* Myers James R
Genl Mgr: Larry Casto
Genl Mgr: John Hopkins
IT Man: Jennifer Rehm

CROWN AUTOMOTIVE
See ASBURY AUTOMOTIVE NORTH CAROLINA LLC

D-U-N-S 00-504-3054 IMP/EXP
CROWN BATTERY MANUFACTURING CO (OH)
1445 Majestic Dr, Fremont, OH 43420-9190
Tel (419) 332-0563 *Founded/Ownrshp* 1926
Sales 222.1MM *EMP* 550
Accts Rsm Us Llp Cleveland Ohio
SIC 3691 Storage batteries
Pr: Hal Hawk
**VP:* JB Blackwelder
CIO: Jeff Mau
Mktg Dir: Mark Kelly

CROWN BOLT
See HD SUPPLY DISTRIBUTION SERVICES LLC

D-U-N-S 05-167-9322
CROWN BUILDING MAINTENANCE CO
ABLE BUILDING MAINTENANCE
868 Folsom St, San Francisco, CA 94107-1123
Tel (415) 981-8070 *Founded/Ownrshp* 1957
Sales 284.2MM^E *EMP* 4,600
SIC 7349 8711 Janitorial service, contract basis; Engineering services
CEO: Paul Bensi
**Owner:* Paul Boschetto
**Pr:* Mark Kelly
CFO: Scott Shephard
**Prin:* Paul Saccone
Opers Mgr: Bill Sivori

CROWN CASTLE
See CROWN COMMUNICATION LLC

D-U-N-S 07-954-9636
▲ CROWN CASTLE INTERNATIONAL CORP
1220 Augusta Dr Ste 600, Houston, TX 77057-6801
Tel (713) 570-3000 *Founded/Ownrshp* 2014
Sales 3.6MMM *EMP* 2,400
Accts Pricewaterhousecoopers Llp Pi
Tkr Sym CCI *Exch* NYS
SIC 6798 4899 7622 4812 Real estate investment trusts; Data communication services; Antenna repair & installation; Radio telephone communication
Ch Bd: J Landis Martin
Pr: W Benjamin Moreland
COO: James D Young
CFO: Jay A Brown
CFO: Daniel K Schlanger
Chf Cred: Patrick Slowey
Sr VP: Andrew Esparza
Sr VP: Philip M Kelley
Sr VP: Kenneth J Simon
VP: Bill Barnett
Prgrm Mgr: Michael Bryant

D-U-N-S 96-914-8220 IMP
CROWN CASTLE INTERNATIONAL CORP
1220 Augusta Dr Ste 600, Houston, TX 77057-6801
Tel (713) 570-3000 *Founded/Ownrshp* 1995
Sales 3.0MMM *EMP* 1,900^E
SIC 4899 7622 4812 6798

D-U-N-S 12-265-3298
■ CROWN CASTLE USA INC
(*Suby of* CROWN CASTLE INTERNATIONAL CORP) ★
2000 Corporate Dr, Canonsburg, PA 15317-8564
Tel (724) 416-2000 *Founded/Ownrshp* 1992
Sales 214.2MM^E *EMP* 500
SIC 4813 Telephone communication, except radio
CEO: John Kelly
**Pr:* Robert A Crown
**Pr:* W Benjamin Moreland
**Treas:* Jay Brown
Ofcr: Benjamin Moreland
**Sr VP:* Jim Quinn
**VP:* E Blake Hawk
**VP:* Patrick Slowey

D-U-N-S 00-308-2401
CROWN CENTRAL PETROLEUM CORP (MD)
(*Suby of* ROSEMORE HOLDINGS INC) ★
1 N Charles St Ste 2100, Baltimore, MD 21201-3759
Tel (410) 539-7400 *Founded/Ownrshp* 1923, 2001
Sales 164.0MM^E *EMP* 2,600
SIC 2911 5171 6794 Petroleum refining; Petroleum terminals; Patent owners & lessors; Selling or licensing
Pr: Thomas L Owsley
CFO: John E Wheeler Jr

D-U-N-S 92-834-0256
■ CROWN COMMUNICATION LLC
CROWN CASTLE
(*Suby of* CROWN CASTLE INTERNATIONAL CORP) ★
2000 Corporate Dr, Canonsburg, PA 15317-8564
Tel (724) 746-3600 *Founded/Ownrshp* 1997
Sales 400.2MM^E *EMP* 1,800
SIC 4812 Radio telephone communication
Ch: Landis Martin
**Pr:* John P Kelly
**VP:* Donald J Reid
VP Mktg: Mike Racippo

D-U-N-S 07-869-3891
■ CROWN CORK & SEAL CO INC
(*Suby of* CROWN HOLDINGS INC) ★
1 Crown Way, Philadelphia, PA 19154-4599
Tel (215) 698-5100 *Founded/Ownrshp* 1989
Sales 179.9MM^E *EMP* 4,400
SIC 3411 Metal cans; Tin cans; Aluminum cans
Pr: John W Conway
**Pr:* Raymond L McGowan

D-U-N-S 00-228-2341 IMP/EXP
■ CROWN CORK & SEAL USA INC
(*Suby of* CROWN HOLDINGS INC) ★
1 Crown Way, Philadelphia, PA 19154-4599
Tel (215) 698-5100 *Founded/Ownrshp* 1892
Sales 2.0MMM^E *EMP* 4,400
SIC 3411 3466 Metal cans; Tin cans; Aluminum cans; Crowns & closures; Jar tops & crowns, stamped metal; Bottle caps & tops, stamped metal
Pr: John W Conway
**Pr:* Raymond L McGowan
Treas: Mike Burn
Ex VP: Ian Carmichael
VP: Larry O Donnell
VP: Joseph C Pearce
VP: Robert Vatistas
VP: Edward C Vesey
Opers Mgr: Rob Ray
Plnt Mgr: Darin Clark
Snr Mgr: Bruce Sandberg

D-U-N-S 04-192-8680 IMP
CROWN CORR INC
7100 W 21st Ave, Gary, IN 46406-2499
Tel (219) 944-7537 *Founded/Ownrshp* 1960
Sales 165.1MM^E *EMP* 199
SIC 1542 1761 Nonresidential construction; Roofing contractor
CEO: Richard J Pellar
Treas: Elaine Pellar
Exec: Erik Bryant
Exec: Kent Oprea
Admn Mgr: Stephen Moell
Brnch Mgr: Michael Price
Sfty Dirs: Richard Marcotte
Opers Mgr: Carl Neilson
Snr PM: David Ford
Snr PM: Mark Rafferty
Snr PM: Brent Reynolds

D-U-N-S 00-332-7616 IMP/EXP
▲ CROWN CRAFTS INC
916 S Burnside Ave, Gonzales, LA 70737-4281
Tel (225) 647-9100 *Founded/Ownrshp* 1957
Sales 84.3MM *EMP* 135
Tkr Sym CRWS *Exch* NAS
SIC 2211 2389 Broadwoven fabric mills, cotton; Disposable garments & accessories
Ch Bd: E Randall Chestnut
Pr: Nanci Freeman
CFO: Olivia W Elliott

D-U-N-S 83-937-4105
CROWN ENERGY SERVICES INC
ABLE ENGINEERING SERVICES
868 Folsom St, San Francisco, CA 94107-1123
Tel (415) 546-6534 *Founded/Ownrshp* 1995
Sales 406.5MM^E *EMP* 3,000
Accts Polly Scatena Vasheresse & M
SIC 8711 Engineering services
CEO: J Paul Saccone
**Ch Bd:* Paul Boschetto
Pr: Aaron Corrales
**CFO:* Jeff Wofford
Rgnl Mgr: Scott Sutherland
Brnch Mgr: Jeff Dachenhaus
Opers Mgr: Carl Kellmyer
Opers Mgr: Mark Nolan

D-U-N-S 84-937-0572
CROWN ENTERPRISES LLC
52410 Clarke Rd, White Castle, LA 70788-4914
Tel (225) 545-3040 *Founded/Ownrshp* 1988
Sales 260.1MM^E *EMP* 1,020
SIC 1541 1791 4212 Industrial buildings & warehouses; Storage tanks, metal: erection; Animal & farm product transportation services
Pr: Ross J Campesi Jr
**Sec:* Juanita Hymel
**VP:* Mike Campesi
**VP:* Pat Campesi
Opers Mgr: Kirk Campesi

D-U-N-S 00-504-0480 EXP
CROWN EQUIPMENT CORP
CROWN LIFT TRUCKS
44 S Washington St, New Bremen, OH 45869-1247
Tel (419) 629-2311 *Founded/Ownrshp* 1988
Sales 5.3MMM^E *EMP* 11,000
SIC 5084 Lift trucks & parts
Ch Bd: James F Dicke II
**Pr:* James F Dicke III
**CFO:* Kent W Spille
Ofcr: Robin Brandt
Ex VP: Lynne Arnold
**Sr VP:* David J Besser
**Sr VP:* James R Mozer
**Sr VP:* Timothy S Quellhorst
**Sr VP:* John Tate
Sr VP: John E Tate
VP: Denise Dix
VP: Ken Dufford
VP: Kyle Falkowski
VP: Michael P Gallagher
VP: James Gaskell
VP: Tom Keller
VP: David Kerr
VP: Don Luebrecht
VP: Mark Manuel
VP: John Maxa
VP: Dave Moran

D-U-N-S 36-397-2415
CROWN GOLF PROPERTIES LP
222 N La Salle St # 2000, Chicago, IL 60601-1109
Tel (312) 395-7701 *Founded/Ownrshp* 1994
Sales 85.5MM^E *EMP* 1,500
SIC 8742 1629 Business consultant; Golf course construction
Pt: Aries Steven Crown
**Pt:* Scott Flynn

CROWN GROUP, THE
See CROWN GROUP CO

D-U-N-S 08-027-8056
CROWN GROUP CO
CROWN GROUP, THE
2111 Walter Reuther Dr, Warren, MI 48091
Tel (586) 575-9800 *Founded/Ownrshp* 2013
Sales 89.3MM^E *EMP* 1,000^E
SIC 3479 Coating of metals & formed products
CFO: Wayne Oliver
**COO:* Jim Keena
VP: Frank Knoth
Admn Mgr: Joan Odonnell

D-U-N-S 80-534-7978
CROWN HOLDING CO
Pasquerilla Plz, Johnstown, PA 15901
Tel (814) 536-4441 *Founded/Ownrshp* 1993
Sales 22.4MM^E *EMP* 1,500
SIC 6512 Shopping center, property operation only
Pr: Mark E Pasquerilla

D-U-N-S 12-997-4270 IMP/EXP
▲ CROWN HOLDINGS INC
1 Crown Way, Philadelphia, PA 19154-4501
Tel (215) 698-5100 *Founded/Ownrshp* 2003
Sales 8.7MMM *EMP* 24,000^E
Tkr Sym CCK *Exch* NYS
SIC 3411 3466 3499 Metal cans; Tin cans; Aluminum cans; Bottle caps & tops, stamped metal; Jar tops & crowns, stamped metal; Closures, stamped metal; Aerosol valves, metal
CEO: Timothy J Donahue
**Ch Bd:* John W Conway
Pr: Robert H Bourque Jr
Pr: Gerard H Gifford
Pr: Djalma Novaes Jr
CFO: Thomas A Kelly
Ex VP: Daniel A Abramowicz
VP: David A Beaver
VP: Christopher A Blaine
VP: Craig Calle
VP: Rick Nunn
Board of Directors: Jim L Turner, Jenne K Britell, William S Urkiel, Arnold W Donald, Rose Lee, William G Little, Hans J Loliger, James H Miller, Josef M Muller, Thomas A Ralph, Caesar F Sweitzer

CROWN HOTEL
See CASINO QUEEN INC

D-U-N-S 14-830-2953 IMP/EXP
■ CROWN IMPORTS LLC
(*Suby of* CONSTELLATION BRANDS INC) ★
1 S Dearborn St Ste 1700, Chicago, IL 60603-2308
Tel (312) 873-9600 *Founded/Ownrshp* 2013
Sales 806.6MM^E *EMP* 325
SIC 5181 Beer & other fermented malt liquors
Pr: Jim Sabia
Sr VP: Natasha Jones
Sr VP: James O'Neil
VP: Fred Berrios
VP: Brian Browne
VP: Nancy Davidson
VP: Fred Graefenhain
VP: Dan Herlihy
VP: Shawn Keller
VP: Ann Legan
VP: Eddie Merideth
VP: Jim Ryan
VP: Charlie Shikany
VP: Paul Verdu
Exec: Melissa Cantalini
Exec: Alan Carter
Exec: Scott Duffey
Exec: Jason Greene
Exec: Scott Klemm
Exec: Henry Schuler

CROWN LIFT TRUCKS
See CROWN EQUIPMENT CORP

D-U-N-S 12-533-4115
CROWN MEDIA HOLDINGS INC
(*Suby of* HALLMARK CARDS INC) ★
12700 Ventura Blvd # 100, Studio City, CA 91604-2469
Tel (888) 390-7474 *Founded/Ownrshp* 2016
Sales 478.7MM *EMP* 208^E
SIC 4841 Cable & other pay television services
Pr: William J Abbott
Pr: Kristen Roberts
Pr: Michelle Vicary
CFO: Andrew Rooke
Ex VP: Andrew P Brilliant
Ex VP: Ed Georger
Ex VP: Annie Howell
Ex VP: Laura Lee
Ex VP: Susanne McAvoy
Ex VP: Charles L Stanford
VP: Jess Aguirre
VP: Chad Harris
VP: Pam Slay
VP: Mark Stolnitz

D-U-N-S 05-021-8114 IMP/EXP
CROWN PACKAGING CORP
17854 Chstrfld Aprt Rd, Chesterfield, MO 63005-1216
Tel (636) 681-8000 *Founded/Ownrshp* 1969
Sales 342.5MM^E *EMP* 340
Accts Lopata Flegel
SIC 5113 5169 5131 5084 Pressure sensitive tape; Corrugated & solid fiber boxes; Polyurethane products; Labels; Packaging machinery & equipment
CEO: Fred L Anthon
**CFO:* Hunt Ray D
**VP:* John J Anthon
**VP:* Hoffmann Donald F
VP: Art Vaughan
Brnch Mgr: Meyer Ken
Dir IT: Terry Dobb
Dir IT: Larry Estas
IT Man: Bill Dotson

Opers Mgr: Dave Konarski
VP Mktg: Ron London

D-U-N-S 78-523-8085
CROWN PAPER GROUP INC
100 Mill Rd, Port Townsend, WA 98368-2246
Tel (770) 330-9137 *Founded/Ownrshp* 2014
Sales 386.5MM[E] *EMP* 1,540[E]
SIC 2621 Paper mills
CEO: Steven Klinger
**CFO:* Matthew Denton

D-U-N-S 78-710-4744 IMP/EXP
CROWN POLY INC
PULL-N-PAC
5700 Bickett St, Huntington Park, CA 90255-2625
Tel (323) 268-1298 *Founded/Ownrshp* 1991
Sales 97.5MM[E] *EMP* 150
SIC 2673 Plastic bags: made from purchased materials
CEO: Ebrahim Simhaee
CFO: Bob Gutterman
VP: David Simhaee
IT Man: Michael Bijelic
Opers Mgr: Mitch Schvab
Manager: Marc Isveck
Sls Mgr: Tom Nelson

CROWN REFRIGERATION SUPPLY
See R E MICHEL CO LLC

CROWN TONKA WALK IN COOLERS
See RAINEY ROAD HOLDINGS INC

D-U-N-S 07-920-2905
CROWNE GROUP LLC
127 Public Sq Ste 5110, Cleveland, OH 44114-1313
Tel (216) 589-0198 *Founded/Ownrshp* 2013
Sales 995.9MM[E] *EMP* 3,343[E]
SIC 3559 8711 Degreasing machines, automotive & industrial; Industrial engineers

D-U-N-S 17-811-5762
CROWNE INVESTMENTS INC
EVERGREEN NURSING HOME
501 Whetstone St, Monroeville, AL 36460-2699
Tel (251) 743-3609 *Founded/Ownrshp* 1986
Sales 60.3MM[E] *EMP* 1,800
SIC 8051 Convalescent home with continuous nursing care
Pr: Joseph W Jones Jr
Ofcr: Rosemary Misencik

D-U-N-S 01-523-5617
CROWNE PLAZA DENVER
(*Suby of* DRIFTWOOD HOSPITALITY GROUP) ★
1450 Glenarm Pl, Denver, CO 80202-5030
Tel (303) 573-1450 *Founded/Ownrshp* 1997
Sales 20.6MM[E] *EMP* 1,323[E]
SIC 7011 Hotels & motels
Genl Mgr: Phyllis Truex
Genl Mgr: Heather Douglas

CROWNE PLAZA SAN ANTONIO ARPRT
See BRE SELECT HOTELS OPERATING LLC

CROWNLINE BOATS
See LEISURE PROPERTIES LLC

D-U-N-S 92-912-8010
CROWNROCK LP
500 W Texas Ave Ste 500, Midland, TX 79701-4211
Tel (432) 818-0300 *Founded/Ownrshp* 2007
Sales 320.0MM *EMP* 140
SIC 1382 Oil & gas exploration services
Pt: Tim Dunn

CROWS AUTO SALES
See CROWS LLC

D-U-N-S 08-001-3427
CROWS LLC (CA)
CROWS AUTO SALES
1141 S 1st St, San Jose, CA 95110-3427
Tel (408) 230-4049 *Founded/Ownrshp* 2014
Sales 150.0MM[E] *EMP* 3,500[E]
SIC 5521 Used car dealers
**Mng Pt:* Rudy Rudolf

CROZER KEYSTONE
See DELAWARE COUNTY MEMORIAL HOSPITAL

CROZER KEYSTONE HEALTH SYSTEMS
See CROZER-CHESTER MEDICAL CENTER

D-U-N-S 07-375-6389
CROZER-CHESTER MEDICAL CENTER
CROZER KEYSTONE HEALTH SYSTEMS
1 Medical Center Blvd, Chester, PA 19013-3995
Tel (610) 447-2000 *Founded/Ownrshp* 1883
Sales 502.0MM *EMP* 3,300
SIC 8011

D-U-N-S 03-223-2477
CROZER-KEYSTONE HEALTH NETWORK
HEALTH ACCESS NETWORK
2602 W 9th St, Chester, PA 19013-2040
Tel (610) 497-7400 *Founded/Ownrshp* 1991
Sales 135.9MM *EMP* 70
Accts Withumsmithbrown Pc Morristow
SIC 8059 Personal care home, with health care
**VP:* James Stuccio

CROZER-KEYSTONE HEALTH SYSTEM
See PROSPECT CROZER LLC

D-U-N-S 11-973-4858
CRR HOLDINGS LLC
1717 Arch St Fl 13, Philadelphia, PA 19103-2844
Tel (215) 209-2000 *Founded/Ownrshp* 1999
Sales 242.9MM[E] *EMP* 7,435
SIC 4011 Railroads, line-haul operating
Pr: Ronald L Batory
**Pr:* Timothy T O'Toole

CRS - USCCB
See CATHOLIC RELIEF SERVICES - UNITED STATES CONFERENCE OF CATHOLIC BISHOPS

CRS AUTOMOTIVE COOLING PDTS
See KSI TRADING CORP

D-U-N-S 00-779-3383
CRST EXPEDITED INC (IA)
(*Suby of* CRST INTERNATIONAL INC) ★
1332 Edgewood Rd Sw, Cedar Rapids, IA 52404-2349
Tel (319) 396-4400 *Founded/Ownrshp* 1953, 1978
Sales 168.1MM[E] *EMP* 3,000
SIC 4213 Trucking, except local
Pr: Cameron Holzer
Ch Bd: John Smith
Pr: Mike Gannon
CEO: David L Rusch
Treas: Wesley L Brackey
VP: Larry Fahvitz

D-U-N-S 10-738-7383
CRST INTERNATIONAL INC
3930 16th Ave Sw, Cedar Rapids, IA 52404-2332
Tel (319) 396-4400 *Founded/Ownrshp* 1978
Sales 2.0MMM[E] *EMP* 5,960
Accts Deloitte & Touche Llp Cedar R
SIC 4213 Trucking, except local
CEO: David Rusch
Pr: Hugh Ekberg
Pr: John Labrie
CFO: Wesley Brackey
VP: Steve Hannah
VP: Bill Kammerer
Sfty Dirs: Laura Wolfe
Board of Directors: John Bowron, Cam Carruth, Robert Lake, Ken Maxfield, Henry Royer, Dyan Smith

D-U-N-S 62-078-7085
CRT CAPITAL GROUP LLC
SHEFFIELD MERCHANT BNKG GROUP
262 Harbor Dr Fl 2, Stamford, CT 06902-7438
Tel (203) 569-6400 *Founded/Ownrshp* 2012
Sales 121.5MM[E] *EMP* 110
SIC 6211

D-U-N-S 36-435-1171
CRT PROPERTIES INC
225 Ne Mizner Blvd # 300, Boca Raton, FL 33432-4078
Tel (561) 395-9666 *Founded/Ownrshp* 1988
Sales 167.2MM *EMP* 140
SIC 6798 Real estate investment trusts
CEO: Thomas Crocker
**Ch Bd:* Victor A Hughes Jr
Sr VP: Christopher L Becker
Sr VP: Thomas C Brockwell
Sr VP: S Mark Cypert
VP: Ben M Wakefield
Board of Directors: D Pike Aloian, Benjamin C Bishop Jr, David Hiley, George F Staudter, J C Teagle

D-U-N-S 96-158-9863 IMP/EXP
CRUCIBLE INDUSTRIES LLC
575 State Fair Blvd, Syracuse, NY 13209-1560
Tel (800) 365-1180 *Founded/Ownrshp* 1876
Sales 92.0MM[E] *EMP* 290
SIC 3312 Bars, iron: made in steel mills
Pr: Jim Beckman
Pr: James Beckman
CFO: William Lester
VP: Lorna Carpenter
VP: Lorna E Carpenter
VP: Joe Nadzan

CRUISER YACHTS
See KCS INTERNATIONAL INC

CRUM & FORSTER
See FAIRFAX INC

D-U-N-S 16-950-7691
CRUM & FORSTER HOLDINGS CORP
CRUM AND FORSTER INSURANCE
(*Suby of* CRUM & FORSTER) ★
305 Madison Ave, Morristown, NJ 07960-6100
Tel (973) 490-6600 *Founded/Ownrshp* 2002
Sales NA *EMP* 1,800
SIC 6331 6321 6351 Fire, marine & casualty insurance; Accident & health insurance; Surety insurance
Pr: Douglas M Libby
Pr: Sid Sumners
COO: Doug Gaudet
CFO: Patrick Rossi
**Ofcr:* Anthony R Slimowicz
**Ex VP:* Stephen M Mulready
**Ex VP:* Mary Jane Robertson
Sr VP: Carl W Berntsen
Sr VP: Peter J Daly
Sr VP: Steve Fomchenko
Sr VP: Mark L Owens
VP: Marc Adee
**VP:* Roberta Aufranc
**VP:* Paul Bassaline
VP: Brian Braden
VP: Rose Ciraulo
VP: Diana Cossetti
VP: Robert Elliot
VP: Steven Fomchenko
VP: Jonathan Godown
VP: Ronald Mongillo
Board of Directors: Anthony F Griffiths, Robert J Gunn, Alan D Horn, Brandon W Sweitzer, V Prem Watsa

D-U-N-S 84-920-2379
CRUM & FORSTER INC
(*Suby of* CRUM AND FORSTER INSURANCE) ★
305 Madison Ave, Morristown, NJ 07960-6100
Tel (973) 490-6600 *Founded/Ownrshp* 2003
Sales NA *EMP* 747
SIC 6311 6321 6331 6411 Life insurance; Accident & health insurance; Fire, marine & casualty insurance; Insurance agents, brokers & service
Ch: Marc Adee
**Pr:* Nicole Bennett
CFO: Howard Debare
**CFO:* Mary Jane Robertson
Ex VP: John Campi
**Ex VP:* Stephen M Mulready
**Sr VP:* Roberta Aufranc
**Sr VP:* Paul Bassaline
Sr VP: Mary Hughes
Sr VP: Mark Srygley
VP: Brian Braden
VP: George Burr
VP: Jorge Echemendia
VP: Robert Elliot
VP: Dennis Hammer
VP: Zach McAbee
VP: Arleen Paladino
VP: Luigi Pedalino
VP: George Roberts
VP: Patrick Rossi
Exec: Nancy Garcia

CRUM AND FORSTER INSURANCE
See CRUM & FORSTER HOLDINGS CORP

D-U-N-S 80-641-6439
CRUMP GROUP INC
105 Eisenhower Pkwy Fl 4, Roseland, NJ 07068-1640
Tel (973) 461-2100 *Founded/Ownrshp* 2005
Sales NA *EMP* 3,028
SIC 6411

D-U-N-S 10-804-9339
■ **CRUMP LIFE INSURANCE SERVICES INC**
INSURENOW DIRECT
(*Suby of* BB&T INSURANCE HOLDINGS INC) ★
4135 N Front St, Harrisburg, PA 17110-1616
Tel (717) 657-2740 *Founded/Ownrshp* 2012
Sales NA *EMP* 1,115
SIC 6411 Insurance brokers
Pr: Brian Winikoff
Pr: Leonard Reynolds
Treas: Michael Galvin
Sr VP: Sherri Lindenberg
Sr VP: Hector Martinez
VP: Michael Folmer
VP: Steven H Turtz
Rgnl Mgr: Adam Herman
VP Opers: Andrea Caruso
Sls Dir: Brent Hughes
Sls Mgr: Cory Mattern
Board of Directors: Bruce D Dalziel

CRUNCH FITNESS
See AGT CRUNCH ACQUISITION LLC

CRUNCH FITNESS CENTER
See BTF/CFI INC

D-U-N-S 83-221-2315 IMP
CRUNCH LLC
220 W 19th St, New York, NY 10011-4035
Tel (212) 993-0300 *Founded/Ownrshp* 2009
Sales 87.0MM[E] *EMP* 1,500
SIC 7991 6794 Physical fitness facilities; Franchises, selling or licensing
Genl Mgr: Charlie Ritchie
**Pr:* Michael R Jacobs
**Pr:* Keith Worts
VP: Kerrie Breslin
Genl Mgr: Tony Auriemma
Genl Mgr: Jason Deraveniere
Genl Mgr: Justin Forcune
Genl Mgr: Eric Foster
Genl Mgr: Donna McGann
Genl Mgr: Sean Young
Dir IT: William Schellhaas

D-U-N-S 01-292-7351 IMP
CRUNCH PAK LLC
300 Sunset Hwy, Cashmere, WA 98815-1327
Tel (509) 782-2807 *Founded/Ownrshp* 1999
Sales 95.7MM *EMP* 700
Accts Homchick Smith And Assoc Wena
SIC 0723 Fruit (fresh) packing services
CEO: Scott Sargent
COO: Rob Sawyer
CFO: Todd Danko
Mktg Dir: Tony Freytag
Mktg Mgr: Krysten Furfaro

D-U-N-S 06-600-0696 IMP/EXP
CRUTCHFIELD CORP
1 Crutchfield Park, Charlottesville, VA 22911-9097
Tel (434) 817-1000 *Founded/Ownrshp* 1974
Sales 152.2MM[E] *EMP* 500
SIC 5961

D-U-N-S 16-281-0720
CRUZ BAY PUBLISHING INC
ACTIVE INTEREST MEDIA
(*Suby of* A I M) ★
300 Continental Blvd # 650, El Segundo, CA 90245-5042
Tel (310) 356-4100 *Founded/Ownrshp* 2003
Sales 115.2MM[E] *EMP* 550
SIC 2721 Magazines: publishing only, not printed on site
Ch: Efrem Zimbalist III
**Pr:* Andrew W Clurman

D-U-N-S 60-646-2182 IMP
CRYDOM INC
(*Suby of* SENSATA TECHNOLOGIES INC) ★
2320 Paseo Delas Amer 2 Ste 201, San Diego, CA 92154
Tel (619) 210-1600 *Founded/Ownrshp* 2005
Sales 117.8MM[E] *EMP* 850[E]
SIC 3625 5065 3674 3643 Relays & industrial controls; Electronic parts & equipment; Semiconductors & related devices; Current-carrying wiring devices
Pr: Martha Sullivan
CFO: Oscar Fernandez
VP: Alison Roelke

D-U-N-S 09-464-7711 IMP/EXP
CRYOGENIC VESSEL ALTERNATIVES INC
CVA
1301 Transport Dr, Baytown, TX 77523-5903
Tel (281) 738-2863 *Founded/Ownrshp* 1999
Sales 164.8MM *EMP* 150
Accts Ratliff & Jentho Cpas Baytow
SIC 3559 Cryogenic machinery, industrial
Pr: Tim Miller
**VP:* Hecter Villarrell
**Prin:* Chris Carr
Admn Mgr: Russ Reder
Genl Mgr: Melynda Wilson
Mfg Mgr: Mike Windham
Mktg Dir: Kellie Hanson
Sales Asso: Gary Vest
Snr Mgr: Devang Patel

D-U-N-S 11-925-3177 IMP/EXP
▲ **CRYOLIFE INC**
1655 Roberts Blvd Nw, Kennesaw, GA 30144-3632
Tel (770) 419-3355 *Founded/Ownrshp* 1984
Sales 145.9MM *EMP* 675[E]
Tkr Sym CRY *Exch* NYS
SIC 3841 Surgical & medical instruments
Ch Bd: J Patrick Mackin
COO: Ashley Lee
COO: D Ashley Lee
Chf Cred: Jean F Holloway
Ofcr: James McDermid
Sr VP: John E Davis
Sr VP: William R Matthews
VP: Albert Heacox
VP: Timothy Neja
VP: William Nortrup III
Genl Mgr: Heather Gordon
Board of Directors: Thomas F Ackerman, James S Benson, Daniel J Bevevino, James W Bullock, Ronald C Elkins, Ronald D McCall, Harvey Morgan, Jon W Salveson

D-U-N-S 03-407-5221 IMP
■ **CRYOVAC INC**
(*Suby of* SEALED AIR CORP) ★
200 Riverfront Blvd, Elmwood Park, NJ 07407-1037
Tel (201) 791-7600 *Founded/Ownrshp* 1981
Sales 2.9MMM[E] *EMP* 25,000[E]
SIC 3086 Packaging & shipping materials, foamed plastic
Treas: Todd Christy
Dir Bus: Jeff Walker

CRYSTAL & COMPANY
See CRYSTAL FRANK & CO INC

CRYSTAL CHEVROLET-CHRYSLER
See CRYSTAL MOTOR CAR CO INC

CRYSTAL CREAMERY
See FOSTER DAIRY FARMS

D-U-N-S 14-815-6649
CRYSTAL DIAMOND BRANDS INC
3000 Tremont Rd, Savannah, GA 31405-1500
Tel (912) 651-5112 *Founded/Ownrshp* 2016
Sales 175.2MM[E] *EMP* 1,000
SIC 7389 2099 Packaging & labeling services; Food preparations
CEO: Anthony Disimone
VP: Robbie Fagundes
VP Opers: Jim Richtman
QC Dir: Greg Bennett
Opers Mgr: Warrick Jones
Plnt Mgr: Mike Osell
Prd Mgr: Dickey Best
Manager: Lisa Barnett
Sls Mgr: Renae Byrd

D-U-N-S 78-206-0826
■ **CRYSTAL FARMS REFRIGERATED DISTRIBUTION CO**
(*Suby of* MICHAEL FOODS OF DELAWARE INC) ★
301 Carlson Pkwy Ste 400, Minnetonka, MN 55305-5370
Tel (800) 672-8260 *Founded/Ownrshp* 1926
Sales 174.1MM[E] *EMP* 500
SIC 5143 5144 Dairy products, except dried or canned; Eggs
CEO: Mark Anderson
CFO: Max Hoffman
VP: Christine Biehl
VP: John D Reedy
Genl Mgr: Jef Johnson

D-U-N-S 83-550-0398 IMP
CRYSTAL FINISHING SYSTEMS INC
4704 Bayberry St, Schofield, WI 54476-6097
Tel (715) 355-5351 *Founded/Ownrshp* 1995
Sales 148.8MM[E] *EMP* 600
Accts Wipfli Llp Wausau Wisconsin
SIC 3479 Painting, coating & hot dipping
Pr: Mark Matthiae
**Ofcr:* Denis Crevier
**VP:* Bob Rhode
QA Dir: Jeffrey Bernas
Sfty Mgr: Ashley Placek
Opers Mgr: Michael Schroedel
Sls Mgr: Terry Lyons

CRYSTAL FLASH ENERGY
See CRYSTAL FLASH LIMITED PARTNERSHIP OF MICHIGAN

D-U-N-S 83-607-0631
CRYSTAL FLASH LIMITED PARTNERSHIP OF MICHIGAN
CRYSTAL FLASH ENERGY
(*Suby of* HERITAGE MANAGEMENT GROUP INC) ★
1754 Alpine Ave Nw, Grand Rapids, MI 49504-2810
Tel (616) 363-4851 *Founded/Ownrshp* 1989
Sales 176.8MM *EMP* 240[E]
SIC 5172 5984 Diesel fuel; Gases, liquefied petroleum (propane); Propane gas, bottled
Pr: Thomas Olive
CFO: Alan Fehsenfeld
VP: John Ertle
VP: David Scigliano
VP Bus Dev: Marc Foerster
Exec: Pam Olson
Dir IT: Daryl Cappon
Mtls Mgr: John Wozniak
Sfty Mgr: Kathrynn Nicholson
Sfty Mgr: Dennis Patrick
Sls Dir: Brad Morrill
Board of Directors: David Armstrong, Thomas Fehsenfeld, William Fehsenfeld, Kenneth Misciewicz, David Scigliano

D-U-N-S 00-798-5567
CRYSTAL FLASH PETROLEUM LLC (IN)
(*Suby of* ASPHALT MATERIALS INC) ★
5221 Ivy Tech Dr, Indianapolis, IN 46268-1016
Tel (317) 879-2849 *Founded/Ownrshp* 1930
Sales 83.3MM[E] *EMP* 400
Accts R J Pile & Company Indianapol
SIC 5541 5411 5171 Filling stations, gasoline; Convenience stores, chain; Petroleum bulk stations

Pr: David Marsh
Treas: Fred M Fehsenfeld Sr

D-U-N-S 07-326-8443
CRYSTAL FRANK & CO INC
CRYSTAL & COMPANY
32 Old Slip, New York, NY 10005-3500
Tel (212) 344-2444 *Founded/Ownrshp* 1933
Sales NA *EMP* 400
SIC 6411 Insurance agents, brokers & service
Ch Bd: James W Crystal
COO: John Cozzi
CFO: Jonathan F Crystal
Ex VP: James F Crystal
Ex VP: Guillaume De Dinechin
Ex VP: John C Smith
Ex VP: Tim Wakeman
Ex VP: Charles Williamson
Sr VP: Richard C Rosen
VP: Christi Chao
VP: Mike Dyas
VP: Matthew Gleeson
VP: Jeffrey Poliseno
VP: Lee Stannard

CRYSTAL GEYSER
See CG ROXANE LLC

D-U-N-S 94-141-9194 IMP
CRYSTAL INC - PMC
(*Suby of* PMC GROUP INC) ★
601 W 8th St, Lansdale, PA 19446-1809
Tel (267) 649-7330 *Founded/Ownrshp* 1995
Sales 90.1MM[E] *EMP* 500
SIC 2899 2842 Chemical preparations; Specialty cleaning, polishes & sanitation goods
Pr: P M Chakrabarti

D-U-N-S 04-703-0341
CRYSTAL LAKE COMMUNITY CONSOLIDATED SCHOOL DISTRICT 47
DISTRICT 47 SCHOOLS
300 Commerce Dr, Crystal Lake, IL 60014-3503
Tel (815) 459-6070 *Founded/Ownrshp* 1920
Sales 76.2MM[E] *EMP* 1,400
SIC 8211 8741 Public elementary school; Public junior high school; Management services
Pr: Jeff Mason
**VP:* Rob Fetzner
MIS Dir: Sandra Correa
Tech Mgr: Bill Schmidt
Pr Dir: Denise Barr
Teacher Pr: Meg Myers

D-U-N-S 11-539-7697 IMP/EXP
CRYSTAL MOTOR CAR CO INC
CRYSTAL CHEVROLET-CHRYSLER
1035 S Suncoast Blvd, Homosassa, FL 34448-1459
Tel (352) 795-1515 *Founded/Ownrshp* 1999
Sales 116.4MM[E] *EMP* 290
SIC 5511 Automobiles, new & used; Pickups, new & used
Pr: Steven D Lamb
**Treas:* Kennedy Smith
**VP:* Jewel Lamb
Sls Mgr: Rob Deliguori

CRYSTAL ODYSSEY
See GLASS GALLERY LTD

CRYSTAL SPRINGS
See DS SERVICES OF AMERICA INC

D-U-N-S 10-772-7919
CRYSTAL STAIRS INC
5110 W Goldleaf Cir # 150, Los Angeles, CA 90056-1287
Tel (323) 299-8998 *Founded/Ownrshp* 1980
Sales 118.2MM *EMP* 356
Accts Gyl Decauwer Llp Ontario Ca
SIC 8322 Individual & family services
CEO: Jackie B Majors
**Ch Bd:* Dianna Torres
**Pr:* Dr Karen Hill-Scott
**COO:* Javier La Fianza
**Treas:* Robert Trujillo
Ex VP: Erma Stewart
VP: Connie Parker
Prgrm Mgr: Grisel Morales
Prgrm Mgr: Yuovene Whistler
CTO: Thomas Carney
Info Man: Robert Georg

D-U-N-S 84-827-8011
CRYSTAL VALLEY FARMS LLC
MILLER MEAT POULTRY
9622 W 350 N, Orland, IN 46776-5468
Tel (260) 829-6550 *Founded/Ownrshp* 2007
Sales 104.2MM[E] *EMP* 560[E]
SIC 5144 Poultry & poultry products
Sales Exec: Len Neeb

D-U-N-S 17-522-7677 IMP
CRYSTAL WINDOW & DOOR SYSTEMS LTD
(*Suby of* CRYSTAL UNION CO., LTD.)
3110 Whitestone Expy, Flushing, NY 11354-2531
Tel (718) 961-7300 *Founded/Ownrshp* 1986
Sales 270.0MM[E] *EMP* 343
SIC 5031 3442 3231 3211 2431 1751 Doors & windows; Metal doors, sash & trim; Doors, glass: made from purchased glass; Window glass, clear & colored; Millwork; Window & door (prefabricated) installation
Pr: Thomas Chen
**CFO:* Sam Chang
**VP:* Steve Chen
Brnch Mgr: Alex Yap
MIS Dir: Mason Wang
QA Dir: Joseph Lin
IT Man: Joseph Chang
Sales Exec: Dong Guo
Manager: Frank Ganninger
Sls Mgr: Mark Lewis
Counsel: Ian Hucul

D-U-N-S 19-071-3797 IMP/EXP
CS ESTATE INC
CARDIAC SCIENCE OPERATING CO
N7w22025 Johnson Dr, Waukesha, WI 53186-1856
Tel (262) 953-3500 *Founded/Ownrshp* 2016
Sales 108.5MM[E] *EMP* 300[E]
SIC 3841 3663 7374

D-U-N-S 00-679-0414
CS MCCROSSAN INC
7865 Jefferson Hwy, Maple Grove, MN 55369-4900
Tel (763) 425-4167 *Founded/Ownrshp* 1953
Sales 175.6MM[E] *EMP* 325
SIC 1611 1622 1799 Highway & street paving contractor; Bridge construction; Insulation of pipes & boilers
Pr: Charles S Mc Crossan
VP: John McCrossan

D-U-N-S 07-390-2207 IMP/EXP
CS&P TECHNOLOGIES LP
C S & P CRYOGENICS
18119 Telge Rd, Cypress, TX 77429-1301
Tel (713) 467-0869 *Founded/Ownrshp* 1973
Sales 84.9MM *EMP* 99
SIC 3561 Pumps & pumping equipment
Pr: Kennis Baskin

D-U-N-S 96-736-4993
CSA ST JOHN MINISTRIES
ST JOHN W SHORE HOSP AUXILLARY
29000 Center Ridge Rd, Cleveland, OH 44145-5219
Tel (440) 835-8000 *Founded/Ownrshp* 1977
Sales 158.2MM *EMP* 2
SIC 5947 Gifts & novelties
**Pr:* Ardis Radik

D-U-N-S 00-791-3890
CSAA AFFINITY INSURANCE CO
(*Suby of* AAA KEYSTONE) ★
2040 Market St, Philadelphia, PA 19103-3302
Tel (215) 864-5000 *Founded/Ownrshp* 1928
Sales NA *EMP* 396
SIC 6331 6321 Fire, marine & casualty insurance & carriers; Accident insurance carriers
Ch Bd: Edward L Jones Jr
Pr: Alice T McLarnon
COO: Spencer Rowan
Treas: William J Clarke
Sr VP: Terry Powers
VP: Dominic J Grosso Jr
VP: William Koch
VP: Ronald Kosh
VP: Frank A Kuehn
VP: Paul Laskow
VP: William Markland
VP: George R Smith
VP: Russ Strover
VP: Robert Woods
Board of Directors: John Healy II, Donald Van Roden, Thomas L Ashbridge III, Richard E Hug, Judith Von Seldeneck, Henry S Baker Jr, Harold S Mc Gay Jr, Bernard C Watson, David W Brenner, Frederick B Miller, Fielding L Williams, L Patrick Deering, William Miller Jr, Raymond R Denworth Jr, Robert B Roth, William K Duncan, Robert R Rugel, Samuel Evans, Michael V Starling, Ruth S Ferber, Rodney G Stieff, William B Graham, Richard G Unruh

D-U-N-S 02-694-3982
CSAA INSURANCE EXCHANGE
3055 Oak Rd, Walnut Creek, CA 94597-2098
Tel (800) 922-8228 *Founded/Ownrshp* 2010
Sales NA *EMP* 3,500[E]
SIC 6411 Insurance agents, brokers & service
Pr: Paula Downey
**COO:* Greg Meyer
**Ofcr:* Marie Andel
**Ofcr:* Michael Zukerman
**CIO:* Stephen O'Connor

CSAA TRAVEL AGENCY
See AMERICAN AUTOMOBILE ASSOCIATION OF NORTHERN CALIFORNIA NEVADA & UTAH

D-U-N-S 83-026-8293
CSAT SOLUTIONS LP
PCS-CTS
(*Suby of* PCS TECHNOLOGY (SUZHOU) CO., LTD.)
4949 Windfern Rd, Houston, TX 77041-7502
Tel (713) 934-5200 *Founded/Ownrshp* 1992
Sales 108.5MM[E] *EMP* 1,000
SIC 7378 Computer maintenance & repair
CFO: Chris Tiesman

CSC
See COMPUTER SCIENCES CORP

D-U-N-S 08-157-6456
■ **CSC CONSULTING INC**
(*Suby of* CSC) ★
404 Wyman St Ste 355, Waltham, MA 02451-1239
Tel (781) 890-7446 *Founded/Ownrshp* 1986
Sales 247.5MM[E] *EMP* 2,300
SIC 7373 7371 8742 Systems integration services; Custom computer programming services; Management consulting services
CEO: Mike Lawrie
**Pr:* Richard F Wunder
**Treas:* Leon J Level
Sr VP: Clive Corscadden

D-U-N-S 14-869-3484
■ **CSC COVANSYS CORP**
(*Suby of* CSC) ★
3170 Fairview Park Dr, Falls Church, VA 22042-4528
Tel (703) 876-1000 *Founded/Ownrshp* 2007
Sales 731.9MM[E] *EMP* 6,800
SIC 7371 Custom computer programming services; Computer software development; Computer software systems analysis & design, custom
Pr: Rajendra B Vattikuti
COO: John Frahlich
**CFO:* James S Trouba
Ex VP: Gerald Massey
**Ex VP:* Siva Velu
Ex VP: Sivaprakasam Velu
Ex VP: Tim Wolfe
**Sr VP:* Muralee Bhaskaran
Sr VP: William R Euller
Sr VP: Mark Gross
Sr VP: Timothy S Manney
**Sr VP:* Stephen P Nicholas
Sr VP: Stephen Nicholas
VP: Barbara Portee
VP: Nathaniel Walker

D-U-N-S 06-129-2587
■ **CSC CREDIT SERVICES INC**
CREDIT BUREAU OF BEAUMONT
(*Suby of* CSC) ★
1775 Tysons Blvd, Tysons, VA 22102-4284
Tel (703) 876-1000 *Founded/Ownrshp* 1967, 1982
Sales 182.9MM[E] *EMP* 1,700
SIC 7323 7322 Credit bureau & agency; Collection agency, except real estate
Pr: John D Dickson
**Treas:* Diao Charles

D-U-N-S 03-346-9946 IMP
■ **CSC DISTRIBUTION INC**
(*Suby of* BIG LOTS INC) ★
300 Phillipi Rd, Columbus, OH 43228-1310
Tel (614) 278-6800 *Founded/Ownrshp* 1998
Sales 146.4MM[E] *EMP* 600[E]
SIC 5092 Toys & games
Pr: Michael J Potter

D-U-N-S 13-088-4570 IMP
CSC HOLDINGS LLC
CABLEVISION
(*Suby of* CABLEVISION SYSTEMS CORP) ★
1111 Stewart Ave, Bethpage, NY 11714-3533
Tel (516) 803-2300 *Founded/Ownrshp* 1985
Sales 6.5MMM *EMP* 12,920
Accts Kpmg Llp Melville New York
SIC 4841 4813 Cable & other pay television services; Cable television services; Subscription television services; Telephone communication, except radio; Local telephone communications; Long distance telephone communications;
CEO: James L Dolan
**Ch Bd:* Charles F Dolan
**Pr:* Brian G Sweeney
**COO:* Kristin A Dolan
Sr VP: Donna Coleman
Sr VP: Victoria M Mink
Board of Directors: Steven J Simmons, Rand Araskog, Deborah Dolan-Sweeney, Edward C Atwood, Vincent Tese, Frank Biondi, Leonard Tow, Patrick F Dolan, Marianne Dolan Weber, Paul J Dolan, Thomas C Dolan, Joseph J Lhota, Thomas V Reifenheiser, John R Ryan

CSC REGULATORY SERVICE GROUP
See IMAGE SOLUTIONS INC

D-U-N-S 07-925-3192
CSC SERVICEWORKS HOLDINGS INC
303 Sunnyside Blvd # 70, Plainview, NY 11803-1597
Tel (516) 349-8555 *Founded/Ownrshp* 2013
Sales 361.1MM[E] *EMP* 805[E]
SIC 3633 5087 Household laundry equipment; Laundry equipment & supplies

D-U-N-S 07-925-3190
CSC SERVICEWORKS INC
(*Suby of* CSC SERVICEWORKS HOLDINGS INC) ★
303 Sunnyside Blvd # 70, Plainview, NY 11803-1597
Tel (516) 349-8555 *Founded/Ownrshp* 2013
Sales 191.9MM[E] *EMP* 805[E]
SIC 3633 5087 Household laundry equipment; Laundry equipment & supplies
CEO: Mark Hjelle
Ex VP: Taylor Doggett
Ex VP: Steve Gallagher
Area Mgr: Kelli Bodinizzo
Area Mgr: Janna Booth
Area Mgr: Nicholas Kotsidis
Area Mgr: Lydia Neal
Admn Mgr: Theresa Vodika
Brnch Mgr: Matthew McManus
Secur Mgr: Otis Sanders
Sls Mgr: Frank Williams

D-U-N-S 06-362-9627
CSC/TECHNOLOGY MGMT GRP
P.O. Box 1728 (20167-1728)
Tel (703) 876-3636 *Founded/Ownrshp* 2011
Sales 197.7MM[E] *EMP* 153[E]
SIC 5112 Office supplies

CSCC
See COLUMBUS STATE COMMUNITY COLLEGE

CSCU
See CONNECTICUT STATE COLLEGES & UNIVERSITIES BOARD OF REGENTS FOR HIGHER EDUCATION

CSD
See CENTENNIAL SCHOOL DISTRICT

D-U-N-S 02-232-3844 IMP
CSD INC
CONSUMERS SUPPLY DISTRIBUTING
5101 Harbor Dr, Sioux City, IA 51111-1109
Tel (712) 255-6927 *Founded/Ownrshp* 1964
Sales 107.5MM[E] *EMP* 70
SIC 5191 Feed
Pr: David B Patee
**CFO:* Glen Poehner
**Sec:* Marilyn J Patee
**VP:* Daniel Patee
VP: Keith Snyder
IT Man: David Taylor
Sls Mgr: Michael Hall
Sls Mgr: Ron Rottmann
Sls Mgr: Ted Wise

CSE
See CENTRAL STATES ENTERPRISES LLC

D-U-N-S 02-929-9856 IMP
■ **CSE HOLDINGS INC**
(*Suby of* INTERLINE BRANDS INC) ★
650 Brennan St, San Jose, CA 95131-1204
Tel (408) 436-1907 *Founded/Ownrshp* 2010
Sales 195.2MM[E] *EMP* 250
SIC 5087 5084 7699 5113 5199 5112 Janitors' supplies; Cleaning equipment, high pressure, sand or steam; Industrial machinery & equipment repair; Industrial & personal service paper; Packaging materials; Office supplies
Pr: Gary Fredkin
**COO:* Marvin Wenger
VP Sls: Bob Friedman
Manager: Tim Chism

CSEA
See CIVIL SERVICE EMPLOYEES ASSOCIATION INC

CSG INTERACTIVE MESSAGING
See CSG SYSTEMS INC

D-U-N-S 87-825-0059
■ **CSG SYSTEMS INC**
CSG INTERACTIVE MESSAGING
(*Suby of* CSG SYSTEMS INTERNATIONAL INC) ★
18020 Burt St, Elkhorn, NE 68022-4406
Tel (402) 431-7000 *Founded/Ownrshp* 1993
Sales 226.0MM[E] *EMP* 1,540
SIC 7374 Data processing service
Pr: Peter E Kalan
Pr: Jeff Schranz
**CFO:* Randy R Wiese
**VP:* Patrick F Costello
VP: Gloria Osborn
VP: Randy Wiese
Ex Dir: Linda Morse
CIO: Bob Donavan
Dir IT: Bob Bischoff
Dir IT: Jeff Willer
IT Man: SAI Renukunta
Board of Directors: George Haddix Phd, Royce J Holland, Janice Obuchowski, Bernard W Reznicek, Rockwell Schnabel, Frank Sica

D-U-N-S 87-811-5161
▲ **CSG SYSTEMS INTERNATIONAL INC**
9555 Maroon Cir, Englewood, CO 80112-5944
Tel (303) 200-2000 *Founded/Ownrshp* 1994
Sales 751.2MM *EMP* 3,277[E]
Tkr Sym CSGS *Exch* NGS
SIC 7374 Data processing & preparation; Computer processing services
Pr: Bret C Griess
Pr: Fred Brott
Pr: Mike Henderson
Pr: Paul Nguyen
Pr: Mike Scott
Pr: Phillip Yoo
CFO: Randy R Wiese
Ex VP: Marwan Fawaz
Ex VP: Ken Kennedy
Ex VP: Alan Michels
Ex VP: Joseph T Ruble
Ex VP: Brian Shepherd
Sr VP: Jerry Baker
Sr VP: Sean Brown
Sr VP: Jay McCracken
VP: Chad Dunavant
VP: Edie Pignotti
Board of Directors: David G Barnes, Ronald H Cooper, John L M Hughes, Janice I Obuchowski, Donald B Reed, Frank V Sica, Donald V Smith, James A Unruh

CSI
See CARDIOVASCULAR SYSTEMS INC

CSI
See COMMUNICATIONS SYSTEMS INC

CSI
See COMPRESSOR SYSTEMS INC

D-U-N-S 83-696-2688
CSI COMPANIES INC
(*Suby of* RECRUIT HOLDINGS CO.,LTD.)
9995 Gate Pkwy N Ste 100, Jacksonville, FL 32246-0800
Tel (904) 338-9515 *Founded/Ownrshp* 2006
Sales 147.8MM[E] *EMP* 150
Accts The Lba Cpa Pa Jacksonville
SIC 7361 Employment agencies
CEO: Raphael Sanson
Pr: Zhawn Stevens
**COO:* Chris Flakus
**CFO:* Shunichi Makita
VP: Kyle Barlow

D-U-N-S 96-251-7616
▲ **CSI COMPRESSCO LP**
3809 S Fm 1788, Midland, TX 79706-2662
Tel (432) 563-1170 *Founded/Ownrshp* 2008
Sales 457.6MM *EMP* 800
Tkr Sym CCLP *Exch* NGS
SIC 1389 3533 Oil field services; Gas field services; Gas field machinery & equipment
Pr: Timothy A Knox
CFO: Derek C Coffie

D-U-N-S 61-292-2286
CSI ELECTRICAL CONTRACTORS INC
C S I
10623 Fulton Wells Ave, Santa Fe Springs, CA 90670-3741
Tel (562) 946-0700 *Founded/Ownrshp* 1990
Sales 111.2MM[E] *EMP* 350
SIC 1731 General electrical contractor
Pr: Steven M Watts
Pr: Paul Pica
**COO:* Craig Epperly
VP: Gene Acosta
VP: Scott Arfsten
VP: Chris Corder
IT Man: Dana Thompson
Mktg Dir: Bonnie Summers
Snr PM: Tyson Bickerstaff
Snr PM: Roger Howard

D-U-N-S 00-261-5610
CSI HOLDINGS INC
4850 E Street Rd Ste 230, Trevose, PA 19053-6655
Tel (215) 357-4400 *Founded/Ownrshp* 1983, 1998
Sales NA *EMP* 350

SIC 6411 7532 Insurance claim processing, except medical; Collision shops, automotive
CEO: Wayne G Smolda
**Treas:* Claudia B Smolda
**Ex VP:* Richard Brigidi
**Ex VP:* Joseph Tornetta
Dir IT: Steve Enoch

CSI IMPORTS
See SAKAR INTERNATIONAL INC

D-U-N-S 62-242-8951
CSI INTERNATIONAL INC
C S I
6700 N Andrews Ave # 400, Fort Lauderdale, FL 33309-2204
Tel (954) 308-4300 *Founded/Ownrshp* 1989
Sales 53.0MM *EMP* 1,917
Accts Buchbinder Tunick & Company Ll
SIC 8744 8711 Facilities support services; Construction & civil engineering
Ch Bd: P Geoffrey Hammond
**Pr:* Jayne Hammond
Pr: Jonathon Pannell
**CEO:* David Hammond
COO: Chuck Wiese
VP: Josh Tomey
Exec: Ann Keenan
Rgnl Mgr: Kathy Gross
Genl Mgr: Martin Feeney
VP Opers: Mike Barile
Opers Mgr: Carlos Alba

D-U-N-S 08-140-2224
CSI LEASING INC
9990 Old Olive Street Rd # 101, Saint Louis, MO 63141-5930
Tel (314) 997-4934 *Founded/Ownrshp* 1972
Sales 577.4MM^E *EMP* 540
SIC 7377 5045 Computer rental & leasing; Computers, peripherals & software
CEO: Bill Gillula
Pr: Bill Elmore
Pr: Steve Hamilton
Pr: Kirk Kasicki
Pr: Matt Kersting
CFO: Fred O'Neal
Ch: Ken Steinback
Ofcr: Don Pratt
Ex VP: Craig Ault
Ex VP: Phil Cagney
Ex VP: Lorraine Cherrick
Sr VP: Paul Keefe
Sr VP: Jonathan Zigman
VP: Eric Ausubel
VP: Tom Brown
VP: Ed Candolini
VP: Mark Crain
VP: Chip Deson
VP: Nikki Douglas
VP: Rick Guilander
VP: Mike Nichter
Board of Directors: Anthony L Guerrerio

CSI ROANOKE CI
See BRENNER HOLDINGS INC

CSID
See LAMAR CONSOLIDATED INDEPENDENT SCHOOL DISTRICT (INC)

D-U-N-S 87-769-6724 IMP
■ **CSK AUTO CORP**
(*Suby of* OREILLY AUTO PARTS) ★
645 E Mazouri Ave Ste 400, Phoenix, AZ 85012
Tel (602) 265-9200 *Founded/Ownrshp* 2008
Sales 1.8MMM^E *EMP* 15,126
SIC 5531 Automotive & home supply stores
Pr: Lawrence Mondry
**CFO:* Steven L Korby
CFO: James Riley
Ex VP: Paul Lehr
**Ex VP:* Dale Ward
**Sr VP:* Larry Buresh
**Sr VP:* Randi Morrison
VP: Lori Muller
CTO: James Foster
CTO: Jim Myers
VP Mktg: Jim Schoenberger

D-U-N-S 04-931-7357 IMP
CSK AUTO INC
CHECKER AUTO PARTS
645 E Missouri Ave # 400, Phoenix, AZ 85012-1373
Tel (602) 265-9200 *Founded/Ownrshp* 2008
Sales NA *EMP* 13,570
SIC 5531

D-U-N-S 93-189-6963 IMP
CSL BEHRING LLC
(*Suby of* CSL LIMITED)
1020 1st Ave, King of Prussia, PA 19406-1310
Tel (610) 878-4000 *Founded/Ownrshp* 2004
Sales 2.5MMM^E *EMP* 5,800
SIC 2836 Blood derivatives; Plasmas
Pr: Paul Perreault
CFO: Jim Fickenscher
CFO: Perry Premdas
**Treas:* Judith Mamora
Ofcr: Andrew Cuthbertson
**Ex VP:* Greg Boss
Ex VP: Gordan Naylor
Ex VP: Bob Repella
Ex VP: Val Romberg
VP: Gary Floyd
VP: Ronan W Gannon
VP: Ronan Gannon
VP: Naylor Gordon
VP: Robert D Lefebvre
VP: Robert Lojewski
VP: Pam Peterson
VP: Rich Walters
VP: Alan Wills
Assoc Dir: Bernadine Dixon
Dir Bus: Stefan Neudoerfer
Comm Man: Greg Healy

D-U-N-S 11-213-2795
CSL PLASMA INC
(*Suby of* CSL LIMITED)
900 Broken Sound Pkwy # 4, Boca Raton, FL 33487-3513
Tel (561) 981-3700 *Founded/Ownrshp* 1998
Sales 245.4MM^E *EMP* 620
SIC 5122 Blood plasma
Treas: Justin Cahill
Exec: Joan Nagel
Genl Mgr: Randy Furby
IT Man: David Bersch
IT Man: James Craig
Snr Mgr: Moshe Vessal

D-U-N-S 08-003-3869
CSLCS LLC (IA)
HEALTH AT HOME
1 10th St Ste 100, Augusta, GA 30901-0100
Tel (855) 458-5500 *Founded/Ownrshp* 2013
Sales 70.4M^E *EMP* 1,000
SIC 8082 Home health care services
Pr: Rick Griffin
**CFO:* John Southern
VP: Bobbi Blair
VP: Walter Wright

CSM AMERICA INC.
See CORBION AMERICA HOLDINGS INC

D-U-N-S 07-490-9086 IMP/EXP
CSM BAKERY SOLUTIONS LLC
(*Suby of* RHONE CAPITAL LLC) ★
5775 Glenridge Dr Bldg A, Sandy Springs, GA 30328-5380
Tel (404) 478-5400 *Founded/Ownrshp* 2013
Sales 675.0MM^E *EMP* 1,000
SIC 2052 Bakery products, dry
Pr: Marianne Kirkegaard
Pr: Rhonda Turner
CFO: Duane Still
VP: Cheryl Barre
VP: Jason Foshaug
VP: Dennis Murphy
VP: Tony Puri
VP: Gretchen Sussman
Genl Mgr: Mark O'Driscoll
Off Mgr: Debbie Major
Opers Mgr: Linh Nguyen
Board of Directors: Michael Rosenzweig

CSM BAKERY SUPPLIES NORTH AMER
See BEST BRANDS CORP

D-U-N-S 09-177-7987
CSM COMPANIES INC
WISCONSIN-KENWORTH
5100 Estpark Blvd Ste 210, Madison, WI 53718
Tel (608) 241-5616 *Founded/Ownrshp* 1978
Sales 214.1MM^E *EMP* 450
SIC 5012 5013 Trucks, commercial; Truck parts & accessories
Pr: James Moeller
VP: Thomas Graves

D-U-N-S 07-961-3328
CSP HOLDING CORP
(*Suby of* CONTINENTAL STRUCTURAL PLASTICS HOLDINGS CORP) ★
255 Rex Blvd, Auburn Hills, MI 48326-2954
Tel (248) 237-7800 *Founded/Ownrshp* 1998
Sales 798.6MM^E *EMP* 2,700^E
SIC 3089 Plastic processing
CEO: Frank Macher

D-U-N-S 04-589-7659
▲ **CSP INC** (MA)
175 Cabot St Ste 210, Lowell, MA 01854-3635
Tel (978) 663-7598 *Founded/Ownrshp* 1968
Sales 89.3MM *EMP* 172^E
Tkr Sym CSPI *Exch* NGM
SIC 3577 7372 7373 Computer peripheral equipment; Prepackaged software; Application computer software; Computer integrated systems design
Pr: Victor Dellovo
**Ch Bd:* C Shelton James
CFO: Gary W Levine
VP: Vijay Aggarwal
VP: William E Bent Jr
VP: Michael M Stern
Board of Directors: Raymond Charles Blackmon, Marilyn T Smith

D-U-N-S 83-557-3452 IMP
■ **CSR TECHNOLOGY INC**
(*Suby of* QUALCOMM TECHNOLOGIES INTERNATIONAL, LTD.)
1060 Rincon Cir, San Jose, CA 95131-1325
Tel (408) 523-6500 *Founded/Ownrshp* 2012
Sales 100.9MM^E *EMP* 500^E
SIC 3679 3812 3674 Electronic circuits; Search & navigation equipment; Semiconductors & related devices
CEO: Brett Gladden
CFO: Geoffrey Ribar
Ch: Ron Mackintosh
Ex VP: Chris Ladas
VP: Babak Bastani
VP: Adam R Dolinko
VP: Warren Hewerdine
VP: Don Leimer
VP: Atul Shingal
Snr Sftwr: Chirag Shah
CIO: Ian Chronister

D-U-N-S 08-001-1988
▲ **CSRA INC**
3170 Fairview Park Dr, Falls Church, VA 22042-4516
Tel (703) 641-2000 *Founded/Ownrshp* 2015
Sales 4.2MMM *EMP* 18,000^E
Accts Deloitte & Touche Llp Mclean
Tkr Sym CSRA *Exch* NYS
SIC 7373 Computer integrated systems design
Pr: Lawrence B Prior III
CFO: David F Keffer
Ofcr: John Reing
Ex VP: William J Haynes II
Ex VP: Catherine Kuenzel
Ex VP: Paul Nedzbala

Board of Directors: Keith B Alexander, Michele A Flournoy, Mark A Frantz, Nancy Killefer, Craig Martin, Sean O'keefe, Michael E Ventling, Billie I Williamson

D-U-N-S 07-835-1306
■ **CSRA INFORMATION SYSTEMS LLC**
(*Suby of* DYNCORP) ★
13857 Mclearen Rd, Herndon, VA 20171-3210
Tel (703) 818-4000 *Founded/Ownrshp* 1999
Sales 16.3MMM *EMP* 905
SIC 7376 Computer facilities management
CEO: Lawrence B Prior
Bd of Dir: Paul Kaminski
VP: Christin Lachance
Dir IT: Fred Mentzel
Netwrk Eng: Pat Hogan

D-U-N-S 07-973-5371
■ **CSRA LLC**
(*Suby of* CSRA INC) ★
3170 Fairview Park Dr, Falls Church, VA 22042-4516
Tel (703) 876-1000 *Founded/Ownrshp* 2015
Sales 622.3MM^E *EMP* 1,000^E
SIC 7371 8733 7376 7374 7379 Custom computer programming services; Scientific research agency; Computer facilities management; Data processing & preparation; Computer processing services; Computer related consulting services
CEO: Lawrence Prior
VP: Helaine Elderkin
Board of Directors: Lannie Elderkin

D-U-N-S 92-792-1627
■ **CSRA SYSTEMS AND SOLUTIONS LLC**
(*Suby of* CSC) ★
15000 Conference Ctr Dr, Chantilly, VA 20151-3819
Tel (703) 641-2213 *Founded/Ownrshp* 1977
Sales 710.6MM^E *EMP* 6,600
SIC 7299 Information services, consumer
CEO: Lawrence B Prior
Bd of Dir: Russell Dougherty
Bd of Dir: Paul Kaminski
Bd of Dir: Dudley Mecum
Plng Mgr: Martin Fulcher
CIO: Venkat Gopalan
IT Man: Nick Moscone
IT Man: Jim Ochse
Board of Directors: Lannie Elderkin

CSS
See CORPORATE SECURITY SOLUTIONS INC

D-U-N-S 01-099-6757
CSS CORP
(*Suby of* C S S) ★
11778 S Election Rd # 160, Draper, UT 84020-6408
Tel (801) 619-4014 *Founded/Ownrshp* 2007
Sales 19.2MM^E *EMP* 3,836^E
SIC 7299 Information services, consumer
Pr: Kevin Betts

D-U-N-S 94-155-4321 IMP
CSS INC
CLOSEOUT SURPLUS & SAVINGS
35 Love Ln, Netcong, NJ 07857-1013
Tel (973) 364-1118 *Founded/Ownrshp* 1988
Sales 90.9MM^E *EMP* 86^E
SIC 5199 General merchandise, non-durable
Pr: Ernest Peia

D-U-N-S 00-698-2003
▲ **CSS INDUSTRIES INC**
450 Plymouth Rd Ste 300, Plymouth Meeting, PA 19462-1644
Tel (610) 729-3959 *Founded/Ownrshp* 1923
Sales 317.0MM *EMP* 1,200^E
Tkr Sym CSS *Exch* NYS
SIC 2771 2679 2389 2396 2621 2865 Greeting cards; Gift wrap & novelties, paper; Gift wrap, paper: made from purchased material; Costumes; Ribbons & bows, cut & sewed; Tissue paper; Dyes & pigments
Pr: Christopher J Munyan
**Ch Bd:* Rebecca C Matthias
CFO: David F McHugh
CFO: Vincent A Paccapaniccia
Ex VP: Carey Edwards
Ex VP: Carey B Edwards
Ex VP: Christian A Sorensen
Sr VP: Cara Farley
Sr VP: Cara L Farley
Sr VP: Lois B Karpinski
VP: Mark Davis
VP: William G Kiesling
Board of Directors: Scott A Beaumont, Robert E Chappell, William Rulon-Miller

D-U-N-S 07-877-1215
▲ **CST BRANDS INC**
19500 Bulverde Rd Ste 100, San Antonio, TX 78259-3768
Tel (210) 692-5000 *Founded/Ownrshp* 2013
Sales 11.4MMM *EMP* 14,517
Tkr Sym CST *Exch* NYS
SIC 5983 5411 Fuel oil dealers; Grocery stores
Ch Bd: Kimberly S Bowers
**Ch Bd:* Kimberly S Lubel
**COO:* Anthony P Bartys
CFO: Clay E Killinger
**CFO:* Clayton E Killinger
**Chf Mktg O:* Charles H Adams
Sr VP: Stephan F Motz
**Sr VP:* Gerard J Sonnier
Sr VP: Stephane Trudel
VP: Peter Brodnitz
VP: Tammy Floyd
VP: Pete Linton
VP: Martin Longpre
VP: Henry Martinez
VP: Warren Maynard
VP: David Mock
VP: Lulu Olson
VP: Mario Sauv
VP: Jeff Truman
Comm Dir: Lisa Koenig
Board of Directors: Joseph V Topper Jr, Donna M Boles, Michael H Wargotz, Roger G Burton, Rocky B Dewbre, Thomas W Dickson, Ruben M Escobedo, Denise Incandela, Joseph E Reece, Alan Schoenbaum, Stephen A Smith

D-U-N-S 61-124-9707 IMP/EXP
CST INDUSTRIES INC
COLUMBIAN TECTANK
903 E 104th St Ste 900, Kansas City, MO 64131-3451
Tel (913) 621-3700 *Founded/Ownrshp* 2012
Sales 271.9MM^E *EMP* 690
SIC 3443 Tanks, standard or custom fabricated: metal plate
Pr: Brian Bauerbach
**Pr:* Declan McLaughlin
**CFO:* Chris Bridgnell
VP: Richard Jarman
**VP:* Rick Wiedemann
MIS Mgr: Celeste Neibarger
Sls Mgr: Scott Berner
Sales Asso: Jill Jones
Sales Asso: Steven Keeler

CSTK
See CENTRAL STATES THERMO KING INC

CSU EAST BAY
See CALIFORNIA STATE UNIVERSITY EAST BAY

CSUSA
See CHARTER SCHOOLS USA INC

CSUSB
See CALIFORNIA STATE UNIVERSITY SAN BERNARDINO

D-U-N-S 07-989-2463
▲ **CSW INDUSTRIALS INC**
5400 Lyndon B Johnson Fwy, Dallas, TX 75240-1000
Tel (972) 233-8242 *Founded/Ownrshp* 2014
Sales 319.8MM *EMP* 725^E
Tkr Sym CSWI *Exch* NGS
SIC 3569 Assembly machines, non-metalworking
Ch Bd: Joseph B Armes
Pr: Christopher J Mudd
CFO: Gregg W Branning
Sr VP: Luke E Alverson
Sr VP: Luke Alverson
Sr VP: Craig J Foster
Sr VP: Mark H Lee
Sr VP: Don J Sullivan

D-U-N-S 03-977-5119
▲ **CSX CORP**
500 Water St Fl 15, Jacksonville, FL 32202-4423
Tel (904) 359-3200 *Founded/Ownrshp* 1978
Sales 11.8MMM *EMP* 29,000
Accts Ernst & Young Llp Jacksonvil
Tkr Sym CSX *Exch* NGS
SIC 4011 Railroads, line-haul operating
Ch Bd: Michael J Ward
Pr: Geoffrey Aughenbaugh
Pr: Peter Burrus
Pr: Bill Clement
Pr: Clarence W Gooden
Pr: Bob Gutman
Pr: Mark Hinsdale
Pr: Mitch Hobbs
Pr: Rick Hood
Pr: Zachery Jones
Pr: Angie Williams
Pr: Duard Williams
COO: Cindy M Sanborn
CFO: Frank A Lonegro
Chf Mktg O: Fredrik J Eliasson
Ofcr: Lisa A Mancini
Ex VP: Ellen M Fitzsimmons
Ex VP: Wendy Hausler
Ex VP: Cindy Sanborn
Sr VP: Kathleen Brandt
Sr VP: Diana Sorfleet
Board of Directors: J Steven Whisler, Donna M Alvarado, John B Breaux, Pamela L Carter, Steven T Halverson, Edward J Kelly III, John D McPherson, Timothy T O'toole, David M Ratcliffe, Donald J Shepard

D-U-N-S 19-428-2745
■ **CSX INTERMODAL INC**
(*Suby of* CSX CORP) ★
500 Water St, Jacksonville, FL 32202-4423
Tel (904) 633-1000 *Founded/Ownrshp* 1980
Sales 146.7MM^E *EMP* 1,000
SIC 4213 4011 4225 Refrigerated products transport; Trailer or container on flat car (TOFC/COFC); Contract haulers; Railroads, line-haul operating; General warehousing
Pr: James R Hertwig
**Pr:* Fredrik Eliasson
**Pr:* Oscar Munoz
**CEO:* Michael J Ward
**Ex VP:* Clarence W Gooden
**Prin:* Alan P Blumenfeld
Rgnl Mgr: Jeff A Heath
Brnch Mgr: Elizabeth Cherry
Brnch Mgr: Larry Noland
Genl Mgr: Scott Setser
Netwrk Mgr: Jim Lubcke

D-U-N-S 18-763-2385
■ **CSX TECHNOLOGY INC**
(*Suby of* CSX CORP) ★
550 Water St, Jacksonville, FL 32202-5177
Tel (904) 633-1000 *Founded/Ownrshp* 1987
Sales 172.3MM^E *EMP* 1,193
SIC 7371 Computer software development
Pr: Kathleen Brandt
**Treas:* David A Boor
**Sr VP:* Mark G Aron
**Sr VP:* James Ermer
**VP:* Patricia J Aftoora
Snr Sftwr: Patricia Imboden

D-U-N-S 00-794-1321
■ **CSX TRANSPORTATION INC** (VA)
(*Suby of* CSX CORP) ★
500 Water St, Jacksonville, FL 32202-4445
Tel (904) 359-3100 *Founded/Ownrshp* 1944, 1980
Sales 3.8MMM^E *EMP* 30,000
SIC 4011 Railroads, line-haul operating
CEO: Michael J Ward
Pr: Fredrik Eliasson
Pr: Clarence Gooden

COO: David A Brown
CFO: Fred Faurner
CFO: Oscar Munoz
Treas: David A Boor
Ofcr: Lisa A Mancini
Assoc VP: Everett Eddy
Ex VP: Frank Lonegro
Sr VP: W Michael Cantrell
VP: James D Bagley
VP: Ed Jenkins
VP: Michele Mastrean
VP: Franklin E Pursley
VP: Cindy Sanborn
VP: Carolyn T Sizemore
VP: Charles Wodehouse
Exec: Jennifer Boyter
Exec: Bob Haulter
Dir Risk M: Deborah Tauro
Board of Directors: Clarence W Gooden

D-U-N-S 60-466-2882
CT ASSOCIATES OF ILLINOIS LP
CAMPBELL TERRACE APARTMENTS
2061 N Campbell Ave Ofc, Chicago, IL 60647-4182
Tel (773) 486-3666 *Founded/Ownrshp* 1986
Sales 43.1MM[E] *EMP* 1,828
SIC 6531 6513 Real estate agents & managers; Apartment building operators
Prin: Stephen Porras
Prin: Larry Lipton

CT FREIGHT
See WEST PLAINS LLC

D-U-N-S 96-543-4751
CT TECHNOLOGIES HOLDINGS INC
875 N Michigan Ave, Chicago, IL 60611-1803
Tel (770) 360-1700 *Founded/Ownrshp* 2010
Sales NA *EMP* 4,000
SIC 6719 Investment holding companies, except banks
CEO: Mike Labetz
**CFO:* Brian Grazzini

CTA
See CHICAGO TRANSIT AUTHORITY

CTA
See CONSUMER TECHNOLOGY ASSOCIATION

D-U-N-S 78-951-9808 IMP/EXP
CTA ACOUSTICS INC
25211 Dequindre Rd, Madison Heights, MI 48071-4211
Tel (248) 544-2580 *Founded/Ownrshp* 1973
Sales 179.1MM[E] *EMP* 560
SIC 3714 Motor vehicle body components & frame
Ch Bd: James J Pike
**Pr:* Thomas Brown
**VP:* Barry Gaines

CTA ARCHITECTS ENGINEERS
See CTA INC

D-U-N-S 06-373-0378
CTA INC
CTA ARCHITECTS ENGINEERS
13 N 23rd St, Billings, MT 59101-2467
Tel (406) 248-7455 *Founded/Ownrshp* 2011
Sales 95.2MM[E] *EMP* 365
Accts Eide Bailly Llp Billings Mon
SIC 8711 8712 Engineering services; Architectural engineering
CEO: Scott Wilson
Bd of Dir: Michael Tuss
Exec: Brad Sperry
Brnch Mgr: Kent Bray
Software D: Laura Ewald

D-U-N-S 96-733-9342
CTAP LLC
2585 Trailridge Dr E # 200, Lafayette, CO 80026-3495
Tel (303) 661-9475 *Founded/Ownrshp* 1995
Sales 139.4MM[E] *EMP* 98
SIC 5082 Oil field equipment
Prin: Duke Altschuler
**Prin:* Ronnie Schwindt
Dir IT: Charles Eickhorst
VP Opers: Stoney McCarrell
Sfty Mgr: Dana Foley
Sls Dir: Mike Booth
Sls Mgr: Zac Cross

D-U-N-S 07-890-7946 IMP/EXP
■ CTB INC
CHORE-TIME PLTY PROD SYSTEMS
(*Suby of* BERKSHIRE HATHAWAY INC) ★
410 N Higbee St, Milford, IN 46542-9147
Tel (574) 658-4191 *Founded/Ownrshp* 2002
Sales 456.4MM[E] *EMP* 1,200
SIC 3443 3523 Bins, prefabricated metal plate; Farm storage tanks, metal plate; Hog feeding, handling & watering equipment; Poultry brooders, feeders & waterers
CEO: Victor A Mancinelli
Pr: Douglas J Niemeyer
VP: Randy S Eveler
VP: William Mabee
Area Mgr: Joe Lockinger
Genl Mgr: Marc Plastow
MIS Dir: Steven Crim
Sls Mgr: Kevin Alger
Sls Mgr: Earl Barrentine
Sls Mgr: Steve Batson
Sls Mgr: Phillip Gilliland

D-U-N-S 07-240-0443
■ CTC COMMUNICATIONS CORP
EARTHLINK BUSINESS
(*Suby of* EARTHLINK HOLDINGS CORP) ★
1170 Peachtree St Ne # 900, Atlanta, GA 30309-7649
Tel (404) 815-0770 *Founded/Ownrshp* 2011
Sales 123.1MM[E] *EMP* 240
SIC 4813
CEO: Kenneth Peterson
Sr Cor Off: Steven Milton
Ex VP: Doug Dalissandro
Ex VP: Russell Oliver
**Ex VP:* John Pittenger
Sr VP: Tony Vermette
VP: Mike Donally

VP: Jeff Howe
VP: Mike Rosato
Ex Dir: Kevin Maroni
Ex Dir: Carl Redfield

CTCA
See CANCER TREATMENT CENTERS OF AMERICA INC

CTDI
See COMMUNICATIONS TEST DESIGN INC

CTE
See CUSTOM TRUCK & EQUIPMENT LLC

D-U-N-S 62-805-6272
CTECU
4800 Fournace Pl, Bellaire, TX 77401-2324
Tel (713) 432-0038 *Founded/Ownrshp* 2006
Sales NA *EMP* 9[E]
SIC 6062 State credit unions
Prin: Jackie Kapalski

CTF
See CALIFORNIA TRUSFRAME LLC

CTG
See COMPUTER TASK GROUP INC

CTG
See ALTA PROPERTIES INC

CTG
See CHANNEL TECHNOLOGIES GROUP LLC

CTI
See CORNET TECHNOLOGY INC

D-U-N-S 96-819-4394
CTI FOODS ACQUISITION LLC
22303 Highway 95, Wilder, ID 83676-5096
Tel (208) 482-7844 *Founded/Ownrshp* 2010
Sales 329.3MM[E] *EMP* 1,503
Accts Deloitte & Touche Llp Boise
SIC 2656 Frozen food containers: made from purchased material
CEO: Sam Rovit
**Ch Bd:* Robert Horowitz
**Pr:* Bobby Horowitz
**CFO:* Horst Sieben
**CFO:* Raymond Silcock
Ql Cn Mgr: Tristan Jennifer

D-U-N-S 80-812-8966 IMP
CTI FOODS HOLDING CO LLC
22303 Highway 95, Wilder, ID 83676-5096
Tel (208) 482-7844 *Founded/Ownrshp* 2013
Sales 587.3MM[E] *EMP* 1,500
SIC 2013 2032 2035 Sausages & other prepared meats; Soups & broths: canned, jarred, etc.; Beans, with meat: packaged in cans, jars, etc.; Beans, without meat: packaged in cans, jars, etc.; Pickles, sauces & salad dressings
CEO: Robert Horowitz
CFO: Raymond Silcock
Ql Cn Mgr: Karen Sanders
VP Sls: Jeff Grohs

D-U-N-S 02-533-1356 IMP
CTI FOODS LLC
CUSTOM FOOD PRODUCTS
(*Suby of* CTI FOODS HOLDING CO LLC) ★
59 Custom Foods Dr, Owingsville, KY 40360-8728
Tel (310) 637-0900 *Founded/Ownrshp* 2007
Sales 89.8MM[E] *EMP* 400
SIC 2013 Prepared beef products from purchased beef

CTI THE LARGEST IN THE WORLD
See CORPORATE TRADE INC

D-U-N-S 12-164-7663 IMP
CTI-SSI FOOD SERVICES LLC
(*Suby of* CTI FOODS HOLDING CO LLC) ★
22303 Highway 95, Wilder, ID 83676-5096
Tel (208) 602-0937 *Founded/Ownrshp* 2003
Sales 134.2MM[E] *EMP* 500
SIC 2013 Cooked meats from purchased meat; Frozen meats from purchased meat
CFO: Horst Sieben
VP Opers: Ben Badiola

D-U-N-S 03-946-1082
CTPARTNERS EXECUTIVE SEARCH INC
1166 Avenue Of The Amrcs, New York, NY 10036-2708
Tel (212) 588-3500 *Founded/Ownrshp* 1980
Sales 176.8MM *EMP* 631
SIC 7361 Employment agencies; Executive placement
CEO: David C Nocifora
Pt: Loran Kaminsky
Pt: Constance Kassouf
Pt: Carrie Pryor
Pt: Rick Sklarin
Mng Pt: Daniel Kaplan
CFO: William J Keneally
Prin: Mark Hexamer
Prin: Noah Schwarz
Board of Directors: Scott M Birnbaum, Michael C Feiner, Betsy L Morgan, Ronald C Parker, Thomas R Testwuide Sr

CTS
See CORE TECHNOLOGY SOLUTIONS LIMITED LIABILITY CO

CTS
See COMMUNICATION TECHNOLOGY SERVICES LLC

CTS
See CREATIVE TESTING SOLUTIONS

D-U-N-S 00-506-8515 IMP
▲ CTS CORP
2375 Cabot Dr, Lisle, IL 60532-3631
Tel (630) 577-8800 *Founded/Ownrshp* 1896
Sales 382.3MM *EMP* 2,883
Tkr Sym CTS *Exch* NYS
SIC 3678 3829 3676 3679 3674 Electronic connectors; Measuring & controlling devices; Aircraft & motor vehicle measurement equipment; Resistor networks; Electronic switches; Switches, stepping; Semiconductors & related devices
Ch Bd: Kieran M O'Sullivan
CFO: Ashish Agrawal
VP: Leslie Lauver
VP: Larry Lyng
VP: Lawrence J Lyng
VP: Luis Francisco Machado
VP: Rajeeb Nath
VP: John Sutter
Genl Mgr: Mario Saucedo
Snr Sftwr: Johnny Gao
DP Dir: Carla Brossman
Board of Directors: Walter S Catlow, Lawrence J Ciancia, Patricia K Collawn, Gordon Hunter, William S Johnson, Diana M Murphy, Robert A Profusek

D-U-N-S 11-447-3460 IMP
■ CTS ELECTRONIC COMPONENTS INC
(*Suby of* CTS CORP) ★
2375 Cabot Dr, Lisle, IL 60532-3631
Tel (630) 577-8800 *Founded/Ownrshp* 1998
Sales 185.4MM[E] *EMP* 1,200
SIC 3724 Research & development on aircraft engines & parts
CEO: Vinod Khilnani
**Pr:* Kieran M O Sullivan
Bd of Dir: Lawrence Ciancia
Bd of Dir: Robert Profusek
VP: Dave Holmes
Opers Mgr: Ken Trippett

D-U-N-S 07-881-9212
▲ CU BANCORP
15821 Ventura Blvd # 100, Encino, CA 91436-2915
Tel (818) 257-7700 *Founded/Ownrshp* 2011
Sales NA *EMP* 112[E]
Accts Rsm Us Llp Los Angeles Calif
Tkr Sym CUNB *Exch* NAS
SIC 6021 6712 National commercial banks; Bank holding companies
Ch Bd: David I Rainer
**Pr:* K Brian Horton
**CFO:* Karen A Schoenbaum
**Ex VP:* Robert E Sjogren
**Ex VP:* Anita Y Wolman

D-U-N-S 15-286-5184
CU COOPERATIVE SYSTEMS INC
CO-OP NETWORK
9692 Haven Ave, Rancho Cucamonga, CA 91730-5891
Tel (909) 948-2500 *Founded/Ownrshp* 1981
Sales NA *EMP* 650
SIC 6099 Automated teller machine (ATM) network; Electronic funds transfer network, including switching
CEO: Stanley Hollen
**Ch Bd:* Tom Sargent
Pr: Annette Bowlick
CFO: Kari Wilfong
**Treas:* John Bommarito
**Ex VP:* James Hanisch
**Ex VP:* Kimberly Hester
**Ex VP:* Eric Porter
Sr VP: Veronica Desrosiers
VP: Ritch Ellis
VP: Linda Pettit
VP: Jackie Scheuerlein
**VP:* Caroline Willard

D-U-N-S 00-323-2688
■ CUB FOODS INC
(*Suby of* SUPERVALU INC) ★
421 3rd St S, Stillwater, MN 55082-4955
Tel (651) 439-7200 *Founded/Ownrshp* 1971, 1968
Sales 768.1MM[E] *EMP* 10,000
SIC 5411

CUBBARD EXPRESS
See BUMGARNER OIL CO INC

D-U-N-S 92-615-3875
CUBE CORP
VT GRIFFIN
(*Suby of* VT SERVICES INC) ★
529 Viking Dr, Virginia Beach, VA 23452-7306
Tel (770) 952-1479 *Founded/Ownrshp* 2005
Sales 93.2MM[E] *EMP* 1,200
SIC 1542 Specialized public building contractors
Pr: Terry M Ryan
**CFO:* Kristin Gawlik
Sr VP: Fran Love
Board of Directors: Kent Bridges, Terry M Ryan

D-U-N-S 08-925-3280 IMP
CUBESMART
CUBESMART SELF STOR LOGISTICS
5 Old Lancaster Rd, Malvern, PA 19355-2132
Tel (610) 535-5000 *Founded/Ownrshp* 2004
Sales 444.5MM *EMP* 1,640
SIC 6798 Real estate investment trusts
Pr: Christopher P Marr
**Ch Bd:* William M Diefenderfer III
CFO: Timothy M Martin
Ofcr: Jeffrey P Foster
VP: Will Hall
VP: Guy Middlebrooks
Dir Risk M: Kathy McElwaine
Area Mgr: Jeannie Cox
Area Mgr: Melinda Lauber
Area Mgr: Kent McInnis
Dist Mgr: Tom Black
Board of Directors: Piero Bussani, John W Fain, Marianne M Keler, John F Remondi, Jeffrey F Rogatz, Deborah R Salzberg

D-U-N-S 78-861-7640
CUBESMART LP
(*Suby of* CUBESMART SELF STOR LOGISTICS) ★
5 Old Lancaster Rd, Malvern, PA 19355-2132
Tel (610) 535-5700 *Founded/Ownrshp* 1996
Sales 444.5MM *EMP* 1,640
SIC 4225 6798 General warehousing & storage; General warehousing; Warehousing, self-storage; Real estate investment trusts

CEO: Christopher P Marr
CFO: Timothy M Martin
VP: Doug Tyrell

CUBESMART SELF STOR LOGISTICS
See CUBESMART

CUBIC APPLICATIONS, INC.
See CUBIC GLOBAL DEFENSE INC

D-U-N-S 00-838-2293 IMP/EXP
▲ CUBIC CORP
9333 Balboa Ave, San Diego, CA 92123-1589
Tel (858) 277-6780 *Founded/Ownrshp* 1951
Sales 1.4MMM *EMP* 8,300
Tkr Sym CUB *Exch* NYS
SIC 3812 3699 7372 Defense systems & equipment; Flight simulators (training aids), electronic; Application computer software
Pr: Bradley H Feldmann
**Ch Bd:* Walter C Zable
CFO: John D Thomas
Treas: Gregory L Tanner
Ofcr: Darryl S Albertson
Ex VP: Roger Crow
Sr VP: Matthew J Cole
Sr VP: James R Edwards
Sr VP: Mark A Harrison
VP: Tom Richards
Mktg Dir: Michael Margro
Board of Directors: Bruce G Blakley, Edwin A Guiles, Janice M Hamby, Steven J Norris, Robert S Sullivan, John H Warner

D-U-N-S 18-606-4960 EXP
■ CUBIC DEFENSE APPLICATIONS INC
(*Suby of* CUBIC CORP) ★
9333 Balboa Ave, San Diego, CA 92123-1515
Tel (858) 277-6780 *Founded/Ownrshp* 1987
Sales 1.3MMM[E] *EMP* 7,800
SIC 3699 3663 3812 Flight simulators (training aids), electronic; Radio & TV communications equipment; Aircraft/aerospace flight instruments & guidance systems; Navigational systems & instruments; Defense systems & equipment; Search & detection systems & instruments
CEO: William J Toti
**CFO:* John D Thomas
**Sr VP:* James R Edwards
**Sr VP:* Mark A Harrison
Sr VP: Joseph Kellogg
**VP:* Norman R Bishop
VP: Randy Shepard
Prgrm Mgr: Jay Bass
Snr Sftwr: Karl Post
Snr Ntwrk: Jeff Cobb
IT Man: Rick Radomski

D-U-N-S 03-374-7226
■ CUBIC GLOBAL DEFENSE INC
(*Suby of* CUBIC CORP) ★
205 Van Buren St Ste 310, Herndon, VA 20170-5336
Tel (703) 821-8930 *Founded/Ownrshp* 2010
Sales 694.4MM[E] *EMP* 3,954
SIC 7379 7371 7373 8711 Computer related consulting services; Custom computer programming services; Computer integrated systems design; Engineering services
Pr: Bill Toti
**Treas:* Gregory L Tanner
Ex VP: David Gokey
**Ex VP:* Ruth Van Sickle
VP: Matthew Broderick
VP: John Etgen
**VP:* Julie M Maloy
**Genl Mgr:* Bill Trikas

D-U-N-S 80-231-6315 IMP
■ CUBIC GLOBAL DEFENSE INC
(*Suby of* CUBIC CORP) ★
9333 Balboa Ave, San Diego, CA 92123-1515
Tel (858) 277-6780 *Founded/Ownrshp* 1951
Sales 353.8MM[E] *EMP* 2,015
SIC 7629 Electrical repair shops
CEO: Jimmie L Balentine
**Pr:* Richard D Koon
**Treas:* Mark A Harrison
Sr VP: James Terry

D-U-N-S 86-862-4214
CUBIC GLOBAL DEFENSE INC
CUBIC APPLICATIONS, INC.
400 Union Ave Se Ste 300, Olympia, WA 98501-2061
Tel (360) 493-6275 *Founded/Ownrshp* 1994
Sales NA *EMP* 1,500
SIC 7373 8744 8711 7376 8748 8741

D-U-N-S 06-447-4778 IMP/EXP
■ CUBIC TRANSPORTATION SYSTEMS INC
(*Suby of* CUBIC CORP) ★
5650 Kearny Mesa Rd, San Diego, CA 92111-1305
Tel (858) 268-3100 *Founded/Ownrshp* 1950
Sales 177.5MM[E] *EMP* 1,011
SIC 3829 1731 Fare registers for street cars, buses, etc.; Toll booths, automatic; Telephone & telephone equipment installation
CEO: Stephen O Shewmaker
**Ch Bd:* Walter C Zable
**Sr VP:* Steve Purcell
VP: Rasheed Behrooznia
VP: Nicole Carroll
**VP:* Raymond De Kozan
VP: Nancy Gilbert
VP: Andy Jaswick
VP: Richard Koon
VP: Doug Morse
VP: Douglas Morse
VP Bus Dev: David Dekozan

D-U-N-S 80-839-4928 IMP/EXP
■ CUBIST PHARMACEUTICALS LLC
(*Suby of* MERCK & CO INC) ★
2000 Galloping Hill Rd, Kenilworth, NJ 07033-1310
Tel (908) 740-4000 *Founded/Ownrshp* 2015
Sales 277.1MM[E] *EMP* 873[E]
SIC 2834 Pharmaceutical preparations
CEO: Michael W Bonney
Owner: Kerry A Flynn
**Pr:* Robert Perez

*CFO: Michael J Tomsicek
Treas: Andrew Vanpraagh
Ofcr: Karen F Anderson
Ex VP: Julian M Davies
*Ex VP: Thomas Desrosier
Ex VP: Tom Desrosier
*Ex VP: Steven Gilman
Ex VP: Steven C Gilman
Ex VP: Clark Golestani
Sr VP: Rancis P Ally
Sr VP: Lindon M Fellows
Sr VP: Robert McCormack
Sr VP: Thomas Rollins
VP: David Lust
VP: David S Mantus
VP: Frederick B Oleson
Board of Directors: Kenneth M Bate, Mark H Corrigan, Jane E Henney, Nancy J Hutson, Alison Lawton, Kenneth J Martin, Martin H Soeters

D-U-N-S 07-928-7774
CUBS ACQUISITION CORP
(Suby of SOUTHWIRE CO LLC) ★
1 Southwire Dr, Carrollton, GA 30119-4400
Tel (770) 832-4242 Founded/Ownrshp 2013
Sales 62.9MM[E] EMP 1,750
SIC 3357 3661 3643 Coaxial cable, nonferrous; Telephone cords, jacks, adapters, etc.; Power line cable

CUDD ENERGY SERVICES
See CUDD PRESSURE CONTROL INC

D-U-N-S 03-930-4662 IMP
■ CUDD PRESSURE CONTROL INC
CUDD ENERGY SERVICES
(Suby of RPC INC) ★
2828 Tech Forest Blvd, The Woodlands, TX 77381-3907
Tel (832) 295-5555 Founded/Ownrshp 1984
Sales 773.3MM[E] EMP 1,100
SIC 1389 Oil field services
Pr: Richard Hubbell
CFO: Ben Palmer
Treas: Ben M Palmer
VP: Dan Edy
VP: Jim Sutton
VP: Clint Walker
Div Mgr: Jesse Carrasco
Off Admin: Treva McReynolds
IT Man: Earl Agan
IT Man: Nicole Kelly
Tech Mgr: David Farrell

D-U-N-S 00-157-3398
▲ CUI GLOBAL INC
20050 Sw 112th Ave, Tualatin, OR 97062-6894
Tel (503) 612-2300 Founded/Ownrshp 1998
Sales 86.6MM EMP 352[E]
Tkr Sym CUI Exch NAS
SIC 3824 8711 Mechanical & electromechanical counters & devices; Electrical or electronic engineering
Ch Bd: William J Clough
*COO: Matthew M McKenzie
CFO: Daniel N Ford
Genl Couns: William Clough
Board of Directors: Corey A Lambrecht, Joseph A Mills, Thomas A Price, Sean P Rooney, Paul D White

D-U-N-S 00-985-5925
CUIVRE RIVER ELECTRIC COOPERATIVE INC
1112 E Cherry St, Troy, MO 63379-1518
Tel (636) 528-8261 Founded/Ownrshp 1941
Sales 110.8MM EMP 138
Accts Botz Deal & Co Pc Saint Charl
SIC 4911 Distribution, electric power
CEO: Dan Brown
IT Man: Mary Clark
Tech Mgr: Anna Pudiwitr
Info Man: Steve Schomburg
Sfty Dirs: Dough Bagby
Opers Supe: Dan Alexander

CULINAIRE FLAIR
See SOUTHERN FOODS INC

D-U-N-S 82-506-1112
CULINAIRE INTERNATIONAL INC
8303 Elmbrook Dr, Dallas, TX 75247-4011
Tel (214) 754-1645 Founded/Ownrshp 1990
Sales 145.0MM[E] EMP 1,200
Accts Howard And Company Dallas Tx
SIC 8742 5812 8741 Restaurant & food services consultants; Caterers; Restaurant management
CEO: Richard N Gussoni
*Pr: Bill Thompson
*CFO: Buz Lafrano
*Sec: Charles P Lafrano
*Sr VP: David Wood
*VP: Kimberly Larsen
VP: James Munoz
VP: Tom Valentin
Exec: Ryan Nagby
Exec: Joey Villarreal
Genl Mgr: Chris Brazzle

D-U-N-S 83-467-9417
CULINART INC
175 Sunnyside Blvd # 200, Plainview, NY 11803-1521
Tel (516) 437-2700 Founded/Ownrshp 1994
Sales 112.7MM[E] EMP 2,000
SIC 5812 Contract food services
CEO: Joseph H Pacifico
*Pr: Thomas R Eich
CFO: Michael Pitkewicz
CFO: Vincent Stracquadanil
*CFO: Vincent Stracquadanio
Genl Mgr: Joe Ginder

CULINARY BEVERAGE
See ADVANCED BEVERAGE INC

D-U-N-S 06-963-4720 IMP
CULINARY HISPANIC FOODS INC
PRODUCTOS CHATA
805 Bow St, Chula Vista, CA 91914
Tel (619) 955-6101 Founded/Ownrshp 2011
Sales 1.0MM EMP 1,458
SIC 5149 Canned goods: fruit, vegetables, seafood, meats, etc.
CEO: Jorge Aguilar
*Prin: Carlos Machado

D-U-N-S 04-412-3420
CULINARY INSTITUTE OF AMERICA
CIA
1946 Campus Dr, Hyde Park, NY 12538-1499
Tel (845) 452-9600 Founded/Ownrshp 1946
Sales 165.4MM EMP 750
SIC 8221 Colleges & universities
CEO: Tim Ryan
Treas: John N Daly
Trst: Charlie Palmer
Ofcr: Michael Brown
Ofcr: Patricia Hamilton
Ofcr: Maura O'Meara
Ofcr: Brad Whitmore
*Sr VP: Charles A O'Mara
VP: Kevin Allan
VP: John Barkley
VP: Susan Dumont-Bengston
VP: Mark Erickson
VP: Victor Gielisse
VP: Maria Krupin
VP: Vance Peterson
VP: Michael Sperling
Exec: Michael Skibitcky
Exec: Brannon Soileau
Assoc Dir: Peg Graham

D-U-N-S 05-756-7158
▲ CULLEN/FROST BANKERS INC
100 W Houston St, San Antonio, TX 78205-1414
Tel (210) 220-4011 Founded/Ownrshp 1966
Sales NA EMP 4,211[E]
Accts Ernst & Young Llp San Antonio
Tkr Sym CFR Exch NYS
SIC 6021 6411 National commercial banks; National trust companies with deposits, commercial; Insurance agents, brokers & service
Ch Bd: Richard W Evans Jr
Pr: Alison Boyd
Pr: Jim Dixon
Pr: Phillip D Green
Pr: David Newman
Pr: Elizabeth Raggio
Pr: Danny Shutt
CFO: Jerry Salinas
Bd of Dir: James A Eckel
Ofcr: Richard Kardys
Ofcr: William L Perotti
Sr Ex VP: William Sirakos
Ex VP: Annette Alonzo
Ex VP: Louis Barton
Ex VP: Robert A Berman
Ex VP: Paul H Bracher
Ex VP: Carl Bush
Ex VP: Jim Crosby
Ex VP: Matt Henson
Ex VP: Cliff McCauley
Ex VP: Gary McKnight
Board of Directors: Richard M Kleberg III, R Denny Alexander, Charles W Matthews, Carlos Alvarez, Ida Clement Steen, Chris Avery, Horace Wilkins Jr, Royce S Caldwell, Jack Wood, Crawford H Edwards, Ruben M Escobedo, Patrick B Frost, David J Haemisegger, Karen E Jennings

D-U-N-S 02-428-6762 IMP/EXP
CULLIGAN INTERNATIONAL CO
(Suby of CULLIGAN INVESTMENTS SARL)
9399 W Higgins Rd # 1100, Rosemont, IL 60018-4940
Tel (847) 430-2800 Founded/Ownrshp 2013
Sales 748.0MM[E] EMP 2,000
SIC 3589 Sewage & water treatment equipment; Water treatment equipment, industrial; Water filters & softeners, household type
CEO: Scott G Clawson
Pr: David Rich
COO: Ruth McDonald
*CFO: Glen Ferguson
Sr VP: Marty Armstrong
VP: Allan Connolly
VP: Nancy Tauber
Admn Mgr: Troy Bergquist
Dept Mgr: Bob Curnell
Genl Mgr: Janet Shawcross
Off Mgr: Melissa Dutcher
Board of Directors: Nathan K Sleeper, David H Wasserman

D-U-N-S 02-288-6360
CULLIGAN SOFT WATER SERVICE CO
6030 Culligan Way, Minnetonka, MN 55345-5917
Tel (952) 933-7200 Founded/Ownrshp 1946
Sales 112.9MM[E] EMP 500
SIC 5999 7389 Water purification equipment; Water softener service
Pr: John P Packard
*Treas: Mark Forsberg
Genl Mgr: Mike Jablonski
Genl Mgr: Steve Wardyn
Sls Mgr: HB Riggs

D-U-N-S 08-576-8604
CULLMAN COUNTY BOARD OF EDUCATION
CULLMAN COUNTY COMM ON EDN
402 Arnold St Ne, Cullman, AL 35055-1964
Tel (256) 734-2933 Founded/Ownrshp 1900
Sales 51.2MM[E] EMP 1,200
SIC 8211 Public elementary & secondary schools

CULLMAN COUNTY COMM ON EDN
See CULLMAN COUNTY BOARD OF EDUCATION

D-U-N-S 07-979-8934
CULLMAN COUNTY SCHOOL DISTRICT
402 Arnold St Ne, Cullman, AL 35055-1964
Tel (256) 734-2933 Founded/Ownrshp 2015
Sales 39.8MM[E] EMP 1,321[E]
SIC 8211 Public elementary & secondary schools

D-U-N-S 00-690-0641
CULLMAN ELECTRIC COOPERATIVE
1749 Eva Rd Ne, Cullman, AL 35055-6031
Tel (256) 737-3200 Founded/Ownrshp 1936
Sales 109.3MM EMP 102[E]
Accts Henderson Hutcherson & Mccullo
SIC 4911 Distribution, electric power
CEO: Grady Smith
*VP: Jerry Weathersby

CULLMAN EMERGENCY MEDICAL SERV
See HEALTH CARE AUTHORITY OF CULLMAN COUNTY

D-U-N-S 07-211-1362
CULLMAN REGIONAL MEDICAL CENTER INC
SPORTS FRST FTNES WELLNESS CTR
1912 Al Highway 157, Cullman, AL 35058-0609
Tel (256) 737-2000 Founded/Ownrshp 1939
Sales 102.9MM EMP 1,015[E]
Accts Draffin & Tucker Llp Albany
SIC 8062 General medical & surgical hospitals
CEO: James Clements
*Pr: Jim Weidner
COO: Jeff Stanley
*CFO: Nesha Donaldson
*Ch: Todd McLeroy
*Treas: Greg Barksdale
*Bd of Dir: Roger Humphrey
*VP: Cheryl Bailey
*VP: Charna Brown
VP: Jim Miller
Dir Rad: Dwayne Denney

D-U-N-S 06-179-8369 IMP/EXP
▲ CULP INC
1823 Eastchester Dr, High Point, NC 27265-1558
Tel (336) 889-5161 Founded/Ownrshp 1972
Sales 312.8MM EMP 1,217[E]
Accts Grant Thornton Llp Raleigh N
Tkr Sym CFI Exch NYS
SIC 2221 Broadwoven fabric mills, manmade; Upholstery fabrics, manmade fiber & silk; Velvets, manmade fiber & silk
Pr: Franklin N Saxon
*Ch Bd: Robert G Culp III
CFO: Kenneth R Bowling
Sales Exec: Ron Edelman
Board of Directors: Patrick B Flavin, Fred A Jackson, Kenneth R Larson, Kenneth W McAllister

D-U-N-S 07-979-9710
CULPEPER COUNTY PUBLIC SCHOOLS
450 Radio Ln, Culpeper, VA 22701-1521
Tel (540) 825-3677 Founded/Ownrshp 2015
Sales 15.8MM[E] EMP 1,141[E]
SIC 8211 Public elementary & secondary schools
DP Exec: Robin Althoff
MIS Dir: Maria Weiss
Teacher Pr: Stacey Timmons

D-U-N-S 04-639-9234
CULVER EDUCATIONAL FOUNDATION
1300 Academy Rd, Culver, IN 46511-1234
Tel (574) 842-8222 Founded/Ownrshp 1894
Sales 95.8MM EMP 500
SIC 8699 Charitable organization

D-U-N-S 80-031-5889
CULWELL HEALTH INC
MERITCARE
4 Widgeon Dr, Pittsburgh, PA 15238-1125
Tel (412) 767-4103 Founded/Ownrshp 1991
Sales 9.2MM[E] EMP 1,200
SIC 8051 Skilled nursing care facilities
CEO: Thomas Konig
*COO: Jan A Beresford
*Treas: Michael Cervo

CUMANCO
See CUTTER MANAGEMENT CO

D-U-N-S 80-560-6571 EXP
CUMBERLAND COAL RESOURCES LP
(Suby of ALPHA NATURAL RESOURCES INC) ★
158 Portal Rd, Waynesburg, PA 15370-2330
Tel (724) 852-5845 Founded/Ownrshp 1993
Sales 112.3MM[E] EMP 569
SIC 1222 Bituminous coal-underground mining
CEO: Richard H Verheij
*VP: James Bryja

CUMBERLAND COUNTY BD EDUCATN
See CUMBERLAND COUNTY SCHOOLS

D-U-N-S 07-200-5705
CUMBERLAND COUNTY HOSPITAL SYSTEM INC
CAPE FEAR VALLEY HEALTH SYSTEM
1638 Owen Dr, Fayetteville, NC 28304-3424
Tel (910) 609-4000 Founded/Ownrshp 1964
Sales 858.0MM EMP 5,000
Accts Deloitte Tax Llp Raleigh Nc
SIC 8062 General medical & surgical hospitals
CEO: Michael Nagowski
*COO: Michael Harrington
*CFO: Sandra Williams
Treas: James Shearer
VP: Lynda Clark
VP: Mashonda Simmons
Exec: Faye Owens
Dir Case M: Cyndy Kern
Dir Rx: Amy Jones
Dir Rx: Thomas Nicholson
Ex Dir: Bart Fiser

D-U-N-S 04-005-0676
CUMBERLAND COUNTY SCHOOLS
CUMBERLAND COUNTY BD EDUCATN
2465 Gillespie St, Fayetteville, NC 28306-3053
Tel (910) 678-2300 Founded/Ownrshp 1903
Sales 413.0MM EMP 6,210
Accts Cherry Bekaert Llp Fayettevi
SIC 8211 Public elementary & secondary schools; Elementary school; Specialty education
Exec: Willie Thomas
Dir Risk M: Henry Smith
Ex Dir: Jane Barnes
DP Exec: Erika White
Dir IT: Jeff McAlister
Mtls Mgr: Margie See-Wai
Sales Exec: Michael Johnson
Pr Dir: Renarta Moyd
Psych: Donna Cooper-Graig
Psych: Leigh Faircloth
Psych: Johnny Jackson

D-U-N-S 00-792-0945
CUMBERLAND ELECTRIC MEMBERSHIP CORP (TN)
C E M C
1940 Madison St, Clarksville, TN 37043-6500
Tel (931) 645-2481 Founded/Ownrshp 1938
Sales 251.2MM EMP 206
SIC 4911

D-U-N-S 00-100-9828 IMP
CUMBERLAND FARMS INC (MA)
100 Crossing Blvd, Framingham, MA 01702-5401
Tel (508) 270-1400 Founded/Ownrshp 1938
Sales 1.4MMM[E] EMP 7,000
SIC 5411 5541 5172 2086 2051 2026 Convenience stores, chain; Filling stations, gasoline; Gasoline; Bottled & canned soft drinks; Bread, cake & related products; Fluid milk
Pr: ARI Haseotes
Pr: Harry J Brenner
CFO: Howard Rosenstein
Treas: Howard Rosenbean
VP: Stephanie Caldwell
VP: Jeff Cutting
VP: Dino DeThomas
VP: Ron Delsapio
VP: Dino Dethomas
VP: Lars Hilgen
VP: Lawrence Kennedy
VP: Raymond Leather
VP: Foster Macrides
VP: Laura Scott

CUMBERLAND INSURANCE GROUP
See CUMBERLAND MUTUAL FIRE INSURANCE CO (INC)

D-U-N-S 07-490-2479
CUMBERLAND MEDICAL CENTER INC
421 S Main St, Crossville, TN 38555-5031
Tel (931) 484-9511 Founded/Ownrshp 1967
Sales 78.9MM EMP 1,000
SIC 8062 General medical & surgical hospitals
Pr: Edwin S Anderson
*Ex VP: Ken Stephens
VP: Jinger Loggins
Dir Lab: Carolyn Smith
Dir Rad: Barbara Sanders
Dir Rx: David Kellogg
Chf Nrs Of: Perri Lynn Capps
Off Mgr: Sharon Bell
Mtls Dir: Thom Hassler
Secur Mgr: James Williams
Doctor: Oscar Mendez

D-U-N-S 02-007-0090
CUMBERLAND MUTUAL FIRE INSURANCE CO (INC)
CUMBERLAND INSURANCE GROUP
633 Shiloh Pike, Bridgeton, NJ 08302-1479
Tel (856) 451-4050 Founded/Ownrshp 1844
Sales NA EMP 195[E]
SIC 6331 6411 Fire, marine & casualty insurance & carriers; Burglary & theft insurance; Insurance agents, brokers & service
Pr: Paul J Ritter III
Ofcr: Matthew J Brasch
*Ex VP: Richard M Ritter
*Sr VP: Steve J Catranis
*Sr VP: Harold P Gunning
Sr VP: Harold Gunning
*Sr VP: Keith A Maxfield
Sr VP: Keith Maxfield
Sr VP: Rob Musick
Sr VP: Paul Ritter
VP: Lisa C Koelln
VP: Linda May
VP: Roby L Musick
VP: Patrick Padalik

D-U-N-S 00-165-0274 IMP/EXP
CUMBERLAND PACKING CORP
2 Cumberland St, Brooklyn, NY 11205-1000
Tel (718) 858-4200 Founded/Ownrshp 1946
Sales 150.0MM EMP 436
SIC 2869 Sweeteners, synthetic; Flavors or flavoring materials, synthetic
CEO: Steven Eisenstadt
CFO: Mary Carpenito
*CFO: Peter Marshall
Ex VP: Rob Bowen
Ex VP: Michael Briskey
*Sr VP: Ira Eisenstadt
VP: Steve Eisenstadt
Exec: Marilyn Jack
Exec: Maria L Wilborn
*Prin: Jeffrey Eisenstadt
QA Dir: Marie Mobarek

CUMBERLAND STONE
See WASCO INC

D-U-N-S 07-284-9946
CUMBERLAND VALLEY SCHOOL DISTRICT
6746 Carlisle Pike, Mechanicsburg, PA 17050-1711
Tel (717) 697-1167 Founded/Ownrshp 1952
Sales 107.1MM EMP 1,600
Accts Boyer & Ritter Camp Hill Pen
SIC 8211 Public elementary & secondary schools
IT Man: Barbara Fickes
Pr Dir: Tracy Panzer
Teacher Pr: Michelle Zettlemoyer
Psych: Garry Maus
HC Dir: Kathy Pollock

D-U-N-S 05-876-7641 IMP
CUMING CORP
(Suby of AMERIFORGE CORP) ★
225 Bodwell St, Avon, MA 02322-1121
Tel (508) 580-2660 Founded/Ownrshp 2011
Sales 113.0MM[E] EMP 239
SIC 3533 3679 Oil & gas field machinery; Microwave components
Pr: Mark Schlegel
*Treas: Perry Ewing
*VP: Lou Watkins

CIO: Robert Gallegher
S&M/VP: Michael Caputo

CUMMIN INDUSTRIAL DIVISION
See CUMMINS CENTRAL POWER LLC

D-U-N-S 00-231-3542
CUMMINGS ELECTRICAL LP (TX)
14900 Grand River Rd # 124, Fort Worth, TX 76155-2749
Tel (817) 355-5300 *Founded/Ownrshp* 1974, 2002
Sales 158.5MM[E] *EMP* 450
SIC 1731 General electrical contractor
Pr: Tim Cummings
**Ex VP:* Chris Lasater
VP: Jerry Beighey
**VP:* Scott Gross
**VP:* Todd Ruddell
**VP:* Scott Smith
Off Mgr: Nicole Karaali
Snr Ntwrk: Alex Sanchez
Dir IT: Daniel Johnson
IT Man: Michele Cote
IT Man: Clay Hazlewood

D-U-N-S 61-032-2836
CUMMINGS FOUNDATION INC
200 W Cummings Park, Woburn, MA 01801-6333
Tel (781) 935-8000 *Founded/Ownrshp* 1990
Sales 174.1MM *EMP* 295
SIC 8361 6512 Geriatric residential care; Nonresidential building operators
Ex Dir: Joel Swets
**Pr:* William S Cummings
**CFO:* William Grant
**Treas:* Joyce M Cummings

CUMMINGS GENERAL CONTRACTORS
See JAMES A CUMMINGS INC

D-U-N-S 00-506-9760 IMP/EXP
CUMMINS - ALLISON CORP
852 Feehanville Dr, Mount Prospect, IL 60056-6001
Tel (847) 759-6403 *Founded/Ownrshp* 1887, 1921
Sales 383.3MM[E] *EMP* 900
SIC 3578 3519 Automatic teller machines (ATM); Internal combustion engines
Ch Bd: William J Jones
**Pr:* Douglas U Mennie
CFO: John Diedrich
**CFO:* Robert Jordan
**Ch:* John E Jones
**Ex VP:* James Stearns
**Sr VP:* Tim Minor
VP: Carol Moore
**Dir Surg:* Tom Conroy
**Dir Surg:* Mark Tankle
Corp Couns: Jeffrey G Knoll

CUMMINS BRIDGEWAY
See K & S PROPERTY INC

D-U-N-S 12-753-9034 EXP
■ **CUMMINS BRIDGEWAY LLC**
(*Suby of* CUMMINS INC) ★
21810 Clessie Ct, New Hudson, MI 48165-8573
Tel (248) 573-1600 *Founded/Ownrshp* 2002
Sales 219.5MM[E] *EMP* 650
SIC 5084 7538 3519 Engines & parts, diesel; Diesel engine repair: automotive; Internal combustion engines
VP: Joseph Bernot
VP: Nathan Kent
VP: Norberto Nunes
VP: Rachita Pandey
VP: Paul Rauch
IT Man: Jeff Ayers
Mtls Mgr: Richelle Hoobler
Opers Mgr: Charlene Ackerson
Ql Cn Mgr: Abhishek Satham
Mktg Dir: Karen Boll
Sls Mgr: Michael Murry

D-U-N-S 08-957-3588 IMP
■ **CUMMINS CENTRAL POWER LLC**
CUMMIN INDUSTRIAL DIVISION
(*Suby of* CUMMINS INC) ★
10088 S 136th St, Omaha, NE 68138-3902
Tel (402) 551-7678 *Founded/Ownrshp* 2005
Sales 118.6MM[E] *EMP* 435
SIC 5084 7538 5999 3519 Engines & parts, diesel; Diesel engine repair: automotive; Engines & parts, air-cooled; Internal combustion engines
**Pr:* Rafa Dorador
VP: Donald W Baldwin
**Prin:* James Czyz
CTO: Jim Czyz
Opers Mgr: Dale Koenig

D-U-N-S 00-605-2245
■ **CUMMINS CROSSPOINT LLC**
(*Suby of* CUMMINS INC) ★
2601 Fortune Cir E 300c, Indianapolis, IN 46241-5548
Tel (317) 243-7979 *Founded/Ownrshp* 1981, 2006
Sales 139.0MM[E] *EMP* 600
SIC 5084 7538 5063 3519 Engines & parts, diesel; Diesel engine repair: automotive; Generators; Internal combustion engines
Pr: R David Smitson
**VP:* Chris Harlow
VP: Mike Patterson
**VP:* John R Smitson
IT Man: Terri Coles
Opers Mgr: Sarah Jarrett

D-U-N-S 00-700-1969 IMP
■ **CUMMINS CROSSPOINT LLC**
(*Suby of* CUMMINS INC) ★
2601 Fortune Cir E Ste 30, Indianapolis, IN 46241-5548
Tel (317) 243-7979 *Founded/Ownrshp* 2006
Sales 104.2MM[E] *EMP* 330
SIC 5084 7538 3519 Engines & parts, diesel; Diesel engine repair: automotive; Internal combustion engines
Pr: Vipul Tandon
**Pr:* P Jack Apple
**Pr:* Dave Smitson
**VP:* Greg Gilmore
**VP:* Jay Goad
**VP:* John Smitson
**VP:* L A Willinger

CUMMINS DIESEL SALES
See CUMMINS NPOWER LLC

D-U-N-S 04-293-9959 IMP/EXP
■ **CUMMINS FILTRATION INC**
FLEETGUARD
(*Suby of* CUMMINS INC) ★
26 Century Blvd Ste 500, Nashville, TN 37214-3683
Tel (615) 367-0040 *Founded/Ownrshp* 1973
Sales 875.7MM[E] *EMP* 3,005
SIC 3714 Filters: oil, fuel & air, motor vehicle
Pr: Joseph Saoud
VP: Vikrant Aggarwal
VP: Pamela Carter
VP: Melanie Hendricks
VP: Sam Hires
VP: Daryl Johnston
VP: John Swaim
Exec: Maria Bailey
Ex Dir: Michael Breedan
Mng Dir: Peter Stone
Genl Mgr: Prashanth RAO

D-U-N-S 00-641-5160 IMP/EXP
▲ **CUMMINS INC**
500 Jackson St, Columbus, IN 47201-6258
Tel (812) 377-5000 *Founded/Ownrshp* 1919
Sales 19.1MMM *EMP* 55,200[E]
Accts Pricewaterhousecoopers Llp In
Tkr Sym CMI *Exch* NYS
SIC 3519 3714 3694 3621 Internal combustion engines; Engines, diesel & semi-diesel or dual-fuel; Diesel engine rebuilding; Motor vehicle parts & accessories; Motor vehicle engines & parts; Crankshaft assemblies, motor vehicle; Filters: oil, fuel & air, motor vehicle; Engine electrical equipment; Generator sets: gasoline, diesel or dual-fuel
Ch Bd: N Thomas Linebarger
Pr: Dave J Crompton
Pr: Tracy A Embree
Pr: Thaddeaus B Ewald
Pr: Richard J Freeland
Pr: Antonio Leitao
Pr: Livingston L Satterthwaite
CFO: Patrick J Ward
Treas: Donald G Jackson
Bd of Dir: Ian Kohen
Ofcr: Jill E Cook
Ofcr: Marya M Rose
VP: Sherry A Aaholm
VP: Sharon R Barner
VP: Merritt Becker
VP: Abhay Bhagwat
VP: Lillia Bromley
VP: Bruce Carver
VP: Steven M Chapman
VP: Pam Donohoe-Duncan
VP: Wayne Eckerle
Board of Directors: Bruno V Di Leo Allen, Robert J Bernhard, Franklin R Chang-Diaz, Stephen B Dobbs, Robert K Herdman, Alexis M Herman, Thomas J Lynch, William I Miller, Georgia R Nelson

D-U-N-S 05-379-4533 IMP/EXP
■ **CUMMINS MID-SOUTH LLC**
(*Suby of* CUMMINS INC) ★
3770 S Perkins Rd, Memphis, TN 38118-6328
Tel (901) 577-0600 *Founded/Ownrshp* 1999
Sales 169.9MM[E] *EMP* 510
SIC 5999 5013

D-U-N-S 00-621-3177 IMP
■ **CUMMINS NPOWER LLC**
CUMMINS DIESEL SALES
(*Suby of* CUMMINS INC) ★
1600 Buerkle Rd, White Bear Lake, MN 55110-5217
Tel (800) 642-0085 *Founded/Ownrshp* 1945, 1996
Sales 143.7MM[E] *EMP* 450
SIC 5084 5063 7538 3519 Engines & parts, diesel; Generators; Diesel engine repair: automotive; Internal combustion engines
Pr: James Andrews
**VP:* Jeff Boelsen
**VP:* Russell Sheaffer

D-U-N-S 78-722-3296 IMP
■ **CUMMINS PACIFIC LLC**
(*Suby of* CUMMINS INC) ★
1939 Deere Ave, Irvine, CA 92606-4818
Tel (949) 253-6000 *Founded/Ownrshp* 2002
Sales 98.2MM[E] *EMP* 300
SIC 3519 5063 7538 Internal combustion engines; Generators; General automotive repair shops
Pr: Mark Yragui
Genl Mgr: Jennifer Vuong
S&M/VP: Jonathan Evans
Sls Mgr: Scott Ruhlen

D-U-N-S 05-341-7515 IMP/EXP
■ **CUMMINS POWER GENERATION INC**
(*Suby of* CUMMINS INC) ★
1400 73rd Ave Ne, Minneapolis, MN 55432-3702
Tel (763) 574-5000 *Founded/Ownrshp* 1986
Sales 531.3MM[E] *EMP* 1,800
SIC 3621 3519 Generators & sets, electric; Gasoline engines
Pr: Tony Satterthwaite
Pr: Jack Edwards
VP: Ronald Moore
Exec: Donna Meier
Prin: Ray Makepeace
Genl Mgr: Trevor Passmore
IT Man: Luiz Lopes
Tech Mgr: John Weippert
Sftwr Eng: Praveen Radhakrishnan
Mtls Mgr: Mike Laciskey
Sfty Mgr: Mark Dhennin
Board of Directors: F Joseph Loughrey, Rick Mills

D-U-N-S 00-232-1420 IMP/EXP
■ **CUMMINS POWER SYSTEMS LLC**
(*Suby of* CUMMINS INC) ★
2727 Ford Rd, Bristol, PA 19007-6805
Tel (215) 785-6005 *Founded/Ownrshp* 1937, 1994
Sales 376.5MM *EMP* 770
SIC 5084 5063 7538 7629 3519 Engines & parts, diesel; Generators; Diesel engine repair: automotive; Generator repair; Internal combustion engines
Pr: Kelley D Tate
**CFO:* James J Schrack
**VP:* John Casey
**VP:* Ellen A Diorio
**VP:* Karl Gontkof
**VP:* Jay Tee White
**Prin:* Robert Hanson
**Genl Mgr:* Gary Pakosky
Off Mgr: DOT Calhoun
Sfty Mgr: Bob Gayle
Sfty Mgr: Aaron Morris

D-U-N-S 88-349-8305
■ **CUMMINS ROCKY MOUNTAIN LLC**
(*Suby of* CUMMINS INC) ★
390 Interlocken Cres # 200, Broomfield, CO 80021-8051
Tel (800) 927-7201 *Founded/Ownrshp* 2001
Sales 279.4MM[E] *EMP* 690
SIC 5084 3519 Engines & parts, diesel; Internal combustion engines

D-U-N-S 15-348-0058 IMP/EXP
■ **CUMMINS SOUTHERN PLAINS LLC**
(*Suby of* CUMMINS INC) ★
600 N Watson Rd, Arlington, TX 76011-5377
Tel (817) 640-6801 *Founded/Ownrshp* 2002
Sales 321.8MM[E] *EMP* 498
SIC 5084 3519 Engines & parts, diesel; Internal combustion engines
Pr: Raj Menon
**CFO:* Chuck Funai
Genl Mgr: Kelly Gorham
Sls Mgr: Chris O'Neal

D-U-N-S 00-886-0298
CUMMINS-WAGNER CO INC
10901 Pump House Rd, Annapolis Junction, MD 20701-1206
Tel (410) 792-4230 *Founded/Ownrshp* 1985
Sales 83.3MM *EMP* 200
SIC 5046

D-U-N-S 11-109-1286
■ **CUMULUS BROADCASTING LLC**
(*Suby of* CUMULUS MEDIA INC) ★
3280 Peachtree Rd Nw Ste, Atlanta, GA 30305
Tel (404) 949-0700 *Founded/Ownrshp* 1997
Sales 83.3MM[E] *EMP* 250
SIC 4832 Radio broadcasting stations
Pr: William M Bungeroth
**Treas:* Richard Bonick

D-U-N-S 07-888-9448
■ **CUMULUS MEDIA HOLDINGS INC**
(*Suby of* CUMULUS MEDIA INC) ★
3280 Peachtree Rd Ne # 2300, Atlanta, GA 30305-2455
Tel (404) 949-0700 *Founded/Ownrshp* 2013
Sales 216.2MM[E] *EMP* 5,618
SIC 4832 Radio broadcasting stations; Radio broadcasting stations, music format
Pr: Mary G Berner

D-U-N-S 01-964-1997
▲ **CUMULUS MEDIA INC**
3280 Peachtree Rd Ne Ne2300, Atlanta, GA 30305-2430
Tel (404) 949-0700 *Founded/Ownrshp* 1997
Sales 1.1MMM *EMP* 5,618[E]
Tkr Sym CMLS *Exch* NGS
SIC 4832 Radio broadcasting stations; Radio broadcasting stations, music format
Pr: Mary G Berner
**Ch Bd:* Jeffrey A Marcus
CFO: Joseph P Hannan
**V Ch Bd:* Lewis W Dickey Jr
Ex VP: Suzanne M Grimes
Sr VP: Richard S Denning
Board of Directors: Brian Cassidy, Ralph B Everett, Alexis Glick, David M Tolley

CUNA MUTUAL GROUP
See CMFG LIFE INSURANCE CO

D-U-N-S 01-174-4232
CUNA MUTUAL GROUP
(*Suby of* CUNA MUTUAL GROUP) ★
5910 Mineral Point Rd, Madison, WI 53705-4498
Tel (608) 238-5851 *Founded/Ownrshp* 1935
Sales NA *EMP* 4,000
SIC 6331 6311 6351 6411 7515 Property damage insurance; Fire, marine & casualty insurance & carriers; Life insurance; Credit & other financial responsibility insurance; Insurance agents, brokers & service; Passenger car leasing
CEO: Jeffrey H Post
Pr: Steve S Bosack
CFO: Alastair Shore
Bd of Dir: Wood M Miller
Sr VP: Paul Chong
Sr VP: David Cry
Sr VP: Ken Otsuka
Sr VP: David Wade
Dir IT: Rick Good
Dir IT: Ken McCullough
Dir IT: Dan Mica

D-U-N-S 01-160-4915
CUNA MUTUAL INSURANCE AGENCY INC
(*Suby of* CUNA MUTUAL GROUP) ★
5910 Mineral Point Rd, Madison, WI 53705-4498
Tel (608) 238-5851 *Founded/Ownrshp* 1974
Sales NA *EMP* 110
SIC 6411 Insurance brokers
Pr: Jeff Post
VP: Thomas Merfeld
Dir Risk M: Kevin Sisler
Dir IT: Steven Haroldson

D-U-N-S 00-694-2338
CUNA MUTUAL LIFE INSURANCE CO
(*Suby of* CUNA MUTUAL GROUP) ★
2000 Heritage Way, Waverly, IA 50677-9208
Tel (319) 352-4090 *Founded/Ownrshp* 1879, 1896
Sales NA *EMP* 1,000
Accts Deloitte & Touche Llp Chicago
SIC 6411 6321 8742 Life insurance agents; Accident & health insurance; Banking & finance consultant
Pr: Jeff Post
**Treas:* Jeffrey D Holley
Exec: Mark McNish
**Prin:* Daniel E Meylink Sr
Div Mgr: Rachel Miller
Dir IT: Nancy Osterman

D-U-N-S 06-897-9863
CUNNINGHAM LINDSEY US INC
(*Suby of* CUNNINGHAM LINDSEY US INC) ★
405 State Highway 121 Byp A100, Lewisville, TX 75067-8107
Tel (214) 488-5139 *Founded/Ownrshp* 2007
Sales NA *EMP* 400
SIC 6411 Insurance claim adjusters, not employed by insurance company; Advisory services, insurance
Pr: James Sirard
VP: David A Rodgers
Exec: Jimmy Smith
**Genl Couns:* Daniel Schulz

D-U-N-S 07-869-4701
CUNNINGHAM LINDSEY US INC
3030 N Rocky Point Dr W # 530, Rocky Point, FL 33607-5905
Tel (813) 830-7100 *Founded/Ownrshp* 2012
Sales 1.4MMM[E] *EMP* 7,000[E]
SIC 6719 Personal holding companies, except banks
Ch: Richard Ward
**Pr:* Philippe Bes
**COO:* David Radcliff
CFO: Nicholas Hinton
**CFO:* Ed Mullen
VP: Shawn Burger
VP: Roger Eiler
QA Dir: Ron Myers
Opers Mgr: Steph Taylor
Sls&Mrk Ex: Anneka Phakey
Snr Mgr: Richard Barker

D-U-N-S 13-161-9637
CUPERTINO ELECTRIC INC
CEI
1132 N 7th St, San Jose, CA 95112-4438
Tel (408) 808-8000 *Founded/Ownrshp* 2000
Sales 686.7MM[E] *EMP* 2,500
SIC 1731 General electrical contractor
Pr: John Boncher
**COO:* Tom Schott
CFO: Marjorie Goss
**CFO:* Bill Slakey
**Chf Cred:* John Curcio
**VP:* Paul Aggarwal
VP: Eileen Nelson
**VP:* John Sales
VP: Steve Schumer
Exec: Donna Kaneko
Dir Risk M: Laura Latshaw

D-U-N-S 07-047-3350
CUPERTINO UNION SCHOOL DISTRICT
10301 Vista Dr, Cupertino, CA 95014-2040
Tel (408) 252-3000 *Founded/Ownrshp* 1930
Sales 79.8MM[E] *EMP* 1,250
SIC 8211 Public elementary & secondary schools
Pr Dir: Jeremy Nishihara
Schl Brd P: Phyllis Vogel
Teacher Pr: Doug Baughn

CURANT HEALTH GEORGA
See CURANT INC

D-U-N-S 04-549-7132
CURANT HEALTH GEORGIA LLC
(*Suby of* CURANT HEALTH GEORGA) ★
200 Technology Ct Se B, Smyrna, GA 30082-5201
Tel (770) 437-8040 *Founded/Ownrshp* 2000
Sales 90.0MM *EMP* 60
SIC 5122 Drugs & drug proprietaries
Pr: Patrick Dunham
Mng Pt: Pankaj Patel
Cert Phar: Melanie Donaldson

D-U-N-S 00-310-6312
CURANT INC (FL)
CURANT HEALTH GEORGA
11001 Roosevelt Blvd N # 1400, Saint Petersburg, FL 33716-2338
Tel (770) 437-8040 *Founded/Ownrshp* 2000
Sales 143.0MM *EMP* 113[E]
SIC 5912 Drug stores
CEO: Patrick Dunham
**Ex VP:* Marc Oconnor
**Ex VP:* Scott Zepp

D-U-N-S 80-642-7709
■ **CURASCRIPT INC**
(*Suby of* EXPRESS SCRIPTS INC) ★
6272 Lee Vista Blvd, Orlando, FL 32822-5148
Tel (407) 852-4903 *Founded/Ownrshp* 2004
Sales 684.9MM[E] *EMP* 2,500
SIC 5122 Drugs, proprietaries & sundries
CEO: Dom Meffe
**Pr:* Gayle Johnston
**Pr:* Patrick R McNamee
**COO:* Don Howard
**CFO:* Claudia Griffith
**CFO:* Steve Jenson
**Treas:* Kelley Elliott
**VP:* Keith Ebling
VP: Chai Gadde
VP: Senaida Hamidovic
**VP:* Chris Houston

CURASCRIPT SPECIALTY DIST
See PRIORITY HEALTHCARE DISTRIBUTION INC

CURATE SNACKS
See ABBOTT LABORATORIES

CURATORS OF THE UNIVERSITY MO
See UNIVERSITY OF MISSOURI SYSTEM

D-U-N-S 00-211-4411 IMP/EXP
CURBELL INC (NY)
7 Cobham Dr, Orchard Park, NY 14127-4180
Tel (716) 667-3377 *Founded/Ownrshp* 1947
Sales 190.5MM *EMP* 445
Accts Dopkins & Company Llp Buffal
SIC 5162 3669 3842 Plastics materials & basic shapes; Plastics sheets & rods; Plastics materials; Plastics film; Intercommunication systems, electric; Surgical appliances & supplies
Pr: Thomas E Leone
V Ch: Tina Sabuda
Pr: William Brennan
Pr: Scott Palka
**CFO:* Arthur J Weibel
**V Ch Bd:* Christine L Sabuda
**Ofcr:* Christopher Schenk
VP: Liz Grimes
Genl Mgr: Douglas Rockwood
IT Man: Robert Lorenz
Mtls Mgr: Larry Pennell

D-U-N-S 79-645-1024
CURBELL PLASTICS INC
(*Suby of* CURBELL INC) ★
7 Cobham Dr, Orchard Park, NY 14127-4180
Tel (716) 667-3377 *Founded/Ownrshp* 2006
Sales 140.1MM *EMP* 221
Accts Dopkins & Company Llp Buffal
SIC 5162 Plastics materials & basic shapes; Plastics sheets & rods; Plastics materials; Plastics film
Ch Bd: Thomas E Leone
**Pr:* Gerald Helbig
**CFO:* Arthur Weibel
**V Ch Bd:* Christine L Sabuda
Assoc Dir: Patrick Hatfield
Mfg Mgr: Angelo Miranda
Opers Mgr: Lisa Percival
Manager: Jeff Rogers
Sls Mgr: Karl Bargmann
Sales Asso: Daniel Clarke
Sales Asso: Angela Colon

D-U-N-S 18-061-6674
CURLYS FOODS INC
(*Suby of* MORRELL JOHN & CO) ★
5201 Eden Ave Ste 370, Minneapolis, MN 55436-2350
Tel (612) 920-3400 *Founded/Ownrshp* 1997
Sales 22.0MM[E] *EMP* 1,000
SIC 2011 Meat packing plants
Pr: John M Pauley
**VP:* Robert Brady

D-U-N-S 13-071-0812
■ **CUROTTO-CAN LLC**
(*Suby of* HEIL ENVIRONMENTAL) ★
4301 Gault Ave N, Fort Payne, AL 35967-8121
Tel (256) 845-8359 *Founded/Ownrshp* 2003
Sales 147.1MM[E] *EMP* 1,523[E]
SIC 4953 Refuse collection & disposal services
CFO: Darren Bird
Sls Dir: Frank Kennedy

D-U-N-S 04-390-7005 IMP/EXP
CURRAN GROUP INC
286 Memorial Ct, Crystal Lake, IL 60014-6277
Tel (815) 455-5100 *Founded/Ownrshp* 1998
Sales 558.9MM[E] *EMP* 2,200[E]
SIC 1799 3253 1611 Welding on site; Wall tile, ceramic; Highway & street paving contractor
Pr: Timothy Curran
CFO: Todd Gierke
Treas: Jordan Wolf

D-U-N-S 01-643-0828
■ **CURRENEX INC**
(*Suby of* STATE STREET BANK AND TRUST CO) ★
1230 Ave Of, New York, NY 10020
Tel (212) 340-1780 *Founded/Ownrshp* 1999
Sales NA *EMP* 500
SIC 6099 Foreign currency exchange
CEO: Clifford Lewis
COO: Chip Lowry
**CFO:* Rodney Yoshida
Ofcr: Joseph Turco
VP: Brian Gibson
VP: Uri Lerman
VP: Chad Parris
Mng Dir: Sean Cleary
Mng Dir: Jeff Cooperstein
Snr Ntwrk: Gary Guan
CTO: Harsha Bhat

D-U-N-S 82-841-3703
CURRENT BUILDERS CONSTRUCTION SERVICES INC
2251 Blount Rd, Pompano Beach, FL 33069-5114
Tel (954) 977-4211 *Founded/Ownrshp* 2004
Sales 148.5MM *EMP* 90[E]
Accts Brunt Sweeney Matz Pa Ho
SIC 1522 1542 Residential construction; Nonresidential construction
CEO: Charles P Reid
**Pr:* Michael C Taylor
**CFO:* Frederick A Colandreo
**Sr VP:* Henry Huisman

D-U-N-S 12-275-0979
CURRIER MCCABE & ASSOCIATES INC
C M A CONSULTING SERVICES
700 Troy Schenectady Rd, Latham, NY 12110-2460
Tel (518) 783-9003 *Founded/Ownrshp* 1984
Sales 94.5MM[E] *EMP* 375[E]
SIC 7371 7379 Computer software development; Computer related consulting services
CEO: Kay Stafford
VP: Peter Chynoweth
VP: Ron Cuneo
VP: Gary Davis
VP: Liz Fitz
**VP:* Ken Romanski
VP: Bob Samson
VP: Steve Zizzi
IT Man: Raj Sinha
Sftwr Eng: Gunasekaran Eswaran
VP Sls: Chynoweth Peter

CURRIES COMPANY INC.
See AADG INC

D-U-N-S 07-381-6597
CURRY COLLEGE
1071 Blue Hill Ave, Milton, MA 02186-2395
Tel (617) 333-0500 *Founded/Ownrshp* 1879
Sales 119.9MM *EMP* 335
Accts Grant Thornton Llp Boston Ma
SIC 8221 College, except junior
Pr: Kenneth K Quigley
CFO: Gerard Linskey
**CFO:* Richard F Sullivan Jr
Sr Cor Off: Christina Broderick
Ofcr: Irina Deane-Costa
Genl Mgr: Kevin Burchill
Genl Mgr: Keith Neal
CIO: Dennis Thibeault
Netwrk Mgr: Kerry Antunes

D-U-N-S 00-610-3394 IMP
CURT G JOA INC
100 Crocker Ave, Sheboygan Falls, WI 53085-1141
Tel (920) 467-6136 *Founded/Ownrshp* 1932
Sales 115.2MM[E] *EMP* 415
Accts Schecnk Sc Sheboygan Wi
SIC 3554 Paper industries machinery; Die cutting & stamping machinery, paper converting
Pr: Gene F Kiela II
**CFO:* Michael J Brookins
VP: Robert Andrews
MIS Dir: Patricia Wagner
Board of Directors: Curt G Joa III, Timothy Kenney, Donald Lammers, Bea J Miley

D-U-N-S 80-998-8975 IMP/EXP
CURT MANUFACTURING LLC
(*Suby of* AUDAX GROUP LP) ★
6208 Industrial Dr, Eau Claire, WI 54701-8493
Tel (715) 831-8713 *Founded/Ownrshp* 2014
Sales 140.5MM[E] *EMP* 300
SIC 3799 Trailer hitches
CEO: Gregory Hooks
CFO: Scott Morrison
VP: David Calloway
VP: David Troup

D-U-N-S 00-330-3369
CURTIS 1000 INC
(*Suby of* C G I) ★
1725 Breckinridge Park, Duluth, GA 30096
Tel (770) 925-4500 *Founded/Ownrshp* 2002
Sales 200.7MM[E] *EMP* 1,000
SIC 2761 2759 2791 2789 2752 Computer forms, manifold or continuous; Business forms: printing; Typesetting; Bookbinding & related work; Commercial printing, lithographic
Pr: Steve Geiger
CFO: Glenn E Kidd
VP: Steve Lawrence
VP: Larry Wagner
Exec: Pl Cobert
Dir Bus: Susan Akins
Dir Bus: Bob Danehy
Dir IT: Ozie Adams
Mktg Mgr: Ryan Morris
Sls Mgr: Tom McCleery
Sls Mgr: Mark Meyer

D-U-N-S 08-027-1869
CURTIS C GUNN INC (DE)
GUNN AUTOMOTIVE GROUP
227 Broadway St, San Antonio, TX 78205-1923
Tel (210) 472-2501 *Founded/Ownrshp* 1980
Sales 192.0MM[E] *EMP* 810
SIC 5511 6531 Automobiles, new & used; Pickups, new & used; Real estate leasing & rentals
Ch Bd: Curtis C Gunn Jr
**CFO:* Kelly Collins
**Treas:* Lee Ellen Gunn
**Ex VP:* Paul M Young
**VP:* Wesley Burke
**VP:* Michael Kane
**VP:* Chris Karcher
Sales Asso: Paul Anderson
Sales Asso: Minnie Talamantez

D-U-N-S 04-768-0392 IMP/EXP
CURTIS CIRCULATION CO
(*Suby of* LAGARDERE TRAVEL RETAIL)
730 River Rd Ste 2, New Milford, NJ 07646-9901
Tel (201) 634-7400 *Founded/Ownrshp* 1986
Sales 114.0MM[E] *EMP* 325
SIC 5192 Magazines
Ch Bd: Joseph M Walsh
**Pr:* Robert Castardi
Ex VP: Dennis Porti
Exec: Jaime Carey
Netwrk Mgr: Harold Kaplan
VP Opers: Scott Largey
Opers Mgr: Glenn Battiste
Natl Sales: Pamela Redig
Mktg Dir: Richard Trummer
Mktg Mgr: Tom Lipski

D-U-N-S 00-202-0477 IMP
CURTIS INSTRUMENTS INC (NY)
CURTIS PMC DIVISION
200 Kisco Ave, Mount Kisco, NY 10549-1400
Tel (914) 666-2971 *Founded/Ownrshp* 1960
Sales 289.1MM[E] *EMP* 1,000
SIC 3825 3824 3629 Elapsed time meters, electronic; Speed indicators & recorders, vehicle; Electronic generation equipment
Ch Bd: Stuart Marwell
**CFO:* Frank Fiumara CPA
VP: Mark Ankers
**VP:* Jim Byrnes
VP: Erland Hagman
**VP:* Dennis Houghton
**VP:* David Mathews
VP: Anthony McCoy
VP: Richard McFarlane
**VP:* Steven Post
**VP:* Richard Sadler
**VP:* Steve Tomafiewicz
**VP:* Steve Waite
**Exec:* Anne Papaelias
Exec: Laura Wilhelm

D-U-N-S 01-364-5551 IMP
CURTIS LUMBER CO INC
885 State Route 67, Ballston Spa, NY 12020-3689
Tel (518) 885-5311 *Founded/Ownrshp* 1948
Sales 185.3MM *EMP* 560
Accts Bonadio & Co Llp Albany Ne
SIC 5211 Lumber & other building materials; Home centers
Ch Bd: Jay S Curtis
**CFO:* Sandy Zelka
**Sec:* James Delaney
**VP:* Richard Colyer
**VP:* Jon Hallgren
Brnch Mgr: Darin Taber
Genl Mgr: Frank Pudney
Genl Mgr: Joe Sanchez
Off Mgr: Lori Dubois
Store Mgr: Bob Eakin
Store Mgr: Jessica Sears

CURTIS PMC DIVISION
See CURTIS INSTRUMENTS INC

D-U-N-S 13-160-3599 IMP
CURTIS-MARUYASU AMERICA INC
(*Suby of* MARUYASU INDUSTRIES CO.,LTD.)
665 Metts Dr, Lebanon, KY 40033-1909
Tel (270) 692-2109 *Founded/Ownrshp* 1984
Sales 154.6MM[E] *EMP* 601
SIC 3714 3498 Fuel systems & parts, motor vehicle; Motor vehicle brake systems & parts; Fabricated pipe & fittings
CEO: Takeji Yazawa
**Pr:* Doug Vyverberg
**VP:* Satoshi Hattori
**VP:* David Sparks
Dir IT: Mike Huff
Sfty Dirs: Jay Batt
Sls Mgr: Kristin Dykstra

CURTISS-WRIGHT
See METAL IMPROVEMENT CO LLC

D-U-N-S 01-188-0077 IMP
■ **CURTISS-WRIGHT CONTROLS INC**
(*Suby of* CURTISS-WRIGHT CORP) ★
15801 Brixham Hill Ave # 200, Charlotte, NC 28277-4792
Tel (704) 869-4600 *Founded/Ownrshp* 1945
Sales 707.0MM[E] *EMP* 2,880
SIC 3728 Aircraft assemblies, subassemblies & parts
Pr: Tom Quinly
**VP:* Brian Freeman
Genl Mgr: Mark Baker
Genl Mgr: Gorky Chin
Genl Mgr: David Dietz
Dir IT: Michelle Stalder
IT Man: Paul Bubendorf
Mktg Dir: Chris Thomson
Sls Mgr: Andrew Clarke
Sls Mgr: Cliff Durling
Sls Mgr: Mervyn Reese

D-U-N-S 00-201-3522 IMP/EXP
▲ **CURTISS-WRIGHT CORP**
13925 Balntyn Corp Pl, Charlotte, NC 28277-2704
Tel (704) 869-4600 *Founded/Ownrshp* 1929
Sales 2.2MMM *EMP* 8,400
Accts Deloitte & Touche Llp Parsip
Tkr Sym CW *Exch* NYS
SIC 3491 3621 3812 Industrial valves; Motors & generators; Aircraft control systems, electronic
Pr: David C Adams
Pr: David J Linton
COO: Thomas P Quinly
CFO: Glenn E Tynan
Treas: Harry S Jakubowitz
Sr VP: Parker B Miller III
VP: Michael J Denton
VP: Jay McMurray
CTO: Johnston Julao
IT Man: Blechinger Todd
Netwrk Eng: Tod Herchenroether
Board of Directors: Dean M Flatt, S Marce Fuller, Allen A Kozinski, John R Myers, John B Nathman, Robert J Rivet, William W Sihler, Albert E Smith, Stuart W Thorn

D-U-N-S 12-611-1348 IMP
■ **CURTISS-WRIGHT ELECTRO-MECHANICAL CORP**
ELECTRO-MECHANICAL DIVISION
(*Suby of* CURTISS-WRIGHT CORP) ★
1000 Wright Way, Cheswick, PA 15024-1008
Tel (724) 275-5000 *Founded/Ownrshp* 2002
Sales 205.3MM[E] *EMP* 900
SIC 3561 3621 3511 Pumps & pumping equipment; Motors & generators; Turbines & turbine generator sets
Ch: Martin R Benante
**Pr:* David C Linton
**CFO:* Yvonne Rupert
VP: Terri Marts
**VP:* Glenn E Tynan
**Genl Mgr:* James Drake
QA Dir: Larry Gilliam
Opers Mgr: Keith Hensler

D-U-N-S 00-203-4056 IMP/EXP
■ **CURTISS-WRIGHT FLOW CONTROL CORP** (NY)
TARGET ROCK
(*Suby of* CURTISS-WRIGHT CORP) ★
1966 Broadhollow Rd Ste E, Farmingdale, NY 11735-1726
Tel (631) 293-3800 *Founded/Ownrshp* 1950
Sales 455.2MM[E] *EMP* 1,942
SIC 3491 3494 Industrial valves; Valves & pipe fittings
Ch Bd: Martin Benante
**Pr:* David Linton
**COO:* David C Adams
**VP:* Joseph Callaghan
**VP:* Greg Hempfling
Exec: Gina Fortunato
Exec: Raymond Kou
QA Dir: Pedro Estrada
Dir IT: Ed Angelo

Ql Cn Mgr: John Debonis
Ql Cn Mgr: Ed Schultz
Board of Directors: David Lasky

CURTZE FOOD SERVICE
See CA CURTZE CO

D-U-N-S 07-833-8768
CURVATURE LLC
(*Suby of* NHR NEWCO HOLDINGS LLC) ★
6500 Hollister Ave # 210, Goleta, CA 93117-3011
Tel (805) 964-9975 *Founded/Ownrshp* 2001
Sales 198.0MM[E] *EMP* 501[E]
SIC 4813
CEO: Mike Sheldon
COO: Terry Stone
CFO: Andrea Greene
Ch: Chuck Sheldon
Ofcr: Jesse Newton
Sr VP: Michael Lodato
Sr VP: Steven McIntosh
VP: Mark Kelly
VP Bus Dev: Jeff Zanardi
Exec: Ezra Stern
Mng Dir: Juan Obispo

CUSD 200
See COMMUNITY UNIT SCHOOL DISTRICT 200

CUSHING CAMPUS
See TAS-CGSMC INC

D-U-N-S 07-096-4841
CUSHMAN & WAKEFIELD HOLDINGS INC
1290 Ave Of The Americas, New York, NY 10104-6178
Tel (212) 841-7500 *Founded/Ownrshp* 1998, 2015
Sales 5.0MMM *EMP* 43,000
SIC 6531 8742 8732 Real estate brokers & agents; Real estate agent, commercial; Real estate managers; Real estate consultant; Market analysis, business & economic research
Ch Bd: Brett White
V Ch: Lou Cushman
Pr: Tod Lickerman
CFO: Duncan Palmer
CFO: Roxane Russel
Ofcr: John Santora
Ex VP: Robert Lowe
Sr VP: Robert Miller
Ex Dir: Andy May
Off Mgr: Patricia Nayer
CIO: Adam Stanley

D-U-N-S 00-179-3470
CUSHMAN & WAKEFIELD INC (NY)
(*Suby of* CUSHMAN & WAKEFIELD HOLDINGS INC) ★
77 W Wacker Dr Ste 1800, Chicago, IL 60601-1714
Tel (312) 424-8000 *Founded/Ownrshp* 1917
Sales 2.5MMM[E] *EMP* 12,655
SIC 6531 8742 8732 Real estate brokers & agents; Real estate agent, commercial; Real estate managers; Real estate consultant; Market analysis, business & economic research
CEO: Brett White
Ch Bd: Edward C Forst
Pr: Tod Lickerman
Pr: John Santora
CEO: Carlo Sant' Albano
CEO: Paul Bedborough
CEO: Chris Lowery
CEO: John C Santora
CEO: Michael Thompson
CEO: James M Underhill
CEO: Jill Underhill
CEO: Sanjay Verma
COO: Franklin L Lavin
COO: Stacey Wallach
CFO: Michael Bartolotta
CFO: Duncan J Palmer
CFO: John Quinn
Treas: Francis P Clerkin
Bd of Dir: Kristoffer Kalmbach
Bd of Dir: Scott Kirkpatrick
Assoc VP: Nancy Carter

D-U-N-S 00-398-5280
CUSHMAN & WAKEFIELD OF CALIFORNIA INC (CA)
(*Suby of* CUSHMAN & WAKEFIELD INC) ★
1 Maritime Plz Ste 900, San Francisco, CA 94111-3412
Tel (408) 275-6730 *Founded/Ownrshp* 1887, 1990
Sales 259.8MM[E] *EMP* 9,000
SIC 6531 Real estate brokers & agents; Real estate agent, commercial; Real estate managers; Appraiser, real estate
CEO: Joseph Stettinius Jr
COO: Anthony Sirianni
Ex VP: Robert Ballard
Ex VP: Robert Rudin
Sr VP: Todd Anderson
Sr VP: Russ Stai
VP: Robert Alperin
VP: Eric Duncanson
VP: Rob Ippolito
VP: Marc Trevisan
Exec: Joe Cook
Assoc Dir: Sean Austin
Assoc Dir: Kenneth Delvillar
Assoc Dir: Jodie Dostal
Assoc Dir: Michael Dyer
Assoc Dir: Caroline Fleischer
Assoc Dir: Andrew Kahn
Assoc Dir: Sean Kern
Assoc Dir: Robert Mangino
Dir Bus: Robin Addams

D-U-N-S 07-890-1014 IMP
CUSTARD INSURANCE ADJUSTERS INC (GA)
CIA
4875 Avalon Ridge Pkwy, Peachtree Corners, GA 30071-4712
Tel (770) 263-6800 *Founded/Ownrshp* 1962
Sales NA *EMP* 700
SIC 6411 Insurance claim adjusters, not employed by insurance company
Pr: Rick Lindille
**CEO:* Robert Soby
**Treas:* Pam State

Ex VP: David White
Sr VP: Michael J Arendt
Sr VP: Shane Carney
Sr VP: Michael Reed
VP: Teresa McKenzie
Rgnl Mgr: Mark Pytel
Brnch Mgr: Scott Barrows
Brnch Mgr: Davis Kathleen

CUSTOM ALLOY LIGHT METALS
See CUSTOM ALLOY SALES INC

D-U-N-S 06-383-2455 IMP/EXP
CUSTOM ALLOY SALES INC
CUSTOM ALLOY LIGHT METALS
13191 Crssrds Pkwy N 37, City of Industry, CA 91746
Tel (626) 369-3641 *Founded/Ownrshp* 1969
Sales 150.0MM *EMP* 132
SIC 3341 5051 Aluminum smelting & refining (secondary); Zinc
CEO: Brandon J Cox
**Pr:* Kenneth J Cox
**CFO:* Tim Chisum
**VP:* Nicholas Drakos

CUSTOM AUTO EQP SPECIALISTS
See APOLLO OIL LLC

CUSTOM AUTO FINISH
See DNIS DLN ATOPRK&TRCK CNTR

D-U-N-S 04-168-8284 IMP/EXP
CUSTOM BUILDING PRODUCTS INC
C-CURE
7711 Center Ave Fl 5, Huntington Beach, CA 92647-3069
Tel (800) 272-8786 *Founded/Ownrshp* 2005
Sales 342.4MM^E *EMP* 1,200
SIC 2891 Adhesives & sealants
CEO: Don Devine
**Pr:* Thomas R Peck Jr
COO: Mike Bilek
CFO: Bill Klein
Assoc VP: A Ignacio
VP: John McMullen
**VP:* Marc Powell
Off Mgr: Kriss Harris
CIO: Kien Trinh
Opers Mgr: Virginia Milella
Sls&Mrk Ex: Diane Stewart

CUSTOM CARTAGE
See CUSTOM COMPANIES INC

D-U-N-S 14-752-4185
CUSTOM COMPANIES INC
CUSTOM CARTAGE
317 W Lake St, Northlake, IL 60164-2433
Tel (708) 344-5555 *Founded/Ownrshp* 1986
Sales 112.2MM *EMP* 350
SIC 4731 4214 Transportation agents & brokers; Freight forwarding; Local trucking with storage
Pr: Perry Mandera
CFO: John Donnelly
CFO: Clete Janik
**CFO:* Tom Roz
Ex VP: Rocky Caylor
Ex VP: Dorland Henderson
VP: Thomas Boyle
VP: Eric Pocious
MIS Dir: Dan Mason
Trfc Dir: John Valente
Sls Mgr: Joe Klikas

D-U-N-S 14-606-6209 IMP
CUSTOM COMPUTER CABLES OF AMERICA INC
2901 Summit Ave Ste 400, Plano, TX 75074-7468
Tel (972) 638-9309 *Founded/Ownrshp* 1999
Sales 207.7MM^E *EMP* 300
SIC 5051 3357 Cable, wire; Communication wire
Pr: Jay Chenault
**CFO:* Olga Tellef
CFO: Olga Telles
**Ex VP:* Kenneth Atkins
**VP:* Robbie Chenault
**VP:* Vince Schlueter

D-U-N-S 09-753-3350
CUSTOM COMPUTER SPECIALISTS INC
EDUCATIONAL TECH ASSOC DIV
70 Suffolk Ct Ste 100, Hauppauge, NY 11788-3744
Tel (800) 598-8989 *Founded/Ownrshp* 1979
Sales 124.8MM^E *EMP* 300
SIC 7379 7373 7378 Computer related consulting services; Computer integrated systems design; Computer maintenance & repair
Ch Bd: Gregory G Galdi
**Pr:* Alan Lacher
**CEO:* John McSweeney
CFO: Rich Kohlberg
**CFO:* Richard Kolberg
CFO: Richard J Kolberg
**CFO:* Paul Sebetic
**Ex VP:* Michael Davis
**Sr VP:* Dennis Callagy
Sr VP: Donald Gracy
**VP:* Linda Miller Galdi
VP: Michael Waldman
Exec: Melissa Demrest
Exec: Dottie Hickey
Exec: Mike Schmutz
Exec: Ru Thomesen
Exec: Matthew Zurawel
Dir Bus: Kenneth Wygand

D-U-N-S 05-637-0869 IMP/EXP
CUSTOM CRETE INC
CUSTOM STONE SUPPLY
(*Suby of* OLDCASTLE INC) ★
2624 Joe Field Rd, Dallas, TX 75229-4601
Tel (972) 243-4466 *Founded/Ownrshp* 2000
Sales 149.6MM^E *EMP* 320
SIC 5032 3273 Building stone; Ready-mixed concrete
Pr: Steve Bond
VP: Keith Schatzle
Sls Mgr: Kevin Nerrie

D-U-N-S 06-291-7179
CUSTOM FOOD GROUP LP
12221 Merit Dr Ste 975, Dallas, TX 75251-2236
Tel (214) 273-0500 *Founded/Ownrshp* 1998
Sales 126.6MM^E *EMP* 750
SIC 5962 Food vending machines
Pt: Chuck Stephenson
Pt: Stan Simms
Exec: Nancy Wincon

CUSTOM FOOD PRODUCTS
See CTI FOODS LLC

CUSTOM FOODS DIVISION
See CUSTOM FOODS OF AMERICA INC

D-U-N-S 10-205-9615
CUSTOM FOODS OF AMERICA INC
CUSTOM FOODS DIVISION
3600 Pleasant Ridge Rd, Knoxville, TN 37921-1737
Tel (865) 525-0401 *Founded/Ownrshp* 1982
Sales 85.0MM^E *EMP* 300
SIC 2038 Soups, frozen
Pr: Graham Hunter
**Pr:* Roger Edens
**VP:* Michael Britton
**VP:* Craig Snow
**VP:* Tony Williams

D-U-N-S 17-759-9784 IMP
CUSTOM SENSORS & TECHNOLOGIES INC
C S T
14401 Princeton Ave, Moorpark, CA 93021-1483
Tel (805) 523-2000 *Founded/Ownrshp* 1997
Sales 639.2MM^E *EMP* 5,268^E
SIC 3679 Electronic circuits
Pr: Martha Sullivan
VP: Horst Obermeier
VP: Tae Rhee
VP: Alison Roelke
Prgrm Mgr: Frances Ressler
Mfg Mgr: Francisco Diaz
VP Sls: Andrew Dyer
Manager: Randy White
Sls Mgr: Jim Brahney

CUSTOM SHIPPING SOLUTIONS
See TRANSPORTATION INSIGHT LLC

D-U-N-S 12-257-4598
CUSTOM STEEL PROCESSING INC
1001 College St, Madison, IL 62060-1084
Tel (618) 876-7276 *Founded/Ownrshp* 2002
Sales 112.3MM *EMP* 50
SIC 5051 Metals service centers & offices
Pr: Pat Notestine
Sls Mgr: Gary McNulty

CUSTOM STONE SUPPLY
See CUSTOM CRETE INC

D-U-N-S 94-218-9507 IMP/EXP
CUSTOM TRUCK & EQUIPMENT LLC
CTE
(*Suby of* UTILITY ONE SOURCE LP) ★
7701 Independence Ave, Kansas City, MO 64125-1300
Tel (816) 241-4888 *Founded/Ownrshp* 2002
Sales 88.9MM^E *EMP* 210
SIC 3713 Specialty motor vehicle bodies
IT Man: Carolyn Ross

CUSTOM WINDOW SYSTEMS
See CWS HOLDING CO LLC

D-U-N-S 15-476-6703 IMP
CUSTOM WINDOW SYSTEMS INC
(*Suby of* CUSTOM WINDOW SYSTEMS) ★
1900 Sw 44th Ave, Ocala, FL 34474-8743
Tel (352) 368-6922 *Founded/Ownrshp* 2014
Sales 114.7MM^E *EMP* 600
SIC 3442 Window & door frames
CEO: Greg Schorr
**CFO:* Matthew Shaw
VP: Patricia Champeau

D-U-N-S 06-994-1151 IMP/EXP
CUSTOM-PAK INC
86 16th Ave N, Clinton, IA 52732-2864
Tel (563) 659-2100 *Founded/Ownrshp* 1974
Sales 207.0MM^E *EMP* 700
SIC 3089 Blow molded finished plastic products; Plastic processing
Pr: Jeffrey S Anderson
Treas: Louise M Laurent
VP: Jeff Anderson
VP: Steven P Guidebeck
VP: Boni Hugunin
VP: Paul Nugent
VP: Mark Rutenbeck
VP: Jim Wiese
Prin: Dick Olsen
IT Man: Mike Grinnall
IT Man: Jack Morgan

D-U-N-S 96-676-5828 EXP
CUSTOM-PAK INC
LIPMAN PRODUCE
315 New Market Rd E, Immokalee, FL 34142-3509
Tel (239) 657-4421 *Founded/Ownrshp* 1994
Sales 187.0MM^E *EMP* 350
SIC 0161 Vegetables & melons; Tomato farm
Pr: Kent Shoemaker
**Pr:* Sheryl Weisinger
**VP:* Darren Micelle
Exec: Joanna Hazel
Genl Mgr: Michael Beasley
Genl Mgr: Ben Branscomb
Opers Mgr: Bob Lamere
Plnt Mgr: Juan Vila
Prd Mgr: Jeff Bennett
Sales Asso: Joseph Staniszewski

D-U-N-S 03-924-1119
▲ CUSTOMERS BANCORP INC
1015 Penn Ave Ste 103, Wyomissing, PA 19610-2006
Tel (610) 933-2000 *Founded/Ownrshp* 2011
Sales NA *EMP* 517^E
Tkr Sym CUBI *Exch* NYS
SIC 6022 State commercial banks
Ch Bd: Jay S Sidhu
Pr: Richard A Ehst
Pr: Glenn A Hedde
CFO: Robert E Wahlman
Ofcr: Steven J Issa

D-U-N-S 09-096-5765
CUSTOMERS BANK
99 Bridge St, Phoenixville, PA 19460-3411
Tel (610) 933-2000 *Founded/Ownrshp* 1997
Sales NA *EMP* 189
SIC 6022 State commercial banks
Ch Bd: Jay S Sidhu
**Pr:* Richard A Ehst
**Pr:* James W McKeighan III
CFO: Thomas Brugger
**CFO:* Robert Wahlman
**Ofcr:* Steven J Issa
**Ofcr:* Robert White
**Ex VP:* Glenn A Hedde
**Ex VP:* James D Hogan
**Ex VP:* Thomas Jastrem
Ex VP: Christopher McGowan
Ex VP: Tim Romig
**Ex VP:* Warren Taylor
Sr VP: Jeff Dickey
Sr VP: Roddrick E Lynch
Sr VP: Anthony P MAI
Sr VP: Joseph Schupp
VP: James B Daley
VP: Richard Ehst
VP: Richard Hood
VP: Ann Steadman

D-U-N-S 86-860-2108 EXP
CUSTOMINK LLC
CUSTOMINK.COM
2910 District Ave Ste 100, Fairfax, VA 22031-2283
Tel (703) 891-2273 *Founded/Ownrshp* 2000
Sales 133.2MM^E *EMP* 500
SIC 2759 5699 5941 Screen printing; Customized clothing & apparel; Specialty sport supplies
Pr: Marc Katz
CFO: Kevin Cheetham
Sr Ex VP: Sean Murphy
Sftwr Eng: Steven Arsena
Sftwr Eng: Ryan Billings
Sftwr Eng: Karle Durante
Sftwr Eng: John B Hall
Sftwr Eng: Mark Jarrell
Sftwr Eng: Andrew Kolas
Sftwr Eng: Christopher Murphy
Sftwr Eng: Rj Pittman

CUSTOMINK.COM
See CUSTOMINK LLC

D-U-N-S 13-323-3531 EXP
CUSTOMIZED DISTRIBUTION LLC
5545 Shawland Rd, Jacksonville, FL 32254-1673
Tel (904) 783-0848 *Founded/Ownrshp* 2000
Sales 237.9MM^E *EMP* 120
Accts Faucett Taylor And Associates
SIC 5141 7319 Food brokers; Sample distribution
**CFO:* August Wingo
Opers Mgr: Roderick Frierson

D-U-N-S 01-557-2548
CUSTOMIZED DISTRIBUTION SERVICES INC
C D S
20 Harry Shupe Blvd, Wharton, NJ 07885-1646
Tel (973) 366-5090 *Founded/Ownrshp* 1995
Sales 104.0MM^E *EMP* 450
SIC 4225 General warehousing & storage
Pr: John Sanacore
CFO: Robert Colletti
**VP:* Adalberto Guerra
**VP:* David Turo
IT Man: Mark Miller
Opers Mgr: Angelo Laporta

D-U-N-S 96-817-4594
CUTCHALL MANAGEMENT CO INC
LO LO CHICKEN AND WAFFLES
13305 Birch Dr Ste 201, Omaha, NE 68164-5451
Tel (402) 558-3333 *Founded/Ownrshp* 2010
Sales 31.6MM^E *EMP* 1,200
SIC 5812 American restaurant
Pr: Greg Cutchall
**CFO:* Bill Nervig
VP: Michelle Diede

D-U-N-S 00-210-0618 IMP
CUTCO CORP
1116 E State St, Olean, NY 14760-3814
Tel (716) 372-3111 *Founded/Ownrshp* 1948
Sales 158.3MM^E *EMP* 835
SIC 5963 3421 Houseware sales, house-to-house; Cutlery
Ch Bd: James E Stitt
**CFO:* Brent Driscoll
CFO: Mark D Heister
Ex VP: Amar Dav
**Ex VP:* James M Stitt
**Ex VP:* John W Whelpley
Store Mgr: Nicholas Boercker
Sfty Dirs: Don Sutton
Ql Cn Mgr: CJ Mackey
VP Sls: Mark A George
Mktg Mgr: Danyle Magiera

D-U-N-S 04-107-1643 IMP
▲ CUTERA INC
3240 Bayshore Blvd, Brisbane, CA 94005-1021
Tel (415) 657-5500 *Founded/Ownrshp* 1998
Sales 94.7MM *EMP* 262^E
Tkr Sym CUTR *Exch* NGS
SIC 3845 Electromedical equipment; Laser systems & equipment, medical
CEO: Ronald J Santilli
**Ch Bd:* J Daniel Plants
COO: Barry Stadler
Ex VP: Jonathan Pearson
VP: Michael Karavitis
Exec: Stuart Mohr
Exec: Chris West
Area Mgr: David Khodayar
Sls Mgr: Kyle Shapero
Snr Mgr: Robert Naidu
Board of Directors: David B Apfelberg, Gregory A Barrett, David A Gollnick, Timothy J O'shea, James A Reinstein, Clint Severson, Jerry P Widman

D-U-N-S 93-252-3863 IMP
CUTLER-HAMMER DE PUERTO RICO INC
(*Suby of* EATON CORP) ★
Carr 2 Km 67 6 Santana In St Ca, Arecibo, PR 00612
Tel (787) 881-3640 *Founded/Ownrshp* 1994
Sales 284.0MM^E *EMP* 3,000
SIC 3613 Switchgear & switchboard apparatus
Pr: Alexander M Cutler

D-U-N-S 95-854-7432 IMP/EXP
CUTRALE CITRUS JUICES USA INC
(*Suby of* SUCOCITRICO CUTRALE LTDA)
602 Mckean St, Auburndale, FL 33823-4070
Tel (863) 528-0396 *Founded/Ownrshp* 1996
Sales 173.1MM^E *EMP* 1,000
SIC 2037 Fruit juices
Pr: Hugh Thompson III
**CFO:* Joe Birge
**Treas:* Jose L Cutrale
Dir Lab: Alez Souza
IT Man: Bill Angerson
Opers Mgr: Orestes Luciano
Plnt Mgr: Reinaldo Kabyashi
Plnt Mgr: Renaldo Kobayashi
Plnt Mgr: Daniel Marques

D-U-N-S 01-068-7866
CUTTER AVIATION
CUTTER TRAVEL
2802 E Old Tower Rd, Phoenix, AZ 85034-6007
Tel (602) 273-1237 *Founded/Ownrshp* 1998
Sales 102.8MM^E *EMP* 250
SIC 5599 5088 4522 5172 4581 Aircraft, self-propelled; Aircraft instruments, equipment or parts; Aircraft & parts; Flying charter service; Aircraft fueling services; Aircraft cleaning & janitorial service
Pr: Will Cutter
CFO: Steve Price

D-U-N-S 07-726-1519
CUTTER MANAGEMENT CO
CUMANCO
1100 Alakea St Steth2, Honolulu, HI 96814
Tel (808) 529-2000 *Founded/Ownrshp* 1970
Sales 176.4MM^E *EMP* 642
SIC 5511 7515 Automobiles, new & used; Passenger car leasing
Pr: Nick Cutter
**CFO:* Herman Jones

CUTTER TRAVEL
See CUTTER AVIATION

CUW
See CONCORDIA UNIVERSITY WISCONSIN INC

D-U-N-S 06-890-7765
CUYAHOGA COMMUNITY COLLEGE
700 Carnegie Ave, Cleveland, OH 44115-2878
Tel (216) 987-6000 *Founded/Ownrshp* 1963
Sales 90.2MM^E *EMP* 1,900
SIC 8222 Community college
Pr: Jerry S Thornton
**Ex VP:* Craig Fulton
**Ex VP:* Jacquelyn A Joseph
Ex VP: Clara Kirk
**Ex VP:* Eric Radtkey
VP: Jennifer Spielvogel
Exec: Michael K Benz
Prgrm Mgr: Lisa Rear-Lassen
Genl Couns: Rebecca R McMahon

D-U-N-S 01-084-9131
CUYAHOGA FALLS GENERAL HOSPITAL
1900 23rd St, Cuyahoga Falls, OH 44223-1404
Tel (330) 971-7000 *Founded/Ownrshp* 2009
Sales 93.8MM^E *EMP* 825^E
SIC 8062

CUYAHOGA FALLS NATATORIUM
See CITY OF CUYAHOGA FALLS

D-U-N-S 07-774-8028
CUYAHOGA METROPOLITAN HOUSING AUTHORITY
CMHA
8120 Kinsman Rd, Cleveland, OH 44104-4310
Tel (216) 348-5000 *Founded/Ownrshp* 1934
Sales NA *EMP* 1,065
Accts James G Zupka Cpa Inc
SIC 9532
CEO: Jeffery K Patterson

D-U-N-S 01-085-5393
CUYAHOGA VALLEY CHRISTIAN ACADEMY ENDOWMENT FUND
CVCA
4687 Wyoga Lake Rd, Cuyahoga Falls, OH 44224-1011
Tel (330) 929-0575 *Founded/Ownrshp* 1968
Sales 514.2M *EMP* 1,150
SIC 8211 Private senior high school; Private junior high school
Pr: Roger Taylor
CFO: Jim Gaul
Bd of Dir: Maribeth Newland

D-U-N-S 07-648-6620
CUYUNA RANGE HOSPITAL INC
CUYUNA REGIONAL MEDICAL CENTER
320 E Main St, Crosby, MN 56441-1645
Tel (218) 546-7000 *Founded/Ownrshp* 1957
Sales 100.4MM *EMP* 900
Accts Mcgladery Llp Duluth Minneso
SIC 8062 8051 General medical & surgical hospitals; Hospital, medical school affiliation; Skilled nursing care facilities
CEO: John Solheim
Pr: Marcella Hanson
CFO: Kyle Bauer
Dir Risk M: Wendi Andersohn
Dir Lab: Russ Miner
CTO: Lisa Hennen-Pupy
Dir IT: Ken Mackley
Sfty Mgr: Rob Almendinger
Mktg Mgr: Theresa Sullivan

Doctor: Linda Distad
Doctor: Paul Severson

CUYUNA REGIONAL MEDICAL CENTER
See CUYUNA RANGE HOSPITAL INC

D-U-N-S 10-738-7156 EXP
CV HOLDINGS LLC
1030 Riverfront Ctr, Amsterdam, NY 12010-4616
Tel (518) 627-0051 *Founded/Ownrshp* 2000
Sales 127.3MM^E *EMP* 400
SIC 5162 3089 Plastics products; Injection molded finished plastic products
CEO: Robert Abrams

D-U-N-S 60-990-4305 IMP/EXP
CV INDUSTRIES INC
CENTURY FURNITURE INDUSTRIES
401 11th St Nw, Hickory, NC 28601-4750
Tel (828) 328-1851 *Founded/Ownrshp* 1973
Sales 415.1MM^E *EMP* 2,100
SIC 2511 2512 2211 Wood household furniture; Upholstered household furniture; Upholstery fabrics, cotton
Pr: A Alex Shuford II
**Ch Bd:* Harley F Shuford Jr
**CFO:* Brandon Hucks
**Sec:* Richard L Reese
**VP:* Nancy S Dowdy
VP: Roger Jones
VP: Corner Wear
IT Man: Michelle Roll
Web Dev: Joe Kelly
QC Dir: Terry Moore

CVA
See CRYOGENIC VESSEL ALTERNATIVES INC

D-U-N-S 60-589-7123
▲ CVB FINANCIAL CORP
701 N Haven Ave Ste 350, Ontario, CA 91764-4920
Tel (909) 980-4030 *Founded/Ownrshp* 1981
Sales NA *EMP* 804^E
Tkr Sym CVBF *Exch* NGS
SIC 6022 State commercial banks
Pr: Christopher D Myers
**Ch Bd:* Raymond V O'Brien III
CFO: E Allen Nicholson
**V Ch Bd:* George A Borba Jr
Chf Cred: David F Farnsworth

D-U-N-S 14-075-5864
CVC HOLDING CO INC
28 Industrial Way, Rochester, NH 03867-4296
Tel (603) 332-2080 *Founded/Ownrshp* 2003
Sales 146.7MM *EMP* 330
Accts Maloney & Kennedy Pllc
SIC 5984 Propane gas, bottled
Pr: Charles V Clement III
**CFO:* Peter Gowell
**VP:* Brian Boudreau
**VP:* Denis Gagne

CVCA
See CUYAHOGA VALLEY CHRISTIAN ACADEMY ENDOWMENT FUND

D-U-N-S 12-904-3142 IMP
CVE TECHNOLOGY GROUP INC
915 Enterprise Blvd, Allen, TX 75013-8003
Tel (972) 424-6606 *Founded/Ownrshp* 2002
Sales 227.1MM^E *EMP* 700^E
SIC 3663 Radio & TV communications equipment
Pr: Edward Cho
**Pr:* Kyu Taek Cho

D-U-N-S 12-548-0892
CVENT INC
1765 Grnsboro Stn Pl Fl 7, Tysons Corner, VA 22102-3467
Tel (703) 226-3500 *Founded/Ownrshp* 1999
Sales 187.7MM *EMP* 1,910
SIC 7372 Prepackaged software
Ch Bd: Rajeev K Aggarwal
Pr: Saurabh Singh
CFO: Cynthia Russo
VP: Kevin Fliess
VP: Pete Floros
VP: David Johnson
CIO: Dwayne J Sye
CTO: David Quattrone
Sales Exec: Carla Perez
Sales Exec: Timothy Sutter
Sls Dir: Peter Kaandorp

CVG
See COMMERCIAL VEHICLE GROUP INC

CVG TRIM SYSTEMS
See TRIM SYSTEMS OPERATING CORP

D-U-N-S 06-491-2348 IMP
■ CVI LASER LLC
CVI LASER OPTICS
(*Suby of* IDEX CORP) ★
200 Dorado Pl Se, Albuquerque, NM 87123-3605
Tel (505) 296-9541 *Founded/Ownrshp* 2011
Sales 112.5MM^E *EMP* 738
SIC 3827 3851 3826 Optical instruments & apparatus; Ophthalmic goods; Analytical instruments
Sr Cor Off: Bill Peters
VP: Mark West
Genl Mgr: Helmut Kessler
CIO: Marcus Barber
CTO: Matt Larsen
IT Man: Hope Kaysaywaysemat
QC Dir: Kathy Lowrey
Opers Mgr: A Quan
VP Mktg: Kinji Yamasaki
Mktg Mgr: Douglas Wolk

CVI LASER OPTICS
See CVI LASER LLC

CVL LOGISTICS
See CROSSVILLE INC

CVPH
See UNIVERSITY OF VERMONT CHAMPLAIN VALLEY PHYSICIANS HOSPITAL

CVPH MEDICAL CENTER
See CHAMPLAIN VALLEY PHYSICIANS HOSPITAL

D-U-N-S 79-541-6135
▲ CVR ENERGY INC
2277 Plaza Dr Ste 500, Sugar Land, TX 77479-6602
Tel (281) 207-3200 *Founded/Ownrshp* 1906
Sales 5.4MMM *EMP* 2,259
Tkr Sym CVI *Exch* NYS
SIC 2911 2873 Petroleum refining; Nitrogenous fertilizers
Pr: John J Lipinski
**Ch Bd:* Carl C Icahn
COO: Stanley George
CFO: Susan M Ball
Chf Cred: Martin J Power
Ex VP: Robert W Haugen
Ex VP: Randal Maffett
Ex VP: Bill White
Sr VP: John R Walter
VP: Tim Kirwin
Board of Directors: Bob G Alexander, Jonathan Frates, Andrew Langham, Stephen Mongillo, James M Strock

D-U-N-S 80-973-6668
■ CVR PARTNERS LP
(*Suby of* COFFEYVILLE RESOURCES LLC) ★
2277 Plaza Dr Ste 500, Sugar Land, TX 77479-6602
Tel (281) 207-3200 *Founded/Ownrshp* 2011
Sales 289.1MM *EMP* 149
Tkr Sym UAN *Exch* NYS
SIC 2873 Nitrogenous fertilizers
Pr: Mark A Pytosh
Genl Pt: Cvr GP
Ch Bd: John Lipinski
CFO: Susan M Ball
Ex VP: Randal Maffett
Ex VP: William White
Sr VP: John R Walter
VP: Steve Eames

D-U-N-S 07-878-9738
■ CVR REFINING HOLDINGS LLC
(*Suby of* COFFEYVILLE RESOURCES LLC) ★
2277 Plaza Dr Ste 500, Sugar Land, TX 77479-6602
Tel (281) 207-3200 *Founded/Ownrshp* 2012
Sales 5.1MMM^E *EMP* 1,622^E
SIC 2911 4612 Petroleum refining; Crude petroleum pipelines
Pr: John J Lipinski
**COO:* Stanley A Riemann

D-U-N-S 07-871-6866
■ CVR REFINING LLC
(*Suby of* CVR REFINING LP) ★
2277 Plaza Dr Ste 500, Sugar Land, TX 77479-6602
Tel (281) 207-3200 *Founded/Ownrshp* 2012
Sales 200.8MM^E *EMP* 550
SIC 2911 Petroleum refining
Pr: John J Lipinski
**COO:* Mark Pytosh
**COO:* Stanley A Riemann

D-U-N-S 07-867-1056
■ CVR REFINING LP
(*Suby of* CVR REFINING HOLDINGS LLC) ★
2277 Plaza Dr Ste 500, Sugar Land, TX 77479-6602
Tel (281) 207-3200 *Founded/Ownrshp* 2012
Sales 5.1MMM *EMP* 968^E
Tkr Sym CVRR *Exch* NYS
SIC 2911 4612 Petroleum refining; Crude petroleum pipelines
Pr: John J Lipinski
Genl Pt: Cvr Refining GP
CFO: Susan M Ball

CVS
See ARBOR DRUGS INC

CVS
See REVCO DISCOUNT DRUG CENTERS INC

D-U-N-S 07-943-0050
■ CVS CAREMARK PART D SERVICES LLC
(*Suby of* CVS HEALTH CORP) ★
1 Cvs Dr, Woonsocket, RI 02895-6195
Tel (401) 770-3317 *Founded/Ownrshp* 2005
Sales NA *EMP* 1,441^E
SIC 6411 Insurance agents, brokers & service

D-U-N-S 80-849-1554
■ CVS CENTER INC
(*Suby of* CVS HEALTH CORP) ★
1 Cvs Dr, Woonsocket, RI 02895-6195
Tel (401) 765-1500 *Founded/Ownrshp* 2007
Sales 46.3MM^E *EMP* 2,522^E
SIC 5912 Drug stores & proprietary stores
Prin: Thomas Ryan

D-U-N-S 00-133-8912
▲ CVS HEALTH CORP
1 Cvs Dr, Woonsocket, RI 02895-6195
Tel (401) 765-1500 *Founded/Ownrshp* 1963
Sales 153.2MMM *EMP* 243,000
Tkr Sym CVS *Exch* NYS
SIC 5912 5961 8099 Drug stores & proprietary stores; Pharmaceuticals, mail order; Medical services organization
Pr: Larry J Merlo
Ch Bd: David W Dorman
Pr: Chris Bodine
Pr: Doug Callihan
Pr: Hank Mullany
CFO: David M Denton
Chf Mktg O: Troyen A Brennan
Ex VP: Tracy Bahl
Ex VP: Scott Baker
Ex VP: Lisa Bisaccia
Ex VP: Jack Bruner
Ex VP: Joshua Flum
Ex VP: Stephen J Gold
Ex VP: Alan Lotvin
Ex VP: Thomas M Moriarty
Ex VP: Jonathan C Roberts
Sr VP: Eva C Boratto
Sr VP: Norman De Greve
Sr VP: Kevin Smith
VP: Mike Bloom
VP: Tony Caskey
Board of Directors: Richard M Bracken, C David Brown II, Anne M Finucane, Richard J Swift, William C Weldon, Tony L White

D-U-N-S 00-692-0268 IMP
■ CVS OF DC AND VA INC
(*Suby of* NASHUA HOLLIS CVS INC) ★
1 Cvs Dr, Woonsocket, RI 02895-6195
Tel (401) 765-1500 *Founded/Ownrshp* 1905, 1990
Sales 194.4MM^E *EMP* 655
SIC 5912 Drug stores & proprietary stores
Pr: Thomas Ryan

D-U-N-S 79-075-3946
■ CVS OF VIRGINIA INC
(*Suby of* CVS HEALTH CORP) ★
1 Cvs Dr, Woonsocket, RI 02895-6195
Tel (401) 765-1500 *Founded/Ownrshp* 2007
Sales 43.0MM^E *EMP* 1,801^E
SIC 5912 Drug stores & proprietary stores
Prin: Zenon Lankowsky

D-U-N-S 17-672-9788 IMP/EXP
■ CVS PHARMACY INC
(*Suby of* CVS HEALTH CORP) ★
1 Cvs Dr, Woonsocket, RI 02895-6195
Tel (401) 765-1500 *Founded/Ownrshp* 1969
Sales 13.8MMM^E *EMP* 66,783
SIC 5912 5122 Drug stores & proprietary stores; Patent medicines
CEO: Larry J Merlo
Pr: Christopher Bos
**Pr:* Mark S Cosby
Pr: Tom Sarro
**Treas:* Carol A Denale
**Ex VP:* Troyen B D
**Ex VP:* David M Denton
**Ex VP:* Helena B Foulkes
**Ex VP:* Jonathan C Roberts
Sr VP: Robert Blyskal
Sr VP: Larry D Burton
Sr VP: Andrew J Sussman
VP: Asif Ally
VP: Neal Baker
VP: Scott Baker
VP: Kirby Bessant
VP: Daniel Best
VP: Pierrette Kelly
VP: Dan Kline
VP: Anne Klis
VP: Teresa Mitchelson
Board of Directors: Laird K Daniels

D-U-N-S 00-890-0938 IMP/EXP
■ CVS REVCO DS INC
(*Suby of* CVS HEALTH CORP) ★
1 Cvs Dr, Woonsocket, RI 02895-6195
Tel (401) 765-1500 *Founded/Ownrshp* 1997
Sales 2.2MMM^E *EMP* 28,000
SIC 5912 Drug stores & proprietary stores
CEO: Larry Merlo
Treas: Carol Danele
**Treas:* Phillip Galbo

D-U-N-S 11-284-6352 IMP
■ CVS VA DISTRIBUTION INC
(*Suby of* CVS OF DC AND VA INC) ★
1 Cvs Dr, Woonsocket, RI 02895-6195
Tel (401) 765-1500 *Founded/Ownrshp* 1998
Sales 194.4MM^E *EMP* 650
SIC 5122 Drugs, proprietaries & sundries
Pr: Thomas M Ryan
**Treas:* Larry Solberg
**VP:* Zenon P Lankowsky

D-U-N-S 00-330-8723 IMP
CW MATTHEWS CONTRACTING CO INC
1600 Kenview Dr Nw, Marietta, GA 30060-1086
Tel (770) 422-7520 *Founded/Ownrshp* 1946
Sales 321.1MM^E *EMP* 930
SIC 2891 2951 Sealants; Asphalt paving mixtures & blocks
CEO: Q William Hammack Jr
COO: Dan Garcia
**CFO:* Bell Michael D
**Ex VP:* Charles E Matthews
**Ex VP:* Jeff Shropshire
VP: Matthew Burton
Div Mgr: Adam Grist
Div Mgr: Paul Register
Div Mgr: Lee Smith
Genl Mgr: Matt Soignet
IT Man: Sharen Alfano

D-U-N-S 78-510-6894
CW NETWORK LLC
CWTV
3300 W Olive Ave Fl 3, Burbank, CA 91505-4640
Tel (818) 977-2500 *Founded/Ownrshp* 2006
Sales 112.3MM^E *EMP* 210^E
SIC 4833 Television broadcasting stations
COO: John Maatta
CFO: Dana Abel
Ex VP: Robert Tuck
VP: Pamela Morrison
VP: Leonard Richardson
VP: Barbra Robin
VP: Justin Rosenblatt
Creative D: Rick Frey
Ex Dir: David Karkenny
VP Prd: Maureen Milmore
Art Dir: Brian Hunt

D-U-N-S 07-929-8230
CW PROFESSIONAL SERVICES LLC
LOCHBRIDGE
150 W Jefferson Ave # 1200, Detroit, MI 48226-4447
Tel (313) 416-1011 *Founded/Ownrshp* 2014
Sales 125.5MM *EMP* 750
SIC 8748 Business consulting
Pr: Romil Bahl
Pr: Dan Hughes
**CEO:* James Byrnes
**CFO:* Robert Garragh
VP: Jerri Baker
VP: William Ball
Dir Bus: Allan Techko
Mktg Dir: Matthew Mowat

CW SERVICE
See MERCER LANDMARK INC

C.W. WRIGHTS
See C W WRIGHT CONSTRUCTION CO INC

CWA
See COMMUNICATIONS WORKERS OF AMERICA AFL-CIO CLC

D-U-N-S 82-469-0494 IMP/EXP
CWD LLC
WDSOURCE.COM
21046 Figueroa St Ste B, Carson, CA 90745-1906
Tel (310) 218-1082 *Founded/Ownrshp* 2000
Sales 169.0MM^E *EMP* 375
SIC 3714 Air brakes, motor vehicle
CFO: Estelle Cohen
VP Opers: Sal Bora
Natl Sales: John Marshall

CWI
See COLLEGE OF WESTERN IDAHO

D-U-N-S 05-001-2582 IMP
CWI INC
NATIONAL SUPPLY
(*Suby of* RV DEALERS MARKETPLACE) ★
650 Three Springs Rd, Bowling Green, KY 42104-7520
Tel (270) 781-2718 *Founded/Ownrshp* 1980
Sales 136.6MM^E *EMP* 1,200
SIC 5941 Specialty sport supplies
Ch Bd: Steve Adams
Pr: Mark Boggess
CEO: Marcus Lemonis
VP: David McKillip

D-U-N-S 01-811-2586
CWPM LLC
25 Norton Pl, Plainville, CT 06062-1258
Tel (860) 747-1335 *Founded/Ownrshp* 2000
Sales 175.5MM^E *EMP* 200
SIC 4953 Recycling, waste materials
Pr: Richard Gaudio
CFO: Steve Rewenko
IT Man: Murphy Naomi

D-U-N-S 05-954-3764
CWS HOLDING CO LLC
CUSTOM WINDOW SYSTEMS
(*Suby of* NAUTIC PARTNERS LLC) ★
1900 Sw 44th Ave, Ocala, FL 34474-8743
Tel (352) 368-6922 *Founded/Ownrshp* 2014
Sales 176.1MM^E *EMP* 915^E
SIC 2431 3211 Window frames, wood; Window glass, clear & colored
CEO: Greg Schorr

CWT
See CARLSON WAGONLIT TRAVEL INC

CWTV
See CW NETWORK LLC

D-U-N-S 79-428-7636
CYAN INC
1383 N Mcdowell Blvd # 300, Petaluma, CA 94954-1190
Tel (707) 735-2300 *Founded/Ownrshp* 2000
Sales 100.4MM *EMP* 200
SIC 5065

D-U-N-S 02-523-6875
CYANCO CORP
1920 Country Place Pkwy # 400, Pearland, TX 77584-2289
Tel (775) 853-4300 *Founded/Ownrshp* 2002
Sales 261.0MM^E *EMP* 64^E
SIC 1081 Metal mining services
Pr: Jeff Davis
CFO: William S Scott
VP: Greg Mitch
VP: Bob Warriner
Prin: John Burrows

D-U-N-S 12-625-6382
CYBER CITY TELESERVICES MARKETING INC
401 Hackensack Ave Fl 3, Hackensack, NJ 07601-6405
Tel (201) 487-1616 *Founded/Ownrshp* 2012
Sales 82.7MM^E *EMP* 2,722^E
SIC 7389 Telemarketing services
Pr: Richard Eychner
COO: Almerita D Leung

D-U-N-S 00-274-0723
CYBERCORE TECHNOLOGIES LLC
6605 Business Pkwy, Elkridge, MD 21075-6349
Tel (410) 561-7177 *Founded/Ownrshp* 2011
Sales 436.2MM^E *EMP* 180^E
SIC 5045 Computers & accessories, personal & home entertainment
Ch: Kevin Powderly
Prgrm Mgr: Lisa Summersgill
CTO: Orson Hsiung
Dir IT: Jason Mullholland

D-U-N-S 96-879-3380 IMP
CYBERNET MANUFACTURING INC
5 Holland Ste 201, Irvine, CA 92618-2574
Tel (949) 600-8000 *Founded/Ownrshp* 1996
Sales 136.3MM^E *EMP* 720
SIC 3571 3577 Electronic computers; Computer peripheral equipment
CEO: Pouran Shoaee
VP: Ali Bagheri
**VP Mktg:* Joe Divino
Mktg Dir: Tim Dalke

D-U-N-S 01-758-0361
CYBERNET SOFTWARE SYSTEMS INC
C S S
1900 Mccarthy Blvd # 210, Milpitas, CA 95035-7414
Tel (408) 615-5700 *Founded/Ownrshp* 2013
Sales 206.0MM^E *EMP* 4,500
Accts Benson & Neff Cpa

SIC 7371 Computer software development & applications
CEO: Suranjan Pramanik
CFO: Bob Steelhammer
CFO: Sivaramakrishnan Sundaram
Chf Mktg O: Ajmal Noorani
Ex VP: Chris Horning
VP: Amar Aswatha
VP: Suresh Babu
VP: Paul Bernhardt
VP: Charles Cohen
VP: Norma Heller
VP: Tony Redding
VP: Ravi Shankar
Exec: Kishorekumar Vasudev

D-U-N-S 19-456-8978
CYBERONICS INC
(*Suby of* LIVANOVA PLC)
100 Cyberonics Blvd # 600, Houston, TX 77058-2017
Tel (281) 228-7200 *Founded/Ownrshp* 2015
Sales 291.5MM *EMP* 639
SIC 3845 Transcutaneous electrical nerve stimulators (TENS)
Pr: Daniel J Moore
**COO:* Rohan H Hoare
COO: Rohan J Hoare
**CFO:* Gregory H Browne
Ofcr: Kim Mumby
**Ofcr:* David S Wise
VP: William H Duffell Jr
VP: Bruce H Kenknight
VP: Milton Morris
VP: John M Murphy
VP: Mark S Verratti

D-U-N-S 02-363-6256 IMP
CYBERPOWER INC
730 Baldwin Park Blvd, City of Industry, CA 91746-1503
Tel (626) 813-7730 *Founded/Ownrshp* 1998
Sales 92.7MM^E *EMP* 91
SIC 5045 Computer peripheral equipment
CEO: Stanley Kwong Ho
**Pr:* Eric Cheung
Exec: Nelson Chui
Dir Bus: Andy Kwok
Genl Mgr: Nelson Chiu
Info Man: Tjandra Afandi
VP Advt: Eddie Vong
Mktg Mgr: Clara Lai
Mktg Mgr: Anson Loh
Mktg Mgr: Joey Wang

D-U-N-S 00-292-4509 IMP
CYBERPOWER SYSTEMS (USA) INC
(*Suby of* CYBER POWER SYSTEMS INC.)
4241 12th Ave E Ste 400, Shakopee, MN 55379-2026
Tel (952) 403-9500 *Founded/Ownrshp* 1997
Sales 182.0MM^E *EMP* 1,160
SIC 3679 Electronic circuits
Pr: Bob Lovett
CFO: Tom Vo
Sr VP: Dan Ayala
**VP:* Doug Summers
Exec: Sarah Oliver
Dir IT: Bob Wallick
IT Man: Jason Halle
VP Sls: Doug Summer
Mktg Dir: Jonah Cagley
Sls Dir: Jeff Backman
Art Dir: Chad Sicard

D-U-N-S 01-966-4528
■ **CYBERSOURCE CORP**
(*Suby of* VISA INC) ★
900 Metro Center Blvd, Foster City, CA 94404-2172
Tel (650) 432-7350 *Founded/Ownrshp* 2010
Sales 162.0MM^E *EMP* 614
SIC 7374 Data processing & preparation
Pr: Michael Walsh
**Pr:* Scott R Cruickshank
**CFO:* Steven D Pellizzer
**Ex VP:* Robert J Ford
Ex VP: Robert Ford
**Sr VP:* Perry Dembner
**VP:* John Bodine
**VP:* Carolyn Brackett
**VP:* Neil Buckley
VP: Patricia Martin
VP: Trish B Martin
VP: John McDonnell
VP: Greg Pappas

D-U-N-S 00-203-6606 IMP/EXP
■ **CYBEX INTERNATIONAL INC** (NY)
(*Suby of* LIFE FITNESS INC) ★
10 Trotter Dr, Medway, MA 02053-2275
Tel (508) 533-4300 *Founded/Ownrshp* 2014
Sales 175.0MM *EMP* 563
SIC 3949 Exercise equipment; Exercising cycles; Treadmills; Dumbbells & other weightlifting equipment
CEO: Christopher Clawson
Recvr: Dale Anderson
Pr: Glenn Colarossi
**CFO:* Todd Davenport
Treas: Jim Ahearn
Sr VP: Raymond Giannelli
Sr VP: John P Young
VP: Paul Dolan
VP: Thomas Gordhamer
Rgnl Mgr: Luke Berry
Off Mgr: Sophie Bailey

D-U-N-S 06-657-2835 IMP
CYCLE GEAR INC
4705 Industrial Way, Benicia, CA 94510-1040
Tel (707) 747-5053 *Founded/Ownrshp* 1995
Sales 267.2MM^E *EMP* 520
SIC 5571 Motorcycle parts & accessories
Pr: David Bertram
COO: Tracy Wan
CFO: Jeff Forgan
**Sec:* Henry Desjardins
Dist Mgr: David Burrow
Store Mgr: Oscar Acosta
Software D: Randy Katsura
Netwrk Eng: Robert Jablonski
Opers Mgr: Cecilia Lara

D-U-N-S 80-286-4582 IMP/EXP
CYCLE LINK (USA) INC
(*Suby of* ANHUI SHANYING PAPER INDUSTRY CO., LTD.)
1330 Valley Vista Dr, Diamond Bar, CA 91765-3910
Tel (909) 861-5888 *Founded/Ownrshp* 2007
Sales 432.1MM *EMP* 35
SIC 5093 Waste paper
CEO: Ming Hua Wu
**VP:* Mandy Che

D-U-N-S 61-533-4864 IMP/EXP
CYCLING SPORTS GROUP INC
CANNONDALE SPORTS GROUP
(*Suby of* DOREL INDUSTRIES INC)
16 Trowbridge Dr, Bedford, PA 15522
Tel (203) 749-7000 *Founded/Ownrshp* 2008
Sales 173.6MM^E *EMP* 635
SIC 3751 2329 Bicycles & related parts; Men's & boys' sportswear & athletic clothing; Athletic (warmup, sweat & jogging) suits: men's & boys'
**CFO:* Ron Lombardi
VP: Daniel Alloway
Mktg Mgr: James Lalonde
Sls Mgr: Matthew Cappiello
Sls Mgr: Rob Voorhees

D-U-N-S 05-402-2421 IMP
CYCLONE ENTERPRISES INC
BOS PADRES
146 Knobcrest Dr, Houston, TX 77060-1213
Tel (281) 872-0087 *Founded/Ownrshp* 1979
Sales 138.8MM^E *EMP* 145
SIC 5141 Groceries, general line
Pr: Henry D Alston III
**VP:* Michael O Mendenhall

CYDI
See CONRAD YELVINGTON DISTRIBUTORS INC

CYGNUS BUSINESS MEDIA
See COMMERCE CONNECT MEDIA INC

D-U-N-S 06-195-8005
CYGNUS BUSINESS MEDIA INC
MODERN JEWELER MAGAZINE
1233 Janesville Ave, Fort Atkinson, WI 53538-2794
Tel (920) 563-6388 *Founded/Ownrshp* 2000
Sales NA *EMP* 2,188
SIC 2721 7389 7319

D-U-N-S 09-005-9713
CYIENT INC (CA)
(*Suby of* CYIENT LIMITED)
330 Roberts St Ste 400, East Hartford, CT 06108-3654
Tel (860) 528-5430 *Founded/Ownrshp* 1991
Sales 231.1MM *EMP* 1,200
SIC 8711 Engineering services
CEO: Thomas M Edwards
CFO: Jeremy C Norton
**Ch:* Krishna Bodanapu
Sr VP: Brian Wyatt
VP: Solomon Joseph
Dir Bus: Michael McCaffrey
Prin: Mm Murugappan
Mng Dir: Sunish Sharma
Genl Mgr: Kenneth Sigmund
Snr Sftwr: Srinath Adipudi
MIS Mgr: Kumar Podila

D-U-N-S 07-857-9219
CYLANCE INC
18201 Von Karman Ave # 700, Irvine, CA 92612-1058
Tel (949) 375-3380 *Founded/Ownrshp* 2012
Sales 183.9MM^E *EMP* 540^E
SIC 3825 7379 Network analyzers; Computer related maintenance services
Pr: Stuart McClure
Pr: Felix Marquardt
**CFO:* Jeff Ishmael
**Chf Mktg O:* Gregory Fitzgerald
**Ofcr:* Vina Leite
**Sr VP:* Braden Russell
VP: Joel Bauman
VP: Glenn L Chisholm
VP: Jon Miller
**VP:* Keith Palumbo
VP: Raj Rajamani
**VP:* Shane Shook
VP: Holly Whalen
**VP:* Corey White
VP: Chris Zimmerman
Board of Directors: Art Coviello, Alex Doll, William J Fallon, Patrick Heim

D-U-N-S 17-714-0688 IMP
CYMER INC
17075 Thornmint Ct, San Diego, CA 92127-2413
Tel (858) 385-7300 *Founded/Ownrshp* 2013
Sales NA *EMP* 1,240
SIC 3699 3827

D-U-N-S 07-912-7712 IMP
CYMER LLC
ASML USA
(*Suby of* ASML HOLDING N.V.)
17075 Thornmint Ct, San Diego, CA 92127-2413
Tel (858) 385-7300 *Founded/Ownrshp* 1986
Sales 456.2MM^E *EMP* 1,240
SIC 3699 3827 Laser systems & equipment; Lens mounts
CEO: Edward J Brown Jr
**CEO:* Jim Koonmen
CFO: Paul B Bowman
Sr VP: Robert P Akins
**Sr VP:* Richard L Sandstrom PHD
**VP:* Daniel Brown PHD
VP: David Knowles
VP: Blake Miller
Comm Man: Brittney Wolff
Genl Mgr: Andy McQuarrie
Sftwr Eng: John Schmucky

D-U-N-S 07-840-7816
CYMI INDUSTRIAL INC
12400 Coit Rd Ste 700, Dallas, TX 75251-2059
Tel (214) 276-8950 *Founded/Ownrshp* 1962
Sales 144.0MM^E *EMP* 500
SIC 1541 Industrial buildings, new construction

CEO: Brad Johnson
**Ch Bd:* Jose Matrinez-Amor
**COO:* Issa Dadoush
**CFO:* Mar Ruperez
**VP:* Wase Beasley
**VP:* Cliff Tubbs

D-U-N-S 13-778-5155
CYMSTAR LLC
1700 W Albany St Ste 500, Broken Arrow, OK 74012-1482
Tel (918) 251-8100 *Founded/Ownrshp* 2003
Sales 96.8MM *EMP* 246
Accts Cross & Robinson Tulsa Oklah
SIC 3699 3728 Flight simulators (training aids), electronic; Aircraft parts & equipment
CEO: John Corder
Prgrm Mgr: Will White
Site Mgr: Derrick Ball

CYNEL
See ALLNEX USA INC

D-U-N-S 78-031-8028 IMP
▲ **CYNOSURE INC**
5 Carlisle Rd, Westford, MA 01886-3601
Tel (978) 256-4200 *Founded/Ownrshp* 1991
Sales 339.4MM *EMP* 755^E
Tkr Sym CYNO *Exch* NGM
SIC 3845 Electromedical equipment; Laser systems & equipment, medical
Ch Bd: Michael R Davin
Bd of Dir: Brian Barefoot
Ex VP: Douglas J Delaney
Ex VP: David Mackie
VP: James Boll
VP: George Cho
VP: Shaun Welches
VP: Stewart Wilson
Dir Soc: Jennifer Dupont
Area Mgr: Jason Grisnik
Area Mgr: Frank Spallitta
Board of Directors: Brian M Barefoot, William O Flannery, Marina Hatsopoulos, Thomas H Robinson

D-U-N-S 00-730-4269 EXP
CYOPTICS INC
(*Suby of* BROADCOM) ★
9999 Hamilton Blvd # 250, Breinigsville, PA 18031-9301
Tel (484) 397-2000 *Founded/Ownrshp* 2013
Sales 161.4MM^E *EMP* 550
SIC 3827 Optical instruments & lenses
CEO: Ed J Coringrato Jr
**CFO:* Warren Barratt
**VP:* Joseph P Keska
**CTO:* Uzi Koren
Mtls Mgr: Cristina Fararoni

D-U-N-S 00-312-7193
CYPRESS BAYOU CASINO
(*Suby of* CHITIMACHA TRIBE OF LOUISIANA) ★
832 Martin Luther King Rd, Charenton, LA 70523
Tel (337) 923-7284 *Founded/Ownrshp* 1993
Sales 53.7MM^E *EMP* 1,100
SIC 7999 Gambling establishment
CFO: Michael Allen
CFO: Montie Spivey
Exec: Willie Gaspard
Exec: David Laszczak
Exec: Scott McCue
**Prin:* Tara Trahan
Ex Dir: Lori Horrell
Dir IT: Mikki Smigielski
Sales Exec: Shannon Redmond

CYPRESS COLLEGE
See NORTH ORANGE COUNTY COMMUNITY COLLEGE DISTRICT

D-U-N-S 07-921-6464
▲ **CYPRESS ENERGY PARTNERS LP**
5727 S Lewis Ave Ste 300, Tulsa, OK 74105-7144
Tel (918) 748-3900 *Founded/Ownrshp* 2012
Sales 371.1MM *EMP* 1,127
Tkr Sym CELP *Exch* NYS
SIC 1389 7389 Impounding & storing salt water, oil & gas field; Pipeline & power line inspection service
Ch Bd: Peter C Boylan III
Genl Pt: Cypress E GP
CFO: G Les Austin
CIO: Ben Stout

D-U-N-S 10-713-9870
CYPRESS FAIRBANKS MEDICAL CENTER
10655 Steepletop Dr, Houston, TX 77065-4222
Tel (281) 897-3172 *Founded/Ownrshp* 2002
Sales 163.9MM *EMP* 15
SIC 5912 Drug stores
Owner: Tony Ng

CYPRESS FAIRBANKS MEDICAL CENTER HOSPITAL
See CYPRESS FAIRBANKS MEDICAL CENTER INC

D-U-N-S 03-884-0492
■ **CYPRESS FAIRBANKS MEDICAL CENTER INC**
CYPRESS FAIRBANKS MEDICAL CENTER HOSPITAL
(*Suby of* TENET HEALTHCARE CORP) ★
10655 Steepletop Dr, Houston, TX 77065-4222
Tel (281) 890-4285 *Founded/Ownrshp* 1979
Sales 191.4MM *EMP* 850
SIC 8062 General medical & surgical hospitals
Pr: Terry J Wheeler
Pr: Alice Elledge
COO: Sheriev Boctor
**CFO:* James Wright
Dir Rx: Danny Babin
CTO: Lorinnsa Key
Opers Mgr: Ralph Finnegan
Mktg Mgr: Nadia Saqr
HC Dir: Michelle Moore
HC Dir: Ron Tuell

D-U-N-S 00-712-9729 IMP
■ **CYPRESS MEDIA LLC**
KANSAS CITY STAR, THE
(*Suby of* MCCLATCHY CO) ★
1729 Grand Blvd, Kansas City, MO 64108-1413
Tel (816) 234-4141 *Founded/Ownrshp* 1926
Sales 245.2MM^E *EMP* 1,300^E
SIC 2711 Newspapers, publishing & printing
Pr: Mark Zieman
CFO: Bryan Harbison
VP: Arthur Brisbane
Board of Directors: Daniel B Burke, Phil Meek

D-U-N-S 79-066-4510 IMP
■ **CYPRESS SEMICONDUCTOR (MINNESOTA) INC**
(*Suby of* CYPRESS SEMICONDUCTOR CORP) ★
2401 E 86th St, Bloomington, MN 55425-2705
Tel (952) 851-5200 *Founded/Ownrshp* 1990
Sales 100.7MM^E *EMP* 450
SIC 3674 Integrated circuits, semiconductor networks, etc.; Microprocessors; Computer logic modules; Random access memory (RAM)
Genl Mgr: Bradley Ferguson

D-U-N-S 10-210-8446 IMP/EXP
▲ **CYPRESS SEMICONDUCTOR CORP**
5883 Rue Ferrari Ste 100, San Jose, CA 95138-1861
Tel (408) 943-2600 *Founded/Ownrshp* 1982
Sales 1.6MMM *EMP* 6,279
Tkr Sym CY *Exch* NGS
SIC 3674 Semiconductors & related devices; Integrated circuits, semiconductor networks, etc.; Random access memory (RAM); Read-only memory (ROM)
Pr: Hassane El-Khoury
**Ch Bd:* H Raymond Bingham
Pr: Dhwani Vyas
CFO: Thad Trent
Ex VP: Dana C Nazarian
VP: Clinton Carlisle
VP: Tom Davenport
VP: Ali Keshavarzi
VP: Jeff Lee
VP: Milton Ribeiro
Mng Dir: Minh Phan
Board of Directors: W Steve Albrecht, Eric A Benhamou, O C Kwon, Michael S Wishart, Wilbert G M Van Den Hoek

D-U-N-S 82-553-3896
CYPRESS SEMICONDUCTOR INTERNATIONAL INC
4001 N 1st St, San Jose, CA 95134-1503
Tel (408) 943-2600 *Founded/Ownrshp* 1987
Sales 727.5MM^E *EMP* 5,000^E
SIC 5065 Semiconductor devices
CFO: Brad Bu
Ex VP: Cathal Phelan
Sr VP: Arthur C Woodward
VP: Bob Blazer
VP: David Kranzler
CTO: Dick Swanson
CTO: John Torode

D-U-N-S 11-516-2471
CYPRESS TRUCK LINES INC
JAX BROKERAGE
1414 Lindrose St, Jacksonville, FL 32206-1616
Tel (904) 353-8641 *Founded/Ownrshp* 1980
Sales 89.1MM^E *EMP* 600
Accts Smoak Davis & Nixon Llp Jack
SIC 4213 Heavy hauling
Pr: David V Penland Sr
CFO: Dave Knaak
Ofcr: W Copeland
**Sr VP:* Pete Peterson
**VP:* Aaron Penland
Off Mgr: Erin Sloan
Trfc Dir: Kelley Wilkerson

CYPRESS-FAIRBANKS I. S. D.
See CYPRESS-FAIRBANKS INDEPENDENT SCHOOL DISTRICT

D-U-N-S 07-391-2156
CYPRESS-FAIRBANKS INDEPENDENT SCHOOL DISTRICT
CYPRESS-FAIRBANKS I. S. D.
10300 Jones Rd, Houston, TX 77065-4208
Tel (281) 897-4000 *Founded/Ownrshp* 1939
Sales 977.1MM *EMP* 13,000
Accts Hereford Lynch Sellars & Kir
SIC 8211 Public elementary & secondary schools; Elementary school; Specialty education
VP: Susan Pavliska
VP: David Taylor
Dir Sec: Alan Bragg
Netwrk Mgr: Fred Brenz
HC Dir: Bevin Gordon
Snr PM: Jim Vangorder

D-U-N-S 06-850-0420
■ **CYPRUS AMAX MINERALS CO**
(*Suby of* FREEPORT-MCMORAN INC) ★
333 N Central Ave, Phoenix, AZ 85004-2121
Tel (602) 366-8100 *Founded/Ownrshp* 1969
Sales 541.5MM^E *EMP* 13,500
SIC 1221 1222 1021 1061 1479 1041 Bituminous coal & lignite-surface mining; Bituminous coal-underground mining; Copper ore mining & preparation; Molybdenum ores mining; Lithium mineral mining; Gold ores
Ch Bd: J Steven Whisler
Pr: S David Colton
CFO: Ramiro G Peru
**Sr VP:* Manuel J Iraola
VP: Gerald Gluscic
IT Man: Jarmo Paukkunen

D-U-N-S 60-520-4536
■ **CYPRUS CLIMAX METALS CO**
(*Suby of* CYPRUS AMAX MINERALS CO) ★
333 N Central Ave, Phoenix, AZ 85004-2121
Tel (928) 473-7000 *Founded/Ownrshp* 1988
Sales 279.1MM^E *EMP* 13,500

SIC 6719 Investment holding companies, except banks
Pr: Richard C Adkerson

D-U-N-S 12-182-1495
■ CYPRUS METALS CO
(*Suby of* CYPRUS AMAX MINERALS CO) ★
333 N Central Ave, Phoenix, AZ 85004-2121
Tel (928) 473-7000 *Founded/Ownrshp* 1986
Sales 168.3MM^E *EMP* 13,500^E
SIC 1021 Copper ores
Pr: J Steven Whisler

D-U-N-S 00-838-4208
■ CYPRUS MINES CORP
(*Suby of* CYPRUS AMAX MINERALS CO) ★
1 N Central Ave, Phoenix, AZ 85004-4414
Tel (602) 366-8100 *Founded/Ownrshp* 2002
Sales 66.3MM^E *EMP* 2,500
SIC 1221 1021 1031 1061 Surface mining, bituminous; Copper ore mining & preparation; Zinc ores mining; Lead ores mining; Molybdenum ores mining
Pr: Milton Ward
Treas: Dennis C Haugh
**Ex VP:* Chester B Stone
VP: Gerald J Malys

D-U-N-S 00-736-0527
CYRACOM INTERNATIONAL INC
5780 N Swan Rd, Tucson, AZ 85718-4527
Tel (520) 745-9447 *Founded/Ownrshp* 1995, 2002
Sales 216.7MM^E *EMP* 1,000^E
Accts Beachfleischman Pc Tucson
SIC 7389 Translation services
CEO: Jeremy Woan
VP: Best Ihegborow
Exec: Carmen Michaud
Snr Sftwr: Mick McGrellis
IT Man: Michael Mygrant
IT Man: Tara M Turner
Prd Mgr: Chris White
Natl Sales: Mario Leon
Natl Sales: Jing Liu
Natl Sales: Andrew Roush
VP Sls: Stephen McNeil

D-U-N-S 01-912-7739
▲ CYRUSONE INC
1649 W Frankford Rd, Carrollton, TX 75007-4605
Tel (972) 350-0060 *Founded/Ownrshp* 2012
Sales 399.3MM *EMP* 580^E
Tkr Sym CONE *Exch* NGS
SIC 6798 Real estate investment trusts
Pr: Gary J Wojtaszek
**Ch Bd:* Alex Shumate
CFO: Gregory R Andrews
Chf Cred: Venkatesh S Durvasula
Ex VP: Brent Behrman
Ex VP: John Gould
Ex VP: Robert M Jackson
Sr VP: Amitabh Rai
VP: Blake Hankins
VP: Amaya Souarez
Div Mgr: Alex Bron
Board of Directors: David H Ferdman, John W Gamble Jr, Michael A Klayko, T Tod Nielsen, William E Sullivan, Lynn A Wentworth

D-U-N-S 78-656-8183
CYS INVESTMENTS INC
500 Totten Pond Rd Ste 6, Waltham, MA 02451-1924
Tel (617) 639-0440 *Founded/Ownrshp* 2006
Sales 331.2MM *EMP* 15
Tkr Sym CYS *Exch* NYS
SIC 6798 Real estate investment trusts
Ch Bd: Kevin E Grant
COO: Richard E Cleary
CFO: Jack Decicco
Ex VP: Thomas A Rosenbloom

D-U-N-S 07-248-0304
CYSTIC FIBROSIS FOUNDATION
6931 Arlington Rd Fl 2, Bethesda, MD 20814-5231
Tel (301) 951-4422 *Founded/Ownrshp* 1955
Sales 405.5MM *EMP* 550
Accts Kpmg Llp Washington Dc
SIC 8733 8399 Medical research; Fund raising organization, non-fee basis
CEO: Preston W Campbell III
COO: Marc Ginsky
VP: Suzanne R Pattee J D
Ex Dir: Sissy Boyd
Ex Dir: Sherri Hahn
Ex Dir: Traci Shur
CIO: Jack Mahler

D-U-N-S 80-998-4230 IMP/EXP
CYTEC ENGINEERED MATERIALS INC
(*Suby of* CYTEC SOLVAY GROUP) ★
2085 E Tech Cir Ste 300, Tempe, AZ 85284
Tel (480) 730-2000 *Founded/Ownrshp* 1993
Sales 614.9MM^E *EMP* 2,000
SIC 3769 5085 2821 Guided missile & space vehicle parts & auxiliary equipment; Abrasives & adhesives; Plastics materials & resins
CEO: David Drillock
**Pr:* William Wood
**Treas:* Jeffrey Fitzgerald
**Treas:* Thomas P Wozniak
**VP:* Roy Smith

D-U-N-S 80-974-9948 EXP
CYTEC INDUSTRIES INC
CYTEC SOLVAY GROUP
(*Suby of* SOLVAY SA)
5 Garret Mountain Plz, Woodland Park, NJ 07424-3300
Tel (973) 357-3100 *Founded/Ownrshp* 2015
Sales 2.0MMM *EMP* 4,600
SIC 2899 2821 2672 2851 2823 2819 Chemical preparations; Water treating compounds; Plastics materials & resins; Adhesive backed films, foams & foils; Paints & allied products; Cellulosic manmade fibers; Industrial inorganic chemicals
Ch Bd: Shane D Fleming
Pr: Frank Aranzana
**CFO:* Daniel G Darazsdi
VP: Andrew Burke
VP: Marc Macaulay
**VP:* Roy D Smith
VP: Dave Snyder
VP: Ying Meng Song
VP: Jan Vandendriessche
Off Mgr: Cheryle Telesco
Sys Admin: Chris Gaffney
Board of Directors: Chris A Davis, Anthony G Fernandes, David P Hess, Louis L Hoynes Jr, Carol P Lowe, William P Powell, Thomas W Rabaut, Raymond P Sharpe

CYTEC SOLVAY GROUP
See CYTEC INDUSTRIES INC

D-U-N-S 06-924-7948 IMP
CYTEC SURFACE SPECIALTIES INC
(*Suby of* CYTEC SOLVAY GROUP) ★
1950 Lake Park Dr Se, Smyrna, GA 30080-7648
Tel (770) 434-6188 *Founded/Ownrshp* 1997, 2005
Sales 102.9MM^E *EMP* 650
SIC 3086 5169 5191 5162 3081 2823 Packaging & shipping materials, foamed plastic; Synthetic rubber; Chemicals, agricultural; Resins; Unsupported plastics film & sheet; Cellulosic manmade fibers
Pr: Larry Golen
**VP:* Tom Kelly

D-U-N-S 00-834-2664 IMP
■ CYTOSPORT INC
(*Suby of* HORMEL FOODS CORP) ★
1340 Treat Blvd Ste 350, Walnut Creek, CA 94597-7581
Tel (707) 751-3942 *Founded/Ownrshp* 2014
Sales 104.9MM^E *EMP* 190
SIC 2023 2086 Dry, condensed, evaporated dairy products; Soft drinks: packaged in cans, bottles, etc.
CEO: Rob King
Ch Bd: Greg Pickett
Pr: Mike Pickett
COO: David Weber
CFO: Mike Dittman
CFO: David Webber
**Chf Mktg O:* Nikki Brown
Ex VP: Wil Holsworth
VP: Gary Garland
VP: Ralph Knights
VP: Ed Lilly
VP: Nick Schott
Exec: Stephanie Madrid
Exec: Dean Pulver
Exec: Chris Running
Exec: Tim Wersel
Comm Man: Brittany Cranston

D-U-N-S 60-123-1475 IMP
■ CYTYC CORP
(*Suby of* HOLOGIC INC) ★
250 Campus Dr, Marlborough, MA 01752-3020
Tel (508) 263-2900 *Founded/Ownrshp* 2007
Sales 156.6MM^E *EMP* 1,530
SIC 3841 Surgical & medical instruments
Ch Bd: Patrick Sullivan
Pr: Robert A Cascella
CFO: Timothy M Adams
CFO: Timothy M Adas
Treas: Glenn P Muir
Ex VP: Daniel J Levangie
Sr VP: A Meszner Eltrich
Sr VP: David P Harding
Sr VP: A Suzanne Mesner-Eltrich
VP: Robert H Lavallee
VP: Eugene Skalnyi

D-U-N-S 05-942-0752
CZARNOWSKI DISPLAY SERVICE INC
CZARNOWSKI EXHIBIT SERVICES
2287 S Blue Island Ave, Chicago, IL 60608-4393
Tel (773) 247-1500 *Founded/Ownrshp* 1973
Sales 396.1MM^E *EMP* 1,500
SIC 7389 Exhibit construction by industrial contractors
Pr: Mark Nagle
**CFO:* Scott Levitt
CFO: Tim Oughton
Ex VP: Kc Nagel
**Ex VP:* Kim Nagle
VP: Jeffrey Brozek
VP: Ed Douglass
VP: Douglas Shockley
VP: Ron Stovall
Dir Bus: Sina Hanson
Genl Mgr: David Maday

CZARNOWSKI EXHIBIT SERVICES
See CZARNOWSKI DISPLAY SERVICE INC

D

D-U-N-S 78-733-4650
D & D DISTRIBUTORS LLLP
GREY EAGLE DISTRIBUTORS
2340 Millpark Dr, Maryland Heights, MO 63043-3530
Tel (314) 429-9100 *Founded/Ownrshp* 2005
Sales 100.3MM^E *EMP* 220
SIC 5182 5149 Wine & distilled beverages; Soft drinks
CEO: Grey Eagle
**Genl Pt:* David M Sokes
COO: Neil G Komadoski
CFO: Jerom P Jasiek
VP: Karen Davis
Exec: Barbara Felling
Adm Dir: Terry J Toennies
Area Mgr: Jim Burke
Area Mgr: Chad Luther
Sales Exec: Frank W Roach
Sls&Mrk Ex: James L Bannes

D-U-N-S 19-472-3008
D & G ELECTRIC CO LLC
8297 Old Tenn Pike Rd, Pinson, AL 35126-3814
Tel (205) 365-4074 *Founded/Ownrshp* 1976
Sales 300.0MM *EMP* 8
SIC 1731 Electrical work
Prin: Gary Mills

D-U-N-S 00-791-1209 IMP/EXP
D & H DISTRIBUTING CO (PA)
2525 N 7th St, Harrisburg, PA 17110-2511
Tel (717) 236-8001 *Founded/Ownrshp* 1918, 1943
Sales 501.2MM^E *EMP* 950
SIC 5045 5065 5064 5063 5044

D-U-N-S 80-312-1180
■ D & I SILICA LLC
PROPN RAIL
(*Suby of* HI-CRUSH PARTNERS LP) ★
3 Riverway Ste 1350, Houston, TX 77056-1982
Tel (713) 980-6200 *Founded/Ownrshp* 2006
Sales 90.2MM^E *EMP* 75^E
SIC 5032 Sand, construction
CEO: Robert Rasmus
**COO:* Jay Alston
**CFO:* Laura Fulton
**Ex VP:* William Fehr
**VP:* Chad McEver
Off Mgr: Emily Rosala
Opers Mgr: Glenn S Carlson

D-U-N-S 06-814-8261 IMP/EXP
D & J PRINTING INC
BANG PRINTING
3323 Oak St, Brainerd, MN 56401-3807
Tel (218) 829-2877 *Founded/Ownrshp* 2000
Sales 89.7MM^E *EMP* 180
SIC 2752 2789 2732 Commercial printing, lithographic; Bookbinding & related work; Book printing
CEO: Chris Kurtzman
CFO: Tom Campian
Sr VP: Tom Knettel
**VP:* Tom Campion
**VP:* Eric Loney
**VP:* Jim Lorentz
**VP:* Todd Vanek
VP: Alice Zumstein
VP Opers: Josh Franzen
Plnt Mgr: Joe Saiko
VP Sls: Thomas Hix

D & K HEALTHCARE RESOURCES INC
See D & K HEALTHCARE RESOURCES LLC

D-U-N-S 18-393-6525
■ D & K HEALTHCARE RESOURCES LLC
D & K HEALTHCARE RESOURCES INC
(*Suby of* MCKESSON CORP) ★
8235 Forsyth Blvd, Saint Louis, MO 63105-1623
Tel (888) 727-3485 *Founded/Ownrshp* 2005
Sales 97.3MM^E *EMP* 819
SIC 5122 Drugs, proprietaries & sundries; Cosmetics, perfumes & hair products; Toiletries; Druggists' sundries
Ch Bd: J Hord Armstrong III
Pr: Martin D Wilson
CFO: Thomas S Hilton
VP: Kim Diemand
VP: Michael Graves
VP: Bill Jarvey
VP: William Jarvey
VP: Rick Jeter
VP: Richard Keffer
VP: Brian G Landry
VP: Jody Lindsey
VP: Terry McKinley
VP: Lewis E Mead
VP: Rick Plotnick
VP: Molly Salky
VP: Denise Wiesemann
Board of Directors: Richard F Ford, Harvey C Jewett IV, Bryan H Lawrence, Thomas F Patton, Louis B Susman, Mary Ann Van Lokeren

D-U-N-S 96-229-0110
D & M CARRIERS LLC
D & M LOGISTICS
8125 Sw 15th St, Oklahoma City, OK 73128-9505
Tel (405) 491-2800 *Founded/Ownrshp* 1996
Sales 83.3MM^E *EMP* 185
SIC 4213 Trucking, except local
CEO: David R Freymiller
COO: Jennifer Laguna
CFO: John McLaughlin
IT Man: Scot Wooldridge

D-U-N-S 13-094-8958 IMP
D & M HOLDINGS US INC
DM GROUP
(*Suby of* D&M HOLDINGS INC.)
100 Corporate Dr, Mahwah, NJ 07430-2041
Tel (201) 762-6500 *Founded/Ownrshp* 2002
Sales 386.8MM^E *EMP* 2,004
SIC 5065 3651 Electronic parts & equipment; Electronic kits for home assembly: radio, TV, phonograph
CEO: Jim Caudill
**CFO:* Jorge Garcia
Sr VP: Bob Zierk
VP: Alex Alexandrou
VP: Jeffrey N Cowan
Off Mgr: Sheryl Chin
VP Mktg: Keyla Velazquez
Mktg Mgr: Rick Hagelauer
Mktg Mgr: Jeffrey Loman

D & M LOGISTICS
See D & M CARRIERS LLC

D-U-N-S 79-224-4097
D & S CONSULTANTS INC
DSCI
40 Christopher Way, Eatontown, NJ 07724-3327
Tel (732) 389-2140 *Founded/Ownrshp* 1992
Sales 103.5MM^E *EMP* 760
SIC 8711
Ch Bd: Steven A Dechiaro
**Pr:* Eric Wagner
**COO:* Mathew Weltman
CFO: James Seary
CFO: Leanard Williams
Ofcr: Peter Major
Sr VP: Tania Filak
VP: Tim Battles
VP: Mike Ferraro
Prgrm Mgr: Robert McHale
Prgrm Mgr: Tom Wasilewski

D-U-N-S 07-113-1866
D & S CREATIVE COMMUNICATIONS INC
BLACK RIVER DISPLAY GROUP
140 Park Ave E, Mansfield, OH 44902-1830
Tel (419) 524-6699 *Founded/Ownrshp* 1960
Sales 120.0MM *EMP* 65^E
SIC 7311 2752 2791 2789 Advertising agencies; Commercial printing, lithographic; Typesetting; Bookbinding & related work
Pr: Terry Neff
Creative D: Tim Sinchok
Dir Bus: Marci Grzelecki
IT Man: Bob Hanes
Sfty Mgr: Steve Winters
Art Dir: Kristi Biglin
Art Dir: Marty Hoenes

D-U-N-S 09-557-2418 IMP
D & W DIESEL INC
1503 Clark Street Rd, Auburn, NY 13021-9526
Tel (315) 253-5300 *Founded/Ownrshp* 1976
Sales 86.9MM^E *EMP* 207
SIC 5013 5531 Motor vehicle supplies & new parts; Automotive supplies; Truck parts & accessories; Automobile & truck equipment & parts; Automotive parts; Truck equipment & parts
CEO: Douglas J Wayne
**VP:* David Wayne
Brnch Mgr: Leo McCaffrey
Brnch Mgr: Tom Ruppelli
Brnch Mgr: Gerald Siconolfi
Genl Mgr: Peter Koon
Mtls Mgr: Kristen Marks
Snr Mgr: Mark Cole

D-U-N-S 79-028-6012
D & Y CHEESES INC
20 N Broadway Ste 5, Nyack, NY 10960-2644
Tel (845) 353-4570 *Founded/Ownrshp* 2007
Sales 106.9MM^E *EMP* 156^E
SIC 7389
CEO: Wayne Henry

D - LINK
See D-LINK SYSTEMS INC

D A V
See DISABLED AMERICAN VETERANS

D' ANGELO'S SANDWICH SHOP
See DELOPS INC

D' ANGELO'S SANDWICH SHOP
See PAPA GINOS HOLDINGS CORP

D-U-N-S 07-134-0806 IMP
■ D B INDUSTRIES INC
CAPITAL SAFETY
(*Suby of* 3M CO) ★
3833 Sala Way, Red Wing, MN 55066-5005
Tel (651) 388-8282 *Founded/Ownrshp* 2007
Sales 160.6MM^E *EMP* 500
SIC 5099 5084 7352 Safety equipment & supplies; Safety equipment; Medical equipment rental
Pr: Kevin Coplan
**CEO:* Stephen Oswald
**CFO:* Paul Andrew Binfield
**Ch:* Pat Velasco
**VP:* Bruce Larson
Mktg Mgr: Jeff Halbach
Board of Directors: Stephen Oswald, Pat Velasco

D B L
See DBL DISTRIBUTING LLC

D. B. ROBERTS COMPANY
See D B ROBERTS INC

D-U-N-S 00-245-8821
D B ROBERTS INC (DE)
D. B. ROBERTS COMPANY
30 Upton Dr Ste 3, Wilmington, MA 01887-1076
Tel (978) 988-5777 *Founded/Ownrshp* 1982
Sales 116.4MM^E *EMP* 230
SIC 5065 Electronic parts & equipment
Pr: Robert W Clapp
Div Mgr: Robert H Landau
Genl Mgr: Charles Garry
Sls Dir: Mike Laurence
Sales Asso: Kelley Burgess
Sales Asso: Bruce Langdon

D BT
See CATERPILLAR GLOBAL MINING AMERICA LLC

D C C
See DUTCHESS COMMUNITY COLLEGE

D C S
See PERFORMANT RECOVERY INC

D-U-N-S 00-383-0668
D C TAYLOR CO (IA)
TAYLOR ROOFING CO
312 29th St Ne, Cedar Rapids, IA 52402-4816
Tel (319) 363-2073 *Founded/Ownrshp* 1949, 1985
Sales 96.9MM^E *EMP* 350
Accts The Vanderbloemen Group Llc W
SIC 1761 Roofing contractor
CEO: William W Taylor
**Pr:* Philip J Suess
VP: Ben Fashimpaur
VP: James Rosetti
**VP:* Jenny Steuri
VP: Gregory J Thirnbeck
VP: Gregory Thirnbeck
VP: Jon Weston
VP Bus Dev: Eric Hasselbusch
IT Man: Rob Moore
Sales Exec: Ron Gibbons

D-U-N-S 04-110-6790
D CONSTRUCTION INC
1488 S Broadway St, Coal City, IL 60416-9443
Tel (815) 634-2555 *Founded/Ownrshp* 1982
Sales 249.8MM *EMP* 40
Accts Brian Zabel & Associates Pc M
SIC 1611 Highway & street construction
Pr: Kenneth T Sandeno
Treas: Michael Treacy
**VP:* Todd M Sandeno

D-U-N-S 61-295-3208 IMP
D D G INC
1955 Shermer Rd Ste 300, Northbrook, IL 60062-5363
Tel (847) 412-0277 *Founded/Ownrshp* 1989
Sales 226.7MM^E *EMP* 400
SIC 3317 2511 6512 Steel pipe & tubes; Wood bedroom furniture; Nonresidential building operators
Ch Bd: E A Goodman
* *Pr:* Dd Goodman

D D I
See DEVELOPMENT DIMENSIONS INTERNATIONAL INC

D D I
See DEVELOPMENTAL DISABILITIES INSTITUTE INC

D D N
See DATADIRECT NETWORKS INC

D E A
See DRUG ENFORCEMENT ADMINISTRATION

D E C
See DELAWARE ELECTRIC COOPERATIVE INC

D E C A
See DEFENSE COMMISSARY AGENCY

D E HARVEY BUILDERS
See DAVID E HARVEY BUILDERS INC

D. E. SHAW GROUP
See D E SHAW INVESTMENTS LP

D-U-N-S 78-680-0508
D E SHAW INVESTMENTS LP
D. E. SHAW GROUP
1166 Avenue Of The Americ, New York, NY 10036-2737
Tel (212) 478-0000 *Founded/Ownrshp* 1988
Sales 416.5MM^E *EMP* 999
SIC 6211

D-U-N-S 13-873-6397
D E SHAW LAMINAR PORTFOLIOS LLC
120 W 45th St Fl 22, New York, NY 10036-4041
Tel (212) 478-0000 *Founded/Ownrshp* 2002
Sales 152.1MM^E *EMP* 700
SIC 6282 2392 5945 Investment advisory service; Slip covers & pads; Toys & games
Mng Dir: Anne Dinning
Mng Dir: Julius Gaudio

D E X
See DATA EXCHANGE CORP

D-U-N-S 00-300-2102 IMP
D F STAUFFER BISCUIT CO INC (PA)
(*Suby of* MEIJI CO., LTD.)
360 S Belmont St, York, PA 17403-2616
Tel (717) 815-4600 *Founded/Ownrshp* 2008
Sales 150.0MM *EMP* 650
SIC 2052 Cookies; Crackers, dry
Pr: Shun Yoshioka
COO: Scott Stauffer
COO: James L Wilson
Treas: David E Stauffer Jr
Ex VP: Tom Gandolfi
IT Man: Craig Hoin
IT Man: Lloyd Myers
VP Opers: George Tucker

D-U-N-S 00-347-0564 IMP/EXP
D H GRIFFIN WRECKING CO INC (NC)
4716 Hilltop Rd, Greensboro, NC 27407-5217
Tel (336) 855-7030 *Founded/Ownrshp* 1959
Sales 370.2MM^E *EMP* 1,200
SIC 1795 5093 Wrecking & demolition work; Metal scrap & waste materials
Pr: David H Griffin Sr
* *CFO:* Jennifer Arndt
* *Treas:* Bonita Mitchell
* *VP:* David Griffin Jr
Dir Bus: Bill Sinclair
Dir Bus: Brocke Walker
Rgnl Mgr: Gene Ingram
Brnch Mgr: Rose M Williams
Div Mgr: Brian Alexander
Div Mgr: Tyler Bivins
Div Mgr: Chris Carter

D H P
See DIAMOND HILL PLYWOOD CO INC

D-U-N-S 06-574-6984 IMP
D H PACE CO INC
D H PACE DOOR SERVICES
(*Suby of* EE NEWCOMER ENTERPRISES INC) ★
1901 E 119th St, Olathe, KS 66061-9502
Tel (816) 221-0543 *Founded/Ownrshp* 1977
Sales 289.5MM *EMP* 900
SIC 5031 7699 Lumber & other building materials; Door & window repair
CEO: Rex E Newcomer
* *Pr:* Steve Pascuzzi
* *CFO:* Brian Gillespie
* *Ex VP:* Emily J Bailey
* *Ex VP:* Chris Mann
* *Ex VP:* N Nelson Newcomer
* *Sr VP:* Rhonda Johnson
VP: Mike Maloney
VP: Rick Martin
* *Exec:* Thomas S Palmer
Off Mgr: Pris Pettol

D H PACE DOOR SERVICES
See D H PACE CO INC

D I I
See DAMONS INTERNATIONAL INC

D-U-N-S 02-683-7067
D L J MERCHANT BANKING PARTNERS I I LP
(*Suby of* CREDIT SUISSE FIRST BOSTON) ★
11 Madison Ave, New York, NY 10010-3643
Tel (212) 325-2000 *Founded/Ownrshp* 1996
Sales 376.7MM^E *EMP* 8,287
SIC 6211 Security brokers & dealers
Mng Pt: Steve Rattner
Pt: Kamil Marc Salame

D-U-N-S 13-921-7392
D L ROGERS CORP
SONIC DRIVE-IN
5013 Davis Blvd, North Richland Hills, TX 76180-6874
Tel (817) 428-2077 *Founded/Ownrshp* 1976
Sales 109.8MM^E *EMP* 3,000
SIC 5812 6552 6799 Drive-in restaurant; Land subdividers & developers, commercial; Real estate investors, except property operators
CEO: Darrell L Rogers
* *Pr:* Shawn Rogers
* *COO:* James C Junkin
CFO: Ron Arrington
* *CFO:* Mark Berger

D M B
See DMB ASSOCIATES INC

D M G
See DISTRICT MEDICAL GROUP INC

D-U-N-S 05-275-5170
D M G INC (SD)
MALLOY ELECTRIC BEARING & SUP
809 W Russell St, Sioux Falls, SD 57104-1360
Tel (605) 336-3693 *Founded/Ownrshp* 1945, 1971
Sales 96.0MM^E *EMP* 195
SIC 5063 7694 3599 1731 Motors, electric; Electric motor repair; Machine shop, jobbing & repair; General electrical contractor
Pr: Gary Jacobson
Sec: Dianne Jacobson
VP: Dawn Gerner
VP: Chris Houwman

D M I
See DISTRIBUTION MANAGEMENT INC

D M P
See DIGITAL MONITORING PRODUCTS INC

D M S
See DMS FACILITY SERVICES INC

D N A
See BURTON CORP

D N R
See MINNESOTA DEPARTMENT OF NATURAL RESOURCES

D N R
See WASHINGTON STATE DEPARTMENT OF NATURAL RESOURCES

D P A
See DEERE PARK ASSOCIATES INC

D P I
See DECORATIVE PANELS INTERNATIONAL INC

D P I
See ELTM LP

D P I
See DPI SPECIALTY FOODS INC

D P S
See DURHAM PUBLIC SCHOOLS

D P X
See DPI NEWCO LLC

D R A
See DRA ADVISORS LLC

D-U-N-S 07-080-5536 IMP
D REYNOLDS CO LLC (TX)
REYNOLDS COMPANY, THE
2680 Sylvania Cross Dr, Fort Worth, TX 76137-5023
Tel (214) 630-9000 *Founded/Ownrshp* 1976, 1984
Sales 503.6MM^E *EMP* 360
SIC 5063 Electrical apparatus & equipment; Wiring devices; Control & signal wire & cable, including coaxial
* *Ex VP:* David Dozier
VP: Steven Guidry
VP: Lavonda Harrison
Sls Mgr: Weldon Laurence
Sls Mgr: Randy Sutton

D S & D
See DANCKER SELLEW & DOUGLAS INC

D S I
See DYNAMIC SYSTEMS INC

D S M
See DSM NUTRITIONAL PRODUCTS LLC

D S M
See DSM ENGINEERING PLASTICS INC

D SOLARIS FOUNDATION
See SOLARIS FOUNDATION INC

D T I
See DOCUMENT TECHNOLOGIES LLC

D W PACKAGING SOLUTIONS
See D&W FINE PACK LLC

D&B
See DUN & BRADSTREET INTERNATIONAL LTD

D&B
See DUN & BRADSTREET INC

D&B
See DUN & BRADSTREET CORP

D-U-N-S 03-394-9397 IMP
D&B SUPPLY CO (ID)
3303 E Linden St, Caldwell, ID 83605-6077
Tel (208) 459-7446 *Founded/Ownrshp* 1959, 1985
Sales 100.0MM *EMP* 50
SIC 5191 5699 5251 5261 5999 5531 Farm supplies; Work clothing; Builders' hardware; Tools, hand; Tools, power; Nurseries & garden centers; Plumbing & heating supplies; Automotive parts
Pr: Mark Schmidt
* *VP:* Kelly Hendrix
* *VP:* Neil Ruzicka

D-U-N-S 95-696-4365
■ **D&E COMMUNICATIONS INC**
(*Suby of* WINDSTREAM SERVICES LLC) ★
124 E Main St Fl 6, Ephrata, PA 17522-2775
Tel (717) 733-4101 *Founded/Ownrshp* 2009
Sales 93.7MM^E *EMP* 506
SIC 4813 4841 Local telephone communications; ; ; Cable television services
Pr: James W Morozzi
CFO: Thomas E Morell
Sr VP: Albert H Kramer

D-U-N-S 18-307-4889
D&M HOLDING INC
DE GOLYER AND MC MAUGHTON
5001 Spring Valley Rd 800e, Dallas, TX 75244-8212
Tel (214) 368-6391 *Founded/Ownrshp* 1945
Sales 165.9MM^E *EMP* 236
SIC 8748 Business consulting
Pr: W Gary McGilvray
Treas: R Michael Shuck
Ex VP: Charles Bryan
Sr VP: Paul J Szatkowski
Sr VP: John W Wallace
* *VP:* James W Hail
VP: Robert Johnston
VP: Matthew Wilson

D-U-N-S 82-628-3301
D&S RESIDENTIAL SERVICES LP
PEACHTREE HOME
8911 N Capital Of Texas H, Austin, TX 78759-7203
Tel (512) 327-2325 *Founded/Ownrshp* 2016
Sales 71.4MM^E *EMP* 1,450
SIC 8059 Home for the mentally retarded, exc. skilled or intermediate
CEO: Mickey Atkins
Pr: George Harold Davis Jr
CFO: Michael Clark
Treas: Harold Davis
Ofcr: Robert Ham
VP: Fred C Allan

D-U-N-S 01-530-5799
D&W FINE PACK HOLDINGS LLC
(*Suby of* MID OAKS INVESTMENTS LLC) ★
1900 Pratt Blvd, Elk Grove Village, IL 60007-5906
Tel (847) 378-1200 *Founded/Ownrshp* 2009
Sales 678.7MM^E *EMP* 1,300
SIC 3089 Plastic kitchenware, tableware & houseware
Pr: David H Randall

D-U-N-S 96-773-5957 IMP
D&W FINE PACK LLC
D W PACKAGING SOLUTIONS
(*Suby of* D&W FINE PACK HOLDINGS LLC) ★
1900 Pratt Blvd, Elk Grove Village, IL 60007-5906
Tel (847) 378-1200 *Founded/Ownrshp* 2009
Sales 676.6MM^E *EMP* 1,300
SIC 3089 Plastic kitchenware, tableware & houseware
CEO: Dave Randall
* *CEO:* Kevin Andrews
* *CFO:* Jim Japczyk
* *Sr VP:* Clay Davis
* *Sr VP:* Jay Dubois
* *VP:* Michael Casula
* *VP:* Kate Daly
* *VP:* Russ Stephens

D-U-N-S 09-129-3753
D+H USA CORP (OR)
(*Suby of* D+H USA HOLDINGS INC) ★
605 Crescent Executive Ct # 600, Lake Mary, FL 32746-2106
Tel (407) 804-6600 *Founded/Ownrshp* 1978, 2013
Sales 420.6MM^E *EMP* 1,300
SIC 7372 Prepackaged software
Pr: William W Neville
* *COO:* Bill Zayas
* *CFO:* Eric Cummins
Ex VP: Yves Denomme
* *Ex VP:* Scott Hansen
* *Sr VP:* Michael Dionne
* *Sr VP:* Carina Le
VP: Joe Plavetic
Mng Dir: Charles Savage
Snr Sftwr: Sanghamitra Borgohain
Snr Sftwr: Tony Harold

D-U-N-S 03-606-2237
D+H USA HOLDINGS INC
(*Suby of* DH CORPORATION)
605 Crescent Executive Ct # 600, Lake Mary, FL 32746-2106
Tel (407) 804-6600 *Founded/Ownrshp* 2001
Sales 366.0MM^E *EMP* 1,300^E
SIC 6719 Personal holding companies, except banks
CEO: Gerrard Schmid
* *CFO:* Brian Kyle
Bd of Dir: Henry Santana
* *Chf Mktg O:* Carrie Russell
* *Ex VP:* Yves Denomme
* *Ex VP:* Bob Noftall
* *Ex VP:* Young Park
Mng Dir: David Caldwell

D-U-N-S 15-395-0274 IMP
D-LINK SYSTEMS INC
D - LINK
(*Suby of* D-LINK CORPORATION)
17595 Mount Herrmann St, Fountain Valley, CA 92708-4160
Tel (714) 885-6000 *Founded/Ownrshp* 1986
Sales 122.0MM *EMP* 164
SIC 5045 3577 Computers; Computer peripheral equipment
Pr: Steven Joe
Pr: Carlos Casassus Fontecilla
* *Pr:* A J Wang
Assoc VP: William C Brown
Ex VP: Daniel Kelley
VP: Michael Fox
VP: Michael Hardy
VP: Sam Liang
VP: Nick Tidd
Exec: April Richardson
Exec: Premal Somani

D-U-N-S 01-628-7112
D-PATRICK INC
D-PATRICK MOTOPLEX
200 N Green River Rd, Evansville, IN 47715-2486
Tel (812) 473-6500 *Founded/Ownrshp* 1998
Sales 145.5MM *EMP* 250
Accts Crowe Horwath Llp Columbus O
SIC 5511 Automobiles, new & used
CEO: Raymond Farabaugh
* *Pr:* Michael O Daniel
* *Sec:* Jane Magary
VP: Charlie Crabtree
Sales Asso: Freddy Ghiai
Sales Asso: Tim Wargel

D-PATRICK MOTOPLEX
See D-PATRICK INC

D-U-N-S 09-758-7877
D-S PIPE & STEEL SUPPLY LLC
1301 Wicomico St Ste 3, Baltimore, MD 21230-2000
Tel (410) 837-1717 *Founded/Ownrshp* 2006
Sales 132.8MM^E *EMP* 110
SIC 5085 5051 Valves & fittings; Copper sheets, plates, bars, rods, pipes, etc.
* *VP:* Sean Keehner
Plnt Mgr: Robert Dillon
Sls Dir: Steven Stroud
Sls Mgr: Eric Frank
Sales Asso: Cross Doug
Sales Asso: Ryan Miller

D11 SCHOOL
See COLORADO SPRINGS SCHOOL DISTRICT 11

D300
See COMMUNITY UNIT SCHOOL DISTRICT 300

D-U-N-S 05-592-3668
DA DAVIDSON & CO (MT)
(*Suby of* DA DAVIDSON COMPANIES) ★
8 3rd St N, Great Falls, MT 59401-3155
Tel (406) 727-4200 *Founded/Ownrshp* 1935, 1986
Sales 326.4MM^E *EMP* 863
SIC 6211 Investment firm, general brokerage
Ch Bd: William Johnstone
Pr: Monte Giese
Pr: Michael Purpura
* *Treas:* Tom Nelson
Assoc VP: Stephen Frahm
Assoc VP: Ken Galimanis
Sr VP: Sean Ryan
Sr VP: Mark Stephenson
Sr VP: John Thompson
VP: Tammy R Beaver
VP: Frank Da Angelo
* *VP:* Ian B Davidson
VP: Julie Genjac
VP: Eric Gottlieb
VP: Dean Hall
VP: Mary Hurley
VP: Jim Lykins
VP: Michael D Maloney
VP: Jim McCarthy
VP: Dan McLaughlin
VP: Jeff Osborne

D-U-N-S 19-845-6691
DA DAVIDSON COMPANIES
8 3rd St N, Great Falls, MT 59401-3155
Tel (406) 727-4200 *Founded/Ownrshp* 1986
Sales 435.0MM^E *EMP* 1,300
SIC 6211 6733 8741 Investment firm, general brokerage; Trusts, except educational, religious, charity: management; Financial management for business
CEO: William Johnstone
* *Pr:* Larry Martinez
Pr: Karen Schaefer
* *CEO:* James Kerr
* *CFO:* Thomas Nelson
Sr Cor Off: Jean Hua
Chf Inves: Edward P Crotty
Assoc VP: Stacey Alderson
Assoc VP: Amanda Burr
Assoc VP: Jason Hufford
Assoc VP: Trisha Mingo
Sr VP: Jack Eaton
VP: Jeffrey Banks
VP: Christopher K Blackwood
VP: Cindy M Burg
VP: Cindy Burg
VP: Russell Caldwell
VP: Charlesf Cameron
VP: Teresa Cohea
VP: Chad Cowan
VP: Elliott De Bruin
Board of Directors: Ian B Davidson, Chet Helck

D-U-N-S 94-680-3459 IMP
DAA DRAEXLMAIER AUTOMOTIVE OF AMERICA LLC
(*Suby of* LISA DRAXLMAIER GMBH)
1751 E Main St, Duncan, SC 29334-9216
Tel (864) 433-8910 *Founded/Ownrshp* 1995
Sales 280.0MM^E *EMP* 1,080
SIC 3714 Motor vehicle parts & accessories
CEO: Martin Gall
* *Pr:* Stephan Bade
* *Pr:* Ulrich Eichler
Prgrm Mgr: Steve Asaro
Prgrm Mgr: Frederik Baelen
Dir IT: Corinne Maday
IT Man: Bill Linville
Opers Supe: Cynthia Todd
Mfg Mgr: Chip Vogal
Opers Mgr: Leslie Hurst
Opers Mgr: Laurie Wimmer

D-U-N-S 01-845-4108 IMP/EXP
DACCO INC
TRANSPARTS OF CHICAGO
(*Suby of* ETX HOLDINGS INC) ★
741 Dacco Dr, Cookeville, TN 38506-6272
Tel (931) 303-0112 *Founded/Ownrshp* 1965
Sales 122.7MM^E *EMP* 500
SIC 3714 5013 Motor vehicle parts & accessories; Automotive supplies & parts
CEO: Steven L Rist
* *CFO:* Andy Gasser

VP: Sam Lugo
**Genl Mgr:* Harry Schmick

D-U-N-S 03-583-4753
DACOTAH BANK
(*Suby of* DACOTAH BANKS INC) ★
308 S Main St, Aberdeen, SD 57401-4146
Tel (605) 225-5611 *Founded/Ownrshp* 1969
Sales NA *EMP* 280
SIC 6022 State commercial banks
Pr: Daniel L Baumgarten
Pr: David W Bangasser
CFO: Chad Bergan
Ofcr: Roy Becker
Ofcr: Nicole Jacobsen
Sr VP: Joe Senger
VP: Patrick Dalzell
VP: Paul Fauth
VP: Timothy Gossman
VP: Dick Gulmon
VP: Kip Hansen
VP: Phoebe Kuntz
VP: Brad Moore
VP: Diana Pfister

D-U-N-S 07-649-0580
DACOTAH BANKS INC
401 S Main St Ste 212, Aberdeen, SD 57401-4363
Tel (605) 225-1300 *Founded/Ownrshp* 1964
Sales NA *EMP* 599
SIC 6712 Bank holding companies
CEO: Richard Westra
**Pr:* Michael Hollan
**CFO:* Chad Bergan
**Sr VP:* Bob Compton
**Sr VP:* Robert Fouberg
**Sr VP:* Joe Senger
VP: Kevin Burckhard
**VP:* Kent Edson
VP: Greg Guhin
VP: Richard Holland
**VP:* Steven Schaefer

DADANCO - MESTEK
See MESTEK INC

D-U-N-S 06-801-2434 IMP/EXP
DADDARIO & CO INC
595 Smith St, Farmingdale, NY 11735-1120
Tel (631) 439-3300 *Founded/Ownrshp* 1973
Sales 221.7MM[E] *EMP* 1,100
SIC 3931 String instruments & parts; Strings, musical instrument
Ch Bd: James D'Addario
Pr: Rick Drumm
CFO: Robert Dodaro
Ex VP: John D'Addario III
VP: John D'Addario Jr
VP: David Via
Exec: Trish Johnson
Sls Mgr: Jess Gonzales

D-U-N-S 00-444-6662 IMP/EXP
DADE PAPER & BAG CO (FL)
DADE PAPER CO
9601 Nw 112th Ave, Medley, FL 33178-2521
Tel (305) 805-2600 *Founded/Ownrshp* 1939
Sales 511.0MM *EMP* 1,070
SIC 5113 Industrial & personal service paper
Pr: Lenny Genet
**COO:* Frank Sansone
**CFO:* Walter Thompson
CFO: Ann Marie Wood
Comm Dir: Laura Craven
**Brnch Mgr:* Andy Baltzell
Brnch Mgr: W A Baltzell
Genl Mgr: Chuck Howard
Genl Mgr: Scott Meltz
Genl Mgr: Thomas Wright
Off Mgr: Carmen Tuesca

DADE PAPER CO
See DADE PAPER & BAG CO

D-U-N-S 16-052-2087 IMP
DAEHAN SOLUTION ALABAMA LLC
(*Suby of* DAEHAN SOLUTION CO., LTD.)
9101 County Road 26, Hope Hull, AL 36043-6222
Tel (334) 404-5000 *Founded/Ownrshp* 2003
Sales 112.9MM *EMP* 310
SIC 3625 2273 Noise control equipment; Carpets & rugs
Pr: Yong Kee Chun
Genl Mgr: Sungtaek Kim
Ql Cn Mgr: Bong Kim

D-U-N-S 02-404-7364 IMP
DAEHAN SOLUTION GEORGIA LLC (GA)
(*Suby of* DAEHAN SOLUTION CO., LTD.)
791 S Progress Pkwy, West Point, GA 31833-5453
Tel (706) 902-5200 *Founded/Ownrshp* 2008
Sales 138.0MM *EMP* 300
Accts Choi Kim & Park Llp Lagrang
SIC 5013 8711 3714 Automotive supplies & parts; Engineering services; Motor vehicle engines & parts
Ch: Hoehyun Kwon
**CEO:* Kangog Lim
COO: Youngki Kim

D-U-N-S 07-976-7726
DAELIM USA INC
1200 International Blvd, Clarksville, TN 37040-6392
Tel (770) 530-3489 *Founded/Ownrshp* 2012
Sales 100.0MM *EMP* 20
SIC 1541

D-U-N-S 79-911-7036 IMP/EXP
DAEWON AMERICA INC
(*Suby of* DAE WON KANG UP CO., LTD.)
4600 N Park Dr, Opelika, AL 36801-9687
Tel (334) 364-1600 *Founded/Ownrshp* 2007
Sales 104.9MM *EMP* 350
SIC 3493 Automobile springs
Pr: Hee Yong Bang
CFO: Duk OH

DAEWOO ELECTRONICS MARKETING
See CNA INTERNATIONAL INC

D-U-N-S 01-123-3509 IMP
DAFFYS INC
DAFFY'S, INC AND AFFLIATE
Daffys Way, Secaucus, NJ 07094
Tel (201) 902-0800 *Founded/Ownrshp* 1961
Sales NA *EMP* 1,400
SIC 5651

DAFFY'S, INC AND AFFLIATE
See DAFFYS INC

D-U-N-S 01-197-5059
DAGOSTINO SUPERMARKETS INC
D'AGOSTINO'S
1385 Boston Post Rd Ste 1, Larchmont, NY 10538-3954
Tel (914) 833-4000 *Founded/Ownrshp* 1936
Sales 160.6MM[E] *EMP* 1,100
SIC 5411 Supermarkets, chain
Ch Bd: Nicholas D'Agostino III
Mktg Dir: Suzanne Cecchi

D'AGOSTINO'S
See DAGOSTINO SUPERMARKETS INC

D-U-N-S 12-150-6281 IMP/EXP
■ **DAHILL OFFICE TECHNOLOGY CORP**
(*Suby of* GLOBAL IMAGING SYSTEMS INC) ★
8200 W Interstate 10 # 400, San Antonio, TX 78230-3876
Tel (210) 805-8200 *Founded/Ownrshp* 2008
Sales 116.7MM[E] *EMP* 492
SIC 5999 3861 2759 Business machines & equipment; Photocopy machines; Facsimile equipment; Photographic equipment & supplies; Commercial printing; Laser printing
CEO: Bradley Rollins
**CFO:* Robert Vandever
**VP:* Tony Damaini
IT Man: Thomas Brownson
Sales Exec: David Riener
Sls Dir: Rick Mailand

DAHL'S FOODS
See FOODS INC

D-U-N-S 05-578-2361 IMP
DAHN CORP (CA)
MINI U STORAGE
18552 Macarthur Blvd # 495, Irvine, CA 92612-1271
Tel (949) 752-1282 *Founded/Ownrshp* 1944, 1968
Sales 120.5MM[E] *EMP* 215
SIC 1531 6531 4225 Operative builders; Real estate managers; Warehousing, self-storage
Pr: Brian A Dahn
**Sec:* Nancy Nave
**Ex VP:* Robert Bradley

D-U-N-S 96-866-6979
DAHUA ELECTRONICS CORP
13412 59th Ave, Flushing, NY 11355-5244
Tel (718) 886-2188 *Founded/Ownrshp* 2011
Sales 156.0MM *EMP* 20
SIC 3676 Electronic resistors
Pr: Gomita Junkiji

D-U-N-S 06-678-1956
DAI GLOBAL LLC
7600 Wisconsin Ave # 200, Bethesda, MD 20814-3657
Tel (301) 771-7600 *Founded/Ownrshp* 1970
Sales 186.6MM[E] *EMP* 1,500
SIC 8748 Economic consultant
Pr: James Boomgard
**CFO:* Michael Jakobowski
**Sr VP:* Jean Gilson
**Sr VP:* Christopher Legrand
**Sr VP:* Christopher Lockett
**Sr VP:* Laura Viehmyer
**Sr VP:* Helle Weeke
VP: Gary Kinney
VP: Betsy Marcotte
**VP:* Zan Northrip
Mng Dir: Claudia Manning
Board of Directors: James Boomgard, Daniel Hearney, Elizabeth Nelson, Maria Otero, Gail Steinel

D-U-N-S 13-940-6391
DAICEL AMERICA HOLDINGS INC
(*Suby of* DAICEL CORPORATION)
1 Parker Plz, Fort Lee, NJ 07024-2920
Tel (201) 461-4466 *Founded/Ownrshp* 1992
Sales 113.1MM[E] *EMP* 344
SIC 8741 Administrative management
Pr: Masato Sakai
**Treas:* Kunio Fukui

D-U-N-S 10-835-7059 IMP/EXP
DAICEL SAFETY SYSTEMS AMERICA LLC
(*Suby of* DAICEL AMERICA HOLDINGS INC) ★
720 Old Liberty Church Rd, Beaver Dam, KY 42320-9130
Tel (270) 274-0062 *Founded/Ownrshp* 2001
Sales 110.7MM[E] *EMP* 340
SIC 3069 Life jackets, inflatable: rubberized fabric
Ql Cn Mgr: Kevin Autry

D-U-N-S 10-217-6674 IMP
DAIFUKU AMERICA CORP
DAIFUKU CO
(*Suby of* DAIFUKU CO., LTD.)
6700 Tussing Rd, Reynoldsburg, OH 43068-5083
Tel (614) 863-1888 *Founded/Ownrshp* 1986
Sales 276.1MM[E] *EMP* 300
SIC 5084 Materials handling machinery; Conveyor systems
Pr: Nobo Morita
**Pr:* Mike Conner
**Pr:* Ken Hamel
**Pr:* Akihiko Nishimura
**Sec:* Tetsuya Hibi
**Sr VP:* John Doychich
VP: Bob Huffman
**VP:* Tomoaki Terai
Ex Dir: Mark Bentley
Snr Sftwr: Tracy Larson
Snr Mgr: Kenji Uemura

DAIFUKU CO
See DAIFUKU AMERICA CORP

D-U-N-S 07-853-3881
DAIFUKU WEBB HOLDING CO
(*Suby of* DAIFUKU CO., LTD.)
34375 W 12 Mile Rd, Farmington Hills, MI 48331-3375
Tel (248) 553-1000 *Founded/Ownrshp* 2011
Sales 518.6MM[E] *EMP* 1,000[E]
SIC 3695 Computer software tape & disks: blank, rigid & floppy
Pr: Aki Nishimura
**Pr:* Noburo Morita
Ex VP: Bill Kline
**VP:* John Doychish
Mng Dir: Brent Brosch
Snr Sftwr: Christopher Simon
Site Mgr: Harvey Henning
Genl Couns: Michael Farley

D-U-N-S 06-860-5067 IMP
DAIICHI SANKYO INC
(*Suby of* DAIICHI SANKYO COMPANY, LIMITED)
2 Hilton Ct Ste 1, Parsippany, NJ 07054-4411
Tel (973) 359-2600 *Founded/Ownrshp* 1996
Sales 868.6MM[E] *EMP* 1,500
SIC 5122 8731 Pharmaceuticals; Commercial physical research
Pr: Glenn Gormley
**Ch Bd:* Susumu Kawabe
**Treas:* Hisao Koshino
Acting Pr: Greg Barrett
Ex VP: Marielle Cohard-Radice
Ex VP: Mahmoud Ghazzi
Sr VP: James Giordano
VP: Leigh Ann Errico
VP: Jay M Feingold
Assoc Dir: Kathleen Chavanu
Assoc Dir: Akihiro Inoguchi
Assoc Dir: Janet Weiss

D-U-N-S 80-002-0604 IMP/EXP
DAIKIN AMERICA INC
(*Suby of* DAIKIN INDUSTRIES, LTD.)
20 Olympic Dr, Orangeburg, NY 10962-2511
Tel (845) 365-9500 *Founded/Ownrshp* 1991
Sales 92.4MM[E] *EMP* 320
SIC 3081 2821

D-U-N-S 00-624-9791 IMP/EXP
DAIKIN APPLIED AMERICAS INC
(*Suby of* AMERICAN AIR FILTER) ★
13600 Industrial Pk Blvd, Minneapolis, MN 55441-3743
Tel (763) 553-5330 *Founded/Ownrshp* 2007
Sales 1.5MMM[E] *EMP* 3,500
SIC 5075 3585 Warm air heating & air conditioning; Refrigeration & heating equipment
CEO: Katsuhiko Takagi
**COO:* Michael G Schwartz
**CFO:* Clayton Jacoby
**Treas:* Ronald J Pederson
Ex VP: Kevin Facinelli
VP: Susan Kaufman
Exec: David Diaz
Exec: Prem Shetty
Prgrm Mgr: Aaron Stonestreet
Dist Mgr: John Adam
Dist Mgr: Scott Schomburg

D-U-N-S 05-074-4557
DAIKIN MANUFACTURING CO LP
5151 San Felipe St # 500, Houston, TX 77056-3607
Tel (972) 245-1510 *Founded/Ownrshp* 1993
Sales 100.0MM *EMP* 9[E]
SIC 3585 Heating & air conditioning combination units
Prin: Kimberly Fields
Exec: Lisa Boemmel
Mktg Dir: Marc Bellanger

DAILY CAMERA
See PRAIRIE MOUNTAIN PUBLISHING CO LLC

DAILY COURIER
See TRIBUNE REVIEW PUBLISHING CO

D-U-N-S 00-302-9345
DAILY EXPRESS INC (PA)
1072 Harrisburg Pike, Carlisle, PA 17013-1615
Tel (717) 243-5757 *Founded/Ownrshp* 1931, 1976
Sales 92.0MM[E] *EMP* 200
SIC 4213 Trucking, except local
CEO: Todd Long
**Pr:* Robert F Long
**Treas:* Michael McGeory
VP Opers: Mike Howard
**VP Sls:* Michael D Howard
Board of Directors: Katherine Long, Tara Long, Todd R Long, Dennis I Meyer, Rita Meyer

DAILY GRILL
See GRILL CONCEPTS-DC INC

DAILY GRILL ENCINO PLACE
See GRILL CONCEPTS INC

DAILY HERALD
See PADDOCK PUBLICATIONS INC

D-U-N-S 79-870-1538 IMP
DAILY NEWS LP
NEW YORK DAILY NEWS
4 New York Plz Fl 6, New York, NY 10004-2828
Tel (212) 210-2100 *Founded/Ownrshp* 1993
Sales 351.9MM[E] *EMP* 1,600
SIC 2711 Commercial printing & newspaper publishing combined
Genl Pt: Marc Kramer
Pt: Mort Zuckerman
CFO: Tom Peck
VP: Michael Flaminio
VP: Matthew Leish
VP: Andrew Reale
Creative D: Paul Kim
Netwrk Eng: David Chan
Opers Mgr: Sherryl Connelly
Mktg Mgr: Ken Marco

DAILY OKLAHOMAN, THE
See OKLAHOMA PUBLISHING CO OF OKLAHOMA

D-U-N-S 00-311-5037
■ **DAILY PRESS INC**
(*Suby of* TRONC INC) ★
703 Mariners Row, Newport News, VA 23606-4432
Tel (757) 245-3737 *Founded/Ownrshp* 2014
Sales 132.9MM[E] *EMP* 575[E]
SIC 2711 Job printing & newspaper publishing combined
Pr: Digby A Solomon Diez
**CFO:* Ann Wilson
VP: Orestes Baez
**VP:* Gregory Pedersen
VP: Mike Petters
Ex Dir: Paula Otto
VP Mktg: Lisa Bohnaker
Assoc Ed: Carol Capo

D-U-N-S 87-812-0120 IMP
DAIMLER PURCHASING COORDINATION CORP
(*Suby of* DAIMLER AG)
36455 Corporate Dr, Farmington Hills, MI 48331-3552
Tel (248) 991-6700 *Founded/Ownrshp* 1992
Sales 155.8MM[E] *EMP* 700
SIC 5012 5013 Automobiles; Trucks, noncommercial; Motor vehicle supplies & new parts
Pr: Michael Jackson

DAIMLER TRUCK FINANCIAL
See MERCEDES-BENZ FINANCIAL SERVICES USA LLC

D-U-N-S 00-902-9687 IMP/EXP
DAIMLER TRUCKS NORTH AMERICA LLC
(*Suby of* DAIMLER AG)
4747 N Channel Ave, Portland, OR 97217-7613
Tel (503) 745-8011 *Founded/Ownrshp* 2007
Sales 8.8MMM[E] *EMP* 20,000
SIC 3711 4789

D-U-N-S 10-300-6649
DAIMLER TRUCKS REMARKETING CORP
(*Suby of* DAIMLER TRUCKS NORTH AMERICA LLC) ★
4747 N Channel Ave, Portland, OR 97217-7613
Tel (503) 745-8000 *Founded/Ownrshp* 1977
Sales NA *EMP* 520
SIC 6153 Financing of dealers by motor vehicle manufacturers organ.
Pr: Richard Simons
**Pr:* Rainer Schmueckle
**Treas:* Kelley Platt
**VP:* Juergen Kritschgau
Snr Mgr: Nicole Kennedy

D-U-N-S 04-177-3912
DAIN RAUSCHER INC
(*Suby of* RBC WEALTH MANAGEMENT) ★
60 S 6th St Ste 700, Minneapolis, MN 55402-4413
Tel (704) 377-4300 *Founded/Ownrshp* 1973
Sales 100.3MM[E] *EMP* 3,000
SIC 6211 Brokers, security; Dealers, security; Investment bankers; Underwriters, security
Ch Bd: Irving Weiser
Pr: Peter Armenio
**CEO:* John Taft
CFO: Dave J Parrin
Treas: Theodore Ceglia
Ofcr: Bob Schneebeck
Ex VP: Paula H Philippe
Sr VP: Daniel Collins
Sr VP: Daniel B Marcotte
VP: Dorothy Marden
VP: Jerry Stratman

D-U-N-S 83-264-8286 IMP
DAINIPPON SUMITOMO PHARMA AMERICA HOLDINGS INC
(*Suby of* SUMITOMO DAINIPPON PHARMA CO., LTD.)
1 Bridge Plz N Ste 510, Fort Lee, NJ 07024-7102
Tel (201) 592-2050 *Founded/Ownrshp* 2009
Sales 645.9MM[E] *EMP* 2,400[E]
SIC 2834 Pharmaceutical preparations
Pr: Shunsuke Sami

D-U-N-S 15-787-3659 IMP/EXP
DAIRICONCEPTS LP
3253 E Chestnut Expy, Springfield, MO 65802-2540
Tel (417) 829-3400 *Founded/Ownrshp* 2000
Sales 316.2MM[E] *EMP* 490
SIC 2022 Cheese spreads, dips, pastes & other cheese products
Pr: Jeff Miyake
VP: Brian Bonebright
VP: Kris Clemenpf
Tech Mgr: Chad Mitchell

D-U-N-S 08-519-5766
DAIRY EXPORT CO INC
(*Suby of* DARIGOLD INC) ★
635 Elliott Ave W, Seattle, WA 98119-3911
Tel (206) 284-7220 *Founded/Ownrshp* 1966
Sales 1.4MMM *EMP* 1,100
SIC 5191 5083 2033 Animal feeds; Farm implements; Fruit juices: packaged in cans, jars, etc.
VP: Steven Rowe
**VP:* Stephen R Boyd

D-U-N-S 02-985-5640 IMP/EXP
DAIRY FARMERS OF AMERICA INC
10220 N Ambassador Dr, Kansas City, MO 64153-1367
Tel (816) 801-6455 *Founded/Ownrshp* 1968
Sales 13.8MMM *EMP* 3,500
Accts Kpmg Llp Kansas City Missour
SIC 2026 2023 2021 2022 5083 2024 Creamery butter; Natural cheese; Processed cheese; Condensed milk; Powdered milk; Fluid milk; Milk processing (pasteurizing, homogenizing, bottling); Ice cream & ice milk; Dairy machinery & equipment
Pr: Rick Smith
V Ch: Steve Hofman
COO: John Collins
COO: Gregory I Wickham
COO: William Phipps
COO: John Stephens
Bd of Dir: Ed Schoen
Ex VP: Doug Glade
Ex VP: Donald Schriver

*Sr VP: Alex Bachelor
*Sr VP: Joel Clark
*Sr VP: David Meyer
VP: Lavonne Dietrich
VP: David Geisler
VP: Bruce Hageman
VP: Randy Harman
VP: Monica Massey
VP: Randall McGinnis
VP: Ernie Napoles
VP: Chris Newman
VP: Pat Panko

D-U-N-S 07-926-6474
DAIRY FRESH FARMS INC
9636 Blomberg St Sw, Olympia, WA 98512-8999
Tel (360) 357-9411 Founded/Ownrshp 1963
Sales 86.2MM[E] EMP 68
SIC 5143 Dairy products, except dried or canned; Ice cream & ices; Milk
Pr: Jerry Clark
*Sec: Marilyn Clark
Genl Mgr: Dean Heggie

DAIRY FRESH FOOD
See DETROIT CITY DAIRY

D-U-N-S 83-606-3438
DAIRY MANAGEMENT INC
(Suby of UNITED DAIRY INDUSTRY ASSOCIATION, INC.)
10255 W Higgins Rd # 900, Rosemont, IL 60018-5638
Tel (847) 803-2000 Founded/Ownrshp 1994
Sales 141.0MM EMP 80
Accts Ernst & Young Us Llp Indianap
SIC 8611 Trade associations
CEO: Thomas Gallagher
Pr: Mark Leitner
Pr: David Pelzer
Ex VP: Greg Miller
Ex VP: Jean Ragalie
Ex VP: Mollie Waller
Sr VP: Daniel Chavka
Sr VP: Sarah Hanson
Sr VP: Sherri Maxson
VP: Sarah Baird
VP: Jessica Learman
VP: Rebecca Mackay
VP: Laura Mandell
VP: Wesley Matthews
VP: Jill Nicholls
VP: Juan Tricarico

DAIRY QUEEN
See M & R UNITED INC

D-U-N-S 93-299-0286 IMP/EXP
DAIRYAMERICA INC
7815 N Palm Ave Ste 250, Fresno, CA 93711-5528
Tel (559) 251-0992 Founded/Ownrshp 1995
Sales 1.6MMM EMP 51
Accts Deloitte & Touche Llp Fresno
SIC 5143 Dairy products, except dried or canned
CEO: Hoyt Huffman
*Treas: Craig Alexander

D-U-N-S 00-610-2784 IMP
DAIRYFOOD USA INC
2819 County Road F, Blue Mounds, WI 53517-9587
Tel (608) 437-5598 Founded/Ownrshp 2002
Sales 103.0MM[E] EMP 115
SIC 5143 2022 2023 Cheese; Processed cheese; Dry, condensed, evaporated dairy products
Pr: Daniel R Culligan
Ql Cn Mgr: Vern Winker

D-U-N-S 05-083-2096
DAIRYLAND INSURANCE CO
(Suby of SENTRY INSURANCE A MUTUAL CO) ★
1800 Northpoint Dr, Stevens Point, WI 54481-1253
Tel (715) 346-6000 Founded/Ownrshp 1991
Sales NA EMP 400
SIC 6331 Automobile insurance
Ch Bd: Dale Schuh
*Pr: Thomas M Lamb
*Pr: Robert Mueller
*COO: Peter Pelizza
*Treas: William Lohr
*Treas: David Rosin
*VP: Janet Fagan
VP: Gregory Pfluger
IT Man: Robert Jakusz
Snr PM: Barb Tuen

D-U-N-S 00-794-6171
DAIRYLAND POWER COOPERATIVE (WI)
3200 East Ave S, La Crosse, WI 54601-7291
Tel (608) 788-4000 Founded/Ownrshp 1941
Sales 418.3MM EMP 500
Accts Deloitte & Touche Llp Minneap
SIC 4911 ; Generation, electric power; Transmission, electric power; Distribution, electric power
Pr: Barbara Nick
*VP: John Carr
*VP: Mary Lund
*VP: Phillip Moilien
*VP: Rob Palmberg
*VP: Ben Porath

D-U-N-S 13-169-8615 IMP
■ **DAIRYLAND USA CORP**
CHEFS' WAREHOUSE, THE
(Suby of CHEFS WAREHOUSE INC) ★
1250 Waters Pl Ste 704, Bronx, NY 10461-2732
Tel (718) 842-8700 Founded/Ownrshp 1985
Sales 313.7MM[E] EMP 310[E]
SIC 5141 Groceries, general line
Ch: Chris Pappas
Pr: Dimitri Papadopoulis
Pr: Kelly Romano
*CFO: Ken Clark
VP: Ed Kauffeld
CIO: Frank Odowd
Sls Dir: Matias Lagos
Sls Mgr: Caryn Gordon
Sls Mgr: Steve Kass
Sls Mgr: Ian Taylor
Sls Mgr: Frank Vitale

D-U-N-S 00-799-3033
DAIRYMANS SUPPLY CO INC (KY)
DSC
3114 State Route 45 S, Mayfield, KY 42066-6133
Tel (270) 247-5641 Founded/Ownrshp 1925
Sales 141.5MM EMP 97
Accts Moffit & Company Pllc David R
SIC 5031 Building materials, exterior; Building materials, interior
*Pr: Greg Cook
*CFO: Jeff Boyd
VP: Lynn-Gregory G Cook
Sales Asso: Jeremy Wheeler
Sales Asso: Larry Williams

D-U-N-S 05-741-7776 IMP
DAISY BRAND LLC
12750 Merit Dr Ste 600, Dallas, TX 75251-1261
Tel (972) 726-0800 Founded/Ownrshp 1971
Sales 179.7MM[E] EMP 400
SIC 2026 Milk processing (pasteurizing, homogenizing, bottling); Cream, sour
CEO: David M Sokolsky
*Pr: Vince Taylor
*CFO: Stu Grubbs
Exec: David Sokolsky
Rgnl Mgr: Chuck Forehand
Genl Mgr: Emily Aguilar
Genl Mgr: Rick Fagan
Genl Mgr: Derek Garwood
Genl Mgr: Mark Schultz
IT Man: Angela Ripley
Opers Mgr: Christopher Brown

D-U-N-S 04-797-9579
DAISY CHAIN DESIGNS
2743 Goneaway Rd, Charlotte, NC 28210-6113
Tel (704) 517-8591 Founded/Ownrshp 2010
Sales 102.7MM EMP 1
Accts Larson & Company Pa Wichit
SIC 7389

D-U-N-S 61-484-4249
DAIWA CAPITAL MARKETS AMERICA HOLDINGS INC
(Suby of DAIWA INTERNATIONAL HOLDINGS, K.K.)
32 Old Slip Fl 14, New York, NY 10005-3518
Tel (212) 612-7000 Founded/Ownrshp 1990
Sales 84.5MM[E] EMP 600
SIC 6211 Dealers, security
Ch: Masayasu Ohi
*Pr: Shuji Nishyama
*COO: Ikou Mori
*Ex VP: Richard Beggs
*Ex VP: Hiroki Numora
DP Exec: Jim Lei
MIS Dir: Jeffrey Borror

D-U-N-S 06-981-9972 IMP/EXP
DAK AMERICAS LLC
(Suby of ALPEK, S.A.B. DE C.V.)
5925 Carnegie Blvd # 500, Charlotte, NC 28209-4671
Tel (704) 940-7500 Founded/Ownrshp 2001
Sales 686.4MM[E] EMP 1,300
SIC 2821 Thermoplastic materials
Pr: Jorge Young
Treas: Christy McCrary
CTO: Jose Cazariego
Cmptr Lab: Judith Bryant
Tech Mgr: Alex Nieuwland
Tech Mgr: Barry West
Netwrk Eng: Johnny Driggers
Site Mgr: John Oladele
Opers Mgr: Louis Hall
Plnt Mgr: Leroy Butler
Plnt Mgr: Antonia Garza

D-U-N-S 02-792-9459 IMP
DAKKOTA INTEGRATED SYSTEMS LLC
1875 Holloway Dr, Holt, MI 48842-9435
Tel (517) 694-6500 Founded/Ownrshp 2001
Sales 269.9MM[E] EMP 670
SIC 3711 Automobile assembly, including specialty automobiles
Ch: Andra Rush
*COO: Peter Goguen
IT Man: Nick Hammond

D-U-N-S 09-999-9732 IMP/EXP
DAKO NORTH AMERICA INC
6392 Via Real, Carpinteria, CA 93013-2921
Tel (805) 566-6655 Founded/Ownrshp 2012
Sales 132.3MM[E] EMP 325
SIC 5122 3841

DAKOTA BLOCK CO
See PETE LIEN & SONS INC

D-U-N-S 19-733-6423
DAKOTA COAL CO
(Suby of BASIN ELECTRIC POWER COOPERATIVE) ★
1717 E Interstate Ave, Bismarck, ND 58503-0542
Tel (701) 223-0441 Founded/Ownrshp 1988
Sales 214.0MM EMP 15
Accts Deloitte & Touche Llp Minneap
SIC 6519 7353 3274 Mine property leasing; Heavy construction equipment rental; Lime
Ch Bd: Roberta Rohrer
CEO: Paul M Sukut
COO: Robert Bartosh
CFO: Steve Johnson

DAKOTA COUNTY COURTHOUSE
See COUNTY OF DAKOTA

D-U-N-S 01-020-0103 IMP/EXP
DAKOTA CREEK INDUSTRIES INC
820 4th St, Anacortes, WA 98221-1507
Tel (360) 293-9575 Founded/Ownrshp 1975
Sales 117.2MM[E] EMP 600
SIC 3732 3731 Boat building & repairing; Ferryboats, building & repairing
Pr: Richard N Nelson
*Treas: Nancy Loftis
*VP: Rick Kirschman
*VP: Mike Nelson
Prgrm Mgr: Hollie Anthonysz
IT Man: Jim Carver
Sales Exec: David Longdale

D-U-N-S 00-696-1346
DAKOTA ELECTRIC ASSOCIATION
4300 220th St W, Farmington, MN 55024-9583
Tel (651) 463-6212 Founded/Ownrshp 1937
Sales 209.2MM EMP 100,000
Accts Cliftonlarsonallen Llp Austin
SIC 8611 Trade associations
CEO: Greg Miller
*Ch Bd: Jim Sheldon
*V Ch: Bill Holton
*Treas: Clay De Bogart
Bd of Dir: David Jones
VP: Doug Larson
VP: Stan McNeil
VP: Dirk Rotty
IT Man: Vicki Aubrecht

DAKOTA ELECTRIC SUPPLY COMPANY
See DAKOTA SUPPLY GROUP INC

D-U-N-S 61-193-5339 IMP
DAKOTA GASIFICATION CO INC
(Suby of BASIN ELECTRIC POWER COOPERATIVE) ★
1717 E Interstate Ave, Bismarck, ND 58503-0542
Tel (701) 223-0441 Founded/Ownrshp 1988
Sales 582.7MM EMP 725
Accts Deloitte & Touche Llp Minneap
SIC 2873 5169 1311 Nitrogenous fertilizers; Chemicals & allied products; Coal gasification
Ch Bd: Don Applegate
*CEO: Paul M Sukut
*COO: David Sauer
*CFO: Steve Johnson

D-U-N-S 79-621-9376 IMP
■ **DAKOTA GROWERS PASTA CO INC**
(Suby of AGRICORE UNITED HOLDINGS INC.)
1 Pasta Ave, Carrington, ND 58421-2500
Tel (701) 652-2855 Founded/Ownrshp 2010
Sales 137.2MM[E] EMP 439[E]
SIC 2098 Macaroni & spaghetti
Pr: Timothy J Dodd
COO: David E Tressler
CFO: Edward O Irin
*CFO: Edward O Irion
VP: Radwan Ibrahim
VP: Gary Mackintosh
Sfty Dirs: Jason Wolsky
Sfty Mgr: Robert Buskness
Prd Mgr: Jerome Sharper
Sales Exec: Denise Shipman
Mktg Dir: Liz Reinhiller

D-U-N-S 15-454-8093
DAKOTA KING INC
BURGER KING
3800 W 53rd St, Sioux Falls, SD 57106-4223
Tel (605) 361-7714 Founded/Ownrshp 1976
Sales 42.2MM[E] EMP 1,100
SIC 5812 Fast-food restaurant, chain
Pr: Tom Walsh

D-U-N-S 02-437-2310
DAKOTA NEWS INC (SD)
COVER TO COVER
221 S Petro Ave, Sioux Falls, SD 57107-0572
Tel (605) 336-3000 Founded/Ownrshp 1958, 2009
Sales 123.9MM[E] EMP 220
SIC 5192 Books, periodicals & newspapers
Pr: Teryl Bourne
VP: Jerome Freese
Genl Mgr: George Mitchell

D-U-N-S 08-039-0381
DAKOTA PARENT INC
9 W 57th St Fl 43, New York, NY 10019-2700
Tel (212) 515-3200 Founded/Ownrshp 2016
Sales 155.8MM[E] EMP 8,174[E]
SIC 6719 Investment holding companies, except banks
CEO: Leon Black

DAKOTA PROVISIONS
See DAKOTA TURKEY GROWERS LLC

D-U-N-S 62-612-0117 IMP
DAKOTA SUPPLY GROUP INC
DAKOTA ELECTRIC SUPPLY COMPANY
2601 3rd Ave N, Fargo, ND 58102-4016
Tel (701) 237-9440 Founded/Ownrshp 1991
Sales 401.1MM EMP 720
Accts Eide Bailly Llp Fargo North
SIC 5063 Electrical apparatus & equipment
CEO: Todd Kumm
*Pr: Tom Rosendahl
*COO: Dan Mille
*CFO: Mark Feeney
*VP: Mike Tupa

D-U-N-S 13-832-3881
DAKOTA TURKEY GROWERS LLC
DAKOTA PROVISIONS
40253 Us Highway 14, Huron, SD 57350-7913
Tel (605) 352-1519 Founded/Ownrshp 2003
Sales 176.5MM[E] EMP 600
SIC 2015 Turkey processing & slaughtering
CEO: Kenneth D Rutledge
IT Man: Karen Snow

D-U-N-S 04-952-1511 IMP/EXP
▲ **DAKTRONICS INC** (SD)
201 Daktronics Dr, Brookings, SD 57006-2359
Tel (605) 692-0200 Founded/Ownrshp 1968
Sales 570.1MM EMP 2,785[E]
Tkr Sym DAKT Exch NGS
SIC 3993 7372 Scoreboards, electric; Application computer software
Pr: Reece A Kurtenbach
Pr: Steven Scarbrough
*CFO: Sheila M Anderson
*Ex VP: Bradley T Wiemann
VP: Bob Dibiasio
*VP: Carla S Gatzke
VP: Seth Hansen
VP: Rich E Hinz
VP: Greg Hoop
*VP: Matthew J Kurtenbach
VP: David Young

Creative D: Danielle Galbavy
Comm Man: Staci Perry
Board of Directors: Byron J Anderson, Robert G Dutcher, Nancy D Frame, John P Friel, Kevin P McDermott, James B Morgan, John L Mulligan

D-U-N-S 01-139-4330
■ **DAL GLOBAL SERVICES LLC**
DELTA GLOBAL SERVICES
(Suby of DELTA AIRLINES) ★
980 Virginia Ave 4th, Atlanta, GA 30354-1389
Tel (404) 715-4300 Founded/Ownrshp 1995
Sales 198.0MM[E] EMP 7,000
SIC 7361 8331 7382 5088 Executive placement; Job training & vocational rehabilitation services; Security systems services; Aeronautical equipment & supplies
Pr: Cyryl Terner
Genl Mgr: Peter Dicarlo
VP Mktg: Phillip Skinner

D-U-N-S 00-234-7003 IMP/EXP
■ **DAL-TILE CORP**
DALTILE
(Suby of MOHAWK INDUSTRIES INC) ★
7834 C F Hawn Fwy, Dallas, TX 75217-6544
Tel (214) 398-1411 Founded/Ownrshp 2002
Sales 1.8MMM[E] EMP 8,600
SIC 3253

D-U-N-S 96-441-1479
■ **DAL-TILE DISTRIBUTION INC**
(Suby of MOHAWK INDUSTRIES INC) ★
7834 C F Hawn Fwy, Dallas, TX 75217-6544
Tel (214) 398-1411 Founded/Ownrshp 2004
Sales 188.2MM[E] EMP 1,856
SIC 5032 Marble building stone; Granite building stone
CEO: Jeffrey S Lorberbaum
*Pr: John Turner
*CFO: Mike McGlophlin
IT Man: Jay Mori
VP Sls: John Cousins

D-U-N-S 60-919-3602 IMP/EXP
■ **DAL-TILE GROUP INC**
(Suby of MOHAWK INDUSTRIES INC) ★
7834 C F Hawn Fwy, Dallas, TX 75217-6544
Tel (214) 398-1411 Founded/Ownrshp 2002
Sales 423.3MM[E] EMP 7,524
SIC 3253 Wall tile, ceramic; Floor tile, ceramic
Pr: Chris Wellborn
Bd of Dir: Jeff Lorberbaum
VP: Barry J Kulpa
VP: John Turmer
Opers Mgr: Andrea Nipp

D-U-N-S 80-800-2240
■ **DAL-TILE SERVICES INC**
(Suby of MOHAWK INDUSTRIES INC) ★
160 S Industrial Blvd, Calhoun, GA 30701-3030
Tel (706) 629-7721 Founded/Ownrshp 2002
Sales 686.4MM[E] EMP 7,524
SIC 3253 Ceramic wall & floor tile
Pr: John Turner Jr
CFO: Frank Boikin
*CFO: James Brunk
*CFO: Mike McGlothlin
*Treas: Scott Veldman
*VP: John Swift
*Prin: Barbara M Goetz

D-U-N-S 00-726-5382 IMP/EXP
■ **DALE VISHAY ELECTRONICS LLC**
VISHAY INTERTECHNOLOGY
(Suby of VISHAY INTERTECHNOLOGY INC) ★
1122 23rd St, Columbus, NE 68601-3647
Tel (605) 665-9301 Founded/Ownrshp 1951, 1985
Sales 288.7MM[E] EMP 4,200
SIC 3676 3679 3677 3678 Electronic resistors; Electronic circuits; Inductors, electronic; Transformers power supply, electronic type; Electronic connectors
Pr: Roland Rueschhoff
*Treas: David McConnell
*Sr VP: Robert A Freece
*Prin: Carl Fritz
Snr Mgr: Dave Richardson

D-U-N-S 00-780-4651
DALHART CONSUMERS FUEL ASSOCIATION INC
919 Liberal St, Dalhart, TX 79022-2928
Tel (806) 249-4660 Founded/Ownrshp 1933
Sales 103.7MM EMP 40
Accts Lindburg Vogel Pierce Faris H
SIC 5153 5172 5191 5541 Grains; Gasoline; Diesel fuel; Lubricating oils & greases; Chemicals, agricultural; Fertilizer & fertilizer materials; Filling stations, gasoline
Treas: Jim Turner

D-U-N-S 96-707-0298
DALIO FOUNDATION INC
1 Glendinning Pl, Westport, CT 06880-1242
Tel (203) 291-5130 Founded/Ownrshp 2002
Sales 398.0MM[E] EMP 14[E]
SIC 8699 Charitable organization
Prin: Raymond T Dalio

D-U-N-S 12-707-5893 IMP
DALLAS AIRMOTIVE INC
PREMIER TURBINES
(Suby of BBA AVIATION PLC)
900 Nolen Dr Ste 100, Grapevine, TX 76051-8641
Tel (214) 956-3001 Founded/Ownrshp 1997
Sales 155.9MM[E] EMP 1,569
SIC 7699 Aircraft & heavy equipment repair services
Pr: Allan Douglas Meador
CFO: Bruce Weaver
*Treas: Mark K Moyer
*VP: Michael T Cumnock
*VP: Nandakumar Madireddi
VP: Hugh McElroy
VP: Tim Ramsey
Genl Mgr: Dan Avicola
Genl Mgr: John Fox
Genl Mgr: Francis Martin
IT Man: Larry Cobbs

Board of Directors: Bruce Van Allen

D-U-N-S 05-109-7897
DALLAS AREA RAPID TRANSIT
DART
1401 Pacific Ave, Dallas, TX 75202-2732
Tel (214) 979-1111 *Founded/Ownrshp* 1997
Sales 85.4MM *EMP* 3,600
Accts Crowe Horwath Llp Dallas Tex
SIC 4111 Bus line operations
Pr: Gary C Thomas
**CFO:* David Leininger
**Treas:* Nate Hallett
Bd of Dir: Daniel Perez
Ofcr: Derrick Angle
Ofcr: Nan Collier
Ofcr: Teresa Silvers
Ofcr: Brent Thompson
Ex VP: Nicole Fontayne
VP: Jeffery Franklin
VP: Michael Hubbell
VP: Timothy Newby

D-U-N-S 07-138-1685
DALLAS BAPTIST UNIVERSITY
DBU
3000 Mountain Creek Pkwy, Dallas, TX 75211-6700
Tel (214) 333-5360 *Founded/Ownrshp* 1898
Sales 93.1MM *EMP* 1,500[E]
Accts Weaver & Tidwell Llp Dalla
SIC 8221 University
Pr: Gary Cook
**CFO:* Eric Bruntmyer
**CFO:* Eric Bruntnyer
Sr VP: Harold Norris
VP: Matt Murrah
Dir IT: Kevin Deaton
Info Man: Mendi McMahan
Web Dev: Kathleen Perdue
Sales Exec: Debbie Leonard
Genl Couns: Dan Malone
Pgrm Dir: Tam Jones

DALLAS CITY HALL
See CITY OF DALLAS

D-U-N-S 06-637-6278
DALLAS COUNTY COMMUNITY COLLEGE DISTRICT
4343 Interstate 30, Mesquite, TX 75150-2018
Tel (972) 860-7700 *Founded/Ownrshp* 1966
Sales 106.5MM *EMP* 200[E]
Accts Grant Thornton Llp Dallas Tx
SIC 8222 Community college
Ch Bd: Jerry Prater
Ex Dir: Iris Bechtol
Dir IT: Michael Burke
IT Man: Jamie Templeton

D-U-N-S 04-904-6527 IMP
DALLAS COUNTY HOSPITAL DISTRICT
PARKLAND HEALTH & HOSPITAL SYS
5200 Harry Hines Blvd, Dallas, TX 75235-7709
Tel (214) 590-8000 *Founded/Ownrshp* 1941
Sales 665.8MM *EMP* 9,500
SIC 8062 General medical & surgical hospitals
CEO: Frederick Cerise
**COO:* Ron Laxton
COO: Sue Pickens
COO: Marcene Royster
CFO: John Dragovits
**CFO:* John Moore
Ofcr: Ciel Murphy
Ex VP: Josh Floren
**Sr VP:* James R Johnson
VP: Joe Chang
VP: Barbara Crutcher
VP: Marnese Elder
VP: Mary Findley
VP: Judy Herrington
**VP:* Paul S Leslie
VP: Richard Massouh
VP: Clifann McCarley
VP: Bob Reed
VP: Paula Turicchi
VP: Katherine Yoder
Dir Rx: Vicki Johnson

D-U-N-S 07-670-8494
DALLAS COUNTY MENTAL HEALTH & MENTAL RETARDATION CENTER (INC)
DALLAS METROCARE SERVICES
1345 River Bend Dr # 200, Dallas, TX 75247-6945
Tel (214) 743-1200 *Founded/Ownrshp* 1965
Sales 64.6MM[E] *EMP* 1,200[E]
SIC 8361 Home for the mentally handicapped
CEO: John Burruss
**CFO:* Kyle Munson
VP: Charlene Stark
Dir IT: Jeff Griffin
MIS Mgr: Kristy Nobele

D-U-N-S 11-743-9141
DALLAS COUNTY SCHOOLS
5151 Samuell Blvd, Dallas, TX 75228-6939
Tel (214) 944-4545 *Founded/Ownrshp* 1846
Sales 120.3MM[E] *EMP* 1,500
SIC 8211 Public elementary & secondary schools
Dir IT: Oscar McCawley

DALLAS GOLD AND SILVER EXCH
See DGSE CORP

D-U-N-S 07-509-6347
DALLAS INDEPENDENT SCHOOL DISTRICT
3700 Ross Ave, Dallas, TX 75204-5491
Tel (972) 925-3700 *Founded/Ownrshp* 1867
Sales 1.6MMM[E] *EMP* 24,937
Accts Deloitte & Touche Llp Dallas
SIC 8211 Public elementary school; Public junior high school; Public senior high school; Public vocational/technical school
CFO: Calvin Holmes
**CFO:* James Terry
**Treas:* Darlene Williams
Trst: Maria Moreno
Prin: Clifford Greer
Prin: Bill Quinones
Ex Dir: Lee Allen
Ex Dir: Pam Carroll
Ex Dir: Jack Chrisman
Ex Dir: Suzanne Davidson
Ex Dir: Leng Fritsche

D-U-N-S 09-136-3242
DALLAS MARKET CENTER DEVELOPMENT CO LTD (TX)
WYNDHAM ANATOLE HOTEL
2201 N Stemmons Fwy, Dallas, TX 75207-2801
Tel (214) 748-1200 *Founded/Ownrshp* 1978
Sales 10.3MM[E] *EMP* 1,500
SIC 7011 Hotels
Ltd Pt: Robert T Crow
Ltd Pt: Lucy Crow Billingsley
Off Mgr: Jay Stirewlt

D-U-N-S 13-170-8687
DALLAS MEDICAL CENTER LLC
(*Suby of* PRIME HEALTHCARE SERVICES INC) ★
7 Medical Pkwy, Dallas, TX 75234-7829
Tel (972) 888-7000 *Founded/Ownrshp* 2009
Sales 220.0MM[E] *EMP* 1,345
SIC 8062 General medical & surgical hospitals
**Pr:* Prem Reddy
**CFO:* Ron Collins
Surg Cl Rc: Elli Kaivan

DALLAS METROCARE SERVICES
See DALLAS COUNTY MENTAL HEALTH & MENTAL RETARDATION CENTER (INC)

DALLAS MORNING NEWS
See DMN INC

D-U-N-S 05-085-0775
DALLAS PRODUCTION INC
PITTS ENERGY GROUP
4600 Greenville Ave # 300, Dallas, TX 75206-5038
Tel (214) 369-9266 *Founded/Ownrshp* 1968
Sales 92.4MM[E] *EMP* 120
SIC 1311 Crude petroleum production; Natural gas production
**Pr:* William A Custard
**CFO:* Ron D Johnson
**VP:* Douglas Sheetz
IT Man: Barbara Chapman

D-U-N-S 01-296-9401
DALLAS REGIONAL MEDICAL CENTER
(*Suby of* PRIME HEALTHCARE SERVICES INC) ★
1011 N Galloway Ave, Mesquite, TX 75149-2433
Tel (214) 320-7000 *Founded/Ownrshp* 1964, 2015
Sales 89.5MM *EMP* 1[E]
SIC 8099 Health screening service
CEO: Tina Pollock
**CFO:* John Irby
Exec: Alayne Sewick
Pathlgst: Dennis R Askins

DALLAS WHOLESALE DISTRIBUTION
See DW DISTRIBUTION INC

D-U-N-S 06-898-6314 IMP
DALLAS/FORT WORTH INTERNATIONAL AIRPORT
DFW INTERNATIONAL AIRPORT
3200 E Airfield Dr, Dfw Airport, TX 75261-4904
Tel (972) 973-8888 *Founded/Ownrshp* 1967
Sales 214.4MM[E] *EMP* 1,700
SIC 4581 Airport
CEO: Jeff P Fegan
Bd of Dir: Richard Hunt
Ofcr: Angela Garza
Ofcr: Kurt Kimmons
Ofcr: Wallace Meeks
Ofcr: Christopher Rhoades
Ofcr: Justin Turner
Ex VP: James Crites
Ex VP: Khaled Naja
VP: Carol Davis
Exec: Janis Moore

D-U-N-S 03-596-3370
DALLASTOWN AREA SCHOOL DISTRICT (PA)
700 New School Ln, Dallastown, PA 17313-9242
Tel (717) 244-4021 *Founded/Ownrshp* 1955
Sales 96.2MM *EMP* 575
Accts Boyer & Ritter Llc Camp Hill
SIC 8211 Public elementary school; Public junior high school; Public senior high school

D-U-N-S 04-835-3734
DALRYMPLE HOLDING CORP
2105 S Broadway, Pine City, NY 14871-9700
Tel (607) 737-6200 *Founded/Ownrshp* 1979
Sales 108.4MM[E] *EMP* 828
SIC 3273 1611 1442 1622 3281 Ready-mixed concrete; Highway & street construction; Construction sand & gravel; Bridge construction; Stone, quarrying & processing of own stone products
Pr: David J Dalrymple
**VP:* Edward C Dalrymple Jr

DALTILE
See DAL-TILE CORP

DALTON BOARD OF EDUCATION
See DALTON PUBLIC SCHOOLS

D-U-N-S 00-514-6022 EXP
DALTON CORP
(*Suby of* NEW DALTON FOUNDRY LLC) ★
1900 E Jefferson St, Warsaw, IN 46580-3761
Tel (574) 267-8111 *Founded/Ownrshp* 1910, 2016
Sales 104.4MM[E] *EMP* 300
SIC 3321

D-U-N-S 02-840-6361
DALTON PUBLIC SCHOOLS
DALTON BOARD OF EDUCATION
300 W Waugh St, Dalton, GA 30720-3143
Tel (706) 876-4000 *Founded/Ownrshp* 1881
Sales 75.3MM *EMP* 1,250
Accts Estes & Williams Dalton Geor
SIC 8211 Public elementary & secondary schools
Pr: Bob Bethel
**CFO:* Theresa Perry
Teacher Pr: Mindy Woods

D-U-N-S 07-448-3298
DALY SEVEN INC
4829 Riverside Dr, Danville, VA 24541-5537
Tel (434) 822-2161 *Founded/Ownrshp* 1981
Sales 90.7MM[E] *EMP* 1,000
SIC 8741 1522 6531 Hotel or motel management; Hotel/motel & multi-family home construction; Real estate agents & managers; Cemetery management service
CEO: Niles Daly
**Pr:* Patrick L Daly
CFO: Carolyn Whitlock
**Ch:* Jon Daly
**VP:* James F Daly
**VP:* Charisse D Kleinman
VP: Stan Webb
Genl Mgr: Christy Beal
Genl Mgr: Kermit Beard
Genl Mgr: Arti Desai
Genl Mgr: Andrew Gorman

D-U-N-S 07-934-1341 IMP
DAMAO LUGGAGE INTERNATIONAL INC
CHARIOT TRAVELWARE
1909 S Vineyard Ave, Ontario, CA 91761-7747
Tel (909) 923-6531 *Founded/Ownrshp* 2014
Sales 161.4MM[E] *EMP* 3,014
SIC 5099 3161 Luggage; Luggage
Pr: Moon Woo
**CFO:* Wendy Fan

D-U-N-S 10-298-3657
DAMCO DISTRIBUTION SERVICES INC
HUDD TRANSPORATION
(*Suby of* DAMCO USA INC) ★
180 Park Ave Ste 105, Florham Park, NJ 07932-1054
Tel (973) 514-5000 *Founded/Ownrshp* 1997
Sales 139.5MM[E] *EMP* 400
SIC 4214 4225 Local trucking with storage; General warehousing
Pr: Nicholas Taro
**CFO:* Colin Green
Treas: Jan K Andersen
**VP:* Brett Bennett
VP: Hans S Moller
Mktg Mgr: Timothy Simpson

D-U-N-S 83-297-7107
DAMCO SOLUTIONS INC
3240 E Estate St Ext, Hamilton, NJ 08619
Tel (609) 632-0350 *Founded/Ownrshp* 2006
Sales 25.0MM *EMP* 1,000
SIC 7371 Computer software development
Pr: Mohid Gupta
VP: Sachin Bedi

D-U-N-S 94-152-2831
DAMCO USA INC
(*Suby of* DAMCO INTERNATIONAL B.V.)
180 Park Ave Ste 105, Florham Park, NJ 07932-1054
Tel (973) 514-5000 *Founded/Ownrshp* 1988
Sales 207.1MM[E] *EMP* 727
SIC 4412 4491 4731 Deep sea foreign transportation of freight; Stevedoring; Agents, shipping
Pr: Jeremy T Haycock
**CFO:* Jan K Andersen
CFO: Michael McDonough
**VP:* Simon Preisler
**VP:* Kurt Pruitt
**Dir Surg:* Nick Fafoutis

D-U-N-S 07-466-5001
DAMERON HOSPITAL ASSOCIATION INC
525 W Acacia St, Stockton, CA 95203-2484
Tel (209) 944-5550 *Founded/Ownrshp* 1943
Sales 190.4MM *EMP* 1,003
Accts Moss Adams Llp Stockton Ca
SIC 8621 Professional membership organizations
CEO: Lorraine Auerbach
Dir Vol: Debbie Grooms
COO: Nicholas Arismendi
**CFO:* David Kerrins
Exec: Maria Junez
Dir Lab: Richard Wong
Dir Rad: Tom Beck
Dir Rx: Gerald Downs
Dir Sec: Brian McClory
Off Mgr: Scott Scanlan
Off Mgr: Juanita Zuniga

D-U-N-S 19-313-8583
DAMICO & PARTNERS INC
LURCAT
211 N 1st St Ste 175, Minneapolis, MN 55401-1480
Tel (612) 317-4223 *Founded/Ownrshp* 1984
Sales 64.9MM[E] *EMP* 1,000
SIC 8741 Restaurant management
CEO: Paul J Smith
**Pr:* Richard D'Amico
**VP:* Larry D'Amico
Exec: Jay Sparks
Genl Mgr: Dan Nelsen

D'AMICO & SONS
See DAMICO HOLDING CO

D-U-N-S 83-499-0483
DAMICO HOLDING CO
D'AMICO & SONS
275 Market St Ste 117, Minneapolis, MN 55405-1622
Tel (612) 374-1776 *Founded/Ownrshp* 1992
Sales 47.0MM[E] *EMP* 1,083
SIC 5812 Restaurant, family: independent; Cafe
Pr: Richard D'Amico
**CFO:* Paul Smith
Genl Mgr: Scott V Maten

DAMON'S
See ALLIANCE DEVELOPMENT GROUP LLC

D-U-N-S 14-721-1098
DAMONS INTERNATIONAL INC
D I I
(*Suby of* G&R ACQUISITION, INC.)
4645 Executive Dr, Columbus, OH 43220-3601
Tel (614) 442-7900 *Founded/Ownrshp* 2008
Sales 119.6MM[E] *EMP* 1,849
SIC 6794 8741 5812 Franchises, selling or licensing; Restaurant management; American restaurant
Ch Bd: William Burke
**Ch Bd:* Benoist Ray
**Pr:* Carl Howard
**Pr:* Charles Kelshaw
CFO: Stu Law
**CFO:* Stuart Laws
**VP:* Jim Meaney
**Prin:* David L Brown

D-U-N-S 13-464-6546
DAN ENNIS FARMS INC
6910 Egbert Rd, Martinsville, IN 46151-8484
Tel (765) 342-2711 *Founded/Ownrshp* 1975
Sales 125.0MM *EMP* 5
SIC 0191 General farms, primarily crop
Pr: Daniel Ennis
**Sec:* Monica Ennis

D-U-N-S 07-858-2229 IMP/EXP
DAN-BUNKERING (AMERICA) INC
(*Suby of* A/S DAN-BUNKERING LTD)
840 Gessner Rd Ste 210, Houston, TX 77024-4154
Tel (281) 833-5801 *Founded/Ownrshp* 1981
Sales 120.0MM *EMP* 12
SIC 5172 Fuel oil
Mng Dir: Mikkel S Vestergaard
VP: Claus Bulch Klausen
Sls Mgr: Jim Jensen

D-U-N-S 00-179-4023 IMP
DAN-DEE INTERNATIONAL LIMITED
106 Harbor Dr, Jersey City, NJ 07305-4506
Tel (201) 332-7600 *Founded/Ownrshp* 1954
Sales 98.2MM *EMP* 17
Accts Eisneramper Llp Bridgewater
SIC 5092 Toys & hobby goods & supplies
CEO: Margaret Ranzman
**Pr:* Gary Holcomb
Software D: Carol Liu

D-U-N-S 80-922-4848 IMP
■ DANA AUTOMOTIVE SYSTEMS GROUP LLC
(*Suby of* DANA LIMITED) ★
3939 Technology Dr, Maumee, OH 43537-9194
Tel (419) 887-3000 *Founded/Ownrshp* 2007
Sales 293.6MM[E] *EMP* 5,242[E]
SIC 3714 Motor vehicle parts & accessories

D-U-N-S 80-924-7732 IMP
■ DANA DRIVESHAFT PRODUCTS LLC
(*Suby of* DANA AUTOMOTIVE SYSTEMS GROUP LLC) ★
3939 Technology Dr, Maumee, OH 43537-9194
Tel (419) 887-3000 *Founded/Ownrshp* 2007
Sales 41.1MM[E] *EMP* 1,847[E]
SIC 3714 Motor vehicle parts & accessories

D-U-N-S 80-922-4640 IMP/EXP
■ DANA HEAVY VEHICLE SYSTEMS GROUP LLC
DANA HEAVY VHCL SYSTEMS GROUP
(*Suby of* DANA LIMITED) ★
3939 Technology Dr, Maumee, OH 43537-9194
Tel (419) 887-3000 *Founded/Ownrshp* 2007
Sales 174.0MM[E] *EMP* 1,691[E]
SIC 3714 Motor vehicle parts & accessories

DANA HEAVY VHCL SYSTEMS GROUP
See DANA HEAVY VEHICLE SYSTEMS GROUP LLC

D-U-N-S 80-910-5351 IMP
▲ DANA INC
3939 Technology Dr, Maumee, OH 43537-9194
Tel (419) 887-3000 *Founded/Ownrshp* 1904
Sales 6.0MMM *EMP* 23,100
Tkr Sym DAN *Exch* NYS
SIC 3714 3053 3593 3492 Motor vehicle parts & accessories; Motor vehicle transmissions, drive assemblies & parts; Axles, motor vehicle; Clutches, motor vehicle; Gaskets & sealing devices; Fluid power cylinders, hydraulic or pneumatic; Control valves, fluid power: hydraulic & pneumatic
Pr: James K Kamsickas
**Ch Bd:* Joseph C Muscari
**Ch Bd:* Keith E Wandell
CFO: Jonathan M Collins
Ofcr: Jeffrey S Bowen
Ofcr: George T Constand
Sr VP: Rodney R Filcek
Sr VP: Marc S Levin
Sr VP: ARI Papadakos
VP: Alfredo Alonso
VP: Ken Koncilja
Board of Directors: Virginia A Kamsky, Terrence J Keating, R Bruce McDonald, Mark A Schulz

D-U-N-S 80-925-5560 IMP
■ DANA LIGHT AXLE MANUFACTURING LLC
DANA LIGHT AXLE PRODUCTS
(*Suby of* DANA LIGHT AXLE PRODUCTS LLC) ★
3939 Technology Dr, Maumee, OH 43537-9194
Tel (419) 887-3000 *Founded/Ownrshp* 2007
Sales 130.0MM *EMP* 812[E]
SIC 3714 Motor vehicle parts & accessories

DANA LIGHT AXLE PRODUCTS
See DANA LIGHT AXLE MANUFACTURING LLC

D-U-N-S 80-924-7641 IMP/EXP
■ DANA LIGHT AXLE PRODUCTS LLC
(*Suby of* DANA AUTOMOTIVE SYSTEMS GROUP LLC) ★
2100 W State Blvd, Fort Wayne, IN 46808-1937
Tel (260) 483-7174 *Founded/Ownrshp* 2007
Sales 130.0MM[E] *EMP* 1,342[E]
SIC 3714 Motor vehicle parts & accessories
CFO: Shirly Baer

D-U-N-S 80-921-4971 IMP
■ DANA LIMITED
(*Suby of* DANA INC) ★
3939 Technology Dr, Maumee, OH 43537-9194
Tel (630) 697-3783 *Founded/Ownrshp* 2007
Sales 6.0MMM[E] *EMP* 22,500

SIC 3714 3053 3593 3492 Motor vehicle parts & accessories; Gaskets & sealing devices; Fluid power cylinders, hydraulic or pneumatic; Control valves, fluid power: hydraulic & pneumatic
Ch: John Devine
**Pr:* James Sweetnam
CFO: Muriel Alvarez
**CFO:* James Yost
**Sr VP:* Marc S Levin
VP: Bob Silcek
VP: Dean Wilson
Corp Couns: Paul Fudacz

D-U-N-S 80-924-7807
■ DANA SEALING PRODUCTS LLC
(*Suby of* DANA AUTOMOTIVE SYSTEMS GROUP LLC) ★
3939 Technology Dr, Maumee, OH 43537-9194
Tel (419) 887-3000 *Founded/Ownrshp* 2007
Sales 88.3MM[E] *EMP* 535[E]
SIC 3714 Motor vehicle parts & accessories

D-U-N-S 06-496-5230
DANA TRANSPORT INC (NJ)
10837 Highway 43, Creola, AL 36525-4560
Tel (732) 750-9100 *Founded/Ownrshp* 2011
Sales 250.0MM *EMP* 2,100[E]
SIC 4213 Liquid petroleum transport, non-local
Pr: Ronald Dana

D-U-N-S 06-313-7640
DANA TRANSPORT SYSTEM INC
210 Essex Ave E, Avenel, NJ 07001-2045
Tel (732) 750-9100 *Founded/Ownrshp* 1972
Sales 223.0MM[E] *EMP* 375
SIC 4213 7513 Contract haulers; Truck leasing, without drivers
Pr: Ron Dana
VP: Gene Patten
Plnt Mgr: Jennings Nichols

D-U-N-S 07-658-0745
DANA-FARBER CANCER INSTITUTE INC
DFCI PEDIATRIC ONCOLOGY
450 Brookline Ave, Boston, MA 02215-5450
Tel (617) 632-3000 *Founded/Ownrshp* 1951
Sales 739.0MM *EMP* 3,000
SIC 8733 8069 Medical research; Cancer hospital
Ch Bd: Gary L Countryman
**Pr:* David G Nathan
Pr: Berenice Ronthal
**CEO:* Edward J Benz Jr
**COO:* Dorothy E Puhy
CFO: Michael L Reney
**Treas:* Richard K Lubin
Ofcr: Amy Carlezon
Ofcr: Barrett J Rollins
Ofcr: Scott J Swanson
Sr VP: Patricia Reid Ponte
**VP:* Richard S Boskey
VP: Lori Buswell
VP: Mark Daniel
VP: Deborah Hicks
VP: Elizabeth Liebow
VP: Maria Papola
VP: Steven Singer
VP: John Stewart
Dir Inf Cn: Susan O'Rourke
Assoc Dir: Christine Cleary

D-U-N-S 02-474-4476 IMP
▲ DANAHER CORP
2200 Penn Ave Nw Ste 800w, Washington, DC 20037-1731
Tel (202) 828-0850 *Founded/Ownrshp* 1980
Sales 20.5MMM *EMP* 81,000[E]
Accts Ernst & Young Llp Mclean Vi
Tkr Sym DHR *Exch* NYS
SIC 3845 3829 3577 3823 3843 Electromedical equipment; Electromedical apparatus; Measuring & controlling devices; Printers & plotters; Printers, computer; Bar code (magnetic ink) printers; Water quality monitoring & control systems; Dental equipment & supplies
Pr: Thomas P Joyce Jr
Ch Bd: Steven M Rales
CFO: Daniel L Comas
Ex VP: James A Lico
Sr VP: Brian W Ellis
Sr VP: William H King
Sr VP: Angela S Lalor
Sr VP: Robert S Lutz
Sr VP: Daniel A Raskas
VP: Larry Byrnes
VP: Andrew Clark
VP: Patrick Donahue
VP: James Eder
VP: Peter Fjellman
VP: Jonathan Graham
VP: Mark Hamberlin
VP: Samuel Liao
VP: Andrew McCauley
VP: Kevin Oconnor
Exec: Joakim Weidemanis
Board of Directors: Donald J Ehrlich, Linda Hefner Filler, Robert J Hugin, Walter G Lohr Jr, Mitchell P Rales, John T Schwieters, Alan G Spoon, Teri List-Stoll, Elias A Zerhouni

DANAHER INDUS SENSORS CONTRLS
See DYNAPAR CORP

DANAHER MOTION
See KOLLMORGEN CORP

DANAHER TOOL GROUP
See EASCO HAND TOOLS INC

DANBURY MINT
See MBI INC

D-U-N-S 19-904-1245
DANBURY OFFICE OF PHYSICIAN SERVICES PC
25 Germantown Rd, Danbury, CT 06810-5036
Tel (203) 794-0090 *Founded/Ownrshp* 1985
Sales 121.6MM *EMP* 300
Accts Ernst & Young Llp Hartford C
SIC 8011 Physicians' office, including specialists
Pr: Patrick Broderick

D-U-N-S 14-159-9154
DANBURY SCHOOL DISTRICT
63 Beaver Brook Rd, Danbury, CT 06810-6211
Tel (203) 797-4701 *Founded/Ownrshp* 2012
Sales 47.8MM[E] *EMP* 1,200[E]
SIC 8211 Public elementary & secondary schools; Public elementary school; Public junior high school; Public senior high school

D-U-N-S 79-604-0673 IMP/EXP
DANBY PRODUCTS INC
(*Suby of* COLDPOINT HOLDINGS LIMITED)
1800 Production Dr, Findlay, OH 45840-5445
Tel (519) 837-0920 *Founded/Ownrshp* 2016
Sales 145.0MM *EMP* 70
SIC 5064 Electrical appliances, major
Pr: James Estill
VP: Andrew Raymond
Opers Mgr: Eian Campbell
Opers Mgr: Doug Chandler

D-U-N-S 00-182-5629 IMP
DANCKER SELLEW & DOUGLAS INC (NY)
D S & D
291 Evans Way, Branchburg, NJ 08876-3766
Tel (908) 429-1200 *Founded/Ownrshp* 1829
Sales 181.7MM[E] *EMP* 150
SIC 5021 5083 5049 Office furniture; Lighting fixtures, commercial & industrial; Laboratory equipment, except medical or dental
**CFO:* Bill Hendry
CFO: Benjamin Klowalczyk
**Ex VP:* Steve Bleiweiss
**VP:* Rob Culvert
**VP:* Manie Fahey
**VP:* Kevin Klier
Admn Mgr: Dolores Mulligan
Genl Mgr: Nancy Cadrera
IT Man: Raj Patel
Opers Mgr: Lou Anselmi

D-U-N-S 01-138-5481 IMP
DANDREA PRODUCE INC
3665 N Mill Rd, Vineland, NJ 08360-1527
Tel (856) 205-1830 *Founded/Ownrshp* 1982, 2006
Sales 97.2MM[E] *EMP* 87[E]
SIC 5148

DANE COUNTY CITY HALL
See COUNTY OF DANE

D-U-N-S 05-899-8675
DANELLA COMPANIES INC
DANELLA CONSTRUCTION
2290 Butler Pike, Plymouth Meeting, PA 19462-1436
Tel (610) 828-6200 *Founded/Ownrshp* 1972
Sales 196.0MM[E] *EMP* 2,000
SIC 7513 7353 8711 1623 8748

DANELLA CONSTRUCTION
See DANELLA COMPANIES INC

D-U-N-S 07-381-1515
DANFORTH ASSOCIATES INC
20 Wight Ave Ste 155, Cockeysville, MD 21030-2064
Tel (781) 235-9100 *Founded/Ownrshp* 1957
Sales 100.0MM *EMP* 8
SIC 6282 Investment advice
Pr: George Padula
CFO: Harry Dulgarian
**Ch:* Stuart Danforth
Sr VP: Mary Piecewicz

DANFOSS AUTOMATIC CONTROLS
See DANFOSS LLC

D-U-N-S 05-351-6055 IMP
DANFOSS LLC
DANFOSS AUTOMATIC CONTROLS
(*Suby of* SAUER-DANFOSS US CO) ★
11655 Crossroads Cir A, Baltimore, MD 21220-9916
Tel (410) 931-8250 *Founded/Ownrshp* 1987
Sales 176.1MM[E] *EMP* 488
SIC 3585 3625 3822 Refrigeration & heating equipment; Relays & industrial controls; Auto controls regulating residntl & coml environmt & applncs
Pr: John Galyen
VP: Michael Beuke
**VP:* Lyle Moroz
Genl Mgr: Sean Kurtz
Off Mgr: Tara Cichetti
IT Man: Adam Decastro
IT Man: Stefan Jost
Sls&Mrk Ex: Petersen Jan
Pr Dir: Mark Menzer
Manager: Dan Patterson
Manager: Gregg Porter
Board of Directors: Ole Steen Anderson

D-U-N-S 17-479-9254 IMP
DANFOSS POWER SOLUTIONS (US) CO
SAUER-DANFOSS US COMPANY
(*Suby of* DANFOSS POWER SOLUTIONS INC) ★
2800 E 13th St, Ames, IA 50010-8600
Tel (515) 239-6000 *Founded/Ownrshp* 1990
Sales 377.2MM[E] *EMP* 1,750
SIC 3594 Pumps, hydraulic power transfer
Pr: Charles Kells Hall
**Treas:* James T Remus
**VP:* Kenneth D McCuskey
VP: James R Wilcox

D-U-N-S 60-735-6649 IMP
DANFOSS POWER SOLUTIONS INC
(*Suby of* DANFOSS A/S)
2800 E 13th St, Ames, IA 50010-8600
Tel (515) 239-6000 *Founded/Ownrshp* 1986
Sales 1.5MMM[E] *EMP* 6,400[E]
Accts Kpmg Llp Des Moines Iowa
SIC 1731 Switchgear & related devices installation
Pr: Eric Alstrom
**Ch Bd:* Jorgen M Clausen
Pr: Helge Jorgensen
CFO: Jesper V Christensen
Chf Mktg O: Marc A Weston
Ex VP: Anne Wilkinson
VP: Kenneth D McCuskey
Sls Mgr: Graham Milne
Snr Mgr: Ed Wiedmann

Board of Directors: Niels B Christiansen, Kim Fausing, Richard J Freeland, Per Have, William E Hoover Jr, Johannes F Kirchhoff, Anders Stahlschmidt, Steven H Wood

D-U-N-S 12-974-6280 IMP
DANFOSS SCROLL TECHNOLOGIES LLC
(*Suby of* DANFOSS A/S)
1 Scroll Dr, Arkadelphia, AR 71923-8813
Tel (870) 246-0700 *Founded/Ownrshp* 1995
Sales 217.4MM[E] *EMP* 600
SIC 3679 3563 Hermetic seals for electronic equipment; Air & gas compressors
MIS Dir: Janet Brady

D-U-N-S 07-197-6609
DANIEL & HENRY CO
1001 Highlands Plaza Dr W # 500, Saint Louis, MO 63110-9917
Tel (314) 421-1525 *Founded/Ownrshp* 1921
Sales NA *EMP* 200
SIC 6411 Insurance agents
CEO: Thomas J Purcell Jr
**Pr:* James N Blaine
COO: Kay J Johnson
**Sec:* James A Samson
Bd of Dir: Barb Morrison
**Ex VP:* Bruce J Abernathy
Ex VP: James N Blaie
Ex VP: John R Dew
**Ex VP:* John R Drew
Ex VP: Richard Halpern
**Ex VP:* Kenneth B Preis
Sr VP: John McLaughlin
Sr VP: Stephen Wicker
**VP:* Stacey W Braswell
VP: Leo Cremins
VP: Joe Duncan
VP: Bill Durkin
VP: Cory Hartung
VP: Jeanne Jones
VP: Steven Lorenzini
VP: Jim Ruebsam

D-U-N-S 07-827-8611
DANIEL G SCHUSTER LLC
SCHUSTER CONCRETE
3717 Crondall Ln Ste B, Owings Mills, MD 21117-6207
Tel (410) 363-9620 *Founded/Ownrshp* 1975
Sales 217.5MM[E] *EMP* 450
SIC 5032 1771 Concrete mixtures; Concrete work
Pr: Daniel G Schuster
CFO: Corine Schuster
Genl Mgr: Beth Schoberg
IT Man: Chris Blanchard
Plnt Mgr: Jay J Harmon
Sales Exec: Dan Hess

DANIEL INDUSTRIES
See DANIEL MEASUREMENT AND CONTROL INC

D-U-N-S 00-808-4634
■ DANIEL INDUSTRIES INC
(*Suby of* EMERSON ELECTRIC CO) ★
11100 Brittmoore Park Dr, Houston, TX 77041-6930
Tel (713) 467-6000 *Founded/Ownrshp* 2013
Sales 482.2MM[E] *EMP* 1,319[E]
SIC 3823 3824 3494 3829 3826 3571 Industrial flow & liquid measuring instruments; Turbine flow meters, industrial process type; Flow instruments, industrial process type; Turbine meters; Positive displacement meters; Plumbing & heating valves; Measuring & controlling devices; Analytical instruments; Electronic computers
CEO: Dennis G Perkins
VP: W A Griffin III
Dept Mgr: Auralicia Oropeza
Sls&Mrk Ex: Dave Seiler

D-U-N-S 17-926-0703
■ DANIEL INDUSTRIES INC
(*Suby of* EMERSON ELECTRIC CO) ★
8460 Valley View Dr, Martinsville, IN 46151-8362
Tel (317) 442-5294 *Founded/Ownrshp* 2000
Sales 100.0M *EMP* 1,065
SIC 1522 Residential construction
Pr: Danny Owens
**Sec:* Crissy Owens

D-U-N-S 07-914-0735
DANIEL J EDELMAN HOLDINGS INC
200 E Randolph St Fl 63, Chicago, IL 60601-6705
Tel (312) 240-3000 *Founded/Ownrshp* 2012
Sales 781.8MM[E] *EMP* 4,045
SIC 7313 8743 Electronic media advertising representatives; Printed media advertising representatives; Public relations & publicity
Ch Bd: Richard W Edelman
V Ch: Ruth A Edelman
COO: Matthew J Harrington
CFO: Victor A Malanga
Ofcr: John D Edelman
Ofcr: Steve Felsher

D-U-N-S 07-232-4379
DANIEL J EDELMAN INC
(*Suby of* DANIEL J EDELMAN HOLDINGS INC) ★
200 E Randolph St Fl 63, Chicago, IL 60601-6705
Tel (312) 240-3000 *Founded/Ownrshp* 1952
Sales 781.4MM[E] *EMP* 4,000
SIC 7313 8743 Electronic media advertising representatives; Printed media advertising representatives; Public relations & publicity
CEO: Matthew Jharrington
Ch Bd: Daniel J Edelman
Pr: Richard Edelman
Pr: Rick Murray
CFO: Mario Cordeiro
CFO: Victor Malanga
CFO: Michael Sloan
V Ch Bd: Alan Vandermolen
Ex VP: Pauline Draper-Watts
Ex VP: Brad Jamison
Ex VP: Bob Knott
Ex VP: Kathryn Kranhold
Ex VP: Christin Palmer
Ex VP: Mark Shadle
Ex VP: Steve Singerman
Sr VP: Gregory Lee Hendricks

Sr VP: Tamara Kruger
Sr VP: Tricia Murphy
Sr VP: Roy Peters
Sr VP: Lee Teller
VP: Steve Bauer

D-U-N-S 08-477-6343
■ DANIEL J KEATING CONSTRUCTION CO
KEATING BUILDING COMPANY
(*Suby of* TUTOR PERINI CORP) ★
130 N 18th St Ste 1500, Philadelphia, PA 19103-2757
Tel (610) 668-4100 *Founded/Ownrshp* 1976, 2009
Sales 154.1MM *EMP* 65
Accts Deloitte & Touche Llp Los Ang
SIC 1542 Commercial & office building contractors
Pr: Bradley W B Statler
**CFO:* Peter Cocchia
**Ch:* Ronald N Tutor
**Sec:* William B Spark
**Ex VP:* Dennis A Martin

D-U-N-S 02-808-1421
DANIEL J NEWLIN PA
LAW OFFCES DAN NEWLIN PARTNERS
7335 W Sand Lake Rd # 200, Orlando, FL 32819-5539
Tel (407) 888-8000 *Founded/Ownrshp* 2010
Sales 100.0MM *EMP* 140[E]
SIC 8111 General practice law office
CEO: Daniel Newlin

D-U-N-S 01-927-0081
DANIEL J QUIRK INC
QUIRK MAZDA
372 Quincy Ave, Braintree, MA 02184-1344
Tel (781) 843-4800 *Founded/Ownrshp* 1974
Sales 186.5MM[E] *EMP* 425
SIC 5511 5013 5531 7538 5521 7515 New & used car dealers; Motor vehicle supplies & new parts; Automotive & home supply stores; General automotive repair shops; Used car dealers; Passenger car leasing
Pr: Daniel J Quirk
Genl Mgr: Eric Ao
Genl Mgr: Paul Butts
Genl Mgr: Michael Piccirilli
Genl Mgr: Corey Williams
Store Mgr: Ken Ux
Dir IT: Dave Thomas
Sls Dir: Greg Merchanthouse
Mktg Mgr: Michael Visconti
Mktg Mgr: Sean Western
Sls Mgr: Wissam S Bassil

D-U-N-S 13-339-9550 IMP/EXP
■ DANIEL MEASUREMENT AND CONTROL INC
DANIEL INDUSTRIES
(*Suby of* DANIEL INDUSTRIES INC) ★
11100 Brittmoore Park Dr, Houston, TX 77041-6930
Tel (713) 467-6000 *Founded/Ownrshp* 2013
Sales 317.7MM[E] *EMP* 892
SIC 3824 3498 3499 3823 3571 3491 Gas meters, domestic & large capacity: industrial; Turbine meters; Pipe sections fabricated from purchased pipe; Machine bases, metal; Industrial instrmnts msrmnt display/control process variable; Electronic computers; Industrial valves
Pr: Jon Stokes
**VP:* John J Kadera
**VP:* Robin C Palmer
VP: John T Seng
Mng Dir: Kevin Jackson
Dir IT: Garet Hall
Sls Dir: Larry Irving
Sls Mgr: Jim Tadvick

D-U-N-S 00-695-4689 IMP
DANIEL OCONNELLS SONS INC (MA)
(*Suby of* OCONNELL COMPANIES INC) ★
480 Hampden St, Holyoke, MA 01040-3309
Tel (413) 534-5667 *Founded/Ownrshp* 1879
Sales 139.6MM[E] *EMP* 250
SIC 1541 1542 1522 1611 1622 1629 Industrial buildings, new construction; Renovation, remodeling & repairs: industrial buildings; Commercial & office building, new construction; Commercial & office buildings, renovation & repair; Multi-family dwellings, new construction; Remodeling, multi-family dwellings; Dormitory construction; General contractor, highway & street construction; Bridge construction; Highway construction, elevated; Waste water & sewage treatment plant construction
Pr: Jeffrey C Bardell
**Treas:* Dennis A Fitzpatrick
VP: Matt Campano
**VP:* Dennis C Cavanaugh
**VP:* Stephen A Maiorano
Dir Bus: Tom Walsh
Dir IT: Jeremy Smith
Mktg Mgr: Mary Shea
Snr PM: Maria Donahue
Snr PM: Chris Jablonski

D-U-N-S 13-595-8887 IMP
DANIELS SHARPSMART INC
(*Suby of* DANIELS CORPORATION INTERNATIONAL PTY LTD)
111 W Jackson Blvd # 720, Chicago, IL 60604-3589
Tel (312) 546-8900 *Founded/Ownrshp* 2002
Sales 210.5MM[E] *EMP* 470
SIC 4953 2834 Medical waste disposal; Pharmaceutical preparations
Pr: Dan Daniels
**CFO:* Dean McPhee
Genl Mgr: Marla Licht
Plnt Mgr: Mike Dabu
Plnt Mgr: Guy Grieco
Manager: Gordon Snelgrove
Sls Mgr: Jose Torres

D-U-N-S 79-296-1542
DANIS BUILDING CONSTRUCTION CO
3233 Newmark Dr, Miamisburg, OH 45342-5422
Tel (937) 228-1225 *Founded/Ownrshp* 1997
Sales 267.2MM[E] *EMP* 475
Accts Barnes Dennig & Co Ltd Ci
SIC 1542 1541 Commercial & office building contractors; Hospital construction; Industrial buildings & warehouses

Pr: John Danis
**Pr:* Thomas P Hammelrath
**CFO:* Tim Carlson
VP: Cory Farmer
Exec: Kevin O'Brien
Exec: Dustin Rohrbach
CTO: Eddie Hamann
Info Man: Ed Bellman
Sfty Mgr: Steve Duff
Sales Exec: Jud Wallner
Sls&Mrk Ex: Mark Graeser

D-U-N-S 61-145-4406 IMP/EXP
■ DANISCO US INC
GENENCOR INTERNATIONAL
(*Suby of* E I DU PONT DE NEMOURS AND CO) ★
925 Page Mill Rd, Palo Alto, CA 94304-1013
Tel (650) 846-7500 *Founded/Ownrshp* 2005
Sales 282.3MM^E *EMP* 1,098
SIC 2835 8731 2899 2869 In vitro & in vivo diagnostic substances; Commercial physical research; Chemical preparations; Industrial organic chemicals
CEO: James C Collins
Sr Cor Off: Jean-Jacques Bienaime
Sr Cor Off: Mogens Granborg
Bd of Dir: Peter Hojland
Bd of Dir: Anders Knutsen
Bd of Dir: Flemming Kristensen
Bd of Dir: Joseph Millica
Bd of Dir: Julie Quist
Bd of Dir: Jorgen Rosenlund
Bd of Dir: Matti Vuoria
Sr VP: Michael Arbige
Sr VP: Michael W Brooks
**Sr VP:* Mark A Goldsmith
Sr VP: Ken F Herfert
VP: Darryl L Canfield
VP: Mark Goldsmith
VP: Floris Luger
VP: Tom Pekich
VP: David Thomaen
VP: David Thomassen
Exec: W Mitchell

D-U-N-S 07-987-4863 IMP/EXP
■ DANISCO USA INC
(*Suby of* E I DU PONT DE NEMOURS AND CO) ★
4 New Century Pkwy, New Century, KS 66031-1144
Tel (913) 764-8100 *Founded/Ownrshp* 2002
Sales 146.5MM^E *EMP* 500
SIC 2099 Food preparations; Emulsifiers, food; Pectin
Pr: Germain Despres
Ex VP: Mogens Granborg
VP: Palle Ikkala
VP: Poul Jensen
VP: Leif Kjrgaard
VP: Stanley Mainzer
VP: Hjuler Vogelsang
Exec: Tom Dalfonso
Exec: Eija Kemppila
Exec: Tuija Laitinen
Exec: Lars M Petersen
Dir Bus: Chris Lehman

DANLY IEM
See CONNELL LIMITED PARTNERSHIP

D-U-N-S 05-745-4019 IMP/EXP
DANNON CO INC
(*Suby of* DANONE)
100 Hillside Ave Fl 3, White Plains, NY 10603-2863
Tel (914) 872-8400 *Founded/Ownrshp* 1981
Sales 854.7MM^E *EMP* 2,400
SIC 2026 Yogurt
CEO: Gustavo Valle
**Ch:* Frank Riboud
**Sr VP:* Sergio Fuster
**VP:* Tony Cicio
**VP:* Francis Gautier
VP: Robert Mozdean
**VP:* Theo Razzuok
**VP:* Antoine Remy
Dir Surg: Joe Oliveri
**Prin:* Thomas Kunz
Genl Mgr: Didier Menu

D-U-N-S 18-337-3880
DANONE HOLDINGS INC
(*Suby of* DANNON CO INC) ★
208 Harbor Dr Fl 3, Stamford, CT 06902-7467
Tel (203) 229-7000 *Founded/Ownrshp* 2001
Sales 16.3M^E *EMP* 1,300
SIC 2086 Pasteurized & mineral waters, bottled & canned
CEO: Jim Stevens
CFO: Michel Botboil
Treas: Seth Marlowe
VP: Michael J Harrison
VP: Gregory Sea
Genl Mgr: Lorenzo Muratore
Mktg Mgr: Christine Mathis
Genl Couns: Donna R Besteiro

D-U-N-S 07-944-0812
DANONE NORTH AMERICA LLC
(*Suby of* DANONE)
100 Hillside Ave, White Plains, NY 10603-2861
Tel (212) 441-1000 *Founded/Ownrshp* 2004
Sales 126.0MM^E *EMP* 70^E
SIC 5149 Natural & organic foods
VP: Philippe Bassin
VP: Gilles Ghnassia
VP: Roland Murray
Mktg Mgr: Angela McGee

D-U-N-S 08-344-0487
DANOS AND CUROLE MARINE CONTRACTORS LLC
3878 W Main St, Gray, LA 70359-6203
Tel (985) 693-3313 *Founded/Ownrshp* 2001
Sales 515.0MM^E *EMP* 900
SIC 1389 Oil field services
CEO: Garret Hank Danos
Pr: Silas W Kelly
CFO: Steve Radatovich
**Ex VP:* Eric Danos
Ex VP: Eric R Danos
Genl Mgr: Marcel Danos
Genl Mgr: Glenn Gros

VP Prd: Reed Pere
Opers Supe: Scott Tew
Sfty Mgr: Issac Dantin
Sfty Mgr: Jim Leblanc

D-U-N-S 00-697-7565
DANS SUPREME SUPER MARKETS INC (NY)
KEY FOOD
474 Fulton Ave Fl 3, Hempstead, NY 11550-4101
Tel (516) 483-2400 *Founded/Ownrshp* 1948, 1985
Sales 93.0MM^E *EMP* 700
SIC 5411

DANSK
See LENOX HOLDINGS INC

D-U-N-S 80-903-3277 IMP
DANSKO HOLDINGS INC
33 Federal Rd, West Grove, PA 19390-9182
Tel (610) 869-8335 *Founded/Ownrshp* 1990
Sales 150.0MM *EMP* 160^E
SIC 5139 Shoes
CEO: Amanda Cabot
**CFO:* Jim Fox
**VP:* Peter Kjellerup

D-U-N-S 61-631-8783
DANUBE PRIVATE HOLDINGS II LLC
601 Lexington Ave, New York, NY 10022-4611
Tel (212) 231-0095 *Founded/Ownrshp* 2014
Sales 1.2MMM^E *EMP* 451^E
SIC 7371 Computer software systems analysis & design, custom
Pt: Frank Baker
Pt: Peter Berger
Pt: Jeffrey Hendren

D-U-N-S 19-499-5957 IMP/EXP
■ DANVILLE LEAF TOBACCO CO INC
(*Suby of* UNIVERSAL CORP) ★
9201 Forest Hill Ave Fl 1, Richmond, VA 23235-6865
Tel (804) 359-9311 *Founded/Ownrshp* 1972
Sales 504.5MM^E *EMP* 24,000
SIC 2141 Tobacco stemming & redrying
Pr: George C Freeman III
**CFO:* David C Moore
**Treas:* Candace C Formacek
**Treas:* Karen M L Whelan
**VP:* Preston D Wigner

D-U-N-S 96-193-6671
DANVILLE REGIONAL HEALTH FOUNDATION
142 S Main St, Danville, VA 24541-2922
Tel (434) 799-2100 *Founded/Ownrshp* 1996
Sales 45.3MM^E *EMP* 1,700
SIC 8741 8062 8051 8011 Nursing & personal care facility management; General medical & surgical hospitals; Skilled nursing care facilities; Offices & clinics of medical doctors
Prin: Dr BR Ashby
V Ch: Carolyn Evans
**Pr:* Warren E Callaway
COO: William Isemann
CFO: Dennis Eith
**Ch:* Dr Betty Jo Foster
Treas: Aubrey Dodson
Bd of Dir: Gregory Hairston
Comm Dir: Kelly Fitzgerald
Dir Rx: Paul O'Brien
Sfty Dirs: Clint Treadway

D-U-N-S 06-601-1255
■ DANVILLE REGIONAL MEDICAL CENTER
(*Suby of* LIFEPOINT HEALTH INC) ★
142 S Main St, Danville, VA 24541-2922
Tel (434) 799-2100 *Founded/Ownrshp* 1993
Sales 172.1MM *EMP* 1,400
SIC 8062 8011 8093 8069 8051 General medical & surgical hospitals; Offices & clinics of medical doctors; Specialty outpatient clinics; Specialty hospitals, except psychiatric; Skilled nursing care facilities
CEO: Eric Deaton
**COO:* Cherie Sibley
**Prin:* Dennis Eith
**Prin:* Saria Saccocio
Dir IT: Yolanda Pool
Mtls Dir: Danny Cline
Nrsg Dir: Debra Clark
Pharmcst: Sherri Francisco

DAPS DCUMENT AUTOMTN PROD SVCS
See DLA DOCUMENT SERVICES

D-U-N-S 96-405-0376
DAPTIV SOLUTIONS LLC
(*Suby of* CHANGEPOINT CANADA ULC)
1111 3rd Ave Ste 700, Seattle, WA 98101-3210
Tel (206) 341-9117 *Founded/Ownrshp* 2014
Sales 103.3MM^E *EMP* 92^E
SIC 5045 Computer software
CEO: Jim Byrnes
CFO: Roger Maloch

D-U-N-S 02-425-0854
DAR CARS DODGE INC
KAPLAN & CRAWFORD DODGE WORLD
(*Suby of* DARCAR) ★
5060 Auth Way, Suitland, MD 20746-4217
Tel (301) 423-5111 *Founded/Ownrshp* 1946
Sales 236.0MM *EMP* 59
SIC 5511 Automobiles, new & used
Genl Mgr: Sam Darvish
**Pr:* John Darvish
**Treas:* Earl Hudson
**VP:* Dan Noel

DAR PRO SOLUTIONS
See GRIFFIN INDUSTRIES LLC

D-U-N-S 87-898-0069 EXP
DARAMIC LLC
(*Suby of* POLYPORE INTERNATIONAL INC) ★
11430 N Cmnity Hse Rd # 350, Charlotte, NC 28277-0454
Tel (704) 587-8599 *Founded/Ownrshp* 1936
Sales 219.7MM^E *EMP* 850
SIC 3069 2499 3269 Roofing, membrane rubber; Battery separators, wood; Filtering media, pottery
CEO: Robert B Toth
Ql Cn Mgr: Mike Lett
Sales Exec: Tucker Roe

D-U-N-S 82-513-7818 IMP/EXP
DARBY DENTAL SUPPLY LLC
300 Jericho Quadrangle Ll, Jericho, NY 11753-2704
Tel (516) 688-6252 *Founded/Ownrshp* 2006
Sales 127.0MM^E *EMP* 400
SIC 5047 Dental equipment & supplies
Pr: Gary Rosenberg
VP: Tucker Craig
VP: Scott Walsh
Genl Mgr: Richard Burke
Genl Mgr: Melody Scott
IT Man: Kevin Brown
IT Man: Kelly Jorgensen
Opers Mgr: Michael Fox
S&M/VP: Chris Reynolds

DARCAR
See MARIAM INC

D-U-N-S 88-370-4959 IMP/EXP
▲ DARDEN RESTAURANTS INC
1000 Darden Center Dr, Orlando, FL 32837-4032
Tel (407) 245-4000 *Founded/Ownrshp* 1968
Sales 6.9MMM *EMP* 150,000
Tkr Sym DRI *Exch* NYS
SIC 5812 Steak restaurant; Italian restaurant
CEO: Eugene I Lee Jr
**Ch Bd:* Charles M Sonsteby
Pr: Todd A Burrowes
Pr: David C George
CFO: Ricardo Cardenas
Ofcr: Danielle L Kirgan
Sr VP: Chris Chang
Sr VP: Danielle Kirgan
Sr VP: John W Madonna
VP: Ana Hooper
VP: Norma Sica
VP: Dan Williams
Board of Directors: Margaret Shan Atkins, Jean M Birch, Bradley D Blum, James P Fogarty, Cynthia T Jamison, Nana Mensah, Lionel C Nowell III, William S Simon, Alan N Stillman

DARICE
See LAMRITE WEST INC

D-U-N-S 80-138-6608 IMP/EXP
■ DARICE INC
PAT CATAN'S CRAFT CENTERS
(*Suby of* MICHAELS STORES INC) ★
13000 Darice Pkwy 82, Strongsville, OH 44149-3800
Tel (440) 238-9150 *Founded/Ownrshp* 2016
Sales 295.6MM^E *EMP* 1,800
SIC 5945 5193 5999 Arts & crafts supplies; Flowers & florists' supplies; Picture frames, ready made
Pr: Michael Catanzarite
Dir IT: Bill Santos
VP Opers: Kevin Kilbane
Sales Exec: Ray Young
Sls Dir: Scott Catan
Snr Mgr: Eric Davenport

D-U-N-S 00-926-0449 IMP/EXP
DARIGOLD INC
(*Suby of* NORTHWEST DAIRY ASSOCIATION) ★
1130 Rainier Ave S, Seattle, WA 98144-2842
Tel (206) 284-7220 *Founded/Ownrshp* 1918
Sales 1.4MMM^E *EMP* 1,240
SIC 2023 2026 2022 5143

D-U-N-S 07-969-4256
DARKA HOLDINGS LLC
1528 Taylor Farm Rd # 105, Virginia Beach, VA 23453-2980
Tel (757) 689-4400 *Founded/Ownrshp* 2013
Sales 100.0MM *EMP* 4
SIC 6719 Investment holding companies, except banks
CEO: William Somerindyke Jr
**Pr:* Lee Tolleson
**CFO:* Daniel Cronin

D-U-N-S 00-509-2358
▲ DARLING INGREDIENTS INC
251 Oconnor Ridge Blvd, Irving, TX 75038
Tel (972) 717-0300 *Founded/Ownrshp* 1882
Sales 3.4MMM *EMP* 10,000
Tkr Sym DAR *Exch* NYS
SIC 2077 Animal & marine fats & oils; Grease rendering, inedible; Tallow rendering, inedible; Bone meal, except as animal feed
Ch Bd: Randall C Stuewe
COO: Eugenie Darling
COO: Martin W Griffin
**COO:* Dirk Kloosterboer
**CFO:* John O Muse
**Ex VP:* John Bullock
Ex VP: Jim Ranswieller
**Ex VP:* John F Sterling
VP: Shirley Elliott
Off Mgr: Christine Hill
Opers Mgr: Ed Frakes
Board of Directors: D Eugene Ewing, Mary R Korby, Charles Macaluso, John D March, Michael Urbut

D-U-N-S 01-898-2678
DARLINGS
DARLING'S HONDA/NISSAN
96 Parkway S Unit 1, Brewer, ME 04412-1686
Tel (207) 992-1720 *Founded/Ownrshp* 1976
Sales 142.6MM^E *EMP* 400
Accts Tyler Simms & St Sauveur P
SIC 5511 6411 Automobiles, new & used; Insurance agents, brokers & service
Pr: John B Darling II
**Treas:* Timothy Dougherty
**VP:* Carry Meo
**VP:* Charles Rohn
Sls Mgr: Ryan Pelkey

DARLING'S HONDA/NISSAN
See DARLINGS

D-U-N-S 07-806-5455
DARLINGTON COUNTY SCHOOL DISTRICT
120 E Smith Ave, Darlington, SC 29532-2120
Tel (843) 398-5100 *Founded/Ownrshp* 1771
Sales 101.5MM *EMP* 1,544
SIC 8211 Public elementary & secondary schools
CFO: Ashley Smith
Schl Brd P: Carnell Delane

D-U-N-S 00-335-4222 IMP/EXP
DARLINGTON VENEER CO INC (SC)
225 4th St, Darlington, SC 29532-4025
Tel (843) 393-3861 *Founded/Ownrshp* 1918
Sales 147.1MM^E *EMP* 200^E
SIC 2426 Hardwood dimension & flooring mills
Pr: John C Ramsey
**VP:* Reginald H Hubbard

D-U-N-S 83-132-1992
DARNGAVIL ENTERPRISES LLC
3103 Riachuelo Ln, Kissimmee, FL 34744-4118
Tel (407) 288-2776 *Founded/Ownrshp* 2009
Sales 130.0MM *EMP* 6
SIC 4213 Trucking, except local

DARR EQUIPMENT CO
See DARR EQUIPMENT LP

D-U-N-S 78-403-6274
DARR EQUIPMENT LP
DARR EQUIPMENT CO
350 Bank St, Southlake, TX 76092-9122
Tel (254) 420-2650 *Founded/Ownrshp* 2005
Sales 133.7MM^E *EMP* 260^E
SIC 5084 7353 5013 4959 Materials handling machinery; Heavy construction equipment rental; Motor vehicle supplies & new parts; Sweeping service: road, airport, parking lot, etc.
Genl Pt: Randy Engstrom
Pt: Steve Brooks
CFO: Gary Brigham
VP Admn: Rick Scripps
IT Man: Brenda Barnes
Sls Mgr: Jamie Freeman
Sls Mgr: Brian Grice
Sls Mgr: Cliff Peterson
Sls Mgr: Tim Zimmerman

D-U-N-S 00-167-3904 IMP
DARRIGO BROS CO OF NEW YORK INC (MA)
D'ARRIGO BROTHERS COMPANY
315 Nyc Terminal Mkt, Bronx, NY 10474
Tel (718) 991-5900 *Founded/Ownrshp* 1948, 2001
Sales 241.6MM *EMP* 170
Accts Rsm Us Llp Stamford Connect
SIC 5148 Fruits, fresh; Vegetables, fresh
Pr: Paul D'Arrigo
**CFO:* David Bub
**VP:* Matthew D'Arrigo
**VP:* Michael D'Arrigo

D-U-N-S 00-691-1176
DARRIGO BROSCOOF CALIFORNIA
ANDY BOY
21777 Harris Rd, Salinas, CA 93908-8609
Tel (831) 455-4500 *Founded/Ownrshp* 1922
Sales 241.6MM^E *EMP* 935
SIC 0161 Broccoli farm; Carrot farm; Lettuce farm; Celery farm
Ch Bd: Andrew A D'Arrigo
**Pr:* John C D'Arrigo
Sec: E John Culligan

D'ARRIGO BROTHERS COMPANY
See DARRIGO BROS CO OF NEW YORK INC

D-U-N-S 06-044-5236
DARROW RUSS GROUP INC (WI)
W133n8569 Executive Pkwy, Menomonee Falls, WI 53051-3344
Tel (262) 250-9600 *Founded/Ownrshp* 1970, 2005
Sales 318.7MM^E *EMP* 1,000
SIC 5511 7538 Automobiles, new & used; General automotive repair shops
CEO: Russell M Darrow Jr
**CEO:* Michael Darrow
**CFO:* Phillip Harrington
**VP:* Dorothy Feest
VP: James Taylor
Advt Mgr: Colleen Kellen

DART
See DALLAS AREA RAPID TRANSIT

D-U-N-S 80-398-9768 IMP/EXP
DART CONTAINER CORP
500 Hogsback Rd, Mason, MI 48854-9547
Tel (800) 248-5960 *Founded/Ownrshp* 1937
Sales 2.4MMM^E *EMP* 8,250
SIC 3086 Plastics foam products
Pr: Robert C Dart
VP: Gary Climes
VP: Roger L Johnson
**VP:* James D Lammers
VP: Dan May
VP: Andrew Serratelli
Exec: Kathy Warren
Dir Risk M: Dan Ide
Off Mgr: Bob West
CTO: Dave Templeton
IT Man: Alison Furton

D-U-N-S 01-086-2035 IMP
DART CONTAINER CORP OF CALIFORNIA
150 S Maple St, Corona, CA 92880
Tel (951) 739-7791 *Founded/Ownrshp* 2016
Sales 96.6MM^E *EMP* 640
SIC 3086 Cups & plates, foamed plastic
CEO: Kenneth B Dart
**Treas:* Kevin Fox

D-U-N-S 04-181-2298 IMP/EXP
DART CONTAINER CORP OF GEORGIA
500 Hogsback Rd, Mason, MI 48854-9547
Tel (517) 676-3800 *Founded/Ownrshp* 1983
Sales 180.8MM^E *EMP* 1,000
SIC 3089 Cups, plastic, except foam
Pr: Robert C Dart
**Treas:* Kevin Fox

Board of Directors: William A Dart

D-U-N-S 09-912-5114 IMP/EXP
DART CONTAINER CORP OF KENTUCKY
DART POLYMERS
500 Hogsback Rd, Mason, MI 48854-9547
Tel (517) 676-3800 *Founded/Ownrshp* 1960
Sales 114.0MM^E *EMP* 682^E
SIC 2821 3086 Plastics materials & resins; Cups & plates, foamed plastic
Ch Bd: William A Dart
* *Pr:* Kenneth B Dart
* *Treas:* Kevin Fox

D-U-N-S 00-652-2890 IMP/EXP
DART CONTAINER CORP OF PENNSYLVANIA
60 E Main St, Leola, PA 17540-1940
Tel (717) 656-2236 *Founded/Ownrshp* 2008
Sales 228.8MM^E *EMP* 1,450
SIC 3086 Cups & plates, foamed plastic
Pr: Robert Dart
VP Mfg: John Murray
Plnt Mgr: Clarence Wenger

D-U-N-S 17-520-6820 IMP/EXP
DART CONTAINER OF MICHIGAN LLC
DART DEVELOPMENT GROUP
(*Suby of* DART CONTAINER CORP) ★
3120 Sovereign Dr Ste 4b, Lansing, MI 48911-4227
Tel (888) 327-8001 *Founded/Ownrshp* 2003
Sales 245.0MM^E *EMP* 760
SIC 3086 Cups & plates, foamed plastic
CEO: Robert C Dart
V Ch: Kami McKenna
Pr: Kenneth Dart
Treas: Kevin Fox
Treas: Jane Samson
VP: William A Dart

DART DEVELOPMENT GROUP
See DART CONTAINER OF MICHIGAN LLC

D-U-N-S 02-412-9611
DART ENERGY CORP (MI)
DART OIL & GAS
600 Dart Rd, Mason, MI 48854-9327
Tel (517) 676-2900 *Founded/Ownrshp* 1976
Sales 388.0MM^E *EMP* 550
SIC 1311 1382 Crude petroleum production; Natural gas production; Oil & gas exploration services
Pr: Phil Leece
CFO: Jim Weigand
Treas: Tom Stapf
Ofcr: Robert Nemeth
VP: Deb Fennell
CTO: Ellen W Franzen
CTO: Bob Nemeth
DP Exec: Brazil Chris
Netwrk Mgr: Brian Verburg

DART ENTITIES
See DART TRANSPORTATION SERVICE A CORP

D-U-N-S 00-833-7057 IMP
■ **DART INDUSTRIES INC**
(*Suby of* TUPPERWARE BRANDS CORP) ★
14901 S Orange Blossom Tr, Orlando, FL 32837-6600
Tel (407) 826-5050 *Founded/Ownrshp* 1996
Sales 624.2MM^E *EMP* 5,800
SIC 3089 Plastic containers, except foam; Kitchenware, plastic
Pr: E V Goings
VP: Nicole Decker
* *VP:* Richard A Lisec

DART OIL & GAS
See DART ENERGY CORP

DART POLYMERS
See DART CONTAINER CORP OF KENTUCKY

D-U-N-S 00-977-4241
DART TRANSPORTATION SERVICE A CORP (CA)
DART ENTITIES
1430 S Eastman Ave Ste 1, Commerce, CA 90023-4096
Tel (323) 981-8205 *Founded/Ownrshp* 1938
Sales 98.1MM^E *EMP* 640^E
SIC 6798 7513 Real estate investment trusts; Realty investment trusts; Truck leasing, without drivers
Pr: Terrence Dedeaux
Treas: Ashok Aggarwal
VP: Joseph M Medlin

D-U-N-S 12-215-1673 IMP
DARTAGNAN INC
600 Green Ln, Union, NJ 07083-8074
Tel (973) 344-0565 *Founded/Ownrshp* 1983
Sales 99.3MM^E *EMP* 85
SIC 5147 5148 5149 2011 Meats, fresh; Vegetables; Natural & organic foods; Canned meats (except baby food), meat slaughtered on site
Pr: Ariane Daguin
* *Pr:* Andy Wertheim
VP: Padraic Doherty
VP: Bob Dunn
VP Sls: Pierre Moreira
Sls Dir: Kevin O'Donnell
Sales Asso: Jamie Busch

D-U-N-S 93-143-4083
DARTMOUTH COLLEGE
(*Suby of* TRUSTEES OF DARTMOUTH COLLEGE) ★
6193 Hinman, Hanover, NH 03755-4007
Tel (603) 646-2191 *Founded/Ownrshp* 1972
Sales 859.5MM *EMP* 10^E
Accts Pricewaterhousecoopers Llp Bo
SIC 8231 College or university library
Assoc Dir: Philip E Barta
Assoc Dir: Seabrook Leslie
Assoc Dir: Stephen Pidgeon
Dept Mgr: Cheryl A Bush
CTO: Geg Husband
Pr Mgr: Michael Barwell
Snr PM: Joe Broemel
Snr PM: Joy Clark

DARTMOUTH-HITCHCOCK
See MARY HITCHCOCK MEMORIAL HOSPITAL

DARTMOUTH-HITCHCOCK KEENE
See CHESHIRE MEDICAL CENTER

D-U-N-S 15-088-3460
DARTMOUTH-HITCHCOCK MEDICAL CENTER
DARTMTH-HTCHCOCK OBLGTED GROUP
1 Medical Center Dr, Lebanon, NH 03756-0001
Tel (603) 650-5000 *Founded/Ownrshp* 1890
Sales 6.9MM *EMP* 9,300
Accts Pricewaterhousecoopers Llp B
SIC 8062 8011 8051 General medical & surgical hospitals; Offices & clinics of medical doctors; Skilled nursing care facilities
* *Pr:* Nancy Sormella
* *CEO:* James N Weinstein
* *COO:* Dan Jantzen
COO: Stephen Leblanc
* *CFO:* Robin Mackey
VP: Karen Buttrey
VP: Deanna Howard
Dir Risk M: Jim Gregoire
CIO: Darcy Dowd
Dir IT: David Roberts
Tech Mgr: Dennis Cogan

D-U-N-S 79-917-5195 IMP
DARTMOUTH-HITCHCOCK MEDICAL CENTER
MAXIFACIAL DENTAL SURGERY
1 Medical Center Dr, Lebanon, NH 03756-0001
Tel (603) 650-5150 *Founded/Ownrshp* 1983
Sales 397.6MM *EMP* 3
SIC 8021 Offices & clinics of dentists; Maxillofacial specialist
Pr: James W Varnum
CFO: Jill Batty
Top Exec: Joseph Paydarfar
Comm Dir: Rosemary Keane
Info Man: Scott Farr
Surgeon: Paul Kispert
Obsttrcn: Leslie Demars
Obsttrcn: Loyd West
Snr PM: Brenda Montagna
Snr Mgr: William Nugent

DARTMTH-HTCHCOCK OBLGTED GROUP
See DARTMOUTH-HITCHCOCK MEDICAL CENTER

DAS
See DEPENDABLE AUTO SHIPPERS INC

D-U-N-S 02-144-9251 IMP
DAS COMPANIES INC
DAS DISTRIBUTORS
724 Lawn Rd, Palmyra, PA 17078-8379
Tel (717) 964-3642 *Founded/Ownrshp* 1978
Sales 501.6MM^E *EMP* 450
SIC 5064 Radios; Radios, motor vehicle; Television sets; Video cassette recorders & accessories
Pr: Michael Z Abel
Pr: Anthony Scicchitano
CFO: John Borst
CFO: Ryan Sanders
VP: Steve Birli
VP: Stephen Sobotta
VP: Wendy Stoviak
VP: Chuck White
VP: Les Willson
Rgnl Mgr: Shawn Malley
Off Mgr: Christine Peppers

DAS DISTRIBUTORS
See DAS COMPANIES INC

D-U-N-S 02-361-6670
■ **DAS HOLDINGS INC**
DIVERSIFIED AGENCY SERVICES
(*Suby of* OMNICOM GROUP INC) ★
437 Madison Ave, New York, NY 10022-7001
Tel (212) 415-3700 *Founded/Ownrshp* 1999
Sales 223.7MM^E *EMP* 482
SIC 7311 Advertising consultant
Pr: Dale A Adams
* *Ch Bd:* Thomas L Harrison
COO: Ceci Zak
Ex VP: Bob Norsworthy
VP: Greg Bedard
VP: Donna Granato
VP Opers: Min Chang
Sls Dir: Darcy Wonsor
Snr Mgr: Kevin Comerford

D-U-N-S 00-541-6611 IMP
DAS NORTH AMERICA INC
(*Suby of* DAS CORPORATION)
840 Industrial Park Blvd, Montgomery, AL 36117-5528
Tel (334) 694-5335 *Founded/Ownrshp* 2004
Sales 182.7MM *EMP* 500
Accts Warren Averett Cpa S Montgome
SIC 2211 Seat cover cloth, automobile: cotton
Pr: Jongmin Uhm
* *COO:* James Uhm

D-U-N-S 03-674-2062 IMP/EXP
■ **DASAN ZHONE SOLUTIONS INC**
(*Suby of* DASAN NETWORKS, INC.)
7195 Oakport St, Oakland, CA 94621-1947
Tel (510) 777-7000 *Founded/Ownrshp* 2016
Sales 100.7MM *EMP* 246
Tkr Sym DZSI *Exch* NAS
SIC 3661 Fiber optics communications equipment
Co-CEO: James Norrod
CFO: Kirk Misaka
Co-CEO: IL Yung Kim
CTO: Eric Presworsky
Board of Directors: Michael Connors, Richard Kramlich

D-U-N-S 95-903-5262 IMP/EXP
DASCO INC
DEARING AGRI-SALES COMPANY
9785 Maroon Cir Ste 110, Englewood, CO 80112-2692
Tel (303) 350-5050 *Founded/Ownrshp* 1996
Sales 148.8MM *EMP* 25
Accts Charles F Roland Cpa Colora
SIC 5191 Fertilizers & agricultural chemicals
Pr: Larry Dearing
* *Sec:* Bonita Dearing
* *VP:* John Ringkob

D-U-N-S 07-870-3707
DASEKE INC
15455 Dallas Pkwy Ste 440, Addison, TX 75001-6764
Tel (972) 248-0412 *Founded/Ownrshp* 2012
Sales 672.7MM^E *EMP* 1,400
SIC 4789 Cargo loading & unloading services
Ch Bd: Don Daseke
* *Pr:* Richard Bailey
* *COO:* Chris Cooper
* *CFO:* R Scott Wheeler

D-U-N-S 06-063-0257
DASEKE LONE STAR INC
(*Suby of* DASEKE INC) ★
15455 Dallas Pkwy, Addison, TX 75001-4690
Tel (972) 248-0412 *Founded/Ownrshp* 2014
Sales 134.8MM^E *EMP* 620^E
SIC 4212 Truck rental with drivers
CEO: Don Daseke
CFO: R Scott Wheeler

D-U-N-S 15-698-2852
DASH IN FOOD STORES INC
(*Suby of* WILLS GROUP INC) ★
6355 Crain Hwy, La Plata, MD 20646-4267
Tel (301) 932-3600 *Founded/Ownrshp* 1986
Sales 160.5MM *EMP* 280
SIC 5541 5411 6794 Filling stations, gasoline; Convenience stores, independent; Franchises, selling or licensing
Pr: Mel Strine
VP: J Blacklock Wills Jr

D-U-N-S 06-465-2266 IMP/EXP
DASH MULTI-CORP INC
(*Suby of* ACCELLA PERFORMANCE MATERIALS INC.)
2500 Adie Rd, Maryland Heights, MO 63043-3525
Tel (314) 432-3200 *Founded/Ownrshp* 1973
Sales 107.9MM^E *EMP* 450
SIC 2821 3069 6512 5169 7359

D-U-N-S 06-133-7663 IMP
DASSAULT FALCON JET CORP
(*Suby of* DASSAULT AVIATION)
200 Riser Rd, Little Ferry, NJ 07643-1226
Tel (201) 440-6700 *Founded/Ownrshp* 1972
Sales 798.7MM^E *EMP* 3,000
SIC 5088 3721

D-U-N-S 02-087-8042
DASSAULT SYSTEMES AMERICAS CORP (DE)
(*Suby of* DASSAULT SYSTEMES)
175 Wyman St, Waltham, MA 02451-1223
Tel (781) 810-3000 *Founded/Ownrshp* 1998
Sales 411.9MM^E *EMP* 1,161
SIC 7371 Computer software systems analysis & design, custom
Pr: Bernard Charls
* *Ch Bd:* Charles Edelstenne
* *Pr:* Bernard Charles
Pr: Jean Grimaud
COO: Keith A Charron
* *CFO:* Thibault De Tersant
* *Ex VP:* Monica Menghini
* *Sr VP:* Al Bunshaft
VP: Alain Houard
VP: Dave Tewksbary
Exec: Treena Landers
Board of Directors: Mark Goldstein, Marcelo Lemos, Michel Tellier

D-U-N-S 80-857-2044
DASSAULT SYSTEMES BIOVIA CORP
(*Suby of* 3DS ACQUISITION CORP) ★
5005 Wateridge Vista Dr # 2, San Diego, CA 92121-5784
Tel (858) 799-5000 *Founded/Ownrshp* 2014
Sales 122.1MM^E *EMP* 647^E
SIC 7372 Application computer software; Business oriented computer software
CEO: Max Carnecchia
* *CFO:* John Pecoraro
* *CFO:* Michael Piraino
* *Sr VP:* Jason Gray
* *Sr VP:* Mathew Hahn
* *Sr VP:* Judith Ohrn Hicks
* *Sr VP:* Scott Hiraoka
* *Sr VP:* Mollie Hunter
Sr VP: Richard Murphy
* *Sr VP:* Leif Pedersen
Sr VP: Brian Stafford
VP: John McCarthy

D-U-N-S 87-814-1795
DASSAULT SYSTEMES SOLIDWORKS CORP
(*Suby of* DASSAULT SYSTEMES)
175 Wyman St, Waltham, MA 02451-1223
Tel (781) 810-3000 *Founded/Ownrshp* 1993
Sales 90.9MM *EMP* 655
Accts Deloitte & Touche Llp Boston
SIC 7371 Computer software development
CEO: Bertrand Sicot
Ex VP: Birtrand Sitcot
VP: Gian P Bassi
VP: Brian Houle
VP: Rachel Simone
Exec: Gian Bartlett
Ex Dir: Mark Norris
CTO: Nikhil Kulkarni
DP Exec: Chilton Jim
Dir IT: Thomas Jun
Sftwr Eng: Fred Dollen

D-U-N-S 03-780-4317 IMP/EXP
DASTECH INTERNATIONAL INC (NY)
10 Cuttermill Rd Ste 400, Great Neck, NY 11021-3201
Tel (516) 466-7676 *Founded/Ownrshp* 1980
Sales 100.0MM *EMP* 15
SIC 5169 Chemicals & allied products
Ch Bd: Robert Kahen
* *Pr:* Moussa Kahen
* *Treas:* Simone Kahen

D-U-N-S 12-086-1042
DATA ANALYSIS INC
12655 Beatrice St, Los Angeles, CA 90066-7300
Tel (310) 448-6800 *Founded/Ownrshp* 1984
Sales 287.7MM^E *EMP* 800
Accts Pricewaterhousecoopers Los An
SIC 6211 2711 7374 Security brokers & dealers; Newspapers, publishing & printing; Data processing service
CEO: Steve S Birchc
Pr: William J O'Neil
CFO: Don Drake

D-U-N-S 06-326-3371
DATA BLUE LLC
1117 Perimeter Ctr, Atlanta, GA 30338-5451
Tel (727) 412-8470 *Founded/Ownrshp* 2011
Sales 90.0MM^E *EMP* 20
SIC 7379 Data processing consultant;
CEO: Kelly Steinberger
* *Pr:* Stephen Ayoub
CFO: Joseph Ayoub

D-U-N-S 05-497-8952 IMP
■ **DATA DEVICE CORP**
(*Suby of* I L C) ★
105 Wilbur Pl, Bohemia, NY 11716-2426
Tel (631) 567-5600 *Founded/Ownrshp* 1964
Sales 144.4MM^E *EMP* 343
SIC 3577 3674 3677 Data conversion equipment, media-to-media: computer; Modules, solid state; Electronic transformers
Pr: Vincent Buffa
Pr: Charles Frazer
VP: Frank Bloomfield
VP: Tammy Huml
* *VP:* William Riley
VP: Martha Solowey
VP: Bill Wagner
Snr Sftwr: Vincent Ballarano
Snr Sftwr: Jeff Nuccio
Snr Sftwr: Charles Saperstein
QA Dir: Gabriela Manugas

D-U-N-S 04-307-4269 IMP
DATA EXCHANGE CORP
D E X
3600 Via Pescador, Camarillo, CA 93012-5035
Tel (805) 388-1711 *Founded/Ownrshp* 1980
Sales 201.9MM^E *EMP* 500
SIC 5045 7378 Computers, peripherals & software; Computer & data processing equipment repair/maintenance; Computer peripheral equipment repair & maintenance
* *CFO:* Shawn Howie
Ch: Tony Harris
* *Ex VP:* Paul Gettings
VP: Dale Cohen
Opers Mgr: Marcelino Guzman

D-U-N-S 01-861-9986
DATA LINK SOLUTIONS LLC
350 Collins Rd Ne, Cedar Rapids, IA 52498-0508
Tel (319) 295-8144 *Founded/Ownrshp* 1996
Sales 150.0MM *EMP* 19^E
SIC 3812 Search & navigation equipment

D-U-N-S 04-837-0548
DATA LISTING SERVICES LLC
CONNECTION, THE
11351 Rupp Dr, Burnsville, MN 55337-1200
Tel (952) 948-5488 *Founded/Ownrshp* 1997
Sales 98.6MM^E *EMP* 1,400
SIC 7389 Telemarketing services
CEO: Fred Weiner
CFO: John Meyer
VP: Paul Howe
Genl Mgr: Ken Unruh
MIS Dir: Bruce Anderson
Sls Dir: Michael McMillan

D-U-N-S 02-157-4967
DATA RECOGNITION CORP
DRC
13490 Bass Lake Rd, Maple Grove, MN 55311-3634
Tel (763) 268-2000 *Founded/Ownrshp* 1976
Sales 201.0MM *EMP* 629
Accts Copeland Buhl & Company Pllp
SIC 8732 2752 Educational research; Commercial printing, offset
CEO: Susan Shannon Engeleiter
* *CFO:* Lany Wittnebel
* *Ch:* Russ Hagen
* *Sr VP:* Dave Chayer
VP: Deanna Hudella
VP: Sherri Woolf
* *CIO:* John Bandy
DP Dir: Scott Linder
QA Dir: Justin Hillesheim
QA Dir: Melody Kelly
QA Dir: Chad Swenson

D-U-N-S 07-176-3155
DATA SALES CO INC
3450 W Burnsville Pkwy, Burnsville, MN 55337-4203
Tel (952) 890-8838 *Founded/Ownrshp* 1973
Sales 160.9MM^E *EMP* 98
SIC 5045 7377 Computers, peripherals & software; Computer hardware rental or leasing, except finance leasing; Computer peripheral equipment rental & leasing
Pr: Paul Breckner
CFO: Gary Finigan
* *Sec:* Judith Breckner
VP: Bill Breckner
VP: Stu Hall
VP: Peter Johnson
VP Admn: Leigh Middag

D-U-N-S 96-543-2920
DATA STRATEGY LLC
4020 E Beltline Ave Ne # 201, Grand Rapids, MI 49525-9324
Tel (616) 281-5566 *Founded/Ownrshp* 2010
Sales 331.4MM^E *EMP* 100^E

SIC 5045 Computers, peripherals & software
Pr: Gregg Dewitt
VP: Bill Hussain
VP: Jason Kuipers
VP: Jim Loznak
Sls Mgr: Pam Eaglen
Sls Mgr: Thomas Finnie
Sales Asso: Aj Heyboer

D-U-N-S 03-513-6936
DATA SYSTEMS INC
RETAIL DATA SYSTEM
6515 S 118th St Ste 100, Omaha, NE 68137-3588
Tel (402) 597-6477 *Founded/Ownrshp* 1992
Sales 142.5MM[E] *EMP* 350
SIC 5044 Cash registers
Pr: Robert Seider
Exec: Paul Stelmachers
Genl Mgr: Larry Frazer
Genl Mgr: Mike Hughes
Genl Mgr: Mike Verwey
Genl Mgr: John Wilkerson
IT Man: Ben Hardy
Software D: Jerry Hobson
VP Opers: Brian Podraza

D-U-N-S 80-858-2811
DATA VISION COMPUTER VIDEO INC
50 W 23rd St, New York, NY 10010-5205
Tel (212) 689-1111 *Founded/Ownrshp* 1993
Sales 95.6MM[E] *EMP* 90
Accts Teich Beim & Moro Pc Suff
SIC 5045 5961 Computers, peripherals & software; Computer equipment & electronics, mail order
Ch Bd: James Garson
VP: Padraic Boyle
VP: ARI Klein
Exec: Seth Brown
Mng Dir: Tim Liggins
Dept Mgr: Sam Cwilich
Store Mgr: Robert Bechan
Tech Mgr: Abu Belal

D-U-N-S 02-181-0908
DATA-MAIL INC
240 Hartford Ave, Newington, CT 06111-2054
Tel (860) 666-0399 *Founded/Ownrshp* 1971
Sales 98.4MM[E] *EMP* 700
SIC 7371 Custom computer programming services
Pr: Andrew Mandell
Sr VP: Scott Braunstein
**VP:* Bruce Mandell
Snr Mgr: Michael Gambaccini

D-U-N-S 09-072-9682
DATAART SOLUTIONS INC
475 Park Ave S Fl 15, New York, NY 10016-6901
Tel (212) 378-4108 *Founded/Ownrshp* 1997
Sales 78.9MM[E] *EMP* 1,208
SIC 7371 Computer software development
Pr: Eugene Goland
**CFO:* Luba Kabrits
**Ex VP:* Alex Miller
Sr VP: Artyom Afanassiev
Sr VP: Artyom Astafurovsenior
Sr VP: Dmitry Dataart
Sr VP: Girish Nairsenior
VP: Roman Chernyshevvice
VP: Simon Cox
VP: Oleg Komissarov
VP: Denis Margolin
VP: Dmitry Stillermannvice
**VP:* Michael Zaitsev
Board of Directors: Mikhail Zavileysky

D-U-N-S 60-599-8587
DATABANK IMX LLC
620 Freedom Business Ctr, King of Prussia, PA 19406-1330
Tel (610) 233-0251 *Founded/Ownrshp* 2005
Sales 111.2MM[E] *EMP* 400
SIC 7374 5044 Optical scanning data service; Microfilm equipment
CEO: Charles Bauer
**CFO:* Sandy Brunner
**Sr VP:* Ken Bozler
**VP:* David Godiksen
Off Mgr: Monique Hyde
CIO: Chad Van Norman
Snr Mgr: Margaret Murray

D-U-N-S 19-480-6634 IMP
DATADIRECT NETWORKS INC
D D N
9351 Deering Ave, Chatsworth, CA 91311-5858
Tel (818) 700-7600 *Founded/Ownrshp* 1988
Sales 223.5MM[E] *EMP* 600
SIC 3572 7374 Computer auxiliary storage units; Data processing service
CEO: Alex Bouzari
**Pr:* Paul Bloch
Pr: Gordon Manning
**CFO:* Ian Angelo
**Chf Mktg O:* Molly Rector
Ex VP: Jean-Luc Chatelain
Sr VP: Robert Triendl
Sr VP: Paul M Whitney
VP: Pascal Barbolosi
VP: Bill Cox
**VP:* Sandra Pak Knox
VP: Bob Merkert
VP: Rich Pappas
VP: Laura Thommen
VP: Bret Weber
Exec: Jason Lewis
Board of Directors: Roger Biscay, Joseph L Cowan, John Dorman

D-U-N-S 04-539-0531
▲ DATALINK CORP
10050 Crosstown Cir # 500, Eden Prairie, MN 55344-3346
Tel (952) 944-3462 *Founded/Ownrshp* 1963
Sales 764.7MM *EMP* 633
Tkr Sym DTLK *Exch* NGM
SIC 5045 7371 7373 Computers, peripherals & software; Computer software systems analysis & design, custom; Computer integrated systems design; Computer systems analysis & design; Systems integration services
Pr: Paul F Lidsky
**Ch Bd:* James E Ousley
COO: M Shawn O'Grady
COO: Krista Schrom
CFO: Gregory T Barnum
CFO: Jim Vonier
Ex VP: Patricia A Hamm
VP: Denise M Westenfield
Exec: Jon Siegel
CIO: Stu Missling
Software D: Derek Brusegard
Board of Directors: Brent G Blackey, Greg R Meland, J Patrick O'halloran, Mercedes A Walton, James L Zucco Jr

D-U-N-S 78-580-9948 IMP
DATALOGIC ADC INC
(*Suby of* DATALOGIC HOLDINGS INC) ★
959 Terry St, Eugene, OR 97402-9150
Tel (541) 683-5700 *Founded/Ownrshp* 1996
Sales 103.7MM[E] *EMP* 788
SIC 3577 Magnetic ink & optical scanning devices; Bar code (magnetic ink) printers
Pr: William L Parnell
Pr: David Richards
Pr: Pietro Todescato
Treas: Heber Wygant
**Sr VP:* David Sullivan
**Sr VP:* Brad West
VP: Matt Kuznicki
VP: Brad Reddersen
VP: Matt Schler
Dir Surg: Roger McComas
Mng Dir: Anthony Beevis
Board of Directors: John O'brien, Roberto Tunioli

D-U-N-S 05-330-5801 IMP
DATALOGIC AUTOMATION INC (GA)
(*Suby of* DATALOGIC SPA)
511 School House Rd, Telford, PA 18969-1148
Tel (215) 723-0981 *Founded/Ownrshp* 1971, 2012
Sales 127.3MM[E] *EMP* 260
SIC 3577 Optical scanning devices; Input/output equipment, computer
CEO: Gian Paolo Fedrigo
**Sec:* Valerie Borchevsky
VP: Alberto Bertomeu
**VP:* Todd Hagerich
Area Mgr: Seth Coleman
Area Mgr: Randy Goltz
Snr Sftwr: Paul Demicco
Snr Sftwr: Srinivasa Divi
Sftwr Eng: Bryan Glaudel
Sftwr Eng: Anne Kelley
Sftwr Eng: William Kurth

D-U-N-S 04-922-3357 IMP
DATALOGIC HOLDINGS INC
(*Suby of* DATALOGIC SPA)
959 Terry St, Eugene, OR 97402-9150
Tel (541) 683-5700 *Founded/Ownrshp* 2005
Sales 164.2MM[E] *EMP* 809
SIC 3577 Magnetic ink recognition devices; Readers, sorters or inscribers, magnetic ink; Optical scanning devices
Ch Bd: William L Parnell Jr
**Pr:* William Parnell
CFO: Stefano Biordi
**VP:* Chester Galka
VP: Matt D Schler
VP: Stan Sroka
**VP:* Dave Sullivan
**VP:* Brad West
Genl Mgr: Nick Tabet
Snr Sftwr: Ron Barnwell
Snr Sftwr: Keith Rogers

D-U-N-S 60-885-9880
DATAMARK INC
123 W Mills Ave Ste 400, El Paso, TX 79901-1674
Tel (915) 778-1944 *Founded/Ownrshp* 1989
Sales 28.0MM *EMP* 2,100
Accts Schmid Broaddus Nugent & Gan
SIC 7374 Data entry service
Ch Bd: William J Holmes
**Pr:* William F Randag Jr
**Sr VP:* John A Holmes
**VP:* Carl Heinlein
**VP:* Matt Lochausen
Exec: Bill Randag
IT Man: Stephen Parker
Sales Exec: Jerry Sarabia
Mktg Dir: Robert Munoz
Sls Dir: Stephen Darling
Mktg Mgr: Lisa Bond

D-U-N-S 84-241-6658 IMP
■ DATAMAX-ONEIL CORP
(*Suby of* HONEYWELL INTERNATIONAL INC) ★
4501 Pkwy Commerce Blvd, Orlando, FL 32808-1013
Tel (407) 578-8007 *Founded/Ownrshp* 2015
Sales 146.3MM *EMP* 440
SIC 3577 2754 Input/output equipment, computer; Labels: gravure printing
Pr: Michael Savignac
**CFO:* John Yuncza
VP: Stephanie U Ulmer
Snr Sftwr: Dan Truong
IT Man: Jacklyn Daniels-Jones
IT Man: Courtney Duerig
Sftwr Eng: Yuechun Chu
Sftwr Eng: Albert Goehring
Plnt Mgr: Keith Jones
Ql Cn Mgr: Sandra Papp
VP Mktg: Doug Hall

D-U-N-S 01-557-0583 IMP
DATAPATH INC
(*Suby of* DPII HOLDINGS, LLC)
2205 Northmont Pkwy 100, Duluth, GA 30096-5892
Tel (678) 597-0300 *Founded/Ownrshp* 2014
Sales 162.8MM[E] *EMP* 568
SIC 3663 Space satellite communications equipment
Pr: David Myers
**CFO:* Emmett Moore
Sr VP: Kevin Benedict
VP: Michael Barnes
VP: Carsten Drachmann
VP: Roger Ramos
VP: Peggy Rowe
VP: George Tong
Genl Mgr: David Hall
Snr Sftwr: Andrew Gomez
Snr Sftwr: Seth Ogram
Board of Directors: David Myers

D-U-N-S 00-721-0714
DATAPIPE INC
10 Exchange Pl, Jersey City, NJ 07302-3918
Tel (201) 792-1918 *Founded/Ownrshp* 2006
Sales 339.4MM[E] *EMP* 575
SIC 7374 Data processing & preparation; Data entry service
**COO:* Daniel Newton
CFO: Bruce Katz
**CFO:* Ed O'Hara
**Sr VP:* Michael Bross
Sr VP: Craig Sowell
VP: Colin Chan
VP: Edvan Chan
VP: David Horowitz
VP: Ed Laczinsky
VP: Ed Laczynski
VP: Chris Mooney
VP: Robert Rorro
VP: Brian St Jean
VP: Mark Underwood
Exec: Ron Campbell
Board of Directors: Michael Parks, Michael Tobin

D-U-N-S 00-166-0786 IMP
DATASCOPE CORP
MAQUET
(*Suby of* GETINGE AB)
15 Law Dr, Fairfield, NJ 07004-3206
Tel (973) 244-6100 *Founded/Ownrshp* 1964, 2009
Sales 115.2MM[E] *EMP* 500
SIC 3845 Electrotherapeutic apparatus; Electromedical apparatus
VP: Donald R Lemma
CFO: Leonard Goodman
CFO: Murray Pitkowsky
**CFO:* Henry M Scaramelli
Treas: Eric H Neitsch
Bd of Dir: David Gibson
VP: Nick Barker
VP: Paul Fein
VP: Jeffrey L Purvin
VP: Mark Rappaport
VP: Donald Southard
VP: Paul J Southworth
**VP:* S Arieh Zak

D-U-N-S 07-958-7857
DATASPAN HOLDINGS INC
1245 Viceroy Dr, Dallas, TX 75247-3908
Tel (214) 905-1882 *Founded/Ownrshp* 2014
Sales 146.1MM[E] *EMP* 578[E]
SIC 6719 7375 Investment holding companies, except banks; Data base information retrieval
Pr: Micky Tsui
**Ch Bd:* Paul Zaidins
**COO:* Nancy Shemwell
**VP:* John Bates

D-U-N-S 82-883-6895
DATASPAN INC
(*Suby of* DATASPAN HOLDINGS INC) ★
1245 Viceroy Dr, Dallas, TX 75247-3908
Tel (800) 660-3586 *Founded/Ownrshp* 2014
Sales 88.8MM[E] *EMP* 85
SIC 5045 7375 Computers, peripherals & software; Data base information retrieval
CEO: Paul Zaidins
COO: Nancy Shemwell
VP: Tonya Lowe
CTO: Chris Gray
Dir IT: Anthony Johnson
Tech Mgr: Frank Dendish
VP Mktg: Jeff Kilpatrick
Mktg Dir: Sherry Pipkin
Sls Mgr: Michael White
Sales Asso: Beth Hoven

DATATEL
See MIDDLE ATLANTIC PRODUCTS INC

D-U-N-S 18-618-3075
■ DATATRAC INFORMATION SERVICES INC
(*Suby of* CSC) ★
3170 Fairview Park Dr, Falls Church, VA 22042-4516
Tel (703) 876-1000 *Founded/Ownrshp* 2006
Sales 215.3MM[E] *EMP* 2,000
SIC 8742 0781 8721 Training & development consultant
Pr: Jose Jimenez

D-U-N-S 12-950-1685 IMP/EXP
■ DATEX-OHMEDA INC
GE HEALTHCARE BSCNCE BIOPROCESS
(*Suby of* GE HEALTHCARE LIFE SCIENCES) ★
3030 Ohmeda Dr, Madison, WI 53718-6704
Tel (608) 221-1551 *Founded/Ownrshp* 2006
Sales 283.4MM[E] *EMP* 1,400
SIC 3845 Electrotherapeutic apparatus
Pr: Richard Atkin
Ex VP: Mark Blair
**VP:* Lori Cross
**VP:* Thierry Leclercq
Ql Cn Mgr: Jason Kelly
Snr Mgr: Monica Morrison
Snr Mgr: Kevin Tissot

D-U-N-S 60-647-1613
DATS TRUCKING INC
OVERLAND PETROLEUM
321 N Old Highway 91, Hurricane, UT 84737-3194
Tel (435) 673-1886 *Founded/Ownrshp* 1988
Sales 89.3MM[E] *EMP* 475
SIC 4212 4213 5171 Local trucking, without storage; Contract haulers; Petroleum bulk stations & terminals
Prin: Don L Ipson
**Sec:* Stanley Snow
VP: David Ipson

DATTO BACKUP
See DATTO INC

D-U-N-S 02-295-1348 EXP
DATTO INC
DATTO BACKUP
101 Merritt 7 Ste 7, Norwalk, CT 06851-1061
Tel (203) 665-6423 *Founded/Ownrshp* 2013
Sales 139.7MM[E] *EMP* 430
SIC 7375 Data base information retrieval
Pr: Austin McChord
CFO: Michelle McComb
**Ofcr:* R Brooks Borcherding
Ofcr: Bill Falk
VP: Carrie Reber
VP: Josh Tamarkin
Off Mgr: Nick Fletcher
Snr Ntwrk: Austin Wilson
**CIO:* Loic Vienne
QA Dir: Jay Lee
Tech Mgr: Jason Elston
Board of Directors: Pat Gray, Steve Herrod, Paul Sagan

D-U-N-S 04-632-1048 IMP/EXP
DATWYLER PHARMA PACKAGING USA REALTY INC
(*Suby of* DATWYLER HOLDING AG)
9012 Pennsauken Hwy, Pennsauken, NJ 08110-1204
Tel (856) 663-2202 *Founded/Ownrshp* 1981
Sales 124.4MM[E] *EMP* 350
SIC 5047 3841

DAUGHERTY BUSINESS SOLUTIONS
See DAUGHERTY SYSTEMS INC

D-U-N-S 17-844-0707
DAUGHERTY SYSTEMS INC
DAUGHERTY BUSINESS SOLUTIONS
3 Cityplace Dr Ste 400, Saint Louis, MO 63141-7087
Tel (314) 432-8200 *Founded/Ownrshp* 1985
Sales 169.6MM *EMP* 475
Accts Cliftonlarsonallen Llp St Lo
SIC 7379 7371 8742 7373 7372 Computer related consulting services; Custom computer programming services; Management consulting services; Computer integrated systems design; Prepackaged software
CEO: Ron Daugherty
VP: Andrea Avery
VP: Clay Brice
VP: Duane Davis
VP: Dave Hoyt
VP: Matt Kimball
VP: Lee J Metcalf
VP: Bill Richards
Exec: Nathan Orwig
Mng Dir: Joe Rutili
Rgnl Mgr: Paul Jakaitis

D-U-N-S 07-588-6218
DAUGHTERS OF CHARITY PROVINCE OF ST LOUISE (MO)
WEST CENTRAL PROVINCE OF THE
4330 Olive St, Saint Louis, MO 63108-2622
Tel (314) 533-4770 *Founded/Ownrshp* 1910
Sales 26.0MM[E] *EMP* 5,500
SIC 8661 5912 Religious organizations; Drug stores
Pr: Sr Marie Theresa Sedgwick

D-U-N-S 07-196-8200
DAUGHTERS OF CHARITY SERVICES OF ST LOUIS
DE PAUL HOSPITAL
12303 De Paul Dr, Bridgeton, MO 63044-2512
Tel (314) 344-6000 *Founded/Ownrshp* 1828
Sales 396.4MM *EMP* 1,550
SIC 8062 8051 8063 8069 General medical & surgical hospitals; Extended care facility; Psychiatric hospitals; Specialty hospitals, except psychiatric
Pr: Robert G Porter
CFO: Mark Oconnor
Adm/Dir: Glenn Kraft

DAV EL WOLDWIDE
See MTG ACQUISITIONS LLC

D-U-N-S 94-746-8286
DAVACO INC
6688 N Cntrl Expy Ste 100, Dallas, TX 75206-3925
Tel (214) 373-4700 *Founded/Ownrshp* 1993
Sales 142.6MM[E] *EMP* 900
Accts Grant Thorton Llp
SIC 1751 1799 1542 1796 Store fixture installation; Home/office interiors finishing, furnishing & remodeling; Commercial & office buildings, renovation & repair; Store front construction; Installing building equipment
CEO: Rick Davis
**Pr:* Gerry Geddis
**CFO:* Lamar Roberts
**Ex VP:* Paul Hamer
Sr VP: Michael Murray
**Sr VP:* Mike Murray
Sr VP: Shelly Vandeven
VP: Roberto Arrocha
VP: Steve Hall
VP: Sheryl Koehn
VP: Kathy Merani
VP: Tom Motschull
VP: Brian Reilly
VP: Thomas Sacco

DAVALAN FRESH
See DAVALAN SALES INC

D-U-N-S 12-204-6048 IMP
DAVALAN SALES INC
DAVALAN FRESH
1601 E Olympic Blvd # 325, Los Angeles, CA 90021-1957
Tel (213) 623-2500 *Founded/Ownrshp* 1983
Sales 119.0MM[E] *EMP* 200
SIC 5148 Fruits; Vegetables
Pr: Alan Frick
**CEO:* Dave Bouton

D-U-N-S 04-268-9070
DAVCO ACQUISITION HOLDING INC
WENDY'S
1657 Crofton Blvd, Crofton, MD 21114-1305
Tel (410) 721-3770 *Founded/Ownrshp* 1998
Sales 177.4MM^E *EMP* 6,575
Accts Independent
SIC 5812 Fast-food restaurant, chain
Ch Bd: Harvey Rothstein
**Pr:* Joseph F Cunnane III
CFO: Charles McGuire
**CFO:* David J Norman
Div VP: Lester Pollitt
**Ex VP:* Richard H Borchers
**VP:* Charles Mc Guire
Dist Mgr: Syed Bukhari

D-U-N-S 19-327-2432
DAVCO RESTAURANTS INC
WENDY'S
(*Suby of* WENDYS) ★
1657 Crofton Blvd, Crofton, MD 21114-1305
Tel (410) 721-3770 *Founded/Ownrshp* 1969
Sales 160.9MM^E *EMP* 4,500
SIC 5812 Fast-food restaurant, chain
CEO: Harvey Rothstein
**Pr:* David J Norman
**COO:* Richard H Borchers
CFO: Charles C McGuire
**Sr VP:* Stacey Jackson
**Sr VP:* Charles Mc Guire
**VP:* David Carpenter
VP: Stacy Duncan
VP: Tom Hughes
VP: Ann Portnow
VP: John Schmidt

D-U-N-S 07-862-5930
▲ DAVE & BUSTERS ENTERTAINMENT INC
2481 Manana Dr, Dallas, TX 75220-1203
Tel (214) 357-9588 *Founded/Ownrshp* 1982
Sales 866.9MM *EMP* 10,961
Tkr Sym PLAY *Exch* NGS
SIC 5812 7993 Eating places; Coin-operated amusement devices; Game machines
CEO: Stephen M King
**Ch Bd:* Alan J Lacy
Pr: Dolf Berle
COO: Margo Manning
CFO: Brian A Jenkins
Sr VP: Sean Gleason
Sr VP: Jay L Tobin
Dir Soc: Evelyn Carrillo
Genl Mgr: Daniel Eurell
Board of Directors: J Taylor Crandall, Michael J Griffith, Jonathan S Halkyard, David A Jones, Kevin M Mailender, Patricia H Mueller, Kevin M Sheehan, Jennifer Storms, Tyler J Wolfram

D-U-N-S 83-069-3722
■ DAVE & BUSTERS HOLDINGS INC
(*Suby of* DAVE & BUSTERS ENTERTAINMENT INC) ★
2481 Manana Dr, Dallas, TX 75220-1203
Tel (214) 357-9588 *Founded/Ownrshp* 2010
Sales 635.5MM^E *EMP* 9,864^E
SIC 5812 Eating places
Chf Mktg O: Sean Gleason
VP: Lisa Warren
Dir Soc: Heather Bernardi
Dir Soc: Julie Detwiler
Dir Soc: Amy Jones
Dir Soc: Kathy Kowalski
Dir Soc: Peggy Sparks
Dir Sec: James Brussow
Genl Mgr: Esther Gomez
Genl Mgr: Eric Landsman
Genl Mgr: Matt Luckett

D-U-N-S 78-371-8216 IMP
■ DAVE & BUSTERS INC
(*Suby of* DAVE & BUSTERS HOLDINGS INC) ★
2481 Manana Dr, Dallas, TX 75220-1203
Tel (214) 357-9588 *Founded/Ownrshp* 2006
Sales 635.5MM *EMP* 9,864
SIC 5812 5813 7999 7993 Eating places; Bar (drinking places); Billiard parlor; Coin-operated amusement devices
Ch Bd: Tyler J Wolfram
Pr: Dolf Berle
Pr: Greg Lecorgne
Pr: Sam Nwachukwu
**CEO:* Stephen M King
CFO: Brian A Jenkins
Chf Mktg O: Sean Gleason
Ex VP: Greg Clore
Sr VP: Kevin Bachus
Sr VP: Nancy Duricic
Sr VP: John B Mulleady
Sr VP: J Michael Plunkett
Sr VP: Bryan L Spain
Sr VP: Jay L Tobin
VP: Barry N Carter
VP: Edward Forler
VP: Corey J Haynes
VP: Vicki Johnson
VP: Mike Kane
VP: Kulsoom Klavon
VP: Nancy Litzler
Board of Directors: J Taylor Crandall, Michael J Griffith, Jonathan S Halkyard, David A Jones, Alan J Lacy, Kevin M Mailender, Kevin M Sheehan

D-U-N-S 09-665-3902 IMP
DAVE CARTER & ASSOCIATES INC (FL)
3530 Sw 7th St, Ocala, FL 34474-1953
Tel (352) 732-3317 *Founded/Ownrshp* 1977
Sales 128.9MM^E *EMP* 95
SIC 5063 5039 Electrical supplies; Prefabricated structures
Pr: John Curran
**Ch Bd:* David J Carter Sr
Admn Mgr: Chris Dyer
Dir IT: Rita Baggerly
Dir IT: Cheryl Wilson
Sales Exec: Rick Deleon
Sales Exec: Mike Kantor
Sls Mgr: David Froom

DAVE SINCLAIR AUTOMOTIVE GROUP
See DAVE SINCLAIR FORD WEST

D-U-N-S 03-109-6829
DAVE SINCLAIR FORD WEST
DAVE SINCLAIR AUTOMOTIVE GROUP
7466 S Lindbergh Blvd, Saint Louis, MO 63125-4898
Tel (314) 892-2600 *Founded/Ownrshp* 1966
Sales 108.2MM^E *EMP* 264
SIC 5511 7538 5521 5012 Automobiles, new & used; General automotive repair shops; Used car dealers; Automobiles & other motor vehicles
Pr: James Sinclair
**VP:* Michael Detwiler
**VP:* John Willett
DP Dir: Megan Hagerty
IT Man: Tim Ruddy
Sls Mgr: Michael Beckman
Sls Mgr: Jim Culp
Sls Mgr: Stephanie Detwiler
Sales Asso: Tom Biermann
Sales Asso: Angela Bonfanti
Sales Asso: Scott Braun

D-U-N-S 05-317-8778
DAVENPORT & CO LLC (VA)
901 E Cary St Ste 1200, Richmond, VA 23219-4037
Tel (804) 780-2000 *Founded/Ownrshp* 1863
Sales 137.0MM^E *EMP* 348
Accts Kpmg Llp Richmond Va
SIC 6211 6282 Investment firm, general brokerage; Underwriters, security; Investment advisory service
Pr: Lee Chapman IV
Ofcr: Kathleen Holman
Ofcr: Brian McCormack
Assoc VP: William Charlet
Assoc VP: Sharon Jett
Assoc VP: Garrett Nelson
Assoc VP: Alan Vaughan
Assoc VP: Sam Waddell
Ex VP: Mike Beall
Ex VP: Robert Giles
Ex VP: Robert Mizell
Sr VP: John Ackerly
Sr VP: David Anderson
Sr VP: D A Armistead
Sr VP: Julie Beck
Sr VP: Christopher Blair
Sr VP: Garry Clay
Sr VP: Eddie Eddins
Sr VP: Moncure Geho
Sr VP: William Hershey
Sr VP: Andrew Jowdy

D-U-N-S 07-584-6832
DAVENPORT COMMUNITY SCHOOL DISTRICT
1606 Brady St Ste 100, Davenport, IA 52803-4709
Tel (563) 336-5000 *Founded/Ownrshp* 1858
Sales 113.3MM^E *EMP* 2,450
SIC 8211 Public elementary & secondary schools
**Pr:* Tony Williams
CFO: Linda Mordhorst
Dir IT: Rudy Schellekens
Teacher Pr: Deb Miller
Teacher Pr: Virginia Weipert

D-U-N-S 07-960-2079
DAVENPORT EDUCATIONAL SYSTEMS INC
DAVENPORT UNIVERSITY
6191 Kraft Ave Se, Grand Rapids, MI 49512-9396
Tel (616) 698-7111 *Founded/Ownrshp* 1997
Sales 29.3MM^E *EMP* 2,000^E
SIC 8221 College, except junior
**VP:* Michael Volk

D-U-N-S 02-368-2586
DAVENPORT ENERGY INC
108 Main St, Chatham, VA 24531
Tel (434) 432-0251 *Founded/Ownrshp* 1941
Sales 106.5MM *EMP* 96
SIC 5172 5983 5984

DAVENPORT ROLLING MILL
See NICHOLS ALUMINUM LLC

DAVENPORT UNIVERSITY
See DAVENPORT EDUCATIONAL SYSTEMS INC

D-U-N-S 04-752-9995
DAVENPORT UNIVERSITY
6191 Kraft Ave Se, Grand Rapids, MI 49512-9396
Tel (616) 698-7111 *Founded/Ownrshp* 2002
Sales 102.7MM^E *EMP* 927
Accts Plante & Moran Pllc Portage
SIC 8221 College, except junior
Pr: Richard J Pappas
Ex VP: Barbara Mieras
Ex VP: Linda Rinker
Ex VP: David Veneklase
VP: Michelle Georgevich
VP: David Lawrence
Creative D: Richard Crispo
Comm Dir: Lyndsie Post
Ex Dir: Sandra Burmeister
Ex Dir: David Deboer
Ex Dir: Steve Landrum

DAVE'S MARKET
See DAVES SUPERMARKET INC

D-U-N-S 01-773-7966
DAVES SUPERMARKET INC
DAVE'S MARKET
5300 Richmond Rd, Bedford, OH 44146-1335
Tel (216) 361-5130 *Founded/Ownrshp* 1933
Sales 233.6MM^E *EMP* 1,500
SIC 5411 Supermarkets
Ch: Burton Saltzman
**CEO:* Dan Saltzman
**CFO:* Tom Thiry
VP: Tony Marlette
**VP:* Rob Miller
**VP:* Steven Saltzman
Exec: Bonnie Stobierski
Genl Mgr: Dan Laubenthal
Store Mgr: Sal Albanese

DAVESTATES
See DAVOIL INC

D-U-N-S 00-790-3180
DAVEY TREE EXPERT CO
1500 N Mantua St, Kent, OH 44240-2399
Tel (330) 673-9511 *Founded/Ownrshp* 1909
Sales 821.9MM *EMP* 8,000
SIC 0783 0782 0811 0181 Removal services, bush & tree; Lawn care services; Tree farm; Nursery stock, growing of
Ch Bd: Karl J Warnke
**COO:* Patrick M Covey
**CFO:* Joseph R Paul
**Treas:* Christopher J Bast
Treas: Bradley L Comport
Ex VP: Pat Covey
VP: Julie Blower
VP: Raminder Braich
VP: Harry Claypool
VP: Greg INA
VP: Anthony Kerosky
VP: Steve Marshall
VP: Richard A Ramsey
**VP:* Nicholas R Sucic
VP: Nicholas Sucic
VP: Don Winsett
Exec: C Celmer
Board of Directors: J Dawson Cunningham, William J Ginn, Douglas K Hall, Sandra W Harbrecht, John E Warfel

D-U-N-S 02-917-6740
DAVEY TREE SURGERY CO
(*Suby of* DAVEY TREE EXPERT CO) ★
2617 S Vasco Rd, Livermore, CA 94550-8322
Tel (925) 443-1723 *Founded/Ownrshp* 1969
Sales 12.4MM *EMP* 1,155
SIC 0783 Ornamental shrub & tree services; Tree trimming services for public utility lines; Surgery services, ornamental tree
CEO: Karl J Warnke
**Pr:* R Douglas Cowan
**CFO:* David Adante
**Sr VP:* Howard Bowles
Genl Mgr: Larry Abernathy

D-U-N-S 08-359-5199
DAVID A CAMPBELL CORP
B M W OF RIVERSIDE
3060 Adams St, Riverside, CA 92504-4014
Tel (951) 785-4444 *Founded/Ownrshp* 1975
Sales 133.2MM^E *EMP* 150
SIC 5511 7538 Automobiles, new & used; General automotive repair shops
CEO: Allen David Franklin
CFO: Chris Ruppert
**VP:* Patrick Campbell
Sls Mgr: Tye Gilbert
Sls Mgr: Jim Hutton
Sls Mgr: Emil Iltchi
Sls Mgr: George Mattei

D-U-N-S 07-988-1880
DAVID AND LILY PENN INC
10201 Wayzata Blvd, Minnetonka, MN 55305-5507
Tel (763) 746-0410 *Founded/Ownrshp* 1992
Sales 120.0MM *EMP* 9^E
SIC 5014 Automobile tires & tubes
CEO: David Penn

D-U-N-S 07-982-6516
DAVID AND LUCILE PACKARD FOUNDATION
343 2nd St, Los Altos, CA 94022-3696
Tel (650) 948-7658 *Founded/Ownrshp* 2015
Sales 333.7MM *EMP* 4^E
SIC 2515 Foundations & platforms
Chf Inves: John Moehling

D-U-N-S 11-816-6990
DAVID AND LUCILE PACKARD FOUNDATION
300 2nd St, Los Altos, CA 94022-3694
Tel (650) 917-7167 *Founded/Ownrshp* 1964
Sales 283.0MM *EMP* 85
Accts Pricewaterhousecoopers Llp
SIC 8699 Personal interest organization
Pr: Carol S Larson
**Prin:* Katy Lnp
**Ex Dir:* Julie Packard
Prgrm Mgr: Gene Lewit
IT Man: Pat Kane
Opers Mgr: Nora Prentice
Pgrm Dir: Linda Baker

DAVID CITY MANUFACTURING
See FARGO ASSEMBLY OF PA INC

DAVID DOUGLAS PUBLIC SCHOOLS
See DAVID DOUGLAS SCHOOOL DISTRICT

D-U-N-S 07-073-1518
DAVID DOUGLAS SCHOOL DISTRICT
DAVID DOUGLAS PUBLIC SCHOOLS
11300 Ne Halsey St # 100, Portland, OR 97220-2013
Tel (503) 252-2900 *Founded/Ownrshp* 1954
Sales 149.9MM *EMP* 2,200
Accts Pauly Rogers And Co Pc
SIC 8211 Public elementary & secondary schools
Ch Bd: Cheryl A Scarcelli Ancheta
Bd of Dir: Christine Larsen
VP: Dennis Hankins
VP: Leslie Jones
Comm Dir: Dan McCue
Dir IT: Derek Edens
IT Man: Colleen Hathaway
IT Man: Greg Lind
Psych: Sherry Dudrey
HC Dir: Brooke O'Neill

D-U-N-S 00-389-7774
DAVID E HARVEY BUILDERS INC (TX)
D E HARVEY BUILDERS
3630 Westchase Dr, Houston, TX 77042-5224
Tel (713) 783-8710 *Founded/Ownrshp* 1958
Sales 521.7MM^E *EMP* 600
Accts Weaver And Tidwell Llp Ho
SIC 1542 Commercial & office building, new construction; Commercial & office buildings, renovation & repair
Pr: David Harvey Jr

CFO: Rodney Finke
Ex VP: Joseph A Cleary Jr
VP: Guy Cook
VP: Rusty Gorman
VP: Kelly Hall
VP: Mark Hammer
VP: Michael Harvey
VP: Dennis Kikolla
VP: Douglas Losey
VP: Bruce Mattila
VP: William McCloud
Assoc Dir: Patrick Byle

D-U-N-S 08-661-2439
DAVID EVANS AND ASSOCIATES INC
2100 Sw River Pkwy, Portland, OR 97201-8070
Tel (503) 223-6663 *Founded/Ownrshp* 1976
Sales 146.0MM^E *EMP* 708
SIC 8711 8713 8741

D-U-N-S 09-787-8664
DAVID H MARTIN EXCAVATING INC
4961 Cumberland Hwy, Chambersburg, PA 17202-9655
Tel (717) 264-1312 *Founded/Ownrshp* 1988
Sales 86.8MM^E *EMP* 205^E
Accts Smith Elliott Kearns & Company
SIC 1623 1794 1711 Water main construction; Excavation work; Septic system construction
Pr: Edwin Martin
CFO: Terry Armstrong
CFO: Phylis Martin
**Treas:* Kirk Martin
**VP:* Jeryl Martin
DP Exec: Grant Benedict
Sfty Dirs: Tom Collins
Sfty Dirs: Debra Partridge

DAVID HIRSH
See ATRIUM BUYING CORP

DAVID J JOSEPH COMPANY, THE
See DJJ HOLDING CORP

D-U-N-S 00-699-9502 IMP/EXP
■ DAVID J JOSEPH CO
(*Suby of* DAVID J JOSEPH CO) ★
300 Pike St Fl 3, Cincinnati, OH 45202-4222
Tel (513) 621-8770 *Founded/Ownrshp* 1937, 1986
Sales 754.8MM^E *EMP* 2,013
SIC 5093

DAVID LIPSCOMB CAMPUS SCHOOL
See LIPSCOMB UNIVERSITY

D-U-N-S 16-697-4477
DAVID M DORSETT HEALTH CARE
1020 N 10th St, Spearfish, SD 57783-2203
Tel (605) 642-2716 *Founded/Ownrshp* 1995
Sales 602.3MM *EMP* 115
SIC 8051 Convalescent home with continuous nursing care

DAVID MCDAVID AUTO GROUP
See MCDAVID IRVING-HON LP

D-U-N-S 07-633-5889 IMP/EXP
DAVID OPPENHEIMER & CO I LLC
OPPENHEIMER GROUP
(*Suby of* OPPENHEIMER, DAVID AND COMPANY I, LLC)
180 Nickerson St Ste 211, Seattle, WA 98109-1631
Tel (206) 284-1705 *Founded/Ownrshp* 1997
Sales 800.0MM *EMP* 290
SIC 5141 Food brokers
CEO: John Anderson

D-U-N-S 05-059-2633 IMP
DAVID PEYSER SPORTSWEAR INC
WEATHERPROOF
88 Spence St, Bay Shore, NY 11706-2229
Tel (631) 231-7788 *Founded/Ownrshp* 1954
Sales 103.7MM^E *EMP* 260
SIC 2329 Men's & boys' sportswear & athletic clothing
Ch Bd: Paul Peyser
CFO: Bruce Lerit
**Sec:* Irwin Peyser
Chf Mktg O: Byron Reed
VP: Irwin Hosea
**VP:* Alan Peyser
IT Man: Rick Pyatt

D-U-N-S 08-206-0880
DAVID VOLKERT & ASSOCIATES INC
3809 Moffett Rd, Mobile, AL 36618-1209
Tel (251) 342-1070 *Founded/Ownrshp* 1975
Sales 87.9MM *EMP* 800
SIC 8711 Consulting engineer
CEO: Perry Hand
**CFO:* Thomas Zoghby
Pr Dir: Suzanne Fornaro
Mktg Mgr: Patricia Rochford

DAVID WEEKLEY HOMES
See WEEKLEY HOMES LLC

D-U-N-S 07-542-9282 IMP/EXP
DAVID YURMAN ENTERPRISES LLC
24 Vestry St, New York, NY 10013-1903
Tel (212) 896-1550 *Founded/Ownrshp* 2012
Sales 268.2MM^E *EMP* 800
SIC 3911 Jewelry, precious metal
CEO: Gabriella Forte
COO: Terry Eagle
CFO: Adrianne Shapira
**CFO:* Victor Wong
Ex VP: Carol Pennelli
Sr VP: Cece Coffin
VP: Kate Harrison
Comm Man: Enjoli Duval
Genl Mgr: Melissa Anastasia
Dir IT: Tino Oliveri
Dir IT: Barbara Orourke

D-U-N-S 78-281-6466 IMP
DAVIDS BRIDAL INC
(*Suby of* LEONARD GREEN & PARTNERS LP) ★
1001 Washington St, Conshohocken, PA 19428-2356
Tel (610) 943-5000 *Founded/Ownrshp* 1990

Sales 1.6MMM[E] *EMP* 12,500
SIC 5621 Women's clothing stores; Dress shops
CEO: Pamela Wallack
Treas: Philip C Galbo
Ofcr: Caryn Furtaw
Ex VP: Ann Acierno
Ex VP: Brian Beitler
Ex VP: Cynthia Harriss
Ex VP: Philip Youtie
VP: Jacqualin Athay
VP: Tony Coccerino
VP: Greg S Pffer
VP: Gary Walker
Comm Man: Jen Hausman

DAVIDSON COMPANY
See ROWE BROTHERS

D-U-N-S 08-990-1029
DAVIDSON COUNTY BOARD OF EDUCATION
DAVIDSON COUNTY SCHOOLS
250 County School Rd, Lexington, NC 27292-5670
Tel (336) 249-6704 *Founded/Ownrshp* 1921
Sales 150.7MM *EMP* 2,500
Accts Rick Allred Cpa Pa Lexingto
SIC 8211 Public elementary & secondary schools
CFO: Pam W Sink
Treas: Amy Kearns
Adm Dir: Jay Temple

DAVIDSON COUNTY SCHOOLS
See DAVIDSON COUNTY BOARD OF EDUCATION

D-U-N-S 07-979-8905
DAVIDSON COUNTY SCHOOLS
250 County School Rd, Lexington, NC 27292-5670
Tel (336) 249-8181 *Founded/Ownrshp* 2015
Sales 68.7MM[E] *EMP* 2,527[E]
SIC 8211 Public elementary & secondary schools
Info Man: Melanie Yarborough

D-U-N-S 17-540-5646
DAVIDSON HEALTH CARE INC
250 Hospital Dr, Lexington, NC 27292-6792
Tel (336) 248-5161 *Founded/Ownrshp* 1985
Sales 88.4MM *EMP* 650[E]
Accts Turlington And Company Llp Wi
SIC 5912 8062 Drug stores & proprietary stores; General medical & surgical hospitals
Pr: Donny Lambeth
**Pr:* Dennis Ayers
CIO: Kevin Buchanan
Netwrk Mgr: Melody Desnoyers

D-U-N-S 08-133-9301
DAVIDSON HOTEL CO
DAVIDSON HOTELS & RESORTS
1 Ravinia Dr Ste 1600, Atlanta, GA 30346-2109
Tel (678) 349-0909 *Founded/Ownrshp* 1991
Sales 23.9MM *EMP* 5,000
Accts Warren Averett Llc Atlanta G
SIC 8741 7011 Hotel or motel management; Hotels & motels
CEO: John Belden
Mng Pt: Buddy Metcalf
COO: Thomas M Geshay
COO: Patrick Lupsha
Chf Inves: Steven A Margol
Chf Inves: Steven Margolto
Sr VP: Stephanie Shenas
VP: Hank Artime
VP: Edie Bates
VP: Kyle Bowman
VP Bus Dev: Jason Rabidoux
Exec: Don Mueller

D-U-N-S 62-377-6387
DAVIDSON HOTEL CO LLC
1 Ravinia Dr Ste 1600, Atlanta, GA 30346-2109
Tel (901) 821-4117 *Founded/Ownrshp* 2005
Sales 164.9MM[E] *EMP* 5,400
SIC 7011 Hotels
Pr: John Belden
**Ex VP:* Patrick Lupsha
**Ex VP:* Barry E Wabler
**Sr VP:* Crystal Beasley
**Sr VP:* Thom Geshay
Sr VP: Larry Mills
VP Bus Dev: Ronald Kim
Genl Mgr: Tim Adams
Genl Mgr: Paul Jordan
VP Sls: Mark Simmons
Sls Mgr: Melissa Berman

D-U-N-S 80-785-5820
DAVIDSON HOTEL PARTNERS LP
1 Ravinia Dr Ste 1600, Atlanta, GA 30346-2109
Tel (901) 761-4664 *Founded/Ownrshp* 1993
Sales 105.4MM[E] *EMP* 5,000
SIC 7011 Hotels
Pt: John Belden
Pt: J J Brown
CFO: Larry M Mills
VP: David Beaulieu

DAVIDSON HOTELS & RESORTS
See DAVIDSON HOTEL CO

D-U-N-S 00-347-0325
DAVIDSONS INC (AZ)
6100 Wilkinson Dr, Prescott, AZ 86301-6162
Tel (928) 776-8055 *Founded/Ownrshp* 1932, 1997
Sales 342.9MM *EMP* 89
Accts Eide Bailly Llp Phoenix Ariz
SIC 5091 Firearms, sporting
Ch: Bryan Tucker
**Pr:* Tim Mulder
CFO: Drew Kramer
**VP:* Daniel Leonard
**VP:* Larry M Massimo
Dir IT: Richard Gutierrez
IT Man: John Giek
IT Man: Sheril Manz
IT Man: David Richardson
IT Man: Josh Tucker
Web Dev: Diane Anderson

D-U-N-S 07-786-8156
DAVIESS COUNTY BOARD OF EDUCATION
DAVIESS COUNTY SCHOOLS
1622 Southeastern Pkwy, Owensboro, KY 42303-1826
Tel (270) 852-7000 *Founded/Ownrshp* 1989
Sales 103.5MM *EMP* 1,898
Accts Riney Hancock Cpas Psc Owens
SIC 8211 Public elementary & secondary schools; High school, junior or senior; School board
Pr: Frank Riney III
HC Dir: Wendy Morgan

DAVIESS COUNTY SCHOOLS
See DAVIESS COUNTY BOARD OF EDUCATION

D-U-N-S 00-590-7621 IMP/EXP
DAVIS & WARSHOW INC
(*Suby of* FERGUSON ENTERPRISES INC) ★
5722 49th St, Maspeth, NY 11378-2107
Tel (718) 937-9500 *Founded/Ownrshp* 1925, 2012
Sales 103.2MM[E] *EMP* 250
SIC 5074 Plumbing & hydronic heating supplies
Ch Bd: Frank Finkel
VP: Mark Bembia
VP: Sheldon Malc
**VP:* Joel Sandberg
Dir IT: Marlene Engelmyer

D-U-N-S 00-326-3167
DAVIS CONSTRUCTION CORP JAMES G
12530 Parklawn Dr Ste 100, Rockville, MD 20852-1762
Tel (301) 881-2990 *Founded/Ownrshp* 1986
Sales 869.3MM *EMP* 350
SIC 1542

D-U-N-S 07-664-1224
DAVIS CONSTRUCTORS & ENGINEERS INC
6591 A St Ste 300, Anchorage, AK 99518-1866
Tel (907) 562-2336 *Founded/Ownrshp* 1976
Sales 196.8MM[E] *EMP* 150
Accts Fm Strand & Associates Pc
SIC 1542 Commercial & office building, new construction
Pr: Joshua M Pepperd
**VP:* Carl A Swanson
Genl Mgr: Jenith Flynn
Sales Exec: Darla Hall

DAVIS COUNTY SCHOOL DISTRICT
See DAVIS SCHOOL DISTRICT

D-U-N-S 00-684-9962
DAVIS H ELLIOT CONSTRUCTION CO INC (VA)
(*Suby of* AEW FOUNDATION) ★
673 Blue Sky Pkwy, Lexington, KY 40509-9459
Tel (859) 263-5148 *Founded/Ownrshp* 1946
Sales 264.2MM[E] *EMP* 700
SIC 1623 1731 Water, sewer & utility lines; Electric power line construction; General electrical contractor
Pr: David S Haskins
**VP:* Glenn F Thomsen

D-U-N-S 07-093-0391
DAVIS HOSPITAL & MEDICAL CENTER INC
(*Suby of* IASIS HEALTHCARE CORP) ★
1600 W Antelope Dr, Layton, UT 84041-1120
Tel (801) 807-1000 *Founded/Ownrshp* 1976, 1999
Sales 118.7MM[E] *EMP* 700[E]
SIC 8062

D-U-N-S 15-179-9111 IMP/EXP
DAVIS MINING & MANUFACTURING INC
613 Front St E, Coeburn, VA 24230-4108
Tel (276) 395-3354 *Founded/Ownrshp* 1985
Sales 504.6MM[E] *EMP* 1,800
SIC 2892 5082 2426 1221 1222 Explosives; Mining machinery & equipment, except petroleum; Turnings, furniture: wood; Strip mining, bituminous; Bituminous coal-underground mining
Ch Bd: W Jack Davis
**Treas:* Deborah Karen Davis
**VP:* L Jack Davis

D-U-N-S 01-672-6895
DAVIS OIL CO
C STORES
1265 Columbia Ave E, Battle Creek, MI 49014-5192
Tel (269) 965-2201 *Founded/Ownrshp* 1990
Sales 84.1MM *EMP* 11
SIC 5541 Filling stations, gasoline
Pr: James P Davis
**VP:* Michael Uldriks

D-U-N-S 06-493-2551
DAVIS POLK & WARDWELL LLP
450 Lexington Ave Fl 10, New York, NY 10017-3982
Tel (212) 450-4000 *Founded/Ownrshp* 1849
Sales 301.4MM[E] *EMP* 1,500
SIC 8111 General practice attorney, lawyer
Mng Pt: Tom Reid
Pt: Jeffrey P Crandall
Pt: John Douglas
Pt: Annette Nazareth
COO: Bob Dermik
CFO: Robin Griffiths
Ex VP: Joe Russo
Exec: Charles Hoppin
Exec: Donna Lucas
Exec: Patricia McGrath
Exec: James Windels

DAVIS REGIONAL MEDICAL CENTER
See STATESVILLE HMA LLC

D-U-N-S 02-309-7694
DAVIS RUSS WHOLESALE INC
266 4th St Ne, Wadena, MN 56482-1205
Tel (218) 631-3078 *Founded/Ownrshp* 1968
Sales 277.0MM[E] *EMP* 525
SIC 5148 Fruits, fresh; Vegetables, fresh
Pr: Adam Gamble
**Sec:* Randy Graham
**VP:* Patrick Miller
Exec: Patrick Titterman

D-U-N-S 01-697-6649
DAVIS SCHOOL DISTRICT
DAVIS COUNTY SCHOOL DISTRICT
45 E St St, Farmington, UT 84025
Tel (801) 402-5261 *Founded/Ownrshp* 1911
Sales 509.5MM *EMP* 6,310
Accts Squire & Company Pc Orem Ut
SIC 8211 Public elementary & secondary schools
Pr: Tamara Lowe
VP: Mona Andrus
**VP:* Burke Larsen
Exec: Steven Snow
CTO: Duane Singleton
DP Dir: Mark Reid
IT Man: Twyla Coleman

DAVIS TRUCKING SERVICES
See KEITH DAVIS

D-U-N-S 62-774-5276 IMP
DAVIS VISION INC
(*Suby of* HVHC INC) ★
159 Express St, Plainview, NY 11803-2404
Tel (210) 245-2200 *Founded/Ownrshp* 2016
Sales 123.0MM[E] *EMP* 1,127[E]
SIC 8011 Medical insurance plan
Pr: Danny Bentley
Pr: Lora Shumate
**CFO:* Christopher Hamey
CFO: Scott Hamey
**Treas:* Michael Kincaid
Ofcr: Michael Ehrle
VP: Paul Ennis
VP: Scott Mallonee
VP: Paul Montuori
VP: Dale Paustian
VP: Terence Ward
Board of Directors: John Baum, Danny Bentley, David Blandino, Nanette Deturk, Karen Hanlon, Deborah Rice-Johnson

D-U-N-S 05-730-7704
DAVIS WRIGHT TREMAINE LLP
1201 3rd Ave Ste 2200, Seattle, WA 98101-3045
Tel (206) 622-3150 *Founded/Ownrshp* 1990
Sales 149.6MM[E] *EMP* 928
SIC 8111 General practice law office
Mng Pt: Richard D Ellingsen
Pt: Sandra Gallagher Alford
Pt: Karen Andersen
Pt: Gary Bergquist
Pt: Robert A Blackstone
Pt: Jason Farber
Pt: Bradley Fisher
Pt: Sandra Gallagher-Alford
Pt: Monica Brown Gianni
Pt: James Greenfield
Pt: Christopher Helm
Pt: Cassandra Kinkead
Pt: Jason Klein
Pt: Harry Korrell
Pt: Randall B Lowe
Pt: R Z Margaret Lu
Pt: Jonathan Michaels
Pt: Martin Morfield
Pt: Peter Mucklestone
Pt: Jeffrey Oster
Pt: Elizabeth Sullivan

D-U-N-S 88-490-1794 IMP
■ **DAVIS ZIFF PUBLISHING INC**
ZIFF-DAVIS PUBLISHING
(*Suby of* ZIFF DAVIS LLC) ★
28 E 28th St Fl 10, New York, NY 10016-7939
Tel (212) 503-3500 *Founded/Ownrshp* 2010
Sales 58.5MM[E] *EMP* 1,000
SIC 2721 2731 7371 Periodicals; Book publishing; Custom computer programming services
Ex VP: Tom McGrade
**Ex VP:* Michael J Miller
VP: Steve Gladysewski
VP: Fredrick Rolff
VP: Bennett Zucker
Creative D: Sean Collins
Ex Dir: John Fraissinet
Genl Mgr: James Whitehead
VP Inf Sys: Jasmine Alexander
IT Man: Jill Leger
Sls Dir: Jacqueline Natz

D-U-N-S 83-712-0591 IMP/EXP
DAVIS-STANDARD HOLDINGS INC
EGAN, STERLING, NRM, BROOKES
1 Extrusion Dr, Pawcatuck, CT 06379-2327
Tel (860) 599-1010 *Founded/Ownrshp* 2005
Sales 283.4MM[E] *EMP* 650
SIC 3559 Plastics working machinery
Pr: James Murphy
**Pr:* Charles Buckley
**CFO:* Robert Armstrong
**Ex VP:* Hassan Helmy
**Ex VP:* Mark Panozzo
**Ex VP:* Ernest Plasse
VP: Alfred J Hodge

D-U-N-S 82-830-8929 IMP/EXP
DAVIS-STANDARD LLC
HARREL
(*Suby of* EGAN STERLING NRM BROOKES) ★
1 Extrusion Dr, Pawcatuck, CT 06379-2327
Tel (860) 599-1010 *Founded/Ownrshp* 1995
Sales 178.2MM[E] *EMP* 400
SIC 3089 Extruded finished plastic products
CEO: James Murphy
**CEO:* Robert Preston
**CFO:* Kevin Coghlan
Plnt Mgr: Earl Clymer
Sls Mgr: Paul Banks

D-U-N-S 05-342-1806 IMP/EXP
DAVISCO FOODS INTERNATIONAL INC
LE SUEUR CHEESE DIVISION
704 Mainstreet, Eden Prairie, MN 55343-7625
Tel (952) 914-0400 *Founded/Ownrshp* 1970
Sales 142.0MM[E] *EMP* 385
SIC 2023 2022 Dried & powdered milk & milk products; Dried whey; Powdered whey; Natural cheese
Ch Bd: Mark Davis
**Pr:* Jonathon W Davis

**Treas:* James Ward
**VP:* Marty Davis
Sls Mgr: Enrique Pedroza

D-U-N-S 01-573-1449
■ **DAVITA ARLINGTON HEIGHTS RENAL CENTER**
ARLINGTON HEIGHTS PD
(*Suby of* DAVITA INC) ★
17 W Golf Rd, Arlington Heights, IL 60005-3905
Tel (847) 437-2188 *Founded/Ownrshp* 2008
Sales 8.3MM[E] *EMP* 1,525
SIC 8092 Kidney dialysis centers

D-U-N-S 88-307-3371
▲ **DAVITA INC**
2000 16th St, Denver, CO 80202-5117
Tel (303) 405-2100 *Founded/Ownrshp* 1994
Sales 13.7MMM *EMP* 60,400
Tkr Sym DVA *Exch* NYS
SIC 8092 8093 Kidney dialysis centers; Specialty outpatient clinics
Ch Bd: Kent J Thiry
Pt: Dennis L Kogod
Pt: Joseph C Mello
CEO: Javier J Rodriguez
COO: Michael D Staffieri
CFO: James K Hilger
Chf Cred: Jeanine M Jiganti
Ofcr: Derek Schoonover
Div VP: Sarah Beidelschies
Div VP: Cassie McLean
VP: Peggy Beyer
VP: Dave Hoerman
VP: Mark Kaplan
VP: Jacqueline Quam
VP: James Rechtin
VP: Martha Wofford
VP: Leanne M Zumwalt
VP Bus Dev: Robert O'Sullivan
Board of Directors: Roger J Valine, Pamela M Arway, Phyllis R Yale, Charles G Berg, Carol Anthony Davidson, Barbara J Desoer, Pascal Desroches, Paul J Diaz, Peter T Grauer, John M Nehra, William L Roper

D-U-N-S 08-579-5433 IMP/EXP
DAVOIL INC
DAVESTATES
6300 Ridglea Pl Ste 1208, Fort Worth, TX 76116-5738
Tel (817) 737-6678 *Founded/Ownrshp* 1976
Sales 160.4MM[E] *EMP* 230
SIC 1382 Oil & gas exploration services
Ch Bd: William S Davis Sr
**Treas:* Richard Fleck
**VP:* William S Davis Jr

D-U-N-S 78-764-6322
DAWN EQUIPMENT CO INC
DAWN FOOD PRODUCTS
(*Suby of* DAWN FOODS INC) ★
2021 Micor Dr, Jackson, MI 49203-3473
Tel (517) 789-4500 *Founded/Ownrshp* 1993
Sales 140.7MM[E] *EMP* 120
SIC 5046 3556 Bakery equipment & supplies; Bakery machinery
Pr: Carrie Barber Jones
**CFO:* Dave Knowlton
Sr VP: Richard Spencer
Sr VP: Gina Troutman
VP: Rick Dahlin
VP: Mary J Schultz
VP: Marcus Slaughter
VP: Francine Steuernagel
Opers Mgr: Cedric Smith
Prd Mgr: Steve Lyerla
VP Sls: Paul Caske

DAWN FOOD PRODUCTS
See DAWN EQUIPMENT CO INC

D-U-N-S 82-676-1207 IMP/EXP
DAWN FOOD PRODUCTS INC
(*Suby of* DAWN FOODS INC) ★
3333 Sargent Rd, Jackson, MI 49201-8847
Tel (517) 789-4400 *Founded/Ownrshp* 1993
Sales 1.0MMM[E] *EMP* 3,150
SIC 2045 5046 3556 Doughnut mixes, prepared: from purchased flour; Cake mixes, prepared: from purchased flour; Bakery equipment & supplies; Bakery machinery
CEO: Carrie L Barber
**Ch Bd:* Miles E Jones
Ch Bd: Stephen Socha
Pr: Phil Batty
**Pr:* Carey Dassatti
Pr: Ken Hall
Pr: Dave Kowal
Pr: Eric Metzendorf
**CFO:* Jerry Baglien
**CFO:* Dave Knowlton
Treas: Frank Hurbis
**Treas:* Stuart Smith
**Sr VP:* Jon Friedholm
VP: Roger Hipwell
VP: Bill McClellan
VP: Mark McFadden
VP: Robert Olender
VP: Bill Palmer
VP: Teri Wolvin

D-U-N-S 00-536-2975 EXP
DAWN FOODS INC (MI)
3333 Sargent Rd, Jackson, MI 49201-8847
Tel (517) 789-4400 *Founded/Ownrshp* 1925, 1985
Sales 1.9MMM[E] *EMP* 4,000
SIC 2053 2045 3556 5046 6719 Cakes, bakery: frozen; Pastries (danish): frozen; Doughnut mixes, prepared: from purchased flour; Bakery machinery; Bakery equipment & supplies; Investment holding companies, except banks
CEO: Carrie Jones-Barber
**CFO:* David Knowlton
**Ch:* Miles E Jones
Treas: Stuart Smith
Ex VP: Phil Crow
CIO: Charlie Massaglia
Mfg Dir: Christopher Lam
Opers Mgr: Chris Devader

D-U-N-S 13-957-1194
▲ DAWSON GEOPHYSICAL CO
508 W Wall St Ste 800, Midland, TX 79701-5010
Tel (432) 684-3000 Founded/Ownrshp 1980
Sales 234.6MM EMP 1,802[E]
Accts Ernst & Young Llp Dallas Tex
SIC 1382 8713 Geophysical exploration, oil & gas field; Surveying services
Ch Bd: Stephen C Jumper
COO: C Ray Tobias
CFO: James K Brata
Treas: Ken Uselton
*V Ch Bd: Wayne A Whitener
Ex VP: Christina W Hagan
Ex VP: Howell Pardue
Ex VP: James W Thomas
VP: K Forsdick
VP: George McDonald
VP: Mark Nelson
Exec: Sammy Barnhill
Board of Directors: William J Barrett, Craig W Cooper, Gary M Hoover, Allen T McInnes, Ted R North, Mark A Vander Ploeg

D-U-N-S 07-455-3397
DAWSON INSURANCE INC (OH)
(Suby of ASSUREDPARTNERS INC) ★
1340 Depot St Ste 300, Cleveland, OH 44116-1799
Tel (440) 333-9000 Founded/Ownrshp 1931, 2012
Sales NA EMP 270[E]
SIC 6411 Insurance brokers
CEO: D Michael Sherman
CFO: Fred Gross
*Sr VP: Robert Lampus
*Sr VP: David Myer
VP: Steven Shechter

D-U-N-S 92-844-5774
DAWSON MARINE INC
4230 College St, Beaumont, TX 77707-3904
Tel (409) 840-4111 Founded/Ownrshp 1995
Sales 23.6MM[E] EMP 1,000[E]
SIC 4499 Water transportation cleaning services
Pr: Doyle E Dawson
Owner: Doyle Dawson

D-U-N-S 18-023-7112
DAWSON TECHNICAL LLC
(Suby of HAWAIIAN NATIVE CORP) ★
900 Fort Street Mall # 1850, Honolulu, HI 96813-3721
Tel (808) 536-5500 Founded/Ownrshp 2006
Sales 404.0MM EMP 25[E]
SIC 8711 1542 Engineering services; Commercial & office buildings, renovation & repair
Pr: Christopher Dawson

D-U-N-S 00-791-3486
DAY & ZIMMERMANN GROUP INC (DE)
1500 Spring Garden St # 900, Philadelphia, PA 19130-4067
Tel (215) 299-8000 Founded/Ownrshp 1901, 1999
Sales 2.0MMM[E] EMP 24,000
SIC 8711 8712 8741 7381 7382 3489 Consulting engineer; Construction & civil engineering; Architectural engineering; Construction management; Industrial management; Security guard service; Security systems services; Protective devices, security; Ordnance & accessories
Ch Bd: Harold L Yoh III
Pr: John Dimarco
*CFO: Joseph Ritzel
CFO: Joseph W Ritzel
*Treas: James Strauss
*Chf Cred: William C Yoh
Ex VP: Rick Domyslawski
*Sr VP: Sankara Viswanathan
VP: Anthony J Bosco
*VP: James Estabrooks
VP: Larry Fanning
VP: Darren Gale
*VP: William R Hamm
VP: Joe Mahaley

D-U-N-S 17-728-9923
DAY & ZIMMERMANN INTERNATIONAL INC
(Suby of DAY & ZIMMERMANN GROUP INC) ★
1500 Spring Garden St # 900, Philadelphia, PA 19130-4067
Tel (215) 299-8000 Founded/Ownrshp 1987
Sales 632.6MM[E] EMP 6,000
SIC 8711 1541 8741 Building construction consultant; Pharmaceutical manufacturing plant construction; Construction management
CEO: Harold L Yoh III
*Pr: Michael P McMahon
Pr: Gary Wittie
*Treas: Gary Cristini
*Sec: Scott L Fast
*Ex VP: Larry Fanning
*VP: Robert J Fitzsimmons
CIO: Brad King
Mktg Mgr: Greg Hallquist

D-U-N-S 87-272-9215
DAY & ZIMMERMANN LLC CO
DAY & ZIMMERMANN SECURITY SVCS
(Suby of DAY & ZIMMERMANN GROUP INC) ★
1500 Spring Garden St # 900, Philadelphia, PA 19130-4067
Tel (215) 299-8000 Founded/Ownrshp 1992
Sales 365.9MM[E] EMP 5,690
SIC 7381 Security guard service
CEO: Harold L Yoh III
Pr: Lawrence J Ames
Pr: John Dimarco
Pr: John Sacht
Sr VP: Beth Albright
Sr VP: Anthony Bosco Jr
Sr VP: William Hamm
Sr VP: Don Hanson
Sr VP: Joesph Ritzel
VP: Dale Biegelman
VP: Lisa Carr
VP: James Hickey
VP: Lee Lawton
VP: Joseph McKinney
VP: William Remphrey
VP: Thomas Rudy
VP: Guy Starr
VP: Debra Stehman
VP: Chris Trevisan
VP: Paul Williams
Div/Sub He: Lawrence Suwak

D-U-N-S 12-719-6426
DAY & ZIMMERMANN NPS INC
N P S SERVICES
(Suby of DAY & ZIMMERMANN INTERNATIONAL INC) ★
1827 Freedom Rd Ste 101, Lancaster, PA 17601-6759
Tel (717) 299-3754 Founded/Ownrshp 1987
Sales 136.3MM[E] EMP 3,100
SIC 7361 Labor contractors (employment agency)
*Pr: Gary McKinney
*CEO: Harold L Yoh
*CFO: Joseph Ritzel
*Treas: Marion Hawkins
Sr Cor Off: Brian Hart
*Sr VP: Beth Albright
VP: Robert Faull
*VP: Robert Fitzsimmons
VP: Greg Kern
VP: Jeffery D Tompkins
Telecom Ex: Michael Wilchek

DAY & ZIMMERMANN SECURITY SVCS
See DAY & ZIMMERMANN LLC CO

DAY & ZIMMERMANN SERVICES
See DAY AND ZIMMERMANN INC

D-U-N-S 03-939-8487
DAY AND ZIMMERMANN INC
DAY & ZIMMERMANN SERVICES
(Suby of DAY & ZIMMERMANN GROUP INC) ★
1500 Spring Garden St # 900, Philadelphia, PA 19130-4067
Tel (215) 299-8000 Founded/Ownrshp 1933
Sales 226.4MM[E] EMP 2,700
SIC 8744 8712 8711 3559 3483 Facilities support services; Architectural services; Engineering services; Ammunition & explosives, loading machinery; Ammunition, except for small arms
CEO: Harold L Yoh III
Pr: Walter M Sanders IV
*Pr: Steve Selfridge
Sr VP: Frances Coady
*Sr VP: William Hamm
*Sr VP: Sankara Viswanathan
VP: Kris Cravey
VP: Jay Crilley
VP: Thomas W Ensminger
*VP: Larry Fanning
VP: Diana McConnell
VP: Doug Napodano
Comm Man: Jayesh Kothari

D-U-N-S 62-089-4803
DAY EL PASO SURGERY LP
1300 Murchison Dr Ste 200, El Paso, TX 79902-4838
Tel (915) 225-7600 Founded/Ownrshp 2003
Sales 62.2MM[E] EMP 2,000
SIC 8011 Ambulatory surgical center
Treas: Scott Christ
Ch Bd: Mark Landeros

D-U-N-S 88-427-4242 EXP
DAY INTERNATIONAL GROUP INC
(Suby of CDR PIGMENTS & DISPERSIONS) ★
14909 N Beck Rd, Plymouth, MI 48170-2411
Tel (734) 781-4600 Founded/Ownrshp 1938
Sales 160.8MM[E] EMP 1,470
SIC 3069 Printers' rolls & blankets: rubber or rubberized fabric
Ch Bd: William C Ferguson
*Pr: Dennis R Wolters
*VP: Dwaine R Brooks
*VP: David B Freimuth
*VP: Thomas J Koenig
Mng Dir: Brent A Stephen

D-U-N-S 06-924-4937
DAY KIMBALL HEALTHCARE INC
DAY KIMBALL HOSPITAL
320 Pomfret St, Putnam, CT 06260-1836
Tel (860) 928-6541 Founded/Ownrshp 1982
Sales 99.8MM EMP 900[E]
SIC 8062 General medical & surgical hospitals
CEO: Robert Smanik
Dir Recs: Angela Levesque
COO: Donald St Onge
Bd of Dir: Jack Burke
Dir Rad: Douglas Gibson
*Prin: Judith Blackmore
CTO: Charles F Schneider
MIS Dir: Odile Romanick
Sfty Dirs: Sharon Sawyer
Surgeon: David R McCallum
Podiatrist: Sean Colsen

DAY KIMBALL HOSPITAL
See DAY KIMBALL HEALTHCARE INC

D-U-N-S 12-322-8376
DAY PITNEY LLP
242 Trumbull St Fl 5, Hartford, CT 06103-1212
Tel (617) 345-4600 Founded/Ownrshp 2006
Sales 101.9MM[E] EMP 950
SIC 8111 Legal services
Ch: Stanley Twardy
Pt: Christopher M Rider
Pt: William S Rogers
Pt: James Sicilian
COO: Kirk R Rossi
COO: Kirk Rossi
CFO: Paul Lach
Ex Dir: Steven M Mauro
Ex Dir: Howard Shaffer
Admn Mgr: Lisa Notarangelo
Dir IT: Tracy Hillhouse

D-U-N-S 07-940-8239
DAY STAR RESTAURANT GROUP INC
5055 W Park Blvd Ste 500, Plano, TX 75093-2587
Tel (972) 295-8600 Founded/Ownrshp 2013
Sales 203.0MM EMP 4,500
SIC 6719 Investment holding companies, except banks
CEO: Scott Smith
*Pr: Tim Dungan

D-U-N-S 02-848-4566 IMP
DAY-LEE FOODS INC
(Suby of NH FOODS LTD.)
10350 Hritg Pk Dr Ste 111, Santa Fe Springs, CA 90670
Tel (562) 903-3020 Founded/Ownrshp 1958
Sales 148.1MM[E] EMP 324
SIC 5147 5144 5146 Meats, fresh; Poultry & poultry products; Fish & seafoods
CEO: Hironobu Yamane
*VP: Kiyoshi Zobe

D-U-N-S 92-789-3602
DAYBREAK FOODS INC
533 E Tyranena Park Rd, Lake Mills, WI 53551-9683
Tel (920) 648-8341 Founded/Ownrshp 1994
Sales 137.8MM[E] EMP 260
SIC 5144 Poultry & poultry products
Pr: William Rehm
CFO: Dick Herman
Genl Mgr: Lee Klug
Genl Mgr: Mark Valen
VP Opers: Bobby Harris

D-U-N-S 78-059-5794 IMP
DAYBREAK GAME CO LLC
15051 Avenue Of Science, San Diego, CA 92128-3430
Tel (858) 577-3100 Founded/Ownrshp 2015
Sales 93.4MM[E] EMP 450
SIC 7371 Computer software development
Pr: John Smedley
*Pr: Russell Shanks
Sr VP: Don Vercelli
Creative D: Jens Andersen
Dir Bus: Louis A Figueroa
Snr Ntwrk: Jason Fermo
Snr Mgr: Tony Eastman
Snr Mgr: Mohammed Khan

D-U-N-S 13-350-7934
DAYBREAK VENTURE LLC
401 N Elm St, Denton, TX 76201-4137
Tel (940) 387-4388 Founded/Ownrshp 2001
Sales 293.5MM[E] EMP 5,500
SIC 8051 8099

D-U-N-S 80-998-4938
DAYCO GLOBAL HOLDING CORP
111 8th Ave, New York, NY 10011-5201
Tel (716) 689-4972 Founded/Ownrshp 2011
Sales 1.1MMM[E] EMP 8,001
SIC 6719 Personal holding companies, except banks
Pr: Mark Barberio

D-U-N-S 05-530-3853 IMP/EXP
DAYCO INC
(Suby of DAYCO GLOBAL HOLDING CORP) ★
1650 Research Dr Ste 200, Troy, MI 48083-2143
Tel (716) 689-4972 Founded/Ownrshp 1978
Sales 1.2MMM[E] EMP 8,000
SIC 3641 3646 3643 3625 3613 Electric lamps; Commercial indusl & institutional electric lighting fixtures; Current-carrying wiring devices; Relays & industrial controls; Switchgear & switchboard apparatus
Ch Bd: Kurt J Johansson
*Pr: Richard Grenolds
*Pr: Giuliano A Zucco
*CEO: Mark G Barberio
CFO: Joe Greco
Sr VP: Thomas Hart
Sr VP: Gordon Hensley
VP: Dan Engler
VP: Jonathon Levine
Dir Risk M: Chris Worth
Genl Mgr: Joe Niederstadt

D-U-N-S 80-197-8037
DAYCO PRODUCTS LLC
(Suby of DAYCO HOLDINGS FINANCE SCS)
1650 Research Dr Ste 200, Troy, MI 48083-2143
Tel (248) 404-6500 Founded/Ownrshp 1986
Sales 192.0MM[E] EMP 350[E]
SIC 3568 Power transmission equipment
CEO: John T Bohenick
Pr: Doug Bowen
CFO: Jonathon Levine
CFO: Peter Nurge
VP: Al Devore
VP: Dan Engler
VP: Edward Steele

DAYCON PRODUCTS COMPANY
See P4 CORP

D-U-N-S 80-882-2618
DAYHAGAN FINANCIAL RJFS
DAYHAYGAN ASSETS MANAGEMENT
1000 S Tamiami Trl, Sarasota, FL 34236-9116
Tel (941) 330-1702 Founded/Ownrshp 2007
Sales 200.0MM EMP 10
SIC 6282 Investment advice
Pt: Arthur S Day
*Pt: Donald Hagan
*Sr VP: Gordon E Jones

DAYHAYGAN ASSETS MANAGEMENT
See DAYHAGAN FINANCIAL RJFS

D-U-N-S 04-766-5245
DAYMON WORLDWIDE INC
700 Fairfield Ave Ste 1, Stamford, CT 06902-7541
Tel (203) 352-7500 Founded/Ownrshp 1970
Sales 1.6MMM[E] EMP 16,000
SIC 8742 Marketing consulting services; Retail trade consultant
Ch Bd: Milton Sender
*Pr: Carla Cooper
COO: Bob Rentz
*CFO: Brian Bensen
*Ofcr: Rhonda Levene
Sr VP: Michael Hankins
Sr VP: Tami Polmanteer
VP: Bob Kaminska
*VP: Kimberlee Marsh
VP: Glenn Pfeifer
*VP: Bharat Rupani
Dir Soc: Jessica Jackson
Dir Bus: Anna Jacobs
Dir Bus: Jim Kirby
Dir Bus: Bruce Parker
Dir Bus: Cliff Peske
Dir Bus: Doug Rhoads

D-U-N-S 03-347-6938
DAYS CHEVROLET INC
3693 Cobb Pkwy Nw, Acworth, GA 30101-5740
Tel (770) 974-4242 Founded/Ownrshp 1959
Sales 95.9MM EMP 105
SIC 5511 Automobiles, new & used
CEO: Calvin L Diemer
*CFO: Rebecca D Diemer
*VP: Andrew Diemer
Exec: Julie Litton

DAYSPRING HEALTHCARE CENTER
See APPALACHIAN RESPITE CARE LTD

D-U-N-S 79-054-0855
DAYSPRING SERVICES OF ARKANSAS LLC
1610 W 3rd St, Little Rock, AR 72201-1815
Tel (501) 372-4440 Founded/Ownrshp 2007
Sales 8.5MM[E] EMP 3,000
SIC 8093 Specialty outpatient clinics

DAYSTAR TELEVISION NETWORK
See WORD OF GOD FELLOWSHIP INC

D-U-N-S 07-127-2124
DAYTON BOARD OF EDUCATION
156 Grant St, Dayton, OH 45404-1819
Tel (937) 226-1084 Founded/Ownrshp 1857
Sales 185.5MM[E] EMP 3,500
SIC 8211 School board
Pr: Robert Walker
Assoc Dir: Julia Beck
Assoc Dir: Patti Daggett
Assoc Dir: Mary Henderson
Assoc Dir: Roberta Williams
Adm Dir: Theodore Newton
Ex Dir: Margaret Sandberg
Ex Dir: Bonnie Strykowski
Dir Sec: Ray Hollis
CIO: Percy Mack
MIS Dir: Richard Melson

DAYTON CHILDREN
See CHILDRENS MEDICAL CENTER TOLEDO

D-U-N-S 07-128-9326 IMP
DAYTON CHILDRENS HOSPITAL (OH)
CHILDREN'S MEDICAL CENTER
1 Childrens Plz, Dayton, OH 45404-1873
Tel (937) 641-3000 Founded/Ownrshp 1919
Sales 233.1MM EMP 1,081
SIC 8069 Children's hospital
CEO: Deborah A Feldman
*Pr: David Kinsaul
*COO: Matt Graybill
*CFO: David Miller
VP: Lisa Coffey
VP: Dana Drazner
VP: Brett Lee
VP: John Pascoe
VP: C Phillips
Dir Inf Cn: Sherman Alter
Dir Risk M: Sue Childs
Dir Rx: Patricia Christoff

D-U-N-S 00-885-2212
■ DAYTON ELECTRIC MFG CO
(Suby of WW GRAINGER INC) ★
100 Grainger Pkwy, Lake Forest, IL 60045-5202
Tel (847) 535-1000 Founded/Ownrshp 1938
Sales 120.3MM[E] EMP 2,337
SIC 5063 5084 5072 Motors, electric; Motor controls, starters & relays: electric; Fans, industrial; Pumps & pumping equipment; Compressors, except air conditioning; Paint spray equipment, industrial; Hand tools
Pr: Richard L Keyser
CFO: P Odgen Loux
Treas: Phillip West
*VP: John L Howard

D-U-N-S 04-538-0458
DAYTON FREIGHT LINES INC
6450 Poe Ave Ste 311, Dayton, OH 45414-2647
Tel (937) 264-4060 Founded/Ownrshp 1981
Sales 921.5MM[E] EMP 4,000
SIC 4213 4212

D-U-N-S 01-795-3712 IMP/EXP
DAYTON HEIDELBERG DISTRIBUTING CO
HEIDELBERG DISTRIBUTING DIV
3601 Dryden Rd, Moraine, OH 45439-1411
Tel (937) 222-8692 Founded/Ownrshp 1959
Sales 386.9MM[E] EMP 1,600
SIC 5181 Beer & other fermented malt liquors
Pr: Steve Lowrey
*Ch Bd: Vail Miller
*CEO: Albert W Vontz III
*CFO: Tom Rouse
Ex VP: Tom McHugh
Ex VP: Patrick O'Sullivan
VP: Daniel Isenbarger
IT Man: Daniel Burgess
Opers Mgr: Brian Oakes
Sales Exec: Mike Ross
Sls Mgr: Dj Homan

D-U-N-S 07-930-5607
DAYTON LAMINA CORP
ANCHOR LAMINA AMERICA
(Suby of MISUMI INVESTMENT USA CORP) ★
500 Progress Rd, Dayton, OH 45449-2326
Tel (937) 859-5111 Founded/Ownrshp 2008
Sales 256.2MM[E] EMP 1,397
SIC 3544 6719 Special dies, tools, jigs & fixtures; Investment holding companies, except banks
Pr: David Turpin
Rgnl Mgr: Rick Chapman

D-U-N-S 07-468-2931
DAYTON OSTEOPATHIC HOSPITAL
GRANDVIEW HOSPITAL & MED CTR
405 W Grand Ave, Dayton, OH 45405-7538
Tel (937) 762-1629 *Founded/Ownrshp* 1999
Sales 115.0MM[E] *EMP* 1,800
Accts Ernst & Young Llp
SIC 8062 General medical & surgical hospitals
CEO: Fred Manchur
**Pr:* Russell J Wetherell
**CFO:* Todd Anderson
**Treas:* Edward Mann
Mktg Mgr: Frank Engler
Surgeon: Marilyn J Borst

D-U-N-S 00-790-2430
■ **DAYTON POWER AND LIGHT CO** (OH)
(*Suby of* DPL INC) ★
1065 Woodman Dr, Dayton, OH 45432-1423
Tel (937) 224-6000 *Founded/Ownrshp* 1911
Sales 1.5MMM *EMP* 595
Accts Ernst & Young Llp Indianapol
SIC 4911 4931 Generation, electric power; Transmission, electric power; Distribution, electric power; ; Electric & other services combined
Pr: Tom Raga
**Ch Bd:* Andrew M Vesey
CFO: Craig L Jackson
VP: Dave Crusey
VP: H Ted Santo
Prgrm Mgr: Shanda Donley
CTO: Karen Garrison
Dir IT: Tom Tatham
VP Sls: Daniel Schilens
Board of Directors: Elizabeth Hackenson, Willard C Hoagland III, Vincent W Mathis, Brian A Miller, Thomas M O'flynn, Kenneth J Zagzebski

D-U-N-S 00-447-5083 IMP
DAYTON PROGRESS CORP
(*Suby of* ANCHOR LAMINA AMERICA) ★
500 Progress Rd, Dayton, OH 45449-2351
Tel (937) 859-5111 *Founded/Ownrshp* 2012
Sales 185.0MM[E] *EMP* 750
SIC 3544 3545 3495 3493 Punches, forming & stamping; Machine tool accessories; Wire springs; Steel springs, except wire
Pr: David Turpin
Pr: Timothy Burkhart
VP: Barb Lipps
Exec: Rosemary D Domansky
Rgnl Mgr: Tommy Baughman
Rgnl Mgr: Rick Chapman
Rgnl Mgr: Sam Dangelo
Rgnl Mgr: Gregory Sullivan
Rgnl Mgr: Gary Wilson
Genl Mgr: John Vecore
Netwrk Eng: Matt Gore

D-U-N-S 00-516-3449 IMP/EXP
DAYTON SUPERIOR CORP
METAL ACESORIES
(*Suby of* DAYTON SUPERIOR CORP) ★
2400 Arthur Ave, Elk Grove Village, IL 60007-6017
Tel (847) 391-4700 *Founded/Ownrshp* 1901
Sales 157.7MM[E] *EMP* 864
SIC 3444 Concrete forms, sheet metal
Pr: John Ciccarelli
CFO: Jim Benka
**VP:* Jim Eenka
VP: Steven Huston
Prgrm Mgr: Catherine Gilbert

D-U-N-S 04-160-4463 IMP
DAYTON SUPERIOR CORP
1125 Byers Rd, Miamisburg, OH 45342-5765
Tel (937) 866-0711 *Founded/Ownrshp* 1997
Sales 2.3MMM[E] *EMP* 1,200
Accts Deloitte & Touche Llp Dayton
SIC 3315 3452 3462 3089 2899 Steel wire & related products; Dowel pins, metal; Construction or mining equipment forgings, ferrous; Plastic hardware & building products; Chemical preparations
CEO: James McRickard
**CEO:* Lutz Richter
Treas: Paul Fisher
**Sr VP:* Randy Brown
**Sr VP:* Peter Viens
VP: Mary Ahrns
VP: Andy Cannon
VP: Mike Deis
VP: John Payne Jr
VP: Thomas Roehrig
VP: James Stewart
**VP:* Kenneth Tynes
Exec: Ken Tynes

D-U-N-S 79-785-4593 IMP
DAYTON-PHOENIX GROUP INC
1619 Kuntz Rd, Dayton, OH 45404-1240
Tel (937) 496-3900 *Founded/Ownrshp* 1992
Sales 142.8MM[E] *EMP* 400[E]
SIC 3621 3743 Motors & generators; Railroad equipment; Locomotives & parts
Pr: Gale Kooken
**VP:* Roger Fleming
**VP:* John Murphy

D-U-N-S 96-439-0616
DAYTONA BEACH AREA ASSOCIATION OF REALTORS FOUNDATION INC
1716 Ridgewood Ave, Holly Hill, FL 32117-1736
Tel (386) 677-7131 *Founded/Ownrshp* 1922
Sales 1.5MM *EMP* 1,300
SIC 8611 Real Estate Board
Pr: Theresa E Geyer
**Treas:* Dorothy L Byrne
**VP:* Ian E Anderson

DAZIAN FABRICS
See DAZIAN LLC

D-U-N-S 00-126-6048 IMP
DAZIAN LLC
DAZIAN FABRICS
18 Central Blvd, South Hackensack, NJ 07606-1802
Tel (877) 232-9426 *Founded/Ownrshp* 1842, 1998
Sales 91.0MM[E] *EMP* 80
SIC 5131 Piece goods & notions
CEO: Jon Weingarten
**CFO:* Chris Diaz

D-U-N-S 06-382-1743
DB CONSULTING GROUP INC
8401 Colesville Rd # 300, Silver Spring, MD 20910-3363
Tel (301) 589-4020 *Founded/Ownrshp* 2002
Sales 92.1MM[E] *EMP* 480
Accts Penan & Scott Pc
SIC 8748 Business consulting
Pr: Gerald Boyd Jr
**COO:* Gerald Boyd Sr
COO: Richard Stalnaker
Ofcr: Reese Squires
VP: Aaron Crossland
VP: Scott Davidow
VP: Glenn Wright
Exec: Iesha Boling
Exec: Genatia Finney
Prgrm Mgr: Allan Small
Prgrm Mgr: Maurice Thompson

DB SCHENKER
See BAX GLOBAL INC

D-U-N-S 15-177-3178
DB SERVICES NEW JERSEY INC
(*Suby of* DEUTSCHE BANKTRUST CO AMERICAS) ★
100 Plaza One, Jersey City, NJ 07311-3934
Tel (201) 593-4183 *Founded/Ownrshp* 1983
Sales NA *EMP* 1,300
SIC 8744 Facilities support services
CEO: Robert Frier
**VP:* Foy Hester

D-U-N-S 07-855-6317
DB US CORP
120 White Plains Rd, Tarrytown, NY 10591-5526
Tel (914) 366-7200 *Founded/Ownrshp* 1998
Sales 48.1MM[E] *EMP* 6,315
SIC 4789 4731 Passenger train services; Domestic freight forwarding
Pr: Dr Christoph Bohl
**CFO:* Joseph L Groneman
**VP:* Brian P Lynch

D-U-N-S 00-896-3332
DB US HOLDING CORP (DE)
(*Suby of* DEUTSCHE BAHN AG)
120 White Plains Rd, Tarrytown, NY 10591-5526
Tel (914) 366-7203 *Founded/Ownrshp* 1926, 1999
Sales 1.7MMM *EMP* 6,300
Accts Pricewaterhousecoopers Llp N
SIC 4731 Freight transportation arrangement
Pr: Dr Josef Blank
**CFO:* Joseph L Groneman
**VP:* Brian P Lynch
Counsel: Dennis St George

D-U-N-S 07-533-2523
DB USA CORP
(*Suby of* DEUTSCHE BANK AG)
60 Wall St, New York, NY 10005-2836
Tel (212) 250-2500 *Founded/Ownrshp* 1999
Sales NA *EMP* 23,000
SIC 6141 6153 Personal credit institutions; Short-term business credit

DBHDD
See DEPARTMENT OF BEHAVIORAL HEALTH AND DEVELOPMENTAL DISABILITIES

DBHIDS
See COMMUNITY BEHAVIORAL HEALTH

D-U-N-S 17-458-9304 IMP
DBI BEVERAGE INC
2 Ingram Blvd, La Vergne, TN 37089-2000
Tel (615) 793-2337 *Founded/Ownrshp* 2002
Sales 206.7MM[E] *EMP* 452[E]
SIC 5149 Beverages, except coffee & tea
CEO: Jeffrey D Skinner
Pr: David B Ingram
V Ch Bd: W Donnie Daniel
Ex VP: Robert W Webb
Sr VP: John J Fletcher
Sr VP: Mark D Ramer

D-U-N-S 07-880-6501 IMP
DBI BEVERAGE SACRAMENTO
(*Suby of* DBI BEVERAGE INC) ★
3500 Carlin Dr, West Sacramento, CA 95691-5872
Tel (916) 373-5700 *Founded/Ownrshp* 2007
Sales 87.1MM[E] *EMP* 290[E]
SIC 5182 5149 Wine & distilled beverages; Beverages, except coffee & tea
CEO: Jeff Skinner
VP: John J Janosko
Dist Mgr: Bob Beviacqua

D-U-N-S 60-410-2574 IMP/EXP
■ **DBL DISTRIBUTING LLC**
D B L
(*Suby of* INGRAM MICRO INC) ★
15880 N Greenwy Hdn Loop # 150, Scottsdale, AZ 85260-1648
Tel (480) 419-3559 *Founded/Ownrshp* 2007
Sales 197.7MM[E] *EMP* 375
SIC 5065 Electronic parts & equipment
Pr: Henry Chiarelli
**COO:* Timothy Butler
Ex VP: Don Anderson
VP: Pat Capparelli
VP: Kurt Kilgast
VP: Brent McCarty
Opers Mgr: Matt Amenson

D-U-N-S 03-505-4928 IMP
■ **DBM GLOBAL INC** (DE)
(*Suby of* HC2 HOLDINGS INC) ★
3020 E Camelback Rd # 100, Phoenix, AZ 85016-4417
Tel (602) 252-7787 *Founded/Ownrshp* 2001, 2014
Sales 577.6MM[E] *EMP* 1,500
SIC 3441 1791 Building components, structural steel; Structural steel erection
Pr: Rustin Roach
**CFO:* Michael R Hill
Plnt Mgr: Tommy Roberts

DBU
See DALLAS BAPTIST UNIVERSITY

DC WATER
See DISTRICT OF COLUMBIA WATER & SEWER AUTHORITY

D-U-N-S 07-654-1056 IMP
DC WATER AND SEWER AUTHORITY
5000 Overlook Ave Sw, Washington, DC 20032-5212
Tel (202) 787-2000 *Founded/Ownrshp* 1997
Sales 473.8MM *EMP* 1,000
Accts Kpmg Llp Washington Dc
SIC 4952 4941 Sewerage systems; Water supply
Ch: William Walker
**CFO:* Olo Adebo
**Treas:* Robert Hunt
Bd of Dir: Glenn S Gerstell
Bd of Dir: Anthony H Griffin
Prgrm Mgr: Bill Levy
Genl Mgr: David Cross
Genl Mgr: Jerry Johnson
Off Admin: Latonya McMillan
CIO: Mujib Lodhi
**CIO:* Omer Siddiqui

DCA
See DEPT OF CORRECTIONS ARIZONA

D-U-N-S 13-326-5855
■ **DCH AUTO GROUP (USA) INC**
(*Suby of* LITHIA MOTORS INC) ★
955 Route 9 N, South Amboy, NJ 08879
Tel (732) 727-9168 *Founded/Ownrshp* 2014
Sales 421.5MM[E] *EMP* 200
SIC 5511 7515 6512 6514 Automobiles, new & used; Passenger car leasing; Commercial & industrial building operation; Residential building, four or fewer units: operation
Pr: Shau W Lam
**Pr:* Chun-Wai Liang
**CFO:* Mark Slosberg
IT Man: Les Jez
Netwrk Eng: Hong Lam
Sls Mgr: Dori Dado
Sls Mgr: John McBride

D-U-N-S 07-209-4311
DCH HEALTH CARE AUTHORITY
DCH HEALTH SYSTEM
809 University Blvd E, Tuscaloosa, AL 35401-2029
Tel (205) 759-7111 *Founded/Ownrshp* 1947
Sales 468.5MM *EMP* 4,683
Accts Morrison & Smith Llp Tuscalo
SIC 8062 8093 General medical & surgical hospitals; Rehabilitation center, outpatient treatment
Ch Bd: J Barry Mason PHD
**Pr:* Bryan Kindred
COO: Joseph Williamson
**CFO:* John W Winfrey
**Treas:* W Paul Ray
Ex VP: Robin Holmes
VP: Anand Pandey
**VP:* Janet Teer
Exec: Gary Lane
Exec: Lindy Noland
Comm Dir: Bradley Fisher
Dir Rad: Hugh Borak
Board of Directors: Joseph A Colquitt, Harvey A Edwards III MD, John Mize, Caroline Powell, Herbert Ragsdale, Ronald P Turner

DCH HEALTH SYSTEM
See DCH HEALTH CARE AUTHORITY

DCH REGIONAL MEDICAL CENTER
See CENTURY HEALTH ALLIANCE JOINT VENTURE

D-U-N-S 93-075-5181
DCHS MEDICAL FOUNDATION
625 Lincoln Ave, San Jose, CA 95126-3785
Tel (408) 278-3000 *Founded/Ownrshp* 2011
Sales 114.1MM *EMP* 9
Accts Lb Grant Thornton Llp San Fra
SIC 8641 Civic social & fraternal associations
CEO: Ernest Wallerstein
Dir IT: Robert Barr

DCIS
See OFFICE OF THE INSPECTOR GENERAL

D-U-N-S 82-854-7757
DCK PACIFIC CONSTRUCTION LLC
(*Suby of* DCK WORLDWIDE LLC) ★
707 Richards St Ste 410, Honolulu, HI 96813-4623
Tel (808) 533-5000 *Founded/Ownrshp* 2008
Sales 99.5MM[E] *EMP* 200[E]
SIC 1542 Nonresidential construction; Design & erection, combined: non-residential
Ofcr: John T O'Reilly
Ofcr: Stephen F D'Angelo

D-U-N-S 82-687-9426
DCK WORLDWIDE LLC
6 Ppg Pl Ste 710, Pittsburgh, PA 15222-5406
Tel (412) 384-1000 *Founded/Ownrshp* 2008
Sales 488.2MM[E] *EMP* 1,000
SIC 1542 Nonresidential construction
CEO: Stephen F D'Angelo
**COO:* Joseph G Belechak
**CFO:* John T O'Reilly
Ofcr: David Hubble
Sr VP: Wil Ideue
Exec: Robert Hartelust
Comm Dir: Laurie Bowers
Off Mgr: Jackie Honn
Off Admin: Jeanne Kemmler
Mktg Dir: Andrea Gardner

DCNA
See FIBRANT LLC

D-U-N-S 36-176-3225
DCOR LLC
290 Maple Ct Ste 290, Ventura, CA 93003-9144
Tel (805) 535-2000 *Founded/Ownrshp* 2001
Sales 171.2MM[E] *EMP* 215[E]
SIC 1382 Oil & gas exploration services
Genl Mgr: Bill Templeton
**Pr:* Andrew Prestridge
**CFO:* Alan C Templeton
**VP:* Greg Cavette
**VP:* Dennis Conley
**VP:* Bob Garcia
**VP:* Khris Kircher
**VP:* Jeff Warren

D-U-N-S 17-437-7197
DCP HOLDING CO
DENTAL CARE PLUS GROUP DCPG
100 Crowne Point Pl, Sharonville, OH 45241-5427
Tel (513) 554-1100 *Founded/Ownrshp* 1986
Sales NA *EMP* 77
Accts Deloitte & Touche Llp Cincinn
SIC 6324 Hospital & medical service plans; Dental insurance; Health maintenance organization (HMO), insurance only
Pr: Anthony A Cook
**Ch Bd:* Stephen T Schuler
COO: Jodi M Fronczek
CFO: Robert C Hodgkins Jr
Board of Directors: Ronald L Poulos, Mark E Bronson, Molly M Rogers, Michael J Carl, Jack M Cook, James T Foley, Robert E Hamilton, David A Kreyling, James E Kroeger, Donald J Peak, Fred H Pack

D-U-N-S 00-711-8276
DCP MIDSTREAM LLC
370 17th St Ste 2500, Denver, CO 80202-5604
Tel (303) 633-2900 *Founded/Ownrshp* 1957, 2007
Sales 2.7MMM[E] *EMP* 3,575
SIC 5172 Gases
Pr: Wouter Van Kempen
**Ch Bd:* Thomas C Oconnor
Pr: Richard Cargile
**CFO:* Rose M Robeson
**Treas:* D Robert Sadler
**VP:* Brent L Backes
**VP:* Chris Lewis
VP: Rose Robeson
**VP:* Bill Waldheim
VP: William Waldheim
Dir Bus: Christer Rundlof

D-U-N-S 00-304-8753
DCP MIDSTREAM LP
(*Suby of* DCP MIDSTREAM LLC) ★
370 17th St Ste 2500, Denver, CO 80202-5604
Tel (303) 595-3331 *Founded/Ownrshp* 2000
Sales 2.7MMM[E] *EMP* 2,700
SIC 4925 Gas production and/or distribution
CEO: Wouter Van Kempen
Pr: Quay Chan
Pr: William Johnson
Pr: Susie Sjulin
Pr: Bill Waldheim
Pr: Floyd Webb
CFO: Sean O'Brien
Ofcr: Chris Lewis
Ex VP: Patrick Greetan
VP: Brent Backes
VP: Scott Delmoro
VP: Irene G Lofland
VP: Bill Prentice
VP: Michael S Richards
VP: Greg Smith

D-U-N-S 61-043-7142
▲ **DCP MIDSTREAM PARTNERS LP**
370 17th St Ste 2500, Denver, CO 80202-5604
Tel (303) 595-3331 *Founded/Ownrshp* 2005
Sales 1.9MMM *EMP* 628[E]
Tkr Sym DPM *Exch* NYS
SIC 4922 4924 Natural gas transmission; Pipelines, natural gas; Storage, natural gas; Natural gas distribution
Ch Bd: Wouter T Van Kempen
Genl Pt: Dcp Midstream GP
CFO: Sean P O'Brien

D-U-N-S 80-786-0262
DCR SYSTEM HOUSE INC
7795 Nw Beacon Sq Blvd, Boca Raton, FL 33487-1392
Tel (561) 998-3737 *Founded/Ownrshp* 2007
Sales 484.8MM *EMP* 85
Accts John Kammerer Boca Raton Flo
SIC 7373 Systems software development services
Pr: Ammu Warrier

D-U-N-S 92-851-2219
DCR WORKFORCE INC
7795 Nw Beacon Sq 201, Boca Raton, FL 33487-1394
Tel (561) 998-3737 *Founded/Ownrshp* 1995
Sales 702.0MM *EMP* 82
Accts John Kammerer Boca Raton Flo
SIC 7379 7363 8742 Computer related consulting services; Help supply services; Human resource consulting services
**Pr:* Ammu Warrier
Ex VP: Chris Mortonson
Sr VP: Timothy Holland
VP: Michele Gibbons
Dir Bus: Tracy White
Snr Sftwr: Umut Deniz
Sftwr Eng: Umut Celik
Sftwr Eng: Sonali Kshirsagar

D-U-N-S 08-366-2916
DCS CORP (VA)
6909 Metro Park Dr # 500, Alexandria, VA 22310-3267
Tel (571) 227-6000 *Founded/Ownrshp* 1977
Sales 315.8MM[E] *EMP* 940[E]
SIC 7373 Computer integrated systems design
CEO: Jim Benbow
Pr: James Benpow
**Pr:* David E Russell
**CFO:* Tom R Fradette
**Ch:* Jim Wood
VP: Tom Gallagher
VP: Arne Johnson
VP: Timothy Phelps
**VP:* Curtis Schehr
**Prin:* James T Wood
Prgrm Mgr: John Hessey

D-U-N-S 10-149-2908
DCS SANITATION MANAGEMENT INC
7864 Camargo Rd, Cincinnati, OH 45243-4300
Tel (513) 891-4980 *Founded/Ownrshp* 1986
Sales 38.5MM^E *EMP* 1,700
SIC 7349 7342 Building cleaning service; Disinfecting services
CEO: Lance White
**Pr:* Thomas Murray
**CFO:* James Gillespie

D-U-N-S 12-510-3205
DCT INDUSTRIAL TRUST INC
518 17th St Ste 800, Denver, CO 80202-4124
Tel (303) 597-2400 *Founded/Ownrshp* 2002
Sales 354.7MM *EMP* 136
Accts Ernst & Young Llp Denver Col
SIC 6798 Real estate investment trusts
CEO: Philip L Hawkins
Ch Bd: Thomas G Wattles
Pr: Jeffrey F Phelan
CFO: Matthew T Murphy
Ex VP: Teresa L Corral
Ex VP: Charla K Rios
Ex VP: John G Spiegleman
Sr VP: Jay Mitchell
Sr VP: Thomas Tucci
Sr VP: Todd Vezza
VP: Frank Petkunas
VP: Lisa Ward
Board of Directors: Marilyn A Alexander, Thomas F August, John S Gates Jr, Raymond B Greer, John C O'keeffe, Bruce L Warwick

D-U-N-S 03-109-8531 IMP
DCX-CHOL ENTERPRISES INC
TELETRONICS/PMP
12831 S Figueroa St, Los Angeles, CA 90061-1157
Tel (310) 516-1692 *Founded/Ownrshp* 1997
Sales 138.4MM^E *EMP* 350
SIC 3671 Electron tubes
Pr: Neal Castleman
VP: Jack Cate
**VP:* Brian Gamberg
VP: Lola Herron
**VP:* Garret Hoffman
Natl Sales: Travis Cooper
Manager: Tim Shantry

DD RESORTS
See DOUBLE DIAMOND INC

D-U-N-S 16-013-5075 IMP/EXP
DD TRADERS INC
DEMDACO
5000 W 134th St, Leawood, KS 66209-7806
Tel (913) 402-6800 *Founded/Ownrshp* 1991
Sales 126.8MM^E *EMP* 285
SIC 5199 Gifts & novelties
Ch: David Kiersznowski
**Pr:* Lawrence W Hart
Pr: Christine Lien
**COO:* Steve Fowler
**CFO:* Stephen J Fowler
**CFO:* Eileen Marshall
CFO: Eileen Marshall
**Treas:* Demi Lloyd
**Treas:* Eileen M Marshall
Bd of Dir: Laura McMillan
VP: Pete Malone
Exec: Linda Bailey
Creative D: Ingrid Liss
Creative D: Julie Puntch

D-U-N-S 08-895-6859
■ **DDB WORLDWIDE COMMUNICATIONS GROUP INC**
(*Suby of* OMNICOM GROUP INC) ★
437 Madison Ave Fl 11, New York, NY 10022-7043
Tel (212) 415-2000 *Founded/Ownrshp* 1986
Sales 385.0MM^E *EMP* 8,833
SIC 7311 Advertising agencies
Pr: Chuck Brymer
Ch Bd: Charles Brymer
Pr: John Bradstock
Pr: Bernard Brochand
Pr: Mike Harris
Pr: Peter McGuinness
Ofcr: Amir Kassaei
Ofcr: Paul Price
Ex VP: Gwendolyn Basinger
Ex VP: Jeffrey Berger
Ex VP: Marc Schwartz
Sr VP: Marcia Iacobucci
VP: Philip Angelastro
Creative D: Matthew Christiansen
Creative D: Vida Cornelious
Creative D: Helene Cote
Creative D: Kuijpers Joris
Creative D: Andy Langer
Creative D: Mark Monteiro
Creative D: Marcia Murray
Dir Bus: Maria Tender

D-U-N-S 05-901-2075
DDH INC
DOMINION DIAGNOSTICS
211 Circuit Dr, North Kingstown, RI 02852-7440
Tel (401) 667-0800 *Founded/Ownrshp* 2010
Sales 91.0MM^E *EMP* 205
SIC 5047 Diagnostic equipment, medical
CEO: Frank Fornari
Manager: Michael Johnson

DDIC
See DELTA DENTAL INSURANCE CO

D-U-N-S 96-492-8402
DDJ CAPITAL MANAGEMENT LLC
DDJ TOTAL RETURN FUND
130 Turner St Ste 600, Waltham, MA 02453-8943
Tel (781) 283-8500 *Founded/Ownrshp* 1996
Sales 628.4MM^E *EMP* 4,048^E
SIC 6282 5094 5812 Investment advice; Jewelry & precious stones; Restaurant, family: chain; Mexican restaurant; Italian restaurant; Fast-food restaurant, chain
CFO: Brian Jacobson
CFO: John Russell
Sr VP: John O'Connor
Mng Dir: Scott McAdam

DDJ TOTAL RETURN FUND
See DDJ CAPITAL MANAGEMENT LLC

DDN PHARMACEUTICAL LOGISTICS
See DDN/OBERGFEL LLC

D-U-N-S 14-165-6244 IMP
DDN/OBERGFEL LLC
DDN PHARMACEUTICAL LOGISTICS
(*Suby of* F DOHMEN CO) ★
4580 S Mendenhall Rd, Memphis, TN 38141-6700
Tel (901) 795-7117 *Founded/Ownrshp* 1995
Sales 113.4MM^E *EMP* 300
SIC 5122 Pharmaceuticals
COO: Mark Wiesman
**CFO:* John Vaughan
VP: Bruce Chiriani
VP: Tom Donahue
VP: Pat P McGinn

D-U-N-S 06-408-2100
▲ **DDR CORP**
3300 Enterprise Pkwy, Beachwood, OH 44122-7200
Tel (216) 755-5500 *Founded/Ownrshp* 1965
Sales 1.0MMM *EMP* 576
Tkr Sym DDR *Exch* NYS
SIC 6798 Real estate investment trusts
Pr: Thomas F August
**Ch Bd:* Terrance R Ahern
CFO: Christa A Vesy
Ex VP: Vincent Corno
Ex VP: James Farrell
Ex VP: Robi Walker-Gibbons
Ex VP: David E Weiss
VP: Gary Ceepo
VP: Joe Chura
VP: David Dieterle
VP: Jennifer Flickinger
VP: James Grafmeyer
VP: Brigette Johnson
VP: Dale Johnson
VP: Benjamin Snyder
VP: Jason Vipperman
VP: Evan Vlaeminck
Exec: Paul W Freddo
Board of Directors: Thomas Finne, Robert H Gidel, Victor B Macfarlane, Alexander Otto, Scott D Roulston, Barry A Sholem

DDS
See DIVERSIFIED DISTRIBUTION SYSTEMS LLC

D-U-N-S 01-746-4025 IMP
DE BRUYN PRODUCE CO
DEBCO
26 Fm 491, La Villa, TX 78562
Tel (956) 262-6286 *Founded/Ownrshp* 1958
Sales 96.9MM^E *EMP* 400
SIC 5148 Vegetables, fresh
Pr: Margret De Bruyn

DE COSTER EGG FARMS
See AUSTIN JACK DE COSTER

D-U-N-S 11-623-5003
DE FOXX & ASSOCIATES INC
VALIDEX
324 W 9th St Fl 5, Cincinnati, OH 45202-2043
Tel (513) 621-5522 *Founded/Ownrshp* 1981
Sales 103.2MM^E *EMP* 1,500
SIC 8742 8741 Business consultant; General management consultant; Construction management
Pr: David E Foxx
COO: Levon Thompson
Opers Mgr: Ken Cartwright
Genl Couns: Constance Hill

DE GOL BROS CARPET DIV
See DEGOL ORGANIZATION L P

DE GOLYER AND MC MAUGHTON
See D&M HOLDING INC

D-U-N-S 05-469-3809
DE LAGE LANDEN FINANCIAL SERVICES INC
AMSOUTH LEASING
(*Suby of* DE LAGE LANDEN INTERNATIONAL B.V.)
1111 Old Eagle School Rd, Wayne, PA 19087-1453
Tel (610) 386-5000 *Founded/Ownrshp* 1999
Sales NA *EMP* 750
SIC 6159 Machinery & equipment finance leasing
Ch Bd: Ronald Slaats
Pr: William Stephenson
COO: Rita Di Di Matino
COO: Rita D Di Matino
COO: Cootjans Marc
CFO: Jim M Caughan
Treas: Denis McCafferty
Ofcr: Chris Cunningham
Ofcr: John Ionata
Ex VP: Bill Hall
Sr VP: Neal Garnett
Sr VP: Maneesh Jhunjhunwala
Sr VP: Lou Maslowe
Sr VP: Mark McGovern
Sr VP: Thomas A Sciorilli
VP: Christiaan Bouhuys
VP: Gary Davis
VP: Rita Dimartino
VP: Paula Dorazio
VP: Edward Gresh
VP: Anand Subramaniam
Board of Directors: Takashi Inouchi

DE LALLO ITALIAN FOODS
See GEORGE DELALLO CO INC

DE LAND TOYOTA
See LONGWOOD LINCOLN-MERCURY INC

D-U-N-S 15-131-2568
DE MOYA GROUP INC
14600 Sw 136th St, Miami, FL 33186-6762
Tel (305) 255-5713 *Founded/Ownrshp* 1986
Sales 83.4MM^E *EMP* 230
SIC 1611 1622 Concrete construction: roads, highways, sidewalks, etc.; Bridge construction
Pr: Armando De Moya
**Sec:* Alisa De Moya
**VP:* Aj De Moya

DE PAUL HOSPITAL
See DAUGHTERS OF CHARITY SERVICES OF ST LOUIS

D-U-N-S 04-569-4130
DE PAUL UNIVERSITY
DEPAUL UNIVERSITY
1 E Jackson Blvd, Chicago, IL 60604-2287
Tel (312) 362-6714 *Founded/Ownrshp* 1907
Sales 562.4MM *EMP* 3,895
Accts Kpmg Llp Chicago Il
SIC 8221 University
Pr: Dennis H Holtschneider
Pr: David Aborgealt
Pr: Guillermo Acampuzano
Pr: David Atharp
Pr: Linda Blakley
Pr: Caryn Chaden
Pr: Gwyn Friend
Pr: Barbara M Schaffer
**CFO:* Bonnie Frankel
**Treas:* Jeffrey Bethke
Ofcr: Susan M Wachowski
Ex VP: Susan Carolan
Ex VP: John Kozak
**Ex VP:* Robert Kozoman
Ex VP: Jose D Padilla
Sr VP: David Kalsbeek
VP: Asher Adiaz
VP: Joann Alulla
VP: Abena Apea
VP: Rebecca Awells
VP: Amanda Azonta

DE-STA-CO
See DOVER ENERGY INC

D-U-N-S 00-249-1645 IMP
DEACON INDUSTRIAL SUPPLY CO INC
1510 Gehman Rd, Harleysville, PA 19438-2929
Tel (215) 256-1715 *Founded/Ownrshp* 1990
Sales 174.4MM^E *EMP* 81
Accts Maillie Falconiero & Company
SIC 5074 5085 Plumbing & hydronic heating supplies; Industrial supplies
Pr: William S Vail
**CFO:* Bill Hardie
CFO: Michael Pavis
VP: Bill Dunne
**VP:* John J Fries
**VP:* Scott Tollefson
Brnch Mgr: Christopher Casey
IT Man: Leo Foster

DEACONESS COUNSELING ASSOC
See DEACONESS HOSPITAL INC

DEACONESS GATEWAY GIFT SHOP
See DEACONESS GATEWAY HOSPITAL

D-U-N-S 07-921-3322
DEACONESS GATEWAY HOSPITAL
DEACONESS GATEWAY GIFT SHOP
4011 Gateway Blvd, Newburgh, IN 47630-8947
Tel (812) 842-2000 *Founded/Ownrshp* 2013
Sales 83.7MM *EMP* 92^E
SIC 8062 General medical & surgical hospitals
CEO: Linda E White
COO: Shawn McCoy
Prin: David Christeson
Prin: Christina M Ryan
Surgeon: Philip B Hurley

D-U-N-S 14-779-9423
DEACONESS HEALTH SYSTEM INC
GATEWAY HEALTH CENTER
600 Mary St, Evansville, IN 47710-1658
Tel (812) 450-5000 *Founded/Ownrshp* 1982
Sales 2.7MM *EMP* 6,086
Accts Blue & Co Llc Indianapolis I
SIC 8741 Hospital management
Pr: Linda E White
**COO:* Shawn McCoy
COO: Tammy Stamp
**CFO:* Cheryl Wathen
Ofcr: Vicki Belangee
Sr VP: Richard Stivers
VP: Bruce Etneier
**VP:* Cherona J Hajewski
**VP:* Lynn Lingafelter
VP: Cheryl A Wathen
Exec: Carl Brueggemeyer
Exec: Jenny Cash
Assoc Dir: Gregory Hindahl

D-U-N-S 05-694-3277 IMP
■ **DEACONESS HEALTH SYSTEM LLC**
DEACONESS HOSPITAL
(*Suby of* COMMUNITY HEALTH SYSTEMS INC) ★
5501 N Portland Ave, Oklahoma City, OK 73112-2074
Tel (405) 604-6000 *Founded/Ownrshp* 2005
Sales 112.5MM *EMP* 1,400
SIC 8062 8051 8011 8361 General medical & surgical hospitals; Skilled nursing care facilities; Radiologist; Self-help group home
Ex Dir: Devin Hyde
Chf Rad: Van A Hooser
CFO: Larry Stevens
VP: Bruce Epmeier
Dir Case M: Priscilla Pierce
Dir Lab: Peyton Jackson
Dir Rx: Joele Harmon
Mng Dir: Farzad R Null
Prac Mgr: Judy Vance
Nurse Mgr: Dawn Purvis
Pathlgst: Peter Brumbaugh

DEACONESS HOSPITAL
See DEACONESS HEALTH SYSTEM LLC

DEACONESS HOSPITAL
See DEACONESS MEDICAL CENTER

DEACONESS HOSPITAL
See SPOKANE WASHINGTON HOSPITAL CO LLC

D-U-N-S 05-682-6456
DEACONESS HOSPITAL INC
DEACONESS COUNSELING ASSOC
(*Suby of* GATEWAY HEALTH CENTER) ★
600 Mary St, Evansville, IN 47710-1674
Tel (812) 450-5000 *Founded/Ownrshp* 1892
Sales 680.9MM *EMP* 5,300
SIC 8062 Hospital, professional nursing school
Pr: Linda E White
**Ch Bd:* John Lipert
COO: Christina Ryan
**CFO:* Richard Stivers
VP: Bruce Epmeier
Adm Dir: Gregory Folz
Dept Mgr: Marlene Waller
Off Mgr: Terry Meadows
IT Man: Kenny Klein
Ansthlgy: Tony Hood
Ansthlgy: Rajesh J Patel

D-U-N-S 83-943-7753
DEACONESS LONG TERM CARE OF MISSOURI INC
CAMDEN HEALTH CENTER
330 Straight St Ste 310, Cincinnati, OH 45219-1068
Tel (513) 487-3600 *Founded/Ownrshp* 1995
Sales 16.8M *EMP* 1,850
SIC 8059 8361 8052 8051 Nursing home, except skilled & intermediate care facility; Residential care; Intermediate care facilities; Skilled nursing care facilities
COO: Ken Raupach

D-U-N-S 80-853-7344
DEACONESS LONG TERM CARE OF MO INC
(*Suby of* DEACONESS LONG TERM CARE, INC.)
8540 Blue Ridge Blvd, Raytown, MO 64138-2959
Tel (816) 380-3319 *Founded/Ownrshp* 1991
Sales 28.1M^E *EMP* 1,500
SIC 8051 Convalescent home with continuous nursing care

DEACONESS MEDICAL CENTER
See EMPIRE HEALTH CENTERS GROUP

D-U-N-S 11-112-9479
■ **DEACONESS MEDICAL CENTER**
DEACONESS HOSPITAL
(*Suby of* DEACONESS HOSPITAL) ★
800 W 5th Ave, Spokane, WA 99204-2803
Tel (509) 458-5800 *Founded/Ownrshp* 1896
Sales 252.3MM *EMP* 888
SIC 8062 General medical & surgical hospitals
CEO: Jeff A Nelson
VP: Ginger Cohen
CIO: Bryan Hillstaead
HC Dir: Heidi Tucker

D-U-N-S 02-234-2153
DEACONESS WOMENS HOSPITAL OF SOUTHERN INDIANA LLC
WOMEN'S HOSPITAL, THE
4199 Gateway Blvd, Newburgh, IN 47630-8940
Tel (812) 842-4200 *Founded/Ownrshp* 2001
Sales 87.3MM^E *EMP* 600
SIC 8062 General medical & surgical hospitals
CEO: Chris Ryan
Pr: Jessica Thornton
Ofcr: Vicki Belange
Ofcr: Melissa Gough
Dir Rad: Denise Lofton
Mng Dir: Anvita Sinha
Obsttrcn: Allen L Walker
Doctor: Phil Gamble
Nrsg Dir: Julia Baumeyer

D-U-N-S 01-188-8328
DEAD RIVER CO (ME)
80 Exchange St Ste 3, Bangor, ME 04401-5200
Tel (207) 947-8641 *Founded/Ownrshp* 1909
Sales 34.2MM^E *EMP* 1,023
SIC 6512 5172 5983 5541 5411 Commercial & industrial building operation; Petroleum products; Fuel oil dealers; Gasoline service stations; Convenience stores
Pr: Robert A Moore
**CFO:* Richard M Roderick
**Treas:* James Burns
VP: Deanna Sherman
VP: Janet Timmins
Brnch Mgr: Melissa Caron
Brnch Mgr: Steve Martin
Dist Mgr: Mark Wilcox
Genl Mgr: Tim Malikowski
CTO: Steve Jacobs
Software D: Mitchell C Preble

D-U-N-S 12-910-3086
DEALER DOT COM INC
DEALER DOT COM WEBSYSTEMS
(*Suby of* DEALERTRACK TECHNOLOGIES INC) ★
1 Howard St, Burlington, VT 05401-4817
Tel (888) 894-8989 *Founded/Ownrshp* 2014
Sales 129.9MM^E *EMP* 540
SIC 7374 Computer graphics service
Pr: Richard Gibbs
Pr: Normand Theberge
**COO:* Michael Lane
COO: Mike Lane
**CFO:* David Stetson
**Chf Mktg O:* Dean Evans
VP: Tim Cornish
VP: Kristin Halpin
VP: Dan Jackson
VP: Kate Paradee
VP: David Parker
VP: Chris Stephenson
Comm Dir: Alison Von Puschendorf

DEALER DOT COM WEBSYSTEMS
See DEALER DOT COM INC

D-U-N-S 00-587-0212 IMP
DEALER TIRE LLC
3711 Chester Ave, Cleveland, OH 44114-4623
Tel (216) 432-0088 *Founded/Ownrshp* 2000
Sales 2.0MMM^E *EMP* 800

SIC 5014 Tires & tubes
CEO: Scott Mueller
**Pr:* Dean T Mueller
CFO: Steve Raguz
Ofcr: Francisco Codina
Ofcr: Jill Marcotte
VP: Andes Candies
VP: Orlando Dangond
VP: Jim Grant
VP: Kevin Peters
VP: Scott Sandifeer
Prgrm Mgr: Stephanie Badza

D-U-N-S 00-737-2543
DEALERS ELECTRICAL SUPPLY CO
2320 Columbus Ave, Waco, TX 76701-1041
Tel (254) 756-7251 *Founded/Ownrshp* 1985
Sales 470.6MM^E *EMP* 50
SIC 5063 5719 Electrical apparatus & equipment; Wire & cable; Cable conduit; Boxes & fittings, electrical; Lighting fixtures
CEO: Morris W Bracey
**Pr:* Scott Bracey
**VP:* Chris Lanham
**VP:* Steve Woznuck

D-U-N-S 18-672-1408
DEALERSOCKET INC
100 Avenida La Pata, San Clemente, CA 92673-6304
Tel (949) 900-0300 *Founded/Ownrshp* 2005
Sales 112.0MM^E *EMP* 470
SIC 7371 Computer software systems analysis & design, custom
Pr: Jonathan Ord
**COO:* Cameron Darby
VP: Jim Habig
**VP:* Matthew Redden

D-U-N-S 16-961-1667
DEALERTRACK INC
(*Suby of* DEALERTRACK TECHNOLOGIES INC) ★
1111 Marcus Ave Ste M04, New Hyde Park, NY 11042-1034
Tel (516) 734-3600 *Founded/Ownrshp* 2000
Sales 496.5MM^E *EMP* 2,000
SIC 7374 Computer graphics service
Ch Bd: Mark O'Neil
Pr: Allen Gerlings
Pr: Charles Giglia
CFO: Paul Heynderickx
**CFO:* Eric Jacobs
Sr VP: Ana Herrera
Sr VP: Rajesh Sundaram
Sr VP: Rick Von Pusch
VP: Mark Brown
VP: Ken Engber
VP: Mitchell Margolis
**VP:* Gary Papilsky
Dir Soc: Mariana Giamundo

D-U-N-S 07-590-0162
DEALERTRACK TECHNOLOGIES INC
(*Suby of* COX AUTOMOTIVE INC) ★
1111 Marcus Ave Ste M04, New Hyde Park, NY 11042-1034
Tel (516) 734-3600 *Founded/Ownrshp* 2001, 2015
Sales 854.4MM *EMP* 2,500^E
SIC 7373 Computer integrated systems design
CEO: Mark F O'Neil
Pr: Richard Gibbs
Pr: Rajesh Sundaram
CFO: Eric D Jacobs
Ex VP: Richard McLeer
Ex VP: Barry Zwarenstein
Sr VP: Ana M Herrera
Sr VP: Amit Maheshwari
Sr VP: David P Trinder
Sr VP: Rick G Von Pusch
VP: Hugh Abernethy
VP: Greg Bauer
VP: Mark Brown
VP: Alison Comolli
VP: Jane Dalzell
VP: Kristin Halpin
VP: Angie Haycock
VP: Ana Herrera
VP: Donal McGranaghan
VP: Kelly Mulroney
VP: Rick Pusch

D-U-N-S 00-890-6497
■ DEALS-NOTHING OVER A DOLLAR LLC
(*Suby of* SAVE-A-LOT LIMITED) ★
12100 St Charles Rock Rd, Bridgeton, MO 63044-2601
Tel (314) 291-5081 *Founded/Ownrshp* 2002
Sales 45.3MM^E *EMP* 1,000
SIC 5311 Department stores, discount

DEAN
See FRYMASTER LLC

D-U-N-S 14-784-3916 IMP/EXP
DEAN & DE LUCA BRANDS INC
(*Suby of* DEAN & DELUCA INC) ★
560 Broadway Frnt 2, New York, NY 10012-3990
Tel (212) 226-6800 *Founded/Ownrshp* 1999
Sales 84.2MM^E *EMP* 352
SIC 5499 5812 2099 Gourmet food stores; Coffee shop; Food preparations
Pr: Dane Neller
**CFO:* Howard P Goodman

D-U-N-S 16-480-3830 IMP/EXP
DEAN & DELUCA INC
560 Broadway Frnt 2, New York, NY 10012-3990
Tel (212) 226-6800 *Founded/Ownrshp* 1977
Sales 110.4MM^E *EMP* 765^E
Accts Kpmg
SIC 5499 5812 5961 2099 Gourmet food stores; Box lunch stand; Food, mail order; Food preparations
Ch: Leslie G Rudd
**CEO:* Mark Daley
Genl Mgr: Dan Kelly

DEAN CLINIC
See DEAN HEALTH SYSTEMS INC

D-U-N-S 00-692-2603 IMP/EXP
■ DEAN DAIRY HOLDINGS LLC
MCARTHUR DAIRY
(*Suby of* DEAN FOODS CO) ★
6851 Ne 2nd Ave, Miami, FL 33138-5503
Tel (305) 795-7700 *Founded/Ownrshp* 1922, 1981
Sales 132.1MM^E *EMP* 437
SIC 5143 Dairy products, except dried or canned
Prin: Tom Davis
Genl Mgr: Bill Giovanetti

D-U-N-S 61-955-7734
■ DEAN DAIRY HOLDINGS LLC
CREAMLAND DAIRIES
(*Suby of* DEAN HOLDING CO) ★
2515 Mckinney Ave # 1100, Dallas, TX 75201-1945
Tel (214) 303-3400 *Founded/Ownrshp* 2001
Sales 411.0MM^E *EMP* 10,000^E
SIC 6719 2026 Investment holding companies, except banks; Fluid milk
Pr: Harrald F K Kroeker
Treas: Timothy A Smith
VP: John F Callahan Jr
VP: Rachel A Gonzalez

D-U-N-S 11-911-5715 IMP
■ DEAN DAIRY PRODUCTS CO
DEAN FOODS COMPANY
(*Suby of* DEAN HOLDING CO) ★
1690 Oneida Ln, Sharpsville, PA 16150-9665
Tel (724) 962-7801 *Founded/Ownrshp* 1984
Sales 98.2MM^E *EMP* 350
SIC 2026 Milk processing (pasteurizing, homogenizing, bottling)
Pr: Gregg L Engles
**VP:* Frank Crastina
Exec: Phil Miller
Mktg Mgr: Betsy Jackson

DEAN FOODS COMPANY
See DEAN DAIRY PRODUCTS CO

D-U-N-S 92-918-2210
▲ DEAN FOODS CO
2711 N Haskell Ave, Dallas, TX 75204-2911
Tel (214) 303-3400 *Founded/Ownrshp* 1988
Sales 8.1MMM *EMP* 16,960
Accts Deloitte & Touche Llp Dallas
Tkr Sym DF *Exch* NYS
SIC 2026 2033 5143 Fluid milk; Milk processing (pasteurizing, homogenizing, bottling); Fruit juices: packaged in cans, jars, etc.; Ice cream & ices
CEO: Gregg A Tanner
Ch Bd: Jim L Turner
COO: Ralph P Scozzafava
CFO: Chris Bellairs
Treas: Tim Smith
Ofcr: Kimberly Warmbier
Ex VP: Marc Kesselman
Ex VP: Gregory A McKelvey
Ex VP: Tommy Zanetich
Sr VP: Debra B Carosella
Sr VP: Edward F Fugger Jr
Sr VP: Brad Holcomb
Sr VP: Brian Murphy
Sr VP: Williams C Tinklepaugh
VP: Sean Bressler
VP: Dave Broughton
VP: Jack Jeffers
VP: Shane Keith
VP: Don Klein
VP: Dean Lippold
VP: Shan Luton

D-U-N-S 07-384-7998
DEAN HEALTH SYSTEMS INC
DEAN CLINIC
(*Suby of* SSM HEALTH CARE CORP) ★
1808 W Beltline Hwy, Madison, WI 53713-2334
Tel (608) 250-1435 *Founded/Ownrshp* 1969
Sales 70.7MM^E *EMP* 3,000
SIC 8099 Medical services organization
Pr: Gregory S Allen
V Ch: Richard W Glad
V Ch: Gerald Lefert
**CFO:* Steve Caldwell
Sec: Robert Gilbert
Ofcr: Rebecca Carlson
**Sr VP:* John L McWilliams
**Sr VP:* Allison A Mooney
**VP:* Todd C Burchill
VP: Jennifer L Close
VP: Charles Deshazer
VP: Deborah Hutchinson
VP: Thomas Kirschbaum
VP: Allison Mooney
VP: Carolyn Ogland
VP: Doug Pillar

D-U-N-S 00-510-4815 IMP
■ DEAN HOLDING CO (DE)
(*Suby of* DEAN FOODS CO) ★
2711 N Haskell Ave, Dallas, TX 75204-2911
Tel (214) 303-3400 *Founded/Ownrshp* 1921, 2001
Sales 1.9MMM^E *EMP* 10,080^E
SIC 2023 5143 5451 Dry, condensed, evaporated dairy products; Dairy products, except dried or canned; Dairy products stores
CEO: Gregg L Engles
**CFO:* Barry A Fromberg
Ex VP: Jack F Callahan Jr
VP: Daniel R Morrison
VP Opers: Alan W Hooper
Board of Directors: Steven J Kemps

D-U-N-S 19-066-7691
DEAN SNYDER CONSTRUCTION CO
913 N 14th St, Clear Lake, IA 50428-2138
Tel (641) 357-2283 *Founded/Ownrshp* 1958
Sales 87.6MM^E *EMP* 190
Accts Hogan-Hansen Mason City Iowa
SIC 1542 1521 1541 Commercial & office building, new construction; New construction, single-family houses; Industrial buildings & warehouses
CEO: Dale A Snyder
**Pr:* Donald D Snyder
**VP:* David L Snyder

D-U-N-S 83-188-1227
■ DEAN WEST II LLC
(*Suby of* CREAMLAND DAIRIES) ★
2515 Mckinney Ave # 1100, Dallas, TX 75201-1945
Tel (214) 303-3400 *Founded/Ownrshp* 2001
Sales 183.4MM^E *EMP* 430^E
SIC 2026 Fluid milk
Pr: Harrald Kroeker

D-U-N-S 04-087-1283
DEANCO HEALTHCARE LLC
MISSION COMMUNITY HOSPITAL
14850 Roscoe Blvd, Panorama City, CA 91402-4618
Tel (818) 787-2222 *Founded/Ownrshp* 2010
Sales 103.4MM^E *EMP* 700
SIC 8063 Psychiatric hospitals
Dir Lab: Joe Magpantay
Dir IT: Erick Rivers
IT Man: Ishmael Silla
QC Dir: Diane Wagner
Mktg Dir: Nate Hart
Mktg Dir: Julie Powers

D-U-N-S 80-748-2294 IMP
DEANGELO BROTHERS LLC
ALENZA
100 N Conahan Dr, Hazleton, PA 18201-7355
Tel (570) 459-5800 *Founded/Ownrshp* 1985
Sales 262.6MM^E *EMP* 450
SIC 0782 Lawn care services
CEO: Roger Zino
**Pr:* Paul D Deangelo
Pr: Jim Faust
**CFO:* Neal A Deangelo
CFO: Ralph Hromisin
Treas: Margurite Routson
Sr VP: Mark Robinson
VP: Wayne Hug
Exec: Richard Baker
Dir Risk M: Cynthia Paisley
Rgnl Mgr: Scott Pedigo

DEARBORN CASH & CARRY
See DEARBORN WHOLESALE GROCERS LP

D-U-N-S 07-974-6428
DEARBORN MID-WEST CO LLC
20334 Superior Rd, Taylor, MI 48180-6301
Tel (734) 288-4400 *Founded/Ownrshp* 2015
Sales 108.0MM^E *EMP* 150^E
SIC 3535 Conveyors & conveying equipment
CEO: Anthony L Rosati
**Pr:* Jeff Homenik
CFO: David Cosgrove
Sr VP: Katarina Katsavrias
VP: C Bagierek
VP: Jeff Brinker
VP: Steve Dorchak
VP: Sudy Vohra
Exec: Jason Benson
MIS Dir: Robert Underwood
Mfg Mgr: Al Chaffin

DEARBORN PUB SCHOLS BD EDUCATN
See DEARBORN PUBLIC SCHOOLS

D-U-N-S 06-983-3390
DEARBORN PUBLIC SCHOOLS
DEARBORN PUB SCHOLS BD EDUCATN
18700 Audette St, Dearborn, MI 48124-4222
Tel (313) 827-3000 *Founded/Ownrshp* 1917
Sales 204.2M *EMP* 2,448
Accts Heller & Wetzler Pc Ypsilanti
SIC 8211 8222 Public elementary & secondary schools; Public junior high school; Public senior high school; Community college
Dir Sec: Don Ball
IT Man: Elaine Starrett
Schl Brd P: Hussein Berry
Schl Brd P: Roxanne McDonald
Psych: Fay Kafi

D-U-N-S 82-795-7783
DEARBORN RESOURCES INC
2130 Inwood Dr, Houston, TX 77019-3523
Tel (713) 521-1950 *Founded/Ownrshp* 2006
Sales 557.6MM^E *EMP* 1,500
SIC 1623 Oil & gas pipeline construction
Pr: Gregory S V Curran

D-U-N-S 02-509-9144 IMP
DEARBORN WHOLESALE GROCERS LP
DEARBORN CASH & CARRY
2455 S Damen Ave Ste 100, Chicago, IL 60608-5233
Tel (773) 254-4300 *Founded/Ownrshp* 1938
Sales 301.2MM^E *EMP* 500
Accts Warady & Davis Llp Deerfield
SIC 5141 Groceries, general line
Mng Pt: Sherwin Friedman
**Pt:* Leonard Friedman

D-U-N-S 00-969-9810 IMP
DEARDENS
DEARDEN'S HOME FURNISHINGS
700 S Main St, Los Angeles, CA 90014-2094
Tel (213) 362-9600 *Founded/Ownrshp* 1959
Sales 135.4MM^E *EMP* 500
SIC 5712 5722 5731 5944 Furniture stores; Electric household appliances; Gas household appliances; Radio, television & electronic stores; Jewelry stores
Ch Bd: Raquel Bensimon
**CEO:* Ronny Bensimon
CFO: James Anderson
VP: Angel Lopez
IT Man: Sam Munoz
Info Man: John Wheatley
Site Mgr: Martin Madrigal
VP Mktg: Eric Lopez

DEARDEN'S HOME FURNISHINGS
See DEARDENS

DEARING AGRI-SALES COMPANY
See DASCO INC

D-U-N-S 03-612-8148
DEARYBURY OIL & GAS INC
2560 Southport Rd, Spartanburg, SC 29302-2982
Tel (864) 585-6226 *Founded/Ownrshp* 1996
Sales 368.2MM *EMP* 35

SIC 5172 5983 4212

DEB SHOPS
See DSI INC

D-U-N-S 78-605-2548
DEBBIES STAFFING SERVICES INC
4431 Cherry St Ste 50, Winston Salem, NC 27105-2562
Tel (336) 744-2393 *Founded/Ownrshp* 1986
Sales 167.9MM^E *EMP* 9,000
SIC 7363 Temporary help service
CEO: Debbie P Little
**Pr:* Heinz W Little
VP: Pam Payne

DEBCO
See DE BRUYN PRODUCE CO

D-U-N-S 07-282-4592 IMP
DEBEVOISE & PLIMPTON LLP
919 3rd Ave Lbby 2, New York, NY 10022-3916
Tel (212) 909-6000 *Founded/Ownrshp* 1931
Sales 303.0MM^E *EMP* 2,130
SIC 8111 General practice attorney, lawyer
Pt: Michael W Blair
Pt: Robert R Bruce
Pt: Anne Cohen
Pt: Frederick T Davis
Pt: Donald F Donovan
Pt: Martin F Evans
Pt: Friedrich Hey
Pt: David Rivkin
Pt: Robert N Shwartz
Pt: Gregory H Woods
Mng Pt: Pierre Clermontel
Mng Pt: Jeffrey P Cunard
Mng Pt: Edward Dutton
Mng Pt: Dmitri V Nikiforov
Mng Pt: Andrew M Ostrognai
Mng Pt: Thomas Sch Rrle
Mng Pt: James C Scoville
VP: Heather D Loeffler
Dir Teleco: Ben Randazzo
Assoc Dir: Paul R Berger

D-U-N-S 07-145-7964 IMP
DEBORAH HEART AND LUNG CENTER
200 Trenton Rd, Browns Mills, NJ 08015-1764
Tel (609) 893-6611 *Founded/Ownrshp* 1923
Sales 163.2MM *EMP* 1,000
SIC 8062 General medical & surgical hospitals
CEO: Joseph Chirichella
Pr: Susan Bonfield
CFO: Grant Leidy
**VP:* R Grant Leidy
VP: Lauren McCormick
Dir Rx: Maryanne C Vanpelt
Ex Dir: Christine Golia
Genl Mgr: David New
CIO: John Ernst
IT Man: Andrew Carr
Mtls Dir: Michele Ingling

D-U-N-S 06-474-3912
■ DECARE DENTAL LLC
(*Suby of* ANTHEM HOLDING CORP) ★
3560 Delta Dental Dr, Saint Paul, MN 55122-3166
Tel (800) 371-6561 *Founded/Ownrshp* 1987
Sales NA *EMP* 700^E
SIC 6324 8621 Dental insurance; Professional membership organizations
Pr: Michael F Walsh
Ex VP: Norman Storbakken
VP: Mark Moksnes
IT Man: Douglas Harrison

D-U-N-S 07-897-2478
DECATUR CITY BOARD OF EDUCATION
302 4th Ave Ne, Decatur, AL 35601-1972
Tel (256) 552-3000 *Founded/Ownrshp* 1927
Sales 97.1MM *EMP* 1,285
Accts Byrd Smalley & Adams Pc Dec
SIC 8211 School board
Pr: Karen Duke
**CFO:* Melanie Maples
Treas: Julian Harris
**VP:* Donnie Lane

D-U-N-S 07-989-3891
DECATUR CITY SCHOOLS
302 4th Ave Ne, Decatur, AL 35601-1972
Tel (256) 552-3000 *Founded/Ownrshp* 2015
Sales 12.0MM^E *EMP* 1,078^E
SIC 8211 Public elementary & secondary schools
Pr Dir: Dwight Satterfield
Teacher Pr: Yvette Evans
Psych: Debbie Dunlap

D-U-N-S 96-288-6516
DECATUR COUNTY SCHOOL DISTRICT
100 S West St, Bainbridge, GA 39817-3680
Tel (229) 248-2200 *Founded/Ownrshp* 2010
Sales 1.7MM^E *EMP* 1,000^E
SIC 8211 Elementary & secondary schools
Prin: Linda Lumpkin
Mfg Dir: Raymond Powell
Schl Brd P: Sydney Cochran
Psych: Susan Lanier
HC Dir: Christy Harrell

D-U-N-S 82-821-8698
DECATUR HOSPITAL AUTHORITY
DFW NURSING AND REHAB
900 W Leuda St, Fort Worth, TX 76104-3002
Tel (817) 332-7003
Sales 124.0MM *EMP* 17^E
Accts Bkd Llp Waco Tx
SIC 8062 General medical & surgical hospitals

D-U-N-S 88-373-2646
DECATUR MEMORIAL FOUNDATION
(*Suby of* DECATUR MEMORIAL HOSPITAL) ★
2300 N Edward St, Decatur, IL 62526-4163
Tel (217) 876-8121 *Founded/Ownrshp* 1984
Sales 3.0MM *EMP* 1,311^E
Accts La Rosa & Co Llc Indianapolis
SIC 6732 Trusts: educational, religious, etc.
CEO: Terry Myers
**Pr:* Kenneth Smith Mier

Dir Lab: John Little
Off Mgr: Nancy Flisher

D-U-N-S 04-658-4991
DECATUR MEMORIAL HOSPITAL
(*Suby of* DMH CORPORATE HEALTH SERVICES) ★
2300 N Edward St, Decatur, IL 62526-4192
Tel (217) 877-8121 *Founded/Ownrshp* 1984
Sales 258.6MM *EMP* 1,311
SIC 8062 General medical & surgical hospitals
Pr: Ken Smithmier
COO: Tim Stone
* *VP:* Gary G Peacock
VP: Kim Stone
Exec: Jon Locke
Dir Rx: Kandie Dino
Ex Dir: John Ridley
Pathlgst: Mark C Clarke
Nrsg Dir: Joan Bricker
Phys Thrpy: Jeff Brown

DECATUR MORGAN HOSPITAL
See HEALTH CARE AUTHORITY OF MORGAN COUNTY - CITY OF DECATUR

D-U-N-S 07-561-4370
DECATUR SCHOOL DISTRICT 61 INC
101 W Cerro Gordo St, Decatur, IL 62523-1001
Tel (217) 362-3000 *Founded/Ownrshp* 1865
Sales 116.0MM *EMP* 2,000
Accts Bkd Llp Decatur Illinois
SIC 8211 Public elementary & secondary schools; Secondary school
Pr Dir: Maria Ford

DECATUR UTILITIES
See MUNICIPAL UTILITIES BOARD OF DECATUR MORGAN COUNTY ALABAMA

D-U-N-S 01-300-3863 IMP
DECEUNINCK NORTH AMERICA LLC
351 N Garver Rd, Monroe, OH 45050-1233
Tel (513) 539-5466 *Founded/Ownrshp* 1969, 2012
Sales 116.4MM^E *EMP* 269^E
SIC 3082 Unsupported plastics profile shapes
Pr: Filip Geeraert
VP: Scott Sheffield
Mng Dir: Roy Frost
Dir IT: Dan Shull
Sfty Dirs: Heather Slaton
Ql Cn Mgr: Don Manning
Sls Dir: Mark Lipsius
Mktg Mgr: Helen L Peyton

D-U-N-S 07-549-0920
DECHERT LLP (PA)
2929 Arch St Ste 400, Philadelphia, PA 19104-2808
Tel (202) 261-3300 *Founded/Ownrshp* 1875
Sales 328.9MM^E *EMP* 1,782
SIC 8111 Malpractice & negligence law; General practice attorney, lawyer
Pt: Barton J Winokur
Pt: M Joel Bolstein
Pt: Lew Burleigh
Pt: Bruce Hickey
Pt: Michael L Kichline
Pt: Edward P Lemanowicz
Pt: Ross Pascal
* *Pt:* Richard C Rizzo
Pt: Louise G Roman
* *Pt:* Michael Vankralingen
Pt: Cindy Williams
Mng Pt: Timothy C Blank
Mng Pt: Laura M Brank
Mng Pt: James R Bryant
Mng Pt: Laura G Ciabarra
Mng Pt: Dean Collins
Mng Pt: Douglas Dick
Mng Pt: William K Dodds
Mng Pt: Paul H Friedman
Mng Pt: Ren H Gonne
Mng Pt: Frederick G Herold

DECISION RESOURCES GROUP
See DECISION RESOURCES INC

D-U-N-S 61-497-1026
DECISION RESOURCES INC
DECISION RESOURCES GROUP
(*Suby of* PIRAMAL ENTERPRISES LIMITED)
800 District Ave Ste 600, Burlington, MA 01803-5062
Tel (781) 993-2500 *Founded/Ownrshp* 2012
Sales 132.2MM^E *EMP* 700
SIC 8732 2721 Market analysis, business & economic research; Periodicals
CEO: Jonathan Sandler
Pr: Mark Meek
Pr: Mark Luck Olson
* *CFO:* Anup Gupta
CFO: John Schuetz
Sr Cor Off: Joseph McDonough
* *Ex VP:* Kyle Bettigole
Ex VP: Tracy Degregorio
* *Sr VP:* Marc Krellenstein
VP: Eric Matckie
VP: Joe Reis

D-U-N-S 19-500-7570
DECISIONONE CORP
(*Suby of* D1 HOLDINGS, LLC)
426 W Lancaster Ave, Devon, PA 19333-1510
Tel (610) 296-6000 *Founded/Ownrshp* 2015
Sales 226.9MM^E *EMP* 1,600^E
SIC 7378 Computer & data processing equipment repair/maintenance
CEO: William F Comfort
COO: Sproxton Howard
COO: Christopher Larsen
CFO: Thomas Darling
Treas: Joseph Ticknor
Ex VP: Robert Schultz
Sr VP: Thomas M Molchan
VP: Dan Cruise
VP: Tait Frank
VP: Mark Friedman
VP: Eric Robertson
VP: Bryan Tesh
Mgt/VP: Kevin Dean
Dir Bus: Janet Kanick

D-U-N-S 94-238-8604
DECKER COMPANIES
4000 5th Ave S, Fort Dodge, IA 50501-6450
Tel (515) 576-4141 *Founded/Ownrshp* 1994
Sales 86.5MM^E *EMP* 750^E
SIC 4213 Refrigerated products transport; Building materials transport; Heavy hauling
Pr: Donald L Decker
* *Treas:* Timothy J Burns

D-U-N-S 02-917-7326 IMP
DECKER ELECTRIC CO INC ELECTRICAL CONTRACTORS (CA)
1282 Folsom St, San Francisco, CA 94103-3817
Tel (415) 552-1622 *Founded/Ownrshp* 1896, 1950
Sales 112.3MM *EMP* 117
SIC 1731

D-U-N-S 07-292-9078
▲ DECKERS OUTDOOR CORP
250 Coromar Dr, Goleta, CA 93117-3697
Tel (805) 967-7611 *Founded/Ownrshp* 1975
Sales 1.8MMM *EMP* 3,500^E
Accts Kpmg Llp Los Angeles Califor
Tkr Sym DECK *Exch* NYS
SIC 3021 2389 2339 Rubber & plastics footwear; Sandals, rubber; Shoes, rubber or rubber soled fabric uppers; Men's miscellaneous accessories; Women's & misses' accessories
Ch Bd: Angel R Martinez
Pr: Jeffrey Bua
Pr: Stefano Caroti
COO: David E Lafitte
CFO: Thomas A George
Sr VP: John Kalinich
VP: Graciela Montgomery
VP: Daniel Petta
VP: Charlotte Russe
Web Dev: Justin Tiernan
Sftwr Eng: Randy Kinsel
Board of Directors: Karyn O Barsa, Nelson C Chan, Michael F Devine III, John M Gibbons, John G Perenchio, James E Quinn, Lauri M Shanahan, Bonita C Stewart

DECO DIVISION
See AMSCAN INC

D-U-N-S 04-525-6000
DECO INC
DECO SECURITY SERVICES
11156 Zealand Ave N, Champlin, MN 55316-3594
Tel (763) 576-9572 *Founded/Ownrshp* 1986
Sales 126.6MM *EMP* 1,600
Accts Cliftonlarsonallen Llp Braine
SIC 7381 Security guard service; Protective services, guard
CEO: Robert A Dorr
* *Pr:* Derek J Dorr
* *CFO:* Tom Buckingham
* *Sr VP:* Jeff Gibson

DECO SECURITY SERVICES
See DECO INC

DECOMA ADMARK
See MAGNA EXTERIORS OF AMERICA INC

D-U-N-S 03-766-6117 IMP
DECOPAC INC
3500 Thurston Ave Ste 200, Anoka, MN 55303-1066
Tel (763) 574-0091 *Founded/Ownrshp* 1992
Sales 96.7MM^E *EMP* 370
SIC 5999 Cake decorating supplies
CEO: Michael J McGlynn
* *Pr:* Christine McKenna
Admn Mgr: Karen Murphy
Dir IT: Val Arntson
VP Opers: Kim Roy
Sales Exec: Marty Krause
VP Mktg: Dewey Wahlin
VP Sls: Steve Buffington
Mktg Mgr: Heather Corbin
Mktg Mgr: John Gardner
Mktg Mgr: Barbara Hiller

D-U-N-S 12-380-6320 IMP/EXP
DECOR HOLDINGS INC
225 Foxboro Blvd, Foxboro, MA 02035-2854
Tel (508) 339-9151 *Founded/Ownrshp* 2002
Sales 295.3MM^E *EMP* 600
SIC 5023 Home furnishings; Bedspreads
Pr: Ron Kass
VP: Peter Routsis

D-U-N-S 14-828-8868 EXP
DECORATIVE PANELS INTERNATIONAL INC
D P I
(*Suby of* AMERICAN STANDARD BRANDS) ★
2900 Hill Ave, Toledo, OH 43607-2929
Tel (419) 535-5921 *Founded/Ownrshp* 2010
Sales 83.8MM^E *EMP* 325
SIC 2435 Hardwood plywood, prefinished; Panels, hardwood plywood
Pr: Tim Clark
Opers Mgr: Mike Norman
Plnt Mgr: Mike Kilbane

D-U-N-S 00-960-1006 IMP
DECORE-ATIVE SPECIALTIES
2772 Peck Rd, Monrovia, CA 91016-5005
Tel (626) 254-9191 *Founded/Ownrshp* 1965
Sales 193.0MM^E *EMP* 1,100
SIC 2431 Doors, wood
CEO: Jack Lansford Sr
* *Pr:* Jack Lansford Jr
* *Treas:* Billie Lansford
* *Sr VP:* Eric Lansford
VP: Jim Allen
VP: David Thomson
Ex Dir: Jesus Rodriguez
Opers Mgr: William Mize
Mktg Dir: Chanda Erselius
Mktg Dir: Todd Warner
Mktg Mgr: Ed Anderson

D-U-N-S 79-065-8905 IMP
DECOSTAR INDUSTRIES INC
(*Suby of* DECOMA ADMARK) ★
1 Decoma Dr, Carrollton, GA 30117-5274
Tel (770) 801-2900 *Founded/Ownrshp* 2013
Sales 392.6MM^E *EMP* 1,100^E
SIC 3714 Motor vehicle parts & accessories
CEO: Joseph P Pittel
* *CFO:* Michael McCarthy
Genl Mgr: David Meier

D-U-N-S 07-532-2404
DECURION CORP
120 N Robertson Blvd Fl 3, Los Angeles, CA 90048-3115
Tel (310) 659-9432 *Founded/Ownrshp* 1966
Sales 200.2MM^E *EMP* 4,386
SIC 7832 7833 Motion picture theaters, except drive-in; Drive-in motion picture theaters
Pr: Michael R Forman
COO: Bryan Ungard
CFO: Bill Boersma
* *VP:* James Cotter
* *VP:* Jerome Forman
VP: James D Vandever
MIS Dir: David Denoy
Opers Mgr: Hina Rizvi
Snr Mgr: Jill Saperstein

D-U-N-S 02-382-7566 EXP
DEDC INC
DOW ELECTRONICS
8603 E Adamo Dr, Tampa, FL 33619-3521
Tel (813) 626-5195 *Founded/Ownrshp* 1959
Sales 141.5MM^E *EMP* 150
SIC 5065 Electronic parts
Pr: John J Yodzis
* *CFO:* Daniel T Carr
* *Treas:* Gregory Buffington
* *Ex VP:* John P Yodzis
* *VP:* Stephen O Decker
Brnch Mgr: David Best
IT Man: Csobanczi Joseph
IT Man: Phillip Partain
Mktg Dir: Jay Johnson
Sales Asso: Cheryl Butler

D-U-N-S 07-953-2008
DEDHAM MEDICAL ASSOCIATES INC
D.M.A.
1 Lyons St, Dedham, MA 02026-5599
Tel (781) 329-1400 *Founded/Ownrshp* 1937
Sales 143.3MM *EMP* 400
Accts Pkf Pc Quincy Ma
SIC 8011 8021 Physicians' office, including specialists; Group & corporate practice dentists
Pr: Barry J Benjamin
* *Pr:* Andrew Gillief MD
Treas: Andrew D Dorr
Trst: Arthur Deloca
Off Mgr: Roberta Sarragher
Obsttrcn: Monica S Ruehli
Opthamlgy: Andrew J Gillies
Podiatrist: Terri Loewenthal
Doctor: Lisa Ferzoco
Doctor: Elizabeth Foley
Doctor: James Goldman

D-U-N-S 03-067-8494 IMP
DEDICATED COMPUTING LLC
N26w23880 Commerce Cir B, Waukesha, WI 53188-1020
Tel (262) 951-7200 *Founded/Ownrshp* 1978
Sales 84.3MM^E *EMP* 240
SIC 3571 3577 5045

D-U-N-S 63-828-0899
DEDICATED LOGISTICS INC
(*Suby of* TOTAL LOGISTIC, INC.)
2900 Granada Ln N, Oakdale, MN 55128-3607
Tel (651) 631-5918 *Founded/Ownrshp* 2014
Sales 212.8MM^E *EMP* 800^E
SIC 4213 4212 4225 Trucking, except local; Local trucking, without storage; General warehousing & storage
CEO: Thomas Wintz
CFO: Keath E Young
Opers Mgr: Nicholas Calafati
Sls Mgr: Scott Carlson

DEE & BEE FASTENERS
See FASTENERS INC

D-U-N-S 00-814-2911
DEE HOWARD CO
9610 John Saunders Rd, San Antonio, TX 78216-4206
Tel (210) 828-1341 *Founded/Ownrshp* 1988
Sales 69.4MM^E *EMP* 1,100
SIC 3721 3724 4581 Aircraft; Motorized aircraft; Aircraft engines & engine parts; Aircraft maintenance & repair services; Aircraft servicing & repairing; Aircraft cleaning & janitorial service
CEO: P L Ughi
VP: J Furnish
VP: Russell McKenzie
VP: Philip O'Connor
VP: A Sassoli
Dir IT: Karl Zonow

D-U-N-S 00-279-7629
DEE PEE ELECTRIC COOPERATIVE INC (SC)
1355 E Mciver Rd, Darlington, SC 29532-8112
Tel (843) 665-4070 *Founded/Ownrshp* 1939
Sales 84.7MM *EMP* 110
Accts Mcnair Mclemore Middlebrooks &
SIC 4911 8611 Distribution, electric power; Business associations
Pr: James Goodson
* *CFO:* Deborah Osterberg
* *VP:* Doran Dennis
VP: Jessica Mason
VP: Lori Stuckey
Sfty Dirs: Terry Thompson

D-U-N-S 06-686-6963
DEE SPEE DELIVERY SERVICE INC
4101 Clearwater Rd, Saint Cloud, MN 56301-9635
Tel (320) 251-6697 *Founded/Ownrshp* 1978
Sales 89.2MM^E *EMP* 1,700
SIC 4212 Delivery service, vehicular
Pr: Donald Weeres
* *Treas:* Curtis Herbes
* *VP:* Tim Papesch

D-U-N-S 62-249-5034 IMP
DEE ZEE INC
DEE ZEE MANUFACTURING
1572 Ne 58th Ave, Des Moines, IA 50313-1622
Tel (515) 265-7331 *Founded/Ownrshp* 1986
Sales 248.2MM^E *EMP* 1,112
SIC 3714 Motor vehicle body components & frame
Pr: Kelli A Gallagher
* *COO:* Michael A Moyer
* *CFO:* Del Lasswell
CFO: Bill McDermott
VP: Brian Nicolet
Exec: Shawn Schulz
Prgrm Mgr: Leandra Holland
Dir IT: Dave Kalwishy
Software D: Bob Anderson
Opers Mgr: Jody West
Sales Exec: Achina Jason
Board of Directors: John B Gerlach Jr

DEE ZEE MANUFACTURING
See DEE ZEE INC

DEED
See MINNESOTA DEPARTMENT OF EMPLOYMENT AND ECONOMIC DEVELOPMENT

D-U-N-S 12-317-5726 IMP
DEEM INC
642 Harrison St Fl 2, San Francisco, CA 94107-1323
Tel (415) 590-8300 *Founded/Ownrshp* 2001
Sales 84.8MM^E *EMP* 360
SIC 5961 Computer software, mail order
Genl Pt: Alex Mendez
Pt: Barry Newman
Pr: Mark Biestman
COO: Brian Kuhn
* *CFO:* Carol Gray
CFO: Mark Rubash
* *CFO:* David Shiba
* *Chf Cred:* Tony D'Astolfo
* *Sr VP:* Tom Allen
Sr VP: Chetan Visweswar
Sr VP: Peg Wynn
Sr VP: Elizabeth Xu
VP: Tony Dastolfo
VP: George Gould
VP: Gary Hanna
* *VP:* Simon Luthi
VP: Thomas Meredith
VP: Marc Spier
* *VP:* Chethan Visweswar
VP: Trina Ward
Exec: Leland Hambley
Board of Directors: Gary Crittenden, Terrell Jones

D-U-N-S 13-228-4030
DEEM LLC
6831 E 32nd St Ste 200, Indianapolis, IN 46226-6195
Tel (317) 860-2990 *Founded/Ownrshp* 2002
Sales 104.5MM^E *EMP* 220^E
SIC 1731 1711 General electrical contractor; Mechanical contractor
Genl Mgr: Chad Gooding
Genl Mgr: Jan Laughlin
Sys Mgr: Greg Wellings
Sls Dir: Jim Skwarczynski
Genl Couns: Christopher Fey

D-U-N-S 01-330-8758
DEEP EAST TEXAS ELECTRIC
880 State Highway 21 E, San Augustine, TX 75972-2534
Tel (936) 275-2314 *Founded/Ownrshp* 2014
Sales 99.1MM *EMP* 17^E
SIC 4911 Electric services
Pr: Larry Warren

D-U-N-S 04-784-5623
DEEP EAST TEXAS ELECTRIC COOPERATIVE INC
U S Hwy 21 E, San Augustine, TX 75972
Tel (936) 275-2314 *Founded/Ownrshp* 1938
Sales 95.3MM *EMP* 113
Accts Knuckols Duvall Hallum & Co M
SIC 4911 Distribution, electric power; Generation, electric power
Genl Mgr: Larry Warren
VP: P Dobbs
Off Mgr: Gina Evett

D-U-N-S 05-846-8372 IMP
DEEP SOUTH CRANE AND RIGGING LLC
15324 Airline Hwy, Baton Rouge, LA 70817-7311
Tel (225) 753-4371 *Founded/Ownrshp* 1968
Sales 165.0MM *EMP* 650
SIC 7353

D-U-N-S 13-197-9713
DEEP SOUTH HOLDING INC
7701 Las Colinas Rdg # 600, Irving, TX 75063-7555
Tel (214) 493-4200 *Founded/Ownrshp* 2002
Sales NA *EMP* 340
SIC 6411 Insurance agents, brokers & service
Pr: David Disiere
* *CFO:* Michael Trotter

D-U-N-S 07-416-4047
DEER PARK INDEPENDENT SCHOOL DISTRICT (INC)
DPISD
2800 Texas Ave, Deer Park, TX 77536-4797
Tel (832) 668-7080 *Founded/Ownrshp* 1929
Sales 195.8MM *EMP* 1,625
Accts Whitley Penn Llp Houston Tex
SIC 8211 Public elementary & secondary schools
Psych: Donna Chamblee

DEER PARK PHARMACY
See ST HELENA HOSPITAL

D-U-N-S 94-930-1337
DEER VALLEY RESORT
DEER VLY RSORT CTRG BNQETS WED
2250 Deer Valley Dr, Park City, UT 84060-5102
Tel (435) 649-1000 *Founded/Ownrshp* 1980
Sales 75.1MM^E *EMP* 2,000^E
SIC 7999 Ski rental concession
Pr: Robert Wheaton
Ofcr: Debbie Barnes
VP: Louise Walton
Exec: Clark Norris
Exec: Jodi Rogers
CTO: Steve McCormick
Dir IT: Tom Stecki
IT Man: Jeannie Lambert
Software D: Phillip Griffin
Sales Exec: Terry Beckman
VP Sls: Dirk Beal

D-U-N-S 00-290-2112
DEER VALLEY SCHOOL DISTRICT 97
DEER VALLEY UNIFIED SCHOOL DST
20402 N 15th Ave, Phoenix, AZ 85027-3636
Tel (623) 445-5000 *Founded/Ownrshp* 1978
Sales 222.6MM^E *EMP* 3,500
Accts Heinfeld Meech & Co Pc P
SIC 8211 Public elementary school; Public junior high school; Public senior high school
Pr Dir: Monica Allread
Pr Dir: Gary McSpadden
Schl Brd P: Ann Ordway
Teacher Pr: Kristi Bushnell
Teacher Pr: Jenna Moffitt
HC Dir: Melissa McCusker

DEER VALLEY UNIFIED SCHOOL DST
See DEER VALLEY SCHOOL DISTRICT 97

DEER VLY RSORT CTRG BNQETS WED
See DEER VALLEY RESORT

D-U-N-S 00-526-7471
▲ DEERE & CO
1 John Deere Pl, Moline, IL 61265-8098
Tel (309) 765-8000 *Founded/Ownrshp* 1837
Sales 26.6MMM *EMP* 57,200
Accts Deloitte & Touche Llp Chicago
Tkr Sym DE *Exch* NYS
SIC 3523 3531 3524 6159 Farm machinery & equipment; Tractors, farm; Harrows: disc, spring, tine, etc.; Plows, agricultural: disc, moldboard, chisel, listers, etc.; Construction machinery; Tractors, crawler; Dozers, tractor mounted: material moving; Bulldozers (construction machinery); Lawn & garden tractors & equipment; Lawnmowers, residential: hand or power; Rollers, lawn; Agricultural credit institutions
Ch Bd: Samuel R Allen
Pr: James M Field
Pr: Max A Guinn
Pr: Michael J Mack Jr
Pr: John C May
Pr: Markwart Von Pentz
CFO: Rajesh Kalathur
Treas: Michael Despain
Treas: Candace Schnoor
Bd of Dir: Brandt Boland
Bd of Dir: Sherry Smith
Ofcr: Thomas Annis
Ex VP: Robert Perez
Sr VP: Jean H Gilles
Sr VP: Mary K W Jones
VP: Paul Bauer
VP: Scott Clarke
VP: Carolyn Clementes
VP: Chuck Dupree
VP: Chris Giles
VP: Pierre Guyot
Board of Directors: Dmitri L Stockton, Crandall C Bowles, Sheila G Talton, Vance D Coffman, Alan C Heuberger, Alan C Heuberger, Michael O Johanns, Clayton M Jones, Brian M Krzanich, Gregory R Page, Sherry M Smith

D-U-N-S 61-203-3357
■ DEERE CREDIT INC
JOHN DEERE
(*Suby of* JOHN DEERE FINANCIAL) ★
6400 Nw 86th St, Johnston, IA 50131-2945
Tel (515) 224-2800 *Founded/Ownrshp* 1978
Sales NA *EMP* 308
SIC 6153 Short-term business credit
Pr: John Volkert
Sr VP: Martin Wilkinson
**VP:* Lyle Feld
**VP:* Henry E Schwabrow
IT Man: Kyle McManus
IT Man: Todd Snell
IT Man: Holly Tigges
Sls Mgr: Gasser Kevin

D-U-N-S 01-857-4058
DEERE PARK ASSOCIATES INC
D P A
240 N Deere Park Dr W, Highland Park, IL 60035-5364
Tel (847) 509-1000 *Founded/Ownrshp* 1997
Sales 175.0MM *EMP* 750
Accts Ostrow Reisin Berk & Abrams Lt
SIC 8742 Business planning & organizing services
Pr: Richard Glabman

D-U-N-S 61-715-0982
■ DEERE PAYROLL SERVICES INC
(*Suby of* DEERE & CO) ★
1 John Deere Pl, Moline, IL 61265-8010
Tel (309) 765-8000 *Founded/Ownrshp* 1999
Sales 25.3MM^E *EMP* 1,000
SIC 8721 Payroll accounting service
CEO: Robert Lane

D-U-N-S 55-707-4379 IMP
DEERE-HITACHI CONSTRUCTION MACHINERY CORP
1000 Deere Hitachi Rd, Kernersville, NC 27284-2275
Tel (336) 996-8100 *Founded/Ownrshp* 1988
Sales 228.8MM^E *EMP* 800
SIC 3531 Bituminous, cement & concrete related products & equipment
Pr: Alan Seeba
**CFO:* Bryan Swerbinsky
**Ex VP:* Kazuhiko Hirayama
IT Man: Terry Coyle
Plnt Mgr: Ron Morrison

D-U-N-S 00-334-3217
DEFENDER SERVICES INC (SC)
SERVE SOURCE STAFFING
9031 Garners Ferry Rd, Hopkins, SC 29061-9540
Tel (803) 776-4220 *Founded/Ownrshp* 1958
Sales 161.0MM^E *EMP* 4,500
Accts Grant Thornton Llp Columbia
SIC 7349 7361 7382 Cleaning service, industrial or commercial; Executive placement; Security systems services
CEO: John Nicholas McCarter Jr
**CEO:* Hollis Cone
**Ex VP:* Aaron Crowe
Board of Directors: James F Kane

D-U-N-S 05-291-2099
DEFENDERS INC
DSC ALARMS
3750 Priority Way S Dr, Indianapolis, IN 46240-3831
Tel (317) 810-4720 *Founded/Ownrshp* 1999
Sales 278.9MM^E *EMP* 2,200
SIC 7382 Security systems services
Pr: Jim Boyce
**Ch Bd:* Dave Lindsey
**Pr:* Marcia Barnes
COO: Bill Barns
**COO:* John Corliss
**CFO:* Bart Shroyer
VP: Dave Beasley
VP: Mark Colucci
**VP:* Scott Denardin
VP: Scott Galovic
VP: Joe Huck
**VP:* Bob Keck
VP: Michael Lantz
VP: Ryan Michalowski
**VP:* Mark Nazarenus
**VP:* Misti Simpson

DEFENSE
See NORTHROP GRUMMAN INFORMATION TECHNOLOGY GLOBAL CORP

DEFENSE & GOVERNMENT SERVICES
See DEFENSE SECURITY SERVICE

D-U-N-S 83-594-9082 IMP/EXP
■ DEFENSE COMMISSARY AGENCY
D E C A
(*Suby of* OFFICE OF THE SECRETARY OF DEFENSE) ★
1300 E Ave, Fort Lee, VA 23801-1800
Tel (804) 734-8000 *Founded/Ownrshp* 1991
Sales NA *EMP* 17,000
SIC 9711 National security;
Pr: Nicholas Shaw
Ofcr: Becky Sipes
VP: Shaffer Michael
Ex Dir: Rogers Campbell
Store Dir: Donna Baird
Store Dir: Scott Harmon
IT Man: Michael Cassun
Netwrk Eng: Raymond Mason
Genl Couns: Thomas Rathgeb
Snr Mgr: James Estrada

D-U-N-S 83-601-5990
■ DEFENSE FINANCE & ACCOUNTING SERVICE
(*Suby of* OFFICE OF THE SECRETARY OF DEFENSE) ★
8899 E 56th St, Indianapolis, IN 46249-0002
Tel (317) 212-0585 *Founded/Ownrshp* 1991
Sales NA *EMP* 18,000
SIC 9311 Public finance & monetary policy;
MIS Dir: Sherman Johnson

D-U-N-S 02-670-0448
■ DEFENSE HEALTH AGENCY
TRICARE MANAGEMENT ACTIVITY
(*Suby of* OFFICE OF THE SECRETARY OF DEFENSE) ★
7700 Arlington Blvd # 5101, Falls Church, VA 22042-5190
Tel (703) 681-1730 *Founded/Ownrshp* 1998
Sales NA *EMP* 1,404
SIC 9431 9711 Administration of public health programs; ; National security;
Opers Mgr: John Morse

D-U-N-S 07-652-3617
■ DEFENSE HUMAN RESOURCES ACTIVITY
(*Suby of* OFFICE OF THE SECRETARY OF DEFENSE) ★
4800 Mark Center Dr D, Alexandria, VA 22350-0002
Tel (571) 372-1949 *Founded/Ownrshp* 2004
Sales NA *EMP* 1,170
SIC 9711 National security;

D-U-N-S 83-601-6741
■ DEFENSE INFORMATION SYSTEMS AGENCY
DISA
(*Suby of* OFFICE OF THE SECRETARY OF DEFENSE) ★
6910 Cooper Rd, Fort Meade, MD 20755-7088
Tel (301) 225-1474 *Founded/Ownrshp* 1960
Sales NA *EMP* 8,500^E
SIC 9711 National security;
Svc Ex: Jason G Martin

D-U-N-S 83-601-9208 IMP/EXP
■ DEFENSE LOGISTICS AGENCY
DLA
(*Suby of* OFFICE OF THE SECRETARY OF DEFENSE) ★
Andrew T Mcnamara Bld, Fort Belvoir, VA 22060
Tel (703) 767-4012 *Founded/Ownrshp* 1961
Sales NA *EMP* 26,000
SIC 9711 National security;
Ofcr: Ed Butzirus
Ofcr: Allen Lans
Ofcr: Terence Lewis
Ofcr: Sandy Power
Ofcr: William Tinston
Ofcr: Brad Von Oven
Ofcr: David Young
VP: Edward J Case
Exec: Robert Foster
Prin: Sultan A Muhammad
Prin: Renee L Roman

D-U-N-S 05-547-8349
■ DEFENSE MEDIA ACTIVITY
DMA
(*Suby of* OFFICE OF THE SECRETARY OF DEFENSE) ★
6700 Taylor Ave, Fort Meade, MD 20755
Tel (301) 222-6000 *Founded/Ownrshp* 2012
Sales NA *EMP* 5,033^E
SIC 9711 National security;
Prin: Ray B Shepherd
Ofcr: Eric Johnson
Genl Couns: Alan Kaufman

D-U-N-S 83-601-7814
■ DEFENSE SECURITY SERVICE
DEFENSE & GOVERNMENT SERVICES
(*Suby of* OFFICE OF THE SECRETARY OF DEFENSE) ★
27130 Telegraph Rd, Quantico, VA 22134-2253
Tel (571) 305-6751 *Founded/Ownrshp* 1972
Sales NA *EMP* 2,600
SIC 9711 National security;
Ex Dir: Charles Cunningham
Ofcr: Byron Jenkins
Ofcr: Maria Ong
VP: Lea Gallogly
VP: Michael Hicks
CIO: John P Skudlarek
Netwrk Mgr: Adam McBride

D-U-N-S 14-332-4726
■ DEFENSE TECHNOLOGY SECURITY ADMINISTRATION
DTSA
(*Suby of* OFFICE OF THE SECRETARY OF DEFENSE) ★
2000 Defense Pentagon 4b661, Washington, DC 20301-2000
Tel (703) 697-3249 *Founded/Ownrshp* 2004
Sales NA *EMP* 5,011^E
SIC 9711 National security;

DEFFENBAUGH DISPOSAL SERVICE
See DEFFENBAUGH INDUSTRIES INC

D-U-N-S 07-302-7609 EXP
■ DEFFENBAUGH INDUSTRIES INC
DEFFENBAUGH DISPOSAL SERVICE
(*Suby of* WM) ★
2601 Midwest Dr, Kansas City, KS 66111-8801
Tel (913) 631-3300 *Founded/Ownrshp* 2015
Sales 469.2MM^E *EMP* 1,500
SIC 4212 4953 Local trucking, without storage; Sanitary landfill operation; Refuse collection & disposal services
Pr: Jim Donahue
**CFO:* Ron Anderson
VP: Tom Coffman
VP: Paul Howe
VP: John King
Genl Mgr: Venus Hegle
Off Mgr: Cindy Crowe
Sales Exec: Jim Stroup
Sls Mgr: Mike Dale
Sls Mgr: Bryce Thompson

DEFIANCE GROUP THE
See GT TECHNOLOGIES INC

D-U-N-S 00-504-1272 IMP
DEFIANCE METAL PRODUCTS CO
21 Seneca St, Defiance, OH 43512-2274
Tel (419) 784-5332 *Founded/Ownrshp* 2006
Sales 373.9MM^E *EMP* 1,115
SIC 3465 3443 3544 Automotive stampings; Fabricated plate work (boiler shop); Special dies & tools
CEO: Stephen Mance
**Pr:* Sam Strausbaugh
**CFO:* Ken Daiss
**CFO:* Jim Hileman
**VP:* Rick Creedmore
VP: Peggy Smith
Exec: Brent Davis
Genl Mgr: Robert Thomas
Info Man: Rick Holler
Opers Mgr: Scott Dickinson
Opers Mgr: Becky Gutman

D-U-N-S 03-647-4625 IMP
DEFIANCE METAL PRODUCTS OF ARKANSAS INC
(*Suby of* DEFIANCE METAL PRODUCTS CO) ★
944 By Pass Rd, Heber Springs, AR 72543-9122
Tel (501) 362-1919 *Founded/Ownrshp* 1997
Sales 184.3MM^E *EMP* 900
SIC 3465 3443 3544 3469 Automotive stampings; Fabricated plate work (boiler shop); Special dies & tools; Metal stampings
Pr: Sam Straubaugh
**Pr:* Stephen Mance
**Treas:* Ken Daiss
**VP:* Dennis Weaver
Exec: Karin Conradson

DEFLECTA SHIELD
See LUND INC

D-U-N-S 00-605-0520 IMP
DEFLECTO LLC
(*Suby of* JORDAN SPECIALTY PLASTICS INC) ★
7035 E 86th St, Indianapolis, IN 46250-1547
Tel (317) 849-9555 *Founded/Ownrshp* 2006
Sales 151.1MM^E *EMP* 726
SIC 3089 Plastic hardware & building products; Ducting, plastic
CEO: Paul Thompson
**Pr:* Thomas H Quinn
**Treas:* Wayne Daege
**VP:* Keith Huffman
VP: Bill Schwartz
QA Dir: Tim Fike
Plnt Mgr: Tom Crockett
Plnt Mgr: Rob Rafter
Ql Cn Mgr: Kyle Pulley
Natl Sales: Frank Coletto
Natl Sales: Chris Grow

D-U-N-S 84-959-9410
DEFORD LUMBER CO LTD
1018 N Duncanville Rd, Duncanville, TX 75116-2202
Tel (972) 298-7121 *Founded/Ownrshp* 1992
Sales 105.8MM^E *EMP* 190
SIC 5031 5211 Lumber: rough, dressed & finished; Plywood; Millwork; Lumber & other building materials
Pt: Homer H De Ford
CFO: Danny Davis
VP: Patrick Davidson
Genl Mgr: Karl Wills
Sales Asso: Sandra Rodermund

D-U-N-S 88-438-6277
DEGC ENTERPRISES (US) INC
CCS MEDICAL
(*Suby of* CCS MEDICAL INC) ★
14255 49th St N Ste 301, Clearwater, FL 33762-2813
Tel (727) 531-9161 *Founded/Ownrshp* 2005
Sales 71.8MM^E *EMP* 1,400
SIC 5999 5912 5961 Convalescent equipment & supplies; Hospital equipment & supplies; Orthopedic & prosthesis applications; Drug stores; Proprietary (non-prescription medicine) stores; Pharmaceuticals, mail order
Pr: John L Miclot
Ex VP: Mike Geldart
Ex VP: Mike Oconnor
Sr VP: Bob Hansen
VP: Linda Langiotti
Natl Sales: Kassem Dickens
Genl Couns: Monica Raines

D-U-N-S 07-862-3785
DEGENCO MANAGEMENT LLC
(*Suby of* MOUNTAIN RANGE RESTAURANTS LLC) ★
825 S 48th St, Tempe, AZ 85281-5101
Tel (480) 829-5090 *Founded/Ownrshp* 2010
Sales 11.0MM^E *EMP* 1,567^E
SIC 5812 Eating places

D-U-N-S 01-413-6519
DEGOL ORGANIZATION L P
DE GOL BROS CARPET DIV
3229 Pleasant Valley Blvd, Altoona, PA 16602-4435
Tel (814) 941-7777 *Founded/Ownrshp* 1950
Sales 231.8MM^E *EMP* 290
Accts Richard Burgan Gallitzin Pa
SIC 5031 5033 5211 5023 5713 Lumber: rough, dressed & finished; Plywood; Roofing, asphalt & sheet metal; Insulation materials; Lumber products; Roofing material; Bathroom fixtures, equipment & supplies; Electrical construction materials; Carpets; Resilient floor coverings: tile or sheet; Carpets; Floor tile; Linoleum
Genl Pt: Donald A Degol Sr
Pt: Gloria Degol Burgan
Pt: Bruno Degol Jr
Pt: David Degol

D-U-N-S 06-899-5513
DEGOLYER AND MACNAUGHTON CORP
(*Suby of* DE GOLYER AND MC MAUGHTON) ★
5001 Spring Valley Rd 800e, Dallas, TX 75244-8212
Tel (214) 368-6391 *Founded/Ownrshp* 1985
Sales 165.9MM^E *EMP* 185^E
SIC 1389

DEGUSSA
See EVONIK CORP

DEGUSSA CONSTRUCTION
See BASF CONSTRUCTION CHEMICALS LLC

D-U-N-S 09-563-4825 IMP
DEHCO INC
RECREATION NATION
3601 Charlotte Ave, Elkhart, IN 46517-1192
Tel (574) 294-2684 *Founded/Ownrshp* 1999
Sales 86.6MM^E *EMP* 180
SIC 2891 5031 5074 5014 5084 Adhesives & sealants; Caulking compounds; Adhesives; Sealants; Lumber, plywood & millwork; Building materials, exterior; Plumbing fittings & supplies; Tires & tubes; Instruments & control equipment
CEO: James T Schwartz
**Pr:* Thomas J Nagy
Ex VP: Ron Wenger

D-U-N-S 14-855-3662 IMP/EXP
DEI HOLDINGS INC
DIRECTED ELECTRONICS
(*Suby of* VIPER HOLDINGS CORP) ★
1 Viper Way Ste 3, Vista, CA 92081-7811
Tel (760) 598-6200 *Founded/Ownrshp* 1999
Sales 172.4MM^E *EMP* 581^E
SIC 3669 3651 Burglar alarm apparatus, electric; Amplifiers: radio, public address or musical instrument
CEO: Kevin P Duffy
COO: Julien Joly
**CFO:* Veysel Goker
**Treas:* Dan Brockman
Chf Mktg O: Blair Tripodi
Ex VP: Richard Rubalcaba
**Ex VP:* Michael S Simmons
**VP:* Michael N Smith
Dir IT: Geoff Augenstein
QC Dir: Mark Chasey
Ql Cn Mgr: Paul Boyer

D-U-N-S 05-059-0926
DEJANA INDUSTRIES INC
30 Sagamore Hill Dr, Port Washington, NY 11050-2110
Tel (516) 944-3100 *Founded/Ownrshp* 1962
Sales 95.4MM^E *EMP* 130
SIC 4959 Sweeping service: road, airport, parking lot, etc.

CEO: Peter Dejana
**Ex VP:* William Wynperle Jr
**VP:* Philip Dejana
**VP:* Fred Gonzalez
Genl Mgr: George Laudermith
IT Man: Mike Inger
Opers Mgr: John Hogan
VP Sls: Edward McDonald

DEKA BATTERIES & CABLES
See EAST PENN MANUFACTURING CO

D-U-N-S 06-647-1582
DEKALB COUNTY BOARD OF EDUCATION
1701 Mountain Indus Blvd, Stone Mountain, GA 30083-1027
Tel (678) 676-1200 *Founded/Ownrshp* 1946
Sales 569.8MM^E *EMP* 16,000
Accts Russell W Hinton Cpa Cgfm
SIC 8211 Public elementary & secondary schools; School board
Mng Pt: Sam Bryant
CFO: Susan Hurst

D-U-N-S 87-796-1193
DEKALB COUNTY BOARD OF EDUCATION
DEKALB COUNTY SCHOOL DISTRICT
306 Main St W, Rainsville, AL 35986-5902
Tel (256) 638-7265 *Founded/Ownrshp* 1970
Sales NA *EMP* 1,100
SIC 9411
Schl Brd P: Matt Sharp

DEKALB COUNTY SCHOOL DISTRICT
See DEKALB COUNTY SCHOOLS

DEKALB COUNTY SCHOOL DISTRICT
See DEKALB COUNTY BOARD OF EDUCATION

D-U-N-S 07-979-8969
DEKALB COUNTY SCHOOLS
DEKALB COUNTY SCHOOL DISTRICT
1701 Mountain Indus Blvd, Stone Mountain, GA 30083-1027
Tel (678) 676-1200 *Founded/Ownrshp* 2015
Sales 70.5MM^E *EMP* 13,596^E
SIC 8211 Public elementary & secondary schools
V Ch: Michael Erwin
Dir Sec: Donald Smith
Off Mgr: Nadine Ali
MIS Dir: Gary Brantley

D-U-N-S 08-696-8112 IMP/EXP
DEKALB FARMERS MARKET INC (GA)
3000 E Ponce De Leon Ave, Decatur, GA 30030-2295
Tel (404) 377-6400 *Founded/Ownrshp* 1977, 1978
Sales 94.0MM^E *EMP* 750^E
SIC 5431 5421 5461 5451 5921 5812 Fruit stands or markets; Vegetable stands or markets; Meat & fish markets; Cakes; Cookies; Dairy products stores; Cheese; Beer (packaged); Wine; Delicatessen (eating places); Restaurant, family: chain
Pr: Robert W Blazer

D-U-N-S 07-586-5766
DEKALB MEDICAL CENTER INC
(*Suby of* DEKALB REGIONAL HEALTH SYSTEM INC) ★
2701 N Decatur Rd, Decatur, GA 30033-5918
Tel (404) 501-1000 *Founded/Ownrshp* 1961
Sales 303.0MM *EMP* 2,700
Accts Pershing Yoakley & Associates
SIC 8062 General medical & surgical hospitals
CEO: John A Shelton Jr
**Ch Bd:* Duane Blair MD
**CEO:* Eric Norwood
**COO:* Dane Henry
**CFO:* Susan Sciullo
Bd of Dir: Beverly Hutchinson
Bd of Dir: Nancy Lawson
VP: C Duane Barclay
VP: Duane Barclay
**VP:* Kim Bentley
**VP:* Cheryl Iverson
**VP:* John Katsianis
**VP:* Deanne Mance
**VP:* Margie Maxey
VP: Cynthia Perley
Dir Lab: Roz Heath
Dir Rx: Carol Story
Board of Directors: Laureen Irving

D-U-N-S 93-911-3494
DEKALB REGIONAL HEALTH SYSTEM INC
2701 N Decatur Rd, Decatur, GA 30033-5918
Tel (404) 501-1000 *Founded/Ownrshp* 1961
Sales 4.9MM *EMP* 2,827
Accts Pershing Yoakley & Associates
SIC 8741 Hospital management; Nursing & personal care facility management
CEO: Eric Norwood
**CEO:* John A Shelton
COO: John Shlton
**CFO:* Diane Harden
Prd Mgr: Melanie Nelson

D-U-N-S 80-794-6038 IMP
DEKKO ACQUISITION PARENT INC
6928 N 400 E, Kendallville, IN 46755-9346
Tel (260) 347-0700 *Founded/Ownrshp* 2006
Sales 179.1MM^E *EMP* 1,400
SIC 3496 Wire fasteners
Pr: Robert Bergmann
VP: Eric Helfrich
VP: Teresea Petersen
**VP:* Gerald Whiteford

D-U-N-S 07-933-9622
■ DEL FRISCOS GRILLE OF TEXAS LLC
(*Suby of* DEL FRISCOS RESTAURANT GROUP INC) ★
1200 E Southlake Blvd, Southlake, TX 76092-6416
Tel (817) 410-3777 *Founded/Ownrshp* 2011
Sales 31.1MM^E *EMP* 1,919^E
SIC 5812 5813 Eating places; Steak restaurant; Drinking places

D-U-N-S 07-911-9506
■ DEL FRISCOS OF NORTH CAROLINA INC
(*Suby of* DEL FRISCOS RESTAURANT GROUP INC) ★
930 S Kimball Ave, Southlake, TX 76092-9021
Tel (817) 601-3421 *Founded/Ownrshp* 2013
Sales 10.5MM^E *EMP* 1,221^E
SIC 5812 Eating places

D-U-N-S 02-641-3215
▲ DEL FRISCOS RESTAURANT GROUP INC
920 S Kimball Ave Ste 100, Southlake, TX 76092-9019
Tel (817) 601-3421 *Founded/Ownrshp* 1981
Sales 331.6MM *EMP* 4,921
Tkr Sym DFRG *Exch* NGS
SIC 5812 5813 Eating places; Steak restaurant; Drinking places
CEO: Norman J Abdallah
**Ch Bd:* Ian R Carter
CFO: Thomas J Pennison Jr
Sr VP: Ray D Risley
VP: Thomas G Dritsas
VP: James W Kirkpatrick
VP: Lisa H Kislak
VP: William S Martens III
Exec: Kevin Favinger
Genl Mgr: Arthur Mooradian
Genl Couns: Lane A Deyoung

D-U-N-S 06-306-7359
DEL MAR COLLEGE DISTRICT
101 Baldwin Blvd, Corpus Christi, TX 78404-3894
Tel (361) 698-1259 *Founded/Ownrshp* 1935
Sales 19.7MM *EMP* 1,200
Accts Collier Johnson & Woods Pc
SIC 8222 Junior college
Pr: Dr Mark Escamilla
COO: Louie Asuncion
CFO: Jessica Alaniz
Exec: Dusty Finch

D-U-N-S 14-205-8069 EXP
DEL MAR DESIGNS INC
1821 Holsonback Dr, Daytona Beach, FL 32117-5113
Tel (386) 767-1997 *Founded/Ownrshp* 2003
Sales 152.6MM *EMP* 5
SIC 5719 Lighting, lamps & accessories
Pr: Colby Harris
**VP:* Ron Harris
Mktg Mgr: Laurie Driggs

D-U-N-S 00-912-5949 IMP/EXP
DEL MAR FOOD PRODUCTS CORP
1720 Beach Rd, Watsonville, CA 95076-9536
Tel (831) 722-3516 *Founded/Ownrshp* 1987
Sales 104.0MM^E *EMP* 500
Accts Hutchinson & Bloodgood Llp Wa
SIC 2033 2099 Canned fruits & specialties; Food preparations
CEO: P J Mecozzi
**CFO:* Paul Wendt
**Treas:* Carolyn Mecozzi
Sls&Mrk Ex: Rhonda Murray

D-U-N-S 07-870-4328 EXP
DEL MONTE
1200 Market St Ne, Decatur, AL 35601-2616
Tel (256) 552-7453 *Founded/Ownrshp* 1982
Sales 500.0MM *EMP* 500
SIC 2047 Dog & cat food
CEO: Rick Walford

D-U-N-S 07-917-6828 IMP/EXP
DEL MONTE FOODS INC
(*Suby of* DEL MONTE PACIFIC LIMITED)
3003 Oak Rd Ste 600, Walnut Creek, CA 94597-4541
Tel (925) 949-2772 *Founded/Ownrshp* 2013
Sales 1.4MMM^E *EMP* 2,500
SIC 2033 5149 Canned fruits & specialties; Groceries & related products
CEO: Nils Lommerin
CFO: Bryan Cullen
**CFO:* Paul Miller
VP: Mario Carrington
**VP:* Robert Long
Exec: Connie Carothers
Rgnl Mgr: Glenn Durflinger
CIO: Timothy Weaver
Natl Sales: Charlie Lyle
Mktg Dir: Brian Ely
Sls Dir: Pam Brown

D-U-N-S 01-805-0919 IMP/EXP
DEL MONTE FRESH PRODUCE CO
(*Suby of* FRESH DEL MONTE PRODUCE INC.)
241 Sevilla Ave Ste 200, Coral Gables, FL 33134-6600
Tel (305) 520-8400 *Founded/Ownrshp* 1996
Sales 1.2MMM^E *EMP* 1,750
SIC 5148 Fruits
CEO: Mohammad Abu-Ghazaleh
**Pr:* Hani El Naffy
Sr VP: Louie Tenazas
**VP:* John Inserra
**VP:* Bruce A Jordan
VP: Skip Marlin
**VP:* Paul J Rice
**VP:* Marissa R Tenazas
**VP:* Peter M Thompson
VP: Michael Walsh
Off Mgr: Mary Bolzenius

D-U-N-S 04-255-9138 IMP/EXP
DEL MONTE FRESH PRODUCE NA INC (FL)
(*Suby of* DEL MONTE FRESH PRODUCE CO) ★
241 Sevilla Ave Ste 200, Coral Gables, FL 33134-6600
Tel (305) 520-8400 *Founded/Ownrshp* 1952, 1996
Sales 910.6MM^E *EMP* 1,050
SIC 5148 Fruits, fresh
CEO: Mohammad Abu-Ghazaleh
**Pr:* Hani El Naffy

DEL MONTE HOTEL GROUP
See EJ DEL MONTE CORP

D-U-N-S 02-605-0856
DEL PAPA DISTRIBUTING CO LP
120 Gulf Fwy, Texas City, TX 77591
Tel (409) 842-5215 *Founded/Ownrshp* 1910
Sales 108.1MM^E *EMP* 300
SIC 5181 Beer & other fermented malt liquors
Ch: Lawrence J Del Papa Sr
**Pr:* Lawrence Del Papa Jr
**CFO:* William Falkenhagen
VP: Danny Dickson

DEL SOL MARKET
See FACTOR SALES INC

DEL SOL MEDICAL CENTER
See EL PASO HEALTHCARE SYSTEM LTD

D-U-N-S 19-036-8852
■ DEL TACO LLC
(*Suby of* DEL TACO HOLDINGS INC) ★
25521 Commercentre Dr # 200, Lake Forest, CA 92630-8872
Tel (949) 462-9300 *Founded/Ownrshp* 2006
Sales 233.9MM^E *EMP* 5,599
SIC 5812

D-U-N-S 62-461-8398
■ DEL TACO HOLDINGS INC
(*Suby of* DEL TACO RESTAURANTS INC) ★
25521 Commercentre Dr # 200, Lake Forest, CA 92630-8872
Tel (949) 462-7324 *Founded/Ownrshp* 1964
Sales 233.9MM^E *EMP* 5,600
SIC 5812 Fast-food restaurant, chain
Pr: Paul J B Murphy III
**CFO:* Steven L Brake
**CFO:* Michael Payne
Ex VP: Steven Brake
**Ex VP:* John D Cappasola Jr
Sr VP: David Pear
VP: Eric Grundmeier
VP: Mike Lucero
VP: David Wetzel
Dir Risk M: Marcus McLaughlin
Site Mgr: Samuel Ambriz

D-U-N-S 07-921-7085
▲ DEL TACO RESTAURANTS INC
25521 Commercentre Dr # 200, Lake Forest, CA 92630-8872
Tel (949) 462-9300 *Founded/Ownrshp* 1964
Sales 233.9MM^E *EMP* 6,690
Tkr Sym TACO *Exch* NAS
SIC 5812 6794 Eating places; American restaurant; Mexican restaurant; Franchises, selling or licensing
Pr: Paul J B Murphy III
**Ch Bd:* Lawrence F Levy
CFO: Steven L Brake
Ex VP: John D Cappasola Jr
Sr VP: David A Pear
VP: David Snyder
Board of Directors: Eileen Aptman, Ari B Levy, Richard J Melman, Joseph Stein, Patrick D Walsh

DEL TECH TERRY CAMPUS
See DELAWARE TECHNICAL & COMMUNITY COLLEGE

D-U-N-S 15-257-6716
■ DEL WEBB COMMUNITIES INC
(*Suby of* DEL WEBB CORP) ★
15333 N Pima Rd Ste 300, Scottsdale, AZ 85260-2717
Tel (602) 808-8000 *Founded/Ownrshp* 2001
Sales 94.8MM^E *EMP* 934
SIC 6552 Subdividers & developers
Pr: Leroy C Hanneman Jr
Treas: Donald V Mickus
Sr VP: John Spencer
VP: Mary S Alexander
VP: Robertson C Jones

D-U-N-S 00-690-2431
■ DEL WEBB CORP
(*Suby of* PULTEGROUP INC) ★
15111 N Pima Rd, Scottsdale, AZ 85260-0002
Tel (480) 391-6000 *Founded/Ownrshp* 1928, 2001
Sales 218.4MM^E *EMP* 3,579
SIC 6552 Land subdividers & developers, residential
Reg Pr: Frank D Pankratz
**Sr VP:* John R Stoller
Off Mgr: Linda Moody

D-U-N-S 10-182-0918
DEL-AIR HEATING AIR CONDITIONING & REFRIGERATION CORP
DELAIR
531 Codisco Way, Sanford, FL 32771-6618
Tel (866) 796-4874 *Founded/Ownrshp* 1983
Sales 148.2MM^E *EMP* 480
SIC 1711 Warm air heating & air conditioning contractor; Refrigeration contractor
Pr: Robert Gene Dello Russo
Pr: Richard Fortin
**CEO:* Bob Dello Russo
CFO: George Sheldon
**Sec:* Diane Dello Russo
Exec: Robert Oliver
Mktg Dir: Joe Strada

D-U-N-S 03-970-3053 IMP/EXP
DEL-JEN INC
4465 Guthrie Hwy, Clarksville, TN 37040-5422
Tel (931) 552-0232 *Founded/Ownrshp* 2003
Sales NA *EMP* 2,500
SIC 8744

DELAIR
See DEL-AIR HEATING AIR CONDITIONING & REFRIGERATION CORP

DELANCEY STREET COACH SERVICE
See DELANCEY STREET FOUNDATION

D-U-N-S 06-885-0890
DELANCEY STREET FOUNDATION
DELANCEY STREET COACH SERVICE
600 The Embarcadero, San Francisco, CA 94107-2116
Tel (415) 957-9800 *Founded/Ownrshp* 1971
Sales 46.4MM^E *EMP* 1,000
SIC 8361 5199 8322 4212 5812 Rehabilitation center, residential: health care incidental; Advertising specialties; Individual & family services; Moving services; Eating places; Caterers
Pr: Mimi Silbert
**Treas:* Jerry Raymond

D-U-N-S 17-370-4867 IMP/EXP
DELAVAL INC
DELAVAL MFG
(*Suby of* DELAVAL HOLDING AB)
11100 N Congress Ave, Kansas City, MO 64153-1222
Tel (816) 891-7700 *Founded/Ownrshp* 1985
Sales 366.3MM^E *EMP* 600
SIC 5083 3523 2842 0241 Dairy machinery & equipment; Dairy equipment (farm); Specialty cleaning, polishes & sanitation goods; Milk production
Pr: Christian Poggensee
COO: Mike Pedrigi
CFO: Larry Skisak
Treas: Jana Hessemyer
Ex VP: G Donald Calhoun
VP: John Benjamin
VP: Thomas C Hemling
Mng Dir: Peter Jorgensen
Mng Dir: Andrew Ritchie
Dist Mgr: Richard Gill
Dist Mgr: Jason Huffman

DELAVAL MFG
See DELAVAL INC

D-U-N-S 00-227-6053 EXP
DELAVAU LLC
10101 Roosevelt Blvd, Philadelphia, PA 19154-2105
Tel (215) 671-1400 *Founded/Ownrshp* 2002
Sales 84.7MM^E *EMP* 350^E
SIC 2087 2834 Flavoring extracts & syrups; Vitamin preparations
Netwrk Eng: Alex Yevtushenko
VP Opers: Jay Jones
QC Dir: Kim Anderson

D-U-N-S 19-482-0163
■ DELAWARE CAPITAL FORMATION INC
(*Suby of* DOVER CORP) ★
501 Silverside Rd Ste 5, Wilmington, DE 19809-1375
Tel (302) 793-4921 *Founded/Ownrshp* 1985
Sales 1.5MMM^E *EMP* 8,387
SIC 5084 3463 3542 3823 Food product manufacturing machinery; Packaging machinery & equipment; Bearing & bearing race forgings, nonferrous; Machine tools, metal forming type; Flow instruments, industrial process type
Pr: Amy Ward
Treas: Jeremiah Mulligan
VP: Lloyd Martin
VP: Alfred Suesser

D-U-N-S 19-482-0775 IMP/EXP
■ DELAWARE CAPITAL HOLDINGS INC
(*Suby of* DELAWARE CAPITAL FORMATION INC) ★
501 Silverside Rd Ste 5, Wilmington, DE 19809-1375
Tel (302) 793-4921 *Founded/Ownrshp* 1985
Sales 1.5MMM^E *EMP* 7,915
SIC 5084 3533 7699 Food product manufacturing machinery; Packaging machinery & equipment; Oil field machinery & equipment; Elevators: inspection, service & repair
Pr: John F Mc Niff
**Treas:* Alfred Suesser

D-U-N-S 96-240-6281 IMP
■ DELAWARE CITY REFINING CO LLC
(*Suby of* PBF HOLDING CO LLC) ★
1 Sylvan Way Ste 2, Parsippany, NJ 07054-3879
Tel (320) 834-6000 *Founded/Ownrshp* 2010
Sales 160.0MM^E *EMP* 500^E
SIC 1629 Oil refinery construction

DELAWARE COUNTY INTERMDIATE UN
See DELAWARE COUNTY INTERMEDIATE UNIT EDUCATION FOUNDATION

D-U-N-S 07-554-1094
DELAWARE COUNTY INTERMEDIATE UNIT EDUCATION FOUNDATION
DELAWARE COUNTY INTERMDIATE UN
200 Yale Ave, Morton, PA 19070-1918
Tel (610) 938-9000 *Founded/Ownrshp* 1971
Sales 97.7M *EMP* 1,000
Accts Maulo & Company Ltd West Ches
SIC 8211 Public elementary & secondary schools
Ex Dir: Lawrence O'Shea
**Pr:* Edward Cardow
**VP:* Maureen Carey
CTO: Laura Dubois
MIS Dir: Ira Warnick
Dir IT: Don Ash
Teacher Pr: Rosemary Fiumisa
Psych: Jaclyn Leotta
Psych: Lisa Monacello
Psych: Gregory Naylor
Psych: Evan Skolnik

D-U-N-S 06-987-7926
DELAWARE COUNTY MEMORIAL HOSPITAL
CROZER KEYSTONE
501 N Lansdowne Ave, Drexel Hill, PA 19026-1191
Tel (610) 284-8100 *Founded/Ownrshp* 1990
Sales 168.2MM *EMP* 1,300
SIC 8062 General medical & surgical hospitals
Pr: Joan K Richards
**Treas:* Robert B Hemphill
**Treas:* Ann F Swann
**Ex VP:* Gerald Miller
Pharmcst: Sandra Flagiello

D-U-N-S 07-695-4890
DELAWARE COUNTY PENNSYLVANIA
201 W Front St, Media, PA 19063-2708
Tel (610) 891-4000 *Founded/Ownrshp* 1789
Sales NA *EMP* 3,100
Accts Baker Tilly Virchow Krause Ll
SIC 9111
Ch: Tom McGarrigle
Ofcr: Frank Ruffo
**Ex Dir:* Marianne Grace
Dir IT: Jerry O'Connor

D-U-N-S 80-985-0910
DELAWARE DEPARTMENT OF CORRECTION
(Suby of EXECUTIVE OFFICE OF GOVERNOR OF DELAWARE) ★
245 Mckee Rd, Dover, DE 19904-2232
Tel (302) 857-5317 Founded/Ownrshp 1975
Sales NA EMP 2,624
SIC 9223 Prison, government;
Snr Mgr: Ed Synoski

D-U-N-S 80-985-6008
DELAWARE DEPARTMENT OF TRANSPORTATION
DELDOT
(Suby of EXECUTIVE OFFICE OF GOVERNOR OF DELAWARE) ★
800 S Bay Rd Ste 1, Dover, DE 19901-4677
Tel (302) 760-2080 Founded/Ownrshp 1917
Sales NA EMP 2,500
SIC 9621 Regulation, administration of transportation;
Prin: Nathan Hayward
Ex Dir: Lauren Skiver
Genl Mgr: Charlanne Thornton
CIO: Tara L Stewart

D-U-N-S 80-985-1041
DELAWARE DEPT OF HEALTH AND SOCIAL SERVICES
(Suby of EXECUTIVE OFFICE OF GOVERNOR OF DELAWARE) ★
1901 N Dupont Hwy, New Castle, DE 19720-1100
Tel (302) 255-9040 Founded/Ownrshp 1972
Sales NA EMP 4,000
SIC 9431 9441 Administration of public health programs; ; Administration of social & manpower programs;
Ofcr: Joe Loureiro
VP: Joan Elston
Ex Dir: Luz Vasquez-Guzman
Prgrm Mgr: Norma Testa
IT Man: Mary Peterson

DELAWARE DIVISION OF REVENUE
See CITY OF WILMINGTON

D-U-N-S 00-691-8643
DELAWARE ELECTRIC COOPERATIVE INC
D E C
14198 Sussex Hwy, Greenwood, DE 19950-6009
Tel (302) 349-9090 Founded/Ownrshp 1936
Sales 154.1MM EMP 141
SIC 4911

D-U-N-S 07-912-1343
DELAWARE LIFE HOLDINGS LLC
1601 Trapelo Rd Ste 30, Waltham, MA 02451-7360
Tel (877) 253-2323 Founded/Ownrshp 2012
Sales NA EMP 3E
SIC 6311 Life insurance
CEO: David Sams
*Pr: Daniel J Towriss

D-U-N-S 05-696-5015
DELAWARE NORTH COMPANIES GAMING & ENTERTAINMENT INC
(Suby of DELAWARE NORTH COMPANIES INC) ★
250 Delaware Ave Ste 3, Buffalo, NY 14202-2014
Tel (716) 858-5000 Founded/Ownrshp 1980
Sales 596.6MM EMP 3,000
SIC 7948 Dog race track operation; Horse race track operation
Pr: E B Hansberry
*Treas: Mike Corbin
*VP: Wendy Watkins

D-U-N-S 05-996-0914
DELAWARE NORTH COMPANIES INC
250 Delaware Ave, Buffalo, NY 14202-2014
Tel (716) 858-5000 Founded/Ownrshp 1915
Sales 2.9MMM EMP 30,135
SIC 5461 7011 7993 7999 Doughnuts; Hotels; Game machines; Recreation services
Co-CEO: Louis Jacobs
Ch Bd: Jeremy M Jacobs Sr
Pr: Louis M Jacobs
Pr: Kevin Kelly
Pr: Matt King
Pr: Matthew King
Pr: Charles E Moran Jr
Pr: Jack Onyett
Pr: John Wentzell
COO: Carlos Bernal
CFO: Christopher J Feeney
Treas: Scott Socha
Treas: Scott P Socha
Co-CEO: Jeremy Jacobs Jr
VP: Tom Barney
VP: Francine Booth
VP: Scott Cooper
VP: John R Digiovanni
VP: John Graham
VP: Camille Jackson
VP: Cynthia Johnson

D-U-N-S 07-658-6346 IMP
DELAWARE NORTH COMPANIES INC - BOSTON
TD BANKNORTH GARDEN
(Suby of DELAWARE NORTH COMPANIES INC) ★
100 Legends Way Ste 100, Boston, MA 02114-1303
Tel (617) 624-1000 Founded/Ownrshp 1975
Sales 91.1MM EMP 25
SIC 5812 5994 6512 7311 Eating places; Newsstand; Commercial & industrial building operation; Advertising agencies
Pr: John Wentzell
*Ch Bd: Harry Sinden
*Pr: Amy Latimer
*Treas: James K Bednarek
*VP: Jennifer Compton
Sls Mgr: Annemarie Kennedy

D-U-N-S 83-930-3518
DELAWARE NORTH COMPANIES PARKS & RESORTS INC
(Suby of DELAWARE NORTH COMPANIES INC) ★
250 Delaware Ave Ste 3, Buffalo, NY 14202-2014
Tel (716) 858-5000 Founded/Ownrshp 1992
Sales 455.8MM EMP 4,000
SIC 7011 Resort hotel
Pr: James W Houser
Pr: Brett Fuller
Pr: Tim Maloney
*Treas: Thomas Barney
*Sr VP: Barry H Freilicher
*VP: Richard Ayson
*VP: Christian Devos
VP: Richard Dobransky
VP: Gerald Gadsden
*VP: Donna Genesky
*VP: Andrew Grinsfelder
VP: Paula Halligan
*VP: Kenneth Leone Jr
VP: Terry Ryan
*VP: Derek Zwickey
Exec: John Morey

D-U-N-S 01-376-8627
DELAWARE NORTH COMPANIES SPORTSERVICE INC
(Suby of DELAWARE NORTH COMPANIES INC) ★
250 Delaware Ave, Buffalo, NY 14202-2014
Tel (716) 858-5000 Founded/Ownrshp 1961
Sales 857.9MM EMP 3,500
SIC 5812 Concessionaire
CEO: John Wentzell
*Co-Ownr: Charlie Jacobs
*Owner: Jeremy Jacobs
*Pr: Rick D Abramson
*Pr: Carlos Bernal
*COO: Larry Wittenberg
*VP: Stephen Nowaczik
VP: Deborah Robinson

D-U-N-S 15-745-9348
DELAWARE NORTH COMPANIES TRAVEL HOSPITALITY SERVICES INC
(Suby of DELAWARE NORTH COMPANIES INC) ★
250 Delaware Ave Ste 3, Buffalo, NY 14202-2014
Tel (716) 858-5000 Founded/Ownrshp 1915
Sales 317.4MM EMP 5,000
SIC 5812 5947 5813 Concessionaire; Gift shop; Souvenirs; Bar (drinking places)
Pr: Kevin Kelly
*Ch Bd: Jeremy M Jacobs
*Pr: Matt King
*Prin: Lou Jacobs
IT Man: Sheri Spinale-Rose

DELAWARE PARK
See DELAWARE RACING ASSOCIATION

D-U-N-S 07-706-2974 IMP
DELAWARE RACING ASSOCIATION
DELAWARE PARK
777 Delaware Park Blvd, Wilmington, DE 19804-4122
Tel (302) 994-2521 Founded/Ownrshp 1937
Sales 86.1MME EMP 1,600
SIC 7948 7993 Horse race track operation; Slot machines
CEO: William M Rickman Jr
Pr: Christopher Farr
*Pr: William Fasy
Exec: Lynda Furlong
Ex Dir: Mike Barrett
Advt Dir: Jennifer Oberle

D-U-N-S 04-733-1624
DELAWARE RIVER PORT AUTHORITY
2 Riverside Dr Ste 603, Camden, NJ 08103-1019
Tel (856) 968-2000 Founded/Ownrshp 1931
Sales 341.2MM EMP 900
SIC 4111 4785 Local & suburban transit; Toll operations
CEO: John T Hanson
Ch Bd: Ryan Boyer
CFO: James M White
Dept Mgr: William Anderson
Genl Mgr: Barbara Holcomb
Dir IT: Michael Duralja
Genl Couns: Richard Brown
Counsel: Roxanne La ROC

D-U-N-S 11-806-2678
DELAWARE SOLID WASTE AUTHORITY
1128 S Bradford St, Dover, DE 19904-6919
Tel (302) 739-5361 Founded/Ownrshp 1975
Sales 93.4MME EMP 150
SIC 4953 Refuse systems
Ch Bd: Richard V Pryor
*CEO: Pasquale S Canzano Pe Dee
*COO: Robin M Roddy
Ch: Ronald G McCabe
Ofcr: Fred Oehler
*Prin: Toby Ryan
*Prin: Tim Sheldon
IT Man: Sarah Gilfus

D-U-N-S 01-104-6943
DELAWARE SUPERMARKETS INC
SHOP RITE
501 S Walnut St, Wilmington, DE 19801-5286
Tel (302) 652-3412 Founded/Ownrshp 1941, 1994
Sales 90.2MME EMP 700
SIC 5411 Supermarkets
Ch Bd: Bernard F Kenny Jr
*CFO: Christopher Kenny

D-U-N-S 93-336-1693
DELAWARE TECHNICAL & COMMUNITY COLLEGE
DEL TECH TERRY CAMPUS
100 Campus Dr, Dover, DE 19904-1383
Tel (302) 857-1000 Founded/Ownrshp 1967
Sales 39.2MME EMP 1,200
SIC 8222 Junior colleges & technical institutes
Ch: Scott A Green
*Pr: Orlando J George Jr
CFO: Robert Hearn
CFO: Jim Samans
Ofcr: Ruth Clarke
VP: Anthony Digenakis
VP: Ginne Emanuel
VP: Irma Giglia
VP: Kevin Marshall
VP: Hope Murray
VP: Karen Stone
Comm Dir: Dana Sawyer
Board of Directors: A Six Member Board of Trus

D-U-N-S 17-505-7892 IMP
DELAWARE VALLEY FLORAL GROUP INC
FRESHBLOOMS
520 Mantua Blvd, Sewell, NJ 08080-1022
Tel (800) 676-1212 Founded/Ownrshp 1987
Sales 178.2MME EMP 625E
SIC 5193 4213 4214 Flowers & florists' supplies; Trucking, except local; Local trucking with storage
Ch Bd: Robert M Wilkins
CEO: John Jack Chidester
Ex VP: Henry Bowen
VP: Rene Quinn
VP: Randy Schenauer
Dir Bus: Nylsa Arce
Prin: John R Wilkins
Genl Mgr: Douglas H Carey
Off Mgr: Sindy Richert
VP Opers: Kevin Clifford
Opers Mgr: Joe Ott

D-U-N-S 01-172-9761 IMP/EXP
DELAWARE VALLEY WHOLESALE FLORIST INC
DVFLORA
(Suby of FRESHBLOOMS) ★
520 Mantua Blvd, Sewell, NJ 08080-1022
Tel (856) 468-7000 Founded/Ownrshp 1959
Sales 176.2MME EMP 450E
SIC 5193 Flowers & florists' supplies
CEO: Jack Chidester
CFO: Gene Owens
VP: Paul Fowle
*VP: John Richards
*VP: John S Wilkins

DELCO REMY AMERICA
See BALLANTRAE INC

DELCOR INC.
See DELCOR INC

D-U-N-S 92-773-3733 IMP/EXP
DELCOR INC
DELCOR INC.
(Suby of SPANGLER COMPANIES INC) ★
834 Rivit St, Greenville, NC 27834-0846
Tel (252) 321-8868 Founded/Ownrshp 1984
Sales 618.8MME EMP 2,100E
SIC 1711 Plumbing, heating, air-conditioning contractors
Pr: W D Cornwell Jr
*Ex VP: Anna S Nelson
*Sr VP: Stephen W Dixon

DELDOT
See DELAWARE DEPARTMENT OF TRANSPORTATION

D-U-N-S 07-855-4624
■ DELEK LOGISTICS PARTNERS LP
(Suby of DELEK LOGISTICS SERVICES COMPANY)
7102 Commerce Way, Brentwood, TN 37027-2896
Tel (615) 771-6701 Founded/Ownrshp 2012
Sales 589.6MM EMP 117E
Tkr Sym DKL Exch NYS
SIC 4612 4613 Crude petroleum pipelines; Gasoline pipelines (common carriers)
Ch Bd: Ezra Uzi Yemin
Genl Pt: Delek Logistics GP
CFO: Assaf Ginzburg

D-U-N-S 00-809-3528
■ DELEK REFINING LIMITED PARTNERSHIP
DELEK REFINING, LTD.
(Suby of DELEK US HOLDINGS INC) ★
7102 Commerce Way, Brentwood, TN 37027-2896
Tel (615) 771-6701 Founded/Ownrshp 2005
Sales 791.4MM EMP 2,500
SIC 4612 2911 Crude petroleum pipelines; Petroleum refining
Genl Pt: Fred Green
*Pt: John Colling
*Pt: Edward Morgan
*Pr: Frederec Green
Treas: Greg Intemann
VP: Mark Davison
VP: Alan Fox

DELEK REFINING, LTD.
See DELEK REFINING LIMITED PARTNERSHIP

D-U-N-S 62-443-8219
▲ DELEK US HOLDINGS INC
7102 Commerce Way, Brentwood, TN 37027-2896
Tel (615) 771-6701 Founded/Ownrshp 2001
Sales 5.7MMM EMP 4,584
Tkr Sym DK Exch NYS
SIC 2911 4612 5541 5411 Petroleum refining; Crude petroleum pipelines; Gasoline service stations; Filling stations, gasoline; Convenience stores; Convenience stores, chain
Ch Bd: Ezra Uzi Yemin
CFO: Assaf Ginzburg
CFO: Uzi Yemin
Treas: Greg Intemann
Ex VP: Harry P Daily
Ex VP: Pete Daily
Ex VP: Daniel L Gordon
Ex VP: Frederec Green
Ex VP: Donald N Holmes
Ex VP: Anthony L Miller
Ex VP: Mark D Smith
Ex VP: Avigal Soreq
Ex VP: Kent B Thomas
VP: Dave Deserio
VP: Assi Ginzburg
VP: Scott McCrary
VP: Danny Norris
Board of Directors: William J Finnerty, Carlos E Jorda, Charles H Leonard, Gary M Sullivan Jr, Shlomo Zohar

D-U-N-S 62-522-6386 IMP/EXP
■ DELFIELD CO LLC
(Suby of MANITOWOC CO INC) ★
980 S Isabella Rd, Mount Pleasant, MI 48858-9200
Tel (989) 773-7981 Founded/Ownrshp 1949
Sales 196.1MME EMP 875
SIC 3589 Commercial cooking & foodwarming equipment
Ex VP: Graham Tillotson
VP: Marcy Malson
VP: Wayne Smith
Dir Lab: Justin Nottingham
Mfg Dir: Michael Curtis
Snr Mgr: Tommy Lancaster

D-U-N-S 09-032-2194
DELHAIZE AMERICA LLC (NC)
FOOD LION
(Suby of DELHAIZE THE LION COORDINATION CENTER SA)
2110 Executive Dr, Salisbury, NC 28147-9007
Tel (704) 633-8250 Founded/Ownrshp 1999
Sales 15.3MMME EMP 109,000E
Accts Deloitte & Touche Llp Charlot
SIC 5411 Grocery stores
CEO: Frans W H Muller
*Pr: Meg Ham
*Sec: Richard A James
*Ex VP: Marc Croonen
*Ex VP: Maura Abeln Smith
*Ex VP: Michael Rex Waller
Sr VP: Cindy Schlaetfer
VP: Odile Ducatez
VP: John Garlick
VP: Chris Lewis
*VP: Kostas Macheras
VP: Dewey Preslar
VP: Geert Verellen
VP: Tony Willia
Dir Risk M: Mary C Kossel

DELI EXPRESS
See E A SWEEN CO

D-U-N-S 08-647-3394
DELI MANAGEMENT INC
JASON'S DELI
2400 Broadway St, Beaumont, TX 77702-1904
Tel (409) 838-1976 Founded/Ownrshp 1976
Sales 229.7MME EMP 6,000
Accts Wathen Deshong & Juncker Cpa
SIC 5812 Delicatessen (eating places); American restaurant
Ch: Joe Tortorice Jr
Mng Pt: Brad Owens
*Pr: Robert Tortorice
*CFO: Troy Cormier
*VP: Anthony Coco
*VP: Ragan Edgerly
*VP: Keith Kemplay
*VP: Wade Sterns
Dist Mgr: Michael Gibson
Dist Mgr: Rachel Huerta
Dist Mgr: Nick Roark

D-U-N-S 15-935-9897 IMP
DELIAS INC
50 W 23rd St, New York, NY 10010-5205
Tel (212) 590-6200 Founded/Ownrshp 1997
Sales 136.6MM EMP 1,689
SIC 5632 5611 Women's accessory & specialty stores; Apparel accessories; Men's & boys' clothing stores; Clothing accessories: men's & boys'
CEO: Tracy Gardner
Ex VP: Daphne Smith
Exec: Molly Gamble
Area Mgr: Kelly Packer
Natl Sales: Terry Pizzarello
Mktg Dir: Amy Tissot
Sls Mgr: Wanda Torress
Genl Couns: Edward D Taffet
Snr Mgr: Prakash Chakraborty

D-U-N-S 15-711-0862
■ DELIGHT PRODUCTS CO
(Suby of KROGER CO) ★
1200 Industrial Dr, Springfield, TN 37172-3328
Tel (615) 384-7546 Founded/Ownrshp 1980
Sales 166.8MME EMP 1E
SIC 2047 Dog & cat food
Pr: Jeff Pahl
Exec: Erica Gibson
IT Man: Craig McDuffie

DELIVERY SYSTEMS AND SERVICES
See VERSUM MATERIALS US LLC

DELL
See FORCE10 NETWORKS INC

DELL COMPELLENT
See COMPELLENT TECHNOLOGIES INC

DELL COMPUTER
See DELL INTERNATIONAL INC

DELL COMPUTER
See DELL INC

DELL EMC
See EMC CORP

D-U-N-S 00-759-4492
■ DELL FINANCIAL SERVICES LLC
DFS
(Suby of DELL COMPUTER) ★
1 Dell Way, Round Rock, TX 78682-7000
Tel (800) 283-2210 Founded/Ownrshp 1997
Sales 90.5MME EMP 230
SIC 7389 Financial services
CEO: Michael Dell
*Treas: Tyler W Johnson
*VP: Brian Gladden
VP: Dennis Gudenau
Dir Bus: Edward Jagt
Ex Dir: Ryan Broadwell
Prgrm Mgr: Ryan C Brown
IT Man: Vivek Naik
IT Man: Robert Rhode
Mktg Mgr: Kevin Choate
Mktg Mgr: Amit Dhar

D-U-N-S 11-431-5195 IMP/EXP
■ DELL INC
DELL COMPUTER
(*Suby of* DENALI INTERMEDIATE INC) ★
1 Dell Way, Round Rock, TX 78682-7000
Tel (512) 338-4400 *Founded/Ownrshp* 1987
Sales 46.2MMM[E] *EMP* 101,800
SIC 3571 3572 3575 3577 7372 7379 Electronic computers; Minicomputers; Personal computers (microcomputers); Computer storage devices; Computer terminals, monitors & components; Computer peripheral equipment; Printers, computer; Application computer software; Computer related consulting services; Computer related maintenance services
Ch Bd: Michael S Dell
**V Ch:* Jeffrey W Clarke
**CFO:* Thomas W Sweet
**Ofcr:* Marius A Haas
Ofcr: Karen H Quintos
Ofcr: Rory P Read
VP: Neeta Balsaver
VP: Kimberly Brown
VP: Cheryl Cook
VP: Joanne Gruber
VP: Gerry Hackett
VP: Neil Hall
VP: Dave Hansen
VP: Janice Jacobs
VP: John Maxwell
VP: Mark Pringle
**VP:* Richard J Rothberg
VP: Janet Smith
Comm Man: Janet Berlind

D-U-N-S 05-433-9994 EXP
■ DELL INTERNATIONAL INC
DELL COMPUTER
(*Suby of* DELL COMPUTER) ★
1 Dell Way, Round Rock, TX 78682-7000
Tel (512) 728-3500 *Founded/Ownrshp* 1987
Sales 225.3MM[E] *EMP* 8[E]
SIC 3571 Personal computers (microcomputers)
Pr: Thomas Green
**Ch Bd:* Michael S Dell
**Treas:* Thomas Luttrell
**Treas:* Brian P Macdonald
**VP:* James L Fitzgerald
**VP:* Yvonne McGill
**VP:* Thomas J Vallone
Ex Dir: Ben Fuentes
Manager: Mike Machado
Sls Mgr: Steve Cockrell

D-U-N-S 87-793-6518 IMP
■ DELL MARKETING LP
(*Suby of* DELL COMPUTER) ★
1 Dell Way, Round Rock, TX 78682-7000
Tel (512) 338-4400 *Founded/Ownrshp* 1991
Sales 6.5MMM[E] *EMP* 1,500[E]
SIC 5045 Computers & accessories, personal & home entertainment
Ch Bd: Michael S Dell

D-U-N-S 80-008-5763 IMP/EXP
■ DELL PRODUCTS LP
(*Suby of* DELL COMPUTER) ★
1 Dell Way, Round Rock, TX 78682-7000
Tel (512) 338-4400 *Founded/Ownrshp* 1999
Sales 228.8MM[E] *EMP* 1,000
SIC 3571 Electronic computers
IT Man: Adrian Soule
Prd Mgr: David Woodhams

DELL SECUREWORKS
See SECUREWORKS INC

DELL SONICWALL
See SONICWALL LLC

DELL SVCS FDRAL GOVERNMENT INC
See NTT DATA SERVICES FEDERAL GOVERNMENT INC

D-U-N-S 60-183-9660
▲ DELL TECHNOLOGIES INC
1 Dell Way, Round Rock, TX 78682-7000
Tel (800) 289-3355 *Founded/Ownrshp* 2013
Sales 70.9MMM[E] *EMP* 101,800[E]
Accts Securities And Exchange Commis
Tkr Sym DVMT *Exch* NYS
SIC 8731 5734 Computer (hardware) development; Computer software & accessories
Ch Bd: Michael S Dell
**Pr:* Jeffrey W Clarke
Pr: David I Goulden
Pr: Howard D Elias
**Pr:* Marius Haas
Pr: John A Swainson
Pr: Suresh C Vaswani
**CFO:* Thomas W Sweet
**Chf Mktg O:* Jeremy Burton
Ofcr: Steven H Price
Ofcr: Karen H Quintos
Ofcr: Rory Read
VP: Lorna Wisham

D-U-N-S 60-304-6210
■ DELL USA CORP
(*Suby of* DELL COMPUTER) ★
1 Dell Way, Round Rock, TX 78682-7000
Tel (512) 338-4400 *Founded/Ownrshp* 1989
Sales 98.4MM[E] *EMP* 5,000
SIC 8741 5045 Business management; Computers & accessories, personal & home entertainment; Computer peripheral equipment
Ch Bd: Michael S Dell
**CFO:* Thomas Meredith

DELL WYSE
See WYSE TECHNOLOGY LLC

D-U-N-S 07-385-5322
■ DELLONA ENTERPRISES INC
CHRISTMAS MOUNTAIN VILLAGE
(*Suby of* BLUEGREEN CORP) ★
S944 Christmas Mtn Rd, Wisconsin Dells, WI 53965-9608
Tel (608) 253-1000 *Founded/Ownrshp* 1980
Sales 50.0MM[E] *EMP* 2,372[E]
SIC 7011 7992 5812 Resort hotel; Ski lodge; Public golf courses; Eating places
Pr: George Donovan
Board of Directors: Tod Escude

DELMAR DISTRIBUTING
See COLUMBUS DISTRIBUTING CO

D-U-N-S 10-656-9999
DELMAR GARDENS ENTERPRISES INC
14805 North Outer 40 Rd # 300, Chesterfield, MO 63017-6060
Tel (636) 733-7000 *Founded/Ownrshp* 1965
Sales 204.6MM[E] *EMP* 30
SIC 8741 Nursing & personal care facility management
Ch Bd: Barbara Grossberg
**Pr:* Gabe Grossberg
**CFO:* Paul Wentzien
**Treas:* Gail Hartmann
**V Ch Bd:* Yetra Goldberg
**Ex VP:* Howard Oppenheimer
VP: Howard Openheimer
Exec: Theda Cohen
CTO: Debbie Huber
Advt Dir: Patricia Muich
Nrsg Dir: Judy Schubert

D-U-N-S 08-983-5318 IMP/EXP
DELMAR SYSTEMS INC (LA)
8114 Highway 90 E, Broussard, LA 70518-8215
Tel (337) 365-0180 *Founded/Ownrshp* 1968
Sales 179.7MM[E] *EMP* 270
SIC 1389 Oil field services
Pr: Sherman A Scott
**Treas:* Danny Pontiff
**Ex VP:* Brady Como
**VP:* Matthew Smith
Board of Directors: Sherman A Scott

D-U-N-S 00-691-8882
■ DELMARVA POWER & LIGHT CO
(*Suby of* CONECTIV LLC) ★
500 N Wakefield Dr Fl 2, Newark, DE 19702-5440
Tel (202) 872-2000 *Founded/Ownrshp* 1909
Sales 1.3MMM *EMP* 880[E]
Accts Pricewaterhousecoopers Llp W
SIC 4939 Combination utilities
Pr: David M Velazquez
CFO: Frederick J Boyle
Sr VP: Joseph W Ford
VP: Ronald K Clark
VP: Albert Kirby
VP: Ed R Mayberry
VP: Glenn Moore
VP: William J Sim
Opers Mgr: Tae Koh
Board of Directors: Kevin C Fitzgerald, Joseph M Rigby

DELNET
See DELSTAR TECHNOLOGIES INC

D-U-N-S 07-458-8567
DELNOR-COMMUNITY HOSPITAL (IL)
CENTRAL DUPAGE HEALTH
(*Suby of* CENTRAL DUPAGE HEALTH) ★
300 Randall Rd, Geneva, IL 60134-4202
Tel (630) 208-3000 *Founded/Ownrshp* 1940, 1986
Sales 305.1MM *EMP* 1,600
Accts Crowe Horwath Ll Chicago Il
SIC 8062 General medical & surgical hospitals
Pr: Craig Livermore
**COO:* Tom Wright
**CFO:* Michael Kittoe
**Treas:* Bob White
VP: Mark Daniels
Dir Risk M: Donna Stueber
Dir Rx: Barbara Hagemann
Nurse Mgr: Gina Malamos
Doctor: Brian S Chang MD
Doctor: Brian Chang
Doctor: Mark A Staudacher

D-U-N-S 00-166-4820 IMP
DELOITTE & TOUCHE LLP
(*Suby of* DELOITTE LLP) ★
30 Rockefeller Plz # 4350, New York, NY 10112-4399
Tel (212) 492-4000 *Founded/Ownrshp* 1997
Sales 6.7MMM[E] *EMP* 42,367
SIC 8721 Certified public accountant; Auditing services
Ch Bd: Joseph Ucuzoglu
Mng Pt: Barry Salzberg
V Ch Bd: Nick Tommasino
VP: Jackie Atkins
VP: Marilynj Cason
VP: Brettj Gilliland
VP: R T Hisey
VP: Karen Hughes
VP: Donald Ibach
VP: Chip Luman
VP: Michellee Norman
VP: Karen Reser
VP: John Ruconich
VP: Jonathan Schoonmaker
VP: Waynet Szmyt

D-U-N-S 00-256-3455
DELOITTE CONSULTING LLP
(*Suby of* DELOITTE LLP) ★
30 Rockefeller Plz, New York, NY 10112-0015
Tel (212) 492-4000 *Founded/Ownrshp* 2000
Sales 864.4MM[E] *EMP* 6,535
SIC 8742 Financial consultant
CEO: Jim Moffatt
Mng Dir: Manoj Singh
Counsel: Victor Stojanow
Snr Mgr: Tanyth Lloyd

D-U-N-S 07-960-8603
DELOITTE CORPORATE FINANCE LLC
(*Suby of* DELOITTE FINANCIAL ADVISORY SERVICES LLP) ★
111 S Wacker Dr, Chicago, IL 60606-4302
Tel (312) 486-1400 *Founded/Ownrshp* 2014
Sales 78.3MM[E] *EMP* 1,114[E]
SIC 7389 Financial services

D-U-N-S 60-379-5159
DELOITTE FINANCIAL ADVISORY SERVICES LLP
(*Suby of* DELOITTE LLP) ★
30 Rockefeller Plz, New York, NY 10112-0015
Tel (212) 492-4000 *Founded/Ownrshp* 2003
Sales 112.6MM[E] *EMP* 1,351
SIC 8721 Certified public accountant
CEO: David S Williams
COO: Nick Florio
Ch: Punit Renjen
Assoc VP: Gautam Pandey
IT Man: Ian Tod
Snr Mgr: Gregory Adamiec
Snr Mgr: Rana Khasnavis
Snr Mgr: ABS Kotulski
Snr Mgr: Scott Stanley

D-U-N-S 01-412-7109 IMP
DELOITTE LLP
30 Rockefeller Plz, New York, NY 10112-0015
Tel (212) 492-4000 *Founded/Ownrshp* 1994
Sales 7.8MMM[E] *EMP* 65,000[E]
SIC 8742 8721 Management consulting services; Certified public accountant
Ch Bd: Mike Fucci
Pt: Teresa Briggs
Pt: Henry Phillips
V Ch: Jeff Bradfield
Pr: Max Hood
CEO: Cathy Engelbert
COO: Frank Friedman
CFO: Gabriele Fraschini
CFO: Peter A Shimer
VP: Swapna Allapur
VP: Kurt Babe
VP: Peter Baljet
VP: Ben Chesters
VP: Nathaniel H Clarkson
VP: Andrew L Feller
VP: Faith Judah
VP: Isaac K Kim
VP: Jaekwon Lee
VP: Jatin Mehta
VP: Jeffrey Morgan
VP: Thomas Nasca

D-U-N-S 82-546-0145
DELOITTE SERVICES LP
(*Suby of* DELOITTE LLP) ★
1633 Broadway Fl 35, New York, NY 10019-6753
Tel (212) 492-2000 *Founded/Ownrshp* 2000
Sales 46.6MM[E] *EMP* 1,135[E]
SIC 8721 Accounting, auditing & bookkeeping
Prin: Lisa Dane

D-U-N-S 00-642-7256 IMP/EXP
DELONG CO INC
513 Front St, Clinton, WI 53525
Tel (800) 356-0784 *Founded/Ownrshp* 1952
Sales 1.3MMM *EMP* 250
Accts Baker Tilly Virchow Krause Ll
SIC 5153 Grain & field beans
Pr: David De Long
Treas: William C De Long
Exec: David Delong
CTO: Brandon Bickham

D-U-N-S 05-972-3643
DELOPS INC
D' ANGELO'S SANDWICH SHOP
(*Suby of* D ANGELOS SANDWICH SHOP) ★
600 Providence Hwy, Dedham, MA 02026-6804
Tel (508) 697-7742 *Founded/Ownrshp* 1993
Sales 49.0MM[E] *EMP* 2,400
SIC 5812 Sandwiches & submarines shop
Pr: Thomas Galligan
Board of Directors: Theresa A Nibi

D-U-N-S 17-030-6331 IMP/EXP
DELORO STELLITE HOLDINGS CORP
1201 Eisenhower Dr N, Goshen, IN 46526-5311
Tel (574) 534-2585 *Founded/Ownrshp* 1986
Sales NA *EMP* 1,000
SIC 3479

DELPHI
See DPH HOLDINGS CORP

DELPHI
See DPH LLC

DELPHI AUTOMOTIVE
See DELPHI CONNECTION SYSTEMS LLC

D-U-N-S 07-951-3129
DELPHI AUTOMOTIVE LLP
(*Suby of* DELPHI AUTOMOTIVE PLC)
5725 Delphi Dr, Troy, MI 48098-2815
Tel (248) 813-2494 *Founded/Ownrshp* 2014
Sales 17.0MMM *EMP* 54[E]
SIC 5065 5012 Electronic parts & equipment; Commercial vehicles
CFO: Kevin Clark

D-U-N-S 02-001-3316
DELPHI AUTOMOTIVE SYSTEMS CORP
12170 Rojas Dr, El Paso, TX 79936-7766
Tel (915) 612-2855 *Founded/Ownrshp* 2008
Sales NA *EMP* 2,500
SIC 3694

D-U-N-S 83-212-1797 IMP/EXP
DELPHI AUTOMOTIVE SYSTEMS LLC
(*Suby of* DELPHI HOLDINGS LLC) ★
5725 Delphi Dr, Troy, MI 48098-2815
Tel (248) 813-2000 *Founded/Ownrshp* 2009
Sales 4.4MMM[E] *EMP* 9,300[E]
SIC 3714 Motor vehicle parts & accessories
Ofcr: Kevin P Clark
Treas: Keith D Stipp
**Ofcr:* Jeffrey J Owens
**Sr VP:* Majdi B Abulaban
**Sr VP:* Kevin M Butler
Sr VP: Timothy C McCabe
VP: James A Bertrnd
VP: Raymond Campbell
**VP:* Michael Gassen
**VP:* Jessica L Holscott
VP: L CIA V Moretti
VP: Donald L Runke

D-U-N-S 83-212-1904 IMP
DELPHI CONNECTION SYSTEMS LLC
DELPHI AUTOMOTIVE
(*Suby of* DELPHI HOLDINGS LLC) ★
30 Corporate Park Ste 303, Irvine, CA 92606-5133
Tel (949) 458-3100 *Founded/Ownrshp* 2010
Sales 111.9MM[E] *EMP* 450[E]
SIC 3714 Motor vehicle parts & accessories
Ch Bd: Kevin Clark
Genl Mgr: Steven Willing

D-U-N-S 83-205-2034 IMP/EXP
DELPHI CORP
(*Suby of* DELPHI AUTOMOTIVE LLP)
5725 Delphi Dr, Troy, MI 48098-2815
Tel (248) 813-2000 *Founded/Ownrshp* 2009
Sales 4.7MMM[E] *EMP* 10,133
SIC 3714 Motor vehicle parts & accessories
Pr: Rodney O'Neal
COO: Brad Wolfert
CFO: Robert J Dellinger
Treas: Thomas Burghart
Bd of Dir: Nicholas Donofrio
VP: Dennis Buser
VP: Laurence Daurelle
VP: Matthew Fortney
VP: Guy Hachey
VP: John R Jewell
VP: Sidney Johnson
VP: Timothy F Richards
VP: Logan G Robinson

D-U-N-S 18-857-4214
DELPHI FINANCIAL GROUP INC
(*Suby of* TOKIO MARINE HOLDINGS, INC.)
1105 N Market St Ste 1230, Wilmington, DE 19801-1216
Tel (302) 478-5142 *Founded/Ownrshp* 1987
Sales NA *EMP* 1,885[E]
SIC 6321 Accident & health insurance; Disability health insurance
CEO: Robert Rosenkranz
**Pr:* Donald A Sherman
**Treas:* Thomas W Burghart
**Ex VP:* Harold F Ilg
Ex VP: Gerald R Scott
Ex VP: Gerald Scott
Ex VP: Robert M Smith
**Sr VP:* Chad W Coulter
VP: Chad Coulter
VP: David M Finkelstein
VP: Carleton S Reynolds

D-U-N-S 83-206-2066
DELPHI HOLDINGS LLC
(*Suby of* DELPHI CORP) ★
5725 Delphi Dr, Troy, MI 48098-2815
Tel (248) 813-2000 *Founded/Ownrshp* 2009
Sales 4.5MMM[E] *EMP* 9,300[E]
SIC 3714 Motor vehicle parts & accessories
Pr: Rodney O'Neal

D-U-N-S 88-447-3398
DELPHINUS ENGINEERING INC
1510 Chester Pike Ste 380, Eddystone, PA 19022-1375
Tel (610) 874-9160 *Founded/Ownrshp* 1994
Sales 89.7MM[E] *EMP* 370
SIC 8711 Construction & civil engineering
Pr: Ranjit K Das
**CFO:* Barbara Prestianne
Ofcr: Linda Woodward
**VP:* Roby C Lentz
VP: Kevin Stewart
Prgrm Mgr: Jack Lucas
Off Mgr: Marilou Jones
Snr Sftwr: Ed Suarez
Sfty Mgr: Michael Potter

D-U-N-S 36-265-5396
■ DELRAY MEDICAL CENTER INC
(*Suby of* TENET HEALTHCARE CORP) ★
5352 Linton Blvd, Delray Beach, FL 33484-6514
Tel (561) 498-4440 *Founded/Ownrshp* 2001
Sales 313.2MM *EMP* 10[E]
SIC 8062 General medical & surgical hospitals
Pr: Mark H Bryan
Dir Vol: Becky McCoy
**Treas:* Tyler Murphy
Dir Lab: Michael Ligotti
Dir Rad: Theresa Griffith
Dir Rad: Judith Zavatsky
Off Mgr: Janice Berry
Dir IT: Robens Rosena
Pathlgst: Albert Cohen
Ansthlgy: Eric Freeman
Ansthlgy: Todd Horowitz

D-U-N-S 05-134-7987 IMP
DELRAY PLANTS CO
956 Old State Road 8, Venus, FL 33960-2137
Tel (800) 854-5393 *Founded/Ownrshp* 2000
Sales 452.5MM[E] *EMP* 300
SIC 5193 Flowers & florists' supplies
Pr: Randolph P Gilde
**Treas:* Marian Gilde
**VP:* Edward W Koornneef

D-U-N-S 05-496-6705 IMP/EXP
■ DELSTAR TECHNOLOGIES INC
DELNET
(*Suby of* SWM INTL) ★
601 Industrial Rd, Middletown, DE 19709-1083
Tel (302) 378-8888 *Founded/Ownrshp* 1946
Sales 130.5MM[E] *EMP* 375
SIC 3081 Polypropylene film & sheet
Pr: Mark Abrahams
**VP:* James Dickson
VP: Jim Dixon
**VP:* Dennis Eckels
**VP:* William Geissler
VP: Michael Miller
VP: John Ribsam
Dir IT: Harry Faulkner
Software D: Jeff Billimek
Mtls Mgr: Philip Hill
Prd Mgr: Robert Packer

D-U-N-S 00-692-4872 IMP/EXP
▲ DELTA AIR LINES INC (GA)
DELTA AIRLINES
1030 Delta Blvd, Atlanta, GA 30354-1989
Tel (404) 715-2600 *Founded/Ownrshp* 1929
Sales 40.7MMM *EMP* 83,000
Accts Ernst & Young Llp Atlanta Ge
Tkr Sym DAL *Exch* NYS
SIC 4512 Air cargo carrier, scheduled; Air passenger carrier, scheduled
CEO: Richard H Anderson
**Pr:* Edward H Bastian
Pr: Timothy Harms
COO: W Gil West
COO: Wayne G West
CFO: Paul A Jacobson
Bd of Dir: Alessio Beldomenico
Bd of Dir: Rodney E Slater
Bd of Dir: Douglas Steenland
Ofcr: Peter Carter
Ex VP: Michael Campbell
Ex VP: Glen W Hauenstein
Ex VP: Joanne Smith
Sr VP: Gary Chase
Sr VP: Mark A P Drusch
Sr VP: Samuel H Halter Jr
Sr VP: Lee Macenczak
Sr VP: Tim Mapes
Sr VP: Rahul Samant
VP: Robert Adams
VP: Donald Bornhorst
Board of Directors: David R Goode, Francis S Blake, George N Mattson, Roy J Bostock, Paula Rosput Reynolds, John S Brinzo, Sergio Rial, Daniel A Carp, Kenneth C Rogers, David G Dewalt, Kathy N Waller, Thomas E Donilon, Kenneth B Woodrow, William H Easter III, Mickey P Foret, Shirley C Franklin

DELTA AIRLINES
See DELTA AIR LINES INC

D-U-N-S 60-360-8167 IMP/EXP
DELTA AMERICA LTD
DELTA PRODUCTS
(*Suby of* DELTA ELECTRONICS, INC.)
46101 Fremont Blvd, Fremont, CA 94538-6468
Tel (510) 668-5100 *Founded/Ownrshp* 2009
Sales 126.3MM^E *EMP* 360
SIC 5065 3679 8731 Electronic parts & equipment; Switches, stepping; Power supplies, all types: static; Electronic research
Pr: Ming H Huang
Dir IT: Sreeni Vemuri

D-U-N-S 00-181-6409
▲ DELTA APPAREL INC (GA)
322 S Main St, Greenville, SC 29601-2606
Tel (864) 232-5200 *Founded/Ownrshp* 1999
Sales 425.2MM *EMP* 7,400
Accts Kpmg Llp Greenville South Ca
Tkr Sym DLA *Exch* ASE
SIC 2321 2369 2339 2253 Sport shirts, men's & boys': from purchased materials; Girls' & children's outerwear; Women's & misses' outerwear; Hats & headwear, knit
Ch Bd: Robert W Humphreys
Pr: Rod McGeachy
CFO: Deborah H Merrill
Ofcr: Martha M Watson
VP: Eric Crocker
VP: Elisa Palefsky
Board of Directors: J Bradley Campbell, Sam P Cortez, Elizabeth J Gatewood, G Jay Gogue, Suzanne B Rudy, Robert E Staton Sr

D-U-N-S 06-289-2708 IMP
DELTA CENTRIFUGAL CORP
3402 Center St, Temple, TX 76504-1207
Tel (254) 773-9055 *Founded/Ownrshp* 1968
Sales 92.6MM^E *EMP* 140
SIC 5051 3325 3369 Sheets, galvanized or other coated; Alloy steel castings, except investment; Nonferrous foundries
Pr: Robert Rose
**Sec:* Ruth Allen
**VP:* Chris Anderson
**VP:* Mark Anderson
VP: Michael Drybola
**VP:* Hope Luther
Off Mgr: Adam Fenyves
Dir IT: Tomas Ball

DELTA CHILDREN'S PRODUCTS
See DELTA ENTERPRISE CORP

D-U-N-S 79-652-9907
DELTA COMMUNITY CREDIT UNION
1025 Virginia Ave, Atlanta, GA 30354-1319
Tel (404) 715-4725 *Founded/Ownrshp* 1940
Sales NA *EMP* 800
Accts Cliftonlarsonallen Llp Baltim
SIC 6061 6163 Federal credit unions; Loan brokers
CEO: Hank Halter
Pr: Russell Copeland
Pr: Anika Davis
Pr: Sujatha Rayburn
**CFO:* Jay Gratwick
Treas: Linda B Oshea
Ofcr: Kimberly Hoovestol
Ex VP: Todd Marksberry
Sr VP: Bill Mesplay
Sr VP: Jason Osterhage
VP: June Albright
VP: Charlotte Bennett
VP: Becky Davis
VP: Pam Davis
VP: Matthew Knighton
VP: Robert Moye
VP: Matthew Shepherd
VP: Jan Tripp
Board of Directors: Matthew J Sullivan

D-U-N-S 82-611-3722 IMP
DELTA COMPANIES INC
(*Suby of* COLAS INC) ★
114 S Silver Springs Rd, Cape Girardeau, MO 63703-5063
Tel (573) 334-5261 *Founded/Ownrshp* 1992
Sales 167.7MM^E *EMP* 643
Accts Pricewaterhousecoopers Llp
SIC 2951 1611 Asphalt paving mixtures & blocks; Highway & street paving contractor; Resurfacing contractor
Pr: Ric Neubert
**Ch Bd:* James Weeks
VP: Paul Ebaugh
**VP:* Del Efrink
VP: Rick Moody
Dir Risk M: Linda Johnson
CTO: Carolyn Torbet
Opers Mgr: Dan Grier
Plnt Mgr: David Brady
Plnt Mgr: Gerald Farnham

DELTA CONNECTION
See MESABA AVIATION INC

D-U-N-S 05-604-6865
DELTA DENTAL INSURANCE CO
DDIC
(*Suby of* DELTA DENTAL OF CALIFORNIA) ★
100 1st St Fl 4, San Francisco, CA 94105-2657
Tel (415) 972-8400 *Founded/Ownrshp* 1970
Sales NA *EMP* 115
Accts Armanino Mckenna Llp San Ram
SIC 6411 Insurance brokers
CEO: Anthony S Barth
**Pr:* Bob Elliott
**COO:* Belinda Martinez
**Sr VP:* Toni Barth
**VP:* Debbie Reeves
VP Sls: Melissa Fullerton

DELTA DENTAL OF ARIZONA
See ARIZONA DENTAL INSURANCE SERVICE INC

D-U-N-S 07-876-0071
DELTA DENTAL OF CALIFORNIA
100 1st St Fl 4, San Francisco, CA 94105-2657
Tel (415) 972-8300 *Founded/Ownrshp* 1955
Sales NA *EMP* 2,925
Accts Cbiz Mhm Llc Smyrna Ga
SIC 6324 Dental insurance
Pr: Gary D Radine
Dir Vol: Sandy Trent
COO: Nilesh Patel
CFO: Michael J Castro
CFO: Mike Castro
Ofcr: Michael G Hankinson
Ofcr: Charles Lamont
Ex VP: Belinda Martinez
Sr VP: Tony Barth
Sr VP: Marilynn Belek
Sr VP: Patrick S Steele
Sr VP: Alicia Weber
VP: Andrea Fegley
VP: Kathy B Jonzzon
VP: Tom Leibowitz
VP: Hari Makkala
VP: Jamal Nasr
VP: Mohammad Reza Navid
VP: Joe Ruiz
VP: Thomas Wong

DELTA DENTAL OF COLORADO
See COLORADO DENTAL SERVICE INC

D-U-N-S 06-999-9399
DELTA DENTAL OF ILLINOIS
111 Shuman Blvd Ste 100, Naperville, IL 60563-8678
Tel (630) 718-4700 *Founded/Ownrshp* 1999
Sales NA *EMP* 150
Accts Plante & Moran Pllc Chicago
SIC 6324 Dental insurance
Pr: Bernard Glossy
COO: Stacey Bonn
VP: Karyn Glogowski
VP: Nancy Karasek
Dir Bus: Jane Ross
Prgrm Mgr: Daniel Lee
Sales Exec: Bob Maxwell
Sales Exec: Steve Soyke
Counsel: Alexandra Kotelon

D-U-N-S 84-761-0995
DELTA DENTAL OF IOWA
9000 Northpark Dr, Johnston, IA 50131-4817
Tel (515) 331-4594 *Founded/Ownrshp* 1970
Sales NA *EMP* 120
Accts Brooks Lodden Pc West Des Moi
SIC 6321 Accident & health insurance
Ex Dir: Suzanne Heckenlaible
**CEO:* Jeff Russell
**COO:* Cheryl Harding

D-U-N-S 07-331-2746
DELTA DENTAL OF KANSAS INC
1619 N Waterfront Pkwy, Wichita, KS 67206-6602
Tel (316) 264-4511 *Founded/Ownrshp* 1972
Sales NA *EMP* 100
Accts Bkd Llp Wichita Ks
SIC 6324 Dental insurance
CEO: Michael Herbert
**CEO:* Linda Branter
VP: Jon Tilton
**Mng Dir:* Dean Newton
CIO: Amy Ellison
IT Man: Robert Ebenkamp
Sales Exec: Jim Davis
Sales Exec: Steve Peppes

D-U-N-S 17-415-4013
DELTA DENTAL OF KENTUCKY INC
DENTAL CHOICE
10100 Linn Station Rd # 700, Louisville, KY 40223-3861
Tel (502) 736-5000 *Founded/Ownrshp* 1966
Sales NA *EMP* 85^E
Accts Plante & Moran Pllc East Lans
SIC 6324 Dental insurance
Pr: John Norton Williams Jr
**CEO:* Clifford T Maesaka Jr DDS
**CFO:* Curtis R Ladig
**Ch:* Carrie B Brown DMD
Ofcr: Ron Story
VP: Dick Aracich
**VP:* Stephen C Day
**VP:* Angela J Nenni
**VP:* John L Weeks III
**Prin:* Carrie Bell Brown
**Prin:* Michael Childers

D-U-N-S 09-863-6459
DELTA DENTAL OF MISSOURI (MO)
12399 Gravois Rd Fl 2, Saint Louis, MO 63127-1761
Tel (314) 656-3000 *Founded/Ownrshp* 1958
Sales NA *EMP* 138
Accts Bkd Llp Cincinnati Oh
SIC 6324 6321 Dental insurance; Accident & health insurance
CEO: David Haynes
**Pr:* Steve P Gaal III
**COO:* Pam Martin
CFO: Barbara Bentrup
**VP:* Richard Klassen
VP: Spann Laffitte
**VP:* Al Martinez
CIO: Karl Mudra
Sftwr Eng: Mike Dietrich
Netwrk Eng: Donald Fitzgerald
Mktg Mgr: Jeanne Aubuchon

DELTA DENTAL OF PENNSYLVANIA
See PENNSYLVANIA DENTAL SERVICE CORP

D-U-N-S 09-321-7230
DELTA DENTAL OF RHODE ISLAND
10 Charles St Ste 100, Providence, RI 02904-2220
Tel (401) 752-6246 *Founded/Ownrshp* 1959
Sales NA *EMP* 115
SIC 6324 8021 Dental insurance; Offices & clinics of dentists
Pr: Joseph A Nagle
**Ch Bd:* Colin Mac Gillivray
**CFO:* Richard A Fritz
**V Ch Bd:* Tom Correia
Chf Cred: James Balujian
Ofcr: Ken Fisher
VP: Kerrie Bennett
VP: Richard Twomey
CIO: Thomas Chase
Snr PM: Diane Gervasio

D-U-N-S 09-568-1748
DELTA DENTAL OF TENNESSEE
240 Venture Cir, Nashville, TN 37228-1604
Tel (615) 255-3175 *Founded/Ownrshp* 1965
Sales NA *EMP* 92
Accts Plante & Moran Pllc East Lans
SIC 6324 Dental insurance
CEO: Phillip Wenk DDS
**CFO:* J Thomas Perry
CFO: Tom Perry
Bd of Dir: Jim Davis
**VP:* Pam Dishman
**Exec:* Kay Martin
Software D: Chris Wood
VP Opers: Melissa Huschke
Sales Exec: Perry Baines
VP Sls: Jay Reavis
Mktg Mgr: Rocio Haskell

D-U-N-S 07-793-2226
DELTA DENTAL OF VIRGINIA
4818 Starkey Rd, Roanoke, VA 24018-8542
Tel (540) 989-8000 *Founded/Ownrshp* 1965
Sales NA *EMP* 190
Accts Brown Edwards & Company Llp R
SIC 6411 6321 Insurance agents; Accident & health insurance carriers
Pr: George A Levicki
**CFO:* Michael Wise
**Treas:* Thomas Nardo
VP: Stacy Campbell
**VP:* Peter V Davies II
VP: Chris Pyle
Exec: Liz Burford
Comm Man: Jamie Akersa
**VP Admn:* Oscar Bryant
Snr Sftwr: Prasad Jampana
QA Dir: Martha Womack

D-U-N-S 05-525-6916
DELTA DENTAL OF WASHINGTON
DELTA DENTAL/WASHINGTON
(*Suby of* WASHINGTON DENTAL SERVICE)
9706 4th Ave Ne Ste 100, Seattle, WA 98115-2199
Tel (206) 522-2300 *Founded/Ownrshp* 1954
Sales NA *EMP* 350^E
Accts Kpmg Llp Seattle Wa
SIC 6324 Dental insurance
CEO: James Dwyer
Ofcr: Maureen Finneran
Ofcr: Laura Flores
**VP:* Kristin Merlo
Prgrm Mgr: Chad Lennox

D-U-N-S 07-478-1378
DELTA DENTAL OF WISCONSIN INC
2801 Hoover Rd, Stevens Point, WI 54481-7100
Tel (715) 344-6087 *Founded/Ownrshp* 1967
Sales NA *EMP* 154
Accts Crowe Horwath Llp Chicago Il
SIC 6324 Dental insurance
CEO: Dennis Peterson
CFO: Timothy Krull
Exec: Pamela Gartmann
CIO: Steve Allen
DP Dir: John O'Keefe
IT Man: Jeff Lutgen
Netwrk Eng: John Okeefe
Mktg Dir: Jennifer Wydeven

DELTA DENTAL PLAN MASS
See DENTAL SERVICE OF MASSACHUSETTS INC

D-U-N-S 03-234-9987
DELTA DENTAL PLAN OF ARKANSAS INC
1513 Country Club Rd, Sherwood, AR 72120-5076
Tel (501) 992-1666 *Founded/Ownrshp* 2000
Sales NA *EMP* 170
SIC 6324 Dental insurance
Pr: Ed Choate
COO: Shana Nolen
**CFO:* Phyllis Rogers
**Sr VP:* Tim Carney
**Sr VP:* Lynn Harbert
**Sr VP:* Jim Johnson
**VP:* Herman Hurd
**VP:* Allen Moore
Sls Dir: Christi Pittman

D-U-N-S 80-075-9136
DELTA DENTAL PLAN OF IDAHO INC
555 E Parkcenter Blvd, Boise, ID 83706-6503
Tel (208) 489-3580 *Founded/Ownrshp* 1971
Sales NA *EMP* 27
Accts Delta Dental Of Idaho Boise
SIC 6324 8021 Dental insurance; Offices & clinics of dentists
Pr: Tamara C Brandstetter
**COO:* Robert Tierney
**Ch:* Steve Nielsen
**Treas:* Park Price
Ofcr: Roxanne Joyner

D-U-N-S 07-633-4622
DELTA DENTAL PLAN OF MICHIGAN INC
4100 Okemos Rd, Okemos, MI 48864-3296
Tel (517) 349-6000 *Founded/Ownrshp* 1964
Sales NA *EMP* 645
Accts Plante & Moranpllc East Lansi
SIC 6324 Dental insurance
VP: Thomas J Fleszar
V Ch: Terence R Comar
**Pr:* Laura L Czelada
Ex VP: Edward Zobeck
**VP:* Wael Awad
**VP:* David Fitzke
**VP:* Karen M Green
Snr Ntwrk: Dave Baldwin
IT Man: Steve Bundick
S&M/VP: Richard Kent
Mktg Dir: Steven Stegmeyer

D-U-N-S 07-398-4510
DELTA DENTAL PLAN OF NEW HAMPSHIRE INC
NORTHEAST DELTA DENTAL
1 Delta Dr, Concord, NH 03301-7406
Tel (800) 537-1715 *Founded/Ownrshp* 1961
Sales NA *EMP* 178
Accts Baker Newman & Noyes Llc Manc
SIC 6324 8021 Dental insurance; Offices & clinics of dentists
Ch: David Hedstrom
V Ch: Melvin J Severamce
**Pr:* Thomas Raffio
**Treas:* Helen T Biglin

D-U-N-S 04-361-7471
DELTA DENTAL PLAN OF NEW MEXICO INC (NM)
(*Suby of* DELTA DENTAL PLAN OF MICHIGAN INC) ★
2500 La Blvd Ne Ste 600, Albuquerque, NM 87110-4302
Tel (505) 883-4777 *Founded/Ownrshp* 1971
Sales NA *EMP* 645
Accts Plante & Moran Pllc East Lan
SIC 6324 Dental insurance
Pr: Walter S Bolic
**CFO:* Edwin Harris
VP: Gerald Stephens
CIO: Mike Maynard

D-U-N-S 07-944-4212
DELTA DENTAL PLAN OF OHIO INC
5600 Blazer Pkwy Ste 150, Dublin, OH 43017-7554
Tel (614) 776-2300 *Founded/Ownrshp* 1960
Sales NA *EMP* 13
SIC 6324 Dental insurance
Sls Mgr: Gerald Kucan
Pr: Michael B Clark
**Pr:* Dr Thomas Fleaszar
Genl Couns: Jonathan S Groat

D-U-N-S 07-429-1972
DELTA DENTAL PLAN OF OKLAHOMA
16 Nw 63rd St Ste 301, Oklahoma City, OK 73116-9115
Tel (405) 607-2100 *Founded/Ownrshp* 1973
Sales NA *EMP* 2
Accts Mcgladrey Llp Oklahoma City
SIC 6411 Insurance agents
Pr: John Gladden
CFO: Stephanie Elliot
**CFO:* Stephanie Elliott
**VP:* Barbara Fennell
Ex Dir: Shelly Perkins
CTO: David Emigh
Opers Mgr: Roger Garms
Sls Dir: Steve Danielsen

D-U-N-S 09-789-3226
DELTA DENTAL PLAN OF SOUTH DAKOTA
720 N Euclid Ave, Pierre, SD 57501-1717
Tel (605) 224-7345 *Founded/Ownrshp* 1963
Sales NA *EMP* 32
Accts Stulken Petersen Lingle Walti
SIC 6411 Insurance agents
Pr: Scott O Jones
Dir IT: Gene Tetzlaff
VP Opers: Mick Heckenlaible
Mktg Dir: Jeff Miller
Pr Dir: Chris Pyle

DELTA DENTAL/WASHINGTON
See DELTA DENTAL OF WASHINGTON

D-U-N-S 04-132-6865 IMP
■ DELTA DESIGN INC
(*Suby of* COHU INC) ★
12367 Crosthwaite Cir, Poway, CA 92064-6817
Tel (858) 848-8000 *Founded/Ownrshp* 1967
Sales 130.0MM^E *EMP* 700
SIC 3569 3825 3674 Testing chambers for altitude, temperature, ordnance, power; Test equipment for electronic & electrical circuits; Semiconductors & related devices
Pr: Samer Aabbani
**Pr:* James A Donahue
CFO: John Allen
**CFO:* Jeff Jose
**Ch:* Charles A Schwan
**Sr VP:* James McFarlane
Sr VP: Shay Torton
VP: Raymond Allen
VP: Roger J Hopkins

VP: Thomas Lightner
Snr Ntwrk: Russ Smith

D-U-N-S 05-690-1192
DELTA DIVERSIFIED ENTERPRISES INC
425 W Gemini Dr, Tempe, AZ 85283-1709
Tel (480) 831-0532 *Founded/Ownrshp* 1982
Sales 121.7MM *EMP* 495
Accts Morrison & Associates Cpas Pl
SIC 1731 General electrical contractor
Pr: Larry Donelson
**CFO:* John Bradley Berry
**VP:* Duane Bushnell
**VP:* Leo D Correll

D-U-N-S 07-434-7303 IMP/EXP
DELTA ENTERPRISE CORP
DELTA CHILDREN'S PRODUCTS
114 W 26th St Fl 11, New York, NY 10001-6812
Tel (212) 736-7000 *Founded/Ownrshp* 1968
Sales 99.2MM[E] *EMP* 115
SIC 5021 5099 Juvenile furniture; Baby carriages, strollers & related products
Ch Bd: Joseph Shamie
**VP:* Sam Shamie
VP: Phil Todaro
Sls Mgr: Louis Hoffstein

D-U-N-S 03-882-0981 IMP
DELTA FABRICATION AND MACHINE INC
1379 County Road 2110, Daingerfield, TX 75638-4421
Tel (903) 645-3994 *Founded/Ownrshp* 1989
Sales 86.1MM[E] *EMP* 150
SIC 1541 3599 3441 Industrial buildings, new construction; Paper/pulp mill construction; Machine shop, jobbing & repair; Fabricated structural metal
Pr: Gerald W Williams
**Sec:* Paula Williams
Sales Exec: Mack Ingram

D-U-N-S 13-134-9557 IMP
DELTA GALIL USA INC
WUNDIES KICKAWAY INNER SECRETS
(*Suby of* DELTA GALIL INDUSTRIES LTD.)
1 Harmon Plz Fl 5, Secaucus, NJ 07094-2800
Tel (201) 392-9098 *Founded/Ownrshp* 2000
Sales 341.1MM[E] *EMP* 2,350
SIC 2341 Women's & children's undergarments; Women's & children's nightwear
CEO: Isaac Dabah
COO: Itzhak Weinstock
CFO: Yossi Hajaj
Ch: Noam Lautman
Sr VP: Robin Costa
Sr VP: Michael Fitzgerald
Sr VP: Esti Maoz
VP: Einat Amitay
VP: Craig Johnson
VP: Alan Lewis
VP: Oz Saar
VP: Steven Seidman

DELTA GLOBAL SERVICES
See DAL GLOBAL SERVICES LLC

D-U-N-S 15-357-8695 IMP
DELTA GROUP ELECTRONICS INC
4521a Osuna Rd Ne, Albuquerque, NM 87109-4467
Tel (505) 883-7674 *Founded/Ownrshp* 1987
Sales 98.6MM[E] *EMP* 390
SIC 3643 3679 Current-carrying wiring devices; Electronic circuits; Harness assemblies for electronic use: wire or cable
CEO: Herald C Mueller
Pr: Sherman Feelin
**VP:* Sherman P Freelin
Exec: Carla Tennyson
Genl Mgr: Mike Prieskorn
Genl Mgr: Bill West
Prd Mgr: Shannon Larrow
Ql Cn Mgr: Lee Edrington
Ql Cn Mgr: Carl Ritnour
Sls Mgr: Allen Gillengerten
Sls Mgr: Roger Haynes

DELTA HOSPITAL
See YUKON-KUSKOKWIM HEALTH CORP

D-U-N-S 05-259-3480 IMP
DELTA MARINE INDUSTRIES INC (WA)
1608 S 96th St, Seattle, WA 98108-5198
Tel (206) 763-0760 *Founded/Ownrshp* 1967
Sales 101.0MM[E] *EMP* 300
SIC 3732 Yachts, building & repairing; Boats, fiberglass: building & repairing
Dir IT: Alan Hartley
Mktg Dir: Paola Ballato

DELTA PRODUCTS
See DELTA AMERICA LTD

D-U-N-S 10-345-6190 IMP/EXP
DELTA PRODUCTS CORP
(*Suby of* DELTA PRODUCTS) ★
46101 Fremont Blvd, Fremont, CA 94538-6468
Tel (510) 668-5100 *Founded/Ownrshp* 1988
Sales 126.3MM[E] *EMP* 292
SIC 5065 5045 8741 5063 3577 Electronic parts & equipment; Computer peripheral equipment; Management services; Electrical apparatus & equipment; Computer peripheral equipment
Pr: Ming H Huang
CFO: Sheryl Chen
Bd of Dir: Julia Yu
VP: Andrew Lee
Div Mgr: Elson Chang
DP Exec: Sreenivasa Vemuri
IT Man: Sam Gonzales
Sys/Mgr: Eunice Lin
Mktg Dir: Shawn Butcher
Mktg Dir: Douglas Hsia
Manager: Matt Bradshaw
Board of Directors: Milan Miodrag

D-U-N-S 06-771-8981
DELTA REGIONAL MEDICAL CENTER
1400 E Union St, Greenville, MS 38703-3246
Tel (662) 378-3783 *Founded/Ownrshp* 1953
Sales 123.3MM *EMP* 800
SIC 8062 General medical & surgical hospitals
CEO: J Stansel Harvey
Trst: Mildred Crockett
**Sr VP:* Mazie B Whalen
VP: Chandler Ewing
VP: Lisa M Zepponi
VP: Lisa Zepponi
Exec: Courtney Phillips
Exec: John Phillips
Dir Rad: Richard C Smith
Ex Dir: Janet Benzing
IT Man: Thomas Moore

D-U-N-S 96-524-0302 IMP/EXP
DELTA RIGGING & TOOLS INC
(*Suby of* BISHOP LIFTING PRODUCTS INC) ★
125 Mccarty St, Houston, TX 77029-1135
Tel (713) 512-1700 *Founded/Ownrshp* 2014
Sales 84.2MM[E] *EMP* 483[E]
SIC 7359 2298 3496 Equipment rental & leasing; Slings, rope; Slings, lifting: made from purchased wire
Pr: Derrick Deakins
VP: Doug Smith
Dir IT: Wally Whitley
Dir IT: Allen Willis
VP Sls: Anthony Piwonka
Sales Asso: Kevin Bock

D-U-N-S 18-953-4969 IMP
DELTA STAR INC
3550 Mayflower Dr, Lynchburg, VA 24501-5019
Tel (434) 845-0921 *Founded/Ownrshp* 1988
Sales 162.5MM[E] *EMP* 443
Accts Mcleod & Company Roanoke Va
SIC 3612 Transformers, except electric
Pr: Ivan Tepper
CFO: Steve Jones
Dept Mgr: Jim Curtis
Genl Mgr: Jeremy Roe
QC Dir: Shane Smith
Sfty Mgr: Mike McDaniel
Mfg Mgr: Greg Halsey
Opers Mgr: Tim Harris
Opers Mgr: Marcia Mayen
Ql Cn Mgr: Ken Burke
Board of Directors: Janet Collins, John Nickels, Ivan Tepper, Wendy Tepper

D-U-N-S 00-842-6413 IMP
■ **DELTA STEEL INC**
(*Suby of* RELIANCE STEEL & ALUMINUM CO) ★
7355 Roundhouse Ln, Houston, TX 77078-4500
Tel (713) 635-1200 *Founded/Ownrshp* 1962, 1963
Sales 217.9MM[E] *EMP* 300
SIC 5051 Metals service centers & offices; Structural shapes, iron or steel; Wire
Pr: Eric Offenberger
**CFO:* V Thomas Rudd
VP: Pam Cervantes
VP Inf Sys: Kelly Foster
Sales Exec: Cindy Aldridge
Sls Mgr: Gary Horne
Sls Mgr: Brian Kalinec
Sales Asso: Jeff Bradford
Sales Asso: Tipper Henderson
Sales Asso: Shannon Martin

D-U-N-S 06-606-8719 IMP
DELTA SYSTEMS INC
1734 Frost Rd, Streetsboro, OH 44241-5008
Tel (330) 626-2811 *Founded/Ownrshp* 1973
Sales 103.9MM[E] *EMP* 200
SIC 3613 3625 Switchgear & switchboard apparatus; Relays & industrial controls
Pr: Elizabeth M Barry
**COO:* Mark J Fechtel
**CFO:* Michael R Jeziorski
Ql Cn Mgr: Adrian Cowan
Sls Mgr: Bill Michaels

D-U-N-S 94-901-6539
■ **DELTA TECHNOLOGY LLC**
(*Suby of* DELTA AIRLINES) ★
1001 International Blvd, Atlanta, GA 30354-1802
Tel (404) 714-1500 *Founded/Ownrshp* 1996
Sales 150.2MM[E] *EMP* 1,917
SIC 7373 Computer integrated systems design
VP: Allison Ausband
VP: Kathy McLeod
Mng Dir: Theresa Keaveny
Genl Mgr: Mark Fogle
Genl Mgr: Khai Phan
IT Man: Doug Wilkin
Info Man: Dean Compton
Software D: Praveen Akula
Software D: Beth Anderson
Software D: Andrew Clarkson
Software D: Roy Ellikkulathu

D-U-N-S 16-949-0625
DELTA WESTERN INC
(*Suby of* NORTH STAR UTILITIES GROUP INC) ★
1177 Fairview Ave N, Seattle, WA 98109-4418
Tel (907) 276-2688 *Founded/Ownrshp* 2000
Sales 110.7MM[E] *EMP* 70[E]
SIC 5171 5251 5411 Petroleum bulk stations & terminals; Hardware; Grocery stores
Pr: Kirk Payne
**Pr:* Brian Bogen
**VP:* Norma Barco

D-U-N-S 05-875-0514 IMP
DELTA WOODSIDE INDUSTRIES INC
700 N Woods Dr, Fountain Inn, SC 29644-9789
Tel (864) 255-4100 *Founded/Ownrshp* 1972
Sales 157.8MM *EMP* 1,000
SIC 2221 Manmade & synthetic broadwoven fabrics
Pr: William F Garrett
CFO: William H Hardman Jr
VP Opers: Donald C Walker

DELTA-HA, INC.
See HA-USA INC

D-U-N-S 06-365-1517
DELTA-SONIC CARWASH SYSTEMS INC
570 Delaware Ave, Buffalo, NY 14202-1206
Tel (716) 874-5668 *Founded/Ownrshp* 1967
Sales 534.9MM[E] *EMP* 3,000
SIC 5461 7542 Doughnuts; Carwash, automatic
Ch Bd: Ronald Benderson
Pr: Dale Wittlief
CFO: Brian Evers
VP: Bob Fisher
VP: Robert Klien
VP: Dale Wittlef
Telecom Ex: Dave Hyzy
Dir IT: Christopher Boebel
VP Opers: Robert Fischer
Mktg Dir: Kim Canna

D-U-N-S 79-643-0536
DELTA-T GROUP INC
950 E Haverford Rd # 200, Bryn Mawr, PA 19010-3851
Tel (610) 527-0830 *Founded/Ownrshp* 1989
Sales 88.4MM[E] *EMP* 2,000
SIC 7363 Medical help service
Pr: Joanne W McAndrews
COO: Patty Welch
**CFO:* Bert Nawn
**Treas:* Scott R McAndrews
VP: Dean Jackson
VP: Rachana Patel
Off Mgr: Phillip Rosanio
Off Mgr: Stephanie Spallino
QA Dir: Maryanne Mabery
IT Man: Paul Smith
S&M/VP: Christopher Mc Andrews

D-U-N-S 14-194-6322
■ **DELTACOM LLC**
EARTHLINK BUSINESS
(*Suby of* EARTHLINK BUSINESS LLC) ★
7037 Old Madison Pike Nw, Huntsville, AL 35806-2107
Tel (256) 382-2100 *Founded/Ownrshp* 1982
Sales 865.5MM[E] *EMP* 2,000
SIC 4813 Long distance telephone communications
Pr: Joseph F Eazor
V Ch: Campbell B Lanier III
**CFO:* Bradley A Ferguson
Chf Cred: Robert W Smith Jr
Sr VP: Thomas Schroeder
Sr VP: Roger F Woodward
VP: Susan Corley
VP: Skip Hinshaw
VP: David McPeters
Area Mgr: Anthony Cox
Genl Mgr: CAM Beckum

DELTACRAFT
See MILLCRAFT GROUP LLC

D-U-N-S 15-699-1705
DELTEK INC
DELTEK SYSTEMS
(*Suby of* THOMA BRAVO LLC) ★
2291 Wood Oak Dr Ste 100, Herndon, VA 20171-6008
Tel (703) 734-8606 *Founded/Ownrshp* 2012
Sales 748.0MM[E] *EMP* 1,800[E]
SIC 7371 7379 Computer software development; Computer related consulting services
CEO: Mike Corkery
CFO: Michael Krone
CFO: Michael L Krone
Ofcr: K A Farber
Ofcr: Kevin Iaquinto
Ex VP: Eric Brehm
Ex VP: Namita Dhallan
Ex VP: Brown Eric
Ex VP: David Hare
Ex VP: Rick Lowenstein
Ex VP: Tom Mazich
Ex VP: Claus Thorsgaard
Sr VP: Deborah K Fitzgerald
Sr VP: Matt Fogo
Sr VP: Holly Kortright
Sr VP: Duane Kotsen
Sr VP: Michael L Krone
VP: Timothy Bailey
VP: Warren Brown
VP: Kevin Carr
VP: Cian Chang

DELTEK SYSTEMS
See DELTEK INC

D-U-N-S 00-690-2878
▲ **DELTIC TIMBER CORP**
210 E Elm St, El Dorado, AR 71730-6104
Tel (870) 881-9400 *Founded/Ownrshp* 1996
Sales 193.8MM *EMP* 536[E]
Tkr Sym DEL *Exch* NYS
SIC 0811 2411 6531 8741 Timber tracts; Timber tracts, softwood; Logging; Real estate agent, commercial; Real estate agent, residential; Real estate managers; Business management; Administrative management; Financial management for business; Industrial management
CEO: D Mark Leland
**Ch Bd:* Robert C Nolann
CFO: Kenneth D Mann
VP: Jim F Andrews Jr
VP: David V Meghreblian
VP: Kent L Streeter
Exec: Angela Gates
Exec: Miranda Lee
Ql Cn Mgr: Chris Brown
Board of Directors: Robert B Tudor III, Randolph C Coley, Bert H Jones, Christoph Keller III, D Mark Leland, David L Lemmon, Robert Madison Murphy, R Hunter Pierson Jr, J Thurston Roach, Lenore M Sullivan

D-U-N-S 06-481-8875 EXP
DELUCA INC
DELUCA TOYOTA
1719 Sw College Rd, Ocala, FL 34471-1623
Tel (352) 732-0770 *Founded/Ownrshp* 1988
Sales 126.0MM *EMP* 103[E]
SIC 5511 Automobiles, new & used
Pr: Frank Deluca
COO: Lori Horner
Treas: Sandy Ingraham
**VP:* Vera Sandiford
Exec: Bill Berry
Mktg Dir: Bryan Denney

DELUCA TOYOTA
See DELUCA INC

D-U-N-S 00-614-8597
▲ **DELUXE CORP** (MN)
3680 Victoria St N, Shoreview, MN 55126-2906
Tel (651) 483-7111 *Founded/Ownrshp* 1915
Sales 1.7MMM *EMP* 5,830
Accts Pricewaterhousecoopers Llp Mi
Tkr Sym DLX *Exch* NYS
SIC 2782 2761 7389 Checkbooks; Computer forms, manifold or continuous; Continuous forms, office & business; Strip forms (manifold business forms); Financial services; Check validation service; Charge account service
CEO: Lee J Schram
CFO: Edward A Merritt
Ofcr: Mike Mathews
Sr VP: John Filby
Sr VP: Pete Godich
Sr VP: Julie Loosbrock
Sr VP: Malcolm McRoberts
Sr VP: Anthony C Scarfone
VP: Amanda Brinkman
VP: Tracey Engelhardt
VP: Michael Mathews
VP: George May
VP: Edward Merritt
VP: Michael O'Keefe
VP: Ilan Sasson
Board of Directors: Ronald C Baldwin, Charles A Haggerty, Don J McGrath, Cheryl E Mayberry McKissac, Neil J Metviner, Stephen P Nachtsheim, Mary Ann O'dwyer, Thomas J Reddin, John L Stauch

D-U-N-S 80-286-2545
DELUXE ENTERTAINMENT SERVICES GROUP INC
(*Suby of* MACANDREWS & FORBES HOLDINGS INC) ★
2400 W Empire Ave, Los Angeles, CA 90027
Tel (323) 462-6171 *Founded/Ownrshp* 2007
Sales 115.5MM[E] *EMP* 808
SIC 7819 7313 Film processing, editing & titling: motion picture; Electronic media advertising representatives
CEO: Cyril Drabinsky
V Ch: Barry Cottle
Pr: Frank Cardello
**CFO:* Neil Davidson
**CFO:* Mike Gunter
Ofcr: Stefan Sonnenfeld
**Ex VP:* Warren Stein
Sr VP: Sean Coughlin
VP: Jay Chicoy
VP: Michael Jackman
VP: Alex Mark
VP: Matthew Ruffi
Creative D: Lindsey Kaiser
Dir Bus: Patrick Vonsychowski

D-U-N-S 03-218-3394
DELUXE MEDIA SERVICES INC
568 Atrium Dr, Vernon Hills, IL 60061-1731
Tel (847) 990-4100 *Founded/Ownrshp* 2008
Sales NA *EMP* 1,200
SIC 7819 7822

D-U-N-S 17-523-3618
DELUXE MOTEL
2700 N Main St, Sumter, SC 29153-8662
Tel (803) 469-0236 *Founded/Ownrshp* 1987
Sales 140.0MM *EMP* 2
SIC 7011 Motels
Owner: Sam Patel

D-U-N-S 78-021-0394
▲ **DEMAND MEDIA INC**
1655 26th St, Santa Monica, CA 90404-4016
Tel (310) 656-6253 *Founded/Ownrshp* 2006
Sales 125.9MM *EMP* 350[E]
Tkr Sym DMD *Exch* NYS
SIC 7313 7336 Electronic media advertising representatives; Creative services to advertisers, except writers
CEO: Sean Moriarty
**Ch Bd:* James R Quandt
COO: Brian Pike
CFO: Rachel Glaser
Ex VP: Daniel Weinrot
VP: Jill Angel
VP: Daniel Bornstein
VP: Rachel F Lee
VP: Mitchell Pavao
VP: Michael Tanaka
Snr Sftwr: Nikhil Almeida
Board of Directors: Fredric W Harman, John A Hawkins, Victor E Parker, Brian M Regan, Mitchell Stern

D-U-N-S 17-335-9683
■ **DEMANDWARE INC**
(*Suby of* SALESFORCE.COM INC) ★
5 Wall St Fl 2, Burlington, MA 01803-4774
Tel (888) 553-9216 *Founded/Ownrshp* 2016
Sales 237.2MM *EMP* 765[E]
SIC 7371 7372 Computer software systems analysis & design, custom; Computer software development & applications; Prepackaged software
Pr: Thomas D Ebling
COO: Jeffrey Barnett
CFO: Timothy M Adams
Ofcr: Nick Camelio
Sr VP: Elana Anderson
Sr VP: Brian Callahan
Sr VP: Jamus Driscoll
Sr VP: Rohit Goyal
Sr VP: Tom Griffin
Sr VP: Kathleen Patton
Sr VP: Rick Welch
VP: Nate Lewis
VP: David Port
Board of Directors: Lawrence S Bohn, Linda Crawford, Jill Granoff, Charles F Kane, Leonard A Schlesinger

D-U-N-S 61-537-1932 IMP/EXP
DEMATIC CORP
DEMATIC GROUP
(*Suby of* DEMATIC HOLDING SARL)
507 Plymouth Ave Ne, Grand Rapids, MI 49505-6029
Tel (678) 695-4500 *Founded/Ownrshp* 2015
Sales 1.2MMM^E *EMP* 2,402
SIC 3535 1796 8711 Conveyors & conveying equipment; Machinery installation; Engineering services
CEO: John Baysore
**CFO:* Dan Killeen
CFO: Richard S Paradise
Ex VP: Robert Arg Elles
Ex VP: Anthony Gajadharsingh
Ex VP: Jeffrey Moss
Ex VP: Jim Stollberg
**Sr VP:* David Berghorn
VP: Dave Berghorn
**VP:* Robert Bork
VP: Michael Dolfin
VP: Cesar Epifanio
VP: Cheryl M Falk
**VP:* Herbert Fitzon
VP: Scott Hinke
**VP:* Aysha Maqbool
VP: Curtis Robbins
VP: Scott Watts
VP: Katie Wierengo
**VP:* Timothy Wolf
Board of Directors: Thomas Klanderman, Doug Schram

DEMATIC GROUP
See DEMATIC CORP

DEMCO
See DIXIE ELECTRIC MEMBERSHIP CORP

D-U-N-S 00-655-2483 IMP/EXP
DEMCO INC (WI)
4810 Forest Run Rd, Madison, WI 53704-7338
Tel (800) 356-1200 *Founded/Ownrshp* 1905, 1978
Sales 117.0MM^E *EMP* 305
SIC 5021 2521

DEMDACO
See DD TRADERS INC

D-U-N-S 08-478-1368
DEMENT CONSTRUCTION CO
96 Smith Ln, Jackson, TN 38301-9669
Tel (731) 424-6306 *Founded/Ownrshp* 1977
Sales 124.0MM^E *EMP* 350^E
SIC 1622 1611 Bridge construction; General contractor, highway & street construction
Pr: William Dement
**Pr:* William Dementt
CFO: Jay Woodall
**Treas:* James Newman
Ex VP: Alan Dement
VP: Wayne Brackeen
**VP:* W D Dement
Genl Mgr: Cindy Taylor

D-U-N-S 00-532-3670 IMP
DEMMER CORP
1600 N Larch St Ste 1, Lansing, MI 48906-4168
Tel (517) 321-3600 *Founded/Ownrshp* 1951
Sales 166.1MM^E *EMP* 475
SIC 3795 3812 3544 3465 3441 Tanks & tank components; Acceleration indicators & systems components, aerospace; Special dies, tools, jigs & fixtures; Automotive stampings; Fabricated structural metal
Ch Bd: John E Demmer
**Pr:* William A Demmer
COO: Sten Sjoberg
**CFO:* Heather Shawa De Cook
CFO: Heather S De Cook
CFO: Heather S Decook
Mng Dir: Matt Heppler
Prgrm Mgr: Brian Engelhardt
Prgrm Mgr: Casey McKinney
Prgrm Mgr: Chad Taylor
Genl Mgr: Timothy McKenna

DEMO DELUXE
See IMG

D-U-N-S 02-658-3997
DEMONTROND BUICK CO (TX)
GOODWRENCH SERVICE CENTER
14101 North Fwy, Houston, TX 77090-6998
Tel (281) 872-7200 *Founded/Ownrshp* 1953
Sales 101.9MM^E *EMP* 220
SIC 5511 Automobiles, new & used
Pr: George A Demontrond III

D-U-N-S 00-786-9647 IMP
DEMOULAS SUPER MARKETS INC (MA)
MARKET BASKET
875 East St, Tewksbury, MA 01876-1495
Tel (978) 640-8100 *Founded/Ownrshp* 1910
Sales 4.8MM *EMP* 19,000
SIC 5411 Supermarkets, 55,000-65,000 square feet (superstore); Supermarkets
Pr: Arthur T Demoulas
**CEO:* Felicia Thornton
COO: Bill Marsden
**CFO:* Donald T Mulligan
**Co-CEO:* James Gooch
**Ex VP:* James D Miamis
**VP:* James Mianis
**VP:* Joseph L Rockwell
Dir IT: Peter Moretti
Dir IT: Cindy Renaud
VP Mktg: Kathy McGovern

D-U-N-S 07-228-8681 IMP
DEN-MAT CORP
(*Suby of* DEN-MAT HOLDINGS LLC) ★
236 S Broadway St, Orcutt, CA 93455-4605
Tel (805) 922-8491 *Founded/Ownrshp* 1972
Sales 90.5MM^E *EMP* 700
SIC 2844 3843 Toothpastes or powders, dentifrices; Dental materials
CEO: Robert L Ibsen
**Ex VP:* Noreen Freitas
Prd Mgr: Eric Codazzi

D-U-N-S 80-985-7704 IMP
DEN-MAT HOLDINGS LLC
(*Suby of* CP DENTAL LLC) ★
1017 W Central Ave, Lompoc, CA 93436-2701
Tel (805) 346-3700 *Founded/Ownrshp* 2011
Sales 151.7MM^E *EMP* 702
SIC 3843 Dental materials
CEO: Steven J Semmelmayer
**COO:* Robert Cartagena
**CFO:* Trevor Roots
VP: Scott Mejia
**Prin:* Todd J Tiberi

D-U-N-S 07-184-5358
DENA NENA HENASH
TANANA CHIEFS CONFERENCE
122 1st Ave Ste 600, Fairbanks, AK 99701-4871
Tel (907) 452-8251 *Founded/Ownrshp* 1971
Sales 123.5MM *EMP* 650
SIC 8011 8331 8322 8093

DENALI ADVNCED INTEGRATION DIV
See 3MD INC

D-U-N-S 93-896-9540
DENALI INC
550 Westcott St Ste 450, Houston, TX 77007-5099
Tel (713) 627-0933 *Founded/Ownrshp* 1995
Sales 7.1MMM^E *EMP* 111,301
SIC 3089 Plastic & fiberglass tanks
Pr: Robert B Bennett
**Ch Bd:* Richard W Volk
**CFO:* Timothy D Maynard
**VP:* Lee W Orr
**VP:* Cathy L Smith
VP: Cathy Smith
VP: Peter M Young
Dir IT: Reagan Franklin

D-U-N-S 07-920-2976
■ **DENALI INTERMEDIATE INC**
(*Suby of* DELL TECHNOLOGIES INC) ★
1 Dell Way, Round Rock, TX 78682-7000
Tel (713) 627-0933 *Founded/Ownrshp* 2013
Sales 46.2MMM^E *EMP* 101,800
SIC 3571 3572 3577 7372 Electronic computers; Minicomputers; Personal computers (microcomputers); Computer storage devices; Computer peripheral equipment; Printers, computer; Application computer software
CEO: Michael S Dell

D-U-N-S 06-105-2986
■ **DENBURY ONSHORE LLC**
(*Suby of* DENBURY RESOURCES INC) ★
5320 Legacy Dr, Plano, TX 75024-3127
Tel (972) 673-2000 *Founded/Ownrshp* 1999
Sales 626.5MM^E *EMP* 345
SIC 1311 1382 Crude petroleum production; Crude petroleum & natural gas production; Oil & gas exploration services
Sr VP: Robert Cornelius
VP: Tracy Evans
VP: Steve McLaurin
Ex Dir: David Miller
Dir IT: Don Purvis
IT Man: Sara Afshar
VP Mktg: Ron Gamling

D-U-N-S 14-753-3025
▲ **DENBURY RESOURCES INC**
5320 Legacy Dr, Plano, TX 75024-3127
Tel (972) 673-2000 *Founded/Ownrshp* 1951
Sales 1.2MMM *EMP* 1,356
Tkr Sym DNR *Exch* NYS
SIC 1311 Crude petroleum & natural gas production; Crude petroleum production
Pr: Phil Rykhoek
Ch Bd: John P Dielwart
Pr: Christian S Kendall
CFO: Mark C Allen
Sr VP: Jim Matthews
VP: Matthew Dahan
VP: Matthew W Dahan
VP: John Filiatrault
VP: Barbara Lathrup
VP: Steve McLaurin
VP: Alan Rhoades
VP: Scott Rodgers
VP: Whitney Shelley
VP: David Sheppard

D-U-N-S 00-943-8490 IMP
DENCO SALES CO
55 S Yuma St, Denver, CO 80223-1207
Tel (303) 733-0607 *Founded/Ownrshp* 1999
Sales 121.0MM^E *EMP* 150
SIC 5199 5084 Variety store merchandise; Printing trades machinery, equipment & supplies
Pr: Ken Von Wald
**CFO:* Jack Lanz
**VP:* Mike Hobbs
**VP:* Gary Lewis
**Prin:* Dave Smith
Brnch Mgr: Scott Campbell

D-U-N-S 80-541-8993 EXP
DENDREON CORP
601 Union St Ste 4900, Seattle, WA 98101-3906
Tel (206) 256-4545 *Founded/Ownrshp* 2015
Sales 213.2MM^E *EMP* 755^E
SIC 2834 Pharmaceutical preparations
COO: John Zeng
CFO: Gregory Cox
Sr VP: David Snyder
Sr VP: David L Urdal PHD
CTO: Jim Devitt
QA Dir: Ahmadullah Mohammad
QA Dir: David Monarrez
QA Dir: Darrell Ransom
IT Man: Brian Kollar
Ql Cn Mgr: Jamie Isonhood
Sls Dir: Dan Duran

D-U-N-S 07-987-9298
DENDREON PHARMACEUTICALS INC
(*Suby of* VALEANT PHARMACEUTICALS INTERNATIONAL, INC)
400 Somerset Corp Blvd # 500, Bridgewater, NJ 08807-2867
Tel (908) 927-1400 *Founded/Ownrshp* 2015
Sales 114.6MM^E *EMP* 460
SIC 2834 Pharmaceutical preparations
CEO: Laizer Kornwasser
Pr: Steven Sembler
**Ex VP:* Robert Chai-Onn
**VP:* Linda Lagorga

D-U-N-S 08-100-3527
DENHAM-BLYTHE CO INC
100 Trade St Ste 250, Lexington, KY 40511-2634
Tel (859) 255-7405 *Founded/Ownrshp* 2006
Sales 94.3MM *EMP* 200
SIC 1541 1542

DENISE ANN HARRIS ESTATE
See HARRIS DENISE ANN TRUST

D-U-N-S 05-825-4217
DENISE THRASHER
THRASHERS TOOLS AND TOYS
959 E Axton Rd, Bellingham, WA 98226-9711
Tel (360) 223-4917 *Founded/Ownrshp* 2012
Sales 240.0MM *EMP* 2
SIC 5945 Toys & games
Owner: Denise Thrasher
Co-Ownr: Sean Job

D-U-N-S 06-905-9111
DENISON UNIVERSITY
100 W College St, Granville, OH 43023-1100
Tel (740) 587-0810 *Founded/Ownrshp* 1831
Sales 128.6MM *EMP* 757^E
Accts Maloney & Novotny Llc Clevela
SIC 8221 College, except junior
Pr: Dale T Knobel
**CFO:* David English
VP: Ken Espinosa
**VP:* Julie Houpt
**VP:* Dr Laurel Kennedy
Dir Risk M: Steven Gauger
Assoc Dir: Bill Robbins
DP Exec: Denise Teesdale
Dir IT: Frank Y Anderson
Prd Mgr: James Hale
Mktg Dir: Scott Tribble

D-U-N-S 11-898-8963
DENMISS LLC
1368 Old Fannin Rd # 100, Brandon, MS 39047-8024
Tel (601) 919-1757 *Founded/Ownrshp* 1971
Sales 237.5MM^E *EMP* 2,812^E
SIC 6211 6531 Mineral leasing dealers; Oil royalties dealers; Real estate leasing & rentals

D-U-N-S 03-468-6942
DENN-OHIO LLC
1002 Armstrong Dr, Willard, OH 44890-9154
Tel (419) 544-4030 *Founded/Ownrshp* 2010
Sales 20.0MM *EMP* 1,000
SIC 5812 Family restaurants

D-U-N-S 04-325-3665
DENNIS BEVERAGE CO
DENNIS PAPER & FOOD SERVICE
101 Mecaw Rd, Bangor, ME 04401
Tel (207) 947-0321 *Founded/Ownrshp* 2015
Sales 131.7MM^E *EMP* 115
SIC 5141 5113 Food brokers; Cups, disposable plastic & paper; Dishes, disposable plastic & paper; Napkins, paper
Pr: Ronald B Dennis
**CFO:* Tom Gagne
Sls&Mrk Ex: Chris Caler
Manager: Zachary Hess
Sls Mgr: Dave McNally

D-U-N-S 19-480-2674
DENNIS GROUP INC
1537 Main St Fl 2, Springfield, MA 01103-1463
Tel (413) 787-1785 *Founded/Ownrshp* 1987
Sales 153.2MM^E *EMP* 270
SIC 8711 Engineering services
Pr: Thomas P Dennis Jr

D-U-N-S 01-918-7053
DENNIS K BURKE INC
284 Eastern Ave, Chelsea, MA 02150-3318
Tel (617) 884-7800 *Founded/Ownrshp* 1961
Sales 933.5MM *EMP* 110
Accts Tonneson & Company Inc Wake
SIC 5172 5541 Gasoline; Diesel fuel; Lubricating oils & greases; Gasoline service stations
Ch Bd: Edmund F Burke
**CFO:* Joe Cote
Exec: Meaghan Burke

DENNIS PAPER & FOOD SERVICE
See DENNIS BEVERAGE CO

D-U-N-S 60-938-1124
DENNISON LUBRICANTS INC
DENNISON LUBRICANTS WA WOOD CO
102 Charles Eldridge Rd, Lakeville, MA 02347-1377
Tel (508) 946-0500 *Founded/Ownrshp* 1988
Sales 105.0MM^E *EMP* 60
SIC 5172 Lubricating oils & greases
Pr: Timothy Dennison
**VP:* Brian Dennison
**VP:* Karen Dennison
**VP:* Barry Macarthur

DENNISON LUBRICANTS WA WOOD CO
See DENNISON LUBRICANTS INC

DENNY'S
See SERVUS

DENNY'S
See RREMC LLC

D-U-N-S 60-816-3747 IMP
▲ **DENNYS CORP**
203 E Main St, Spartanburg, SC 29319-0003
Tel (864) 597-8000 *Founded/Ownrshp* 1988
Sales 491.2MM *EMP* 8,500
Tkr Sym DENN *Exch* NAS
SIC 5812 6794 Restaurant, family: chain; Franchises, selling or licensing
Pr: John C Miller
**Ch Bd:* Brenda J Lauderback
COO: Christopher D Bode
Chf Mktg O: John W Dillon
Ofcr: Jill A Van Pelt
**Ofcr:* F Mark Wolfinger
Ex VP: Laysha L Ward
Sr VP: Stephen C Dunn
VP: Jay Gilmore
VP: William Ruby
VP: Jill Van Pelt
Board of Directors: Gregg R Dedrick, Jose M Gutierrez, George W Haywood, Robert E Marks, Debra Smithart-Oglesby, Donald C Robinson

D-U-N-S 02-636-5807 IMP
■ **DENNYS INC**
(*Suby of* DENNYS INC) ★
2306 Reidville Rd, Spartanburg, SC 29301-3650
Tel (864) 597-8532 *Founded/Ownrshp* 1959
Sales 259.2MM^E *EMP* 8,000
SIC 5812 6794

D-U-N-S 61-030-3596
■ **DENNYS INC**
(*Suby of* DENNYS CORP) ★
203 E Main St P-73, Spartanburg, SC 29319-0003
Tel (864) 597-8000 *Founded/Ownrshp* 1953
Sales 266.4MM^E *EMP* 8,000
SIC 5812 Restaurant, family: chain
Pr: Nelson Marchioli
**Pr:* John C Miller
**CEO:* John Miller
**CFO:* Mark Wolfinger
**Chf Mktg O:* Frances Allen
Opers Mgr: Becky Cudd

DENOVA
See MASCO CABINETRY LLC

D-U-N-S 55-602-7456 IMP
DENSO AIR SYSTEMS MICHIGAN INC
(*Suby of* DENSO AIR SYSTEMS CORPORATION)
300 Fritz Keiper Blvd, Battle Creek, MI 49037-5607
Tel (269) 962-9676 *Founded/Ownrshp* 2009
Sales 83.9MM^E *EMP* 345^E
SIC 3714 3498 Air conditioner parts, motor vehicle; Fabricated pipe & fittings
VP: Katsuaki Kawai
Genl Mgr: Yoshi Saitoh
Snr Mgr: Steve Clement
Snr Mgr: John Thawnghmung

D-U-N-S 15-136-9881 IMP/EXP
DENSO INTERNATIONAL AMERICA INC
(*Suby of* DENSO CORPORATION)
24777 Denso Dr, Southfield, MI 48033-5244
Tel (248) 350-7500 *Founded/Ownrshp* 1949
Sales 2.9MMM^E *EMP* 12,000
SIC 3714 5013 Motor vehicle parts & accessories; Motor vehicle engines & parts; Radiators & radiator shells & cores, motor vehicle; Motor vehicle electrical equipment; Motor vehicle supplies & new parts
Pr: Hikaru Sugi
**COO:* Kazumasa Kimura
COO: Stephen Milam
Ex VP: Atsuhiko Shimmura
VP: Pat Bassett
VP: Roger Berg
VP: Mike Brackett
VP: Dave Ewing
**VP:* Bill Foy
VP: Itsushi Kawamoto
VP: Fran Labun
VP: Koji Mori
VP: Shigeki Nishiyama
VP: Bassett Patrick
VP: Douglas Patton
VP: Nobuhiro Sugawara
VP: Michael Winkler
Exec: Yoshiki Sekiguchi

D-U-N-S 14-369-4201 EXP
DENSO MANUFACTURING ARKANSAS INC
(*Suby of* DENSO INTERNATIONAL AMERICA INC) ★
100 Denso Rd, Osceola, AR 72370-3849
Tel (870) 622-9500 *Founded/Ownrshp* 2003
Sales 91.2MM^E *EMP* 438
SIC 3089 7539 Automotive parts, plastic; Radiator repair shop, automotive
Pr: Andris Staltmanis
**Treas:* Seiji Maeda
**Treas:* Yoshihiko Yoshikawa
Admn Mgr: John Beal
Genl Mgr: George Harguess

D-U-N-S 12-762-5478 IMP/EXP
DENSO MANUFACTURING ATHENS TENNESSEE INC
(*Suby of* DENSO INTERNATIONAL AMERICA INC) ★
2400 Denso Dr, Athens, TN 37303-7835
Tel (423) 746-0000 *Founded/Ownrshp* 2003
Sales 293.1MM^E *EMP* 1,000
SIC 3694 3714 Alternators, automotive; Motors, starting: automotive & aircraft; Motor vehicle electrical equipment; Instrument board assemblies, motor vehicle
Pr: Kazuhiko Miura
**Pr:* Youichi Yamashita
Treas: Marc Allyn
Treas: Analiza Schmidt
VP: Robyn Abbott
VP: David Hollomon
Genl Mgr: Brian Nolen
IT Man: Atul Giri
VP Opers: Robert Hull
Sls Mgr: Alex Merlina

D-U-N-S 14-775-4931 IMP/EXP
DENSO MANUFACTURING MICHIGAN INC
DMMI
(*Suby of* DENSO INTERNATIONAL AMERICA INC) ★
1 Denso Rd, Battle Creek, MI 49037-7313
Tel (269) 965-3322 *Founded/Ownrshp* 1984
Sales 71.8MM^E *EMP* 2,500
SIC 5531 Automotive accessories; Automotive parts
CEO: Hikaru Howard Sugi
Pr: Kazutaka Nimura
**COO:* Kazumasa Kimura
**Treas:* Masato Yamada
**Ex VP:* Atsuhiko Art Shimmura
Genl Mgr: Karen Cooper-Boyer
Genl Mgr: Greg Lampert
Genl Mgr: Joe Stich
Snr Mgr: Darren Hervey
Board of Directors: M Kawai

D-U-N-S 60-226-2990 IMP/EXP
DENSO MANUFACTURING TENNESSEE INC
(*Suby of* DENSO INTERNATIONAL AMERICA INC) ★
1720 Robert C Jackson Dr, Maryville, TN 37801-3748
Tel (865) 982-7000 *Founded/Ownrshp* 1988
Sales 530.5MM^E *EMP* 2,393
SIC 3694 3714 Alternators, automotive; Motors, starting: automotive & aircraft; Motor vehicle electrical equipment; Instrument board assemblies, motor vehicle
Pr: Van Saka
**Ex VP:* Toshimitsu Kosaka
**Ex VP:* Hisao Oita
Sr VP: Jim Woroniecki
VP: Randy Adams
VP: Britt Autry
VP: Troy Bigelow
VP: Tammy Jurinsky
**VP:* Tsutomu Maekawa
Genl Mgr: Steven Seagle
QA Dir: Jack Martin

D-U-N-S 05-735-7196 IMP/EXP
DENSO PRODUCTS AND SERVICES AMERICAS INC
DSCA
(*Suby of* DENSO INTERNATIONAL AMERICA INC) ★
3900 Via Oro Ave, Long Beach, CA 90810-1868
Tel (310) 834-6352 *Founded/Ownrshp* 1985
Sales 187.5MM^E *EMP* 504^E
SIC 5013 7361 5075 3714 Automotive supplies & parts; Employment agencies; Warm air heating & air conditioning; Motor vehicle parts & accessories
CEO: Yoshihiko Yamada
Pr: Hisashi Matsunobu
Ex VP: Roy Nakaue
VP: Peter Clotz
VP: Fran Labun
VP: Jeff Rogers
VP: Susan Wright
Exec: Yoshiaki Sugiyama
QA Dir: Adam Martin
Info Man: Ruth Canloba
VP Prd: Eugene Stark

D-U-N-S 03-523-7614
DENT J GREGG & ASSOSICATES PLC (FL)
400 Health Park Blvd, Saint Augustine, FL 32086-5784
Tel (904) 819-4565 *Founded/Ownrshp* 2001
Sales 207.5MM *EMP* 2
SIC 8031 Offices & clinics of osteopathic physicians
Pr: James G Dent

D-U-N-S 86-132-0919
DENTAL CARE ALLIANCE LLC
6240 Lake Osprey Dr, Lakewood Ranch, FL 34240-8421
Tel (888) 876-4531 *Founded/Ownrshp* 2002
Sales 80.7MM^E *EMP* 1,100
SIC 8021 Dental clinics & offices
CEO: Mitchell B Olan
**Pr:* Michael Bileca
**CEO:* David P Nichols
CFO: David Nichols
Ex VP: Kevin Webb
Sr VP: Dwain Shearer
Rgnl Mgr: Robin Leavitt
Off Mgr: Heather Smith
Mktg Mgr: Jeannie Smith-Rosenberg

DENTAL CARE PLUS GROUP DCPG
See DCP HOLDING CO

DENTAL CHOICE
See DELTA DENTAL OF KENTUCKY INC

D-U-N-S 80-011-1106
DENTAL IMAGING TECHNOLOGIES CORP
IMAGING SCIENCES INTERNATIONAL
2800 Crystal Dr, Hatfield, PA 19440-1944
Tel (215) 997-5666 *Founded/Ownrshp* 1992
Sales 200.0MM *EMP* 200^E
SIC 3843 5047 Dental equipment; X-ray machines & tubes
Pr: Amir Aghbabi
**CFO:* Marc Pensa
**Treas:* Frank McFaden
VP: Tony Reynolds
Sftwr Eng: Leonid Khatutskiy
Ql Cn Mgr: David Appleton
Sales Exec: Christopher Scharff
Sls Dir: Ty Ramsey
Snr PM: Kartik B Damany

D-U-N-S 11-820-2696
DENTAL NETWORK OF AMERICA LLC
HEALTH CARE SERVICE
(*Suby of* BLUE CROSS AND BLUE SHIELD) ★
701 E 22nd St Ste 300, Lombard, IL 60148-5097
Tel (630) 691-0290 *Founded/Ownrshp* 2001
Sales NA *EMP* 366
SIC 6324 Dental insurance
Sls Mgr: John Doyle
CFO: Jerry Mallen
Sr VP: Shreyas Shah
IT Man: David Frasca

D-U-N-S 13-166-8600
DENTAL SERVICE OF MASSACHUSETTS INC
DELTA DENTAL PLAN MASS
465 Medford St Ste 150, Charlestown, MA 02129-1457
Tel (617) 886-1000 *Founded/Ownrshp* 1970
Sales NA *EMP* 400
Accts Ernst & Young Us Llp Cincinna
SIC 6324 Dental insurance
CEO: Steven Pollock
**Pr:* Kathy O'Loughlin
**Sr VP:* Fay Donohue-Rolfe
CTO: Sandy Patterson
Dir IT: Steve Robinson

D-U-N-S 11-928-8934
DENTALCARE PARTNERS INC
SEARS DENTAL CENTER
6200 Oak Tree Blvd # 200, Independence, OH 44131-6933
Tel (216) 584-1000 *Founded/Ownrshp* 1997
Sales 55.6MM^E *EMP* 1,000
SIC 8021

D-U-N-S 08-023-7131
DENTALONE PARTNERS INC
DENTALWORKS
7160 Dallas Pkwy Ste 400, Plano, TX 75024-7111
Tel (972) 755-0800 *Founded/Ownrshp* 2008
Sales 6.8MM^E *EMP* 2,300
SIC 8621 Professional membership organizations
Ch Bd: Edward Meckler
**CEO:* Thomas J Marler

DENTALWORKS
See DENTALONE PARTNERS INC

D-U-N-S 93-823-8821
DENTAQUEST LLC
(*Suby of* DENTAQUEST VENTURES LLC) ★
12121 Corporate Pkwy, Mequon, WI 53092-3332
Tel (262) 241-7140 *Founded/Ownrshp* 2004
Sales NA *EMP* 240
SIC 6324 Hospital & medical service plans

D-U-N-S 11-184-9621
DENTAQUEST VENTURES LLC
465 Medford St Ste 150, Boston, MA 02129-1457
Tel (617) 886-1818 *Founded/Ownrshp* 2006
Sales NA *EMP* 1,000^E
SIC 6324 Dental insurance
Pr: Steven Pollock
**CFO:* James Collins
Treas: Scott O Gorman
VP: Brett Bostrack
VP: Sheryl Trylor

D-U-N-S 00-894-7913
DENTON COUNTY ELECTRIC COOPERATIVE INC
COSERV ELECTRIC
7701 S Stemmons Fwy, Corinth, TX 76210
Tel (940) 321-7800 *Founded/Ownrshp* 1937
Sales 511.9MM *EMP* 900
Accts Bolinger Segars Gilbert And Mo
SIC 4911 Distribution, electric power
Pr: Michael A Dreyspring
**CFO:* Donnie Clary
Treas: Bill Ragsdale
**Sr VP:* Joe R Forman
**Sr VP:* Stacia Sims
Exec: Leon Pelzel
Dir Risk M: Dan Lemons
Dir IT: Jeff McNeal

D-U-N-S 05-531-1104
DENTON INDEPENDENT SCHOOL DISTRICT
1307 N Locust St, Denton, TX 76201-3037
Tel (940) 369-0000 *Founded/Ownrshp* 1884
Sales 313.4MM *EMP* 3,300
Accts Hankins Eastup Deaton Tonn
SIC 8211 Public elementary & secondary schools
Pr: Mia Price
**VP:* Glenna G Harris
Pr Dir: Mario Zavala
Schl Brd P: Charles Stafford
HC Dir: Kathy Malmberg

D-U-N-S 78-141-4248
■ **DENTON REGIONAL MEDICAL CENTER INC**
(*Suby of* HOSPITAL CORPORATION OF AMERICA) ★
3535 S Interstate 35 E, Denton, TX 76210-6850
Tel (940) 384-3535 *Founded/Ownrshp* 1991
Sales 157.9MM *EMP* 900
SIC 8062 8011 General medical & surgical hospitals; Offices & clinics of medical doctors
**CFO:* Brad Shultz
Dir Rad: Richard R Reinholtz
CTO: Lester Jerone
Dir IT: Rex Conatser
Mktg Dir: Kathy Sims
Board of Directors: Candice L Beard

D-U-N-S 78-454-0812
DENTON TRANSITIONAL LTCH LP
INTEGRITY TRANSITIONAL HOSP
2813 S Mayhill Rd, Denton, TX 76208-5910
Tel (940) 320-2300 *Founded/Ownrshp* 2005
Sales 106.2MM^E *EMP* 1,054^E
SIC 8062 General medical & surgical hospitals
Prin: Benjamin Patton
Dir IT: Florence Dickerson
Opers Mgr: Ken Fitzgerald

D-U-N-S 07-704-1697
DENTONS US LLP
233 S Wacker Dr Ste 5900, Chicago, IL 60606-6404
Tel (312) 876-8000 *Founded/Ownrshp* 1906
Sales 505.0MM^E *EMP* 1,576
SIC 8111 General practice law office
Genl Pt: Duane C Quaini
Pt: Karen Gifford
Pt: Daniel E McCann
Pt: David Schadler
Pt: Darry Sragow
Pt: Clinton A Vince
Pt: Mary G Wilson
Mng Pt: Frank Shisler
Pr: Kim Arrington
CEO: Jorge Alers
CFO: David Nelson

D-U-N-S 10-222-1942 IMP/EXP
▲ **DENTSPLY SIRONA INC**
221 W Philadelphia St, York, PA 17401-2991
Tel (717) 845-7511 *Founded/Ownrshp* 1899
Sales 2.6MMM *EMP* 11,400
Accts Pricewaterhousecoopers Llp Ha
Tkr Sym XRAY *Exch* NGS
SIC 3843 Dental equipment & supplies; Impression material, dental; Denture materials; Teeth, artificial (not made in dental laboratories)
CEO: Jeffrey T Slovin
Ch Bd: Bret W Wise
Pr: Christopher T Clark
Pr: James G Mosch
CFO: Ulrich Michel
CFO: Kelley Quinn
Sr VP: Robert J Size
Sr VP: Albert J Sterkenburg
VP: Todd Gunter
VP: Andrew Lichkus
VP: Bill Schlageter
Exec: Kelly Koehler
Exec: Danny Zanotti
Board of Directors: Michael C Alfano, David K Beecken, Eric K Brandt, Michael J Coleman, Willie A Deese, Thomas Jetter, Arthur D Kowaloff, Francis J Lunger

DENTSU AEGIS NETWORK USA
See AEGIS MEDIA AMERICAS INC

D-U-N-S 00-709-0269
DENVER BOARD OF WATER COMMISSIONERS
DENVER WATER
1600 W 12th Ave, Denver, CO 80204-3412
Tel (303) 893-2444 *Founded/Ownrshp* 1918
Sales 810.5MM^E *EMP* 1,100^E
Accts Kpmg Llp Denver Co
SIC 4941 Water supply
CEO: James Loughhead
**CFO:* Angela Bircmont
Bd of Dir: Lindsay Weber
VP: Alan Chotiner
VP: Eric Gordon
VP: Laurna Kaatz
VP: Penfield Tate
Sys Mgr: Patrick O'Malley
Info Man: John Nelson
Software D: Carol Austin
Software D: Jeff Cook

DENVER COUNTRY STORES
See SAFEWAY STORES 46 INC

D-U-N-S 08-868-2539
DENVER FOUNDATION
55 Madison St Ste 800, Denver, CO 80206-5423
Tel (303) 300-1790 *Founded/Ownrshp* 1925
Sales 127.9MM *EMP* 25
Accts Eks&H Lllp Denver Co
SIC 6732 Trusts: educational, religious, etc.
Pr: David Miller
Bd of Dir: Tucker Adams
Ofcr: Charmaine Brown
Ofcr: Harold Fields
Ofcr: Niki Herrera
Ofcr: Kelly Purdy
Ofcr: Emily Stanley
VP: Barbara Berv
VP: Lauren Casteel
VP: Sarah Harrison
Ex Dir: Kim Hacker

D-U-N-S 09-356-4180
DENVER HEALTH AND HOSPITALS AUTHORITY INC
777 Bannock St, Denver, CO 80204-4597
Tel (720) 956-2580 *Founded/Ownrshp* 1999
Sales 449.8MM *EMP* 3,541^E
SIC 8062 General medical & surgical hospitals
CEO: Arthur Gonzalez
**Pr:* Patricia Gabow
**COO:* Stephanie Thomas
CFO: Peg Burnette
CFO: Lorraine Montoya
VP: Jennifer Crebs
Dir Risk M: Angelita Valdez
Chf Nrs Of: Kathy Boyle
Ex Dir: Leann Donovan
Ex Dir: Paula Herzmark
Mtls Dir: Philip Pettigrew

D-U-N-S 00-706-0817
DENVER POST CORP
(*Suby of* DIGITAL FIRST MEDIA) ★
1560 Broadway Fl 4, Denver, CO 80202-5108
Tel (303) 321-7012 *Founded/Ownrshp* 1892
Sales 141.1MM^E *EMP* 1,107
SIC 2711 Newspapers, publishing & printing
Ch Bd: W Dean Singleton
VP: Dmitry Primachenko
Dir IT: Justin Lee

D-U-N-S 01-914-5460 IMP
DENVER POST LLC
ROCKY MOUNTAIN NEWS
(*Suby of* DIGITAL FIRST MEDIA) ★
101 W Colfax Ave, Denver, CO 80202-5315
Tel (303) 892-5000 *Founded/Ownrshp* 2001
Sales 191.4MM^E *EMP* 1,700
SIC 2711 Newspapers, publishing & printing
Mng Pt: Harry Whipple
**Pr:* Mac Tully
**Ofcr:* David P Murphy
Sr VP: Bernie Rakowsky
Sr VP: Bill Reynolds
VP: Ryan Moffat
VP: Marty Sokoler
Admn Mgr: Ken Killpack
Off Mgr: Joni Dougherty
CTO: Zach Johnson
Web Dev: Joe Murphy

D-U-N-S 04-109-9334
DENVER PUBLIC SCHOOLS
1860 N Lincoln St, Denver, CO 80203-2996
Tel (720) 423-3200 *Founded/Ownrshp* 1902
Sales 389.0MM^E *EMP* 99
Accts Cliftonlarsonallen Llp Greenw
SIC 8211 Public elementary & secondary schools; Public junior high school; Public senior high school
Pr: Gary Losh
COO: Craig Cook
Prin: Emillo Esquibel
Ex Dir: John Simmons
Ex Dir: Jennifer Stern
Dir Sec: Michael Eaton
Dir IT: Bobby Williams
Pr Dir: Nancy Michelle
Schl Brd P: Happy Hyanes
Teacher Pr: Shayne Spalten
Instr Medi: Dave Sanger

DENVER WATER
See DENVER BOARD OF WATER COMMISSIONERS

D-U-N-S 00-797-0064
DENVER WHOLESALE FLORISTS CO
DWF WHOLESALE FLORISTS
4800 Dahlia St Ste A, Denver, CO 80216-3121
Tel (303) 399-0970 *Founded/Ownrshp* 1909
Sales 105.9MM^E *EMP* 285
SIC 5193 Flowers, fresh; Plants, potted; Florists' supplies
Sr Cor Off: Marion Elliott
**V Ch Bd:* Kenneth Tagawa
**VP:* David Gaul

DEPARTAMENTO DE HACIENDA DE PR
See PUERTO RICO DEPARTMENT OF TREASURY

DEPARTAMENTO DE INSTRCCN
See DEPARTMENT OF EDUCATION OF PUERTO RICO

DEPARTAMENTO DEL TRABAJO
See PUERTO RICO DEPARTMENT OF LABOR AND HUMAN RESOURCES

DEPARTMENT MANAGEMENT SERVICES
See FLORIDA DIVISION OF ADMINISTRATIVE HEARINGS

D-U-N-S 96-573-6635
DEPARTMENT OF BEHAVIORAL HEALTH AND DEVELOPMENTAL DISABILITIES
DBHDD
(*Suby of* EXECUTIVE OFFICE OF STATE OF GEORGIA) ★
2 Peachtree St Nw, Atlanta, GA 30303-3141
Tel (404) 657-1650 *Founded/Ownrshp* 2009
Sales NA *EMP* 8,561
SIC 9431 Administration of public health programs;
CFO: Lee Wright
IT Man: Shawn Dupree

D-U-N-S 78-191-2886
DEPARTMENT OF BEHAVIORAL HEALTHCARE DEVELOPMENTAL DISABILITIES AND HOSPITALS
BHDDH
(*Suby of* EXECUTIVE OFFICE OF STATE OF RHODE ISLAND) ★
14 Harrington Rd, Cranston, RI 02920-3080
Tel (401) 462-3201 *Founded/Ownrshp* 1995
Sales NA *EMP* 1,600
SIC 9431 Mental health agency administration, government;
IT Man: Melanie Wilson

D-U-N-S 07-941-9705
DEPARTMENT OF CHILD SERVICES
302 W Washington St E306, Indianapolis, IN 46204-2738
Tel (317) 234-5739 *Founded/Ownrshp* 2014
Sales NA *EMP* 1,500
SIC 9611

D-U-N-S 80-884-7735
DEPARTMENT OF COMMERCE OHIO
(*Suby of* SECRETARY OF STATE OHIO) ★
6606 Tussing Rd, Reynoldsburg, OH 43068-4175
Tel (614) 644-2223 *Founded/Ownrshp* 1920
Sales NA *EMP* 1,200
SIC 9611 Administration of general economic programs;
Ofcr: Lisa Caldwell

D-U-N-S 92-699-4492
DEPARTMENT OF COMMUNITY BASED SERVICES
(*Suby of* HEALTH & FAMILY SERVICES KENTUCKY CABINET FOR) ★
275 E Main St Ste 3wa, Frankfort, KY 40601-2321
Tel (502) 564-3703 *Founded/Ownrshp* 1996
Sales NA *EMP* 4,690^E
SIC 9431 9441 Administration of public health programs; ; Administration of social & manpower programs;

D-U-N-S 80-987-2831
DEPARTMENT OF CORRECTION ARKANSAS
(*Suby of* GOVERNERS OFFICE) ★
6814 Princeton Pike, White Hall, AR 71602-9411
Tel (870) 267-6999 *Founded/Ownrshp* 1968
Sales NA *EMP* 3,688
SIC 9223 Prison, government;
Ex Dir: Ray Hobbs
**Ex Dir:* Larry Norris

D-U-N-S 82-520-1205
DEPARTMENT OF CORRECTION IDAHO
(*Suby of* EXECUTIVE OFFICE OF STATE OF IDAHO) ★
1299 N Orchard St Ste 110, Boise, ID 83706-2266
Tel (208) 658-2000 *Founded/Ownrshp* 1865
Sales NA *EMP* 1,950
SIC 9223 Prison, government
**CFO:* Lisa Johnson
IT Man: Derrick Georgiades
Board of Directors: Thomas Beauelaire, Brent Reinke,

James Spalding

D-U-N-S 93-369-8409
DEPARTMENT OF CORRECTIONS ALABAMA
(*Suby of* OFFICE OF SECRETARY STATE) ★
301 S Ripley St, Montgomery, AL 36104-4425
Tel (334) 353-3844 *Founded/Ownrshp* 1996
Sales NA *EMP* 3,626
SIC 9222 Attorney General's office;

D-U-N-S 80-938-6410
DEPARTMENT OF CORRECTIONS ALASKA
(*Suby of* OFFICE OF GOVERNOR) ★
802 3rd St, Douglas, AK 99824-5412
Tel (907) 465-4652 *Founded/Ownrshp* 1995
Sales NA *EMP* 1,861
SIC 9223 8322 9441 8299 Prison, government; ; Parole office; Probation office; Substance abuse counseling; Medical assistance program administration, government; Educational services
**CFO:* Amy Moselle

D-U-N-S 80-681-1808
DEPARTMENT OF CORRECTIONS ILLINOIS
(*Suby of* EXECUTIVE OFFICE OF GOVERNOR) ★
1301 Concordia Ct, Springfield, IL 62702-5699
Tel (217) 557-1030 *Founded/Ownrshp* 1970
Sales NA *EMP* 11,900
SIC 9223 9111 Prison, government; ; Executive offices;
CFO: Bill Edleyl
Genl Mgr: John Baldwin
IT Man: Jared Brunk
Mktg Mgr: Richard Hampton

D-U-N-S 92-699-5812
DEPARTMENT OF CORRECTIONS KENTUCKY
(*Suby of* JUSTICE AND PUBLIC SAFETY CABINET OF KENTUCKY) ★
275 E Main St Rm 36, Frankfort, KY 40601-2321
Tel (502) 564-4726 *Founded/Ownrshp* 1792
Sales NA *EMP* 4,000
SIC 9223 Prison, government;
Genl Mgr: Hilarye Dailey
IT Man: Danny Norris
IT Man: Terry Terrell
Netwrk Mgr: Marvin Todd

D-U-N-S 80-904-5438
DEPARTMENT OF CORRECTIONS MAINE
(*Suby of* EXECUTIVE OFFICE OF STATE OF MAINE) ★
25 Tyson Dr 3rd Flr, Augusta, ME 04333-0001
Tel (207) 287-2711 *Founded/Ownrshp* 1982
Sales NA *EMP* 1,325[E]
SIC 9223 Correctional institutions;

D-U-N-S 80-533-6526
DEPARTMENT OF CORRECTIONS MICHIGAN
MDOC
(*Suby of* EXECUTIVE OFFICE OF STATE OF MICHIGAN) ★
206 E Michigan Ave, Lansing, MI 48933-1431
Tel (517) 373-0720 *Founded/Ownrshp* 1900
Sales NA *EMP* 13,500
SIC 9223 Prison, government;

D-U-N-S 80-479-3511
DEPARTMENT OF CORRECTIONS MINNESOTA
CENTRAL OFFICE
(*Suby of* GOVERNORS OFFICE) ★
1450 Energy Park Dr # 200, Saint Paul, MN 55108-5219
Tel (651) 361-7200 *Founded/Ownrshp* 1889
Sales NA *EMP* 3,700
SIC 9223 Prison, government;
**CFO:* Chris Dodge
CFO: Rich Schoenthaler
**VP:* Guy Piras
**Prin:* Tom Roy
Brnch Mgr: Jeff Martin

D-U-N-S 80-939-9678
DEPARTMENT OF CORRECTIONS MISSISSIPPI
(*Suby of* EXECUTIVE OFFICE OF STATE OF MISSISSIPPI) ★
633 N State St Ste 208, Jackson, MS 39202-3306
Tel (601) 359-5600 *Founded/Ownrshp* 1976
Sales NA *EMP* 3,037
SIC 9223 Prison, government;
MIS Mgr: Audrey McAfee

D-U-N-S 87-900-2251
DEPARTMENT OF CORRECTIONS MISSOURI
EXECUTV OFC OF THE STATE OF MO
(*Suby of* EXECUTIVE OFFICE OF STATE OF MISSOURI) ★
2729 Plaza Dr, Jefferson City, MO 65109-1146
Tel (573) 751-2389 *Founded/Ownrshp* 1821
Sales NA *EMP* 10,883
SIC 9223 Correctional institutions;

D-U-N-S 80-979-0587
DEPARTMENT OF CORRECTIONS MONTANA
(*Suby of* EXECUTIVE OFFICE OF STATE OF MONTANA) ★
5 S Last Chance Gulch, Helena, MT 59601-4178
Tel (406) 444-3930 *Founded/Ownrshp* 1967
Sales NA *EMP* 1,000
SIC 9223 Prison, government;
Genl Mgr: Kara Sperle
IT Man: Diane Jones
Board of Directors: Mike Ferriter

D-U-N-S 83-556-9716
DEPARTMENT OF CORRECTIONS UTAH
(*Suby of* EXECUTIVE OFFICE OF STATE OF UTAH) ★
14717 S Minuteman Dr, Draper, UT 84020-9549
Tel (801) 545-5500 *Founded/Ownrshp* 1850
Sales NA *EMP* 2,300
SIC 9223 Prison, government;
Ex Dir: Rollin E Cook
Genl Mgr: David Worthington

D-U-N-S 80-888-2310
DEPARTMENT OF CORRECTIONS WASHINGTON STATE
DIVISION OF PRISONS
(*Suby of* STATE OF WASH OFFICE OF GVRNOR) ★
7345 Linderson Way Sw, Tumwater, WA 98501-6504
Tel (360) 725-8213 *Founded/Ownrshp* 1981
Sales NA *EMP* 8,000
SIC 9223
Top Exec: Richard Baldwin
IT Man: Kevin Grover
IT Man: Carolyn House-Higgins

D-U-N-S 80-991-5408
DEPARTMENT OF CORRECTIONS WYOMING
(*Suby of* EXECUTIVE OFFICE OF STATE OF WYOMING) ★
1934 Wyott Dr Ste 100, Cheyenne, WY 82007-2123
Tel (307) 777-7208 *Founded/Ownrshp* 1991
Sales NA *EMP* 1,304
SIC 9223 Prison, government;
**CFO:* Clarance Carpenter

D-U-N-S 01-719-3702
■ **DEPARTMENT OF DEFENSE EDUCATION ACTIVITY**
DODEA
(*Suby of* OFFICE OF THE SECRETARY OF DEFENSE) ★
4800 Mark Center Dr, Alexandria, VA 22350-0002
Tel (571) 372-1337 *Founded/Ownrshp* 1992
Sales NA *EMP* 8,785[E]
SIC 9711 9411 National security; Administration of educational programs

D-U-N-S 05-341-2198
DEPARTMENT OF ECONOMIC AND SOCIAL AFFAIRS
(*Suby of* UNITED NATIONS SECRETARIAT) ★
Secretariat Bldg Unitedn, New York, NY 10003
Tel (212) 963-1707 *Founded/Ownrshp* 1999
Sales NA *EMP* 5,314[E]
SIC 9721 United Nations
Prin: Sha Zukang
Ex Dir: Amir Dossal

DEPARTMENT OF EDUCATION
See NEW YORK CITY BOARD OF EDUCATION

DEPARTMENT OF EDUCATION
See AUBURN SCHOOL DEPARTMENT

D-U-N-S 09-014-2522
DEPARTMENT OF EDUCATION OF PUERTO RICO
DEPARTAMENTO DE INSTRCCN
150 Calle Federico Costa, San Juan, PR 00918-1339
Tel (787) 759-2000 *Founded/Ownrshp* 1952
Sales NA *EMP* 45,000
SIC 9411 State education department

D-U-N-S 93-299-9758
DEPARTMENT OF EMPLOYMENT OREGON
(*Suby of* EXECUTIVE OFFICE OF STATE OF OREGON) ★
875 Union St Ne, Salem, OR 97311-0800
Tel (503) 947-1470 *Founded/Ownrshp* 1987
Sales NA *EMP* 1,382
SIC 9441 Administration of social & manpower programs;
Genl Mgr: Rich Rowzee

D-U-N-S 09-040-6737
DEPARTMENT OF FAMILY
FAMILIA
(*Suby of* SECRETARY OF COMMONWEALTH) ★
Sevilla Plz Bldg Se, San Juan, PR 00919
Tel (787) 643-1855 *Founded/Ownrshp* 1968
Sales NA *EMP* 11,000
SIC 9441 8331 Public welfare administration: nonoperating, government; Vocational rehabilitation agency

D-U-N-S 02-369-9320
DEPARTMENT OF HEALTH AND HUMAN SERVICES
8000 N Stadium Dr Fl 8, Houston, TX 77054-1823
Tel (713) 794-9370 *Founded/Ownrshp* 2001
Sales NA *EMP* 1,200
SIC 9431
Dir Vol: Cydney Cameron

D-U-N-S 79-652-8263
DEPARTMENT OF HEALTH CARE SERVICES
(*Suby of* CHHS) ★
1501 Capitol Ave, Sacramento, CA 95814-5005
Tel (916) 445-4171 *Founded/Ownrshp* 1998
Sales NA *EMP* 3,500
SIC 9431 Administration of public health programs;
Genl Mgr: Jennifer Kent
IT Man: Angeli Lee
Info Man: Loretta Wallis

D-U-N-S 80-488-7321
DEPARTMENT OF HEALTH MINNESOTA
(*Suby of* GOVERNORS OFFICE) ★
625 Robert St N, Saint Paul, MN 55155-2538
Tel (651) 201-5000 *Founded/Ownrshp* 1977
Sales NA *EMP* 1,300
SIC 9431 Administration of public health programs;
**Prin:* Sanne Magnan
Genl Mgr: Carolyn Hoel
IT Man: Marita Bliven
IT Man: Wendy Melki

D-U-N-S 80-884-7933
DEPARTMENT OF HEALTH OHIO
ODH
(*Suby of* EXECUTIVE OFFICE STATE OF OHIO) ★
246 N High St, Columbus, OH 43215-2406
Tel (614) 466-3543 *Founded/Ownrshp* 1886
Sales NA *EMP* 2,400
SIC 9431 Administration of public health programs;
**Pr:* Richard Hodges
CFO: Harold Vermillion
Exec: Bret Atkins
CIO: Gil Vincent
DP Exec: Chris Slee
Snr Mgr: Amadou Diallo

D-U-N-S 61-448-9839
DEPARTMENT OF HEALTH PENNSYLVANIA
(*Suby of* GOVERNORS OFFICE) ★
625 Forster St, Harrisburg, PA 17120-0701
Tel (717) 787-6325 *Founded/Ownrshp* 1929
Sales NA *EMP* 1,403
SIC 9431 Administration of public health programs;

D-U-N-S 95-934-7972
DEPARTMENT OF HEALTH UTAH
(*Suby of* EXECUTIVE OFFICE OF STATE OF UTAH) ★
288 N 1460 W, Salt Lake City, UT 84116-3231
Tel (801) 538-6111 *Founded/Ownrshp* 1980
Sales NA *EMP* 1,500
SIC 9431 Administration of public health programs;
Ex Dir: Joe Miner
Dir IT: Michael Allred

D-U-N-S 96-656-2894
DEPARTMENT OF HIGHWAYS KENTUCKY
(*Suby of* TRANSPORTATION CABINET KENTUCKY) ★
200 Mero St, Frankfort, KY 40601-1920
Tel (502) 564-4890 *Founded/Ownrshp* 1837
Sales NA *EMP* 2,500
SIC 9621 Bureau of public roads;

D-U-N-S 92-995-6548
DEPARTMENT OF MILITARY ALABAMA
(*Suby of* OFFICE OF SECRETARY STATE) ★
1720 Congsman Wl Dksn Dr, Montgomery, AL 36109
Tel (334) 271-7435 *Founded/Ownrshp* 1946
Sales NA *EMP* 3,000
SIC 9711 National Guard

D-U-N-S 80-748-7863
DEPARTMENT OF MILITARY CALIFORNIA
ADJUTANT GENERAL'S OFFICE
(*Suby of* EXECUTIVE OFFICE OF STATE OF CALIFORNIA) ★
9800 Goethe Rd 10, Sacramento, CA 95827-3561
Tel (916) 854-3500 *Founded/Ownrshp* 1850
Sales NA *EMP* 1,600[E]
SIC 9711 National Guard;
Prin: David Baldwin

D-U-N-S 80-958-0343
DEPARTMENT OF MILITARY OREGON
(*Suby of* EXECUTIVE OFFICE OF STATE OF OREGON) ★
1776 Militia Way Se, Salem, OR 97301-6888
Tel (503) 584-3910 *Founded/Ownrshp* 1859
Sales NA *EMP* 1,220
SIC 9711 National security;
Prin: Raymond F Rees
**Prin:* Tracy Ann Gill
**Prin:* Peter R Wood

D-U-N-S 80-937-6668
DEPARTMENT OF MILITARY VERMONT
VERMONT NATIONAL GUARD
(*Suby of* GOVERNORS OFFICE) ★
789 National Guard Rd, Colchester, VT 05446-3046
Tel (802) 338-3310 *Founded/Ownrshp* 1791
Sales NA *EMP* 4,000
SIC 9711 Army;
**Prin:* Joseph T Quick
IT Man: Tiffany Davis

D-U-N-S 80-991-5960
DEPARTMENT OF MILITARY WYOMING
ADJUTANT GENERAL'S OFFICE
(*Suby of* EXECUTIVE OFFICE OF STATE OF WYOMING) ★
5500 Bishop Blvd, Cheyenne, WY 82009-3320
Tel (307) 772-6201 *Founded/Ownrshp* 1890
Sales NA *EMP* 3,741
SIC 9711 National security;

DEPARTMENT OF PSYCHIATR
See MEDICAL UNIVERSITY OF SOUTH CAROLINA

DEPARTMENT OF REVENUE
See STATE OF WISCONSIN

D-U-N-S 80-634-7274
DEPARTMENT OF REVENUE ILLINOIS
(*Suby of* EXECUTIVE OFFICE OF GOVERNOR) ★
101 W Jefferson St, Springfield, IL 62702-5145
Tel (217) 782-3336 *Founded/Ownrshp* 1818
Sales NA *EMP* 1,800[E]
SIC 9311 Finance, taxation & monetary policy;
Ex Dir: Michael Malone

D-U-N-S 80-483-2376
DEPARTMENT OF REVENUE MINNESOTA
SALES & USE TAX
(*Suby of* GOVERNORS OFFICE) ★
600 Robert St N, Saint Paul, MN 55101-2228
Tel (651) 556-3000 *Founded/Ownrshp* 1858
Sales NA *EMP* 1,560
SIC 9311 Taxation department, government;

D-U-N-S 87-804-7620
DEPARTMENT OF REVENUE MISSOURI
(*Suby of* EXECUTIVE OFFICE OF STATE OF MISSOURI) ★
301 W High St, Jefferson City, MO 65101-1517
Tel (573) 751-4450 *Founded/Ownrshp* 1821
Sales NA *EMP* 2,000
SIC 9311 Finance, taxation & monetary policy;
Comm Dir: Michelle Gleba
IT Man: Jeff Falter

D-U-N-S 80-979-1270
DEPARTMENT OF REVENUE MONTANA
(*Suby of* EXECUTIVE OFFICE OF STATE OF MONTANA) ★
125 N Roberts St Fl 34, Helena, MT 59601-4559
Tel (406) 444-2460 *Founded/Ownrshp* 1972
Sales NA *EMP* 1,219
SIC 9311 Finance, taxation & monetary policy;

D-U-N-S 80-985-5554
DEPARTMENT OF SAFETY AND HOMELAND SECURITY (DSHS)
(*Suby of* EXECUTIVE OFFICE OF GOVERNOR OF DELAWARE) ★
303 Transportation Cir, Dover, DE 19901-4671
Tel (302) 744-2672 *Founded/Ownrshp* 1970
Sales NA *EMP* 1,033
SIC 9221 9229 State police; ; Public order & safety statistics centers;

D-U-N-S 18-631-3342 IMP
DEPARTMENT OF STATE MICHIGAN
(*Suby of* EXECUTIVE OFFICE OF STATE OF MICHIGAN) ★
430 W Allegan St, Lansing, MI 48933-1592
Tel (517) 373-2510 *Founded/Ownrshp* 1837
Sales NA *EMP* 2,200[E]
SIC 9199 General government administration;

DEPARTMENT OF SURGERY
See HOWARD UNIVERSITY HOSPITAL

D-U-N-S 03-079-1966
DEPAUL INDUSTRIES
TEMPORARY STAFFING
4950 Ne Martin Luther Ki, Portland, OR 97211-3354
Tel (503) 281-1289 *Founded/Ownrshp* 1971
Sales 92.8MM[E] *EMP* 1,020
Accts Moss Adams Llp Portland Or
SIC 7361 8331 Placement agencies; Vocational rehabilitation agency
Pr: Travis Pearson
CFO: Thomas Horey
Ofcr: Dean Stearman
VP: Katy Daughn
VP: Thomas Gornick
VP: Jon Ulsh
Prgrm Mgr: Carol Simon-Perry
Rgnl Mgr: Joshua Latshaw
IT Man: Irina Bennington
Ql Cn Mgr: Randy Peterson
Sls Mgr: Bryan Baker

DEPAUL UNIVERSITY
See DE PAUL UNIVERSITY

D-U-N-S 00-494-3114
DEPAUW UNIVERSITY
313 S Locust St, Greencastle, IN 46135-1736
Tel (765) 658-4800 *Founded/Ownrshp* 1837
Sales 180.3MM *EMP* 652
Accts Crowe Horwath Llp Chicago Il
SIC 8221 University
Pr: Brian W Casey
Genl Pt: Tom Porter
**Pr:* Robert G Bottoms
Bd of Dir: Tobias Butler
Bd of Dir: Annie John
Trst: James R Batlett
Trst: Thomas W Bosell
Trst: Rhett Butler
Trst: Nicholas Chabraja
Trst: John Christensen
Trst: James Cornelius
Trst: Glady Faires
Trst: Charles Grannon
Trst: David Greising
Trst: Kathryn Hubbard
Trst: Charles Iikubo
Trst: Hirotsugu Iikubo
Trst: Arthur Klauser
Trst: Michael Maine
Trst: David Morehead
Trst: David Posegay
Board of Directors: Tom Dicson

D-U-N-S 07-944-4151
DEPCOM POWER INC
9200 E Pima Center Pkwy # 180, Scottsdale, AZ 85258-4398
Tel (480) 270-6910 *Founded/Ownrshp* 2013
Sales 195.6MM *EMP* 30
SIC 1623 5211 Electric power line construction; Solar heating equipment
CEO: Jim Lamon
Genl Couns: Tracy Morehouse

D-U-N-S 80-856-6723 IMP/EXP
DEPENDABLE AUTO SHIPPERS INC
DAS
3020 U S 80 Frontage Rd, Mesquite, TX 75149
Tel (214) 381-0181 *Founded/Ownrshp* 1989
Sales 101.0MM[E] *EMP* 375
SIC 4213 Automobiles, transport & delivery
Pr: Tina Azzarella
Ex VP: Earl Daniel
VP: Jim Brown
Dir Bus: Jim Mueller
Genl Mgr: Michael Liquori
Genl Mgr: Clifford Schwichow
CIO: Erik Weinkam
IT Man: Yao-WEI Hung
Netwrk Mgr: Harnett Grewal
Info Man: Louis Carpenter
VP Opers: Ken Phillips

D-U-N-S 15-750-9373 IMP/EXP
DEPENDABLE HIGHWAY EXPRESS INC
2555 E Olympic Blvd, Los Angeles, CA 90023-2605
Tel (323) 526-2200 *Founded/Ownrshp* 1986
Sales 303.0MM[E] *EMP* 1,000
SIC 4213 4225 Trucking, except local; General warehousing & storage
Pr: Ronald Massman
**CFO:* Michael Dougan
VP: Bob Massman
**VP:* Robert Massman
Brnch Mgr: Bill Butler
Sfty Dirs: Wayne Carson
Opers Mgr: Jose Estrada
Opers Mgr: AVI Singh
VP Sls: Sal Ioele
VP Sls: Bruce Lensch
VP Sls: Allen Wizelman

D-U-N-S 93-756-2890
▲ DEPOMED INC
7999 Gateway Blvd Ste 300, Newark, CA 94560-1188
Tel (510) 744-8000 Founded/Ownrshp 1995
Sales 342.7MM EMP 494E
Tkr Sym DEPO Exch NGS
SIC 2834 Drugs acting on the central nervous system & sense organs
Pr: James A Schoeneck
Ch Bd: Peter D Staple
CFO: August J Moretti
Chf Cred: R Scott Shively
Chf Mktg O: Srinivas G RAO
Sr VP: Matthew M Gosling
VP: Jeff Coon
VP: Amar Murugan
VP: Michael M Sweeney
Assoc Dir: Kathleen Bennett
Assoc Dir: Singh Noel
Assoc Dir: Sumant Rajendran
Board of Directors: Vicente Anido Jr, Karen A Dawes, Louis J Lavigne Jr, Samuel R Saks, David B Zenoff

D-U-N-S 00-982-7874
■ DEPOSIT TELEPHONE CO INC
TDS
(Suby of TDS TELECOMMUNICATIONS CORP) ★
87 Front St, Deposit, NY 13754-1023
Tel (607) 467-2111 Founded/Ownrshp 1996
Sales 302.2MME EMP 2,700
SIC 4813 Local telephone communications
Pr: David A Wittwer
VP: Mike Pandow

D-U-N-S 07-324-9799 IMP
▲ DEPOSITORY TRUST & CLEARING CORP
CEDE AND COMPANY
55 Water St Ste Conc3, New York, NY 10041-0024
Tel (212) 855-1000 Founded/Ownrshp 1973
Sales 1.2MMM EMP 5,000
Accts Deloitte & Touche Llp New Yor
SIC 6289 6211 7389 Security custodians; Security brokers & dealers; Financial services
Ch Bd: Robert Druskin
Pr: Michael C Bodson
COO: Darryll Hendricks
Ofcr: Pablo Cubi
Sr VP: Neil Brander
VP: Mark Bramante
VP: Gary Burkhardt
VP: Frank Gaffney
VP: Sal Matera
VP: Vivek Pabby
VP: Cory Stark
Dir Bus: Susan Nugent

D-U-N-S 03-519-3742
■ DEPOSITORY TRUST CO INC
DTCC
(Suby of CEDE AND CO) ★
55 Water St Ste Conc4, New York, NY 10041-0099
Tel (212) 855-1000 Founded/Ownrshp 1999
Sales NA EMP 2,500
SIC 6289 Security custodians
Pr: Michael C Bodson
*Ch Bd: Jill M Considine
CFO: Ellen Fine Levine
Bd of Dir: Robin Vince
Sr VP: Patricia Reilly
VP: John Abel
VP: George M Forte
VP: Steve Mandras
VP: Jim Spangler
VP: Sara Stonner
*Prin: Robert Druskin
Board of Directors: Peter B Madoff, James W Zeigon, Bradley Abelow, James H Messenger, Jeffrey C Bernstein, Eileen K Murray, Stephen P Casper, Thomas J Perna, Frank J Decongelio, Ronald Purpora, Dennis J Dirks, Peter Quick, Mary M Fenoglio, Robert H Silver, George Hrabovsky, Thompson M Swayne, Ronald J Kessler, Melvin B Taub, Edward A Kwalwasser, Arthur L Thomas

DEPOT INTERNATIONAL
See CLOVER TECHNOLOGIES GROUP LLC

D-U-N-S 60-454-6273
DEPT OF CORRECTIONS ARIZONA
DCA
(Suby of EXECUTIVE OFFICE OF STATE OF ARIZONA) ★
1601 W Jefferson St, Phoenix, AZ 85007-3056
Tel (602) 542-5225 Founded/Ownrshp 1912
Sales NA EMP 10,000
SIC 9223

D-U-N-S 83-555-1037
DEPT OF CORRECTIONS OKLAHOMA
(Suby of EXECUTIVE OFFICE OF STATE OF OKLAHOMA) ★
3400 N Mtn Lthr Kng Ave, Oklahoma City, OK 73111-4219
Tel (405) 425-2500 Founded/Ownrshp 1967
Sales NA EMP 4,000
SIC 9223 Prison, government;
CEO: Robert Patton
CFO: Jim Harris
*CFO: Tom James
*Ex Dir: Justin Jones
Netwrk Mgr: Jim Glover

D-U-N-S 79-514-5705
DEPT OF EDUCATION PENNSYLVANIA
EXECUTIVE OFC OF THE COMMNWLTH
(Suby of GOVERNORS OFFICE) ★
333 Market St, Harrisburg, PA 17101-2210
Tel (717) 787-5820 Founded/Ownrshp 1834
Sales NA EMP 1,100
SIC 9411 Administration of educational programs;
Dir Sec: Michael Kozup
Pr Dir: Casey Smith
Pr Dir: Kirk Wilson
Teacher Pr: Diana Hershey
HC Dir: Nicholas Lotterback

DEPT OF PHYSICS
See BOSTON UNIVERISTY

D-U-N-S 92-992-9693
DEPT OF REVENUE ALABAMA
(Suby of OFFICE OF SECRETARY STATE) ★
50 N Ripley St Fl 4, Montgomery, AL 36130-1001
Tel (334) 242-1170 Founded/Ownrshp 1898
Sales NA EMP 1,198
SIC 9311 Finance, taxation & monetary policy;
Prin: Tim Russell
IT Man: Phillip Wellman
Netwrk Mgr: Scott Crews

D-U-N-S 80-479-4857
DEPT OF REVENUE ARIZONA
RVA
(Suby of EXECUTIVE OFFICE OF STATE OF ARIZONA) ★
1600 W Monroe St, Phoenix, AZ 85007-2650
Tel (602) 542-2054 Founded/Ownrshp 1974
Sales NA EMP 1,238
SIC 9311

DEPUTY COMMISSIONER
See VIRGINIA DEPARTMENT OF SOCIAL SERVICES

DEPUY ACE MEDICAL
See DEPUY INC

D-U-N-S 79-478-2409
DEPUY INC
DEPUY ACE MEDICAL
1 Johnson And Johnson Plz, New Brunswick, NJ 08901-1241
Tel (732) 524-0400 Founded/Ownrshp 2002
Sales NA EMP 5,140
SIC 3842

D-U-N-S 85-939-5428 IMP
■ DEPUY ORTHOPAEDICS INC
(Suby of JOHNSON & JOHNSON) ★
700 Orthopaedic Dr, Warsaw, IN 46582-3900
Tel (574) 267-8143 Founded/Ownrshp 1998
Sales 443.4MME EMP 3,500
SIC 3842 Surgical appliances & supplies
Pr: Andrew Ekdahl
Ex VP: Larry Williamson
VP: Peter Batesko III
VP: Thomas Guest
VP: Rick Sedlatschek
Off Mgr: Micheael Kasehub
Ql Cn Mgr: Kyle Flakne
Ql Cn Mgr: Brian Nichols
Sls&Mrk Ex: Kent Anderson
VP Mktg: Gordon Van Ummerson
Sls Dir: Raghavendra Shenoy

D-U-N-S 06-639-5992
■ DEPUY PRODUCTS INC
(Suby of JOHNSON & JOHNSON) ★
700 Orthopaedic Dr, Warsaw, IN 46582-3900
Tel (574) 267-8143 Founded/Ownrshp 2000
Sales 1.4MMME EMP 12,000E
SIC 3842 Surgical appliances & supplies
Pr: Andrew Ekdahl
Treas: Peter Batesko III
Ql Cn Mgr: William Fausey

D-U-N-S 78-023-1150
■ DEPUY SYNTHES INC
SYNTHES USA
(Suby of DEPUY PRODUCTS INC) ★
1302 Wrights Ln E, West Chester, PA 19380-3417
Tel (610) 719-5000 Founded/Ownrshp 2009
Sales 1.4MMME EMP 12,000E
SIC 3841 Medical instruments & equipment, blood & bone work
CEO: Michel Orsinger
Rgnl Mgr: Steve Hare
QA Dir: Dave Flett
Netwrk Eng: Jo Kramer
Opers Mgr: Sandeep Ghosh
Opers Mgr: Marco Tamburini
Sales Asso: Jason Buran
Sales Asso: David Coppola
Sales Asso: Joshua Dickerson
Sales Asso: Lori Fletcher
Sales Asso: Brian Gustafson

DER DUTCHMAN RESTAURANTS
See DUTCHMAN HOSPITALITY GROUP INC

D-U-N-S 79-987-4982
DERBY INDUSTRIES LLC
4451 Robards Ln, Louisville, KY 40218-4572
Tel (502) 451-7373 Founded/Ownrshp 2001
Sales 99.3MME EMP 350
SIC 4225 7389 4222 4226 General warehousing & storage; Packaging & labeling services; Refrigerated warehousing & storage; Special warehousing & storage
Pr: Diana Herold
VP: Renee Hunt

D-U-N-S 03-061-6486
DERBY PUBLIC SCHOOLS
DERBY UNIFIED SCHL DST NO 260
120 E Washington St, Derby, KS 67037-1435
Tel (316) 788-8400 Founded/Ownrshp 1872
Sales 59.9MME EMP 1,100
Accts George Bowerman & Noel Pa
SIC 8211 Public elementary school; Public junior high school; Public senior high school
*Treas: Donald Adkisson
Assoc Dir: Travis Keller
DP Exec: Trishia Ferguson
Pr Dir: Heather Bohaty
Mktg Mgr: Gayle Cox
Schl Brd P: Janet Sprecker

DERBY UNIFIED SCHL DST NO 260
See DERBY PUBLIC SCHOOLS

D-U-N-S 01-238-6405 IMP/EXP
■ DERCO AEROSPACE INC
(Suby of SIKORSKY AIRCRAFT CORP) ★
8000 W Tower Ave, Milwaukee, WI 53223-3216
Tel (414) 355-3066 Founded/Ownrshp 2002
Sales 124.3MME EMP 247E
SIC 5065 5088 Electronic parts; Aircraft & parts
Pr: Mark Hoehnen
CFO: Amy Skaar
VP: Kathy Busch
VP: Markus Heinrich
QA Dir: Scott Gluck
VP Opers: Steve Nelson

D-U-N-S 05-853-3977 IMP
DERICHEBOURG RECYCLING USA INC
OKLAHOMA METAL PROCESSSING CO.
7501 Wallisville Rd, Houston, TX 77020-3543
Tel (713) 675-2281 Founded/Ownrshp 1975
Sales 232.8MM EMP 153
Accts Uhy Llp Houston Texas
SIC 5093 Scrap & waste materials
CEO: Philippe Leonard
*Pr: Daniel Derichebourg
VP: Francis Garrigues
VP: Desprez Stephane

D-U-N-S 00-507-3895 IMP
DERINGER-NEY INC
616 Atrium Dr Ste 100, Vernon Hills, IL 60061-1713
Tel (847) 566-4100 Founded/Ownrshp 1950
Sales 110.6MME EMP 396
SIC 3643 3542 3469 3452 3316 Contacts, electrical; Machine tools, metal forming type; Metal stampings; Bolts, nuts, rivets & washers; Cold finishing of steel shapes
Pr: Rod Lamm
*Pr: John L Wallace
*VP: Robert Deringer
*VP: Lee Trimble
Ex Dir: Gary Mowder
Dir IT: Anne Seaver
Plnt Mgr: Richard Rzeszotarski
Mktg Dir: Bruce Quimby

DERIVAMAR
See LAWRENCE WHOLESALE LLC

D-U-N-S 05-462-9373
DERLE FARMS INC
15602 Liberty Ave, Jamaica, NY 11433-1004
Tel (718) 257-2040 Founded/Ownrshp 1954
Sales 146.9MME EMP 96E
SIC 5143 Milk
Ch Bd: Nathan Abramson
*VP: Louis Abramson

D-U-N-S 14-428-0088 IMP
▲ DERMA SCIENCES INC
214 Carnegie Ctr Ste 300, Princeton, NJ 08540-6237
Tel (609) 514-4744 Founded/Ownrshp 1984
Sales 84.4MM EMP 260E
Tkr Sym DSCI Exch NAS
SIC 3842 2211 2834 Surgical appliances & supplies; Bandages & dressings; Bandages, gauzes & surgical fabrics, cotton; Pharmaceutical preparations; Ointments
Prin: Stephen T Wills
CFO: John E Yetter
Ex VP: Frederic Eigner
Ql Cn Mgr: Frank Antonetti
Manager: Bill Schneider
Board of Directors: Brett D Hewlett, Robert G Moussa, Samuel E Navarro

DERMAL GROUP, THE
See DERMALOGICA LLC

D-U-N-S 17-769-8560 IMP
DERMALOGICA LLC
DERMAL GROUP, THE
(Suby of UNILEVER PLC)
1535 Beachey Pl, Carson, CA 90746-4005
Tel (310) 900-4000 Founded/Ownrshp 2015
Sales 123.8MME EMP 400
SIC 2844 Cosmetic preparations
Pr: Aurelian Lis
Creative D: Armand Tatis
Mktg Mgr: Lindsay Cruz

D-U-N-S 09-637-2255 IMP/EXP
DEROYAL INDUSTRIES INC (TN)
200 Debusk Ln, Powell, TN 37849-4703
Tel (865) 938-7828 Founded/Ownrshp 1973
Sales 461.9MME EMP 2,000
SIC 3841 Surgical & medical instruments
Prin: Pete Debusk
Pr: Richard Nichols
*Pr: Bill Pittman
*CEO: Brian C Debusk
VP: Mario Gaztambide
VP: Jeb Hopper
VP: Michael Iekeler
*VP: Michael Lekeler
VP: Mark Mabry
VP: Kristen Rogers
VP: Angie Sewell
VP: Tim Wine
Exec: Melinda Catron
Dir Risk M: Deborah Witt

D-U-N-S 00-211-0864 IMP/EXP
DERRICK CORP (NY)
DERRICK EQUIPMENT
590 Duke Rd, Buffalo, NY 14225-5102
Tel (716) 683-9010 Founded/Ownrshp 1951, 1960
Sales 215.5MME EMP 695
SIC 3533 Oil & gas field machinery
Ch Bd: James W Derrick
*Pr: William W Derrick
*CFO: Frank R Knuth
*Ex VP: John J Bakula
Ex VP: John Bakula
*Ex VP: Robert G Derrick
VP: Dan Carroll
VP: Mutahare Engin
Opers Mgr: Tim Rosen
Opers Mgr: Bob Walczyk
Mktg Dir: Frank Russom

DERRICK EQUIPMENT
See DERRICK CORP

D-U-N-S 08-915-9230 IMP/EXP
DERROUGH AND TALLEY INC
EARTH FARE
(Suby of OAK HILL CAPITAL PARTNERS LP) ★
145 Cane Cr Ind P Rd 15, Fletcher, NC 28732
Tel (828) 281-4800 Founded/Ownrshp 2012
Sales 87.8MME EMP 350
SIC 5499 Health foods
CEO: Jack Murphy
*CFO: Gary Jones
Ofcr: Caroline Skinner
VP Opers: Ronald Henderson

D-U-N-S 02-337-8730 IMP
DERSE INC
3800 W Canal St, Milwaukee, WI 53208-4150
Tel (414) 257-2000 Founded/Ownrshp 1989
Sales 111.3MME EMP 435
SIC 3993 7312 Displays & cutouts, window & lobby; Outdoor advertising services
Owner: William F Haney
*Owner: William M McNamara
*Ch Bd: Bill Haney
*CEO: Adam Beckett
*Ex VP: James Elser
Ex VP: David Sherman
Creative D: Dan Cieciwa
Creative D: Michael Cutchins
Creative D: Robert Herdman
Dir Bus: Beck Wentz
Genl Mgr: Ken Aden-Buie

D-U-N-S 00-329-6043
■ DERST BAKING CO LLC (GA)
(Suby of FLOWERS FOODS INC) ★
1311 W 52nd St, Savannah, GA 31405-3078
Tel (912) 233-2235 Founded/Ownrshp 1867, 2006
Sales 176.1MME EMP 508
SIC 2051 5461

D-U-N-S 87-813-9492
DES MOINES AREA COMMUNITY COLLEGE
DMACC
2006 S Ankeny Blvd, Ankeny, IA 50023-8995
Tel (515) 964-6214 Founded/Ownrshp 1966
Sales 98.9MME EMP 850
SIC 8221 Colleges universities & professional schools
Pr: Robert Denson
V Ch: Kevin Halterman
*Sr VP: Kim Linduska
Store Mgr: Linda Cummings
Psych: Jennifer Wollesen

D-U-N-S 07-807-2899
DES MOINES INDEPENDENT COMMUNITY SCHOOL DISTRICT
DES MOINES PUBLIC SCHOOLS
2323 Grand Ave, Des Moines, IA 50312-5307
Tel (515) 242-7911 Founded/Ownrshp 1913
Sales 381.3MME EMP 5,000E
SIC 8211 Public elementary & secondary schools
VP: Katie Hentges
Instr Medi: Debra Augspurger
Psych: Taylor Bryant
Psych: Julia Minnehan

DES MOINES PUBLIC SCHOOLS
See DES MOINES INDEPENDENT COMMUNITY SCHOOL DISTRICT

D-U-N-S 04-572-6650
■ DES PERES HOSPITAL INC
TENET
(Suby of TENET HEALTHCARE CORP) ★
2345 Dougherty Ferry Rd, Saint Louis, MO 63122-3313
Tel (314) 966-9100 Founded/Ownrshp 1997
Sales 140.9MME EMP 1,410
SIC 8062 General medical & surgical hospitals
Ch Bd: Jeffrey C Barbakow
*CFO: David Byrd
Exec: Kathaleen Clutts
Dir Rx: Steve Schoenekase
Doctor: Victor Rivera
Doctor: Nicole Roedel
Pharmcst: Todd Schrewe
HC Dir: Barbara Schmidt

D-U-N-S 07-448-9474
DESA AGI LLC
1450 Brickell Ave # 2080, Miami, FL 33131-3444
Tel (786) 315-4680 Founded/Ownrshp 2012
Sales 100.0MM EMP 4
SIC 6221 Commodity traders, contracts

D-U-N-S 07-361-7227
DESALES UNIVERSITY
2755 Station Ave, Center Valley, PA 18034-9568
Tel (610) 282-1100 Founded/Ownrshp 1964
Sales 96.8MME EMP 580
SIC 8221 College, except junior
Pr: Rev Bernard O'Connor
*CFO: Robert Snyder
Trst: Scott V Fainor
Trst: James F Kilcur
Trst: Alex L Maggitti
Trst: Charles McIntyre
Ofcr: Dennis Csensits
*VP: Thomas Campbell
VP: Michelle Traub
*VP: Dr Karen Walton
Assoc Dir: Mary Falk
Assoc Dir: Ramona Hollie-Major

D-U-N-S 96-815-6153
DESCO ACQUISITION LLC
BLACKEAGLE ENERGY SERVICES
(Suby of DESCO CORP) ★
230 Commerce Rd, Berthoud, CO 80513-9186
Tel (970) 532-0600 Founded/Ownrshp 1967
Sales 132.4MME EMP 509
Accts Bkd Llp Denver Colorado
SIC 1796 3533 1389 Machinery installation; Oil & gas field machinery; Building oil & gas well foundations on site

CFO: Roger Bailey
**VP:* David Mayo

D-U-N-S 04-081-6399
DESCO CORP
7795 Walton Pkwy Ste 175, New Albany, OH 43054-0002
Tel (614) 888-8855 *Founded/Ownrshp* 1975
Sales 205.6MM^E *EMP* 759
SIC 3442 3825 3643 3531 3429 Window & door frames; Metal doors; Instruments to measure electricity; Current-carrying wiring devices; Construction machinery; Manufactured hardware (general)
Pr: Arnold B Siemer
**CFO:* Roger Bailey
**VP:* Thomas Villano
**Prin:* Mc Connell A Coakwell
**Prin:* James M Smith
Sales Asso: Sandra Lopez

D-U-N-S 00-895-4554 IMP
DESERET BOOK CO
MORMON HANDICRAFT
(*Suby of* CHURCH OF JSUS CHRST OF LD STS) ★
57 W South Temple, Salt Lake City, UT 84101-1511
Tel (801) 517-3294 *Founded/Ownrshp* 1932
Sales 363.8MM^E *EMP* 700
SIC 5192 5942 2731 Books; Book stores; Books, religious; Book publishing
Pr: Sheri L Dew
VP: Jeffrey Gillette
**VP:* Keith Hunter
VP: Ryan Miller
Dir Soc: Luanne Banks
Mng Dir: Cathy Chamberlain
Genl Mgr: Greg Gorzitze
Store Mgr: Tim Bennett
Store Mgr: Darrin Sneddon
Dir IT: Julie Hill
Mktg Dir: Gail Halladay

D-U-N-S 09-881-4395
DESERET GENERATION AND TRANSMISSION CO-OPERATIVE
DESERET POWER
10714 S Jordan Gtwy # 300, South Jordan, UT 84095-3922
Tel (435) 781-5737 *Founded/Ownrshp* 1978
Sales 154.5MM^E *EMP* 250
Accts Deloitte & Touche Llp Salt L
SIC 4911 Generation, electric power; Transmission, electric power
Pr: Kimball Rasmussen
CFO: Robert Dalley
**Sec:* Mark Anderson
Opers Mgr: Marilyn Long
VP Mktg: Curt Winterfeld
Mktg Mgr: Clay Macarthur

D-U-N-S 80-054-6207
DESERET HEALTH GROUP LLC
190 S Main St, Bountiful, UT 84010-6234
Tel (801) 296-5105 *Founded/Ownrshp* 2006
Sales 88.6MM^E *EMP* 1,600
SIC 8051 Skilled nursing care facilities
CEO: Garett Robertson
COO: Skyler Robertson
COO: Scott Stringham
CFO: Richard Berman
CFO: Lars Elliot

D-U-N-S 07-295-8770 IMP
DESERET MANAGEMENT CORP
CHURCH OF JSUS CHRST OF LD STS
(*Suby of* CHURCH OF JSUS CHRST OF LD STS) ★
55 N 300 W Ste 800, Salt Lake City, UT 84101-3580
Tel (801) 538-0651 *Founded/Ownrshp* 1966
Sales 851.9MM^E *EMP* 3,210
SIC 4832 4833 5932 6512 6531 6411 Radio broadcasting stations; Television broadcasting stations; Used merchandise stores; Nonresidential building operators; Real estate managers; Insurance agents, brokers & service
CEO: Keith B McMullin
**Treas:* Scott Florence
VP: Dale Bailey
**VP Admn:* Roland A Radack
VP Admn: Roland Radack
CIO: Steve Tolman
Genl Couns: Robert Hyde

DESERET POWER
See DESERET GENERATION AND TRANSMISSION CO-OPERATIVE

DESERT DIAMND CASINOS & ENTRMT
See TOHONO ODHAM GAMING ENTERPRISE

D-U-N-S 17-080-8484
DESERT FUELS INC
4421 Irving Blvd Nw Ste A, Albuquerque, NM 87114-5919
Tel (505) 750-3835 *Founded/Ownrshp* 2004
Sales 120.0MM *EMP* 15
SIC 5172 5171

D-U-N-S 08-839-1883
■ DESERT MECHANICAL INC
DMI
(*Suby of* TUTOR PERINI CORP) ★
15870 Olden St, Sylmar, CA 91342-1241
Tel (702) 873-7333 *Founded/Ownrshp* 1977
Sales 43.4MM *EMP* 1,100
Accts Deloitte & Touche Llp Los Ang
SIC 1711 Plumbing contractors
Pr: Casey M Condron
**Sr VP:* Joseph Guglielmo
**VP:* Andre Burnthon
**VP:* Alex L Hodson
**VP:* Dan Naylor
IT Man: Chris J Pettigrew

D-U-N-S 60-653-4105
DESERT MOUNTAIN PROPERTIES LIMITED PARTNERSHIP
GOLF CLUB AT DESERT MOUNTAIN
37700 N Desert Mtn Pkwy, Scottsdale, AZ 85262-3100
Tel (480) 595-4000 *Founded/Ownrshp* 1997
Sales 103.2MM^E *EMP* 675
SIC 6552 7997 Land subdividers & developers, commercial; Golf club, membership
Pt: Lyle Anderson
CFO: Richard Yehling
Ex Dir: Keli Greenberg
Dir IT: Linda Leinwand

D-U-N-S 83-208-9705
■ DESERT PALACE INC
CAESARS PALACE HOTEL & CASINO
(*Suby of* CAESARS) ★
1 Caesars Palace Dr, Las Vegas, NV 89109-8969
Tel (702) 407-6289 *Founded/Ownrshp* 2009
Sales 21.9MM^E *EMP* 5,025^E
SIC 7011 Hotels & motels
Pr: Gary W Loveman
Exec: Frank Nguyen
VP Sls: Tammy Puchliakow

DESERT PARADISE RESORT
See EPIC RESORTS LLC

D-U-N-S 07-357-9336
■ DESERT REGIONAL MEDICAL CENTER INC
TENET HEALTHSYSTEM DESERT INC
(*Suby of* TENET HEALTHCARE CORP) ★
1150 N Indian Canyon Dr, Palm Springs, CA 92262-4872
Tel (760) 323-6374 *Founded/Ownrshp* 1997
Sales 206.5MM^E *EMP* 1,400
Accts Jonathan Stone Joshua Tree C
SIC 8062 General medical & surgical hospitals
CEO: Carolyn Caldwell
Chf Path: Robert Rosser
Pr: Lisa Wilson
CFO: Ken Wheat
**Ch:* Frank Ercoli
Ofcr: Cheryl Busch
Dir Rad: Raymond Foster
Dir Rad: Peter Greenberg
Dir Rx: Tim Perlick
**Prin:* Ralph M Steiger
CIO: Robert Klingseis

D-U-N-S 06-615-3875
DESERT SANDS UNIFIED SCHOOL DISTRICT SCHOOL BUILDING CORP
47950 Dune Palms Rd, La Quinta, CA 92253-4000
Tel (760) 771-8567 *Founded/Ownrshp* 1965
Sales 189.7MM^E *EMP* 3,200
Accts Vavrinek Trine Day & Co Ll
SIC 8211 Public elementary & secondary schools
CEO: Richard Oliphant
Exec: Blanche Ramirez
Dir Sec: Jeff Kaye
IT Man: Jim Novak

D-U-N-S 07-445-0453
DESERT SCHOOLS FEDERAL CREDIT UNION
148 N 48th St, Phoenix, AZ 85034-1900
Tel (602) 433-7000 *Founded/Ownrshp* 1939
Sales NA *EMP* 900
SIC 6062 State credit unions
CEO: Susan Frank
COO: Mike Donofrio
CFO: David Dick
Sr Cor Off: Mary Garry
Bd of Dir: Michael Konen
Ofcr: Anita Lopez
Ofcr: Sulie Richardson
Ofcr: Earl Young
**Ex VP:* Jeff Meshey
VP: C Brice
VP: Thomas Marlowe
VP: Mark Olague
VP: Beth Schnell
Mng Ofcr: Joe Greenberg

D-U-N-S 14-556-4295
■ DESERT SPRINGS HOSPITAL MEDICAL CENTER
(*Suby of* VALLEY HOSPITAL MEDICAL CENTER) ★
2075 E Flamingo Rd, Las Vegas, NV 89119-5188
Tel (702) 733-8800 *Founded/Ownrshp* 1971
Sales 243.7MM *EMP* 12
SIC 8062 General medical & surgical hospitals
CEO: Sam Kaufman
**COO:* Ryan Jensen
CFO: Jeffrey Blomeley
Dir Rad: Matt Grimes

DESHAZO CRANE COMPANY
See DESHAZO LLC

D-U-N-S 07-545-7432 IMP
DESHAZO LLC
DESHAZO CRANE COMPANY
190 Airpark Industrial Rd, Alabaster, AL 35007-9597
Tel (205) 664-2006 *Founded/Ownrshp* 1996
Sales 93.5MM *EMP* 275
SIC 3536 Cranes, overhead traveling
Pr: Guy K Mitchell LII
**Ch Bd:* Guy K Mitchell III
**VP:* Charles Tucker
Genl Mgr: Kevin Calma
Genl Mgr: Steve Holcomb
IT Man: Chris Boyd
Sfty Dirs: Nick Vincent
Manager: Kelly Coons

D-U-N-S 00-397-1926 IMP/EXP
DESIGN HOMES INC (WI)
DH SATELLITE
600 N Marquette Rd, Prairie Du Chien, WI 53821-1127
Tel (608) 326-8406 *Founded/Ownrshp* 1966
Sales 107.0MM^E *EMP* 428
SIC 2452 3663 5211 Modular homes, prefabricated, wood; Antennas, transmitting & communications; Lumber & other building materials
Pr: Randy Weeks
**CFO:* Franklin A Weeks
**Sr VP:* Jeff Irvine
Sfty Mgr: Dave Parks
Sales Exec: Kurt Smith
Sls&Mrk Ex: Tom Bennett

DESIGN IMAGES
See PEARL ARTIST & CRAFT SUPPLY CORP

DESIGN MADE EASY
See EMSER TILE LLC

D-U-N-S 60-630-9789 IMP
DESIGN READY CONTROLS INC
9325 Winnetka Ave N, Minneapolis, MN 55445-1617
Tel (763) 565-3000 *Founded/Ownrshp* 1989
Sales 139.1MM^E *EMP* 160^E
SIC 5084 3613 3561 Pollution control equipment, air (environmental); Pollution control equipment, water (environmental); Control panels, electric; Pumps & pumping equipment
CEO: Troy Schmidtke
**Pr:* Mark Whitten
**VP:* David Peterson
IT Man: Jason Hudson
**VP Mfg:* Pete Steil
Mfg Mgr: Paul Goldashkin
Sls Dir: Diane Morando

DESIGN SYSTEMS BUILDERS
See TWFRIERSON CONTRACTOR INC

D-U-N-S 00-591-6374 IMP/EXP
■ DESIGNTEX GROUP INC
DESIGNTEX
(*Suby of* STEELCASE INC) ★
200 Varick St Fl 8, New York, NY 10014-7433
Tel (212) 886-8100 *Founded/Ownrshp* 1961
Sales 92.5MM^E *EMP* 100
SIC 5131 Drapery material, woven; Upholstery fabrics, woven
Pr: Thomas Hamilton
CFO: George Whalen
IT Man: Jodi McIntyre
VP Sls: Lonnie Fogg
Sls Dir: Carmen Martinez

D-U-N-S 05-360-6534 IMP/EXP
■ DESIGN WITHIN REACH INC
DWR
(*Suby of* HERMAN MILLER INC) ★
711 Canal St Ste 3, Stamford, CT 06902-6094
Tel (203) 614-0600 *Founded/Ownrshp* 2014
Sales 309.1MM^E *EMP* 423
SIC 5021 5719 Furniture; Household furniture; Office furniture; Lighting, lamps & accessories
CEO: John Edelman
**Pr:* John McPhee
**CFO:* Anthony Deluca
Sr VP: Christine Lumpkins
VP: Carmela Krantz
VP: Tara Poseley
VP: Laura Reynolds
VP: Elizabeth Rivera
VP: Kari Woldum
Creative D: Alain Capretz
Area Mgr: Curtis Lee

D-U-N-S 00-203-7190 IMP/EXP
DESIGNATRONICS INC
SDP/SI
2101 Jericho Tpke Ste 1, New Hyde Park, NY 11040-4702
Tel (516) 328-3300 *Founded/Ownrshp* 1995
Sales 112.1MM^E *EMP* 400
SIC 3824 3559 3545 3625 3462 Mechanical & electromechanical counters & devices; Electronic component making machinery; Cams (machine tool accessories); Relays & industrial controls; Iron & steel forgings
Pr: Richard Kufner
**CFO:* Richard Desantis
Ex VP: Sue Anderson
Sr VP: Hitoshi Tanaka
**VP:* Robert Lindemann
VP: Daniel Raleigh
Exec: Meghan Altilio
Software D: Mark Koyenov
Sfty Mgr: Pat Miele
Natl Sales: James Mastrorilli

D-U-N-S 17-218-2482 IMP
■ DESIGNED METAL CONNECTIONS INC
PERMASWAGE USA
(*Suby of* PCC) ★
14800 S Figueroa St, Gardena, CA 90248-1719
Tel (310) 323-6200 *Founded/Ownrshp* 2013
Sales 208.2MM^E *EMP* 550
SIC 3451 Screw machine products
VP: Thomas McDonnell
QA Dir: Gil Sassoon
Dir IT: Cecille Hayes
Dir IT: Brian Parks

DESIGNTEX
See DESIGNTEX GROUP INC

D-U-N-S 96-195-2199
DESILVA GATES CONSTRUCTION LP
11555 Dublin Blvd, Dublin, CA 94568-2854
Tel (925) 361-1380 *Founded/Ownrshp* 1932
Sales 139.0MM^E *EMP* 235
SIC 1611 1794 1542 General contractor, highway & street construction; Excavation & grading, building construction; Nonresidential construction
Pr: Edwin O Desilva
Ex VP: David Desilva
Ex VP: Richard B Gates
VP: J Scott Archibald
VP: Pete Davos
VP: Mike Kloos
VP: William Kuchulis

D-U-N-S 07-997-6799
DESK BC MERGER LLC
333 W State St, Milwaukee, WI 53203-1305
Tel (414) 224-2000 *Founded/Ownrshp* 2014
Sales 732.8MM^E *EMP* 6,865^E
SIC 4832 Radio broadcasting stations

DESKTYPE
See RICHARDS GROUP INC

D-U-N-S 00-619-5077
DESOTO INDEPENDENT SCHOOL DISTRICT
200 E Belt Line Rd, Desoto, TX 75115-5704
Tel (972) 223-6666 *Founded/Ownrshp* 1923
Sales 110.0MM *EMP* 1,172
Accts Hankins Eastup Deaton Tonn
SIC 8211 Public senior high school; Public junior high school; Public elementary school
CFO: Bobby Laborde
Ex Dir: Jim Cockrell
Schl Brd P: Carl Sherman
Teacher Pr: Larry Phillips
Psych: Robert Jones

D-U-N-S 60-626-1568 IMP/EXP
DESSERT SERVICE INC
(*Suby of* SOCIETA' ITALIANA PRODOTTI ALIMENTARI S.I.P.A. SPA)
630 Belleville Tpke, Kearny, NJ 07032-4407
Tel (201) 246-7292 *Founded/Ownrshp* 1989
Sales 84.4MM^E *EMP* 75
SIC 5142 Packaged frozen goods; Bakery products, frozen
Pr: Attilio Bindi
Sales Exec: Ken Kaprowski
Mktg Mgr: Yolanda Defilippis

D-U-N-S 09-045-2624 IMP
DESTILERIA SERRALLES INC
Calle Central 1, Mercedita, PR 00715
Tel (787) 840-1000 *Founded/Ownrshp* 1949, 1996
Sales 85.0MM^E *EMP* 292
Accts Kevane Grant Thornton Llp San
SIC 2085 2084 5141 Rum (alcoholic beverage); Rye whiskey; Vodka (alcoholic beverage); Gin (alcoholic beverage); Wines, brandy & brandy spirits; Groceries, general line
Pr: Felix S Nevares
**VP:* Roberto Serrallez
**VP:* Jorge A Vazquez

DESTINATION HOTELS
See DESTINATION RESIDENCES LLC

D-U-N-S 05-531-6459
▲ DESTINATION MATERNITY CORP
232 Strawbridge Dr # 100, Moorestown, NJ 08057-4603
Tel (856) 291-9700 *Founded/Ownrshp* 1982
Sales 498.7MM *EMP* 4,200^E
Accts Kpmg Llp Philadelphia Pennsy
Tkr Sym DEST *Exch* NGS
SIC 5621 Maternity wear; Ready-to-wear apparel, women's
Pr: Anthony M Romano
**Ch Bd:* Arnaud Ajdler
CFO: David Stern
CFO: David R Stern
CFO: Judd P Tirnauer
Ofcr: Ronald J Masciantonio
Creative D: Christine Johnston
Genl Couns: Janine Petit
Board of Directors: Michael J Blitzer, Barry Erdos, Melissa Payner-Gregor, William A Schwartz Jr, B Allen Weinstein

D-U-N-S 02-185-9616
DESTINATION RESIDENCES LLC
DESTINATION HOTELS
(*Suby of* LEI AG SEATTLE) ★
10333 E Dry Creek Rd, Englewood, CO 80112-1560
Tel (303) 799-3830 *Founded/Ownrshp* 1972
Sales 176.7MM^E *EMP* 4,120
SIC 7011 8741 Resort hotel; Management services
Pr: John B Platt
Ch Bd: Robert J Lowe
CEO: Jamie Sabatier
Sr VP: Peter A Delfranco
VP: Peter R O Keeffe

D-U-N-S 08-653-0011 IMP
▲ DESTINATION XL GROUP INC
555 Turnpike St, Canton, MA 02021-2724
Tel (781) 828-9300 *Founded/Ownrshp* 1976
Sales 442.2MM *EMP* 2,567
Accts Kpmg Llp Boston Massachuset
Tkr Sym DXLG *Exch* NGS
SIC 5699 Designers, apparel
Pr: David A Levin
**Ch Bd:* Seymour Holtzman
CFO: Peter H Stratton Jr
Sr Cor Off: Elizabeth White
Ofcr: Angela Chew
Ofcr: Kenneth M Ederle
Ofcr: Brian S Reaves
Ofcr: Peter E Schmitz
Ofcr: Derrick Walker
Ex VP: Dennis R Hernreich
Sr VP: Francis Chane
Sr VP: Jack R McKinney
Sr VP: Robert S Molloy
Sr VP: Walter E Sprague
VP: Mark Albert
VP: Mark Bean
VP: Jeff Cavicchi
VP: Frank Chane
VP: Heather Hintlian
VP: Debbie McCarthy
VP: Robert Molloy
Board of Directors: Alan S Bernikow, Jesse H Choper, John E Kyees, Willem Mesdag, Ward K Mooney, George T Porter Jr, Mitchell S Presser, Ivy Ross

D-U-N-S 08-049-9606
DESTINY HEALTH INC
VITALITY GROUP, THE
(*Suby of* DISCOVERY LTD)
200 W Monroe St Ste 1900, Chicago, IL 60606-5072
Tel (312) 224-7100 *Founded/Ownrshp* 2006
Sales NA *EMP* 170
SIC 6321 8399 Accident & health insurance carriers; Health & welfare council
Pr: Arthur Carlos
Ofcr: Mark Smith
**Sr VP:* Tom Lerche
**VP:* Bob Carter
VP: Leesa Tori

Exec: Linda Simms
Off Mgr: Farah Williams
Software D: Pranen Reddy
Manager: Kristin Jordal
Board of Directors: Kenneth Linde

D-U-N-S 06-583-7619 IMP
DET DISTRIBUTING CO (TN)
301 Great Circle Rd, Nashville, TN 37228-1789
Tel (615) 244-4113 *Founded/Ownrshp* 1951
Sales 134.5MM *EMP* 150^E
Accts Lbmc Pc Brentwood Tennessee
SIC 5181 Beer & other fermented malt liquors
Pr: G Fred Dettwiller
VP: Ken Draper
VP: Marc Miller
Opers Mgr: Tim Estes
VP Sls: John Curley
Mktg Mgr: David Cain

D-U-N-S 12-524-1906 IMP
DET LOGISTICS USA CORP
46101 Fremont Blvd, Fremont, CA 94538-6468
Tel (510) 668-5100 *Founded/Ownrshp* 2000
Sales 250.3MM *EMP* 12
SIC 5065 Electronic parts
Pr: Yao Chou
**CFO:* Jean Huang

D-U-N-S 18-223-9921
DET NORSKE VERITAS HOLDING (USA) INC
(*Suby of* DNV GL AS)
1400 Ravello Rd, Katy, TX 77449-5164
Tel (281) 396-1000 *Founded/Ownrshp* 1981
Sales 185.9MM^E *EMP* 690^E
SIC 8711 7389 5734 8741 Consulting engineer; Inspection & testing services; Software, business & non-game; Management services
Pr: Kenneth Vareide
**Treas:* Wade Tettleton

DETECTO SCALE
See CARDINAL SCALE MANUFACTURING CO

D-U-N-S 06-338-0497
DETERVILLE LUMBER & SUPPLY LLC
3749 S County Road T, Denmark, WI 54208-8843
Tel (920) 863-2191 *Founded/Ownrshp* 2014
Sales 125.0MM *EMP* 3
SIC 5211 Lumber & other building materials

D-U-N-S 01-685-9308 IMP
DETROIT CITY DAIRY
DAIRY FRESH FOOD
21405 Trolley Indus Dr, Taylor, MI 48180-1811
Tel (313) 295-6300 *Founded/Ownrshp* 1960
Sales 201.9MM^E *EMP* 190
SIC 5143 5141 5147 5149 Dairy products, except dried or canned; Cheese; Groceries, general line; Meats, fresh; Bakery products
Pr: Alan Must
**Ch Bd:* Meyer Must
**VP:* H Joel Must
Sls Mgr: Jay Must

D-U-N-S 07-845-7877
DETROIT CITY SCHOOL DISTRICT
3011 W Grand Blvd Fl 14, Detroit, MI 48202-3096
Tel (313) 873-7553 *Founded/Ownrshp* 2012
Sales 8.4MM^E *EMP* 19,893^E
SIC 8211 Public elementary & secondary schools
CFO: Delores Brown

DETROIT DESL MTU RMNUFACTURING
See DETROIT DIESEL REMANUFACTURING-WEST INC

D-U-N-S 18-181-7628 IMP/EXP
DETROIT DIESEL CORP
DETROIT DIESEL USA
(*Suby of* DAIMLER AG)
13400 W Outer Dr, Detroit, MI 48239-1309
Tel (313) 592-5000 *Founded/Ownrshp* 2007
Sales 2.3MMM^E *EMP* 6,660
SIC 3519 3714 7538 Engines, diesel & semi-diesel or dual-fuel; Diesel engine rebuilding; Motor vehicle engines & parts; Diesel engine repair: automotive
Ch Bd: Eckhard Cordes
CFO: Bob Simonds
Treas: Nelson A Dworack
**Ex VP:* J James Morrow
VP: David Dumbrell
VP: John F Farmer
VP: Erich Neukirchner
VP: Dominick Vermet
VP Bus Dev: Wood Craig
Exec: Keith Vaughn
Dir Lab: Tony Bozaan
Board of Directors: Dr Eckhard Cordes, John E Doddridge, Richard M Donnelly, William E Hoglund, Gary G Jacobs, Joseph F Welch, R Jamison Williams Jr, Dieter E Zetsche

D-U-N-S 85-845-4101 IMP
DETROIT DIESEL REMANUFACTURING CORP
(*Suby of* DETROIT DIESEL USA) ★
13400 W Outer Dr, Detroit, MI 48239-1309
Tel (313) 592-5000 *Founded/Ownrshp* 1996
Sales 313.6MM *EMP* 1,095
SIC 3519 Diesel engine rebuilding
Ch: Roger S Penske
**VP:* Jeb Berg

D-U-N-S 61-792-0350 IMP
DETROIT DIESEL REMANUFACTURING-EAST INC
(*Suby of* DETROIT DIESEL REMANUFACTURING CORP) ★
60703 Country Club Rd, Byesville, OH 43723-9730
Tel (740) 439-7701 *Founded/Ownrshp* 1991
Sales 174.2MM^E *EMP* 500
SIC 3519 Diesel engine rebuilding
Ch Bd: Roger S Penske
**Pr:* James Morrow
COO: Michelle Delong
**VP:* Mike Chuich

D-U-N-S 06-332-4354 IMP/EXP
DETROIT DIESEL REMANUFACTURING-WEST INC
DETROIT DESL MTU RMNUFACTURING
(*Suby of* DETROIT DIESEL REMANUFACTURING CORP) ★
100 Lodestone Way, Tooele, UT 84074-5100
Tel (435) 843-6000 *Founded/Ownrshp* 1992
Sales 105.6MM^E *EMP* 385
SIC 3519 3714 5013 Diesel engine rebuilding; Motor vehicle parts & accessories; Truck parts & accessories
Pr: John Morrow
**Pr:* Friedrich Baumann
**Pr:* Jim Morrow
**Ch:* Roger S Penske
**Treas:* Paulo Silvestri
**VP:* Jeb Berg
**VP:* Gary Dassenko
**VP:* William H Micholls
VP: Volker Rathmann
VP: Joseph Turturica
**VP:* Douglas Wolma

DETROIT DIESEL USA
See DETROIT DIESEL CORP

D-U-N-S 04-892-4232
DETROIT ENTERTAINMENT LLC
MOTORCITY CASINO & HOTEL
2901 Grand River Ave, Detroit, MI 48201-2907
Tel (313) 237-7711 *Founded/Ownrshp* 1997
Sales 84.6MM^E *EMP* 2,750
SIC 7999 Gambling establishment
VP: Stacey Young
Netwrk Mgr: Ralph Bowlen
Genl Couns: Cheryl S Dube

DETROIT MEDIA PARTNERSHIP
See DETROIT NEWSPAPER PARTNERSHIP LP

DETROIT MEDICAL CENTER
See VHS OF MICHIGAN INC

DETROIT METROPOLITAN AIRPORT
See WAYNE COUNTY AIRPORT AUTHORITY

D-U-N-S 60-729-9526
■ **DETROIT NEWSPAPER PARTNERSHIP LP**
DETROIT MEDIA PARTNERSHIP
(*Suby of* GANNETT CO INC) ★
160 W Fort St, Detroit, MI 48226-3700
Tel (313) 222-2300 *Founded/Ownrshp* 2015
Sales 291.8MM^E *EMP* 2,600
SIC 2711 Newspapers: publishing only, not printed on site
Pt: Joyce Jenereaux
Pt: David Hunke
Pt: Tracey M Medley
Sr Cor Off: John Wise
Sr VP: Randall S Brant
VP: Mark J Brown
VP: Henry S Ford
Exec: Janet Hasson
IT Man: Krystal Rucker
Opers Mgr: Mark Vines

D-U-N-S 94-311-0296
DETROIT TECHNOLOGIES INC
CONFORM GROUP
32500 Telg Rd Ste 207, Bingham Farms, MI 48025
Tel (248) 647-0400 *Founded/Ownrshp* 1996
Sales 177.1MM^E *EMP* 1,000
SIC 3714 Motor vehicle parts & accessories
CEO: Steven Phillips
**CFO:* Gary M Stanis
**Ex VP:* William Vaughn
VP: Gary Stanis

D-U-N-S 04-350-2715
■ **DETROIT TELEVISION STATION WKBD INC**
PARAMOUNT TELEVISION DIVISON
(*Suby of* CBS CORP) ★
5555 Melrose Ave, Los Angeles, CA 90038-3989
Tel (323) 956-5000 *Founded/Ownrshp* 2006
Sales 194.4MM^E *EMP* 2,500
SIC 4833 Television broadcasting stations
Pr: John Severino
**Ex VP:* Ray Rajewski
**VP:* Tom Zappala
Prd Mgr: Caroline Neal

D-U-N-S 00-626-3925
DETROIT TOOL METAL PRODUCTS CO
DTMP
949 Bethel Rd, Lebanon, MO 65536-9020
Tel (417) 532-2142 *Founded/Ownrshp* 2013
Sales 107.3MM^E *EMP* 350
SIC 3469 3444 Metal stampings; Sheet metalwork
CEO: Steven Westfall
**CEO:* Terry Wogan
**VP:* Don Miller
Exec: Chris McElroy
**VP Sls:* Marty Kozarec
Board of Directors: Bart S Bergman, Stephen B Broun, William Scruggs

D-U-N-S 06-982-9729
DETROIT-MACOMB HOSPITAL CORP
ST JOHN HOSPITAL
28000 Dequindre Rd, Warren, MI 48092-2468
Tel (313) 499-3000 *Founded/Ownrshp* 2001
Sales NA *EMP* 4,030
SIC 8062

D-U-N-S 00-335-0782 IMP
DETYENS SHIPYARDS INC (SC)
1670 Dry Dock Ave # 236, North Charleston, SC 29405-2121
Tel (843) 746-1603 *Founded/Ownrshp* 1956, 1982
Sales 119.6MM^E *EMP* 589^E
SIC 4499 Ship cleaning
Ch Bd: D Loy Stewart Sr
**Pr:* D Loy Stewart Jr
**Sec:* Leo A Fary Jr
VP: Peter Browne
Dir IT: Petty Talamayan
Genl Couns: Randy Horner
Board of Directors: D Loy Stewart Sr

D-U-N-S 00-518-0195 IMP/EXP
DEUBLIN CO (IL)
2050 Norman Dr, Waukegan, IL 60085-8270
Tel (847) 689-8600 *Founded/Ownrshp* 1945
Sales 131.9MM^E *EMP* 500
SIC 3498 3492 3568 3494 Fabricated pipe & fittings; Fluid power valves & hose fittings; Power transmission equipment; Valves & pipe fittings
Ch Bd: Donald Deubler
**Pr:* Ronald Kelner
**CFO:* Ed Lerner
Dist Mgr: Matt Bell
Netwrk Eng: Steve Kim
Plnt Mgr: Dave Short
Snr Mgr: Andrew Shaub

DEUTSCH FAMILY WINE & SPIRITS
See WJ DEUTSCH & SONS LTD

D-U-N-S 07-524-9854
■ **DEUTSCH INC**
INTERPUBLIC GROUP OF COMPANIES
(*Suby of* INTERPUBLIC GROUP OF COMPANIES INC) ★
6 E 78th St, New York, NY 10075-1706
Tel (212) 981-7600 *Founded/Ownrshp* 2000
Sales 102.8MM^E *EMP* 850
SIC 7311 Advertising agencies
Ch Bd: Linda Sawyer
Pt: Val Difebo
**Pt:* Michael Duda
COO: Erica Grau
CFO: Thomas Entrup
CFO: Nina Werner
Ofcr: Winston Binch
Ofcr: Pete Favat
Ex VP: Mike Bryce
Ex VP: Zach Gallagher
Ex VP: Kris Weiner
Sr VP: Cathy Carr
Sr VP: Victor Kimble
Sr VP: Amy Liebesman
Sr VP: Dick Rinehimer
Sr VP: Melanie Steinbach
VP: Bryan Blackhave
VP: Karen Deluca
VP: Mike Depirroand
VP: Martin Dix
VP: Bill Fitzgerald

DEUTSCHE BANK A G
See DEUTSCHE BANK US FINANCIAL MARKETS HOLDING CORP

D-U-N-S 79-078-6891
DEUTSCHE BANK AMERICAS HOLDING CORP
DEUTSCHE BANK CAPITAL
(*Suby of* DB USA CORP) ★
60 Wall St, New York, NY 10005-2858
Tel (212) 250-2500 *Founded/Ownrshp* 1991
Sales NA *EMP* 3,031
SIC 6141 6153 6211 Personal credit institutions; Short-term business credit; Investment bankers
Ch Bd: Seth H Waugh
**CEO:* Jim Ziolkowski
VP: Timothy Donmoyer
VP: David G Hill
VP: Suzanne Rice
VP: Robert Simmons
Dir IT: Christian Ashmore
IT Man: Grant Holland
IT Man: Peter Skouteris

DEUTSCHE BANK CAPITAL
See DEUTSCHE BANK AMERICAS HOLDING CORP

D-U-N-S 12-156-6350
DEUTSCHE BANK SECURITIES INC
(*Suby of* DEUTSCHE BANK A G) ★
60 Wall St Bsmt 1, New York, NY 10005-2858
Tel (212) 250-2500 *Founded/Ownrshp* 1986
Sales 342.9MM^E *EMP* 720^E
SIC 6211 6036 Brokers, security; Dealers, security; Savings institutions, not federally chartered
Pr: Robert B Allardice III
**Ch Bd:* Richard Byrne
V Ch: Jeff Rosichan
**CFO:* Doug Barnard
CFO: Robert J Pearce
Treas: Chris Demaio
Chf Inves: Vinay Pande
Ofcr: Jane Carner
Ofcr: Alessandra Digiusto
Ofcr: George Hornig
Ofcr: Troland Link
Ofcr: Mark J Palma
Top Exec: David Pearson
Top Exec: Tony Whittemore
Assoc VP: Maria N Babek
Assoc VP: Raman Kapil
Assoc VP: Sally K Waller
Assoc VP: Marianne R Westerfield
Ex VP: Mark Cullen
Ex VP: Emron Goolcharran
Ex VP: Gurinder Johar

D-U-N-S 17-334-6941
DEUTSCHE BANK TRUST CO AMERICAS
(*Suby of* DB USA CORP) ★
60 Wall St Bsmt 1, New York, NY 10005-2858
Tel (212) 250-2500 *Founded/Ownrshp* 1999
Sales NA *EMP* 1,585
SIC 6021 6211 National commercial banks; Security brokers & dealers
V Ch Bd: Yves De Balmann
**V Ch:* Saman Majd
**V Ch:* Sir Robert Smith
**CEO:* Udo Behrenwaldt
**CEO:* James Goulding
**CEO:* Brian Scullin
COO: Karen Bell
**COO:* Mark Gelnaw
CFO: Douglas R Banad
**CFO:* Douglas R Barnard
**Treas:* Donna M Milrod
**V Ch Bd:* Eugene A Ludwig
**V Ch Bd:* Mayo A Shattuck III
**Ex VP:* Rodney McLauchlan
**Sr VP:* Jeffrey J Glibert

D-U-N-S 79-650-7663
DEUTSCHE BANK US FINANCIAL MARKETS HOLDING CORP
DEUTSCHE BANK A G
(*Suby of* DB USA CORP) ★
60 Wall St Bsmt 1, New York, NY 10005-2858
Tel (212) 250-2500 *Founded/Ownrshp* 1986
Sales 657.8MM^E *EMP* 721
SIC 6211 Brokers, security; Dealers, security
CEO: Stephan Leithner
V Ch: Saman Majd
V Ch: Mayo A Shttuck
V Ch: R Smith
Pr: Chris Konopelko
COO: Christian Ricken
COO: Henry Ritchotte
CFO: Stefan Krause
**Ch:* John Rolls
Ofcr: Jorge Arce
Assoc VP: Brian Baugh
VP: Karthic Babu
VP: Kenneth Bacow
VP: Kevin Carney
VP: Anthony Depeppo
VP: Nick Desantis
VP: Timothy Dohrmann
VP: David Feng
VP: Eugene Geltser
VP: Scott Habura
VP: Alex Merced

D-U-N-S 04-296-6044 IMP
DEUTZ CORP
(*Suby of* DEUTZ AG)
3883 Steve Reynolds Blvd, Norcross, GA 30093-3066
Tel (770) 564-7100 *Founded/Ownrshp* 1966
Sales 306.0MM *EMP* 115
SIC 5084 Engines & parts, diesel
CEO: Robert Mann
**Pr:* Steve Corley
CFO: Mark Kliendienst
**CFO:* Christian Vorspel-Rueter
**Treas:* Wallace Evans III
Sr VP: Martin Strecker
VP: Stephen J Corley
VP: Georg Diderich
VP: Bernd Freudenmann
VP: Arthur Northover
Exec: Patricia Rhoades

D-U-N-S 07-046-8210
DEVCON CONSTRUCTION INC
690 Gibraltar Dr, Milpitas, CA 95035-6317
Tel (408) 942-8200 *Founded/Ownrshp* 1976
Sales 1.2MMM *EMP* 350
Accts Johanson & Yau Accountancy Cor
SIC 1541 Industrial buildings, new construction
Pr: Gary Filizetti
CFO: Keith Offill
**CFO:* Brett Sisney
VP: Jonathan Harvey
VP: Daisy Pereira
CIO: Eric Holland
Manager: Jim Dunn
Snr PM: Susan Becher
Snr PM: Trina Warren
Snr PM: Kevin White

D-U-N-S 00-192-7474 IMP/EXP
DEVCON INTERNATIONAL CORP (FL)
(*Suby of* GOLDEN GATE CAPITAL) ★
595 S Federal Hwy Ste 500, Boca Raton, FL 33432-5542
Tel (954) 926-5200 *Founded/Ownrshp* 1951, 2009
Sales 147.9MM^E *EMP* 591^E
SIC 3699 3273 3281 3271 2951 5032 Security devices; Ready-mixed concrete; Stone, quarrying & processing of own stone products; Concrete block & brick; Asphalt paving mixtures & blocks; Cement
CEO: Mr Steve Hafen
CFO: Robert Ferro
CFO: Mr Sean Forrest
CFO: Mark McIntosh
Sr VP: Ms Ann Macdonald
Sr VP: Mr Mark M McIntosh
Prin: Mr Donald L Smith

D-U-N-S 05-481-9743 IMP/EXP
DEVELOPMENT DIMENSIONS INTERNATIONAL INC (DE)
D D I
1225 Washington Pike, Bridgeville, PA 15017-2825
Tel (412) 257-0600 *Founded/Ownrshp* 1970
Sales 219.9MM^E *EMP* 1,100
SIC 8742 Training & development consultant
CEO: Tacy M Byham
**Pr:* Ronald R Dalesio
**Pr:* Robert W Rogers
**Ch:* William C Byham
Treas: Barry Williams
**Treas:* William Finnbar Butler William
**VP:* Carolyn Byham
VP: Jim Concelman
**VP:* William D Koch
VP: Douglas Reynolds
Exec: Gil Duncan
Board of Directors: Carolyn Byham, William Byham

D-U-N-S 06-807-7452
DEVELOPMENTAL DISABILITIES INSTITUTE INC
D D I
99 Hollywood Dr, Smithtown, NY 11787-3135
Tel (631) 366-2900 *Founded/Ownrshp* 1961
Sales 88.5MM *EMP* 1,500
Accts Bdo Usa Llp New York Ny
SIC 8211 8052 Specialty education; Intermediate care facilities
Ex Dir: Peter Pierri
**CFO:* Marie Roza
**Prin:* David Bartash
**Prin:* William Kacin
MIS Dir: Bill Barbar
Software D: Larry Carella

D-U-N-S 06-309-7679
DEVERE CONSTRUCTION CO INC
1030 Devere Dr, Alpena, MI 49707-8163
Tel (989) 356-4411 *Founded/Ownrshp* 1980

Sales 92.2MM *EMP* 175
Accts Rehmann Robson Cheboygan Mi
SIC 1542 1541 1629 8741 Commercial & office building, new construction; Industrial buildings & warehouses; Renovation, remodeling & repairs: industrial buildings; Waste water & sewage treatment plant construction; Construction management
Pr: Richard Crittenden
**Treas:* Cheryl Lumsden
**Prin:* Michael Crittenden

DEVEREUX FLORIDA
See DEVEREUX FOUNDATION

D-U-N-S 00-251-4420
DEVEREUX FOUNDATION
DEVEREUX FLORIDA
444 Devereux Dr, Villanova, PA 19085-1932
Tel (610) 520-3000 *Founded/Ownrshp* 1912, 1938
Sales 391.5MM *EMP* 6,000
Accts Ernst & Young Llp Philadelph
SIC 8361 Residential care
Pr: Robert Q Kreider
V Ch: Samuel Coppersmith
V Ch: Thomas Hays
COO: Carl Clark
**COO:* Margaret McGill
COO: Molly Watson
**Treas:* Stanley Kopala
**Chf Cred:* Marilyn Benoit MD
Trst: Elva B Ferrari
Trst: Marguerite Hark
**Sr VP:* Robert C Dunne
**Sr VP:* Dolores McLaughin
**VP:* Sarah Lenahan
VP: Martha Lindsay
VP: Howard Savin
**VP:* Leah Yaw
Exec: Matthew Babin

D-U-N-S 96-183-2156
DEVICOR MEDICAL PRODUCTS INC
MAMMOTONE
(*Suby of* LEICA BIOSYSTEMS RICHMOND INC) ★
300 E Business Way Fl 5, Cincinnati, OH 45241-2384
Tel (513) 864-9000 *Founded/Ownrshp* 2014
Sales 234.0MM[E] *EMP* 550
SIC 3841 Surgical & medical instruments
CEO: Tom Daulton
**CFO:* Robert Goss
**Sr VP:* Jim Frontero
**Sr VP:* Gene Schrecengost
VP: Sean Burke
**VP:* Chip Clark
VP: Bruce Marchioni

D-U-N-S 93-360-4571 EXP
■ **DEVILBISS AIR POWER CO**
(*Suby of* BLACK & DECKER CORP) ★
4825 Highway 45 N, Jackson, TN 38305-7900
Tel (800) 888-2468 *Founded/Ownrshp* 1999
Sales 130.3MM[E] *EMP* 870
SIC 3563 3621 3589 Air & gas compressors; Electric motor & generator parts; High pressure cleaning equipment
Pr: Tom Dewitt
VP: Gus J Athas
**VP:* Robert Bukholder
VP: Mike Hibbison
Genl Mgr: Clyde Swoger

D-U-N-S 96-217-5894 IMP/EXP
DEVILBISS HEALTHCARE LLC
(*Suby of* MEDICAL DEPOT, INC.)
100 Devilbiss Dr, Somerset, PA 15501-2125
Tel (814) 443-4881 *Founded/Ownrshp* 2015
Sales 100.0MM *EMP* 273
SIC 3845 Electromedical equipment
Pr: Rich Kocinski
**CFO:* Tim Walsh
**VP:* Joe Lewarski
**VP:* Mike Marcinek
VP: Oliver Niemann
CTO: Dave Greene
Sftwr Eng: Pete Tataliba
Ql Cn Mgr: Dourene Gobbel
Sls Mgr: Rebecca Parise
Sls Mgr: Michael Ring
Sales Asso: Lucy Kelley

DEVON
See ENLINK MIDSTREAM LLC

D-U-N-S 04-940-1565 IMP/EXP
▲ **DEVON ENERGY CORP**
333 W Sheridan Ave, Oklahoma City, OK 73102-5015
Tel (405) 235-3611 *Founded/Ownrshp* 1971
Sales 13.1MMM *EMP* 6,600[E]
Tkr Sym DVN *Exch* NYS
SIC 1311 1382 Crude petroleum & natural gas; Crude petroleum & natural gas production; Oil & gas exploration services
Pr: David A Hager
Ch Bd: J Larry Nichols
COO: Tony D Vaughn
CFO: Thomas L Mitchell
V Ch Bd: John Richels
Ex VP: R Alan Marcum
Ex VP: Frank W Rudolph
Ex VP: Frank Rudolph
Ex VP: Darryl G Smette
Ex VP: Lyndon C Taylor
Sr VP: Rick Gideon
Sr VP: Kevin Lafferty
VP: Carla Brockman
VP: Sewell Gina
VP: Gregg Henson
VP: Gilbert Horton
VP: John Raines
VP: Jeff Ritenour
VP: Frank Schroeder
Board of Directors: Barbara M Baumann, John E Bethancourt, Robert H Henry, Michael M Kanovsky, Robert A Mosbacher, Duane C Radtke, Mary P Ricciardello

D-U-N-S 93-110-4632
■ **DEVON ENERGY INTERNATIONAL CO**
(*Suby of* DEVON ENERGY CORP) ★
20 N Broadway Ave # 1500, Oklahoma City, OK 73102-8296
Tel (405) 235-3611 *Founded/Ownrshp* 1999
Sales 107.1MM[E] *EMP* 4,000
SIC 2911 Petroleum refining; Gasoline; Diesel fuels; Oils, lubricating
VP: Rebecca Rosen

D-U-N-S 08-800-3756 IMP
■ **DEVON ENERGY PRODUCTION CO LP**
(*Suby of* DEVON ENERGY CORP) ★
333 W Sheridan Ave, Oklahoma City, OK 73102-5015
Tel (405) 235-3611 *Founded/Ownrshp* 1999
Sales 3.9MMM[E] *EMP* 4,600
SIC 1311 5172 Crude petroleum production; Natural gas production; Crude oil
Ch: J Larry Nichols
Sr VP: Stephen J Hadden
Sr VP: Duke R Ligon
VP: Darryl G Smette
Prin: John Richels
Board of Directors: Thomas Ferguson, David Gavrin, Michael Gellert, John Hill, William Johnson, Michael Kanovsky, Robert Mosbacher Jr, Robert Weaver

D-U-N-S 00-508-8856
■ **DEVON GAS SERVICES LP** (TX)
(*Suby of* DEVON ENERGY CORP) ★
333 W Sheridan Ave, Oklahoma City, OK 73102-5010
Tel (405) 235-3611 *Founded/Ownrshp* 1998
Sales 138.4MM[E] *EMP* 143
SIC 4922 Natural gas transmission
Pt: George P Mitchell
Ltd Pt: Liquid Energy Fuel Corporation
Ltd Pt: Mitchell Marketing Corporation

D-U-N-S 04-783-7765
DEVON INDUSTRIAL GROUP
(*Suby of* DEVON CONTRACTING, INC.)
535 Griswold St Ste 2050, Detroit, MI 48226-3680
Tel (313) 965-3455 *Founded/Ownrshp* 2015
Sales 112.3MM[E] *EMP* 428
Accts Doeren Mayhew Troy Michigan
SIC 1541 Industrial buildings, new construction
VP: Stella Burnley
Opers Mgr: Tom Roelofs
Snr PM: David Green

D-U-N-S 06-726-6551 IMP/EXP
■ **DEVON OEI OPERATING INC**
(*Suby of* DEVON ENERGY CORP) ★
20 N Broadway, Oklahoma City, OK 73102-9213
Tel (405) 235-3611 *Founded/Ownrshp* 2003
Sales 418.2MM[E] *EMP* 5,000
SIC 4922 4924 1311 4613 Natural gas transmission; Pipelines, natural gas; Natural gas distribution; Crude petroleum production; Natural gas production; Refined petroleum pipelines

D-U-N-S 01-362-7294
▲ **DEVRY EDUCATION GROUP INC**
DEVRY GROUP
3005 Highland Pkwy # 700, Downers Grove, IL 60515-5798
Tel (630) 515-7700 *Founded/Ownrshp* 1931
Sales 1.8MMM *EMP* 13,404[E]
Tkr Sym DV *Exch* NYS
SIC 8221 8299 8249 8243 Professional schools; Educational services; Vocational schools; Data processing schools
Pr: Lisa W Wardell
**Ch Bd:* Christopher B Begley
Pr: Jeffrey R Akens
Pr: Eric P Dirst
Pr: Carlos Degas Filgueiras
Pr: Susan L Groenwald
Pr: Robert A Paul
Pr: Steven P Riehs
Pr: John P Roselli
CFO: Patrick J Unzicker
Chf Mktg O: Melissa Esbenshade
Sr VP: Gregory S Davis
Sr VP: Donna N Jennings
Sr VP: Christopher C Nash
Sr VP: Lisa M Sodeika
VP: Adriano Allegrini
VP: Joseph Cantoni
Board of Directors: David S Brown, Ann Weaver Hart, Lyle Logan, Michael W Malafronte, Alan G Merten, Fernando Ruiz, Ronald L Taylor, James D White

DEVRY GROUP
See DEVRY EDUCATION GROUP INC

D-U-N-S 06-998-2445
■ **DEVRY UNIVERSITY INC**
KELLER GRADUATE SCHOOL MGT
(*Suby of* DEVRY GROUP) ★
3005 Highland Pkwy # 700, Downers Grove, IL 60515-5799
Tel (630) 515-7700 *Founded/Ownrshp* 1987
Sales 329.6MM[E] *EMP* 4,800
SIC 8221 Professional schools
Pr: Robert Paul
Pr: John Ballheim
Pr: Steven Brooks
Pr: James Caldwell
Pr: Michael Cubbin
Pr: Pamela Daly
Pr: Maria Dezenberg
Pr: Darryl W Field
Pr: Susan Lerner Friedberg
Pr: Scarlett Howery
Pr: Craig Jacob
Pr: Kevin Lamountain
Pr: Steven Nelson
Pr: Kim Nugent
Pr: Joseph Onorio
Pr: Joshua Ben Michael Padron
Pr: Joyce Wheatley
VP: Shantanu Bose
VP: John Holbrook
VP: Joe Mozden
Exec: Kaye Segreti

D-U-N-S 62-368-7444
DEVTEK INC
220 Cedar St Nw, Hartselle, AL 35640-2404
Tel (256) 751-9441 *Founded/Ownrshp* 2006
Sales 200.0MM *EMP* 3
SIC 5091 Sporting & recreation goods
Pr: Larry A Coulter
**VP:* Dewayne Raines
Off Mgr: Larry Ziegler

D-U-N-S 62-131-7770
DEWBERRY COMPANIES INC
(*Suby of* DEWBERRY COMPANIES LC) ★
8401 Arlington Blvd, Fairfax, VA 22031-4619
Tel (703) 849-0100 *Founded/Ownrshp* 2000
Sales 213.0MM *EMP* 700
SIC 6719 Investment holding companies, except banks
Ch: Barry K Dewberry
**CEO:* Gary Neuwerth
**CEO:* Donald E Stone Jr
COO: Dan M Pleasant
**CFO:* Mark H Reiner
Assoc VP: Denice Bracey
Assoc VP: Steven Kuntz
Assoc VP: Dan Williams
Assoc VP: Kevin Wood
VP: Richard Cawley
VP: Bryon Griffith
VP: Robert Grimm
VP: Dennis H Kwiatkowski
VP: Tim McCormick
VP: Mark Montgomery
VP: Jerome Strauss
Assoc Dir: Phillip Condley

D-U-N-S 62-131-6814
DEWBERRY COMPANIES LC
8401 Arlington Blvd Ste 1, Fairfax, VA 22031-4619
Tel (703) 849-0100 *Founded/Ownrshp* 1956
Sales 143.0MM *EMP* 2,000
SIC 8711 Engineering services
Ch: Barry Dewberry
**CEO:* Donald E Stone Jr
**COO:* Dan Pleasant
**CFO:* Mark H Reiner
**Chf Cred:* Gary Neuwerth

D-U-N-S 05-175-8449
DEWBERRY CONSULTANTS LLC
(*Suby of* DEWBERRY COMPANIES LC) ★
8401 Arlington Blvd Ste 1, Fairfax, VA 22031-4619
Tel (703) 849-0311 *Founded/Ownrshp* 1956
Sales 151.0MM *EMP* 885
Accts Kpmg Peat Marwick Llp Vienna
SIC 8711 8712 8731 Engineering services; Architectural services; Commercial physical research
Ch Bd: Barry Dewberry
**CEO:* Donald Stone
CFO: Mark Reiner
Ex VP: Lawrence Olinger
CIO: Henry Tyler
Counsel: Mark Davis

D-U-N-S 04-579-3460
DEWBERRY ENGINEERS INC
(*Suby of* DEWBERRY COMPANIES INC) ★
200 Broadacres Dr Ste 410, Bloomfield, NJ 07003-3177
Tel (973) 338-9100 *Founded/Ownrshp* 2006
Sales 168.0MM *EMP* 120
SIC 8711 Consulting engineer
Ch: Barry Dewberry
**CEO:* Gary Neuwerth
**CEO:* Donald E Stone Jr
**COO:* Dan Pleasant
**CFO:* Mark H Reiner
Sr VP: William Pl
CIO: Henry Taylor

DEWEY CHEETHAM & HOWE
See TAPPET BROTHERS ASSOCIATES

D-U-N-S 15-526-6364
DEWEY CORP
5500 Highway 80 W, Jackson, MS 39209-3507
Tel (601) 922-8331 *Founded/Ownrshp* 1942
Sales 101.9MM *EMP* 1,000
Accts Horne Llp Ridgeland Mississi
SIC 4213 6719 Liquid petroleum transport, non-local; Investment holding companies, except banks
Pr: Lee Miller
**Ex VP:* Hal Miller
**VP:* Joe Hegi
**VP:* Terry Malone
Board of Directors: Dennis M Miller, Harold D Miller Jr, Richard L Miller, Scott F Miller

D-U-N-S 07-101-8659
DEWITT STERN GROUP INC
420 Lexington Ave Rm 2700, New York, NY 10170-0199
Tel (212) 867-3550 *Founded/Ownrshp* 1899
Sales NA *EMP* 224
SIC 6411 Insurance agents & brokers
Ch: Jolyon F Stern
**Pr:* Charles R Johnson Jr
**Treas:* Kevin P Walker
Sr VP: Timothy Devin
Sr VP: Peter Marshall
**Sr VP:* Margaret J O'Brien
Sr VP: Margaret O'Brien
Sr VP: Anthony Pittari
VP: David Benoit
**VP:* Maureen Devoe
**VP:* David S Flecker
VP: Roger Kluge
VP: Rona Lind
VP: Carol Lipnik
VP: Marilyn Quinlan
VP: Janice Ruiz
VP: Christopher Sam

D-U-N-S 13-038-9112
DEX IMAGING INC
5109 W Lemon St, Tampa, FL 33609-1105
Tel (813) 288-8080 *Founded/Ownrshp* 1994
Sales 229.1MM[E] *EMP* 450[E]
SIC 5044 Copying equipment
CEO: Dan Doyle
**Sec:* Daniel M Doyle Sr
Off Mgr: Debra Eichhammer
Off Mgr: Cher Grigsby

D-U-N-S 13-735-1727
DEX MEDIA HOLDINGS INC
QWEST
(*Suby of* DEX MEDIA INC) ★
2200 W Airfield Dr, Dfw Airport, TX 75261-4008
Tel (972) 453-7000 *Founded/Ownrshp* 2006
Sales 132.5MM[E] *EMP* 1,000[E]
SIC 8742 Marketing consulting services
CEO: Joe Walsh
CFO: Robert Neumeister
**CFO:* Paul Rouse
**Ex VP:* Mark Cairns
**Ex VP:* John Wholey

D-U-N-S 07-878-0377
DEX MEDIA INC
2200 W Airfield Dr, Dfw Airport, TX 75261-4008
Tel (972) 453-7000 *Founded/Ownrshp* 2012
Sales 1.8MMM *EMP* 3,500[E]
SIC 2741 7311 Miscellaneous publishing; Directories: publishing & printing; Advertising agencies
Pr: Joseph A Walsh
**Ch Bd:* Alan F Schultz
CFO: Paul D Rouse
Chf Mktg O: Gordon Henry
Ofcr: Andrew Dj Hede
Ofcr: Debra M Ryan
Ex VP: Mark Cairns
Ex VP: Michael N Dunn
Ex VP: Raymond R Ferrell
Ex VP: Carleton G Shaw
Ex VP: John F Wholey
VP: Mike Massing
VP: Kevin O'Connor
VP: Gregory Sirianni
VP: Richard Wall
VP: Cody Wilbanks
Board of Directors: Jonathan B Bulkeley, Thomas D Gardner, Douglas D Wheat

D-U-N-S 00-192-2111
DEX ONE CORP
1001 Winstead Dr Ste 100, Cary, NC 27513-2117
Tel (919) 297-1600 *Founded/Ownrshp* 1973
Sales 1.3MMM *EMP* 2,300
SIC 2741 8732

D-U-N-S 12-316-0736
▲ **DEXCOM INC**
6340 Sequence Dr, San Diego, CA 92121-4356
Tel (858) 200-0200 *Founded/Ownrshp* 1999
Sales 400.7MM *EMP* 1,212[E]
Tkr Sym DXCM *Exch* NGS
SIC 3841 Surgical & medical instruments
Pr: Kevin Sayer
**Ch Bd:* Terrance H Gregg
CFO: Jess Roper
Chf Cred: Richard Doubleday
Chf Mktg O: Claudia Graham
Ex VP: Andrew K Balo
Ex VP: Richard B Doubleday
Ex VP: Jorge Valdes
VP: David Carner
VP: Richard C Yang
Prgrm Mgr: Jim Galloway

D-U-N-S 02-230-8964
DEXIA CREDIT LOCAL (INC)
(*Suby of* DEXIA SA)
445 Park Ave Fl 8, New York, NY 10022-8645
Tel (212) 515-7000 *Founded/Ownrshp* 2012
Sales NA *EMP* 150
SIC 6082 Foreign trade & international banking institutions
Pr: Guy Cools
**CFO:* Anthony Mauro
**VP:* Michael Midden
VP: Jonathan Rodrigues
VP: Alban Selle
VP: Kevin Soucy
Exec: John Flaherty

DEXT COMPANY
See RECONSERVE INC

D-U-N-S 05-791-6173 IMP/EXP
DEXTER APACHE HOLDINGS INC
2211 W Grimes Ave, Fairfield, IA 52556-2681
Tel (641) 472-5131 *Founded/Ownrshp* 1912
Sales 164.3MM[E] *EMP* 750
SIC 3321 3582 Gray iron castings; Drycleaning equipment & machinery, commercial
Pr: Patrick D Albregts
VP: Jim N Freeze
VP: Frank D Fritz
VP: Tom Jones
Dir IT: Paul Bakutis
Mfg Mgr: Daniel Smithburg
VP Sls: Paul Thurman
Sls Dir: Susan McPherson
Sls Dir: Mike Sabbatis
Sls Mgr: Bud Clapsaddle
Sls Mgr: Shanna Judit

D-U-N-S 78-394-3710 IMP/EXP
DEXTER AXLE CO
2900 Industrial Pkwy, Elkhart, IN 46516-5491
Tel (574) 295-7888 *Founded/Ownrshp* 1999
Sales 353.0MM[E] *EMP* 735
SIC 3714 Axles, motor vehicle
Pr: Adam W Dexter
Pr: Tim Meckstroth
COO: Edward Kopkowski
CFO: Bernie Bolka
Chf Mktg O: Steve Kildow
VP: Tom Kelly
IT Man: Brian Bowman
Opers Mgr: Chip Durren
Plnt Mgr: Dwight Busche
Plnt Mgr: George Tierce
Ql Cn Mgr: Tammy Charters

DEXTRYS
See NEWBURYPORT HOLDINGS INC

D-U-N-S 12-997-5392 IMP/EXP
DEZURIK INC
HILTON
250 Riverside Ave N, Sartell, MN 56377-2129
Tel (320) 259-2000 *Founded/Ownrshp* 2009
Sales 149.9MM^E *EMP* 500
SIC 3491 Water works valves
Pr: Bryan Burns
CFO: Scott Crane
VP: Bonnie Funk
Exec: George Lancaster
Sfty Mgr: Dan Metoyer

D-U-N-S 00-255-8039
DF PRAY INC (RI)
25 Anthony St, Seekonk, MA 02771-3701
Tel (508) 336-3366 *Founded/Ownrshp* 1959, 1982
Sales 102.2MM^E *EMP* 140
Accts William A Wooley Cpa Wrenth
SIC 1542 1541 Commercial & office building, new construction; Industrial buildings, new construction
Pr: Scott W Pray
CFO: Jim Waterman
**Ex VP:* Mike Burke
**Sr VP:* Ronald Laprise
**Sr VP:* Vincent Villella
**VP:* William Hoffmann
VP: Kevin Lagasse
**VP:* Gary Smith

D-U-N-S 09-483-7841 IMP
DFA HOLDINGS INC
6100 Hllywood Blvd Fl 7, Miami, FL 33180
Tel (954) 986-7700 *Founded/Ownrshp* 2002
Sales 322.8MM^E *EMP* 1,300
SIC 5182 5399 Liquor; Duty-free goods
CEO: Jerome Falic
**Pr:* Leon Falic
**Treas:* Simon Falic

D-U-N-S 96-551-6164
DFB PHARMACEUTICALS LLC
3909 Hulen St, Fort Worth, TX 76107-7253
Tel (817) 900-4050 *Founded/Ownrshp* 1997
Sales 174.0MM^E *EMP* 700
Accts Ernst & Young Llp San Antonio
SIC 2834 Pharmaceutical preparations
CEO: H Paul Dorman
Pr: Michael E Steadman
Chf Mktg O: Herbert B Slade
VP: Phil Brandazio
**VP:* Maxwell Lea
VP: Maxwell A Lea
VP: Braham Shroot
Genl Mgr: Harald Heckenm Ller
Prd Mgr: Kai Sch Tte
VP Sls: Hal McLeod

D-U-N-S 80-762-9399
DFC GLOBAL CORP
74 E Swedesford Rd # 150, Malvern, PA 19355-1488
Tel (610) 296-3400 *Founded/Ownrshp* 1990
Sales NA *EMP* 6,600^E
SIC 6099 6141 Check cashing agencies; Money order issuance; Personal credit institutions
CEO: Jeffrey A Weiss
**COO:* Michael Hudachek
**CFO:* Randy Underwood
**Ex VP:* Michael Coury
Snr PM: Virginia Schock

D-U-N-S 07-920-4106
DFC HOLDINGS LLC (KS)
1 Dole Dr, Westlake Village, CA 91362-7300
Tel (818) 879-6600 *Founded/Ownrshp* 2013
Sales 9.8MMM^E *EMP* 34,800^E
SIC 0174 0175 0161 5148 2033 Citrus fruits; Deciduous tree fruits; Lettuce farm; Celery farm; Cauliflower farm; Broccoli farm; Fruits; Vegetables; Fruit juices: fresh; Fruit juices: packaged in cans, jars, etc.
Ch Bd: David H Murdock

DFCI PEDIATRIC ONCOLOGY
See DANA-FARBER CANCER INSTITUTE INC

D-U-N-S 17-217-9280
DFG WORLD INC
DOLLAR FINANCIAL
(*Suby of* DOLLAR FINANCIAL GROUP INC) ★
74 E Swedesford Rd, Malvern, PA 19355-1488
Tel (610) 296-3400 *Founded/Ownrshp* 1999
Sales NA *EMP* 800
SIC 6099 Check cashing agencies
Ch Bd: Jeffery Weiss
**Pr:* Donald Gayhardt
**CFO:* Randall Underwood
Sr VP: David Alexander
Sr VP: Eric Erickson
Sr VP: Peggy Kile
Sr VP: Carl Spilker
VP: Ira Distenfield
VP: Tim Hickey
VP: Jim Higgins
VP: Brett Horrocks
VP: Mike Hudachek
VP: Jeff Knapp
**VP:* Peter Sokolowski
VP: Gillian Wilmot

D-U-N-S 03-874-6938
DFI HOLDINGS LLC
3179 Deer Creek Rd, Collegeville, PA 19426-1449
Tel (610) 584-5836 *Founded/Ownrshp* 2015
Sales 109.9MM^E *EMP* 1,010^E
SIC 6719 Personal holding companies, except banks

DFS
See DELL FINANCIAL SERVICES LLC

D-U-N-S 13-970-9075
■ **DFS CORPORATE SERVICES LLC**
DISCOVERY NETWORK
(*Suby of* DISCOVER FINANCIAL SERVICES) ★
2500 Lake Cook Rd 2, Riverwoods, IL 60015-3851
Tel (224) 405-0900 *Founded/Ownrshp* 2007
Sales NA *EMP* 9,139
SIC 6153 Credit card services, central agency collection
CEO: David W Nelms
Pr: Roger C Hochschild
COO: R Mark Graf
CFO: Mark R Graf
Mktg Dir: Tory Jarvis
Snr Mgr: Jay Kulesza
Board of Directors: Lawrence A Weinbach, Jeffrey S Aronin, Mary K Bush, Gregory C Case, Dennis D Dammerman, Robert M Devlin, Philip A Laskawy, Michael H Moskow, Michael Rankowitz, E Folin Smith

DFS FOOD SERVICE
See DI CARLO DISTRIBUTORS INC

D-U-N-S 10-291-6426 IMP/EXP
DFS GROUP LP
(*Suby of* MOET HENNESSY USA INC) ★
525 Market St Fl 33, San Francisco, CA 94105-2769
Tel (415) 977-2701 *Founded/Ownrshp* 1986
Sales 343.1MM^E *EMP* 3,190
SIC 5944 5948 5921 5993 5947 5999 Jewelry stores; Leather goods, except luggage & shoes; Luggage, except footlockers & trunks; Liquor stores; Tobacco stores & stands; Gift, novelty & souvenir shop; Toiletries, cosmetics & perfumes
Pt: Ed Brennan
**Pt:* Keith Harrison
**Pt:* John Kresich
**Pt:* Steve Mangum
**Pt:* Michael Schriver
Sr VP: Peggy Tate
VP: Mike Osorio
Genl Mgr: June Guzman
Genl Mgr: Nina Zieling
Plng Mgr: Denise Jernas
Dir IT: Eric Davis

DFT
See DUPONT FABROS TECHNOLOGY INC

DFW AIRPORT
See AVIALL SERVICES INC

DFW INTERNATIONAL AIRPORT
See DALLAS/FORT WORTH INTERNATIONAL AIRPORT

DFW NURSING AND REHAB
See DECATUR HOSPITAL AUTHORITY

D-U-N-S 04-936-5591
DG21 LLC
(*Suby of* PARSONS GOVERNMENT SUPPORT SERVICES INC) ★
14900 Landmark Blvd # 400, Dallas, TX 75254-6783
Tel (972) 774-8850 *Founded/Ownrshp* 1999
Sales 35.6MM^E *EMP* 1,950
SIC 8744 Facilities support services
Ch: Robert W Unger
Ofcr: Gary Billions
IT Man: Derek Lowe

D-U-N-S 62-128-2867
DG3 GROUP AMERICA INC
CGI NORTH AMERICA
(*Suby of* DIVERSFIED GLOBL GRPHICS GROUP) ★
100 Burma Rd, Jersey City, NJ 07305-4623
Tel (201) 793-5000 *Founded/Ownrshp* 2006
Sales 160.0MM^E *EMP* 406^E
SIC 2752 Commercial printing, offset
CEO: Tom Saggiomo
**Pr:* Michael Cunningham
**CFO:* Gerald Baillargeon
Ex VP: Fred Gorra

D-U-N-S 07-849-3495
DG3 HOLDINGS LLC
DIVERSFIED GLOBL GRPHICS GROUP
(*Suby of* ARSENAL CAPITAL PARTNERS LP) ★
100 Burma Rd, Jersey City, NJ 07305-4623
Tel (201) 793-5000 *Founded/Ownrshp* 2008, 2016
Sales 160.0MM^E *EMP* 880^E
SIC 2752 Commercial printing, offset
CEO: Tom Saggiomo
**CFO:* Gerald Baillargeon
Exec: Mike Morin
Mng Dir: Victor Lee
VP Sls: Brian C Paoli

D-U-N-S 16-785-4678
DG3 NORTH AMERICA INC
DIVERSFIED GLOBL GRPHICS GROUP
(*Suby of* CGI NORTH AMERICA) ★
100 Burma Rd, Jersey City, NJ 07305-4623
Tel (201) 793-5000 *Founded/Ownrshp* 2005
Sales 160.0MM *EMP* 405
SIC 2752 Commercial printing, offset
CEO: Tom Saggiomo
Pr: Jim Molloy
**CFO:* Gerald Baillargeon
Bd of Dir: Mary Driscoll
Ex VP: Robert Bocksel
Ex VP: Joe Lindfeldg
Ex VP: Joe Lindfeldt
Ex VP: Gordon Mays
Sr VP: Michael D'Onofrio
Sr VP: Seth Diamond
Sr VP: Fred Gorra
Sr VP: Phil Rybecky
Sr VP: Bob Zanisnik
VP: Angelo Autiero
VP: John Tenwinkel
Exec: Sean Murphy

DGI SUPPLY
See DOALL INDUSTRIAL SUPPLY CORP

DGI SUPPLY
See DOALL CO

D-U-N-S 06-640-4232 IMP
DGL GROUP LTD
195 Raritan Center Pkwy, Edison, NJ 08837-3650
Tel (718) 499-1000 *Founded/Ownrshp* 2001
Sales 96.7MM *EMP* 47
Accts Mayer Rispler & Company Pc
SIC 5731 5065 Consumer electronic equipment; Mobile telephone equipment
Ch Bd: Ezra Zaafarani
**CFO:* Mured Nakash
**VP:* Zack Massre
**VP:* Victor Sardar
Creative D: Amy Rosemberg

DGMB CASINO
See RESORTS CASINO HOTEL

D-U-N-S 96-700-0600
DGMB CASINO LLC
RESORTS CASINO HOTEL
1133 Boardwalk, Atlantic City, NJ 08401-7329
Tel (800) 772-9000 *Founded/Ownrshp* 1978
Sales 134.8MM^E *EMP* 1,400^E
SIC 7011 Casino hotel; Resort hotel
CEO: Mark Giannantonio
**CFO:* Tim Ebling

D-U-N-S 14-493-2183 IMP
■ **DGPM INVESTMENTS INC**
RED THREAD
(*Suby of* RED THREAD SPACES LLC) ★
300 E River Dr, East Hartford, CT 06108-4205
Tel (860) 528-9981 *Founded/Ownrshp* 1981
Sales 195.9MM^E *EMP* 450
SIC 5044 5021 5713 1752 Office equipment; Office furniture; Floor covering stores; Floor laying & floor work
Pr: Larry Levine
**CEO:* Jenny Niemann
**CFO:* Orlando Corsi Jr
**Ex VP:* Casey Kalman
**Ex VP:* Don Marshall
Genl Mgr: Gordon Muir
Genl Mgr: Tom Perrone
Site Mgr: Tammy Horn
Sales Exec: Tim Bycholski
Mktg Mgr: David Jackson
Sls Mgr: Abbie Prevost

D-U-N-S 08-647-3050
■ **DGSE CORP**
DALLAS GOLD AND SILVER EXCH
(*Suby of* DGSE COMPANIES, INC.)
15850 Dallas Pkwy, Dallas, TX 75248-3308
Tel (972) 484-3662 *Founded/Ownrshp* 1987
Sales 85.0MM *EMP* 82
SIC 5094 Jewelry
CEO: Lynn Smith
**Pr:* William Oyster
**CFO:* John Benson

D-U-N-S 18-290-2536 IMP
■ **DH HOLDINGS CORP**
(*Suby of* DANAHER CORP) ★
1250 24th St Nw, Washington, DC 20037-1124
Tel (202) 828-0850 *Founded/Ownrshp* 1986
Sales 174.8MM^E *EMP* 1,400
SIC 3545 Machine tool accessories
Ch Bd: Steven M Rales
**Pr:* George M Sherman
**Treas:* Patrick W Allender
Sfty Mgr: Sean Melville

DH SATELLITE
See DESIGN HOMES INC

D-U-N-S 04-024-5779
DHARM INTERNATIONAL LLC
DHARMANANDAN DIAMONDS
(*Suby of* DHARMANANDAN DIAMONDS PRIVATE LIMITED)
15 W 47th St Ste 506, New York, NY 10036-5704
Tel (212) 398-7777 *Founded/Ownrshp* 2010
Sales 169.8MM *EMP* 17
Accts Shah & Pandya Cpa Pc Lake S
SIC 5094 Diamonds (gems)

DHARMANANDAN DIAMONDS
See DHARM INTERNATIONAL LLC

DHCUS
See DSM HOLDING CO USA INC

D-U-N-S 03-959-4247
DHG MANAGEMENT CO LLC
551 5th Ave Fl 10, New York, NY 10176-0901
Tel (212) 465-3700 *Founded/Ownrshp* 1999
Sales 93.3MM^E *EMP* 1,200
SIC 8741 Hotel or motel management
CEO: Benjamin Denihan
**CEO:* Brooke Barrett
COO: Brad Wilson
**CFO:* Glenn Wasserman
Ex VP: Ellen Brown
VP: Tom Feldgerman

DHHS
See NEW HAMPSHIRE DEPT OF HEALTH AND HUMAN SERVICES

D-U-N-S 14-457-6399
DHHS-BROUGHTON HOSPITAL
1000 S Sterling St, Morganton, NC 28655-3938
Tel (828) 433-2516 *Founded/Ownrshp* 1887
Sales 183.9MM^E *EMP* 1,200
SIC 5122 Pharmaceuticals

D-U-N-S 80-440-4494
▲ **DHI GROUP INC**
1040 Avenue Of The Amrcas, New York, NY 10018-3703
Tel (212) 725-6550 *Founded/Ownrshp* 2005
Sales 259.7MM *EMP* 861^E
Tkr Sym DHX *Exch* NYS
SIC 7361 4813 7375 Employment agencies; ; Online data base information retrieval
Pr: Michael P Durney
**Ch Bd:* John W Barter
Pr: Shravan Goli
CFO: John Roberts
Sr VP: Pam Bilash
VP: Jennifer Bewley
VP: Brian P Campbell
VP: Greg Schippers
Mng Dir: Bryan Bassett
Mng Dir: James Bennett
Mng Dir: Evan H Lesser
Board of Directors: Carol Carpenter, Jennifer Deason, Jim Friedlich, Burton M Goldfield, David S Gordon, Scot W Melland, Brian Schipper

D-U-N-S 02-282-4192
■ **DHI HOLDINGS INC**
DIVERSCO INTEGRATED SERVICES
(*Suby of* ABM INDUSTRIES INC) ★
105 Diversco Dr, Spartanburg, SC 29307-5408
Tel (864) 579-3420 *Founded/Ownrshp* 2010
Sales 139.4MM^E *EMP* 11,000
SIC 7361 Employment agencies
Pr: Mike Price
**Pr:* Gary Hentschel
**CFO:* Rhonda Thompson
**Sr VP:* John Demarest
Sr VP: Apple Richardson
VP: Ed Holland
**VP Mktg:* Adair Watters

D-U-N-S 78-740-2163
■ **DHI MORTGAGE CO LTD**
(*Suby of* DR HORTON INC) ★
10700 Pecan Park Blvd # 450, Austin, TX 78750-1227
Tel (512) 502-0545 *Founded/Ownrshp* 1997
Sales NA *EMP* 842
SIC 6162 Mortgage bankers & correspondents; Mortgage bankers
Pr: Randall C Present
Rgnl Mgr: Amy Keen
Brnch Mgr: Karen Leedholm

DHL
See DPWN HOLDINGS (USA) INC

DHL ECOMMERCE
See GLOBAL MAIL INC

D-U-N-S 10-223-1276 IMP
DHL EXPRESS (USA) INC
(*Suby of* DHL) ★
1210 S Pine Island Rd, Plantation, FL 33324-4402
Tel (954) 888-7000 *Founded/Ownrshp* 2004
Sales 350.9MM^E *EMP* 400
SIC 4513 7389 4731 Air courier services; Courier or messenger service; Freight transportation arrangement
CEO: Mike Parra
**CFO:* Rafael Estevez
CFO: Terry Hilsman
**Treas:* Robert Whitaker
Ex VP: Dianne Leblanc
Ex VP: Keith E Lovetro
Sr VP: Karsten Aufgebauer
Sr VP: John Cornish
VP: Ian Carey
VP: John Fox
**VP:* Josh Frank
VP: Cain Moodie
**VP:* Jon Olin
VP: Darren Plested
Exec: Joseph Miller
Dir Bus: Alberto Hallivas

DHL GLOBAL FORWARDING
See AIR EXPRESS INTERNATIONAL USA INC

D-U-N-S 78-875-8790
DHM HOLDING CO INC
1 Dole Dr, Westlake Village, CA 91362-7300
Tel (818) 879-6600 *Founded/Ownrshp* 2001
Sales 521.8MM^E *EMP* 75,000
SIC 0179 0174 0175 0161 5148 2033 Pineapple farm; Banana grove; Citrus fruits; Deciduous tree fruits; Lettuce farm; Celery farm; Cauliflower farm; Broccoli farm; Fruits; Vegetables; Fruit juices: fresh; Fruit juices: packaged in cans, jars, etc.
Ch Bd: David H Murdock
VP: Joseph Tesoriero

D-U-N-S 80-792-1531
DHS OF BLUNT COUNTY LLC
TLC NURSING CENTER
212 Ellen St, Oneonta, AL 35121-2720
Tel (205) 625-3520 *Founded/Ownrshp* 2001
Sales 667.1MM^E *EMP* 130
SIC 8051 Convalescent home with continuous nursing care
Nrsg Dir: Angela Stone
HC Dir: Joann Powers

D-U-N-S 80-820-3553 IMP
■ **DHSC LLC**
AFFINITY MEDICAL CENTER
(*Suby of* QUORUM HEALTH CORP) ★
875 8th St Ne, Massillon, OH 44646-8503
Tel (330) 832-8761 *Founded/Ownrshp* 2016
Sales 101.2MM *EMP* 500
SIC 8062 General medical & surgical hospitals
CEO: Elizabeth Pruitt
**CFO:* Micheal Holt
Web Dev: Pamela Hughes
Sls&Mrk Ex: Susan Koosh

D-U-N-S 96-340-3790
DHW LEASING LLC
230 S Phillips Ave # 202, Sioux Falls, SD 57104-6354
Tel (605) 330-9414 *Founded/Ownrshp* 2010
Sales 64.1MM^E *EMP* 2,323
SIC 6799 Investors

D-U-N-S 03-970-6981 IMP/EXP
DHX-DEPENDABLE HAWAIIAN EXPRESS INC
19201 S Susana Rd, Rancho Dominguez, CA 90220
Tel (310) 537-2000 *Founded/Ownrshp* 1980
Sales 109.3MM^E *EMP* 480
SIC 4731 Freight forwarding
Ch: Ronald Massman
Pr: Gerard Crisostomo
Pr: Cammie Laster
CFO: Tim Rice
VP: Ralph Merolla
Exec: Josetta Lyons
Genl Mgr: Paje Butler
Genl Mgr: Kane McEwen
Genl Mgr: Nery Vellman
Off Mgr: Melissa Katada
Off Mgr: Karron K Lualemaga

D-U-N-S 05-499-6590 IMP
DI CARLO DISTRIBUTORS INC
DFS FOOD SERVICE
1630 N Ocean Ave, Holtsville, NY 11742-1838
Tel (800) 342-2756 *Founded/Ownrshp* 1964
Sales 250.0MM[E] *EMP* 240
Accts Albrecht Viggiano Zureck & C
SIC 5142 5141 5143 Packaged frozen goods; Groceries, general line; Dairy products, except dried or canned
Ch Bd: Vincent Di Carlo
**Sec:* Michael Di Carlo
**Sr VP:* John Di Carlo
Exec: Michael Dicarlo
MIS Dir: Bill Schlageter
Opers Mgr: Martin Minogue
Sls Mgr: Bonnie Savel
Sales Asso: Anthony Bianco

D-U-N-S 82-716-2855 IMP/EXP
DI GIORGIO CORP
WHITE ROSE FOODS
(*Suby of* C&S WHOLESALE PRODUCE) ★
160 Fieldcrest Ave Ste A, Edison, NJ 08837-3642
Tel (718) 470-1744 *Founded/Ownrshp* 2006
Sales 207.6MM[E] *EMP* 2,450[E]
SIC 5149 Specialty food items
Pr: Stephen R Bokser
Sr VP: John J Becker
Sr VP: Lawrence S Grossman
VP: Harlan Lcnie
Genl Mgr: Angela Decicco
Genl Mgr: James Miller

DIABETES CARE LINK
See MERLE WEST MEDICAL CENTER

DIABETES MGT PRGRAM SPTSYLVNIA
See WASHINGTON HOSPITAL INC MARY

D-U-N-S 03-440-7395
DIABLO VALLEY COLLEGE FOUNDATION
321 Golf Club Rd, Pleasant Hill, CA 94523-1544
Tel (925) 685-1230 *Founded/Ownrshp* 1949
Sales 1.3MM *EMP* 2,000[E]
Accts Burr Pilger Mayer Inc San Fra
SIC 7389 8221 Fund raising organizations; Colleges universities & professional schools
Pr: Mark G Edelstein
**CEO:* Katherine Guptill
Off Admin: Mianmian Ding
Mktg Dir: Chrisanne Knox

D-U-N-S 04-415-9234 IMP/EXP
DIAGEO NORTH AMERICA INC (CT)
(*Suby of* DIAGEO PLC)
801 Main Ave, Norwalk, CT 06851-1127
Tel (203) 229-2100 *Founded/Ownrshp* 1997
Sales 2.1MMM[E] *EMP* 8,040
SIC 2084 2085 Wines, brandy & brandy spirits; Cordials, alcoholic
CEO: Ivan Menezes
Pr: Alberta Hawkins
Pr: Maggie Lapcewich
Pr: Larry Schwartz
CFO: Chris Davies
**CFO:* Greg Kryder
**CFO:* Deirdre Mahlan
**Treas:* James D Ricci
Chf Mktg O: Debra J Kellyennis
VP: Simon Burch
VP: Dan Buttling
VP: Christian Giorgio
VP: Sandra Lalli
VP: Zsoka McDonald
VP: John Mooney
VP: Michael O'Reilly
VP: Steve Spadarotto
VP: Steve Wallet
Mng Ofcr: Ron Anderson

D-U-N-S 79-010-3980
DIAGNOSTIC HEALTH CORP
(*Suby of* DIAGNOSTIC HEALTH HOLDINGS, INC.)
22 Inverness Pkwy Ste 425, Birmingham, AL 35242
Tel (205) 980-2500 *Founded/Ownrshp* 1991
Sales 34.7MM[E] *EMP* 1,200
SIC 8742 Hospital & health services consultant
Pr: Diane Munson
**Pr:* Russell H Maddox
**COO:* Robert E Gontarek
**CFO:* Steven A McPherson
**Sr VP:* Lucy Hicks
**VP:* Kurt Hans
**VP:* Nancy McNee Newell
**VP:* Jeff Parks
Off Mgr: Jennifer Grupp
Dir IT: Mark Bodden
IT Man: Maurizio Corrao

DIAGNOSTIC LABS & RDLGY
See KAN-DI-KI LLC

D-U-N-S 01-016-9253
DIAKON
DIAKON LTHRAN SCIAL MINISTRIES
798 Hausman Rd Ste 300, Allentown, PA 18104-9108
Tel (610) 682-1262 *Founded/Ownrshp* 2000
Sales 442.8MM[E] *EMP* 4,600
Accts Kpmg Llp Philadelphia Pa
SIC 8322 Individual & family services
CEO: Mark T Pile
**CFO:* Richard Barger
VP: John Polkovitz
Ex Dir: Karen Wood

DIAKON LTHRAN SCIAL MINISTRIES
See DIAKON

D-U-N-S 07-144-5951
DIAKON LUTHERAN SOCIAL MINISTRIES
(*Suby of* DIAKON LTHRAN SCIAL MINISTRIES) ★
1022 N Union St, Middletown, PA 17057-2158
Tel (610) 682-1262 *Founded/Ownrshp* 1974
Sales 219.0MM *EMP* 4,300
Accts Kpmg Llp Mc Lean Va
SIC 8051 8322 Skilled nursing care facilities; Social service center
**CFO:* Rick Barger
Sr Cor Off: Carol Ferrera
Ofcr: Alex Dapkewicz
Sr VP: Jarrod Leo
Ex Dir: Terry Lieb
Off Mgr: Barb Gilbert
Off Mgr: Cindy Rothermel
CTO: Denise Roe
IT Man: Susan Hurst
VP Opers: Stephen A McShane
Mktg Dir: Erin Smith

D-U-N-S 14-105-6601
DIAKON LUTHERAN SOCIAL MINISTRIES
(*Suby of* DIAKON LTHRAN SCIAL MINISTRIES) ★
1022 N Union St, Middletown, PA 17057-2158
Tel (610) 682-1262 *Founded/Ownrshp* 1974
Sales 207.7MM *EMP* 2,300
Accts Kpmg Llp
SIC 8322 8051 Individual & family services; Skilled nursing care facilities
Pr: Daun E McKee
**CEO:* Rev Dr Don E McKee

DIAL ADJUSTMENT BUREAU
See DIALAMERICA MARKETING INC

D-U-N-S 00-693-0366 IMP/EXP
DIAL CORP
(*Suby of* HENKEL CONSUMER GOODS INC) ★
7201 E Henkel Way, Scottsdale, AZ 85255-9678
Tel (480) 754-3425 *Founded/Ownrshp* 1996
Sales 1.0MMM[E] *EMP* 2,900
SIC 2841 2844 2842 2032 2013 Soap & other detergents; Soap: granulated, liquid, cake, flaked or chip; Detergents, synthetic organic or inorganic alkaline; Dishwashing compounds; Toilet preparations; Deodorants, personal; Hair preparations, including shampoos; Face creams or lotions; Specialty cleaning, polishes & sanitation goods; Bleaches, household: dry or liquid; Ammonia, household; Fabric softeners; Canned specialties; Chili with or without meat: packaged in cans, jars, etc.; Spaghetti: packaged in cans, jars, etc.; Sausages & other prepared meats
Pr: Bradley A Casper
**CFO:* Jack Tierney
Treas: David M Riddiford
**Treas:* James R Terrel
**Sr VP:* Keith Davis
**Sr VP:* Brian T Shook
**Sr VP:* Richard Theiler
**Sr VP:* Mitchell D Tinnan
**Sr VP:* Greg A Tipsord
VP: Shari Brickin
VP: Bob Forte
VP: Scott Symons

D-U-N-S 07-056-7300
DIALAMERICA MARKETING INC
DIAL ADJUSTMENT BUREAU
960 Macarthur Blvd, Mahwah, NJ 07430-2040
Tel (201) 327-0200 *Founded/Ownrshp* 1975
Sales 440.6MM[E] *EMP* 5,000
SIC 7389 Telemarketing services; Telephone services
Pr: Arthur W Conway
**CFO:* Christopher W Conway
**Sr VP:* Mary Conway
**Sr VP:* Laurence H Kyse
**Sr VP:* John Redinger
Brnch Mgr: Karen Segers
CIO: Gerhard Lyndenmayer

D-U-N-S 03-273-5603
DIALECTIC DISTRIBUTION LLC
1275 Bloomfield Ave # 66, Fairfield, NJ 07004-2728
Tel (973) 870-0250 *Founded/Ownrshp* 2013
Sales 95.1MM *EMP* 22
SIC 5065 Intercommunication equipment, electronic
Pr: Zachary Zeltzer

D-U-N-S 10-653-9174 IMP
DIALIGHT CORP
(*Suby of* ROXBORO HOLDINGS INC) ★
1501 State Route 34, Wall Township, NJ 07727-3932
Tel (732) 919-3119 *Founded/Ownrshp* 1988
Sales 302.0MM[E] *EMP* 1,040
SIC 3679 3674 Liquid crystal displays (LCD); Electronic circuits; Semiconductors & related devices
CEO: Roy Burton
**Ch:* Bill Ronald
Snr Sftwr: Paul Geisler
Dir IT: Tracy Kozinski
IT Man: Barbara Angley
Sftwr Eng: Matt Keith
Sftwr Eng: Allan Kramer
Mktg Mgr: Kellie Connors
Mktg Mgr: Michael Schratz
Manager: Christopher Carpenter
Manager: Phil Hausman

D-U-N-S 07-935-6592
DIALOGDIRECT INC
(*Suby of* DIALOGDIRECT LLC) ★
13700 Oakland St, Highland Park, MI 48203-3173
Tel (313) 957-5100 *Founded/Ownrshp* 2012
Sales 262.1MM *EMP* 5,700
Accts Uhy Llp Sterling Heights Mic
SIC 8742 Marketing consulting services
Pr: Doug Kearney
**Ch Bd:* Ron Risher
**Chf Mktg O:* Jack Wilkie

D-U-N-S 07-955-2876
DIALOGDIRECT LLC
13700 Oakland St, Highland Park, MI 48203-3173
Tel (313) 957-5100 *Founded/Ownrshp* 2014
Sales 262.1MM *EMP* 3,500
SIC 6799 8742 Venture capital companies; Marketing consulting services
Pr: Doug Kearney
Pr: Peter Cartwright
Pr: Keir Rothnie
COO: Jason Lancaster
CFO: Patrick Murphy
Ofcr: Michael Pavan
Ex VP: Jim Guillaumin
Sr VP: Patrick Hughes
VP: Jim Fritner
CIO: Thomas Denomme
QC Dir: Lisa Hunzicker

D-U-N-S 11-887-9667
DIALOGIC INC
(*Suby of* GROUPE DIALOGIC INC)
4 Gatehall Dr, Parsippany, NJ 07054-4518
Tel (973) 967-6000 *Founded/Ownrshp* 2014
Sales 132.0MM *EMP* 539[E]
SIC 3661 3577 7371 Telephone & telegraph apparatus; Data conversion equipment, media-to-media: computer; Computer software development & applications
Pr: Bill Crank
COO: Christian Primeau
CFO: Bob Dennerlein
Ex VP: Anthony Housefather
Sr VP: Kevin Gould
Sr VP: Jim Machi
VP: Laszlo Meszaros
Netwrk Mgr: Robert Yuen
Opers Mgr: Steve Moninghoff
Mktg Dir: John Porter
Board of Directors: Chris Burke

DIALOGUE BUSINESS SOLUTIONS
See DIALOGUE MARKETING INC

D-U-N-S 15-136-5004
DIALOGUE MARKETING INC
DIALOGUE BUSINESS SOLUTIONS
800 Tower Dr Ste 200, Troy, MI 48098-2843
Tel (800) 523-5867 *Founded/Ownrshp* 1985
Sales NA *EMP* 1,100
SIC 7389

D-U-N-S 03-810-7744
DIALYSIS CLINIC INC
1633 Church St Ste 500, Nashville, TN 37203-2948
Tel (615) 327-3061 *Founded/Ownrshp* 1971
Sales 712.6MM *EMP* 5,000
Accts Deloitte & Touche Llp Nashvil
SIC 8092 5047 8071 Kidney dialysis centers; Medical & hospital equipment; Medical laboratories
Ch Bd: H Keith Johnson
**Pr:* Ed Attrill
**Sec:* William Wood
Trst: Nancy N Johnson
Ofcr: Peggy Williams
VP: Teresa Yates
Off Mgr: Sondra Payne
Nurse Mgr: Michelle Perry
CTO: Donovan Schultz
DP Dir: Stanley Wasserman
Software D: Allen Burnett

D-U-N-S 96-980-7580
DIALYSIS NEWCO INC
DSI RENAL
(*Suby of* USRC) ★
424 Church St Ste 1900, Nashville, TN 37219-2387
Tel (615) 777-8200 *Founded/Ownrshp* 2016
Sales 380.1MM *EMP* 1,803
SIC 8092 Kidney dialysis centers
CEO: Craig Goguen
**COO:* Jason Gunter
**Ex VP:* Jay Yalowitz
Sr VP: Ben Croce
VP: Fran Attrill
VP: Johnie Flotte
VP: Mary Reeves
VP: Dawn Twardy
VP: Giles Ward
VP: Dewitt Warren
Tech Mgr: Eric Foster

DIAM INTERNATIONAL
See CREATIVE SOLUTIONS GROUP INC

D-U-N-S 08-456-2748 IMP
DIAMLINK INC
JEWELERY MARKETING COMPANY
25 W 45th St Ste 1406, New York, NY 10036-4902
Tel (212) 704-0777 *Founded/Ownrshp* 1984
Sales 90.0MM[E] *EMP* 16
SIC 5094

D-U-N-S 03-725-4760
DIAMOND B CONSTRUCTION CO INC
2090 Industrial Park Rd, Alexandria, LA 71303-4567
Tel (318) 427-1300 *Founded/Ownrshp* 1978
Sales 94.4MM[E] *EMP* 150
SIC 1611 General contractor, highway & street construction
Pr: Bryan L Bossier
COO: Phillip Bossier
**VP:* Renee Bossier
**Prin:* Gary Lewis
Sfty Mgr: Adrian Bell

D-U-N-S 79-129-7658
▲ DIAMOND BLACK INC
BLACK DIAMOND
2084 E 3900 S, Salt Lake City, UT 84124-1723
Tel (801) 278-5552 *Founded/Ownrshp* 1957
Sales 155.2MM *EMP* 400[E]
Tkr Sym BDE *Exch* NGS
SIC 3949 2329 2339 Sporting & athletic goods; Helmets, athletic; Men's & boys' sportswear & athletic clothing; Sportswear, women's
Ch Bd: Warren B Kanders
COO: Mark Ritchie
Ofcr: Aaron J Kuehne
Board of Directors: Michael A Henning, Nicholas Sokolow, Donald L House

D-U-N-S 00-691-0954 IMP/EXP
DIAMOND BLUE GROWERS (CA)
CALIFORNIA ALMOND GROWERS EXCH
1802 C St, Sacramento, CA 95811-1099
Tel (916) 442-0771 *Founded/Ownrshp* 1910
Sales 1.6MMM *EMP* 1,500
SIC 2099

D-U-N-S 15-177-6341
DIAMOND BRANDS INC
1800 Cloquet Ave, Cloquet, MN 55720-2141
Tel (218) 879-6700 *Founded/Ownrshp* 1989
Sales 104.6MM *EMP* 700
SIC 2499 Toothpicks, wood; Handles, poles, dowels & stakes: wood
Pr: Dr Naresh K Nakra
VP: Fred Chalk
VP: Peter R Lynn
VP: Chris Mathews
VP: William Olsen
Plnt Mgr: Carolyn Meysenborg
VP Sls: James M Lincoln
VP Sls: John Young
Sls Mgr: Philip Dvorak
Pgrm Dir: Naresh Nakra
Pgrm Dir: Tim Peleski
Board of Directors: Alfred Aragona, Bradley R Kent, Terry R Peets, Alexander M Seaver

D-U-N-S 17-712-4380
DIAMOND CASTLE HOLDINGS LLC
280 Pk Ave Fl 25 E Tower, New York, NY 10017
Tel (212) 300-1900 *Founded/Ownrshp* 2004
Sales 387.7MM[E] *EMP* 1,100[E]
SIC 7353 7699 5082 Heavy construction equipment rental; Industrial machinery & equipment repair; Construction & mining machinery
Pt: ARI Benacerraf
**Pt:* Michael Ranger
**Pt:* Andrew Rush
VP: Rudolf Herrmann
VP: John McNiff
VP: George Pompetzki
CTO: Mike Kulsziski

D-U-N-S 04-880-1401 IMP
DIAMOND COMIC DISTRIBUTORS INC
ALLIANCE GAME DISTRIBUTORS
10150 York Rd Ste 300, Cockeysville, MD 21030-3344
Tel (443) 318-8001 *Founded/Ownrshp* 1982
Sales 625.2MM[E] *EMP* 622
SIC 5192 Books, periodicals & newspapers
Pr: Stephen Geppi
**Treas:* Larry Swanson
**VP:* Charles Parker
Mktg Mgr: Daria Medved
Sls Mgr: Terry Helman
Sls Mgr: Joe Lunday

D-U-N-S 05-112-8163
DIAMOND DRUGS INC
DIAMOND MEDICAL SUPPLY
645 Kolter Dr, Indiana, PA 15701-3522
Tel (724) 349-1111 *Founded/Ownrshp* 1970
Sales 153.0MM[E] *EMP* 750
SIC 5912 5999

D-U-N-S 60-775-8000 IMP/EXP
DIAMOND ELECTRIC MFG CORP
(*Suby of* DIAMOND ELECTRIC MFG. CO., LTD.)
Hc 62, Eleanor, WV 25070
Tel (304) 586-0070 *Founded/Ownrshp* 1987
Sales 85.6MM[E] *EMP* 360
SIC 3694 Ignition coils, automotive
Pr: Scott Hogan
Ch: Shigehiko Ikenaga
Treas: Gene Bialy
Ql Cn Mgr: Jerry Maxwell

D-U-N-S 00-691-4352
■ DIAMOND FOODS LLC
(*Suby of* SNYDERS-LANCE INC) ★
1050 Diamond St, Stockton, CA 95205-7020
Tel (415) 445-7444 *Founded/Ownrshp* 2015
Sales 864.1MM *EMP* 1,696
SIC 2068 2096 Salted & roasted nuts & seeds; Potato chips & similar snacks
Pr: Carl E Lee
Genl Mgr: Gail Myers

D-U-N-S 80-988-9652
▲ DIAMOND HILL INVESTMENT GROUP INC
325 John H Mcconnell Blvd # 200, Columbus, OH 43215-2677
Tel (614) 255-3333 *Founded/Ownrshp* 1990
Sales 124.4MM *EMP* 126[E]
Tkr Sym DHIL *Exch* NGS
SIC 6282 Investment advice; Investment advisory service; Investment counselors
Ch Bd: Roderick H Dillon Jr
Pr: Christopher M Bingaman
COO: Lisa M Wesolek
CFO: Thomas E Line
Chf Cred: Gary R Young
Ofcr: Austin Hawley
Assoc Dir: Alex Gardner
Dir Bus: Faith Stevenson
Mng Dir: Chuck Bath
Mktg Dir: Susan Stuart

D-U-N-S 00-791-9624 IMP
DIAMOND HILL PLYWOOD CO INC
D H P
(*Suby of* DARLINGTON VENEER CO INC) ★
600 E Broad St, Darlington, SC 29532-2900
Tel (843) 393-4036 *Founded/Ownrshp* 1945
Sales 147.1MM[E] *EMP* 200
SIC 5031 Lumber, plywood & millwork; Plywood; Paneling, wood; Siding, wood
Ch Bd: John C Ramsey
Pr: James H Ramsey
COO: Joseph Walsh
CFO: Kennedy Breeden
VP: Bill Abbott
VP: Geary Sharber
Dir Risk M: Ken Hardee
Mktg Dir: Johnny Smith

D-U-N-S 92-687-2409
DIAMOND HOSPITALITY ENTERPRISES
HARDEE'S
5 Mystic Isle Rd, Edgemont, AR 72044-9547
Tel (501) 723-5150 *Founded/Ownrshp* 1993
Sales 39.8MM[E] *EMP* 1,300
SIC 5812 5541 5411 Fast-food restaurant, chain; Filling stations, gasoline; Convenience stores, independent
Pr: Stacy Schmidt
**VP:* Dolores Schmidt

D-U-N-S 14-255-4901 IMP
DIAMOND INNOVATIONS INC
(Suby of SANRIP AB)
6325 Huntley Rd, Columbus, OH 43229-1007
Tel (614) 438-2000 Founded/Ownrshp 2003
Sales 136.0MM^E EMP 550
SIC 3291 Abrasive products
Pr: Mark Schweizer
COO: John Thompson
*CFO: Paula Miller
CFO: Rick Willet
Ofcr: Martin Deakins
VP: Susan Mann
Exec: Steve Wood
IT Man: John Rhoads
Info Man: Ernie Hickman
Info Man: Frank Sgandurra
Mfg Mgr: Carl Liebert

DIAMOND JACKS CASINO & RESORT
See LOUISIANA RIVERBOAT GAMING PARTNERSHIP

D-U-N-S 00-303-8031 IMP
■ **DIAMOND MANUFACTURING CO**
(Suby of RELIANCE STEEL & ALUMINUM CO) ★
243 W Eigth St, Wyoming, PA 18644
Tel (570) 693-0300 Founded/Ownrshp 1915
Sales 99.2MM^E EMP 380
SIC 3469 3471 3479 3089 Perforated metal, stamped; Cleaning, polishing & finishing; Coating of metals & formed products; Plastic processing
CEO: Charles D Flack Jr
*Pr: Harold E Flack II
*Pr: David L Simpson
*CEO: Rusty Flack
*COO: Lee Plank
*Treas: Keith A Zinn
Genl Mgr: Jim Murphy
VP Mfg: Robert Ubsidas
Mktg Mgr: Karen Kelly

DIAMOND MEDICAL SUPPLY
See DIAMOND DRUGS INC

D-U-N-S 10-210-1888
DIAMOND MULTIMEDIA SYSTEMS INC
2880 Junction Ave, San Jose, CA 95134-1922
Tel (408) 868-9613 Founded/Ownrshp 1973
Sales 608.5MM EMP 290
SIC 3672 3577 3661 Printed circuit boards; Computer peripheral equipment; Modems
Pr: William J Schroeder
Pr: Franz Fichtner
CFO: James M Walker
Sr VP: C Scott Holt
Sr VP: Hyung Hwe Huh
Sr VP: Wade Meyercord
Sr VP: Dennis D Praske
VP: David Bates
VP: David Bonaker
VP: James K Gifford
VP: Daniel B Gochnauer
VP: Frank G Hausmann
VP: Jack E Kister
Board of Directors: Bruce C Edwards, Carl W Neun, Gregorio Reyes, Jeffrey D Saper, James T Schraith

D-U-N-S 61-277-0396
■ **DIAMOND OFFSHORE DRILLING INC**
LOEWS
(Suby of LOEWS CORP) ★
15415 Katy Fwy Ste 400, Houston, TX 77094-1812
Tel (281) 492-5300 Founded/Ownrshp 1989
Sales 2.4MMM EMP 3,400^E
Tkr Sym DO Exch NYS
SIC 1381 Drilling oil & gas wells
Pr: Marc Edwards
*Ch Bd: James S Tisch
CFO: Kelly Youngblood
Chf Cred: Ronald Woll
Sr VP: Lyndol L Dew
Sr VP: David L Roland
VP: Richard L Male
Opers Mgr: Ian Clubb
Opers Mgr: Randy Earl
Opers Mgr: Jeramie James
Ql Cn Mgr: Benjamin Devlin
Board of Directors: John R Bolton, Charles L Fabrikant, Paul G Gaffney II, Edward Grebow, Herbert C Hofmann, Kenneth I Siegel, Clifford M Sobel, Andrew H Tisch, Raymond S Troubh

DIAMOND OIL DISTRIBUTORS
See VESCO OIL CORP

D-U-N-S 02-742-4712
DIAMOND PARKING SERVICES LLC
PAULSEN CENTER
605 1st Ave Ste 600, Seattle, WA 98104-2224
Tel (206) 284-2732 Founded/Ownrshp 1922
Sales 80.6MM^E EMP 1,100
SIC 7521 6512 Parking lots; Commercial & industrial building operation; Property operation, retail establishment
CEO: Jonathon D Diamond
*Pr: Jonathon Diamond
*CFO: Robert Turley
*Treas: Greg Matous
*Sr VP: Dave Watson

D-U-N-S 07-962-7212
DIAMOND PLASTICS CORP
1212 Johnstown Rd, Grand Island, NE 68803-5011
Tel (765) 287-9234 Founded/Ownrshp 1982
Sales 135.0MM^E EMP 450
SIC 3084 Plastics pipe
Ch Bd: T Nakamura
*Pr: John Britton
CFO: Peggy Skaggs
Off Mgr: Cindy Kemp
CTO: Scott Clark
IT Man: Joe Dye
Opers Mgr: Dedrick Broussard
Opers Mgr: Robert Gilbreath
Prd Mgr: Tom Brewer
Ql Cn Mgr: Brad Bannister
Sls Dir: Skip Yentes

D-U-N-S 12-765-5731 IMP/EXP
■ **DIAMOND POWER INTERNATIONAL INC**
DIAMOND POWER SPECIALTY
(Suby of BABCOCK & WILCOX CO) ★
2600 E Main St, Lancaster, OH 43130-9366
Tel (740) 687-6500 Founded/Ownrshp 1922
Sales 131.9MM^E EMP 500^E
SIC 3564 Blowers & fans
Pr: Eileen M Competti
Treas: Robert Honaker
Treas: William Powers
Sr VP: Laura S Karch
VP: William Wright
Dir Soc: Marguerite Gossel
Mng Dir: Thomas Moskal
Genl Mgr: Mark Bunton
Genl Mgr: Randal Dortch
IT Man: Mark Adkins
IT Man: Steve Sullivan

DIAMOND POWER SPECIALTY
See DIAMOND POWER INTERNATIONAL INC

D-U-N-S 88-476-2006
DIAMOND RESORTS CORP
(Suby of DIAMOND RESORTS HOLDINGS LLC) ★
10600 W Charleston Blvd, Las Vegas, NV 89135-1014
Tel (702) 684-8000 Founded/Ownrshp 2007
Sales 270.5MM EMP 5,100
Accts Bdo Usa Llp Las Vegas Nevad
SIC 7041 6141 8741 Membership-basis organization hotels; Consumer finance companies; Hotel or motel management
Ch Bd: Stephen J Cloobeck
*Pr: Simon Crawford-Welch PHD Rrp
COO: Mark Ordan
*CFO: David Palmer
*Ex VP: Steven F Bell
*Ex VP: C Alan Bentley CPA
VP: Steve Hicks
*VP: Barry Parrish
Opers Mgr: Bill Driver

D-U-N-S 16-972-6697
DIAMOND RESORTS HOLDINGS LLC
10600 W Charleston Blvd, Las Vegas, NV 89135-1014
Tel (877) 787-0906 Founded/Ownrshp 2007
Sales 271.4MM^E EMP 5,100
SIC 7011 6141 8741 Hotels; Personal credit institutions; Hotel or motel management
Ch Bd: Stephen J Cloobeck
V Ch: Lowell D Kraff
*Pr: David F Palmer
Ex VP: Steve Bell
Ex VP: Michael Flaskey
Ex VP: Howard S Lanznar
*Sr VP: Frank T Goeckel
VP: Sarah Hulme
VP: Keith Marcos
IT Man: Marla Tompkins
IT Man: Michael Wilson

D-U-N-S 07-887-8507
DIAMOND RESORTS INTERNATIONAL INC
(Suby of DAKOTA PARENT INC) ★
10600 W Charleston Blvd, Las Vegas, NV 89135-1014
Tel (702) 798-8840 Founded/Ownrshp 2016
Sales 954.0MM EMP 8,174
SIC 7011 Resort hotel
Pr: David F Palmer
CFO: Al Bentley
Ex VP: Steven F Bell
Ex VP: Michael Flaskey
Ex VP: Brian Garavuso
Ex VP: Howard S Lanznar
VP: Nizar Jabara
VP: Dave Womer
Dir Sec: Steve Hinson
Genl Mgr: James Dinnall
Genl Mgr: Dennis Strait

D-U-N-S 02-279-5384
DIAMOND RESORTS MANAGEMENT INC
(Suby of DIAMOND RESORTS CORP) ★
10600 W Charleston Blvd, Las Vegas, NV 89135-1014
Tel (702) 240-9712 Founded/Ownrshp 1991
Sales 15.5MM^E EMP 1,000
SIC 7011 Resort hotel
CEO: Simon Crawford-Welch
CIO: Brian Garavuso

DIAMOND RIDGE HEALTHCARE CTR
See SSC PITTSBURG OPERATING CO LP

D-U-N-S 19-475-4719
■ **DIAMOND SHAMROCK REFINING AND MARKETING CO**
(Suby of VALERO ENERGY CORP) ★
6000 N Loop 1604 W, San Antonio, TX 78249-1100
Tel (210) 345-2000 Founded/Ownrshp 1983
Sales 3.9MMM^E EMP 20,313
SIC 5541 5171 2911 Gasoline service stations; Petroleum bulk stations & terminals; Petroleum refining
CEO: William E Greehey
Ex VP: John D Gibbons
Ex VP: Gregory C King
Ex VP: William R Klesse
Sr VP: Gary L Arthur Jr
Sr VP: Timothy J Fretthold
VP: John V Cottle
VP: Roger Hemminghaus

D-U-N-S 10-145-1110
DIAMOND STATE INSURANCE CO
(Suby of UNITED NATIONAL INSURANCE CO) ★
3 Bala Plz E Ste 300, Bala Cynwyd, PA 19004-3406
Tel (610) 664-1500 Founded/Ownrshp 1982
Sales NA EMP 240
SIC 6331 6411 Fire, marine & casualty insurance: mutual; Insurance agents, brokers & service
Pr: Bill Smith
*Ch Bd: Raymond L Freudberg
*Treas: Tom McGeehan
*VP: Gerard J Durkin
*VP: Richard March
VP: Noreen Marshall
*VP: John F Yaglenski Jr
IT Man: Brit Brashear

D-U-N-S 07-947-7832
DIAMOND TOOL & FASTENERS INC
2800 Grays Ferry Ave, Philadelphia, PA 19146-3695
Tel (215) 952-1919 Founded/Ownrshp 1993
Sales 84.0MM^E EMP 80
SIC 5082 Masonry equipment & supplies
Prin: Brandon Kelley
CFO: Louis Butcher
*CFO: Tom Kelly
*Prin: Ed Kelley
Dir IT: Charlie Shag
Genl Couns: Monica Lawrence

DIAMOND VOGEL PAINT
See VOGEL PAINT & WAX CO INC

D-U-N-S 10-322-4999
DIAMOND WIRELESS LLC
VERIZON WIRELESS AUTHORIZED RET
(Suby of GLENTEL INC)
10450 S State St, Sandy, UT 84070-4164
Tel (801) 501-7683 Founded/Ownrshp 2010
Sales 279.0MM^E EMP 750
SIC 4812 Cellular telephone services
Sls Dir: Michael Thompson

D-U-N-S 02-957-0200
DIAMOND WIRELESS-OREGON LLC
7927 High Point Pkwy # 300, Sandy, UT 84094-5573
Tel (801) 733-6929 Founded/Ownrshp 2012
Sales 211.9MM^E EMP 265^E
SIC 4812 Cellular telephone services
Prin: Troy Crosland
Exec: Raul Castillo
Exec: Ryan Gunn
Exec: Ryan Souza
Exec: Chris Wiser
Creative D: Dan Kimball
Dir Bus: Parker Smith
Admn Mgr: Dan Smith
Dist Mgr: Ruth Caforio
Dist Mgr: Dominick Caracillo
Dist Mgr: Rick Casassa

D-U-N-S 05-605-1568 EXP
DIAMOND-VOGEL PAINT CO
1110 Albany Pl Se, Orange City, IA 51041-1982
Tel (712) 737-8880 Founded/Ownrshp 1971
Sales 166.3MM^E EMP 500
SIC 2851 5231 Paints & paint additives; Lacquers, varnishes, enamels & other coatings; Removers & cleaners; Paint, glass & wallpaper
Pr: Drew F Vogel
*Treas: Aarsen Bert
*Sec: Bert Aarsen
*VP: Mark Vogel
VP Mktg: Dale Hays

D-U-N-S 07-853-6538
▲ **DIAMONDBACK ENERGY INC**
500 W Texas Ave Ste 1200, Midland, TX 79701-4203
Tel (432) 221-7400 Founded/Ownrshp 2007
Sales 446.7MM EMP 141
Tkr Sym FANG Exch NGS
SIC 1311 Crude petroleum & natural gas; Crude petroleum & natural gas production; Natural gas production
CEO: Travis D Stice
*Ch Bd: Steven E West
COO: Michael L Hollis
CFO: Teresa L Dick
VP: Randall J Holder
VP: Paul S Molnar
VP: Elizabeth E Moses
VP: Russell D Pantermuehl

D-U-N-S 15-222-9162
▲ **DIAMONDROCK HOSPITALITY CO**
3 Bethesda Metro Ctr # 1500, Bethesda, MD 20814-5330
Tel (240) 744-1150 Founded/Ownrshp 2004
Sales 930.9MM EMP 26
Tkr Sym DRH Exch NYS
SIC 6798 Real estate investment trusts
Pr: Mark W Brugger
Ch Bd: William W McCarten
COO: Robert D Tanenbaum
CFO: Sean M Mahoney
Ex VP: Troy G Furbay
Ex VP: William J Tennis
VP: Diem Larsen

DIAMONDS INTERNATIONAL
See ALMOD DIAMONDS LTD

D-U-N-S 15-464-8018
DIANA FOODS INC
GOYA FOODS OF FLORIDA
(Suby of GOYA FOODS INC) ★
13300 Nw 25th St, Miami, FL 33182-1510
Tel (305) 593-8317 Founded/Ownrshp 1938
Sales 221.8MM^E EMP 725
SIC 5141 5149 Groceries, general line; Groceries & related products
Ch Bd: Joseph Unanue
*Sec: Frank Unanue
*VP: Ruben Chavez
*VP Sls: Jose Maria Perez

DIANA'S BAKERY
See CONNECTICUT PIE INC

D-U-N-S 07-797-4475
DIANAS MEXICAN FOOD PRODUCTS INC
LA BONITA
16330 Pioneer Blvd, Norwalk, CA 90650-7042
Tel (562) 926-5802 Founded/Ownrshp 1975
Sales 104.5MM^E EMP 300
SIC 2099 5812 Food preparations; Ethnic food restaurants
CEO: Samuel Magana
Chf Mktg O: Elmer Guzman
*VP: Hortensia Magana
Sales Exec: Victor Salazar

D-U-N-S 07-846-8234
DIANNES FINE DESSERT INC
4 Graf Rd, Newburyport, MA 01950-4015
Tel (978) 463-3832 Founded/Ownrshp 2016
Sales 104.5MM^E EMP 500
SIC 2024 Dairy based frozen desserts
CEO: Mike Knowles
*Pr: Daniel Scales
*CFO: Tom Lundquist

D-U-N-S 10-133-7863
■ **DIANON SYSTEMS INC**
(Suby of LABORATORY CORP OF AMERICA HOLDINGS) ★
1 Forest Pkwy, Shelton, CT 06484-6147
Tel (203) 926-7100 Founded/Ownrshp 1984
Sales 31.6MM^E EMP 2,000
SIC 8071 Testing laboratories
Pr: Thomas Macmahon
CFO: Anne Lash
CFO: David Shriber
Bd of Dir: Arundhati Chatterjee
Bd of Dir: Emma E Diaz
Bd of Dir: Margaret Johnson
Ex VP: Myla Lai
VP: Steven Gersen
*VP: Valerie B Palmieri
VP: Marty Philips
VP: Christopher J Rausch
Dir Lab: Honggang Shen
Assoc Dir: Edward Poole
Assoc Dir: Usha Vasa

DIAPERS.COM
See QUIDSI INC

D-U-N-S 03-342-9783 IMP
DIASORIN INC
(Suby of DIASORIN SPA)
1951 Northwestern Ave S, Stillwater, MN 55082-7536
Tel (651) 439-9710 Founded/Ownrshp 1999
Sales 92.1MM^E EMP 550
SIC 2835 5047

D-U-N-S 08-027-1715
DIASORIN MOLECULAR LLC
(Suby of DIASORIN INC) ★
11331 Valley View St, Cypress, CA 90630-5366
Tel (562) 240-6500 Founded/Ownrshp 2016
Sales 90.0MM EMP 200
SIC 2835 5047 In vitro diagnostics; Diagnostic equipment, medical
CEO: Carlo Rosa

DIAZ FOODS
See DIAZ WHOLESALE & MFG CO INC

D-U-N-S 07-967-3382
DIAZ FOODS
4 Rosol Ln, Saddle Brook, NJ 07663-5503
Tel (404) 629-3616 Founded/Ownrshp 2014
Sales 200.0MM EMP 100
SIC 2038 Frozen specialties
CEO: Rene M Diaz
*V Ch: Marsh Selaya

D-U-N-S 04-396-1754 IMP
DIAZ WHOLESALE & MFG CO INC
DIAZ FOODS
5501 Fulton Indus Blvd Sw, Atlanta, GA 30336-2677
Tel (404) 346-9312 Founded/Ownrshp 1980
Sales 388.4MM^E EMP 375^E
SIC 5141 Groceries, general line
CEO: Rene M Diaz
*CFO: Eric Newberg
CFO: Eric Nuberg
Ex VP: Jorge Antona
*Ex VP: Barbarella Diaz
Ex VP: Lisa Lee
*Ex VP: Carmen Saldana
VP: Liliana Bejarano
VP: Susana Sotoliu
*VP: Lourdes Winkelmann
VP Opers: Jeff Lee

D-U-N-S 09-706-2111
DIBUDUO & DEFENDIS INSURANCE BROKERS LLC
6873 N West Ave, Fresno, CA 93711-4308
Tel (559) 432-0222 Founded/Ownrshp 1960
Sales NA EMP 127
SIC 6411 Insurance agents
Pt: Matt Defendis
Pt: Mike De Fendis
VP: Tony Canizales
VP: Ron Lamm
Dir IT: John McNally
Mktg Mgr: Linda Euler
Mktg Mgr: Nancy Westcott

D-U-N-S 01-877-6997
DICHELLO DISTRIBUTORS INC (CT)
55 Marsh Hill Rd, Orange, CT 06477-3648
Tel (203) 891-2100 Founded/Ownrshp 1933
Sales 97.6MM^E EMP 205
SIC 5182 5181 Wine & distilled beverages; Beer & ale
CEO: Gloria Dichello Hall
*Pr: Edward M Crowley
CFO: Robert Simon
*Sec: John Dichello Jr
Area Mgr: Joe Belcourt
Genl Mgr: Peter Deane
Sls Dir: Kevin Gaetano

D-U-N-S 08-951-4434
DICK ANDERSON CONSTRUCTION INC
3424 E Us Highway 12, Helena, MT 59601-9708
Tel (406) 443-3225 Founded/Ownrshp 1975
Sales 185.4MM EMP 160
Accts Anderson Zurmuehlen & Co Pc
SIC 1542 1622 1611 Commercial & office building contractors; Bridge construction; Highway & street construction
Pr: Martin Schuma
*CEO: Dick Anderson
CFO: Sarah EBY
CFO: Jan Taylor
*Treas: Kathryn Smith
*Sec: Regan Meredith
*VP: Derek Didriksen
*VP: Allan Frankl
VP: Kevin Hintt
*VP: Ed Venetz

D-U-N-S 00-193-3258 IMP/EXP
DICK BLICK CO (IL)
BLICK DICK ART MATERIALS STORE
(*Suby of* DICK BLICK HOLDINGS INC) ★
1849 Green Bay Rd Ste 310, Highland Park, IL 60035-3168
Tel (847) 681-6800 *Founded/Ownrshp* 1921, 1947
Sales 96.4MM[E] *EMP* 700
SIC 5945 Arts & crafts supplies
CEO: Bob Buchsbaum
CFO: Ed Ogorzaly
VP: Lanny Rosenbaum
VP: Winnie Tuszynski
Board of Directors: Andrew Morrill, Craig Buchsbaum, Richard Morrill, Samuel Buchsbaum, Laurie Stevens, Tom Buchsbaum, Sarah Gilchrist, Jenny Liddle, Howard Metzenberg, Robert Metzenberg Jr, Stan Metzenberg, Aaron Morrill

D-U-N-S 00-585-6666 IMP/EXP
DICK BLICK HOLDINGS INC (DE)
1849 Green Bay Rd Ste 310, Highland Park, IL 60035-3168
Tel (847) 681-6800 *Founded/Ownrshp* 1991
Sales 150.5MM[E] *EMP* 900[E]
SIC 5961 Arts & crafts equipment & supplies, mail order
Ch: Jack Wyatt
**Pr:* Robert Buchsbaum
**CEO:* Bob Buchsbaum
**CFO:* Ed Ogorzaly
Genl Mgr: Joyce Del
Genl Mgr: Susan Walsh
Off Mgr: Megan Cartwright
Board of Directors: Andrew Morrill, Craig Buchsbaum, Richard Morrill, Samuel Buchsbaum, Laurie Stevens, Tom Buchsbaum, Sarah Gilchrist, Jenny Liddle, Howard Metzenberg, Robert Metzenberg Jr, Stan Metzenberg, Aaron Morrill

DICK DYER TOYOTA
See DYER INC

D-U-N-S 60-654-2934
DICK SMITH AUTOMOTIVE GROUP INC
9940 Two Notch Rd, Columbia, SC 29223-4381
Tel (800) 944-8570 *Founded/Ownrshp* 1987
Sales 112.6MM[E] *EMP* 350
SIC 5511 7515 New & used car dealers; Passenger car leasing
Pr: Brian Smith
**Ch:* Richard Smith
**Sec:* Wilma Smith
**VP:* David Smith
Genl Mgr: Greg Messenger
Sales Exec: Joel Thompson
VP Sls: Joby Webster

D-U-N-S 05-587-4564
DICKERSON PETROLEUM INC
920 N Illinois St, Belleville, IL 62220-4346
Tel (618) 233-0786 *Founded/Ownrshp* 1971
Sales 151.4MM *EMP* 17
Accts Voellinger Simpson Dolan & A
SIC 5172 Petroleum products
Pr: Steven R Dickerson
**Treas:* Alison Fournier
**Sec:* Lajuana J Dickerson
**VP:* Thomas H Wuller
Sales Exec: James Fournier

D-U-N-S 06-377-6785
DICKERSON STATIONS INC
GAS MART
920 N Illinois St, Belleville, IL 62220-4374
Tel (618) 233-0786 *Founded/Ownrshp* 1977
Sales 183.5MM *EMP* 275
Accts Voellinger Simpson Dolan & A
SIC 5541 5411 Filling stations, gasoline; Grocery stores
Pr: Steve Dickerson
**VP:* Allen Bocker
**VP:* James Fournier

DICKEY'S BARBECUE PIT
See DICKEYS BARBECUE RESTAURANTS INC

D-U-N-S 04-783-9089
DICKEYS BARBECUE RESTAURANTS INC
DICKEY'S BARBECUE PIT
4514 Cole Ave Ste 1015, Dallas, TX 75205-5449
Tel (972) 248-9899 *Founded/Ownrshp* 1967
Sales 70.9MM[E] *EMP* 1,018
SIC 5812 Barbecue restaurant
CEO: Jay Grewal
COO: Andy Abbajay
COO: Barry Barron Sr
CFO: Roland Dickey Jr
Chf Mktg O: Diana Larocca
Ofcr: Christie Finley
Dist Mgr: Henry Lara
CIO: Brian Maupin
Art Dir: Jamie K Henretta

D-U-N-S 13-018-4856
■ **DICKEYVILLE TELEPHONE LLC**
TDS
(*Suby of* TDS TELECOMMUNICATIONS CORP) ★
200 W Main St, Dickeyville, WI 53808-9700
Tel (608) 831-1000 *Founded/Ownrshp* 2001
Sales 135.2MM[E] *EMP* 2,700
SIC 4813 Local & long distance telephone communications
Pr: David Wittwer

DICKIES
See WILLIAMSON-DICKIE MANUFACTURING CO

D-U-N-S 00-302-9253 IMP
DICKINSON COLLEGE
College & Louther St, Carlisle, PA 17013
Tel (717) 245-1010 *Founded/Ownrshp* 1773
Sales 102.7MM[E] *EMP* 632
Accts Kpmg Llp Harrisburg Pennsylv
SIC 8221 College, except junior
Pr: Nancy Roseman
**VP:* Joyce Bylander
**VP:* Bront Jones
Exec: Nancy Edlin
**Prin:* Cathy McDonald Davenport
CTO: Jennifer Love

D-U-N-S 07-479-2540
DICKINSON COUNTY HEALTHCARE SYSTEM
DICKINSON MEMORIAL HOSPITAL
1721 S Stephenson Ave, Iron Mountain, MI 49801-3637
Tel (906) 774-1313 *Founded/Ownrshp* 1930
Sales 110.7MM *EMP* 798
Accts Eide Bailly Llp Fargo North
SIC 8062 General medical & surgical hospitals
CEO: John Schon
Chf Path: Peter C Hamel
Natl Sales: Jackson Edmund
Doctor: Donald J Acobs MD
Doctor: Emma Diponio

D-U-N-S 96-647-6202
DICKINSON FINANCIAL CORP II
1111 Main St Ste 1600, Kansas City, MO 64105-2116
Tel (816) 472-5244 *Founded/Ownrshp* 1992
Sales NA *EMP* 1,240[E]
Accts Kpmg Llp Kansas City Missour
SIC 6712 Bank holding companies
Ch Bd: Ann Dickinson
Pr: Rick Smalley
CEO: Paul P Holewinski
Treas: Dennis P Ambroske
Ofcr: Steve Hutcheson
Ex VP: Dan Dickinson
VP: Daniel L Dickinson
VP: Lisa Germonprez
VP: George Harrison
VP: Stacey L Lucas
VP: Brent Parsons
VP: Mike Schwarz
Exec: Steven Mallory

D-U-N-S 15-397-2922 IMP
DICKINSON FROZEN FOODS INC
NORSUN
(*Suby of* WASHINGTON POTATO CO) ★
1205 E Iron Eagle Dr B, Eagle, ID 83616-6725
Tel (208) 938-7540 *Founded/Ownrshp* 1986
Sales 228.8MM[E] *EMP* 220
SIC 5142 Vegetables, frozen
Pr: Paul Fox
**CFO:* Doug Reader
**Ex VP:* Butch Wilson
Exec: Jeff Hymas

D-U-N-S 07-416-7529
DICKINSON INDEPENDENT SCHOOL DISTRICT
2218 Fm 517 Rd E, Dickinson, TX 77539-8661
Tel (281) 229-6000 *Founded/Ownrshp* 1941
Sales 111.8MM *EMP* 750
Accts Start Garcia & Stanley Llc
SIC 8211 Public elementary & secondary schools
Ex Dir: Jeannie Thielemann
Pr Dir: Tammy Dowdy
Teacher Pr: Kimberly Rich

DICKINSON MEMORIAL HOSPITAL
See DICKINSON COUNTY HEALTHCARE SYSTEM

D-U-N-S 01-665-9112
DICKMAN SUPPLY INC
1991 St Marys Ave, Sidney, OH 45365
Tel (937) 492-6166 *Founded/Ownrshp* 1953
Sales 120.2MM[E] *EMP* 110
SIC 5063 5084 Electrical apparatus & equipment; Drilling bits; Paper, sawmill & woodworking machinery
Pr: Tim Geise
**Pr:* Timothy Geise
**CFO:* Luke Allen
**Sec:* Marla Geise
**VP:* Chris Geise
Off Mgr: Rick Lunsford
Sls Mgr: Mario Nova
Sales Asso: Jon Wente

D-U-N-S 08-028-3036
■ **DICKS MERCHANDISING & SUPPLY CHAIN INC**
(*Suby of* DICKS SPORTING GOODS INC) ★
345 Court St, Coraopolis, PA 15108-3817
Tel (724) 723-3400 *Founded/Ownrshp* 2015
Sales 32.6MM[E] *EMP* 1,800
SIC 5941 Sporting goods & bicycle shops
Pr: Lee Belitsky

D-U-N-S 15-732-2272 IMP
▲ **DICKS SPORTING GOODS INC**
345 Court St, Coraopolis, PA 15108-3817
Tel (724) 273-3400 *Founded/Ownrshp* 1948
Sales 7.2MMM *EMP* 37,200
Accts Deloitte & Touche Llp Pittsbu
Tkr Sym DKS *Exch* NYS
SIC 5941 5699 Sporting goods & bicycle shops; Sports apparel
Ch Bd: Edward W Stack
COO: Andr J Hawaux
COO: Andre J Hawaux
CFO: Lee J Belitsky
CFO: Teri L List-Stoll
CFO: Garth Murszewski
**V Ch Bd:* William J Colombo
Chf Mktg O: Lauren R Hobart
Ex VP: Michele B Willoughby
Sr VP: John E Hayes III
Sr VP: Joseph R Oliver
VP: Scott Blyze
VP: Jim Braim
VP: Moussa Coulibaly
VP: Ryan Eckel
VP: George Giacobbe
VP: Todd Hipwell
VP: Jonathan Husted
Board of Directors: Mark J Barrenechea, Vincent C Byrd, Emanuel Chirico, Lawrence J Schorr, Larry D Stone, Allen R Weiss

D-U-N-S 07-483-4839
DICKSTEIN SHAPIRO LLP (DC)
1825 Eye St Nw Fl 1200, Washington, DC 20006-5417
Tel (202) 420-2200 *Founded/Ownrshp* 1953
Sales 98.4MM[E] *EMP* 800
SIC 8111

DICKTEN MASCH PLASTICS
See TECHNIPLAS LLC

D-U-N-S 00-129-0691 IMP
■ **DICTAPHONE CORP** (DE)
(*Suby of* NUANCE COMMUNICATIONS INC) ★
3191 Broadbridge Ave, Stratford, CT 06614-2559
Tel (203) 381-7000 *Founded/Ownrshp* 1881, 2006
Sales 115.3MM[E] *EMP* 1,650
SIC 3579 3825 3695 3577 Dictating machines; Instruments to measure electricity; Magnetic & optical recording media; Computer peripheral equipment
Sr VP: Daniel P Hart
**Ch Bd:* Robert Schwager
Ex VP: Jon Tropsa
**Sr VP:* Joseph Delaney
**Sr VP:* Thomas C Hodge
**Sr VP:* Ed Rucinski
VP: Lawrence E Bergeron

D-U-N-S 07-115-4678
DIDION MILLING INC (WI)
520 Hartwig Blvd Ste C, Johnson Creek, WI 53038-9315
Tel (920) 348-5868 *Founded/Ownrshp* 1972
Sales 120.7MM[E] *EMP* 130
SIC 5153 2041 Corn; Flour & other grain mill products
CEO: John Didion
**Pr:* Dow Didion
**CFO:* Luke Burmeister
VP: Dale Drachenberg
Prgrm Mgr: Tonya Umbarger
Dir IT: Jim Dingnan
IT Man: James Dingman
Sfty Mgr: Scott Hulsey

D-U-N-S 09-541-7929
DIDLAKE INC
DIDLAKE OCCUPATIONAL CENTER
8641 Breeden Ave Ste 101, Manassas, VA 20110-8431
Tel (703) 361-4195 *Founded/Ownrshp* 1965
Sales 63.8MM *EMP* 1,700
Accts Bennett Atkinson And Associate
SIC 8331 7331 7349 7334 Job training services; Vocational rehabilitation agency; Direct mail advertising services; Building maintenance services; Photocopying & duplicating services
Pr: Rexford G Parr Jr
**Ch:* Richard Ratcliffe
Bd of Dir: Jackie White
VP: John Craig
VP: Bruce Gross
VP: Donna Hollis
Exec: Karen Ford
Exec: Heidi Thornlow
Dir Bus: Valerie Spencer
Prgrm Mgr: Emily Gebhart
Dir IT: Ivy Tetreault

DIDLAKE OCCUPATIONAL CENTER
See DIDLAKE INC

D-U-N-S 00-446-9300
▲ **DIEBOLD INC** (OH)
DIEBOLD NIXDORF
5995 Mayfair Rd, North Canton, OH 44720-1597
Tel (330) 490-4000 *Founded/Ownrshp* 1859
Sales 2.4MMM *EMP* 16,000
Tkr Sym DBD *Exch* NYS
SIC 3578 3699 3499 Automatic teller machines (ATM); Banking machines; Security control equipment & systems; Safes & vaults, metal; Safe deposit boxes or chests, metal
Pr: Andreas W Mattes
**Ch Bd:* Henry D G Wallace
**CFO:* Christopher A Chapman
Treas: Robert Warren
**Chf Cred:* John D Kristoff
Bd of Dir: John Gall
**Ofcr:* Sheila M Rutt
Ex VP: James L M Chen
Ex VP: Roy Lu
Ex VP: George S Mayes
Ex VP: George Mayes
Ex VP: Frank A Natoli Jr
Ex VP: Charles Scheuer
Sr VP: Bassem Bouzid
Sr VP: Neil Emerson
Sr VP: Octavio Marquez
**Sr VP:* Stefan E Merz
Sr VP: Tom Signorello
VP: Scott M Angelo
VP: Antonio Antonuccio
VP: Elias R Da Silva
Board of Directors: Alan Weber, Patrick W Alexander, Phillip R Cox, Richard L Crandall, Gale S Fitzgerald, Gary G Greenfield, Andy W Mattes, Robert S Prather Jr, Rajesh K Soin, Henry Dg Wallace

DIEBOLD NIXDORF
See DIEBOLD INC

D-U-N-S 62-534-2787 IMP
DIEBOLD SELF SERVICE SYSTEMS
5995 Mayfair Rd, Canton, OH 44720-1550
Tel (330) 490-5099 *Founded/Ownrshp* 1990
Sales 300.0MM *EMP* 620
SIC 3578 Automatic teller machines (ATM)
CEO: Thomas Swidarski
CFO: Gregory T Geswein
Treas: Robert J Warren
VP: Daniel J Brien
VP: James L Chen
VP: Larry D Ingram
VP: Dennis M Moriarty
VP: Anthony J Rusciano
VP: Charles B Scheurer
VP: Ernesto R Unanue
VP: Jeffrey J Vancleve

D-U-N-S 82-611-0330
DIEOMATIC INC
BENCO MANUFACTURING
(*Suby of* COSMA ENGINEERING) ★
750 Tower Dr Mail 7000 Mail Code, Troy, MI 48098
Tel (319) 668-2031 *Founded/Ownrshp* 1972
Sales 168.1MM[E] *EMP* 1,500[E]
SIC 3714 Motor vehicle parts & accessories
Pr: Tommy Skudutis
**Treas:* Richard J Smith
**Prin:* Brian Duivesteyn

DIERBERG'S CENTRAL OFFICE
See DIERBERGS MARKETS INC

D-U-N-S 03-102-7303
DIERBERGS INC
16690 Swingley Ridge Rd # 300, Chesterfield, MO 63017-0758
Tel (636) 532-8884 *Founded/Ownrshp* 1959
Sales 512.2MM[E] *EMP* 5,000
SIC 5411 5992 Supermarkets, chain; Flowers, fresh; Plants, potted
Pr: Greg Dierberg
**VP:* Robert Dierberg
Exec: Melvie Nunn
Dir Risk M: Steven Radcliff
Dept Mgr: Angie Kauffmann
IT Man: Gary Sanguinett

D-U-N-S 02-972-6239
DIERBERGS MARKETS INC
DIERBERG'S CENTRAL OFFICE
16690 Swingley Ridge Rd # 300, Chesterfield, MO 63017-0767
Tel (636) 532-8884 *Founded/Ownrshp* 1854
Sales 579.6MM[E] *EMP* 4,126
SIC 5411 Supermarkets, chain
Pr: Greg Dierberg
**Ch Bd:* Robert J Dierberg
VP: Dave Madeor
Store Dir: Jamar Jones
CIO: Jim Shipley
Board of Directors: Ron Edelen, Mike Hanny

D-U-N-S 11-421-1543
DIERBERGS OFALLON LLC
16690 Swingley Ridge Rd, Chesterfield, MO 63017-0758
Tel (636) 532-8884 *Founded/Ownrshp* 1983
Sales 147.4M[E] *EMP* 4,126
SIC 5411 Supermarkets
Treas: Robert J Dierberg
CEO: Greg Dierberg

DIERKS WAUKESHA
See WAUKESHA WHOLESALE FOODS INC

D-U-N-S 95-738-5958 IMP
DIESEL USA INC
(*Suby of* OTB SPA)
220 W 19th St Fl 5, New York, NY 10011-4035
Tel (212) 755-9200 *Founded/Ownrshp* 1995
Sales 288.2MM[E] *EMP* 1,000
SIC 5137 5136 5621 5632 5611 Women's & children's clothing; Women's & children's accessories; Men's & boys' clothing; Women's clothing stores; Women's accessory & specialty stores; Men's & boys' clothing stores; Clothing accessories: men's & boys'
CEO: Panayiotis Phillippou
CEO: Renzo Rosso
COO: Bob Almerini
CFO: Donateller Bordigion
Treas: Nitin Patel
Sr Cor Off: Antonio Ruffoni
VP: Francis Pierrel
Opers Mgr: Sergio Caredda

D-U-N-S 00-227-3340 IMP
DIETZ & WATSON INC (NJ)
BLACK BEAR DELI MEATS
5701 Tacony St, Philadelphia, PA 19135-4394
Tel (800) 333-1974 *Founded/Ownrshp* 1939
Sales 234.5MM[E] *EMP* 900
SIC 2011 2013 Beef products from beef slaughtered on site; Pork products from pork slaughtered on site; Sausages & other prepared meats
CEO: Louis Eni Jr
Pr: John Schoenfellinger
**COO:* Christopher Eni
**CFO:* Sandy Eni
**Treas:* Cynthia Yingling
Genl Mgr: Carl Fann
CTO: Mark Rubin
Plnt Mgr: Tony Alvarez
Sls&Mrk Ex: John Oberg
VP Sls: Thom Nardi
Mktg Dir: Steve Riley

D-U-N-S 62-644-3204
▲ **DIFFERENTIAL BRANDS GROUP INC**
1231 S Gerhart Ave, Commerce, CA 90022-4255
Tel (323) 890-1800 *Founded/Ownrshp* 1987
Sales 250.7MM[E] *EMP* 588
Tkr Sym DFBG *Exch* NAS
SIC 2337 2339 2311 2325 3111 2387 Women's & misses' suits & coats; Women's & misses' suits & skirts; Women's & misses' capes & jackets; Jeans: women's, misses' & juniors'; Men's & boys' suits & coats; Jeans: men's, youths' & boys'; Accessory products, leather; Handbag leather; Shoe leather; Apparel belts
CEO: Michael Buckley
**Ch Bd:* William Sweedler
CFO: Hamish Sandhu
Ex VP: Tom Nevell
VP: Tracy Fung
VP: Elena Pickett
VP: Dolores Rykowski
Creative D: Joseph Dahan
Store Mgr: Carrie Sandelin
Board of Directors: Matthew Eby, Kelly Hoffman, Walter McLallen, Kent Savage, Andrew Tarshis

D-U-N-S 14-465-5669 IMP
▲ **DIGI INTERNATIONAL INC**
11001 Bren Rd E, Minnetonka, MN 55343-9685
Tel (952) 912-3444 *Founded/Ownrshp* 1985

Sales 203.0MM *EMP* 565[E]
Accts Pricewaterhousecoopers Llp Mi
Tkr Sym DGII *Exch* NGS
SIC 3577 3575 7374 7371 Computer peripheral equipment; Computer terminals; Computer processing services; Computer software development & applications
Pr: Ronald E Konezny
COO: Kevin C Riley
CFO: Michael C Goergen
CFO: Mike Goergen
Treas: Chris Lappi
Chf Mktg O: Jeff Liebl
Sr VP: Joel K Young
VP: Shawn Ivey
VP: Larry Kraft
VP: Jon A Nyland
VP: David H Sampsell
Exec: Venetia Silva
Board of Directors: Spiro C Lazarakis, Ahmed Nawaz, William N Priesmeyer, Girish Rishi

D-U-N-S 00-932-1542
DIGI-KEY CORP
1393 E Powell Way, Chandler, AZ 85249-4733
Tel (480) 294-5709 *Founded/Ownrshp* 2010
Sales 17.0MM[E] *EMP* 1,150
SIC 7389
Prin: John Crawford

D-U-N-S 05-760-2120 IMP/EXP
DIGI-KEY CORP
DIGI-KEY ELECTRONICS
701 Brooks Ave S, Thief River Falls, MN 56701-2757
Tel (800) 344-4539 *Founded/Ownrshp* 1973
Sales 1.5MMM *EMP* 3,100
SIC 5065 Electronic parts
CEO: Ronald A Stordahl
**Pr:* David Doherty
**Ex VP:* Chris Beeson
VP: Todd Bill
VP: Dave Doherty
VP: Tom Dusher
VP: Marie Finney
VP: Kris Haggstorm
VP: Kris Haggstrom
VP: Teri Ivaniszyn
**VP:* Roy Lunde
VP: Jeff Shafer
VP: Steve Vecchiarelli
VP: Lorae Wendlandt
VP: Mark Zack

DIGI-KEY ELECTRONICS
See DIGI-KEY CORP

D-U-N-S 00-238-3701 IMP
DIGIORGIO MUSHROOM CORP (PA)
GIORGIO FOODS
1161 Park Rd, Reading, PA 19605
Tel (610) 926-2139 *Founded/Ownrshp* 1960
Sales 94.5MM[E] *EMP* 282[E]
SIC 2033 5148 2037 6512 Mushrooms: packaged in cans, jars, etc.; Vegetables, fresh; Vegetables, quick frozen & cold pack, excl. potato products; Commercial & industrial building operation
Pr: Peter F Giorgi
**Sec:* Philip M Impink
**VP:* John Majaewski

D-U-N-S 08-040-5064
DIGIPAS TECHNOLOGIES INC
200 Spectrum Center Dr, Irvine, CA 92618-5003
Tel (949) 558-0160 *Founded/Ownrshp* 2016
Sales 250.0MM *EMP* 3
SIC 3429 3499 3699 Security cable locking system; Locks, safe & vault: metal; Security control equipment & systems; Security devices
CEO: Jim LI Hui Hong
CFO: Ellyta Yauwan Yauw

D-U-N-S 05-248-9051
DIGITAL EMPLOYEES FEDERAL CREDIT UNION (MA)
DIGITAL FEDERAL CREDIT UNION
220 Donald Lynch Blvd, Marlborough, MA 01752-4708
Tel (508) 263-6700 *Founded/Ownrshp* 1979
Sales NA *EMP* 875
SIC 6061 Federal credit unions
Pr: James Regan
VP: Edward Crisci
**VP:* Richard Hayward
VP: Phil Moor
CIO: Nancy Bryant
IT Man: Patrick Kelley
IT Man: Ben Sum
IT Man: Dan Toohey
IT Man: Francis Zdrojkowski
Opers Mgr: Yadama Unikama

DIGITAL FEDERAL CREDIT UNION
See DIGITAL EMPLOYEES FEDERAL CREDIT UNION

DIGITAL FIRST MEDIA
See MEDIANEWS GROUP INC

D-U-N-S 01-104-3677
DIGITAL FIRST MEDIA LLC
20 W 33rd St Fl 7, New York, NY 10001-3305
Tel (212) 257-7212 *Founded/Ownrshp* 2013
Sales 4.7MMM[E] *EMP* 12,953[E]
SIC 2711 Commercial printing & newspaper publishing combined
CEO: John Paton
Pr: Kevin Corrado
Pr: Steve Rossi
CFO: Barbara Bennett
Ofcr: Arturo Duran
Ofcr: Robert Monteleone
Ex VP: Guy Gilmore
Ex VP: William J Higginson
Ex VP: Mac Tully
Ex VP: Tom Wiley
Sr VP: Maryann Kiley
Sr VP: Chris Loretto
Sr VP: Jeannie Parent
VP: Jonathan Cooper
VP: Christian De Gennaro
VP: Joe Miller
VP: Bruce Spiro

DIGITAL HIGH POINT
See CAROLINA CONTAINER CO

D-U-N-S 93-359-5886
■ **DIGITAL INSIGHT CORP**
INTUIT FINANCIAL SERVICES
(*Suby of* NCR CORP) ★
1300 Seaport Blvd Ste 300, Redwood City, CA 94063-5591
Tel (818) 879-1010 *Founded/Ownrshp* 2014
Sales 202.4MM[E] *EMP* 800
SIC 7375 7372 7371 Information retrieval services; Prepackaged software; Custom computer programming services
Pr: Jeffrey E Stiefler
**Ex VP:* Joseph M McDoniel
**Ex VP:* Tom Shen
Sr VP: Vincent R Brennan
**Sr VP:* Robert R Surridge
VP: Thomas Blass
VP: Paul Campbell
VP: Meheriar Hasan
VP: Katherine Jansen
VP: Joe McDaniel
VP: Scott Pranger
VP: Steven Reich
VP: Stephen Zarate

D-U-N-S 93-832-0280
DIGITAL INTELLIGENCE SYSTEMS LLC
DISYS
8270 Greensboro Dr # 1000, Mc Lean, VA 22102-4910
Tel (703) 752-7900 *Founded/Ownrshp* 1994
Sales 805.6MM[E] *EMP* 4,000
SIC 7373 7371 Computer integrated systems design; Computer software development & applications
CEO: Mahfuz Ahmed
**Pr:* Maruf Ahmed
**CFO:* Michael Bolton
VP: Curry Nichols
VP: Paul Pinto
Ex Dir: Firas Al-Hindi
Ex Dir: Peter Meister
Ex Dir: Lily Yeh
Mng Dir: Bob Quinn
Mng Dir: Larry Thompson
Brnch Mgr: Tim Laughlin
Board of Directors: Tom Van Horn

D-U-N-S 83-121-5988
■ **DIGITAL LEASH LLC**
PROTECT CELL
(*Suby of* FORTEGRA FINANCIAL CORP) ★
39500 High Pointe Blvd # 250, Novi, MI 48375-5508
Tel (877) 775-3274 *Founded/Ownrshp* 2006
Sales NA *EMP* 236[E]
SIC 6331 6411 Burglary & theft insurance; Property & casualty insurance agent
Prin: Richard Kahlbaugh
COO: Chris Beyersdorff
**CFO:* Walter Mascherin
**Treas:* George Freeman
Software D: Abiyu Getahun
Sls Mgr: Doug Horiski

D-U-N-S 11-351-2359
DIGITAL MANAGEMENT LLC
DMI
6550 Rock Spring Dr Fl 7, Bethesda, MD 20817-1124
Tel (240) 223-4800 *Founded/Ownrshp* 2002
Sales 384.2MM[E] *EMP* 1,812
Accts Grant Thornton Llp Mclean V
SIC 7371 Computer software development & applications
Pr: Jay Sunny Bajaj
COO: Ken S Bajaj
CFO: Noah S Asher
Ex VP: Charles Thompson
Sr VP: Collin Dretsch
VP: Mark Beekman
VP: Mark Bui
VP: John Buscher
VP: Steve Cooper
VP: Linda Gillen
VP: Shaji Joseph
VP: Suzanne Mauro
VP: John McDermott
VP: Erika Peace
VP: Larry Silver
Comm Dir: Lori Brooks
Dir Bus: Basil Parker

D-U-N-S 03-829-5382 IMP
DIGITAL MONITORING PRODUCTS INC
D M P
2500 N Partnership Blvd, Springfield, MO 65803-8877
Tel (417) 831-9362 *Founded/Ownrshp* 1974
Sales 106.5MM[E] *EMP* 210
SIC 3669 Burglar alarm apparatus, electric; Fire alarm apparatus, electric; Intercommunication systems, electric
Pr: Rick Britton
**Pr:* David Roberts
**COO:* Marc Mills
**CFO:* Chris Stange
Treas: Bob Spencer
VP: David Peebles
**VP:* Joseph Reynolds
Exec: Joan Hounslow
Exec: Lola Johnson
Dir Soc: Jan Britton
Ex Dir: Pat Tobin

D-U-N-S 17-078-1038
▲ **DIGITAL REALTY TRUST INC**
4 Embarcadero Ctr # 3200, San Francisco, CA 94111-4106
Tel (415) 738-6500 *Founded/Ownrshp* 2004
Sales 1.7MMM *EMP* 1,604
Accts Kpmg Llp San Francisco Calif
Tkr Sym DLR *Exch* NYS
SIC 6798 Real estate investment trusts
Ch Bd: Dennis E Singleton
V Ch: Laurence A Chapman
CEO: A William Stein
COO: Jarrett B Appleby
CFO: Andrew P Power
CFO: William Stein
Sr VP: Ellen Jacobs
Sr VP: Chris Kenney
Sr VP: Joshua A Mills
Sr VP: Daniel Papes
VP: Dana Adams
VP: Rita Da
VP: Brian Keyser
VP: John Kuchachik
VP: Craig McGahey
VP: Sara Mooradian
VP: Krupal Raval
VP: David Robertson
VP: John Sarkis
VP: Jennifer Xiao

D-U-N-S 60-747-5667
DIGITAL RISK LLC
(*Suby of* MPHASIS CORP) ★
2301 Maitland Center Pkwy # 165, Maitland, FL 32751-7465
Tel (407) 215-2900 *Founded/Ownrshp* 2005
Sales 150.0MM *EMP* 1,400
Accts Kpmg Llp Orlando Fl
SIC 8748 Business consulting
CEO: Peter Kassabov
**Mng Pt:* Jeffrey C Taylor
Pr: Kristina Cmorey
Pr: Maria Pennington
**Pr:* Omar Quddus
**Pr:* Edward A Santos
**CEO:* Sesha Dhanyamraju
**CFO:* Mark Hinshaw
Ex VP: Dave Lucchino
Ex VP: Gary Manfredi
Ex VP: Earl Smith
Sr VP: Chris Castoro
VP: David C Cash
VP: James Held

D-U-N-S 96-260-8972
DIGITAL RIVER INC
(*Suby of* DANUBE PRIVATE HOLDINGS II LLC) ★
10380 Bren Rd W, Minnetonka, MN 55343-9072
Tel (952) 253-1234 *Founded/Ownrshp* 2015
Sales 1.0MMM[E] *EMP* 1,317[E]
SIC 4813
CEO: David C Dobson
Pr: Rita Khan
**COO:* Theodore R Cahall Jr
**CFO:* Hoke Horne
CFO: Sue Michal
**CFO:* Stefan Shulz
**Ex VP:* Thomas E Peterson
Ex VP: Tom Peterson
**Sr VP:* Kevin L Crudden
Sr VP: Peterson Don
Sr VP: Joydeep Haldar
Sr VP: Rob Hines
Sr VP: Hayden Reed
Sr VP: Stewart Sagastume
Sr VP: Scott Scazafavo
Sr VP: Glenn Stolar
Sr VP: David Woolenberg
VP: Tara Baynes
VP: Jack Brau
VP: Paul Bridgewater
VP: Mark Iverson

D-U-N-S 80-731-4617
▲ **DIGITAL TURBINE INC**
1300 Guadalupe St Ste 302, Austin, TX 78701-1607
Tel (512) 387-7717 *Founded/Ownrshp* 1998
Sales 86.5MM *EMP* 161[E]
Tkr Sym APPS *Exch* NAS
SIC 7373 Computer integrated systems design
CEO: William Stone III
**Ch Bd:* Robert Deutschman
CFO: Barrett Garrison
Sr VP: Brian Bartholomew
VP: Harris Thurmond
Snr Sftwr: Rob Cecchino
Software D: Frank Curcio

D-U-N-S 78-963-8418
▲ **DIGITALGLOBE INC**
1300 W 120th Ave, Westminster, CO 80234-2726
Tel (303) 684-4000 *Founded/Ownrshp* 1995
Sales 702.4MM *EMP* 1,319[E]
Tkr Sym DGI *Exch* NYS
SIC 4899

D-U-N-S 02-850-8612
DIGITAS INC
DIGITASLBI
(*Suby of* PUBLICIS GROUPE S A)
33 Arch St Fl 8, Boston, MA 02110-1437
Tel (617) 369-8000 *Founded/Ownrshp* 2006
Sales 308.4MM[E] *EMP* 1,740
SIC 8742 Marketing consulting services
CEO: David W Kenny
CFO: Michael Goss
CFO: Amy Murphy-Dowd
CFO: Joe Tomasulo
CFO: Joseph Tomasulu
Ofcr: Mark Beeching
Ofcr: Lincoln Bjorkman
Ofcr: Renato Fabri
Ofcr: Cella M Irvine
Ofcr: Judy Jackson
Ofcr: Paul Kitcatt
Ex VP: Barbara Goose
Ex VP: Dave Marsey
Sr VP: Ernest W Cloutier
Sr VP: Anthony Gandia
Sr VP: Joe Lin
Sr VP: Sarah Montague
Sr VP: Mark Nolan
Sr VP: Anita Puri
Sr VP: Ashley Swartz
VP: Amit Awasthi

DIGITASLBI
See DIGITAS INC

DIGITEK COMPUTER PRODUCTS INC
See DIGITEK IMAGING PRODUCTS INC

D-U-N-S 01-618-6814 IMP/EXP
DIGITEK IMAGING PRODUCTS INC
DIGITEK COMPUTER PRODUCTS INC
(*Suby of* ARLINGTON INDUSTRIES) ★
44258 Mercure Cir, Dulles, VA 20166-2025
Tel (703) 421-0300 *Founded/Ownrshp* 2016
Sales 163.7MM[E] *EMP* 50[E]
SIC 5045 Computers, peripherals & software; Computer peripheral equipment; Computers & accessories, personal & home entertainment
CEO: Paul Martorana
CFO: Sarah Bulver

D-U-N-S 07-930-9887
DIGITY COMPANIES LLC
701 Nrthpint Pkwy Ste 500, West Palm Beach, FL 33407
Tel (561) 616-4600 *Founded/Ownrshp* 2013
Sales 80.4MM *EMP* 1,100
SIC 4832 Radio broadcasting stations
CEO: Dean Goodman
COO: George Pelletier
CFO: Lenny Brandon

D-U-N-S 13-160-6022 IMP
DIGNITY HEALTH
185 Berry St Ste 300, San Francisco, CA 94107-1773
Tel (415) 438-5500 *Founded/Ownrshp* 1984
Sales 7.1MMM[E] *EMP* 49,363
Accts Deloitte & Touche Llp San Fra
SIC 8062 General medical & surgical hospitals
Pr: Lloyd Dean
**COO:* Marvin O'Quinn
**CFO:* Michael Blaszyk
CFO: Michael Blazysk
CFO: Daniel J Morissette
CFO: Ani Varro
CFO: Harold Way
**Treas:* Lisa Zuckerman
Bd of Dir: Barbara Pelletreau
Ex VP: Rick Grossman
Ex VP: Darryl L Robinson
**Ex VP:* Elizabeth Shih
Ex VP: Robert L Wiebe
Ex VP: Deanna L Wise
VP: Jackie Aragon
VP: Julie Bietsch
VP: Pablo Bravo
VP: Sherri Comaianni
**VP:* Derek Covert
VP: Rod Davis
VP: Abel Garcia

D-U-N-S 79-783-8505
DIGNITY HEALTH MEDICAL FOUNDATION
DIGNITY HLTH MED GRP-DOMINICAN
3400 Data Dr, Rancho Cordova, CA 95670-7956
Tel (916) 379-2840 *Founded/Ownrshp* 1990
Sales 570.1MM *EMP* 1,000
Accts Kpmg Llp San Francisco Ca
SIC 8099 Medical services organization
Pr: Laurie Schwarctz
CFO: Sue Haddad
Counsel: C Evans

DIGNITY HLTH MED GRP-DOMINICAN
See DIGNITY HEALTH MEDICAL FOUNDATION

D-U-N-S 82-710-1960
DILIGENT CORP
1385 Brdwy Fl 19, New York, NY 10018
Tel (212) 741-8181 *Founded/Ownrshp* 2016
Sales 99.3MM[E] *EMP* 264[E]
SIC 7372 Prepackaged software
Pr: Brian Stafford
CFO: Michael Stanton
Chf Cred: Jeffrey Hilk
Chf Mktg O: Amada Carty
Chf Mktg O: Shawn Lankton
Ex VP: Thomas N Tartaro
Sr VP: Johnson Garrett
VP: Dennis Comma
Snr Sftwr: Paul Faid
CTO: Michael Flickman
QA Dir: Wilson Rodriguez

D-U-N-S 00-486-7198 IMP
▲ **DILLARDS INC**
1600 Cantrell Rd, Little Rock, AR 72201-1145
Tel (501) 376-5200 *Founded/Ownrshp* 1938
Sales 6.7MMM *EMP* 40,000
Accts Kpmg Llp Dallas Texas
Tkr Sym DDS *Exch* NYS
SIC 5311 5611 5621 5641 5712 Department stores; Men's & boys' clothing stores; Women's clothing stores; Children's & infants' wear stores; Furniture stores
Ch Bd: William Dillard III
Pr: Theodore Callier
**Pr:* Alex Dillard
Treas: Sherrill Wise
**Ex VP:* Mike Dillard
**Ex VP:* Drue Matheny
Sr VP: Chris B Johnson
Sr VP: Denise Mahaffy
Sr VP: Phillip R Watts
VP: Mike McNiff
VP: Brant Musgrave
VP: Louise Platt
VP: David Terry
VP: Dean L Worley
Board of Directors: Robert C Connor, James I Freeman, H Lee Hastings, Frank R Mori, Warren A Stephens, J C Watts Jr, Nick White

DILLON
See AVERY WEIGH-TRONIX LLC

D-U-N-S 00-694-2882 IMP/EXP
■ **DILLON COMPANIES INC**
GERBES SPRMKT / KING SOOPERS
(*Suby of* KROGER CO) ★
2700 E 4th Ave, Hutchinson, KS 67501-1903
Tel (620) 665-5511 *Founded/Ownrshp* 1921
Sales 4.3MMM[E] *EMP* 47,000
SIC 5411 Supermarkets, chain
Pr: David Dillon
Dist Mgr: Kim Svoboda
Genl Mgr: Kay Tomasu

IT Man: Jay Yoder
VP Opers: Ken Deluca
Trfc Mgr: Christy Bugg

D-U-N-S 00-318-7515 IMP
DILLON SUPPLY CO (NC)
MILES JENNINGS INDUSTRIAL SUP
(*Suby of* DESCOURS ET CABAUD SA)
440 Civic Blvd, Raleigh, NC 27610-2967
Tel (919) 838-4200 *Founded/Ownrshp* 1914, 1979
Sales 216.5MM^E *EMP* 370
SIC 5084 5085 5051 5074 5072 Industrial machinery & equipment; Materials handling machinery; Lift trucks & parts; Industrial machine parts; Industrial supplies; Mill supplies; Steel; Boilers, power (industrial); Hardware
Pr: Dean Wagoner
**VP:* Eric Dillon
**VP:* Joseph Zinaich
Rgnl Mgr: Jeff Hagar
Board of Directors: Pierre De Limairac, Marc Debollardiere

D-U-N-S 10-319-3504
DILLON TRANSPORT INC
901 Mcclintock Dr Ste 300, Burr Ridge, IL 60527-7941
Tel (630) 281-7093 *Founded/Ownrshp* 1980
Sales 157.9MM^E *EMP* 480
SIC 4212 Local trucking, without storage
Pr: Jeff Dillon
**COO:* Charles Musgrove
**CFO:* Don Tomes
VP: Eric Peterson
**VP Admn:* Sue Crofts
Sfty Mgr: Rich Wagner
Snr Mgr: Billy Alford
Snr Mgr: Dallas Hamilton
Snr Mgr: Phil Nutter

D-U-N-S 04-493-7431 IMP
DILMAR OIL CO INC
1951 W Darlington St, Florence, SC 29501-2050
Tel (843) 662-4179 *Founded/Ownrshp* 1970
Sales 101.6MM *EMP* 120
Accts Burch Oxner Seale Co Cpa S
SIC 5172 2819 Petroleum products; Industrial inorganic chemicals
Ch: W Gray Atkinson
**CFO:* R Earle Atkinson Jr
CFO: Rob Campbell
**Sec:* Vicky Jackson
VP: Robert Scott
**VP:* David N Tart
Manager: Aaron Dameron

D-U-N-S 00-799-7224
DIMARE BROTHERS INC
84 New England Prod Ctr, Chelsea, MA 02150-1703
Tel (617) 889-3800 *Founded/Ownrshp* 1926, 1928
Sales 180.1MM^E *EMP* 522
SIC 5148 Fruits, fresh; Vegetables, fresh
Pr: Paul Dimare
**Treas:* Thomas Dimare

D-U-N-S 60-406-8874
DIMARE FRESH INC
(*Suby of* DIMARE BROTHERS INC) ★
4629 Diplomacy Rd, Fort Worth, TX 76155-2621
Tel (817) 385-3000 *Founded/Ownrshp* 2003
Sales 109.2MM^E *EMP* 233
SIC 5148 Fruits, fresh
Pr: Paul Dimare
**CFO:* Cheryl Taylor
**VP:* Eric Janke
Exec: Bonnie Jordan
DP Exec: Hope Sanchez
Sls Mgr: Faye Westfall

DIMAS DIVISION
See HUSQVARNA CONSTRUCTION PRODUCTS NORTH AMERICA INC

D-U-N-S 94-937-6792
▲ DIME COMMUNITY BANCSHARES INC
209 Havemeyer St, Brooklyn, NY 11211-6206
Tel (718) 782-6200 *Founded/Ownrshp* 1996
Sales NA *EMP* 409^E
Accts Crowe Horwath Llp New York N
Tkr Sym DCOM *Exch* NGS
SIC 6035 Federal savings & loan associations
Ch Bd: Vincent F Palagiano
**V Ch:* Michael P Devine
**COO:* Kenneth J Mahon
CFO: Michael Pucella
Chf Inves: Robert Volino
Ofcr: Timothy B King
Ofcr: Terence J Mitchell
Ex VP: Lance J Bennett
Ex VP: Timothy Lenhoff
Ex VP: Anthony J Rose

D-U-N-S 00-697-8928
■ DIME COMMUNITY BANK
(*Suby of* DIME COMMUNITY BANCSHARES INC) ★
209 Havemeyer St, Brooklyn, NY 11211-6206
Tel (718) 782-6200 *Founded/Ownrshp* 1864
Sales NA *EMP* 394
SIC 6035 Federal savings banks
Ch Bd: Vincent Palagiano
**Pr:* Michael Devine
**COO:* Kenneth Mahon
**Ex VP:* William E Brown
**Ex VP:* Timothy King
**Ex VP:* Timothy Lenhoff
**Ex VP:* Christopher Maher
**Ex VP:* Michael Pucella
**Ex VP:* Robert Volino
**Sr VP:* James Rizzo
VP: Lamar Hall

D-U-N-S 14-240-6334
DIMENSION DATA
(*Suby of* DIMENSION DATA (PTY) LTD)
27202 Turnberry Ln # 100, Valencia, CA 91355-1023
Tel (661) 257-1500 *Founded/Ownrshp* 2014
Sales 211.8MM^E *EMP* 340
SIC 4899 Data communication services
CEO: Deron Pearson
Pr: Waheed Choudhry
CFO: Dan Dougherty
VP: Sabrina Anderson
VP: Dale Hardy
VP: Mike Heiman
VP: Tom Lyon
VP: Tom Lyons
VP: Joy W Wong
Exec: Todd Caporal
Prac Mgr: Ted Alben

D-U-N-S 00-391-4454
DIMENSION DATA NORTH AMERICA INC
(*Suby of* DIMENSION DATA HOLDINGS PLC)
1 Penn Plz Ste 1600, New York, NY 10119-1600
Tel (212) 613-1220 *Founded/Ownrshp* 2003
Sales 329.7MM^E *EMP* 700
Accts Peter O Donoghue Fca London
SIC 7373 Computer integrated systems design; Systems integration services
CEO: Mark Slaga
**COO:* Scott Macfee
**CFO:* Eric Gibson
**Sr VP:* Denise Messineo
Sr VP: Mark Zerbe
VP: Stephen Bloom
VP: Greg Bowden
VP: Tina Gravel
Off Mgr: Sue Atwood
Off Mgr: Lynne Steinhart
Netwrk Eng: Jim Strong

DIMENSION FOR LIVING
See UNITED METHODIST PUBLISHING HOUSE

D-U-N-S 04-942-4435
DIMENSIONAL FUND ADVISORS LP
6300 Fm 2244 Rd Bldg 1, Austin, TX 78746-5833
Tel (512) 306-7400 *Founded/Ownrshp* 1981
Sales 179.7MM^E *EMP* 300
SIC 6722 Management investment, open-end
Pt: David Booth
CEO: Eduardo Repetto
COO: Patrick Keating
CFO: Christopher Crossan
Bd of Dir: Eugene F Fama
Bd of Dir: John A McQuown
Bd of Dir: Rex A Sinquefield
Ofcr: April A Aandal
VP: Akbar Ali
VP: Darryl D Avery
VP: Stanley Black
VP: Scott A Bosworth
VP: Valerie A Brown
VP: Patrick E Carter
VP: Stephen A Clark
VP: Robert Cornell
VP: Christopher S Crossan
VP: Christopher Crossan
VP: James L Davis
VP: Richard A Eustice
VP: Gretchen A Flicker

D-U-N-S 08-235-0422
DIMENSIONS HEALTH CORP
DIMENSIONS HEALTHCARE SYSTEM
3001 Hospital Dr, Cheverly, MD 20785-1189
Tel (301) 618-2000 *Founded/Ownrshp* 1982
Sales 365.9MM *EMP* 2,800
Accts Gohen Rutherford & Knight P
SIC 8062 8059 Hospital, affiliated with AMA residency; Nursing home, except skilled & intermediate care facility
Pr: Neil J Moore
Chf OB: Lauren R Rodgers
Chf Rad: Gurmeet Sidhu
Dir Recs: Stephanie Jordan
Pr: Juliet Gomez
**COO:* John A Obrien
Ofcr: Lauren Russell
VP: Suresh Gupta
VP: Nellie Sain
VP: Aletha Walker
Dir Inf Cn: Abdul Zafar
Dir Risk M: Eslanda Dasher
Dir Rad: Donna Lanier
Dir Rad: Joe Wheeler
Dir Env Sv: Azizur Khan

DIMENSIONS HEALTHCARE SYSTEM
See DIMENSIONS HEALTH CORP

D-U-N-S 00-159-1999
DIMEO CONSTRUCTION CO
DIMEO GROUP OF COMPANIES
75 Chapman St, Providence, RI 02905-5496
Tel (401) 781-9800 *Founded/Ownrshp* 1981
Sales 272.1MM^E *EMP* 300
Accts Stowe & Degon Llc Westborough
SIC 1542 1522 7353 Commercial & office building, new construction; Hospital construction; School building construction; Multi-family dwellings, new construction; Heavy construction equipment rental
Pr: Bradford S Dimeo
COO: Stephen F Rutledge
CFO: Steven B Avery
Ch: Thomas P Dimeo
Exec: Terri Maclean
IT Man: Marianna Zotos
Sys Mgr: Jonathan Santos
Sfty Dirs: Bob Kunz
Snr PM: Frank Allard
Snr PM: Steven Banak

DIMEO GROUP OF COMPANIES
See DIMEO CONSTRUCTION CO

D-U-N-S 02-810-0782 IMP
DIMETRI GARDIKAS PRODUCE CO INC
14811 Marquardt Ave, Santa Fe Springs, CA 90670-5126
Tel (562) 404-4779 *Founded/Ownrshp* 1983
Sales 87.2MM *EMP* 40
Accts Bernotas Accountancy Corporati
SIC 5148 Fruits, fresh
Pr: Dimetri Gardikas
**Sec:* Mary B Gardikas
**VP:* Tashi Zouras

D-U-N-S 80-009-0219 IMP
DINCO INC
(*Suby of* DIN GLOBAL CORP.)
27520 Hawthorne Blvd # 180, Rllng HLS Est, CA 90274-3542
Tel (424) 331-1200 *Founded/Ownrshp* 2009
Sales 246.6MM^E *EMP* 200
SIC 4899 Data communication services; Satellite earth stations
Pr: Attiazaz Din
CEO: Kevin Schatzle
CFO: Javed Latif
Ofcr: Fida Abbas
**Sr VP:* Robert A Mercer
VP: Ali M Din
VP: Tom Versfelt
Exec: Ali Mubashir
Prgrm Mgr: Vamsi Madasu
Genl Mgr: Gail Oreilly
Dir IT: Ernesto Saucedo
Board of Directors: Mark R Briggs, Edward O Hunter, Timothy J Lilligren, Mansoor S Shah

D-U-N-S 03-086-5711
▲ DINEEQUITY INC
450 N Brand Blvd, Glendale, CA 91203-2347
Tel (818) 240-6055 *Founded/Ownrshp* 1976
Sales 681.1MM *EMP* 975
Tkr Sym DIN *Exch* NYS
SIC 5812 6794 Restaurant, family: chain; Franchises, selling or licensing
Ch Bd: Julia A Stewart
CFO: Thomas W Emrey
CFO: Gregg Kalvin
Ex VP: Jonathan Fitzpatrick
Sr VP: Bryan R Adel
Sr VP: John B Jakubek
Sr VP: Greggory W Kalvin
VP: Patrick Dandino
Ex Dir: Randy Bogart
Ex Dir: Paul Zolnowski
CTO: Ann Hackett
Board of Directors: Howard M Berk, Daniel J Brestle, Richard J Dahl, Stephen P Joyce, Larry A Kay, Caroline W Nahas, Douglas M Pasquale, Gilbert T Ray, Patrick W Rose

D-U-N-S 60-970-0083
DINGMAN GROUP INC
1051 W Webster Ave, Winter Park, FL 32789-3033
Tel (407) 644-6043 *Founded/Ownrshp* 1984
Sales 111.1MM^E *EMP* 200
SIC 5511 5531 7539 Automobiles, new & used; Automotive parts; Automotive repair shops
Pr: William E Dingman

D-U-N-S 07-286-2691
DINSMORE & SHOHL LLP
255 E 5th St Ste 1900, Cincinnati, OH 45202-1971
Tel (513) 977-8200 *Founded/Ownrshp* 1996
Sales 151.6MM^E *EMP* 890
SIC 8111 General practice law office
Mng Pt: Doug Feichtner
Mng Pt: Peter Georgiton
Mng Pt: David R Monohan
Mng Pt: George H Vincent
Mng Pt: Kirk Wall
Exec: Faith Isenhath
Opers Mgr: Michelle Miller
Counsel: Patrick D Lane
Counsel: Harry Riggs
Counsel: Jan H Steinher
Counsel: Alex M Triantafilou

D-U-N-S 15-518-4732
DIOCESAN HEALTH FACILITIES OFFICE
368 N Main St, Fall River, MA 02720-2406
Tel (508) 679-8154 *Founded/Ownrshp* 1987
Sales 59.6MM^E *EMP* 1,200
SIC 8051 Skilled nursing care facilities
Ex Dir: Rev Edmund J Fitzgerald

DIOCESAN MEDIA CENTER, THE
See DIOCESE OF CAMDEN NEW JERSEY

DIOCESE LFYTTE CATHLIC SCHOOLS
See DIOCESE OF LAFAYETTE

D-U-N-S 07-365-9617
DIOCESE OF ALLENTOWN
4029 W Tilghman St Ste 3, Allentown, PA 18104-4400
Tel (610) 437-0755 *Founded/Ownrshp* 1961
Sales 46.9MM^E *EMP* 1,250
SIC 8661 Catholic Church

D-U-N-S 07-495-6632
DIOCESE OF ALTOONA-JOHNSTOWN
927 S Logan Blvd, Hollidaysburg, PA 16648-2699
Tel (814) 695-5579 *Founded/Ownrshp* 1901
Sales 37.2MM^E *EMP* 1,400
SIC 8661 Religious organizations
Prin: Mark L Bartchak

D-U-N-S 06-905-0029
DIOCESE OF CAMDEN NEW JERSEY (NJ)
DIOCESAN MEDIA CENTER, THE
631 Market St, Camden, NJ 08102-1103
Tel (856) 756-7900 *Founded/Ownrshp* 1937
Sales 348.5MM^E *EMP* 3,000
SIC 2711 8661 Newspapers: publishing only, not printed on site; Catholic Church
Pr Dir: Peter Feuerherd

D-U-N-S 09-520-2917
DIOCESE OF COVINGTON
ROMAN CTHLIC DIOCESE COVINGTON
1125 Madison Ave, Covington, KY 41011-3115
Tel (859) 392-1500 *Founded/Ownrshp* 1852, 1972
Sales 92.6MM^E *EMP* 1,800
SIC 8211 8661 Catholic combined elementary & secondary school; Catholic Church
**CFO:* Dale Henson

D-U-N-S 07-892-1038
DIOCESE OF FORT WAYNE-SOUTH BEND INVESTMENT TRUST INC
915 S Clinton St, Fort Wayne, IN 46802-2601
Tel (260) 422-4611 *Founded/Ownrshp* 1857
Sales 29.6MM *EMP* 1,750
Accts Leonardo J Andorfer & Co Ll
SIC 8661 Catholic Church
Pr: Kevin C Rhoades
**CFO:* Joseph Ryan
**VP:* John M D'Arcy
Teacher Pr: Stephanie Howe
Board of Directors: Harry Verhiley

D-U-N-S 06-885-8919
DIOCESE OF FRESNO EDUCATION CORP
ROMAN CATHOLIC BISHOP FRESNO
1550 N Fresno St, Fresno, CA 93703-3711
Tel (559) 488-7400 *Founded/Ownrshp* 1967
Sales 60.5MM^E *EMP* 1,200
SIC 8211 8661 Catholic elementary & secondary schools; Catholic Church
CEO: Armando X Ochoa
COO: Richard Sexton

D-U-N-S 07-390-6083
DIOCESE OF GALVESTON-HOUSTON EDUCATION FOUNDATION
1700 San Jacinto St, Houston, TX 77002-8216
Tel (713) 652-8248 *Founded/Ownrshp* 1847
Sales 222.3MM^E *EMP* 6,000
SIC 8661 Religious organizations

DIOCESE OF HELENA
See ROMAN CATHOLIC BISHOP OF HELENA MONTANA

D-U-N-S 07-945-4153
DIOCESE OF LAFAYETTE
DIOCESE LFYTTE CATHLIC SCHOOLS
1408 Carmel Dr, Lafayette, LA 70501-5215
Tel (337) 261-5652 *Founded/Ownrshp* 1918
Sales 43.8MM^E *EMP* 1,566
SIC 8661 Catholic Church

D-U-N-S 07-563-7736
DIOCESE OF LANSING
228 N Walnut St, Lansing, MI 48933-1122
Tel (517) 342-2440 *Founded/Ownrshp* 1865
Sales 45.9MM^E *EMP* 1,300
Accts Plante & Moran Pllc East Lan
SIC 8661 Catholic Church

D-U-N-S 05-051-7366
DIOCESE OF METUCHEN INC
146 Metlars Ln, Piscataway, NJ 08854-4303
Tel (732) 562-1990 *Founded/Ownrshp* 1982
Sales 73.9MM^E *EMP* 2,300
SIC 8661 Religious organizations
Pr: Paul G Bootkoski
**Sec:* Tom Toolan
**VP:* William Benwell
Off Mgr: Monica Danquiz

DIOCESE OF OAKLAND
See ROMAN CATHOLIC BISHOP OF OAKLAND

D-U-N-S 07-921-3278
DIOCESE OF ORLANDO HUMAN CONCERNS FOUNDATION INC
50 E Robinson St, Orlando, FL 32801-1619
Tel (407) 246-4800 *Founded/Ownrshp* 1968
Sales 85.4MM^E *EMP* 3,000
SIC 8661 Catholic Church
Prin: Bishop John Noonan
CFO: Jerry Hilbirch
**CFO:* Gerald F Hilbrich

D-U-N-S 06-872-4442
DIOCESE OF PITTSBURGH
111 Blvd Of The Allies, Pittsburgh, PA 15222-1618
Tel (412) 456-3000 *Founded/Ownrshp* 1843
Sales 184.2MM^E *EMP* 8,300
SIC 8661 Catholic Church
**CFO:* Frederick P O'Brien
Opers Mgr: Jim Tancosh

D-U-N-S 19-331-0778
DIOCESE OF PORTLAND SCHOOL OFFICE
510 Ocean Ave, Portland, ME 04103-4900
Tel (207) 773-6471 *Founded/Ownrshp* 1853
Sales 27.0MM^E *EMP* 1,200
SIC 8211 Catholic elementary & secondary schools

DIOCESE OF SAN BERNARDINO
See ROMAN CATHOLIC BISHOP OF SAN BERNARDINO

DIOCESE OF SAN JOSE
See ROMAN CATHOLIC BISHOP OF SAN JOSE

DIOCESE OF SCRANTON, THE
See CATHOLIC SOCIAL SERVICES OF DIOCESE OF SCRANTON INC

D-U-N-S 08-272-9260
DIOCESE OF SIOUX CITY (IA)
1821 Jackson St, Sioux City, IA 51105-1055
Tel (712) 255-7933 *Founded/Ownrshp* 1902
Sales 21.6MM^E *EMP* 1,000
SIC 8661 Catholic Church
Prin: Linda Ebel
Prin: Lorie Nussbaum
Prin: Ronald Olberding
Prin: Michael Pavik

DIOCESE OF SPRINGFIELD
See ROMAN CATHOLIC BISHOP OF SPRINGFIELD

D-U-N-S 06-588-7390
DIOCESE OF ST AUGUSTINE INC
MARYWOOD RETREAT CENTER
11625 Old St Augustine Rd, Jacksonville, FL 32258-2056
Tel (904) 824-2806 *Founded/Ownrshp* 1995
Sales 49.1MM^E *EMP* 1,050
SIC 8661 6531 Catholic Church; Real estate managers
Ch: James Marx
**Pr:* Felipe J Estvez
**CFO:* Catherine A Macina
Assoc Dir: Anita Hassell
Comm Dir: Kathleen Bagg-Morgan
Ex Dir: Andy Duran

DIOCESE OF ST PETERSBURG
See DIOCESE OF ST PETERSBURG INC

D-U-N-S 06-965-7682
DIOCESE OF ST PETERSBURG INC
DIOCESE OF ST PETERSBURG
6363 9th Ave N, Saint Petersburg, FL 33710-6212
Tel (727) 345-3338 *Founded/Ownrshp* 1968
Sales 90.9MM[E] *EMP* 1,700
SIC 8661 Catholic Church
Ch Bd: Robert Lynch
COO: Betty Deptula
* *Treas:* Philip Signore
* *VP:* Robert R Morris
* *VP:* Frank V Murphy
* *VP:* Michael Tkacik
Ex Dir: Paul Ward
VP Mktg: Sharon Larson

D-U-N-S 01-697-5914
DIOCESE OF STEUBENVILLE CATHOLIC CHARITIES
422 Washington St Ste 1, Steubenville, OH 43952-2159
Tel (740) 282-3631 *Founded/Ownrshp* 1944
Sales 28.3MM[E] *EMP* 1,500
SIC 8661 Catholic Church

D-U-N-S 18-933-6837
DIOCESE OF STOCKTON EDUCATIONAL OFFICE
CATHOLIC SCHOOLS OFFICE, THE
212 N San Joaquin St, Stockton, CA 95202-2409
Tel (209) 466-0636 *Founded/Ownrshp* 1994
Sales 61.7MM[E] *EMP* 1,500
SIC 8211 Catholic elementary & secondary schools
V Ch: David Springer

D-U-N-S 07-757-2253
DIOCESE OF TOLEDO
1933 Spielbusch Ave, Toledo, OH 43604-5360
Tel (419) 244-6711 *Founded/Ownrshp* 1910
Sales 88.4MM[E] *EMP* 2,444
SIC 8661 Religious organizations
* *CFO:* Walter Nevolis

D-U-N-S 07-706-5258
DIOCESE OF TRENTON
CATHOLIC DIOCESE OF TRENTON
701 Lawrenceville Rd, Trenton, NJ 08648-4295
Tel (609) 406-7400 *Founded/Ownrshp* 1881
Sales 145.9MM[E] *EMP* 3,000
SIC 8661 Religious organizations
Pr: Bishop John M Smith
Assoc Dir: Mariann Gilbride
Assoc Dir: Rosemary Kimball
Assoc Dir: Michael Riley
* *Prin:* Bishop David M O'Connell
* *Prin:* Katherine Soss Prihoda
Off Mgr: Linda Mullin
Advt Mgr: Edward Heffernan

D-U-N-S 04-096-8968
DIOCESE OF WINONA FOUNDATION
55 W Sanborn St, Winona, MN 55987-3655
Tel (507) 454-4643 *Founded/Ownrshp* 1889
Sales 32.3MM[E] *EMP* 1,800
SIC 8661 Religious organizations

DIOCESE OF WORCESTER
See ROMAN CATHOLIC BISHOP OF WORCESTER

DIOCESE PHOENIX SCHOOL OFFICE
See ROMAN CATHOLIC CHURCH OF DIOCESE OF PHOENIX

D-U-N-S 04-935-0432 IMP
▲ DIODES INC
4949 Hedgcoxe Rd Ste 200, Plano, TX 75024-3935
Tel (972) 987-3900 *Founded/Ownrshp* 1959
Sales 848.9MM *EMP* 6,695
Tkr Sym DIOD *Exch* NGS
SIC 3674 Semiconductors & related devices
Pr: Keh-Shew Lu
* *Ch Bd:* Raymond Soong
CFO: Richard D White
* *V Ch Bd:* C H Chen
Sr VP: Hans Rohrer
VP: Clemente Beltran
VP: Julie Holland
VP: Alex CHI Ming Hui
VP: Edmund Tang
VP: Francis Tang
Counsel: Sam Tung
Board of Directors: Michael R Giordano, L P Hsu, John M Stich, Michael K C Tsai

D-U-N-S 05-539-5487
■ DIONEX CORP
(*Suby of* THERMO FISHER SCIENTIFIC INC) ★
1228 Titan Way Ste 1002, Sunnyvale, CA 94085-4074
Tel (408) 737-0700 *Founded/Ownrshp* 2011
Sales 279.2MM[E] *EMP* 1,550
SIC 3826 2819 3087 3841 Chromatographic equipment, laboratory type; Chemicals, reagent grade: refined from technical grade; Custom compound purchased resins; Surgical & medical instruments
Pr: Mark Casper
* *CFO:* Craig A McCollam
* *Ex VP:* Bruce Barton
Sr VP: Peter Jochum PHD
VP: Dermin Fan
VP: Jasmine Gruia Gray PHD
Exec: Phillip Deland
Tech Mgr: Srinivasa RAO
VP Mktg: Curtis Beeman
VP Mktg: Mike Pettigrew
Mktg Mgr: Linda Lopez

D-U-N-S 80-889-7631 EXP
DIPLOMAT
501 Diplomat Pkwy, Hallandale Beach, FL 33009-3710
Tel (954) 883-4000 *Founded/Ownrshp* 1991
Sales 53.8MM[E] *EMP* 1,500
SIC 7997 Country club, membership
Genl Mgr: Mark Kukulski
Treas: Gerald Laduco
VP: Silvio Silveira
Exec: Paul Riso
Ex Dir: Marjorie Cowan
Genl Mgr: Paul Asciotí
Dir IT: Steve Hicks

D-U-N-S 07-423-2695
▲ DIPLOMAT PHARMACY INC
4100 S Saginaw St Ste A, Flint, MI 48507-2687
Tel (888) 720-4450 *Founded/Ownrshp* 1975
Sales 3.3MMM *EMP* 1,667[E]
Tkr Sym DPLO *Exch* NYS
SIC 5912

D-U-N-S 10-193-1335
DIPLOMAT PROPERTIES LIMITED PARTNERSHIP
DIPLOMAT RESORT & COUNTRY CLUB
(*Suby of* THAYER LODGING GROUP INC) ★
3555 S Ocean Dr, Hollywood, FL 33019-2827
Tel (954) 602-6000 *Founded/Ownrshp* 1997
Sales 89.7MM[E] *EMP* 1,500
SIC 7011 7997 Hotels & motels; Country club, membership; Golf club, membership
Mng Pt: Mark Kukulski
Genl Mgr: Ed Walls

DIPLOMAT RESORT & COUNTRY CLUB
See DIPLOMAT PROPERTIES LIMITED PARTNERSHIP

D-U-N-S 04-609-3284
DIRECT AUCTION SERVICES LLC
101 Jessica Lauren Ct, Hendersonville, TN 37075-9619
Tel (678) 570-3493 *Founded/Ownrshp* 2010
Sales 48.5MM[E] *EMP* 1,700
SIC 5012 7539 7549 7542 7361 Automobile auction; Automotive repair shops; Automotive maintenance services; Washing & polishing, automotive; Labor contractors (employment agency)
CEO: David Nutter
* *Pr:* David Young
* *COO:* David Rush
* *Treas:* Donald Cameron
* *Prin:* Jack Garrett

DIRECT AUTO INSURANCE
See DIRECT GENERAL INSURANCE AGENCY INC

D-U-N-S 07-958-1061
DIRECT BEAUTY INC
33 Estate Fryndendahl, St Thomas, VI 00802
Tel (340) 775-4612 *Founded/Ownrshp* 1993
Sales 200.0MM *EMP* 2
SIC 7231 Beauty shops
Pr: Louvina Ramsay

D-U-N-S 61-858-4569 IMP
DIRECT CABINET SALES - US LBM LLC
(*Suby of* US LBM HOLDINGS LLC) ★
180 Herrod Blvd, Dayton, NJ 08810-1562
Tel (908) 587-9577 *Founded/Ownrshp* 2015
Sales 83.8MM[E] *EMP* 95
SIC 5031 5064 Kitchen cabinets; Electrical appliances, major
Pr: Joe Demussi

D-U-N-S 84-052-7415
■ DIRECT CHECKS UNLIMITED LLC
(*Suby of* DELUXE CORP) ★
8245 N Union Blvd, Colorado Springs, CO 80920-4456
Tel (719) 531-3900 *Founded/Ownrshp* 1997
Sales 144.7MM[E] *EMP* 1,400
SIC 2782 Checkbooks
Chf Mktg O: Tiffany Runge
IT Man: Dan Van Wijk

DIRECT CONTAINER LINE
See NACA HOLDINGS INC

DIRECT DISTRIBUTORS
See BOUMA CORP

D-U-N-S 80-077-0810
DIRECT ENERGY BUSINESS LLC
(*Suby of* DIRECT ENERGY SERVICES LLC) ★
1001 Liberty Ave Ste 1200, Pittsburgh, PA 15222-3728
Tel (800) 830-5923 *Founded/Ownrshp* 2008
Sales 6.2MMM[E] *EMP* 14,608
SIC 4911
Ex VP: Adele Malo
CIO: Kim McIntyre

D-U-N-S 07-879-0103
DIRECT ENERGY BUSINESS MARKETING LLC
(*Suby of* DIRECT ENERGY BUSINESS LLC) ★
194 Wood Ave S Fl 2, Iselin, NJ 08830-2710
Tel (732) 516-7500 *Founded/Ownrshp* 2013
Sales 98.4MM[E] *EMP* 5,025[E]
SIC 8742 Marketing consulting services
Pr: Maura Clark

D-U-N-S 14-875-8951 IMP
DIRECT ENERGY INC
(*Suby of* CENTRICA PLC)
263 Tresser Blvd Fl 8, Stamford, CT 06901-3236
Tel (800) 260-0300 *Founded/Ownrshp* 2004
Sales 287.0MM[E] *EMP* 357[E]
SIC 4911 1311 Electric services; Natural gas production
CEO: Deryk King
CFO: David Clarke
* *Sr VP:* Badar Khan

D-U-N-S 03-971-3354 IMP
DIRECT ENERGY LP
(*Suby of* CENTRICA PLC)
12 Greenway Plz Ste 250, Houston, TX 77046-1211
Tel (713) 877-3500 *Founded/Ownrshp* 2001
Sales 503.6MM[E] *EMP* 325
SIC 4911 Distribution, electric power
Pr: Badar Khan
Pr: Manu Asthana
Pr: Phillip W Tonge
COO: Steven Murray
CFO: David Clark
VP: Benjamin Davis
VP: Bill Fortner
VP: Mike Housh
Exec: Grace Gonzalez
Off Mgr: Herman Lam
Dir IT: Dirk Shatsby

D-U-N-S 15-235-8441
DIRECT ENERGY SERVICES LLC
(*Suby of* CENTRICA PLC)
12 Greenway Plz Ste 250, Houston, TX 77046-1211
Tel (713) 877-3500 *Founded/Ownrshp* 2004
Sales 6.1MMM[E] *EMP* 20,350
SIC 4931 Electric & other services combined
CEO: Badar Khan
Pr: Manu Asthana
Pr: John Schultz
* *COO:* Paul Dobson
* *CFO:* Andrew Sunderman
Ex VP: Melinda Guerra-Reeves
* *Ex VP:* Thomas Smith
Ex VP: Jim Steffes

D-U-N-S 13-292-9097
DIRECT ENERGY US HOME SERVICES INC
(*Suby of* CENTRICA PLC)
9260 Marketplace Dr, Miamisburg, OH 45342-4478
Tel (937) 898-0826 *Founded/Ownrshp* 2011
Sales 242.1MM[E] *EMP* 1,900
SIC 1711 Plumbing contractors; Warm air heating & air conditioning contractor
CEO: Eric Salzer
* *CFO:* Victor Ragucci

D-U-N-S 62-757-9555
DIRECT FINANCIAL SOLUTIONS LLC
CASH CENTRAL
(*Suby of* EASY MONEY) ★
84 E 2400 N, Logan, UT 84341-2902
Tel (435) 774-8207 *Founded/Ownrshp* 2012
Sales 88.5MM[E] *EMP* 46[E]
SIC 7389 Financial services
VP: Angela Thompson
Netwrk Eng: Keith Wood

D-U-N-S 92-615-3271
■ DIRECT GENERAL CORP
FLORIDA NO - FAULT
(*Suby of* ELARA HOLDINGS INC) ★
1281 Murfreesboro Pike # 150, Nashville, TN 37217-2437
Tel (615) 399-4700 *Founded/Ownrshp* 2007
Sales NA *EMP* 2,453
SIC 6311 6321 6331 6411 Life insurance; Health insurance carriers; Automobile insurance; Property & casualty insurance agent
CEO: John W Mullen
* *COO:* Jacqueline C Adair
CFO: J Todd Hagely
CFO: J T Hagley
Ch: Robert M Sandler
Sr VP: Barry D Elkins
Sr VP: Kim W Noell
Sls Mgr: Jennifer Y Ordonez

D-U-N-S 88-476-8953
■ DIRECT GENERAL INSURANCE AGENCY INC
DIRECT AUTO INSURANCE
(*Suby of* FLORIDA NO - FAULT) ★
1281 Murfreesboro Pike, Nashville, TN 37217-2423
Tel (615) 226-2550 *Founded/Ownrshp* 1991
Sales NA *EMP* 530
SIC 6411 Insurance agents, brokers & service
Pr: Jackie Adair
Sls Dir: Ken Hampton
Sls Mgr: Alberto Garza

D-U-N-S 17-780-5389
■ DIRECT GENERAL INSURANCE CO
CASH REGISTER
(*Suby of* FLORIDA NO - FAULT) ★
1281 Murfreesboro Pike # 150, Nashville, TN 37217-2437
Tel (615) 399-4700 *Founded/Ownrshp* 1997
Sales NA *EMP* 145
SIC 6411 Insurance agents, brokers & service
CEO: Dan Tarantin
* *Pr:* James Dickson
CFO: Barry Elkins
CFO: Todd Hogely
* *Treas:* J Todd Hagely
* *VP:* Scott Johnson
* *VP:* Jonathan Walters

D-U-N-S 08-269-6691 IMP/EXP
DIRECT RELIEF
DIRECT RELIEF USA
27 S La Patera Ln, Goleta, CA 93117-3214
Tel (805) 964-4767 *Founded/Ownrshp* 1948
Sales 388.3MM *EMP* 2
SIC 8322 Disaster service
CEO: Thomas Tighe
* *CFO:* Bhupi Singh
Prgrm Mgr: Jessica Koval
Software D: Jon Zaid
Opers Mgr: Sean Copeland

DIRECT RELIEF USA
See DIRECT RELIEF

D-U-N-S 79-677-7212
DIRECT SAT TV LLC
1930 N Poplar St Ste 21, Southern Pines, NC 28387-7092
Tel (910) 693-3000 *Founded/Ownrshp* 2004
Sales 104.1MM[E] *EMP* 250[E]
SIC 4841 Cable & other pay television services

D-U-N-S 80-632-3358
DIRECT SOURCE INC
8176 Mallory Ct, Chanhassen, MN 55317-8586
Tel (952) 934-8000 *Founded/Ownrshp* 1992
Sales 196.7MM[E] *EMP* 80[E]
Accts Abdo Eick & Meyers Llp Mank
SIC 5046 5045 Commercial equipment; Computer software
CEO: John Hillen
* *Pr:* Brad Fick
* *CTO:* Dan Charbonneau
Sftwr Eng: Dave Ranzau
VP Sls: Bob Kilby

D-U-N-S 03-139-9878 IMP
DIRECT SOURCE SEAFOOD LLC
840 140th Ave Ne, Bellevue, WA 98005-5223
Tel (908) 240-9374 *Founded/Ownrshp* 2010
Sales 90.0MM *EMP* 10
SIC 5146 Seafoods
Pr: David Almeda
* *COO:* Roman Tkachendo
* *CFO:* Takako Yamamoto
* *VP:* Joe Crowe
* *VP:* Ian Kennaway

DIRECT SUPPLY EQUIPMENT
See DIRECT SUPPLY INC

D-U-N-S 12-159-7595
DIRECT SUPPLY INC
DIRECT SUPPLY EQUIPMENT
6767 N Industrial Rd, Milwaukee, WI 53223-5815
Tel (414) 358-2805 *Founded/Ownrshp* 1985
Sales 800.0MM *EMP* 1,500
SIC 5047 Medical equipment & supplies; Hospital furniture
Pr: Robert J Hillis
CFO: John Lewis
Ex VP: Bill Avery
* *Ex VP:* Corey G Denman
* *Ex VP:* Randall S Kirk
* *Ex VP:* Kevin J Peters
VP: Brett A Gardner
* *VP:* Robert H Klein Jr
VP: Brad Klitsch
VP: Joel Treffert
Assoc Dir: Angela Eslinger
Assoc Dir: Matt Kwapis
Assoc Dir: Patrick Mahoney
Creative D: Brian Visser

DIRECT SYSTEMS SUPPORT
See ABF DATA SYSTEMS INC

D-U-N-S 07-937-3670
DIRECT TRAVEL INC
DTI
7430 E Caley Ave Ste 220, Centennial, CO 80111-6717
Tel (952) 746-3575 *Founded/Ownrshp* 1993, 2015
Sales 119.3MM[E] *EMP* 576[E]
SIC 4724 Travel agencies
Pr: Lisa Buckner
Pr: Sam Defranco
Sr VP: Ronda Shipley
Sr VP: Christine Sikes
VP: Gerard Bellino
VP: Michael Nelson
VP: John Townes
Dir Bus: Tyler Poynton
Opers Mgr: Karen Rogers
VP Sls: Chris Welch

DIRECT TV HOME SVCS SOUTHEAST
See SOUTHEASTERN VENTURES INC

D-U-N-S 05-786-7939 IMP/EXP
DIRECTBUY INC
UCC TOTALHOME
8450 Broadway, Merrillville, IN 46410-6221
Tel (219) 736-1100 *Founded/Ownrshp* 2007
Sales 275.3MM[E] *EMP* 250
SIC 5021 5064 5023 5961 6794 7299 Furniture; Electrical appliances, television & radio; Home furnishings; Carpets; Catalog & mail-order houses; Franchises, selling or licensing; Buyers' club
Pr: Michael P Bornhorst
V Ch: James L Gagan
* *Pr:* Scott M Powell
* *CFO:* Mark J Boggess
Chf Mktg O: Mark Gonsalves
Ex VP: Sarah Durkel
* *Ex VP:* Bart Fesperman
Ex VP: Curt Hilliard
VP: Frank Ball
* *VP:* Debbie Bowen
* *VP:* John Meyer
* *VP:* Patrick Sanford
* *VP:* Joseph Yast

D-U-N-S 19-656-0192
DIRECTECH HOLDING CO INC
(*Suby of* MULTIBAND CORP) ★
33 W 2nd St Ste 504, Maysville, KY 41056-1166
Tel (606) 564-0007 *Founded/Ownrshp* 2009
Sales 99.9MM[E] *EMP* 2,600
SIC 5731 Antennas, satellite dish
CEO: Thomas Beaudreau
* *CFO:* David Wallingford
* *VP:* Henry Block
* *VP:* Bernard Schafer

D-U-N-S 18-938-8825
DIRECTECH OF KENTUCKY INC
33 W 2nd St Ste 504, Maysville, KY 41056-1166
Tel (606) 564-0007 *Founded/Ownrshp* 2003
Sales 48.2MM[E] *EMP* 3,000
SIC 7389 Accomodation locating services
Pr: Jay Bassel Mattingly

DIRECTED ELECTRONICS
See DEI HOLDINGS INC

DIRECTIONAL AVIATION CAPITAL
See DIRECTIONAL CAPITAL LLC

D-U-N-S 17-439-9639
DIRECTIONAL CAPITAL LLC
DIRECTIONAL AVIATION CAPITAL
355 Richmond Rd Ste 8, Richmond Heights, OH 44143-4404
Tel (216) 261-3000 *Founded/Ownrshp* 2007
Sales 89.4MM[E] *EMP* 250
SIC 6722 Management investment, open-end
Pr: Greg Richman
Exec: Kenneth Ricci

D-U-N-S 83-153-9742 IMP
DIRECTIONAL DRILLING CO LP
CENTERLINE TRUCKING
11390 Fm 830 Rd, Willis, TX 77318-5626
Tel (936) 856-4332 *Founded/Ownrshp* 2004

Sales 268.9MM^E *EMP* 360^E
SIC 1381 Service well drilling
Pr: Jim Beasley
CFO: Gary Hammons
Sfty Mgr: Mike Bourque

D-U-N-S 78-519-0021
DIRECTOR OF V0LUNTEERS SERVICE
2900 1st Ave, Huntington, WV 25702-1241
Tel (304) 526-1400 *Founded/Ownrshp* 2006
Sales 399.4MM *EMP* 1
SIC 8999 Services
Prin: Patricia Chambers
Dir Vol: Linda Tillman
VP: Robin Armstrong
VP: Denise Steffich
VP: Sandra Walker

D-U-N-S 80-856-8047
DIRECTORS GUILD OF AMERICA - PRODUCER PENSION AND HEALTH PLANS
5055 Wilshire Blvd # 600, Los Angeles, CA 90036-6103
Tel (323) 866-2200 *Founded/Ownrshp* 2007
Sales NA *EMP* 27^E
Accts Miller Kaplan Arase & Co Llp
SIC 6371 Pension, health & welfare funds
CEO: Mack Clapp
CFO: Jean Sommerville

D-U-N-S 82-640-4444
DIRECTORS INVESTMENT GROUP INC
955 S Virginia St Ste 116, Reno, NV 89502-0413
Tel (775) 329-3311 *Founded/Ownrshp* 1992
Sales NA *EMP* 103
SIC 6311 Life insurance; Life reinsurance
Pr: Billy Kris Seale
**CFO:* Terry Groban
**VP:* Clay Peterson
VP Mktg: Jeff Stewart

DIRECTOR'S OFFICE
See NEVADA DEPARTMENT OF HEALTH AND HUMAN SERVICES

D-U-N-S 18-728-5890
DIRECTSAT USA LLC
(*Suby of* UNITEK USA LLC) ★
2010 Renaissance Blvd, King of Prussia, PA 19406-2746
Tel (267) 464-1700 *Founded/Ownrshp* 2004
Sales 96.7MM^E *EMP* 1,290^E
SIC 1731 Communications specialization
Pr: Daniel Yannantuono
CFO: Jeffrey Theisen
VP: John Gatta

D-U-N-S 96-166-7177
■ **DIRECTV ENTERPRISES LLC**
(*Suby of* DIRECTV HOLDINGS LLC) ★
2230 E Imperial Hwy, El Segundo, CA 90245-3504
Tel (310) 535-5000 *Founded/Ownrshp* 1995
Sales 120.3MM^E *EMP* 1,500
SIC 4841 Direct broadcast satellite services (DBS)
Site Mgr: Michael D White
**Ch Bd:* Eddy W Hartenstein
**Pr:* Odie C Donald
**CFO:* R L Myers
CFO: Mike Palkovic
CFO: Barbara Simon
Ex VP: Joe Bosch
Ex VP: Patrick T Doyle

D-U-N-S 83-306-1081 IMP
■ **DIRECTV GROUP HOLDINGS LLC**
(*Suby of* AT&T INC) ★
2260 E Imperial Hwy, El Segundo, CA 90245-3501
Tel (310) 964-5000 *Founded/Ownrshp* 2015
Sales 15.9MMM^E *EMP* 31,700
SIC 4841 Cable & other pay television services
Pr: Michael White
CFO: Patrick Doyle
Treas: Fazal Merchant
Ofcr: Joseph Bosch
Ex VP: William Casamo
Ex VP: Paul Guyardo
Ex VP: Larry Hunter
Ex VP: R Mulo C Pontual
Sr VP: Steven Adams
Sr VP: Robert Thun
VP: Lisa Caputo
VP: Amy Leifer
VP: Michelle Wolloff
Board of Directors: Lorrie Norrington, Neil Austrian, Anthony Vinciquerra, Ralph Boyd Jr, Abelardo Bru, David Dillon, Samuel Dipiazza Jr, Dixon Doll, Charles Lee, Peter Lund, Nancy Newcomb

D-U-N-S 05-518-5102 IMP
■ **DIRECTV GROUP INC**
(*Suby of* DIRECTV GROUP HOLDINGS LLC) ★
2260 E Imperial Hwy, El Segundo, CA 90245-3501
Tel (310) 964-5000 *Founded/Ownrshp* 1977
Sales 5.7MMM^E *EMP* 18,900
SIC 4841 Cable & other pay television services
CEO: Michael White
CFO: Fred Christensen
**CFO:* Patrick T Doyle
**Treas:* J William Little
**Ex VP:* Romulo Pontual
Sr VP: Sandra L Harrison
Sr VP: Steve Hindman
**Sr VP:* John F Murphy
VP: Tom Barrett
VP: Mufit Cinali
VP: Odie C Donald
VP: Susan Eid
VP: Stacy Fuller
VP: Evan R Grayer
VP: Kenneth N Heintz
VP: Pamela Hymel
VP: Theodore Jackson
VP: George Jaison
VP: Don Jones
VP: Mark McEachen
VP: Kevin Moncrief

D-U-N-S 04-061-4948 IMP/EXP
■ **DIRECTV HOLDINGS LLC**
(*Suby of* DIRECTV GROUP INC) ★
2230 E Imperial Hwy, El Segundo, CA 90245-3504
Tel (310) 964-5000 *Founded/Ownrshp* 2011
Sales 1.7MMM *EMP* 16,300^E
SIC 4841 Direct broadcast satellite services (DBS)
Pr: Michael D White
**CFO:* Patrick T Doyle
Treas: Patrick Doyle
**Ex VP:* Larry D Hunter
**Sr VP:* John F Murphy
Exec: John Norin
Dir IT: Howard Buckley

DISA
See DEFENSE INFORMATION SYSTEMS AGENCY

D-U-N-S 92-931-2106 IMP
DISABILITY SERVICES OF SOUTHWEST INC
6243 W Interstate 10 # 395, San Antonio, TX 78201-2086
Tel (210) 798-0123 *Founded/Ownrshp* 1991
Sales 29.1MM *EMP* 1,000
Accts Weaver And Tidwell Llp San A
SIC 8093

D-U-N-S 04-661-6983
DISABLED AMERICAN VETERANS
D A V
3725 Alexandria Pike, Cold Spring, KY 41076-1712
Tel (859) 441-7300 *Founded/Ownrshp* 1920
Sales 114.0MM *EMP* 615
SIC 8641 Veterans' organization
**Pr:* Larry Polvin
Ofcr: Arthur Jones
Ofcr: Matthew Paige
Ofcr: Royden Shelton
**VP:* Donald L Samuels
Assoc Dir: Steven Wilson
CTO: Clare Dan
IT Man: Greg Nichols
Web Dev: Ryan Hildebrandt
Netwrk Eng: Kathy Walker
Opers Mgr: Kevin Garvey

D-U-N-S 05-939-7919 IMP/EXP
■ **DISCOUNT AUTO PARTS LLC**
ADVANCE AUTO PARTS
(*Suby of* ADVANCE AUTO PARTS) ★
4900 Frontage Rd S, Lakeland, FL 33815-3193
Tel (863) 248-2056 *Founded/Ownrshp* 2001
Sales 1.1MMM^E *EMP* 6,460
SIC 5531 Automobile & truck equipment & parts
Ch Bd: Peter J Fontaine
**CFO:* C Michael Moore
VP: Kurt Schumacher
IT Man: Chad Peters

D-U-N-S 04-774-1335 IMP
DISCOUNT DRUG MART INC
211 Commerce Dr, Medina, OH 44256-1398
Tel (330) 725-2340 *Founded/Ownrshp* 1968
Sales 780.1MM^E *EMP* 2,700
Accts Grant Thorton Cpa Medina Oh
SIC 5912 5331 5411 5451 5122 8082 Drug stores & proprietary stores; Variety stores; Grocery stores; Dairy products stores; Pharmaceuticals; Home health care services
CEO: Donald Boodjeh
**Ch Bd:* Parviz Boodjeh
**Pr:* John Gains
**COO:* Dough Boodjeh
**CFO:* Thomas McConnell
Genl Mgr: Heather Ashburn
Store Mgr: Matt Troup
IT Man: Keith Miller
Software D: Jacob Schneck
Sftwr Eng: Jaison Lee
VP Opers: Michael McIntire

DISCOUNT FOOD MART
See WILLIAMSON OIL CO INC

D-U-N-S 13-550-4863 IMP
DISCOUNT MEDIA PRODUCTS LLC
MEDIA DISTRIBUTORS
845 N Church Ct, Elmhurst, IL 60126-1036
Tel (630) 834-3113 *Founded/Ownrshp* 2003
Sales 103.4MM^E *EMP* 75
SIC 5065 5999 Tapes, audio & video recording; Electronic parts & equipment

DISCOUNT MOTORS
See MORITZ PARTNERS LP

DISCOUNT SCHOOL SUPPLY
See EXCELLIGENCE LEARNING CORP

DISCOUNT TIRE
See REINALT-THOMAS CORP

D-U-N-S 05-053-6911
DISCOUNT TIRE CO INC (AZ)
(*Suby of* DISCOUNT TIRE) ★
20225 N Scottsdale Rd, Scottsdale, AZ 85255-6456
Tel (480) 606-6000 *Founded/Ownrshp* 1969
Sales 488.4MM^E *EMP* 1,093
SIC 5531 Automotive tires
Pr: Michael S Zuieback
Pr: Lori Governale
COO: John McPherson
**CFO:* Christian Roe
**Ex VP:* Robert H Holman Jr
Ex VP: Matt Malley
**Ex VP:* James Silhasek
**Ex VP:* Gary T Van Brumt
Ex VP: Kyle Ward
VP: Mike Bailey
VP: Steve Beiser
VP: Al Hatfield
VP: Dean Muglia
VP: Coleen Scott
VP: Jeff Stein
VP: Rob Wise
Exec: Carolyn Henderson

D-U-N-S 79-116-1045 IMP
DISCOUNT TIRE CO OF NEW MEXICO INC
(*Suby of* DISCOUNT TIRE) ★
20225 N Scottsdale Rd, Scottsdale, AZ 85255-6456
Tel (480) 606-6000 *Founded/Ownrshp* 1980
Sales 418.0MM^E *EMP* 4,000
SIC 5531 Automotive tires; Automotive accessories
Pr: Bruce T Halle
**Treas:* Robert H Holman Jr
**Ex VP:* Theodor Von Voigtlander
Ex VP: Doug Wilson
VP: Steve Beiser

D-U-N-S 10-900-4564
DISCOUNT TIRE CO OF TEXAS INC
(*Suby of* DISCOUNT TIRE) ★
20225 N Scottsdale Rd, Scottsdale, AZ 85255-6456
Tel (817) 460-0162 *Founded/Ownrshp* 1980
Sales 207.5MM^E *EMP* 1,338
SIC 5531 Automotive tires
Pr: Bruce Halle
**Treas:* Timothy J Schafer
**Sec:* Robert Holman
**Ex VP:* Theodor Von Voigtlander

D-U-N-S 96-725-7648
■ **DISCOVER BANK**
(*Suby of* DISCOVER FINANCIAL SERVICES) ★
502 E Market St, Greenwood, DE 19950-9700
Tel (302) 349-4512 *Founded/Ownrshp* 1986
Sales NA *EMP* 249^E
SIC 6022 State commercial banks
Pr: Christina Favilla
**Pr:* James J Roszkowski
Genl Mgr: Amy Schneider
Snr Mgr: David Dreytser

D-U-N-S 04-980-9676
▲ **DISCOVER FINANCIAL SERVICES**
2500 Lake Cook Rd, Riverwoods, IL 60015-1838
Tel (224) 405-0900 *Founded/Ownrshp* 1960
Sales NA *EMP* 15,036
Tkr Sym DFS *Exch* NYS
SIC 6022 6141 7389 State commercial banks; Personal credit institutions; Financial services
Ch Bd: David W Nelms
Pr: Roger C Hochschild
Pr: Carlos M Minetti
Pr: Diane E Offereins
Pr: James V Panzarino
CFO: R Mark Graf
Chf Mktg O: Julie A Loeger
Ofcr: R Douglas Rose
Ex VP: Kathryn McNamara Corley
Ex VP: Mark Graf
Ex VP: Glenn P Schneider
Sr VP: Steven E Cunningham
Sr VP: Julie Loeger
VP: Steve Bayans
VP: Joseph Bonefas
VP: Steve Butler
VP: Nicole Carroll
VP: Gerald Egner
VP: William Franklin
VP: Jack Garland
VP: Dale Newland
Board of Directors: Mark A Thierer, Jeffrey S Aronin, Lawrence A Weinbach, Mary K Bush, Gregory C Case, Candace H Duncan, Joseph F Eazor, Cynthia A Glassman, Richard H Lenny, Thomas G Maheras, Michael H Moskow

D-U-N-S 01-063-3766
DISCOVER GOODWILL OF SOUTHERN & WESTERN COLORADO
1460 Grdn Of The Gods Rd, Colorado Springs, CO 80907-3414
Tel (719) 635-4483 *Founded/Ownrshp* 1961
Sales 168.1MM^E *EMP* 1,173
Accts Stockman Kast Ryan & Co Llp
SIC 5932 8331 Used merchandise stores; Job training & vocational rehabilitation services
Pr: Karla Trazier
VP: Denise Krug
Exec: Karen Gordon
Assoc Dir: Ellen Burkart
**Prin:* Indy Fraze
Prgrm Mgr: Tina Argus
Prgrm Mgr: Billie Starr
IT Man: Mike Garner

D-U-N-S 80-126-9577
■ **DISCOVER RE MANAGERS INC**
(*Suby of* UNITED STATES FIDELITY AND GUARANTY COMPANY)
5 Batterson Park Rd, Farmington, CT 06032-2501
Tel (860) 674-2660 *Founded/Ownrshp* 1999
Sales NA *EMP* 1,990^E
SIC 6311 Life insurance
CEO: Arthur W Wright

DISCOVERY CHANNEL, THE
See DISCOVERY COMMUNICATIONS LLC

DISCOVERY CLOTHING COMPANY
See R & R GOLDMAN & ASSOCIATES INC

D-U-N-S 82-841-1897
▲ **DISCOVERY COMMUNICATIONS INC**
1 Discovery Pl, Silver Spring, MD 20910-3354
Tel (240) 662-2000 *Founded/Ownrshp* 2008
Sales 6.3MMM *EMP* 7,000
Tkr Sym DISCA *Exch* NGS
SIC 4841 7812 7922

D-U-N-S 12-154-5180 IMP
■ **DISCOVERY COMMUNICATIONS LLC**
DISCOVERY CHANNEL, THE
(*Suby of* DISCOVERY COMMUNICATIONS INC) ★
1 Discovery Pl, Silver Spring, MD 20910-3354
Tel (240) 662-2000 *Founded/Ownrshp* 1991
Sales 771.2MM^E *EMP* 4,500
SIC 4841

D-U-N-S 62-282-9653
DISCOVERY MARKETING AND DISTRIBUTING INC
RAINSOFT WATER TREATMENT
6505 Edgewater Dr, Orlando, FL 32810-4205
Tel (407) 523-0775 *Founded/Ownrshp* 1990
Sales 86.3MM^E *EMP* 500
SIC 5999 7389 Water purification equipment; Water softener service
Pr: Timothy V Randolph III
**Treas:* Margaret D Randolph
**VP:* Robert J Hogan
**VP:* John Lister II

DISCOVERY NETWORK
See DFS CORPORATE SERVICES LLC

D-U-N-S 10-741-1977 IMP
■ **DISH DBS CORP**
(*Suby of* DISH ORBITAL CORP) ★
9601 S Meridian Blvd, Englewood, CO 80112-5905
Tel (303) 723-1000 *Founded/Ownrshp* 1996
Sales 14.6MMM *EMP* 400^E
SIC 4841 Cable & other pay television services
Ch Bd: Charles W Ergen
CFO: Steven E Swain
Ex VP: Erik Carlson
VP: Andrew R Cipra
VP: Paul Mino
CIO: Michael McClaskey
IT Man: Eric Moore
Snr Mgr: Michael Covard
Snr Mgr: Michael Fox
Snr Mgr: Duncan McCloud
Snr Mgr: Allen Rensel
Board of Directors: James Defranco, R Stanton Dodge

DISH NETWORK
See SOUTHERN STAR INC

D-U-N-S 82-702-8143
▲ **DISH NETWORK CORP**
9601 S Meridian Blvd, Englewood, CO 80112-5905
Tel (303) 723-1000 *Founded/Ownrshp* 1995
Sales 15.0MMM *EMP* 18,000
Tkr Sym DISH *Exch* NGS
SIC 4841 Direct broadcast satellite services (DBS)
Pr: Joseph P Clayton
**Ch Bd:* Charles W Ergen
Pr: W Erik Carlson
CFO: Robert Olson
CFO: Steven E Swain
Bd of Dir: Hazel Quiambao
Ofcr: Michael K McClaskey
Ofcr: Jay Roth
Ex VP: Erik Carlson
Ex VP: Thomas A Cullen
Ex VP: James Defranco
Ex VP: R Stanton Dodge
Ex VP: Bernie Han
Ex VP: Vivek Khemka
Ex VP: Warren Schlichting
Ex VP: John Swieringa
Sr VP: Rob Dravenstott
VP: Amir Ahmed
VP: Anthony Bowling
VP: Kathy Buff
VP: Andy Cipra
Board of Directors: George R Brokaw, James Defranco, Steven R Goodbarn, Charles M Lillis, David K Moskowitz, Tom A Ortolf, Carl E Vogel

D-U-N-S 60-366-6202
■ **DISH NETWORK LLC**
DISH NETWORK SERVICE
(*Suby of* DISH NETWORK CORP) ★
9601 S Meridian Blvd, Englewood, CO 80112-5905
Tel (303) 723-1000 *Founded/Ownrshp* 1987
Sales 418.5MM^E *EMP* 500^E
SIC 1799 Antenna installation
CEO: Joe Clayton
**CFO:* David J Rayner
**Ex VP:* James Defranco
**Sr VP:* David K Moskowitz
VP: John Kennedy
VP: Martin Lenoir
Prin: Jason Leer
Genl Mgr: Jason Klipp
VP Opers: Nick Rossetti
Sls&Mrk Ex: Lorilynne Ross
Mktg Mgr: Bill Everett

DISH NETWORK SERVICE
See DISH NETWORK LLC

D-U-N-S 83-469-6411
■ **DISH NETWORK SERVICE LLC**
(*Suby of* DISH NETWORK CORP) ★
9601 S Meridian Blvd, Englewood, CO 80112-5905
Tel (303) 723-1000 *Founded/Ownrshp* 1992
Sales 4.3MMM^E *EMP* 5,200
SIC 1799 4841 Antenna installation; Cable television services
CEO: Charles Ergen

D-U-N-S 61-627-9068
■ **DISH ORBITAL CORP**
(*Suby of* DISH NETWORK CORP) ★
9601 S Meridian Blvd, Englewood, CO 80112-5905
Tel (303) 723-1000 *Founded/Ownrshp* 2000
Sales 14.6MMM^E *EMP* 400^E
SIC 3663 4841 Radio & TV communications equipment; Direct broadcast satellite services (DBS)
Ch Bd: Charles W Ergen
**Pr:* Mike Dugan
**COO:* Bernie Han
**CFO:* Robert Olson
Bd of Dir: Gary S Howard
VP: Stanton Dodge
VP: Nicholas Sayeedi
Mng Dir: Dave Shull
Prgrm Mgr: Charlotte Champigny
Prgrm Mgr: Shannon Kuhn
Prgrm Mgr: Ross Meachum

D-U-N-S 00-690-4700 IMP
■ **DISNEY ENTERPRISES INC** (DE)
(*Suby of* WALT DISNEY CO) ★
500 S Buena Vista St, Burbank, CA 91521-0001
Tel (818) 560-1000 *Founded/Ownrshp* 1986
Sales 5.0MMM[E] *EMP* 133,000
SIC 7812 6794 5331 7996 7941 Motion picture production & distribution; Motion picture production & distribution, television; Video tape production; Television film production; Copyright buying & licensing; Music royalties, sheet & record; Performance rights, publishing & licensing; Variety stores; Theme park, amusement; Ice hockey club
Pr: Robert Iger
CFO: Thomas O Staggs
Sr Ex VP: Alan Braverman
Ex VP: Mary Parker
Ex VP: Anne Sweeney
Sr VP: Kathy Clark
Sr VP: Robert Langer
Sr VP: Kevin Mayer
Sr VP: Cathy Roy
Sr VP: Paul Steinke
Sr VP: Tracy Sutherland
VP: Rilous Carter
VP: Gary Courtland
VP: Kevin Ellman
VP: Adriana Jaramillo
VP: Michele Kane

D-U-N-S 05-802-5797
■ **DISNEY INTERACTIVE STUDIOS INC**
(*Suby of* WALT DISNEY CO) ★
500 S Buena Vista St, Burbank, CA 91521-0001
Tel (818) 560-1000 *Founded/Ownrshp* 1988
Sales 107.5MM[E] *EMP* 1,080
SIC 7371 Computer software development
CEO: John Pleasants
**CFO:* Gary Sproule
**Sr VP:* Graham Hopper
**VP:* Bruce Austin
**VP:* Sanjeev Lamba
**VP:* Akira Matsumoto
VP: Raj Murari

D-U-N-S 96-564-5468
■ **DISNEY REGIONAL ENTERTAINMENT INC**
(*Suby of* WALT DISNEY CO) ★
500 S Buena Vista St, Burbank, CA 91521-0001
Tel (818) 560-1000 *Founded/Ownrshp* 1996
Sales 30.3MM[E] *EMP* 1,000
SIC 7999 5812 5813 Recreation center; Eating places; American restaurant; Drinking places; Bar (drinking places)
Pr: Arthur Levitt
**CFO:* Gary Marcotte
VP: Julie Hodges
VP: Mike Morrison
Assoc Ed: David Auguste

D-U-N-S 61-591-2292 IMP
■ **DISNEY WORLDWIDE SERVICES INC**
(*Suby of* DISNEY ENTERPRISES INC) ★
500 S Buena Vista St, Burbank, CA 91521-0001
Tel (877) 466-6669 *Founded/Ownrshp* 1989
Sales 549.7MM[E] *EMP* 5,044
SIC 7812 5736 Motion picture & video production; Cartoon motion picture production; Musical instrument stores
Pr: Jeffrey H Smith
**Treas:* James S Hunt
**VP:* James H Kapenstein
Board of Directors: Donald Clark

DISNEYLAND HOTEL
See WCO HOTELS INC

D-U-N-S 14-870-8241
■ **DISNEYLAND INTERNATIONAL INC**
(*Suby of* DISNEY ENTERPRISES INC) ★
500 S Buena Vista St, Burbank, CA 91521-0001
Tel (818) 560-1000 *Founded/Ownrshp* 1961
Sales 180.5MM[E] *EMP* 20,200
SIC 7996 Theme park, amusement
Pr: James Thomas
Ch Bd: James Cora
**Treas:* Robert S Risteen
Sr VP: Brent Woodford
Prin: Michael Eisner
Prin: Richard Nunis
Board of Directors: Sanford M Litvack

D-U-N-S 00-428-8254
DISPATCH PRINTING CO
COLUMBUS DISPATCH THE
62 E Broad St, Columbus, OH 43215-3500
Tel (614) 461-5000 *Founded/Ownrshp* 1903
Sales 671.8MM[E] *EMP* 2,100
SIC 4833 Television broadcasting stations
CEO: Michael J Fiorile
**Ch Bd:* John F Wolfe
**Pr:* Joseph Y Gallo
CFO: Poe A Timmons
VP: Brad Campbell
VP: James Gilmore
**Prin:* J H Peterson Et Al
**Prin:* Joseph J Gill
**Prin:* Charles D Simeral
Dist Mgr: Jill Laudermilch
MIS Mgr: Janis Bobb
Board of Directors: Preston Wolfe

D-U-N-S 05-094-8623
DISPLAY PACK INC
1340 Monroe Ave Nw Ste 1, Grand Rapids, MI 49505-4694
Tel (616) 451-3061 *Founded/Ownrshp* 1967
Sales 163.3MM[E] *EMP* 750
SIC 3089 2759 7389 Plastic processing; Commercial printing; Packaging & labeling services
Pr: Victor Hansen
**Pr:* Jim Woodcock
VP: Jonathan Hansen
Dir Bus: David Korhorn
MIS Dir: Holly Coppock
Dir IT: Mike Hansen
IT Man: Mike Hanson

Web Dev: Joel Schelhaas
Mfg Dir: Jason Rose
Prd Mgr: Brian Alicki
Trfc Mgr: Nate Briggs

DISTANT LANDS COFFEE
See JAVA TRADING CO LLC

DISTIRC24J-MRYNNE CNTRY-OREGON
See SALEM-KEIZER SCHOOL DISTRICT 24J

D-U-N-S 02-305-6096 IMP
DISTRIBUTION ALTERNATIVES INC
SCHOLL'S
435 Park Ct, Lino Lakes, MN 55014-2073
Tel (651) 636-9167 *Founded/Ownrshp* 1996
Sales 85.3MM[E] *EMP* 230
SIC 5122 5912

D-U-N-S 02-312-6647 IMP/EXP
DISTRIBUTION INTERNATIONAL INC
9000 Railwood Dr, Houston, TX 77078-4518
Tel (713) 428-3740 *Founded/Ownrshp* 2014
Sales 508.2MM[E] *EMP* 389
SIC 5033 5099 Roofing, siding & insulation; Insulation materials; Firearms & ammunition, except sporting
CEO: Celeste Beeks Mastin
CFO: Tim Reed
**Treas:* Dana Vlk
VP: Brad Farrimond
VP: George Franciscus
**VP:* Korey Haun
**VP:* Paco Sinta
VP Bus Dev: Bill Rodger
Rgnl Mgr: George Lionikis
Brnch Mgr: Jerry Malter
Brnch Mgr: Nancy Muller

D-U-N-S 15-429-7774
DISTRIBUTION INTERNATIONAL SOUTHWEST INC
M I T INTERNATIONAL
(*Suby of* DISTRIBUTION INTERNATIONAL INC) ★
9000 Railwood Dr, Houston, TX 77078-4518
Tel (713) 428-3900 *Founded/Ownrshp* 1997
Sales 255.4MM[E] *EMP* 225
SIC 5087 5047 Carpet installation equipment; Industrial safety devices: first aid kits & masks
Ex VP: Frank Farese
**CFO:* Doug Waugaman
Brnch Mgr: Gerald Blevins

D-U-N-S 83-106-6188 IMP
DISTRIBUTION MANAGEMENT INC
D M I
5 Research Park Dr, Saint Charles, MO 63304-5685
Tel (636) 300-4000 *Founded/Ownrshp* 1971
Sales 235.4MM[E] *EMP* 200
SIC 5112 Stationery & office supplies; Computer paper; Data processing supplies; Photocopying supplies
Pr: Thomas M Fleming
COO: Jack E Easterling
VP: Sean C Fleming
VP: Ken Heberer
Opers Mgr: Daniel Shipley

DISTRICT 196
See ROSEMOUNT-APPLE VALLEY-EAGAN SCHOOL DISTRICT

DISTRICT 47 SCHOOLS
See CRYSTAL LAKE COMMUNITY CONSOLIDATED SCHOOL DISTRICT 47

D-U-N-S 83-753-9972
DISTRICT ATTORNEYS GENERAL CONFERENCE TENNESSEE
(*Suby of* SUPREME COURT OF STATE OF TENNESSEE) ★
226 Capitol Blvd Ste 800, Nashville, TN 37219-1804
Tel (615) 741-1696 *Founded/Ownrshp* 1972
Sales NA *EMP* 1,000
SIC 9222 District Attorneys' offices;
Ex Dir: William Whitesell
**Prin:* Nancy White
Genl Mgr: Tammy Hancock
Genl Mgr: David Hicks
Genl Mgr: Guy Jones

DISTRICT BRD TRUSTEES HILLSBOR
See HILLSBOROUGH COMMUNITY COLLEGE INC

D-U-N-S 07-869-8004
DISTRICT COUNCIL 37 BENEFITS FUND TRUST
125 Barclay St Bsmt B, New York, NY 10007-2179
Tel (917) 716-2097 *Founded/Ownrshp* 1979
Sales NA *EMP* 25
Accts Manfre Cpa Pc New York Ny
SIC 6371 Union welfare, benefit & health funds
**Ch:* Lillian Roberts

D-U-N-S 96-489-2348
DISTRICT COUNCIL 37 HEALTH & SECURITY PLAN TRUST
125 Barclay St, New York, NY 10007-2233
Tel (212) 815-1305 *Founded/Ownrshp* 1967
Sales 239.4MM[E] *EMP* 2
Accts Manfre Cpa Pc New York Ny
SIC 8699 Charitable organization
Ex Dir: Henry Garrido

D-U-N-S 17-667-7920
DISTRICT MEDICAL GROUP INC
D M G
2929 E Thomas Rd, Phoenix, AZ 85016-8034
Tel (602) 274-8859 *Founded/Ownrshp* 2006
Sales 141.9MM[E] *EMP* 460
SIC 8011 Offices & clinics of medical doctors
CEO: Kote R Chundu
**COO:* Peg Loos
CFO: Jones Craig
**CFO:* Craig Jones
QA Dir: Daina Mason

D-U-N-S 12-209-5102
DISTRICT OF COLUMBIA PUBLIC SCHOOLS
1200 1st St Ne Fl 9, Washington, DC 20002-7953
Tel (202) 442-5885 *Founded/Ownrshp* 2009
Sales 334.7MM[E] *EMP* 8,000
SIC 8211 Elementary & secondary schools
Genl Mgr: Kisha Kantasingh
CTO: Jennifer Boudrye
MIS Dir: Simone Andrews
Software D: Merlene Vassall
Pr Dir: Josephine Bias Robinson
Sls Mgr: Grace Manubay
Teacher Pr: Crystal Jefferson
Instr Medi: David Rose
Psych: Sherema Copes
HC Dir: Diana Bruce

D-U-N-S 07-979-4740
DISTRICT OF COLUMBIA WATER & SEWER AUTHORITY
DC WATER
5000 Overlook Ave Sw, Washington, DC 20032-5212
Tel (202) 787-2000 *Founded/Ownrshp* 2015
Sales NA *EMP* 1,100
SIC 9511
CEO: George Hawkins
CFO: Olu Adebo
Treas: Robert Hunt
DP Dir: Eric Euell
Snr Mgr: Cheryl Jackson

D-U-N-S 01-829-9511
DISTRICT PETROLEUM PRODUCTS INC
HY-MILER
1814 River Rd, Huron, OH 44839-9522
Tel (419) 433-8373 *Founded/Ownrshp* 1963
Sales 88.1MM[E] *EMP* 230
SIC 5541 5171 5172 Filling stations, gasoline; Petroleum bulk stations; Petroleum products
Pr: Scott L Stipp
**CFO:* Timothy J Donnelly
**Sec:* Robert J Fast
**VP:* Gary Gockstetter
**VP:* Mike Stipp

D-U-N-S 02-254-6840
DISTRICT PHOTO INC
CLARK COLOR LABS
10501 Rhode Island Ave, Beltsville, MD 20705-2389
Tel (301) 595-5300 *Founded/Ownrshp* 1949
Sales 148.1MM[E] *EMP* 1,200[E]
SIC 7384 5043 5946 Photofinishing laboratory; Photographic equipment & supplies; Cameras; Photographic supplies
Pr: Neil Cohen
CFO: Wayne Boggs
**Ex VP:* Robert E Friend

D-U-N-S 78-571-4239
DISTRICT PUBLIC DEFENDERS CONFERENCE TENNESSEE
(*Suby of* SUPREME COURT OF STATE OF TENNESSEE) ★
211 7th Ave N Ste 320, Nashville, TN 37219-1811
Tel (615) 741-5562 *Founded/Ownrshp* 1989
Sales NA *EMP* 1,500
SIC 9222 Public defenders' offices;
Ex Dir: Jeffrey Henry

DISTRICT SCHOOL BOARD OF HENDR
See HENDRY COUNTY SCHOOL DISTRICT

D-U-N-S 79-436-7227
DISTRICT SCHOOL BOARD OF PASCO COUNTY
7227 Land O Lakes Blvd, Land O Lakes, FL 34638-2826
Tel (813) 794-2000 *Founded/Ownrshp* 1887
Sales 669.3MM[E] *EMP* 19,000
Accts Moore Stephens Lovelace Pa
SIC 8211 School board
Ch Bd: Steve Luikart
CFO: Olga Swinson
Prin: Yvonne Reins
Plnt Mgr: Micheal Desiante

DISTRICT SCHOOL ESCAMBIA CNTY
See ESCAMBIA COUNTY SCHOOL DISTRICT

D-U-N-S 00-283-4919
DISTTECH INC
4366 Mount Pleasant St Nw, North Canton, OH 44720-5446
Tel (800) 969-5419 *Founded/Ownrshp* 1992
Sales 85.4MM[E] *EMP* 675
SIC 4213

DISYS
See DIGITAL INTELLIGENCE SYSTEMS LLC

DITCH WITCH INTERMOUNTAIN
See ARNOLD MACHINERY CO

D-U-N-S 13-989-4690 IMP
DITECH FINANCIAL LLC
345 Sint Peter St Ste 300, Saint Paul, MN 55102
Tel (651) 293-4800 *Founded/Ownrshp* 1994
Sales NA *EMP* 1,800
SIC 6162 Loan correspondents
Sr VP: Brian Corey
CFO: Cheryl Collins
Sr VP: Matthew Detwiler
VP: Bill Ashley
VP: Martin Burd
VP: Michael Donnelly
QA Dir: Rachana Thapa
Ql Cn Mgr: Paula Wahl
Sls Dir: Chris Nobile

D-U-N-S 06-221-3483
DITTMAN AND GREER INC
270 Park Ave, New Hyde Park, NY 11040-5318
Tel (860) 347-4655 *Founded/Ownrshp* 1990
Sales 150.0MM *EMP* 20
SIC 5063 Electrical apparatus & equipment; Electrical supplies
Pr: Paul Lewis
**VP:* Gerald Dieundolo

D-U-N-S 13-674-1027
DITTO II LLC
MEGA PICK N SAVE
1201 S Hastings Way, Eau Claire, WI 54701-4459
Tel (715) 836-8710 *Founded/Ownrshp* 2002
Sales 92.7MM[E] *EMP* 700
SIC 5541 5411 Gasoline service stations; Grocery stores
Genl Mgr: Rick Lambrecht

DIVAC
See DOOSAN INDUSTRIAL VEHICLE AMERICA CORP

D-U-N-S 08-352-9651 IMP
DIVAL SAFETY EQUIPMENT INC
1721 Niagara St, Buffalo, NY 14207-3188
Tel (716) 874-9060 *Founded/Ownrshp* 1977
Sales 110.0MM[E] *EMP* 155
SIC 5099 8748 8734 5047 5136 5661 Safety equipment & supplies; Fire extinguishers; Lifesaving & survival equipment (non-medical); Safety training service; Product testing laboratory, safety or performance; Industrial safety devices: first aid kits & masks; Men's & boys' hats, scarves & gloves; Men's shoes
CEO: Charles Vallone Sr
**Pr:* C J Vallone
**Ex VP:* Chris Werner
Genl Mgr: Jay Spencer
IT Man: Matt Weick
Sls Mgr: Dave Grabowski
Sls Mgr: Eric Krueger
Sls Mgr: Steve Wheeler
Sales Asso: Liz Eyrick
Sales Asso: Morgan Krauss
Sales Asso: Scott Wierzbicki

D-U-N-S 80-738-7600
DIVERSCO HOLDINGS INC
105 Diversco Dr, Spartanburg, SC 29307-5408
Tel (864) 579-3420 *Founded/Ownrshp* 1993
Sales 53.4MM[E] *EMP* 8,000
SIC 7381 7349 Security guard service; Building maintenance services
V Ch Bd: William A Hudson

DIVERSCO INTEGRATED SERVICES
See DHI HOLDINGS INC

D-U-N-S 00-481-1543
DIVERSE POWER INC AN ELECTRIC MEMBERSHIP CORP (GA)
1400 S Davis Rd, Lagrange, GA 30241-6112
Tel (706) 845-2000 *Founded/Ownrshp* 1936
Sales 85.7MM *EMP* 90
Accts Mcnair Mclemore Middlebrooks
SIC 4911 Distribution, electric power
Pr: Wayne Livingston
**Ch Bd:* Charles Knight
**Sr VP:* Wade Hall
VP: Randy Pruett

D-U-N-S 15-847-0224
DIVERSE STAFFING INC
DIVERSE STAFFING SOLUTIONS
1800 E Lambert Rd Ste 100, Brea, CA 92821-4370
Tel (714) 482-0499 *Founded/Ownrshp* 2008
Sales 26.8MM[E] *EMP* 1,200
SIC 7361 Employment agencies
Pr: Fred S Flores
**VP:* Cesar Hindu
Brnch Mgr: James Pahl

DIVERSE STAFFING SOLUTIONS
See DIVERSE STAFFING INC

D-U-N-S 12-076-2617 IMP/EXP
■ **DIVERSEY HOLDINGS INC**
(*Suby of* SEALED AIR CORP) ★
8310 16th St, Sturtevant, WI 53177-1964
Tel (262) 631-4001 *Founded/Ownrshp* 2011
Sales 585.2MM[E] *EMP* 10,400[E]
SIC 2842 Cleaning or polishing preparations
Pr: Edward F Lonergan
**CFO:* Norman Clubb
VP: Wim Callens
VP: Carolyn Cooke
**VP:* Scott D Russell
Sales Exec: Scott Horlbogen
Mktg Dir: Katie Das

D-U-N-S 01-824-0817 IMP/EXP
■ **DIVERSEY INC**
(*Suby of* SEALED AIR CORP) ★
2415 Cascade Pointe Blvd, Charlotte, NC 28208-6899
Tel (262) 631-4001 *Founded/Ownrshp* 1997
Sales 2.6MMM[E] *EMP* 10,170
SIC 2842 Cleaning or polishing preparations
Ch Bd: Helen P Johnson-Leipold
Pr: Edward F Lonergan
CFO: Norman Clubb
Ex VP: Scott D Russell
Sr VP: Gregory F Clark
VP: Carolyn Cooke
VP: Rob Kohlhagen
VP: Christopher J Slusar
Board of Directors: Todd C Brown, Robert M Howe, George K Jaquette, Philip W Knisely, Clifton D Louis, Winifred J Marquart, Richard J Schnall

DIVERSFIED GLOBL GRPHICS GROUP
See DG3 HOLDINGS LLC

DIVERSFIED GLOBL GRPHICS GROUP
See DG3 NORTH AMERICA INC

DIVERSFIED SPCIALTY INSTITUTES
See DSI RENAL HOLDINGS LLC

D-U-N-S 62-142-2708
▲ **DIVERSICARE HEALTHCARE SERVICES INC**
1621 Galleria Blvd, Brentwood, TN 37027-2926
Tel (615) 771-7575 *Founded/Ownrshp* 1994
Sales 387.6MM *EMP* 6,300[E]
Tkr Sym DVCR *Exch* NAS
SIC 8051 8322 Skilled nursing care facilities; Extended care facility; Rehabilitation services

Pr: Kelly J Gill
**Ch Bd:* Chad A McCurdy
COO: Leslie Campbell
CFO: James R McKnight Jr
VP: Tina Blahofski
VP: Clint Hill
VP: Matthew Weishaar
CIO: April Marbury
Sls&Mrk Ex: Larry Reger
Board of Directors: Richard M Brame, Robert Z Hensley, Robert A McCabe Jr, William C O'neil Jr, Wallace E Olson

D-U-N-S 88-347-6376
■ DIVERSICARE MANAGEMENT SERVICES CO
DIVERSICARE MGT SVCS ALA
(*Suby of* DIVERSICARE HEALTHCARE SERVICES INC) ★
277 Mallory Station Rd # 130, Franklin, TN 37067-8207
Tel (615) 771-7575 *Founded/Ownrshp* 1994
Sales 83.3MM^E *EMP* 4,600
SIC 8741 Management services
**Pr:* William Council III
**Pr:* Charles Rinne
**CFO:* Glyn Riddle
Bd of Dir: William C O Neil

DIVERSICARE MGT SVCS ALA
See DIVERSICARE MANAGEMENT SERVICES CO

DIVERSIFIED
See EDM AMERICAS INC

DIVERSIFIED AGENCY SERVICES
See DAS HOLDINGS INC

DIVERSIFIED BUS COMMUNICATIONS
See DIVERSIFIED BUSINESS COMMUNICATIONS

D-U-N-S 05-571-6039
DIVERSIFIED BUSINESS COMMUNICATIONS (ME)
DIVERSIFIED BUS COMMUNICATIONS
121 Free St, Portland, ME 04101-3919
Tel (207) 842-5400 *Founded/Ownrshp* 1970, 2009
Sales 182.1MM^E *EMP* 412
SIC 4833 4841 2721 7389 Television broadcasting stations; Cable television services; Magazines: publishing only, not printed on site; Trade show arrangement
Pr: Nancy Hasselback
**Pr:* Theodore Wirth
CFO: Kathy Willing
**Ch:* Horace A Hildreth Jr
**Treas:* Paul G Clancy
VP: Veronica Fossett
Ex Dir: Rd Whitney
Software D: Timothy Eichfeld
Opers Mgr: Imani Clark
Prd Mgr: Stephanie Scherer
Sls Dir: Brian Cuthbert

D-U-N-S 05-334-6508
DIVERSIFIED CHEMICAL TECHNOLOGIES INC (MI)
15477 Woodrow Wilson St, Detroit, MI 48238-1586
Tel (313) 867-5444 *Founded/Ownrshp* 1971
Sales 94.1MM^E *EMP* 225
Accts Porvin Burnstein & Garelik P
SIC 2891 2992 2899 2842 2841 Sealing compounds, synthetic rubber or plastic; Glue; Epoxy adhesives; Lubricating oils & greases; Chemical preparations; Specialty cleaning, polishes & sanitation goods; Soap & other detergents
Pr: George H Hill
**VP:* Arnold F Joseff

D-U-N-S 05-220-9298
DIVERSIFIED CONVEYORS INC
2163 Airways Blvd Ste 300, Memphis, TN 38114-5208
Tel (901) 333-8346 *Founded/Ownrshp* 2000
Sales 153.1MM *EMP* 140
Accts Stallings & Associates Cpa S
SIC 8711 Engineering services
Ch Bd: Elizabeth Phillips
**COO:* Thomas Phillips
**CFO:* Hubert McManus
Dist Mgr: Bob Owens

D-U-N-S 04-505-6082 IMP/EXP
DIVERSIFIED CPC INTERNATIONAL INC
(*Suby of* SUMITOMO CORP OF AMERICAS) ★
24338 W Durkee Rd, Channahon, IL 60410-9719
Tel (815) 423-5991 *Founded/Ownrshp* 1995
Sales 145.0MM *EMP* 66
SIC 2813 5169 Industrial gases; Aerosols
CEO: Bill Auriemma
**CFO:* Paul Caponigri
**VP:* John P Dowd II
**VP:* William A Frauenheim III
VP: William Frauenheim
**VP:* Bill Madigan
**VP:* William E Madigan
VP: John G North
VP: Akira Sugimoto
Sfty Mgr: Steve Graham
Plnt Mgr: Devin Dransfeldt

D-U-N-S 19-687-7906 IMP
DIVERSIFIED DISTRIBUTION SYSTEMS LLC
DDS
7351 Boone Ave N, Brooklyn Park, MN 55428-1009
Tel (612) 813-5200 *Founded/Ownrshp* 1986
Sales 734.0MM^E *EMP* 400
SIC 5112 Office supplies
Mktg Mgr: James Murphy
**CFO:* Jim Kozicky
Software D: Todd Haehn
Natl Sales: Jill Courtney
Natl Sales: Edward Kirchberger

D-U-N-S 61-089-7308 EXP
DIVERSIFIED FOODS AND SEASONINGS LLC
1115 N Causeway Blvd # 200, Mandeville, LA 70471-3441
Tel (985) 809-3600 *Founded/Ownrshp* 1981
Sales 166.9MM^E *EMP* 457
SIC 2099 2034 Food preparations; Seasonings & spices; Sauces: dry mixes; Soup mixes
**Pr:* Peter F Smith
Exec: Paul Rockwell
**Prin:* Andrew Mitts
Plnt Mgr: John Werner

D-U-N-S 96-286-3895
DIVERSIFIED FOODSERVICE SUPPLY INC
607 Dempster St, Mount Prospect, IL 60056-4585
Tel (847) 966-9700 *Founded/Ownrshp* 2015
Sales 397.4MM^E *EMP* 230^E
SIC 5046 7699 Cooking equipment, commercial; Restaurant equipment & supplies; Restaurant equipment repair
CEO: Mike Cate

D-U-N-S 79-054-3193
DIVERSIFIED HEALTH SERVICES INC
(*Suby of* BLUE CROSS AND BLUE SHIELD OF FLORIDA INC) ★
4800 Deerwood Campus Pkwy, Jacksonville, FL 32246-6498
Tel (904) 791-6111 *Founded/Ownrshp* 1985
Sales NA *EMP* 450
SIC 6311 Life insurance carriers
Pr: Michael Cascone Jr

D-U-N-S 80-014-4243 IMP
DIVERSIFIED MACHINE BRISTOL LLC
DMI
(*Suby of* DIVERSIFIED MACHINE INC) ★
51650 County Road 133, Bristol, IN 46507-9800
Tel (248) 728-8642 *Founded/Ownrshp* 2007
Sales 208.9MM^E *EMP* 884
SIC 3465 Body parts, automobile: stamped metal
CEO: Douglas Delgrosso
**VP:* Eva M Kalawski
**VP:* Mary Ann Sigler
**VP:* Stephen Zollo
Ql Cn Mgr: Jean Brewer

D-U-N-S 61-182-8695 IMP
DIVERSIFIED MACHINE INC
(*Suby of* CHASSIX INC) ★
300 Galleria Officentre # 501, Southfield, MI 48034-8460
Tel (248) 728-8642 *Founded/Ownrshp* 1988
Sales 991.9MM^E *EMP* 1,700
SIC 3465 Body parts, automobile: stamped metal
CEO: Douglas Delgrosso
**Pr:* Robert J Remenar

D-U-N-S 79-795-0982
DIVERSIFIED MAINTENANCE SYSTEMS LLC
5110 Sunforest Dr Ste 250, Tampa, FL 33634-6307
Tel (800) 351-1557 *Founded/Ownrshp* 2001
Sales 200.0MM^E *EMP* 10,000
SIC 7349 Chemical cleaning services
VP: Susan Salzsieder
Pr: Angie Bennett
Pr: Bob Duncan
Pr: Burney Veazey
**CEO:* David Ramon
COO: Pete Belusic
COO: Jeremy Dieterle
**COO:* Bobby Duncan
**COO:* Keith McAlpin
Sr VP: Robert Natale
VP: Amy Chasse
VP: Kelly Devin
Board of Directors: Coby Orr, Mitchell Spurlock

DIVERSIFIED MEDIA GROUP
See ONE DIVERSIFIED LLC

D-U-N-S 14-758-0195
DIVERSIFIED MOTEL PROPERTIES LIMITED PARTNERSHIP
ZENITH MERCHANDISING
2305 W Superior St, Duluth, MN 55806-1931
Tel (218) 723-8433 *Founded/Ownrshp* 1984
Sales 30.6MM^E *EMP* 1,655
SIC 6512 Nonresidential building operators
CEO: Kenneth Goldfine
Genl Pt: Edgewater Investors
Pr: John Goldfine
CFO: Todd Torvinen
Advt Dir: Kate Katich

D-U-N-S 01-475-9027
▲ DIVERSIFIED RESTAURANT HOLDINGS INC
DRH
27680 Franklin Rd, Southfield, MI 48034-8203
Tel (248) 223-9160 *Founded/Ownrshp* 1999
Sales 172.4MM *EMP* 2,200^E
Tkr Sym SAUC *Exch* NAS
SIC 5812 5813 6794 Eating places; Drinking places; Tavern (drinking places); Franchises, selling or licensing
CEO: David G Burke
Mng Pt: Drew Hundley
Ch Bd: T Michael Ansley
COO: Jason Curtis
CFO: Phyllis A Knight
Board of Directors: Jay Alan Dusenberry, Philip Friedman, David Ligotti, Joseph M Nowicki, Gregory J Stevens

D-U-N-S 07-651-1257
DIVERSIFIED RETIREMENT CORP
(*Suby of* AEGON USA, INC.)
440 Mamaroneck Ave, Harrison, NY 10528-2418
Tel (914) 627-3000 *Founded/Ownrshp* 1993
Sales 133.5MM^E *EMP* 900
SIC 6282 Investment advice
Ch Bd: Peter Kunkel
**Pr:* Mark Mullin
CFO: Marteena Rodriguez
VP: Brian Gupton
VP: Robert McBride
VP: Renee Onorato
VP: Charlie Powers
VP: Steve Smith
Exec: Mark Pilkington
Web Dev: Helen Leykin
VP Sls: Joe Fournier

D-U-N-S 18-705-1156
DIVERSIFIED ROOFING CORP
2015 W Mountain View Rd, Phoenix, AZ 85021-1922
Tel (602) 850-8218 *Founded/Ownrshp* 1988
Sales 98.3MM^E *EMP* 350
SIC 1761 Roofing contractor
Pr: Mark Schouten
**Treas:* William J Moroney

D-U-N-S 12-915-0111
DIVERSIFIED SERVICE OPTIONS INC
GUIDEWELL SOURCE
(*Suby of* BLUE CROSS AND BLUE SHIELD OF FLORIDA INC) ★
532 Riverside Ave, Jacksonville, FL 32202-4914
Tel (904) 791-6305 *Founded/Ownrshp* 1998
Sales 141.4MM^E *EMP* 800^E
SIC 6719 Investment holding companies, except banks
CEO: Patrick J Geraghty
**Ch Bd:* Deanna McDonald
**Treas:* Jonathan Hogan

D-U-N-S 79-109-9948
DIVERSIFIED WELL LOGGING INC
711 W 10th St, Reserve, LA 70084-6919
Tel (985) 536-4143 *Founded/Ownrshp* 1991
Sales 86.2MM^E *EMP* 200^E
SIC 1389 Well logging
Pr: Richard Klibert
CFO: Paz Nair
Genl Mgr: Scott Bentley
Opers Mgr: Damon Milioto

DIVERSIONS GIFT SHOP
See SAINT ANNS HOSPITAL AUXILIARY

D-U-N-S 08-937-1728 IMP/EXP
DIVERSITECH CORP
6650 Sugarloaf Pkwy # 100, Duluth, GA 30097-4364
Tel (678) 542-3600 *Founded/Ownrshp* 2015
Sales 197.9MM^E *EMP* 400
SIC 3272

D-U-N-S 82-907-5832 EXP
DIVERSITY-VUTEQ LLC
2300 Munsford Dr, New Albany, MS 38652-7415
Tel (662) 534-9250 *Founded/Ownrshp* 2008
Sales 177.2MM^E *EMP* 750
SIC 3089 Automotive parts, plastic
Pr: Christopher Spence

D-U-N-S 06-680-0244
DIVI HOTELS MARKETING INC
DIVI RESORT
6320 Quadrangle Dr # 210, Chapel Hill, NC 27517-7815
Tel (919) 419-3484 *Founded/Ownrshp* 1992
Sales 62.6MM^E *EMP* 1,000
SIC 7011 7999 6531 Resort hotel; Gambling establishment; Time-sharing real estate sales, leasing & rentals
Pr: Ej Schan Farber
**CFO:* Mike Walsnovich
Genl Couns: Charles Munn

DIVI RESORT
See DIVI HOTELS MARKETING INC

D-U-N-S 83-050-6783
DIVIDEND CAPITAL DIVERSIFIED PROPERTY FUND INC
518 17th St Ste 1200, Denver, CO 80202-4108
Tel (303) 228-2200 *Founded/Ownrshp* 2010
Sales 225.2MM *EMP* 142^E
SIC 6798 Real estate investment trusts

D-U-N-S 85-867-2749 IMP/EXP
DIVINE FLAVOR LLC
766 N Target Range Rd, Nogales, AZ 85621-2400
Tel (520) 281-8328 *Founded/Ownrshp* 2007
Sales 90.5MM *EMP* 20
SIC 5148 Fresh fruits & vegetables
**CFO:* David Bon
Trfc Dir: Ulysses Morales
Opers Mgr: Oliver Sanchez
Sales Exec: Luis Batiz
VP Sls: Pedro Batiz

D-U-N-S 06-960-2571
DIVINE PROVIDENCE HOSPITAL OF SISTERS OF CHRISTIAN CHARITY
1100 Grampian Blvd, Williamsport, PA 17701-1995
Tel (570) 321-1000 *Founded/Ownrshp* 1951
Sales 92.9MM *EMP* 332^E
Accts Bkd Llp Springfield Mo
SIC 8062 General medical & surgical hospitals
Pr: Steve Johnson
**Sr VP:* George A Manchester MD
**Sr VP:* Glenn Mechling
**VP:* Candy Dewar
Off Mgr: Cicily Nonemaker

D-U-N-S 07-115-2086 IMP
DIVINE SAVIOR HEALTHCARE INC
2817 New Pinery Rd # 202, Portage, WI 53901-9296
Tel (608) 745-4598 *Founded/Ownrshp* 1916
Sales 88.2MM *EMP* 725
Accts Wipfli Llp Eau Claire Wiscon
SIC 8062 8011 8051 General medical & surgical hospitals; Primary care medical clinic; Skilled nursing care facilities
CEO: Michael T Decker
**CFO:* Marlin Nelson
VP: Jennifer Bieno
VP: Jackie Sill
VP: Stewart Taylor
Dir Lab: Joann Taylor
Dir Rx: Brent Isensee
Dir Sec: Jeff Thompson
CTO: Jon Erdmann
Dir IT: Brad Davidson
Sfty Dirs: Judy Decker

DIVISADERO TOUCHLESS CAR WASH
See CANADIAN AMERICAN OIL CO INC

DIVISION C
See ZF CHASSIS COMPONENTS LLC

DIVISION OF ENERGY AND CLIMATE
See STATE OF DELAWARE DNREC

DIVISION OF FISCAL SERVICES
See TENNESSEE DEPT OF HEALTH

DIVISION OF LABOR STANDARDS
See TENNESSEE DEPARTMENT OF LABOR AND WORKFORCE DEVELOPMENT

DIVISION OF NATURAL AREAS
See EASTERN KENTUCKY UNIVERSITY

DIVISION OF PRISONS
See DEPARTMENT OF CORRECTIONS WASHINGTON STATE

DIVISION OF PUBLIC HEALTH
See HEALTH & HOSPITAL CORP OF MARION COUNTY

DIVISION P
See ZF TRANSMISSIONS GRAY COURT LLC

DIVISION P
See ZF AXLE DRIVES MARYSVILLE LLC

DIVISION Z
See ZF NORTH AMERICA INC

D-U-N-S 02-321-5135
DIVISIONS INC
DIVISIONS MAINTENANCE GROUP
1 Riverfront Pl Ste 500, Newport, KY 41071-4573
Tel (859) 448-9730 *Founded/Ownrshp* 1999
Sales 117.0MM *EMP* 120^E
SIC 7349 Building maintenance services
Owner: Gary Mitchell
**Owner:* Kyle Murray
**VP:* Doug Lackey
VP: Greg Menetrey
**VP:* Grant Mitchell
**VP:* Mike Pederson
**VP:* Andy Smith
VP: John Thompson
**VP:* Bill Volz
**VP:* Brian Wint
Rgnl Mgr: Eric Ray

DIVISIONS MAINTENANCE GROUP
See DIVISIONS INC

D-U-N-S 61-352-2895
■ DIVOSTA HOMES LP
(*Suby of* PULTE DIVERSIFIED COMPANIES INC) ★
4500 Pga Blvd Ste 400, Palm Beach Gardens, FL 33418-3995
Tel (561) 691-9050 *Founded/Ownrshp* 1998
Sales 7.1MM^E *EMP* 2,000
SIC 6552 Land subdividers & developers, residential
Pt: Harmon Smith
**Pt:* Rick Green
**Pt:* William Shannon
Pr: Curtis Ring
MIS Dir: Bill Weir
Sfty Dirs: Chris Brew
Sales Asso: Jaymie Catalano
Sales Asso: Debra Ponder

DIXIE CAFE THE
See DIXIE RESTAURANTS INC

D-U-N-S 04-567-7333
DIXIE CONSTRUCTION CO INC
260 Hopewell Rd, Churchville, MD 21028-1914
Tel (410) 879-8055 *Founded/Ownrshp* 1983
Sales 90.0MM *EMP* 275
SIC 1611 1623

DIXIE EGG COMPANY
See FOODONICS INTERNATIONAL INC

D-U-N-S 05-946-0352 IMP
DIXIE ELECTRIC LLC
EPIC INTEGRATED SERVICES
701 Tradewinds Blvd, Midland, TX 79706-3148
Tel (432) 580-7095 *Founded/Ownrshp* 2013
Sales 234.9MM^E *EMP* 800
SIC 1731

D-U-N-S 00-878-3656
DIXIE ELECTRIC MEMBERSHIP CORP (LA)
DEMCO
16262 Wax Rd, Greenwell Springs, LA 70739-4964
Tel (225) 261-1221 *Founded/Ownrshp* 1938
Sales 206.0MM *EMP* 230
SIC 4911 Distribution, electric power
CEO: John Vranic

D-U-N-S 00-333-0016
▲ DIXIE GROUP INC (TN)
475 Reed Rd, Dalton, GA 30720-6307
Tel (706) 876-5800 *Founded/Ownrshp* 1920
Sales 422.4MM *EMP* 1,822^E
Accts Dixon Hughes Goodman Llp Atla
Tkr Sym DXYN *Exch* NGM
SIC 2273 Carpets & rugs
Ch Bd: Daniel K Frierson
Pr: E David Hobbs
Pr: Vinson Lee Martin
**COO:* D Kennedy Frierson Jr
CFO: Jon A Faulkner
VP: Paul B Comiskey
Board of Directors: William F Blue Jr, Charles E Brock, Walter W Hubbard, Lowry F Kline, Hilda S Murray, John W Murrey III, Michael L Owens

D-U-N-S 09-816-8917 IMP
DIXIE MAT AND HARDWOOD CO
YAK MAT
236 Herring Rd, Sandy Hook, MS 39478-9680
Tel (601) 876-2427 *Founded/Ownrshp* 1982
Sales 162.0MM^E *EMP* 50^E
Accts Alford Holloway & Co Pa
SIC 2448 2426 Wood pallets & skids; Hardwood dimension & flooring mills
Pr: Jonathan Jones
**Sec:* Jonathan Duhon
**Sec:* Lisa Jones

**VP:* Bret Jones
Opers Mgr: Hayden Verucchi
Sls Dir: Scott Ervin
Sls Mgr: Jason Dunn
Board of Directors: Sherman Ponds

DIXIE MEDICAL CENTER
See IHC HEALTH SERVICES INC

DIXIE PLYWOOD & LBR CO ATLANTA
See BRADLEY PLYWOOD CORP

D-U-N-S 15-424-7530
DIXIE RESTAURANTS INC
DIXIE CAFE THE
1215 Rebsamen Park Rd, Little Rock, AR 72202-1819
Tel (501) 666-3494 *Founded/Ownrshp* 1982
Sales 29.4MM[E] *EMP* 1,200
SIC 5812 5813 Restaurant, family: independent; Drinking places
Pr: Frank Bestro
**VP:* Gordon Gondek

D-U-N-S 02-458-8030 IMP
DIXIE SERVANTAGE SALES INC
(*Suby of* BARRETT CORPORATION)
5920 Summit Ave, Browns Summit, NC 27214-9704
Tel (336) 375-7500 *Founded/Ownrshp* 1950
Sales 103.3MM[E] *EMP* 250
SIC 5083 Lawn machinery & equipment
CEO: Harold Reiter
**Pr:* Michael Rounsavall
**CFO:* Laura Garrett

D-U-N-S 00-306-2650 IMP
■ DIXIE-NARCO INC
(*Suby of* CRANE NATIONAL VENDERS) ★
3330 Dixie Narco Blvd, Williston, SC 29853-6008
Tel (803) 266-5000 *Founded/Ownrshp* 1957
Sales 129.5MM[E] *EMP* 850[E]
SIC 3581 Automatic vending machines
Pr: R W Downing
**Treas:* D D Urbani
VP: Doug Dranton
VP: Jon Nicholas
Snr Sftwr: Talbert Black
DP Exec: Bryan Staubs
QC Dir: John Balsam
Sls Dir: Rick Tarleton

D-U-N-S 00-329-0533 IMP
DIXIEN LLC (GA)
5286 Circle Dr, Lake City, GA 30260-3548
Tel (478) 929-4121 *Founded/Ownrshp* 1961, 1996
Sales 95.0MM[E] *EMP* 350
SIC 3089 Injection molding of plastics; Blow molded finished plastic products
CEO: Juan R Garcia
Exec: Rafael Garcia
Plnt Mgr: Billy Holley
Ql Cn Mgr: Brian Belom
Ql Cn Mgr: Jim Gebhard
Sls Mgr: Alex Garcia
Snr Mgr: Stephen Geyer

D-U-N-S 09-378-1201
DIXON HUGHES GOODMAN LLP
4350 Congress St Ste 900, Charlotte, NC 28209-4866
Tel (704) 367-7760 *Founded/Ownrshp* 2004
Sales 341.9MM[E] *EMP* 1,850
SIC 8721 Certified public accountant
Pt: Matt Snow
Pt: Kenneth M Hughes
Pt: Kent Satterfield
Pt: Martin Schlaeppi
Pt: Tricia Wilson
COO: Mike Crawford
CFO: Lynn Kline
Dir Bus: Craig Lundgren
Dir Bus: Robert Roth
Dir IT: Nick Layes
Mktg Mgr: Anne Banez

DIXON VALVE & COUPLING
See DVCC INC

D-U-N-S 94-821-8102 IMP
DIXON VALVE & COUPLING CO
(*Suby of* DIXON VALVE & COUPLING) ★
800 High St, Chestertown, MD 21620-1105
Tel (410) 778-2000 *Founded/Ownrshp* 1995
Sales 95.4MM[E] *EMP* 350[E]
SIC 3492 5085 Fluid power valves & hose fittings; Hose, belting & packing; Valves, pistons & fittings
Pr: Bob Grace
Pr: Brian Zottarelli
**CFO:* James Canalichio
CFO: Johan Trumpy
Ex VP: Douglas K Goodall
Ex VP: Scott Spurrier
VP: Dick Conard
**VP:* Jim McCuligan
Brnch Mgr: Bryan Love
Div Mgr: Paul Grant
Sys Mgr: April Plummer

D-U-N-S 10-364-2070 IMP
DIY/GROUP INC
2401 W 26th St, Muncie, IN 47302-9548
Tel (765) 284-9000 *Founded/Ownrshp* 1983
Sales 121.7MM[E] *EMP* 265
SIC 1541 Industrial buildings & warehouses
CEO: Finley D Durham
**Pr:* Philip F Durham
**Prin:* Brian Lough
IT Man: Kristy Abbett
Site Mgr: Aaraka Case
Ql Cn Mgr: Tricia Buchanan

D-U-N-S 15-960-8756
DJ PROPERTY INVESTMENTS INC
JENKINS HYUNDAI
1602 Sw College Rd, Ocala, FL 34471-1644
Tel (352) 620-2264 *Founded/Ownrshp* 2004
Sales 126.7MM[E] *EMP* 350[E]
SIC 5511 Automobiles, new & used
Pr: Donald R Jenkins
**CEO:* Tom Formanek
Sls Mgr: Carolyn Davis

D-U-N-S 06-299-7812 IMP/EXP
■ DJJ HOLDING CORP
DAVID J JOSEPH COMPANY, THE
(*Suby of* NUCOR CORP) ★
300 Pike St, Cincinnati, OH 45202-4222
Tel (513) 621-8770 *Founded/Ownrshp* 2008
Sales 754.9MM[E] *EMP* 2,015
Accts Pricewaterhousecoopers Llp
SIC 5093 5088 4741 Ferrous metal scrap & waste; Nonferrous metals scrap; Railroad equipment & supplies; Rental of railroad cars
Pr: Craig A Feldman
**CFO:* David J Steigerwald
**Ex VP:* Robert L Angotti
**Ex VP:* Mark D Schaefer
**Sr VP:* Karen A Arnold
**Sr VP:* Christopher J Bedel
**Sr VP:* Michael H Knellinger
Genl Mgr: Pat Wells
Board of Directors: John J Ferriola, R Joseph Stratman

D-U-N-S 80-789-1085
■ DJO FINANCE LLC
(*Suby of* DJO HOLDINGS LLC) ★
1430 Decision St, Vista, CA 92081-8553
Tel (760) 727-1280 *Founded/Ownrshp* 2006
Sales 1.1MMM *EMP* 4,940
Accts Ernst & Young Llp San Diego
SIC 3842 Surgical appliances & supplies
Pr: Michael P Mogul
CFO: Susan M Crawford
Ex VP: Thomas A Capizzi
Ex VP: Gerry McDonnell
Ex VP: Donald M Roberts

DJO GLOBAL
See DJO LLC

D-U-N-S 96-874-5497 IMP
■ DJO GLOBAL INC
(*Suby of* BLACKSTONE GROUP) ★
1430 Decision St, Vista, CA 92081-8553
Tel (760) 727-1280 *Founded/Ownrshp* 2006
Sales 1.5MMM[E] *EMP* 5,470
SIC 3842 Surgical appliances & supplies; Implants, surgical
Pr: Michael P Mogul
Ch Bd: Kenneth W Davidson
Pr: Christina McMahon
Pr: Brady Shirley
Pr: Sharon Wolfington
COO: Scott Rogow
CFO: Vickie L Capps
Ex VP: Tom Capizzi
Ex VP: Andrew Holman
Ex VP: Jeanine Kestler
Ex VP: Stephen Murphy
Ex VP: Donald M Roberts
VP: Curtis Cox
VP: Kristin Grit
VP: John Liedtky
VP: Bryan Monroe
VP: Paul Rolle
VP: Efrain S Sotelo
VP: Birt Stem
Exec: Tonya Dubrish
Board of Directors: James R Lawson, John R Murphy, James Quella

D-U-N-S 06-590-9073 EXP
■ DJO HOLDINGS LLC
(*Suby of* DJO GLOBAL INC) ★
1430 Decision St, Vista, CA 92081-8553
Tel (760) 727-1280 *Founded/Ownrshp* 2006
Sales 1.1MMM[E] *EMP* 5,470[E]
SIC 3842 Surgical appliances & supplies
CFO: Vickie Capps
Sls Mgr: Danielle Basile

D-U-N-S 08-184-0873 IMP/EXP
■ DJO LLC
DJO GLOBAL
(*Suby of* DJO FINANCE LLC) ★
1430 Decision St, Vista, CA 92081-8553
Tel (760) 727-1280 *Founded/Ownrshp* 2011
Sales 405.4MM[E] *EMP* 1,132
SIC 3842 Adhesive tape & plasters, medicated or non-medicated
CEO: Michael P Mogul
Sr VP: Michael R McBaye
VP: Marsh Moore
VP: Margaret Sheehan
Exec: Philip Westhoff
Sls Mgr: Camilla Haynes

DJO SURGICAL
See ENCORE MEDICAL LP

D-U-N-S 00-936-2767 IMP
DK MAGAZINES CORP (NY)
24 Meadow St, Brooklyn, NY 11206-1708
Tel (718) 417-3573 *Founded/Ownrshp* 2008
Sales 712.6MM *EMP* 3
SIC 5199 Packaging materials
Pr: Vikas Madan

D-U-N-S 36-225-8873
DKM LTD
(*Suby of* DYSON-KISSNER-MORAN CORP) ★
2515 South Rd, Poughkeepsie, NY 12601-5473
Tel (212) 661-4600 *Founded/Ownrshp* 1991
Sales 173.0MM[E] *EMP* 419
SIC 6211 Investment firm, general brokerage
Ch Bd: Robert R Dyson
Pr: Joseph L Aurichio
CFO: Matthew J Zilinskas
Treas: Mark Feldman
Ofcr: John A Moran
VP: Robert Farley

DKNY
See DONNA KARAN CO LLC

D-U-N-S 84-708-0963
DKR CAPITAL INC
10 Glenville St Ste 5, Greenwich, CT 06831-3680
Tel (203) 324-8352 *Founded/Ownrshp* 1992
Sales 90.1MM[E] *EMP* 85
SIC 6722 Management investment, open-end
CEO: Gary Davis
**CFO:* Frederic Leif
Dir Risk M: Xiaoping Zhang

D-U-N-S 78-882-5896
DKR OASIS MANAGEMENT CO LP
(*Suby of* DKR CAPITAL INC) ★
1281 E Main St Ste 3, Stamford, CT 06902-3553
Tel (203) 324-8400 *Founded/Ownrshp* 2002
Sales 85.0MM *EMP* 1
SIC 6722 Management investment, open-end
Pt: Fredrick Leif

D-U-N-S 96-276-0872
DKT INTERNATIONAL INC
1701 K St Nw Ste 900, Washington, DC 20006-1513
Tel (202) 223-8780 *Founded/Ownrshp* 1990
Sales 148.1MM *EMP* 80[E]
SIC 8322 Individual & family services
Pr: Philip D Harvey
Bd of Dir: Christopher Purdy
Ofcr: Phoebe Chastain
Ofcr: Katarina Swanson
IT Man: Jeff Bryant

DLA
See DEFENSE LOGISTICS AGENCY

D-U-N-S 04-944-2473
■ DLA DOCUMENT SERVICES
DAPS DCUMENT AUTOMTN PROD SVCS
(*Suby of* DLA) ★
5450 Carlisle Pike Bldg 9, Mechanicsburg, PA 17050-2411
Tel (717) 605-2362 *Founded/Ownrshp* 1949
Sales NA *EMP* 1,400
SIC 9711 National security;
Genl Mgr: Joseph Fagan
IT Man: Michael Daft

D-U-N-S 06-937-1797
DLA PIPER LLP (US) (MD)
6225 Smith Ave Ste 200, Baltimore, MD 21209-3635
Tel (410) 580-3000 *Founded/Ownrshp* 1854, 1956
Sales 5.1MM[E] *EMP* 3,323
SIC 8111 General practice law office
Pt: Kenneth S Aneckstein
Pt: Juan M Alcal
Pt: Orson Alcocer
**Pt:* Anthony P Ashton
**Pt:* Francis B Burch Jr
Pt: Roy Chan
Pt: David Church
**Pt:* Stephen R Colgate
**Pt:* Raymond A Dearchs
Pt: Karol K Denniston
Pt: Ivo Deskovic
Pt: Paul Firth
Pt: Deborah E Jennings
**Pt:* Jordan I Bailowitz
**Pt:* Nigel Knowles
Pt: Neil McLean
Pt: Bruce C Mee
Pt: Lance Miller
**Pt:* Lee Miller
Pt: Espen Moe
Pt: Bruce Mullins

DLC
See DUQUESNE LIGHT CO

D-U-N-S 05-941-5604 IMP/EXP
DLF PICKSEED USA INC
SEED RESEARCH OF OREGON
(*Suby of* DLF SEEDS A/S)
175 W H St, Halsey, OR 97348-2297
Tel (541) 369-2251 *Founded/Ownrshp* 1972
Sales 100.0MM *EMP* 83
SIC 5191 Farm supplies; Seeds: field, garden & flower
Genl Mgr: Clauss Ikjaer
**Pr:* Claus Ikjaer
**Ex VP:* William Dunn
**Ex VP:* Brian Free
**VP:* Roeland Kapsenberg
**VP:* Richard Myers
Sales Asso: Jason Mikkelsen

D-U-N-S 06-867-8788
▲ DLH HOLDINGS CORP
3565 Piedmont Rd Ne, Atlanta, GA 30305-8202
Tel (770) 554-3545 *Founded/Ownrshp* 1969
Sales 85.6MM *EMP* 1,459[E]
Tkr Sym DLHC *Exch* NAS
SIC 7363 8742 Medical help service; Management consulting services
Pr: Zachary C Parker
**Ch Bd:* Frederick G Wasserman
Pr: Helene Fisher
**CFO:* Kathryn M Johnbull
Ofcr: Bob Coffman
**Ex VP:* John F Armstrong
CTO: Gregory J Haygood
Board of Directors: William H Alderman, Martin J Delaney, Elder Granger, T Stephen Johnson, Austin J Yerks III

D-U-N-S 08-016-1136 IMP/EXP
DLHBOWLES INC
2422 Leo Ave Sw, Canton, OH 44706-2344
Tel (330) 478-2503 *Founded/Ownrshp* 2015
Sales 139.3MM[E] *EMP* 1,200
SIC 8711 3089 3082 Engineering services; Injection molding of plastics; Tubes, unsupported plastic
CEO: John W Saxon
**Pr:* SRI Sridhara
**CFO:* Mike Ramsay
VP: Matthew Reese

D-U-N-S 00-984-6558
■ DLP HEALTHCARE LLC
DUKE LIFEPOINT HEALTHCARE
(*Suby of* LIFEPOINT HEALTH INC) ★
330 Seven Springs Way, Brentwood, TN 37027-5098
Tel (615) 372-8500 *Founded/Ownrshp* 2011
Sales 1.1MMM[E] *EMP* 2,626[E]
SIC 8062 General medical & surgical hospitals
CEO: William F Carpenter III

**Pr:* Jon Law Koford
**Sr VP:* Paul Hannah

D-U-N-S 07-972-0068
DLT MERGERCO LLC
2411 Dulles Corner Park, Herndon, VA 20171-3431
Tel (800) 262-4358 *Founded/Ownrshp* 2013
Sales 144.4MM[E] *EMP* 260
SIC 7373 Value-added resellers, computer systems; Systems integration services
CEO: Alan Marcsmith
CFO: Craig Adler
VP: Julie Bintzler

D-U-N-S 80-788-8388
DLT SOLUTIONS HOLDINGS INC
13861 Sunrise Valley Dr # 400, Herndon, VA 20171-6126
Tel (800) 262-4358 *Founded/Ownrshp* 2007
Sales 825.2MM *EMP* 67[E]
SIC 7371 Custom computer programming services
Pr: Rick Marcotte
CFO: Iain Slimmon
Ex VP: Larry Allen
Ex VP: Terri Allen
VP: Don Simpson
VP: Ron Tucker
IT Man: Nick Hamner
Sls Mgr: Carolyn Harrell
Sls Mgr: Jason Quinn
Sales Asso: Seth Goldman
Sales Asso: Ken Parrotte

D-U-N-S 78-646-8199
DLT SOLUTIONS LLC
(*Suby of* DLT MERGERCO LLC) ★
2411 Dulles Corner Park # 800, Herndon, VA 20171-6168
Tel (703) 709-7172 *Founded/Ownrshp* 2015
Sales 144.4MM[E] *EMP* 254
SIC 7373 Value-added resellers, computer systems; Systems integration services
Pr: Alan Marc Smith
CFO: Craig Adler
Ex VP: Brian Strosser
Sr VP: Gary Danoff
VP: Julie Bintzler
VP: Kim Boarts
VP: Jim Helou
VP: Jim Propps
CTO: David Blankenhorn
VP Mktg: Kristin Oelke

D-U-N-S 60-939-3657
DLZ CORP
6121 Huntley Rd, Columbus, OH 43229-1003
Tel (614) 888-0040 *Founded/Ownrshp* 1996
Sales 93.0MM[E] *EMP* 625
SIC 1623 8713 8712 Underground utilities contractor; Surveying services; Architectural engineering
Pr: Vikram Rajadhyaksha
**CFO:* James May
CFO: Jim May
**CFO:* Joe Zowrenski
Sr VP: Joseph Zwierzynski
**VP:* Robert Kirkley
VP: Farid Pezeshk
**VP:* Ram Rajadhyaksha
VP: William E Sampson
**VP:* A James Siebert
VP: Thomas Sisley

DM GROUP
See D & M HOLDINGS US INC

DMA
See DEFENSE MEDIA ACTIVITY

D.M.A.
See DEDHAM MEDICAL ASSOCIATES INC

D-U-N-S 04-440-2980
DMA CLAIMS INC
DMA CLAIMS SERVICES
330 N Brand Blvd Ste 230, Glendale, CA 91203-2380
Tel (323) 342-6800 *Founded/Ownrshp* 1993
Sales NA *EMP* 475[E]
SIC 6411 Insurance adjusters
Pr: Thomas J Reitze
COO: Charles N Ohl
Brnch Mgr: Brad Balentine

DMA CLAIMS SERVICES
See DMA CLAIMS INC

DMACC
See DES MOINES AREA COMMUNITY COLLEGE

D-U-N-S 07-925-3428 IMP/EXP
■ DMAX LTD
(*Suby of* GENERAL MOTORS LLC) ★
3100 Dryden Rd, Moraine, OH 45439-1622
Tel (937) 425-9700 *Founded/Ownrshp* 2009
Sales 127.1MM[E] *EMP* 100[E]
SIC 3519 Engines, diesel & semi-diesel or dual-fuel
IT Man: Dwayne Hopkins
Sfty Mgr: Debbie Fisher
Ql Cn Mgr: Matthew Swart

D-U-N-S 61-470-9459
DMB ASSOCIATES INC
D M B
7600 E Doubletree Ste 300, Scottsdale, AZ 85258
Tel (480) 367-6874 *Founded/Ownrshp* 1985
Sales 122.5MM[E] *EMP* 600
SIC 5999 6512 5961 1542 3446 Artificial flowers; Commercial & industrial building operation; Catalog & mail-order houses; Nonresidential construction; Architectural metalwork
Pr: Charley Freericks
**Ch Bd:* Drew M Brown
Ex VP: Eneas Kane
**VP:* Bennett Dorrance
VP: Robert Mayhew
Genl Mgr: John L Bradley
CIO: Terry Kading
S&M/VP: Bennett Dorance
Snr PM: Nancy Alexander

D-U-N-S 60-120-9463
DMC BUILDERS CO INC
(*Suby of* DMC CONSOLIDATED INC)
3411 Richmond Ave Ste 200, Houston, TX 77046-3412
Tel (832) 209-1200 *Founded/Ownrshp* 1988
Sales 112.0MM *EMP* 55
SIC 1522 Apartment building construction; Remodeling, multi-family dwellings
Pr: Jack Dinerstein
**Ch Bd:* T H Dinerstein
**COO:* Tom Calgagirone
**CFO:* Randall Husman

D-U-N-S 00-709-4105 EXP
▲ DMC GLOBAL INC
5405 Spine Rd, Boulder, CO 80301-3389
Tel (303) 665-5700 *Founded/Ownrshp* 1965
Sales 166.9MM *EMP* 424[E]
Accts Ernst & Young Llp Denver Col
Tkr Sym BOOM *Exch* NGS
SIC 3399 Metal powders, pastes & flakes; Powder, metal; Laminating steel
Pr: Kevin T Longe
**Ch Bd:* Gerard Munera
Pr: Ian Grieves
Pr: Jeff Nicol
CFO: Michael Kuta
VP: Jeff Fithian
Exec: Tom Morey
Off Admin: Christa Steenwerth
Dir IT: Matthew Bartels
VP Opers: Gary Burke
Board of Directors: David Aldous, Yvon Pierre Cariou, Robert A Cohen, James J Ferris, Richard P Graff, Peter Rose, Rolf Rospek

D-U-N-S 01-333-0704
DMD INC
LABOR FINDERS
1309 W Detroit St, Broken Arrow, OK 74012-3608
Tel (918) 250-5521 *Founded/Ownrshp* 1996
Sales 53.2MM[E] *EMP* 9,015
SIC 7361 Employment agencies
Pr: David McDaniel
**Sec:* Sandra McDaniel
**VP:* Douglas McCarty

D-U-N-S 79-337-0073
DMD MANAGEMENT INC
LEGACY HEALTH SERVICES
12380 Plaza Dr, Cleveland, OH 44130-1043
Tel (216) 898-8399 *Founded/Ownrshp* 1990
Sales 112.3MM[E] *EMP* 1,400
SIC 8741 Nursing & personal care facility management
CEO: Bruce Daskal
**COO:* Jim Taylor
COO: Jim Wilson
**CFO:* Barry Stump
**Treas:* Larry Dancziger
Ofcr: Rey Nevarez
**VP:* Harold Shachter
Ex Dir: Vanessa Pappalardo
Off Mgr: Linda Anderson
Netwrk Mgr: Rob Buzaleski
HC Dir: Legacy P Twinsburg

D-U-N-S 04-554-9193
DMG CORP
SHARP HTG VENTILATION DIV DMG
1110 W Taft Ave Ste A, Orange, CA 92865-4141
Tel (562) 692-1277 *Founded/Ownrshp* 1979
Sales 103.0MM[E] *EMP* 55
SIC 5075 5078 Air conditioning equipment, except room units; Refrigeration equipment & supplies
CEO: Ronald D Sweet
**CFO:* Jeff Bulkin
**VP:* Will Clark
VP: Victor Murphy
**VP:* Steve Weston
Sls Mgr: Jordan Jones
Sales Asso: Terri Chumbley

D-U-N-S 00-493-2091 IMP
DMG EQUIPMENT CO LTD (TX)
PAVERS SUPPLY COMPANY
1575 Fm 1485 Rd, Conroe, TX 77301-6839
Tel (936) 756-6960 *Founded/Ownrshp* 1946
Sales 100.2MM *EMP* 225
Accts Hereford Lynch Sellars & Kir
SIC 1611 2951 Highway & street paving contractor; Asphalt & asphaltic paving mixtures (not from refineries)
Genl Pt: Mike C Smith
Pt: Dave Smith
Pt: Gene Smith

D-U-N-S 02-056-8874
DMG INFORMATION INC (DE)
(*Suby of* DAILY MAIL AND GENERAL TRUST P L C)
46 Southfield Ave Ste 400, Stamford, CT 06902-7236
Tel (203) 973-2940 *Founded/Ownrshp* 1997
Sales 201.6MM[E] *EMP* 1,476[E]
SIC 6719 1731 8748 Personal holding companies, except banks; Energy management controls; Telecommunications consultant
CEO: Suresh Kavan
**CEO:* Suresh Kavam
**CFO:* Paul Sykes
**Ex VP:* Martha Notaras
**VP:* Erik Levy

DMG MORI SEIKI U.S.A
See DMG MORI USA INC

D-U-N-S 10-262-1943 IMP
DMG MORI USA INC
DMG MORI SEIKI U.S.A
(*Suby of* DMG MORI CO., LTD.)
2400 Huntington Blvd, Hoffman Estates, IL 60192-1564
Tel (847) 593-5400 *Founded/Ownrshp* 2006
Sales 506.1MM *EMP* 260
SIC 3541 3545 Machine tools, metal cutting type; Machine tool accessories
Pr: Thorsten Schmidt
**Sec:* Brian McGirk
**Ex VP:* Randall Harland
**Ex VP:* Marlow Knabach
VP: Volker Stitz
**Prin:* Mark H Mohr
IT Man: Lawrence Chan

D-U-N-S 18-056-7232
DMH CORPORATE HEALTH SERVICES
2300 N Edward St, Decatur, IL 62526-4192
Tel (217) 876-8121 *Founded/Ownrshp* 1984
Sales 419.7MM[E] *EMP* 2,300[E]
SIC 8062 General medical & surgical hospitals
Pr: Kenneth Smithmier
**COO:* Tim Stone
**CFO:* Al Naqvi
**Ex VP:* Gary Peacock
Exec: Jeanine Garner
Doctor: Cesar Arguelles
Doctor: Cohen Carol
Doctor: Arguelles Cesar
Doctor: Ellington Charles
Doctor: Facchini Frank
Doctor: Gordon Gregory

DMI
See DESERT MECHANICAL INC

DMI
See DIGITAL MANAGEMENT LLC

DMI
See DIVERSIFIED MACHINE BRISTOL LLC

D-U-N-S 83-260-5641 IMP
DMI COLUMBUS LLC
COLUMBUS FOUNDRY
(*Suby of* DIVERSIFIED MACHINE INC) ★
1600 Northside Indus Blvd, Columbus, GA 31904-4444
Tel (248) 728-8642 *Founded/Ownrshp* 2013
Sales 157.9MM[E] *EMP* 482
SIC 3465 Body parts, automobile: stamped metal
CEO: Douglas Delgrosso
**Pr:* Chad Bullock
**CFO:* Shankar Kiro
**Treas:* Kelly Burchart
**VP:* Katia Moraes
Dir IT: Greg Buxkemper

D-U-N-S 18-505-5217 IMP
■ DMI HOLDING CORP
(*Suby of* THOR INDUSTRIES INC) ★
2164 Caragana Ct, Goshen, IN 46526-9149
Tel (574) 534-1224 *Founded/Ownrshp* 1991
Sales 86.4MM[E] *EMP* 1,200
SIC 3792 5012 Travel trailers & campers; Travel trailer chassis; Recreational vehicles, motor homes & trailers
Pr: David Hoefer
**Pr:* Richard W Florea
**CFO:* Bill Maki
Sr VP: Walter Bennett
**VP:* Steve Paul

D-U-N-S 62-346-6682
DMI TECHNOLOGY CORP
1 Progress Dr, Dover, NH 03820-5450
Tel (603) 742-3330 *Founded/Ownrshp* 1994
Sales 137.8MM[E] *EMP* 423[E]
SIC 3625 3621 Relays & industrial controls; Electric motor & generator parts
Pr: James Elsner
**Ch:* Logan D Delany Jr

DMMI
See DENSO MANUFACTURING MICHIGAN INC

D-U-N-S 80-387-1938 IMP
■ DMN INC
DALLAS MORNING NEWS
(*Suby of* A H BELO CORP) ★
508 Young St, Dallas, TX 75202-4808
Tel (214) 977-8222 *Founded/Ownrshp* 1885
Sales 279.1MM[E] *EMP* 1,190
SIC 2711 Newspapers, publishing & printing
CEO: James M Moroney III
Pt: Priscilla Presley
Pt: Jason Taylor
**Pr:* Robert W Mong Jr
**Chf Mktg O:* Philipp Von Holtzendorff Fehli
**Ex VP:* Evelyn H Miller
**VP:* Gilbert Bailon
VP: Cyndy Carr
**VP:* Mike Lavy
VP: Jacquelyn U Smith
**Dir Risk M:* Dan Phelan

D-U-N-S 08-048-4082
DMN MANAGEMENT SERVICES LLC
CAPITAL CARE RHBILITATION SVCS
26 N Broadway, Schenectady, NY 12305-1932
Tel (518) 346-9640 *Founded/Ownrshp* 2003
Sales 50.9MM[E] *EMP* 1,000
SIC 8051 Skilled nursing care facilities
Pr: James Durante
CFO: Anthony Durante

DMR METRO REGION
See MASSACHUSETTS DEPT OF MENTAL RETARDATION

D-U-N-S 07-530-0624
DMS FACILITY SERVICES INC
D M S
1040 Arroyo Dr, South Pasadena, CA 91030-2908
Tel (626) 305-8500 *Founded/Ownrshp* 1967
Sales 60.6MM *EMP* 2,600
SIC 7349

D-U-N-S 79-044-5444
DMS FACILITY SERVICES LLC
1040 Arroyo Dr, South Pasadena, CA 91030-2908
Tel (626) 305-8500 *Founded/Ownrshp* 1998
Sales 43.8MM[E] *EMP* 1,500
SIC 8711 7349 0781 Engineering services; Janitorial service, contract basis; Landscape services

DMS HOLDINGS
See BRIGGS MEDICAL SERVICE CO

DMV
See DRIVER & MOTOR VEHICLE SERVICES OREGON

DMV BUDGET AND ANALYSIS
See CALIFORNIA DEPARTMENT OF MOTOR VEHICLES

D-U-N-S 80-373-2366
DNC LANDMARK HOLDINGS LLC
PATINA RESTAURANT GROUP
(*Suby of* DELAWARE NORTH COMPANIES INC) ★
40 Fountain Plz, Buffalo, NY 14202-2229
Tel (716) 858-5000 *Founded/Ownrshp* 2007
Sales 259.6MM *EMP* 195[E]
SIC 5812 American restaurant

D-U-N-S 06-610-9141
DNC PARKS & RESORTS AT YOSEMITE INC
YOSEMITE CONCESSION SERVICES
(*Suby of* DELAWARE NORTH COMPANIES PARKS & RESORTS INC) ★
9001 Village Dr, Yosemite Ntpk, CA 95389-9912
Tel (209) 372-1001 *Founded/Ownrshp* 1993
Sales 63.6MM[E] *EMP* 1,100
SIC 7011 5399 5812 5947 5541 4725 Hotels; Vacation lodges; Country general stores; Eating places; Snack shop; Gift shop; Gasoline service stations; Tours, conducted
Pr: Dan Jensen
**VP:* Paul Jensen
**VP:* Paul Jeppson
Area Mgr: Christy Contreras

D-U-N-S 07-839-8657
DNC/MFS FOOD GROUP
RICHMOND AIRPORT
(*Suby of* DELAWARE NORTH COMPANIES TRAVEL HOSPITALITY SERVICES INC) ★
1 Richard E Byrd Trml Dr, Richmond, VA 23250-2450
Tel (804) 222-1227 *Founded/Ownrshp* 2012
Sales 20.5MM[E] *EMP* 1,161[E]
SIC 5812 Concessionaire
Pr: Cain Bassett

DNE WORLD FRUIT
See BERNARD EGAN & CO

D-U-N-S 06-980-7345 IMP
DNIS DLN ATOPRK&TRCK CNTR
CUSTOM AUTO FINISH
2573 S Orchard St, Boise, ID 83705
Tel (208) 336-6000 *Founded/Ownrshp* 1975
Sales 88.0MM[E] *EMP* 200
SIC 5511 Automobiles, new & used; Pickups, new & used
Pr: Dennis E Dillon
CFO: David Booher
**Treas:* Joan Dillon
Genl Mgr: Jason Wood
Dir IT: Chris Wood
IT Man: Tom Browning
IT Man: Patsy Price
Mktg Dir: Jason Erickson
Sls Mgr: Ruell Antonucci
Sls Mgr: Joe Bocci
Sls Mgr: Keith Boyer

D-U-N-S 06-790-8183
DNK SALES LLC
949 Stephenson Rd Ste B, Stone Mountain, GA 30087-4620
Tel (678) 704-7300 *Founded/Ownrshp* 2013
Sales NA *EMP* 4
SIC 6311 7291 5699 Life insurance; Tax return preparation services; Customized clothing & apparel
Pr: Cicley T Hudson
**Sec:* Na'ilah Muhammad

D-U-N-S 00-809-8212 IMP
■ DNOW LP (TX)
WILSON EXPORTS
(*Suby of* NOW INC) ★
7402 N Eldridge Pkwy, Houston, TX 77041-1902
Tel (281) 823-4700 *Founded/Ownrshp* 1862, 2014
Sales 3.0MMM[E] *EMP* 5,000
SIC 5084 7353 3533 Oil well machinery, equipment & supplies; Oil field equipment, rental or leasing; Drilling tools for gas, oil or water wells
CEO: Robert Workman
CFO: Daniel Molinaro
Ofcr: Michelle A Lewis
VP: Neal Meadows
VP: Brad B Wise
Exec: Lara Isaacs
Rgnl Mgr: Don Ard
Rgnl Mgr: Stu Goehring
Rgnl Mgr: Mark Riggs
Dept Mgr: Mark Napier
Brnch Mgr: Ryan Hill

D-U-N-S 79-974-5302 IMP
DNP CORP USA
(*Suby of* DAI NIPPON PRINTING CO., LTD.)
335 Madison Ave Fl 3, New York, NY 10017-4616
Tel (212) 503-1060 *Founded/Ownrshp* 1997
Sales 274.8MM[E] *EMP* 263[E]
SIC 5111 Printing paper
CEO: Masahiko Koizumi
**Sec:* Kunihiko Takemura

D-U-N-S 87-926-9918 IMP
DNP IMAGINGCOMM AMERICA CORP
(*Suby of* DNP CORP USA) ★
4524 Enterprise Dr Nw, Concord, NC 28027-6437
Tel (704) 784-8100 *Founded/Ownrshp* 2001
Sales 250.0MM *EMP* 263[E]
SIC 3955 Ribbons, inked: typewriter, adding machine, register, etc.
CEO: Katsyuki Oshima
**CFO:* Kojie Kuzusako
QA Dir: Bhanu Tatineni
Dir IT: Cory Rice
Sftwr Eng: Jim Burgess
VP Sls: James Rowley

DNR
See UTAH DEPARTMENT OF NATURAL RESOURCES

D-U-N-S 95-975-0949
DNT CONSTRUCTION LLC
2300 Picadilly Dr, Round Rock, TX 78664-8642
Tel (512) 837-6700 *Founded/Ownrshp* 2009
Sales 230.0MM *EMP* 700
SIC 1623 1794 1611 Water, sewer & utility lines; Excavation & grading, building construction; Highway & street construction
CFO: Dean Tomme
CFO: Jack Brown
Off Mgr: Jessica McCourt
Mtls Mgr: Hunter Drummond
Snr PM: Jason Gray
Snr PM: Grant Robinson

DO IT BEST
See NATIONAL LUMBER CO

DO IT BEST
See FARMERS COOPERATIVE SOCIETY

DO IT BEST
See EFFINGHAM EQUITY

DO IT BEST
See TURNER SUPPLY CO

DO IT BEST
See MILLARD LUMBER INC

DO IT BEST
See CENTRAL MISSOURI AGRISERVICE LLC

DO IT BEST
See FOXWORTH GALBRAITH LUMBER CO

DO IT BEST
See CITY MILL CO LIMITED

DO IT BEST
See WESTERN RESERVE FARM COOPERATIVE INC

DO IT BEST
See PREMIER COOPERATIVE

DO IT BEST
See COUNTRY PRIDE COOPERATIVE INC

DO IT BEST
See R P LUMBER CO INC

DO IT BEST
See SIMONSON PROPERTIES CO

DO IT BEST
See VALU HOME CENTERS INC

DO IT BEST
See RAKS BUILDING SUPPLY INC

DO IT BEST
See MEAD HOLDING CO INC

D-U-N-S 00-693-7130 IMP/EXP
DO IT BEST CORP
6502 Nelson Rd, Fort Wayne, IN 46803-1947
Tel (260) 748-5300 *Founded/Ownrshp* 1945
Sales 2.9MMM *EMP* 1,519
Accts Crowe Horwath Llp
SIC 5072 5031 5063 Hardware; Builders' hardware; Lumber, plywood & millwork; Electrical apparatus & equipment
Pr: Daniel B Starr
**COO:* Dave Haist
CFO: Doug Roth
VP: Michael J Altendorf
**VP:* Jay Brown
**VP:* David W Dietz
**VP:* Steve Markley
VP: Dori Meighan
**VP:* Tim Miller
VP: Timothy Miller
VP: Gary Nackers
VP: Bill Zilke
Exec: Patricia Jackson
Comm Man: Gonzeez Kim

DOAK WALKER CARE CENTER
See YAMPA VALLEY MEDICAL CENTER

D-U-N-S 00-896-4736 IMP
DOALL CO (IL)
DGI SUPPLY
1480 S Wolf Rd, Wheeling, IL 60090-6514
Tel (847) 495-6800 *Founded/Ownrshp* 1927
Sales 464.8MM[E] *EMP* 800
SIC 5085 5084 Industrial supplies; Machine tools & accessories
Pr: Michael Wilkie
**Ch Bd:* Jon Henricks
**COO:* William Henricks
CFO: Jim Japczyk
**Sr VP:* David Crawford
**VP:* Mickey Davis
VP: Jim Rudolph
Exec: Don Muller
Dir Bus: Gregg Muntean
IT Man: Todd Mills
IT Man: Carol Shannon

D-U-N-S 00-886-0421 IMP
DOALL INDUSTRIAL SUPPLY CORP (IL)
DGI SUPPLY
1480 S Wolf Rd, Wheeling, IL 60090-6514
Tel (800) 923-6255 *Founded/Ownrshp* 1946, 1963
Sales 141.0MM[E] *EMP* 500
SIC 5085 Industrial supplies; Industrial tools
Ch Bd: Michael Wilkie
**COO:* Bill Henricks
**V Ch Bd:* Jon Henricks
**Sr VP:* David Crawford
Prgrm Mgr: Rich Hermann
IT Man: Darryl Thompson
Sales Asso: John Sparkman
Genl Couns: Timothy Moran

D-U-N-S 07-713-5333
DOBBS TIRE & AUTO CENTERS INC
DOBBS TIRE CENTER
1983 Brennan Plz, High Ridge, MO 63049-1893
Tel (636) 677-2101 *Founded/Ownrshp* 1974
Sales 199.1MM[E] *EMP* 650
SIC 5531

DOBBS TIRE CENTER
See DOBBS TIRE & AUTO CENTERS INC

D-U-N-S 01-916-5406 IMP
■ **DOBLE ENGINEERING CO**
(*Suby of* ESCO TECHNOLOGIES INC) ★
85 Walnut St, Watertown, MA 02472-4037
Tel (617) 926-4900 *Founded/Ownrshp* 1920
Sales 129.4MM[E] *EMP* 386
SIC 3825 7359 3829 3826 Electrical power measuring equipment; Business machine & electronic equipment rental services; Measuring & controlling devices; Analytical instruments
Pr: David B Zabetakis
COO: Bill Fernihough
COO: Richard Heywood
**Treas:* Lawrence H Nordt
**VP:* Don Angell
VP: Alyson Barclay
VP: Edward Condit
**VP:* Jay Cunningham
VP: John Gagnon
**VP:* Paul Griffin
VP: Dennis Kopaczynski
**VP:* Vegard Larsen
**VP:* Joseph McCadden
**VP:* Rob Ryan
VP: Robert Ryan
**VP:* Julie Crisafulli Brown Sphr

D-U-N-S 96-643-5190
■ **DOBSON COMMUNICATIONS CORP**
(*Suby of* AT&T INC) ★
14201 Wireless Way, Oklahoma City, OK 73134-2512
Tel (405) 529-8500 *Founded/Ownrshp* 2007
Sales 576.4MM[E] *EMP* 2,500[E]
SIC 4812

DOBY BUILDING SUPPLY
See L & W SUPPLY CORP

D-U-N-S 60-194-8339
DOCKWISE USA LLC
(*Suby of* DOCKWISE TRANSPORT N.V.)
16340 Park Ten Pl Ste 200, Houston, TX 77084-5185
Tel (713) 934-7300 *Founded/Ownrshp* 1978
Sales 539.4MM *EMP* 20
SIC 4493 Marinas
Off Mgr: Amanda Brown
IT Man: Robb Erickson

DOCTORS CARE
See UCI MEDICAL AFFILIATES INC

D-U-N-S 07-021-5157
DOCTORS CO AN INTERINSURANCE EXCHANGE (CA)
185 Greenwood Rd, NAPA, CA 94558-6270
Tel (707) 226-0100 *Founded/Ownrshp* 1976
Sales NA *EMP* 704
SIC 6321 Reciprocal interinsurance exchanges
Ch Bd: Richard E Anderson
**Pr:* Manuel Puebla
Sr VP: David A McHale

DOCTORS COMMUNITY HOSPITAL
See DOCTORS HOSPITAL INC

DOCTORS FOSTER AND SMITH
See FOSTER AND SMITH INC

DOCTOR'S HOSPITAL
See DOCTORS HOSPITAL OF AUGUSTA LLC

D-U-N-S 96-303-5084
DOCTORS HOSPITAL AT RENAISSANCE LTD
5501 S Mccoll Rd, Edinburg, TX 78539-5503
Tel (956) 362-8677 *Founded/Ownrshp* 1997
Sales 436.5MM *EMP* 176
SIC 8062 General medical & surgical hospitals
CEO: Lawrence Gelman
**Pr:* Susan Turley
Dir Rx: Gabino Garza
CIO: Dean Besley

D-U-N-S 14-420-6315
DOCTORS HOSPITAL INC
DOCTORS COMMUNITY HOSPITAL
8118 Good Luck Rd, Lanham, MD 20706-3574
Tel (301) 552-8118 *Founded/Ownrshp* 1975
Sales 197.1MM *EMP* 1,200
SIC 8062 Hospital, affiliated with AMA residency
CEO: Philip B Down
CFO: Jennifer Dunphy
Chf Mktg O: John Watovish
**Ex VP:* Thomas Crowley
**Ex VP:* Paul R Grenaldo
**VP:* Camille R Bash
**VP:* Paula L Bruening
**VP:* Patricia Christensen
**VP:* Gabriel Jaffe
**VP:* Charlene Lundgren
**VP:* Robyn M Webb Williams
VP: Robyn Williams
Exec: Maria Hunt

D-U-N-S 18-930-6566
DOCTORS HOSPITAL INC
(*Suby of* BAPTIST HEALTH SOUTH FLORIDA INC) ★
5000 University Dr, Coral Gables, FL 33146-2008
Tel (305) 666-2111 *Founded/Ownrshp* 2010
Sales 191.3MM *EMP* 717
Accts Deloitte & Touche Llp
SIC 8062 General medical & surgical hospitals
CEO: Brian E Keeley
Chf Rad: Michael Thorpe
**COO:* Douglas J Jolly
VP: Sandra Hyatt

DOCTORS HOSPITAL NORTH
See DOCTORS OHIOHEALTH CORP

D-U-N-S 06-760-4405
■ **DOCTORS HOSPITAL OF AUGUSTA LLC**
DOCTOR'S HOSPITAL
(*Suby of* HOSPITAL COPORATION OF AMERICA) ★
3651 Wheeler Rd, Augusta, GA 30909-6426
Tel (706) 651-3232 *Founded/Ownrshp* 1993
Sales 281.6MM[E] *EMP* 1,300
SIC 8062 8049 General medical & surgical hospitals; Physical therapist
Prin: Doug Welch
Chf Rad: Hal Hobbs
COO: Paul Bonucci
CFO: Robert C Paris
Ofcr: Kelly Penton
VP: Lee Gray MD
Exec: Christopher Henry
Dir Bus: Bill Byars
Prin: Sondra Smith
Prin: William Ziesmer
CIO: Ronald Hall

DOCTORS HOSPITAL OF LAREDO
See LAREDO REGIONAL MEDICAL CENTER L P

D-U-N-S 00-479-9644
■ **DOCTORS HOSPITAL OF MANTECA INC** (CA)
(*Suby of* TENET HEALTHCARE CORP) ★
1205 E North St, Manteca, CA 95336-4900
Tel (209) 823-3111 *Founded/Ownrshp* 2001
Sales 90.8MM *EMP* 400
SIC 8069 Specialty hospitals, except psychiatric
CEO: Nicholas Tejeda
**Pr:* Mark Lisa
**Pr:* Katherine Medeiros
**CFO:* Tracy Roman

DOCTORS' HOSPITAL OF MICHIGAN
See OAKLAND PHYSICIANS MEDICAL CENTER LLC

D-U-N-S 08-005-6708
DOCTORS MANAGEMENT CO
(*Suby of* DOCTORS CO AN INTERINSURANCE EXCHANGE) ★
185 Greenwood Rd, NAPA, CA 94558-6270
Tel (707) 226-0100 *Founded/Ownrshp* 1982
Sales NA *EMP* 300
SIC 6411 Insurance information & consulting services; Insurance claim processing, except medical
CEO: Richard E Anderson
COO: Robert Francis
**CFO:* Eugene M Bullis
**Ex VP:* Kenneth R Chrisman
Ex VP: Bruce Crile
**Sr VP:* William J Gallagher
**Prin:* Michael Yacob
Board of Directors: David M Charles, Kenneth R Chrisman, Charles R Kossman, Donald J Palmisano, Robert B Sheppard, Diana L Starcher, David B Troxel, Thomas A Waltz, Randall K Zeller

D-U-N-S 07-464-3735
DOCTORS MEDICAL CENTER LLC
(*Suby of* WCCHD) ★
2000 Vale Rd, San Pablo, CA 94806-3808
Tel (510) 970-5000 *Founded/Ownrshp* 2001
Sales 90.7MM[E] *EMP* 937[E]
SIC 8062 General medical & surgical hospitals
Pr: Jo Stuart
**COO:* Candy Markwith
Ql Cn Mgr: Kari Kuenzinger
Mktg Dir: Paula Ferron
Doctor: Carol Towarnick
HC Dir: Jody Popke

D-U-N-S 11-554-1547
■ **DOCTORS MEDICAL CENTER OF MODESTO INC**
(*Suby of* TENET HEALTHCARE CORP) ★
1441 Florida Ave, Modesto, CA 95350-4404
Tel (209) 578-1211 *Founded/Ownrshp* 2003
Sales 236.2MM[E] *EMP* 2,000[E]
SIC 8062 General medical & surgical hospitals
CEO: Warren J Kirk
**CFO:* Greg Berry

D-U-N-S 07-165-4172
DOCTORS OHIOHEALTH CORP
DOCTORS HOSPITAL NORTH
(*Suby of* OHIOHEALTH CORP) ★
5100 W Broad St, Columbus, OH 43228-1607
Tel (614) 544-5424 *Founded/Ownrshp* 1987
Sales 321.9MM[E] *EMP* 9,000
SIC 8062 8011 Hospital, medical school affiliated with residency; Medical insurance plan
CEO: David Blom
Bd of Dir: Carl A Krantz Jr
Bd of Dir: Chester P Porembski
Bd of Dir: Joseph Ruane
Bd of Dir: Michael P Scott
**Ofcr:* Frank T Pandora II
**Sr VP:* Michael Bernstein
**Sr VP:* Steve Garlock
**Sr VP:* Cheryl Herbert
**Sr VP:* Barbara Otey
**VP:* Ed Cotter
**VP:* Cheryl Hodges
VP: Jon M Joffe
VP: Jill Willen Kennelly
**VP:* Mike Louge
VP: Mary Jo McElroy
**VP:* David Morehead
VP: Keith R Vesper
VP: Mary Wilcox

D-U-N-S 61-643-7240
DOCTORS OSTEOPATHIC MEDICAL CENTER INC
GULF COAST HOSPITAL
13681 Doctors Way, Fort Myers, FL 33912-4300
Tel (239) 768-5000 *Founded/Ownrshp* 2006
Sales 296.2MM *EMP* 1,530
SIC 8062 General medical & surgical hospitals
CEO: Jim Nathan
COO: Larry Antonucci
CFO: John West
Treas: Nancy Elkin
VP: Joan Newman
Dir Lab: Steve Daugherty
IT Man: Benefiel Greg
Mktg Dir: Karen Krieger
Doctor: Richard Davis

DOCTORS REGIONAL CAMPUS
See BAY AREA HEALTHCARE GROUP LTD

DOCTORS WITHOUT BORDERS USA
See MEDECINS SANS FRONTIERES USA INC

D-U-N-S 05-223-1169
DOCUMENT TECHNOLOGIES LLC
D T I
2 Ravinia Dr Ste 850, Atlanta, GA 30346-2126
Tel (770) 390-2700 *Founded/Ownrshp* 1998
Sales 593.8MM[E] *EMP* 2,500
SIC 7389 Document storage service
CEO: John Davenport Jr
**Pr:* Christopher Aronson
**CFO:* Chris Henderson
CFO: Edward James
**Sr VP:* Jackie Bebczuk
**VP:* David Barrett
Exec: Gina Joshua
Off Mgr: Alicen Matthews
Sftwr Eng: Matthew Guenther

D-U-N-S 78-933-5809
■ **DOCUMENTUM INC**
(*Suby of* DELL EMC) ★
6801 Koll Center Pkwy, Pleasanton, CA 94566-7047
Tel (925) 600-6800 *Founded/Ownrshp* 2003
Sales 61.8MM[E] *EMP* 1,155
SIC 7372 7371 Business oriented computer software; Custom computer programming services
Pr: David Dewalt
Ex VP: Rob Tarkoff
**VP:* Michael Decesare
**VP:* Mark Garrett
CTO: Razmik Abnous
Mktg Dir: Lothar Hnle

D-U-N-S 04-947-0162
DOCUSIGN INC
221 Main St Ste 1000, San Francisco, CA 94105-1925
Tel (415) 489-4940 *Founded/Ownrshp* 2010
Sales 115.5MM[E] *EMP* 213[E]
SIC 7373

D-U-N-S 13-591-5101
DOCUSIGN INC
221 Main St Ste 1000, San Francisco, CA 94105-1925
Tel (415) 489-4940 *Founded/Ownrshp* 2003
Sales 259.1MM[E] *EMP* 1,500
SIC 7373 Systems software development services
CEO: Keith Krach
**COO:* Gordon Payne
**CFO:* Mike Dinsdale
**CFO:* Michael Sheridan
**Chf Mktg O:* Brad Brooks
**Chf Mktg O:* Dustin Grosse
**Ex VP:* Tom Gonser
Sr VP: Tom Casey
Sr VP: Lambert Walsh
VP: Cynthia Ashworth
VP: Bob Desantis
**VP:* Robin Ducot
VP: Ron Hirson
**VP:* Ken Moyle
Dir Bus: Helen Joo

D-U-N-S 96-597-0994
■ **DOD PATIENT SAFETY PROGRAM**
(*Suby of* OFFICE OF THE SECRETARY OF DEFENSE) ★
5111 Leesburg Pike # 810, Falls Church, VA 22041-3251
Tel (703) 681-0064 *Founded/Ownrshp* 2001
Sales NA *EMP* 5,010[E]
SIC 9711 National security;

D-U-N-S 07-981-2246
■ **DOD TEST RESOURCE MANGEMENT CENTER**
(*Suby of* OFFICE OF THE SECRETARY OF DEFENSE) ★
3000 Defense Pentagon, Washington, DC 20301-3000
Tel (571) 372-2700 *Founded/Ownrshp* 2015
Sales NA *EMP* 4,052[E]
SIC 9711 National security;

DODD
See OHIO DEPARTMENT OF DEVELOPMENTAL DISABILITIES

DODEA
See DEPARTMENT OF DEFENSE EDUCATION ACTIVITY

D-U-N-S 06-885-9693
DODGE & COX (CA)
555 California St Fl 40, San Francisco, CA 94104-1538
Tel (415) 981-1710 *Founded/Ownrshp* 1930
Sales 216.8MM[E] *EMP* 195
SIC 6722 Management investment, open-end
CEO: Dana M Emery
**Ch:* John A Gunn
**Treas:* John Loll
**Sr VP:* C Bryan Cameron
**Sr VP:* Thomas S Dugan
**Sr VP:* David C Hoeft
**Sr VP:* Charles Poll
**Sr VP:* Gregory R Serrurier
Sr VP: Horton Shapiro
**Sr VP:* Diana S Strandberg
VP: Steve Gorski
**VP:* Roberta Rw Kameda
VP: Mary Klabunde
VP: Jane F Larrow
VP: Laura Leung
VP: Ria Nickens
VP: Lynn Poole
VP: Gregory Serrurier
VP: Jay J Stock
VP: Naveen Verma
VP: Steven Voorhis

DODGE DAKOTA
See OLD CARCO INTERNATIONAL CORP

DODGER STADIUM
See FOX BSB HOLDCO INC

D-U-N-S 02-207-9323
DOE FL SMIDTH
7158 Fl Smidth Dr, Midvale, UT 84047
Tel (801) 526-2500 *Founded/Ownrshp* 2009
Sales 122.4MM[E] *EMP* 400
SIC 5039 Prefabricated structures
Pr: Peter J Flanagan
**VP:* Brian M Day
**VP:* Brian Field
**VP:* Bernard Zavatone

DOE RUN COMPANY, THE
See DOE RUN RESOURCES CORP

D-U-N-S 16-135-9302 IMP/EXP
DOE RUN RESOURCES CORP
DOE RUN COMPANY, THE
(*Suby of* RENCO GROUP INC) ★
1801 Park 270 Dr Ste 300, Saint Louis, MO 63146-4040
Tel (314) 453-7100 *Founded/Ownrshp* 1994
Sales 58.6MM[E] *EMP* 1,400
SIC 1031 1021 3339 Lead ores mining; Zinc ores mining; Copper ore mining & preparation; Copper ore milling & preparation; Primary nonferrous metals
Pr: Jerry Lpyatt
CFO: Terry P Fox
VP: Jeff Gibson
VP: Sharon Gietl
VP: Jose Hansen
VP: Richard Wagner
VP: Matthew D Wohl
VP: Mark Yingling
Exec: James Conner
Exec: Ross Conner
Creative D: Adam Kresler

D-U-N-S 03-436-0644
DOERLE FOOD SERVICES LLC
113 Kol Dr, Broussard, LA 70518-3825
Tel (337) 252-8551 *Founded/Ownrshp* 1954
Sales 470.0MM[E] *EMP* 404
SIC 5142 5141 5087 5148 Meat, frozen: packaged; Vegetables, frozen; Fish, frozen: packaged; Groceries, general line; Janitors' supplies; Fresh fruits & vegetables
CEO: Carolyn Doerle
Genl Pt: Paul A Doerle Sr
**Sr VP:* Allen Boudreaux
**Sr VP:* Robert Woodburn
**VP:* Rick Blum
**VP:* Charlie Martin
**VP:* John Romero
VP: Woody Woodburn

DOH
See STATE HAWAII DEPARTMENT OF HEALTH

DOJ
See NORTH CAROLINA DEPARTMENT OF JUSTICE

D-U-N-S 04-641-1898
DOLAN FOSTER ENTERPRISES LLC
TACO BELL
5635 W Las Positas Blvd # 406, Pleasanton, CA 94588-4076
Tel (925) 621-2600 *Founded/Ownrshp* 1968
Sales 46.8MM[E] *EMP* 1,300
SIC 5812 Fast-food restaurant, chain
CFO: Paul Luce
VP: Lorna Evans
Area Supr: Robert Millhouse
Genl Mgr: Monica Schneider

D-U-N-S 80-592-2143
DOLAN LLC
(*Suby of* BAYSIDE CAPITAL INC) ★
222 S 9th St Ste 2300, Minneapolis, MN 55402-3363
Tel (612) 317-9420 *Founded/Ownrshp* 2014
Sales 127.1MM[E] *EMP* 350
SIC 7375 2741 2711 2752 Data base information retrieval; Miscellaneous publishing; Newspapers; Commercial printing, offset
CEO: Mark McEachen
**COO:* Scott J Pollei
**CFO:* Vicki J Duncomb
**Ofcr:* Kevin Nystrom
IT Man: Stephanie Thompsen

D-U-N-S 94-725-6236 IMP
DOLAN NORTHWEST LLC
SEATTLE LIGHTING FIXTURE
1919 Nw 19th Ave, Portland, OR 97209-1735
Tel (503) 221-1919 *Founded/Ownrshp* 1996
Sales 129.9MM[E] *EMP* 342
SIC 5063 5719 Lighting fixtures, commercial & industrial; Lighting fixtures, residential; Lighting fixtures
Sales Exec: Sherry Medhaug

D-U-N-S 08-385-7383
▲ **DOLBY LABORATORIES INC**
1275 Market St, San Francisco, CA 94103-1410
Tel (415) 558-0200 *Founded/Ownrshp* 1965
Sales 1.0MMM *EMP* 1,867[E]
Tkr Sym DLB *Exch* NYS
SIC 3663 6794 Radio broadcasting & communications equipment; Patent buying, licensing, leasing
Pr: Kevin Yeaman
**Ch Bd:* Peter Gotcher
CFO: Lewis Chew
Chf Mktg O: Robert Borchers
Ex VP: Michael J Rockwell
Ex VP: Andy Sherman
Sr VP: Giles Baker
Sr VP: Michael Bergeron
Sr VP: John Couling
Sr VP: Doug Darrow
Sr VP: Steven E Forshay
Sr VP: Craig Todd
Sr VP: David Watts
VP: Mary Anderson
VP: Michael Archer
VP: Carlo Basile

VP: Richard Bell
VP: Jennifer Bowcock
VP: Shawn Ellis
VP: Ariel Fischer
VP: J Stuart Mitchell

DOLCE HOTELS & RESORTS
See DOLCE INTERNATIONAL HOLDINGS INC

DOLCE HOTELS AND RESORTS
See DOLCE INTERNATIONAL HOSPITALITY LLC

D-U-N-S 05-869-3433
■ DOLCE INTERNATIONAL HOLDINGS INC
DOLCE HOTELS & RESORTS
(*Suby of* DOLCE HOTELS AND RESORTS) ★
22 Sylvan Way, Parsippany, NJ 07054-3801
Tel (201) 307-8700 *Founded/Ownrshp* 2015
Sales 125.9MM^E^ *EMP* 4,000
SIC 7011 8741 Resort hotel; Hotel or motel management
Pr: Steven A Rudnitsky
**CFO:* Debra Bates
Ofcr: Barry Goldstein
IT Man: Karin Reynolds
Sls Dir: Mike Tidwell
Sls Mgr: Danny Dolce
Board of Directors: Jeff Barone, John Foster, Phillip Maritz

D-U-N-S 96-952-2387
■ DOLCE INTERNATIONAL HOSPITALITY LLC
DOLCE HOTELS AND RESORTS
(*Suby of* KNIGHTS INN) ★
22 Sylvan Way, Parsippany, NJ 07054-3801
Tel (201) 307-8700 *Founded/Ownrshp* 2007
Sales 125.9MM^E^ *EMP* 4,010
SIC 7011 Hotels
Pr: Steven A Rudnitsky
**COO:* Richard Maxfield
**CFO:* Debra Bates
**Sr VP:* John Betancourt

D-U-N-S 12-276-2771
DOLCE SALON & SPA LLC
7898 E Acoma Dr Ste 108, Scottsdale, AZ 85260-3480
Tel (602) 515-0420 *Founded/Ownrshp* 2000
Sales 99.5MM^E^ *EMP* 350^E^
SIC 5087 Beauty salon & barber shop equipment & supplies

D-U-N-S 00-896-5428 IMP/EXP
DOLE FOOD CO INC
(*Suby of* DFC HOLDINGS LLC) ★
1 Dole Dr, Westlake Village, CA 91362-7300
Tel (818) 874-4000 *Founded/Ownrshp* 2013
Sales 1.1MMM^E^ *EMP* 1,534^E^
SIC 0179 0174 0175 0161 5148 2033 Pineapple farm; Banana grove; Citrus fruits; Deciduous tree fruits; Lettuce farm; Celery farm; Cauliflower farm; Broccoli farm; Fruits; Vegetables; Fruit juices: fresh; Fruit juices: packaged in cans, jars, etc.
Ch Bd: David H Murdock
**Pr:* Johan Linden
**CFO:* Johan Malmqvist
**Sr VP:* Yoon J Hugh
**Sr VP:* Charlene Mims
VP: Leigh Billingsley
**VP:* Ron Bouchard
**VP:* Jay Esban
**VP:* Jared Gale
VP: Javier Idrovo
VP: Glenn Wells
VP: Dan Winans
VP: Terry Young

D-U-N-S 06-610-9869 IMP
DOLE FRESH FRUIT CO
(*Suby of* DOLE FOOD CO INC) ★
1 Dole Dr, Westlake Village, CA 91362-7300
Tel (818) 874-4000 *Founded/Ownrshp* 1995
Sales 948.8MM^E^ *EMP* 1,234
SIC 5148 Fruits, fresh; Banana ripening
Pr: Johan Linden
Pr: John Trummel
**Treas:* Johan L Malmqvist
VP: Ronald D Bouchard
VP: David Bright
VP: Todd Camel
VP: Brad Cantwell
VP: Jared Gale
VP: Pay Jaeger
VP: Barry Jung
VP: Charlene Mims
VP: Cynthia Nunes

D-U-N-S 61-905-4208 EXP
DOLE FRESH VEGETABLES INC
(*Suby of* DOLE FOOD CO INC) ★
2959 Salinas Hwy, Monterey, CA 93940-6400
Tel (831) 422-8871 *Founded/Ownrshp* 1983
Sales 122.6MM^E^ *EMP* 300
SIC 2099 0723 Food preparations; Fruit (fresh) packing services
CEO: Howard Roeder
**Pr:* David H Murdock
**Pr:* Ray Riggi
**Ex VP:* Roger Billingsly
Sr VP: Tim Stejskal
VP: Dawn Valenta
QA Dir: Ashley Anderson
QA Dir: Nita Corbett
Sfty Mgr: Griselda Lopez
VP Mktg: Julie Poduch
Mktg Dir: David Austin

D-U-N-S 78-877-2064
DOLE HOLDING CO LLC
(*Suby of* DHM HOLDING CO INC) ★
1 Dole Dr, Westlake Village, CA 91362-7300
Tel (818) 879-6600 *Founded/Ownrshp* 2004
Sales 57.6MM *EMP* 74,999
SIC 0179 0174 0175 0161 5148 2033 Pineapple farm; Banana grove; Citrus fruits; Deciduous tree fruits; Lettuce farm; Celery farm; Cauliflower farm; Broccoli farm; Fruits; Vegetables; Fruit juices: fresh; Fruit juices: packaged in cans, jars, etc.
Ch Bd: David H Murdock

D-U-N-S 04-651-5557 IMP/EXP
DOLE PACKAGED FOODS LLC
GLACIER FOODS DIVISION
(*Suby of* ITOCHU CORPORATION)
3059 Townsgate Rd, Westlake Village, CA 91361-5861
Tel (805) 601-5500 *Founded/Ownrshp* 2013
Sales 246.8MM^E^ *EMP* 800
SIC 2037 Fruits, quick frozen & cold pack (frozen); Vegetables, quick frozen & cold pack, excl. potato products
Treas: Dorothy Johnston
VP: Robert Barnhouse
VP: Hany Farag
VP: Jennifer Grossman
**VP:* Jon Rodacy
VP: Denise Rohm
Exec: Nancy Mackey
Genl Mgr: Gerald Widick
CIO: Jonathon Moldenhauer
Dir IT: Joe Valdez

D-U-N-S 00-718-9202 IMP
DOLESE BROS CO
20 Nw 13th St, Oklahoma City, OK 73103-4806
Tel (405) 235-2311 *Founded/Ownrshp* 1907
Sales 8.5MM *EMP* 1,100
Accts Cole & Reed Pc Oklahoma City
SIC 3273 1422 1442 Ready-mixed concrete; Crushed & broken limestone; Construction sand mining
Pr: Mark Helm
IT Man: Angie Wall
Sfty Dirs: Jimmy Hatch
Opers Mgr: Kevin Mueggenborg
Plnt Mgr: Jim Knowles

D-U-N-S 09-062-0725
DOLEX DOLLAR EXPRESS INC
700 Highlander Blvd # 450, Arlington, TX 76015-4329
Tel (817) 548-4700 *Founded/Ownrshp* 2010
Sales NA *EMP* 3,300
SIC 6099 Check clearing services
Pr: Mario Trujillo
**Pr:* Raul Limon
**COO:* Laybaa Hernandez
**CFO:* Patrick Bates
**Treas:* James Kelly
**Ex VP:* Eduardo Villalobos
**Sr VP:* Joseph Venezia

D-U-N-S 06-833-1990 IMP
■ DOLGENCORP LLC
DOLLAR GENERAL
(*Suby of* DOLLAR GENERAL CORP) ★
100 Mission Rdg, Goodlettsville, TN 37072-2171
Tel (615) 855-4000 *Founded/Ownrshp* 1973
Sales 8.7MMM^E^ *EMP* 71,500
SIC 5331 Variety stores
Pr: Don Shaffer
**Pr:* David L Bere
**CFO:* David Tehle
**Treas:* Wade Smith
**VP:* Anita C Elliott

D-U-N-S 78-330-8240 IMP
■ DOLGENCORP OF TEXAS INC
DOLLAR GENERAL
(*Suby of* DOLLAR GENERAL) ★
100 Mission Rdg, Goodlettsville, TN 37072-2171
Tel (615) 855-4000 *Founded/Ownrshp* 2007
Sales 330.2MM^E^ *EMP* 5,379
SIC 5331 Variety stores
Ch Bd: David Perdue
**CEO:* Steven R Deckard
**CFO:* David Tehle
**VP:* Larry P Gatta
**VP:* James P Smits

D-U-N-S 00-791-5580
DOLLAR BANK FEDERAL SAVINGS BANK (PA)
401 Liberty Ave, Pittsburgh, PA 15222-1000
Tel (412) 261-4900 *Founded/Ownrshp* 1855
Sales NA *EMP* 1,200
SIC 6035 7359 Federal savings banks; Equipment rental & leasing
CEO: Robert Oeler
**CFO:* Thomas A Kobus
Ex VP: Wayne Mannella
**Ex VP:* Jeffrey Morrow
**Sr VP:* John F Shelley III
VP: Donna Beacom
**VP:* James F Carroll Jr
VP: Wayne Gillam
VP: Jeffery Heald
VP: Brian D Tucker
VP: Alfred Williams

D-U-N-S 19-460-7883
DOLLAR BANK LEASING CORP
(*Suby of* DOLLAR BANK FEDERAL SAVINGS BANK) ★
401 Liberty Ave Lobby, Pittsburgh, PA 15222-1000
Tel (412) 261-4900 *Founded/Ownrshp* 1982
Sales NA *EMP* 15
SIC 6035 7359 Federal savings banks; Equipment rental & leasing
Pr: James Wheeler
**Pr:* Robert Oeler
**Treas:* Tom Kobus
**VP:* Robert Dentino
**Prin:* Ralph J Horne
**Prin:* Thomas A Kobus

DOLLAR FINANCIAL
See DFG WORLD INC

D-U-N-S 13-921-2609
DOLLAR FINANCIAL GROUP INC
(*Suby of* DFC GLOBAL CORP) ★
74 E Swedesford Rd, Malvern, PA 19355-1488
Tel (610) 296-3400 *Founded/Ownrshp* 1990
Sales NA *EMP* 4,226
SIC 6099 8721 Check clearing services; Accounting, auditing & bookkeeping
Pr: Jeffrey A Weiss
**CFO:* Randy Underwood
Treas: Evan Guengerich
**Treas:* Peter J Sokolowski
VP: Bill Athas
VP: Matt Pasch
VP: Patti Smith
VP: David Zarski
Dist Mgr: MAI Yang
Dir IT: Bruce Cummings
IT Man: Anant Kumar

DOLLAR GENERAL
See DOLGENCORP LLC

DOLLAR GENERAL
See DOLGENCORP OF TEXAS INC

D-U-N-S 00-694-6172 IMP
▲ DOLLAR GENERAL CORP (TN)
100 Mission Rdg, Goodlettsville, TN 37072-2171
Tel (615) 855-4000 *Founded/Ownrshp* 1955
Sales 20.3MMM *EMP* 113,400
Accts Ernst & Young Llp Nashville
Tkr Sym DG *Exch* NYS
SIC 5331 Variety stores
CEO: Todd J Vasos
**Ch Bd:* Michael M Calbert
CFO: John W Garratt
Ex VP: John W Flanigan
Ex VP: Jeffery C Owen
Ex VP: Robert D Ravener
Ex VP: Rhonda M Taylor
Ex VP: David Tehle
Ex VP: James W Thorpe
VP: Bruce Ash
VP: John Cosma
VP: Cris Debord
VP: Mike Dysinger
VP: John Flanigan
VP: Brian Hartshorn
VP: Adam Janastch
VP: Susan S Lanigan
VP: Jeff Owen
VP: Jerry Reinhardt
VP: Gary Stephens
VP: Tony Zuazo
Board of Directors: Warren F Bryant, Sandra B Cochran, Patricia D Fili-Krushel, Paula A Price, William C Rhodes III, David B Rickard

D-U-N-S 13-243-5442
DOLLAR PHONE CORP
(*Suby of* GLOBAL SWITCHING INC) ★
34 Franklin Ave Ste 220, Brooklyn, NY 11205-1221
Tel (718) 889-1100 *Founded/Ownrshp* 1999
Sales 122.2MM *EMP* 47
Accts Saul N Friedman & Company Br
SIC 4813 Telephone communications broker
Ch Bd: Moses Greenfield
Pr: AVI Horowitz
Pr: AVI Klinger
**CFO:* Rachel Klein
Sr VP: Abish Landau
**VP:* Abraham Greenfield
Creative D: Michael Bajraktari
**Dir IT:* Jennifer Delcielo
Sls Mgr: Alex Gomez

D-U-N-S 18-797-1411 EXP
■ DOLLAR RENT A CAR INC
(*Suby of* DOLLAR THRIFTY AUTOMOTIVE GROUP INC) ★
5330 E 31st St Ste 100, Tulsa, OK 74135-5023
Tel (918) 669-3000 *Founded/Ownrshp* 1990
Sales 98.0MM^E^ *EMP* 2,500
SIC 7514 Rent-a-car service
Pr: Gary L Paxton
**CFO:* H Clifford Buster
CFO: Robert Drvostep
CFO: Sidney Harris
**Treas:* Michael H McMahon
Treas: Pamela S Peck
Sr Ex VP: Scott Anderson
Ex VP: Clair Lloyd
**Ex VP:* David W Sparkman
Sr VP: Charlie Coniglio
**VP:* R Scott Anderson
VP: Richard Halbrook
VP: Kimberly D Paul
VP: Shannon Ryan
**VP:* Vicki J Vaniman
Exec: John Potter

D-U-N-S 61-123-9542
■ DOLLAR THRIFTY AUTOMOTIVE GROUP INC
(*Suby of* HERC HOLDINGS INC) ★
5330 E 31st St, Tulsa, OK 74135-5076
Tel (918) 660-7700 *Founded/Ownrshp* 2012
Sales 1.8MMM^E^ *EMP* 4,600
SIC 6794 7514 Franchises, selling or licensing; Rent-a-car service
Ex VP: Rick L Morris
CFO: Steven B Hildebrand
Bd of Dir: Anthony Rhodes
Ofcr: Donald M Hielfarb
Sr Ex VP: Scott Thompson
Ex VP: Jim Duffy
Ex VP: G L Paxton
Ex VP: Dan Regan
Ex VP: Lloyd Stclair
Ex VP: Vicki J Vaniman
Ex VP: Vicki Vaniman
Sr VP: Jeff Cerefice
VP: Jim Bowen
VP: Brian Carpenter
VP: Charlie Coniglio
VP: Lou Desotel
VP: Steve Hoy
VP: Tim Oldfield
VP: James R Ryan
VP: Robert Smith
VP: Peter Sokolowski

D-U-N-S 96-061-8171
■ DOLLAR TREE DISTRIBUTION INC
(*Suby of* DOLLAR TREE INC) ★
500 Volvo Pkwy, Chesapeake, VA 23320-1604
Tel (757) 321-5000 *Founded/Ownrshp* 1994
Sales 96.8MM^E^ *EMP* 600
SIC 4225 General warehousing & storage
Ch Bd: J Douglas Perry
**Pr:* Macon F Brock Jr
**Pr:* Stephen White
**COO:* Bob Sasser
**CFO:* H Ray Compton
**Sr VP:* Frederick C Coble
**VP:* K Bryan Bagwell
**VP:* Kathleen Mallas
**VP:* Kevin Wampler
Genl Mgr: Sam Hammond

D-U-N-S 18-895-5553 IMP
▲ DOLLAR TREE INC
500 Volvo Pkwy, Chesapeake, VA 23320-1604
Tel (757) 321-5000 *Founded/Ownrshp* 1986
Sales 15.5MMM *EMP* 167,800^E^
Accts Kpmg Llp Norfolk Virginia
Tkr Sym DLTR *Exch* NGS
SIC 5331 Variety stores
Ch Bd: Macon F Brock Jr
CEO: Bob Sasser
COO: Michael A Witynski
CFO: Kevin S Wampler
Ofcr: David Jacobs
Ofcr: Michael Matacunas
Ofcr: Gary A Maxwell
Ofcr: William A Old Jr
Ofcr: Robert H Rudman
CIO: Joshua Jewett

DOLLAR TREE MDSG CHESAPEAKE CI
See GREENBRIER INTERNATIONAL INC

D-U-N-S 82-893-9640 IMP/EXP
■ DOLLAR TREE STORES INC
(*Suby of* DOLLAR TREE INC) ★
500 Volvo Pkwy, Chesapeake, VA 23320-1604
Tel (757) 321-5000 *Founded/Ownrshp* 1986
Sales 2.8MMM^E^ *EMP* 20,000
SIC 5331 Variety stores
Pr: Gary Philbin
CFO: Frederick Coble
**CFO:* Kevin Wampler
Ex VP: Ray H Compton
Sr VP: Thomas Bowyer
Sr VP: David E Hnsly
Sr VP: Arvil Priode
Sr VP: Mike Witynski
**VP:* Roger Dean
VP: David Jewell
**VP:* Deborah E Miller
VP: Robert G Urnee
VP: Bruce Walters
Dir Risk M: Nancy Norman-Powell

D-U-N-S 60-737-6477
DOLMAR GMBH (INC)
1005 Alderman Dr Ste 106, Alpharetta, GA 30005-3825
Tel (770) 569-4945 *Founded/Ownrshp* 2006
Sales 165.0MM *EMP* 4
SIC 5072 Power tools & accessories
Pr: Tray Brown

D-U-N-S 05-017-4291
DOLSEN COMPANIES
DOLSEN LEASING COMPANY
301 N 3rd St, Yakima, WA 98901-2340
Tel (509) 248-2831 *Founded/Ownrshp* 1958
Sales 750.7MM^E^ *EMP* 200
SIC 0241 0211 2086 7359

DOLSEN LEASING COMPANY
See DOLSEN COMPANIES

D-U-N-S 04-740-0601
DOME CONSTRUCTION CORP
393 E Grand Ave, South San Francisco, CA 94080-6233
Tel (650) 416-5600 *Founded/Ownrshp* 1969
Sales 251.0MM *EMP* 180
SIC 1542 1541

D-U-N-S 12-255-4868 IMP
DOME CORP
JOHNS HOPKINS REAL ESTATE
(*Suby of* JOHNS HOPKINS UNIVERSITY) ★
1101 E 33rd St Ste E100, Baltimore, MD 21218-3637
Tel (443) 997-3737 *Founded/Ownrshp* 1984
Sales 74.2MM *EMP* 1,800
Accts Kpmg Llp Baltimore Md
SIC 8741 Management services
Pr: Brian Dembeck
IT Man: Lonnell Brooks

D-U-N-S 01-686-2336
DOMESTIC LINEN SUPPLY AND LAUNDRY CO
DOMESTIC UNIFORM RENTAL
30555 Northwestern Hwy, Farmington Hills, MI 48334-3160
Tel (248) 737-2000 *Founded/Ownrshp* 1926
Sales 34.5MM^E^ *EMP* 1,000
SIC 7213 Uniform supply; Linen supply, non-clothing
Pr: Bruce L Colton
**CFO:* George Collet
**Treas:* Leonard H Colton
VP: Richard Dix
**VP Admn:* Michael Defortuna
Genl Mgr: Steven Campbell
Genl Mgr: Mark Colton
Sales Exec: Evan Lacross
Sales Exec: Dennis Soloway
VP Mktg: Evan Colton
Mktg Dir: Christine Sarver

DOMESTIC UNIFORM RENTAL
See DOMESTIC LINEN SUPPLY AND LAUNDRY CO

D-U-N-S 04-107-6981 IMP/EXP
DOMETIC CORP
DOMETIC GROUP
(*Suby of* DOMETIC GROUP AB (PUBL))
13551 Triton Park Blvd # 1000, Louisville, KY 40223-4196
Tel (502) 873-3524 *Founded/Ownrshp* 2005
Sales 459.0MM *EMP* 1,050^E^

SIC 3089 3443 3444 3822 3823 3999 Plastic boats & other marine equipment; Heat exchangers, condensers & components; Sheet metalwork; Auto controls regulating residntl & coml environmt & applncs; Industrial instrmnts msrmnt display/control process variable; Combs, except hard rubber
CEO: Roger Johannson
**Pr:* Frank Marciano
**Treas:* Steve McElwain
VP: Mark Minatel

D-U-N-S 83-052-0065 IMP/EXP
DOMETIC CORP
(*Suby of* DOMETIC HOLDING AB)
2320 Industrial Pkwy, Elkhart, IN 46516-5407
Tel (574) 294-2511 *Founded/Ownrshp* 2005
Sales 394.3MM^E *EMP* 1,000^E
SIC 5561 Camper & travel trailer dealers
Pr: Frank Marciano
CFO: Beth Martin
VP: Dave Schutz
Sfty Mgr: Tom Christophel
Manager: Ned Green
Sls Mgr: Joe Costa
Sls Mgr: Tiffany McLaughlin
Sales Asso: Jennifer Peck

DOMETIC GROUP
See DOMETIC CORP

D-U-N-S 06-958-0199
DOMINICAN HEALTH SERVICES
5633 N Lidgerwood St, Spokane, WA 99208-1224
Tel (509) 482-0111 *Founded/Ownrshp* 1988
Sales NA *EMP* 1,300
SIC 8062

D-U-N-S 11-780-9314
DOMINICAN HOSPITAL
SANTA CRUZ SPORTS MEDICINE CEN
1555 Soquel Dr, Santa Cruz, CA 95065-1794
Tel (831) 462-7700 *Founded/Ownrshp* 2000
Sales 418.1MM *EMP* 6
SIC 8062 General medical & surgical hospitals
COO: Roger Hite
Dir Lab: Steve McCarthy
Mtls Dir: Jevon Todd
Plnt Mgr: Kevin Keith
Pathlgst: Paula Quinn
Ansthlgy: John C Glina
Ansthlgy: Linda L Leum
Ansthlgy: Mark L Rigler
Dir Health: Vicki Carlisle

D-U-N-S 06-439-0230
DOMINICAN UNIVERSITY
ROSARY COLLEGE
7900 Division St, River Forest, IL 60305-1066
Tel (708) 366-2490 *Founded/Ownrshp* 1901
Sales 98.3MM *EMP* 500
Accts Plante & Moran Pllc Portage
SIC 8221 College, except junior
Pr: Donna Carroll
Ofcr: Melanie Dykstra
Sr VP: Amy McCormack
VP: Pamela A Johnson
VP: Cheryl Odim
Assoc Dir: Darren Robards
CIO: Jill A Hill
IT Man: Haley Smith
Psych: Jason Bonick

D-U-N-S 07-466-4855
DOMINICAN UNIVERSITY OF CALIFORNIA (CA)
50 Acacia Ave, San Rafael, CA 94901-2298
Tel (415) 457-4440 *Founded/Ownrshp* 1890
Sales 94.0MM *EMP* 300
Accts Grant Thornton Llp San Franci
SIC 8221 College, except junior
Pr: Mary B Marcy
**Pr:* Joseph Fink
**Ch:* Andrew P Barowsky
Ofcr: Xiomara Garcia
**VP:* Michele Hinken
**VP:* Peter Johnson
**VP:* Kathy Krueger Park
**VP:* Nicola Pitchford
Assoc Dir: David Albee
Assoc Dir: Michael Henkes
Ex Dir: Gary Gorka

D-U-N-S 00-798-2465
DOMINICKS FINER FOODS INC
711 Jorie Blvd Ms-4000, Oak Brook, IL 60523-4425
Tel (630) 891-5000 *Founded/Ownrshp* 1998
Sales NA *EMP* 18,000
SIC 5411

D-U-N-S 92-983-6153
DOMINICKS FINER FOODS LLC
(*Suby of* SAFEWAY INC) ★
150 E Pierce Rd Ste 400, Itasca, IL 60143-1231
Tel (630) 990-2880 *Founded/Ownrshp* 1995
Sales 71.8MM^E *EMP* 18,000
SIC 5411 Supermarkets, chain
Exec: Mike McCue
Pharmcst: Magdalene Ladas

DOMINION
See VIRGINIA ELECTRIC AND POWER CO

D-U-N-S 14-986-1437
■ **DOMINION CAPITAL INC**
(*Suby of* DOMINION RESOURCES INC) ★
120 Tredegar St, Richmond, VA 23219-4306
Tel (804) 819-2000 *Founded/Ownrshp* 1985
Sales 204.7MM^E *EMP* 1,700
Accts Deloitte & Touche Llp
SIC 4911 Generation, electric power
Prin: Thomas N Chewning
**Pr:* Charlie Coudriet
**Sr VP:* Bill Mistr
**VP:* Mark Mikuta

D-U-N-S 08-046-8744
■ **DOMINION COVE POINT INC** (VA)
(*Suby of* DOMINION RESOURCES INC) ★
120 Tredegar St, Richmond, VA 23219-4306
Tel (804) 819-2000 *Founded/Ownrshp* 2002
Sales 369.6MM^E *EMP* 115^E
SIC 4911 4923 1311 Generation, electric power; Transmission, electric power; Distribution, electric power; Gas transmission & distribution; Natural gas production
Pr: Thomas F Farrell II

DOMINION DIAGNOSTICS
See DDH INC

DOMINION DX1
See DOMINION ENTERPRISES

DOMINION EAST OHIO
See EAST OHIO GAS CO

D-U-N-S 00-895-5221
DOMINION ELECTRIC SUPPLY CO INC
5053 Lee Hwy, Arlington, VA 22207-2513
Tel (703) 532-0741 *Founded/Ownrshp* 1940
Sales 349.7MM^E *EMP* 245
SIC 5063 5719 Electrical supplies; Lighting fixtures; Lighting, lamps & accessories
Ch: Richard S Sharlin
**Pr:* Stephen Krooth
**CEO:* Richard A Williams
COO: Richard A Willims
CFO: Grace Kwong
Ex VP: James Pishner
**Ex VP:* Jim Pishner
**Ex VP:* Sam S Stotler
VP: Mike O'Donnell
VP: Mike Odonnell
**VP:* James J Pishner

D-U-N-S 19-657-9130
■ **DOMINION ENERGY INC**
(*Suby of* DOMINION RESOURCES INC) ★
120 Tredegar St, Richmond, VA 23219-4306
Tel (804) 819-2000 *Founded/Ownrshp* 1980
Sales 481.0MM^E *EMP* 3,995
SIC 4911

D-U-N-S 62-369-9436
DOMINION ENTERPRISES
DOMINION DX1
(*Suby of* LANDMARK MEDIA ENTERPRISES LLC) ★
150 Granby St Ste 150, Norfolk, VA 23510-1688
Tel (757) 351-7000 *Founded/Ownrshp* 2006
Sales 536.7MM^E *EMP* 3,100
SIC 7374 2721 2741 Data processing & preparation; Computer graphics service; Periodicals;
Pr: Jack J Ross
Pr: Anita Williams
**CEO:* Frank Batten Jr
COO: Judy Jewell
CFO: Teresa S Blevins
Ofcr: Erin Heischober
**Ex VP:* Teresa F Blevins
**Ex VP:* Guy Friddell III
Ex VP: Guy R Friddell III
Ex VP: Brock Maclean
VP: Amanda Ayala
VP: Paige Bouma
VP: Adam Dennis
VP: Harry Flaris
VP: Joe Fuller
VP: Bill Leek
VP: Susan Moll
VP: William Owens
**VP:* Colleen Pittman
VP: Grant Simmons
VP: Lori Stacy

D-U-N-S 07-499-2967
DOMINION EXPLORATION & PRODUCTION INC
1250 Poydras St Ste 2000, New Orleans, LA 70113-1821
Tel (504) 593-7000 *Founded/Ownrshp* 2000
Sales NA *EMP* 1,310^E
SIC 1382

D-U-N-S 82-871-5644
DOMINION HOLDING CORP
4900 Tuttle Crossing Blvd, Dublin, OH 43016-1532
Tel (614) 356-5000 *Founded/Ownrshp* 2008
Sales 91.8MM^E *EMP* 194
SIC 1521 Single-family housing construction
CEO: Douglas G Borror
Sr VP: Lori Steiner

D-U-N-S 84-207-4510
DOMINION HOMES INC
(*Suby of* DOMINION HOLDING CORP) ★
4900 Tuttle Crossing Blvd, Dublin, OH 43016-1532
Tel (614) 356-5000 *Founded/Ownrshp* 2008
Sales 91.8MM^E *EMP* 193
SIC 1521 Single-family housing construction
Ch Bd: Donn Borror
Pr: Jeffrey Croft
COO: Holly Fasone
CFO: William G Cornely
Ex VP: David S Borror
Sr VP: Lori M Steiner
VP: Eric S Allion
VP: Allison Eric
Ex Dir: Tom Hart
Ql Cn Mgr: Dave Casey
Sales Exec: Mike Archer

D-U-N-S 07-939-6632
■ **DOMINION MIDSTREAM PARTNERS LP**
(*Suby of* DOMINION MLP HOLDING CO LLC) ★
120 Tredegar St, Richmond, VA 23219-4306
Tel (804) 819-2000 *Founded/Ownrshp* 2014
Sales 369.6MM *EMP* 115^E
Tkr Sym DM *Exch* NYS
SIC 4925 4922 Gas production and/or distribution; Liquefied petroleum gas, distribution through mains; Pipelines, natural gas
Genl Pt: Dominion Midstream GP
Ch Bd: Thomas F Farrell II
CFO: Mark F McGettrick

D-U-N-S 08-046-8953
■ **DOMINION MLP HOLDING CO LLC**
(*Suby of* DOMINION COVE POINT INC) ★
120 Tredegar St, Richmond, VA 23219-4306
Tel (804) 819-2000 *Founded/Ownrshp* 2014
Sales 369.6MM^E *EMP* 115^E
SIC 4911 4923 1311 Generation, electric power; Transmission, electric power; Distribution, electric power; Gas transmission & distribution; Natural gas production
Pr: Thomas F Farrell II

D-U-N-S 01-561-4543 IMP
■ **DOMINION NUCLEAR CONNECTICUT INC**
MILLSTONE POWER STATION
(*Suby of* DOMINION RESOURCES INC) ★
120 Tredegar St, Richmond, VA 23219-4306
Tel (866) 366-4357 *Founded/Ownrshp* 2000
Sales 198.6MM^E *EMP* 1,650
SIC 4931 Electric & other services combined
CEO: Thomas F Farrell II
**Pr:* David A Heacock
**Ex VP:* David A Christian
**Ex VP:* Mark F McGettrick
**Sr VP:* Mary C Doswell
**Sr VP:* G Scott Hetzer
**VP:* William Matthews
**VP:* Alan Price

D-U-N-S 10-171-5035 IMP
▲ **DOMINION RESOURCES INC**
120 Tredegar St, Richmond, VA 23219-4306
Tel (804) 819-2000 *Founded/Ownrshp* 1983
Sales 11.6MMM *EMP* 24,300
Tkr Sym D *Exch* NYS
SIC 4911 4923 1311 Generation, electric power; Transmission, electric power; Distribution, electric power; Gas transmission & distribution; Natural gas production
Pr: Thomas F Farrell II
CFO: Mark F McGettrick
Treas: G Scott Hetzer
Ex VP: Eva Teig Hardy
Sr VP: Robert M Blue
Sr VP: Anne E Bomar
Sr VP: Katheryn B Curtis
Sr VP: Scot C Hathaway
Sr VP: Mark O Webb
VP: Michele L Cardiff
Snr Mgr: Diane Simon

D-U-N-S 13-589-6798
■ **DOMINION RESOURCES SERVICES INC**
(*Suby of* DOMINION RESOURCES INC) ★
120 Tredegar St, Richmond, VA 23219-4306
Tel (804) 775-2500 *Founded/Ownrshp* 1999
Sales 2.0MMM^E *EMP* 17,000
Accts Ernst & Young Us Llp Salt Lak
SIC 4911 Generation, electric power
Ch Bd: Thomas E Capps
Pr: Rogers Steven A
CEO: Mary C Doswell
CEO: Thomas F Farrell II
CFO: Thomas N Chewning
Chf Cred: Sarah Cosby
Ex VP: Gary Sypolt
Sr VP: David A Christian
Sr VP: Margaret McDermin
Sr VP: Wohlfarth Thomas P
VP: Jim Eck
VP: April Fisher
VP: Baine Edward H
VP: James Martin
VP: Carter Reid
VP: Sharonda Shepard
VP: Patricia A Wilkerson
Dir Bus: Jeffrey Keister

D-U-N-S 11-602-5180
■ **DOMINION TRANSMISSION INC**
(*Suby of* DOMINION RESOURCES INC) ★
120 Tredegar St, Richmond, VA 23219-4306
Tel (804) 771-4795 *Founded/Ownrshp* 2000
Sales 155.8MM^E *EMP* 1,294
SIC 4922 4923 Pipelines, natural gas; Storage, natural gas; Gas transmission & distribution
CEO: Thomas F Farrell II
VP: Georgia Carter

D-U-N-S 10-903-9925
DOMINO FOOD AND FUEL INC
(*Suby of* ELMER SMITH OIL CO) ★
Hwy 183 S, Clinton, OK 73601
Tel (580) 323-0341 *Founded/Ownrshp* 1984
Sales 92.2MM *EMP* 150
Accts Smith Carney & Co Pc Okl
SIC 5411 Convenience stores
CEO: Elmer Smith
**Pr:* Martin Smith
**Sec:* James A Harris
**VP:* Amy Smith

D-U-N-S 19-930-9118
DOMINO FOODS INC
DOMINO SUGAR
99 Wood Ave S Ste 901, Iselin, NJ 08830-2733
Tel (732) 590-1173 *Founded/Ownrshp* 2001
Sales 125.6MM^E *EMP* 122^E
SIC 5149 Sugar, refined; Specialty food items
CEO: Brian O' Malley
Natl Sales: John Damiano
Mktg Dir: Tom Gould
Sls Mgr: David Poust

DOMINO SUGAR
See AMERICAN SUGAR REFINING INC

DOMINO SUGAR
See DOMINO FOODS INC

DOMINO'S
See RPM PIZZA LLC

DOMINO'S PIZZA
See TEAM WASHINGTON INC

D-U-N-S 10-917-7576 IMP/EXP
▲ **DOMINOS PIZZA INC**
30 Frank Lloyd Wright Dr, Ann Arbor, MI 48105-9757
Tel (734) 930-3030 *Founded/Ownrshp* 1960
Sales 2.2MMM *EMP* 11,900
Tkr Sym DPZ *Exch* NYS
SIC 5812 5149 6794 Pizzeria, chain; Pizza supplies; Franchises, selling or licensing
Pr: J Patrick Doyle
**Ch Bd:* David A Brandon
Pr: Richard E Allison
Pr: Russell J Weiner
CFO: Jeffrey D Lawrence
Ex VP: Eric B Anderson
Ex VP: Troy A Ellis
Ex VP: Stanley J Gage
Ex VP: Scott R Hinshaw
Ex VP: Kenneth B Rollin
Ex VP: James G Stansik
Ex VP: J Kevin Vasconi
Ex VP: Judith L Werthauser
Board of Directors: C Andrew Ballard, Andrew B Balson, Diana F Cantor, Richard L Federico, James A Goldman, Gregory A Trojan

D-U-N-S 01-746-0668 IMP
■ **DOMINOS PIZZA LLC**
(*Suby of* DOMINOS PIZZA INC) ★
30 Frank Lloyd Wright Dr, Ann Arbor, MI 48105-9757
Tel (734) 930-3030 *Founded/Ownrshp* 1998
Sales 514.0MM^E *EMP* 10,000
Accts Pricewaterhousecooopers Llp D
SIC 5812 6794 5046 5149 8741 2045 Pizzeria, chain; Franchises, selling or licensing; Restaurant equipment & supplies; Pizza supplies; Management services; Prepared flour mixes & doughs
CFO: David Mounts
Chf Mktg O: Russell J Weiner
Ex VP: Michael Lawton
VP: Marci Smith
VP: Brandon Solano
Brnch Mgr: Christine Jones
Genl Mgr: Bob Calder
Genl Mgr: Brent Gutierrez
Genl Mgr: Conrad Vessey
Snr Ntwrk: Jason McCracken
QA Dir: Bill Holmberg
Board of Directors: Dennis F Hightower, Robert Ruggiero

D-U-N-S 11-441-5925 IMP
DOMTAR AW LLC
(*Suby of* DOMTAR INC)
285 Highway 71 S, Ashdown, AR 71822-8356
Tel (870) 898-2711 *Founded/Ownrshp* 2001
Sales 228.8MM^E *EMP* 1,125
SIC 2611 Pulp mills

DOMTAR EDDY SPECIALTY PAPERS
See E B EDDY PAPER INC

D-U-N-S 11-472-6214 EXP
DOMTAR INDUSTRIES LLC
(*Suby of* DOMTAR INC)
100 Kingsley Park Dr, Fort Mill, SC 29715-6476
Tel (803) 802-7500 *Founded/Ownrshp* 1965
Sales 433.4MM^E *EMP* 2,700
SIC 2621 5111 Printing paper; Printing & writing paper
Pr: John D Williams
**VP:* Roger Brear

D-U-N-S 78-924-5110 IMP/EXP
DOMTAR PAPER CO LLC
(*Suby of* DOMTAR CORPORATION)
100 Kingsley Park Dr, Fort Mill, SC 29715-6476
Tel (803) 802-7500 *Founded/Ownrshp* 2006
Sales 324.5MM^E *EMP* 656
SIC 2421 2621 Sawmills & planing mills, general; Paper mills
Pr: John D Williams
**CFO:* Daniel Buron
**Sr VP:* Melissa Anderson
**Sr VP:* Michael Fagan
**Sr VP:* Zygmunt Jablonski
IT Man: Chelsie Norton
Sls Mgr: Tim Spencer

D-U-N-S 09-220-5202
DON CHAPIN CO INC
TOM SEPTIC CONSTRUCTION
560 Crazy Horse Canyon Rd, Salinas, CA 93907-8434
Tel (831) 449-4273 *Founded/Ownrshp* 1978
Sales 91.6MM^E *EMP* 200
SIC 1623 1611 1771 Sewer line construction; Surfacing & paving; Concrete work
Pr: Donald Chapin Jr
VP: Caroline Chapin
**VP:* Sam Funk
IT Man: David Drueding
Sfty Dirs: Craig Norleen

D-U-N-S 15-052-6143
DON DAVIS AUTO GROUP INC
DON DAVIS DODGE CHRYSLER JEEP
1901 N Collins St, Arlington, TX 76011-4399
Tel (817) 461-1000 *Founded/Ownrshp* 1979
Sales 272.8MM^E *EMP* 865
SIC 5511 Automobiles, new & used
Pr: Robert B Howard
**CFO:* Jim Brown
**VP:* Lisa Howard Robertson

DON DAVIS DODGE CHRYSLER JEEP
See DON DAVIS AUTO GROUP INC

D-U-N-S 00-692-9814 IMP/EXP
DON EDWARD & CO (IL)
9801 Adam Don Pkwy, Woodridge, IL 60517-8136
Tel (708) 442-9400 *Founded/Ownrshp* 1921
Sales 753.1MM^E *EMP* 1,000
SIC 5021 5046 5087 5113 5169 Restaurant furniture; Restaurant equipment & supplies; Service establishment equipment; Disposable plates, cups, napkins & eating utensils; Napkins, paper; Towels, paper; Cups, disposable plastic & paper; Sanitation preparations; Specialty cleaning & sanitation preparations

Ch Bd: Robert E Don
**Pr:* Steven R Don
COO: Jim Jones
VP: Rick Wiley
Exec: Bob Lelingis
MIS Dir: Frank Yi
Sales Exec: Danny Lewis
Sales Exec: Donald Weaver
Mktg Mgr: Kris Laszczewski
Mktg Mgr: Larry Shrout
Manager: Bill Davis

D-U-N-S 00-643-3346 IMP/EXP
DON EVANS INC (WI)
EVCO PLASTICS
100 W North St, Deforest, WI 53532-1147
Tel (608) 846-6000 *Founded/Ownrshp* 1960
Sales 164.7MM^E *EMP* 395
SIC 3089 Injection molding of plastics; Plastic containers, except foam
Pr: Dale Evans
CFO: John Caruso
CFO: Paul Mueller
**Treas:* Chris Evans
**VP:* Steven Evans
Prd Mgr: Troy Frantzen
Ql Cn Mgr: Laura Gavins
Ql Cn Mgr: Jonathan Knoblett
Ql Cn Mgr: Tim Linzner
Mktg Mgr: Anna Bartz
Snr Mgr: Carrie Woltman

D-U-N-S 03-586-5096
DON FORD SANDERSON INC (AZ)
SANDERSON FORD
6400 N 51st Ave, Glendale, AZ 85301-4600
Tel (623) 842-8600 *Founded/Ownrshp* 1955
Sales 679.3MM *EMP* 416^E
SIC 5511 Automobiles, new & used; Pickups, new & used
Pr: David Kimmerle
**Ch Bd:* La Verne Sanderson
**Sec:* Stephen C Wendt
Exec: Leslie Sanches
**Prin:* Sandra Sue Kimmerle
IT Man: Mark Crites
VP Mktg: Bob McKinzey
Advt Dir: Max Sirstins
Sls Mgr: Tony Komadina
Sls Mgr: John Pratt
Sales Asso: Brad Bailey

D-U-N-S 10-886-8969
DON HENRY JR & SONS
BUILDING CLEANING CONTRACTORS
Rr Box 12a, Plainfield, NH 03781
Tel (603) 298-8551 *Founded/Ownrshp* 1980
Sales 1.0MM *EMP* 1,520
SIC 7349 Janitorial service, contract basis
Pt: Daniel Henry

DON LEE FARMS
See GOODMAN FOOD PRODUCTS INC

D-U-N-S 05-188-1290
DON MCGILL TOYOTA INC
11800 Katy Fwy I10, Houston, TX 77079-1299
Tel (281) 496-2000 *Founded/Ownrshp* 1970
Sales 99.0MM^E *EMP* 300
SIC 5511 5521 Automobiles, new & used; Pickups, new & used; Vans, new & used; Used car dealers
Pr: Donald R McGill
**Sec:* Kathryn McGill
Genl Mgr: Mike Mynagt
IT Man: Michael Binkley
Sales Exec: Ferol Morris
Sales Asso: Amos Alvarez
Sales Asso: Anthony Hoang

DON MIGUEL FOODS
See DON MIGUEL MEXICAN FOODS INC

D-U-N-S 00-834-1331 IMP
DON MIGUEL MEXICAN FOODS INC (CA)
DON MIGUEL FOODS
(*Suby of* MEGAMEX FOODS LLC) ★
333 S Anita Dr Ste 1000, Orange, CA 92868-3318
Tel (714) 385-4500 *Founded/Ownrshp* 1908, 2010
Sales 178.1MM^E *EMP* 600
SIC 2038 Frozen specialties
CEO: Jeff Frank
COO: Richard Swanson
CFO: Dori Reap
**VP:* Saralyn Brown
**CTO:* Terry Girch
**VP Mfg:* Donald Goglia
VP Opers: Mike Morales
Sls&Mrk Ex: Ryan Meitzler
**VP Mktg:* Mike Elliott

DON PABLO'S
See RITA RESTAURANT CORP

D-U-N-S 05-948-0228 IMP
DON QUIJOTE (USA) CO LTD
GOOD NEIGHBOR PHARMACY
(*Suby of* DON QUIJOTE HOLDINGS CO., LTD.)
801 Kaheka St, Honolulu, HI 96814-3798
Tel (808) 973-4800 *Founded/Ownrshp* 2006
Sales 124.6MM^E *EMP* 800^E
SIC 5411 5331 6512 5912 Supermarkets, independent; Variety stores; Shopping center, property operation only; Drug stores
Treas: Herbert Gushikuma
**Pr:* Takao Yasuda
**CFO:* Mitsuo Takahashi
**VP:* Koji Oohara
Board of Directors: Junji Narusawa

D-U-N-S 00-905-5336
DON RASMUSSEN CO
MERCEDES-BENZ OF WILSONVILLE
720 Ne Grand Ave, Portland, OR 97232-2744
Tel (503) 230-7700 *Founded/Ownrshp* 1950
Sales 183.8MM *EMP* 304
SIC 5511 Automobiles, new & used
Pr: Gregory S Rasmussen
**CFO:* Christopher T Foy
CFO: Michael Krautscheid

**VP:* Amy D Nieto
**VP:* Mikkel Nieto

DON-NAN MACHINE & MFG
See DON-NAN PUMP AND SUPPLY CO INC

D-U-N-S 02-684-0256 IMP/EXP
DON-NAN PUMP AND SUPPLY CO INC
DON-NAN MACHINE & MFG
3427 E Garden Cy Hwy 158, Midland, TX 79706
Tel (432) 682-7742 *Founded/Ownrshp* 1978
Sales 172.2MM^E *EMP* 146
SIC 1389 3599 3561 Oil field services; Custom machinery; Pumps & pumping equipment
Pr: Don V Carruth
**CFO:* Rick Burden
Exec: Katie Swezy
Store Mgr: Jeff Beal
Sfty Dirs: Jesse Rogers
Mktg Mgr: Jason Dominguez

D-U-N-S 04-864-1229 IMP
DONAGHY SALES INC
2363 S Cedar Ave, Fresno, CA 93725-1078
Tel (559) 486-0901 *Founded/Ownrshp* 1966
Sales 102.1MM^E *EMP* 150
SIC 5181 Beer & other fermented malt liquors
CEO: Edward Donaghy

D-U-N-S 07-526-2691
DONALD J FAGER & ASSOCIATES INC
2 Park Ave Fl 25, New York, NY 10016-9394
Tel (212) 576-9800 *Founded/Ownrshp* 1975
Sales NA *EMP* 475
SIC 6411 Insurance brokers
Pr: Donald Fager
VP: Bill Fellner
CTO: Susan Friedman
Dir IT: Hung Vu

D-U-N-S 03-495-0428
DONALD J LAUGHLIN
RIVERSIDE RESORT AND HOTEL
1650 S Casino Dr Pmb 500, Laughlin, NV 89029-1512
Tel (702) 298-2535 *Founded/Ownrshp* 1967
Sales 64.7MM^E *EMP* 2,010
SIC 7993 5812 Gambling machines, coin-operated; Eating places
Owner: Donald J Laughlin
Exec: Herve Allain
Sfty Mgr: Valerie Lopez
Opers Mgr: Dell Newman
Mktg Mgr: Diana Fuchs
Genl Couns: Herm Walker

D-U-N-S 00-647-7301
▲ DONALDSON CO INC
1400 W 94th St, Minneapolis, MN 55431-2370
Tel (952) 887-3131 *Founded/Ownrshp* 1915
Sales 2.2MMM *EMP* 12,500
Tkr Sym DCI *Exch* NYS
SIC 3599 3569 3714 3564 Air intake filters, internal combustion engine, except auto; Filters; Filter elements, fluid, hydraulic line; Filters, general line: industrial; Motor vehicle engines & parts; Mufflers (exhaust), motor vehicle; Exhaust systems & parts, motor vehicle; Dust or fume collecting equipment, industrial; Air cleaning systems
Pr: Tod E Carpenter
CFO: Scott J Robinson
Sr VP: Thomas R Scalf
Sr VP: Jeffrey E Spethmann
VP: Amy C Becker
VP: Franklin G Cardenas
VP: Timothy H Grafe
VP: Peggy Herrmann
VP: Dennis D Jandik
VP: Richard B Lewis
VP: Mary Lynne Perushek
VP: Sheila C Peyraud
VP: Jim Shaw
VP: Wim J Vermeersch
VP: Fred Wahlquist
VP: Jay Ward
Board of Directors: Andrew Cecere, Michael J Hoffman, Douglas A Milroy, Jeffrey Noddle, Willard D Oberton, James J Owens, Trudy A Rautio, John P Wiehoff

DONATO'S PIZZA
See DONATOS PIZZERIA LLC

D-U-N-S 10-769-9183
DONATOS PIZZERIA LLC
DONATO'S PIZZA
935 Taylor Station Rd, Columbus, OH 43230-6657
Tel (614) 864-2444 *Founded/Ownrshp* 1999
Sales 117.9MM^E *EMP* 2,200
SIC 5812 Pizzeria, chain
COO: Thomas Pendrey
VP: Craig Burt
Ex Dir: Carolyn Butler
Ex Dir: Tom Santor
Genl Mgr: Beth Keesling
MIS Dir: Jeff Davis
Site Mgr: Jason Marksberry
Secur Mgr: John Conway

D-U-N-S 78-718-5651 IMP/EXP
DONCASTERS INC
(*Suby of* DONCASTERS GROUP LIMITED)
36 Spring Ln, Farmington, CT 06032-3140
Tel (860) 677-1376 *Founded/Ownrshp* 2006
Sales 182.9MM^E *EMP* 500
SIC 3511 3356 3728 7699 Turbines & turbine generator sets; Turbines & turbine generator sets & parts; Titanium; Aircraft parts & equipment; Aircraft propellers & associated equipment; Aircraft & heavy equipment repair services
CEO: Tariq Jesrai
COO: Raymond Mitchell
Sr VP: William Traynor
VP: Tim Martin
Prgrm Mgr: Eric Lawson
QA Dir: Florin Alexandru
Dir IT: John Cyr
Dir IT: Jim Fiorentino
IT Man: Harry Jernigan

Sfty Mgr: Ben Siap
Opers Mgr: Alan Erickson

D-U-N-S 00-724-6747
DONDLINGER & SONS CONSTRUCTION CO INC
2656 S Sheridan Ave, Wichita, KS 67217-1341
Tel (316) 945-0555 *Founded/Ownrshp* 1898
Sales 119.1MM *EMP* 180^E
Accts Bkd Llp
SIC 1622 1541 1542 Bridge construction; Industrial buildings, new construction; Warehouse construction; Commercial & office building contractors
Pr: Thomas Dondlinger
Sec: Greg Phillips
VP: James Dondlinger
VP: Martin C Dondlinger Jr
VP: Troy Kapels
Genl Mgr: Raymond Dondlinger

D-U-N-S 15-214-3913
▲ DONEGAL GROUP INC
1195 River Rd, Marietta, PA 17547-1628
Tel (717) 426-1931 *Founded/Ownrshp* 1986
Sales NA *EMP* 800^E
Tkr Sym DGICA *Exch* NGS
SIC 6331 Fire, marine & casualty insurance
Pr: Kevin G Burke
**Ch Bd:* Donald H Nikolaus
CFO: Jeffrey D Miller
Treas: Daniel J Wagner
Sr VP: Cyril J Greenya
Sr VP: Sanjay Pandey
Sr VP: Robert G Shenk
VP: K R McNees
VP: Chet Szczepanski
VP: M A Zimmerman
Board of Directors: Richard D Wampler II, Scott A Berlucchi, Robert S Bolinger, Patricia A Gilmartin, Philip H Glatfelter II, Jack L Hess, Barry C Huber, Kevin M Kraft Sr, Jon M Mahan, S Trezevant Moore Jr

DONEGAL INSURANCE
See DONEGAL MUTUAL INSURANCE CO

D-U-N-S 00-302-8545
■ DONEGAL MUTUAL INSURANCE CO
DONEGAL INSURANCE
(*Suby of* DONEGAL GROUP INC) ★
1195 River Rd, Marietta, PA 17547-1638
Tel (717) 426-1931 *Founded/Ownrshp* 1889
Sales NA *EMP* 800^E
SIC 6331 Fire, marine & casualty insurance
Pr: Donald H Nikolaus
**Ch Bd:* Philip Hughes Glatfelter II
**Treas:* Daniel J Wagner
**Ex VP:* Kevin G Burke
**Ex VP:* Jeffrey D Miller
**Sr VP:* Cyril J Greenya
**Sr VP:* Francis J Haefner Jr
VP: George Blosser
VP: Jeff Jacobsen
VP: David Johnson
VP: Kenneth P Kirchner
VP: George A Ludwig Jr
**VP:* Christina M Springer
**VP:* Chester J Szczepanski

D-U-N-S 07-929-5224
■ DONER PARTNERS LLC
(*Suby of* MDC PARTNERS INC) ★
25900 Northwestern Hwy, Southfield, MI 48075-1067
Tel (248) 354-9700 *Founded/Ownrshp* 2012
Sales 98.4MM^E *EMP* 600
SIC 7311 Advertising agencies
**COO:* Naveen Passey
Ex VP: Craig Conrad
Ex VP: Mike Flynn
Ex VP: Sue Guise
Ex VP: Cindy Kenety
Ex VP: Alison Taubman
Sr VP: Karen Cathel
Sr VP: Larry Deangelis
Sr VP: Gary Gonya
Sr VP: Gail Offen
Sr VP: Bob Tacy
VP: Ann Antonini
VP: Karyn Bylinowski
VP: Tim Coughlin
VP: Wendy Dewindt
VP: John Garlock
VP: Shelby Rauen
VP: Barbara Walker
Assoc Dir: Susan Carey
Creative D: Stephen Bantien
Creative D: Jason Bergeron

D-U-N-S 06-500-0127 IMP
DONGALEN ENTERPRISES INC
INTERSTATE PLASTICS
330 Commerce Cir, Sacramento, CA 95815-4213
Tel (916) 422-3110 *Founded/Ownrshp* 1981
Sales 124.6MM^E *EMP* 165
SIC 5162 Plastics products
Pr: Mark Courtright
**CFO:* Cole Klokkevold
IT Man: Chris Isar

D-U-N-S 07-943-4371
DONGHEE ALABAMA LLC
(*Suby of* DONGHEE AMERICA)
2550 Innovation Dr, Auburn, AL 36832-8069
Tel (334) 321-2756 *Founded/Ownrshp* 2013
Sales 83.7MM *EMP* 127
SIC 3443 Fuel tanks (oil, gas, etc.): metal plate
CEO: Sun Sub Kwat
CFO: Nam Kyu Hong

DONGHIA FURNITURE AND TEXTILES
See DONGHIA INC

D-U-N-S 05-030-2207 IMP/EXP
DONGHIA INC
DONGHIA FURNITURE AND TEXTILES
500 Bic Dr Ste 20, Milford, CT 06461-1777
Tel (800) 366-4442 *Founded/Ownrshp* 2005
Sales 89.4MM^E *EMP* 200

SIC 5198 5131 5021 2342 Wallcoverings; Piece goods & other fabrics; Furniture; Corset accessories: clasps, stays, etc.
Pr: Rose Crans Baldwin
**CFO:* William Peterson
Creative D: Charles Chewning
IT Man: Allan Chernak
Sales Asso: Winston Frazier
Sales Asso: Anna Green
Sales Asso: Heather Myers
Sales Asso: Jose Rolon

D-U-N-S 15-709-5543 IMP
DONGWON AUTOPART TECHNOLOGY ALABAMA LLC
(*Suby of* DONGWON AUTOPART TECHNOLOGY INC)
★
12970 Montgomery Hwy, Luverne, AL 36049-5260
Tel (334) 537-5000 *Founded/Ownrshp* 2003
Sales 106.8MM *EMP* 287
Accts Choie Kim & Park Llp Montgo
SIC 3465 Body parts, automobile: stamped metal
Pr: Jung-Kwon Kim
Sfty Dirs: Donna Russell

D-U-N-S 07-941-1644
DONGWON AUTOPART TECHNOLOGY INC
(*Suby of* DONGWON METAL.CO.,LTD.)
12970 Montgomery Hwy, Luverne, AL 36049-5260
Tel (706) 637-9735 *Founded/Ownrshp* 2003
Sales 133.4MM *EMP* 287^E
Accts Choikim & Park Llp Montgome
SIC 3465 Body parts, automobile: stamped metal
Pr: Jung-Kwon Kim
Plnt Mgr: Yong Kim

D-U-N-S 00-892-7972
DONLEYS INC (OH)
5430 Warner Rd, Cleveland, OH 44125-1140
Tel (216) 524-6800 *Founded/Ownrshp* 1941
Sales 155.8MM^E *EMP* 200^E
SIC 1542 Commercial & office building, new construction
Pr: Malcolm M Donley
Ch Bd: Terrance K Donley
COO: Mark Hoenk
CFO: Patrick J Powers
Ex VP: Don K Dreier
VP: Jeff Hamburg
VP: Tom Heginbotham
VP: Kurt Weinfurther
Exec: Jeff Dentzer
CIO: Joe Fiore
CTO: Matthew Friedman
Board of Directors: James Bigger, James Hill, Al Klavora, Charles E Zumkehr, Phil Kaszar Are Outside Di

D-U-N-S 02-344-8491
DONNA INDEPENDENT SCHOOL DISTRICT
116 N 10th St, Donna, TX 78537-2799
Tel (956) 464-1600 *Founded/Ownrshp* 1907
Sales 165.0MM *EMP* 2,400
Accts Pattillo Brown & Hill Llp
SIC 8211 Public elementary school; Public junior high school; Public senior high school
**CFO:* David Robledo
Dir Sec: Roy Padia

D-U-N-S 06-621-8892 IMP
DONNA KARAN CO LLC
DKNY
(*Suby of* DONNA KARAN INTERNATIONAL INC) ★
240 W 40th St, New York, NY 10018-1533
Tel (212) 789-1500 *Founded/Ownrshp* 2003
Sales 514.5MM^E *EMP* 1,300
SIC 2335 2337 2331 2339 2311 2325 Women's, juniors' & misses' dresses; Suits: women's, misses' & juniors'; Skirts, separate: women's, misses' & juniors'; Pantsuits: women's, misses' & juniors'; Blouses, women's & juniors': made from purchased material; Women's & misses' jackets & coats, except sportswear; Suits, men's & boys': made from purchased materials; Coats, tailored, men's & boys': from purchased materials; Slacks, dress: men's, youths' & boys'
CEO: Donna Karan
Pr: Carolyn Mariani
Treas: Anthony Farese
Ex VP: Patti Cohen
Sr VP: Andrew Lee
Sr VP: James Thompson
Sr VP: Lynn Usdan
VP: Jacki Bouza
VP: Neil Bracco
VP: Caren Cheung
VP: Elizabeth Costa
VP: Doreen W Ritter
VP: Martha Silva-Porteus
Creative D: Lindsay Ackroyd

D-U-N-S 00-772-7639 IMP/EXP
DONNA KARAN INTERNATIONAL INC
(*Suby of* LVMH MOET HENNESSY LOUIS VUITTON)
240 W 40th St, New York, NY 10018-1533
Tel (212) 789-1500 *Founded/Ownrshp* 2016
Sales 514.5MM^E *EMP* 10^E
SIC 2335 2337 2331 2339 2321 2325 Women's, juniors' & misses' dresses; Jackets & vests, except fur & leather: women's; Skirts, separate: women's, misses' & juniors'; Suits: women's, misses' & juniors'; Blouses, women's & juniors': made from purchased material; Shirts, women's & juniors': made from purchased materials; Women's & misses' outerwear; Slacks: women's, misses' & juniors'; Jeans: women's, misses' & juniors'; Athletic clothing: women's, misses' & juniors'; Men's & boys' furnishings; Slacks, dress: men's, youths' & boys'; Jeans: men's, youths' & boys'
Ch Bd: Mark Weber
Founder: Donna Karan
Ofcr: Mark Cox
Ofcr: Tisha Kalberer
Ex VP: Patti Cohen
Ex VP: Lee Goldenberg
Sr VP: Louis Praino
Sr VP: Lynn E Usdan
VP: Martha Porteus
Board of Directors: M William Benedetto, John Eyler,

Ann McLaughlin, Frank R Mori

D-U-N-S 04-617-2797 IMP
■ DONNELLEY FINANCIAL LLC
RR DONNELLEY FINANCIAL, INC.
(*Suby of* RR DONNELLEY) ★
55 Water St Lowr L1, New York, NY 10041-0005
Tel (212) 425-0298 *Founded/Ownrshp* 2010
Sales 1.0MMM^E *EMP* 2,800
SIC 2752 Commercial printing, lithographic; Business forms, lithographed
CEO: Thomas J Quinlan III
* *Pr:* William P Penders
* *CFO:* John J Walker
* *Treas:* Bryan Berndt
Sr VP: Sandy McGee
Sr VP: Jim Palmiter
* *Sr VP:* Scott L Spitzer
VP: Tim Maclean
VP: Gerard Phelan
Exec: Louis Rojas
Assoc Dir: Michellel Smith

D-U-N-S 07-966-1780
DONNIE SHONOBI BRAND NAME TRADEMARK COLLECTION CORP
160 Town Park Dr, Advance, NC 27006-8605
Tel (336) 940-5682 *Founded/Ownrshp* 2014
Sales 100.0MM *EMP* 8
SIC 5699 7389 Designers, apparel;
CEO: Stylesz Patterson

D-U-N-S 00-325-1220
DONOHOE COMPANIES INC
2101 Wisconsin Ave Nw, Washington, DC 20007-2395
Tel (202) 333-0880 *Founded/Ownrshp* 1884, 1998
Sales 6.9MM *EMP* 1,400
Accts Bdo Usa Llp Mc Lean Va
SIC 6552 1542 Subdividers & developers; Commercial & office buildings, renovation & repair; Commercial & office building, new construction
V Ch: Steven J Donohoe
* *CFO:* Gerard M Goeke
* *Sr VP:* David Barry
* *Sr VP:* Steven Donohoe
* *Sr VP:* Peter Gartlan
VP: Mohamed Allibhai
* *VP:* Philip Carrescia
VP: Robert F Donohoe Jr
VP: Brian Gianfelice
VP: Paul Harris
VP: George Heacox
VP: Don Konz
VP: George Labarraque
VP: John Newell
Exec: Cheryl Haughton
Board of Directors: Robert Donohoe Jr

D-U-N-S 01-621-7361
DONORS TRUST INC
1800 Diagonal Rd Ste 280, Alexandria, VA 22314-2840
Tel (703) 535-3563 *Founded/Ownrshp* 1999
Sales 104.5MM *EMP* 3
SIC 6732 8733 Trusts: educational, religious, etc.; Noncommercial research organizations
Ex Dir: Whitney Ball
* *Pr:* Kimberly Dennis

D-U-N-S 00-785-9457 IMP/EXP
DONOVAN MARINE INC (LA)
6316 Humphreys St, Harahan, LA 70123-3159
Tel (504) 729-2520 *Founded/Ownrshp* 1950
Sales 154.4MM^E *EMP* 420
SIC 5088

D-U-N-S 06-977-6987 IMP
DONSCO INC
REGISTRY FOR EXCELLENCE
124 N Front St, Wrightsville, PA 17368-1374
Tel (717) 252-0690 *Founded/Ownrshp* 1970
Sales 92.2MM^E *EMP* 375
SIC 3398 3321 Metal heat treating; Gray iron castings
Pr: Arthur K Mann
* *Pr:* Arthur Mann Jr
* *CFO:* Wayne Kaufman
* *VP:* Chris Buck
* *VP:* Michael Day
* *VP:* John Smeltzer
Prgrm Mgr: Gabriel Bertini
Mfg Mgr: Larry Gilbert
Ql Cn Mgr: Bob King
Sls Dir: Suzette Cover
Mktg Mgr: Joanna Miles

D-U-N-S 94-352-6947
DONUT MANAGEMENT INC
DUNKIN' DONUTS
3 Pluff Ave, Haverhill, MA 01835
Tel (978) 664-2854 *Founded/Ownrshp* 1992
Sales 98.4MM^E *EMP* 1,600
SIC 5461 Doughnuts
Pr: Constantine Scrivanos

D-U-N-S 96-910-7973 IMP/EXP
DOOSAN INDUSTRIAL VEHICLE AMERICA CORP
DIVAC
2905 Shawnee Indus Way, Suwanee, GA 30024-4645
Tel (770) 831-2200 *Founded/Ownrshp* 2011
Sales 119.3MM *EMP* 45
Accts Deloitte & Touche Llp New Yor
SIC 5084 Lift trucks & parts
CEO: Tony Jones

D-U-N-S 80-938-2880 IMP/EXP
DOOSAN INFRACORE AMERICA CORP
(*Suby of* DOOSAN INFRACORE CO., LTD.)
2905 Shawnee Industrial W, Suwanee, GA 30024-4647
Tel (770) 831-2200 *Founded/Ownrshp* 1992
Sales 214.7MM^E *EMP* 150
Accts Deloitte & Touche Llp New Yo
SIC 5084 5082 Machine tools & accessories; Lift trucks & parts; Construction & mining machinery
CEO: Hyeong Joo Kim
V Ch: Yongmaan Park
* *Pr:* Michael P Stanley
COO: John Bandy
* *COO:* Kim Parkinson
* *CFO:* H S Lee
* *CFO:* Yeong Su Yoon
VP: Sanghoon Lee
VP: Agripino Serrano
Area Mgr: Lyndle McCurley
IT Man: Brian Grellinger

D-U-N-S 80-087-7479
DOOSAN INFRACORE INTERNATIONAL INC
2905 Shawnee Industrial W, Suwanee, GA 30024-4647
Tel (770) 831-2200 *Founded/Ownrshp* 2007
Sales 2.6MMM *EMP* 5,000
SIC 3531

D-U-N-S 09-684-0616 IMP/EXP
DOPACO INC
461 Boot Rd, Downingtown, PA 19335-3043
Tel (610) 269-6048 *Founded/Ownrshp* 2011
Sales NA *EMP* 1,300
SIC 2657 2656 3089 3792

D-U-N-S 09-000-6339
■ DORADO BEACH HOTEL CORP (DE)
HYATT CENTER
(*Suby of* HYATT CENTER) ★
Km 12 7 Rr 693, Dorado, PR 00646
Tel (787) 796-1234 *Founded/Ownrshp* 1961, 1985
Sales 19.5MM^E *EMP* 1,440
SIC 7011 Hotels & motels
Ch Bd: Jay A Pritzker
* *Pr:* Thomas J Pritzker

D-U-N-S 80-122-7476
DORADO HEALTH INC
MANATI MEDICAL CENTER
Carrion Hernandez St Urb, Manati, PR 00674
Tel (787) 621-3700 *Founded/Ownrshp* 1998
Sales 58.0MM^E *EMP* 1,049
SIC 8011 Health maintenance organization
Pr: Jose Quiros
* *Treas:* Jose A Faura
* *VP:* Carlos Disdier
VP: Noriselle Rivera

D-U-N-S 09-043-7831
DORAL FINANCIAL CORP
200 Park Ave Ste 1700, New York, NY 10166-0005
Tel (646) 632-3700 *Founded/Ownrshp* 1972
Sales NA *EMP* 1,333^E
Accts Pricewaterhousecoopers Llp Sa
SIC 6029 6162 6035 6211 6411 Commercial banks; Mortgage bankers; Federal savings banks; Investment bankers; Insurance agents, brokers & service
Dir Risk M: Carol Flaton
* *Ch Bd:* Dennis G Buchert
CFO: David Hooston
Chf Cred: Andrew Bastone
Ex VP: Ilia Rodriguez
Ex VP: Enrique R Ubarri
Sr VP: Louis Aponte
Sr VP: Denise Segarra Sacarello
Sr VP: Laura V Zquez

D-U-N-S 80-780-7883
DORAL HOLDINGS DELAWARE LLC
1451 Frnklin D Rsvelt Ave, San Juan, PR 00920
Tel (787) 474-6700 *Founded/Ownrshp* 2007
Sales NA *EMP* 1,372
SIC 6162 6035 6211 6411 Mortgage bankers; Federal savings banks; Investment bankers; Insurance agents, brokers & service
Prin: David King

D-U-N-S 11-884-6034
DORAS NATURALS INC
21 Empire Blvd, South Hackensack, NJ 07606-1805
Tel (201) 229-0500 *Founded/Ownrshp* 1999
Sales 135.4MM^E *EMP* 140^E
SIC 5149 Natural & organic foods
Pr: Cyrus Schwartz
VP Sls: Mike Taroli
Sales Asso: Nicole Lugo

D-U-N-S 08-637-7595
DORCHESTER SCHOOL DISTRICT TWO
102 Greenwave Blvd, Summerville, SC 29483-2455
Tel (843) 873-2901 *Founded/Ownrshp* 1935
Sales 91.8MM^E *EMP* 2,000
Accts Greene Finney & Horton Llp
SIC 8211 Public elementary & secondary schools
Exec: Pat Raynor

D-U-N-S 08-439-5607 IMP
DOREL HOME FURNISHINGS INC
AMERIWOOD INDUSTRIES, INC.
(*Suby of* DOREL INDUSTRIES INC)
410 E 1st St S, Wright City, MO 63390-1335
Tel (636) 745-3351 *Founded/Ownrshp* 1990
Sales 464.3MM^E *EMP* 1,300
SIC 2511 Console tables: wood; Coffee tables: wood; Tea wagons: wood
Pr: Rick Jackson
VP: Steve Harris
VP: James Kimminau
Info Man: Steve Brankmann
Plnt Mgr: Mark Thomas

DOREL JUVENILE GROUP
See DOREL USA INC

D-U-N-S 11-884-1501 IMP/EXP
DOREL JUVENILE GROUP INC
COSCO HOME & OFFICE PDTS DIV
(*Suby of* DOREL JUVENILE GROUP) ★
2525 State St, Columbus, IN 47201-7494
Tel (800) 457-5276 *Founded/Ownrshp* 2000
Sales 177.3MM^E *EMP* 320
SIC 3089 3069 3429 3699 3648 Plastic kitchenware, tableware & houseware; Baby pacifiers, rubber; Teething rings, rubber; Manufactured hardware (general); Door locks, bolts & checks; Security devices; Lighting equipment
Pr: David Taylor
Ex VP: Mark Evanko
* *VP:* Jay Caron
* *VP:* Steven E Willeke
Creative D: Lynn Dowling
Netwrk Mgr: Timothy Pickett
Mktg Dir: Jason Owens

D-U-N-S 80-590-3754 IMP
DOREL USA INC
DOREL JUVENILE GROUP
(*Suby of* DOREL INDUSTRIES INC)
2525 State St, Columbus, IN 47201-7443
Tel (812) 372-0141 *Founded/Ownrshp* 1991
Sales 533.2MM^E *EMP* 1,287
SIC 3944 2511 2514 Strollers, baby (vehicle); Child restraint seats, automotive; Walkers, baby (vehicle); High chairs, children's: wood; Cribs: wood; Cribs: metal; Stools, household, padded or plain: metal; Serving carts & tea wagons: metal; Tables, household: metal
Pr: Nick Costides
* *Ex VP:* Tim Ferguson
* *Ex VP:* Steve Willeke

DORFMAN PACIFIC
See DORFMAN-PACIFIC CO

D-U-N-S 00-922-6952 IMP/EXP
DORFMAN-PACIFIC CO
DORFMAN PACIFIC
2615 Boeing Way, Stockton, CA 95206-3984
Tel (209) 982-1400 *Founded/Ownrshp* 1990
Sales 83.5MM^E *EMP* 155
SIC 5136 5137 Caps, men's & boys'; Hats, men's & boys'; Men's & boys' outerwear; Caps & gowns; Hats: women's, children's & infants'; Women's & children's outerwear
CEO: Douglas Highsmith

D-U-N-S 15-548-9219 IMP/EXP
DORMA USA INC
(*Suby of* DORMA NEDERLAND B.V.)
1 Dorma Dr, Reamstown, PA 17567
Tel (717) 336-3881 *Founded/Ownrshp* 1944
Sales 174.2MM^E *EMP* 494
SIC 3429 Builders' hardware
Pr: Michael Kincaid
* *CFO:* Bernard Brinker
CFO: Dan Connor
* *CFO:* Oliver Schubert
* *Treas:* Kevin Hollenbach
VP: Paul Kesaris
* *VP:* Ashley Prall
Dir Bus: Celine Nair
Genl Mgr: Andrew Knarvik
Off Mgr: Eric Lim
Opers Mgr: Emile Newchurch
Board of Directors: Reed Buettner, Michael Kincaid

D-U-N-S 09-371-5316 IMP/EXP
▲ DORMAN PRODUCTS INC
3400 E Walnut St, Colmar, PA 18915-9768
Tel (215) 997-1800 *Founded/Ownrshp* 1978
Sales 802.9MM *EMP* 1,846
Tkr Sym DORM *Exch* NGS
SIC 3714 3231 3965 Motor vehicle parts & accessories; Mirrors, truck & automobile: made from purchased glass; Fasteners
Pr: Mathias J Barton
CFO: Michael P Ginnetti
CFO: Matt Kohnke
Sec: Steven L Berman
Sr VP: Jeffrey L Darby
Sr VP: Michael B Kealey
VP: Jeff Darby
Dist Mgr: Stanford Burrell
IT Man: Scott Thiel
Info Man: Andrea Getty
Mktg Dir: Daniel Brown
Board of Directors: John J Gavin

DORMITORY AUTH OF THE STATE NY
See DORMITORY AUTHORITY - STATE OF NEW YORK

D-U-N-S 07-108-8736
DORMITORY AUTHORITY - STATE OF NEW YORK
DORMITORY AUTH OF THE STATE NY
515 Broadway Ste 100, Albany, NY 12207-2964
Tel (518) 257-3000 *Founded/Ownrshp* 1946
Sales 2.1MMM *EMP* 625
Accts Kpmg Llp Albany Ny
SIC 8611 Business associations
Ex Dir: Paul T Williams
* *CFO:* Kim Nadeau
* *CFO:* John G Pasicznyk
* *Ex VP:* Maryanne Gridley
Assoc Dir: Marilyn Fountain
* *Ex Dir:* Micheal Coorigan
Off Mgr: Delores Bates
Off Admin: Jeanne Jones
Off Admin: Kimberly Kreski
Dir IT: Arthur Miller
IT Man: Michael Tanzman

D-U-N-S 02-287-5694
DORO INC
HARDEE'S
3112 Golf Rd, Eau Claire, WI 54701-8013
Tel (715) 836-6800 *Founded/Ownrshp* 1968
Sales 43.4MM^E *EMP* 1,250
SIC 5812 Fast-food restaurant, chain
Pr: Jon J Munger
* *VP:* Paul F Koch

D-U-N-S 06-541-7050
DOROTHEA HOPFER SCHOOL OF NURSING
53 Valentine St, Mount Vernon, NY 10550-2009
Tel (914) 361-6221 *Founded/Ownrshp* 2011
Sales 94.5MM *EMP* 12^E
Accts Pricewaterhousecoopers Llp Ne
SIC 8099 Health & allied services
Prin: Salvatore Quaranta

D-U-N-S 00-447-1074 IMP
DOROTHY LANE MARKET INC (OH)
2710 Far Hills Ave, Oakwood, OH 45419-1636
Tel (937) 299-3561 *Founded/Ownrshp* 1953
Sales 114.8MM^E *EMP* 700
SIC 5411 Supermarkets, independent
CEO: Norman Mayne
* *Pr:* Calvin Mayne
* *CEO:* Norman Mayne
* *CFO:* Kent Dimbath
VP: Jack Gridley
Sftwr Eng: Marcus Levin
Board of Directors: Norman Mayne

DORSCHEL BUICK
See DORSCHEL REALTY CORP

D-U-N-S 17-502-4488
DORSCHEL REALTY CORP
DORSCHEL BUICK
3817 W Henrietta Rd, Rochester, NY 14623-3703
Tel (585) 475-1700 *Founded/Ownrshp* 1977
Sales 123.0MM^E *EMP* 419
SIC 5511 7538 7549 New & used car dealers; General automotive repair shops; Automotive maintenance services
CEO: Richard J Dorschel
* *CFO:* Albert J Baronas
* *Treas:* Nancy J Dorschel
Sales Asso: Natalya Depasse

D-U-N-S 07-178-1090
DORSEY & WHITNEY LLP
50 S 6th St Ste 1500, Minneapolis, MN 55402-1553
Tel (612) 340-2600 *Founded/Ownrshp* 2001
Sales 757.6MM^E *EMP* 11,060
SIC 8111 Legal services
Mng Pt: Kenneth L Cutler
Pt: Peter Bado
Pt: Ellen J Bickal
Pt: B Andrew Brown
Pt: Zachary Carter
Pt: Frances P Doherty
Pt: Robert J Dwyer
Pt: David J Fernandez
Pt: L J Genereux
Pt: Anthony M Harvin
Pt: Peter Hendrixson
Pt: Annette W Jarvis
Pt: E Michael Johnson
Pt: Paul Klaas
Pt: Michael A Piazza
Pt: Stanley M Rein
Pt: Steven R Schoenfeld
Pt: Marcus Sisk
Pt: Thomas W Tinkham
Mng Pt: Marianne D Short
Ch Bd: Christopher J Barry

D-U-N-S 01-144-4823
DORTCH ENTERPRISES LLC
8487 Retreat Dr, Grand Blanc, MI 48439-2564
Tel (810) 771-4500 *Founded/Ownrshp* 2009
Sales 79.3MM^E *EMP* 2,000
SIC 5812 Fast food restaurants & stands
Ch Bd: Louis Dortch Jr
* *CFO:* Robert Grabowski
* *VP:* Jeff Bedolla
Area Mgr: Lena Sadik
Area Mgr: Justin Shipman
Area Mgr: Jim Sutherland
Off Mgr: Angie Kulza

D-U-N-S 00-803-1015 IMP/EXP
DOSKOCIL MANUFACTURING CO INC (TX)
PETMATE
(*Suby of* PETMATE HOLDINGS CO) ★
2300 E Randol Mill Rd, Arlington, TX 76011-6333
Tel (877) 738-6283 *Founded/Ownrshp* 1968, 2011
Sales 121.0MM^E *EMP* 650^E
SIC 3999 5999

D-U-N-S 01-833-9952
DOSS AVIATION INC (TX)
(*Suby of* JF LEHMAN & CO INC) ★
3670 Rebecca Ln Ste 100, Colorado Springs, CO 80917-5080
Tel (719) 570-9804 *Founded/Ownrshp* 1969, 2011
Sales 142.4MM^E *EMP* 500
Accts Brunson Wilkerson Bowden & A
SIC 5172 4581 Aircraft fueling services; Aircraft maintenance & repair services; Airport control tower operation, except government
Pr: Kenneth S Smith Jr
Pr: Jim Dormer
* *CFO:* Luann Hanson
Treas: Bent Liechty
Dir Bus: Bobby Goodman
Brnch Mgr: Vic Leeman
CIO: Daniel Ellis
IT Man: Jamie Trujillo
VP Opers: Paul Walker

D-U-N-S 05-016-2650
DOSTER CONSTRUCTION CO INC
2100 International Pk Dr, Birmingham, AL 35243-4209
Tel (205) 443-3800 *Founded/Ownrshp* 1969
Sales 196.4MM *EMP* 175^E
SIC 1542 Commercial & office building, new construction
CEO: Thomas E Doster III
* *Pr:* Walton C Doster
VP: Charles Harland
Opers Mgr: Joseph Schneider

D-U-N-S 02-567-1256 IMP/EXP
DOT FOODS INC
1 Dot Way, Mount Sterling, IL 62353-1664
Tel (217) 773-4411 *Founded/Ownrshp* 1960
Sales 5.6MMM^E *EMP* 2,550
SIC 5141 5142 Groceries, general line; Packaged frozen goods
CEO: John Tracy
* *Pr:* Joseph P Tracy
* *COO:* Dick Tracy
* *CFO:* William H Metzinger
Treas: Pete Jinkens
* *VP:* George Eversman
VP: Anita Montgomery
VP: Becky Reynolds
VP: Scott Stmaerjohn
VP: Jim Tracy
Genl Mgr: Bill King

D-U-N-S 19-616-9437 IMP
DOT HILL SYSTEMS CORP
(*Suby of* SEAGATE HDD CAYMAN)
1351 S Sunset St, Longmont, CO 80501-6533
Tel (303) 845-3200 *Founded/Ownrshp* 2015
Sales 217.6MM *EMP* 324ᴱ
SIC 3572 7371 Computer storage devices; Custom computer programming services; Custom computer programming services; Computer software development & applications; Computer software development
Pr: Phil Brace
**Treas:* Patrick J O'Malley
Sr VP: William Haskins
VP: Cooper Cowart
VP: Ernest Hafersat
VP: Eileen Jonikas
VP: James Kuenzel
Exec: Lenise Erich
Prgrm Mgr: Gary Clauson
Snr Sftwr: Michael Barrell
Snr Sftwr: Walter Ramsey

DOTERRA ESSENTIAL WELLNESS
See DOTERRA INTERNATIONAL LLC

D-U-N-S 83-227-4935 IMP
DOTERRA INTERNATIONAL LLC
DOTERRA ESSENTIAL WELLNESS
389 S 1300 W, Pleasant Grove, UT 84062-3761
Tel (801) 615-7200 *Founded/Ownrshp* 2007
Sales 685.0MM *EMP* 1,500ᴱ
Accts Hawkins Cloward & Simister Lc
SIC 2899 Oils & essential oils
**VP:* Emily Wright
Web Dev: Varvara Jones
**VP Opers:* Gregory Cook
Mktg Mgr: Arturo Soza

D-U-N-S 14-807-4743
DOTHAN CITY BOARD OF EDUCATION
500 Dusy St, Dothan, AL 36301-2500
Tel (334) 793-1397 *Founded/Ownrshp* 1905
Sales 84.9MM *EMP* 1,100
Accts Parsonsgroup Llc Dothan Ala
SIC 8211 Public elementary school; Public junior high school; Public senior high school; Public vocational/technical school
Ch Bd: Harry Parrish
**CEO:* Tim Wilder
**CFO:* Michael Manuel

D-U-N-S 07-872-5547
DOTHAN CITY SCHOOLS
500 Dusy St, Dothan, AL 36301-2500
Tel (334) 793-1397 *Founded/Ownrshp* 2015
Sales 75.5MMᴱ *EMP* 1,971ᴱ
SIC 8211 Public elementary & secondary schools
Psych: Angelia Brown
HC Dir: Todd Weeks

D-U-N-S 05-491-0658
DOTHAN SECURITY INC
DSI SECURITY SERVICES
600 W Adams St, Dothan, AL 36303-4306
Tel (334) 793-5720 *Founded/Ownrshp* 2010
Sales 83.8MMᴱ *EMP* 2,000
SIC 7381 Security guard service
Ch Bd: Alan Clark
**Pr:* Marsha Clark
CFO: Mike Hallford
Exec: Gwendolyn Bell
Rgnl Mgr: James L Delaney Jr
Brnch Mgr: Rich Hunter
Brnch Mgr: Michael Ollie
Brnch Mgr: Darnell Sanders
CTO: Leslie Fulton
IT Man: Larry Davis
Ql Cn Mgr: Clay Jordan

D-U-N-S 19-236-5161 IMP
DOTS LLC
30300 Emerald Valley Pkwy, Solon, OH 44139-4394
Tel (440) 349-7900 *Founded/Ownrshp* 2011
Sales 71.8MMᴱ *EMP* 2,500
SIC 5621 Ready-to-wear apparel, women's
Treas: Janey Kelley
Sr Cor Off: Rosalind Thompson
VP: Tiina Kaltot
Brnch Mgr: Heather Allsman
Brnch Mgr: Stephanie Gillette
Brnch Mgr: Melissa Iverson
Brnch Mgr: Margarita Mendez
Brnch Mgr: Dorothy Reed
Brnch Mgr: Michelle Smith
Genl Mgr: Amy Clark
Genl Mgr: Caryn Korbert

D-U-N-S 00-513-3124
DOTSTER INC
HOST LANE
8100 Ne Parkway Dr # 300, Vancouver, WA 98662-7954
Tel (360) 883-5589 *Founded/Ownrshp* 2004
Sales 84.6MMᴱ *EMP* 515ᴱ
SIC 4813
Pr: Hari Ravichandran
**Pr:* Clint Page
**Treas:* Jeremy Goodson
**VP:* Tom Bennet
**VP:* George Decarlo
**VP:* Christina Lane

D-U-N-S 00-477-8957
DOTY BROS EQUIPMENT CO
(*Suby of* MERUELO ENTERPRISES INC) ★
11232 Firestone Blvd, Norwalk, CA 90650-2201
Tel (562) 864-6566 *Founded/Ownrshp* 1959
Sales 92.8MMᴱ *EMP* 300
SIC 1623

D-U-N-S 01-505-1258
DOUBLE DIAMOND - DELAWARE INC
5495 Belt Line Rd Ste 200, Dallas, TX 75254-7658
Tel (214) 706-9831 *Founded/Ownrshp* 1972
Sales 111.3MMᴱ *EMP* 545
SIC 6552 7992 Subdividers & developers; Public golf courses
Pr: R Mike Ward

D-U-N-S 09-351-5104
DOUBLE DIAMOND INC
DD RESORTS
(*Suby of* DOUBLE DIAMOND - DELAWARE INC) ★
5495 Belt Line Rd Ste 200, Dallas, TX 75254-7658
Tel (214) 706-9801 *Founded/Ownrshp* 1997
Sales 90.3MMᴱ *EMP* 211
Accts Grant Thornton Dallastx
SIC 6552 Subdividers & developers
Pr: R Mike Ward
COO: Cindy Clark
**Treas:* Fred K Curran
Sr VP: Randy Gracy
Sr VP: Jeff Schmidt
Info Man: Brian Fiske
VP Mktg: Keith Brock

D-U-N-S 00-491-0030
DOUBLE E FOODS LLC (WA)
(*Suby of* E & E FOODS CORPORATION)
801 S Fidalgo St Ste 100, Seattle, WA 98108-2613
Tel (206) 768-8979 *Founded/Ownrshp* 1931
Sales 110.0MM *EMP* 2
SIC 8741 Management services
CFO: Yuk Li

D-U-N-S 08-047-8739
DOUBLE EAGLE PARENT INC
(*Suby of* ADVENT INTERNATIONAL GPE VII LLC) ★
75 State St Fl 29, Boston, MA 02109-1827
Tel (617) 951-0555 *Founded/Ownrshp* 2016
Sales NA *EMP* 7,112
SIC 6719 Investment holding companies, except banks
Prin: Ernest G Bachrach

DOUBLE KWIK
See HOMETOWN CONVENIENCE LLC

DOUBLE KWIK MARKET
See CHILDERS OIL CO

DOUBLETREE HOTEL
See DOUBLETREE INC

DOUBLETREE HOTEL
See BURRUS INVESTMENT GROUP INC

D-U-N-S 04-837-8293 IMP
■ **DOUBLETREE INC**
DOUBLETREE HOTEL
(*Suby of* HILTON) ★
755 Crossover Ln, Memphis, TN 38117-4906
Tel (901) 374-5000 *Founded/Ownrshp* 2000
Sales 143.9MMᴱ *EMP* 7,140
SIC 7011 5812 5813 Hotels & motels; Eating places; Cocktail lounge
Pr: Richard Kelleher
Ex VP: Ralph B Lake
Ex VP: William L Perocchi
Sr VP: M Ronald Halpern
Sr VP: Ronald M Halpern
Sr VP: Robert Provost
VP: R Brian Mulroy Jr
Dir Surg: Tom Befreece

D-U-N-S 84-999-7069 IMP
■ **DOUBLETREE LLC**
EMBASSY SUITES
(*Suby of* HILTON) ★
7930 Jones Branch Dr, Mc Lean, VA 22102-3388
Tel (703) 883-1000 *Founded/Ownrshp* 2011
Sales 340.9MMᴱ *EMP* 12,115ᴱ
SIC 7011 Hotels & motels
Pr: Richard M Kelleher
CFO: Robert Laforgia
CFO: William Perocchi
**Ex VP:* Dave Horton
**Ex VP:* Thomas L Keltner
**Ex VP:* Ralph B Lake
**Ex VP:* Margaret Ann Rhoades
**Sr VP:* James T Harvey
VP: Bill Space
Snr Mgr: Nancy Nusrally

D-U-N-S 03-396-2663
DOUG ANDRUS DISTRIBUTING LLC
6300 S 45th W, Idaho Falls, ID 83402-5771
Tel (208) 523-1034 *Founded/Ownrshp* 2002
Sales 91.1MMᴱ *EMP* 300
SIC 4213 Trucking, except local; Contract haulers
CEO: Clay Murdoch
**V Ch:* Jason Andrus
Exec: Craig Ritchie
CTO: Shane Peterson
IT Man: Peterson Shane
Opers Mgr: Virgil Baldwin

DOUGHERTY COUNTY BOARD EDUCATN
See DOUGHERTY COUNTY SCHOOL SYSTEM

D-U-N-S 03-005-0629
DOUGHERTY COUNTY SCHOOL SYSTEM
DOUGHERTY COUNTY BOARD EDUCATN
200 Pine Ave, Albany, GA 31701-2531
Tel (229) 431-1264 *Founded/Ownrshp* 1951
Sales 143.9MMᴱ *EMP* 2,500
Accts Russell W Hinton State Audit
SIC 8211 Public elementary & secondary schools
Ch Bd: David Maschke
**Ch Bd:* Micheal Windom
Bd of Dir: Velvet Riggins
Ex Dir: Dianne Daniels
**Ex Dir:* Robert Lloyd
Dir Sec: Troy Conley
Prgrm Mgr: Dwala Nobles
Dist Mgr: Julius Corker
Off Mgr: Tonia Moore
Web Dev: J Sumner
Teacher Pr: Sheila Marshal

D-U-N-S 00-624-9056 IMP
DOUGLAS CORP (MN)
9650 Valley View Rd, Eden Prairie, MN 55344-3507
Tel (800) 806-6113 *Founded/Ownrshp* 1932, 1933
Sales 123.8MMᴱ *EMP* 450ᴱ
SIC 3089 2759 Injection molding of plastics; Screen printing
CEO: Douglas R Skanse
Dir IT: Bruce Kuehl
VP Mktg: Jim Rinck
VP Sls: Joseph Hamein
VP Sls: Joseph L Hamelin
Sls Mgr: Kevin Waggoner
Orthpdst: Steven Berglund

D-U-N-S 09-779-1032
DOUGLAS COUNTY BOARD OF EDUCATION
9030 Highway 5, Douglasville, GA 30134-1539
Tel (770) 651-2000 *Founded/Ownrshp* 1956
Sales 256.3MM *EMP* 3,947
Accts Mauldin & Jenkins Llc Atlant
SIC 8211 School board
Ch Bd: DT Jackson

D-U-N-S 06-863-7693
DOUGLAS COUNTY NEBRASKA
Omaha Douglas Civic Cente, Omaha, NE 68183-0001
Tel (402) 444-7025 *Founded/Ownrshp* 1894
Sales NA *EMP* 2,200
Accts Hayes & Associatres Llc O
SIC 9111 Executive offices;
V Ch: Mike Boyle
Ofcr: Karen Curry
Ofcr: Mary Herres

D-U-N-S 03-950-9609
DOUGLAS COUNTY SCHOOL DISTRICT
620 Wilcox St, Castle Rock, CO 80104-1730
Tel (303) 387-0100 *Founded/Ownrshp* 1958
Sales NA *EMP* 7,000
Accts Mcgladrey Llp Denver Colorad
SIC 9411
Pr: Kevin Larsen
COO: William Moffitt
CFO: Chris Stutler
**VP:* Emily Hanson
Exec: Randy Barber
Exec: Brian Cesare
**Prin:* Christine Turner
Ex Dir: Alyson Reynolds
Psych: Sherrie Langston
Psych: Laura Portman
Counsel: Robert Ross

D-U-N-S 07-979-9690
DOUGLAS COUNTY SCHOOL SYSTEM
9030 Highway 5, Douglasville, GA 30134-1539
Tel (770) 651-2000 *Founded/Ownrshp* 2015
Sales 29.8MMᴱ *EMP* 2,598ᴱ
SIC 8211 Public elementary & secondary schools
CFO: Bonnie Betz
Dir Sec: Tim Scott
MIS Dir: Todd Hindmon
Pr Dir: Karen Stroud
Teacher Pr: Michelle Ruble

D-U-N-S 14-419-9114
DOUGLAS DEVELOPMENT CORP
702 H St Nw Ste 400, Washington, DC 20001-3875
Tel (202) 638-6300 *Founded/Ownrshp* 1985
Sales 100.2MMᴱ *EMP* 85
SIC 6552 6531 Land subdividers & developers, commercial; Land subdividers & developers, residential; Real estate agents & managers; Multiple listing service, real estate; Real estate agent, residential
Pr: Douglas Jemal
**CFO:* George Hardos
**Sr VP:* Norman Jemal
**VP:* Paul Millstein

DOUGLAS DISTRIBUTING
See W DOUGLASS DISTRIBUTING LTD

D-U-N-S 96-214-1466 IMP
▲ **DOUGLAS DYNAMICS INC**
7777 N 73rd St, Milwaukee, WI 53223-4021
Tel (414) 354-2310 *Founded/Ownrshp* 2004
Sales 400.4MM *EMP* 1,104ᴱ
Tkr Sym PLOW *Exch* NYS
SIC 3531 Snow plow attachments; Blades for graders, scrapers, dozers & snow plows; Finishers & spreaders (construction equipment)
Ch Bd: James L Janik
CFO: Robert L McCormick
Sr VP: Mark Adamson
Sr VP: Keith Hagelin
Board of Directors: Margaret S Dano, Kenneth W Krueger, James L Packard, James D Staley, Donald W Sturdivant

D-U-N-S 00-609-3199 IMP
■ **DOUGLAS DYNAMICS LLC**
WESTERN PRODUCTS
(*Suby of* DOUGLAS DYNAMICS INC) ★
7777 N 73rd St, Milwaukee, WI 53223-4021
Tel (414) 354-2310 *Founded/Ownrshp* 1950, 2004
Sales 142.7MMᴱ *EMP* 450
SIC 3531 Construction machinery attachments; Snow plow attachments
Pr: James L Janik
**VP:* Mark Adamson
VP: Ralph Gould
**VP:* Robert McCormick
Exec: Theresa Keosheyan
Exec: Joyce Monast
Genl Mgr: Klug Steve
Dir IT: Joseph Raml
Web Prj Mg: Scott Fischer
Sfty Mgr: Peter Stark
VP Mktg: Richard Burkhardt

D-U-N-S 06-777-7458
DOUGLAS EMMETT INC
808 Wilshire Blvd Ste 200, Santa Monica, CA 90401-1889
Tel (310) 255-7700 *Founded/Ownrshp* 1971
Sales 635.7MM *EMP* 560
Accts Ernst & Young Llp Los Angeles
SIC 6798 Real estate investment trusts
Pr: Jordan L Kaplan
**Ch Bd:* Dan A Emmett
**COO:* Kenneth M Panzer
CFO: Theodore E Guth
CFO: Theodore Guth
Chf Inves: Kevin A Crummy
Ofcr: Mona Gisler
Sr VP: Allan B Golad
Sr VP: Michael J Means
VP: Mary Jensen
VP: Kevin Kuritani

D-U-N-S 00-831-7414 IMP
DOUGLAS FURNITURE OF CALIFORNIA LLC
809 Tyburn Rd, Palos Verdes Estates, CA 90274-2843
Tel (310) 749-0003 *Founded/Ownrshp* 2000
Sales NA *EMP* 2,400
SIC 2514 2512

DOUGLAS GAS & OIL
See BRENNER OIL CO

D-U-N-S 13-078-3541
DOUGLAS HOSPITAL INC
WELLSTAR DOUGLAS HOSPITAL
8954 Hospital Dr Frnt, Douglasville, GA 30134-5604
Tel (770) 949-1500 *Founded/Ownrshp* 2004
Sales 117.1MM *EMP* 313
SIC 8062 Hospital, affiliated with AMA residency
CEO: Reynold J Jennings
Chf Path: Cesar Angeletti
**COO:* Mike Graue
**CFO:* Jim Budzinski
**Ex VP:* David Anderson
**Ex VP:* Leo E Reichert
Dir Lab: Laura Boynton
Dir Lab: Linda Faulkner
Dir Lab: Kathy Harville
Chf Nrs Of: Millisa Box
Genl Mgr: Christopher Greene

D-U-N-S 96-961-2865
DOUGLAS HOSPITAL INC
805 Sandy Plains Rd, Marietta, GA 30066-6340
Tel (770) 792-5023 *Founded/Ownrshp* 2011
Sales 126.2MM *EMP* 14ᴱ
Accts Pricewaterhousecoopers Llp Ph
SIC 8062 General medical & surgical hospitals
Prin: Linda Clark

D-U-N-S 00-620-3277 IMP
DOUGLAS MACHINE INC
3404 Iowa St, Alexandria, MN 56308-3399
Tel (320) 763-6587 *Founded/Ownrshp* 1964
Sales 121.6MMᴱ *EMP* 483
SIC 3565 Carton packing machines; Wrapping machines
Ch Bd: Vernon J Anderson
**Pr:* Rick Paulsen
**CFO:* Thomas Wosepka
**VP:* Jon Ballou

D-U-N-S 79-080-3352
DOUGLAS REALTY LLC
8096 Edwin Raynor Blvd C, Pasadena, MD 21122-6837
Tel (410) 255-3690 *Founded/Ownrshp* 2006
Sales 95.0MM *EMP* 100
SIC 6531 Real estate brokers & agents
CFO: Jennifer Smith

D-U-N-S 02-332-7588 IMP
DOUGLAS STEWART CO INC
2402 Advance Rd, Madison, WI 53718-6737
Tel (608) 221-1155 *Founded/Ownrshp* 2000
Sales 164.0MMᴱ *EMP* 105
Accts Cliftonlarsonallen Llp Milwau
SIC 5045 5044 5049 Computers, peripherals & software; Computer peripheral equipment; Computer software; Calculating machines; School supplies
CEO: Cheryl R Weston
Pr: Craig Stewart
COO: Robert Bernier
**COO:* Charles Hulan
**VP:* John A Thomson
Prgrm Mgr: Melissa Henke
Web Dev: Matt Martindale
Natl Sales: Amy Amegashie
Mktg Dir: Beth Lunde
Mktg Mgr: Angela Bluhm

D-U-N-S 00-979-3886 IMP
DOUGLASS COLONY GROUP INC
DOUGLASS ROOFING
5901 E 58th Ave, Commerce City, CO 80022-3917
Tel (303) 288-2635 *Founded/Ownrshp* 1947, 1983
Sales 85.6MMᴱ *EMP* 350
Accts Bauerle And Company Pc Den
SIC 1761 Roofing contractor
Pr: Robert Bechtholdt
**VP:* Steve Bechtholdt
**VP:* Gary Degenhart
**VP:* Patrick Wolach
Off Mgr: Dave Kellogg
Mktg Dir: Alexis Smith
Sls Mgr: Mark Lloyd

D-U-N-S 15-759-3039
DOUGLASS DISTRIBUTING RETAIL CO INC
LONESTAR
325 E Forest Ave, Sherman, TX 75090-8832
Tel (903) 893-1181 *Founded/Ownrshp* 1984
Sales 107.4MM *EMP* 150
SIC 5411 5541 Convenience stores; Filling stations, gasoline
Ch Bd: William P Douglass
VP: Madalyne Lange
Off Mgr: Rena Balbwin

DOUGLASS ROOFING
See DOUGLASS COLONY GROUP INC

D-U-N-S 05-663-1518
DOVENMUEHLE MORTGAGE INC
1 Corporate Dr Ste 360, Lake Zurich, IL 60047-8945
Tel (847) 550-7300 *Founded/Ownrshp* 1990
Sales NA *EMP* 494
SIC 6162 6411 Mortgage companies, urban; Insurance agents, brokers & service
Pr: William A Mynatt Jr
Pr: Vincent Nicoll
**CFO:* Glen S Braun
Treas: H Griswold
Sr VP: Mary K Przybyla
**VP:* David Allison
VP: Greg Frost
Dept Mgr: Ron Malik

QA Dir: Kimberly Grote
Dir IT: Engstrom Todd
Software D: Gurvinder Rajput

D-U-N-S 14-831-9874 IMP
■ DOVER ARTIFICIAL LIFT INTERNATIONAL LLC
NORRIS PRODUCTION SOLUTIONS
(*Suby of* DOVER CORP) ★
3005 Highland Pkwy, Downers Grove, IL 60515-5682
Tel (630) 743-2563 *Founded/Ownrshp* 1985
Sales 1.3MMM[E] *EMP* 6,000
SIC 3559 3535 3533 3561 Automotive related machinery; Bulk handling conveyor systems; Oil field machinery & equipment; Industrial pumps & parts
Pr: William C Johnson
**CEO:* Robert A Livingston
**CFO:* Brad M Cerepak
CFO: Gary Larson
**VP:* Kevin P Buchanan

D-U-N-S 04-708-2443
■ DOVER ARTIFICIAL LIFT SYSTEMS LLC
(*Suby of* DOVER CORP) ★
15 E 5th St Ste 1421, Tulsa, OK 74103-4363
Tel (918) 396-0558 *Founded/Ownrshp* 2013
Sales 100.0MM *EMP* 122
SIC 1389 Construction, repair & dismantling services

D-U-N-S 00-421-0563 IMP
DOVER CHEMICAL CORP (OH)
(*Suby of* ICC INDUSTRIES INC) ★
3676 Davis Rd Nw, Dover, OH 44622-9771
Tel (330) 343-7711 *Founded/Ownrshp* 1949, 1975
Sales 113.2MM[E] *EMP* 270
SIC 2819 2869 2899 Industrial inorganic chemicals; Industrial organic chemicals; Chemical preparations
Pr: Dwain S Colvin
**CFO:* Darren Schwede
VP: Charles Fletcher
**VP:* Chuck Fletcher
VP: Kim Sangha
VP: Don Stevenson
Tech Mgr: Daryl Stein
Sfty Dirs: Jiim Moore
Sfty Mgr: Steven Hartford
Sfty Mgr: Gary Thornton
Prd Mgr: Larry Spore

D-U-N-S 00-324-5271 IMP/EXP
▲ DOVER CORP
3005 Highland Pkwy # 200, Downers Grove, IL 60515-5655
Tel (630) 541-1540 *Founded/Ownrshp* 1947
Sales 6.9MMM *EMP* 26,000
Tkr Sym DOV *Exch* NYS
SIC 3632 3586 3533 3577 3674 Household refrigerators & freezers; Measuring & dispensing pumps; Oil & gas drilling rigs & equipment; Computer peripheral equipment; Bar code (magnetic ink) printers; Semiconductors & related devices
Pr: Robert A Livingston
Ch Bd: Robert W Cremin
Pr: C Anderson Fincher
Pr: William C Johnson
Pr: Sivasankaran Somasundaram
Pr: William W Spurgeon Jr
CFO: Brad M Cerepak
CFO: Robert Scheuer
Treas: James M Moran
Bd of Dir: Mary Winston
Sr VP: Ivonne M Cabrera
Sr VP: Jay L Kloosterboer
Sr VP: Stephen R Sellhausen
Sr VP: Russell E Toney
VP: Sandra A Arkell
VP: Ann Miller
Exec: Dorothy Aloma

D-U-N-S 09-290-2266
▲ DOVER DOWNS GAMING & ENTERTAINMENT INC
1131 N Dupont Hwy, Dover, DE 19901-2008
Tel (302) 674-4600 *Founded/Ownrshp* 1969
Sales 182.9MM *EMP* 1,407[E]
Tkr Sym DDE *Exch* NYS
SIC 7929 7999 7011 7948 Entertainment service; Card & game services; Hotels; Racing, including track operation; Harness horse racing
Pr: Denis McGlynn
**Ch Bd:* Henry B Tippie
COO: Edward J Sutor
**CFO:* Timothy R Horne
Sr VP: Klaus M Belohoubek
Board of Directors: Patrick J Bagley, Jeffrey W Rollins, R Randall Rollins, Richard K Struthers

D-U-N-S 10-652-1458 IMP
■ DOVER ENERGY INC
DE-STA-CO
(*Suby of* DOVER CORP) ★
15 Corporate Dr, Auburn Hills, MI 48326-2919
Tel (248) 836-6700 *Founded/Ownrshp* 1985
Sales 199.6MM[E] *EMP* 650
SIC 3429 Clamps, metal
Pr: Byron Paul
VP: Lisa Bell
Dir Bus: Leo McAuliffe
Off Mgr: Patrick Bourdon
Manager: Dustin Hrubetz

D-U-N-S 18-670-9457 IMP/EXP
■ DOVER ENGINEERED SYSTEMS INC
(*Suby of* DELAWARE CAPITAL HOLDINGS INC) ★
3005 Highland Pkwy # 200, Downers Grove, IL 60515-5682
Tel (630) 743-2505 *Founded/Ownrshp* 1984
Sales 1.5MMM[E] *EMP* 7,165
SIC 3568 3443 3441 3561 3491 3492

D-U-N-S 07-514-1788
DOVER GENERAL HOSPITAL & MEDICAL CENTER (INC)
400 W Blackwell St, Dover, NJ 07801-2525
Tel (973) 989-3000 *Founded/Ownrshp* 1909
Sales 88.4MM *EMP* 1,400
SIC 8062 General medical & surgical hospitals
Pr: Wayne C Schiffner
**Ch Bd:* John C Bermingham
**Ch Bd:* Jay Singleton
**Treas:* Michael Halpin
**V Ch Bd:* Ira M Ayers Jr

D-U-N-S 15-261-1042 IMP/EXP
■ DOVER PRINTING & IDENTIFICATION INC
DOVER RFRGN & FD EQP INC
(*Suby of* DOVER CORP) ★
3005 Highland Pkwy # 200, Downers Grove, IL 60515-5682
Tel (630) 541-1540 *Founded/Ownrshp* 1985
Sales 1.9MMM[E] *EMP* 5,595
SIC 3556 3565 3593 7699 Food products machinery; Packaging machinery; Fluid power cylinders, hydraulic or pneumatic; Industrial equipment services
CEO: Lewis Burns
**Pr:* John F Hartner
VP: Peter Downe
VP: Daniel McCourt
VP: Bob Schewer

DOVER RFRGN & FD EQP INC
See DOVER PRINTING & IDENTIFICATION INC

D-U-N-S 07-951-7447 IMP
DOVER SADDLERY INC (MA)
525 Great Rd, Littleton, MA 01460-6221
Tel (978) 952-8062 *Founded/Ownrshp* 1975
Sales 101.8MM *EMP* 777[E]
SIC 5941 Saddlery & equestrian equipment
Ch Bd: Stephen L Day
COO: William G Schmidt
CFO: David R Pearce
Ex VP: James Cullen
**VP:* Jonathan A R Grylls
Software D: Erin Burke
Manager: Paul Horsmann
Board of Directors: Kevin K Albert, John W Mitchell, Gregory F Mulligan, David J Powers, James F Powers

DOW
See ANGUS CHEMICAL CO

D-U-N-S 60-548-2694 IMP/EXP
■ DOW AGROSCIENCES LLC
(*Suby of* DOW CHEMICAL CO) ★
9330 Zionsville Rd, Indianapolis, IN 46268-1053
Tel (317) 337-3000 *Founded/Ownrshp* 2003
Sales 88.5MM[E] *EMP* 3,518
SIC 2879 5191 0721 8731 Agricultural chemicals; Insecticides & pesticides; Fungicides, herbicides; Seeds & bulbs; Crop protecting services; Agricultural research
VP: Janet Giesselman
Exec: Mark Jackson
Ql Cn Mgr: Tumey Mark
Sls&Mrk Ex: Ben Kaehler
Sales Asso: Gary Burton
Sales Asso: Renee Stoneman

D-U-N-S 00-138-1581 IMP/EXP
▲ DOW CHEMICAL CO
2030 Dow Ctr, Midland, MI 48674-1500
Tel (989) 636-1000 *Founded/Ownrshp* 1897
Sales 48.7MMM *EMP* 49,500[E]
Accts Deloitte & Touche Llp Midlan
Tkr Sym DOW *Exch* NYS
SIC 2821 3081 3086 2812 2879 Thermoplastic materials; Thermosetting materials; Plasticizer/additive based plastic materials; Molding compounds, plastics; Plastic film & sheet; Plastics foam products; Insulation or cushioning material, foamed plastic; Alkalies & chlorine; Fungicides, herbicides; Insecticides, agricultural or household; Pesticides, agricultural or household
Ch Bd: Andrew N Liveris
V Ch: Howard I Ungerleider
Pr: James R Fitterling
Treas: Gary McGuire
Chf Cred: Joe E Harlan
Ofcr: Wanda Fischer
Ex VP: Charles J Kalil
Sr VP: Attiganal N Sreeram
VP: Ronald C Edmonds
VP: Neil C Hawkins
VP: Julie Monson
VP: Fernando Ruiz
Board of Directors: James M Ringler, Jacqueline K Barton, Ruth G Shaw, James A Bell, Richard K Davis, Jeff M Fettig, Mark Loughridge, Raymond J Milchovich, Robert S Miller, Paul Polman, Dennis H Reilley

D-U-N-S 61-895-3868 IMP/EXP
■ DOW CHEMICAL CO
(*Suby of* ROHM AND HAAS CO) ★
25500 Whitesell St, Hayward, CA 94545-3615
Tel (510) 786-0100 *Founded/Ownrshp* 1947
Sales 92.8MM[E] *EMP* 2,393[E]
SIC 2819 2821

D-U-N-S 00-535-3487 IMP/EXP
■ DOW CORNING CORP
(*Suby of* DOW CHEMICAL CO) ★
2200 W Salzburg Rd, Auburn, MI 48611-9548
Tel (989) 496-4000 *Founded/Ownrshp* 2016
Sales 2.5MMM[E] *EMP* 9,000
Accts Pricewaterhousecoopers Llp D
SIC 2821 2869 Silicone resins; Silicones
CEO: Robert Bob Henson
**CFO:* Joseph D Sheets
Treas: Jan Hjalber
**Ex VP:* J Donald Sheets
Sr VP: Kristy J Folkwein
**Sr VP:* Ganesh Kailasam
Sr VP: Kenneth P Kaufman
Sr VP: Andrew E Tometich
**VP:* Sue K McDonnell
VP: Paul Pretzer
VP: Kevin W Scroggin
Exec: Angelo Bianchini
Exec: Jeroen Bloemhard
Exec: Peter Cartwright
Exec: Klaus Hoffmann
Exec: Eriko Sakurai
Exec: SOO Kee Wang
Comm Man: Agnes Khu

D-U-N-S 62-620-2360
■ DOW CORNING SILICON ENERGY SYSTEMS INC
(*Suby of* DOW CORNING CORP) ★
2200 Salzburg St, Midland, MI 48640-8531
Tel (989) 496-4000 *Founded/Ownrshp* 1992
Sales NA *EMP* 1,500
SIC 6719 Investment holding companies, except banks
Pr: Gary Anderson
**Prin:* Richard Hazelton

DOW ELECTRONICS
See DEDC INC

DOW GARDENS
See DOW HERBERT H & GRACE A FOUNDATION

D-U-N-S 09-631-8613
DOW HERBERT H & GRACE A FOUNDATION (MI)
DOW GARDENS
1809 Eastman Ave, Midland, MI 48640-2641
Tel (989) 631-2677 *Founded/Ownrshp* 1936
Sales 97.5MM *EMP* 4
SIC 6732 Charitable trust management
Pr: Margaret A Riecker
**Ch:* Herbert D Doan
**Treas:* Michael L Dow
Dir Soc: Carolynn Paten

D-U-N-S 87-283-5350
■ DOW HOLDINGS LLC
(*Suby of* DOW CHEMICAL CO) ★
2030 Dow Ctr, Midland, MI 48674-1500
Tel (989) 636-1000 *Founded/Ownrshp* 1994
Sales 142.7MM[E] *EMP* 129[E]
SIC 8748

D-U-N-S 05-346-7713
DOW HOTEL CO LLC
16400 Southcenter Pkwy # 208, Tukwila, WA 98188-3335
Tel (206) 575-3600 *Founded/Ownrshp* 1998
Sales 153.9MM[E] *EMP* 3,000
SIC 7011 Hotels & motels
CFO: Louis W Sanford
Sr VP: Greg Denton
Sr VP: Robert Levy
Rgnl Mgr: Jay Hadsell
Genl Mgr: Kevin Schjei
VP Opers: Ernest Catanzaro

D-U-N-S 00-131-6702 IMP
■ DOW JONES & CO INC
(*Suby of* NEWS CORP) ★
1211 Avenue Of The Americ, New York, NY 10036-8711
Tel (609) 627-2999 *Founded/Ownrshp* 1882, 2007
Sales 2.5MMM[E] *EMP* 8,000
SIC 2711 2721 Newspapers; Magazines: publishing & printing
CEO: William Lewis
Pr: Edwin Finn Jr
**CFO:* Anna Sedgley
**Ofcr:* Ashley Huston
Ofcr: Michael Rooney
**Ex VP:* Mark Jackson
VP: Andy Baez
VP: Michael B Buchanan
VP: Chris Collins
VP: Lisa Fleischman
VP: Eric Mandrackie
VP: Viv Wang
Comm Dir: Janet Mayo

D-U-N-S 84-967-9188
■ DOW JONES AER CO INC
(*Suby of* DOW JONES & CO INC) ★
1211 Av Of The Am Lwr C3r, New York, NY 10036
Tel (212) 416-2000 *Founded/Ownrshp* 2001
Sales 155.2MM[E] *EMP* 865[E]
SIC 2721 Periodicals
Ex VP: Mark Kirkhart
Ex VP: Patrick Purcell
Sr VP: Paul Meller
VP: Joseph Baio
VP: Frank Barnako
VP: Dick Levine
Exec: Mark Musgrave
Dir Soc: Angus Peckham-Cooper
Genl Mgr: Sharon Terlep
CTO: Christopher Nelligan
IT Man: Michael Bird

D-U-N-S 06-472-4917
DOWLING COLLEGE INC
DOWLING INSTITUTE
150 Idle Hour Blvd, Oakdale, NY 11769-1999
Tel (631) 244-3000 *Founded/Ownrshp* 1968
Sales 78.1MM *EMP* 1,030
Accts Kpmg Llp New York Ny
SIC 8221 Colleges universities & professional schools
Pr: Bob Gafney
**Pr:* Dr Norman R Smith
Pr: Jonathan White
Treas: Amanda Johnson
**Sr VP:* Dr Elana Zolfo
VP: Maria Brown
Ex Dir: Antonia Loschiavo
MIS Dir: Walter Benka
HC Dir: Suzanne Voss

DOWLING INSTITUTE
See DOWLING COLLEGE INC

D-U-N-S 11-853-4809 IMP/EXP
DOWLING TEXTILE CO
DOWLING TEXTILE MFG CO
615 Macon Rd, McDonough, GA 30253-3533
Tel (770) 957-3981 *Founded/Ownrshp* 1946
Sales 166.3MM[E] *EMP* 800
SIC 2326 2337 2389 Medical & hospital uniforms, men's; Uniforms, except athletic: women's, misses' & juniors'; Hospital gowns
Ch Bd: William A Hanger Sr
Pr: David A Huelsbeck
CFO: Gregory N Duggar
Ex VP: Daniel C Wright
VP: Robert Fogel
VP: John M Hanger
VP: Vijay Shah

DOWLING TEXTILE MFG CO
See DOWLING TEXTILE CO

DOWN EAST MEDICAL SUPPLY
See LENOIR MEMORIAL HOSPITAL INC

D-U-N-S 06-892-9686 IMP
DOWN-LITE INTERNATIONAL INC
DOWNLITE
8153 Duke Blvd, Mason, OH 45040-8104
Tel (513) 229-3696 *Founded/Ownrshp* 1983
Sales 92.6MM[E] *EMP* 235
SIC 2392 5719 Pillows, bed: made from purchased materials; Comforters & quilts: made from purchased materials; Bedding (sheets, blankets, spreads & pillows)
CEO: James P Lape
**CFO:* Janna Ragan
CFO: Josh Werthaiser
VP: Bob Altbaier
**VP:* Chad Altbaier
VP: Chuck Northcutt
Genl Mgr: Frank Corella
CIO: Brian Levy
Dir IT: Larry Werthaiser
Sls&Mrk Ex: Jyl Davis

D-U-N-S 79-363-1078 IMP
DOWNEAST OUTFITTERS INC
NAMEBRAND OUTLET
375 W Hope Ave, Salt Lake City, UT 84115-5116
Tel (801) 467-7520 *Founded/Ownrshp* 1991
Sales 97.7MM[E] *EMP* 750
SIC 5611 5621 5963 2512 Men's & boys' clothing stores; Women's clothing stores; Furnishings, including furniture, house-to-house; Living room furniture: upholstered on wood frames
CEO: Klane Murphy
Pr: Eugene Freedman
COO: Rich Israelsen
Treas: Bill Freedman
VP: Jonathan Freedman

D-U-N-S 06-619-0547
DOWNERS GROVE IMPORTS LTD
PUGI OF CHICAGOLAND
2020 Ogden Ave, Downers Grove, IL 60515-2620
Tel (630) 964-9500 *Founded/Ownrshp* 1990
Sales 96.0MM *EMP* 63[E]
Accts Jerry J Sarcia Cpa Libertyv
SIC 5511 Automobiles, new & used
Pr: Dominic Pugliani
CFO: Victor Perez
Off Mgr: Terry Carlson

DOWNEY CMNTY HOSP AUX GIFT SP
See DRMC PROPERTIES INC

D-U-N-S 04-743-7306
DOWNEY REGIONAL MEDICAL CENTER-HOSPITAL INC
PIH HOME HEALTH SERVICES
(*Suby of* PIH HOME HEALTH SERVICES) ★
11500 Brookshire Ave, Downey, CA 90241-4990
Tel (562) 698-0811 *Founded/Ownrshp* 2013
Sales 126.8MM *EMP* 1,150
SIC 8062 General medical & surgical hospitals
Pr: James R West
Chf Path: Parakrama T Chandrasoma
Chf OB: David G Aguilar
COO: Bryan Smolskis
CFO: Greg Williams
Treas: Kenton Woods
Sr VP: Rosalio Lopez MD
Off Mgr: Teresa Guardino
Off Mgr: Tiffany A Mendoza
IT Man: Popo Chung
IT Man: Shaun Holliday

D-U-N-S 07-795-5813
DOWNEY UNIFIED SCHOOL DISTRICT
D.U.S.D
11627 Brookshire Ave, Downey, CA 90241-4911
Tel (562) 904-3500 *Founded/Ownrshp* 2000
Sales 126.8MM[E] *EMP* 2,900
SIC 8211 Public elementary & secondary schools
CFO: Kevin Condon
**Ch:* Dianne Lumsdaine
Off Mgr: Linda James
MIS Dir: John Varak
Pr Dir: Ashley Greaney
Teacher Pr: Bethann Arko
Teacher Pr: Kenneth Kato
Teacher Pr: Rena Thompson

D-U-N-S 08-880-7029
DOWNINGTOWN AREA SCHOOL DISTRICT
540 Trestle Pl, Downingtown, PA 19335-3459
Tel (610) 269-8460 *Founded/Ownrshp* 1900
Sales 204.8MM *EMP* 1,300
Accts Rainer & Company Newtown Squa
SIC 8211 Public elementary & secondary schools
**CFO:* Richard Fazio
MIS Dir: Colleen Yenser
Dir IT: Buck Jones
Info Man: Alicia Liermann
Pr Dir: Patricia McGrown
Psych: Georgia Soley

DOWNLITE
See DOWN-LITE INTERNATIONAL INC

D-U-N-S 11-861-5848
DOWNRITE HOLDINGS INC
14241 Sw 143rd Ct, Miami, FL 33186-5695
Tel (305) 232-2340 *Founded/Ownrshp* 2001
Sales 83.5MM[E] *EMP* 378[E]
SIC 1611 1623 8711 1794 Surfacing & paving; Water & sewer line construction; Engineering services; Excavation work
Pr: Samuel J Lo Bue
**VP:* Joseph Lo Bue

DOWNS FOOD GROUP
See TONY DOWNS FOODS CO

DOWNTOWN MUNICIPAL AIRPORT
See CITY OF SHREVEPORT

D-U-N-S 07-374-9640
DOYLESTOWN HOSPITAL HEALTH AND WELLNESS CENTER INC
595 W State St, Doylestown, PA 18901-2597
Tel (215) 345-2200 Founded/Ownrshp 1923
Sales 211.1MM EMP 2,853
SIC 8051 8062 Skilled nursing care facilities; General medical & surgical hospitals
Pr: James Brexler
Dir Vol: Karen Langley
*Pr: Richard A Reif
COO: James Browlow
*CFO: Dan Upton
Bd of Dir: Gregory Gallant
Bd of Dir: Richard Lambert
VP: Scott Levy
*VP: Eleanor Wilson
Comm Dir: Ron E Watson
Dir Rad: William Corse
Dir Rad: Ronald Costanzo

D-U-N-S 06-394-1033
DOYON DRILLING INC
(Suby of DOYON LIMITED) ★
11500 C St Ste 200, Anchorage, AK 99515-2693
Tel (907) 563-5530 Founded/Ownrshp 1981
Sales 90.0MM^E EMP 450
SIC 1381 Drilling oil & gas wells; Directional drilling oil & gas wells; Redrilling oil & gas wells; Reworking oil & gas wells
Pr: Aaron Schutt
*Genl Mgr: Ron Wilson

D-U-N-S 07-819-7928
DOYON LIMITED
1 Doyon Pl Ste 300, Fairbanks, AK 99701-2941
Tel (907) 459-2000 Founded/Ownrshp 2008
Sales 1.6MMM^E EMP 1,200
Accts Kpmg
SIC 1381 1382 Drilling oil & gas wells; Oil & gas exploration services
CEO: Aaron M Schutt
*Ch Bd: Robert Brean
*Pr: Norm Phillips Jr
COO: Aaron M Schutt
COO: Aaron Schutt
*CFO: Daniel Osborn
*Treas: Miranda Wright
*Sr VP: Patrick W Duke
*Sr VP: Roberta Bobbi Quintavell
*Sr VP: Geraldine Geri Simon
*VP: Julie L Biddle
VP: Kelly Brooks
*VP: Charlene R Marth
*VP: James Mery
VP: Sarah Obed
VP: Kevin Slattery
Exec: Jeff Filut

D-U-N-S 80-637-3259 EXP
DP DISTRIBUTION LLC
(Suby of DADE PAPER CO) ★
9601 Nw 112th Ave, Medley, FL 33178-2521
Tel (305) 777-6108 Founded/Ownrshp 1939
Sales 142.0MM^E EMP 690
SIC 5149 5963 Groceries & related products; Health foods; Home related products, direct sales
Prin: Robert A Whitebook

DPC INSTRUMENT SYSTEMS
See SIEMENS MEDICAL SOLUTIONS DIAGNOSTICS

D-U-N-S 04-389-8092 IMP/EXP
DPH HOLDINGS CORP
DELPHI
(Suby of DELPHI AUTOMOTIVE LLP)
5725 Delphi Dr, Troy, MI 48098-2815
Tel (248) 813-2000 Founded/Ownrshp 1999
Sales 1.7MMM^E EMP 11,900^E
SIC 3714 Motor vehicle parts & accessories
CEO: Rodney O'Neal
Pr: Kenneth Ian
Sr Cor Off: Renee George
Sr VP: Majdi B Abulaban
Sr VP: Kevin M Butler
Sr VP: Liam Butterworth
Sr VP: Kevin P Clark
VP: John P Arle
VP: Ray C Campbell
VP: Jessica L Holscott
VP: Timothy Richards
VP: Logan G Robinson
VP: Michael Troisi

D-U-N-S 60-731-4031 IMP/EXP
DPH LLC
DELPHI
(Suby of DELPHI CORP) ★
5725 Delphi Dr, Troy, MI 48098-2815
Tel (248) 813-2000 Founded/Ownrshp 2009
Sales 136.0MM^E EMP 1,000
SIC 3714 Motor vehicle parts & accessories
Prin: Robert Brust

D-U-N-S 10-520-4155 IMP
DPH-DAS GLOBAL (HOLDINGS) LLC
(Suby of DELPHI) ★
5725 Delphi Dr, Troy, MI 48098-2815
Tel (248) 813-2000 Founded/Ownrshp 2005
Sales 52.7MM^E EMP 1,000
SIC 3714 Motor vehicle parts & accessories
Prin: Bette Walker
Pr Mgr: Lindsey Williams

D-U-N-S 16-275-7723 IMP
DPH-DAS LLC
(Suby of DELPHI) ★
5725 Delphi Dr, Troy, MI 48098-2815
Tel (248) 813-2000 Founded/Ownrshp 1998
Sales 1.0MMM^E EMP 9,500
SIC 3714 Motor vehicle parts & accessories
V Ch: Donald Runkle
Dir: William Herren
Brnch Mgr: Jack Hulfe
QC Dir: John Moulds
Advt Dir: Joe Martin

DPI
See DSM PHARMACEUTICALS INC

DPI MID ATLANTIC DIVISION
See DPI SPECIALTY FOODS MID ATLANTIC INC

D-U-N-S 07-832-0833
DPI NEWCO LLC
D P X
(Suby of ACE CASH EXPRESS) ★
45 Waterview Blvd, Parsippany, NJ 07054-7611
Tel (973) 257-8113 Founded/Ownrshp 1994, 2014
Sales 99.2MM^E EMP 159^E
SIC 2834 Pharmaceutical preparations
Exec: Doreen Guastini
Sls Mgr: Bernt Schober

D-U-N-S 07-936-3286
DPI NEWCO LLC
(Suby of PATHEON HOLDINGS I B.V.)
5900 Martin Luther King, Greenville, NC 27834-8628
Tel (252) 758-3436 Founded/Ownrshp 2014
Sales 113.9MM EMP 1,200
SIC 2834 Pharmaceutical preparations
CEO: Jim Mullen

DPI ROCKY MOUNTAIN
See DPI SPECIALTY FOODS ROCKY MOUNTAIN INC

D-U-N-S 60-343-3723 IMP/EXP
DPI SPECIALTY FOODS INC
D P I
(Suby of IDB HOLDINGS INC) ★
601 S Rockefeller Ave, Ontario, CA 91761-7871
Tel (909) 390-0892 Founded/Ownrshp 1990
Sales 1.0MMM^E EMP 1,450
SIC 5149 5143

D-U-N-S 06-928-4123 IMP
DPI SPECIALTY FOODS MID ATLANTIC INC
DPI MID ATLANTIC DIVISION
(Suby of D P I) ★
1000 Prince Georges Blvd, Upper Marlboro, MD 20774-8705
Tel (301) 430-2200 Founded/Ownrshp 1974
Sales 183.5MM^E EMP 220
SIC 5149 Health foods; Natural & organic foods
CEO: John Jordan
*Pr: Jayson Folus
*CFO: David Doggin
*CFO: Rick Pitts
Treas: Clary Cheryl
VP: Beth Haley
VP: Joe Oflynn
*VP: Allen Sabry
VP: Ron Stone
Genl Mgr: Bill Barrett

D-U-N-S 03-197-7929 IMP
DPI SPECIALTY FOODS ROCKY MOUNTAIN INC
DPI ROCKY MOUNTAIN
(Suby of D P I) ★
8125 E 88th Ave, Henderson, CO 80640-8121
Tel (303) 301-1226 Founded/Ownrshp 1996
Sales 98.1MM^E EMP 320
SIC 5141

D-U-N-S 04-115-8668 IMP
DPI SPECIALTY FOODS WEST INC
(Suby of D P I) ★
601 S Rockefeller Ave, Ontario, CA 91761-7871
Tel (909) 975-1019 Founded/Ownrshp 1990
Sales 662.5MM^E EMP 800^E
SIC 5141 Groceries, general line
CEO: John Jordan
*Pr: James De Keyser
*Pr: Donna Robbins
*COO: Francis Haren
*CFO: Conor Crowley
*Sr VP: Larry Noble
VP: Bob Adams
VP Opers: Sam Lopez
S&M/VP: Paul Miller
Mktg Dir: Betty Gregory

DPISD
See DEER PARK INDEPENDENT SCHOOL DISTRICT (INC)

D-U-N-S 14-721-2336
■ **DPL INC**
(Suby of AES DPL HOLDINGS LLC) ★
1065 Woodman Dr, Dayton, OH 45432-1438
Tel (937) 331-4063 Founded/Ownrshp 1985
Sales 1.6MMM EMP 1,182^E
Accts Ernst & Young Llp Indianapoli
SIC 4911 Generation, electric power; Transmission, electric power; Distribution, electric power
Pr: Phil Herrington
Pr: Derek Porter
CFO: Craig Jackson
Treas: Jeffrey K Mackay
VP: Gregory S Campbell
VP: Shirish Desai
VP: Timothy G Rice
Genl Mgr: Mike Russ
CIO: Cedric Oluoch
Sfty Mgr: Georgene Dawson
Opers Mgr: Jeff Tauscher
Board of Directors: Brian Miller, Mary Stawikey, Andrew Vesey

D-U-N-S 96-443-8530
DPR CONSTRUCTION A GENERAL PARTNERSHIP
(Suby of DPR CONSTRUCTION INC) ★
1450 Veterans Blvd, Redwood City, CA 94063-2617
Tel (650) 474-1450 Founded/Ownrshp 1990
Sales 2.6MMM EMP 2,300
SIC 1541 Industrial buildings & warehouses
Pr: Douglas E Woods
CFO: Michele Leiva
Sec: Ron J Davidowski
Ex VP: James F Dolen
Ex VP: Michael Ford
Ex VP: Eric R Lamb
Ex VP: George J Pfeffer
Ex VP: Peter A Salvati
Prin: Peter C Nosler
Dir IT: Everardo Villasenor

D-U-N-S 61-780-1915 IMP
DPR CONSTRUCTION INC
1450 Veterans Blvd Ofc, Redwood City, CA 94063-2618
Tel (650) 474-1450 Founded/Ownrshp 1990
Sales 3.1MMM EMP 4,500
Accts Pricewaterhousecoopers Llp Lo
SIC 1541 1542 Industrial buildings & warehouses; Commercial & office building contractors
CEO: Douglas E Woods
V Ch: Daniel Valentine
Pr: Alison Lyons
*CFO: Michele Leiva
*Treas: Ron J Davidowski
*Ex VP: James F Dolen
*Ex VP: Michael Ford
*Ex VP: Eric R Lamb
*Ex VP: George J Pfeffer
*Ex VP: Peter A Salvati
Exec: Aric Preisendorf
Exec: Michael Saks
Board of Directors: Peter C Nosler

DPSCS
See MARYLAND DEPT OF PUBLIC SAFETY & CORRECTIONAL SERVICES

D-U-N-S 62-178-2218 IMP
DPT LABORATORIES LTD
(Suby of RENAISSANCE ACQUISITION HOLDINGS LLC) ★
318 Mccullough Ave, San Antonio, TX 78215-1833
Tel (866) 225-5378 Founded/Ownrshp 2012
Sales 519.8MM^E EMP 1,774
Accts Ernst & Young Llp San Antonio
SIC 2834 Pharmaceutical preparations
Pr: Paul H Johnson
Treas: Belinda Arcos
Sr VP: Mark Fite
Sr VP: Paul Josephs
Sr VP: Glenn Kues
VP: Rick Bentzinger
VP: Kuljit Bhatia
VP: Gene Ciolfi
VP: Lyle Flom
VP: Nick Walp
VP Bus Dev: Kay Harrell
Dir Bus: Lynn Allen

D-U-N-S 07-169-5233
DPWN HOLDINGS (USA) INC
DHL
(Suby of DHL FINANCE SERVICES B.V.)
1210 S Pine Island Rd, Plantation, FL 33324-4402
Tel (954) 888-7000 Founded/Ownrshp 2005
Sales 3.5MMM^E EMP 30,000
SIC 4513 4731 Air courier services; Freight forwarding
Pr: Robert Whitaker
*CEO: Mike Parra
*CFO: Rafael Estevez
CFO: Fabio Manca
CFO: Rick Turner
Treas: Robert Whitaker
Ex VP: Brian Lindholm
Ex VP: Steve Wells
Sr VP: Chee K Lin
*VP: David Brown
VP: Shanon Duthie
*VP: Josh Frank
*VP: Jon Olin
VP: Christopher Ong
VP: Cindy Smith
Dir Bus: Richard Jones
Dir Bus: Jean-Marc Lami

D-U-N-S 07-954-7846
DPX HOLDINGS INC
(Suby of ACE CASH EXPRESS) ★
4307 Emperor Blvd Ste 140, Durham, NC 27703-8080
Tel (919) 226-3200 Founded/Ownrshp 2014
Sales 250.3MM^E EMP 8,000
SIC 6799 Investors
Pr: Paul Levy

D-U-N-S 83-053-8893
DQE HOLDINGS LLC
411 7th Ave Ste 3, Pittsburgh, PA 15219-1905
Tel (412) 393-7100 Founded/Ownrshp 2006
Sales 350.7MM^E EMP 1,400^E
SIC 6719 Investment holding companies, except banks
Secur Mgr: Dale Flaherty

DR. BRONNER'S SOAPS
See ALL ONE GOD FAITH INC

D-U-N-S 07-850-8990 IMP/EXP
DR FRESH LLC
FRESH MERGE
6645 Caballero Blvd, Buena Park, CA 90620-1131
Tel (714) 690-1573 Founded/Ownrshp 2012
Sales 110.3MM EMP 100^E
Accts Crowe Horwath Llp Costa Mesa
SIC 5047 3843 Medical & hospital equipment; Dental equipment

D-U-N-S 07-498-8221
DR GERTRUDE A BARBER CENTER INC
DR GERTRUDE A BARBER NATIONAL
100 Barber Pl, Erie, PA 16507-1899
Tel (814) 453-7661 Founded/Ownrshp 1954
Sales 68.4MM EMP 1,100^E
Accts Bkd Llp Erie Pa
SIC 8361 8211 Residential care; School for physically handicapped
CEO: John J Barber
CFO: Karen M McElhinny
Ofcr: Chris Curcio
Ex VP: Maureen Barber-Carey
Exec: Lauren Glass
Dept Mgr: Paul Causgrove
Off Mgr: Julie Deangelo
CIO: Jane Davis
IT Man: Laurie Callaghan
IT Man: Mike Dugan
IT Man: Greg Stubits

DR GERTRUDE A BARBER NATIONAL
See DR GERTRUDE A BARBER CENTER INC

D-U-N-S 92-976-5030
■ **DR HORTON - TEXAS LTD**
(Suby of DR HORTON INC) ★
301 Commerce St Ste 500, Fort Worth, TX 76102-4178
Tel (817) 856-8200 Founded/Ownrshp 1979
Sales 4.3MMM EMP 3,477
SIC 1521 Single-family housing construction
Ch Bd: Donald R Horton

D-U-N-S 09-704-7369
▲ **DR HORTON INC**
301 Commerce St Ste 500, Fort Worth, TX 76102-4178
Tel (817) 390-8200 Founded/Ownrshp 1978
Sales 11.8MMM EMP 6,976
Accts Pricewaterhousecoopers Llp Fo
Tkr Sym DHI Exch NYS
SIC 1531 6162 Speculative builder, single-family houses; Condominium developers; Speculative builder, multi-family dwellings; Townhouse developers; Mortgage bankers
Pr: David V Auld
*Ch Bd: Donald R Horton
COO: Michael J Murray
CFO: Bill W Wheat
Board of Directors: Barbara K Allen, Brad S Anderson, Michael R Buchanan, Michael W Hewatt

D-U-N-S 01-199-9190 IMP
DR JAYS INC
STEEV WEST FOURTH
15 W 37th St Fl 11, New York, NY 10018-5391
Tel (212) 239-3355 Founded/Ownrshp 1991
Sales 105.1MM^E EMP 700^E
Accts Levine & Granet New York Ny
SIC 5611 5661 Clothing, sportswear, men's & boys'; Footwear, athletic
Pr: Elliot Betesh
*CFO: Darlene Sauder
*VP: Raymond Betesh

DR LEONARD HEALTH CARE PDTS
See DR LEONARDS HEALTHCARE CORP

D-U-N-S 03-929-0887 IMP/EXP
DR LEONARDS HEALTHCARE CORP
DR LEONARD HEALTH CARE PDTS
(Suby of AMERIMARK HOLDINGS LLC) ★
100 Nixon Ln, Edison, NJ 08837-3804
Tel (732) 572-0900 Founded/Ownrshp 2007
Sales 168.5MM^E EMP 600
SIC 5961 Catalog sales
CEO: Gary Geisler
COO: Donna Elliott
*CFO: Joseph Albanese
Chf Mktg O: Leigh Tricamo
Ex VP: Joe Albanese
*Ex VP: Diane Huzaer
*VP: Gary Porto
Exec: Susanna Englert
Exec: Jeffrey Feierstein
*Prin: Mark Ethier
Genl Mgr: Peter Reno

DR PEPPER SNAPPLE GROUP
See AMERICAN BOTTLING CO

D-U-N-S 80-791-9571 IMP
▲ **DR PEPPER SNAPPLE GROUP INC**
5301 Legacy Dr, Plano, TX 75024-3109
Tel (972) 673-7000 Founded/Ownrshp 2003
Sales 6.2MMM EMP 19,000
Accts Deloitte & Touche Llp Dallas
Tkr Sym DPS Exch NYS
SIC 2086 Bottled & canned soft drinks; Carbonated beverages, nonalcoholic: bottled & canned; Iced tea & fruit drinks, bottled & canned; Mineral water, carbonated: packaged in cans, bottles, etc.
Pr: Larry D Young
*Ch Bd: Wayne R Sanders
Pr: Rodger L Collins
Pr: James J Johnston Jr
CFO: Martin M Ellen
Ex VP: James L Baldwin Jr
Ex VP: Tina Barry
Ex VP: Philip L Hancock
Ex VP: Derry L Hobson
Ex VP: John Stewart
Ex VP: James R Trebilcock
Sr VP: Dana Berghorn
VP: Debra Benovitz
VP: Victor Cosentino
VP: Randy Downing
VP: Vicki Draughn
VP: Thomas Farrah
VP: Dan Flowers
VP: Kelton Graham
VP: Pablo Guzman
VP: Terry Hollister
Board of Directors: David E Alexander, Antonio Carillo, Jos Gutirrez, Pamela H Patsley, Joyce M Roche, Ronald G Rogers, M Anne Szostak

D-U-N-S 00-733-2273 IMP/EXP
■ **DR PEPPER/SEVEN UP INC** (DE)
(Suby of DR PEPPER SNAPPLE GROUP INC) ★
5301 Legacy Dr Fl 1, Plano, TX 75024-3109
Tel (972) 673-7000 Founded/Ownrshp 1885
Sales 535.4MM^E EMP 1,869
SIC 2087 Flavoring extracts & syrups
CEO: Larry D Young
*Pr: Douglas Tough
*Sr VP: Taun Dimatteo
*Sr VP: Tom Farrah
*Sr VP: William M Nelson
*Sr VP: Angela Stephens
*VP: Jeff Altizer
IT Man: Debbie Depasquale

D-U-N-S 80-231-5887 IMP/EXP
DR REDDYS LABORATORIES INC
(*Suby of* DR REDDY'S LABORATORIES LIMITED)
107 College Rd E Ste 100, Princeton, NJ 08540-6623
Tel (908) 203-4900 *Founded/Ownrshp* 2000
Sales 278.5MM^E *EMP* 485
SIC 5122 3089 Pharmaceuticals; Cases, plastic
CEO: G V Prasad
**Sec:* Vishwanatha R Bonthu
**Ex VP:* Umang Vohra
Sr VP: Raghav Chari
VP: Kenneth Surowitz
Assoc Dir: Abhishek Mukhopadhyay

DR WILLIAM SCHOLL COLLEGE OF P
See ROSALIND FRANKLIN UNIVERSITY OF MEDICINE AND SCIENCE

D-U-N-S 19-396-6157
DRA ADVISORS LLC
D R A
220 E 42nd St Fl 27, New York, NY 10017-5829
Tel (212) 697-4740 *Founded/Ownrshp* 1994
Sales 204.0MM^E *EMP* 177
SIC 6282 Investment advisory service
Pt: Francis X Tansey
**Pt:* Janine Roberts
**Pt:* Dean Sickles
**Pt:* Brian T Summers
**Pt:* Diana Tully
CFO: Brian Summers
Ex VP: Glen Besser
VP: Peter Janoff
Dir Risk M: Brad Boyle
Dir Risk M: Jodi Santi
Mng Dir: Jean-Marie Apruzzese

D-U-N-S 01-754-4514 IMP
DRA TAGGART LLC
4000 Town Center Way # 200, Canonsburg, PA 15317-5837
Tel (724) 754-9800 *Founded/Ownrshp* 1999
Sales 221.8MM^E *EMP* 750
SIC 5052 Coal & other minerals & ores
VP Mktg: Dennis Davis

D-U-N-S 04-454-9434 IMP
DRAEGER INC
NORTH AMERICAN DRAGER
(*Suby of* DRAGERWERK AG & CO. KGAA)
3135 Quarry Rd, Telford, PA 18969-1042
Tel (215) 721-5400 *Founded/Ownrshp* 1993
Sales 209.3MM^E *EMP* 800
SIC 3841

D-U-N-S 02-866-5404
DRAEGERS SUPER MARKETS
VIOGNIER
291 Utah Ave, South San Francisco, CA 94080-6802
Tel (650) 244-6500 *Founded/Ownrshp* 1953
Sales 89.7MM^E *EMP* 550
SIC 5411 Supermarkets, independent
CEO: James M Draeger
Pr: Andy Butera
**CFO:* Peter Draeger
**Treas:* Richard Draeger
**VP:* John Draeger
Exec: Chris Aquino
IT Man: Roger Martin
VP Opers: F Draeger
Sales Asso: Lisa Jensen
Sales Asso: Beverly Townsley
Pgrm Dir: Mia Chambers

D-U-N-S 61-668-5355 EXP
DRAGADOS USA INC
(*Suby of* DRAGADOS SA FCC CONSTRUCCION SA UTE BOETTICHER LEY 18-1982)
810 7th Ave Fl 9, New York, NY 10019-9003
Tel (212) 779-0900 *Founded/Ownrshp* 2005
Sales 756.2MM^E *EMP* 1,100
SIC 1611 General contractor, highway & street construction
CEO: Ignacio Segura
**CFO:* Fernando G Alcaniz
Treas: Sully Chen
Ex VP: Larry Hurley
Genl Couns: Joseph Portela

D-U-N-S 08-032-0523
DRAGON CLOUD INC
1 Commerce St, Wilmington, DE 19801
Tel (702) 508-2676 *Founded/Ownrshp* 2014
Sales 15.8MM^E *EMP* 1,200
SIC 2731 Books: publishing & printing

DRAGON ESP
See MODERN AG PRODUCTS LTD

D-U-N-S 05-458-9481
DRAGON PRODUCTS LTD
(*Suby of* DRAGON ESP) ★
1655 Louisiana St, Beaumont, TX 77701-1120
Tel (409) 833-2665 *Founded/Ownrshp* 1998
Sales 288.1MM^E *EMP* 1,000^E
SIC 3443 Fuel tanks (oil, gas, etc.): metal plate
Genl Pt: Will Crenshaw
CFO: Brian Bommer
Genl Mgr: Jimmy Jones

DRAINAGE PROTECTION SYSTEMS
See OLDCASTLE PRECAST INC

D-U-N-S 60-399-1949 IMP/EXP
DRAKA CABLETEQ USA INC
(*Suby of* PRYSMIAN CABLES & SYSTEMS USA) ★
22 Joseph E Warner Blvd, North Dighton, MA 02764-1300
Tel (508) 822-5444 *Founded/Ownrshp* 1992
Sales 184.7MM^E *EMP* 384
SIC 3357 Building wire & cable, nonferrous
Pr: Hakan Ozmen
**Treas:* Daniele Mazzarella
VP: Andrew Hemingway
VP: Mark Lowell

D-U-N-S 19-275-0412 IMP
DRAKA HOLDINGS USA INC
PRYSMIAN CABLES & SYSTEMS USA
(*Suby of* DRAKA HOLDING B.V.)
2512 Penny Rd, Claremont, NC 28610-8634
Tel (828) 459-8550 *Founded/Ownrshp* 1988
Sales 315.4MM^E *EMP* 1,130
SIC 3357 Communication wire
**Pr:* F Douglas Barbe
**Treas:* Gary R Wilbur
Dir IT: Martin Scholte

D-U-N-S 01-198-8045
■ **DRAKE PETROLEUM CO INC**
XTRA MART
(*Suby of* WARREN EQUITIES INC) ★
221 Quinebaug Rd, North Grosvenordale, CT 06255-1123
Tel (860) 935-5200 *Founded/Ownrshp* 1958
Sales 789.6MM^E *EMP* 1,200
SIC 5541 5411 Gasoline service stations; Grocery stores
Pr: David Preble
**Ch Bd:* Herbert M Kaplan
**Treas:* Amato Dibiasio
**Ex VP:* Paul Samar
Ex VP: Paul Sammara
**Prin:* John Dziedzic
Dir IT: Tom Flanagan
Site Mgr: Allauddin Chaudhry
Mktg Mgr: John Genovesi

D-U-N-S 01-711-0030
DRAKE REHAB WEST CHESTER
7700 University Ct # 1600, West Chester, OH 45069-7202
Tel (513) 475-7454 *Founded/Ownrshp* 2008
Sales 141.1MM *EMP* 2
SIC 8049 Physical therapist
Prin: Carol A King

D-U-N-S 04-110-3730
DRAKE UNIVERSITY
2507 University Ave, Des Moines, IA 50311-4505
Tel (515) 271-2011 *Founded/Ownrshp* 1881
Sales 224.6MM *EMP* 830
Accts Denman & Company Llp West Des
SIC 8221 University
Pr: David Maxwell
COO: Sandra Ries-Wandrey
COO: Melissa Van
**Treas:* Victoria E Payseur
Ofcr: Nicole McAllister
Ofcr: Meaghan Tigges
VP: Angela Accurso
VP: Don Adams
VP: Nicholas Cooling
Exec: Elise Beacom
Exec: Sarah Hite
Exec: Maria Reyes

DRAKENFELD PRODUCTS
See FERRO COLOR & GLASS CORP

D-U-N-S 00-641-8164 IMP/EXP
DRAPER INC
411 S Pearl St, Spiceland, IN 47385-9637
Tel (765) 987-7999 *Founded/Ownrshp* 1902
Sales 133.4MM^E *EMP* 500^E
SIC 3861 2591 3651 Photographic equipment & supplies; Drapery hardware & blinds & shades; Household audio & video equipment
Pr: John D Pidgeon
Pr: Terry Coffey
**Treas:* Gary Knowles
**VP:* Michael D Broome
VP: Eric Guffey
Exec: Gini Deaton
Exec: Amy Magee
Exec: Eric McDaniel
Rgnl Mgr: Todd Garner
Rgnl Mgr: Ross Rhoades
Dir IT: Dave Elliott

DRAPER VALLEY FARMS
See DRAPER VALLEY HOLDINGS LLC

D-U-N-S 02-734-7483
DRAPER VALLEY HOLDINGS LLC
DRAPER VALLEY FARMS
1000 Jason Ln, Mount Vernon, WA 98273-2490
Tel (360) 424-7947 *Founded/Ownrshp* 2007
Sales 138.3MM^E *EMP* 475
SIC 0254 2015

D-U-N-S 08-445-5153 IMP/EXP
DRAPERS & DAMONS LLC
DRAPERS DAMONS FINE LADIES AP
(*Suby of* BEDFORD FAIR APPAREL) ★
9 Pasteur Ste 200, Irvine, CA 92618-3817
Tel (949) 784-3000 *Founded/Ownrshp* 2008
Sales 137.6MM^E *EMP* 634
SIC 5961 5621 5632 Catalog & mail-order houses; Clothing, mail order (except women's); Women's apparel, mail order; Ready-to-wear apparel, women's; Apparel accessories
CEO: Naomi Langdecker
**Pr:* Jeff Farmer
**Co-Pr:* Brent Bostwick
**Co-Pr:* Brad Farmer
Snr Mgr: Mary Lowrance

DRAPERS DAMONS FINE LADIES AP
See DRAPERS & DAMONS LLC

D-U-N-S 07-948-7728
DRAW ANOTHER CIRCLE LLC
3601 Plains Blvd, Amarillo, TX 79102-1004
Tel (806) 351-2300 *Founded/Ownrshp* 2014
Sales 1.2MMM^E *EMP* 200^E
SIC 5735 Video discs & tapes, prerecorded; Records, audio discs & tapes

D-U-N-S 14-048-5116
■ **DRAYER PHYSICAL THERAPY INSTITUTE LLC**
ADVANTAGE SPORTS PERFORMANCE
(*Suby of* GOLDMAN SACHS) ★
8205 Presidents Dr Fl 2, Hummelstown, PA 17036-8621
Tel (717) 220-2100 *Founded/Ownrshp* 2002
Sales 108.3MM^E *EMP* 1,800
SIC 8049 Physical therapist
Ch Bd: Luke Drayer
**CEO:* Eric Williams
**COO:* Ron Baum
CFO: Scott Cielewich
**CFO:* Kyle Conlee
Ex VP: Greg Bennett
Genl Mgr: Robyn Bailey
Genl Mgr: Terri Miller
Off Mgr: Suzi Spadonee
Info Man: Wade Doyle
Sls Dir: Beth Mason

DRC
See DATA RECOGNITION CORP

D-U-N-S 82-534-1709
DREAM MARRIAGE GROUP INC
2533 N Carson St Ste 3988, Carson City, NV 89706-0242
Tel (310) 200-8875 *Founded/Ownrshp* 2006
Sales 7.5MM^E *EMP* 1,500
SIC 8322 Family (marriage) counseling
Pr: Ilia Zavialov

D-U-N-S 14-558-4897
DREAMERS TRAVELS LLC
BRI FREE TOURS
830 E Sherman St, Phoenix, AZ 85034-4024
Tel (602) 305-6414 *Founded/Ownrshp* 2002
Sales 975.0MM *EMP* 27
SIC 7999 Tour & guide services

DREAMWORKS SKG
See DW STUDIOS LLC

D-U-N-S 00-382-6641
DREES CO
DREES HOMES COMPANY
211 Grandview Dr Ste 300, Fort Mitchell, KY 41017-2790
Tel (859) 578-4200 *Founded/Ownrshp* 1959
Sales 722.6MM *EMP* 549
Accts Deloitte & Touche Llp Cincinn
SIC 1531 1522 1521 Speculative builder, single-family houses; Apartment building construction; Condominium construction; New construction, single-family houses; Townhouse construction
Ch Bd: Ralph Drees
Pr: David Drees
VP: Lawrence Herbst
IT Man: Connie Thornton
Sls Mgr: Kristie Webber

DREES HOMES COMPANY
See DREES CO

D-U-N-S 01-881-6942 IMP
■ **DRESS BARN INC**
(*Suby of* ASCENA RETAIL GROUP INC) ★
933 Macarthur Blvd, Mahwah, NJ 07430-2045
Tel (800) 373-7722 *Founded/Ownrshp* 2011
Sales 4.3MMM^E *EMP* 30,000
SIC 5621 5632 Women's specialty clothing stores; Apparel accessories
Ch: Elliot Jaffe
Pr: Jeff Gerstel
Pr: John Sullivan
CFO: Robb Giammatteo
VP: John Pershing

D-U-N-S 07-320-5796 IMP/EXP
■ **DRESSER INC**
(*Suby of* GENERAL ELECTRIC CO) ★
601 Shiloh Rd, Plano, TX 75074-7210
Tel (262) 549-2626 *Founded/Ownrshp* 2011
Sales 73.8MM^E *EMP* 6,300
SIC 3491 3825 3594 3593 3561 3494 Industrial valves; Instruments to measure electricity; Fluid power pumps & motors; Fluid power cylinders & actuators; Pumps & pumping equipment; Valves & pipe fittings
CEO: Greg Cominos
Pr: R Michael Carlson
Pr: Bruce D Coventry
Pr: Daniel E Jezerinac
Pr: John T McKenna
CFO: James Nattier
Ex VP: Jacqueta Bradley
Ex VP: Randy Richoux
Sr VP: Linda Rutherford
VP: Tom Barrett
VP: Martha Bixby
**VP:* Dylan Cannon
**VP:* Robbie Marshall
**VP:* Linda L Rutherford
**VP:* Neil Thomas
**VP:* Brian White

DRESSER-RAND
See SIEMENS GOVERNMENT TECHNOLOGIES INC

D-U-N-S 16-118-7539 IMP/EXP
DRESSER-RAND CO
(*Suby of* DRESSER-RAND LLC) ★
500 Paul Clark Dr, Olean, NY 14760-9560
Tel (716) 375-3000 *Founded/Ownrshp* 1992
Sales 55.0MM^E *EMP* 2,297
SIC 3563 3511 3621

D-U-N-S 60-312-7825 IMP
DRESSER-RAND GROUP INC
(*Suby of* SIEMENS AG)
10205 Westheimer Rd # 1000, Houston, TX 77042-3139
Tel (713) 354-6100 *Founded/Ownrshp* 2015
Sales 3.4MMM^E *EMP* 7,900^E
SIC 3563 3511 Air & gas compressors; Steam turbines; Turbo-generators
CFO: Heribert Stumpf
CFO: Waleed M Sheikh
Ex VP: Pascal Lardy
Ex VP: Luciano Mozzato
Ex VP: Christopher Rossi
VP: Steve Brady
VP: Raymond L Carney Jr
VP: Claude Cordery
VP: Raimondo Giavi
VP: Terje Jensen
VP: Maged Mikhaeil
VP: Mark F MAI
VP: Martin Pfund
VP: Rajesh Vyas
Board of Directors: Steven Conner, Randy Zwirn

D-U-N-S 62-498-8726 IMP
DRESSER-RAND LLC
(*Suby of* DRESSER-RAND GROUP INC) ★
1200 W Sam Houston Pkwy N, Houston, TX 77043-4009
Tel (713) 354-6100 *Founded/Ownrshp* 2006
Sales 218.0MM^E *EMP* 3,197
SIC 3563 Air & gas compressors
Pr: Vincent R Volpe Jr
**CFO:* Mark E Baldwin
Ex VP: Luciano Mozzato
**VP:* Ann Ackerson
**VP:* Sammy Antoun
VP: Marco Rossi
Exec: Bradford Dickson
Genl Mgr: Nicolas Samson
IT Man: Alkesh Oza
Plnt Mgr: Somsanouk Khammivong
Sales Exec: Robert Marsters

D-U-N-S 00-787-1643
▲ **DREW INDUSTRIES INC**
3501 County Road 6 E, Elkhart, IN 46514-7663
Tel (574) 535-1125 *Founded/Ownrshp* 1984
Sales 1.4MMM *EMP* 6,576^E
Accts Kpmg Llp Chicago Illinois
Tkr Sym DW *Exch* NYS
SIC 3711 3714 3715 3442 3431 Chassis, motor vehicle; Motor vehicle parts & accessories; Trailer bodies; Window & door frames; Shower stalls, metal
CEO: Jason D Lippert
Ch Bd: James F Gero
Pr: Scott T Mereness
CFO: Brian M Hall
CFO: David M Smith
Board of Directors: Leigh J Abrams, Frank J Crespo, Brendan J Deely, Tracy D Graham, Frederick B Hegi Jr, John B Lowe Jr, Kieran M O'sullivan, David A Reed

D-U-N-S 08-022-3461
DREW MARINE GROUP INC
(*Suby of* DREW MARINE GROUP COOPERATIEF U.A.)
100 S Jefferson Rd # 204, Whippany, NJ 07981-1009
Tel (973) 526-5700 *Founded/Ownrshp* 2013
Sales 231.7MM^E *EMP* 500^E
SIC 8999 5169 Search & rescue service; Chemicals & allied products
Pr: Leonard Gelosa
**CFO:* Doug Grierson
**Treas:* Francis Quinn

D-U-N-S 07-925-8423
DREW MARINE PARTNERS LP
(*Suby of* JORDAN CO L P) ★
100 S Jefferson Rd # 102, Whippany, NJ 07981-1009
Tel (973) 526-5700 *Founded/Ownrshp* 2009
Sales 144.2MM^E *EMP* 47^E
SIC 5169 Chemicals & allied products
CEO: Leonard Gelosa

D-U-N-S 83-170-4429 IMP
DREW MARINE USA INC
(*Suby of* DREW MARINE GROUP INC) ★
100 S Jefferson Rd # 204, Whippany, NJ 07981-1009
Tel (973) 526-5700 *Founded/Ownrshp* 2013
Sales 234.6MM^E *EMP* 399
SIC 5169 Chemicals & allied products
CEO: Leonard Gelosa
**Treas:* Francis Queen
Ex VP: Jerry Hamby
Sr VP: Thomas Cessario
Sr VP: Daniel Kelleher
VP: Dan Kelleher
Genl Mgr: Steven Medved
CTO: Mark Ippolito
IT Man: Ken Amron
VP Opers: James Chandler
Opers Mgr: Jasmine Daniel

D-U-N-S 00-256-1868
DREW UNIVERSITY
DREW UNIVERSITY GRADUATE SCHOO
36 Madison Ave, Madison, NJ 07940-1493
Tel (973) 408-3000 *Founded/Ownrshp* 1867
Sales 128.2MM *EMP* 550^E
SIC 8221 University; Theological seminary
Ch Bd: Lewis Andrews
Pr: Jill Anderson
**Pr:* Maryann Baenninger
**Pr:* Dr Vivian Bull
Pr: Tom Harris
**Pr:* Thomas Kean
**V Ch Bd:* Barbara Casperson
**V Ch Bd:* Nancy Schaenen
Trst: Jordan Glatt
Trst: Ernest Lyght
Trst: Nancy Priest
Trst: Jeanne Zenker
Ofcr: George-Har Jennings
**VP:* Kenneth Alexo
VP: Savanna Arabi-Katbi
VP: Victoria Dayton
**VP:* Michael Groener
**VP:* Margaret E L Howard
**VP:* Mark Kopenski
VP: Robert Massa
**VP:* Michael McKitish

DREW UNIVERSITY GRADUATE SCHOO
See DREW UNIVERSITY

D-U-N-S 07-352-4555 IMP/EXP
DREXEL CHEMICAL CO
1700 Channel Ave, Memphis, TN 38106
Tel (901) 774-4370 *Founded/Ownrshp* 1972
Sales 112.8MM[E] *EMP* 250
SIC 2879 Agricultural chemicals; Fungicides, herbicides; Insecticides, agricultural or household; Plant hormones
Ch Bd: Leigh Shockey
Pr: Ben Johnson
VP: Jimmy Pelt
VP: Robert Shockey
Plnt Mgr: David Parker

DREXEL HERITAGE FURNITURE
See HFI WIND DOWN INC

D-U-N-S 00-260-4817
DREXEL UNIVERSITY (PA)
3141 Chestnut St, Philadelphia, PA 19104-2875
Tel (215) 895-2000 *Founded/Ownrshp* 1891
Sales 569.9MM[E] *EMP* 2,868
Accts Pricewaterhousecoopers Llp Ph
SIC 8221 Colleges & universities
Pr: Constantine N Papdakis
Pr: Michele Rovinsky
CFO: James Archibald
CFO: Daniel Dougherty
**CFO:* Thomas J Elzey
Assoc VP: Donna Frithsen
Assoc VP: Anne Jensen
Assoc VP: Michael N McCabe
Assoc VP: David Toll
**Ex VP:* Carl Oxholm III
Sr VP: Adele Barbat
**Sr VP:* Elizabeth A Dale
Sr VP: Mark L Greenberg
Sr VP: Richard V Homan
**Sr VP:* James R Tucker
VP: John Bielec
VP: M Brian Blake
VP: Michael Exler
VP: Michael J Exter
VP: Brian T Keech
VP: Joan Mc Donald

D-U-N-S 13-350-9237 IMP/EXP
DREYERS GRAND ICE CREAM HOLDINGS INC
(*Suby of* NESTLE PREPARED FOODS CO) ★
5929 College Ave, Oakland, CA 94618-1325
Tel (510) 652-8187 *Founded/Ownrshp* 2003
Sales 655.9MM[E] *EMP* 7,500
SIC 5143 5451 2024 Frozen dairy desserts; Ice cream & ices; Ice cream (packaged); Ice cream & frozen desserts; Ice cream, packaged: molded, on sticks, etc.; Ice cream, bulk; Yogurt desserts, frozen
CEO: Michael T Mitchell
**CFO:* Steve Barbour
Ex VP: Tony Sarsam
Prin: Suzanne Saltzman
CTO: Madelyn Van Der Bokke
DP Exec: Gary Carter
Dir IT: Dave Mack
Ql Cn Mgr: Katie Bracker
VP Mktg: Sally Williams
Mktg Dir: Craig Whitney
Mktg Mgr: Yulanda Young

D-U-N-S 01-198-8441
■ **DREYFUS CORP** (NY)
(*Suby of* BNY MELLON) ★
200 Park Ave Fl 7east, New York, NY 10166-0039
Tel (212) 922-6000 *Founded/Ownrshp* 1947, 2007
Sales 262.7MM[E] *EMP* 1,100
SIC 6211 6282 Dealers, security; Investment advisory service; Manager of mutual funds, contract or fee basis
Pr: J Charles Cardona
**Ch Bd:* Jon Little
**V Ch:* Charles Cardona
**V Ch:* Diane Durnin
Pr: Mike Olson
**CEO:* Jon Baum
CFO: Ernest F Steiner
CFO: William Tunney
Treas: James Windels
**V Ch Bd:* J David Officer
Ex VP: Timothy M McCormick
Sr VP: Michele Molfetta
VP: Mark Abruzzo
VP: Maryalice Bartlett
VP: Ursula Carty
VP: Patricia Gambino
VP: Michael Hall
VP: Brian Jones
**VP:* Patrice M Kozlowski
VP: Ellen Lawrence
VP: Anthony Mayo
Board of Directors: Frank V Cahouet, Alvin E Friedman, Lawrence M Greene, Lawrence S Kash, Douglas D Ramos, Keith Smith, David B Truman, Hilary R Woods

D-U-N-S 06-120-3998
■ **DREYFUS SERVICE ORGANIZATION INC**
(*Suby of* DREYFUS CORP) ★
200 Park Ave, New York, NY 10166-0005
Tel (212) 922-6000 *Founded/Ownrshp* 1968
Sales 78.4MM[E] *EMP* 1,000
Accts Kpmg Llp New York Ny
SIC 6211 Underwriters, security
Ch Bd: Michael G Millard
CFO: William Maresca
Treas: Gary Pierce
Sr VP: David Dipetrillo
VP: Theodore A Schachar

DRH
See DIVERSIFIED RESTAURANT HOLDINGS INC

D-U-N-S 15-395-3930 IMP
DRIESSEN AIRCRAFT INTERIOR SYSTEMS INC
DRIESSEN GALLEYS USA
(*Suby of* DRIESSEN AEROSPACE GROUP N.V.)
17311 Nichols Ln, Huntington Beach, CA 92647-5721
Tel (714) 861-7300 *Founded/Ownrshp* 2000
Sales 149.1MM[E] *EMP* 717[E]
SIC 3728 Aircraft parts & equipment
Genl Mgr: Matt Stafford
**CFO:* Boris Gorelik
Genl Mgr: Alex Johnson
IT Man: Stephen Jones

DRIESSEN GALLEYS USA
See DRIESSEN AIRCRAFT INTERIOR SYSTEMS INC

D-U-N-S 00-831-9311
DRIFTWOOD DAIRY INC
10724 Lower Azusa Rd, El Monte, CA 91731-1390
Tel (626) 444-9591 *Founded/Ownrshp* 1945
Sales 87.1MM[E] *EMP* 165
SIC 2026 Milk processing (pasteurizing, homogenizing, bottling)
CEO: P Kelly Olds
**VP:* Monty Zwieg
Exec: Vince Berrilon
IT Man: Frank Valdonos

DRIFTWOOD HOSPITALITY GROUP
See DRIFTWOOD HOSPITALITY MANAGEMENT LLC

D-U-N-S 07-096-1532
DRIFTWOOD HOSPITALITY MANAGEMENT LLC (FL)
DRIFTWOOD HOSPITALITY GROUP
11770 Us Highway 1 # 202, North Palm Beach, FL 33408-3027
Tel (561) 833-9979 *Founded/Ownrshp* 1998
Sales 296.9MM[E] *EMP* 3,000
SIC 7011 Resort hotel, franchised
Pr: David Buddemeyer
**Ex VP:* Charles Michael Diaz
**Ex VP:* Steven M Johnson
Ex VP: Brian Quinn
**Ex VP:* Carlos J Rodriguez
**Ex VP:* Peter J Walz
VP: Carlos Rodriguez
VP: Mohammad Siddiqui
Genl Mgr: Christy Duprey
Sls Mgr: Dan Deherrera

D-U-N-S 01-687-4125 IMP/EXP
▲ **DRIL-QUIP INC**
6401 N Eldridge Pkwy, Houston, TX 77041-3505
Tel (713) 939-7711 *Founded/Ownrshp* 1981
Sales 844.3MM *EMP* 2,319
Tkr Sym DRQ *Exch* NYS
SIC 3533 Oil & gas field machinery; Drilling tools for gas, oil or water wells; Gas field machinery & equipment
Pr: Blake T Deberry
Ch Bd: John V Lovoi
COO: James A Gariepy
CFO: Jerry M Brooks
VP: Thomas Owen
VP: James C Webster
QA Dir: Lane Keller
QA Dir: Raghu Shivaraj
Sales Asso: Douglas Muchaw
Board of Directors: Terence B Jupp, Steven L Newman, Alexander P Shukis

D-U-N-S 79-800-9234
DRILLING INFO INC
DRILLINGINFO.COM
2901 Via Fortuna Bldg 6, Austin, TX 78746-7565
Tel (512) 477-9200 *Founded/Ownrshp* 1999
Sales 219.5MM[E] *EMP* 231
SIC 1381 Drilling oil & gas wells
CEO: Allen Gilmer
CFO: Dave Piazza
Chf Mktg O: Maria Carballosa
Sr VP: Mike Couvillion
Sr VP: Adam Farris
Sr VP: Rich Herrmann
Sr VP: Corey Rhoden
Sr VP: Dean Witte
VP: Clark Archer
VP: Chris Buoy
VP: John Fierstien
VP: Leann Jeter
VP: Dean Metzger
VP: Martin Payne
VP: Marc Silvia
VP: Cindy Stewart
Board of Directors: Scott Sachs

DRILLINGINFO.COM
See DRILLING INFO INC

D-U-N-S 06-999-0526 IMP/EXP
DRILLMEC INC
(*Suby of* SOILMEC SPA)
16320 Imperial Valley Dr, Houston, TX 77060-6273
Tel (281) 885-0777 *Founded/Ownrshp* 1998
Sales 141.9MM[E] *EMP* 74
Accts Weaver & Tidwell Llp Houston
SIC 3533 Oil & gas drilling rigs & equipment
Pr: Paulo Brando Ballerini
**CFO:* Massimo Tartagni
Exec: Dave Warner
IT Man: Joann Guilbeaux
Sftwr Eng: Mauricio Torres
Snr PM: John Folsom
Snr PM: Alessandro Taccini

D-U-N-S 07-547-6390
DRINKER BIDDLE & REATH LLP
1 Logan Sq Ste 2000, Philadelphia, PA 19103-6996
Tel (215) 988-2700 *Founded/Ownrshp* 1935
Sales 269.3MM[E] *EMP* 1,500
SIC 8111 General practice law office
Ch Bd: Alfred Putnam
Pt: Paul H Saint Antoine
Pt: Bonnie Allyn Barnett
Pt: Gary R Battistoni
Pt: Marsha W Beidler
Pt: Thomas A Belton
Pt: John C Bennett Jr
Pt: James Biehl
Pt: Jill E Bronson
Pt: David J Brooman
Pt: Michael F Brown
Pt: Wilson M Brown III
Pt: David P Bruton
Pt: William C Bullitt
Pt: Harry Sarkis Cherken Jr
Pt: William H Clark Jr
Pt: John J D'Andrea
Pt: Edwin A Getz
Pt: Edward A Gramigna Jr
Pt: Barry Gross
Pt: William A Hanssen

D-U-N-S 14-192-1382
DRISCOLL CHILDRENS HEALTH PLAN
(*Suby of* DRISCOLL CHILDRENS HOSPITAL) ★
615 N Uppr Brdwy 1621, Corpus Christi, TX 78401
Tel (361) 694-6432 *Founded/Ownrshp* 1997
Sales 385.7MM *EMP* 49
Accts Bkd Llp Houston Tx
SIC 8011 6399 Medical insurance plan; Health insurance for pets
Pr: Mary D Peterson MD
Dir Lab: Tecia Carter
Off Mgr: Donna Deeb

D-U-N-S 05-512-8250
DRISCOLL CHILDRENS HOSPITAL
3533 S Alameda St, Corpus Christi, TX 78411-1721
Tel (361) 694-5000 *Founded/Ownrshp* 1945
Sales 262.9MM *EMP* 1,500
SIC 8069 Children's hospital
Pr: Steve Warnaer
**CFO:* Eric Hamon
Ofcr: Matthew Evans
VP: Bill Larsen
Comm Dir: Linda Peterson
Dir Bus: Laura Zamora
Adm Dir: Tecia Carter
Dir Sec: Joe Schumann
Off Mgr: Evette Oriley
Dir IT: Eduardo Gomez
Sys Mgr: Dennis Joaquin

DRISCOLL FOODS
See METROPOLITAN FOODS INC

D-U-N-S 02-823-8699 IMP/EXP
DRISCOLL STRAWBERRY ASSOCIATES INC
345 Westridge Dr, Watsonville, CA 95076-4169
Tel (831) 424-0506 *Founded/Ownrshp* 1961
Sales 511.5MM[E] *EMP* 412
SIC 5148 5431 Fruits, fresh; Fruit & vegetable markets
CEO: Miles Reiter
**Ch Bd:* Joseph Miles Reiter
**CFO:* Sean Martin
Sr VP: Soren Bjorn
Sr VP: Kevin Murphy
Sr VP: Tom O'Brien
Sr VP: Tom Obrien
VP: Kelley Bell
**VP:* Jerry D'Amore
VP: Elly Hoever
**VP:* Michael Hollister
**VP:* Emmett Linder
**VP:* John Siletto
**VP:* Dorn Wenninger
Exec: Lynne Oldham
Board of Directors: Charles Boyles, Neil Defeo, Keith Ford, Larry Ledin, Clint Miller, Garland Reiter, Richard Uyematsu

D-U-N-S 94-558-2054 IMP
DRIVE AUTOMOTIVE INDUSTRIES OF AMERICA INC
MAGNA DRIVE AUTO AMER DIV
(*Suby of* MAGNA INTERNATIONAL INC)
120 Moon Acres Rd, Piedmont, SC 29673-8693
Tel (864) 299-1349 *Founded/Ownrshp* 1993
Sales 228.8MM[E] *EMP* 500
SIC 3465 3714 3711 3469 Automotive stampings; Motor vehicle parts & accessories; Motor vehicles & car bodies; Metal stampings
CEO: Donald J Walker
Genl Mgr: David Meier
Genl Mgr: David Meyer
Ql Cn Mgr: Craig Hall

DRIVE FINANCIAL SERVICES
See SANTANDER CONSUMER USA INC FOUNDATION

D-U-N-S 79-128-0782
■ **DRIVE INSURANCE HOLDINGS INC**
(*Suby of* PROGRESSIVE INSURANCE) ★
6300 Wilson Mills Rd, Cleveland, OH 44143-2109
Tel (440) 461-5000 *Founded/Ownrshp* 2007
Sales NA *EMP* 2,591[E]
SIC 6331 6351 Fire, marine & casualty insurance; Surety insurance
Pr: Leslie Kolleda

D-U-N-S 07-513-9816
DRIVELINE RETAIL MERCHANDISING INC
DRIVELINE RETAIL SOLUTIONS
1141 E 1500 North Rd, Taylorville, IL 62568-7950
Tel (704) 663-7741 *Founded/Ownrshp* 1976
Sales NA *EMP* 12,000
SIC 8742 Merchandising consultant; Food & beverage consultant
CEO: Loyd R Wilson
CFO: Lori Bennett
Sr VP: Dan Colvard
VP: Jim Swanson
Dist Mgr: Jill Dye

DRIVELINE RETAIL SOLUTIONS
See DRIVELINE RETAIL MERCHANDISING INC

D-U-N-S 60-262-2925
DRIVEN BRANDS INC
MEINEKE DISCOUNT MUFFLERS
440 S Church St Ste 700, Charlotte, NC 28202-2059
Tel (704) 337-8855 *Founded/Ownrshp* 2015
Sales 107.3MM[E] *EMP* 776[E]
SIC 7533 Muffler shop, sale or repair & installation
CEO: Jonathan Fitzpatrick
Pr: Jose Costa
Pr: Jose R Costa
Pr: Danny Rivera
CFO: Steve Jackson
Ex VP: Noah Pollack
IT Man: Heather Masterson
Mktg Mgr: Sydney Weaver-Bey

D-U-N-S 93-295-4241
DRIVER & MOTOR VEHICLE SERVICES OREGON
DMV
(*Suby of* OREGON DEPARTMENT OF TRANSPORTATION) ★
1905 Lana Ave Ne, Salem, OR 97314-5000
Tel (503) 945-5000 *Founded/Ownrshp* 1969
Sales NA *EMP* 1,500
SIC 9621 Regulation, administration of transportation;
Pt: Lorna Youngs
IT Man: Virginia Alster
Netwrk Mgr: Tom McClellan

D-U-N-S 05-532-4701
DRIVER PIPELINE CO INC
1200 N Union Bower Rd, Irving, TX 75061-5828
Tel (214) 638-7131 *Founded/Ownrshp* 1970
Sales 88.2MM *EMP* 830
Accts Hein & Associates Llp Dallas
SIC 1623 Oil & gas pipeline construction
CEO: James T Driver
**Pr:* Bradford C Walker
CFO: Bobby Farrell
Dir Bus: Mike Norris
Sfty Dirs: Lee Laxson

D-U-N-S 12-201-6504
■ **DRIVERS MANAGEMENT LLC**
(*Suby of* WERNER ENTERPRISES INC) ★
14507 Frontier Rd, Omaha, NE 68138-3808
Tel (402) 895-6640 *Founded/Ownrshp* 1986
Sales 98.4MM[E] *EMP* 9,500
SIC 7363 Truck driver services

DRIVES & MOTION DIVISION
See YASKAWA AMERICA INC

D-U-N-S 80-075-5402
DRIVESOL WORLDWIDE HOLDING CORP
(*Suby of* SUN CAPITAL PARTNERS INC) ★
1104 W Maple Rd, Troy, MI 48084-5352
Tel (248) 729-2222 *Founded/Ownrshp* 2005
Sales 77.6MM[E] *EMP* 1,800
SIC 5013 Motor vehicle supplies & new parts
Pr: Mark Simon
VP: Joseph Gonnella

D-U-N-S 84-062-6691
DRIVETIME AUTOMOTIVE GROUP INC
1720 W Rio Salado Pkwy, Tempe, AZ 85281-6590
Tel (602) 852-6600 *Founded/Ownrshp* 1992
Sales 2.3MMM *EMP* 3,165[E]
SIC 5521 Used car dealers
Pr: Raymond C Fidel
**Ch Bd:* Ernest C Garcia II
COO: Ray Fidel
**CFO:* Mark G Sauder
Ofcr: Alan J Appelman
**Ex VP:* Jon D Ehlinger
**Sr VP:* Paul I Kaplan
VP: Jon Ehunger
VP: Jeanne Madsen
Admn Mgr: Taylor Hooks
Genl Mgr: Andrew McMurtrie
Board of Directors: Maryann N Keller, Ira J Platt, Donald J Sanders, Gregg E Tryhus

D-U-N-S 94-059-2116
DRIVING MOMENTUM INC
17024 Butte Creek Rd # 107, Houston, TX 77090-2347
Tel (281) 893-3390 *Founded/Ownrshp* 1991
Sales 493.1MM[E] *EMP* 186
SIC 7363 Employee leasing service
Pr: William R Graham
**VP:* Paul M Rahn

D-U-N-S 01-105-6780
DRIVING MOMENTUM USA INC
(*Suby of* DRIVING MOMENTUM INC) ★
2025 Irving Blvd Ste 102, Dallas, TX 75207-6617
Tel (214) 651-1031 *Founded/Ownrshp* 1996
Sales 493.1MM *EMP* 3
Accts Kpmg Llp Dallas Tx
SIC 7361 Employment agencies
Pr: William Graham

D-U-N-S 09-339-6570
DRM INC
5324 N 134th Ave, Omaha, NE 68164-6326
Tel (402) 573-1216 *Founded/Ownrshp* 1978
Sales 66.5MM[E] *EMP* 1,500
SIC 5812 Fast-food restaurant, chain
Pr: Matthew Johnson
**Pr:* Marc Johnson
**Ch:* Dean C Johnson
Dir IT: Kevin Dabbs

D-U-N-S 08-377-8936
DRMC PROPERTIES INC
DOWNEY CMNTY HOSP AUX GIFT SP
11500 Brookshire Ave, Downey, CA 90241-4917
Tel (562) 904-5464 *Founded/Ownrshp* 1957
Sales 173.9MM *EMP* 30
SIC 5947 Gift shop
Ex Dir: Nancy Stiles
Ofcr: Allen Acree

D-U-N-S 09-013-1905 IMP/EXP
DROGUERIA BETANCES LLC (FL)
Luis Munoz Marin Ave Esq, Caguas, PR 00725
Tel (787) 653-1200 *Founded/Ownrshp* 1982
Sales 358.6MM[E] *EMP* 291
Accts Jover & Leon Cpa Llc San Juan
SIC 5122 Pharmaceuticals
Pr: Raul Rodriguez
VP: Rafael Rodriguez

DROGUERIA CASTILLO
See CESAR CASTILLO INC

DROP LOT SERVICES
See MERIT INTEGRATED LOGISTICS LLC

D-U-N-S 08-482-4499
DRS CONSOLIDATED CONTROLS INC
(*Suby of* DRS DS) ★
21 South St, Danbury, CT 06810-8147
Tel (203) 798-3000 *Founded/Ownrshp* 2009
Sales 139.1MM^E *EMP* 600^E
SIC 3823 Nuclear reactor controls
Pr: Jimmy Baird
**CFO:* Robert Dann
**VP:* Jeff Armstrong
**Prin:* Richard Danforth

D-U-N-S 82-951-8328
DRS DEFENSE SOLUTIONS LLC
DRS DS
(*Suby of* DRS TECHNOLOGIES INC) ★
1 Milestone Center Ct, Germantown, MD 20876-7106
Tel (240) 238-3900 *Founded/Ownrshp* 2008
Sales 285.0MM^E *EMP* 6,000
SIC 3812 Defense systems & equipment
CEO: William J Lynn III
Pr: Mike Morningstar
**CEO:* Dill Lynn
**COO:* Terence J Murphy
CFO: Robert Dann
VP: Gary Marble
Genl Mgr: David Kee
Genl Mgr: Ira Krowitz
Snr Mgr: Gregory Pitts

DRS DS
See DRS DEFENSE SOLUTIONS LLC

D-U-N-S 10-191-8811
DRS GLOBAL ENTERPRISE SOLUTIONS INC
(*Suby of* DRS TECHNOLOGIES INC) ★
12930 Worldgate Dr, Herndon, VA 20170-6011
Tel (703) 896-7100 *Founded/Ownrshp* 2006
Sales 218.3MM^E *EMP* 901
SIC 7371 8731 Computer software development; Commercial physical research
CEO: William J Lynn III
**Pr:* Sandra L Hodgkinson
**Pr:* Terence J Murphy
**Pr:* Mitchell B Rambler
**Pr:* Jim Scott
**Pr:* Roger N Sexauer
Sr VP: Jason Rinsky
VP: Matt Gent
VP: Phillip Sandmann
Exec: Debbie Brazil
Genl Mgr: Patricia Chandler

D-U-N-S 83-307-6883
DRS ICAS LLC
TECHNOLOGIES INC ARLINGTON VA
(*Suby of* DRS DS) ★
2601 Mission Point Blvd, Beavercreek, OH 45431-6600
Tel (937) 429-7408 *Founded/Ownrshp* 2009
Sales 107.7MM^E *EMP* 350
SIC 3812 Search & navigation equipment
**CEO:* William J Lynn III
**COO:* Terence J Murphy
**VP:* Sandra L Hodgkinson
VP: Gary Marble
Exec: Rob Pietsch
Ex Dir: Fred Gooding

D-U-N-S 19-395-5036
DRS LAUREL TECHNOLOGIES
(*Suby of* DRS TECHNOLOGIES INC) ★
246 Airport Rd, Johnstown, PA 15904-7224
Tel (814) 534-8900 *Founded/Ownrshp* 1993
Sales 122.6MM^E *EMP* 300^E
SIC 3672 3315 Printed circuit boards; Cable, steel: insulated or armored; Wire products, ferrous/iron: made in wiredrawing plants
CEO: William J Lynn
Pr: Nick Angelini
**Sr VP:* Joseph Militano
VP: Blake M Guy
VP: Sandra L Hodgkinson
**VP:* Patrick R Marion
VP: Michael Schwarm
VP: Richard Sparks
Prgrm Mgr: Gary Disbrow
Prgrm Mgr: Marc Elbaz
Prgrm Mgr: Michael Gregory

D-U-N-S 88-463-4718
DRS NETWORK & IMAGING SYSTEMS LLC
(*Suby of* DRS TECHNOLOGIES INC) ★
100 N Babcock St, Melbourne, FL 32935-6715
Tel (321) 309-1500 *Founded/Ownrshp* 1995
Sales 268.1MM^E *EMP* 1,000
SIC 3674 Infrared sensors, solid state
Pr: Michael Sarrica
**Treas:* Thomas P Crimmins
**VP:* Toby Mannheimer
**VP:* Jason Rinsky
**Prin:* Fred Marion

D-U-N-S 10-182-1531
DRS POWER & CONTROL TECHNOLOGIES INC
(*Suby of* DRS TECHNOLOGIES INC) ★
4265 N 30th St, Milwaukee, WI 53216-1821
Tel (414) 875-4314 *Founded/Ownrshp* 1911
Sales 127.4MM^E *EMP* 478
SIC 3812 Nautical instruments
Pr: Mark S Newman

DRS TECHNOLOGIES
See SYSTEMS DRS SUSTAINMENT INC

DRS TECHNOLOGIES
See DRS TRAINING & CONTROL SYSTEMS LLC

D-U-N-S 06-134-5351 IMP
DRS TECHNOLOGIES INC
(*Suby of* LEONARDO - FINMECCANICA - SPA)
2345 Crystal Dr Ste 1000, Arlington, VA 22202-4801
Tel (973) 898-1500 *Founded/Ownrshp* 1968
Sales 2.0MMM *EMP* 6,000
SIC 3812 3699 3572 3669 3679 8741 Navigational systems & instruments; Electronic training devices; Computer storage devices; Intercommunication systems, electric; Harness assemblies for electronic use: wire or cable; Management services
CEO: William J Lynn III
Pr: Jim Scott
Pr: Sally A Wallace
COO: Robert Mehmel
**COO:* Terence J Murphy
COO: Terence J Murphy
**CFO:* Thomas Crimmins
Ofcr: Jason Rinsky
**Ex VP:* Steve Cortese
**Ex VP:* Mark A Dorfman
Ex VP: Mark Wiggins
Sr VP: Lary Beaulieu
Sr VP: John G Cotton
Sr VP: Robert Russo
Sr VP: Mark Williams
VP: Robert Acker
VP: John Flagg
VP: Raymond G Goldstein
**VP:* Sandra L Hodgkinson
VP: Wayne Sauer
VP: Ron Sepe

D-U-N-S 00-816-9708
DRS TRAINING & CONTROL SYSTEMS LLC
DRS TECHNOLOGIES
(*Suby of* DRS TECHNOLOGIES INC) ★
645 Anchors St Nw, Fort Walton Beach, FL 32548-3803
Tel (850) 302-3000 *Founded/Ownrshp* 2003
Sales 96.7MM^E *EMP* 338
SIC 3812 8713 Radar systems & equipment;
CEO: William J Lynn III
**Pr:* Edwin R Epstein
**Pr:* Jim Scott
**Pr:* Robert Viviano
**Ex VP:* Terence J Murphy
**VP:* Sandra L Hodgkinson
VP: Steven Potts- Vp-Bus Ops
**Genl Mgr:* Larry Azelle
IT Man: Nicole Svetz
Netwrk Mgr: William Miller

D-U-N-S 96-191-8831
DRT HOLDINGS INC
618 Greenmount Blvd, Dayton, OH 45419-3271
Tel (937) 298-7391 *Founded/Ownrshp* 2008
Sales 181.9MM^E *EMP* 549
SIC 6719 Investment holding companies, except banks
Pr: Gary Van Gundy
**CFO:* Joseph Zehenny
**Sr VP:* Greg Martin

DRUG EMPORIUM
See GIBSON SALES LP

D-U-N-S 87-888-1879
■ DRUG ENFORCEMENT ADMINISTRATION
DEA
(*Suby of* UNITED STATES DEPARTMENT OF JUSTICE) ★
8701 Morrissette Dr, Springfield, VA 22152-1080
Tel (202) 307-1000 *Founded/Ownrshp* 1973
Sales NA *EMP* 9,100
Accts Kpmg Llp Washington Dc
SIC 9229 Public order & safety statistics centers;
CFO: Frank M Kalder
Ofcr: Najma Begum
CIO: Thomas Neal

D-U-N-S 01-388-7161 EXP
DRUG PLASTICS AND GLASS CO INC
1 Bottle Dr, Boyertown, PA 19512-8623
Tel (610) 367-5000 *Founded/Ownrshp* 1963
Sales 138.0MM^E *EMP* 700
SIC 3085

D-U-N-S 13-648-3505
DRUG SHOPPE INC
DRUG STORE
4060 N Armenia Ave, Tampa, FL 33607-1002
Tel (813) 870-3939 *Founded/Ownrshp* 2003
Sales 400.0MM *EMP* 19
SIC 5912 Drug stores
Pr: Bhupendra Agravat

DRUG STORE
See DRUG SHOPPE INC

D-U-N-S 06-710-3432 IMP/EXP
DRUMMOND CO INC
1000 Urban Center Dr # 300, Vestavia, AL 35242-2532
Tel (205) 945-6500 *Founded/Ownrshp* 1935
Sales 5.8MMM^E *EMP* 6,800
SIC 1221 1222 3312 5052 5085 5172 Surface mining, bituminous; Bituminous coal-underground mining; Coke oven products (chemical recovery); Coal; Coke; Industrial supplies; Petroleum products
CEO: Mike Tracy
**Ch Bd:* John Howard Drummond Sr
**Pr:* Richard Mullen
**Pr:* Richard R Owens
**Pr:* George Wilbanks
CFO: Ken Dortch
**CFO:* Alan Lang
Treas: Scott O Stanfield
**Sr VP:* John Coffey
Sr VP: Nathaniel Drummond
Sr VP: Carolina Riao
**VP:* Blake Andrews
VP: Gary Lacaze
VP: Ken Maddox
VP: Catherine W Pecher
VP: Matt Rohling
Board of Directors: Charles Bishop, John R Davidson, Bryan Drummond, Herman Lin Drummond, Patrick Drummond, Beth Stukes

D-U-N-S 80-630-4101
DRURY DEVELOPMENT CORP
721 Emerson Rd Ste 200, Saint Louis, MO 63141-6755
Tel (314) 423-6698 *Founded/Ownrshp* 1985
Sales 300.0MM^E *EMP* 150
SIC 6512 1542 5812 Commercial & industrial building operation; Commercial & office building contractors; Fast food restaurants & stands
Ch Bd: Charles Drury Sr
**Pr:* Timothy Drury
**CFO:* Larry Hasselfeld
Sr VP: Shirley Drury
**Sr VP:* Jacqueline D Pollvogt
**VP:* Charles Drury Jr
**VP:* Charles Lee
Exec: Tony Right
Genl Mgr: Thomas Milford

D-U-N-S 06-463-6863
DRURY HOTELS CO LLC
MANAGEMENT CO
721 Emerson Rd Ste 400, Saint Louis, MO 63141-6770
Tel (314) 429-2255 *Founded/Ownrshp* 2008
Sales 391.4MM^E *EMP* 4,200
SIC 7011 Hotels & motels
CEO: Charles L Drury Jr
Pr: Jayne Nicholson
**CFO:* Carr Trovillion
**Treas:* Robert S Rhoads
**VP:* Stephen R Bollinger
**VP:* Joseph B Pereles
**VP:* Eric Strand
VP: Tom Walsh
**Prin:* Bruce K Edwards
**Prin:* Thomas B Walsh
Area Mgr: Tammy Bizzle

D-U-N-S 80-809-7013
DRW HOLDINGS LLC
540 W Madison St Ste 2500, Chicago, IL 60661-2555
Tel (312) 542-1000 *Founded/Ownrshp* 1999
Sales 191.9MM^E *EMP* 460^E
SIC 6719 Investment holding companies, except banks
COO: Erin Brown
CFO: James Lange
CFO: Craig Saltzman
Dir Risk M: Jeremy Vosko
Off Admin: James Coddington
Snr Sftwr: Jay Fields
Snr Sftwr: Vijay Govindarajan
Snr Sftwr: Oren Miller
Snr Sftwr: Derek Passen
Snr Sftwr: Kurt Stephens
Snr Sftwr: Ed Taylor

D-U-N-S 03-240-4726
DRYBAR HOLDINGS LLC
125 Technology Dr Ste 150, Irvine, CA 92618-2477
Tel (310) 776-6330 *Founded/Ownrshp* 2010
Sales 322.8MM^E *EMP* 906^E
SIC 6719 Investment holding companies, except banks
CFO: Mitch Reback
CFO: Diego Vidal
VP: Menal Parikh
CIO: Steve Labrie
Mktg Mgr: Tessa Johnson
Art Dir: Jane Moon

D-U-N-S 16-086-0417
DRYCO CONSTRUCTION INC
42745 Boscell Rd, Fremont, CA 94538-3106
Tel (510) 438-6500 *Founded/Ownrshp* 1985
Sales 96.8MM^E *EMP* 180^E
SIC 1611 1721 5211 Surfacing & paving; Pavement marking contractor; Lumber & other building materials
Pr: Daren R Young
**CFO:* David Henke
**VP:* William McCrea
**VP:* Kevin Mitchell
**VP:* Rafael Torres
Dir Bus: Diane Rebecchi
Dir IT: Brian Robertson
Trfc Dir: Gina Chase
Sfty Mgr: Gary Hamamoto
Opers Mgr: Alan Berger

D-U-N-S 94-455-3528
DRYER CANCER CENTER
1221 N Highland Ave, Aurora, IL 60506-1404
Tel (630) 264-8656 *Founded/Ownrshp* 1999
Sales 37.5MM^E *EMP* 1,100
SIC 5047 8011 Medical & hospital equipment; Offices & clinics of medical doctors
Owner: John Potter

D-U-N-S 05-856-0426
DRYMALLA CONSTRUCTION CO INC
608 Harbert St, Columbus, TX 78934-2812
Tel (281) 342-3853 *Founded/Ownrshp* 1946
Sales 220.2MM *EMP* 105
Accts Desroches Partners Llp Houst
SIC 1542 Institutional building construction; Commercial & office building, new construction
Chf Mktg O: Jay W Altieri
**VP:* Rusty Klaus
**VP:* Charles Labay
VP: Robert Scronce
VP: Bob R Sronce
**VP:* W R Sronce IV
IT Man: Janna Christoph
Snr Mgr: Bill Breen

D-U-N-S 62-055-8866 IMP/EXP
■ DRYVIT HOLDINGS INC
(*Suby of* REPUBLIC POWDERED METALS INC) ★
1 Energy Way, Providence, RI 02903
Tel (401) 822-4100 *Founded/Ownrshp* 1995
Sales 87.6MM^E *EMP* 365
SIC 2822 2899 Synthetic rubber; Chemical preparations
Pr: Peter Balint
**Treas:* Dennis M Dallman

D-U-N-S 04-897-3150 IMP/EXP
■ DRYVIT SYSTEMS INC
(*Suby of* DRYVIT HOLDINGS INC) ★
1 Energy Way, West Warwick, RI 02893-2322
Tel (401) 822-4100 *Founded/Ownrshp* 1969
Sales 87.6MM^E *EMP* 361
SIC 2899 Chemical preparations
Pr: Robert Michael Murphy
**VP:* Dennis Dallman
Genl Mgr: Roger Peevler
IT Man: Maureen Charello
Mktg Mgr: Peter Culyer
Mktg Mgr: Robert Dazel

DS SCREEN PRINTING & EMB
See SAMUEL VAZQUEZ

D-U-N-S 14-182-7480
DS SERVICES HOLDINGS INC
(*Suby of* DS WATERS HOLDINGS LLC) ★
5660 New Northside Dr # 500, Atlanta, GA 30328-5826
Tel (770) 933-1400 *Founded/Ownrshp* 2005
Sales 342.1MM^E *EMP* 5,350
SIC 5499 5149 Water: distilled mineral or spring; Water, distilled; Mineral or spring water bottling
Pr: Pete Maclean
**Prin:* Stewart E Allen
**Prin:* K Dillon Schickli
Opers Mgr: Scott Herzog
Mktg Mgr: Troy Cox

D-U-N-S 19-674-9550 IMP/EXP
DS SERVICES OF AMERICA INC
CRYSTAL SPRINGS
(*Suby of* COTT CORPORATION)
2300 Windy Ridge Pkwy Se 500n, Atlanta, GA 30339-8577
Tel (770) 933-1400 *Founded/Ownrshp* 2014
Sales 1.3MMM^E *EMP* 5,500
SIC 5963 Beverage services, direct sales
Ch: Jerry Fowden
**CEO:* Tom Harrington
**CFO:* Ron Z Frieman
**Treas:* Shane Perkey
VP: Darin Ball
VP: Larry Brookes
VP: James Higgins
VP: Mark McCaulissa
**VP:* Marni Morgan Poe
Genl Mgr: Mike Moffenbier
CTO: Ccory Fleming

D-U-N-S 14-867-4521 IMP/EXP
DS WATERS HOLDINGS LLC
5660 New Northside Dr # 500, Atlanta, GA 30328-5826
Tel (770) 933-1400 *Founded/Ownrshp* 2003
Sales 856.7MM^E *EMP* 5,500
SIC 2086 Pasteurized & mineral waters, bottled & canned; Mineral water, carbonated: packaged in cans, bottles, etc.
CIO: Robert Bramski

DSC
See DAIRYMANS SUPPLY CO INC

DSC ALARMS
See DEFENDERS INC

DSC LGSTICS SUP CHAIN MNAGMENT
See DSC LOGISTICS INC

D-U-N-S 62-644-2750
DSC LOGISTICS INC
DSC LGSTICS SUP CHAIN MNAGMENT
1750 S Wolf Rd, Des Plaines, IL 60018-1924
Tel (847) 390-6800 *Founded/Ownrshp* 1989
Sales 355.0MM *EMP* 3,500
SIC 4225 4213 4212 4731 General warehousing & storage; Trucking, except local; Local trucking, without storage; Freight consolidation
Pr: Ann Drake
Pr: Ritchie Paik
**CFO:* Joann Lilek
**Ofcr:* Greg Goluska
**Ex VP:* Michael Weinstock
Sr VP: Edward Bowersox
Sr VP: Ken Heller
VP: Dave Bode
VP: Dale Carpenter
**VP:* Kevin Coleman
VP: Jeff Conover
**VP:* David Copeland
VP: Karin Kaspar
VP: Beth Wong

DSCA
See DENSO PRODUCTS AND SERVICES AMERICAS INC

DSCI
See D & S CONSULTANTS INC

DSG PITTSBURGH
See SENTAGE CORP

DSHS
See TEXAS DEPARTMENT OF STATE HEALTH SERVICES

DSHS
See WASHINGTON STATE DEPARTMENT OF SOCIAL AND HEALTH SERVICES

D-U-N-S 10-734-6827 IMP/EXP
DSI DISTRIBUTING INC
DSI SYSTEMS
3601 109th St, Urbandale, IA 50322-8102
Tel (515) 276-9181 *Founded/Ownrshp* 1998
Sales 139.2MM^E *EMP* 250
SIC 5063 5731 Antennas, receiving, satellite dishes; Consumer electronic equipment
**Ch Bd:* Charles Robison
**Pr:* Douglas H Robison
**CFO:* Craig Anderson
Dist Mgr: Vince Cisneros
Dist Mgr: Steven Frank
Sls Mgr: Shane Vetter
Board of Directors: Charles Robison, Janice Schroeder, Michael Schroeder

D-U-N-S 12-475-9312
DSI HOLDING CO INC
DSI HOLDINGS
424 Church St Ste 1900, Nashville, TN 37219-2387
Tel (615) 777-8201 *Founded/Ownrshp* 2003
Sales 48.0MM^E *EMP* 2,300

SIC 8092 8069 8742 Kidney dialysis centers; Cancer hospital; Management consulting services
Pr: Craig Goguen
Ex VP: Stephen Harrison
Ex VP: Judy Lefkovitz
Ex VP: Judy W Lefkovitz
Ex VP: Jay A Yalowitz
*Sr VP: Ben Croce
*Sr VP: Jimmy Cummings
*VP: Fran Attrill
*VP: Penny Deblois

DSI HOLDINGS
See DSI HOLDING CO INC

D-U-N-S 01-472-6038 IMP/EXP
DSI INC
DEB SHOPS
9401 Blue Grass Rd, Philadelphia, PA 19114-2305
Tel (215) 676-6000 *Founded/Ownrshp* 2011
Sales 399.2MM^E *EMP* 5,000
SIC 5621 Women's clothing stores
Pr: Mark Hoffman
CFO: Tom Zambelli
*Treas: Barry S Susson
*Treas: Barry J Susson
VP: John Oconnor
*VP: Anthony J Vitullo Jr
VP: Tony Vitullo
Dist Mgr: Judy Duncan
Info Man: Christian Collazo
Mktg Dir: Dina Katz

DSI RENAL
See DIALYSIS NEWCO INC

D-U-N-S 96-500-6807
DSI RENAL HOLDINGS LLC
DIVERSFIED SPCIALTY INSTITUTES
424 Church St Ste 1900, Nashville, TN 37219-2387
Tel (615) 777-8201 *Founded/Ownrshp* 2006
Sales 36.6MM^E *EMP* 2,300
SIC 8092 8069 8742 Kidney dialysis centers; Cancer hospital; Management consulting services
Ex VP: Stephen Harrison
Ex VP: Judy Lefkovitz
Ex VP: Judy W Lefkovitz
Ex VP: Jay Yalowitz

DSI SECURITY SERVICES
See DOTHAN SECURITY INC

DSI SYSTEMS
See DSI DISTRIBUTING INC

DSI USA
See DYWIDAG SYSTEMS INTERNATIONAL USA INC

D-U-N-S 07-298-7910
DSJS INC
16 W 36th St Rm 901, New York, NY 10018-5205
Tel (212) 564-9326 *Founded/Ownrshp* 1980
Sales 107.7MM^E *EMP* 51
SIC 5199 General merchandise, non-durable
Pr: Jay Small

D-U-N-S 15-942-1960
DSK GROUP INC
6715 W Grver Clvland Blvd, Homosassa, FL 34446-1306
Tel (352) 628-9800 *Founded/Ownrshp* 1993
Sales 37.8MM^E *EMP* 1,200
SIC 7363 Employee leasing service
Pr: Jeff Connley
VP: Patty Connley

DSK INDUSTRIES
See TOMMY HILFIGER USA INC

D-U-N-S 96-909-5574
DSL XPRESS LLC
2006 Karl Dr Apt 1602, Warner Robins, GA 31088-9423
Tel (706) 945-9542 *Founded/Ownrshp* 2011
Sales 200.0MM^E *EMP* 2
SIC 4213 Trucking, except local

DSM BIOMEDICAL
See NASH KENSEY CORP

D-U-N-S 78-478-7459 IMP/EXP
DSM ENGINEERING PLASTICS INC
D S M
(*Suby of* DSM FINANCE USA INC) ★
2267 W Mill Rd, Evansville, IN 47720-6902
Tel (812) 435-7500 *Founded/Ownrshp* 1991
Sales 99.2MM^E *EMP* 300
SIC 2821 3087 3083 Acrylonitrile-butadiene-styrene resins (ABS resins); Custom compound purchased resins; Laminated plastics plate & sheet
Pr: Richard Pieters
VP: Rob Crowell
*VP: Debra Dykema
VP: Robert Evans
VP: Kent Johnson
VP: Richard Wenger
Opers Mgr: Carol Reising

D-U-N-S 60-823-3961 IMP/EXP
DSM FINANCE USA INC
(*Suby of* DHCUS) ★
1408 Columbia Nitrogen Dr, Augusta, GA 30901-2000
Tel (706) 849-6515 *Founded/Ownrshp* 2005
Sales 427.2MM^E *EMP* 3,000
SIC 2891 2816 3089 3083 5169 Adhesives; Inorganic pigments; Synthetic resin finished products; Thermoplastic laminates: rods, tubes, plates & sheet; Chemicals & allied products
CEO: J W Price
*Pr: A H P Gratama Van Andel
*Treas: David W Leach
*Prin: William P Bivins

D-U-N-S 09-226-3636 IMP
DSM FOOD SPECIALTIES USA INC
(*Suby of* DHCUS) ★
45 Waterview Blvd, Parsippany, NJ 07054-7611
Tel (973) 257-1063 *Founded/Ownrshp* 1999
Sales 123.7MM^E *EMP* 184
SIC 5149 Groceries & related products
Treas: Jack Dijk

D-U-N-S 82-502-9234 IMP/EXP
DSM HOLDING CO USA INC
DHCUS
(*Suby of* DSM FINANCE B.V.)
45 Waterview Blvd, Parsippany, NJ 07054-7611
Tel (973) 257-1063 *Founded/Ownrshp* 1991
Sales 1.0MMM^E *EMP* 3,000
SIC 2891 2816 3089 3083 5169 Adhesives; Inorganic pigments; Synthetic resin finished products; Thermoplastic laminates: rods, tubes, plates & sheet; Chemicals & allied products
Pr: A H P Gratama Van Andel
*Treas: Patrick F Peters

D-U-N-S 16-014-7252 IMP/EXP
DSM NUTRITIONAL PRODUCTS LLC
D S M
(*Suby of* DHCUS) ★
2105 Technology Dr, Schenectady, NY 12308-1143
Tel (518) 372-5155 *Founded/Ownrshp* 2003
Sales 468.3MM^E *EMP* 1,265^E
SIC 2834 2836 Pharmaceutical preparations; Vitamin, nutrient & hematinic preparations for human use; Biological products, except diagnostic; Veterinary biological products
Pr: Richard Polacek
*Treas: Patrick Weinberg
VP: David Cordova
VP: Pierre Y Hardy
Mng Dir: Michael Effing
Mng Dir: Nitin Kothari
Area Mgr: Luis Pereira
Genl Mgr: Dorothy Y Towns
Software D: John Forbes
Netwrk Eng: Raymond Rook
Plnt Mgr: David Brennan

D-U-N-S 07-630-1910 IMP
DSM PHARMACEUTICALS INC
DPI
5900 M L King Jr Hwy, Greenville, NC 27834
Tel (252) 758-3436 *Founded/Ownrshp* 2000
Sales 174.7MM^E *EMP* 1,200
SIC 2834

D-U-N-S 18-190-7312
▲ DSP GROUP INC
161 S San Antonio Rd # 10, Los Altos, CA 94022-3031
Tel (408) 986-4300 *Founded/Ownrshp* 1987
Sales 144.2MM *EMP* 314
Tkr Sym DSPG *Exch* NGS
SIC 3674 7371 Semiconductors & related devices; Integrated circuits, semiconductor networks, etc.; Computer software development
CEO: Ofer Elyakim
*Ch Bd: Patrick Tanguy
CFO: Dror Levy
Board of Directors: Thomas A Lacey, Gabi Seligsohn, Norman P Taffe, Kenneth H Traub

DSS
See SOCIAL SERVICES SOUTH CAROLINA DEPARTMENT

D-U-N-S 02-615-3416
■ DST HEALTH SOLUTIONS INC
(*Suby of* DST SYSTEMS INC) ★
2500 Corporate Dr, Birmingham, AL 35242-2729
Tel (205) 437-6204 *Founded/Ownrshp* 2005
Sales 152.8MM^E *EMP* 2,945
SIC 8742 Management consulting services
Pr: Teri Mullaney
Ex VP: John Gray
Ex VP: Tom Hurley
Sr VP: Rick Austin
Sr VP: Curtis Palmer
Sr VP: John Tobin
VP: Jay Flounlacker
VP: Stan Lewallyn
VP: Ejay Lockwood
Exec: Cindy Franks
Mng Dir: Lisa Crymes

DST OUTPUT CENTRAL, LLC
See BROADRIDGE CUSTOMER COMMUNICATIONS CENTRAL LLC

D-U-N-S 07-303-1197
▲ DST SYSTEMS INC
333 W 11th St, Kansas City, MO 64105-1773
Tel (816) 435-1000 *Founded/Ownrshp* 1969
Sales 2.8MMM *EMP* 13,420
Tkr Sym DST *Exch* NYS
SIC 7374 7371 7331 7372 Data processing service; Software programming applications; Mailing service; Prepackaged software
Ch Bd: Stephen C Hooley
CFO: Gregg Wm Givens
CFO: Brad Walker
Treas: Ted Carlton
Ofcr: Beth Sweetman
Ex VP: Jonathan J Boehm
Ex VP: Edmund J Burke
Ex VP: Simon N Hudson-Lund
Ex VP: Vercie L Lark
Ex VP: Mike Tobin
Sr VP: Randall D Young
VP: Don Ainslie
VP: Bill Chisholm
VP: Susan Hubbell
VP: Michael Huffer
VP: Lee Kowarski
VP: Thomas Rozman
VP Bus Dev: Lawrence Kiefer
Board of Directors: Joseph C Antonellis, Jerome H Bailey, Lynn Dorsey Bleil, Lowell L Bryan, Gary D Forsee, Charles E Haldeman Jr, Samuel G Liss

D-U-N-S 83-236-3969
DSV AIR & SEA HOLDING INC
(*Suby of* DSV AIR & SEA HOLDING A/S)
100 Walnut Ave Ste 405, Clark, NJ 07066-1247
Tel (732) 850-8000 *Founded/Ownrshp* 2009
Sales 621.8MM^E *EMP* 500
SIC 4731 Foreign freight forwarding
COO: Ken Witkowski

D-U-N-S 04-642-4990 IMP
▲ DSW INC
810 Dsw Dr, Columbus, OH 43219-1828
Tel (614) 237-7100 *Founded/Ownrshp* 1969
Sales 2.6MMM *EMP* 11,900
Tkr Sym DSW *Exch* NYS
SIC 5661 Shoe stores; Children's shoes; Men's shoes; Women's shoes
Pr: Michael R Macdonald
*Ch Bd: Jay L Schottenstein
*CEO: Roger Rawlins
CFO: Jared A Poff
Chf Cred: Simon R Nankervis
Chf Mktg O: Deborah L Ferree
Ofcr: William L Jordan
Ex VP: Bill Jordan
Ex VP: Kevin M Lonergan
Ex VP: Harris Mustafa
Sr VP: Richard Golden
VP: Antoinette Carter
VP: Dave Crawford
VP: Laura Cross
VP: Mark Delcher
VP: Jeff Espersen
VP: Barry Esposito
VP: Allison Pignatelli
Comm Dir: Stacey Marshall
Board of Directors: Joanne Zaiac, Henry Aaron, Elaine J Eisenman, Carolee Friedlander, Joanna T Lau, Philip B Miller, James O'donnell, Joseph A Schottenstein, Harvey L Sonnenberg, Allan J Tanenbaum

D-U-N-S 00-890-9137 IMP
■ DSW SHOE WAREHOUSE INC
(*Suby of* DSW INC) ★
4314 E 5th Ave, Columbus, OH 43219-1816
Tel (614) 237-7100 *Founded/Ownrshp* 1986
Sales 286.1MM^E *EMP* 2,500
SIC 5661

DTCC
See DEPOSITORY TRUST CO INC

D-U-N-S 15-089-5316 IMP
■ DTE COAL SERVICES INC
(*Suby of* DTE ENERGY CO) ★
414 S Main St Ste 600, Ann Arbor, MI 48104-2398
Tel (734) 913-2080 *Founded/Ownrshp* 1996
Sales 129.3MM^E *EMP* 154
SIC 5052 4212 Coal; Coal haulage, local
Pr: Matt T Paul
*VP: Stephen Braverman

D-U-N-S 00-695-7872
■ DTE ELECTRIC CO (MI)
(*Suby of* DTE ENERGY CO) ★
1 Energy Plz, Detroit, MI 48226-1221
Tel (313) 235-4000 *Founded/Ownrshp* 1903
Sales 4.9MMM *EMP* 4,500
SIC 4911 Electric services; Distribution, electric power; Generation, electric power; Transmission, electric power
Ch Bd: Gerard M Anderson
CFO: Peter B Oleksiak
Sr VP: Joyce V Hayes-Giles
Board of Directors: David E Meador, Lisa A Muschong, Bruce D Peterson

D-U-N-S 83-932-9158 EXP
▲ DTE ENERGY CO
1 Energy Plz, Detroit, MI 48226-1221
Tel (313) 235-4000 *Founded/Ownrshp* 1995
Sales 10.3MMM *EMP* 10,000
Tkr Sym DTE *Exch* NYS
SIC 4911 4923 1311 ; Generation, electric power; Transmission, electric power; ; Gas transmission & distribution; Crude petroleum & natural gas
Ch Bd: Gerard M Anderson
*V Ch: Steven E Kurmas
CFO: Mansour Allaf
*CFO: Peter B Oleksiak
Bd of Dir: Mark A Murray
*Ofcr: David E Meador
Ex VP: Ron May
*Sr VP: Bruce D Peterson
Sr VP: Heather Rivard
VP: Daniel Brudzynski
VP: Marco Bruzzano
VP: Rodney Christian
VP: Gail Fielder
VP: Joyce Hayes Giles
VP: Renze Hoeksema
VP: Jeffrey Papineau
VP: Matthew Paul
VP: Paula Silver
VP: Mark W Stiers
Comm Man: Ronald Plooster

D-U-N-S 96-139-7692 EXP
■ DTE ENERGY RESOURCES INC
(*Suby of* DTE ENERGY CO) ★
414 S Main St Ste 600, Ann Arbor, MI 48104-2398
Tel (734) 302-4800 *Founded/Ownrshp* 1994
Sales 202.2MM^E *EMP* 215
SIC 4911 1389 Electric services; Gas field services
CEO: Gerard M Anderson
Pr: Karl Wittbold
*CEO: Gerald M Anderson
*VP: Lillian Bauder
VP: Steve Earhart
VP: Gary Quantock

D-U-N-S 87-623-5490 EXP
■ DTE ENERGY SERVICES INC
(*Suby of* DTE ENERGY RESOURCES INC) ★
414 S Main St Ste 600, Ann Arbor, MI 48104-2398
Tel (734) 302-4800 *Founded/Ownrshp* 1994
Sales 169.3MM^E *EMP* 215
SIC 4911 Electric services
Ch Bd: Gerard M Anderson
Pr: Gerald Endler
CFO: Kent L McCargar
Ex VP: Jack Sullivan
VP: Christopher Davis
VP: Jerry Endler
VP: Charles Holt
VP: Gary Quantock
VP: Steve Sorrentino
Exec: Kurt Christian
Exec: Carl Nystrom

D-U-N-S 17-998-9231
■ DTE ENERGY TRADING INC
(*Suby of* DTE ENERGY CO) ★
414 S Main St Ste 200, Ann Arbor, MI 48104-2397
Tel (734) 887-2000 *Founded/Ownrshp* 1999
Sales 316.8MM^E *EMP* 200
SIC 4911 4923 Distribution, electric power; Gas transmission & distribution
Pr: Mark Cousino
Sr VP: Ron May
*VP: Michael Kotyk
VP: Peter Oleksiak
*VP: Gary S Quantock
*Prin: Steve Mabry

D-U-N-S 00-695-8540
■ DTE GAS CO (MI)
(*Suby of* DTE ENERGY CO) ★
1 Energy Plz Rm 1600, Detroit, MI 48226-1221
Tel (313) 235-4000 *Founded/Ownrshp* 1898
Sales 2.9MMM^E *EMP* 7,946
SIC 4924 4922 Natural gas distribution; Natural gas transmission; Storage, natural gas
Ch Bd: Gerard M Anderson
*Ch Bd: Anthony F Earley Jr
*Pr: Jerry Norcia
*CFO: David E Meador
VP: Sharon Niel
*VP: Peter B Oleksiak
VP: Larry Steward
Dir IT: Rosa Lacass
Dir IT: Susan Walsh
Sls Mgr: Collene Taylor
Board of Directors: Bruce D Peterson

DTI
See DIRECT TRAVEL INC

DTI FOR GOVERNMENT
See DULUTH TRAVEL INC

D-U-N-S 10-148-2578
DTLR INC
(*Suby of* B R S) ★
1300 Mercedes Dr, Hanover, MD 21076-3140
Tel (410) 850-5900 *Founded/Ownrshp* 2005
Sales 122.2MM^E *EMP* 1,000
SIC 5611 5661 Clothing, sportswear, men's & boys'; Shoe stores
*CFO: Richard E Pitts

DTMP
See DETROIT TOOL METAL PRODUCTS CO

D-U-N-S 18-382-4903 IMP
DTR INDUSTRIES INC
(*Suby of* SUMITOMO RIKO COMPANY LIMITED)
320 Snider Rd, Bluffton, OH 45817-9573
Tel (419) 358-2121 *Founded/Ownrshp* 2013
Sales 180.0MM^E *EMP* 750^E
SIC 3052 3069 3829 3714 Automobile hose, rubber; Molded rubber products; Measuring & controlling devices; Motor vehicle parts & accessories
Pr: Akira Kikuta
*Ch Bd: M Fujiwara
*Treas: Yuichi Ariga
Sr VP: Bill Yokas
Exec: Mikiro Sato
Genl Mgr: Peter Byrne
QA Dir: Chris Motoki
Sfty Mgr: Laura Jones
Sls Mgr: Jeff Vennekotter

D-U-N-S 79-924-1476 IMP
■ DTS INC
(*Suby of* TESSERA HOLDING CORP) ★
5220 Las Virgenes Rd, Calabasas, CA 91302-1064
Tel (818) 436-1000 *Founded/Ownrshp* 2016
Sales 138.2MM *EMP* 484
SIC 7819 3651 Services allied to motion pictures; Household audio & video equipment
CEO: Jon E Kirchner
Pr: Brian D Towne
CFO: Melvin L Flanigan
Chf Mktg O: Kevin Doohan
Ofcr: Frederick L Kitson
Ex VP: Kris M Graves
Ex VP: Geir Skaaden
Ex VP: Patrick J Watson
Ex VP: Blake A Welcher
Sftwr Eng: Mat Rizzo

DTSA
See DEFENSE TECHNOLOGY SECURITY ADMINISTRATION

DTZ
See CASSIDY TURLEY INC

D-U-N-S 06-822-4385
DTZ GOVERNMENT SERVICES INC (DE)
(*Suby of* CUSHMAN & WAKEFIELD INC) ★
275 Grove St Ste 3-200, Auburndale, MA 02466-2274
Tel (617) 527-5222 *Founded/Ownrshp* 1962, 2001
Sales 180.7MM^E *EMP* 673^E
SIC 7349 Building maintenance, except repairs
Pr: George A Keches
V Ch: Louis J Lanzillo Jr
*Treas: James E Lawlor
Sr VP: Michael Dunn
VP: Walter W Cro
VP: Jonica Preite
Dir Risk M: Tammie Pannone
Dir Bus: Jonathan A Peck

D-U-N-S 05-320-2271
DU PAGE MEDICAL GROUP LTD
GLEN ELLYN CLINIC
1100 31st St Ste 300, Downers Grove, IL 60515-5512
Tel (630) 545-6000 *Founded/Ownrshp* 1994
Sales 268.7MM^E *EMP* 1,500
SIC 8011 Medical centers
CEO: Michael Kasper
*Pr: Paul Merrick
*COO: Dennis Fine
*CFO: Mike Pacetti
*Treas: John Porcelli

*VP: Brian Oleary
Prac Mgr: Corie Rectenwald
Off Mgr: Sue Alberto
Off Mgr: Christyne Strutynsky
Off Mgr: WarnerTine
Dir IT: Karen Adamson

D-U-N-S 80-442-2509
■ DU PONT FOREIGN SALES CORP
(Suby of E I DU PONT DE NEMOURS AND CO) ★
974 Centre Rd, Wilmington, DE 19805-1269
Tel (302) 774-1000 Founded/Ownrshp 1995
Sales 17.0MM^E EMP 2,000
SIC 7389 Personal service agents, brokers & bureaus
CEO: Charles Holliday

D-U-N-S 00-120-5595 IMP/EXP
DU PONT TEIJIN FILMS US LIMITED PARTNERSHIP
3600 Discovery Dr, Chester, VA 23836-6436
Tel (804) 530-4076 Founded/Ownrshp 1993
Sales 264.8MM^E EMP 1,400^E
SIC 3081 Unsupported plastics film & sheet
CEO: Masaaki Hojo
*Pr: Jean-Philippe Azoulay
*COO: John C Groves
CIO: Joseph Racette

D-U-N-S 07-551-8134
DUANE MORRIS LLP
30 S 17th St Fl 5, Philadelphia, PA 19103-4196
Tel (215) 979-1000 Founded/Ownrshp 1932
Sales 335.8MM^E EMP 1,450
SIC 8111 General practice attorney, lawyer
Ch Bd: John J Soroko
Pt: Kimball Ann
Pt: William M Bagliebter
Pt: John H Barron Jr
Pt: Demetrios C Batsides
Pt: Andres C Benach
Pt: Joseph M Bennett-Paris
Pt: Mark A Canizio
Pt: Vincent L Capuano
Pt: Jeffrey Chamberlain
Pt: Michael L Chartan
Pt: Frederick Cohen
Pt: Preston C Delashmit
Pt: Richard P Dyer
Pt: Anthony J Fitzpatrick
Pt: Michael D Grohman
Pt: Harvey W Gurland Jr
Pt: James P Hollihan
Pt: Amelia Huskins
Pt: L N Jameson
Pt: J Colin Knisely

D-U-N-S 01-198-8995 IMP
■ DUANE READE INC
(Suby of WALGREENS) ★
40 Wall St Fl 22, New York, NY 10005-1340
Tel (212) 273-5700 Founded/Ownrshp 2010
Sales 840.5MM^E EMP 6,000
SIC 5912 Drug stores
CEO: John A Lederer
CFO: John Fishkin
*CFO: John K Henry
CFO: Sharon Savary
Sr VP: Joseph C Magnacca
Sr VP: Jenna Merch
VP: Chris Darrow
VP: Anthony M Goldrick
Dir Rx: Tony Riso
Pr Mgr: Calvin Peters
Mktg Mgr: Lauren Purdo

D-U-N-S 15-765-1410 IMP
■ DUANE READE SHAREHOLDERS LLC
(Suby of WALGREENS) ★
40 Wall St Fl 22, New York, NY 10005-1340
Tel (212) 273-5700 Founded/Ownrshp 2011
Sales 52.8MM^E EMP 1,000
SIC 5912 Drug stores

D-U-N-S 36-168-7080
DUARTE NURSERY INC
DUARTE PROPERTIES
1555 Baldwin Rd, Hughson, CA 95326-9522
Tel (209) 531-0351 Founded/Ownrshp 1989
Sales 85.0MM^E EMP 400
SIC 0181 Ornamental nursery products
Pr: John Duarte
*Treas: Anita Duarte
*VP: Jeff Duarte

DUARTE PROPERTIES
See DUARTE NURSERY INC

D-U-N-S 06-435-8989
DUBELL LUMBER CO
148 Route 70, Medford, NJ 08055-2373
Tel (609) 654-4143 Founded/Ownrshp 1972
Sales 119.7MM^E EMP 155
SIC 5031 5211 Lumber: rough, dressed & finished; Lumber & other building materials
Pr: Gene S Dimedio
*Sec: Dennis Dimedio
*VP: David Dimedio
MIS Dir: Bill Sauser
Board of Directors: Anthony A Di Medio, Gabriel Di Medio, Michael Di Medio, Renato Di Medio

D-U-N-S 05-838-7275
DUBLIN CITY SCHOOLS
7030 Coffman Rd, Dublin, OH 43017-1008
Tel (614) 764-5913 Founded/Ownrshp 1922
Sales 218.8MM EMP 1,110
Accts Plattenburg & Associates Inc
SIC 8211 Public elementary school; Public junior high school; Public senior high school
*Pr: Chris Valentine
Treas: Chris Mohr
*VP: Mark Holderman
Prin: Timothy Barton
Prin: Thomas Bates
Prin: Marina Davis
Prin: Henry Griffith Sr
Prin: Douglas Heuer
Prin: Carol King
Prin: Philip Niemie
Prin: David Nosker

DUBLIN HONDA
See HARVEY & MADDING INC

D-U-N-S 19-350-8470
DUBLIN UNIFIED SCHOOL DISTRICT
7471 Larkdale Ave, Dublin, CA 94568-1500
Tel (925) 828-2551 Founded/Ownrshp 1933
Sales 104.8MM EMP 600
Accts Crowe Horwath Llp Sacramento
SIC 8211 Public elementary & secondary schools; Public elementary school; Public junior high school; Public senior high school
Trst: Greg Tomlinson
MIS Dir: Custer Rodriguez
Psych: Sara Brown
Psych: Winston Wong
HC Dir: Tim McCarty
Snr Mgr: Dharini Baskaran

DUBLINAIRE
See AGE GOLDEN PROPERTIES LTD

D-U-N-S 94-145-4639
DUBOIS CHEMICALS
FOOD GROUP ENGINEERING
3630 E Kemper Rd, Cincinnati, OH 45241-2011
Tel (800) 438-2647 Founded/Ownrshp 2007
Sales 174.0MM^E EMP 1,400
SIC 2842 Cleaning or polishing preparations
Pr: V Kasturirangan
VP: Jeff Berresford
VP: Ronald J Christensen
*VP: Bernard Damon
VP: Jim Forrester
VP: Tom Gartland
VP: Gary Prampero
VP: Jim Walker
VP: Jeff Welsh
Brnch Mgr: Steve Moser
Genl Mgr: Peter A Misslin
Board of Directors: Jeff Berresford, Tom Gartland, Jim Walker, Jeff Welsh

D-U-N-S 82-823-5445 EXP
DUBOIS CHEMICALS INC
3630 E Kemper Rd, Sharonville, OH 45241-2011
Tel (800) 438-2647 Founded/Ownrshp 2012
Sales 233.4MM^E EMP 516^E
SIC 2869 Industrial organic chemicals
CEO: Jeff Welsh
Pr: Eric Dill
VP: Jake Harris
Exec: Ronnie Padgett
CIO: Jim Flynn
Dir IT: Scott Leonard
Tech Mgr: Matthew Hall
QI Cn Mgr: Chris Strub
VP Mktg: Blair Imbody
Mktg Dir: Kevin Davis
Sls Mgr: Eric Retzlaff

D-U-N-S 94-614-0886
DUBOIS REGIONAL MEDICAL CENTER INC
PENN HIGHLANDS DUBOIS
100 Hospital Ave, Du Bois, PA 15801-1499
Tel (814) 371-2200 Founded/Ownrshp 1995
Sales 248.6MM EMP 1,400^E
SIC 8093 8011 Rehabilitation center, outpatient treatment; Offices & clinics of medical doctors
Pr: Raymond Graeca
Chf Rad: Ali Shaw
COO: Gary Macioce Fache
CFO: John Sutika
Sr VP: Raymond Greg
Sr VP: Debbie Wayne
VP: Dan Ahern
Dir Risk M: Greg Volpe
Dir Lab: Karen Abogast
Dir Rad: Michael Sands
Chf Nrs Of: Kim Grossman

D-U-N-S 78-733-5835
DUBOSE STEEL INC OF NORTH CAROLINA
767 Dr Mlk Jr Blvd, Roseboro, NC 28382
Tel (910) 525-4161 Founded/Ownrshp 1990
Sales 155.4MM^E EMP 140^E
SIC 5051 Metals service centers & offices; Structural shapes, iron or steel; Tubing, metal; Plates, metal
Pr: Thomas L Harrington
*VP: J R Fischer
*VP: Steve Johnson
*VP: Leonard Lynch

D-U-N-S 87-819-4406
DUBUIS HEALTH SYSTEM INC
2707 North Loop W Ste 7, Houston, TX 77008-1048
Tel (713) 277-2300 Founded/Ownrshp 1994
Sales 45.4MM^E EMP 1,300
Accts Deloitte Tax Llp Houston Tx
SIC 8069 Specialty hospitals, except psychiatric
CEO: Stephen Mills
*COO: Tracey Richard
CFO: Charles Soster
Ofcr: Gary Kempf
VP: Tim Freeman
*VP: Paul Veillon
Exec: Judy Boudreaux
Exec: Chad Brisendine
Exec: George Garrett
*Prin: Ellen Smith
CIO: Wayman Thurman

DUBUQUE BANK & TRUST
See DUBUQUE BANK AND TRUST CO

D-U-N-S 00-694-1512
■ DUBUQUE BANK AND TRUST CO
DUBUQUE BANK & TRUST
(Suby of HEARTLAND FINANCIAL USA INC) ★
1398 Central Ave, Dubuque, IA 52001-5021
Tel (563) 589-2000 Founded/Ownrshp 1935
Sales NA EMP 272
SIC 6022 State trust companies accepting deposits, commercial
Pr: Douglas J Horstmann
Pr: Deb Siegworth
*COO: John K Schmidt
Chf Mktg O: John Berg
Sr VP: David Gaylor
Sr VP: Polly Hauser
VP: Shari Bartels
VP: Wayne Breckon
VP: Lynne Juergens
VP: Rita McCarthy
VP: Karen Olson
VP: Sarah Ross
VP: Ron Sterr
VP: Doug Stillings
VP: Jeffrey Timmerman
Dir Bus: Jeffrey Vaassen

D-U-N-S 04-059-5803
DUBUQUE COMMUNITY SCHOOL DISTRICT
2300 Chaney Rd, Dubuque, IA 52001-3059
Tel (563) 552-3000 Founded/Ownrshp 1856
Sales 106.5MM^E EMP 1,800
SIC 8211 Public elementary & secondary schools; Elementary school
Ex Dir: Betty Hogan
Pr Dir: Mike Cyze
Teacher Pr: Phil Kramer
HC Dir: Rhonda Ramler

D-U-N-S 10-693-7436 IMP/EXP
DUCHOSSOIS GROUP INC
845 N Larch Ave, Elmhurst, IL 60126-1114
Tel (630) 279-3600 Founded/Ownrshp 1983
Sales 1.7MMM^E EMP 6,222
SIC 3699 Household electrical equipment
Ch Bd: Robert L Fealy
CEO: Craig J Duchossois
CFO: Michael E Flannery
IT Man: Shannon Lange

D-U-N-S 06-060-6092
DUCK DELIVERY PRODUCE INC
(Suby of UNITED SALAD CO) ★
8448 Ne 33rd Dr Ste 120, Portland, OR 97211-2105
Tel (503) 288-9380 Founded/Ownrshp 1985
Sales 87.1MM^E EMP 193
SIC 5148 4212 Fruits, fresh; Vegetables, fresh; Delivery service, vehicular
Pr: Ernest Spada J
VP: Ron Carlston
Off Admin: Claire Allen
Sfty Mgr: Liliya Pirumova
Sales Asso: Trent Gay

D-U-N-S 00-792-2966
DUCK RIVER ELECTRIC MEMBERSHIP CORP (TN)
1411 Madison St, Shelbyville, TN 37160-3629
Tel (931) 684-4621 Founded/Ownrshp 1935
Sales 178.9MM EMP 160
Accts Winnett Associates Pllc Shelb
SIC 4911 Distribution, electric power
Pr: Michael Watson
*Ch Bd: Brent Willis
*Treas: John Moses
Ex Dir: Bobby Vannatta
Dist Mgr: Michael Millraney
Dist Mgr: Timmy Terry
Dist Mgr: Michael Trew
IT Man: Doug Snyder
Sfty Dirs: Timmy Orrell
Opers Supe: Rob Edde
Sfty Mgr: Steven Hopkins

DUCK TAPE
See SHURTECH BRANDS LLC

DUCK THRU FOOD STORES
See JERNIGAN OIL CO INC

D-U-N-S 06-857-7741 IMP
DUCKS UNLIMITED INC
1 Waterfowl Way, Memphis, TN 38120-2351
Tel (901) 758-3825 Founded/Ownrshp 1937
Sales 209.6MM EMP 500
Accts Kpmg Llp Memphis Tennessee
SIC 0971 Wildlife management
Pr: Bruce Lewis
Pr: Eric Rudgers
COO: Scott Yaich
CFO: Randy L Graves
CFO: Adam Webster
Treas: Robert S Hester Jr
Ofcr: Loni Lindsey
Ex VP: D A Young
VP: Paul Boehne
VP: Jared Brown
VP: Andrew Gregory
VP: A Long

D-U-N-S 00-828-6494 EXP
■ DUCOMMUN AEROSTRUCTURES INC
(Suby of DUCOMMUN INC) ★
268 E Gardena Blvd, Gardena, CA 90248-2814
Tel (310) 380-5390 Founded/Ownrshp 1949
Sales 298.5MM^E EMP 1,300
SIC 3724 3812 3728 Aircraft engines & engine parts; Search & navigation equipment; Aircraft parts & equipment
CEO: Anthony J Reardon
QI Cn Mgr: Alfredo Sandoval

DUCOMMUN AROSTRUCTURES-GARDENA
See AHF-DUCOMMUN INC

D-U-N-S 00-690-7042 IMP
▲ DUCOMMUN INC
23301 Wilmington Ave, Carson, CA 90745-6209
Tel (310) 513-7200 Founded/Ownrshp 1849
Sales 666.0MM EMP 2,900^E
Tkr Sym DCO Exch NYS
SIC 3728 3679 Aircraft parts & equipment; Aircraft body & wing assemblies & parts; Aircraft assemblies, subassemblies & parts; Microwave components
Ch Bd: Anthony J Reardon
CFO: Douglas L Groves
Ofcr: Rosalie F Rogers
VP: Kathryn M Andrus
VP: James S Heiser
VP: Jerry L Redondo
VP: Christopher D Wampler
Board of Directors: Richard A Baldridge, Joseph C Berenato, Gregory S Churchill, Robert C Ducommun, Dean M Flatt, Jay L Haberland, Robert D Paulson

D-U-N-S 00-721-7805 IMP
■ DUCOMMUN LABARGETECHNOLOGIES INC
(Suby of DUCOMMUN INC) ★
689 Craig Rd 200, Saint Louis, MO 63141-7112
Tel (314) 997-0800 Founded/Ownrshp 1953, 1968
Sales 358.2MM^E EMP 1,560
SIC 3812 3699 Aircraft/aerospace flight instruments & guidance systems; Electrical equipment & supplies
Pr: Anthony Reardon
COO: Randy L Buschling
CFO: Joseph Bellino
CFO: Leonard Michael
CFO: Todd Quernheim
CFO: Bill Wagner
Bd of Dir: Dorothy Legrand
VP: Barry Pipkin
VP: Rosalie Rogers
Ex Dir: Jim Key
Genl Mgr: Scott Gustafson

D-U-N-S 01-645-0244 IMP/EXP
DUCON TECHNOLOGIES INC
5 Penn Plz Ste 2403, New York, NY 10001-1848
Tel (631) 694-1700 Founded/Ownrshp 1996
Sales 479.4MM EMP 471
Accts Salboro And Associates New Yo
SIC 3537 3564 Industrial trucks & tractors; Blowers & fans
Ch: Aron Govil
*Ch: William Papa
*VP: Renato Delarama
*VP: Bob Gupta

DUCT DIRECT
See MCCORVEY SHEET METAL WORKS LP

D-U-N-S 80-120-8971 IMP/EXP
DUDA FARM FRESH FOODS INC
(Suby of A DUDA & SONS INC) ★
1200 Duda Trl, Oviedo, FL 32765-4507
Tel (407) 365-2111 Founded/Ownrshp 1972
Sales 143.3MM^E EMP 500
SIC 5148 0161 0174 Fresh fruits & vegetables; Vegetables & melons; Citrus fruits
Pr: David Duda
*Treas: Mark E Engwall
*Sr VP: Mark Bassetti
*VP: Richard Alcocer
*VP: Dean Diefenthaler
*VP: Carol Barrell L Duda
*VP: Samuel D Duda
*VP: Mike Robinson
*VP: Palmer Weeks
Snr Mgr: Rick Hanas

D-U-N-S 80-788-2845
DUFF & PHELPS CORP
(Suby of DAKOTA HOLDING CORPORATION)
55 E 52nd St Fl 31, New York, NY 10055-0004
Tel (212) 871-2000 Founded/Ownrshp 2013
Sales 924.7MM^E EMP 1,453^E
Accts Kpmg Llp New York New York
SIC 6282 6211 Investment advice; Investment bankers
Ch Bd: Noah Gottdiener
Pr: Jacob L Silverman
COO: Joseph R Greiner
COO: Brett A Marschke
CFO: Patrick M Puzzuoli
CFO: Patrick Puzzuoli
Chf Mktg O: Marty Garofalo
Ex VP: Edward S Forman
Ex VP: William P Hall
Ex VP: Kimberly Russo
Ex VP: Mimi Song
VP: Jason Albert
VP: Federico Azpiazu
VP: Michael Berbari
VP: Eric Bringer
VP: Joyolin Brown
VP: Iris Cao
VP: Sherri Davis
VP: Eric Elvekrog
VP: Max Fan
VP: Mike Ferrara

D-U-N-S 55-650-1708
DUFF & PHELPS LLC
(Suby of DUFF & PHELPS CORP) ★
55 E 52nd St Fl 31, New York, NY 10055-0004
Tel (212) 871-2000 Founded/Ownrshp 2004
Sales 134.9MM^E EMP 1,054
SIC 8742 Financial consultant
CEO: Noah Gottdiener
*Pr: Jacob Silverman
*COO: Brett Marschke
*CFO: Patrick Puzzuoli
Ofcr: Catherine Makstenieks
VP: Matt Abhalter
VP: Mark Brashear
VP: Steve Burt
VP: Betty Daum
VP: Mike Dotson
VP: Daniel Eliades
VP: Laura Horstmann
VP: Kelly Hunter
VP: Manasi Kapadia
VP: Roger Ketron
VP: Larry Kohn
VP: Patty Mosley
VP: Michael Snowdon
VP: Marybeth Temmallo
VP: Cristobal Valencia
VP: Michael Van Donselaar

DUFFENS OPTICAL
See ESSILOR LABORATORIES OF AMERICA INC

D-U-N-S 19-807-0141
DUFFYS HOLDINGS INC
4440 Pga Blvd Ste 201, Palm Beach Gardens, FL 33410-6540
Tel (561) 804-7676 Founded/Ownrshp 2002
Sales 40.9MM^E EMP 1,100
SIC 5812 Eating places
Pr: Paul Emmett

*VP: Steve Cournoyer
Mktg Dir: Sandy Nelson

D-U-N-S 00-380-5256
DUGAN & MEYERS CONSTRUCTION CO
(Suby of DUGAN & MEYERS INTERESTS INC) ★
11110 Kenwood Rd, Blue Ash, OH 45242-1818
Tel (513) 891-4300 Founded/Ownrshp 1984
Sales 102.5MM^E EMP 150
SIC 1541 1542 1522 Industrial buildings, new construction; Commercial & office building, new construction; Institutional building construction; Condominium construction
CEO: Francis Dugan
*Pr: Jerome E Meyers Jr
*Treas: Jeffrey Kelly
Sr VP: Steven Klinker
*VP: Tim Dugan

D-U-N-S 11-288-8912
DUGAN & MEYERS INTERESTS INC
11110 Kenwood Rd, Blue Ash, OH 45242-1818
Tel (513) 891-4300 Founded/Ownrshp 1935
Sales 103.1MM^E EMP 200
Accts Clark Schaefer Hackett Cincin
SIC 1541 1542 1522 Industrial buildings, new construction; Renovation, remodeling & repairs: industrial buildings; Commercial & office building, new construction; Commercial & office buildings, renovation & repair; Institutional building construction; Condominium construction
CEO: Jerome E Meyers Jr
*CFO: Jeffrey Kelly

DUGGAN AND MARCON
See MARCON & BOYER INC

D-U-N-S 02-297-7813
DUININCK INC (MN)
408 6th St, Prinsburg, MN 56281-9738
Tel (320) 978-6011 Founded/Ownrshp 1940, 1962
Sales 156.0MM EMP 1,000
Accts Grant Thornton Llp Minneapoli
SIC 1629 1611 Golf course construction; General contractor, highway & street construction
CEO: Trevor Duininck
Mng Pt: Norman Duininck
*CEO: Willis Duininck
*Treas: Curtis Duininck
*VP: Christian Duininck
Div Mgr: Jerome Vikse
Genl Mgr: Dave Munkvold
IT Man: Rochelle Anderson

D-U-N-S 92-927-7390
DUKE CLINICAL RESEARCH INSTITUTE
DUKE MEDICAL CENTER
2400 Pratt St, Durham, NC 27705-3976
Tel (919) 668-8725 Founded/Ownrshp 2000
Sales 47.8MM EMP 1,000^E
SIC 8071 Medical laboratories
Ex Dir: Robert Califf MD
COO: Elizabeth B Reid
Exec: Nicole Hedrick
Assoc Dir: John Norman
Assoc Dir: Jack Shostak
Assoc Dir: Brian Smith
Assoc Dir: David Wright
Off Mgr: Joy Lopez
Off Mgr: Diane Uzarski
IT Man: Donna Taylor
Opers Mgr: Nancy Newark

D-U-N-S 07-866-3132
■ **DUKE ENERGY BECKJORD LLC**
(Suby of DUKE ENERGY OHIO INC) ★
139 E 4th St, Cincinnati, OH 45202-4034
Tel (513) 287-2561 Founded/Ownrshp 2012
Sales 59.3MM^E EMP 4,738^E
SIC 4911 Electric services
Prin: Charles Whitlock

D-U-N-S 83-076-0216
■ **DUKE ENERGY BUSINESS SERVICES LLC**
(Suby of DUKE ENERGY CORPORATE SERVICES INC) ★
526 S Church St Ec-03t, Charlotte, NC 28202-1802
Tel (704) 594-6200 Founded/Ownrshp 1998
Sales 2.6MMM^E EMP 6,884^E
SIC 4911 4922 Electric services; Pipelines, natural gas
CEO: James E Rogers
*CEO: Lynn J Good
*COO: B Keith Trent
Ex VP: Richard Blackburn

D-U-N-S 61-459-7974
■ **DUKE ENERGY CAROLINAS LLC**
(Suby of DUKE ENERGY CORP) ★
410 S Wilmington St, Raleigh, NC 27601-1849
Tel (704) 382-3853 Founded/Ownrshp 2006
Sales 7.2MMM EMP 29,188^E
SIC 4911 Electric services
Ch Bd: Lynn J Good
CFO: Steven K Young
Ofcr: Melissa H Anderson
Sr VP: Brian D Savoy
Prgrm Mgr: Wanda Evans
Prgrm Mgr: Rob Robertson
IT Man: Floyd Phillips
VP Opers: Michael Williams
Opers Mgr: Dan Beahan
Secur Mgr: Lisa Suggs
Snr PM: Christy Johnston
Board of Directors: Lloyd M Yates

DUKE ENERGY COML ASSET MGT LLC
See DYNEGY COMMERCIAL ASSET MANAGEMENT LLC

DUKE ENERGY CONESVILLE, LLC
See DYNEGY CONESVILLE LLC

D-U-N-S 00-699-6052 IMP/EXP
▲ **DUKE ENERGY CORP**
550 S Tryon St, Charlotte, NC 28202-4200
Tel (704) 382-3853 Founded/Ownrshp 1904
Sales 23.4MMM EMP 31,131
Accts Deloitte & Touche Llp Charlot
Tkr Sym DUK Exch NYS
SIC 4911 4924 4931 Electric services; Natural gas distribution; Electric & other services combined
Pr: Lynn J Good
V Ch: Charlie Nartker
Pr: Kodwo Ghartey-Tagoe
Pr: Harry Sideris
COO: Dhiaa Jamil
COO: Dhiaa M Jamil
CFO: Steven K Young
Treas: Robert Combs
Treas: William Mayhew
Ofcr: Melissa H Anderson
Ex VP: Melissa Anderson
Ex VP: A Mullinax
Sr VP: Keith G Butler
Sr VP: Paul Draovitch
Sr VP: Alex Glenn
Sr VP: Michael A Lewis
Sr VP: Regis T Repko
Sr VP: Brian Savoy
VP: Lee E Barrett
VP: Elliott Batson
VP: Jane Brown
Board of Directors: William E Kennard, Michael J Angelakis, E Marie McKee, Michael G Browning, Richard A Meserve, Harris E Deloach Jr, Charles W Moorman, Daniel R Dimicco, James T Rhodes, John H Forsgren, Carlos A Saladrigas, Ann Maynard Gray, James H Hance Jr, John T Herron, James B Hyler Jr

D-U-N-S 07-848-3671
■ **DUKE ENERGY CORPORATE SERVICES INC**
(Suby of DUKE ENERGY CORP) ★
526 S Church St, Charlotte, NC 28202-1802
Tel (704) 594-6200 Founded/Ownrshp 2008
Sales 2.6MMM^E EMP 6,926^E
SIC 4911 Electric services
Ch Bd: James E Rogers

D-U-N-S 00-692-3700 IMP/EXP
■ **DUKE ENERGY FLORIDA LLC** (FL)
PROGRESS ENERGY FLORIDA
(Suby of PROGRESS ENERGY FLORIDA) ★
299 1st Ave N, Saint Petersburg, FL 33701-3308
Tel (704) 382-3853 Founded/Ownrshp 1899, 2000
Sales 4.9MMM EMP 100
SIC 4911 Electric services
CEO: Lynn J Good
CFO: Jeff Foster
CFO: Steven K Young
Ofcr: C S Hinnant
Sr VP: E Michael Williams
VP: Jackie Joyner
VP: Michael Lewis
VP: Brian D Savoy
VP: Jennifer Stenger

D-U-N-S 00-693-9540
■ **DUKE ENERGY INDIANA LLC** (IN)
(Suby of DUKE ENERGY CORP) ★
1000 E Main St, Plainfield, IN 46168-1782
Tel (704) 382-3853 Founded/Ownrshp 1941
Sales 2.8MMM EMP 197
SIC 4911 Electric services; Distribution, electric power; Generation, electric power; Transmission, electric power
CEO: Lynn J Good
*CFO: Steven K Young
*Sr VP: Brian D Savoy
Software D: Carla Evans

DUKE ENERGY MIAMI FORT, LLC
See DYNEGY MIAMI FORT LLC

D-U-N-S 16-090-0189
DUKE ENERGY NATURAL GAS CORP
(Suby of DCP MIDSTREAM LP) ★
5400 Westheimer Ct, Houston, TX 77056-5353
Tel (713) 627-5400 Founded/Ownrshp 2000
Sales 143.1MM^E EMP 300^E
SIC 4923 Gas transmission & distribution
Ch Bd: David Hauser
CFO: Murray Bennett
CFO: Greg Rizzo
Genl Mgr: Roy Breen
CIO: Gayle Puterbough

D-U-N-S 00-699-9189 IMP
■ **DUKE ENERGY OHIO INC**
(Suby of DUKE ENERGY CORP) ★
400 S Tryon, Charlotte, NC 28285-1900
Tel (704) 382-3853 Founded/Ownrshp 1837
Sales 1.9MMM EMP 28,344
Accts Deloitte & Touche Llp Charlot
SIC 4911 4922 4924 4931 Electric services; Distribution, electric power; Generation, electric power; Transmission, electric power; Natural gas transmission; Natural gas distribution; Electric & other services combined
CEO: Lynn J Good
CFO: Steven K Young
Ex VP: Fred Newton
VP: Brian D Savoy
Board of Directors: B Keith Trent, Lloyd M Yates

D-U-N-S 00-699-7217 IMP
■ **DUKE ENERGY PROGRESS LLC**
(Suby of PROGRESS ENERGY INC) ★
410 S Wilmington St, Raleigh, NC 27601-1849
Tel (704) 382-3853 Founded/Ownrshp 1899
Sales 5.2MMM EMP 28,344
SIC 4911 Electric services; Generation, electric power; Transmission, electric power; Distribution, electric power
CEO: Lynn J Good
Pr: Tom D Kilgore
Pr: William S Orser
CFO: Steven K Young
Ofcr: C S Hinnant
Sr VP: E Michael Williams
Prgrm Mgr: Gubelli Gary
Board of Directors: Julia S Janson

D-U-N-S 07-844-7089
■ **DUKE ENERGY REGISTRATION SERVICES INC**
(Suby of DUKE ENERGY CORP) ★
526 S Church St, Charlotte, NC 28202-1802
Tel (704) 594-6200 Founded/Ownrshp 1998
Sales 605.1MM^E EMP 6,028^E
SIC 4922 Natural gas transmission
CEO: James E Rogers

D-U-N-S 07-848-4736
■ **DUKE ENERGY SERVICES INC**
(Suby of DUKE ENERGY REGISTRATION SERVICES INC) ★
526 S Church St, Charlotte, NC 28202-1802
Tel (704) 594-6200 Founded/Ownrshp 1997
Sales 341.3MM^E EMP 1,022^E
SIC 4911 Electric services
Ch Bd: James E Rogers
Sr VP: Paul R Newton
Sr VP: Sara S Whitney
VP: Jeff Almond
VP: Myron Caldwell
VP: William McCabe
IT Man: Joseph Adams
IT Man: Steve Blackburn
IT Man: Tom Harrington
IT Man: Sam Holeman
IT Man: Liem Tran

DUKE ENERGY ZIMMER, LLC
See DYNEGY ZIMMER LLC

D-U-N-S 84-196-5676
DUKE HEALTH RALEIGH HOSPITAL GUILD
DUKE RALEIGH HOSPITAL
(Suby of DUKE UNIVERSITY HOSPITAL) ★
3400 Wake Forest Rd, Raleigh, NC 27609-7317
Tel (919) 954-3000 Founded/Ownrshp 1982
Sales 348.8MM EMP 600
SIC 8062 General medical & surgical hospitals
Pr: David Zaas
*CEO: Doug Dinsel
*COO: Rick Gannotta
*CFO: Terri Newsom
VP: Teresa Todd
Sfty Mgr: Kenneth Eatman
Mktg Mgr: Carla Parker-Hollis
Pharmcst: Christopher Stein
Occ Thrpy: Liz Jackson

DUKE LIFEPOINT HEALTHCARE
See DLP HEALTHCARE LLC

DUKE LIFEPOINT HEALTHCARE
See FRYE REGIONAL MEDICAL CENTER INC

DUKE LIFEPOINT HEALTHCARE
See LIFEPOINT OF LAKE CUMBERLAND LLC

DUKE MANUFACTURING
See DUKE MFG PROPERTIES LLC

DUKE MEDICAL CENTER
See DUKE CLINICAL RESEARCH INSTITUTE

D-U-N-S 00-627-6026 IMP/EXP
DUKE MFG PROPERTIES LLC
DUKE MANUFACTURING
2224 N 10th St, Saint Louis, MO 63102-1421
Tel (800) 735-3853 Founded/Ownrshp 2003
Sales 150.8MM^E EMP 520
SIC 3589 3556 Food warming equipment, commercial; Cooking equipment, commercial; Food products machinery
Pr: John J Hake
COO: David Marvel
*CFO: Lawrence Reader
VP: Christine Freed
VP: Brian Heuckroth
VP: Jim Klimt
VP: Tom Lamantia
VP: Todd Taylor
VP: Kathy Veder
Rgnl Mgr: Joe Rennon
IT Man: Sheldon Coach

DUKE RALEIGH HOSPITAL
See DUKE HEALTH RALEIGH HOSPITAL GUILD

D-U-N-S 11-530-8553 IMP
DUKE REALTY CORP
600 E 96th St Ste 100, Indianapolis, IN 46240-3792
Tel (317) 808-6000 Founded/Ownrshp 1986
Sales 949.4MM EMP 500^E
SIC 6798 1542 Real estate investment trusts; Nonresidential construction
Ofcr: Dennis D Oklak
V Ch: Gary Burk
*Pr: James B Connor
Pr: Sandy Hege
Pr: Tim Hoffman
Pr: Gladys Tejada
CFO: Mark A Denien
CFO: Gene Zink
Treas: Chris Donovan
Ofcr: Jack W Guinee III
Ex VP: Nick Anthony
Ex VP: James B Conner
Ex VP: Ann C Dee
Ex VP: Ann Dee
Ex VP: Donald J Hunter
Ex VP: Steve Kennedy
Ex VP: Samuel O'Briant
Ex VP: Steven W Schnur
Sr VP: Chris Brown
Sr VP: J K Dehner
Sr VP: Paul R Quinn
Board of Directors: Lynn C Thurber, Thomas J Baltimore Jr, Robert J Woodward Jr, William Cavanaugh III, Alan H Cohen, Charles R Eitel, Martin C Jischke, Melanie R Sabelhaus, Peter M Scott III, Jack R Shaw, Michael E Szymanczyk

D-U-N-S 17-471-4787
DUKE REALTY LIMITED PARTNERSHIP
(Suby of DUKE REALTY CORP) ★
600 E 96th St Ste 100, Indianapolis, IN 46240-3792
Tel (317) 808-6000 Founded/Ownrshp 1972
Sales 949.4MM EMP 99^E
SIC 6798 Real estate investment trusts
Genl Pt: Duke Realty Corp
Ltd Pt: Dennis D Oklak

D-U-N-S 04-438-7793 IMP/EXP
DUKE UNIVERSITY
2200 W Main St Ste 710, Durham, NC 27705-4677
Tel (919) 684-3030 Founded/Ownrshp 1841
Sales 4.8MMM EMP 26,000
Accts Kpmg Llp Greensboro Nc
SIC 8221 University
Pr: Richard Brodhead
Pr: Colleen Fitzpatrick
Pr: CAM Kelly
*CFO: Kenneth Morris
Trst: David Gergen
Trst: Kimberly J Jenkins
Trst: John J Mack
Trst: Nancy A Nasher
Trst: Ann Pelham
Trst: Charles M Smith
Trst: Ryan Todd
Trst: Xing Zong
Ofcr: Angel Wingate
Assoc VP: Victoria Nevois
*Ex VP: Tallman Trask III
*VP: Pamela J Bernard
*VP: Kyle Cavanaugh
VP: Greg Jones
VP: Wendy Kuran
VP: Larry Moneta
VP: Marsha Perry

D-U-N-S 00-164-2367 IMP/EXP
DUKE UNIVERSITY HEALTH SYSTEM INC
DUKE UNIVERSITY HOSPITAL
(Suby of DUKE UNIVERSITY) ★
2301 Erwin Rd, Durham, NC 27705-4699
Tel (919) 684-8111 Founded/Ownrshp 2001
Sales 2.6MMM EMP 16,627^E
Accts Kpmg Llp Norfolk Virginia
SIC 8062 General medical & surgical hospitals
Doctor: Victor Dzau
CFO: Kenneth C Morris
Ofcr: Karen Frush
Ofcr: Tin Tyson
VP: Mary Ann Fuchs
VP: Philip Stern
Dir Case M: Donna Peter
Dir Rx: Kirby D Contracting
Ex Dir: Paul R Newman
Prgrm Mgr: Paula Herber
Off Mgr: Cherie Sumner

DUKE UNIVERSITY HOSPITAL
See DUKE UNIVERSITY HEALTH SYSTEM INC

DULANEY STATION
See MOSAIC COMMUNITY SERVICES INC

D-U-N-S 15-116-5404
DULCICH INC
PACIFIC SEAFOOD GROUP
16797 Se 130th Ave, Clackamas, OR 97015-8966
Tel (503) 226-2200 Founded/Ownrshp 1985
Sales 476.0MM^E EMP 1,090
SIC 5146 2092 Seafoods; Seafoods, fresh: prepared; Seafoods, frozen: prepared
Pr: Frank Dominic Dulcic
VP: Jim Lanter
Genl Mgr: Anwer Haider
*Genl Mgr: Joe O'Halloran
Genl Mgr: Mary Schaffhausen
Ql Cn Mgr: David Doble
Mktg Mgr: Kira Kuetgens
Sls Mgr: Grant Larson
Sls Mgr: Jamie Watson

DULCINEA FARMS
See PACIFIC TRELLIS FRUIT LLC

DULLES INTERNATIONAL AIRPORT
See METROPOLITAN WASHINGTON AIRPORTS AUTHORITY

D-U-N-S 00-728-3823 IMP/EXP
DULTMEIER SALES LIMITED LIABILITY CO
13808 Industrial Rd, Omaha, NE 68137-1104
Tel (402) 333-1444 Founded/Ownrshp 1992
Sales 84.1MM^E EMP 70
Accts Masimore Magnuson & Associate
SIC 5083 5084 Agricultural machinery & equipment; Cleaning equipment, high pressure, sand or steam
COO: Mike Hansen
*Treas: R J Sall
Exec: R Sall

D-U-N-S 36-107-8798
DULUTH CLINIC LTD
(Suby of ESSENTIA HEALTH) ★
400 E 3rd St, Duluth, MN 55805-1983
Tel (218) 786-3600 Founded/Ownrshp 2005
Sales 128.8MM EMP 3
SIC 8011 Neurosurgeon
CEO: Peter Person
VP: Diane Davidson
Dir Rx: Stephanie Anderson
Dir Rx: Dianne Witten
Off Mgr: Gwen Cressman
Off Mgr: Cindy Sorenson
IT Man: Keavin Bostrom
IT Man: Eric Hill
Opthamlgy: Thomas F Shuey
Doctor: Rahul Aggarwal
Doctor: Brooks S Edward MD

D-U-N-S 15-697-3323
▲ **DULUTH HOLDINGS INC**
170 Countryside Dr, Belleville, WI 53508-9739
Tel (608) 424-1544 Founded/Ownrshp 1986
Sales 304.1MM EMP 1,187
Tkr Sym DLTH Exch NGS
SIC 5961 5611 5621 Catalog & mail-order houses; Catalog sales; Men's & boys' clothing stores; Women's clothing stores
Pr: Stephanie L Pugliese
*Ch Bd: Stephen L Schlecht
CFO: Mark M Deorio
Sr VP: Allen L Dittrich
Exec: John Wilson
Board of Directors: E David Coolidge III, Francesca M Edwardson, William E Ferry, David C Finch, Thomas G

Folliard, C Roger Lewis, Brenda I Morris

DULUTH PUBLIC SCHOOLS
See INDEPENDENT SCHOOL DISTRICT 709

DULUTHTEACHRS RTMNT FUND ASSN
SeeTEACHERS RETIREMENT FUND

D-U-N-S 82-723-5110
DULUTHTRAVEL INC
DTI FOR GOVERNMENT
2860 Peachtree Industrial, Duluth, GA 30097-7906
Tel (770) 813-9895 *Founded/Ownrshp* 1993
Sales 210.7MM *EMP* 60
SIC 4724 Travel agencies; Tourist agency arranging transport, lodging & car rental
CEO: Arthur Salus
**Ofcr:* John Lawless
Prgrm Mgr: Cookie Jenkins
Off Admin: Miryam Gonzalez

D-U-N-S 00-225-5776
DUMAC BUSINESS SYSTEMS INC (NY)
19 Corporate Cir Ste 1, East Syracuse, NY 13057-1129
Tel (315) 463-1010 *Founded/Ownrshp* 1952
Sales 128.1MM^E *EMP* 284
SIC 5045 7699 3578 Computers, peripherals & software; Cash register repair; Point-of-sale devices
CFO: David Mc Carthy
**Pr:* Shaun O Brien
**CEO:* Howard Mc Carthy
COO: Scott Smith
**Treas:* Phillip Mc Carthy
VP: Michael Kress
VP: Shaun Obrien
VP: Stephen Williams
Exec: Kathy Hanley
Exec: Kathy Leach-Hanley
Sales Exec: Phil McCarthy

DUMP, THE
See HAYNES FURNITURE CO INC

D-U-N-S 88-411-4609
▲ DUN & BRADSTREET CORP
D&B
103 Jfk Pkwy, Short Hills, NJ 07078-2708
Tel (973) 921-5500 *Founded/Ownrshp* 1841
Sales 1.6MMM *EMP* 4,600
Tkr Sym DNB *Exch* NYS
SIC 7323 Commercial (mercantile) credit reporting bureau
CEO: Robert Carrigan
Pr: Joshua L Peirez
CFO: Richard H Veldran
Chf Mktg O: Rishi Dave
Ofcr: Christie Hill
Ofcr: Peter Lehmann
Board of Directors: Christopher J Coughlin Ch, Cindy Christy, L Gordon Crovitz, James N Fernandez, Paul R Garcia, Anastassia Lauterbach, Thomas J Manning, Randall D Mott, Judith A Reinsdorf

D-U-N-S 96-465-2973
■ DUN & BRADSTREET EMERGING BUSINESSES CORP
DUN & BRDSTREET CRDBILITY CORP
(*Suby of* D&B) ★
22761 Pacific Coast Hwy # 226, Malibu, CA 90265-5064
Tel (310) 456-8271 *Founded/Ownrshp* 2010
Sales 101.7MM^E *EMP* 722
SIC 7389 Financial services
CEO: Robert Carrigan
**CFO:* Wisdom Lu
**Treas:* Kathleen M Guinnessey
**VP:* Susan D Beriont
QA Dir: Lucky Islam
Sftwr Eng: Rashmi Prasad
Mktg Mgr: Dorothy Kiniti
Mktg Mgr: Mindy Sartori
**Genl Couns:* Moujan Kazerani

D-U-N-S 15-048-3782
■ DUN & BRADSTREET INC
D&B
(*Suby of* D&B) ★
103 Jfk Pkwy, Short Hills, NJ 07078-2708
Tel (973) 921-5500 *Founded/Ownrshp* 1841
Sales 574.7MM^E *EMP* 3,000
SIC 7323 Commercial (mercantile) credit reporting bureau
CEO: Robert Carrigan
**Pr:* Joshua L Peirez
**CFO:* Richard H Veldran
**Treas:* Kathleen Guinnessey
**Chf Mktg O:* Rishi Dave
**Ofcr:* Christie Hill
**Ofcr:* Peter Lehmann
Ofcr: Anthony Pietrontone Jr
Ofcr: Louis Sapirman
VP: John F Cinque
VP: Richard S Mattessich
VP: Janet Parkhurst
VP: Michael G Sabin
VP: Susan D Veriont

D-U-N-S 04-997-7515
■ DUN & BRADSTREET INTERNATIONAL LTD
D&B
(*Suby of* D&B) ★
103 Jfk Pkwy, Short Hills, NJ 07078-2708
Tel (973) 921-5500 *Founded/Ownrshp* 1933
Sales 90.8MM^E *EMP* 2,750
SIC 7323 8741 Commercial (mercantile) credit reporting bureau; Management services
CEO: Robert Carrigan
**Pr:* Josh L Peirez
**Treas:* Kathleen M Guinnessey
Treas: Michael Muller
Ofcr: Peter Lehmann
VP: Susan D Beriont
**VP:* Christie Hill
VP: Anthony Pietrontone Jr
VP: Richard H Veldran
VP: Piers Woolston

DUN & BRDSTREET CRDBILITY CORP
See DUN & BRADSTREET EMERGING BUSINESSES CORP

D-U-N-S 00-894-3284 IMP/EXP
DUNAVANT ENTERPRISES INC
DUNAVANT, W B & CO
959 Ridg Loop Rd Ste 200, Memphis, TN 38120
Tel (901) 369-1500 *Founded/Ownrshp* 1957
Sales 397.3MM^E *EMP* 1,722
SIC 5159 4221 4731 0131

DUNAVANT, W B & CO
See DUNAVANT ENTERPRISES INC

D-U-N-S 02-243-6992
DUNBAR ARMORED INC
50 Schilling Rd, Hunt Valley, MD 21031-1424
Tel (410) 584-9800 *Founded/Ownrshp* 1956
Sales 612.0MM^E *EMP* 4,075
SIC 7381 Armored car services
Pr: Kevin Dunbar
Pr: Jose Montesino
CFO: Willie Roach
VP: Mark Basso
VP: Wayne Birely
VP: Brian Cain
VP: Dan Greif
VP: Bruce Nolan
VP: Ed Walsh
VP: Doug White
VP: Debra Wisner
Exec: Frank Costantino
Exec: Bruce Micale

D-U-N-S 00-480-6550
DUNBAR MECHANICAL INC (OH)
2806 N Reynolds Rd, Toledo, OH 43615-2034
Tel (734) 856-6601 *Founded/Ownrshp* 1956, 2005
Sales 379.0MM^E *EMP* 200
SIC 1711 Mechanical contractor
Pr: Stephen E Dunbar
**CFO:* Todd Friesner
VP: Aaron Lewis
**Prin:* Dale R Dunbar
**Prin:* Delbert R Dunbar
Genl Mgr: Jean Elkins
IT Man: Dana Newhouse
Sfty Dirs: Dan Worstein
Ql Cn Mgr: Tony Koepfer
Mktg Mgr: Pauline Glaza
Sls Mgr: Daniel Brown

D-U-N-S 62-613-6238 IMP
DUNCAN AVIATION INC
3701 Aviation Rd, Lincoln, NE 68524-2415
Tel (402) 479-1616 *Founded/Ownrshp* 1963
Sales 209.1MM^E *EMP* 1,751
Accts Hancock & Dana Pc
SIC 7699 5088 4522 4512 Aircraft & heavy equipment repair services; Aircraft equipment & supplies; Air transportation, nonscheduled; Air transportation, scheduled
CEO: Aaron C Hilkemann
Pr: J R Duncan
**COO:* Jeff Lake
Ex VP: Tom Burt
**VP:* Rich Baeder
**VP:* Todd Duncan
**VP:* Gary Hartwig
**VP:* Mark Matthes
VP: Andy Richards
**VP:* John Slieter
VP Bus Dev: Jeannine Falter
Exec: Linda Smith

D-U-N-S 79-103-8834
■ DUNCAN ENERGY PARTNERS LP
(*Suby of* ENTERPRISE PRODUCTS PARTNERS LP) ★
1100 Louisiana St Fl 10, Houston, TX 77002-5432
Tel (713) 381-6500 *Founded/Ownrshp* 2011
Sales 372.9MM^E *EMP* 1,900^E
SIC 4922 Natural gas transmission
Pr: W Randall Fowler
CFO: Bryan F Bulawa
Bd of Dir: Michael Creel
Ex VP: William Ordemann
Ex VP: A James Teague
Sr VP: Michael J Knesek
VP: John R Burkhalter

DUNCAN INDUSTRIAL SOLUTIONS
See BLACKHAWK INDUSTRIAL DISTRIBUTION INC

D-U-N-S 04-160-8118
DUNCAN OIL CO
849 Factory Rd, Dayton, OH 45434-6134
Tel (937) 426-5945 *Founded/Ownrshp* 1960
Sales 142.7MM^E *EMP* 85
SIC 5172 5411 5983 1542 Petroleum products; Fuel oil; Convenience stores; Fuel oil dealers; Service station construction
Pr: Roger McDaniel
**COO:* Ryan McDaniel
CFO: Terry Domer
**CFO:* Steven Heck
**Treas:* Steven A Wells
**VP:* Dan Gose
Dir Bus: Ryan Burba
Dir IT: Zach Demeter
Sfty Dirs: Dave Propst
Trfc Dir: Jessica McGrew

D-U-N-S 08-247-0576
DUNCAN REGIONAL HOSPITAL INC
1407 N Whisenant Dr, Duncan, OK 73533-1698
Tel (580) 252-5300 *Founded/Ownrshp* 1976
Sales 123.2MM *EMP* 780
Accts Bkd Llp Tulsa Ok
SIC 8062 General medical & surgical hospitals
CEO: Jay R Johnson
**CFO:* Douglas Volinski
CFO: Melissa Walker
**VP:* Roger L Neal
**VP:* Cynthia M Rauh
**VP:* Mark W Rhoades
**VP:* Deborah G Rodgers
VP: William Stewart
Dir OR: Kristen Webb
Dir Lab: Patricia Linam
CTO: Betty Beck

D-U-N-S 08-155-1483
DUNCANVILLE INDEPENDENT SCHOOL DISTRICT
710 S Cedar Ridge Dr, Duncanville, TX 75137-2204
Tel (972) 708-2000 *Founded/Ownrshp* 1890
Sales 132.4MM *EMP* 1,650
Accts Hankins Eastup Deaton Tonn
SIC 8211 Public elementary & secondary schools
Dir Sec: Chad Wilhelm
Pr Dir: Tiara Richard
Psych: Tijuana Hudson

D-U-N-S 83-906-6458
DUNES POINT CAPITAL LLC
411 Theodore Fremd Ave # 125, Rye, NY 10580-1450
Tel (914) 967-1390 *Founded/Ownrshp* 2012
Sales 154.1MM^E *EMP* 491^E
SIC 6799 Investors
CEO: Timothy J White
Mng Dir: James Clark
Mng Dir: Paul R Cox

D-U-N-S 08-113-2128
DUNGARVIN GROUP INC
1444 Northland Dr Ste 200, Mendota Heights, MN 55120-1032
Tel (651) 699-6050 *Founded/Ownrshp* 1975
Sales 148.1MM^E *EMP* 3,070
SIC 7389 Financial services
Pr: David R Toeniskoetter
Ch Bd: Timothy Madden
COO: Michael N Holmes
Sec: Joseph W Regenscheid

DUNHAM BOOTMAKERS
See NEW BALANCE ATHLETICS INC

D-U-N-S 13-063-0494 IMP
DUNHAMS ATHLEISURE CORP
DUNHAM'S SPORTS
(*Suby of* DUNHAMS SPORTS) ★
5607 New King Dr Ste 125, Troy, MI 48098-2654
Tel (248) 674-4991 *Founded/Ownrshp* 1985
Sales 362.7MM^E *EMP* 2,000
SIC 5699 5661 5941 5961 Sports apparel; Footwear, athletic; Men's boots; Specialty sport supplies; Team sports equipment; Water sport equipment; Fitness & sporting goods, mail order
Ch Bd: Jeffrey G Lynn
**Pr:* Kenneth R Meehan
**Sr VP:* John H Palmer
VP: Daniel Cieslak
**VP:* Steven J Sander
**VP:* Marshall Sosne

DUNHAM'S SPORTS
See DUNHAMS ATHLEISURE CORP

DUNHAMS SPORTS
See AMERICAN SPECIALTY RETAILING GROUP INC

D-U-N-S 96-858-0550
▲ DUNKIN BRANDS GROUP INC
130 Royall St, Canton, MA 02021-1010
Tel (781) 737-3000 *Founded/Ownrshp* 1940
Sales 810.9MM *EMP* 1,145
Tkr Sym DNKN *Exch* NGS
SIC 5461 5499 6794 5812 Doughnuts; Bagels; Coffee; Franchises, selling or licensing; Eating places
Ch Bd: Nigel Travis
Pr: John Costello
Pr: Bill Mitchell
Pr: Paul Twohig
COO: Leigh Fuller
COO: Paul E Twohig
CFO: Paul Carbone
Chf Cred: Karen Raskopf
Ofcr: Richard Emmett
Ofcr: William M Mitchell
Sr VP: Scott Murphy
Sr VP: Weldon Spangler
VP: Maryanne Knott
VP: Ted Manley
VP: Lynette McKee
VP: John Varughese
VP: Rick Woods
Board of Directors: Raul Alvarez, Irene Chang Britt, Anthony Dinovi, Michael Hines, Sandra Horbach, Mark Nunnelly, Carl Sparks

D-U-N-S 00-537-9128 IMP/EXP
■ DUNKIN BRANDS INC
DUNKIN' DONUTS
(*Suby of* DUNKIN BRANDS GROUP INC) ★
130 Royall St, Canton, MA 02021-1010
Tel (781) 737-5200 *Founded/Ownrshp* 1961, 2006
Sales 303.3MM^E *EMP* 1,075
SIC 5461 5812 Doughnuts; Ice cream stands or dairy bars
Pr: John Costello
Pr: Giorgio Minardi
Pr: Neal Yanofsky
**CEO:* Nigel Travis
**CFO:* Paul Carbone
**CFO:* Cornelius F Moses
Treas: Kieth Cavella
Treas: Gina Powers
**Chf Cred:* Karen Raskopf
Sr VP: Rojean Dechantal
**Sr VP:* Christine Deputy
**Sr VP:* Richard Emmett
VP: Marc Cote
VP: Jonathan Gaiman
VP: John Gilbert
VP: Kevin Houser
Dir Surg: Walter Erwin
Board of Directors: Todd Abbrecht, Anita Balaji, Andrew Balson, Anthony Dinovi, Michael Hines, Sandra Horbach, Mark Nunnelly, Joe Uva

DUNKIN' DONUTS
See DUNKIN BRANDS INC

DUNKIN' DONUTS
See CAP GROUP INC

DUNKIN' DONUTS
See NATIONAL DCP LLC

DUNKIN' DONUTS
See DONUT MANAGEMENT INC

D-U-N-S 00-704-1593 IMP/EXP
DUNLAP & KYLE CO INC
GATEWAY TIRE & SERVICE CENTER
280 Eureka St, Batesville, MS 38606-2624
Tel (662) 563-7601 *Founded/Ownrshp* 1966
Sales 106.0MM *EMP* 1,000
SIC 5014 5531 5013

D-U-N-S 00-793-3906 IMP
DUNLAP CO (DE)
DUNLAP'S
200 Bailey Ave Ste 100, Fort Worth, TX 76107-1219
Tel (817) 336-4985 *Founded/Ownrshp* 1890, 1947
Sales 67.9MM^E *EMP* 1,200
SIC 5311

DUNLAP'S
See DUNLAP CO

DUNN BLACKTOP DIVISION
See MATHY CONSTRUCTION CO

D-U-N-S 00-896-4728
DUNN CONSTRUCTION CO INC
(*Suby of* DUNN INVESTMENT CO) ★
3905 Airport Hwy, Birmingham, AL 35222-1419
Tel (205) 592-3866 *Founded/Ownrshp* 1977
Sales 84.1MM^E *EMP* 225
SIC 1611 2951

D-U-N-S 09-569-1085
DUNN INVESTMENT CO
3900 Messer Airport Hwy, Birmingham, AL 35222-1420
Tel (205) 592-3866 *Founded/Ownrshp* 1977
Sales 285.8MM^E *EMP* 992
SIC 1542 1611 3273 Nonresidential construction; Highway & street paving contractor; Ready-mixed concrete
CEO: James S M French
**Pr:* Craig Fleming
**Pr:* Daniel Rodgers
CFO: Al Caskey
**CFO:* William French
**VP:* Harry Thomas

D-U-N-S 07-995-0066
DUNN PAPER HOLDINGS INC
218 Riverview St, Port Huron, MI 48060-2976
Tel (810) 984-5521 *Founded/Ownrshp* 2010
Sales 206.4MM^E *EMP* 648
SIC 2621 2672 Paper mills; Coated & laminated paper
Pr: Brent Earnshaw
**CFO:* Gregory Howe
**VP:* Richard Voss

D-U-N-S 13-825-9440 IMP/EXP
DUNN PAPER INC
(*Suby of* DUNN PAPER HOLDINGS INC) ★
218 Riverview St, Port Huron, MI 48060-2996
Tel (810) 984-5521 *Founded/Ownrshp* 2016
Sales 206.4MM^E *EMP* 223
SIC 2671 2672 Paper coated or laminated for packaging; Coated & laminated paper
Pr: Brent Earnshaw
**COO:* Wade Kemnitz
**CFO:* Al Magnan
VP: Scott McNutt
VP: Rick Voss
IT Man: Kathy Johnston
Mill Mgr: Sherrill Mayton
Plnt Mgr: Kevin French
Sls Mgr: Joe Doyle

D-U-N-S 07-148-1832 IMP
DUNN TIRE LLC
EXPRESS TIRE DELIVERY
475 Cayuga Rd Ste 500, Buffalo, NY 14225-1309
Tel (716) 683-3910 *Founded/Ownrshp* 1974
Sales 100.0MM^E *EMP* 400
SIC 5531 5014 Automotive tires; Tires & tubes
CEO: Randall L Clark
**Pr:* Randy Jones
**CFO:* David Simons
Genl Mgr: Frank Georgetti
Store Mgr: Scott Osborne
IT Man: Tim Paige
Board of Directors: Herbert J Heimerl

DUNN-DWRDS PINTS WALLCOVERINGS
See DUNN-EDWARDS CORP

D-U-N-S 00-823-6648 IMP/EXP
DUNN-EDWARDS CORP
DUNN-DWRDS PINTS WALLCOVERINGS
4885 E 52nd Pl, Vernon, CA 90058-5584
Tel (323) 771-3330 *Founded/Ownrshp* 1925
Sales 581.6MM^E *EMP* 1,500
SIC 2851 5231 Paints & allied products; Lacquer: bases, dopes, thinner; Varnishes; Enamels; Paint
CEO: Michael G Rose
Pr: Michael Badar
CFO: Dennis Kromer
VP: Nick Hess
Exec: Joyce Childs
Exec: Danny Lilly
Area Mgr: Oscar Ochoa
Store Mgr: Cory Cheng
Store Mgr: Henry Lopez
Store Mgr: Paul Staub
VP Mktg: Tim Bosvelb

D-U-N-S 15-730-8560 IMP
■ DUNSIRN INDUSTRIES INC
(*Suby of* AVERY DENNISON CORP) ★
2415 Industrial Dr, Neenah, WI 54956-4858
Tel (920) 725-3814 *Founded/Ownrshp* 2001
Sales 103.5MM^E *EMP* 400
SIC 2671 5113 3081 2672 2621 Packaging paper & plastics film, coated & laminated; Industrial & personal service paper; Unsupported plastics film & sheet; Coated & laminated paper; Paper mills

Ch Bd: Duane Dunsirn
**Pr:* Brian Dunsirn

D-U-N-S 01-639-0045
DUPAGE HIGH SCHOOL DISTRICT 88
2 Friendship Plz, Addison, IL 60101-2787
Tel (630) 530-3990 *Founded/Ownrshp* 2009
Sales 89.3MM *EMP* 17E
Accts Mathieson Moyski Celer & Co
SIC 8211 Elementary & secondary schools
Schl Brd P: Donna Cain

D-U-N-S 06-129-0706
DUPHIL INC (LA)
6608 Interstate 10 W, Orange, TX 77632-8350
Tel (409) 883-8550 *Founded/Ownrshp* 1968, 1995
Sales 108.7MME *EMP* 260
SIC 1542 Nonresidential construction
Pr: Jennie Scalfano
**Treas:* Carol Flannigan
**VP:* Ron Redkey
Genl Mgr: Robert James

D-U-N-S 07-555-0988
DUPLIN COUNTY BOARD OF EDUCATION
315 N Main St, Kenansville, NC 28349
Tel (910) 293-4218 *Founded/Ownrshp* 1960
Sales 53.7MME *EMP* 1,200
SIC 8211 Public elementary & secondary schools
CFO: Joann Hartley
**Prin:* Carolyn Olivarez
Dir IT: Kara Lee

DUPONT COATING SOLUTIONS
See AXALTA POWDER COATING SYSTEMS USA INC

D-U-N-S 80-902-3091
▲ DUPONT FABROS TECHNOLOGY INC
DFT
1212 New York Ave Nw # 900, Washington, DC 20005-6600
Tel (202) 728-0044 *Founded/Ownrshp* 2007
Sales 452.4MM *EMP* 113
Tkr Sym DFT *Exch* NYS
SIC 6798 7374 Real estate investment trusts; Data processing & preparation
Pr: Christopher P Eldredge
**Ch Bd:* Lammot J Du Pont
CFO: Jeffrey H Foster
Ofcr: Brian D Doricko
Ofcr: Maria Kenny
Ex VP: Scott A Davis
Ex VP: Richard A Montfort Jr
Dir IT: Melvin Bellamy
Board of Directors: Michael A Coke, Thomas D Eckert, Frederic V Malek, John T Roberts Jr, Mary M Styer, John H Toole

D-U-N-S 82-692-3216
■ DUPONT FABROS TECHNOLOGY LP
(*Suby of* DFT) ★
1212 New York Ave Nw # 900, Washington, DC 20005-6600
Tel (202) 728-0044 *Founded/Ownrshp* 2007
Sales 452.4MM *EMP* 97
SIC 6798 Real estate investment trusts
Pr: Hossein Fateh
Genl Pt: Dupont Fabros Technology
CFO: Jeffrey H Foster

D-U-N-S 07-950-0111
DUPONT PERFORMANCE COATINGS INC
4417 Lncaster Pike Barley, Wilmington, DE 19805
Tel (302) 892-1064 *Founded/Ownrshp* 1998
Sales 98.4MME *EMP* 1,449E
SIC 8711 Engineering services
CEO: Ellen Kullman
VP: Nicholas Fanandakis
VP: Shelley Stewart
Genl Mgr: Guo Miao
IT Man: David Giacomini
IT Man: Carol Lowrie
IT Man: Suneet Ranganath
IT Man: Mark Rowan
Tech Mgr: Hjalti Skulason
Ql Cn Mgr: Larry Pritchard
Mktg Dir: Raul B Kasat

D-U-N-S 93-319-4151 EXP
■ DUPONT PERFORMANCE ELASTOMERS LLC
(*Suby of* E I DU PONT DE NEMOURS AND CO) ★
4417 Lancaster Pike, Wilmington, DE 19805-1523
Tel (302) 774-1000 *Founded/Ownrshp* 1996
Sales 284.7MM *EMP* 1,400
SIC 2822 Synthetic rubber
Dir IT: Pascal Ferrandez

D-U-N-S 18-296-6648
DUPRE INVESTMENTS INC
DUPRE LOGISTICS
201 Energy Pkwy Ste 500, Lafayette, LA 70508-3851
Tel (337) 237-8471 *Founded/Ownrshp* 1979
Sales 225.3MM *EMP* 1,400
Accts Grant Thornton Llp Tulsa Ok
SIC 4212 4213 4731 Local trucking, without storage; Petroleum haulage, local; Trucking, except local; Truck transportation brokers
CEO: Coty Dupre Jr
**Pr:* Tom Voelkel
**CFO:* Doug Place

DUPRE LOGISTICS
See DUPRE INVESTMENTS INC

D-U-N-S 03-917-6904
DUPRE LOGISTICS LLC
(*Suby of* DUPRE LOGISTICS) ★
201 Energy Pkwy Ste 500, Lafayette, LA 70508-3851
Tel (337) 237-8471 *Founded/Ownrshp* 1979
Sales 225.3MM *EMP* 1,100
Accts Grant Thornton Llp Tulsa Ok
SIC 4213 4212 Trucking, except local; Local trucking, without storage
CEO: Coty R Dupre Jr
**CFO:* Douglas Place
VP: Dan Schinke

Dir Bus: Chuck Toledo
Dir IT: Melissa Olivier
Dir IT: Stuart Suffren
IT Man: Jarrett Glatiolais
IT Man: Stuart Suffren
Sfty Dirs: Bob Coussan
Sfty Dirs: Al Lacombe
Opers Supe: Chance Lafleur

D-U-N-S 08-005-5811
DUQUESNE ENERGY SERVCES LLC
4949 S Syracuse St # 550, Denver, CO 80237-2714
Tel (832) 278-5980 *Founded/Ownrshp* 2012
Sales 195.0MM *EMP* 11
SIC 2911 5142 Gasoline; Packaged frozen goods

D-U-N-S 00-791-5606
DUQUESNE LIGHT CO (PA)
DLC
(*Suby of* DUQUESNE LIGHT HOLDINGS INC) ★
411 7th Ave 6-1, Pittsburgh, PA 15219-1942
Tel (412) 393-6000 *Founded/Ownrshp* 1912
Sales 828.5MME *EMP* 1,000
SIC 4911 Generation, electric power; Transmission, electric power; Distribution, electric power
Pr: Morgan K O'Brien
Pr: Anthony Pekny
**COO:* Joseph G Belechak
COO: Joe Dickson
**CFO:* Mark E Kaplan
**Treas:* William F Fields
VP: Dave Bordo
VP: Jim Gariepy
VP: Hogel Maureen
Genl Mgr: Tim Kuruce
QA Dir: Laura M Alberghini

D-U-N-S 60-873-8464 IMP
DUQUESNE LIGHT HOLDINGS INC
(*Suby of* DQE HOLDINGS LLC) ★
411 7th Ave Ste 3, Pittsburgh, PA 15219-1905
Tel (412) 393-6000 *Founded/Ownrshp* 2007
Sales 848.0MME *EMP* 1,200
SIC 4911 Generation, electric power; Transmission, electric power; Distribution, electric power
Pr: Morgan K O'Brien
**Ch Bd:* Robert P Bozzone
COO: Joseph G Belechak
**CFO:* Mark E Kaplan
CFO: Mark Kaplan
**Treas:* William F Fields
**V Ch Bd:* Doreen E Boyce
Ex VP: Gary Schwass
Sr VP: Philip J Damiani
VP: William J Deleo
VP: Lora Dikun
VP: Thomas W Hubbell
VP: Jack Saxer Jr
VP: John Schmidt

D-U-N-S 00-450-1193
DUQUESNE UNIVERSITY OF HOLY SPIRIT
600 Forbes Ave, Pittsburgh, PA 15219-3016
Tel (412) 396-6000 *Founded/Ownrshp* 1878
Sales 400.4MM *EMP* 3,601
Accts Schneider Downs & Co Inc Pitt
SIC 8221 University
Pr: Charles J Dougherty
Treas: Antony Davies
**Ex VP:* Father S Hogan
Ex VP: Carly Koza
VP: Timothy Austin
VP: David Beaupri
VP: Melanie Eberhardt
VP: Zachary Galloway
VP: Rachael Gerstein
VP: Ralph L Pearson
VP: Stephen Schillo
VP: Zachery West
Assoc Dir: Jeremy Mayernik
Comm Dir: Colleen C Derda

DURA AUTOMOTIVE SYSTEMS
See DURA OPERATING LLC

D-U-N-S 83-199-4228 IMP/EXP
DURA AUTOMOTIVE SYSTEMS LLC
(*Suby of* PATRIARCH PARTNERS LLC) ★
1780 Pond Run, Auburn Hills, MI 48326-2752
Tel (248) 299-7500 *Founded/Ownrshp* 2008
Sales 3.3MMME *EMP* 10,000
SIC 3714 Motor vehicle parts & accessories; Motor vehicle brake systems & parts; Anti-sway devices, motor vehicle
CEO: Lynn Tilton
**CEO:* Jeffrey M Stafeil
**COO:* Martin Becker
**CFO:* Jim Gregory
Ex VP: Pierre Beyer
Ex VP: Jerry Lavine
Ex VP: Fran Ois Stouvenot
**Ex VP:* Franois Stouvenot
**Ex VP:* Nizar Trigui
**VP:* Kathleen Birney
VP: Rick Kelly
VP: Matti Masanovich
**VP:* Theresa L Skotak
VP: Francois Stouvenot

D-U-N-S 17-451-9306 IMP/EXP
DURA COAT PRODUCTS INC
5361 Via Ricardo, Riverside, CA 92509-2414
Tel (951) 341-6500 *Founded/Ownrshp* 1986
Sales 100.0MME *EMP* 120
SIC 3479 2851 Aluminum coating of metal products; Coating of metals & formed products; Paints & allied products
CEO: Myung K Hong
**CFO:* Suzanne Faust
VP Admn: John Suh
Sls Mgr: Richard Papin

D-U-N-S 62-069-7136 IMP/EXP
DURA OPERATING LLC
DURA AUTOMOTIVE SYSTEMS
(*Suby of* DURA AUTOMOTIVE SYSTEMS LLC) ★
1780 Pond Run, Auburn Hills, MI 48326-2752
Tel (248) 299-7500 *Founded/Ownrshp* 2008
Sales 1.0MMME *EMP* 8,500

SIC 3429 3714 Motor vehicle hardware; Motor vehicle electrical equipment
CEO: Lyn Tilton
**Ch Bd:* Scott D Rued
**COO:* Martin Becker
**CFO:* Jim Gregory
**CFO:* Keith Marchianbo
Treas: Kathy Birney
**VP:* Robert R Hibbs
**VP:* Theresa L Skotak

D-U-N-S 00-437-3981
DURA-BOND INDUSTRIES INC (PA)
2658 Puckety Dr, Export, PA 15632-1234
Tel (724) 327-0280 *Founded/Ownrshp* 1960
Sales 107.3MME *EMP* 349
SIC 3441 3479

D-U-N-S 05-427-7561 IMP
DURA-LINE CORP (DE)
MEXICHEM SHARED SERVICES
(*Suby of* MEXICHEM, S.A.B. DE C.V.)
11400 Parkside Dr Ste 300, Knoxville, TN 37934-1917
Tel (865) 218-3460 *Founded/Ownrshp* 1971, 2014
Sales 478.3MME *EMP* 650
SIC 3644 Electric conduits & fittings
CEO: Paresh Chari
Pr: Vince Dimino
**CFO:* David Schaufel
**Ex VP:* Wes Tomaszek
Ex VP: Wesley Tomaszek
**Ex VP:* Dale Wilson
Sr VP: Timothy A Grimsley
**Sr VP:* Michael S Hilliard
**Sr VP:* Anil Pande
Sr VP: Chuck Parke
**VP:* Wayne Byrne
**VP:* Randi Misher
**VP:* Robert J Morita
**VP:* Kurt Yeeger

D-U-N-S 00-512-1470 IMP
DURABLE INC (IL)
DURABLE PACKAGING INTL
750 Northgate Pkwy, Wheeling, IL 60090-2660
Tel (847) 541-4400 *Founded/Ownrshp* 1943, 1946
Sales 111.3MME *EMP* 800
SIC 3497 3354 Foil containers for bakery goods & frozen foods; Aluminum extruded products
Pr: Scott Anders
CFO: Michael Rabin
Plnt Mgr: John Biel
Natl Sales: Todd Dery
Natl Sales: Gina Deutsch
Natl Sales: John Goggin
Natl Sales: Len Kleinhans
Sls Dir: Dave Saunders

DURABLE PACKAGING INTL
See DURABLE INC

D-U-N-S 60-997-8267 IMP/EXP
■ DURACELL INC
(*Suby of* DURACELL INTERNATIONAL INC) ★
14 Research Dr, Bethel, CT 06801-1040
Tel (203) 796-4000 *Founded/Ownrshp* 1920
Sales 537.9MME *EMP* 7,700
SIC 3691 Storage batteries
Ch Bd: Charles R Perrin
Board of Directors: Kevin A Bousquette, Thomas W Hudson Jr, Henry R Kravis, George R Roberts

D-U-N-S 00-603-7774 IMP
■ DURACELL INTERNATIONAL INC
(*Suby of* BERKSHIRE HATHAWAY INC) ★
14 Research Dr, Bethel, CT 06801-1040
Tel (203) 796-4000 *Founded/Ownrshp* 1916, 2016
Sales 1.8MMME *EMP* 8,000
SIC 3691 Storage batteries; Alkaline cell storage batteries; Batteries, rechargeable
Pr: Mark Leckie
Sr VP: Gregg A Dwyer
Sr VP: Wade G Lewis
VP: Edward Graan
VP Mktg: John Bickney
VP Mktg: Robert Giaclonone
VP Mktg: Margie Smith
Mktg Mgr: Tom Murray

DURACITE
See HALABI INC

D-U-N-S 17-020-7000 IMP/EXP
DURAFIBER TECHNOLOGIES (DFT) ENTERPRISES INC
(*Suby of* SUN CAPITAL PARTNERS INC) ★
13620 Reese Blvd E # 400, Huntersville, NC 28078-6417
Tel (704) 912-3770 *Founded/Ownrshp* 2004
Sales 400.0MM *EMP* 1,200
SIC 2824 Nylon fibers; Polyester fibers
CEO: Frank Papa
CFO: Erwin Bette
VP: Rick Spurlock

D-U-N-S 07-992-3007
DURAFIBER TECHNOLOGIES (DFT) HOLDINGS II LLC
(*Suby of* SUN PERFORMANCE FIBERS, LLC)
13620 Reese Blvd E # 400, Huntersville, NC 28078-6417
Tel (704) 912-3700 *Founded/Ownrshp* 2004
Sales 78.1ME *EMP* 1,500
SIC 2824 Organic fibers, noncellulosic
Pr: Frank Papa
VP: Jim Tuttle

D-U-N-S 02-365-8991 IMP
DURAFIBER TECHNOLOGIES (DFT) INC
(*Suby of* DURAFIBER TECHNOLOGIES (DFT) ENTERPRISES INC) ★
13620 Reese Blvd E # 400, Huntersville, NC 28078-6417
Tel (704) 912-3700 *Founded/Ownrshp* 2004
Sales 400.0MME *EMP* 1,200
SIC 2824 Organic fibers, noncellulosic
CEO: Frank Papa
CFO: Erwin Bette

VP: Rick Spurlock
Snr Mgr: Van Towle

D-U-N-S 80-298-7433 IMP/EXP
DURAFIBER TECHNOLOGIES (DFT) OPERATIONS LLC
(*Suby of* DURAFIBER TECHNOLOGIES (DFT) ENTERPRISES INC) ★
13620 Reese Blvd E # 400, Huntersville, NC 28078-6417
Tel (704) 912-3770 *Founded/Ownrshp* 2008
Sales 216.6MME *EMP* 650
SIC 2824 Organic fibers, noncellulosic
CEO: Frank Papa
**CFO:* Erwin Bette
**VP:* Rick Spurlock
Board of Directors: Mike Agler, T Scott King

D-U-N-S 07-323-3504 IMP/EXP
DURAFLAME INC
2894 Monte Diablo Ave, Stockton, CA 95203-1143
Tel (209) 461-6600 *Founded/Ownrshp* 1982
Sales 105.0MME *EMP* 307
SIC 5099

D-U-N-S 05-772-0856 IMP/EXP
DURALEE FABRICS LTD
49 Wireless Blvd Ste 150, Hauppauge, NY 11788-3950
Tel (631) 273-8800 *Founded/Ownrshp* 1952
Sales 276.0MME *EMP* 300
SIC 5199 Fabrics, yarns & knit goods
Ch Bd: Leonard Silberman
**Pr:* Martin Rosenberger
CFO: Bill Fuches
**Ex VP:* Lee Silberman
**Sr VP:* Amy Silberman-Benjamin
VP: Gary Rosenthal
CIO: Bill Kelly
IT Man: Denise Loughrey
IT Man: Joe Muscarella
Mktg Mgr: Robin Gordon

DURAMATIC PRODUCTS
See ROTARY CORP

D-U-N-S 05-148-1257 IMP
DURAND GLASS MANUFACTURING CO INC
(*Suby of* ARC INTERNATIONAL NORTH AMERICA INC) ★
901 S Wade Blvd, Millville, NJ 08332-3531
Tel (856) 327-1850 *Founded/Ownrshp* 1982
Sales 228.8MME *EMP* 1,100
SIC 3229 3269 5023 Tableware, glass or glass ceramic; Kitchen articles, coarse earthenware; Glassware
CEO: Susan Saidman
**CFO:* Timothy S Bell
**VP:* Ken Bell
VP: Emmanuel Gauffeny
VP: Shannon Merson
**VP:* Steve Obrian
**VP:* Sherry Perley
Sfty Mgr: John Thein

D-U-N-S 62-076-9844
DURANT BANCORP INC
FIRST UNITED BANK AND TRUST CO
1400 W Main St, Durant, OK 74701-4906
Tel (580) 924-2211 *Founded/Ownrshp* 1980
Sales NA *EMP* 450
SIC 6022 State commercial banks
Pr: John Massey
**Pr:* Greg John Massey
**Treas:* William Fahrendorf

D-U-N-S 12-237-5595
■ DURANT HMA INC
MEDICAL CTR SOUTHEASTERN OKLA
(*Suby of* HMA) ★
1800 W University Blvd, Durant, OK 74701-3006
Tel (580) 924-3080 *Founded/Ownrshp* 1987
Sales 114.0MM *EMP* 520E
SIC 8062 General medical & surgical hospitals
CEO: Pat Dorris
COO: Eric Burch
CFO: Phillip Baker
CFO: Toby Butler
Dir Lab: Becky Dyer
Dir Env Sv: Linda Kelso
Chf Nrs Of: Corinne Hunter
**Prin:* John Harms
Mktg Mgr: Linda French
Doctor: Bob Burlison
Doctor: Scott Renfro

D-U-N-S 00-630-1519
DURHAM CO
722 Durham Rd, Lebanon, MO 65536-3405
Tel (417) 532-7121 *Founded/Ownrshp* 1959
Sales 121.4MME *EMP* 353
SIC 3644 3643 3613 Junction boxes, electric; Outlet boxes (electric wiring devices); Current-carrying wiring devices; Switchgear & switchboard apparatus
Ch Bd: George E Carr
**Pr:* J Douglas Russell
CFO: Joe Foster
Ex VP: G T Carr
Ex VP: George Carr
VP: Jenny Carr
VP: Jim Carr
VP: Jim Tucker
QA Dir: Simon Westerfield
IT Man: Jeff Stokes
Prd Mgr: Michael Mulligan
Board of Directors: Steve Carr

D-U-N-S 06-529-9851
DURHAM COUNTY HOSPITAL CORP
DURHAM REGIONAL HOSPITAL
(*Suby of* DUKE UNIVERSITY HOSPITAL) ★
3643 N Roxboro St, Durham, NC 27704-2702
Tel (919) 470-4000 *Founded/Ownrshp* 1971
Sales 178.2MME *EMP* 1,918
SIC 8062 General medical & surgical hospitals
Pr: Katie Galbraith
Chf Rad: Diane Voorhees
**Ch Bd:* George K Quick
Pr: Richard L Myers

COO: Larry T Suitt
CFO: Jonathan Hoy
*Treas: Charles Blackman
*V Ch Bd: Eugene Staples
Chf Mktg O: Elizabeth Henke
Exec: Brian Callahan
Dir Rad: Gary Abode
Dir Rx: Lynn Whitt
Board of Directors: Carolyn I Thorton, William V Bell, Charles Blackman, Dr John T Daniel Jr, Dr James E Davis, Deborah G Giles, M Anita Page Holmes, Elizabeth H Maxwell, Linda Chandler-Rhodes, David P Shaw

D-U-N-S 10-005-8429
DURHAM PUBLIC SCHOOLS
D P S
511 Cleveland St, Durham, NC 27701-3334
Tel (919) 560-2000 Founded/Ownrshp 1869
Sales 230.8MM[E] EMP 4,500
Accts Rives & Associates Llp Ralei
SIC 8211 Public elementary & secondary schools
*CFO: Aaron Beaulieu
VP: Charles Douglass
Ex Dir: Brian Letourneau
Dir Sec: Terry Brown
MIS Dir: Perry Dixon
IT Man: Lorraine Rice
Pr Dir: Jason Hare
Pr Dir: William Sudderth
Teacher Pr: Freddie McNeil
HC Dir: Wade Gulledge

DURHAM REGIONAL HOSPITAL
See DURHAM COUNTY HOSPITAL CORP

D-U-N-S 03-762-6629
DURHAM SCHOOL SERVICES L P
(Suby of NATIONAL EXPRESS GROUP PLC)
4300 Weaver Pkwy Ste 100, Warrenville, IL 60555-3920
Tel (630) 836-0292 Founded/Ownrshp 2002
Sales 1.2MMM[E] EMP 17,551
SIC 4151 School buses
CEO: David Duke
CEO: John A Elliott
CFO: Judith Crawford
Sr VP: Michele McDermott
Sr VP: GP Singh

D-U-N-S 00-423-7319 IMP/EXP
DURO BAG MANUFACTURING CO (KY)
(Suby of NOVOLEX) ★
7600 Empire Dr, Florence, KY 41042-2920
Tel (859) 371-2150 Founded/Ownrshp 1953, 2014
Sales 1.1MMM[E] EMP 3,000
SIC 2674 Paper bags: made from purchased materials; Grocers' bags: made from purchased materials; Shipping bags or sacks, including multiwall & heavy duty; Shopping bags: made from purchased materials
Pr: Charles Shor
Pr: Jim Berry
*COO: Don Breen
*Sec: Robert Desrochers
Ex VP: Paul Feldman
Ex VP: Douglas Leland
Ex VP: Scott Murchison
VP: Steve Champion
VP: Nick Duren
VP: William Forstrom
VP: Debbie Harmon
VP: Bob Leblanc

D-U-N-S 12-252-4916 IMP/EXP
DURO TEXTILES LLC
110 Chace St, Fall River, MA 02724-1416
Tel (508) 675-0102 Founded/Ownrshp 2002
Sales 90.9MM[E] EMP 234
SIC 2261 2262 Finishing plants, cotton; Dyeing cotton broadwoven fabrics; Printing of cotton broadwoven fabrics; Chemical coating or treating of cotton broadwoven fabrics; Finishing plants, manmade fiber & silk fabrics; Dyeing: manmade fiber & silk broadwoven fabrics; Printing: manmade fiber & silk broadwoven fabrics; Chemical coating or treating: manmade broadwoven fabrics
CEO: Stewart Little
*CFO: Frank Tarantino
*Sr VP: Joseph Gatta
*VP: Peter Ricci
*VP: Steve Schroeder
*VP: Ron Souza
IT Man: Joe Catalfano
IT Man: James Souza
Opers Mgr: Joe Melo
Sls Dir: John Machado
Pr Mgr: Brenda Schieri

D-U-N-S 06-517-3064 EXP
DURO-LAST INC
DURO-LAST ROOFING
525 E Morley Dr, Saginaw, MI 48601
Tel (800) 248-0280 Founded/Ownrshp 1981
Sales 180.0MM[E] EMP 525
Accts Bdo Usa Llp Troy Mi
SIC 2295 Resin or plastic coated fabrics
CEO: Tom Saeli
*Pr: Tom Hollingsworth
*CFO: Cory Gergar
Bd of Dir: Mike Krug
Ex VP: Linda Buaer
*Ex VP: Shawn Sny
*Ex VP: Jason Tunney
Sr VP: Tom Lawler
*VP: Bill Carroll
VP: Scott Ostrom
Dir IT: John Greko

DURO-LAST ROOFING
See DURO-LAST INC

D-U-N-S 05-567-2315 IMP
DURR SYSTEMS INC
PFS - PNT FNAL ASSMBLY SYSTEMS
(Suby of DURR—INC) ★
26801 Northwestern Hwy, Southfield, MI 48033-6251
Tel (248) 450-2000 Founded/Ownrshp 1992
Sales 149.0MM[E] EMP 400
SIC 3559 3567 Metal finishing equipment for plating, etc.; Incinerators, metal: domestic or commercial
CEO: Ralf W Dieter
*CFO: Ralph Heuwing
CFO: David Williams
Ofcr: Cecil Kroswell
VP: Dave Ciuffoletti
Genl Mgr: Garry Oliver
CIO: Dianna Thomas
IT Man: Washington Harry
Sftwr Eng: Collin Smyth
Mfg Mgr: Bill Stoltz
Snr PM: Marc Brill

D-U-N-S 78-934-7572 IMP
DURR—INC
(Suby of DURR AG)
26801 Northwestern Hwy, Southfield, MI 48033-6251
Tel (734) 459-6800 Founded/Ownrshp 1991
Sales 149.0MM[E] EMP 550
SIC 3559 3567 Metal finishing equipment for plating, etc.; Incinerators, metal: domestic or commercial
Pr: Bruno Welsch
CFO: Ken Banach
CFO: Steve Heinrich
CFO: Mateusz Nowakowski
VP: Andreas Schaal
MIS Dir: Gerry Cox
VP Opers: Ken Chandler
VP Opers: Keith Coe
Sls&Mrk Ex: Schaffer Leanna

D-U-N-S 92-716-5431
DURST ORGANIZATION INC
1 Bryant Park Fl 49, New York, NY 10036-6744
Tel (212) 257-6600 Founded/Ownrshp 1980
Sales 203.6MM[E] EMP 550[E]
SIC 6512 Nonresidential building operators
Ch Bd: Douglas Durst
*Pr: Jonathan Durst
CFO: Gijs F Van Thiel
Ofcr: Natalie Gill
Ex VP: Lisa Cintron
Ex VP: Louis Esposito
*Sr VP: Kristoffer Durst
VP: Tom Duff
*VP: Alexander Durst
*VP: Helena Rose Durst
VP: Frank Giuliano
VP: Helena Mocher
VP: Michael Rhee
Exec: Jimi Sangster

D-U-N-S 05-638-7798 IMP
DURVET INC
100 Se Magellan Dr, Blue Springs, MO 64014-5909
Tel (816) 229-9101 Founded/Ownrshp 1970
Sales 171.4MM EMP 30
Accts Hsmc Orizon Llc Lee S Summit
SIC 5122 Animal medicines
Pr: Robert Hormann
*Pr: Robert Horman

D.U.S.D
See DOWNEY UNIFIED SCHOOL DISTRICT

D-U-N-S 18-216-3469 IMP/EXP
DUTCH FARMS INC
700 E 107th St, Chicago, IL 60628-3806
Tel (773) 660-0900 Founded/Ownrshp 1987
Sales 190.8MM[E] EMP 165[E]
SIC 5143 Dairy products, except dried or canned
Pr: Brian Boomsma
Exec: Rachelle Knapper
VP Sls: Jeffrey Centerino

D-U-N-S 00-253-3222 IMP/EXP
DUTCH GOLD HONEY INC
2220 Dutch Gold Dr, Lancaster, PA 17601-1997
Tel (717) 393-1716 Founded/Ownrshp 1946
Sales 199.2MM EMP 85
Accts Baker Tilly Virchow Krause Llp
SIC 2099 5149 Honey, strained & bottled; Honey
Pr: Nancy J Gamber
*Ch: William R Gamber II
*Ch: William Gamber
*Sec: Marianne M Gamber
VP: Norman Randall
CTO: Tony Pantano
Sls Dir: Ted Shear

D-U-N-S 03-345-2959 IMP
DUTCH LLC
JOIE
(Suby of TA) ★
5301 S Santa Fe Ave, Vernon, CA 90058-3519
Tel (323) 277-3900 Founded/Ownrshp 2001
Sales 251.5MM[E] EMP 200[E]
SIC 5137 Women's & children's clothing

D-U-N-S 09-535-7398 IMP/EXP
DUTCH VALLEY FOOD DISTRIBUTORS INC
7615 Lancaster Ave, Myerstown, PA 17067-2004
Tel (717) 933-4191 Founded/Ownrshp 1988
Sales 131.9MM[E] EMP 125[E]
Accts Good Firestone & Remliber My
SIC 5141 Groceries, general line
Pr: Melvin S Burkholder
VP: Mathew Burkholder
Telecom Ex: John Sheaffer
VP Opers: Steve Wills
S&M/VP: George Mobarak
Mktg Mgr: Daryl Musser
Sls Mgr: Ryan Miller

D-U-N-S 08-407-0952
DUTCHESS COMMUNITY COLLEGE
D C C
(Suby of SUNY ADMINISTRATION) ★
53 Pendell Rd, Poughkeepsie, NY 12601-1595
Tel (845) 431-8000 Founded/Ownrshp 1992
Sales 48.2MM[E] EMP 1,700
SIC 8222 9411 Community college;
Pr: D David Conklin PHD
Pr: Linda Beasimer
*Ch: Thomas E Legrand
Bd of Dir: Nancy Clancy
*VP: Dr William F Anderson
VP: Patrick Griffin
Assoc Dir: Chrisie Mitchell
*Prin: Vincent J Dimaso
Off Admin: Pamela Osterhoudt
Dir IT: Christopher Brellochs
Nrsg Dir: Robert J Zasso

D-U-N-S 08-228-2195
DUTCHESS COUNTY OF (INC)
626 Dutchess Tpke, Poughkeepsie, NY 12603-1906
Tel (845) 486-2000 Founded/Ownrshp 1683
Sales NA EMP 1,852
SIC 9111 Executive offices;
Exec: Marcus J Molinaro
Comm Dir: Colleen Pillus
Genl Mgr: Rosemary Lamadore

D-U-N-S 96-957-4594
DUTCHESS EDUCATIONAL HEALTH INSURAN
5 Boces Rd, Poughkeepsie, NY 12601-6565
Tel (845) 486-4800 Founded/Ownrshp 2011
Sales 177.1MM EMP 7[E]
Accts Sicklertorchiaallen&Churchillc
SIC 8211 Elementary school
Prin: John Pennoyer

D-U-N-S 00-726-0235 IMP
DUTCHLAND PLASTICS LLC
54 Enterprise Ct, Oostburg, WI 53070-1656
Tel (920) 564-3633 Founded/Ownrshp 2013
Sales 109.9MM[E] EMP 445
SIC 3089 3544 Plastic processing; Special dies, tools, jigs & fixtures
CEO: Carl Claerbout
*Pr: Daven Claerbout
*VP: Nancy Claerbout

D-U-N-S 04-842-9344
DUTCHMAN HOSPITALITY GROUP INC
DER DUTCHMAN RESTAURANTS
4985 State Rte 515, Walnut Creek, OH 44687
Tel (330) 893-2926 Founded/Ownrshp 1969
Sales 43.1MM[E] EMP 1,000[E]
SIC 5812

D-U-N-S 96-187-4182
■ **DUTCHMEN MANUFACTURING INC**
(Suby of THOR INDUSTRIES INC) ★
2164 Caragana Ct, Goshen, IN 46526-9149
Tel (574) 537-0600 Founded/Ownrshp 1991
Sales 353.4MM[E] EMP 1,400[E]
SIC 5511 New & used car dealers
Pr: Rich Florea
*Pr: Matthew Zimmerman
*VP: Mark Schwartzhoff
Brnch Mgr: Keth Wever
CIO: Jeff Diel
IT Man: Jeff Diehl

DUTRA DREDGING
See DUTRA GROUP

D-U-N-S 05-913-3509 IMP
DUTRA GROUP
DUTRA DREDGING
2350 Kerner Blvd Ste 200, San Rafael, CA 94901-5595
Tel (415) 258-6876 Founded/Ownrshp 1998
Sales 179.0MM[E] EMP 240
SIC 1629 8711 1429 Marine construction; Dredging contractor; Earthmoving contractor; Civil engineering; Igneous rock, crushed & broken-quarrying
CEO: Bill T Dutra
*COO: Harry Stewart
*CFO: James Hagood
Dir Bus: Denise Dutra
Mtls Mgr: Steve Lee
Genl Couns: Molly Jacobson-Greany

D-U-N-S 00-726-6059 IMP/EXP
DUTTON-LAINSON CO
CORNHUSKER PRESS
451 W 2nd St, Hastings, NE 68901-7598
Tel (402) 463-6702 Founded/Ownrshp 1886
Sales 85.6MM[E] EMP 300
SIC 3531 5999 5063 5074 Construction machinery; Winches; Plumbing & heating supplies; Electrical apparatus & equipment; Plumbing fittings & supplies
Ch Bd: Gretchen H Lainson
Pr: William Hermes
CFO: David N Brandt
Sr VP: Ron Haase
VP: Mark Bliss
VP: Jorn C Olsen

D-U-N-S 08-068-3048
DUVAL COUNTY PUBLIC SCHOOLS
DUVAL COUNTY SCHOOL BOARD
1701 Prudential Dr, Jacksonville, FL 32207-8152
Tel (904) 390-2000 Founded/Ownrshp 1900
Sales 1.0MMM EMP 13,000
SIC 8211 Public elementary & secondary schools
V Ch: Cheryl Grymes
CFO: Lee Legutko
Ofcr: Sonita Young
Exec: Saundra Moore
Ex Dir: Stephen Bright
Ex Dir: Michelle Gabertan
Ex Dir: Pearl Roziers
Ex Dir: Arlinda Smith
Admn Mgr: Christina Lord
Genl Mgr: Adora Davis
CIO: Kirk Altman

DUVAL COUNTY SCHOOL BOARD
See DUVAL COUNTY PUBLIC SCHOOLS

D-U-N-S 00-692-1522 EXP
DUVAL MOTOR CO INC
TAMPA HONDALAND
(Suby of SCOTT-MCRAE GROUP) ★
1616 Cassat Ave, Jacksonville, FL 32210-1600
Tel (904) 387-6541 Founded/Ownrshp 1980
Sales 148.6MM[E] EMP 300
SIC 5521 5511 Used car dealers; Automobiles, new & used
Pr: David C Hodges Jr
*Ch Bd: Walter A Mc Rae Jr
*Pr: Henry H Graham Jr
*Sec: Lawrence Matheny
*VP: Bruce Divey
VP: Mark Lacovara
*VP: William A Long
Pr Mgr: Tami Peavy
Sls Mgr: Rodney Brown
Sales Asso: Curtis Brown
Sales Asso: Susan Crawford

D-U-N-S 08-041-6817
■ **DVA HEALTHCARE RENAL CARE INC**
(Suby of DAVITA INC) ★
2000 16th St, Denver, CO 80202-5117
Tel (253) 280-9501 Founded/Ownrshp 1976
Sales 109.5MM[E] EMP 12,000[E]
SIC 8092 Kidney dialysis centers
Pr: Javier J Rodriguez
*Treas: James K Hilger

D-U-N-S 15-201-2134 IMP/EXP
■ **DVA RENAL HEALTHCARE INC**
(Suby of DAVITA INC) ★
5200 Virginia Way, Brentwood, TN 37027-7569
Tel (615) 320-4200 Founded/Ownrshp 1992
Sales 124.1MM[E] EMP 4,000
SIC 8092 8071 Kidney dialysis centers; Medical laboratories
Pr: Kent Thiry
CFO: Tom Kelly
VP: Larry Centella
VP: Brian Gauger

D-U-N-S 00-229-6713 IMP/EXP
DVCC INC (PA)
DIXON VALVE & COUPLING
800 High St, Chestertown, MD 21620-1105
Tel (410) 778-2000 Founded/Ownrshp 1916
Sales 269.2MM[E] EMP 1,329
SIC 3492 5085 3535 3321 3364 Fluid power valves & hose fittings; Hose, belting & packing; Valves, pistons & fittings; Conveyors & conveying equipment; Gray & ductile iron foundries; Nonferrous die-castings except aluminum
*Treas: James F Canalichio
VP: James McColigan

DVFLORA
See DELAWARE VALLEY WHOLESALE FLORIST INC

DVM INSURANCE AGENCY
See VETERINARY PET INSURANCE SERVICES INC

D-U-N-S 02-622-7868 IMP
DW DISTRIBUTION INC (TX)
DALLAS WHOLESALE DISTRIBUTION
1200 E Centre Park Blvd, Desoto, TX 75115-2536
Tel (214) 381-2200 Founded/Ownrshp 1955
Sales 250.0MM EMP 150
SIC 5033 5031 5072

D-U-N-S 08-024-4534
DW SAWMILL LLC
N8972 County Road Jj, Westfield, WI 53964-8487
Tel (608) 296-1863 Founded/Ownrshp 2005
Sales 170.0MM EMP 6
SIC 5099 2491 5211 Wood & wood by-products; Structural lumber & timber, treated wood; Lumber products
Pr: David Borntrager

D-U-N-S 94-173-5102 IMP
DW STUDIOS LLC
DREAMWORKS SKG
100 Universal City Plz, Universal City, CA 91608-1002
Tel (818) 695-5000 Founded/Ownrshp 2008
Sales 69.1MM[E] EMP 1,200
SIC 7812 Motion picture & video production
CEO: Michael Wright
COO: Matt Baer
*CFO: Jeff Small
VP: Jonathan Eirich
VP: Jeff Hare
VP: Anthony Jackson
VP: Yoshi Maruyama
VP: Joshua Ravetch
Creative D: Philippe Gluckman
IT Man: Victor Guest
Info Man: Eric Valdes

D-U-N-S 96-399-8583 IMP
DW-NATIONAL STANDARD-STILLWATER LLC
(Suby of HEICO COMPANIES L L C) ★
3602 N Perkins Rd, Stillwater, OK 74075-2221
Tel (405) 377-5050 Founded/Ownrshp 2010
Sales 125.2MM[E] EMP 200
SIC 3315 Steel wire & related products
Exec: Danny Miller

D-U-N-S 15-766-4579
■ **DWA HOLDINGS LLC**
(Suby of NECN) ★
1000 Flower St, Glendale, CA 91201-3007
Tel (818) 695-5000 Founded/Ownrshp 2016
Sales 915.8MM EMP 2,300[E]
SIC 7812 Cartoon motion picture production
Ch Bd: Mellody Hobson
Pr: Ann Daly
CEO: Jeffrey Katzenberg
COO: Matt Baer
CFO: Fazal Merchant
VP: Julie Butchko
VP: Juan Lora
VP: Gia Russo
Exec: Sunny Park
Dir Sec: Matthew Bogaard
Snr Sftwr: Mark Lee

DWF WHOLESALE FLORISTS
See DENVER WHOLESALE FLORISTS CO

DWL INDUSTRIES
See DWL INTERNATIONAL TRADING INC

D-U-N-S 92-620-3084 IMP/EXP
DWL INTERNATIONAL TRADING INC
DWL INDUSTRIES
65 Industrial Rd, Lodi, NJ 07644-2607
Tel (973) 916-9958 Founded/Ownrshp 1991
Sales 83.1MM[E] EMP 250

SIC 5023 5046 Kitchenware; Linens, table; Commercial cooking & food service equipment; Bakery equipment & supplies; Cooking equipment, commercial; Restaurant equipment & supplies
Pr: David W LI
CFO: Peggy J Ding

DWR
See DESIGN WITHIN REACH INC

D-U-N-S 14-458-1001
DWW AZ INC
7875 E Frank Lloyd Wright, Scottsdale, AZ 85260-1002
Tel (480) 778-2440 *Founded/Ownrshp* 1998
Sales 125.7MM *EMP* 6[E]
SIC 7389 Business services
Prin: Jay Francis

D-U-N-S 00-508-1237 IMP/EXP
DWYER INSTRUMENTS INC
JOHNSON CONTROLS
102 Indiana Highway 212, Michigan City, IN 46360-1956
Tel (219) 879-8868 *Founded/Ownrshp* 1966
Sales 100.0MM *EMP* 700
SIC 3823 3824 3822 3829 3491 3625

D-U-N-S 62-331-4515
DX HOLDING CO INC
300 Jackson Hill St, Houston, TX 77007-7430
Tel (713) 863-1947 *Founded/Ownrshp* 1980
Sales 173.4MM[E] *EMP* 657
SIC 2869 2819 5169 Industrial organic chemicals; Industrial inorganic chemicals; Drilling mud; Industrial gases
Ch Bd: S Reed Morian
Dir Risk M: Jack Holcomb

D-U-N-S 96-729-6120
▲ DXP ENTERPRISES INC
7272 Pinemont Dr, Houston, TX 77040-6606
Tel (713) 996-4700 *Founded/Ownrshp* 1908
Sales 1.2MMM *EMP* 3,241
Accts Grant Thornton Llp Houston T
Tkr Sym DXPE *Exch* NGS
SIC 5084 5063 Materials handling machinery; Pumps & pumping equipment; Machine tools & metalworking machinery; Machine tools & accessories; Electrical apparatus & equipment
Ch Bd: David R Little
**CFO:* Mac McConnell
**Sr VP:* Wayne Crane
Sr VP: John J Jeffery
**Sr VP:* Gary Messersmith
Sr VP: David C Vinson
**Sr VP:* Kent Yee
VP: Tom Atkinson
VP: Fred Blevins
VP: Howard Gainey
VP: Todd Hamlin
VP: Mark Johnson
VP: Bill Kiefer
VP: Nick Little
VP: Dan Pavlik
VP: Chuck Rod
Board of Directors: Cletus Davis, Timothy P Halter, David Patton, Bryan Wimberly

D-U-N-S 05-376-3637
▲ DYCOM INDUSTRIES INC (FL)
11780 Us Highway 1 # 600, Palm Beach Gardens, FL 33408-3043
Tel (561) 627-7171 *Founded/Ownrshp* 1969
Sales 2.6MMM *EMP* 11,902
Tkr Sym DY *Exch* NYS
SIC 1623 1731 Communication line & transmission tower construction; Cable laying construction; Cable television line construction; Telephone & communication line construction; Communications specialization
Ch Bd: Steven E Nielsen
COO: Timothy R Estes
CFO: H Andrew Deferrari
Ch: Kimberly L Dickens
VP: Rebecca Brightly
VP: Richard Vilsoet
Dir Risk M: Philip Mullis
CIO: Curtis Chambers
Dir IT: Eric Morlang
IT Man: Amber Glover
Info Man: Paul Chaney

D-U-N-S 79-715-0633
■ DYCOM INVESTMENTS INC
(*Suby of* DYCOM INDUSTRIES INC) ★
11770 Us Highway 1 # 101, Palm Beach Gardens, FL 33408-3000
Tel (561) 627-7171 *Founded/Ownrshp* 2003
Sales 95.4MM[E] *EMP* 1,900
SIC 1623 Underground utilities contractor
Pr: Steven E Nielsen
**VP:* Timothy R Estes

D-U-N-S 19-371-4177
DYER INC
DICK DYER TOYOTA
240 Killian Commons Pkwy, Columbia, SC 29203-9131
Tel (803) 691-5602 *Founded/Ownrshp* 1969
Sales 98.4MM *EMP* 100
SIC 5511 7532 Automobiles, new & used; Body shop, automotive
Pr: Bruce Dyer
**Treas:* Ginger Dyer
**VP:* Richard S Dyer Sr
Dir IT: Shelley Fentress
Sls Mgr: Jeffrey Bowers
Sls Mgr: Chris Cagno
Sls Mgr: John Herring
Sls Mgr: Adam Whisenand
Sales Asso: Xavier Bailey
Sales Asso: Zackery Bayone
Sales Asso: Bill Buschmann

D-U-N-S 83-022-8511
DYK AUTOMOTIVE LLC
ATLANTIC PACIFIC AUTOMOTIVE
1900 Exeter Rd Ste 200, Germantown, TN 38138-2954
Tel (763) 478-2360 *Founded/Ownrshp* 2009
Sales 165.0MM[E] *EMP* 230
SIC 6719 Investment holding companies, except banks
Pr: Donald Youngblood
Sales Exec: Mike Opiel

DYKE BROTHERS
See DYKE INDUSTRIES INC

D-U-N-S 00-635-8865 IMP
DYKE INDUSTRIES INC (AR)
DYKE BROTHERS
309 Center St, Little Rock, AR 72201-2603
Tel (501) 376-2921 *Founded/Ownrshp* 1860, 1965
Sales 192.9MM[E] *EMP* 500
SIC 5031 Lumber: rough, dressed & finished; Millwork; Plywood
Pr: Fred Edick
**Ch Bd:* James T Dyke
CFO: Dyke James
**Sec:* Wendy Bush
VP: Carl D McVay
Brnch Mgr: Robin Parker
Genl Mgr: Albert Fulgham
**VP Opers:* Carl D Mc Vay
Opers Mgr: William Wmitchum
Sales Asso: Danny Larios

D-U-N-S 06-983-9975
DYKEMA GOSSETT PLLC
400 Renaissance Ctr, Detroit, MI 48243-1502
Tel (313) 568-6800 *Founded/Ownrshp* 1926
Sales 113.2MM[E] *EMP* 746
SIC 8111 8742

D-U-N-S 92-978-5350
■ DYN SPECIALTY CONTRACTING INC
(*Suby of* EMCOR GROUP INC) ★
1420 Spring Hill Rd # 500, Mc Lean, VA 22102-3006
Tel (703) 556-8000 *Founded/Ownrshp* 1986
Sales 149.9MM[E] *EMP* 3,986
SIC 1711 1731 Plumbing, heating, air-conditioning contractors; Electrical work
Pr: Jeffrey M Levy
**CFO:* John E Warga Jr
**Ex VP:* Frank Macinnis
**Sr VP:* Joseph McCormick

D-U-N-S 09-521-2023
■ DYNA TEN CORP
DYNATEN
(*Suby of* COMFORT SYSTEMS USA INC) ★
4375 Diplomacy Rd, Fort Worth, TX 76155-2635
Tel (817) 616-2200 *Founded/Ownrshp* 2014
Sales 114.1MM[E] *EMP* 550
SIC 1711 Mechanical contractor
CEO: Mark Nyquist
**Pr:* Scott Brady
Treas: Dewayne White
VP: Doug Pritchard
VP: Dave Recca
Ql Cn Mgr: Henry Jarvis

D-U-N-S 07-856-7973
DYNACAST INTERNATIONAL INC
(*Suby of* PARTNERS GROUP AG)
14045 Ballantyne Ste 400, Charlotte, NC 28277
Tel (704) 927-2790 *Founded/Ownrshp* 2011, 2015
Sales 641.2MM[E] *EMP* 5,510
SIC 3364 Nonferrous die-castings except aluminum; Zinc & zinc-base alloy die-castings; Brass & bronze die-castings; Copper & copper alloy die-castings
Pr: Simon J Newman
**COO:* David Angell
**CFO:* Adrian Murphy
**Ex VP:* Josef Ungerhofer
**Dir Sec:* Tom Kerscher
Genl Mgr: Thinh Pho

D-U-N-S 17-855-6093
DYNAFIRE INC
109 Concord Dr Ste B, Casselberry, FL 32707-3219
Tel (407) 740-0232 *Founded/Ownrshp* 2004
Sales 105.6MM[E] *EMP* 150
Accts Grennan Fender Orlando Fl
SIC 5063 Fire alarm systems
Pr: Steven F Hatch
**VP:* Kenneth L Hoffmann
VP: Joann Lane
Genl Mgr: Mary Galloway
IT Man: Kelly Gazaway
Sls Dir: Eric Simmons

D-U-N-S 08-351-1345
■ DYNALECTRIC CO
DYNATRAN
(*Suby of* EMCOR GROUP INC) ★
22930 Shaw Rd Ste 100, Dulles, VA 20166-9448
Tel (703) 288-2866 *Founded/Ownrshp* 2007
Sales 565.3MM[E] *EMP* 3,245
SIC 1731 General electrical contractor
Pr: J Brian Burns
CFO: Yates Robert
Treas: Doug Myers
Sr VP: Paul Mella
VP: Paul J Fracassini
VP: Matz Kevin
Brnch Mgr: Brian Burns
DP Exec: Shenton Roger

DYNAMEX OR HAZEN FINAL MILE
See TF FINAL MILE LLC

D-U-N-S 15-449-9099 IMP/EXP
DYNAMIC AVIATION GROUP INC
1402 Airport Rd, Bridgewater, VA 22812-3534
Tel (540) 828-6070 *Founded/Ownrshp* 1936
Sales 178.7MM[E] *EMP* 561[E]
SIC 5088 Aircraft & parts
Pr: Michael Stoltzfus
Pr: Aaron Lorson
CFO: Guy Cannady
CFO: David Schneeman
Treas: Barbara Stoltzfus
Ofcr: Garrett Jacobsen
Ofcr: Ken Misiak
Ofcr: Ben Shreve
Ofcr: Matthew Stoker
Ofcr: Tom Turner
Ex VP: J Merla Zook
Sr VP: Ralph Alderson
Sr VP: Cris Benavides
Sr VP: Michael George
Sr VP: Shannon Wagner
VP: Glen Ackermann
VP: David P Hoyt
VP: Darrell Pope

D-U-N-S 19-413-2098 IMP
DYNAMIC COOKING SYSTEMS INC
FISHER & PAYKEL
(*Suby of* FISHER & PAYKEL APPLIANCES USA HOLDINGS INC) ★
695 Town Center Dr # 180, Costa Mesa, CA 92626-1924
Tel (714) 372-7000 *Founded/Ownrshp* 2004
Sales 170.1MM[E] *EMP* 700
SIC 3589 Cooking equipment, commercial
CEO: Laurence Mawhinney
**CEO:* Stuart Broadhurst
CFO: Jeff Elder
Bd of Dir: Marty Carrillo
Sr VP: Jamie Simmonds
VP: Andrew Cooke
VP: Eric Deng
VP: Peter Klein
VP: Daniel Witten
CIO: Mark Mourd
Natl Sales: Scott Monroe

DYNAMIC EXPRESS
See DYNAMIC INTERNATIONAL USA INC

D-U-N-S 08-226-4615 IMP/EXP
DYNAMIC FASTENER SERVICE INC
9911 E 53rd St, Raytown, MO 64133-2242
Tel (816) 358-9898 *Founded/Ownrshp* 1968
Sales 94.9MM[E] *EMP* 130
SIC 5072 Hardware; Miscellaneous fasteners; Power tools & accessories
Ch Bd: Kevin Perz
**VP:* Dennis Perz
Sales Asso: Bob Monnich

DYNAMIC FOODS
See FRESH ACQUISITIONS LLC

D-U-N-S 14-772-7820 IMP
DYNAMIC INDUSTRIES INC
400 Poydras St Ste 1800, New Orleans, LA 70130-3223
Tel (504) 684-1305 *Founded/Ownrshp* 1985
Sales 288.5MM[E] *EMP* 999
SIC 3441 Fabricated structural metal
VP: Martin Bech
Mfg Dir: George Muffoletto
Opers Mgr: Bobby Miller

D-U-N-S 82-494-1111
DYNAMIC INTERNATIONAL USA INC
DYNAMIC EXPRESS
2501 71st St, North Bergen, NJ 07047-6406
Tel (973) 344-6300 *Founded/Ownrshp* 1994
Sales 100.0MM *EMP* 100[E]
SIC 4214 Local trucking with storage
Pr: Thomas C Gambino Jr
COO: Ralph Sangillo
VP: Leis Arntzen
Genl Mgr: Amy Depack
IT Man: Joe Weingar
Sls Mgr: Frank Genova

D-U-N-S 05-945-5170 IMP
DYNAMIC MANUFACTURING INC
1930 N Mannheim Rd, Melrose Park, IL 60160-1013
Tel (708) 343-8753 *Founded/Ownrshp* 1967
Sales 166.9MM[E] *EMP* 550
SIC 3714 Transmissions, motor vehicle
Pr: Nancy Partipilo
**Ch:* Gary R Noel
**Ex VP:* Tony Partipilo
Genl Mgr: Tony Falco
Dir IT: Nestor Angel

D-U-N-S 07-876-9683
DYNAMIC PRECISION GROUP INC
3651 Se Commerce Ave, Stuart, FL 34997-4967
Tel (772) 287-7770 *Founded/Ownrshp* 2011
Sales 217.0MM[E] *EMP* 968[E]
SIC 3724 3444 Engine mount parts, aircraft; Sheet metalwork
Prin: Greg Bennett
CFO: Diane Lockhart

D-U-N-S 11-491-4349
DYNAMIC RESTAURANTS LLC
BLACK-EYED PEAS RESTAURANTS
313 E Mn St, Hendersonville, TN 37075
Tel (615) 277-1234 *Founded/Ownrshp* 2002
Sales 28.5MM[E] *EMP* 2,500
SIC 5812 Restaurant, family: chain

D-U-N-S 03-825-7952
DYNAMIC SECURITY INC
1102 Woodward Ave, Muscle Shoals, AL 35661-2232
Tel (256) 383-5798 *Founded/Ownrshp* 1976
Sales 60.7MM[E] *EMP* 2,000
SIC 7381 Security guard service
Pr: John C Riddle Sr
**CFO:* Robert Nicholson
**Sec:* Mary Ann Riddle
**Ex VP:* Scott A Riddle
Rgnl Mgr: Glenn Brown
Genl Mgr: Kristal Riddle

D-U-N-S 19-775-3015
DYNAMIC SYSTEMS INC
D S I
(*Suby of* FGI GROUP INC) ★
3901 S Lamar Blvd Ste 300, Austin, TX 78704-8718
Tel (512) 443-4848 *Founded/Ownrshp* 1988
Sales 283.0MM[E] *EMP* 1,000
SIC 1711 Mechanical contractor
Ch: Royce W Faulkner
**Pr:* Randy J Rehmann
**Treas:* Charles D Schmidt
VP: Travis Everett
VP: Gary Kau
VP: Mark Kelly
**VP:* Mark D Ridley
VP Bus Dev: Rick Gopffarth
Genl Mgr: John Marchand
Genl Mgr: Glen McManus
Genl Mgr: Greg Seiter

D-U-N-S 00-101-4182
■ DYNAMICS RESEARCH CORP (MA)
(*Suby of* ENGILITY LLC) ★
2 Tech Dr, Andover, MA 01810-2434
Tel (978) 289-1500 *Founded/Ownrshp* 1955, 2014
Sales 232.6MM[E] *EMP* 2,698
SIC 7373 7379 8711 Computer integrated systems design; Computer-aided engineering (CAE) systems service; Computer related consulting services; Consulting engineer; Electrical or electronic engineering
Pr: Anthony Smeraglinolo
**CFO:* Michael Alber
**CFO:* David Keleher
**Ofcr:* Helen E Tsingos
Ex VP: Trisha Jones
Sr VP: Thomas J Connell
**Sr VP:* Kirk Dye
Sr VP: Jeanne D Lefevre
**Sr VP:* Thomas Miiller
**Sr VP:* Lawrence H O'Brien Jr
**Sr VP:* Craig Reed
**Sr VP:* Steven P Wentzell
VP: Barry L Aldrich
VP: Barry Aldrich
VP: Randy Sablich
VP: Eric Wolf

D-U-N-S 83-750-1899
DYNAMIX GROUP INC
1905 Woodstock Rd # 4150, Roswell, GA 30075-5625
Tel (770) 643-8877 *Founded/Ownrshp* 1995
Sales 140.8MM *EMP* 93
Accts Helton/Schuetze Cpa Llc Rosw
SIC 7373 8731 Systems software development services; Computer-aided system services; Computer (hardware) development
Pr: Charles E Hawkins Jr
**COO:* David A Delong
CFO: Dave Delong
Tech Mgr: Rick Scott

D-U-N-S 05-543-4062 IMP
■ DYNAPAR CORP
DANAHER INDUS SENSORS CONTRLS
(*Suby of* FORTIVE CORP) ★
1675 N Delany Rd, Gurnee, IL 60031-1237
Tel (847) 662-2666 *Founded/Ownrshp* 2016
Sales 305.7MM[E] *EMP* 1,500
SIC 3824 Controls, revolution & timing instruments; Electronic totalizing counters; Mechanical counters
Pr: Joseph Alexander
Ex VP: Thomas P Joyce
VP: Chet Kwasniak
VP: Craig T Paulson
VP Mktg: Andrew Ross

D-U-N-S 15-444-8625
DYNASTY FARMS INC
11900 Big Tujunga Cyn Rd, Tujunga, CA 91042-1129
Tel (831) 755-1398 *Founded/Ownrshp* 1981
Sales 363.2MM *EMP* 100
SIC 5148 Fresh fruits & vegetables
Pr: Thomas G Russell

D-U-N-S 00-609-0583 IMP/EXP
DYNATECT MANUFACTURING INC
GORTITE
(*Suby of* AUDAX GROUP LP) ★
2300 S Calhoun Rd, New Berlin, WI 53151-2708
Tel (262) 786-1500 *Founded/Ownrshp* 2007
Sales 148.9MM[E] *EMP* 535
SIC 3069 3499 3714 3599 Molded rubber products; Aerosol valves, metal; Motor vehicle body components & frame; Flexible metal hose, tubing & bellows
CEO: James O'Rourke
**VP:* Daniel Croal
Genl Mgr: George Hamzik
Ql Cn Mgr: Michael Rowe
Sls Mgr: Wade Van Harpen

DYNATEN
See DYNA TEN CORP

D-U-N-S 07-981-0687
DYNATRACE LLC
404 Wyman St Ste 500, Waltham, MA 02451-1250
Tel (781) 530-1000 *Founded/Ownrshp* 2014
Sales 11.3MM[E] *EMP* 1,500
SIC 7372 5045 Prepackaged software; Computer software
CEO: John Van Siclen
**CFO:* Ken Stillwell
**VP:* Steve Tack
Off Mgr: Jill Cochran
Software D: Robin Bothwell
Software D: Paul Hurley
Mktg Mgr: Megan Campbell

DYNATRAN
See DYNALECTRIC CO

D-U-N-S 96-776-3152 IMP
DYNAX AMERICA CORP
(*Suby of* DYNAX CORPORATION)
568 Eastpark Dr, Roanoke, VA 24019-8229
Tel (540) 966-6010 *Founded/Ownrshp* 1999
Sales 130.5MM[E] *EMP* 600
SIC 3714 Motor vehicle transmissions, drive assemblies & parts; Transmissions, motor vehicle; Transmission housings or parts, motor vehicle
Pr: Tatsuo Kuroda
**Pr:* Koji Akita
**Treas:* Takahiro Kobayashi
**Ex VP:* Masamitsu Kubota
**Ex VP:* Masaki Motomura
VP: Douglas J Feuerbach
Prd Mgr: Debra Cook
Prd Mgr: Michael Hinkley
Ql Cn Mgr: Deanna Surratt
Sales Exec: Keith Barker

D-U-N-S 00-324-2013
■ DYNCORP
(Suby of CSC) ★
1700 Old Meadow Rd, Mc Lean, VA 22102-4302
Tel (571) 722-0210 Founded/Ownrshp 1946, 2005
Sales 16.3MMM^E EMP 23,300
SIC 7373 7371 7374 7375 8744 4581 Systems software development services; Computer software development; Data processing service; Information retrieval services; Facilities support services; Airports, flying fields & services; Aircraft servicing & repairing
Pr: James Schaeffer
CFO: Christin Bailey
VP: Mark W Andresen
VP: Michael Boltan
VP: Gordon K Meriwether
Corp Couns: Carl J Peckinpaugh

D-U-N-S 61-533-5804
■ DYNCORP INTERNATIONAL INC
(Suby of DELTA TUCKER HOLDINGS, INC.)
1700 Old Meadow Rd, Mc Lean, VA 22102-4302
Tel (571) 722-0210 Founded/Ownrshp 2010
Sales 1.9MMM^E EMP 22,000^E
Accts Deloitte & Touche Llp
SIC 8741 7371 7381 7361 7363 Management services; Computer software development & applications; Protective services, guard; Labor contractors (employment agency); Employee leasing service
CEO: Lewis Von Thaer
CFO: Bill Kansky
Mktg Mgr: Heather Laudo
Board of Directors: Jim Geisler

D-U-N-S 10-122-1174 IMP
DYNE DURO NATIONAL CORP
81 Spence St, Bay Shore, NY 11706-2206
Tel (631) 249-9000 Founded/Ownrshp 1952
Sales 120.9MM^E EMP 290
SIC 3585 Air conditioning equipment, complete; Heating equipment, complete
Pr: Randall Hinden
CFO: Steve Friedstein
Genl Mgr: Eric Johannesen
Dir IT: Raanan Bar-Cohen
Dir IT: Julie Diehl
Plnt Mgr: Bob Ramotor
Board of Directors: Bernard Hinden

D-U-N-S 83-049-2844
■ DYNEGY COMMERCIAL ASSET MANAGEMENT LLC
DUKE ENERGY COML ASSET MGT LLC
(Suby of DYNEGY RESOURCE I LLC) ★
139 E 4th St, Cincinnati, OH 45202-4003
Tel (704) 382-5460 Founded/Ownrshp 2015
Sales 3.5MMM^E EMP 1^E
SIC 4924 4911 Natural gas distribution; Generation, electric power
Pr: Charles Whitlock
Treas: Stephen Gerard De May
VP: Keith Gerard Butler
VP: Larry Eiser
VP: Bob Ringel
Exec: Lynn J Good
Dir Risk M: Ryan Gentil
Genl Mgr: Jayne Cook
Genl Mgr: Gary Hebbeler
Genl Mgr: Kimberly Timmons
Dir IT: Mark Rogers

D-U-N-S 07-866-3086
■ DYNEGY CONESVILLE LLC
DUKE ENERGY CONESVILLE, LLC
(Suby of DYNEGY RESOURCE I LLC) ★
601 Travis St Ste 1400, Houston, TX 77002-3253
Tel (713) 507-6400 Founded/Ownrshp 2012
Sales 3.5MMM^E EMP 2^E
SIC 4911 Electric services
Pr: Robert C Flexon

D-U-N-S 80-440-5074 IMP/EXP
■ DYNEGY HOLDINGS LLC
(Suby of DYNEGY INC) ★
601 Travis St Ste 1400, Houston, TX 77002-3253
Tel (713) 507-6400 Founded/Ownrshp 1996
Sales 406.0MM^E EMP 400
SIC 4911 4923 5172 Electric services; Gas transmission & distribution; Petroleum products
Pr: Robert C Flexon
*COO: Kevin T Howell
*CFO: Clint C Freeland
*Ex VP: Carolyn J Burke
*VP: J Clint Walden

D-U-N-S 12-563-6345 IMP
▲ DYNEGY INC
601 Travis St Ste 1400, Houston, TX 77002-3253
Tel (713) 507-6400 Founded/Ownrshp 1984
Sales 1.4MMM EMP 1,679
Tkr Sym DYN Exch NYS
SIC 4911 Electric services; Generation, electric power
Pr: Robert C Flexon
COO: Martin Daley
CFO: Clint C Freeland
Ofcr: Carolyn J Burke
Ex VP: Mario Alonso
Ex VP: Mario E Alonso
Ex VP: Carolyn Burke
Ex VP: Carolyn J Burke
Ex VP: Catherine B Callaway
Ex VP: Julius Cox
Ex VP: Martin W Daley
Ex VP: Richard W Eimer
Ex VP: Jason A Hochberg
Ex VP: Catherine C James
Ex VP: Henry D Jones
Ex VP: Sheree M Petrone
Sr VP: Charles C Cook
Sr VP: Dean Ellis
VP: Rob Hardman
VP: John Johnson
VP: Sam Krueger
Board of Directors: Hilary E Ackermann, Paul M Barbas, Richard Lee Kuersteiner, Jeffrey S Stein, John R Sult, Pat Wood III

D-U-N-S 13-761-9136
■ DYNEGY MARKETING & TRADE LLC
(Suby of DYNEGY INC) ★
601 Travis St Ste 1400, Houston, TX 77002-3253
Tel (713) 507-6400 Founded/Ownrshp 2008
Sales 349.2MM^E EMP 400
SIC 4911 4924 ;
Ch: Pat Wood III
*Ex VP: Carolyn Burke
Ex VP: Henry D Jones

D-U-N-S 07-866-3113
■ DYNEGY MIAMI FORT LLC
DUKE ENERGY MIAMI FORT, LLC
(Suby of DYNEGY RESOURCE I LLC) ★
601 Travis St Ste 1400, Houston, TX 77002-3253
Tel (713) 507-6400 Founded/Ownrshp 2014
Sales 92.7MM^E EMP 1^E
SIC 4911 Electric services
Pr: Robert C Flexon

D-U-N-S 11-442-9496
■ DYNEGY MIDWEST GENERATION LLC
(Suby of DYNEGY INC) ★
10901 Baldwin Rd, Baldwin, IL 62217-1549
Tel (618) 785-2294 Founded/Ownrshp 1999
Sales 161.5MM^E EMP 185
SIC 4911 Electric services
Int Pr: Hunter Harrison

D-U-N-S 80-181-4344 IMP
■ DYNEGY MIDWEST GENERATION LLC
(Suby of DYNEGY HOLDINGS LLC) ★
601 Travis St Ste 1400, Houston, TX 77002-3253
Tel (713) 507-6400 Founded/Ownrshp 2011
Sales 201.1MM^E EMP 253
SIC 4911 Generation, electric power
CEO: Robert C Flexon
*CFO: Clint Freeland

D-U-N-S 60-285-5843
■ DYNEGY POWER CORP
(Suby of DYNEGY HOLDINGS LLC) ★
601 Travis St Ste 1400, Houston, TX 77002-3253
Tel (713) 507-6400 Founded/Ownrshp 1997
Sales 161.5MM^E EMP 400
SIC 4911 Generation, electric power
CEO: Robert C Flexon
*Pr: Burch Williamson
*Treas: Robert Doty
*Ex VP: Mario E Alonso
*Ex VP: Carolyn J Burke
*Ex VP: Catherine B Callaway
*Ex VP: Julius Cox
*Sr VP: Kenneth Randolph

D-U-N-S 07-979-5636
■ DYNEGY RESOURCE I LLC
(Suby of DYNEGY INC) ★
601 Travis St Ste 1400, Houston, TX 77002-3253
Tel (713) 507-6400 Founded/Ownrshp 2014
Sales 7.4MMM^E EMP 10^E
SIC 4911 4924 4931 Electric services; Natural gas distribution; Electric & other services combined
Pr: Robert Flexon

D-U-N-S 07-941-4326
■ DYNEGY RESOURCES GENERATING HOLDCO LLC
EQUIPWER RSOURCES HOLDINGS LLC
(Suby of DYNEGY INC) ★
601 Travis St Ste 1400, Houston, TX 77002-3253
Tel (713) 507-6400 Founded/Ownrshp 2010
Sales 349.2MM^E EMP 400
SIC 4911 Generation, electric power
CEO: Robert C Flexon
*CFO: Karl Ebert
*Ex VP: Alan P Dunlea
*Sr VP: John P Campbell
*Sr VP: Donna M Poresky

D-U-N-S 07-993-1151
DYNEGY ZIMMER LLC
1781 Us Rte 52, Moscow, OH 45153
Tel (713) 767-0483 Founded/Ownrshp 2012
Sales 34.5MM^E EMP 1,200
SIC 1731 Electric power systems contractors
CEO: Bob Foeson

D-U-N-S 07-866-3090
■ DYNEGY ZIMMER LLC
DUKE ENERGY ZIMMER, LLC
(Suby of DYNEGY RESOURCE I LLC) ★
601 Travis St Ste 1400, Houston, TX 77002-3253
Tel (713) 507-6400 Founded/Ownrshp 2014
Sales 83.5MM^E EMP 1^E
SIC 4911 Electric services
Pr: Robert C Flexon

D-U-N-S 07-545-8455
DYNETICS INC
1002 Explorer Blvd Nw, Huntsville, AL 35806-2806
Tel (256) 964-4000 Founded/Ownrshp 1974
Sales 275.5MM EMP 1,532
SIC 8731 Engineering laboratory, except testing
CEO: Marcus J Bendickson
*Pr: Thomas A Baumbach
COO: Vicki Kittrell
CFO: Fred Kummer
*CFO: Randy Reynolds
*Ex VP: David King
*VP: Michael A Demaioribus
*VP: Greg Lester
VP: Phyllis Nicaise
*VP: Jonathan Whitcomb
Dir Bus: Robert Dowling

D-U-N-S 19-643-5440
▲ DYNEX CAPITAL INC
4991 Lake Brook Dr # 100, Glen Allen, VA 23060-9245
Tel (804) 217-5800 Founded/Ownrshp 1988
Sales 101.1MM EMP 20
Tkr Sym DX Exch NYS
SIC 6798 Real estate investment trusts
Pr: Byron L Boston
*Ch Bd: Thomas B Akin
COO: Stephen J Benedetti

Ex VP: Smriti L Popenoe
VP: Robert Nilson

D-U-N-S 10-839-8462
DYNIX CORP
(Suby of SIRSIDYNIX) ★
400 W 5050 N, Provo, UT 84604-5650
Tel (800) 288-8820 Founded/Ownrshp 1999
Sales 110.0MM EMP 500
SIC 8231 Library services
Pr: Gary Rautenstrauch
COO: Matthew Hawkins
Mktg Mgr: Steve Donoghue

DYNO NOBEL HOLDINGS USA, INC.
See DYNO NOBEL HOLDINGS USA INC

D-U-N-S 94-596-8246 IMP/EXP
DYNO NOBEL HOLDINGS USA INC
DYNO NOBEL HOLDINGS USA, INC.
(Suby of INCITEC PIVOT LIMITED)
2795 E Cottonwood Pkwy # 500, Salt Lake City, UT 84121-5695
Tel (801) 364-4800 Founded/Ownrshp 2001
Sales 236.0MM EMP 2,701
SIC 2892 Explosives
VP: Kelly Arnold
*CFO: Lars Johansen
VP: Sergio Lafratta
*Prin: Alfred Nobel
Mktg Dir: Steven Walker

D-U-N-S 00-909-1257 IMP/EXP
DYNO NOBEL INC
(Suby of DYNO NOBEL HOLDINGS USA INC) ★
2795 E Cottonwood Pkwy # 500, Salt Lake City, UT 84121-5695
Tel (801) 364-4800 Founded/Ownrshp 1962, 1996
Sales 236.0MM^E EMP 2,701
SIC 2892 Slurries (explosive); Nitroglycerin (explosive)
VP: Kelly G Arnold
CFO: Nick Stratford
*Sr VP: Robert A Bingham
*Sr VP: Seth Hobby
VP: Kelly Arnold
VP: Robert Brouwer
VP: David Bullis
Genl Mgr: Patrick Barrett
Genl Mgr: Tony Francelj
Genl Mgr: Richard B Gotcher
Genl Mgr: Pat Nill

DYSART ISCHOOL
See DYSART UNIFIED SCHOOL DISTRICT

D-U-N-S 00-290-1544
DYSART UNIFIED SCHOOL DISTRICT
DYSART ISCHOOL
15802 N Parkview Pl, Surprise, AZ 85374-7466
Tel (623) 876-7000 Founded/Ownrshp 1945
Sales 193.3MM EMP 2,000
Accts Heinfeld Meech & Co Pc Pho
SIC 8211 Public elementary & secondary schools; Public junior high school
Dir Vol: Sharon Boersma
*Pr: Traci Sawyer-S
Dir Sec: Karen Winterstein
Genl Mgr: Linda Price
Off Mgr: Tamara Ansbach
Off Mgr: Jeannette Schurke
CTO: Diana Hawari
Schl Brd P: Traci Sawyer-Sinkbel
Teacher Pr: Patti Buck
HC Dir: Clark Crace

D-U-N-S 00-896-5659 IMP/EXP
DYSON-KISSNER-MORAN CORP
2515 South Rd Ste 5, Poughkeepsie, NY 12601-5474
Tel (212) 661-4600 Founded/Ownrshp 1954
Sales 530.0MM^E EMP 2,500
SIC 3433 3625 3699 Gas burners, industrial; Motor controls, electric; Security devices
Ch Bd: Robert R Dyson
*Pr: Michael J Harris
Genl Couns: John H Fitzsimons
Board of Directors: Henry Beistein, Anne E Dyson MD, Joseph V Mariner

D-U-N-S 15-428-2263 IMP/EXP
DYWIDAG SYSTEMS INTERNATIONAL USA INC
DSI USA
(Suby of DSI INTERNATIONAL LUXEMBOURG SARL)
320 Marmon Dr, Bolingbrook, IL 60440-3078
Tel (630) 739-1100 Founded/Ownrshp 1969
Sales 95.8MM^E EMP 180
SIC 5051

E

D-U-N-S 79-717-5627
E & B NATURAL RESOURCES MANAGEMENT CORP
1600 Norris Rd, Bakersfield, CA 93308-2234
Tel (661) 679-1714 Founded/Ownrshp 2003
Sales 326.3MM EMP 250
SIC 1311 Crude petroleum & natural gas
Pr: Steve Layton
*CFO: Frank J Ronkese
*Sr VP: Jeff Blesener
VP: Joyce Holtzclaw
*VP: Jeff Jones
Genl Mgr: Christy Swatzeel

D-U-N-S 04-282-9630
E & B PAVING INC
(Suby of I M I) ★
286 W 300 N, Anderson, IN 46012-1200
Tel (765) 643-5358 Founded/Ownrshp 1967
Sales 275.7MM^E EMP 550
SIC 1611 2951 1794 Highway & street paving contractor; Asphalt & asphaltic paving mixtures (not from refineries); Excavation work
Pr: Gary Stebbins
*Sec: Richard Knief
*VP: Larry Canterbury

*VP: John Eller
*VP: Ron Zink
Off Admin: Angie Riddle
Off Admin: Paula Sloan

D-U-N-S 80-564-5983
E & C ENTERPRISES INC
TEXACO
2359 Research Ct, Woodbridge, VA 22192-4632
Tel (703) 494-5800 Founded/Ownrshp 1992
Sales 171.6MM^E EMP 500
SIC 5541 Filling stations, gasoline
Pr: Abdolhossein Ejtemai
*VP: Julio Cornejo
Off Mgr: Tiffany Longo
CIO: Andrew Zaleski
Mktg Dir: Mark Hall
Mktg Mgr: Jaime Maldonado

D-U-N-S 87-754-2951 IMP/EXP
E & E CO LTD
JLA HOME
45875 Northport Loop E, Fremont, CA 94538-6414
Tel (510) 490-9788 Founded/Ownrshp 1992
Sales 219.7MM^E EMP 800
SIC 5023 Sheets, textile
CEO: Edmund Jin
VP: Susan Wang
IT Man: Jeremy Xu
Prd Mgr: Anne Hu

D-U-N-S 08-041-8667
E & E FOODS INC (WA)
PACIFIC STAR SEAFOODS
801 S Fidalgo St Ste 100, Seattle, WA 98108-2613
Tel (206) 768-8979 Founded/Ownrshp 2016
Sales 120.0MM EMP 100
SIC 5146 2092 Fish & seafoods; Seafoods, fresh: prepared
Pr: Randy Patrick
CFO: Yuk Lan Li
*VP: Tadayuki Goto

E & G TRADING
See QUIRCH FOODS CO

D-U-N-S 96-210-0710
■ E & H DISTRIBUTING LLC
U.S. FOODSERVICE
(Suby of US FOODS INC) ★
1685 W Cheyenne Ave, North Las Vegas, NV 89032-7764
Tel (702) 636-3663 Founded/Ownrshp 1955
Sales 189.4MM^E EMP 473
SIC 5113 5141 5142 5149 Industrial & personal service paper; Groceries, general line; Packaged frozen goods; Bakery products
COO: Stuart Schuette
*Ex VP: Juliette Pryor
*Ex VP: David Schreibman
*Sr VP: Tom Lynch
Sls Mgr: Nicole Johnston

D-U-N-S 00-920-0056 IMP/EXP
E & J GALLO WINERY
SAN JOAQUIN VLY CONCENTRATES
600 Yosemite Blvd, Modesto, CA 95354-2760
Tel (209) 341-3111 Founded/Ownrshp 1942
Sales 4.1MMM EMP 6,300
SIC 2084 0172 Wines; Grapes
CEO: Joseph E Gallo
CFO: Anthony Youga
Ex VP: Robert Gallo
Sr VP: Roger Nabedian
VP: Peter Abate
VP: Bill Backus
VP: Ben Bisordi
VP: Robert Donoho
VP: Allen Doty
VP: Matt Gallo
VP: Chris Kalabokes
VP: Phillip Klein
VP: Anne Kraus
VP: George Neveling
VP: Jose Reyes
VP: Anna Roberts
VP: Peter Vella
Dir Lab: Steven Tallman

D-U-N-S 06-384-8253 IMP
E & J LAWRENCE CORP
HYPERACTIVE
85 Metro Way, Secaucus, NJ 07094-1905
Tel (201) 210-5577 Founded/Ownrshp 1972
Sales 213.3MM^E EMP 2,000
Accts David H Gordon Cpa Pllc Gr
SIC 5651 Family clothing stores
Pr: James Khezrie
*Treas: Gabriel Khezrie
Dir IT: Bilal Ahmad

D-U-N-S 04-928-1702 IMP
■ E & R INDUSTRIAL SALES INC
ER INDUSTRIAL
(Suby of WW GRAINGER INC) ★
40800 Enterprise Dr, Sterling Heights, MI 48314-3761
Tel (586) 795-2400 Founded/Ownrshp 2013
Sales 405.4MM^E EMP 400
SIC 5085 Mill supplies
CEO: Ernest I Pizzimenti
*Pr: Jerry Pizzimenti
Genl Mgr: Heather Murphy
IT Man: Prasad Romawickrama
Natl Sales: Randy Miller
Mktg Dir: Gerald Pizzimenti
Mktg Dir: Katy Trionfi
Mktg Dir: Cathy Veri
Manager: Scott Beck
Sls Mgr: David Hustwick
Sls Mgr: Michele May

D-U-N-S 02-893-5179 IMP/EXP
E & S INTERNATIONAL ENTERPRISES INC
IMPORT DIRECT
7801 Hayvenhurst Ave, Van Nuys, CA 91406-1712
Tel (818) 702-2207 Founded/Ownrshp 1978
Sales 124.7MM^E EMP 135
SIC 5064 Electrical appliances, television & radio
Ch: Ehsan Asherian

*Pr: Farshad Asherian
*CEO: Phillip Asherian
*COO: Mike RAD
*CFO: Mark W Barron
Ex VP: Brandon Wolsic
VP: Nathan Thinnes
Natl Sales: Sean Mann
VP Sls: Eli Chorbajian
VP Sls: Rodney RAD

E A G L E
See EVERGREEN AVIATION GROUND LOGISTICS ENTERPRISE INC

D-U-N-S 00-621-7517 IMP
E A SWEEN CO
DELI EXPRESS
16101 W 78th St, Eden Prairie, MN 55344-5798
Tel (952) 937-9440 Founded/Ownrshp 1964
Sales 275.5MM[E] EMP 900
SIC 2099 5142 Sandwiches, assembled & packaged: for wholesale market; Salads, fresh or refrigerated; Packaged frozen goods
Ch Bd: Tom E Sween
*Pr: Robert Linner
*CFO: John Davis
*Sr VP: Rob Linner
Sr VP: Tom Nientimp
VP: Mary Kelly
VP: William Lewis
Exec: John Miller
Genl Mgr: Mark Gray
Telecom Ex: Jeff Denzer
QA Dir: Jacki Lemus

D-U-N-S 36-171-0163 IMP
E AARON ENTERPRISES INC
AARON GROUP OF COMPANIES, THE
161 Wshington St Fl 11, Conshohocken, PA 19428
Tel (610) 940-0800 Founded/Ownrshp 1988
Sales 85.2MM[E] EMP 70
SIC 5111 Printing paper; Fine paper
Ch Bd: Eugene Aaron
*CEO: Drew Aaron
*COO: Brent Aaron
*Sec: Mindy Aaron
VP: Franco Dorzaio
VP: Greg Giller
Board of Directors: Dick O'brien

D-U-N-S 01-190-4604 IMP
E ARMATA INC (NY)
114 Nyc Term Mkt, Bronx, NY 10474-7303
Tel (718) 991-5600 Founded/Ownrshp 1911
Sales 90.2MM[E] EMP 180
SIC 5148 Fruits, fresh; Vegetables, fresh
Pr: Chris Armata
*Treas: Paul Armata
Dir IT: Chris Lion

D-U-N-S 00-796-5023 IMP
E B BRADLEY CO (CA)
5602 Bickett St, Vernon, CA 90058-2826
Tel (323) 585-9917 Founded/Ownrshp 1946, 2014
Sales 116.7MM[E] EMP 250
SIC 5072 2452 Hardware; Panels & sections, prefabricated, wood
Pr: Don Lorey
*CFO: Scott Simons
Opers Mgr: Casey Lemke
Sls Mgr: Ron Taisey
Sales Asso: Joel Ballard
Sales Asso: Mark Walder

D-U-N-S 17-830-1230
E B EDDY PAPER INC
DOMTAR EDDY SPECIALTY PAPERS
(Suby of DOMTAR INC)
1700 Washington Ave, Port Huron, MI 48060-3462
Tel (810) 982-0191 Founded/Ownrshp 1998
Sales 117.0MM[E] EMP 324
SIC 2621 Packaging paper; Specialty papers; Offset paper; Fine paper
CEO: John Williams
*VP: Gilles Pharand

D-U-N-S 62-141-4648
■ **E C AVIATION SERVICES INC**
(Suby of GENTEX CORP) ★
600 N Centennial St, Zeeland, MI 49464-1318
Tel (616) 772-1800 Founded/Ownrshp 1990
Sales 52.8MM[E] EMP 1,400
SIC 4522 Air passenger carriers, nonscheduled
Pr: Thomas Ludema
*Sec: Enoch Jen
VP: Dennis Alexejun
Sftwr Eng: Greg Pattok
Board of Directors: Fred Bauer, Ken Lagrand

D-U-N-S 00-690-3199 IMP/EXP
E C BARTON & CO
BARTON'S
2929 Browns Ln, Jonesboro, AR 72401-7208
Tel (870) 932-6673 Founded/Ownrshp 1967
Sales 269.8MM EMP 700
Accts Jones & Company Ltd Jonesbo
SIC 5031 5211 5713 Lumber: rough, dressed & finished; Millwork; Plywood; Millwork & lumber; Roofing material; Paneling; Floor covering stores
Ch Bd: Neil Crowson
*Treas: Gary Beasley
*Treas: Tom Rainwater
Chf Mktg O: H R McDonough
*Ofcr: Greg Smith
VP: Ron Bellas
VP: Larry Chance
VP: Kevin Pierce
VP: Bill Ringelstein
Dist Mgr: Bob Brown
Dist Mgr: Sean Fitzpatrick

E C C INTEGRATED
See EPLUS TECHNOLOGY OF PENNSYLVANIA INC

E C I
See ELECTRICAL CONSULTANTS INC

E C R M C
See EL CENTRO REGIONAL MEDICAL CENTER INC

E C S
See ENGINEERING CONSULTING SERVICES LTD

E C S
See ECS FEDERAL LLC

E D C
See EDUCATION DEVELOPMENT CENTER INC

D-U-N-S 05-240-9596
E D D INVESTMENT CO
14325 Iseli Rd, Santa Fe Springs, CA 90670-5203
Tel (562) 921-5410 Founded/Ownrshp 1968
Sales 32.4MM[E] EMP 1,219
SIC 5812 Fast-food restaurant, chain
Pt: Donald Sheldrake

D-U-N-S 00-507-0511 IMP/EXP
E D ETNYRE & CO (IL)
EDETNYRE
1333 S Daysville Rd, Oregon, IL 61061-9778
Tel (815) 732-2116 Founded/Ownrshp 1898
Sales 94.5MM[E] EMP 380
SIC 3531 Road construction & maintenance machinery
Ch Bd: Roger L Etnyre
*Pr: Thomas Brown
CFO: Lane Zerbe
VP: Steve Carr
*VP: Sharon Engel
Rgnl Mgr: Brian Horner
Rgnl Mgr: Dennis Muse
Genl Mgr: Brian Clark
Genl Mgr: Tim Krueger
Genl Mgr: Terry Stone
Netwrk Mgr: Dave Sloman

E D I
See SHEALY ELECTRICAL WHOLESALERS INC

E E I
See EDISON ELECTRIC INSTITUTE INC

E E M C O
See EATON AEROSPACE LLC

D-U-N-S 04-908-2985
E E R INC (TX)
MCDONALD'S
3000 W Cedar St, Beaumont, TX 77702-2528
Tel (409) 838-2002 Founded/Ownrshp 1969
Sales 142.4MM[E] EMP 3,325
SIC 5812 Fast-food restaurant, chain
Pr: Rodger Ellis
*VP: Russell W Ellis

E E REED CONSTRUCTION CO
See E E REED CONSTRUCTION LP

D-U-N-S 01-687-4757
E E REED CONSTRUCTION LP
E E REED CONSTRUCTION CO
333 Commerce Green Blvd, Sugar Land, TX 77478-3596
Tel (281) 933-4000 Founded/Ownrshp 1997
Sales 116.5MM[E] EMP 150
SIC 1542 Nonresidential construction
CEO: Gene Reed
*Pt: Terry D Early
*Pt: Mike Jones
*Pt: Jim Owrey
*Pt: Douglas Peterson
*Pt: Curtis D Rakosi
*Pt: Marty Tilts
*Pt: John Waltz
*Pr: Mark Reed
CFO: Mike Denherder
*VP: David Clowers

D-U-N-S 16-160-5647
E ENTERTAINMENT TELEVISION INC
STYLE NETWORK
5750 Wilshire Blvd # 500, Los Angeles, CA 90036-3635
Tel (323) 954-2400 Founded/Ownrshp 1985
Sales 234.8MM[E] EMP 900
SIC 4841 4833

E F D
See NORDSON EFD LLC

E FUN
See YIFANG USA INC

D-U-N-S 02-488-5048
E G FORREST CO (NC)
E G FRREST FD SVC DISTRIBUTERS
1023 N Chestnut St, Winston Salem, NC 27101-1519
Tel (336) 723-9151 Founded/Ownrshp 1920
Sales 88.8MM[E] EMP 108
Accts Dixon Huges Pllc Winston-Sale
SIC 5142 5141 Packaged frozen goods; Groceries, general line
Ch Bd: Louis P Forrest
*Pr: Jeffrey J Holderfield
*Treas: Robin E Heflin
Treas: Robin E Hflin

E G FRREST FD SVC DISTRIBUTERS
See E G FORREST CO

D-U-N-S 08-740-3341 IMP/EXP
E GLUCK CORP (NY)
ARMITRON WATCH DIV
6015 Little Neck Pkwy, Little Neck, NY 11362-2500
Tel (718) 784-0700 Founded/Ownrshp 1957, 1977
Sales 85.1MM[E] EMP 400[E]
SIC 3873 5094 Watches & parts, except crystals & jewels; Clocks, assembly of; Watches & parts; Clocks
Pr: Eugen Gluck
*CFO: Renee Jacobs
Sr VP: Mark Odenheimer
VP: Jerry Dikowitz
VP: Michael Feagan
VP: Michael Feagen
*VP: Sidney Gluck
VP: Michael Kronenberg
VP: Bob Nublin
VP: Rob Robertaccio
Creative D: Mark Chang

E GRAPHICS
See TBWA WORLDWIDE INC

D-U-N-S 00-131-5704 IMP/EXP
▲ **E I DU PONT DE NEMOURS AND CO**
974 Centre Rd, Wilmington, DE 19805-1269
Tel (302) 774-1000 Founded/Ownrshp 1802
Sales 25.1MMM EMP 52,000
Accts Pricewaterhousecoopers Llp Ph
Tkr Sym DD Exch NYS
SIC 2879 2824 2865 2821 2834 Agricultural chemicals; Nylon fibers; Polyester fibers; Dyes & pigments; Thermoplastic materials; Pharmaceutical preparations
Ch Bd: Edward D Breen
Pr: Balvinder Singh Kalsi
Pr: Patrick Lindner
Pr: Randy L Stone
CFO: Nicholas C Fanandakis
Sr VP: Benito Cachinero-Sanchez
Sr VP: Marc Doyle
Sr VP: Stacy L Fox
Sr VP: Douglas Muzyka
VP: Krysta Harden
Ql Cn Mgr: Giannis Katsiamouris
Board of Directors: Lamberto Andreotti, Robert A Brown, Bertrand P Collomb, Alexander M Cutler, James L Gallogly, Lois D Juliber, Ulf M Schneider, Lee M Thomas, Patrick J Ward

E J P
See EVERETT J PRESCOTT INC

D-U-N-S 14-020-4640
■ **E K HOLDINGS INC**
(Suby of HAIN CELESTIAL GROUP INC) ★
Rr 5, Mifflintown, PA 17059-9805
Tel (717) 436-5921 Founded/Ownrshp 2015
Sales 197.3MM[E] EMP 1,500[E]
SIC 2015 Poultry slaughtering & processing; Chicken, processed; Turkey, processed
CEO: Jeff Brown

D-U-N-S 09-506-7898 IMP/EXP
E K SUCCESS LTD
EK SUCCESS BRANDS
(Suby of EK SUCCESS BRANDS) ★
2240 75th St, Woodridge, IL 60517-2333
Tel (630) 963-7100 Founded/Ownrshp 2007
Sales 85.0MM EMP 400
SIC 5199 2679

E K U
See EASTERN KENTUCKY UNIVERSITY

E L F
See E L FARMER & CO

D-U-N-S 00-877-7310
E L FARMER & CO (TX)
E L F
3800 E 42nd St Ste 417, Odessa, TX 79762-5928
Tel (432) 366-2010 Founded/Ownrshp 1910
Sales 94.5MM[E] EMP 110
SIC 1389 Haulage, oil field
Pr: Jimmie B Todd
*VP: Carroll Brents
*VP: David Musgraves

D-U-N-S 00-686-7675
E L HOLLINGSWORTH & CO (MI)
CHIEFTAIN CONTRACT SERVICES
3039 Airpark Dr N, Flint, MI 48507-3471
Tel (810) 233-7331 Founded/Ownrshp 1965, 1987
Sales 95.2MM[E] EMP 675
SIC 4212 4213 Local trucking, without storage; Trucking, except local
Ch: Stephen Barr
*Pr: Michael T McNamara
*CFO: Jeff Berlin
*Ch: R James Lapointe
Dir Bus: Curtis Bull
Dir IT: Sean Goldie
Sftwr Eng: Bryan English
Sfty Mgr: Scott Wiegers
Opers Mgr: Justin Hermanson
Mktg Mgr: Scott McNiel

E L I
See ENERGY LABS INC

E LEND
See AMERICAN FINANCIAL RESOURCES INC

E M
See ELECTRIC MACHINERY CO INC

E M C
See WALTON ELECTRIC MEMBERSHIP CORP

D-U-N-S 13-465-8181
E M C NATIONAL LIFE MUTUAL HOLDING CO
699 Walnut St, Des Moines, IA 50309-3929
Tel (515) 225-8197 Founded/Ownrshp 1999
Sales NA EMP 119
SIC 6311 Life insurance
Ch Bd: Bruce G Kelley
*Pr: Alan D Huisinga
CFO: Keith R Troester
Board of Directors: Lawrence K Hedlin, Robert L Howe, Richard D Johnson, Frederick H Lock, Robert W Murray, Fredrick A Schiek, Gretchen H Tegeler

E M D
See CAPITOL-EMI MUSIC INC

D-U-N-S 05-180-8988
E M DUGGAN INC
140 Will Dr, Canton, MA 02021-3704
Tel (781) 828-2292 Founded/Ownrshp 1891
Sales 175.6MM EMP 400
SIC 1711

E M P
See ENGINEERED MACHINED PRODUCTS INC

D-U-N-S 80-844-1653
E M P INTERIORS INC
STANDARD DRY WALL
9902 Channel Rd, Lakeside, CA 92040-3042
Tel (619) 443-7034 Founded/Ownrshp 1990
Sales 133.7MM[E] EMP 1,251
SIC 1742 Drywall
Pr: Robert Caya
*VP: Blaine Caya
Exec: Letty Perez

E M S
See E MAIL SOLUTIONS INC

E M S
See EASTERN METAL SUPPLY OF NORTH CAROLINA INC

E M S I
See EMSI HOLDING CO

E M S I
See EXAMINATION MANAGEMENT SERVICES INC

D-U-N-S 07-620-0190
E MAIL SOLUTIONS INC
E M S
12111 Emmet St, Omaha, NE 68164-4264
Tel (402) 496-2223 Founded/Ownrshp 1998
Sales 125.2MM[E] EMP 500
SIC 4822 Electronic mail
Pr: Mitch Johnson
Opers Mgr: Linda Colton
Mktg Mgr: James Weis

D-U-N-S 94-226-5778
E MASON ROBERT & ASSOCIATES INC
1726 N Graham St, Charlotte, NC 28206-3026
Tel (704) 375-4465 Founded/Ownrshp 1992
Sales 100.3MM[E] EMP 100
SIC 5085 7699 Valves, pistons & fittings; Valve repair, industrial
Ch Bd: Robert E Mason III
*Pr: Robert E Mason IV
*Sr VP: Michael G Griffith
IT Man: Walter Weber

D-U-N-S 02-359-9939
E O JOHNSON CO INC
8400 Stewart Ave, Wausau, WI 54401-9047
Tel (715) 842-9999 Founded/Ownrshp 1957
Sales 100.8MM[E] EMP 122
SIC 5112 7699 5045 Office supplies; Fountain pen repair shop; Computer software
CEO: Mary Jo Johnson
*Pr: Roger King
*Treas: Ronald Dustan
*VP: Dave Johnson
Exec: Sharon J Zwicky
*Prin: Emery O Johnson
Brnch Mgr: Patrick McCabe
CIO: Dan Rickert
Natl Sales: Mike Derleth
Sls Mgr: Todd Brost

E P
See EMERALD PACKAGING INC

E P B
See ELECTRIC POWER BOARD OF CHATTANOOGA

E P I
See EDUCATIONAL PRODUCTS INC

E R C
See ERC PROPERTIES INC

E R C
See ENHANCED RECOVERY CO LLC

E R M
See ERM-NA HOLDINGS CORP

E R M
See ENVIRONMENTAL RESOURCES MANAGEMENT - NORTH CENTRAL INC

D-U-N-S 00-348-1397
E R SNELL CONTRACTOR INC
ERS ROADS AND BRIDGES
1785 Oak Rd, Snellville, GA 30078-2233
Tel (770) 985-0600 Founded/Ownrshp 1940
Sales 234.6MM[E] EMP 388
SIC 1611 Highway & street paving contractor; Grading
CEO: Robin J Snell
*CFO: Christopher L Snell
VP: Kenneth Blizzard
VP: Thomas Byrd
VP: Randy Griffin
VP: Terry Hollis
IT Man: Kevin Moon
IT Man: Jared Snell
Sfty Mgr: Roger Goodwin

E R T
See ENERGY RESOURCE TECHNOLOGY GOM LLC

D-U-N-S 00-190-9464
E RITTER & CO
10 Elm St, Marked Tree, AR 72365-2211
Tel (870) 358-7333 Founded/Ownrshp 1907
Sales 201.3MM EMP 175
Accts Kpmg Llp Memphis Tn
SIC 0131 0116 0724 4813 5211 5083 Cotton; Soybeans; Cotton ginning; Telephone communication, except radio; Lumber & other building materials; Farm implements
Ch: Daniel B Hatzenbuehler
Pr: Charles R Dickinson Jr
VP: E Ritter Arnold
Genl Mgr: Dan Kennedy
Board of Directors: Jane Ritter Clawson, Walter B Howell, George W Johnston, Roderick E Kesting, John M Vines

D-U-N-S 96-721-8657
E RITTER AGRIBUSINESS HOLDINGS INC
(Suby of E RITTER & CO) ★
10 Elm St, Marked Tree, AR 72365-2211
Tel (870) 336-7310 Founded/Ownrshp 2010
Sales 108.3MM EMP 104[E]

Accts Kpmg Llp Memphis Tn
SIC 0131 4813 Cotton; Telephone communication, except radio
Pr: Ritter Arnold
*COO: Kenny Traynon
*CFO: L Alan Wright
*Sec: Bill Harrison

D-U-N-S 62-226-1527
E RITTER COMMUNICATIONS HOLDINGS INC
(Suby of E RITTER & CO) ★
2400 Ritter Dr, Jonesboro, AR 72401-6241
Tel (870) 336-3434 Founded/Ownrshp 1990
Sales 92.6MM EMP 81[E]
Accts Kpmg Llp Memphis Tn
SIC 4813 4812 5045 Telephone communication, except radio; Cellular telephone services; Computer software
Pr: Alan G Morse
*VP: Susan Christian
*VP: Robert G Mouser
*VP: Clinton N Orr
VP: Jim Roberts
VP: Becky Smith
Genl Mgr: Mike Thompson
Board of Directors: William F Harrison, Alan G Morse

E RITTER SEED
See E RITTER SEED CO

D-U-N-S 03-557-6628
E RITTER SEED CO
E RITTER SEED
(Suby of E RITTER AGRIBUSINESS HOLDINGS INC) ★
300 Adamson St, Marked Tree, AR 72365-1631
Tel (870) 358-2130 Founded/Ownrshp 1969
Sales 107.3MM EMP 14
Accts Kpmg Llp Memphis Tn
SIC 5153 5191 Field beans; Grains; Rice, unpolished; Chemicals, agricultural
Pr: Kevin Wright
*Sec: William F Harrison

E S I
See ELECTRONIC SYSTEMS INC

E. S. SUTTON EXTRA SPORTSWEAR
See E S SUTTON INC

D-U-N-S 88-490-3246 IMP/EXP
E S SUTTON INC
E. S. SUTTON EXTRA SPORTSWEAR
1400 Broadway Fl 26, New York, NY 10018-5396
Tel (212) 944-9494 Founded/Ownrshp 1991
Sales 119.6MM[E] EMP 256
SIC 5137 Sportswear, women's & children's
Pr: Joseph Sutton
*VP: Sam Sasson
*VP: Albert Sutton

E S U
See EAST STROUDSBURG UNIVERSITY

ET C
See ELECTRONIC THEATRE CONTROLS INC

D-U-N-S 00-959-7733 IMP/EXP
ET HORN CO (CA)
16050 Canary Ave, La Mirada, CA 90638-5585
Tel (714) 523-8050 Founded/Ownrshp 1961
Sales 290.0MM EMP 150
SIC 5169 Industrial chemicals
Ch Bd: Gene Alley
*Pr: Bob Ahn
*Pr: Jeff Martin
*Pr: Kevin Salerno
*Pr: Mike Zarkades
CFO: Sam Orpilla
*Ofcr: Roger Clemens
VP: Jim Berg
VP: Bob Blackford
VP: Cecilia Chavez
VP: Patty Degrazzio
VP: Adam Ernst
VP: Mario Kuhn
VP: Jack Lawrence
VP: Christopher G Lesko
VP: Julie Wubbana
*VP: Julie Wubbena

ET M C SPECIALTY HOSPITAL
See EAST TEXAS SPECIALTY HOSP

ET S
See EDUCATIONAL TESTING SERVICE INC

D-U-N-S 02-423-7489
▲ ETRADE FINANCIAL CORP
1271 Ave Of The Americas, New York, NY 10020-1300
Tel (646) 521-4300 Founded/Ownrshp 1982
Sales 1.4MMM EMP 3,400
Accts Deloitte & Touche Llp Mclean
Tkr Sym ETFC Exch NGS
SIC 6211 6035 Brokers, security; Dealers, security; Federal savings & loan associations
Ch Bd: Rodger A Lawson
Pr: Judy Balint
CEO: Paul T Idzik
CFO: Michael A Pizzi
Ofcr: Thomas A Bevilacqua
Ofcr: Michael J Curcio
Ofcr: Michael E Foley
Ofcr: Ellen Koebler
Ofcr: Joshua S Levine
Ofcr: Charles Nalbone
Ex VP: Karl A Roessner
Sr VP: Hartley Caldwell
Sr VP: David S Herbert
VP: John Davidson

E V O
See EVO MERCHANT SERVICES LLC

E W A
See ELECTRONIC WARFARE ASSOCIATES INC

D-U-N-S 19-601-3718
▲ E W SCRIPPS CO
312 Walnut St Ste 2800, Cincinnati, OH 45202-4067
Tel (513) 977-3000 Founded/Ownrshp 1878
Sales 715.6MM EMP 3,800
Tkr Sym SSP Exch NYS
SIC 4841 2711 4833 7375 Cable & other pay television services; Newspapers; Television broadcasting stations; On-line data base information retrieval
Ch Bd: Richard A Boehne
*CFO: Timothy M Wesolowski
*Ofcr: Lisa A Knutson
*Sr VP: William Appleton
Sr VP: Chad Boydston
Sr VP: Brian G Lawlor
Sr VP: Jonathan Sichel
Sr VP: Adam Symson
VP: Greg Curling
VP: Robbin Holliday
*VP: Douglas F Lyons
VP: Bob Sullivan

D-U-N-S 01-033-2120
E W WYLIE CORP (ND)
(Suby of DASEKE INC) ★
1520 2nd Ave Nw, West Fargo, ND 58078-1161
Tel (701) 277-7540 Founded/Ownrshp 1938, 1999
Sales 90.2MM[E] EMP 215
SIC 4213 Contract haulers
CEO: Shane Waslaski
*Pr: Brian Gast
*Treas: Kevin Moug
*VP: Michelle Kommer

D-U-N-S 05-223-4014
E WALSH MANAGEMENT CORP
PREFERRED HOME HEALTH CARE OF
45 Main St, Eatontown, NJ 07724-3919
Tel (732) 443-8100 Founded/Ownrshp 2004
Sales 71.3MM[E] EMP 1,418
SIC 5999 8082 Medical apparatus & supplies; Home health care services
Pr: Joel Markel
COO: Jonathan Herman
*CFO: Todd Thiede

D-U-N-S 07-934-9773
E&H FAMILY GROUP INC
1401 Old Mansfield Rd, Wooster, OH 44691-9050
Tel (330) 264-4355 Founded/Ownrshp 2011
Sales 382.1MM[E] EMP 2,700
SIC 5411 Supermarkets
Pr: Dan Shanahan

D-U-N-S 55-695-5966
E-BRANDS RESTAURANTS LLC
SAMBA ROOM
6475 Christie Ave Ste 300, Emeryville, CA 94608-2263
Tel (407) 226-1433 Founded/Ownrshp 2002
Sales 19.3MM[E] EMP 1,000
SIC 5812 Eating places
COO: Charly Robinson
*Prin: Alexander Urrunaga
Mktg Dir: Lindsey Kurtz
Sls Mgr: Jackie Gale
Sls Mgr: Amy Jones

D-U-N-S 14-957-9901
E-INFOCHIPS INC
(Suby of E-INFOCHIPS LIMITED)
2025 Gateway Pl Ste 270, San Jose, CA 95110-1007
Tel (408) 496-1882 Founded/Ownrshp 1998
Sales 2.4MMM[E] EMP 149
SIC 7371 7373 Computer software development; Systems software development services; Computer systems analysis & design; Computer-aided system services; Computer-aided design (CAD) systems service
CEO: Pratul Shroff
COO: Raj Sirohi
*VP: Sribash Dey
Snr Sftwr: Vijayaragavan Krishnaswamy
Snr Sftwr: Girish Sharma
QA Dir: Jimit Doshi
IT Man: Heena Mankad
Software D: Smitha Maganahalli
Sftwr Eng: Deval Sheth
Mktg Dir: Nirav Shah

E-J COMMUNICATION SYSTEMS
See E-J ELECTRIC INSTALLATION CO INC

D-U-N-S 00-197-1324
E-J ELECTRIC INSTALLATION CO INC (NY)
E-J COMMUNICATION SYSTEMS
4641 Vernon Blvd, Long Island City, NY 11101-5308
Tel (718) 786-9400 Founded/Ownrshp 1912, 1966
Sales 238.8MM[E] EMP 800
SIC 1731 Electrical work; Communications specialization; Safety & security specialization
CEO: Anthony E Mann
*Ch: J Robert Mann Jr
*Treas: Leslie Blacksburg
VP: Fred Kinn
VP: Alan Norden
Exec: Alan Doubert
Genl Mgr: Beatrice Constantine
Opers Mgr: Matthew Duffy
Snr PM: Anthony Badalamenti
Snr PM: Angelo Economou
Snr PM: Patricia Mohiuddin

D-U-N-S 08-247-5364 IMP
E-LO SPORTSWEAR LLC
SHARAGANO STUDIO
500 Fashion Ave, New York, NY 10018-4502
Tel (862) 902-5225 Founded/Ownrshp 1999
Sales 138.0MM EMP 160
Accts Cohn Reznick Llp Roseland Ne
SIC 5137 5621 Sportswear, women's & children's; Women's clothing stores
Pr: Eli Lomita
CFO: Sam Kaplan
VP: David Lomita
Off Mgr: Olga Alulma
Off Mgr: Virginia Grayson

D-U-N-S 82-541-6423
■ E-LOAN INC
(Suby of POPULAR FINANCE INC) ★
6230 Stoneridge Mall Rd, Pleasanton, CA 94588-3260
Tel (925) 847-6200 Founded/Ownrshp 2005
Sales NA EMP 1,000
SIC 6163 6162 Mortgage brokers arranging for loans, using money of others; Mortgage bankers & correspondents
Pr: Mark E Lefanowicz
Sr VP: Cameron King
VP: David Drow
VP: Geoff Halverson
CTO: Etienne Handman
Sls&Mrk Ex: Eduardo Pretell
Mktg Mgr: Matt Nesbitt
Mktg Mgr: Salil Shah

D-U-N-S 06-785-1683 IMP/EXP
E-ONE INC
E-ONE PARTS CENTRAL
(Suby of ASV) ★
1601 Sw 37th Ave, Ocala, FL 34474-2829
Tel (352) 237-1122 Founded/Ownrshp 1967, 2008
Sales 188.8MM EMP 704[E]
SIC 3711 Fire department vehicles (motor vehicles), assembly of
CEO: Tim Sullivan
Pr: Dan Peters
Pr: Kent Tyler
COO: James Meyer
CFO: Chris Eppel
Chf Cred: Marcus Berto
VP: Dino Cusumano
VP: Oussama Itani
VP: Dirk Steyn
Area Mgr: David Perkins
Admn Mgr: George Beckwith
Board of Directors: Paul Barnatter, John Becker

E-ONE PARTS CENTRAL
See E-ONE INC

D-U-N-S 96-735-3645
E-T-T LLC
3440 W Russell Rd, Las Vegas, NV 89118-2495
Tel (877) 736-5388 Founded/Ownrshp 2010
Sales 18.4MM[E] EMP 5,000
SIC 7993 Slot machines

D-U-N-S 08-331-4161 EXP
E-Z MART STORES INC (TX)
602 Falvey Ave, Texarkana, TX 75501-6677
Tel (903) 832-6502 Founded/Ownrshp 1970
Sales 827.8MM EMP 2,100
Accts Bkd Llp Port Smith Arkansas
SIC 5541 5411 Gasoline service stations; Grocery stores
CEO: Sonja Hubbard
*Pr: Bob Hubbard
CFO: Stacy Y Flod
*CFO: Stacy Yates
CTO: Bubba Kirkland

E-ZBENEFITS
See KEY BENEFIT ADMINISTRATORS INC

D-U-N-S 80-778-0924
E2 ACQUISITION CORP
MARYLAND STEEL SPARROWS POINT
1430 Sparrows Point Blvd, Baltimore, MD 21219-1039
Tel (410) 388-3000 Founded/Ownrshp 2007
Sales 180.2MM[E] EMP 2,500
SIC 3325 Steel foundries
CEO: Craig Bouchard
*COO: David Luptak
Ex VP: David Pryzbylski

E3 CAROLINA SALES & SERVICE
See E3 DIAGNOSTICS INC

D-U-N-S 02-569-1171
E3 DIAGNOSTICS INC
E3 CAROLINA SALES & SERVICE
(Suby of WILLIAM DEMANT HOLDING A/S)
3333 N Kennicott Ave, Arlington Heights, IL 60004-1429
Tel (847) 459-1770 Founded/Ownrshp 1990
Sales 440.4MM[E] EMP 53
SIC 5999

E3 MED-ACOUSTICS
See MED-ACOUSTICS INC

D-U-N-S 17-530-4679
E4E INC
502 Washington Ave # 200, Towson, MD 21204-4530
Tel (443) 275-1632 Founded/Ownrshp 2000
Sales 48.6MM[E] EMP 3,000
SIC 7389 Telephone services
Pr: Bhaskar Menon
Pr: Deborah Kirkham
Pr: Geoff Smyth
Pr: Sivakumar Thiyagarajan
COO: Madhav Halbe
COO: Deepa Haridas
CFO: Steve Moseley
Bd of Dir: Bill Melton
Sr VP: Sam Mohamad
Netwrk Eng: John Hardman
Board of Directors: Bill Melton

EA
See EVERGREEN INTERNATIONAL AVIATION INC

EA ELECTRIC
See JMEG LP

EA SPORTS
See ELECTRONIC ARTS REDWOOD INC

D-U-N-S 14-864-9288 IMP
▲ EACO CORP
1500 N Lakeview Ave, Anaheim, CA 92807-1819
Tel (714) 876-2490 Founded/Ownrshp 1974
Sales 148.5MM EMP 426[E]
Tkr Sym EACO Exch OTO
SIC 5065 Electronic parts & equipment
Ch Bd: Glen F Ceiley
Dir IT: Brian Stover
S&M/VP: Zachary Ceiley
S&M/VP: Robert Rist

EADS COMPANY, THE
See EADS DISTRIBUTION LLC

D-U-N-S 00-389-7048 IMP
EADS DISTRIBUTION LLC
EADS COMPANY, THE
13843 N Promenade Blvd, Stafford, TX 77477-4047
Tel (281) 243-2900 Founded/Ownrshp 1953, 2012
Sales 121.0MM[E] EMP 220
SIC 5085 Industrial supplies; Filters, industrial; Valves & fittings
Pr: Steve Albert
*CFO: Dejan Gagic
*VP: Tim Smith
Sales Asso: Jerae Brown

D-U-N-S 09-486-6142
EAG INC
2710 Walsh Ave, Santa Clara, CA 95051-0963
Tel (408) 454-4600 Founded/Ownrshp 2007
Sales 294.9MM[E] EMP 1,157[E]
SIC 8734 Product testing laboratories
CEO: Siddhartha Kadia
Pr: Lance Jones
CFO: Christeen Russel
*Ex VP: Patricia M Lindley
Genl Mgr: Randall S Francisco
*Genl Mgr: Aram Sarkissian
Board of Directors: John Newman

EAGLE
See CEVA LOGISTICS LLC

D-U-N-S 00-879-1217
▲ EAGLE BANCORP INC
7830 Old Georgtwn Rd Fl 3, Bethesda, MD 20814-2432
Tel (301) 986-1800 Founded/Ownrshp 1997
Sales NA EMP 434
Tkr Sym EGBN Exch NAS
SIC 6022 State commercial banks
Ch Bd: Ronald D Paul
CFO: James H Langmead
*V Ch Bd: Robert P Pincus
Ofcr: Lucy Lu
Ofcr: Bill Sherrill
Ex VP: Laurence E Bensignor
Ex VP: Antonio F Marquez
Ex VP: Lindsey Rheaume
Ex VP: Susan G Riel
VP: Michael Benedict
VP: Deborah Cabala-Moshides
VP: Lawrence Dunford
VP: Joan Grant
VP: Archisha Mehan
Board of Directors: Leslie M Alperstein, Dudley C Dworken, Harvey M Goodman, Norman R Pozez, Donald R Rogers, Leland M Weinstein

EAGLE BANK
See EAGLEBANK

D-U-N-S 17-343-3624 IMP
EAGLE BEND MFG INC
MAGNA COSMA BDY CHASSIS GROUP
(Suby of MAGNA INTERNATIONAL INC)
1000 Jd Yrnell Indus Pkwy, Clinton, TN 37716-4036
Tel (865) 457-3800 Founded/Ownrshp 1986
Sales 195.9MM[E] EMP 600
SIC 3465 3714 Automotive stampings; Motor vehicle parts & accessories
Dir IT: Marty Rowat
IT Man: Liuba Lupasco
Netwrk Mgr: Jody Taylor

EAGLE BRANDS SALES
See EAGLE BRANDS WEDCO LIMITED PARTNERSHIP

D-U-N-S 80-779-7167 IMP
EAGLE BRANDS WEDCO LIMITED PARTNERSHIP
EAGLE BRANDS SALES
(Suby of ANHEUSER-BUSCH COMPANIES LLC) ★
3201 Nw 72nd Ave, Miami, FL 33122-1337
Tel (305) 599-2337 Founded/Ownrshp 2007
Sales 87.0MM[E] EMP 246
SIC 5182 Liquor
Genl Mgr: George Halper
MIS Mgr: Herberto Montenegro
Sales Exec: George Hoyos

D-U-N-S 36-069-4686
▲ EAGLE BULK SHIPPING INC
300 Frst Stamford Pl Fl 5, Stamford, CT 06902
Tel (203) 276-8100 Founded/Ownrshp 2005
Sales 103.8MM EMP 900[E]
Tkr Sym EGLE Exch NGS
SIC 4412 Deep sea foreign transportation of freight
CEO: Gary Vogel
*Ch Bd: Paul M Leand Jr
CFO: Frank De Costanzo
Board of Directors: Justin A Knowles, Casey Shanley, Bart Veldhuizen, Gary Weston

D-U-N-S 82-908-1822
EAGLE CANYON CAPITAL LLC
MY GOODS MARKET
3130 Crow Canyon Pl # 240, San Ramon, CA 94583-1346
Tel (925) 884-0800 Founded/Ownrshp 2007
Sales 2.3MMM EMP 2,800[E]
SIC 5411 5499 2092 Convenience stores; Beverage stores; Coffee; Crab meat, fresh: packaged in non-sealed containers
Mktg Dir: Charlene Kovacsik

D-U-N-S 96-642-7155
EAGLE CARE
6900 Gray Rd, Indianapolis, IN 46237-3209
Tel (317) 788-2500 Founded/Ownrshp 1996
Sales 42.4MM[E] EMP 2,500
SIC 6512 Nonresidential building operators
Pr: James Burkhart
*VP: Daniel S Benson
*VP: Blake A Jackson

*VP: Roger E Werner
IT Man: David Justice
IT Man: Jeremy Lane
IT Man: John H Suterlin
IT Man: John Sutherlin
Mktg Mgr: Sherri Davies

D-U-N-S 02-669-9085
EAGLE CONSTRUCTION & ENVIRONMENTAL SERVICES LLC
(Suby of SWS ENVIRONMENTAL SERVICES) ★
600 Grand Panama Blvd, Panama City Beach, FL 32407-3459
Tel (254) 442-1553 Founded/Ownrshp 2008
Sales 435.0MM EMP 500
SIC 8744
*CEO: Jim Weber Jr
*CFO: Robert Coston

D-U-N-S 02-453-4703 IMP/EXP
EAGLE CORP
1020 Harris St, Charlottesville, VA 22903-5315
Tel (434) 971-2686 Founded/Ownrshp 1979
Sales 210.1MM^E EMP 1,115^E
SIC 3272 3271 3273

D-U-N-S 95-975-3278
EAGLE EXPRESS LINES INC
925 175th St, Homewood, IL 60430-2048
Tel (708) 333-8401 Founded/Ownrshp 1996
Sales 100.5MM^E EMP 525
SIC 4213 4215 4212 Contract haulers; Courier services, except by air; Local trucking, without storage
Pr: Wayne Hoovestol
*VP: Tim Pals
Div Mgr: Glen Gearhart
IT Man: Adam Clark
Trfc Dir: David Prater
Opers Mgr: Harvey Verhaegen

EAGLE EYE GRAPE GUYS
See EAGLE EYE PRODUCE INC

D-U-N-S 11-207-7649 IMP/EXP
EAGLE EYE PRODUCE INC
EAGLE EYE GRAPE GUYS
4050 E Lincoln Rd, Idaho Falls, ID 83401-1826
Tel (208) 522-2343 Founded/Ownrshp 1996
Sales 97.6MM^E EMP 80
SIC 5148 Vegetables
Pr: Newman Giles
*Sec: Kathy Giles
Sr VP: Oscar Melara
VP: Justin Clement
Genl Mgr: Joey Anticevich
Telecom Ex: Garn Herrick
IT Man: Joe Davis
IT Man: Laurie Steele
Sales Exec: Jared Neville
Mktg Mgr: Lance Poole
Sls Mgr: Shawn Bittle

D-U-N-S 08-022-7357
EAGLE FAMILY FOODS GROUP LLC
4020 Kinross Lakes Pkwy, Richfield, OH 44286-9084
Tel (330) 382-3725 Founded/Ownrshp 2015
Sales 200.0MM EMP 235
SIC 2023 Condensed milk
CEO: Paul Smucker Wagstaff
*COO: Larry Herman

EAGLE FOODSERVICE
See METAL MASTERS FOODSERVICE EQUIPMENT CO INC

EAGLE GOLF
See EVERGREEN ALLIANCE GOLF LIMITED LP

D-U-N-S 07-837-2461 IMP
EAGLE GROUP INC
100 Industrial Blvd, Clayton, DE 19938-8903
Tel (302) 653-3000 Founded/Ownrshp 1985
Sales 113.5MM^E EMP 547^E
SIC 3589 8099 Commercial cooking & foodwarming equipment; Blood related health services
Pr: Larry McAllister
VP: Glenn Dorris

D-U-N-S 92-688-1327
■ **EAGLE GROUP INTERNATIONAL LLC**
(Suby of LEIDOS HOLDINGS INC) ★
10530 Rosehaven St # 500, Fairfax, VA 22030-2840
Tel (703) 272-6161 Founded/Ownrshp 2016
Sales 31.7MM^E EMP 1,400
SIC 8742 Hospital & health services consultant
VP: Mark Norris

D-U-N-S 96-322-0012
EAGLE GROUP SYSTEMS INC
230 Grant Rd, East Wenatchee, WA 98802-5383
Tel (509) 665-0319 Founded/Ownrshp 1996
Sales 101.4MM^E EMP 650^E
SIC 4214 4119 4522 7373 7374 8741 Local trucking with storage; Furniture moving & storage, local; Household goods moving & storage, local; Ambulance service; Ambulance services, air; Computer integrated systems design; Data processing & preparation; Administrative management
Ch Bd: Michael Walker
*Pr: Greg Olshavsky
*CEO: Gerry Aits
*CFO: Cindy Rudolph
Ex VP: Jeff Lang

D-U-N-S 79-649-9671
EAGLE HEALTHCARE INC
PINEHURST PARK TERRACE
12015 115th Ave Ne, Kirkland, WA 98034-6940
Tel (425) 285-3880 Founded/Ownrshp 1991
Sales 30.1MM^E EMP 1,500
SIC 8051

D-U-N-S 02-722-2751 IMP
■ **EAGLE INDUSTRIES UNLIMITED INC**
(Suby of VISTA OUTDOOR INC) ★
2645 Intl Pkwy Ste 102, Virginia Beach, VA 23454
Tel (888) 343-7547 Founded/Ownrshp 1982
Sales 113.6MM^E EMP 400
SIC 3842 Bulletproof vests

CEO: Mark W Deyoung
*CFO: Stephen M Nolan
Sfty Mgr: Phillip Couto

D-U-N-S 86-875-6438
■ **EAGLE INVESTMENT SYSTEMS LLC**
(Suby of BNY MELLON) ★
45 William St Ste 200, Wellesley, MA 02481-4004
Tel (781) 943-2200 Founded/Ownrshp 2007
Sales 91.7MM^E EMP 400
SIC 6722 6282 8721 7372 Management investment, open-end; Investment advisory service; Accounting services, except auditing; Business oriented computer software
Ch Bd: Mal Cullen
*Ch Bd: John J Lehner
Sr VP: Robert Erman
Sr VP: Robert Leaper
VP: Greg Gruber
VP: Stephen Piraino
*CTO: Marc Firenze
QA Dir: Lana Shumakina

EAGLE MANUFACTURING GROUP
See U S HOLDINGS INC

D-U-N-S 07-935-5194 IMP
▲ **EAGLE MATERIALS INC**
3811 Turtle Creek Blvd # 1100, Dallas, TX 75219-4487
Tel (214) 432-2000 Founded/Ownrshp 1963
Sales 1.1MMM EMP 2,050^E
Accts Ernst & Young Llp Dallas Tex
Tkr Sym EXP Exch NYS
SIC 3241 3275 3273 Cement, hydraulic; Wallboard, gypsum; Cement, keene's; Plaster & plasterboard, gypsum; Ready-mixed concrete
Pr: David B Powers
*Ch Bd: Laurence E Hirsch
COO: Michael Haack
CFO: D Craig Kesler
*V Ch Bd: Richard R Stewart
Ex VP: Gerald J Essl
Ex VP: James H Graass
Ex VP: Robert S Stewart
Sr VP: Rahul Desai
Sr VP: William R Devlin
Board of Directors: F William Barnett, Richard Beckwitt, Ed H Bowman Jr, George Damiris, Martin M Ellen, Michael R Nicolais

D-U-N-S 08-107-6648
EAGLE MOUNTAIN-SAGINAW INDEPENDENT SCHOOL DISTRICT
1200 Old Decatur Rd, Fort Worth, TX 76179-4300
Tel (817) 232-0123 Founded/Ownrshp 1958
Sales 191.8MM EMP 139
Accts Hankins Eastup Deaton Tonn
SIC 8211 Public elementary school; Public junior high school; Public senior high school
V Ch: Dick Elkins
Dir Bus: Shane Valdez
MIS Dir: Belinda Newman
Psych: Carol Rivers
HC Dir: Cheryl Phalen

EAGLE OTTAWA LEATHER
See EAGLE OTTAWA LLC

D-U-N-S 07-131-9128 IMP/EXP
■ **EAGLE OTTAWA LLC**
EAGLE OTTAWA LEATHER
(Suby of LEAR CORP) ★
21557 Telegraph Rd, Southfield, MI 48033-4248
Tel (248) 364-7400 Founded/Ownrshp 2003, 2015
Sales 1.0MMM^E EMP 4,250
SIC 3111 2399 2396 Leather tanning & finishing; Automotive covers, except seat & tire covers; Automotive & apparel trimmings
Pr: Jerry Sumpter
*Ch Bd: J Douglas Gray
*Pr: Cary Bean
*Pr: Udo Schnell
*Pr: Craig Tonti
*CFO: Bob F Carlo
VP: Eric Brooke
*VP: Steven Hartung
VP: Randall Johnson
VP: Steve Korc
Prgrm Mgr: Mark Best

D-U-N-S 08-731-1411
EAGLE PASS INDEPENDENT SCHOOL DISTRICT
1420 Eidson Rd, Eagle Pass, TX 78852-5410
Tel (830) 773-5181 Founded/Ownrshp 1900
Sales 150.0MM EMP 2,481
Accts Leal & Cater Pc San Antoni
SIC 8211 Public senior high school; Public vocational/technical school; Public junior high school; Public elementary school
VP: Patrick Birch
*Ex Dir: Jesus A Costilla
IT Man: Rudy Benavidez
VP Mktg: Michelle Graham
VP Mktg: Horacio Sanchez
Pr Dir: Melissa Gratkowski
Psych: Toyoko Rivera

D-U-N-S 07-885-3800
EAGLE PIPE LLC
9525 Katy Fwy Ste 306, Houston, TX 77024-1468
Tel (713) 464-7473 Founded/Ownrshp 2013
Sales 200.0MM^E EMP 9
SIC 3533 5082 Oil & gas drilling rigs & equipment; Oil field equipment
Pr: Brandon Dewan
COO: Jared Light
VP: Scott Lawler
Dir IT: Daniel Johnson

D-U-N-S 78-726-6311 IMP
EAGLE PRODUCE LLC
MARTORI FARMS
7332 E Butherus Dr # 200, Scottsdale, AZ 85260-2426
Tel (480) 998-1444 Founded/Ownrshp 1992
Sales 106.0MM^E EMP 400
SIC 0161 Vegetables & melons

D-U-N-S 15-721-0977 IMP
EAGLE ROCK DISTRIBUTING CO LLC
6205 Best Friend Rd, Norcross, GA 30071-2910
Tel (770) 498-5500 Founded/Ownrshp 2000
Sales 209.4MM^E EMP 300
SIC 5181 5182 Beer & other fermented malt liquors; Wine
Pr: Steve Economos
*CEO: John Economos
COO: Alton Danielson
COO: Charles Martin
CIO: Ron Ward

D-U-N-S 78-781-1715
■ **EAGLE ROCK ENERGY PARTNERS LP**
(Suby of VANGUARD NATURAL RESOURCES LLC) ★
5847 San Felipe St # 3000, Houston, TX 77057-3399
Tel (281) 408-1200 Founded/Ownrshp 2015
Sales 298.2MM EMP 159^E
SIC 1311 1321 Natural gas production; Liquefied petroleum gases (natural) production
Pr: Scott W Smith
CFO: Richard A Robert
Ex VP: Britt Pence
Sr VP: Robert D Hallett

D-U-N-S 07-873-7896
■ **EAGLE SPINCO INC**
SPLITCO
(Suby of AXIALL CORP) ★
115 Perimeter Center Pl, Atlanta, GA 30346-1249
Tel (770) 395-4500 Founded/Ownrshp 2013
Sales 80.5MM^E EMP 2,000
SIC 2812 5169 Alkalies & chlorine; Alkalines & chlorine
CFO: Gregory Thompson
*VP: Joseph Breunig

D-U-N-S 05-486-7848
EAGLE TOPCO LP
18200 Von Karman Ave, Irvine, CA 92612-1023
Tel (949) 585-4329 Founded/Ownrshp 2011
Sales 185.6MM^E EMP 4,000^E
SIC 7372

D-U-N-S 02-465-9906
EAGLE TRANSPORT CORP (NC)
300 S Wesleyan Blvd # 200, Rocky Mount, NC 27804-4215
Tel (252) 937-2464 Founded/Ownrshp 1964
Sales 134.6MM^E EMP 600
SIC 4213 Liquid petroleum transport, non-local; Contract haulers
Ch: Donald Stallings
*Pr: Bill George
Ofcr: Pat Holland
*Ex VP: Herb Evans
*VP: Ed Chahoc
*VP: Lance Collette
*VP: Joe Duncan
*VP: Edwin Teeny Jones
VP: Teeny Jones
VP: Richard Overman
Ex Dir: Hugh Shearin

D-U-N-S 07-845-4395
EAGLE US SUB INC
(Suby of GRUPO ELEKTRA, S.A.B. DE C.V.)
135 N Church St, Spartanburg, SC 29306-5138
Tel (864) 515-5600 Founded/Ownrshp 2012
Sales NA EMP 6,443^E
SIC 6141 6153 Personal credit institutions; Consumer finance companies; Short-term business credit

D-U-N-S 10-991-6432 IMP
EAGLE WINDOW & DOOR INC
ANDERSEN E SERIES
(Suby of ANDERSEN CORP) ★
2045 Kerper Blvd, Dubuque, IA 52001-3669
Tel (563) 556-2270 Founded/Ownrshp 2005
Sales 114.9MM^E EMP 700^E
SIC 2431 Millwork
CEO: Jay Laund
*Pr: David Beeken
CFO: Bob Penvose
*VP: Ron Vander Weerd
*Genl Mgr: Sandy Peters
Off Mgr: Ellen Neese
QA Dir: Jason Kretz
Dir IT: Chris Paulsen
Dir IT: Dan Sheehan
VP Sls: Kent Johnson
Snr Mgr: Chad Roberts

D-U-N-S 00-105-3206
EAGLE-TRIBUNE PUBLISHING CO
ANDOVER TOWNSMAN
(Suby of JOHNSTOWN TRIBUNE DEMOCRAT) ★
100 Turnpike St, North Andover, MA 01845-5033
Tel (978) 946-2000 Founded/Ownrshp 1940
Sales 120.3MM^E EMP 522
SIC 2711 Newspapers, publishing & printing
*Pr: Donna J Barrett
VP: Vincent Cottone
VP: John Gregory
Assoc Dir: Shiela Smith
VP Opers: Dennis Turmel
Mktg Dir: Steve Baskin
Sls Mgr: Peter Reiser

D-U-N-S 02-275-7962
■ **EAGLEBANK**
EAGLE BANK
(Suby of EAGLE BANCORP INC) ★
7830 Old Georgtwn Rd Fl 3, Bethesda, MD 20814-2432
Tel (301) 986-1800 Founded/Ownrshp 1998
Sales NA EMP 410
SIC 6022 State commercial banks
Pr: Ronald D Paul
*Pr: Michael T Flynn
Pr: Thomas D Murphy
*COO: Christopher J Ewing
*COO: Susan G Riel
Ofcr: Christine Andrukitis
Ofcr: Bryan Leigh
Ofcr: Catherine McNamee
*Ofcr: Steven A Reeder
*Ofcr: Lindsey S Rheaume
Ofcr: Jenny A Shtipelman
Ofcr: Jackie Starr
Ex VP: Mark S Merrill
*Ex VP: Thomas Murphy
*Sr VP: Richard Bernardi
*Sr VP: Martha Foulon-Tonat
Sr VP: Robert F Hickey
*Sr VP: William Tinely
Sr VP: Douglas L Vigen
Sr VP: John Vogt
VP: Renee Aldrich
Board of Directors: Thomas E Burdette, Joann Kay Dimeglio, Susan Lacz, Norman R Pozez, Kathy A Raffa, Thomas W Roberson, David P Summers, Steven M Wiltse

D-U-N-S 07-869-6339
EAGLEBURGMANN KE INC
EXPANSION JOINT SOLUTIONS
(Suby of EAGLEBURGMANN GERMANY GMBH & CO. KG)
10038 Marathon Pkwy, Lakeside, CA 92040-2771
Tel (619) 562-6083 Founded/Ownrshp 2000
Sales 412.5MM^E EMP 6,000
SIC 3441 Expansion joints (structural shapes), iron or steel

D-U-N-S 78-810-4334 EXP
EAGLEPICHER TECHNOLOGIES LLC
(Suby of VECTRA CO) ★
C & Porter Sts, Joplin, MO 64802
Tel (417) 623-8000 Founded/Ownrshp 2006
Sales 288.5MM^E EMP 800
SIC 3691 3629 3599 2892 Storage batteries; Battery chargers, rectifying or nonrotating; Bellows, industrial: metal; Squibbs, electric
Pr: John Bennett
CFO: Neil Thomas
*Treas: Joe Herndon
*VP: Dave Lucero
*VP: Greg Miller
*VP: Ron Nowlin
Exec: Creed Jones
Prgrm Mgr: Jackie Kennedy
*Dir IT: David Ryan
Opers Mgr: Arturo Ibarra
QI Cn Mgr: Heather Mauk

D-U-N-S 62-202-8587 IMP
EAKAS CORP
(Suby of SAKAE RIKEN KOGYO CO.,LTD.)
6251 State Route 251, Peru, IL 61354-9711
Tel (815) 223-8811 Founded/Ownrshp 1989
Sales 94.0MM^E EMP 275
SIC 3089 Injection molding of plastics
Pr: Tomohisa Mori
Genl Mgr: Tom Shores
Plnt Mgr: Cary Miller
Plnt Mgr: Jeff Wagner
QI Cn Mgr: John Lamps
Board of Directors: Tomohisa Mori

D-U-N-S 83-157-2958
EAN HOLDINGS LLC
ENTERPRISE RENT-A-CAR
(Suby of ENTERPRISE RENT-A-CAR) ★
600 Corporate Park Dr, Saint Louis, MO 63105-4204
Tel (314) 512-5000 Founded/Ownrshp 2008
Sales 189.7MM^E EMP 2,184^E
SIC 7514 7515 Rent-a-car service; Passenger car leasing
Pr: Pamela M Nicholson
Dir IT: Dave Hoover

EANES ADMINISTRATIVE OFFICE
See EANES INDEPENDENT SCHOOL DISTRICT

D-U-N-S 08-027-1448
EANES INDEPENDENT SCHOOL DISTRICT
EANES ADMINISTRATIVE OFFICE
601 Camp Craft Rd, West Lake Hills, TX 78746-6511
Tel (512) 732-9000 Founded/Ownrshp 1890
Sales 140.1MM EMP 1,100
Accts Maxwell Locke & Ritter Llp Au
SIC 8211 Public elementary & secondary schools
Pr: Dr Colleen Jones
*CEO: David Edgar
VP: Jennifer Salas
Mng Dir: David Poole
Pr Dir: Claudia McWhorter
Teacher Pr: Lester Wolff
Board of Directors: Cynthia Hayden

D-U-N-S 05-753-8365
EARHART PETROLEUM INC
1494 Lytle Rd, Troy, OH 45373-8925
Tel (937) 335-2928 Founded/Ownrshp 1998
Sales 89.2MM^E EMP 85
SIC 5172 5541 5983 Fuel oil; Lubricating oils & greases; Gasoline; Filling stations, gasoline; Fuel oil dealers
Pr: Jeffrey W Earhart
*Treas: Michael W Earhart
Exec: Karla Jones
Dir Bus: Mark Brewer
VP Sls: Dan Mader

D-U-N-S 04-705-9076 EXP
EARL W COLVARD INC
BOULEVARD TIRE CENTER
816 S Woodland Blvd, Deland, FL 32720-6836
Tel (386) 734-6447 Founded/Ownrshp 1982
Sales 134.0MM^E EMP 349
SIC 5531 7534 Automotive tires; Tire retreading & repair shops
Pr: Earl W Colvard
*Sec: Patricia B Colvard
Trfc Dir: Ismael Marcelo
Sfty Mgr: Mike Gray

D-U-N-S 00-825-3718 IMP/EXP
■ **EARLE M JORGENSEN CO**
JORGENSEN STEEL AND ALUMINUM
(Suby of RELIANCE STEEL & ALUMINUM CO) ★
10650 Alameda St, Lynwood, CA 90262-1754
Tel (323) 567-1122 Founded/Ownrshp 1921, 2006

Sales 470.4MM^E *EMP* 1,586
SIC 5051

D-U-N-S 04-112-9669
EARLHAM COLLEGE
801 National Rd W, Richmond, IN 47374-4095
Tel (765) 983-1200 *Founded/Ownrshp* 1847
Sales 88.3MM *EMP* 365^E
Accts Capin Crouse Llp Greenwood I
SIC 8221 College, except junior
Pr: J David Dawson
Pr: Dana North
VP: Nelson Bingham
**VP:* Sena Klandey
**VP:* Greg Mahler
**VP:* Jay Marshall
**VP:* Jim McKey
VP: Richard Smith
**VP:* Avis Stewart
VP: Jonathan Stroud
Assoc Dir: Polly Albright

D-U-N-S 05-422-0475
EARLY BLOOM LEARNING
17805 County Road 6, Minneapolis, MN 55447-2904
Tel (763) 449-0600 *Founded/Ownrshp* 1998
Sales 693.7M^E *EMP* 1,523
Accts Roxbury Incorporated Minneapo
SIC 8351 Child day care services
CEO: Melissa Musliner
Ex Dir: Judy Reckner

D-U-N-S 12-296-2165
EARLY LEARNING COALITION OF BROWARD COUNTY INC
6301 Nw 5th Way Ste 3400, Fort Lauderdale, FL 33309-6183
Tel (954) 377-2188 *Founded/Ownrshp* 2005
Sales 88.5MM *EMP* 12
Accts Bca Watson Rice Llp Miami Fl
SIC 8299 Educational services
**CFO:* Andrea Braynon
**Ofcr:* K LeeTirpak
Ex Dir: Debbie Bainton
**Ex Dir:* Charles Hood
Genl Mgr: Renee Jaffe

D-U-N-S 60-362-8285
EARLY LEARNING COALITION OF MIAMI-DADE MONROE INC
2555 Ponce De Leon Blvd # 5, Coral Gables, FL 33134-6010
Tel (305) 646-7220 *Founded/Ownrshp* 2005
Sales 165.9MM *EMP* 155
Accts Morrison Brown Argiz And Farra
SIC 8351 Child day care services
Pr: Evelio Torres
**CEO:* Evelio C Torres
Ofcr: Tamara Garcia
**Ofcr:* Angelo Parrino
Ofcr: Stephanie Smith
Sr VP: Pamela Hollingsworth
Sr VP: Yusneli Martinez
Mng Dir: Mary Williams
CIO: Fred Hicks

D-U-N-S 60-752-7475
EARLY LEARNING COALITION OF PALM BEACH COUNTY INC
2300 High Ridge Rd # 115, Boynton Beach, FL 33426-8795
Tel (561) 214-8000 *Founded/Ownrshp* 2005
Sales 99.1MM *EMP* 2
Accts Caler Donten Levine Et Al Pa
SIC 8351 Child day care services
Ch: Adam Hasner
**CEO:* Dr Barbara Weinstein
**CEO:* Lisa Williams-Taylor
**COO:* Michael J Napoleone
**COO:* Christie L Young
**Treas:* Howard Burnston

D-U-N-S 03-585-1419
EARNHARDT FORD SALES CO INC
EARNHARDT'S FORD
7300 W Orchid Ln, Tempe, AZ 85284
Tel (480) 893-0000 *Founded/Ownrshp* 1951
Sales 97.4MM *EMP* 520
SIC 5511 5531 7538 5561 Automobiles, new & used; Pickups, new & used; Vans, new & used; Automotive parts; General automotive repair shops; Motor homes
Ch Bd: Hal J Earnhardt Jr
**Pr:* Hal J Earnhardt III
**Sec:* Jim Babe Earnhardt
Genl Mgr: Jerry Brown
Dir IT: Nature Winters
IT Man: Don Speen
Sales Exec: Larry Storjohann

EARNHARDT'S FORD
See EARNHARDT FORD SALES CO INC

EARP DISTRIBUTION
See EARP MEAT CO

D-U-N-S 02-983-5477
EARP MEAT CO
EARP DISTRIBUTION
2730 S 98th St, Edwardsville, KS 66111-3507
Tel (913) 287-3311 *Founded/Ownrshp* 1966
Sales 208.3MM^E *EMP* 250
SIC 5142 5141 5113 Packaged frozen goods; Groceries, general line; Industrial & personal service paper
Pr: Donald C Earp
COO: Thom Bear
CFO: Steven Henry
Manager: Shelly Watson

EARTH DIGITAL
See EARTHCOLOR INC

EARTH FARE
See DERROUGH AND TALLEY INC

D-U-N-S 04-949-2638
EARTH FARE INC
220 Continuum Dr, Fletcher, NC 28732-7444
Tel (828) 281-4800 *Founded/Ownrshp* 1984
Sales 85.9MM^E *EMP* 627^E
SIC 5499 Health & dietetic food stores
CEO: Frank Scorpiniti
**CEO:* Jack Murphy
CFO: Scott Little
Sr VP: Steven Jarvis
VP: Jeff Jones
Genl Mgr: Henry Kugler
Genl Mgr: Bill Sutara
Off Admin: Tara Escobar
IT Man: Eric Richbourg
Pr Mgr: Brooke Dickens
Art Dir: Tanya Johnson

EARTH FRIENDLY PRODUCTS
See VENUS LABORATORIES INC

D-U-N-S 19-714-0171 IMP/EXP
EARTH SUPPORT SERVICES INC
MICON
25 Allegheny Sq, Glassport, PA 15045-1649
Tel (412) 664-7788 *Founded/Ownrshp* 1988
Sales 183.3MM^E *EMP* 65
SIC 1241

D-U-N-S 05-162-2272
■ EARTH TECH (INFRASTRUCTURE) INC
(*Suby of* AECOM TECHNICAL SERVICES INC) ★
300 Oceangate Ste 700, Long Beach, CA 90802-4391
Tel (562) 951-2000 *Founded/Ownrshp* 1998
Sales 44.3MM^E *EMP* 1,500
SIC 8711 8712 Consulting engineer; Energy conservation engineering; Architectural engineering
Pr: Alan Krusi
Pr: Joe Burton
**VP:* Creighton K Early
VP: Jerry B Farrar
VP: Terry Krause
VP: Lou Tortora
Exec: Robert Cochran
CIO: Georgia Perky
IT Man: Becky Danbara
IT Man: Lynette Engelke
IT Man: Julie Hassle

D-U-N-S 80-650-9126
■ EARTH TECHNOLOGY CORP USA
(*Suby of* AECOM) ★
1999 Avenue Of Ste 2600, Los Angeles, CA 90067
Tel (213) 593-8000 *Founded/Ownrshp* 1998
Sales 880.8MM^E *EMP* 4,655
SIC 4953 8748 8742 8711 Refuse systems; Environmental consultant; Management consulting services; Engineering services
Ch Bd: Michael S Burke
Ex VP: Bill Webb
VP: Paul Bassi
VP: Brian Burgher
VP: Robert Johnston
VP: Erin Mahoney
VP: Keith Oldewurtel
VP: Dale Sands
VP: Ken Vinson
VP: Phil Watts
Snr Mgr: Maria Garcia

D-U-N-S 05-967-6181
EARTHBEND LLC
2300 E 54th St N Ste 3, Sioux Falls, SD 57104-8810
Tel (605) 789-5700 *Founded/Ownrshp* 2012
Sales 102.8MM^E *EMP* 57
SIC 5065 Mobile telephone equipment; Telephone & telegraphic equipment
CEO: Robert Beyer
VP: Ryan Donovan
CTO: Wade Hoffman
Sales Asso: Stephanie Cox
Sales Asso: Rebecca Wright

D-U-N-S 85-855-6517 IMP/EXP
■ EARTHBOUND FARM LLC
(*Suby of* EARTHBOUND HOLDINGS III LLC) ★
1721 San Juan Hwy, San Juan Bautista, CA 95045-9780
Tel (831) 623-7880 *Founded/Ownrshp* 1995
Sales 189.8MM^E *EMP* 1,025
SIC 0723 2037 2099 Vegetable packing services; Fruit crops market preparation services; Frozen fruits & vegetables; Food preparations
Pr: Kevin C Yost
Ex VP: Myra Goodman
Exec: Sarah Lacasse
Mtls Mgr: Elsa Arteaga
Opers Mgr: Sulema Armenta
Opers Mgr: Eric Arriaga
Mktg Dir: Nicole Glenn
Mktg Mgr: Laura Hubrich
Sls Mgr: Crystal Magdaleno
Sls Mgr: Katie McDermott
Sls Mgr: Adrian Paco

D-U-N-S 03-200-7209
EARTHBOUND HOLDING LLC
EARTHBOUND TRADING COMPANY
4051 Freport Pkwy Ste 400, Grapevine, TX 76051
Tel (972) 248-0228 *Founded/Ownrshp* 1994
Sales 275.1MM^E *EMP* 1,775^E
SIC 5632 Women's accessory & specialty stores
Rgnl Mgr: Clayton Young
Dist Mgr: Alisha Gresham
Dist Mgr: Rebecca Kemper
Dist Mgr: Leah King
Manager: Marcio Oliveira
Opers Mgr: Melanie Kendrick

D-U-N-S 07-846-8152
■ EARTHBOUND HOLDINGS I LLC
(*Suby of* EB SAV INC) ★
1721 San Juan Hwy, San Juan Bautista, CA 95045-9780
Tel (831) 623-2767 *Founded/Ownrshp* 2009, 2014
Sales 226.9MM^E *EMP* 1,025^E
SIC 0723 2099 Vegetable packing services; Fruit crops market preparation services; Food preparations

D-U-N-S 07-846-8186
■ EARTHBOUND HOLDINGS II LLC
(*Suby of* EARTHBOUND HOLDINGS I LLC) ★
1721 San Juan Hwy, San Juan Bautista, CA 95045-9780
Tel (831) 623-2767 *Founded/Ownrshp* 2009
Sales 226.9MM^E *EMP* 1,045^E
SIC 0723 2099 Vegetable packing services; Fruit crops market preparation services; Food preparations

D-U-N-S 07-846-8192
■ EARTHBOUND HOLDINGS III LLC
(*Suby of* EARTHBOUND HOLDINGS II LLC) ★
1721 San Juan Hwy, San Juan Bautista, CA 95045-9780
Tel (831) 623-7880 *Founded/Ownrshp* 2014
Sales 226.9MM^E *EMP* 1,042^E
SIC 0723 2099 6719 Vegetable packing services; Fruit crops market preparation services; Food preparations; Investment holding companies, except banks
Pr: Kevin C Yost

EARTHBOUND TRADING COMPANY
See EARTHBOUND HOLDING LLC

D-U-N-S 77-993-4970
■ EARTHCOLOR INC
EARTH DIGITAL
(*Suby of* ARES CAPITAL CORP) ★
249 Pomeroy Rd, Parsippany, NJ 07054-3727
Tel (973) 884-1300 *Founded/Ownrshp* 1999
Sales 97.4MM^E *EMP* 235^E
SIC 2752 2759 Commercial printing, lithographic; Business forms: printing; Laser printing
CEO: Robert Kashan
Pr: Lucille Ben-Ezra
**Pr:* Bruce Wexler
**CFO:* Dennis Ganzak
Ex VP: Frank Brusco
**Ex VP:* Cheryl Kahanec
Exec: Todd Martin
Netwrk Mgr: Darryl Sokolowski
VP Mfg: Dominick Maria
Prd Mgr: Chip Quayle
VP Sls: Tripp Johnson

D-U-N-S 00-732-2340
EARTHGRAINS BAKERY GROUP INC (DE)
3470 Rider Trl S, Earth City, MO 63045-1109
Tel (314) 291-5480 *Founded/Ownrshp* 2011
Sales NA *EMP* 21,000
SIC 2051

EARTHLINK BUSINESS
See ONE COMMUNICATIONS CORP

EARTHLINK BUSINESS
See CTC COMMUNICATIONS CORP

EARTHLINK BUSINESS
See DELTACOM LLC

D-U-N-S 08-110-8172
■ EARTHLINK BUSINESS LLC
(*Suby of* EARTHLINK LLC) ★
1170 Pchtree S Ne Ste 900, Atlanta, GA 30309
Tel (404) 815-0770 *Founded/Ownrshp* 2006
Sales 997.7MM^E *EMP* 2,000
SIC 4899 Data communication services
Pr: Joseph F Eazor
CFO: Bradley A Ferguson

D-U-N-S 07-929-1889
▲ EARTHLINK HOLDINGS CORP
1170 Peachtree St Ne # 900, Atlanta, GA 30309-3100
Tel (404) 815-0770 *Founded/Ownrshp* 1994
Sales 1.1MMM *EMP* 2,138^E
Tkr Sym ELNK *Exch* NGS
SIC 4813
Pr: Joseph F Eazor
Ch Bd: Julie A Shimer
CFO: Louis M Alterman
Chf Cred: Richard C Froehlich
Ex VP: Gerard Brossard
Ex VP: Samuel R Desimone Jr
Ex VP: John T Dobbins
Ex VP: Bradley A Ferguson
Sr VP: Valerie C Benjamin
Board of Directors: Susan D Bowick, Kathy S Lane, Garry K McGuire, R Gerard Salemme, Marc F Stoll, Walter L Turek

D-U-N-S 84-741-2368
EARTHLINK INC
1375 Peachtree St Ne A9, Atlanta, GA 30309-3117
Tel (404) 815-0770 *Founded/Ownrshp* 1994
Sales 136.6MM^E *EMP* 3,034^E
SIC 4813

D-U-N-S 07-929-2762
■ EARTHLINK LLC
(*Suby of* EARTHLINK HOLDINGS CORP) ★
1170 Peachtree St Ne # 900, Atlanta, GA 30309-3100
Tel (877) 355-1501 *Founded/Ownrshp* 2013
Sales 1.3MMM^E *EMP* 2,659^E
SIC 4813
Pr: Joseph F Eazor
CFO: Bradley A Ferguson
Ex VP: Samuel R Desimone Jr
Ex VP: Rick Froehlich
Ex VP: Stacie S Hagan
VP: William Billbrough
VP: Michael Flanagan
Off Admin: Becky Knowles
CTO: Brian F President
IT Man: Elizabeth Cunningham

EARTHWERKS
See SWIFF-TRAIN CO LLC

D-U-N-S 14-725-6424 IMP/EXP
EASCO HAND TOOLS INC
DANAHER TOOL GROUP
125 Powder Forest Dr, Simsbury, CT 06070
Tel (860) 843-7351 *Founded/Ownrshp* 1990
Sales NA *EMP* 1,400
SIC 3423

EAST 95TH STREET APARTMENTS
See 95TH IH ASSOCIATES LLC

D-U-N-S 06-645-9843 EXP
EAST ALABAMA HEALTH CARE AUTHORITY
EAST ALABAMA MEDICAL CENTER
2000 Pepperell Pkwy, Opelika, AL 36801-5452
Tel (334) 749-3411 *Founded/Ownrshp* 1952
Sales 288.9MM *EMP* 2,250
SIC 8062 General medical & surgical hospitals
Pr: Terry Andrus
Chf OB: George R Jones
Chf Rad: David C Montiel
Dir Recs: Kathryn Mc Millian
V Ch: Joel Pittard
Pr: Greg Nichols
Pr: Dennis Thrasher
Ofcr: Janice Baker
Assoc VP: Susan Johnson
Assoc VP: Roben Nutter
Ex VP: Chris Clark
**Ex VP:* Laura D Grill
**Ex VP:* Sam Price
**VP:* Michael Lisenby
VP: Ken Lott
VP: Carey Owen
VP: Carey Owens
VP: Darby Womelsdorf
Dir Rad: Melinda Johnson
Comm Man: Sharon Pouncey

EAST ALABAMA MEDICAL CENTER
See EAST ALABAMA HEALTH CARE AUTHORITY

D-U-N-S 07-098-0388
EAST ALLEN COUNTY SCHOOLS
1240 State Road 930 E, New Haven, IN 46774-1732
Tel (260) 446-0100 *Founded/Ownrshp* 1969
Sales 62.3MM^E *EMP* 1,100
SIC 8211 Public elementary & secondary schools
Ofcr: Darren Peterson
Schl Brd P: Chris Baker

D-U-N-S 03-961-7600
EAST AURORA SCHOOL DISTRICT 131
417 5th St, Aurora, IL 60505-4700
Tel (630) 299-8355 *Founded/Ownrshp* 1835
Sales 96.0MM^E *EMP* 1,175
SIC 8211 Public elementary & secondary schools; Public junior high school; Public senior high school
Pr: Raymond Hull
**VP:* Kirsten Strand
Teacher Pr: Steve Megazzini

D-U-N-S 13-665-7157
EAST BATON ROUGE MEDICAL CENTER LLC
OCHSNER MEDICAL CENTER - BATON
17000 Medical Center Dr, Baton Rouge, LA 70816-3246
Tel (225) 752-2470 *Founded/Ownrshp* 2001
Sales 213.0MM *EMP* 500^E
SIC 8062 General medical & surgical hospitals
Chf Path: Leo Pei
CEO: Mitch Wasden
COO: Eric Mc Millen
Dir Rad: Dana Guilory
Chf Nrs Of: Dawn Pevey
Dir QC: Erin Ray
Dir IT: Charlotte Crummey
Web Dev: Jeffrey Pisto
Opers Mgr: Amy Chauffe
Obsttrcn: Margaret S Miklic
Obsttrcn: Melanie Weaver

D-U-N-S 07-945-7941
EAST BATON ROUGE PARISH SCHOOL DISTRICT
1050 S Foster Dr, Baton Rouge, LA 70806-7221
Tel (225) 922-5400 *Founded/Ownrshp* 1877
Sales 372.9MM^E *EMP* 6,800
SIC 8211 Public elementary & secondary schools
Ofcr: Peggy Lede
Dir Sec: Dewayne Wells
Instr Medi: Susan Gauthier

EAST BAY MUN UTILITY DIST WTR
See EAST BAY MUNICIPAL UTILITY DISTRICT WASTEWATER SYSTEM

D-U-N-S 62-015-9012
EAST BAY MUNICIPAL UTILITY DISTRICT WASTEWATER SYSTEM
EAST BAY MUN UTILITY DIST WTR
(*Suby of* EBMUD) ★
375 111th St, Oakland, CA 94607
Tel (866) 403-2683 *Founded/Ownrshp* 1944
Sales 461.7MM *EMP* 241
Accts Maze & Associates Pleasant Hi
SIC 4952 4953 Sewerage systems;
Genl Mgr: Alexander Coate

D-U-N-S 05-190-4423
EAST BAY MUNICIPAL UTILITY DISTRICT WATER SYSTEM
EBMUD
375 11th St, Oakland, CA 94607-4246
Tel (866) 403-2683 *Founded/Ownrshp* 1923
Sales 525.4MM *EMP* 1,511
Accts Maze & Associates Walnut Cree
SIC 4941 Water supply
Genl Mgr: Alexander Coate
**Treas:* Sophia Skoda
VP: Andy Katz
CTO: Bryan Marini
IT Man: Andrew Levine
IT Man: Darryl Yee
Netwrk Mgr: Syed Rahman
Opers Mgr: Dan Ohara
**Genl Couns:* Jylnana Collins
Snr Mgr: Thomas Fox
Board of Directors: Lesa Mc Intoshjohn Coleman, Andy Katz, Douglas Linney, Lesa Mc Intosh, Frank Mellon, Katy Foulkes,william Patte

D-U-N-S 07-629-2515
EAST BAY REGIONAL PARK DISTRICT
2950 Peralta Oaks Ct, Oakland, CA 94605-5320
Tel (888) 327-2757 *Founded/Ownrshp* 1934
Sales 176.0MM *EMP* 750E
SIC 7999

D-U-N-S 19-060-4744
EAST BOSTON NEIGHBORHOOD HEALTH CENTER CORP
URGENT CARE/WALK IN SERVICE
10 Gove St, Boston, MA 02128-1920
Tel (617) 567-3600 *Founded/Ownrshp* 1970
Sales 83.9MME *EMP* 450
SIC 8062 General medical & surgical hospitals
CEO: Manny Lopes
**Pr:* John P Cradock
VP: Stephen Fraser
VP: Michael Mancusi
VP: Lili Silva
VP: Laura Wagner
CIO: Manuel Lopes
CTO: Jim Hill
IT Man: Liz Desisto
Doctor: Michael Chin
Doctor: Margareth Chua

D-U-N-S 01-975-9497
■ **EAST BOSTON SAVING BANK**
(*Suby of* MERIDIAN BANCORP INC) ★
10 Meridian St, Boston, MA 02128-1963
Tel (617) 567-1500 *Founded/Ownrshp* 1848, 1991
Sales NA *EMP* 401E
SIC 6029 6141 Commercial banks; Financing: automobiles, furniture, etc., not a deposit bank
CEO: Richard J Gavegnano
**Pr:* Deborah J Jackson
**CFO:* Mark L Abbate
**CFO:* Leonard Siuda
Ofcr: Pebbles Bethel
**Sr VP:* Keith D Armstrong
**Sr VP:* Paula M Cotter
Sr VP: James Morgan
VP: Tatiana Bougdaeva
VP: Debby Chui
VP: Lisa Dunlea
VP: David Fama
VP: Donna Finnerty
**VP:* Michael Flynn
VP: Philip Freehan
VP: Michele Pergola
VP: Brian Slater
**VP:* John Tirrusa
VP: Jonathan Towslee
Board of Directors: Richard Gavegnano

D-U-N-S 01-674-6653
EAST BRUNSWICK BOARD OF EDUCATION (INC)
760 State Route 18, East Brunswick, NJ 08816-4907
Tel (732) 613-6700 *Founded/Ownrshp* 1894
Sales 87.3MME *EMP* 1,600
SIC 8211 Public elementary & secondary schools; Elementary school; High school, junior or senior
Pr: Todd Simmens
VP: Katie Spiegler

D-U-N-S 80-981-3913
EAST BRUNSWICK PUBLIC SCHOOLS
760 Highway 18, East Brunswick, NJ 08816-4907
Tel (732) 613-6700 *Founded/Ownrshp* 1894
Sales 13.8MME *EMP* 1,219E
SIC 8211 Public elementary & secondary schools
Dir Sec: Paul Natalicchio
MIS Dir: Edward Leypoldt
Pr Dir: Beth Warren
Teacher Pr: Danielle Ruggiero
HC Dir: Danielle Blalock

D-U-N-S 96-685-6317
EAST CAROLINA HEALTH INC
2100 Stantonsburg Rd, Greenville, NC 27834-2818
Tel (252) 847-6156 *Founded/Ownrshp* 2011
Sales 366.5MM *EMP* 2
Accts Mcgladrey Llp Chicago Il
SIC 8099 Health & allied services
Prin: Anita Hunt

D-U-N-S 07-555-7926
EAST CAROLINA UNIVERSITY
ECU
(*Suby of* OFFICE OF PRESIDENT) ★
E Fifth St, Greenville, NC 27858
Tel (252) 328-6131 *Founded/Ownrshp* 2000
Sales 500.8MM *EMP* 4,837E
SIC 8221

D-U-N-S 07-848-8327
EAST CENTRAL INDEPENDENT SCHOOL DISTRICT
6634 New Sulphur Sprng Rd, San Antonio, TX 78263-2500
Tel (210) 648-7861 *Founded/Ownrshp* 1949
Sales 72.8MME *EMP* 1,086
Accts Coleman Horton & Company Llp
SIC 8211 Public elementary school; Public junior high school; Public senior high school; Public special education school
Dir Bus: Jim Selpy
HC Dir: Linda Bailey

D-U-N-S 02-219-4138
EAST CENTRAL IOWA COOP
ECIS
602 Washington St, Hudson, IA 50643-7751
Tel (319) 988-3257 *Founded/Ownrshp* 1947
Sales 155.2MM *EMP* 54
Accts Gardiner Thomsen Charles City
SIC 5153 5191 Grain elevators; Grains; Feed; Seeds: field, garden & flower; Fertilizer & fertilizer materials
Pr: Denise Maas
**CFO:* Joel Murphy
VP: Jason Trumbauer

D-U-N-S 36-115-0126
EAST CENTRAL REGIONAL HOSPITAL
3405 Mike Padgett Hwy, Augusta, GA 30906-3815
Tel (706) 792-7105 *Founded/Ownrshp* 2005
Sales 63.4MME *EMP* 1,267E
SIC 8062 General medical & surgical hospitals
Prin: David Bate

D-U-N-S 10-131-0951
EAST COAST DISTRIBUTORS INC
1705 Broad St, Cranston, RI 02905-2724
Tel (401) 780-8800 *Founded/Ownrshp* 1989
Sales 130.9MM *EMP* 10
Accts Delgrande & Montefusco Inc
SIC 5147 Meat brokers
Pr: Geoffrey Tapper
**VP:* Frank De Anglis

D-U-N-S 02-452-3243
■ **EAST COAST METAL DISTRIBUTORS LLC**
(*Suby of* WATSCO INC) ★
1313 S Briggs Ave, Durham, NC 27703-5049
Tel (919) 598-5030 *Founded/Ownrshp* 1954, 2005
Sales 135.3MME *EMP* 350
SIC 5075

EAST COAST MOULDINGS
See ECMD INC

EAST COAST SEAFOOD
See AMERICAN HOLDCO LLC

D-U-N-S 12-098-8746 IMP
EAST COAST SEAFOOD INC
(*Suby of* EAST COAST SEAFOOD) ★
448 Boston St, Topsfield, MA 01983-1216
Tel (978) 561-3800 *Founded/Ownrshp* 1992
Sales 104.6MME *EMP* 50
SIC 5146 Seafoods
Pr: Michael J Tourkistas
**CFO:* James C Bouras
Ex VP: Willard Fehr
**Ex VP:* Spiros Tourkakis
VP: Frank De Anglis
VP: Linzy Lopez
QC Dir: Tad Pawlowski

D-U-N-S 10-583-7702 IMP/EXP
EAST COAST TILE IMPORTS INC
BESTTILE DISTRIBUTORS
8 Stony Brook St Ste 1, Ludlow, MA 01056-1239
Tel (518) 344-7000 *Founded/Ownrshp* 1981
Sales 129.1MME *EMP* 500
SIC 5032 8741 Ceramic wall & floor tile; Business management
Mng Pt: Brian Ford
Treas: William Dupuis
VP: Brian Knies
VP: John M Knies Jr
VP: Steven Marcus
Genl Mgr: Kevin Pasu
Mktg Mgr: Lindsey Diflorio

D-U-N-S 06-837-8058
EAST COKE COUNTY HOSPITAL DISTRICT
BRONTE NURSING HOME
900 S State St, Bronte, TX 76933-5717
Tel (325) 473-3621 *Founded/Ownrshp* 1971
Sales 173.0MME *EMP* 45
SIC 8059 8051 Nursing home, except skilled & intermediate care facility; Skilled nursing care facilities
Off Mgr: Andra Arrot

D-U-N-S 14-793-7213 IMP
■ **EAST COOPER COMMUNITY HOSPITAL INC**
EAST COOPER MEDICAL CENTER
(*Suby of* TENET HEALTHSYSTEM MEDICAL INC) ★
2000 Hospital Dr, Mount Pleasant, SC 29464-3764
Tel (843) 881-0100 *Founded/Ownrshp* 1984
Sales 152.1MM *EMP* 600
Accts Andrew C Smith Cpa Mt Pleasan
SIC 8062 8011 General medical & surgical hospitals; Offices & clinics of medical doctors
CEO: Jason Alexander
CIO: David Karinshak
Ansthlgy: Charles Weinheimer

EAST COOPER MEDICAL CENTER
See EAST COOPER COMMUNITY HOSPITAL INC

D-U-N-S 07-277-3658
EAST DETROIT PUBLIC SCHOOLS
24685 Kelly Rd, Eastpointe, MI 48021-1399
Tel (586) 445-4400 *Founded/Ownrshp* 1920
Sales 42.2MME *EMP* 1,000
Accts Yeo & Yeo Pc Flint Michig
SIC 8211 Public elementary & secondary schools

D-U-N-S 07-839-8135
■ **EAST DUBUQUE NITROGEN PARTNERS LP**
(*Suby of* CVR PARTNERS LP) ★
10877 Wilshire Blvd Fl 10, Los Angeles, CA 90024-4251
Tel (310) 571-9800 *Founded/Ownrshp* 2015
Sales 340.7MM *EMP* 145E
Accts Pricewaterhousecoopers Llp Lo
SIC 2873 Nitrogenous fertilizers
CEO: Keith B Forman
Pr: Colin Campbell
Pr: John H Diesch
CFO: Jeffrey R Spain
Sr VP: Wilfred Bahl Jr
Sr VP: Joe Herold
Sr VP: Colin Morris
Sr VP: Marc Wallis
VP: Julie Dawoodjee Cafarella
VP: Eileen Ney

D-U-N-S 96-294-9574
EAST GEORGIA REGIONAL MEDICAL CENTER
1499 Fair Rd, Statesboro, GA 30458-1683
Tel (912) 486-1000 *Founded/Ownrshp* 2000
Sales 210.0MM *EMP* 750
SIC 8748 Business consulting
CEO: Bob Bigley
Dir Vol: Daryl Waters
CFO: Scott Whittemore
**VP:* Page Vaughn
Pharmcst: Robin Thompson

D-U-N-S 05-271-0357
EAST HAVEN BUILDERS SUPPLY - US LBM LLC (CT)
KITCHEN FACTOR , THE
(*Suby of* US LBM HOLDINGS LLC) ★
193 Silver Sands Rd, East Haven, CT 06512-4124
Tel (203) 469-2394 *Founded/Ownrshp* 1971
Sales 142.3MME *EMP* 192
SIC 5031 5211 Building materials, exterior; Building materials, interior; Kitchen cabinets; Lumber & other building materials; Cabinets, kitchen
Pr: Antonio Rossano
Opers Mgr: Michael Monico
Mktg Dir: Neil Frederick
Sales Asso: Ray Halliday
Sales Asso: Don Kellam
Sales Asso: Michael Salva
Sales Asso: Scott Wetmore

D-U-N-S 08-278-1212
EAST ISLIP UNION FREE SCHOOL DISTRICT 3
1 Craig B Gariepy Ave, Islip Terrace, NY 11752-2820
Tel (631) 224-2000 *Founded/Ownrshp* 1929
Sales 104.1MM *EMP* 850
Accts Cullen & Danowski Llp
SIC 8211 Public elementary & secondary schools
Schl Brd P: Steven Behan

D-U-N-S 07-193-9722
EAST JEFFERSON GENERAL HOSPITAL
EJGH
4200 Houma Blvd, Metairie, LA 70006-2996
Tel (504) 454-4000 *Founded/Ownrshp* 1965
Sales 322.5MM *EMP* 3,436
SIC 8062 General medical & surgical hospitals
CEO: Mark J Peters
Chf OB: Steven J Herron
Chf Rad: John N Joslyn
Dir Vol: Nina Victory
Pt: Martin H Klein
Pt: Dr Reita Lawrence
CFO: Marianne Call
Ch: Jim M Hudson
Treas: Ashton J Ryan Jr
Chf Mktg O: Renee Hooter
Ex VP: Judy Brown
VP: Steve Baker
VP: Paula Kensler
VP: Ann Seal
Dir Inf Cn: Carol Scioneaux
Dir Lab: Linda Daigle
Dir Rad: Dan Fertel

D-U-N-S 13-150-4941
EAST KENTUCKY NETWORK LLC
APPALACHIAN WIRELESS
101 Technology Trl, Ivel, KY 41642-9057
Tel (606) 477-2355 *Founded/Ownrshp* 1998
Sales 102.1MM *EMP* 165
Accts Jones Nale & Mattingly Plc
SIC 4812 1731 Cellular telephone services; Fiber optic cable installation
CEO: Gerald Robinette
CFO: John Arnhold
Exec: John Willogby

D-U-N-S 07-287-8432
EAST KENTUCKY POWER COOPERATIVE
(*Suby of* EKP COOPERATIVE) ★
4775 Lexington Rd, Winchester, KY 40391-9709
Tel (859) 744-4812 *Founded/Ownrshp* 1971
Sales 93.1MME *EMP* 283
SIC 4911 Generation, electric power
Pr: Robert Marshall

D-U-N-S 00-777-9416 IMP
EAST KENTUCKY POWER COOPERATIVE INC
EKP COOPERATIVE
4775 Lexington Rd, Winchester, KY 40391-9709
Tel (859) 744-4812 *Founded/Ownrshp* 1941
Sales 819.0MME *EMP* 655
SIC 4911 Generation, electric power; Transmission, electric power
Ch Bd: Paul Hawkins
**CEO:* Anthony Campbell
Chf Mktg O: Gary Crawford
VP: Stacy Barker
VP: David Eames
VP: Bo Miller
Dir IT: Eddy McNaught
Software D: Steve Weaver
Sfty Mgr: Vernon Sherer
Opers Mgr: Bob Tegge
Sls&Mrk Ex: Dan Playforth

EAST MEADOW PUBLIC SCHOOLS
See EAST MEADOW UFSD (INC)

D-U-N-S 06-807-4921
EAST MEADOW UFSD (INC)
EAST MEADOW PUBLIC SCHOOLS
718 The Plain Rd Ste 1, Westbury, NY 11590-5956
Tel (516) 478-5730 *Founded/Ownrshp* 1948
Sales 50.2MME *EMP* 1,013
SIC 8211 Public elementary & secondary schools
**Pr:* Joseph Parisi
**VP:* Walter Skinner
HC Dir: Kristi Decor

D-U-N-S 00-480-3680
EAST MISSISSIPPI ELECTRIC POWER ASSN INC
EMEPA
2128 Highway 39 N, Meridian, MS 39301-2723
Tel (601) 581-8600 *Founded/Ownrshp* 1938
Sales 87.8MM *EMP* 180
Accts Wilson & Biggs Pllc Ridgeland
SIC 4911 Distribution, electric power
Pr: Larry Pace
**Treas:* Chester Willis
Genl Mgr: H Wayne Henson
IT Man: Kevin Hedgpeth

D-U-N-S 00-790-0475
■ **EAST OHIO GAS CO**
DOMINION EAST OHIO
(*Suby of* DOMINION RESOURCES INC) ★
19701 Libby Rd, Maple Heights, OH 44137-2371
Tel (800) 362-7557 *Founded/Ownrshp* 1942
Sales 240.8MME *EMP* 2,000
SIC 4923 Gas transmission & distribution
Pr: Tom D Newland
**Treas:* Michael G Bartels
**Sr VP:* Anne E Bomar
**VP:* Brian Brakeman
**VP:* B C Klink Sr
**VP:* Ron Kovach

D-U-N-S 06-752-1070
EAST ORANGE GENERAL HOSPITAL (INC)
300 Central Ave, East Orange, NJ 07018-2897
Tel (973) 672-8400 *Founded/Ownrshp* 1903
Sales 109.9MME *EMP* 801
SIC 8062

D-U-N-S 08-299-7214
EAST ORANGE SCHOOL DISTRICT
199 4th Ave, East Orange, NJ 07017-4803
Tel (862) 233-7300 *Founded/Ownrshp* 1880
Sales 77.9MME *EMP* 1,421
SIC 8211 9111 Public elementary & secondary schools; Mayors' offices
Schl Brd P: Bergson Leneus
HC Dir: Tonya Santos

D-U-N-S 06-439-6336
EAST ORLANDO HEALTH & REHAB CENTER INC
ADVENTIST HEALTH SYSTEM SUNBEL
(*Suby of* ADVENTST HLTH SYSTM SUNBELT H) ★
250 S Chickasaw Trl, Orlando, FL 32825-3503
Tel (407) 380-3466 *Founded/Ownrshp* 1981
Sales 12.5MM *EMP* 2,230
SIC 8051 Skilled nursing care facilities
Ch Bd: Robert R Henderschedt
**Pr:* Michelle Fetters
Off Mgr: Wallie Villafane

D-U-N-S 00-679-0521
EAST OTTER TAIL TELEPHONE CO (MN)
ARVIG COMMUNICATION SYSTEM ACS
(*Suby of* ACS) ★
150 2nd Ave Sw, Perham, MN 56573-1409
Tel (218) 346-5500 *Founded/Ownrshp* 1950
Sales 89.3MME *EMP* 240
SIC 4813 Local telephone communications
Pr: Allen R Arvig
**Treas:* Rick Vyskocil
**VP:* David Arvig

D-U-N-S 00-233-0165 IMP/EXP
EAST PENN MANUFACTURING CO (PA)
DEKA BATTERIES & CABLES
102 Deka Rd, Lyon Station, PA 19536-5001
Tel (610) 682-6361 *Founded/Ownrshp* 1946
Sales 2.2MMME *EMP* 8,000
SIC 3694 3691 5063 4225

D-U-N-S 07-366-5234
EAST PENN SCHOOL DISTRICT
EPSD
800 Pine St, Emmaus, PA 18049-2100
Tel (610) 966-8300 *Founded/Ownrshp* 1966
Sales 86.2MME *EMP* 1,057
SIC 8211 Public elementary & secondary schools
Bd of Dir: Ann L Thompson
MIS Dir: Michael Mohn
Teacher Pr: Jessica Afflerbach

D-U-N-S 11-731-9962
EAST RAMAPO CENTRAL SCHOOL DISTRICT
105 S Madison Ave, Spring Valley, NY 10977-5474
Tel (845) 577-6000 *Founded/Ownrshp* 1952
Sales 81.0MME *EMP* 1,400
SIC 8211 Public elementary & secondary schools
Treas: Israel Bier
Genl Mgr: Merritte Mellion
MIS Dir: Azhar Ahmad
IT Man: Riva Fishbeyn
Teacher Pr: M Sculnick
Snr Mgr: Ellen Andriello
Board of Directors: Roy Belser, David Leis, Brian Molloy

EAST REGIONAL OFFICE
See LHOIST NORTH AMERICA OF TENNESSEE INC

D-U-N-S 00-894-1882 IMP
EAST RIVER ELECTRIC POWER COOPERATIVE INC (SD)
211 S Harth Ave, Madison, SD 57042-2905
Tel (605) 256-4536 *Founded/Ownrshp* 1949
Sales 231.9MM *EMP* 126
Accts Eide Bailly Llp Sioux Falls
SIC 4911 6163 Distribution, electric power; Loan brokers
CEO: Jeffrey L Nelson
**Pr:* James Ryken
**Treas:* Bert Rogness
**VP:* Vic Gross
Sls&Mrk Ex: Holt Tom

D-U-N-S 07-992-6424
EAST ST LOUIS SCHOOL DISTRICT 189
1005 State St, East Saint Louis, IL 62201-1907
Tel (618) 646-3000 *Founded/Ownrshp* 1890
Sales 78.6MME *EMP* 1,198
SIC 8211 Public elementary & secondary schools; Public junior high school; Public senior high school
**CFO:* Adil Khan
VP: Kinnis Williams
Comm Dir: Kelli Hawkins
Dir Sec: Joe Haskell
Pr Dir: Crystal Thompson
Instr Medi: Yvette Jackson
HC Dir: Alonzo Nelson

D-U-N-S 08-672-3277
EAST STROUDSBURG AREA SCHOOL DISTRICT
ESASD
50 Vine St, East Stroudsburg, PA 18301-2150
Tel (570) 424-8500 *Founded/Ownrshp* 1959
Sales 59.5MM^E *EMP* 1,200
Accts Kirk Summa & Co Llp East S
SIC 8211 Public elementary school; Public junior high school; Public senior high school
HC Dir: Sue Cole

D-U-N-S 78-666-1629
EAST STROUDSBURG UNIVERSITY
E S U
(*Suby of* STATE SYSTEM HIGHER EDUCATN PA) ★
200 Prospect St Ste 1, East Stroudsburg, PA 18301-2956
Tel (570) 422-3211 *Founded/Ownrshp* 1893
Sales 89.2MM^E *EMP* 726
SIC 8221 9411 University; Administration of educational programs;
Pr: Robert J Dillman
**Pr:* Marcia Welsh
COO: Mary Postupack
Bd of Dir: Mary Devito
Ofcr: Carlos Assi
**VP:* Richard A Staneski
Exec: Caryn Fogel
Exec: Sandra Mosher
Ex Dir: Frederick Moses
Dir IT: Tami Moffett
IT Man: Lavar Peterson

D-U-N-S 07-490-9540
EAST TENNESSEE CHILDRENS HOSPITAL ASSOCIATION INC
2018 W Clinch Ave, Knoxville, TN 37916-2301
Tel (865) 541-8000 *Founded/Ownrshp* 1937
Sales 219.5MM *EMP* 1,500
Accts Pershing Yoakley & Associates
SIC 8069 Children's hospital
Pr: Keith Goodwin
Chf Rad: Clifford J Meservy
COO: Rudy McKinnley
VP: Joe Childs
VP: Philip Tregoning
Dir OR: Sherry Larue
Dir Lab: Bob Stewart
Off Mgr: Angela Connors
Netwrk Eng: David McHone
Mktg Dir: Bill Gooch
Doctor: John Ambrosia

D-U-N-S 00-792-1323
■ **EAST TENNESSEE NATURAL GAS LLC** (TN)
(*Suby of* SPECTRA ENERGY CORP) ★
5400 Westheimer Ct, Houston, TX 77056-5353
Tel (713) 627-5400 *Founded/Ownrshp* 1992
Sales 152.4MM *EMP* 2,400
Accts Deloitte & Touche Llp Housto
SIC 4923 Gas transmission & distribution

D-U-N-S 05-112-5037
EAST TENNESSEE STATE UNIVERSITY (TN)
(*Suby of* UNIVERSITY AND COMMUNITY COLLEGE SYSTEM TENNESSEE STATE) ★
1276 Gilbreath Dr, Johnson City, TN 37614-6503
Tel (423) 439-1000 *Founded/Ownrshp* 1909
Sales 186.5MM *EMP* 2,400
Accts Deborah V Loveless Cpa Nash
SIC 8221 University
Pr: Brian Noland
Assoc VP: Jeremy Ro
VP: Sherry Armitage
**VP:* Bert C Bach
VP: Steven S Bader
**VP:* David Collins
**VP:* Richard A Manahan
VP: Whitney Martin
VP: William Miller
VP: Gary D Taylor
Exec: Susan Gardner
Exec: Ruth Hausman
Assoc Dir: Wayne L Miller
Comm Dir: Robert Russell

EAST TENNESSEE STEEL SUPPLY CO
See SISKIN STEEL & SUPPLY CO INC

D-U-N-S 94-853-5265
EAST TEXAS ELECTRIC COOPERATIVE INC
2905 Westward Dr, Nacogdoches, TX 75964-1231
Tel (936) 560-9532 *Founded/Ownrshp* 1987
Sales 281.8MM *EMP* 7
Accts Goff & Herrington Pc Lufkin
SIC 4939 Combination utilities
Pr: Debra Robinson
**CFO:* Ryan Thomas
**VP:* John Dugan

D-U-N-S 18-313-2794
EAST TEXAS MEDICAL CENTER
EMS
(*Suby of* ETMC REGIONAL HEALTH SYSTEM) ★
1000 S Beckham Ave, Tyler, TX 75701-1908
Tel (903) 597-0351 *Founded/Ownrshp* 1951
Sales 378.1MM *EMP* 2,500^E
SIC 8062 8011 General medical & surgical hospitals; Clinic, operated by physicians
Pr: Elmer G Ellis
VP: Ralph Carroll
VP: Jon Ledlie
Dir OR: Chris Davis
QA Dir: Robert Tippens
Orthpdst: Jan H Garrett
Surgeon: Vivek Patel

D-U-N-S 13-039-7573 IMP
EAST TEXAS MEDICAL CENTER REGIONAL HEALTH SERVICES INC
(*Suby of* ETMC REGIONAL HEALTH SYSTEM) ★
1000 S Beckham Ave, Tyler, TX 75701-1908
Tel (903) 597-0351 *Founded/Ownrshp* 1970
Sales 398.7MM^E *EMP* 2,600
SIC 8062 General medical & surgical hospitals
CEO: Elmer G Ellis
COO: Jerry Massey
**CFO:* Anthony L Wahl
**Sr VP:* Robert E Evans
Sr VP: Byron C Hale
VP: Eddie Howard
Nurse Mgr: Robert Collyer
CTO: Lacie Massingill
Sfty Dirs: Dick Delk
Sfty Dirs: Pat Poole
Orthpdst: Anthony Anderson

D-U-N-S 05-312-5936
EAST TEXAS MEDICAL CENTER REGIONAL HEALTHCARE SYST
ETMC REGIONAL HEALTH SYSTEM
1000 S Beckham Ave, Tyler, TX 75701-1908
Tel (866) 333-3862 *Founded/Ownrshp* 1947
Sales 871.3MM^E *EMP* 7,600
SIC 8062 8741 General medical & surgical hospitals; Management services
Pr: Elmer G Ellis
Ofcr: Rose Gray
**Sr VP:* Robert E Evans
**Sr VP:* Jerry L Massey
VP: Larry Davis
**VP:* Cherie Martin
VP: Jerry Massey
Exec: Lori Neubauer
Dir Inf Cn: Amber Sims
Dir Lab: Tauniya White
Dir Rad: Donald Clark
Dir Rx: Brooks McGinnis

D-U-N-S 14-187-1116
EAST TEXAS SPECIALTY HOSP
E T M C SPECIALTY HOSPITAL
(*Suby of* EAST TEXAS MEDICAL CENTER REGIONAL HEALTH SERVICES INC) ★
1000 S Beckham Ave Fl 5, Tyler, TX 75701-1908
Tel (903) 596-3600 *Founded/Ownrshp* 1981
Sales 365.8MM *EMP* 80
SIC 8062 General medical & surgical hospitals
VP: Eddie Howard

D-U-N-S 11-505-0619
EAST VALLEY TOURIST DEVELOPMENT AUTHORITY
FANTASY SPRINGS RESORT CASINO
84245 Indio Springs Dr, Indio, CA 92203-3405
Tel (760) 342-5000 *Founded/Ownrshp* 1983
Sales 60.5MM^E *EMP* 1,200
SIC 7999 Gambling establishment; Off-track betting
Ch Bd: John James
Treas: Angela Rosevelt
**Sec:* Angela Roosevelt
**V Ch Bd:* Mark Benitez
**V Ch Bd:* Brenda Soulliere
VP: Dan London
VP: Steve Oskiera
VP: Royce Wilkinson
Exec: Sylvia Pershing
Exec: Freddy Rieger
Ex Dir: Lou Crescenzo
Board of Directors: John Welmas, Elisa Welmas-Wildman

D-U-N-S 04-911-3074
▲ **EAST WEST BANCORP INC**
135 N Los Robles Ave Fl 7, Pasadena, CA 91101-4525
Tel (626) 768-6000 *Founded/Ownrshp* 1998
Sales NA *EMP* 2,833^E
Tkr Sym EWBC *Exch* NGS
SIC 6022 State commercial banks
Ch Bd: Dominic Ng
Pr: Gregory L Guyett
CFO: Irene H OH
**V Ch Bd:* John M Lee
Ex VP: Douglas P Krause
Sr VP: Gary Teo

D-U-N-S 07-411-4620
■ **EAST WEST BANK**
(*Suby of* EAST WEST BANCORP INC) ★
135 N Ls Rbls Ave 100, Pasadena, CA 91101
Tel (626) 768-6000 *Founded/Ownrshp* 1998
Sales NA *EMP* 1,310
SIC 6022 State commercial banks
Ch Bd: Dominic Ng
V Ch: John Lee
Pr: Donald S Chow
Pr: Maureen Finn
Pr: Gregory L Guyett
CFO: Thomas J Tolda
Ofcr: Damon Ho
Ofcr: John Meyer
Ex VP: William Fong
Ex VP: Karen Fukumura
Ex VP: Douglas P Krause
Ex VP: Andy Yen
Sr VP: Ming L Chen
Sr VP: Sharon Cheung
Sr VP: Bennett Chui
Sr VP: Don Danh
Sr VP: Gordon Delang
Sr VP: Paul Liaw
Sr VP: Irene OH
VP: Jila Ahdot
VP: Wendy Anderson
Board of Directors: Molly Campbell

D-U-N-S 60-963-8593 IMP/EXP
EAST WEST COPOLYMER LLC
5955 Scenic Hwy, Baton Rouge, LA 70805-2044
Tel (225) 267-3400 *Founded/Ownrshp* 2014
Sales 290.6MM^E *EMP* 153^E
SIC 2822 Synthetic rubber
Pr: Gregory Nelson
CFO: Celso Goncalves
VP: Patrick Bowers
VP: Dana Coody
VP: Bobby Rikhoff

D-U-N-S 07-551-4976 IMP
EAST WEST INDUSTRIAL ENGINEERING CO
EWIE CO
1099 Highland Dr Ste D, Ann Arbor, MI 48108-5002
Tel (734) 971-6265 *Founded/Ownrshp* 1981
Sales 179.9MM^E *EMP* 160
SIC 5085 5172 Industrial supplies; Industrial tools; Abrasives & adhesives; Tools; Lubricating oils & greases
Pr: Dilip Mullick
**COO:* Tom Connelly
**Treas:* Poonam Sachdeva
**VP:* Manoj K Sachdeva
Mktg Mgr: Shoki Mullick

EASTAR HEALTH SYSTEM
See MUSKOGEE REGIONAL MEDICAL CENTER LLC

D-U-N-S 03-876-4411 IMP/EXP
■ **EASTBAY INC**
(*Suby of* FOOTLOCKER.COM INC) ★
111 S 1st Ave, Wausau, WI 54401-4625
Tel (800) 826-2205 *Founded/Ownrshp* 1982
Sales 192.8MM^E *EMP* 2,000
SIC 5699 5661 5941 Sports apparel; Footwear, athletic; Sporting goods & bicycle shops
Pr: Dowe S Tillema
VP: David Lokes
VP: Pat Schmidt
Dir IT: Todd Schmidt
Sys Mgr: Craig Gadke
Web Dev: Steve Cerny
Mktg Dir: Dawn Lacy
Mktg Mgr: Kathie Morgen

D-U-N-S 00-782-2448
■ **EASTCOAST TELECOM OF WISCONSIN LLC**
TDS
(*Suby of* TDS TELECOMMUNICATIONS CORP) ★
1140 W Washington Ave, Cleveland, WI 53015-1423
Tel (920) 693-8121 *Founded/Ownrshp* 1991
Sales 853.0MM *EMP* 8^E
SIC 4813 Telephone communication, except radio
Pr: Dave Wittwer

EASTER SEAL MINNESOTA
See GOODWILL INDUSTRIES INC

D-U-N-S 08-557-3467
EASTER SEAL NEW HAMPSHIRE INC
555 Auburn St, Manchester, NH 03103-4803
Tel (603) 623-8863 *Founded/Ownrshp* 1967
Sales 104.9MM *EMP* 2,000
Accts Baker Newman & Noyes Llc Man
SIC 8331 8399 4119 8322 Vocational rehabilitation agency; Community action agency; Local passenger transportation; Individual & family services
Pr: Larry J Gammon
Treas: Elin Treanor
Sr VP: Michael Bonfanti
Sr VP: Sue Silsby

EASTER SEAL TEACHING FMLY CTR
See EASTER SEALS VERMONT INC

EASTER SEALS DISABILITY SERVIC
See EASTER SEALS SOUTHERN CALIFORNIA INC

D-U-N-S 02-035-0476
EASTER SEALS MIDWEST
13545 Barrett Parkway Dr, Ballwin, MO 63021-3822
Tel (314) 394-7026 *Founded/Ownrshp* 1964
Sales 49.0MM *EMP* 1,400^E
Accts Rubinbrown Llp Saint Louis M
SIC 8361 8331 8322 8052 Residential care for the handicapped; Job training services; Individual & family services; Intermediate care facilities
Ex Dir: Windy Buehler
CFO: John Adkins
Treas: Gwen Knight
Ofcr: Jeanne Marshall
VP: Shana Albright
VP: Amanda Bartosch
VP: Tom Bay
VP: Bill Eastman
VP: William Eastman
VP: Nicole Johnson
VP: Micki Keim

D-U-N-S 06-870-8213 IMP
EASTER SEALS NEW JERSEY
25 Kennedy Blvd Ste 600, East Brunswick, NJ 08816-1262
Tel (732) 257-6662 *Founded/Ownrshp* 1948
Sales 127.0MM *EMP* 1,000
Accts Cohnreznick Llp Roseland Nj
SIC 8322 Social service center
Pr: Brian Fitzgerald
**CFO:* Cheryl Young
VP Admn: Helen Drobnis

D-U-N-S 16-867-5759
EASTER SEALS SOUTHERN CALIFORNIA INC
EASTER SEALS DISABILITY SERVIC
1570 E 17th St, Santa Ana, CA 92705-8502
Tel (714) 834-1111 *Founded/Ownrshp* 1988
Sales 140.0MM *EMP* 640
Accts Mcgladrey Llp Los Angeles Ca
SIC 8399 Fund raising organization, non-fee basis
CEO: Mark Whitley
CFO: Susan Berglund
**Ex VP:* Carlene Holden
**VP:* Terry McCormick
Prgrm Mgr: Carlie Robitaille
Off Mgr: April Montgomery

D-U-N-S 04-003-8531
EASTER SEALS UCP NORTH CAROLINA & VIRGINIA INC
5171 Glenwood Ave Ste 400, Raleigh, NC 27612-3266
Tel (919) 832-3787 *Founded/Ownrshp* 1952
Sales 82.7MM^E *EMP* 2,600
Accts Langdon & Company Cpas Garne
SIC 8322 Association for the handicapped
CEO: Luanne Welch
**CFO:* Joyce Stevens
Prgrm Mgr: Dean Ewart
Prgrm Mgr: Aimee Izawa
Prgrm Mgr: Sheila Reeves
Prgrm Mgr: Jeremy Wagoner
Genl Mgr: Jacqueline Cavadi

D-U-N-S 01-996-8585
EASTER SEALS VERMONT INC
EASTER SEAL TEACHING FMLY CTR
641 Comstock Rd Ste 1, Berlin, VT 05602-9611
Tel (802) 223-4744 *Founded/Ownrshp* 1985
Sales 104.9MM *EMP* 15
SIC 8322 Individual & family services
VP: Mark Johnson

D-U-N-S 08-459-9208
EASTERN AMERICAN ENERGY CORP
ECA
(*Suby of* ECA HOLDING) ★
500 Corporate Lndg, Charleston, WV 25311-1264
Tel (304) 925-6100 *Founded/Ownrshp* 1973
Sales 195.1MM^E *EMP* 190
SIC 1311 4922 5172 1321 Crude petroleum production; Natural gas production; Pipelines, natural gas; Gases; Natural gas liquids
Pr: John Mork
**COO:* Kyle M Mork
**CFO:* Michael S Fletcher
Treas: Rodney Cox
**Ex VP:* Joseph Casabona
**VP:* J Michael Forbes
**VP:* George O'Malley
VP: Don Supcoe
Exec: Peter A Sullivan
Genl Couns: Robert M Adkins

D-U-N-S 01-860-7887 IMP/EXP
EASTERN BAG AND PAPER CO INC
EBP SUPPLY SOLUTIONS
200 Research Dr, Milford, CT 06460-2880
Tel (203) 878-1814 *Founded/Ownrshp* 1918
Sales 192.0MM *EMP* 285
Accts Blum Shapiro & Company Pc
SIC 5113 5087 5046 Bags, paper & disposable plastic; Napkins, paper; Cups, disposable plastic & paper; Janitors' supplies; Restaurant equipment & supplies
CEO: Meredith Reuben
**Pr:* Eric Peabody
**CFO:* William J O Donnell
VP: Walt Ancker
VP: Michael Kaplan
VP: Joseph Lopresti
VP: Joe Ondriezek
VP: Andrew Reuben
VP: Ken Rosenberg
VP: Alan Schachter
CIO: Jack Jurkowski

EASTERN BAND CHEROKEE INDIANS
See EASTERN BAND OF CHEROKEE INDIANS

D-U-N-S 07-451-1999
EASTERN BAND OF CHEROKEE INDIANS
EASTERN BAND CHEROKEE INDIANS
88 Council House Loop, Cherokee, NC 28719
Tel (828) 497-2771 *Founded/Ownrshp* 1885
Sales NA *EMP* 1,500
Accts Dixon Hughes Pllc Asheville
SIC 9131 Indian reservation
CEO: Michell Hicks
**Pr:* Michael Bolt
CFO: Kim Peone
**Treas:* Calvin Blanksteen
Ofcr: Lisa Penick
Ofcr: Curtis Wildcatt
**Exec:* Larry Blythe
Prgrm Mgr: Julie Maney
Off Admin: Marsha Jackson
Mktg Dir: Mary J Ferguson
Pr Mgr: Robert Jumper

D-U-N-S 00-695-5009 IMP
EASTERN BANK
(*Suby of* EASTERN BANK CORP) ★
265 Franklin St Fl 2, Boston, MA 02110-3120
Tel (617) 897-1100 *Founded/Ownrshp* 1818
Sales NA *EMP* 1,330
SIC 6036 Savings institutions, not federally chartered
CEO: Richard E Holbrook
V Ch: Thomas S Olen
**Pr:* Robert F Rivers
Pr: Chrissie Stevens
**CFO:* Charles Johnston
**Treas:* John F McKinlay
Ex VP: Barbara Heinemann
Ex VP: Carol McMullen
Sr VP: Jonathan Marcus
Sr VP: Richard F Moore
Sr VP: Karen E Quinn
Sr VP: Joseph Richardi
VP: John Doherty
VP: Ernest Jones
VP: Paula Murphy-Roux
VP: Catherine Scherer
VP: William H Tomas
VP: Donald M Urano

D-U-N-S 55-689-4459
EASTERN BANK CORP
265 Franklin St Fl 2, Boston, MA 02110-3120
Tel (617) 897-1100 *Founded/Ownrshp* 1989
Sales NA *EMP* 1,635
Accts Ernst & Young Llp Boston Ma
SIC 6036 6022 6282 State savings banks, not federally chartered; State commercial banks; Investment advisory service
CEO: Richard Holbrook
Pr: Paul Cullen
**Pr:* Jan A Miller
**CFO:* Charles M Johnston
**Treas:* James B Fitzgerald
**Trst:* Mark R Albrecht
**Trst:* Ferdinand Alvaro Jr
Trst: Robert V Antonucci
Trst: Roger Redfield
**Ofcr:* Steven L Antonakes
**Ex VP:* Robert Griffin
**Ex VP:* K Mark Primeau
Sr VP: Mark J Boss
VP: Lisa Carbone
VP: Stacey A Jackson
VP: Sumner Jones
VP: Paul Mollica
VP: Robert Moodie
VP: Richard Moore

VP: Shelley Murray
VP: Maureen Pacella

D-U-N-S 19-786-5889
EASTERN CAROLINA ORGANICS LLC
2210 E Pettigrew St, Durham, NC 27703-4279
Tel (919) 542-3264 *Founded/Ownrshp* 2007
Sales 55.0MM[E] *EMP* 2,007
SIC 0723 Crop preparation services for market
Opers Mgr: David Altshuler

D-U-N-S 00-116-5679 IMP/EXP
▲ EASTERN CO (CT)
112 Bridge St, Naugatuck, CT 06770-2903
Tel (203) 729-2255 *Founded/Ownrshp* 1912
Sales 144.5MM *EMP* 911
Tkr Sym EML *Exch* NGM
SIC 3429 3452 3316 2439 Manufactured hardware (general); Locks or lock sets; Keys & key blanks; Metal fasteners; Bolts, nuts, rivets & washers; Cold finishing of steel shapes; Structural wood members
Ch Bd: Leonard F Leganza
**Ch Bd:* James A Mitarotonda
Pr: August M Vlak
COO: Angelo M Labbadia
CFO: John L Sullivan III
Treas: Gene Finelli
VP: R Wright
Board of Directors: John W Everets, Charles W Henry, Leonard F Leganza, Michael A McManus

D-U-N-S 04-191-4487
EASTERN COLORADO WELL SERVICE LLC
1400 W 122nd Ave Ste 120, Denver, CO 80234-3499
Tel (719) 767-5100 *Founded/Ownrshp* 1997
Sales 152.3MM[E] *EMP* 250
SIC 1389 Oil field services
Ch Bd: Jack Ryser
**Pr:* Randal J Ryser
**CEO:* Jeff Brines

D-U-N-S 18-950-7577
EASTERN CONNECTICUT HEALTH NETWORK INC
ECHN
71 Haynes St, Manchester, CT 06040-4131
Tel (860) 533-6565 *Founded/Ownrshp* 1985
Sales 33.4MM *EMP* 2,600
SIC 8062 General medical & surgical hospitals
Pr: Peter J Karl
**Ch Bd:* Dennis O'Neill
Pr: Marge Letitia
**Treas:* Craig Lappen
**Treas:* Kevin Murphy
Treas: Dennis G O'Neill
**Sr VP:* Deb R Gogliettino
**Sr VP:* Dennis P McConville
Sr VP: Dennis McConville
**VP:* Charles Covin
**VP:* Leona Crosskey
**VP:* Nina Kruse
**VP:* Robin Murdock-Meggers
VP: Jim Weeks
Exec: Michaelj Deangelis
Dir Risk M: Ann Donahue
Dir Rad: Daniel Delgallo

D-U-N-S 10-793-1271
EASTERN CONNECTION OPERATING INC
60 Olympia Ave Ste 2, Woburn, MA 01801-6818
Tel (800) 795-2872 *Founded/Ownrshp* 1986
Sales 84.8MM[E] *EMP* 325[E]
SIC 4215 Package delivery, vehicular
CEO: Jim Berluti
**Ch:* Ted Kauffman
**VP:* Steve Lavigne
**VP:* Kevin Mallory
Opers Mgr: Lynsey Fitzgerald
Opers Mgr: Michael Paolini

D-U-N-S 12-210-7519
EASTERN FARMERS COOPERATIVE
CHS
26033 482nd Ave, Brandon, SD 57005-6670
Tel (605) 582-2415 *Founded/Ownrshp* 2000
Sales 135.2MM[E] *EMP* 88
SIC 5191 5171 5541 Fertilizer & fertilizer materials; Petroleum bulk stations; Filling stations, gasoline
Prin: Randy Kringen
Genl Mgr: Stanley Hippe

EASTERN FENCE
See EASTERN WHOLESALE FENCE CO INC

EASTERN FINANCIAL FLORIDA CRED
See SPACE COAST CREDIT UNION

D-U-N-S 08-135-4318
EASTERN FLORIDA STATE COLLEGE
EFSC
1519 Clearlake Rd, Cocoa, FL 32922-6598
Tel (321) 433-7345 *Founded/Ownrshp* 1960
Sales 173.7MM[E] *EMP* 2,154
SIC 8221 Colleges universities & professional schools
Ch Bd: Stephen Charpentier
Pr: John Glisch
**Pr:* James H Richey
**CFO:* Mark Cherry
VP: Jack Parker
Assoc Dir: Suzanne Leslie
Ex Dir: Frank Margiotta

D-U-N-S 15-102-2464
EASTERN HEALTH SYSTEM INC
Medical Park E Dr Bldg 1, Birmingham, AL 35235
Tel (205) 838-3996 *Founded/Ownrshp* 1985
Sales 52.7MM[E] *EMP* 2,800
SIC 8062 8082 8051 8011 8322 8093 General medical & surgical hospitals; Home health care services; Skilled nursing care facilities; Medical centers; Outreach program; Specialty outpatient clinics
Pr: Robert C Chapman

D-U-N-S 86-870-9726
EASTERN IDAHO REGIONAL MEDICAL CENTER AUXILIARY INC
3100 Channing Way, Idaho Falls, ID 83404-7533
Tel (208) 529-6111 *Founded/Ownrshp* 1977
Sales 259.9MM *EMP* 1,700
SIC 8011 General & family practice, physician/surgeon
Pr: Shirley Lords
COO: Sandee Moore
**Treas:* Norrine Parkinson
Ofcr: Jan Romrell
Ex Dir: Pete Snyder
CIO: Joe Vilvig
QA Dir: Cindy Christensen

D-U-N-S 62-484-7984
EASTERN ILLINOIS UNIVERSITY
600 Lincoln Ave, Charleston, IL 61920-3099
Tel (217) 581-5000 *Founded/Ownrshp* 1895
Sales 117.7MM *EMP* 2,178
Accts Cliftonlarsonallen Llp Peoria
SIC 8221 5812 Colleges universities & professional schools; Caterers
Pr: William Perry
Pr: Sherry Unkraut
Ofcr: Monty Bennett
Ofcr: Jennifer Spracklen
Assoc VP: Jeffrey Cross
Ex VP: Eric Schultz
**VP:* Jeff Cooley
VP: Samuel Slaven
Off Mgr: Richelle Heise
Off Mgr: Jane Johnson
Off Mgr: Jennifer Porter

D-U-N-S 09-987-7524 IMP
EASTERN INDUSTRIAL SUPPLIES INC
11 Caledon Ct Ste A, Greenville, SC 29615-3170
Tel (864) 451-5285 *Founded/Ownrshp* 1987
Sales 123.0MM[E] *EMP* 200
SIC 5085 5051 Valves & fittings; Pipe & tubing, steel
CEO: Kip Miller
**CFO:* Robby Davis
**VP:* Alyn Judkins
**VP:* Richy Milligan
Rgnl Mgr: Jack Sullivan
Brnch Mgr: Ray Fields
Brnch Mgr: Nathan Hampton
Brnch Mgr: Randy Lee
Opers Mgr: Tex Ramey
Opers Mgr: Andy Ray
Sls Mgr: Rob Livingston

D-U-N-S 00-193-7010
EASTERN INDUSTRIES INC
(*Suby of* STABLER COMPANIES INC) ★
3724 Crescent Ct W 200, Whitehall, PA 18052-3446
Tel (610) 866-0932 *Founded/Ownrshp* 1976
Sales 151.5MM[E] *EMP* 500
SIC 5032 3273 1611 Paving mixtures; Concrete & cinder block; Stone, crushed or broken; Ready-mixed concrete; Highway & street paving contractor
Ch Bd: Cyril C Dunmire Jr
**Pr:* Snyder Kim
**Pr:* Paul I Detwiler III
**Treas:* Thomas G Frye
**V Ch Bd:* Paul B Shannon
**Ex VP:* Robert M Mc Cann
**VP:* Dick Holderman
**VP:* James W Vanburen
Opers Mgr: Richard Holderman
Plnt Mgr: Jim Delong

D-U-N-S 61-779-3067
■ EASTERN INSURANCE HOLDINGS INC
(*Suby of* PROASSURANCE CORP) ★
25 Race Ave, Lancaster, PA 17603-3179
Tel (717) 239-1641 *Founded/Ownrshp* 2014
Sales NA *EMP* 220[E]
SIC 6311 6331 Life insurance; Mutual association life insurance; Fire, marine & casualty insurance & carriers
Pr: Michael L Boguski
V Ch: Bruce M Eckert
Ofcr: Judy Bowman
**Ofcr:* Kevin M Shook
VP: Suzanne Emmet
Exec: Noreen U Dishart
**CIO:* Harry Talbert
IT Man: Andrew Lefever
Software D: Glenn Bobb
VP Mktg: Robert A Gilpin
Mktg Mgr: Donna Nardy

D-U-N-S 87-977-2614
EASTERN IOWA COMMUNITY COLLEGE DISTRICT
SCOTT COMMUNITY COLLEGE
(*Suby of* EASTERN IOWA COMMUNITY COLLEGES)
152 Colorado St, Muscatine, IA 52761-5329
Tel (563) 264-2088 *Founded/Ownrshp* 1960
Sales 849.8M *EMP* 1,050
SIC 8222 8221 Junior colleges & technical institutes; Colleges universities & professional schools
Pr: Robert Allbee
**Pr:* Jeff Armstrong
Assoc Dir: Marvin Smith

D-U-N-S 07-405-1269
EASTERN KENTUCKY UNIVERSITY
E K U
521 Lancaster Ave, Richmond, KY 40475-3102
Tel (859) 622-1791 *Founded/Ownrshp* 1906
Sales 158.7MM *EMP* 2,100
Accts Crowe Horwath Llp Louisville
SIC 8221 University
Pr: Michael T Benson
**Ch Bd:* Gary Adney
COO: Susan Cornelius
**Treas:* Debbie Newson
Ofcr: Hal Boyd
**Ofcr:* Virginia Underwood
Ex VP: Collin Potter
VP: Jonathan Collins
VP: Donald Feltner
VP: Deborah Newsom
VP: Nick Perlick
Exec: Michelle Goda
Assoc Dir: Angela Burrows

D-U-N-S 94-474-0117
EASTERN KENTUCKY UNIVERSITY
DIVISION OF NATURAL AREAS
(*Suby of* E K U) ★
91 Lilley Cornett Br, Hallie, KY 41821-8953
Tel (606) 633-5828 *Founded/Ownrshp* 1977
Sales 164.6MM *EMP* 2
Accts Deloitte & Touche Llp Louisvi
SIC 8221 Colleges universities & professional schools; University
Genl Mgr: Robert Watts

D-U-N-S 06-738-5393 IMP
EASTERN LIFT TRUCK CO INC
549 E Linwood Ave, Maple Shade, NJ 08052-1209
Tel (856) 779-8880 *Founded/Ownrshp* 1974
Sales 120.0MM *EMP* 425
SIC 5084 7699 7359

D-U-N-S 16-101-8676
EASTERN LOS ANGELES REGIONAL CENTER FOR DEVELOPMENTALLY DISABLED INC
1000 S Fremont Ave # 23, Alhambra, CA 91803-8800
Tel (626) 299-4700 *Founded/Ownrshp* 1986
Sales 184.0MM *EMP* 287
Accts Lautze & Lautze San Francisco
SIC 8322 Association for the handicapped
Ex Dir: Gloria Wong
Bd of Dir: Theresa Chen
Sales Exec: Adriana Hernandez
Psych: Heike I Ballmaier

D-U-N-S 10-818-0597
EASTERN MAINE HEALTHCARE SYSTEMS
EMHS
43 Whiting Hill Rd # 500, Brewer, ME 04412-1005
Tel (207) 973-7050 *Founded/Ownrshp* 1982
Sales 1.3MMM *EMP* 8,175
Accts Berry Dunn Mcneil & Parker
SIC 8621 8062 Health association; General medical & surgical hospitals
Pr: Terri Vieira
CEO: M Michelle Hood
CFO: Derrick Hollings
VP: Elmer Doucette
VP: John Doyle
VP: Glenn Martin
VP: Jill McDonald
VP: Deborah Sanford
Exec: David Zelz
Dir Rx: Frank McGrady
Prgrm Mgr: Kate Bartley

D-U-N-S 07-173-5682
EASTERN MAINE MEDICAL CENTER
(*Suby of* EMHS) ★
489 State St, Bangor, ME 04401-6674
Tel (207) 973-7000 *Founded/Ownrshp* 1891
Sales 720.2MM *EMP* 1,119
Accts Berry Dunn Mcneil & Parker Ll
SIC 8062 General medical & surgical hospitals
CEO: Deborah C Johnson
**CFO:* Elmer Doucette
Ofcr: Deborah Sanford
VP: Mer Doucette
**VP:* John Doyle
VP Admn: Paul Kelly
Opers Supe: Sheila Thibodeau
Ansthlgy: Jay L Nei
Doctor: Izzeldin Abdalla
Doctor: David T Ahola
Doctor: Robert Anderson

D-U-N-S 62-282-4647 IMP
EASTERN METAL SUPPLY OF NORTH CAROLINA INC
E M S
2925 Stewart Creek Blvd, Charlotte, NC 28216-3593
Tel (704) 391-2266 *Founded/Ownrshp* 1989
Sales 130.3MM[E] *EMP* 75
SIC 5051 Aluminum bars, rods, ingots, sheets, pipes, plates, etc.
Pr: Susan Walsh
**Sec:* Keith Crowell
**VP:* Greg Weekes
Manager: Thomas Long
Sls Mgr: Jerry Aucoin
Sales Asso: Judd Cantley
Sales Asso: Greg Gregor
Sales Asso: Allison Honeycutt
Sales Asso: Russ Lamb

D-U-N-S 07-313-2136
EASTERN MICHIGAN UNIVERSITY
202 Welch Hall, Ypsilanti, MI 48197-2214
Tel (734) 487-2031 *Founded/Ownrshp* 1849
Sales 229.5MM *EMP* 2,000
Accts Plante & Moran Pllc Portage
SIC 8221 College, except junior
Pr: Dr Susan W Martin
Pr: David Woike
VP: David Carroll
VP: Theodore Coutilish
VP: Calvin Phillips
Prin: Joshua D Morast
Ex Dir: Laura A Wilbanks Jr
Dir IT: Dennis Stolte
Mktg Dir: Kevin Devine
Pgrm Dir: Wendy Beattie

EASTERN MOUNTAIN SPORTS
See SME HOLDING CO LLC

D-U-N-S 04-778-9870 IMP
EASTERN MUNICIPAL WATER DISTRICT
2270 Trumble Rd, Perris, CA 92572
Tel (951) 928-3777 *Founded/Ownrshp* 1950
Sales 206.2MM *EMP* 620
Accts Davis Farr Llp Irvine Califo
SIC 4941 4952 Water supply; Sewerage systems
CEO: Paul D Jones II
CFO: Charles M Rathbone Jr
Bd of Dir: Ronald Sullivan
Exec: Doug Hefley
Exec: Roxanne Rountree
Genl Mgr: Mike Dad
Genl Mgr: Anthony Pack
Dir IT: Keith Bratisax
Dir IT: Jayne Joy
Dir IT: Mike Maraffi
IT Man: Rob Behrens

EASTERN NEW MEXICO MEDICAL CENTER
See ROSWELL HOSPITAL CORP

D-U-N-S 08-033-2194
EASTERN OUTFITTERS LLC
160 Corporate Ct, Meriden, CT 06450-7177
Tel (203) 235-5775 *Founded/Ownrshp* 2016
Sales 604.5MM[E] *EMP* 3,700[E]
SIC 5611 6719 Clothing, sportswear, men's & boys'; Investment holding companies, except banks
CEO: Mark Walsh

D-U-N-S 61-043-0519
EASTERN REGIONAL MEDICAL CENTER INC
CANCER TREATMENT CENTERS AMER
(*Suby of* CTCA) ★
1331 E Wyoming Ave, Philadelphia, PA 19124-3808
Tel (215) 537-7400 *Founded/Ownrshp* 2005
Sales 85.3MM[E] *EMP* 400
SIC 8069 Cancer hospital
Pr: John M McNeil
Bd of Dir: Aroop Banerji
VP: Diane Denny
Dir Risk M: Theresa Flack
Nurse Mgr: Marie Decker
IT Man: Stacey M Beagel
Secur Mgr: Lee Bernhang
Mktg Dir: John Goodchild

D-U-N-S 00-709-9914 IMP
EASTERN SHIPBUILDING GROUP INC (FL)
2200 Nelson Ave, Panama City, FL 32401-4969
Tel (850) 763-1900 *Founded/Ownrshp* 1996
Sales 318.3MM *EMP* 975
Accts Carr Riggs & Ingram Llc Ridge
SIC 3731 Shipbuilding & repairing
Pr: Brian D Isernia
Pr: Fernando Malabet
Ofcr: Kenneth R Munroe
Sr VP: Kenneth Monroe
Exec: Mark McGruder
Prgrm Mgr: Rick Cunningham
Genl Mgr: Rudy Sistrunk
Dir IT: Justin Smith
Sfty Mgr: Rick Antes
Sfty Mgr: Lisa Mayo
Sfty Mgr: William Spence

D-U-N-S 00-311-1747 IMP/EXP
EASTERN SLEEP PRODUCTS CO (VA)
SYMBOL MATTRESS
4901 Fitzhugh Ave, Richmond, VA 23230-3531
Tel (804) 254-1711 *Founded/Ownrshp* 1961, 2002
Sales 102.7MM[E] *EMP* 450
SIC 2515 2512 7641 4213

EASTERN SPORTS
See EASTON HOCKEY INC

D-U-N-S 07-145-0480
EASTERN UNIVERSITY
1300 Eagle Rd, Wayne, PA 19087-3617
Tel (610) 341-5800 *Founded/Ownrshp* 1932
Sales 89.3MM *EMP* 970[E]
Accts Capin Crouse Lp Greenwood In
SIC 8221 College, except junior
Pr: Dr Robert G Duffett
CFO: Francisco Milan
Ofcr: Lauren White
**Sr VP:* Thomas Ridington
**VP:* Diana Bacci
**VP:* Bettie Ann Brigham
**VP:* Rev Elizabeth Conde-Frazier
**VP:* J Pernell Jones
VP: Pernell Jones
**VP:* Derek Ritchie
**Prin:* David Black

D-U-N-S 05-862-5146
EASTERN VIRGINIA MEDICAL SCHOOL
714 Woodis Ave, Norfolk, VA 23510-1026
Tel (757) 446-6052 *Founded/Ownrshp* 1964
Sales 234.9MM *EMP* 1,500
Accts Kpmg Llp Norfolk Va
SIC 8221 8099 Colleges universities & professional schools; Physical examination & testing services
Pr: Richard V Homan
**Ch Bd:* Richard C Zoretic
**Pr:* Harry T Lester
Treas: John Hitt
Ofcr: Bruce Finlay
Ofcr: Amanda Mitchell
Ofcr: Stacy Purcell
VP: Nell M Reece
Comm Dir: Christine Butler
**VP Admn:* Mark Babashanian
Adm Dir: Robert J Alpino

D-U-N-S 60-309-9904 IMP
EASTERN WAREHOUSE DISTRIBUTORS INC
AUTO PARTS WAREHOUSE
355 S Flowers Mill Rd, Langhorne, PA 19047-2939
Tel (215) 741-4228 *Founded/Ownrshp* 1995
Sales 112.3MM[E] *EMP* 400
SIC 5013

D-U-N-S 06-150-7273
EASTERN WASHINGTON UNIVERSITY INC
307 Showalter Hall, Cheney, WA 99004-2445
Tel (509) 359-6200 *Founded/Ownrshp* 1882
Sales 147.3MM[E] *EMP* 1,550
Accts Brian Sonntag Cgfm State Aud
SIC 8221 University
Pr: Dr Rodolfo Arvalo
V Ch: Kris Mikkelsen
CFO: Toni Habegge
CFO: Toni Habegger
**CFO:* Toni Havegger
Assoc VP: Neil Woolf
VP: David French
VP: Stacy Morgan
VP: Heather Schmitt
**VP:* Mary Voves
VP: Michael Westfall

D-U-N-S 10-900-1271 IMP
EASTERN WHOLESALE FENCE CO INC
EASTERN FENCE
274 Middle Island Rd, Medford, NY 11763-1510
Tel (631) 698-0900 *Founded/Ownrshp* 1971
Sales 97.5MM^E *EMP* 300^E
SIC 5039 5031 5051 3496 Wire fence, gates & accessories; Fencing, wood; Piling, iron & steel; Miscellaneous fabricated wire products
Ch Bd: Peter E Williams
**CFO:* Peter E Williams Jr

EASTERNS AUTOMOTIVE GROUP
See SABMD LLC

D-U-N-S 15-155-9531
EASTGATE VILLAGE RETIREMENT CENTER
3500 Haskell Blvd, Muskogee, OK 74403-3915
Tel (918) 682-3191 *Founded/Ownrshp* 1986
Sales 576.7MM^E *EMP* 75
SIC 8052 8051 Intermediate care facilities; Skilled nursing care facilities
Pt: Sam Scott
Pt: Jim Breshears
Pt: Phillip Green

D-U-N-S 07-279-5834
▲ EASTGROUP PROPERTIES INC
190 E Capitol St Ste 400, Jackson, MS 39201-2152
Tel (601) 354-3555 *Founded/Ownrshp* 1969
Sales 235.0MM *EMP* 73^E
Tkr Sym EGP *Exch* NYS
SIC 6798 Real estate investment trusts
Pr: Marshall A Loeb
**Ch Bd:* David H Hoster II
CFO: N Keith McKey
Sr VP: John F Coleman
Sr VP: Bruce Corkern
Sr VP: William D Petsas
Sr VP: Brent W Wood
Board of Directors: D Pike Aloian, H C Bailey Jr, H Eric Bolton Jr, Hayden C Eaves III, Fredric H Gould, Mary E McCormick, Leland R Speed

D-U-N-S 02-582-9862
EASTLAND FEED AND GRAIN INC (IL)
EFGI
210 N Stanton St, Shannon, IL 61078-9325
Tel (815) 864-2723 *Founded/Ownrshp* 1960, 1990
Sales 182.1MM *EMP* 16
SIC 5191 5153

D-U-N-S 80-889-8381
▲ EASTMAN CHEMICAL CO
200 S Wilcox Dr, Kingsport, TN 37660-5147
Tel (423) 229-2000 *Founded/Ownrshp* 1920
Sales 9.6MMM *EMP* 15,000
Tkr Sym EMN *Exch* NYS
SIC 2821 2869 2865 2823 Plastics materials & resins; Polyethylene resins; Polypropylene resins; Industrial organic chemicals; Cyclic crudes & intermediates; Cellulosic manmade fibers
Ch Bd: Mark J Costa
COO: Ronald C Lindsay
CFO: Curtis E Espeland
Treas: Greg Allen
Treas: Mary D Hall
Treas: Jim Maitland
Ofcr: Perry Stuckey III
Ex VP: Brad A Lich
Sr VP: Michael H K Chung
Sr VP: Mark K Cox
Sr VP: Stephen G Crawford
Sr VP: Godefroy A F E Motte
VP: Don Cleek
VP: Deana Collins
VP: Richard Johnson
VP: Scott V King
Board of Directors: James J O'brien, Humberto P Alfonso, David W Raisbeck, Gary E Anderson, Brett D Begemann, Michael P Connors, Stephen R Demeritt, Robert M Hernandez, Julie F Holder, Renee J Hornbaker, Lewis M Kling

D-U-N-S 04-548-3088 EXP
■ EASTMAN CHEMICAL LTD CORP
(*Suby of* EASTMAN CHEMICAL CO) ★
200 S Wilcox Dr, Kingsport, TN 37660-5147
Tel (423) 229-2000 *Founded/Ownrshp* 1994
Sales 5.1MMM^E *EMP* 13,500
SIC 5169 8742 Industrial chemicals; Manmade fibers; Management consulting services
Ch Bd: James Rogers
**Pr:* Mark Costa
**CFO:* Curt Espeland
**Treas:* Mary Hall
**Ex VP:* Ron Linsey
Exec: Katherine K Hall
Dir IT: Roger Chadwell

D-U-N-S 12-711-1862
EASTMAN CREDIT UNION
2021 Meadowview Ln # 200, Kingsport, TN 37660-7468
Tel (423) 229-8200 *Founded/Ownrshp* 1934
Sales NA *EMP* 372
SIC 6062 State credit unions
Pr: Olan O Jones Jr
**Ch:* B F Rolston
Treas: Tonja Fish
Ofcr: Ryan Powell
Sr VP: Debra Bridwell
Sr VP: Gary Tucker
**Sr VP:* B G Viers
VP: Tammie Blakeley
VP: Darrell Dinsmore
Rgnl Mgr: Pam Mahaffey
Rgnl Mgr: Lynn Osborne

D-U-N-S 00-220-6183
■ EASTMAN KODAK CO (NJ)
(*Suby of* NANOCO GROUP PLC)
343 State St, Rochester, NY 14650-0001
Tel (585) 724-4000 *Founded/Ownrshp* 1880, 2016
Sales 1.8MMM *EMP* 6,400^E
Tkr Sym KODK *Exch* NYS
SIC 3861 3577 7384 Film, sensitized motion picture, X-ray, still camera, etc.; Cameras, still & motion picture (all types); Photographic paper & cloth, all types; Computer peripheral equipment; Graphic displays, except graphic terminals; Optical scanning devices; Photofinish laboratories
CEO: Jeffrey J Clarke
CFO: John N McMullen
Ex VP: John McMullen
Sr VP: Philip Cullimore
Sr VP: Brad W Kruchten
Sr VP: Eric-Yves Mahe
Sr VP: Steven Overman
Sr VP: Sharon E Underberg
VP: Natasha M Adams
VP: Brian Burr
VP: Michael Korizno
VP: Lo S Lebegue
VP: Michael Lo
VP: Mike Massey
VP: John O'Grady
VP: Timothy Smith
Board of Directors: Mark S Burgess, Matthew A Doheny, John A Janitz, George Karfunkel, Jason New, William G Parrett, Derek Smith

EASTON BELL SPORTS
See BELL SPORTS INC

D-U-N-S 00-922-3983 IMP/EXP
EASTON HOCKEY INC
EASTERN SPORTS
(*Suby of* BRG SPORTS INC) ★
7855 Haskell Ave Ste 200, Van Nuys, CA 91406-1935
Tel (818) 782-6445 *Founded/Ownrshp* 2006
Sales 247.2MM^E *EMP* 1,500
SIC 5091 Sporting & recreation goods
CEO: Mary George
**Pr:* Anthony Palma
CFO: Mark Tripp
Sr VP: Duke Stump
VP: Mike Zlaket
**Prin:* Paul E Harrington
Off Admin: Ron Thomas
CTO: Gerry Maurizio
MIS Dir: Jerry Mauricio
Dir IT: Hari Rayapati
IT Man: Kerry Jarrell

EASTON HOME, THE
See PRESBYTERIAN HOMES INC

EASTON HOSPITAL
See NORTHAMPTON HOSPITAL CORP

EASTRIDGE ADM STAFFING
See EPLICA INC

EASTRIDGE NURSING CENTER
See ARKANSAS ELDER OUTREACH OF LITTLE ROCK

D-U-N-S 08-291-3567
EASTSIDE UNION HIGH SCHOOL DISTRICT
830 N Capitol Ave, San Jose, CA 95133-1316
Tel (408) 347-5000 *Founded/Ownrshp* 1940
Sales 181.3MM^E *EMP* 2,666
Accts Vavrinek Trine Day & Co Ll
SIC 8211 Public senior high school
VP: Lan Nguyen
Ex Dir: Mary Jacobs
Netwrk Eng: Gilbert Gaska
Sls&Mrk Ex: Silvia Pelayo
Snr Mgr: Kelly Kwong

D-U-N-S 08-507-3856
EASTWOOD CONSTRUCTION LLC
EASTWOOD HOMES
2857 Westport Rd, Charlotte, NC 28208-3647
Tel (704) 399-4663 *Founded/Ownrshp* 1977
Sales 113.1MM^E *EMP* 185
SIC 1521 New construction, single-family houses
Pr: Clark Stewart
**CFO:* Kevin Hutchins
VP: Max Thomason
Admn Mgr: Heather Lambert
VP Opers: Mike Conley
Sls&Mrk Ex: Michael Obrien

EASTWOOD HOMES
See EASTWOOD CONSTRUCTION LLC

EASY GARDENER
See UNITED AMERICAN ACQUISITION CORP

EASY MASK
See LOPAREX LLC

EASY MONEY
See COMMUNITY CHOICE FINANCIAL INC

D-U-N-S 00-426-1335 EXP
EASY WAY LEISURE CORP
EASY WAY PRODUCTS
8950 Rossash Rd, Cincinnati, OH 45236-1210
Tel (513) 731-5640 *Founded/Ownrshp* 1996
Sales 99.3MM^E *EMP* 500
SIC 2392 Cushions & pillows; Chair covers & pads: made from purchased materials
Pr: Jon D Randman
**VP:* Steve Coppel
Prd Mgr: Joe Carchedi
Prd Mgr: Jeff Luke
**VP Sls:* Scott Szymkowicz

EASY WAY PRODUCTS
See EASY WAY LEISURE CORP

D-U-N-S 79-111-0810
EASYLINK SERVICES INTERNATIONAL CORP
OPENTEXT
(*Suby of* OPEN TEXT CORPORATION)
11720 Amberpark Dr # 200, Alpharetta, GA 30009-2275
Tel (678) 533-8000 *Founded/Ownrshp* 2012
Sales 296.9MM^E *EMP* 541^E
SIC 4813
Pr: Mark J Barrenechea
Pr: Richard Shriver
**CFO:* Paul McFeeters
**Chf Mktg O:* James Latham
**Ofcr:* Gordon A Davies
**Ex VP:* Gregory W Corgan
Ex VP: Teresa A Deuel
**Ex VP:* Jonathan Hunter
Ex VP: Chris Parker
**Ex VP:* David Wareham
**Sr VP:* Steve Best
**Sr VP:* Walter Kohler
**Sr VP:* Muhi Majzoub
Sr VP: Kevin Maloney
**Sr VP:* James McGourlay
**Sr VP:* Louis Mousseau
**Sr VP:* Tony Preston
**Sr VP:* Graham Pullen
VP: Richard Blume
VP: Jack Harwood
VP: John Harwood

EATEL PUBLISHING
See EATELCORP LLC

D-U-N-S 36-165-7265
EATELCORP LLC
EATEL PUBLISHING
913 S Burnside Ave, Gonzales, LA 70737-4258
Tel (225) 621-4300 *Founded/Ownrshp* 1983
Sales 120.7MM^E *EMP* 434
SIC 5731 Radio, television & electronic stores
Pr: John D Scanlan
**Pr:* Kevin E Dolan
**Ch:* Ruth B Scanlan
**Prin:* A G Scanlan II
Mktg Mgr: Evan Gonzales
Mktg Mgr: Doug Luke

D-U-N-S 11-905-4187
EATERIES INC
GARFIELDS RESTAURANT & PUB
1220 S Santa Fe Ave, Edmond, OK 73003-5904
Tel (480) 347-3800 *Founded/Ownrshp* 2006
Sales 79.1MM^E *EMP* 2,889
SIC 5812 5813 6794 American restaurant; Bar (drinking places); Franchises, selling or licensing
Pr: Preston Stockton
**CEO:* Richard Cervera
**CFO:* Adam Romo
**VP:* James M Burke
VP: August Hehemann
VP: Meline Towler
Board of Directors: Marc Buehler, Joli Cooper, Carl Cordova, Thomas F Golden, Bradley L Grow, Edward D Orza, Vincent F Orza Jr

D-U-N-S 04-529-2711
EATN PARK HOSPITALITY GROUP INC
PARKHURST DINING SERVICES
285 E Waterfront Dr # 200, Homestead, PA 15120-5017
Tel (412) 461-2000 *Founded/Ownrshp* 1989
Sales 883.4MM^E *EMP* 10,000
SIC 8741

EATON
See COOPER B-LINE INC

D-U-N-S 11-833-2969 IMP
EATON AEROSPACE LLC
E E M C O
(*Suby of* EATON HYDRAULICS GROUP USA) ★
1000 Eaton Blvd, Cleveland, OH 44122-6058
Tel (216) 523-5000 *Founded/Ownrshp* 2000
Sales 224.4MM^E *EMP* 1,000
SIC 3812 Acceleration indicators & systems components, aerospace
CEO: Alexander M Cutler
**CFO:* R H Fearon
Sr VP: Randy W Carson
Mng Dir: Bob Brlas

EATON COOPER LIGHTING
See COOPER LIGHTING LLC

D-U-N-S 00-415-5818 IMP/EXP
EATON CORP
(*Suby of* EATON CORPORATION PUBLIC LIMITED COMPANY)
1000 Eaton Blvd, Cleveland, OH 44122-6058
Tel (216) 523-5000 *Founded/Ownrshp* 1911
Sales 6.9MMM *EMP* 73,000
Accts Ernst & Young Llp Cleveland
SIC 3625 3714 3594 3559 3571 Motor controls & accessories; Motor starters & controllers, electric; Actuators, industrial; Motor vehicle engines & parts; Motor vehicle transmissions, drive assemblies & parts; Motor vehicle steering systems & parts; Pumps, hydraulic power transfer; Motors: hydraulic, fluid power or air; Semiconductor manufacturing machinery; Personal computers (microcomputers)
Ch Bd: Alexander Cutler
CFO: Richard Fearon
Treas: David Foster
Ex VP: Mark McGuire
Sr VP: Craig Arnold
Sr VP: Thomas Moran
Sr VP: Ram Ramakrishnan
Sr VP: Billie Rawot
VP: Scott Krueger
IT Man: Nan Sambandan
Sls Mgr: Paul Parubrub

D-U-N-S 36-294-3706
EATON CORP
(*Suby of* COOPER POWER SYSTEMS LLC) ★
505 Hghway 169 N Ste 1200, Minneapolis, MN 55441
Tel (763) 595-7777 *Founded/Ownrshp* 2006
Sales 122.0MM^E *EMP* 1,000
SIC 5084 Measuring & testing equipment, electrical
CEO: Alexander Cutler
Treas: Tyler Johnson
VP: Melissa Scheppele
Mktg Mgr: Rochelle Filiowich

D-U-N-S 60-275-5428 IMP
EATON ELECTRIC HOLDINGS LLC
(*Suby of* EATON CORPORATION PUBLIC LIMITED COMPANY)
600 Travis St Ste 5600, Houston, TX 77002-2909
Tel (713) 209-8400 *Founded/Ownrshp* 2012
Sales 3.7MMM^E *EMP* 26,860^E
SIC 3646 3612 3613 3644 3536 3423 Commercial indusl & institutional electric lighting fixtures; Ceiling systems, luminous; Fluorescent lighting fixtures, commercial; Transformers, except electric; Power & distribution transformers; Power transformers, electric; Voltage regulators, transmission & distribution; Panel & distribution boards & other related apparatus; Power circuit breakers; Switches, electric power except snap, push button, etc.; Fuses & fuse equipment; Noncurrent-carrying wiring services; Electric outlet, switch & fuse boxes; Electric conduits & fittings; Hoists, cranes & monorails; Hoists; Hand & edge tools; Wrenches, hand tools; Hammers (hand tools); Soldering tools
Pr: Kirk Hachigian
CFO: David Barta
Treas: Tyler Johnson
Sr VP: Bruce M Taten
IT Man: Steven Hill
Prd Mgr: Manuel Cruz
Ql Cn Mgr: Frank Domingo
Ql Cn Mgr: Amy Poole
VP Sls: John Kerkhove

EATON GLOBAL HOSE
See EATON-AEROQUIP LLC

EATON HYDRAULICS GROUP USA
See EATON HYDRAULICS LLC

D-U-N-S 07-908-9128 IMP/EXP
EATON HYDRAULICS INC
(*Suby of* EATON HYDRAULICS GROUP USA) ★
803 32nd Ave W, Spencer, IA 51301-6122
Tel (712) 264-3269 *Founded/Ownrshp* 2013
Sales 694.0M^E *EMP* 1,821^E
SIC 1799 Hydraulic equipment, installation & service
Prin: Tony Niese

D-U-N-S 00-504-5000 IMP/EXP
EATON HYDRAULICS LLC
EATON HYDRAULICS GROUP USA
(*Suby of* EATON CORP) ★
14615 Lone Oak Rd, Eden Prairie, MN 55344-2200
Tel (952) 937-9800 *Founded/Ownrshp* 2008
Sales 1.3MMM^E *EMP* 14,568
SIC 3089 3052 3568 3492 3594 3728 Injection molded finished plastic products; Injection molding of plastics; Rubber hose; Plastic hose; Power transmission equipment; Hose & tube fittings & assemblies, hydraulic/pneumatic; Hose & tube couplings, hydraulic/pneumatic; Fluid power pumps; Aircraft parts & equipment; Aircraft assemblies, subassemblies & parts
CEO: Alexander M Cutler
VP: J Robert Horst
VP: Deb Lauer
VP: Matt Mehlbrech
VP: Ruppert Russoniello
VP: William Vanarsdale
Comm Dir: Lynn Soule
Prgrm Mgr: Richard France
Dir IT: Michael Rainwater
Netwrk Eng: Steve Adolphin
Mtls Mgr: Gregory Eatmon

D-U-N-S 15-736-7301
EATON INDUSTRIAL CORP
ARGO-TECH
(*Suby of* AT HOLDINGS CORP) ★
23555 Euclid Ave, Cleveland, OH 44117-1703
Tel (216) 692-5456 *Founded/Ownrshp* 1990
Sales 95.3MM^E *EMP* 736
SIC 3724 3728 Pumps, aircraft engine; Aircraft parts & equipment
CEO: Alexander M Cutler
CFO: John S Glover
Ex VP: Paul R Keen
VP: James Cunningham
VP: Earl R Franklin
Prgrm Mgr: Michael Amrine
Genl Mgr: Ken Kovalchik
IT Man: Lawrence Frank
IT Man: Jeffrey Tomson

EATON STEEL BAR COMPANY
See EATON STEEL CORP

D-U-N-S 01-728-7566 IMP
EATON STEEL CORP
EATON STEEL BAR COMPANY
10221 Capital St, Oak Park, MI 48237-3103
Tel (248) 398-3434 *Founded/Ownrshp* 1953
Sales 87.9MM^E *EMP* 210
SIC 5051 3312 Structural shapes, iron or steel; Bars & bar shapes, steel, cold-finished: own hot-rolled
Owner: Mark Goodman
**VP:* Mark Candy
**VP:* Gary Goodman
VP: Glen Huber
VP: Rod Machak

D-U-N-S 94-287-4462
EATON USEV HOLDING CO INC
(*Suby of* EATON CORP) ★
1111 Suprr Eatn Ctr 173, Cleveland, OH 44114
Tel (216) 523-5000 *Founded/Ownrshp* 1990
Sales 106.0MM^E *EMP* 286^E
SIC 3592 Valves, engine
CEO: Alexander M Cutler

D-U-N-S 09-586-1001
▲ EATON VANCE CORP
2 International Pl # 1400, Boston, MA 02110-4101
Tel (617) 482-8260 *Founded/Ownrshp* 1924
Sales 1.4MMM *EMP* 1,473
Tkr Sym EV *Exch* NYS
SIC 6282 Investment advice; Investment advisory service; Investment counselors
Ch Bd: Thomas E Faust Jr
Pr: Sean Broussard
Pr: Rick Coscia
Pr: Eric Filkins
Pr: Lisa Flynn
Pr: Grant Howes
Pr: Jennifer Klempa
Pr: Linda Nishi
Pr: Jeff Norton
Pr: Lisa Smith

Pr: Andrew Szczurowski
CFO: Laurie G Hylton
Ofcr: Jeffrey P Beale
Sr VP: Paul Nobile
VP: Robb Allen
VP: Kristin Anagnost
VP: David Barr
VP: Jackson Bennett
VP: Christopher Berry
VP: Michael Botthof
VP: John Brodbine
Board of Directors: Ann E Berman, Leo I Higdon Jr, Brian D Langstraat, Dorothy E Puhy, Winthrop H Smith Jr, Richard A Spillane Jr

D-U-N-S 04-480-9994

■ EATON VANCE MANAGEMENT INC
(*Suby of* EATON VANCE CORP) ★
2 International Pl # 1400, Boston, MA 02110-4101
Tel (617) 482-8260 *Founded/Ownrshp* 1981
Sales 284.5MM^E *EMP* 700
SIC 6282 Investment advisory service
CEO: Thomas E Faust Jr
**Pr:* M Dozier Gardner
**Pr:* James B Hawkes
Pr: Jane Rudnick
**Treas:* Curtis H Jones
VP: Kelley Baccei
**VP:* Jeffrey P Beale
VP: Robert Bortnick
VP: Jeremiah Casey
VP: John Crowley
VP: Alan Dynner
VP: Daniel Ethier
VP: Charles Gaffney
VP: Kathleen C Gaffney
**VP:* M Katharine Kasper
VP: Kwang Kim
VP: Coreen Kraysler
VP: Jason Kritzer
VP: Walter L Lindsay
VP: Catherine McDermott
VP: Michael McLean

D-U-N-S 00-535-6498 IMP

EATON-AEROQUIP LLC
EATON GLOBAL HOSE
(*Suby of* AEROQUIP-VICKERS INC) ★
1000 Eaton Blvd, Cleveland, OH 44122-6058
Tel (216) 523-5000 *Founded/Ownrshp* 1940
Sales 1.0MMM^E *EMP* 8,000
SIC 3052 3492 3429 3069 3585 3728 Rubber hose; Plastic hose; Hose & tube fittings & assemblies, hydraulic/pneumatic; Clamps & couplings, hose; Clamps, metal; Molded rubber products; Parts for heating, cooling & refrigerating equipment; Aircraft parts & equipment
CEO: Alexander M Cutler
**VP:* E R Franklin

D-U-N-S 07-650-5734

EAU CLAIRE AREA SCHOOL DISTRICT
500 Main St, Eau Claire, WI 54701-3770
Tel (715) 852-3000 *Founded/Ownrshp* 1901
Sales 57.6MM^E *EMP* 1,491
SIC 8211 Public elementary & secondary schools
Genl Mgr: Scott Noffke
IT Man: Abigail Johnson

EAU CLAIRE HOSPITAL
See MAYO CLINIC HEALTH SYSTEM-NORTHWEST WISCONSIN REGION INC

EB
See EXCHANGE BANK

D-U-N-S 09-541-8377

EB ACQUISITION CO LLC
(*Suby of* FORD FINANCIAL FUND II LP) ★
200 Crescent Ct, Dallas, TX 75201-1834
Tel (214) 871-5151 *Founded/Ownrshp* 2014
Sales NA *EMP* 921^E
SIC 6029 Commercial banks
Prin: Kenneth Russell

D-U-N-S 09-156-6708

■ EB INVESTMENT CORP
(*Suby of* ELECTRONICS BOUTIQUE AMERICA INC) ★
931 S Matlack St, West Chester, PA 19382-5521
Tel (610) 430-8100 *Founded/Ownrshp* 2001
Sales 2.0MMM *EMP* 1,400
SIC 5734 5945 Software, computer games; Software, business & non-game; Hobby, toy & game shops
CEO: Jeffrey Griffiths

D-U-N-S 07-986-5024

■ EB SAV INC
(*Suby of* WWF OPERATING CO) ★
1721 San Juan Hwy, San Juan Bautista, CA 95045-9780
Tel (303) 635-4500 *Founded/Ownrshp* 2013
Sales 226.9MM^E *EMP* 1,028^E
SIC 0723 2099 Vegetable packing services; Food preparations

D-U-N-S 96-887-9887

EB SUBHOLDINGS I INC
(*Suby of* SELECT STAFFING) ★
1040 Crown Pointe Pkwy, Atlanta, GA 30338-6908
Tel (770) 671-1900 *Founded/Ownrshp* 2011
Sales 15.3MM^E *EMP* 1,500^E
SIC 7363 Temporary help service
Pr: Tom Bickes
Ch Bd: James M Holland

EBA&D
See ENSIGN-BICKFORD AEROSPACE & DEFENSE CO

D-U-N-S 83-156-1428 IMP/EXP

EBARA AMERICA CORP
(*Suby of* EBARA CORPORATION)
809 Walker Ave Apt 1, Oakland, CA 94610-2018
Tel (510) 251-0500 *Founded/Ownrshp* 1993
Sales 129.3MM^E *EMP* 331
SIC 3492 Fluid power valves & hose fittings
Pr: Mitsuhiro Kochi
**CEO:* Kengo Choki
**Sec:* Kazuhiro Nakamura

D-U-N-S 96-382-3786 IMP/EXP

▲ EBAY INC
2065 Hamilton Ave, San Jose, CA 95125-5904
Tel (408) 376-7400 *Founded/Ownrshp* 1995
Sales 8.5MMM *EMP* 11,600^E
Accts Pricewaterhousecoopers Llp Sa
Tkr Sym EBAY *Exch* NGS
SIC 5961 Catalog & mail-order houses; ;
Pr: Devin N Wenig
CFO: Leigh Gui
CFO: Scott Schenkel
CFO: Scott F Schenkel
Treas: Louise Curtis
Treas: Anthony Glasby
Bd of Dir: John Donahoe
Bd of Dir: Scott Shipman
Bd of Dir: Max Stanford
Ex VP: Molly Smith
Sr VP: Stephen Fisher
Sr VP: Marie OH Huber
Sr VP: Harry A Lawton
Sr VP: Jay Lee
Sr VP: Rj Pittman
Sr VP: Paul Todd
VP: Don Albert
VP: Gyla Becks
VP: Paul Cataldo
VP: Jean-Marc Codsi
VP: Anjli Dudani
Board of Directors: Perry M Traquina, Fred D Anderson, Edward W Barnholt, Anthony J Bates, Bonnie S Hammer, Kathleen C Mitic, Pierre M Omidyar, Paul S Pressler, Robert H Swan, Thomas J Tierney

D-U-N-S 01-596-7771

EBCO GENERAL CONTRACTOR LTD
305 W Gillis Ave, Cameron, TX 76520-3930
Tel (254) 697-8516 *Founded/Ownrshp* 2003
Sales 87.0MM *EMP* 76
SIC 1542 8741 Commercial & office building, new construction; Construction management
Pt: John Egger
Snr PM: Gene Rigby

D-U-N-S 07-763-3451

EBENEZER SOCIETY
OUTPATIENT CHEMICAL DEPENDENCY
(*Suby of* OUTPATENT CHEM DPNDNCY PROGRAM) ★
2722 Park Ave, Minneapolis, MN 55407-1009
Tel (612) 874-3460 *Founded/Ownrshp* 1917
Sales 72.7MM *EMP* 1,505
SIC 8051 8741 Skilled nursing care facilities; Management services
Pr: Mark Thomas
**CFO:* Steve Gryger
VP: Susan Farr
VP: Gary Lewis
VP: Susan Olson
MIS Dir: Roger Hennen
VP Opers: Sharon Klefsaas

D-U-N-S 07-996-9669

EBERL CLAIMS SERVICE LLC
(*Suby of* EM) ★
7276 W Mansfield Ave, Lakewood, CO 80235-2201
Tel (303) 988-6286 *Founded/Ownrshp* 2015
Sales NA *EMP* 1,300
SIC 6411 Insurance claim adjusters, not employed by insurance company
CEO: Gerrad Brigham
Ex Dir: Jennifer Hevelone

D-U-N-S 78-349-8967

EBERSEN INC
7401 Central Ave Ne Ste 2, Minneapolis, MN 55432-3572
Tel (763) 572-2661 *Founded/Ownrshp* 1987
Sales 1.4MMM^E *EMP* 1,500
SIC 4911 1521 6211 1382 4731 8711 Electric services; Single-family housing construction; Security brokers & dealers; Oil & gas exploration services; Freight transportation arrangement; Engineering services
Pr: Chidi N Anunka

D-U-N-S 12-058-1132 IMP

EBERSPAECHER NORTH AMERICA INC
CATEM NORTH AMERICA
(*Suby of* EBERSPACHER CLIMATE CONTROL SYSTEMS GMBH & CO. KG)
29101 Haggerty Rd, Novi, MI 48377-2913
Tel (248) 994-7010 *Founded/Ownrshp* 1999
Sales 268.1MM^E *EMP* 630
SIC 3714 Exhaust systems & parts, motor vehicle
CFO: Martin Peters
**COO:* Heinrich Baumann
**COO:* Klaus Beetz
**COO:* Thomas Waldhier
**Ch:* Gunter Baumann

D-U-N-S 55-741-2041

EBHI HOLDINGS INC
(*Suby of* GOLDEN GATE CAPITAL LP) ★
1000 Field Dr Ste 240, Lake Forest, IL 60045
Tel (312) 251-3430 *Founded/Ownrshp* 2005
Sales 546.9MM^E *EMP* 7,427
SIC 5611 5699 5941 5719 5947 5961 Men's & boys' clothing stores; Sports apparel; Sporting goods & bicycle shops; Housewares; Gift shop; Clothing, mail order (except women's); Fishing, hunting & camping equipment & supplies: mail order; Furniture & furnishings, mail order; Women's apparel, mail order
Pr: Neil Fiske
CFO: Marv Toland
Ofcr: R Thomas Helton
Ofcr: Brent Kugman
Sr VP: Kimberly Berg
Sr VP: Freya R Brier
VP: Tony Krohn
Dir IT: Karen Kaup
Board of Directors: Edward M Straw, John C Brouillard, Stephen E Watson, Jerry M Comstock Jr, William T End, Scott Galloway, Howard Gross, Paul E Kirincic, William E Redmond, Kenneth M Reiss, Laurie M Shahon

EBI CONSULTING
See ENVIROBUSINESS INC

D-U-N-S 05-041-0323 IMP

■ EBI LLC
BIOMET BONE HEALING TECH
(*Suby of* ZIMMER BIOMET) ★
399 Jefferson Rd, Parsippany, NJ 07054-3707
Tel (973) 299-9300 *Founded/Ownrshp* 1999
Sales 400.0MM^E *EMP* 1,504
SIC 5047 Medical equipment & supplies
Pr: Bob Phelp
VP: John Blumers
DP Dir: Lisa Viele
VP Mktg: Marshall Perez

D-U-N-S 08-270-3679

▲ EBIX INC (GA)
1 Ebix Way Ste 100, Duluth, GA 30097-2463
Tel (678) 281-2020 *Founded/Ownrshp* 1976
Sales 265.4MM *EMP* 2,707^E
Tkr Sym EBIX *Exch* NGS
SIC 7371 7372 Computer software development & applications; Prepackaged software
Ch Bd: Robin Raina
CFO: Robert F Kerris
Ex VP: Leon D'Apice
Ex VP: Graham Prior
Sr VP: James Senge Sr
VP: Rahul Raina
Snr Sftwr: Rajnish Khungar
IT Man: Robert Rodriguez
Software D: Ramesh Thatavarty
VP Sls: Jose Lopez
VP Sls: Larry Panetta
Board of Directors: Hans U Benz, Neil D Eckert, George W Hebard III, Rolf Herter, Hans Ueli Keller, Joseph R Wright Jr

D-U-N-S 94-272-2885 IMP

EBM INDUSTRIES MANAGEMENT GROUP INC
(*Suby of* EBM BETEILIGUNGS-GMBH)
100 Hyde Rd, Farmington, CT 06032-2835
Tel (860) 674-1515 *Founded/Ownrshp* 1995
Sales 152.6MM^E *EMP* 450^E
SIC 5084 Fans, industrial
Pr: Robert Sobolewski
**Ch:* Gerhard Sturm
IT Man: Jamie Perkins

D-U-N-S 05-443-2893 IMP

EBM-PAPST INC (CT)
(*Suby of* EBM INDUSTRIES MANAGEMENT GROUP INC) ★
100 Hyde Rd, Farmington, CT 06032-2835
Tel (860) 674-1515 *Founded/Ownrshp* 1981, 1995
Sales 152.6MM^E *EMP* 450
SIC 5084 3564 Fans, industrial; Blowers & fans
CEO: Robert Sobolewski
**Ch Bd:* Gerhard Sturm
Pr: Scott Beauchemin
Sr VP: Bill John
**Sr VP:* William T John
VP: William John
Mng Dir: Mark Hill
Ql Cn Mgr: Jack Derewonko
Sls Dir: James Pisano
Mktg Mgr: Stan Barbas

EBMUD
See EAST BAY MUNICIPAL UTILITY DISTRICT WATER SYSTEM

EBP SUPPLY SOLUTIONS
See EASTERN BAG AND PAPER CO INC

D-U-N-S 00-339-6256 IMP/EXP

EBSCO INDUSTRIES INC
VULCAN INFORMATION PACKAGING
5724 Highway 280 E, Birmingham, AL 35242-6818
Tel (205) 991-6600 *Founded/Ownrshp* 1944, 1952
Sales 2.0MMM^E *EMP* 6,032
SIC 7389 2782 3949 7375 2721 6552 Subscription fulfillment services: magazine, newspaper, etc.; Blankbooks & looseleaf binders; Sporting & athletic goods; Lures, fishing: artificial; Information retrieval services; Periodicals; Subdividers & developers
Pr: Timothy R Collins
**Ch Bd:* James T Stephens
Pr: Steve Hill
Pr: Kim James
Pr: Greg Robb
CFO: Richard Bozzelli
**CFO:* David Walker
**Ex VP:* Sam Brooks
Ex VP: Michael Gorrell
Ex VP: Stratton Lloyd
**Sr VP:* John Atkins
VP: Gary Balentine
VP: Tamir Borensztajn
VP: Becky Caldarello
VP: Iveta Chuda
VP: Tad Goltra
VP: Kai Haatainen
VP: Tracy Housch
VP: Michael Humber
VP: William Hutson
VP: Doug Jenkins

D-U-N-S 16-951-9837

EBSCO PUBLISHING INC
EBSCOHOST
(*Suby of* VULCAN INFORMATION PACKAGING) ★
10 Estes St, Ipswich, MA 01938-2106
Tel (978) 356-6500 *Founded/Ownrshp* 1995
Sales 247.1MM^E *EMP* 1,278
SIC 2741 7375 2731 2721 Miscellaneous publishing; Information retrieval services; Book publishing; Periodicals
Pr: Tim Collins
CFO: Rick N Bozellie
CFO: David Walker
Ex VP: Samuel Brooks
Ex VP: Michael Gorrell
Sr VP: Mark Herrick
Sr VP: Doug Jenkins
Sr VP: Stratton Lloyd
Sr VP: David Mangione
Sr VP: Oliver Pesch
VP: Brad Buckley
VP: Paul Donovan
VP: Brad Rich
VP: Mike Wallis
Exec: Nancy Gormley
Exec: Deborah Lapierre
Dir Bus: Randy Lyle

EBSCOHOST
See EBSCO PUBLISHING INC

D-U-N-S 04-452-0877 IMP

■ EBV EXPLOSIVES ENVIRONMENTAL CO
GENERAL DYNAMICS ORDNANCE AND
(*Suby of* GENERAL DYNAMICS ORDNANCE AND TACTICAL SYSTEMS INC) ★
4174 County Road 180, Carthage, MO 64836-4002
Tel (417) 624-0212 *Founded/Ownrshp* 2010
Sales 89.3MM^E *EMP* 130^E
SIC 4953 Refuse systems
Pr: Frank Winkler
**CFO:* Shyla Schilling
**VP Sls:* David R Zoghby

D-U-N-S 15-409-0385

EBY CORP
2525 E 36th Cir N, Wichita, KS 67219-2303
Tel (316) 268-3500 *Founded/Ownrshp* 1986
Sales 93.2MM *EMP* 150^E
SIC 1629 1623 1622 1541 1542 7353 Dam construction; Dock construction; Waterway construction; Waste water & sewage treatment plant construction; Sewer line construction; Bridge construction; Tunnel construction; Industrial buildings, new construction; Warehouse construction; Commercial & office building, new construction; Heavy construction equipment rental
Pr: Michael A Grier
**Ch Bd:* James R Greir III
**Ch Bd:* James R Grier III
**Ex VP:* Kurt T Grier
VP: Larry Cheatham

D-U-N-S 09-259-5557

EBY GROUP INC
EBY HOLDINGS
13795 S Mur Len Rd # 301, Olathe, KS 66062-1675
Tel (913) 782-3200 *Founded/Ownrshp* 1991
Sales NA *EMP* 1,300
SIC 6719 Personal holding companies, except banks
Pr: Joe EBY
**Pr:* Andy EBY
**CFO:* Mike EBY
Sr VP: Alan Fairbanks
Dir IT: Chris Steger

EBY HOLDINGS
See EBY GROUP INC

D-U-N-S 80-971-1898

EBY-BROWN CO LLC
1415 W Diehl Rd Ste 300, Naperville, IL 60563-1153
Tel (630) 778-2800 *Founded/Ownrshp* 2000
Sales 2.4MMM^E *EMP* 2,500
SIC 5194 5145 5141 5122 5149 Cigarettes; Cigars; Snuff; Confectionery; Groceries, general line; Drugs, proprietaries & sundries; Groceries & related products
CFO: Mark Smetana
Sr VP: Scott Kolat
VP: Lee Canon
VP: Brady Freeman
VP: James Hachtel
VP: Shirley Jaehrling
VP: Dennie Jezior
VP: Christina Larson
VP: Joe Pfeifer
VP: Joe Roenna
VP: John Scardina
VP: Mike Wierzbicki
VP Bus Dev: Kenneth Denney
VP Bus Dev: Dustin Snyder

D-U-N-S 01-757-3259

■ EC AMERICA INC (VA)
(*Suby of* IMMIXGROUP INC) ★
8444 Westpark Dr Ste 200, Mc Lean, VA 22102-5112
Tel (703) 752-0610 *Founded/Ownrshp* 1998, 2008
Sales 187.4MM^E *EMP* 201
SIC 5045 Computers, peripherals & software
CEO: Jeffrey Copeland
**Pr:* Arthur Richer
Opers Mgr: Vikek Gupta

D-U-N-S 00-961-1484

EC CO
ELECTRICAL CONSTRUCTION CO
2121 Nw Thurman St, Portland, OR 97210-2517
Tel (503) 224-3511 *Founded/Ownrshp* 2003
Sales 169.5MM *EMP* 800
Accts Moss Adams Llp Portland Oreg
SIC 1731 7694 5063 5084 General electrical contractor; Electric motor repair; Rewinding stators; Generators; Motors, electric; Engines & parts, diesel; Engines, gasoline
Pr: George H Adams
Pr: Jon Orrell
COO: Rick Rinehart
**CFO:* Joel J Scroggy
Bd of Dir: Eric Bender
VP: Mike Douglas
VP: Kelly Grant
VP: Steve Schmitz
Dept Mgr: Bill Coburn
Brnch Mgr: Mark Seeronen
Sfty Dirs: Jolene Burum

D-U-N-S 80-857-8814

■ EC SOURCE SERVICES LLC
(*Suby of* MASTEC INC) ★
16055 Space Center Blvd # 700, Houston, TX 77062-6266
Tel (281) 480-4600 *Founded/Ownrshp* 2011
Sales 290.4MM^E *EMP* 517
SIC 1623 8742 Electric power line construction; Construction project management consultant
Pr: Brian E Bratton

Genl Mgr: Doug Link
Off Mgr: Liz Higgins

EC WASTE
See EC WASTE LLC

D-U-N-S 10-409-7993
■ EC WASTE LLC
EC WASTE
(*Suby of* WM) ★
Int 923 Km 1/7 Rr 3, Humacao, PR 00791
Tel (787) 852-4444 *Founded/Ownrshp* 1995
Sales 97.1MM[E] *EMP* 305
SIC 4953 Non-hazardous waste disposal sites
CEO: Randy Jensen

ECA
See EASTERN AMERICAN ENERGY CORP

ECA HOLDING
See ENERGY CORP OF AMERICA

ECC
See ENVIRONMENTAL CHEMICAL CORP

D-U-N-S 60-100-7946
ECCA HOLDINGS CORP
EYE CARE CENTERS OF AMERICA
(*Suby of* HVHC INC) ★
175 E Houston St Fl 6, San Antonio, TX 78205-2210
Tel (210) 340-3531 *Founded/Ownrshp* 2004
Sales 1.0MMM[E] *EMP* 5,601
SIC 5995 3851 Optical goods stores; Eyeglasses, prescription; Ophthalmic goods
Ch Bd: David McComas
**Pr:* James J Denny
Pr: Vincent Iavarone
Pr: J Llanes
COO: Robert Gross
CFO: Mark Pearson
**CFO:* Douglas C Shepard
**Ex VP:* George E Gebhardt
Ex VP: Jennifer Taylor
Sr VP: Robert Niemiec
VP: Chad Hayes

ECCLESTONE ORGANIZATION
See PGA RESORT & SPA

ECCO RETAIL
See ECCO USA INC

D-U-N-S 55-604-3982 IMP
ECCO USA INC
ECCO RETAIL
(*Suby of* ECCO SKO A/S)
16 Delta Dr, Londonderry, NH 03053-2382
Tel (603) 537-7300 *Founded/Ownrshp* 2007
Sales 95.2MM[E] *EMP* 277[E]
SIC 5139 5661 Shoes; Shoe stores
Pr: David Quel
**Sec:* Claus Ipsen
VP: Barbara Brigugio
Sftwr Eng: Enzo Chiariotti

ECENTRIA
See OPTICSPLANET INC

D-U-N-S 02-498-2166
ECHELON CAPITAL LLC
121 W Wacker Dr, Chicago, IL 60601-1781
Tel (312) 263-0263 *Founded/Ownrshp* 2010
Sales 114.5MM[E] *EMP* 3[E]
SIC 6799 Investors
Prin: Louis E Berg

ECHN
See MANCHESTER MEMORIAL HOSPITAL INC

ECHN
See EASTERN CONNECTICUT HEALTH NETWORK INC

D-U-N-S 93-233-5367
ECHN ENTERPRISES INC
(*Suby of* ECHN) ★
71 Haynes St, Manchester, CT 06040-4131
Tel (860) 646-1222 *Founded/Ownrshp* 1984
Sales 27.1MM *EMP* 2,400
SIC 8741 Hospital management
CEO: Peter J Karl
**Pr:* Peter Cholera

ECHO ELECTRIC SUPPLY
See ECHO GROUP INC

D-U-N-S 55-564-8455
▲ ECHO GLOBAL LOGISTICS INC
600 W Chicago Ave Ste 725, Chicago, IL 60654-2522
Tel (800) 354-7993 *Founded/Ownrshp* 2005
Sales 1.5MMM *EMP* 2,335
Tkr Sym ECHO *Exch* NGS
SIC 4731 4813 Freight transportation arrangement;
Ch Bd: Douglas R Waggoner
Pr: David B Menzel
CFO: Kyle L Sauers
Ex VP: Scott Boyer
Sr VP: Christopher N Clemmensen
VP: Jay Gustafson
VP: Nick Hannigan
VP: John Mims
VP: Myron Ronay
Off Mgr: Helene Paul
IT Man: Michael Calvert
Board of Directors: Nelda J Connors, Matthew Ferguson, David Habiger, Bradley A Keywell, Paul Loeb, Samuel K Skinner

D-U-N-S 92-649-0715
ECHO GROUP INC
ECHO ELECTRIC SUPPLY
1851 Madison Ave Ste 710, Council Bluffs, IA 51503-3602
Tel (712) 322-4120 *Founded/Ownrshp* 1949
Sales 417.8MM[E] *EMP* 400
SIC 5063 Electrical apparatus & equipment; Wire & cable; Lighting fixtures; Electrical fittings & construction materials
CEO: Mitch Lane
**CFO:* Greg Johnson
Brnch Mgr: Rick Williams

D-U-N-S 06-247-5090 IMP/EXP
ECHO INC (IL)
(*Suby of* YAMABIKO CORPORATION)
400 Oakwood Rd, Lake Zurich, IL 60047-1564
Tel (847) 540-8400 *Founded/Ownrshp* 1972
Sales 246.2MM[E] *EMP* 1,108
SIC 3524 Lawn & garden equipment
Pr: Dan Obringer
Treas: J Tanaka
VP: Takashi Harada
CIO: Tim Dorsey
MIS Dir: Kim Dorsey
MIS Mgr: Jeff Garver
Web Dev: Aaron Cook
Sales Asso: Mayra Saucedo
Pgrm Dir: Lorri Murray

D-U-N-S 79-925-5989
ECHO MAINTENANCE LLC
6711 N Twin City Hwy, Port Arthur, TX 77642-6423
Tel (409) 724-0456 *Founded/Ownrshp* 2006
Sales 134.6MM[E] *EMP* 200
SIC 1541 3498 1623 Industrial buildings, new construction; Steel building construction; Renovation, remodeling & repairs: industrial buildings; Fabricated pipe & fittings; Water, sewer & utility lines
Pr: Michael P Roebuck
**VP:* Andy Brisendine
Off Mgr: Clara Obannon
Sfty Dirs: Paul Seward
Sfty Mgr: Dwight Dugas
Ql Cn Mgr: Jesse Comeaux
Ql Cn Mgr: Hamp Lewis

D-U-N-S 02-030-7185
ECHOPOWER CORP
3720 Baseline Ave, Santa Ynez, CA 93460-9773
Tel (805) 729-4473 *Founded/Ownrshp* 2006
Sales 100.0MM *EMP* 5
SIC 4953 5331 Recycling, waste materials; Variety stores
Pr: Joaquin F Bin

D-U-N-S 03-487-9007
■ ECHOSPHERE LLC
ECHOSTAR SATELLITE PRODUCTIONS
(*Suby of* DISH NETWORK CORP) ★
9601 S Meridian Blvd, Englewood, CO 80112-5905
Tel (303) 723-1000 *Founded/Ownrshp* 1993
Sales 83.7MM[E] *EMP* 100
SIC 5065 4841 Communication equipment; Cable & other pay television services
Genl Mgr: Greg Sheldon

D-U-N-S 80-125-9180 IMP
▲ ECHOSTAR CORP
100 Inverness Ter E, Englewood, CO 80112-5308
Tel (303) 706-4000 *Founded/Ownrshp* 2008
Sales 3.1MMM *EMP* 4,400[E]
Tkr Sym SATS *Exch* NGS
SIC 3663 4841 Space satellite communications equipment; Direct broadcast satellite services (DBS)
Pr: Michael T Dugan
**Ch Bd:* Charles W Ergen
Pr: Mark W Jackson
Pr: Anders N Johnson
CFO: David J Rayner
Ex VP: Kenneth G Carroll
Ex VP: Sandra L Kerentoff
Ex VP: Kranti K Kilaru
Ex VP: Dean A Manson
Sr VP: Gareth Hughes
VP: Shah Behzadi
VP: Navaid Mufti
VP: Gustavo Nader
VP: Trip Von Minden
Board of Directors: R Stanton Dodge, Anthony M Federico, Tom A Ortolf, C Michael Schroeder

ECHOSTAR SATELLITE PRODUCTIONS
See ECHOSPHERE LLC

D-U-N-S 96-859-6846
■ ECHOSTAR SATELLITE SERVICES LLC
(*Suby of* ECHOSTAR CORP) ★
100 Inverness Ter E, Englewood, CO 80112-5308
Tel (866) 359-8804 *Founded/Ownrshp* 2011
Sales 289.2MM[E] *EMP* 2,255[E]
SIC 4841 Direct broadcast satellite services (DBS)
Pr: Dean Olmstead
**COO:* Ken Carroll
Sr VP: Richard Mortellaro
Sr VP: Vernon Smith
VP: Jerry Jason
**CTO:* Derek De Bastos

ECI GROUP
See EICHELBERGER CONSTRUCTION INC

D-U-N-S 62-667-3771
ECI HOLDING INC
ECI HOLDINGS COMPANY
1 Cityplace Dr Ste 450, Saint Louis, MO 63141-7060
Tel (314) 692-4204 *Founded/Ownrshp* 1969
Sales 2.1MMM[E] *EMP* 12,000[E]
SIC 3643 Current-carrying wiring devices
CEO: David J Webster
**CFO:* Mitch Leonard
VP: Ken Partewka

ECI HOLDINGS COMPANY
See ECI HOLDING INC

ECI2
See ECOMMERCE INDUSTRIES INC

D-U-N-S 12-998-3339
ECICONSTRUCTION LLC
124 W Church St, Dillsburg, PA 17019-1200
Tel (717) 638-3000 *Founded/Ownrshp* 2003
Sales 87.2MM[E] *EMP* 180[E]
SIC 1542 Nonresidential construction
VP: Scott Feaser
VP: David Noss
VP: Jason Rimmer
Genl Mgr: Mark Yinger
IT Man: Jonra Feldman
IT Man: Jennifer Smith

ECIS
See EAST CENTRAL IOWA COOP

ECISD
See ECTOR COUNTY INDEPENDENT SCHOOL DISTRICT

D-U-N-S 15-449-1336
ECK ENTERPRISES INC
EEI
1405 W Main St, Richmond, VA 23220-4629
Tel (804) 359-5781 *Founded/Ownrshp* 1958
Sales 151.3MM[E] *EMP* 350
SIC 5063 6512 Electrical supplies; Commercial & industrial building operation
Pr: Edgar C Eck Jr
**Treas:* Bruce H Boykin
**VP:* Francis Eck
DP Exec: Charlie Smith
IT Man: Mike Crowder
IT Man: Kevin Williams

D-U-N-S 02-392-5233
ECK SUPPLY CO
ESC
1405 W Main St, Richmond, VA 23220-4629
Tel (804) 359-5781 *Founded/Ownrshp* 2015
Sales 332.2MM[E] *EMP* 325
SIC 5063

D-U-N-S 08-068-1158
ECKERD YOUTH ALTERNATIVES INC (FL)
EWES-ECKERD YOUTH CHALLENGE
100 Starcrest Dr, Clearwater, FL 33765-3224
Tel (727) 461-2990 *Founded/Ownrshp* 1964
Sales 172.1MM *EMP* 1,400
Accts Crowe Horwath Llp Fort Lauder
SIC 8211 Public senior high school
Pr: David Dennis
**Ch:* V Raymond Ferrara
**Treas:* Randall Luecke
Ofcr: Pam Griffith
Genl Mgr: Ellyn Evans
IT Man: Stuart Towery
IT Man: Tony Vasilakis
IT Man: Ray Wright
Netwrk Eng: Ehren Cline
Psych: Brandi Meese
Pgrm Dir: Sonya Graham

D-U-N-S 07-497-5061
ECKERT SEAMANS CHERIN & MELLOTT LLC
600 Grant St Fl 44, Pittsburgh, PA 15219-2713
Tel (412) 566-6000 *Founded/Ownrshp* 1958
Sales 122.6MM[E] *EMP* 740
SIC 8111 General practice law office
Treas: Myra D Kilgore
VP: Bridget Montgomery
VP: Lori L Moran
Exec: Kristin Howells
Off Mgr: Donna Frati
IT Man: Candaceaa Gottschall
Counsel: Michael Kinkopf
Counsel: Edward Kuna
Counsel: Willis Siegfried
Counsel: David Strasser

ECKLERS
See SMART CHOICE AUTOMOTIVE GROUP INC

D-U-N-S 79-056-9003
ECLINICAL WORKS LLC
COCOWEB.COM, LLC
2 Technology Dr, Westborough, MA 01581-1727
Tel (508) 366-8301 *Founded/Ownrshp* 2007
Sales 167.6MM[E] *EMP* 2,200
SIC 7371

D-U-N-S 13-681-5235
ECLINICALWORKS LLC
2 Technology Dr, Westborough, MA 01581-1727
Tel (508) 475-0450 *Founded/Ownrshp* 1999
Sales 334.8MM[E] *EMP* 2,800
SIC 7371 Computer software development
CEO: Girish Navani
**COO:* Mahesh Kumar Navani
**Founder:* Asharani Navani
**Chf Mktg O:* Rajesh Dharampuriya
Dir Bus: Kapil Langer
Genl Mgr: Timothy Nason
Snr Sftwr: Shilpa Hegde
Snr Sftwr: Kulwinder Kapoor
IT Man: Aum Patel
Software D: Arjun Srinivasan
Sftwr Eng: Jalaj Asher

D-U-N-S 83-750-2657 IMP
■ ECLIPSE COMBUSTION INC
(*Suby of* ELSTER THERMAL SOLUTIONS) ★
1665 Elmwood Rd, Rockford, IL 61103-1299
Tel (815) 877-3031 *Founded/Ownrshp* 1994
Sales 86.6MM[E] *EMP* 452
SIC 3433 Gas burners, industrial; Gas-oil burners, combination; Oil burners, domestic or industrial
CEO: Douglas Perks
**Pr:* Lachlan L Perks
**VP:* Chet Allen
**VP:* Greg Bubp

D-U-N-S 00-510-1266 IMP/EXP
■ ECLIPSE INC
ELSTER THERMAL SOLUTIONS
(*Suby of* HONEYWELL INTERNATIONAL INC) ★
1665 Elmwood Rd, Rockford, IL 61103-1299
Tel (815) 877-3031 *Founded/Ownrshp* 2015
Sales 125.0MM[E] *EMP* 520
SIC 3564 3433 3822 3823 3443 3494 Blowing fans: industrial or commercial; Gas-oil burners, combination; Gas burners, industrial; Gas burner, automatic controls; Flame safety controls for furnaces & boilers; Temperature instruments: industrial process type; Heat exchangers, condensers & components; Valves & pipe fittings
Ch Bd: David M Cote
**CFO:* Thomas A Szlosek
**Sr VP:* Katherine L Adams
Genl Mgr: Donald Darrell
Genl Mgr: Timothy Lee

Off Mgr: Sharon Wolfe
Software D: Ralf Sternberg
VP Opers: Dan Mills
Mktg Mgr: Mike Milinkovich

D-U-N-S 07-940-3711
■ ECLIPSE RESOURCES CORP
(*Suby of* ECLIPSE RESOURCES HOLDINGS LP) ★
2121 Old Gatesburg Rd # 110, State College, PA 16803-2290
Tel (814) 308-9754 *Founded/Ownrshp* 2011
Sales 255.3MM *EMP* 210[E]
Tkr Sym ECR *Exch* NYS
SIC 1311 Crude petroleum & natural gas
Ch Bd: Benjamin W Hulburt
COO: Thomas S Liberatore
CFO: Matthew R Denezza
**Ex VP:* Christopher K Hulburt

D-U-N-S 07-945-3815
▲ ECLIPSE RESOURCES HOLDINGS LP
2121 Old Gatesburg Rd # 110, State College, PA 16803-2290
Tel (814) 308-9754 *Founded/Ownrshp* 2014
Sales 255.3MM[E] *EMP* 227[E]
SIC 1311 Crude petroleum & natural gas
Prin: Benjamin W Hulburt

D-U-N-S 03-272-9470
■ ECLIPSE RESOURCES I LP
(*Suby of* ECLIPSE RESOURCES CORP) ★
2121 Old Gteburg Rd Ste 1, State College, PA 16803
Tel (814) 308-9754 *Founded/Ownrshp* 1998
Sales 248.5MM[E] *EMP* 159[E]
SIC 1311 1382 Crude petroleum & natural gas; Oil & gas exploration services
CEO: Benjamin W Hulburt
**Ex VP:* Matthew R Denezza
**Ex VP:* Christopher K Hulburt
**Ex VP:* Thomas S Liberatore
VP: Marty L Byrd
VP: Timothy Loos
Genl Couns: Dan Sweeney

ECM DISTRIBUTION
See ECM PUBLISHERS INC

D-U-N-S 07-134-9518
ECM PUBLISHERS INC
ECM DISTRIBUTION
4095 Coon Rapids Blvd Nw, Minneapolis, MN 55433-2523
Tel (763) 712-2400 *Founded/Ownrshp* 1976
Sales 96.5MM[E] *EMP* 550
SIC 2711 2741 7319 2789 2752 Commercial printing & newspaper publishing combined; Shopping news: publishing & printing; Distribution of advertising material or sample services; Shopping news, advertising & distributing service; Bookbinding & related work; Commercial printing, lithographic
Ch Bd: Julian L Andersen
**Pr:* Jeff Athmann
CFO: John McGraw
**Treas:* Maxine Gift
**VP:* Eleanor J Andersen
VP: Rod Decker
Genl Mgr: Steve Rajtar
Off Mgr: Annette Gruber
Dir IT: Kirk Valisk
Prd Mgr: Sarah Foote
Mktg Mgr: Bridget Kasper

D-U-N-S 61-147-8595
ECM TRANSPORT LLC
1 Rich Hill Rd, Cheswick, PA 15024-2120
Tel (724) 339-8800 *Founded/Ownrshp* 2004
Sales 94.0MM[E] *EMP* 500
SIC 4214 4213 Local trucking with storage; Trucking, except local
Area Mgr: Stella Davis
Off Mgr: Phyllis Meier
CTO: Adam Ciancio
Opers Mgr: Mary Williams
Board of Directors: Michael Sisczyzewski

ECMC
See EDUCATIONAL CREDIT MANAGEMENT CORP

ECMC
See ERIE COUNTY MEDICAL CENTER CORP

D-U-N-S 07-962-8205
ECMC GROUP INC
111 Washington Ave S # 1400, Minneapolis, MN 55401-2108
Tel (651) 325-3652 *Founded/Ownrshp* 2000
Sales NA *EMP* 9,000[E]
SIC 6111 Student Loan Marketing Association
Pr: Dave Hawn
**CFO:* Greg Van Guilder

D-U-N-S 03-584-4976 IMP
ECMD INC (NC)
EAST COAST MOULDINGS
2 Grandview St, North Wilkesboro, NC 28659-3109
Tel (336) 667-5976 *Founded/Ownrshp* 1981
Sales 141.6MM[E] *EMP* 515
SIC 2431 5031

D-U-N-S 96-805-0042
ECO GSI CONSTRUCTION AND MAINTENANCE LLC
6917 Arlington Rd, Bethesda, MD 20814-5211
Tel (240) 832-8035 *Founded/Ownrshp* 2011
Sales 9.9MM[E] *EMP* 1,700
SIC 7349 Building maintenance services
Ex VP: Arthur C Stecklow

D-U-N-S 01-065-8014
ECO SERVICES OPERATIONS LLC
2002 Timberloch Pl # 300, Spring, TX 77380-1171
Tel (800) 642-4200 *Founded/Ownrshp* 2011
Sales 390.8MM *EMP* 500
Accts Pricewaterhousecoopers Llp Fl
SIC 2819
Ch Bd: James Harton

D-U-N-S 18-163-7047 IMP
ECO-BAT AMERICA LLC
(*Suby of* ECO-BAT TECHNOLOGIES LIMITED)
2777 N Stemmons Fwy, Dallas, TX 75207-2277
Tel (214) 688-4000 *Founded/Ownrshp* 2000
Sales 126.7MM[E] *EMP* 602
SIC 3356 Nonferrous rolling & drawing

D-U-N-S 13-547-5023 IMP/EXP
ECO-PAK
(*Suby of* KELLY ELECTRIC) ★
9211 E Jackson St, Selma, IN 47383-9598
Tel (765) 287-2093 *Founded/Ownrshp* 2003
Sales 71.3MM[E] *EMP* 1,357[E]
SIC 5999 Art & architectural supplies
Prin: Gary Townsend

ECOG-ACRIN CANCER RES GROUP
See ECOG-ACRIN MEDICAL RESEARCH FOUNDATION INC

D-U-N-S 07-857-9855
ECOG-ACRIN MEDICAL RESEARCH FOUNDATION INC
ECOG-ACRIN CANCER RES GROUP
1818 Market St, Philadelphia, PA 19103-3638
Tel (215) 789-3600 *Founded/Ownrshp* 2012
Sales 306.8M[E] *EMP* 6,000
SIC 8731 Commercial physical research
Pr: Robert L Comis
**VP:* Mitchell Schnall
Comm Dir: Diane M Dragaud

D-U-N-S 00-615-4611 IMP/EXP
▲ ECOLAB INC
370 Wabasha St N, Saint Paul, MN 55102-1349
Tel (800) 232-6522 *Founded/Ownrshp* 1924
Sales 13.5MMM *EMP* 47,015
Accts Pricewaterhousecoopers Llp Mi
Tkr Sym ECL *Exch* NYS
SIC 2841 2842 7342 Soap & other detergents; Dishwashing compounds; Textile soap; Specialty cleaning, polishes & sanitation goods; Specialty cleaning preparations; Sanitation preparations, disinfectants & deodorants; Disinfecting & pest control services; Pest control services
Ch Bd: Douglas M Baker Jr
Pr: Theresa Foss
Pr: Thomas W Handley
Pr: Kenneth Iverson
Pr: Tim Rathje
Pr: Randy Wade
CFO: Daniel J Schmechel
Ex VP: Nicholas Alfano
Ex VP: Larry L Berger
Ex VP: Alex Blanco
Ex VP: Michael A Hickey
Ex VP: Luciano Iannuzzi
Ex VP: Luciano Lannuzzi
Ex VP: Richard Marcantonio
Ex VP: Stewart H McCutcheon
Ex VP: James Miller
Ex VP: James J Seifert
Sr VP: Elizabeth A Simermeyer
VP: Kathy Adams
VP: Anil Arcalgud
VP: Paul B Chaffin
Board of Directors: Jerry W Levin, Barbara J Beck, Robert L Lumpkins, Leslie S Biller, David W Maclennan, Carl M Casale, Tracy B McKibben, Stephen I Chazen, Victoria J Reich, Jeffrey M Ettinger, Suzanne M Vautrino, Jerry A Grundhofer, John J Zillmer, Arthur J Higgins, Joel W Johnson, Michael Larson

D-U-N-S 05-864-8312
▲ ECOLOGY AND ENVIRONMENT INC
368 Pleasant View Dr, Lancaster, NY 14086-1397
Tel (716) 684-8060 *Founded/Ownrshp* 1970
Sales 105.8MM *EMP* 893[E]
Tkr Sym EEI *Exch* NGM
SIC 8748 8734 8711 Environmental consultant; Hazardous waste testing; Pollution testing; Pollution control engineering
Pr: Gerard A Gallagher III
**Ch Bd:* Frank B Silvestro
COO: Fred J McKosky
CFO: H John Mye III
**Ex VP:* Ronald L Frank
Sr VP: Nancy J Aungst
Sr VP: Laurence M Brickman
VP: Dan Castle
VP: Mike Donnelly
VP: Doug Heatwole
VP: Mike Kane
VP: Dan Sewall
Board of Directors: Michael S Betrus, Michael R Cellino, Gerard A Gallagher Jr, Michael C Gross, Gerald A Strobel

D-U-N-S 06-459-0375 IMP
ECOLOGY AUTO PARTS INC
14150 Vine Pl, Cerritos, CA 90703-2416
Tel (562) 404-2277 *Founded/Ownrshp* 1966
Sales 104.6MM[E] *EMP* 142
SIC 5531 Automotive parts
Pr: Charles B Siroonian
CFO: Paul Macleith
**Sec:* Charles D Pratty II
**VP:* Jeanne Pratty
Exec: Ron Coffman

D-U-N-S 08-513-4211 IMP/EXP
ECOM ATLANTIC INC
(*Suby of* ECOM AGROINDUSTRIAL CORP. LIMITED)
13760 Noel Rd Ste 500, Dallas, TX 75240-1362
Tel (214) 520-1717 *Founded/Ownrshp* 1885
Sales 102.4MM *EMP* 80
SIC 5159 5149 Cotton merchants; Coffee, green or roasted
Pr: Jennifer Allen
VP: EMI Kamura
VP: Dan Luby
Mng Dir: Eduardo Esteve
Dir IT: Henry Liverpool
Netwrk Mgr: Alexander Mendoza
Opers Mgr: Patrick Mitchell
Sls Dir: Justin Archer

D-U-N-S 14-711-6420 EXP
ECOM USA INC
ESTAVE COTTON
(*Suby of* ECOM ATLANTIC INC) ★
13760 Noel Rd Ste 500, Dallas, TX 75240-1362
Tel (214) 520-1717 *Founded/Ownrshp* 1988
Sales 87.6MM[E] *EMP* 80
SIC 5159 Cotton merchants
Pr: Eduardo Esteve
**Treas:* Cindy Parrish
**VP:* Andrew P Halle

D-U-N-S 13-451-1414
ECOMMERCE INDUSTRIES INC
ECI2
4400 Alliance Gateway Fwy # 154, Fort Worth, TX 76177-3706
Tel (682) 831-0827 *Founded/Ownrshp* 2014
Sales 160.8MM[E] *EMP* 440
SIC 7373 Computer integrated systems design
Pr: Ron Books
**COO:* Trevor Gruenewald
**CFO:* Glen Etherington
CFO: Tom Gerrity
**Sr VP:* Mike Gibson
**Sr VP:* David Lipetz
QA Dir: James Regan
Dir IT: Andy Wheeler
Web Dev: Gretchen Hughes
Software D: Gautam Dharmapuri
Software D: Lori Heather

D-U-N-S 08-416-2577 EXP
ECONOLITE CONTROL PRODUCTS INC
3360 E La Palma Ave, Anaheim, CA 92806-2814
Tel (714) 630-3700 *Founded/Ownrshp* 1977
Sales 83.0MM[E] *EMP* 225
SIC 3669 Traffic signals, electric
CEO: Michael C Doyle
**Pr:* David St Amant
CFO: John Tracey
VP: Andy Burke
VP: Mark Nogaki
CIO: Keith Golden
MIS Dir: Adolf Hoskis
QA Dir: Jose Mejia
Sys Mgr: Greg Mizell
VP Prd: Wayne Hagewood

ECONOMIST GROUP, THE
See ECONOMIST NEWSPAPER GROUP INC

D-U-N-S 61-511-9708 IMP
ECONOMIST NEWSPAPER GROUP INC
ECONOMIST GROUP, THE
(*Suby of* ECONOMIST NEWSPAPER LIMITED(THE))
750 3rd Ave Fl 5, New York, NY 10017-2723
Tel (212) 541-0500 *Founded/Ownrshp* 1977
Sales 134.5MM[E] *EMP* 350
SIC 2721 7313 5963 Periodicals: publishing & printing; Magazines: publishing & printing; Printed media advertising representatives; Magazine advertising representative; Newspaper advertising representative; Encyclopedias & publications, direct sales; Magazine subscription sales, excl. mail order, house sales
CEO: Chris Stibbs
VP: Tony Tran
Assoc Dir: Lucy Hurst
Mng Dir: James Myers
Mktg Mgr: Zohray Brennan

D-U-N-S 16-528-1267
ECONOMOS PROPERTIES INC
4000 N Federal Hwy # 206, Boca Raton, FL 33431-4527
Tel (561) 361-2504 *Founded/Ownrshp* 1969
Sales 42.0MM *EMP* 1,500[E]
SIC 8741 Hotel or motel management
Pr: Nick Economos

ECONOMY BOAT STR CO-WOOD RIVER
See MERS LLC

D-U-N-S 00-808-7603 IMP/EXP
ECONOMY MUD PRODUCTS CO
ECONOMY POLYMERS & CHEMICAL
435 E Anderson Rd, Houston, TX 77047-5016
Tel (800) 231-2066 *Founded/Ownrshp* 1951
Sales 150.0MM *EMP* 98[E]
SIC 2869 2899 Hydraulic fluids, synthetic base; Chemical preparations
Pr: Lawrence E Walton
**Treas:* Walter M White

ECONOMY POLYMERS & CHEMICAL
See ECONOMY MUD PRODUCTS CO

D-U-N-S 02-337-5964
ECOSERV LLC
207 Towncenter Pkwy Fl 2, Lafayette, LA 70506-7507
Tel (337) 984-4445 *Founded/Ownrshp* 2014
Sales 83.1MM[E] *EMP* 325
SIC 4959 7699 Environmental cleanup services; Waste cleaning services
CEO: Kenny Desormeaux
**CFO:* Rob Driskell

ECOT
See ELECTRONIC CLASSROOM OF TOMORROW

D-U-N-S 94-541-4530
ECOVA INC
(*Suby of* ENGIE HOLDINGS INC) ★
1313 N Atl St Ste 5000, Spokane, WA 99201
Tel (509) 747-5069 *Founded/Ownrshp* 2014
Sales 368.0MM[E] *EMP* 1,400
SIC 8742 Public utilities consultant
Pr: Jana Schmidt
COO: Jeffrey W Hart
**CFO:* Olivier De Jonghe Dardoye
**Treas:* John Robison
Treas: Craig O Urdahl
Ex VP: David Porter
**Ex VP:* Ed Schlect
**Sr VP:* Donato Capobianco
**Sr VP:* Julie Kearney
**Sr VP:* Seth Nesbitt
**Sr VP:* Jana Miller Schmidt
**Sr VP:* Ted Schultz
**Sr VP:* Bob Zak
VP: Ivan Bel
VP: Mary Braunstein
**VP:* Marian Durkin
VP: Jim Hendricks
VP: Chris Jernigan
**VP:* Lauren Kirkley
VP: Tony Presho
Exec: Kelly Chapin

D-U-N-S 61-057-8684 IMP/EXP
■ ECOWATER SYSTEMS LLC
(*Suby of* MARMON INDUSTRIAL LLC) ★
1890 Woodlane Dr, Saint Paul, MN 55125-2980
Tel (651) 731-7401 *Founded/Ownrshp* 1981
Sales 174.8MM[E] *EMP* 475
SIC 5074 3589 Water softeners; Water purification equipment; Water filters & softeners, household type; Water treatment equipment, industrial
Pr: Donald Brockley
**Co-Ownr:* Terry Reeh
VP: Al Dennis
Genl Mgr: Greg Reese
Dir IT: Will Wiestert
Plnt Mgr: Dave Kell

D-U-N-S 02-827-9966
ECPH MANAGEMENT INC
PIZZA HUT
2317 Professional Dr, Rocky Mount, NC 27804-2252
Tel (252) 443-4028 *Founded/Ownrshp* 1971
Sales 26.2MM[E] *EMP* 1,200
SIC 5812 Pizzeria, chain
Pr: Theron Riley

D-U-N-S 00-210-1137 IMP/EXP
ECR INTERNATIONAL INC (NY)
UTICA BOILERS
2201 Dwyer Ave, Utica, NY 13501-1101
Tel (315) 797-1310 *Founded/Ownrshp* 1928
Sales 112.1MM[E] *EMP* 500
SIC 3433 3443 Boilers, low-pressure heating: steam or hot water; Fabricated plate work (boiler shop)
Pr: Ronald J Passafaro
V Ch: Earle C Reed
Pr: Timothy R Reed
Treas: John J Lauchert
VP: James Benson
VP: Paul Totaro
Sfty Mgr: Eric Dorozynski
Mktg Dir: Thomas Legutko
Board of Directors: Andrew Burns, Andrew Dorn, Dr Richard Foss, Frederick Hayes, Stephen Sweet, Parker Weld

D-U-N-S 80-602-6852
ECS FEDERAL LLC
E C S
2750 Prosperity Ave # 600, Fairfax, VA 22031-4312
Tel (703) 270-1540 *Founded/Ownrshp* 2000
Sales 233.4MM *EMP* 1,184
Accts Aronson Llc Rockville Maryl
SIC 7371 7379 8742 Custom computer programming services; Computer related consulting services; Management consulting services
Pr: George Wilson
**Ch Bd:* Roy Kapani
CFO: Anthony Schulien
VP: Simone Acha
VP: Amie Bothwell
VP: John Magee
Exec: Victoria Kruk
Exec: Stephen Parra
Prgrm Mgr: Jeff Wu
Div Mgr: James Okeefe
Genl Mgr: Brett Surbey

D-U-N-S 78-057-8014
ECS REFINING LLC
705 Reed St, Santa Clara, CA 95050-3980
Tel (408) 988-4386 *Founded/Ownrshp* 1980
Sales 126.7MM[E] *EMP* 250
SIC 5093 Metal scrap & waste materials
CFO: Jeff Lewis
**VP:* Mark Robards
VP: Diane Walsh
Genl Mgr: Jim Nelson
Dir IT: Matt Hewitt
VP Opers: Michael Costello
Plnt Mgr: Marty Veloz
Manager: Jim Anglum
Manager: Chris Ellis
Manager: Sylvia Jasso

ECS-CHART RETRIEVAL SERVICES
See ENTERPRISE CONSULTING SOLUTIONS INC

D-U-N-S 07-854-6348
ECTOR COUNTY HOSPITAL DISTRICT
MEDICAL CENTER HEALTH SYSTEM
500 W 4th St, Odessa, TX 79761-5001
Tel (432) 640-4000 *Founded/Ownrshp* 1949
Sales 189.9MM *EMP* 1,630
SIC 8062 General medical & surgical hospitals
Pr: William Webster
**CFO:* Robert Abernathy
Dir Rx: Jean Estime
Ex Dir: Robbi Banks
Ex Dir: Harvey Hudspeth
**CIO:* Gary Barnes
CTO: Daniel Ohearn
Opers Mgr: Lewis Dingman
Ansthlgy: Mark L Johnson
Snr Mgr: Peter Crisanti

D-U-N-S 07-855-8467
ECTOR COUNTY INDEPENDENT SCHOOL DISTRICT
ECISD
802 N Sam Houston Ave, Odessa, TX 79761-3973
Tel (432) 456-0002 *Founded/Ownrshp* 1921
Sales 264.5MM *EMP* 3,900
Accts Johnson Miller & Co Cpa S P
SIC 8211 Public elementary school; Public junior high school; Public senior high school; Public vocational/technical school
CEO: Brian Moersch
**Pr:* Nelson Minyard
**VP:* Teri Ervin
Genl Mgr: Sherrill Watson
Netwrk Mgr: Toby L La Fee Vers
Plnt Mgr: David D Ilbeck
Teacher Pr: Keith Garinger

ECU
See EAST CAROLINA UNIVERSITY

D-U-N-S 17-175-7433
ECUMEN
3530 Lexington Ave N Fl 2, Saint Paul, MN 55126-8191
Tel (651) 766-4300 *Founded/Ownrshp* 1863
Sales 145.9MM *EMP* 3,400
Accts Cliftonlarsonallen Llp Minne
SIC 8051 Skilled nursing care facilities
Pr: Kathryn Roberts
**CFO:* Dennis Johnson
Ofcr: Stacy Hanley
**Ex VP:* Judy Blaseg
**Sr VP:* Robin Dunbar
**Sr VP:* Steve Ordahl
**VP:* Larry Jorgensen
Dir Soc: Nicole Hendrickson
Dir Bus: Anne Stanfield
Ex Dir: Nathan Johnson
Genl Mgr: Lori Lewis

D-U-N-S 78-467-4835 IMP/EXP
ED & F MAN HOLDINGS INC
(*Suby of* E D & F MAN HOLDINGS LIMITED)
33 Whitehall St Broad, New York, NY 10004
Tel (212) 618-2802 *Founded/Ownrshp* 2000
Sales 267.7MM[E] *EMP* 600
SIC 5149 Cocoa; Coffee & tea; Molasses, industrial; Spices & seasonings
Pr: Daniel Rosenblum
**Treas:* Ian Falshaw
**VP:* Donald Galante
**VP:* Geoffrey C Kent
**VP:* Bridgette Pla
**VP:* Anthony B Stillitano

D-U-N-S 13-956-5774
ED BELL INVESTMENTS INC
10605 Harry Hines Blvd, Dallas, TX 75220-2634
Tel (214) 358-3414 *Founded/Ownrshp* 1973
Sales 100.2MM[E] *EMP* 250
SIC 1611 5082 4424 General contractor, highway & street construction; General construction machinery & equipment; Intercoastal transportation, freight
Pr: Edwin S Bell Sr
**VP:* Gus Brair

D-U-N-S 78-032-7339
ED HIGHER HOLDINGS LLC
600 N Pearl St Ste 900, Dallas, TX 75201-2872
Tel (214) 210-7300 *Founded/Ownrshp* 2004
Sales 66.4MM[E] *EMP* 2,000
SIC 8211 Elementary & secondary schools

D-U-N-S 15-817-6623
ED MAP INC
296 S Harper St Ste 1, Nelsonville, OH 45764-1600
Tel (740) 753-3439 *Founded/Ownrshp* 2001
Sales 83.0MM[E] *EMP* 83
SIC 5192 Books
CEO: Michael Mark
**Pr:* Kerry Stoessel Pigman
**CFO:* Greg Smith
**CFO:* Micah Zimmerman
**VP:* Andrew J Herd
VP: Andrew Herd
**VP:* Kelby Kostival
VP: Sarah Riddlebarger
VP: Anna Wilson
Dir IT: Corey West
Software D: Matthew Henry

D-U-N-S 02-523-3107
ED MINIAT LLC (IL)
(*Suby of* MINIAT HOLDINGS LLC) ★
16250 Vincennes Ave, South Holland, IL 60473-1260
Tel (708) 589-2400 *Founded/Ownrshp* 1923, 2013
Sales 269.4MM[E] *EMP* 360[E]
SIC 5147 5144 Meats & meat products; Poultry & poultry products
CEO: David J Miniat
**Ch Bd:* Ronald Miniat
**VP:* G Michael Botelho
VP: Michael Botelho
**VP:* Charles Nalon
Dir Surg: Curt Hyzy
Opers Mgr: Lucio Fragoso
Plnt Mgr: Chuck Hunka
Trfc Mgr: Alphonso Magana
Sales Exec: Chuck Nailon

ED MORSE AUTOMOTIVE GROUP
See MORSE OPERATIONS INC

D-U-N-S 07-048-7921
ED RACHAL FOUNDATION INC
500 N Shoreline Blvd # 606, Corpus Christi, TX 78401-0323
Tel (361) 881-9040 *Founded/Ownrshp* 1965
Sales 87.0MM *EMP* 3
SIC 8322 Social service center
CEO: Paul D Altheide

D-U-N-S 05-181-4341
ED SHULTS CHEVROLET INC
300 Fluvanna Ave, Jamestown, NY 14701-2032
Tel (716) 484-7151 *Founded/Ownrshp* 1970
Sales 170.4MM[E] *EMP* 600
SIC 5511

D-U-N-S 06-500-4277
ED STAUB & SONS PETROLEUM INC
1301 Esplanade Ave, Klamath Falls, OR 97601-5902
Tel (541) 887-8900 *Founded/Ownrshp* 1952
Sales 327.9MM *EMP* 300
SIC 5172 5541 5411

D-U-N-S 04-559-2995 IMP/EXP
ED TUCKER DISTRIBUTOR INC
TUCKER ROCKY DISTRIBUTING
(*Suby of* MOTORSPORT AFTERMARKET GROUP INC) ★
4900 Alliance Gateway Fwy, Fort Worth, TX 76177-3722
Tel (817) 258-9000 *Founded/Ownrshp* 2014
Sales 616.9MM^E *EMP* 700
SIC 5013 Automotive supplies
Pr: Erick Cagel
CFO: Jay Goldstein
**Treas:* J William Himebrook
VP: Bruce Baker
**VP:* Thomas M Boehner
Telecom Ex: Ken Lauder
Opers Mgr: Mike Ries
**VP Mktg:* Hank Defardins
Manager: Dennis Kurtjian
Manager: Fred Oberer
Manager: Tim Walsworth

EDAC MACHINERY
See EDAC TECHNOLOGIES LLC

D-U-N-S 14-492-1780
EDAC TECHNOLOGIES LLC
EDAC MACHINERY
(*Suby of* MEGGITT PLC)
5 Mckee Pl, Cheshire, CT 06410-1119
Tel (203) 806-2090 *Founded/Ownrshp* 1970
Sales 147.7MM^E *EMP* 390^E
SIC 3769 3541 3724 Guided missile & space vehicle parts & auxiliary equipment; Machine tools, metal cutting type; Aircraft engines & engine parts
Pr: Terry Bruni
**CFO:* Mike Debolt
VP: John Dossmann
Sls Mgr: Gerry Sandstrom
Snr Mgr: Brian Ives

D-U-N-S 04-652-4013 IMP
■ **EDAW INC**
(*Suby of* AECOM) ★
300 California St Fl 5, San Francisco, CA 94104-1411
Tel (415) 955-2800 *Founded/Ownrshp* 2005
Sales 151.3MM^E *EMP* 800
SIC 6552 0781 Subdividers & developers; Landscape architects
CEO: Joseph E Brown
Pr: Jason Prior
CFO: Dana Waymire
VP: Dennis Carmichael
VP: Richard Dorrier
Prin: Vaughan Davies
Admn Mgr: Dean Dipietrantonio
CIO: Jeremy Verba
Snr PM: Chris Moore

D-U-N-S 04-292-7152
EDCO DISPOSAL CORP INC (CA)
LA MESA DISPOSAL
2755 California Ave, Signal Hill, CA 90755-3304
Tel (619) 287-7555 *Founded/Ownrshp* 1967
Sales 411.3MM^E *EMP* 600
SIC 4953 Garbage: collecting, destroying & processing
CEO: Steve South
**Pr:* Edward Burr
Bd of Dir: Octavio Duran
**VP:* Sandra Burr
Ex Dir: Don Harris
Dist Mgr: Carl Scherbaum
Div Mgr: Elmer Heap

D-U-N-S 05-478-0051
EDCO WASTE & RECYCLING SERVICES INC (CA)
SOLID WASTE SERVICES
(*Suby of* LA MESA DISPOSAL) ★
224 S Las Posas Rd, San Marcos, CA 92078-2421
Tel (760) 744-2700 *Founded/Ownrshp* 1954, 1998
Sales 140.0MM^E *EMP* 250^E
SIC 4953 4212 Rubbish collection & disposal; Garbage: collecting, destroying & processing; Local trucking, without storage
CEO: Steve South
**Pr:* Edward Burr
CFO: Alan Walsh
**Sec:* Sandra Burr
**VP:* Jeffrey Ritchie
Comm Dir: Yvette Snyder
Mktg Dir: Bob Hill

EDDIE BAUER
See EVEREST HOLDINGS LLC

EDDIE BAUER
See AMARGOSA INC

D-U-N-S 83-175-3665 IMP
EDDIE BAUER LLC
(*Suby of* GOLDEN GATE CAPITAL LP) ★
10401 Ne 8th St Ste 500, Bellevue, WA 98004-4346
Tel (425) 755-6100 *Founded/Ownrshp* 2009
Sales 1.2MMM^E *EMP* 8,000^E
SIC 5611 5961 5621 Men's & boys' clothing stores; Clothing accessories: men's & boys'; Clothing, sportswear, men's & boys'; Clothing, mail order (except women's); Fishing, hunting & camping equipment & supplies: mail order; Furniture & furnishings, mail order; Women's apparel, mail order; Women's clothing stores
CEO: Michael R Egeck
**COO:* Daniel E Templin
COO: Daniel Templin
**Ch:* David Chamberlain
Ex VP: Paul Bundonis
Sr VP: Steve Hartman
VP: Jos Cabao
**VP:* Vivian Gysler
VP: Steve Venegas
Exec: David Kardesh
Dist Mgr: Marilisa Commerford
Board of Directors: David Chamberlain

D-U-N-S 00-812-1220 IMP
EDDY PACKING CO INC
404 Airport Rd, Yoakum, TX 77995-4801
Tel (361) 580-3800 *Founded/Ownrshp* 2012
Sales 134.2MM^E *EMP* 400
SIC 2011 2013 Meat packing plants; Sausages & other prepared meats
Pr: Hans-Peter Ryholt
**CFO:* Carol Brown
**Sec:* P Keith O'Gorman
Exec: Kieley Stibich

D-U-N-S 61-891-3107
EDELBROCK FOUNDRY CORP
(*Suby of* EDELBROCK LLC) ★
1320 S Buena Vista St, San Jacinto, CA 92583-4665
Tel (951) 654-6677 *Founded/Ownrshp* 1938
Sales 95.6MM^E *EMP* 691
SIC 3363 3365 3325 Aluminum die-castings; Aluminum foundries; Steel foundries
Pr: Otis Victor Edelbrock
**Treas:* Nancy Edelbrock
**Ex VP:* Ronald L Webb
VP: Aristedes Feles
**VP:* Aristedes Seles
Off Mgr: Julia Montano
Plnt Mgr: Mike Covington

D-U-N-S 78-810-5463 IMP/EXP
EDELBROCK HOLDINGS INC
2700 California St, Torrance, CA 90503-3907
Tel (310) 781-2222 *Founded/Ownrshp* 2004
Sales 116.4MM^E *EMP* 722
SIC 3714 3751 Motor vehicle parts & accessories; Manifolds, motor vehicle; Cylinder heads, motor vehicle; Exhaust systems & parts, motor vehicle; Motorcycle accessories
Pr: O Victor Edelbrock
**CFO:* Norman Judd

D-U-N-S 00-837-5750 IMP
EDELBROCK LLC
(*Suby of* EDELBROCK HOLDINGS INC) ★
2700 California St, Torrance, CA 90503-3907
Tel (310) 781-2222 *Founded/Ownrshp* 1994, 2010
Sales 116.4MM^E *EMP* 400
SIC 3714 3751 Motor vehicle parts & accessories; Manifolds, motor vehicle; Cylinder heads, motor vehicle; Exhaust systems & parts, motor vehicle; Motorcycle accessories
CEO: John Colaianne
Pr: Wayne Murray
CFO: Steve Zitkus
VP: Rob Simons
Natl Sales: Cary Redman
Manager: Shane Turner

D-U-N-S 10-788-6483
EDEN OIL CO INC
RENTZ OIL
2507 Richardson Dr, Reidsville, NC 27320-5901
Tel (336) 349-8228 *Founded/Ownrshp* 1977
Sales 103.2MM *EMP* 19
Accts Cherry Bekaert Llp Asheboro
SIC 5171 5983 Petroleum bulk stations & terminals; Fuel oil dealers
Pr: Reid Teague
**VP:* Cynthia Teague

D-U-N-S 06-683-0423 IMP
EDEN PARK MANAGEMENT INC
22 Holland Ave, Albany, NY 12209-1713
Tel (518) 729-5230 *Founded/Ownrshp* 1970
Sales 47.5MM^E *EMP* 2,257
SIC 8051 Skilled nursing care facilities
Ch: Scott H Hoffman
**Pr:* Alton P Mendleson

D-U-N-S 05-268-4206
EDEN PRAIRIE SCHOOLS
8100 School Rd, Eden Prairie, MN 55344-2292
Tel (952) 975-7000 *Founded/Ownrshp* 1915
Sales 71.5MM^E *EMP* 1,400
SIC 8211 Public elementary school; Public junior high school; Public senior high school
Dir Vol: Lisa Wood
Treas: Karla Bratrud
Bd of Dir: Cathy Bockenstedt
Bd of Dir: Dave Espe
Bd of Dir: Ranee Jacobus
Ex Dir: Tricia Clair
Ex Dir: Mary Lenker
Ex Dir: Joshua Swanson
Dir IT: Michelle Ament
Dir IT: Joe Brazil
Dir IT: Kathy Palmer

D-U-N-S 00-578-1075
EDEN STONE CO INC (WI)
W4520 Lime Rd, Eden, WI 53019-1108
Tel (920) 477-2521 *Founded/Ownrshp* 1952, 1999
Sales 95.7MM^E *EMP* 190
Accts Huberty & Associates Sc Fo
SIC 1411 5032 Limestone, dimension-quarrying; Building stone
Pr: Dave Wirtz
**VP:* Richard Corser
**VP:* Peter Roehrig
Sls Mgr: John Fahser

D-U-N-S 07-653-8214
EDEN TOWNSHIP HOSPITAL DISTRICT INC
EDEN TOWNSHIP HOSPITAL DST
(*Suby of* SUTTER C H S) ★
20400 Lake Chabot Rd # 303, Castro Valley, CA 94546-5316
Tel (510) 538-2031 *Founded/Ownrshp* 1948
Sales 334.5MM *EMP* 968
SIC 8062 8011 General medical & surgical hospitals; Offices & clinics of medical doctors
Pr: Terry Glubka
Treas: Nadder Mirsepassi
VP: Rose Corcoran
Dir Risk M: Deborah Henderson
Dir Rx: Jan Hoang
CIO: Carol Sandoval
Mktg Dir: Cindy Dove
Doctor: Nancy Dyar
Doctor: Sidney E Wanetick
Nrsg Dir: Kathy Lawrence

EDEN TOWNSHIP HOSPITAL DST
See EDEN TOWNSHIP HOSPITAL DISTRICT INC

D-U-N-S 02-357-7336
EDENS & AVANT INC
1221 Main St Ste 1000, Columbia, SC 29201-3255
Tel (803) 779-4420 *Founded/Ownrshp* 1979
Sales 198.8MM^E *EMP* 240
SIC 6798 Real estate investment trusts
CEO: Terry S Brown
**Ch Bd:* Joe Edens
**Pr:* Jodi Mc Lean
**COO:* Rob Wyant
**CFO:* Mark Garside
**CFO:* Jason Tompkins
**Chf Inves:* Jami Passer
Sr VP: Lloyd Kapp
Sr VP: Jeff Kaufman
VP: Reynolds Allen
**VP:* Jessica Bruner
VP: Hal Cottingham
**VP:* Keith Davidson
VP: Brad Dumont
**VP:* Dale Johnston
**VP:* Maria Smith
VP: Lowell K Vice

EDETNYRE
See E D ETNYRE & CO

D-U-N-S 07-954-8227
EDF RENEWABLE ASSET HOLDINGS INC
15445 Innovation Dr, San Diego, CA 92128-3432
Tel (888) 903-6926 *Founded/Ownrshp* 2009
Sales 288.4MM^E *EMP* 826
SIC 4911 Electric services
Pr: Tristan Grimbert
**VP:* Richard Jigarjian

D-U-N-S 61-765-0189 IMP
EDF RENEWABLE ENERGY INC
15445 Innovation Dr, San Diego, CA 92128-3432
Tel (858) 521-3300 *Founded/Ownrshp* 1987
Sales 915.1MM^E *EMP* 877
SIC 4911 Generation, electric power
Pr: Tristan Grimbert
**CFO:* Luis Silva
Treas: Todd Benett
**Treas:* Kara Vongphakdy
**Ex VP:* Ryan Pfaff
Sr VP: Kristine N Yancey
**VP:* Larry Barr
VP: Matthias Beier
VP: Jeff Ghilardi
VP: Rich Jigarjian
VP: Kristina Peterson
VP: James Schretter
VP: Mark Tholke
Dir Risk M: Janet Richardson

D-U-N-S 36-256-5905
EDF RENEWABLE SERVICES INC
ENXCO
(*Suby of* EDF RENEWABLE ENERGY INC) ★
15445 Innovation Dr, San Diego, CA 92128-3432
Tel (858) 521-3575 *Founded/Ownrshp* 1992
Sales 85.9MM^E *EMP* 361
SIC 7539 Alternators & generators, rebuilding & repair
Pr: Tristan Grimbert
Pr: John Marchand
CFO: Jean Roche
Ex VP: Larry Barr
Ex VP: Deborah Gronvold
Ex VP: Ryan Pfaff
VP: Jeff Ghilardi
VP: Richard Jigarjian
VP: Tad Miller
Prgrm Mgr: Art Rio
Rgnl Mgr: Larry Freeman

D-U-N-S 13-038-5763
EDF TRADING NORTH AMERICA LLC
(*Suby of* E D F TRADING LIMITED)
4700 W Sam Houston Pkwy N, Houston, TX 77041-8210
Tel (281) 781-0333 *Founded/Ownrshp* 2009
Sales 279.5MM *EMP* 250
Accts Deloitte & Touche Llp Houston
SIC 6799 Commodity contract trading companies
COO: Justin Rowland
**CFO:* Michelle Barreda
**CFO:* Batrice Bigois
CFO: Beatrice Bigois
**Ch:* Philippe Torrion
Sr VP: Brett McCarroll
VP: Arun Eamani
VP: Stan Horton
Exec: Shannon Turner
Mng Dir: Philippe Mugnier
Dir IT: Kurt Wissner

D-U-N-S 79-545-3542
EDFINANCIAL SERVICES LLC
298 N Seven Oaks Dr, Knoxville, TN 37922-2369
Tel (865) 342-5500 *Founded/Ownrshp* 2006
Sales NA *EMP* 350
SIC 6111 Student Loan Marketing Association
CEO: William Hollin
COO: Farinella John
**CFO:* Steven Beasley
**Ex VP:* John Farinella
Sr VP: Wanda Hall
**Sr VP:* Elena Lubimstev
Sr VP: Judith B Witherspoon
VP: Connie Gibson
VP: Vicki Summers
Genl Mgr: Kim Watson

D-U-N-S 80-197-4721
EDGE ACQUISITION LLC
1001 Fleet St, Baltimore, MD 21202-4346
Tel (410) 843-8000 *Founded/Ownrshp* 2006
Sales 194.5MM^E *EMP* 10,461
SIC 8299 8748 Tutoring school; Testing service, educational or personnel; Educational consultant
Ch Bd: Christopher Hoehn-Saric
**Pr:* Peter Cohen

D-U-N-S 05-228-8529
EDGECOMBE COUNTY SCHOOLS
2311 N Main St, Tarboro, NC 27886-2108
Tel (252) 641-2600 *Founded/Ownrshp* 1993
Sales 56.3MM^E *EMP* 1,051
SIC 8211 Public elementary & secondary schools
Info Man: Cynthia Bridgers
Pr Dir: Susan Hock

EDGELL GROVE CEMETERY
See TOWN OF FRAMINGHAM

D-U-N-S 07-843-2514
EDGEN GROUP INC
(*Suby of* SUMITOMO CORP OF AMERICAS) ★
18444 Highland Rd, Baton Rouge, LA 70809-6105
Tel (225) 756-9868 *Founded/Ownrshp* 2011, 2013
Sales 461.5MM^E *EMP* 1,635^E
SIC 5051 Metals service centers & offices; Pipe & tubing, steel; Plates, metal; Steel
CEO: Daniel J O'Leary
**Pr:* Robert Dvorak
**Pr:* Craig Kiefer
**CFO:* David L Laxton III
Sr VP: Dan Keaton
VP: Jerry Daly
Dir Bus: Alex Collazo

D-U-N-S 07-962-2834
EDGES ELECTRICAL GROUP LLC
(*Suby of* ELECTRICAL DISTRIBUTORS CO) ★
1135 Auzerais Ave, San Jose, CA 95126-3402
Tel (408) 293-5818 *Founded/Ownrshp* 2014
Sales 171.3MM^E *EMP* 110^E
SIC 5063 Electrical apparatus & equipment
CFO: Mark Arndt

D-U-N-S 04-283-9857
EDGEWATER BEACH RESORT LLC
11212 Front Beach Rd, Panama City, FL 32407-3668
Tel (850) 235-4044 *Founded/Ownrshp* 1984
Sales 122.2MM^E *EMP* 529
SIC 1531 7011 5813 5812 Condominium developers; Hotels & motels; Drinking places; Eating places
Sr VP: Mike Stange
VP: Heem Chee
VP: Stacey Herndon
VP: Mike Wray
Exec: Philippe Robles
CTO: Ken Floyd
Dir IT: Kurt Weller
IT Man: Cathy Paddock
IT Man: Jeannie Quave
Sls&Mrk Ex: Wohlford Paul
Mktg Mgr: Catherine Collins

D-U-N-S 80-433-6055
■ **EDGEWATER TECHNOLOGY**
(*Suby of* EDGEWATER TECHNOLOGY INC) ★
200 Harvard Mill Sq # 210, Wakefield, MA 01880-3239
Tel (781) 246-3343 *Founded/Ownrshp* 1993
Sales 102.4MM *EMP* 220
Accts Deloitte & Touche Llp Boston
SIC 7371 Computer software development
CEO: Shirley Singleton
**COO:* David Gallo
**CFO:* Kevin R Rhodes
**VP:* Kris Zaepfel
VP: Kristen Zapro
**CTO:* David Clancey

D-U-N-S 95-745-5132
▲ **EDGEWATER TECHNOLOGY INC**
200 Harvard Mill Sq # 210, Wakefield, MA 01880-3239
Tel (781) 246-3343 *Founded/Ownrshp* 1992
Sales 116.7MM *EMP* 414^E
Accts Bdo Usa Llp Boston Massachu
Tkr Sym EDGW *Exch* NGM
SIC 7379 8742 ; Management consulting services
Ch Bd: Shirley Singleton
CFO: Timothy R Oakes
Ex VP: David Clancey
IT Man: Alysa Gilman
Sftwr Eng: Brandon Levasseur
Board of Directors: Stephen Bova, Paul E Flynn, Paul Guzzi, Nancy L Leaming, Michael Loeb, Timothy Whelan, Wayne Wilson

D-U-N-S 15-117-9769 IMP/EXP
■ **EDGEWELL PERSONAL CARE BRANDS LLC**
(*Suby of* EDGEWELL PERSONAL CARE CO) ★
6 Research Dr, Shelton, CT 06484-6228
Tel (203) 944-5500 *Founded/Ownrshp* 2000
Sales 3.8MMM^E *EMP* 9,800
SIC 3421 2844 2676 Razor blades & razors; Lotions, shaving; Tampons, sanitary: made from purchased paper
Ch Bd: Ward Klein
**CEO:* David Hatfield
Chf Mktg O: Al Robertson
**Ex VP:* Daniel J Sescleifer
VP: Peter Conrad
VP: Perry Morton
VP: Luis Plana
VP: Linda Price
VP: Terrence Schulke
VP: Joseph Tisone
VP: David Wagner
VP: Jeff Ziminski
VP: Robert Zimmermann

D-U-N-S 13-318-4171
▲ **EDGEWELL PERSONAL CARE CO**
1350 Tmberlake Manor Pkwy, Chesterfield, MO 63017-6042
Tel (314) 594-1900 *Founded/Ownrshp* 1999
Sales 2.3MMM *EMP* 6,000
Accts Pricewaterhousecoopers Llp St
Tkr Sym EPC *Exch* NYS
SIC 3421 2844 2676 3069 Razor blades & razors; Shaving preparations; Lotions, shaving; Suntan lotions & oils; Hair preparations, including shampoos; Tampons, sanitary: made from purchased paper; Diapers, paper (disposable): made from purchased paper; Nipples, rubber; Baby pacifiers, rubber; Bibs, vulcanized rubber or rubberized fabric; Water bottles, rubber

Pr: David P Hatfield
Ch Bd: Ward M Klein
CFO: Sandra J Sheldon
Ofcr: Peter J Conrad
Ex VP: Daniel Corbin
VP: Anthony J Bender
VP: Harry Strachan
VP: David S Vernooy

D-U-N-S 02-171-8141 IMP/EXP
■ EDGEWELL PERSONAL CARE LLC
(*Suby of* EDGEWELL PERSONAL CARE CO) ★
1350 Timberlake Mano, Chesterfield, MO 63017-6042
Tel (314) 594-1900 *Founded/Ownrshp* 2008
Sales 314.1MM^E *EMP* 798
SIC 2844 Shaving preparations; Lotions, shaving; Suntan lotions & oils; Hair preparations, including shampoos
Pr: David P Hatfield

D-U-N-S 01-054-1092
EDGEWOOD INDEPENDENT SCHOOL DISTRICT
5358 W Comm St, San Antonio, TX 78237
Tel (210) 444-4500 *Founded/Ownrshp* 1910
Sales 135.5MM *EMP* 2,000
Accts Garza/Gonzalez & Associates S
SIC 8211 Public combined elementary & secondary school; High school, junior or senior
Pr: Joseph M Guerra
Bd of Dir: Dorothy Dursky
Bd of Dir: Lisa Gonzalez
Bd of Dir: Thom Hanson
Bd of Dir: Marissa Martinez
Bd of Dir: Christopher Padilla
Bd of Dir: Lisa Segovia
Ofcr: Alberto Barrientos
Ofcr: Genevieve Guerra
Ofcr: Gloria Martinez
VP: Mark Cox
**VP:* Tina Moralesm

D-U-N-S 04-795-6487
EDGEWOOD INDEPENDENT SCHOOL DISTRICT 903
804 E Pine St, Edgewood, TX 75117-3347
Tel (903) 896-4332 *Founded/Ownrshp* 1990
Sales 135.5MM *EMP* 120^E
SIC 8211 9411 Public elementary & secondary schools; Administration of educational programs
**Prin:* Blake Cooper
**Prin:* Carolyn James
**Prin:* Terry Phillips

EDGEWOOD MANOR OF WESTERVILLE
See CONSULATE MANAGEMENT CO LLC

D-U-N-S 95-859-9144
EDGEWOOD PARTNERS INSURANCE CENTER
EPIC
135 Main St 21f, San Francisco, CA 94105-1812
Tel (415) 356-3900 *Founded/Ownrshp* 1994
Sales NA *EMP* 550
SIC 6411 Insurance brokers
CEO: Dan Francis
**Pr:* John Hahn
COO: Stephen Adkins
**COO:* Peter Garvey
CFO: Karman Chan
**CFO:* Michael Gonthier
Ofcr: Phil Grove
Ofcr: Patrick McCaleb
Sr VP: Diane Browne
**Sr VP:* Jim Gillette
Sr VP: James N Johnson
Sr VP: Christopher R Mitchell
Sr VP: Hali Nielson
VP: David Bloodgood
VP: Judi Bolanos
VP: Robert Carrington
VP: Susan Cereghino
VP: Ricky Choi
VP: Joe Dunn
VP: Joan Frenz
VP: Adam Heher

D-U-N-S 85-904-8662
EDGEWOOD PROPERTIES INC
1260 Stelton Rd, Piscataway, NJ 08854-5282
Tel (732) 985-1900 *Founded/Ownrshp* 1992
Sales 211.6MM^E *EMP* 150
SIC 6552 6531 Subdividers & developers; Real estate agents & managers
Pr: Jack Morris
Sr VP: John Birnbaum
Sr VP: Jim Towle
**VP:* Sheryl Weingarten
Sls Mgr: Sue Vernon
Sls Mgr: Susan Yoder

D-U-N-S 08-998-9859
EDIFICE INC (NC)
1401 W Morehead St Ste A, Charlotte, NC 28208-5262
Tel (704) 332-0900 *Founded/Ownrshp* 1978
Sales 92.9MM *EMP* 54
Accts Elliott Davis Decosimo Charlo
SIC 1542 Commercial & office building, new construction
CEO: Eric Laster
**CFO:* Tod Creech
Treas: Michael Dyer
**Ex VP:* Bryan Knupp
**VP:* Gary W Creed
**VP:* Scott Fandel
Off Mgr: Rose Tuttle

EDINA PUBLIC SCHOOLS
See INDEPENDENT SCHOOL DISTRICT 273

D-U-N-S 07-848-5455
EDINBURG CONSOLIDATED INDEPENDENT SCHOOL DISTRICT
411 N 8th Ave, Edinburg, TX 78541-3309
Tel (956) 289-2300 *Founded/Ownrshp* 1997
Sales 219.0MM^E *EMP* 3,779
Accts Luis C Orozco Pharr Tx
SIC 8211 Public elementary & secondary schools
Pr: Carmen Gonzalez

**CFO:* Melissa Salina
**VP:* Omar Palacios
IT Man: Stella Lopez
IT Man: Elida Martinez
Prd Mgr: Pearl A Benavides
Prd Mgr: Hector Gonzalez
Pr Dir: Gilbert Dagler
Psych: Juanita Fong

EDISON CHOUEST OFFSHORE
See OFFSHORE SERVICE VESSELS LLC

D-U-N-S 06-496-8670
EDISON ELECTRIC INSTITUTE INC (VA)
E E I
701 Pennsylv Ave Nw Fl 3, Washington, DC 20004
Tel (202) 508-5000 *Founded/Ownrshp* 1933
Sales 85.2MM *EMP* 197
Accts Cliftonlarsonallen Llp Arling
SIC 8611 Trade associations
Ch Bd: Theodore F Craver Jr
**Ch Bd:* Jeffry E Sterba
Pr: Jim Owen
COO: Tony Odett
CFO: John Schlenker
**V Ch Bd:* Anthony F Earley Jr
**V Ch Bd:* David M Ratcliffe
Bd of Dir: Brad Whitcomb
Sr VP: Karl Stahlkopf
**Sr VP:* Brian L Wolff
**VP:* Edward H Comer
VP: John J Easton Jr
VP: James Fama
VP: Lawrence E Jones
VP: Brian McCormack
VP: James B Robb

D-U-N-S 19-513-8458 IMP
▲ EDISON INTERNATIONAL
2244 Walnut Grove Ave, Rosemead, CA 91770-3714
Tel (626) 302-2222 *Founded/Ownrshp* 1987
Sales 11.5MMM *EMP* 12,768
Tkr Sym EIX *Exch* NYS
SIC 4911 Electric services; Distribution, electric power; Generation, electric power; Transmission, electric power
Ch Bd: Theodore F Craver Jr
**Pr:* Pedro J Pizarro
CFO: Maria Rigatti
CFO: W James Scilacci
Ex VP: Ronald L Litzinger
Ex VP: Adam S Umanoff
Sr VP: Janet T Clayton
Sr VP: Janet Clayton
Sr VP: J Andrew Murphy
Sr VP: Gaddi H Vasquez
VP: David Heller
VP: Andrew McMillan
VP: Aaron D Moss
VP: Joseph Ruiz
Board of Directors: Vanessa C L Chang, Louis Hernandez Jr, James T Morris, Richard T Schlosberg III, Linda G Stuntz, William P Sullivan, Ellen O Tauscher, Peter J Taylor, Brett White

D-U-N-S 60-156-4086
■ EDISON MATERIAL SUPPLY LLC
(*Suby of* SOUTHERN CALIFORNIA EDISON CO) ★
125 Elm Ave, Long Beach, CA 90802-4918
Tel (562) 491-2341 *Founded/Ownrshp* 1999
Sales 147.3MM^E *EMP* 43^E
SIC 5031 Building materials, exterior

D-U-N-S 15-427-2918 IMP
■ EDISON MISSION ENERGY
(*Suby of* NRG ENERGY HOLDINGS INC.)
3 Macarthur Pl Ste 100, Santa Ana, CA 92707-6068
Tel (714) 513-8000 *Founded/Ownrshp* 2014
Sales 1.9MMM^E *EMP* 1,047^E
SIC 4931 Electric & other services combined
Pr: Pedro J Pizarro
Sr VP: Daryl David
**Sr VP:* Andrew J Hertneky
**Sr VP:* Paul Jacob
**Sr VP:* John C Kennedy
Sr VP: S Daniel Melita
Sr VP: Georgia R Nelson
Sr VP: Bertrand Valdman
**VP:* Guy F Gorney
Board of Directors: Frederic F Brace, Hugh E Sawyer

D-U-N-S 18-313-0228
■ EDISON MISSION GROUP INC
(*Suby of* EDISON INTERNATIONAL) ★
2244 Walnut Grove Ave, Rosemead, CA 91770-3714
Tel (626) 302-2222 *Founded/Ownrshp* 1987
Sales 3.9MMM^E *EMP* 2,746
SIC 4931 6799 1629 1531 Electric & other services combined; Investors; Venture capital companies; Power plant construction; Operative builders
CEO: Mark C Clarke
**Pr:* Ronald L Litzinger
**Treas:* Theodore F Craver
Sr VP: Janet Clayton

D-U-N-S 80-312-4804
■ EDISON MISSION MIDWEST HOLDINGS CO
(*Suby of* EDISON MISSION GROUP INC) ★
2244 Walnut Grove Ave, Rosemead, CA 91770-3714
Tel (626) 302-2222 *Founded/Ownrshp* 2012
Sales 3.9MMM^E *EMP* 2,483
SIC 4911 Electric services
Pr: Guy F Gorney
IT Man: Jeffrey Balaban
IT Man: Efrain Gonzalez
IT Man: Kenneth Pramana
IT Man: Kristina Quick

EDISON SCHOOLS
See EDISONLEARNING INC

D-U-N-S 06-072-7864
EDISON TOWNSHIP PUBLIC SCHOOLS
312 Pierson Ave, Edison, NJ 08837-3106
Tel (732) 452-4900 *Founded/Ownrshp* 1898
Sales 98.4MM^E *EMP* 1,698
Accts Hodulik & Morrison Pa
SIC 8211 Public elementary & secondary schools

Dir Sec: Richard Adams
MIS Dir: Emilio Barca
HC Dir: James Muldowney

D-U-N-S 79-261-6245
EDISONLEARNING INC
EDISON SCHOOLS
Harborside Financial Center 2910, Jersey City, NJ 07311
Tel (201) 630-2600 *Founded/Ownrshp* 2003
Sales 14.6MM *EMP* 1,400
Accts Rainer & Company Newtown Squa
SIC 8211 Private elementary & secondary schools
Pr: Thomas Jackson
**Pr:* Jodi Mastronardi
**CFO:* Maureen Ryan
Treas: Mike McInerney
VP: Suzanne Glass
Mktg Mgr: Jennifer Pricci
Snr Mgr: Ranald Hopkins

D-U-N-S 06-408-8073
EDM AMERICAS INC
DIVERSIFIED
(*Suby of* EDM GROUP LIMITED)
10 Ed Preate Dr, Moosic, PA 18507-1755
Tel (800) 852-9809 *Founded/Ownrshp* 2013
Sales 209.5MM^E *EMP* 1,590
SIC 4226 7389 7334 8741 Document & office records storage; Microfilm recording & developing service; Photocopying & duplicating services; Management services
CEO: Scott A Byers
**CFO:* Jimmy Eyerman
**CFO:* Joseph Murray
**Sr VP:* Leo Malsky
VP: Julie Calabro
**VP:* Warren Lederer
VP: Joseph O'Boyle
**VP:* Arun Singh
Genl Mgr: Mike Balberchak
Genl Mgr: Jen Praefke
Dir IT: Jason Washo
Board of Directors: William R Gruver

EDMANAGE
See SOUTH CAROLINA STUDENT LOAN CORP

D-U-N-S 61-319-6567
EDMENTUM INC
PLATO LEARNING
(*Suby of* THOMA BRAVO LLC) ★
5600 W 83rd St 3008200, Bloomington, MN 55437-1000
Tel (800) 447-5286 *Founded/Ownrshp* 1989
Sales 93.4MM^E *EMP* 380^E
SIC 7372 Educational computer software
Pr: Robert J Rueckl
**Sr VP:* Jamie Candee
**VP:* Dave Adams
VP: Tom Bukowski
VP: Mike Duffy
VP: Sergio Garcia
**VP:* Stacey Herteux
VP: Ian Kees
VP: Dan Kelly
VP: Carol Loomis
VP: Libby Preble
VP: Jeff Reistad

D-U-N-S 07-427-7724
EDMOND PUBLIC SCHOOLS
ISD 12
1001 W Danforth Rd, Edmond, OK 73003-4801
Tel (405) 340-2800 *Founded/Ownrshp* 1897
Sales 196.4MM *EMP* 2,276
Accts Rehhal Henderson Johnson Pllc
SIC 8211 Public combined elementary & secondary school
**CFO:* Lori Smith
Off Mgr: Judy Pendergraft
MIS Dir: Stacie Vincent
Pr Dir: Susan P Schlepp

D-U-N-S 02-357-1974
EDMONDS COMMUNITY COLLEGE FOUNDATION
20000 68th Ave W, Lynnwood, WA 98036-5912
Tel (425) 640-1459 *Founded/Ownrshp* 1967
Sales 1.0MM *EMP* 1,372
Accts Vine Dahlen Pllc Lynnwood Wa
SIC 8222 Community college
Pr: Jean Hernandez
**Treas:* Diana Clay
VP: Mark Cassidy
VP: Christina Castorena
VP: Terry Cox
VP: Tonya Drake
VP: Joseph Duggan
VP: Vu Linh
VP: Kevin McKay
VP: Lynne Rigoroso
VP: George Smith
VP: Mary Zickafoose
Assoc Dir: Miki Aspree
Assoc Dir: Janie Barnett
Assoc Dir: Lucy Quek-Tait

D-U-N-S 02-025-6996
EDMONDS SCHOOL DISTRICT 15
20420 68th Ave W, Lynnwood, WA 98036-7400
Tel (425) 431-7000 *Founded/Ownrshp* 1900
Sales 207.7MM *EMP* 2,800
SIC 8211 Public elementary & secondary schools
Genl Mgr: Manny Juzon
CTO: Nancy Sutherland
IT Man: Stewart Mhyre

D-U-N-S 00-233-3870 IMP/EXP
EDMUND OPTICS INC
EDMUND SCIENTIFIC CO
101 E Gloucester Pike, Barrington, NJ 08007-1331
Tel (856) 547-3488 *Founded/Ownrshp* 1942
Sales 118.8MM^E *EMP* 400
SIC 3211 5961 Flat glass; Catalog sales
CEO: Robert Edmund
**Treas:* Marissa Edmund
Ex VP: Susan O'Keefe
Exec: Susan Tunney

Off Mgr: Regina Brophy
QA Dir: Howard Zwick
Dir IT: Margie Chiaravolloti
Web Dev: David Schrenker
Sfty Mgr: Jay Budd
Prd Mgr: Paula Bao
QI Cn Mgr: William Daley

EDMUND SCIENTIFIC CO
See EDMUND OPTICS INC

D-U-N-S 85-971-3179
EDMUNDS HOLDING CO
EDMUNDS.COM
1620 26th St Ste 400s, Santa Monica, CA 90404-4063
Tel (310) 309-6300 *Founded/Ownrshp* 1988
Sales 102.5MM^E *EMP* 650
SIC 7375 Information retrieval services
CEO: AVI Steinlauf
Pr: Seth Berkowitz
CFO: Charles Farrell
VP: Laura Perlman
Assoc Dir: Megan Jay
Snr Sftwr: Matt Altermatt

EDMUNDS.COM
See EDMUNDS HOLDING CO

D-U-N-S 04-197-1722 IMP
EDMUNDS.COM INC
(*Suby of* EDMUNDS.COM) ★
2401 Colorado Ave, Santa Monica, CA 90404-3585
Tel (310) 309-6300 *Founded/Ownrshp* 1988
Sales 102.5MM^E *EMP* 400
SIC 2731 Book publishing
Ch Bd: Peter Steinlauf
Pr: Seth Berkowitz
CEO: AVI Steinlauf
CFO: Allen Steinlauf
V Ch Bd: Jeremy Anwyl
Chf Mktg O: Nathalie Lubensky
Ex VP: Ken Levin
VP: Katti Fields
VP: Michael Kilander
VP: Mark Rankin
VP: Sven Wood

EDO CORPORATION
See EDO LLC

D-U-N-S 00-187-6440 IMP/EXP
■ EDO LLC
EDO CORPORATION
(*Suby of* HARRIS CORP) ★
1500 New Horizons Blvd, Amityville, NY 11701-1130
Tel (631) 630-4000 *Founded/Ownrshp* 1925, 2015
Sales 956.8MM^E *EMP* 4,000
SIC 3812 3728 3663 3679 Search & navigation equipment; Sonar systems & equipment; Warfare counter-measure equipment; Detection apparatus: electronic/magnetic field, light/heat; Military aircraft equipment & armament; Countermeasure dispensers, aircraft; Research & dev by manuf., aircraft parts & auxiliary equip; Antennas, transmitting & communications; Satellites, communications; Electronic crystals; Piezoelectric crystals
CEO: Charles Greene
CFO: Frederic B Bassett
Sr VP: Jon A Anderson
Sr VP: Frank W Otto
VP: Roy R Byrd
VP: Joe Carnevale
VP: Patricia D Comiskey
VP: George P Fox
VP: Peter Martin
VP: Lisa M Palumbo
Prin: Lawrence Schwartz

D-U-N-S 01-800-9738
EDON FARMERS COOPERATIVE ASSOCIATION
205 S Michigan St, Edon, OH 43518-9697
Tel (419) 272-2121 *Founded/Ownrshp* 1919
Sales 89.1MM *EMP* 30
Accts Bashore Reineck Stoller & Wate
SIC 5153 5191 Grain & field beans; Farm supplies
Ch: Robert Waltz
**Prin:* David Brigle
**Prin:* John Ingram
Genl Mgr: Richard Dunbar

D-U-N-S 01-553-4469
EDP RENEWABLES NORTH AMERICA LLC
(*Suby of* EDP RENOVAVEIS, SA)
808 Travis St Ste 700, Houston, TX 77002-5774
Tel (713) 265-0350 *Founded/Ownrshp* 2007
Sales 571.7MM^E *EMP* 300
SIC 4911
Ex VP: Andrew Young
VP: Howard A Huckins
VP: Fritz Richard
Dir IT: David Edwards
Site Mgr: Jack Frosh
Opers Mgr: Kevin Davis
Opers Mgr: Justin Steinbrock
Opers Mgr: Gary Webb
Counsel: John McMullan

EDR
See EDUCATION REALTYTRUST INC

D-U-N-S 78-214-4349
■ EDS ELECTRONIC FINANCIAL SERVICES INC
(*Suby of* ELECTRONIC DATA SYSTEMS) ★
5400 Legacy Dr, Plano, TX 75024-3199
Tel (972) 378-6985 *Founded/Ownrshp* 1989
Sales 91.0MM^E *EMP* 539
SIC 7374 Data processing service
CFO: Bob Swan
Treas: Scott J Krenz
Ex VP: Bruce N Hawthorne
VP: James E Daley
VP: R J Smith
Prgrm Mgr: Cathy Wolanzyk
Genl Mgr: Mark Makowski
IT Man: Rafael N Almeida
IT Man: Cliff Engle
IT Man: Dennis Lackey
Netwrk Mgr: Derek Meller

D-U-N-S 78-840-4598 IMP
EDS MANUFACTURING INC
765 N Target Range Rd, Nogales, AZ 85621-2490
Tel (520) 287-9711 *Founded/Ownrshp* 1991
Sales 322.0MM[E] *EMP* 1,900[E]
SIC 3679 Harness assemblies for electronic use: wire or cable; Electronic switches; Electronic circuits
Pr: Luis Moreno Sr
* *Treas:* Robert C Milo Sr
Ex VP: John Roderick
* *VP:* Luis Moreno Jr
CIO: Hector R Leyva

D-U-N-S 00-514-0603 IMP/EXP
EDSAL MANUFACTURING CO INC (IL)
4400 S Packers Ave, Chicago, IL 60609-3388
Tel (773) 475-3020 *Founded/Ownrshp* 1952
Sales 339.4MM[E] *EMP* 1,300
SIC 2599 2542 2522 Factory furniture & fixtures; Shelving, office & store: except wood; Cabinets: show, display or storage: except wood; Office furniture, except wood
Chf Mktg O: Scott Henry
MIS Dir: Art Courtney
Sfty Dirs: Bruce Murray
Mtls Mgr: Joseph Zaplatosch
Opers Mgr: James Chruszczyk

D-U-N-S 09-800-7867
EDSEL & ELEANOR FORD HOUSE
1100 Lake Shore Rd, Grosse Pointe Shores, MI 48236-4106
Tel (313) 884-4222 *Founded/Ownrshp* 1978
Sales 104.6MM *EMP* 90
SIC 8412 Museum
Pr: Kathleen Stiso Mullins
VP: Ann Fitzpatrick

EDSOUTH
See EDUCATIONAL FUNDING OF SOUTH INC

EDSOUTH SERVICES
See EDUCATIONAL SERVICES OF AMERICA INC

EDUBUYERS
See M&A TECHNOLOGY INC

D-U-N-S 13-411-0555
EDUCATE INC
SYLVAN LEARNING CENTERS
(*Suby of* EDGE ACQUISITION LLC) ★
4 North Park Dr Ste 500, Hunt Valley, MD 21030-1810
Tel (410) 843-8000 *Founded/Ownrshp* 2003
Sales 194.5MM[E] *EMP* 10,161
SIC 8299 Educational services
CEO: Christopher Hoehn-Saric
Pr: Peter J Cohen
Pr: Chip Paucek
COO: William Rieders
CFO: Kevin Shaffer
Bd of Dir: Douglas Becker
Ofcr: Kevin E Shaffer
VP: Nancy Fowler
VP: Mary Giermek
VP: Patricia Miller
Mng Dir: Neil Boylan

D-U-N-S 96-291-5224
EDUCATION AFFILIATES INC
(*Suby of* EDUCATION AFFILIATES LLC) ★
5026 Campbell Blvd, Baltimore, MD 21236-4966
Tel (410) 633-2929 *Founded/Ownrshp* 2004
Sales 159.3MM[E] *EMP* 3,700[E]
SIC 8221 Colleges universities & professional schools
Pr: Duncan M Anderson
Pr: Bill Polmear
Pr: Glen Tharp
* *CFO:* Stephen J Budosh
Sr VP: Jerry Smith
VP: Eric Jacobs
VP: Alex Teitelbaum
Dir Bus: Dan York
DP Exec: Marino Joe
IT Man: Mark Van Bemmel
HC Dir: Lee Nelly

D-U-N-S 78-443-3836
EDUCATION AFFILIATES LLC
(*Suby of* ACE CASH EXPRESS) ★
5204 Campbell Blvd Ste A, Baltimore, MD 21236
Tel (410) 633-2929 *Founded/Ownrshp* 2004
Sales 165.3MM[E] *EMP* 4,000
SIC 8222 6211 Technical institute; Security brokers & dealers
CEO: Duncan Anderson
Pr: Cary Metz
VP: Robert L Anders
VP: Stephen Budosh
VP: Maryse Levy
VP: Alex Teitelbaum
Exec: Jim Herbst
Off Mgr: Shelley Faytak
Dir IT: Joe Marino
IT Man: Mike Thompson
Pgrm Dir: Marie Gillis

D-U-N-S 12-866-7599
EDUCATION AGENCY TEXAS
(*Suby of* EXECUTIVE OFFICE OF STATE OF TEXAS) ★
1701 Congress Ave, Austin, TX 78701-1402
Tel (512) 463-9734 *Founded/Ownrshp* 2003
Sales 235.2MM[E] *EMP* 844
Accts Bolinger Segars Gilbert & Mo
SIC 8211 9411 Public elementary & secondary schools; Administration of educational programs;
Pr: James Gonzalez
* *Treas:* Mae Murray
* *Prin:* Robert Duron
* *Prin:* Bill Parker
* *Prin:* Lizzette Gonzalez Reynolds
Prgrm Mgr: Howard Morrison
CTO: Susanna Garza
MIS Dir: Meloddy Parrish
QA Dir: Shobha Sety
IT Man: Sharon Lewellyn
Opers Mgr: Mark Wallace

D-U-N-S 15-424-1558
EDUCATION AMERICA INC
REMINGTON COLLEGE
7131 Bus Pk Ln Ste 300, Lake Mary, FL 32746
Tel (407) 562-5500 *Founded/Ownrshp* 1985
Sales 252.6MM[E] *EMP* 1,200
SIC 8222 Technical institute
Ch: Jerald M Barnett Jr
* *CEO:* Jack W Forrest
* *CFO:* Reid Allison
CFO: Jack Forest

EDUCATION CENTER
See POCATELLO/CHUBBUCK SCHOOL DISTRICT 25

EDUCATION CENTER
See BETHLEHEM AREA SCHOOL DISTRICT

D-U-N-S 79-712-3259
EDUCATION CORP OF AMERICA
BRIGHTWOOD COLLEGE
3660 Grandview Pkwy # 300, Birmingham, AL 35243-3340
Tel (205) 329-7900 *Founded/Ownrshp* 1999
Sales 131.5MM[E] *EMP* 2,000[E]
SIC 8299 Educational services
V Ch Bd: Tom Moore
Mng Pt: John Willis
* *Pr:* Geoffrey Baird
* *Pr:* Deb Lenart
* *CEO:* Stu Reed
* *CFO:* Roger M Miller
* *Ex VP:* Christopher Boehm
* *Ex VP:* Gregory Fern
* *Ex VP:* Sara Lawhorne
* *Ex VP:* William R Owens
* *Sr VP:* Ryan Brewer
Sr VP: David Kahn
Sr VP: Scot Stapleton
VP: Rita Chubick
VP: Robert Landman
Exec: John Cardona
Exec: Christian Lara

D-U-N-S 80-678-2173
EDUCATION DEPARTMENT NEW YORK STATE
EXECUTV OFC OF THE STATE OF NY
(*Suby of* EXECUTIVE OFFICE OF STATE OF NEW YORK) ★
89 Washington Ave, Albany, NY 12234-1000
Tel (518) 474-3852 *Founded/Ownrshp* 1784
Sales 155.6MM[E] *EMP* 2,964
SIC 8299 9411 Educational services;
Pr: Maryellen Elia
Ofcr: Maria McCashion
VP: Catalina Fortino
Dir: Carolee Smith
Dir Sec: Linda Seaman
HC Dir: Karen Hollowood

D-U-N-S 07-658-3830
EDUCATION DEVELOPMENT CENTER INC
E D C
43 Foundry Ave, Waltham, MA 02453-8313
Tel (617) 969-7100 *Founded/Ownrshp* 1958
Sales 143.3MM *EMP* 600
SIC 8732 2741 Educational research; Miscellaneous publishing
Pr: Luther S Luedtke
CFO: Cheryl Hoffman
* *CFO:* Cheryl Hoffman-Bray
* *CFO:* Robert Rotner
Bd of Dir: Deborah Spencer
* *Sr VP:* Joanne Brady
* *Sr VP:* Larry C Lai
VP: Doryn D Chervin
* *VP:* Christine Filosa
VP: Rebecca Jacksonstoeckle
* *VP:* Siobhan Murhphy
VP: Robyn Priest
VP: Mildred Solomon
Assoc Dir: Gayle Oulighan
Comm Dir: Peter Orne

D-U-N-S 06-872-8039
▲ EDUCATION MANAGEMENT CORP
210 6th Ave Fl 33, Pittsburgh, PA 15222-2602
Tel (412) 562-0900 *Founded/Ownrshp* 1962
Sales 2.2MMM *EMP* 20,800
Accts Ernst & Young Llp Pittsburgh
Tkr Sym EDMC *Exch* OTO
SIC 8299 Educational services
Pr: Edward H West
Ch Bd: John T South III
Pr: Mitchell Gilbert
Pr: Joseph Marsico
Pr: Charles Restivo
Pr: Ronald Riel
Pr: Leanne Wruck
CFO: Mick J Beekhuizen
CFO: Frank Jalufka
Chf Cred: Donna A Bucella
Act CFO: Randall J Killeen
Ex VP: Carol A Dibattiste
Ex VP: James Hobby
Ex VP: James C Hobby
Sr VP: John M Azzoni
Sr VP: Robert E Barr
Sr VP: Tyler D Gronbach
Sr VP: Devitt Kramer
Sr VP: J Devitt Kramer
Sr VP: Mark S Miko
Sr VP: Ronald W Ogrodnik
Board of Directors: Samuel C Cowley, Adrian M Jones, Jeffrey T Leeds, John R McKernan Jr, Leo F Mullin, Brian A Napack, Paul J Salem, Peter O Wilde

D-U-N-S 61-908-3160
■ EDUCATION MANAGEMENT CORP
(*Suby of* EDUCATION MANAGEMENT CORP) ★
210 6th Ave Ste 3300, Pittsburgh, PA 15222-2603
Tel (412) 562-0900 *Founded/Ownrshp* 2006
Sales 599.3MM[E] *EMP* 11,300
Accts Ernst & Young Llp Pittsburgh
SIC 8221 Colleges universities & professional schools
CEO: Todd S Nelson
Pr: John Kline
* *Pr:* Edward H West
* *Chf Mktg O:* Anthony F Digiovanni
* *Ex VP:* Mick J Beekhuizen
* *Ex VP:* Carol Dibattiste
* *Sr VP:* John M Bowen
* *Sr VP:* Donna Bucella
* *Sr VP:* Robert A Carroll
* *Sr VP:* J Devitt Kramer
VP: Jeffrey Durosko
VP: Daniel Levinson
VP: Mary McCollough
VP: Frederick Steinberg
Board of Directors: Adrian M Jones, Jeffrey T Leeds, John R McKernan Jr, Leo F Mullin, Paul J Salem, Peter O Wilde

D-U-N-S 04-911-5157 IMP
EDUCATION REALTY TRUST INC
EDR
999 Shady Grove Rd S # 600, Memphis, TN 38120-4130
Tel (901) 259-2500 *Founded/Ownrshp* 2004
Sales 225.7MM *EMP* 1,283
SIC 6798

EDUCATION SERVICE CENTER
See WATERLOO COMMUNITY SCHOOL DISTRICT INC

EDUCATION SERVICE CENTERS RISK
See BARTHOLOMEW CONSOLIDATED SCHOOL FOUNDATION INC

EDUCATION SUPPORT CENTER
See AMARILLO INDEPENDENT SCHOOL DISTRICT

D-U-N-S 13-061-5354
EDUCATION TRAINING CORP
FLORIDA CAREER COLLEGE
3383 N State Road 7, Lauderdale Lakes, FL 33319-5617
Tel (954) 400-2000 *Founded/Ownrshp* 1994
Sales 87.9MM[E] *EMP* 1,800
SIC 8243

D-U-N-S 07-834-6249
EDUCATION UNLIMITED OF OHIO INC
ELCOLE FRANCAISE
8216 Kennedy Rd, Blacklick, OH 43004-9707
Tel (614) 451-1309 *Founded/Ownrshp* 1995
Sales 22.3MM[E] *EMP* 1,126
SIC 8211 Private elementary & secondary schools
Pr: Ron Flynn
* *Pr:* June Flynn

D-U-N-S 07-100-8932
EDUCATIONAL ALLIANCE INC
197 E Brdwy, New York, NY 10002
Tel (646) 654-1297 *Founded/Ownrshp* 1889
Sales 42.7MM *EMP* 1,000
Accts Cohnreznick Llp New York Ny
SIC 8399 Community development groups; Social service information exchange
Pr: Robin Bernstein
* *Ch:* Russell Makowsky
* *Treas:* Jonathan Rosenweig
Sr VP: Maidelle Benamy
* *VP:* Edger Eisner
VP: Danny Rosenthal
CTO: Carl Feinman
MIS Dir: Dov Nierman
Dir IT: Piotr Ziarnik

D-U-N-S 00-795-8366
EDUCATIONAL CREDIT MANAGEMENT CORP (MN)
ECMC
111 Wshngton Ave Ste 1400, Minneapolis, MN 55401
Tel (651) 221-0566 *Founded/Ownrshp* 1994
Sales NA *EMP* 634
Accts Baker Tilly Virchow Krause Llp
SIC 6111 Federal & federally sponsored credit agencies
CEO: Jan Hines
* *Pr:* Richard J Boyle
Pr: Morgan Pinckney
* *COO:* Dave Hawn
COO: Roberta Sweeney
CFO: Cathleen King
* *CFO:* Greg Van Guilder
* *Ex VP:* Dan Fisher
* *Ex VP:* Heather Renner
Sr VP: Matt Mikulski
VP: Geri Gjesdahl
VP: Hugh McSherry
Board of Directors: Kathy McCutchen, Jack O'connell, Maurice M Salter

D-U-N-S 60-691-2947
EDUCATIONAL FUNDING OF SOUTH INC
EDSOUTH
12700 Kingston Pike, Knoxville, TN 37934-0917
Tel (865) 342-0684 *Founded/Ownrshp* 1985
Sales NA *EMP* 3
Accts Kraft Cpas Nashville Tenness
SIC 6141 Personal credit institutions
CEO: Ron Gambill

D-U-N-S 14-795-4127
EDUCATIONAL MANAGEMENT CORP
HARRISON COLLEGE
550 E Washington St, Indianapolis, IN 46204-2611
Tel (317) 264-5656 *Founded/Ownrshp* 1986
Sales 116.8MM[E] *EMP* 950
SIC 8221 College, except junior
* *Pr:* Jason T Konesco
Ex VP: Kevin Hesler
Assoc Dir: Becky Polston
IT Man: Greg Harris
IT Man: Nikall Miller
HC Dir: Sarah Stultz

D-U-N-S 18-052-7392
EDUCATIONAL MEDIA FOUNDATION
K-LOVE RADIO NETWORK
5700 West Oaks Blvd, Rocklin, CA 95765-3719
Tel (916) 251-1600 *Founded/Ownrshp* 1981
Sales 155.2MM *EMP* 325
Accts Kcoe Isom Llp Chico Ca
SIC 4832 Radio broadcasting stations
Ch Bd: Darrell Chambliss
* *Pr:* Richard Jenkins
Pr: Bill Lyons
* *CEO:* Mike Novak
CFO: Eric Moser
* *CFO:* Jon Taylor
* *VP:* David Atkinson
VP: Randy Rich
VP: Sam Wallington
Creative D: Shawn Farrington
Rgnl Mgr: Anne Tata

D-U-N-S 03-721-9847 IMP
EDUCATIONAL PRODUCTS INC
E P I
(*Suby of* DISCOUNT SCHOOL SUPPLY) ★
4100 N Sam Houston Pkwy W P, Houston, TX 77086-1465
Tel (800) 365-5345 *Founded/Ownrshp* 1999
Sales 116.6MM[E] *EMP* 100
SIC 5112 5049 Stationery & office supplies; School supplies
CEO: Ron Phelan
CFO: Jim Faryewicz
* *Treas:* Mike Gaitley
* *VP:* Rick Phelan

EDUCATIONAL SERVICE CENTER
See LAKE STEVENS SCHOOL DISTRICT

EDUCATIONAL SERVICES AMERICA
See CHANCELIGHT INC

D-U-N-S 09-424-9026
EDUCATIONAL SERVICES COMMISSION OF NEW JERSEY (NJ)
1660 Stelton Rd, Piscataway, NJ 08854-4973
Tel (732) 777-9848 *Founded/Ownrshp* 1978
Sales NA *EMP* 1,000
Accts Ernst & Young Llp
SIC 9411 Administration of educational programs
Genl Mgr: Patrick Moran
Dir IT: Bob Reinke
Board of Directors: Patrick Moran

D-U-N-S 93-831-4317
EDUCATIONAL SERVICES OF AMERICA INC
EDSOUTH SERVICES
12700 Kingston Pike, Farragut, TN 37934-0917
Tel (865) 824-3051 *Founded/Ownrshp* 1995
Sales 118.5MM *EMP* 20[E]
SIC 7389 Financial services
CEO: John Arnold Jr
Genl Mgr: Greg Sawyers

EDUCATIONAL TECH ASSOC DIV
See CUSTOM COMPUTER SPECIALISTS INC

D-U-N-S 00-250-8463
EDUCATIONAL TESTING SERVICE INC (NY)
E T S
660 Rosedale Rd, Princeton, NJ 08540-2218
Tel (609) 921-9000 *Founded/Ownrshp* 1947
Sales 1.5MMM *EMP* 2,614
Accts Deloitte & Touche Llp
SIC 8748 8732 Testing service, educational or personnel; Test development & evaluation service; Educational research
Pr: Walt Macdonald
* *CFO:* Jack Hayon
* *Treas:* John Basehore
Sr VP: David Hunt
Sr VP: Scott Nelson
Sr VP: Michael T Nettles
VP: Charles Cascio
VP: Kadriye Ercikan
VP: Sheree Johnson-Gregory
Prin: Diana Schmelzer
VP Admn: Bruce Gilbertson
Board of Directors: Walt Macdonald

EDUK GROUP
See GRUPO EDUK INC

D-U-N-S 83-142-1792
EDURO HEALTHCARE LLC
1376 E 3300 S, Salt Lake City, UT 84106-3069
Tel (801) 601-1450 *Founded/Ownrshp* 2009
Sales 37.1MM *EMP* 1,100
SIC 8051 Skilled nursing care facilities

D-U-N-S 00-535-4816 IMP
EDW C LEVY CO (MI)
ACE ASPHALT PRODUCTS COMPANY
9300 Dix, Dearborn, MI 48120-1528
Tel (313) 429-2200 *Founded/Ownrshp* 1918, 1987
Sales 388.3MM[E] *EMP* 1,200
SIC 3295 5032 2951 Minerals, ground or treated; Blast furnace slag; Aggregate; Asphalt & asphaltic paving mixtures (not from refineries)
Pr: Edward C Levy Jr
CFO: Robert Scholz
VP: Malcom Dunbar
VP: S E Weiner
Netwrk Eng: Dan Crain
Ql Cn Mgr: Katie Schroeder

D-U-N-S 04-350-8290 IMP
EDWARD D JONES & CO LP
EDWARD JONES INVESTMENTS
(*Suby of* JONES FINANCIAL COMPANIES LLLP) ★
12555 Manchester Rd, Saint Louis, MO 63131-3729
Tel (314) 515-2000 *Founded/Ownrshp* 1987
Sales 44.5MM *EMP* 36,000
SIC 6211 Brokers, security
Genl Pt: Jim Weddle
* *Sr Pt:* John W Bachmann
* *Pt:* Douglas E Hill
Mng Pt: James D Weddle
CFO: Kevin D Bastien
CFO: Linda Becker
* *CFO:* Steve Novik
CFO: Kevin Vastien
Ofcr: Norman L Eaker
Ex VP: Thomas Butler
Ex VP: Ann Lenihan
Exec: Matt Mikula

D-U-N-S 13-087-8713 EXP
EDWARD HINES LUMBER CO
EHLCO WHOLESALE CHICAGO
(*Suby of* US LBM HOLDINGS LLC) ★
1050 Corporate Grove Dr, Buffalo Grove, IL 60089-4550
Tel (847) 353-7700 *Founded/Ownrshp* 2010
Sales 270.6MM[E] *EMP* 800
SIC 5031 5211 Lumber, plywood & millwork; Building materials, exterior; Building materials, interior; Lumber & other building materials; Door & window products
Pr: Edward Hines
**CFO:* Steven T Svendsen
VP: Mac Hines
**VP:* John P Vetter
**VP:* Gerry Wille

D-U-N-S 06-847-8155
EDWARD HOSPITAL
EDWARD HOSPITAL AND HLTH SVCS
(*Suby of* EDWARD-ELMHURST HEALTHCARE) ★
801 S Washington St, Naperville, IL 60540-7499
Tel (630) 355-0450 *Founded/Ownrshp* 1987
Sales 567.7MM *EMP* 4,700
Accts Crowe Horwath Llp Chicago Il
SIC 8062 General medical & surgical hospitals
CEO: Pamela Davis
Chf OB: Linda A A Anderson
Pr: Nancy Bork
CFO: William Devoney
Chf Mktg O: Brian Davis
Assoc VP: Yvette Saba
Ex VP: Susan Mitchell
Ex VP: Chris Mollet
Ex VP: Richard W Pehlke
Ex VP: Vince Pryor
Sr VP: Dwight Monson
VP: Hoda Asmar
VP: Barbara Byrne
VP: Bobbie Byrne
VP: Marilyn Daley
VP: Alan S Kaplan
VP: Bill Kottman
VP: William Kottmann
VP: Patti Ludwig-Beymer
VP: Mary Lou Mastro
VP: Gary Mielak

EDWARD HOSPITAL AND HLTH SVCS
See EDWARD HOSPITAL

EDWARD JONES INVESTMENTS
See EDWARD D JONES & CO LP

D-U-N-S 00-794-7559 IMP
EDWARD KRAEMER & SONS INC (WI)
1 Plainview Rd, Plain, WI 53577-9694
Tel (608) 546-2311 *Founded/Ownrshp* 1949, 1986
Sales 547.5MM[E] *EMP* 1,000
SIC 1622 1442 Bridge construction; Gravel mining
Pr: Scott Peterson
**Treas:* Tina H Johansen
**Sr VP:* Fred E Lueck
**VP:* Robert J Beckel
**VP:* Timothy J Maloney
**VP:* Dennis M Maney

D-U-N-S 00-655-2245
EDWARD MEDICAL GROUP
(*Suby of* EDWARD HOSPITAL AND HLTH SVCS) ★
16151 Weber Rd Ste 201, Crest Hill, IL 60403-0865
Tel (815) 773-7827 *Founded/Ownrshp* 2010
Sales 6.8MM[E] *EMP* 1,364[E]
SIC 8099 Health & allied services
Prin: William Kottman

D-U-N-S 12-256-6560
EDWARD VIA VIRGINIA COLLEGE OF OSTEOPATHIC MEDICINE
VCOM-VIRGINIA CAMPUS
2265 Kraft Dr, Blacksburg, VA 24060-6360
Tel (540) 231-4000 *Founded/Ownrshp* 2002
Sales 135.2MM *EMP* 170
Accts Kpmg Llp Richmond Va
SIC 8733 Noncommercial research organizations
Prin: Dixie Tooke-Rawlins
CFO: Mark Hammerick
**CFO:* Mark Hamric
VP: Marianne Baernholdt
VP: Mark Rolfs
Assoc Dir: Jean Harris
**Prin:* John Rocovich Jr
**Prin:* James Wolfe
Dir IT: Gary Brewer
Obsttrcn: Diane Aslanis
Obsttrcn: Mark Austin

D-U-N-S 04-180-7777
EDWARD W SPARROW HOSPITAL ASSOCIATION
(*Suby of* SPARROW HEALTH SYSTEM) ★
1215 E Michigan Ave, Lansing, MI 48912-1896
Tel (517) 364-1000 *Founded/Ownrshp* 1984
Sales 857.8MM *EMP* 3,400
SIC 8062 General medical & surgical hospitals
Pr: Dennis Swan
CFO: Chris Bergman
**CFO:* James Budzinski
VP: Don Davis
VP: Andrea Price
VP: Larry Rawsthrone
VP Admn: Ira Ginsburg
Obsttrcn: Michael C Garbaccio
Obsttrcn: Joseph J Kochan
Ansthlgy: Wenshu L Liu
Doctor: Mark A Cook

D-U-N-S 80-935-3816
EDWARD-ELMHURST HEALTHCARE
801 S Washington St, Naperville, IL 60540-7430
Tel (630) 355-0450 *Founded/Ownrshp* 1987
Sales 75.8MM *EMP* 6,500[E]
Accts Crowe Horwath Llp Chicago Il
SIC 8062 General medical & surgical hospitals
Pr: Pamela Meyer-Davis
V Ch: Richard Pehlke
**CFO:* Vince Pryor
**Ex VP:* Susan Mitchell
**Ex VP:* Chris Mollet
**VP:* Bobbie Byrne
VP: William Devoney
VP: Hoda El-Asmar
VP: Marylou Mastro
VP: Gary Mielak
Dir Lab: Mathew Keloeher

D-U-N-S 00-535-5037 IMP
EDWARDS BROTHERS INC (MI)
EDWARDS BROTHERS MALLOY
(*Suby of* EDWARDS BROTHERS MALLOY INC) ★
5411 Jackson Rd, Ann Arbor, MI 48103-1861
Tel (800) 722-3231 *Founded/Ownrshp* 1893, 2012
Sales 252.6MM[E] *EMP* 600[E]
SIC 2732 2789 Books: printing & binding; Bookbinding & related work
Pr: John Edwards
**CFO:* William Upton
VP: Dave Mead
IT Man: Tawnya McKinzie
Mfg Mgr: John Welton

EDWARDS BROTHERS MALLOY
See EDWARDS BROTHERS INC

D-U-N-S 07-850-8433
EDWARDS BROTHERS MALLOY INC
5411 Jackson Rd, Ann Arbor, MI 48103-1861
Tel (734) 665-6113 *Founded/Ownrshp* 2012
Sales 323.0MM[E] *EMP* 600
SIC 2732 Book printing; Books: printing only
Pr: John Edwards
**CFO:* William Upton
IT Man: Gordon Richards
Sys Mgr: Steve Mattison
Netwrk Eng: Tom Rice
Plnt Mgr: John Welton
Mktg Dir: Donna Coleman
Sls Dir: Robert Durgy
Sls Mgr: Bob Durgy

EDWARDS CANCER CENTER
See TEXAS HLTH HRS MTHDT HSPTL HEB

D-U-N-S 13-167-4371 IMP
▲ EDWARDS LIFESCIENCES CORP
1 Edwards Way, Irvine, CA 92614-5688
Tel (949) 250-2500 *Founded/Ownrshp* 1999
Sales 2.4MMM *EMP* 9,800
Tkr Sym EW *Exch* NYS
SIC 3842 Surgical appliances & supplies
Ch Bd: Michael A Mussallem
CFO: Scott B Ullem
VP: Diane Biagianti
VP: Donald E Bobo Jr
VP: Denise E Botticelli
VP: Francis Duhay
VP: Stuart Foster
VP: Caroline Hagemeier
VP: Brian Heyland
VP: John Kehl
VP: Dirksen Lehman
VP: Steven Lewis
VP: John P McGrath
VP: Thomas Morissey
VP: Keith Newburry
VP: Margie O'Jea
VP: Vikas Patel
VP: Stan Rabinovich
VP: Paul R Redmond
VP: Keith A Reisinger
VP: Stanton J Rowe
Board of Directors: John T Cardis, Kieran T Gallahue, Leslie S Heisz, William J Link, Steven R Loranger, Martha H Marsh, Nicholas J Valeriani, Wesley W Von Schack

D-U-N-S 13-413-9174 IMP
■ EDWARDS LIFESCIENCES LLC
(*Suby of* EDWARDS LIFESCIENCES CORP) ★
1 Edwards Way, Irvine, CA 92614-5688
Tel (949) 250-2500 *Founded/Ownrshp* 1958
Sales 406.7MM[E] *EMP* 5,000
SIC 8011 Cardiologist & cardio-vascular specialist
CEO: Michael A Mussallem
Pr: Huimin Wang MD
Treas: Dennis Popovic
VP: Thomas Abate
VP: Anita Bessler
VP: Stuart Foster
VP: Bruce Garren
VP: Patricia Garvey
**VP:* John H Kehl Jr
VP: John Kehl Jr
VP: Alex Martin
VP: Robert Reindl
VP: Randel Woodgrift

D-U-N-S 03-471-7421
EDWARDS OIL CO OF LAWRENCEBURG INC
105 Helton Dr, Lawrenceburg, TN 38464-2253
Tel (931) 762-5531 *Founded/Ownrshp* 1955
Sales 105.5MM *EMP* 15[E]
Accts A D Regeon & Associates Cpa
SIC 5172 Petroleum products
Pr: Jonathan M Edwards
**Sec:* Connie Lynn Cooper
Ofcr: Oneal Stanford

D-U-N-S 05-035-8360
EDWARDS TELEPHONE CO INC
159 Main St, Edwards, NY 13635-4114
Tel (315) 562-9913 *Founded/Ownrshp* 2009
Sales 48.3MM[E] *EMP* 2,700
SIC 1731 4813 Electrical work; Telephone communication, except radio
Pr: David A Wittwer

D-U-N-S 07-527-8440
■ EDWARDS THEATRES CIRCUIT INC
(*Suby of* REGAL ENTERTAINMENT) ★
300 Newport Center Dr, Newport Beach, CA 92660-7529
Tel (949) 640-4600 *Founded/Ownrshp* 1930
Sales 78.4MM[E] *EMP* 3,700
SIC 7832 Motion picture theaters, except drive-in
Ch Bd: W James Edwards III
**Pr:* Steve Coffey
VP: Kevin Frabotta
**VP:* Joan Randolph
CIO: John Carpenter

D-U-N-S 01-194-5391 IMP
EDWARDS VACUUM LLC
(*Suby of* EDWARDS LIMITED)
6416 Inducon Dr W, Sanborn, NY 14132-9019
Tel (800) 848-9800 *Founded/Ownrshp* 2006
Sales 163.1MM[E] *EMP* 600
SIC 3563 Vacuum (air extraction) systems, industrial
CEO: Matthew Taylor
**Ch Bd:* John O'Sullivan
**Pr:* Butch Paddock
Ofcr: Chris Case
**VP:* Michael Allison
**VP:* Nigel Wenden
Dir IT: Donnelly Mike
IT Man: Charlene Kelly
Mktg Mgr: Don Collins

D-U-N-S 36-120-7116
EDWARDS WILDMAN PALMER LLP
111 Huntington Ave, Boston, MA 02199-7610
Tel (617) 239-0100 *Founded/Ownrshp* 2005
Sales NA *EMP* 1,140
SIC 8111

D-U-N-S 09-153-2986
EDWARDSVILLE COMMUNITY SCHOOL DISTRICT 7
708 Saint Louis St, Edwardsville, IL 62025-1427
Tel (618) 659-3672 *Founded/Ownrshp* 1951
Sales 89.2MM *EMP* 600
Accts Schowalter & Jabouri Pc St
SIC 8211 Public combined elementary & secondary school; School board
VP: Debbie Gaughan
Prin: William P Macdonald

D-U-N-S 05-278-0392 IMP
EDWIN B STIMPSON CO INC
1515 Sw 13th Ct, Pompano Beach, FL 33069-4710
Tel (954) 946-3500 *Founded/Ownrshp* 1852, 1943
Sales 86.3MM[E] *EMP* 394[E]
SIC 3452 3469 Washers, metal; Rivets, metal; Electronic enclosures, stamped or pressed metal
CEO: Howard C Rau
**Pr:* Ralph E Rau Jr
**Pr:* Scott H Thomas
**CFO:* George A Fortmuller
**Treas:* Peter Albano
**VP:* James E Cuenin
**VP:* John H Rau
**VP:* William G Rauss
Sales Exec: Keith Gentilin
Sls Mgr: Valerie D'Alessandro

D-U-N-S 11-509-0870 EXP
EDYS GRAND ICE CREAM
WINDY CITY EXPRESS
(*Suby of* HAAGEN-DAZS) ★
5929 College Ave, Oakland, CA 94618-1325
Tel (510) 652-8187 *Founded/Ownrshp* 1981
Sales 228.8MM[E] *EMP* 3,700
SIC 2024 5143 Ice cream & ice milk; Ice cream & ices
Pr: William F Cronk III
IT Man: Mark Myers

D-U-N-S 17-370-3885
EE NEWCOMER ENTERPRISES INC
1901 E 119th St, Olathe, KS 66061-9502
Tel (816) 221-0543 *Founded/Ownrshp* 1980
Sales 289.5MM[E] *EMP* 900
SIC 5031 5211 7699 Doors, garage; Doors; Door frames, all materials; Building materials, interior; Garage doors, sale & installation; Doors, wood or metal, except storm; Door & window repair; Garage door repair
Pr: Rex E Newcomer
**Ch Bd:* Eric Hanson
CFO: Larry Miller
**Ex VP:* Brian C Gillespie
**Ex VP:* N Nelson Newcomer
Board of Directors: Edward E Newcomer

EECO
See ELECTRICAL EQUIPMENT CO INC

D-U-N-S 96-747-1694
■ EECO INC
(*Suby of* EMERSON ELECTRIC CO) ★
850 Library Ave Ste 204c, Newark, DE 19711-7170
Tel (302) 456-1448 *Founded/Ownrshp* 1978
Sales 5.0MMM[E] *EMP* 4,877
SIC 3823 3491 3621 3585 3546 3679 Industrial instrmnts msrmnt display/control process variable; Industrial flow & liquid measuring instruments; Industrial process measurement equipment; Temperature measurement instruments, industrial; Industrial valves; Automatic regulating & control valves; Process control regulator valves; Valves, automatic control; Motors & generators; Motors, electric; Refrigeration & heating equipment; Heating equipment, complete; Refrigeration equipment, complete; Parts for heating, cooling & refrigerating equipment; Power-driven handtools; Saws & sawing equipment; Drills & drilling tools; Grinders, portable: electric or pneumatic; Electronic circuits
CFO: Michael Lefkowitz

D-U-N-S 80-819-0701
■ EEG INC
EMPIRE EDUCATION GROUP
(*Suby of* REGIS CORP) ★
396 Pttsvlle St Clair Hwy, Pottsville, PA 17901
Tel (570) 429-4321 *Founded/Ownrshp* 2008
Sales 43.7MM[E] *EMP* 1,900
SIC 8299 Educational services
CEO: Franklin K Schoeneman
Pr: Michael D Bouman
CFO: James A Wunderle
Ex VP: Joseph A Carretta
Ex VP: Bruce R Schmidt

EEI
See ECK ENTERPRISES INC

D-U-N-S 84-334-3075
EEMPLOYERS SOLUTIONS INC
12211 Huebner Rd, San Antonio, TX 78230-1207
Tel (210) 495-1171 *Founded/Ownrshp* 1988
Sales 2.0MM *EMP* 3,000
SIC 8742 6411 Human resource consulting services; Insurance agents, brokers & service
Pr: Tanya A Perez
**VP:* Donald G Kremmel
Dir Risk M: John Titus

EEOC
See EQUAL EMPLOYMENT OPPORTUNITY COMMISSION

D-U-N-S 61-893-1039
EEP HOLDINGS LLC
4626 Eucalyptus Ave, Chino, CA 91710-9215
Tel (909) 597-7861 *Founded/Ownrshp* 2002
Sales 144.5MM[E] *EMP* 1,400[E]
SIC 3089 3544 Molding primary plastic; Special dies, tools, jigs & fixtures
CEO: Earl E Payton

EFCO
See WILIAN HOLDING CO

D-U-N-S 00-527-8494 IMP/EXP
EFCO CORP (IA)
(*Suby of* EFCO) ★
1800 Ne 46th Ave, Des Moines, IA 50313-2655
Tel (515) 266-1141 *Founded/Ownrshp* 1936
Sales 95.3MM[E] *EMP* 500
SIC 3523 Cabs, tractors & agricultural machinery
Pr: A L Jennings
COO: Jim Davis
**CFO:* Ryan Loecher
**CFO:* Brad Schefold
**Sec:* Michael J Timmins
**Ex VP:* Bob Jennings
**VP:* Curt Bennethum
VP: David Drees
VP: Jim Johnson
VP: Brian West
Genl Mgr: Robert Kacher

D-U-N-S 00-715-7829 EXP
EFCO CORP (MO)
(*Suby of* PELLA CORP) ★
1000 County Rd, Monett, MO 65708-9214
Tel (800) 221-4169 *Founded/Ownrshp* 1953, 2007
Sales 305.4MM[E] *EMP* 1,750
SIC 3442 3449 Window & door frames; Store fronts, prefabricated, metal; Curtain wall, metal
Pr: Cameron McGinley
**Pr:* Michael J Farquhar
IT Man: Tony Kennedy
Opers Mgr: Greg Arnold
Opers Mgr: Brian Salsman
Prd Mgr: Robert Hartley
Mktg Dir: Jack Williams

EFD
See EFUNDS CORP

EFFICIENCY VERMONT
See VERMONT ENERGY INVESTMENT CORP

D-U-N-S 06-919-3258
EFFINGHAM COUNTY BOARD OF EDUCATION (GA)
EFFINGHAM COUNTY SCHOOL
405 N Ash St, Springfield, GA 31329-4958
Tel (912) 754-6491 *Founded/Ownrshp* 1777
Sales 67.0MM[E] *EMP* 1,250
SIC 8211 Public elementary & secondary schools

EFFINGHAM COUNTY SCHOOL
See EFFINGHAM COUNTY BOARD OF EDUCATION

D-U-N-S 07-979-8751
EFFINGHAM COUNTY SCHOOLS
405 N Ash St, Springfield, GA 31329-4958
Tel (912) 754-6491 *Founded/Ownrshp* 2015
Sales 10.2MM[E] *EMP* 1,175[E]
SIC 8211 Public elementary & secondary schools
Bd of Dir: Tina Birthisel
Bd of Dir: Karen Bright
MIS Dir: Noralee Deason
Teacher Pr: Susan Hartzog
Instr Medi: Gregg Miles
Psych: Tonya Ward

D-U-N-S 00-627-3924
EFFINGHAM EQUITY
DO IT BEST
201 W Roadway Ave, Effingham, IL 62401-2101
Tel (217) 342-4101 *Founded/Ownrshp* 1919
Sales 322.5MM *EMP* 348
Accts Blue & Company Llc Seymour
SIC 5999 5251 Feed & farm supply; Hardware
CEO: Bruce Vernon
**CFO:* Karen Whitt
**Treas:* Patricia Wente
Genl Mgr: Tim Bence
**Genl Mgr:* Dennis Montavon
Sales Asso: Dirk Hockman

D-U-N-S 02-095-2017
EFG HOLDINGS INC
10217 Brecksville Rd, Brecksville, OH 44141-3207
Tel (812) 717-2544 *Founded/Ownrshp* 2009
Sales 126.1MM[E] *EMP* 655[E]
SIC 3452 Bolts, nuts, rivets & washers
Pr: Ronald J Kiter
**CFO:* Ian McKenna

EFGI
See EASTLAND FEED AND GRAIN INC

EFI
See ELECTRONICS FOR IMAGING INC

D-U-N-S 14-902-4585
EFINANCIAL LLC
TERMFINDER.COM
13810 Se Eastgate Way # 300, Bellevue, WA 98005-4400
Tel (800) 482-6616 *Founded/Ownrshp* 2000
Sales NA *EMP* 150[E]

SIC 6411 Insurance brokers
Mktg Mgr: Bill Cox

D-U-N-S 79-227-1988
■ EFS TRANSPORTATION SERVICES INC
(Suby of CONCORD EFS NATIONAL BANK) ★
2525 Horizon Lake Dr # 120, Memphis, TN 38133-8117
Tel (901) 371-8000 Founded/Ownrshp 2000
Sales 73.8MM[E] EMP 2,000
SIC 4731 Transportation agents & brokers
CEO: Charles T Fote

EFSC
See EASTERN FLORIDA STATE COLLEGE

D-U-N-S 18-966-3206 IMP
EFTEC NORTH AMERICA LLC
(Suby of EMS-CHEMIE HOLDING AG)
31601 Research Park Dr, Madison Heights, MI 48071-4626
Tel (248) 526-4565 Founded/Ownrshp 2007
Sales 104.9MM[E] EMP 250
SIC 2891 8731 3296 2899 2851 Adhesives & sealants; Commercial physical research; Mineral wool; Chemical preparations; Paints & allied products
VP: Tony Brens

D-U-N-S 16-102-0151
■ EFUNDS CORP
EFD
(Suby of FIS) ★
4900 N Scottsdale Rd # 1000, Scottsdale, AZ 85251-7652
Tel (602) 431-2700 Founded/Ownrshp 2007
Sales 178.3MM[E] EMP 5,300
SIC 7374 7372 7371 Data processing service; Business oriented computer software; Computer software development
Pr: Gary A Norcross
Ch Bd: Paul F Walsh
Pr: Nelson G Eng
CFO: George W Gresham
Ex VP: Tommy L Andrews
Ex VP: Steven F Coleman
Ex VP: Kay J Nichols
Ex VP: Clyde L Thomas
VP: Scott Anders
VP: Dvorak Jim
IT Man: Jon Vemo

D-U-N-S 80-076-5331 IMP/EXP
EFW INC
(Suby of ELBIT SYSTEMS OF AMERICA LLC) ★
4700 Marine Creek Pkwy, Fort Worth, TX 76179-3598
Tel (817) 916-1359 Founded/Ownrshp 2007
Sales 247.2MM[E] EMP 1,100
SIC 3812 Search & navigation equipment
Pr: Raanan Horowitz
CFO: William Augat
Ofcr: Dennis Klix
VP: Gary Quarve
Prgrm Mgr: Bill Johnson
Prgrm Mgr: Brad Morian
Prgrm Mgr: John Murphy
Prgrm Mgr: Brandon Sanders
Prgrm Mgr: Dan Wright
Brnch Mgr: Richard Brandorff
CIO: Max Horne

EG INDUSTRIES
See ERNIE GREEN INDUSTRIES INC

D-U-N-S 79-831-7756
■ EG&G SPECIAL PROJECTS INC
(Suby of PERKINELMER INC) ★
811 Grier Dr Ste A, Las Vegas, NV 89119-3705
Tel (702) 492-7800 Founded/Ownrshp 1983
Sales 54.7MM[E] EMP 1,350
SIC 8741 Personnel management
Pr: Gary Fitzgerald

D-U-N-S 14-850-8351
EGAN CO
7625 Boone Ave N, Brooklyn Park, MN 55428-1011
Tel (763) 595-4358 Founded/Ownrshp 1948
Sales 212.0MM EMP 648
Accts Redpath And Company Ltd St
SIC 1711 1731 3444 7623 1793 Plumbing contractors; Warm air heating & air conditioning contractor; General electrical contractor; Safety & security specialization; Metal ventilating equipment; Refrigeration service & repair; Glass & glazing work
CEO: James J Malecha
*CFO: James Johnson
Chf Mktg O: Bruce Young
*Ex VP: Jack Galvin
*Ex VP: Duane Hendricks
*Ex VP: Jim Paul
Sr VP: Bob Gorg
Sr VP: Tim Woolworth
Div Mgr: Brad Drews
Genl Mgr: Dan Wilson
Dir IT: Jim Nonn

EGAN, STERLING, NRM, BROOKES
See DAVIS-STANDARD HOLDINGS INC

D-U-N-S 00-958-4835
EGENERA INC
80 Central St Ste 300, Boxborough, MA 01719-1245
Tel (978) 206-6300 Founded/Ownrshp 2000
Sales 97.6MM[E] EMP 305
SIC 7373 1731 8741 Computer integrated systems design; Electrical work; Management services
Pr: Pete Manca
*Pr: Michael Thompson
CFO: Donald R Peck
*CFO: Thomas Sheehan
*Treas: Kevin Kerrigan
*Ex VP: Jim Bandanza
*Ex VP: Scott Geng
Sr VP: Subo Guha
*VP: Susan Davis
VP: Tom Ganley
*VP: Chris Hill
VP: Gerry Murray
VP: Benjamin Sprachman
VP: Cecil C Umberger

Exec: Mike Farina
Dir Bus: Shirley Yee

D-U-N-S 14-440-1304
EGG HARBOR TOWNSHIP BOARD OF EDUCATION INC
EGG HARBOR TOWNSHIP SCHOOL DST
13 Swift Ave, Egg Harbor Township, NJ 08234-9477
Tel (609) 646-7911 Founded/Ownrshp 1900
Sales 47.8MM[E] EMP 1,000[E]
SIC 8211 School board
Bd of Dir: Kristy Benton
Bd of Dir: Chris Lane
VP: Betsy Hires
Teacher Pr: Carolyn Gibson
HC Dir: Karen Semet

EGG HARBOR TOWNSHIP SCHOOL DST
See EGG HARBOR TOWNSHIP BOARD OF EDUCATION INC

D-U-N-S 00-607-6947 IMP
EGGERS INDUSTRIES INC (WI)
1 Eggers Dr, Two Rivers, WI 54241
Tel (920) 793-1351 Founded/Ownrshp 1884, 1937
Sales 107.6MM[E] EMP 500
SIC 2431 2435 Doors, wood; Hardwood veneer & plywood
Ch Bd: Jay Streu
*CFO: Jeff Simons
*Ex VP: Harold A Reichwald
*VP: Ann Duebner
CIO: Cindy Latour
*VP Opers: Mary Streu

EGI
See ERGONOMIC GROUP INC

D-U-N-S 03-479-3501
EGL HOLDCO INC
18200 Von Karman Ave # 1000, Irvine, CA 92612-1023
Tel (800) 678-7423 Founded/Ownrshp 2011
Sales 98.4MM[E] EMP 4,000
SIC 7372

EGLESTON CHILDRENS HEALTH CTR
See CHILDRENS HEALTHCARE OF ATLANTA FOUNDATION INC

D-U-N-S 04-380-8385 IMP/EXP
EGO NORTH AMERICA INC (GA)
(Suby of E.G.O. ELEKTRO - GERATE AG)
83 Hillwood Cir, Newnan, GA 30263-5858
Tel (770) 251-3980 Founded/Ownrshp 1980
Sales 88.9MM[E] EMP 300
SIC 3634 5065 Broilers, electric; Electronic parts
CEO: Glen M Butler
VP: Frank Jensen
*VP: David Keller
Snr Sftwr: Erick Vargas
CTO: Annie Haynes
Sales Asso: Bianca Baxter

D-U-N-S 02-003-7248
EGS CUSTOMER CARE INC (PA)
(Suby of EXPERT GLOBAL SOLUTIONS INC) ★
5085 W Park Blvd Ste 300, Plano, TX 75093-2599
Tel (972) 943-7000 Founded/Ownrshp 1973, 2013
Sales 299.0MM[E] EMP 2,901
SIC 7389 Telephone services; Telemarketing services; Telephone solicitation service
Pr: Jay King
*CFO: Andrew B Szafran
Sr Cor Off: Don Grooms
Bd of Dir: Joe Tabarangao
Bd of Dir: John L Workman
Ofcr: Jack Jones
Sr VP: Mark K Anderson
*Sr VP: Greg Carr
Sr VP: Christopher H Crowley
*Sr VP: Arthur D Dibari
*Sr VP: Mark E McDermott
*Sr VP: Robert B Nachwalter
Sr VP: Patrick S Ohara
*VP: Joseph R Doolan
*VP: Jennifer Young

D-U-N-S 07-401-7021 IMP
EGS FINANCIAL CARE INC (PA)
(Suby of EXPERT GLOBAL SOLUTIONS INC) ★
507 Prudential Rd, Horsham, PA 19044-2308
Tel (877) 217-4423 Founded/Ownrshp 1966
Sales 384.5MM[E] EMP 2,901
SIC 7322 Collection agency, except real estate
Pr: Jay King
CFO: Nancy McCrary
*CFO: Steven Winokur
Sr VP: Brad Campbell
Sr VP: Richard Davis
Sr VP: Bob Hodges
Sr VP: Vania Lively
VP: James Heron
VP: Michael G Noah
VP: Steven L Winokur
Genl Mgr: Andrew Quinn
Board of Directors: Charles Piola Jr

D-U-N-S 82-640-6592
■ EGS HOLDINGS INC
(Suby of ENTERGY CORP) ★
2001 Timberloch Pl, Spring, TX 77380-1335
Tel (409) 981-2000 Founded/Ownrshp 2007
Sales 2.1MM[E] EMP 763[E]
SIC 4911 4924 Electric services; Generation, electric power; Transmission, electric power; Distribution, electric power; Natural gas distribution
Ch Bd: Phillip R May Jr

D-U-N-S 03-258-2430
EGT LLC
150 E Mill Rd, Longview, WA 98632-8980
Tel (503) 827-4066 Founded/Ownrshp 1991
Sales 112.7MM[E] EMP 62
SIC 5153 Grains
Genl Mgr: Adam Johnson

EGUSD
See GROVE ELK UNIFIED SCHOOL DISTRICT

D-U-N-S 96-485-2516
EGYPTIAN AREA SCHOOLS EMPLOYEE BENEFIT TRUST
1109 Hartman Ln, Belleville, IL 62221-7916
Tel (618) 973-8221 Founded/Ownrshp 2010
Sales 91.1MM EMP 12[E]
Accts Rice Sullivan Llc Swansea Il
SIC 8211 Elementary & secondary schools
Prin: Matt Klosterman

D-U-N-S 78-740-0712
■ EHCA EASTSIDE OCCUPATIONAL MEDICINE CENTER LLC
EMORY EASTSIDE MEDICAL CENTER
(Suby of HOSPITAL COPORATION OF AMERICA) ★
1700 Medical Way, Snellville, GA 30078-2195
Tel (770) 979-0200 Founded/Ownrshp 1999
Sales 177.4MM[E] EMP 1,500
SIC 8062 General medical & surgical hospitals
CFO: Tom Jackson
VP: Seretha Crayton
Dir Inf Cn: Helen Ebaugh
Dir Bus: Heather Hogan
Dir Env Sv: Eric Roman
CIO: David Kornelius
Tech Mgr: McCreary Michael
Doctor: Joseph Chandler
Doctor: Sreeni Gangasani

D-U-N-S 78-355-0036
EHCA JOHNS CREEK LLC
EMORY JOHN CREEK HOSPITAL
6325 Hospital Pkwy, Johns Creek, GA 30097-5775
Tel (770) 813-0438 Founded/Ownrshp 1998
Sales 104.4MM[E] EMP 495
SIC 8062 General medical & surgical hospitals
Chf Path: Robert Harrell
COO: Gregory Caples
COO: Laurie Hansen
CFO: Joann Manning
VP: Helen Gidey
VP: Staci Smith
Dir Rx: Beth Delrossi
VP Admn: Tyrone Baines
Dir IT: Brad Foresythe
IT Man: Susan Widmayer
Tech Mgr: Ramiro Duran

D-U-N-S 62-357-9955
▲ EHEALTH INC
440 E Middlefield Rd, Mountain View, CA 94043-4006
Tel (650) 584-2700 Founded/Ownrshp 1997
Sales NA EMP 869[E]
Tkr Sym EHTH Exch NGS
SIC 6411 Insurance agents, brokers & service; Insurance agents & brokers; Insurance information & consulting services
CEO: Scott N Flanders
*Ch Bd: Ellen O Tauscher
COO: David Francis
Ex VP: Robert S Hurley
Sr VP: Jay Jennings
VP: Bob Hurley
Prgrm Mgr: Michael Chen
Software D: Julius Mendoza
Opers Mgr: Tami Doyle
Opers Mgr: Oscar Espinoza
Mktg Mgr: Andrew Naber
Board of Directors: Scott N Flanders, Michael D Goldberg, Randall S Livingston, Jack L Oliver III

D-U-N-S 96-313-0526
■ EHHI HOLDINGS INC
ENCOMPASS HOME HLTH & HOSPICE
(Suby of HEALTHSOUTH HOME HEALTH CORP) ★
6688 N Cntrl Expy # 1300, Dallas, TX 75206-3914
Tel (877) 330-7657 Founded/Ownrshp 2014
Sales 4.5MM[E] EMP 3,800[E]
SIC 8082 Home health care services
CEO: April Anthony

EHLCO WHOLESALE CHICAGO
See EDWARD HINES LUMBER CO

D-U-N-S 96-847-4390
EHW CONSTRUCTORS A JOINT VENTURE
295 Bendix Rd Ste 400, Virginia Beach, VA 23452-1295
Tel (757) 420-4140 Founded/Ownrshp 2012
Sales 97.5MM EMP 220
SIC 1629 Dams, waterways, docks & other marine construction
Ex VP: Sal Taddeo
*Sr VP: Stephen Davis

EI, A PHRM SOLUTIONWORKS
See EI LLC

D-U-N-S 10-580-3274 IMP
EI LLC
EI, A PHRM SOLUTIONWORKS
(Suby of PRODUCT QUEST MANUFACTURING LLC) ★
2865 N Cannon Blvd, Kannapolis, NC 28083-9124
Tel (704) 939-4300 Founded/Ownrshp 2003
Sales 130.0MM[E] EMP 300
SIC 2834 2844 Pharmaceutical preparations; Cosmetic preparations
CEO: Michael Kane
*Pr: Roger Martin
*CFO: Steve Havala
*Sr VP: Charles Gray
*VP: Darin Downs
VP Opers: Matt Augustine
Ql Cn Mgr: Kevin Feezor

D-U-N-S 80-770-2253
EI TAPATIO MARKETS INC
13635 Freeway Dr, Santa Fe Springs, CA 90670-5622
Tel (562) 293-4200 Founded/Ownrshp 1980
Sales 85.7MM[E] EMP 500
SIC 5411 Supermarkets
Pr: Larry Flores
*CFO: Arthur Flores
*VP: David Flores

D-U-N-S 80-010-5900
EICHELBERGER CONSTRUCTION INC
ECI GROUP
124 W Church St, Dillsburg, PA 17019-1232
Tel (717) 638-2000 Founded/Ownrshp 1992
Sales 101.3MM EMP 255[E]
SIC 1542 Commercial & office building contractors; Commercial & office buildings, renovation & repair
Pr: William P Eichelberger
Pr: Fred Feldman
COO: Bill Freeman
*VP: Todd Rothermel
*VP: Mark Yinger
Sfty Dirs: Vince Magaro
Ql Cn Mgr: William Blackwood

D-U-N-S 09-709-8065
EIDE BAILLY LLP
4310 17th Ave S, Fargo, ND 58103-3339
Tel (701) 239-8500 Founded/Ownrshp 1998
Sales 259.4MM EMP 1,720
SIC 8721 Certified public accountant
Mng Pt: Dave Stende
COO: Michael Astrup
COO: Lisa Giles
CFO: Steve Troyer
Treas: Rhonda Nance
Off Mgr: Lori Leidholt
Off Admin: Anna Roling
Off Admin: Diane Whipple
CIO: Aaron Ness
Snr Mgr: Brad Dejong
Snr Mgr: Toby Hazen

D-U-N-S 83-075-6792
EIGER HOLDCO LLC
(Suby of LUTHER KING CAPITAL MANAGEMENT CORP) ★
301 Commerce St Ste 1600, Fort Worth, TX 76102-4116
Tel (817) 332-3235 Founded/Ownrshp 2008
Sales NA EMP 1,240
SIC 6719 Investment holding companies, except banks

D-U-N-S 14-144-8576
EIGHT OCLOCK COFFEE CO
(Suby of TATA COFFEE LIMITED)
155 Chestnut Ridge Rd # 2, Montvale, NJ 07645-1156
Tel (201) 571-9214 Founded/Ownrshp 2006
Sales 149.4MM[E] EMP 215[E]
SIC 5149 2095 Coffee & tea; Roasted coffee
Pr: Barbara Roth
Chf Mktg O: Don Sommerville

EIGHT STAR EQUIPMENT
See NOBLESSE OBLIGE INC

D-U-N-S 00-682-7419
EIGHT-O MANAGEMENT INC (TX)
1722 S Harwood St, Dallas, TX 75215-1221
Tel (214) 969-9321 Founded/Ownrshp 1994
Sales 74.8MM[E] EMP 1,400
SIC 8741 Restaurant management
Pr: Shannon Wynne
*CFO: Michael Byres
*VP: Larry Richardson
*VP: Mark Siegel
IT Man: Keith Schlabs

D-U-N-S 03-914-2970
EIGHTH & EATON PROFESSIONAL BUILDING LP
(Suby of ST LUKES HOSPITAL & HEALTH NE) ★
801 Ostrum St, Bethlehem, PA 18015-1000
Tel (610) 954-4000 Founded/Ownrshp 2010
Sales 2.5MM[E] EMP 1,252[E]
SIC 8062 Hospital, professional nursing school

D-U-N-S 13-047-4265
EII INC
530 South Ave E, Cranford, NJ 07016-3208
Tel (908) 276-1000 Founded/Ownrshp 1984
Sales 128.1MM EMP 310
Accts Robert A Crystal Cpa Pscata
SIC 1731 Electrical work
CEO: Richard Guempel
*Pr: John T Guempel
Treas: Arthur J Flinn
VP: Scott Alling
VP: Doreen Macauley
*VP: Richard Wood Jr
Sfty Mgr: Michael Adelsohn

D-U-N-S 11-750-3656 IMP
EILEEN FISHER INC
EILEEN FISHER WOMENS APPAREL
2 Bridge St Ste 230, Irvington, NY 10533-3500
Tel (914) 591-5700 Founded/Ownrshp 1984
Sales 350.0MM EMP 1,000
SIC 2339 Sportswear, women's
Ch Bd: Eileen Fisher
CFO: Kenneth Pollak
VP: Hillary Old
VP: Mariclare Vanbergen
Exec: Cynthia Malm
Exec: Jena Pace
Exec: Milena Smolen
Creative D: Peter Scavuzzo
Genl Mgr: Christine Beisiegel
Store Mgr: John Aguilera
Dir IT: Bill Miller

EILEEN FISHER WOMENS APPAREL
See EILEEN FISHER INC

D-U-N-S 02-324-5632 IMP
EILLIENS CANDIES INC
1301 Waube Ln, Green Bay, WI 54304-5655
Tel (920) 336-7549 Founded/Ownrshp 1959
Sales 123.5MM[E] EMP 150
SIC 5145 Candy; Nuts, salted or roasted
Pr: John P Burke
Pr: Jerry Buresh
Trfc Dir: Rick Freitag
Trfc Mgr: Lorne Bries
Sales Exec: Pat Burke

EIMICKE
See CARLSON CRAFT INC

D-U-N-S 02-844-5554
EINSTEIN AND NOAH CORP
EINSTEIN BROTHERS BAGELS
(*Suby of* EINSTEIN NOAH RESTAURANT GROUP INC) ★
555 Zang St Ste 300, Lakewood, CO 80228-1013
Tel (303) 568-8000 *Founded/Ownrshp* 2001
Sales 248.3MM[E] *EMP* 7,937[E]
SIC 5812 Cafe
CEO: Michael W Arthur
**Pr:* Ginger Torsell
**VP:* Michael Serchia
Mktg Dir: Alex Sterling

EINSTEIN BROTHERS BAGELS
See EINSTEIN AND NOAH CORP

D-U-N-S 95-983-2304
EINSTEIN COMMUNITY HEALTH ASSOCIATES
EINSTEIN MEDICAL CENTER
5501 Old York Rd, Philadelphia, PA 19141-3018
Tel (215) 456-7890 *Founded/Ownrshp* 1994
Sales 65.1MM[E] *EMP* 6,000
Accts Pricewaterhousecoopers Llp Ph
SIC 8011 Offices & clinics of medical doctors

EINSTEIN MEDICAL CENTER
See EINSTEIN COMMUNITY HEALTH ASSOCIATES

D-U-N-S 07-924-4479
EINSTEIN MEDICAL CENTER MONTGOMERY
559 W Germantown Pike, East Norriton, PA 19403-4250
Tel (484) 622-1000 *Founded/Ownrshp* 2014
Sales 182.0MM *EMP* 3
SIC 8011 Offices & clinics of medical doctors
Pr: Richard H Greenberg
VP: Richard L Allman

D-U-N-S 80-382-9258
EINSTEIN NOAH RESTAURANT GROUP INC
(*Suby of* JAB BEECH INC) ★
555 Zang St Ste 300, Lakewood, CO 80228-1013
Tel (303) 568-8000 *Founded/Ownrshp* 2014
Sales 282.7MM[E] *EMP* 6,000
SIC 5812 6794 Eating places; Franchises, selling or licensing
Pr: Frank G Paci
**COO:* Emanuel P N Hilario
**CFO:* John A Coletta
**Chf Cred:* Glenn Lunde
Ofcr: Rhonda Parish
VP: Gerardo Donatiello
Creative D: Moya Suddaby
Area Mgr: Alex Ramirez
Genl Mgr: Gina McConahy
Mfg Dir: Marci Navarro
Mktg Mgr: Angie Hoagland

D-U-N-S 01-638-5358
EINSTEIN PRACTICE PLAN INC
5501 Old York Rd Ste 2, Philadelphia, PA 19141-3018
Tel (215) 456-6070 *Founded/Ownrshp* 1992
Sales 127.6MM *EMP* 3
SIC 8741 Hospital management
CEO: Martin Goldsmith
**Treas:* John Murino

D-U-N-S 00-331-3590 IMP/EXP
■ EIS INC
ELECTRICAL INSUL SUPPLIERS
(*Suby of* GENUINE PARTS CO) ★
2018 Powers Ferry Rd Se # 500, Atlanta, GA 30339-7202
Tel (678) 255-3600 *Founded/Ownrshp* 1998
Sales 755.7MM[E] *EMP* 812
SIC 5065 Electronic parts
CEO: Robert W Thomas
**Pr:* Larry Griffin
Pr: Darrell Reid
CFO: Matthew Tyser
**Sr VP:* Alex Gonzalez
**Sr VP:* Bill Knight
**Sr VP:* Peter Sheehan
**Sr VP:* Matt Tyser
VP: Bill M Knight
VP: Lee Linder
Prgrm Mgr: Michelle Stewart

D-U-N-S 79-454-0609 IMP
EISAI CORP OF NORTH AMERICA
(*Suby of* EISAI CO., LTD.)
100 Tice Blvd, Woodcliff Lake, NJ 07677-8404
Tel (201) 692-1100 *Founded/Ownrshp* 1992
Sales 538.0MM[E] *EMP* 900
SIC 5169 8731 Chemicals & allied products; Medical research, commercial
CEO: Hajime Shimiae
**COO:* Lonnel Coats
VP: Robert Scala
Netwrk Eng: Nelson Rodriguez

D-U-N-S 02-157-4355
EISAI INC
(*Suby of* EISAI CORP OF NORTH AMERICA) ★
100 Tice Blvd, Woodcliff Lake, NJ 07677-8404
Tel (919) 941-6920 *Founded/Ownrshp* 1995
Sales 211.5MM[E] *EMP* 553
SIC 2834 Pharmaceutical preparations
Pr: Lonnel Coats
CFO: Junichi Asatani
CFO: Barry Lederman
CFO: Ivor Macleod
CFO: Shaji Procida
CFO: William F Spengler
Treas: Kenneth R Klauser Sr
Bd of Dir: Gilla Kaplan
Ex VP: Eric P Loukas
Ex VP: Andrew Satlin
Sr VP: John R Macdonald
VP: Kristin Ficks
VP: Mary Lynne Hedley
VP: Robert M Johnson
VP: David Martin
VP: Joe Stich
Exec: Valerie Cooper
Dir Surg: Charles Pigneri
Assoc Dir: Anthony Critelli
Assoc Dir: Douglas Dorfman
Assoc Dir: Kenan Gu

EISENHOWER BANK
See BROADWAY NATIONAL BANK

D-U-N-S 07-814-0845 IMP
EISENHOWER MEDICAL CENTER (CA)
39000 Bob Hope Dr, Rancho Mirage, CA 92270-3221
Tel (760) 340-3911 *Founded/Ownrshp* 1971
Sales 571.7MM *EMP* 3,000
Accts Ernst & Young Us Llp San Dieg
SIC 8062 8082 General medical & surgical hospitals; Home health care services
CEO: G Aubrey Serfling
Chf Path: Barbara Comess
COO: Martin Massielo
**CFO:* Kimberly Osborne
CFO: Tom Tokheim
VP: Keenan Barber
VP: Laura Fritz
**VP:* Liz Guignier
VP: Julie Haas
VP: Thomas Johnston
**VP:* Martin Massiello
**VP:* Ann Mostofi
VP: Randy Mueller
**VP:* David Perez
**VP:* Joseph Scherger
VP: Barbara Sinatra
VP: Ali Tourkaman
VP: Ken Wheat
VP: Louise White
VP: Alan Williamson
VP Bus: Mary Ellen Fontana

D-U-N-S 04-835-2397
EISNERAMPER LLP
750 3rd Ave, New York, NY 10017-2703
Tel (212) 949-8700 *Founded/Ownrshp* 1963
Sales 276.3MM *EMP* 1,895
SIC 8742 8721 Management consulting services; Certified public accountant
Mng Pt: Charles Weinstein
Pt: Richard A Eisner
Pt: Theodore Levine
CFO: Jeffrey Melnick
CFO: Kimberly Mumme
Bd of Dir: Michael Morris
Div Mgr: Susan Wolfman
Off Mgr: Eli Hoffman
Off Mgr: Diane Rubin
Telecom Ex: Carolyn Smith
CIO: Amir Segev

D-U-N-S 96-712-3436
EJ AMERICAS LLC
(*Suby of* EJ GROUP INC) ★
301 Spring St, East Jordan, MI 49727-5128
Tel (231) 536-2261 *Founded/Ownrshp* 2009
Sales 135.4MM[E] *EMP* 840[E]
SIC 6719 3321 Investment holding companies, except banks; Manhole covers, metal
Prin: Lori Willis

EJ BARTELLS
See RHEM LLC

D-U-N-S 00-215-9978 IMP/EXP
EJ BROOKS CO
TYDENBROOKS
(*Suby of* TYDEN GROUP HOLDINGS CORP) ★
409 Hoosier Dr, Angola, IN 46703-9335
Tel (800) 348-4777 *Founded/Ownrshp* 1873, 2009
Sales 269.4MM[E] *EMP* 1,200
SIC 3679 Hermetic seals for electronic equipment
CEO: Trent Jensen
**Pr:* Alexander Shen
CFO: Bruce Heinemann
VP: Phil Whitley
IT Man: Al Marshall
Plnt Mgr: Bob Triano

D-U-N-S 00-282-0793
EJ DEL MONTE CORP (NY)
DEL MONTE HOTEL GROUP
909 Linden Ave Ste 1, Rochester, NY 14625-2711
Tel (585) 586-3121 *Founded/Ownrshp* 1953
Sales 266.6MM[E] *EMP* 600
SIC 6552 8741 6512 6799 7011 Subdividers & developers; Management services; Commercial & industrial building operation; Investors; Hotels & motels
CEO: Ernest J Del Monte Sr
**Pr:* E John Del Monte Jr
Pr: Michael Soto
**CFO:* Mike Mercier
**VP:* Michael A Mercier
**VP:* James L Pestke
IT Man: Jason Chester
IT Man: Jonathan Coupal
**VP Mfg:* John M Tengeres
Opers Mgr: Matt Wilde
Sls Mgr: Alicia Moorman

D-U-N-S 96-712-3063
EJ GROUP INC
301 Spring St, East Jordan, MI 49727-5128
Tel (231) 536-2261 *Founded/Ownrshp* 2009
Sales 320.1MM *EMP* 2,000
SIC 3321 Manhole covers, metal
CEO: Tracey K Malpass
VP: Kevin Keane
VP: Thomas Teske
Sales Asso: Jennifer Cox
Sales Asso: Tim Powell
Sales Asso: Bill Stup
Sales Asso: Derek Wickman

D-U-N-S 00-602-0309 EXP
EJ USA INC
(*Suby of* EJ AMERICAS LLC) ★
301 Spring St, East Jordan, MI 49727-5128
Tel (800) 874-4100 *Founded/Ownrshp* 1883
Sales 263.7MM[E] *EMP* 835
SIC 3321 Gray & ductile iron foundries; Pressure pipe & fittings, cast iron; Gray iron castings; Manhole covers, metal
Pr: Fred Malpass
COO: Marie Eckstein
**CFO:* Jack Poindexter
Chf Mktg O: Nancy Tyree
Ex VP: Tad M Alpass
Off Mgr: Jerry Lynch
IT Man: Carl Barnum

EJGH
See EAST JEFFERSON GENERAL HOSPITAL

EK SUCCESS BRANDS
See E K SUCCESS LTD

EK SUCCESS BRANDS
See WILTON BRANDS LLC

D-U-N-S 06-022-3708 IMP/EXP
EKMAN & CO INC
INTERCONTINENTAL CELLULOSE SLS
(*Suby of* EKMAN HOLDING INC) ★
8750 Nw 36th St Ste 400, Doral, FL 33178-2499
Tel (305) 579-1200 *Founded/Ownrshp* 1992
Sales 167.8MM[E] *EMP* 30
SIC 5099 Pulpwood
Pr: Jan Svensson
**Ch Bd:* Matts Ekman
**CFO:* Annie Edvardsen
**Ex VP:* Fredrik Trgrdh
**VP:* Michael Flynn

D-U-N-S 61-286-6863 IMP/EXP
EKMAN HOLDING INC
(*Suby of* EKMAN & CO AB)
8750 Nw 36th St Ste 400, Doral, FL 33178-2499
Tel (305) 579-1200 *Founded/Ownrshp* 1985
Sales 167.8MM[E] *EMP* 31
SIC 5099 Pulpwood
CEO: Jan Svensson

EKMAN RECYCLING
See K-C INTERNATIONAL LLC

D-U-N-S 19-395-2884 IMP
EKORNES INC
(*Suby of* EKORNES ASA)
615 Pierce St, Somerset, NJ 08873-1262
Tel (732) 302-0097 *Founded/Ownrshp* 1985
Sales 95.2MM *EMP* 40
Accts Werdann Devito Llc Clark Nj
SIC 5021 Furniture
Ch Bd: Peter Bjerregaard
CFO: Trine-Marie Hagen
**Treas:* Nils Tore Lande
Treas: Hideki Yamauchi
CTO: Lance Kelley
MIS Dir: Malvin Newman
Prd Mgr: Rolf Aarseth
Prd Mgr: Jarle Hoydal
Sls Mgr: Todd Swiler

EKP COOPERATIVE
See EAST KENTUCKY POWER COOPERATIVE INC

D-U-N-S 05-010-0650 IMP
EL & EL WOOD PRODUCTS CORP (CA)
6011 Schaefer Ave, Chino, CA 91710-7043
Tel (909) 591-0339 *Founded/Ownrshp* 1963
Sales 89.5MM[E] *EMP* 140[E]
Accts White Nelson & Co Llp Irvi
SIC 5031 Millwork
Pr: Cathy Vidas
Creative D: Asha Darbeau
Sales Asso: Al Bhakta
Sales Asso: Rick Hegemier
Sales Asso: Leah Longacre
Sales Asso: Jessika Skillern

EL CAMINO COLLEGE
See EL CAMINO COMMUNITY COLLEGE DISTRICT

D-U-N-S 07-879-9616
EL CAMINO COMMUNITY COLLEGE DISTRICT (CA)
EL CAMINO COLLEGE
16007 Crenshaw Blvd, Torrance, CA 90506-0001
Tel (310) 532-3670 *Founded/Ownrshp* 1947
Sales 1.5MM *EMP* 1,100
SIC 8222

D-U-N-S 07-630-9442
EL CAMINO HOSPITAL
2500 Grant Rd, Mountain View, CA 94040-4378
Tel (408) 224-6660 *Founded/Ownrshp* 1961
Sales 795.6MM *EMP* 2,145[E]
SIC 8062

EL CAMINO RESOURCES
See CHG-MERIDIAN US HOLDING INC

D-U-N-S 60-895-7254
EL CENTRO REGIONAL MEDICAL CENTER INC
E C R M C
1415 Ross Ave, El Centro, CA 92243-4306
Tel (760) 339-7100 *Founded/Ownrshp* 2005
Sales 127.8MM *EMP* 673
Accts Hutchinson And Bloodgood Llpec
SIC 8062 General medical & surgical hospitals
Pr: Robert R Frantz
**Pr:* Barbara Blevins
Pr: Claudia Dubbe
**CFO:* Kathy Farmer
CFO: Alex Wells
Treas: Irene Shelton
Trst: Amanda Brooke
**Ex VP:* David Jones
**Sr VP:* Heidi Allen
**VP:* Debra Drifkill
VP: Rosa Gamboa
Exec: Jim Dikes
Dir Inf Cn: Brenda Rivera
Dir Lab: David Mohlenhoff

EL CHEAPO FUEL STOPS
See SOMMERS CO

EL CHICO RESTAURANT
See CONSOLIDATED RESTAURANT COMPANIES INC

D-U-N-S 00-732-4890
EL CHICO RESTAURANTS INC
(*Suby of* EL CHICO RESTAURANT) ★
12200 N Stemmons Fwy, Dallas, TX 75234-5897
Tel (972) 241-5500 *Founded/Ownrshp* 1998
Sales 124.1MM[E] *EMP* 4,500
SIC 5812 6794 5046 Mexican restaurant; Franchises, selling or licensing; Commercial cooking & food service equipment
CEO: John D Harkey
**Ch Bd:* E Jene Street
**Treas:* Sue Wymond
Genl Mgr: Sean Wright

D-U-N-S 80-159-2080
EL CONQUISTADOR PARTNERSHIP LPSE (DE)
EL CONQUISTADOR RESORT & SPA
1000 Ave El Conquistador, Fajardo, PR 00738-3711
Tel (787) 863-1000 *Founded/Ownrshp* 1990
Sales 31.3MM[E] *EMP* 1,000
SIC 7011 Resort hotel
Pt: Stan Soroka

EL CONQUISTADOR RESORT & SPA
See EL CONQUISTADOR PARTNERSHIP LPSE (DE)

EL CORTEZ HOTEL
See IKE GAMING INC

EL DESCANSO
See PLEASANT VALLEY SCHOOL DISTRICT

D-U-N-S 10-397-0307
■ EL DORADO CHEMICAL CO INC
(*Suby of* LSB CHEMICAL LLC) ★
16 S Pennsylvania Ave, Oklahoma City, OK 73107-7024
Tel (405) 235-4546 *Founded/Ownrshp* 1984
Sales 107.9MM[E] *EMP* 350
SIC 2819 2875 2892 Inorganic acids, except nitric & phosphoric; Fertilizers, mixing only; Explosives
Sr VP: Paul Rydlund
**CFO:* Matt Mann
Ofcr: Cunny Broun
**Sr VP:* Larry Fitzwater
**Sr VP:* Phil Gough
VP: Robert Giovando
VP: Barry Golsen
**VP:* Brian Lewis
VP: Paul Nylund
**VP:* Anne O Rendon
VP: Heidi Shear
**VP:* Mike Wolfe

D-U-N-S 04-546-7230 EXP
EL DORADO FURNITURE CORP
4200 Nw 167th St, Miami Gardens, FL 33054-6112
Tel (305) 624-9700 *Founded/Ownrshp* 1967
Sales 212.6MM *EMP* 705
SIC 5712 Furniture stores
Pr: Luis E Capo
**COO:* Pedro Capo
Treas: Gerardo Capo Jr
**Treas:* Julio Capo
Ofcr: Carlos Cap
**Sr VP:* Carlos Capo
**VP:* Robert Capo
**VP:* Henry E Hererro
**VP:* Ivan Trabal
Exec: Suen Capo
Exec: Lorenzo Fior

EL DORADO HOTEL & CASINO
See ELDORADO RESORTS LLC

D-U-N-S 00-710-5281
EL ENCANTO INC (NM)
BUENO FOODS
2001 4th St Sw, Albuquerque, NM 87102-4520
Tel (505) 243-2722 *Founded/Ownrshp* 1957
Sales 91.4MM[E] *EMP* 400
SIC 2038 2099 Frozen specialties; Seasonings & spices
Pr: Jacqueline J Baca
**Sr VP:* Gene Baca
IT Man: Kendra Karp
Mfg Dir: Sergio Lopez
Sls&Mrk Ex: Frank Lucero
Sls Mgr: Bryan Vice

D-U-N-S 06-578-3813 IMP
EL HARVEY & SONS INC
HARVEY EXPORT
68 Hopkinton Rd, Westborough, MA 01581-2126
Tel (508) 836-3000 *Founded/Ownrshp* 1956
Sales 121.2MM[E] *EMP* 195[E]
SIC 4953 Sanitary landfill operation; Rubbish collection & disposal; Recycling, waste materials
CEO: James Harvey
**Pr:* Robert Harvey
CFO: Pam Jernberg
Ex VP: Lynda Harvey
**VP:* Benjamin Harvey
VP: Ellen Harvey
**VP:* Steve Harvey
Dir IT: Dean Polamerius
IT Man: Chris George
VP Sls: Lynda Harvey-Fletcher
Sls Mgr: Anthony Cerqueira

D-U-N-S 00-694-7717
■ EL INVESTMENT CO LLC
(*Suby of* ENTERGY LOUISIANA HOLDINGS INC) ★
4809 Jefferson Hwy, Jefferson, LA 70121-3122
Tel (504) 576-4000 *Founded/Ownrshp* 2005
Sales 4.4MMM *EMP* 923
SIC 4911 4922 Electric services; Distribution, electric power; Generation, electric power; Transmission, electric power; Natural gas transmission; Pipelines, natural gas
Ch Bd: Phillip R May Jr
**Pr:* Theodore H Bunting Jr
**CFO:* Andrew S Marsh
Ofcr: Jeffrey S Forbes
Ex VP: Marcus V Brown
Ex VP: Leo Denault
Ex VP: Curtis L Hebert
Ex VP: Michael R Kansler

Ex VP: Mark T Savoff
Sr VP: Alyson M Mount
Board of Directors: Mark T Savoff

D-U-N-S 01-264-7277
EL MONTE CITY SCHOOL DISTRICT
3540 Lexington Ave, El Monte, CA 91731-2608
Tel (626) 453-3700 *Founded/Ownrshp* 1851
Sales 82.0MM *EMP* 1,046
SIC 8211 Public elementary & secondary schools
Bd of Dir: Carlos Salcedo
Exec: Jeff Seymour
Prin: Liz Bass
Prin: Cynthia Flores
Prin: Adriana Garcia
Prin: Erick Hansen
Prin: Carole Key
Prin: Lance Lawston
Prin: Carole McLean
Prin: Lillian Prince
Prin: Liz Raymond

D-U-N-S 08-650-2903
EL MONTE UNION HIGH SCHOOL DISTRICT
3537 Johnson Ave, El Monte, CA 91731-3211
Tel (626) 258-4905 *Founded/Ownrshp* 1901
Sales 93.1MM *EMP* 1,100
SIC 8211 Public senior high school
Bd of Dir: Juanita Gonzales
Bd of Dir: Ricardo Padilla
Bd of Dir: Salvador Ramirez
IT Man: Merlina Loh
Psych: Stephanie Deering
Psych: Valerie Sadler

EL NUEVO DIA
See GFR MEDIA LLC

D-U-N-S 06-288-3079 IMP/EXP
■ **EL PASO CGP CO LLC**
(*Suby of* EL PASO LLC) ★
1001 Louisiana St, Houston, TX 77002-5089
Tel (713) 420-2600 *Founded/Ownrshp* 2001
Sales 352.7MM^E *EMP* 2,984
SIC 2911 1311 4613 4612 5541 4922 Petroleum refining; Crude petroleum & natural gas; Refined petroleum pipelines; Crude petroleum pipelines; Gasoline service stations; Natural gas transmission
Ch Bd: Ronald L Kuehn Jr
**Pr:* H Brent Austin
**CFO:* D Dwight Scott
**Ex VP:* Peggy A Heeg

EL PASO COMMUNITY COLLEGE
See EL PASO COUNTY COMMUNITY COLLEGE DISTRICT

D-U-N-S 03-016-0782
EL PASO COUNTY COMMUNITY COLLEGE DISTRICT
EL PASO COMMUNITY COLLEGE
9050 Viscount Blvd, El Paso, TX 79925-6511
Tel (915) 831-3722 *Founded/Ownrshp* 1971
Sales 33.3MM *EMP* 2,499
Accts Pena Briones Mcdaniel & Co E
SIC 8222 Community college
Pr: Richard Rhodes
**Pr:* William Serrata
VP: Nancy Nelson
**VP:* Josette Shaughnessy
Ex Dir: Daryl Hendry
CTO: Debbie Aguitera
Psych: Ana Guerrero
Psych: Marta Olivares

D-U-N-S 07-508-9953
EL PASO COUNTY HOSPITAL DISTRICT
UNIVERSITY MEDICAL CTR EL PASO
4815 Alameda Ave, El Paso, TX 79905-2705
Tel (915) 544-1200 *Founded/Ownrshp* 1941
Sales 177.1MM *EMP* 1,898
SIC 8062 General medical & surgical hospitals
CEO: James N Valenti
COO: Dennece Knight
**COO:* Maria Zampini
CFO: Michael Nu EZ
**CFO:* Michael Nunez
Dir Lab: David Stevens
Dir Rx: Myron Lewis
Chf Nrs Of: Dian Cassidy
Genl Mgr: Diana Ramirez
Nurse Mgr: Elisa Garcia
Nurse Mgr: Ray Gonzalez

D-U-N-S 07-037-8344
EL PASO COUNTY SCHOOL DISTRICT 8
FOUNTAIN-FORT CARSON SCHOOL DI
10665 Jimmy Camp Rd, Fountain, CO 80817-4175
Tel (719) 382-1300 *Founded/Ownrshp* 1901
Sales 93.3MM *EMP* 950
Accts Swanhorst & Company Llc Green
SIC 8211 Public elementary school; Public junior high school; Public senior high school

D-U-N-S 00-792-8955
▲ **EL PASO ELECTRIC CO** (TX)
Stanton Twr 100 N Stanton, El Paso, TX 79901
Tel (915) 543-5711 *Founded/Ownrshp* 1901
Sales 849.8MM *EMP* 1,100
Accts Kpmg Llp Kansas City Missour
Tkr Sym EE *Exch* NYS
SIC 4911 Generation, electric power; Transmission, electric power; Distribution, electric power
CEO: Mary E Kipp
**Ch Bd:* Charles A Yamarone
Pr: Joe Nevarez
COO: Rose Lowe
CFO: Nathan T Hirschi
**V Ch Bd:* Edward Escudero
Sr VP: John R Boomer
Sr VP: Steven T Buraczyk
VP: Michael D Blanchard
VP: Russell G Gibson
VP: Richard G Gonzalez
VP: David Hawkins
VP: Kerry Lore
Dir Risk M: Henry Hernandez
Board of Directors: Catherine A Allen, John Robert Brown, James W Cicconi, James W Harris, Woody L Hunt, Thomas V Shockley, Eric V Siegel, Stephen N Wertheimer

D-U-N-S 09-013-2569
EL PASO FIRST HEALTH PLANS INC (TX)
(*Suby of* UNIVERSITY MEDICAL CTR EL PASO) ★
1145 Westmoreland Dr, El Paso, TX 79925-5637
Tel (915) 298-7198 *Founded/Ownrshp* 1996
Sales 88.4MM *EMP* 140
SIC 8741 Administrative management
CEO: James Valenti
**CFO:* Phil Rivera
Dir QC: Don Gillis
Mktg Dir: Don Gilmore

D-U-N-S 19-491-8876
■ **EL PASO HEALTHCARE SYSTEM LTD**
DEL SOL MEDICAL CENTER
(*Suby of* HOSPITAL CORPORATION OF AMERICA) ★
10301 Gateway Blvd W, El Paso, TX 79925-7701
Tel (915) 595-9000 *Founded/Ownrshp* 1988
Sales 270.2MM^E *EMP* 3,000
SIC 8062 General medical & surgical hospitals
CEO: Jacob Cintron
Chf Rad: Vishan Giyanani
Dir Recs: Enrique Bernal
COO: Elizabeth Carroll Gonzalez
COO: Gary Purushotham
CFO: Luanne Campbell
Ofcr: Ken Massie
Dir Lab: Gracy Urias
Adm Dir: Deborah Tappen
MIS Dir: Terri Cummings
QA Dir: Irma Montezgomez

D-U-N-S 07-874-3760
■ **EL PASO HOLDCO LLC**
(*Suby of* KMI) ★
1001 Louisiana St, Houston, TX 77002-5089
Tel (713) 420-2600 *Founded/Ownrshp* 2011
Sales 362.5MM^E *EMP* 4,858^E
SIC 6719 Investment holding companies, except banks

D-U-N-S 07-984-1979
EL PASO INDEPENDENT SCHOOL DISTRICT
6531 Boeing Dr, El Paso, TX 79925-1008
Tel (915) 230-2000 *Founded/Ownrshp* 1920
Sales 651.8MM *EMP* 9,000
Accts Gibson Ruddock Patterson Llc
SIC 8211 Public elementary & secondary schools
Dir Sec: Victor Araiza
Psych: Michael McCormack
HC Dir: Alana Bejarano

D-U-N-S 02-951-4077 IMP
■ **EL PASO LLC**
(*Suby of* EL PASO HOLDCO LLC) ★
1001 Louisiana St, Houston, TX 77002-5089
Tel (713) 420-2600 *Founded/Ownrshp* 2012
Sales 3.1MMM^E *EMP* 4,858^E
SIC 4922 1311 Natural gas transmission; Natural gas production
CEO: Richard D Kinder
**Pr:* C Park Shaper
**Pr:* Brent J Smolik
**Pr:* Jim Yardley
COO: Richard Lietz
**CFO:* John R Sult
Ofcr: Carol Shanks
Ex VP: Brent H Austin
**Ex VP:* Robert Baker
**Ex VP:* James King
**Ex VP:* D Mark Leland
**Ex VP:* James C Yardley
VP: Stephen Beasley
VP: Gregory Clark
VP: James Coulter
VP: William Healy Jr
**VP:* Joseph Listengart
VP: Grace Martinez
Dir Risk M: Ginny Penzell
Dir Risk M: Anthony Trinko

D-U-N-S 80-175-4073
EL PASO PIPELINE PARTNERS LP
1001 La St Ste 1000, Houston, TX 77002
Tel (713) 369-9000 *Founded/Ownrshp* 2007
Sales 1.5MMM *EMP* 8^E
SIC 4922

D-U-N-S 00-795-7871
■ **EL PASO TENNESSEE PIPELINE CO LLC**
KINDER MORGAN
(*Suby of* EL PASO LLC) ★
1001 Louisiana St, Houston, TX 77002-5089
Tel (713) 420-2131 *Founded/Ownrshp* 1987
Sales 973.0MM^E *EMP* 2,200
SIC 4922 Natural gas transmission
Ch Bd: William A Wise
Mng Pt: Timmie Smith
**VP:* H Brent Austin
**VP:* Joel Richards III
**VP:* Britton White
Exec: Sylvia Aguilar
Exec: Amy Lujan
Dir IT: Rick Diaz
Dir IT: Jim Noot
IT Man: Anthony Chisesi
IT Man: John Gray

D-U-N-S 14-867-8837
EL PASO WATER UTILITIES PUBLIC SERVICE BOARD
1154 Hawkins Blvd, El Paso, TX 79925-6436
Tel (915) 594-5500 *Founded/Ownrshp* 2004
Sales 215.2MM *EMP* 850
Accts Gibson Ruddock Patterson Llc
SIC 4941 1623 Water supply; Water, sewer & utility lines
Ch: Richard T Schoephoerster
**CEO:* John Balliew
CFO: Marcela Navarette
VP: Gloria Fredricks
VP: Steve Teran
CTO: Humberto Juarez
MIS Dir: Ross Swall

D-U-N-S 78-546-7163
▲ **EL POLLO LOCO HOLDINGS INC**
3535 Harbor Blvd Ste 100, Costa Mesa, CA 92626-1494
Tel (714) 599-5000 *Founded/Ownrshp* 1980
Sales 355.0MM *EMP* 5,171
Tkr Sym LOCO *Exch* NGS
SIC 5812 6794 Eating places; Mexican restaurant; Fast-food restaurant, chain; Grills (eating places); Franchises, selling or licensing
Pr: Stephen J Sather
**Ch Bd:* Michael G Maselli
CFO: Laurance Roberts
Chf Mktg O: Edward Valle
VP: Gustavo Siade
Board of Directors: Douglas K Ammerman, Samuel N Borgese, Mark Buller, William R Floyd, Dean C Kehler, Carol Lynton John M Roth

D-U-N-S 12-274-0921
■ **EL POLLO LOCO INC**
(*Suby of* EL POLLO LOCO HOLDINGS INC) ★
3535 Harbor Blvd Ste 100, Costa Mesa, CA 92626-1494
Tel (714) 599-5000 *Founded/Ownrshp* 1980
Sales 64.8MM^E *EMP* 4,000
SIC 5812 Mexican restaurant
Pr: Steve Sather
**Ch Bd:* Samuel N Borgese
**COO:* Kay Bogeajis
**COO:* Dennis Farrow
COO: Raymond Perry
CFO: Larry Roberts
**CFO:* Joseph Stein
Sr Cor Off: Francisco P Ochoa
**Chf Mktg O:* Karen Eadon
**Chf Mktg O:* Ed Valle
Ex VP: Julius Christensen
**Sr VP:* Jeanne Scott
VP: Dale Burke
**VP:* Patsy Estis
**VP:* Heather Gardea
**VP:* Mark Hardison
**VP:* Richard Pineda
VP: Mike Wildman
Dir Risk M: Kelly Morgan

EL RIO HEALTH CENTER
See EL RIO SANTA CRUZ NEIGHBORHOOD HEALTH CENTER INC

D-U-N-S 07-751-9122
EL RIO SANTA CRUZ NEIGHBORHOOD HEALTH CENTER INC
EL RIO HEALTH CENTER
839 W Congress St, Tucson, AZ 85745-2819
Tel (520) 792-9890 *Founded/Ownrshp* 1970
Sales 107.3MM *EMP* 732
Accts Fester & Chapman Pc Phoenix
SIC 8093 Specialty outpatient clinics
Ex Dir: Kathy Byrne
**COO:* Nancy Metzger Johnson
**CFO:* Celia Hightower
Ofcr: Nancy Johnson
Ofcr: Mary Spoerl
VP: Pete Reisinger
Dir Rx: Anthony Felix
Doctor: Edgardo Laguillo MD
Pharmcst: Melissa Thiessen Warken
Med Dir: Arthur Martinez

EL SOL
See CARIBBEAN FINANCIAL GROUP INC

EL SUPER
See BODEGA LATINA CORP

EL TORITO MEXICAN RESTAURANT
See EL TORITO RESTAURANTS INC

EL TORITO MEXICAN RESTAURANT
See REAL MEX RESTAURANTS INC

D-U-N-S 08-391-1875
EL TORITO RESTAURANTS INC (DE)
EL TORITO MEXICAN RESTAURANT
(*Suby of* EL TORITO MEXICAN RESTAURANT) ★
4001 Via Oro Ave Ste 200, Long Beach, CA 90810-1400
Tel (562) 346-1200 *Founded/Ownrshp* 1954, 2000
Sales 160.6MM^E *EMP* 5,800
SIC 5812 Mexican restaurant
Pr: Fred Wolfe
COO: Chuck Rink
CFO: Steve Tanner
VP: Mark Turpin
VP Mktg: Julie Koenig

EL-BEE
See ELDER-BEERMAN STORES CORP

D-U-N-S 05-109-1544 IMP
EL-MILAGRO INC
3050 W 26th St, Chicago, IL 60623-4130
Tel (773) 579-6120 *Founded/Ownrshp* 1976
Sales 122.9MM^E *EMP* 540
SIC 2099 5812 Tortillas, fresh or refrigerated; Mexican restaurant
Pr: Raphael Lopez
Off Mgr: Raulinda Sierra
Board of Directors: Raul Lopez

D-U-N-S 13-190-5940
ELAMEX USA CORP
(*Suby of* ELAMEX, S.A. DE C.V.)
1800 Northwestern Dr, El Paso, TX 79912-1122
Tel (915) 298-3061 *Founded/Ownrshp* 1998
Sales 128.0MM^E *EMP* 600
SIC 3694 2068 2064 Engine electrical equipment; Salted & roasted nuts & seeds; Candy & other confectionery products
Pr: Richard Spencer
**CFO:* Sam L Henry

ELAMF
See MOUNT FRANKLIN FOODS LLC

D-U-N-S 92-778-2912
ELAN CHATEAU RESORTS LLC
INN AT CHATEAU ELAN
(*Suby of* CHATEAU ELAN GOLF) ★
100 Rue Charlemagne Dr, Braselton, GA 30517-2435
Tel (678) 425-0900 *Founded/Ownrshp* 2004
Sales 104.5MM^E *EMP* 500
SIC 2084 5812 7992 7011 Wines, brandy & brandy spirits; Eating places; Public golf courses; Hotels & motels
**CFO:* David Ostrander
Genl Mgr: Steve Contos
VP Mktg: Doug Rollins

D-U-N-S 60-677-9429 IMP
■ **ELAN NUTRITION INC**
(*Suby of* TREEHOUSE FOODS INC) ★
21325 Hamburg Ave, Lakeville, MN 55044-8341
Tel (616) 940-6000 *Founded/Ownrshp* 2010
Sales 108.7MM^E *EMP* 200
SIC 2099 Food preparations
Pr: David F Finnigan
**CFO:* Tom W Olive
**VP:* Randy Olshen
**Prin:* Bob Ferguson

D-U-N-S 96-698-5624 IMP
■ **ELANCO US INC**
NOVARTIS ANIMAL HEALTH US INC
(*Suby of* ELI LILLY AND CO) ★
3200 Northline Ave # 300, Greensboro, NC 27408-7616
Tel (877) 352-6261 *Founded/Ownrshp* 2015
Sales 87.8MM^E *EMP* 230
SIC 2834 Pharmaceutical preparations
CEO: Joseph Burkett
**Pr:* Robert Jones
VP: Virginia Lizala
**VP:* Brian Reeve
Dir Soc: Kelley Rickard
Dir IT: Tim Hawks
Dir IT: Eric Lapp
IT Man: Dan Mars
Corp Couns: Beverley Crump

D-U-N-S 10-320-1567
ELANDIA INTERNATIONAL INC
(*Suby of* AMPER SA)
8333 Nw 53rd St Ste 400, Miami, FL 33166-4787
Tel (305) 415-8830 *Founded/Ownrshp* 2011
Sales 110.7MM^E *EMP* 905
SIC 4813 4899 7371 5044 Telephone communication, except radio; ;Telephone/video communications; Voice telephone communications; Data communication services; Software programming applications; Office equipment
CEO: Pedro R Pizarro
**CFO:* Harley Rollins
VP: Carlos Apollonio

D-U-N-S 16-991-9425
■ **ELARA HOLDINGS INC**
(*Suby of* NATIONAL GENERAL HOLDINGS CORP) ★
1281 Murfreesboro Pike, Nashville, TN 37217-2423
Tel (615) 366-3723 *Founded/Ownrshp* 2016
Sales 137.8MM^E *EMP* 2,453^E
SIC 6719 Investment holding companies, except banks

D-U-N-S 62-489-7013
■ **ELAVON INC**
(*Suby of* US BANCORP) ★
2 Cncourse Pkwy Ste 800, Atlanta, GA 30328
Tel (678) 731-5000 *Founded/Ownrshp* 2002
Sales 12.7MM^E *EMP* 2,000
SIC 7375 7374 Information retrieval services; Data processing & preparation
CEO: Simon Haslam
V Ch: Pam Joseph
Pr: Antonio Castilho
**Pr:* Guy Harris
**Pr:* Pamela A Joseph
Pr: Brett Turner
**COO:* Elaine Thompson Baker
CFO: Bradley Herring
**CFO:* James Steawart Walker
Ofcr: Brian Mahony
Ex VP: Ian Drysdale
Ex VP: Laura Willson
**Sr VP:* Shanon Carpenter
**Sr VP:* Mindy Doster
Sr VP: David McAlhaney
VP: Jeff Afonso
VP: Phil Agcaoili
VP: Eric Barfield
VP: Frank Bolling
VP: Rhonda Capone
VP: Sara Cichoski

D-U-N-S 00-326-4942 IMP/EXP
ELBERTA CRATE & BOX CO (GA)
606 Dothan Rd, Bainbridge, GA 39817-3053
Tel (229) 243-1268 *Founded/Ownrshp* 1905, 1976
Sales 137.8MM^E *EMP* 740
SIC 2449 5023 2448 Vegetable crates, wood: wirebound; Fruit crates, wood: wirebound; Boxes, wood: wirebound; Wood flooring; Pallets, wood
Ch Bd: John M Simmons
**Pr:* D Ramsay Simmons Jr
**CEO:* Tom Simmons
**CFO:* Steve Williams
**VP:* D Ramsay Simmons III
**VP Sls:* Todd Mills

D-U-N-S 79-318-3794 IMP
ELBIT SYSTEMS OF AMERICA LLC
(*Suby of* ELBIT SYSTEMS LTD)
4700 Marine Creek Pkwy, Fort Worth, TX 76179-3505
Tel (817) 234-6600 *Founded/Ownrshp* 2007
Sales 663.1MM^E *EMP* 1,905
SIC 3827 Optical instruments & apparatus
Pr: Raanan Horowitz
CFO: Cletus Glasener
Ofcr: Chad Ramsay
Ofcr: Lorraine Wall
Ex VP: Gideon Sheffer
Sr VP: David Rogers
VP: Tom Carter

VP: Brett Cohen
VP: Leanne Collazzo
VP: Kelly Dameron
VP: Joel Friederich
VP: Chris Hickey
VP: Kendra Luker
VP: Tiffany Nesbit
VP: R Chris Puffer
VP: Kenneth Quinlan
VP: Douglas Sandklev
VP: Amela Wilson
Dir Bus: Rafael De
Dir Bus: Bob Sandt

ELCOLE FRANCAISE
See EDUCATION UNLIMITED OF OHIO INC

D-U-N-S 55-591-4779 IMP
ELCOM INC
(*Suby of* YAZAKI INTERNATIONAL CORP) ★
20 Butterfield Trail Blvd, El Paso, TX 79906-5254
Tel (915) 298-2000 *Founded/Ownrshp* 1988
Sales 604.2MM[E] *EMP* 2,900[E]
SIC 3679 3694 Electronic circuits; Engine electrical equipment
**Treas:* Don Winn
VP: Sheldon Paul
Mktg Dir: Olga Koksharova

D-U-N-S 00-925-1042 IMP/EXP
■ **ELDEC CORP**
CRANE AEROSPACE & ELECTRONICS
(*Suby of* CRANE AEROSPACE INC) ★
16700 13th Ave W, Lynnwood, WA 98037-8503
Tel (425) 743-8362 *Founded/Ownrshp* 1994
Sales 197.8MM[E] *EMP* 815
SIC 3812 3728 3824 3769 3674 3613 Search & navigation equipment; Aircraft control instruments; Aircraft control systems, electronic; Aircraft parts & equipment; Fluid meters & counting devices; Guided missile & space vehicle parts & auxiliary equipment; Semiconductors & related devices; Switchgear & switchboard apparatus
Ch: Max Mitchell
**Pr:* Brendan Curran
**Treas:* Sina A Passarelli
Sr VP: Rick Jones
**VP:* Michael Brady
VP: Chris Cook
Dir Rx: Jerome Bowler
Dir Rx: Mark Stefanich
IT Man: Mohammed Ali
Sftwr Eng: Ming Yue

ELDER CARE HOUSE PLAN
See CARE WISCONSIN FIRST INC

D-U-N-S 07-956-1724
ELDER LIVING CONCEPTS INC (MA)
51 Summer St, Rowley, MA 01969-1835
Tel (978) 948-7383 *Founded/Ownrshp* 1992
Sales 8.4MM[E] *EMP* 1,200
SIC 8051 Skilled nursing care facilities
Pr: Frank Romano

D-U-N-S 00-628-7171 IMP/EXP
ELDER MANUFACTURING CO INC
ELDERWEAR
999 Executive Parkway Dr # 300, Saint Louis, MO 63141-6336
Tel (314) 469-1120 *Founded/Ownrshp* 1917, 1983
Sales 157.4MM[E] *EMP* 600
SIC 2321 2361 2253 Polo shirts, men's & boys': made from purchased materials; Blouses: girls', children's & infants'; Shirts: girls', children's & infants'; Knit outerwear mills
Pr: Perry Sarinsky
**CFO:* Bob Branstetter
Ex VP: Gregory Beile
Off Mgr: Mary Burns
Off Mgr: Lisa Roberts
Store Mgr: Regina Everett
VP Opers: Gregg Hanson

D-U-N-S 00-790-2463 IMP
■ **ELDER-BEERMAN STORES CORP**
EL-BEE
(*Suby of* BON-TON STORES INC) ★
3155 Elbee Rd Ste 201, Moraine, OH 45439-2046
Tel (937) 296-2700 *Founded/Ownrshp* 2003
Sales 394.1MM[E] *EMP* 6,053
SIC 5311 5661 7389 Department stores, non-discount; Shoe stores; Credit card service
Pr: Byron Bergren
Ex VP: Leonard Peal
Ex VP: Charles P Shaffer
**Ex VP:* James M Zamberlan
Sr VP: Darlen Denman Jones
Sr VP: Guenter C Kass
Sr VP: James A Lance
Sr VP: Jeffrey D Skoglind
Sr VP: Timothy L Worcester
Sr VP: Mork Zwerner
Sales Exec: David Biundo

D-U-N-S 11-521-5857
ELDERPLAN INC
6323 7th Ave Ste 3, Brooklyn, NY 11220-4719
Tel (800) 353-3765 *Founded/Ownrshp* 1982
Sales NA *EMP* 100
SIC 6324 Hospital & medical service plans
**Pr:* Martin Simon
CFO: Daniel Kasle

ELDERWEAR
See ELDER MANUFACTURING CO INC

D-U-N-S 00-530-3284 IMP
ELDON C STUTSMAN INC (IA)
121 Lassie, Hills, IA 52235-7734
Tel (319) 679-2281 *Founded/Ownrshp* 1940
Sales 204.1MM[E] *EMP* 117
SIC 5191 3523 Farm supplies; Fertilizer & fertilizer materials; Chemicals, agricultural; Feed; Farm machinery & equipment
Pr: Roger A Slaughter
CFO: Scott Szymanek
**CFO:* Scott Zymananek
**Treas:* Mark A Stutsman

VP: Jediah French
**VP:* James R Stutsman

D-U-N-S 07-829-6112
ELDORADO CASINO SHREVEPORT JOINT VENTURE
(*Suby of* EL DORADO HOTEL & CASINO) ★
451 Clyde Fant Pkwy, Shreveport, LA 71101-3206
Tel (877) 602-0711 *Founded/Ownrshp* 2011, 2005
Sales 15.9MM[E] *EMP* 2,032[E]
SIC 7011 Casino hotel
Dir IT: Charles Lancaster

ELDORADO HOTEL CASINO
See RECREATIONAL ENTERPRISES INC

D-U-N-S 55-643-9917 IMP/EXP
ELDORADO NATIONAL (CALIFORNIA) INC
(*Suby of* ASV) ★
9670 Galena St, Riverside, CA 92509-3089
Tel (951) 727-9300 *Founded/Ownrshp* 2013
Sales 96.8MM[E] *EMP* 351
SIC 3711 Buses, all types, assembly of
CEO: Peter Orthwein
Genl Mgr: Dan Daniels

D-U-N-S 07-956-3153
▲ **ELDORADO RESORTS INC**
100 W Liberty St Ste 1150, Reno, NV 89501-1960
Tel (775) 328-0100 *Founded/Ownrshp* 2013
Sales 719.7MM *EMP* 7,800[E]
Tkr Sym ERI *Exch* NGS
SIC 7011 Hotels & motels
Ch Bd: Gary L Carano
**Pr:* Thomas Reeg
CFO: Robert M Jones
Ex VP: Anthony Carano
Ex VP: Anthony L Carano
VP: Gene R Carano
Board of Directors: Frank J Fahrenkopf Jr, James B Hawkins, Michael E Pegram, David P Tomick, Roger P Wagner

D-U-N-S 06-294-6637
ELDORADO RESORTS LLC
EL DORADO HOTEL & CASINO
345 N Virginia St, Reno, NV 89501-1136
Tel (775) 786-5700 *Founded/Ownrshp* 1973
Sales 159.2MM[E] *EMP* 2,200[E]
SIC 7011 5812 5813 Casino hotel; Eating places; Bar (drinking places)
Pr: Peter Broughton
Treas: Gary Carano
Ofcr: Raymond J Poncia Jr
**VP:* Rhonda Carano
**VP:* Rob Mouchou
Ex Dir: Linda Seidl
IT Man: Irene Dominguez
IT Man: Peter Larragueta
Natl Sales: El D Reno
Sls&Mrk Ex: Peggy Selvey
Mktg Mgr: Donald Carano

D-U-N-S 10-340-6695 IMP
■ **ELDORADO STONE LLC**
(*Suby of* HEADWATERS INC) ★
1370 Grand Ave Bldg B, San Marcos, CA 92078-2404
Tel (800) 925-1491 *Founded/Ownrshp* 2000
Sales 537.6MM *EMP* 1,700
SIC 3272 Concrete products, precast
Mktg Mgr: Alice Faggi

ELE INTERNATIONAL
See HACH CO

ELEAD
See FRESH BEGINNINGS INC

D-U-N-S 03-766-1667 IMP
ELECTION SYSTEMS & SOFTWARE LLC
ES&S
11208 John Galt Blvd, Omaha, NE 68137-2320
Tel (402) 593-0101 *Founded/Ownrshp* 1979
Sales 116.7MM[E] *EMP* 350
SIC 3577 Optical scanning devices
Ch Bd: Michael McCarthy
**Pr:* Tom Burt
**Pr:* Aldo Tesi
**CFO:* Tom O'Brien
Treas: Richard Jablonski
Ofcr: William F Welsh II
Sr VP: John Groh
**Sr VP:* Kathy Rogers
Sr VP: Geoff Ryan
VP: Val Guyett
VP: Bryan Hoffman
**VP:* Richard J Jablonski
VP: Thomas Obrien
**VP:* Gary Weber
VP: Peter Zelechoski
Exec: Mark Norris
Board of Directors: John Gottschalk, Pat Jung, Mike Mc Carthy, Manny Quevedo, Steve Seline, Bill Welsh

D-U-N-S 13-759-3687
ELECTRA LINK INC
21755 Interstate 45 # 10, Spring, TX 77388-3621
Tel (281) 350-6096 *Founded/Ownrshp* 1999
Sales 189.4MM[E] *EMP* 345
SIC 1623 Cable laying construction; Telephone & communication line construction
Pr: Ernest D Antoni
**CFO:* Joan McKinney
**VP:* Pearson Dale
**VP:* Dale Pearson
Sls Mgr: Bob Wiliamson

D-U-N-S 36-171-2540
ELECTRIC & WATER PLANT BOARD OF CITY OF FRANKFORT KY
FRANKFORT ELC & WTR PLANT BD
317 W 2nd St, Frankfort, KY 40601-2645
Tel (502) 352-4372 *Founded/Ownrshp* 1943
Sales 84.8MM *EMP* 202
SIC 4941 4911 7382 5063 4841 4813 Water supply; Electric services; Security systems services; Burglar alarm systems; Cable television services; Telephone communication, except radio
Genl Mgr: Warner J Caines

D-U-N-S 96-373-7366 IMP/EXP
■ **ELECTRIC BOAT CORP**
GENERAL DYNAMICS ELECTRIC BOAT
(*Suby of* GENERAL DYNAMICS CORP) ★
75 Eastern Point Rd, Groton, CT 06340-4905
Tel (860) 433-3000 *Founded/Ownrshp* 1899
Sales 2.9MMM[E] *EMP* 10,500
SIC 3731 8711 Submarines, building & repairing; Engineering services
Pr: John P Casey
CFO: John V Leonard
**Treas:* David H Fogg
Ex VP: Gerard J Demuro
Sr VP: Kevin J Poitras
VP: Joseph E Chontos
VP: Robert Dinapoli
VP: Kristin L Fletcher
**VP:* Gregory S Gallopoulos
VP: Craig Haines
VP: Kurt A Hesch
VP: Robert H Nardone
VP: Devin Poitras
VP: Roger Sexauer
VP: Joseph A Walsh
Exec: Charles Lombardi
Dir: Harry Winthrop

D-U-N-S 00-197-9350 IMP
■ **ELECTRIC ENERGY INC** (IL)
(*Suby of* ILLINOIS POWER HOLDINGS LLC) ★
2100 Portland Rd, Joppa, IL 62953
Tel (618) 543-7531 *Founded/Ownrshp* 1950, 2013
Sales 194.8MM[E] *EMP* 179
Accts Pricewaterhousecoopers Llp S
SIC 4911 ; Generation, electric power; Distribution, electric power
Pr: Christopher A Iselin
**Prin:* James M Helm

D-U-N-S 13-912-7117
ELECTRIC LIGHTWAVE COMMUNICATIONS INC
18110 Se 34th St Bldg 1s, Vancouver, WA 98683-9440
Tel (360) 558-6900 *Founded/Ownrshp* 1996
Sales 434.3MM[E] *EMP* 1,446
SIC 7389 4813 Telephone services; Telephone communication, except radio
CEO: Mark Willency
COO: Michael Sharpe
CFO: Jesse Selnick
Treas: Mark Roskopf
Sr VP: Karen L Clauson
Sr VP: Felicity O'Herron
Sr VP: Daniel Stoll
VP: Brady Adams
VP: Aaron Capsel
VP: Stephen Fisher
VP: Steven Fisher
VP: Rob Hamer
VP: Cindy Leiser
Dir Surg: Jim Nieuwstraten
Dir Surg: Chris Pike
Board of Directors: Craig Pierce, Jesse Selnick, Mark Willency

D-U-N-S 16-012-2222
ELECTRIC LIGHTWAVE HOLDINGS INC
INTEGRA TELECOM
18110 Se 34th St, Vancouver, WA 98683-9418
Tel (360) 558-6900 *Founded/Ownrshp* 2014
Sales 353.4MM[E] *EMP* 1,400
SIC 4813 Local & long distance telephone communications;
CEO: Mark Willency
**Pr:* Daniel Stoll
**CFO:* Jesse Selnick
**Treas:* Mark Roskopf
Chf Mktg O: Joseph Harding
Ofcr: Jason Koenders
Sr VP: Claire Schulte
**VP:* Brady Adams
**VP:* Aaron Capsel
**VP:* Stephen Fisher
VP: Steven Fisher
**VP:* Rob Hamer
VP: Cindy Leiser
**VP:* Cynthia Leiser
VP: Martha Tate
Dir Surg: Jim Nieuwstraten

D-U-N-S 17-858-5113
ELECTRIC LIGHTWAVE LLC
INTEGRA TELECOM
(*Suby of* INTEGRA TELECOM) ★
18110 Se 34th St Bldg 1s, Vancouver, WA 98683-9440
Tel (360) 558-6900 *Founded/Ownrshp* 2006
Sales 133.4MM[E] *EMP* 823
SIC 4813 Local & long distance telephone communications;
CEO: Mark Willency
Ex VP: Jeff Oxley
Sr VP: Mike Daniel
VP Mktg: Trent Anderson
VP Sls: Jay Dirkmaat
VP Sls: Ray Napoletano
Sls Mgr: Frank Cotroneo
Board of Directors: Mark Willency

D-U-N-S 10-153-6626 IMP/EXP
ELECTRIC MACHINERY CO INC
E M
(*Suby of* WEG EQUIPAMENTOS ELETRICOS S/A.)
800 Central Ave Ne, Minneapolis, MN 55413-2400
Tel (612) 378-8000 *Founded/Ownrshp* 1891
Sales 122.6MM[E] *EMP* 410
SIC 3621 Motors & generators
Pr: Richard Fesmire
IT Man: Patty Wallin
Sls Mgr: Evandro Bulling

ELECTRIC METER DIVISION
See ELSTER SOLUTIONS LLC

ELECTRIC MOTOR & SUPPLY
See ELECTRIC MOTOR SHOP

D-U-N-S 02-818-5718
ELECTRIC MOTOR SHOP
ELECTRIC MOTOR & SUPPLY
253 Fulton St, Fresno, CA 93721-3164
Tel (559) 233-1153 *Founded/Ownrshp* 1913
Sales 116.2MM[E] *EMP* 182
Accts Diebert And Associates Cpas F
SIC 5063 1731 7694 7922 Motor controls, starters & relays: electric; Motors, electric; Electrical work; Electric motor repair; Theatrical producers & services
Pr: Richard M Caglia
CFO: Derek Larsen
**Sec:* Sally M Caglia
Ofcr: Steven Ray
Off Mgr: Glenda Ritter
Sls Mgr: Raymond Keith
Sls Mgr: Larry Negrete
Sales Asso: Darrell Duchscher
Sales Asso: Larry Meyer

D-U-N-S 00-792-0739
ELECTRIC POWER BOARD OF CHATTANOOGA (TN)
E P B
10 W Martin Luther King B, Chattanooga, TN 37402-1813
Tel (423) 756-2706 *Founded/Ownrshp* 1935
Sales 671.0MM *EMP* 400
Accts Henderson Hutcherson & Mccullo
SIC 4911 Distribution, electric power
Pr: Harold De Priest
**COO:* David Wade
**CFO:* Greg Eaves
**Sr VP:* Steve Clark
**VP:* Diana Bullock
Snr Ntwrk: Dale McLeod
Software D: Leslie Wortman
Netwrk Eng: Nidhi Agarwal
Netwrk Eng: John Alcock
VP Legal: Aaron Webb

D-U-N-S 07-537-9156 IMP
ELECTRIC POWER BOARD OF METROPOLITAN GOVERNMENT OF NASHVILLE & DAVIDSON COUNTY (TN)
NASHVILLE ELECTRIC SERVICE
1214 Church St, Nashville, TN 37246-0001
Tel (615) 747-3831 *Founded/Ownrshp* 1939
Sales 1.2MMM *EMP* 950
Accts Pricewaterhousecoopers Llp N
SIC 4911 ; Distribution, electric power
Pr: Decosta Jenkins
**Pt:* Robert Campbell
CFO: Teresa Broyles Aplin
VP: Kate Tallmadge
CIO: Vic Hatridge
Opers Mgr: Frank Travis
Snr Mgr: Ricky Davis

D-U-N-S 06-251-1126
ELECTRIC POWER RESEARCH INSTITUTE INC
3420 Hillview Ave, Palo Alto, CA 94304-1382
Tel (650) 855-2000 *Founded/Ownrshp* 1973
Sales 406.0MM *EMP* 891
Accts Deloitte & Touche Llp San Fr
SIC 8731 Energy research
CEO: Michael Howard
**Ch Bd:* Gil C Quiniones
**Pr:* Terry Boston
CFO: Steve Yamamoto
**V Ch Bd:* Patricia Vincent-Collawn
Ofcr: Clark Gellings
VP: C T Alley
VP: Henry Courtright
VP: Pamela Keefe
VP: Christian Larsen
VP: Mark F McGranaghan
VP: Neil Wilmshurst
Board of Directors: Lord John Mogg, Terry Bassham, Pedro J Pizarro, Terry Boston, Rod West, Kenneth W Cornew, Doug Esamann, Thomas J Heller, Jim Kerr, James H Lash, Allen L Leverett, Jeff Lyash

D-U-N-S 18-352-9049
ELECTRIC RELIABILITY COUNCIL OF TEXAS INC
ERCOT ISO
7620 Metro Center Dr, Austin, TX 78744-1613
Tel (512) 225-7000 *Founded/Ownrshp* 1986
Sales 156.5MM *EMP* 625
SIC 4911 Distribution, electric power; Generation, electric power; Transmission, electric power
CEO: Bill Magness
CEO: Tammy Porter
CFO: Maxine N Buckles
Treas: James Nield
**VP:* Jerry Dryer
VP: Mark Ruane
Comm Man: Robbie Searcy
**Prin:* Betty Day
Snr Ntwrk: John Fisher
Dir IT: Richard Howard
IT Man: Tamara Bunner
Board of Directors: Alton D Patton, Don Ballard, Barry T Smitherman, Andrew J Dalton, William J Taylor, Miguel W Espinosa, Robert P Thomas, Nikolaus Fehrenbach, Dan Wilkerson, Bob Helton, Eric Hendrick, Charles W Jenkins III, Clifton B Karnei, Jan L Newton

D-U-N-S 05-868-8698
ELECTRIC RESEARCH AND MANUFACTURING COOPERATIVE INC
ERMCO
(*Suby of* AECI) ★
2225 Industrial Rd, Dyersburg, TN 38024-2344
Tel (731) 285-9121 *Founded/Ownrshp* 1964
Sales 154.4MM[E] *EMP* 579
SIC 3612 Distribution transformers, electric; Voltage regulating transformers, electric power
CEO: William Reffert
**Sr VP:* Kent D Raffath
VP Opers: Bob Grunert
Mktg Mgr: Craig Tennant
Sales Asso: Carre Gordon

D-U-N-S 05-069-2920 IMP/EXP
ELECTRIC SUPPLY OF TAMPA INC
4407 N Manhattan Ave, Tampa, FL 33614-7626
Tel (813) 872-1894 *Founded/Ownrshp* 1969
Sales 167.8MM^E *EMP* 120
Accts Dwight Darby & Company Tampa
SIC 5063 Electrical supplies
Pr: George M Adams Jr
COO: Matt Coffey
**CFO:* Harry Irwin
Exec: Donna Holcomb
Div Mgr: Bruce Montgomery
Genl Mgr: Frank Burgess
IT Man: Jason Tregler
Sls Mgr: Rick Atkinson
Sales Asso: Jerry Meguiar

ELECTRIC SYSTEM
See PUBLIC UTILITY DISTRICT 2 GRANT COUNTY

ELECTRIC UTILITY
See PUBLIC UTILITY DISTRICT 1 OF BENTON COUNTY

D-U-N-S 62-613-7504 IMP
ELECTRICAL COMPONENTS INTERNATIONAL INC
WHITEHOUSE ACQUISITION CO
(*Suby of* ECI HOLDINGS CO) ★
1 Cityplace Dr Ste 450, Saint Louis, MO 63141-7060
Tel (314) 692-4204 *Founded/Ownrshp* 2005
Sales 2.1MMM^E *EMP* 12,000
SIC 3679 Harness assemblies for electronic use: wire or cable
Prin: David J Webster
Pr: Ken Treftz
**CFO:* Mitch Leonard
Software D: Miguel Osorio

ELECTRICAL CONSTRUCTION CO
See EC CO

D-U-N-S 18-250-5636
ELECTRICAL CONSULTANTS INC
E C I
3521 Gabel Rd Ste A, Billings, MT 59102-7310
Tel (406) 259-9933 *Founded/Ownrshp* 1985
Sales 225.0MM *EMP* 358
SIC 8711

D-U-N-S 05-789-0204
ELECTRICAL CORP OF AMERICA INC
7320 Arlington Ave, Raytown, MO 64133-6567
Tel (816) 737-3206 *Founded/Ownrshp* 1970
Sales 90.8MM^E *EMP* 420
Accts Boan Connealy & Houlehan Llc
SIC 1731 Electrical work
Ch: James W Lacy
**Pr:* Donald Laffoon
Rgnl Mgr: Bruce Turpin
Info Man: Michael Crone

ELECTRICAL DISTRIBUTORS CO
See CHESTER C LEHMANN CO INC

D-U-N-S 82-756-9018
ELECTRICAL DISTRIBUTORS LLC
2301 Century Cir, Irving, TX 75062-4918
Tel (469) 533-6250 *Founded/Ownrshp* 2008
Sales 106.4MM^E *EMP* 48^E
SIC 5063 5999 Electrical apparatus & equipment; Electronic parts & equipment
Ch: Tim Cappelli
CEO: Jesse Jacobi
VP: Wendy Bartlet
VP: Martin Martinez
VP: Jimmy Ross

D-U-N-S 79-119-4454
ELECTRICAL EMPLOYERS SELF INSURANCE SAFETY PLAN
15811 Jewel Ave, Fresh Meadows, NY 11365-3085
Tel (718) 591-2000 *Founded/Ownrshp* 2007
Sales NA *EMP* 2
SIC 6311 Life insurance

D-U-N-S 00-528-0102
ELECTRICAL ENGINEERING AND EQUIPMENT CO (IA)
3E
953 73rd St, Windsor Heights, IA 50324-1031
Tel (515) 273-0100 *Founded/Ownrshp* 1920
Sales 449.7MM^E *EMP* 430^E
SIC 5063 8711 Electrical supplies; Engineering services
Pr: Jeff Stroud
**Pr:* Steve Vanbrocklin
**CFO:* Dave Moench
**Ex VP:* John Pilmer
**VP:* Mike Ahlrichs
Sales Asso: Shane Brown

D-U-N-S 00-320-2488 IMP/EXP
ELECTRICAL EQUIPMENT CO INC (NC)
EECO
1440 Diggs Dr, Raleigh, NC 27603-2755
Tel (919) 828-5411 *Founded/Ownrshp* 1926
Sales 139.9MM^E *EMP* 307
SIC 5063 7699

ELECTRICAL INSUL SUPPLIERS
See EIS INC

D-U-N-S 06-950-1195
ELECTRICAL INSURANCE TRUSTEES
JOINT PENSION TRUST OF CHICAGO
221 N La Salle St Ste 200, Chicago, IL 60601-1273
Tel (312) 782-5442 *Founded/Ownrshp* 1931
Sales NA *EMP* 27
SIC 6371 6282 Pension funds; Investment advice
Ch: William T Devane Jr

ELECTRICAL WHOLESALERS
See US ELECTRICAL SERVICES INC

D-U-N-S 82-883-3629
ELECTRICAL WHOLESALERS METRO DC INC
MAURICE ELECTRICAL SUPPLY CO.
6500a Sheriff Rd, Landover, MD 20785-4362
Tel (301) 333-5990 *Founded/Ownrshp* 2008
Sales 106.7MM^E *EMP* 131
SIC 5063

ELECTRO KINETICS DIVISION
See PACIFIC SCIENTIFIC CO INC

D-U-N-S 10-739-2060
ELECTRO MANAGEMENT CORP
111 Jackson Ave, Des Moines, IA 50315-1226
Tel (515) 288-6774 *Founded/Ownrshp* 1935
Sales 141.4MM^E *EMP* 532
SIC 1731 General electrical contractor
Pr: Britt Baker
**Pr:* Dave Hearn
**CFO:* Patty Skokan
**Treas:* Patty J Skokan
**Ex VP:* John Layland
**VP:* Don Stockton

D-U-N-S 05-399-9009
ELECTRO RENT CORP
6060 Sepulveda Blvd # 300, Van Nuys, CA 91411-2512
Tel (818) 786-2525 *Founded/Ownrshp* 2016
Sales 175.3MM *EMP* 410^E
Accts Deloitte & Touche Llp Los Ang
SIC 7359 7377 5065 5045 Electronic equipment rental, except computers; Computer rental & leasing; Electronic parts & equipment; Computers & accessories, personal & home entertainment
CEO: Steven Markheim
**CFO:* Allen Sciarillo

D-U-N-S 00-903-1485 IMP
▲ ELECTRO SCIENTIFIC INDUSTRIES INC
13900 Nw Science Park Dr, Portland, OR 97229-5411
Tel (503) 641-4141 *Founded/Ownrshp* 1944
Sales 184.3MM *EMP* 698
Accts Deloitte & Touche Llp Portlan
Tkr Sym ESIO *Exch* NGS
SIC 3826 Laser scientific & engineering instruments
Pr: Edward C Grady
**Ch Bd:* Richard H Wills
CFO: Paul Oldham
Chf Mktg O: James Latham
Sr VP: Robert Debakker
Sr VP: Robert M Debakker
VP: Michael Darwin
VP: Bing-FAI Wong
Snr Sftwr: Tobin Hall
Snr Sftwr: Alexander Myachin
Dir IT: Lance Litmer
Board of Directors: Frederick A Ball, Laurence E Cramer, Raymond A Link, John Medica, Robert R Walker

ELECTRO SWITCH BUSINESS TRUST
See ELECTRO SWITCH CORP

D-U-N-S 08-042-0475
ELECTRO SWITCH BUSINESS TRUST
775 Pleasant St Ste 1, Weymouth, MA 02189-2301
Tel (781) 335-1195 *Founded/Ownrshp* 2000
Sales 93.8MM^E *EMP* 504^E
SIC 6733 Trusts
Prin: Robert Pineau
Prin: David Donovan
Prin: Robert James
Prin: Ken Lloyd
Prin: Lisa Richardson

D-U-N-S 00-104-0542
ELECTRO SWITCH CORP
ELECTRO SWITCH BUSINESS TRUST
(*Suby of* ELECTRO SWITCH BUSINESS TRUST) ★
775 Pleasant St Ste 1, Weymouth, MA 02189-2301
Tel (781) 335-1195 *Founded/Ownrshp* 1946, 2000
Sales 92.3MM^E *EMP* 450
SIC 3613 3625

D-U-N-S 06-081-5503
■ ELECTRO-BIOLOGY INC
(*Suby of* ZIMMER BIOMET) ★
100 Interpace Pkwy Ste 1, Parsippany, NJ 07054-1149
Tel (973) 299-9022 *Founded/Ownrshp* 1987
Sales 120.1MM^E *EMP* 1,504
SIC 3841 Surgical & medical instruments
Pr: James R Pastena
VP: Peter Dambach
**VP:* Bartolome Gamundi
VP: Sue Greenspan
VP: Marshall Perez
VP Sls: Chris Denicola

ELECTRO-MATIC PRODUCTS
See ELECTRO-MATIC VENTURES INC

D-U-N-S 06-558-4195 IMP
ELECTRO-MATIC VENTURES INC
ELECTRO-MATIC PRODUCTS
23409 Industrial Park Ct, Farmington Hills, MI 48335-2849
Tel (248) 478-1182 *Founded/Ownrshp* 1972
Sales 133.0MM^E *EMP* 111
Accts Metzler Locricchio Serra & Com
SIC 5063 3674 Electrical apparatus & equipment; Semiconductors & related devices
Pr: James C Baker Jr
**Treas:* David Scaglione
Sls Mgr: Mike Longo
Board of Directors: Tom C Moore, Raymond J Persia

D-U-N-S 02-366-5995 EXP
ELECTRO-MECHANICAL CORP
METAL CASTINGS CO
329 Williams St, Bristol, VA 24201-4558
Tel (276) 669-9428 *Founded/Ownrshp* 1958
Sales 208.3MM^E *EMP* 636
SIC 3612 5063 3829 3822 3613 3354 Transformers, except electric; Electrical apparatus & equipment; Measuring & controlling devices; Auto controls regulating residntl & coml environmt & applncs; Switchgear & switchboard apparatus; Aluminum extruded products
Pr: Russell F Leonard
**Pr:* Morris Arnold
**CFO:* Neil Richards
**Ch:* Francis L Leonard
**VP:* Tom Davenport
**VP:* Roger L Leonard
VP: Russell Leonard
VP: Steve Park
Genl Mgr: Scott Bullock
CIO: Mary Burkhammer
QA Dir: Robert Spiegel

ELECTRO-MECHANICAL DIVISION
See CURTISS-WRIGHT ELECTRO-MECHANICAL CORP

D-U-N-S 62-346-6773 IMP
ELECTROCRAFT INC
(*Suby of* DMI TECHNOLOGY CORP) ★
1 Progress Dr, Dover, NH 03820-5450
Tel (603) 742-3330 *Founded/Ownrshp* 2004
Sales 137.8MM^E *EMP* 408
SIC 3625 3621 Relays & industrial controls; Electric motor & generator parts
Pr: James Elsner
VP: Kelly Wilks
**Prin:* Logan D Delany Jr
Genl Mgr: Philip Martin
Mfg Dir: Richard Nelson
Mtls Mgr: Michael Smith
Opers Mgr: Melissa Rhodes
Plnt Mgr: Douglas Cook
VP Sls: Rob Kerber
VP Sls: Stephen Prochazka

D-U-N-S 15-147-3063 IMP/EXP
ELECTROIMPACT INC
4413 Chennault Beach Rd, Mukilteo, WA 98275-5048
Tel (425) 348-8090 *Founded/Ownrshp* 1986
Sales 192.9MM^E *EMP* 600
SIC 3542 Machine tools, metal forming type; Riveting machines
Pr: Peter Zieve
**VP:* John Hartmann

D-U-N-S 83-118-6890 IMP/EXP
ELECTROLUX HOME CARE PRODUCTS INC
AB ELECTROLUX
(*Suby of* ELECTROLUX INTERNATIONAL CO) ★
10200 David Taylor Dr, Charlotte, NC 28262-2373
Tel (980) 236-2000 *Founded/Ownrshp* 2001
Sales 165.1MM^E *EMP* 323
SIC 5064 Electric household appliances; Vacuum cleaners, household
Sr VP: Marty O'Gorman
VP: Tony Ritter
**VP:* G C Weigand
VP Sls: Micheal Piraino
Manager: Jay Rollie

D-U-N-S 80-483-3564 IMP/EXP
ELECTROLUX HOME PRODUCTS INC
(*Suby of* ELECTROLUX INTERNATIONAL CO) ★
10200 David Taylor Dr, Charlotte, NC 28262-2373
Tel (980) 236-2000 *Founded/Ownrshp* 2000
Sales 3.8MMM^E *EMP* 8,000
SIC 5064 Electric household appliances
Prin: Keith McLoughlins
COO: Jan Brockmann
CFO: Tomas Eliasson
Ex VP: Henrik Bergstrm
Sr VP: Marykay Kopf
**Sr VP:* Richard Pietch
VP: Catarina Ihre
VP: Mary Kopf
VP: Ronald E Zajaczkowski
Dir Risk M: Stephen Brown
Div Mgr: Steven Mahler

ELECTROLUX INTERNATIONAL CO
See ELECTROLUX NORTH AMERICA INC

D-U-N-S 02-850-9094 EXP
ELECTROLUX NORTH AMERICA INC
ELECTROLUX INTERNATIONAL CO
(*Suby of* AB ELECTROLUX)
10200 David Taylor Dr, Charlotte, NC 28262-2373
Tel (980) 236-2000 *Founded/Ownrshp* 1999
Sales 7.1MMM^E *EMP* 22,000
SIC 3631 3585 3632 3633 3635 3639 Electric ranges, domestic; Air conditioning units, complete: domestic or industrial; Freezers, home & farm; Household laundry equipment; Household vacuum cleaners; Dishwashing machines, household
CEO: Keith McLoughlin
**Pr:* Johan Bygge
**CFO:* George Weigand
**Sr VP:* Robert E Cook
Sr VP: Nolan Pike
**Sr VP:* Olle Wallen
Sr VP: John Weinstock
**Sr VP:* Ron Zajaczkowski
VP: Robert Brunozzi
VP: Bjorn V Jensen
VP: Kenn Maas
**VP:* Mark W Russell
VP: Joon So

ELECTROMARK COMPANY
See BRADY WORLDWIDE INC

D-U-N-S 05-244-3652
ELECTROMOTIVE INC
4880 Hudson Dr, Stow, OH 44224-1708
Tel (330) 688-6494 *Founded/Ownrshp* 2016
Sales 158.3MM^E *EMP* 400^E
SIC 3679 3677 Solenoids for electronic applications; Electronic coils, transformers & other inductors
CEO: Michael Piglia
**CFO:* Jeffrey Bissell

D-U-N-S 07-319-9531
▲ ELECTRONIC ARTS INC
209 Redwood Shores Pkwy, Redwood City, CA 94065-1175
Tel (650) 628-1500 *Founded/Ownrshp* 1982
Sales 4.4MMM *EMP* 8,500
Accts Kpmg Llp Santa Clara Califor
Tkr Sym EA *Exch* NGS
SIC 7372 Home entertainment computer software
CEO: Andrew Wilson
**Ch Bd:* Lawrence F Probst III
CFO: Blake Jorgensen
Chf Cred: Peter R Moore
Chf Mktg O: Christopher Bruzzo
Ofcr: Gabrielle Toledano
Ex VP: Joel Linzner
Ex VP: Laura Miele
Ex VP: Patrick Soderlund
Sr VP: Kenneth A Barker
Sr VP: Jacob J Schatz
Sr VP: Samantha Smith
VP: Steve Bena
VP: Steve Bene
VP: Bill Mooney
VP: Samantha Ryan
VP: Mike Williams
Board of Directors: Leonard S Coleman, Jay C Hoag, Jeffrey T Huber, Richard A Simonson, Luis A Ubinas, Denise F Warren

D-U-N-S 13-539-6237
■ ELECTRONIC ARTS REDWOOD INC
EA SPORTS
(*Suby of* ELECTRONIC ARTS INC) ★
209 Redwood Shores Pkwy, Redwood City, CA 94065-1175
Tel (650) 628-1500 *Founded/Ownrshp* 2001
Sales 2.9MM *EMP* 1,000^E
SIC 3695 Video recording tape, blank
CEO: Larry Probst
Mktg Mgr: Elon Cohen
Mktg Mgr: Christy Huender
Mktg Mgr: Michael Johnson

D-U-N-S 09-436-5772 IMP
■ ELECTRONIC ASSEMBLY CORP (NC)
(*Suby of* PLEXUS CORP) ★
55 Jewelers Park Dr, Neenah, WI 54956-3768
Tel (920) 722-3451 *Founded/Ownrshp* 1970
Sales 338.5MM^E *EMP* 2,500^E
SIC 3672 3679 3825 3841 Printed circuit boards; Power supplies, all types: static; Test equipment for electronic & electric measurement; Meters: electric, pocket, portable, panelboard, etc.; Surgical & medical instruments
Pr: Dean Foate
**Pr:* Peter Strandwitz
COO: Steve Gresl
CFO: Steve Deleretto
CFO: Michael T Verstegen
VP: Dave Clark
**Prin:* John Nussbaum
CIO: Timothy Sheraden
CTO: Tom Decoe
Corp Couns: Heather Deneys

D-U-N-S 83-820-7020
ELECTRONIC CLASSROOM OF TOMORROW
ECOT
3700 S High St Ste 95, Columbus, OH 43207-4083
Tel (888) 326-8395 *Founded/Ownrshp* 2000
Sales 105.8MM *EMP* 850
Accts Dave Yost Columbus Ohio
SIC 8211 Public combined elementary & secondary school
COO: Steve Sellers
VP: Christopher Meister
**Prin:* Amy J Borman
Mktg Mgr: Travis Foegler

ELECTRONIC DATA SYSTEMS
See HP ENTERPRISE SERVICES LLC

D-U-N-S 13-036-6172 IMP
ELECTRONIC EXPRESS INC
418 Harding Industrial Dr, Nashville, TN 37211-3106
Tel (615) 259-2031 *Founded/Ownrshp* 1983
Sales 218.2MM^E *EMP* 100
SIC 5064 Electrical appliances, television & radio
Pr: Sam Yazdian
Treas: Ramin Hanai
**Sec:* Abe Yazdian
Doctor: Stephen Dorning

D-U-N-S 00-974-7122
■ ELECTRONIC FUNDS SOURCE LLC
TCH
(*Suby of* WEX INC) ★
3100 West End Ave # 1150, Nashville, TN 37203-1320
Tel (888) 824-7378 *Founded/Ownrshp* 2016
Sales 83.4MM^E *EMP* 7^E
SIC 7371 6099 Custom computer programming services; Electronic funds transfer network, including switching
Pr: Scott R Phillips
COO: Ted D Jones
CFO: Ed Morgan
Treas: Bethany Malakelis
Ex VP: Sott J Bojczuk
Ex VP: Cindy Gamble O'Neill
VP: Linda Byington
CIO: Kevin Farnsworth
Opers Mgr: Kelly Pardee
VP Mktg: Kellie Jones

ELECTRONIC RECYCLERS AMERICA
See ELECTRONIC RECYCLERS INTERNATIONAL INC

D-U-N-S 60-968-0397 IMP
ELECTRONIC RECYCLERS INTERNATIONAL INC
ELECTRONIC RECYCLERS AMERICA
7815 N Palm Ave Ste 140, Fresno, CA 93711-5531
Tel (800) 884-8466 *Founded/Ownrshp* 2006
Sales 551.9MM^E *EMP* 800^E
SIC 4953 Recycling, waste materials
CEO: John S Shegerian

*Pr: Dann V Angeloff
*COO: Kelly Thomas
*CFO: James Kim
Ofcr: Aaron Blum
*Ofcr: Rich Calzada
*Ofcr: Tammy Shegerian
*Prin: Kevin J Anton
*Prin: Keith D Bronstein
*Prin: Yong Seok Jeong
*Prin: Matthew McGovern

D-U-N-S 05-342-6946 IMP
■ ELECTRONIC SYSTEMS INC
E S I
(Suby of GLOBAL IMAGING SYSTEMS INC) ★
369 Edwin Dr, Virginia Beach, VA 23462-4522
Tel (757) 497-8000 Founded/Ownrshp 1997
Sales 516.6MM^E EMP 508
SIC 5044 Office equipment
CEO: Daniel Robert Cooper
Pr: Anthony Lane
Treas: Bob Smith
VP: R Edward Bass
VP: Kevin Kendall
VP: Roxanne Kosarzycki
VP: Jarek Mlodzinski
VP: Andrew Zipprich
Sls Dir: Susan Kreikamp

D-U-N-S 78-935-0154 IMP
ELECTRONIC TECHNOLOGIES CORP USA
(Suby of SCHLAGE LOCK CO LLC) ★
11819 N Pennsylvania St, Carmel, IN 46032-4555
Tel (317) 810-3177 Founded/Ownrshp 2013
Sales 97.4MM^E EMP 600
SIC 5065 5063 7382 Security control equipment & systems; Fire alarm systems; Burglar alarm maintenance & monitoring
Ch: Michael W Lamach
*Treas: Derrick Goins
*Sr VP: Paul Camuti
VP: Howard A Berkof
*VP: Scott Deininger
IT Man: Gary Otto
Sales Exec: Ross Linville

D-U-N-S 08-985-2826 IMP
ELECTRONIC THEATRE CONTROLS INC (WI)
E T C
3031 Pleasant View Rd, Middleton, WI 53562-4809
Tel (608) 831-4116 Founded/Ownrshp 1977
Sales 437.9MM^E EMP 600
SIC 5063 Lighting fixtures, commercial & industrial
CEO: Fred Foster
*Pr: Richard L Titus
COO: Corey Evert
*Treas: Dr Robert E Gilson
VP: Joe Bokelman
VP: Wynne Cheung
VP: Julianne Cymbalak
*VP: Sarah Danke
VP: Dale Hopman
VP: Tera Johnson
VP: Mark Vassallo
Exec: Erik Larsen

D-U-N-S 16-925-1720
ELECTRONIC TRANSACTION CONSULTANTS CORP
ETCC
1705 N Plano Rd, Richardson, TX 75081-1915
Tel (972) 470-5873 Founded/Ownrshp 1999
Sales 139.9MM^E EMP 350
SIC 7371 Computer software development & applications
Pr: Timothy O Gallagher
COO: Giorgio Frondoni
CFO: Jenny Darling
VP: Simon Cheng
VP: Boni Danner
VP: Karen Falk
*VP: Tim Gallagher
*VP: Mickey Myers
VP: Francis O'Connor
Exec: Geoff Spillane
Prgrm Mgr: Jack Rudzinski

D-U-N-S 08-635-2689
ELECTRONIC WARFARE ASSOCIATES INC
E W A
13873 Park Center Rd # 500, Herndon, VA 20171-3223
Tel (703) 904-5700 Founded/Ownrshp 1977
Sales 98.6MM^E EMP 400^E
SIC 7373 7374 3672 3699 3643 3441

D-U-N-S 02-008-1423
■ ELECTRONICS BOUTIQUE AMERICA INC
(Suby of GAMESTOP CORP) ★
625 Westport Pkwy, Grapevine, TX 76051-6740
Tel (817) 424-2000 Founded/Ownrshp 1998, 2005
Sales 2.0MMM^E EMP 280
SIC 5734 Computer & software stores
Pr: Jeffrey W Griffiths
*COO: John R Panichello
*CFO: James A Smith
*Sr VP: Seth P Levy
*Sr VP: Steve Morgan

D-U-N-S 00-731-3440
■ ELECTRONICS BOUTIQUE HOLDINGS CORP
(Suby of GAMESTOP CORP) ★
625 Westport Pkwy, Grapevine, TX 76051-6740
Tel (817) 424-2000 Founded/Ownrshp 2010
Sales 849.9MM^E EMP 30,794^E
SIC 5734 Software, computer games

D-U-N-S 09-176-2547
■ ELECTRONICS BOUTIQUE OF AMERICA INC
(Suby of EB INVESTMENT CORP) ★
625 Westport Pkwy, Grapevine, TX 76051-6740
Tel (817) 424-2000 Founded/Ownrshp 1998
Sales 122.8MM^E EMP 1,400
SIC 5734 5945 Software, computer games; Software, business & non-game; Hobby, toy & game shops
Pr: Joseph J Firestone
*COO: John Panichello
*Sr VP: Jeffrey Griffiths

D-U-N-S 60-232-5755 EXP
▲ ELECTRONICS FOR IMAGING INC
EFI
6750 Dumbarton Cir, Fremont, CA 94555-3616
Tel (650) 357-3500 Founded/Ownrshp 1989
Sales 882.5MM EMP 3,136
Accts Deloitte & Touche Llp San Jos
Tkr Sym EFII Exch NGS
SIC 3577 2899 Computer peripheral equipment; Printers & plotters; Ink or writing fluids
Pr: Guy Gecht
*Ch Bd: Gill Cogan
CFO: Marc Olin
Sr VP: Gabriel Matsliach
VP: Waiman Cho
VP: Frank Tuckmantel
VP: Frank Tueckmantel
Mng Dir: Paul Cripps
Prgrm Mgr: Brian Dahlquist
Dist Mgr: Eddie Wood
Off Mgr: Jo Wakenigg
Board of Directors: Eric Brown, Thomas Georgens, Richard A Kashnow, Dan Maydan

D-U-N-S 07-974-1283
ELECTRONICS ROW LLC
10601 W I 70 Frntage Rd N, Wheat Ridge, CO 80033-2285
Tel (720) 728-5420 Founded/Ownrshp 2015
Sales 225.0MM EMP 10
SIC 5731 Radio, television & electronic stores

ELEGANT BATH, THE
See CENTRAL SUPPLY CO INC

D-U-N-S 79-343-6445 IMP/EXP
ELEKTA HOLDINGS US INC
(Suby of ELEKTA AB (PUBL))
400 Perimeter Center Ter, Atlanta, GA 30346-1227
Tel (770) 300-9725 Founded/Ownrshp 1987
Sales 112.0MM^E EMP 471
SIC 5047 3841 Instruments, surgical & medical; Surgical & medical instruments
Ch Bd: Laurent Leksell
*Pr: Niklas Savander
*Pr: Hans Von Celsing
*CEO: Jay Hoey
*CFO: Hkan Bergstrm
*Ex VP: Ian Alexander
*Ex VP: SA Hedin
*Ex VP: James P Hoey
*VP: Catherine Gilmore

D-U-N-S 02-233-3491
ELEMENT CARE INC
37 Friend St, Lynn, MA 01902-3068
Tel (781) 715-6608 Founded/Ownrshp 1994
Sales 84.1MM EMP 300
Accts Moody Famiguetti & Andronico
SIC 8399 Health & welfare council
Pr: Robert D Wakefield Jr
*CFO: Bob Durante
CFO: Robert Durante
*Treas: John Feehan
Ex Dir: Patti Malinowski
CIO: John Coolong
Mktg Dir: Linda Leblanc
Doctor: Elisabeth Broderick
Doctor: Joanna Duby
Doctor: Eric Reines
Doctor: David Wahl

ELEMENT FINANCIAL US CORP.
See ELEMENT FLEET MANAGEMENT (US) CORP

D-U-N-S 79-021-2125
ELEMENT FLEET MANAGEMENT (US) CORP
ELEMENT FINANCIAL US CORP.
(Suby of ELEMENT FLEET MANAGEMENT CORP)
655 Business Center Dr, Horsham, PA 19044-3409
Tel (267) 960-4000 Founded/Ownrshp 2012
Sales NA EMP 95^E
SIC 6159 Equipment & vehicle finance leasing companies
CEO: Steven Hudson
*CFO: Michel Beland
*CFO: Bruce Smith
Chf Cred: Bruce Ells
Ex VP: Dan Kramer
Sr VP: Patrick Neary
VP: Rick Atherholt
*VP: Mr Curt Freifelder
VP: Matthew Hieber
VP: Craig Jackson
VP: Dennis Johnson
VP: Robert Levitsky

D-U-N-S 01-483-7902
ELEMENT VEHICLE MANAGEMENT SERVICES GROUP LLC
PHH ARVAL
(Suby of ELEMENT FINANCIAL US CORP) ★
940 Ridgebrook Rd, Sparks, MD 21152-9390
Tel (410) 771-1900 Founded/Ownrshp 2014
Sales NA EMP 1,216^E
SIC 6141 Financing: automobiles, furniture, etc., not a deposit bank
Pr: James Halliday
*COO: Thomas Keilty
*CFO: John Yeldezian
*Sr VP: Gary Anderson
*Sr VP: Ted Carter
Sr VP: James R Halliday
VP: David J Zuidema

D-U-N-S 03-886-4682
ELEMENT VEHICLE MANAGEMENT SERVICES LLC
PHH ARVAL
(Suby of PHH ARVAL) ★
940 Ridgebrook Rd, Sparks, MD 21152-9390
Tel (410) 771-1900 Founded/Ownrshp 2005
Sales 157.4MM^E EMP 1,200^E
SIC 7513 7515

D-U-N-S 07-955-5191
■ ELEMENT14 US HOLDINGS INC
(Suby of PREMIER FARNELL LIMITED)
4180 Highlander Pkwy, Richfield, OH 44286-9352
Tel (330) 523-4280 Founded/Ownrshp 2012
Sales 598.0MM EMP 1,043
SIC 5065 3429 Electronic parts & equipment; Nozzles, fire fighting
Pr: Ralf Buehler
*Treas: Paul M Barlak
*VP: Joseph R Daprile

D-U-N-S 60-606-5936 IMP/EXP
ELEMENTIS GLOBAL LLC
ELEMENTIS SPECIALITIES
(Suby of ELEMENTIS PLC)
469 Old Trenton Rd, East Windsor, NJ 08512-5601
Tel (609) 443-2000 Founded/Ownrshp 1994
Sales 184.2MM^E EMP 513
SIC 2899 Vegetable oils, vulcanized or sulfurized
Pr: Dennis Valentino
*Pr: Greg McClatchy
*VP: Gary Castellino
*VP: Ling Dawes

ELEMENTIS SPECIALITIES
See ELEMENTIS GLOBAL LLC

D-U-N-S 60-945-4954 IMP/EXP
ELEMENTIS SPECIALTIES INC
(Suby of ELEMENTIS PLC)
469 Old Trenton Rd, East Windsor, NJ 08512-5601
Tel (609) 443-2000 Founded/Ownrshp 1997
Sales 154.8MM^E EMP 572
SIC 2851 8731 2899 2865 2816 Paints & paint additives; Commercial physical research; Chemical preparations; Cyclic crudes & intermediates; Inorganic pigments
Pr: Neil Carr
*COO: William J French
VP: Jim Gambino
Genl Mgr: Eric Post
CIO: Brad Rector
IT Man: Grant Rauch
Site Mgr: Steven Payne
Mktg Mgr: Rose Burke

D-U-N-S 07-850-4660
ELEMETAL LLC
15850 Dallas Pkwy, Dallas, TX 75248-3308
Tel (214) 956-7600 Founded/Ownrshp 2008
Sales 129.7MM^E EMP 350
SIC 3341 3356 3339 Secondary precious metals; Nonferrous rolling & drawing; Primary nonferrous metals
*CFO: Alan Buehler

ELEPHANT BAR RESTAURANT
See SB RESTAURANT CO

ELEPHANT STRUCTURES
See CMD SALES LLC

D-U-N-S 07-943-2096
ELEVATE CREDIT INC
4150 Intl Plz Ste 300, Fort Worth, TX 76109
Tel (817) 928-1500 Founded/Ownrshp 2014
Sales NA EMP 445
SIC 6141 Licensed loan companies, small
Ch Bd: Kenneth E Rees
*COO: Jason Harvison
CFO: Christopher Lutes
Chf Cred: Walt Ramsey
Chf Mktg O: Greg Hall
Sr VP: Rex Northen
CIO: Joan Kuehl
Board of Directors: John C Dean, Stephen B Galasso, Michael L Goguen, Tyler Head, Robert L Johnson, John C Rosenberg, Saundra Schrock, Stephen J Shaper

D-U-N-S 07-949-7537
ELF BEAUTY INC
570 10th St, Oakland, CA 94607-4038
Tel (510) 778-7787 Founded/Ownrshp 2004
Sales 191.4MM EMP 231
Tkr Sym ELF Exch NYS
SIC 5999 Cosmetics
*Ch Bd: Tarang P Amin
*Pr: John P Bailey
*Chf Cred: Richard F Baruch Jr
*Chf Mktg O: Erin C Daley
*Sr VP: Jonathan T Fieldman
*Sr VP: Scott K Milsten
Board of Directors: Lauren Cooks Levitan, William E McGlashan Jr, Kirk L Perry, Joseph A Shamah, Sabrina L Simmons, Maureen C Watson, Richard G Wolford

ELFORD CONSTRUCTION SERVICES
See ELFORD INC

D-U-N-S 00-885-0414
ELFORD INC (OH)
ELFORD CONSTRUCTION SERVICES
1220 Dublin Rd, Columbus, OH 43215-1008
Tel (614) 488-4000 Founded/Ownrshp 1910, 1986
Sales 150.7MM^E EMP 200
SIC 1542 1541 8741 Commercial & office building, new construction; Institutional building construction; Industrial buildings, new construction; Construction management
Ch Bd: Jeffrey L Copeland
*Pr: James W Smith
*CFO: Edward Straub
*Treas: Christopher J Fisher
Ex VP: Timothy Davis
Ex VP: James R Johnson
VP: Robert Butler
VP: Kristy Daniel

D-U-N-S 14-464-1867 IMP/EXP
ELG HANIEL METALS CORP
(Suby of ELG HANIEL GMBH)
369 River Rd, McKeesport, PA 15132-3882
Tel (412) 672-9200 Founded/Ownrshp 2008
Sales 83.7MM^E EMP 235
SIC 5093 5051 Ferrous metal scrap & waste; Steel
CEO: Simon Merrills
*Sec: David R Reichenecker
*VP: Brown Terence
Genl Mgr: Andres Montes
IT Man: Rick Landram

D-U-N-S 01-501-7395 IMP/EXP
ELG METALS INC
(Suby of ELG HANIEL METALS CORP) ★
369 River Rd, McKeesport, PA 15132-3882
Tel (412) 672-9200 Founded/Ownrshp 1985
Sales 83.5MM^E EMP 225
SIC 5093 3341

D-U-N-S 06-800-7491
ELGIN COMMUNITY COLLEGE
(Suby of ILLINOIS COMMUNITY COLLEGE BD) ★
1700 Spartan Dr, Elgin, IL 60123-7193
Tel (847) 697-1000 Founded/Ownrshp 1949
Sales 24.2MM EMP 1,300^E
Accts Sikich Naperville Illinois
SIC 8222 8221 9411 Junior college; Colleges universities & professional schools; Administration of educational programs
Pr: David Sam
Pr: Kathleen J Stover
Bd of Dir: Clare Ollayos
Ofcr: Christopher J Springborn
VP: David Bluestein
VP: Rose Digerlando
Exec: Janelle Crowley
Ex Dir: Philip Garber
Mng Dir: Andrea Lehmacher
Store Mgr: Kelly Strossner
Off Admin: Cynthia A Luc

D-U-N-S 96-770-7659
ELGIN EQUIPMENT GROUP LLC
(Suby of AUDAX GROUP LP) ★
2001 Bttrfeld Rd Ste 1020, Downers Grove, IL 60515
Tel (630) 434-7200 Founded/Ownrshp 2011
Sales 150.9MM^E EMP 518
SIC 3532 Mining machinery
Pr: David Hall
*VP: Kerry Koch
IT Man: Rick Schulte
VP Opers: Tim Lilly
Opers Mgr: Jason Hairston
Opers Mgr: Keith Wilkerson
Prd Mgr: Randy Finney

D-U-N-S 96-983-4204
ELGIN FASTENER GROUP LLC
(Suby of EFG HOLDINGS INC) ★
10217 Brecksville Rd, Brecksville, OH 44141-3207
Tel (812) 717-2544 Founded/Ownrshp 2009
Sales 126.1MM^E EMP 655
SIC 3399 3452 Metal fasteners; Bolts, metal
CEO: Ron Auletta
*COO: Gary Goodwin
Treas: Tena Heller
*VP: Marty Goeree
VP Sls: Pete Chojnacki

D-U-N-S 04-682-2896 IMP/EXP
ELGIN NATIONAL INDUSTRIES INC
2001 Bttrfeld Rd Ste 1020, Downers Grove, IL 60515
Tel (630) 434-7200 Founded/Ownrshp 1962
Sales 92.8MM^E EMP 600
SIC 3532 8711 Mining machinery; Crushing, pulverizing & screening equipment; Engineering services
Pr: David Hall
*Ch Bd: Fred C Schulte
*Pr: Charles D Hall
*CFO: Wayne J Conner
Sr Ex VP: Umberto Vergine
*VP: Lynn C Batory

D-U-N-S 00-521-2303 IMP/EXP
■ ELGIN SWEEPER CO
(Suby of FEDERAL SIGNAL CORP) ★
1300 W Bartlett Rd, Elgin, IL 60120-7529
Tel (847) 741-5370 Founded/Ownrshp 1903, 1982
Sales 194.0MM^E EMP 425
SIC 3711 Street sprinklers & sweepers (motor vehicles), assembly of
CEO: Robert Welding
*Pr: Mark Weber
*CFO: Charles Avery
*VP: Julie Cook
VP: Michael Kim
VP: John Riedemann
VP: Ronald Schmidt
VP: Bev Thies
Rgnl Mgr: Roger Himrod
Genl Mgr: Gary Gembala
Dir IT: Sheila Gee

ELGIN WATCH
See MZ BERGER & CO INC

D-U-N-S 13-329-8427
ELI AND EDYTHE BROAD FOUNDATION
2121 Avenue Of The Stars 30t, Los Angeles, CA 90067-5010
Tel (310) 954-5050 Founded/Ownrshp 1999
Sales 226.7MM EMP 12^E
SIC 8299 Educational services
CEO: Eli Broad
Pr: Joe Biden
Pr: Gerun Riley
Assoc Dir: Emily Gerry
Mng Dir: Dan Katzir
Mng Dir: Gregory McGinity
Off Mgr: Nancy Tierney

D-U-N-S 00-642-1325
▲ ELI LILLY AND CO
Lilly Corporate Center, Indianapolis, IN 46285-0001
Tel (317) 276-2000 Founded/Ownrshp 1876
Sales 19.9MMM EMP 41,275
Tkr Sym LLY Exch NYS
SIC 2834 Pharmaceutical preparations; Drugs affecting parasitic & infective diseases; Analgesics; Veterinery pharmaceutical preparations
Ch Bd: John C Lechleiter
Pr: Sue Mahony
Pr: Jeff Simmons
COO: Joe Meyer
Treas: Thomas Grein

Bd of Dir: Kathryn E Broderick
Bd of Dir: Mark Miklinski
Bd of Dir: Jessi Pitrelli
Ofcr: Timothy Garnett
Assoc VP: Michael Dowd
Ex VP: Mark A Deeg
Ex VP: Steven Paul
Ex VP: Derica W Rice
Ex VP: Johnathan Schilling
Ex VP: Matthew Yates
Sr VP: Alex M Azar
Sr VP: Melissa S Barnes
Sr VP: Timothy J Garnett
Sr VP: Michael J Harrington
Sr VP: Barton R Peterson
Sr VP: Aarti Shah
Board of Directors: Franklyn G Prendergast, Ralph Alvarez, Marchall S Runge, Katherine Baicker, Kathi P Seifert, Michael L Eskew, Jackson Pei Tai, J Erik Fyrwald, R David Hoover, Karen N Horn, William G Kaelin Jr, Juan R Luciano, Ellen R Marram

D-U-N-S 09-000-9457 IMP
■ ELI LILLY INDUSTRIES INC
LILLY DEL CARIBE
(*Suby of* ELI LILLY AND CO) ★
430 Calle Fabril, Carolina, PR 00987-2705
Tel (787) 257-5555 *Founded/Ownrshp* 1965
Sales 150.1MM^E *EMP* 900
SIC 2834 Pharmaceutical preparations
**Pr:* Maria Crowe
**Treas:* Phil Johnson
Ql Cn Mgr: Rey Cordova
Mktg Dir: Martin Consuegra
Sls Dir: Dave Hall

D-U-N-S 07-595-7928
■ ELI LILLY INTERNATIONAL CORP
(*Suby of* ELI LILLY AND CO) ★
893 S Delaware St, Indianapolis, IN 46225-1782
Tel (317) 276-2000 *Founded/Ownrshp* 1943
Sales 310.7MM^E *EMP* 5,500
SIC 8742 2834 8731 3841 2879 Business consultant; Pharmaceutical preparations; Commercial physical research; Surgical & medical instruments; Agricultural chemicals
Pr: David Ricks
**VP:* J A Harper
**VP:* Mark Ryan
**VP:* Richard Smith
**Prin:* James B Lootens

D-U-N-S 01-199-7921 IMP
ELIAS BEN INDUSTRIES CORP
TEMPO INTERNATIONAL
550 Fashion Ave Fl 12, New York, NY 10018-3230
Tel (212) 354-8300 *Founded/Ownrshp* 1962
Sales 165.0MM^E *EMP* 250
SIC 5137 5136 Women's & children's clothing; Men's & boys' clothing
Ch: Irving Elias
**Pr:* Butch Elias
CFO: Susan Witt
**Treas:* Allan Elias
**Exec:* Bobby Elias
Genl Mgr: Howard Sachs

D-U-N-S 09-199-8054 IMP/EXP
ELIASON & KNUTH COMPANIES INC
13324 Chandler Rd, Omaha, NE 68138-3701
Tel (402) 896-1614 *Founded/Ownrshp* 1977
Sales 72.3MM^E *EMP* 1,200
SIC 1742 5032 Drywall; Drywall materials
Pr: Kent Vipond
**Treas:* Brian Baumert
Off Mgr: Lynn Ryan
Prd Mgr: Pat Logelin

D-U-N-S 07-328-9704 IMP
ELIETAHARI LTD
16 Bleeker St, Millburn, NJ 07041-1415
Tel (973) 671-6300 *Founded/Ownrshp* 1987
Sales 257.2MM^E *EMP* 700
SIC 2331 2339 2335 2337 5621 5611 Blouses, women's & juniors': made from purchased material; Slacks: women's, misses' & juniors'; Women's, juniors' & misses' dresses; Suits: women's, misses' & juniors'; Jackets & vests, except fur & leather: women's; Women's clothing stores; Men's & boys' clothing stores
Ch Bd: Elie Tahari
COO: Arthur Bargonetti
CFO: Gera Davidson
VP: Scott Herckis
Rgnl Mgr: Lauren Brodie
Store Mgr: Tasha Hill
Mktg Dir: Dina Koutroumanis
Sls Mgr: Ryan Hansen

D-U-N-S 80-513-4608
ELIM CARE INC
ELIM CARE MINISTRIES
7485 Office Ridge Cir, Eden Prairie, MN 55344-3690
Tel (952) 259-4500 *Founded/Ownrshp* 1927
Sales 121.8MM *EMP* 2,070
Accts Cliftonlarsonallen Llp Minnea
SIC 8051 8322 Skilled nursing care facilities; Individual & family services; General counseling services
CEO: Robert M Dahl
**Pr:* Ronald Sanford
Pr: Jeffrey Wipf
**CFO:* Kathy Youngquist
VP: Dave Kiel
VP: Linda Leitch
Mktg Dir: Joyce Eisenbraun

ELIM CARE MINISTRIES
See ELIM CARE INC

D-U-N-S 07-952-5101
ELIOT COMMUNITY HUMAN SERVICES INC
186 Bedford St, Lexington, MA 02420-4436
Tel (781) 861-0890 *Founded/Ownrshp* 1958
Sales 92.8MM *EMP* 1,300
SIC 8361 8322 Residential care; Individual & family services
Ex Dir: Kate Markarian

**Pr:* Barry Collamore
**Treas:* Ann Duffy
**Sr VP:* Ellen Dalton
**VP:* Joseph Dodd
**VP:* Sheila Ghazarian
**VP:* Melinda Matthews
**VP:* Tammy Odonnell
VP: Kristen Sault
**Prin:* Edward Gaffey
Prgrm Mgr: Lisa Banks

D-U-N-S 04-167-0711
ELITE COMPRESSION SERVICES LLC
10375 Richmond Ave Ste 450, Victoria, TX 77901
Tel (361) 894-6320 *Founded/Ownrshp* 2011
Sales 107.3MM^E *EMP* 78
SIC 1389 Gas compressing (natural gas) at the fields
Pr: Jerry Blackmon
**CFO:* Daniel Savitz

D-U-N-S 02-180-3627 IMP
ELITE FLOWER SERVICES INC (FL)
3200 Nw 67th Ave Bldg 2s, Miami, FL 33122-2239
Tel (305) 436-7400 *Founded/Ownrshp* 1987, 2002
Sales 150.0MM *EMP* 120
SIC 5193 Flowers & florists' supplies
Pr: Juan Carlos Hannaford
**VP:* Sebastian Serrano

D-U-N-S 11-850-7581
ELITE INVESTIGATIONS LTD
538 W 29th St, New York, NY 10001-1308
Tel (212) 629-3131 *Founded/Ownrshp* 1981
Sales 29.4MM^E *EMP* 1,000
SIC 7381 Protective services, guard
Pr: Joseph Saponaro
**Ex VP:* Gary E Weksler
Board of Directors: Kevin Clark

D-U-N-S 79-798-3145
ELITE LABOR SERVICES LTD
ELITE STAFFING
1400 W Hubbard St Ste 2, Chicago, IL 60642-8196
Tel (773) 235-3000 *Founded/Ownrshp* 1997
Sales 497.1MM^E *EMP* 32,000
SIC 7363

D-U-N-S 08-008-4491
ELITE ONE SOURCE NUTRISCIENCES INC
13840 Magnolia Ave, Chino, CA 91710-7027
Tel (909) 902-5005 *Founded/Ownrshp* 2013
Sales 127.6MM^E *EMP* 204^E
SIC 8049 8099 3999 Nutritionist; Nutrition services; Atomizers, toiletry
Pr: Tom Burnell

D-U-N-S 04-673-3265
ELITE PACIFIC PROPERTIES LLC
4211 Waialae Ave Ste 106, Honolulu, HI 96816-5300
Tel (808) 589-2040 *Founded/Ownrshp* 2014
Sales 561.0MM *EMP* 13
SIC 6512 6531 Nonresidential building operators; Real estate agents & managers

D-U-N-S 01-565-1631
ELITE SHOW SERVICES INC
2878 Camino Del Rio S # 260, San Diego, CA 92108-3855
Tel (619) 574-1589 *Founded/Ownrshp* 1995
Sales 69.4MM^E *EMP* 3,123
SIC 7381 Security guard service
Pr: John Kontopuls
Sr VP: Nicole Stichka
**VP:* Gus Kontopuls
Sales Exec: Diane Yoshida

D-U-N-S 18-289-3370 IMP/EXP
ELITE SPICE INC
7151 Montevideo Rd, Jessup, MD 20794-9308
Tel (410) 796-1900 *Founded/Ownrshp* 1988
Sales 115.6MM^E *EMP* 410
SIC 2099 Spices, including grinding; Chili pepper or powder; Seasonings: dry mixes
**Treas:* Anton Samuel
VP: Paul Kurpe
VP: George Meyer
Rgnl Mgr: Joe Freiert
Rgnl Mgr: Andrew Wales
Telecom Ex: Donna Duvall
MIS Dir: Robert Cloney
Dir IT: Bob Clooney
Dir IT: Peter Gyening
Ql Cn Mgr: Ginny Kunkel
Sls Mgr: Tony Grenis

ELITE STAFFING
See ELITE LABOR SERVICES LTD

ELITELCKCOM WE SIMPLIFY GAMING
See ELITELUCK.COM INC

D-U-N-S 07-978-4502
ELITELUCK.COM INC
ELITELCKCOM WE SIMPLIFY GAMING
10510 62nd Rd Apt 1d, Forest Hills, NY 11375-1120
Tel (718) 938-1203 *Founded/Ownrshp* 2013
Sales 384.0MM *EMP* 4
SIC 7311 Advertising agencies
Pr: Victor Daniel

D-U-N-S 01-085-6514
ELIZA COFFEE MEMORIAL HOSPITAL
205 Marengo St, Florence, AL 35630-6033
Tel (256) 768-9191 *Founded/Ownrshp* 2010
Sales 144.4MM *EMP* 100
SIC 8062 General medical & surgical hospitals
Prin: Diane Myrick
**CEO:* Russell Pigg
Exec: Hisham Baalbaki
Nurse Mgr: Terrie McAnally
Doctor: John Reinke
Pharmcst: Mark Donaldson

D-U-N-S 12-101-2645
ELIZA CORP
75 Sylvan St Ste B205, Danvers, MA 01923-2764
Tel (978) 921-2700 *Founded/Ownrshp* 1983
Sales 102.7MM^E *EMP* 201
SIC 5045 Computers, peripherals & software

Pr: John Shagoury
**CFO:* Mark Beucler
CFO: Dawn Chyten
CFO: Jeff Patulak
**Founder:* Lucas Merrow
Sr VP: Chris Couch
Sr VP: Ellen Harrison
Sr VP: Lee Horner
Sr VP: Marc Jeffreys
Sr VP: John Puopolo
VP: Chris Flieger
VP: Bill Meehan
VP: Christopher O'Reilly
VP: Allison Unger
VP: Ian Watters
Dir Teleco: John Hopwood
Dir Bus: Cathy Shea
Board of Directors: David Ament, Kurt Brumme, Alexandra Drane, William Kessinger, Lucas Merrow, John Shagoury

D-U-N-S 79-433-7337 IMP/EXP
■ ELIZABETH ARDEN INC
(*Suby of* REVLON CONSUMER PRODUCTS CORP) ★
880 Sw 145th Ave Ste 200, Pembroke Pines, FL 33027-6171
Tel (954) 364-6900 *Founded/Ownrshp* 2016
Sales 966.7MM^E *EMP* 2,419^E
SIC 2844 Toilet preparations; Perfumes, natural or synthetic; Colognes; Lotions, shaving
Ch Bd: E Scott Beattie
Pr: George Cleary
Pr: Eric Lauzat
Pr: Jue Wong
**CFO:* Rod R Little
**Ex VP:* Oscar E Marina
Ex VP: Marina Oscar
**Ex VP:* Pierre Pirard
Genl Mgr: Robin Mitchell
Genl Mgr: Valerie Riley
Genl Mgr: Natalie Sella
Board of Directors: Fred Berens, Maura J Clark, M Steven Langman, Edward D Shirley, William M Tatham

D-U-N-S 80-267-5447
■ ELIZABETH ARDEN SALON-HOLDINGS INC
RED DOOR SPA
(*Suby of* ELIZABETH ARDEN INC) ★
222 S Mill Ave Ste 201, Tempe, AZ 85281-3738
Tel (602) 864-8191 *Founded/Ownrshp* 2000
Sales 54.5MM^E *EMP* 2,000
SIC 7231 5999 7299 Beauty shops; Cosmetics; Massage parlor
**Pr:* Todd Walter
**CEO:* John Richards
**CFO:* Robert Broadhead
**Sr VP:* Debbie Foi
**Sr VP:* Charles Ieni
**Sr VP:* Kelly Weber
**VP:* Tad Kossak
VP: Deborah Venuti
Rgnl Mgr: Bruce Valade
CIO: Paul Kaczmarek
Mktg Dir: Inga Pross

D-U-N-S 00-704-1168
ELIZABETH GLASER PEDIATRIC AIDS FOUNDATION (CA)
1140 Conn Ave Nw Ste 200, Washington, DC 20036-4028
Tel (310) 314-1459 *Founded/Ownrshp* 1988
Sales 126.0MM *EMP* 1,000
Accts Lb Bdo Usa Llp Bethesda Md
SIC 8099 8733 Medical services organization; Noncommercial research organizations
Pr: Charles Lyons
COO: Bradley Kiley
Ofcr: Olena Gaponenko
Ex VP: Philip O Brien
Ex VP: Nicholas Hellmann
VP: Laura Guay
VP: R J Simonds
Prin: Nigel Barker
Prgrm Mgr: Thembie Masuku
Snr Ntwrk: Kevin Burr
Board of Directors: Nigel Barker

D-U-N-S 09-221-8882
ELIZABETH PUBLIC SCHOOLS
500 N Broad St, Elizabeth, NJ 07208-3302
Tel (908) 436-5010 *Founded/Ownrshp* 1825
Sales 261.6MM^E *EMP* 4,200
SIC 8211 Public elementary & secondary schools
Board of Directors: Carole Cascio, Carlos Cedeno, Armando Da Silvia, Rafael J Fajardo, Edmund Proctor, Edward R Whelan, Cherry Davis Wilcots

D-U-N-S 07-284-0838
ELIZABETHTOWN COLLEGE
1 Alpha Dr, Elizabethtown, PA 17022-2297
Tel (717) 361-1000 *Founded/Ownrshp* 1899
Sales 108.1MM *EMP* 470^E
Accts Baker Tilly Virchow Krause Ll
SIC 8221 College, except junior
Ch Bd: James Shriener
**Pr:* Theodore E Long
**Treas:* Richard E Jordan
Sr VP: Marty Thomas-Brumme
**VP:* Richard Bailey
VP: David Beidleman
VP: Paul Cramer
VP: David Dentler
**VP:* Susan Traverso
Assoc Dir: Benjamin Goodhart
Ex Dir: Elizabeth Dahmus

D-U-N-S 00-697-2236
■ ELIZABETHTOWN GAS CO
NEW JERSEY DIVISION
(*Suby of* SOUTHERN CO GAS) ★
1 Elizabethtown Plz, Union, NJ 07083-7138
Tel (908) 289-5000 *Founded/Ownrshp* 2004
Sales 223.4MM^E *EMP* 295
SIC 4932 4924 Gas & other services combined; Natural gas distribution

Pr: Hank Linginfelter
Exec: Donald Carter

D-U-N-S 00-697-2244
ELIZABETHTOWN WATER CO INC (NJ)
(*Suby of* ETOWN CORP) ★
7303 Plantation Rd, Pensacola, FL 32504-6335
Tel (251) 656-9857 *Founded/Ownrshp* 1854, 1985
Sales 89.9MM^E *EMP* 427
Accts Pricewaterhousecoopers Llp
SIC 4941 Water supply
Ch Bd: Ann Evans-Estabrook
**Pr:* Andrew M Chapman
CFO: Gail P Brady
Sr VP: Henry S Patterson III
Sr VP: Norbert Wagner
VP: Walter M Braswell
**VP:* James Cowley
VP: Dennis W Doll
VP: Edward D Mullen
Board of Directors: Thomas J Cawley, Anthony S Cicatiello, Edward Clerico, James Hughes, John Kean, Barry T Parker, Hugo M Pfaltz Jr, Chester A Ring III, Joan Verplanck

D-U-N-S 13-575-1936
ELK GROVE AUTO GROUP INC
ELK GROVE DODGE
8575 Laguna Grove Dr, Elk Grove, CA 95757-8711
Tel (916) 405-2600 *Founded/Ownrshp* 2003
Sales 189.0MM^E *EMP* 330
SIC 5511 Automobiles, new & used
Prin: Mark Lasher
Chf Mktg O: Vince Bloom
**VP:* Scott Lasher
Off Mgr: Cindy Emerick-Khan
Sls Mgr: Massad Saeed
Sales Asso: Richard Brown
Sales Asso: Elijah Evans
Sales Asso: Curtis Jare
Sales Asso: Gabe Morales
Sales Asso: Mir Sabir

ELK GROVE DODGE
See ELK GROVE AUTO GROUP INC

D-U-N-S 62-420-4947 IMP
ELK PREMIUM BUILDING PRODUCTS INC
(*Suby of* GAF MATERIALS) ★
14911 Quorum Dr Ste 600, Dallas, TX 75254-1491
Tel (972) 851-0400 *Founded/Ownrshp* 1989
Sales 693.6MM *EMP* 930
SIC 2952 2273 Roofing materials; Carpets & rugs
Pr: Richard A Nowak
**Ch Bd:* Thomas D Karol
**VP:* Gregory J Fisher

D-U-N-S 85-925-2777
ELK REGIONAL HEALTH SYSTEM
763 Johnsonburg Rd, Saint Marys, PA 15857-3417
Tel (814) 788-8000 *Founded/Ownrshp* 1990
Sales 66.0MM^E *EMP* 1,000
Accts Bkd Llp Springfield Mo
SIC 8062 8051 8361 8399 General medical & surgical hospitals; Skilled nursing care facilities; Home for the aged; Fund raising organization, non-fee basis
CEO: Gregory Bauer

D-U-N-S 09-595-8187
ELK RIVER AREA SCHOOL DISTRICT 728
815 Highway 10, Elk River, MN 55330-2549
Tel (763) 241-3400 *Founded/Ownrshp* 1890
Sales 90.1MM^E *EMP* 2,000
SIC 8211 Public elementary & secondary schools
Dir Sec: Laura Masley
Pr Dir: Cory Famson
Teacher Pr: Timothy Caskey

D-U-N-S 05-833-0218 IMP
ELK RIVER MACHINE CO
(*Suby of* CRETEX COMPANIES INC) ★
828 4th St Nw, Elk River, MN 55330-1394
Tel (763) 441-1581 *Founded/Ownrshp* 1972
Sales 95.7MM^E *EMP* 610^E
SIC 3599 Machine & other job shop work
**Pr:* James M Barthel
Dir IT: Bob Becker

D-U-N-S 00-508-0429 IMP/EXP
ELKAY MANUFACTURING CO INC
NEPTUNE LIFETIME SINKS
2222 Camden Ct, Oak Brook, IL 60523-1248
Tel (630) 574-8484 *Founded/Ownrshp* 2008
Sales 849.1MM^E *EMP* 4,300
SIC 3431 3585 3432 2434

D-U-N-S 05-387-6397 IMP
ELKAY PLASTICS CO INC
6000 Sheila St, Commerce, CA 90040-2405
Tel (323) 722-7073 *Founded/Ownrshp* 1990
Sales 114.1MM^E *EMP* 190
SIC 5113 Bags, paper & disposable plastic
Pr: Louis Chertkow
**CFO:* Geoffrey Pankau
IT Man: Vickie Gosnell
MIS Mgr: Vicki Gosnell
Natl Sales: Matthew Banghart
S&M/VP: Dan Kniola
Mktg Dir: Bill Lindamood
Sls Dir: David Bronstein
Mktg Mgr: Jason Kang
Manager: Matt Allen
Sales Asso: Melissa Aguirre

D-U-N-S 09-981-7397 IMP/EXP
ELKAY PLUMBING PRODUCTS CO
(*Suby of* NEPTUNE LIFETIME SINKS) ★
2222 Camden Ct, Oak Brook, IL 60523-1248
Tel (630) 574-8484 *Founded/Ownrshp* 1979
Sales 228.8MM^E *EMP* 3,700
SIC 3431 Sinks: enameled iron, cast iron or pressed metal
CEO: Timothy J Jahnke
**Ch Bd:* Ronald C Katz
Mktg Mgr: Rod Magnuson

D-U-N-S 36-185-3229 IMP
ELKAY WOOD PRODUCTS CO
YORKTOWNE CABINETRY
(*Suby of* NEPTUNE LIFETIME SINKS) ★
1 Medallion Way, Waconia, MN 55387-7000
Tel (952) 442-5171 *Founded/Ownrshp* 1993
Sales 40.0MM^E *EMP* 1,746^E
SIC 2434 Wood kitchen cabinets; Vanities, bathroom: wood
Pr: Thomas Beyer
**Pr:* Tom Cook
**Pr:* Stephen C Rogers
**CFO:* Phil Olphin
Sr VP: Dottie Howard
**VP:* Leslie S Clark
Board of Directors: Stuart Dunnigan

D-U-N-S 00-840-9070 EXP
ELKCORP (DE)
GAF MATERIALS
(*Suby of* BMCA) ★
14911 Quorum Dr Ste 600, Dallas, TX 75254-1491
Tel (972) 851-0500 *Founded/Ownrshp* 1956
Sales 699.7MM^E *EMP* 1,496
SIC 2952 5033 2426 2431 3471 Roofing materials; Roofing, asphalt & sheet metal; Flooring, hardwood; Stair railings, wood; Plating & polishing
Ch Bd: Thomas D Karol
**Pr:* Richard A Nowak
**CFO:* Gregory J Fisher
**Sr VP:* Matti Kiik
VP: Raul Holguin
IT Man: Heath Johnson

D-U-N-S 17-781-6766 IMP/EXP
ELKEM HOLDING INC
ELKEM METAL
(*Suby of* NEH INC) ★
Airport Office Park Bldg, Coraopolis, PA 15108
Tel (412) 299-7200 *Founded/Ownrshp* 2001
Sales 91.0MM *EMP* 337
SIC 3313 Ferroalloys
Mng Dir: Helge Aasen
Off Mgr: Patricia Zyroll

ELKEM METAL
See ELKEM HOLDING INC

D-U-N-S 07-430-6465
ELKHART COMMUNITY SCHOOLS
2720 California Rd, Elkhart, IN 46514-1220
Tel (574) 262-5500 *Founded/Ownrshp* 1997
Sales 201.0MM *EMP* 1,700
SIC 8211 Kindergarten; Public vocational/technical school; Public elementary school; Public senior high school
**Treas:* Douglas Hasler
Dir Sec: James Snyder
Pr Dir: Shawn Hannon
Teacher Pr: W Douglas Thorne
Psych: Annetta Ropp
HC Dir: Anthony England

D-U-N-S 06-470-5015
ELKHART GENERAL HOSPITAL INC
BEACON HEALTH SYSTEM
(*Suby of* MEMORIAL HOSPITAL SOUTH BEND) ★
600 East Blvd, Elkhart, IN 46514-2499
Tel (574) 294-2621 *Founded/Ownrshp* 1909
Sales 274.0MM *EMP* 1,900
SIC 8062 General medical & surgical hospitals
Pr: Gregory W Lintjer
Pr: Diana Stammich
**CFO:* Kevin Higdon
**Ch:* John Martin
**Treas:* Pam Hluchota
**VP:* Danielle Dyer
**VP:* Gregory Losasso
Exec: Jason Oppenheim
Ex Dir: Cindy Hayes
Off Admin: Grace Carpenter
Pharmcst: Darra Cover

D-U-N-S 05-199-5404
ELKHART PLASTICS
PORTLAND PLASTICS
3300 N Kenmore St, South Bend, IN 46628-4314
Tel (574) 232-8066 *Founded/Ownrshp* 2011
Sales 158.2MM^E *EMP* 500
SIC 3089 Plastic containers, except foam
CEO: Jack Welter
**CFO:* Jon Wyngarden
**VP:* Frank Ermeti
**VP:* Chuck Huston
**VP:* Todd Outman
Off Mgr: Cindy Tucker
QA Dir: Janice Woyksnar

D-U-N-S 05-365-8654 IMP/EXP
ELKHART PRODUCTS CORP
(*Suby of* AALBERTS INDUSTRIES N.V.)
1255 Oak St, Elkhart, IN 46514-2277
Tel (574) 264-3181 *Founded/Ownrshp* 2004
Sales 124.3MM^E *EMP* 500
SIC 3498 Tube fabricating (contract bending & shaping)
Pr: Glenn Mosack
**CFO:* Sean P O'Connell
VP: Dale Dieckbernd
**VP:* Larry Johnson
VP: Elaine Laux
VP: Sean Oconnell
Genl Mgr: J M Davis

D-U-N-S 10-840-0292
ELKHORN CONSTRUCTION INC
PROSAFE
(*Suby of* JOHN WOOD GROUP P.L.C.)
71 Allegiance Cir, Evanston, WY 82930-3823
Tel (307) 789-1595 *Founded/Ownrshp* 1995
Sales 306.9MM^E *EMP* 1,300
SIC 1629 1731 1623

ELKHORN PUBLIC SCHOOLS
See ELKHORN SCHOOL DISTRICT 010

D-U-N-S 10-004-8081
ELKHORN SCHOOL DISTRICT 010
ELKHORN PUBLIC SCHOOLS
20650 Glenn St, Elkhorn, NE 68022-2324
Tel (402) 289-2579 *Founded/Ownrshp* 1900
Sales 95.3MM *EMP* 600
Accts Dana F Cole & Company Llp Li
SIC 8211 Public elementary & secondary schools; School board
Ex Dir: Stacey Falk
Pr Dir: Janna Anderson
Teacher Pr: Donald Pechous

D-U-N-S 00-408-3234
ELKINS CONSTRUCTORS INC (FL)
701 W Adams St Ste 1, Jacksonville, FL 32204-1600
Tel (904) 353-6500 *Founded/Ownrshp* 1955, 1986
Sales 144.3MM *EMP* 55^E
Accts Ennis Pellum & Associates Cpa
SIC 1542 Commercial & office building, new construction; Specialized public building contractors
CEO: Barry L Allred
**Pr:* Matthew D Welch
**Sr VP:* J Bill Stinson
VP: Robert Crowe
**VP:* David W Hamilton
**VP:* W Scott Parker
**Prin:* Joseph Newell
Mktg Mgr: Tabatha Collins

D-U-N-S 10-066-2469
ELKO COUNTY SCHOOL DISTRICT
850 Elm St, Elko, NV 89801-3349
Tel (775) 738-5196 *Founded/Ownrshp* 1954
Sales 105.9MM^E *EMP* 2,000
Accts Kafoury Armstrong & Co Elko
SIC 8211 Public elementary & secondary schools
Psych: Tracy Hamilton
HC Dir: Karen Branzell

D-U-N-S 07-258-7736
ELLA E M BROWN CHARITABLE CIRCLE
OAKLAWN HOSPITAL
200 N Madison St, Marshall, MI 49068-1143
Tel (269) 781-4271 *Founded/Ownrshp* 1912
Sales 121.0MM *EMP* 450
Accts Plante & Moran Pllc Portage
SIC 8062 8049 General medical & surgical hospitals; Psychologist, psychotherapist & hypnotist
CFO: Colleen Koppenhaver
Chf OB: David Bryens
Dir Lab: Chris Wetzel
Opers Mgr: John Miller
Orthpdst: Anoop Thakur
Obsttrcn: Mark Walker
Doctor: Rick Gorham
Nrsg Dir: Nan Brown
Pharmcst: James Gardner

D-U-N-S 14-411-1598
ELLER-ITO STEVEDORING CO LLC
1007 N America Way # 501, Miami, FL 33132-2603
Tel (305) 379-3700 *Founded/Ownrshp* 1998
Sales 38.0MM *EMP* 1,500
SIC 7999 4491 Pleasure boat rental; Marine cargo handling; Stevedoring
Sr VP: Christopher Arrocha
VP: Sylvia Guardado
Dir Risk M: Alfonso Johnson
Opers Mgr: Charles Schroeder

D-U-N-S 11-492-5076
■ **ELLERBE BECKET INC**
(*Suby of* AECOM) ★
800 Lasalle Ave Fl 5, Minneapolis, MN 55402-2006
Tel (612) 376-2000 *Founded/Ownrshp* 1976
Sales 110.7MM^E *EMP* 585
SIC 8712 8711 Architectural services; Engineering services
Pr: Mike Just
**VP:* Steve Lichtenberger
**VP:* Steve Loomis
VP: Frank Mastel
VP: Jon Niemuth
VP: Lewis Robinson
VP: Michael C Wood
Prin: Jonathan Hopwood

ELLETT BROTHERS
See UNITED SPORTING COMPANIES INC

D-U-N-S 17-403-5410 IMP
ELLETT BROTHERS LLC
(*Suby of* ELLETT BROTHERS) ★
267 Columbia Ave, Chapin, SC 29036-8322
Tel (803) 345-3751 *Founded/Ownrshp* 2002
Sales 276.9MM^E *EMP* 500
SIC 5091 3949 2499 2541 Sporting & recreation goods; Firearms, sporting; Ammunition, sporting; Camping equipment & supplies; Sporting & athletic goods; Decorative wood & woodwork; Display fixtures, wood
CEO: F Hewitt Grant
**CEO:* Bradley Johnson
**CFO:* Jim McCrudden
Sr VP: Chuck Walker
Prgrm Mgr: Cary Wells
Genl Mgr: Mary Lynn
Dir IT: Mike Eargle
Sales Asso: Beverly Boulware
Sales Asso: Rose Meadows
Board of Directors: Wayne Gibson, Robert Gorham

D-U-N-S 16-014-4044
ELLICOTT DEVELOPMENT OF BUFFALO LLC
295 Main St Rm 210, Buffalo, NY 14203-2402
Tel (716) 854-0060 *Founded/Ownrshp* 1979
Sales 90.5MM^E *EMP* 249^E
SIC 1522 1542 6531 Residential construction; Nonresidential construction; Real estate managers
CEO: William Paladino
**Ch Bd:* Carl Paladino
**Pr:* Joseph Hannon
VP: Sarah Couch
VP: Kirk Fitscher
VP: Kathy Linhardt
VP: William A Paladino
Genl Mgr: George Letina
IT Man: Joe Hannon
Mktg Dir: David Lacki
Mktg Mgr: Caitlin Krumm

D-U-N-S 83-031-6043
■ **ELLICOTT DREDGE ENTERPRISES LLC**
(*Suby of* MARKEL VENTURES INC) ★
1611 Bush St, Baltimore, MD 21230-2020
Tel (410) 625-0808 *Founded/Ownrshp* 2003
Sales 103.5MM^E *EMP* 200^E
SIC 3731 Dredges, building & repairing
Pr: Peter Bowe
**CFO:* Joseph Wendel

D-U-N-S 10-237-3300 IMP/EXP
■ **ELLICOTT DREDGES LLC**
(*Suby of* ELLICOTT DREDGE ENTERPRISES LLC) ★
1611 Bush St, Baltimore, MD 21230-2020
Tel (410) 625-0808 *Founded/Ownrshp* 2002
Sales 93.1MM^E *EMP* 127^E
SIC 3731 Dredges, building & repairing
CFO: Joe Wendel
COO: Martin Barnes
Opers Mgr: Omar Eid
Sls Mgr: Walter Mather

D-U-N-S 01-825-7472
▲ **ELLIE MAE INC**
4420 Rosewood Dr Ste 500, Pleasanton, CA 94588-3059
Tel (925) 227-7000 *Founded/Ownrshp* 1997
Sales 253.9MM *EMP* 857^E
Tkr Sym ELLI *Exch* NYS
SIC 7371 Computer software systems analysis & design, custom; Computer software development & applications
Pr: Jonathan H Corr
**Ch Bd:* Sigmund Anderman
CFO: Edgar A Luce
Ex VP: Cathleen Schreiner Gates
Ex VP: Limin Hu
Ex VP: Melanie Simpson
Ex VP: Joseph Tyrrell
Sr VP: Brian Brown
Sr VP: Lester Liu
VP: John Aslanian
VP: Lisa Bruun
VP: Susan Chenoweth
VP: Michelle Gable
VP: Wendy Nemeroff
Board of Directors: Karen Blasing, Carl Buccellato, Craig Davis, A Barr Dolan, Robert J Levin, Marina Levinson, Frank Schultz, Jeb S Spencer

D-U-N-S 82-871-5990
ELLINGTON FINANCIAL LLC
53 Forest Ave, Old Greenwich, CT 06870-1526
Tel (203) 698-1200 *Founded/Ownrshp* 2007
Sales NA *EMP* 130
Accts Pricewaterhousecoopers Llp Ne
Tkr Sym EFC *Exch* NYS
SIC 6162 Mortgage bankers & correspondents
Pr: Laurence Penn
**Ch Bd:* Thomas F Robards
CFO: Lisa Mumford
Genl Couns: Daniel Margolis
Snr Mgr: Michael Vranos
Board of Directors: Edward Resendez, Ronald I Simon

ELLIOT, THE
See ELLIOT HEALTH SYSTEM

ELLIOT BEECHCRAFT
See ELLIOTT AVIATION INC

D-U-N-S 13-185-2394
ELLIOT HEALTH SYSTEM
ELLIOT, THE
1 Elliot Way, Manchester, NH 03103-3502
Tel (603) 663-1600 *Founded/Ownrshp* 1890
Sales 206.1MM^E *EMP* 3,400
SIC 8062 General medical & surgical hospitals
Pr: Doug Dean
Trst: Robert Lavery
Sr VP: Joseph Kulle
VP: Michelle Drewniak
VP: Susanna Fier
VP: Sabrina Granville
VP: Susanna Whitcher
Ex Dir: Darrell Grande
Genl Mgr: Michael Deblasi
Off Mgr: April Toomey
Doctor: Garrett Bomba

D-U-N-S 07-399-1085
ELLIOT HOSPITAL OF CITY OF MANCHESTER
1 Elliot Way, Manchester, NH 03103-3502
Tel (603) 669-5300 *Founded/Ownrshp* 1890
Sales 400.6MM *EMP* 2,000
Accts Baker Newman & Noyes Llc Manc
SIC 8062 General medical & surgical hospitals
Pr: Douglas Dean
**CFO:* Richard Elwell
VP: Tate Curti
Dir Rx: Stephen Kavadias
Mng Dir: Lisa Williams
Off Mgr: Joanne O'Connell
IT Man: Eric Johannesson
Software D: Bill Farrell
Opers Mgr: Graham Thompson
VP Mktg: Jennifer Coeman
Pathlgst: John Bissonnette

D-U-N-S 00-972-6399
ELLIOTT ASSOCIATES LP
712 5th Ave Fl 36, New York, NY 10019-4108
Tel (212) 586-9431 *Founded/Ownrshp* 1986
Sales 124.1MM^E *EMP* 1,520
SIC 6282 1382 Investment advisory service; Seismograph surveys
Pt: Paul Singer

D-U-N-S 00-621-3391 IMP/EXP
ELLIOTT AUTO SUPPLY CO INC (MN)
FACTORY MOTOR PARTS
1380 Corporate Center Cur, Eagan, MN 55121-1200
Tel (651) 454-4100 *Founded/Ownrshp* 1945
Sales 466.6MM^E *EMP* 1,200^E
SIC 5013

D-U-N-S 00-677-3691
ELLIOTT AVIATION INC (IA)
ELLIOT BEECHCRAFT
6601 74th Ave, Milan, IL 61264-3203
Tel (309) 799-3183 *Founded/Ownrshp* 1936
Sales 101.2MM^E *EMP* 350
Accts Anderson Lower Whitlow Pc
SIC 4581 5599 Aircraft servicing & repairing; Aircraft, self-propelled
CEO: Wynn Elliott
**Pr:* Greg Sahr
**COO:* Alan Nitchman
**CFO:* Jeff Hyland
**VP:* Richard Baeder
**VP:* Ed Chevrestt
**VP:* Rick Michalski

D-U-N-S 10-631-3851 IMP/EXP
ELLIOTT CO
ELLIOTT SUPPORT SERVICES
(*Suby of* EBARA CORPORATION)
901 N 4th St, Jeannette, PA 15644-1474
Tel (724) 527-2811 *Founded/Ownrshp* 1985
Sales 402.1MM^E *EMP* 1,297
Accts Ernst & Young Llp Pittsburgh
SIC 3563 3511 Air & gas compressors; Steam turbines
Pr: Antonio Casillo
COO: Art Titus
**Treas:* Charles Steinmetz
**Sr VP:* Yasuyuki Uruma
VP: George Adda
**VP:* William K Cox
VP: Brian Lapp
**VP:* Eugene O Sullivan
Area Mgr: Matthew Stitt
QA Dir: John Diethorn
QA Dir: Thomas Ridenour

D-U-N-S 05-718-5928
ELLIOTT ELECTRIC SUPPLY INC
2526 N Stallings Dr, Nacogdoches, TX 75964-1201
Tel (936) 569-1184 *Founded/Ownrshp* 1972
Sales 959.9MM^E *EMP* 1,200
SIC 5063 5084

D-U-N-S 06-223-6989 EXP
ELLIOTT EQUIPMENT CO
4427 S 76th Cir, Omaha, NE 68127-1806
Tel (402) 592-4500 *Founded/Ownrshp* 1990
Sales 105.0MM^E *EMP* 235
SIC 3531 Aerial work platforms: hydraulic/elec. truck/carrier mounted
CEO: James M Glazer
**Ch Bd:* Richard S Glazer
**CFO:* Jamie Hudson
**Ex VP:* John M Glazer
VP: Jonathan Ehly
QA Dir: Nathan Novotny

ELLIOTT SUPPORT SERVICES
See ELLIOTT CO

D-U-N-S 00-893-7641
ELLIOTT-LEWIS CORP
2900 Black Lake Pl, Philadelphia, PA 19154-1018
Tel (215) 698-4400 *Founded/Ownrshp* 1998
Sales 200.0MM^E *EMP* 550
SIC 1711 7349 7353 Plumbing contractors; Ventilation & duct work contractor; Warm air heating & air conditioning contractor; Refrigeration contractor; Building maintenance, except repairs; Cranes & aerial lift equipment, rental or leasing
CEO: Bill Sautter
**Pr:* William R Sautter
**COO:* James A Pizzi
**Sec:* Kenneth G Meehan
**VP:* Stephen D Dadio
**VP:* James A Gentile
**VP:* Joseph J Merkel
Sfty Dirs: Dan Mullen
Sls Mgr: Matt Sutherland
Sales Asso: Rita Reith

D-U-N-S 05-620-7954
ELLIS ATLANTA JIM INC
JIM ELLIS DIRECT
5901 Peachtree Indus Blvd, Atlanta, GA 30341-1630
Tel (770) 454-8200 *Founded/Ownrshp* 1983
Sales 305.9MM^E *EMP* 800^E
SIC 5511 5521 Automobiles, new & used; Used car dealers
CEO: Ellis James W Jr
**Sec:* Billie S Ellis
VP: Wesley Ellis
Exec: Mary Cole
Dir Bus: Ayonna Webb
Genl Mgr: Doug McIntyre
Genl Mgr: David Miles
Off Mgr: Katrina Cole
MIS Dir: Wayne Usserly
Dir IT: Wayne Uery
Sales Exec: William Farmer

D-U-N-S 05-051-5170
ELLIS COMMUNICATIONS KDOC LLC
CHANNEL 56 KDOC
625 N Grand Ave Fl 1, Santa Ana, CA 92701-4347
Tel (949) 442-9800 *Founded/Ownrshp* 1988, 2006
Sales 150.0MM *EMP* 40
SIC 4833 Television broadcasting stations
Sls Mgr: Jeremy Berk

D-U-N-S 06-682-2784
ELLIS HOSPITAL
ELLIS RESIDENTIAL AND REHABILI
1101 Nott St, Schenectady, NY 12308-2489
Tel (518) 243-4000 *Founded/Ownrshp* 1891
Sales 377.9MM *EMP* 3,000^E

SIC 8062 8051 General medical & surgical hospitals; Hospital, professional nursing school; Skilled nursing care facilities
Ch: Deborah Mullaney
Chf Rad: Gary Wood
**CEO:* James W Connolly
Bd of Dir: Linda Breault
Trst: Suzanne C Smith
VP: Patti Hammond
**VP:* Daniel Rinaldi
VP: Paul Segovis
VP: Colleen Susko
Exec: John Barnett
Dir Rx: Martin Killian

ELLIS RESIDENTIAL AND REHABILI
See ELLIS HOSPITAL

D-U-N-S 04-522-9887
ELLISON MACHINERY CO
ELLISON TECHNOLOGIES
(*Suby of* ELLISON TECHNOLOGIES INC) ★
9912 Pioneer Blvd, Santa Fe Springs, CA 90670-3257
Tel (562) 949-8311 *Founded/Ownrshp* 1985
Sales 117.0MM[E] *EMP* 283
SIC 5084 Metalworking machinery
Pr: W J Ellison
**Sec:* Donald Bendix
**VP:* Leonard C Atkins
**VP:* Klaus Rindt

ELLISON TECHNOLOGIES
See ELLISON MACHINERY CO

D-U-N-S 03-970-4135 IMP
ELLISON TECHNOLOGIES INC
(*Suby of* MITSUI & CO (USA) INC) ★
9912 Pioneer Blvd, Santa Fe Springs, CA 90670-3250
Tel (562) 949-8311 *Founded/Ownrshp* 2006
Sales 200.2MM[E] *EMP* 500
SIC 5084 Metalworking machinery
CEO: Timothy Kilty
CFO: Charles Cusumano
VP: Doug Harbord
Genl Mgr: Erick Mustifisch
MIS Dir: Scott Doorne
Tech Mgr: Patrick Ofenloch
VP Opers: Kevin Cruz
Sls Dir: Fraser Marshall
Manager: Tim Tilton

ELLSWORTH ADHESIVS SPCLTY CHEM
See ELLSWORTH CORP

D-U-N-S 08-281-5226 IMP/EXP
ELLSWORTH CORP
ELLSWORTH ADHESIVS SPCLTY CHEM
W129n10825 Washington Dr, Germantown, WI 53022-4446
Tel (262) 253-8600 *Founded/Ownrshp* 1975
Sales 217.9MM[E] *EMP* 172
SIC 5169 5085 Adhesives, chemical; Industrial supplies
CEO: Paul Ellsworth
**Pr:* Paul R Ellsworth III
**CFO:* Dave Woloszyk
**Treas:* Patricia F Ellsworth
VP: Mike McCourt
IT Man: Matt Gilbertson
Mktg Mgr: James P Ellsworth

D-U-N-S 07-865-4603
ELLUCIAN CO LP
4 Country View Rd, Malvern, PA 19355-1408
Tel (610) 647-5930 *Founded/Ownrshp* 2011
Sales 28.8MM[E] *EMP* 1,660[E]
SIC 7373 8741 Systems software development services; Management services
Ch Bd: John F Speer III
Pr: Jeff Ray
CFO: Kevin Boyce
Treas: John T Georges
Treas: Mary Ellen Roth
Sr VP: Paul Cunningham
Sr VP: Jorge Green
Sr VP: Mark D Jones
Sr VP: Holly Kortright
Sr VP: Jack A Kramer
Sr VP: Amy A Turner Ladow
Sr VP: Michelle Lynn Reed
Sr VP: Michael H Wallesen
Sr VP: Darren L Wesemann
Sr VP: Toby Williams
VP: Joshua Eric Dietrich
VP: Valerie L Mead
VP: Thomas Reynolds
VP: Susan L Stern
Board of Directors: Kevin M Boyce

D-U-N-S 02-187-1306
ELLUCIAN INC
4375 Fair Lakes Ct, Fairfax, VA 22033-4234
Tel (407) 660-1199 *Founded/Ownrshp* 2015
Sales 758.0MM[E] *EMP* 3,090
SIC 7371 7373 Custom computer programming services; Systems software development services
Pr: Jeff Ray
Ch Bd: John F Speer III
CFO: Kevin M Boyce
Bd of Dir: Jeff Butera
Ex VP: Alvin Pollard
Sr VP: Paul Cunningham
Sr VP: Joshua E Dietrich
Sr VP: Jonathan Garnett
Sr VP: John T Georges
Sr VP: William H Graves
Sr VP: Jorge Green
Sr VP: Mark Jones
Sr VP: Mark D Jones
Sr VP: John L Kopcke
Sr VP: Holly Kortright
Sr VP: Jack A Kramer
Sr VP: Amy A Turner Ladow
Sr VP: Brent A McCracken
Sr VP: Michelle Reed
Sr VP: Michael H Wallesen
Sr VP: Darren L Wesemann

ELLWOOD CITY FORGE CO
See ELLWOOD GROUP INC

D-U-N-S 00-434-1087 IMP/EXP
ELLWOOD GROUP INC (PA)
ELLWOOD CITY FORGE CO
600 Commercial Ave, Ellwood City, PA 16117
Tel (724) 752-3680 *Founded/Ownrshp* 1910
Sales 774.9MM[E] *EMP* 2,400
SIC 3312 3462

D-U-N-S 94-092-1083 IMP
ELLWOOD QUALITY STEELS CO
(*Suby of* ELLWOOD CITY FORGE CO) ★
700 Moravia St Ste 7, New Castle, PA 16101-3950
Tel (724) 658-6502 *Founded/Ownrshp* 1985
Sales 94.9MM[E] *EMP* 178
SIC 3312 Blast furnaces & steel mills
Pr: Robert E Rumcik
**Treas:* Bentraum D Huffman
**VP:* David E Barensfeld
VP: Richard Schochet
IT Man: Rich Owry
Sls Dir: Mark Martonik

D-U-N-S 79-917-9226 IMP/EXP
ELLWOOD TEXAS FORGE NAVASOTA LLC
(*Suby of* ELLWOOD CITY FORGE CO) ★
10908 County Road 419, Navasota, TX 77868-2379
Tel (936) 825-7531 *Founded/Ownrshp* 2006
Sales 136.3MM[E] *EMP* 340
SIC 3462 Iron & steel forgings
Pr: Richard Allender
VP: Valli Senthilnathan

ELM CONSULTING
See ELM ENTERPRISES LLC

D-U-N-S 15-456-7171
ELM ENTERPRISES LLC
ELM CONSULTING
60 State St Ste 201, Peoria, IL 61602-5154
Tel (309) 671-4300 *Founded/Ownrshp* 1999
Sales 111.8MM[E] *EMP* 1,140
SIC 8748 8713 Environmental consultant; Surveying services
CEO: Lee C Graves
**Pr:* Matt Quinn
**COO:* James Richmond

D-U-N-S 02-545-3440
ELM HURST AUTO GROUP
466 W Lake St, Elmhurst, IL 60126-1418
Tel (630) 833-7945 *Founded/Ownrshp* 1961
Sales 93.2MM[E] *EMP* 300
SIC 5511 Automobiles, new & used
Pr: Hj Schiele
Genl Mgr: Brian Schiele
Sales Exec: Bill Pfeffer
Sls Mgr: Tim Baber
Sls Mgr: Irv Chenderowsky
Sls Mgr: Jack Metz

ELM LOCATING & UTILITY SERVICE
See ONE CALL LOCATORS LTD

ELMCROFT SENIOR LIVING
See SENIOR CARE INC

ELMER A. KNOPF LEARNING CENTER
See GENESEE INTERMEDIATE SCHOOL DISTRICT

D-U-N-S 00-814-9627 IMP
ELMER CANDY CORP
ELMER CHOCOLATE
401 N 5th St, Ponchatoula, LA 70454-2458
Tel (985) 386-6166 *Founded/Ownrshp* 1963
Sales 97.6MM[E] *EMP* 300
SIC 2066 2064 Chocolate candy, solid; Candy & other confectionery products
Pr: Robert A Nelson
COO: Diane Bankston
**CFO:* Robert J Barousse Jr
**VP:* Roch Lemieux
**VP:* Michael J Nelson
**VP:* Michael Sitarz
MIS Dir: Paul Hanson
Dir IT: Dale Flanagan
Sfty Mgr: Jeffrey Bell
Sfty Mgr: Teri Hoover
Manager: Aaron Camp

ELMER CHOCOLATE
See ELMER CANDY CORP

D-U-N-S 03-290-9285
ELMER SMITH OIL CO (OK)
Hwy 183 S, Clinton, OK 73601
Tel (580) 323-2929 *Founded/Ownrshp* 1955
Sales 152.9MM *EMP* 162
Accts Smith Carney & Co Pc Okl
SIC 5171 5411 Petroleum bulk stations; Convenience stores, independent
Pr: Elmer Smith
**Sec:* James A Harris
**VP:* Amy Ross

D-U-N-S 02-772-1612
ELMERS RESTAURANTS INC
MITZEL'S AMERICAN KITCHENS
8338 Ne Alderwood Rd, Portland, OR 97220-6809
Tel (503) 252-1485 *Founded/Ownrshp* 1960
Sales 128.7MM[E] *EMP* 783
SIC 6794 5812 Franchises, selling or licensing; Restaurant, family: chain
Ch Bd: Bruce N Davis
Pr: Dennis Waldron
VP: Jerry Scott

D-U-N-S 06-846-7208
ELMHURST COLLEGE (IL)
190 S Prospect Ave, Elmhurst, IL 60126-3296
Tel (630) 279-4100 *Founded/Ownrshp* 1871
Sales 115.0MM *EMP* 1,055
Accts Grant Thornton Llp Elmhurst
SIC 8221 College, except junior
Pr: Alan Ray
Trst: Harold Mayer
Trst: John Popp
Ex VP: James Kulich
VP: Kenneth E Bartels
VP: Peggy Sandgren
VP: Tina Smith
Exec: John Newton
Sfty Dirs: Tony Leggett
Mktg Dir: Jim Winters

D-U-N-S 80-654-6730
ELMHURST HOSPITAL CENTER
(*Suby of* NEW YORK CITY HLTH & HOSPITALS) ★
7901 Broadway, Elmhurst, NY 11373-1329
Tel (718) 334-2424 *Founded/Ownrshp* 1918
Sales 687.6MM *EMP* 1[E]
SIC 8062 General medical & surgical hospitals
Sr VP: C Constantino
Dir Lab: Sylvia Chin
Assoc Dir: Jackie McCann
Assoc Dir: Dean Mihaltses

D-U-N-S 00-395-3605
ELMHURST MEMORIAL HEALTHCARE
PROFESSIONAL PROGRAM
(*Suby of* EDWARD-ELMHURST HEALTHCARE) ★
155 E Brush Hill Rd, Elmhurst, IL 60126-5658
Tel (331) 221-1000 *Founded/Ownrshp* 2013
Sales 78.8MM *EMP* 2,450[E]
Accts Crowe Horwath Llp Chicago Il
SIC 8011 Health maintenance organization
Pr: Mary Lou Matro
VP: Ken Fishbain
Software D: Shelly Myers
Pharmcst: Amy Johnson
Pgrm Dir: Mike McKenna

D-U-N-S 05-192-1161 EXP
ELMHURST MEMORIAL HOSPITAL INC
(*Suby of* PROFESSIONAL PROGRAM) ★
133 E Brush Hill Rd, Elmhurst, IL 60126-5659
Tel (331) 221-9003 *Founded/Ownrshp* 1926
Sales 379.8MM *EMP* 2,444
SIC 8062 General medical & surgical hospitals
CEO: Pamela Davis
Dir Vol: Denise Panek
**CEO:* Mary Lou Mastro
**CFO:* James Doyle
Sr VP: Lambert Matthew III
**VP:* Pamela Dunley
Dir Lab: Perulle Patel
Off Mgr: Donna Liepe
Software D: Philip Cozzi
Site Mgr: Diane Hein
Pr Mgr: Polly Lleras

D-U-N-S 00-510-0508
ELMHURST-CHICAGO STONE CO
400 W 1st St, Elmhurst, IL 60126-2604
Tel (630) 832-4000 *Founded/Ownrshp* 1960
Sales 136.3MM[E] *EMP* 125
SIC 1442 3273 3272 Gravel mining; Ready-mixed concrete; Pipe, concrete or lined with concrete
Pr: Charles Hammersmith Jr
Ch: Charles Hammersmith Sr
VP: Jeff Brown
VP: Kenneth J Lahner
Off Mgr: Joe Mateas

ELMIRA CITY SCHOOL DISTRICT
See CITY SCHOOL DISTRICT OF CITY OF ELMIRA NY

D-U-N-S 06-833-7708
ELMO GREER & SONS LLC (KY)
3138 N Us Highway 25, East Bernstadt, KY 40729-6139
Tel (606) 862-4233 *Founded/Ownrshp* 1999
Sales 127.9MM[E] *EMP* 300
SIC 1611 2951

D-U-N-S 10-000-0355
ELMORE COUNTY SCHOOL DISTRICT
100 H H Robinson Dr, Wetumpka, AL 36092-5701
Tel (334) 567-1200 *Founded/Ownrshp* 1911
Sales 47.5MM[E] *EMP* 1,200
SIC 8211 Public elementary & secondary schools
Pr Dir: June Serpack
Teacher Pr: Celeste Tilley

ELMWOOD APARTMENTS
See ELMWOOD SQUARE PRESERVATION LP

D-U-N-S 83-253-3017
ELMWOOD SQUARE PRESERVATION LP
ELMWOOD APARTMENTS
(*Suby of* RELATED COMPANIES L P) ★
505 Elmwood Ave, Buffalo, NY 14222-2051
Tel (716) 881-6662 *Founded/Ownrshp* 2009
Sales 28.4MM[E] *EMP* 1,828
SIC 6531 Real estate agents & managers
Prin: Larry Lipton
Prin: Michael Herrington

D-U-N-S 07-854-3133 IMP/EXP
ELO TOUCH SOLUTIONS INC
(*Suby of* GORES GROUP LLC) ★
1033 Mccarthy Blvd, Milpitas, CA 95035-7920
Tel (408) 597-8000 *Founded/Ownrshp* 2012
Sales 152.0MM[E] *EMP* 400[E]
SIC 3575 Computer terminals, monitors & components
CEO: Craig A Witsoe
CFO: Jeff Harrison
**CFO:* Roxi Wen
Chf Mktg O: Trent Waterhouse
**VP:* Kevin Cole
VP: Mike Moran
VP: Randi Moran
VP: Chris Sullivan
VP: Bronwyn Syiek
**Prin:* Bruno Thuillier
Manager: Raimon Chikhani

D-U-N-S 07-157-4552
ELON UNIVERSITY (NC)
100 Campus Dr, Elon, NC 27244-9423
Tel (336) 278-2000 *Founded/Ownrshp* 1889
Sales 262.6MM *EMP* 1,200[E]
Accts Grant Thornton Llp Charlotte
SIC 8221 University
Pr: Leo M Lambert
**Ch Bd:* William NP Herbert
**V Ch Bd:* Kerrii Brown Anderson
**Ex VP:* Gerald Francis
**Sr VP:* Gerald Whittington
**VP:* Holly Berry
Exec: Donna Van Bodegraven
Assoc Dir: Andrus Jim
Assoc Dir: Melissa Jordan
Assoc Dir: Catherine King
Assoc Dir: Zaire McCoy
Assoc Dir: Carolyn Nelson

D-U-N-S 19-144-1500 IMP
ELRAC LLC
(*Suby of* ENTERPRISE RENT-A-CAR) ★
1550 Route 23, Wayne, NJ 07470-7516
Tel (973) 709-2499 *Founded/Ownrshp* 1988
Sales 91.2MM[E] *EMP* 1,800
SIC 7514 7515 5511 5521 Rent-a-car service; Passenger car leasing; Automobiles, new & used; Used car dealers
Genl Mgr: Pam Nicholson
Treas: Andrew Taylor
Manager: Carl Grady

D-U-N-S 11-857-5963 IMP
ELSA CORP
(*Suby of* SAKAMOTO INDUSTRY CO., LTD.)
1240 S State Road 37, Elwood, IN 46036-3023
Tel (765) 552-5200 *Founded/Ownrshp* 1987
Sales 130.0MM *EMP* 500
SIC 3714 Exhaust systems & parts, motor vehicle; Gas tanks, motor vehicle; Cleaners, air, motor vehicle; Motor vehicle body components & frame
CEO: Kiyokazu Sakamoto
**Pr:* Yasuhiko Matsuoka
COO: Earl Land
**VP:* Hideo Nakamura
**Prin:* Takuya Yoshida
Ql Cn Mgr: Michael Derry
Sls Dir: Brad Stewart
Snr Mgr: Scott Pierce

D-U-N-S 00-193-7218 IMP/EXP
ELSEVIER INC
(*Suby of* ELSEVIER LIMITED)
230 Park Ave Fl 7, New York, NY 10169-0935
Tel (212) 633-3773 *Founded/Ownrshp* 1962, 1998
Sales 203.7MM[E] *EMP* 425[E]
SIC 2741 Technical manuals: publishing only, not printed on site
Ch: Youngsuk CHI
Pr: Matt Dobski
Pr: Hajo Oltmanns
**CEO:* Ron Mobed
**CFO:* David Lomas
**CFO:* Stuart Whayman
**Chf Mktg O:* Peter Edelstein
Ex VP: Gerrit Bos
**Ex VP:* Gavin Howe
**Ex VP:* Adriaan Roosen
Sr VP: Tommy Doyle
Sr VP: Anne Kitson
Sr VP: Karthik Krishnan
Sr VP: Sumita Singh
Sr VP: Philippe Terheggen
VP: Yasushi Adachi
VP: Rusty Bausch
VP: David Hamre
VP: Philip Ramey
Exec: Peggy Freeman
Exec: Jennifer Janson

D-U-N-S 12-174-3298 IMP/EXP
■ **ELSTER AMERICAN METER CO LLC**
(*Suby of* HONEYWELL INTERNATIONAL INC) ★
208 S Rogers Ln, Raleigh, NC 27610-2144
Tel (800) 257-9754 *Founded/Ownrshp* 2016
Sales 113.5MM[E] *EMP* 750
SIC 3824 3613

D-U-N-S 80-803-1962 IMP
■ **ELSTER AMERICAN METER CO LLC**
(*Suby of* ELSTER GMBH)
2221 Industrial Rd, Nebraska City, NE 68410-6886
Tel (402) 873-8200 *Founded/Ownrshp* 1984
Sales 176.7MM[E] *EMP* 738[E]
SIC 3829 Measuring & controlling devices
COO: Scott Lohmann
Sls Mgr: Steve Johnson

D-U-N-S 12-598-3887 IMP/EXP
■ **ELSTER SOLUTIONS LLC**
ELECTRIC METER DIVISION
(*Suby of* ELSTER GMBH)
208 S Rogers Ln, Raleigh, NC 27610-2144
Tel (919) 212-4800 *Founded/Ownrshp* 2002
Sales 152.6MM[E] *EMP* 545
SIC 3825 Meters: electric, pocket, portable, panelboard, etc.
Pr: Mark Munday
**Pr:* Mark Fronmuller
CFO: Raymond L Schmidt
Ex VP: Jerry Lauzze
Sr VP: Tom Van Denover
VP: Pat Corrigan
**VP:* Patrick Corrigan
VP: David Hart
VP: John Shumate
VP: Deborah Sinclair
VP: Paul Yarka

ELSTER THERMAL SOLUTIONS
See ECLIPSE INC

ELTECH
See GUNZE ELECTRONICS USA CORP

D-U-N-S 18-629-3577
ELTM LP
D P I
1374 Highway 11, Petal, MS 39465-2140
Tel (601) 583-9991 *Founded/Ownrshp* 2002
Sales 150.6MM[E] *EMP* 200
SIC 5172 Gases, liquefied petroleum (propane)
Pt: Curtis J Dufour
Pt: Mike Howell
Genl Mgr: Melaine Walker

D-U-N-S 16-380-9122
ELWOOD STAFFING SERVICES INC
4111 Central Ave, Columbus, IN 47203-1854
Tel (812) 372-6200 *Founded/Ownrshp* 1995
Sales 145.2MM^E *EMP* 980
SIC 7361 Employment agencies
Ch: David L Elwood PHD
**Pr:* John Elwood
**CEO:* Mark S Elwood
**Treas:* Steven J Hunnicutt
Ex VP: John A Elwood
**VP:* Ella Elwood
**VP:* Michael D Elwood
VP: Brett Flora
VP: David Meyercord
VP: John Morrison
Area Mgr: Robin Killeen

D-U-N-S 07-373-7918
ELWYN
111 Elwyn Rd, Media, PA 19063-4622
Tel (610) 891-2000 *Founded/Ownrshp* 1991
Sales 268.3MM *EMP* 2,500
SIC 8211 Private special education school
Pr: Sandra Cornelius
V Ch: J R Leaman Jr
Treas: William J Dixon
Ofcr: James R Duthie
**VP:* H Scott Campbell
VP: Scott Campbell
**VP:* Daniel Reardon
**VP:* Richard T Smith
Dir Risk M: Marie Johnson
Assoc Dir: Erin Gallagher
Assoc Dir: Angela Sands

D-U-N-S 16-961-5569
ELYRIA CITY SCHOOL DISTRICT
42101 Griswold Rd, Elyria, OH 44035-2117
Tel (440) 284-8000 *Founded/Ownrshp* 2004
Sales 10.0MM^E *EMP* 1,100^E
Accts Rea & Associates Inc
SIC 8211 Public elementary & secondary schools
Psych: Judy Giannuzzi

D-U-N-S 05-434-6887
ELYRIA FOUNDRY CO LLC
120 Filbert St, Elyria, OH 44035-5357
Tel (440) 322-4657 *Founded/Ownrshp* 1905, 1983
Sales 85.3MM *EMP* 350^E
SIC 3321 3369 3325 2821

EM
See MARTIN ENGLE & ASSOCIATES INC

D-U-N-S 16-277-3092 IMP/EXP
■ **EM CLARCOR HOLDINGS INC**
ENGINE MOBILE SOLUTIONS EMS
(*Suby of* CLARCOR INC) ★
60 Prestige Park Rd, East Hartford, CT 06108-1919
Tel (860) 920-4200 *Founded/Ownrshp* 2014
Sales 417.3MM^E *EMP* 1,730
SIC 3714 3492 Fuel systems & parts, motor vehicle; Control valves, fluid power: hydraulic & pneumatic
CEO: Christopher Conway
CFO: Stephen S Langin
CIO: George Taylor

D-U-N-S 18-444-1269
EMANUEL MEDICAL CENTER AUXILLARY
825 Delbon Ave, Turlock, CA 95382-2016
Tel (209) 667-4200 *Founded/Ownrshp* 1970
Sales 234.1MM *EMP* 6
SIC 5932 5947 8699 Used merchandise stores; Gift shop; Charitable organization
CEO: Robert Moen
**Pr:* Jonette Crowell

D-U-N-S 07-465-3270
■ **EMANUEL MEDICAL CENTER INC**
(*Suby of* DOCTORS MEDICAL CENTER OF MODESTO INC) ★
825 Delbon Ave, Turlock, CA 95382-2016
Tel (209) 667-4200 *Founded/Ownrshp* 2014
Sales 236.2MM *EMP* 878
SIC 8062 General medical & surgical hospitals
CEO: Susan Micheletti
**Chf Rad:* Joseph L Higgins
Exec: Misty Terry
Dir Rx: Cindy Lai
**CTO:* Beth Walker
IT Man: Carlos Shepherd
VP Mktg: David Jones
Pharmcst: Tom Sperry

D-U-N-S 07-877-4375
EMARICO INC (AL)
146 Resource Center Pkwy, Birmingham, AL 35242-8095
Tel (205) 545-9362 *Founded/Ownrshp* 2006
Sales 101.5MM^E *EMP* 131
SIC 2392 Cushions & pillows
CEO: E J Marino Jr

EMAS AMC
See EMAS CHIYODA SUBSEA INC

D-U-N-S 96-333-3450 IMP/EXP
EMAS CHIYODA SUBSEA INC
EMAS AMC
(*Suby of* EZRA HOLDINGS LIMITED)
825 Town And Country Ln, Houston, TX 77024-2238
Tel (832) 487-7300 *Founded/Ownrshp* 2011
Sales 205.7MM^E *EMP* 275^E
SIC 1381 Drilling oil & gas wells
Ch: Lionel Lee
COO: Daniel Sack
**Treas:* See Foon Leong
VP: Kenny Campbell
Exec: Darryn Lim
Plng Mgr: Steven Scanlan
VP Opers: Greg Donnelly
Snr Mgr: Haiyan Zhang

D-U-N-S 86-844-9893
EMBARCADERO TECHNOLOGIES INC
(*Suby of* POINTSECURE) ★
10801 N Mopac Expy 1-100, Austin, TX 78759-5460
Tel (415) 834-3131 *Founded/Ownrshp* 2001
Sales 107.8MM^E *EMP* 404
SIC 7371 7372 Computer software development & applications; Software programming applications; Business oriented computer software
CEO: Wayne Williams
COO: Chris Smith
**CFO:* Robert Levin
**CFO:* Michael Shahbazian
**Sr VP:* Nigel Brown
**Sr VP:* Tony De La Lama
**Sr VP:* Raj P Sabhlok
**Sr VP:* Michael Swindell
VP: Lorraine Genecco
**VP:* Steve Haney
**VP:* Robert Lamvik
VP: Nigel C Myers
VP: Jaywant Singh RAO
VP: Robin Schumacher

EMBARQ
See CENTEL CORP

D-U-N-S 62-374-5499
■ **EMBARQ CORP**
CENTURYLINK
(*Suby of* CENTURYLINK INC) ★
100 Centurylink Dr, Monroe, LA 71203-2041
Tel (318) 388-9000 *Founded/Ownrshp* 2009
Sales 2.3MMM^E *EMP* 16,000
SIC 4813 Telephone communication, except radio; Local & long distance telephone communications; Data telephone communications
Pr: Thomas A Gerke
**CFO:* Gene M Betts
Bd of Dir: Thomas Gerke
**Sr VP:* Dennis G Huber
**VP:* Richard B Green
VP: Bob Gronert
VP: Jonathan Robinson
Natl Sales: Darryl Lynn
Pr Mgr: Pat Elmore

D-U-N-S 00-692-1092
■ **EMBARQ FLORIDA INC**
CENTURYLINK
(*Suby of* CENTURYLINK) ★
100 Centurylink Dr, Monroe, LA 71203-2041
Tel (318) 388-9000 *Founded/Ownrshp* 1967
Sales 117.3MM^E *EMP* 1,000^E
Accts Ernst & Young Kansas City Mo
SIC 4813 Local telephone communications; Long distance telephone communications; Voice telephone communications; Data telephone communications
CEO: Glen Post
Pr: William E Cheek
COO: Michael Fuller
Sr VP: Kim McNees
VP: Jeffrey Lynch
Prin: Shelley Obringer
Genl Mgr: Monique Montanino
Genl Mgr: Traci Thornton
Mktg Mgr: Laura Mortick
Counsel: Torry Somers

D-U-N-S 61-005-9482
■ **EMBARQ MANAGEMENT CO**
CENTURYLINK
(*Suby of* CENTURYLINK) ★
5454 W 110th St, Shawnee Mission, KS 66211-1204
Tel (913) 323-4637 *Founded/Ownrshp* 2006
Sales 721.1MM^E *EMP* 5,600^E
SIC 4813 4812 Local telephone communications; Long distance telephone communications; Radio telephone communication
Pr: William E Cheek
Dir IT: Ike Salter
Sftwr Eng: Ravi Baburajan

D-U-N-S 86-744-2295
■ **EMBARQ MID-ATLANTIC MANAGEMENT SERVICES INC**
(*Suby of* CENTURYLINK) ★
100 Centurylink Dr, Monroe, LA 71203-2041
Tel (318) 388-9000 *Founded/Ownrshp* 2006
Sales 148.2MM^E *EMP* 1,059^E
SIC 4813 Telephone communication, except radio
Pr: William E Cheek
VP: Loren Sprouse
IT Man: Hanbin Pang

D-U-N-S 07-873-5272
EMBASSY MANAGEMENT LLC
AACRES
5709 W Sunset Hwy Ste 100, Spokane, WA 99224-9446
Tel (509) 328-2740 *Founded/Ownrshp* 2007
Sales 97.1MM^E *EMP* 2,800
SIC 8741 Management services
Pr: Martin Favis
CFO: Sean Lyman
Exec: Robert Efford

D-U-N-S 02-496-4954
■ **EMBASSY OF UNITED STATES OF AMERICA**
(*Suby of* UNITED STATES DEPT OF STATE) ★
2201 C St Nw, Washington, DC 20520-0099
Tel (202) 895-3500 *Founded/Ownrshp* 1789
Sales NA *EMP* 1,596^E
SIC 9721 Embassies;
**Ex Dir:* Robert M Orr

EMBASSY SUITES
See DOUBLETREE LLC

D-U-N-S 07-922-6832
■ **EMBASSY SUITES CLUB NO 1 INC**
(*Suby of* HILTON WORLDWIDE HOLDINGS INC) ★
7930 Jones Branch Dr, Mc Lean, VA 22102-3388
Tel (703) 883-1000 *Founded/Ownrshp* 2013
Sales 3.8MM^E *EMP* 5,003^E
SIC 7011 Hotels & motels

EMBCC
See SCHUMACHER GROUP OF LOUISIANA INC

D-U-N-S 07-519-9265
EMBLEMHEALTH INC
55 Water St Ste Conc1, New York, NY 10041-0014
Tel (646) 447-5000 *Founded/Ownrshp* 1944
Sales NA *EMP* 5,000^E
Accts Grant Thornton Llp New York
SIC 6324 Health maintenance organization (HMO), insurance only
CEO: Anthony L Watson
**CFO:* Arthur Byrd
Ex VP: William C Lamoreaux
Ex VP: Russell C Petrella
**Ex VP:* John Steber
VP: Jim Albano
VP: Fred Blickman
VP: Jeffrey Chansler
VP: Douglas Cowieson
VP: Shawn Fitzgibbon
VP: Amanda Michelson
VP: David Morin
VP: Michele Podolak
VP: Magali Santacruz
Dir Risk M: Paulette Taylor
Board of Directors: Carl Haynes, Dr Kirtikumar Patel, Richard Berman, Stanley Hill, Catherine Ruiz, Dr Amarliys Cortijo, Ronald Jones, Dr Reza Sabet, Karen J Davis, Judith Keiler, Peter Sacriatos, Dr Alexander Ellman, Dr Gordon Koota, Charles P Wang, John Gallagher, Dr Moshe Labi, Roslyn Yasser, Kevin Gallagher, Morris Lee, Paula Gavin, Dr Margaret Pan-Loo, Paul Gibson, John J O'connor, Sonny Hall, Carol Parry

D-U-N-S 10-619-0127
EMBRACE HOME LOANS INC
25 Enterprise Ctr, Middletown, RI 02842-5201
Tel (401) 846-3100 *Founded/Ownrshp* 1983
Sales NA *EMP* 525
Accts Richey May & Co Englewood C
SIC 6162 Bond & mortgage companies
CEO: Dennis F Hardiman
Pr: Joseph Beacher
**Pr:* Kurt Noyce
**Treas:* Robert Barber
**Ofcr:* Anthony Branda
Ofcr: Bernie Motta
Ex VP: Kenneth Kasnett
Sr VP: Randy Johnson
VP: Kevin Brennan
VP: Jeffrey Cordeiro
VP: Brian Gilpin
VP: Carlos Hernandez
VP: Craig McManus
VP: Joe Veitch
Creative D: Jennifer A O'Neil

D-U-N-S 06-928-3893 IMP/EXP
EMBRAER AIRCRAFT CUSTOMER SERVICES INC (FL)
EMBRAER AIRCRAFT HOLDING
(*Suby of* EMBRAER AIRCRAFT HOLDING INC) ★
276 Sw 34th St, Fort Lauderdale, FL 33315-3603
Tel (954) 359-3700 *Founded/Ownrshp* 1979, 2002
Sales 138.1MM^E *EMP* 420
SIC 5088

EMBRAER AIRCRAFT HOLDING
See EMBRAER AIRCRAFT CUSTOMER SERVICES INC

D-U-N-S 62-015-6260
EMBRAER AIRCRAFT HOLDING INC
(*Suby of* EMBRAER S/A.)
276 Sw 34th St, Fort Lauderdale, FL 33315-3688
Tel (954) 359-3700 *Founded/Ownrshp* 2001
Sales 410.6MM^E *EMP* 1,200
SIC 7699 Aircraft & heavy equipment repair services; Aircraft flight instrument repair
Pr: Gary J Spulak
**CFO:* Christopher J Appleton
**Ch:* Frederico Curado
VP: David Balloff
VP: Scott Kalister
Mng Dir: Phil Krull
Prgrm Mgr: Chris Murrah
CIO: Gilbert Reyes
Dir IT: Gary Spulak
Opers Mgr: Michael Barbagallo
Opers Mgr: Leonardo Itaborahy

D-U-N-S 05-241-9871 IMP
EMBRAER SERVICES INC
(*Suby of* EMBRAER AIRCRAFT HOLDING INC) ★
276 Sw 34th St, Fort Lauderdale, FL 33315-3603
Tel (954) 359-3700 *Founded/Ownrshp* 2008
Sales 191.6MM^E *EMP* 600
SIC 3721 Aircraft
CEO: Gary Spulak
**COO:* Gary J Spulak
Ex VP: Hermann Ponte
Ex VP: Gary Spuluk
VP: Horacio Forjaz
VP: Luiz Lima
VP: Antonio Manso
VP: Carlos Villela
Sls Dir: Patrice Candeten
Sls Dir: Luis Lopes

D-U-N-S 09-847-2947
EMBREE CONSTRUCTION GROUP INC
EMBREE GROUP
4747 Williams Dr, Georgetown, TX 78633-3799
Tel (512) 819-4700 *Founded/Ownrshp* 1979
Sales 190.3MM *EMP* 175^E
Accts Padgett Stratemann & Co Llp
SIC 1542 Restaurant construction; Commercial & office building, new construction; Commercial & office buildings, renovation & repair; Bank building construction
CEO: Jim Embree
V Ch: Rick Crowe
Pr: Frank Krenek
Ex VP: Philip Annis
VP: Josiah Byrnes
VP: Beau Embree
VP: Mark Henderson
VP: Bill Paetznick
Genl Couns: Richard Crowe
Snr PM: Allen Baran

EMBREE GROUP
See EMBREE CONSTRUCTION GROUP INC

D-U-N-S 05-210-4791
EMBRY-RIDDLE AERONAUTICAL UNIVERSITY INC
600 S Clyde Morris Blvd, Daytona Beach, FL 32114-3966
Tel (386) 226-6000 *Founded/Ownrshp* 1960
Sales 340.9MM *EMP* 4,719
Accts Bdo Usa Llp Miami Florida
SIC 8221 Professional schools
Pr: John P Johnson
**CFO:* Eric B Weekes
Trst: Joseph R Martin
Ofcr: Thomas Rice
Ex VP: Marty Smith
VP: Rodney Cruise
VP: Karen Jans
VP: Rick Larsen
VP: Dan McCune
VP: Daniel McCune
VP: Irene C McReynolds
VP: Daniel Montplaisir
Exec: John Watret
Assoc Dir: Eve Fouratt

EMC
See EMERGING MARKETS COMMUNICATIONS LLC

D-U-N-S 09-744-7148 EXP
■ **EMC CORP**
DELL EMC
(*Suby of* DELL TECHNOLOGIES INC) ★
176 South St, Hopkinton, MA 01748-2230
Tel (508) 435-1000 *Founded/Ownrshp* 2016
Sales 24.7MMM *EMP* 72,000
SIC 3572 7372 7371 3577 Computer storage devices; Prepackaged software; Custom computer programming services; Computer peripheral equipment
Pr: David I Goulden
Pr: Jeremy Burton
Pr: Arthur W Coviello Jr
Pr: Chirantan Desai
Pr: Rick Devenuti
Pr: Howard Elias
Pr: Rainer Erlat
Pr: Pat Gelsinger
Pr: Tom Heiser
Pr: William Jenkins
Pr: Harel Kodesh
Pr: Steve Leonard
Pr: Toshio Morohoshi
CEO: David Goulden
COO: Joe Eazor
CFO: Denis Cashman
Treas: Tyler W Johnson
Chf Cred: Marius Haas
Chf Mktg O: Nina Hargus
Chf Mktg O: Jonathan Martin
Ofcr: Mark Lewis

EMC INSURANCE COMPANIES
See EMPLOYERS MUTUAL CASUALTY CO

D-U-N-S 04-152-3598
■ **EMC INSURANCE GROUP INC**
(*Suby of* EMC INSURANCE COMPANIES) ★
717 Mulberry St, Des Moines, IA 50309-3810
Tel (515) 345-2902 *Founded/Ownrshp* 1974
Sales NA *EMP* 2,160^E
Tkr Sym EMCI *Exch* NGS
SIC 6331 6351 6321 Fire, marine & casualty insurance; Property damage insurance; Fire, marine & casualty insurance & carriers; Surety insurance; Accident & health insurance; Reinsurance carriers, accident & health
Pr: Bruce G Kelley
**Ch Bd:* Stephen A Crane
COO: Kevin J Hovick
CFO: Mark E Reese
Chf Inves: Bradley J Fredericks
Ex VP: Scott R Jean
Ex VP: Mick A Lovell
Sr VP: Jason R Bogart
Sr VP: Rodney D Hanson
Sr VP: Aaron M Larson
Sr VP: Robert L Link
Sr VP: Elizabeth A Nigut
Sr VP: Larry W Phillips
Sr VP: Lisa A Simonetta
VP: Ian C Asplund
VP: Richard W Hoffmann
Board of Directors: Jonathan R Fletcher, Robert L Howe, Gretchen H Tegeler

D-U-N-S 60-408-6132
■ **EMC INTERNATIONAL HOLDINGS INC**
EMC2
(*Suby of* DELL EMC) ★
176 South St, Hopkinton, MA 01748-2230
Tel (508) 435-1000 *Founded/Ownrshp* 1986
Sales 20.0MMM *EMP* 60,000
SIC 3572 3577 Computer storage devices; Computer peripheral equipment
Pr: Joseph Tucci
CFO: Stormy Dean
CFO: Colin Patterson
**Treas:* William J Tauber
VP: Andy Bass
**VP:* W Paul Fitzgerald
Dir IT: Bryan Whitehead
IT Man: Joe Bowling
Pgrm Dir: Pellegrini Judith

D-U-N-S 55-627-0528
■ **EMC MORTGAGE LLC**
(*Suby of* BEAR STEARNS COMPANIES LLC) ★
2780 Lake Vista Dr, Lewisville, TX 75067-3884
Tel (214) 626-2735 *Founded/Ownrshp* 1990
Sales NA *EMP* 1,800
SIC 6162 Mortgage bankers & correspondents
CEO: Ralene Ruyle
**Pr:* John Vella
**Sr VP:* Sue Stapanek

D-U-N-S 01-026-5601
EMC NATIONAL LIFE CO
(Suby of E M C NATIONAL LIFE MUTUAL HOLDING CO) ★
699 Walnut St Ste 1100, Des Moines, IA 50309-3965
Tel (515) 237-2000 Founded/Ownrshp 2003
Sales NA EMP 117
SIC 6311 6411 Life insurance carriers; Insurance agents, brokers & service
CEO: Bruce Gunn Kelley
Pr: Alan Dale Huisinga
COO: Eric J Faust
CFO: Keith Roger Troester
Ex VP: John R Kelley
VP: Barbara Williams

D-U-N-S 62-605-9224
■ **EMC REINSURANCE CO**
(Suby of EMC INSURANCE GROUP INC) ★
717 Mulberry St, Des Moines, IA 50309-3810
Tel (515) 345-4541 Founded/Ownrshp 2008
Sales NA EMP 21
SIC 6411 Insurance agents
Pr: Ron Hallenbeck
Brnch Mgr: Jim Fontanini
Tech Mgr: Ronald Zoss

EMC2
See EMC INTERNATIONAL HOLDINGS INC

D-U-N-S 55-647-7982 IMP
■ **EMCARE HOLDINGS INC**
(Suby of ENVISION HEALTHCARE HOLDINGS INC) ★
13737 Noel Rd Ste 1600, Dallas, TX 75240-1374
Tel (214) 712-2000 Founded/Ownrshp 1972
Sales 53.4MM^E EMP 1,500
SIC 7363 Medical help service
CEO: William Sanger
*Pr: Don S Harvey
COO: David Singley
*CFO: Randel G Owen
*Sr VP: Steve Murphy
*Sr VP: Kimberly Norman
VP: Karen Thornton
*VP: Todd G Zimmerman
Obsttrcn: Angel L Iscovich

D-U-N-S 07-256-8108
■ **EMCARE INC**
(Suby of ENVISION HEALTHCARE HOLDINGS INC) ★
13737 Noel Rd Ste 1600, Dallas, TX 75240-1374
Tel (214) 712-2000 Founded/Ownrshp 2005
Sales 304.0MM^E EMP 8,054
SIC 7363 Medical help service
CEO: William A Sanger
*Pr: Todd G Zimmerman
*COO: David Singley
*CFO: Randel G Owen
*CFO: Steve Ratton
*Treas: Kent Fannon
Ex VP: Brit Ferrell
Ex VP: Kirk Jensen
Ex VP: Ross Ronan
VP: Stephen Carson
VP: Lisa Kerich

D-U-N-S 05-664-7050 IMP
EMCO CHEMICAL DISTRIBUTORS INC
8601 95th St, Pleasant Prairie, WI 53158-2205
Tel (262) 427-0400 Founded/Ownrshp 1971
Sales 535.8MM^E EMP 400
SIC 5169 7389 2819 Chemicals & allied products; Packaging & labeling services; Industrial inorganic chemicals
Pr: Edward Polen
*VP: J Korman
*VP: Stuart Levy
*VP: Randy Polen
Cmptr Lab: Adrian Cook
Ql Cn Mgr: David Jepsen

D-U-N-S 15-115-1362 IMP
EMCO ENTERPRISES INC
EMCO SPECIALTIES
(Suby of ANDERSEN CORP) ★
2121 E Walnut St, Des Moines, IA 50317-2264
Tel (515) 264-4283 Founded/Ownrshp 2001
Sales 129.1MM^E EMP 700
SIC 5031 Doors, combination, screen-storm
Pr: Jay R Lund
Prgrm Mgr: Debra Cowling
Dir IT: Hobie Vanvalkenburg
IT Man: Jeff Weeks
Mktg Mgr: Kelly Bakerink
Sls Mgr: Brenda Haney

EMCO SPECIALTIES
See EMCO ENTERPRISES INC

D-U-N-S 07-631-0556
EMCON INC
(Suby of CB&I GOVERNMENT SOLUTIONS INC) ★
2790 Mosside Blvd, Monroeville, PA 15146-2743
Tel (412) 372-7701 Founded/Ownrshp 2003
Sales 21.8MM^E EMP 1,088
SIC 8711 8999 Engineering services; Consulting engineer; Geological consultant
Pr: Eugene M Herson
CFO: R Michael Momboisse
*VP: Donald Andres
*VP: Richard A Peluso

EMCOR CONSTRUCTION SERVICES
See M E S HOLDING CORP

D-U-N-S 92-978-5541
■ **EMCOR CONSTRUCTION SERVICES INC**
(Suby of EMCOR CONSTRUCTION SERVICES) ★
301 Merritt 7 Fl 6, Norwalk, CT 06851-1052
Tel (203) 849-7800 Founded/Ownrshp 1992
Sales 313.4MM^E EMP 700
SIC 1711 1731 Plumbing, heating, air-conditioning contractors; Electrical work
Pr: Jeffrey M Levy

D-U-N-S 05-307-5149
■ **EMCOR FACILITIES SERVICES INC**
VIOX SERVICES
(Suby of EMCOR GROUP INC) ★
15 W Voorhees St, Cincinnati, OH 45215-4834
Tel (888) 846-9462 Founded/Ownrshp 1965
Sales 206.8MM^E EMP 800
SIC 8744 Facilities support services
Pr: Mike Viox
*CFO: Jim Ebenschweiger
*VP: Frank Riley
*VP: Dan Viox
VP: Joan Woodward
Opers Supe: Brian Vandergriff
Opers Mgr: Rick Stahl
Snr Mgr: Larry Dye
Snr Mgr: Denny Harvey

D-U-N-S 85-888-8761
■ **EMCOR GOVERNMENT SERVICES INC**
(Suby of EMCOR GROUP INC) ★
2800 Crystal Dr Ste 600, Arlington, VA 22202-3590
Tel (571) 403-8900 Founded/Ownrshp 2001
Sales 199.6MM^E EMP 1,141
SIC 8741 8711 1731 Management services; Engineering services; Electrical work
Ch Bd: Michael W Shelton
*Pr: Joseph M Gleeson
Pr: Doug Rowles
*VP: Robert Currier
*VP: Edward Dabrowski
*VP: Leara Dory
*VP: Douglas Kachadorian
*VP: R Kevin Matz
*VP: Michael L Rodgers
*VP: Joseph Serino
Exec: John Egan

D-U-N-S 01-710-6386 IMP/EXP
▲ **EMCOR GROUP INC**
301 Merritt 7 Fl 6, Norwalk, CT 06851-1092
Tel (203) 849-7800 Founded/Ownrshp 1987
Sales 6.7MMM EMP 29,000
Tkr Sym EME Exch NYS
SIC 1731 1711 7349 Electrical work; General electrical contractor; Electric power systems contractors; Mechanical contractor; Heating & air conditioning contractors; Ventilation & duct work contractor; Plumbing contractors; Building maintenance services
Pr: Anthony J Guzzi
*Ch Bd: Stephen W Bershad
V Ch: Sheldon I Cammaker
CFO: Mark A Pompa
Ofcr: Richard Franklin
Ex VP: R Kevin Matz
Sr VP: Maxine L Mauricio
VP: Peter Baker
VP: Jeff Budzinski
VP: Mava K Heffler
VP: Rob Krawic
VP: Ron Lemke
VP: Maxine Mauricio
Exec: Hanna Dabrowska
Creative D: Serge Ghio
Board of Directors: Michael T Yonker, John W Altmeyer, David A B Brown, Larry J Bump, Richard F Hamm Jr, David H Laidley, M Kevin McEvoy, M Kevin McEvoy, Jerry E Ryan, Steven B Schwarzwaelder

D-U-N-S 92-978-5806
■ **EMCOR MECHANICAL/ELECTRICAL SERVICES (WEST) INC**
(Suby of EMCOR CONSTRUCTION SERVICES INC) ★
301 Merritt 7, Norwalk, CT 06851-1070
Tel (203) 849-7800 Founded/Ownrshp 1992
Sales 99.0MM^E EMP 506^E
SIC 1711 1731 Plumbing, heating, air-conditioning contractors; Electrical work
Pr: Jeffrey M Levy
IT Man: Sarah Barnes

EMCOR SERVICES
See MESA ENERGY SYSTEMS INC

D-U-N-S 12-224-5046 IMP
▲ **EMCORE CORP**
2015 Chestnut St, Alhambra, CA 91803-1542
Tel (626) 293-3400 Founded/Ownrshp 1984
Sales 92.0MM EMP 543
Accts Kpmg Llp Albuquerque New Mex
Tkr Sym EMKR Exch NGM
SIC 3674 3559 Integrated circuits, semiconductor networks, etc.; Metal oxide silicon (MOS) devices; Wafers (semiconductor devices); Semiconductor manufacturing machinery
CEO: Jeffrey Rittichier
*Ch Bd: Gerald J Fine
CFO: Jikun Kim
CFO: Mark Weinswig
VP: Robert P Bryan PHD
VP: Craig W Farley PHD
VP: William J Kroll
VP: Shane Mortazavi
VP: Paul Rotella
CTO: Hank Blauvelt
VP Sls: David Wojciechowski
Board of Directors: Robert L Bogomolny, Ed Coringrato, Stephen L Domenik, Rex S Jackson, Charles T Scott

EMD
See PROGRESS RAIL LOCOMOTIVE INC

D-U-N-S 00-105-0152 IMP/EXP
EMD MILLIPORE CORP (MA)
(Suby of EMD HOLDING CORP)
290 Concord Rd, Billerica, MA 01821-3405
Tel (781) 533-6000 Founded/Ownrshp 1954, 2010
Sales 1.9MMM^E EMP 6,100
SIC 3559 1541 3999 Pharmaceutical machinery; Pharmaceutical manufacturing plant construction; Atomizers, toiletry
Pr: Udit Batra
Pr: Jean-Paul Mangeolle
Pr: Kevin Sanborn
Pr: Hideo Takahashi
*CFO: Anthony L Mattacchione
*Treas: Monica Elliott
Treas: Paul O'Connor
*Sr VP: David P Hutchinson
VP: Bruce Bonnevier
VP: Andrew Bulpin
VP: James Buntaine
VP: Thomas Cicale
VP: Christophe Couturier
*VP: Dennis W Harris
VP: Roland Heinrich
VP: Geoff Ide
*VP: Peter C Kershaw
VP: Jean-Marc Pandraud
*VP: Jeffrey Rudin
VP: Bob Saturley
VP: Charles F Wagner Jr
Board of Directors: David P Hutchinson, Gerhard Schmitz

D-U-N-S 16-952-0462 IMP/EXP
EMD PERFORMANCE MATERIALS CORP
(Suby of MERCK KG AUF AKTIEN)
1 International Plz # 300, Philadelphia, PA 19113-1510
Tel (484) 652-5600 Founded/Ownrshp 2014
Sales 200.1MM^E EMP 500
SIC 2819 2816 Industrial inorganic chemicals; Inorganic pigments
Pr: Luiz G Vieira

EMD PHARMACEUTICALS
See EMD SERONO INC

D-U-N-S 08-851-4898 IMP
EMD SERONO INC
EMD PHARMACEUTICALS
(Suby of MERCK SERONO SA)
1 Technology Pl, Rockland, MA 02370-1071
Tel (781) 982-9000 Founded/Ownrshp 1982
Sales 262.0MM^E EMP 1,000
SIC 2834 Pharmaceutical preparations
Pr: James Hoyes
Pr: Yariv Hefez
CFO: Lisa Costantino
*Treas: Monica Elliot
*Chf Cred: Gary Zieziula
*Chf Mktg O: Joseph Leveque
Ofcr: Daniel Moynihan
Top Exec: INA Sungaila
Ex VP: Annalisa Jenkins
Sr VP: Allene Diaz
Sr VP: Scott Filosi
Sr VP: Craig Millian
Sr VP: Alise Reicin
Sr VP: David Trexler
Sr VP: Drew Young
VP: Annetta Beauregard
VP: Amy Broidrick
VP: Renee Connolly
VP: Andrew Galazka
VP: Jeanna Guthrie
VP: Alexander Kuta

D-U-N-S 36-462-8420
EMDEON CORP
MEDICAL MANAGER
669 River Dr Ste 240, Elmwood Park, NJ 07407-1361
Tel (201) 703-3400 Founded/Ownrshp 2009
Sales 92.6MM^E EMP 2,258
SIC 7373 3089 Systems software development services; Injection molded finished plastic products; Synthetic resin finished products
Ch Bd: Martin J Wygod
Pr: Roger Holstein
CFO: James R Love
V Ch Bd: James V Manning
Ex VP: Mark D Funston
Ex VP: David A Gang
*Ex VP: Charles A Mele
Sr VP: Lewis H Leicher
Sr VP: Anthony Vuolo
VP: Todd Evans
VP: William Midgette
VP: Scott Shaffmaster

EMEPA
See EAST MISSISSIPPI ELECTRIC POWER ASSN INC

D-U-N-S 00-694-9002
EMERA MAINE (ME)
(Suby of BANGOR HYDRO ELECTRIC) ★
21 Telcom Dr, Bangor, ME 04401-3392
Tel (207) 945-5621 Founded/Ownrshp 1924, 2001
Sales 169.9MM^E EMP 250
SIC 4911 Transmission, electric power; Distribution, electric power; Generation, electric power;
Pr: Jerry Chasse
CFO: Rod Black
CFO: Peter Dawes
Prin: Rob Bennett
Sls Mgr: Calvin Luther
Board of Directors: Robert S Briggs, Jane J Bush, Norman A Ledwin, Elizabeth A Macdonald, Richard J Smith, Ronald E Smith

EMERALD CITY PIZZA HUT
See EMERALD CITY PIZZA LLC

D-U-N-S 03-999-4665
EMERALD CITY PIZZA LLC
EMERALD CITY PIZZA HUT
12121 Harbour Rch Dr 20 Ste 200, Mukilteo, WA 98275
Tel (425) 493-8077 Founded/Ownrshp 2000
Sales 58.2MM^E EMP 1,900
SIC 5812 Pizzeria, chain

D-U-N-S 12-242-3668
EMERALD COAST UTILITIES AUTHORITY
ESCAMBIA COUNTY UTILITIES AUTH
9255 Sturdevant St, Pensacola, FL 32514-7038
Tel (850) 476-5110 Founded/Ownrshp 1981
Sales 118.4MM EMP 537
Accts Saltmarsh Cleaveland & Gund
SIC 4959 4952 4941 Sanitary services; Sewerage systems; Water supply
Ex Dir: Stephen E Sorrell
Genl Mgr: Sarah Seymour
Dir IT: David Roberts

D-U-N-S 82-693-2886
EMERALD DAIRY INC
11990 Market St Unit 205, Reston, VA 20190-6001
Tel (703) 867-9247 Founded/Ownrshp 2007
Sales 27.7MM^E EMP 1,449
SIC 5451 Dairy products stores
Ch Bd: Yang Yong Shan
*CFO: Shu Kaneko
VP: Qin Si
*VP: Yuan Yong WEI
*VP Prd: Qin Si Bo

D-U-N-S 93-929-2780
EMERALD EXPOSITIONS LLC
CONTRACT
(Suby of ONEX CORPORATION)
31910 Del Obispo St # 200, San Juan Capistrano, CA 92675-3195
Tel (949) 226-5700 Founded/Ownrshp 2013
Sales 197.1MM^E EMP 1,028
SIC 7389 Advertising, promotional & trade show services
CEO: Kosty Gilis
Sr VP: Sabrina Crow
Sr VP: Darrell Denny
VP: Howard Appelbaum
VP: Rob Carstens
VP: Christine Cassidy
VP: Joe Miranda
VP: Tina Nicholson
VP: Scott Pierce
VP: David Rector
VP: K Schlager

D-U-N-S 79-465-4871
EMERALD FOODS INC
WENDY'S
6300 West Loop S, Bellaire, TX 77401-2900
Tel (713) 791-9167 Founded/Ownrshp 1991
Sales 45.9MM^E EMP 1,350
Accts Norman Jones Enlow & Co Colu
SIC 5812 Fast-food restaurant, chain
Ch: Donald L Feinstein
*Pr: Mark J George
CFO: David Godfrey
VP: Ty Miyahara
VP: Ellen Ruth

D-U-N-S 16-718-5953
EMERALD OIL INC
200 Columbine St Ste 500, Denver, CO 80206-4736
Tel (303) 595-5600 Founded/Ownrshp 2002
Sales 112.6MM EMP 42
SIC 1311 Crude petroleum & natural gas; Oil shale mining
CEO: McAndrew Rudisill
*Ch Bd: Daniel L Spears
CFO: Ryan Smith
Ex VP: Andy Goetsch
Board of Directors: Duke R Ligon, Seth Setrakian, Matthew Sheehy

D-U-N-S 00-920-2417 IMP
EMERALD PACKAGING INC
E P
33050 Western Ave, Union City, CA 94587-2157
Tel (510) 429-5700 Founded/Ownrshp 1963
Sales 109.4MM^E EMP 250
SIC 2673 Plastic bags: made from purchased materials
CEO: Kevin Kelly
Ch Bd: James P Kelly Sr
COO: Mike Dorthick
Ex VP: James M Kelly Jr
VP: Maura Kelly Koberlein
Opers Mgr: Darin Wilson
Ql Cn Mgr: Louise Perez
Sls Mgr: Todd Sommers

D-U-N-S 61-938-5586 IMP/EXP
EMERALD PERFORMANCE MATERIALS LLC
1499 Se Tech Center Pl, Vancouver, WA 98683-5528
Tel (330) 916-6700 Founded/Ownrshp 2014
Sales 364.4MM^E EMP 750
SIC 2821 Plastics materials & resins; Thermosetting materials
CFO: Becki L Watson
*Treas: Jim Warholic
*VP: Robert Culp
VP: Daniel Emmett
VP: Joseph Marshaleck
*VP: Chris O'Neil
*VP: Julie O Vaughn

EMERALD RECYCLING
See EMERALD SERVICES INC

D-U-N-S 82-505-4810 IMP
EMERALD SERVICES INC
EMERALD RECYCLING
7343 E Marginal Way S, Seattle, WA 98108-3513
Tel (206) 430-7795 Founded/Ownrshp 1938
Sales 170.0MM^E EMP 260
SIC 4953 7699 2911 8748 7359 Refuse collection & disposal services; Waste cleaning services; Petroleum refining; Environmental consultant; Portable toilet rental
Pr: J Stephan Banchero Jr
*COO: Dean Kattler
*CFO: Kurt Frost
*Treas: Catherine Malshuk
*Ex VP: Clue Westmoreland
*Sr VP: John Brigham
Comm Dir: Susan Thoman
Brnch Mgr: Todd Hurn
Genl Mgr: Steve Banchero
Genl Mgr: Marc McReynolds
Genl Mgr: Jim Munnell

D-U-N-S 07-882-7527
▲ **EMERGE ENERGY SERVICES LP**
180 State St Ste 225, Southlake, TX 76092-7632
Tel (817) 865-5830 Founded/Ownrshp 2012
Sales 1.1MMM EMP 487
Tkr Sym EMES Exch NYS
SIC 1311 1389 4613 Oil sand mining; Sand & shale oil mining; Oil field services; Processing service, gas; Refined petroleum pipelines

CEO: Rick Shearer
Genl Pt: Emerge Energy Services GP LLC
CFO: Deborah Deibert

EMERGENCY HOSPITAL EASTON MD
See SHORE HEALTH SYSTEM INC

D-U-N-S 02-648-9018
■ EMERGENT BIODEFENSE OPERATIONS LANSING LLC
(*Suby of* EMERGENT BIOSOLUTIONS INC) ★
3500 N Martin Luther King, Lansing, MI 48906-2933
Tel (517) 327-1500 *Founded/Ownrshp* 1998
Sales 107.0MM^E *EMP* 300
SIC 2836 2834 Vaccines; Pharmaceutical preparations
Ch Bd: Fuad El-Hibri
**CFO:* Robert Kramer
**Ex VP:* Robert Myers
VP: Thomas A Waytes

D-U-N-S 17-357-0271
▲ EMERGENT BIOSOLUTIONS INC
400 Professional Dr # 400, Gaithersburg, MD 20879-3457
Tel (240) 631-3200 *Founded/Ownrshp* 1998
Sales 522.7MM *EMP* 1,292^E
Tkr Sym EBS *Exch* NYS
SIC 2834 2836 Pharmaceutical preparations; Drugs affecting parasitic & infective diseases; Bacterial vaccines
Ch Bd: Fuad El-Hibri
Pr: Danial J Abdun-Nabi
CFO: Robert G Kramer
Ex VP: Adam Havey
VP: James Jackson
VP: Robert Myers
VP: Scott Stromatt
Dir Risk M: Colleen Larson
QA Dir: Brian Gronowski
Counsel: Emma Falsey
Snr Mgr: Amanda Ball

D-U-N-S 08-365-1406 IMP/EXP
EMERGING ACQUISITIONS LLC (IL)
BULK HANDLING SYSTEMS
3592 W 5th Ave, Eugene, OR 97402-5338
Tel (541) 485-0999 *Founded/Ownrshp* 1976, 2005
Sales 83.5MM^E *EMP* 231^E
SIC 3535 Conveyors & conveying equipment
Mktg Mgr: Amanda Davidson

D-U-N-S 11-083-5779 IMP
■ EMERGING MARKETS COMMUNICATIONS LLC
EMC
(*Suby of* GLOBAL EAGLE ENTERTAINMENT INC) ★
3044 N Commerce Pkwy, Miramar, FL 33025-3969
Tel (954) 538-4000 *Founded/Ownrshp* 2016
Sales 125.5MM^E *EMP* 349
SIC 4841 Satellite master antenna systems services (SMATV)
CEO: Abel Avellan
Sr Pt: Victor H Rodriguez
Pr: Livio Arleo
CFO: Richard Hadsall
**CFO:* Thomas E Severson
Ex VP: Susan Miller
Sr VP: Jan Kjaer
Sr VP: Bill Madden
VP: Frank Pacella
VP: Joe Wright
Mng Dir: Joe Kamau

D-U-N-S 11-209-0779 IMP/EXP
EMERGING POWER INC
(*Suby of* ENER1 INC) ★
200 Holt St, Hackensack, NJ 07601-5244
Tel (201) 441-3590 *Founded/Ownrshp* 2002
Sales 94.8MM^E *EMP* 501^E
Accts Sejong Llp Fort Lee Nj
SIC 5063 Batteries
CEO: Tom Corbett
**Treas:* Carlos Rojas
Genl Mgr: Tom McGee
Genl Mgr: Jennifer Williams
Manager: Khanh Hoang

D-U-N-S 84-729-5722
■ EMERITUS CORP
BROOKDALE SENIOR LIVING
(*Suby of* BROOKDALE SENIOR LIVING) ★
3131 Elliott Ave Ste 500, Milwaukee, WI 53214
Tel (206) 298-2909 *Founded/Ownrshp* 1993
Sales 1.0MMM^E *EMP* 30,236
SIC 8052 Personal care facility
Pr: Mark Ohlendorf
**COO:* James Christopher Hyatt
**CFO:* Robert C Bateman
**Treas:* Kristin Ferge
**Ex VP:* Budgie Amparo
**Ex VP:* Mark A Finkelstein
**Ex VP:* Bill Sivill
**Ex VP:* Steve Tarr
**Ex VP:* Melanie Werdel
Sr VP: John Cincotta
VP: Tony Sanford
**VP:* Chad White

D-U-N-S 00-426-8884 IMP/EXP
■ EMERSON CLIMATE TECHNOLOGIES INC
(*Suby of* EECO INC) ★
1675 Campbell Rd, Sidney, OH 45365-2479
Tel (937) 498-3011 *Founded/Ownrshp* 2006
Sales 1.4MMM^E *EMP* 4,877
SIC 3585 Compressors for refrigeration & air conditioning equipment; Condensers, refrigeration
Pr: Ed Purvis Jr
Pr: Ken Monnier
Pr: William Ragon
**CFO:* Richard Denuzzo
Ofcr: Tom Shimp
**VP:* Jean Caillt
**VP:* Tom Croone
**VP:* Art Gabbard
VP: Frank Landwehr
VP: Brandy Powell
VP: Clyde Verhoff
**VP:* Marjorie Wallman
VP: John Ward

D-U-N-S 04-341-1438
EMERSON COLLEGE
120 Boylston St Ste 414, Boston, MA 02116-4624
Tel (617) 824-8500 *Founded/Ownrshp* 1886
Sales 200.0MM *EMP* 425^E
Accts Kpmg Llp Hartford Ct
SIC 8221 College, except junior
Pr: Lee Pelton
**Ch Bd:* Ted Benard-Cutler
Pr: Keira McClain
**Treas:* Jeffrey Greenhawt
Ofcr: Carl Yancey
VP: Gwendolyn Bates
VP: Loretta Bemis
VP: Michael Duggan
VP: Mj Knoll Finn
VP: Donna Heiland
VP: Christine Hughes
VP: Margaret Ann Ings
VP: Margaret Ings
VP: Alexa Jackson
VP: Ruthanne Madsen
VP: Jay Phillips
VP: Anthony Pinder
VP: Barbara Rutberg
VP: Sylvia Spears
VP: Richard Zauft
Exec: William Anderson

D-U-N-S 61-535-2465 IMP
■ EMERSON ELECTRIC (US) HOLDING CORP
(*Suby of* EECO INC) ★
850 Library Ave Ste 204c, Saint Louis, MO 63136
Tel (314) 553-2000 *Founded/Ownrshp* 1984
Sales 1.7MMM^E *EMP* 4,876
SIC 3824 Fluid meters & counting devices
Ch Bd: Charles F Knight
**Ch Bd:* David N Farr
VP: Jake Fritz
Sls Dir: Bryan Mueller

D-U-N-S 00-626-9633 IMP/EXP
▲ EMERSON ELECTRIC CO (MO)
8000 W Florissant Ave, Saint Louis, MO 63136-1415
Tel (314) 553-2000 *Founded/Ownrshp* 1890
Sales 14.5MMM *EMP* 110,800
Accts Kpmg Llp St Louis Missouri
Tkr Sym EMR *Exch* NYS
SIC 3823 3491 3621 3585 3679 Industrial instrmnts msrmnt display/control process variable; Industrial flow & liquid measuring instruments; Industrial process measurement equipment; Temperature measurement instruments, industrial; Industrial valves; Automatic regulating & control valves; Process control regulator valves; Valves, automatic control; Motors & generators; Motors, electric; Refrigeration & heating equipment; Heating equipment, complete; Refrigeration equipment, complete; Parts for heating, cooling & refrigerating equipment; Electronic circuits
Ch Bd: David N Farr
Pr: Tim Ferry
Pr: Edward L Monser
Pr: Robert T Sharp
Pr: Michael H Train
COO: Edgar M Purvis
CFO: Frank J Dellaquila
Treas: David Rabe
Bd of Dir: Joe Morris
Chf Mktg O: Katherine Bell
Trst Ofcr: Patrick J Sly
Ex VP: Craig Ashmore
Ex VP: Jay L Geldmacher
VP: Tim Backs
VP: David Baker
VP: Jan L Bansch
VP: David Bersaglini
VP: Cathy Bevan
VP: John Bingham
VP: Kevin Bjork
VP: Jim Bolit
Board of Directors: Clemens A H Boersig, Joshua B Bolten, Arthur F Golden, William R Johnson, Candace Kendle, Matthew S Levatich, Joseph W Prueher, Randall L Stephenson, James S Turley

D-U-N-S 61-531-4960
■ EMERSON ELECTRIC OVERSEAS FINANCE CORP
(*Suby of* EMERSON ELECTRIC (US) HOLDING CORP) ★
8000 W Florissant Ave, Saint Louis, MO 63136-1415
Tel (314) 553-2000 *Founded/Ownrshp* 1971
Sales NA *EMP* 300
SIC 6153 Short-term business credit
Pr: Charles Knight
**CEO:* D N Farr
Treas: Alan Mielcuszny
VP: Keith Browning
VP: David Gerhart
VP: Dave Proffitt
Exec: Joan Coleman
Exec: Diane Morris
Dir Rx: Greg Romanchuk
Prgrm Mgr: Kar Chan
Rgnl Mgr: Russell Liner

D-U-N-S 06-935-6467
EMERSON HOSPITAL
133 Old Rd To 9 Acre Cor, Concord, MA 01742-4169
Tel (978) 369-1400 *Founded/Ownrshp* 1911
Sales 201.3MM *EMP* 1,450
Accts Pricewaterhousecooper Llp Bos
SIC 8062 General medical & surgical hospitals
Chf Rad: David Rose
**Pr:* Ronald H Johnson
COO: Tom Kleinhanzl
**CFO:* Dana Diggins
**Treas:* Paul D Birch
Treas: Mark A Connaughton
Bd of Dir: Joan Litle
Ofcr: C G Martin
**VP:* John Dresser
**VP:* Christine Gallery
VP: Karl Kussin
**VP:* Gregory Martin
VP: Eric Stastney
**VP:* Eric Stastny
**VP:* Kevin Whitney
Dir Lab: Gene Dibenedetto
Comm Man: Lara Ellis
Board of Directors: Charles Bauer

EMERSON INDUSTRIAL AUTOMATION
See KATO ENGINEERING INC

D-U-N-S 16-725-3504 IMP/EXP
EMERSON NETWORK POWER ENERGY SYSTEMS NORTH AMERICA INC
(*Suby of* CORTES NP ACQUISITION CORP) ★
1510 Kansas Ave, Lorain, OH 44052-3364
Tel (440) 288-1122 *Founded/Ownrshp* 2016
Sales 203.6MM^E *EMP* 800
SIC 3661 3644 7629 Telephone & telegraph apparatus; Noncurrent-carrying wiring services; Telecommunication equipment repair (except telephones)
Opers Mgr: Dave Smith
**CFO:* Michael Neeley
VP: Dennis Del Campo
IT Man: Andy Doud

D-U-N-S 02-204-1318
EMERSON NETWORK POWER LIEBERT SERVICES INC
(*Suby of* VERTIV) ★
610 Executive Campus Dr, Westerville, OH 43082-8870
Tel (614) 841-6400 *Founded/Ownrshp* 1997
Sales 158.2MM^E *EMP* 592
SIC 7378

D-U-N-S 05-890-0606 IMP/EXP
EMERSON POWER TRANSMISSION CORP
7120 New Buffington Rd, Florence, KY 41042-2841
Tel (859) 342-7900 *Founded/Ownrshp* 1983
Sales NA *EMP* 3,000
SIC 3429 3052 3568 3562 3566 3462

EMERSON PRCESS MGT SHFER DVSON
See EMERSON PROCESS MANAGEMENT VALVE AUTOMATION INC

EMERSON PROCESS MANAGEMENT
See TESCOM CORP

D-U-N-S 80-082-8548
■ EMERSON PROCESS MANAGEMENT LLLP
(*Suby of* FISHER-ROSEMOUNT SYSTEMS INC) ★
1100 W Louis Henna Blvd, Round Rock, TX 78681-9921
Tel (512) 835-2190 *Founded/Ownrshp* 2002
Sales 121.4MM^E *EMP* 684^E
SIC 8742 Automation & robotics consultant
Pr: Steve Sonnenberg
Pr: Eric Wilcox
Exec: Florence Black
Snr Sftwr: Prasanthi Ballada
Software D: Deji Chen
Sftwr Eng: Brent Betts
Sftwr Eng: Joe Murphy
Sftwr Eng: Daniel Orozco
Sftwr Eng: Jared Stokes
Sftwr Eng: Kevin Webb
Mktg Mgr: Matthew Cate

D-U-N-S 09-290-3751 IMP/EXP
■ EMERSON PROCESS MANAGEMENT POWER & WATER SOLUTIONS INC
(*Suby of* FISHER-ROSEMOUNT SYSTEMS INC) ★
200 Beta Dr, Pittsburgh, PA 15238-2918
Tel (412) 963-4000 *Founded/Ownrshp* 2007
Sales 238.4MM^E *EMP* 990
SIC 3823 5063 Industrial instrmnts msrmnt display/control process variable; Generators
Pr: Robert Yeager
COO: Bob Yeager
**Treas:* Teresa A Burnett
**VP:* Denis Lawlor
VP: Steven Schilling
Exec: Michele Horsley
IT Man: Pam Knox
IT Man: Alan White
Sftwr Eng: Pankaj Mishra
Opers Mgr: Ray Overmyer
Sls Mgr: Richard Stafford

D-U-N-S 82-877-4518 IMP/EXP
■ EMERSON PROCESS MANAGEMENT REGULATOR TECHNOLOGIES INC
(*Suby of* EPMCO HOLDINGS, INC.)
3200 Emerson Way, McKinney, TX 75069-7918
Tel (972) 548-3585 *Founded/Ownrshp* 2008
Sales 84.6MM^E *EMP* 400^E
SIC 3491 Pressure valves & regulators, industrial
Pr: Surendralal Karsanbhai
**Pr:* Earle L Weaver
**Treas:* Teresa A Burnett
Plnt Mgr: Michael Douglas
Plnt Mgr: Ed Herron
Sls Mgr: Curtis Bagby

D-U-N-S 00-415-6733 IMP/EXP
■ EMERSON PROCESS MANAGEMENT VALVE AUTOMATION INC
EMERSON PRCESS MGT SHFER DVSON
(*Suby of* DANIEL INDUSTRIES INC) ★
8000 W Florissant Ave, Saint Louis, MO 63136-1414
Tel (314) 553-2000 *Founded/Ownrshp* 1946, 1999
Sales 164.4MM^E *EMP* 400
SIC 3594 3593 Fluid power pumps & motors; Fluid power actuators, hydraulic or pneumatic
Pr: John Kurtz
**CEO:* David Farr
VP: Michael McQuade
Rgnl Mgr: Steve Burke
Sls Dir: Doug Viafora

EMERSON RMOTE AUTOMTN SOLUTION
See BRISTOL INC

EMERSON SWAN COMMERCIAL
See EMERSON-SWAN INC

D-U-N-S 01-920-3694 IMP
EMERSON-SWAN INC (MA)
EMERSON SWAN COMMERCIAL
300 Pond St Ste 1, Randolph, MA 02368-2663
Tel (781) 986-2000 *Founded/Ownrshp* 2009
Sales 91.2MM^E *EMP* 126
SIC 5084 5074 Industrial machinery & equipment; Plumbing & hydronic heating supplies
Ch: Joseph Swan
**Pr:* George Simas III
**Pr:* Parker Wheat
**VP:* Delancey Davis
**VP:* Bill Kohl
Mktg Dir: Carrol Geray
Sls Mgr: Tom Brown
Sales Asso: Peter Froment
Sales Asso: Ryan Jacobs

D-U-N-S 07-963-5662
■ EMERSUB 14 LLC
(*Suby of* EMERSON ELECTRIC CO) ★
8000 W Florissant Ave, Saint Louis, MO 63136-1414
Tel (314) 553-2000 *Founded/Ownrshp* 2009
Sales 164.2MM^E *EMP* 232^E
SIC 3823 Industrial instrmnts msrmnt display/control process variable
Pr: David N Farr

D-U-N-S 07-945-4107
EMERY AIR INC (IL)
CHAUTAUQUA
46 Airport Dr, Rockford, IL 61109-2902
Tel (815) 987-4100 *Founded/Ownrshp* 2014
Sales 3.7MM^E *EMP* 1,000
SIC 4731 Freight transportation arrangement
Pr: John C Emery

D-U-N-S 61-401-0838 IMP
EMERY OLEOCHEMICALS LLC
(*Suby of* EMERY OLEOCHEMICALS (M) SDN. BHD.)
4900 Este Ave, Cincinnati, OH 45232-1491
Tel (513) 762-2500 *Founded/Ownrshp* 1850
Sales 104.6MM^E *EMP* 300^E
SIC 2899 Chemical preparations; Acids
CEO: Ramesh Kana
Sr VP: Azuddin Rahman
VP: Shamsol Anuar
Dir Rx: Allan Chiu
Dir Rx: Mark Kinkelaar
Area Mgr: Bill Kafiti
Tech Mgr: Chad Walker
Ql Cn Mgr: Kevin George
Snr Mgr: Faroze Nadar

D-U-N-S 07-588-7059
EMERY SAPP & SONS INC
2301 Interstate 70 Dr Nw, Columbia, MO 65202-1347
Tel (573) 445-8331 *Founded/Ownrshp* 1972
Sales 125.5MM^E *EMP* 250^E
SIC 1622 1629 1611 Bridge construction; Blasting contractor, except building demolition; Highway & street construction
Exec: Billy Sapp
**Exec:* Keith Bennett
**Exec:* Glen Robertson
**Exec:* Shawn Sapp
Brnch Mgr: Justin Gay
Genl Mgr: Angie Regan
Dir IT: Steve Hinz
Mtls Mgr: Scott Zepp
Opers Mgr: Blake Hustedde
Opers Mgr: Tim Paulson

D-U-N-S 00-694-9309 IMP
EMERY-WATERHOUSE CO (ME)
GOLDEN RULE STORES
(*Suby of* ACE HARDWARE CORP) ★
7 Rand Rd, Portland, ME 04102-1433
Tel (207) 775-2371 *Founded/Ownrshp* 1892, 2014
Sales 448.7MM^E *EMP* 410
SIC 5072 Hardware
Pr: Stephen M Frawley
**COO:* Don Dickson
**CFO:* Gary Merrill
**Ch:* Charles H Hildreth Jr
Bd of Dir: Nicole Levesque
Sr VP: Bobby Kinchla
VP: Bruce Sherman
Dir IT: Jeff Fisher
Tech Mgr: Dennis Hawkins
VP Sls: Charles Chibante
Sls Dir: Jim Cook

EMFCO
See EXOTIC METALS FORMING CO LLC

EMG
See CLAMPETT INDUSTRIES LLC

EMH REGIONAL HEALTHCARE SYSTEM
See COMPREHENSIVE HEALTH CARE OF OHIO INC

D-U-N-S 01-084-4959
EMH REGIONAL MEDICAL CENTER
(*Suby of* EMH REGIONAL HEALTHCARE SYSTEM) ★
630 E River St, Elyria, OH 44035-5902
Tel (440) 329-7500 *Founded/Ownrshp* 1907
Sales 16.7MM^E *EMP* 1,712
SIC 8062

D-U-N-S 00-114-3528
EMHART TEKNOLOGIES LLC
STANLEY ENGINEERED FASTENING
480 Myrtle St, New Britain, CT 06053-4018
Tel (800) 783-6427 *Founded/Ownrshp* 1902
Sales 318.1MM^E *EMP* 3,165
SIC 8711 3541 Engineering services; Machine tools, metal cutting type
Pr: Michael A Tyll
**VP:* Ed Delterio
**VP:* Charles Fenton
Prd Mgr: Donald White

EMHS
See EASTERN MAINE HEALTHCARE SYSTEMS

EMI MUSIC DISTRIBUTION
See CAPITOL RECORDS LLC

D-U-N-S 05-156-1876
EMIGRANT SAVINGS BANK
5 E 42nd St Fl 5, New York, NY 10017-6904
Tel (212) 850-4000 Founded/Ownrshp 1986
Sales NA EMP 1,375
SIC 6036 6311 6512 6514

D-U-N-S 14-255-4885
EMILY DICKINSON MUSEUM
TRUSTEES OF AMHERST COLLEGE
280 Main St, Amherst, MA 01002-2349
Tel (413) 542-8161 Founded/Ownrshp 2004
Sales 511.9MM EMP 4
SIC 8412 Museum
*Treas: Shannon Gurek
*Ex Dir: Jane Wald
Pgrm Dir: Brooke Steinhauser

D-U-N-S 09-637-8187
EMJ CORP
2034 Hamilton Place Blvd # 400, Chattanooga, TN 37421-6102
Tel (423) 855-1550 Founded/Ownrshp 1978
Sales 339.0MME EMP 210
SIC 1542 Commercial & office building contractors
CEO: James Jolley
*Pr: Burt Odom
*COO: Doug Martin
CFO: David Keller
*CFO: Chuck McGlothlen
Ex VP: Alex Grace
VP: Philip Augustino
VP: Earl Carstens
VP: Ray Catlin
VP: Clint Dean
VP: Christopher Hall
VP: Drew Halsey
VP: Ed Jolley
VP: Drew Smith
VP: James T Tyson
Dir Bus: Sam Wills

EMMANUEL COLLEGE
See INTERNATIONAL PENTECOSTAL HOLINESS CHURCH

D-U-N-S 09-150-3201
EMMANUEL COLLEGE (INC)
400 Fenway, Boston, MA 02115-5798
Tel (617) 277-9340 Founded/Ownrshp 1919
Sales 95.1MM EMP 449
Accts Kpmg Llp Boston Ma
SIC 8221 College, except junior
Pr: Sister Janet Eisner
*COO: Eleanor Mulvaney Seamans
*CFO: Neil Buckley
*Treas: Anne M Donovan
Assoc VP: Kristen Conroy
*Ex VP: James L Elcock
*Ex VP: Margaret L McKenna
*Sr VP: John F Burke
*VP: Frank Fcully
VP: Patricia Rimeyer
*VP: Patricia Rissmeyer
Assoc Dir: Andrew Yosinoff

D-U-N-S 02-666-2379
▲ EMMIS COMMUNICATIONS CORP
40 Monument Cir Ste 700, Indianapolis, IN 46204-3017
Tel (317) 266-0100 Founded/Ownrshp 1981
Sales 231.4MM EMP 1,085
Tkr Sym EMMS Exch NGS
SIC 4832 2721 Radio broadcasting stations; Periodicals: publishing & printing
Ch Bd: Jeffrey H Smulyan
Pr: Gregory T Loewen
*Pr: Patrick M Walsh
CFO: Ryan A Hornaday
Board of Directors: Susan B Bayh, James M Dubin, Gary L Kaseff, Richard A Leventhal, Peter A Lund, Greg A Nathanson, Lawrence B Sorrel

D-U-N-S 06-696-1608 IMP/EXP
EMO-TRANS INC
135 Guy Lombardo Ave, Freeport, NY 11520-4457
Tel (516) 867-6800 Founded/Ownrshp 1965
Sales 162.3MME EMP 300
SIC 4731 Foreign freight forwarding
CEO: Joachim Frigger
*Pr: Marco Rohrer
*Ex VP: Wick Campbell
*VP: Thomas Harlin
Rgnl Mgr: Gisela Beckermann
Off Mgr: Phyllis Kephart
Sls Mgr: Lindy Marshall

D-U-N-S 06-918-0529
EMORY CLINIC INC (GA)
(Suby of EMORY HEALTHCARE INC) ★
1365 Clifton Rd Ne, Atlanta, GA 30322-1013
Tel (404) 778-5000 Founded/Ownrshp 1953
Sales 169.7MME EMP 1,600
SIC 8062

EMORY EASTSIDE MEDICAL CENTER
See EHCA EASTSIDE OCCUPATIONAL MEDICINE CENTER LLC

D-U-N-S 03-528-0853
EMORY HEALTHCARE INC
(Suby of EMORY UNIVERSITY) ★
1440 Clifton Rd Ne, Atlanta, GA 30322-1053
Tel (404) 778-7777 Founded/Ownrshp 1994
Sales 1.1MMME EMP 16,000
SIC 8062 General medical & surgical hospitals
CEO: Micheal Johns
*Pr: Jonathan S Lewin
COO: Pete A Basler
COO: Albert K Blackwelder
COO: John Temple
CFO: Micki Begitschke
CFO: Barbara Channell
CFO: James T Hacher
*CFO: James Hatcher
CFO: Carol Hazen
CFO: David Stein
Bd of Dir: Ellen A Bailey
Bd of Dir: Sarah Berga
Bd of Dir: Norman Elliott
Bd of Dir: Russell R French
Bd of Dir: Charles B Ginden
Bd of Dir: Joseph Gladden
Bd of Dir: John T Glover
Bd of Dir: Robert C Goddard III
Bd of Dir: Lucky Jain
Bd of Dir: Christian P Larsen

EMORY JOHN CREEK HOSPITAL
See EHCA JOHNS CREEK LLC

D-U-N-S 06-646-9933 IMP
EMORY UNIVERSITY
201 Dowman Dr Ne, Atlanta, GA 30322-1061
Tel (404) 727-6013 Founded/Ownrshp 1836
Sales 4.4MMM EMP 22,000E
SIC 8221 8082

D-U-N-S 62-692-7966
EMORY UNIVERSITY HOSPITAL MIDTOWN
(Suby of EMORY UNIVERSITY) ★
550 Peachtree St Ne, Atlanta, GA 30308-2212
Tel (404) 686-7100 Founded/Ownrshp 1974
Sales 641.2MM EMP 2,500
SIC 8062 General medical & surgical hospitals
CEO: Robert J Bachman
*Pr: John T Fox
*Ex VP: S Wright Caughman
VP: Franchot Mackin
VP: Henry Marshall
VP: Marion Melani
VP: David Smith
Dir Rad: Jamilk-Omari Johnson
Genl Mgr: Deborah Plement
Off Mgr: Vickie Russell
CTO: Annette Warbel

D-U-N-S 03-937-5910 IMP/EXP
EMPI INC
599 Cardigan Rd, Saint Paul, MN 55126-4099
Tel (651) 415-9000 Founded/Ownrshp 2004
Sales 84.2MME EMP 780
SIC 3845

EMPIRE
See WELLCHOICE INC

D-U-N-S 06-979-3826
EMPIRE BEAUTY SCHOOL INC
EMPIRE EDUCATION GROUP
396 Pttsvlle St Clair Hwy, Pottsville, PA 17901
Tel (570) 429-4321 Founded/Ownrshp 1956
Sales 61.7MME EMP 1,900
SIC 8249

D-U-N-S 13-074-6001
EMPIRE CHEESE INC
(Suby of GREAT LAKES CHEESE CO INC) ★
4520 County Road 6, Cuba, NY 14727-9598
Tel (585) 968-1552 Founded/Ownrshp 1993
Sales 92.8MME EMP 175
SIC 2022 Cheese, natural & processed
CEO: Gary Vanic
*Sec: John Epprecht
*VP: Russell Mullins
Plnt Mgr: Thomas Eastham
QI Cn Mgr: Bozena Lukomski

D-U-N-S 00-890-1811 IMP
EMPIRE CO LLC
EMPIRE DISTRIBUTORS
(Suby of TENON LIMITED)
8181 Logistics Dr, Zeeland, MI 49464-9378
Tel (616) 772-7272 Founded/Ownrshp 1993
Sales 106.0MME EMP 237
SIC 5031 2431 Lumber, plywood & millwork; Millwork; Molding, all materials; Staircases, stairs & railings
Pr: Thomas H Highley
*CFO: Stephen J Johandes
VP: Richard Carlson
*VP: Stephen R Grossman
S&M/VP: Dennis Berry
Mktg Mgr: Scott Bos
Mktg Mgr: Jeff Leys

EMPIRE CREDIT COMPANY
See SIOUX STEEL CO

EMPIRE DISTRIBUTORS
See EMPIRE CO LLC

D-U-N-S 00-884-7030 IMP
■ EMPIRE DISTRIBUTORS INC
(Suby of BERKSHIRE HATHAWAY INC) ★
3755 Atlanta Indus Pkwy, Atlanta, GA 30331-1027
Tel (404) 572-4100 Founded/Ownrshp 1940
Sales 284.1MME EMP 397
SIC 5182 Liquor; Wine
Pr: David Kahn
*CFO: Michael Kahn
*CFO: Jim Schwarzkopf
Dist Mgr: Mike Ray
Dist Mgr: Alex Smith
Dist Mgr: Ray Stevenson
Dist Mgr: Jason Turner
Genl Mgr: Art Gennari
Off Mgr: Matthew Garrett
Sls Mgr: Tripp Adams
Sls Mgr: Todd Cox

D-U-N-S 94-559-0305 IMP
■ EMPIRE DISTRIBUTORS OF NORTH CAROLINA INC
(Suby of EMPIRE DISTRIBUTORS INC) ★
13833 Carowinds Blvd, Charlotte, NC 28273-4736
Tel (704) 588-9463 Founded/Ownrshp 1983
Sales 147.1MME EMP 397
SIC 5182 5181 Wine & distilled beverages; Beer & ale
CEO: David Kahn
*CFO: Jim Schwarzkopf
*VP: Michael Kahn
Dist Mgr: Brian Clayton
Dist Mgr: Heath Truelove
Sls Mgr: Brian Sun

D-U-N-S 00-696-5305
▲ EMPIRE DISTRICT ELECTRIC CO (KS)
602 S Joplin Ave, Joplin, MO 64801-2337
Tel (417) 625-5100 Founded/Ownrshp 1909
Sales 605.5MM EMP 749
Tkr Sym EDE Exch NYS
SIC 4911 4941 Electric services; Transmission, electric power; Distribution, electric power; Water supply
Pr: Bradley P Beecher
CFO: Laurie A Delano
Treas: Mark T Timpe
Dir: Scott Keith
Off Mgr: Jeff Lebeda
IT Man: Chase Shelley
IT Man: Jared Wicklund
Web Dev: Glen West
Sfty Dirs: Tina Montez
Sfty Mgr: Pete Babb
Sfty Mgr: Wayne Hartin

EMPIRE EDUCATION GROUP
See EMPIRE BEAUTY SCHOOL INC

EMPIRE EDUCATION GROUP
See EEG INC

D-U-N-S 04-738-0894 IMP/EXP
EMPIRE ELECTRONICS INC
214 E Maple Rd, Troy, MI 48083-2716
Tel (248) 585-8130 Founded/Ownrshp 1993
Sales 462.5MME EMP 3,300E
SIC 3679

D-U-N-S 60-566-7716
EMPIRE EXPRESS INC
999 Channel Ave, Memphis, TN 38106
Tel (901) 942-3300 Founded/Ownrshp 1985
Sales 86.4MME EMP 235
SIC 4213 Trucking, except local
Pr: Tim Gatlin
*Co-Ownr: Ed Gatlin
Pr: Don Stroud
COO: Mike Reaves
*Sec: Linda Gatlin
VP: Bruce Erlandson
VP: Donna Nicholas
Exec: Jera Skaggs
Off Mgr: Irish Chapman
Dir IT: Travis Stone
Opers Mgr: Terri Hollowell

D-U-N-S 79-610-9874
EMPIRE HEALTH CENTERS GROUP
DEACONESS MEDICAL CENTER
800 W 5th Ave, Spokane, WA 99204-2803
Tel (509) 473-5800 Founded/Ownrshp 1985
Sales 249.2MM EMP 2,020
SIC 8062 General medical & surgical hospitals
CEO: Linda E White
*COO: Shawn McCoy
Off Mgr: Liz Haller
Opthamlgy: William H Bray
Opthamlgy: Jane F Durcan
Opthamlgy: Robert W Hander
Opthamlgy: Jason H Jones
Opthamlgy: Erik D Skoog

D-U-N-S 15-686-1481
EMPIRE INVESTMENT HOLDINGS LLC
1220 Malaga Ave, Coral Gables, FL 33134-6322
Tel (305) 403-1111 Founded/Ownrshp 2003
Sales 135.8MME EMP 950
SIC 6799 Investors
CEO: David F Alfonso
*Pt: Dennis M Mahoney
Sr VP: Paul H Miller

D-U-N-S 06-889-0839
EMPIRE IRON MINING PARTNERSHIP
1100 Superior Ave E Fl 15, Cleveland, OH 44114-2530
Tel (216) 694-5700 Founded/Ownrshp 1959, 1983
Sales 93.8MME EMP 628
SIC 1011 Iron ore mining; Iron ore pelletizing; Iron ore beneficiating
Genl Mgr: David B Blake
Genl Pt: The Cleveland-Cliffs Iron Comp
Genl Pt: Mittal Steel USA

D-U-N-S 00-304-4567 EXP
■ EMPIRE KOSHER POULTRY INC
MATTERNS HATCHERY
(Suby of E K HOLDINGS INC) ★
Chicken Plant Rd, Mifflintown, PA 17059
Tel (717) 436-5921 Founded/Ownrshp 1992
Sales 197.3MME EMP 1,000
SIC 2015 5812 Poultry slaughtering & processing; Chicken, processed; Turkey, processed; Eating places
CEO: Greg Rosenbaum
*Ex VP: Paul Simkus
*Sr VP: Lisa Nelson
Sales Exec: Harry Geedey
VP Mktg: Janice Price
Manager: John Boggs

D-U-N-S 19-733-2687
EMPIRE MARKETING STRATEGIES INC
11243 Cornell Park Dr, Blue Ash, OH 45242-1811
Tel (513) 793-6241 Founded/Ownrshp 1984
Sales 167.1MME EMP 600
SIC 5141 Food brokers
CEO: Danny Harris Sr
*Pr: Brent Beerens
*Pr: Paul Towle
*COO: Len Marek
*CFO: Michael Marek
Genl Mgr: Todd Lockhart
Dir IT: Ryan Koster
Sls Dir: Mary Botha

D-U-N-S 79-113-9087 IMP
EMPIRE MERCHANTS LLC
EMPIRE NEW YORK
(Suby of BREAKTHRU BEVERAGE GROUP) ★
16 Bridgewater St, Brooklyn, NY 11222-3804
Tel (718) 383-5500 Founded/Ownrshp 2006
Sales 572.5MME EMP 1,452E
SIC 5182 Wine & distilled beverages
*Pr: E Lloyd Sobel
COO: Anthony Magliocco Jr
*COO: Tony Magliocco
CFO: Terrance Arlotta
*CFO: Terrence A Arlotta
VP: Josip Jurkovic
*Genl Mgr: David C Drucker
CIO: Ed Lederer

D-U-N-S 00-385-1912 IMP
EMPIRE MERCHANTS NORTH LLC
16 Houghtaling Rd, Coxsackie, NY 12051
Tel (518) 731-5200 Founded/Ownrshp 2007
Sales 260.6MME EMP 630
SIC 5182 Wine; Liquor
Pr: Vincent Andretta III
*CFO: William F Simpson
*Treas: Paul Wilburger
*VP: Jay Andretta
DP Mgr: Douglas Davis
*VP Sls: Kevin Tucker
Sls Dir: David Puorto
Sls Mgr: Larry Scanio
Sales Asso: Rick Abraham

EMPIRE NEW YORK
See EMPIRE MERCHANTS LLC

D-U-N-S 00-254-0375 IMP
EMPIRE OFFICE INC (NY)
105 Madison Ave Fl 15, New York, NY 10016-7418
Tel (212) 607-5500 Founded/Ownrshp 1946
Sales 400.0MM EMP 413
SIC 5021 Office furniture
Ch Bd: Larry Gaslow
*CEO: Peter Gaslow
COO: Richard Gulardo
CFO: Martin Hills

D-U-N-S 03-477-6393
EMPIRE PACKING CO LP
LEDBETTER PACKING
1837 Harbor Ave, Memphis, TN 38113
Tel (901) 948-4788 Founded/Ownrshp 1948
Sales 110.7MM EMP 300
Accts Del Brocco & Associates Pllc
SIC 5147 2011 Meats, fresh; Meat packing plants
CEO: Danny Harris
Pt: Len Marek

D-U-N-S 06-904-1763
EMPIRE PETROLEUM PARTNERS LLC
SHELL
8350 N Central Expy M2175, Dallas, TX 75206-1648
Tel (214) 750-9313 Founded/Ownrshp 2011
Sales 90.9MME EMP 121E
SIC 4924 5172 Natural gas distribution; Petroleum products
CEO: Hank Heithaus
*COO: Michael Diebus
*CFO: Atanas H Atanasov
*CFO: David Potter
*Ex VP: Rick Golman
Sr VP: David Rabe

D-U-N-S 13-192-2734 IMP
▲ EMPIRE RESOURCES INC
2115 Linwood Ave Ste 200, Fort Lee, NJ 07024-5022
Tel (201) 944-2200 Founded/Ownrshp 1999
Sales 521.7MM EMP 60E
Tkr Sym ERS Exch NAS
SIC 5051 Aluminum bars, rods, ingots, sheets, pipes, plates, etc.; Copper sheets, plates, bars, rods, pipes, etc.; Nonferrous metal sheets, bars, rods, etc.
Pr: Nathan Kahn
*Ch Bd: William Spier
*CFO: Sandra Kahn
*Ex VP: Harvey Wrubel
Board of Directors: Jack Bendheim, Peter G Howard, Douglas Kass, Nathan Mazurek, Morris J Smith

D-U-N-S 00-773-7518
EMPIRE SCAFFOLD LLC
(Suby of SUNBELT RENTALS INDUSTRIAL SERVICES LLC) ★
9680 S Choctaw Dr, Baton Rouge, LA 70815-1204
Tel (225) 924-3170 Founded/Ownrshp 2001
Sales 78.6MME EMP 1,000
SIC 1799 Scaffolding construction
Pr: David Starkey
*VP: Robert Kusch

D-U-N-S 01-347-5020 IMP/EXP
EMPIRE SOUTHWEST LLC
1725 S Country Club Dr, Mesa, AZ 85210-6099
Tel (480) 633-4000 Founded/Ownrshp 1950
Sales 881.9MM EMP 1,450
SIC 5082 7353 7699 Construction & mining machinery; Heavy construction equipment rental; Aircraft & heavy equipment repair services; Agricultural equipment repair services
CEO: Jeffrey S Whiteman
CFO: Chris Zaharas
Ex Dir: Molly Trivers
Genl Mgr: Mike Brannon
Snr Sftwr: Robert Haasch
Dir IT: Ruben Rivera
Sls Mgr: Rick Scott
Board of Directors: Jim E Smith

D-U-N-S 07-839-8094
EMPIRE STATE REALTY TRUST INC (MD)
60 E 42nd St, New York, NY 10165-0006
Tel (212) 687-8700 Founded/Ownrshp 2013
Sales 657.6MM EMP 862E
Accts Ernst & Young Llp New York N
SIC 6798 Real estate investment trusts
Ch Bd: Anthony E Malkin
Pr: John B Kessler
Pr: Lotfollah Rezvan
CFO: David A Karp
Ex VP: Thomas P Durels
Ex VP: Thomas N Keltner Jr
Sr VP: Mark Labell
VP: Ryan Kass
VP: Fred C Posniak
VP: Vincent Sultana
Board of Directors: William H Berkman, Alice M Connell, Thomas J Derosa, Steven J Gilbert, S Michael Giliberto, James D Robinson IV

D-U-N-S 94-097-2011
EMPIRE TECHNOLOGIES LLC
(Suby of CONVERGEONE HOLDINGS CORP) ★
246 Industrial Way W # 1, Eatontown, NJ 07724-4240
Tel (732) 625-3200 Founded/Ownrshp 2009
Sales 115.3MM^E EMP 165^E
SIC 5065 1731 5999 Communication equipment; Communications specialization; Fiber optic cable installation; Telephone equipment & systems

D-U-N-S 02-511-5833 IMP
EMPIRE TODAY LLC
(Suby of HIG CAPITAL INC) ★
333 Northwest Ave, Northlake, IL 60164-1604
Tel (847) 583-5238 Founded/Ownrshp 2016
Sales 613.4MM^E EMP 2,000
SIC 5713

D-U-N-S 08-047-5569
EMPIRE VISION CENTER INC
(Suby of DAVIS VISION INC) ★
2921 Erie Blvd E, Syracuse, NY 13224-1432
Tel (315) 446-3145 Founded/Ownrshp 1997
Sales 82.8MM^E EMP 1,000^E
SIC 5995 Optical goods stores; Contact lenses, prescription; Eyeglasses, prescription
CEO: David L Holmberg
*Pr: Walter Froh
Sr VP: Alan Thrower
*VP: Paul Anderson

D-U-N-S 86-853-2131
EMPIRIX INC
600 Technology Park Dr # 1, Billerica, MA 01821-4130
Tel (978) 313-7000 Founded/Ownrshp 2013
Sales 102.4MM^E EMP 380^E
SIC 7371 8734 Custom computer programming services; Testing laboratories
CEO: John Danna
*Pr: Gregor N Ferguson
*CFO: Ray Dezenzo
Treas: Raymond Dezenzo
*Ex VP: Matthew Ainsworth
*Sr VP: Vijay Malik
*VP: Brigid Macdonald
*VP: Tim Moynihan
*VP: Andre Serpa
VP: Walter G Vahey
Dir Bus: John Schmottlach
Board of Directors: Cynthia M Deysher

EMPLOY AMERICA
See SOCIAL VOCATIONAL SERVICES INC

EMPLOYBRIDGE
See EMPLOYMENT SOLUTIONS MANAGEMENT INC

D-U-N-S 02-604-8517
EMPLOYBRIDGE HOLDING CO (GA)
SELECT STAFFING
1040 Crown Pointe Pkwy # 1040, Atlanta, GA 30338-6908
Tel (770) 671-1900 Founded/Ownrshp 2000, 2006
Sales 458.6MM^E EMP 3,186^E
SIC 7361 Employment agencies
CEO: Thomas A Bickes
Pr: Joanie Courtney
Pr: Shawn Poole
Board of Directors: Michael Miles

D-U-N-S 87-739-9998
EMPLOYBRIDGE LLC
SELECT STAFFING
(Suby of SELECT STAFFING) ★
3820 State St, Santa Barbara, CA 93105-3182
Tel (805) 882-2200 Founded/Ownrshp 2010
Sales 322.3MM^E EMP 1,500^E
SIC 7363 Temporary help service
Pr: Thomas A Bickes
Pr: Fred R Herbert
Pr: Steve Mills
*Pr: Paul J Sorensen
*COO: Mark R McComb
*CFO: Shawn Poole
Bd of Dir: Stephen Sorensen
*Sr VP: Lisa Cooney
*Sr VP: Gunnar Gooding
*Sr VP: Michael J Parrish
*Sr VP: Rachelle Vargas
VP: Donna Boyson
VP: Steve Grimaud
VP: Laurie Maxwell
VP: Fred Pachon
Board of Directors: David Stephen Sorensen

D-U-N-S 96-888-0174
EMPLOYBRIDGE SOUTHWEST LLC
(Suby of PROLOGISTIX) ★
3050 Peachtree Rd Nw, Atlanta, GA 30305-2212
Tel (404) 816-3255 Founded/Ownrshp 2011
Sales 7.1MM^E EMP 2,459^E
SIC 7363 Temporary help service
Pr: Thomas A Bickes
CFO: Shawn W Poole
Board of Directors: Chip Grissom Vp, Lisa Powell Vp, Sharon Greenbaum Assistan, Fred Herbert Vp, John Rosenbaum Vp, Michael Baer Vp, Keith Kislow Vp, Paul Seymour Vp, Ken Christensen Vp, Dan Lieblich Vp, Carolyn Silvey Vp, Jim Cleary Vp, Chris Loope Vp, Paul Sorensen Vp, Lisa Cooney Vp, Mark McComb Vp, Jeannie Davis Vp, Theresa McDannald Vp, Brian Devine Vp, Steve Mills Vp, Gunnar Gooding Vp, Michael Mitchell Vp, Steven Grimaud Vp, Melissa Porter Vp

D-U-N-S 96-995-6221
EMPLOYCO USA II INC
350 E Ogden Ave, Westmont, IL 60559-5534
Tel (630) 920-0000 Founded/Ownrshp 2009
Sales 45.0MM^E EMP 5,000
SIC 7361 Labor contractors (employment agency)
Pr: Robert W Wilson
CFO: Mike Dougalar
Ex VP: Scott Wilson
Sr VP: Michael Leach
*VP: Scott R Wilson

D-U-N-S 96-981-0642
EMPLOYEE BENEFIT TR OF EASTERN PA
6 Danforth Dr, Easton, PA 18045-7820
Tel (610) 515-6412 Founded/Ownrshp 2011
Sales NA EMP 2
Accts Palmer And Company Easton Pa
SIC 6351 8699 6321 Surety insurance; Charitable organization; Health insurance carriers
Off Mgr: Hans Ealtzersen

EMPLOYEE CMPT PRCHASE PROGRAMS
See PURCHASING POWER LLC

D-U-N-S 93-227-5878
EMPLOYEE LEASING SOLUTIONS INC
1401 Manatee Ave W # 600, Bradenton, FL 34205-6708
Tel (941) 746-6567 Founded/Ownrshp 2004
Sales 23.8MM^E EMP 1,500^E
Accts Hevia Beagles & Company Pa
SIC 7363 Employee leasing service
Pr: William Mullis
Sr VP: R T Nipper
Sr VP: C E Southwick
VP: Ed Richardson
VP: Brian R Varnadore

D-U-N-S 82-803-4327
EMPLOYEE OWNED HOLDINGS INC
HYDRAQUIP
5500 N Sam Houston Pkwy W # 100, Houston, TX 77086-1572
Tel (281) 569-7000 Founded/Ownrshp 2006
Sales 246.8MM^E EMP 282
SIC 5084 Hydraulic systems equipment & supplies
Pr: Richard Neels
Brnch Mgr: Gordon Shellhaas
Dir IT: Jason Burger
Dir IT: Chad Ferreira
Mktg Dir: Jennifer Werth
Sales Asso: Marty Briles

D-U-N-S 13-614-0295
EMPLOYEES ONLY INC
805 Oakwood Dr Ste 100, Rochester, MI 48307-6206
Tel (248) 276-0950 Founded/Ownrshp 1996
Sales 71.5MM^E EMP 3,500
SIC 5812 Cafe
Pr: Mario D Apruzzese
Ql Cn Mgr: Joe Deehan

D-U-N-S 09-157-8711
EMPLOYEES RETIREMENT SYSTEM OF TEXAS
EXECUTV OFC OF THE STATE OF TX
(Suby of EXECUTIVE OFFICE OF STATE OF TEXAS) ★
200 E 18th St, Austin, TX 78701-1400
Tel (512) 867-7199 Founded/Ownrshp 1947
Sales NA EMP 400
Accts John Keel Cpa-State Auditor S
SIC 6371 9441 Pension funds; Administration of social & manpower programs;
Ex Dir: Porter Wilson
Pr: Dayna Trotter
COO: Larry Zeplin
Sr VP: Caandra Cooper
Exec: Cathy Terrell
*Ex Dir: Ann S Bishop
MIS Dir: Rob Robinson
Pr Dir: Mary Wardlow

D-U-N-S 92-778-0791
EMPLOYER SERVICES CORP
20 Pineview Dr Ste 3, Amherst, NY 14228-2122
Tel (716) 691-4455 Founded/Ownrshp 1995
Sales 88.9MM^E EMP 6,000
SIC 7363 8721 Employee leasing service; Accounting, auditing & bookkeeping
Pr: Greg Bauer
*VP: Kim Bartolotti
*VP: Jan Owczarzak
*VP: Jan Owczarzak
VP: Elizabeth Warren
*VP: Liz Warren

D-U-N-S 11-413-5796
■ EMPLOYERS COMPENSATION INSURANCE CO INC
(Suby of EMPLOYERS INSURANCE CO OF NEVADA) ★
500 N Brand Blvd Ste 800, Glendale, CA 91203-4707
Tel (818) 549-4600 Founded/Ownrshp 2002
Sales NA EMP 210^E
SIC 6411 Insurance agents, brokers & service
Pr: Douglas Dirks
*CFO: William E Yocke
Ex VP: Ann W Nelson
Sr VP: Allyson Simpson

D-U-N-S 78-813-2637
■ EMPLOYERS GENERAL INSURANCE GROUP INC
(Suby of OLD REPUBLIC INTERNATIONAL CORP) ★
1700 Pacific Ave Ste 1600, Dallas, TX 75201-4677
Tel (214) 665-6100 Founded/Ownrshp 1992
Sales NA EMP 172
SIC 6331 8742 Property damage insurance; Industry specialist consultants
Pr: Robert C Ramsower
Ch Bd: Aldo C Zucaro
Pr: Bob Johnson
VP: Phyllis Cawan
VP: Phyllis Cowan
VP: Michael Klink
VP: Gerald R Stell
VP: Kevin W Uzzle
VP: Thomas R Vick
Genl Mgr: H Dortc
Board of Directors: John H Binning, Wilbur S Legg, John W Popp, Arnold L Steiner, William R Stover

D-U-N-S 18-418-2009
■ EMPLOYERS GROUP INC
(Suby of EMPLOYERS HOLDINGS INC) ★
9790 Gateway Dr, Reno, NV 89521-8921
Tel (775) 327-6000 Founded/Ownrshp 2000
Sales NA EMP 628
SIC 6331 Workers' compensation insurance
Pr: Douglas Dirks
*Treas: William E Yocke

D-U-N-S 79-116-1347
▲ EMPLOYERS HOLDINGS INC
10375 Professional Cir, Reno, NV 89521-4802
Tel (888) 682-6671 Founded/Ownrshp 2005
Sales NA EMP 716^E
Tkr Sym EIG Exch NYS
SIC 6331 Workers' compensation insurance
Pr: Douglas D Dirks
*Ch Bd: Robert J Kolesar
COO: Stephen V Festa
CFO: Terry Eleftheriou
CFO: William E Yocke
Ofcr: Richard P Hallman
Ofcr: John P Nelson
Ex VP: Ann Nelson
Ex VP: Bryan C Ware
Sr VP: Cecelia M Abraham
Sr VP: Lori A Brown
Sr VP: Mark Hogle
Sr VP: Mark R Hogle
Sr VP: David M Quezada
Sr VP: Bryan Ware
Sr VP: Ray Wise
VP: Frank Buonomo
VP: Vicki Erickson
VP: Matthew H Hendricksen
VP: Kimberly K Hulse
VP: Samuel V King

D-U-N-S 87-864-0861
■ EMPLOYERS INSURANCE CO OF NEVADA
(Suby of EMPLOYERS GROUP INC) ★
10375 Professional Cir, Reno, NV 89521-4802
Tel (775) 327-2700 Founded/Ownrshp 2005
Sales NA EMP 620
SIC 6331 Workers' compensation insurance
CEO: John Donaldson
*Pr: Douglas D Dirks
*CEO: Leslie Mallonee
*CEO: Mary-Lou Misrahy
Sr VP: Aaron Mikulsky
Sr VP: Barry Vogt
VP: Celia Colling
VP: Martha Collins
VP: Kimberly Hulse
VP: David Macy
VP: Doug Zearfoss
Board of Directors: Richard Blakey, Rose James, Ronald Mosher

D-U-N-S 00-794-7872
EMPLOYERS INSURANCE OF WAUSAU A MUTUAL CO (WI)
LIBERTY MUTUAL
(Suby of LIBERTY MUTUAL GROUP INC) ★
2000 Westwood Dr, Wausau, WI 54401-7802
Tel (715) 845-5211 Founded/Ownrshp 1911, 1999
Sales NA EMP 3,500
SIC 6331 6311 Workers' compensation insurance; Fire, marine & casualty insurance: mutual; Automobile insurance; Life insurance carriers
Pr: Susan M Doyle
Pr: Mr Joe Gilles
CEO: Edmund F Kelly
CFO: Scott W Hogan
Treas: Laurance H S Yahia
Ex VP: James J McIntyre
Sr VP: Jay M Anliker
Sr VP: John D Crosby
Sr VP: Bob D Effinger
Sr VP: Eugene B Kelly
Sr VP: David L Lancaster
Sr VP: Harold W Larson
Sr VP: Michael H Mayers
Sr VP: Alfred P Moore
Sr VP: Francis W Robinson
Sr VP: James P Vaneyck
Sr VP: Martin J Welch
VP: Steve Kurtenbach
VP: Samuel McKnight
Comm Dir: Paul Hunsanger

D-U-N-S 00-694-1066
▲ EMPLOYERS MUTUAL CASUALTY CO
EMC INSURANCE COMPANIES
717 Mulberry St, Des Moines, IA 50309-3810
Tel (515) 280-2511 Founded/Ownrshp 1911
Sales NA EMP 2,338
SIC 6411 6321 6311 6519 Insurance agents, brokers & service; Reinsurance carriers, accident & health; Life insurance carriers; Real property lessors
CEO: Bruce G Kelley
Pr: Harold Capps
Pr: Rod Hanson
*CFO: Mark Reese
*Ex VP: Ronald W Jean
*Sr VP: Ray Davis
*VP: Kevin J Hovick
VP: Elizabeth Nigut
VP: Tom Oconnell
VP: Bryon Snethen
Exec: Linda Hoffmann

D-U-N-S 15-449-1757
EMPLOYERS RESOURCE MANAGEMENT CO
1301 S Vista Ave Ste 200, Boise, ID 83705-2576
Tel (208) 376-3000 Founded/Ownrshp 1985
Sales 456.8MM EMP 95
SIC 7363 Employee leasing service
Ch Bd: George H Gersema
*Pr: Ray O'Leary
*Ex VP: Mary D Gersema
*VP: Douglas W Gersema
VP: Douglas C Neve
IT Man: David Collette
Manager: Jim Grimm

D-U-N-S 87-813-6894 IMP
■ EMPLOYMENT AND TRAINING ADMINISTRATION
OFFICE OF NATIONAL RESPONSE
(Suby of UNITED STATES DEPARTMENT OF LABOR) ★
200 Constitution Ave Nw S2307, Washington, DC 20210-0001
Tel (202) 693-3500 Founded/Ownrshp 1935
Sales NA EMP 1,200
SIC 9441 Income maintenance programs; Administration of social & human resources;
Adm Dir: Mary Young
IT Man: Jeffery Hoskins
IT Man: Shawn Isaac

D-U-N-S 87-807-1547
EMPLOYMENT COMMISSION VIRGINIA
STATE DATA CENTER
(Suby of VIRGINIA SECRETARY OF COMMERCE AND TRADE) ★
703 E Main St, Richmond, VA 23219-3315
Tel (804) 786-3021 Founded/Ownrshp 1990
Sales NA EMP 1,000
SIC 9441 Administration of social & manpower programs;
Ex Dir: Roberto Pineda
Plng Mgr: Lynn Bradford
CIO: Linda Belflower
MIS Dir: Jim Peters
QA Dir: Wellford Dowdy
IT Man: Shirley Bray-Sledge
IT Man: Harry Holt
IT Man: David Portner

D-U-N-S 03-892-8615
EMPLOYMENT SOLUTIONS MANAGEMENT INC
EMPLOYBRIDGE
(Suby of EB SUBHOLDINGS II, INC.)
1040 Crown Pointe Pkwy, Atlanta, GA 30338-6908
Tel (770) 671-1900 Founded/Ownrshp 2000
Sales 169.9MM^E EMP 1,100^E
SIC 8741 Financial management for business
Pr: Thomas A Bickes
Pr: Debbie Worley
*CFO: Shawn W Poole
Ex VP: Shawn Poole
VP: Sharon Greenbaum
Exec: Beth Beidler
Area Mgr: Roxie Puente
Area Mgr: Ashley Stringfield
Brnch Mgr: Jennifer Wilson
Opers Supe: Johna Martinez
Opers Mgr: Rick Jones
Board of Directors: Chip Grissom Vp, Lisa Powell Vp, Sharon Greenbaum Assistan, Fred Herbert Vp, John Rosenbaum Vp, Michael Baer Vp, Keith Kislow Vp, Paul Seymour Vp, Ken Christensen Vp, Dan Lieblich Vp, Carolyn Silvey Vp, Jim Cleary Vp, Chris Loope Vp, Paul Sorensen Vp, Lisa Cooney Vp, Mark McComb Vp, Jeannie Davis Vp, Theresa McDannald Vp, Brian Devine Vp, Steve Mills Vp, Gunnar Gooding Vp, Michael Mitchell Vp, Steven Grimaud Vp, Melissa Porter Vp

D-U-N-S 87-870-4030
■ EMPLOYMENT STANDARDS ADMINISTRATION
OFFICE WKRS CMPNSTION PROGRAMS
(Suby of UNITED STATES DEPARTMENT OF LABOR) ★
200 Constitution Ave Nw, Washington, DC 20210-0001
Tel (202) 541-3610 Founded/Ownrshp 1971
Sales NA EMP 3,570
SIC 9651 Labor regulatory agency;
Prin: Bernard E Anderson

D-U-N-S 88-368-7568
EMPLOYMENT TRADITIONS INC
10045 E Rivershore Dr Se, Alto, MI 49302-9683
Tel (616) 891-9194 Founded/Ownrshp 1993
Sales 26.0MM EMP 1,000
SIC 7363 Help supply services
CEO: Patrick L Montgomery
*VP: Chandy Colley

D-U-N-S 03-070-0793
EMPORIA STATE UNIVERSITY
1 Kellogg Cir, Emporia, KS 66801-5087
Tel (620) 341-1200 Founded/Ownrshp 1863
Sales 48.3MM EMP 1,700^E
SIC 8221 University
Pr: Allison D Garrett
Bd of Dir: Jean Schulenberg
VP: David Cordle
VP: Jennifer Denton
VP: Olga Garay
VP: Allison Garrett
*VP: Werner Golling
VP: Natasha McCurdy
VP: Marsha Moulton
VP: Micheal Torres
VP: James Williams
Comm Man: Amanda Dura

D-U-N-S 07-988-1678
EMPORIA UNIFIED SCHOOL DISTRICT 253
1700 W 7th Ave, Emporia, KS 66801-2461
Tel (620) 341-2200 Founded/Ownrshp 1964
Sales 69.8MM EMP 1,100
SIC 8211 Public elementary & secondary schools; Elementary school; Secondary school; Vocational high school
*Prin: Marie Hazlett
Pr Dir: Nancy Horst
Teacher Pr: Andy Koenigs
HC Dir: Elena Lincoln

D-U-N-S 00-989-0922
EMPRES FINANCIAL SERVICES LLC (WA)
EVERGREEN HEALTHCARE
4601 Ne 77th Ave Ste 300, Vancouver, WA 98662-6736
Tel (360) 892-6628 Founded/Ownrshp 1997
Sales 124.2MM^E EMP 4,500
SIC 8051 Skilled nursing care facilities

Pr: Dale Patterson
COO: Anne Nipp
COO: Brent Weil
CFO: Michael Miller
VP: Jonathan Allred
Dir IT: Mike Eaton

EMPRESAS MUNICIPALES DEPT.
See MUNICIPIO DE SAN JUAN

D-U-N-S 78-812-0574
■ EMPRESS CASINO JOLIET CORP
HOLLYWOOD CASINO JOLIET
(*Suby of* PENN NATIONAL GAMING INC) ★
777 Hollywood Blvd, Joliet, IL 60436-1097
Tel (815) 744-9400 *Founded/Ownrshp* 1990
Sales 253.3MM[E] *EMP* 16,000
SIC 7999 Gambling establishment
Pr: Timothy J Wilmott
**CEO:* Peter Carlino
**CFO:* William Clifford
**VP:* Jeff Pfeiffer
VP Mktg: Chris Rellinger

EMR
See SOUTHERN RECYCLING LLC

D-U-N-S 82-845-4079
EMR (USA HOLDINGS) INC
(*Suby of* EUROPEAN METAL RECYCLING LIMITED)
143 Harding Ave Ste 1, Bellmawr, NJ 08031-2430
Tel (856) 365-7500 *Founded/Ownrshp* 2006
Sales 281.9MM[E] *EMP* 2,027
SIC 6719 Investment holding companies, except banks
CEO: Colin Iles
**Prin:* Stephanie Cion
**Prin:* Eric Ripoli

D-U-N-S 07-953-4845
EMR GOLD RECYCLING LLC
(*Suby of* EMR (USA HOLDINGS) INC) ★
4305 S Lamar St, Dallas, TX 75215-4108
Tel (214) 421-0247 *Founded/Ownrshp* 2011
Sales 122.5MM[E] *EMP* 153[E]
SIC 5093 6719 Scrap & waste materials; Metal scrap & waste materials; Investment holding companies, except banks

EMS
See EAST TEXAS MEDICAL CENTER

D-U-N-S 11-842-0046
EMS ASSEMBLY LLC
(*Suby of* HON HAI PRECISION INDUSTRY CO., LTD.)
8807 Fallbrook Dr, Houston, TX 77064-4856
Tel (281) 668-1551 *Founded/Ownrshp* 2002
Sales 100.0MM *EMP* 80
SIC 3575 Computer terminals, monitors & components
Prin: Fooming Fu

D-U-N-S 00-231-6342 IMP
EMS ENGINEERED MATERIALS SOLUTIONS LLC
(*Suby of* WICKEDER WESTFALENSTAHL GMBH)
39 Perry Ave, Attleboro, MA 02703-2417
Tel (508) 342-2100 *Founded/Ownrshp* 2000, 2007
Sales 98.2MM[E] *EMP* 306
SIC 3351 Copper & copper alloy sheet, strip, plate & products
CFO: Kevin Folan
COO: Paul Duffy
Opers Mgr: Joseph Roy

EMS GROUP
See ENERGY MAINTENANCE SERVICES GROUP I INC

D-U-N-S 04-794-9979 IMP
■ EMS TECHNOLOGIES INC
(*Suby of* HONEYWELL INTERNATIONAL INC) ★
660 Engineering Dr, Norcross, GA 30092-2821
Tel (770) 263-9200 *Founded/Ownrshp* 2011
Sales 261.9MM[E] *EMP* 1,300[E]
SIC 3663 7373 Microwave communication equipment; Space satellite communications equipment; Antennas, transmitting & communications; Receiver-transmitter units (transceiver); Systems integration services
CEO: Darius Adamczyk
Pr: Norman N Eldridge
Pr: Dick Sorenson
COO: Wiley Loughran
COO: Neilson A McKy
COO: Don T Scarz
**CFO:* John J Tus
Treas: Walter Plevyak
Treas: D T Scarz
Bd of Dir: Thomas W Connell
Sr VP: John J Farrell
Sr VP: Mike Guller
Sr VP: Donald Osborne
VP: Linda Cook
VP: Paul R Cox
VP: Kai Figwer
VP: Gary Hebb
VP: T Gerald Hickman
VP: Jon Holmes
VP: Bill Jacobs
VP: Jim Kershaw

D-U-N-S 02-040-4047
EMS USA INC
(*Suby of* EMS GROUP) ★
2000 Bering Dr Ste 600, Houston, TX 77057-3835
Tel (713) 595-7600 *Founded/Ownrshp* 2006
Sales 163.5MM *EMP* 1,200[E]
Accts Deloitte & Touche Llp Houston
SIC 1389 Construction, repair & dismantling services
CEO: Alexander J Buehler
**Pr:* James S Schroder
**CFO:* Steve List
**Sr VP:* Mark S Campbell
VP: William E Rom
VP: William Rome
VP: Jon D Simunek
Genl Mgr: Craig Wing
Off Mgr: Desiree Horton

Board of Directors: Steve List, Steve Schroder

D-U-N-S 12-193-2755 IMP
EMSER INTERNATIONAL LLC
EMSER TILE
8431 Santa Monica Blvd, Los Angeles, CA 90069-4294
Tel (323) 650-2000 *Founded/Ownrshp* 2000
Sales 164.0MM[E] *EMP* 300
SIC 5032 Ceramic wall & floor tile

EMSER TILE
See EMSER INTERNATIONAL LLC

D-U-N-S 04-935-1117 IMP/EXP
EMSER TILE LLC
DESIGN MADE EASY
8431 Santa Monica Blvd, Los Angeles, CA 90069-4209
Tel (323) 650-2000 *Founded/Ownrshp* 2000
Sales 160.7MM[E] *EMP* 300
SIC 5032 5211

D-U-N-S 00-949-6758
EMSI HOLDING CO
E M S I
3050 Regent Blvd Ste 400, Irving, TX 75063-5808
Tel (602) 288-4488 *Founded/Ownrshp* 1975
Sales 193.9MM[E] *EMP* 5,000
SIC 8099 Physical examination & testing services
Pr: Mark S Davis
**Pr:* Richard Peranton
**CFO:* Jon Gruenhagen
**CFO:* Keith Lieberman
**Ex VP:* Robert P Brooks
**Sr VP:* Tom Rubenstein

D-U-N-S 14-732-6540
EMSL ANALYTICAL INC
LA TESTING
200 Route 130 N, Cinnaminson, NJ 08077-2892
Tel (856) 858-4800 *Founded/Ownrshp* 1981
Sales 123.6MM[E] *EMP* 513
SIC 8734 Testing laboratories
Pr: Peter Frasca
**Sr VP:* Rob Demalo
**VP:* Luc Boisclair
**VP:* Carmela Frasca
Dir Lab: Michelle McGowan
Brnch Mgr: Kimberly Wallace
QA Dir: Bill Chamberlin
Manager: Melissa Helmick
Sls Mgr: Joseph Frasca
Sls Mgr: Deepa Thakar
Snr Mgr: Andrea Norman

D-U-N-S 05-609-0210
▲ EMTEC INC
150 N Radnor, Radnor, PA 19087
Tel (973) 376-4242 *Founded/Ownrshp* 2001
Sales 223.1MM[E] *EMP* 751[E]
Tkr Sym ETEC *Exch* OTO
SIC 7371 7379 Custom computer programming services; Software programming applications; Computer related consulting services
Ch Bd: Dinesh R Desai
Pr: Gregory P Chandler
Ex VP: Ronald A Seitz
VP: Sam Bhatt
VP: Sunil Misra
Mng Dir: Siva Arunachalam
Mng Dir: Don Sweeney
Prgrm Mgr: Narayan Ranganathan
CIO: Bart H De Maertelaere
CTO: Anshoom Jain
Board of Directors: Gregory L Cowan, Christopher M Formant, Robert Mannarino

D-U-N-S 02-185-5424 IMP/EXP
EMTEK PRODUCTS INC
(*Suby of* ASSA ABLOY AB)
15250 Stafford St, City of Industry, CA 91744-4418
Tel (626) 961-0413 *Founded/Ownrshp* 1999
Sales 104.0MM[E] *EMP* 797
SIC 3429 Manufactured hardware (general)
Pr: Thomas Millar
Sls Dir: Bill Schmidt

D-U-N-S 94-525-1924
■ EMTEQ LLC
(*Suby of* B/E AEROSPACE INC) ★
5349 S Emmer Dr, New Berlin, WI 53151-7302
Tel (262) 679-6170 *Founded/Ownrshp* 2014
Sales 113.6MM[E] *EMP* 400
SIC 8711 Aviation &/or aeronautical engineering
CEO: Jerry Jendusa
**COO:* Mark Ciepluch
**CFO:* Roger Naniot
**Ex VP:* James Harasha
Prgrm Mgr: Beverly Ronge
Dir IT: Josh Moore
Sls&Mrk Ex: Jeff Rozewicz

D-U-N-S 09-324-4218 IMP
EMULEX CORP
(*Suby of* BROADCOM) ★
3333 Susan St, Costa Mesa, CA 92626-1632
Tel (714) 662-5600 *Founded/Ownrshp* 2015
Sales 447.3MM *EMP* 1,122
SIC 3577 3661 Input/output equipment, computer; Telephone & telegraph apparatus
Pr: Hock E Tan
Pr: Dave Crespi
CFO: Kyle Wescoat
Treas: Anthony E Maslowski
Ex VP: Sadie A Herrera
Sr VP: Ali Hedayati
Sr VP: Perry Mulligan
Sr VP: Perry M Mulligan
VP: Jon Affeld
VP: Elmer Arment
VP: Rob Atherton
VP: Bill Caldwell
VP: Paul Ely
VP: Joseph J Garvey
VP: Mark Karnowski
VP: Michael Kelley
VP: Patricia H McCall
VP: Matt McSweeney

VP: Karen Mulvany
VP: Charlie Nogales
VP: Brian Reed
Board of Directors: Eugene J Frantz

D-U-N-S 02-958-3320
EN ENGINEERING LLC
(*Suby of* CIVC PARTNERS LP) ★
28100 Torch Pkwy Ste 400, Warrenville, IL 60555-3938
Tel (630) 353-4000 *Founded/Ownrshp* 2001
Sales 142.0MM[E] *EMP* 400[E]
SIC 8711 Engineering services
CFO: Ed Cvekej
CFO: Kevin Krueger
Dir IT: Amie Haltom
Software D: Jeff Sampson
Snr PM: John Brady
Snr Mgr: John Davis

D-U-N-S 87-267-0161
■ ENABLE GAS TRANSMISSION LLC
(*Suby of* ENABLE MIDSTREAM PARTNERS LP) ★
1111 Louisiana St, Houston, TX 77002-5230
Tel (713) 207-1111 *Founded/Ownrshp* 1992
Sales 232.6MM[E] *EMP* 310
SIC 4922 Pipelines, natural gas
Pr: David McClanahan
**Pr:* Gregory Harper
**Treas:* Marc Kilbride
VP: Doyle McQuillon
VP: Cy Zebot
Dist Mgr: Jay Reber
MIS Dir: Frank Hughes

D-U-N-S 83-568-7930
■ ENABLE MIDSTREAM PARTNERS LP
(*Suby of* CENTERPOINT ENERGY INC) ★
211 N Robinson Ave S410, Oklahoma City, OK 73102-7260
Tel (405) 525-7788 *Founded/Ownrshp* 1993
Sales 2.4MMM *EMP* 1,640
Tkr Sym ENBL *Exch* NYS
SIC 4922 4612 4619 Natural gas transmission; Pipelines, natural gas; Crude petroleum pipelines; Coal pipeline operation
Pr: Rodney J Sailor
Genl Pt: Enable GP
CFO: John P Laws
CFO: John Laws
Ex VP: Paul M Brewer
Ex VP: Deanna J Farmer
Ex VP: Mark C Schroeder

D-U-N-S 07-984-2988
■ ENABLE MISSISSIPPI RIVER TRANSMISSION LLC
(*Suby of* CENTERPOINT ENERGY INC) ★
211 N Robinson Ave N950, Oklahoma City, OK 73102-7109
Tel (405) 557-5271 *Founded/Ownrshp* 2013
Sales 1.3MMM[E] *EMP* 2,000
SIC 4619 Pipelines
Sr VP: Paul Brewer

D-U-N-S 00-720-5412
■ ENABLE OKLAHOMA INTRASTATE TRANSMISSION LLC
OGE ENERGY
(*Suby of* ENABLE MIDSTREAM PARTNERS LP) ★
211 N Robinson Ave N950, Oklahoma City, OK 73102-7109
Tel (405) 525-7788 *Founded/Ownrshp* 1997
Sales 702.7MM[E] *EMP* 500
SIC 4922 1321 4923 2911 Pipelines, natural gas; Natural gas liquids production; Gas transmission & distribution; Petroleum refining
Pr: E Keith Mitchell
**COO:* Stephen E Merrill
**VP:* Jon E Hanna
**VP:* Patricia D Horn
VP: John Laws
VP: Jean C Leger
VP: John McDougal
**VP:* Ramiro F Rangel
Snr Mgr: Celso Alonso

D-U-N-S 94-356-5028
ENANTA PHARMACEUTICALS INC
500 Arsenal St, Watertown, MA 02472-2806
Tel (617) 607-0800 *Founded/Ownrshp* 1995
Sales 88.2MM *EMP* 69
Tkr Sym ENTA *Exch* NGS
SIC 2834 8731 Pharmaceutical preparations; Biotechnical research, commercial
Pr: Jay R Luly
CFO: Paul J Mellett
Chf Mktg O: Nathalie Adda
Sr VP: Yat Sun or
Sr VP: Nathaniel S Gardiner
Sr VP: Timothy D Ocain
Assoc Dir: Guoqiang Wang
Board of Directors: Stephen Buckley Jr, Bruce L A Carter, George S Golumbeski, Terry C Vance

ENAP
See LBM ADVANTAGE INC

D-U-N-S 94-995-4002 IMP
ENBRIDGE (US) INC
(*Suby of* ENBRIDGE INC)
1100 Louisiana St # 3300, Houston, TX 77002-5227
Tel (713) 821-2000 *Founded/Ownrshp* 1995
Sales 231.6MM[E] *EMP* 1,000
SIC 4612 Crude petroleum pipelines
CEO: Al Monaco
**Pr:* Terry McGill
**CFO:* Stephen J Wuori
Ex VP: Leon A Zupan
**Sr VP:* Doug Krenz
**VP:* J Richard Bird

D-U-N-S 80-287-3125
▲ ENBRIDGE ENERGY PARTNERS LP
1100 La St Ste 3300, Houston, TX 77002
Tel (713) 821-2000 *Founded/Ownrshp* 1991
Sales 5.1MMM *EMP* 13[E]
Tkr Sym EEP *Exch* NYS
SIC 4612 4922 4924 Crude petroleum pipelines; Pipelines, natural gas; Natural gas distribution
Pr: Mark A Maki
Genl Pt: Lynn L Bourdon
CFO: Stephen J Neyland
VP: R L Adams
VP: Janet L Coy
VP: Chris Kaitson
Prgrm Mgr: Karen Dickson
IT Man: Terry Register
Counsel: Mollie Merritt
Snr Mgr: Rick Rakus

D-U-N-S 07-026-8537
■ ENBRIDGE MIDCOAST ENERGY INC
(*Suby of* ENBRIDGE ENERGY PARTNERS LP) ★
1100 La St Ste 3300, Houston, TX 77002
Tel (713) 650-8900 *Founded/Ownrshp* 1999
Sales 348.5MM[E] *EMP* 352[E]
SIC 4923 Gas transmission & distribution
Pr: Dan C Tutcher
**COO:* Terrance L McGill

D-U-N-S 60-640-2993 IMP
ENBRIDGE OFFSHORE (GAS TRANSMISSION) LLC
(*Suby of* ENBRIDGE (US) INC) ★
1100 La St Ste 3300, Houston, TX 77002
Tel (713) 821-2000 *Founded/Ownrshp* 1998
Sales 225.1MM[E] *EMP* 500[E]
SIC 4922 Natural gas transmission
Pr: Douglas V Krenz
**Treas:* Stephen J Neyland
**VP:* Heather Breitenbach
**VP:* Kenneth C Lanik
**VP:* Bradley C Petzolo
**VP:* Michael Shannon

D-U-N-S 03-000-7947
ENCANA OIL & GAS (USA) INC
(*Suby of* ENCANA CORPORATION)
370 17th St Ste 1700, Denver, CO 80202-5632
Tel (303) 623-2300 *Founded/Ownrshp* 1987, 1970
Sales 4.4MMM *EMP* 7,000
SIC 2911 1311 Petroleum refining; Crude petroleum & natural gas production
Pr: Doug Suttles
**COO:* Michael McAllister
**CFO:* Sherri Brillon
CFO: Alan Webb
**Ex VP:* Joanne Alexander
**Ex VP:* David Hill
**Ex VP:* Mike Williams
**Ex VP:* Rene Zemljak

D-U-N-S 03-615-5612 IMP
ENCLOS CORP
(*Suby of* ENCLOSE) ★
2770 Blue Waters Rd # 100, Saint Paul, MN 55121-1671
Tel (651) 796-6100 *Founded/Ownrshp* 1999
Sales 149.7MM[E] *EMP* 500
SIC 1741 Foundation & retaining wall construction
Pr: Gregg Sage
**CFO:* David Coleman
CFO: Dan Green
VP: Pam Dewall
**VP:* E J Kelley
**VP:* Tom Kretschmer
VP: Kevin Lamay
Exec: John McElroy
Exec: Bryan Wedan
**Prin:* John Jeske
Genl Mgr: Kevin Gross

ENCLOSE
See CH HOLDINGS USA INC

D-U-N-S 82-710-2810
ENCOMPASS DIGITAL MEDIA INC
(*Suby of* COURT SQUARE CAPITAL PARTNERS LP) ★
250 Harbor Dr, Stamford, CT 06902-7444
Tel (203) 965-6000 *Founded/Ownrshp* 2012
Sales 290.2MM[E] *EMP* 1,250
SIC 4841 8742 Cable television services; Direct broadcast satellite services (DBS); Multipoint distribution systems services (MDS); Distribution channels consultant
Co-CEO: William Tillson
CFO: Kenneth Sexton
**CFO:* Brian Stewart
**Co-CEO:* Ed Horowitz
**Chf Cred:* Barrie Woolston
Ex VP: Sarah Foss
Ex VP: Jon Rees
Ex VP: Jim Schuster
Sr VP: Jonathan Goldstein
Sr VP: Jay Laprise
Sr VP: Vince Matherne
VP: Louisa Brennan
VP: Richard Cline
VP: Mary Dahlke
VP: Jean Darold
VP: Ed Deckert
VP: Joe Garzillo
VP: Chere Johnson
VP: Jarred Kennedy
VP: Steve Mankowski

D-U-N-S 12-178-8819 IMP/EXP
ENCOMPASS GROUP LLC
ENCOMPASS TEXTILES & INTERIORS
(*Suby of* DOWLING TEXTILE MFG CO) ★
615 Macon St, McDonough, GA 30253-3531
Tel (770) 957-3981 *Founded/Ownrshp* 1999
Sales 166.3MM[E] *EMP* 489
SIC 2326 2337 2389 Medical & hospital uniforms, men's; Uniforms, except athletic: women's, misses' & juniors'; Hospital gowns
CEO: Michael L Spurlock
**Pr:* Tom Langdon
Pr: Melissa Warren
**CFO:* Alan V Davis
VP: Denise Formisano
VP: Katie Friedman
VP: Joe Przepiorka
Exec: Bob Fogle
Exec: Brian Hirz
Exec: Tom Sweatt
Exec: John Wood

ENCOMPASS HOME HEALTH
See ADVANCED HOMECARE MANAGEMENT INC

ENCOMPASS HOME HLTH & HOSPICE
See EHHI HOLDINGS INC

ENCOMPASS LIGHTING GROUP
See TECH LIGHTING LLC

ENCOMPASS PART DISTRIBUTION
See ENCOMPASS SUPPLY CHAIN SOLUTIONS INC

D-U-N-S 07-827-6306
ENCOMPASS SUPPLY CHAIN SOLUTIONS INC
ENCOMPASS PART DISTRIBUTION
775 Tipton Industrial Dr, Lawrenceville, GA 30046-2886
Tel (800) 432-8542 *Founded/Ownrshp* 2012
Sales 99.4MM[E] *EMP* 505[E]
SIC 8741 Business management
Pr: Robert Coolidge
**CFO:* Lanier Bivings
Sr VP: Scott Cameron
Sr VP: Joe Hurley
Sales Asso: Eddie Cafferty

ENCOMPASS TEXTILES & INTERIORS
See ENCOMPASS GROUP LLC

D-U-N-S 00-507-6497
ENCORE BANCSHARES INC
(*Suby of* CADENCE BANCORP LLC) ★
9 Greenway Plz Ste 1000, Houston, TX 77046-0900
Tel (713) 787-3100 *Founded/Ownrshp* 2000
Sales NA *EMP* 293[E]
SIC 6021 National commercial banks
Ch Bd: James S D'Agostino Jr
**Pr:* Preston Moore
**CFO:* Patrick T Oakes
Ex VP: Daryl Frevert
**Ex VP:* Carmen A Jordan
**Ex VP:* J Harold Williams
Sr VP: John D Caley
**Sr VP:* Stephanie R Pollock

D-U-N-S 07-512-1582
ENCORE BANK
(*Suby of* CADENCE BANK NA) ★
9 Greenway Plz Ste 1000, Houston, TX 77046-0900
Tel (713) 787-3100 *Founded/Ownrshp* 2000
Sales NA *EMP* 214
Accts Deloitte & Touche Llp Houston
SIC 6021 6035 National commercial banks; Federal savings & loan associations
Ch Bd: James D'Agostino
CFO: Anderson L Cree
**CFO:* L Anderson Creel
**Sr VP:* John D Caley
**Sr VP:* Rhonda Carroll
Sr VP: Derek Munger
VP: Greg Jahnke
VP: Jim Wilmouth

D-U-N-S 02-921-1260
▲ ENCORE CAPITAL GROUP INC
3111 Camino Del Rio N # 103, San Diego, CA 92108-5720
Tel (877) 445-4581 *Founded/Ownrshp* 1998
Sales NA *EMP* 6,700[E]
Tkr Sym ECPG *Exch* NGS
SIC 6153 Short-term business credit; Purchasers of accounts receivable & commercial paper
Pr: Kenneth A Vecchione
**Ch Bd:* Willem Mesdag
Pr: Amy Anuk
CFO: Jonathan Clark
Ex VP: Ashish Masih
Sr VP: Gregory L Call
VP: Barbara Kennedy
Prgrm Mgr: Rachel Nieting
Snr Mgr: Blake Hern
Board of Directors: Wendy Hannam, Michael P Monaco, Laura Newman Olle, Francis E Quinlan, Norman R Sorensen, Richard J Srednicki

D-U-N-S 13-251-1440
ENCORE ELECTRIC INC
7125 W Jefferson Ave # 400, Lakewood, CO 80235-2333
Tel (303) 934-1234 *Founded/Ownrshp* 2002
Sales 83.1MM[E] *EMP* 300
SIC 1731 Electrical work
Pr: Willis Wiedel
**CFO:* Vicki Waters
VP: Justin Godwin
**VP:* Garry Lawrenz
VP: Jim Nottingham
VP: Jeff Thompson
**VP:* David White
Genl Mgr: Marlin Linder
CTO: George Moore
IT Man: John J Pl
Natl Sales: Mitchell Avis

D-U-N-S 62-700-5320
ENCORE ENTERPRISES INC
ENCORE HOSPITALITY
5005 L B Johnson Fwy 12 Ste 1200, Dallas, TX 75244
Tel (214) 259-7009 *Founded/Ownrshp* 1999
Sales 190.9MM[E] *EMP* 500[E]
SIC 6531 6512 Real estate agent, commercial; Nonresidential building operators
Pr: Patrick J Barber
**Ch Bd:* Bharat H Sangani
Pr: D Stephen Donosky
**COO:* Mahesh Shetty
**Ex VP:* Charles A Omage
Sr VP: Mark Avis
**Sr VP:* Yatin Gandhi
VP: Scot Clevenger
**VP:* Smita Sangani
VP: Mark Stevenson

ENCORE HOSPITALITY
See ENCORE ENTERPRISES INC

D-U-N-S 15-407-4504 IMP
■ ENCORE MEDICAL LP
DJO SURGICAL
(*Suby of* DJO GLOBAL) ★
9800 Metric Blvd, Austin, TX 78758-5445
Tel (512) 832-9500 *Founded/Ownrshp* 2011
Sales 228.8MM[E] *EMP* 1,000
SIC 3842 5047 Surgical appliances & supplies; Implants, surgical; Medical equipment & supplies
CEO: Michael P Mogul
Pr: Toby Bost
Pr: Steven Ingel
Ex VP: Susan Crawford
Ex VP: Jeanine Kestler
VP: Al Alonzo
VP: William Fain
VP: Sam Son
Plnt Mgr: Dan Stump
Board of Directors: John Abeles MD, Kenneth Davidson, Dennis J Enright, Jay Haft, Joel Kanter, Richard Martin

D-U-N-S 15-902-7833
■ ENCORE RECEIVABLE MANAGEMENT INC
(*Suby of* CONVERGYS CUSTOMER MANAGEMENT GROUP INC) ★
400 N Rogers Rd, Olathe, KS 66062-1212
Tel (913) 782-3333 *Founded/Ownrshp* 2000
Sales 47.5MM[E] *EMP* 1,000
SIC 7322 Adjustment & collection services
Pr: Doug Jones
VP: Kathy Cooley
VP: Tom Jordan
VP: Teri Strahine

D-U-N-S 80-965-5090
ENCORE REHABILITATION SERVICES LLC
33533 W 12 Mile Rd # 290, Farmington Hills, MI 48331-5635
Tel (248) 865-1177 *Founded/Ownrshp* 2015
Sales 105.2MM[E] *EMP* 2,988[E]
SIC 8093 8049 Rehabilitation center, outpatient treatment; Occupational therapist; Physical therapist; Speech therapist
Pr: Linda Shackelford
VP: Don Cook
VP: John Rubino
Mktg Dir: Robin Penn
Board of Directors: Eric A Shuey

D-U-N-S 36-409-5273
▲ ENCORE WIRE CORP
1329 Millwood Rd, McKinney, TX 75069-7157
Tel (972) 562-9473 *Founded/Ownrshp* 1989
Sales 1.0MMM *EMP* 1,182[E]
Accts Ernst & Young Llp Dallas Tex
Tkr Sym WIRE *Exch* NGS
SIC 3357 Building wire & cable, nonferrous
Ch Bd: Daniel L Jones
CFO: Frank J Bilban
VP: Todd Clayton
VP: David Smith
VP: Gary Spence
IT Man: Jay Cutrona
Sls&Mrk Ex: Kevin Kieffer
Sls Dir: Landon B Hartwick
Mktg Mgr: Karolina Zuraw
Board of Directors: Donald E Courtney, Gregory J Fisher, William R Thomas III, Scott D Weaver, John H Wilson

D-U-N-S 00-516-2904 IMP
ENCYCLOPAEDIA BRITANNICA INC
(*Suby of* ENCYCLOPAEDIA BRITANNICA HOLDING SA)
325 N Lasalle St Ste 200, Chicago, IL 60654
Tel (847) 777-2241 *Founded/Ownrshp* 1768, 1996
Sales 109.3MM[E] *EMP* 439[E]
SIC 2731 Book publishing
Pr: Jorge Cauz
**CFO:* Maria Fiore
**Ch:* Jacob Safra
**Sr VP:* Leah Mansoor
**Sr VP:* Michael Ross
Comm Dir: Tom Panelas
Ex Dir: Je Luebering
Web Dev: Frank Radostits
Genl Couns: Cyrl Carifa
Assoc Ed: Marino Pebenito

D-U-N-S 13-080-5948
■ ENDEAVOR AIR INC
(*Suby of* DELTA AIRLINES) ★
7500 Airline Dr, Minneapolis, MN 55450-1101
Tel (901) 348-4100 *Founded/Ownrshp* 2013
Sales 577.6MM[E] *EMP* 5,000
SIC 4512 Air passenger carrier, scheduled
CEO: Ryan Gumm
**COO:* Barry Wilbur
**CFO:* Loren Neuenschwander
CFO: Curtis Sawyer
Ofcr: Brent Skillings
**VP:* Bill Donohue
**VP:* L Russell Elander III
**Prin:* Mike Becker

D-U-N-S 06-212-2114 IMP
ENDEAVOR ENERGY RESOURCES LP (TX)
110 N Marienfeld St # 200, Midland, TX 79701-4400
Tel (432) 687-1575 *Founded/Ownrshp* 2000
Sales 293.5MM[E] *EMP* 300
SIC 1311 8748 Crude petroleum production; Business consulting
Pt: Autry C Stephens
**CFO:* Damon Button
CFO: Doug Feldman
CTO: Joe Stephens
Dir IT: Michael Hillebrand

ENDEAVOUR
See ASPIRE HOLDINGS LLC

D-U-N-S 55-606-2750
ENDEAVOUR CAPITAL FUND LIMITED PARTNERSHIP
920 Sw 6th Ave Ste 1400, Portland, OR 97204-1241
Tel (503) 223-2721 *Founded/Ownrshp* 1991
Sales 94.5MM[E] *EMP* 508
SIC 4213 4731 6799

D-U-N-S 60-194-6291 IMP
ENDEAVOUR INTERNATIONAL CORP
811 Main St Ste 2100, Houston, TX 77002-6128
Tel (713) 307-8700 *Founded/Ownrshp* 2002
Sales 316.0MM *EMP* 38[E]
SIC 1311 Crude petroleum & natural gas
Co-CEO: Catherine L Stubbs
**Ch Bd:* William L Transier
**V Ch Bd:* John N Seitz
Ex VP: James J Emme
Ex VP: H Teague
VP: Julie Ferro
Board of Directors: James H Browning, John B Connally III, Sheldon R Erikson, William D Lancaster, Nancy K Quinn

D-U-N-S 07-873-3846
ENDEMOL
9255 W Sunset Blvd # 1100, West Hollywood, CA 90069-3309
Tel (310) 860-9914 *Founded/Ownrshp* 2012
Sales 170.0MM *EMP* 70
SIC 7922 Television program, including commercial producers
Ch: David Goldberg

D-U-N-S 02-611-7433
ENDICOTT COLLEGE
376 Hale St, Beverly, MA 01915-2098
Tel (978) 927-0585 *Founded/Ownrshp* 1939
Sales 121.5MM *EMP* 782
Accts Kpmg Llp Boston Ma
SIC 8221 Colleges universities & professional schools
Pr: Richard Wylie
Pr: Joanne L Waldner
Ofcr: Robert Allen
**Ex VP:* Lynne O'Toole
VP: Lynne Otoole
VP: Thomas J Redman
VP: David Vigneron
Assoc Dir: Donald Femino
Assoc Dir: George Sherman
**Prin:* Todd J Wemmer
Dir IT: Gary Kelley

D-U-N-S 07-381-7603
ENDICOTT COLLEGE
376 Hale St, Beverly, MA 01915-2098
Tel (978) 927-0585 *Founded/Ownrshp* 1987
Sales 95.7MM *EMP* 62
Accts Kpmg Llp Boston Ma
SIC 8221 College, except junior
Pr: Dr Richard E Wylie
CFO: Danni Dragonas
**Treas:* Donna Couture

ENDNOTE
See THOMSON REUTERS (SCIENTIFIC) LLC

ENDO CHOICE PATHOLOGY
See ENDOCHOICE INC

D-U-N-S 00-120-1735
ENDO HEALTH SOLUTIONS INC (DE)
(*Suby of* ENDO INTERNATIONAL PUBLIC LIMITED COMPANY)
1400 Atwater Dr, Malvern, PA 19355-8701
Tel (484) 216-0000 *Founded/Ownrshp* 1997, 2014
Sales 1.2MMM[E] *EMP* 6,119
SIC 2834 Pharmaceutical preparations; Analgesics
Pr: Rajiv De Silva
Pr: Joseph J Ciaffoni
COO: Don Degolyer
CFO: Suketu P Upadhyay
Treas: Andrew Saik
Ex VP: Susan Hall PHD
Sr VP: Marc Kustoff
VP: Julie H McHugh
VP: Brian Munroe
VP: Dan A Rudio
VP: George Vargo
Assoc Dir: Dennis Baker

D-U-N-S 17-807-4951 IMP
ENDO PHARMACEUTICALS INC
(*Suby of* ENDO HEALTH SOLUTIONS INC) ★
1400 Atwater Dr, Malvern, PA 19355-8701
Tel (484) 216-0000 *Founded/Ownrshp* 1997
Sales 668.3MM[E] *EMP* 1,858[E]
SIC 2834 Pharmaceutical preparations
CEO: Rajiv De Silva
**Treas:* Karen C Adler
Treas: Charles A Rowland Jr
Sr VP: Colleen A Pero
VP: Armando Cortaas
VP: Blaine Davis
VP: Jennifer Dubas
**VP:* Ivan Gergel
VP: Sanjay Patel
Dir Risk M: Veronica Urdaneta
Genl Mgr: Darnell Turner

D-U-N-S 01-415-4279 IMP
ENDOCHOICE INC
ENDO CHOICE PATHOLOGY
11405 Old Roswell Rd, Alpharetta, GA 30009-2054
Tel (888) 682-3636 *Founded/Ownrshp* 2008
Sales 115.0MM[E] *EMP* 210[E]
SIC 5047 Medical & hospital equipment
CEO: Mark Gilreath
**Ch Bd:* Scott Huennekens
Pr: Yoram Ashery
**COO:* Lou Malice
**COO:* Kevin Rubey
**CFO:* David N Gill
**CFO:* Mike Lambert
**Chf Mktg O:* Douglas N Ladd
**Sr VP:* Gregg Costantino
**Sr VP:* Will Parks
**VP:* Yaniv Kirma
**VP:* Tolan E Mitchell
**VP:* George Pratt
**VP:* Kristen J Schuller
VP: Vince Turturro
**VP:* Nigel Wilkinson

D-U-N-S 85-856-0477 IMP
▲ ENDOLOGIX INC
2 Musick, Irvine, CA 92618-1631
Tel (949) 595-7200 *Founded/Ownrshp* 1992
Sales 153.6MM *EMP* 619[E]
Tkr Sym ELGX *Exch* NGS
SIC 3841 Surgical & medical instruments; Catheters
Ch Bd: John McDermott
Pr: Robert D Mitchell
CFO: Vaseem Mahboob
VP: Amanda L Depalma
VP: Dave Jennings
VP: Jose Lima
VP: James Machek
VP: Shari L O'Quinn
Assoc Dir: Julia Dunham
Genl Mgr: Joseph A Dejohn
Genl Mgr: Cecile Ferracci
Board of Directors: Christopher G Chavez, Daniel Lemaitre, Guido J Neels, Leslie Norwalk, Gregory D Waller, Thomas C Wilder III, Thomas F Zenty III

D-U-N-S 60-302-7801 IMP
ENDRESS + HAUSER FLOWTEC AG INC
ENDRESSHAUSER
(*Suby of* ENDRESS+HAUSER (INTERNATIONAL) HOLDING AG)
2330 Endress Pl, Greenwood, IN 46143-9772
Tel (317) 535-7138 *Founded/Ownrshp* 1995
Sales 228.8MM[E] *EMP* 8,500
SIC 3823 Flow instruments, industrial process type
CEO: Gerhard Jost
Exec: Luc Schultheiss
**Genl Mgr:* Hans-Peter Blaser
Genl Mgr: Patrick Ncglothen
Opers Mgr: Joe Clarke

D-U-N-S 05-347-2650 IMP
ENDRESS + HAUSER INC
(*Suby of* ENDRESS+HAUSER (INTERNATIONAL) HOLDING AG)
2350 Endress Pl, Greenwood, IN 46143-9672
Tel (317) 535-7138 *Founded/Ownrshp* 1970
Sales 173.2MM[E] *EMP* 250
SIC 8711 Engineering services
Pr: Klaus Endress
CFO: Luc Schultheiss
VP: Chris English
VP: Brian Hoover
VP: Phil Pescitelli
VP: Keith Riley
**Prin:* Todd Lucey
Div Mgr: Jurgen Schrempp
Genl Mgr: Peter Blaser-Hans
Genl Mgr: Codd Lucey
Genl Mgr: Tod Lucey

ENDRESSHAUSER
See ENDRESS + HAUSER FLOWTEC AG INC

D-U-N-S 04-901-8237 IMP
ENDRIES INTERNATIONAL INC (WI)
(*Suby of* FERGUSON ENTERPRISES INC) ★
714 W Ryan St, Brillion, WI 54110-1045
Tel (920) 756-2174 *Founded/Ownrshp* 1969, 2005
Sales 310.2MM[E] *EMP* 464
SIC 5085 5072 Fasteners & fastening equipment; Fasteners, industrial: nuts, bolts, screws, etc.; Industrial tools; Hardware
Pr: Steven R Endries
**CFO:* Matthew Vechart
**VP:* Edward T Fischer
VP: Rich Shovick
**VP:* Dan Stieber
Dist Mgr: Steven Larson
Dist Mgr: Byron O Olson
CIO: Todd Fischer
IT Man: Sarah Gruber
**VP Opers:* Daniel Stieber
Plnt Mgr: Randy Loppnow

ENDURA HEALTHCARE
See ENSIGN GROUP INC

D-U-N-S 00-321-3279 IMP
ENDURA PRODUCTS INC (NC)
8817 W Market St, Colfax, NC 27235-9419
Tel (336) 668-2472 *Founded/Ownrshp* 1954
Sales 1.2MMM *EMP* 350
SIC 3429

D-U-N-S 02-521-5570
ENDURACARE THERAPY MANAGEMENT INC
3765a Government Blvd, Mobile, AL 36693-4307
Tel (251) 666-7867 *Founded/Ownrshp* 2002
Sales 82.8MM[E] *EMP* 4,000
SIC 8049 8741 Physical therapist; Speech specialist; Occupational therapist; Nursing & personal care facility management
Ch: Andrew Turner
V Ch: James Martin IV
**Pr:* Tom Dixon
**COO:* Tom Mack

ENDURANCE AMERICAN INSUR CO
See ENDURANCE SERVICES LIMITED

D-U-N-S 12-422-8920
ENDURANCE ASSURANCE CORP
(*Suby of* ENDURANCE SPECIALTY HOLDINGS LTD)
750 3rd Ave Fl 1819, New York, NY 10017-2703
Tel (212) 471-2800 *Founded/Ownrshp* 2002
Sales NA *EMP* 85[E]
SIC 6351 Surety insurance
Pr: Steve Carlsen
**CFO:* Bill Babcock
Chf Inves: Mark Silverstein
VP: Pat Corless
**VP:* David Palastro
Exec: Ron Koch
CIO: Tom Terry
Software D: Deepak Walia
**Genl Couns:* Emily Canelo

D-U-N-S 07-917-1550
▲ ENDURANCE INTERNATIONAL GROUP HOLDINGS INC
10 Corporate Dr Ste 300, Burlington, MA 01803-4200
Tel (781) 852-3200 *Founded/Ownrshp* 1997
Sales 741.3MM *EMP* 2,593[E]
Tkr Sym EIGI *Exch* NGS
SIC 7372 Prepackaged software
CEO: Hari Ravichandran
**Ch Bd:* James C Neary
Pr: Ronald Lasalvia
CFO: Marc Montagner
Ofcr: Kathy Andreasen
VP: Michael Powderly

D-U-N-S 11-201-6985
■ ENDURANCE INTERNATIONAL GROUP INC
BIZLAND
(*Suby of* ENDURANCE INTERNATIONAL GROUP HOLDINGS INC) ★
10 Corporate Dr Ste 300, Burlington, MA 01803-4200
Tel (866) 897-5421 *Founded/Ownrshp* 1997
Sales 97.9MM[E] *EMP* 250
SIC 8732 Market analysis, business & economic research
CEO: Hari Ravichandran
Pt: Neil Shetty
**CEO:* Steve Sydness
**CFO:* Tivanka Ellawala
**CFO:* Christina Lane
CFO: Marc Montagner
Bd of Dir: John Doggett
Ex VP: Brian Unruh
Sr VP: Jean McCarthy
VP: Craig Millman
Sftwr Eng: Quinn Jones

D-U-N-S 79-093-5626
ENDURANCE SERVICES LIMITED
ENDURANCE AMERICAN INSUR CO
(*Suby of* ENDURANCE U.S. HOLDINGS CORP.)
750 3rd Ave 210, New York, NY 10017-2703
Tel (212) 471-2800 *Founded/Ownrshp* 2005
Sales NA *EMP* 200
SIC 6411 Property & casualty insurance agent
CEO: John Charman
**Pr:* Michael Fujii
**CFO:* Brian Nolan
VP: Sharon Herbert
**VP:* Michael Sovern
CIO: Tom Terry

D-U-N-S 83-703-7816 IMP
ENDURO COMPOSITES INC
16602 Central Green Blvd, Houston, TX 77032-5131
Tel (713) 358-4000 *Founded/Ownrshp* 2009
Sales 118.2MM[E] *EMP* 200
SIC 5033 Fiberglass building materials
Ch Bd: Walter C Greig
Pr: Flavio Ortiz
**Pr:* Wallace Woodlief
**CFO:* Timothy Broussard
CFO: Tim Grussard
Mng Dir: Kyle Montgomery
Rgnl Mgr: Paul Whiteman
Mktg Dir: Deborah Newby
Manager: Blake Heger

D-U-N-S 14-492-7415
ENEL GREEN POWER NORTH AMERICA INC
(*Suby of* ENEL GREEN POWER SPA)
1 Tech Dr Ste 220, Andover, MA 01810-2452
Tel (978) 681-1900 *Founded/Ownrshp* 2000
Sales 579.7MM[E] *EMP* 370
Accts Ernst & Young Llp
SIC 4911 Generation, electric power
Pr: Francesco Venturini
CFO: Gianfranco Butera
**CFO:* Marco Fossataro
**Treas:* Rodolfo Martinvilla Pena
VP: Stephen Champagne
VP: Amea L Desjourdy
VP: Stephen Pike
VP: David Post
Netwrk Eng: Chad Rian

ENEOS
See JX NIPPON OIL & ENERGY USA INC

D-U-N-S 00-409-5442
ENER-G GROUP INC
1261 Broadway Fl 6, New York, NY 10001-3506
Tel (917) 281-0020 *Founded/Ownrshp* 2010
Sales 25.6MM[E] *EMP* 1,200
SIC 8711 Energy conservation engineering
Ch Bd: Tim Scott
**CEO:* Chris Hayton

D-U-N-S 10-372-7124 IMP
ENER1 GROUP INC
550 W Cypress Creek Rd, Fort Lauderdale, FL 33309-6168
Tel (954) 202-4442 *Founded/Ownrshp* 2001
Sales 134.9MM[E] *EMP* 769[E]
SIC 3577 3069 Computer peripheral equipment; Graphic displays, except graphic terminals; Input/output equipment, computer; Battery boxes, jars or parts, hard rubber
Pr: Mike Zoi
**COO:* Ronald Stewart
**CFO:* Anthony Castano
**VP:* Peter Novan

D-U-N-S 13-178-8879
ENER1 INC
(*Suby of* ENER1 GROUP INC) ★
1540 Broadway Fl 25c, New York, NY 10036-4039
Tel (212) 920-3500 *Founded/Ownrshp* 2002
Sales 132.3MM[E] *EMP* 769[E]
SIC 3691 Storage batteries
CEO: Alex Sorokin
**Ch Bd:* Melissa Debes
**Ch Bd:* Thomas Snyder
Ch Bd: Tae-Hee Yoon
**Pr:* Christopher L Cowger
Pr: Bruce Curtis
Pr: Ulrik Grape
**Pr:* David Roberts
**CEO:* Michael Alma
**CFO:* Dale E Parker
**Treas:* Richard Quirin
VP: Thomas C Goesch
**Int Pr:* Nicholas Brunero
Board of Directors: Kenneth Baker, Nora Brownell, Elliot Fuhr, William E James, Greg Kasagawa, Stanislav Shekshnia, Boris Zingarevich

D-U-N-S 07-212-0215
ENERCON SERVICES INC
500 Townpark Ln Nw # 275, Kennesaw, GA 30144-3707
Tel (770) 919-1930 *Founded/Ownrshp* 1982
Sales 291.9MM *EMP* 1,833
SIC 8711 Engineering services
Pr: John Richardson
COO: Robert Bryan
Sec: James M Marshall
VP: Pete Capponi
VP: John Corn
VP: Jerry Curreri
VP: Ray Dremel
VP: Bob Evans
VP: Robert Evans
VP: Jim Gannon
VP: Mike Manski
VP: Pete Nast
VP: J Aaron Smith
VP: David Studley
VP: Michelle Zerkle

D-U-N-S 03-093-8732 IMP/EXP
ENERFAB INC
4955 Spring Grove Ave, Cincinnati, OH 45232-1925
Tel (513) 641-0500 *Founded/Ownrshp* 1988
Sales 669.6MM[E] *EMP* 2,200
SIC 3443 1629 1541 1711 3479 Tanks, standard or custom fabricated: metal plate; Power plant construction; Land reclamation; Industrial buildings & warehouses; Mechanical contractor; Process piping contractor; Painting, coating & hot dipping
CEO: Wendell R Bell
**Pr:* Jeffrey P Hock
**CFO:* Daniel J Sillies
**Ch:* Dave Herche
Ex VP: Jeffrey R Aasch
**VP:* Mark Schoettmer
VP: Daniel Sillies
Sales Exec: Jerry Ankenbauer

D-U-N-S 16-167-8966 IMP/EXP
ENERFLEX ENERGY SYSTEMS INC
(*Suby of* ENERFLEX LTD.)
10815 Telge Rd, Houston, TX 77095-5038
Tel (281) 345-9300 *Founded/Ownrshp* 1986
Sales 330.3MM[E] *EMP* 500
SIC 3585 7623 7699 3563 Refrigeration equipment, complete; Compressors for refrigeration & air conditioning equipment; Refrigeration repair service; Compressor repair; Air & gas compressors
Pr: Jerry Fraelic
**Sec:* Anna M Paravi
**VP:* James Harbilas
VP: Rick Holbrook
MIS Dir: Bruce Hawk
IT Man: Bruce Hock
Sfty Mgr: Rob Morton

D-U-N-S 07-888-6170
ENERFO USA INC
(*Suby of* ENERFO PTE. LTD.)
16934 Frances St Ste 105, Omaha, NE 68130-2397
Tel (402) 401-6300 *Founded/Ownrshp* 2013
Sales 250.0MM *EMP* 30
SIC 6221 Commodity traders, contracts
**COO:* Aaron Campbell

D-U-N-S 09-570-6032
▲ ENERGEN CORP
605 Richard Arrington Jr, Birmingham, AL 35203-2777
Tel (205) 326-2700 *Founded/Ownrshp* 1978
Sales 878.5MM *EMP* 470[E]
Tkr Sym EGN *Exch* NYS
SIC 1311 4924 4922 1321 Crude petroleum & natural gas; Natural gas distribution; Natural gas transmission; Natural gas liquids; Natural gas liquids production
Ch Bd: James T McManus II
CFO: Charles W Porter Jr
Sr VP: David A Godsey
VP: Russell E Lynch Jr
VP: John S Richardson
VP: J David Woodruff Jr
Exec: Tammy Finch
Info Man: Keith Brown
Prd Mgr: Paul Callaway
Mktg Dir: Cindy Smith
Mktg Mgr: Greg Bomar
Board of Directors: Kenneth W Dewey, T Michael Goodrich, M James Gorrie, Jay Grinney, William G Hargett, Frances Powell Hawes, Alan A Kleier, Stephen A Snider

D-U-N-S 14-787-1420
■ ENERGEN RESOURCES CORP
(*Suby of* ENERGEN CORP) ★
605 Richard Arrington Jr, Birmingham, AL 35203-2777
Tel (205) 326-2710 *Founded/Ownrshp* 1979
Sales 700.4MM[E] *EMP* 353
SIC 1382 1321 Oil & gas exploration services; Natural gas liquids
Ch Bd: James T McManus
**Pr:* John S Richardson
Sr VP: Joe E Cook
**VP:* William K Bibb
VP: Russell E Lynch Jr
VP: Cindy Rayburn
VP: Linda Sewell
VP: David Woodruff
VP: J D Woodruff Jr
Exec: Charles E Saltzer
CIO: William L Brunson Jr

ENERGEX TUBE
See ZEKELMAN INDUSTRIES INC

D-U-N-S 83-149-7792 EXP
■ ENERGIZER BATTERY INC
(*Suby of* ENERGIZER HOLDINGS INC) ★
533 Maryville Univ Dr, Saint Louis, MO 63141-5801
Tel (314) 985-2000 *Founded/Ownrshp* 2003
Sales 96.2MM[E] *EMP* 300
SIC 3691 Storage batteries
CEO: Ward M Klein
VP Mktg: David Hatfield
VP Mktg: Jeff Ziminski

ENERGIZER BATTERY MFG INC
See ENERGIZER MANUFACTURING INC

D-U-N-S 07-987-8676
■ ENERGIZER BRANDS LLC
(*Suby of* ENERGIZER HOLDINGS INC) ★
533 Maryville Univ Dr, Saint Louis, MO 63141-5801
Tel (314) 985-2000 *Founded/Ownrshp* 2015
Sales 221.8MM[E] *EMP* 5,500
SIC 5063 Flashlights
CEO: Alan Hoskins

D-U-N-S 07-981-5248
▲ ENERGIZER HOLDINGS INC
533 Maryville Univ Dr, Saint Louis, MO 63141-5801
Tel (314) 985-2000 *Founded/Ownrshp* 2015
Sales 1.6MMM *EMP* 11,292
Tkr Sym ENR *Exch* NYS
SIC 3691 Storage batteries; Alkaline cell storage batteries; Batteries, rechargeable; Lead acid batteries (storage batteries)
Pr: Alan R Hoskins
**Ch Bd:* J Patrick Mulcahy
COO: Mark S Lavigne
CFO: Brian K Hamm
Ofcr: Sue K Drath
Ex VP: Gregory T Kinder
VP: Emily K Boss
Mktg Mgr: Kathy Spencer
Board of Directors: Bill G Armstrong, Cynthia J Brinkley, Kevin J Hunt, James C Johnson, John E Klein, W Patrick McGinnis, Patrick J Moore, John R Roberts

D-U-N-S 60-245-5516 IMP/EXP
■ ENERGIZER MANUFACTURING INC
ENERGIZER BATTERY MFG INC
(*Suby of* ENERGIZER HOLDINGS INC) ★
25225 Detroit Rd, Westlake, OH 44145-2536
Tel (440) 835-7866 *Founded/Ownrshp* 2002
Sales 145.6MM[E] *EMP* 325
SIC 3691 Storage batteries
Pr: Sam Johnson
Corp Couns: Brian Foster

D-U-N-S 88-495-1849 IMP/EXP
ENERGY ALLOYS LLC
3 Waterway Square Pl # 600, The Woodlands, TX 77380-3489
Tel (832) 601-5800 *Founded/Ownrshp* 1995
Sales 222.1MM[E] *EMP* 500
SIC 5051 Tubing, metal; Bars, metal
CEO: Dave Warren
**CFO:* Paul F Patek
**Treas:* Mary Magin
VP: Michael Gray
IT Man: Kaushik Ray
Mtls Mgr: Grant Landry
Mktg Mgr: Marty Westbeld
Sls Mgr: Cheryl Gilmore
Sls Mgr: Rich Steinkirchner
Sls Mgr: Edward Yates

ENERGY AND CHEMICALS GROUP
See CHART ENERGY & CHEMICALS INC

D-U-N-S 92-732-4749
ENERGY AND ENVIRONMENT CABINET
(*Suby of* EXECUTIVE OFFICE OF COMMONWEALTH OF KENTUCKY) ★
500 Mero St Ste 4, Frankfort, KY 40601-1957
Tel (502) 564-3350 *Founded/Ownrshp* 1973
Sales 29.9MM[E] *EMP* 1,700
SIC 8641 9611 Environmental protection organization; Energy development & conservation agency, government

D-U-N-S 07-889-1647
ENERGY CAPITAL PARTNERS II LLC
51 John F Kennedy Pkwy # 200, Short Hills, NJ 07078-2702
Tel (973) 671-6100 *Founded/Ownrshp* 2009
Sales 212.2MM[E] *EMP* 5,701
SIC 6799 4953 8711 Investors; Radioactive waste materials, disposal; Engineering services
Prin: Doug Kimmenlman

D-U-N-S 07-929-1789
ENERGY CAPITAL PARTNERS III LLC
51 John F Kennedy Pkwy, Short Hills, NJ 07078-2704
Tel (973) 671-6100 *Founded/Ownrshp* 2013
Sales 211.2MM[E] *EMP* 1,590[E]
SIC 5211 Energy conservation products
Sr Pt: Doug Kimmelman
Pt: Pete Labbat
Pt: Tom Lane
Pt: Tyler Reeder
Pt: Andrew Singer
VP: Matt Denichilo
VP: Andrew Gilbert
VP: Sara Graziano
Snr Mgr: Rosanne Migliorino

D-U-N-S 04-273-9759
ENERGY CONSULTING GROUP
1000 Emc Pkwy Ne, Marietta, GA 30060-7908
Tel (678) 355-3190 *Founded/Ownrshp* 2010
Sales 433.7MM *EMP* 1
SIC 8748 Business consulting
CEO: Anis Sherali

D-U-N-S 00-652-2080 IMP
ENERGY CONVERSION DEVICES INC
1441 E Maple Rd Ste 301, Troy, MI 48083-4027
Tel (248) 293-8772 *Founded/Ownrshp* 1960
Sales 124.8MM[E] *EMP* 1,300
SIC 3674 Semiconductors & related devices; Solar cells

Pr: Julian Hawkins
Pr: Ted Amyuni
**CFO:* William C Andrews
CFO: Stephan W Zumsteg
**Ex VP:* Joseph P Conroy
**Ex VP:* Jay B Knoll
Sr VP: Jeffrey P Harvey
Sr VP: Jeffrey Yang
VP: Hellmut Fritzsche
VP: Marcelino Susas
Dir Bus: Peter Gibson
Board of Directors: Joseph A Avila, Alan E Barton, Robert I Frey, William J Ketelhut, Stephen Rabinowitz, George A Schreiber Jr

D-U-N-S 83-447-5691
ENERGY CORP OF AMERICA
ECA HOLDING
4643 S Ulster St Ste 1100, Denver, CO 80237-2867
Tel (303) 694-2667 *Founded/Ownrshp* 1992
Sales 340.5MM[E] *EMP* 300
SIC 4924 4932 1382 4922 5172 Natural gas distribution; Gas & other services combined; Oil & gas exploration services; Natural gas transmission; Petroleum products
Pr: John Mork
COO: Joseph E Casabona
**CFO:* Michael Fletcher
**Treas:* J Michael Forbes
**Sr VP:* Donald C Supcoe
VP: Clark Clement
VP: David Jordan
VP: Dennis McGowan
VP: George V O'Malley
VP: Ranson K Ralph
VP: Peter Sullivan
Dir Bus: Matt Flavin

D-U-N-S 61-079-5622 IMP
■ ENERGY DUANE ARNOLD LLC
(*Suby of* NEXTERA ENERGY INC) ★
700 Universe Blvd, Juno Beach, FL 33408-2657
Tel (561) 691-7171 *Founded/Ownrshp* 2005
Sales 239.5MM[E] *EMP* 550
SIC 4911 Electric services
CEO: James L Robo

D-U-N-S 10-399-4067
ENERGY FUTURE COMPETITIVE HOLDINGS CO LLC
(*Suby of* ENERGY FUTURE HOLDINGS CORP) ★
1601 Bryan St Ste 510, Dallas, TX 75201-3483
Tel (214) 812-4600 *Founded/Ownrshp* 1982
Sales 5.3MMM *EMP* 5,060[E]
Accts Deloitte & Touche Llp Dallas
SIC 4911 Electric services; Distribution, electric power; Generation, electric power; Transmission, electric power
CFO: Paul M Keglevic
Ex VP: Stacey H Dore
Board of Directors: Scott Lebovitz, Michael Macdougall, Hugh E Sawyer, Jonathan D Smidt

ENERGY FUTURE HOLDINGS
See LUMINANT GENERATION CO LLC

D-U-N-S 16-014-1222
ENERGY FUTURE HOLDINGS CORP
(*Suby of* T P G) ★
1601 Bryan St Ste 510, Dallas, TX 75201-3483
Tel (214) 812-4600 *Founded/Ownrshp* 2007
Sales 5.3MMM *EMP* 8,860
SIC 4911 Electric services; Distribution, electric power; Generation, electric power; Transmission, electric power
CEO: Paul M Keglevic
**Ch Bd:* Donald L Evans
CFO: Anthony R Horton
Ofcr: Kim K W Rucker
Ex VP: James Browne
Ex VP: James A Burke
Ex VP: Stacey H Dor
Ex VP: Stacey Dore
Ex VP: Carrie L Kirby
Ex VP: Jack Redding
Ex VP: Andrew M Wright
Sr VP: Vinay Gadiyar
VP: Drew Cameron
VP: Tony Horton
VP: Daniel J Kelly
VP: Brian Kerrigan
VP: Susan Maurer
VP: Terry Nutt
Exec: Sano Blocker
Exec: Don Lowry

D-U-N-S 83-245-4529
ENERGY FUTURE INTERMEDIATE HOLDING CO LLC
(*Suby of* ENERGY FUTURE HOLDINGS CORP) ★
1601 Bryan St Ste 510, Dallas, TX 75201-3483
Tel (214) 812-4600 *Founded/Ownrshp* 2009
Sales 392.3MM[E] *EMP* 1[E]
Accts Deloitte & Touche Llp Dallas
SIC 4911 Electric services

ENERGY INSULATION SYSTEMS
See HENRIETTA BUILDING SUPPLIES INC

D-U-N-S 09-862-1220 IMP
ENERGY LABS INC
E L I
1695 Cactus Rd, San Diego, CA 92154-8102
Tel (619) 671-0100 *Founded/Ownrshp* 1974
Sales 288.0MM[E] *EMP* 800
SIC 3585 Heating & air conditioning combination units
Ch Bd: Bob Leclercq
**Pr:* Ray Irani
**CEO:* Reza K Irani
**VP:* Ward Hotze
Mktg Dir: Miguel Reyes

D-U-N-S 14-499-3784
ENERGY MAINTENANCE SERVICES GROUP I INC
EMS GROUP
2000 Bering Dr Ste 600, Houston, TX 77057-3835
Tel (713) 595-7600 *Founded/Ownrshp* 2003

Sales 1.9MMM^E *EMP* 1,650
SIC 1389 Measurement of well flow rates, oil & gas
CEO: James S Schroder
**CFO:* Steven List
**CFO:* Harvey Schnitzer
Bd of Dir: Steve Schroder
**Sr VP:* Troy Lee
VP: Trever Eade
VP: Arthur Robbins
VP: William Rowe
VP: John Simunek
VP: Sumner White
CIO: William Miller

D-U-N-S 06-166-6103 IMP
ENERGY NORTHWEST
76 N Power Plant Loop, Richland, WA 99354
Tel (509) 372-5000 *Founded/Ownrshp* 1957
Sales 3.2MM^E *EMP* 1,098^E
SIC 4911 7699 ; Generation, electric power; Transmission, electric power; Industrial equipment services
CEO: Mark Reddemann
**Pr:* Terry Brewer
**CFO:* Brent Ridge
Sr Cor Off: Bob Boyd
Bd of Dir: Ronald Hatfield
Ofcr: Sherri Schwartz
VP: James Garrett
Exec: Mike Paoli
Rgnl Mgr: Earl Terwilliger
IT Man: Adrian Corpus
Genl Couns: Robert Dutton

D-U-N-S 80-489-1849
■ ENERGY PLUS HOLDINGS LLC
(*Suby of* NRG ENERGY INC) ★
3711 Market St Ste 1000, Philadelphia, PA 19104-5537
Tel (877) 320-0356 *Founded/Ownrshp* 2007
Sales 179.7MM^E *EMP* 200^E
SIC 4911 Distribution, electric power
Pr: Steve Barnes
**Pr:* Stephen H Barnes
**CFO:* Paul Ricci

D-U-N-S 80-990-4865
ENERGY RESOURCE TECHNOLOGY GOM LLC
E RT
(*Suby of* TALOS PRODUCTION LLC) ★
500 Dallas St Ste 2000, Houston, TX 77002-4727
Tel (281) 618-0590 *Founded/Ownrshp* 2013
Sales 350.8MM^E *EMP* 130
SIC 1311 1389 Crude petroleum production; Natural gas production; Processing service, gas; Pumping of oil & gas wells
Pr: Timothy S Duncan
**Ex VP:* Stephen E Heitzman
**Ex VP:* John A Parker
**Sr VP:* Shannon E Young III

D-U-N-S 79-704-7540
▲ ENERGY SERVICES OF AMERICA CORP
75 3rd Ave W, Huntington, WV 25701-1116
Tel (304) 522-3868 *Founded/Ownrshp* 2008
Sales 155.4MM *EMP* 612
Accts Arnett Carbis Toothman Llp Ch
Tkr Sym ESOA *Exch* OTO
SIC 1623 1731 Pipe laying construction; General electrical contractor
Pr: Douglas V Reynolds
CFO: Charles P Crimmel
VP: Jim Poling
Dir IT: Chris White

D-U-N-S 79-049-6892
■ ENERGY SERVICES PROVIDERS INC
(*Suby of* USG&E) ★
3700 Lakeside Dr 6, Miramar, FL 33027-3264
Tel (305) 947-7880 *Founded/Ownrshp* 2009
Sales 96.4MM^E *EMP* 13^E
SIC 2211 Broadwoven fabric mills, cotton
CEO: Douglas W Marcille
**Treas:* David Weinberg
**VP:* Brian Rose

ENERGY SOLUTIONS
See ENERGYSOLUTIONS LLC

D-U-N-S 07-827-8865
ENERGY SPECTRUM PARTNERS VI LP
5956 Sherry Ln Ste 900, Dallas, TX 75225-8020
Tel (214) 987-6100 *Founded/Ownrshp* 2010
Sales 98.1MM^E *EMP* 128^E
SIC 6722 Management investment, open-end

D-U-N-S 10-717-5358
■ ENERGY SYSTEMS GROUP LLC
ESG
(*Suby of* VECTREN ENERGY SERVICES CORP) ★
4655 Rosebud Ln, Newburgh, IN 47630-9366
Tel (812) 492-3734 *Founded/Ownrshp* 1997
Sales 199.9MM *EMP* 238
Accts Harding Shymanski & Company
SIC 8711 1711 1629 Energy conservation engineering; Plumbing, heating, air-conditioning contractors; Dams, waterways, docks & other marine construction
Pr: Gregory F Collins
**Treas:* Dennis Perrey
Sr VP: Ken Ormsbee
**Sr VP:* Steve Pride
**Sr VP:* Lawrence Roth
VP: Luke Brockman
**VP:* W Luke Brockman
**VP:* Jonathan D Shell
Ex Dir: Karen Galindo-White
Genl Mgr: Mike Nasiatka
IT Man: Joshua Ackerman
Board of Directors: Jerome A Benkert Jr, Daniel C Bugher, Carl L Chapman, Gregory F Collins, M Susan Hardwick, Jon K Luttrell, Eric J Schach

ENERGY TRANSFER COMPANY
See ETC INTRASTATE PROCUREMENT CO LLC

ENERGY TRANSFER COMPANY
See LA GRANGE ACQUISITION LP

D-U-N-S 07-976-3340
■ ENERGY TRANSFER CRUDE OIL CO LLC
(*Suby of* ENERGY TRANSFER EQUITY LP) ★
800 E Sonterra Blvd, San Antonio, TX 78258-3940
Tel (210) 403-7300 *Founded/Ownrshp* 2012
Sales 20.4MM^E *EMP* 2,484^E
SIC 4612 Crude petroleum pipelines
CEO: Kelcy L Warren
**Pr:* Marshall S McCrea

D-U-N-S 61-079-2264
▲ ENERGY TRANSFER EQUITY LP
8111 Westchester Dr # 600, Dallas, TX 75225-6142
Tel (214) 981-0700 *Founded/Ownrshp* 2002
Sales 42.1MMM *EMP* 30,078^E
Tkr Sym ETE *Exch* NYS
SIC 4922 Natural gas transmission; Pipelines, natural gas; Storage, natural gas
Pr: John W McReynolds
CFO: Thomas E Long
Ex VP: Thomas P Mason
VP: Renee Lorenz
VP Bus Dev: Coby Washburn
Snr PM: Jim Cremer
Snr PM: Danny Grantham

D-U-N-S 07-936-0305
ENERGY TRANSFER PARTNERS GP LP
8111 Westchester Dr # 600, Dallas, TX 75225-6142
Tel (214) 981-0700 *Founded/Ownrshp* 2000
Sales 1.0MM^E *EMP* 25,682
SIC 4922 Natural gas transmission; Pipelines, natural gas; Storage, natural gas
Ch Bd: Kelcy L Warren

D-U-N-S 55-637-1545
■ ENERGY TRANSFER PARTNERS LLC
(*Suby of* ENERGY TRANSFER EQUITY LP) ★
8111 Westchester Dr # 600, Dallas, TX 75225-6142
Tel (214) 981-0700 *Founded/Ownrshp* 2002
Sales 98.4MM^E *EMP* 13,573
SIC 8748 Business consulting
Pr: John W McReynolds
**Ch Bd:* Kelcy L Warren
**CFO:* Jamie Welch

D-U-N-S 36-444-5767
▲ ENERGY TRANSFER PARTNERS LP
8111 Westchester Dr # 600, Dallas, TX 75225-6142
Tel (214) 981-0700 *Founded/Ownrshp* 1989
Sales 34.2MMM *EMP* 9,466^E
Tkr Sym ETP *Exch* NYS
SIC 4922 5984 Natural gas transmission; Pipelines, natural gas; Storage, natural gas; Propane gas, bottled
Ch Bd: Kelcy L Warren
Genl Pt: Energy T LP
Pr: Matthew S Ramsey
VP: Steven Breckon
VP: Roy Patton
VP: Valerie White
Dir Risk M: Todd Frazee
Opers Mgr: Louis Cappiello
VP Mktg: Brad Holmes
Snr Mgr: Robert Bandel

D-U-N-S 12-942-3112
ENERGY TRUST OF OREGON INC
421 Sw Oak St Ste 300, Portland, OR 97204-1810
Tel (866) 368-7878 *Founded/Ownrshp* 2001
Sales 163.6MM *EMP* 59
Accts Moss Adams Llp Portland Or
SIC 8699 Charitable organization
Ch Bd: John Reynolds
**CFO:* Susanne Sample
Bd of Dir: Jason Eisdorfer
Bd of Dir: Julie Hammond
Bd of Dir: Alan Meyer
VP: Rick Applegate
VP: Kathleen Belkhayat
Dir: Fred Gordon
Comm Dir: Amber Cole
**Ex Dir:* Margie Harris
Prgrm Mgr: Adam Serchuk
Board of Directors: Monica Gruher, Steve Lacey

ENERGY UNITED
See ENERGYUNITED ELECTRIC MEMBERSHIP CORP

D-U-N-S 62-377-6916
■ ENERGY XXI GULF COAST INC
(*Suby of* ENERGY XXI USA INC) ★
1021 Main St Ste 2626, Houston, TX 77002-6516
Tel (713) 351-3000 *Founded/Ownrshp* 2006
Sales 577.7MM^E *EMP* 450
SIC 4424 1311 Coastwide transportation, freight; Crude petroleum & natural gas production
Ch Bd: John D Schiller Jr
**CFO:* David West Griffin
**Treas:* Bobby Poirrier
**Ex VP:* Ben Marchive
**Sr VP:* Hugh Menown
**Sr VP:* Todd Reid

D-U-N-S 62-377-6841
ENERGY XXI USA INC
(*Suby of* ENERGY XXI (BERMUDA) LIMITED)
1021 Main St Ste 2626, Houston, TX 77002-6516
Tel (713) 351-3000 *Founded/Ownrshp* 2006
Sales 595.7MM^E *EMP* 450^E
SIC 1311 Crude petroleum & natural gas
Pr: John Schiller
**Pr:* Granger Anderson
**CEO:* Ben Marchive
**CFO:* Rick Fox
**CFO:* David Griffin
VP: Stewart Lawrence
**VP:* Steve Nelson

ENERGYNORTH NATURAL GAS, INC.
See LIBERTY UTILITIES (ENERGYNORTH NATURAL GAS) CORP

D-U-N-S 80-826-5917
ENERGYSOLUTIONS INC
299 S Main St Ste 1700, Salt Lake City, UT 84111-2279
Tel (801) 649-2000 *Founded/Ownrshp* 1988
Sales 2.9MMM^E *EMP* 5,000
SIC 4953 8711 Radioactive waste materials, disposal; Engineering services
Pr: David Lockwood
CFO: Greg Wood
Sr VP: Brent H Shimada

D-U-N-S 18-378-6607
ENERGYSOLUTIONS LLC
ENERGY SOLUTIONS
(*Suby of* ENERGYSOLUTIONS INC) ★
299 Suth Main St Ste 1700, Salt Lake City, UT 84111
Tel (801) 649-2000 *Founded/Ownrshp* 2005
Sales 2.9MMM^E *EMP* 5,000
SIC 4953 8711 Hazardous waste collection & disposal; Engineering services
Pr: David J Lockwood
**Pr:* John A Christian
**Pr:* Mark Morant
**Pr:* Alan Parker
CFO: Chip Everest
**Ex VP:* Greg Wood
Sr VP: John Ward
Mng Dir: David L Johnson
Off Mgr: Sharon Howells

D-U-N-S 13-950-8212 IMP
ENERGYSOLUTIONS SERVICES INC
(*Suby of* ENERGY SOLUTIONS) ★
299 S Main St Ste 1700, Salt Lake City, UT 84111-2279
Tel (801) 649-2000 *Founded/Ownrshp* 2006
Sales 650.0MM *EMP* 1,800
SIC 4953 Radioactive waste materials, disposal
CEO: David Lockwood
**Pr:* Greg Wood
**Treas:* David Nelson
Board of Directors: David Lockwood Gregory Woo

D-U-N-S 05-908-5568
■ ENERGYSOUTH INC
(*Suby of* SPIRE INC) ★
2828 Dauphin St, Mobile, AL 36606-2457
Tel (251) 450-4774 *Founded/Ownrshp* 2016
Sales 182.5MM^E *EMP* 266^E
SIC 4924 4922 Natural gas distribution; Storage, natural gas
Pr: Constantine S Liollio
CFO: Charles P Huffman
VP: Edgar Downing
Sys/Mgr: Sherry Garner

D-U-N-S 03-049-4488
ENERGYUNITED ELECTRIC MEMBERSHIP CORP
ENERGY UNITED
567 Mocksville Hwy, Statesville, NC 28625-8269
Tel (704) 873-5241 *Founded/Ownrshp* 1998
Sales 274.8MM *EMP* 175
SIC 4911 Distribution, electric power
CEO: H Wayne Wilkins
Bd of Dir: N M Shoaf
VP: Eric McIntire
Exec: Johnny Mabe
Exec: Wes Smith
DP Exec: Wayne Wilkins

D-U-N-S 13-716-1548
▲ ENERNOC INC
1 Marina Park Dr Ste 400, Boston, MA 02210-1643
Tel (617) 224-9900 *Founded/Ownrshp* 2001
Sales 399.5MM *EMP* 1,366^E
Tkr Sym ENOC *Exch* NGS
SIC 7371 Custom computer programming services; Computer software development; Software programming applications
Ch Bd: Timothy G Healy
Pr: David Brewster
COO: Neil Moses
CFO: William Sorenson
Sr VP: Eric Erston
Sr VP: Micah Remley
VP: Michael Berdik
QA Dir: Carol Morgan
Sftwr Eng: John Blakeney
Sftwr Eng: Michael McAvoy
Sls Dir: Scott Martin
Board of Directors: Kirk Arnold, James Baum, Arthur Coviello, Gary Haroian

D-U-N-S 05-241-2533 IMP/EXP
▲ ENERSYS
2366 Bernville Rd, Reading, PA 19605-9457
Tel (610) 208-1991 *Founded/Ownrshp* 2000
Sales 2.3MMM *EMP* 9,400
Tkr Sym ENS *Exch* NYS
SIC 3691 3699 Lead acid batteries (storage batteries); Electrical equipment & supplies
Pr: David M Shaffer
**Ch Bd:* Arthur T Katsaros
Pr: Holger P Aschke
Pr: Jeffrey W Long
COO: Todd M Sechrist
CFO: Michael J Schmidtlein
Dist Mgr: Russ Johnson
Board of Directors: Howard I Hoffen, John F Lehman, Robert Magnus, Dennis S Marlo, Joseph C Muscari, Paul J Tufano

D-U-N-S 96-363-8452 IMP
■ ENERSYS DELAWARE INC
(*Suby of* ENERSYS) ★
2366 Bernville Rd, Reading, PA 19605-9457
Tel (214) 324-8990 *Founded/Ownrshp* 1998
Sales 1.1MMM^E *EMP* 9,000^E
SIC 3691 5063 Lead acid batteries (storage batteries); Electrical apparatus & equipment
VP: Michael J Schmidtlein
**Treas:* Thomas L Oneill
**Ex VP:* Richard W Zuidema

D-U-N-S 83-214-4422
ENERVEST LTD
1001 Fannin St Ste 800, Houston, TX 77002-6707
Tel (713) 659-3500 *Founded/Ownrshp* 1992
Sales 495.4MM^E *EMP* 300
SIC 1311 1382 Crude petroleum & natural gas production; Oil & gas exploration services
CEO: John B Walker
Pt: L Todd Guest
Pt: Mark A Houser
Pt: Jon Rex Jones
Pt: James M Vanderhider
Pr: Ken Mariani
CFO: Micheal Mercer
Ex VP: Phil C Delozier
Sr VP: Stephen A McDaniel
VP: Harvey Barney
VP: Michael Cheng
VP: Bryan Ginsburg
VP: David G Kyte
VP: Johnny Lockett
VP: Polly Schott
VP: Karen Taylor
VP: Fabene Welch
VP: Alison Whiteley
VP Bus Dev: Luke Albrecht
Exec: Stephen Jones

D-U-N-S 92-902-2069
ENERVEST OPERATING LLC
(*Suby of* ENERVEST LTD) ★
1001 Fannin St Ste 800, Houston, TX 77002-6707
Tel (713) 659-3500 *Founded/Ownrshp* 1995
Sales 137.9MM *EMP* 125
SIC 1311 Crude petroleum & natural gas production
CEO: John B Walker
CFO: Michael E Mercer
**VP:* Mark Houser
IT Man: Sean Cooper

D-U-N-S 79-348-0919 IMP/EXP
ENESCO LLC
225 Windsor Dr, Itasca, IL 60143-1225
Tel (630) 875-5300 *Founded/Ownrshp* 2015
Sales 113.5MM^E *EMP* 850
SIC 5947 Gifts & novelties; Souvenirs
CEO: Todd Mavis
Pr: Molly C Kinney
Pr: Bruce S Raiffe
COO: Theodore Eischeid
Chf Mktg O: Kathi P Lentzsch
Sr VP: Ricky T Chan
Sr VP: Jeffrey S Mith
Sr VP: Matt Myren
VP: Michael Rumak
IT Man: Matt Litchfield
VP Opers: H Riechers

ENGAGE PEO
See S2 HR SOLUTIONS 1A LLC

ENGAGE2EXCEL
See THARPE CO INC

D-U-N-S 82-469-3881 IMP
ENGEL MACHINERY INC
(*Suby of* ENGEL AUSTRIA GMBH)
3740 Board Rd, York, PA 17406-8425
Tel (717) 764-6818 *Founded/Ownrshp* 2013
Sales 190.4MM *EMP* 140
Accts Kpmg Llp Waterloo Canada
SIC 5084 7699 Industrial machinery & equipment; Industrial machinery & equipment repair
Pr: Mark Sankovitch
COO: Jeff Hershey
VP: Mike Petrides
Rgnl Mgr: Jim Bell
Sls Dir: Jim Moran
Mktg Mgr: Kleta Childs
Mktg Mgr: Anthony Thompson
Manager: Markus Lettau

ENGELHARD
See BASF CATALYSTS LLC

D-U-N-S 12-221-6948
ENGHOUSE INTERACTIVE INC
ARC
(*Suby of* ENGHOUSE SYSTEMS LIMITED)
2095 W Pinnacle Peak Rd, Phoenix, AZ 85027-1247
Tel (602) 789-2800 *Founded/Ownrshp* 1984
Sales 215.0MM^E *EMP* 900
SIC 3571 3661 3663 7372 7374 Computers, digital, analog or hybrid; Telephones & telephone apparatus; Telephone dialing devices, automatic; Electronic secretary; Message concentrators; Cable television equipment; Application computer software; Calculating service (computer)
CEO: Stephen Sadler
**COO:* Craig Wallace
**CFO:* Douglas Bryson
**VP:* Sam Anidjar
VP: John Cray
Admn Mgr: Megan Chapman
Genl Mgr: Laura Gettler
IT Man: Ariella Zaarur
Sftwr Eng: Larry Duran
Netwrk Eng: Michael Gonzalez
Manager: Julie McLane

D-U-N-S 07-947-6555
ENGIE HOLDINGS INC
(*Suby of* ENGIE ENERGY SERVICES INTERNATIONAL SA)
1313 N Atl St Ste 5000, Spokane, WA 99201
Tel (509) 329-7600 *Founded/Ownrshp* 2014
Sales 636.9MM^E *EMP* 1,400^E
SIC 8742 Public utilities consultant
Pr: Etienne Jacolin

D-U-N-S 08-006-2796
ENGIE NORTH AMERICA INC
(*Suby of* ENGIE HOLDINGS INC) ★
1990 Post Oak Blvd # 1900, Houston, TX 77056-3831
Tel (713) 636-0000 *Founded/Ownrshp* 2015
Sales 268.9MM^E *EMP* 237^E
SIC 4911
CEO: Frank Demaille
CFO: Patrick Gaussent

D-U-N-S 09-966-8332
ENGIE RESOURCES LLC
(*Suby of* ENGIE NORTH AMERICA INC) ★
1990 Post Oak Blvd # 1900, Houston, TX 77056-3818
Tel (713) 636-0000 *Founded/Ownrshp* 2001
Sales 205.9MM^E *EMP* 190
SIC 4911 Generation, electric power
Pr: Sayun Sukduang
VP: Jay Bell

VP: John Henderson
VP: Helen Lo
VP: Danielle R Wilks
Dir IT: Mark Brown
Dir IT: Jeff Dorsey
Dir IT: Sean McClure
Sls Dir: Alejandra Hidalgo
Mktg Mgr: Kevin Stafford
Manager: Mary B Caldwell

D-U-N-S 06-934-1972
■ ENGILITY CORP
TASC
(*Suby of* ENGILITY HOLDINGS INC) ★
35 New Engld Busctr Dr200, Andover, MA 01810
Tel (978) 749-2100 *Founded/Ownrshp* 1966, 2015
Sales 876.8MM[E] *EMP* 4,120
SIC 8711 Engineering services
Pr: Anthony Smeraglinolo
**COO:* John P Hynes Jr
**CFO:* Wayne Rehberger
Treas: Nicole Faxon
VP: Amanda Brownfield
VP: Mark Bruno
VP: Mark A Forman
VP: Thomas J Kilcline Jr
VP: Joseph Pacileo
VP: Bob Pattishall
VP: Terry Roberts
VP: Bob Silsby

D-U-N-S 78-383-7672
▲ ENGILITY HOLDINGS INC
3750 Centerview Dr, Chantilly, VA 20151-3200
Tel (703) 708-1400 *Founded/Ownrshp* 1969
Sales 2.0MMM *EMP* 9,800[E]
Tkr Sym EGL *Exch* NYS
SIC 8711 8741 Engineering services; Management services
CEO: Lynn A Dugle
**Ch Bd:* Peter A Marino
**Ch Bd:* David A Savner
Pr: John P Hynes Jr
CFO: Wayne M Rehberger
Sr VP: Thomas O Miiller
Board of Directors: John Barter, Steven A Denning, David M Kerko, Darryll J Pines, Anthony Principi, Charles S Ream, William G Tobin

D-U-N-S 04-834-1838 IMP
■ ENGILITY LLC
(*Suby of* ENGILITY HOLDINGS INC) ★
4803 Stonecroft Blvd, Chantilly, VA 20151-3822
Tel (703) 708-1400 *Founded/Ownrshp* 2012
Sales 2.0MMM[E] *EMP* 9,800
SIC 8711 Engineering services
CEO: Lynn Dugle
Pr: Gregory Carper
Pr: Timothy Gillespie
Pr: John Heller
**Pr:* John Hynes
**CFO:* Wayne Rehberger
**Treas:* Ray H Guillaume
Ofcr: Tracey Thompson
Ofcr: William Tobin
Sr VP: Christine Bailey
Sr VP: Jim Campbell
**Sr VP:* Kirk Dye
Sr VP: Pearl Mihara
Sr VP: Thomas O Miller
**Sr VP:* Craig S Reed
Sr VP: Craig Reed
VP: Philip Decosse
VP: Kristin Dufrene
VP: Rich Harkey
VP: Thomas J Murray
VP: Joanne B Newman

ENGINE MOBILE SOLUTIONS EMS
See EM CLARCOR HOLDINGS INC

ENGINEERED AIR
See AIRTEX MANUFACTURING LLLP

D-U-N-S 96-384-2963 IMP/EXP
ENGINEERED CONTROLS INTERNATIONAL LLC
(*Suby of* WINDJAMMER CAPITAL INVESTORS IV LP) ★
100 Rego Dr, Elon, NC 27244-9159
Tel (336) 449-7707 *Founded/Ownrshp* 2010
Sales 139.7MM[E] *EMP* 450
SIC 3491 Pressure valves & regulators, industrial; Compressed gas cylinder valves
Pr: Thomas Farrel

D-U-N-S 02-074-3442 IMP
ENGINEERED FLOORS LLC (GA)
3510 Corporate Dr, Dalton, GA 30721-4900
Tel (706) 625-4334 *Founded/Ownrshp* 2009
Sales 266.0MM[E] *EMP* 3,000
SIC 2273 Floor coverings, textile fiber
CEO: Robert Shaw
CFO: Tommy Johnson
VP: Mitch Land
Plnt Mgr: Terry Harper

D-U-N-S 78-152-0283 IMP/EXP
ENGINEERED MACHINED PRODUCTS INC
E M P
3111 N 28th St, Escanaba, MI 49829-9324
Tel (906) 786-8404 *Founded/Ownrshp* 1981
Sales 115.3MM[E] *EMP* 420
SIC 3519 3714 3568 3599 3561 Internal combustion engines; Water pump, motor vehicle; Pulleys, power transmission; Air intake filters, internal combustion engine, except auto; Pumps & pumping equipment
CEO: Brian K Larche
CFO: Rick Nardi
VP: Mark Bader
VP: Ralph Bedogne
VP: Jerry Guindon
IT Man: Mark Whitens

ENGINEERED PLASTIC COMPONENTS
See AEES POWER SYSTEMS LIMITED PARTNERSHIP

D-U-N-S 87-426-9483 IMP
ENGINEERED PLASTIC COMPONENTS INC
1408 Zimmerman Dr, Grinnell, IA 50112-9703
Tel (641) 236-3100 *Founded/Ownrshp* 1994
Sales 190.8MM[E] *EMP* 528
Accts Lwvj Llp West Des Moines Io
SIC 3089 Injection molding of plastics
CEO: Reza Kargarzadeh
Prd Mgr: Rob Rich

D-U-N-S 61-193-1650 IMP
ENGINEERED POLYMERS CORP
(*Suby of* IMPERIAL PLASTICS INC) ★
1020 Maple Ave E, Mora, MN 55051-1217
Tel (320) 679-3232 *Founded/Ownrshp* 2014
Sales 114.6MM[E] *EMP* 350
SIC 3086 3089 Plastics foam products; Injection molded finished plastic products
Pr: Andy Eckert
VP: Jeff Fackler
VP: Gary Whitcher
IT Man: Nick Radich
Ql Cn Mgr: Bruce Hiles
Snr Mgr: Doug Price

D-U-N-S 07-312-7409
ENGINEERED STRUCTURES INC
ESI CONSTRUCTION
3330 E Louise Dr Ste 300, Meridian, ID 83642-5123
Tel (208) 362-3040 *Founded/Ownrshp* 1992
Sales 295.7MM *EMP* 250
Accts Harris & Co Pllc Meridian I
SIC 1542 1531 Commercial & office building contractors; Speculative builder, multi-family dwellings
CEO: Thomas D Hill
**Pr:* Neil W Nelson
VP: Elizabeth Brockway
Snr PM: Kelly Davis

D-U-N-S 06-932-9316
ENGINEERED SYSTEMS INC
1121 Duncan Reidville Rd, Duncan, SC 29334-9740
Tel (864) 879-7438 *Founded/Ownrshp* 1996
Sales 94.9MM[E] *EMP* 120
SIC 5084 Materials handling machinery; Cranes, industrial
Pr: Don Wilson
**VP:* Ray L Wilson III
Genl Mgr: Paul Wilson
CIO: Randy Garrick
Sls Mgr: Ricky Carroll

ENGINEERING & INDSTRL EQPMT
See UNIVERSITY OF FLORIDA

D-U-N-S 19-502-8642
ENGINEERING CONSULTING SERVICES LTD
E C S
14026 Thunderbolt Pl, Chantilly, VA 20151-3295
Tel (703) 471-8400 *Founded/Ownrshp* 1987
Sales 120.1MM *EMP* 1,000[E]
Accts Homes Lowry Horn & Johnson L
SIC 8711 Consulting engineer
Pr: Henry L Lucas
**Treas:* James A Eckert
VP: Ron Basso
**VP:* James Carpenter
**VP:* Douglas Cole
Brnch Mgr: Sun Breza
Off Mgr: Linsey Armstrong
Off Mgr: Keri Cummings
VP Sls: Eric Slatten

D-U-N-S 09-567-3521
ENGINEERING RESEARCH AND CONSULTING INC (TN)
ERC, INC FOR PURP DO BUS IN AL
308 Voyager Way Nw # 200, Huntsville, AL 35806-3206
Tel (256) 430-3080 *Founded/Ownrshp* 1988
Sales 185.4MM[E] *EMP* 768[E]
Accts Brumbelow & Barnes Pc
SIC 8731 8711 Commercial physical research; Engineering services
CEO: Ernest Wu
**Pr:* Kenny Frame
**CFO:* Stacey Riley
**Ch:* Susan Wu
Comm Man: Mark Jones
Prgrm Mgr: Van Chatraw
Prgrm Mgr: Darrell Shoup
Prgrm Mgr: Darryl Smith
IT Man: Kendyl Wilbanks

D-U-N-S 02-181-5113 IMP
ENGINEERING SERVICES & PRODUCTS CO
CLEARSPAN
1395 John Fitch Blvd, South Windsor, CT 06074-1029
Tel (860) 528-1119 *Founded/Ownrshp* 1981
Sales 96.9MM[E] *EMP* 320
Accts Sheptoff Reuber & Company Pc
SIC 3523 5083 3081 Dairy equipment (farm); Hog feeding, handling & watering equipment; Poultry brooders, feeders & waterers; Poultry equipment; Agricultural machinery; Polyethylene film
Pr: Barry Goldsher
**Sec:* Charles R Clark Jr
**VP:* Matthew K Niaura
Exec: Marge Spinella
Dir Teleco: Alice Brown
Creative D: Tania Tomoroga
Mng Dir: Charles Clark
Genl Mgr: Martina Bockenstedt
Genl Mgr: Geoffrey Ching
IT Man: Dave Cochefski
Sys Mgr: Paul Espeseth

ENGINEERING SOLUTIONS & PDTS
See ENGINEERING SOLUTIONS & PRODUCTS LLC

D-U-N-S 93-122-1258
ENGINEERING SOLUTIONS & PRODUCTS LLC
ENGINEERING SOLUTIONS & PDTS
14566 Lee Rd, Chantilly, VA 20151-1684
Tel (571) 375-1400 *Founded/Ownrshp* 2000
Sales 134.3MM[E] *EMP* 1,200
SIC 8711 7379 4813 8742 8748 Electrical or electronic engineering; Computer related maintenance services; Telephone communication, except radio; Management consulting services; Business consulting
Pr: James E Hoffman Jr

ENGINEERING TECHNICAL GROUP
See ENTEGEE INC

D-U-N-S 00-338-6927 IMP/EXP
■ ENGLAND INC (TN)
(*Suby of* LA-Z-BOY INC) ★
1 La Z Boy Dr, Monroe, MI 48162
Tel (734) 242-1444 *Founded/Ownrshp* 1964, 1995
Sales 208.4MM[E] *EMP* 1,600
SIC 2512 Upholstered household furniture; Living room furniture: upholstered on wood frames; Recliners: upholstered on wood frames
CEO: Kurt L Darrow
Treas: James P Klarr

D-U-N-S 94-390-3823
ENGLAND LOGISTICS INC
(*Suby of* CR ENGLAND INC) ★
1325 S 4700 W, Salt Lake City, UT 84104-4431
Tel (801) 656-4500 *Founded/Ownrshp* 1994
Sales 130.6MM[E] *EMP* 700
SIC 8742 Transportation consultant
Pr: Jason Beardall
Sec: Keith C Wallace Jr
VP: David Akers
VP: Coby Bullard
VP: Daniel E England
VP: Josh England
VP: Lance Evenson
VP: Kirk Freimuth
VP: Justin Olsen
VP: Thom Pronk
VP: Dave Robbins
Exec: Jennifer Skinner

D-U-N-S 61-032-1671
ENGLEFIELD INC
ENGLEFIELD OIL CO
447 James Pkwy, Heath, OH 43056-1030
Tel (740) 928-8215 *Founded/Ownrshp* 1988
Sales 234.8MM[E] *EMP* 1,200
SIC 5541 Filling stations, gasoline
Ch Bd: J Robert Beam
**Ch Bd:* F William Englefield III
**Pr:* Frederick W Englefield IV
CFO: Chris Beem
VP: Ed Canter
**VP:* Greg Ehrlich
**VP:* Will Englefield
VP: John Epstein
VP: John Gordon
VP: Fred Kaseman
**Prin:* Ben B Englefield

ENGLEFIELD OIL CO
See ENGLEFIELD INC

D-U-N-S 00-191-1833 IMP/EXP
ENGLERT INC (NJ)
1200 Amboy Ave, Perth Amboy, NJ 08861-1956
Tel (800) 364-5378 *Founded/Ownrshp* 1966
Sales 90.8MM[E] *EMP* 250
SIC 3444 5033 Gutters, sheet metal; Siding, sheet metal; Roof deck, sheet metal; Roofing, siding & insulation
CEO: Debra Harnett
VP: Brian Englert
**VP:* Joseph Turovach
VP: John Williams
Plnt Mgr: Tom Harnett

D-U-N-S 09-447-9383
ENGLEWOOD HEALTH CARE CENTER LLC
2046 S Alabama Ave, Monroeville, AL 36460-3097
Tel (251) 575-3285 *Founded/Ownrshp* 1971
Sales 586.7MM *EMP* 107
SIC 8051 Skilled nursing care facilities
VP: Keith Baggett
Off Mgr: June Skinner

D-U-N-S 05-628-9481 EXP
ENGLEWOOD HOSPITAL AND MEDICAL CENTER FOUNDATION INC
350 Engle St, Englewood, NJ 07631-1808
Tel (201) 894-3000 *Founded/Ownrshp* 1888
Sales 480.1MM *EMP* 2,200
SIC 8062 8011 Hospital, medical school affiliation; Hospital, professional nursing school; Medical centers
VP: Anthony T Orlando
Treas: Mike Schirk
**VP:* Dimitri J Cruz
VP: Sarah Humme
VP: Daniel Markum
VP: Ann Shears
Dir Risk M: Sherry Grumet
Dir Lab: Cioco Delara
Dir Env Sv: Phill Irwin
Prin: Phil Maneri
Adm Dir: Lori Horton

D-U-N-S 94-172-4502 IMP
ENGLEWOOD MARKETING GROUP INC
(*Suby of* LAUREN HOLDING INC) ★
1471 Partnership Rd, Green Bay, WI 54304-5685
Tel (920) 337-9800 *Founded/Ownrshp* 2004
Sales 162.0MM[E] *EMP* 95
SIC 5064

ENGLISH AS A SECOND LANGUAGE
See ROGERS PUBLIC SCHOOLS

D-U-N-S 05-013-9922
ENGLISH COLOR & SUPPLY INC
806 N Grove Rd, Richardson, TX 75081-2747
Tel (972) 235-3108 *Founded/Ownrshp* 1946
Sales 161.0MM[E] *EMP* 235
SIC 5198 5231 Paints; Paint
CEO: Jim English III
**VP:* Robert Burns
VP: Jeff King
Rgnl Mgr: Richey Gentry
Area Mgr: Marvin Williams
Opers Mgr: Tonya Rimbey
Manager: Scott Conaway
Manager: Brent Fox
Manager: Jim Rimbey
Sls Mgr: Chad Francis
Sls Mgr: Jeremi Holmes

D-U-N-S 00-793-9804
ENGLISH CONSTRUCTION CO INC (VA)
615 Church St Ste 2, Lynchburg, VA 24504-1314
Tel (434) 845-0301 *Founded/Ownrshp* 1947, 1997
Sales 158.8MM[E] *EMP* 200
SIC 1611 1629 1623 1542 General contractor, highway & street construction; Waste water & sewage treatment plant construction; Sewer line construction; School building construction; Hospital construction; Religious building construction
Pr: A Douglas Dalton Jr
**CFO:* Garry A Collie
**VP:* John M Jordan Jr
**VP:* Maurice C Law
Off Mgr: Whitney Melton
Sfty Mgr: Michael Scott
Sales Exec: Carla Hart

ENGLISH VLG MANOR NURSING HM
See WCR ENTERPRISES INC

D-U-N-S 02-338-2807
ENGMAN-TAYLOR CO INC
W142n9351 Fountain Blvd, Menomonee Falls, WI 53051-1624
Tel (262) 255-9300 *Founded/Ownrshp* 1994
Sales 93.3MM[E] *EMP* 125
SIC 5084 5085 Industrial machinery & equipment; Industrial supplies
Pr: Rich Star
CFO: Lee Moter
VP: Jim Mueller
Mfg Dir: Connie Bock
**VP Sls:* Mark Sauer
Sales Asso: Steve Malisow

ENHANCE
See AINSWORTH PET NUTRITION LLC

D-U-N-S 12-336-2639
ENHANCED RECOVERY CO LLC
E R C
8014 Bayberry Rd, Jacksonville, FL 32256-7412
Tel (904) 371-1005 *Founded/Ownrshp* 1999
Sales 64.0MM *EMP* 1,394
SIC 7322 Adjustment & collection services
CEO: Mark Thompson
**Pr:* Marty Sarim
Pr: Thomas York
**CEO:* Kirk Moquin
**CFO:* Michael Harrison
VP: Jason Davis
VP: Trish Johnson
Dir Bus: Jamie Jutte
Genl Mgr: Kelly Paul
Genl Mgr: Scott Rozier
Software D: Robert Harris

ENI PETROLEUM CO., INC.
See ENI PETROLEUM CO INC

D-U-N-S 09-508-3044 IMP
ENI PETROLEUM CO INC
ENI PETROLEUM CO., INC.
(*Suby of* ENI SPA)
1201 La St Ste 3500, Houston, TX 77002
Tel (713) 393-6100 *Founded/Ownrshp* 1966
Sales 698.6MM[E] *EMP* 320
SIC 1311 Crude petroleum production; Natural gas production
CEO: Leonardo Stefani
**Pr:* Roberto Dall'omo
**Ch:* Enzo Viscusi
**Treas:* Brian Lloyd
**Treas:* Roberto Pasqua
Sr VP: Giuseppe Bellussi
VP: Paolo Linzi
Rgnl Mgr: Stefano Giani
Genl Mgr: Joe V Davidson
IT Man: Thomas Browning
IT Man: Kelly Hansbro

D-U-N-S 82-994-2593 IMP
ENI TRADING & SHIPPING INC
(*Suby of* ENI TRADING & SHIPPING SPA)
1200 Smith St Ste 1707, Houston, TX 77002-4372
Tel (713) 393-6340 *Founded/Ownrshp* 2008
Sales 87.9MM[E] *EMP* 35
SIC 5172 Crude oil; Engine fuels & oils; Fuel oil; Lubricating oils & greases
Ch: Antonio Ruggiero
**Ch Bd:* Franco Magnani
**Pr:* Emanuele Carviello
**CEO:* Giorgio Mari
**CFO:* Paolo De Juliis
**CFO:* Renato Squadrone
Board of Directors: Roberto Dall'omo, Cosimo Imperiale

ENIVATE - AEROSPACE DIVISION
See ITT ENIDINE INC

D-U-N-S 05-875-6586 IMP/EXP
ENJET LLC
(*Suby of* APEX OIL CO INC) ★
5373 W Alabama St Ste 502, Houston, TX 77056-5923
Tel (713) 552-1559 *Founded/Ownrshp* 2002
Sales 109.4MM[E] *EMP* 27
SIC 5172 Petroleum products
Pr: L Peter Byler
**Treas:* Christine H Hughes
**VP:* John L Hank Jr
**VP:* GT Mercier
Opers Mgr: John Kennelly

D-U-N-S 14-708-0022 IMP
ENKEI AMERICA INC
2900 Inwood Dr, Columbus, IN 47201-9758
Tel (812) 373-7000 *Founded/Ownrshp* 1985
Sales 166.1MM[E] *EMP* 800
SIC 3714 3365 Wheels, motor vehicle; Aluminum foundries

CEO: Makoto Miura
Ex VP: Rick Merkel
VP: Jun Banno
VP: Mike Boggs
VP: Theodore Schorn
Genl Mgr: Dave Galle
Genl Mgr: Larry Skyler
IT Man: Gary Cavanauh

D-U-N-S 04-249-4450
ENLARGED CITY SCHOOL DISTRICT OF TROY
TROY CITY SCHOOLS
2920 5th Ave, Troy, NY 12180-1294
Tel (518) 328-5005 *Founded/Ownrshp* 1854
Sales 92.2MM *EMP* 700[E]
Accts Cusack & Company Latham New
SIC 8211 Public elementary & secondary schools

D-U-N-S 08-033-4499
ENLIGHTEN AIR INC
23 E 81st St Apt 10, New York, NY 10028-0225
Tel (917) 656-1248 *Founded/Ownrshp* 2016
Sales 392.0MM *EMP* 5
SIC 3728 Target drones
CEO: William O'Boyle

D-U-N-S 80-453-8960
■ ENLINK MIDSTREAM GP LLC
CROSSTEX ENERGY GP
(*Suby of* ENLINK MIDSTREAM INC) ★
2501 Cedar Springs Rd, Dallas, TX 75201-1409
Tel (214) 953-9500 *Founded/Ownrshp* 2002
Sales 108.5MM[E] *EMP* 216[E]
SIC 5172 Gases

D-U-N-S 13-106-5398
■ ENLINK MIDSTREAM INC
(*Suby of* DEVON) ★
2501 Cedar Springs Rd, Dallas, TX 75201-1409
Tel (214) 953-9500 *Founded/Ownrshp* 2014
Sales 599.5MM[E] *EMP* 736[E]
Accts Kpmg Llp Dallas Texas
SIC 1311 5712 Natural gas production; Mattresses
Ch Bd: Barry E Davis
*COO: William W Davis
*CFO: Michael J Garberding
Ex VP: Chris Auibs
Ex VP: A Chris Aulds
*Ex VP: Joe A Davis
*Sr VP: Stan Golemon
Sr VP: Paul A Weissgarber
Board of Directors: James C Crain, Bryan H Lawrence, Cecil E Martin Jr, Robert F Murchison

D-U-N-S 07-926-8238
■ ENLINK MIDSTREAM LLC
DEVON
(*Suby of* DEVON ENERGY CORP) ★
2501 Cedar Springs Rd, Dallas, TX 75201-1409
Tel (214) 953-9500 *Founded/Ownrshp* 2013
Sales 4.4MMM *EMP* 1,432[E]
Tkr Sym ENLC *Exch* NYS
SIC 1311 Crude petroleum & natural gas; Crude petroleum & natural gas production
Ch Bd: Barry E Davis
Pr: Michael J Garberding
Ex VP: Michael Garberding
Ex VP: Steve J Hoppe
Ex VP: Benjamin D Lamb
VP: Joel Gonzales

D-U-N-S 87-863-6729
▲ ENLINK MIDSTREAM PARTNERS LP
2501 Cedar Springs Rd, Dallas, TX 75201-1409
Tel (214) 953-9500 *Founded/Ownrshp* 2002
Sales 4.4MMM *EMP* 1,432
Accts Kpmg Llp Dallas Texas
Tkr Sym ENLK *Exch* NYS
SIC 4922 1321 Pipelines, natural gas; Natural gas liquids production
Pr: Barry E Davis
Genl Pt: Enlink Midstream GP LLC
CFO: Michael J Garberding
Sr VP: Cynthia Jaggi
Sr VP: Benjamin D Lamb
Sr VP: Michael Leblanc
Sr VP: Royston Lightfoot
Sr VP: Stephen McNair
Sr VP: Michael P Scott
Sr VP: Paul A Weissgarber
VP: Sean Atkins
VP: Stan Golemon
VP: Jennifer Johnson

ENLIVANT
See ASSISTED LIVING CONCEPTS LLC

D-U-N-S 07-611-8900
ENLOE MEDICAL CENTER
1531 Esplanade, Chico, CA 95926-3310
Tel (530) 332-7300 *Founded/Ownrshp* 1913
Sales 505.9MM *EMP* 2,500
SIC 8062

ENMR PLATEAU
See ENMR TELEPHONE COOPERATIVE

D-U-N-S 00-984-8524
ENMR TELEPHONE COOPERATIVE
ENMR PLATEAU
7111 N Prince St, Clovis, NM 88101-9730
Tel (575) 389-5100 *Founded/Ownrshp* 1949
Sales 91.6MM[E] *EMP* 270
Accts Moss Adams Llp Spokane Washi
SIC 4813 Telephone communication, except radio
CEO: Tom Phelps
*Pr: Frank H Blackburn
*CFO: David Robinson
*Sec: Powhattan Carter III
*VP: Kenny Wilhite
Genl Mgr: Shannon Bufkin
Opers Mgr: Ken Betz

D-U-N-S 00-731-9445 IMP/EXP
▲ ENNIS INC (TX)
2441 Presidential Pkwy, Midlothian, TX 76065-3723
Tel (972) 775-9801 *Founded/Ownrshp* 1909
Sales 568.9MM *EMP* 6,018
Accts Grant Thornton Llp Dallas Te
Tkr Sym EBF *Exch* NYS
SIC 2761 2759 2331 2329 Manifold business forms; Business forms: printing; T-shirts & tops, women's: made from purchased materials; Men's & boys' sportswear & athletic clothing
Ch Bd: Keith S Walters
CFO: Richard L Travis Jr
*Ex VP: Michael D Magill
Ex VP: Michael Magill
VP: Ronald M Graham
Genl Mgr: Mark Beamesderfer
Board of Directors: John R Blind, Frank D Bracken, Godfrey M Long Jr, Michael D Magill, Thomas R Price, Kenneth G Pritchett, Alejandro Quiroz, Michael J Schaefer, James C Taylor

D-U-N-S 16-015-7624 IMP
ENNIS PAINT INC
ENNIS TRAFFIC SAFETY SOLUTIONS
115 Todd Ct, Thomasville, NC 27360-3233
Tel (800) 331-8118 *Founded/Ownrshp* 2016
Sales 136.8MM[E] *EMP* 198
SIC 2851 3953 Paints & allied products; Marking devices
CEO: Bryce Anderson
*Pr: Matt Soule
*Pr: Steven Vetter
*CFO: Michael Murren
*Treas: Tom Hoolan
*VP: Vagn Askjaer
*VP Sls: Andrew Liebert

D-U-N-S 09-971-3174
ENNIS STEEL INDUSTRIES INC
204 Metro Park Blvd, Ennis, TX 75119-7031
Tel (972) 878-0400 *Founded/Ownrshp* 1980
Sales 99.0MM *EMP* 175
SIC 3312 3441 1791 Structural shapes & pilings, steel; Hoops, iron & steel; Fabricated structural metal; Structural steel erection; Iron work, structural
CEO: W Bryce Anderson
*Ch Bd: Sandra Anderson
*Pr: Robert E Jones
*VP: Wayne Wood
*Prin: Paul Tomberlin

ENNIS TRAFFIC SAFETY SOLUTIONS
See ENNIS PAINT INC

D-U-N-S 83-750-9157
■ ENOVA CORP
(*Suby of* SEMPRA ENERGY) ★
101 Ash St, San Diego, CA 92101-3017
Tel (619) 239-7700 *Founded/Ownrshp* 1994
Sales 4.2MMM[E] *EMP* 5,008[E]
SIC 4911 4924 Distribution, electric power; Generation, electric power; Transmission, electric power; ;
Pr: Stephen L Baun
VP: Ryan O'Neal

D-U-N-S 83-308-8516
■ ENOVA FINANCIAL HOLDINGS LLC
(*Suby of* CASH AMERICA) ★
200 W Jackson Blvd # 2400, Chicago, IL 60606-6941
Tel (312) 568-4200 *Founded/Ownrshp* 2009
Sales NA *EMP* 366
SIC 6163 Loan brokers
Pr: Timothy Ho
CEO: David A Fisher
VP: Robert S Clifton
VP: Arad Levertov
Snr Sftwr: Aaron Pavely
Snr Sftwr: Emmanuel Sambo
IT Man: Andrew Dyminskiy
Software D: Srikanth Astaputhra
Mktg Dir: Briana J Fabbri
Mktg Mgr: Tesha Choi
Snr Mgr: Karyln Callahan

D-U-N-S 07-860-6400
▲ ENOVA INTERNATIONAL INC
175 W Jackson Blvd Fl 10, Chicago, IL 60604-2863
Tel (312) 568-4200 *Founded/Ownrshp* 2011
Sales 652.6MM *EMP* 1,132[E]
Tkr Sym ENVA *Exch* NYS
SIC 7389 Financial services
Ch Bd: David A Fisher
COO: Greg Zeeman
COO: Gregory Zeeman
CFO: Robert S Clifton
CFO: Steve Cunningham
Chf Mktg O: Kirk Chartier
Ofcr: Sean Rahilly
Ofcr: Tj Williams
Top Exec: Briana Fabbri
Sr VP: Kirk L Chartier
Sr VP: Alex T King
VP: Rob Clifton
VP: John J Higginson
VP: Lisa M Young
Board of Directors: Ellen Carnahan, Daniel R Feehan, William M Goodyear, James A Gray, David C Habiger, Gregg A Kaplan, Mark P McGowan, Mark A Tebbe

D-U-N-S 80-829-0436 IMP
ENOVAPREMIER LLC
1630 Lyndon Farm Ct # 100, Louisville, KY 40223-4086
Tel (502) 412-4406 *Founded/Ownrshp* 2007
Sales 197.4MM[E] *EMP* 300
SIC 3089 Automotive parts, plastic
Ch: Edwin Rigaud
COO: Byron Meyer
CFO: David Dudding
Dir IT: John Chumney
Dir IT: Gus Malawi
IT Man: Rachel Pasha
Plnt Mgr: Stephan Sherrick
Prd Mgr: Steven Harry
Ql Cn Mgr: Don Armstrong
Ql Cn Mgr: Chad Brooks
Ql Cn Mgr: Chris Masten

D-U-N-S 86-956-6992 IMP
ENOVATE MEDICAL LLC
1152 Park Ave, Murfreesboro, TN 37129-4912
Tel (615) 896-1652 *Founded/Ownrshp* 2012
Sales 89.5MM[E] *EMP* 250
SIC 3441 Fabricated structural metal
Dir IT: Larry Slavick
Mktg Dir: Kevin Bridges

D-U-N-S 07-878-4082 IMP
ENOVATION CONTROLS LLC
5311 S 122nd East Ave, Tulsa, OK 74146-6006
Tel (918) 317-4100 *Founded/Ownrshp* 2009
Sales 161.6MM[E] *EMP* 392
SIC 3625 3714 3694 8711 Motor starters & controllers, electric; Motor vehicle steering systems & parts; Ignition apparatus, internal combustion engines; Mechanical engineering
Pr: Patrick W Cavanagh
VP: Brad Beaird
Dir IT: Aaron McDaniel
Sls Mgr: Tom Hamilton

D-U-N-S 78-082-5530 IMP
▲ ENPHASE ENERGY INC
1420 N Mcdowell Blvd, Petaluma, CA 94954-6515
Tel (707) 774-7000 *Founded/Ownrshp* 2006
Sales 357.2MM *EMP* 543[E]
Tkr Sym ENPH *Exch* NGM
SIC 3674 Semiconductors & related devices
Pr: Paul B Nahi
CFO: Bert Garcia
VP: Ciaran Fox
Exec: Liz Winstanley
Prgrm Mgr: Curtis Kahnberg
Snr Sftwr: Sean Straw
QA Dir: Andy Hohenner
Sftwr Eng: Brenda Strech
Sls Dir: Diane Boudreault
Sls Dir: Mike Haines
Mktg Mgr: Anna Porta
Board of Directors: Neal Dempsey, Steven J Gomo, Benjamin Kortlang, Richard Mora, John H Weber

D-U-N-S 03-393-7074 IMP/EXP
▲ ENPRO INDUSTRIES INC
5605 Carnegie Blvd # 500, Charlotte, NC 28209-4674
Tel (704) 731-1500 *Founded/Ownrshp* 2002
Sales 1.2MMM *EMP* 5,400[E]
Accts Pricewaterhousecoopers Llp Ch
Tkr Sym NPO *Exch* NYS
SIC 3053 3519 3089 Gaskets & sealing devices; Engines, diesel & semi-diesel or dual-fuel; Marine engines; Gasoline engines; Bearings, plastic
Pr: Stephen E Macadam
*Ch Bd: Gordon D Harnett
Pr: Todd L Anderson
Pr: William A Favenesi
Pr: Gilles Hudon
Pr: Marvin A Riley
Pr: Susan E Sweeney
Pr: Eric A Vaillancourt
COO: Kenneth D Walker
CFO: J Milton Childress II
Ofcr: Jon A Cox
Ofcr: Robert S McLean
VP: Steven R Bower
VP: David S Burnett
VP: William C O'Neal
VP: Ali Pektas
VP: William L Sparks
Board of Directors: Thomas M Botts, Felix M Brueck, B Bernard Burns Jr, Diane C Creel, David L Hauser, John Humphrey, Kees Van Der Graaf

D-U-N-S 15-399-8539 IMP
ENPROTECH CORP
(*Suby of* ITOCHU INTERNATIONAL INC) ★
4259 E 49th St, Cleveland, OH 44125-1001
Tel (216) 206-0080 *Founded/Ownrshp* 1984
Sales 111.8MM[E] *EMP* 410
SIC 5084 Industrial machinery & equipment
Pr: Pedro Garcia
CFO: Donald Albert
VP Opers: Hiroshi Aida

D-U-N-S 01-109-3975
ENRIQUE MENDOZA (IL)
OLLIN TECHNOLOGY
2350 Nantucket Ln, Elgin, IL 60123-8579
Tel (630) 364-1808 *Founded/Ownrshp* 1999
Sales 300.0MM *EMP* 10
SIC 7379 5045 Computer related consulting services; Computer hardware requirements analysis; Computer software
Owner: Enrique Mendoza

D-U-N-S 00-697-0404 IMP
ENRON CREDITORS RECOVERY CORP
ENRON STEEL PRODUCTS SERVICES
1221 Lamar St Ste 1325, Houston, TX 77010-3050
Tel (713) 853-6161 *Founded/Ownrshp* 1996
Sales 2.9MMM[E] *EMP* 10,000
SIC 5172 4922 4911 1311 1321 2911 Gases; Pipelines, natural gas; Electric services; Natural gas production; Crude petroleum production; Natural gas liquids; Petroleum refining
Pr: John J Ray I
*CFO: Raymond M Bowen
*Ex VP: Robert H Walls Jr
Sls&Mrk Ex: Janet McQuade

D-U-N-S 00-432-8568 EXP
ENRON ENERGY SERVICES INC (DE)
(*Suby of* ENRON STEEL PRODUCTS SERVICES) ★
1400 Smith St Ste 501, Houston, TX 77002-7342
Tel (713) 853-6161 *Founded/Ownrshp* 1997
Sales 137.9MM[E] *EMP* 538
SIC 4924 4911 Natural gas distribution; Electric services; Distribution, electric power
Ch Bd: Lou L Pai
Ex VP: J C Baxter
Ex VP: Richard A Causey
Ex VP: J V Derrick
Ex VP: Steven J Kern
Ex VP: Mark E Koenig
Ex VP: Cindy K Olson
Mng Dir: Richard Shapiro
Netwrk Eng: Scott Shishido
VP Pub Rls: Mark Palmer

D-U-N-S 03-776-0043
ENRON NETWORKS LLC
1400 Smith St, Houston, TX 77002-7327
Tel (713) 853-6161 *Founded/Ownrshp* 2007
Sales 28.1MM[E] *EMP* 1,600
SIC 7389 Financial services
Pr: Greg Piper
*COO: Sally Beck

D-U-N-S 60-924-8265
ENRON POWER CORP
(*Suby of* ENRON STEEL PRODUCTS SERVICES) ★
333 Clay St 400, Houston, TX 77002-4000
Tel (713) 853-6161 *Founded/Ownrshp* 1989
Sales 241.7MM[E] *EMP* 650
SIC 4911 Generation, electric power
Ch Bd: Thomas E White
*Pr: Larry Izzo
*CFO: Keith Marlow
Mng Dir: Joseph Sutton

ENRON STEEL PRODUCTS SERVICES
See ENRON CREDITORS RECOVERY CORP

D-U-N-S 62-308-3565
ENRON TRANSPORTATION SERVICES CO
(*Suby of* ENRON STEEL PRODUCTS SERVICES) ★
1400 Smith St, Houston, TX 77002-7327
Tel (713) 853-6161 *Founded/Ownrshp* 1990
Sales 2.4MMM[E] *EMP* 2,932
SIC 4922 Pipelines, natural gas
Ch Bd: Stanley Horton
Ex Dir: Ron Hagge

D-U-N-S 12-231-4651
ENSCO INC
3110 Frview Pk Dr Ste 300, Falls Church, VA 22042
Tel (703) 321-4713 *Founded/Ownrshp* 1983
Sales 88.1MM *EMP* 700
Accts Bdo Usa Llp Mclean Virginia
SIC 8731 Commercial physical research
Ch: Paul W Broome III
*CEO: Gregory B Young
COO: Mike Dirkes
*CFO: Milan Mike Bogdanovic
CFO: Bogdanovic M Mike
VP: James Barton
VP: Ted Freeman
VP: Joe French
VP: Deborah Hall-Greene
VP: Vernon Joyner
VP: David Macaluso
VP: Boris Nejikovky
VP: Karl E Nell
VP: Jay Paccione
VP: Ta-Lun Yang
Exec: Doug Baumgardt

D-U-N-S 08-974-3280 IMP
ENSCO INTERNATIONAL INC
(*Suby of* ENSCO PLC)
5847 San Felipe St # 3300, Houston, TX 77057-3000
Tel (800) 423-8006 *Founded/Ownrshp* 1987
Sales 57.6MM[E] *EMP* 3,947
SIC 1381 Drilling oil & gas wells
Ch Bd: Daniel W Rabun
*Pr: Carl Trowll
*COO: William Chadwick
*CFO: James Swent
*VP: Brady Long

D-U-N-S 96-869-1308
ENSEMBLE PARENT LLC
345 Park Ave, New York, NY 10154-0004
Tel (212) 583-5000 *Founded/Ownrshp* 2005
Sales 37.1MM[E] *EMP* 6,800
SIC 7363 8741

D-U-N-S 95-719-4541
ENSERCO ENERGY LLC
ENSERCO MIDSTREAM
(*Suby of* TWIN EAGLE RESOURCE MANAGEMENT LLC) ★
1900 16th St Ste 450, Denver, CO 80202-5219
Tel (303) 568-3242 *Founded/Ownrshp* 2012
Sales 89.2MM *EMP* 40[E]
SIC 5172 Crude oil
CEO: Griff Jones
Treas: Chris Elwess
*VP: Victoria Campbell
*VP: Jeff Price
*VP: Cole Stanley
*Genl Mgr: Eric Watts

ENSERCO MIDSTREAM
See ENSERCO ENERGY LLC

D-U-N-S 12-739-1279
▲ ENSIGN GROUP INC
ENDURA HEALTHCARE
27101 Puerta Real Ste 450, Mission Viejo, CA 92691-8566
Tel (949) 487-9500 *Founded/Ownrshp* 1999
Sales 1.3MMM *EMP* 16,494
Accts Deloitte & Touche Llp Costa M
Tkr Sym ENSG *Exch* NGS
SIC 8051 Skilled nursing care facilities
Pr: Christopher R Christensen
Ch Bd: Roy E Christensen
COO: Barry R Port
CFO: Suzanne D Snapper
Ofcr: Ellen Cote
Ex VP: Chad A Keetch
VP: Cory R Monette
VP: Gregory K Stapley
VP: Beverly B Wittekind
Dir Soc: Cassandra Jenkins
Mktg Dir: Kendra Vallone

D-U-N-S 17-489-0608 EXP
ENSIGN UNITED STATES DRILLING INC
(*Suby of* ENSIGN ENERGY SERVICES INC)
410 17th St Ste 1200, Denver, CO 80202-4425
Tel (303) 292-1206 *Founded/Ownrshp* 1994
Sales 1.2MMM[E] *EMP* 2,000
SIC 1381 Drilling oil & gas wells
Ch: N Murray Edwards
*Pr: Edward D Kautz
*Ex VP: Glenn O J Dagenais

Ex VP: Ed Kautz
**VP:* Tom Schledwitz
**Prin:* Selby W Porter
Dir IT: Bill Vaccaro

D-U-N-S 03-911-9057 IMP
ENSIGN-BICKFORD AEROSPACE & DEFENSE CO
EBA&D
(*Suby of* AEROSPACE) ★
640 Hopmeadow St, Simsbury, CT 06070-2420
Tel (860) 843-2289 *Founded/Ownrshp* 2009
Sales 130.6MM^E *EMP* 435^E
SIC 2892 Detonators & detonating caps
Pr: Brendan Walsh
**Pr:* Brendan M Walsh
Prgrm Mgr: Kenneth Stonebraker
IT Man: Mario Colon
Ql Cn Mgr: Michael Bendas
Ql Cn Mgr: Geoff Cordeiro
Ql Cn Mgr: Jennifer Stiffen
Mktg Dir: Samantha Turbarg

D-U-N-S 05-850-9654 IMP/EXP
ENSIGN-BICKFORD INDUSTRIES INC
AEROSPACE
125 Pwder Frest Dr Fl 3, Simsbury, CT 06070
Tel (860) 843-2000 *Founded/Ownrshp* 1836
Sales 400.0M *EMP* 1,600
SIC 3764 2047 2835 3829 2499 6552 Guided missile & space vehicle propulsion unit parts; Dog & cat food; In vitro & in vivo diagnostic substances; Measuring & controlling devices; Laundry products, wood; Land subdividers & developers, commercial; Land subdividers & developers, residential
CEO: Caleb E White
CFO: Scott Deakin
Snr Mgr: Jim Murphy

D-U-N-S 14-864-5229 IMP
ENSINGER INDUSTRIES INC
(*Suby of* ENSINGER GMBH)
365 Meadowlands Blvd, Washington, PA 15301-8904
Tel (724) 746-6050 *Founded/Ownrshp* 1991
Sales 159.5MM^E *EMP* 500
SIC 2821 Plastics materials & resins
Pr: Warren J Phillips
CFO: Bob Racchini
VP: Lawrence Resavage
Rgnl Mgr: Martin Wood
Genl Mgr: Fred Nass
CTO: Lubeth Manzo
Sales Exec: Jim Jones
Mktg Mgr: Bruce Dickinson
Manager: Lance Nixon
Sls Mgr: German Baur
Sls Mgr: Mike Ferreira

D-U-N-S 09-372-8012
ENSR INTL CORP
250 Apollo Dr, Chelmsford, MA 01824-3627
Tel (978) 589-3000 *Founded/Ownrshp* 1998
Sales NA *EMP* 2,601
SIC 8748 8711

ENSTAR NATURAL GAS
See NORSTAR PIPELINE CO INC

D-U-N-S 05-165-4379
■ **ENSYNCH INC**
(*Suby of* INSIGHT ENTERPRISES INC) ★
6820 S Harl Ave, Tempe, AZ 85283-4318
Tel (480) 894-3500 *Founded/Ownrshp* 2011
Sales 198.7MM^E *EMP* 200
SIC 8748 Business consulting
CEO: Gene Holmquist
**COO:* Stan Lequin
**CFO:* Rick Winterich
VP: Joel Fricker
VP: Tobias Johansson
**Dir Sec:* Lynn Blecha
**CTO:* Hunter Bennett
Snr PM: Jed Lazzeri

D-U-N-S 03-043-7586
ENT FEDERAL CREDIT UNION
7250 Campus Dr Ste 200, Colorado Springs, CO 80920-6532
Tel (719) 574-1100 *Founded/Ownrshp* 1957
Sales NA *EMP* 530
SIC 6061 Federal credit unions
Ch: Tim E Rickert
V Ch: Lori Kurtz
**Pr:* Randy Bernstein
**CEO:* Charles F Emmer
**CFO:* Mj Coon
Treas: Richard Discenza
Ofcr: Judy Blotz
Ofcr: Marcus Brown
Ofcr: Jack Hook
Ofcr: Mike Steppenbacker
Sr VP: Rich Scholes
Sr VP: Barbara Winter
**VP:* Sharie Flanagan
VP: Cathy Grossman
VP: Steven Post
VP: William Vogeney
VP: Jeff Wilkins
Exec: Paula Pollet
Dir Risk M: Jay Olson

D-U-N-S 16-285-2359
ENTACT LLC
3129 Bass Pro Dr, Grapevine, TX 76051-1987
Tel (972) 580-1323 *Founded/Ownrshp* 2015
Sales 203.4MM^E *EMP* 450
SIC 1629 Earthmoving contractor
CEO: Dean Pisani
**Pr:* Greg Tunstall
**CFO:* Thomas Frawley
Ofcr: Jake Grieco
Ofcr: Jamie Stiehl
Snr PM: Jim Satkoski

ENTEC ENGINEERED RESINS
See ENTEC POLYMERS LLC

D-U-N-S 14-810-5315 IMP/EXP
ENTEC POLYMERS LLC
ENTEC ENGINEERED RESINS
(*Suby of* RAVAGO AMERICAS) ★
1900 Summit Tower Blvd # 900, Orlando, FL 32810-5925
Tel (407) 875-9595 *Founded/Ownrshp* 2006
Sales 653.3MM^E *EMP* 365
SIC 5162 1459 Plastics resins; Plastic fire clay mining
Pr: David Hagopian
**CFO:* James Ashton
**Ex VP:* Michael Clifton
Sls Mgr: Tom Haughey

D-U-N-S 02-357-3108
ENTECH SALES AND SERVICE INC
3404 Garden Brook Dr, Dallas, TX 75234-2496
Tel (972) 241-8188 *Founded/Ownrshp* 1981
Sales 105.5MM^E *EMP* 290
Accts Burch Fincher & Co Llc Dalla
SIC 1731 7623 1711 Electronic controls installation; Energy management controls; Refrigeration service & repair; Air conditioning repair; Plumbing, heating, air-conditioning contractors
Pr: Gale P Rucker
COO: Vince Fabry
**CFO:* Bernetta Rucker
Ex VP: John Mattes
**VP:* Rob Emmert
**VP:* Nick J Kollasch
**VP:* Bruce Long
Exec: Sandy Riley
Dir Bus: Chet Kieselhorst
Prgrm Mgr: Michael Chavez
Div Mgr: Sonny Goodwin

D-U-N-S 08-852-4111
ENTEGEE INC
ENGINEERING TECHNICAL GROUP
(*Suby of* ADECCO TECHNICAL) ★
70 Blanchard Rd Ste 102, Burlington, MA 01803-5100
Tel (781) 221-5800 *Founded/Ownrshp* 1996
Sales 87.4MM^E *EMP* 2,629
SIC 7363 5045 Engineering help service; Computer software
Pr: Robert P Crouch
**COO:* Timothy Payne
**CFO:* J Todd King
**Treas:* Lorelei Depalo
**VP:* Diane Howell

D-U-N-S 10-324-4773 IMP/EXP
▲ **ENTEGRIS INC**
129 Concord Rd, Billerica, MA 01821-4600
Tel (978) 436-6500 *Founded/Ownrshp* 2005
Sales 1.0MMM *EMP* 3,419
Tkr Sym ENTG *Exch* NGS
SIC 3089 3081 3674 Plastic processing; Plastic film & sheet; Packing materials, plastic sheet; Semiconductors & related devices
Pr: Bertrand Loy
**Ch Bd:* Paul L H Olson
COO: Todd Edlund
CFO: Gregory B Graves
Sr VP: John J Murphy
Sr VP: William Shaner
Sr VP: Peter W Walcott
VP: Jack Barker
VP: Steve Cantor
VP: Wai Choi
VP: Gregory Marshall
VP: Corey Rucci
VP: Michael D Sauer
VP Bus Dev: Stuart Tison
Board of Directors: Michael A Bradley, Marvin D Burkett, R Nicholas Burns, Daniel W Christman, James F Gentilcore, James P Lederer, Brian F Sullivan

D-U-N-S 18-682-0155 IMP/EXP
ENTEK INTERNATIONAL LLC
250 Hansard Ave, Lebanon, OR 97355-2218
Tel (541) 259-3901 *Founded/Ownrshp* 1983
Sales 102.2MM^E *EMP* 225
SIC 3089 Plastic processing
CEO: Larry Keith
**Pr:* Rob Keith
CFO: Jeff Grimm
VP: Tony Vander Heide
VP: Joel Kuntz
Exec: Jennifer Stock
CIO: Ed Marantz
VP Mktg: Dan Weerts
Sls Mgr: Dan Powell
Genl Couns: Kimberly Medford
Snr Mgr: Arthur Seavy

ENTENMANNS BAKERY
See ENTENMANNS INC

D-U-N-S 00-205-4880
ENTENMANNS INC (DE)
ENTENMANNS BAKERY
1724 5th Ave, Bay Shore, NY 11706-3487
Tel (631) 273-6000 *Founded/Ownrshp* 1995
Sales NA *EMP* 3,000
SIC 2051

D-U-N-S 14-425-9876 IMP
■ **ENTERASYS NETWORKS INC**
CABLETRON
(*Suby of* EXTREME NETWORKS INC) ★
9 Northstern Blvd Ste 300, Salem, NH 03079
Tel (603) 952-5000 *Founded/Ownrshp* 2013
Sales 131.4MM^E *EMP* 668
SIC 3577 7373 3357 5045 Computer peripheral equipment; Local area network (LAN) systems integrator; Communication wire; Coaxial cable, nonferrous; Fiber optic cable (insulated); Computers, peripherals & software
CEO: Ed Meyercord
**Pr:* Michael Fabiaschi
**CFO:* Terry Schmid
**Ex VP:* Chris Crowell
**VP:* Ken Arola
**VP:* Frank Blohm
**VP:* Bob Gault
**VP:* Katy Motiey
Sftwr Eng: Larry Walker
Sftwr Eng: Dave White
Opers Mgr: Ronald Baron

D-U-N-S 05-899-4237
▲ **ENTERCOM COMMUNICATIONS CORP**
401 E City Ave Ste 809, Bala Cynwyd, PA 19004-1130
Tel (610) 660-5610 *Founded/Ownrshp* 1968
Sales 411.3MM *EMP* 2,529^E
Tkr Sym ETM *Exch* NYS
SIC 4832 Radio broadcasting stations
Pr: David J Field
**Ch Bd:* Joseph M Field
COO: Louise C Kramer
CFO: Stephen F Fisher
Treas: Eugene D Levin
Chf Mktg O: Ruth Gaviria
Sr VP: Pat Paxton
Sr VP: Andrew P Sutor IV
VP: Tim Murphy
VP: Lance Richard
VP: Andrew Sutor
VP: Don Tomasulo
VP: Phil Zachary
Board of Directors: David J Berkman, Joel Hollander, Mark Laneve, David Levy

D-U-N-S 36-155-1331
■ **ENTERCOM RADIO LLC**
(*Suby of* ENTERCOM COMMUNICATIONS CORP) ★
401 E City Ave Ste 409, Bala Cynwyd, PA 19004-1121
Tel (610) 660-5610 *Founded/Ownrshp* 1999
Sales 793.1MM^E *EMP* 1,110
SIC 4832 Radio broadcasting stations
Prin: David Field
VP: Gene Levin
Prd Dir: Richard Murphy
Sls&Mrk Ex: Andrew Ellenberg

D-U-N-S 00-690-3298
■ **ENTERGY ARKANSAS INC** (AR)
(*Suby of* ENTERGY CORP) ★
425 W Capitol Ave Fl 20, Little Rock, AR 72201-3471
Tel (501) 377-4000 *Founded/Ownrshp* 1926
Sales 2.2MMM *EMP* 1,217^E
Tkr Sym EAI *Exch* NYS
SIC 4911 Electric services; Distribution, electric power; Generation, electric power; Transmission, electric power
Ch Bd: Hugh T McDonald
**CFO:* Andrew S Marsh
Sr VP: Alyson M Mount
VP: Oscar Washington
Snr Mgr: Bill Parker
Board of Directors: Theodore H Bunting Jr, Paul D Hinnenkamp

D-U-N-S 80-974-9005
▲ **ENTERGY CORP**
639 Loyola Ave Ste 300, New Orleans, LA 70113-7106
Tel (504) 576-4000 *Founded/Ownrshp* 1989
Sales 11.5MMM *EMP* 13,579^E
Tkr Sym ETR *Exch* NYS
SIC 4931 Electric & other services combined;
Ch Bd: Leo P Denault
COO: Paul D Hinnenkamp
CFO: Andrew S Marsh
Treas: Steven McNeal
Bd of Dir: Charles Watkins
Ofcr: Roderick K West
Ex VP: Steven Agresta
Ex VP: Christopher Bakken
Ex VP: Marcus V Brown
Ex VP: Renae Conley
Ex VP: Jerry D Jackson
Ex VP: Michael Kansler
Ex VP: Brionn Stephens
Ex VP: Don Vinci
Sr VP: Andrea Coughlin Rowley
VP: Jack Balla
VP: Kimberly Buckhalter
VP: Michela Darville
VP: Ed Davis
VP: Kimberly Despeaux
VP: Daniel Falstad
Board of Directors: Karen A Puckett, Maureen S Bateman, W J Tauzin, Patrick J Condon, Steven V Wilkinson, Kirkland H Donald, Gary W Edwards, Philip L Frederickson, Alexis M Herman, Donald C Hintz, Stuart L Levenick, Blanche L Lincoln

D-U-N-S 11-898-6819
■ **ENTERGY ENTERPRISES INC**
(*Suby of* ENTERGY CORP) ★
905 Highway 80 E, Clinton, MS 39056-5244
Tel (601) 925-6504 *Founded/Ownrshp* 1993
Sales 289.4MM^E *EMP* 810
Accts Deloitte & Touche Llp
SIC 4931 Electric & other services combined
Ch Bd: Edwin Lupberger
**Sr VP:* Michael Thompson
VP: Dennis Walsh
Dir IT: Robin Woods

D-U-N-S 00-792-4251
■ **ENTERGY GULF STATES LOUISIANA LLC**
(*Suby of* EGS HOLDINGS INC) ★
4809 Jefferson Hwy, Jefferson, LA 70121-3122
Tel (504) 576-4000 *Founded/Ownrshp* 1925
Sales 2.1MMM *EMP* 763^E
SIC 4911 4924 Generation, electric power; Transmission, electric power; Distribution, electric power; Natural gas distribution
Ch Bd: Phillip R May Jr
**Pr:* Theodore H Bunting Jr
Ex VP: Marcus V Brown
Ex VP: Jeffrey S Forbes
Sr VP: Alyson M Mount
Board of Directors: Andrew S Marsh, Mark T Savof

D-U-N-S 78-943-7188
■ **ENTERGY LOUISIANA HOLDINGS INC**
(*Suby of* ENTERGY CORP) ★
4809 Jefferson Hwy, Jefferson, LA 70121-3122
Tel (504) 840-2734 *Founded/Ownrshp* 2005
Sales 4.4MMM^E *EMP* 923^E
SIC 4911 4922 Electric services; Distribution, electric power; Generation, electric power; Transmission, electric power; Pipelines, natural gas
Ch Bd: Phillip R May Jr

D-U-N-S 08-002-1872
■ **ENTERGY LOUISIANA LLC**
(*Suby of* ENTERGY UTILITY HOLDING CO LLC) ★
4809 Jefferson Hwy, Jefferson, LA 70121-3122
Tel (504) 576-4000 *Founded/Ownrshp* 2015
Sales 373.4MM^E *EMP* 1,686
SIC 4911 4922 Electric services; Distribution, electric power; Generation, electric power; Transmission, electric power; Natural gas transmission; Pipelines, natural gas
Ch Bd: Phillip R May Jr
Pr: Theodore H Bunting Jr
CFO: Andrew S Marsh
Ofcr: Jeffrey S Forbes
Ex VP: Marcus V Brown
Sr VP: Alyson M Mount

D-U-N-S 00-696-4381
■ **ENTERGY MISSISSIPPI INC**
(*Suby of* ENTERGY CORP) ★
308 E Pearl St, Jackson, MS 39201-3419
Tel (601) 368-5000 *Founded/Ownrshp* 1963
Sales 1.4MMM *EMP* 724
Accts Deloitte & Touche Llp New Orl
SIC 4911 Electric services; Generation, electric power; Distribution, electric power
Ch Bd: Haley R Fisackerly
**Pr:* Theodore H Bunting Jr
Ex VP: Marcus V Brown
Sr VP: Alyson M Mount
IT Man: Don Little
IT Man: Charlie Sanders
Board of Directors: Andrew S Marsh, Mark T Savoff

D-U-N-S 00-694-7824
■ **ENTERGY NEW ORLEANS INC** (LA)
(*Suby of* ENTERGY CORP) ★
1600 Perdido St Bldg 505, New Orleans, LA 70112-1208
Tel (504) 670-3700 *Founded/Ownrshp* 1926
Sales 671.4MM *EMP* 292
Accts Deloitte & Touche Llp New Orl
Tkr Sym ENJ *Exch* NYS
SIC 4931 Electric & other services combined
Pr: Charles L Rice Jr
CFO: Leo Denault
Ex VP: Marcus V Brown
Sr VP: Alyson M Mount
Opers Mgr: Frank Wilson
Board of Directors: Theodore H Bunting Jr, Paul D Hinnenkamp, Andrew S Marsh

D-U-N-S 08-031-2295
■ **ENTERGY NEW ORLEANS TRANSMISSION OWNER**
(*Suby of* ENTERGY NEW ORLEANS INC) ★
1600 Perdido St Bldg 505, New Orleans, LA 70112-1208
Tel (501) 228-2888 *Founded/Ownrshp* 2016
Sales 700.0MM *EMP* 2
SIC 4931 Electric & other services combined
Pr: Charles L Rice Jr

D-U-N-S 05-328-7889 IMP/EXP
■ **ENTERGY NUCLEAR GENERATION CO** (MA)
(*Suby of* ENTERGY CORP) ★
1340 Echelon Pkwy Ste 100, Jackson, MS 39213-8210
Tel (601) 368-5000 *Founded/Ownrshp* 1998, 1999
Sales 777.1MM^E *EMP* 2,175
SIC 4911 Generation, electric power
CEO: John Herron
**Treas:* Steven C McNeal
VP: Michael L Balduzzi
VP: Tim Mitchell
**VP:* John C Wilder

D-U-N-S 80-919-9297
■ **ENTERGY NUCLEAR HOLDING CO**
(*Suby of* ENTERGY CORP) ★
639 Loyola Ave, New Orleans, LA 70113-3125
Tel (504) 576-4000 *Founded/Ownrshp* 2000
Sales 985.8MM^E *EMP* 536^E
SIC 4911
Ch Bd: J Wayne Leonard
VP: Joseph T Henderson
VP: Neal Jansonius
VP: Kenneth R Theobalds

D-U-N-S 80-921-6885 IMP
■ **ENTERGY NUCLEAR PALISADES LLC**
PALISADES NUCLEAR PLANT
(*Suby of* ENTERGY NUCLEAR HOLDING CO) ★
27780 Blue Star Hwy, Covert, MI 49043-9530
Tel (269) 764-2000 *Founded/Ownrshp* 2007
Sales 985.8MM^E *EMP* 500
SIC 4911
Pr: Mike Kansler

D-U-N-S 61-616-9751
■ **ENTERGY OPERATIONS INC**
(*Suby of* ENTERGY CORP) ★
1340 Echelon Pkwy Ste 100, Jackson, MS 39213-8210
Tel (601) 366-2727 *Founded/Ownrshp* 1990
Sales 1.2MMM^E *EMP* 3,600
SIC 4911 Generation, electric power
Pr: Jeff S Forbes
Sr VP: Marcus Brown
VP: Robyn Bentley
**VP:* Wanda C Curry
**VP:* Clifford Eubanks
VP: John Herron
Exec: Cindy Rambin
VP Opers: Joseph P Deroy
VP Opers: John Ventosa
Opers Mgr: Steve Beagles
Counsel: Chuck Barlow

D-U-N-S 05-252-4212
■ **ENTERGY SERVICES INC**
(*Suby of* ENTERGY CORP) ★
639 Loyola Ave Ste 300, New Orleans, LA 70113-7106
Tel (504) 576-4000 *Founded/Ownrshp* 1963
Sales 473.4MM^E *EMP* 1,325

SIC 8741 8711 Administrative management; Industrial engineers
CEO: Leo P Denault
*Pr: Marcus V Brown
*Pr: Theo Bunting Jr
*COO: Mark T Savoff
*CFO: Andrew Marsh
Treas: Mary A Valladares
*VP: Jere M Ahrens
*VP: Kay K Arnold
*VP: Michael A Balduzzi
*VP: Kelle J Barfield
VP: Theodore H Bunting
*VP: Kimberly H Despeaux
VP: Michael R Kansler
VP: Robert D Sloan

D-U-N-S 61-725-1533
■ ENTERGY TEXAS INC
(Suby of ENTERGY CORP) ★
350 Pine St, Beaumont, TX 77701-2437
Tel (409) 981-2000 Founded/Ownrshp 2007
Sales 1.7MMM EMP 608E
Tkr Sym EZT Exch NYS
SIC 4911 Electric services; Distribution, electric power; Generation, electric power; Transmission, electric power
Ch Bd: Sallie T Rainer
*CFO: Andrew S Marsh
Ex VP: Marcus V Brown
Sr VP: Alyson M Mount
Board of Directors: Theodore H Bunting Jr, Mark T Savoff

D-U-N-S 80-998-5083
ENTERGY TEXAS INC
446 North Blvd, Baton Rouge, LA 70802-5717
Tel (800) 368-3749 Founded/Ownrshp 2008
Sales 2.3MMME EMP 1,595
SIC 4911 Electric services
CEO: Joseph F Domino

D-U-N-S 08-002-2102
■ ENTERGY UTILITY HOLDING CO LLC
(Suby of ENTERGY CORP) ★
4809 Jefferson Hwy, Jefferson, LA 70121-3122
Tel (504) 576-4000 Founded/Ownrshp 2014
Sales 602.3MME EMP 1,686E
SIC 4911 4922 Electric services; Distribution, electric power; Generation, electric power; Transmission, electric power; Natural gas transmission; Pipelines, natural gas
Ch Bd: Phillip R May Jr

D-U-N-S 00-934-9692 IMP
ENTERGY-KOCH L P
20 Greenway Plz Ste 950, Houston, TX 77046-2008
Tel (713) 544-6000 Founded/Ownrshp 2001
Sales 306.5MME EMP 600
Accts Deloitte & Touche Llp
SIC 4923 4911 Gas transmission & distribution; Electric services
CEO: Kyle D Vann
Pr: David Sobotka
CFO: Dennis Albrecht
Ex VP: Ronald S Oppenheimer
IT Man: Chris Bauer

ENTERPRISE, THE
See ENTERPRISE PUBLISHING CO LLC

D-U-N-S 09-544-8309
▲ ENTERPRISE BANCORP INC
222 Merrimack St, Lowell, MA 01852-5913
Tel (978) 459-9000 Founded/Ownrshp 1996
Sales NA EMP 412
Tkr Sym EBTC Exch NGS
SIC 6022 State commercial banks
CEO: John P Clancy Jr
*Ch Bd: George L Duncan
Pr: Joy Beaubien-Harmer
Pr: David Brown
Pr: Lauretta Doyle
*Pr: Richard W Main
COO: Stephen J Irish
CFO: James A Marcotte
*V Ch Bd: Arnold S Lerner
Ex VP: Brian H Bullock
Ex VP: Chester J Szablak Jr
Sr VP: William Collins
Sr VP: Steven R Larochelle
VP: Tracy Clement
VP: Diane Jeray
VP: Edith Joyce
VP: Carolyn Mansour
VP: Cheryl Serpe
Dir Risk M: Michael Gallagher
Board of Directors: Jacqueline F Moloney, Gino J Baroni, Luis M Pedroso, John R Clementi, Michael T Putziger, James F Conway III, Carol L Reid, Carole A Cowan, Michael A Spinelli, Normand E Deschene, John T Grady Jr, Eric W Hanson, Mary Jane King, John A Koutsos

D-U-N-S 18-481-8466
■ ENTERPRISE BANK & TRUST
(Suby of ENTERPRISE FINANCIAL SERVICES CORP) ★
150 N Meramec Ave Ste 300, Saint Louis, MO 63105-3765
Tel (314) 725-5500 Founded/Ownrshp 1988
Sales NA EMP 450
SIC 6022 State commercial banks
Ch: Stephen Marsh
*Pr: Peter Benoit
*Pr: Scott Goodman
Pr: Mark Gorman
Pr: James Graser
Pr: Tina Gray
*CFO: Frank Sanfilippo
*CFO: Keene Turner
Chf Inves: Michael Kowalkowski
Ofcr: Ralph Hultin
Ofcr: Peg Kirkman
Ofcr: Kyle Koupal
Ofcr: Joe Mark
Ofcr: Deanna Pfaff
Ofcr: Kara Schultze
Ofcr: Alex Stack
Ofcr: Denise Tuhill
Sr VP: Ellen Jordan
Sr VP: Steven Middelkamp
Sr VP: Steve Middendorf
Sr VP: Sherri Nordgren
Board of Directors: Benjamin Ola Akande

D-U-N-S 61-410-6896
■ ENTERPRISE BANK AND TRUST CO
(Suby of ENTERPRISE BANCORP INC) ★
222 Merrimack St Fl 1, Lowell, MA 01852-5994
Tel (978) 459-9000 Founded/Ownrshp 1989
Sales NA EMP 226
SIC 6022 State commercial banks
CEO: John P Clancy Jr
*Ch Bd: George L Duncan
*Pr: Richard W Main
*CFO: James Marcotte
Ofcr: Wendy Foster
*Ex VP: Brian H Bullock
*Ex VP: Stephen J Irish
Sr VP: Clayton Mersereau
Sr VP: Diane Silva
VP: Pamela Anastasi
VP: J M Coggins
VP: Patrick Connerty
VP: Susan Covey
VP: Erica Eftimoff
VP: Darlene Hagan
VP: George Kriegshauser
VP: Michael Sullivan

D-U-N-S 96-201-6049
ENTERPRISE CONSULTING SOLUTIONS INC
ECS-CHART RETRIEVAL SERVICES
(Suby of HEALTHPORT) ★
15458 N 28th Ave, Phoenix, AZ 85053-4076
Tel (623) 207-5600 Founded/Ownrshp 2015
Sales NA EMP 2,500
SIC 7375 Information retrieval services
CEO: Tim Poehling
*Pr: Craig Mercure
VP: Jason Grendahl
VP: Pamela Hulse
VP Opers: Jason Schmidt

D-U-N-S 04-819-3077 IMP
■ ENTERPRISE CRUDE OIL LLC
(Suby of ENTERPRISE OFFSHORE PORT SYS) ★
1100 Louisiana St, Houston, TX 77002-5227
Tel (713) 381-6500 Founded/Ownrshp 2014
Sales 20.9MMME EMP 69E
SIC 5172 Petroleum brokers
Ex VP: Larry Fenity
Off Mgr: Diane Steven

D-U-N-S 88-479-3472
▲ ENTERPRISE FINANCIAL SERVICES CORP
150 N Meramec Ave Ste 350, Saint Louis, MO 63105-3874
Tel (314) 725-5500 Founded/Ownrshp 1994
Sales NA EMP 459E
Accts Deloitte & Touche Llp St Lou
Tkr Sym EFSC Exch NGS
SIC 6022 State commercial banks
CEO: Peter F Benoist
*Ch Bd: James J Murphy Jr
Pr: James B Lally
CFO: Keene S Turner
Sr VP: Mark G Ponder

D-U-N-S 17-238-5994
ENTERPRISE FLEET MANAGEMENT INC
(Suby of CRAWFORD GROUP INC) ★
2600 S Hanley Rd Ste 460, Saint Louis, MO 63144-2594
Tel (314) 256-5100 Founded/Ownrshp 1971
Sales 186.1MME EMP 308
SIC 7515 7514 Passenger car leasing; Rent-a-car service
Pr: Bob Schurwan

D-U-N-S 04-638-0093 IMP/EXP
ENTERPRISE HOLDINGS INC
ENTERPRISE RENT-A-CAR
(Suby of CRAWFORD GROUP INC) ★
600 Corporate Park Dr, Saint Louis, MO 63105-4204
Tel (314) 512-5000 Founded/Ownrshp 1980
Sales 5.8MMME EMP 68,993
SIC 7514 7515 Rent-a-car service; Passenger car leasing
Pr: Pamela M Nicholson
Ch Bd: Andrew C Taylor
Pr: Greg Stubblefield
COO: Christine Taylor
CFO: Jeffer Berry
CFO: Virginia Halbert
CFO: William W Snyder
CFO: Mark Strong
Treas: Rose Langhorst
Assoc VP: Steven Kluesner
Ex VP: Travis Tanner
Sr VP: Edward Adams
Sr VP: Steve Bloom
Sr VP: Matthew G Darrah
Sr VP: Lee Kaplan
Sr VP: Craig Kennedy
Sr VP: Christine Taylor-Broughton
Comm Man: Jaime Perez
Comm Man: Chad Stiltener
Comm Man: Bryan Watson

D-U-N-S 83-643-4290
■ ENTERPRISE HYDROCARBONS LP
(Suby of ENTERPRISE OFFSHORE PORT SYS) ★
1100 La St Fl 10, San Antonio, TX 78209
Tel (713) 381-6500 Founded/Ownrshp 2004
Sales 382.0MM EMP 69
SIC 1389 Processing service, gas
CEO: Michael Creel

D-U-N-S 79-690-3094
ENTERPRISE LEASING CO OF CHICAGO LLC
(Suby of ENTERPRISE RENT-A-CAR) ★
1050 N Lombard Rd, Lombard, IL 60148-1232
Tel (630) 693-2916 Founded/Ownrshp 1984
Sales 61.3MME EMP 1,400
SIC 7515 7514 Passenger car leasing; Rent-a-car service
Pr: Jeffrey D Wilder

D-U-N-S 08-502-0154 IMP/EXP
ENTERPRISE LEASING CO OF FLORIDA LLC
(Suby of ENTERPRISE RENT-A-CAR) ★
3505 E Fontage Ste 200 Rd, Tampa, FL 33607
Tel (813) 887-4299 Founded/Ownrshp 1975
Sales 81.1MME EMP 2,000
SIC 7514 7515 Rent-a-car service; Passenger car leasing
CFO: William Snyder
*VP: Richard Allen
VP: Joseph Jacobs
*VP: William Lafferty
*VP: Donald Ross
*Prin: Pam M Nicholson
*Prin: William W Snyder

D-U-N-S 04-883-2018
ENTERPRISE LEASING CO OF GEORGIA LLC
ENTERPRISE RENT A CAR
(Suby of ENTERPRISE RENT-A-CAR) ★
5909 Peachtree Ind, Atlanta, GA 30341-1630
Tel (770) 821-0399 Founded/Ownrshp 1969
Sales 41.6MME EMP 1,000
SIC 7514 7515 5521

D-U-N-S 14-340-5095
■ ENTERPRISE NEWSMEDIA LLC
(Suby of NEW MEDIA INVESTMENT GROUP INC) ★
400 Crown Colony Dr, Quincy, MA 02169-0930
Tel (585) 598-0030 Founded/Ownrshp 2013
Sales 135.7MME EMP 950
SIC 2711 Commercial printing & newspaper publishing combined

ENTERPRISE OFFSHORE PORT SYS
See ENTERPRISE PRODUCTS OPERATING LLC

D-U-N-S 04-821-0686 IMP
ENTERPRISE PRODUCTS CO
1100 Louisiana St, Houston, TX 77002-5227
Tel (713) 880-6500 Founded/Ownrshp 1998
Sales 3.9MMME EMP 6,900E
SIC 1321 4925 Natural gas liquids; Gas production and/or distribution
CEO: Michael A Creel
*Pr: Randa L Duncan
*CEO: Michael J Knesek
COO: Bill Ordermann
*COO: A J Jim Teague
*Ofcr: Richard A Bachmann
Sr VP: James M Collingsworth
Sr VP: Mark Hurley
Sr VP: Leonard W Mallett
*VP: Dannine D Avara
*VP: Lynn L Bourdon III
*VP: Terry L Hurlburt
VP: Bryan Oliver
Exec: Max Blackwood

D-U-N-S 60-380-4548
ENTERPRISE PRODUCTS HOLDINGS LLC
1100 Louisiana St Fl 10, Houston, TX 77002-5432
Tel (713) 381-6500 Founded/Ownrshp 2010
Sales 773.6MME EMP 4,800
SIC 4922 4925 4923 Pipelines, natural gas; Storage, natural gas; Liquefied petroleum gas, distribution through mains; Gas transmission & distribution
CEO: Ralph S Cunningham
*Ch Bd: Randa Duncan Williams
COO: William Ordemann
CFO: Randall W Foler
CFO: Randall W Fowler
Ex VP: Richard H Bachmann
Sr VP: Lynn L Bourdon
Board of Directors: Carin M Barth, William C Montgomery

D-U-N-S 84-152-8859 IMP
■ ENTERPRISE PRODUCTS OPERATING LLC
ENTERPRISE OFFSHORE PORT SYS
(Suby of ENTERPRISE PRODUCTS PARTNERS LP) ★
1100 La St Ste 1000, Houston, TX 77002
Tel (713) 381-6500 Founded/Ownrshp 1998
Sales 21.3MMME EMP 69
Accts Deloitte & Touche Llp Houston
SIC 4923 Gas transmission & distribution
CEO: A James Teague
*Pr: Richard H Bachmann
*Pr: Lynn L Bourdon III
*Pr: James A Cisarik
*Pr: Michael A Creel
*Pr: Randall W Fowler
*CEO: Ralph S Cunnigham
*CFO: Bryan F Bulawa
*Ex VP: W Randall Fowler
Ex VP: Willam Ordemann
*Sr VP: Kevin C Bodenhamer
Sr VP: Stephanie C Hildebrandt
*VP: Graham W Bacon
VP: Gene Petru
VP: Monty Wells
VP: Fay Wood
Dir Bus: Michael Deprang

D-U-N-S 02-795-3129
▲ ENTERPRISE PRODUCTS PARTNERS LP
1100 Louisiana St Fl 10, Houston, TX 77002-5432
Tel (713) 381-6500 Founded/Ownrshp 1968
Sales 27.0MMM EMP 6,800E
Tkr Sym EPD Exch NYS
SIC 4922 4925 4923 Pipelines, natural gas; Gas production and/or distribution; Liquefied petroleum gas, distribution through mains; Gas transmission & distribution
CEO: Michael A Creel
Genl Pt: Enterprise Products Holdings L
Pr: W Randall Fowler
CEO: A James Teague
COO: Jim A Teague
CFO: Bryan F Bulawa
Ex VP: Bob Sanders
Ex VP: Aj Teague
Sr VP: Graham W Bacon
Sr VP: Charles M Brabson
Sr VP: Jerry Cardillo
Sr VP: Paul G Flynn
Sr VP: Mark A Hurley
Sr VP: Robbie L Leffel
Sr VP: Leonard W Mallett
Sr VP: Craig W Murray
Sr VP: William Ordemann
Sr VP: Gary P Smith
Sr VP: Michael C Smith
VP: James Cisrik
VP: Angela Deloach
Board of Directors: Harry P Weitzel

D-U-N-S 00-104-4080
■ ENTERPRISE PUBLISHING CO LLC
ENTERPRISE, THE
(Suby of NEW MEDIA INVESTMENT GROUP INC) ★
10 Purchase St, Fall River, MA 02720-3100
Tel (585) 598-0030 Founded/Ownrshp 2013
Sales 125.9MME EMP 881
SIC 2711 Commercial printing & newspaper publishing combined
MIS Mgr: Jeff Wheaton

ENTERPRISE RENT A CAR
See ENTERPRISE LEASING CO OF GEORGIA LLC

ENTERPRISE RENT-A-CAR
See ENTERPRISE HOLDINGS INC

ENTERPRISE RENT-A-CAR
See EAN HOLDINGS LLC

D-U-N-S 02-186-5050
ENTERPRISE RENT-A-CAR CO OF LOS ANGELES LLC
(Suby of ENTERPRISE RENT-A-CAR) ★
333 City Blvd W Ste 1000, Orange, CA 92868-5917
Tel (657) 221-4400 Founded/Ownrshp 1980
Sales 135.6MME EMP 1,600
SIC 7515 7513 5511 7514 Passenger car leasing; Truck rental & leasing, no drivers; Trucks, tractors & trailers: new & used; Passenger car rental
Ch Bd: Jack C Taylor
COO: Pamela Nicholson
CFO: William W Snyder
Ch: Andrew C Taylor
Treas: Rose Langhorst
Ex VP: Greg Stubblefield
VP: Katherine Turner
Genl Mgr: Joe Kalman
Dir IT: Jason Sonboul
IT Man: Miguel Arroyo
IT Man: Brian Schlueter

D-U-N-S 79-690-3805 IMP
ENTERPRISE RENT-A-CAR CO OF SACRAMENTO LLC
(Suby of ENTERPRISE RENT-A-CAR) ★
150 N Sunrise Ave, Roseville, CA 95661-2905
Tel (916) 787-4500 Founded/Ownrshp 1989
Sales 63.5MME EMP 1,000
SIC 7515 7514 5511 Passenger car leasing; Rent-a-car service; Automobiles, new & used
VP: Susan M Irwin
Board of Directors: Jack C Taylor

D-U-N-S 10-339-8608
ENTERPRISE RENT-A-CAR CO OF SAN FRANCISCO LLC
(Suby of ENTERPRISE RENT-A-CAR) ★
2633 Camino Ramon Ste 400, San Ramon, CA 94583-2176
Tel (925) 464-5100 Founded/Ownrshp 1980
Sales 35.1MME EMP 1,000
SIC 7514

ENTERTAINMENT
See HSP EPI ACQUISITION LLC

D-U-N-S 78-501-1508
ENTERTAINMENT CRUISES INC
455 N Ctyfrnt Plz Dr # 2600, Chicago, IL 60611-5503
Tel (312) 321-7600 Founded/Ownrshp 2005
Sales 177.1MME EMP 1,404
SIC 4489 Excursion boat operators
CEO: Kenneth Svendsen
*Pr: Michael W Higgins
CFO: Baran Lauren
*VP: Bob Tantonast
Assoc Dir: Kimi Williams
IT Man: Dawn Gregory
VP Mktg: Carolyn Crafts
Sls Dir: Anthony Regucci

D-U-N-S 94-785-6464
▲ ENTRAVISION COMMUNICATIONS CORP
2425 Olympic Blvd Ste 600, Santa Monica, CA 90404-4030
Tel (310) 447-3870 Founded/Ownrshp 1996
Sales 254.1MM EMP 1,010E
Tkr Sym EVC Exch NYS
SIC 4833 4832 Television broadcasting stations; Radio broadcasting stations
Ch Bd: Walter F Ulloa
COO: Jeffery A Liberman
CFO: Christopher T Young
Ofcr: Esteban Lopez Blanco
Dir Risk M: Mario M Carrera
Board of Directors: Patricia Diaz Dennis, Martha Elena Diaz, Gilbert R Vasquez, Juan Saldivar Von Wuthenau, Paul A Zevnik

D-U-N-S 96-666-6740
ENTRIX HOLDING CO
(Suby of CARDNO USA INC) ★
5252 Westchester St # 250, Houston, TX 77005-4141
Tel (713) 666-6223 Founded/Ownrshp 2010
Sales 39.3MME EMP 1,000

SIC 8748

D-U-N-S 92-864-1708 IMP
■ ENTROPIC COMMUNICATIONS LLC
(Suby of MAXLINEAR INC) ★
5966 La Place Ct Ste 100, Carlsbad, CA 92008-8830
Tel (858) 768-3600 Founded/Ownrshp 2015
Sales 139.6MM[E] EMP 300[E]
SIC 3674 7372 Semiconductor circuit networks; Prepackaged software
Pr: Kishore Seendripu
Pr: Andrew Chartrand
Pr: Vernon Cheng
Treas: Adam Spice
Bd of Dir: Patrick Henry
Sr VP: William R Bradford
Sr VP: Michael Farese
Sr VP: Matthew Rhodes
VP: Michael J Lachance
VP: Madhukar Reddy
VP: Will Torgerson
Exec: Kent Vandenberg

D-U-N-S 04-671-3244 IMP/EXP
ENTRUST DATACARD CORP
1187 Park Pl, Shakopee, MN 55379-3817
Tel (952) 933-1223 Founded/Ownrshp 1987
Sales 1.0MMM[E] EMP 2,000
SIC 3579 3089 7373 7372 Embossing machines for store & office use; Addressing machines, plates & plate embossers; Identification cards, plastic; Computer integrated systems design; Turnkey vendors, computer systems; Prepackaged software; Application computer software
Pr: Todd G Wilkinson
Pr: Timothy Cheung
CFO: Kurt Ishaug
Bd of Dir: Jim Beatty
Ofcr: Ray Wizbowski
Sr VP: Tony Ball
Sr VP: John Di Leo
Sr VP: Chris Pelletier
Sr VP: Kent Shields
Sr VP: Jeffrey L Smolinski
Sr VP: Andrea Snook
Sr VP: Lisa Tibbits
VP: Mike Baxter
VP: Brian Beech
VP: Mike Boucher
VP: Joe L Gilligan
VP: Lynnette Heath
VP: Jabs Joshua
VP: Joe Lee-Gilligan
VP: John Leo
VP: Michael J Schnaus
Board of Directors: Ken Berryman, Lars Nyberg, Sheila A Penrose, Stefan Quandt, Todd Wilkinson

D-U-N-S 06-472-8738
ENTRUST ENERGY INC (TX)
1301 Mckinney St Ste 1200, Houston, TX 77010-3064
Tel (713) 338-2601 Founded/Ownrshp 2010
Sales 87.6MM[E] EMP 115
SIC 4911 Electric services
Pr: Tom Gilpin
*CFO: John Edgar
*VP: Chuck Cavin
Off Mgr: Ashley Barham

D-U-N-S 79-945-4061
ENTRUST INC
(Suby of ENTRUST DATACARD CORP) ★
5430 Lyndon B Johnson Fwy, Dallas, TX 75240-2601
Tel (972) 728-0447 Founded/Ownrshp 2013
Sales 92.0MM[E] EMP 411
SIC 7371 Computer software development
Pr: David Wagner
CFO: David Thompson
Sr VP: Peter Bello
Sr VP: Hansen Downer
VP: Terrie Anderson
VP: Rusty Atkinson
VP: Ian Curry
VP: Rockvam David
VP: Jim Fields
VP: Mark Reeves
VP: David Rockvam
VP: Robert Vankirk
VP: Robert B Vankirk
VP: Colin Wyatt
Board of Directors: James H Dennedy, Jerry C Jones, Michael E McGrath, Michael P Ressner, Douglas Schloss, Ray W Washburne

D-U-N-S 07-919-9263 IMP
ENVELOPE 1 INC
41969 State Route 344, Columbiana, OH 44408-9421
Tel (330) 482-3900 Founded/Ownrshp 2012
Sales 102.9MM[E] EMP 236[E]
SIC 2677 Envelopes
CEO: Tarry Pidgeon

D-U-N-S 04-672-5321 IMP/EXP
ENVELOPES UNLIMITED INC
EU SERVICES
649 N Horners Ln, Rockville, MD 20850-1299
Tel (301) 424-3300 Founded/Ownrshp 1971
Sales 114.4MM[E] EMP 372
SIC 2759 7331 Envelopes: printing; Invitation & stationery printing & engraving; Mailing service
CEO: Clif McDougall
*COO: Russ Stewart
*CFO: Christopher P Bean
*VP: David Loudon
*VP: Tom Loudon
VP: Heather Macomber
Genl Mgr: Steve Rudman
Mktg Mgr: Justin Hersh
Mktg Mgr: Crystal Uppercue

D-U-N-S 14-758-7554
ENVENTIS CORP
221 E Hickory St, Mankato, MN 56001-3610
Tel (507) 387-1151 Founded/Ownrshp 2014
Sales 225.3MM[E] EMP 518
SIC 4813

D-U-N-S 07-979-2722
■ ENVENTIS TELECOM INC
CONSOLIDATED COMMUNICATIONS
(Suby of CONSOLDTED CMMNCTIONS HOLDINGS) ★
2950 Xenium Ln N Ste 138, Minneapolis, MN 55441-8759
Tel (763) 577-3900 Founded/Ownrshp 2016
Sales 143.6MM[E] EMP 489
SIC 4813
CEO: C Robert Udell Jr
VP: Steve Larson
Snr Ntwrk: Tom Delaney
CIO: Lane Nordquist
Dir IT: Dan Beddow
IT Man: Kirk Allbutt

D-U-N-S 07-457-5767
ENVENTURE GLOBAL TECHNOLOGY INC
(Suby of SHELL OIL CO) ★
15995 N Barkers Landing R, Houston, TX 77079-2493
Tel (281) 552-2200 Founded/Ownrshp 2004
Sales 127.4MM EMP 211
Accts Pricewaterhousecoopers Llp Ho
SIC 7353 Oil field equipment, rental or leasing
CEO: Ray Ballantyne
*Pr: Eugene Jorgensen
*CFO: Kevin Knight
Bd of Dir: Rob McNally
Bd of Dir: Amy Nelson
Bd of Dir: Martin Vos
VP: Kirk Heinritz
VP: Alastair McClean
*VP: Richard Sherry
Dir Risk M: Kevin Waddell
*Prin: Rob E Mc Kee III

D-U-N-S 00-470-7860
■ ENVESTNET ASSET MANAGEMENT INC
(Suby of ENVESTNET INC) ★
35 E Wacker Dr Ste 2400, Chicago, IL 60601-2310
Tel (312) 827-2800 Founded/Ownrshp 1999
Sales 99.6MM[E] EMP 447
SIC 6282 Investment advisory service
CEO: Judson Bergman
*Pr: Bill Crager
COO: Charles Tennant
*CFO: Peter D'Arrigo
Sr VP: Karen Lanzetta
*Sr VP: Dale Seier
VP: William Cragle
Genl Couns: Shelly Starr

D-U-N-S 15-461-4916
▲ ENVESTNET INC
35 E Wacker Dr Ste 2400, Chicago, IL 60601-2310
Tel (312) 827-2800 Founded/Ownrshp 1999
Sales 348.7MM EMP 1,708
Tkr Sym ENV Exch NYS
SIC 7389 6282 7372 Financial services; Investment advice; Prepackaged software; Business oriented computer software
Ch Bd: Judson Bergman
Pr: Kristin Allard
Pr: Michael Chrisler
Pr: William Crager
Pr: Lisa Mark
Pr: Regan Ryan
COO: Josh Mayer
CFO: Peter D'Arrigo
Ofcr: Jennifer Tarnoff
Assoc VP: Stephen Vacanti
Ex VP: Mike Apker
Ex VP: Ajit Kumar
Ex VP: James Lumberg
Ex VP: Karen McCue
Ex VP: Viggy Mokkarala
Ex VP: Kevin Osborn
Ex VP: James Patrick
Ex VP: Ron Pruitt
Ex VP: Anilal Ravi
Ex VP: Lincoln Ross
Sr VP: Gregory Classen

D-U-N-S 61-276-1304
ENVIROBUSINESS INC
EBI CONSULTING
21 B St, Burlington, MA 01803-3485
Tel (781) 273-2500 Founded/Ownrshp 1989
Sales 109.4MM[E] EMP 405
Accts Nardella & Taylor Llp Lexing
SIC 8748 Environmental consultant
Pr: Frank E Previte
CFO: Mathieu Gagne
CFO: Dan Tollman
Ex VP: Chris Barrile
Ex VP: Glen Elias
Sr VP: Jeffrey Cprevite
Sr VP: Nolan Pprevite
VP: Bryan Bakis
VP: Joseph Campisi
VP: Russell Gordon
VP: John Hession
VP: John H Hovsepian
VP: Josh Simon
VP: Kathleen Treat
Exec: Charles Losinger
Board of Directors: Frank Previte, Jeffrey Previte, Nolan Previte

D-U-N-S 61-503-0137
ENVIROCON INC
101 International Dr, Missoula, MT 59808-1549
Tel (406) 523-1150 Founded/Ownrshp 1985
Sales 110.5MM[E] EMP 250
SIC 1795 Wrecking & demolition work
Pr: Jack Gilbraith
COO: Paul Halliday
*COO: Kris Kok
*CFO: Earl McCall
Ofcr: Dave Vanbebber
*Sr VP: Jack Maserejian
*VP: Kristina L Paffhausen
*VP: Charlie Wells
Mtls Mgr: Marty Bishop
Mtls Mgr: Cayce Jones

ENVIRON INTERNATIONAL
See RAMBOLL ENVIRON INC

D-U-N-S 02-139-6577
ENVIRONAMICS INC (NC)
13935 S Point Blvd, Charlotte, NC 28273-7716
Tel (704) 376-3613 Founded/Ownrshp 1980
Sales 94.0MM[E] EMP 175
SIC 1542 Commercial & office building contractors
Pr: Louis Santospago
Off Admin: Mary Watts
IT Man: Edward Taylor
Board of Directors: Harry Johnson

D-U-N-S 16-964-0062 IMP
ENVIRONMENT MARYLAND DEPARTMENT OF
MARYLAND EXEC OFC OF THE STATE
(Suby of EXECUTIVE OFFICE OF STATE OF MARYLAND) ★
1800 Washington Blvd A, Baltimore, MD 21230-1717
Tel (410) 537-3000 Founded/Ownrshp 1987
Sales NA EMP 1,650
SIC 9511 Air, water & solid waste management;
CFO: Thomas French
CFO: Richard Pencek
Adm Dir: Mark Jacobs
Adm Dir: Georgette Pettit
Adm Dir: Paul Sodeman
Dist Mgr: Heather Nelson
IT Man: Sandra Velez
Snr Mgr: Brian Clevenger
Snr Mgr: Peggy Courtright
Snr Mgr: Paula Montgomery
Snr Mgr: Michael Richardson

D-U-N-S 05-230-0798
■ ENVIRONMENTAL AIR SYSTEMS LLC
(Suby of COMFORT SYSTEMS USA INC) ★
521 Banner Ave, Greensboro, NC 27401-4300
Tel (336) 273-1975 Founded/Ownrshp 2011
Sales 126.1MM EMP 1
SIC 1711 Plumbing, heating, air-conditioning contractors

D-U-N-S 60-129-3962 EXP
ENVIRONMENTAL CHEMICAL CORP
ECC
1240 Bayshore Hwy, Burlingame, CA 94010-1805
Tel (650) 347-1555 Founded/Ownrshp 1985
Sales 178.0MM[E] EMP 350
SIC 8711 1542 8744 Engineering services; Commercial & office building contractors;
Pr: Manjiv Vohra
CFO: Steve Anderson
Treas: Tom Delmastro
VP: Terry Kohl
VP: August Ochabauer
VP: Patrick Scher
Genl Mgr: Rick Ebel
VP Mktg: Mitch Clark

D-U-N-S 07-982-2748
ENVIRONMENTAL DEFENSE FUND INC (NY)
257 Park Ave S Fl 17, New York, NY 10010-7386
Tel (212) 505-2100 Founded/Ownrshp 1967
Sales 147.1MM EMP 450
Accts Eisneramper Llp New York Ny
SIC 8641 8748 Environmental protection organization; Business consulting
Pr: Fred Krupp
COO: Elizabeth Henshaw
*COO: Liza Henshaw
*CFO: Peter Accinno
CFO: Cynthia Hallenbeck
*Ch: Carl Ferenbach
Trst: Norman Christensen Jr
Ofcr: Barbara McCullough
Assoc VP: Keely Henderson
Assoc VP: Amanda Leland
*Sr VP: Diana H Josephson
Sr VP: Eric Pooley
VP: Cynthia Hampton
*VP: Debbie McGinn
VP: Gernot Wagner
Assoc Dir: Michael Pohlmann
Comm Dir: Tiana Norgren

D-U-N-S 03-231-9712 IMP
ENVIRONMENTAL FILTRATION TECHNOLOGIES LLC
(Suby of NEDERMAN HOLDING AB)
4404a Chesapeake Dr, Charlotte, NC 28216-3413
Tel (704) 399-7441 Founded/Ownrshp 2012
Sales 291.1MM[E] EMP 1,743
SIC 3569 5085 3564 3444 3469 3561 Filters; Filters, industrial; Valves & fittings; Air cleaning systems; Ducts, sheet metal; Metal stampings; Cylinders, pump
Pr: Douglas Albert
Genl Mgr: Ken Smith

D-U-N-S 17-030-8956
ENVIRONMENTAL MATERIALS LLC
ENVIRONMENTAL STONEWORKS
7306 S Alton Way Ste B, Centennial, CO 80112-2346
Tel (303) 309-6610 Founded/Ownrshp 2001
Sales 252.4MM[E] EMP 812
SIC 3281 Stone, quarrying & processing of own stone products
Ex VP: Lanson Sutter
IT Man: Markida Massey
Plnt Mgr: Paul Simmons
Natl Sales: Kevin McNally

D-U-N-S 05-794-4910
■ ENVIRONMENTAL PROTECTION AGENCY
US EPA
(Suby of EXECUTIVE OFFICE OF UNITED STATES GOVERNMENT) ★
1200 Pennsylvania Ave Nw, Washington, DC 20460-0003
Tel (202) 272-0167 Founded/Ownrshp 1970
Sales NA EMP 18,000
SIC 9511 Environmental protection agency, government;
CFO: Maryann Froehlich
Ofcr: Kristian Buschmann
Ofcr: Rocco Fiato
Ofcr: Susan Wickwire
Ex VP: Diane Lynne
VP: Patrick Reiten
VP: Brian Shrager
Assoc Dir: Peter Celone
Assoc Dir: Yvetter Hellyer
Assoc Dir: Van Housman
Assoc Dir: Penny Lassiter
Assoc Dir: David McGuigan
Assoc Dir: Cheryl Wasserman

D-U-N-S 80-880-5154
ENVIRONMENTAL QUALITY TEXAS COMMISSION ON
(Suby of EXECUTIVE OFFICE OF STATE OF TEXAS) ★
12100 Pk Thirty Five Cir, Austin, TX 78753-1808
Tel (512) 239-5500 Founded/Ownrshp 1993
Sales NA EMP 3,000
SIC 9511 Air, water & solid waste management;
CFO: Liz Day
CFO: Linda Flores
Sec: Doretta Conrad
IT Man: Susan Franks

D-U-N-S 78-810-2213
ENVIRONMENTAL RESOURCES MANAGEMENT - NORTH CENTRAL INC
E R M
(Suby of ERM GROUP HOLDINGS LIMITED)
1701 Golf Rd Ste 1-700, Rolling Meadows, IL 60008-4249
Tel (610) 524-3500 Founded/Ownrshp 1976
Sales 98.4MM[E] EMP 3,500
SIC 8748 Environmental consultant
Pr: Michael O'Shaughnessy
*Ch Bd: Robin Bidwell
*VP: David Dusing
Off Mgr: Nadia Ali

D-U-N-S 11-707-6203
ENVIRONMENTAL RESOURCES MANAGEMENT INC
ERM
(Suby of ERM-DELAWARE, INC.)
75 Valley Stream Pkwy # 200, Malvern, PA 19355-1480
Tel (484) 913-0300 Founded/Ownrshp 1977
Sales 137.6MM EMP 146
SIC 8748 Environmental consultant
Pr: Michael O'Shaughnessy
CFO: Patrick Heenan
Treas: John C Stipa
VP: David Dusing
VP: Julia B Ross
CTO: Joe Amatrudo
CTO: Ru Hobaugh
Board of Directors: John E Deal Jr, David Edwards, Edward M Simek

ENVIRONMENTAL RESOURCES MGT
See ERM-WEST INC

D-U-N-S 00-819-8421
ENVIRONMENTAL RESTORATION LLC (MO)
1666 Fabick Dr, Fenton, MO 63026-2926
Tel (636) 227-7477 Founded/Ownrshp 1997
Sales 118.7MM[E] EMP 325
Accts Wilhelm & Wilhelm Llc St Lo
SIC 8744
COO: Steve Jackson
CFO: Steve Wilheln
*VP: Jim Davis
*VP: Mark Ruck
VP: Steven Wilhelm
CTO: Lonnie Wright

ENVIRONMENTAL STONEWORKS
See ENVIRONMENTAL MATERIALS LLC

ENVIRONMENTAL SYSTEMS PRODUCTS
See OPUS INSPECTION INC

D-U-N-S 06-313-4175
ENVIRONMENTAL SYSTEMS RESEARCH INSTITUTE INC
ESRI
380 New York St, Redlands, CA 92373-8118
Tel (909) 793-2853 Founded/Ownrshp 1973
Sales 830.9MM[E] EMP 3,200
SIC 5045

D-U-N-S 04-964-1798 IMP/EXP
▲ ENVIRONMENTAL TECTONICS CORP
ETC
125 James Way, Southampton, PA 18966-3817
Tel (215) 355-9100 Founded/Ownrshp 1969
Sales 88.2MM[E] EMP 336
Tkr Sym ETCC Exch OTO
SIC 3728 3842 3826 3823 3841 Aircraft training equipment; Sterilizers, hospital & surgical; Environmental testing equipment; Industrial instrmnts msrmnt display/control process variable; Surgical & medical instruments
Pr: William F Mitchell
Pr: Gene Davis
Pr: Robert L Laurent Jr
Pr: Bernhard H Ricter
Pr: Marco Van Wijngaarden
Pr: Steve Wood
Treas: Lee Greenfield
VP: Richard Burley
VP: Alper Kus
VP: James Wells
Prin: Gerry H F Lenfest
Board of Directors: George K Anderson MD, Linda J Brent, Roger Colley, Gerry H F Lenfest, George A Sawyer, Winston E Scott

D-U-N-S 80-340-0964
ENVIROSOLUTIONS HOLDINGS INC
9650 Hawkins Dr, Manassas, VA 20109-4501
Tel (703) 633-3000 Founded/Ownrshp 2003
Sales 135.1MM EMP 400[E]
Accts Mcgladrey Llp Vienna Virgini
SIC 8748 Environmental consultant

D-U-N-S 14-523-7512 IMP
ENVIROSOLUTIONS INC
ESI
9650 Hawkins Dr, Manassas, VA 20109-4501
Tel (703) 633-3000 Founded/Ownrshp 2003

Sales 487.3MM^E *EMP* 350^E
Accts Mcgladrey & Pullen Llp Vienna
SIC 4953 Street refuse systems; Sanitary landfill operation
Pr: Eric Wallace
**CFO:* Marc Bourhis
VP: Scott Cunningham
VP: Bob Gretz
VP: Gary Hewes
VP: Clayton Walton
Dir Bus: Kirk Nimtz
Dist Mgr: Mal Granville
Genl Mgr: Derek D Shreves
CIO: Tim Kyle
IT Man: Michael Kim

D-U-N-S 87-436-0381 IMP/EXP
ENVIROTECH PUMPSYSTEMS INC
CHAS S LEWIS & CO
(*Suby of* WEIR SPM) ★
440 W 800 S, Salt Lake City, UT 84101-2229
Tel (801) 359-8731 *Founded/Ownrshp* 1994
Sales 126.2MM^E *EMP* 500
SIC 3561 3491 3089 Pumps & pumping equipment; Industrial valves; Molding primary plastic
Pr: William J Fath
**Pr:* James G Board
CFO: Ted Kellog
Treas: Mark White
**Sec:* Dennis Carder
**VP:* Linda Beal
VP: Charlie Horne
VP: Jim Mangano
**VP:* R Lynn Marlow
MIS Dir: Dana Jeffs
IT Man: Ray Vweirzycki

ENVISION HEALTHCARE
See AMERICAN MEDICAL RESPONSE INC

D-U-N-S 60-687-7830
■ **ENVISION HEALTHCARE CORP**
(*Suby of* ENVISION HEALTHCARE HOLDINGS INC) ★
6363 S Fiddlers Green Cir # 1400, Greenwood Village, CO 80111-5024
Tel (303) 495-1200 *Founded/Ownrshp* 2005
Sales 3.6MMM^E *EMP* 12,562^E
SIC 4119 7363 Ambulance service; Medical help service
Pr: William A Sanger
**Ch Bd:* Ronald A Williams
Pr: James Murphy
**COO:* Randel G Owen
COO: Robert Zuckswert
CFO: Julia Byrne
**Treas:* Steve W Ratton Jr
Chf Mktg O: Janell Marshall
Ofcr: Ross Ronan
**Sr VP:* Nicholas A Poan
**Sr VP:* Craig A Wilson
VP: Eric Foust
VP: Tricia Frachetti
VP: Valerie Gaither

D-U-N-S 96-895-3450
▲ **ENVISION HEALTHCARE HOLDINGS INC**
6200 S Syracuse Way, Greenwood Village, CO 80111-4737
Tel (303) 495-1200 *Founded/Ownrshp* 1972
Sales 5.4MMM *EMP* 22,049^E
Tkr Sym EVHC *Exch* NYS
SIC 8062 4119 General medical & surgical hospitals; Ambulance service
Ch Bd: William A Sanger
COO: Randel G Owen
Ex VP: Steve W Ratton Jr
Sr VP: Thomas F Bongiorno
Sr VP: Craig A Wilson
Netwrk Eng: Jason Cobb
Board of Directors: Carol J Burt, Mark V Mactas, Leonard M Riggs Jr, Richard J Schnall, James D Shelton, Michael L Smith, Ronald A Williams

D-U-N-S 00-724-2498 IMP
ENVISION INC
2301 S Water St, Wichita, KS 67213-4819
Tel (316) 267-2244 *Founded/Ownrshp* 1933
Sales 108.6MM^E *EMP* 400
SIC 2673 2676

D-U-N-S 62-510-7003
■ **ENVISION PHARMACEUTICAL SERVICES LLC**
ENVISION RX OPTIONS
(*Suby of* RITE AID CORP) ★
2181 E Aurora Rd Ste 201, Twinsburg, OH 44087-1974
Tel (330) 405-8080 *Founded/Ownrshp* 2015
Sales NA *EMP* 320
SIC 6411 Insurance claim processing, except medical
CEO: Frank Sheehy
Genl Couns: Eugene P Samuels

ENVISION RX OPTIONS
See ENVISION PHARMACEUTICAL SERVICES LLC

D-U-N-S 07-981-5144
ENVIVA PARTNERS LP
7200 Wscnsin Ave Ste 1000, Bethesda, MD 20814
Tel (301) 657-5660 *Founded/Ownrshp* 2010
Sales 457.3MM *EMP* 569
Tkr Sym EVA *Exch* NYS
SIC 2421 Wood chips, produced at mill
Ch Bd: John K Keppler
Genl Pt: Enviva P GP
CFO: Stephen F Reeves

D-U-N-S 02-237-7357
■ **ENVOY AIR INC**
AMR EAGLE
(*Suby of* AMERICAN EAGLE HOLDING LLC) ★
4301 Regent Blvd, Irving, TX 75063-2253
Tel (972) 374-5200 *Founded/Ownrshp* 1920
Sales 130.3M *EMP* 12,000
SIC 4512 Air passenger carrier, scheduled
CEO: Pedro Fbregas
**Pr:* Daniel P Garton
**CEO:* Gerard Arpey
**CFO:* John T Hutchinson
CFO: John Hutchinson
**Ch:* Thomas W Horton
Sr VP: David Campbell
**Sr VP:* John Jaynes
Sr VP: Steve Jennings
**Sr VP:* Maya Leibman
**Sr VP:* Dee Temples
**VP:* Gregg Formella
VP: Joe Reedy

ENXCO
See EDF RENEWABLE SERVICES INC

ENZO ANGIOLINI
See JAG FOOTWEAR ACCESSORIES AND RETAIL CORP

D-U-N-S 08-166-4328
▲ **ENZO BIOCHEM INC** (NY)
527 Madison Ave Rm 901, New York, NY 10022-4373
Tel (212) 583-0100 *Founded/Ownrshp* 1976
Sales 102.7MM *EMP* 483
Tkr Sym ENZ *Exch* NYS
SIC 8071 8731 Medical laboratories; Biological laboratory; Commercial physical research; Biotechnical research, commercial
Ch Bd: Elazar Rabbani
**Pr:* Barry W Weiner
Treas: Shahram Rabbani
Ex VP: James M O'Brien
VP: David C Goldberg
VP: Barbara Thalenfeld

D-U-N-S 05-654-4166 EXP
ENZYMATIC THERAPY LLC
825 Challenger Dr, Green Bay, WI 54311-8328
Tel (920) 469-1313 *Founded/Ownrshp* 2008
Sales 120.6MM^E *EMP* 320
SIC 2834

D-U-N-S 18-683-0733 IMP/EXP
▲ **EOG RESOURCES INC**
1111 Bagby St Lbby 2, Houston, TX 77002-2589
Tel (713) 651-7000 *Founded/Ownrshp* 1985
Sales 8.7MMM *EMP* 2,760^E
Tkr Sym EOG *Exch* NYS
SIC 1311 Crude petroleum production; Natural gas production
Ch Bd: William R Thomas
Pr: Lindell Looger
COO: Ted Kelly
COO: Gary L Thomas
CFO: Timothy K Driggers
Bd of Dir: Megan Lewis
Ex VP: Michael P Donaldson
Ex VP: Robert K Garrison
Ex VP: Lloyd W Helms Jr
Ex VP: Rick Plaeger
Ex VP: David W Trice
VP: Nathan J Andrews
VP: Sandeep Bhakhri
VP: John J Boyd III
VP: Cedric Burgher
VP: Kenneth E Dunn
VP: Kevin Hanzel
VP: Kenneth D Marbach
VP: Sara Miller
VP: Ronald D Oden
VP: Frederick J Plaeger
Board of Directors: Janet F Clark, Charles R Crisp, James C Day, H Leighton Steward, Donald F Textor, Frank G Wisner

EOHHS
See MASSACHUSETTS EXECUTIVE OFFICE OF HEALTH AND HUMAN SERVICES

D-U-N-S 06-345-5190 IMP
EOIR TECHNOLOGIES INC
10300 Spotsylvania Ave, Fredericksburg, VA 22408-2697
Tel (540) 834-4888 *Founded/Ownrshp* 2016
Sales 113.2MM^E *EMP* 425
SIC 8711 7371 8731 8742 Engineering services; Computer software systems analysis & design, custom; Commercial physical research; Manufacturing management consultant
Pr: Peter Cannito
**CFO:* Scott Crane
**Ex VP:* Diane Deterline
**Ex VP:* Ricardo Lorenzo
Sr VP: Joseph S Zirilli
Sftwr Eng: Richard Chan

D-U-N-S 16-806-2540
EON CLIMATE & RENEWABLES NORTH AMERICA LLC
(*Suby of* E.ON SE)
353 N Clark St Fl 30, Chicago, IL 60654-4704
Tel (312) 245-3035 *Founded/Ownrshp* 2007
Sales 165.0MM *EMP* 230
SIC 4911 Generation, electric power
Ch: Patrick Woodson
**Ch Bd:* Steve Trenholm
**CFO:* Tom Festle
VP: John Bodeusz
**VP:* Robert Bellingham
VP: Dawn Bugbee
VP: Jeff Huang

D-U-N-S 84-792-5062
EOS PARTNERS LP
320 Park Ave Rm 900, New York, NY 10022-6838
Tel (212) 832-5800 *Founded/Ownrshp* 1993
Sales 158.3MM^E *EMP* 1,315
SIC 6211 Investment firm, general brokerage
Genl Pt: Brian D Young
Genl Pt: Steven M Friedman
CFO: Beth Bernstein
VP: Abigail Cohen
VP: Trey Lee
VP: Aakash Patel
VP: Jason Pike
Mng Dir: Brian Machale
Mng Dir: Evan Steen
Opers Mgr: Jay Appel
Opers Mgr: Frank Moy

D-U-N-S 61-291-1284
EP BOLLINGER LLC
MYRLEN
2664 Saint Georges Ct, Cincinnati, OH 45233-4290
Tel (513) 941-1101 *Founded/Ownrshp* 2015
Sales 220.5M^E *EMP* 32,000
SIC 2821 Plastics materials & resins

D-U-N-S 07-923-9456
▲ **EP ENERGY CORP**
1001 Louisiana St, Houston, TX 77002-5089
Tel (713) 997-1200 *Founded/Ownrshp* 2012
Sales 1.9MMM *EMP* 665^E
Tkr Sym EPE *Exch* NYS
SIC 1311 Crude petroleum & natural gas; Natural gas production
Ch Bd: Brent J Smolik
COO: Clayton A Carrell
CFO: Dane E Whitehead
Sr VP: Joan M Gallagher
Sr VP: Marguerite N Woung-Chapman

D-U-N-S 61-537-1312
■ **EP ENERGY E&P CO LP**
(*Suby of* EP ENERGY GLOBAL LLC) ★
1001 Louisiana St, Houston, TX 77002-5089
Tel (713) 997-4858 *Founded/Ownrshp* 2012
Sales 559.8MM^E *EMP* 770^E
SIC 1382 Oil & gas exploration services
CFO: Dane E Whitehead
Ex VP: Clayton A Carrell
Ex VP: John D Jensen
Sr VP: Joan M Gallagher

D-U-N-S 96-897-3094
■ **EP ENERGY GLOBAL LLC**
(*Suby of* EP ENERGY LLC) ★
1001 Louisiana St, Houston, TX 77002-5089
Tel (713) 420-2600 *Founded/Ownrshp* 1999
Sales 559.8MM^E *EMP* 116^E
SIC 8748 Energy conservation consultant
Pr: Brent J Smolik
**VP:* Francis C Olmsted III

D-U-N-S 07-854-4943
■ **EP ENERGY LLC**
(*Suby of* EP ENERGY CORP) ★
1001 Louisiana St, Houston, TX 77002-5089
Tel (713) 997-1200 *Founded/Ownrshp* 2012
Sales 1.9MMM *EMP* 748^E
SIC 1311 1382 Crude petroleum & natural gas; Crude petroleum production; Natural gas production; Oil & gas exploration services
Pr: Brent J Smolik
COO: Clayton A Carrell
CFO: Dane E Whitehead
Sr VP: Joan Gallagher
Sr VP: Marguerite N Woung-Chapman
VP: Greg Givens
VP: Francis C Olmsted III
Opers Supe: Carr Garrison
Mktg Mgr: Cathy Bulf

D-U-N-S 62-641-0935
EP ENERGY MANAGEMENT LLC
1001 Louisiana St, Houston, TX 77002-5089
Tel (713) 997-1000 *Founded/Ownrshp* 1964
Sales 262.8MM^E *EMP* 1,000^E
SIC 4922 1321 Natural gas transmission; Natural gas liquids production
Pr: Brent Smolik
**CFO:* Dane Whitehead
**Sr VP:* William Griffin
**Sr VP:* Thomas Hart
**Sr VP:* William Smolik

D-U-N-S 07-860-3588
EP ENERGY RESALE CO LLC
(*Suby of* EP ENERGY MANAGEMENT LLC) ★
1001 Louisiana St, Houston, TX 77002-5089
Tel (713) 997-1000 *Founded/Ownrshp* 1994
Sales 84.0MM^E *EMP* 1,000^E
SIC 2911 Petroleum refining
CEO: Brent J Smolik

D-U-N-S 62-155-6344 IMP/EXP
EP MANAGEMENT CORP
801 W Ann Arbor Trl # 220, Plymouth, MI 48170-6224
Tel (313) 749-5500 *Founded/Ownrshp* 2006
Sales 185.7MM^E *EMP* 1,400
SIC 3692 3661 2834 3674 3691 Primary batteries, dry & wet; Telephone & telegraph apparatus; Pharmaceutical preparations; Semiconductors & related devices; Storage batteries
Pr: David Treadwell
**CFO:* Patrick S Aubry
**VP:* Benjamin A Depompei
QA Dir: Dale Crane
Plnt Mgr: Bob Berberich
Plnt Mgr: Terry Ray
VP Sls: Joseph Marotta
Mktg Dir: Jennifer Warmoth

D-U-N-S 78-810-4672 IMP/EXP
EP MINERALS LLC
(*Suby of* GOLDEN GATE CAPITAL LP) ★
9785 Gateway Dr Ste 1000, Reno, NV 89521-2991
Tel (775) 824-7600 *Founded/Ownrshp* 2011
Sales 285.0MM^E *EMP* 563^E
SIC 1481 Nonmetallic mineral services
Pr: Gregg Jones
**CFO:* Tammi Scott
VP: Kurt Jones
VP: Jeff Kitchens
VP: Scott Palm
Prd Mgr: Jonas Pearce
Mktg Dir: Jneal Hachquet
Manager: Reid Wetherell
Sls Mgr: Gary G Smith

D-U-N-S 12-386-9799
▲ **EPAM SYSTEMS INC**
41 University Dr Ste 202, Newtown, PA 18940-1873
Tel (267) 759-9000 *Founded/Ownrshp* 1993
Sales 914.1MM *EMP* 18,354
Tkr Sym EPAM *Exch* NYS
SIC 7371 8742 Computer software development & applications; Management consulting services
Ch Bd: Arkadiy Dobkin
CFO: Anthony Conte
Chf Mktg O: Elaina Shekhter
Top Exec: Vasily Agafonov
Sr VP: Balazs Fejes
Sr VP: Ginger Mosier
VP: Anatoliy Chudnovskiy
VP: Alan Harlan
VP: John Shane
Snr Sftwr: Alexander Leonenko
Snr Sftwr: Monica Marinescu
Board of Directors: Peter Kuerpick, Richard Michael Mayoras, Karl Robb, Robert E Segert, Jill B Smart, Ronald P Vargo

D-U-N-S 02-220-0656
EPANTRY LLC
GROVE COLLABORATIVE
1770 Union St, San Francisco, CA 94123-4407
Tel (657) 444-7837 *Founded/Ownrshp* 2012
Sales 1.0MMM *EMP* 50
SIC 5961 Catalog & mail-order houses
CEO: Stuart Landesberg

D-U-N-S 10-425-0829
EPC SERVICES CO
(*Suby of* E C I) ★
3521 Gabel Rd Ste B, Billings, MT 59102-7310
Tel (406) 294-8544 *Founded/Ownrshp* 2000
Sales 160.3MM *EMP* 30
Accts Summers Mcnea & Company Pc
SIC 1731 8711 Electric power systems contractors; Electrical or electronic engineering
Pr: Richard L McComish
Sec: John Satchell
Genl Mgr: Lynn Larson

D-U-N-S 82-686-8064
EPCO HOLDINGS INC
1100 Louisiana St Fl 10, Houston, TX 77002-5432
Tel (713) 880-6500 *Founded/Ownrshp* 2005
Sales 103.8MM^E *EMP* 4,802
SIC 7299 Debt counseling or adjustment service, individuals
CEO: W Randall Fowler
**Sr VP:* Thomas M Zulim
VP: Michael Knesek

D-U-N-S 03-454-7200
EPCOR WATER (USA) INC
(*Suby of* EPCOR UTILITIES INC)
2355 W Pinnacle Peak Rd # 300, Phoenix, AZ 85027-1282
Tel (623) 445-2400 *Founded/Ownrshp* 2010
Sales 244.8MM^E *EMP* 285^E
SIC 4941 Water supply
CEO: Joseph Gysel
**Treas:* Sam Myers
**VP:* Jim McKee

D-U-N-S 04-788-3926 IMP
EPCOS INC
(*Suby of* EPCOS AG)
485b Route 1 S Ste 200, Iselin, NJ 08830-3013
Tel (732) 906-4300 *Founded/Ownrshp* 1999
Sales 250.0MM^E *EMP* 300
SIC 3679 3546 5065 3671 Electronic crystals; Power-driven handtools; Electronic parts & equipment; Electron tubes
Pr: Achim Buecklers
Genl Mgr: Tracey Dewitt

EPCOT CENTER
See WALT DISNEY PARKS AND RESORTS US INC

D-U-N-S 18-275-4572
EPES CARRIERS INC
3400 Edgefield Ct, Greensboro, NC 27409-9663
Tel (336) 668-3358 *Founded/Ownrshp* 1990
Sales 218.4MM *EMP* 1,100
SIC 4213

D-U-N-S 62-488-8459
EPES LOGISTICS SERVICES INC
(*Suby of* EPES CARRIERS INC) ★
538 N Regional Rd, Greensboro, NC 27409-9085
Tel (336) 665-1553 *Founded/Ownrshp* 1987
Sales 106.1MM *EMP* 135
SIC 4731

D-U-N-S 00-793-9960
EPES TRANSPORT SYSTEM INC (NC)
(*Suby of* EPES CARRIERS INC) ★
3400 Edgefield Ct, Greensboro, NC 27409-9663
Tel (336) 668-3358 *Founded/Ownrshp* 1931, 1987
Sales 44.1MM^E *EMP* 1,100
SIC 4213

EPHRAIM MCDOWELL HEALTH
See EPHRAIM MCDOWELL REGIONAL MEDICAL CENTER INC

D-U-N-S 07-786-0526
EPHRAIM MCDOWELL REGIONAL MEDICAL CENTER INC (KY)
EPHRAIM MCDOWELL HEALTH
217 S 3rd St, Danville, KY 40422-1823
Tel (859) 239-1000 *Founded/Ownrshp* 1912
Sales 159.1MM *EMP* 950
SIC 8062 General medical & surgical hospitals
Ch: Dale Kihlman
**Pr:* Vicki A Darnell
Pr: Marilyn Peterson
**CFO:* Bill Snapp
**VP:* Sally Davenport
VP: Jim Tune
Dir Rx: Joan Haltom
CIO: Angela Allen
QA Dir: Debbie Clark
Netwrk Mgr: Chris Poarch
Sls&Mrk Ex: Keith Bridges

D-U-N-S 07-285-6651
EPHRATA COMMUNITY HOSPITAL INC
169 Martin Ave, Ephrata, PA 17522-1755
Tel (717) 721-5883 *Founded/Ownrshp* 1940
Sales 190.6MM *EMP* 1,894
Accts Ernst & Young Llp

SIC 8062 General medical & surgical hospitals
Pr: John Porter
**Ch Bd:* Gilbert Sager
Pr: Kathy Edwards
**Treas:* Ronald L Miller
**Treas:* Dick Young
Ofcr: Sue Shollenberger
Ex VP: Robert Graupensperger
**VP:* John Holmes
VP: Mark Jacobson
Dir Risk M: Leslie Kuipers
Off Mgr: Cindy Rutt
Board of Directors: Patricia Windham

EPI BREADS
See LAVOI CORP

D-U-N-S 00-334-5139 IMP
EPI GROUP LLC (SC)
POST & COURIER, THE
134 Columbus St, Charleston, SC 29403-4809
Tel (843) 577-7111 *Founded/Ownrshp* 1894
Sales 47.0MM *EMP* 1,515
SIC 2711 Newspapers, publishing & printing
Ch Bd: John P Barnwell
**Ch Bd:* Pierre Manigault
**Ex VP:* Daniel P Herres
Ex VP: Travis O Rckey
**Sr VP:* Roger A Berardinis
Assoc Dir: Joe Waring
**Prin:* Edward M Gilbreth

D-U-N-S 00-537-3527 IMP/EXP
EPI PRINTERS INC (MI)
HEALTH SEMINARS
5404 Wayne Rd, Battle Creek, MI 49037-7300
Tel (800) 562-9733 *Founded/Ownrshp* 1959, 1960
Sales 175.2MM[E] *EMP* 650
SIC 2752 Commercial printing, offset
Pr: William Guzy
COO: Wende Swanson
CFO: Tim Czerney
**Treas:* La Verne De Young
Ex VP: Thomas Epi
VP: Craig Langbo
**VP:* Ivan Mellema
VP: Steve Walker
Dir Bus: Stephanie Engle
Genl Mgr: Dennis Bridges
CTO: Terri Etter

EPIC
See EDGEWOOD PARTNERS INSURANCE CENTER

D-U-N-S 80-454-4724
EPIC AVIATION LLC
3841 Fairview Indust 15, Salem, OR 97302-1179
Tel (503) 362-3633 *Founded/Ownrshp* 2002
Sales 1.4MMM[E] *EMP* 144
Accts Pricewaterhousecoopers Llp Po
SIC 5172 Engine fuels & oils
Pr: Kevin Cox
**COO:* James E Green
Genl Mgr: Gregory Miller

D-U-N-S 05-123-0956
EPIC HEALTH SERVICES INC
5220 Spring Valley Rd, Dallas, TX 75254-3099
Tel (214) 466-1340 *Founded/Ownrshp* 2003
Sales 346.6MM[E] *EMP* 8,041
SIC 8082 Home health care services
Pr: Charlie E Price III
CFO: David Hagey
VP: Christopher P Christian
Opers Mgr: Maleta Carter
Opers Mgr: Matt Peterson

EPIC INTEGRATED SERVICES
See DIXIE ELECTRIC LLC

D-U-N-S 12-126-1122
EPIC RESORTS - SCOTTSDALE LINKS RESORT LLC
(*Suby of* DESERT PARADISE RESORT) ★
3865 W Cheyenne Ave, North Las Vegas, NV 89032-3431
Tel (610) 992-0100 *Founded/Ownrshp* 2002
Sales 15.3MM[E] *EMP* 1,763[E]
SIC 7011 Hotels & motels
Ex VP: Frederick Bauman

D-U-N-S 04-604-1021
EPIC RESORTS LLC
DESERT PARADISE RESORT
(*Suby of* DIAMOND RESORTS CORP) ★
1150 1st Ave Ste 900, King of Prussia, PA 19406-1338
Tel (610) 992-0100 *Founded/Ownrshp* 1998
Sales 24.0MM[E] *EMP* 2,600
SIC 7011 Hotels
CFO: Helen Brady
CFO: Scott Egelkamp

D-U-N-S 10-829-9124
EPIC SYSTEMS CORP
1979 Milky Way, Verona, WI 53593-9179
Tel (608) 271-9000 *Founded/Ownrshp* 1979
Sales 2.0MMM *EMP* 9,900
SIC 7371 Custom computer programming services
CEO: Judith R Faulkner
**Pr:* Carl Dvorak
CFO: Peter Cyffka
Ofcr: Steve Dickman
Ofcr: Steve Dickmann
Sr VP: Sumit Rana
VP: Brad Eichhorst
VP: Alan Feinberg
VP: Tina Graham
VP: Kelly Parrish
CIO: Aaron Cornelius

D-U-N-S 13-793-3169 IMP
EPIC TECHNOLOGIES LLC
NATEL
(*Suby of* NEOTECH) ★
9340 Owensmouth Ave, Chatsworth, CA 91311-6915
Tel (818) 734-6500 *Founded/Ownrshp* 2013
Sales 667.4MM[E] *EMP* 1,750
SIC 3661 3577 3679 Telephone & telegraph apparatus; Computer peripheral equipment; Electronic circuits

VP: Wally Johnson
IT Man: Jeff Cuen
Mtls Mgr: Sabino Nevarez

EPICOR
See APTOS INC

D-U-N-S 96-818-8693
EPICOR SOFTWARE CORP
804 Las Cimas Pkwy, Austin, TX 78746-5150
Tel (512) 328-2300 *Founded/Ownrshp* 2016
Sales 994.9MM[E] *EMP* 4,000
SIC 7372 Prepackaged software
Pr: Joe Cowan
COO: Kathleen Crusco
Chf Mktg O: Celia Fleischaker
Ofcr: Amanda Ruiz
Ex VP: Sabby Gill
Ex VP: Craig McCollum
Ex VP: Mark Mincin
Ex VP: Himanshu Palsule
Ex VP: Donna Troy
Sr VP: Steve Bieszczat
Sr VP: Noel Goggin
VP: Christopher Orr
VP: Scott Roush
VP: Scott Thompson
Board of Directors: Will Chen, Peter Gyenes, Roy Mackenzie, Paul Walker, Jason Wright

D-U-N-S 06-577-0638
EPIQ SYSTEMS INC
(*Suby of* DT I) ★
501 Kansas Ave, Kansas City, KS 66105-1300
Tel (913) 621-9500 *Founded/Ownrshp* 2016
Sales 544.2MM *EMP* 1,300[E]
SIC 7371 8748 Computer software development & applications; Business consulting
Pr: Brad D Scott
Pr: Andrew Shimek
Sr VP: Terry Gaylord
VP: Nicole Hamann

D-U-N-S 07-815-9456
EPISCOPAL HEALTH SERVICES INC
700 Hicksville Rd Ste 210, Bethpage, NY 11714-3473
Tel (516) 349-6100 *Founded/Ownrshp* 1851
Sales 176.1MM *EMP* 1,800
Accts Charles A Barragato & Co Llp
SIC 8062 8051 General medical & surgical hospitals; Skilled nursing care facilities
Pr: Richard Brown
Ch Bd: Corbett A Price
Ch Bd: Lawrence Provenzano
Treas: Ronald Cole
VP: Lynore Dupiton
Dir IT: Alan Walker
IT Man: Jeanne Anderson

D-U-N-S 01-473-1489
EPISCOPAL HOMES FOUNDATION
2185 N Calif Blvd Ste 275, Walnut Creek, CA 94596-3508
Tel (925) 956-7400 *Founded/Ownrshp* 2009
Sales 104.5MM *EMP* 29[E]
SIC 1521 Single-family housing construction
Pr: Lawrence Pratt
VP: Nadine Alcorne
VP: Julie Erdmann

D-U-N-S 07-169-5449
EPISCOPAL SENIOR COMMUNITIES (CA)
2185 N Calif Blvd Ste 575, Walnut Creek, CA 94596-7323
Tel (925) 956-7400 *Founded/Ownrshp* 1965
Sales 106.3MM *EMP* 800
Accts Moss Adams Llp San Francisco
SIC 8361 Geriatric residential care
Pr: Kevin J Gerber
CFO: William Tobein
Bd of Dir: Wendy Howe
VP: Chris Dana
Prgrm Mgr: Susan Lindeman
IT Man: Larry Klein

D-U-N-S 09-911-4795
EPITEC INC
24800 Denso Dr Ste 150, Southfield, MI 48033-7464
Tel (248) 353-6800 *Founded/Ownrshp* 1978
Sales 67.0MM *EMP* 1,800
Accts Plante & Moran Pllc Ann Arbor
SIC 7371 7379 7373 8748 8711 Computer software systems analysis & design, custom; Computer related consulting services; Computer integrated systems design; Systems engineering, computer related; Systems engineering consultant, ex. computer or professional; Consulting engineer
CEO: Jerome Sheppard
**Pr:* Josephine Sheppard
**CFO:* Mark J Ruma
**Ofcr:* Rebecca Bray
**Ex VP:* Anthony Hollamon
CTO: Timothy Steffes
Sls Mgr: Drew Satterley
Sls Mgr: Hannah Schneider

EPIX
See STUDIO 3 PARTNERS LLC

D-U-N-S 00-512-3567 IMP/EXP
EPKO INDUSTRIES INC
MDC WALLCOVERINGS
400 High Grove Blvd, Glendale Heights, IL 60139-4019
Tel (847) 437-4000 *Founded/Ownrshp* 1970
Sales 101.8MM[E] *EMP* 250
SIC 5198 Wallcoverings
Pr: Albert G Rothschild
CFO: Albert Rothchild
Exec: Maritza Vega
VP Sls: Greg Wittlinger
Mktg Dir: Dan Brandt
Mktg Dir: Patrick Glynn
Sls Mgr: McKenzie Swihart

D-U-N-S 78-962-7887
■ **EPL INTERMEDIATE INC**
(*Suby of* EL POLLO LOCO HOLDINGS INC) ★
3535 Harbor Blvd Ste 100, Costa Mesa, CA 92626-1494
Tel (714) 599-5000 *Founded/Ownrshp* 2006
Sales 271.2MM *EMP* 3,998
SIC 5812 Chicken restaurant
Pr: Stephen E Carley
Pr: Steve Sather
CFO: Gary Campanaro
Sr VP: Karen B Eadon
Sr VP: Jeanne A Scott
Sr VP: Joseph N Stein
Board of Directors: Douglas K Ammerman, Andrew R Heyer, Dean C Kehler, Jeffrey J Naumowitz, Alberto Robaina, John M Roth, Griffin Whitney

D-U-N-S 02-311-3140 EXP
EPL OIL & GAS INC
(*Suby of* ENERGY XXI GULF COAST INC) ★
1021 Main St Ste 2626, Houston, TX 77002-6516
Tel (713) 351-3000 *Founded/Ownrshp* 2014
Sales 542.8MM *EMP* 2[E]
SIC 1311 Crude petroleum & natural gas; Crude petroleum production; Natural gas production
Pr: Antonio De Pinho
Pr: Chad E Williams
**CFO:* Rick Fox
Sr VP: Javan D Ottoson
Sr VP: L Keith Vincent
VP: Edmond Mcllhenny

D-U-N-S 04-130-3728
EPLICA INC (CA)
EASTRIDGE ADM STAFFING
2355 Northside Dr Ste 120, San Diego, CA 92108-2714
Tel (619) 260-2000 *Founded/Ownrshp* 1971
Sales 179.9MM[E] *EMP* 4,600
SIC 7363 7361 Temporary help service; Employment agencies
Pr: Robert Svet
Ex VP: Seth Stein
Mng Dir: Brian Schultz
Manager: Jessica Kane

D-U-N-S 78-217-6531
■ **EPLUS GROUP INC**
(*Suby of* EPLUS INC) ★
13595 Dulles Tech Dr, Herndon, VA 20171-3413
Tel (703) 984-8400 *Founded/Ownrshp* 1996
Sales 304.9MM[E] *EMP* 272[E]
Accts Deloitte & Touche Llp
SIC 7377 5734 5045 Computer hardware rental or leasing, except finance leasing; Computer peripheral equipment rental & leasing; Computer & software stores; Computer peripheral equipment; Computer software & accessories; Computers, peripherals & software; Computer peripheral equipment; Computer software
Ch: Phillip G Norton
**Pr:* Chad Fredrick
**Sec:* Kleyton Parkhurst
**VP:* Thomas B Howard
Board of Directors: Bruce Bowen

D-U-N-S 96-152-3214
▲ **EPLUS INC**
13595 Dulles Tech Dr, Herndon, VA 20171-3413
Tel (703) 984-8400 *Founded/Ownrshp* 1990
Sales 1.2MMM *EMP* 1,074
Accts Deloitte & Touche Llp Mclean
Tkr Sym PLUS *Exch* NGS
SIC 5045 7377 7379 7372 Computers, peripherals & software; Computer rental & leasing; Computer peripheral equipment rental & leasing; Computer related consulting services; Prepackaged software
Ch Bd: Phillip G Norton
COO: Thomas Howard Jr
COO: Mark P Marron
CFO: Elaine D Marion
Ex VP: Darren Raiguel
Ex VP: John Reilly
Sr VP: William R Crocker
Sr VP: Tony Mazzullo
Sr VP: Steven J Mencarini
VP: Jim Belger
VP: John Bengivenni
VP: Herbert Brown
VP: Jay Farrell
VP: Robert Filaski
VP: Chris Finney
VP: Burt Gastonguay
VP: Mark Gonzalez
VP: Gary Miglicco
VP: Lisa Neal
VP: Andy Shulman
VP: Jim Solomone
Board of Directors: Bruce M Bowen, John E Callies, C Thomas Faulders III, Lawrence S Herman, Eric D Hovde, Ira A Hunt III, Terrence O'donnell

D-U-N-S 61-851-0192
■ **EPLUS TECHNOLOGY INC**
(*Suby of* EPLUS INC) ★
13595 Dulles Tech Dr, Herndon, VA 20171-3413
Tel (703) 984-8400 *Founded/Ownrshp* 1998
Sales 757.9MM[E] *EMP* 676
SIC 5045 5734 Computers; Computer software; Computer peripheral equipment; Personal computers; Computer software & accessories
Pr: Phillip G Norton
**Pr:* Bruce M Bowen
**Pr:* Phillip G Norton
Pr: Gene Ratto
**COO:* Mark P Marron
**CFO:* Elaine D Marion
Sr Cor Off: Stewart Curley
**Ex VP:* Darren Raiguel
Ex VP: Sam Taylor
**Sr VP:* Steven J Mencarini
**Sr VP:* Kleyton L Parkhurst
VP: Herbert R Brown
VP: Joel Gilbert
VP: Daniel Zapatka
Exec: Raj Ananthanpillai
Dir Bus: Frank Barnes

D-U-N-S 17-345-7805
■ **EPLUS TECHNOLOGY OF PENNSYLVANIA INC**
E C C INTEGRATED
(*Suby of* EPLUS INC) ★
130 Futura Dr, Pottstown, PA 19464-3480
Tel (610) 495-7800 *Founded/Ownrshp* 1997
Sales 117.7MM[E] *EMP* 105
SIC 5734 7378 8243 Computer peripheral equipment; Computer software & accessories; Computer maintenance & repair; Software training, computer
Pr: Vincent W Marino
Netwrk Eng: Joe Cooke
Sales Asso: Stacy Szczepanski
Sales Asso: Holly Wilkie

EPOCH ROBOTICS
See JR AUTOMATION TECHNOLOGIES LLC

D-U-N-S 01-900-6134
EPOCH SL III INC
51 Sawyer Rd Ste 500, Waltham, MA 02453-3461
Tel (781) 891-0777 *Founded/Ownrshp* 1997
Sales 81.1MM[E] *EMP* 3,500
SIC 8059 8051 Nursing home, except skilled & intermediate care facility; Skilled nursing care facilities
Pr: Lawrence Gerber
Ex Dir: Todd Werthman
Mktg Dir: Amy McNally
HC Dir: Sharyn Greenleaf

EPOXY CHEMICALS
See EUCLID CHEMICAL CO

D-U-N-S 80-781-2354 IMP
EPPENDORF HOLDING INC
(*Suby of* EPPENDORF AG)
175 Freshwater Blvd, Enfield, CT 06082-4444
Tel (860) 253-3417 *Founded/Ownrshp* 2007
Sales 87.7MM[E] *EMP* 437[E]
SIC 3821 Laboratory apparatus & furniture; Shakers & stirrers; Sterilizers; Chemical laboratory apparatus
CEO: Martin Farb
**CFO:* Christian Jaaks

D-U-N-S 04-224-1369
EPR PROPERTIES (MD)
909 Walnut St Ste 200, Kansas City, MO 64106-2003
Tel (816) 472-1700 *Founded/Ownrshp* 1997
Sales 421.0MM *EMP* 180
Accts Kpmg Llp Kansas City Missour
SIC 6798 Real estate investment trusts
Pr: Gregory K Silvers
CFO: Mark A Peterson
Chf Inves: Jerry Ernest
Sr VP: Morgan G Earnest II
Sr VP: Craig L Evans
Sr VP: Neil E Sprague
Sr VP: Thomas B Wright
VP: Michael L Hirons
VP: Michael Hirons
VP: Brian Moriarty
Exec: Peter Brown
Exec: Nilda Morell
Exec: Katie Reichenberger

D-U-N-S 04-046-0672 IMP/EXP
EPRODUCTION SOLUTIONS LLC
WEATHERFORD ARTIFICIAL LIFT
(*Suby of* WEATHERFORD INTERNATIONAL LLC) ★
22001 Northpark Dr, Kingwood, TX 77339-3804
Tel (281) 348-1000 *Founded/Ownrshp* 2013
Sales 135.1MM *EMP* 276
SIC 3491 5084 1389 Automatic regulating & control valves; Safety equipment; Oil field services
Pr: Dharmesh Bhupatrai Mehta
**Ex VP:* Krishna Shivram
**VP:* Douglas James Lukey
**VP:* Danielle J Nicholas
**VP:* Dianne B Ralston
VP: James Williams
VP Mktg: Karl Sakocius
VP Sls: Scott Weatherill

D-U-N-S 04-077-5822
EPS SOLUTIONS INC
1525 W Lake Shore Dr, Woodstock, IL 60098-6917
Tel (815) 206-0868 *Founded/Ownrshp* 2004
Sales 141.5MM[E] *EMP* 606
SIC 2676 Towels, napkins & tissue paper products
CEO: David H Hoffmann
Pr: Mark C Coleman
Pr: Jeffrey A Richardson
Sr VP: Michael G Goldstein
Prin: Christopher P Massey
Prin: Erik R Watts
Board of Directors: John Aylsworth, Gary C Grom, Early Price Pritchett III

EPSD
See EAST PENN SCHOOL DISTRICT

D-U-N-S 06-215-8480
■ **EPSILON DATA MANAGEMENT LLC**
(*Suby of* ALLIANCE DATA SYSTEMS CORP) ★
6021 Connection Dr, Irving, TX 75039-2607
Tel (972) 582-9600 *Founded/Ownrshp* 2004
Sales 769.7MM[E] *EMP* 1,450
SIC 7375 Data base information retrieval
CEO: Bryan Kennedy
**Pr:* Andrew Frawley
Pr: Ravi Karumuru
**CFO:* Paul Dundon
Bd of Dir: Cathy Horn
Ex VP: Taleen Ghazarian
Ex VP: Stacia Goddard
Ex VP: Michael Penney
Ex VP: Timothy Prunk
**Ex VP:* Eric Stein
Ex VP: John Vierheller
VP: Greg Akouris
VP: Bryan Anderson
VP: John Bartold
VP: Andrew Bast
VP: Dan Beder
VP: Mathias Berg
VP: Stephen Bernstein
VP: Chris Blumhagen
VP: Liz Buderus
VP: Heather Costello

D-U-N-S 03-552-9804
EPSILON SYSTEMS SOLUTIONS INC
9242 Lightwave Ave # 100, San Diego, CA 92123-6402
Tel (619) 702-1700 *Founded/Ownrshp* 1990
Sales 110.0MM *EMP* 887
SIC 8711 Engineering services
CEO: Bryan Min
**CFO:* Stuart Teshima
Ex VP: Joe Quinn
Sr VP: Ralph Staples
VP: Jeff Giglio
VP: Larry Ingels
VP: Bill Lapsansky
VP: Robin Nordberg
VP: John Sellers
Prgrm Mgr: Betsy Cottle
Prgrm Mgr: Barbara Glasco

EPSON AMERICA
See US EPSON INC

D-U-N-S 02-075-4396 IMP/EXP
EPSON AMERICA INC (CA)
SEIKO EPSON
(*Suby of* EPSON AMERICA) ★
3840 Kilroy Airport Way, Long Beach, CA 90806-2452
Tel (800) 463-7766 *Founded/Ownrshp* 1975, 2007
Sales 343.8MM^E *EMP* 832
SIC 3577 Computer peripheral equipment
Pr: John Lang
CFO: Andrea Zoeckler
Sr VP: Keith Kratzberg
VP: Agustin Chacon
VP: Tadaaki Hagata
VP: Miko Sion
**VP:* Genevieve Walker
Dir Sec: Herman Figueroa
CIO: Cornel Ruston
CTO: Alan Pound
QA Dir: Vincent Lam

D-U-N-S 15-116-0934 IMP/EXP
EPSON PORTLAND INC
(*Suby of* EPSON AMERICA) ★
3950 Nw Aloclek Pl, Hillsboro, OR 97124-7199
Tel (503) 645-1118 *Founded/Ownrshp* 1985
Sales 84.5MM^E *EMP* 400
SIC 3577 Printers, computer
Pr: David Graham
COO: Matt Markunas
**VP:* Tak Shiozaki
CTO: Muneer Koborsi
IT Man: Randal McEvers
Mtls Mgr: Al Fella
Opers Mgr: Larry Halverson
Prd Mgr: Kimball McKeehan

D-U-N-S 00-791-5663
▲ EQT CORP (PA)
625 Liberty Ave Ste 1700, Pittsburgh, PA 15222-3114
Tel (412) 553-5700 *Founded/Ownrshp* 1888
Sales 2.3MMM *EMP* 1,914^E
Accts Ernst & Young Llp Pittsburgh
Tkr Sym EQT *Exch* NYS
SIC 1311 4923 4924 4925 Crude petroleum & natural gas; Gas transmission & distribution; Natural gas distribution; Gas production and/or distribution
Ch Bd: David L Porges
Pr: Steven T Schlotterbeck
CFO: Robert J McNally
Ofcr: Charlene Petrelli
Ex VP: Ken Kirk
Sr VP: Philip P Conti
Sr VP: Randall L Crawford
VP: Cliff Baker
VP: Michael Butcher
VP: Carol Caracciolo
VP: Michael Conn
VP: Lewis B Gardner
VP: Jim Helmick
VP: Natalie Jefferis
VP: Steven Prelipp
VP: John Quinn
VP: David Schlosser
VP: Jimmi Smith
Board of Directors: Lee T Todd Jr, Vicky A Bailey, Christine J Toretti, Philip G Behrman, Kenneth M Burke, A Bray Cary Jr, Margaret K Dorman, George L Miles Jr, James E Rohr, David S Shapira, Stephen A Thorington

D-U-N-S 08-018-1356
■ EQT GATHERING HOLDINGS LLC
(*Suby of* EQT CORP) ★
625 Liberty Ave Ste 1700, Pittsburgh, PA 15222-3114
Tel (412) 553-5700 *Founded/Ownrshp* 2013
Sales 614.1MM^E *EMP* 3^E
SIC 4922 Natural gas transmission
Ch Bd: David L Porges
**CFO:* Philip P Conti

D-U-N-S 07-972-9131
■ EQT GP HOLDINGS LP
(*Suby of* EQT GATHERING HOLDINGS LLC) ★
625 Liberty Ave Ste 1700, Pittsburgh, PA 15222-3114
Tel (412) 553-5700 *Founded/Ownrshp* 2015
Sales 614.1MM *EMP* 3
Accts Ernst & Young Llp Pittsburgh
Tkr Sym EQGP *Exch* NYS
SIC 4922 Natural gas transmission
Ch Bd: David L Porges
Genl Pt: Eqt GP Services
CFO: Philip P Conti

D-U-N-S 07-843-2607
EQT MIDSTREAM PARTNERS LP
625 Liberty Ave Ste 1700, Pittsburgh, PA 15222-3114
Tel (412) 553-5700 *Founded/Ownrshp* 2012
Sales 614.1MM *EMP* 4
Accts Ernst & Young Llp Pittsburgh
Tkr Sym EQM *Exch* NYS
SIC 4922 Natural gas transmission; Pipelines, natural gas
Pr: David L Porges
Genl Pt: Eqt Midstream Services
CFO: Philip P Conti

D-U-N-S 10-468-0777
■ EQT PRODUCTION CO
(*Suby of* EQT CORP) ★
625 Liberty Ave Ste 1700, Pittsburgh, PA 15222-3114
Tel (412) 553-5700 *Founded/Ownrshp* 2000
Sales 615.8MM^E *EMP* 400
SIC 4911 Generation, electric power
Pr: Diane Prier
**CEO:* David L Porges
**Sr VP:* Philip P Conti
Snr Mgr: Rob Kovacevic

D-U-N-S 08-919-1928
■ EQUAL EMPLOYMENT OPPORTUNITY COMMISSION
EEOC
(*Suby of* EXECUTIVE OFFICE OF UNITED STATES GOVERNMENT) ★
131 M St Ne, Washington, DC 20507-0003
Tel (202) 663-4519 *Founded/Ownrshp* 1964
Sales NA *EMP* 2,255
SIC 9441 Equal employment opportunity office, government;
Ch: Jenny R Yang
**COO:* Claudia Withers
**CFO:* Jeffrey A Smith
Ofcr: Bernadette Wilson
Prgrm Mgr: Len Worley
Sales Exec: Kendall Cooper
Genl Couns: David Lopez
Counsel: Christopher Lage

D-U-N-S 14-970-2966
EQUIAN LLC
5975 Castle Crk Pkwy 10 Ste 100, Indianapolis, IN 46250
Tel (800) 962-6831 *Founded/Ownrshp* 2015
Sales NA *EMP* 180
SIC 6324 Hospital & medical service plans
CEO: Scott Mingee
Pr: Chris Reed
COO: Shankar Narayanan
CFO: Jeff Martin
Ofcr: Sameer Mishra
Ofcr: Mike Morrison
VP: Brad Devorkin
Prd Mgr: Shannon Quijano

D-U-N-S 83-060-0016
EQUICORP PARTNERS LLC
75 14th St Ne Unit 4610, Atlanta, GA 30309-7621
Tel (404) 442-1530 *Founded/Ownrshp* 2005
Sales 90.1MM^E *EMP* 1,705
SIC 6282 Investment advice

D-U-N-S 04-581-2369
▲ EQUIFAX INC
1550 Peachtree St Nw, Atlanta, GA 30309
Tel (404) 885-8000 *Founded/Ownrshp* 1899
Sales 2.6MMM *EMP* 8,000^E
Tkr Sym EFX *Exch* NYS
SIC 7323 7389 8732 8741 Credit reporting services; Credit bureau & agency; Commercial (mercantile) credit reporting bureau; Credit investigation service; Financial services; Credit card service; Market analysis, business & economic research; Market analysis or research; Management services; Financial management for business
Ch Bd: Richard F Smith
Pr: Dann Adams
Pr: Chad Barker
Pr: Paulino Barros
Pr: John Breen
Pr: Dennis Cerullo
Pr: Adam Corsi
Pr: Heath Eckert
Pr: David Frankel
Pr: John Hartman
Pr: Clay Irwin
Pr: Rakesh Patel
Pr: Rudy Ploder
Pr: Zachary Schneider
Pr: Shannon Strachan
Pr: Jonathan Zurick
**CFO:* John W Gamble Jr
Treas: Mark E Young
Bd of Dir: John A McKinley
Chf Mktg O: Dianne Runnebohm
Sr VP: Frank Blaul
Board of Directors: James E Copeland Jr, Robert D Daleo, Walter W Driver Jr, Mark L Feidler, L Philip Humann, Robert D Marcus, John A McKinley, Mark B Templeton

D-U-N-S 05-953-8249
■ EQUIFAX INFORMATION SERVICES LLC
(*Suby of* EQUIFAX INC) ★
1550 Peachtree St Ne, Atlanta, GA 30309-2468
Tel (404) 885-8000 *Founded/Ownrshp* 1967
Sales 171.8MM^E *EMP* 2,700
SIC 7323 Commercial (mercantile) credit reporting bureau; Credit bureau & agency
CEO: Richard F Smith
**Treas:* Michael G Schirk
**Exec:* James Dann Adams
MIS Dir: Charles Reid

EQUIFAX WORKFORCE SOLUTIONS
See TALX CORP

D-U-N-S 00-429-4737 IMP/EXP
EQUILON ENTERPRISES LLC
SHELL OIL PRODUCTS U S
(*Suby of* SHELL OIL CO) ★
910 Louisiana St Ste 2, Houston, TX 77002-4906
Tel (713) 241-6161 *Founded/Ownrshp* 1998
Sales 780.1MM^E *EMP* 1,449
SIC 2911 4612 2992 5172 Petroleum refining; Crude petroleum pipelines; Lubricating oils; Petroleum products
Pr: Lynn Elsenhans
**Pr:* Lisa A Davis
**CFO:* K M Fisher
**VP:* R R Caplan
VP: Lee Gaspard Jr
**VP:* S P Methvin
**VP:* D J Pirret
Plnt Mgr: Elijah Finister
**Genl Couns:* D E Kinnan

D-U-N-S 04-526-7338
▲ EQUINIX INC
1 Lagoon Dr Ste 400, Redwood City, CA 94065-1564
Tel (650) 598-6000 *Founded/Ownrshp* 1998
Sales 2.7MMM *EMP* 5,042
Tkr Sym EQIX *Exch* NGS
SIC 4813 Telephone communication, except radio; Data telephone communications
Pr: Stephen Smith
Pt: Greg Adgate
COO: Charles Meyers
CFO: Keith Taylor
Ch: Peter Van Camp
Treas: Melanie Mock
Chf Cred: Brian Lillie
Bd of Dir: Marcia Britton
Chf Mktg O: Jarrett Appleby
Chf Mktg O: Sara Baack
Ofcr: Michael Campbell
Ofcr: Peter Ferris
Ofcr: Ravi Ravishankar
Sr VP: Daniel C Walker
VP: Monica Andrews
VP: Biju Baby
VP: Diraj Bamola
VP: Andy Castle
VP: Bill Dembinski
VP: Gus Ezcurra
VP: Teri Francis
Board of Directors: Thomas Bartlett, Nanci Caldwell, Gary Hromadko, John Hughes, Scott Kriens, William Luby, Irving Lyons III, Christopher Paisley

EQUINOX 19TH ST
See EQUINOX HOLDINGS INC

EQUINOX FITNESS CLUB
See EQUINOX-76TH STREET INC

D-U-N-S 09-250-2694
EQUINOX HOLDINGS INC
EQUINOX 19TH ST
(*Suby of* RELATED COMPANIES L P) ★
895 Broadway Fl 3, New York, NY 10003-1281
Tel (212) 677-0180 *Founded/Ownrshp* 1998
Sales 845.0MM^E *EMP* 18,000
SIC 7991 Physical fitness facilities
CEO: Harvey J Spevak
Pr: Josh Wyatt
COO: Sarah Robb O Hagan
COO: Scott M Rosen
CFO: Larry M Segall
CFO: Larry Seigal
CFO: Paul Tizik
Ex VP: Todd Magazine
VP: Jeff Grayson
VP: Patrik Hellstrand
VP: Lisa Tharps
VP Bus Dev: Liz Henning
Board of Directors: Douglas W Lehrman, Stephen M Ross

D-U-N-S 78-270-3284
EQUINOX-76TH STREET INC
EQUINOX FITNESS CLUB
(*Suby of* EQUINOX 19TH ST) ★
895 Broadway Fl 3, New York, NY 10003-1281
Tel (212) 677-0180 *Founded/Ownrshp* 2006
Sales 167.3MM^E *EMP* 4,000
SIC 7991 Physical fitness clubs with training equipment
CEO: Harvey Spevak
**COO:* Scott Rosen
**CFO:* Larry Seigal
VP: Vito Errico
VP: Jack Gannon
Dir IT: Christian Fortucci

D-U-N-S 05-213-7866 IMP/EXP
EQUIPMENT DEPOT LTD (TX)
(*Suby of* PON MATERIAL HANDLING NA INC) ★
840 Gessner Rd Ste 950, Houston, TX 77024-4593
Tel (713) 365-2547 *Founded/Ownrshp* 1965, 2015
Sales 191.0MM^E *EMP* 300
SIC 5083 5084 7359 7699 7353 Farm implements; Lift trucks & parts; Industrial truck rental; Industrial truck repair; Tractor repair; Industrial machinery & equipment repair; Cranes & aerial lift equipment, rental or leasing; Earth moving equipment, rental or leasing
Pr: David Turner
**CFO:* Marcel Broeshart
Sr VP: Jack Whitney
**VP:* John Kilbride
**VP:* Bryan Monk
VP: Rick Scott
Exec: Diana Torrez
Genl Mgr: Kevin Harris
Genl Mgr: Scott Hendrickson
Dir IT: Kevin Corley
Sfty Dirs: Michael Hassell
Board of Directors: Marcel Broeshart, David Turner

D-U-N-S 02-579-4215 IMP
EQUIPMENT DEPOT OF ILLINOIS INC
(*Suby of* PON NORTH AMERICA INC) ★
751 Expressway Dr, Itasca, IL 60143-1321
Tel (847) 836-5005 *Founded/Ownrshp* 1956, 1999
Sales 93.1MM^E *EMP* 250
SIC 5084 5087 5063 7699 Materials handling machinery; Floor machinery, maintenance; Storage batteries, industrial; Industrial machinery & equipment repair
Pr: David Turner
**Pr:* Donald G Moes
**COO:* Frank C Ricciardi
**CFO:* Kenneth E Miller
IT Man: John Amidei

D-U-N-S 00-886-2369 IMP
EQUIPMENT DEPOT OHIO INC
(*Suby of* PON NORTH AMERICA INC) ★
4331 Rossplain Dr, Blue Ash, OH 45236-1207
Tel (513) 891-0600 *Founded/Ownrshp* 2008
Sales 115.3MM^E *EMP* 325
SIC 5084 Industrial machinery & equipment
Pr: Edward Neyer
**VP:* John Ventre
Genl Mgr: John Herrmann
Genl Mgr: Randy Reece
CIO: Tim Orr
Sls Mgr: David Connell

D-U-N-S 96-272-0772
■ EQUIPOWER RESOURCES CORP
(*Suby of* DYNEGY INC) ★
100 Constitution Plz # 10, Hartford, CT 06103-1702
Tel (203) 676-6700 *Founded/Ownrshp* 2010
Sales 92.5MM^E *EMP* 106^E
SIC 4911 Generation, electric power
CEO: Curtis A Morgan
**CFO:* Alan P Dunlea
**Chf Cred:* Robert A Hayes
**Ex VP:* Bryan Fisher
**Ex VP:* Dave Freysinger
Sr VP: John P Campbell
Sr VP: James A Ginnetti
Sr VP: Donna M Poresky
**VP:* Mary K Kennedy

EQUIPWER RSOURCES HOLDINGS LLC
See DYNEGY RESOURCES GENERATING HOLDCO LLC

D-U-N-S 96-955-7263 IMP/EXP
EQUISTAR CHEMICALS LP
(*Suby of* LYONDELL CHEMICAL CO) ★
1221 Mckinney St Ste 700, Houston, TX 77010-2045
Tel (713) 309-7200 *Founded/Ownrshp* 2002
Sales 1.2MMM^E *EMP* 3,330
SIC 2869 2822 Olefins; Ethylene; Butadiene (industrial organic chemical); Ethylene oxide; Polyethylene, chlorosulfonated (hypalon)
CEO: James L Gallogly
Pt: Eberhard Faller
V Ch: Jay Miller
CFO: Robert T Blakely
Ex VP: Craig Glidden
Ex VP: Karyn Ovelmen
Ex VP: Bhavesh V Patel
Ex VP: Tim Roberts
Sr VP: Bart C De Jong
Sr VP: John A Hollinshead
VP: Dave Balderston
VP: Rick Fontenot
VP: Susan Moore
VP: Gerald A O'Brien
VP: Jose L Rodriguez
VP: Michael White

D-U-N-S 07-301-1462
EQUITABLE LIFE & CASUALTY INSURANCE CO
EQUITABLE LIFE ASSURANCE
3 Triad Ctr, Salt Lake City, UT 84180-1211
Tel (801) 579-3400 *Founded/Ownrshp* 1935
Sales NA *EMP* 188
SIC 6411 6311 Insurance agents, brokers & service; Life insurance carriers
CEO: Bill Prouty
**Pr:* Kendall Surfass
**Treas:* Daran Hackett
Sr Cor Off: Scott Hansen
Sr VP: Ravinder Singh
Creative D: Christine Trani
**Prin:* Stephanie Lunt
CTO: Christopher Jordan
Sales Asso: Gene Lieberman
Board of Directors: E Rod Ross

EQUITABLE LIFE ASSURANCE
See EQUITABLE LIFE & CASUALTY INSURANCE CO

D-U-N-S 18-956-9585
■ EQUITRANS LP
(*Suby of* KENTUCKY WEST VIRGINIA GAS CO) ★
625 Liberty Ave Ste 1700, Pittsburgh, PA 15222-3114
Tel (412) 553-5700 *Founded/Ownrshp* 1986
Sales 99.2MM^E *EMP* 231
SIC 4922 Pipelines, natural gas; Storage, natural gas
**Pt:* James E Crockard
Board of Directors: Cliff Baker, Diana Charletta, Robert Frankhouser, Chris Klemstine, Charlene Petrelli

D-U-N-S 04-854-3107
EQUITRUST LIFE INSURANCE CO INC (IA)
(*Suby of* MAGIC JOHNSON ENTERPRISES INC) ★
7100 Westown Pkwy Ste 200, West Des Moines, IA 50266-2521
Tel (888) 400-5759 *Founded/Ownrshp* 1986, 2015
Sales NA *EMP* 1,000
SIC 6411 Insurance agents, brokers & service
CEO: James Hohmann
**Pr:* Jeffrey S Lang
**CFO:* James Brannen
**Treas:* James D Purvis
VP: Ana Bumgardner
VP: Brian Mamola
Genl Couns: David McNeill

D-U-N-S 15-519-1299
EQUITY COMMONWEALTH
2 N Riverside Plz Ste 600, Chicago, IL 60606-2627
Tel (312) 646-2800 *Founded/Ownrshp* 1986
Sales 714.8MM *EMP* 62
SIC 6798 Real estate investment trusts
Pr: David Helfand
COO: David S Weinberg
CFO: Adam S Markman
Ex VP: Orrin S Shifrin
VP: Tim Bonang
VP: Bob Johnson
VP: Danny Kuo
VP: David M Lepore
VP: Dov Pinchot

D-U-N-S 95-883-7775
EQUITY GROUP - GEORGIA DIVISION LLC
7220 Us Highway 19, Camilla, GA 31730-7432
Tel (229) 336-1001 *Founded/Ownrshp* 1972
Sales 228.8MM^E *EMP* 2,900
SIC 2015 0254 2048 Chicken, slaughtered & dressed; Chicken hatchery; Chicken feeds, prepared

Genl Mgr: Tim Lawson
**Genl Mgr:* Clay Banks

D-U-N-S 01-211-7060 EXP
EQUITY GROUP - KENTUCKY DIVISION LLC
2294 Ky Highway 90W, Albany, KY 42602-7537
Tel (606) 387-2300 *Founded/Ownrshp* 1998
Sales 175.3MM^E *EMP* 1,540
SIC 2048 5144 Prepared feeds; Poultry & poultry products
Ex VP: Greg Clayborn
Exec: Ken McCratic

D-U-N-S 14-472-9469 IMP
EQUITY GROUP EUFAULA DIVISION LLC
KEYSTONE FOODS
(*Suby of* M & M RESTAURANT SUPPLY) ★
57 Melvin Clark Rd, Eufaula, AL 36027-4938
Tel (334) 687-7790 *Founded/Ownrshp* 1960
Sales 228.8MM^E *EMP* 1,200
SIC 2015 2048 2041 2011 Poultry slaughtering & processing; Prepared feeds; Flour & other grain mill products; Meat packing plants
**CFO:* Eduardo Miron
**Genl Mgr:* Tim Asslinger

D-U-N-S 62-460-6588
EQUITY INTERNATIONAL INC
B & W
(*Suby of* B & W GROUP LTD)
54 Concord St, North Reading, MA 01864-2699
Tel (978) 664-2712 *Founded/Ownrshp* 1993
Sales 200.0MM *EMP* 574
SIC 5065 Radio & television equipment & parts
Pr: Joseph Atkins
**Treas:* Cindy Hughes
**VP:* Stephen Curran

D-U-N-S 80-208-9169
▲ EQUITY LIFESTYLE PROPERTIES INC
2 N Riverside Plz Ste 800, Chicago, IL 60606-2682
Tel (312) 279-1400 *Founded/Ownrshp* 1969
Sales 821.6MM *EMP* 4,100
Tkr Sym ELS *Exch* NYS
SIC 6798 6531 Real estate investment trusts; Real estate agents & managers; Real estate agent, commercial; Real estate agent, residential
Pr: Marguerite Nader
**Ch Bd:* Thomas Heneghan
**Ch Bd:* Howard Walker
**Ch Bd:* Samuel Zell
COO: Patrick Waite
CFO: Paul Seavey
Ex VP: Roger Maynard
Genl Mgr: Bill Krzyston
Board of Directors: Philip Calian, David Contis, Thomas Dobrowski, William Young

D-U-N-S 96-545-1441
EQUITY MSOUTH PARTNERS L P
MSOUTH EQUITY PARTNERS
3050 Peachtree Rd Nw, Atlanta, GA 30305-2212
Tel (404) 816-3255 *Founded/Ownrshp* 2008
Sales 239.2MM^E *EMP* 5,688
SIC 6799 7363 Venture capital companies; Temporary help service
Pt: Mark L Feidler
Pt: Barry L Boniface
Pt: Michael D Long
Pt: Bart A McLean
Pt: Peter S Pettit
CFO: Wanda R Morgan

D-U-N-S 80-414-4970
▲ EQUITY ONE INC
410 Park Ave Ste 1220, New York, NY 10022-9461
Tel (212) 796-1760 *Founded/Ownrshp* 1992
Sales 353.1MM *EMP* 155^E
Tkr Sym EQY *Exch* NYS
SIC 6798 Real estate investment trusts
CEO: David R Lukes
**Ch Bd:* Chaim Katzman
Pr: Thomas Caputo
**CEO:* David Lukes
COO: Michael Makinen
CFO: Mark Langer
CFO: Matthew Ostrower
**V Ch Bd:* Dori Segal
Ex VP: William L Brown
Ex VP: Lauren Holden
VP: Aaron M Kitlowski
Board of Directors: Cynthia R Cohen, David Fischel, Neil Flanzraich, Jordan Heller, Peter Linneman, Galia Maor

D-U-N-S 80-562-1927
EQUITY RESIDENTIAL
2 N Rverside Plz Ste 1100, Chicago, IL 60606
Tel (312) 474-1300 *Founded/Ownrshp* 1993
Sales 2.7MMM *EMP* 3,500
SIC 6798 Real estate investment trusts
Pr: David J Neithercut
**Ch Bd:* Samuel Zell
COO: David S Santee
CFO: Mark J Parrell
**V Ch Bd:* Gerald A Spector
Chf Inves: Alan W George
Ex VP: Barry S Altshuler
Ex VP: Alexander Brackenridge
Ex VP: John Powers
Ex VP: Christa L Sorenson
Ex VP: Bruce C Strohm
VP: Barry Altshuler
VP: Bradley Karvasek
VP: Edward Leigh
VP: John Lennox
VP: Mark Trager
VP: Corey Warren
VP: Susan Zumph
Board of Directors: B Joseph White, John W Alexander, Charles L Atwood, Linda Walker Bynoe, Connie K Duckworth, Mary Kay Haben, Bradley A Keywell, John E Neal, Mark S Shapiro, Stephen E Sterrett

EQUITY TITLE COMPANY AMERICA
See NETCO INC (IL)

D-U-N-S 02-389-2198
EQUIVA SERVICES LLC
SHELL
(*Suby of* ROYAL DUTCH SHELL PLC)
1100 La St Ste 3030, Houston, TX 77002
Tel (713) 241-6161 *Founded/Ownrshp* 1998
Sales 72.4MM^E *EMP* 1,449
SIC 8741 Management services; Administrative management; Financial management for business; Personnel management
Treas: M V Michael Carlucci
VP: S B Bruce Culpepper

D-U-N-S 78-204-2188 IMP
EQUUS COMPUTER SYSTEMS INC
7725 Washington Ave S, Edina, MN 55439-2422
Tel (612) 617-6200 *Founded/Ownrshp* 1996
Sales 500.0MM *EMP* 400^E
SIC 3571 Computers, digital, analog or hybrid
CEO: Andy S Juang
Pr: Dave Guzzi
**CFO:* Howard Gilles
**Prin:* Diane L Ketcher
Genl Mgr: Michael Foley
Opers Mgr: Brian Orazio

D-U-N-S 96-818-5996
ER EQUIPMENT INC
Calle Sur Num 10 Mariani St Calle Sur N, Ponce, PR 00730
Tel (787) 841-2743 *Founded/Ownrshp* 2011
Sales 262.3MM^E *EMP* 3,531
SIC 3531

ER INDUSTRIAL
See E & R INDUSTRIAL SALES INC

D-U-N-S 07-864-0374
▲ ERA GROUP INC
818 Town And Country Blvd, Houston, TX 77024-4550
Tel (713) 369-4700 *Founded/Ownrshp* 1948
Sales 281.8MM *EMP* 936^E
Tkr Sym ERA *Exch* NYS
SIC 4512 Helicopter carrier, scheduled
Pr: Christopher S Bradshaw
**Ch Bd:* Charles Fabrikant
CFO: Andrew L Puhala
Sr VP: Shefali A Shah
Sr VP: Stuart Stavley
Sr VP: Paul White
VP: Anna Goss
VP: Jennifer Whalen
Board of Directors: Ann Fairbanks, Blaine Fogg, Christopher P Papouras, Steven Webster

D-U-N-S 55-683-0912
ERA RIZZO REALTY LLC
244 Us Highway 46 Ste 6, Fairfield, NJ 07004-2300
Tel (973) 575-1155 *Founded/Ownrshp* 2005
Sales 90.0MM *EMP* 28
SIC 6531 Real estate brokers & agents

D-U-N-S 80-404-4907
ERASE INC
107 Myrtle Ave 27, Ramsey, NJ 07446-1017
Tel (201) 760-0189 *Founded/Ownrshp* 1987
Sales 85.0MM *EMP* 45
SIC 8748 Environmental consultant
Pr: Paul Leonard

D-U-N-S 03-103-1594
ERB EQUIPMENT CO INC
JOHN DEERE AUTHORIZED DEALER
200 Erb Industrial Dr, Fenton, MO 63026-4640
Tel (636) 349-0200 *Founded/Ownrshp* 1973
Sales 130.2MM *EMP* 120
Accts Cliftonlarsonallen Llp St Lo
SIC 5082 7353 5084 Road construction equipment; General construction machinery & equipment; Heavy construction equipment rental; Industrial machinery & equipment
Ch Bd: Robert Erb
**Pr:* Gregg Erb
**CEO:* Carrie Roider
Dept Mgr: Montey Johnson
Genl Mgr: Diane Konradi
Sls Mgr: Scott Crean
Sales Asso: Mike Lamp

ERC, INC FOR PURP DO BUS IN AL
See ENGINEERING RESEARCH AND CONSULTING INC

D-U-N-S 08-923-6798
ERC PROPERTIES INC
E R C
4107 Massard Rd, Fort Smith, AR 72903-6223
Tel (479) 478-5103 *Founded/Ownrshp* 1997
Sales 167.9MM^E *EMP* 250
SIC 1522 6552 6513 Multi-family dwelling construction; Land subdividers & developers, residential; Apartment building operators
Pr: Rod Coleman
**Treas:* Lyndon Morris
**Sr VP:* John Clayton
**Sr VP:* David Needham
**Sr VP:* Jim Phelan
Rgnl Mgr: Barbara Jarvis
Sfty Dirs: Linda Udoj

ERCOT ISO
See ELECTRIC RELIABILITY COUNCIL OF TEXAS INC

D-U-N-S 15-098-7316
ERDMAN CO
(*Suby of* LUBAR & CO INC) ★
1 Erdman Pl, Madison, WI 53717-2100
Tel (608) 410-8000 *Founded/Ownrshp* 1951
Sales 186.1MM^E *EMP* 398
SIC 1542 Hospital construction; Specialized public building contractors
**COO:* Tyler Vassar
**Ch:* Frank Spencer
**Ex VP:* Rustin Becker
Ex VP: Eli Woyke
Sr VP: Dave Scott
**Exec:* Andrea Hopkins
CTO: Andrea Andrews
Dir IT: Erik Lewis

D-U-N-S 00-610-2834 IMP
ERDMAN HOLDINGS INC (WI)
ERDMAN REAL STATE HOLDINGS
6720 Frank Llyd Wright Av, Middleton, WI 53562-1753
Tel (608) 662-2205 *Founded/Ownrshp* 1946
Sales 130.0MM^E *EMP* 500
SIC 1542 2599 Hospital construction; Specialized public building contractors; Commercial & office buildings, prefabricated erection; Cabinets, factory
Pr: Timothy B Erdman
**Sec:* Alan Hembel
**Sr VP:* Steve Roth
**VP:* Jerry Sholts
**VP:* Sam Smith
Snr PM: Charles Falk

ERDMAN REAL STATE HOLDINGS
See ERDMAN HOLDINGS INC

D-U-N-S 86-728-8557
ERESEARCHTECHNOLOGY INC
(*Suby of* NORDIC CAPITAL LIMITED)
1818 Market St Ste 1000, Philadelphia, PA 19103-3647
Tel (215) 972-0420 *Founded/Ownrshp* 2016
Sales 126.6MM^E *EMP* 680
SIC 8734 Testing laboratories
Pr: James Corrigan
**CFO:* Waqar Nasim
**Chf Cred:* Steve Nuckols
**Ex VP:* Amy Furlong
**Ex VP:* Achim Schlkem
**Ex VP:* Ron Sullivan
**Ex VP:* Andrea Valente
VP: Werner Buerk
VP: David Coman
VP: Scott Dixon
VP: Jason Eger
VP: Steven Geffon
VP: Michael Harte
VP: Robert Jacobs
VP: Valerie Mattern
VP: Richard Miller
VP: Tammy Miller
VP: Steven Silber
Dir Bus: Leslie Reimer

ERGODYNE
See TENACIOUS HOLDINGS INC

D-U-N-S 12-269-5240 IMP
ERGON ASPHALT & EMULSIONS INC
(*Suby of* ERGON INC) ★
2829 Lakeland Dr Ste 2000, Flowood, MS 39232-7611
Tel (601) 933-3000 *Founded/Ownrshp* 1982
Sales 169.3MM^E *EMP* 75
SIC 5172 2951

D-U-N-S 08-702-3743 IMP/EXP
ERGON INC
2829 Lakeland Dr Ste 2000, Flowood, MS 39232-7611
Tel (601) 933-3000 *Founded/Ownrshp* 1970
Sales 1.1MMM^E *EMP* 2,330
SIC 2911 4213 4449 4613 5171 5172 Gases & liquefied petroleum gases; Greases, lubricating; Asphalt or asphaltic materials, made in refineries; Liquid petroleum transport, non-local; River transportation, except on the St. Lawrence Seaway; Intracoastal (freight) transportation; Refined petroleum pipelines; Petroleum bulk stations; Petroleum terminals; Petroleum products
Pr: Leslie B Lampton Sr
**Treas:* Jimmy Clunan
VP: Lee Adams
VP: Steve Adams
VP: Gaylon Baumgardner
**VP:* Baxter Burns
VP: Craig Busbea
**VP:* A Patrick Busby
VP: Keith Clair
VP: Mark Clark
VP: Tony Doblado
VP: Janis Erikson
VP: Bill Grubba
VP: Jamie Harris
**VP:* Ken Hodges
VP: Jeff Kerkove
**VP:* Lee C Lampton
**VP:* Leslie B Lampton III
**VP:* Robert H Lampton
VP: Jimmy Langdon
VP: Jimmy Lingdon

D-U-N-S 15-138-2793
ERGONOMIC GROUP INC
EGI
609 Cantiague Rock Rd # 3, Westbury, NY 11590-1721
Tel (516) 746-7777 *Founded/Ownrshp* 1984
Sales 311.9MM^E *EMP* 165
SIC 5045 7373 7374 7376 7379 Computers; Systems integration services; Computer processing services; Computer facilities management; Computer related maintenance services
Ch Bd: Karen Girards
COO: Robert Gerards
COO: Bob Girards
Sales Exec: Chris Kerwin
Sls Dir: Chris Dichiara
Sales Asso: Mike Allen
Pgrm Dir: Robert Packer

D-U-N-S 06-264-4448 IMP
ERGOTRON INC
(*Suby of* NORTEK INC) ★
1181 Trapp Rd Ste 100, Saint Paul, MN 55121-1266
Tel (651) 681-7600 *Founded/Ownrshp* 2010
Sales 83.1MM^E *EMP* 375^E
SIC 7373 3577 Computer integrated systems design; Computer peripheral equipment
Pr: Joel Hazzard
**COO:* Dan Miller
CFO: Scott Lunger
**CFO:* Greg A Mohwinkel
Ofcr: Jane Payfer
Sr VP: Mark Ellson
Sr VP: Melody J McKay
Sr VP: Pete Segar
VP: John Deutsch
VP: Ken Jensen
VP: Daneen J Kiger
VP: James Noreault
VP: Craig Thomas
VP: David Wardleworth
Exec: Sam Schmidt

D-U-N-S 94-969-1695
■ ERI INVESTMENTS INC
(*Suby of* EQT CORP) ★
801 N West St Fl 2, Wilmington, DE 19801-1525
Tel (302) 656-8089 *Founded/Ownrshp* 2003
Sales 569.2MM *EMP* 10
SIC 6719 Investment holding companies, except banks
Pr: John Bergonzi
**Pr:* Philip Conti
**Treas:* Claire A Paschitti
**VP:* Kenneth Kubacki

D-U-N-S 19-497-8920
■ ERICKSON BUILDING COMPONENTS LLC
(*Suby of* MASCO CORP) ★
250 N Beck Ave, Chandler, AZ 85226-1701
Tel (480) 627-1100 *Founded/Ownrshp* 2007
Sales 86.8MM^E *EMP* 381
SIC 2439 2452 Trusses, wooden roof; Panels & sections, prefabricated, wood

D-U-N-S 07-641-4135
ERICKSON INC
5550 Sw Mcdam Ave Ste 200, Portland, OR 97239
Tel (503) 505-5800 *Founded/Ownrshp* 1971
Sales 297.5MM *EMP* 819
SIC 7363 4581 3721 7359 5599 3728 Help supply services; Aircraft maintenance & repair services; Aircraft servicing & repairing; Aircraft; Aircraft rental; Aircraft dealers; Aircraft parts & equipment
CFO: David Lancelot
Ch Bd: Gary R Scott
Pr: Jeffrey Roberts
CFO: David W Lancelot
Ofcr: Chris Erickson
VP: Eric Fraenkel
VP: Robert Lewis
VP: Brian Pierson
Exec: Brenda Peterson
Genl Mgr: Ray Byrd
VP Mfg: Kerry Jarandson
Board of Directors: Glenn Johnson, Meredith Siegfried Madden, Quinn Morgan, James L Welch

D-U-N-S 96-595-3396
ERICKSON LIVING MANAGEMENT LLC
701 Maiden Choice Ln, Catonsville, MD 21228-5968
Tel (410) 402-2097 *Founded/Ownrshp* 2009
Sales 1.2MMM *EMP* 12,000
SIC 8741 Nursing & personal care facility management
CEO: Alan R Butler
**Pr:* William J Butz
**COO:* Debra B Doyle
CFO: William Butz
**CFO:* Todd A Matthiesen
**Ch:* Jim Davis
Ex VP: Mary Wagner
**Sr VP:* Adam Kane
VP: Russ Caccamisi
VP: Scott Gensler
VP: Jeff Hofstetter
VP: Hans Keller
VP: Matt Neville
VP: Darah Okeke

D-U-N-S 05-903-2078
■ ERICKSON OIL PRODUCTS INC
FREEDOM VALU CENTER
(*Suby of* CROSSAMERICA PARTNERS LP) ★
1231 Industrial St, Hudson, WI 54016-9301
Tel (715) 386-8241 *Founded/Ownrshp* 1959
Sales 222.4MM^E *EMP* 700
SIC 5541 5411 Filling stations, gasoline; Convenience stores
CEO: Claire L Erickson
**CFO:* Gary Vander Vorst
VP: Darren Forbes
VP: Gary Vorst
Telecom Ex: Sherry Jerry

D-U-N-S 00-446-0671 IMP
ERICO INTERNATIONAL CORP (OH)
(*Suby of* PENTAIR PUBLIC LIMITED COMPANY)
31700 Solon Rd, Solon, OH 44139-3532
Tel (440) 349-2630 *Founded/Ownrshp* 1903, 2015
Sales 428.7MM^E *EMP* 1,230
SIC 3441 Fabricated structural metal
Pr: William Roj
CFO: Jeffrey R Steinhilber
Ex VP: Andy Henderson
VP: William A Fullmer
VP: Peter B Korte
VP: Dan Lister
Dir IT: Karen Nelson
Mktg Mgr: Jen Znidarsk
Manager: James Kane
Snr Mgr: Jeff Neer

ERICSSON GE MBL COMMUNICATIONS
See ERICSSON INC

D-U-N-S 87-898-3378 IMP
ERICSSON HOLDING II INC
(*Suby of* TELEFON AB LM ERICSSON)
6300 Legacy Dr, Plano, TX 75024-3607
Tel (972) 398-0183 *Founded/Ownrshp* 1992
Sales 4.0MMM^E *EMP* 8,529
SIC 3663 Radio broadcasting & communications equipment; Cellular radio telephone; Mobile communication equipment
CEO: Kurt Hellstrom
**Pr:* Angel Ruiz
CFO: Hans Vestberg
VP: Franck Bouetard
VP: George Fath
**VP:* Jane Frykhammar
VP: Petter Jartby
VP: Gary Pinkham
VP: Nils Rydbeck

VP: Anders Torstensson
Exec: John Moon

D-U-N-S 13-955-7425 IMP
ERICSSON INC
ERICSSON GE MBL COMMUNICATIONS
(*Suby of* ERICSSON HOLDING II INC) ★
6300 Legacy Dr, Plano, TX 75024-3607
Tel (972) 583-0000 *Founded/Ownrshp* 1984
Sales 4.0MMM[E] *EMP* 8,275
SIC 4899 Communication signal enhancement network system
Pr: Angel Ruiz
COO: Mark Leifer
CFO: Pavi Binning
CFO: Jan Frykhammer
CFO: Ben Harris
CFO: Timothy Lucie
CFO: Jan Ogren
CFO: Lindner Rick
CFO: Karl-Henrik Sundstrom
**CFO:* Hans Vestberg
Bd of Dir: Zibber Mohiuddin
Ex VP: Daniel Caruso
Ex VP: Magnus Mandersson
VP: Dennis C Connors
**VP:* John Moore
VP: Chris Ross
Exec: Erwin Leichtle
Exec: Mark Selfon
Dir Risk M: Susan Cox
Comm Dir: Bitopi D Chowdhury
Comm Dir: Borbla Szkely

D-U-N-S 07-402-1932
ERIE 1 BOARD OF COOPERATIVE EDUCATIONAL SERVICES
ERIE 1 BOCES
355 Harlem Rd, West Seneca, NY 14224-1825
Tel (716) 821-7000 *Founded/Ownrshp* 1965
Sales 89.7MM[E] *EMP* 1,300
SIC 8211 Public elementary & secondary schools
CEO: Lynn M Fusco
COO: David Brace
Treas: Doreen Kausner
Assoc Dir: Rosanne Huffcut
IT Man: Kay Beyea
IT Man: Robert Rossi
Netwrk Mgr: Lynn Reed
Netwrk Eng: Joseph Hejna

ERIE 1 BOCES
See ERIE 1 BOARD OF COOPERATIVE EDUCATIONAL SERVICES

D-U-N-S 60-633-8887
ERIE COMMUNITY COLLEGE
FSA OF ECC
(*Suby of* SUNY ADMINISTRATION) ★
121 Ellicott St, Buffalo, NY 14203-2601
Tel (716) 842-2770 *Founded/Ownrshp* 1946
Sales 30.9MM[E] *EMP* 1,400[E]
SIC 5942 8222 College book stores; Community college

ERIE COUNTY
See COUNTY OF ERIE

ERIE COUNTY COURTHOUSE
See COUNTY OF ERIE

D-U-N-S 01-829-9651
ERIE COUNTY INVESTMENT CO
ARBY'S
601 Corporate Cir, Golden, CO 80401-5607
Tel (303) 384-0200 *Founded/Ownrshp* 1899
Sales 41.8MM[E] *EMP* 1,400
SIC 5812 6794 6531 6552 1542 1521 Fast-food restaurant, chain; Franchises, selling or licensing; Real estate managers; Subdividers & developers; Commercial & office building contractors; Single-family housing construction
Pr: David Bailey
**CFO:* William D Whitehurst
**VP:* Geoffrey R Bailey

D-U-N-S 87-919-6178
ERIE COUNTY MEDICAL CENTER CORP
ECMC
462 Grider St, Buffalo, NY 14215-3098
Tel (716) 898-3000 *Founded/Ownrshp* 2004
Sales 514.6MM *EMP* 3,300[E]
Accts Freedmaxick Cpas Pc Buffal
SIC 8062 General medical & surgical hospitals
CEO: Jody L Lomeo
Dir Vol: Kathi Mitri
**COO:* Richard C Cleland
**CFO:* Steven Gary
**CFO:* Michael J Sammarco
Ofcr: Bryan Mayer
Top Exec: Nestor R Rigual
Sr VP: Susan Gonzalez
**Sr VP:* Ronald Krawiec
Sr VP: Thomas J Quatroche Jr
**Sr VP:* Karen Ziemianski
Dir Inf Cn: Kathleen Seibel

D-U-N-S 07-147-8119
ERIE COUNTY WATER AUTHORITY
295 Main St Rm 350, Buffalo, NY 14203-2494
Tel (716) 849-8484 *Founded/Ownrshp* 1949
Sales 136.3MM[E] *EMP* 271
Accts Lumsden & Mccormick Llp Buffa
SIC 4941 Water supply
Ch Bd: Francis G Warthling
**Treas:* John F O Donnell Jr
Treas: Acea Moseypawlowski
**Treas:* Jerome D Schad
**V Ch Bd:* Earl L Jann Jr
**Ex VP:* Robert F Gaylord
**Ex Dir:* Robert A Mendez
IT Man: Susan Rinaldo

D-U-N-S 06-068-2572
ERIE FAMILY LIFE INSURANCE CO INC (PA)
ERIE INSURANCE GROUP
(*Suby of* ERIE INSURANCE EXCHANGE ACTIVITIES ASSOCIATION INC) ★
100 Erie Insurance Pl, Erie, PA 16530-0001
Tel (814) 870-2000 *Founded/Ownrshp* 1967
Sales NA *EMP* 2,500
SIC 6331 Reciprocal interinsurance exchanges: fire, marine, casualty
Pr: Jeffrey A Ludrof
**Pr:* Terry Cavanaugh
**Treas:* Douglas F Ziegler
VP: Jay V Mauri
Board of Directors: Jeffrey A Ludrof, John T Baily, Robert C Wilburn, J Ralph Borneman Jr, Wilson C Cooney, Patricia Garrison-Corbin, John R Graham, Susan Hirt Hagen, C Scott Hartz, F William Hirt, Claude C Lilly III

ERIE INDEMNITY COMPANY
See ERIE INSURANCE GROUP EMPLOYEES

D-U-N-S 00-503-3741
ERIE INSURANCE EXCHANGE ACTIVITIES ASSOCIATION INC
100 Erie Insurance Pl, Erie, PA 16530-9000
Tel (800) 458-0811 *Founded/Ownrshp* 1925
Sales NA *EMP* 3,500
SIC 6331

ERIE INSURANCE GROUP
See ERIE FAMILY LIFE INSURANCE CO INC

D-U-N-S 05-909-1918
▲ ERIE INSURANCE GROUP EMPLOYEES
ERIE INDEMNITY COMPANY
100 Erie Insurance Pl, Erie, PA 16530-9000
Tel (814) 870-2000 *Founded/Ownrshp* 1925
Sales NA *EMP* 4,800[E]
Tkr Sym ERIE *Exch* NGS
SIC 6411 8741 Insurance agents, brokers & service; Property & casualty insurance agent; Management services
Pr: Timothy G Necastro
**Ch Bd:* Thomas B Hagen
CFO: Gregory Gutting
**V Ch Bd:* Jonathan Hirt Hagen
Ex VP: Robert C Ingram III
Ex VP: Sean J McLaughlin
Sr VP: Julie Pelkowski
VP: Scott Schnars
Board of Directors: Robert C Wilburn, J Ralph Borneman Jr, Luann Datesh, C Scott Hartz, Claude C Lilly III, George R Lucore, Thomas W Palmer, Martin P Sheffield, Richard L Stover, Elizabeth Hirt Vorsheck

D-U-N-S 00-453-6116
ERIE LAKE ELECTRIC INC (OH)
25730 1st St, Westlake, OH 44145-1432
Tel (440) 835-5565 *Founded/Ownrshp* 1952
Sales 153.2MM[E] *EMP* 525
SIC 1731 Electrical work
Pr: Peter J Corogin
**Sr VP:* Kenneth R Beck
**VP:* Armando Francisco
VP: John Kellamis
**Prin:* Linda L Bottegal
Off Mgr: Judy Sippola
Off Admin: Tracy Knowles
IT Man: Joe Pinter
IT Man: Timothy Smitley
Sfty Dirs: Ned Dooley

D-U-N-S 06-305-5511
ERIE MATERIALS INC (NY)
500 Factory Ave, Syracuse, NY 13208-1439
Tel (315) 455-7434 *Founded/Ownrshp* 1950, 1973
Sales 167.4MM[E] *EMP* 149
SIC 5033 5031 Roofing & siding materials; Millwork
Pr: Robert S Neumann
**Treas:* Michael J Shorney
**VP:* John Johnson
**VP:* Randy Moore
Opers Mgr: Chris Kittelson

ERIE SCIENTIFIC COMPANY
See ERIE SCIENTIFIC LLC

D-U-N-S 36-160-5223 IMP
■ ERIE SCIENTIFIC LLC
ERIE SCIENTIFIC COMPANY
(*Suby of* FISHER SCIENTIFIC INTERNATIONAL LLC) ★
20 Post Rd, Portsmouth, NH 03801-5622
Tel (603) 430-6859 *Founded/Ownrshp* 2006
Sales 150.3MM[E] *EMP* 1,167
SIC 3231 3821 3229 3221 3211 Products of purchased glass; Laboratory apparatus & furniture; Pressed & blown glass; Glass containers; Flat glass
Ex VP: Stephen K Wiatt
VP: Gary J Marmontello
Genl Mgr: Colm Geraghty

ERIE'S PUBLIC SCHOOL
See SCHOOL DISTRICT OF CITY OF ERIE

ERIEZ MAGNETICS
See ERIEZ MANUFACTURING CO

D-U-N-S 00-502-8089 IMP/EXP
ERIEZ MANUFACTURING CO (PA)
ERIEZ MAGNETICS
2200 Asbury Rd, Erie, PA 16506-1402
Tel (814) 835-6000 *Founded/Ownrshp* 1942
Sales 140.1MM *EMP* 980
SIC 3559 Separation equipment, magnetic
Pr: Timothy G Shuttleworth
**CFO:* Mark Mandel
**Treas:* Dennis L Salsbury
Treas: Joyce Versaw
Ex VP: Lukas Guenthardt
**VP:* Charlie Ingram
**VP:* Andy Lewis
**VP:* Mike Mankosa
CTO: Timothy Gland
Dir IT: Dan Ester
QC Dir: J Snyder
Board of Directors: Richard A Merwin

ERLANGER HEALTH SYSTEM
See HAMILTON CHATTANOOGA COUNTY HOSPITAL AUTHORITY

ERM
See ENVIRONMENTAL RESOURCES MANAGEMENT INC

D-U-N-S 07-937-1598
ERM NORTH AMERICA INC (PA)
(*Suby of* E R M) ★
75 Valley Stream Pkwy, Malvern, PA 19355-1459
Tel (484) 913-0300 *Founded/Ownrshp* 1993
Sales 202.9MM[E] *EMP* 785[E]
SIC 8748 Environmental consultant
Pr: John Stipa
Ex VP: John Alexander

D-U-N-S 09-371-8021
ERM-NA HOLDINGS CORP
E R M
(*Suby of* EAGLE 5 LIMITED)
75 Valley Stream Pkwy # 200, Malvern, PA 19355-1459
Tel (484) 913-0300 *Founded/Ownrshp* 2001
Sales 388.9MM *EMP* 1,573
Accts Kpmg Llp Philadelphia Pa
SIC 8711 8748 8742 Consulting engineer; Environmental consultant; Industry specialist consultants
CEO: David McArthur
**CFO:* John Stipa
Dir IT: Richard Brown
Sls Mgr: Melinda Stephens

D-U-N-S 14-470-9672
ERM-WEST INC
ENVIRONMENTAL RESOURCES MGT
(*Suby of* ERM NORTH AMERICA INC) ★
1277 Treat Blvd Ste 500, Walnut Creek, CA 94597-7989
Tel (925) 946-0455 *Founded/Ownrshp* 1984
Sales 120.9MM *EMP* 460
SIC 8711 8742 Consulting engineer; Management consulting services
Pr: Jonathan Beevers
Mng Pt: Paul Douglass
CFO: Josie Rosidi
Treas: Cindy Buitrago
**Sec:* Rita Harvey
Ofcr: Eric Graham
**VP:* John Kinsella
IT Man: Janice Davis
Mktg Mgr: Katie Garlewicz
Mktg Mgr: Orli Vanmourik
Snr Mgr: James Leist
Board of Directors: William Lorenz, Paul Woodruff

D-U-N-S 80-015-4437
ERMC II LP
1 Park Pl 6148, Chattanooga, TN 37421
Tel (423) 899-2753 *Founded/Ownrshp* 1998
Sales 318.6MM[E] *EMP* 3,900
SIC 7349 7382 Janitorial service, contract basis; Security systems services
Pt: Emerson Russell
Pr: Stephanie Hall
**Pr:* Eddie Russell
CFO: Tommy Kranz
VP: Hal Bowling
**VP:* Jeff Brewer
VP: Bill Capps
**VP:* Larry Dismukes
VP: Rodney Jackson
**VP:* Angela S Russell
**VP:* Kathryn Russell

D-U-N-S 07-870-6909
ERMC III PROPERTY MANAGEMENT CO LLC
6148 Lee Hwy Ste 300, Chattanooga, TN 37421-2941
Tel (423) 899-2753 *Founded/Ownrshp* 2007
Sales 46.4MM[E] *EMP* 5,000
SIC 7349 Janitorial service, contract basis
CEO: Emerson Russell
**Pr:* Eddie Russell

ERMCO
See ELECTRIC RESEARCH AND MANUFACTURING COOPERATIVE INC

D-U-N-S 00-681-1798
ERMCO INC
1625 W Thompson Rd, Indianapolis, IN 46217-9289
Tel (317) 780-2923 *Founded/Ownrshp* 1962
Sales 105.3MM[E] *EMP* 300
SIC 1731

D-U-N-S 07-860-4808 IMP
ERMENEGILDO ZEGNA CORP
ZEGNA SPORT
(*Suby of* LANIFICIO ERMENEGILDO ZEGNA E FIGLI SPA)
100 W Forest Ave Ste A, Englewood, NJ 07631-4033
Tel (201) 816-0921 *Founded/Ownrshp* 1975
Sales 86.7MM[E] *EMP* 220
SIC 5136 5611 Men's & boys' clothing; Men's & boys' clothing stores
Pr: Robert Ackerman
CFO: Carlo Cavalleri
**Treas:* John Haddad
Treas: Jennifer Mead
**VP:* Richard Wolf
Ex Dir: Djordje Stefanovic
Mng Dir: Ken Kress

D-U-N-S 14-477-7526 IMP
ERNEST HEALTH INC
7770 Jefferson St Ne # 320, Albuquerque, NM 87109-4386
Tel (505) 856-5300 *Founded/Ownrshp* 2003
Sales 175.1MM[E] *EMP* 3,800[E]
SIC 8069 Specialty hospitals, except psychiatric
Pr: Darby Brockette
COO: Claudia Saiz
CFO: Mark E Liebner
CFO: Mars P Patricio Jr
Ofcr: Paula Clymore
Sr VP: Tony Hernandez
VP: Danny Banks
VP: Kristi Duncan
VP: Denise Kann
Dir Case M: Corina Humphreys
Dir Rx: Amy Ross
Board of Directors: Denise Kann

ERNEST MARIO SCHOOL PHARMACY
See RUTGERS STATE UNIVERSITY

D-U-N-S 00-958-2271 IMP
ERNEST PACKAGING SOLUTIONS INC
ERNEST PAPER
5777 Smithway St, Commerce, CA 90040-1507
Tel (800) 233-7788 *Founded/Ownrshp* 1990
Sales 270.6MM[E] *EMP* 325
SIC 5113 5199 7389 Industrial & personal service paper; Shipping supplies; Packaging materials; Cosmetic kits, assembling & packaging
Ch Bd: Charles Wilson
**Pr:* Timothy Wilson

ERNEST PAPER
See ERNEST PACKAGING SOLUTIONS INC

D-U-N-S 03-231-3694 IMP
ERNIE GREEN INDUSTRIES INC
EG INDUSTRIES
2030 Dividend Dr, Columbus, OH 43228-3847
Tel (614) 219-1423 *Founded/Ownrshp* 1981
Sales 575.1MM[E] *EMP* 1,000
SIC 3714 3089 3471 3469 Motor vehicle wheels & parts; Motor vehicle body components & frame; Motor vehicle engines & parts; Motor vehicle transmissions, drive assemblies & parts; Injection molded finished plastic products; Automotive parts, plastic; Chromium plating of metals or formed products; Metal stampings
Pr: Ernie Green
**Ex VP:* Samuel Morgan

D-U-N-S 05-836-9562 IMP
ERNST & YOUNG LLP
5 Times Sq Fl Conlv1, New York, NY 10036-6530
Tel (212) 773-3000 *Founded/Ownrshp* 1894
Sales 6.1MMM[E] *EMP* 27,390
SIC 8721 Certified public accountant; Auditing services
Ch Bd: James Turley
Pt: Anthony K Anderson
Pt: David B Benjamin
Pt: Jeffrey C Bilek
Pt: Arend W Boterenbrood
Pt: Todd B Cameron
Pt: Victoria Cochrane
Pt: Marios Damianides
Pt: Dennis J Deutmeyer
Pt: Cynthia T Fletcher
Pt: Robert J Forbes
Pt: Robert D Foster
Pt: Aubie Goldenberg
Pt: Peter Griffith
Pt: Mark F Halliwell
Pt: Jim Hassett
Pt: Calliope B Henkel
Pt: David Heselton
Pt: Thomas A Hogenkamp
Pt: Steve Howe
Pt: Matthew C Howley

D-U-N-S 04-449-7691
ERNST ENTERPRISES INC
ERNST READY MIX DIVISION
3361 Successful Way, Dayton, OH 45414-4317
Tel (937) 233-5555 *Founded/Ownrshp* 1946
Sales 173.6MM[E] *EMP* 550
SIC 3273 Ready-mixed concrete
Pr: John C Ernst Jr
Bd of Dir: Adam Kress
**VP:* David Ernst
**Prin:* Bob Hines

ERNST READY MIX DIVISION
See ERNST ENTERPRISES INC

D-U-N-S 94-195-2335
ERP OPERATING LIMITED PARTNERSHIP
(*Suby of* EQUITY RESIDENTIAL) ★
2 N Riverside Plz Ste 400, Chicago, IL 60606-2624
Tel (312) 474-1300 *Founded/Ownrshp* 1993
Sales 2.7MMM *EMP* 3,500[E]
Accts Ernst & Young Llp Chicago I
SIC 6798 Real estate investment trusts
Pr: David J Neithercut
Genl Pt: Equity Residential
CFO: Mark J Parrell

ERS ROADS AND BRIDGES
See E R SNELL CONTRACTOR INC

D-U-N-S 61-298-6356
■ ERVIN CABLE CONSTRUCTION LLC
(*Suby of* DYCOM INDUSTRIES INC) ★
450 Pryor Blvd, Sturgis, KY 42459-7996
Tel (270) 333-3366 *Founded/Ownrshp* 1999
Sales 90.3MM[E] *EMP* 400
SIC 1623

D-U-N-S 00-533-7738 IMP/EXP
ERVIN INDUSTRIES INC
ERVIN INTERNATIONAL
3893 Research Park Dr, Ann Arbor, MI 48108-2267
Tel (734) 769-4600 *Founded/Ownrshp* 1920
Sales 116.8MM[E] *EMP* 400
SIC 3291 6159 Steel shot abrasive; Grit, steel; Machinery & equipment finance leasing
Pr: John E Pearson
CFO: Richard Conn
VP: Roger Nash
VP: James Pearson
VP: William L Rhodaberger
IT Man: Sharon Noffze
Netwrk Eng: Brian Kleinschmidt
VP Mfg: Ken Prior
VP Mfg: Kenneth R Prior
Plnt Mgr: Trent Pearson
Prd Mgr: Mark Dinius

ERVIN INTERNATIONAL
See ERVIN INDUSTRIES INC

D-U-N-S 04-836-9284
■ ERWIN-PENLAND INC
(*Suby of* HILL HOLLIDAY) ★
125 E Broad St Ste 300, Greenville, SC 29601-2834
Tel (864) 271-0500 *Founded/Ownrshp* 2004
Sales 98.0MM[E] *EMP* 380
SIC 7311 Advertising agencies
Sr VP: John Cornette

Sr VP: Curtis Rose
Sr VP: Kat Shafer
VP: Wesley Westenberg
Creative D: Mark Bazil
Creative D: Jimmy Collins
Creative D: Andy Mendelsohn
Creative D: Erwin Penland
IT Man: Bobby Gallagher
Web Dev: Lee Duran
Prd Mgr: Jamie Clark

ES&S
See ELECTION SYSTEMS & SOFTWARE LLC

D-U-N-S 08-365-1042
ES-O-EN CORP
TACO BELL
455 W Amity Rd, Meridian, ID 83642-6921
Tel (208) 888-6428 *Founded/Ownrshp* 1969
Sales 40.5MM^E *EMP* 1,310
SIC 5812 Fast-food restaurant, chain
Pr: S Carl Nicolaysen
COO: Dennis Meister
COO: Dennis Miester
**VP:* Duane Nicolaysen

D-U-N-S 83-101-5552
■ ESA 2007 OPERATING LESSEE LLC
(*Suby of* ESA MANAGEMENT LLC) ★
11525 N Cmnity Hse Rd R, Charlotte, NC 28277-3609
Tel (980) 345-1600 *Founded/Ownrshp* 2014
Sales 18.9MM^E *EMP* 2,000^E
SIC 7011 Hotels & motels
IT Man: Nancy Smith

ESA MANAGEMENT, LLC
See ESA MANAGEMENT LLC

D-U-N-S 07-920-9455
■ ESA MANAGEMENT LLC
ESA MANAGEMENT, LLC
(*Suby of* EXTENDED STAY AMERICA INC) ★
11525 N Community House R, Charlotte, NC 28277-3609
Tel (980) 345-1600 *Founded/Ownrshp* 2013
Sales 476.8MM^E *EMP* 9,300^E
SIC 8741 Hotel or motel management
Chf Mktg O: Tom Seddon
Ex VP: Mark Mahoney

D-U-N-S 13-041-8346 IMP/EXP
■ ESAB GROUP INC
ESAB WELDING & CUTTING PDTS
(*Suby of* COLFAX CORP) ★
2800 Airport Rd, Denton, TX 76207-2100
Tel (843) 669-4411 *Founded/Ownrshp* 1984
Sales 217.9MM^E *EMP* 400^E
SIC 3548 2899 Welding apparatus; Electrodes, electric welding; Fluxes: brazing, soldering, galvanizing & welding
VP: Michael Castner
**Founder:* Oscar Kjellberg
Sr VP: Dick Powell
IT Man: Glen Langston
VP Sls: Jerry Gleisner

ESAB WELDING & CUTTING PDTS
See ESAB GROUP INC

ESASD
See EAST STROUDSBURG AREA SCHOOL DISTRICT

ESC
See ECK SUPPLY CO

D-U-N-S 83-326-1378 IMP
ESCADA US SUBCO LLC
26 Main St, Chatham, NJ 07928-2425
Tel (212) 852-5300 *Founded/Ownrshp* 2009
Sales 213.9MM^E *EMP* 1,000
SIC 5137 5621 5632 5099 Sportswear, women's & children's; Women's sportswear; Handbags; Luggage
CEO: Anthony Lucia
Pr: Richard Gonzalez
CEO: Nancy Creaturo
COO: Beate Rapp
CFO: Markus Schurholz
Sr VP: Suzanne Humbert
Sr VP: Kimberly Jetnil
Dir: John Wilson
Genl Mgr: Jennifer Bailey
Genl Mgr: Ann Wallace
Sales Exec: Julie Boucherit

D-U-N-S 11-147-6313
ESCAL INSTITUTE OF ADVANCED TECHNOLOGIES INC
SANS INSTITUTE
8120 Woodmont Ave Ste 310, Bethesda, MD 20814-2743
Tel (301) 951-0102 *Founded/Ownrshp* 1995
Sales 132.4MM^E *EMP* 80
SIC 8732 Educational research
Pr: Alan Paller
**Prin:* Moe Aye
Mng Dir: Scott Cassity
Genl Mgr: Nimar Maung
IT Man: Tin Aye
Opers Mgr: Jackie Houston
Sls Mgr: Jay Armstrong

D-U-N-S 05-831-2877
▲ ESCALADE INC
817 Maxwell Ave, Evansville, IN 47711-3847
Tel (812) 467-4449 *Founded/Ownrshp* 1922
Sales 155.5MM *EMP* 522^E
Tkr Sym ESCA *Exch* NGM
SIC 3949 3579 Sporting & athletic goods; Ping-pong tables; Billiard & pool equipment & supplies, general; Basketball equipment & supplies, general; Paper cutters, trimmers & punches; Collating machines for store & office use; Perforators (office machines)
Pr: David L Fetherman
**Ch Bd:* Richard D White
CFO: Stephen R Wawrin
**VP:* Patrick J Griffin
Sls Mgr: Brad Elpers
Board of Directors: Richard F Baalmann Jr, Walter P Glazer Jr, George Savitsky, Edward E Williams

ESCALADE SPORTS
See INDIAN INDUSTRIES INC

D-U-N-S 07-261-2120
ESCAMBIA COUNTY SCHOOL BOARD
75 N Pace Blvd, Pensacola, FL 32505-7965
Tel (850) 432-6121 *Founded/Ownrshp* 1900
Sales 137.5MM^E *EMP* 6,000
SIC 8211 Public elementary & secondary schools
Psych: Holly Busse
Psych: Amy Engesser

D-U-N-S 80-897-3353
ESCAMBIA COUNTY SCHOOL DISTRICT
DISTRICT SCHOOL ESCAMBIA CNTY
75 N Pace Blvd, Pensacola, FL 32505-7965
Tel (850) 432-6121 *Founded/Ownrshp* 2008
Sales 321.7MM^E *EMP* 5,000
SIC 8211 Public elementary & secondary schools
Dir Sec: Jennifer Ellis
Area Mgr: Donna Burks
Area Mgr: Anitta Nordstrom
Teacher Pr: Keith Leonard
Instr Medi: Sheila Brandt
HC Dir: Martha Hanna

ESCAMBIA COUNTY UTILITIES AUTH
See EMERALD COAST UTILITIES AUTHORITY

D-U-N-S 03-017-9782
ESCANABA PAPER CO
7100 County Rd 426, Escanaba, MI 49829
Tel (906) 786-1660 *Founded/Ownrshp* 2005
Sales NA *EMP* 1,200
SIC 2611 2621 2672

D-U-N-S 00-902-8259 IMP/EXP
ESCO CORP
2141 Nw 25th Ave, Portland, OR 97210-2597
Tel (360) 690-0074 *Founded/Ownrshp* 1988
Sales 1.5MMM^E *EMP* 5,200
SIC 3535 3545 3325 3531 Conveyors & conveying equipment; Machine tool accessories; Steel foundries; Draglines, powered; Scrapers, graders, rollers & similar equipment
Pr: Calvin W Collins
**Pr:* Jon Owens
**CFO:* Ray Verlinich
**Ch:* Steven Pratt
Treas: Betty Abel
Treas: Michael Fortwengler
**Sr VP:* Eric Blackburn
**Sr VP:* Nick Blauwiekel
**Sr VP:* Kevin Thomas
VP: Rob Cornilles
VP: Bradley Hahn
VP: John Henningsen
VP: Elizabeth King
VP: Doug Macgowan
VP: Mike Tanner
Dir Risk M: Cheryl Arpan
Comm Dir: Kelley Egre

D-U-N-S 00-610-1229
ESCO MARINE INC
16200 Jose Garza Rd, Brownsville, TX 78521-9207
Tel (956) 554-5300 *Founded/Ownrshp* 1996
Sales 89.1MM^E *EMP* 530
Accts Kpmg Llp
SIC 4499 5093 7389 Marine dismantling & scrapping services; Metal scrap & waste materials; Metal cutting services
Pr: Richard Jaross
**Ch Bd:* Andrew Levy
**CEO:* Keith Rhodes
**VP:* Tim Bernstein
**VP:* Joshua Greenberg
**VP:* Kris Wood

D-U-N-S 07-927-7144
■ ESCO TECHNOLOGIES HOLDING LLC
(*Suby of* ESCO TECHNOLOGIES INC) ★
9900 Clayton Rd Ste A, Saint Louis, MO 63124-1186
Tel (314) 213-7200 *Founded/Ownrshp* 2012
Sales 120.3MM^E *EMP* 620^E
SIC 3825 3492 3812 3711 3663 Radar testing instruments, electric; Fluid power valves & hose fittings; Radar systems & equipment; Military motor vehicle assembly; Microwave communication equipment

D-U-N-S 61-895-7153
▲ ESCO TECHNOLOGIES INC
9900 Clayton Rd Ste A, Saint Louis, MO 63124-1186
Tel (314) 213-7200 *Founded/Ownrshp* 1990
Sales 571.4MM *EMP* 2,323
Accts Kpmg Llp St Louis Missouri
Tkr Sym ESE *Exch* NYS
SIC 3669 3569 3825 Intercommunication systems, electric; Filters; Radar testing instruments, electric; Test equipment for electronic & electrical circuits
Ch Bd: Victor L Richey
COO: Charles Kretschmer
CFO: Gary E Muenster
Sr VP: Alyson S Barclay
VP: Richard Garretson
Exec: Elizabeth Hughes
Counsel: Michael Cooney
Counsel: Jeffrey Fisher

D-U-N-S 07-336-8284
ESCONDIDO UNION SCHOOL DISTRICT
EUSD
2310 Aldergrove Ave, Escondido, CA 92029-1935
Tel (760) 432-2400 *Founded/Ownrshp* 1890
Sales 181.0MM *EMP* 1,925
Accts Wilkinson Hadley King & Co Ll
SIC 8211 Public elementary & secondary schools
VP: Zesty Harper
Psych: Lauren Berliner
HC Dir: Narciso Iglesias
Board of Directors: John F Laing, Kathy Marler, Linda Woods, Mark Wyland

D-U-N-S 01-433-0174 EXP
ESD WASTE2WATER INC (FL)
495 Oak Rd, Ocala, FL 34472-3005
Tel (800) 277-3279 *Founded/Ownrshp* 1993
Sales 115.3MM *EMP* 85
SIC 3589 Water treatment equipment, industrial
Pr: Jon E Houchens
Pr: Ed Tierney
Genl Mgr: Kevin Hawkins
Genl Mgr: Gary Palmeri

ESG
See ENERGY SYSTEMS GROUP LLC

D-U-N-S 07-835-6001
■ ESH HOSPITALITY INC
(*Suby of* EXTENDED STAY AMERICA INC) ★
11525 N Community Hse Rd, Charlotte, NC 28277-3609
Tel (980) 345-1600 *Founded/Ownrshp* 2010
Sales 1.0MMM *EMP* 10,400
SIC 6798 Real estate investment trusts
Ch Bd: Douglas G Geoga
**CEO:* James L Donald
**CFO:* Peter J Crage
**Ofcr:* Ross W McCanless
**Prin:* Chris Daniello
**Prin:* Kevin Dinnie
**Prin:* Lisa Palmer
**Prin:* Ty Wallach
**Prin:* Richard F Wallman
Board of Directors: Chris Daniello, Kevin Dinnie, Lisa Palmer, Ty Wallach, Richard F Wallman

ESI
See ENVIROSOLUTIONS INC

ESI CONSTRUCTION
See ENGINEERED STRUCTURES INC

D-U-N-S 16-721-2823
ESI ENERGY LLC
700 Universe Blvd, Juno Beach, FL 33408-2657
Tel (561) 691-7171 *Founded/Ownrshp* 1999
Sales 131.5MM^E *EMP* 77
SIC 4911 Electric services
Pr: James L Robo
**Treas:* Paul I Cutler
**VP:* F Mitchell Davidson
**VP:* Dean R Gosselin
**VP:* James A Keener
**VP:* Michael L Leighton
**VP:* Charles J Muoio
**VP:* Michael O'Sullivan
VP: Michael Osullivan
**VP:* Mark R Sorensen

D-U-N-S 05-644-7618
ESIS INC (PA)
CHUBB
436 Walnut St, Philadelphia, PA 19106-3703
Tel (215) 640-1000 *Founded/Ownrshp* 1953, 2002
Sales NA *EMP* 162
SIC 6411 Advisory services, insurance
CEO: Joe Vasquez
**Pr:* David Patterson
**CFO:* Brian O'Hara
Ex VP: Ellen Townsend
Sr VP: Lee W Farrow
Sr VP: Michael J Hoberman
Sr VP: Michael R Richardson
**VP:* Ray Hafner
**VP:* Paul Holden
VP: David Landrum
VP: Robin M Mountain
VP: Gerald Rojewski
**VP:* Sharon E Simpson
VP: Frank Westfall

D-U-N-S 11-908-6551
ESKATON
5105 Manzanita Ave Ste D, Carmichael, CA 95608-0523
Tel (916) 334-0296 *Founded/Ownrshp* 1968
Sales 1.4MM *EMP* 1,400
Accts Moss Adams Llp Stockton Ca
SIC 6512 8051 Commercial & industrial building operation; Convalescent home with continuous nursing care
CEO: Todd Murch
**COO:* Trevor Hammond
CFO: Bill Pace
**CFO:* William Pace
VP: Kim Rhinehelder
Ex Dir: Theresa Harrison
Ex Dir: Suzanne Olson
Off Mgr: Elisabeth M Koester
Off Mgr: Donna Medina
CIO: Jere Fass
Sfty Mgr: Kenneth J Fisher

D-U-N-S 62-150-6310 IMP
ESKATON PROPERTIES INC
OEPI
5105 Manzanita Ave Ste A, Carmichael, CA 95608-0523
Tel (916) 334-0810 *Founded/Ownrshp* 1983
Sales 90.6MM *EMP* 1,400
Accts Moss Adams Llp Stockton Ca
SIC 8361 Home for the aged
Pr: Todd Murch
**Sr VP:* Betsy Donovan
**Sr VP:* Bill Pace
**Sr VP:* Sheri Peifer
**VP:* Charles Garcia
Genl Mgr: Cindy Powell
Mktg Dir: Jill Baughman

D-U-N-S 07-928-5791
ESKENAZI HEALTH CENTER INC
720 Eskenazi Ave Fl 2, Indianapolis, IN 46202-5189
Tel (317) 880-0000 *Founded/Ownrshp* 2012
Sales 28.8MM^E *EMP* 2,000
SIC 8062 8093 8099 General medical & surgical hospitals; Mental health clinic, outpatient; Blood related health services
Pr: Ellen Hawkins
**CEO:* Mark A Bustamante
**CEO:* Matthew Gutwein
Assoc VP: Julie Szempruch
VP: Jessica Barth
VP: Michelle O'Keefe
Assoc Dir: John Reynolds
Assoc Dir: Anita Sears
Assoc Dir: Kevin Swing
Dir Rx: Christopher Scott
Comm Man: Allison Hoyt

D-U-N-S 79-768-7717 IMP
■ ESKO-GRAPHICS INC
ESKOARTWORK
(*Suby of* ESKO-GRAPHICS BVBA)
8535 Gander Creek Dr, Miamisburg, OH 45342-5436
Tel (937) 454-1721 *Founded/Ownrshp* 2011
Sales 119.3MM^E *EMP* 250
SIC 5084 7372 Printing trades machinery, equipment & supplies; Prepackaged software
CEO: Kurt Demeuleneere
**Pr:* Mark Quinlan
**Pr:* Tony Wiley
**CFO:* Frank McFaden
**VP:* Gary Evers
VP: Ian Hole
VP: Guy Puyvelde
Opers Mgr: Joe Cross
Mktg Mgr: Marcos Cardinale
Sls Mgr: Ron Larry

ESKOARTWORK
See ESKO-GRAPHICS INC

D-U-N-S 07-969-7397
ESL FEDERAL CREDIT UNION
225 Chestnut St, Rochester, NY 14604-2426
Tel (585) 336-1000 *Founded/Ownrshp* 1920
Sales NA *EMP* 560
SIC 6061 Federal credit unions
Pr: D L Fiedler
CFO: Jim Darcy
CFO: Walter F Rufnak
Sr VP: Faheem A R Masood
VP: Donald Aldred
VP: Cynthia Flannigan
VP: Ted Heinrich
Brnch Mgr: Linda Dove
Brnch Mgr: Debbie Hoffman
Brnch Mgr: Kris Prince
IT Man: Lou Fracassi

ESMARK
See SEVERSTAL US HOLDINGS II INC

D-U-N-S 01-350-3010
ESMARK INC
100 Hazel Ln Ste 300, Sewickley, PA 15143-1249
Tel (412) 259-8868 *Founded/Ownrshp* 2008
Sales 205.8MM^E *EMP* 350^E
SIC 1382 3324 Oil & gas exploration services; Steel investment foundries
CEO: James P Bouchard
**Pr:* J Gregory Pilewicz
**CFO:* Karl F Csensich
CFO: Brian Dettmann
**Treas:* Michael P Diclemente
**Ex VP:* Stephen W Powers

D-U-N-S 96-269-1544
ESMARK STEEL GROUP LLC
2500 Euclid Ave, Chicago Heights, IL 60411-4019
Tel (708) 756-0400 *Founded/Ownrshp* 2009
Sales 141.7MM^E *EMP* 340^E
SIC 5051 Sheets, metal
CEO: John Godwin
Pr: Peter Doyle
Ex VP: Mark Schwertner

D-U-N-S 60-299-0129
■ ESOTERIX GENETIC LABORATORIES LLC
INTEGRATED GENETICS
(*Suby of* LABORATORY CORP OF AMERICA HOLDINGS) ★
3400 Computer Dr, Westborough, MA 01581-1771
Tel (508) 389-6650 *Founded/Ownrshp* 2010
Sales 52.3MM^E *EMP* 1,886^E
SIC 8731 2835 8071 Commercial physical research; In vitro & in vivo diagnostic substances; Testing laboratories
Sr VP: Michael F Minahan
Dir Lab: Jin-Chen C Wang
IT Man: Michael Minahan

D-U-N-S 00-522-4402
ESPARZA ENTERPRISES INC
3851 Fruitvale Ave Ste A, Bakersfield, CA 93308-5111
Tel (661) 831-0002 *Founded/Ownrshp* 1999
Sales 56.6MM^E *EMP* 2,400^E
SIC 7361 7363 Labor contractors (employment agency); Help supply services
Pr: Luis Esparza

D-U-N-S 61-726-4288
■ ESPN HOLDING CO INC
(*Suby of* ABC HOLDING CO INC) ★
77 W 66th St, New York, NY 10023-6201
Tel (212) 916-9200 *Founded/Ownrshp* 1985
Sales 570.5MM^E *EMP* 1,507
SIC 4841 Cable television services
CEO: Robert A Iger

D-U-N-S 09-207-7171 EXP
■ ESPN INC
(*Suby of* ESPN HOLDING CO INC) ★
Espn Plz, Bristol, CT 06010
Tel (860) 766-2000 *Founded/Ownrshp* 1985
Sales 570.5MM^E *EMP* 1,250
SIC 4841 4832 Cable television services; Radio broadcasting stations
Ch Bd: John D Skipper
**CEO:* Pittsburgh Penguins
**CFO:* Christine F Driessen
Ex VP: Justin Connolly
Ex VP: Edwin M Durso
Ex VP: Eric Johnson
Ex VP: Aaron Laberge
Ex VP: Jodi Markley
Ex VP: John Wildhack
Sr VP: Marie Donoghue
Sr VP: Norby Williamson
Sr VP: Russell Wolff
Sr VP: Wanda Young

D-U-N-S 80-804-0971
■ ESPN PRODUCTIONS INC
(Suby of ESPN INC) ★
545 Middle St, Bristol, CT 06010-8413
Tel (860) 766-2000 Founded/Ownrshp 1994
Sales 365.9MM[E] EMP 1,250[E]
SIC 4833 Television broadcasting stations
Pr: George Bodenheimer
*Treas: Anne L Buettner
*Ex VP: Edwin M Durso
*VP: Griffith W Foxley
VP: Gary Perrelli
Exec: Sara Held
IT Man: Neila Witter

D-U-N-S 01-460-6946
ESQUIRE DEPOSITION SERVICES LLC (GA)
2700 Centennial Twr, Atlanta, GA 30303
Tel (404) 495-0777 Founded/Ownrshp 1997, 2001
Sales 99.6MM[E] EMP 600
SIC 7338 Court reporting service
Pr: Tony Vaglica
COO: Terrie Campbell
*CFO: Lisa Passero
VP: Keith Brenda
VP: Perry Solomon
Genl Mgr: Michelle Dennison
Genl Mgr: Sandra Humenny
Genl Mgr: Sara McDonald
CIO: Jim Ballowe
Web Dev: Matthew De Mello
VP Sls: Gina Carlson

ESRI
See ENVIRONMENTAL SYSTEMS RESEARCH INSTITUTE INC

D-U-N-S 07-999-3421
ESSAR PROJECTS (USA) LLC
(Suby of ESSAR GLOBAL FUND LIMITED)
555 W 27th St, Hibbing, MN 55746-2050
Tel (218) 263-3331 Founded/Ownrshp 2012
Sales 500.0MM EMP 60
SIC 1542 Commercial & office building, new construction
Ex Dir: Steve Rutherford
CFO: Narasimhan Ramakrishnan
VP: Ravi Muthreja

D-U-N-S 01-710-8929 IMP
ESSELTE HOLDINGS INC
48 S Service Rd Ste 400, Melville, NY 11747-2335
Tel (631) 675-5700 Founded/Ownrshp 1989
Sales NA EMP 13,125
SIC 2675 2782 3579 2672 3953 3596

D-U-N-S 00-798-1038 IMP/EXP
■ ESSENDANT CO (IL)
MICROUNITED DIVISION
(Suby of ESSENDANT INC) ★
1 Parkway North Blvd # 100, Deerfield, IL 60015-2554
Tel (847) 627-7000 Founded/Ownrshp 1922, 1981
Sales 4.1MMM[E] EMP 5,000
SIC 5112 Stationery & office supplies; Office supplies
Ch Bd: Charles Crovitz
*Sr VP: Ronald Berg
Sr VP: Patrick T Collins
*Sr VP: Brian Cooper
*Sr VP: Kathleen Dvorak
*Sr VP: James Fahey
*Sr VP: Deidra Gold
*Sr VP: Mark Hampton
Sr VP: Joseph R Templet
VP: Laura Gale
*VP: Robert J Kelderhouse
*VP: Barbara Kennedy
*VP: Fareed Khan
*VP: Kenneth M Nickel
VP: Paul Rickerhauser

D-U-N-S 01-897-8783 IMP/EXP
▲ ESSENDANT INC
1 Parkway North Blvd # 100, Deerfield, IL 60015-2554
Tel (847) 627-7000 Founded/Ownrshp 1922
Sales 5.3MMM EMP 6,400
Tkr Sym ESND Exch NGS
SIC 5112 5111 5021 5044 5087 5045 Stationery & office supplies; Business forms; Writing instruments & supplies; Office filing supplies; Printing & writing paper; Desks; Filing units; Office & public building furniture; Office equipment; Janitors' supplies; Computer peripheral equipment; Disk drives; Computers & accessories, personal & home entertainment
Pr: Robert B Aiken Jr
*Ch Bd: Charles K Crovitz
Pr: Richard D Phillips
COO: Timothy P Connolly
CFO: Jean Blackwell
CFO: Earl Shanks
CFO: Earl C Shanks
Ofcr: Girisha Chandraraj
Ofcr: Carole Tomko
Sr VP: Eric A Blanchard
Sr VP: Janet Zelenka
Dir Risk M: John Constabileo

D-U-N-S 14-684-3169
■ ESSENDANT MANAGEMENT SERVICES LLC
(Suby of ESSENDANT INC) ★
1 Parkway N Ste 100, Deerfield, IL 60015-2559
Tel (847) 627-7000 Founded/Ownrshp 2001
Sales 226.2MM[E] EMP 270[E]
SIC 5943 7373 Office forms & supplies; Computer-aided design (CAD) systems service
Pr: Dave Bent

ESSENT HEALTHCARE
See REGIONAL CARE HOSPITAL PARTNERS INC

D-U-N-S 86-958-6599
ESSENT PRMC LP
PARIS REGIONAL MEDICAL CENTER
865 Deshong Dr, Paris, TX 75460-9313
Tel (903) 785-9082 Founded/Ownrshp 1916
Sales 93.7MM[E] EMP 750[E]
SIC 8062 General medical & surgical hospitals
CEO: Bill Porter
*CEO: Stephen Grubbs
*COO: Patti Monczewski
Exec: Cheryl Perry
Software D: Boris Chavis

ESSENTIA HEALTH
See SMDC MEDICAL CENTER

ESSENTIA HEALTH
See ST MARYS MEDICAL CENTER

ESSENTIA HEALTH
See INNOVIS HEALTH LLC

D-U-N-S 61-904-2760
ESSENTIA HEALTH
502 E 2nd St, Duluth, MN 55805-1913
Tel (218) 786-8376 Founded/Ownrshp 2003
Sales 131.7MM EMP 18,177
Accts Ernst & Young Us Llp Columbus
SIC 8062 8051 Hospital management
CEO: Peter Person
COO: Laura Ackman
COO: John C Smylie
Treas: Bert Norman
Ofcr: Teresa Toole
Ex VP: Teresa O'Toole
VP: Vicki Clevenger
VP: Thomas Crook
VP: Sheila Hart
VP: Mark Hayward
VP: Michael J Mahoney
VP: Ann Malmberg
VP: Steven Mattson
VP: Traci Morris
VP: Kristi Schmidt
VP: Ann Watkins
VP: Rebecca Watkins
VP: Kim Wolf
Dir Rx: Dianne Witten

D-U-N-S 07-149-9628
ESSENTIA HEALTH LLC
(Suby of ESSENTIA HEALTH) ★
1702 University Dr S, Fargo, ND 58103-4940
Tel (701) 364-8900 Founded/Ownrshp 2008
Sales 228.7MM[E] EMP 2,000
SIC 8011 Clinic, operated by physicians
CEO: Greg Glasner
*CEO: Peter Person
*COO: Kevin Pitzer
*COO: John Smylie
*CFO: Bert Norman
Chf Mktg O: Timothy J Mahoney
Exec: Jan Bexell-Gierke
Exec: Terry Burrell
Exec: Crystal Cossette
Exec: Ali Khan
Exec: Scott Mutchler
Dir OR: Racehl Boyer
Dir Lab: Shirlene Nitzel
Dir Lab: Greig Schuer

ESSENTIA HLTH ST JSPHS MED CTR
See ST JOSEPHS MEDICAL CENTER

ESSENTIAL ENTERPRISE SOLUTIONS
See ESSINTIAL ENTERPRISE SOLUTIONS LLC

D-U-N-S 12-380-5595
■ ESSENTIAL POWER NEWINGTON ENERGY LLC
(Suby of CONSOLIDATED EDISON INC) ★
200 Shattuck Way, Newington, NH 03801-7869
Tel (603) 766-1880 Founded/Ownrshp 1996
Sales 121.8MM[E] EMP 120
SIC 4911
Pr: Tom Rainwater
Pr: Lisa Krueger
VP: John Bahrs
VP: Steven Birchfield
VP: Timothy Pearce
VP: David Rosenstein
VP: Jeffery Spencer
VP: Rick White

D-U-N-S 00-518-1623 IMP
ESSENTRA COMPONENTS INC
(Suby of ESSENTRA PLC)
7400 Industrial Dr, Forest Park, IL 60130-2536
Tel (773) 539-4060 Founded/Ownrshp 1955, 2011
Sales 83.4MM[E] EMP 500
SIC 3089

D-U-N-S 17-760-2927 IMP
ESSENTRA HOLDINGS CORP
(Suby of ESSENTRA PLC)
1625 Ashton Park Dr Ste A, South Chesterfield, VA 23834-5908
Tel (804) 518-0322 Founded/Ownrshp 1997
Sales 248.7MM[E] EMP 1,200
SIC 3081 3082 3999 3951 2823 Unsupported plastics film & sheet; Unsupported plastics profile shapes; Cigarette filters; Pens & mechanical pencils; Cigarette tow, cellulosic fiber
Pr: Russell P Rogers
IT Man: Greg Bartlett
VP Opers: Walter Adams
Manager: Susan Cranford

ESSENTRA MOORESTOWN
See CLONDALKIN PHARMA & HEALTHCARE LLC

D-U-N-S 00-312-1324 IMP
ESSENTRA POROUS TECHNOLOGIES CORP
ALLIANCE PLASTICS
(Suby of ESSENTRA HOLDINGS CORP) ★
1625 Ashton Park Dr Ste A, South Chesterfield, VA 23834-5908
Tel (804) 524-4983 Founded/Ownrshp 2009
Sales 156.6MM[E] EMP 350
SIC 3081 3951 3082 2823 3999 Unsupported plastics film & sheet; Pens & mechanical pencils; Unsupported plastics profile shapes; Cigarette tow, cellulosic fiber; Cigarette filters
Pr: Russell P Rogers
Ex VP: Jeff Green
VP: Jeff Shugart
Exec: Julie Hill
Div/Sub He: Randall Hagan
Mng Dir: Matthew Taylor
CTO: Greg Bartlett
Board of Directors: Don Nelson

D-U-N-S 07-877-6430
ESSEX BROKERAGE
57 Center Church Rd, Grove City, PA 16127-3417
Tel (724) 748-3126 Founded/Ownrshp 2003
Sales 3.3MMM EMP 1
SIC 4731 Brokers, shipping

ESSEX COUNTY HOSPITAL CENTER
See COUNTY OF ESSEX

D-U-N-S 08-061-7335
ESSEX COUNTY WELFARE BOARD INC (NJ)
18 Rector St Ste 9, Newark, NJ 07102-4585
Tel (973) 733-3326 Founded/Ownrshp 1935
Sales 13.7MM[E] EMP 1,000
SIC 8322 8399 Aid to families with dependent children (AFDC); Association for the handicapped; Senior citizens' center or association; Refugee service; Health & welfare council
Pr: Bruce Nigro

D-U-N-S 00-506-8952 IMP
ESSEX GROUP INC (MI)
SUPERIOR ESSEX
(Suby of SUPERIOR ESSEX INC) ★
1601 Wall St, Fort Wayne, IN 46802-4352
Tel (260) 461-4000 Founded/Ownrshp 1930, 2003
Sales 521.6MM[E] EMP 1,619
SIC 3357 Communication wire; Fiber optic cable (insulated)
Pr: Justin F Deedy Jr
*Pr: Stephen M Carter
*Ex VP: David S Aldridge
*Sr VP: Debbie Baker-Oliver
*Sr VP: Matt Odonnell
*Sr VP: Mary Love Sullenberger
Ex Dir: Douglas Pett
Prd Mgr: Rodney Arthur
Natl Sales: Stuart Karpy
Manager: Steve Strawn

D-U-N-S 14-824-4213
■ ESSEX INSURANCE CO
(Suby of MARKEL CORP) ★
4521 Highwoods Pkwy, Glen Allen, VA 23060-6148
Tel (804) 273-1400 Founded/Ownrshp 1980
Sales NA EMP 340
SIC 6331 Fire, marine & casualty insurance
Pr: W Bradley Dickler

D-U-N-S 96-464-8695
ESSEX PORTFOLIO LP
925 E Meadow Dr, Palo Alto, CA 94303-4299
Tel (650) 494-3700 Founded/Ownrshp 1994
Sales 1.1MMM EMP 869
Accts Kpmg Llp San Francisco Calif
SIC 6798 6513 Real estate investment trusts; Apartment building operators
Pr: Keith R Guericke
*Ch Bd: George M Marcus
Pr: Michael J Schall
CFO: Michael T Dance
Ex VP: John D Eudy
Ex VP: Craig K Zimmerman
Board of Directors: David W Brady, Robert E Larson, Gary P Martin, William A Millichap, Thomas E Randlett, Willard H Smith Jr

D-U-N-S 07-718-6500
ESSEX PROPERTY TRUST INC
1100 Park Pl Ste 200, San Mateo, CA 94403-7107
Tel (650) 655-7800 Founded/Ownrshp 1994
Sales 1.1MMM EMP 1,725[E]
Accts Kpmg Llp San Francisco Calif
SIC 6798 Real estate investment trusts
Pr: Michael J Schall
*Ch Bd: George M Marcus
CFO: Michael T Dance
*V Ch Bd: Keith R Guericke
Bd of Dir: Janice Sears
Ofcr: Barb Pak
Ex VP: John F Burkart
Ex VP: John F Burkart
Ex VP: John D Eudy
Ex VP: John D Euy
Ex VP: Craig K Zimmerman
Sr VP: John Burkart
VP: Casey Adams
VP: Gerald Bryan
VP: Gerald Kelly
VP: Donald Kinney
VP: Angela L Kleiman
VP: Bruce Knoblock
VP: Mark J Mikl
VP: Jo Ann Petrie
Board of Directors: Claude J Zinngrabe Jr, David W Brady, Irving F Lyons III, George M Marcus, Gary P Martin, Thomas E Randlett, Thomas E Robinson, Byron A Scordelis, Janice L Sears, Thomas P Sullivan

D-U-N-S 82-877-8824
ESSEX RENTAL CORP
1110 W Lake Cook Rd # 220, Buffalo Grove, IL 60089-1958
Tel (847) 215-6500 Founded/Ownrshp 2008
Sales 103.4MM EMP 260[E]
SIC 7353 5082 Cranes & aerial lift equipment, rental or leasing; Cranes, construction
Pr: Nicholas J Matthews
*Ch Bd: Laurence S Levy
CFO: Kory M Glen
Opers Mgr: Mike Munson
Sls Mgr: Chris Power

D-U-N-S 84-859-6362 EXP
ESSEX TECHNOLOGY GROUP INC
BARGAIN HUNT CORPORATE
455 Industrial Blvd Ste C, La Vergne, TN 37086-4196
Tel (615) 620-5444 Founded/Ownrshp 2000
Sales 115.9MM[E] EMP 130[E]
SIC 5045 8732 5261 Computers; Research services, except laboratory; Nurseries & garden centers
Ch Bd: Phil Pfeffer
*Pr: Robert Echols
CFO: David Aldridge
*VP: Eric Crawford
*VP: Don Gozzard
*VP: Gregg Whittaker
IT Man: Peter Adams
VP Opers: Gary Rossier
Sales Exec: Todd Pewitt

D-U-N-S 55-590-0927
ESSEX VALLEY HEALTHCARE INC
ESSEX VALLEY MEDICAL TRNSP SVC
300 Central Ave, East Orange, NJ 07018-2819
Tel (973) 672-8400 Founded/Ownrshp 1987
Sales 60.0MM[E] EMP 1,200
SIC 8741 Hospital management; Nursing & personal care facility management
Pr: Darlene Cox
*Ch Bd: George M Wallhauser
*CFO: Frank Andreola
Dir Pat Ac: Warren Miller

ESSEX VALLEY MEDICAL TRNSP SVC
See ESSEX VALLEY HEALTHCARE INC

D-U-N-S 87-792-3235 IMP
ESSICK AIR PRODUCTS INC
5800 Murray St, Little Rock, AR 72209-2543
Tel (501) 562-1094 Founded/Ownrshp 1978
Sales 92.9MM[E] EMP 400
SIC 3534 3585 3634 Elevators & equipment; Air conditioning equipment, complete; Electric household fans, heaters & humidifiers
Pr: Kim Stafford
*VP: Mark Ulrey
Brnch Mgr: Eric Harrawood
Netwrk Eng: Daniel Fraley
Ql Cn Mgr: Harry Moore
Natl Sales: Chad Long

D-U-N-S 06-411-4564 IMP/EXP
ESSILOR LABORATORIES OF AMERICA INC
DUFFENS OPTICAL
(Suby of OMEGA DALLAS) ★
13515 N Stemmons Fwy, Dallas, TX 75234-5765
Tel (972) 241-4141 Founded/Ownrshp 1996
Sales 631.6MM[E] EMP 3,032
SIC 3851 5048 Eyeglasses, lenses & frames; Contact lenses; Ophthalmic goods; Frames, ophthalmic; Lenses, ophthalmic
CEO: Hubert Sagni RES
*Pr: Weldon Lucas
Sr VP: Eric Javellaud
VP: R M Daley
VP: Herv De La Sayette
VP: Gerard Malledant
VP: Karen Unzueta
VP: John Walborn
Ex Dir: Audrey Reed
*VP Sls: William Clove
Mktg Dir: Traci Nelson

D-U-N-S 60-807-0900 IMP
ESSILOR OF AMERICA INC
OMEGA DALLAS
(Suby of ESSILOR INTERNATIONAL)
13555 N Stemmons Fwy, Dallas, TX 75234-5765
Tel (214) 496-4000 Founded/Ownrshp 1999
Sales 3.3MMM[E] EMP 8,700
SIC 3851 5048 Ophthalmic goods; Ophthalmic goods
Pr: John Carrier
*CFO: Kevin Rupp
Sr VP: Theresa Agnew
Sr VP: Daniel Liberman
*Sr VP: David Milan
VP: Rick Bannon
VP: Colin Clair
VP: Gregory Ericson
VP: Carl Joseph
VP: Jean Leroy
VP: Phil Miller
VP: James Schrick
VP: Marty Whalen
VP Bus Dev: Maria Barnwell
Exec: Lisa Scacco
Assoc Dir: Sheree E Rajan
Board of Directors: Philippe Alfroid, Claude Brignon, Bernard Hours, Hubert Sagnieres, Jacques Stoerr, Laurent Vacherot

D-U-N-S 83-155-3156
ESSINTIAL ENTERPRISE SOLUTIONS LLC
ESSENTIAL ENTERPRISE SOLUTIONS
100 Sterling Pkwy Ste 307, Mechanicsburg, PA 17050-2903
Tel (717) 610-3200 Founded/Ownrshp 2009
Sales 92.8MM[E] EMP 537
SIC 8742 Materials mgmt. (purchasing, handling, inventory) consultant
CEO: Tom York
COO: Matt Mannix
*CFO: Dale Drendall
CFO: Joseph Sciacca
*VP: Jennifer Currao
VP: Robert Drennen
*VP: Craig Heck
VP: Greg Lorenzen
VP: Doug Reece
VP: Joseph Rowley
VP: Arthur Whalen

D-U-N-S 00-238-9625 IMP/EXP
ESSROC CEMENT CORP
ITALCEMENTI GROUP
(Suby of ESSROC CORP) ★
3251 Bath Pike, Nazareth, PA 18064-8999
Tel (610) 837-6725 Founded/Ownrshp 1866
Sales 396.0MM[E] EMP 1,100
Accts Ernst & Young Llp Philadelphi
SIC 3241 Cement, hydraulic; Masonry cement; Portland cement
Pr: Silvio Panseri
*Treas: Kevin A Jones
*Sr VP: Craig Becker
*Sr VP: Alexander Car
*Sr VP: Glenn Dalrymple

D-U-N-S 60-448-0541 IMP/EXP
ESSROC CORP
(*Suby of* ITALCEMENTI FABBRICHE RIUNITE CEMENTO SPA BERGAMO)
3251 Bath Pike, Nazareth, PA 18064-8999
Tel (610) 837-6725 *Founded/Ownrshp* 1976
Sales 746.0MM[E] *EMP* 2,000
Accts Ernst & Young Llp Philadelphi
SIC 3241 5032 3273 Cement, hydraulic; Masonry cement; Portland cement; Cement; Ready-mixed concrete
Pr: Alex Car
**CFO:* Glenn R Dalrymple
**Treas:* Kevin A Jones
**Sr VP:* Craig C Becker
**Sr VP:* Roberto Fedi
**Sr VP:* Francois M Perrin
VP: Oliver Apruzzese
**VP:* Carol Lowry
VP: Gary Molchan
VP: James Russ
VP Sls: Anthony C Rudy

ESTAVE COTTON
See ECOM USA INC

ESTEE LAUDER
See ARAMIS INC

ESTEE LAUDER
See ORIGINS NATURAL RESOURCES INC

D-U-N-S 79-080-2086 IMP/EXP
▲ **ESTEE LAUDER COMPANIES INC**
767 5th Ave Fl 37, New York, NY 10153-0003
Tel (212) 572-4200 *Founded/Ownrshp* 1946
Sales 11.2MMM *EMP* 46,000
Accts Kpmg Llp New York New York
Tkr Sym EL *Exch* NYS
SIC 2844 Toilet preparations; Cosmetic preparations; Perfumes & colognes
Pr: Fabrizio Freda
Ch Bd: William P Lauder
Pr: John Demsey
Pr: Cedric Prouve
CFO: Tracey T Travis
Ex VP: Carl Haney
Ex VP: Sara E Moss
Ex VP: Michael O'Hare
Ex VP: Gregory F Polcer
Ex VP: Alexandra Ctrower
Sr VP: Barbara De Laere
Sr VP: Julie Van Ongevalle
VP: George H Eisenbach
Board of Directors: Richard F Zannino, Charlene Barshefsky, Rose Marie Bravo,wei Sun C, Lynn Forester De Rothschil, Paul J Fribourg, Irvine O Hockaday Jr, Jane Lauder, Leonard A Lauder, Ronald S Lauder, Richard D Parsons, Barry S Sternlicht

D-U-N-S 00-591-4387 IMP
■ **ESTEE LAUDER INC**
(*Suby of* ESTEE LAUDER COMPANIES INC) ★
767 5th Ave Fl 37, New York, NY 10153-0003
Tel (212) 572-4200 *Founded/Ownrshp* 1944
Sales 10.7MMM *EMP* 9,525
SIC 2844 5999 Toilet preparations; Cosmetic preparations; Perfumes & colognes; Toiletries, cosmetics & perfumes; Cosmetics; Perfumes & colognes
CEO: Freda Fabrizio
**Ch Bd:* Leonard A Lauder
**Pr:* John Demsey
**Pr:* Ed Straw
CFO: Malcolm Bond
**CFO:* Richard Kuens
**Ch:* William P Lauder
**Ex VP:* Amy Digeso
**Ex VP:* Carl Haney

D-U-N-S 93-394-7699 IMP
■ **ESTEE LAUDER INTERNATIONAL INC**
(*Suby of* ESTEE LAUDER INC) ★
767 5th Ave Bsmt 1, New York, NY 10153-0003
Tel (212) 572-4200 *Founded/Ownrshp* 1995
Sales 175.2MM[E] *EMP* 2,403
SIC 2844 Toilet preparations; Face creams or lotions; Lipsticks; Perfumes & colognes
Pr: Patrick Bousquet-Chavanne
Pr: Joel Bramble
CFO: Rick Kunes
Ex VP: Larry Berger
Ex VP: Nancy Castro
Ex VP: Amy Digeso
Ex VP: Michael Meyer
Ex VP: Sara Moss
Ex VP: Michael O'Hare
Ex VP: Gregory F Polcer
Ex VP: Sally Susman
Ex VP: Tracey T Travis
Ex VP: Alexandra Trower
VP: Sara Beaney
VP: Gerry Berg
VP: Andy Bevacqua
VP: Bill Borland
VP: Herve Bouix
VP: Kelly Brice
VP: Lisa Cappell
VP: Jamal Chamariq

ESTERLINE POWER SYSTEMS
See LEACH INTERNATIONAL CORP

D-U-N-S 04-319-0826 EXP
▲ **ESTERLINE TECHNOLOGIES CORP**
500 108th Ave Ne Ste 1500, Bellevue, WA 98004-5500
Tel (425) 453-9400 *Founded/Ownrshp* 1967
Sales 1.9MMM *EMP* 13,290
Tkr Sym ESL *Exch* NYS
SIC 3728 3812 3429 Aircraft assemblies, subassemblies & parts; Panel assembly (hydromatic propeller test stands), aircraft; Aircraft control instruments; Radar systems & equipment; Aircraft hardware
Ch Bd: Curtis C Reusser
Pr: Roger A Ross
Pr: Pierre Rossignol
Pr: Albert S Yost
CFO: Robert D George
Ofcr: Paul P Benson
VP: Andy Buchan
VP: Marcia J Mason
VP: Mike Mason
Mng Dir: Gary Kasten
VP Mfg: Daniel Luzi
Board of Directors: Michael J Cave, Delores M Etter, Anthony P Franceschini, Paul V Haack, Mary L Howell, Scott E Kuechle, Nils Larsen, James J Morris, Gary E Pruitt

D-U-N-S 00-278-0633
ESTES EXPRESS LINES INC
3901 W Broad St, Richmond, VA 23230-3962
Tel (804) 353-1900 *Founded/Ownrshp* 1931
Sales 2.3MMM *EMP* 14,000
SIC 4213 Less-than-truckload (LTL) transport
Pr: Robey W Estes Jr
COO: Billy Hupp
**Treas:* Gary D Okes
**Ex VP:* William T Hupp
VP: Al Bucher
VP: John Buffington
VP: Mike Campese
VP: Curtis Carr
VP: Bob Fowler
**VP:* Patricia A Garland
VP: Trish Garland
VP: Francis Glidewell
Dir Bus: Henry Brawley

D-U-N-S 79-094-3646
ESTRELLA BANNER MEDICAL CENTER
9201 W Thomas Rd, Phoenix, AZ 85037-3332
Tel (623) 327-4000 *Founded/Ownrshp* 2005
Sales 268.4MM *EMP* 1,400
SIC 8011 Medical centers
CEO: Deb Krmpotic
**CFO:* Patti Rhoden
Dir Inf Cn: Toni Lee
Dir Rx: John Placko
Nrsg Dir: Nancy Adamson
Nrsg Dir: Davey Ellison

D-U-N-S 60-989-2638
ESTRELLA BANNER SURGERY CENTER
(*Suby of* BANNER RESEARCH INSTITUTE) ★
9301 W Thomas Rd, Phoenix, AZ 85037-3327
Tel (623) 388-5700 *Founded/Ownrshp* 2004
Sales 42.2MM[E] *EMP* 1,029[E]
SIC 8062 General medical & surgical hospitals

D-U-N-S 00-521-2394 IMP
ESTWING MANUFACTURING CO INC
2647 8th St, Rockford, IL 61109-1190
Tel (815) 397-9521 *Founded/Ownrshp* 1923
Sales 101.7MM[E] *EMP* 500
SIC 3423 3546 3545 3429 3421 3425 Hammers (hand tools); Axes & hatchets; Garden & farm tools, including shovels; Power-driven handtools; Machine tool accessories; Manufactured hardware (general); Cutlery; Saw blades & handsaws
Pr: Robert H Youngren
**CFO:* Sharon L Phillips
**Treas:* Susan J Nunez
**VP:* John Ryan
**VP:* Mark Youngren
Ex Dir: Paul Gallant

ESURANCE INC.
See ESURANCE INSURANCE SERVICES INC

D-U-N-S 09-519-3236
■ **ESURANCE INSURANCE SERVICES INC**
ESURANCE INC.
(*Suby of* ALLSTATE CORP) ★
650 Davis St, San Francisco, CA 94111-1981
Tel (415) 875-4500 *Founded/Ownrshp* 2011
Sales NA *EMP* 140[E]
SIC 6411 Insurance agents, brokers & service
CEO: Gary C Tolman
**CFO:* Jonathan Adkisson
**Chf Mktg O:* Alan Gellman
**Ofcr:* Eric Brandt
Ofcr: Wayne Sharrah
VP: Nancy Abraham
**VP:* Kerian Bunch
VP: Melissa Eaton
VP: Jeff Huebbers
VP: Eric Madia
VP: Blair Rumbaugh

D-U-N-S 07-270-9231 IMP/EXP
ET BROWNE DRUG CO INC
PALMER'S COCOA BUTTER FORMULA
440 Sylvan Ave, Englewood Cliffs, NJ 07632-2727
Tel (201) 894-9020 *Founded/Ownrshp* 1840
Sales 94.9MM[E] *EMP* 220
SIC 2844 Cosmetic preparations; Face creams or lotions; Toilet preparations
Ch Bd: Arnold Hayward Neis
**Pr:* Robert Neis

D-U-N-S 00-209-5296 IMP
ET SOLAR INC (CA)
4900 Hopyard Rd Ste 310, Pleasanton, CA 94588-7100
Tel (925) 460-9898 *Founded/Ownrshp* 2007
Sales 84.8MM[E] *EMP* 20
SIC 1711 Solar energy contractor
CEO: Patrick Guo
**Pr:* Xinghua Wang
VP: Linhui Sui
Mktg Mgr: Leon Wang
Manager: Ricki Lee
Sls Mgr: May Khasem

D-U-N-S 00-661-9316
ETAS INC
(*Suby of* ETAS GMBH)
3021 Miller Rd, Ann Arbor, MI 48103-2122
Tel (734) 997-9393 *Founded/Ownrshp* 1997, 2003
Sales 126.3MM[E] *EMP* 650
SIC 5049 Engineers' equipment & supplies
Pr: Jeff Cason
Prgrm Mgr: Rose Ryan
Sls&Mrk Ex: Rod Line

ETC
See ENVIRONMENTAL TECTONICS CORP

D-U-N-S 08-002-7763
■ **ETC INTRASTATE PROCUREMENT CO LLC**
ENERGY TRANSFER COMPANY
(*Suby of* ENERGY TRANSFER EQUITY LP) ★
1300 Main St, Houston, TX 77002-6803
Tel (713) 989-2688 *Founded/Ownrshp* 2009
Sales 8.0MM[E] *EMP* 1,200
SIC 1311

ETCC
See ELECTRONIC TRANSACTION CONSULTANTS CORP

D-U-N-S 12-626-0319
ETECH GLOBAL SERVICES LLC
1903 Berry Dr, Nacogdoches, TX 75964-1206
Tel (936) 559-2200 *Founded/Ownrshp* 2010
Sales 183.2MM[E] *EMP* 2,500
SIC 7389 8742 7373 8741 8721 7374 Telemarketing services; Quality assurance consultant; Systems software development services; Management services; Accounting services, except auditing; Data processing & preparation
Pr: Matthew Rocco
Ch Bd: Dilip Barot
CFO: Ashok Kumar
Sr VP: Ronnie Mize
VP: Kaylene Eckels
VP: Patrick Reynolds
Sales Asso: Treshayla Wilson
Snr Mgr: Keyur Dave

ETHAN ALLEN GALLERY
See KITTLES HOME FURNISHINGS CENTER INC

D-U-N-S 60-594-0324
■ **ETHAN ALLEN GLOBAL INC**
(*Suby of* ETHAN ALLEN INTERIORS INC) ★
25 Lake Ave, Danbury, CT 06810-6338
Tel (203) 743-8000 *Founded/Ownrshp* 2005
Sales 655.1MM[E] *EMP* 4,290
SIC 5712 Furniture stores
Ch: M Farooq Kathwari
**Treas:* David R Callen
**VP:* Pamela A Banks
**VP:* Eric D Kostec

ETHAN ALLEN IMPORT DEPARTMENT
See ETHAN ALLEN OPERATIONS INC

D-U-N-S 60-250-3013 IMP/EXP
▲ **ETHAN ALLEN INTERIORS INC**
Ethan Allen Dr, Danbury, CT 06811
Tel (203) 743-8000 *Founded/Ownrshp* 1932
Sales 794.2MM *EMP* 5,200[E]
Accts Kpmg Llp
Tkr Sym ETH *Exch* NYS
SIC 2511 2512 5712 Wood household furniture; Wood bedroom furniture; Kitchen & dining room furniture; Bookcases, household: wood; Upholstered household furniture; Furniture stores
Ch Bd: M Farooq Kathwari
CFO: Corey Whitely
Sr VP: Daniel M Grow
VP: Eric D Koster
VP: Tracy Paccione
VP: Clifford Thorn
Board of Directors: James B Carlson, Clinton A Clark, John J Dooner Jr, Domenick J Esposito, Mary Garrett, James W Schmotter, Tara I Stacom

D-U-N-S 62-110-4301 IMP
■ **ETHAN ALLEN OPERATIONS INC**
ETHAN ALLEN IMPORT DEPARTMENT
(*Suby of* ETHAN ALLEN INTERIORS INC) ★
Ethan Allen Dr, Danbury, CT 06813
Tel (203) 743-8496 *Founded/Ownrshp* 1994
Sales 305.4MM[E] *EMP* 2,000
SIC 2511 Wood household furniture
Pr: Farooq M Kathwari
**VP:* Pamela A Banks
**VP:* David R Callen
**VP:* Jeffrey Hoyt
**VP:* Eric D Koster

D-U-N-S 00-121-3545 IMP/EXP
■ **ETHAN ALLEN RETAIL INC**
(*Suby of* ETHAN ALLEN INTERIORS INC) ★
Ethan Allen Dr, Danbury, CT 06811
Tel (203) 743-8000 *Founded/Ownrshp* 1989
Sales 649.0MM[E] *EMP* 4,250
SIC 5712 5719 5713 5231 2273 Furniture stores; Bedding (sheets, blankets, spreads & pillows); Lighting fixtures; Carpets; Rugs; Wallpaper; Carpets & rugs
Ch Bd: Farooq Kathwari
**Treas:* Geoffrey White
**Ex VP:* Ed Teplitz
**Ex VP:* Corey Whitely
**VP:* John Derrett
**VP:* Cliff Good
**VP:* Don McCreary
**VP:* Tracey Paccione
**VP:* N Zaccaria
Board of Directors: Peg Lupton

D-U-N-S 93-021-2456
ETHANOL PRODUCTS LLC
POET ETHANOL PRODUCTS
3939 N Webb Rd, Wichita, KS 67226-8100
Tel (316) 303-1380 *Founded/Ownrshp* 2000
Sales 221.8MM[E] *EMP* 245
SIC 5172 5169 Gasoline; Alcohols
CEO: Robert Casper
**CFO:* Bob Whiteman
VP: Steve Seabrook
Mktg Mgr: Marcus Lara

D-U-N-S 06-671-4577
ETHICA HEALTH & RETIREMENT COMMUNITIES
1005 Boulder Dr, Gray, GA 31032-6141
Tel (478) 621-2100 *Founded/Ownrshp* 1986
Sales 52.6MM[E] *EMP* 1,000
SIC 8051 Skilled nursing care facilities
Pr: Ron Rollins
VP: Jim Gilliam
Exec: Dawn Clifton
Exec: Tina Fowler
Exec: Tammy Ladford
Exec: April Shiver
Exec: Sharon West
Exec: Jolie Worthy
Genl Mgr: Kim Sheffield
Telecom Ex: Troy Churchill
IT Man: Tina Lane

D-U-N-S 07-521-0252
ETHICAL CULTURE FIELDSTON SCHOOL
33 Central Park W, New York, NY 10023-6001
Tel (212) 712-6220 *Founded/Ownrshp* 1878
Sales 100.3MM *EMP* 613
Accts Eisneramper Llp New York Ny
SIC 8211 Elementary school
Prin: Damian Fernandez
CFO: Sun A Yoon
Prin: Ann Vershbow

D-U-N-S 12-340-7392
■ **ETHICON ENDO-SURGERY INC**
(*Suby of* JOHNSON & JOHNSON) ★
4545 Creek Rd, Blue Ash, OH 45242-2839
Tel (513) 337-7000 *Founded/Ownrshp* 1992
Sales 245.4MM[E] *EMP* 1,494
SIC 3841 Surgical instruments & apparatus
Ch: Karen Licitra
**Pr:* Tim Schmid
VP: Oray Boston
VP: Ed Dormier
VP: Jacob Drapkin
VP: Rey Leon
Exec: Anne Buck
Exec: Julie Crawford
Assoc Dir: Reinhard Juraschek
Assoc Dir: Rengin Konuk
**Prin:* S M Rosenberg

D-U-N-S 00-214-4145 IMP/EXP
■ **ETHICON INC**
(*Suby of* JOHNSON & JOHNSON) ★
Us Route 22, Somerville, NJ 08876
Tel (732) 524-0400 *Founded/Ownrshp* 1945
Sales 1.6MMM[E] *EMP* 5,382
SIC 3842 Sutures, absorbable & non-absorbable; Ligatures, medical
Pr: Steven Henn
Ch: Philip Carne
Treas: Kendall O Brien
Treas: Robert J Decker
VP: Sarah G Brennan
Assoc Dir: Irene Dris
IT Man: Maryanne Hamlin
IT Man: Jennifer Nahvi-Sickles
Mktg Dir: Chris Teasdale
Snr Mgr: Adrian Enriquez
Board of Directors: Andrew K Ekdahl

ETHICS POINT
See NAVEX GLOBAL INC

D-U-N-S 17-198-7837
ETHOS GROUP INC
5215 N O Connor Blvd # 1450, Irving, TX 75039-3742
Tel (972) 331-1000 *Founded/Ownrshp* 1996
Sales NA *EMP* 275
SIC 6411 Insurance information & consulting services
Pr: David Terek
VP: Steven Lliod
**VP:* Jeff Lukash
CIO: Kenneth Huntley
Dir IT: John Wacholtz

D-U-N-S 94-500-5267
ETHOSENERGY GTS HOLDINGS (US) LLC
(*Suby of* WG) ★
2800 North Loop W # 1100, Houston, TX 77092-8825
Tel (281) 227-5600 *Founded/Ownrshp* 1994
Sales 184.1MM[E] *EMP* 420
SIC 1731 7699 4581 Electrical work; Aircraft flight instrument repair; Aircraft servicing & repairing

D-U-N-S 00-313-2222 IMP/EXP
■ **ETHYL CORP** (VA)
(*Suby of* NEWMARKET CORP) ★
330 S 4th St, Richmond, VA 23219-4304
Tel (804) 788-5000 *Founded/Ownrshp* 1887
Sales 117.4MM[E] *EMP* 467
SIC 2869 5169 2899 2841 2865 Industrial organic chemicals; Chemicals & allied products; Corrosion preventive lubricant; Soap & other detergents; Cyclic crudes & intermediates
Pr: Azfar A Choudhury
**Pr:* Russell L Gottwald Jr
**CEO:* Thomas E Gottwald
**Ch:* T E Gottwald
VP: Damian Barnes
**VP:* W C Drinkwater
**VP:* Bruce R Hazelgrove III
VP: C S Warren Huang
VP: Donald R Lynam
VP: Shawn McGowan
VP: A Prescott Rowe
VP: Roger H Venable

D-U-N-S 00-465-5916
ETIWANDA SCHOOL DISTRICT
6061 East Ave, Etiwanda, CA 91739-2218
Tel (909) 899-2451 *Founded/Ownrshp* 1883
Sales 107.9MM *EMP* 1,400
Accts Vavrinek Trine Day & Co Ll
SIC 8211 Public elementary & secondary schools
MIS Dir: Bob Joseph
Instr Medi: Amber Claflin
Psych: Janet Riddall
Psych: Shannon Watkins

ETMC REGIONAL HEALTH SYSTEM
See EAST TEXAS MEDICAL CENTER REGIONAL HEALTHCARE SYST

D-U-N-S 01-708-1407 IMP
ETNA DISTRIBUTORS LLC
ETNA SUPPLY COMPANY
529 32nd St Se, Grand Rapids, MI 49548-2303
Tel (616) 245-4373 *Founded/Ownrshp* 1965

Sales 180.6MM[E] *EMP* 285
Accts Bdo Usa Llp Grand Rapids Mi
SIC 5074 Plumbing fittings & supplies
Exec: David Faas
VP Mktg: Ben J Potgeter
Sales Asso: Jared Rose

ETNA SUPPLY COMPANY
See ETNA DISTRIBUTORS LLC

D-U-N-S 07-765-0794
ETOWAH COUNTY BOARD OF EDUCATION
3200 W Meighan Blvd, Gadsden, AL 35904-1732
Tel (256) 549-7560 *Founded/Ownrshp* 1918
Sales 58.1MM[E] *EMP* 1,100
Accts Ronald L Jones
SIC 8211 School board
Pr: Danny Golden

D-U-N-S 07-979-9675
ETOWAH COUNTY SCHOOLS
3200 W Meighan Blvd, Gadsden, AL 35904-1732
Tel (256) 549-7560 *Founded/Ownrshp* 2015
Sales 11.4MM[E] *EMP* 1,195[E]
SIC 8211 Public elementary & secondary schools
HC Dir: Rita King
Snr Mgr: Cory Nickels

D-U-N-S 15-058-6014
ETOWN CORP
(*Suby of* THAMES WATER LIMITED)
989 Lenox Dr Ste 224, Lawrenceville, NJ 08648-2315
Tel (609) 512-9400 *Founded/Ownrshp* 2000
Sales 116.1MM[E] *EMP* 427
Accts Deloitte & Touche Llp
SIC 4941 Water supply
Ch Bd: Jeremy D Pelczer
**Pr:* Andrew M Chapman
CFO: Elaine Margette
VP: Dennis Doll
Pr Dir: Donna Gregory

D-U-N-S 36-365-1324
ETRALI NORTH AMERICA LLC
1500 Broadway Ste 708, New York, NY 10036-4055
Tel (212) 418-9328 *Founded/Ownrshp* 1987
Sales 223.0MM[E] *EMP* 385[E]
SIC 5045 7378 1731

D-U-N-S 78-968-9416
▲ ETSY INC
117 Adams St, Brooklyn, NY 11201-1401
Tel (718) 855-7955 *Founded/Ownrshp* 2005
Sales 273.5MM *EMP* 829
Tkr Sym ETSY *Exch* NGS
SIC 5961 5947 7319 Catalog & mail-order houses; Artcraft & carvings; Media buying service
Ch Bd: Chad Dickerson
COO: Mary Underwood
CFO: Kristina Salen
Dir Bus: Morgan Blake
Prgrm Mgr: Gabrielle Gianelli
Snr Sftwr: Keyur Govande
Snr Sftwr: Anthony Hersey
Snr Sftwr: Kyle Seever
CTO: John Allspaw
Sftwr Eng: Fiona Condon
Sftwr Eng: Wayne Gerard
Board of Directors: M Michele Burns, Jonathan D Klein, Melissa Reiff, Josh Silverman, Margaret M Smyth, Fred Wilson

D-U-N-S 01-514-7499
ETTLINE FOODS CORP
525 N State St, York, PA 17403-1029
Tel (717) 848-1564 *Founded/Ownrshp* 1989
Sales 202.8MM[E] *EMP* 160
SIC 5141 Groceries, general line
Pr: N Joseph Ayoub
**Treas:* William J Houghton
**VP:* Robert J Kranz
**VP:* Steven Smith
**VP:* John J Tassia
Dir Bus: Ron Miller
Sls&Mrk Ex: Tracie Ekas
VP Sls: Greg Pondolfino
Mktg Mgr: Jennifer Sim
Sales Asso: Bobbie Johnson

D-U-N-S 79-707-1086 EXP
ETX HOLDINGS INC
(*Suby of* NICKELS PERFORMANCE) ★
2000 Michigan Ave, Alma, MI 48801-9703
Tel (989) 463-1151 *Founded/Ownrshp* 2014
Sales 154.9MM[E] *EMP* 1,100
SIC 3585 3621 3714 5013 3089 Compressors for refrigeration & air conditioning equipment; Motors & generators; Motor vehicle parts & accessories; Automotive supplies & parts; Fittings for pipe, plastic
Pr: Alan Gatlin
**Ch Bd:* Thomas H Quinn
**CFO:* Andy Gasser

D-U-N-S 96-858-7928
ETX INC
ALMA PRODUCTS COMPANY
(*Suby of* NICKELS PERFORMANCE) ★
2000 Michigan Ave, Alma, MI 48801-9703
Tel (989) 463-1151 *Founded/Ownrshp* 2014
Sales 21.7MM[E] *EMP* 2,300[E]
SIC 7549 Automotive maintenance services
Pr: Alan Gatlin

EU SERVICES
See ENVELOPES UNLIMITED INC

D-U-N-S 00-420-1042 IMP/EXP
■ EUCLID CHEMICAL CO (OH)
EPOXY CHEMICALS
(*Suby of* TREMCO INC) ★
19218 Redwood Rd, Cleveland, OH 44110-2799
Tel (800) 321-7628 *Founded/Ownrshp* 1965, 1984
Sales 129.1MM[E] *EMP* 310
SIC 2899 4213 Chemical preparations; Trucking, except local
Pr: Moorman L Scott Jr
VP: Phillip Brandt
VP: MA Drolet
VP: Volkmar Harnischmacher
Genl Mgr: Carol Rode
IT Man: Robert Scott
Tech Mgr: Bruce Berglund
Sls Dir: Paul Albright
Mktg Mgr: Diego Lopez
Mktg Mgr: Kenneth Sroka
Manager: Michael Welch

D-U-N-S 07-097-5060
EUCLID HOSPITAL
CLEVELAND CLINIC HEALTH SYSTEM
(*Suby of* CLEVELAND CLINIC HEALTH SYSTEM) ★
18901 Lake Shore Blvd, Euclid, OH 44119-1078
Tel (216) 531-9000 *Founded/Ownrshp* 2003
Sales 109.8MM *EMP* 1,000[E]
SIC 8062 General medical & surgical hospitals
CEO: Tom Selden
**Pr:* Mark Froimson
**COO:* Lauren Rock
Dir Rad: Kathy Rood
Mng Dir: Warren Rock
Surgeon: Maggie Eberhard

D-U-N-S 09-364-0639
EUCON CORP
4201 Snake River Ave, Lewiston, ID 83501-6252
Tel (509) 533-1615 *Founded/Ownrshp* 1973
Sales 96.0MM[E] *EMP* 242
SIC 1442 1611 Gravel mining; General contractor, highway & street construction
CEO: A Neil Deatley
**VP:* John Hjaltalin

EUGENE PUBLIC SCHOOL
See EUGENE SCHOOL DISTRICT 4J

D-U-N-S 09-699-8661
EUGENE SCHOOL DISTRICT 4J
EUGENE PUBLIC SCHOOL
200 N Monroe St, Eugene, OR 97402-4243
Tel (541) 790-7600 *Founded/Ownrshp* 1910
Sales 193.0MM *EMP* 2,000
Accts Grove Mueller & Swank Pc
SIC 8211 Public elementary school; Public junior high school; Public senior high school
Dir Sec: Randi Bowers-Payn
MIS Dir: Steve Menachemson
Dir IT: Jocelyn Harley
Netwrk Mgr: Roger Morris
Teacher Pr: Cydney Vandercar
HC Dir: Maxine Proskurowski
Counsel: Janice Hornsby

D-U-N-S 00-790-8304
EUGENE WATER & ELECTRIC BOARD
500 E 4th Ave, Eugene, OR 97401-2465
Tel (541) 685-7000 *Founded/Ownrshp* 1911
Sales 276.5MM *EMP* 460
Accts Moss-Adams Llp Portland Ore
SIC 4931 9641 Electric & other services combined; Agriculture fair board, government
Genl Pt: Randy Berggren
Prgrm Mgr: Gene Austin
Genl Mgr: Roger J Gray
Genl Mgr: Roger Gray
Dir IT: Patty Brown
IT Man: Gregory Armstead
Netwrk Mgr: Rick Riley
Sls Mgr: Quentin Furrow
Snr PM: Todd Wallace
Snr PM: Maria Wren
Snr Mgr: Mark Tuffo

D-U-N-S 05-983-1615
EUGENIA CHANG MD
HARWOOD, EMMA L MD
100 E Idaho St, Boise, ID 83712-6267
Tel (208) 381-2711 *Founded/Ownrshp* 1999
Sales 141.9MM *EMP* 20
Accts Tax Llp San Jose Ca
SIC 8011 Pediatrician
CEO: Ed Dahlberg

D-U-N-S 02-602-9202
EUGENIO MARIA DEHOSTOS COMMUNITY COLLEGE
500 Grand Concourse, Bronx, NY 10451-5323
Tel (718) 518-4444 *Founded/Ownrshp* 1968
Sales 928.6M *EMP* 1,200[E]
SIC 8222 Community college
Pr: Felix Matos Rodriguez
CFO: Martin Onikute
CFO: Manuel Ramirez
Sr VP: Astor Rederigoz-Chardavoyne
Exec: Glenda Grace
Exec: Jose Ryan
Assoc Dir: Marisa Rodriguez
Telecom Ex: Daniel Ramirez
Dir IT: Llinet Beltre

EULEN AMERICA
See AMERICAN SALES AND MANAGEMENT ORGANIZATION LLC

EULER HERMES A C I
See EULER HERMES NORTH AMERICA INSURANCE CO

D-U-N-S 96-049-4243
EULER HERMES ACI HOLDING INC
800 Red Brook Blvd # 400, Owings Mills, MD 21117-5190
Tel (410) 753-0753 *Founded/Ownrshp* 1998
Sales 180.4MM[E] *EMP* 400
SIC 7322 6351 6719 Collection agency, except real estate; Credit & other financial responsibility insurance; Personal holding companies, except banks
CEO: Jochen Dumler
**CFO:* Bert Emerson
**Ex VP:* Joseph Ketzner
**Ex VP:* Gary Shapiro
VP Sls: Tim Huber

D-U-N-S 00-694-9648
EULER HERMES NORTH AMERICA INSURANCE CO
EULER HERMES A C I
(*Suby of* EULER HERMES ACI HOLDING INC) ★
800 Red Brook Blvd, Owings Mills, MD 21117-5173
Tel (410) 753-0753 *Founded/Ownrshp* 1893
Sales NA *EMP* 300
SIC 6351 6411 Credit & other financial responsibility insurance; Insurance information & consulting services
Pr: Jochen Dumler
**CFO:* Karl Coutet
**CFO:* Bertrand M Emerson
**Ex VP:* Joe Ketzner
**Sr VP:* Kevin McCann
VP: Daniel C North

D-U-N-S 09-851-1249 IMP/EXP
EURAMAX HOLDINGS INC
303 Research Dr Ste 400, Norcross, GA 30092-2926
Tel (770) 449-7066 *Founded/Ownrshp* 1999
Sales 854.7MM *EMP* 1,784
SIC 3444 Sheet metalwork; Metal flooring & siding; Metal roofing & roof drainage equipment
Ch Bd: Michael D Lundin
Pr: R Scott Vansant
CFO: Mary S Cullin
Ofcr: John F Blount
Int Pr: Hugh Sawyer

D-U-N-S 80-040-1734
EURAMAX INTERNATIONAL INC
(*Suby of* EURAMAX HOLDINGS INC) ★
303 Research Dr Ste 400, Norcross, GA 30092-2926
Tel (770) 449-7066 *Founded/Ownrshp* 2005
Sales 546.9MM[E] *EMP* 1,650[E]
SIC 3471 Decorative plating & finishing of formed products
CEO: Hugh Sawyer
**CFO:* Mary S Cullin
**CFO:* R Scott Vansant
Ex VP: Neil Bashore
Ex VP: Frank Geist
**VP:* Noel Gayle
VP: Chester Klos
VP: Frank McDermott
Dir: Ravi Patil
**Prin:* Mitchell B Lewis
Admn Mgr: Linda Austin

D-U-N-S 11-396-7082
EUREKA BROADBAND CORP
EUREKA GGN
39 Broad St Fl 19, New York, NY 10004-2513
Tel (212) 404-5000 *Founded/Ownrshp* 2004
Sales 115.0MM *EMP* 207
SIC 4822 Telegraph & other communications
Pr: Raul Martynek

EUREKA GGN
See EUREKA BROADBAND CORP

D-U-N-S 93-326-7122
EUREKA REALTY PARTNERS INC
CRAIG REALTY GROUP
4100 Macarthur Blvd # 200, Newport Beach, CA 92660-2064
Tel (949) 224-4100 *Founded/Ownrshp* 1996
Sales 158.5MM[E] *EMP* 280
SIC 6552 Subdividers & developers
CEO: Steven L Craig
**VP:* Donna Balderrama
**VP:* Rino Larosa
**VP:* Lori Smith
**VP:* Sally Terando
Dir Soc: Karen Chan
Genl Mgr: Randy Berman
Genl Mgr: Brad Gunn
Genl Mgr: Margie Munoz
Genl Mgr: Jennifer Rodriguez
Genl Mgr: Rob Snowden

D-U-N-S 08-000-3701
EUREKA RESTAURANT GROUP LLC
12101 Crenshaw Blvd, Hawthorne, CA 90250-3369
Tel (310) 331-8233 *Founded/Ownrshp* 2014
Sales 50.0MM *EMP* 1,200[E]
SIC 5812 8741 Fast-food restaurant, independent; Restaurant management
CEO: Justin Nedelman
Ofcr: Robert Suzuki

EUREST DINING SERVICES
See COMPASS GROUP USA INC

D-U-N-S 03-796-3592
EUREST SUPPORT SERVICES
EUREST SUPPORT SERVICES E.S.S
(*Suby of* EUREST DINING SERVICES) ★
207 Towncenter Pkwy, Lafayette, LA 70506-7507
Tel (337) 233-9153 *Founded/Ownrshp* 1978
Sales 42.5MM *EMP* 1,200
SIC 5812 Caterers
Pr: Erin Meehan
**CFO:* Philip Fremin

EUREST SUPPORT SERVICES E.S.S
See EUREST SUPPORT SERVICES

EURO CLEAN
See NILFISK INC

D-U-N-S 84-706-4581
EURO MOTORCARS INC
7020 Arlington Rd, Bethesda, MD 20814-5229
Tel (888) 250-2987 *Founded/Ownrshp* 1990
Sales 110.1MM[E] *EMP* 250[E]
SIC 5511 Automobiles, new & used
COO: Nick Scanniello
COO: Melvyn Douglas
VP: Akmal Tareen
Sls Mgr: Charlie Harmel
Sls Mgr: Gil Hofheimer
Sales Asso: Mohammed Ahmed
Sales Asso: Mike Anderson
Sales Asso: Frederick Gordon
Sales Asso: Dorota Gorzala
Sales Asso: Ramesh Kapoor
Sales Asso: Aref Saeydie

D-U-N-S 60-275-7119
EURO RSCG LATINO
(*Suby of* HAVAS NORTH AMERICA INC) ★
350 Hudson St Fl 6, New York, NY 10014-4506
Tel (212) 345-6383 *Founded/Ownrshp* 2005
Sales 98.4MM[E] *EMP* 5,006[E]
SIC 7311 Advertising agencies
Prin: Craig Thomas

EURO SPORT
See SPORTS ENDEAVORS INC

D-U-N-S 14-945-6159
EUROBANCSHARES INC
State Rd Pr 1 Km 24 5, San Juan, PR 00926
Tel (787) 751-7340 *Founded/Ownrshp* 2001
Sales NA *EMP* 477[E]
SIC 6022 State commercial banks
Pr: R Arrillaga-Torrens Jr
Pr: Rafael Arrillaga-Torrens Jr
CFO: Yadira R Mercado Pineiro
Treas: Jorge E Sepulveda-Estrada
Ofcr: Luis J Berrios L Pez
Ex VP: Felix M Le N Le N
Ex VP: Felix M Len Len
Sr VP: Jaime A Borges Bonilla
Sr VP: Jaime N Fernndez
Sr VP: Jaime Noble Fern Ndez
Sr VP: Luis S Suau Hern Ndez
Sr VP: Jos M Del R O Jim Nez
Sr VP: Fausto P Villegas
Sr VP: Fausto Pe A Villegas
VP: Rafael L Pez
VP: Jorge P Rez

D-U-N-S 06-977-7290
EUROFINS LANCASTER LABORATORIES INC
(*Suby of* EUROFINS SCIENTIFIC SE SOC. EUROP.)
2425 New Holland Pike, Lancaster, PA 17601-5946
Tel (717) 656-2300 *Founded/Ownrshp* 2011
Sales 125.1MM *EMP* 1,500
SIC 8731 8734 Commercial research laboratory; Testing laboratories
CEO: Timothy S Oostdyk
**Pr:* Gilles Martin
CFO: Charles Bagi
Exec: Beth Dipaolo
Exec: Carol Miller
Exec: Karen Semper
CTO: Susan Guarducci
Software D: Harry Thompson
Ql Cn Mgr: Dorothy Love
Mktg Dir: Doug Hostetler
Mktg Dir: Michael Kramer

D-U-N-S 82-861-5034
EUROHEALTH (USA) INC
(*Suby of* HIKMA PHARMACEUTICALS PUBLIC LIMITED COMPANY)
401 Industrial Way W, Eatontown, NJ 07724-2209
Tel (732) 542-1191 *Founded/Ownrshp* 1991
Sales 78.6MM[E] *EMP* 1,100
SIC 6719 Investment holding companies, except banks
Pr: Said Darwazah
**CFO:* Mohammed Obeidat
**Treas:* George J Muench III
**VP:* Micheal Raya

D-U-N-S 02-511-7953 IMP/EXP
EUROMARKET DESIGNS INC (IL)
CRATE & BARREL
(*Suby of* OTTO (GMBH & CO KG))
1250 Techny Rd, Northbrook, IL 60062-5419
Tel (847) 272-2888 *Founded/Ownrshp* 1962, 1998
Sales 1.9MMM[E] *EMP* 7,500
SIC 5719 5947 5712 5961 2599 Kitchenware; Beddings & linens; Gift shop; Furniture stores; Mail order house; Boards: planning, display, notice
Pr: Steve Woodward
CFO: Diane Pearce
VP: Kasey Hooper
VP: Chris Kaye
VP: Suzanne Muellman
Creative D: Annie Oneil
Area Mgr: Kim Kite
CTO: Lue Tucker
Dir IT: Pandora Brewer
Dir IT: Patrick E McManus
Telecom Mg: Mark Carrier

D-U-N-S 83-085-4829
EUROMONEY US HOLDINGS LP
225 Park Ave S Fl 7, New York, NY 10003-1611
Tel (212) 224-3300 *Founded/Ownrshp* 1997
Sales 100.0MM *EMP* 0[E]
SIC 6719 Personal holding companies, except banks

D-U-N-S 02-918-3225
EUROMOTORS INC
MERCEDES-BENZ OF SAN FRANCISCO
500 8th St, San Francisco, CA 94103-4409
Tel (415) 673-1700 *Founded/Ownrshp* 1954
Sales 110.6MM[E] *EMP* 125
Accts Sundberg Martinelli Novy & W
SIC 5511 Automobiles, new & used
Pr: David Barsotti

D-U-N-S 92-986-2647
▲ EURONET WORLDWIDE INC
3500 College Blvd, Leawood, KS 66211-1901
Tel (913) 327-4200 *Founded/Ownrshp* 1995
Sales NA *EMP* 5,600[E]
Accts Kpmg Llp Kansas City Missour
Tkr Sym EEFT *Exch* NGS
SIC 6099 7372 4813 Automated teller machine (ATM) network; Business oriented computer software; Telephone communications broker
Ch Bd: Michael J Brown
COO: Miro I Bergman
CFO: Rick L Weller
Ex VP: Jeffrey B Newman
Sr VP: Martin L Bruckner
Sr VP: Karyn Clewes Zaborny
Exec: Sujatha Saraff
Mng Dir: Jason C Thompson
Software D: Prachi Khadilkar

Sftwr Eng: Vamsi K Inturi
Sftwr Eng: Tushar Patel
Board of Directors: Paul S Althasen, Mark R Callegari, Thomas A McDonnell, Andrew B Schmitt, M Jeannine Strandjord

D-U-N-S 62-188-8833 EXP
EUROPA SPORTS PRODUCTS INC
11401 Granite St Ste H, Charlotte, NC 28273-6401
Tel (704) 405-2022 *Founded/Ownrshp* 1990
Sales 296.1MM *EMP* 250ᴱ
Accts Mcgladrey Llp Charlotte Nort
SIC 5122 5149 5941 Vitamins & minerals; Health foods; Specialty food items; Sporting goods & bicycle shops
CEO: Eric Hillman
**COO:* Jeffrey Compton
Chf Mktg O: Marcus Hermens
Genl Mgr: Frankie Rocha
Telecom Ex: Winston Edmiston
Software D: Seth Campbell
Opers Mgr: Tim Williams
Sales Exec: Daniel Moore
Sales Asso: Mike Gargiulo
Sales Asso: Jason Hammond

D-U-N-S 09-473-0298 IMP/EXP
■ **EUROPEAN IMPORTS INC**
(*Suby of* SYSCO CORP) ★
600 E Brook Dr, Arlington Heights, IL 60005-4622
Tel (800) 323-3464 *Founded/Ownrshp* 2012
Sales 120.0MM *EMP* 200ᴱ
SIC 5141 5149 5147 Groceries, general line; Groceries & related products; Meats & meat products
CFO: Adrian Goetz
**Genl Mgr:* Kevin Piscitello

D-U-N-S 03-337-6612
EUROPEAN UNION DELEGATION TO UNITED NATION
666 3rd Ave Fl 31, New York, NY 10017-4009
Tel (212) 401-0117 *Founded/Ownrshp* 1959
Sales NA *EMP* 2,700
SIC 9721 United Nations
VP: Karel Van

D-U-N-S 12-087-7865 IMP
EUROSTAR INC
WAREHOUSE SHOE SALE
13425 S Figueroa St, Los Angeles, CA 90061-1143
Tel (310) 715-9300 *Founded/Ownrshp* 1979
Sales 167.4MMᴱ *EMP* 700
SIC 5661 Shoe stores
Pr: Eric Alon
CFO: Jim Miele
VP: Garry Rau

D-U-N-S 79-003-2762 IMP
EUROTIRE INC
200 S Biscayne Blvd # 5500, Miami, FL 33131-2333
Tel (212) 262-2251 *Founded/Ownrshp* 2006
Sales 93.9MMᴱ *EMP* 2,000
SIC 3011 Tire & inner tube materials & related products
CEO: Uri Laber
COO: Meir Dubinsky
**VP:* Shimon Laber

D-U-N-S 04-120-6798
EURPAC SERVICE INC
MID VALLEY PRODUCTS
101 Merritt 7 Corp Park 7 Corporate, Norwalk, CT 06851
Tel (203) 847-0800 *Founded/Ownrshp* 1961
Sales 302.1MMᴱ *EMP* 700
SIC 5141 5122

EUSD
See ESCONDIDO UNION SCHOOL DISTRICT

D-U-N-S 03-940-9651
EUTAW CONSTRUCTION CO INC
109 W Commerce St, Aberdeen, MS 39730-2631
Tel (662) 369-7121 *Founded/Ownrshp* 1980
Sales 92.2MM *EMP* 225
Accts Carr Riggs & Ingram Llc Ridg
SIC 1611 1623 1794 General contractor, highway & street construction; Water & sewer line construction; Excavation & grading, building construction
Pr: Tom Elmore
**Pr:* William E Cox
**COO:* Robert T Elmore
**Treas:* James G Long
Div Mgr: Matt McQueen
Mtls Mgr: Don K Stewart
Snr PM: Scott Carter
Snr Mgr: Jerome Cox

D-U-N-S 78-583-3513
▲ **EV ENERGY PARTNERS LP**
1001 Fannin St Ste 800, Houston, TX 77002-6707
Tel (713) 651-1144 *Founded/Ownrshp* 2006
Sales 177.9MM *EMP* 1,207ᴱ
Tkr Sym EVEP *Exch* NGS
SIC 1311 Crude petroleum & natural gas
Pr: Michael E Mercer
Genl Pt: Ev Energy GP
Ch Bd: John B Walker
CFO: Nicholas P Bobrowski

D-U-N-S 60-702-1003
EV3 ENDOVASCULAR INC
COVIDIEN
3033 Campus Dr Ste W550, Plymouth, MN 55441-2654
Tel (763) 398-7000 *Founded/Ownrshp* 2010
Sales 351.4MMᴱ *EMP* 1,350ᴱ
SIC 3841

D-U-N-S 12-222-4090 EXP
EVAERO INC
3807 E Kleindale Rd, Tucson, AZ 85716-1465
Tel (520) 327-0053 *Founded/Ownrshp* 1982
Sales 6.1MMM *EMP* 44
SIC 3599

EVANGELICAL COMMUNITY HOSPITAL
See EVANGELICAL MEDICAL SERVICES ORGANIZATION

D-U-N-S 07-144-5985
EVANGELICAL COMMUNITY HOSPITAL
1 Hospital Dr, Lewisburg, PA 17837-9350
Tel (570) 522-2000 *Founded/Ownrshp* 1926
Sales 163.5MM *EMP* 1,360
SIC 8062 General medical & surgical hospitals
Pr: Michael O'Keefe
Dir Recs: Joyce Telatovich
V Ch: Martha A Barrick
COO: Kendra Aucker
COO: Richard E Smith Jr
**CFO:* Christine Martin
**CFO:* James Stopper
Ofcr: Christin Kieffer
VP: Andrew Gibbons
VP: Paul Tarves
Dir Lab: Brian Kerstetter
Dir Lab: Steven King
Dir Rad: Ron R Caldwell

D-U-N-S 04-901-4509
EVANGELICAL COVENANT CHURCH (IL)
8303 W Higgins Rd Fl 1, Chicago, IL 60631-2949
Tel (773) 907-3303 *Founded/Ownrshp* 1885
Sales 88.0MMᴱ *EMP* 1,506
SIC 8661 Covenant & Evangelical Church
Pr: Gary B Walter
**Treas:* Dean Lundgren
Ex VP: Peter Hedstrom
**VP:* Donn Engerbertson
Exec: Meagan Gillan
Exec: Al Tizon
Assoc Dir: Patty Shepherd
Ex Dir: Rebecca Gonzalez
Ex Dir: Dick Lucco
Snr Mgr: Tim Ciccone
Snr Mgr: Beth Seversen

D-U-N-S 06-866-7906
EVANGELICAL LUTHERAN GOOD SAMARITAN SOCIETY
4800 W 57th St, Sioux Falls, SD 57108-2239
Tel (866) 928-1635 *Founded/Ownrshp* 1922
Sales 979.7MM *EMP* 24,000
Accts Cliftonlarsonallen Llp Minnea
SIC 8051 8052 8059 Skilled nursing care facilities; Intermediate care facilities; Rest home, with health care; Personal care home, with health care
Pr: David J Horazdovsky
**CFO:* Raye Nae Nylander
Ex VP: Rayenae Nylander
VP: Dan Fosness
VP: Thomas J Kapusta
VP: William Kubat
VP: Suzie O'Meara
VP: Mark A Scharnberg
VP: Greg Wilcox
**Prin:* Diane M Cummins
Dir IT: Nancy Wepplo

D-U-N-S 00-784-0205
EVANGELICAL MEDICAL SERVICES ORGANIZATION
EVANGELICAL COMMUNITY HOSPITAL
1 Hospital Dr, Lewisburg, PA 17837-9350
Tel (570) 522-2000 *Founded/Ownrshp* 1998
Sales 30.8MMᴱ *EMP* 1,600
SIC 8011 General & family practice, physician/surgeon
CEO: Michael N O'Keefe
**VP:* Kendra A Aucker
**VP:* J Lawrence Ginsburg
**VP:* Dale Moyer

D-U-N-S 13-972-2800
EVANGELICAL SERVICES CORP
(*Suby of* ADVOCATE HEALTH CARE NETWORK) ★
2025 Windsor Dr, Oak Brook, IL 60523-1586
Tel (630) 572-9393 *Founded/Ownrshp* 1982
Sales 40.2MMᴱ *EMP* 2,500ᴱ
SIC 8741 Management services
Pr: James Dan
**Pr:* Donald M Hallberg

D-U-N-S 08-909-5830
EVANS & ASSOCIATES ENTERPRISES INC
3320 N 14th St, Ponca City, OK 74601-1036
Tel (580) 765-6693 *Founded/Ownrshp* 2002
Sales 96.3MMᴱ *EMP* 300
SIC 5032 2951 1442 1611 3273 1311 Brick, stone & related material; Asphalt & asphaltic paving mixtures (not from refineries); Construction sand mining; Gravel mining; Highway & street paving contractor; Ready-mixed concrete; Crude petroleum production; Natural gas production
Pr: Linda Brown
**CFO:* Mandy Morris
**VP:* Jimmie Bentley
**VP:* Bruce Evans
**VP:* Lee Evans
**VP:* Glen Nickles
CTO: Mike Rozell
Plnt Mgr: Tom Riggle
Plnt Mgr: Jody Vance

D-U-N-S 00-878-1833
EVANS DELIVERY CO INC
ALL POINTS TRANSPORT
100 W Columbia St Ste 110, Schuylkill Haven, PA 17972-1934
Tel (570) 385-9048 *Founded/Ownrshp* 1939
Sales 173.6MMᴱ *EMP* 85
SIC 4213 Trucking, except local
Pr: Matthew Bates
**Pr:* Albert Evans Jr
**VP:* William Hohn
**VP:* Jorge Oliu
**VP:* Ed Zaun

D-U-N-S 00-948-6903 IMP/EXP
EVANS FRUIT CO INC
11R SALES
200 Cowiche City Rd, Cowiche, WA 98923
Tel (509) 678-4127 *Founded/Ownrshp* 1949
Sales 100.0MMᴱ *EMP* 500
SIC 0175 Apple orchard
Pr: William G Evans
**Sec:* Jeanette Evans

D-U-N-S 04-343-3259
EVANS OIL CO LLC
8450 Millhaven Rd, Monroe, LA 71203-8927
Tel (318) 345-1502 *Founded/Ownrshp* 1966
Sales 102.5MM *EMP* 27
Accts Johnston Perry Johnson & Ass
SIC 5172 Petroleum products
Treas: James Evans

D-U-N-S 07-702-4354
EVANSTON CONSOLIDATED COMMUNITY SCHOOL DISTRICT 65
COMMUNITY CNSLD SCHL DST 65
1500 Mcdaniel Ave, Evanston, IL 60201-3976
Tel (847) 859-8000 *Founded/Ownrshp* 1800
Sales 113.9MM *EMP* 1,100
Accts Rsm Us Llp Chicago Illinois
SIC 8211 Public elementary & secondary schools
Teacher Pr: Beatrice Davis
Instr Medi: Patty Tzortzif
Psych: Nicole Lown
Psych: Lyn Wilkins
HC Dir: Mary Larson

EVANSTON HOSPITAL
See NORTHSHORE UNIVERSITY HEALTHSYSTEM

D-U-N-S 09-474-9470
■ **EVANSTON INSURANCE CO**
(*Suby of* MARKEL MIDWEST) ★
10 Parkway N Ste 100, Deerfield, IL 60015-2526
Tel (847) 572-6000 *Founded/Ownrshp* 1990
Sales NA *EMP* 213
SIC 6351 6331 Liability insurance; Property damage insurance; Fire, marine & casualty insurance & carriers
Pr: Michael A Rozenberg
Sec: Fran Hanson
VP: Paul Chuchel

D-U-N-S 01-832-7791
EVANSTON TOWNSHIP HIGH SCHOOL DISTRICT 202
EVANSTON TWP HIGH SCHOOL
1600 Dodge Ave, Evanston, IL 60201-3449
Tel (847) 424-7000 *Founded/Ownrshp* 1883
Sales 87.5MM *EMP* 540
Accts Miller Cooper & Co Ltd Deerf
SIC 8211 Public senior high school
Bd of Dir: Jonathan Baum
Ofcr: Charlie Milam
**Prin:* Marcus A Campbell
Dir Sec: Matthew Driscoll
Site Mgr: Matthew Bufis
Schl Brd P: Mark Metz
HC Dir: Lisa Walter

EVANSTON TWP HIGH SCHOOL
See EVANSTON TOWNSHIP HIGH SCHOOL DISTRICT 202

EVANSVILLE CIVIC CTR COMPLEX
See CITY OF EVANSVILLE

D-U-N-S 04-041-8626
EVANSVILLE-VANDERBURGH SCHOOL DISTRICT
951 Walnut St, Evansville, IN 47713-1850
Tel (812) 435-8477 *Founded/Ownrshp* 1962
Sales 151.6MMᴱ *EMP* 3,160
SIC 8211 Public senior high school; Public junior high school; Public elementary school
Pr: Jonathan Ruthenburg
**CFO:* Carl Underwood
Treas: Debra Wells
Schl Brd P: Mike Duckworth
Schl Brd P: Christopher Kiefer

D-U-N-S 08-054-6625 IMP
EVAPCO INC
5151 Allendale Ln, Taneytown, MD 21787-2155
Tel (410) 756-2600 *Founded/Ownrshp* 1976
Sales 432.8MMᴱ *EMP* 1,122
SIC 3443 3585 Cooling towers, metal plate; Air coolers, metal plate; Evaporative condensers, heat transfer equipment
Ch Bd: Wilson E Bradley
Pr: Toby Athron
**Pr:* William Bartley
**Ch:* William E Kahlert
Sr VP: Jay Calkins
**Sr VP:* Harold W Walsh
VP: Walter Altman
VP: Jamie Facius
VP: John Kollasch
VP: Kurt Liebendorfer
Genl Mgr: Bruce Schehlein

EVCO PLASTICS
See DON EVANS INC

D-U-N-S 80-005-6558 IMP/EXP
EVENFLO CO INC
(*Suby of* WESTON PRESIDIO CAPITAL) ★
225 Byers Rd, Miamisburg, OH 45342-3614
Tel (937) 415-3300 *Founded/Ownrshp* 2004
Sales 278.9MMᴱ *EMP* 800
SIC 3944 2519 Games, toys & children's vehicles; Child restraint seats, automotive; Fiberglass & plastic furniture
CEO: Scott Weiss
**CFO:* Josh Korth
**Treas:* David McGillivary
VP: Andy Antil
**VP:* Peter Banat
Assoc Dir: Jodi Cranston
Snr Ntwrk: James Lilley
Dir IT: Anthony Chip Gaetano
Ql Cn Mgr: Jason Riehle
VP Sls: Brian Moore
Mktg Dir: Elise Ring

D-U-N-S 00-619-1613
EVENING TELEGRAM CO (WI)
1226 Ogden Ave, Superior, WI 54880-1584
Tel (715) 394-4411 *Founded/Ownrshp* 1890
Sales 200.7MMᴱ *EMP* 600
SIC 4833 Television broadcasting stations
Pr: John B Murphy
**CFO:* Bob Wallace
**VP:* Elizabeth Burns
**VP:* George Nelson

D-U-N-S 79-703-3313 IMP
EVENT NETWORK INC
9606 Aero Dr Ste 1000, San Diego, CA 92123-1869
Tel (858) 222-6100 *Founded/Ownrshp* 1998
Sales 123.8MMᴱ *EMP* 900
Accts Moss-Adams Llp San Diego Ca
SIC 5947 Gift, novelty & souvenir shop; Gift shop
Pr: Larry Gilbert
**CFO:* Larry Eyler
Ofcr: Steve Petersen
**Ex VP:* Lorena Bubel
Ex VP: Ryan Close
**Ex VP:* Helen Sherman
VP: Brian Archibald
VP: Don Boas
VP: Lorna Davis
VP: Eric Flanigan
VP: Toby Mensforth
Board of Directors: Rachel Gilbert

EVER PURE
See PENTAIR FILTRATION INC

D-U-N-S 80-807-5282
■ **EVERBANK**
(*Suby of* EVERBANK FINANCIAL CORP) ★
501 Riverside Ave Fl 1, Jacksonville, FL 32202-4934
Tel (904) 623-8408 *Founded/Ownrshp* 2007
Sales NA *EMP* 1,400
SIC 6035 Federal savings banks
CEO: Robert M Clements
Chf Mktg O: Lisa Johnston
Ex VP: Michael C Koster
Sr VP: Cameron Beane
Sr VP: Janice Butler
Sr VP: Judy Hughes
Sr VP: Brian Kukwa
VP: Katie D'Arcy
VP: Gayle Edwards
VP: Jane Gielincki
VP: Troy Haeggberg
VP: Kari Laboe
VP: Scott Miller
VP: Keith Pearson
VP: Angie Roberts
VP: Jim Stjohn
VP: Linda Tassinari
VP: Andrew Tynan
VP: James Vozza
VP: Valerie Zart

D-U-N-S 08-621-8158
▲ **EVERBANK FINANCIAL CORP**
501 Riverside Ave, Jacksonville, FL 32202-4934
Tel (904) 281-6000 *Founded/Ownrshp* 2010
Sales NA *EMP* 3,000
Tkr Sym EVER *Exch* NYS
SIC 6035 7389 Savings institutions, federally chartered; Financial services
Ch Bd: Robert M Clements
**Pr:* W Blake Wilson
CFO: Steven J Fischer
Ex VP: Francis X Ervin Jr
Ex VP: James R Hubbard
Ex VP: Michael C Koster
VP: Scott Miller
Exec: John S Surface
Board of Directors: Joseph D Hinkel, Marrick R Kleeman, W Radford Lovett II, Russell B Newton III, William Sanford, Richard P Schifter, Scott M Stuart

D-U-N-S 04-513-1182 IMP
EVERBRITE LLC
4949 S 110th St, Greenfield, WI 53228-3100
Tel (414) 529-3500 *Founded/Ownrshp* 1927
Sales 223.5MMᴱ *EMP* 850
SIC 3993 Signs & advertising specialties
Ch Bd: Judith M Wamser
VP: Barbara Cameron
VP: Robert Mathson
Dir IT: Mark Latus
Sys Mgr: Timothy Oconnor
Software D: Selina Powell
Mtls Mgr: Scott Branch
Sfty Mgr: Neal Fuchs
Opers Mgr: Keith Lemere
Ql Cn Mgr: Marcy Bayon
Ql Cn Mgr: Dave Turner

D-U-N-S 00-536-2629 IMP
EVERCARE CO
ONECARE COMPANY, THE
3885 Crestwd Pkwy Nw # 175, Duluth, GA 30096-5004
Tel (770) 570-5000 *Founded/Ownrshp* 1952, 1997
Sales 163.9MMᴱ *EMP* 700
SIC 3991 Brooms & brushes
Ch Bd: Robert B Kay
**Pr:* Tom Penner
**COO:* Tim Simmone
CFO: Don Mills
**CFO:* David Stover
**VP:* Grant Anderson
VP: Mike Jewell
**CIO:* Lee Macdonald
Prd Mgr: Peter Williamson
VP Sls: Scott Edwards
VP Sls: Mike Ortale

D-U-N-S 96-572-7498
EVERCOM SYSTEMS INC
P-NETIX
(*Suby of* SECURUS TECHNOLOGIES INC) ★
14651 Dallas Pkwy Ste 600, Dallas, TX 75254-8815
Tel (972) 277-0300 *Founded/Ownrshp* 2005
Sales 100.8MMᴱ *EMP* 600
SIC 4813 Telephone communication, except radio
CEO: Richard A Smith
**CFO:* Keith Kelson

*CFO: William D Markert
*VP: Dennis J Reinhold

D-U-N-S 96-438-2423
EVERCORE LP
55 E 52nd St Fl 35, New York, NY 10055-0110
Tel (212) 857-3100 Founded/Ownrshp 2006
Sales 122.2MM^E EMP 274^E
SIC 6282 6211 Investment advice; Investment counselors; Manager of mutual funds, contract or fee basis; Security brokers & dealers; Security brokers & dealers; Flotation companies
Prin: Joseph Campbell

D-U-N-S 78-610-1035
▲ EVERCORE PARTNERS INC
55 E 52nd St Fl 35, New York, NY 10055-0110
Tel (212) 857-3100 Founded/Ownrshp 1996
Sales 1.2MMM EMP 1,400^E
Tkr Sym EVR Exch NYS
SIC 6282 6211 Investment advice; Investment counselors; Manager of mutual funds, contract or fee basis; Security brokers & dealers; Security brokers & dealers
Pr: Ralph L Schlosstein
Ch Bd: John S Weinberg
CEO: Augusto Arellano
CFO: Robert B Walsh
VP: Fausto Borotto
VP: Jay Mirostaw
Mng Dir: Nicole Cost
Mng Dir: Chris Freudenreich
Sales Asso: Hira Mahmood
Genl Couns: Adam B Frankel
Board of Directors: Richard I Beattie, Gail B Harris, Curt Hessler, Robert B Millard, Willard J Overlock Jr, Francois De Saint Phalle, William J Wheeler

D-U-N-S 07-373-8077
EVERCORE PARTNERS SERVICES EAST LLC
55 E 52nd St, New York, NY 10055-0002
Tel (212) 857-3100 Founded/Ownrshp 2003
Sales 128.3MM^E EMP 2,460
SIC 2711 Newspapers, publishing & printing
VP: Stacy Dick
VP: Edward Merrell
VP: Shinji Sugiyama
Board of Directors: Ezra Field, John Honts, Eugene Lee, Craig Moore, Bill Owens, Gregory Warner

D-U-N-S 79-823-9518
■ EVEREN CAPITAL CORP
(Suby of WELLS FARGO & CO) ★
301 S College St, Charlotte, NC 28202-6000
Tel (704) 374-6565 Founded/Ownrshp 2008
Sales 159.2MM^E EMP 2,500^E
SIC 6211 Security brokers & dealers
Pr: Scott Ilario

D-U-N-S 11-530-4081
EVERENCE ASSOCIATION INC
1110 N Main St, Goshen, IN 46528-2638
Tel (574) 533-9511 Founded/Ownrshp 1945
Sales NA EMP 275
SIC 6321 Accident & health insurance
CEO: Larry Miller
*Pr: Howard Brenneman
Treas: James E Beitler
*Treas: John Liechty
*Sr VP: Jim Alvarez
*VP: Steve Garboden

EVEREST COLLEGE
See RHODES COLLEGES INC

D-U-N-S 02-074-3547
EVEREST HOLDINGS LLC
EDDIE BAUER
(Suby of GOLDEN GATE CAPITAL LP) ★
10401 Ne 8th St Ste 500, Bellevue, WA 98004-4346
Tel (425) 755-6544 Founded/Ownrshp 2009
Sales 71.8MM^E EMP 8,000
SIC 5699 5611 5961 Sports apparel; Men's & boys' clothing stores; Clothing, mail order (except women's)

D-U-N-S 07-953-4668
EVEREST MERGER SUB INC
(Suby of VESTIS RETAIL GROUP LLC) ★
160 Corporate Ct, Meriden, CT 06450-7177
Tel (203) 235-5775 Founded/Ownrshp 2014
Sales 503.4MM^E EMP 2,800
SIC 5699 Sports apparel
CEO: Mark Walsh

D-U-N-S 08-062-8993
EVEREST REINSURANCE CO
(Suby of EVEREST REINSURANCE HOLDINGS INC) ★
477 Martinsville Rd, Liberty Corner, NJ 07938
Tel (908) 604-3000 Founded/Ownrshp 1995
Sales NA EMP 377
SIC 6331 Fire, marine & casualty insurance; Property damage insurance
Ex VP: John Doucette
Pr: Peggy House
CFO: Craig E Eisenacher
*CFO: Craig Howie
*Ch: Dominic Addesso
Bd of Dir: Thomas Gallagher
Bd of Dir: William F Galtney
Ofcr: Barry H Smith
Ex VP: Steven Mestman
Sr VP: Gail Vanbeveren
Sr VP: Dennis Alba
Sr VP: Ronald D Diaz
VP: Daryl Bradley
VP: Roberto Brandon
VP: Billy Bugarin
VP: Robert Capicchioni
VP: Don Delgrosso
VP: Mark Digaetano
VP: Frank Eustace
VP: Beth Farrell
VP: Melissa Ford

D-U-N-S 88-468-4648
EVEREST REINSURANCE HOLDINGS INC
(Suby of EVEREST UNDERWRITING GROUP (IRELAND) LIMITED)
477 Martinsville Rd, Liberty Corner, NJ 07938
Tel (908) 604-3000 Founded/Ownrshp 1993
Sales NA EMP 695^E
Accts Pricewaterhousecoopers Llp Ne
SIC 6411 6331 6321 Property & casualty insurance agent; Fire, marine & casualty insurance; Accident & health insurance
Ch Bd: Dominic J Addesso
CFO: Craig W Howie
Treas: Ron Cenzano
Ex VP: Scott P Callahan
Ex VP: David Schmitt
Sr VP: Gail Beveren
Sr VP: Chip Craze
VP: Richard Yien
Area Mgr: Michael Ruck
Dir IT: Afzal Khan

D-U-N-S 07-666-4176
■ EVERETT CLINIC PLLC
(Suby of DAVITA INC) ★
3901 Hoyt Ave, Everett, WA 98201-4988
Tel (425) 339-5465 Founded/Ownrshp 2016
Sales 201.7MM^E EMP 1,500
Accts Moss Adams Llp Everett Washi
SIC 8011 Clinic, operated by physicians
CEO: Chris Knapp
Pr: Harold Dash
COO: Jeff Bissey
COO: Mark Mantei
CFO: Andrea Rodewald
Bd of Dir: Deanna Hartsock
Bd of Dir: Priscilla Thompson
Chf Mktg O: Albert W Fisk
Ofcr: Janneen Lambert
VP: Shawn Slack
Exec: Colleen Hernandez
Exec: Shashank Kalokhe
Comm Dir: April Zepeda

D-U-N-S 06-567-6177
EVERETT FINANCIAL INC
SUPREME LENDING
14801 Quorum Dr Ste 300, Dallas, TX 75254-1422
Tel (214) 340-5225 Founded/Ownrshp 1997
Sales NA EMP 500
SIC 6163 Loan brokers
Pr: Scott Everett
*CFO: Anthony G Schmeck
CFO: Tony Schmeck
Ofcr: Jason Murphy
VP: Steve Shuart
Ex Dir: Rodney Anderson
Brnch Mgr: Jeff Aldredge
Brnch Mgr: Brad Boswell
Brnch Mgr: Casey Cooke
Brnch Mgr: Drew Davis
Brnch Mgr: Nancy Davis

D-U-N-S 83-196-2654
EVERETT HOSPITAL
OU MEDICAL CENTER
1200 Everett Dr, Oklahoma City, OK 73104-5047
Tel (405) 271-4700 Founded/Ownrshp 1999
Sales 137.3MM^E EMP 2,800
SIC 8062 General medical & surgical hospitals
CEO: Jerry Maier
COO: David Shimp
COO: Don Whitehead
CFO: Jim Watson
Bd of Dir: Elizabeth S Smoots
Ofcr: Valerie Henson
Ofcr: Joan Krall
VP: Chuck Spicer
Exec: Eric Ferguson
Netwrk Mgr: Kirk Smith
Obsttrcn: Michael Glass

D-U-N-S 01-901-5544 IMP
EVERETT J PRESCOTT INC
E J P
32 Prescott St Libby Libby Hill, Gardiner, ME 04345
Tel (207) 582-2006 Founded/Ownrshp 1958
Sales 128.9MM^E EMP 275
SIC 5074 Plumbing fittings & supplies
CEO: Peter E Prescott
*Pr: Steven E Prescott
*COO: Stanley G Mc Curdy
COO: Stanley McCurdy
*VP: Edward Boudreau
Div Mgr: Rod Dubois
Div Mgr: John Meador
Opers Supe: Derek Session
Sls Mgr: John Flagg
Sls Mgr: Frank Gibson
Sales Asso: Butch Conover

D-U-N-S 08-039-1151
EVERETT MSO INC
3901 Hoyt Ave, Everett, WA 98201-4918
Tel (425) 339-5465 Founded/Ownrshp 2016
Sales 2.6MM^E EMP 2,500
SIC 8011 General & family practice, physician/surgeon
Pr: Rick Cooper

D-U-N-S 05-036-2268
EVERETT PUBLIC SCHOOLS (WA)
EVERETT SCHOOL DISTRICT 2
3900 Broadway, Everett, WA 98201-5033
Tel (425) 385-4000 Founded/Ownrshp 1985
Sales 103.6MM^E EMP 2,500
SIC 8211 Public elementary school; Public junior high school; Public senior high school
Pr: Pam Lesesne
*VP: Carol Andrews
*Prin: Brittni Burgess
*Prin: Caroline Mason
*Prin: Ted Wenta
Genl Mgr: Gina Zeutenhorst
CTO: Carol Stolz
DP Dir: Terry Miller
DP Dir: William Nelson
Dir IT: Kim Metcalfe
IT Man: Darla Van Duren

D-U-N-S 07-979-9225
EVERETT PUBLIC SCHOOLS
121 Vine St, Everett, MA 02149-4827
Tel (617) 394-2400 Founded/Ownrshp 2015
Sales 10.2MM^E EMP 1,694^E
SIC 8211 Public elementary & secondary schools
Teacher Pr: Louise Genualdo
HC Dir: Laura Boni

EVERETT SCHOOL DISTRICT 2
See EVERETT PUBLIC SCHOOLS

D-U-N-S 07-615-3147 IMP/EXP
EVERETT SMITH GROUP LTD
330 E Kilbourn Ave # 1400, Milwaukee, WI 53202-3170
Tel (414) 223-1560 Founded/Ownrshp 1974
Sales 750.7MM^E EMP 6,396
SIC 3111 6282 Leather tanning & finishing; Investment advice
*Pr: J Douglas Gray
*CFO: Bruce J Betters
*CFO: Charles D Krull
*VP: Todd J Flunker

EVERETT/KITSAP PRESS
See SOUND PUBLISHING INC

D-U-N-S 00-698-3464 IMP
EVERFAST INC
CALICO CORNERS
203 Gale Ln, Kennett Square, PA 19348-1735
Tel (610) 444-9700 Founded/Ownrshp 1936
Sales 513.3MM^E EMP 1,600
SIC 5023 Decorative home furnishings & supplies
Pr: Roy B Simpson Jr
*Ch Bd: Bert G Kerstetter
*VP: Scott Berman
*VP: Laura Grier
Store Mgr: Susan Kahut
Store Mgr: Donna Lanney
Store Mgr: Vince McKenna
Sales Asso: Pamela Johns
Snr Mgr: Stephen Bash

D-U-N-S 09-961-7847
EVERGLADES COLLEGE INC
KEISER UNIVERSITY
1900 W Coml Blvd Ste 180, Fort Lauderdale, FL 33309
Tel (954) 776-4476 Founded/Ownrshp 1978
Sales 220.6MM^E EMP 3,500
SIC 8221 Colleges universities & professional schools
CFO: Joseph Berardinelli
CIO: Andrew Lee
Mktg Dir: Brian Woods
Sls Mgr: Fred Pfeffer
Pgrm Dir: Cynthia Cruz
Pgrm Dir: Kathleen Drotar

D-U-N-S 19-598-1055
EVERGREEN ALLIANCE GOLF LIMITED LP
EAGLE GOLF
4851 Lydon B Johnson Ste 600, Dallas, TX 75244
Tel (214) 722-6000 Founded/Ownrshp 1988
Sales 50.0MM EMP 1,200
SIC 7992 5091 Public golf courses; Golf & skiing equipment & supplies
Pr: Joe Munsch
CFO: John Curreri
CFO: Eric T Logan
CFO: Patrick G Mackey
Treas: Stephanie Scroggins
Ex VP: Dale Folmar
Ex VP: Rob Larkin
Sr VP: Scott Carrier
Sr VP: Kathryn Comfort
VP: John Corcoran
VP: Lynn M Mallery
VP: Sharon Szymanski

D-U-N-S 17-697-1299
EVERGREEN AVIATION GROUND LOGISTICS ENTERPRISE INC
E A G L E
3850 Three Mile Ln, McMinnville, OR 97128
Tel (503) 472-9361 Founded/Ownrshp 1987
Sales NA EMP 3,153
SIC 4581

D-U-N-S 07-915-1733
EVERGREEN CAPITAL LP
21st Fl 551 5th Ave, New York, NY 10176
Tel (914) 400-4277 Founded/Ownrshp 2003
Sales 125.0MM EMP 20^E
SIC 6211 Investment firm, general brokerage
Mng Pt: Gavin Wolfe
Mng Pt: Hope Wolfe

D-U-N-S 83-936-9857 IMP/EXP
EVERGREEN ENTERPRISES INC
ASHFORD COURT RICHMOND CI
5915 Midlothian Tpke, Richmond, VA 23225-5917
Tel (804) 231-1800 Founded/Ownrshp 1993
Sales 140.8MM^E EMP 400
SIC 3253 2399 5193 5999 Ceramic wall & floor tile; Flags, fabric; Flowers & florists' supplies; Banners, flags, decals & posters
CEO: Frank Qiu
*Pr: Ting Xu
*COO: John Toler
VP: Chuck Fraelich
*VP: James Xu
VP: Yongjie Xu
Sls&Mrk Ex: John Shannon
Sls Mgr: Lori Bettinghaus
Sls Mgr: Robbin Carver
Sls Mgr: Teresa Copenhaver
Sls Mgr: Kimberly Hawk

EVERGREEN HEALTHCARE
See EMPRES FINANCIAL SERVICES LLC

EVERGREEN HEALTHCARE
See KING COUNTY PUBLIC HOSPITAL DISTRICT NO 2

D-U-N-S 07-072-0412
EVERGREEN HEALTHCARE INC
4601 Ne 77th Ave Ste 300, Vancouver, WA 98662-6736
Tel (360) 892-6472 Founded/Ownrshp 1963
Sales 103.4MM^E EMP 4,000
SIC 8051 6513 8059 8741 Extended care facility; Retirement hotel operation; Personal care home, with health care; Management services
Pr: Andrew V Martini
VP Mktg: Kay Taylor
Mktg Dir: Celeste McBee

D-U-N-S 09-700-9625 EXP
EVERGREEN HOLDINGS INC
EVERGREEN INTL AVI GROUP
3850 Ne Three Mile Ln, McMinnville, OR 97128-9402
Tel (503) 472-0011 Founded/Ownrshp 1997
Sales NA EMP 3,942
SIC 4522 4513 4215

EVERGREEN HOSPITAL MEDICAL CEN
See KING COUNTY PUBLIC HOSPITAL DISTRICT 2

D-U-N-S 80-613-8447
EVERGREEN INTERNATIONAL AVIATION INC
EA
3850 Ne Three Mile Ln, McMinnville, OR 97128-9402
Tel (503) 472-0011 Founded/Ownrshp 1978
Sales NA EMP 3,942
SIC 4522 4513 4215

EVERGREEN INTL AVI GROUP
See EVERGREEN HOLDINGS INC

D-U-N-S 07-382-3460
■ EVERGREEN INVESTMENT MANAGEMENT CO LLC
(Suby of WELLS FARGO BANK NATIONAL ASSOCIATION) ★
200 Berkeley St Ste 22, Boston, MA 02116-5035
Tel (617) 210-3200 Founded/Ownrshp 1989
Sales 140.0MM^E EMP 1,800
SIC 6282 Investment advisory service
Sr VP: Mike Koontz
VP: Michael Bradshaw
VP: Karenne N Fru
VP: Darcy Morrison
VP: Madhuleena Saha
VP: Riza Sychangco
VP: Kevin Waldeck
Dir Soc: Jennifer Falvey
Mng Dir: Reid Kilberg
Mng Dir: James Tringas
Mng Dir: Jerry Zhang

EVERGREEN LIFE SERVICES
See EVERGREEN PRESBYTERIAN MINISTRIES INC

EVERGREEN MILLS DIVISION
See KENT NUTRITION GROUP INC

EVERGREEN NURSING HOME
See CROWNE INVESTMENTS INC

D-U-N-S 16-726-8312
EVERGREEN PACIFIC PARTNERS MANAGEMENT CO INC
1700 7th Ave Ste 2300, Seattle, WA 98101-1387
Tel (206) 262-4709 Founded/Ownrshp 2004
Sales 82.8MM^E EMP 1,304
SIC 7389 6282 Financial services; Investment advice
Co-Pr: Tim Bernardez
CFO: Timothy Brillon
*Treas: Michael Nibarger
*Co-Pr: Thoms McGill
*Sr VP: Dave Dandel
*Sr VP: Ty Schultz
*Sr VP: Edward A Whatley Jr
Sr VP: Steve Wiesner
*VP: Chris Brenes

EVERGREEN PACKAGING
See BLUE RIDGE PAPER PRODUCTS INC

D-U-N-S 79-114-3972
EVERGREEN PACKAGING INC
(Suby of CARTER HOLT HARVEY LIMITED)
5350 Poplar Ave Ste 600, Memphis, TN 38119-3697
Tel (901) 821-5350 Founded/Ownrshp 2006
Sales 491.6MM^E EMP 2,109
SIC 7389 2621 Packaging & labeling services; Fine paper; Kraft paper
Pr: John Rooney
Pr: John Pekar
CFO: Ricardo Alvergue
VP: Jim Coe
VP: Allan Lips
VP: Tobi Merschat
VP: James C Oe
Snr Ntwrk: Colin Whittington
CIO: Larry Shutzberg
Dir IT: Tim Camp
IT Man: Sanjay Srivastava

D-U-N-S 06-703-9909
EVERGREEN PRESBYTERIAN MINISTRIES INC
EVERGREEN LIFE SERVICES
2101 Highway 80, Haughton, LA 71037-9488
Tel (318) 949-5500 Founded/Ownrshp 1959
Sales 76.5MM EMP 2,400
Accts Heard Mcelroy & Vestal Shre
SIC 8331 8361 Vocational training agency; Home for the mentally handicapped
Pr: Susan Buchholtz
*CFO: Kent Craft
*VP: Beth Ann Holmes
VP: Beth Holmes
VP: Corey Shadd
Ex Dir: Doug Ryland
Area Supr: Katie Conner
Area Supr: Rebecca Williams
IT Man: Audrey Blagg

D-U-N-S 05-596-7327
EVERGREEN PUBLIC SCHOOLS
13501 Ne 28th St, Vancouver, WA 98682-8091
Tel (360) 604-4000 Founded/Ownrshp 1945
Sales 176.9MM^E EMP 3,200

Accts Troy Kelley
SIC 8211 Public elementary & secondary schools; Public elementary school; Public junior high school; Public senior high school
Pr: Jennifer Weber
**COO:* Mike Merlino
Comm Dir: Gail Spolar
Prin: Alicia Brown
Dir Sec: Scott Deutch
Dir Sec: Scott Dowt
Admn Mgr: Jeff Evans
Admn Mgr: Lisa Wagner
Pr Dir: Gail Spoler

D-U-N-S 16-700-8544
EVERGREEN REHABILITATION LLC
136 Saint Matthews Ave # 300, Louisville, KY 40207-3193
Tel (502) 897-1700 *Founded/Ownrshp* 1999
Sales 55.5MM[E] *EMP* 1,400[E]
SIC 8049

D-U-N-S 02-846-9039
■ **EVERGREEN RESOURCES INC**
(*Suby of* PIONEER NATURAL RESOURCES CO) ★
1401 17th St Ste 1200, Denver, CO 80202-5928
Tel (303) 298-8100 *Founded/Ownrshp* 2004
Sales 457.6MM[E] *EMP* 354
SIC 1311 1382 1381 Natural gas production; Geological exploration, oil & gas field; Drilling oil & gas wells
Pr: Mark S Sexton

D-U-N-S 07-716-3384
EVERGREEN SCHOOL DISTRICT
3188 Quimby Rd, San Jose, CA 95148-3099
Tel (408) 270-6800 *Founded/Ownrshp* 1860, 1880
Sales 51.5MM[E] *EMP* 1,200
Accts Vavrinek Trine Day & Co Ll
SIC 8211 Public elementary & secondary schools
Prin: Jozie Autry
Prin: Christopher Corpus
Prin: Carole Greenwald
Prin: Rick Miller
Prin: Robert Pruitt
IT Man: Tina Cuneo

D-U-N-S 17-429-9743
EVERGREEN SHIPPING AGENCY (AMERICA) CORP
(*Suby of* EVERGREEN MARINE CORPORATION (TAIWAN) LTD.)
1 Evertrust Plz, Jersey City, NJ 07302-3051
Tel (201) 761-3000 *Founded/Ownrshp* 1986
Sales 175.4MM[E] *EMP* 700
SIC 4731 Agents, shipping
Pr: Wesley J Brunson
**Ch Bd:* Marcel Ming B Chang
**Ch Bd:* Y F Chang
Ex VP: Yih-Jong Chen
**Ex VP:* Jimmy Kuo
**VP:* Jay Buckley
VP: Terry Chang
**VP:* Jason Wu
Genl Mgr: James Chien
Dir IT: Lee Thach
IT Man: Randy Huang

D-U-N-S 00-407-7350
■ **EVERHOME MORTGAGE CO**
(*Suby of* EVERBANK) ★
301 W Bay St Ste 2600, Jacksonville, FL 32202-5103
Tel (904) 281-6000 *Founded/Ownrshp* 1960
Sales NA *EMP* 1,000
Accts Deloitte & Touche Llp Jackson
SIC 6162 Mortgage companies, urban
Ch Bd: Robert Clements
CFO: Blake Wilson
VP: Drew Walthall
Info Man: Diane Hunter

D-U-N-S 80-321-2356 IMP
■ **EVERI GAMES HOLDING INC**
(*Suby of* EVERI HOLDINGS INC) ★
206 Wild Basin Rd, West Lake Hills, TX 78746-3344
Tel (512) 334-7500 *Founded/Ownrshp* 2014
Sales 126.5MM[E] *EMP* 280[E]
SIC 3944 Electronic game machines, except coin-operated; Video game machines, except coin-operated
CFO: Adam Chibib
Sr VP: Mickey D Roemer
VP: Valerie Siegrist
Sls&Mrk Ex: Tommy Gassick

D-U-N-S 14-454-1559
▲ **EVERI HOLDINGS INC**
7250 S Tenaya Way Ste 100, Las Vegas, NV 89113-2175
Tel (800) 833-7110 *Founded/Ownrshp* 1998
Sales 827.0MM *EMP* 900[E]
Tkr Sym EVRI *Exch* NYS
SIC 7389 Financial services; Charge account service; Check validation service; Credit card service
Pr: Michael D Rumbolz
**Ch Bd:* E Miles Kilburn
CFO: Randy L Taylor
Ex VP: Juliet A Lim
Ex VP: David Lucchese
Ex VP: Edward A Peters
Sr VP: Jay Koldus
Sr VP: Mark Labay
Prgrm Mgr: Marcella Williams
Board of Directors: Ronald Congemi, Geoff Judge, Eileen F Raney

D-U-N-S 07-147-2836
■ **EVERI PAYMENTS INC**
(*Suby of* EVERI HOLDINGS INC) ★
7250 S Tenaya Way Ste 100, Las Vegas, NV 89113-2175
Tel (702) 855-3000 *Founded/Ownrshp* 1998
Sales 89.8MM[E] *EMP* 280
SIC 7389 6099 Financial services; Charge account service; Check validation service; Check cashing agencies; Money order issuance
Co-Ch Bd: Karim Maskatiya
Ch Bd: Walter Kortschak
Pr: Scott H Betts
CEO: Ram V Chary
CFO: George W Gresham
Treas: Mary E Higgins
Treas: Cal Roskeland
Ex VP: Morry Goldstein
Ex VP: Harry Hagerty
Ex VP: David D Johnson
Ex VP: Diran Kludjian
Ex VP: Juliet A Lim
Ex VP: David Lucchese
Ex VP: Robert Myhre
Ex VP: Robert A Myhre
Ex VP: Tom Sears
Ex VP: Kurt Sullivan
Ex VP: Randy L Taylor
Sr VP: Jay Koldus
Sr VP: Darren Simmons
VP: Harry Demaria
Board of Directors: Eileen F Raney

D-U-N-S 00-986-9480 IMP
EVERNOTE CORP
SKITCH
305 Walnut St, Redwood City, CA 94063-1731
Tel (650) 216-7700 *Founded/Ownrshp* 2004
Sales 175.5MM[E] *EMP* 400[E]
SIC 4813
CEO: Phil Libin
**CEO:* Chris O'Neill
**COO:* Ken Gullicksen
**COO:* Linda Kozlowski
**CFO:* Jeff Shotts
**Ch:* Hitoshi Hokamura
Bd of Dir: Esther Dyson
**VP:* Bethany Brodsky
VP: Zeesha Currimbhoy
VP: Jeff Zwerner
Creative D: John Barretto
Dir Bus: John Hoye

D-U-N-S 08-024-9818
EVEROSE HEALTHCARE INC
11200 Westheimer Rd # 100, Houston, TX 77042-3227
Tel (919) 482-9036 *Founded/Ownrshp* 2009
Sales 1.1MM[E] *EMP* 1,500
SIC 8082 Home health care services
CEO: Ted Nguyen

EVERSOURCE ENERGY
See NSTAR ELECTRIC CO

EVERSOURCE ENERGY
See WESTERN MASSACHUSETTS ELECTRIC CO

EVERSOURCE ENERGY
See PUBLIC SERVICE CO OF NEW HAMPSHIRE

EVERSOURCE ENERGY
See YANKEE GAS SERVICES CO

D-U-N-S 00-695-3418 IMP
▲ **EVERSOURCE ENERGY**
300 Cadwell Dr, Springfield, MA 01104-1742
Tel (413) 785-5871 *Founded/Ownrshp* 1927
Sales 7.9MMM *EMP* 7,943[E]
Accts Deloitte & Touche Llp Hartfor
Tkr Sym ES *Exch* NYS
SIC 4911 4924 Electric services; Distribution, electric power; Generation, electric power; Transmission, electric power; Natural gas distribution
Ch Bd: Thomas J May
COO: Werner J Schweiger
CFO: James J Judge
CFO: Phil Lembo
Trst: Sanford Cloud
Ofcr: David R McHale
Sr VP: Gregory B Butler
Sr VP: Christine M Carmody
Sr VP: Joseph R Nolan Jr
VP: Jay S Buth
VP: Joseph Nolan
Board of Directors: Frederica M Williams, John S Clarkeson, Dennis R Wraase, Cotton M Cleveland, Sanford Cloud Jr, James S Distasio, Francis A Doyle, Charles K Gifford, Paul A La Camera, Kenneth R Leibler, William C Van Faasen

D-U-N-S 05-254-3980 IMP
■ **EVERSOURCE ENERGY SERVICE CO**
NORTHEAST UTILITIES
(*Suby of* EVERSOURCE ENERGY) ★
107 Selden St, Berlin, CT 06037-1616
Tel (860) 665-5000 *Founded/Ownrshp* 1965
Sales 2.1MMM[E] *EMP* 4,550
SIC 1623 Underground utilities contractor
CEO: Thomas J May
V Ch: Guy Carpenter
COO: Leon Olivier
**CFO:* James Judge
Treas: Linda A Jensen
**Sr VP:* Gregory B Butler
VP: Marc Andrukiewicz
VP: David H Boguslawski
VP: Christine M Carmody
VP: Robert Coatesjr
VP: Mary J Keating
VP: Margaret Morton
VP: James A Muntz
VP: Joseph Nolan
VP: John Serrantino
VP: Steve Smith
VP: Dennis Welch

EVERSPRING ENTERPRISES
See NORTH FOOD GROUP INC

D-U-N-S 09-046-6525
▲ **EVERTEC INC**
Km 1/3 Rr 176, San Juan, PR 00926
Tel (787) 759-9999 *Founded/Ownrshp* 2012
Sales 373.5MM *EMP* 1,680
Tkr Sym EVTC *Exch* NYS
SIC 8741 8748 7379 8721 Business management; Financial management for business; Business consulting; Computer related consulting services; Payroll accounting service
Pr: Morgan M Schuessler
**Ch Bd:* Frank G D Angelo
COO: Philip E Steurer
CFO: Juan Jimenez
CFO: Juan J Rom N-Jim Nez
CFO: Peter J S Smith
Ofcr: Miguel Colon
Ofcr: Maricarmen Rivera
Ex VP: Alan I Cohen
Ex VP: Carlos J Ramirez
Ex VP: Carlos J Ram Rez
Ex VP: Miguel Vizcarrondo
Sr VP: Wanda Betancourt
Sr VP: Jose L Casas
Sr VP: Jorge R Hernandez
Sr VP: Lisa Wert
VP: Jorge R Hern Ndez
Board of Directors: Olga Botero, Jorge Junquera, Teresita Loubriel, Nestor O Rivera, Alan H Schumacher, Brian J Smith, Thomas W Swidarski

D-U-N-S 09-687-1822
▲ **EVERYDAY HEALTH INC**
345 Hudson St Rm 1600, New York, NY 10014-7120
Tel (646) 728-9500 *Founded/Ownrshp* 2002, 2016
Sales 231.9MM *EMP* 700
Tkr Sym EVDY *Exch* NYS
SIC 8099 7319 Physical examination & testing services; Media buying service
CEO: Benjamin Wolin
**Ch Bd:* Douglas McCormick
Pr: Michael Du Toit
Pr: Miki Kapoor
CFO: Brian Cooper
Ex VP: Alan Shapiro
VP: Melanie Chang
VP: Carolina Petrini
VP: Carole Sizemore

D-U-N-S 07-839-8205
EVERYWARE GLOBAL INC
519 N Pierce Ave, Lancaster, OH 43130-2927
Tel (740) 687-2500 *Founded/Ownrshp* 2011
Sales 526.8MM[E] *EMP* 1,663[E]
Accts Bdo Usa Llp New York New Yo
SIC 3469 3089 Kitchen fixtures & equipment, porcelain enameled; Plastic kitchenware, tableware & houseware
CEO: Patrick Lockwood-Taylor
**Ch Bd:* Daniel J Collin
**CFO:* Robert M Ginnan
**V Ch Bd:* Thomas J Baldwin
**Chf Mktg O:* Jeffrey W Jarrett
**Sr VP:* Anthony Reisig
Sr VP: Michael J Sullivan
**Sr VP:* Colin Walker
VP: Michael Bohland
VP: Mark Cornelius
**Prin:* Erika Schoenberger

EVICORE HEALTHCARE
See MEDSOLUTIONS INC

EVICORE HEALTHCARE
See CARECORE NATIONAL LLC

D-U-N-S 62-114-2579 IMP
▲ **EVINE LIVE INC**
6740 Shady Oak Rd, Eden Prairie, MN 55344-3433
Tel (952) 943-6000 *Founded/Ownrshp* 1990
Sales 693.3MM *EMP* 1,300
Accts Deloitte & Touche Llp Minneap
Tkr Sym EVLV *Exch* NGS
SIC 5961 Television, home shopping; Jewelry, mail order; Women's apparel, mail order; Computer equipment & electronics, mail order
CEO: Bob Rosenblatt
Ch Bd: Landel Hobbs
CFO: Timothy A Peterman
Chf Mktg O: Michael Henry
Ofcr: Lori Riley
Ex VP: Scott Danielson
Ex VP: John Ryan
Sr VP: Kevin Hanson
Sr VP: Jaime B Nielsen
Sr VP: Jean-Guillaume Sabatier
Sr VP: Damon E Schramm
Sr VP: Nicholas J Vassallo
VP: Ashish G Akolkar
VP: Amy Anding
VP: Bjorn Behlau
VP: Lee Goehring
VP: Tom Long
VP: Beth K McCartan
VP: Linh Phan
VP: Kelly Thorp
Board of Directors: Thomas D Beers, Lisa Litizio, Lowell W Robinson, Fred R Siegel

D-U-N-S 78-306-7531
EVO MERCHANT SERVICES LLC
E V O
(*Suby of* EVO MERCHANT SERVICES CORP. CANADA)
515 Broadhollow Rd # 100, Melville, NY 11747-3709
Tel (516) 479-9000 *Founded/Ownrshp* 2011
Sales 85.9MM[E] *EMP* 900
SIC 7389 Credit card service
CEO: Jim Kelly
**Pr:* Ayman Ibrahim
**Pr:* Kevin Lambrix
Pr: Eileen Mark
**Pr:* Jeff Rosenblatt
COO: Jeffery Roseblatt
**CFO:* Kevin M Hodges
**CFO:* Alon Kindler
**Ch:* Ray Sidhom

D-U-N-S 07-908-9096
EVO PAYMENTS INTERNATIONAL LLC
515 Broadhollow Rd # 100, Melville, NY 11747-3705
Tel (800) 227-3794 *Founded/Ownrshp* 2011
Sales 100.8MM[E] *EMP* 800[E]
SIC 8721 Payroll accounting service
Pr: Darren Wilson
CFO: Kevin Hodges
Ex VP: Steven J De Groot
Ex VP: Brendan F Tansill
Sr VP: Kelvin Arcelay
Sr VP: Steve Callis
Sr VP: Thomas Koerner
Sr VP: Peter Osberg
VP: Curtis Desilva
VP: Donald Hughes
VP: Ayman Ibrahim
VP: Mahesh Joshi
VP: Barry Levenson

D-U-N-S 96-245-6898
EVOKE NEUROSCIENCE INC
200 Valencia Dr Ste 109, Jacksonville, NC 28546-6312
Tel (910) 353-1760 *Founded/Ownrshp* 2009
Sales 140.0MM *EMP* 13
SIC 3845 Electromedical equipment
CEO: David Hagedorn
**Prin:* Nicole Hagedorn
**Prin:* James Thompson

D-U-N-S 04-520-5511
▲ **EVOLENT HEALTH INC**
800 N Glebe Rd Ste 500, Arlington, VA 22203-2151
Tel (571) 389-6000 *Founded/Ownrshp* 2011
Sales 96.8MM *EMP* 946
Tkr Sym EVH *Exch* NYS
SIC 8099 Medical services organization
CEO: Frank Williams
Pr: Seth Blackley
COO: Tom Peterson
CFO: Nicholas McGrane
Sr VP: Asit Gosar
VP: Tahasin Alam
Assoc Dir: Yiliu Chen
Assoc Dir: Jonathan Collins
Mng Dir: Katie Cook
Off Admin: Amanda Zeitler
QA Dir: Sirisha Kusuma
Board of Directors: Michael D'amato, David Farner, Bruce Felt, Matthew Hobart, Dian Holder, Michael Kirshbaum, Norman Payson, Kenneth Samet, Cheryl Scott

D-U-N-S 02-803-4921 IMP
■ **EVOLUTION FRESH INC**
EVOLUTION JUICE
(*Suby of* STARBUCKS CORP) ★
11655 Jersey Blvd, Rancho Cucamonga, CA 91730-4903
Tel (909) 478-0895 *Founded/Ownrshp* 2011
Sales 424.9MM[E] *EMP* 180[E]
SIC 5148 Fruits, fresh; Vegetables, fresh
CEO: Chris Bruzzo
**Ch Bd:* James Rosenberg
**CFO:* Ricki Reves

D-U-N-S 05-495-4390
EVOLUTION HOSPITALITY LLC (CA)
1211 Puerta Del Sol # 170, San Clemente, CA 92673-6353
Tel (949) 325-1350 *Founded/Ownrshp* 2010, 2011
Sales 243.9MM[E] *EMP* 2,600[E]
SIC 8741 7011 Hotel or motel management; Hotels & motels
Pr: John Murphy
Sr VP: Bhavesh Patel
VP: Matt Greene
VP: Gary J Spencer
Exec: Dalia Aguilar
Exec: Jon Eyer
Exec: Joshua Phillips
Dir Risk M: Conrad Riddle
Dir Soc: Michelle Aceves
Rgnl Mgr: John Blem
Admn Mgr: Summer Pettus

EVOLUTION JUICE
See EVOLUTION FRESH INC

EVOLVE FURNITURE GROUP
See GLOBAL INDUSTRIES INC

D-U-N-S 06-820-9295 IMP/EXP
EVONIK CORP
DEGUSSA
(*Suby of* EVONIK INDUSTRIES AG)
299 Jefferson Rd, Parsippany, NJ 07054-2827
Tel (973) 929-8000 *Founded/Ownrshp* 2007
Sales 2.5MMM[E] *EMP* 3,720
SIC 2819 2869 2851 2816 Industrial inorganic chemicals; Industrial organic chemicals; Paints & allied products; Inorganic pigments
Pr: John Rolando
**CFO:* Wolfgang Colberg
**CFO:* B Sigg
**CFO:* Burkhard Zoller
**Treas:* Mary R Zehnde
Ofcr: Alexandra Boy
Ofcr: Lee Braem
Ofcr: Edda Schulze
Ofcr: Ruben Thiel
**Sr VP:* Hans-Josef Ritzert
Sr VP: Armgard Von Burgsdorff
**VP:* Kenneth M Bittner
VP: Cornelia Borgmann
VP: Alan Brewer
VP: Jack Chenault
VP: John Kennedy
VP: Elias Lacerda
**VP:* John Luppino
VP: Bernfried Messner
**VP:* Gregory Mulligan
VP: Helena Pott

D-U-N-S 07-880-5307 IMP
EVONIK CORP
4201 Degussa Rd, Theodore, AL 36582-7284
Tel (251) 443-4000 *Founded/Ownrshp* 1973
Sales 127.0MM[E] *EMP* 116[E]
SIC 5169 Chemicals & allied products
CEO: Dr Klaus Engel
**COO:* Patrik Wohlhauser
**CFO:* Roger Avery
**CFO:* Dr Wolfgang Colberg
Top Exec: Jeff Adams
Snr Mgr: Mark Olsen

D-U-N-S 06-080-9647 IMP/EXP
EVONIK CYRO LLC
ROHM AMERICA
(*Suby of* DEGUSSA) ★
299 Jefferson Rd, Parsippany, NJ 07054-2827
Tel (973) 929-8000 *Founded/Ownrshp* 2008
Sales 216.1MM[E] *EMP* 700
SIC 2821 Plastics materials & resins; Acrylic resins; Molding compounds, plastics
Pr: John Rolando
Genl Mgr: Stephen J Costanzo
Mktg Mgr: Johan Holleman

D-U-N-S 08-990-6614 IMP/EXP
EVONIK STOCKHAUSEN LLC
(*Suby of* EVONIK INDUSTRIES AG)
2401 Doyle St, Greensboro, NC 27406-2911
Tel (336) 333-3500 *Founded/Ownrshp* 2009
Sales 149.2MM[E] *EMP* 358
SIC 2869 2899 Industrial organic chemicals; Chemical preparations
Pr: Reinhold Brand
**Sec:* Susan Duncan
VP Opers: Dieter Bettinger

D-U-N-S 15-079-5342 IMP/EXP
EVOQUA WATER TECHNOLOGIES LLC
(*Suby of* EWT HOLDINGS III CORP) ★
181 Thorn Hill Rd, Warrendale, PA 15086-7527
Tel (724) 772-0044 *Founded/Ownrshp* 2014
Sales 1.2MMM[E] *EMP* 2,898
SIC 3589 3569 3823 3826 4941

D-U-N-S 00-910-6055 IMP/EXP
EVRAZ INC NA
EVRAZ OREGON STEEL
(*Suby of* EVRAZ GROUP SA)
200 E Randolph St # 7800, Chicago, IL 60601-7703
Tel (312) 533-3621 *Founded/Ownrshp* 1986, 2007
Sales 1.6MMM[E] *EMP* 1,000
SIC 3312 3317 3325 Plate, steel; Bar, rod & wire products; Rails, steel or iron; Steel pipe & tubes; Tubes, seamless steel; Railroad car wheels, cast steel
Pr: Conrad Winkler
**CFO:* Glenda Minor
Ex VP: Tigran Atayan
**Ex VP:* Jerry Reed
**Ex VP:* John Zanieski
**Sr VP:* Jacob Lubbe
VP: Brad Ewers
VP: Jerry E Reed
VP: Michael Shuble
Genl Mgr: Sonya M Pease
CIO: Richard Guetzloff

EVRAZ OREGON STEEL
See EVRAZ INC NA

EVRAZ ROCKY MOUNTAIN STL MILLS
See CF&I STEEL LP

EWES-ECKERD YOUTH CHALLENGE
See ECKERD YOUTH ALTERNATIVES INC

EWI WORLDWIDE
See EXHIBIT WORKS INC

EWIE CO
See EAST WEST INDUSTRIAL ENGINEERING CO

D-U-N-S 05-878-4679 IMP
EWING IRRIGATION PRODUCTS INC
3441 E Harbour Dr, Phoenix, AZ 85034-0908
Tel (602) 437-9530 *Founded/Ownrshp* 1963
Sales 767.9MM[E] *EMP* 850
Accts Cliftonlarsonallen Llp Phoen
SIC 5085 5087 5074 Industrial supplies; Sprinkler systems; Pipes & fittings, plastic
Pr: Douglas W York
Pr: Jay Riviere
**Ch:* Susan E York
**Treas:* Raymon A York
**Ex VP:* Richard A York
**Sr VP:* Rilus A Graham III
**Sr VP:* Clifford P Woodbury
VP: Andrew Bell
**VP:* James A Borneman
VP: Mark Creighton
VP: Raul Gonzales
VP: Raul Gonzalez
**VP:* Warren Gorowitz

D-U-N-S 96-875-4366
EWING MARION KAUFFMAN FOUNDATION
4801 Rockhill Rd, Kansas City, MO 64110-2046
Tel (816) 932-1000 *Founded/Ownrshp* 1916
Sales 154.8MM *EMP* 85
SIC 8699 Charitable organization
Pr: Benno Schmidt
**Pr:* Thomas A McDonnell
Ofcr: Derek Ozkal
Ofcr: Wendy Shaull
Exec: Wanda Bentrop
Snr Ntwrk: Rob White
Netwrk Mgr: John Hilton
Sls&Mrk Ex: Aaron North
Doctor: Mary McLean
Genl Couns: Tim Racer
Genl Couns: John Tyler

D-U-N-S 07-942-7087
EWT HOLDINGS I CORP
666 5th Ave Fl 36, New York, NY 10103-3102
Tel (212) 644-5900 *Founded/Ownrshp* 2013
Sales 1.2MMM[E] *EMP* 4,957[E]
SIC 8748 Business consulting

D-U-N-S 07-923-4861
EWT HOLDINGS III CORP
(*Suby of* EWT HOLDINGS I CORP) ★
666 5th Ave Fl 36, New York, NY 10103-3102
Tel (212) 644-5900 *Founded/Ownrshp* 2013
Sales 1.2MMM[E] *EMP* 4,953[E]
SIC 3589 3823 3826 4941 5051 Sewage & water treatment equipment; Water treatment equipment, industrial; Sewage treatment equipment; Water purification equipment, household type; Water quality monitoring & control systems; Water testing apparatus; Water supply; Iron & steel (ferrous) products; Cast iron pipe; Piling, iron & steel

D-U-N-S 15-756-5946 IMP
▲ EXACTECH INC
2320 Nw 66th Ct, Gainesville, FL 32653-1630
Tel (352) 377-1140 *Founded/Ownrshp* 1985
Sales 241.8MM *EMP* 674[E]
Tkr Sym EXAC *Exch* NGS
SIC 3842 Surgical appliances & supplies; Implants, surgical; Orthopedic appliances; Trusses, orthopedic & surgical
Pr: David W Petty
**Ch Bd:* William Petty
CFO: Dave Grant
CFO: Joel C Phillips
Bd of Dir: Richard Smith
Ex VP: Gary J Miller
Sr VP: Bruce Thompson
VP: Donna Edwards
VP: Darin Johnson
VP: Darrell Lackey
VP: John Pelc
VP: Betty Petty
VP: Bob Roesler
VP: Bill Shopoff
VP: Steve Szabo
Dir Soc: Alissa Stokes
Dir Soc: Aliya Webb
Board of Directors: James G Binch, W Andrew Krusen Jr, William B Locander, Richard C Smith, Fern S Watts

D-U-N-S 00-252-6627
■ EXACTTARGET INC
(*Suby of* SALESFORCE.COM INC) ★
20 N Meridian St Ste 200, Indianapolis, IN 46204-3023
Tel (317) 423-3928 *Founded/Ownrshp* 2000, 2013
Sales 5.1MM[E] *EMP* 1,679[E]
SIC 7372 Prepackaged software
Ch Bd: Marc Benioff
**COO:* Andrew J Kofoid
**CFO:* Steven A Collins
**Chf Mktg O:* Timothy B Kopp
Ofcr: Traci Dolan
Sftwr Eng: Jason Pardieck

D-U-N-S 14-219-7867
EXAGRID SYSTEMS INC
2000 W Park Dr Ste 110, Westborough, MA 01581-3990
Tel (508) 898-2872 *Founded/Ownrshp* 2002
Sales 142.2MM[E] *EMP* 200
SIC 5045 Computers, peripherals & software
CEO: Edward Eyring
Pr: Domingo Gonzalez
COO: Tom Driscoll
**CFO:* Paul M Bernard
Bd of Dir: Robert E Davoli
**Sr VP:* Yee-Ching Chao
Sr VP: Dana Prestigiacomo
VP: Richard Pearce
**VP:* Dave Therrien
VP: Andy Walsky
QA Dir: Tom Andresen
Board of Directors: Brian Paul

D-U-N-S 80-227-8580 IMP
EXAL CORP
1 Performance Pl, Youngstown, OH 44502-2099
Tel (330) 744-9505 *Founded/Ownrshp* 1992
Sales 120.6MM[E] *EMP* 385[E]
SIC 3411 3354 Aluminum cans; Aluminum extruded products
CEO: Michael Mapes
**Pr:* Delfin Gibert
CFO: Ruben Yantorno
**VP:* Brenda Oman
QA Dir: Woodrow Booth
IT Man: Tom Chupak
Tech Mgr: Edward Carhart
Opers Mgr: Ignacio Menescardi
Sls Dir: Susan Chupak

D-U-N-S 07-933-5493
EXAMINATION MANAGEMENT SERVICES INC
E M S I
(*Suby of* E M S I) ★
3050 Regent Blvd Ste 100, Irving, TX 75063-3107
Tel (214) 689-3600 *Founded/Ownrshp* 1974, 1999
Sales 188.3MM[E] *EMP* 2,500
SIC 8099 Physical examination & testing services; Physical examination service, insurance
Pr: Mark S Davis
**Pr:* Tom Rubenstein
**CFO:* John Gruenhagen
Ex VP: Louis Beniamino
**Ex VP:* Robert P Brooks
**Sr VP:* Jane Severson Kelly
**CIO:* Chad Gross

D-U-N-S 96-499-9978
EXAMWORKS GROUP INC
(*Suby of* GOLD PARENT LP) ★
3280 Peachtree Rd Ne # 2625, Atlanta, GA 30305-2457
Tel (404) 952-2400 *Founded/Ownrshp* 2016
Sales 819.5MM *EMP* 3,400[E]
SIC 8099 Medical services organization
CEO: James K Price
**Ch Bd:* Richard E Perlman
Pr: Wesley J Campbell
CFO: J Miguel Fernandez De Castro
Ex VP: Clare Y Arguedas
CIO: Kevin J Kozlowski
Board of Directors: William A Shutzer

D-U-N-S 83-047-0915
EXAMWORKS INC
(*Suby of* EXAMWORKS GROUP INC) ★
3280 Peachtree Rd Ne # 2625, Atlanta, GA 30305-2457
Tel (404) 952-2400 *Founded/Ownrshp* 2008
Sales 85.8MM[E] *EMP* 455[E]
SIC 7389 Inspection & testing services
CEO: Richard E Perlman
Pr: Kevin Bird
Pr: Damien Caldwell
Pr: Kayla McCain
**CFO:* J Miguel Fernandez De Castro
Ex VP: Clare Arguedas
Ex VP: Wallace Logie
VP: Stuart Girard
VP: Scott Green
VP: Carianne Mazur
VP: Mark McCormick
**VP:* Crystal Patmore
VP: Fran Slansky
VP: Deborah Stoico

D-U-N-S 05-949-5325
▲ EXAR CORP
48720 Kato Rd, Fremont, CA 94538-7312
Tel (510) 668-7000 *Founded/Ownrshp* 1971
Sales 149.3MM *EMP* 269[E]
Accts Bdo Usa Llp San Jose Califo
Tkr Sym EXAR *Exch* NYS
SIC 3674 Integrated circuits, semiconductor networks, etc.; Metal oxide silicon (MOS) devices; Microcircuits, integrated (semiconductor)
CEO: Ryan A Benton
Ch Bd: Richard L Leza
CEO: Ryan A Benton
CFO: Keith Tainsky
Ch: Gary Meyers
Ex VP: Paul Pickering
Sr VP: Hung P Le
Sr VP: James Lougheed
VP: Dimitry Goder
VP: Nikhil Kelkar
VP: Tim Lu
VP: Ali Sahin
VP: Dan Wark
Board of Directors: Pierre Guilbault, Brian Hilton

EXCALIBUR HOTEL & CASINO
See NEW CASTLE CORP

D-U-N-S 13-108-8817
■ EXCALIBUR REINSURANCE CORP
PMA CAPITAL INSURANCE COMPANY
(*Suby of* PMA CAPITAL) ★
1735 Market St Fl 30, Philadelphia, PA 19103-7510
Tel (215) 665-5000 *Founded/Ownrshp* 1981
Sales NA *EMP* 408[E]
SIC 6331 Fire, marine & casualty insurance & carriers; Property damage insurance
CEO: John W Smithson
**Pr:* Stephen G Tirney
COO: Vincent Donnelly
**Sr VP:* Richard Decoux
**Sr VP:* Anthony J Grosso
**Sr VP:* David C Snow

EXCAVATING SPECIALISTS
See HEAVY CONSTRUCTORS INC

D-U-N-S 02-039-1215
EXCAVATORS 731 PROPERTY CORP (NY)
EXCAVATORS UNION LOCAL 731
3411 35th Ave, Astoria, NY 11106-1222
Tel (718) 706-0720 *Founded/Ownrshp* 1939
Sales 149.6MM *EMP* 4
Accts Battaglia Avellino & Co Pc Hu
SIC 6512 Commercial & industrial building operation
Pr: Andrew Arena

EXCAVATORS UNION LOCAL 731
See EXCAVATORS 731 PROPERTY CORP

D-U-N-S 09-049-5925
EXCEL BUILDING SERVICES LLC (CA)
1061 Serpentine Ln Ste H, Pleasanton, CA 94566-4793
Tel (650) 755-0900 *Founded/Ownrshp* 1998
Sales 52.8MM[E] *EMP* 1,300
SIC 7349 Janitorial service, contract basis
CEO: Jenn Fabrique
**Pr:* Jack Fabrique
**CFO:* Steve Sui
**Ex VP:* Gabe Costello
**Ex VP:* Scott Henley
Ex VP: Jeremi Pulido
VP Opers: Joe Persico

D-U-N-S 10-245-0335 IMP
EXCEL CONTRACTORS INC
EXCEL USA
8641 United Plaza Blvd, Baton Rouge, LA 70809-7032
Tel (225) 408-1300 *Founded/Ownrshp* 1992
Sales 200.4MM[E] *EMP* 850
SIC 1731 General electrical contractor
Pr: David E Roberts
COO: Jeff Smith
**Sec:* William M Knobles Jr
Ofcr: Bob Hicks
VP: Rusty Brown
VP: Stacie Lacour
VP: Joseph Wiley
VP Opers: Jeff Pruitt
Mktg Dir: Jessica Johnson
Snr PM: Jim Jackson

D-U-N-S 61-291-5467 IMP
■ EXCEL GARDEN PRODUCTS
CENTRAL GARDEN DISTRIBUTION
(*Suby of* CENTRAL GARDEN & PET CO) ★
10708 Norwalk Blvd, Santa Fe Springs, CA 90670-3824
Tel (562) 567-2000 *Founded/Ownrshp* 2007
Sales 175.1MM[E] *EMP* 450[E]
SIC 5191 Garden supplies
Prin: Charlie Naush

D-U-N-S 94-909-6002
EXCEL MODULAR SCAFFOLD AND LEASING CORP
720 Washington St Unit 5, Hanover, MA 02339-2369
Tel (508) 830-1111 *Founded/Ownrshp* 1996
Sales 150.0MM *EMP* 2,500
SIC 1799 Rigging & scaffolding
Pr: Bruce R Bartlett
**Ex VP:* Brandon Munn

D-U-N-S 08-526-1048
EXCEL STAFFING COMPANIES LLC
2100 Osuna Rd Ne Ste 100, Albuquerque, NM 87113-1040
Tel (505) 262-1871 *Founded/Ownrshp* 2014
Sales 13.0MM *EMP* 1,400
SIC 7361 7363 Executive placement; Labor contractors (employment agency); Temporary help service
Pr: Virginia Buckmelter

D-U-N-S 02-394-4218
EXCEL TRUCK GROUP
267 Lee Hwy, Roanoke, VA 24019-8568
Tel (540) 777-7700 *Founded/Ownrshp* 1947
Sales 104.6MM[E] *EMP* 221
SIC 5511 5013 7538 5012 Trucks, tractors & trailers: new & used; Truck parts & accessories; General truck repair; Automobiles & other motor vehicles
Ch: Frank R Ellett
**VP:* Greg Witt
Store Mgr: Brian Carey
Dir IT: Rass Spears
IT Man: Donald Stuart
Mktg Dir: Vicki Cromer
Sales Asso: James Germann
Sales Asso: James Kyle

D-U-N-S 96-164-4718
EXCEL TRUST INC
17140 Bernardo Center Dr, San Diego, CA 92128-2093
Tel (858) 613-1800 *Founded/Ownrshp* 2009
Sales 130.3MM *EMP* 67[E]
SIC 6798

EXCEL TRUST, L.P.
See SHOPCORE PROPERTIES LP

EXCEL USA
See EXCEL CONTRACTORS INC

EXCELA HEALTH
See WESTMORELAND REGIONAL HOSPITAL

D-U-N-S 10-733-0342
EXCELA HEALTH HOLDING CO INC
532 W Pittsburgh St, Greensburg, PA 15601-2239
Tel (724) 832-4000 *Founded/Ownrshp* 1984
Sales 358.4MM[E] *EMP* 2,548
Accts Carbis Walker Llp Pittsburgh
SIC 8062 8093 5999 7363 7322 8361 General medical & surgical hospitals; Rehabilitation center, outpatient treatment; Hospital equipment & supplies; Domestic help service; Collection agency, except real estate; Residential care
CEO: David S Gallatin
V Ch: James R Breisinger
**COO:* Michael D Busch
**CFO:* Jeffrey Curry
**Treas:* John Robertshaw Jr
Treas: Thomas L Sochacki
VP: Tim Fedele
VP: Gary Metcalfe
VP: Jennifer Miele
VP: Kirk L Miller
Exec: Norma Samide
Exec: Eric Wissinger

D-U-N-S 08-000-9270
EXCELA HEALTH LATROBE AREA HOSPITAL
1 Mellon Way, Latrobe, PA 15650-1197
Tel (877) 771-1234 *Founded/Ownrshp* 2015
Sales 134.0MM *EMP* 10[E]
SIC 8062 General medical & surgical hospitals

D-U-N-S 96-582-9216
EXCELITAS TECHNOLOGIES CORP
(*Suby of* EXCELITAS TECHNOLOGIES HOLDING CORP) ★
200 West St, Waltham, MA 02451-1121
Tel (781) 522-5910 *Founded/Ownrshp* 2004
Sales 1.1MMM[E] *EMP* 5,500
Accts Pricewaterhousecoopers Llp Bo
SIC 3648 3845 Lighting equipment; Electromedical apparatus
Pr: David Nislick
**COO:* Joel Falcone
**CFO:* James RAO
**Ex VP:* Doug Benner
**Ex VP:* Michael Ersoni
**Sr VP:* Steven Boyce
Sr VP: Chris Wright
VP: Joe Delfino
VP: Dan Iadonisi
VP: Wolfgang Schmidt
Dir Bus: Todd Brainard
Dir Bus: Ben Standish

D-U-N-S 96-582-5487
EXCELITAS TECHNOLOGIES HOLDING CORP
(*Suby of* EXCELITAS TECHNOLOGIES HOLDINGS LLC) ★
200 West St Ste E403, Waltham, MA 02451-1121
Tel (781) 522-5914 *Founded/Ownrshp* 2010
Sales 1.3MMM[E] *EMP* 5,500[E]
SIC 3648 3845 Lighting equipment; Electromedical apparatus
Ch: Robert McKeon
**Pr:* David Nislick
**Ex VP:* Joel Falcone
**Ex VP:* Michael Messier
**Ex VP:* James RAO

D-U-N-S 96-578-1300
EXCELITAS TECHNOLOGIES HOLDINGS LLC
200 West St Ste E403, Waltham, MA 02451-1121
Tel (781) 522-5900 *Founded/Ownrshp* 2010
Sales 1.1MMM[E] *EMP* 5,500
SIC 3648 Lighting equipment

D-U-N-S 08-258-6421 IMP
EXCELLED SHEEPSKIN & LEATHER COAT CORP (NJ)
RG APPAREL GROUP
1400 Brdwy Fl 31, New York, NY 10018
Tel (212) 594-5843 *Founded/Ownrshp* 1927, 1976
Sales 84.9MM[E] *EMP* 383
SIC 2386 3172 2337 2311 Coats & jackets, leather & sheep-lined; Personal leather goods; Women's & misses' suits & coats; Men's & boys' suits & coats
Ch: Myron Goldman
**Pr:* William Goldman
**CFO:* Ken Walton
**VP:* Michael Holzberg
Netwrk Mgr: Enrico Bizetti

D-U-N-S 02-179-9486 IMP
EXCELLIGENCE LEARNING CORP
DISCOUNT SCHOOL SUPPLY
2 Lower Ragsda Dr Ste 200, Monterey, CA 93940
Tel (831) 333-2000 *Founded/Ownrshp* 2015
Sales 241.2MM[E] *EMP* 398
SIC 3944 5999 Games, toys & children's vehicles; Craft & hobby kits & sets; Puzzles; Dollhouses & furniture; Education aids, devices & supplies
CEO: Kelly Crampton
**Pr:* Dipak Golechha

*COO: Judith McGuinn
VP: Gina Van De Vort
VP: Don Hahn
VP: Jihan Thissel
CIO: David Jennings
Web Dev: Patrick Rocchi
Ql Cn Mgr: Mario Sanchez
VP Sls: Tim Lynch
Mktg Mgr: Joey Cassidy

D-U-N-S 06-680-2257
EXCELLUS HEALTH PLAN INC
(Suby of LIFETIME HEALTH COMPANIES) ★
165 Court St, Rochester, NY 14647-0001
Tel (585) 454-1700 Founded/Ownrshp 1936
Sales NA EMP 6,000
SIC 6321 Accident & health insurance
CEO: David H Klein
*Pr: Kevin Hill
*CEO: Christopher C Booth
*CFO: Dorothy A Coleman
*CFO: Emil D Duda
Treas: Jim Haefner
Ex VP: Dorothy Coleman
Ex VP: Stephen R Sloan
*Sr VP: James Heafner
*Sr VP: James R Reed
VP: Zeke Duda
VP: Mindy Gray
VP: John Griffith
VP: Mark Harris
VP: Mary Moynihan
VP: Daniel Owen
VP: Lynn M Persi
VP: Doug Porter
VP: Tove Stigum
VP: Geoff Taylor
VP: Robert Thompson

D-U-N-S 14-353-2294
EXCELSIOR COLLEGE
7 Columbia Cir, Albany, NY 12203-5159
Tel (518) 464-8500 Founded/Ownrshp 1971
Sales 97.4MM EMP 400
SIC 8221 Colleges & universities
Pr: John F Ebersole
*CFO: John Pontius
*VP: Wayne Brown
*VP: Steve Ernst
*VP: Edmund J McTernan
*VP: Susan O'Hern
*Prin: Douglas Tucker

D-U-N-S 55-617-6555
EXCEPTIONAL EDUCATIONAL SERVICES LLC
5960 S Cooper Rd Ste 1, Chandler, AZ 85249-5392
Tel (480) 398-1994 Founded/Ownrshp 2005
Sales 1.4MMM EMP 30
SIC 8748 Educational consultant

D-U-N-S 79-501-2624
EXCEPTIONAL INC
111 Hana Hwy Ste 111, Kahului, HI 96732-2300
Tel (808) 877-6555 Founded/Ownrshp 1982
Sales 320.2MM EMP 300
SIC 7363 5941 7361 Temporary help service; Saddlery & equestrian equipment; Employment agencies
Pr: Jennifer Brittin

EXCEPTIONAL LIVING CENTERS
See MEDICAL REHABILITATION CENTERS LLC

D-U-N-S 00-691-4139
EXCHANGE BANK
EB
(Suby of FRANK P. DOYLE TRUST, ARTICLE IX)
440 Aviation Blvd, Santa Rosa, CA 95403-1069
Tel (707) 524-3000 Founded/Ownrshp 1890
Sales NA EMP 453
SIC 6036 8741 6022 State savings banks, not federally chartered; Management services; State commercial banks
CEO: Gary T Hartwick
Ch Bd: C William Reinking
Pr: Linda Burille
Pr: Jane Daniel
Pr: Pam Maslak
Pr: Eugene Patterson
Pr: William R Schrader
Pr: Stacy Small
Pr: Sally Traughber
Pr: Byron Webb
COO: Bruce Decrona
CFO: Greg Jahn
Sr Cor Off: Ricky Ray
Bd of Dir: Michael Morgan
Ofcr: Beth Ryan
Trst Ofcr: Toni Elordi
Assoc VP: Polly Novak
Ex VP: William Badstubner
Ex VP: David Voss
Sr VP: Peggy Betchley
Sr VP: Ann Hudson
Board of Directors: Marlene Barney, Charles R Bartley, Jean Dusty Destruel, Samuel L Jones III, John E Mc Donald, James Ryan, Robert G Stone

D-U-N-S 11-830-0735
EXCLUSIVE STAFFING LTD
8774 Yates Dr Ste 210, Westminster, CO 80031-6906
Tel (303) 430-1700 Founded/Ownrshp 2004
Sales 22.7MM^E EMP 1,000
SIC 7363 Help supply services
Pr: Diane Astley
*CEO: Walter Goozh

D-U-N-S 08-024-5877
EXCO INC
(Suby of EXCO TECHNOLOGIES LIMITED)
1007 N Orange St, Wilmington, DE 19801-1239
Tel (905) 477-3065 Founded/Ownrshp 1983
Sales 50.3MM^E EMP 3,000^E
SIC 6719 Public utility holding companies
Prin: Brian Robbins
Prin: Drew Knight
Prin: Paul Riganelli

D-U-N-S 79-700-3402
■ **EXCO OPERATING CO LP**
EXCO RESOURCES
(Suby of EXCO RESOURCES INC) ★
12377 Merit Dr Ste 1700, Dallas, TX 75251-2256
Tel (214) 368-2084 Founded/Ownrshp 2006
Sales 444.2MM^E EMP 755^E
SIC 1382 Oil & gas exploration services
Prin: Harold L Hickey
VP: William L Boeing
VP: Michael R Chambers
VP: Ronald G Edelen

EXCO RESOURCES
See EXCO OPERATING CO LP

D-U-N-S 61-348-0854
■ **EXCO RESOURCES (PA) LLC**
(Suby of EXCO RESOURCES INC) ★
260 Executive Dr Ste 100, Cranberry Township, PA 16066-6446
Tel (724) 720-2500 Founded/Ownrshp 2004
Sales 128.8MM^E EMP 219^E
SIC 1382 1381 1311 8741 6211 Oil & gas exploration services; Drilling oil & gas wells; Crude petroleum & natural gas; Management services; Brokers, security
Pr: Stephen F Smith
*Ch Bd: Douglas H Miller
*COO: Harold L Hickey
*Treas: Andrew C Springer
*VP: William L Boeing
*VP: Ronald G Edelen
*VP: Steve Estes
*VP: Russell D Griffin
*VP: Richard L Hodges
*VP: John D Jacobi
*VP: Harold H Jameson
*VP: Tommy Knowles
*VP: Stephen E Puckett
*VP: J Douglas Ramsey
*VP: Paul B Rudnicki
*VP: Marcia R Simpson
*VP: Mark E Wilson

D-U-N-S 07-855-0639 IMP
▲ **EXCO RESOURCES INC**
12377 Merit Dr Ste 1700, Dallas, TX 75251-2256
Tel (214) 368-2084 Founded/Ownrshp 1955
Sales 328.3MM EMP 558^E
Accts Kpmg Llp Dallas Texas
Tkr Sym XCO Exch NYS
SIC 1311 Crude petroleum & natural gas
Pr: Harold L Hickey
*Ch Bd: C John Wilder
V Ch: Stephen Smith
COO: Harold H Jameson
COO: Harold Jameson
CFO: Mark F Mulhern
CFO: Chris Peracchi
VP: William L Boeing
VP: Michael R Chambers
VP: Tyler Farquharson
VP: Heather Lamparter
VP: Stephen E Puckett
VP: Mark Wilson
Board of Directors: Jeffrey D Benjamin, B James Ford, Samuel A Mitchell, Wilbur L Ross Jr, Jeffrey S Serota, Robert L Stillwell

D-U-N-S 00-416-8899
EXECUSOURCE INC
5925 Carnegie Blvd # 350, Charlotte, NC 28209-4655
Tel (704) 483-9800 Founded/Ownrshp 1997
Sales 29.0MM EMP 1,200
SIC 8742 Management consulting services
Pr: Russ Salerno Sr
VP: Jennifer Gabrenas

D-U-N-S 10-408-8141
■ **EXECUTIVE AIR LINES INC**
AMERICAN EAGLE
(Suby of AMERICAN AIRLINES GROUP INC) ★
Lmm Int Airport Central, Carolina, PR 00983
Tel (787) 253-6401 Founded/Ownrshp 1989
Sales 41.4MM^E EMP 1,509
SIC 4512 4212 Air passenger carrier, scheduled; Air cargo carrier, scheduled; Mail carriers, contract
Pr: Pedro Fabregas

EXECUTIVE BEECHCRAFT
See SIGNATURE FLIGHT SUPPORT CORP

EXECUTIVE DIRECTOR'S OFFICE
See COLORADO DEPARTMENT OF NATURAL RESOURCES

D-U-N-S 60-659-5312
EXECUTIVE MANAGEMENT SERVICES OF INDIANA INC
4177 N Ems Blvd, Indianapolis, IN 46250
Tel (317) 813-1490 Founded/Ownrshp 1989
Sales 182.8MM^E EMP 4,000
SIC 7349 Office cleaning or charring
Pr: David A Bego
Pr: Erick Nichols
Ex VP: Ray Mourey
VP: Steven Evans
Rgnl Mgr: Steve Lowder
Rgnl Mgr: Kelly Simerly
Brnch Mgr: Tom Byerlly
Brnch Mgr: Hugh Chapman
Genl Mgr: Tom Byerly
Opers Supe: Jennifer Magers
Opers Mgr: Chad Miller

EXECUTIVE OFC OF THE COMMNWLTH
See DEPT OF EDUCATION PENNSYLVANIA

EXECUTIVE OFC OF THE STATE ARK
See ARKANSAS DEPARTMENT OF PARKS AND TOURISM

EXECUTIVE OFFC OF AR
See ARKANSAS DEPARTMENT OF HEALTH

EXECUTIVE OFFC OF THE ST OF OK
See OKLAHOMA DEPT OF TOURISM AND RECREATION

EXECUTIVE OFFCE
See COUNTY OF ST LOUIS

EXECUTIVE OFFCE OF THE STATE
See KANSAS DEPARTMENT OF TRANSPORTATION

EXECUTIVE OFFCE OF THE STATE
See ALABAMA DEPT OF PUBLIC SAFETY

EXECUTIVE OFFICE
See PUBLIC EMPLOYEE DEFERRED COMPENSATION OHIO

EXECUTIVE OFFICE OF THE
See HAWAII DEPARTMENT OF TRANSPORTATION

D-U-N-S 18-859-3644
EXECUTIVE OFFICE OF COMMONWEALTH OF KENTUCKY
(Suby of COMMONWEALTH OF KENTUCKY) ★
State Cptl 700 Cpitol Ave State Capitol, Frankfort, KY 40601
Tel (502) 564-2611 Founded/Ownrshp 1792
Sales NA EMP 22,185
SIC 9111 Governors' offices;

D-U-N-S 82-520-1924
EXECUTIVE OFFICE OF COMMONWEALTH OF MASSACHUSETTS
(Suby of COMMONWEALTH OF MASSACHUSETTS) ★
24 Beacon St Rm 360, Boston, MA 02133-1099
Tel (617) 727-3600 Founded/Ownrshp 1788
Sales NA EMP 59,000
SIC 9111 Executive offices;
CFO: Lawrence Behan
Ofcr: Richard Currier
CIO: Joan Clark
Dir IT: Michael Barrows
IT Man: Tom Lee
IT Man: Jim Nally
Genl Couns: David Hoover
Counsel: William Cowan

D-U-N-S 18-865-5898
EXECUTIVE OFFICE OF COMMONWEALTH OF PENNSYLVANIA
GOVERNOR'S OFFICE, THE
(Suby of COMMONWEALTH OF PENNSYLVANIA) ★
225 Capitol Bldg, Harrisburg, PA 17120-0001
Tel (717) 787-5962 Founded/Ownrshp 1776
Sales NA EMP 78,547
SIC 9111 Executive offices;
IT Man: Margaret Hively

D-U-N-S 36-175-9707
EXECUTIVE OFFICE OF COMMONWEALTH OF PUERTO RICO
SECRETARY OF THE COMMONWEALTH
(Suby of COMMONWEALTH OF PUERTO RICO) ★
San Jose St Crn San, San Juan, PR 00901
Tel (787) 722-2121 Founded/Ownrshp 1967
Sales NA EMP 17,500
SIC 9111 Executive offices, state & local;

D-U-N-S 80-641-9131
EXECUTIVE OFFICE OF GOVERNOR
(Suby of STATE OF ILLINOIS) ★
207 S State St, Springfield, IL 62704-1754
Tel (217) 782-6832 Founded/Ownrshp 1818
Sales NA EMP 39,402
SIC 9111 Executive offices;
Treas: Alexi Giannoulias

D-U-N-S 80-939-8084
EXECUTIVE OFFICE OF GOVERNOR OF DELAWARE
(Suby of STATE OF DELAWARE)
150 Mlk Jr Blvd S Fl 2, Dover, DE 19901
Tel (302) 744-4101 Founded/Ownrshp 1787
Sales NA EMP 16,024
SIC 9111 Executive offices;
Prin: Jack A Markell

D-U-N-S 80-955-9248
EXECUTIVE OFFICE OF GOVERNOR OF FLORIDA
(Suby of STATE OF FLORIDA) ★
400 S Monroe St, Tallahassee, FL 32399-6536
Tel (850) 488-4505 Founded/Ownrshp 1845
Sales NA EMP 105,847
SIC 9111 Executive offices;
CFO: Tom Gallagher
Exec: Fleming Phil
Sls&Mrk Ex: Bronson Charles

D-U-N-S 94-758-1567
EXECUTIVE OFFICE OF LABOR AND WORKFORCE DEVELOPMENT
(Suby of MASSACHUSETTS DEPT OF WORKFORCE DEVELOPMENT) ★
19 Staniford St, Boston, MA 02114-2502
Tel (617) 626-5680 Founded/Ownrshp 1935
Sales NA EMP 1,400
SIC 9441 Unemployment insurance office, government
*CFO: Barbara McDonough

EXECUTIVE OFFICE OF THE STATE
See MILITARY DEPARTMENT MISSISSIPPI

EXECUTIVE OFFICE OF THE STATE
See ARKANSAS DEPARTMENT OF EDUCATION

EXECUTIVE OFFICE OF THE STATE
See IDAHO DEPARTMENT OF TRANSPORTATION

EXECUTIVE OFFICE OF THE STATE
See MISSOURI OFFICE OF ADMINISTRATION

D-U-N-S 19-999-3528
EXECUTIVE OFFICE OF STATE OF ALABAMA
OFFICE OF THE SECRETARY STATE
(Suby of STATE OF ALABAMA) ★
600 Dexter Ave Ste S105, Montgomery, AL 36130-3024
Tel (334) 242-7205 Founded/Ownrshp 1819
Sales NA EMP 6,609
SIC 9111 Executive offices, state & local

D-U-N-S 80-956-0345
EXECUTIVE OFFICE OF STATE OF ALASKA
OFFICE OF THE GOVERNOR
(Suby of STATE OF ALASKA) ★
Capitol Bldg Fl 3, Juneau, AK 99811
Tel (907) 465-3500 Founded/Ownrshp 1959
Sales NA EMP 4,300
SIC 9111 Executive offices;

D-U-N-S 80-444-2010
EXECUTIVE OFFICE OF STATE OF ARIZONA
(Suby of GOVERNORS OFFICE) ★
1700 W Washington St # 602, Phoenix, AZ 85007-2812
Tel (602) 542-4331 Founded/Ownrshp 1912
Sales NA EMP 28,000
SIC 9111 Governors' offices;
Treas: Dean Martin

D-U-N-S 80-974-7660
EXECUTIVE OFFICE OF STATE OF ARKANSAS
GOVERNERS OFFICE, THE
(Suby of STATE OF ARKANSAS) ★
State Capitol Ste 250, Little Rock, AR 72201
Tel (501) 682-2345 Founded/Ownrshp 1836
Sales NA EMP 3,688
SIC 9111 Executive offices;
Off Mgr: Howard Himmelbaum
Counsel: Betty Dickey

D-U-N-S 80-738-6123
EXECUTIVE OFFICE OF STATE OF CALIFORNIA
(Suby of STATE OF CALIFORNIA) ★
Governors Ofc, Sacramento, CA 95814
Tel (916) 445-2841 Founded/Ownrshp 1850
Sales NA EMP 181,617
Accts John F Collins Ii Cpa
SIC 9111 Executive offices;
*Treas: Phil Angelides
Exec: Deborah Holstein
Exec: Jane Pruitt
Admn Mgr: Guy Blair
Brnch Mgr: Shirley Willd-Wagner
CIO: Chris Crossley
DP Exec: Theresa Bober
DP Exec: Melody Ogara
IT Man: Roberta Mangini

D-U-N-S 18-858-9402
EXECUTIVE OFFICE OF STATE OF COLORADO
GOVERNORS OFFICE
(Suby of STATE OF COLORADO) ★
136 State Capitol Bldg, Denver, CO 80203
Tel (303) 866-2471 Founded/Ownrshp 1876
Sales NA EMP 6,000
Accts Nancy Lee Couse Cpa
SIC 9111 9223 Governors' offices; ; Correctional institutions
Ex Dir: Dennis Ellis

D-U-N-S 80-729-2099
EXECUTIVE OFFICE OF STATE OF GEORGIA
(Suby of STATE OF GEORGIA) ★
203 State Capitol Sw, Atlanta, GA 30334-1600
Tel (404) 656-1776 Founded/Ownrshp 1788
Sales NA EMP 66,176
SIC 9111 Executive offices;
V Ch: David L Burge

D-U-N-S 80-993-0217
EXECUTIVE OFFICE OF STATE OF HAWAII
(Suby of STATE OF HAWAII) ★
415 S Beretania St Fl 5, Honolulu, HI 96813-2407
Tel (808) 586-0034 Founded/Ownrshp 1959
Sales NA EMP 44,201
SIC 9111 Executive offices;
IT Man: Ming Wang

D-U-N-S 82-469-7726
EXECUTIVE OFFICE OF STATE OF IDAHO
(Suby of STATE OF IDAHO DEPARTMENT OF LANDS)
700 W Jefferson St, Boise, ID 83720-0001
Tel (208) 334-2100 Founded/Ownrshp 1890
Sales NA EMP 6,541
SIC 9111 Executive offices;

D-U-N-S 80-994-2899
EXECUTIVE OFFICE OF STATE OF INDIANA
(Suby of STATE OF INDIANA) ★
200 W Washington St # 206, Indianapolis, IN 46204-2728
Tel (317) 232-4567 Founded/Ownrshp 1816
Sales NA EMP 29,143
SIC 9111 Executive offices;
Prin: Mike Pence

D-U-N-S 36-074-3462
EXECUTIVE OFFICE OF STATE OF KANSAS
(Suby of STATE OF KANSAS) ★
300 Sw 10th Ave, Topeka, KS 66612-1504
Tel (785) 296-6240 Founded/Ownrshp 1861
Sales NA EMP 15,000
SIC 9111 Executive offices, state & local;
*CFO: Jill Stewart
Netwrk Mgr: Donald King

D-U-N-S 80-974-7785
EXECUTIVE OFFICE OF STATE OF LOUISIANA
(Suby of STATE OF LOUISIANA) ★
900 N 3rd St Fl 4, Baton Rouge, LA 70802-5236
Tel (225) 342-7015 Founded/Ownrshp 1812
Sales NA EMP 47,837
SIC 9111 Executive offices;
Pr: Frank Collins III
Ofcr: Danielle Babineaux
Comm Dir: Kyle Plotkin

D-U-N-S 80-917-4659
EXECUTIVE OFFICE OF STATE OF MAINE
(*Suby of* STATE OF MAINE) ★
1 Stathuse Stn 2nd Fl 236, Augusta, ME 04333-0001
Tel (207) 287-3531 *Founded/Ownrshp* 1820
Sales NA *EMP* 13,089
SIC 9111 Governors' offices
Ex Dir: Victor Horton
Ex Dir: Lynn Rubinstein
Ex Dir: Gaile Wright

D-U-N-S 87-802-2847
EXECUTIVE OFFICE OF STATE OF MARYLAND
(*Suby of* STATE OF MARYLAND) ★
100 State Cir, Annapolis, MD 21401-1924
Tel (410) 974-3901 *Founded/Ownrshp* 1776
Sales NA *EMP* 11,626
SIC 9111 Governors' offices;
Ofcr: Joseph C Bryce
Exec: Wendy Hershey
**Prin:* Martin J O'Malley
Counsel: Elizabeth F Harris
Snr Mgr: Amanda O'Malley

D-U-N-S 80-388-9070
EXECUTIVE OFFICE OF STATE OF MICHIGAN
(*Suby of* STATE OF MICHIGAN) ★
Romne Bldg 111 S Cap, Lansing, MI 48933
Tel (517) 373-3400 *Founded/Ownrshp* 1837
Sales NA *EMP* 30,195
SIC 9111 Executive offices;
**Treas:* Robert J Kleine
**Off Mgr:* Judy Chapman

D-U-N-S 80-450-8372
EXECUTIVE OFFICE OF STATE OF MINNESOTA
GOVERNOR'S OFFICE
(*Suby of* STATE OF MINNESOTA) ★
75 Rev Doc Martin Luther, Saint Paul, MN 55155-0001
Tel (651) 201-3400 *Founded/Ownrshp* 1858
Sales NA *EMP* 35,217
SIC 9111 Executive offices;
IT Man: Lisa Dobias

D-U-N-S 80-939-8399
EXECUTIVE OFFICE OF STATE OF MISSISSIPPI
(*Suby of* STATE OF MISSISSIPPI) ★
550 High St, Jackson, MS 39201-1111
Tel (601) 359-3100 *Founded/Ownrshp* 1817
Sales NA *EMP* 21,000
SIC 9111 Executive offices;

D-U-N-S 19-999-5176
EXECUTIVE OFFICE OF STATE OF MISSOURI
(*Suby of* STATE OF MISSOURI) ★
201 W Capitol Ave Rm 216, Jefferson City, MO 65101-1556
Tel (573) 751-1851 *Founded/Ownrshp* 1821
Sales NA *EMP* 19,600
SIC 9111 Executive offices, state & local;

D-U-N-S 80-958-0442
EXECUTIVE OFFICE OF STATE OF MONTANA
(*Suby of* STATE OF MONTANA)
State Capitol Rm 204, Helena, MT 59620
Tel (406) 444-3111 *Founded/Ownrshp* 1889
Sales NA *EMP* 10,000
Accts James Gillett Cpa
SIC 9111 Executive offices;

D-U-N-S 80-994-2782
EXECUTIVE OFFICE OF STATE OF NEVADA
(*Suby of* STATE OF NEVADA) ★
101 N Carson St, Carson City, NV 89701-3713
Tel (775) 684-5670 *Founded/Ownrshp* 1864
Sales NA *EMP* 13,539
SIC 9111 Executive offices;
**Treas:* Brian Krolicki

D-U-N-S 80-839-0330
EXECUTIVE OFFICE OF STATE OF NEW HAMPSHIRE
OFFICE OF ECONOMIC STIMULUS
(*Suby of* STATE OF NEW HAMPSHIRE) ★
107 N Main St Rm 208, Concord, NH 03301-4951
Tel (603) 271-2121 *Founded/Ownrshp* 1788
Sales NA *EMP* 3,000
SIC 9111 Governors' offices;
Mktg Dir: Stuart Arnett

D-U-N-S 80-670-4391
EXECUTIVE OFFICE OF STATE OF NEW JERSEY
(*Suby of* STATE OF NEW JERSEY) ★
125 W State St, Trenton, NJ 08608-1101
Tel (609) 292-6000 *Founded/Ownrshp* 1787
Sales NA *EMP* 81,836
SIC 9111 Governors' offices;
CIO: E Steven Emanuel
IT Man: Vicki Fallon
IT Man: Robert Sherman
Snr Mgr: Kevin May

D-U-N-S 36-073-9262
EXECUTIVE OFFICE OF STATE OF NEW YORK
(*Suby of* STATE OF NEW YORK) ★
Executive Chamber Capitol, Albany, NY 12224
Tel (518) 474-8390 *Founded/Ownrshp* 1788
Sales NA *EMP* 105,019
SIC 9111 Governors' offices;
Comm Dir: Christene Anderson
Ex Dir: Mario Musolino
MIS Dir: Tom Irvin
Counsel: Maria Colavito

D-U-N-S 80-939-4513
EXECUTIVE OFFICE OF STATE OF NORTH CAROLINA
NORTH CRLINA OFFICE OF GVERNOR
(*Suby of* STATE OF NORTH CAROLINA) ★
20301 Mail Svc Ctr, Raleigh, NC 27699-0001
Tel (919) 814-2000 *Founded/Ownrshp* 1789
Sales NA *EMP* 67,097
SIC 9111 Governors' offices;
Pr: Crystal Feldman
Pr: Jenny Steele
CFO: David Rossi
Off Mgr: Amy Blinson
Board of Directors: Jerry Spangler

D-U-N-S 80-273-2941
EXECUTIVE OFFICE OF STATE OF NORTH DAKOTA
(*Suby of* STATE OF NORTH DAKOTA) ★
600 E Boulevard Ave, Bismarck, ND 58505-0601
Tel (701) 328-2680 *Founded/Ownrshp* 1889
Sales NA *EMP* 8,726
SIC 9111 Executive offices;
Prin: William R Strader
IT Man: Monte Krebsbach

D-U-N-S 80-991-6190
EXECUTIVE OFFICE OF STATE OF OKLAHOMA
(*Suby of* STATE OF OKLAHOMA) ★
2300 N Lincoln Blvd, Oklahoma City, OK 73105-4805
Tel (405) 521-2342 *Founded/Ownrshp* 1907
Sales NA *EMP* 20,400
SIC 9111 Governors' offices;

D-U-N-S 80-939-4125
EXECUTIVE OFFICE OF STATE OF OREGON
(*Suby of* STATE OF OREGON) ★
900 Court St Ne, Salem, OR 97301-4042
Tel (503) 378-3111 *Founded/Ownrshp* 1859
Sales NA *EMP* 36,176
SIC 9111 Executive offices;

D-U-N-S 18-395-6978
EXECUTIVE OFFICE OF STATE OF RHODE ISLAND
(*Suby of* STATE OF RHODE ISLAND AND PROVIDENCE PLANTATIONS) ★
82 Smith St Ste 217, Providence, RI 02903-1120
Tel (401) 574-8423 *Founded/Ownrshp* 1636
Sales NA *EMP* 2,228
SIC 9111 Executive offices, state & local;

D-U-N-S 80-851-4830
EXECUTIVE OFFICE OF STATE OF SOUTH CAROLINA
BUDGET & CTRL BD EXEC DIRS OFF
(*Suby of* STATE OF SOUTH CAROLINA) ★
Wade Hampton Bldg Fl 6, Columbia, SC 29211
Tel (803) 734-2320 *Founded/Ownrshp* 1788
Sales NA *EMP* 5,500
SIC 9111 Executive offices;
Ex Dir: Marcia Adams
Treas: Converse A Chellis

D-U-N-S 80-957-9030
EXECUTIVE OFFICE OF STATE OF SOUTH DAKOTA
(*Suby of* STATE OF SOUTH DAKOTA) ★
500 E Capitol Ave, Pierre, SD 57501-5007
Tel (605) 773-3411 *Founded/Ownrshp* 1889
Sales NA *EMP* 8,256
Accts Maurice C Christiansen Cpa Au
SIC 9111 Executive offices;

D-U-N-S 60-555-1126
EXECUTIVE OFFICE OF STATE OF TENNESSEE
(*Suby of* STATE OF TENNESSEE) ★
600 Charlotte Ave, Nashville, TN 37243-9034
Tel (615) 741-2001 *Founded/Ownrshp* 1796
Sales NA *EMP* 4,967
SIC 9111 Executive offices, state & local;
Bd of Dir: Bill Knapp
Ofcr: Peter Gallinari
Ex Dir: Ronald Grove
Prgrm Mgr: Jim Winters
Rgnl Mgr: Eddie Graham
Pgrm Dir: Jimmy Simerly

D-U-N-S 80-719-6449
EXECUTIVE OFFICE OF STATE OF TEXAS
(*Suby of* STATE OF TEXAS) ★
1100 San Jacinto Blvd, Austin, TX 78701-1935
Tel (512) 463-2000 *Founded/Ownrshp* 1845
Sales NA *EMP* 108,285
SIC 9111 Executive offices;
Mktg Dir: Carla Click

D-U-N-S 36-074-9162
EXECUTIVE OFFICE OF STATE OF UTAH
(*Suby of* GOVERNORS OFFICE) ★
2110 State Ofc Bldg, Salt Lake City, UT 84114-1206
Tel (801) 538-3020 *Founded/Ownrshp* 1851
Sales NA *EMP* 28,445
Accts Auston G Johnson Salt Lake C
SIC 9111 Governors' offices;
**Treas:* Richard K Ellis

D-U-N-S 80-904-9943
EXECUTIVE OFFICE OF STATE OF VERMONT
GOVERNOR'S OFFICE
(*Suby of* STATE OF VERMONT) ★
109 State St Ste 5, Montpelier, VT 05609-0003
Tel (802) 828-3333 *Founded/Ownrshp* 1791
Sales NA *EMP* 6,900
SIC 9111 Executive offices;

D-U-N-S 80-897-2970
EXECUTIVE OFFICE OF STATE OF WASHINGTON
STATE OF WASH OFFICE OF GVRNOR
(*Suby of* GOVERNORS OFFICE) ★
1115 Washington St Se, Olympia, WA 98501-2283
Tel (360) 753-6780 *Founded/Ownrshp* 1889
Sales NA *EMP* 57,659
SIC 9111 Executive offices;
Ex Dir: David Postman
Ex Dir: Ted Sturdevant

D-U-N-S 80-889-2475
EXECUTIVE OFFICE OF STATE OF WISCONSIN
GOVERNER'S OFFICE
(*Suby of* STATE OF WISCONSIN) ★
115 E State Capitol, Madison, WI 53702-0001
Tel (608) 266-1212 *Founded/Ownrshp* 1848
Sales NA *EMP* 30,279
SIC 9111 Executive offices;
Opers Mgr: Teri Divine

D-U-N-S 80-974-7959
EXECUTIVE OFFICE OF STATE OF WYOMING
(*Suby of* STATE OF WYOMING) ★
200 W 24th St Rm 124, Cheyenne, WY 82001-3642
Tel (307) 777-7434 *Founded/Ownrshp* 1890
Sales NA *EMP* 6,153
SIC 9111 Executive offices;

EXECUTIVE OFFICE OF THE STATE
See ATTORNEY GENERAL TEXAS

D-U-N-S 16-190-6078
■ EXECUTIVE OFFICE OF UNITED STATES GOVERNMENT
(*Suby of* U S GOVERNMENT) ★
1600 Pennsylvania Ave Nw, Washington, DC 20006
Tel (202) 456-1414 *Founded/Ownrshp* 1787
Sales NA *EMP* 1,917,456
SIC 9111 President's office;
Pr: Barack Obama
**VP:* Joseph Biden

D-U-N-S 80-938-7079
EXECUTIVE OFFICE OF VIRGINIA
OFFICE OF THE GOVERNOR
(*Suby of* COMMONWEALTH OF VIRGINIA) ★
1111 E Broad St Fl 3, Richmond, VA 23219-1934
Tel (804) 225-4534 *Founded/Ownrshp* 1788
Sales NA *EMP* 98,075
Accts Walter J Kucharski Auditor R
SIC 9111 Executive offices;
Ofcr: Barnette Coleman

D-U-N-S 80-903-1776
EXECUTIVE OFFICE STATE OF OHIO
(*Suby of* STATE OF OHIO) ★
30 E Broad St, Columbus, OH 43215-3414
Tel (614) 466-3555 *Founded/Ownrshp* 1803
Sales NA *EMP* 51,879
SIC 9111 Executive offices;
**Prin:* Mary Taylor

D-U-N-S 80-959-4377
EXECUTIVE OFFICE STATE OF WEST VIRGINIA
(*Suby of* GOVERNORS OFFICE) ★
1900 Kanawha Blvd E, Charleston, WV 25305-0009
Tel (304) 558-2000 *Founded/Ownrshp* 1863
Sales NA *EMP* 17,129
SIC 9111 Governors' offices;

EXECUTIVE OFFICES
See SHAW INDUSTRIES INC

EXECUTIVE SECRETARY
See JUDICIARY COURTS OF COMMONWEALTH OF VIRGINIA

EXECUTRAIN
See INTERNATIONAL DATA GROUP INC

D-U-N-S 15-694-7012
EXECUTRAIN CORP
2500 Northwinds Pkwy # 460, Alpharetta, GA 30009-2247
Tel (770) 667-7700 *Founded/Ownrshp* 2002
Sales 84.4MM[E] *EMP* 530
SIC 6794 8243 Franchises, selling or licensing; Software training, computer
CEO: Ronald Grawert
**VP:* Christopher Bloor
**VP:* Steve Gilroy
Dir Bus: Amy Spears
Manager: Brandon Nakamura

EXECUTV OFC OF THE STATE OF AL
See ALABAMA DEPT OF TRANSPORTATION

EXECUTV OFC OF THE STATE OF AR
See ARKANSAS DEPT OF FINANCE AND ADMINISTRATION

EXECUTV OFC OF THE STATE OF AR
See ARKANSAS DEPARTMENT OF HUMAN SERVICES

EXECUTV OFC OF THE STATE OF MO
See DEPARTMENT OF CORRECTIONS MISSOURI

EXECUTV OFC OF THE STATE OF NY
See EDUCATION DEPARTMENT NEW YORK STATE

EXECUTV OFC OF THE STATE OF TX
See EMPLOYEES RETIREMENT SYSTEM OF TEXAS

EXECUTVE OFC OF THE GOV OF FL
See FLORIDA DEPARTMENT OF JUVENILE JUSTICE

EXECUTVE OFC OF THE US GOVT
See UNITED STATES DEPARTMENT OF HOMELAND SECURITY

D-U-N-S 88-365-9419 IMP
EXEDY AMERICA CORP
(*Suby of* EXEDY CORPORATION)
2121 Holston Bend Dr, Mascot, TN 37806-1524
Tel (865) 932-3700 *Founded/Ownrshp* 2003
Sales 133.5MM[E] *EMP* 550
SIC 3714 Motor vehicle transmissions, drive assemblies & parts
Pr: Ted T Yoshinaga
**VP:* Sean Kawalura

D-U-N-S 09-127-7186 IMP/EXP
EXEL GLOBAL LOGISTICS INC (NY)
(*Suby of* DHL) ★
22879 Glenn Dr Ste 100, Sterling, VA 20164-4493
Tel (703) 350-1298 *Founded/Ownrshp* 1970, 2005
Sales 88.1MM[E] *EMP* 1,300
SIC 4731 4225 Domestic freight forwarding; Foreign freight forwarding; Customhouse brokers; General warehousing
Pr: Sueann Fulton
Pr: Edward Marrin
Treas: Jon McCaman

D-U-N-S 15-685-6387 IMP/EXP
EXEL HOLDINGS (USA) INC
(*Suby of* EXEL LIMITED)
570 Polaris Pkwy Ste 110, Westerville, OH 43082-7902
Tel (614) 865-8500 *Founded/Ownrshp* 1984
Sales 7.2MMM[E] *EMP* 16,600
SIC 4226 4213 Special warehousing & storage; Household goods transport
CEO: Scott Sureddin
**CEO:* Jose Fernando Nava
CEO: Jose Nava
**CFO:* Scot Hofacker
**Treas:* Duncan McGrath
**Treas:* George Meechan
**VP:* Lynn Anderson
**VP:* Tim Sprosty

D-U-N-S 03-623-5240 IMP/EXP
EXEL INC
EXEL LOGISTICS
(*Suby of* EXEL HOLDINGS (USA) INC) ★
570 Polaris Pkwy, Westerville, OH 43082-7900
Tel (614) 865-8500 *Founded/Ownrshp* 1989
Sales 7.2MMM[E] *EMP* 16,600
SIC 4213 4225 4581 Trucking, except local; General warehousing; Air freight handling at airports
CEO: Scott Sureddin
**Pr:* Scott Cubbler
**Pr:* Luis Eraa
**Pr:* Jim Gehr
**Pr:* Gordon Gruszka
**Pr:* Mark Kunar
**CFO:* Scot Hofacker
Ofcr: Robert E Liss
**Ofcr:* Joe Puleo
**Sr VP:* Val Hoge
Sr VP: Marvin Larger
**Sr VP:* Tim Sprosty
Sr VP: Fred Takavitz
VP: Patrick Bennett
VP: Claudius Christmas Jr
VP: Ron Davis
VP: Brian Deffet
**VP:* Jaime Hooker
VP: Patrick Kelleher
VP: Thomas Kimball
VP: Rick Macdonald

EXEL LOGISTICS
See EXEL INC

D-U-N-S 60-712-6026 IMP/EXP
EXEL NORTH AMERICAN LOGISTICS INC
(*Suby of* EXEL FREIGHT MANAGEMENT (UK) LIMITED)
570 Players Pkwy, Westerville, OH 43081
Tel (800) 272-1052 *Founded/Ownrshp* 2000
Sales 123.6MM[E] *EMP* 800
SIC 4731 Freight forwarding
Pr: Randy Briggs
**VP:* Hugh Evans
VP Sls: Michael Steen

EXELIS
See ITT CORP

D-U-N-S 96-931-6046
EXELIS INC
2235 Monroe St, Herndon, VA 20171-2824
Tel (703) 790-6300 *Founded/Ownrshp* 2015
Sales 3.9MMM[E] *EMP* 14,000
SIC 3669 3823 3812

EXELON
See PECO ENERGY CO

EXELON
See PEPCO HOLDINGS LLC

D-U-N-S 03-942-4721 IMP
■ EXELON BUSINESS SERVICES CO LLC
(*Suby of* EXELON CORP) ★
10 S Dearborn St, Chicago, IL 60603-2300
Tel (800) 483-3220 *Founded/Ownrshp* 2001
Sales 181.5MM[E] *EMP* 1,000[E]
SIC 7389 Financial services; Legal & tax services
Pr: Ruth Ann M Gillis
**Treas:* J Barry Mitchell
**VP:* Matthew R Galvanoni
**VP:* Raymond Tyne
Exec: Arthur Barsema
Snr Mgr: Connie Fisher

D-U-N-S 00-180-7150 IMP/EXP
▲ EXELON CORP (PA)
10 S Dearborn St Fl 53, Chicago, IL 60603-2398
Tel (800) 483-3220 *Founded/Ownrshp* 1999
Sales 29.4MMM *EMP* 29,762[E]
Accts Pricewaterhousecoopers Llp Ch
Tkr Sym EXC *Exch* NYS
SIC 4911 4924 Generation, electric power; Transmission, electric power; Distribution, electric power; Natural gas distribution
Pr: Christopher M Crane
COO: Michael J Pacilio

CFO: Jonathan W Thayer
Ofcr: Kenneth W Cornew
Ex VP: Paymon Aliabadi
Sr VP: Darryl M Bradford
Sr VP: Duane M Desparte
Sr VP: Mike Koehler
Sr VP: Mike Kormos
VP: Kathleen Barron
VP: David C Brown
VP: Stacie Frank
VP: Dean Hengst
VP: Christopher Mudrick
VP: Mark Newcomer
VP: Chris Symonds
Exec: William A Von Hoene Jr
Comm Dir: Denis Eischen
Comm Dir: Marshall Murphy
Board of Directors: Richard W Mies, Anthony K Anderson, John W Rogers Jr, Ann C Berzin, Mayo A Shattuck III, John A Canning Jr, Stephen D Steinour, Yves C De Balmann, Nicholas Debenedictis, Nancy L Gioia, Linda P Jojo, Paul L Joskow, Robert J Lawless

D-U-N-S 13-527-2271 IMP
■ EXELON ENERGY DELIVERY CO LLC
(*Suby of* EXELON CORP) ★
10 S Dearborn St Fl 53, Chicago, IL 60603-2398
Tel (312) 394-7399 *Founded/Ownrshp* 2001
Sales 6.1MMM[E] *EMP* 16,087[E]
SIC 4931 Electric & other services combined
Ofcr: Robert McDonald
Ofcr: Pamela B Strobel
VP: Duane Desparte
VP: Joseph Dominguez
VP: Mary Ludford
VP: Anne Pramaggiore
VP: George Williams

D-U-N-S 19-674-8938 IMP
■ EXELON GENERATION CO LLC
CONSTELLATION ENERGY
(*Suby of* EXELON CORP) ★
300 Exelon Way, Kennett Square, PA 19348-2473
Tel (215) 841-4000 *Founded/Ownrshp* 2000
Sales 19.1MMM *EMP* 3,000
Accts Pricewaterhousecoopers Llp Ba
SIC 4911 Generation, electric power
Pr: Bryan C Hanson
CEO: Christopher M Crane
Ch: Mayo A Shattuck III
Sr VP: Doyle N Beneby
Sr VP: Bryan Hanson
Sr VP: Thomas S O'Neill

D-U-N-S 16-185-0685
■ EXELON POWER CORP
(*Suby of* CONSTELLATION ENERGY) ★
2233 Mountain Creek Pkwy A, Dallas, TX 75211-6716
Tel (214) 623-1051 *Founded/Ownrshp* 2004
Sales 415.8MM[E] *EMP* 270[E]
SIC 4911 ; Generation, electric power
Prin: Jim Byrd
Sr VP: Doyle N Beneby

EXEMPLA SAINT JOSEPH HOSPITAL
See ST JOSEPH HOSPITAL INC

D-U-N-S 93-365-2414 IMP/EXP
EXEMPLIS LLC
SITONIT
6415 Katella Ave, Cypress, CA 90630-5245
Tel (714) 995-4800 *Founded/Ownrshp* 1996
Sales 122.0MM[E] *EMP* 300
SIC 2522 Chairs, office: padded or plain, except wood
CEO: Paul Devries
**Pr:* Mike Mekjian
**CFO:* Mike Phelan
**Ex VP:* Patrick Sommerfield
VP: Karen Robinson
CTO: Jeffrey Blum
Dir IT: Dale Minney
Natl Sales: Timothy Travis
VP Sls: Todd Holderness
Mktg Mgr: Scott Brickin
Mktg Mgr: Jennifer Chaffins

D-U-N-S 80-900-8613
■ EXETER FINANCE CORP
(*Suby of* BLACKSTONE GROUP L P) ★
222 Las Colinas Blvd W, Irving, TX 75039-5421
Tel (214) 572-8276 *Founded/Ownrshp* 2011
Sales NA *EMP* 1,026[E]
SIC 6153

D-U-N-S 07-397-8389
EXETER HOSPITAL INC
5 Alumni Dr, Exeter, NH 03833-2160
Tel (603) 778-7311 *Founded/Ownrshp* 1891
Sales 186.7MM *EMP* 740[E]
SIC 8062 General medical & surgical hospitals
Pr: Kevin Callahan
**CFO:* Kevin O'Leary
**VP:* Allison Casassa
IT Man: Ken Kuster
Sfty Dirs: Katelyn Galante
Surgeon: Roderick Mkee
Doctor: Maribeth Dinicola
Doctor: Gary Proulx
Pharmcst: Karen Cue
Pgrm Dir: Richard Hollister
Snr Mgr: Jill Kennedy

D-U-N-S 09-274-6551 IMP/EXP
EXETER PACKERS INC
SUN PACIFIC PACKERS
1250 E Myer Ave, Exeter, CA 93221-9345
Tel (559) 592-5168 *Founded/Ownrshp* 1975
Sales 131.9MM[E] *EMP* 585
SIC 0723 Fruit (fresh) packing services
CEO: Berne H Evans III
**Pr:* Robert Reniers
**CFO:* Ernie Larsen
CFO: Toby Lewis

D-U-N-S 13-411-4230
EXETER SCHOOL DISTRICT
STRATHAM MEMORIAL SCHOOL
(*Suby of* SAU 16) ★
24 Front St Ste 111, Exeter, NH 03833-2773
Tel (603) 778-7772 *Founded/Ownrshp* 2012
Sales 15.6MM *EMP* 1,185[E]
Accts Plodzik & Sanderson Concord
SIC 8211 Public elementary & secondary schools; Public junior high school; Public senior high school
CFO: Nathan Lunney
IT Man: Art Reardon

D-U-N-S 80-955-5584
EXFO AMERICA INC
(*Suby of* EXFO INC)
3400 Waterview Pkwy # 100, Richardson, TX 75080-1472
Tel (972) 761-9271 *Founded/Ownrshp* 1993
Sales 172.8MM[E] *EMP* 24[E]
Accts Pricewaterhouse Coopers Llp
SIC 3825 8734 Instruments to measure electricity; Testing laboratories
CEO: Germain Lamonde
**CFO:* Pierre Plamondon
Genl Mgr: Dave Norman
IT Man: Ayodhya Paikaray
Sls Mgr: Geoff Galligher
Sls Mgr: Christian Steube

D-U-N-S 12-147-8825
EXHALE ENTERPRISES INC
250 W 57th St Ste 1901, New York, NY 10107-1902
Tel (212) 300-2310 *Founded/Ownrshp* 2001
Sales 30.8MM[E] *EMP* 1,000[E]
SIC 7991 Spas
CEO: Annbeth Eschbach
**COO:* Julia Sutton
**VP:* Fred Devito

EXHIBIDORES UNIVERSALES
See RACKS INC

D-U-N-S 09-695-8533 IMP
EXHIBIT WORKS INC (MI)
EWI WORLDWIDE
27777 Inkster Rd Ste 200, Farmington Hills, MI 48334-5326
Tel (734) 525-9010 *Founded/Ownrshp* 1979
Sales 141.8MM[E] *EMP* 450
Accts Wright Griffin Davis And Co P
SIC 7389 Advertising, promotional & trade show services; Interior design services; Lettering & sign painting services; Design services
Pr: Dominic Silvio
**Pr:* Andrew P Austin
**Pr:* David Brown
Pr: Josh Mooney
**CFO:* Ronald Gasparotto
Treas: Douglas Turkington
**Sr VP:* Larry Parrott
**Sr VP:* Mike Rosenau
Sr VP: Sheri Sullivan
VP: Andrew Austin
VP: Jerry Deeney
VP: Ben Einer
VP: Hilary Read
VP: Jeff Smith
VP: Danelle Xu
Assoc Dir: Angela Heiple
Creative D: Chris Petit

D-U-N-S 03-800-9866 IMP/EXP
EXIDE TECHNOLOGIES
13000 Deerfield Pkwy # 200, Milton, GA 30004-6118
Tel (678) 566-9000 *Founded/Ownrshp* 1966
Sales 2.8MMM[E] *EMP* 8,986
SIC 3691 Lead acid batteries (storage batteries)
Pr: Vic Koelsch
Pr: Luke Lu
Pr: Yates Moosic
COO: Brad Wheelus
**CFO:* Phillip A Damaska
**CFO:* Anthony Genito
CFO: Anthony L Genito
Ch: Albrecht K M Leuschner
**Ofcr:* Edgar W Mosley Jr
Ofcr: Jeff Nordling
Ex VP: Phillip Damaska
**Ex VP:* Barbara A Hatcher
Ex VP: George S Jones Jr
**Ex VP:* Brad S Kalter
Sr VP: Ted Becker
VP: Jeff Barna
VP: Charles Giesige
**VP:* Louis E Martinez
VP: Kevin McMahon
VP: Steve O'Leary
VP: Lily Prost
Board of Directors: Herbert F Aspbury, Michael R D'appolonia, David S Ferguson, John O'higgins, Dominic J Pileggi, Michael P Ressner, Carroll R Wetzel Jr

D-U-N-S 96-153-7966
EXIT 76 CORP
J&H FAMILY STORES
2696 Chicago Dr Sw, Grand Rapids, MI 49519-1628
Tel (616) 534-2181 *Founded/Ownrshp* 1987
Sales 265.0MM *EMP* 600
Accts Uhy Llp Sterling Heights Mic
SIC 5812 Sandwiches & submarines shop
Pr: Craig Hoppen
**CFO:* Joe Albers
CFO: Michael Obrien
**VP:* Sandra Arrasmith

D-U-N-S 07-935-1721
■ EXLP FINANCE CORP
(*Suby of* EXTERRAN CORP) ★
16666 Northchase Dr, Houston, TX 77060-6014
Tel (281) 836-7000 *Founded/Ownrshp* 2014
Sales 168.4M[E] *EMP* 5,009[E]
SIC 3533 Oil & gas field machinery

D-U-N-S 12-690-1029 IMP
▲ EXLSERVICE HOLDINGS INC
280 Park Ave Fl 38, New York, NY 10017-1216
Tel (212) 277-7100 *Founded/Ownrshp* 1999
Sales 628.4MM *EMP* 24,100[E]
Tkr Sym EXLS *Exch* NGS
SIC 7389 Telemarketing services
CEO: Rohit Kapoor
Ch Bd: Garen K Staglin
Pr: Pavan Bagai
Pr: Arun Kumar
CFO: Vishal Chhibbar
Ofcr: Nalin Miglani
Ex VP: Rembert De Villa
Ex VP: Nancy Saltzman
Ex VP: Amit Shashank
VP: Vikas Bhalla
CTO: Mike Toma
Board of Directors: David B Kelso, Deborah Kerr, Anne E Minto, Clyde W Ostler, Nitin Sahney

D-U-N-S 00-721-1993
■ EXLSERVICE.COM LLC (DE)
(*Suby of* EXLSERVICE HOLDINGS INC) ★
280 Park Ave, New York, NY 10017-1216
Tel (212) 277-7100 *Founded/Ownrshp* 1996
Sales 48.3MM[E] *EMP* 1,900
SIC 7389 Telemarketing services
Pr: Rohit Kapoor
VP: Kal Bittianda
VP: Cindy Carpenter
VP: Amitabh Hajela
VP: Pramode Metre
VP: Alka Misra
VP: Baljinder Singh
VP: Lalit Vij
Prin: Nikhil Anand
Genl Mgr: Kulpreet Singh
Snr Mgr: Leah Holton

D-U-N-S 60-302-0855 IMP/EXP
EXO-S US LLC
CAMOPLAST CROCKER
(*Suby of* EXO-S INC)
6505 N State Road 9, Howe, IN 46746-9702
Tel (260) 562-4100 *Founded/Ownrshp* 2005
Sales 86.5MM[E] *EMP* 381
SIC 3089 Injection molding of plastics
CEO: Emmanuel Duchesne
**Pr:* Sylvain Dupuis
**CFO:* Daniel Denault
Exec: Ron Lebiecki
Plnt Mgr: Craig Mohney

D-U-N-S 07-351-2048
EXODYNE INC
8433 N Black Canyon Hwy # 100, Phoenix, AZ 85021-4859
Tel (602) 995-3700 *Founded/Ownrshp* 1982
Sales 142.1MM[E] *EMP* 1,350
SIC 8711 8731 8741 8744 8748 Engineering services; Commercial physical research; Management services; Facilities support services; Business consulting
Ch Bd: Ralph A Rockow
**CFO:* Robert Swank
Genl Mgr: Clint Bateman
Genl Mgr: Mark Clapp
Genl Mgr: Frank Merritt
Opers Mgr: Rene Arkin
Opers Mgr: Angie Ryan
Snr Mgr: Julie Rossignol

EXOPACK HOLDING
See COVERIS HOLDING CORP

EXOS PROMAT SYSTEMS
See HOLLINGSWORTH LOGISTICS MANAGEMENT LLC

D-U-N-S 00-948-1078 IMP
EXOTIC METALS FORMING CO LLC
EMFCO
5411 S 226th St, Kent, WA 98032-4842
Tel (253) 220-5900 *Founded/Ownrshp* 1963
Sales 150.5MM[E] *EMP* 300
SIC 3728 3724 Aircraft parts & equipment; Aircraft engines & engine parts
COO: Tim Kurnik
**Treas:* Terry Osthus
VP: Bill Binder
Prgrm Mgr: Chris Schatz
Genl Mgr: Mark Simon
Sfty Mgr: Vince Firlotte
Prd Mgr: Dan Marden
Ql Cn Mgr: Jon Butler
Sls&Mrk Ex: Chris Capuano

D-U-N-S 12-660-1801
EXOVA INC
194 Internationale Blvd, Glendale Heights, IL 60139-2094
Tel (630) 221-0385 *Founded/Ownrshp* 2009
Sales 372.9MM[E] *EMP* 4,000
SIC 8734 Metallurgical testing laboratory
CEO: Grant Rumbles
**Pr:* Ravijit Paintal
VP: Bobby Archibald
Genl Mgr: Michael FEC
Dir IT: Corwyn Berger
Tech Mgr: Rocco Rizzo
Opers Mgr: Steven Scarborough

D-U-N-S 10-094-3047
EXP US SERVICES INC
(*Suby of* EXP GLOBAL INC)
205 N Mich Aveste 3600, Chicago, IL 60601
Tel (312) 616-0000 *Founded/Ownrshp* 2009
Sales 128.4MM[E] *EMP* 800
SIC 8711 8712 Engineering services; Architectural services
CEO: Vladimir Stritesky
**CFO:* Greg Henderson
VP: Neal Boothe
Netwrk Eng: Fernando Jimenez

EXPANSION JOINT SOLUTIONS
See EAGLEBURGMANN KE INC

D-U-N-S 18-554-6405
EXPANSION STRATEGIES INC
17 Rollingwood Dr, New Hartford, NY 13413-2707
Tel (315) 793-3137 *Founded/Ownrshp* 1986
Sales 57.6MM[E] *EMP* 2,700
SIC 8742 Management consulting services; Marketing consulting services
Pr: Neville Barnett
**VP:* Helen Barnett

D-U-N-S 09-218-0517
▲ EXPEDIA INC
333 108th Ave Ne, Bellevue, WA 98004-5703
Tel (425) 679-7200 *Founded/Ownrshp* 1996
Sales 6.6MMM *EMP* 18,730
Accts Ernst & Young Llp Seattle Wa
Tkr Sym EXPE *Exch* NGS
SIC 4724 Travel agencies
Pr: Dara Khosrowshahi
Ch Bd: Barry Diller
CFO: Mark D Okerstrom
V Ch Bd: Victor A Kaufman
Ex VP: Robert J Dzielak
VP: Tom Colandrea
VP: Bruce Freeman
VP: Kristin Graham
VP: Mark Hollyhead
VP: Julie Kyse
VP: Eric Nicholson
VP: Mark Rowland
VP: Sean C Shannon
VP: Lance A Soliday
Dir Rx: Mark Moseley
Board of Directors: Alexander Von Furstenberg, Susan C Athey, A George Battle, Pamela L Coe, Jonathan L Dolgen, Craig A Jacobson, Peter M Kern, John C Malone, Christopher W Shean, Jose A Tazon

D-U-N-S 04-685-8820
EXPEDITED LOGISTICS AND FREIGHT SERVICES LLC
4740 Consulate Plaza Dr, Houston, TX 77032-2671
Tel (281) 442-3323 *Founded/Ownrshp* 2014
Sales 106.7MM[E] *EMP* 175
SIC 4731 Freight forwarding
Genl Pt: Fred Lalumandier
Pt: Randy Cockrell
Pt: David Flake
Pt: Steven Lalumandier

D-U-N-S 03-523-9425 IMP/EXP
▲ EXPEDITORS INTERNATIONAL OF WASHINGTON INC
1015 3rd Ave Fl 12, Seattle, WA 98104-1184
Tel (206) 674-3400 *Founded/Ownrshp* 1979
Sales 6.6MMM *EMP* 15,397
Tkr Sym EXPD *Exch* NGS
SIC 4731 Freight transportation arrangement; Domestic freight forwarding; Foreign freight forwarding; Customhouse brokers
Pr: Jeffrey S Musser
**Ch Bd:* Robert R Wright
Pr: Philip M Coughlin
Pr: Daniel R Wall
Sr VP: Benjamin G Clark
Sr VP: Charles Lynch
Sr VP: Christopher J McClincy
IT Man: Eric Woodbury
Software D: Srikanth Akkiraju
Software D: Uchendu Awa
Software D: Dan Clark
Board of Directors: James M Dubois, Mark A Emmert, Diane H Gulyas, Dan P Kourkoumelis, Michael J Malone, Richard B McCune, Liane J Pelletier, James Li Kou Wang

D-U-N-S 79-044-3449 IMP/EXP
EXPERA SPECIALTY SOLUTIONS LLC
THILMANY PAPERS
600 Thilmany Rd, Kaukauna, WI 54130-2164
Tel (920) 766-4611 *Founded/Ownrshp* 2013
Sales 804.2MM[E] *EMP* 1,800
SIC 2621 Paper mills
Pr: Russ Wanke
**Pr:* Ann Funk
**CFO:* Rob McNutt
**VP:* Robyn Buss
VP: Richard Cote
**VP:* John Katchko
Dir IT: Roderick Glauser
Sls Mgr: Robin Buff
Sls Mgr: Debra Stacy
Pgrm Dir: Jean Rusch

D-U-N-S 95-805-1591
EXPERIAN CORP
(*Suby of* EXPERIAN NA UNLIMITED)
475 Anton Blvd, Santa Ana, CA 92704
Tel (714) 830-7000 *Founded/Ownrshp* 1996
Sales 98.4MM[E] *EMP* 7,710
SIC 7323 Credit bureau & agency; Commercial (mercantile) credit reporting bureau
CEO: Rick Cortese
**Ch Bd:* Craig Smith
V Ch: Thomas Newkirk
Pr: Chris Callero
Pr: Margaret B Smith
Pr: Deborah Zuccarini
CEO: Scot Thomas
CFO: Paul Brooks
Treas: Mark Pepper
Sr VP: Laura Desoto
Sr VP: Patricia Dever
VP: Michael Ceritano
**VP:* Peg Smith

D-U-N-S 96-855-2018
EXPERIAN HEALTH INC
PASSPORT HLTH CMMNICATIONS INC
(*Suby of* EXPERIAN PLC)
720 Cool Springs Blvd, Franklin, TN 37067-2626
Tel (615) 661-5657 *Founded/Ownrshp* 2013
Sales 108.9MM[E] *EMP* 700
SIC 7372 8399 Business oriented computer software; Health & welfare council
Pr: Scott Bagwell
Pr: Heather Lane
Pr: Tom Sale
Pr: Steve Taylor
CFO: Scotte Hudsmith
**Sr VP:* Davd Fox
**Sr VP:* Kevin Gibson
**Sr VP:* Ram Iyengar
**Sr VP:* Marcus Padgett

VP: John Bush
**VP:* Crista Harwood
VP: Kevin Hulvey
VP: Paulette Jaeger
VP: Robert Kinard
VP: Robert Novielli
VP: Peter Savage

D-U-N-S 13-884-4167
EXPERIAN HOLDINGS INC
(*Suby of* EXPERIAN FINANCE PLC)
475 Anton Blvd, Costa Mesa, CA 92626-7037
Tel (714) 830-7000 *Founded/Ownrshp* 2009
Sales 4.2MMM^E *EMP* 6,765^E
SIC 8741 Management services
CEO: Victor Nichols
Pr: Scott Bagwell
Ex VP: Joseph Ervin
VP: Russ Bartlett
**Prin:* Joanna Leivici
**Prin:* Douglass Sturgess
Sls&Mrk Ex: Cheyenne Bertiloni
Mktg Mgr: Mark Dinicola

D-U-N-S 00-864-2530
EXPERIAN INFORMATION SOLUTIONS INC (OH)
(*Suby of* EXPERIAN HOLDINGS INC) ★
475 Anton Blvd, Costa Mesa, CA 92626-7037
Tel (714) 830-7000 *Founded/Ownrshp* 1996, 1999
Sales 4.2MMM^E *EMP* 6,765
Accts Ranjan Sriskandan/Pricewaterho
SIC 7323 Credit bureau & agency; Commercial (mercantile) credit reporting bureau
CEO: Chris Callero
Pr: Craig Halley
Pr: Gary Kearns
Pr: Daniel Schotland
Pr: Jennifer Schulz
Sr VP: Dan Buell
**Sr VP:* Stephen Burnside
Sr VP: Dean Paluch
Sr VP: Joseph M Paulsen
VP: Guy Abramo
VP: Jim Fick
VP: Allison Halley
VP: Heather Lane
VP: Tammy Marge
VP: Joe Moffa
VP: Mark Pepper
VP: Doug Sash
VP: Bill Schneider
VP: Dean Skonieczny
VP: Melanie Sohl
VP: Karen Tatten

D-U-N-S 05-251-5201
■ **EXPERIENCE 1 INC**
(*Suby of* SOLUTIONSTAR HOLDINGS LLC) ★
5000 Birch St Ste 300, Newport Beach, CA 92660-2147
Tel (949) 475-3752 *Founded/Ownrshp* 2015
Sales NA *EMP* 366^E
SIC 6361 6531 Title insurance; Real estate agents & managers
CEO: Michael Tafoya

D-U-N-S 07-010-4203
EXPERIENCE WORKS INC
4401 Wilson Blvd Ste 1100, Arlington, VA 22203-4196
Tel (703) 522-7272 *Founded/Ownrshp* 2005
Sales 104.4MM *EMP* 400
Accts Mcgladrey Llp Gaithersburg M
SIC 8322 8331 Old age assistance; Community center; Community service employment training program
Mng Dir: Shane Bateman
**Ch Bd:* Phillip Klutts
**Treas:* Doug Anderton
Ofcr: Shawn Williams
**Prin:* Sally Boofer
**Ex Dir:* William Wooten
Genl Mgr: Richard Schorr
IT Man: Rosemary Schmidt

D-U-N-S 84-931-3051
EXPERIENCED MAIL TRANSPORT INC
1072 Leeda Dr, Jacksonville, FL 32254-2245
Tel (904) 354-4855 *Founded/Ownrshp* 1994
Sales 150.0MM *EMP* 28
SIC 4212 Mail carriers, contract
Pr: Sidney Saunders

D-U-N-S 06-040-6907
EXPERIENT INC
(*Suby of* MARITZ TRAVEL CO) ★
2500 E Enterprise Pkwy, Twinsburg, OH 44087-2338
Tel (330) 425-8333 *Founded/Ownrshp* 2012
Sales 86.5MM^E *EMP* 540
SIC 8742

D-U-N-S 93-841-3366
■ **EXPERIS FINANCE US LLC**
(*Suby of* MANPOWERGROUP INC) ★
100 W Manpower Pl, Milwaukee, WI 53212-4030
Tel (414) 319-3400 *Founded/Ownrshp* 2001
Sales 113.6MM^E *EMP* 1,700
SIC 8721 Accounting, auditing & bookkeeping
CEO: Owen G Sullivan
**Pr:* Michael Touhey

D-U-N-S 96-336-0623
■ **EXPERIS US INC**
(*Suby of* MANPOWERGROUP INC) ★
100 W Manpower Pl, Milwaukee, WI 53212-4030
Tel (414) 961-1000 *Founded/Ownrshp* 1995
Sales 144.3MM^E *EMP* 850^E
SIC 7361 Employment agencies
Pr: Jeff Joerres
Pr: Perry Wedum
VP: Debra Banning
Mng Dir: Jonathan Evans
Mng Dir: Jason Hogan
Mng Dir: Chris Layden
Mng Dir: John Sullivan
Mng Dir: Steve Young
Tech Mgr: Josh Long
Snr Mgr: Martin Amundson
Snr Mgr: Jamie Grab

D-U-N-S 06-852-3562
EXPERITEC INC
504 Trade Center Blvd, Chesterfield, MO 63005-1253
Tel (636) 681-1500 *Founded/Ownrshp* 1992
Sales 195.3MM^E *EMP* 137
SIC 5085 5084 Industrial supplies; Valves & fittings; Industrial machinery & equipment
Pr: Laurence J Tietjen
CFO: Melody Donovan
Sr VP: Mark Franklin
Dir IT: Rick Meuser
Sls Mgr: Gary Miller
Sls Mgr: Kevin Potter
Sales Asso: Diane Becraft
Sales Asso: Maverick Ford
Sales Asso: Lane Forhetz
Sales Asso: Joshua Lieblong
Sales Asso: Brian Long

EXPERT AIR
See KTB SERVICES LLC

D-U-N-S 96-678-6360
EXPERT GLOBAL SOLUTIONS INC
(*Suby of* PRIORITY ONE SUPPORT) ★
5085 W Park Blvd Ste 300, Plano, TX 75093-2599
Tel (800) 252-3996 *Founded/Ownrshp* 2016
Sales 813.7MM^E *EMP* 40,000
SIC 7322 Adjustment & collection services; Collection agency, except real estate
CEO: Andy Lee
Pr: Bong Borja
COO: Art Dibari
CFO: James Molloy
CIO: Jim Radzicki

D-U-N-S 07-881-3071
EXPOCREDIT LLC
1450 Brickell Ave # 2660, Miami, FL 33131-3458
Tel (305) 347-9222 *Founded/Ownrshp* 2013
Sales NA *EMP* 17
SIC 6153 Short-term business credit
Pr: Carlos Escobar
**Mng Pt:* Alejandro Gonzalez
**Prin:* Nestor Gonzalez
**Prin:* Alfredo Quintero

D-U-N-S 60-406-1267
▲ **EXPONENT INC**
149 Commonwealth Dr, Menlo Park, CA 94025-1133
Tel (650) 326-9400 *Founded/Ownrshp* 1967
Sales 304.7MM *EMP* 999^E
Tkr Sym EXPO *Exch* NGS
SIC 8711 8742 8999 Consulting engineer; Management consulting services; Scientific consulting
Pr: Paul R Johnston
**Ch Bd:* Michael R Gaulke
Pr: Catherine Corrigan
**CEO:* Paul Johnston
CFO: Richard L Schlenker Jr
Bd of Dir: Bernard Ross
Ofcr: Elizabeth L Anderson
Grp VP: Robert D Caligiuri PH
VP: Larry Anderson
VP: Paul D Boehm
VP: Robert Caligiuri
VP: Graeme Fowler
VP: Caroline Harris
VP: Jason L Hertzberg
VP: Brad A James
VP: Steven M Kurtz
VP: Harri K Kytomaa
VP: Robert C Lange
VP: Angela A Meyer
VP: Suresh Moolgavkar
VP: John D Osteraas
Board of Directors: Karen A Richardson, Stephen C Riggins, John B Shoven, Debra L Zumwalt

D-U-N-S 00-292-2110
EXPORT PACKAGING CO INC
XPAC
525 10th Ave E, Milan, IL 61264-3117
Tel (309) 756-4288 *Founded/Ownrshp* 1962, 1996
Sales 110.1MM^E *EMP* 1,000
SIC 4783 2448 2441 Packing & crating; Pallets, wood; Shipping cases, wood: nailed or lock corner
Pr: Gregory A Ruggies
**CEO:* Donald Ruggles
**CFO:* Byron Fernald
**VP:* John Beck
Plnt Mgr: Bob Smith

D-U-N-S 02-626-0096
EXPRESS ENERGY SERVICES OPERATING LP
9800 Richmond Ave Ste 500, Houston, TX 77042-4853
Tel (713) 625-7400 *Founded/Ownrshp* 2006
Sales 1.0MMM^E *EMP* 1,328
SIC 1389 Pipe testing, oil field service
CEO: Stuart Bodden
**Genl Pt:* Darron Anderson
**Pt:* Donnie Goodwin
**COO:* David Brunnert
**CFO:* John Robert Beall
Treas: Ryan Mc Millan
Ex VP: Mark Haubert
Sr VP: Tom B Slocum
VP: Jay Garner
Exec: Kay Hight
CIO: Mike Giles

D-U-N-S 96-372-6984
■ **EXPRESS HOLDING LLC**
(*Suby of* EXPRESS TOPCO LLC) ★
11431 W Airport Svc Rd, Swanton, OH 43558-9389
Tel (614) 474-4001 *Founded/Ownrshp* 2004
Sales 1.4MMM^E *EMP* 17,000^E
SIC 5621 5611 Women's clothing stores; Men's & boys' clothing stores
Pr: Michael A Weiss

D-U-N-S 96-370-4775 IMP/EXP
▲ **EXPRESS INC**
1 Express Dr, Columbus, OH 43230-1496
Tel (614) 474-4001 *Founded/Ownrshp* 1980
Sales 2.3MMM *EMP* 18,000
Tkr Sym EXPR *Exch* NYS
SIC 5621 5632 5611 Women's clothing stores; Ready-to-wear apparel, women's; Women's accessory & specialty stores; Apparel accessories; Men's & boys' clothing stores; Clothing accessories: men's & boys'
Pr: David G Kornberg
Ch Bd: Mylle Mangum
Pr: David Kornberg
COO: Matthew Moellering
CFO: Periclis Pericleous
CFO: Periclis V Pericleous
Chf Mktg O: Jim Hilt
Ex VP: Colin Campbell
Ex VP: Erica A McIntyre
Ex VP: Jeanne St Pierre
Ex VP: Douglas Tilson
VP: Lori Berzow
VP: Keith Pickens
VP: Jack Rafferty
VP: Mary Schutter
VP: Deborah Urton
VP: Carmen Wamre
Board of Directors: Michael Archbold, Terry Davenport, Michael Devine III, Theo Killion, Karen Leever, Peter Swinburn

D-U-N-S 12-055-1143 IMP/EXP
■ **EXPRESS LLC**
(*Suby of* EXPRESS HOLDING LLC) ★
1 Express Dr, Columbus, OH 43230-1496
Tel (614) 474-4001 *Founded/Ownrshp* 1998
Sales 1.4MMM^E *EMP* 17,000
SIC 5621 5611 Ready-to-wear apparel, women's; Men's & boys' clothing stores
VP: Matthew Moellering
**CFO:* Matthew C Moellering
CFO: Todd Painter
**Chf Mktg O:* Lisa A Gavales
**Ex VP:* Colin Campbell
**Ex VP:* Elliott R Tobias

D-U-N-S 11-628-6048 IMP/EXP
EXPRESS MANUFACTURING INC
3519 W Warner Ave, Santa Ana, CA 92704-5214
Tel (714) 979-2228 *Founded/Ownrshp* 1984
Sales 155.7MM^E *EMP* 500^E
SIC 3672 3679 Printed circuit boards; Electronic circuits
Pr: Chauk Pan Chin
**Treas:* Catherine Lee Chin
VP: Mike Chen
**VP:* C M Chin
VP: Stana Marko
Mng Dir: Davone Oudomthavy
Genl Mgr: Reed Chan
Genl Mgr: Bob Cunningham
Info Man: Lia Chin
Ql Cn Mgr: Linwood J Goddard III
Ql Cn Mgr: Jenny Luo

EXPRESS MART
See TRI-CON INC

EXPRESS MART
See PETR-ALL PETROLEUM CONSULTING CORP

D-U-N-S 83-756-3717
EXPRESS MESSENGER SYSTEMS INC
ONTRAC
2501 S Price Rd Ste 201, Chandler, AZ 85286-7897
Tel (800) 334-5000 *Founded/Ownrshp* 1980
Sales 706.7MM^E *EMP* 2,500
SIC 4215 Courier services, except by air
Prin: David Callaway
COO: Robert E Humphrey Jr
**CFO:* Thomas B Fischer
Area Mgr: Brian Schnakenberg
Area Mgr: Joyce Tucker
Genl Mgr: Keenan Moore
Genl Mgr: Charlie Smith
MIS Dir: Diane Palmer
Dir IT: Tim Elder
IT Man: Rob Abel
Sfty Dirs: Mike Pettebone
Board of Directors: John Dir

EXPRESS METALS
See BCH MECHANICAL INC

EXPRESS OIL CHANGE AND SVC CTR
See EXPRESS OIL CHANGE LLC

D-U-N-S 15-530-5154
EXPRESS OIL CHANGE LLC
EXPRESS OIL CHANGE AND SVC CTR
1880 Southpark Dr, Hoover, AL 35244-2094
Tel (205) 945-1771 *Founded/Ownrshp* 2013
Sales 78.2MM^E *EMP* 1,000
SIC 7549 7538 6794 Lubrication service, automotive; General automotive repair shops; Franchises, selling or licensing
CEO: Ricky Brooks
COO: Joseph E Watson
Sr VP: Robert Campbell
Sr VP: Jeremy Persinger
Sr VP: Jason Seeby
VP: Kent Feazell

EXPRESS PERSONNEL SERVICES
See EXPRESS SERVICES INC

EXPRESS POINT
See EXPRESSPOINT TECHNOLOGY SERVICES INC

EXPRESS SCRIPTS HOLDING CO
See MEDCO HEALTH SOLUTIONS INC

D-U-N-S 07-846-1979
▲ **EXPRESS SCRIPTS HOLDING CO**
1 Express Way, Saint Louis, MO 63121-1824
Tel (314) 996-0900 *Founded/Ownrshp* 2011
Sales 101.7MMM *EMP* 25,900
Tkr Sym ESRX *Exch* NGS
SIC 5912 5961 Drug stores & proprietary stores; Pharmaceuticals, mail order
Pr: Timothy Wentworth
**Ch Bd:* George Paz
CFO: Eric Slusser
Chf Mktg O: Phyllis Anderson
Ofcr: Steven Miller
Ofcr: Glen Stettin
Ofcr: Sara Wade
Sr VP: Martin Akins
Sr VP: Don Fotsch
Sr VP: Christine Houston
Sr VP: Everett Neville
Sr VP: David Queller
Sr VP: Neal Sample
Sr VP: Glen D Stettin
VP: Kelley Elliott
VP: Christopher McGinnis

D-U-N-S 17-349-0459
■ **EXPRESS SCRIPTS INC**
(*Suby of* EXPRESS SCRIPTS HOLDING CO) ★
1 Express Way, Saint Louis, MO 63121-1824
Tel (314) 996-0900 *Founded/Ownrshp* 2012
Sales 3.1MMM^E *EMP* 13,120
SIC 5961 Pharmaceuticals, mail order
CEO: George Paz
**CFO:* Jeffrey Hall
Ofcr: Joseph W Plum
Ofcr: Edward J Tenholder
Ofcr: Darryl E Weinrich
**Ex VP:* Keith Ebling
Ex VP: Michael Holmes Sr
**Ex VP:* Ed Ignaczak
**Ex VP:* Patrick McNamee
**Sr VP:* John Henderson
**Sr VP:* Christine Houston
**Sr VP:* Steven Miller
Sr VP: Agnes Rey-Giraud
Sr VP: Larry Zarin
VP: Sumner Charles
**VP:* Kelley Elliott
VP: Ronald Fox
VP: Thomas Hagerman
VP: Sonja Larson
VP: Karen Matteuzzi
VP: David Norton

D-U-N-S 13-106-7282
EXPRESS SERVICES INC
EXPRESS PERSONNEL SERVICES
9701 Boardwalk Blvd, Oklahoma City, OK 73162-6029
Tel (405) 840-5000 *Founded/Ownrshp* 1983
Sales 2.6MMM *EMP* 373,869
Accts Mcgladrey Llp Dallas Texas
SIC 7363 6794 7361 Help supply services; Temporary help service; Franchises, selling or licensing; Employment agencies
CEO: Robert A Funk
COO: Christy Taylor
CFO: Tony Bostwick
CFO: W Anthony Bostwick
Ex VP: Robert E Fellinger
Ex VP: Keith McFall
Ex VP: William H Stoller
Sr VP: Cory Benton
VP: Arthur L Atkinson
VP: Cindy S Fairchild
VP: C Thomas Gunderson
VP: Dave Kuker
VP: Don Lapp
VP: L Edward Taylor
VP: Jonathan Thom
VP: Terry Weldon
VP: Ann West
VP Bus Dev: Framme Cyndi
VP Bus Dev: Holly Doan
VP Bus Dev: Calvin Ishee
Dir Soc: Terese Irwin
Board of Directors: Bob Gibson, Dave Gillogly

EXPRESS SHOPS
See LITCO PETROLEUM INC

EXPRESS STORE
See BEST-WADE PETROLEUM INC

EXPRESS TIRE DELIVERY
See DUNN TIRE LLC

D-U-N-S 96-371-4550 IMP
■ **EXPRESS TOPCO LLC**
(*Suby of* EXPRESS INC) ★
1 Express Dr, Columbus, OH 43230-1496
Tel (614) 474-4001 *Founded/Ownrshp* 2010
Sales 1.2MMM^E *EMP* 17,000^E
SIC 5621 5611 Women's clothing stores; Men's & boys' clothing stores
Pr: Michael A Weiss

D-U-N-S 11-191-5989 IMP
EXPRESS TRADE CAPITAL INC
1410 Broadway Fl 26, New York, NY 10018-5007
Tel (212) 997-0155 *Founded/Ownrshp* 1993
Sales NA *EMP* 18^E
SIC 6153 4731 Direct working capital financing; Customhouse brokers
Ch Bd: Peter Stern
**Ex VP:* Benjamin Ellis
**Sr VP:* Mark Bienstock
VP: David Estrakh

EXPRESS TRUCK CENTER
See OMAHA TRUCK CENTER INC

D-U-N-S 09-584-5095
■ **EXPRESSJET AIRLINES INC**
(*Suby of* SKYWEST INC) ★
100 Hartsfield Ctr 700, Atlanta, GA 30354-1329
Tel (404) 856-1000 *Founded/Ownrshp* 2002
Sales 935.5MM^E *EMP* 9,200
SIC 4512 Air passenger carrier, scheduled; Air cargo carrier, scheduled
CEO: Jerry C Atkin
**Pr:* Brad Holt
**CFO:* Michael J Kraupp
Bd of Dir: Michael K Young
Ofcr: Kyle Barr
Ofcr: Eric Graser
Ofcr: Stephen Rocha
Ofcr: Andrew Webb
VP: Richard L Frymire
VP: Melanee Haywood
VP: Lisa Walker
**VP:* Eric Woodward
Board of Directors: Margaret Billson, Ian M Cumming, Henry J Eyring, Ronald J Mittelstaedt, Keith E Smith

D-U-N-S 03-026-1130
■ **EXPRESSJET HOLDINGS INC**
(*Suby of* EXPRESSJET AIRLINES INC) ★
700 N Sam Hous Pkwy W # 200, Houston, TX 77067-4335
Tel (832) 353-1000 *Founded/Ownrshp* 2012
Sales 155.5MM^E *EMP* 5,600
SIC 4512 Air passenger carrier, scheduled; Air cargo carrier, scheduled
Pr: Brad Holt
**VP:* Ken Ashworth
VP: Fred H Junek Jr
VP: Fred Junek
**VP:* Brandee Reynolds
**VP:* Charlie Tutt
**VP:* Terry Vais
**VP:* Lisa Walker
**VP Admn:* Kevin Wade
Rgnl Mgr: Steven Moore
Genl Mgr: Ron Busch

D-U-N-S 00-260-1768 IMP
EXPRESSPOINT TECHNOLOGY SERVICES INC (DE)
EXPRESS POINT
10900 Wayzata Blvd # 800, Hopkins, MN 55305-5602
Tel (763) 543-6000 *Founded/Ownrshp* 1997
Sales 136.8MM^E *EMP* 300
SIC 5045 7379 7699 8741 7389 7378 Computers, peripherals & software; Computer peripheral equipment; Computer related maintenance services; Automated teller machine (ATM) repair; Management services; Purchasing service; Computer maintenance & repair
CEO: David Anderson
CFO: John March
VP: Kelly Dudek
Prgrm Mgr: Michael Olson
CIO: Terry Waagmeester
IT Man: Jackie Welucox
Plnt Mgr: Matthew Riehl

D-U-N-S 17-330-7240 IMP
EXTECH BUILDING MATERIALS INC
87 Bowne St, Brooklyn, NY 11231-1243
Tel (718) 852-7090 *Founded/Ownrshp* 1987
Sales 148.0MM^E *EMP* 150
SIC 5082 5033 5031 Masonry equipment & supplies; Roofing & siding materials; Trim, sheet metal
Ch Bd: Robert Feury Sr
**VP:* Vito Pela
Brnch Mgr: Jeff Alba
Brnch Mgr: Doug Kisley
Brnch Mgr: C J Pinkney
IT Man: Gautam Bhayana
Sales Exec: Lee Gomes
Sales Asso: Jaikumar Assudani
Sales Asso: Eric Kernisant
Sales Asso: Fernando Pedro

D-U-N-S 14-953-1399
EXTEND HEALTH INC
ONEEXCHANGE
(*Suby of* TOWERS WATSON & CO) ★
2929 Campus Dr Ste 400, San Mateo, CA 94403-2537
Tel (650) 288-4800 *Founded/Ownrshp* 2012
Sales NA *EMP* 283
SIC 6411 Insurance agents, brokers & service
CEO: John J Haley
**Pr:* Bryce Williams
COO: Joseph Murad
**Sr VP:* Joseph J Murad
Sr VP: Richard Wheeler
VP: Ben Miller
Exec: Lourdes Jones
Mng Dir: Bryce A Williams
**CTO:* Cameron Liljenquist
Opers Supe: Max Jackson
Mktg Dir: John Barkett

D-U-N-S 07-909-3017
▲ **EXTENDED STAY AMERICA INC**
11525 N Community House, Charlotte, NC 28277-3609
Tel (980) 345-1600 *Founded/Ownrshp* 1995
Sales 1.2MMM *EMP* 8,500^E
Tkr Sym STAY *Exch* NYS
SIC 7011 Hotels & motels
Pr: Gerardo I Lopez
**Ch Bd:* Douglas G Geoga
COO: Tom Bardenett
CFO: Jonathan S Halkyard
Chf Mktg O: Thomas Seddon
Ofcr: Kevin A Henry
Genl Mgr: Crystal Ford
Sls Dir: Victoria Schaefer
Board of Directors: Michael Barr, William D Rahm, William J Stein, Richard R Wallman

EXTENDED STAY HOTELS
See HVM LLC

D-U-N-S 07-616-4227
EXTENDICARE FOUNDATION INC
111 W Michigan St, Milwaukee, WI 53203-2903
Tel (414) 908-8000 *Founded/Ownrshp* 1983
Sales 94.5MM^E *EMP* 4,591
SIC 8051

D-U-N-S 11-753-1814
EXTENDICARE HEALTH SERVICES INC
MT VERNON NRSING RHBLTTION CTR
111 W Michigan St, Milwaukee, WI 53203-2903
Tel (414) 908-6720 *Founded/Ownrshp* 1989
Sales NA *EMP* 18,970
SIC 8051 7389 5912

EXTENDICARE HOLDINGS, INC.
See EXTENDICARE HOLDINGS LLC

D-U-N-S 04-526-1612
EXTENDICARE HOLDINGS LLC
EXTENDICARE HOLDINGS, INC.
111 W Michigan St, Milwaukee, WI 53203-2903
Tel (414) 908-8000 *Founded/Ownrshp* 2015
Sales NA *EMP* 20,000
SIC 8051

D-U-N-S 10-221-4558
EXTENDICARE HOMES INC
111 W Michigan St, Milwaukee, WI 53203-2903
Tel (414) 908-8000 *Founded/Ownrshp* 2016
Sales 122.8MM^E *EMP* 11,283
SIC 8051 Skilled nursing care facilities
Ch Bd: Frederick B Ladly
**CEO:* Tim Lukenda
**VP:* Robert J Abramowski
**VP:* Leland M Austin
**VP:* Richard L Bertrand
VP: Hugh McManus
VP: William L Wagner
Dir Soc: Nancy Horne

D-U-N-S 15-466-2824
EXTERIOR SERVICES LLC
209 Anderson Dr, Princeton, WV 24739-7418
Tel (304) 487-1503 *Founded/Ownrshp* 1999
Sales 125.0MM *EMP* 10
SIC 1611 Surfacing & paving

D-U-N-S 07-865-9564
▲ **EXTERRAN CORP**
4444 Brittmoore Rd, Houston, TX 77041-8004
Tel (281) 836-7000 *Founded/Ownrshp* 2007
Sales 1.8MMM *EMP* 15,300^E
Accts Deloitte & Touche Llp Houston
Tkr Sym EXTN *Exch* NYS
SIC 7359 Equipment rental & leasing
Pr: Andrew J Way
Ch Bd: Mark R Sotir
Pr: Girish Saligram
Sr VP: Jon C Biro
Sr VP: Christine M Michel
Sr VP: Steven W Muck
Sr VP: Daniel K Schlanger
Sr VP: Christopher T Werner
VP: Valerie L Banner
VP: Ray Carney
VP: Susan Moore
VP: Rob Rice
Board of Directors: William M Goodyear, James C Gouin, John P Ryan, Christopher T Seaver, Richard R Stewart

EXTERRAN ENERGY
See EXTERRAN TRINIDAD LLC

D-U-N-S 14-660-3688 IMP/EXP
■ **EXTERRAN ENERGY SOLUTIONS LP**
(*Suby of* EXTERRAN ENERGY) ★
263 N Sam Houston Pkwy E, Houston, TX 77060-2014
Tel (281) 836-7000 *Founded/Ownrshp* 2000
Sales 342.1MM^E *EMP* 6,000^E
SIC 7353 Oil field equipment, rental or leasing
Mng Pt: Ernie Danner

D-U-N-S 05-109-9141
■ **EXTERRAN INC**
(*Suby of* ARCHROCK INC) ★
16666 Northchase Dr, Houston, TX 77060-6014
Tel (281) 836-7000 *Founded/Ownrshp* 2007
Sales 480.1MM^E *EMP* 3,095
SIC 7353 5084 Oil equipment rental services; Petroleum industry machinery
CEO: D Bradley Childers
Pr: Ernie L Danner
CFO: J Michael Anderson
CFO: William M Austin
Ex VP: Mark R Sotir
Sr VP: Joseph Kishkill
Sr VP: Chris Michel
Sr VP: Daniel K Schlanger
VP: Steven W Muck
VP: Donald C Wayne
Counsel: Bill Bowes

D-U-N-S 62-330-7790
■ **EXTERRAN TRINIDAD LLC**
EXTERRAN ENERGY
(*Suby of* EXTERRAN CORP) ★
12001 N Huston Rosslyn Rd, Houston, TX 77086-3212
Tel (281) 921-9337 *Founded/Ownrshp* 2015
Sales 433.0MM^E *EMP* 8,300
SIC 7353 5084 1389 Oil field equipment, rental or leasing; Petroleum industry machinery; Gas compressing (natural gas) at the fields
Pr: Andrew J Way
Pr: Girish K Saligram
CFO: Jon C Biro
Sr VP: Christine M Michel
Sr VP: Steven W Muck
Sr VP: Christopher T Werner
VP: Valerie L Banner
VP: Ray Carney

D-U-N-S 17-495-6102
■ **EXTRA SPACE MANAGEMENT INC**
STORAGE USA
(*Suby of* EXTRA SPACE STORAGE INC) ★
2795 E Cottonwood Pkwy # 400, Salt Lake City, UT 84121-7033
Tel (801) 562-5556 *Founded/Ownrshp* 1983
Sales 103.0MM^E *EMP* 279
SIC 4225 Warehousing, self-storage
COO: Karl Haas
VP: Buck Brown
**VP:* Gwyn G McNeal
**VP:* David L Rasmussen
Dist Mgr: Shannon Parks
Store Mgr: Joecool Kemper
IT Man: Megan Pidduck
Sftwr Eng: Richard Keeler
Sftwr Eng: Shane Rasband

D-U-N-S 05-129-9258
▲ **EXTRA SPACE STORAGE INC**
2795 E Cottonwood Pkwy # 400, Salt Lake City, UT 84121-7033
Tel (801) 365-4600 *Founded/Ownrshp* 1977
Sales 782.2MM *EMP* 3,209
Tkr Sym EXR *Exch* NYS
SIC 6798 Real estate investment trusts
CEO: Spencer F Kirk
**Ch Bd:* Kenneth M Woolley
COO: Samrat Sondhi
CFO: P Scott Stubbs
Chf Mktg O: James Overturf
Chf Inves: Joseph D Margolis
Ex VP: Kent Christensen
VP: Timothy Arthurs
VP: Stephen Blake
VP: Bret Durfee
VP: Alex Engel
VP: Brent Hardy
VP: Grace Kunde
VP: David Rasmussen
Dir Risk M: Mark Marshall

D-U-N-S 13-955-1485
EXTRACO CORP
1700 N Vly Mills Dr Ste 1, Waco, TX 76710-2569
Tel (254) 776-0330 *Founded/Ownrshp* 1978
Sales NA *EMP* 535
Accts Federal Deposit Insurance Corp
SIC 6712 Bank holding companies
Pr: S Boyce Brown
Ofcr: Tabitha Schuerg
Sr VP: Andy Sheehy
VP: Gary Webb
Brnch Mgr: Linda Shannon
Board of Directors: James Geeslin, C Sam Smith, Michael Thompson

D-U-N-S 02-680-9898
▲ **EXTRACTION OIL & GAS INC**
370 17th St Ste 5300, Denver, CO 80202-5653
Tel (720) 557-8300 *Founded/Ownrshp* 2012
Sales 197.7MM *EMP* 120^E
Tkr Sym XOG *Exch* NGS
SIC 1382 Oil & gas exploration services
Ch Bd: Mark A Erickson
**Pr:* Matthew R Owens
CFO: Russell T Kelley Jr
Dir IT: John Scheier
Board of Directors: Marvin M Chronister, Donald L Evans, John S Gaensbauer, Peter A Leidel, Wayne W Murdy, Patrick D O'brien

D-U-N-S 11-850-3130 EXP
EXTREME ENGINEERING SOLUTIONS INC
X-ES
3225 Deming Way Ste 120, Middleton, WI 53562-1408
Tel (608) 833-1155 *Founded/Ownrshp* 2002
Sales 106.1MM^E *EMP* 165
SIC 5045 Computers, peripherals & software
CEO: Robert S Scidmore
**COO:* David Scidmore
VP Mktg: John Schmoller
Mktg Dir: Dave Barker
Sales Asso: Erin Kind

D-U-N-S 96-016-2576 IMP
▲ **EXTREME NETWORKS INC**
145 Rio Robles, San Jose, CA 95134-1860
Tel (408) 579-2800 *Founded/Ownrshp* 1996
Sales 528.3MM *EMP* 1,378
Tkr Sym EXTR *Exch* NGS
SIC 3661 7373 7372 Telephone & telegraph apparatus; Computer integrated systems design; Systems integration services; Prepackaged software
Pr: Edward B Meyercord
**Ch Bd:* John H Kispert
CFO: Benjamin Drew Davies
Ex VP: Frank Blohm
Ex VP: Robert Gault
VP: Matt Cleaver
VP: Jack Lyon
VP: Joe Novak
VP: Frank Yoshino
Snr Mgr: Rob Hiekel
Board of Directors: Charles P Carinalli, Kathleen M Holmgren, Edward H Kennedy, Raj Khanna, John C Shoemaker

D-U-N-S 07-941-9643
EXTREME PLASTICS PLUS INC
(*Suby of* EPP INTERMEDIATE HOLDINGS INC)
360 Epic Circle Dr, Fairmont, WV 26554-1582
Tel (304) 534-3600 *Founded/Ownrshp* 2007
Sales 130.0MM^E *EMP* 400
SIC 3083 Laminated plastics plate & sheet
CEO: Bennie M Wharry
**Treas:* Steve Biggs
**VP:* Justin Wade Holt
Off Admin: Amy Cunningham
Sfty Dirs: Rick Richards
Sfty Mgr: Bill Westfall
Opers Mgr: Ross Jones

D-U-N-S 92-704-2643
EXTREME REACH INC
75 2nd Ave Ste 720, Needham Heights, MA 02494-2826
Tel (781) 577-2016 *Founded/Ownrshp* 2007
Sales 232.1MM *EMP* 1,000
Accts Ernst & Young Llp Boston Ma
SIC 7311 Advertising agencies
Pr: John Roland
**COO:* Tim Conley
**CFO:* Michael C Greiner
**Chf Mktg O:* Robert Haskitt
**Chf Mktg O:* Melinda McLaughlin
**Sr VP:* Patrick Hanavan
VP: Dascha Bright
VP: Andy Donato
VP: Kris Estrella
VP: Joann Kessler
VP: Chris Lutz
**VP:* Jorge Martell
VP: Kanayochukwu Onwuama
VP: Ryan Pamplin
VP: Chip Scully
VP: David Unsworth

D-U-N-S 07-844-4859
EXTREME STAFFING OF IDAHO LLC (ID)
651 Blue Lakes Blvd N, Twin Falls, ID 83301-4036
Tel (208) 733-5627 *Founded/Ownrshp* 2010
Sales 64.5MM^E *EMP* 2,000
SIC 7363 Help supply services
COO: Joe Visser

EXTRON ELECTRONICS
See RGB SYSTEMS INC

D-U-N-S 06-983-2009
EXULT INC
(*Suby of* AON HEWITT LLC) ★
121 Innovation Dr Ste 200, Irvine, CA 92617-3094
Tel (949) 856-8800 *Founded/Ownrshp* 2004
Sales 83.8MM^E *EMP* 2,424
SIC 8742 Human resource consulting services
Ch Bd: James C Madden
Pt: Jim Aselta
**Pr:* Kevin Campbell
**CFO:* John Adams
Ex VP: Michael Salvino
**Ex VP:* Stephen M Unterberger
VP: Bruce Ferguson
VP: Gerald Williams
Prin: Russell Fradin
Prin: Alexandra Gallo
Corp Couns: Brian Copple

D-U-N-S 83-553-6699 IMP
EXX INC
1350 E Flamingo Rd 689, Las Vegas, NV 89119-5263
Tel (248) 409-1070 *Founded/Ownrshp* 1994
Sales 96.8MM^E *EMP* 875^E
SIC 3621 3669 3714 3944

D-U-N-S 05-047-5016 IMP
EXXEL OUTDOORS INC
300 American Blvd, Haleyville, AL 35565-2338
Tel (205) 486-5258 *Founded/Ownrshp* 1997
Sales 151.2MM^E *EMP* 500^E
SIC 2399 Sleeping bags
CEO: Harry Kazazian
**Pr:* Armen Kouleyan
**VP:* Barbara Garrison
**VP:* Scott Magardichian
VP: Donald Sands
**VP:* Tory H Upham
Exec: Traci U Lovett

D-U-N-S 00-121-3214 EXP
▲ **EXXON MOBIL CORP** (NJ)
EXXONMOBIL
5959 Las Colinas Blvd, Irving, TX 75039-2298
Tel (972) 444-1000 *Founded/Ownrshp* 1882
Sales 268.8MMM *EMP* 73,500
Tkr Sym XOM *Exch* NYS
SIC 2911 4612 5541 5171 4911 Petroleum refining; Light distillates; Aromatic chemical products; Crude petroleum pipelines; Gasoline service stations; Petroleum bulk stations & terminals; Generation, electric power
Ch Bd: Rex W Tillerson
Pr: Darren W Woods
CFO: Andrew P Swiger
Treas: Robert N Schleckser
VP: S Jack Balagia
VP: David S Rosenthal
VP: Jeffrey J Woodbury
Board of Directors: Samuel J Palmisano, Michael J Boskin, Steven S Reinemund, Angela F Braly, William C Weldon, Ursula M Burns, Larry R Faulkner, Jay S Fishman, Henrietta H Fore, Kenneth C Frazier, Peter Brabeck-Letmathe, Douglas R Oberhelman

D-U-N-S 04-058-6120 IMP
■ **EXXON PIPELINE HOLDINGS INC**
(*Suby of* EXXONMOBIL) ★
800 Bell St Rm 2441, Houston, TX 77002-7455
Tel (713) 656-3636 *Founded/Ownrshp* 1995
Sales 149.8MM^E *EMP* 1,200
SIC 4612 4613 Crude petroleum pipelines; Refined petroleum pipelines
Pr: Barbara A Patocka
**Treas:* Deborah Drumheller
**Prin:* Deborah White
Board of Directors: Deborah Taule SEC

EXXONMOBIL
See EXXON MOBIL CORP

D-U-N-S 07-908-2094 IMP/EXP
■ **EXXONMOBIL CHEMICAL CO**
(*Suby of* EXXONMOBIL) ★
22777 Sprngwoods Vlg Pkwy, Spring, TX 77389-1425
Tel (281) 834-5200 *Founded/Ownrshp* 1882
Sales 1.1MMM^E *EMP* 6,660^E
SIC 2821 Plastics materials & resins

D-U-N-S 00-129-4834 IMP/EXP
■ **EXXONMOBIL OIL CORP** (NY)
L & S AVIATION LUBRICANTS
(*Suby of* EXXONMOBIL) ★
2805 Sycamore St, Beaumont, TX 77701
Tel (409) 757-3763 *Founded/Ownrshp* 1882
Sales 3.7MMM^E *EMP* 5^E
SIC 2911 5171 4613 1311 Petroleum refining; Petroleum bulk stations & terminals; Refined petroleum pipelines; Crude petroleum production; Natural gas production
Ch Bd: Stephen M Greenlee
**Ch Bd:* Robert N Schelckser
Plnt Mgr: Mark Beshears

D-U-N-S 00-793-1777 IMP
■ **EXXONMOBIL PIPELINE CO**
(*Suby of* EXXON PIPELINE HOLDINGS INC) ★
22777 Sprngwoods Vlg Pkwy, Spring, TX 77389-1425
Tel (713) 656-3636 *Founded/Ownrshp* 1941, 2002
Sales 149.8MM^E *EMP* 600
SIC 4612 4613 2911 Crude petroleum pipelines; Gasoline pipelines (common carriers); Petroleum refining
Pr: Mike P Tudor

D-U-N-S 00-172-4657 IMP/EXP
■ **EXXONMOBIL SALES AND SUPPLY LLC** (DE)
(*Suby of* EXXONMOBIL) ★
22777 Sprngwoods Vlg Pkwy, Spring, TX 77389-1425
Tel (800) 243-9966 *Founded/Ownrshp* 1963, 1965
Sales 108.1MM^E *EMP* 300^E
SIC 2911 Petroleum refining
Pr: Lance E Johnson
VP: James Rouse
Dir Soc: Kelly Nealon
Off Mgr: Kevin Kinports

D-U-N-S 09-431-8284
■ EXXONMOBIL SAUDI ARABIA INC (DE)
(*Suby of* L & S AVIATION LUBRICANTS) ★
22777 Sprngwoods Vlg Pkwy, Spring, TX 77389-1425
Tel (281) 288-4545 *Founded/Ownrshp* 1976
Sales 87.9MM[E] *EMP* 3,000
SIC 4213 Liquid petroleum transport, non-local
Pr: Curtis Brand
**Treas:* Joseph Sarnowski
VP: S B Finch Jr
VP: Pj Foley
VP: C K Hanna
VP: Rd Nelson
VP: Wh Ritchie
VP: Dt Warden
VP: W Wiggans

D-U-N-S 04-112-3035
■ EXXONMOBIL UPSTREAM RESEARCH CO
EXXONMOBIL UTEC
(*Suby of* EXXONMOBIL) ★
3120 Buffalo Speedway, Houston, TX 77098-1806
Tel (713) 431-4222 *Founded/Ownrshp* 1964
Sales 228.8MM[E] *EMP* 1,000
SIC 2911 Petroleum refining
CEO: Rex W Tillerson
**Treas:* T Crichlow Jr
**Sr VP:* Mark W Albers
VP: Bashar Alramahi
VP: Kara L Guthrie
VP: George Lock
VP: Craig Rapp
VP: William Reese
**VP:* J A Willott
CTO: Fran Stinson
IT Man: Sylvester Wilson

EXXONMOBIL UTEC
See EXXONMOBIL UPSTREAM RESEARCH CO

EYE CARE CENTERS OF AMERICA
See ECCA HOLDINGS CORP

D-U-N-S 62-384-5005
EYE-MART EXPRESS INC
VISION 4 LESS
13800 Senlac Dr Ste 200, Dallas, TX 75234-8823
Tel (972) 488-2002 *Founded/Ownrshp* 1990
Sales 91.3MM[E] *EMP* 700
SIC 5995 Optical goods stores
Pr: H Doug Barnes
**VP:* Thomas C Floyd
Creative D: Kurt Conner
Dist Mgr: Marty Finley
Genl Mgr: Gina McKee
Genl Mgr: Chris Smith
Snr Sftwr: Jennifer Stearns
Software D: Neil Little
Prd Mgr: Mandy Davis
Advt Mgr: Cory Dugas

D-U-N-S 07-835-5156
EYEA LLLP
200 Plaza Dr Ste 2222, Secaucus, NJ 07094-3663
Tel (201) 872-2200 *Founded/Ownrshp* 2012
Sales 105.3MM[E] *EMP* 27,000
SIC 8721 Accounting, auditing & bookkeeping
COO: Peter Griffith
CFO: Michael Ventling
Treas: Jeffrey Dworken

D-U-N-S 07-966-1634
EYEMART EXPRESS LLC
VISION4LESS
13800 Senlac Dr Ste 200, Farmers Branch, TX 75234-8823
Tel (972) 488-2002 *Founded/Ownrshp* 2014
Sales 163.3MM[E] *EMP* 1,228[E]
SIC 5995 Optical goods stores; Eyeglasses, prescription; Opticians
Pr: Hd Barnes
COO: Doug Barnes

D-U-N-S 95-815-8222 IMP
EYEMART EXPRESS LTD
13800 Senlac Dr Ste 200, Dallas, TX 75234-8823
Tel (972) 488-2002 *Founded/Ownrshp* 1996
Sales 71.8MM[E] *EMP* 1,000
SIC 5995 Optical goods stores
Pr: Hernkovitz Jonathan
**COO:* Doug Barnes Jr
VP: Eva Thomas

EYEWAY
See CREATIVE OFFICE ENVIRONMENTS

EZ GO
See CAREY JOHNSON OIL CO INC

D-U-N-S 60-284-2502
▲ EZCORP INC
2500 Bee Caves Rd B1-200, Austin, TX 78746-0016
Tel (512) 314-3400 *Founded/Ownrshp* 1989
Sales 788.3MM *EMP* 7,300[E]
Accts Bdo Usa Llp Dallas Texas
Tkr Sym EZPW *Exch* NGS
SIC 5932 6141 Pawnshop; Personal credit institutions
CEO: Stuart I Grimshaw
Ch Bd: Lachlan P Given
Pr: Joseph L Rotunda
CFO: Mark Ashby
CFO: David McGuire
Ofcr: Scott Alomes
Ofcr: Jodie E B Maccarrone
Ofcr: F Carl Spilker III
Ofcr: Jacob Wedin
Sr VP: Thomas H Welch Jr
VP: Irma Arguijo-Rivera
VP: Susan Baker
VP: Edward Foster
VP: Eric Harrison
VP: Dave Hurrell
VP: Peter McCormick
VP: Tammie Valentini
Board of Directors: Matthew W Appel, Peter Cumins, Pablo Lagos Espinosa, Santiago Creel Miranda, Thomas C Roberts, Joseph L Rotunda

D-U-N-S 01-082-8630
EZRA HEALTH CARE INC
BEACHWOOD NRSING HALTHCARE CTR
23258 Fernwood Dr, Beachwood, OH 44122-1569
Tel (440) 498-3000 *Founded/Ownrshp* 1993
Sales 963.6MM *EMP* 130
SIC 8051 Extended care facility
Pr: Will Grunspan
**VP:* Sharona Grunspan

F

F & E TRADING
See VALOR GROUP LLC

D-U-N-S 80-815-8567
F & H ACQUISITION CORP
200 Crescent Ct Ste 1400, Dallas, TX 75201-7826
Tel (214) 661-7474 *Founded/Ownrshp* 2005
Sales 252.8MM[E] *EMP* 1,029
SIC 6799 Investors
Pr: Mark E Schwarz

D-U-N-S 00-790-7421 IMP
F & M BANK & TRUST CO
1330 S Harvard Ave, Tulsa, OK 74112-5818
Tel (918) 744-1330 *Founded/Ownrshp* 1974
Sales NA *EMP* 240
SIC 6022

D-U-N-S 01-674-5994 IMP/EXP
F & M MAFCO INC
9149 Dry Fork Rd, Harrison, OH 45030-1901
Tel (513) 367-2151 *Founded/Ownrshp* 1946
Sales 102.1MM *EMP* 250
SIC 5085 5072 7353 5082 Welding supplies; Hardware; Heavy construction equipment rental; General construction machinery & equipment
Pr: Daniel Mc Kenna
**CFO:* James Zeisler
Sr Cor Off: Brenda Mittelstadt
**Ex VP:* Pat Mc Kenna
**Ex VP:* Robert W Mc Kenna Jr
Ex VP: Patrick D McKenna
**VP:* Gregory Friedmann
**VP:* William Mc Kenna
VP: Robert McKenna
Genl Mgr: Scott Speigle
MIS Dir: David Norris

D-U-N-S 02-449-8862
F & W FARMS INC
177 Woody Cir, New Hope, AL 35760-8359
Tel (256) 599-8422 *Founded/Ownrshp* 1999
Sales 2.5MMM *EMP* 2
SIC 0116 0115 0131 0111 Soybeans; Corn; Cotton; Wheat
Pr: Jeff Webster

F A A
See FEDERAL AVIATION ADMINISTRATION

D-U-N-S 00-691-8262
F A BARTLETT TREE EXPERT CO
BARTLETT TREE EXPERTS
1290 E Main St Ste 2, Stamford, CT 06902-3556
Tel (203) 323-1131 *Founded/Ownrshp* 1907
Sales 7.6MM[E] *EMP* 1,250
Accts Mercer Health & Benefits Llc
SIC 0783 Spraying services, ornamental tree; Spraying services, ornamental bush; Pruning services, ornamental bush; Pruning services, ornamental tree
Ch Bd: Robert A Bartlett Jr
**Pr:* Gregory S Daniels
**CFO:* John E Signorini
**Sr VP:* John J Bedosky
VP: Patrick Brewer
**VP:* Frank B Heisinger
Exec: Carol Kijek
Div Mgr: Dave Anderson
Genl Mgr: Thomas Mullarney
Off Mgr: Lynn Roberts
Off Mgr: Rich Sala

D-U-N-S 09-210-0833
F A RICHARD & ASSOCIATES INC
FARA
(*Suby of* AVIZENT) ★
1625 W Causeway Approach, Mandeville, LA 70471-2954
Tel (985) 624-8383 *Founded/Ownrshp* 2011
Sales NA *EMP* 482
SIC 6411

F C A
See FIRST COOPERATIVE ASSOCIATION

F C A
See FELLOWSHIP OF CHRISTIAN ATHLETES

F C C
See FCC ENVIRONMENTAL LLC

F C C C
See FREIGHTLINER CUSTOM CHASSIS CORP

F C N
See FCN INC

F C P
See FILLMORE CAPITAL PARTNERS LLC

F CHRISTIANA & CO
See RIVERSIDE FOOD DISTRIBUTORS LLC

D-U-N-S 00-794-6676
F DOHMEN CO (WI)
190 N Milwaukee St, Milwaukee, WI 53202-6013
Tel (414) 299-4913 *Founded/Ownrshp* 1858
Sales 218.2MM[E] *EMP* 355
SIC 5122 5045 7374 Drugs, proprietaries & sundries; Pharmaceuticals; Computer software; Computers; Data processing & preparation
Ch Bd: Robert C Dohmen
Pr: Clay Anselmo
Pr: Mark Helvick
Pr: Dan Johnson
Pr: Herbert Lee
Pr: Joe Nolan
CEO: Cynthia A Laconte
Chf Mktg O: Todd Nash
Ofcr: Joe Hammer
Ofcr: Bill Von Rohr
VP: Patrick K Byrnes
VP: Stephen Delaat
VP: Lora Platt
VP: John Waughan

F E C ELECTRIC
See FARMERS ELECTRIC COOPERATIVE INC

F E I
See FRITZ ENTERPRISES INC

D-U-N-S 00-382-1642
F E MORAN INC (IL)
(*Suby of* ARMON INC) ★
2265 Carlson Dr, Northbrook, IL 60062-6797
Tel (847) 498-4800 *Founded/Ownrshp* 1915, 1957
Sales 108.1MM[E] *EMP* 250
SIC 1711 Warm air heating & air conditioning contractor; Refrigeration contractor; Ventilation & duct work contractor; Plumbing contractors
Pr: Michael V McCombie
**Treas:* Russell Bentley
Dir IT: Mike Carr

F F C
See FARMERS WIN COOPERATIVE

F F G
See FLYING FOOD GROUP INC

F F THOMPSON HOSPITAL
See FREDERICK FERRIS THOMPSON HOSPITAL

F G I C
See FINANCIAL GUARANTY INSURANCE CO

F H I
See FREIGHT HANDLERS INC

F H N
See FAMILY HEALTH NETWORK INC

F I M C
See FINANCIAL INSURANCE MANAGEMENT CORP

F I S
See FIDELITY NATIONAL GLOBAL CARD SERVICES INC

F I S OUTDOOR
See FLORIDA IRRIGATION SUPPLY INC

D-U-N-S 00-913-6920 IMP
F KORBEL & BROS
KORBEL CHAMPAGNE CELLERS
13250 River Rd, Guerneville, CA 95446-9593
Tel (707) 824-7000 *Founded/Ownrshp* 1984
Sales 85.8MM[E] *EMP* 500
SIC 2084 0172 Wines; Grapes
Pr: Gary B Heck
Treas: David Faris
Ofcr: Andrew Matthias
Ex VP: Danny Baker
Sr VP: Harold Duncan
VP: Matthew Healey
Software D: Anthony Mazzola
Sfty Mgr: Sylvia Lopez
Prd Mgr: Rafael Alvarez
Natl Sales: Dick Reeves

D-U-N-S 00-480-2088 IMP
F L CRANE AND SONS INC (MS)
508 S Spring St, Fulton, MS 38843-1710
Tel (662) 862-2172 *Founded/Ownrshp* 1950, 1963
Sales 88.9MM *EMP* 600
Accts R Dale Pierce Aberdeen Miss
SIC 1542 Specialized public building contractors
Prin: Johnny L Crane II
**Pr:* Mike Heering
**CFO:* Evangela Roberts
Ofcr: Justin Beck
Ofcr: Jonathan Heering
Ofcr: Doug Lesley
Sr VP: John Pitts
**VP:* Kevin Payne
Off Mgr: Connie Vicknair
Off Mgr: Ashley Wilson

D-U-N-S 01-449-2847 IMP
F M BROWNS SONS INC
205 Woodrow Ave, Reading, PA 19608-1402
Tel (800) 334-8816 *Founded/Ownrshp* 1843
Sales 134.3MM[E] *EMP* 200
SIC 5191 2041 0723 2048 Farm supplies; Feed; Flour; Crop preparation services for market; Bird food, prepared
Pr: Franklin M Brown Jr
**Treas:* Carl A Brown
VP: Lester Brown
**VP:* Thomas E Brown
Dir IT: Frank May
Sls Mgr: Stephen Deysher

D-U-N-S 00-481-8456
F M SYLVAN INC (MI)
(*Suby of* SYLVAN FM HOLDING LLC) ★
1001 State St, Perth Amboy, NJ 08861-2001
Tel (732) 826-7474 *Founded/Ownrshp* 2001
Sales 121.3MM[E] *EMP* 524
SIC 1711 Mechanical contractor
Pr: Robert H Metz
Sr VP: Kenneth A Giacobbe
Sr VP: Dan Kearney
Sr VP: Matthew Panconi
Sr VP: Bill Proctor
VP: Edward Maier

D-U-N-S 03-058-3298
F M TARBELL CO
TARBELL REALTORS
(*Suby of* TARBELL FINANCIAL CORP) ★
1403 N Tustin Ave Ste 380, Santa Ana, CA 92705-8691
Tel (714) 972-0988 *Founded/Ownrshp* 1982
Sales 28.6MM[E] *EMP* 1,300
SIC 6531 Real estate brokers & agents
Pr: Tina Jimov
**CEO:* Donald M Tarbell
COO: Jin Lee
IT Man: Carol Red

F P M
See FOUNDATION PROPERTY MANAGEMENT INC

F R C
See FRC FOUNDERS CORP

F S C
See FORSYTH COUNTY BOARD OF EDUCATION

F S I
See PALL FILTER SPECIALISTS INC

F S U S D
See FAIRFIELD-SUISUN UNIFIED SCHOOL DISTRICT

D-U-N-S 00-150-2426 IMP/EXP
F SCHUMACHER & CO
875 Ave Of The Amrcs 14, New York, NY 10001-3527
Tel (212) 213-7900 *Founded/Ownrshp* 1889
Sales 98.0MM[E] *EMP* 225
SIC 5131 2299 Broadwoven fabrics; Broadwoven fabrics: linen, jute, hemp & ramie
CEO: Terri Eagle
Pr: Nadille Sondike
**CFO:* Robert G Gerboth
CFO: Deb Klemm
CFO: Joseph Meth
**Ch:* Gerald W Puschel
VP: Dave Hart
Creative D: Dara Caponigro
Mktg Dir: Andrew Puschel
Sales Asso: Camille Madonna
Board of Directors: John S Crowley, Elizabeth R Culligan, Warren Mang

F T E I
See FUTURETECH ENTERPRISE INC

D-U-N-S 00-799-7760 IMP/EXP
F W WEBB CO (MA)
160 Middlesex Tpke, Bedford, MA 01730-1416
Tel (781) 272-6600 *Founded/Ownrshp* 1933
Sales 1.2MMM[E] *EMP* 1,500
SIC 5074 5085 5075 Plumbing fittings & supplies; Heating equipment (hydronic); Industrial supplies; Warm air heating & air conditioning
Pr: Jeff Pope
**COO:* Robert Mucciarone
Sr VP: Michael Michaud
VP: Thomas Grunewald
VP: Robert Michaud
VP: John Provencal
Exec: Ernie Coutermarsh
Rgnl Mgr: Mel Hale
Genl Mgr: Jim Hale
Genl Mgr: Chris Sears
IT Man: Matt Lyons
Board of Directors: Elinor Abel, John Pope, Louise Southwick

D-U-N-S 05-810-8184
F&A FOOD SALES INC
2221 Lincoln St, Concordia, KS 66901-5303
Tel (785) 243-2301 *Founded/Ownrshp* 1970
Sales 101.5MM[E] *EMP* 96
SIC 5141 Food brokers
Pr: Dan R Farha
VP: Frank Headrick
Mktg Dir: Robert Cadamore
Sls Mgr: Virginia Blankenbeckley

F&D CORPORATE GENERAL
See FLOOR AND DECOR OUTLETS OF AMERICA INC

F&M BANK
See FARMERS & MERCHANTS BANK OF CENTRAL CALIFORNIA

F&M BANK
See FARMERS & MERCHANTS BANK OF LONG BEACH

D-U-N-S 82-676-1314 IMP
F&P AMERICA MFG INC
(*Suby of* F-TECH INC.)
2101 Corporate Dr, Troy, OH 45373-1076
Tel (937) 339-0212 *Founded/Ownrshp* 1993
Sales 178.0MM[E] *EMP* 650[E]
SIC 3714 Motor vehicle parts & accessories; Motor vehicle steering systems & parts; Motor vehicle brake systems & parts; Motor vehicle body components & frame
Pr: Masafumi Yamano
**Ch Bd:* Akihide Fukuda

D-U-N-S 15-379-6719 IMP
F&S PRODUCE CO INC
913 Bridgeton Ave, Rosenhayn, NJ 08352
Tel (856) 453-0316 *Founded/Ownrshp* 1989
Sales 85.8MM *EMP* 35
SIC 0723 2099 2032 0181 Vegetable crops market preparation services; Vegetable packing services; Vegetables, peeled for the trade; Canned specialties; Ornamental nursery products
Pr: Salvatore Pipitone Jr

D-U-N-S 04-328-4652 IMP/EXP
F&T APPAREL LLC (PA)
FISHMAN & TOBIN
(*Suby of* MAX LEATHER) ★
4000 Chemical Rd Ste 500, Plymouth Meeting, PA 19462-1713
Tel (610) 828-8400 *Founded/Ownrshp* 2011
Sales 102.0MM *EMP* 400
SIC 2311 2321 2325 Suits, men's & boys': made from purchased materials; Men's & boys' sports & polo shirts; Men's & boys' dress slacks & shorts
Pr: Mark Fishman
Sr VP: Jenny Vitale
VP: Mario Lerias
VP: Charles Tarragano
Dir IT: Joe Demarco
VP Opers: Harry Ciaccio
Opers Mgr: Amanda Lally
Plnt Mgr: Nick Vetere
Prd Mgr: Ramon Rodriguez

D-U-N-S 00-425-3480 IMP
F+W MEDIA INC
NOVEL WRITING WORKSHOP
(*Suby of* NEW PUBLISHING HOLDINGS, LLC)
10151 Carver Rd Ste 200, Blue Ash, OH 45242-4760
Tel (513) 531-2690 *Founded/Ownrshp* 2008, 2014
Sales 220.0MM *EMP* 650
SIC 2731 2721 Books: publishing only; Book clubs: publishing only, not printed on site; Magazines: publishing only, not printed on site; Trade journals: publishing only, not printed on site
Ch Bd: David Nussbaum
**Pr:* Sara Domville
**COO:* Jim Ogle
Ofcr: Chad Phelps
Sr VP: Phil Graham
Sr VP: S B Wallis
VP: David Davel
VP: Sara Decarlo
VP: Helen Gregory
**VP:* Richard Warner
Exec: David Thiel
Dir Soc: Taylor Jacobs
Dir Soc: Barb Klus
Dir Soc: Alicia Newton

F-NOK
See FREUDENBERG-NOK GENERAL PARTNERSHIP

F/K/A RADIATION THERAPY SVCS
See 21ST CENTURY ONCOLOGY INC

F/K/A VEOLIA ES SOLID WASTE
See MWSTAR WASTE HOLDINGS CORP

D-U-N-S 95-844-8920
▲ F5 NETWORKS INC
401 Elliott Ave W Ste 500, Seattle, WA 98119-4003
Tel (206) 272-5555 *Founded/Ownrshp* 1996
Sales 1.9MMM *EMP* 4,178
Accts Pricewaterhousecoopers Llp Se
Tkr Sym FFIV *Exch* NGS
SIC 7373 7372 Computer integrated systems design; Prepackaged software
Pr: John McAdam
COO: Edward J Eames
CFO: Andy Reinland
Treas: David Scharler
Top Exec: Andrew Stern
Ex VP: John Dilullo
Ex VP: John D Dilullo
Ex VP: Kristen Roby Dimlow
Ex VP: Edward Eames
Ex VP: David Feringa
Ex VP: Ryan Kearny
Ex VP: Scot Rogers
Ex VP: Karl Triebes
Sr VP: Tony Bozzuti
Sr VP: Peter Brant
VP: Bill Baumann
VP: Brian Blank
VP: Pat Brennan
VP: Michael Corrigan
VP: Renae Culala
VP: Julian Eames
Board of Directors: A Gary Ames, Sandra Bergeron, Deborah L Bevier, Jonathan Chadwick, Michael Dreyer, Alan J Higginson, Peter Klein, Stephen Smith

F.A. WILHELM CONSTRUCTION
See WILHELM CONSTRUCTION INC

FAB
See FASHION ACCESSORY BAZAAR LLC

D-U-N-S 08-046-6777
▲ FAB HOLDINGS I LP
250 Park Ave Fl 4, New York, NY 10177-0001
Tel (212) 624-1200 *Founded/Ownrshp* 2016
Sales 122.5MM[E] *EMP* 82[E]
SIC 6798 Real estate investment trusts
Pr: Stephen J Vaccaro

D-U-N-S 94-572-3096
▲ FAB UNIVERSAL CORP
5001 Baum Blvd Ste 770, Pittsburgh, PA 15213-1856
Tel (412) 621-0902 *Founded/Ownrshp* 1995
Sales 110.8MM *EMP* 193[E]
Tkr Sym FABU *Exch* OTO
SIC 7371 7372 5735 5942 5994 5099 Custom computer programming services; Software programming applications; Prepackaged software; Compact discs; Book stores; Magazine stand; Compact discs
Pr: Christopher J Spencer
**Ch Bd:* Zhang Hongcheng
CFO: John Busshaus
Sr VP: Skip Fredricks
VP: Rob Walch
Prgrm Mgr: Patrick Grumbar
CTO: Armen Geronian

D-U-N-S 02-997-2684 IMP
FABARC STEEL SUPPLY INC
111 Meadow Ln, Oxford, AL 36203-2644
Tel (256) 831-8770 *Founded/Ownrshp* 1979
Sales 149.8MM[E] *EMP* 300
SIC 3441 Building components, structural steel
Pr: Gene Heathcock
**CFO:* John Pilkington
Ex VP: Jim Potter

D-U-N-S 18-318-2054 IMP
FABCO AUTOMOTIVE CORP
(*Suby of* FABCO AUTOMOTIVE CORP) ★
151 Lawrence Dr, Livermore, CA 94551-5126
Tel (925) 245-4100 *Founded/Ownrshp* 2011
Sales 315.7MM[E] *EMP* 2,420[E]
SIC 3714 Axles, motor vehicle; Gears, motor vehicle; Transmission housings or parts, motor vehicle; Transmissions, motor vehicle
Pr: Allen Sunderland
**VP:* David Doden
VP: Lou Keane

D-U-N-S 96-999-5427 IMP
FABCO AUTOMOTIVE CORP
151 Lawrence Dr, Livermore, CA 94551-5126
Tel (925) 454-9500 *Founded/Ownrshp* 2011
Sales 315.7MM[E] *EMP* 2,635
SIC 3714 Axles, motor vehicle
CEO: Gerard Giucidi
**Pr:* Allen Sunderland
**VP:* David Doden

D-U-N-S 02-846-2101 IMP
FABCO LLC
13835 Beaumont Hwy, Houston, TX 77049-1417
Tel (713) 633-6500 *Founded/Ownrshp* 2009
Sales 98.1MM[E] *EMP* 85[E]
SIC 3441 8741 8711 Fabricated structural metal; Management services; Building construction consultant

D-U-N-S 83-644-1675
FABCON COMPANIES LLC
6111 Highway 13 W, Savage, MN 55378-1298
Tel (952) 890-4444 *Founded/Ownrshp* 1995
Sales 220.0MM *EMP* 600
SIC 3272 1771 Panels & sections, prefabricated concrete; Concrete work
CEO: Michael L Lejeune
**CFO:* Mark Pederson
**VP:* Jim Houtman
IT Man: Matt Smith

D-U-N-S 05-607-0477
FABCON INC
6111 Highway 13 W, Savage, MN 55378-1298
Tel (952) 890-4444 *Founded/Ownrshp* 1970
Sales 100.0MM[E] *EMP* 270
SIC 3272 1771 Panels & sections, prefabricated concrete; Concrete work
CEO: Mike Le Jeune
CFO: Scott Sinjem
**CFO:* Craig Wassenaar
**Sr VP:* Richard Wesen
**VP:* Jim Houtman
**VP:* Tom Kuckhahn
**VP:* Mark Pederson
Dir IT: Kim Capel
IT Man: Mark R Pederson
Mfg Dir: Dave Frykman
Mfg Dir: Brian Kopas

D-U-N-S 00-697-3515
FABER COE & GREGG INC
550 Madowlands Pkwy Ste 2, Secaucus, NJ 07094
Tel (201) 330-1515 *Founded/Ownrshp* 1848
Sales 100.0MM *EMP* 600
SIC 5994 5499 5813 Newsstand; Dried fruit; Bars & lounges
Pr: Charles Finkelstein
Mng Pt: Jess Pilotich
**CFO:* Burton Friedman
**Sr VP:* Roberta Rubin
**VP:* Wally Janokowicz
**VP:* Jan Vernie
**VP Opers:* David Horvat

D-U-N-S 80-318-9521
FABIAN OIL INC
15 Oak St, Oakland, ME 04963-5013
Tel (207) 465-7958 *Founded/Ownrshp* 1988
Sales 97.3MM *EMP* 40
Accts Macpage Llc Augusta Maine
SIC 5541 5983 5984 5411 Filling stations, gasoline; Fuel oil dealers; Liquefied petroleum gas dealers; Convenience stores, independent
Pr: Edward J Fabian Jr
Brnch Mgr: Max Marston

D-U-N-S 01-726-0605 IMP
FABIANO BROS INC
1885 Bevanda Ct, Bay City, MI 48706-8720
Tel (989) 509-0200 *Founded/Ownrshp* 2008
Sales 160.0MM *EMP* 340
SIC 5181 5182 Beer & other fermented malt liquors; Wine
Ch: James C Fabiano
**Pr:* James C Fabiano II
**Pr:* Joseph R Fabiano II
**COO:* John Bicknell
**CFO:* Gerard Witte
Sls Dir: Jamie Farrell
Sls Mgr: Jerry Clairmont

D-U-N-S 08-618-4009 IMP
FABIO PERINI NORTH AMERICA INC
(*Suby of* FABIO PERINI SPA)
3060 S Ridge Rd, Green Bay, WI 54304-5526
Tel (920) 336-5000 *Founded/Ownrshp* 1978
Sales 190.6MM[E] *EMP* 800
SIC 5084

D-U-N-S 00-536-1902 IMP/EXP
FABRI-KAL CORP
FK
(*Suby of* TWO MITTS, INC.)
600 Plastics Pl, Kalamazoo, MI 49001-4882
Tel (269) 385-5050 *Founded/Ownrshp* 1950
Sales 350.0MM *EMP* 1,192[E]
SIC 3089

FABRICLAND
See HOUSE OF FABRICS INC

FABRICUT CONTRACT
See FABRICUT INC

D-U-N-S 00-192-1766 IMP/EXP
FABRICUT INC (OK)
FABRICUT CONTRACT
9303 E 46th St, Tulsa, OK 74145-4895
Tel (918) 622-7700 *Founded/Ownrshp* 1959
Sales 122.0MM *EMP* 378
Accts Grant Thornton Llp Tulsa Okl
SIC 5199 Fabrics, yarns & knit goods
CEO: David Finer
**Pr:* Harvey Nudelman
**CFO:* Ron Graham
**Ex VP:* Michael Guterman
VP: Howard Baratz
VP: Nina Butkin
VP: Ray Sparks
Exec: Sherrie Alexander
CIO: Dale Shrauger
Dir IT: Anna Logsdon
Dir IT: Ben Novak

D-U-N-S 08-204-9552 IMP
FABRIK INDUSTRIES INC
FABRIK MOLDED PLASTICS
5213 Prime Pkwy, McHenry, IL 60050-7038
Tel (815) 385-9480 *Founded/Ownrshp* 1980
Sales 91.9MM[E] *EMP* 280
SIC 3089 3544 Injection molding of plastics; Special dies & tools
Pr: Seth Wagner
VP: Deb Madoni

FABRIK MOLDED PLASTICS
See FABRIK INDUSTRIES INC

FABRISTEEL PRODUCTS
See FASTENTECH INC

D-U-N-S 15-431-8133 IMP/EXP
FABTEX INC
111 Woodbine Ln, Danville, PA 17821-9118
Tel (570) 275-7500 *Founded/Ownrshp* 1986
Sales 100.6MM[E] *EMP* 310
SIC 5072 2221 5023 2512 2392 2391 Miscellaneous fasteners; Draperies & drapery fabrics, manmade fiber & silk; Bedspreads, silk & manmade fiber; Draperies; Upholstered household furniture; Household furnishings; Curtains & draperies
Pr: Robert W Snyder
CFO: Ron Swank
Treas: Glenn E Halterman
VP: Brian P Coughlin
VP: Ralph C Davis
VP: William P Friese
Genl Mgr: Craig R Davis
IT Man: Lee Slowick

D-U-N-S 01-601-5958
FABUWOOD CABINETRY CORP
99 Caven Point Rd, Jersey City, NJ 07305-4605
Tel (201) 432-6555 *Founded/Ownrshp* 2009
Sales 96.9MM[E] *EMP* 350
SIC 2434 Wood kitchen cabinets
CEO: Moshe Panzer
**COO:* Joel Epstein
Sftwr Eng: Yakov Muller
VP Opers: Joel Weinstein

FAC
See FARMERS COOPERATIVE ELEVATOR CO

FAC
See FARGO ASSEMBLY CO

D-U-N-S 18-190-4434 IMP
FACCHINA CONSTRUCTION CO INC
(*Suby of* EMPRESAS ICA, S.A.B. DE C.V.)
102 Centennial St Ste 201, La Plata, MD 20646-5969
Tel (240) 776-7000 *Founded/Ownrshp* 2014
Sales 158.5MM[E] *EMP* 500
SIC 1542 1799 1623 1611 1622 1629 Commercial & office building contractors; Construction site cleanup; Building site preparation; Communication line & transmission tower construction; Highway & street construction; Concrete construction: roads, highways, sidewalks, etc.; Bridge, tunnel & elevated highway; Dams, waterways, docks & other marine construction
Ch Bd: Paul V Facchina Sr
**Pr:* Charles W McPherson
**COO:* Jesus R Vazquez
**CFO:* Robert P Kravic
**Ex VP:* Leslie A Nicholson
**Sr VP:* David E Anderson
Exec: Modesto Millo
Div Mgr: Paul Barry
Div Mgr: Tom Mutchler
IT Man: Jeff Jones
Sfty Mgr: Chst D McMoran

D-U-N-S 19-633-7864
▲ FACEBOOK INC
1 Hacker Way Bldg 10, Menlo Park, CA 94025-1456
Tel (650) 543-4800 *Founded/Ownrshp* 2004
Sales 17.9MMM *EMP* 12,711
Accts Ernst & Young Llp San Francis
Tkr Sym FB *Exch* NGS
SIC 7375 On-line data base information retrieval
Ch Bd: Mark Zuckerberg
COO: Sheryl K Sandberg
Ofcr: Christopher K Cox
Top Exec: Ajay Shah
VP: Jorissen Alexandra
VP: Blake Chandlee
VP: Brandon Pierce
VP: Daniel Rose
VP: Colin S Stretch
VP: David M Wehner
Dir Soc: Joshua Needle
Comm Dir: Brian Thomas

D-U-N-S 07-925-8925
■ FACEBOOK PAYMENTS INC (FL)
(*Suby of* FACEBOOK INC) ★
1601 Willow Rd, Menlo Park, CA 94025-1452
Tel (650) 690-3038 *Founded/Ownrshp* 2011
Sales 98.0MM *EMP* 15
SIC 7389 Financial services
CEO: Deborah Liu
**COO:* John Anderson
**CFO:* JAS Athwal
**Chf Cred:* Benjamin Duranske
**Dir Sec:* Micheal Podobnik

D-U-N-S 07-880-2840
FACEY MEDICAL FOUNDATION
15451 San Fernando Msn, Mission Hills, CA 91345-1368
Tel (818) 365-9531 *Founded/Ownrshp* 1991
Sales 197.1MM *EMP* 1,200
Accts Clark Nuber Ps Bellevue Wa
SIC 8099 Medical services organization
CEO: Bill Gill
COO: Teresa David
**CFO:* Jim Corwin
Exec: Cheryl Dee
Comm Man: Abraham Rakelian
Off Mgr: Alma Garcia
Off Mgr: Pat Mahony
Dir IT: Russel Wilmes
Doctor: Ali Gamini

D-U-N-S 08-576-1492 IMP/EXP
FACIL NORTH AMERICA INC
STREETSBORO OPERATIONS
(*Suby of* FACIL EUROPE BVBA)
2242 Pinnacle Pkwy # 100, Twinsburg, OH 44087-5301
Tel (330) 487-2500 *Founded/Ownrshp* 2011
Sales 171.9MM[E] *EMP* 400
SIC 5072 3452 5085 Nuts (hardware); Bolts; Screws; Nuts, metal; Fasteners, industrial: nuts, bolts, screws, etc.
CEO: Rene Achten
**CFO:* Daniel Michiels

D-U-N-S 04-441-1036
FACILITY DESIGN/BUILDERS INC
(*Suby of* FACILITY GROUP) ★
2233 Lake Park Dr Se # 450, Smyrna, GA 30080-8813
Tel (770) 437-2700 *Founded/Ownrshp* 2001
Sales 150.0MM *EMP* 7
SIC 1541 Industrial buildings & warehouses
Ch: Robert H Moultrie
**Pr:* Nick Cawood
CFO: Jack F Godfrey
VP: Donya Edler

FACILITY GROUP
See FACILITY HOLDINGS CORP

D-U-N-S 62-799-7109
FACILITY HOLDINGS CORP
FACILITY GROUP
2700 Cumberland Pkwy Se, Atlanta, GA 30339-3321
Tel (770) 437-2700 *Founded/Ownrshp* 1897
Sales 199.9MM[E] *EMP* 200
SIC 1541 Industrial buildings & warehouses
CEO: James Strack
**Pr:* William Moultrie
**CEO:* W Ennis Parker Jr
CFO: Jack F Godfrey
**Ch:* Frank E Williams Jr

D-U-N-S 96-868-5052
FACILITY LEADERS IN ARCHITECTURAL/ENGINEERING DESIGN PC
FLAD/LEO A DALY JOINT
1201 Conn Ave Nw Fl 10, Washington, DC 20036-2611
Tel (608) 238-2661 *Founded/Ownrshp* 2011
Sales 18.8MM[E] *EMP* 1,000
SIC 8712 8711 Architectural services; Engineering services
CFO: Anika Radtke

D-U-N-S 06-237-6637
FACILITY SOLUTIONS GROUP INC
FSG LIGHTING
4401 West Gate Blvd # 310, Austin, TX 78745-1493
Tel (512) 440-7985 *Founded/Ownrshp* 2008
Sales 1.4MMM[E] *EMP* 1,500
SIC 5063 1731 Lighting fixtures, commercial & industrial; Light bulbs & related supplies; Electrical work; Lighting contractor
Pr: William Graham
COO: Steve Byrne
CFO: Roxanne Roberts
**Treas:* Steve Bryne
VP: Ron Cleary
**VP:* Robert Graham
VP: Keith Zoellner
Creative D: Brent Young
Ex Dir: Debra Meyer
Dir Sec: Greg Thornbury
Dept Mgr: Chris Wills

D-U-N-S 13-844-9173
■ FACTIVA INC
(*Suby of* DOW JONES & CO INC) ★
4300 N Rt 1 820 Ridge Rd, Monmouth Junction, NJ 08852
Tel (609) 627-2000 *Founded/Ownrshp* 2006
Sales 86.2MM[E] *EMP* 800
SIC 7375 Information retrieval services

D-U-N-S 06-885-8414
FACTOR SALES INC
DEL SOL MARKET
676 N Archibald St, San Luis, AZ 85349
Tel (928) 627-8033 *Founded/Ownrshp* 1982
Sales 87.1MM[E] *EMP* 480
SIC 5411 5651 5141 Grocery stores; Family clothing stores; Groceries, general line
Pr: Victor M Salcido
**Treas:* Alicia Mendoza
Treas: Jose L Mendoza

D-U-N-S 60-283-1703 IMP
■ FACTORY CARD & PARTY OUTLET CORP
(*Suby of* AMSCAN HOLDINGS INC) ★
2727 W Diehl Rd, Naperville, IL 60563-8720
Tel (630) 579-2000 *Founded/Ownrshp* 2007
Sales 155.6MM[E] *EMP* 2,500
SIC 5947 Gift, novelty & souvenir shop; Greeting cards; Party favors; Novelties
Pr: Gary W Rada
CFO: Timothy J Benson
CFO: Fred Kraegel
Sr VP: Timothy F Gower
Sr VP: Michael Perri
VP: Joe Cabon
Dist Mgr: Crystal Freitager
Dist Mgr: Larry Hehl
Dist Mgr: Craig Heinitz
Dist Mgr: Fred Jonasen
Tech Mgr: Ray Laylo

D-U-N-S 08-138-7946 IMP
FACTORY CONNECTION LLC
2300 Highway 79 S, Guntersville, AL 35976-2220
Tel (256) 264-9400 *Founded/Ownrshp* 2004
Sales 128.7MM *EMP* 950
SIC 5621 Women's clothing stores
Pr: Mike Reaves
**Ch Bd:* Terry Lane Scott
CFO: Steve Williams
VP: Kevin Hawk
**VP:* Kenneth Littleton
Dist Mgr: Ebbie Moresco
Store Mgr: Kathy Hughes

Store Mgr: Amy Inmon
Site Mgr: Pat Adams
Site Mgr: Kelly Leoppard
Site Mgr: Shannon Turner

FACTORY MOTOR PARTS
See ELLIOTT AUTO SUPPLY CO INC

D-U-N-S 05-151-1178 IMP
FACTORY MUTUAL INSURANCE CO (RI)
FM GLOBAL
270 Central Ave, Johnston, RI 02919-4923
Tel (401) 275-3000 *Founded/Ownrshp* 1835, 1999
Sales NA *EMP* 5,191
Accts Ernst & Young Llp Boston Mas
SIC 6331 8711 6512 Fire, marine & casualty insurance; Engineering services; Nonresidential building operators
Ch: Shivan S Subramaniam
**Pr:* Thomas A Lawson
**COO:* Jonathan W Hall
**CFO:* Kevin S Ingram
CFO: Jonathan D Mariner
**Treas:* William A Mekrut
Ex VP: Bret Ahell
Sr VP: Roberta H Butler
Sr VP: Brion E Callori
Sr VP: Rodney C Fisher
Sr VP: James R Galloway
**Sr VP:* Paul E La Fleche
Sr VP: Kenneth V Lavigne
Sr VP: Jeanne R Lieb
**Sr VP:* Jonathan L Mishara
Sr VP: Enzo Rebula
Sr VP: Daniel W Schaffer
Sr VP: Ziad Alex S Tadmoury
VP: Richard Baird
VP: Robert Bean
VP: Dennis J Bessant

D-U-N-S 01-073-6867
FACTORYOUTLETSTORE LLC
1407 Broadway Rm 700, New York, NY 10018-3299
Tel (646) 367-6141 *Founded/Ownrshp* 2012
Sales 95.0MM *EMP* 108
SIC 5722 5064 Electric household appliances, small; Answering machines, telephone

D-U-N-S 18-974-0558
▲ FACTSET RESEARCH SYSTEMS INC
601 Merritt 7, Norwalk, CT 06851-1091
Tel (203) 810-1000 *Founded/Ownrshp* 1978
Sales 1.0MMM *EMP* 7,360[E]
Accts Ernst & Young Llp Stamford C
Tkr Sym FDS *Exch* NYS
SIC 7374 Data processing & preparation
Pr: F Philip Snow
**Ch Bd:* Philip A Hadley
V Ch: Michael D Frankenfield
Pr: Shawn Dupont
Pr: Jordan Kamps
Pr: Samuel Lee
Pr: Sean O'Dowd
COO: Mark J Hale
CFO: Maurizio Nicolelli
Ofcr: Edward Baker-Greene
Ex VP: Scott Miller
Sr VP: Rachel R Stern
Sr VP: Daniel Weinstein
VP: Jason Almeter
VP: Colin Armstrong
VP: Keith Baker
VP: Jason Baroni
VP: Rick Barrett
VP: Scott Beyer
VP: Marc Boffardi
VP: Sharon Dipre
Board of Directors: Robin A Abrams, Scott A Billeadeau, Joseph E Laird Jr, James J McGonigle, Walter F Siebecker, Laurie Siegel, Joseph R Zimmel

D-U-N-S 96-953-5546
FACULTY PRACTICE FOUNDATION INC AND AFFILIATES
660 Harrison Ave, Boston, MA 02118-2304
Tel (617) 638-8923 *Founded/Ownrshp* 2011
Sales 339.4MM *EMP* 21[E]
Accts Pricewaterhousecoopers Llp Bo
SIC 8011 General & family practice, physician/surgeon
Prin: Annmarie Cloonan

FADV
See FIRST ADVANTAGE CORP

D-U-N-S 04-030-4073
FAEGRE BAKER DANIELS LLP
300 N Meridian St # 2700, Indianapolis, IN 46204-1750
Tel (317) 237-0300 *Founded/Ownrshp* 1863
Sales 267.9MM[E] *EMP* 1,581
SIC 8111 General practice law office
Mng Pt: Thomas C Froehle
Mng Pt: Andrew Humphrey
COO: Rogor T Flower
Sr VP: Theodore W Bristol
VP: Nicholas Manetto
Counsel: Amy Judge-Prein
Counsel: Suzanne M Oshea
Counsel: James R Pope
Counsel: Mark C Sausser
Counsel: Fred E Schlegel
Counsel: Lee M Tumminello

D-U-N-S 04-853-3657 IMP/EXP
FAG HOLDING CORP
(*Suby of* FAG KUGELFISCHER GMBH)
200 Park Ave, Danbury, CT 06810-7553
Tel (203) 790-5474 *Founded/Ownrshp* 2006
Sales 84.2MM[E] *EMP* 1,602
SIC 3562 Ball bearings & parts; Roller bearings & parts
Pr: Claus Bauer

D-U-N-S 80-565-6514 IMP/EXP
FAGE USA DAIRY INDUSTRY INC
FAGE USA YOGURT MFG PLANT
(*Suby of* FAGE USA HOLDINGS) ★
1 Opportunity Dr, Johnstown, NY 12095-3349
Tel (518) 762-5912 *Founded/Ownrshp* 2015
Sales 100.8MM[E] *EMP* 265
SIC 2026 Yogurt
CEO: Athanasios Filippou
**Sec:* Robert Shea
**VP:* Spyridon Giantatas
**VP:* Jeffrey Scipione
**VP Mfg:* Ioannia Ravania

D-U-N-S 00-602-8974 IMP/EXP
FAGE USA HOLDINGS (NY)
(*Suby of* FAGE DAIRY INDUSTRY S.A.)
1 Opportunity Dr, Johnstown, NY 12095-3349
Tel (518) 762-5912 *Founded/Ownrshp* 2000
Sales 100.8MM[E] *EMP* 270
SIC 2026 5143 Yogurt; Yogurt
CEO: Anthanasios Filippou
**Treas:* Christos Koloventzos
Sfty Mgr: Bernard McConaghy

FAGE USA YOGURT MFG PLANT
See FAGE USA DAIRY INDUSTRY INC

D-U-N-S 18-864-2698
FAGEN INC
501 Highway 212 W, Granite Falls, MN 56241-1308
Tel (320) 564-3324 *Founded/Ownrshp* 1988
Sales 507.1MM[E] *EMP* 750
SIC 1541 1731 1711 Industrial buildings & warehouses; Food products manufacturing or packing plant construction; Paper/pulp mill construction; Electrical work; Mechanical contractor
CEO: Aaron Fagen
**Pr:* Roland Fagen
VP: Walter Kittrell
Exec: Dolores Porter
DP Exec: Rosa Solorzano

D-U-N-S 01-621-4657 IMP
FAGOR ARRASATE USA INC
(*Suby of* FAGOR ARRASATE SDAD COOP)
636 Executive Dr, Willowbrook, IL 60527-5610
Tel (630) 920-0422 *Founded/Ownrshp* 2000
Sales 300.0MM *EMP* 700
SIC 5051 5064 Sheets, metal; Stampings, metal; Electrical appliances, major
CEO: Jose Mari Balzategi
Sls Dir: Robert Budz

D-U-N-S 82-618-3097
FAI ELECTRONICS CORP
FUTURE ACTIVE INDUSTRIAL ELEC
(*Suby of* FUTURE ELECTRONICS CORP) ★
41 Main St, Bolton, MA 01740-1134
Tel (978) 779-3111 *Founded/Ownrshp* 1994
Sales 103.4MM[E] *EMP* 1,400
SIC 5065 Electronic parts & equipment
Prin: Jon Rodman
**CFO:* Tierre Guilbault
**Ch:* Robert Miller
VP: Robert Wheeler
Sls Mgr: Rachel Noce

D-U-N-S 07-552-2888
FAIR ACRES GERIATRIC CENTER
340 N Middletown Rd, Media, PA 19063-5597
Tel (610) 891-5600 *Founded/Ownrshp* 1857
Sales 477.9MM *EMP* 2[E]
Accts Parente Randolph Llc Media
SIC 8361 Rest home, with health care incidental
**CFO:* Jim Gallagher

D-U-N-S 12-364-7182
FAIR ACRES GERIATRIC CENTER
340 N Middletown Rd, Media, PA 19063-5597
Tel (610) 891-5700 *Founded/Ownrshp* 1987
Sales 36.0MM[E] *EMP* 1,100
SIC 8059 Nursing home, except skilled & intermediate care facility
CFO: Jim Gallagher
VP: Cheryl Stank
HC Dir: Lisa Maffei-Hahn

D-U-N-S 07-466-4715
▲ FAIR ISAAC CORP
181 Metro Dr Ste 700, San Jose, CA 95110-1346
Tel (408) 535-1500 *Founded/Ownrshp* 1956
Sales 881.3MM *EMP* 2,803
Tkr Sym FICO *Exch* NYS
SIC 7372 8748 7389 Prepackaged software; Business oriented computer software; Business consulting; Financial services
CEO: William J Lansing
Pt: Robert M Berini
**Ch Bd:* A George Battle
COO: Michael Campbell
CFO: Michael J Pung
Ex VP: Richard S Deal
Ex VP: Wayne Huyard
Ex VP: Mark R Scadina
Ex VP: James M Wehmann
Ex VP: Stuart C Wells
Sr VP: Thomas Hearity
VP: Thomas F Carretta
VP: Michael S Leonard
VP: Carole-Ann Matignon
VP: Ivana Ulivi
Board of Directors: Greg R Gianforte, Braden R Kelly, James D Kirsner, Marc F McMorris, Joanna Rees, David A Rey

D-U-N-S 94-976-9723
■ FAIR ISAAC INTERNATIONAL CORP
(*Suby of* FAIR ISAAC CORP) ★
200 Smith Ranch Rd, San Rafael, CA 94903-5551
Tel (415) 446-6000 *Founded/Ownrshp* 1979
Sales 38.5MM[E] *EMP* 1,500
SIC 7372 Business oriented computer software
Pr: Thomas G Grudnowski
Ch: Robert Oliver
Bd of Dir: George Battle
Bd of Dir: Bryant Brooks
Bd of Dir: Guy Henshaw
Bd of Dir: David Hopkins
Sr VP: Hollis Holstine
Sr VP: Gordon Kaye
Sr VP: Rachel King
Sr VP: Jeffrey Robinson
VP: Robert Duque-Ribeiro
VP: O Nelson
VP: Larry Rosenberger
VP: Sue Simon
VP: Alfred Sowden

D-U-N-S 15-071-6769 EXP
FAIR OAKS FARMS LLC
7600 95th St, Pleasant Prairie, WI 53158-2713
Tel (262) 947-0320 *Founded/Ownrshp* 2003
Sales 112.4MM[E] *EMP* 550
SIC 2013 Sausages & related products, from purchased meat
CEO: Mike Thompson
**VP:* Joe Benedetti
Sfty Dirs: Todd Campbell
Sfty Mgr: Frank Moss
Plnt Mgr: Martin Sievers

FAIRBANKS
See FANCOR INC

FAIRBANKS MEMORIAL HOSPITAL
See BANNER HEALTH SYSTEM

FAIRBANKS MORSE ENGINE
See COLTEC INDUSTRIES INC

D-U-N-S 10-064-2156 IMP
FAIRBANKS NORTH STAR BOROUGH SCHOOL DISTRICT
520 5th Ave, Fairbanks, AK 99701-4718
Tel (907) 452-2000 *Founded/Ownrshp* 1920
Sales 437.5MM *EMP* 2,000
Accts Cook & Haugeberg Llc Fairbank
SIC 8211 Public elementary & secondary schools
Ex Dir: Katherine Wassmann

D-U-N-S 18-308-5091 EXP
FAIRBANKS SCALES INC
(*Suby of* FAIRBANKS) ★
821 Locust St, Kansas City, MO 64106-1925
Tel (816) 471-0231 *Founded/Ownrshp* 1988
Sales 176.6MM[E] *EMP* 656
SIC 3596 Scales & balances, except laboratory; Industrial scales
Ch: F A Norden
**Pr:* Richard Norden
**CFO:* Stephen Wurtzler
CFO: Win Zoellner
VP: Bruce Breeden
Area Mgr: John Forsythe
Area Mgr: Dave Snedden
Admn Mgr: Michael Smith
MIS Dir: Duane Johnson
QA Dir: Harry Byrne
QA Dir: Gene Redfield

D-U-N-S 01-347-5517 IMP
FAIRCHILD PUBLICATIONS INC
WOMENS WEAR DAILY
(*Suby of* CONDE NAST PUBLICATIONS) ★
475 5th Ave, New York, NY 10017-6220
Tel (212) 630-4000 *Founded/Ownrshp* 1999
Sales 133.8MM[E] *EMP* 700
SIC 2721 2711 2731 Periodicals; Newspapers; Book publishing
Pr: Charles H Townsend
Pr: Richard Baylef
Pr: Michael Coady
**CFO:* John Balendo
VP: Oren Klein
**VP:* Donald E Newhouse
Creative D: Holly Dunlap
Creative D: Robert Kline
Ex Dir: Ralph Erardy
Genl Mgr: Bill Andrulevich
Mktg Dir: Stanton Fish

D-U-N-S 00-489-5751 IMP
■ FAIRCHILD SEMICONDUCTOR CORP
(*Suby of* FAIRCHILD SEMICONDUCTOR INTERNATIONAL INC) ★
82 Running Hill Rd, South Portland, ME 04106-3293
Tel (207) 775-8100 *Founded/Ownrshp* 1997
Sales 1.3MMM[E] *EMP* 6,379
SIC 3674 Semiconductors & related devices; Metal oxide silicon (MOS) devices; Hybrid integrated circuits; Transistors
Ch: Mark Thompson
**Pr:* Kevin B London
**CFO:* Mark S Frey
**Ex VP:* Justin Chiang
**Ex VP:* Robin G Goodwin
Ex VP: Allan Lam
Sr VP: Bob Conrad
**Sr VP:* Paul D Delva
Sr VP: Hubertus Englebrechten
Sr VP: Kevin London
**VP:* Dan Janson
VP: Bob Murphy

D-U-N-S 17-622-7148
■ FAIRCHILD SEMICONDUCTOR INTERNATIONAL INC
(*Suby of* ON SEMICONDUCTOR CORP) ★
1272 Borregas Ave, Sunnyvale, CA 94089-1310
Tel (408) 822-2000 *Founded/Ownrshp* 2016
Sales 1.3MMM *EMP* 6,379[E]
SIC 3674 Semiconductors & related devices
Pr: Keith D Jackson
COO: William A Schromm
CFO: Bernard Gutmann
Ex VP: George H Cave
Ex VP: William M Hall
Ex VP: Robert A Klosterboer
Ex VP: Paul Rolls
Sr VP: Taner Ozcelik
Sr VP: Hans Stork

FAIRFAX COUNTY GOVERNMENT
See FAIRFAX COUNTY VIRGINIA

D-U-N-S 14-499-2856
FAIRFAX COUNTY PUBLIC SCHOOLS
8115 Gatehouse Rd, Falls Church, VA 22042-1203
Tel (571) 423-1010 *Founded/Ownrshp* 1958
Sales 659.6MM[E] *EMP* 26,000
SIC 8211

D-U-N-S 07-483-7626
FAIRFAX COUNTY VIRGINIA
FAIRFAX COUNTY GOVERNMENT
12000 Government Ste 214, Fairfax, VA 22035
Tel (703) 324-3126 *Founded/Ownrshp* 1742
Sales NA *EMP* 12,000
Accts Kpmg Llp Washington Dc
SIC 9121
Exec: Anthony H Griffin
Dir Vol: Lisa Callahan
Pr: John Niemiec
Treas: Kevin C Greenlief
Ofcr: Jeffrey Bergman
Exec: Irene Haske
Exec: Robert Stalzer
Exec: Karen Zelonis
Assoc Dir: Marianne Gearhart
Ex Dir: Bonnie Sullivan
Ex Dir: Larry Swartz

D-U-N-S 02-030-0885
FAIRFAX COUNTY WATER AUTHORITY
8570 Executive Park Ave, Fairfax, VA 22031-2218
Tel (703) 698-5600 *Founded/Ownrshp* 1957
Sales 153.1MM *EMP* 390[E]
Accts Pbmares Llp Harrisonburg Vi
SIC 4941 Water supply
Prin: Steven T Edgemon
Treas: Linda A Singer
**Prin:* Steven T Edgemon
Genl Mgr: Steven Edgemon
Snr Ntwrk: Frank Rajendra
Sfty Mgr: Mark Hoke
Snr Mgr: Donald Dickhute
Snr Mgr: Simon Jones
Snr Mgr: Irvin Maupin

D-U-N-S 82-871-3524
FAIRFAX COUNTY WATER AUTHORITY WELFARE BENEFIT TRUST
8570 Executive Park Ave, Fairfax, VA 22031-2218
Tel (703) 698-5600 *Founded/Ownrshp* 1957
Sales NA *EMP* 417
SIC 6371 Pension, health & welfare funds
Genl Mgr: Steven Edgemon
Genl Mgr: Charlie Crowder
Genl Mgr: Steve Edgemon
Genl Mgr: Charles Murry

D-U-N-S 13-384-8346
FAIRFAX INC
CRUM & FORSTER
(*Suby of* FAIRFAX FINANCIAL HOLDINGS LIMITED)
305 Madison Ave, Morristown, NJ 07960-6117
Tel (973) 490-6600 *Founded/Ownrshp* 2002
Sales NA *EMP* 1,800[E]
SIC 6411 Insurance agents, brokers & service
CEO: Marc Adee
**Pr:* Joe Brasutein
Sr VP: Steven Fomchenko
VP: George Burr
CTO: Richard Wien
**CTO:* Ahmed Yaknour
Mktg Mgr: Rosemary Ciraulo

FAIRFAX RADIOLOGY
See RADIOLOGICAL CONSULTANTS FAIRFAX PC

D-U-N-S 00-315-9126 IMP/EXP
FAIRFIELD CHAIR CO (NC)
1331 Harper Ave Sw, Lenoir, NC 28645-5098
Tel (828) 758-5571 *Founded/Ownrshp* 1921, 1967
Sales 125.4MM[E] *EMP* 700
SIC 2512 2511 Chairs: upholstered on wood frames; Couches, sofas & davenports: upholstered on wood frames; Wood household furniture
Ch: J Harper Beall
**Pr:* Dick Posey
**CEO:* J Harper Beall III
**Ex VP:* Larry E Hollar
**VP:* Alvin W Daughtridge
VP: Doug McClurd
**VP:* Gary V Renegar
**VP:* Gary Renegar
Dir IT: Jon Thomson
Mfg Dir: Terry Smith
Plnt Mgr: Rick Pierce

D-U-N-S 08-185-6866
FAIRFIELD CITY SCHOOL DISTRICT (INC)
4641 Bach Ln, Fairfield, OH 45014-1900
Tel (513) 829-6300 *Founded/Ownrshp* 1915
Sales 59.7MM[E] *EMP* 1,022
Accts Clark Schaefer Hackett & Co
SIC 8211 Public elementary & secondary schools
COO: Rachel Haughin
Treas: Nancy Lane
Sec: Deborah Scepp
VP: Don Nuss
Sls&Mrk Ex: Pat Heinrich

D-U-N-S 18-314-9470
FAIRFIELD COUNTRY RADIOOLOGY A
ST. VINCENT'S MEDICAL CENTER
2800 Main St, Bridgeport, CT 06606-4201
Tel (203) 576-5033 *Founded/Ownrshp* 2005
Sales 466.4MM *EMP* 3[E]
SIC 8011 Offices & clinics of medical doctors
Prin: Shashi Chaddha

D-U-N-S 07-807-0828
FAIRFIELD COUNTY SCHOOL DISTRICT
1226 Us Highway 321 Byp S, Winnsboro, SC 29180-7188
Tel (803) 635-4607 *Founded/Ownrshp* 1900
Sales 51.4MM[E] *EMP* 1,165
SIC 8211 Public elementary & secondary schools; High school, junior or senior
Genl Mgr: Veronica Rabb
Genl Mgr: Kevin Robinson
Pr Dir: Jackie Wallace

D-U-N-S 14-434-7614 IMP
FAIRFIELD DEVELOPMENT INC
FFD II
5510 Morehouse Dr Ste 200, San Diego, CA 92121-3722
Tel (858) 457-2123 *Founded/Ownrshp* 1985
Sales 372.0MM[E] *EMP* 1,500

SIC 1522 Multi-family dwelling construction
Pr: Paulette Green
**COO:* Greg Pinkalla
**CFO:* James A Hribar
**Ch:* James L Bosler
Sr VP: Kim Bender
**Sr VP:* Ted Bradford
Sr VP: Terry Phillips
Sr VP: Larry Scott
**VP:* Alan G Bear
**VP:* Benjamin Bennett
VP: Tommy Brunson
**VP:* Liz Culibrk
VP: Zach Johnston
**VP:* Terri Lehnertz
VP: Kevin Maley
**VP:* Cathy Stiles
**VP:* Jay Walker
VP: Sherry Yarborough

FAIRFIELD HIGH SCHOOL
See FAIRFIELD PUBLIC SCHOOLS

D-U-N-S 08-647-5746
FAIRFIELD INDUSTRIES INC
FAIRFIELDNODAL
(*Suby of* FAIRFIELD-MAXWELL LTD) ★
1111 Gillingham Ln, Sugar Land, TX 77478-2865
Tel (281) 275-7627 *Founded/Ownrshp* 1974
Sales 172.9MM^E *EMP* 400
SIC 7374 3829 1382 3429 Data processing service; Geophysical or meteorological electronic equipment; Geophysical exploration, oil & gas field; Manufactured hardware (general)
Ch Bd: Walter D Pharris
**VP:* Marc A Lawrence
**VP:* Steve Mitchell
VP: John Smythe
Off Mgr: Joann Clover
Off Admin: Chantae Adams
QA Dir: Daniel Addessi
Plnt Mgr: Tom Grisham
VP Mktg: Steve McIntosh
Manager: Hugo Villarroel
Sls Mgr: Dennis Clark

D-U-N-S 82-611-8135 IMP/EXP
FAIRFIELD MANUFACTURING CO INC
OERLIKON FAIRFIELD
(*Suby of* OC OERLIKON CORPORATION AG, PFAFFIKON)
2400 Sagamore Pkwy S, Lafayette, IN 47905-5116
Tel (765) 772-4000 *Founded/Ownrshp* 2007
Sales 187.7MM^E *EMP* 840^E
SIC 3462 3714 5085 Gear & chain forgings; Gears, motor vehicle; Gears
Pr: David Evans
Pr: Mike Pyatt
**CFO:* Chad Heathco
**VP:* Garry Francis
**VP:* Dave Martin
VP: Milagros C Perez
Area Mgr: Gary McGrady
Area Mgr: Jose Orozco
Dir IT: Timothy Simpson
Opers Mgr: Bob Anderson
Mktg Mgr: Greg Moreland
Board of Directors: Oliver Dohn, David Evans, Luciano Viaro

D-U-N-S 07-942-8397
FAIRFIELD MEDICAL CENTER (OH)
401 N Ewing St, Lancaster, OH 43130-3371
Tel (740) 687-8000 *Founded/Ownrshp* 1914, 1991
Sales 255.7MM *EMP* 2,200
SIC 8062 7352 5999 General medical & surgical hospitals; Medical equipment rental; Medical apparatus & supplies
CEO: Sky Gettys
Chf Rad: Gerald Smidebush
Dir Recs: Cheryl Henney
CFO: Katie Hannahs
Ofcr: Larry Mitchell
Ofcr: Sonya Poff
Ofcr: Ryan Snider
Exec: Eric Brandt
Dir Lab: Crystal Morris
Ex Dir: Beth Daugherty
Brnch Mgr: Mary Roof
Board of Directors: Robert J Sprouse, A William Bickham, R Dane Swinehart, Lawrence Burgess, David Gallimore, Pat Gilmore, Shashi Gogate MD, D Jane Joos, David Lifer MD, James Parker, Rick L Snider

FAIRFIELD PREP
See FAIRFIELD UNIVERSITY

D-U-N-S 10-001-1592 IMP
FAIRFIELD PUBLIC SCHOOLS
FAIRFIELD HIGH SCHOOL
501 Kings Hwy E Ste 210, Fairfield, CT 06825-4864
Tel (203) 255-7201 *Founded/Ownrshp* 1894
Sales 61.2MM^E *EMP* 1,350
SIC 8211 Public elementary & secondary schools
Dept Mgr: Brenda J Anziano
Dept Mgr: Kevin Chase
IT Man: Elizabeth Lockwood
IT Man: Barbara Merry
Teacher Pr: Ann Leffert
HC Dir: Lori Mediate
Snr Mgr: Gregg Pugliese

D-U-N-S 07-212-0702
FAIRFIELD UNIVERSITY
FAIRFIELD PREP
1073 N Benson Rd, Fairfield, CT 06824-5195
Tel (203) 254-4000 *Founded/Ownrshp* 1942
Sales 213.4MM *EMP* 883
Accts Kpmg Llp New York Ny
SIC 8221 8211 University; Preparatory school
Pr: Rev Jeffrey Von ARX Sj
Pr: Charles H Allen
Pr: Susan Birge
**Treas:* Julie Dolan
Assoc Dir: Alison Hildenbrand
Assoc Dir: Meredith Marquez
**VP Admn:* Dr Mark Reed
Dir Sec: Todd A Pelzz
Prgrm Mgr: Katie Coutu
CIO: Paige Francis
Dir IT: Laura Manolis

D-U-N-S 05-356-5990 IMP/EXP
FAIRFIELD-MAXWELL LTD
60 E 42nd St Fl 55, New York, NY 10165-0035
Tel (212) 297-9030 *Founded/Ownrshp* 1957
Sales 183.3MM^E *EMP* 400
SIC 8741 4731 5172 4412

D-U-N-S 01-463-4976
FAIRFIELD-SUISUN UNIFIED SCHOOL DISTRICT
F S U S D
2490 Hilborn Rd, Fairfield, CA 94534-1072
Tel (707) 399-5000 *Founded/Ownrshp* 1968
Sales 94.3MM^E *EMP* 2,400
SIC 8211 Public elementary & secondary schools
**CEO:* David Isom
Bd of Dir: Kathy Marianno
Bd of Dir: Pat Shamansky
Dir Sec: Jim Walker
MIS Dir: Tim Goree
IT Man: Corie Barloggi
IT Man: Stacy Burke
Trfc Dir: Denise Davis
Opers Supe: Joanne Jarvis
Psych: Nicholas Cheatham
Psych: Kaitlin Richter

FAIRFIELDNODAL
See FAIRFIELD INDUSTRIES INC

D-U-N-S 04-567-1948
FAIRLEIGH DICKINSON UNIVERSITY
BECTON COLLEGE ARTS & SCIENCES
1000 River Rd, Teaneck, NJ 07666-1914
Tel (800) 338-8803 *Founded/Ownrshp* 1941
Sales 237.6MM *EMP* 1,505
Accts Kpmg Llp Short Hills Nj
SIC 8221 University
Pr: Sheldon Drucker
**Ch:* Steve C Tumminello
Trst: Michael J Adams
Trst: Nick Agostino
Trst: Cheryl K Beebe
Trst: Ahmad Kamal
Trst: Molly Smith
**Ex VP:* Carl Viola
VP: Rose D'Ambrosio
VP: Ashly Gomez
VP: Chris Perez
VP: Richard Reiss
VP: Neal Sturm
Assoc Dir: Everard Cowan
Assoc Dir: Laurie Eick
Assoc Dir: Sanaa Hamawi
Dir: Charles Dees

D-U-N-S 05-561-1887
FAIRLIFE LLC
1001 W Adams St, Chicago, IL 60607-2911
Tel (312) 624-9444 *Founded/Ownrshp* 2000
Sales 131.6MM^E *EMP* 150^E
SIC 5149 Dairy products, dried or canned; Beverage concentrates
CEO: Stephen Jones
Dir Bus: Sara Reed
Off Mgr: Talena Bennett
Off Mgr: Talea Bennette

FAIRMONT AND CLARK
See APPA SEAFOOD INC

D-U-N-S 05-603-9050
■ FAIRMONT HOMES LLC
FRIENDSHIP HOMES DIVISION
(*Suby of* FH GROUP LLC) ★
502 S Oakland Ave, Nappanee, IN 46550-2332
Tel (574) 773-7941 *Founded/Ownrshp* 2015
Sales 141.2MM^E *EMP* 600
SIC 2451 Mobile homes, except recreational
Pr: Brian Cira
Recvr: Jennifer Wolford
VP: Steve Maisonneuve
**VP:* Maison Neuve
IT Man: Jeff Klingler
Plnt Mgr: Jason Osborn

D-U-N-S 10-341-8216 IMP/EXP
FAIRMONT HOTEL PARTNERS LLC
(*Suby of* FAIRMONT HOTELS & RESORTS INC)
950 Mason St, San Francisco, CA 94108-2098
Tel (415) 772-5000 *Founded/Ownrshp* 2012
Sales 206.3MM^E *EMP* 2,295
SIC 8741 Hotel or motel management
Genl Mgr: April Sheesley

FAIRMONT SAN FRANCISCO
See MASON STREET OPCO LLC

D-U-N-S 15-754-5138
FAIRMONT SCOTTSDALE PRINCESS
(*Suby of* FAIRMONT HOTELS & RESORTS INC)
7575 E Princess Dr, Scottsdale, AZ 85255-5802
Tel (480) 585-4848 *Founded/Ownrshp* 1998
Sales 74.2MM^E *EMP* 1,150
SIC 7011 5812 5813 Resort hotel; Eating places; Drinking places
Genl Mgr: Jack Miller
Exec: Rosemary Taylor
Genl Mgr: Robert Foster

D-U-N-S 00-842-6959
FAIRMONT SPECIALTY INSURANCE MANAGERS INC
(*Suby of* FAIRMONT SPECIALTY GROUP)
11490 Westheimer Rd # 300, Houston, TX 77077-6841
Tel (713) 954-8100 *Founded/Ownrshp* 1988
Sales NA *EMP* 5
Accts Pricewaterhousecoopers Llp Ho
SIC 6411 Insurance agents, brokers & service
Ch Bd: V Prem Watsa

D-U-N-S 00-786-1107 IMP
FAIRMONT SUPPLY CO
(*Suby of* TENEX CAPITAL MANAGEMENT LP) ★
437 Jefferson Ave, Washington, PA 15301-4273
Tel (724) 223-2200 *Founded/Ownrshp* 1921, 2015
Sales 296.7MM^E *EMP* 300
SIC 5085 5082 Industrial supplies; Mining machinery & equipment, except petroleum
CEO: Rudolph Strobl
**Pr:* Van Compagni
**CFO:* Gary Bench
Ofcr: Colten Sunseri
**VP:* John Floyd
VP: Amy Moser
Genl Mgr: Greg Eustis
Genl Mgr: Monica Marshman
Genl Mgr: Lauren Scarberry
Dir IT: Ron Thompson
IT Man: Amy Martin

FAIRMOUNT MINERALS
See FAIRMOUNT SANTROL INC

D-U-N-S 04-075-7058
FAIRMOUNT MINERALS LLC
FAIRMOUNT SANTROL
8834 Mayfield Rd Ste A, Chesterland, OH 44026-2696
Tel (269) 926-9450 *Founded/Ownrshp* 2011
Sales 988.0MM *EMP* 1,100
SIC 1446 Industrial sand
CEO: Jenniffer Deckard

FAIRMOUNT SANTROL
See FAIRMOUNT MINERALS LLC

D-U-N-S 14-748-0834 IMP/EXP
FAIRMOUNT SANTROL HOLDINGS INC
8834 Mayfield Rd Ste A, Chesterland, OH 44026-2696
Tel (800) 255-7263 *Founded/Ownrshp* 1986
Sales 828.7MM *EMP* 1,113
SIC 1446 Industrial sand
Pr: Jenniffer D Deckard
**Ch Bd:* Matthew F Lebaron
COO: Joseph D Fodo
CFO: Christopher L Nagel
Ex VP: Gerald L Clancey
Ex VP: Van T Smith
VP: David J Crandall

D-U-N-S 01-609-9793 EXP
FAIRMOUNT SANTROL INC
FAIRMOUNT MINERALS
(*Suby of* FAIRMOUNT SANTROL HOLDINGS INC) ★
8834 Mayfield Rd Ste A, Chesterland, OH 44026-2696
Tel (440) 214-3200 *Founded/Ownrshp* 2010
Sales 294.9MM^E *EMP* 296
SIC 2891 Adhesives
Pr: Jenniffer D Deckard
**CEO:* Charles D Fowler
**CFO:* Michael F Biehl
**Ch:* William E Conway
**VP:* Joseph Fodo
VP: Maureen Lynn
Dir IT: Robert Hakenson
Plnt Mgr: Bob Goelz
Plnt Mgr: Jeff Himes
Ql Cn Mgr: William Nevison
Sls&Mrk Ex: Tim Mc Millin

D-U-N-S 08-211-7094 IMP/EXP
FAIRN & SWANSON INC
BAJA DUTY FREE
400 Lancaster St, Oakland, CA 94601-2827
Tel (510) 533-8260 *Founded/Ownrshp* 1949
Sales 183.3MM^E *EMP* 200
Accts Armanino Mckenna Llp San Ramo
SIC 5122 5182 Cosmetics; Perfumes; Liquor
CEO: Achim Fritzen
**Pr:* Nicole Uhlig
VP: Elisa Castro
Brnch Mgr: Ruth Clark
IT Man: Chris Magallanes

FAIRPLAY FINE FOODS
See FAIRPLAY INC

D-U-N-S 14-821-2780
FAIRPLAY INC
FAIRPLAY FINE FOODS
4640 S Halsted St, Chicago, IL 60609-4414
Tel (773) 247-3077 *Founded/Ownrshp* 1985
Sales 83.6MM^E *EMP* 800
SIC 5411 Grocery stores, chain
Pr: Richard Goodrich
**VP:* Michael Kuzlowski

D-U-N-S 86-816-3775
▲ FAIRPOINT COMMUNICATIONS INC
521 E Morehead St Ste 500, Charlotte, NC 28202-2861
Tel (704) 344-8150 *Founded/Ownrshp* 1991
Sales 859.4MM *EMP* 2,700
Tkr Sym FRP *Exch* NAS
SIC 4813 4812 4899 Local & long distance telephone communications; ; Wire telephone; Paging services; Data communication services
CEO: Paul H Sunu
**Ch Bd:* Edward D Horowitz
Pr: Karen Romano
CFO: Karen D Turner
Treas: Jamie Chadbourne
Treas: Tom Griffin
Bd of Dir: Dennis Austin
Bd of Dir: John Cilio
Bd of Dir: Shelley Rudnicki
Ex VP: John J Lunny
Ex VP: Peter G Nixon
Ex VP: Steven Rush
Ex VP: Steven G Rush
Ex VP: Ajay Sabherwal
Ex VP: Tony Tomae
Sr VP: John T Hogshire
VP: Chris Alberding
VP: Dave Remele
VP: Susan Sowell
VP: Garrett Vanosdell
Board of Directors: Peter D Aquino, Dennis J Austin, Peter C Gingold, Michael J Mahoney, Michael K Robinson, David L Treadwell, Wayne Wilson

D-U-N-S 06-819-9611
FAIRVIEW HEALTH SERVICES (MN)
OUTPATENT CHEM DPNDNCY PROGRAM
2450 Riverside Ave, Minneapolis, MN 55454-1450
Tel (612) 672-6300 *Founded/Ownrshp* 1905
Sales 3.3MMM *EMP* 18,000
Accts Ernst & Young Llp
SIC 8062 General medical & surgical hospitals
CEO: Rulon F Stacey
Chf Rad: Chuck Dietz
Chf Rad: James Kirkham
Dir Vol: Pamela N Mills
V Ch: Charles W Mooty
COO: Laura Deneui
COO: Richard Dinter
COO: Dave Dobosenski
COO: Margaret Van Bree
**CFO:* James M Fox
CFO: Jim Fox
Ofcr: Paula H Phillippe
Ex VP: William Maxwell
**Ex VP:* Carolyn Wilson
Sr VP: Terry Carroll
**Sr VP:* Daniel Fromm
Sr VP: Diane Iorfida
**VP:* Bob Beacher
VP: Andy Borland
VP: Leann Born
VP: Mary C Edwards

D-U-N-S 07-676-2988
FAIRVIEW HOSPITAL
CLEVELAND CLINIC HEALTH SYSTEM
(*Suby of* CLEVELAND CLINIC HEALTH SYSTEM) ★
18101 Lorain Ave, Cleveland, OH 44111-5612
Tel (216) 476-7000 *Founded/Ownrshp* 1894
Sales 426.3MM *EMP* 2,364^E
SIC 8062 8011 General medical & surgical hospitals; Offices & clinics of medical doctors
CEO: Toby Cosgrove
**Pr:* Louis Caravella MD
**Pr:* Delos Cosgrove
CFO: Christopher Winter
Ansthlgy: Richard M Hofstra
Pharmcst: Amy Busker
Pharmcst: Jonica Hazaert
Pharmcst: Heidi Mandt

D-U-N-S 00-380-5498
FAIRVIEW MILLS LLC
604 Nemaha St, Seneca, KS 66538-1735
Tel (785) 336-2148 *Founded/Ownrshp* 2006
Sales 132.8MM *EMP* 30
SIC 3999 Pet supplies
CFO: Joseph Kramer
**Treas:* Colleen Terpening

FAIRVIEW PARK HOSPITAL
See FAIRVIEW PARK LIMITED PARTNERSHIP

D-U-N-S 07-810-8206
■ FAIRVIEW PARK LIMITED PARTNERSHIP
FAIRVIEW PARK HOSPITAL
(*Suby of* HOSPITAL COPORATION OF AMERICA) ★
200 Industrial Blvd, Dublin, GA 31021-2981
Tel (478) 274-3990 *Founded/Ownrshp* 2001
Sales 104.4MM *EMP* 675
SIC 8062 General medical & surgical hospitals
Pt: Donald R Avery
Genl Pt: Donald Avery
Pt: Ted Short
Dir Soc: Michael Bland
Dir Bus: Karen Warnock
Chf Nrs Of: Verno Davidson
MIS Dir: Marsha Morris
Ansthlgy: Jim Lane
Doctor: Manuel Vega
HC Dir: Tina Gilbert
HC Dir: Sue Hatem

D-U-N-S 18-475-0714
FAIRVIEW PHARMACY SERVICES LLC
(*Suby of* OUTPATENT CHEM DPNDNCY PROGRAM) ★
711 Kasota Ave Se, Minneapolis, MN 55414-2842
Tel (612) 672-5200 *Founded/Ownrshp* 2005
Sales 560.0MM *EMP* 250^E
SIC 5912 5122 Drug stores & proprietary stores; Drugs, proprietaries & sundries
CEO: Rulon Stacey
**Pr:* Daniel K Anderson
**Pr:* Brent Asplin
**Sr VP:* Daniel Fromm
**VP:* Bob Beacher
Mktg Dir: Dick Schirber

D-U-N-S 80-942-5601 IMP
FAIRWAY GROUP HOLDINGS CORP
2284 12th Ave, New York, NY 10027-2316
Tel (646) 616-8000 *Founded/Ownrshp* 1933
Sales 797.5MM *EMP* 4,300^E
SIC 5411 Grocery stores
CEO: John E Murphy
**Ch Bd:* Charles W Santoro
Pr: Edward C Arditte
Pr: Kevin McDonnell
Chf Mktg O: Dorothy Carlow
Sr VP: Nathalie Augustin
Sr VP: Maureen Minard
VP: Peter Romano
Board of Directors: Michael A Barr, Howard Glickberg, Stephen L Key, Robert Magnus

D-U-N-S 96-051-8827
FAIRWAY INDEPENDENT MORTGAGE CORP
4801 S Biltmore Ln, Madison, WI 53718-2108
Tel (608) 837-4800 *Founded/Ownrshp* 1996
Sales NA *EMP* 3,400
SIC 6162

D-U-N-S 00-997-5173
FAIRWAYS GOLF CORP
(*Suby of* MEADOWBROOK GOLF GROUP INC) ★
5385 Gateway Blvd Ste 12, Lakeland, FL 33811-1785
Tel (407) 589-7200 *Founded/Ownrshp* 1991
Sales 10.1MM^E *EMP* 1,500
SIC 7992 Public golf courses
Pr: Ron Jackson
**CFO:* Calvin Sellers

D-U-N-S 86-142-7805
FAISON ENTERPRISES INC
121 W Trade St Fl 27, Charlotte, NC 28202-5399
Tel (704) 972-2500 Founded/Ownrshp 2002
Sales 138.6MM^E EMP 1,100
SIC 6799 Real estate investors, except property operators
*Ch Bd: Henry J Faison
*CEO: Jay W Faison
CFO: Allen S Jackson Jr
Treas: Chris Poplin
Sr VP: Ken McCoy
Exec: James H Culpepper IV
Mng Dir: Christopher Branch

FAITH REGIONAL HEALTH SERVICES
See REHABILITATION THERAPIST

D-U-N-S 12-432-9231
FAITH TECHNOLOGIES INC
225 Main St, Menasha, WI 54952-3186
Tel (920) 738-1500 Founded/Ownrshp 2002
Sales 467.5MM^E EMP 2,060
Accts Grant Thornton Llp Milwaukee
SIC 1731 Electrical work
CEO: Mike Jansen
*Ch Bd: Rollie Stephenson
*Treas: Diane Schaefer
*Ex VP: Tom Clark
Ex VP: Bob Dakovich
*Ex VP: Robert Dakovich
*Ex VP: David Jahner
*Ex VP: George Vander Linden
*Ex VP: Scott Romenesko
VP: Michael Bowman
VP: Jack Brock
VP: Charlie Fredrickson
VP: Rocky Rowlett
VP: Charles J Seghers
VP: Dan Siebers
Exec: Jeff Heegeman
Dir Risk M: Ken Baumgart

D-U-N-S 16-916-6514
FAK INC
10885 E 51st Ave, Denver, CO 80239-2507
Tel (303) 289-5433 Founded/Ownrshp 1983
Sales 113.6MM EMP 48
SIC 4731 Domestic freight forwarding
Pr: Samuel R Marcove
*CEO: Bobby Marcove
*CFO: Felipe Suaez
VP: Debbie Ogden

FALASCA MECHANICAL CONTRACTORS
See FALASCA MECHANICAL INC

D-U-N-S 05-008-7472
FALASCA MECHANICAL INC
FALASCA MECHANICAL CONTRACTORS
3329 N Mill Rd, Vineland, NJ 08360-1525
Tel (856) 794-2010 Founded/Ownrshp 2001
Sales 126.5MM EMP 80
Accts Fabietti Hale Hammerstedt &
SIC 1711 Plumbing contractors
Pr: Daniel Falasca Jr

D-U-N-S 02-152-3882
FALCK USA INC
(Suby of FALCK DANMARK A/S)
21540 30th Dr Se Ste 250, Bothell, WA 98021-7015
Tel (425) 892-1180 Founded/Ownrshp 2011
Sales 95.4MM^E EMP 100^E
SIC 4119 Ambulance service
Pr: Boo Heffner

FALCO LIME COMPANY
See MISSISSIPPI LIME CO

D-U-N-S 83-032-7438
FALCON AEROSPACE HOLDINGS LLC
WESCO AIRCRAFT
27727 Avenue Scott, Valencia, CA 91355-1219
Tel (661) 775-7200 Founded/Ownrshp 2006
Sales 35.7MM^E EMP 1,250
SIC 8741 Management services
Ch Bd: Randy J Snyder
*Ex VP: Gregory A Hann
*Ex VP: Tommy Lee

D-U-N-S 00-586-0361
■ **FALCON CABLE COMMUNICATIONS LLC**
(Suby of CHARTER COMMUNICATIONS HOLDINGS LLC) ★
12405 Powerscourt Dr, Saint Louis, MO 63131-3673
Tel (314) 965-0555 Founded/Ownrshp 1999
Sales 169.6MM^E EMP 1,000
SIC 4841 Cable television services
Prin: Carl Vogel
IT Man: Marrisha McFoulon

D-U-N-S 19-397-9085 EXP
FALCON FARMS INC
2330 Nw 82nd Ave, Miami, FL 33122-1511
Tel (305) 477-8088 Founded/Ownrshp 1987
Sales 111.8MM^E EMP 544
SIC 5992 5193 Florists; Flowers, fresh
Pr: Jairo Rengifo
Sr VP: Edgar Poveda
Prd Mgr: Alvaro Ucros
Sales Exec: Todd Ingham
Mktg Dir: Juan Alvarez
Board of Directors: Scott Foushee

D-U-N-S 00-673-2861
FALCON HOLDINGS LLC
CHURCH'S CHICKEN
1301 Solana Blvd Ste 2300, Roanoke, TX 76262-1676
Tel (817) 693-5151 Founded/Ownrshp 1999
Sales 65.7MM^E EMP 1,500
SIC 5812 Chicken restaurant
CEO: Aslam Khan
*Pr: Khaled Habash
*Pr: Azam Malik
*CEO: Aslan Khan
*CFO: Jill Filipiak
*CFO: Giovanna Koning
*VP: Mahmood Ahmed
Genl Couns: Dawn Diaz

D-U-N-S 87-764-8949
FALCON PACKAGING LLC
1359 Sater St, Greenville, OH 45331-1640
Tel (937) 547-9800 Founded/Ownrshp 1994
Sales 100.0MM EMP 30
SIC 7389 4225 Packaging & labeling services; General warehousing & storage

D-U-N-S 87-434-5820
FALCON PHARMACEUTICALS LTD
(Suby of ALCON LABORATORIES INC) ★
6201 South Fwy, Fort Worth, TX 76134-2001
Tel (800) 343-2133 Founded/Ownrshp 1995
Sales 207.5MM^E EMP 3,000
SIC 2834 3841 Solutions, pharmaceutical; Ophthalmic instruments & apparatus
Pr: Cary Rayment
*CFO: Jacqualyn Fouse
*Sr VP: Gerald Cagle PHD
*VP: Kevin Buehler
*VP: Andre Bens PHD

D-U-N-S 03-045-7303
FALCON SCHOOL DISTRICT 49 (INC)
10850 E Woodmen Rd, Peyton, CO 80831-8127
Tel (719) 495-3601 Founded/Ownrshp 1920
Sales 100.9MM EMP 1,500
Accts Hoelting & Company Inc Colo
SIC 8211 Public elementary & secondary schools
Pr: Tammy Harold
*Treas: Kevin Butcher
*VP: David Moore
Genl Mgr: Fran Christensen
Pr Dir: Matt Meister
Teacher Pr: Paul Andersen

D-U-N-S 00-740-9550 IMP
FALCON TRADING CO
SUNRIDGE FARMS
423 Salinas Rd, Royal Oaks, CA 95076-5232
Tel (831) 786-7000 Founded/Ownrshp 1977
Sales 169.0MM^E EMP 215
SIC 5149 Natural & organic foods
CEO: Morty Cohen
*VP: Rebecca Cohen
Exec: Maria Marsilio
Exec: Darshan Siegman
Genl Mgr: Ron Giannini

D-U-N-S 03-040-7050
FALCON TRANSPORT CO
4944 Belmont Ave, Youngstown, OH 44505-1055
Tel (330) 793-1345 Founded/Ownrshp 2000
Sales 325.7MM^E EMP 1,490
SIC 4213 Trucking, except local
Pr: Barbara Takach
*Ex VP: Brad Constantini
*VP: Mark Constantini
VP: Steve Olender
*VP: Lee Simmerman
*VP: Tom Welsh
Brnch Mgr: Richard Rose
IT Man: Larry Hamilton
Mktg Dir: John Progar
Mktg Mgr: Rhonda Petruzzi

D-U-N-S 01-128-8201
FALCONHEAD CAPITAL LLC
645 Madison Ave Fl 9, New York, NY 10022-1010
Tel (212) 634-3304 Founded/Ownrshp 1998
Sales 219.3MM^E EMP 2,881
SIC 6722 3812 Management investment, open-end; Radar systems & equipment
CEO: David Moross
Genl Pt: Brian Crosby
Genl Pt: Zuher Ladak
*Pt: Peter Englehart
*Pt: David Gubbay
*Pt: Michael Lorelli
*Pt: Jason Turowsky
*CFO: Glen Bushery
Mng Dir: Robert Fioretti
Mng Dir: Adam Treanor

D-U-N-S 78-502-8395
FALCONHEAD CAPITAL PARTNERS II LP
(Suby of FALCONHEAD CAPITAL LLC) ★
450 Park Ave Bsmt, New York, NY 10022-2630
Tel (212) 634-3304 Founded/Ownrshp 2005
Sales 144.5MM^E EMP 2,001
SIC 6722 7221 7335 Management investment, open-end; Photographic studios, portrait; Commercial photography
Pt: David Moross

D-U-N-S 78-054-9791
FALFURRIAS CAPITAL PARTNERS LP
100 N Tryon St Ste 4100, Charlotte, NC 28202-4034
Tel (704) 371-3220 Founded/Ownrshp 2006
Sales 401.1MM^E EMP 4,645
SIC 6726 Investment offices
Ch Bd: Hugh McColl
Pr: Wilson Sullivan
Prin: Ed McMahan
Off Mgr: Carolyn Hubbard

D-U-N-S 78-780-0507
■ **FALK SERVICE CORP**
(Suby of REXNORD LLC) ★
3001 W Canal St, Milwaukee, WI 53208-4222
Tel (414) 342-3131 Founded/Ownrshp 1896
Sales 91.3MM^E EMP 625^E
SIC 5085 Power transmission equipment & apparatus
Pr: Todd Adams

FALKEN TIRE CORPORATION
See SUMITOMO RUBBER NORTH AMERICA INC

D-U-N-S 01-082-8333
■ **FALKIRK MINING CO**
(Suby of NORTH AMERICAN COAL CORP) ★
2801 1st St Sw, Underwood, ND 58576-9611
Tel (701) 442-5751 Founded/Ownrshp 1913
Sales 168.8MM EMP 253
Accts Ernst & Young Llp Richmond V
SIC 1221 Surface mining, lignite

D-U-N-S 07-979-9251
FALL RIVER PUBLIC SCHOOLS
417 Rock St, Fall River, MA 02720-3344
Tel (508) 675-8420 Founded/Ownrshp 2015
Sales 13.9MM^E EMP 1,112^E
SIC 8211 Public elementary & secondary schools
Psych: Lisa Andrade

FALLAS DISCOUNT STORES
See J & M SALES INC

FALLAS-PAREDES
See NATIONAL STORES INC

D-U-N-S 10-900-2873
FALLON COMMUNITY HEALTH PLAN INC
10 Chestnut St Ste 800, Worcester, MA 01608-2804
Tel (508) 799-2100 Founded/Ownrshp 1975
Sales NA EMP 750^E
Accts Lb Pricewaterhousecoopers Llp
SIC 6324 Health maintenance organization (HMO), insurance only
Pr: Eric H Schultz
COO: Richard Commander
*CFO: Charley Goheen
CFO: Scott Walker
*Treas: Donald Melville
Trst: Dilip Subbarao
Sr VP: Sarika Aggarwal
*Sr VP: Richard Burke
*Sr VP: Anne Doyle
*Sr VP: Patrick Hughes
Sr VP: Jill Lebow
*Sr VP: Teena Osgood
Sr VP: David Przesiek
VP: Beth Foley
VP: Donald Perron
Dir Rx: Sonja Brehm

D-U-N-S 78-475-5519
FALLS CREEK LIVING CENTER LLC
2906 Geer Hwy, Marietta, SC 29661-9517
Tel (864) 836-6381 Founded/Ownrshp 2006
Sales 299.3MM EMP 30
SIC 8051 Skilled nursing care facilities
CFO: John Swift

FALLSINGTON
See PENNSBURY SCHOOL DISTRICT

D-U-N-S 07-380-0302
FALMOUTH HOSPITAL ASSOCIATION INC
(Suby of CAPE COD HEALTHCARE INC) ★
100 Ter Heun Dr, Falmouth, MA 02540-2599
Tel (508) 548-5300 Founded/Ownrshp 1956
Sales 152.6MM EMP 950
SIC 8062 General medical & surgical hospitals
Pr: Michael K Lauf
*Pr: William B Reals
Treas: Malcolm Robertson Jr
*Sr VP: Theresa Ahern
*Sr VP: Michael L Connors
*Sr VP: Jeffrey S Dykens
*Sr VP: Jeanne Fallon
Dir Lab: Richard Corkey
Obsttrcn: Susan Andregg
Opthamlgy: Dale C Oates
Opthamlgy: William H Schutten

FAMILIA
See DEPARTMENT OF FAMILY

D-U-N-S 06-801-2954
FAMILY AIDES INC
120 W John St B, Hicksville, NY 11801-1020
Tel (516) 681-2300 Founded/Ownrshp 1972
Sales 49.0MM^E EMP 3,000
SIC 8082 Home health care services
Ch Bd: Kathleen Crimi
VP: Kristine Mais

D-U-N-S 04-099-4006
FAMILY CENTRAL INC
840 N Lauderdale Ave, North Lauderdale, FL 33068-2001
Tel (954) 720-1000 Founded/Ownrshp 1973
Sales 193.2MM EMP 428
Accts Daszkal Bolton Llp Fort Laude
SIC 8322 Child related social services; Family service agency
Pr: Barbara A Weinstein
*Prin: Ken Dresner

D-U-N-S 87-822-6281 IMP
FAMILY CHRISTIAN STORES LLC
5300 Patterson Ave Se, Grand Rapids, MI 49530-1000
Tel (616) 554-8700 Founded/Ownrshp 2015
Sales 593.7MM^E EMP 4,600
SIC 5942 5735 5947 5699 8741 Book stores; Compact discs; Audio tapes, prerecorded; Greeting cards; Gift shop; Customized clothing & apparel; Management services
CEO: Charles Dengophea
*Pr: Chuck Bengochea
VP: Daniel Jesse
VP: Paul Neitzel
VP: Caroline Sharrow
Genl Mgr: Frederick Smitherman
Store Mgr: Jennifer Triebwasser
Telecom Mg: Nancy Littlefair
Merch Mgr: Susan Hertzmann
Sales Asso: Yvonne Edwards
Sales Asso: Rachel Huffman

D-U-N-S 79-463-6670
FAMILY DINING INC
BURGER KING
(Suby of U S RESTAURANTS INC) ★
1780 Swede Rd, Blue Bell, PA 19422-3522
Tel (610) 277-4200 Founded/Ownrshp 1985
Sales 25.8MM^E EMP 1,000
SIC 5812 Fast-food restaurant, chain
Pr: Steven M Lewis
*Sec: Vernon W Hill II

D-U-N-S 07-053-6458 IMP
■ **FAMILY DOLLAR SERVICES INC**
(Suby of FAMILY DOLLAR STORES INC) ★
10401 Monroe Rd, Matthews, NC 28105-5349
Tel (704) 847-6961 Founded/Ownrshp 1991
Sales 284.4MM^E EMP 3,200
SIC 5331 Variety stores
CEO: Howard R Levine
Pr: R James Kelly
CFO: Mary A Winston
Ex VP: Charles S Gibson Jr
Ex VP: Paul G White
Sr VP: Kevin Boyanowski

D-U-N-S 02-447-2631 IMP/EXP
■ **FAMILY DOLLAR STORES INC**
(Suby of DOLLAR TREE INC) ★
10401 Monroe Rd, Matthews, NC 28105-5349
Tel (704) 847-6961 Founded/Ownrshp 1969, 2015
Sales 10.1MMM^E EMP 60,000
SIC 5331 Variety stores
Pr: Gary Philbin
*CFO: Mary A Winston
*Chf Mktg O: Jason S Reiser
Ex VP: Dorlisa K Flur
*Ex VP: Barry W Sullivan
Sr VP: Bruce E Barkus
Sr VP: Kathi S Child
Sr VP: Tammy L Deboer
Sr VP: Charles S Gibson Jr
Sr VP: Brian D Hancock
Sr VP: Samuel N McPherson
Sr VP: Thomas M Nash
Sr VP: Irv Neger
Sr VP: Brad Rogers
Sr VP: Jeffrey Thomas
Sr VP: Bryan E Venberg
Sr VP: Scott T Zucker
VP: Kevin Boyanowski
VP: Bill Broome
VP: Tim Chew
VP: Odette Cummings
Board of Directors: Pamela L Davies, Sharon Allred Decker, Edward C Dolby, Glenn A Eisenberg, Edward P Garden, George R Mahoney Jr, James G Martin, Harvey Morgan, Dale C Pond

D-U-N-S 08-193-3793 IMP
■ **FAMILY DOLLAR STORES OF LOUISIANA INC**
(Suby of FAMILY DOLLAR STORES INC) ★
10401 Monroe Rd, Matthews, NC 28105-5349
Tel (704) 847-6961 Founded/Ownrshp 1983
Sales 2.6MMM^E EMP 50,000
SIC 5331 Variety stores
Pr: Howard R Levine
*Ch Bd: Leon Levine
*V Ch: R James Kelly
*Pr: Barry Sullivan
Ex VP: Charles Gibson Jr
*Ex VP: George Mahoney
*Ex VP: Mary A Winston
Sr VP: Paul White
*VP: Jonathan E Broz
*VP: Steven E Burt
*VP: Erik Gast
*VP: Jose Luis
VP: Lonnie McCaffety

D-U-N-S 08-228-5730
■ **FAMILY DOLLAR STORES OF MISSOURI INC**
(Suby of FAMILY DOLLAR STORES INC) ★
10401 Monroe Rd, Matthews, NC 28105-5349
Tel (704) 847-6961 Founded/Ownrshp 1971
Sales 137.2MM^E EMP 2,000
SIC 5331 Variety stores
Ch Bd: Leon Levine
*Pr: Howard R Levine
Pr: Jeff Thomas
*COO: R David Alexander Jr
*CFO: R James Kelly
*Ex VP: George R Mahoney Jr
VP: David Easton
VP: Eric C Gordon
VP: Anette Gutierrez
VP: Derek Jones
Brnch Mgr: Keith Leatherberry

D-U-N-S 08-234-0063 IMP/EXP
■ **FAMILY DOLLAR STORES OF VIRGINIA INC**
(Suby of FAMILY DOLLAR STORES INC) ★
10401 Old Monroe St, Matthews, NC 28105
Tel (704) 847-6961 Founded/Ownrshp 2003
Sales 104.5MM^E EMP 1,337
SIC 5331 Variety stores
Prin: Leon Levine

D-U-N-S 05-183-6807
FAMILY EXPRESS CORP
213 S State Road 49, Valparaiso, IN 46383-7976
Tel (219) 531-6490 Founded/Ownrshp 1976
Sales 276.4MM^E EMP 500
Accts Mcmahon & Associates Cpas Pc
SIC 5541 5411 Filling stations, gasoline; Convenience stores, independent
Pr: Gus Olympidis
*Treas: Monique Horn
VP: Bill Nolan
Exec: Cynthia Carlson

D-U-N-S 06-222-6063
FAMILY FARE INC
TRADE STYLE FAMILY FARE SPRMKT
3030 Corporate Grove Dr, Hudsonville, MI 49426-8023
Tel (616) 896-5910 Founded/Ownrshp 1973
Sales 200.0MM EMP 1,500
SIC 5411 Grocery stores
Ch Bd: Donald Koop
*Pr: Robert Kaiser
VP: Rog Bronsink
*VP: David Kraker

D-U-N-S 10-400-1594 IMP
FAMILY FARM & HOME INC
900 3rd St Ste 302, Muskegon, MI 49440-1152
Tel (231) 722-8335 Founded/Ownrshp 2002
Sales 134.2MM EMP 700
Accts Conn Geneva & Robinson Muskeg

SIC 5999 5261 5149 5611 5211 5091 Farm equipment & supplies; Lawn & garden supplies; Pet foods; Clothing accessories: men's & boys'; Lumber & other building materials; Sporting & recreation goods
CEO: Alan Fansler
*Pr: Robert Tarrant
*CFO: Rick McLouch
CFO: Rick McLouth
*Treas: Bob Tarrant
*Chf Mktg O: Tim Fansler

FAMILY FUEL
See R H FOSTER ENERGY LLC

FAMILY GARD/BRK
See BRK BRANDS INC

FAMILY HEALTH CENTER
See ATLANTIC HEALTH

D-U-N-S 13-502-2296
FAMILY HEALTH CENTER OF A MARSHFIELD INC
1000 N Oak Ave, Marshfield, WI 54449-5703
Tel (715) 387-9137 Founded/Ownrshp 1990
Sales 142.8MM EMP 1
Accts Kpmg Llp Chicago Il
SIC 8621 Health association

D-U-N-S 02-053-1893
FAMILY HEALTH CENTERS OF SAN DIEGO INC (CA)
823 Gateway Center Way, San Diego, CA 92102-4541
Tel (619) 515-2303 Founded/Ownrshp 1972
Sales 147.1MM EMP 550
Accts The Pun Group Llp Santa Ana
SIC 8093 Specialty outpatient clinics
Pr: Fran Butler-Cohen
QA Dir: Barbara Greer
Pgrm Dir: Chris Gordon
Board of Directors: Lois Bernstein, Jose R De La Garza, Bertha Garcia, Otto A Hirr, Mercedes Ortiz, Stephanie Perez, Robert Resley, Paula Rotenberg

D-U-N-S 06-718-0786
FAMILY HEALTH INTERNATIONAL INC
FHI 360
359 Blackwell St Ste 200, Durham, NC 27701-2477
Tel (919) 544-7040 Founded/Ownrshp 1971
Sales 653.6MM EMP 4,000
Accts Lb Ernst & Young Us Llp Durha
SIC 8733 Medical research
CEO: Patrick C Fine
V Ch: Edward Whitehorne
*CEO: Albert J Siemens
*COO: Deborah Kennedy
*COO: Marjorie N Williams
*CFO: Hubert C Graves
*CFO: Robert S Murphy
*CFO: Rasika Padmaperuma
*Treas: Martin M Lenkheym
Ofcr: Stephanie Davison
Ofcr: Margaret Hendrickson
Ofcr: Amrita Mathew
Ofcr: Marta Pirzadeh
Ofcr: Kate Plourde
Ofcr: Robinah Sanyangore
*Ofcr: Sean Temeemi
Ofcr: Casey Wilson
Ofcr: Shaha Yakubova
*Ex VP: Robert R Price
*Sr VP: Sheila Mitchell
Sr VP: Gary West

D-U-N-S 15-587-7405
FAMILY HEALTH NETWORK INC
F H N
322 S Green St Ste 400, Chicago, IL 60607-3544
Tel (312) 243-5235 Founded/Ownrshp 1982
Sales 266.0MM EMP 30
SIC 8011 Offices & clinics of medical doctors
CEO: Keith Kudla
*Pr: Philip C Bradley
*CFO: Tom Tennison
VP: James Kiamos
VP: Karen Osuch
Dir QC: Sally Szumlas
IT Man: P J Schmidt

D-U-N-S 17-559-2385
FAMILY HEALTH PLAN INC
(Suby of MERCY HEALTH) ★
2200 Jefferson Ave Fl 6, Toledo, OH 43604-7102
Tel (419) 241-6501 Founded/Ownrshp 1985
Sales NA EMP 170
SIC 6324 8011 Health maintenance organization (HMO), insurance only; Offices & clinics of medical doctors
Pr: Tom Beaty
*CFO: Randy Hoffman
*VP: Lauri Oakes
*Med Dir: Dr Mark Tucker

D-U-N-S 03-232-6548
FAMILY HEALTHCARE NETWORK
305 E Center Ave, Visalia, CA 93291-6331
Tel (559) 737-4700 Founded/Ownrshp 1978
Sales 100.9MM EMP 900
Accts Lb Chw Lp Fresno Ca
SIC 8011 Primary care medical clinic
CEO: Karry Hydash
CFO: Chad Vawter
Off Mgr: Veronica Loya
CIO: Jay Kelley
Dir QC: Marisol De Cardoso
Obsttrcn: Juan C Sabogal Tamayo
Doctor: Maria C Detubio
Pharmcst: Geethanjali S Pandey

D-U-N-S 18-974-1382
■ **FAMILY HOME HEALTH CARE INC**
AMEDYSIS HOME HEALTH
(Suby of AMEDYSIS HOME HEALTH INC OF SOUTH CAROLINA) ★
937 Campbellsville Rd R, Columbia, KY 42728-2265
Tel (270) 384-6411 Founded/Ownrshp 2009
Sales 401.2MM EMP 125[E]
SIC 8082 Home health care services

Pr: Zaheer Sardar
*Sec: John P Coan

FAMILY MARKET
See WAREHOUSE MARKET INC

D-U-N-S 18-059-0838
FAMILY MEDICAL CENTER AT ROCKWALL
HEALTH TEXAS PROVIDE NETWORK
1975 Alpha Dr 204, Rockwall, TX 75087-4951
Tel (972) 771-9155 Founded/Ownrshp 1987
Sales 234.4MM EMP 35
SIC 8011 General & family practice, physician/surgeon
Pt: Dr Greg Muns
Pt: Dr Richard Bellinger
Pt: Dr David Linch
Pt: Dr Jenny Miller
Doctor: Wes Acker

D-U-N-S 10-568-7693
FAMILY MEDICINE NORTH INC
1930 Crown Park Ct # 130, Columbus, OH 43235-2402
Tel (614) 457-1793 Founded/Ownrshp 1978
Sales 309.2MM EMP 18
SIC 8011 General & family practice, physician/surgeon
Pr: Paul C Leidheiser

FAMILY PHYSICIAN HEALTH CENTER
See REGIONS HOSPITAL FOUNDATION

D-U-N-S 80-396-4352
FAMILY PHYSICIANS OF WINTER PARK PA
6416 Old Winter Garden Rd, Orlando, FL 32835-1348
Tel (407) 293-2930 Founded/Ownrshp 1990
Sales 200.4MM EMP 400
Accts Vestal & Wiler Orlando Flori
SIC 8011 General & family practice, physician/surgeon
Pr: Andy Vyas
*CEO: Imtiaz Sattaur
CTO: Amar Bulsara

D-U-N-S 09-560-8808
FAMILY RESIDENCES & ESSENTIAL ENTERPRISES INC
191 Bethpage Sweet Holw, Old Bethpage, NY 11804-1342
Tel (516) 870-1600 Founded/Ownrshp 1977
Sales 88.2MM EMP 1,200
Accts Baker Tilly Virchow Krause Llp
SIC 8399 Health systems agency
CEO: Robert S Budd
*COO: Christopher Long
*CFO: Susan Dickinson
CFO: Dara Gray
VP: Barbara Best
Genl Mgr: Vincent Cona
Genl Mgr: Herbert Reyes
Off Mgr: Kelly Walthour
CTO: Nancy Bugeia
Pgrm Dir: David Barhorne
Pgrm Dir: Laura Graf

FAMILY RESOURCE CENTER
See PROVIDENCE EVERETT MEDICAL CENTER

D-U-N-S 06-639-3706 IMP
FAMILY ROOTS USA INC
4211 Produce Rd, Louisville, KY 40218-3064
Tel (502) 964-0063 Founded/Ownrshp 2007
Sales 54.6MM[E] EMP 1,099
SIC 5999 Heraldic insignia
Prin: Michael Menahan
*Prin: Heather Gaylor

D-U-N-S 06-391-6173
FAMILYCARE INC
(Suby of FAMILYCARE MEDICAL CLINICS INC) ★
825 Ne Multnomah St # 300, Portland, OR 97232-2135
Tel (503) 222-2880 Founded/Ownrshp 1984
Sales 410.4MM EMP 5[E]
Accts Perkins & Company Pc Portland
SIC 8082 Home health care services
Pr: Jeff Heatherington
QC Dir: Mary Brenner

D-U-N-S 18-080-3595
FAMILYCARE MEDICAL CLINICS INC
825 Ne Multnomah St # 300, Portland, OR 97232-2135
Tel (503) 222-3205 Founded/Ownrshp 1984
Sales NA EMP 34
Accts Perkins & Company Pc Portland
SIC 6411 Medical insurance claim processing, contract or fee basis
Pr: Jeff Heatherington
Exec: Carrie Jones
Dir Rx: Alex Bulochnik
Pharmcst: Stacy Eria

D-U-N-S 07-639-3375
FAMILYMEDS GROUP INC
ARROW PRESCRIPTION CENTER
312 Farmington Ave Ste B, Farmington, CT 06032-1913
Tel (888) 787-2800 Founded/Ownrshp 1993
Sales 207.4MM[E] EMP 630[E]
SIC 5912 Drug stores
Ch Bd: Edgardo A Mercadante
*CFO: James E Searson
Sr VP: Lawrence D Kososki
Genl Mgr: David Mallary

D-U-N-S 08-015-0210
FAMOSA NORTH AMERICA INC
1357 Ashford Ave Se, San Juan, PR 00907
Tel (206) 316-8315 Founded/Ownrshp 2011
Sales 100.0MM EMP 5
SIC 5092 Toys
Genl Mgr: Marybeth King

FAMOUS BRANDS
See MRS FIELDS HOLDING CO INC

FAMOUS BRANDS INTERNATIONAL
See MRS FIELDS COMPANIES INC

D-U-N-S 93-260-6262
▲ **FAMOUS DAVES OF AMERICA INC**
12701 Whitewater Dr # 200, Minnetonka, MN 55343-4165
Tel (952) 294-1300 Founded/Ownrshp 1995
Sales 114.2MM EMP 2,585
Tkr Sym DAVE Exch NGS
SIC 5812 6794 Family restaurants; Restaurant, family: independent; Franchises, selling or licensing
CEO: Michael W Lister
*Ch Bd: Joseph M Jacobs
COO: Abelardo Ruiz
CFO: Dexter Newman
Chf Mktg O: Alfredo V Martel
Board of Directors: Anand D Gala, Jonathan P Lennon, Chuck Mooty, Richard A Shapiro, Patrick D Walsh, Bryan L Wolff

D-U-N-S 05-356-1351
FAMOUS DISTRIBUTION INC
FAMOUS SUPPLY COMPANIES
(Suby of FAMOUS MANUFACTURING) ★
2620 Ridgewood Rd Ste 200, Akron, OH 44313-3507
Tel (330) 762-9621 Founded/Ownrshp 1970
Sales 204.3MM[E] EMP 650
SIC 5074 5075 5085 5023 Plumbing & hydronic heating supplies; Furnaces, warm air; Warm air heating equipment & supplies; Valves & fittings; Kitchenware
CEO: Jay Blaushild
*Pr: Marc Blaushild
COO: David Figuly
*Treas: Dale Newman
Opers Mgr: Callie St Clair
Advt Mgr: Eddie Roedig
Sales Asso: Larry Puchajda

D-U-N-S 92-919-8232
FAMOUS ENTERPRISES INC
FAMOUS MANUFACTURING
2620 Ridgewood Rd Ste 200, Akron, OH 44313-3507
Tel (330) 762-9621 Founded/Ownrshp 1933
Sales 293.0MM[E] EMP 650
SIC 5075 5031 5074 7699 Warm air heating equipment & supplies; Lumber, plywood & millwork; Plumbing & hydronic heating supplies; Industrial equipment services
Ch: Jay Blaushild
*Pr: Marc Blaushild
*Treas: Dale J Newman
MIS Dir: Craig Raub

FAMOUS HAIR
See CHICAGO 29 INC

D-U-N-S 00-892-6321
FAMOUS INDUSTRIES INC
JOHNSON CONTRLS AUTHORIZED DLR
(Suby of FAMOUS MANUFACTURING) ★
2620 Ridgewood Rd Ste 200, Akron, OH 44313-3507
Tel (330) 535-1811 Founded/Ownrshp 1982
Sales 84.7MM[E] EMP 300
SIC 5074 3444 5065 Plumbing & hydronic heating supplies; Plumbing & heating valves; Metal ventilating equipment; Telephone equipment; Intercommunication equipment, electronic
Pr: Jay Blaushild
*VP: Marc Blaushild
Tech Mgr: CAM Jordan

FAMOUS MANUFACTURING
See FAMOUS ENTERPRISES INC

FAMOUS SUPPLY COMPANIES
See FAMOUS DISTRIBUTION INC

D-U-N-S 87-738-7048 IMP
FAMSA INC
FAMSA USA
(Suby of GRUPO FAMSA, S.A.B. DE C.V.)
2727 Lyndon B Johnson Fwy, Dallas, TX 75234-7334
Tel (972) 993-5800 Founded/Ownrshp 2000
Sales 140.0MM[E] EMP 700
SIC 5722 5712 Electric household appliances; Furniture stores
Pr: Ignacio Ortiz
*CFO: Gilbert Gomez
CIO: Oscar Recio
Dir IT: Alfredo Farid
IT Man: Francisco Huezo
IT Man: Denisse Medina
Sales Exec: Carlos Martinez

FAMSA USA
See FAMSA INC

D-U-N-S 83-619-2278 IMP
FANATICS INC
FOOTBALL FANATICS
(Suby of KYNETIC LLC) ★
8100 Nations Way, Jacksonville, FL 32256-4405
Tel (904) 421-8143 Founded/Ownrshp 2011
Sales 228.3MM[E] EMP 920
SIC 5941 5699 Sporting goods & bicycle shops; Sports apparel
Ch Bd: Michael Rubin
Pr: Raphael Peck
CEO: Doug Mack
CFO: Thomas Baumlin
CFO: Lauren Cooks Levitan
Ex VP: Victor Shaffer
Ex VP: Stefan Tesoriero
Sr VP: Richard Perel
VP: Robert Barnhart
VP: Ryan Donovan
VP: Jim Gruhn
VP: Scott Gude
VP: Lonnie Philips
VP: Lee Pinkerton
VP: Brian Swallow
VP: Mitchell Trager

D-U-N-S 18-668-6754 IMP/EXP
FANCOR INC
FAIRBANKS
821 Locust St, Kansas City, MO 64106-1908
Tel (816) 471-0231 Founded/Ownrshp 1987
Sales 180.0MM[E] EMP 1,272

SIC 3596 7699 5046 Industrial scales; Weighing machines & apparatus; Industrial machinery & equipment repair; Scales, except laboratory
Ch Bd: F A Norden
*Pr: Richard Norden

D-U-N-S 05-861-3761 IMP
FANCY FOODS INC
21ST CENTURY
Hunts Pt Cooperative Mkt, Bronx, NY 10474
Tel (718) 617-3000 Founded/Ownrshp 1981
Sales 230.3MM EMP 106
Accts Monteverde & Amari Cpas Llp
SIC 5144 5147 Poultry & poultry products; Meats & meat products
CEO: Robert Corazza
*VP: Thomas Corazza
*VP: Robert Dee
*VP: Marian Petrone
IT Man: Jimmy Cancino
Sales Exec: Anthony D'Urso
Mktg Dir: Ed Lopez

FANESTIL MEATS
See S&S QUALITY MEATS LLC

D-U-N-S 92-951-1863 IMP
■ **FANEUIL INC**
(Suby of ALJ REGIONAL HOLDINGS INC) ★
2 Eaton St Ste 1002, Hampton, VA 23669-3979
Tel (757) 722-3235 Founded/Ownrshp 2013
Sales 142.0MM EMP 3,629
Accts Pbmares Llp Norfolk Virgini
SIC 7389 Telemarketing services
Pr: Anna M Van Buren
*CFO: Samuel R Rehm

D-U-N-S 18-328-2128 IMP/EXP
FANJUL CORP
1 N Clematis St Ste 200, West Palm Beach, FL 33401-5551
Tel (561) 655-6303 Founded/Ownrshp 1987
Sales 1.1MMM[E] EMP 3,000
SIC 0133 2061 2099 6552 Sugarcane farm; Raw cane sugar; Sugar grinding; Subdividers & developers
Ch: Alfonso Fanjul
*Pr: Jose F Fanjul
*Pr: Luis Fernandez
COO: Jose Fanjul
*VP: Erik J Blomqvist
*VP: Alexander J Fanjul
*VP: Oscar R Hernandez

FANNIE MAE
See FEDERAL NATIONAL MORTGAGE ASSOCIATION

D-U-N-S 16-367-8621
■ **FANNIE MAY CONFECTIONS BRANDS INC**
(Suby of 1-800-FLOWERS.COM INC) ★
2457 W North Ave, Melrose Park, IL 60160-1120
Tel (773) 693-9100 Founded/Ownrshp 2006
Sales 142.3MM[E] EMP 1,022
SIC 2064 5441 Candy & other confectionery products; Candy, nut & confectionery stores
CEO: David Taiclet
*Pr: Terry Mitchell
*COO: Alan Petrik
Opers Mgr: Tina Johnson
Mktg Dir: Susan Haynie
Mktg Mgr: Jennifer Peterson

D-U-N-S 83-496-2602
■ **FANNIE MAY CONFECTIONS BRANDS INC**
(Suby of FANNIE MAY CONFECTIONS BRANDS INC) ★
5353 Lauby Rd, North Canton, OH 44720-1572
Tel (330) 494-0833 Founded/Ownrshp 2004
Sales 100.0MM[E] EMP 800
SIC 5441 2066 Candy; Chocolate bars, solid
Pr: Terry Michell
Genl Mgr: Gina Miller
Opers Mgr: Vince Grishaber
Plnt Mgr: Calvin Reynolds

D-U-N-S 00-513-0786 IMP
FANSTEEL INC
FANSTEEL INTERCAST
1746 Commerce Rd, Creston, IA 50801-8191
Tel (641) 782-8521 Founded/Ownrshp 1907
Sales 141.2MM[E] EMP 738
SIC 3463 3728 3365 3369 3769 3545 Aircraft forgings, nonferrous; Aircraft assemblies, subassemblies & parts; Aerospace castings, aluminum; Aerospace castings, nonferrous: except aluminum; Guided missile & space vehicle parts & auxiliary equipment; Machine tool accessories; Tools & accessories for machine tools; Machine knives, metalworking
CEO: Brian Cassady
*CFO: Earl F White
*VP: Robert R Compernolle
Board of Directors: Brian F Cassady, Todd M Hymel

FANSTEEL INTERCAST
See FANSTEEL INC

FANTASY SPRINGS RESORT CASINO
See EAST VALLEY TOURIST DEVELOPMENT AUTHORITY

D-U-N-S 05-329-3007 IMP/EXP
FANUC AMERICA CORP (DE)
(Suby of FANUC CORPORATION)
3900 W Hamlin Rd, Rochester Hills, MI 48309-3253
Tel (248) 377-7000 Founded/Ownrshp 1992
Sales 523.8MM[E] EMP 1,100
SIC 3559 3548 3569 3542 Metal finishing equipment for plating, etc.; Electric welding equipment; Robots, assembly line: industrial & commercial; Robots for metal forming: pressing, extruding, etc.
Pr: Mike Cicco
*Ch Bd: Richard E Schneider
*CFO: Steve Stanko
*Treas: William M Owens
VP: Andrew Denny

VP: Jon Karr
VP: Kevin Ostby
**VP:* Niles Kevin Ostby
VP: Denise Scanlon
VP: Gary Zwyiol
VP: Gary Zywiol

D-U-N-S 01-149-3152 IMP
FAPS INC
371 Craneway St, Newark, NJ 07114-3114
Tel (973) 589-5656 *Founded/Ownrshp* 1991
Sales 97.6MM[E] *EMP* 274
SIC 3499 3711 7538 Metal household articles; Motor vehicles & car bodies; General automotive repair shops
Pr: Gary L Lobue
**VP:* August Lobue
Dir IT: Chris Heisman

D-U-N-S 17-122-2656
FAR NORTHERN COORDINATING COUNCIL ON DEVELOPMENTAL DISABILITIES
FAR NORTHERN REGIONAL CENTER
1900 Churn Creek Rd # 31, Redding, CA 96002-0292
Tel (530) 222-4791 *Founded/Ownrshp* 1967
Sales 121.0MM *EMP* 180
Accts Matson & Isom Redding Califo
SIC 8322 Social services for the handicapped
Ex Dir: Laura L Larson
COO: Cynthia Presidio
CFO: Michael Mintline
Off Mgr: Diane Abraham

FAR NORTHERN REGIONAL CENTER
See FAR NORTHERN COORDINATING COUNCIL ON DEVELOPMENTAL DISABILITIES

FARA
See F A RICHARD & ASSOCIATES INC

D-U-N-S 80-840-9643
FARAHMAND ARTA DDS
23326 Hawthorne Blvd # 220, Torrance, CA 90505-3725
Tel (310) 373-3501 *Founded/Ownrshp* 1993
Sales 93.3MM *EMP* 2
SIC 8021 Offices & clinics of dentists
Owner: Arta Farahmand DDS

D-U-N-S 06-298-0412
FARBEST FOODS INC
4689 S 400w, Huntingburg, IN 47542-9199
Tel (812) 683-4200 *Founded/Ownrshp* 1998
Sales 218.0MM[E] *EMP* 900
SIC 2015 Turkey, processed
Pr: Ted J Segar
**VP:* Brian Hawkins
**VP:* Gerald K Jones
VP: Charles Larue
VP: Joseph Michael
Adm Dir: Diane Lindar
Plnt Mgr: Pat Jacobs
Sales Asso: Emily Souders

D-U-N-S 14-526-1223
FAREPORTAL INC
CHEAPOAIR
135 W 50th St Ste 500, New York, NY 10020-1201
Tel (646) 738-7813 *Founded/Ownrshp* 2002
Sales 255.2MM[E] *EMP* 1,400[E]
SIC 7379
Ch Bd: Sam Jain
**COO:* Werner G Kunz
COO: Ravindra Sharma
**CFO:* William Bullard
**Chf Cred:* Chris Cuddy
Sr VP: David Hang
Sr VP: Rocky Kurita
Sr VP: John Rustum
Sr VP: Michelle Toth
Sr VP: Prev Venugopal
Sr VP: Peter White
Sr VP: Yong-Yeow Yeoh
VP: Michael Cherney
VP: Derek Crevello
VP: Nikunj Dhawan
VP: Sarah Johnson
VP: Yury Kalnitsky
VP: Drew Osarchuk
VP: Srinivas Todupunoori
VP: Guarav Uri
Exec: Mary Grasso

D-U-N-S 00-694-0381 IMP
FAREWAY STORES INC
FAREWAY WHOLESALE GROCERY
715 8th St, Boone, IA 50036-2727
Tel (515) 432-2623 *Founded/Ownrshp* 1938
Sales 1.3MMM[E] *EMP* 9,000
SIC 5411 Grocery stores, independent
Pr: Frederick R Greiner
**CFO:* Craig A Shepley
CFO: Craig Shepley
**Ch:* F William Beckwith
**Ch:* Richard P Beckwith
**Treas:* Pat Hagan
Ofcr: Scott Beckwith
**Sr VP:* Richard L Stearns
**VP:* Kip Assis
VP: Aaron Irlbeck
VP: Jeff Stearns

FAREWAY WHOLESALE GROCERY
See FAREWAY STORES INC

D-U-N-S 07-971-7484
FARGO ASSEMBLY CO
FAC
3300 7th Ave N, Fargo, ND 58102-3069
Tel (701) 298-3803 *Founded/Ownrshp* 1975
Sales 171.5MM[E] *EMP* 650
SIC 3643 Current-carrying wiring devices
CEO: Ron Bergan
**Sec:* Mary Alice Bergan
VP: Joan Bommen
VP: Bob Sabre
**VP:* Herb Siemens
Prgrm Mgr: Cameron Pendleton
Brnch Mgr: Tim Pagel
Plnt Mgr: Brad Grosz
Plnt Mgr: Jared Lais
Sales Exec: Jeff Dostal

D-U-N-S 79-806-7864
FARGO ASSEMBLY OF PA INC
DAVID CITY MANUFACTURING
800 W Washington St, Norristown, PA 19401-4535
Tel (610) 272-6850 *Founded/Ownrshp* 1992
Sales 189.4MM[E] *EMP* 700
SIC 3679 Harness assemblies for electronic use: wire or cable
Ch: Ron Bergan
**CEO:* Dennis Rees
Exec: Lorraine Mancini
QA Dir: Tom Ravert
Dir IT: Dave Price
IT Man: Gregory Litwin
Plnt Mgr: Bob Glas
Plnt Mgr: Bruce Hansley
Plnt Mgr: Rob Sell
Sls Mgr: Jack Young

FARGO PUBLIC SCHOOLS
See FARGO SCHOOL DISTRICT NO 1

D-U-N-S 08-023-6219
FARGO SCHOOL DISTRICT NO 1 (ND)
FARGO PUBLIC SCHOOLS
415 4th St N, Fargo, ND 58102-4514
Tel (701) 446-1000 *Founded/Ownrshp* 1879
Sales 150.4MM *EMP* 1,600
Accts Robert R Peterson Fargo Nor
SIC 8211 Public elementary & secondary schools; Public junior high school; Public senior high school
VP: Michelle Martin
Dir Soc: Krista Ulrich
Netwrk Mgr: Terry Cote
Pr Dir: Annmarie Campbell
Schl Brd P: Linda Boyd
Teacher Pr: Britnee Nickle

D-U-N-S 00-647-8903 IMP/EXP
FARIBAULT FOODS INC
BUTTER KERNEL
(*Suby of* LA COSTENA USA INC) ★
222 S 9th St Ste 3380, Minneapolis, MN 55402-3820
Tel (612) 333-6461 *Founded/Ownrshp* 2014
Sales 185.3MM[E] *EMP* 550
SIC 2099 2032 2033 Packaged combination products: pasta, rice & potato; Canned specialties; Vegetables: packaged in cans, jars, etc.
CEO: Albert Hoflack
**CFO:* Michael W Weber
**Ex VP:* Gary Kindseth
**Ex VP:* Scott King
**Ex VP:* James Nelson
Snr Mgr: Carol Harwell

D-U-N-S 03-911-9362 IMP
FARLEYS & SATHERS CANDY CO INC
1 Sather Plz, Round Lake, MN 56167-4006
Tel (507) 945-8181 *Founded/Ownrshp* 2001
Sales NA *EMP* 1,079
SIC 5145

D-U-N-S 06-687-6566 IMP/EXP
FARM & FLEET OF JANESVILLE INC
2421 Old Humes Rd Hwy 14, Janesville, WI 53545
Tel (608) 752-6377 *Founded/Ownrshp* 1955
Sales 89.0MM[E] *EMP* 873
SIC 5331 Variety stores
Pr: Robert Blain
**VP:* Jane Blain Gildertson
Genl Mgr: Paul Stubbens

D-U-N-S 02-327-2610 IMP
FARM & FLEET OF MADISON INC
3507 E Racine St, Janesville, WI 53546-2320
Tel (608) 754-2821 *Founded/Ownrshp* 1962
Sales 371.3MM[E] *EMP* 633
SIC 5199 5531 5251 5261 5039 Pets & pet supplies; Automotive tires; Hardware; Nurseries & garden centers; Wire fence, gates & accessories
Pr: Robert Blain
**Sec:* William Schondt

D-U-N-S 02-327-2636
FARM & FLEET OF RICE LAKE INC
3507 E Racine St, Janesville, WI 53546-2320
Tel (608) 754-2821 *Founded/Ownrshp* 1957
Sales 90.0MM[E] *EMP* 494
SIC 5191 5251 5531 Farm supplies; Hardware; Automotive parts; Truck equipment & parts; Automotive tires
Pr: Robert S Blain
**CFO:* William Schondt
**Ex VP:* Jane Blane Gilbertson
**VP:* Robert Glaser

FARM BUREAU FINANCIAL SERVICES
See FARM BUREAU PROPERTY & CASUALTY INSURANCE CO

D-U-N-S 10-156-4987
FARM BUREAU GENERAL INSURANCE CO OF MICHIGAN
FARM BUREAU INSURANCE
(*Suby of* MICHIGAN FARM BUREAU FINANCIAL CORP) ★
7373 W Saginaw Hwy, Lansing, MI 48917-1124
Tel (517) 323-7000 *Founded/Ownrshp* 1990
Sales NA *EMP* 99
Accts Bdo Seldman Llp Grand Rapids
SIC 6411 Insurance agents, brokers & service
Pr: Wayne Wood
**Pr:* James Robin
**Treas:* Douglas Kammann

FARM BUREAU INSURANCE
See FARM BUREAU MUTUAL INSURANCE CO INC

FARM BUREAU INSURANCE
See FARM BUREAU MUTUAL INSURANCE CO OF MICHIGAN

FARM BUREAU INSURANCE
See SOUTHERN FARM BUREAU CASUALTY INSURANCE CO

FARM BUREAU INSURANCE
See SOUTHERN FARM BUREAU LIFE INSURANCE CO INC

FARM BUREAU INSURANCE
See OKLAHOMA FARM BUREAU MUTUAL INSURANCE CO

FARM BUREAU INSURANCE
See MISSISSIPPI FARM BUREAU MUTUAL INSURANCE CO

FARM BUREAU INSURANCE
See LOUISIANA FARM BUREAU CASUALTY INSURANCE CO

FARM BUREAU INSURANCE
See SOUTH CAROLINA FARM BUREAU MUTUAL INSURANCE CO (INC)

FARM BUREAU INSURANCE
See FARM BUREAU MUTUAL INSURANCE CO OF IDAHO

FARM BUREAU INSURANCE
See FLORIDA FARM BUREAU GENERAL INSURANCE CO

FARM BUREAU INSURANCE
See FARM BUREAU GENERAL INSURANCE CO OF MICHIGAN

FARM BUREAU INSURANCE
See TEXAS FARM BUREAU MUTUAL INSURANCE CO

D-U-N-S 80-570-7317
FARM BUREAU MULTI-STATE SERVICES INC
5400 University Ave, West Des Moines, IA 50266-5997
Tel (515) 225-5400 *Founded/Ownrshp* 2010
Sales NA *EMP* 1,350[E]
SIC 6411 Insurance agents, brokers & service
Prin: Edward G Parker

D-U-N-S 00-694-3336
FARM BUREAU MUTUAL INSURANCE CO INC
FARM BUREAU INSURANCE
2627 Kfb Plz, Manhattan, KS 66503-8116
Tel (785) 587-6000 *Founded/Ownrshp* 1938
Sales NA *EMP* 300
SIC 6331 Fire, marine & casualty insurance
Pr: Steve Baccus
**Treas:* Ron Koester
Ofcr: Jim Chan
**Ex VP:* Michael D Wilds
VP: Terry Arthur
**VP:* Marty Orth
Board of Directors: John R Stegman, Stan Ahlerich, Lenard Stumpff, Fred Askren, Edith M Dahlsten, Gary R Doane, Barbara Gresian, Jeffery Grossenbacher, Duane L McHenry, Helen Norris, Dale G Roberds

D-U-N-S 08-949-0437
FARM BUREAU MUTUAL INSURANCE CO OF IDAHO
FARM BUREAU INSURANCE
275 Tierra Vista Dr, Pocatello, ID 83201-5813
Tel (208) 232-7914 *Founded/Ownrshp* 1947
Sales NA *EMP* 323
SIC 6331 Property damage insurance
Ex Dir: Phillip Joslin
**Pr:* Frank S Priestley
**Treas:* Paul B Roberts
Ex VP: Rick Keller
**VP:* Lex Heyer
**VP:* Richard Petersen
IT Man: Dan Davids
Software D: Robert Catmull
Software D: Rafael Moreira
Software D: John Thompson
Mktg Mgr: Becky Chase

D-U-N-S 00-696-0066
FARM BUREAU MUTUAL INSURANCE CO OF MICHIGAN
FARM BUREAU INSURANCE
7373 W Saginaw Hwy, Lansing, MI 48917-1124
Tel (517) 323-7000 *Founded/Ownrshp* 1949
Sales NA *EMP* 384
SIC 6331 Fire, marine & casualty insurance: mutual
Pr: Barbara Costello
**Pr:* Wayne Woods
**CFO:* Doug Kammann
**Treas:* Steve Rock
Treas: Don Simon
Treas: John Stindt
**Ex VP:* James Robinson
VP: Kim Bailey
VP: Lisa Balderson
**VP:* Joshua Wunfch
**Prin:* Joshua Klee

D-U-N-S 00-694-1090
FARM BUREAU PROPERTY & CASUALTY INSURANCE CO (IA)
FARM BUREAU FINANCIAL SERVICES
(*Suby of* FARM BUREAU MULTI-STATE SERVICES INC) ★
5400 University Ave, West Des Moines, IA 50266-5997
Tel (515) 225-5400 *Founded/Ownrshp* 1939
Sales NA *EMP* 1,800
SIC 6411 2711 6211 Insurance agents, brokers & service; Job printing & newspaper publishing combined; Security brokers & dealers
**Pr:* Steve Baccus
**Pr:* Kevin Rogers
**CFO:* Jim Brannen
CFO: Debra Francis
VP: Laura Beebe
VP: Stan Bergstrom
VP: John Broadrick
VP: Tim Cratch
VP: Dave Dickmeyer
VP: Tricia Erb
VP: Tony Kimmi
VP: Ron Mead
VP: David Oberholtz
**VP:* Dennis J Presnall
VP: Doug Shelton
VP: Scott Shuck
VP: Roger Soener
VP: Christopher Van Note

D-U-N-S 19-668-4666
FARM CREDIT BANK OF TEXAS
AG AGENCIES, THE
4801 Plaza On The Lk # 1200, Austin, TX 78746-1081
Tel (512) 330-9060 *Founded/Ownrshp* 1988
Sales NA *EMP* 200
Accts Pricewaterhousecoopers Llp Au
SIC 6111 Federal & federally sponsored credit agencies
Ch: Jimmy Dodson
Pr: Jeremy Lightfoot
Pr: Jae J Thompson
**CEO:* Larry R Doyle
CFO: Amie Pala
**Chf Cred:* Steven H Fowlkes
**Ofcr:* Thomas W Hill
Ofcr: Manuel Martinez
Ofcr: Ansel McDowell
Sr VP: Gary Blair
VP: Chris Amend
VP: Ed Crawford
VP: Chris Levine
VP: Gary Pickering
VP: Susan Wallar

D-U-N-S 96-782-5428
FARM CREDIT FOUNDATIONS WELFARE BENEFITS
30 7th St E, Saint Paul, MN 55101-4914
Tel (651) 282-8347 *Founded/Ownrshp* 2011
Sales NA *EMP* 2
Accts Agribank Fcb St Paul Mn
SIC 6159 Farm mortgage companies
CEO: Sandy Schmiesing
VP Opers: Teresa Heath-Alva

D-U-N-S 62-544-6257
FARM CREDIT ILLINOIS ACA
FARM CREDIT SERVICES ILL FLCA
1100 Farm Credit Dr, Mahomet, IL 61853-8532
Tel (217) 590-2222 *Founded/Ownrshp* 1916
Sales NA *EMP* 210
Accts Pricewaterhousecoopers Llp Mi
SIC 6159 6153 6111 Farm mortgage companies; Short-term business credit; Federal & federally sponsored credit agencies
Pr: Steve Witges
**CFO:* Steve Ray
Bd of Dir: Lance Beery
Bd of Dir: Kent Brinkmann
Bd of Dir: Mike Carls
Bd of Dir: Dennis Frey
**Sr VP:* Ryan Berg
**Sr VP:* Steve Cason
**Sr VP:* Aaron Johnson
**Sr VP:* Loren J Leskis
VP: Donna Arnold
VP: Ryan Buckles
VP: Gary Denzer
VP: Rob Downs
VP: Chuck Foran
VP: Don Henrichs
VP: Todd Hortin
VP: Carla Lappe
VP: Ron Lintker
VP: Mike Loyd
VP: Martin Meyer

D-U-N-S 15-275-9924 IMP
FARM CREDIT MID-AMERICA
1601 Ups Dr, Louisville, KY 40223-4023
Tel (502) 420-3700 *Founded/Ownrshp* 1985
Sales NA *EMP* 1,150
SIC 6159 6141 Production credit association, agricultural; Personal credit institutions
CEO: Bill Johnson
Pr: Jonathan Carrico
Ofcr: Jerick Abbott
Ofcr: Benjamin Bradley
Ofcr: Ron G Burns
Ofcr: Caitlin Bushman
Ofcr: Jess Campbell
Ofcr: Ken Carrington
Ofcr: Jarrod Crowder
Ofcr: Gabe Curtis
Ofcr: Emily Duckworth
Ofcr: Cody Eaton
Ofcr: Jennifer Ferris
Ofcr: Hart Fledderjohann
Ofcr: Tim Fraley
Ofcr: Devin Gilliam
Ofcr: Andrew Glasscock
Ofcr: Kelli Grice
Ofcr: Jonathan Harrison
Ofcr: Ashley Hayworth-Hopp
Ofcr: Becky Hoffman

D-U-N-S 62-110-6715
FARM CREDIT OF VIRGINIAS ACA
106 Sangers Ln, Staunton, VA 24401-6711
Tel (540) 899-0989 *Founded/Ownrshp* 1917
Sales NA *EMP* 142
Accts Pricewaterhousecoopers Llp Fo
SIC 6159 Farm mortgage companies
CEO: David Lawrence
**CFO:* David Sauer

FARM CREDIT SERVICES ILL FLCA
See FARM CREDIT ILLINOIS ACA

D-U-N-S 08-253-7879
FARM CREDIT SERVICES OF AMERICA PCA/FLCA
5015 S 118th St, Omaha, NE 68137-2210
Tel (800) 884-3276 *Founded/Ownrshp* 1933
Sales NA *EMP* 10,000
Accts Pricewaterhousecoopers Llp M
SIC 6159 Agricultural credit institutions
Pr: Doug Stark
**CFO:* Eugene College
Treas: Tanya Storer
Bd of Dir: John Andrikopoulos
Ofcr: Dianne Jones
**Ex VP:* Neil Olsen
Sr VP: Scott Coziahr

*Sr VP: Michelle Mapes
*Sr VP: David Martin
Sr VP: Bob Schmidt
VP: Bruce Dean
VP: Jason Edleman
VP: Kathy Frahm
VP: Shane Frahm
VP: Anthony Jesina
VP: Dave Kalil
VP: Kurt Kline
VP: Sharlyn Konfrst
VP: Gary Taake
Assoc Dir: Matthew Heimann

D-U-N-S 03-087-2506
FARM CREDIT WEST ACA
1478 Stone Point Dr # 450, Roseville, CA 95661-2869
Tel (916) 724-4800 Founded/Ownrshp 1917
Sales NA EMP 165
Accts Pricewaterhousecoopers Llp Sa
SIC 6159 Farm mortgage companies
Pr: Mark D Littlefield
*CFO: Chris Doherty
*Ex VP: John C Boyes
*Ex VP: Ernest M Hodges
*Sr VP: Chris N Brumfield
Sr VP: Paul Lamothe
Sr VP: Chris Roche
VP: Melissa Gomes
VP: Tom McGuire
VP: Anthony Monaco
VP: Michael Moore
*VP: William M Noland

D-U-N-S 02-613-4051
■ FARM FAMILY HOLDINGS INC
(Suby of ANICO) ★
344 Route 9w, Glenmont, NY 12077-2910
Tel (518) 431-5000 Founded/Ownrshp 2001
Sales NA EMP 500
Accts Pricewater House Coopers Llp
SIC 6331 Property damage insurance; Fire, marine & casualty insurance: mutual
Pr: Timothy A Walsh
*V Ch Bd: G Richard Ferdinandtsen

FARM FRESH DIRECT OF AMERICA
See GROWERS SALES AND MARKETING LLC

FARM LAND FOODS
See FARMLAND FOODS INC

FARM MART 11755
See BINGHAM COOPERATIVE INC

D-U-N-S 92-933-0975
■ FARM SERVICE AGENCY
(Suby of U S D A) ★
1400 Independence Ave Sw # 3086, Washington, DC 20250-0002
Tel (202) 720-6215 Founded/Ownrshp 1961
Sales NA EMP 16,000
SIC 9641 Regulation of agricultural marketing;
Brnch Mgr: Chris Burgess
Brnch Mgr: Cary Tucker
IT Man: James Spurling

D-U-N-S 00-486-9269
FARM SERVICE COOPERATIVE
FSC
2308 Pine St, Harlan, IA 51537-1884
Tel (712) 755-2207 Founded/Ownrshp 1930
Sales 101.2MM^E EMP 110
Accts Meriwether Wilson And Company
SIC 5153 Grains
Genl Mgr: Gary Jahn
Treas: Gary Hall
Bd of Dir: Duane Alff
Off Mgr: Cathy Fenn

FARM SERVICE ELEVATOR CO.
See WILLMAR POULTRY FARMS INC

D-U-N-S 00-361-8738
FARM STORES CORP (FL)
2937 Sw 27th Ave Ste 203, Miami, FL 33133-3772
Tel (800) 726-3276 Founded/Ownrshp 1999
Sales 91.5MM^E EMP 700
SIC 5411 Convenience stores, chain
Pr: Jose Garcia-Pedrosa
*COO: Maurice Bared

D-U-N-S 07-808-4001
FARMCHEM CORP
616 Madison, Floyd, IA 50435
Tel (800) 247-1854 Founded/Ownrshp 1995
Sales 92.1MM^E EMP 75
Accts Marshall Wilson Cpa Charles
SIC 5083 Agricultural machinery & equipment
Ch: Gary Jacques
Pr: Ryan Bergman
*Pr: Dion Buhman
VP: Eric McCann
Rgnl Mgr: Alvin Thompson
Natl Sales: Brian Pieper

D-U-N-S 00-828-8979
▲ FARMER BROS CO
FARMER BROTHERS
13601 North Fwy Ste 200, Fort Worth, TX 76177-3010
Tel (682) 549-6600 Founded/Ownrshp 1912
Sales 544.3MM EMP 1,634
Accts Deloitte & Touche Llp Dallas
Tkr Sym FARM Exch NGM
SIC 2095 5149 Roasted coffee; Coffee & tea; Coffee, green or roasted; Spices & seasonings; Sugar, refined
Pr: Michael H Keown
*Ch Bd: Randy E Clark
CFO: Isaac N Johnston Jr
Sr VP: Scott W Bixby
Sr VP: Barry C Fischetto
Genl Couns: Thomas J Mattei Jr
Board of Directors: Guenter W Berger, Jeanne Farmer Grossman, Charles F Marcy, Christopher P Mottern

FARMER BROTHERS
See FARMER BROS CO

FARMER JOHN BRAND
See CLOUGHERTY PACKING LLC

FARMER MAC
See FEDERAL AGRICULTURAL MORTGAGE CORP

D-U-N-S 00-695-0851
■ FARMERS & MECHANICS BANK
(Suby of PNC FINANCIAL SERVICES GROUP INC) ★
110 Thomas Johnson Dr # 100, Frederick, MD 21702-4400
Tel (301) 694-4050 Founded/Ownrshp 2007
Sales NA EMP 400
SIC 6021 6163 National commercial banks; Loan brokers
Pr: Faye E Cannon
*Ch Bd: R Carl Benna
*CFO: Kaye A Simmons
*Sr VP: John J Joback
*Exec: David R Stauffer

D-U-N-S 14-636-4117
▲ FARMERS & MERCHANTS BANCORP
111 W Pine St, Lodi, CA 95240-2110
Tel (209) 367-2300 Founded/Ownrshp 1999
Sales NA EMP 316^E
Tkr Sym FMCB Exch OTC
SIC 6022 State commercial banks
Ch Bd: Kent A Steinwert
CFO: Stephen W Haley
Ofcr: Kenneth W Smith

D-U-N-S 00-690-5939
■ FARMERS & MERCHANTS BANK OF CENTRAL CALIFORNIA
F&M BANK
(Suby of FARMERS & MERCHANTS BANCORP) ★
121 W Pine St, Lodi, CA 95240-2110
Tel (209) 367-2300 Founded/Ownrshp 1916
Sales NA EMP 298
SIC 6022 6021 State commercial banks; National commercial banks
Pr: Kent A Steinwert
Ch Bd: Ole R Mettler
CFO: Stephen W Haley
Bd of Dir: Stephen Barney
Ofcr: Richard S Erichson
Ofcr: Deborah Skinner
Ex VP: James P Daugherty
Ex VP: Donald H Fraser
Ex VP: Deborah E Hodkin
Ex VP: Ryan J Misasi
Ex VP: Ryan Misasi
Ex VP: Chris C Nelson
Ex VP: Kenneth Smith
Sr VP: Robert Hallquist
Sr VP: Aaron Nissim
Sr VP: Dennis Raymond
VP: Nathan Dellinger
VP: Aubrey Halverson
VP: Bob Harmon
VP: John Meredith
VP: Cheryl Rau

D-U-N-S 00-690-6085 IMP
FARMERS & MERCHANTS BANK OF LONG BEACH (CA)
F&M BANK
(Suby of PALOMAR ENTERPRISES, LLC)
302 Pine Ave, Long Beach, CA 90802-2326
Tel (562) 437-0011 Founded/Ownrshp 1907
Sales NA EMP 700
SIC 6022 6029 State trust companies accepting deposits, commercial; Commercial banks
CEO: W Henry Walker
Pr: Lissette Najarro
*Pr: Kenneth G Walker
*COO: Melissa Lanfre
*Chf Cred: Phillip Bond
Bd of Dir: Sue Wilson
Ofcr: Kirk Erickson
Ofcr: Thylan Nguyen
Trst Ofcr: Garry Baker
*Ex VP: John Hinrichs
*Ex VP: Danile K Walker
Sr VP: Valentina Fiorentina
Sr VP: Andy Gray
Sr VP: Jeff Hahn
Sr VP: Julie Hare
*Sr VP: Jerry Harpstrike
Sr VP: George McFedries
*Sr VP: Ken Nagel
Sr VP: Kathleen Salmons
Sr VP: Darrel Van
Sr VP: Darrel R Van Es
Board of Directors: Timothy M Wilson, Richard Darling, Stanley L Hahn, William G Hayter, Lawrence McLaughlin, Roger Molvar, Frank O'bryan, Charles Z Walker Jr, Daniel K Walker, William Wells

D-U-N-S 04-114-1680
FARMERS ALLIANCE MUTUAL INSURANCE CO
ALLIANCE INSURANCE CO
1122 N Main St, McPherson, KS 67460-2846
Tel (620) 241-2200 Founded/Ownrshp 1888
Sales NA EMP 630
SIC 6331 Fire, marine & casualty insurance
Ch Bd: Keith Birkhead
*Treas: Paul Toliver
VP: Joe Brossard
*VP: Dick Foulke
VP: James Lusk
IT Man: Teresa McCoy

D-U-N-S 00-176-0057
▲ FARMERS AUTOMOBILE INSURANCE ASSOCIATION (INC)
2505 Court St, Pekin, IL 61558-0001
Tel (309) 346-1161 Founded/Ownrshp 1921
Sales NA EMP 750
SIC 6411 6311 Insurance agents, brokers & service; Life insurance carriers
Pr: Gordon Walker
*COO: Scott A Martin
*Treas: Daniel Connell
*VP: Michael Zabinski

D-U-N-S 08-208-7180
■ FARMERS AUTOMOBILE MANAGEMENT CORP
(Suby of FARMERS AUTOMOBILE INSURANCE ASSOCIATION (INC)) ★
2505 Court St, Pekin, IL 61554-5308
Tel (309) 346-1161 Founded/Ownrshp 2008
Sales NA EMP 700
SIC 6311 6321 Life insurance; Accident & health insurance
Pr: Gordan Walker
Board of Directors: Arthur Anderson, Merlyn Lower, Curtis Mahaffey, Walter McCoy, Dale W Sarver, Eugene W Taylor

D-U-N-S 11-596-7135
▲ FARMERS CAPITAL BANK CORP
202 W Main St Ste 100, Frankfort, KY 40601-1811
Tel (502) 227-1668 Founded/Ownrshp 1982
Sales NA EMP 501^E
Tkr Sym FFKT Exch NGS
SIC 6021 7374 6411 National commercial banks; Data processing service; Property & casualty insurance agent
*Ch Bd: R Terry Bennett
*V Ch Bd: David Y Phelps
Board of Directors: J Barry Banker, Michael J Crawford, William C Nash, David R O'bryan, Fred N Parker, David Y Phelps, Marvin E Strong Jr, Fred Sutterlin, Judy Worth

D-U-N-S 79-759-3386
FARMERS CO-OPERATIVE ELEVATOR CO
1972 510th St, Hanley Falls, MN 56245-3082
Tel (507) 768-3448 Founded/Ownrshp 1912
Sales 174.5MM EMP 56
Accts Carlson Highland New Ulm Min
SIC 0723 Cash grain crops market preparation services
CEO: Scott Dubbelde
Sls Dir: Kay Mueller

D-U-N-S 03-501-3556
FARMERS COOPERATIVE
208 W Depot St, Dorchester, NE 68343-2375
Tel (402) 946-4631 Founded/Ownrshp 1914
Sales 830.6MM EMP 470
Accts Gardiner Thomsen Lincoln Ne
SIC 5153 5191 5172 Grains; Fertilizers & agricultural chemicals; Feed; Petroleum products
Pr: Ron Velver
*Sec: Glen Capek
Store Mgr: Sue Lang

D-U-N-S 03-549-5209
FARMERS COOPERATIVE
2105 Industrial Park Rd, Van Buren, AR 72956-6001
Tel (479) 474-8051 Founded/Ownrshp 1944
Sales 125.9MM^E EMP 125
Accts Przybysz & Associates Cpa S
SIC 5191 Farm supplies
CEO: Gene Bruick
*CFO: Charlene Booth
*VP: Allan Hales
Genl Mgr: Renne Chesser
Genl Mgr: Jerri Farrar
Genl Mgr: John Grote
Store Mgr: Danny Brown

D-U-N-S 02-201-3775
FARMERS COOPERATIVE ELEVATOR CO
FAC
12543 190th St, Arcadia, IA 51430
Tel (712) 689-2296 Founded/Ownrshp 1917
Sales 157.9MM^E EMP 85
SIC 5191 5153 Feed; Fertilizer & fertilizer materials; Grains
Pr: Dale Lenz
*VP: Keith Weller
*Prin: Robert Hackfort
Brnch Mgr: Richard Wuebker
Div Mgr: Nathan Fara
*Genl Mgr: David L Leiting

D-U-N-S 00-486-9301
FARMERS COOPERATIVE SOCIETY
DO IT BEST
317 3rd St Nw, Sioux Center, IA 51250-1897
Tel (712) 722-2671 Founded/Ownrshp 1906
Sales 384.1MM EMP 160
SIC 5153 5191 5211 Grain elevators; Feed; Seeds: field, garden & flower; Chemicals, agricultural; Lumber & other building materials
Pr: Marvin Wynia
Ex VP: Steven T White
*VP: Dave Deboer

D-U-N-S 00-984-4234
FARMERS ELECTRIC COOPERATIVE INC
F E C ELECTRIC
2000 I 30 E, Greenville, TX 75402-9084
Tel (903) 455-1715 Founded/Ownrshp 1937
Sales 116.7MM EMP 130
SIC 4911 Electric services; Distribution, electric power
Pr: David Magness
*CFO: Kathy Scroggins
Bd of Dir: Dough Slaubaugh
*VP: Bill Samuels
*Ex Dir: Mark Stubbs
IT Man: Anthony Grant

D-U-N-S 02-560-3291
FARMERS ELEVATOR CO OF LOWDER
10955 North St, Waverly, IL 62692-8520
Tel (217) 435-9023 Founded/Ownrshp 1905
Sales 96.5MM EMP 24
SIC 5153 Grain elevators
Pr: Joseph Murphy
*Treas: Jerry Ackerman
*VP: Gearal Carney

D-U-N-S 04-911-8623
FARMERS GRAIN TERMINAL INC
1977 Harbor Front Rd, Greenville, MS 38701-9588
Tel (662) 332-0987 Founded/Ownrshp 1968
Sales 878.8MM EMP 82
Accts Hudson Cisne & Co Llp Litt
SIC 5153 Grain elevators
Pr: Steve Nail
*CFO: Richard Watkins
*Ex VP: Harvey Parrish
*VP: C C Craig
*VP: John Oakes
Brnch Mgr: Lynn Bowden

D-U-N-S 00-690-7141 IMP
FARMERS GROUP INC (CA)
FARMERS INSURANCE
(Suby of ZURICH INSURANCE GROUP AG)
6301 Owensmouth Ave, Woodland Hills, CA 91367-2216
Tel (323) 932-3200 Founded/Ownrshp 1927, 1998
Sales NA EMP 28,975
SIC 6331 Automobile insurance; Reciprocal interinsurance exchanges: fire, marine, casualty
CEO: Jeff Dailey
Pr: Steve Boshoven
Pr: Tony Desantis
Pr: Mhayse Samalya
CFO: Scott Lindquist
CFO: Scott R Lindquist
Chf Inves: Tom Rogers
Ofcr: Deborah Aldredge
Ofcr: Keith Daly
Ofcr: David Travers
Ex VP: Frank Ceglar
Ex VP: James Mackinnon
Ex VP: C Paul Patsis
Sr VP: Stephen Boshoven
*Sr VP: Stephen J Feely
Sr VP: Peter Teuscher
VP: Mike Cleveland
VP: Kelvin Connally
VP: Martin Leitner
VP: Gilbert Leslie
VP: John Patton
Board of Directors: Dale Marlin, Donnell Reid, James Shiro

FARMERS HOME FURNITURE
See WAREHOUSE HOME FURNISHINGS DISTRIBUTORS INC

FARMERS INSURANCE
See FARMERS GROUP INC

FARMERS INSURANCE
See PEKIN INSURANCE

D-U-N-S 11-267-6093 IMP
FARMERS INSURANCE
(Suby of FARMERS INSURANCE EXCHANGE) ★
23175 Nw Bennett St, Hillsboro, OR 97124-5602
Tel (503) 372-2000 Founded/Ownrshp 1970
Sales NA EMP 1,200
SIC 6411 Insurance agents, brokers & service
Prin: Lonnie Sproat

D-U-N-S 36-394-3788
FARMERS INSURANCE CO OF ARIZONA
(Suby of FARMERS INSURANCE EXCHANGE) ★
16001 N 28th Ave, Phoenix, AZ 85053-4050
Tel (602) 863-8100 Founded/Ownrshp 1980
Sales NA EMP 2,918^E
SIC 6411 8741 Insurance agents, brokers & service; Management services
Ex Dir: Steve Wampler
CFO: Craig Shepley
Ex VP: Pierre Wauthier

D-U-N-S 06-206-3623
FARMERS INSURANCE EXCHANGE
6301 Owensmouth Ave # 300, Woodland Hills, CA 91367-2268
Tel (323) 932-3200 Founded/Ownrshp 1998
Sales NA EMP 18,000
SIC 6311 Life insurance
CEO: Jeff Pailey
Pr: Katie Meyers
*CFO: Ron Myhan
Ofcr: Keith Daly
VP: Mike Cok
VP: Mike Pessetti
VP: Jim Randolph
VP: Russina Sgoureva
VP: Reed Whitlock
Dir Sec: Hermann Tai
Prgrm Mgr: Gary Kokonyan

D-U-N-S 06-031-6106
FARMERS INSURANCE GROUP
(Suby of FARMERS INSURANCE) ★
6301 Owensmouth Ave, Los Angeles, CA 90010
Tel (888) 327-6335 Founded/Ownrshp 1967, 1928
Sales NA EMP 704
SIC 6411 Insurance agents, brokers & service
Ex Dir: Jim Snikeris
Pr: Verginia Lam
Pr: Russina Sgoureva
*Pr: Erik J Snikeris
*Treas: Ronald G Myhan
Sr VP: Mark Martin
Dist Mgr: Naji J Garabet
Dist Mgr: Jodi Webster
Dist Mgr: Matt Wolk
Web Dev: Jill Hageman
Netwrk Eng: Elias Abdella

D-U-N-S 00-530-2823
FARMERS MUTUAL HAIL INSURANCE CO OF IOWA (IA)
6785 Westown Pkwy, West Des Moines, IA 50266-7727
Tel (515) 282-9104 Founded/Ownrshp 1893
Sales NA EMP 348
SIC 6331 Agricultural insurance
Pr: Ron Rutledge
Pr: Karen Daugherty
Pr: Barbara Raife
*Pr: Steve Rutledge
*CFO: Darin L Roggenburg
CFO: Darin Roggenburg
Ex VP: Bruce Vnloenen
VP: Donald Bevins
VP: Francis V Bigley
VP: Frank Bigley

VP: Steve G Fischer
VP: Gregory Meek
VP: Chad Mixdorf

D-U-N-S 05-483-9766
FARMERS NEW WORLD LIFE INSURANCE CO INC (WA)
(*Suby of* FARMERS INSURANCE) ★
3003 77th Ave Se, Mercer Island, WA 98040-2837
Tel (206) 232-1093 *Founded/Ownrshp* 1910, 1928
Sales NA *EMP* 800
SIC 6311 6411 Life insurance; Insurance agents, brokers & service
Pr: Paul Patsis
**Pr:* C Paul Patsis
**CFO:* Katherine P Cody
**Treas:* David A Demmon
Ex VP: Link Murphy
**VP:* Kathryn M Callahan
**VP:* James Randolph
Prgrm Mgr: Scott Zahren
Genl Couns: Garrett Paddor

FARMERS PRIDE
See BATTLE CREEK FARMERS COOPERATIVE NON-STOCK

D-U-N-S 00-893-5892 IMP/EXP
FARMERS PRIDE INC
BELL & EVANS
(*Suby of* SECHLER FAMILY FOODS INC) ★
154 W Main St, Fredericksburg, PA 17026-9510
Tel (717) 865-6626 *Founded/Ownrshp* 1939
Sales 170.3MM[E] *EMP* 1,050
SIC 2015 Chicken, slaughtered & dressed
Pr: Scott Sechler
**CEO:* J Michael Good
COO: Lummy Ythier
**CFO:* Daniel Chirico
VP: Clair Eberly
VP: Bryan Woods
Exec: Thomas Stone
IT Man: Aaron Lettich
Netwrk Mgr: Michael Welch
VP Opers: Joe Gardner
Sfty Dirs: Jerry Reardon

D-U-N-S 07-330-9668
FARMERS RANCHERS LIVSTOCK COMMUNITY INC
1500 W Old Highway 40, Salina, KS 67401-2084
Tel (785) 825-0211 *Founded/Ownrshp* 1987
Sales 135.0MM *EMP* 57
SIC 5154 Auctioning livestock
Pr: Christian C Hoffman III
**Sec:* William C Hoffman
**VP:* Michael T Samples

D-U-N-S 00-914-4031 IMP/EXP
FARMERS RICE COOPERATIVE
FRC
2566 River Plaza Dr, Sacramento, CA 95833-3673
Tel (916) 923-5100 *Founded/Ownrshp* 1944
Sales 110.9MM[E] *EMP* 336
SIC 2044 Rice milling
CEO: Frank Bragg
V Ch: Charles R Hoppin
**CFO:* Bill Tanimoto
Bd of Dir: Andrew Rudd
**Sr VP:* H Kirk Messick
VP: Steve Ellis
**VP:* Keith Hargrove
**VP:* Rob Paschoal
VP: Mike Sandrock
Opers Mgr: Joseph Magliola

D-U-N-S 96-555-2818
FARMERS SERVICES LLC
(*Suby of* FARMERS INSURANCE) ★
4680 Wilshire Blvd, Los Angeles, CA 90010-3807
Tel (323) 932-3200 *Founded/Ownrshp* 2006
Sales NA *EMP* 2,809[E]
SIC 6411 Insurance agents, brokers & service
Prin: Randy Farmer

D-U-N-S 03-550-8688
FARMERS SUPPLY ASSOCIATION
16240 Highway 14 E, Harrisburg, AR 72432-9684
Tel (870) 578-2468 *Founded/Ownrshp* 1962
Sales 168.1MM[E] *EMP* 100
SIC 5191 5172 5261 5541 5999 Farm supplies; Chemicals, agricultural; Fertilizer & fertilizer materials; Petroleum products; Fertilizer; Gasoline service stations; Feed & farm supply
Pr: Roger Pohlner

D-U-N-S 00-978-7623
FARMERS TELEPHONE COOPERATIVE INC
FTC
1101 E Main St, Kingstree, SC 29556-4105
Tel (843) 382-2333 *Founded/Ownrshp* 1952
Sales 188.1MM[E] *EMP* 418
SIC 4813 Telephone communication, except radio
CEO: Bradley Erwin
CFO: James Fogg
**CFO:* Jeffrey Lawrimore
Ex VP: John McDaniel
Off Mgr: Melissa Wiley
IT Man: James Barnard
IT Man: Dwayne Deininger
Sfty Dirs: Ella Mae
Opers Mgr: Tom Czerwinski
Sales Exec: Richard Spangler

D-U-N-S 02-216-5252
FARMERS UNION COOPERATIVE
1913 County Road B32, Ossian, IA 52161-8041
Tel (563) 532-9381 *Founded/Ownrshp* 1912
Sales 94.4MM *EMP* 39
Accts Meriwether Wilson & Company
SIC 5153 5261 5983 Grains; Lawn & garden supplies; Fuel oil dealers
Genl Mgr: David Hemesath

D-U-N-S 78-598-5503 EXP
FARMERS UNION INDUSTRIES LLC
CENTRAL BI-PRODUCTS
590 W Park Rd, Redwood Falls, MN 56283-1431
Tel (507) 637-5210 *Founded/Ownrshp* 2005
Sales 196.1MM *EMP* 320
SIC 2048 2047 Meat meal & tankage: prepared as animal feed; Cat food
CEO: Duane Anderson
**CFO:* William Day

D-U-N-S 02-048-2519
FARMERS UNION OIL CO OF STANLEY
CENEX
8149 Highway 2, Stanley, ND 58784-9404
Tel (701) 628-2322 *Founded/Ownrshp* 1943
Sales 104.8MM *EMP* 250
SIC 5172 5251 5541 5411

D-U-N-S 03-181-6069
FARMERS UNION OIL OF SOUTHERN VALLEY
100 S Front St, Fairmount, ND 58030-4108
Tel (701) 474-5440 *Founded/Ownrshp* 1997
Sales 92.8MM *EMP* 72
Accts Hennen & Associates Plc S
SIC 5171 5191 5541 5251 Petroleum bulk stations; Fertilizer & fertilizer materials; Gasoline service stations; Hardware
Pr: Brad Kubela
**Sec:* Corey Theede
**VP:* Jeff Leinen
**Genl Mgr:* Lynn Nelson

D-U-N-S 08-007-0769
FARMERS UNION OIL OF SOUTHERN VALLEY
107 S Front St, Fairmount, ND 58030
Tel (701) 474-5882 *Founded/Ownrshp* 1935
Sales 89.0MM *EMP* 30
SIC 5999 Feed & farm supply
Genl Mgr: Lynn Nelson

D-U-N-S 02-217-2951
FARMERS WIN COOPERATIVE
F F C
110 N Jefferson Ave, Fredericksburg, IA 50630-7757
Tel (563) 237-5324 *Founded/Ownrshp* 1956
Sales 174.4MM *EMP* 42
Accts Gardiner Thomsen Pc Charle
SIC 5191 Feed; Fertilizer & fertilizer materials; Seeds: field, garden & flower
Pr: Chris Hagedorn
**VP:* Keith Schlatter
Genl Mgr: James Erickson

D-U-N-S 07-115-1740
FARMFIRST DAIRY COOPERATIVE
4001 Nakoosa Trl Ste 100, Madison, WI 53714-1381
Tel (608) 244-3373 *Founded/Ownrshp* 1971
Sales 164.2MM *EMP* 18
Accts Cliftonlarsonallen Llp Middle
SIC 5143 8611 Milk; Trade associations
Pr: Peter Kleiman
Treas: Sharon Laubscher
**Treas:* John Rettler
**VP:* Richard Meyer
Genl Mgr: David Cooper
Genl Mgr: Richard L Klossner

D-U-N-S 62-011-3431
FARMINGTON AREA PUBLIC SCHOOLS
FARMINGTON PUBLIC SCHOOL
20655 Flagstaff Ave, Farmington, MN 55024-9242
Tel (651) 463-5001 *Founded/Ownrshp* 1957
Sales 93.9MM *EMP* 800
Accts Kern Dewenter Viere Ltd M
SIC 8211 Public senior high school; Public junior high school; Public elementary school

D-U-N-S 00-691-6845
■ **FARMINGTON BANK** (CT)
(*Suby of* FIRST CONNECTICUT BANCORP INC) ★
1 Farm Glen Blvd, Farmington, CT 06032-1919
Tel (860) 676-4600 *Founded/Ownrshp* 1851, 2011
Sales NA *EMP* 299
SIC 6036 6163 State savings banks, not federally chartered; Loan brokers
Pr: John Patrick
**Pr:* Eric M Schwab
**CEO:* John J Patrick Jr
**CFO:* Greg White
Ofcr: John Pember
Ex VP: Jim Wilson
**Sr VP:* Kenneth F Burns
**Sr VP:* Robert O Ciraco
Sr VP: Carl N Josephson
Sr VP: Andr Kapetanopoulos
Sr VP: Susan Laberge
Sr VP: Mike Moriarty
**Sr VP:* Catherine E Parente
Sr VP: Bob Surocco
Sr VP: Stacey Uccello
VP: Karen Bixby
VP: Laurie Brooks
VP: Dave Chamberlain
VP: Bob Ciraco
VP: Robert Gruggs
VP: Mecheal Hamilton

D-U-N-S 61-667-3661
■ **FARMINGTON CASUALTY CO**
TRAVELERS INSURANCE
(*Suby of* TRAVELERS INSURANCE) ★
1 Tower Sq, Hartford, CT 06183-0001
Tel (860) 277-0111 *Founded/Ownrshp* 1996
Sales NA *EMP* 31
SIC 6411 Insurance agents, brokers & service
CEO: Jay Fishman

D-U-N-S 06-947-2660 EXP
FARMINGTON FOODS INC
7419 Franklin St, Forest Park, IL 60130-1016
Tel (708) 771-3600 *Founded/Ownrshp* 1972
Sales 101.1MM[E] *EMP* 310
SIC 2013 Prepared beef products from purchased beef; Prepared pork products from purchased pork
Pr: Anthony Dijohn
Sls Dir: Allan Flynn

D-U-N-S 06-972-0043
FARMINGTON MUNICIPAL SCHOOLS (NM)
2001 N Dustin Ave, Farmington, NM 87401-2120
Tel (505) 324-9840 *Founded/Ownrshp* 1925
Sales 123.6MM *EMP* 2,000
Accts Accounting & Financial Solutio
SIC 8211 Public elementary school; Public junior high school; Public senior high school; Public special education school
Dir Sec: Ann Diehl
MIS Dir: Michelle Hill
Teacher Pr: Christopher Pash
HC Dir: Cathy McDonald

FARMINGTON PUBLIC SCHOOL
See FARMINGTON AREA PUBLIC SCHOOLS

D-U-N-S 04-055-9411
FARMINGTON PUBLIC SCHOOL DISTRICT
32500 Shiawassee Rd, Farmington, MI 48336-2338
Tel (248) 489-3300 *Founded/Ownrshp* 1922
Sales 155.7MM *EMP* 1,639
Accts Plante & Moran Pllc Auburn Hi
SIC 8211 Public elementary & secondary schools
Trst: David Turner
Teacher Pr: Jeff Douziger

D-U-N-S 00-896-5774 IMP/EXP
FARMLAND DAIRIES LLC
CLINTON
520 Main Ave, Wallington, NJ 07057-1830
Tel (973) 777-2500 *Founded/Ownrshp* 1914
Sales 212.0MM[E] *EMP* 300[E]
SIC 5143 2026 2023

D-U-N-S 13-943-8258 IMP/EXP
FARMLAND FOODS INC
FARM LAND FOODS
11500 Nw Ambassa Ste 500, Kansas City, MO 64153
Tel (816) 243-2700 *Founded/Ownrshp* 2003
Sales NA *EMP* 6,123
SIC 2011

D-U-N-S 60-946-4495
FARMLAND FOODS INC
COOKS HAM
200 S 2nd St, Lincoln, NE 68508-2407
Tel (402) 475-6700 *Founded/Ownrshp* 2003
Sales NA *EMP* 6,000
SIC 2013

D-U-N-S 15-211-4211
FARMLAND MANAGEMENT SERVICES
301 E Main St, Turlock, CA 95380-4537
Tel (209) 669-0742 *Founded/Ownrshp* 1986
Sales 97.2MM[E] *EMP* 120
SIC 0762 Farm management services
CEO: Oliver S Williams IV
**Pr:* Joseph P Silveira

D-U-N-S 00-694-1108
FARMLAND MUTUAL INSURANCE CO INC
NATIONWIDE MUTUAL INSURANCE
1100 Locust St, Des Moines, IA 50391-1100
Tel (515) 508-3300 *Founded/Ownrshp* 1909
Sales NA *EMP* 240
SIC 6411 Insurance agents, brokers & service
Pr: Kim Austen
**VP:* Wendell Crosser
Netwrk Eng: Perry Barstad
Sales Exec: Tracy Spellman
Sls Mgr: David Wandro

D-U-N-S 10-581-4433 IMP
FARMLAND RESERVE INC
50 E North Temple, Salt Lake City, UT 84150-9001
Tel (801) 240-6301 *Founded/Ownrshp* 2003
Sales 186.0MM[E] *EMP* 802
SIC 0762 Farm management services
Prin: Gordon B Hinckley
**Prin:* Boyd Black
**Prin:* Gordan B Henkley

D-U-N-S 00-531-3382 IMP
FARNER-BOCKEN CO
1751 E Us Highway 30, Carroll, IA 51401-2691
Tel (712) 792-7454 *Founded/Ownrshp* 1949
Sales 841.3MM[E] *EMP* 750
SIC 5145 5194 Candy; Cigarettes
Pr: Dean Onken
CFO: Paul Francis
**Sec:* Dennis L Anderson
Dir IT: Jerry Devore
IT Man: John Perrin
Sls Mgr: Randy Barkema
Sls Mgr: Jim Bocken
Sls Mgr: Wade Fowler
Sls Mgr: Marc Frette
Sls Mgr: Bruce Milbrandt
Sls Mgr: Ryan Owen

D-U-N-S 80-852-8145 IMP
FARO SERVICES INC
7070 Pontius Rd, Groveport, OH 43125-7504
Tel (614) 497-1700 *Founded/Ownrshp* 1988
Sales 104.8MM[E] *EMP* 350
Accts Joseph Decosimo And Company C
SIC 4225 4731 General warehousing & storage; Freight transportation arrangement
Pr: Rich Ashton
Brnch Mgr: Tim Thomas
Sls Mgr: Matthew Shaw

D-U-N-S 61-730-8929 IMP
▲ **FARO TECHNOLOGIES INC**
250 Technology Park, Lake Mary, FL 32746-7115
Tel (407) 333-9911 *Founded/Ownrshp* 1982
Sales 317.5MM *EMP* 1,288[E]
Tkr Sym FARO *Exch* NGS
SIC 3829 Measuring & controlling devices; Medical diagnostic systems, nuclear
Ch Bd: Simon Raab
COO: Kathleen J Hall
Ofcr: Joseph Arezone
Sr VP: Jody Gale
VP: Janet D'Anjou
VP: Robert King
VP: Christopher Scholl
Plnt Mgr: Kenneth Steffey
Sales Asso: Theresa Crisafi
Board of Directors: Lynn Brubaker, John E Caldwell, Stephen R Cole, John Donofrio, Marvin R Sambur

D-U-N-S 13-759-8132 IMP/EXP
FAROUK SYSTEMS INC
880 E Richey Rd, Houston, TX 77073-6325
Tel (281) 876-2000 *Founded/Ownrshp* 1986
Sales 150.6MM[E] *EMP* 600[E]
Accts Pricewaterhousecoopers Llp Ho
SIC 2844 Hair preparations, including shampoos; Hair coloring preparations
Ch Bd: Farouk Shami
**V Ch:* John McCall
**Pr:* Lisa Marie Garcia
**Pr:* Shauky Gulamani
**CEO:* Basim Shami
CFO: Micheal Hausinger
Ex VP: Gregg Emery
**VP:* Heitham Badran
**VP:* Scott Emery
Prin: Bobbi Mihal
**Prin:* Rami Shami

D-U-N-S 13-761-1745 IMP/EXP
FARREL CORP
FARREL POMINI
(*Suby of* HARBURG-FREUDENBERGER MASCHINENBAU GMBH)
1 Farrell Blvd, Ansonia, CT 06401-1256
Tel (203) 736-5500 *Founded/Ownrshp* 2008
Sales 88.8MM[E] *EMP* 256
SIC 3559 1011 3089 Rubber working machinery, including tires; Plastics working machinery; Iron ore pelletizing; Extruded finished plastic products
CEO: Mark Meulbroek
Pr: Steve Peterson
CFO: Paul Zapp
**CFO:* Paul M Zepp
Sr VP: Alberto Shaio
VP: Stephen E Peterson
VP Opers: Stuart Wilson
Board of Directors: Alberto Shaio

FARREL POMINI
See FARREL CORP

D-U-N-S 02-938-6190
FARRELL AREA SCHOOL DISTRICT
1600 Roemer Blvd, Farrell, PA 16121-1754
Tel (724) 346-6585 *Founded/Ownrshp* 1911
Sales 20.2MMM *EMP* 300
SIC 8211 Public elementary & secondary schools
VP: Edward Turosky
IT Man: Steven Benefield

D-U-N-S 07-938-6190
FARREN INTERNATIONAL LLC
1578 Sussex Tpke, Randolph, NJ 07869-1833
Tel (800) 253-3203 *Founded/Ownrshp* 2012, 1959
Sales 88.2MM[E] *EMP* 257
Accts Withumsmith+Brown Pc New Bru
SIC 4213 1796 6719 Contract haulers; Machine moving & rigging; Public utility holding companies

D-U-N-S 03-185-2478
FARSTAD OIL INC
(*Suby of* PARKLAND FUEL CORPORATION)
100 27th St Ne, Minot, ND 58703-5164
Tel (701) 852-1194 *Founded/Ownrshp* 2014
Sales 545.3MM *EMP* 125
SIC 5172 Diesel fuel; Gasoline; Lubricating oils & greases; Gases, liquefied petroleum (propane)
Pr: Merv Carter
**COO:* Dennis Krueger
**CFO:* Bruce Hest
Rgnl Mgr: Eric Lawson
Genl Mgr: Stephen Ronning
Sls Mgr: Dallas Varty

D-U-N-S 00-941-8005 IMP
FARWEST STEEL CORP
2000 Henderson Ave, Eugene, OR 97403-2224
Tel (541) 686-2000 *Founded/Ownrshp* 1991
Sales 589.3MM[E] *EMP* 665
SIC 5051 Steel
Pr: Patrick Eagen
Ch Bd: Robert Buckland
COO: Jennifer Coiner
VP: Chuck Cunning
VP: Robert Patrick
**VP:* Mike Solomon
**VP:* John Worstell
Prgrm Mgr: Matt Curry
Brnch Mgr: Rick Morrison
Genl Mgr: Chuck Leslie
Genl Mgr: Gordon Turnquest

FARWEST TRADING
See ASSOCIATED FEED & SUPPLY CO

FAS MART
See GPM INVESTMENTS LLC

FASCLAMPITT DIVISIONS
See CLAMPITT PAPER CO OF DALLAS GP LLC

FASCORE INSTITUTIONAL SERVICES
See FASCORE LLC

D-U-N-S 82-882-4834
FASCORE LLC
FASCORE INSTITUTIONAL SERVICES
(*Suby of* GREAT-WEST LIFE & ANNUITY INSURANCE CO) ★
8515 E Orchard Rd, Greenwood Village, CO 80111-5002
Tel (303) 737-3600 *Founded/Ownrshp* 1993
Sales 315.8MM *EMP* 1,558[E]
Accts Deloitte & Touche Llp Denver
SIC 8741 Administrative management
Ch: Richard H Linton Jr
Pr: James M Gearin
Treas: Kara S Roe
Sr VP: William S Harmon
Sr VP: Jeffrey W Knight
Sr VP: Ron J Laeyendecker
Sr VP: William J McDermott
Sr VP: Brent P Neese

VP: Jeffrey K Boschen
VP: Donna L Browne
VP: Perry A Christie
VP: Marybeth Daubenspeck
VP: Paul S Dewey Jr
VP: John Fellin
VP: Shane Fitzpatrick
VP: William C Jeffries
VP: Gary D Longwell
VP: William F Porter
VP: Timothy Radebaugh
VP: Todd Sexton
VP: Darlene Soderquist

D-U-N-S 05-969-5317 IMP/EXP
FASHION ACCESSORY BAZAAR LLC
FAB
15 W 34th St Fl 2, New York, NY 10001-3015
Tel (212) 947-9001 Founded/Ownrshp 1997
Sales 83.4MM^E EMP 140
Accts Hecht And Company Pc New Y
SIC 5199 5112 Bags, baskets & cases; Stationery
CFO: Moses Safdieh
Info Man: Adam Jay
Sls Dir: Allan Sasson

D-U-N-S 15-085-8983 IMP
FASHION AVENUE KNITS INC
FASHION AVENUE SWEATER KNITS
525 Fashion Ave Fl 4, New York, NY 10018-4940
Tel (718) 456-9000 Founded/Ownrshp 1985
Sales 125.0MM EMP 106^E
Accts Mahoney Cohen & Compan Cpa P
SIC 5137 Sweaters, women's & children's
CEO: Melvyn Weiss
*CFO: Ronald Hollandsworth
*VP: Sherian Weiss
Exec: Ana Ceruga

FASHION AVENUE SWEATER KNITS
See FASHION AVENUE KNITS INC

FASHION BUG
See CHARMING SHOPPES OF DELAWARE INC

D-U-N-S 05-571-3200
FASHION GALLERY INC
RAINBOW SHOP
(Suby of RAINBOW SHOPS) ★
1000 Pennsylvania Ave, Brooklyn, NY 11207-8417
Tel (718) 485-3000 Founded/Ownrshp 1985
Sales 118.9MM^E EMP 1,900
SIC 5699 Uniforms & work clothing
CEO: Joseph Chehebar
*Pr: Albert Chehebar
COO: Martin Stein
CFO: Jonothan Powell
*Treas: Jack Chehebar
*VP: Issac Chehebar

D-U-N-S 07-103-1504
FASHION INSTITUTE OF TECHNOLOGY
(Suby of SUNY ADMINISTRATION) ★
7th Ave 27th St Rm C908, New York, NY 10001
Tel (212) 217-7999 Founded/Ownrshp 1940
Sales 228.0MM^E EMP 1,212
SIC 8222 9411 Junior colleges & technical institutes;
Pr: Joyce F Brown
Pr: Yasemin Jones
*Treas: Harvey Spector
VP: Kenneth Drayton
VP: Dawn Duncan
CIO: Frank Sirianni
Web Dev: Joseph Lucca
Psych: Fran Kalish
Art Dir: Sondra Graff

FAST
See FENNER ADVANCED SEALING TECHNOLOGIES INC

D-U-N-S 05-041-3657
FAST FARE INC
(Suby of CROWN CENTRAL PETROLEUM CORP) ★
1 N Charles St, Baltimore, MD 21201-3740
Tel (410) 539-7400 Founded/Ownrshp 1983
Sales 110.1MM^E EMP 1,935
SIC 5411 5541 Convenience stores; Gasoline service stations
Ch Bd: Henry Rosenberg
*CFO: John E Wheeler Jr
*VP: Paul Ebner
*VP: Thomas L Owsley

FAST FOOD ENTERPRISES 2 & 3
See PATTERSON-ERIE CORP

D-U-N-S 09-789-3960 IMP/EXP
FAST GLOBAL SOLUTIONS INC
WASP
20631 State Highway 55, Glenwood, MN 56334-5079
Tel (320) 634-5126 Founded/Ownrshp 1997
Sales 101.2MM^E EMP 650
SIC 3537 3565 3523 Trucks: freight, baggage, etc.: industrial, except mining; Packaging machinery; Farm machinery & equipment
Pr: Dane Anderson
*VP: John Hoeper
*VP: Jeanne Kramer
*VP: Dewayne Nelson
*VP Mfg: Eric Kolstoe

FAST STOP FOOD MARKETS
See HIGHLAND CORP

FAST TRACK FOODS
See LAND OSUN MANAGEMENT CORP

FASTBREAK
See REIF OIL CO

D-U-N-S 11-917-4415 IMP
FASTCO THREADED PRODUCTS INC
539 Clemson Rd, Columbia, SC 29229-4307
Tel (803) 788-1000 Founded/Ownrshp 2003
Sales 8.9MM^E EMP 6,329
SIC 5085 Fasteners, industrial: nuts, bolts, screws, etc.
Pr: Christopher Ray

FASTCOR
See BISCO INDUSTRIES INC

D-U-N-S 04-265-3634 IMP/EXP
▲ FASTENAL CO
2001 Theurer Blvd, Winona, MN 55987-1500
Tel (507) 454-5374 Founded/Ownrshp 1967
Sales 3.8MMM EMP 20,746
Tkr Sym FAST Exch NGS
SIC 5085 5072 5063 5169 5198 Fasteners & fastening equipment; Industrial tools; Rope, cord & thread; Chains; Power tools & accessories; Bolts, nuts & screws; Electrical apparatus & equipment; Batteries; Electrical fittings & construction materials; Wire & cable; Adhesives & sealants; Adhesives, chemical; Sealants; Paints, varnishes & supplies; Paints
Pr: Daniel L Florness
*Ch Bd: Willard D Oberton
Pr: Cody Webb
CFO: Sheryl A Lisowski
Bd of Dir: Ryan Walsh
Ex VP: James C Jansen
Ex VP: Nicholas J Lundquist
Ex VP: Charles S Miller
Ex VP: Gary A Polipnick
Ex VP: John L Soderberg
*Ex VP: Reyne K Wisecup
VP: John Barrera
VP: Dawn May
VP: Kirk Talmontas
*Exec: Leland J Hein
Exec: Terry M Owen
Board of Directors: Michael J Ancius, Michael J Dolan, Stephen L Eastman, Rita J Heise, Darren R Jackson, Hugh L Miller, Scott A Satterlee

D-U-N-S 08-017-5246
FASTENER HOLDINGS INC
SOUTHERNCARLSON
10840 Harney St, Omaha, NE 68154-2638
Tel (402) 593-5300 Founded/Ownrshp 2014
Sales 83.2MM^E EMP 700
SIC 6719 Investment holding companies, except banks
CEO: Jim Whitley
*CFO: Don Munchrath

D-U-N-S 01-708-1720 IMP
FASTENERS INC
DEE & BEE FASTENERS
640 44th St Sw Ste 1, Grand Rapids, MI 49548-1053
Tel (616) 241-3448 Founded/Ownrshp 1987
Sales 125.2MM^E EMP 160
SIC 5072 Power tools & accessories
Pr: John Szlenkier
*CFO: Scott Beardsley
*VP: Keith Oosterbaan
Brnch Mgr: Ryan Brink
Mktg Dir: Jake Eller
Sls Mgr: Kurt Rosenberg
Sales Asso: Tom Graney

D-U-N-S 03-405-9410 IMP
FASTENING SOLUTIONS INC
FSI
3075 Selma Hwy, Montgomery, AL 36108-5001
Tel (334) 284-8300 Founded/Ownrshp 1956
Sales 111.1MM^E EMP 130
SIC 5085 5072 5051 Staplers & tackers; Staples; Nails
CEO: Bill Rue Jr
*CFO: Frank M Stewart III
Prin: Ricky Albright
IT Man: Marshall Mims
VP Sls: Les Rue
Board of Directors: William H Rue Jr

FASTENING SYSTEMS
See SFS INTEC INC

D-U-N-S 01-990-9329 IMP/EXP
FASTENTECH INC
FABRISTEEL PRODUCTS
(Suby of DONCASTERS INC) ★
8500 Normandale Lake Blvd, Minneapolis, MN 55437-3813
Tel (952) 921-2090 Founded/Ownrshp 2007
Sales 150.4MM^E EMP 500
SIC 3452 Bolts, nuts, rivets & washers
Pr: Ronald Kalich
*Ch Bd: Richard Puricelli
*CFO: David Harbert
CFO: Michael Jones

FASTMED URGENT CARE
See URGENT CARES OF AMERICA HOLDINGS LLC

D-U-N-S 07-313-6806
FATHER FLANAGANS BOYS HOME
BOYS TOWN
14086 Mother Theresa Ln, Boys Town, NE 68010-7552
Tel (402) 498-1111 Founded/Ownrshp 1917
Sales 465.5MM EMP 2,000
Accts Kpmg Llp Omaha Ne
SIC 8361 Boys' Towns
Pr: Steven E Boes
CFO: David Lesley
Sr VP: Sy Nicholson
VP: Gil Barajas
VP: Jerry Davis
VP: Mike Eglseder
Assoc Dir: Ryan McCreery
*Ex Dir: Rev Steve Boes
Ex Dir: Michael Burke
Ex Dir: Howard Olshansky
Off Mgr: Rick Maki

FATHER'S TABLE, THE
See FATHERSTABLE L L C

D-U-N-S 05-501-9280
FATHERSTABLE L L C
FATHER'S TABLE, THE
2100 Country Club Rd, Sanford, FL 32771-4051
Tel (407) 324-1200 Founded/Ownrshp 1999
Sales 100.7MM^E EMP 300
SIC 2099 Food preparations
VP: John Hicks
VP: Michael Keenan

VP: Fidahussein Khaki
Exec: Daniel Gilardi
QA Dir: Susan Guetschow
QA Dir: Elyse Payne
Mtls Mgr: Michelle Thompson
Opers Mgr: Michael Bishop
Natl Sales: Eric Pasquale
VP Sls: Cheryl Lawton
Sls Dir: David Colvin

D-U-N-S 01-666-0651
FATIMA GIFT SHOP
ST JOSEPH HEALTH SERVICES OF R
200 High Service Ave, North Providence, RI 02904-5113
Tel (401) 456-3448 Founded/Ownrshp 2002
Sales 131.3MM EMP 4
SIC 5947 Gift shop
Dir OR: Denise Demers
Chf Nrs Of: Debra Cathcart

FATZ CAFE
See CAFE ENTERPRISES INC

FAUCETDIRECT.COM
See BUILD.COM INC

FAULCONER CONSTRUCTION COMPANY
See FAULCONER CONSTRUCTION CO INC

D-U-N-S 00-978-1865
FAULCONER CONSTRUCTION CO INC
FAULCONER CONSTRUCTION COMPANY
2496 Old Ivy Rd, Charlottesville, VA 22903-4895
Tel (434) 295-0033 Founded/Ownrshp 1954
Sales 121.5MM^E EMP 250
Accts Shelton & Company Cpas Pc L
SIC 1629 1611 1542 1623 Dams, waterways, docks & other marine construction; Highway & street construction; Shopping center construction; Underground utilities contractor
Pr: Jack Sanford Jr
*Ex VP: FA Burke III
*Ex VP: Vincent H Derr
*VP: Frank Burke III
*VP: David Galloway
*VP: Bruce Kohn
Off Admin: Michelle Kruse
Sfty Dirs: Bob Zehringer
Snr PM: Ray Lindholm

FAULKNER HOSPITAL
See JOHN R GRAHAM HEADACHE CENTER INC

FAUQUIER COUNTY OFFICE OF ADULT COURT SERVICES
See COUNTY OF FAUQUIER

D-U-N-S 78-671-2471
FAUQUIER COUNTY PUBLIC SCHOOLS
320 Hospital Dr Ste 40, Warrenton, VA 20186-3037
Tel (540) 422-7000 Founded/Ownrshp 1895
Sales 140.0MM EMP 1,700
SIC 8211 Public elementary & secondary schools
IT Man: Margaret Williams
Teacher Pr: Janelle Downs

D-U-N-S 18-927-8658
FAUQUIER HEALTH SYSTEM INC
FAUQUIER HOSPITAL
500 Hospital Dr, Warrenton, VA 20186-3027
Tel (540) 316-5000 Founded/Ownrshp 1987
Sales 128.3MM EMP 1,100
SIC 8062 General medical & surgical hospitals
Ch Bd: Robin Gulick
*Pr: Rodger H Baker
CFO: Lionel Phillips
Exec: Laura Welsh
Dir OR: Christy Shaw
Dir Inf Cn: Dorothy Seibert
Dir Case M: Rebecca Wolfrey
Dir Lab: Marybeth Waldeck
Snr Ntwrk: Jim Biecher
CIO: Donna Staton
Netwrk Mgr: Rich Asbell

FAUQUIER HOSPITAL
See FAUQUIER HEALTH SYSTEM INC

D-U-N-S 12-770-9892 IMP
FAURECIA AUTOMOTIVE HOLDINGS INC
(Suby of FAURECIA USA HOLDINGS INC) ★
543 Matzinger Rd, Toledo, OH 43612-2638
Tel (419) 727-5000 Founded/Ownrshp 1999
Sales 80.5MM^E EMP 1,000
SIC 3714 Mufflers (exhaust), motor vehicle
Int Pr: Patrick Szaroletta
Prgrm Mgr: Leonardo Gomes
Sls Mgr: Anna Smith

D-U-N-S 15-529-3749 IMP
FAURECIA AUTOMOTIVE SEATING LLC
(Suby of FAURECIA)
2800 High Meadow Cir, Auburn Hills, MI 48326-2772
Tel (248) 288-1000 Founded/Ownrshp 1989
Sales 1.5MMM^E EMP 1,969
SIC 8711 Designing: ship, boat, machine & product
CEO: Yann Delabriere
*Pr: Thorsten Muschel
Pr: Nicolas Pechnyk
CFO: Gilles Descarsin
*Ex VP: Jean Marc Hannequin
*Ex VP: Frank Imbert
*Ex VP: Patrick Koller
*Ex VP: Kate Philipps
VP: Jean-Luc Daudon
VP: Fernando Gil
Prgrm Mgr: Brian Sowa

D-U-N-S 80-077-0195 IMP/EXP
FAURECIA EMISSIONS CONTROL TECHNOLOGIES USA LLC
FAURECIA EMISSIONS CTRL TECH
(Suby of FAURECIA EXHAUST SYSTEMS INC) ★
950 W 450 S, Columbus, IN 47201-1520
Tel (812) 341-2000 Founded/Ownrshp 2009
Sales 1.7MMM^E EMP 7,500
SIC 3714 Exhaust systems & parts, motor vehicle; Filters: oil, fuel & air, motor vehicle
Pr: Mark Stidham

VP: Patrick Bauer
Exec: Anita Gazaway
Prgrm Mgr: Kyle Jackson
Ql Cn Mgr: Jennifer Fleming
Ql Cn Mgr: Cristina Rakoczy
Ql Cn Mgr: Roxanna Roddy
Snr Mgr: Stephanie Hayes
Snr Mgr: Ryan Knutson
Snr Mgr: Josh Martin
Snr Mgr: Nicolas Rousseaux

FAURECIA EMISSIONS CTRL TECH
See FAURECIA EMISSIONS CONTROL TECHNOLOGIES USA LLC

FAURECIA EXHAUST SYSTEMS, INC.
See FAURECIA EXHAUST SYSTEMS LLC

D-U-N-S 02-300-6286 IMP
FAURECIA EXHAUST SYSTEMS LLC
FAURECIA EXHAUST SYSTEMS, INC.
(Suby of FAURECIA USA HOLDINGS INC) ★
543 Matzinger Rd, Toledo, OH 43612-2638
Tel (419) 727-5000 Founded/Ownrshp 2007
Sales 2.2MMM^E EMP 8,700
SIC 3714 5013 Mufflers (exhaust), motor vehicle; Motor vehicle supplies & new parts
Pr: Mark Stidham
Pr: Andrew Pontius
*CFO: Philippe Vienney
*Treas: Dave Borysiak
VP: Robert Parmann
*VP Sls: Curt Miller

D-U-N-S 00-505-3341 IMP
FAURECIA INTERIOR SYSTEMS INC
(Suby of FAURECIA AUTOMOTIVE SEATING LLC) ★
2500 Executive Hills Dr, Auburn Hills, MI 48326-2983
Tel (248) 409-3500 Founded/Ownrshp 1997
Sales 1.3MMM^E EMP 1,969
SIC 5013 3999 Automotive supplies & parts; Atomizers, toiletry
CEO: Jean Renautie
*CFO: Vincent Leroy
VP: Philippe Bertrand
VP: Mark Jackson
VP: James Loftus
VP: Robert Schnell
VP: Jeff Telder
Prgrm Mgr: Len Capogreco
Prgrm Mgr: Johann Jung
Prgrm Mgr: Jag Mundian
Prgrm Mgr: Neal Thompson

D-U-N-S 92-720-4487 IMP/EXP
FAURECIA INTERIOR SYSTEMS INC
SAI AUTOMOTIVE
(Suby of FAURECIA AUTOMOTIVE SEATING LLC) ★
101 International Blvd, Fountain Inn, SC 29644-7033
Tel (864) 862-1900 Founded/Ownrshp 1994
Sales 159.5MM^E EMP 376
SIC 5013 Automotive supplies & parts
CEO: Jean Renautie
*CFO: Jim Tostine
VP: Scott Cieslak
VP: Todd Fletemier
VP: Patrick Remil
VP: Brad Ring
VP: Matthias Siemer
VP: Giuseppe Zichella
Comm Dir: Thierry Lemane
Prgrm Mgr: Donald Bowling
Prgrm Mgr: Nicolas Lelievre

D-U-N-S 07-849-4662 IMP
FAURECIA INTERIOR SYSTEMS SALINE LLC
(Suby of FAURECIA INTERIOR SYSTEMS INC) ★
7700 E Michigan Ave, Saline, MI 48176-1721
Tel (734) 429-0030 Founded/Ownrshp 2011
Sales 221.8MM^E EMP 802^E
SIC 5013 Automotive supplies & parts

D-U-N-S 12-762-7441 IMP
FAURECIA USA HOLDINGS INC
(Suby of FAURECIA)
2800 High Meadow Cir, Auburn Hills, MI 48326-2772
Tel (248) 724-5100 Founded/Ownrshp 1999
Sales 3.0MMM^E EMP 8,700
SIC 3714 Mufflers (exhaust), motor vehicle
Pr: Patrick Szaroletta
Pr: Christopher Wiegandt
*CFO: Michel Favre
CFO: Vincent Leroy
Sr VP: Sharon Bell
VP: John Burke
Rgnl Mgr: Frank Gora
Genl Mgr: Shawna Smith
IT Man: Shaun Kartje
QC Dir: Boris Kokotovic
VP Sls: Paul Vallis

D-U-N-S 02-604-4065 IMP
FAUST DC LTD (TX)
FAUST DISTRIBUTING COMPANY
10040 East Fwy, Houston, TX 77029-1902
Tel (713) 673-5111 Founded/Ownrshp 1952, 1957
Sales 103.3MM^E EMP 230
SIC 5181 Beer & other fermented malt liquors
*Pr: Tyson Faust
*Ex VP: Skip Chancellor
*Ex VP: Rick Forcier
*VP: Jack Law
VP Sls: Scott Murray
Sls Mgr: Randy Slaton

FAUST DISTRIBUTING COMPANY
See FAUST DC LTD

D-U-N-S 03-228-2659
FAVORITE HEALTHCARE STAFFING INC (KS)
7255 W 98th Ter Ste 150, Overland Park, KS 66212-2215
Tel (913) 383-9733 Founded/Ownrshp 1981
Sales 532.5MM^E EMP 15,000
SIC 7363 Temporary help service
CEO: Gerhard J Kuti
Pr: Jayson Kuti
*CFO: Christopher Brink
Genl Mgr: Kathleen Perry

Snr Sftwr: Bill Marshall
CTO: Brody Whitley
IT Man: Desiree Sutton

D-U-N-S 01-052-0385
■ FAWCETT MEMORIAL HOSPITAL INC
COLUMBIA HCA
(*Suby of* HOSPITAL COPORATION OF AMERICA) ★
21298 Olean Blvd, Port Charlotte, FL 33952-6765
Tel (941) 629-1181 *Founded/Ownrshp* 1991
Sales 165.3MM *EMP* 850
SIC 8062 General medical & surgical hospitals
Pr: John Mll Franck
Chf Rad: Ramanan Venkat
**CFO:* Phil Baker
**VP:* Donald W Stinnett
Dir OR: Vickie Pettigrew
Dir Pat Ca: Kathy Pace
Dir Inf Cn: Melanie Hall
Dir Lab: David Doll
Dir Lab: Jack Hamilton
**Prin:* Jim Burns
Dir Sec: Gerald Mix

D-U-N-S 84-345-8808
FAXTON ST LUKES HEALTH CARE
8411 Seneca Tpke Ste 1, New Hartford, NY 13413-4912
Tel (315) 724-0659 *Founded/Ownrshp* 2000
Sales 281.8MM *EMP* 28
Accts Fust Charles Chambers Llp Syr
SIC 8011 Offices & clinics of medical doctors

D-U-N-S 13-620-4067
FAXTON-ST LUKES HEALTHCARE
(*Suby of* MOHAWK VALLEY NETWORK) ★
1656 Champlin Ave, Utica, NY 13502-4830
Tel (315) 624-6000 *Founded/Ownrshp* 2003
Sales 263.5MM *EMP* 2,980
SIC 8062 General medical & surgical hospitals
CEO: Scott H Perra
Dir Vol: Sue Warwick
COO: Steve Brown
CFO: Michael Haile
Bd of Dir: Mary Schumaci
Ofcr: Nancy Ricci
Sr VP: Carol English
VP: Debra Altdoerffer
VP: David Calabreese
Dir Lab: Jack Zito
Dir Rx: Maria Carucci

D-U-N-S 15-227-9675
FAYETTE COMMUNITY HOSPITAL INC
PIEDMONT FAYETTE HOSPITAL
(*Suby of* PIEDMONT HEALTHCARE) ★
1255 Highway 54 W, Fayetteville, GA 30214-4526
Tel (770) 719-7000 *Founded/Ownrshp* 1992
Sales 306.2MM *EMP* 1,045
Accts Kpmg Llp Greensboro Nc
SIC 8062 General medical & surgical hospitals
CEO: James Michael Burnette
Dir Recs: Pat K Jones
CFO: Sheryl Klink
**CFO:* John Miles
Dir Lab: Vicky Barkely

D-U-N-S 07-938-7411
FAYETTE COUNTY BOARD OF EDUCATION
210 Stonewall Ave W, Fayetteville, GA 30214-1518
Tel (770) 460-3520 *Founded/Ownrshp* 1920
Sales 220.8MM *EMP* 3,500
Accts Mauldin & Jenkins Llc Macon
SIC 8211 Public elementary & secondary schools

D-U-N-S 07-934-4181
FAYETTE COUNTY PUBLIC SCHOOLS
TAX OFFICE
701 E Main St Rm 219, Lexington, KY 40502-1670
Tel (859) 381-4159 *Founded/Ownrshp* 2014
Sales 448.9MM *EMP* 26^E^
Accts Strothman And Company Louisvi
SIC 8211 Public elementary school
Ex Dir: Amanda Ferguson

D-U-N-S 07-979-9679
FAYETTE COUNTY PUBLIC SCHOOLS
210 Stonewall Ave W, Fayetteville, GA 30214-1518
Tel (770) 460-3535 *Founded/Ownrshp* 2015
Sales 21.3MM^E^ *EMP* 2,660^E^
SIC 8211 Public elementary & secondary schools
Dir Sec: Ted Lombard
Pr Dir: Melinda B Dreisbach
HC Dir: Debbie King

D-U-N-S 07-982-7357
FAYETTE COUNTY PUBLIC SCHOOLS
1126 Russell Cave Rd, Lexington, KY 40505-3412
Tel (859) 381-4000 *Founded/Ownrshp* 2015
Sales 141.8MM^E^ *EMP* 4,810^E^
SIC 8211 Public elementary & secondary schools
Dir Sec: Laurence Whethers
MIS Dir: Bob Moore
Pr Dir: Lisa Deffendall
Teacher Pr: Jennifer Dyar
Teacher Pr: Melodee Parker
HC Dir: Debbie Bolan

D-U-N-S 08-667-5626
FAYETTE COUNTY SCHOOLS
111 Fayette Ave, Fayetteville, WV 25840-1219
Tel (304) 574-1176 *Founded/Ownrshp* 1831
Sales NA *EMP* 1,100
SIC 9111 8211 County supervisors' & executives' offices; Public elementary & secondary schools
**Treas:* Paula Fridley
Pr Dir: Joe Dooley

D-U-N-S 96-778-3536
FAYETTE COUNTY SCHOOLS
126 W Market St, Somerville, TN 38068-1401
Tel (901) 465-5260 *Founded/Ownrshp* 1919
Sales 20.6MM^E^ *EMP* 1,017^E^
SIC 8211 Public elementary & secondary schools
**Dir IT:* Richard England
Teacher Pr: Kathy Redditt
Psych: Natasha Reeves

FAYETTE IMPORT
See M B FAYETTE SPECIALISTS INC

FAYETTEVILLE OBSERVER, THE
See FAYETTEVILLE PUBLISHING CO INC

D-U-N-S 00-318-8596 IMP
FAYETTEVILLE PUBLISHING CO INC (NC)
FAYETTEVILLE OBSERVER, THE
458 Whitfield St, Fayetteville, NC 28306-1698
Tel (910) 486-2741 *Founded/Ownrshp* 1817, 1923
Sales 84.0MM^E^ *EMP* 350^E^
SIC 2711 2791 2759 2752 Newspapers, publishing & printing; Typesetting; Commercial printing; Commercial printing, lithographic
Pr: Charles Broadwell
**Treas:* Virginia L Yarborough
**VP:* Ashton L Fox

D-U-N-S 08-258-5720
FAYETTEVILLE SCHOOL DISTRICT 1
1000 W Bulldog Blvd, Fayetteville, AR 72701-4714
Tel (479) 444-3000 *Founded/Ownrshp* 1995
Sales 120.0MM *EMP* 1,400
SIC 8211 Public elementary school; Public junior high school; Public senior high school
**CFO:* Kathy Hanlom
Teacher Pr: Greg Mones
HC Dir: Melissa Thomas

D-U-N-S 06-718-8979
FAYETTEVILLE STATE UNIVERSITY
(*Suby of* OFFICE OF PRESIDENT) ★
1200 Murchison Rd, Fayetteville, NC 28301-4298
Tel (910) 672-1111 *Founded/Ownrshp* 2000
Sales 3.0MM *EMP* 2,000
SIC 8221 Colleges & universities
CEO: James A Anderson
Dir Vol: Marquelle Turner
**Ch Bd:* Terence Murchison
Dir Risk M: Garland Cottrell
Dir Lab: Tony Washington
Assoc Dir: Christine Mitchell
Dir: Wendy Jones
Off Admin: Charity Boozer
Off Admin: Erica Locklear
Sls&Mrk Ex: Ben Minter
Genl Couns: Wanda Jenkins

D-U-N-S 07-784-2797
FAYETTEVILLE TECHNICAL COMMUNITY COLLEGE FOUNDATION INC
(*Suby of* NORTH CAROLINA COMMUNITY COLLEGE SYSTEM) ★
2201 Hull Rd, Fayetteville, NC 28303-4761
Tel (910) 678-8400 *Founded/Ownrshp* 1963
Sales 41.2MM^E^ *EMP* 1,000
SIC 8222 9411 Community college; Administration of educational programs;
Pr: J Larry Keen
Ch Bd: Richard E Eslinger
VP: David Brand
VP: Bob Ervin
VP: Joe Levister
VP: David Sullivan
Exec: Mary Carter
Ex Dir: Brian T Haney
Genl Mgr: Holly Silvey
Genl Mgr: Debbie Todd
DP Dir: Heather Yarborough

D-U-N-S 00-537-8534
■ FAYGO BEVERAGES INC (MI)
(*Suby of* NEWBEVCO INC) ★
3579 Gratiot Ave, Detroit, MI 48207-1892
Tel (313) 925-1600 *Founded/Ownrshp* 1907, 1987
Sales 482.6MM^E^ *EMP* 450
SIC 2086 Soft drinks: packaged in cans, bottles, etc.; Mineral water, carbonated: packaged in cans, bottles, etc.
Ch Bd: Nick A Caporella
**Pr:* Alan Chittaro
**Pr:* Stanley M Sheridan
COO: Don Hernnon
**VP:* David Piontkowski
Area Mgr: Verneice Sparks
Dir IT: Dave Bisdorf
Plnt Mgr: Kerry Kline
Ql Cn Mgr: Ladonna Joseph
Sales Exec: Al Chittaro
Manager: Ed Frost

FAZOLI'S
See SEED RESTAURANT GROUP INC

D-U-N-S 61-523-9506
FAZOLIS RESTAURANTS LLC
2470 Palumbo Dr, Lexington, KY 40509-1117
Tel (859) 268-1668 *Founded/Ownrshp* 2006
Sales 213.4MM^E^ *EMP* 5,500
SIC 5812 Italian restaurant
CEO: Carl Howard
VP: Wayne Albretton
VP: Wayne M Albritton
VP: Rebbecca Fine
VP: James Franks
VP: Kathryn Watkins
VP Opers: Al Hodges

D-U-N-S 60-294-8812
▲ FB FINANCIAL CORP
211 Commerce St Ste 300, Nashville, TN 37201-1810
Tel (615) 313-0080 *Founded/Ownrshp* 1984
Sales NA *EMP* 1,038
Tkr Sym FBK *Exch* NYS
SIC 6022 State commercial banks
Pr: Christopher T Holmes
**Ch Bd:* James Wayers
CFO: James R Gordon

FB INSURANCE COMPANY
See KENTUCKY FARM BUREAU MUTUAL INSURANCE CO

FBFS
See FIRST BUSINESS FINANCIAL SERVICES INC

D-U-N-S 03-511-7787
FBG SERVICE CORP
407 S 27th Ave, Omaha, NE 68131-3609
Tel (402) 346-4422 *Founded/Ownrshp* 1968
Sales 49.2MM *EMP* 1,100
Accts Rsm Us Llp Omaha Nebraska
SIC 7349 Janitorial service, contract basis; Building component cleaning service; Window cleaning
Ch: Wayne E Simmonds
**Pr:* Terri Gogetap
**CFO:* Kathy Clark
**VP:* James Simmonds
Area Mgr: Jamie Losch
Area Mgr: Doug Schnepf
Dist Mgr: Diane McCutcheon
CTO: Steve Firmature

FBI
See FEDERAL BUREAU OF INVESTIGATION

D-U-N-S 00-594-1067
FBI BUILDINGS INC
ASPEN GROUP
3823 W 1800 S, Remington, IN 47977-8831
Tel (219) 261-2157 *Founded/Ownrshp* 1957, 1961
Sales 110.5MM^E^ *EMP* 230
SIC 1542 5031 1541 Commercial & office building contractors; Farm building construction; School building construction; Building materials, exterior; Building materials, interior; Industrial buildings, new construction
CEO: Edwin L Bahler
**Pr:* Miles P Ridgway
**COO:* Don Hoerr
**VP:* Kurt Bahler
VP: Char Shaw
**VP:* Ryan Sutton
IT Man: Ric Twig
Netwrk Mgr: Cynthia Decouto
Sls Mgr: Jeff Neihouser

D-U-N-S 84-743-6052
▲ FBL FINANCIAL GROUP INC
5400 University Ave, West Des Moines, IA 50266-5997
Tel (515) 225-5400 *Founded/Ownrshp* 1993
Sales NA *EMP* 1,637^E^
Tkr Sym FFG *Exch* NYS
SIC 6311 6411 Life insurance; Life insurance agents
CEO: James P Brannen
Ch Bd: Craig D Hill
COO: Daniel D Pitcher
COO: Raymond W Wasilewski
CFO: Donald J Seibel
V Ch Bd: Jerry L Chicoine
Chf Mktg O: D Scott Stice
Chf Inves: Charles T Happel
CIO: Daniel G Greteman
Board of Directors: Roger K Brooks, Richard W Felts, Joe D Heinrich, James A Holte, Paul E Larson, Kevin G Rogers, Scott E Vanderwal

D-U-N-S 05-002-9347
FBM OHIO LLC
(*Suby of* GREAT WESTERN BUILDING MTL) ★
2048 Rolling Hills Dr, Covington, KY 41017-9418
Tel (859) 431-0626 *Founded/Ownrshp* 2016
Sales 84.2MM^E^ *EMP* 90
SIC 5031 Lumber, plywood & millwork; Wallboard
Pr: Ruben Mendoza
Genl Mgr: Dan Guess

D-U-N-S 80-009-3697
▲ FBR & CO
1300 17th St N, Arlington, VA 22209-3811
Tel (703) 312-9500 *Founded/Ownrshp* 2006
Sales 155.4MM *EMP* 303
Tkr Sym FBRC *Exch* NGS
SIC 6211 Security brokers & dealers; Investment bankers
Ch Bd: Richard J Hendrix
CFO: Bradley J Wright
Ex VP: Adam J Fishman
Ex VP: James C Neuhauser
Ex VP: Kenneth P Slosser
Sr VP: Robert J Kiernan
Sr VP: Beverly Taylor
VP: Craig Berger
VP: Tom Hereghty
VP: Margret N Kellems
Mng Dir: Daniel Ives
Board of Directors: Reena Aggarwal, Thomas J Hynes Jr, Richard A Kraemer, Mark R Patterson, Arthur J Reimers, William F Strome, Allison Leopold Tilley, Allison M Leopold Tilley

FC
See FEDERAL COMMUNICATIONS COMMISSION

D-U-N-S 96-892-7421
FC CONTINENTAL LANDLORD LLC
(*Suby of* FOREST CITY ENTERPRISES INC) ★
50 Public Sq Ste 1360, Cleveland, OH 44113-2233
Tel (216) 621-6060 *Founded/Ownrshp* 2010
Sales 5.0MM *EMP* 2,917
SIC 6531 Real estate agents & managers

D-U-N-S 82-747-0613
FC ORGANIZATIONAL PRODUCTS LLC
2250 W Parkway Blvd, Salt Lake City, UT 84119-5038
Tel (801) 817-1776 *Founded/Ownrshp* 2008
Sales 61.5MM^E^ *EMP* 1,000
SIC 5942 5734 Book stores; Computer & software stores
CEO: Sarah Merz Devoll
Genl Mgr: Kim Bourell
VP Mktg: Lareen Strong

D-U-N-S 82-884-8973
■ FC-GEN ACQUISITION INC
GENESIS HEALTHCARE
(*Suby of* GENESIS HEALTHCARE INC) ★
101 E State St, Kennett Square, PA 19348-3109
Tel (610) 444-6350 *Founded/Ownrshp* 2007
Sales 9.1MMM^E^ *EMP* 80,000
SIC 8361 8051 8099 Home for the aged; Skilled nursing care facilities; Medical services organization
CEO: George V Hager Jr
**Pr:* Christopher Smith
**CFO:* Tom Divittorio
**VP:* Paul D Bach
**VP:* Steven E Fishman
**VP:* Serge Learsy
Board of Directors: Serge Learsy, Christopher M Sertich, Frank Small, Arnold M Whitman

D-U-N-S 15-114-8103
FCA INC
FCA PACKAGING PRODUCTS
7601 John Deere Pkwy, Moline, IL 61265-8028
Tel (309) 792-3222 *Founded/Ownrshp* 1985
Sales 114.1MM^E^ *EMP* 550
SIC 5085 5031

D-U-N-S 82-606-3190
FCA LLC
FCA PACKAGING
7601 John Deere Pkwy, Moline, IL 61265-8028
Tel (309) 792-3444 *Founded/Ownrshp* 2015
Sales 156.8MM^E^ *EMP* 600
SIC 4783 5031 5085 2448 Packing goods for shipping; Composite board products, woodboard; Industrial supplies; Pallets, wood
Pr: David Wilsted
VP: Jenny Dormire
VP: Greg King

D-U-N-S 96-889-6105
FCA NORTH AMERICA HOLDINGS LLC
(*Suby of* FIAT CHRYSLER AUTOMOBILES NV)
1000 Chrysler Dr, Auburn Hills, MI 48326-2766
Tel (248) 512-2950 *Founded/Ownrshp* 2014
Sales 31.0MMM^E^ *EMP* 77,817^E^
SIC 3711 3714 Motor vehicles & car bodies; Automobile assembly, including specialty automobiles; Truck & tractor truck assembly; Bus & other large specialty vehicle assembly; Motor vehicle parts & accessories; Motor vehicle engines & parts
Snr Mgr: Larry Abramson
Snr Mgr: Amar Alamin
Snr Mgr: Robert Rabe
Snr Mgr: Elaine Thompson
Snr Mgr: Gary Wade

FCA PACKAGING
See FCA LLC

FCA PACKAGING PRODUCTS
See FCA INC

D-U-N-S 83-096-6904 IMP/EXP
FCA US LLC
(*Suby of* FCA NORTH AMERICA HOLDINGS LLC) ★
1000 Chrysler Dr, Auburn Hills, MI 48326-2766
Tel (248) 512-2950 *Founded/Ownrshp* 2014
Sales 31.0MMM^E^ *EMP* 77,817
SIC 3711 3714 Motor vehicles & car bodies; Automobile assembly, including specialty automobiles; Truck & tractor truck assembly; Bus & other large specialty vehicle assembly; Motor vehicle parts & accessories; Motor vehicle engines & parts
Ch Bd: Sergio Marchionne
Pr: Bruno Cattori
Pr: Fred Diaz
Pr: Al Gardner
Pr: Timothy Kuniskis
CEO: Ralph Gilles
COO: Mark Chernoby
CFO: Richard K Palmer
Chf Cred: David Buckingham
Chf Mktg O: Olivier J Francois
Ex VP: Ross Roy
Sr VP: Douglas D Betts
Sr VP: Marjorie H Loeb
VP: Alistair Gardner
VP: Alessandro Gili
VP: Brian Harlow
VP: Robert Lee
Dir Soc: Lynne Schrage
Comm Man: Nick Cappa
Board of Directors: Reid A Bigland, Giorgio Fossati, Leo W Houle, Michael J Keegan, John B Lanaway, Robert G Liberatore, Michael Manley, Hermann G Waldemer

D-U-N-S 96-914-2491
▲ FCB FINANCIAL HOLDINGS INC
2500 Weston Rd Ste 300, Weston, FL 33331-3617
Tel (954) 984-3313 *Founded/Ownrshp* 2009
Sales NA *EMP* 638^E^
Accts Grant Thornton Llp Fort Laude
Tkr Sym FCB *Exch* NYS
SIC 6022 State commercial banks
Pr: Kent S Ellert
Ch Bd: Vincent S Tese
V Ch: Les J Lieberman
CFO: Paul D Burner
Ofcr: James E Baiter
Ofcr: Stuart I Oran
Ex VP: Juan C Castro

D-U-N-S 18-810-5076
FCB INTERNATIONAL LLC
100 W 23rd St Frnt, New York, NY 10011-2457
Tel (212) 885-3000 *Founded/Ownrshp* 1969
Sales 39.1MM^E^ *EMP* 1,458
SIC 7311 Advertising agencies
Ch Bd: Don Seeley
**CFO:* Ed Harrigan
**Ex VP:* Richard W Cuthbertson
Sr VP: David Bell
Sr VP: Ceren Cubukcu
VP: Anette Avestro
Netwrk Mgr: Mark Anderson
Netwrk Mgr: J Taney

D-U-N-S 04-617-2672
■ FCB WORLDWIDE INC
HEALTHMARK/ATG
(*Suby of* INTERPUBLIC GROUP OF COMPANIES INC) ★
100 W 33rd St Fl 5, New York, NY 10001-2921
Tel (212) 885-3000 *Founded/Ownrshp* 2007
Sales 310.7MM^E^ *EMP* 2,750
SIC 7311 8743

D-U-N-S 05-108-5058
FCC ENTERPRISES INC
FEDERAL BUILDING SERVICES
1641 Barclay Blvd, Buffalo Grove, IL 60089-4544
Tel (847) 279-7360 *Founded/Ownrshp* 1963
Sales 47.0MM *EMP* 2,000
SIC 7349 Janitorial service, contract basis
Pr: Stephen E Kulp
**CEO:* Keith A Anderson
**Ex VP:* Peter F Kulp
**Sr VP:* John Congletons
**VP:* William Hoffman
**VP:* Ken Raffensberger

D-U-N-S 96-027-7692
■ **FCC ENVIRONMENTAL LLC**
F C C
(*Suby of* HERITAGE-CRYSTAL CLEAN LLC) ★
2175 Point Blvd Ste 375, Elgin, IL 60123-9211
Tel (281) 668-3300 *Founded/Ownrshp* 2014
Sales 337.1MM[E] *EMP* 540
SIC 4953 Hazardous waste collection & disposal; Recycling, waste materials;
**Pr:* Aurelio Blasco
**Ex VP:* Ken Cherry

D-U-N-S 80-534-8070
FCC HOLDINGS INC
3383 N State Road 7, Lauderdale Lakes, FL 33319-5617
Tel (954) 535-8700 *Founded/Ownrshp* 2007
Sales 21.1MM[E] *EMP* 3,000
SIC 8243 Data processing schools
CEO: David Knobel
Board of Directors: David Abrams, Kevin Bousquette, Robert Niehaus, Travis Rhodes

D-U-N-S 82-756-3862
FCCI GROUP INC
(*Suby of* FCCI MUTUAL INSURANCE HOLDING CO) ★
6300 University Pkwy, Sarasota, FL 34240-8424
Tel (941) 907-3224 *Founded/Ownrshp* 1998
Sales NA *EMP* 718
SIC 6331 Fire, marine & casualty insurance & carriers
Pr: G W Jacobs
Pr: Carey Geaglone
**CFO:* Craig Johnson
**V Ch Bd:* John T Stafford
**Ex VP:* Debra Douglas
**Ex VP:* Joseph Keene
IT Man: Lori Richards

D-U-N-S 03-956-2335
FCCI INSURANCE CO
(*Suby of* FCCI GROUP INC) ★
6300 University Pkwy, Sarasota, FL 34240-8424
Tel (941) 907-3224 *Founded/Ownrshp* 2008
Sales NA *EMP* 718
SIC 6331 Fire, marine & casualty insurance & carriers; Workers' compensation insurance
CEO: Craig Johnson
Pr: G W Jacobs
COO: Rupert L Willis
CFO: Chris Shoucair
V Ch Bd: John T Stafford
Assoc VP: Ned Wilson
Ex VP: Debra H Douglas
Ex VP: Joseph A Keene
Ex VP: Lisa Krouse

D-U-N-S 79-611-9634
FCCI INSURANCE GROUP INC
(*Suby of* FCCI INSURANCE CO) ★
6300 University Pkwy, Sarasota, FL 34240-8424
Tel (941) 907-2515 *Founded/Ownrshp* 1991
Sales NA *EMP* 700
SIC 6411 Insurance agents, brokers & service
Pr: G W Jacobs
**V Ch Bd:* John T Stafford
Assoc VP: Ned Wilson
**Ex VP:* Debra H Douglas
**Ex VP:* Joseph A Keene
Software D: Doug Rothauser
Opers Supe: Gary Ostrander

D-U-N-S 82-756-3532
FCCI MUTUAL INSURANCE HOLDING CO
6300 University Pkwy, Sarasota, FL 34240-8424
Tel (941) 907-3224 *Founded/Ownrshp* 1998
Sales NA *EMP* 718
SIC 6331 Fire, marine & casualty insurance & carriers
Pr: G W Jacobs
**CFO:* Craig Johnson
**V Ch Bd:* John T Stafford
**Ex VP:* Debra Douglas
**Ex VP:* Joseph Keene

D-U-N-S 04-327-4794
FCCI SERVICES INC
(*Suby of* FCCI INSURANCE GROUP INC) ★
6300 University Pkwy, Sarasota, FL 34240-8424
Tel (941) 556-3345 *Founded/Ownrshp* 1979
Sales NA *EMP* 700
SIC 6411 Insurance agents, brokers & service
V Ch Bd: John T Stafford
CFO: Chris Schoucair
Assoc VP: Ned Wilson
Ex VP: Joseph A Keene
Sr VP: William Speaker

FCD DIVISION
See FLOWSERVE US INC

D-U-N-S 62-596-1024
FCE BENEFIT ADMINISTRATORS INC
887 Mitten Rd Ste 200, Burlingame, CA 94010-1303
Tel (650) 341-0306 *Founded/Ownrshp* 1989
Sales NA *EMP* 150
SIC 6411 Insurance agents, brokers & service
Pr: Gary Beckman
**Ex VP:* Steve Porter

D-U-N-S 03-321-6599
FCH ENTERPRISES INC
ZIPPYS SAIMIN LANAI RESTAURANT
1765 S King St, Honolulu, HI 96826-2134
Tel (808) 973-0877 *Founded/Ownrshp* 1966
Sales 93.5MM[E] *EMP* 2,000
SIC 5812 Fast-food restaurant, chain; Caterers
CEO: Jason Higa
**Pr:* Paul S Yokota
**Treas:* Douglas Shimabukuro
**VP:* Charles A Higa
Adm Dir: Char Kim
Genl Mgr: Michael Kamei
Genl Mgr: Jeff Marcello
Sftwr Eng: Thanh Giang
Mktg Mgr: Jeanine Kalahiki

D-U-N-S 01-126-4421
FCI CONSTRUCTORS INC
3070 I 70 Bus Loop Ste A, Grand Junction, CO 81504-4446
Tel (970) 434-9093 *Founded/Ownrshp* 1991
Sales 221.9MM[E] *EMP* 275
Accts Stanfield & Company Pc Gra
SIC 1542 1541 Institutional building construction; Commercial & office building, new construction; Industrial buildings, new construction; Renovation, remodeling & repairs: industrial buildings
Pr: Ed Forsman
**CFO:* Mark Labere
CFO: Clayton Marshall
Mng Dir: Jason Dill
Off Mgr: Karissa Churchill
Off Mgr: Jamie Larkins

D-U-N-S 11-892-7735
FCI FEDERAL INC
20135 Lakeview Center Plz # 300, Ashburn, VA 20147-5963
Tel (703) 443-1888 *Founded/Ownrshp* 2002
Sales 98.4MM[E] *EMP* 35,000
SIC 8742 8748 Management consulting services; Business consulting
CEO: Scott F Miller
**Ch Bd:* Sharon Virts
Pr: Kevin Mozer
**CFO:* Jeffrey Leong
**Ex VP:* Michael Petrucelli
VP: Eleni Z Antoniou
VP: Sheila S Blackwell
VP: Dawn Lewandowski
VP: Alicia Mallaney
VP: Michael Mikuta
VP: Sean Wilson

FCM TRAVEL SOLUTIONS
See FLIGHT CENTRE USA HOLDING CORP

D-U-N-S 61-537-8007
FCN INC
F C N
12315 Wilkins Ave, Rockville, MD 20852-1827
Tel (301) 770-2925 *Founded/Ownrshp* 1990
Sales 230.0MM[E] *EMP* 105[E]
Accts Sullivan & Company Bethesda
SIC 8748 Systems analysis or design
Pr: Ann Sullivan
**Treas:* George Sullivan
**VP:* Dennis Sullivan
Exec: Brian Lucas
Prgrm Mgr: Kathleen Niedzwick
Opers Mgr: Julie Fragale
Sales Exec: Lucas Arroyo
Sls Mgr: Kirk Fox

FCN WEST
See FOX CABLE NETWORK SERVICES LLC

FCPA
See FLORIDA CLINICAL PRACTICE ASSOCIATION INC

FCPS
See FREDERICK COUNTY PUBLIC SCHOOLS

FCSO
See FIRST COAST SERVICE OPTIONS INC

D-U-N-S 09-802-6008
■ **FCSTONE GROUP INC**
(*Suby of* INTL FCSTONE INC) ★
1251 Nw Briarcliff Pkwy, Kansas City, MO 64116-1786
Tel (816) 410-7120 *Founded/Ownrshp* 2009
Sales 152.7MM[E] *EMP* 448[E]
SIC 6221 Commodity contracts brokers, dealers
Pr: Paul G Anderson
**Pr:* Scott J Branch
**CEO:* Sean O Connor
**COO:* Stephan L Gutierrez
**COO:* Xuong Nguyen
**CFO:* William J Dunaway
Ex VP: Jim Lambert
MIS Dir: Beau McAdams
Dir IT: David Hendrix

D-U-N-S 17-050-4059 IMP/EXP
FCTG HOLDINGS INC
FOREST CITY TRADING GROUP
10250 Sw Greenburg Rd # 200, Portland, OR 97223-5461
Tel (503) 246-8500 *Founded/Ownrshp* 1964
Sales 864.8MM[E] *EMP* 410
SIC 5031 Lumber: rough, dressed & finished; Plywood; Particleboard
Pr: Craig Johnston
**CFO:* Derrick Coder
Board of Directors: Lorin Rydstrom

FCUSD
See FOLSOM-CORDOVA UNIF SCH DIST

D-U-N-S 10-780-6148 IMP
FCX PERFORMANCE INC
JH INSTRUMENTS
3000 E 14th Ave, Columbus, OH 43219-2355
Tel (614) 324-6050 *Founded/Ownrshp* 2012
Sales 212.4MM[E] *EMP* 215
SIC 5084 5085 3494 Instruments & control equipment; Industrial supplies; Valves & fittings; Valves & pipe fittings

CEO: Thomas Cox
**Pr:* Don G Reece
**COO:* Russell S Frazee
CFO: Mark Riordan
Ofcr: Brian Richter
**Ex VP:* Chris Hill
Sr VP: Susan Snowden
VP: Kevin Kenning
Exec: Jay Bush
Area Mgr: Amory Roach
Dir IT: Jon Zygmunt

FDA- OFM
See FOOD & DRUG ADMINISTRATION

FDBL
See FRAGOMEN DEL REY BERNSEN & LOEWY LLP

D-U-N-S 10-147-8977 IMP/EXP
■ **FDC VITAMINS LLC**
NUTRI-FORCE NUTRITION
(*Suby of* NUTRI-FORCE NUTRITION) ★
14620 Nw 60th Ave, Miami Lakes, FL 33014-2811
Tel (305) 468-1600 *Founded/Ownrshp* 2014
Sales 90.3MM[E] *EMP* 400[E]
SIC 2833 Vitamins, natural or synthetic: bulk, uncompounded
Prin: Colin Watts
**COO:* Dan Alhadeff

D-U-N-S 12-652-0449 IMP/EXP
FDG ASSOCIATES LLC
605 3rd Ave Fl 15, New York, NY 10158-0180
Tel (212) 940-6864 *Founded/Ownrshp* 1998
Sales 254.3MM[E] *EMP* 570
SIC 7389

FDH VELOCITEL
See VELOCITEL INC

FDIC
See FEDERAL DEPOSIT INSURANCE CORP

FDOT
See FLORIDA DEPARTMENT OF TRANSPORTATION

FDVA
See FLORIDA DEPARTMENT OF VETERANS AFFAIRS

D-U-N-S 02-888-3486
FEATHER RIVER HOSPITAL
5974 Pentz Rd, Paradise, CA 95969-5593
Tel (530) 877-9361 *Founded/Ownrshp* 1947
Sales 207.0MM *EMP* 925
Accts Ernst & Young Llp Roseville
SIC 8062 8051 General medical & surgical hospitals; Convalescent home with continuous nursing care
CEO: Wayne Ferch
**CFO:* Dan Gordon
Treas: Patricia Sangl
Top Exec: James P Lacey
Dir OR: Randall Cardwell
Dir Lab: Dayne Jones
Dir Rad: Sue Davin-Hancock
Chf Nrs Of: Jackie Fullton
CIO: Adam Benjamin
Sfty Mgr: Carole Mickelson
Mktg Dir: Maureen Wisener

D-U-N-S 19-439-4789
FEATHERLITE INC
(*Suby of* UNIVERSAL TRAILER HOLDINGS CORP) ★
13380 Highways 63 & 9, Cresco, IA 52136
Tel (563) 547-6000 *Founded/Ownrshp* 1988
Sales 210.3MM[E] *EMP* 1,300
SIC 3716 3799 3714 Motor homes; Trailers & trailer equipment; Motor vehicle parts & accessories
Pr: Terry L Carlson
**VP:* Eric P Clement
Dir IT: George Willis
Ql Cn Mgr: Brian Balk
Natl Sales: Randy Lewis

FEC
See FLORIDA EAST COAST RAILWAY LLC

D-U-N-S 00-423-2179 IMP/EXP
■ **FECHHEIMER BROTHERS CO**
(*Suby of* BERKSHIRE HATHAWAY INC) ★
4545 Malsbary Rd, Blue Ash, OH 45242-5624
Tel (513) 793-7819 *Founded/Ownrshp* 1842, 1986
Sales 264.8MM[E] *EMP* 1,000
SIC 2311 2337 2339 5699 Men's & boys' uniforms; Policemen's uniforms: made from purchased materials; Firemen's uniforms: made from purchased materials; Women's & misses' suits & coats; Uniforms, except athletic: women's, misses' & juniors'; Women's & misses' outerwear; Uniforms
CEO: Dan Dudley
**Sr VP:* Fred Heldman
VP: Dan Balzofiore
VP: Chris Gruenke
VP: Angela Milligan
Mng Dir: Steven Riley
Sales Exec: Larry Schmalz

D-U-N-S 07-830-2661
FECR RAIL CORP
(*Suby of* FLORIDA EAST COAST HOLDINGS CORP) ★
7411 Fullerton St Ste 100, Jacksonville, FL 32256-3628
Tel (800) 342-1131 *Founded/Ownrshp* 2007
Sales 112.0MM[E] *EMP* 525[E]
SIC 4011 Railroads, line-haul operating
CEO: James R Hertwig

D-U-N-S 07-101-7115
FEDCAP REHABILITATION SERVICES INC (NY)
633 3rd Ave Fl 6, New York, NY 10017-6733
Tel (212) 727-4200 *Founded/Ownrshp* 1935
Sales 173.8MM *EMP* 1,540
SIC 8093 Rehabilitation center, outpatient treatment
Ch Bd: Mark Odonoghue
**Pr:* Christine McMahon
**COO:* Joseph Giannetto
**VP:* Kenneth Brezenoff
Opers Mgr: Loren Ganoe

D-U-N-S 13-048-8604 IMP/EXP
FEDDERS CORP
13455 Noel Rd Ste 2200, Dallas, TX 75240-6685
Tel (604) 908-8686 *Founded/Ownrshp* 1896
Sales 141.1MM[E] *EMP* 1,664
SIC 3585 3674 3634 3564 Refrigeration & heating equipment; Dehumidifiers electric, except portable; Compressors for refrigeration & air conditioning equipment; Heat pumps, electric; Thermoelectric devices, solid state; Electric housewares & fans; Blowers & fans
CFO: Robert L Laurent Jr
**Treas:* Nancy Digiovanni
**Ex VP:* Kent E Hansen
VP: Richard Essex
**VP:* Judy A Katz
VP Opers: Brown Tim
Manager: David Walsh
Board of Directors: Joseph Giordano, Michael Giordano, Howard S Modlin, Herbert A Morey, S A Muscarnera, Anthony E Puleo

D-U-N-S 01-275-7949
FEDELITY FEDERAL BANK & TRUST
205 Datura St, West Palm Beach, FL 33401-5603
Tel (561) 803-9900 *Founded/Ownrshp* 1956
Sales NA *EMP* 1,000
SIC 6141 Financing: automobiles, furniture, etc., not a deposit bank
CEO: Vince Elhilow
**VP:* Bob Fugate

D-U-N-S 61-296-1276
▲ **FEDERAL AGRICULTURAL MORTGAGE CORP**
FARMER MAC
1999 K St Nw Fl 4, Washington, DC 20006-1118
Tel (202) 872-7700 *Founded/Ownrshp* 1988
Sales NA *EMP* 71[E]
Tkr Sym AGM *Exch* NYS
SIC 6111 6159 Federal & federally sponsored credit agencies; Agricultural credit institutions
Pr: Timothy L Buzby
**Ch Bd:* Lowell L Junkins
CFO: R Dale Lynch
**V Ch Bd:* Myles J Watts
Sr VP: J Curtis Covington
Sr VP: Stephen P Mullery
Dir IT: Mario Maurice
Counsel: Christy Prendergast
Board of Directors: Mitchell A Johnson, Dennis L Brack, Clark B Maxwell, Chester J Culver, Bruce J Sherrick, Richard H Davidson, Douglas E Wilhelm, Sara L Faivre-Davis, James R Engebretsen, Dennis A Everson, Douglas A Felton, Douglas L Flory, Thomas W Hill

D-U-N-S 92-833-8656
■ **FEDERAL AVIATION ADMINISTRATION**
F A A
(*Suby of* UNITED STATES DEPARTMENT OF TRANSPORTATION) ★
800 Independence Ave Sw, Washington, DC 20591-0004
Tel (866) 835-5322 *Founded/Ownrshp* 1958
Sales NA *EMP* 48,799
SIC 9621 Aircraft regulating agencies
Mng Pt: Marlene Wechsler
COO: Russell G Chew
**COO:* Hank Krakowski
Chf Mktg O: Jonathan Goode
Chf Mktg O: Christine Jordan
Chf Mktg O: Mitchell Wagster
Adm Dir: Nicki Duncan
Adm Dir: Pat Hamel
Adm Dir: Harriet Menezes
Adm Dir: Elvie Ranan
Adm Dir: Marilyn Vandalsem

FEDERAL BUILDING SERVICES
See FCC ENTERPRISES INC

D-U-N-S 87-886-5674
■ **FEDERAL BUREAU OF INVESTIGATION**
FBI
(*Suby of* UNITED STATES DEPARTMENT OF JUSTICE) ★
935 Pennsylvania Ave Nw, Washington, DC 20535-0001
Tel (202) 324-3000 *Founded/Ownrshp* 1908
Sales NA *EMP* 9,000
SIC 9221 Bureau of criminal investigation, government;
Ofcr: Patrick Kelley
VP: Anna Chew
VP: Isis Y Jones
VP: Linda McCall
VP: Donna Murphy
Exec: Marilyn Moore
Adm Dir: Donna Judge
Prgrm Mgr: Roger Campbell
Prgrm Mgr: Johnna Hoban
Prgrm Mgr: Paul Morin
Prgrm Mgr: Arnold Pierce

D-U-N-S 87-843-5213
■ **FEDERAL BUREAU OF PRISONS**
CENTRAL OFFICE
(*Suby of* UNITED STATES DEPARTMENT OF JUSTICE) ★
320 1st St Nw Ste 654, Washington, DC 20534-0002
Tel (202) 307-3198 *Founded/Ownrshp* 1930
Sales NA *EMP* 30,000
SIC 9223 Prison, government;
IT Man: John Morris

D-U-N-S 02-030-9969
■ **FEDERAL COMMUNICATIONS COMMISSION**
FC
(*Suby of* EXECUTIVE OFFICE OF UNITED STATES GOVERNMENT) ★
445 12th St Sw, Washington, DC 20554-0004
Tel (202) 418-1925 *Founded/Ownrshp* 1934
Sales NA *EMP* 1,930
Accts Kpmg Llp Washington Dc

SIC 9631 Communications commission, government;
Ch: Tom Wheeler
CFO: Nelson Davis
Adm Dir: John Vance
QA Dir: Jarod Gaspard
Software D: Chris Hall
Opers Mgr: Spenser Stone
Mktg Mgr: John Carey
Snr Mgr: Eric Panketh

FEDERAL COMPANIES
See FEDERAL WAREHOUSE CO

D-U-N-S 00-325-6534
FEDERAL DEPOSIT INSURANCE CORP
FDIC
550 17th St Nw, Washington, DC 20429-0002
Tel (877) 275-3342 *Founded/Ownrshp* 1933
Sales NA *EMP* 7,300
SIC 6399 9311 Federal Deposit Insurance Corporation (FDIC); Finance, taxation & monetary policy;
Ch: Martin J Gruenberg
V Ch: Thomas M Hoenig
V Ch: Thomas Hoenig
COO: John Bovenzi
COO: Gina Sacripanti
CFO: Steven O App
Ch: Martin J Gruenberg
Bd of Dir: James Barker
Bd of Dir: Donna Tanoue
Ofcr: Teresa Perez
Ofcr: Lisa Schra
Ofcr: Beverly Shuck
VP: Keith Armstrong
VP: Jacob Berge
VP: George French
Assoc Dir: Jamal Hindi
Comm Man: Peter Lugo
Board of Directors: Thomas M Hoenig, Jeremiah O Norton

FEDERAL DIVISION
See PHILLIPS CORP

D-U-N-S 03-775-1583 IMP/EXP
■ FEDERAL EMERGENCY MANAGEMENT AGENCY
FEMA
(*Suby of* EXECUTVE OFC OF US GOVT) ★
500 C St Sw Ocfo, Washington, DC 20472-0001
Tel (202) 646-2500 *Founded/Ownrshp* 1979
Sales NA *EMP* 2,400
SIC 9229

D-U-N-S 03-776-0097
■ FEDERAL ENERGY REGULATORY COMMISSION
(*Suby of* EXECUTIVE OFFICE OF UNITED STATES GOVERNMENT) ★
888 1st St Ne, Washington, DC 20426-0002
Tel (202) 502-6629 *Founded/Ownrshp* 1995
Sales NA *EMP* 1,500E
Accts Kpmg Llp Washington Dc
SIC 9611 Energy development & conservation agency, government;
Ch: John Wellinghol
Pr: Mary Odriscoll
Pr: Angela Stokes
CFO: William D Foster Jr
VP: Arthur Reis
Adm Dir: Angela McKnight
Ex Dir: Anton C Porter
Snr Ntwrk: Juned Shaikh
CIO: Sanjay Sardar
Dir IT: Naeem Musa
Software D: Angela Washington

D-U-N-S 05-807-0459
■ FEDERAL EXPRESS CORP
FEDEX
(*Suby of* FEDEX CORP) ★
3610 Hacks Cross Rd, Memphis, TN 38125-8800
Tel (901) 369-3600 *Founded/Ownrshp* 1971
Sales 26.0MMM *EMP* 166,000E
Accts Ernst & Young Llp Memphis Te
SIC 4513 4512 4215 4213 Air courier services; Letter delivery, private air; Package delivery, private air; Parcel delivery, private air; Air cargo carrier, scheduled; Package delivery, vehicular; Parcel delivery, vehicular; Trucking, except local
Pr: David J Bronczek
**Ch Bd:* Frederick W Smith
**COO:* David L Cunningham Jr
CFO: Elise L Jordan
**Ex VP:* James R Parker
VP: Walt Abercrombie
VP: Jerry Beyl
VP: Carol Smith
VP: Gene Sun
Mng Dir: Brian Baucke
Mng Dir: Guy See
Board of Directors: Robert B Carter, T Michael Glenn, Alan B Graf Jr, Christine P Richards

D-U-N-S 07-967-5304
FEDERAL EXPRESS PACIFIC INC
1209 N Orange St, Wilmington, DE 19801-1120
Tel (901) 369-3600 *Founded/Ownrshp* 2014
Sales 273.9MME *EMP* 2,393E
SIC 4513

D-U-N-S 93-359-0056 IMP/EXP
FEDERAL HEATH SIGN CO LLC
4602 North Ave, Oceanside, CA 92056-3509
Tel (760) 941-0715 *Founded/Ownrshp* 2001
Sales 132.4MME *EMP* 500
SIC 3993 Electric signs
Ch Bd: Kenneth A Hendricks
**Pr:* Kevin Stotmeiser
COO: Ken Moultray
**CFO:* James Schmidt
**Sr VP:* Stewart Edinger
**VP:* Thomas Berse
Prgrm Mgr: Kay Bacon
Prgrm Mgr: Peggy Deheck
Prgrm Mgr: Sherri McFadden
Prgrm Mgr: Amy Potter
Mktg Dir: Annette Adams

D-U-N-S 92-833-8219
■ FEDERAL HIGHWAY ADMINISTRATION
(*Suby of* UNITED STATES DEPARTMENT OF TRANSPORTATION) ★
1200 New Jersey Ave Se, Washington, DC 20590-0001
Tel (202) 366-0650 *Founded/Ownrshp* 1967
Sales NA *EMP* 2,925
SIC 9621 Transportation department: government, non-operating;
Pr: Frederick Wright
**CFO:* Albert T Park
Adm Dir: Jewell Bolding
Adm Dir: Lorri Hamn
Adm Dir: Cynthia McDuffie
**Ex Dir:* Jeff Paniati
Prgrm Mgr: Daniel M Ferezan
Prgrm Mgr: Gregory Murrill
Prgrm Mgr: Dean Scott
Rgnl Mgr: Tammy Wagner
Genl Mgr: Terry Weems

D-U-N-S 07-874-7765
FEDERAL HOME LOAN ADMINISTRATION INC
1201 N Orange St Ste 600, Wilmington, DE 19801-1171
Tel (855) 345-2669 *Founded/Ownrshp* 2013
Sales NA *EMP* 55
SIC 6162 Bond & mortgage companies
CEO: Nicholas Krakana

D-U-N-S 84-848-9183
FEDERAL HOME LOAN BANK
FHL BANK
(*Suby of* FEDERAL HOME LOAN BANK - OFFICE OF FINANCE) ★
1 Sw Sec Bnft Pl Ste 100, Topeka, KS 66606-2542
Tel (785) 233-0507 *Founded/Ownrshp* 1989
Sales NA *EMP* 100E
Accts Pricewaterhousecoopers Llp Ka
SIC 6019 Federal home loan banks
Pr: Andrew J Jetter
Bd of Dir: Jenifer Whitehead
Chf Mktg O: Julie Devander
Ofcr: Bobbi Shinn
**Ex VP:* David S Fisher
Ex VP: Mark Yardely
**Ex VP:* Mark E Yardley
**Sr VP:* Patrick C Doran
**Sr VP:* Frank Tiernan
VP: Tom Bliss
VP: Denise Cauthon
VP: Josh Clark
VP: Julie Devader
VP: Dave Fisher
VP: Brad Gentry
VP: Kathleen Grote
VP: Eric Haar
VP: Dan Hess
VP: Lance Liby
VP: Greg McLaren
VP: Don MAI

D-U-N-S 80-600-4404
FEDERAL HOME LOAN BANK - OFFICE OF FINANCE
1818 Library St Ste 200, Reston, VA 20190-6273
Tel (703) 467-3600 *Founded/Ownrshp* 1932
Sales NA *EMP* 100E
SIC 6019 Federal home loan banks
Ch: Jonathan Scott
Bd of Dir: Timothy O'Niel
Ofcr: Ryan Crackel
Ofcr: Megan Dougherty
Ofcr: Violeta Tkachuk
IT Man: Maggie Baran

D-U-N-S 06-536-4069
FEDERAL HOME LOAN BANK OF ATLANTA
1475 Peachtree St Ne # 400, Atlanta, GA 30309-3037
Tel (404) 888-8000 *Founded/Ownrshp* 1932
Sales NA *EMP* 339E
Accts Pricewaterhousecoopers Llp At
SIC 6111 Federal & federally sponsored credit agencies
Pr: W Wesley McMullan
**Ch Bd:* F Gary Garczynski
Pr: Deandra Wulf
COO: Cathy C Adams
CFO: Kirk R Malmberg
CFO: Mike Sims
**V Ch Bd:* Richard A Whaley
Ofcr: Cissy McElvy
Sr VP: Julia S Brown
Sr VP: Reginald T O'Shields
VP: Connie Arnold
VP: Kevin Ashburn
VP: Colin Gatewood
VP: Jennifer Robinson
VP: Leslie Schreiner
VP: Brett Sommerville
VP: Kevin Wyckoff
VP: Mark Zelermyer
Board of Directors: Henry Gary Pannell, Travis Cosby III, Robert L Strickland Jr, Suzanne S Deferie, Michael P Fitzgerald, William C Handorf, J Thomas Johnson, Jonathan Kislak, Kim C Liddell, Miriam Lopez, John C Neal

D-U-N-S 61-919-2529
FEDERAL HOME LOAN BANK OF BOSTON
800 Boylston St Ste 900, Boston, MA 02199-8072
Tel (617) 292-9600 *Founded/Ownrshp* 1932
Sales NA *EMP* 200
Accts Pricewaterhousecoopers Llp Bo
SIC 6111 6019 Federal & federally sponsored credit agencies; Federal Home Loan Mortgage Corporation; Federal home loan banks
Pr: Edward A Hjerpe III
**Ch Bd:* Andrew J Calamare
CFO: Frank Nitkiewicz
Treas: Timothy J Barrett
**V Ch Bd:* Steven A Closson
Ofcr: George H Collins
Ofcr: M Susan Elliott
Sr VP: Brian G Donahue
Sr VP: Barry F Gale
Sr VP: Sean R McRae
Sr VP: Carol Hempfling Pratt
VP: Laura Glowick
Board of Directors: Emil J Ragones, Donna L Boulanger, Gregory R Shook, Joan Carty, Stephen R Theroux, Eric Chatman, John F Treanor, Patrick E Clancy, Michael R Tuttle, Stephen G Crowe, Martin J Geitz, Cornelius K Hurley, Jay F Malcynsky, John W McGeorge

D-U-N-S 03-580-8708
FEDERAL HOME LOAN BANK OF CHICAGO
200 E Randolph St # 1700, Chicago, IL 60601-6428
Tel (312) 565-5700 *Founded/Ownrshp* 1932
Sales NA *EMP* 405
Accts Pricewaterhousecoopers Llp C
SIC 6111 Federal Home Loan Mortgage Corporation
Pr: Matthew R Feldman
**Ch Bd:* Steven F Rosenbaum
Pr: Kevin Erickson
Pr: Sameera Ishaq
Pr: Marlaine McVisk
CFO: Roger D Lundstrom
**V Ch Bd:* William W Sennholz
Sr Inv Off: Andreas Demetis
VP: Troy Bienash
VP: Rene Cornejo
VP: Kimberly Cullotta
VP: Matthew Desmarais
VP: Terry Dugan
VP: Brian Frame
VP: Ed Gomez
VP: Carolyn Jaw
VP: Kathy Rasmussen
VP: Thomas Ruggieri
VP: Matthew Stewart
VP: Benny Tjahjono
VP: Karen Vlcek
Board of Directors: David R Pirsein, Diane M Aigotti, John K Reinke, James T Ashworth, Leo J Ries, Owen E Beacom, Michael G Steelman, Edward P Brady, Gregory A White, Mary J Cahillane, Mark J Eppli, Arthur E Greenbank, Thomas L Herlache, E David Locke

D-U-N-S 07-286-7211
FEDERAL HOME LOAN BANK OF CINCINNATI
600 Atrium Two # 2, Cincinnati, OH 45201
Tel (513) 852-7500 *Founded/Ownrshp* 1932
Sales NA *EMP* 204
Accts Pricewaterhousecoopers Llp Ci
SIC 6019 Federal home loan banks
Pr: Andrew S Howell
**Ch Bd:* Donald J Mullineaux
Pr: Jeffery Berryman
Pr: Paul Doyle
Pr: Thomas Muth
Pr: John Zazycki
COO: Donald R Able
Treas: John Dolan
**V Ch Bd:* William J Small
Ofcr: Janice Weber
Ex VP: Andrew Howell
Ex VP: Kyle Lawler
Ex VP: R Kyle Lawler
Sr VP: Roger B Batsel
Sr VP: Stephen J Sponaugle
VP: Tom Ciresi
VP: John Kozak
VP: Karla Russo
VP: Thomas Schlager
VP: Risk Stephen
VP: Keith B Thurman
Board of Directors: Thomas L Moore, J Lynn Anderson, Alvin J Nance, Grady P Appleton, Charles J Ruma, Greg W Caudill, David E Sartore, James R Deroberts, William S Stuard Jr, Mark N Duhamel, Nancy E Uridil, Leslie D Dunn, James A England, Charles J Koch, Michael R Melvin

D-U-N-S 06-531-4361
FEDERAL HOME LOAN BANK OF DALLAS
8500 Freeport Pkwy # 600, Irving, TX 75063-1938
Tel (214) 441-8500 *Founded/Ownrshp* 1932
Sales NA *EMP* 207
SIC 6111

D-U-N-S 07-347-6624
FEDERAL HOME LOAN BANK OF DES MOINES
801 Walnut St Ste 200, Des Moines, IA 50309-3610
Tel (515) 281-1000 *Founded/Ownrshp* 1932
Sales NA *EMP* 389E
Accts Pricewaterhousecoopers Llp Mi
SIC 6019 Federal home loan banks
CEO: Richard S Swanson
Ch Bd: Dale E Oberkfell
Pr: Michael L Wilson
COO: Steven T Schuler
V Ch Bd: William V Humphreys
Ex VP: Stan Hilst
Ex VP: Steven Schuler
Sr VP: Ardis E Kelley
Sr VP: Aaron B Lee
VP: Mary Cecola
VP: Jennifer Ernst
VP: Curt Heidt
VP: Kelly Rasmuson
VP: Bradley Spears
Assoc Dir: Kimberly Majors
Board of Directors: W Douglas Hile, Cynthia A Parker, Ruth B Bennett, Teresa J Keegan, J Benson Porter, Michael J Blodnick, Michelle M Keeley, Thomas P Potiowsky, David P Bobbitt, John F Kennedy Sr, John P Rigler II, Steven L Bumann, Ellen Z Lamale, John H Robinson, Marianne M Emerson, Russell J Lau, Joseph C Stewart III, David J Ferries, James G Livingston, Robert M Teachworth, Van D Fishback, Michael W McGowan, David F Wilson, Chris D Grimm, Elsie M Meeks, Eric A Hardmeyer

D-U-N-S 07-070-8037
FEDERAL HOME LOAN BANK OF INDIANAPOLIS
8250 Wdfld Xing Blvd, Indianapolis, IN 46240-7324
Tel (317) 465-0200 *Founded/Ownrshp* 1932
Sales NA *EMP* 215
Accts Pricewaterhousecoopers Llp In
SIC 6111 Federal & federally sponsored credit agencies
Pr: Cindy L Konich
**Ch Bd:* James D Macphee
COO: Jonathan R West
CFO: Gregory L Teare
**V Ch Bd:* Michael J Hannigan Jr
Ofcr: Lavonne C Cate
Sr VP: K Lowell Short Jr
VP: Jeff Buttars
VP: Gregory Teare
CIO: Deron Streitenberger
Counsel: Michael Zaradich
Board of Directors: Jeffrey A Poxon, Jonathan P Bradford, John L Skibski, Matthew P Forrester, Elliot A Spoon, Timothy P Gaylord, Thomas R Sullivan, Karen F Gregerson, Larry A Swank, Carl E Liedholm, Maurice F Winkler III, James L Logue III, Robert D Long, Dan L Moore, Christine Coady Narayanan

D-U-N-S 08-042-4484
FEDERAL HOME LOAN BANK OF NEW YORK
101 Park Ave Fl 5, New York, NY 10178-0500
Tel (212) 441-6616 *Founded/Ownrshp* 1932
Sales NA *EMP* 273E
Accts Pricewaterhousecoopers Llp Ne
SIC 6111 Federal & federally sponsored credit agencies
Pr: Alfred A Dellibovi
**Ch Bd:* Michael M Horn
CFO: Kevin M Neylan
**V Ch Bd:* James W Fulmer
Bd of Dir: Carlos Vazquez
Ofcr: Jessey Abraham
Sr VP: John F Edelen
Sr VP: Adam Goldstein
Sr VP: Peter S Leung
Sr VP: Paul B H Roux
VP: Steve Christatos
VP: Bob Fusco
VP: Paul Heroux
VP: Phil Scott
Board of Directors: Monte N Redman, Kevin Cummings, Edwin C Reed, Anne Evans Estabrook, Larry E Thompson, Jay M Ford, Carlos J Vazquez, Gerald H Lipkin, Christopher P Martin, Richard S Mroz, David J Nasca, Vincent F Palagiano, C Cathleen Raffaeli

D-U-N-S 61-919-2800
FEDERAL HOME LOAN BANK OF PITTSBURGH
601 Grant St Ste 1000, Pittsburgh, PA 15219-4420
Tel (412) 288-3400 *Founded/Ownrshp* 1932
Sales NA *EMP* 219E
Accts Pricewaterhousecoopers Llp Pi
SIC 6019 Federal home loan banks
Pr: Winthrop Watson
**Ch Bd:* Patrick A Bond
COO: Kristina K Williams
CFO: David G Paulson
**V Ch Bd:* John K Darr
VP: Vincent Moye
VP: Lawrence Swingle
Dir Risk M: Katie Chieffe
Dir Risk M: Michael A Rizzo
Dir Risk M: Mike Rizzo
Dir Sec: John C Mason
Board of Directors: John S Milinovich, Pamela C Asbury, Charles J Nugent, Joseph M Blaston, James R Reske, Glenn R Brooks, Bradford E Ritchie, Rev Luis A Cortes Jr, Frederick E Schea, Pamela H Godwin, Patrick J Ward, Brian A Hudson, Angela J Yochem, William C Marsh, Charlotte B McLaughlin, Lynda A Messick

D-U-N-S 00-944-9117
FEDERAL HOME LOAN BANK OF SAN FRANCISCO
600 California St, San Francisco, CA 94108-2704
Tel (415) 616-1000 *Founded/Ownrshp* 1932
Sales NA *EMP* 262E
SIC 6111 Federal & federally sponsored credit agencies
Ch Bd: John F Luikart
Pr: Larry Feigenbaum
Pr: Dean Schultz
COO: Lisa B Macmillen
CFO: Kenneth C Miller
Assoc VP: Richard Knowles
Sr VP: David H Martens
Sr VP: Robert Shovlowsky
Sr VP: Suzanne Titus-Johnson
VP: Elena Andreadakis
VP: Suzanne Johnson
VP: Kenneth Miller
VP: Antonio Ruscitti
VP: Tom Wilson
Dir Risk M: David Martens
Board of Directors: Robert F Nielsen, Bradley W Beal, John F Robinson, Craig G Blunden, Scott C Syphax, Steven R Gardner, John T Wasley, Melinda Guzman, Richard A Heldebrant, W Douglas Hile, Simone Lagomarsino, Douglas H Lowrey, Kevin Murray

D-U-N-S 08-373-9763
FEDERAL HOME LOAN BANK OF SEATTLE
1001 4th Ave Ste 2600, Seattle, WA 98154-1005
Tel (206) 340-2421 *Founded/Ownrshp* 1964
Sales NA *EMP* 161E
SIC 6019

D-U-N-S 05-338-2495
▲ FEDERAL HOME LOAN MORTGAGE CORP
FREDDIE MAC
8200 Jones Branch Dr, Mc Lean, VA 22102-3107
Tel (703) 903-2000 *Founded/Ownrshp* 1970
Sales NA *EMP* 5,462
Tkr Sym FMCC *Exch* OTC
SIC 6111 Federal Home Loan Mortgage Corporation
CEO: Donald H Layton
**Ch Bd:* Christopher S Lynch
CFO: James G Mackey
Ofcr: Subha V Barry
Ofcr: Jerry Weiss
Ex VP: Anil Hinduja
Ex VP: Robert Lux

Ex VP: William H McDavid
Ex VP: Joseph A Smilowski
Sr VP: Robert C Dean
Sr VP: Margie Farber
Sr VP: Melvin M Kann
Sr VP: Peter F Maselli
Sr VP: Tracy Mooney
Sr VP: Paul Mullings
Sr VP: David R Polombi
Sr VP: Gregory E Reynolds
Sr VP: Joseph A Rossi
Sr VP: Patrick M Sheehy
Sr VP: Manoj Singh
VP: David M Brickman

D-U-N-S 00-698-3563
FEDERAL INSURANCE CO
CHUBB
(*Suby of* INA CHUBB HOLDINGS INC) ★
15 Mountainview Rd, Warren, NJ 07059-6711
Tel (908) 903-2000 *Founded/Ownrshp* 1901, 2016
Sales NA *EMP* 2,000
SIC 6411 Insurance agents, brokers & service
CEO: John D Finnegan
**Pr:* Thomas F Motamed
**Treas:* Philip John Sempier
Sr VP: Timothy Buckley
Sr VP: Michele Fincher
Sr VP: Keith Spalding
VP: Sybil Baffoe
VP: Peter Barber
VP: Joanne Bober
VP: Roger Charles Prior Brookhouse
VP: Helen Cauthorn
VP: Christopher Cocca
**VP:* Henry Gregory Gulick
VP: Ian Lancaster
VP: Russell Schuren
VP: David Shultz
VP: Bert Wolff
VP: Jack Zacharias

D-U-N-S 00-890-8337 IMP
FEDERAL INTERNATIONAL INC
7935 Clayton Rd Ste A, Saint Louis, MO 63117-1317
Tel (314) 721-3377 *Founded/Ownrshp* 1916
Sales 123.5MM *EMP* 322
SIC 3086 7389 Plastics foam products; Brokers, contract services
Pr: Melvyn Lefkowitz
CFO: Bill Jwanouskos
**VP:* David Charak II
**VP:* Claire Newton
**VP:* Jim Schulz
**VP:* Edgardo Wente
Off Mgr: Crystal Haudrich
Plnt Mgr: Michelle Morin

D-U-N-S 02-371-4660
■ **FEDERAL KEMPER LIFE ASSURANCE CO**
(*Suby of* BANK ONE INSURANCE HOLDINGS, INC)
1600 Mcconnor Pkwy, Schaumburg, IL 60173-6801
Tel (847) 874-4000 *Founded/Ownrshp* 2003
Sales NA *EMP* 1,000
SIC 6311 Life insurance
Pr: Gale Caruso
CFO: Frederick B Blackmon
Ex VP: Adam Braff
Sr VP: Debra P Rezabek
Prgrm Mgr: Jasmin Schenk
CIO: Russell Bostick

FEDERAL MOGUL
See FEDERAL-MOGUL CORP

D-U-N-S 04-951-5430
▲ **FEDERAL NATIONAL MORTGAGE ASSOCIATION**
FANNIE MAE
3900 Wisconsin Ave Nw, Washington, DC 20016-2806
Tel (202) 752-7000 *Founded/Ownrshp* 1938
Sales NA *EMP* 7,300
Tkr Sym FNMA *Exch* OTC
SIC 6111 Federal & federally sponsored credit agencies; Federal Home Loan Mortgage Corporation; Federal National Mortgage Association
Pr: Timothy J Mayopoulos
**Ch Bd:* Egbert L J Perry
CFO: David C Benson
Ofcr: Kimberly H Johnson
Ex VP: Brian P Brooks
Ex VP: Andrew J Bon Salle
Sr VP: Joy C Cianci
Sr VP: Kimberly Johnson
Sr VP: Bruce R Lee
Sr VP: Bruce Lee
Sr VP: Zachary Oppenheimer
Sr VP: Andrew Bon Salle
VP: Nigel D Brazier

D-U-N-S 13-342-4023
■ **FEDERAL NETWORK SYSTEMS LLC**
(*Suby of* JACOBS TECHNOLOGY INC) ★
11710 Plaza America Dr, Reston, VA 20190-4742
Tel (703) 694-7200 *Founded/Ownrshp* 2014
Sales 114.9MM^E *EMP* 1,120
SIC 8748 Communications consulting
Pr: Susan Zeleniak
Sr VP: Michael Maiorana
VP: Sonya Cork
VP: Wesley Jordan Jr
VP: Peter Pin
VP: Jack Walters

D-U-N-S 62-662-7459
■ **FEDERAL PRISON INDUSTRIES INC**
UNICOR
(*Suby of* UNITED STATES DEPARTMENT OF JUSTICE) ★
320 1st St Nw, Washington, DC 20534-0002
Tel (202) 305-3500 *Founded/Ownrshp* 1934
Sales NA *EMP* 1,900
SIC 9223 Correctional institutions
Ch: David D Spears
**CEO:* Steve V Schwalb
**COO:* Paul M Laird
COO: Mary M Mitchell
Prgrm Mgr: John Roderique
Genl Mgr: Brad Beus
Genl Mgr: Jane Eyre

D-U-N-S 07-780-3880
▲ **FEDERAL REALTY INVESTMENT TRUST**
1626 E Jefferson St, Rockville, MD 20852-4041
Tel (301) 998-8100 *Founded/Ownrshp* 1962
Sales 744.0MM *EMP* 436^E
Tkr Sym FRT *Exch* NYS
SIC 6798 Real estate investment trusts
Pr: Donald C Wood
COO: Dawn M Becker
CFO: Dan Guglielmone
CFO: James M Taylor Jr
Trst Ofcr: John R Tschiderer
Ex VP: Don Briggs
Ex VP: Donald T Briggs
Sr VP: Jeff Mooallem
VP: Porter Bellew
VP: Andrea Simpson
Genl Mgr: Mickey Papillon
Board of Directors: Jon E Bortz, David W Faeder, Kristin Gamble, Gail P Steinel, Warren M Thompson, Joseph S Vassalluzzo

D-U-N-S 06-897-2058 IMP
FEDERAL RESERVE BANK DALLAS
(*Suby of* FEDERAL RESERVE SYSTEM) ★
2200 N Pearl St, Dallas, TX 75201-2272
Tel (214) 922-6000 *Founded/Ownrshp* 1913
Sales NA *EMP* 1,474
SIC 6011 Federal reserve branches
**Ch Bd:* Cindy Ramos-Davidson
**Pr:* Lawrence G Rex
Pr: Richard Tong
Pr: Robert L Triplett
**COO:* Meredith N Black
**COO:* Helen E Holcomb
**Ch:* Anthony R Chase
Ch: Manoj Saxena
Bd of Dir: Hugh G Robinson
Ofcr: Karen Gist
Ofcr: Robert L Moore
**Ex VP:* Harvey Rosenblum
Sr VP: Kelly Dubbert
Sr VP: Carl Gambs
**Sr VP:* J Tyrone Gholson
**Sr VP:* Robert Hankins
Sr VP: Barbara Pacheco
Sr VP: Daron Peschel
**Sr VP:* Millard E Sweatt
VP: Ann Dodson
VP: J V Duca
Board of Directors: Dudley K Montgomery, Dan Angel, Patricia M Patterson, Gayle M Earls, Julie Spicer England, Roger R Hemminghaus, Ray L Hunt, Herb Kelleher, James A Martin, Kirk A McLaughlin, Robert McNair

D-U-N-S 18-121-2879
FEDERAL RESERVE BANK OF ATLANTA
BOARD OF GOV OF THE FED RESRVE
(*Suby of* FEDERAL RESERVE SYSTEM) ★
1000 Peachtree St Ne, Atlanta, GA 30309-4470
Tel (404) 498-8500 *Founded/Ownrshp* 1914
Sales NA *EMP* 2,822
SIC 6011 Federal reserve banks
Pr: Dennis P Lockhart
Pr: Blake Lyons
Pr: Clifford S Stanford
**COO:* Marie Gooding
Sr Ex VP: Ben T Roberts
Ex VP: Earl Anderson
Ex VP: Richard R Oliver
Sr VP: Lois C Bethaume
Sr VP: Christopher G Brown
Sr VP: William B Estes III
VP: Andre Anderson
VP: Christopher Brown
VP: Richard Fraher
VP: Mary Kepler
VP: Nellie Liang
VP: Robert Schaub
VP: Robert M Schenk
Assoc Dir: Betsy Cross
Assoc Dir: Thomas Cunningham
Board of Directors: Juanita P Baranco, Suzanne E Boas, John Dane III, Waymon L Hickman, Richard G Hickson, Maria Camila Leiva, Paula Lovell, William G Smith Jr, John Wieland

D-U-N-S 05-180-3229
FEDERAL RESERVE BANK OF BOSTON
BOARD OF GOVS OF THE FED RESRV
(*Suby of* FEDERAL RESERVE SYSTEM) ★
600 Atlantic Ave, Boston, MA 02210-2204
Tel (617) 973-3000 *Founded/Ownrshp* 1913
Sales NA *EMP* 1,200
Accts Deloitte & Touche Llp Boston
SIC 6011 Federal reserve branches
Pr: Eric S Rosengren
Pr: Mary Bickerton
Pr: Scott Schuh
Pr: Joel Werkema
Pr: Lisa Wright
**COO:* Paul M Connolly
Bd of Dir: James Wood
**Ex VP:* William N Mc Donough
**Sr VP:* Lynn E Browne
**Sr VP:* Thomas E Cimeno Jr
**Sr VP:* Thomas E Gagnon
**Sr VP:* Sarah G Green
**Sr VP:* Robert K La Rocca
VP: Robert Augusta Jr
VP: Jon Colvin
**VP:* Cynthia A Conley
VP: Mary Cottman
VP: James Cunha
VP: Jaron Eanes
VP: Christopher Haley
VP: Yolanda Kodrzycki

D-U-N-S 06-845-2135 IMP/EXP
FEDERAL RESERVE BANK OF CHICAGO
(*Suby of* FEDERAL RESERVE SYSTEM) ★
230 S La Salle St Ste 1, Chicago, IL 60604-1413
Tel (312) 322-2128 *Founded/Ownrshp* 1913
Sales NA *EMP* 2,145
Accts Deloitte & Touche Llp Chicago
SIC 6011 Federal reserve banks
CEO: Charles L Evans
Pr: Cynthia Castillo
Pr: Mike Keppler
Pr: Kristin Laporte
Pr: Matthew Larocco
**COO:* Gordon Werkema
Treas: Laura Jean
Ofcr: Deborah Baldwin
**Sr VP:* David R Allardice
**Sr VP:* Richard Anstee
**Sr VP:* William A Barouski
**Sr VP:* Charles W Furbee
**Sr VP:* William H Gram
**Sr VP:* William C Hunter
**Sr VP:* Jerome F John
Sr VP: Elizabeth A Knopse
**Sr VP:* John J Wixted Jr
VP: Williams Alicia
VP: Jeffery Anderson
VP: Wayne Baxter
VP: James Bluemle

D-U-N-S 00-445-4450
FEDERAL RESERVE BANK OF CLEVELAND
(*Suby of* FEDERAL RESERVE SYSTEM) ★
1455 E 6th St, Cleveland, OH 44114-2517
Tel (216) 579-2000 *Founded/Ownrshp* 1914
Sales NA *EMP* 1,400
SIC 6011 Federal reserve banks
CEO: Sandra Pianalto
**Ch Bd:* Alfred M Rankin Jr
Pr: John Lytell
Pr: Henry Shepherd
Pr: Michael Vangelos
Pr: Carolyn Williams
**COO:* Gregory L Stefani
Treas: Glenn Mauder
Bd of Dir: Charlotte Martin
Ofcr: Bert Jenkins
Ofcr: Lori Schumacher
**Ex VP:* Mark S Sniderman
Sr VP: Andrew Burkle Jr
**Sr VP:* Lawrence Cuy
VP: Larry Cuy
VP: Suzanne Howe
VP: Stephen Ong
VP: Terrence Roth
VP: Susan Steinbrick
VP: Lisa Vidacs
VP: Gary Wagner
Board of Directors: C Daniel Delawder, Roy W Haley, Kevin T Kabat, Todd A Mason, Alfred Rankin Jr, Edwin J Rigaud

D-U-N-S 00-717-2729
FEDERAL RESERVE BANK OF KANSAS CITY (INC) (MO)
BOARD OF GOVS OF FED RESERVE S
(*Suby of* FEDERAL RESERVE SYSTEM) ★
1 Memorial Dr, Kansas City, MO 64198-0002
Tel (816) 881-2000 *Founded/Ownrshp* 1914
Sales NA *EMP* 1,645
Accts Deloitte & Touche Llp Kansas
SIC 6011 Federal reserve branches
Pr: Esther George
Pr: Todd Aadland
Pr: San Cannon
Pr: Kelley Courtright
Pr: Kristi Coy
Pr: Kevin Craig
Pr: Tammy Edwards
Pr: Sean Foley
Pr: Ken Green
**Pr:* Thomas M Hoenig
Pr: Melissa Jackson
Pr: Nathan Kauffman
Pr: Garth Larry
Pr: Tom Lombardo
Pr: Renu Mehra
Pr: Erika Ramirez
Pr: Tom Weber
Pr: James Wilkinson
Pr: Jonathan Willis
**COO:* Kelly J Dubbert
Ex VP: Veronica M Sellers

D-U-N-S 00-622-1048
FEDERAL RESERVE BANK OF MINNEAPOLIS
FEDERAL RESERVE SYSTEM, THE
(*Suby of* FEDERAL RESERVE SYSTEM) ★
90 Hennepin Ave, Minneapolis, MN 55401-1804
Tel (612) 204-5000 *Founded/Ownrshp* 1913
Sales NA *EMP* 1,212
Accts Deloitte & Touche Llp Minnea
SIC 6011 Federal reserve branches
CEO: Narayana Kocherlakota
**Ch Bd:* David A Koch
**Pr:* Gary Stern
**Ch:* Mary K Brainerd
Bd of Dir: Samuel Gane
**Ex VP:* Karen L Grandstand
**Sr VP:* Scott Dake
VP: Duane A Carter
VP: Barbara Coyle
VP: Creighton Frichek
VP: Michael Garrett
VP: Caryl Hayward
VP: Mike Johnson
VP: Frederick Miller
VP: Marie Munson
VP: Sam Schulhofer-Wohl
**VP:* Colleen K Strand
VP: Sharon Sylvester
VP: Sam Wohl
Dir Risk M: Scott Larson

D-U-N-S 00-167-3995
FEDERAL RESERVE BANK OF NEW YORK
(*Suby of* FEDERAL RESERVE SYSTEM) ★
33 Liberty St, New York, NY 10045-0001
Tel (212) 720-6130 *Founded/Ownrshp* 1913
Sales NA *EMP* 4,032
Accts Deloitte & Touche Llp New Yo
SIC 6011 Federal reserve banks
V Ch: William C Dudley
Ch Bd: Denis Hughes
V Ch: William C Dudley
Pr: Idanna Appio
Pr: Marilyn Arbuthnott
Pr: Danielle Levitt
Pr: Karen Lynch
Pr: Craig Mazur
Pr: Jacqueline McCormack
Pr: Scott Nesson
Pr: Sean Omalley
Pr: Janine Tramontana
Ofcr: Susan Chase
Ofcr: Hunter Clark
Ex VP: Lee Alexander
Ex VP: Thomas C Baxter Jr
Ex VP: Terrence J Checki
Ex VP: William T Christie
Ex VP: Suzanne Cutler
Ex VP: Russell Goldammer
Ex VP: Krishna Guha
Board of Directors: Sanford I Weill, Jill M Considine, Kathryn Wylde, Ann M Fudge, Richard S Fuld Jr, George W Hamlin IV, Gerald M Levin, Peter G Peterson, Denise Scott, Albert J Simone, Jerry I Speyer

D-U-N-S 00-173-5927
FEDERAL RESERVE BANK OF PHILADELPHIA (INC) (PA)
(*Suby of* FEDERAL RESERVE SYSTEM) ★
100 N Independence Mall W, Philadelphia, PA 19106-1574
Tel (215) 574-6000 *Founded/Ownrshp* 1914
Sales NA *EMP* 1,100^E
Accts Deloitte & Touche Llp Philad
SIC 6011 Federal reserve banks
Pr: Patrick T Harker
Pr: Brian Calderwood
Pr: Jennifer Cardy
Pr: Kori Connelly
Pr: Maryann Connelly
COO: Blake Prichard
**CFO:* Michael J Angelakis
**Ch:* James E Nevels
Ex VP: William Stone
VP: John Ackley
VP: John Bell
VP: Gregory Fanelli
VP: Mary Hood
VP: Alice J Menzano
VP: Blake Prichar
VP: Jeanne Rentezelas
VP: Herbert Taylor
VP: Jim Welch
Board of Directors: Michael F Camardo, Keith S Campbell, Ted T Cecala, Aaron L Groff Jr, William F Hecht, David R Hunsicker, Garry Maddox, Jeremy Nowak, Charles P Pizzi

D-U-N-S 06-237-3840
FEDERAL RESERVE BANK OF RICHMOND (VA)
(*Suby of* FEDERAL RESERVE SYSTEM) ★
701 E Byrd St Fl 2, Richmond, VA 23219-6105
Tel (804) 697-8000 *Founded/Ownrshp* 1914
Sales NA *EMP* 2,500
SIC 6029 Commercial banks
Pr: Jeffrey M Lacker
Pr: Keith Malatesta
Pr: Page Marchetti
Pr: Johnnie Moore
Pr: Susan Moore
**COO:* Janice Clatterbuck
**COO:* Roland Costa
**COO:* Mark Mullinix
COO: Mark L Mullinix
CFO: Michael L Wilder
**Sr VP:* Kartik Athreya
**Sr VP:* Becky Bareford
**Sr VP:* Dave Beck
**Sr VP:* Jennifer Burns
Sr VP: Jennifer J Burns
Sr VP: Jeff Crow
**Sr VP:* Michelle Gluck
**Sr VP:* Matthew Martin
**Sr VP:* Michael Stough
VP: R Ahern
VP: Valerie Freund

D-U-N-S 00-922-6978 IMP/EXP
FEDERAL RESERVE BANK OF SAN FRANCISCO
BOARD OF GOVS OF THE FED RESRV
(*Suby of* FEDERAL RESERVE SYSTEM) ★
101 Market St, San Francisco, CA 94105-1530
Tel (415) 974-2000 *Founded/Ownrshp* 1913
Sales NA *EMP* 2,466
SIC 6011 Federal reserve banks
Pr: John C Williams
**Ch Bd:* Patricia E Yarrington
COO: John F Moore
Ch: Bradley J Wiskirchen
Sr Cor Off: Ching Lee
Sr Cor Off: Candice Mann
Sr VP: Teresa M Curran
Sr VP: Mark A Gould
Sr VP: Stephen M Hoffman
Sr VP: Stephen Hoffman
VP: Bonnie R Allen
VP: Tracy Basinger
VP: Clifford Croxall
VP: Tom Cunningham
VP: Lee C Dwyer
VP: John Fernald
VP: Beverley-Ann Hawkins
VP: Richard B Hornsby
VP: Michael E Johnson
VP: Terry Schwakopf
VP: David Tresmontan
Board of Directors: Joseph C Berenato, Arnold T Grisham, Betsy Lawer, John C Molina, David I Rainer, Douglas W Shorenstein, Nicole Taylor

D-U-N-S 00-632-6359
FEDERAL RESERVE BANK OF ST LOUIS
FEDERAL RESERVE SYSTEM, THE
(*Suby of* FEDERAL RESERVE SYSTEM) ★
1421 Dr Martin Luther, Saint Louis, MO 63106-3716
Tel (314) 444-8444 *Founded/Ownrshp* 1913
Sales NA *EMP* 1,215
Accts Deloitte & Touche Llp St Lou
SIC 6011 Federal reserve banks
Pr: James B Bullard
Pr: Scott Smith
**COO:* David Sapenaro
Ofcr: Terri A Aly

Ofcr: Patricia Goessling
Ofcr: Debra Johnson
Ofcr: Alex Monge
Sr VP: Joan P Cronin
VP: Richard Anderson
VP: Karl Ashman
VP: Fontaine Chapman
VP: Roy Hendin
VP: Mary Karr
VP: Robert Schenk
VP: Matt Torbett
VP: Scott M Trilling
Board of Directors: Joseph E Gliessner Jr, Bert Greenwalt, Gayle W Jackson, Thomas H Jacobsen, Robert L Johnson, Charles W Mueller, Bradley W Small

FEDERAL RESERVE SYSTEM, THE
See BOARD OF GOVERNORS OF FEDERAL RESERVE SYSTEM

FEDERAL RESERVE SYSTEM, THE
See FEDERAL RESERVE BANK OF MINNEAPOLIS

FEDERAL RESERVE SYSTEM, THE
See FEDERAL RESERVE BANK OF ST LOUIS

D-U-N-S 04-525-6666 IMP/EXP
▲ FEDERAL SIGNAL CORP
1415 W 22nd St Ste 1100, Oak Brook, IL 60523-2004
Tel (630) 954-2000 *Founded/Ownrshp* 1901
Sales 768.0MM *EMP* 2,200
Tkr Sym FSS *Exch* NYS
SIC 3711 3647 3669 3559 3544 3545 Motor vehicles & car bodies; Fire department vehicles (motor vehicles), assembly of; Chassis, motor vehicle; Ambulances (motor vehicles), assembly of; Motor vehicle lighting equipment; Dome lights, automotive; Flasher lights, automotive; Sirens, electric: vehicle, marine, industrial & air raid; Parking facility equipment & supplies; Special dies & tools; Die sets for metal stamping (presses); Punches, forming & stamping; Cutting tools for machine tools
Pr: Jennifer L Sherman
Ch Bd: Dennis J Martin
CFO: Brian S Cooper
Sr VP: Samuel E Miceli
VP: Daniel A Dupre
VP: Tony Fuller
VP: Ian A Hudson
Rgnl Mgr: Kevin Bruszewski
Opers Mgr: Earl Begeman
Opers Mgr: Peter Sniadowski
Sls Dir: Dan Federico
Board of Directors: James E Goodwin, Paul W Jones, Bonnie C Lind, Richard R Mudge, William F Owens, Brenda L Reichelderfer, John L Workman

D-U-N-S 00-798-2994 IMP
FEDERAL WAREHOUSE CO (IL)
FEDERAL COMPANIES
200 National St, East Peoria, IL 61611-2030
Tel (309) 694-4500 *Founded/Ownrshp* 1915, 2009
Sales 99.7MM^E *EMP* 350
SIC 4225 4213 4212 General warehousing; Household goods transport; Delivery service, vehicular
Pr: William T Cirone
VP: Jeff Bogdan
VP: Jeffrey R Bogdan
VP: Rick Dokey
VP: Kyle Gordon
Prin: Randall L Schrock
Genl Mgr: James McNeely

FEDERAL WAY PUBLIC SCHL ECEAP
See FEDERAL WAY PUBLIC SCHOOLS

D-U-N-S 09-782-2407
FEDERAL WAY PUBLIC SCHOOLS
FEDERAL WAY PUBLIC SCHL ECEAP
33330 8th Ave S, Federal Way, WA 98003-6325
Tel (253) 830-6246 *Founded/Ownrshp* 1929
Sales 273.9MM *EMP* 2,309
Accts Troy Kelley Olympia Wa
SIC 8211 Public elementary & secondary schools; Public senior high school
Dir Sec: Paul Vang
Off Mgr: Kisha Goings
Off Mgr: Jodi Klettke
Off Mgr: Cathy Parisi
Off Mgr: Sara Peraza
Off Mgr: Christine Young
Pr Dir: Kassie Swenson
Teacher Pr: Vince Blauser
Teacher Pr: Dan Dizon
Teacher Pr: Marion Leech
Psych: Anna Bush

D-U-N-S 82-605-0119 IMP
■ FEDERAL-MOGUL CORP
FEDERAL MOGUL
(*Suby of* FEDERAL-MOGUL HOLDINGS CORP) ★
27300 W 11 Mile Rd, Southfield, MI 48034-6147
Tel (248) 354-7700 *Founded/Ownrshp* 2014
Sales 6.7MMM^E *EMP* 44,275
SIC 3559 3462 3812 3674 3694 Degreasing machines, automotive & industrial; Automotive & internal combustion engine forgings; Acceleration indicators & systems components, aerospace; Computer logic modules; Automotive electrical equipment
CEO: Daniel A Ninivaggi
CEO: Rainer Jueckstock
CFO: Jerome Rouquet
CFO: Rajesh Shah
Co-CEO: Michael Broderick
Sr VP: G Rard Chochoy
Sr VP: Ren L Dalleur
Sr VP: Horst Fischer
Sr VP: Richard Llope
Sr VP: Janice Maiden
Sr VP: Shaun Merry
Sr VP: Bernhard Motel
Sr VP: Scott Pepin
Sr VP: Laura Soave
VP: Mark Bradbury
VP: Ken Burns
VP: Neil Carr
VP: Robert F Egan
VP: Kathleen Johnson
VP: Eric McAlexander
VP: Lori Pitler

D-U-N-S 92-645-4513 IMP
■ FEDERAL-MOGUL FAP INC
(*Suby of* FEDERAL MOGUL) ★
1 Grizzly Ln, Smithville, TN 37166-2810
Tel (615) 597-6700 *Founded/Ownrshp* 2007
Sales 128.5MM^E *EMP* 600^E
SIC 3714 Motor vehicle parts & accessories
Pr: Richard Newson
Board of Directors: Mike Campbell, Dean Campeotto

D-U-N-S 07-939-2936
■ FEDERAL-MOGUL HOLDINGS CORP
(*Suby of* ICAHN) ★
27300 W 11 Mile Rd, Southfield, MI 48034-6147
Tel (248) 354-7700 *Founded/Ownrshp* 1899
Sales 7.4MMM *EMP* 53,700^E
Tkr Sym FDML *Exch* NGS
SIC 3462 3559 3694 3812 3674 3714 Automotive & internal combustion engine forgings; Railroad, construction & mining forgings; Degreasing machines, automotive & industrial; Automotive electrical equipment; Acceleration indicators & systems components, aerospace; Computer logic modules; Motor vehicle parts & accessories
Co-CEO: Rainer Jueckstock
**Ch Bd:* Daniel A Ninivaggi
CFO: Jerome Rouquet
Sr VP: Scott Pepin
Board of Directors: Sung Whan Cho, Thomas W Elward, George Feldenkreis, J Micheal Laisure, Courtney Mather, Michael Nevin, Louis J Pastor, Neil S Subin

D-U-N-S 00-601-5192 IMP
■ FEDERAL-MOGUL PISTON RINGS INC
(*Suby of* FEDERAL MOGUL) ★
26555 Northwestern Hwy, Southfield, MI 48033-2199
Tel (248) 354-7700 *Founded/Ownrshp* 2007
Sales 273.4MM^E *EMP* 1,200
SIC 3592 3053 3369 Pistons & piston rings; Gaskets & sealing devices; Gaskets, all materials; Nonferrous foundries
Pr: David Krohn
**VP:* Dante T Pletcher
Sfty Mgr: Daniel Brumbaugh
Sfty Mgr: Rachel Layman
Sfty Mgr: Joshua Smith

D-U-N-S 00-626-5326 IMP
■ FEDERAL-MOGUL PRODUCTS INC (MO)
(*Suby of* FEDERAL MOGUL) ★
26555 Northwestern Hwy, Southfield, MI 48033-2199
Tel (248) 354-7700 *Founded/Ownrshp* 1919, 2007
Sales 172.3MM^E *EMP* 3,000
SIC 3714 Motor vehicle parts & accessories; Ball joints, motor vehicle; Tie rods, motor vehicle; Universal joints, motor vehicle
Pr: David A Bozynski

D-U-N-S 12-090-1041
FEDERATED INDIANS OF GRATON RANCHERIA
GRATON RESORT & CASINO
6400 Redwood Dr Ste 300, Rohnert Park, CA 94928-2341
Tel (619) 917-9566 *Founded/Ownrshp* 1992
Sales NA *EMP* 1,700^E
SIC 9131 Indian reservation
Ch: Greg Sarris
**V Ch:* Lorelle Ross
CFO: William Lancaster
**Treas:* Gene Buvelot
IT Man: Linda Simenak
Mktg Dir: Mark Ward

FEDERATED INSURANCE COMPANIES
See FEDERATED MUTUAL INSURANCE CO

FEDERATED INSURANCE COMPANIES
See FEDERATED LIFE INSURANCE CO

D-U-N-S 04-819-8188
▲ FEDERATED INVESTORS INC
1001 Liberty Ave Ste 2100, Pittsburgh, PA 15222-3779
Tel (412) 288-1900 *Founded/Ownrshp* 1955
Sales 926.6MM *EMP* 1,443^E
Tkr Sym FII *Exch* NYS
SIC 6282 6722 Investment advisory service; Management investment, open-end
Pr: J Christopher Donahue
Pr: Ken Baber
Pr: Gordon J Ceresino
Pr: Jeff Langer
Pr: Eileen K Mallin
Pr: Marvin McNair
Pr: Paul A Uhlman
CFO: Thomas R Donahue
Chf Cred: Stephen Van Meter
Ex VP: Eugene F Maloney
VP: Todd Abraham
VP: Bryan Burke
VP: Jacqueline Chandler
VP: David Cook
VP: Julie Cummings
VP: Peter Eisenbrandt
VP: Don Ellenberger
VP: John B Fisher
VP: John Gentry
VP: Dayna Haferkamp
VP: Scott Holick
Board of Directors: Joseph C Bartolacci, Michael J Farrell, Marie Milie Jones, David M Kelly

D-U-N-S 95-642-9401
■ FEDERATED INVESTORS SERVICES CORP
(*Suby of* FEDERATED INVESTORS INC) ★
1001 Liberty Ave Ste 2100, Pittsburgh, PA 15222-3779
Tel (412) 288-1900 *Founded/Ownrshp* 1996
Sales 78.6MM^E *EMP* 1,200
SIC 6722 6282 Management investment, open-end; Investment advice
CEO: Thomas R Donahue
**Pr:* Arthur Cherry
**VP:* Denis McAuley III
Sftwr Eng: J Raborn

D-U-N-S 07-134-1283
FEDERATED LIFE INSURANCE CO
FEDERATED INSURANCE COMPANIES
(*Suby of* FEDERATED INSURANCE COMPANIES) ★
121 E Park Sq, Owatonna, MN 55060-3046
Tel (507) 455-5200 *Founded/Ownrshp* 1958
Sales NA *EMP* 2,270
SIC 6311 Life insurance carriers
Pr: Jeffrey Fetters
**Ex VP:* Paul Droher
**Ex VP:* Mark D Scharmer
**VP:* David Broin

D-U-N-S 00-696-2872
FEDERATED MUTUAL INSURANCE CO
FEDERATED INSURANCE COMPANIES
121 E Park Sq, Owatonna, MN 55060-3046
Tel (507) 455-5200 *Founded/Ownrshp* 1904
Sales NA *EMP* 2,270^E
SIC 6331 6321 6311 Fire, marine & casualty insurance: mutual; Accident associations, mutual; Life insurance carriers
Pr: Jeffrey Fetters
Ofcr: Cathy Guimond
**Ex VP:* Mark D Scharmer
Sr VP: Gregory Stroik
VP: Tom Berg
**VP:* David Broin
VP: David Bucher
VP: Patrick Cooper
VP: Bradley Hanson
VP: Daniel Horecka
VP: Doyle Johnson
VP: Michael Keller
VP: Michael Kerr
VP: Amy Knutson
VP: Jeff Kramer
VP: Bridget Lawler
VP: James Leighty
VP: Theodore D Leon
VP: Harlan Moret
VP: David Ramsey
VP: Bob Rinaldi

D-U-N-S 03-584-7446 IMP
▲ FEDERATED NATIONAL HOLDING CO
14050 Nw 14th St Ste 180, Sunrise, FL 33323-2851
Tel (954) 581-9993 *Founded/Ownrshp* 1991
Sales NA *EMP* 297
Tkr Sym FNHC *Exch* NGM
SIC 6331 6411 Fire, marine & casualty insurance; Automobile insurance; Property damage insurance; Insurance agents, brokers & service; Property & casualty insurance agent; Insurance agents & brokers
Pr: Michael H Braun
**Ch Bd:* Bruce F Simberg
CFO: Erick A Fernandez
Sls Mgr: Rebecca Doetsch
Board of Directors: Carl Dorf, Jenifer G Kimbrough, Thomas A Rogers, William G Stewart, Richard W Wilcox Jr

D-U-N-S 05-997-9211
FEDERATED RURAL ELECTRIC INSURANCE EXCHANGE
11875 W 85th St, Lenexa, KS 66214-1519
Tel (913) 541-0150 *Founded/Ownrshp* 1957
Sales NA *EMP* 85
Accts Ernst & Young Kcmo
SIC 6331 Property damage insurance; Fire, marine & casualty insurance & carriers
Pr: Philip Irwin
**CFO:* Kelly Klug
**VP:* Michael Bird
**VP:* Richard Burns
**VP:* Chad Ogren
**VP:* Susan Olander
**VP:* William West
Mktg Mgr: Rich Burns

D-U-N-S 15-758-5050
FEDERATED SERVICE INSURANCE CO
(*Suby of* FEDERATED INSURANCE COMPANIES) ★
121 E Park Sq, Owatonna, MN 55060-3046
Tel (507) 455-5200 *Founded/Ownrshp* 1975
Sales NA *EMP* 2,270
SIC 6331 Fire, marine & casualty insurance
Pr: Jeffrey Fetters
CFO: Gregory Stroik
**Ex VP:* Paul F Droher
Ex VP: Paul F Dr Her
**Ex VP:* Mark D Scharmer
Ex VP: Mark Scharmer
**VP:* David Broin
VP: John H Thompson
VP: James A Thon
Prgrm Mgr: Scott Peterson
Dir IT: Jill Mattone

D-U-N-S 04-007-4502
FEDERATION EMPLOYMENT AND GUIDANCE SERVICE INC (NY)
FEGS
445 Oak St, Copiague, NY 11726-3111
Tel (212) 366-8040 *Founded/Ownrshp* 1934
Sales 185.0MM^E *EMP* 845
SIC 8399 Health systems agency
Ch: Joseph Stein Jr
**Pr:* Stuart Oltchick
**CEO:* Gail A Magaliff
**CFO:* Leonard Silver
**Treas:* Barry Gosin
**Ex VP:* Ira Machowsky
Sr VP: Lee Rambeau
Off Mgr: Kim Bjorklund
IT Man: Howard Chesloff

FEDEX
See FEDERAL EXPRESS CORP

D-U-N-S 00-314-1970
▲ FEDEX CORP
942 Shady Grove Rd S, Memphis, TN 38120-4117
Tel (901) 818-7500 *Founded/Ownrshp* 1971
Sales 50.3MMM *EMP* 166,000
Tkr Sym FDX *Exch* NYS
SIC 4513 4512 4213 4215 7334 Package delivery, private air; Letter delivery, private air; Parcel delivery, private air; Air cargo carrier, scheduled; Trucking, except local; Less-than-truckload (LTL) transport; Package delivery, vehicular; Parcel delivery, vehicular; Photocopying & duplicating services
Ch Bd: Frederick W Smith
Pr: David J Bronczek
Pr: Michael L Ducker
Pr: Henry J Maier
CFO: Alan B Graf Jr
Ex VP: Robert B Carter
Ex VP: Jim French
Ex VP: T Michael Glenn
Ex VP: Christine P Richards
VP: Dale Chrystie
VP: Stephanie Cohen
VP: Mark J Colombo
VP: Glen Corbin
VP: Kristi Emmons
VP: Betty Hale
VP: Julie Henry
VP: Robert E Holcombe
VP: Duuna Kee
VP: Steve Longoria
VP: Sandra V McCurdy
VP: Mariwilda Montalvo
Board of Directors: Susan C Schwab, James L Barksdale, David P Steiner, John A Edwardson, Paul S Walsh, Marvin R Ellison, John C Inglis, Kimberly A Jabal, Shirley Ann Jackson, Gary W Loveman, R Brad Martin, Joshua Cooper Ramo

D-U-N-S 05-582-0518
■ FEDEX CUSTOM CRITICAL INC
(*Suby of* FEDEX CORP) ★
1475 Boettler Rd, Uniontown, OH 44685-9584
Tel (234) 310-4090 *Founded/Ownrshp* 1998
Sales 120.3MM^E *EMP* 600
SIC 4213 Trucking, except local
Ch Bd: Alan B Graf Jr
**CEO:* Virginia Albanese
VP: Christopher N O'Neil
VP: Jim Snider
Rgnl Mgr: Claude Colombo
IT Man: Daniel Lori
Sales Exec: Vince Bradford
Manager: Jeff Cross
Manager: Vince Fiorenza
Manager: Charlie Moss
Snr Mgr: Ramona Hood

D-U-N-S 84-127-0536
■ FEDEX FREIGHT CORP
(*Suby of* FEDEX CORP) ★
1715 Aaron Brenner Dr, Memphis, TN 38120-1442
Tel (901) 434-3100 *Founded/Ownrshp* 2000
Sales 2.5MMM^E *EMP* 26,828
SIC 4213 7513 Less-than-truckload (LTL) transport; Truck leasing, without drivers
Ch: Frederick Smith
**Pr:* William J Logue
**CFO:* Don Brown
Ch: Kenneth Masterson
**Sr VP:* Robert H Rhea
Dir IT: Fred Klemashevich
VP Sls: Patrick Finan
S&M/VP: Charles B Malone
Counsel: Kevin M Derbyshire

D-U-N-S 01-641-4120
■ FEDEX FREIGHT INC
(*Suby of* FEDEX FREIGHT CORP) ★
2200 Forward Dr, Harrison, AR 72601-2234
Tel (870) 741-9000 *Founded/Ownrshp* 2001
Sales 1.2MMM^E *EMP* 13,200
SIC 4213 Less-than-truckload (LTL) transport
Pr: William J Logue
COO: Pat Reed
COO: Pat Reede
CFO: Frank Conner
**Treas:* Sherri R Swindle
VP: Dennis Beal
**VP:* Donald C Brown
**VP:* Randy Gardner
VP: Randy W Gardner
VP: Dennis E Michael
VP: Steven B Moore
**VP:* Greg Satterfield
VP: Jeffrey J Sobecki
Exec: Debbie Peerce
Board of Directors: Melanie Kings

D-U-N-S 05-160-6135 IMP/EXP
FEDEX FREIGHT WEST INC
6411 Guadalupe Mines Rd, San Jose, CA 95120-5000
Tel (775) 356-7600 *Founded/Ownrshp* 1998
Sales 91.1MM^E *EMP* 4,500
SIC 4213 4731 4212

D-U-N-S 11-913-3494 IMP
■ FEDEX GROUND PACKAGE SYSTEM INC
(*Suby of* FEDEX CORP) ★
1000 Fed Ex Dr, Coraopolis, PA 15108-9373
Tel (412) 269-1000 *Founded/Ownrshp* 1985
Sales 2.9MMM^E *EMP* 10,000
SIC 4213 Contract haulers
CEO: Henry J Maier
**Pr:* Paul Esposito
**Pr:* David Rebholz
COO: Michael P Mannion
Ex VP: Don Colleran
**Ex VP:* Bram B Johnson
Ex VP: Rajesh Subramaniam
Sr VP: Leland E Holly III
**Sr VP:* Gretchen G Smarto
VP: Jim Bowman
VP: Shannon Brown
VP: Patrick Fitzgerald
VP: Gretchen Smarto
**VP:* Tretzhen Smarto
VP: Anthony F Spalvieri

D-U-N-S 16-115-2996
■ FEDEX OFFICE AND PRINT SERVICES INC
(*Suby of* FEDEX CORP) ★
7900 Legacy Dr, Plano, TX 75024-4089
Tel (214) 550-7000 *Founded/Ownrshp* 2004

Sales 197.9MM^E *EMP* 60
SIC 7334 Photocopying & duplicating services
Pr: Brandon Knowles
Pr: Michael H Cohn
Ex VP: Allen Dickason
**Sr VP:* Leslie M Benners
Sr VP: Tom Carroll
Sr VP: John McDonald
Sr VP: Laurie Zeitlin
VP: Tracy Brightman
VP: Robert Cooper
VP: Michael Lenz
VP: Lynda Robey
VP: Scott Struminger
Exec: Rhea Caulk
Exec: Charles Smith
Dir Soc: Glenda Slovacek

D-U-N-S 60-936-0342 IMP
■ FEDEX SUPPLY CHAIN SERVICES INC
(*Suby of* FEDEX CORP) ★
5455 Darrow Rd, Hudson, OH 44236-4082
Tel (800) 588-3020 *Founded/Ownrshp* 1998
Sales 98.4MM^E *EMP* 1,800
SIC 8742 4213 8741 4731

D-U-N-S 13-165-7681
■ FEDEX TRADE NETWORKS INC
(*Suby of* FEDEX CORP) ★
6075 Poplar Ave Ste 300, Memphis, TN 38119-1400
Tel (901) 684-4800 *Founded/Ownrshp* 2000
Sales 727.2MM^E *EMP* 3,500
SIC 4731 Customhouse brokers
Pr: James R Muhs
COO: Udo Lange

D-U-N-S 00-213-0219 IMP/EXP
■ FEDEX TRADE NETWORKS TRANSPORT & BROKERAGE INC (NY)
(*Suby of* FEDEX TRADE NETWORKS INC) ★
128 Dearborn St, Buffalo, NY 14207-3122
Tel (716) 879-1300 *Founded/Ownrshp* 1913, 2000
Sales 724.5MM^E *EMP* 3,500
SIC 4731 Customhouse brokers; Customs clearance of freight; Freight forwarding
CEO: Jack Muhs
CFO: Thomas L Holland
CFO: Michelle N Miller
Sr VP: Penelope W Register
VP: Ronald W Berger
VP: David A Henry

FEDLOAN SERVICING
See PENNSYLVANIA HIGHER EDUCATION ASSISTANCE AGENCY

D-U-N-S 00-697-2822 IMP
FEDWAY ASSOCIATES INC (GA)
505 Martinsville Rd Fl 1, Basking Ridge, NJ 07920-4301
Tel (973) 624-6444 *Founded/Ownrshp* 1934, 1978
Sales 289.6MM^E *EMP* 500
SIC 5182 Wine; Liquor
Pr: Richard B Leventhal
**CFO:* Michael Dokachev
Sls Mgr: Gerry Piserchia

D-U-N-S 07-426-8897 IMP/EXP
FEED CHILDREN INC
333 N Meridian Ave, Oklahoma City, OK 73107-6507
Tel (800) 627-4556 *Founded/Ownrshp* 1964
Sales 453.8MM *EMP* 160^E
Accts Hogantaylor Llp Oklahoma City
SIC 8661 8699 4832 Non-church religious organizations; Charitable organization; Radio broadcasting stations
CEO: Vic Diffee
Dir Vol: Kevin Richardson
**Pr:* Travis Arnold
**CEO:* Kevin Hagan
**Ex VP:* Frances Jones
VP: Gary Sloan
VP: Gary Young
Software D: Barrett Cid
Mktg Mgr: Diane Harger
Pgrm Dir: Monica Linville
Board of Directors: Rick England, Leo B Fundaro Jr, Dan Mugg, Linda Schluchter, George Stevens

D-U-N-S 14-359-8527
FEEDCO
521 Wells St, Belgrade, MN 56312-4559
Tel (320) 254-8294 *Founded/Ownrshp* 2004
Sales 85.0MM *EMP* 2
SIC 5999 Feed & farm supply
Owner: Kevin Weller

D-U-N-S 03-954-6494
FEEDING AMERICA
35 E Wacker Dr Ste 2000, Chicago, IL 60601-2200
Tel (312) 263-2303 *Founded/Ownrshp* 1988
Sales 2.4MMM *EMP* 125
SIC 8322

FEESERS FOOD DISTRIBUTORS
See FEESERS INC

D-U-N-S 01-418-0350
FEESERS INC
FEESERS FOOD DISTRIBUTORS
5561 Grayson Rd, Harrisburg, PA 17111-3327
Tel (717) 248-9658 *Founded/Ownrshp* 1952
Sales 221.8MM^E *EMP* 300
SIC 5141 Groceries, general line
Pr: Lester S Miller Jr
**Sec:* John M Tighe
**VP:* Terry L Bowman
**VP:* Terry L Kaufman
VP: Terry Kaufman
VP: Victor Smith
Dir IT: Kerry Shuey
Sls&Mrk Ex: Jennifer Ciotola

FEGS
See FEDERATION EMPLOYMENT AND GUIDANCE SERVICE INC

D-U-N-S 09-914-1541
■ FEI CO
(*Suby of* THERMO FISHER SCIENTIFIC INC) ★
5350 Ne Dawson Creek Dr, Hillsboro, OR 97124-5793
Tel (503) 726-7500 *Founded/Ownrshp* 2016
Sales 930.1MM *EMP* 3,060^E
SIC 3826 Analytical instruments; Specific ion measuring instruments; Microscopes, electron & proton
Ch Bd: Thomas F Kelly
**Pr:* Don R Kania
COO: Neal Landreville
**CFO:* Anthony L Trunzo
Ex VP: Tony Trunzo
**Sr VP:* Bradley J Thies
VP: Jens Greiser
VP: Jiri Ocadlik
VP: Michael R Scheinfein
VP: Baertlein Tom
Area Mgr: L Mendoza

D-U-N-S 10-885-8085
■ FEI CO MEPD PEABODY
(*Suby of* FEI CO) ★
1 Corporation Way Ste 2, Peabody, MA 01960-7925
Tel (978) 538-6700 *Founded/Ownrshp* 1999
Sales 427.2MM *EMP* 232
SIC 3559 3827 3699 Semiconductor manufacturing machinery; Optical instruments & lenses; Electrical equipment & supplies
Pr: Vahe Sarkissian
**Sr VP:* John A Doherty
Netwrk Eng: Chris Schlichten

D-U-N-S 96-676-2630
FEINBERG GRADUATE SCHOOL OF WEIZMANN INSTITUTE OF SCIENCE
633 3rd Ave Fl 20, New York, NY 10017-8156
Tel (212) 895-7900 *Founded/Ownrshp* 2011
Sales NA *EMP* 2
SIC 6411 Insurance agents, brokers & service

D-U-N-S 04-197-0328 IMP
FEINTOOL US OPERATIONS INC
(*Suby of* FEINTOOL TECHNOLOGIE AG)
11280 Cornell Park Dr, Blue Ash, OH 45242-1888
Tel (513) 247-0110 *Founded/Ownrshp* 1978
Sales 96.0MM^E *EMP* 300
SIC 3469 3465 Metal stampings; Automotive stampings
CEO: Richard Surico
**Pr:* Ralph E Hardt
VP: Rick Bachman
**Prin:* Christoph Trachsler
IT Man: Stephan Prebeck

D-U-N-S 04-555-3138 IMP
FELCHAR MANUFACTURING CORP
NORWICH MANUFACTURING DIVISION
(*Suby of* SHOP VAC CORP) ★
196 Corporate Dr, Binghamton, NY 13904-3295
Tel (607) 723-3106 *Founded/Ownrshp* 1962
Sales 222.8MM^E *EMP* 1,600
SIC 3678 3089 3621 Electronic connectors; Injection molding of plastics; Motors & generators
Pr: Jonathan Miller
**VP:* Vince Bungo
VP: Steve Cole
Plnt Mgr: Mike Carr
Plnt Mgr: Ron Sternberg

D-U-N-S 79-577-3360
FELCOR LODGING LIMITED PARTNERSHIP
(*Suby of* FELCOR LODGING TRUST INC) ★
545 E John Carpenter Fwy # 1300, Irving, TX 75062-8188
Tel (972) 444-4900 *Founded/Ownrshp* 1994
Sales 886.2MM *EMP* 61
Accts Pricewaterhousecoopers Llp Da
SIC 7011 Hotels & motels
Pr: Richard A Smith
Genl Pt: Felcor Lodging Trust Incorpora
CFO: Michael C Hughes
VP: Bianca Green

D-U-N-S 84-923-8886
FELCOR LODGING TRUST INC
545 E John Carpenter Fwy # 1300, Irving, TX 75062-8188
Tel (972) 444-4900 *Founded/Ownrshp* 1994
Sales 886.2MM *EMP* 63
SIC 6798 Real estate investment trusts
Pr: Troy A Pentecost
**Ch Bd:* Thomas J Corcoran Jr
CFO: Michael C Hughes
Ex VP: Thomas C Hendrick
Ex VP: Jonathan H Yellen
VP: Melissa Kendrick
VP: Jan Kuehnemann
Board of Directors: Glenn A Carlin, Robert F Cotter, Patricia L Gibson, Dana Hamilton, Christopher J Hartung, Charles A Ledsinger Jr, Robert H Lutz Jr, Mark D Rozells

D-U-N-S 15-770-0980 IMP
FELD ENTERTAINMENT INC
RINGLING BRS-BRNUM BLEY CIRCUS
800 Feld Way, Palmetto, FL 34221-8514
Tel (941) 721-1200 *Founded/Ownrshp* 1982
Sales 327.3MM^E *EMP* 3,000
SIC 7999 7929 5945 Circus company; Entertainers & entertainment groups; Children's toys & games, except dolls
Ch Bd: Kenneth J Feld
**CFO:* Michael Ruch
**Ex VP:* Alana Feld
**Sr VP:* Rob Desatnick
VP: Vincent Foderingham
VP: Sam Gomez
Dir Surg: Russel Ray
Web Dev: Orin Walker
Art Dir: Ryan Bauer

D-U-N-S 00-222-9599
FELDMEIER EQUIPMENT INC (NY)
6800 Townline Rd, Syracuse, NY 13211-1325
Tel (315) 823-2000 *Founded/Ownrshp* 1953
Sales 90.5MM^E *EMP* 350
SIC 3443 Fabricated plate work (boiler shop)
CEO: Robert E Feldmeier
**VP:* Jean Jackson
Dir Bus: Larry Harper
Off Mgr: Jessica Brooks
Telecom Ex: Colby Clark
Software D: Tom King

D-U-N-S 04-104-6707 EXP
FELDSPAR CORP
FELDSPAR CORP POINTE CORP
(*Suby of* IMERYS USA INC) ★
100 Mansell Ct E Ste 300, Roswell, GA 30076-4860
Tel (770) 594-0660 *Founded/Ownrshp* 2007
Sales 208.2MM^E *EMP* 160
SIC 1459 1442

FELDSPAR CORP POINTE CORP
See FELDSPAR CORP

D-U-N-S 14-578-4612 IMP
FELIX SCHOELLER NORTH AMERICA INC
FELIX SCHOELLER TECHNICAL PPRS
(*Suby of* SCHOELLER BETEILIGUNGEN GMBH)
179 County Route 2a, Pulaski, NY 13142-2546
Tel (315) 298-5133 *Founded/Ownrshp* 1961
Sales 168.0MM *EMP* 110
SIC 2679 Paper products, converted
Pr: Michael Szidat
Genl Mgr: Gunter Raabe

FELIX SCHOELLER TECHNICAL PPRS
See FELIX SCHOELLER NORTH AMERICA INC

D-U-N-S 00-507-0008 IMP/EXP
FELLOWES INC
1789 Norwood Ave, Itasca, IL 60143-1059
Tel (630) 893-1600 *Founded/Ownrshp* 1917
Sales 491.5MM^E *EMP* 1,532
SIC 2522 3589 2653 3577 3572 3579

D-U-N-S 07-625-3889
FELLOWSHIP OF CHRISTIAN ATHLETES
8701 Leeds Rd, Kansas City, MO 64129-1680
Tel (816) 921-0909 *Founded/Ownrshp* 1954
Sales 109.0MM *EMP* 1,200
Accts Keller & Owens Llc Overland
SIC 8661 Religious organizations
Pr: Les Steckel
**CFO:* Fred Olson
**Ex VP:* Dan Britton
**Ex VP:* Nancy Hedrick
Exec: Judy Aimers
Exec: Jay Fowler
Ex Dir: Jim Faulk
Ex Dir: Romy Pierce
**Ex Dir:* Ken Williams
**Ex Dir:* Shane Williamson
Opers Mgr: Johanna Meza

D-U-N-S 07-996-0599
FELLOWSHIP OF CHRISTIAN ATHLETES
F C A
8701 Leeds Rd, Kansas City, MO 64129-1680
Tel (816) 921-0909 *Founded/Ownrshp* 2015
Sales 1.0MM^E *EMP* 1,100
SIC 8661 Religious instruction
CFO: Fred Olson
Ex Dir: Gary Beets

FEMA
See FEDERAL EMERGENCY MANAGEMENT AGENCY

FEMCO RADIO CONTROLS
See HUBBELL INDUSTRIAL CONTROLS INC

FENCECONNECT.COM
See FENCES4LESS INC

D-U-N-S 01-433-6627 IMP
FENCES4LESS INC
FENCECONNECT.COM
31290 Manzanita Crest Rd, Valley Center, CA 92082-5072
Tel (760) 749-2069 *Founded/Ownrshp* 1995
Sales 100.0MM *EMP* 5
SIC 8742 Retail trade consultant
Owner: Gary W Ash

D-U-N-S 14-837-7302 IMP
FENCEWORKS INC
GOLDEN STATE FENCE CO.
870 Main St, Riverside, CA 92501-1016
Tel (951) 788-5620 *Founded/Ownrshp* 1998
Sales 119.0MM^E *EMP* 700
SIC 1799 Fence construction
CEO: Jason Ostrander
**Pr:* Mel Kay
CFO: Aaron Garcia
Ofcr: Floyd N Nixon
Genl Mgr: Dawn Smith
VP Sls: Steve Anderson

D-U-N-S 13-124-1135 IMP/EXP
FENDER MUSICAL INSTRUMENTS CORP
17600 N Perimeter Dr # 100, Scottsdale, AZ 85255-5435
Tel (480) 596-7195 *Founded/Ownrshp* 1991
Sales 806.8MM^E *EMP* 3,186
SIC 3651 3931 Amplifiers: radio, public address or musical instrument; Musical instruments; Guitars & parts, electric & nonelectric
CEO: Andrew P Mooney
CFO: Jim Brennan
**CFO:* James Broenen
Sr VP: Ritchie Flieger
VP: Jason Biedimus
VP: Tom Brockman
VP: Jim Broenen
VP: Bill Cummisky
VP: Karen Diepholz
VP: Chuck Hemrich
VP: Dave Lewis
VP: Jeff Moore
VP: Justin Norvell
VP: Brad Saviello
VP: Steve Souers
VP: Ralph Thomas
VP: Paul Yandell
Board of Directors: Kerry Trainor, David Ewans, Mark Fukunaga, Scott Gilbertson, Paul Hewson, Bill Mc Glashan, Andrew Mooney, Robert Roback, Dan Rosensweig, Larry E Thomas

D-U-N-S 00-111-4867 IMP/EXP
FENIX MANUFACTURING SOLUTIONS LLC (SC)
PHELON COMPANY
2063 University Pkwy, Aiken, SC 29801-6343
Tel (803) 649-1381 *Founded/Ownrshp* 1944, 2008
Sales 127.8MM^E *EMP* 490
SIC 3694 3825 3625 3354 Engine electrical equipment; Test equipment for electronic & electrical circuits; Relays & industrial controls; Aluminum extruded products
Pr: David Mosier
**VP:* Doug Azbell
**VP:* Emil Hernandez
**VP:* Kathy Sapp
Genl Mgr: Carl Cartwright
Dir IT: Russell Summer
Plnt Mgr: C Hurst
Ql Cn Mgr: Julius Buenaventura
Ql Cn Mgr: Gary Robinson

FENNER ADVANCED SEALING TECH
See CDI ENERGY PRODUCTS INC

D-U-N-S 96-180-5905 IMP
FENNER ADVANCED SEALING TECHNOLOGIES INC
FAST
(*Suby of* HALL & HALL LIMITED)
975 Market St Ste 201a, Fort Mill, SC 29708-6531
Tel (803) 547-8434 *Founded/Ownrshp* 1996
Sales 172.8MM^E *EMP* 417
SIC 3061

D-U-N-S 87-862-9872 IMP/EXP
FENNER DUNLOP AMERICAS INC
(*Suby of* FENNER PLC)
1000 Omega Dr Ste 1400, Pittsburgh, PA 15205-5001
Tel (412) 249-0700 *Founded/Ownrshp* 2003
Sales 275.0MM^E *EMP* 530
SIC 3496 Conveyor belts
Ex Dir: Edwin Have
COO: Jim Gann
CFO: Raj Gopal
VP: Pamela Minteer
VP: Jim Panter
Genl Mgr: Carrie Busch
Board of Directors: Bill Mooney, Cassandra Pan

D-U-N-S 83-129-2383
FENWAL HOLDINGS INC
(*Suby of* FRESENIUS KABI DEUTSCHLAND GMBH)
3 Corporate Dr Ste 300, Lake Zurich, IL 60047-8930
Tel (847) 550-2300 *Founded/Ownrshp* 2012
Sales 804.1MM^E *EMP* 1,760
SIC 3069 5047 Medical & laboratory rubber sundries & related products; Medical equipment & supplies
Pr: Ron K Labrum
**CFO:* Micheal L Johnson
**Treas:* James McHale
Ofcr: Jo Anne Fasetti
Sr VP: William H Cork
Sr VP: Geoffrey D Fenton
Sr VP: Angela Goodwin
Sr VP: Dean A Gregory
Sr VP: Tony Orsini

D-U-N-S 79-451-9020 IMP
FENWAL INC
(*Suby of* FENWAL HOLDINGS INC) ★
3 Corporate Dr Ste 300, Lake Zurich, IL 60047-8930
Tel (847) 550-2300 *Founded/Ownrshp* 2007
Sales 817.9MM^E *EMP* 1,760
SIC 5047 3069 Medical equipment & supplies; Medical & laboratory rubber sundries & related products
Treas: Jim McHale
Pr: Dean A Gregory
COO: Anthony Orsini
**CFO:* Michael Johnson
**Sr VP:* William H Cork
VP Sls: Jeff Blair

FENWAL SAFETY SYSTEMS
See KIDDE TECHNOLOGIES INC

D-U-N-S 87-972-4565
FENWAY PARTNERS LLC
152 W 57th St Fl 5927, New York, NY 10019-3414
Tel (212) 698-9400 *Founded/Ownrshp* 1994
Sales 798.1MM^E *EMP* 4,388
SIC 6211 Investment firm, general brokerage
CEO: Peter Lamm
**Pr:* Richard C Dresdale
**CFO:* Walter Wiacek
VP: Bill Webb
Mng Dir: Bill Donner
**Mng Dir:* Andrea Geisser
Mng Dir: Timothy P Mayhew

D-U-N-S 07-629-6656
FENWICK & WEST LLP (CA)
801 California St, Mountain View, CA 94041-1990
Tel (650) 988-8500 *Founded/Ownrshp* 1971, 1975
Sales 106.1MM^E *EMP* 605
SIC 8111 Legal services; Patent, trademark & copyright law; Taxation law
Genl Pt: Gordon K Davidson
Pt: Michael R Blum
Pt: Darren E Donnelly
Pt: Dan Dorosin
Pt: Stephen D Gillespie
Pt: Cynthia C Hess
Pt: Andrew J Kim
Pt: Ralph M Pais
Pt: Scott Pine
Pt: Laird H Simons
Pr: Nicole Otis
Pr: Diane Tullman

D-U-N-S 00-510-3189 IMP
■ FERALLOY CORP
(*Suby of* RELIANCE STEEL & ALUMINUM CO) ★
8755 W Higgins Rd Ste 970, Chicago, IL 60631-2735
Tel (503) 286-8869 *Founded/Ownrshp* 1969
Sales 350.3MM^E *EMP* 836

SIC 5051 3471 3444 3312 Iron or steel flat products; Plating & polishing; Sheet metalwork; Blast furnaces & steel mills
Pr: Carlos Rodriguez Borjas
VP: Paul W Abernethy
**VP:* John A Hirt
VP: John Hirt
**VP:* Jack D Love
VP: Michael Messinger
Dir IT: Ken Lyttek
Plnt Mgr: Rick Henke
Snr Mgr: Paul Cusumano

FERGADIS ENTERPRISES
See PERRIN BERNARD SUPOWITZ INC

D-U-N-S 00-782-5185
FERGUSON CONSTRUCTION CO INC (OH)
400 Canal St, Sidney, OH 45365-2312
Tel (937) 498-2381 *Founded/Ownrshp* 1920, 1983
Sales 128.4MM[E] *EMP* 250
SIC 1541 1542 Industrial buildings, new construction; Commercial & office building, new construction
Pr: Martin Given
CFO: Tom Pleman
**Sec:* Thomas Pleiman
**VP:* J Michael Dant
VP: Michael J Dant
VP: Jason Stiver
Genl Mgr: Tom Snapp
VP Opers: Doug Fortkamp
Sfty Mgr: John Brown
Snr PM: Joseph O Reichert
Board of Directors: Mike Dance, Bob Getto

D-U-N-S 00-895-5171 IMP/EXP
FERGUSON ENTERPRISES INC (VA)
(*Suby of* WOLSELEY PLC)
12500 Jefferson Ave, Newport News, VA 23602-4314
Tel (757) 874-7795 *Founded/Ownrshp* 1954, 1982
Sales 13.8MMM *EMP* 23,001[E]
Accts Pricewaterhousecoopers Llp Ri
SIC 5074 5085 5075 5064 Plumbing & hydronic heating supplies; Plumbing & heating valves; Valves & fittings; Industrial tools; Air conditioning & ventilation equipment & supplies; Electrical appliances, major
Pr: Frank W Roach
COO: Kevin M Murphy
CFO: David L Keltner
VP: John Blankinship
VP: Bill Brundage
VP: Jimmy Cross
VP: Mike Grunkemeyer
VP: Scott Russell
VP: John Stegeman
VP: Douglas Strup
Brnch Mgr: Patrick Nugent
Board of Directors: Michael L Grunkemeyer, William S Hargette

D-U-N-S 07-529-3134 IMP
FERGUSON FIRE & FABRICATION INC
PACIFIC FIRE SAFETY
(*Suby of* FERGUSON ENTERPRISES INC) ★
2750 S Towne Ave, Pomona, CA 91766-6205
Tel (909) 517-3085 *Founded/Ownrshp* 1982
Sales 148.3MM[E] *EMP* 600
SIC 5074 5099 Plumbing fittings & supplies; Safety equipment & supplies; Fire extinguishers
Pr: Leo J Klien
**Pr:* Leo J Klein
**CFO:* Dave Keltner
Opers Mgr: Ted Nelson
Sales Exec: Melanie Fitzgearld

D-U-N-S 07-989-6577
FERGUSON REORGANIZED SCHOOL DISTRICT R-2
1005 Waterford Dr, Florissant, MO 63033-3649
Tel (314) 506-9000 *Founded/Ownrshp* 1951
Sales 127.6MM[E] *EMP* 2,000
SIC 8211 Public combined elementary & secondary school
**Treas:* Theresa George
Ex Dir: Doretha Pearson

FERMAN BMW
See FERMAN CHEVROLET OF TARPON SPRINGS

FERMAN CHEVROLET
See FERMAN MOTOR CAR CO INC

D-U-N-S 03-281-2547 IMP
FERMAN CHEVROLET OF TARPON SPRINGS
FERMAN BMW
43520 Us Highway 19 N, Tarpon Springs, FL 34689-6224
Tel (727) 942-4800 *Founded/Ownrshp* 1989
Sales 83.4MM[E] *EMP* 215
SIC 5511 7538 7515 7513 5521 Automobiles, new & used; General automotive repair shops; Passenger car leasing; Truck rental & leasing, no drivers; Used car dealers
CEO: James L Ferman Jr
**VP:* Preston L Farrior
**VP:* Stephen B Straske II
**VP:* Douglas M Tew

D-U-N-S 00-692-4039
FERMAN MOTOR CAR CO INC (FL)
FERMAN CHEVROLET
1306 W Kennedy Blvd, Tampa, FL 33606-1849
Tel (813) 251-2765 *Founded/Ownrshp* 1895
Sales 264.3MM[E] *EMP* 900
SIC 5511 Automobiles, new & used; Pickups, new & used
Pr: James L Ferman
Treas: Steven Straske
**VP:* Stephen B Straske
CIO: Michelle Alexander

D-U-N-S 62-639-9831
FERMI RESEARCH ALLIANCE LLC
Ms 105 Wilson & Kirk Rds, Batavia, IL 60510
Tel (630) 406-7901 *Founded/Ownrshp* 2006
Sales 373.6MM *EMP* 5[E]
Accts Lb Crowe Horwath Llp Chicago
SIC 8731 Energy research
Genl Couns: William Schmidt

D-U-N-S 13-140-8663
FERMILAB
Wilson Str And Kirk Rd, Batavia, IL 60510
Tel (630) 840-3000 *Founded/Ownrshp* 1999
Sales 98.4MM[E] *EMP* 2,000
SIC 8731 Commercial physical research
Prin: Darrell Wohlt
Software D: Qiming Lu

D-U-N-S 00-423-9034 IMP/EXP
FERNO-WASHINGTON INC (OH)
70 Weil Way, Wilmington, OH 45177-9300
Tel (877) 733-0911 *Founded/Ownrshp* 1955, 1956
Sales 90.3MM[E] *EMP* 250[E]
SIC 5047 Medical equipment & supplies
Pr: Joseph Bourgraf
**Ch Bd:* Elroy Bourgraf
VP: Brent Fairweather
VP: Gary C Hiles
VP: Christopher Way
Off Mgr: Carol Williams
Opers Mgr: Cecil Mullins
Plnt Mgr: Willard Self
Ql Cn Mgr: Bruno Tegano
Sls&Mrk Ex: Jerry D Socha
VP Sls: Ron Bellan

FERNWOOD RESORT
See BUSHKILL GROUP INC

D-U-N-S 04-766-5815 IMP
FERRAGAMO U S A INC
SALVATORE FERRAGAMO
700 Castle Rd, Secaucus, NJ 07094-1614
Tel (201) 553-6100 *Founded/Ownrshp* 1956
Sales 154.5MM[E] *EMP* 400
SIC 5139 5136 5137 5621 5632 Shoes; Men's & boys' clothing; Women's & children's clothing; Ready-to-wear apparel, women's; Apparel accessories
Pr: Massimo Ferragamo
**VP:* Frank Torrent
**Prin:* Vincent Ottomanelli
Dir IT: Sandro Biagiotti
Trfc Mgr: Patty Loua

D-U-N-S 95-650-4823
FERRANDINO & SON INC
71 Carolyn Blvd, Farmingdale, NY 11735-1527
Tel (866) 571-4609 *Founded/Ownrshp* 1993
Sales 112.1MM *EMP* 307
Accts Castellano Korenberg & Co H
SIC 1542 0781 3531 7299 Commercial & office building, new construction; Landscape services; Snow plow attachments; Handyman service
Pr: Peter J Ferrandino
**COO:* Kevin Smith
**CFO:* Michael C Rose
VP: David Magill
Dir Bus: Steve Vollrath
Area Mgr: Doug Bock
Area Mgr: Armand Bruno
Area Mgr: Gregory Connors
Area Mgr: Bob Dlouhy
Area Mgr: Bill Laura
Area Mgr: Michael Schafer

D-U-N-S 00-510-6224 IMP/EXP
FERRARA CANDY CO (IL)
1 Tower Ln Ste 2700, Oakbrook Terrace, IL 60181-4641
Tel (708) 366-0500 *Founded/Ownrshp* 1908
Sales 616.5MM[E] *EMP* 1,100
SIC 2064 Candy & other confectionery products; Chewing candy, not chewing gum; Chocolate candy, except solid chocolate; Jellybeans
CEO: Todd Siwak
Pr: James Nicketta
Pr: Thomas P Polke
Pr: Bernie Woziwodzki
COO: Michael Murray
CFO: Stephen Bowater
CFO: James Bufardi
Ch: Cynthia Hiskes
Treas: Carl Gray
Sr Cor Off: Michael Binstein
Chf Cred: Jamie Mattikow
Sr VP: Jon Levin
VP: Hans Becher
VP: Joseph Dileonardo
VP: Jason Havlin
VP: Ronnie Loveless
VP: Tim Murphy
VP: Terry Wagner
Dir: Michael Faron

D-U-N-S 95-811-9026 IMP/EXP
FERRARA FIRE APPARATUS INC
27855 James Chapel Rd N, Holden, LA 70744-5309
Tel (225) 567-7100 *Founded/Ownrshp* 1988
Sales 105.8MM[E] *EMP* 365[E]
SIC 3711 Fire department vehicles (motor vehicles), assembly of
Pr: Christopher Ferrara
**COO:* Bert McCutcheon
**CFO:* Gary Galeziewski
CFO: Benny Gardner
CFO: Benny Guardner
VP: Mark Coley
Rgnl Mgr: Shaun Hanzalik
CTO: Ronnie Gataris
CTO: Glyn Harding
IT Man: Charles Kearney
VP Mktg: Mike Doran

D-U-N-S 05-725-5267
FERRARA FIREFIGHTING EQUIPMENT INC
27855 James Chapel Rd N, Holden, LA 70744-5309
Tel (225) 567-7100 *Founded/Ownrshp* 1979
Sales 155.5MM[E] *EMP* 171
SIC 5087 Firefighting equipment
Pr: Christopher Ferrara
**COO:* Bert McCutcheon
**Sec:* Angela Ferrara
**Sr VP:* Mike Doran

D-U-N-S 07-683-0132 IMP/EXP
FERRARI NORTH AMERICA INC
(*Suby of* FERRARI SPA ESERCIZIO FABBRICHE AUTOMOBILI E CORSE)
250 Sylvan Ave, Englewood Cliffs, NJ 07632-2504
Tel (201) 816-2600 *Founded/Ownrshp* 1971
Sales 93.7MM[E] *EMP* 200
SIC 5511 5012 Automobiles, new & used; Automobiles
Ch: Furio Colombo
Pr: Vittorio C Vellano
CFO: Joseph Mercello
VP: Paul Montopoli
VP: Dave Wertheim
Comm Dir: Krista Florin
Area Mgr: Michael Borelli
Dir IT: Sandro Levati
VP Mktg: Marco Mattiacci

D-U-N-S 05-238-6281 IMP/EXP
FERRARO FOODS INC
287 S Randolphville Rd, Piscataway, NJ 08854-3806
Tel (732) 424-3400 *Founded/Ownrshp* 1957
Sales 156.4MM[E] *EMP* 175
SIC 5149 5812 Pasta & rice; Spaghetti; Pizza supplies; Eating places
Pr: Michael Giammarino
Pr: Eric Eigen
Pr: Wendy Romm
CFO: Don Barron
**VP:* Dean Barcelona
Mng Dir: Lucy Casa
Telecom Ex: Paul Carlet
Sales Exec: Chris Piacentini
VP Sls: Christopher Piacentini
Manager: David Foschini
Sales Asso: John Deak

D-U-N-S 03-176-0697
FERREIRA CONSTRUCTION CO INC
31 Tannery Rd, Branchburg, NJ 08876-6001
Tel (908) 534-8655 *Founded/Ownrshp* 1994
Sales 196.0MM[E] *EMP* 225[E]
Accts Wiss & Company Iselin New Je
SIC 1611 Highway & street construction
Pr: Nelson Ferreira
**Sec:* Lou Pacheco
**Ex VP:* Dictinio Garcia
**VP:* Brian Delpome
**VP:* Tom Groark
**VP:* Nancy Vliet

D-U-N-S 02-996-7569 IMP
FERRELL COMPANIES INC
7500 College Blvd # 1000, Overland Park, KS 66210-4035
Tel (913) 661-1500 *Founded/Ownrshp* 1938
Sales 446.8MM[E] *EMP* 3,922
SIC 1311 5984 Crude petroleum & natural gas production; Liquefied petroleum gas dealers
**Sr VP:* Kenneth A Heinz
**VP:* George Koloroutis
**VP:* Patrick J Walsh

D-U-N-S 05-281-5986
FERRELLGAS INC (DE)
(*Suby of* FERRELL COMPANIES INC) ★
7500 College Blvd # 1000, Overland Park, KS 66210-4035
Tel (913) 661-1500 *Founded/Ownrshp* 1986
Sales 86.4MM[E] *EMP* 3,922
SIC 5084 5172 Propane conversion equipment; Gases, liquefied petroleum (propane)
Pr: Stephen L Wambold
**Ch Bd:* James E Ferrell
CFO: J Ryan Vanwinkle

D-U-N-S 86-101-7291 IMP
■ **FERRELLGAS LP**
(*Suby of* FERRELLGAS PARTNERS LP) ★
7500 College Blvd # 1000, Overland Park, KS 66210-4098
Tel (913) 661-1500 *Founded/Ownrshp* 1994
Sales 2.0MMM *EMP* 3,922[E]
Accts Grant Thornton Llp Kansas Cit
SIC 5984 Liquefied petroleum gas dealers
CEO: Stephen L Wambold
Pr: Tod D Brown
Pr: Julio E Rios II
COO: Jeremy H Gamboa
CFO: Kevin T Kelly
CFO: J Ryan Vanwinkle
Ch: James E Ferrell
Sr VP: James Hacke

D-U-N-S 83-695-4826
▲ **FERRELLGAS PARTNERS LP**
7500 College Blvd # 1000, Overland Park, KS 66210-4098
Tel (913) 661-1500 *Founded/Ownrshp* 1994
Sales 2.0MMM *EMP* 4,028[E]
Tkr Sym FGP *Exch* NYS
SIC 5084 5172 Propane conversion equipment; Petroleum products; Gases, liquefied petroleum (propane)
CEO: James E Ferrell
COO: Jeremy H Gamboa
COO: Todd Saddoris
CFO: Alan C Heitmann
Ex VP: Tod D Brown
Ex VP: Ryan L Vanwinkle
Sr VP: James M Hake
VP: Scott Brockelmeyer
VP: Tom Buren
VP: Bill Evans
VP: George Koloroutis
VP: D Sheldon

D-U-N-S 07-860-9484 IMP
FERRERO U S A INC
(*Suby of* FERRERO SPA)
600 Cottontail Ln, Somerset, NJ 08873-1233
Tel (732) 764-9300 *Founded/Ownrshp* 1969
Sales 207.9MM[E] *EMP* 500
SIC 5145 2064 Candy; Candy & other confectionery products
CEO: Bernard F Kreilmann
**CFO:* Giuseppe Dibernardo
CFO: Vladimiro Sinatti
**Treas:* Frank A Defilippis
Treas: Stefano Lano
Exec: Susan Cortley
Mng Dir: Rudy Sequeira
Opers Mgr: Daniel Degiovanni
Opers Mgr: Francesco Truglia
Opers Mgr: Dave Vennard
Natl Sales: Ted Bailey

D-U-N-S 10-372-2955 IMP
FERRING PHARMACEUTICALS INC
(*Suby of* FERRING B.V.)
100 Interpace Pkwy, Parsippany, NJ 07054-1149
Tel (973) 796-1600 *Founded/Ownrshp* 1980
Sales 125.3MM[E] *EMP* 406[E]
SIC 2834 5122 Pharmaceutical preparations; Pharmaceuticals
Pr: Aaron Graff
**CFO:* Lalit Ahluwalia
**Chf Mktg O:* Pascal Danglas
Ofcr: Brent Ragans
**Ex VP:* Per Falk
VP: William N Garbarini
VP: Ron Hargreaves
VP: Herve Udriot
Rgnl Mgr: Gail Sibert
Dir IT: Vince Mates

D-U-N-S 05-477-5663
FERRIS STATE UNIVERSITY (MI)
1201 S State St, Big Rapids, MI 49307-2714
Tel (231) 591-2000 *Founded/Ownrshp* 1884
Sales 162.2MM *EMP* 1,200
Accts Andrews Hooper Pavlik Plc Gra
SIC 8221 University
Pr: David Eisler
Pr: Rick Brunson
Pr: Kisten Salomanson
Bd of Dir: Linda Kuk
Ofcr: Elizabeth Hawkins
Assoc VP: David Lepper
Assoc VP: Roberta Teahen
VP: Shelly Armstong
VP: Donald Flickinger
VP: Ted Halm
VP: Ronny Latimore
VP: Ruth Ridderman
VP: Eric Szczepanski

D-U-N-S 80-279-7084 IMP/EXP
■ **FERRO COLOR & GLASS CORP**
DRAKENFELD PRODUCTS
(*Suby of* FERRO CORP) ★
251 W Wylie Ave, Washington, PA 15301-2276
Tel (724) 223-5900 *Founded/Ownrshp* 2001
Sales 74.4MM[E] *EMP* 1,030
SIC 3231 Enameled glass

D-U-N-S 00-416-1477 IMP/EXP
▲ **FERRO CORP**
6060 Parkland Blvd # 250, Mayfield Heights, OH 44124-4225
Tel (216) 875-5600 *Founded/Ownrshp* 1919
Sales 1.0MMM *EMP* 4,991
Tkr Sym FOE *Exch* NYS
SIC 3479 2816 2851 3399 2821 2834 Coating of metals & formed products; Color pigments; Enamels; Plastics base paints & varnishes; Paste, metal; Plastics materials & resins; Carbohydrate plastics; Proprietary drug products
Ch Bd: Peter T Thomas
**CFO:* Jeffrey L Rutherford
CFO: Benjamin Schlater
VP: Duke Dellavechio
**VP:* Mark H Duesenberg
VP: Lori Saviers
VP Opers: Jeff Holthus
Genl Couns: Carol Mulac

D-U-N-S 01-682-0565 IMP/EXP
FERROUS PROCESSING AND TRADING CO
FPT CLEVELAND
(*Suby of* SOAVE ENTERPRISES LLC) ★
3400 E Lafayette St, Detroit, MI 48207-4962
Tel (313) 582-2910 *Founded/Ownrshp* 1997
Sales 672.6MM *EMP* 425
Accts Pricewaterhousecoopers Llp De
SIC 5093 Metal scrap & waste materials
Pr: Howard Sherman
Mng Pt: Bill Wild
**CFO:* Joanie Streicher
Treas: Richard Brockhaus
**Treas:* Michael L Piesko
**Ex VP:* Rob Bakotich
**Ex VP:* Tony Benacquisto
**Ex VP:* Jan Hemme
**Ex VP:* AG Hering
Ex VP: Dick Kenny
VP: Dave Dobronos
VP: Daniel Roma
VP: Clarence Watts

D-U-N-S 02-613-6736
FERROVIAL AGROMAN TEXAS LLC
9600 Great Hills Trl 200e, Austin, TX 78759-6387
Tel (512) 637-8587 *Founded/Ownrshp* 2007
Sales 650.0MM *EMP* 2
SIC 8711 Engineering services
COO: Eduardo Gonzales
CFO: Jose M Asensio

D-U-N-S 00-418-6136 IMP
FERRY CAP & SET SCREW CO
(*Suby of* FABRISTEEL PRODUCTS) ★
13300 Bramley Ave, Lakewood, OH 44107-6248
Tel (216) 649-7400 *Founded/Ownrshp* 1998
Sales 88.8MM[E] *EMP* 350
SIC 3452 Bolts, nuts, rivets & washers; Bolts, metal; Nuts, metal; Screws, metal
Pr: Joseph Mc Auliffe
**Sec:* Gerald O Mullin
Sls Mgr: Brock Massullo

D-U-N-S 96-516-2378
FERTITTA GROUP INC
1510 West Loop S, Houston, TX 77027-9505
Tel (713) 850-1010 *Founded/Ownrshp* 2010
Sales 4.3MMM[E] *EMP* 30,544[E]

SIC 6799 Commodity investors
Pr: Tilman J Fertitta

D-U-N-S 00-877-0299
FESCO LTD (TX)
FESCO SUPPLY
1000 Fesco Dr, Alice, TX 78332-7318
Tel (361) 664-3479 *Founded/Ownrshp* 1949
Sales 201.0MM *EMP* 650
SIC 8711 5082 Petroleum engineering; Oil field equipment
CEO: William E Findley Jr
Pr: Steve Findley
CFO: Tom Anderson
VP: Bobby Mandel
VP: Eddie Pickham
Dir Lab: Pat Bickman
Dist Mgr: Joel Morris
IT Man: John Lockman
IT Man: Jon Ripley
Sls Dir: Randy Tarver
Manager: Cody Birden

FESCO SUPPLY
See FESCO LTD

FESTIVAL FOODS
See KNOWLANS SUPER MARKETS INC

D-U-N-S 02-991-2065
FESTIVAL FUN PARKS LLC
PALACE ENTERTAINMENT
4590 Macarthur Blvd # 400, Newport Beach, CA 92660-2027
Tel (949) 261-0404 *Founded/Ownrshp* 1998
Sales 159.7MM^E *EMP* 1,965
SIC 7999 7993 Miniature golf course operation; Arcades
Pr: Fernando Eiroa
Off Mgr: Linda Fittinger
S&M/VP: Michele Wischmeyer

D-U-N-S 06-594-1072 IMP
FESTO CORP
(*Suby of* FESTO AG & CO. KG)
395 Moreland Rd, Hauppauge, NY 11788-3900
Tel (800) 993-3786 *Founded/Ownrshp* 1925
Sales 378.8MM^E *EMP* 400^E
SIC 5085 3593 3566 3492 Industrial supplies; Fluid power cylinders & actuators; Speed changers, drives & gears; Fluid power valves & hose fittings
Ch: Dr Eberhard Veit
**Pr:* Gian Paolo Arosio
Pr: Daniel Rodriguez
**CEO:* Michael Cybulski
**CEO:* Rich Huss
CFO: Ulf Clever
**CFO:* Sven Doerge
Opers Supe: Steven Scolaro
Mktg Dir: Frank Langro
Sls Mgr: Dan Western

D-U-N-S 14-988-7064
■ **FET HOLDINGS LLC**
(*Suby of* FORUM ENERGY TECHNOLOGIES INC) ★
920 Memorial City Way, Houston, TX 77024-2649
Tel (281) 949-2500 *Founded/Ownrshp* 2011
Sales 165.5MM^E *EMP* 215^E
SIC 5084 Oil refining machinery, equipment & supplies; Oil well machinery, equipment & supplies
CFO: James W Harris

D-U-N-S 18-065-3818
FEV NORTH AMERICA INC
(*Suby of* FEV GMBH)
4554 Glenmeade Ln, Auburn Hills, MI 48326-1766
Tel (248) 475-4761 *Founded/Ownrshp* 2008
Sales 127.9MM^E *EMP* 400^E
SIC 8748 8743 Testing services; Sales promotion
Pr: Patrick Hupperich
CFO: Ragnar Bergethon
VP: Joachim Wolschendorf

D-U-N-S 04-461-5545
■ **FF ACQUISITION LLC** (VA)
(*Suby of* SUPERVALU INC) ★
4860 Cox Rd, Glen Allen, VA 23060-9275
Tel (757) 306-7006 *Founded/Ownrshp* 1997
Sales 311.5MM^E *EMP* 5,000
SIC 5411 Grocery stores
**Pr:* Gaelo De La Fuente
**CFO:* Lisa Olverson

FF INTERNATIONAL
See CHEYENNE INDUSTRIES LLC

D-U-N-S 87-933-0967
FF THOMPSON HEALTH SYSTEM INC
350 Parrish St, Canandaigua, NY 14424-1731
Tel (585) 396-6000 *Founded/Ownrshp* 1904
Sales 4.5MM *EMP* 1,000
SIC 8741 8069 Hospital management; Nursing & personal care facility management; Specialty hospitals, except psychiatric
CEO: Michael F Stapleton Jr
**Pr:* Linda Janczack
Ofcr: Bob Locke
Ex VP: Kurt Koczent
Sr VP: Carlos Ortiz
Sr VP: Sharon Pepper
VP: R D Alling
VP: Benjamin L D
VP: Hazel Robertshaw
VP: Elizabeth Talia
Exec: Joan Fulton
Dir Inf Cn: Lynette Ward
Assoc Dir: Anita Pietropaolo

D-U-N-S 82-864-2137
FFC HOLDING CORP AND SUBSIDIARIES
1 Ice Cream Dr, Dunkirk, NY 14048-3300
Tel (716) 366-5400 *Founded/Ownrshp* 2007
Sales 102.3MM^E *EMP* 352^E
SIC 2024 Ice cream & frozen desserts
Pr: Kenneth A Johnson

D-U-N-S 00-844-6619
FFC LIMITED PARTNERSHIP
WENDY'S
166 Southgate Dr Ste 10, Boone, NC 28607-2905
Tel (828) 262-1811 *Founded/Ownrshp* 1997
Sales 73.1MM *EMP* 1,500
SIC 5812 Fast-food restaurant, chain
Pt: James Furman
Pt: Tad Dolbier

FFD II
See FAIRFIELD DEVELOPMENT INC

D-U-N-S 18-996-1100
FFE LOGISTICS INC
3400 Stonewall St, Lancaster, TX 75134-1536
Tel (214) 630-8090 *Founded/Ownrshp* 2005
Sales 89.7MM^E *EMP* 2,400
SIC 4731 Freight transportation arrangement
Pr: S Russell Stubbs Jr
CIO: Nick Cook
Sls Dir: Brad McEachern

D-U-N-S 00-792-6413
FFE TRANSPORTATION SERVICES INC (DE)
AMERICAN EAGLE
(*Suby of* FROZEN FOOD EXPRESS INDUSTRIES INC) ★
3400 Stonewall St, Lancaster, TX 75134-1536
Tel (800) 569-9200 *Founded/Ownrshp* 1945, 1948
Sales 86.0MM^E *EMP* 650
SIC 4213 Refrigerated products transport
Ch Bd: Stoney M Stubbs Jr
**Pr:* S Russell Stubbs
**COO:* John Hickerson
**CFO:* Thomas G Yetter
**VP:* Steve Stedman

D-U-N-S 19-746-8465
FFF ENTERPRISES INC
41093 County Center Dr, Temecula, CA 92591-6025
Tel (951) 296-2500 *Founded/Ownrshp* 1988
Sales 159.7MM^E *EMP* 285
SIC 5122 5047 Pharmaceuticals; Medical equipment & supplies
CEO: Patrick M Schmidt
**COO:* Chris Ground
COO: Kieth Sinclair
**CFO:* Brad Cooper
Sr VP: Jeff Primovic
Sr VP: Nik Vojicic
VP: URS Aeberli
VP: Richard Bagley
VP: Bob Coates
VP: Nancy Creadon
VP: Michelle Greer
VP: Jon Hahn
VP: Michele Hubach
VP: Vanessa Koch
VP: Sue Richter
VP Bus Dev: Greg Neier
Exec: Julie Pitruzzello
Exec: Philip Quarles

FFG
See FLYING FOOD FARE INC

FFNA
See FUJITSU FRONTECH NORTH AMERICA INC

FFO HOME
See FURNITURE FACTORY OUTLET LLC

FGDI
See AGREX INC

D-U-N-S 02-690-7334
FGI ACQUISITION CORP
(*Suby of* FINANCIERE ATLANTIS II)
201 Kingwood Medical Dr B200, Kingwood, TX 77339-6006
Tel (281) 604-2525 *Founded/Ownrshp* 2013
Sales 245.7MM *EMP* 923
SIC 3053 Gaskets & sealing devices
CEO: Jon Stoks
CFO: Jerry Maters

D-U-N-S 19-623-1096 EXP
FGI GROUP INC
3901 S Lamar Blvd Ste 100, Austin, TX 78704-7989
Tel (512) 448-9898 *Founded/Ownrshp* 1984
Sales 336.2MM^E *EMP* 1,800
SIC 1542 1541 1794 1611 7353 1711 Commercial & office building, new construction; Commercial & office buildings, renovation & repair; Institutional building construction; Industrial buildings, new construction; Renovation, remodeling & repairs: industrial buildings; Excavation & grading, building construction; Resurfacing contractor; Heavy construction equipment rental; Mechanical contractor
Ch: Royce W Faulkner
**CEO:* Randy J Rehmann
**Treas:* Joyce Bradley
**VP:* Charles D Schmidt

D-U-N-S 96-532-4267
■ **FGI OPERATING CO LLC**
(*Suby of* FGI HOLDING COMPANY, LLC)
870 Remington Dr, Madison, NC 27025-8331
Tel (336) 548-8700 *Founded/Ownrshp* 2010
Sales 684.1MM^E *EMP* 2,340^E
SIC 3484 3482 Small arms; Small arms ammunition
Prin: Roderick Fgiles

D-U-N-S 10-326-7142
FGIC CORP
125 Park Ave Fl 5, New York, NY 10017-5664
Tel (212) 312-3000 *Founded/Ownrshp* 2005
Sales NA *EMP* 190
SIC 6411 7389 Insurance agents; Purchasing service
CEO: Frank J Bivona
Mng Dir: Richard A Price
Mng Dir: Wilfred Romero

D-U-N-S 15-750-6577 IMP
FGS-WI LLC
FREEDOM GRAPHIC SYSTEMS
1101 S Janesville St, Milton, WI 53563-1838
Tel (608) 373-6500 *Founded/Ownrshp* 1986
Sales 106.7MM^E *EMP* 250
SIC 2752 7331 Commercial printing, offset; Direct mail advertising services
Pr: Martin Liebert
CFO: Terry Brady
**CFO:* William R Greene
Ex VP: Jon Singer
Ex VP: Ingrid Vaisvilaite
VP: Richard Green
CTO: Richard Greene
IT Man: Steve Andersen
IT Man: Darryl Graham
Sfty Mgr: Mark Fero
Opers Mgr: Eric Blohm

D-U-N-S 80-040-3227
FGX INTERNATIONAL HOLDINGS LIMITED
(*Suby of* ESSILOR INTERNATIONAL)
500 Washington Hwy, Smithfield, RI 02917-1926
Tel (401) 231-3800 *Founded/Ownrshp* 2010
Sales 385.0MM^E *EMP* 3,000
SIC 5099 3851 Sunglasses; Eyeglasses, lenses & frames
Pr: John H Flynn Jr
CFO: Anthony Di Paola
Treas: Brian Lagarto
Ex VP: Steven Crellin
Ex VP: Jeffrey J Giguere
VP: Thomas Fernandes
VP: Chris Jones
VP: Idalia Rodriguez
Dist Mgr: Scott Deschner
Dist Mgr: Esther Flanagain
Dist Mgr: Nicole Hasson

D-U-N-S 06-231-2087 IMP/EXP
FGX INTERNATIONAL INC
(*Suby of* FGX INTERNATIONAL HOLDINGS LIMITED) ★
500 George Washington Hwy, Smithfield, RI 02917-1926
Tel (401) 231-3800 *Founded/Ownrshp* 2010
Sales 385.0MM^E *EMP* 1,195
SIC 5099 3851 Sunglasses; Eyeglasses, lenses & frames
CEO: Anthony Di Paola
**Pr:* John H Flynn Jr
Ex VP: Stephen Burbridge
**Ex VP:* Steve Crellin
**Ex VP:* Jeffrey J Giguere
Ex VP: Gerald Kitchen
Ex VP: Gina Lazaro
Ex VP: Ellen Mash
Ex VP: Matthew Panucci
VP: Corinne McCormack
VP Admn: Anne Reed

D-U-N-S 07-984-0395
■ **FH GROUP LLC**
(*Suby of* CAVCO INDUSTRIES INC) ★
1001 N Central Ave # 800, Phoenix, AZ 85004-1935
Tel (574) 773-7941 *Founded/Ownrshp* 2014
Sales 141.2MM^E *EMP* 512^E
SIC 2451 Mobile homes, except recreational
Prin: James Foster Shea

D-U-N-S 87-633-2040
FH PASCHEN SN NIELSEN INC
FHP SNN
5515 N East River Rd, Chicago, IL 60656-1113
Tel (773) 444-3474 *Founded/Ownrshp* 1991
Sales 203.7MM^E *EMP* 260
SIC 1611 1622 1522 1542 Highway & street construction; Bridge construction; Remodeling, multi-family dwellings; Commercial & office buildings, renovation & repair
Pr: James V Blair
**Ch Bd:* Frank Paschen Jr
**CFO:* Carol Einfalt
**Sr VP:* Robert F Zitek
**VP:* Joseph Scarpelli
VP: Leo Wright
Off Mgr: Linda Maresh
QA Dir: Tim Jenkins
Snr PM: Timothy Bea
Snr PM: Scott Bowden
Snr PM: Matt Moss

D-U-N-S 10-870-6771 IMP
FHA/RALEIGH INC
TOYOTA CENTER
9101 Glenwood Ave, Raleigh, NC 27617-7507
Tel (919) 787-0099 *Founded/Ownrshp* 1981
Sales 130.2MM^E *EMP* 400
SIC 5511 5521 5012 Automobiles, new & used; Used car dealers; Automobiles & other motor vehicles
Pr: Fredrick H Anderson
VP: Jim Anderson
**VP:* Michael Anderson
IT Man: Brandon Newnam
Mktg Dir: Alison Anderson
Sales Asso: Kevin Austin

D-U-N-S 10-575-2901
FHC HEALTH SYSTEMS INC
240 Corporate Blvd # 100, Norfolk, VA 23502-4900
Tel (757) 459-5100 *Founded/Ownrshp* 1983
Sales 431.2MM^E *EMP* 3,000
SIC 6719 Investment holding companies, except banks
**Pr:* Timothy Murphy
CTO: Barbara Hill
Info Man: Betty Hernandez
VP Mktg: Tom Warburton
Mktg Dir: Anthony Davis
Sls Dir: Andrea Rizzo

D-U-N-S 94-407-7614 IMP/EXP
FHG CORP
INTEGRITY NUTRACEUTICALS INTL
4637 Port Royal Rd, Spring Hill, TN 37174-2834
Tel (931) 499-7070 *Founded/Ownrshp* 2000
Sales 181.5MM^E *EMP* 400^E
SIC 7389 5122

FHGM
See FLORIDA HOSPITAL MEDICAL GROUP INC

FHI 360
See FAMILY HEALTH INTERNATIONAL INC

FHI FAMILY OF COMPANIES
See FLEXFAB HORIZONS INTERNATIONAL INC

D-U-N-S 06-940-0745
FHI SERVICES (VA)
(*Suby of* FAUQUIER HOSPITAL) ★
500 Hospital Dr, Warrenton, VA 20186-3027
Tel (540) 347-2550 *Founded/Ownrshp* 1954, 1987
Sales 122.9MM^E *EMP* 700
SIC 8062 General medical & surgical hospitals
Pr: Christy Connolly
**Prin:* Rodger H Baker
Prgrm Mgr: Yvonne Mitchell

FHL BANK
See FEDERAL HOME LOAN BANK

FHN FOUNDATION
See FREEPORT REGIONAL HEALTH CARE FOUNDATION

FHN MEMORIAL HOSPITAL
See FREEPORT MEMORIAL HOSPITAL INC

D-U-N-S 60-080-7908 IMP/EXP
FHP MANUFACTURING CO
FLORIDA HEAT PUMP
(*Suby of* BOSCH THERMOTECHNOLOGY CORP) ★
601 Nw 65th Ct, Fort Lauderdale, FL 33309-6109
Tel (954) 776-5471 *Founded/Ownrshp* 2007
Sales 120.2MM^E *EMP* 282
SIC 3585 Heat pumps, electric
Pr: Martin Kueper
**VP:* Albano Magalhaes

FHP SNN
See FH PASCHEN SN NIELSEN INC

FHS ACT 1 TECHNICAL SERVICES
See COVENTRY HEALTH PLAN OF FLORIDA INC

D-U-N-S 04-873-3638
■ **FIA CARD SERVICES NATIONAL ASSOCIATION**
(*Suby of* BANK OF AMERICA CORP) ★
1100 N King St, Wilmington, DE 19884-0011
Tel (800) 362-6255 *Founded/Ownrshp* 1991
Sales 581.7MM^E *EMP* 27,921^E
SIC 7389 Credit card service
Pr: Brian T Moynihan
COO: John Cochran III
**Treas:* Linsz Mark D
VP: William Bailey

FIA FINANCIAL SERVICES GROUP
See ABSCO LTD CORP

D-U-N-S 61-160-2608
FIAT USA INC
375 Park Ave Ste 2703, New York, NY 10152-2704
Tel (212) 355-2600 *Founded/Ownrshp* 2005
Sales NA *EMP* 1,350
SIC 3714 8741 3535 5012 5013 5082

D-U-N-S 01-462-7496 IMP/EXP
FIBER COMPOSITES LLC
FIBERON
181 Random Dr, New London, NC 28127-8735
Tel (704) 463-7120 *Founded/Ownrshp* 1997
Sales 139.7MM^E *EMP* 318
SIC 2899 Plastic wood
**Pr:* Anne-Marie Davis
COO: James Pryzbylinski
CFO: Donald Parish
VP: Mike Karause
Dir IT: Allen Rainwater
Opers Mgr: Debbie Ferr
Plnt Mgr: Larry Gates
Plnt Mgr: Ken Ropski
VP Mktg: Shellie Sellards
VP Sls: Bill Ross
Mktg Dir: Edie Kello

FIBER VISIONS MFG CO
See FIBERVISIONS CORP

FIBERMARK NORTH AMERICA
See NEENAH NORTHEAST LLC

FIBERON
See FIBER COMPOSITES LLC

D-U-N-S 80-659-4487 IMP/EXP
FIBERVISIONS CORP
FIBER VISIONS MFG CO
(*Suby of* INDORAMA VENTURES PUBLIC COMPANY LIMITED)
3700 Crestwood Pkwy Nw, Duluth, GA 30096-5599
Tel (678) 578-7240 *Founded/Ownrshp* 2012
Sales 248.7MM^E *EMP* 550
SIC 2899 Sizes
CEO: Tom J Zaiser
**Pr:* Gary Spitz
**CFO:* A Dale Carter
**Prin:* Stephen Wood
Sfty Dirs: John Humphreys

D-U-N-S 80-658-8646 IMP/EXP
FIBERVISIONS MANUFACTURING CO
(*Suby of* FIBER VISIONS MFG CO) ★
7101 Alcovy Rd Ne, Covington, GA 30014-1373
Tel (770) 784-3402 *Founded/Ownrshp* 1997
Sales 121.6MM^E *EMP* 200
SIC 2821 2823 Polypropylene resins; Cellulosic man-made fibers
Ch: Stephen Wood
**Pr:* Craig Rogerson
**Pr:* Gary Spitz
**CEO:* Tom Zaiser
**CFO:* A Dale Carter
**VP:* Geoffrey Meyer
Board of Directors: Leslie Shorey

D-U-N-S 13-105-6764 IMP/EXP
■ **FIBERWEB INC**
(*Suby of* AVINTIV SPECIALTY MATERIALS INC) ★
9335 Harris Corners Pkwy, Old Hickory, TN 37138
Tel (704) 697-5100 *Founded/Ownrshp* 2013
Sales 321.7MM^E *EMP* 630

SIC 2281 5047 5137 Polyester yarn, spun: made from purchased staple; Polypropylene yarn, spun: made from purchased staple; Industrial safety devices: first aid kits & masks; Diapers
Pr: Dean Gaskins
**Treas:* Michael Maddox
**Treas:* Craig Smith
**VP:* Joe Dyer
VP: Bhavesh Sheth
IT Man: Bob Hunnings
IT Man: Tracy Newton
Opers Mgr: Eric Holloway
Opers Mgr: Stan Wilson

D-U-N-S 05-101-1609 IMP/EXP
FIBRANT LLC
DCNA
(*Suby of* DSM FINANCE USA INC) ★
1408 Columbia Nitrogen Dr, Augusta, GA 30901-2000
Tel (706) 849-6600 *Founded/Ownrshp* 1963
Sales 254.5MM[E] *EMP* 483[E]
SIC 2819 2899 Nonmetallic compounds; Ammonium compounds, except fertilizers; Chemical preparations
CEO: Pol Deturck
**Pr:* David Hitchins
**Pr:* David D Quester
**CFO:* Martijn Amory
**Treas:* David Leach
Bd of Dir: David Quester
**VP:* Hans Op HetVeld
**VP:* Luan Yizheng
Sfty Mgr: Jimmy Cook
Prd Mgr: Jason Hawes

D-U-N-S 07-267-7537 IMP
FIBREBOND CORP
FIBREBOND POWER
1300 Davenport Dr, Minden, LA 71055-3924
Tel (318) 377-1030 *Founded/Ownrshp* 1982
Sales 150.0MM *EMP* 575
SIC 3272

FIBREBOND POWER
See FIBREBOND CORP

D-U-N-S 60-855-9944 IMP/EXP
FIBRO SOURCE USA INC
985 Old Eagle School Rd # 514, Wayne, PA 19087-1712
Tel (610) 293-3200 *Founded/Ownrshp* 1998
Sales 103.6MM *EMP* 50
Accts Eisneramper Llp Jenkintown P
SIC 5099 5113 5141 5112 Wood & wood by-products; Industrial & personal service paper; Groceries, general line; Writing instruments & supplies
Pr: Gyan J Bindra
**VP:* Sarvjeet Bindra

D-U-N-S 83-557-3239
▲ **FIBROGEN INC**
409 Illinois St, San Francisco, CA 94158-2509
Tel (415) 978-1200 *Founded/Ownrshp* 1993
Sales 180.8MM *EMP* 353[E]
Tkr Sym FGEN *Exch* NGS
SIC 2834 Pharmaceutical preparations
Ch Bd: Thomas B Neff
CFO: Pat Cotroneo
Chf Mktg O: K Peony Yu
Assoc Dir: Nils Hauptmann
Prgrm Mgr: Lisa Bacolini
IT Man: Van Gerard
Snr Mgr: Helen DEA
Snr Mgr: Melissa Leon
Board of Directors: Jeffrey L Edwards, Jeffrey W Henderson, Thomas F Kearns Jr, Rory B Riggs, Roberto Pedro Rosenkranz, James A Schoeneck

D-U-N-S 93-225-3628 IMP
FIC AMERICA CORP
(*Suby of* FUTABA INDUSTRIAL CO., LTD.)
485 E Lies Rd, Carol Stream, IL 60188-9422
Tel (630) 871-7609 *Founded/Ownrshp* 1994
Sales 227.1MM[E] *EMP* 685
SIC 3469 Metal stampings
Pr: Kenzo Yanase
**Treas:* Hiroshi Ono
**VP:* William T Murakami
Dir Teleco: Steven Chadra
Genl Mgr: Tsukasa Ishimaru
Snr Mgr: Helmut Seimen

D-U-N-S 93-325-8204 IMP
FICOSA NORTH AMERICA CORP
(*Suby of* FICOSA INTERNATIONAL, SA)
30870 Stephenson Hwy, Madison Heights, MI 48071-1614
Tel (248) 307-2230 *Founded/Ownrshp* 1995
Sales 711.8MM[E] *EMP* 1,509
SIC 5531 Automotive parts
Pr: Javier Pujol
**Treas:* Raul Urbina
Genl Mgr: Frederick Zicard
QA Dir: David Bear
Plnt Mgr: Santiago Martinez

FIDELIS CARE NEW YORK
See NEW YORK STATE CATHOLIC HEALTH PLAN INC

D-U-N-S 16-672-6203
FIDELIS CYBERSECURITY INC
(*Suby of* MARLIN EQUITY PARTNERS LLC) ★
4416 East West Hwy # 310, Bethesda, MD 20814-4565
Tel (617) 275-8800 *Founded/Ownrshp* 2015
Sales 88.9MM[E] *EMP* 300[E]
SIC 7373 Systems software development services
CEO: Peter George
**CFO:* Richard Darer
**Chf Mktg O:* Michael Evans
Sr VP: David Macey
**VP:* Kurt Bertone
VP: Scott Collins
VP: Gerald Mancini
Sls Dir: Matthew Wayland
Manager: Andrew Hood

D-U-N-S 00-507-1766
FIDELITONE INC
BLACK & DECKER
1260 Karl Ct, Wauconda, IL 60084-1094
Tel (847) 487-3300 *Founded/Ownrshp* 1946
Sales 278.2MM[E] *EMP* 600[E]
SIC 4214 Household goods moving & storage, local
CEO: Craig Hudson
**Pr:* Josh Johnson
VP: Scott Deblois
VP: Bruce Massel
VP: Chuck Perry
QA Dir: Ed Burton
IT Man: Leonardus Adisumarta
Opers Mgr: Barry McGreer

D-U-N-S 00-698-3639
■ **FIDELITY & CASUALTY CO OF NEW YORK** (NY)
CNA INSURANCE
(*Suby of* CNA INSURANCE) ★
333 S Wabash Ave Fl 1, Chicago, IL 60604-4250
Tel (312) 822-5000 *Founded/Ownrshp* 1875, 2008
Sales NA *EMP* 1,000
SIC 6411 Insurance agents, brokers & service
CEO: Stephen W Lilienthal
**Ch Bd:* Bernard L Hengesbaugh
**Pr:* William J Adamson
**Pr:* Peter E Jokiel
**Pr:* Michael S McGavick
**Pr:* Gary J Owcar
**Pr:* Jae L Wittlich
**CFO:* Robert V Deutsch
**Treas:* Pamela S Dempsey
**Ex VP:* Thomas F Taylor
**Sr VP:* Jonathan Kantor
**Sr VP:* Thomas Pontarelli
**Sr VP:* Peter Wilson
**Sr VP:* David W Wroe
**VP:* John Squarok

D-U-N-S 04-628-3073
■ **FIDELITY & GUARANTY INSURANCE UNDERWRITERS INC**
(*Suby of* UNITED STATES FIDELITY AND GUARANTY COMPANY)
20800 Swenson Dr Ste 300, Waukesha, WI 53186-4081
Tel (414) 784-5530 *Founded/Ownrshp* 1951
Sales NA *EMP* 2,488[E]
SIC 6331 Property damage insurance; Fire, marine & casualty insurance & carriers
Pr: Douglas Leatherdale

D-U-N-S 07-922-8389
■ **FIDELITY & GUARANTY LIFE**
(*Suby of* HRG GROUP INC) ★
601 Locust St Fl 2, Des Moines, IA 50309-3738
Tel (800) 445-6758 *Founded/Ownrshp* 2011
Sales NA *EMP* 200[E]
SIC 6311 Life insurance
CEO: Leland C Launer Jr
Pr: Christopher J Littlefield
CFO: Dennis Vigneau
Ex VP: Rajesh Krishnan
Ex VP: Eric L Marhoun
Board of Directors: Omar M Asali, William J Bawden, James M Benson, Kostas Cheliotis, Phillip J Gass, Kevin J Gregson, William P Melchionni, L John H Tweedie, Thomas A Williams

D-U-N-S 00-787-1221
■ **FIDELITY & GUARANTY LIFE INSURANCE CO** (MD)
OLD MUTUAL FINANCIAL NETWORK
(*Suby of* HARBINGER OM LLC) ★
1001 Fleet St Fl 7, Baltimore, MD 21202-4363
Tel (410) 895-0100 *Founded/Ownrshp* 1960, 2000
Sales NA *EMP* 300[E]
SIC 6311 Life insurance carriers
Pr: Guy Vincent Barker
**Pr:* Chris Littlefield
**CEO:* Lee Launerce
**COO:* Vic Lumby
**CFO:* John M Varvaris
CFO: Dennis R Vigneau
Ofcr: Wendy J Young
**Ex VP:* Raj Krishnan
Ex VP: Rajesh Krishnan
**Ex VP:* Eric Marhoun
**Ex VP:* Dennis Vigneau
VP: Christopher S Fleming
VP: Steven Kennedy
VP: John A Phelps II

D-U-N-S 00-696-1783
■ **FIDELITY ACCEPTANCE CORP**
(*Suby of* WELLS FARGO BANK NATIONAL ASSOCIATION) ★
800 Walnut St, Des Moines, IA 50309-3605
Tel (515) 557-8279 *Founded/Ownrshp* 1997
Sales NA *EMP* 1,000
SIC 6021 National commercial banks
VP: Dean Anderson
Treas: Michael Matera
VP: Fred Nungesser
Genl Couns: Patricia McFarland

D-U-N-S 79-119-2920
FIDELITY BANCSHARES (NC) INC
100 S Main St, Fuquay Varina, NC 27526-2221
Tel (919) 552-2242 *Founded/Ownrshp* 2007
Sales NA *EMP* 414[E]
SIC 6712 Bank holding companies
CEO: Billy Woodard
**Ch Bd:* Billy T Woodard
VP: Ivy Goodson
VP: Tim Stratton

D-U-N-S 06-649-6175
■ **FIDELITY BANK**
(*Suby of* FIDELITY SOUTHERN CORP) ★
3 Corporate Blvd Ne # 110, Brookhaven, GA 30329-2078
Tel (404) 325-3935 *Founded/Ownrshp* 1979
Sales NA *EMP* 332
SIC 6029 Commercial banks

CEO: James Miller Jr
Pr: Palmer Proctor Jr
CFO: M H Griffith
CFO: B Rodrick Marlow
Treas: Stephen Brolly
Ofcr: Julie Jones
Ex VP: David Buchanan
VP: Stephanie Huckaby
VP: Gloria O'Neal
Prin: Howard Griffith
Rgnl Mgr: Virginia Roberson
Board of Directors: Donald A Harp

D-U-N-S 14-896-5549
FIDELITY CAPITAL INVESTORS INC
FIDELITY INVESTMENTS
(*Suby of* FIDELITY INVESTMENTS) ★
82 Devonshire St, Boston, MA 02109-3614
Tel (617) 563-7000 *Founded/Ownrshp* 2001
Sales 399.2MM[E] *EMP* 17,458
SIC 6282 6211 Investment advisory service; Management of mutual funds, contract or fee basis; Brokers, security
Pr: Abigail P Johnson
**Treas:* Michael B Fox
**Prin:* Steven P Akin
Snr Sftwr: Paul Allard
Sftwr Eng: Joe Brouillard
VP Mktg: Amy Pirozzolo
VP Mktg: Richard Strout
Mktg Dir: Stacey Cappella
Mktg Dir: Tracy Murnahan
Mktg Dir: Tracey Ryan
Mktg Mgr: Josh Britton

D-U-N-S 62-110-3027
FIDELITY COMMUNICATIONS CO
64 N Clark St, Sullivan, MO 63080-1610
Tel (800) 392-8070 *Founded/Ownrshp* 1988
Sales 85.6MM[E] *EMP* 300[E]
SIC 4841 4813 Cable & other pay television services; Local telephone communications; Long distance telephone communications
Pr: John Colbert
Genl Mgr: Darrick Collier
Genl Mgr: Don Knight
Genl Mgr: Kip McVey
MIS Dir: Dennis Watz
Netwrk Mgr: Mark Pashia
Sales Exec: Jill Wagner
Sls Dir: Holly Bryant

D-U-N-S 02-243-7610
FIDELITY ENGINEERING CORP
25 Loveton Cir, Sparks, MD 21152-9201
Tel (410) 771-9400 *Founded/Ownrshp* 2002
Sales 107.7MM[E] *EMP* 460
SIC 1711 5063 1799 8711 Plumbing contractors; Heating & air conditioning contractors; Ventilation & duct work contractor; Refrigeration contractor; Generators; Home/office interiors finishing, furnishing & remodeling; Heating & ventilation engineering
CEO: David Lanphar
VP: Keith Klann
VP: Carmine Mistichelli
Dept Mgr: Bryan Dailey
Brnch Mgr: Miran Vucic
Brnch Mgr: Troy Williams
Off Mgr: Baarbara Bannon
Dir IT: David Deitrich
IT Man: Kathi Meckel
Opers Mgr: Stephen Cook
Opers Mgr: Charles Hicks

D-U-N-S 03-958-2481 IMP
■ **FIDELITY EXPLORATION & PRODUCTION CO**
(*Suby of* CENTENNIAL ENERGY HOLDINGS INC) ★
1801 Calif St Ste 2500, Denver, CO 80202-2638
Tel (303) 893-3133 *Founded/Ownrshp* 2001
Sales 266.9MM[E] *EMP* 170
SIC 1382 Oil & gas exploration services
CEO: J Kent Wells
**CFO:* Darwin Subart
**VP:* Bruce Bowman
VP: Jim Hohenstein
VP: Marv Rygh
Opers Mgr: Dennis Zander

D-U-N-S 18-962-2665
FIDELITY FINANCIAL CORP
100 E English St, Wichita, KS 67202-3706
Tel (316) 265-2261 *Founded/Ownrshp* 1985
Sales NA *EMP* 90
SIC 6035 Savings institutions, federally chartered
Ch Bd: H Marvin Bastian
Sr VP: Albert Sanchez

D-U-N-S 06-530-9544
■ **FIDELITY INFORMATION SERVICES LLC**
FIS
(*Suby of* FIS) ★
601 Riverside Ave, Jacksonville, FL 32204-2946
Tel (888) 323-0310 *Founded/Ownrshp* 2006
Sales 1.3MMM[E] *EMP* 7,000
SIC 7374 Data processing service
CEO: Gary Norcross
Chf Mktg O: Ellyn Raftery
Ex VP: Dean McCreary
**Ex VP:* James Woodall
Dir Soc: Lindsay Taylor
QA Dir: Troy Hallberg
IT Man: Al Lehman
IT Man: Jane Linn
Plnt Mgr: John Rys

D-U-N-S 96-487-7950
FIDELITY INV CHARITABLE GIFT FUND
200 Seaport Blvd Ste 1, Boston, MA 02210-2000
Tel (617) 392-8679 *Founded/Ownrshp* 2010
Sales 1.8MMM *EMP* 1
SIC 5947 Gift shop

FIDELITY INVESTMENTS
See FIDELITY MANAGEMENT & RESEARCH CO

FIDELITY INVESTMENTS
See FMR LLC

FIDELITY INVESTMENTS
See FIDELITY CAPITAL INVESTORS INC

FIDELITY INVESTMENTS
See FMR CORP

D-U-N-S 15-106-7337
FIDELITY INVESTMENTS INSTITUTIONAL OPERATIONS CO INC
(*Suby of* FIDELITY INVESTMENTS) ★
245 Summer St Ste 1100, Boston, MA 02210-1129
Tel (617) 563-7000 *Founded/Ownrshp* 1992
Sales 593.5MM[E] *EMP* 600
SIC 6282 6211 Investment advisory service; Brokers, security
Pr: Robert Adams
CFO: Alan Scheuer
**Treas:* Steven F Schiffman
Ofcr: Stephanie Bailey
Ofcr: Alexandria Cutrone
Ofcr: Tracie Honsberger
Ofcr: Yanting Leite
Ofcr: Daniel Rizk
Ofcr: Deborah Williams
VP: Warren Fagan
VP: Joseph Lorusso
VP: Frank Margiotto
VP: Brad Mondshane

D-U-N-S 04-481-1776
FIDELITY MANAGEMENT & RESEARCH CO
FIDELITY INVESTMENTS
(*Suby of* FIDELITY INVESTMENTS) ★
1 Federal St Fl 33, Boston, MA 02110-2005
Tel (603) 791-5000 *Founded/Ownrshp* 1946
Sales 175.0MM *EMP* 600
SIC 6282 Investment advisory service
Ch Bd: Edward C Johnson III
**Pr:* Walter C Donovan
**Pr:* Jacques P Perold
**Treas:* William E Dailey
**Treas:* Js Wynant
Ex VP: James Speros
Sr VP: Stephen Gresham
VP: Michael Holtschlag
VP: Lori Johnson
VP: Eunice Lee
VP: Kevin Lynch
VP: Thomas Soviero

D-U-N-S 85-920-0438
FIDELITY MANAGEMENT TRUST CO
(*Suby of* FIDELITY INVESTMENTS) ★
82 Devonshire St, Boston, MA 02109-3614
Tel (617) 563-7000 *Founded/Ownrshp* 1981
Sales 193.7MM *EMP* 141
SIC 6282 Investment advice
Pr: Drew Lawton
**CFO:* John Murphy
Treas: Eric Ennes
**Sr VP:* Chris Keating
VP: Brian Cashin
VP: John Danahy
VP: John J Doyle
VP: Maureen Flynn

D-U-N-S 82-587-8379
■ **FIDELITY NATIONAL EUROPE LLC**
(*Suby of* FIDELITY NATIONAL FINANCIAL INC) ★
601 Riverside Ave Fl 4, Jacksonville, FL 32204-2901
Tel (904) 854-8100 *Founded/Ownrshp* 2001
Sales NA *EMP* 1,347[E]
SIC 6361 Title insurance
Pr: Raymond R Quirk
CFO: Jeffrey S Carbiener
CFO: Anthony J Park
**Treas:* Patrick G Farenga
Ofcr: Geraldine Lowe
Ex VP: Brent Bickett
Ex VP: Gerald A Hines
Ex VP: Roger S Jewkes
Ex VP: Peter T Sadowski
Sr VP: Marcia Danzeisen
**Sr VP:* Todd C Johnson
Sr VP: Michele Jorgensen
Sr VP: Daniel Kennedy
VP: Al Bartello
VP: Betsy Thompson
Board of Directors: Alan L Stinson

D-U-N-S 60-452-5241
▲ **FIDELITY NATIONAL FINANCIAL INC**
601 Riverside Ave Fl 4, Jacksonville, FL 32204-2957
Tel (904) 854-8100 *Founded/Ownrshp* 1847
Sales NA *EMP* 54,091[E]
Tkr Sym FNF *Exch* NYS
SIC 6361 6331 6531 8741 3699 Title insurance; Fire, marine & casualty insurance; Escrow agent, real estate; Restaurant management; Electrical equipment & supplies
CEO: Raymond R Quirk
Ch Bd: William P Foley II
Pr: Yvonne Ahsing
Pr: Alicia Buckley
Pr: Erin Campbell
Pr: Wanda Carter
Pr: Anthony Ching
Pr: Dan Cowgill
Pr: Thomas Davidson
Pr: Julie Deal
Pr: Jennifer Douthit
Pr: Jennifer Edwards
Pr: Laura Franceschi
Pr: Kevin Giltmier
Pr: Lorna E Johnson
Pr: Kianna Leomiti
Pr: Bryan McGahan
Pr: Chris Newman
Pr: Michael J Nolan
Pr: Donna Nowlin
Pr: Chris Rouly
Board of Directors: Frank P Willey, Douglas K Ammerman, Willie D Davis, Thomas M Hagerty, Janet Kerr, Daniel D Lane, Richard N Massey, John D Rood, Peter O Shea Jr, Cary H Thompson

D-U-N-S 62-747-3457
■ FIDELITY NATIONAL GLOBAL CARD SERVICES INC
FIS
(*Suby of* FIS) ★
11601 Roosevelt Blvd N, Saint Petersburg, FL 33716-2202
Tel (727) 556-9000 *Founded/Ownrshp* 1990
Sales 96.8MM^E *EMP* 1,785
SIC 7389 Credit card service
CEO: Lee A Kennedy
**Pr:* Gary A Norcross
**Ex VP:* Michael P Oates
Sr VP: Robert Bream
VP: John Broda
VP: Lynn Cravey
**VP:* Kirk T Larsen
Sales Exec: Ken Dickens
Sales Exec: Nathan Giordano
Sls Mgr: Joann Bennett
Sls Mgr: Rick Silva

FIDELITY NATIONAL INFO SVCS
See METAVANTE CORP

D-U-N-S 03-077-2334
▲ FIDELITY NATIONAL INFORMATION SERVICES INC
FIS
601 Riverside Ave, Jacksonville, FL 32204-2946
Tel (904) 438-6000 *Founded/Ownrshp* 1961
Sales 6.6MMM *EMP* 55,000
Accts Kpmg Llp Jacksonville Flori
Tkr Sym FIS *Exch* NYS
SIC 7389 7374 Financial services; Check validation service; Credit card service; Computer processing services
Pr: Gary A Norcross
**Ch Bd:* Frank R Martire
Pr: Theresa Hoskinson
Pr: Eric Kraus
Pr: Paula Orel
Pr: Christine Sterling
COO: Marianne Brown
COO: Marianne C Brown
COO: Anthony M Jabbour
CFO: James W Woodall
**V Ch Bd:* William P Foley II
Ex VP: Cynthia Fitzgerald
Ex VP: Trent Georges
Ex VP: Raja Gopalakrishnan
Ex VP: Gregory G Montana
Ex VP: Kay Nichols
Ex VP: Michael P Oates
Ex VP: Steve Patterson
Sr VP: Don Covey
Sr VP: William D Johnson
VP: Arun Ahuja
Board of Directors: Ellen R Alemany, Thomas M Hagerty, Keith W Hughes, David K Hunt, Stephan A James, Richard N Massey, Leslie M Muma, James B Stallings Jr

D-U-N-S 07-800-0932
■ FIDELITY NATIONAL TITLE INSURANCE CO (CA)
(*Suby of* FIDELITY NATIONAL FINANCIAL INC) ★
3220 El Camino Real, Irvine, CA 92602-1377
Tel (949) 622-4600 *Founded/Ownrshp* 1913
Sales NA *EMP* 500
SIC 6361 8741 6541 6531 Real estate title insurance; Management services; Title abstract offices; Escrow agent, real estate
CEO: Raymond R Quirk
**Ch Bd:* William P Foley II
**Pr:* Frank Willey
**COO:* Pat Stone
Ex VP: Peter Sadowski
**Ex VP:* Alan Stenson
VP: Andy Puzder
VP: Hai Tran
CIO: Tom Ashbrook
MIS Dir: Lori Sanchez
IT Man: Michael Okumura

D-U-N-S 00-699-0188
■ FIDELITY NATIONAL TITLE INSURANCE CO OF NEW YORK
(*Suby of* FIDELITY NATIONAL FINANCIAL INC) ★
1 Pak Ave Ste 1402, New York, NY 10016
Tel (904) 854-8100 *Founded/Ownrshp* 1928, 2013
Sales NA *EMP* 11,147
SIC 6361 Real estate title insurance
Pr: Patrick Francis Stone
**Ch Bd:* William P Foley II
**VP:* Carl Strunk

D-U-N-S 83-103-8075
FIDELITY NEWPORT HOLDINGS LLC
400 W 48th Ave, Denver, CO 80216-1806
Tel (303) 296-2121 *Founded/Ownrshp* 2009
Sales 862.3MM^E *EMP* 15,000^E
Accts Kpmg Llp Nashville Tn
SIC 5812 2051 6719 Restaurant, family: chain; Bread, cake & related products; Investment holding companies, except banks
Pr: Cindy Doyle
**CEO:* Hazem Ouf
**COO:* Robert Kaltenbach

D-U-N-S 10-202-7687
▲ FIDELITY SOUTHERN CORP
3490 Piedmont Rd Ne # 1550, Atlanta, GA 30305-1743
Tel (404) 639-6500 *Founded/Ownrshp* 1979
Sales NA *EMP* 1,242
Tkr Sym LION *Exch* NGS
SIC 6022 State commercial banks
Ch Bd: James B Miller Jr
**Pr:* H Palmer Proctor Jr
CFO: Stephen H Brolly
VP: David Buchanan
VP: Ron Hendrix
VP: Mickey Parker
VP: Kena Powell
Mktg Mgr: Phillip Hilton

D-U-N-S 96-783-6953
FIDELITY WELFARE BENEFIT PLANS VEBA TRUST
82 Devonshire St, Boston, MA 02109-3614
Tel (617) 563-1428 *Founded/Ownrshp* 2011
Sales NA *EMP* 2
Accts Pricewaterhousecoopers Llp Bo
SIC 6411 Pension & retirement plan consultants

D-U-N-S 79-056-2326
FIDELITY/WTC INC
(*Suby of* FIDELITY INVESTMENTS) ★
82 Devonshire St, Boston, MA 02109-3614
Tel (617) 563-8300 *Founded/Ownrshp* 1987
Sales 38.1MM^E *EMP* 1,000
SIC 6282 Investment advice
VP: Beth Flanagan

D-U-N-S 06-149-4606
FIDESSA BUY-SIDE INC
160 Federal St, Boston, MA 02110-1700
Tel (617) 235-1000 *Founded/Ownrshp* 2001
Sales 105.3MM^E *EMP* 2,000
SIC 6726 8742 Investment offices; Financial consultant
Pr: Megan Costello

D-U-N-S 11-412-8577
FIDESSA CORP
(*Suby of* FIDESSA GROUP PLC)
17 State St Fl 18, New York, NY 10004-1563
Tel (212) 269-9000 *Founded/Ownrshp* 1999
Sales 109.8MM^E *EMP* 375^E
SIC 7371 Computer software development
COO: Robert Thompson
**Ch Bd:* Mark Ames
Pr: Martin Hakker
Pr: Anthony Martinez
Pr: Brian Tang
**Ch:* John Hamer
Ex VP: Joy Rosenstein
Sr VP: Dan Smalley
VP: Michael Begic
VP: Nigel Holmes-Mitchell
VP: Kristin Kelly
VP: Adam Levy
**VP:* Justin Llewellyn-Jones
VP: Paul Neumaier
VP: Nevin Patton
VP: Kevin Sacristan
VP: Magaly Sanchez
Assoc Dir: Daniel Delahanty

D-U-N-S 00-698-3654
■ FIDUCIARY TRUST CO INTERNATIONAL (NY)
(*Suby of* FRANKLIN RESOURCES INC) ★
280 Park Ave, New York, NY 10017-1216
Tel (212) 632-3000 *Founded/Ownrshp* 1930
Sales NA *EMP* 300
SIC 6099 Safe deposit companies
CEO: John M Dowd
Ch Bd: Margot Bogert
**Ch Bd:* Gail E Cohen
CFO: Larry Sternkopf
Ex VP: Stephanie Birrell Luedke
Ex VP: J Chisholm Lyons
Ex VP: Michael J Materasso
Ex VP: Ronald J Sanchez
Sr VP: William E Leffingwell
Sr VP: R Ward
Board of Directors: Margot Bogert, James C Goodfellow

D-U-N-S 04-207-2157 IMP
FIELD MUSEUM OF NATURAL HISTORY (IL)
RESEARCH CENTER
1400 S Lake Shore Dr, Chicago, IL 60605-2429
Tel (312) 922-9410 *Founded/Ownrshp* 1893
Sales 95.3MM *EMP* 600^E
Accts Plante & Moran Pllc Chicago
SIC 8412 Museum
Pr: John W McCarter Jr
V Ch: Wilbur H Gantz III
**Pr:* Richard Lariviere
COO: Josh Ostergaard
Bd of Dir: William J White
**Ex VP:* Jim Croft
VP: Lance Grande
VP: R L Grande
**VP:* Charles Katzenmeyer
**VP:* Debra Moskovits
**VP:* Laura Sadler
Exec: Pamela Clayburn

D-U-N-S 00-637-5125
FIELD PACKING CO LLC
SPECIALTY FOODS GROUP
(*Suby of* SPECIALTY FOODS GROUP) ★
6 Dublin Ln, Owensboro, KY 42301-0500
Tel (270) 926-2324 *Founded/Ownrshp* 1914
Sales 121.5MM^E *EMP* 500
SIC 2011 Meat packing plants; Pork products from pork slaughtered on site
Genl Mgr: Aen Sthissler
VP: Steve Knott
Prd Mgr: Glen Harriman
VP Sls: Keith Luedke

FIELD TURF USA
See FIELDTURF USA INC

D-U-N-S 05-726-5027 EXP
FIELDALE FARMS CORP
555 Broiler Blvd, Baldwin, GA 30511-2064
Tel (706) 778-5100 *Founded/Ownrshp* 2000
Sales 1.5MMM^E *EMP* 4,800
SIC 2015 2013 0751 Poultry slaughtering & processing; Poultry, processed: cooked; Sausages & other prepared meats; Poultry services
CEO: Thomas A Arrendale III
**Pr:* Thomas M Hensley Jr
**CFO:* David E Elrod
**Ch:* Gus Arrendale
**Treas:* Eddie Elrod
Info Man: Joe Hatfield

D-U-N-S 10-219-3278 EXP
FIELDBROOK FOODS CORP
(*Suby of* FFC HOLDING CORP AND SUBSIDIARIES) ★
1 Ice Cream Dr, Dunkirk, NY 14048-3300
Tel (716) 366-5400 *Founded/Ownrshp* 2001
Sales 101.8MM^E *EMP* 350^E
SIC 2024 Ice cream & frozen desserts
CEO: Kenneth A Johnson
**Pr:* Robert Griewisch
**Sr VP:* James Masood
**VP:* Ronald Odebralski

FIELDER EQUIPMENT
See ARIZONA PARKING LOT SERVICE

D-U-N-S 00-204-8341
FIELDGLASS INC
(*Suby of* SAP SE)
111 N Canal St Ste 600, Chicago, IL 60606-7221
Tel (312) 763-4800 *Founded/Ownrshp* 2000
Sales 120.0MM *EMP* 637
SIC 7373 Systems software development services
Pr: Rob Brim
**CFO:* John Jennings
VP: Jeff Basso
**CTO:* Sean Chou
QA Dir: Grace Buzzard
QA Dir: Vikram Rudra
Web Dev: Noah Pearson
Software D: Lucas Bivens
Software D: Roshini David
Software D: Yatin Madan
Opers Mgr: Matt Kreh

D-U-N-S 88-340-4998
FIELDSTONE MORTGAGE CO
(*Suby of* FIELDSTONE INVESTMENT CORPORATION)
5094 Dorsey Hall Dr # 104, Ellicott City, MD 21042-7821
Tel (410) 772-7217 *Founded/Ownrshp* 1995
Sales NA *EMP* 730
SIC 6163 Mortgage brokers arranging for loans, using money of others
CEO: Michael J Sonnenfeld
CFO: Teresa McDrmott
Ofcr: Andrew Baraline
Ofcr: Jennifer McGrath
Ofcr: Beau Taylor
Ex VP: Mary Obannon
Sr VP: John J Jacobs
Sr VP: John Kendall
Sr VP: Mary A O'Bannon
VP: John Camarena
VP: Monica Crowther
VP: Tom Gillen
VP: Cynthia Harkness
VP: Cynthia L Harkness
VP: Camp John
VP: Jacobs John
VP: Mark Krebs
VP: Nancy Maradie
VP: Teri Rapp
VP: Diane Slack
**VP:* Gary Uchimoio

D-U-N-S 13-186-2364 IMP
FIELDTURF USA INC
FIELDTURF USA
175 N Industrial Blvd Ne, Calhoun, GA 30701-8651
Tel (706) 625-6533 *Founded/Ownrshp* 1999
Sales 2.7MMM *EMP* 184
SIC 3999 Grasses, artificial & preserved
CEO: Eric Daliere
**CFO:* Pedro Azevedo

FIELDVIEW MANOR
See BEVERLY ENTERPRISES - WISCONSIN INC

D-U-N-S 06-866-3836 EXP
FIELDWOOD ENERGY LLC
2000 W Sam Houston Pkwy S # 1200, Houston, TX 77042-3623
Tel (713) 969-1000 *Founded/Ownrshp* 2012
Sales 1.2MMM^E *EMP* 835^E
SIC 1382 Oil & gas exploration services
Pr: Matt McCarroll
**VP:* Richard Black
VP: Trey Gilmore
VP: Doug Macafee
VP: John Nicholson
VP Opers: Paul Gluth
Counsel: William Getschow

D-U-N-S 05-933-9341 EXP
FIESTA MART INC
5235 Katy Fwy, Houston, TX 77007-2210
Tel (713) 869-5060 *Founded/Ownrshp* 2015
Sales 1.3MMM^E *EMP* 8,000
SIC 5411 Supermarkets, chain
Pr: Michael Byars
**Pr:* Michael Byers
**CFO:* Vicki J Baum
**Treas:* Stacy Walker
Sys Mgr: Connie Richard
Pr Mgr: Elisa Garnica
Pgrm Dir: Jim Pessagno

D-U-N-S 03-874-9111
FIESTA RESTAURANT GROUP INC
968 James St, Syracuse, NY 13203-2503
Tel (315) 424-0513 *Founded/Ownrshp* 2012
Sales 79.8MM^E *EMP* 1,700^E
SIC 5812 Eating places
Pr: Timothy P Taft
**VP:* William E Myers

D-U-N-S 07-831-2330
▲ FIESTA RESTAURANT GROUP INC
14800 Landmark Blvd # 500, Dallas, TX 75254-7013
Tel (972) 702-9300 *Founded/Ownrshp* 2011
Sales 687.3MM *EMP* 11,550
Tkr Sym FRGI *Exch* NGS
SIC 5812 6794 Eating places; Mexican restaurant; Franchises, selling or licensing
CEO: Danny Meisenheimer
**Ch Bd:* Jack A Smith
CFO: Lynn S Schweinfurth
Sr VP: Joseph A Zirkman
VP: John A Todd
Netwrk Eng: Dustin Pike

Board of Directors: Barry J Alperin, Nicholas Daviras, Stephen P Elker, Brian P Friedman, Stacey Rauch

D-U-N-S 62-230-5878 IMP
FIESTA TEXAS INC
SIX FLAGS FESTA TEXAS THEME PK
17000 W Interstate 10, San Antonio, TX 78257-9503
Tel (210) 697-5000 *Founded/Ownrshp* 1990
Sales 58.1MM^E *EMP* 1,775
SIC 7996 Theme park, amusement
Pr: Martin Bozer

D-U-N-S 07-972-7060
FIFTEENINONE OPCO GROUP LLC
7400 New La Grange Rd, Louisville, KY 40222-4870
Tel (502) 429-8062 *Founded/Ownrshp* 2013
Sales 5.3MM^E *EMP* 2,540
SIC 8051 Skilled nursing care facilities
CEO: Bob Norcross
CFO: Stacey Rogers

D-U-N-S 07-957-6977
▲ FIFTH STREET ASSET MANAGEMENT INC
777 W Putnam Ave Ste 3, Greenwich, CT 06830-5014
Tel (203) 681-3600 *Founded/Ownrshp* 1998
Sales 97.7MM *EMP* 70^E
Tkr Sym FSAM *Exch* NGS
SIC 6282 Investment advice; Manager of mutual funds, contract or fee basis
Ch Bd: Leonard M Tannenbaum
**Pr:* Bernard D Berman
Pr: Todd G Owens
**COO:* Alexander C Frank
CIO: Ivelin M Dimitrov

D-U-N-S 80-857-3690
▲ FIFTH STREET FINANCE CORP
777 W Putnam Ave Ste 3, Greenwich, CT 06830-5014
Tel (203) 681-3600 *Founded/Ownrshp* 2007
Sales 247.8MM *EMP* 5^E
Accts Pricewaterhousecoopers Llp Ne
Tkr Sym FSC *Exch* NGS
SIC 6726 Investors syndicates
CEO: Todd G Owens
**Ch Bd:* Bernard D Berman
**Pr:* Ivelin M Dimitrov
CFO: Steven M Noreika
Chf Cred: Kerry S Acocella
VP: Andrew Ippolite
Corp Couns: Steven Magi

D-U-N-S 00-699-9403 IMP
▲ FIFTH THIRD BANCORP (OH)
38 Fountain Square Plz, Cincinnati, OH 45202-3102
Tel (800) 972-3030 *Founded/Ownrshp* 1975
Sales NA *EMP* 18,261^E
Tkr Sym FITB *Exch* NGS
SIC 6022 State commercial banks
Pr: Greg D Carmichael
Pr: Megan Anderson
Pr: Joy Byrwa
Pr: Jim Chandler
Pr: Carolyn Dearmond
Pr: Tom Eldridge
Pr: Cherisse Estes
Pr: Rebecca Gray
Pr: Maria Holmes
Pr: Ben Jenkins
Pr: Cory Kent
Pr: Mark Lamson
Pr: Kevin Mataway
Pr: Michele McDonel
Pr: Jason Parigen
Pr: Peter Richards
Pr: Gregory Sova
Pr: Melissa Stegman
Pr: Richard Steimer
Pr: Monique Suranye
Pr: Michelle Van Dyke
Board of Directors: Jewell D Hoover, Nicholas K Akins, Eileen A Mallesch, B Evan Bayh III, Michael B McCallister, Jorge L Benitez, Hendrick G Meijer, Katherine B Blackburn, Marsha C Williams, Ulysses L Bridgeman Jr, Emerson L Brumback, Jerry W Burris, James P Hackett, Gary R Heminger

D-U-N-S 08-159-0853
■ FIFTH THIRD BANK (OH)
(*Suby of* FIFTH THIRD FINANCIAL CORPORATION)
38 Fountain Square Plz, Cincinnati, OH 45202-3191
Tel (800) 972-3030 *Founded/Ownrshp* 1858, 2001
Sales NA *EMP* 19,446
SIC 6022 State trust companies accepting deposits, commercial
CEO: George A Schaefer
**Pr:* Greg Carmichael
Pr: Thomas R Quinn Jr
Assoc VP: Michael Pento
Ex VP: Debra Arenson
Ex VP: Robert Curry
Ex VP: Olga Demekhin
Ex VP: Gregory Lutz
Sr VP: Mark Bitter
**Sr VP:* Don Coleman
Sr VP: Richard Cushman
Sr VP: Anne L Gehring
Sr VP: Richard D Maxwell
Sr VP: Diana McAfee
Sr VP: Michael Menyhart
Sr VP: Thomas Schiller
Sr VP: John Worthington
VP: Dave Allaire
VP: Joseph Daly
VP: Craig Ellis
VP: Don Figlio

D-U-N-S 78-706-4281
■ FIFTH THIRD BANK
(*Suby of* FIFTH THIRD FINANCIAL CORPORATION)
1 Vandenberg Ctr Nw, Grand Rapids, MI 49503
Tel (616) 653-5900 *Founded/Ownrshp* 1853
Sales NA *EMP* 751
SIC 6022 State commercial banks
Pr: George A Schaefer Jr
Ofcr: Crystal Arnold
Assoc VP: Jennifer Ranville
Assoc VP: Rebecca Sack
VP: Wesley Vanderwilk

D-U-N-S 01-975-6683
■ **FIFTHTHIRD BANK INDIANA**
(Suby of FIFTHTHIRD BANCORP) ★
251 N Illinois St # 1000, Indianapolis, IN 46204-4304
Tel (317) 383-2300 Founded/Ownrshp 1989
Sales NA EMP 830
SIC 6022 State commercial banks
Pr: Michael Alley
*Sr VP: Carol Dienhart
Sr VP: John Edwards
Sr VP: Kyle Fisher
Sr VP: Kevin Hipskind
VP: Steven Alonso
VP: Jeff Craig
VP: Todd Flick
VP: Teresa Shaffer

D-U-N-S 80-979-2513
■ **FIFTHTHIRD BANK NATIONAL ASSOCIATION**
(Suby of FIFTHTHIRD BANCORP) ★
424 Church St Ste 500, Nashville, TN 37219-2391
Tel (615) 687-3100 Founded/Ownrshp 2008
Sales NA EMP 500
SIC 6022 State commercial banks
CFO: Michael Shingleton
Sr VP: Karen Ahern
VP: Brent Michell

D-U-N-S 13-188-9255
■ **FIFTHTHIRD BANK OF COLUMBUS OH**
(Suby of FIFTHTHIRD BANCORP) ★
21 E State St Fl 4, Columbus, OH 43215-4208
Tel (614) 744-7553 Founded/Ownrshp 1985
Sales NA EMP 900
SIC 6022 State trust companies accepting deposits, commercial
Pr: Jordan Miller

D-U-N-S 04-491-0040
■ **FIFTHTHIRD BANK OF KENTUCKY INC**
(Suby of FIFTHTHIRD BANCORP) ★
401 S 4th St Ste 1000, Louisville, KY 40202-3411
Tel (502) 562-5215 Founded/Ownrshp 1886, 1995
Sales NA EMP 501
SIC 6021 National commercial banks
Pr: James R Gaunt
Treas: Paul F Clemens
Sr VP: Robert Banks
Sr VP: Marty Garrity
VP: Philip R McHugh
VP: Sharon Wheat

D-U-N-S 04-226-3934
■ **FIFTHTHIRD BANK OF NORTHEASTERN OHIO**
(Suby of FIFTHTHIRD BANCORP) ★
600 Superior Ave E Fl 5, Cleveland, OH 44114-2621
Tel (216) 274-5533 Founded/Ownrshp 1995
Sales NA EMP 720
SIC 6021 National commercial banks
CEO: George A Schaefer
CFO: Anthony V Cosentino
*Ex VP: Stephen J Schrantz
VP: Dennis Green
VP: Thomas Stuckart

D-U-N-S 18-325-9779
■ **FIFTHTHIRD BANK OF NORTHERN KENTUCKY**
(Suby of FIFTHTHIRD BANCORP) ★
8100 Burlington Pike, Florence, KY 41042-1261
Tel (859) 283-8500 Founded/Ownrshp 1988
Sales NA EMP 300
SIC 6022 State commercial banks
CEO: Timothy Rawe
*CFO: Jason Kaster
VP: William Cochran

D-U-N-S 00-790-4543
■ **FIFTHTHIRD BANK OF NORTHWESTERN OHIO NA**
(Suby of FIFTHTHIRD BANCORP) ★
1 Seagate Ste 2200, Toledo, OH 43604-1525
Tel (419) 259-7820 Founded/Ownrshp 1989
Sales NA EMP 300
SIC 6021 National commercial banks
Pr: Robert Laclair
Off Mgr: Kelly Davidson

D-U-N-S 00-715-1046 IMP/EXP
FIKE CORP (MO)
704 Sw 10th St, Blue Springs, MO 64015-4286
Tel (816) 229-3405 Founded/Ownrshp 1945
Sales 215.0MM^E EMP 930
SIC 3494 3569 3444 2899

D-U-N-S 10-766-9335
FIKES WHOLESALE INC
CORD FINANCIAL SERVICES
6261 Central Pointe Pkwy, Temple, TX 76504-2613
Tel (254) 791-0009 Founded/Ownrshp 1975
Sales 208.3MM^E EMP 1,000
SIC 5411 5171 Convenience stores, independent; Petroleum bulk stations & terminals
CEO: James Fikes
*COO: Raymond Smith CPA
*Sec: Kim Fikes
VP: Kipp Sassaman

FILA FOOTWEAR U S A
See FILA USA INC

D-U-N-S 10-632-6812 IMP
■ **FILA USA INC**
FILA FOOTWEAR U S A
(Suby of FILA KOREA LTD.)
930 Ridgebrook Rd Ste 200, Sparks, MD 21152-9482
Tel (410) 773-3000 Founded/Ownrshp 2007
Sales 324.6MM^E EMP 710
SIC 5139 5131 5137 5611 5621 5632 Footwear, athletic; Piece goods & notions; Women's & children's clothing; Men's & boys' clothing stores; Women's clothing stores; Women's accessory & specialty stores
CEO: Gene Yoon
*Pr: Jon Epstein
COO: Aron Corona
*CFO: Yung Chan Jo
*Treas: Christopher Blumhard
*VP: Andrea Greco
VP: Gary Wakley
Brnch Mgr: Gabrielle Lockhart
Dir IT: Tracy Butler
Dir IT: Sandy Hamilton
IT Man: Dawn Augsburger

D-U-N-S 18-056-3058
■ **FILEMAKER INC**
(Suby of APPLE INC) ★
5201 Patrick Henry Dr, Santa Clara, CA 95054-1164
Tel (408) 987-7000 Founded/Ownrshp 1987
Sales 86.0MM^E EMP 407
SIC 7372 Prepackaged software
Pr: Dominique Philippe Goupil
CFO: Bill Epling
VP: Lucy Chen
VP: Brad Freitag
VP: Scott Lewis
VP: Frank Lu
VP: Takanobu Miyamoto
VP: John F Pinheiro
VP: John Ponheiro
VP: Ryan Rosenberg
VP: Ryanm Rosenberg
VP: Jon Sigler
VP: Simon Thornhill
Dir Soc: Shari Martinez
Comm Man: Kevin Mallon

D-U-N-S 07-495-8679
FILENET CORP
3565 Harbor Blvd, Costa Mesa, CA 92626-1405
Tel (800) 345-3638 Founded/Ownrshp 2006
Sales 89.2MM^E EMP 1,695
SIC 7373 7372

FILET OF CHICKEN
See FOC ACQUISITION LLC

D-U-N-S 62-156-1971
FILLMORE CAPITAL PARTNERS LLC
F C P
4 Embarcadero Ctr Ste 710, San Francisco, CA 94111-4172
Tel (415) 834-1477 Founded/Ownrshp 2003
Sales 2.6MMM^E EMP 35,100
SIC 6799 Real estate investors, except property operators
*Ex VP: Timothy C Getz
*Sr VP: Milton B Patipa
VP: Nicholas Finn
Mktg Dir: Hilary Andron

D-U-N-S 07-920-7332
FILLMORE CCA INVESTMENT LLC
100 Fillmore St Ste 600, Denver, CO 80206-4931
Tel (720) 284-6400 Founded/Ownrshp 2013
Sales 46.9MM^E EMP 16,900
SIC 7997 Membership sports & recreation clubs
Pr: Eric L Affeldt

D-U-N-S 07-860-2543
FILLMORE HOSPITALITY LLC
(Suby of F C P) ★
250 W Old Wilson Bridge R, Worthington, OH 43085-2215
Tel (614) 781-1420 Founded/Ownrshp 2011
Sales 58.0MM^E EMP 12,000
SIC 7041 Lodging house, organization
Sr VP: B Thomas Goodwin

D-U-N-S 02-243-5833
FILM MUSICIANS SECONDARY MARKETS FUND
15910 Ventura Blvd # 900, Encino, CA 91436-2809
Tel (818) 755-7777 Founded/Ownrshp 1975
Sales 93.7MM EMP 39
Accts Miller Kaplan Arase Llp North
SIC 8741 6722 Financial management for business; Management investment, open-end
Ex Dir: Kim Roberts Hedgpeth
Off Mgr: Cathy Chu
Opers Mgr: Chris Kuhrt

D-U-N-S 04-446-7140 IMP
FILMED ENTERTAINMENT INC
BOOK OF THE MONTH CLUB
(Suby of PRIDE TREE HOLDINGS, INC.)
1 Penn Plz Fl 5, New York, NY 10119-0599
Tel (212) 596-2000 Founded/Ownrshp 2012
Sales 117.0MM^E EMP 500
SIC 5961 Book club, mail order; Record &/or tape (music or video) club, mail order; Mail order house
CEO: Deborah I Fine
*Ch Bd: John Lippman
*Ex VP: Beth Goss
Sr VP: Ralph Cuomo
Sr VP: Joanne Pello
VP: Dirk Bouwman
VP: Steve Brita
*VP: Jenn Feldman
VP: Achim Welter
VP Merchng: Ann Axelrod

D-U-N-S 84-800-7910 IMP/EXP
■ **FILTERTEK INC**
ITW FLTER PDTS TRNSM FLTRATION
(Suby of ILLINOIS TOOL WORKS INC) ★
11411 Price Rd, Hebron, IL 60034-8936
Tel (815) 648-2410 Founded/Ownrshp 1965
Sales 171.9MM^E EMP 770
SIC 3089 3564 Plastic processing; Blowers & fans
Pr: Roland Martel
*CEO: David F Atkinson
VP: Larry Larkin
Prd Mgr: Brenda Syevens

D-U-N-S 83-284-2350
FILTRAN HOLDINGS LLC
875 Seegers Rd, Des Plaines, IL 60016-3045
Tel (847) 635-6670 Founded/Ownrshp 2009
Sales 174.9MM^E EMP 606
SIC 3433 Heating equipment, except electric
Pr: Larry W Gies Jr
*CFO: Dennis Baran
*Treas: David J Ball
*VP: John E Udelhofen
*VP: Brett Wall

D-U-N-S 83-280-5159 IMP
FILTRAN LLC
(Suby of FILTRAN HOLDINGS LLC) ★
875 Seegers Rd, Des Plaines, IL 60016-3045
Tel (847) 635-6670 Founded/Ownrshp 2008
Sales 172.4MM^E EMP 605
SIC 3433 Heating equipment, except electric
Pr: Brett Wall
CFO: Dennis Baran
VP: Dennis Barn
VP: John Eleftherakis
VP: John E Udelhofen
Brnch Mgr: Bob Somers
Genl Mgr: Chris Heidemann
Plnt Mgr: Joe Curtin

D-U-N-S 07-915-9345
FILTRATION GROUP CORP
912 E Washington St Ste 1, Joliet, IL 60433-1286
Tel (815) 726-4600 Founded/Ownrshp 2010
Sales 183.1MM^E EMP 674^E
SIC 3564 Blowers & fans
Pr: George Nolen
*CFO: Tim McCarty
*Sr VP: Bill Huber

D-U-N-S 12-128-1083 IMP/EXP
FILTRATION GROUP LLC
912 E Washington St Ste 1, Joliet, IL 60433-1286
Tel (815) 726-4600 Founded/Ownrshp 2010
Sales 271.4MM^E EMP 900
SIC 3564

D-U-N-S 00-749-4024 IMP/EXP
FIMCO INC
FIMCO INDUSTRIES
800 Stevens Port Dr, Dakota Dunes, SD 57049-5005
Tel (605) 232-6800 Founded/Ownrshp 1966
Sales 104.0MM^E EMP 350
SIC 3523 3524

FIMCO INDUSTRIES
See FIMCO INC

D-U-N-S 09-679-0980
FINANCE AMERICA LLC
(Suby of LEHMAN BROTHERS HOLDINGS INC.)
1901 Main St Ste 150, Irvine, CA 92614-0516
Tel (949) 440-1000 Founded/Ownrshp 1999
Sales NA EMP 827
Accts Ernst & Young Llp
SIC 6162 6163 Mortgage bankers; Loan brokers
Ofcr: Leigh Harris
MIS Dir: Jeff Hurley

FINANCE AND ACCOUNTS
See HEALTH MISSISSIPPI ORGANIZATION INC

FINANCE AND ADMINISTRATION
See IDAHO STATE UNIVERSITY

FINANCE DEPARTMENT
See CITY OF MANCHESTER

FINANCE DEPARTMENT
See ATTORNEY GENERAL OF OHIO

D-U-N-S 00-891-2185
▲ **FINANCIAL ENGINES INC**
1050 Enterprise Way Fl 3, Sunnyvale, CA 94089-1411
Tel (408) 498-6000 Founded/Ownrshp 1996
Sales 310.7MM EMP 527
Tkr Sym FNGN Exch NGS
SIC 8742 6282 6411 Management consulting services; Investment advice; Pension & retirement plan consultants
Pr: Lawrence M Raffone
*Ch Bd: Blake R Grossman
CFO: Raymond J Sims
Chf Inves: Christopher L Jones
Ofcr: Dexter Buck
Ex VP: John B Bunch
Ex VP: Michael J Campbell
Ex VP: Gina M Cruse
Ex VP: Paul A Gamble
Ex VP: Paul Gamble
Ex VP: Kelly S O'Donnell
Ex VP: Kelly Odonnell
VP: Chung Cheong
VP: Jeffrey C Grace
VP: Anne Tuttle
Board of Directors: Heidi K Fields, Joseph A Grundfest, Robert A Huret, E Olena Berg-Lacy, Michael E Martin, John B Shoven, David B Yoffie

D-U-N-S 10-328-2604
FINANCIAL GUARANTY INSURANCE CO
F G I C
(Suby of FGIC CORP) ★
521 5th Ave Fl 15, New York, NY 10175-1201
Tel (212) 312-3000 Founded/Ownrshp 2003
Sales NA EMP 189^E
SIC 6351 Surety insurance
Prin: Timothy S Travers
V Ch: Haughton W Roger
*Ex VP: A Edward Turi III
Ex VP: Dennis Uhniat
*VP: Michael C Haines
VP: Elizabeth Menhenett
VP: John Rossi
*Mng Dir: Derek M Donnelly
IT Man: Joseph Fanelli
Mktg Mgr: Riina Rumvolt
Genl Couns: Turi Edward

D-U-N-S 15-043-9800
FINANCIAL HOLDING CORP
IPFS CORPORATION
1055 Broadway Blvd Fl 11, Kansas City, MO 64105-1575
Tel (816) 391-2000 Founded/Ownrshp 1984
Sales NA EMP 971
SIC 6411 6311 6153 Insurance agents, brokers & service; Life insurance; Short-term business credit
Pr: Michael A Merriman
*CFO: Gary E Jenkins
*Ex VP: Gary Muller
*VP: Mark K Fallon

D-U-N-S 06-200-9279
FINANCIAL INDUSTRY REGULATORY AUTHORITY INC
FINRA
1735 K St Nw, Washington, DC 20006-1506
Tel (301) 590-6500 Founded/Ownrshp 1938
Sales 900.7MM EMP 3,400
Accts Ernst & Young Llp Mclean Vir
SIC 8611 Regulatory associations
CEO: Richard G Ketchum
Pr: Linda Fienberg
*CFO: Todd T Diganci
Bd of Dir: Randall L Rubin
Assoc VP: Michael Dillon
Ex VP: Gregory Ahern
Ex VP: Brad Bennett
*Ex VP: J Bradley Bennett
Ex VP: Todd Diganci
Ex VP: Thomas Gira
Ex VP: Steve Joachim
Ex VP: John Malitzis
*Ex VP: Marc Menchel
*Ex VP: Howard M Schloss
*Ex VP: Thomas M Selman
*Sr VP: Marcia E Asquith
Sr VP: Gene Demaio
*Sr VP: Tracy Johnson
VP: Alden Adkins
VP: Katri Arcaro
VP: Nancy Condon

D-U-N-S 08-033-8262
▲ **FINANCIAL INSTITUTIONS INC**
220 Liberty St, Warsaw, NY 14569-1499
Tel (585) 786-1100 Founded/Ownrshp 1931
Sales NA EMP 645^E
Accts Kpmg Llp Rochester New York
Tkr Sym FISI Exch NGS
SIC 6021 7389 National commercial banks; Financial services
Pr: Martin K Birmingham
COO: Richard J Harrison
CFO: Kevin B Klotzbach
Ofcr: Christina George
Ofcr: Kenneth V Winn
Top Exec: Bridget Gandy
Top Exec: Laurie K Hunsicker
Ex VP: William L Kreienberg
Sr VP: Jonathan W Chase
Sr VP: Paula D Dolan
Sr VP: Sonia M Dumbleton
Sr VP: Michael D Grover
VP: Robert Alin
VP: Steven Ambrose
VP: Rita Bartol
VP: Cathy Cary
VP: Alan Conley
VP: Gina Grisaffi
VP: Jennifer Lam
VP: Amy Mathis
VP: Robert McFadden

D-U-N-S 01-058-8754
FINANCIAL INSURANCE MANAGEMENT CORP
F I M C
1440 Main St, Sarasota, FL 34236-5715
Tel (941) 952-5522 Founded/Ownrshp 2001
Sales NA EMP 150^E
SIC 6411 8742 Insurance agents; Marketing consulting services
Pr: Darrell Gambero
*Ch Bd: Douglas S Libertore
*CFO: Denise Leach
Sr VP: Chuck Hosie
Sr VP: Lou-Ann Speed
VP Sls: Claude Borrelli

FINANCIAL OFFICE
See WASHINGTON COUNTY ENDOWMENT FUND (INC)

D-U-N-S 14-784-3361
FINANCIAL SECURITY ASSURANCE HOLDINGS LTD
(Suby of ASSURED GUARANTY US HOLDINGS INC) ★
31 W 52nd St, New York, NY 10019-6118
Tel (212) 826-0100 Founded/Ownrshp 2009
Sales NA EMP 125^E
SIC 6351 Surety insurance
Ch Bd: Dominic Frederico
*Pr: Sean W McCarthy
CFO: Robert Bailenson
*CFO: Robert Mills
VP: Jay Gandhi
VP: Nick Pappadopolis
VP: Steve Tremblay
Dir Risk M: Howard W Albert
Mng Dir: Russell B Brewer
Mng Dir: Christopher Chafizadeh
Mng Dir: Edsel C Langley

D-U-N-S 13-136-4994
FINANCIAL SECURITY ASSURANCE INTERNATIONAL INC
(Suby of FINANCIAL SECURITY ASSURANCE HOLDINGS LTD) ★
350 Park Ave Fl 13, New York, NY 10022-6140
Tel (212) 826-0100 Founded/Ownrshp 1989
Sales NA EMP 346
Accts Pricewaterhousecoopers Llp Ne
SIC 6351 Surety insurance
Ch Bd: Robert P Cochran
*Pr: Sean W McCarthy
*CFO: John A Harrison
Treas: Edsel C Langley Jr
VP: Ryan Ashley
VP: Nick Papadopoulos
Mng Dir: Miguel Abeniacar
*Mng Dir: Russell B Brewer II
Mng Dir: Geoffrey H Durno
Mng Dir: Suzanne Finnegan
*Mng Dir: Peter E Hoey
Board of Directors: Constance A Begelfer, James P Conn, Kathleen A Cullen, Charles D Silberstein

D-U-N-S 60-939-2253
■ **FINANCIAL SERVICE CORP**
(*Suby of* SUNAMERICA INC) ★
2300 Windy Ridge Pkwy Se 1100s, Atlanta, GA 30339-5665
Tel (770) 916-6500 *Founded/Ownrshp* 1997
Sales 194.7MM^E *EMP* 200
SIC 6722 6411 8742 6211 Mutual fund sales, on own account; Life insurance agents; New business start-up consultant; Security brokers & dealers
Pr: Gerald A Geiger
COO: Helen Praiter
Treas: Daniel O Williams
Sr VP: A Geiger
VP: Helen H Prater

FINANCIAL SERVICES
See COUNTY OF MARION

D-U-N-S 02-898-7984
FINANCIALFORCE.COM INC
(*Suby of* UNIT4 N.V.)
595 Market St Ste 2700, San Francisco, CA 94105-2840
Tel (866) 743-2220 *Founded/Ownrshp* 2009
Sales 88.0MM^E *EMP* 650^E
SIC 7371 Computer software development
CEO: Jeremy Roche
Pr: Joe Fuca
CFO: John Bonney
Sr VP: John Moss
VP: Chris Lee
VP: Sam Loveland
Snr Sftwr: Nathan Pepper
Software D: Agustina Garcia
Software D: Paul Lawrence
Software D: Chris Peterson
Pr Dir: Sandra Lo

D-U-N-S 82-956-6855
FINCANTIERI MARINE GROUP HOLDINGS INC
(*Suby of* FINCANTIERI SPA)
605 N 3rd Ave, Sturgeon Bay, WI 54235-2324
Tel (920) 743-3406 *Founded/Ownrshp* 2008
Sales 308.4MM^E *EMP* 1,500
SIC 3731 Shipbuilding & repairing
Pr: Upinder Kamal
Prgrm Mgr: Gordon Lepisto
IT Man: Julie Koch

D-U-N-S 04-439-1712 IMP
FINCANTIERI MARINE GROUP LLC (NV)
BAY SHIPBUILDING
(*Suby of* FINCANTIERI MARINE GROUP HOLDINGS INC) ★
605 N 3rd Ave, Sturgeon Bay, WI 54235-2324
Tel (920) 743-3406 *Founded/Ownrshp* 1959
Sales 277.1MM^E *EMP* 900
SIC 3731 Shipbuilding & repairing
Ch: Corrado Antonini
Pr: Gene Caldwell
**CEO:* Giuseppe Bono
**COO:* Enrico Buschi
**Ch:* Vincenzo Petrone
**Sr VP:* Gabriele Cocco
**Sr VP:* Alberto Maestrini
**Sr VP:* Giorgi Rizzo
Prgrm Mgr: James Lynch
Genl Mgr: Michael Pinkham
Genl Mgr: Todd Thayse

D-U-N-S 11-306-8027 IMP
FINCANTIERI MARINE SYSTEMS NORTH AMERICA INC
(*Suby of* FINCANTIERI SPA)
800 Principal Ct Ste C, Chesapeake, VA 23320-3681
Tel (757) 548-6000 *Founded/Ownrshp* 1996
Sales 34.7MMM *EMP* 56
SIC 7699 5084 Marine engine repair; Engines & parts, diesel
CEO: Dario Deste
**Pr:* Domenico Sorvillo
Treas: Paolo Pezzulo
**VP:* Richard Dinsmore
Board of Directors: Dario Deste, Pier Francesco Ragni, Domenico Sorvillo, Francesco Valente

D-U-N-S 80-202-4955
FINCH PAPER HOLDINGS LLC
1 Sound Shore Dr Ste 302, Greenwich, CT 06830-7251
Tel (203) 622-9138 *Founded/Ownrshp* 2007
Sales 83.7MM^E *EMP* 750
SIC 2621 Paper mills
VP: Edward Fletcher
Genl Mgr: Christine Perigen

D-U-N-S 79-484-0967 IMP
FINDLAY AUTOMOTIVE INC
SATURN
310 N Gibson Rd, Henderson, NV 89014-6702
Tel (702) 558-8888 *Founded/Ownrshp* 1990
Sales 86.3MM^E *EMP* 175
SIC 5511 Automobiles, new & used
Pr: Clifford J Findlay
**CFO:* Tyler Corder
Mktg Mgr: Mike Feeney
Sls Mgr: Jack D Cowell

FINE ART LAMPS
See BLUMBERG INDUSTRIES INC

FINE TEC COMPUTER
See TRIGEM ENTERPRISES INC

D-U-N-S 96-552-3624
FINGER LAKES REGIONAL HEALTH SYSTEM INC
GENEVA GENERAL HOSPITAL
196 North St, Geneva, NY 14456-1651
Tel (315) 787-4000 *Founded/Ownrshp* 1898
Sales 93.3MM *EMP* 160
Accts Bonadio & Co Llp Pittsford
SIC 8051 Skilled nursing care facilities
Pr: Jose Acevedo
**CFO:* Patricia Thompson
Dir Rx: Ted Mitchell
Ansthlgy: Kermit McGinnis
Doctor: Olaf Lieberg
Doctor: Ketul Patel
Doctor: Tamara Prull
Doctor: Mark Ryan

FINGERHUT
See BLUESTEM BRANDS INC

FINGERLAKES CENTER FOR LIVING
See AUBURN COMMUNITY HOSPITAL

D-U-N-S 03-820-4467
FINIAL REINSURANCE CO
(*Suby of* SCOR HOLDING (SWITZERLAND) AG)
100 Stamford Pl Ste 201, Stamford, CT 06902-6747
Tel (203) 564-5273 *Founded/Ownrshp* 2001
Sales NA *EMP* 231
SIC 6411

D-U-N-S 18-508-1635
▲ **FINISAR CORP**
1389 Moffett Park Dr, Sunnyvale, CA 94089-1134
Tel (408) 548-1000 *Founded/Ownrshp* 1987
Sales 1.2MMM *EMP* 13,400
Tkr Sym FNSR *Exch* NGS
SIC 3661 3663 Fiber optics communications equipment; Antennas, transmitting & communications; Receiver-transmitter units (transceiver)
Ch Bd: Jerry S Rawls
CFO: Kurt Adzema
Ex VP: Christopher E Brown
Ex VP: John H Clark
Ex VP: Julie S Eng
Ex VP: Todd Swanson
Ex VP: Joseph A Young
Sr VP: Mark Colyar

D-U-N-S 04-515-5652
▲ **FINISH LINE INC**
3308 N Mitthoefer Rd, Indianapolis, IN 46235-2332
Tel (317) 899-1022 *Founded/Ownrshp* 1976
Sales 1.8MMM *EMP* 14,300
Accts Ernst & Young Llp Indianapoli
Tkr Sym FINL *Exch* NGS
SIC 5661 5699 5941 Shoe stores; Footwear, athletic; Sports apparel; Sporting goods & bicycle shops
CEO: Samuel M Sato
**Ch Bd:* Glenn S Lyon
COO: Melissa A Greenwell
CFO: Edward W Wilhelm
Div Pres: Imran Jooma
Chf Mktg O: John J Hall
Ex VP: Bill Kirkendall
Ex VP: Sam Sato
Ex VP: Albert J Sutera
Sr VP: Steven Schreibman
Sr VP: Roger C Underwood
VP: Greg Davis
VP: Jenni Dillon
VP: Robert Edwards
VP: Teresa Harkness
VP: Jeff Kish
Exec: Jenncy Miller
Comm Dir: Dianna Boyce
Board of Directors: Torrence Boone, William P Carmichael, Richard P Crystal, Stephen Goldsmith, Norman H Gurwitz, Dolores A Kunda, Catherine A Langham

FINISHMASTER AUTO PNT STORES
See FINISHMASTER INC

D-U-N-S 03-774-8092
FINISHMASTER INC
FINISHMASTER AUTO PNT STORES
(*Suby of* UNI-SELECT INC)
115 W Washington St Fl 7, Indianapolis, IN 46204-2979
Tel (317) 237-3678 *Founded/Ownrshp* 1996
Sales 747.6MM^E *EMP* 1,646
SIC 5013 Body repair or paint shop supplies, automotive
Pr: Steve Arndt
COO: Wes N Dearbaugh
Treas: Gary Bilsland
VP: Craig Caudill
VP: Marc D Johnson
VP: Dean Mindestrom
VP: George Rickus
VP: Diane Roberts
VP: Kirk Utemark
Brnch Mgr: Lyndy Boutell
Brnch Mgr: Denise Hess

FINKL STEEL - CHICAGO
See A FINKL & SONS CO

FINLEY HOSPITAL
See CHILDBIRTH EDUCATION

D-U-N-S 06-325-4676
FINLEY HOSPITAL
350 N Grandview Ave, Dubuque, IA 52001-6392
Tel (563) 582-1881 *Founded/Ownrshp* 1987
Sales 110.9MM *EMP* 900
SIC 8011 Medical centers
Pr: David Brandon
Chf OB: Deborah A Labeau
**CFO:* Daniel L Carpenter
Treas: Glenda Egan
VP: Theodore Blanchard
VP: Judy Bredlow
VP: Katie Marchik
Dir Env Sv: Mary Jacobson
Ex Dir: Jim Hallihan
Mktg Mgr: Rod Tokheim

D-U-N-S 96-613-8013
FINN HOLDING CORP
PLATINUM EQUITY
360 N Crescent Dr, Beverly Hills, CA 90210-4874
Tel (310) 712-1850 *Founded/Ownrshp* 2010
Sales 1.1MMM^E *EMP* 8,278
SIC 4449 3731 4491 Canal barge operations; Barges, building & repairing; Marine terminals
Ch Bd: Tom Gores
**CFO:* Mary Ann Sigler
**VP:* Eva M Kalawski

D-U-N-S 07-484-2121
FINNEGAN HENDERSON FARABOW GARRETT & DUNNER LLP
901 New York Ave Nw # 1150, Washington, DC 20001-4435
Tel (202) 408-4000 *Founded/Ownrshp* 1965
Sales 130.3MM^E *EMP* 1,000^E
SIC 8111 General practice law office; Antitrust & trade regulation law; Patent, trademark & copyright law
Mng Pt: Barbara Clarke McCurdy
Pt: Steven M Anzalone
Pt: Robert D Bajefsky
Pt: Thomas Banks
Pt: M Paul Barker
Pt: James R Barney
Pt: John T Battaglia
Pt: Ronald A Bleeker
Pt: Michele Bosch
Pt: Smith R Brittingham IV
Pt: Paul W Browning
Pt: Richard V Burgujian
Pt: Adriana L Burgy
Pt: Elizabeth M Burke
Pt: Don O Burley
Pt: Virginia L Carron
Pt: Robert E Converse Jr
Pt: Patrick J Coyne
Pt: Kathleen A Daley
Pt: Frank A Decosta
Pt: Bryan C Diner

FINRA
See FINANCIAL INDUSTRY REGULATORY AUTHORITY INC

D-U-N-S 04-303-2283
FIP CONSTRUCTION INC
1536 New Britain Ave, Farmington, CT 06032-3112
Tel (860) 470-1800 *Founded/Ownrshp* 1985
Sales 149.5MM *EMP* 60
Accts Budwitz & Meyerjack Pc Chesh
SIC 1542 1541 Nonresidential construction; Commercial & office building, new construction; Industrial buildings & warehouses
Ch Bd: David T Shopis
**Pr:* William G Hardy
**VP:* Daniel Burns
Snr PM: Alan McLellan

D-U-N-S 17-668-0460
FIRE & LIFE SAFETY AMERICA INC
FLSA
(*Suby of* FIRE AND LIFE SAFETY AMERICA HOLDINGS INC) ★
3017 Vernon Rd, Richmond, VA 23228-3737
Tel (804) 222-1381 *Founded/Ownrshp* 1997
Sales 566.7MM^E *EMP* 1,200
SIC 5063 Fire alarm systems
Pr: Tom York
**COO:* Mark Glidewell
**CFO:* John Wolf
Bd of Dir: Gaylon Layfield
Bd of Dir: John Woodfin
**VP:* Ronnie Burkett
**VP:* Tom Coulbourn
**VP:* Jack Medovich
Dist Mgr: Rick Williams
Genl Mgr: Bill Woodcock
Off Mgr: Angela Doyle

D-U-N-S 61-973-3533
FIRE AND LIFE SAFETY AMERICA HOLDINGS INC
3017 Vernon Rd Ste 100, Richmond, VA 23228-3737
Tel (804) 222-1381 *Founded/Ownrshp* 1997
Sales 610.1MM^E *EMP* 1,200^E
SIC 1711 1731 Plumbing, heating, air-conditioning contractors; Sprinkler contractors; Fire sprinkler system installation; Fire detection & burglar alarm systems specialization
Pr: Tom York
**Pr:* James E Toups
**COO:* Ken Bitner
**VP:* Jay Coughlon

D-U-N-S 04-443-5584
FIRE INSURANCE EXCHANGE
4680 Wilshire Blvd, Los Angeles, CA 90010-3807
Tel (323) 932-3200 *Founded/Ownrshp* 1942
Sales NA *EMP* 16,728
SIC 6411 Insurance agents, brokers & service
Pr: Martin Feinstein
**Pr:* John Harrington
**Treas:* Ron Myhan

FIRE KING SECURITY GROUP
See FKI SECURITY GROUP LLC

D-U-N-S 08-269-7913 IMP/EXP
FIRE MOUNTAIN GEMS & BEADS INC (OR)
1 Fire Mountain Way, Grants Pass, OR 97526-2373
Tel (541) 956-7700 *Founded/Ownrshp* 1975
Sales 139.3MM^E *EMP* 450
SIC 5094

D-U-N-S 62-360-3086
FIRE MOUNTAIN RESTAURANTS LLC
(*Suby of* RYANS RESTAURANT GROUP LLC) ★
120 Chula Vis, San Antonio, TX 78232-2234
Tel (651) 994-8608 *Founded/Ownrshp* 1991
Sales 75.3MM^E *EMP* 2,900
SIC 5812 Restaurant, family: chain
CFO: A Wall
CFO: Keith Wall

D-U-N-S 95-991-9098
FIREBIRD RESTAURANT GROUP LLC
1845 Woodall Rodgers Fwy # 1100, Dallas, TX 75201-2239
Tel (972) 241-2171 *Founded/Ownrshp* 2008
Sales 42.2MM^E *EMP* 1,800
SIC 5812 Eating places
Pr: Michael D Karns

D-U-N-S 12-828-0273
FIREBIRDS INTERNATIONAL LLC
FIREBIRDS WOOD FIRED GRILL
13850 Balntyn Corp Pl # 450, Charlotte, NC 28277-2829
Tel (704) 944-5180 *Founded/Ownrshp* 2011
Sales 16.2MM *EMP* 3,550
SIC 5812 Eating places
CEO: Mark Eason
**CFO:* Brian McAlpine
VP: John Fowley
**VP Opers:* Steve Kislow
VP Opers: Gerald Pulsinelli
**VP Mktg:* Stephen Loftis

FIREBIRDS WOOD FIRED GRILL
See FIREBIRDS INTERNATIONAL LLC

D-U-N-S 60-539-2047
▲ **FIREEYE INC**
1440 Mccarthy Blvd, Milpitas, CA 95035-7438
Tel (408) 321-6300 *Founded/Ownrshp* 2004
Sales 622.9MM *EMP* 3,100^E
Tkr Sym FEYE *Exch* NGS
SIC 7372 Prepackaged software
Ch Bd: David G Dewalt
**Pr:* Kevin R Mandia
COO: Michael J Berry
Ex VP: Bill Robbins
Sr VP: Julie Cullivan
Sr VP: Alexa King
Sr VP: John McGee
Sr VP: Grady Summers
Sr VP: Kara Wilson
VP: Vijaya Kaza
VP: Christopher Lehman
VP: Jason Martin
VP: Barbara Massa
Exec: Tyler Hendey
Comm Dir: Dan Wire
Board of Directors: Kimberly Alexy, Ronald E F Codd, William M Coughran Jr, Stephen Pusey, Enrique Salem

D-U-N-S 03-753-4810
FIREFIGHTERS PENSION FUND GEORGIA
(*Suby of* EXECUTIVE OFFICE OF STATE OF GEORGIA) ★
2171 Eastview Pkwy, Conyers, GA 30013-5756
Tel (770) 388-5757 *Founded/Ownrshp* 1955
Sales 133.4MM *EMP* 9
Accts Russell W Hinton Cpa Cgfm
SIC 8631 9651 Labor unions & similar labor organizations; Labor regulatory agency;
Ex Dir: James Meynard

D-U-N-S 94-255-9014
FIREHOUSE SUBS INC
3400-8 Kori Rd, Jacksonville, FL 32257-8884
Tel (904) 886-8300 *Founded/Ownrshp* 1994
Sales 107.9MM^E *EMP* 2,500
SIC 5812 Sandwiches & submarines shop
Pr: Robin Sorensen
**CFO:* Vincent Burchianti
CFO: Schel Collins
VP: Rich Goodman
**VP:* Chris Sorensen
Dist Mgr: Jovon Silkert
Mktg Dir: Sally James
Snr Mgr: Peter Carantza

FIREHOUSE SUBS OF CONYERS
See CLEAR GROUP LLC

D-U-N-S 12-240-0088
FIRELANDS REGIONAL HEALTH SYSTEM
FIRELANDS REGIONAL MEDICAL CTR
1111 Hayes Ave, Sandusky, OH 44870-3323
Tel (419) 557-7400 *Founded/Ownrshp* 1982
Sales 623.4M *EMP* 1,635
SIC 8062 General medical & surgical hospitals
CEO: Martin E Tursky
COO: Robert Aryes
**CFO:* Daniel Moncher
VP: Mike Canfield
VP: Marsha O Mruk
Dir Inf Cn: Susie Kramer
Dir Rx: Jim Spicer
Ex Dir: Julia Colavinvenco
Dir Sec: Terry Bartlett
Off Mgr: Donna Robinson
Telecom Ex: Kevin Slisher

FIRELANDS REGIONAL MEDICAL CTR
See FIRELANDS REGIONAL HEALTH SYSTEM

FIRELINE 520
See INPRO CORP

D-U-N-S 00-691-2414
FIREMANS FUND INSURANCE CO (CA)
(*Suby of* ALLIANZ SE)
777 San Marin Dr Ste 2160, Novato, CA 94945-1352
Tel (415) 899-2000 *Founded/Ownrshp* 1864, 2014
Sales NA *EMP* 4,400
SIC 6331 6351 6321 Fire, marine & casualty insurance & carriers; Property damage insurance; Fire, marine & casualty insurance: stock; Workers' compensation insurance; Surety insurance; Credit & other financial responsibility insurance; Liability insurance; Reinsurance carriers, accident & health
Ch Bd: Gary Bhojwani
**COO:* Antonio Derossi
COO: Bruce Petersen
**CFO:* Kevin Walker
**Chf Mktg O:* Robyn Hahn
**Sr VP:* Christian Kortebein
Sr VP: Peter Lefkin
VP: Tiffany Alvey
VP: Arun Chanana
VP: Jay Dipasupil
VP: John Georgevits
VP: Joey Ghiringhelli
VP: Terry Griffith
**VP:* Jeffrey F Johnson
VP: Bernd Keller
VP: John Looby
VP: Mike Seling
VP: Vijay Singh

Section I
Businesses Alphabetically

VP: Sissi Tchehrazi
VP: Gregory Wacker
Board of Directors: Dale E Lauer, Michael P Sullivan, D Andrew Torrance, Kevin E Walker, Marna C Whittington

FIRESTONE BUILDING PRODUCTS CO
See BFS DIVERSIFIED PRODUCTS INC

D-U-N-S 80-962-2447 IMP/EXP
FIRESTONE BUILDING PRODUCTS CO LLC
FIRESTONE METAL PRODUCTS
(*Suby of* BRIDGESTONE AMERICAS SOURCING) ★
250 W 96th St Ste 150, Indianapolis, IN 46260-1318
Tel (317) 575-7000 *Founded/Ownrshp* 1982
Sales 1.1MMM^E *EMP* 1,500
SIC 5033 Roofing, siding & insulation
Pr: Timothy Dunn
Creative D: Amanda Byer
Off Admin: Jane Kimble
IT Man: Ken Crawford
Netwrk Eng: Mark Fox
Mktg Mgr: Christine Reppert
Manager: Chuck Steiner

D-U-N-S 80-134-1152 IMP/EXP
FIRESTONE FIBERS & TEXTILES CO LLC
(*Suby of* BRIDGESTONE AMERICAS SOURCING) ★
100 Firestone Ln, Kings Mountain, NC 28086-7706
Tel (704) 734-2110 *Founded/Ownrshp* 2007
Sales 200.0MM *EMP* 520
SIC 5531 Automotive & home supply stores
Pr: James Pridgen

D-U-N-S 78-877-4730
FIRESTONE HOLDINGS LLC
6501 W William Cannon Dr, Austin, TX 78735-8523
Tel (512) 895-2000 *Founded/Ownrshp* 2006
Sales 1.6MMM^E *EMP* 24,100^E
SIC 5531 Automotive tires

D-U-N-S 80-962-2835 IMP/EXP
FIRESTONE INDUSTRIAL PRODUCTS CO LLC
(*Suby of* BRIDGESTONE AMERICAS SOURCING) ★
250 W 96th St Ste 150, Indianapolis, IN 46260-1318
Tel (317) 818-8600 *Founded/Ownrshp* 1936
Sales 343.8MM^E *EMP* 686
SIC 5531 3469 3714 3495 Automotive & home supply stores; Metal stampings; Motor vehicle parts & accessories; Wire springs
Pr: Scott Damon
VP: Bob Delaney
Dir IT: Graham Brookes

FIRESTONE METAL PRODUCTS
See FIRESTONE BUILDING PRODUCTS CO LLC

D-U-N-S 80-962-8436 IMP
FIRESTONE NATURAL RUBBER CO LLC
(*Suby of* BRIDGESTONE AMERICAS SOURCING) ★
535 Marriott Dr Fl 3, Nashville, TN 37214-5019
Tel (866) 900-3767 *Founded/Ownrshp* 2008
Sales 125.0MM *EMP* 30^E
SIC 3069 2499 Rubber automotive products; Laundry products, wood
Pr: Steve Shelton
Treas: Marshall Kelley
VP: Jim Crothers
VP: Ed Garcia

D-U-N-S 10-153-8549 IMP/EXP
FIRESTONE POLYMERS LLC
(*Suby of* BRIDGESTONE PROCUREMENT HOLDINGS USA INC) ★
381 W Wilbeth Rd, Akron, OH 44301-2465
Tel (330) 379-7000 *Founded/Ownrshp* 2009
Sales 198.4MM^E *EMP* 567
SIC 3069 Latex, foamed

D-U-N-S 10-839-6904
FIRETROL PROTECTION SYSTEMS INC
(*Suby of* MX HOLDINGS US) ★
3696 W 900 S Ste A, Salt Lake City, UT 84104-4560
Tel (801) 485-6900 *Founded/Ownrshp* 1984
Sales 136.7MM^E *EMP* 721
SIC 1711 1731 Fire sprinkler system installation; Fire detection & burglar alarm systems specialization
Pr: John White
**VP:* Blake A Vance
Dist Mgr: Buck Taylor
Dir IT: Michael Holtorf
Opers Mgr: Steven White
Sales Exec: Raymond Trammel

D-U-N-S 00-182-5892 IMP/EXP
FIRMENICH INC
(*Suby of* FRAGAR (AMERICA) SA)
250 Plainsboro Rd, Plainsboro, NJ 08536-1999
Tel (609) 452-1000 *Founded/Ownrshp* 1950
Sales 218.9MM^E *EMP* 900
SIC 2899 2869

D-U-N-S 14-911-8270
FIRST & GOAL INC
SEAHAWKS STADIUM
800 Occidental Ave S, Seattle, WA 98134-1200
Tel (206) 381-7940 *Founded/Ownrshp* 1997
Sales 141.1MM^E *EMP* 1,055
SIC 1542 7941 Stadium construction; Stadium event operator services
Pr: Bob Whitsitt
**Ch Bd:* Lorraine Hine
**V Ch:* Fred Mendoza
**VP:* Buster Brown
VP: Jeff Klein
Exec: Tyrone Smith
Creative D: John Weaver

D-U-N-S 07-138-8508
▲ FIRST ACCEPTANCE CORP
3813 Green Hills Vlg Dr, Nashville, TN 37215-2610
Tel (615) 844-2800 *Founded/Ownrshp* 1996
Sales NA *EMP* 1,400^E
Tkr Sym FAC *Exch* NYS
SIC 6331 6531 Automobile insurance; Real estate agents & managers
Pr: Joseph S Borbely
Ch Bd: Jeremy B Ford
CFO: Brent J Gay
Board of Directors: Harvey B Cash, Donald J Edwards, Mark A Kelly, Tom C Nichols, Lyndon L Olson Jr, Kenneth D Russell, William A Shipp Jr

D-U-N-S 12-311-7595
FIRST ADVANTAGE CORP
FADV
(*Suby of* SYMPHONYTECHNOLOGY GROUP LLC) ★
1 Concourse Pkwy Ste 200, Atlanta, GA 30328-5346
Tel (800) 888-5773 *Founded/Ownrshp* 1999
Sales 520.7MM^E *EMP* 3,700
SIC 7323 8742 7372 7389 7381 Credit reporting services; Industry specialist consultants; Prepackaged software; Tenant screening service; Detective services
Pr: Mark Parise
Pr: Paul Areida
**COO:* Eric Hess
**CFO:* Michael S Duffey
Ofcr: Richard Heitzmann
Ofcr: Joe Jaeger
Ofcr: David Wachtel
**Ex VP:* Michael Briggs
Ex VP: Navin Chugh
**Ex VP:* Michael Cool
Ex VP: Ron Douglas
**Ex VP:* Dan Filby
**Ex VP:* Bill Franck
Ex VP: Bret Jardine
Ex VP: Todd L Mavis
Sr VP: David Carner
Sr VP: Nick Grecco
Sr VP: Purushotam Savlani
VP: Hal Ghering
VP: Laurie Harris
**VP:* Bret T Jardine

D-U-N-S 07-631-5720
FIRST ALARM
1111 Estates Dr, Aptos, CA 95003-3572
Tel (831) 476-1111 *Founded/Ownrshp* 1982
Sales 66.8MM^E *EMP* 1,027
Accts Hutchinson And Bloodgood Llp
SIC 7382 Burglar alarm maintenance & monitoring
Ch: Jarl E Saal
**Pr:* David Hood
COO: Chris Guzman
Brnch Mgr: Shea Ackerly
Brnch Mgr: Jim Norkoli
Genl Mgr: Jeffrey Samuels
CIO: Erik Haston
IT Man: Marie Malsor
IT Man: John Sullivan
Opers Supe: Romano Clark

D-U-N-S 79-695-4634 IMP
■ FIRST ALERT INC
(*Suby of* SUNBEAM OUTDOOR PRODUCTS) ★
3901 Liberty St, Aurora, IL 60504-8122
Tel (630) 851-7330 *Founded/Ownrshp* 1998
Sales 728.4MM^E *EMP* 3,142
SIC 3669 3999 3446 3499 3829 3648 Smoke detectors; Fire extinguishers, portable; Stairs, fire escapes, balconies, railings & ladders; Safes & vaults, metal; Gas detectors; Flashlights; Lanterns: electric, gas, carbide, kerosene or gasoline
CEO: Joseph Messner
**CFO:* Michael A Rohl
**VP:* Mark A Devine
**VP:* Edward J Tyranski
MIS Dir: Jim Champion
Dir IT: Gene Brooks
VP Opers: Trisha Costello
Ql Cn Mgr: Ed Duran

D-U-N-S 83-511-5726
FIRST ALLIED SECURITIES INC
655 W Broadway Fl 11, San Diego, CA 92101-8487
Tel (619) 702-9600 *Founded/Ownrshp* 2011
Sales 102.3MM^E *EMP* 230
SIC 6211 Security brokers & dealers
CEO: Adam Antoniades
**Pr:* Kevin Keefe
**COO:* Tiy O'Neal
**CFO:* Gregg S Glaser
**Ch:* Joel Marks
Bd of Dir: Trevor Brody
Assoc VP: Anny Choi
Assoc VP: Abbey Eastham
Sr VP: James Reynolds-Hale
Sr VP: Richard Umstead
VP: Michael Chamberlain
VP: Kristin Gang
VP: Aaron Hahn
VP: Scott Hoxie
VP: Lauren Jacobs
VP: Steph Laflamme
VP: Aaron Pearce
VP: Adelaide Pund
VP: L G Ramos
VP: Dan Umansky
VP: Mitchel Wahrman

D-U-N-S 00-695-6858
FIRST ALLMERICA FINANCIAL LIFE INSURANCE CO
(*Suby of* COMMONWEALTH ANNUITY & LIFE INSURANCE) ★
440 Lincoln St, Worcester, MA 01653-0002
Tel (508) 855-1000 *Founded/Ownrshp* 1844, 2009
Sales NA *EMP* 1,400
SIC 6411 6211 6324 Insurance agents, brokers & service; Mutual funds, selling by independent salesperson; Health maintenance organization (HMO), insurance only
Pr: Mark A Hug
**VP:* J Kendall Huber
VP: Jennifer Lauro
**VP:* Gregory D Tranter
IT Man: Patricia Benson

D-U-N-S 00-174-5181 IMP
FIRST AMERICAN BANK (IL)
(*Suby of* FIRST AMERICAN DATA SERVICES) ★
700 Busse Rd, Elk Grove Village, IL 60007-2133
Tel (847) 228-9300 *Founded/Ownrshp* 1957, 1986
Sales NA *EMP* 660
SIC 6022

D-U-N-S 10-762-8323
FIRST AMERICAN BANK CORP (DEL)
FIRST AMERICAN DATA SERVICES
1650 Lewis Ave, Elk Grove Village, IL 60007
Tel (847) 228-5505 *Founded/Ownrshp* 1972
Sales NA *EMP* 660
SIC 6712 Bank holding companies
Ch Bd: Thomas E Wells IV
**Pr:* James M Lynch
**V Ch Bd:* John Ward
Ex VP: Adelbert Spaan

FIRST AMERICAN CASH ADVANCE
See FIRST AMERICAN HOLDING INC

FIRST AMERICAN DATA SERVICES
See FIRST AMERICAN BANK CORP (DEL)

D-U-N-S 96-259-3849
▲ FIRST AMERICAN FINANCIAL CORP
1 First American Way, Santa Ana, CA 92707-5913
Tel (714) 250-3000 *Founded/Ownrshp* 1889
Sales NA *EMP* 17,553^E
Accts Pricewaterhousecoopers Llp Lo
Tkr Sym FAF *Exch* NYS
SIC 6361 6351 Title insurance; Surety insurance
CEO: Dennis J Gilmore
Ch Bd: Parker S Kennedy
Pr: George Livermore
Pr: Kathy Vian
COO: Robert Lawson
COO: Christopher M Leavell
CFO: Mark E Seaton
Ex VP: Kenneth D Degiorgio
Ex VP: Eric R McMullen
Sr VP: Merri Altadonna
Sr VP: Larry W Godec
Sr VP: Mark E Rutherford
Sr VP: Dianna Serio
VP: David Blackman
VP: Chris Clemens
VP: Valerie Kolytiris
VP: Deanna L McCann
VP: Raymond Novi
VP: Michelle Owens
VP: Desai Priti
VP: Robert Richardson
Board of Directors: Anthony K Anderson, George L Argyros, James L Doti, Margaret M McCarthy, Michael D McKee, Thomas V McKernan, Mark C Oman, Herbert B Tasker, Virginia M Ueberroth

D-U-N-S 93-775-8415
FIRST AMERICAN HOLDING INC
FIRST AMERICAN CASH ADVANCE
2504 Cross Winds Ln, Chattanooga, TN 37421-1501
Tel (423) 894-8783 *Founded/Ownrshp* 1996
Sales NA *EMP* 1,000
SIC 6163 Loan brokers
Pr: Larry Kugler

D-U-N-S 12-096-7682
■ FIRST AMERICAN HOME BUYERS PROTECTION CORP
(*Suby of* FIRST AMERICAN TITLE INSURANCE CO) ★
8521 Fallbrook Ave # 340, Canoga Park, CA 91304-3239
Tel (818) 781-5050 *Founded/Ownrshp* 1984
Sales NA *EMP* 27^E
SIC 6351 Warranty insurance, home
CEO: Larry Davidson
**Pr:* Daniel Langston
**COO:* Lawrence F Hariton
**VP:* Ralph Ciaramella
VP: Harold H Sterling III

D-U-N-S 83-070-4230
FIRST AMERICAN MORTGAGE SERVICES
3 First American Way, Santa Ana, CA 92707-5913
Tel (714) 250-4210 *Founded/Ownrshp* 2009
Sales NA *EMP* 350
SIC 6361 Title insurance
Pr: Wes Mee
**Sr VP:* Jeanie Matten
Sr VP: Diana Vazquez
VP: Matt Miller
Snr Mgr: Robert Lay

D-U-N-S 00-420-0445
■ FIRST AMERICAN MORTGAGE SOLUTIONS LLC
(*Suby of* FIRST AMERICAN FINANCIAL CORP) ★
30005 Ladyface Ct, Agoura Hills, CA 91301-2583
Tel (800) 333-4510 *Founded/Ownrshp* 2014
Sales NA *EMP* 700^E
SIC 6163 Mortgage brokers arranging for loans, using money of others
Pr: Jeff Moyer
**Ex VP:* Constance Wilson
**Sr VP:* Paul Harris
**Sr VP:* David G Kittle
**Sr VP:* Brett Waterman
VP: Laura Buser
VP: Shiraz Vartanian
VP: Ilya Verlinsky
VP: Nick Volpe
VP: Ashley Woodworth
Sftwr Eng: Dave Druss

D-U-N-S 79-146-6436
FIRST AMERICAN PAYMENT SYSTEMS LP
100 Throckmorton St # 1800, Fort Worth, TX 76102-2802
Tel (817) 317-9100 *Founded/Ownrshp* 1990
Sales NA *EMP* 1,206
SIC 6153 Credit card services, central agency collection
Pr: Neil Randel
Pr: Debra Bradford
Pr: Brian Dorchester
Pr: Mike Lawrence
Pr: Rick Rizenbergs
Pr: Alan Struble
Ex VP: Howard W Herndon
Sr VP: Michael Lawrence
VP: Michael Byrnes
VP: Rick Diamond
VP: Shawn Dillon
VP: Valerie Grillo
VP: Jonathan Haghtuh
VP: Jonathan Hughes
VP: John Pitarresi
VP: Rhonda Rumbaugh
VP: Linda Young
Exec: Tammy Decker
Dir Bus: Chuck Mooney

D-U-N-S 04-068-1397 IMP
FIRST AMERICAN RESOURCES CO LLC
COIL COATERS OF AMERICA
2030 Rverview Indus Dr Se, Mableton, GA 30126
Tel (404) 505-3499 *Founded/Ownrshp* 2001
Sales 88.2MM^E *EMP* 77
SIC 5051 3479 Iron & steel (ferrous) products; Aluminum bars, rods, ingots, sheets, pipes, plates, etc.; Coating of metals & formed products
CEO: Stan Hollander
**CFO:* Fred Hayse
MIS Dir: Joseph Liotta
Ql Cn Mgr: Gladys Shiosaki

D-U-N-S 07-724-0398
■ FIRST AMERICAN TITLE CO INC
(*Suby of* FIRST AMERICAN FINANCIAL CORP) ★
1 First American Way, Santa Ana, CA 92707-5913
Tel (505) 881-3300 *Founded/Ownrshp* 1965
Sales NA *EMP* 900
SIC 6361 Real estate title insurance
Pr: Robert Schott
Dir Vol: Mick Dolan
Ofcr: Ted Bigornia
Ofcr: Kimberly Delpolito
Ofcr: Mila Wright
VP: Debra Hochman
VP: James Liddle
**VP:* Ronald Olson
Dir IT: Chris Lara
IT Man: Joe Marphis
Opers Mgr: Erica Reid

D-U-N-S 07-169-5464
■ FIRST AMERICAN TITLE GUARANTY CO
(*Suby of* FIRST AMERICAN TITLE INSURANCE CO) ★
1355 Willow Way Ste 100, Concord, CA 94520-5740
Tel (925) 356-7000 *Founded/Ownrshp* 1998
Sales NA *EMP* 276
SIC 6361 6531 Real estate title insurance; Escrow agent, real estate
Pr: Richard Paulitich
CFO: Steven Bramble
**Sr VP:* Mark Sachau

D-U-N-S 07-250-6041
■ FIRST AMERICAN TITLE INSURANCE CO
(*Suby of* FIRST AMERICAN FINANCIAL CORP) ★
1 First American Way, Santa Ana, CA 92707-5913
Tel (800) 854-3643 *Founded/Ownrshp* 1969
Sales NA *EMP* 900^E
SIC 6361 Title insurance
CEO: Dennis J Gilmore
**V Ch:* Kurt Pfotenhauer
Pr: Kevin Wall
**COO:* Curt Caspersen
CFO: Mark E Seaton
**V Ch Bd:* Curt G Johnson
Ofcr: Debbie Duke
Ofcr: Brandon Grajewski
Ofcr: Aaron Hansen
Ofcr: Daisy Howell
Ofcr: Wes Keller
Ofcr: Elizabeth Luna
Ofcr: Gloria Miller
Ofcr: Michelle Schimmelman
Ofcr: Michele Seibold
VP: Janine Andriole
VP: Tiah Brooks
VP: Matthew Cahill
VP: Palma Collins
VP: Deborah Gibson
VP: David Hays

D-U-N-S 06-195-8369
■ FIRST AMERICAN TITLE INSURANCE CO OF NEW YORK
(*Suby of* FIRST AMERICAN TITLE INSURANCE CO) ★
666 3rd Ave Fl 5, New York, NY 10017-4126
Tel (646) 487-5640 *Founded/Ownrshp* 1967
Sales NA *EMP* 450
SIC 6361 Real estate title insurance
Ch Bd: Steve Natolitano
Pr: Jeffrey Mitzner
Pr: Phillip Salomon
COO: David Wanetik
**Ch:* James Orphanides
Ex VP: Helen Powell
Sr VP: Linda Isaacson
Sr VP: Richard Marshall
VP: Joseph Desalvo
VP: Patrica Hutton
**VP:* Paul S Janicke
VP: Randi Munsey
VP: James Thanasules

D-U-N-S 13-754-8749
■ FIRST AMERICAN TITLE INSURANCE CO OF TEXAS
(*Suby of* FIRST AMERICAN TITLE INSURANCE CO) ★
1500 S Dairy Ashford Rd # 300, Houston, TX 77077-3858
Tel (281) 588-2200 *Founded/Ownrshp* 1977
Sales NA *EMP* 21,886
SIC 6361 Real estate title insurance
CEO: Parker S Kennedy
**Pr:* Craig I Deroy
**Ch:* Dp Kennedy
**Ex VP:* Curt A Caspersen
**Ex VP:* Dennis J Gilmore
**Ex VP:* John M Hoolenbeck
**Ex VP:* Gary L Kermott
**VP:* Mark R Arnesen
**VP:* Max O Valdes
Genl Couns: Tim Sullivan

FIRST AMRCN TTLE MIDLAND TITLE
See MIDLAND TITLE SECURITY INC

D-U-N-S 62-281-8813 IMP/EXP
FIRST ATLANTIC CAPITAL LTD
135 E 57th St Rear, New York, NY 10022-2133
Tel (212) 750-0300 *Founded/Ownrshp* 1989
Sales 434.9MM[E] *EMP* 5,073
SIC 6799 Investors
Ch Bd: Roberto Buaron
**Ex VP:* Hiedi Van Evera
Mng Dir: Andrew Cohen

D-U-N-S 12-136-2719
FIRST ATLANTIC CORP
FIRST ATLANTIC HEALTHCARE
100 Waterman Dr Ste 401, South Portland, ME 04106-2880
Tel (207) 874-2700 *Founded/Ownrshp* 1985
Sales 92.9MM[E] *EMP* 1,700
SIC 8741 Management services
CEO: Kenneth Bowden
**Pr:* Ronald Coffin
COO: Craig Coffin

FIRST ATLANTIC HEALTHCARE
See FIRST ATLANTIC CORP

D-U-N-S 05-246-3601
FIRST AUSA LIFE INSURANCE CO
(*Suby of* AEGON USA, INC.)
1111 N Charles St, Baltimore, MD 21201-5505
Tel (410) 576-4571 *Founded/Ownrshp* 1969
Sales NA *EMP* 5,759
SIC 6311 Life insurance carriers
Pr: James Beardsworth
Treas: Brenda Clancy
VP: Robert Kontz
VP: Irv Lamblin
VP: Craig Vermie
Board of Directors: Larry Brown, William Busler

D-U-N-S 09-009-1406 IMP
▲ FIRST BANCORP
FIRST BANK
130 Mnoz Rvera Ave Fl 2, San Juan, PR 00908
Tel (787) 729-8200 *Founded/Ownrshp* 1998
Sales NA *EMP* 2,617
Accts Kpmg Llp San Juan Puerto Ri
Tkr Sym FBP *Exch* NYS
SIC 6022 6411 State commercial banks; Insurance agents, brokers & service
Pr: Aurelio Aleman
**Ch Bd:* Roberto R Herencia
COO: Donald Kafka
CFO: Orlando Berges-Gonzalez
Ex VP: Calixto Garcia-Velez
Ex VP: Ginoris Lopez-Lay
Ex VP: Michael McDonald
Ex VP: Lawrence Odell
Ex VP: Cassan Pancham
Ex VP: Nayda Rivera-Batista
Sr VP: Michael Garc A
Sr VP: Jos H Aponte
Sr VP: Miguel Mej As
Sr VP: Jorge Rend N
Sr VP: Hayde Rivera
Sr VP: Josianne Rossello
Sr VP: H Ctor Santiago
Sr VP: Laura Villarino-Tur
VP: Javier Cabrera
VP: Alfred Massheder
VP: Francisco Pascual
Board of Directors: Jose Menendez-Cortada, Luz A Crespo, Robert T Gormley, Thomas M Hagerty, Michael P Harmon, David I Matson, Juan Acosta Reboyras

D-U-N-S 17-355-2167
▲ FIRST BANCORP
300 Sw Broad St, Southern Pines, NC 28387-5407
Tel (910) 246-2500 *Founded/Ownrshp* 1983
Sales NA *EMP* 873[E]
Accts Elliott Davis Decosimo Pllc
Tkr Sym FBNC *Exch* NGS
SIC 6022 State commercial banks
Pr: Richard H Moore
**Ch Bd:* Mary Clara Capel
CFO: Eric P Credle
Dir Sec: Edward F Soccorso
Board of Directors: Daniel T Blue Jr, James C Crawford III, Thomas F Phillips, O Temple Sloan III, Frederick L Taylor II, Virginia C Thomasson, Dennis A Wicker

D-U-N-S 06-580-1656
FIRST BANCSHARES INC
9701 Indpls Blvd, Highland, IN 46322
Tel (219) 659-0043 *Founded/Ownrshp* 1979
Sales NA *EMP* 350
Accts Crowe Chizek And Company Llp
SIC 6022 State commercial banks
Ch Bd: Michael E Schrage

FIRST BANK
See FIRST BANCORP

D-U-N-S 03-583-3284
■ FIRST BANK
(*Suby of* FIRST BANCORP) ★
341 N Main St, Troy, NC 27371-3017
Tel (910) 576-6171 *Founded/Ownrshp* 1983
Sales NA *EMP* 693
SIC 6022 State commercial banks
Pr: Michael G Mayer
**Ch Bd:* James C Crawford III
**CEO:* Jerry L Ocheltree
**COO:* Anna Hollers
**CFO:* Eric Credle
**Ex VP:* Cathy A Dudley
**Ex VP:* Teresa Nixon
Sr VP: Richard E Clayton
**Sr VP:* Delores George
VP: Patricia Lynch
VP Opers: Galen Hunsucker

D-U-N-S 05-588-7228 IMP
FIRST BANK
FIRST BANK AND TRUST
(*Suby of* FIRST BANKS INC) ★
11901 Olive Blvd Stop 1, Saint Louis, MO 63141-6736
Tel (314) 995-8700 *Founded/Ownrshp* 2002
Sales NA *EMP* 644
SIC 6036 State savings banks, not federally chartered
Pr: Tim Lathe
COO: Sam Rudd
**Ch:* Donald W Williams
Sr VP: Wallace Carter
Sr VP: Scott Corley
Sr VP: Brian Dickmann
VP: Jeff Buettner
VP: Greg Gener
VP: Andy Humphries
VP: Chris Keutzer
VP: Liz Modesitt
Board of Directors: Gordon Gundaker, Robert S Holmes, Daniel W Jasper, Terrance M McCarthy, Christopher McLaughlin, F C McLaughlin, Lisa K Vansikle

FIRST BANK AND TRUST
See FIRST BANK

FIRST BANK, INC.
See FIRSTBANK

D-U-N-S 04-897-3372
▲ FIRST BANK OF NEW JERSEY
2465 Kuser Rd, Trenton, NJ 08690-3303
Tel (609) 528-4400 *Founded/Ownrshp* 2001
Sales NA *EMP* 235[E]
Tkr Sym FRBA *Exch* NGM
SIC 6029 6021 Commercial banks; National commercial banks
COO: Ryan K Manville
VP: Marianne Desimone
Snr Mgr: Sandy Grant

D-U-N-S 78-001-3970
FIRST BANK OF PALM BEACHES
415 5th St, West Palm Beach, FL 33401-3903
Tel (561) 651-7266 *Founded/Ownrshp* 2006
Sales NA *EMP* 1,415
SIC 6022 State commercial banks
CEO: Joseph Shearoufe
Sr VP: Cindy L Sheppard
VP: Dale Boardman

FIRST BANK OF PUERTO RICO
See RICO FIRSTBANK PUERTO

D-U-N-S 07-198-7895
FIRST BANKS INC
135 N Meramec Ave, Saint Louis, MO 63105-3751
Tel (314) 854-4600 *Founded/Ownrshp* 1978
Sales NA *EMP* 1,177[E]
SIC 6021 National commercial banks; National trust companies with deposits, commercial
Pr: Timothy J Lathe
**Ch Bd:* James F Dierberg
V Ch: Michael Dierberg
CFO: Lisa K Vansickle
**V Ch Bd:* Michael J Dierberg
Chf Cred: John H Montgomery
Ex VP: Brenda J Laux
Ex VP: Phillip Lykens
Ex VP: F C Mlaughlin
Sr VP: Patrick S Day
VP: Paul Lints
VP: Renee Montague
VP: James Mosby
VP: Jackie Wilson
Exec: John Grauten
Exec: Kris Wade
Board of Directors: Allen H Blake, James A Cooper, Michael J Dierberg, Ellen Dierberg Milne, John S Poelker, Guy Rounsaville Jr, Douglas H Yaeger

D-U-N-S 94-801-9401
FIRST BOOK
1319 F St Nw Ste 1000, Washington, DC 20004-1155
Tel (202) 393-1222 *Founded/Ownrshp* 1992
Sales 94.5MM *EMP* 50
Accts Mendelson & Mendelson Cpa S A
SIC 8322 Helping hand service (Big Brother, etc.)
Pr: Kyle Zimmer
Pr: Diana Peacock
COO: Chandler Arnold
Prin: John E Harmon Sr
Ex Dir: Roopal Saran
Mktg Dir: Jane Robinson
Snr Mgr: Shannon Burke-Kranzberg
Board of Directors: John E Harmon

D-U-N-S 03-532-0720
▲ FIRST BUSEY CORP
100 W University Ave, Champaign, IL 61820-3910
Tel (217) 365-4544 *Founded/Ownrshp* 1980
Sales NA *EMP* 795[E]
Tkr Sym BUSE *Exch* NGS
SIC 6022 State commercial banks
Pr: Van A Dukeman
**Ch Bd:* Gregory B Lykins
COO: Robin N Elliott
Chf Cred: Robert F Plecki Jr
Ofcr: Amy L Randolph
Sr VP: Sandra Moore
Dir Risk M: Barbara J Harrington
Genl Couns: John J Powers
Board of Directors: Jon D Stewart, Joseph M Ambrose, Phyllis M Wise, Stanley J Bradshaw, David J Downey, Stephen V King, E Phillips Knox, V B Leister Jr, August C Meyer Jr, George T Shapland, Thomas G Sloan

D-U-N-S 62-527-8585
▲ FIRST BUSINESS FINANCIAL SERVICES INC
FBFS
401 Charmany Dr, Madison, WI 53719-1272
Tel (608) 238-8008 *Founded/Ownrshp* 1986
Sales NA *EMP* 258[E]
Tkr Sym FBIZ *Exch* NGM
SIC 6022 State commercial banks
Pr: Corey A Chambas
**Ch Bd:* Jerome J Smith
COO: David R Seiler
CFO: Edward G Sloane Jr
Treas: James F Ropella
Chf Cred: Michael J Losenegger
Sr VP: Jodi A Chandler
Sr VP: Barbara M Conley
VP: Gay Denny
VP: Greg Lherault
CIO: Daniel S Ovokaitys
Board of Directors: Mark D Bugher, Jan A Eddy, John J Harris, Gerald L Kilcoyne, Carol P Sanders, John M Silseth, Barbara H Stephens, Dean W Voeks

D-U-N-S 15-686-2877
FIRST CALL AMBULANCE SERVICE LLC
1930 Air Lane Dr, Nashville, TN 37210-3810
Tel (615) 277-0900 *Founded/Ownrshp* 2004
Sales 112.5MM[E] *EMP* 825[E]
SIC 4119 Ambulance service
CEO: Michael K Ross
**CFO:* Terry Bryant
VP: Joy Ross

D-U-N-S 03-396-5054
FIRST CALL JEWEL INC
1410 Hollipark Dr, Idaho Falls, ID 83401-2100
Tel (208) 522-7777 *Founded/Ownrshp* 1998
Sales 4.1MM *EMP* 2,527
SIC 1731 1711 5078 5063 General electrical contractor; Warm air heating & air conditioning contractor; Refrigeration equipment & supplies; Electrical apparatus & equipment
Pr: Robert Bidstrup
**VP:* Rosslyn Bidstrup

FIRST CARE HEALTH
See ALBANY GENERAL HOSPITAL LIFELINE

FIRST CHICE HLTH ADMNISTRATORS
See FIRST CHOICE HEALTH NETWORK INC

D-U-N-S 78-123-6344
FIRST CHINESE PRESBYTERIAN COMMUNITY AFFAIRS HOME ATTENDANT CORP
30 Broad St Ste 602, New York, NY 10004-2958
Tel (212) 226-4910 *Founded/Ownrshp* 1979
Sales 38.8MM *EMP* 1,100
SIC 8051 Skilled nursing care facilities
Ex Dir: Chuck Mulford
Ex Dir: Arnold Ng

D-U-N-S 80-045-3776
FIRST CHOICE BANK
669 Whitehead Rd, Trenton, NJ 08648-4449
Tel (609) 454-0338 *Founded/Ownrshp* 2009
Sales NA *EMP* 175
SIC 6021 National commercial banks
CEO: Paul Fitzgerald
**CFO:* Howard Hall
Chf Cred: Joanne O'Donnell
VP: Joseph Cavalchire
VP: Hal English
VP: Kevin Gehring
VP: Doreen A Goch
VP: Tom Lanigan
VP: Frank Troilo
VP: Vincent Wong
Brnch Mgr: Gregory Kay

D-U-N-S 14-834-3775
FIRST CHOICE HEALTH NETWORK INC
FIRST CHICE HLTH ADMNISTRATORS
600 University St # 1400, Seattle, WA 98101-3129
Tel (206) 292-8255 *Founded/Ownrshp* 1984
Sales NA *EMP* 160[E]
SIC 6324 Hospital & medical service plans
Pr: Ken Hamm
VP: Ruth Baker
**VP:* Ross Heyl
**VP:* Bob Hinman
Brnch Mgr: Bonnie Blissenbach
Snr Sftwr: Hsuehwen Chiang
Snr Sftwr: Sudhakar Sivalanka
CIO: Greg Palmberg
IT Man: Steve Butler
Software D: Jack Young
Sftwr Eng: Ritu Bindra

D-U-N-S 11-773-4405
FIRST CHOICE MEDICAL SUPPLY LLC
127 Interstate Dr, Richland, MS 39218-9485
Tel (800) 809-4556 *Founded/Ownrshp* 2002
Sales 84.1MM[E] *EMP* 60[E]
SIC 5047 Medical equipment & supplies
CEO: Guy Edwards
**Pr:* Steve Richardson
**CFO:* Stacey Holt
CFO: Louie Vaughan
Sr VP: Shane Holloway
VP: Palmer Dinkel
**VP:* Tommy Hixon
VP: Bill Horne
VP: John Schwartz
VP: John Tipton
VP: Billy Williams
Dir Soc: Kelsey Alford
Dir Soc: Kelsey Pedersen
Creative D: Morrison McSherry

D-U-N-S 11-972-3906
▲ FIRST CITIZENS BANCSHARES INC
FIRST CITIZENS BANK
4300 Six Forks Rd, Raleigh, NC 27609-5718
Tel (919) 716-7000 *Founded/Ownrshp* 1986
Sales NA *EMP* 6,232[E]
Tkr Sym FCNCA *Exch* NGS
SIC 6022 State commercial banks
Ch Bd: Frank B Holding Jr
**Pr:* Peter M Bristow
Pr: Gina Isenhour
Pr: Lorinda Whaley
COO: Edward L Willingham IV
CFO: Craig L Nix
**V Ch Bd:* Hope H Bryant
Ofcr: Ian Bundy
Ofcr: Blake R Coules
Ofcr: Lara Craven
Ofcr: Lisa McCameron
Ofcr: Jeffery L Ward
VP: Hope Bryant
VP: Karen Carver
VP: Wesley Cole
VP: Bill Deleo
VP: Megan Gillikin
VP: Rich Irons
VP: Ken Madden
VP: Sam McClure
VP: Joshua Roehr
Board of Directors: James M Parker, John M Alexander Jr, Victor E Bell III, H Lee Durham Jr, Daniel L Heavner, Robert R Hoppe, Lucius S Jones, Floyd L Keels, Robert E Mason IV, Robert T Newcomb

FIRST CITIZENS BANK
See FIRST-CITIZENS BANK & TRUST CO

FIRST CITIZENS BANK
See FIRST CITIZENS BANCSHARES INC

D-U-N-S 00-791-9392 IMP
FIRST CITIZENS BANK AND TRUST CO INC (SC)
1230 Main St, Columbia, SC 29201-3248
Tel (803) 733-2020 *Founded/Ownrshp* 1982
Sales NA *EMP* 1,784
SIC 6022

D-U-N-S 85-980-6291
FIRST COAST ENERGY LLP
7014 A C Skinner Pkwy # 290, Jacksonville, FL 32256-6940
Tel (904) 596-3200 *Founded/Ownrshp* 1997
Sales 197.3MM[E] *EMP* 500
SIC 5541 5411 5172 Gasoline service stations; Convenience stores, chain; Petroleum products
Genl Pt: J G Ray Jr
**Pt:* Kenneth Allen
**Pt:* Aubrey Edge
**Pt:* Richard H Fornell
COO: John Rodriguez
Area Mgr: Russell Sellars
Mktg Mgr: Trey Byrd

D-U-N-S 05-813-7881
FIRST COAST SERVICE OPTIONS INC
FCSO
(*Suby of* BLUE CROSS AND BLUE SHIELD OF FLORIDA INC) ★
532 Riverside Ave, Jacksonville, FL 32202-4914
Tel (904) 791-8000 *Founded/Ownrshp* 1998
Sales 102.5MM[E] *EMP* 1,500
SIC 8742 Management consulting services
CEO: Sandra L Coston
**COO:* Harvey Dikter
**Ch:* Guy Marvin
**Sr VP:* Diana Haramboure
VP: Michael Davis
VP: Harvey Dikter
Genl Mgr: Gayeta Porter
IT Man: Claudia Bohm
Opers Mgr: Susan Bullard

D-U-N-S 13-697-8595
■ FIRST COLLATERAL SERVICES INC
(*Suby of* CITIMORTGAGE INC) ★
1000 Technology Dr, O Fallon, MO 63368-2239
Tel (813) 604-8143 *Founded/Ownrshp* 2000
Sales NA *EMP* 202[E]
SIC 6162 Mortgage bankers
Pr: Lyndon C Merkle
**CFO:* Paul Hubbard
**VP:* William Gorman
**VP:* Brad Knapp
**VP:* Gino Verza

D-U-N-S 15-154-9607
FIRST COMMAND FINANCIAL PLANNING INC
U S P A
(*Suby of* FIRST COMMAND FINANCIAL SERVICES INC) ★
1 Firstcomm Plz, Fort Worth, TX 76109-4999
Tel (817) 731-8621 *Founded/Ownrshp* 1958
Sales NA *EMP* 1,330
SIC 6311 6211 Life insurance; Mutual funds, selling by independent salesperson
CEO: J Scott Spiker
**Ch Bd:* James N Lanier
**Chf Cred:* Adan Araujo
**Ex VP:* Michael F Morrison
**Ex VP:* Hugh A Simpson
**Sr VP:* Jill Lyttle
**Sr VP:* Joseph R Morrin Jr
VP: Scott Hallock
**VP:* James Peterson
IT Man: Chris Drake
IT Man: Julie Malwitz

D-U-N-S 03-970-8768
FIRST COMMAND FINANCIAL SERVICES INC
1 Firstcomm Plz, Fort Worth, TX 76109-4978
Tel (817) 731-8621 *Founded/Ownrshp* 1958
Sales 435.0MM[E] *EMP* 1,330
SIC 7389 Personal service agents, brokers & bureaus
Ch Bd: James N Lanier
**CEO:* J Scott Spiker
**CEO:* John Spiker
**CFO:* Mike F Morrison
**CFO:* Sandy Rischel
Ofcr: Daniel Behrens
**Ex VP:* Michael J Wheeler
**Sr VP:* Jerry Wackerhagen
VP: Jill Lyttle
Assoc Dir: Brian Dawson
Off Mgr: Husineh Curts

D-U-N-S 00-791-0557
■ FIRST COMMONWEALTH BANK
PITTSBURGH SAVINGS BANK
(*Suby of* FIRST COMMONWEALTH FINANCIAL CORP) ★
601 Philadelphia St, Indiana, PA 15701-3903
Tel (724) 349-7220 *Founded/Ownrshp* 1880
Sales NA *EMP* 937
SIC 6021 National commercial banks
CEO: T Michael Price
Pr: Jane Grebenc
COO: Craig Best
COO: George Dash
Ofcr: Tony E Kallsen
Ex VP: David B Buckiso
Ex VP: Stan Foraker
Sr VP: Larry Kubala

Sr VP: Patrick McMullen
Sr VP: Susan L Nelson
Sr VP: Angela Ritenour
Sr VP: Jim Stevens
Sr VP: James Valletta
VP: James Knipple

D-U-N-S 10-732-3057
▲ FIRST COMMONWEALTH FINANCIAL CORP
601 Philadelphia St, Indiana, PA 15701-3903
Tel (724) 349-7220 *Founded/Ownrshp* 1982
Sales NA *EMP* 1,373
Tkr Sym FCF *Exch* NYS
SIC 6021 National commercial banks
Pr: T Michael Price
CFO: James R Reske
Ofcr: Jane Grebenc
Ex VP: David B Buckiso
Ex VP: Robert Emmerich
Ex VP: Thomas Mathe
Ex VP: Norman Montgomery
Ex VP: J Eric Renner
Ex VP: Carrie L Riggle
Ex VP: Matthew C Tomb
Sr VP: William R Jarrett
Sr VP: Kurt Lamar
Sr VP: Linda M Larotonda
Sr VP: Sue McMurdy
Sr VP: R John Previte
Sr VP: Gregory J Sipos
VP: Chuck Bennett
VP: Bowser Brian
VP: Craig Coon
VP: Morgan Cypher
VP: David Hepler
Board of Directors: Laurie Stern Singer, James G Barone, Robert J Ventura, Julie A Caponi, Ray T Charley, Gary R Claus, David S Dahlmann, Johnston A Glass, Jon L Gorney, David W Greenfield, Luke A Latimer

D-U-N-S 04-846-9253 IMP
FIRST COMMUNICATIONS LLC
3340 W Market St, Fairlawn, OH 44333-3381
Tel (330) 835-2323 *Founded/Ownrshp* 1998
Sales 134.6MM[E] *EMP* 310
SIC 4813 Telephone communication, except radio
CEO: Raymond Hexamer
Mng Pt: Michalyn Ross
Pr: Cindy Butash
**Pr:* Margi Shaw
**CFO:* Mark Sollenberger
Bd of Dir: Eric Feingold
Chf Mktg O: John G Musci
Assoc VP: Ed Reilly
Sr VP: Sandi Murphy
VP: Abby Knowlton
VP: Jessica Newman
VP: Mark Wons
Exec: Harvey Schafle

D-U-N-S 10-630-7432
▲ FIRST COMMUNITY BANCSHARES INC
1 Community Pl, Bluefield, VA 24605-2400
Tel (276) 326-9000 *Founded/Ownrshp* 1989
Sales NA *EMP* 673
Tkr Sym FCBC *Exch* NGS
SIC 6022 State commercial banks
Ch Bd: William P Stafford
Pr: Gary R Mills
COO: E Stephen Lilly
CFO: David D Brown

D-U-N-S 04-202-2942
■ FIRST COMMUNITY BANK
(*Suby of* FIRST COMMUNITY BANCSHARES INC) ★
1 Community Pl, Bluefield, VA 24605-2400
Tel (276) 326-9000 *Founded/Ownrshp* 1999
Sales NA *EMP* 568
SIC 6021 National commercial banks
Pr: Robert Buzzo
**COO:* Stephen Lilly
**CFO:* David Brown
Ofcr: Roger Phipps
**Ex VP:* John M Mendez
**VP:* Garry Stutts
Dir IT: Beverley K Atwell

D-U-N-S 80-673-2710
■ FIRST COMMUNITY BANK NA
(*Suby of* FIRST COMMUNITY BANCSHARES INC) ★
29 College Dr, Bluefield, VA 24605-1736
Tel (304) 323-6300 *Founded/Ownrshp* 2007
Sales NA *EMP* 250[E]
SIC 6021 National commercial banks

D-U-N-S 07-877-4972
▲ FIRST CONNECTICUT BANCORP INC (MD)
1 Farm Glen Blvd, Farmington, CT 06032-1919
Tel (860) 676-4600 *Founded/Ownrshp* 2011
Sales NA *EMP* 337[E]
Accts Pricewaterhousecoopers Llp Ha
Tkr Sym FBNK *Exch* NGM
SIC 6036 State savings banks, not federally chartered
Ch Bd: John J Patrick Jr
CFO: Gregory A White
Ofcr: Michael T Schweighoffer
Ex VP: Catherine M Burns
Ex VP: Kenneth F Burns

D-U-N-S 02-311-4601
FIRST CONTACT LLC
(*Suby of* IQOR US INC) ★
200 Central Ave Ste 600, Saint Petersburg, FL 33701-6323
Tel (727) 369-0850 *Founded/Ownrshp* 1997
Sales 19.9MM[E] *EMP* 2,000
SIC 7389 Personal service agents, brokers & bureaus
Pr: Dan Montenaro
Ofcr: Dawn Lehtinen
**VP:* Grant Newmyer

D-U-N-S 01-984-6203
FIRST COOPERATIVE ASSOCIATION
F C A
960 Riverview Dr, Cherokee, IA 51012-1492
Tel (712) 225-5400 *Founded/Ownrshp* 1912
Sales 390.0MM[E] *EMP* 150
Accts Gardiner Thomsen Pc Des Mo
SIC 5191 5153 Farm supplies; Grains
Pr: Charles Speckter
**Treas:* Mark Johnson
**VP:* David Dean
IT Man: Randy Walton

D-U-N-S 60-436-0081
▲ FIRST DATA CORP
225 Liberty St Fl 29, New York, NY 10281-1049
Tel (800) 735-3362 *Founded/Ownrshp* 1989
Sales 11.4MMM *EMP* 24,000
Tkr Sym FDC *Exch* NYS
SIC 7389 6099 6153 Credit card service; Electronic funds transfer network, including switching; Short-term business credit
Ch Bd: Frank J Bisignano
**V Ch:* Joseph J Plumeri
**Pr:* Guy Chiarello
COO: Jeffrey I Hack
**COO:* Christine E Larsen
**CFO:* Himanshu A Patel
Ofcr: Cynthia Armine-Klein
Ofcr: Cynthia A Armine-Klein
**Ofcr:* Thomas Higgins
Ex VP: Daniel J Charron
Ex VP: Sanjiv Das
Ex VP: Christopher Foskett
Ex VP: Andrew Gelb
Ex VP: Gustavo C Marin
Ex VP: Gustavo Marin
Ex VP: Anthony S Marino
Ex VP: Barry C McCarthy
Ex VP: Michael K Neborak
**Ex VP:* Adam L Rosman
VP: Tiffany Penna
Board of Directors: Joe W Forehand, Henry R Kravis, Heidi G Miller, James E Nevels, Scott C Nuttall, Barbara A Yastine

D-U-N-S 82-589-4319
FIRST DATA HOLDINGS INC
5775 Dtc Blvd Ste 100, Greenwood Village, CO 80111-3209
Tel (303) 967-8000 *Founded/Ownrshp* 2007
Sales NA *EMP* 27,001[E]
SIC 6099 7375 7389 6153

D-U-N-S 12-290-6089
■ FIRST DATA MERCHANT SERVICES CORP
(*Suby of* FIRST DATA CORP) ★
5565 Glenridge Connector, Atlanta, GA 30342-4756
Tel (404) 890-3000 *Founded/Ownrshp* 1981
Sales 563.2MM[E] *EMP* 12,000
SIC 7374 7389 7375 6153 6099 Data processing service; Credit card service; On-line data base information retrieval; Short-term business credit; Electronic funds transfer network, including switching
Ch Bd: Frank J Bisignano
**Ch Bd:* Jonathan Judge
**Pr:* Edward A Labry
**Pr:* John Shlonsky
**Treas:* Michael A Jacobs
**VP:* Stanley J Andersen
VP: Mark Arthus
VP: Christian Pizarro
**Genl Mgr:* Don Esposito
**Genl Mgr:* Joe Locurto

D-U-N-S 05-897-0807
■ FIRST DATA RESOURCES LLC
(*Suby of* FIRST DATA CORP) ★
6855 Pacific St, Omaha, NE 68106-1052
Tel (303) 967-8000 *Founded/Ownrshp* 1989
Sales 577.0MM[E] *EMP* 6,000
SIC 7374 7389 7375 Data processing service; Telemarketing services; On-line data base information retrieval
Pr: Susan Hendricks
Ex VP: Michael L Massey
VP: Jaret Blum
**VP:* John Burkey
VP: Ted Henkenius
VP: Kristi Wolff
Dir IT: Theresa Kraniewski
IT Man: Chris Tyler
Software D: Elliott Hanneman
Board of Directors: David P Bailis, Walter M Hoff, Joseph L Jackson

D-U-N-S 55-651-7258
■ FIRST DATA TECHNOLOGIES INC
(*Suby of* FIRST DATA CORP) ★
6902 Pine St, Omaha, NE 68106-2855
Tel (402) 222-5679 *Founded/Ownrshp* 1993
Sales 143.3MM[E] *EMP* 994
SIC 7374 Data processing & preparation
Ch Bd: Charles T Fote
Pr: Ron Prchal
CFO: Kim Patmore
Ch: Thomas R Bell Jr
Treas: Michael A Jacobs
Ex VP: Mike Dambrose
Ex VP: Michael T Whealy
Sr VP: David Banks
Sr VP: Guy Battista
Sr VP: Christine Carnavos
Sr VP: Matt Figurski
Sr VP: Matt Golub
Sr VP: Kim Mitchell
Sr VP: John Pane
VP: Donald Alvarado
VP: Jeffrey R Billat
VP: Kathy Bowers
VP: Jeff Brown
VP: Jeni Campagna
VP: Todd Cushing
VP: Robert Deschino

D-U-N-S 92-853-8941
▲ FIRST DEFIANCE FINANCIAL CORP
601 Clinton St, Defiance, OH 43512-2636
Tel (419) 782-5015 *Founded/Ownrshp* 1995
Sales NA *EMP* 555[E]
Accts Crowe Horwath Llp South Bend
Tkr Sym FDEF *Exch* NGS
SIC 6035 6331 6321 6311 Savings institutions, federally chartered; Fire, marine & casualty insurance; Accident & health insurance; Life insurance
Ch Bd: William J Small
**Pr:* Donald P Hileman
CFO: Kevin T Thompson
Ofcr: Michael D Mulford
Ex VP: John R Reisner
Ex VP: Dennis Rose
VP: Steve Giesige
Brnch Mgr: Tina Denker
Tech Mgr: Bill Bridenbaugh
Mfg Dir: David Mansell
Sales Exec: Chad Kaup

D-U-N-S 00-615-3597 EXP
FIRST DISTRICT ASSOCIATION (MN)
101 S Swift Ave, Litchfield, MN 55355-2800
Tel (320) 693-3236 *Founded/Ownrshp* 1921, 1986
Sales 615.7MM *EMP* 150
SIC 2023 2022 2026 Concentrated whey; Evaporated whey; Dried whey; Powdered whey; Natural cheese; Fluid milk
CEO: Clinton Fall
Genl Mgr: Doug Anderson

D-U-N-S 78-610-6257
FIRST EAGLE INVESTMENT MANAGEMENT LLC
1345 Ave Of The Americas, New York, NY 10105
Tel (212) 698-3300 *Founded/Ownrshp* 2003
Sales 88.8MM[E] *EMP* 100
SIC 6282 Investment advice
Pr: Polina Feldsher
VP: Suzan Afifi
VP: Heather Beatty
VP: Boris Berlinrut
VP: Kerry Byrne
VP: Greg Cassano
VP: Daniel Declue
VP: Melanie Dow
VP: Jon Flynn
VP: Robert Folino
VP: Chun W Fong
VP: Phillip Marriott
VP: Trey Miller
VP: Sachin Narang
VP: Byron Spivack

D-U-N-S 00-481-6500
FIRST ELECTRIC CO-OPERATIVE CORP
FIRST ELECTRIC COOPERATIVE
1000 S Jp Wright Loop Rd, Jacksonville, AR 72076-5264
Tel (501) 982-4545 *Founded/Ownrshp* 1937
Sales 183.9MM *EMP* 237
Accts Bolinger Segars Gilbert And Mo
SIC 4911 Distribution, electric power
CEO: Don Crabbe
**Ch Bd:* Robert Hil
**COO:* Brad Ford
**CFO:* Bruce Andrews
**Sec:* Robert Maartens
**VP:* Larry Harp
VP: Robert Hill
VP: Jon Joyce
VP: Tonya Sexton
Brnch Mgr: Donna Marty
Genl Mgr: Alton Higginbotham

FIRST ELECTRIC COOPERATIVE
See FIRST ELECTRIC CO-OPERATIVE CORP

D-U-N-S 08-489-2710
FIRST EXCESS AND REINSURANCE CORP
G E REINSURANCE
(*Suby of* SWISS RE SOLUTIONS HOLDING CORP) ★
6329 Glenwood St Ste 300, Shawnee Mission, KS 66202-4291
Tel (913) 676-5524 *Founded/Ownrshp* 1974
Sales NA *EMP* 1,000
SIC 6331 Fire, marine & casualty insurance
Pr: James R Miller
Treas: Alan Ryder
VP: Robert Buckner

FIRST FEDERAL BANK OF MIDWEST
See FIRST FEDERAL BANK OF MIDWEST

D-U-N-S 05-688-6880
■ FIRST FEDERAL BANK OF MIDWEST
FIRST FEDERAL BANK OF MIDWEST
(*Suby of* FIRST DEFIANCE FINANCIAL CORP) ★
601 Clinton St Ste 1, Defiance, OH 43512-2661
Tel (419) 782-5015 *Founded/Ownrshp* 1900
Sales NA *EMP* 500
SIC 6035 Federal savings & loan associations
Ch Bd: William J Small
**Pr:* James L Rohrs
CFO: Donald Hileman
Ofcr: Kimberly Ward
Trst Ofcr: Tom Weber
**Ex VP:* Gregory R Allen
Ex VP: Steve Grosenbacher
Ex VP: Ken Keller
**Ex VP:* Dennis Rose
Ex VP: Kevin Thompson
**Ex VP:* Jeffrey D Vereecke
Ex VP: Tim Whetstone
Ex VP: Larry Woods
**Sr VP:* John Boesling
Sr VP: Linda Moening
Sr VP: Michael Mulford
VP: Tari Christoff
VP: Craig Curtis
VP: Don Flick
VP: Kathy Hoover
VP: Tracy Isaacson
Board of Directors: Charles D Niehaus

D-U-N-S 10-148-8302
▲ FIRST FINANCIAL BANCORP
255 E 5th St Ste 700, Cincinnati, OH 45202-4700
Tel (877) 322-9530 *Founded/Ownrshp* 1982
Sales NA *EMP* 1,471
Tkr Sym FFBC *Exch* NGS
SIC 6021 National commercial banks
CEO: Claude E Davis
**Ch Bd:* Murph Knapke
Pr: Tammy Kinser
Pr: Anthony M Stollings
CFO: John M Gavigan
CFO: John Gavigan
Ofcr: Holly M Foster
Ofcr: Alisa E Poe

D-U-N-S 00-694-0076
■ FIRST FINANCIAL BANK NA
TERRE HAUTE FIRST NATIONAL BANK
(*Suby of* FIRST FINANCIAL CORP) ★
1 First Financial Plz, Terre Haute, IN 47807-3226
Tel (812) 238-6000 *Founded/Ownrshp* 1834
Sales NA *EMP* 760
SIC 6021 National commercial banks
**Pr:* Norman L Lowery
**CFO:* Michael A Carty
CFO: Rodger McHargue
Ofcr: Stephen Browning
Ofcr: Patricia Kirkpatrick
Ofcr: Britt Lowery
Ts Inv Off: Jo E McBeth
**Sr VP:* Tom Clary
**Sr VP:* Cary Sparks
VP: Carl Britton
VP: John D Evans
VP: Steve Herndon
VP: Terry Tevlin

D-U-N-S 00-792-3121
■ FIRST FINANCIAL BANK NATIONAL ASSOCIATION (TX)
(*Suby of* FIRST FINANCIAL BANKSHARES INC) ★
400 Pine St, Abilene, TX 79601-5104
Tel (325) 627-7000 *Founded/Ownrshp* 1889
Sales NA *EMP* 299
SIC 6021 National commercial banks
Ch Bd: Ron Butler
**Pr:* Marelyn B Shedd
**CFO:* Chuck Tennesson
Ofcr: Michelle Fagan
**Ofcr:* Robert Patterson
Ofcr: Terry L Young
Ex VP: Monica Houston
**Ex VP:* John Prince
**Ex VP:* Gary Tucker
Ex VP: Barry A Wellins
Sr VP: Erin Moosbrugger
VP: Steve Cunningham
VP: Vanessa Faz
VP: Evan Harris
VP: Yancey House
VP: Jana Kitchens
VP: Mark McClellan
VP: Daniel Ortiz
VP: Beverly Stevens
VP: Donita Watkins
VP: Larry Williams

D-U-N-S 11-541-3374
■ FIRST FINANCIAL BANK NATIONAL ASSOCIATION
(*Suby of* FIRST FINANCIAL BANCORP) ★
300 High St Side, Hamilton, OH 45011-6045
Tel (513) 867-4700 *Founded/Ownrshp* 2002
Sales NA *EMP* 1,100
SIC 6021 National commercial banks
Pr: Claude E Davis
Ch Bd: Bruce E Leep
Pr: Harry Korros
COO: Michael R Teone
CFO: J Franklin Hall
Ofcr: Mike Pate
Ex VP: Samuel J Munafo
Sr VP: Matthew Marro
VP: Glenn Boone
VP: Adrian O Breen
VP: Carl Britton
VP: Renee Gorbett
VP: Greg Harris
VP: Howard Stammen
VP: Lyneer Straub
Exec: George Brooks
Exec: John Christman
Exec: Richard Erickson
Exec: Steven Gochenour
Board of Directors: David S Barker, Cynthia O Booth, Peter E Geier, Jeffrey D Meyer, Maribeth S Rahe

D-U-N-S 02-033-1286
▲ FIRST FINANCIAL BANKSHARES INC
400 Pine St, Abilene, TX 79601-5108
Tel (325) 627-7155 *Founded/Ownrshp* 1956
Sales NA *EMP* 1,100[E]
Accts Ernst&Young Llp Dallas Texa
Tkr Sym FFIN *Exch* NGS
SIC 6022 State commercial banks
Ch Bd: F Scott Dueser
CFO: J Bruce Hildebrand
Ofcr: Ronald D Butler II
Ex VP: Gary S Gragg
Board of Directors: April Anthony, Steven L Beal, Tucker S Bridwell, David Copeland, Murray Edwards, Ron Giddiens, Tim Lancaster, Ross H Smith Jr, Johnny E Trotter

D-U-N-S 11-733-1447
▲ FIRST FINANCIAL CORP
1 First Financial Plz, Terre Haute, IN 47807-3226
Tel (812) 238-6000 *Founded/Ownrshp* 1984
Sales NA *EMP* 896
Tkr Sym THFF *Exch* NGS
SIC 6022 State commercial banks
Pr: Norman L Lowery
**Ch Bd:* B Guille Cox Jr
COO: Norman D Lowery
CFO: Rodger A McHargue
Chf Cred: Steven H Holliday
VP: Terry Tevlin

IT Man: Kristina Castor
Netwrk Eng: Randy Axe
Board of Directors: W Curtis Brighton, Thomas T Dinkel, Anton H George, Gregory L Gibson, William R Krieble, Ronald K Rich, Virginia L Smith, William J Voges

D-U-N-S 36-230-5120
FIRST FINANCIAL HOLDINGS INC
2440 Mall Dr, North Charleston, SC 29406-6544
Tel (843) 529-5933 *Founded/Ownrshp* 1987
Sales NA *EMP* 880^E
SIC 6035

D-U-N-S 06-619-1305
FIRST FINANCIAL INSURANCE CO INC
IFG COMPANIES
(*Suby of* ISG COMPANIES) ★
238 International Rd, Burlington, NC 27215-5129
Tel (336) 586-2500 *Founded/Ownrshp* 1985
Sales NA *EMP* 300
SIC 6331 Fire, marine & casualty insurance
Pr: Lou Levinson
**Pr:* David A Macleod
**Treas:* Kerry W Fabor
Sr VP: Manuel Almagro Jr
VP: Timothy P Martin
VP: Christopher Strapp
VP: Debra Taylor
**Prin:* Richard C Barbieri
Mng Dir: Elin Walpole

D-U-N-S 02-589-2787
FIRST FINANCIAL RESOURCES INC
611 Kimberly Dr, Denton, TX 76208-6300
Tel (940) 382-4599 *Founded/Ownrshp* 1970, 1968
Sales 411.2MM^E *EMP* 650
SIC 4789 4953

FIRST FLEET
See FIRSTENTERPRISES INC

FIRST FRUITS MARKETING WASH
See BROETJE ORCHARDS LLC

D-U-N-S 60-686-6130
FIRST GROUP INVESTMENT PARTNERSHIP
(*Suby of* FIRSTBUS INVESTMENTS LIMITED)
600 Vine St Ste 1200, Cincinnati, OH 45202-2474
Tel (513) 241-2200 *Founded/Ownrshp* 1999
Sales 257.1MM^E *EMP* 31,250
SIC 7513 4212 4213 4225 4151 4111 Truck leasing, without drivers; Truck rental, without drivers; Local trucking, without storage; Trucking, except local; General warehousing; School buses; Local & suburban transit
Pt: Alton Sloan
Pt: Phil Crookes

FIRST GROUP OF AMERICA
See FIRSTGROUP AMERICA INC

D-U-N-S 79-089-1266
■ **FIRST GUARD INSURANCE CO**
(*Suby of* BIGLARI HOLDINGS INC) ★
200 Nokomis Ave S Fl 4, Venice, FL 34285-2315
Tel (941) 485-6210 *Founded/Ownrshp* 2014
Sales NA *EMP* 1^E
SIC 6411 Insurance agents, brokers & service
CEO: Edmund B Campbell III

D-U-N-S 00-922-7000 IMP
■ **FIRST HAWAIIAN BANK**
(*Suby of* FIRST HAWAIIAN INC) ★
999 Bishop St Ste 3200, Honolulu, HI 96813-4424
Tel (808) 525-6340 *Founded/Ownrshp* 1974
Sales NA *EMP* 2,100
SIC 6022 State commercial banks
Pr: Robert S Harrison-Chm
V Ch: Albert Yamanda
**CEO:* Donald Horner
**COO:* Raymond S Ono
**CFO:* Albert M Yamada
Ofcr: Macy Lee
Ofcr: Sharon Zehner
Trst Ofcr: Mark S Taylor
Assoc VP: Shirley Durham
Ex VP: Robert Alm
Ex VP: Terence Kimura
Ex VP: Michelle Machida
Sr VP: Neill Char
Sr VP: Smith Craig
Sr VP: Ralph M Mesick
Sr VP: Candice Naito
Sr VP: Sherri Yim
VP: Char Ed
VP: Edmund Kajiyama
VP: John Lee
VP: Vernon Omori

D-U-N-S 07-830-0124
FIRST HAWAIIAN BANK
2339 Kamehameha Hwy # 447, Honolulu, HI 96819-2387
Tel (808) 844-4444 *Founded/Ownrshp* 1982
Sales NA *EMP* 99
SIC 6029 Commercial banks
Sr VP: Glen Okazaki
V Ch: Robert Fujioka
Sr VP: Gary Fujitani
VP: Pauline Akiona
VP: Scott Mead
Brnch Mgr: Helen Giron

D-U-N-S 06-628-6865 IMP
■ **FIRST HAWAIIAN INC**
(*Suby of* BNP PARIBAS)
999 Bishop St Fl 29, Honolulu, HI 96813-4423
Tel (808) 525-7000 *Founded/Ownrshp* 1858
Sales NA *EMP* 2,250^E
Accts Pricewaterhousecoopers Llp Sa
Tkr Sym FHB *Exch* NGS
SIC 6022 State commercial banks
Ch Bd: Robert S Harrison
V Ch: Alan H Arizumi
Pr: Eric K Yeaman
CFO: Michael Ching
Ofcr: Ralph M Mesick
Ofcr: Albert M Yamada
VP: Ray Phillips
CIO: Gary Caulfield

D-U-N-S 05-353-4699
■ **FIRST HEALTH GROUP CORP**
(*Suby of* COVENTRY HEALTH CARE INC) ★
3200 Highland Ave, Downers Grove, IL 60515-1282
Tel (630) 737-7900 *Founded/Ownrshp* 1982
Sales 544.4MM^E *EMP* 6,000
SIC 8742 6324 6321 6411 Hospital & health services consultant; Health maintenance organization (HMO), insurance only; Indemnity plans health insurance, except medical service; Medical insurance claim processing, contract or fee basis
Pr: Edward L Wristen
Pr: John Tate
CFO: Dennis Meulemans
Act CFO: Dinusha Perera
Ex VP: Mary Carpenter
**Ex VP:* A Lee Dickerson
**Ex VP:* Patrick G Dills
**Ex VP:* Joseph E Whitters
**Sr VP:* Susan Oberling
VP: Ron Boeving
VP: Greg Hale
VP: Susan Korth
VP: Tamra Lent
VP: Patrick Murray
VP: Scott P Smith
VP: Lynn Williamson

D-U-N-S 07-309-0623
■ **FIRST HEALTH STRATEGIES INC**
(*Suby of* FIRST HEALTH GROUP CORP) ★
3200 Highland Ave, Downers Grove, IL 60515-1282
Tel (630) 737-7900 *Founded/Ownrshp* 1986
Sales NA *EMP* 3,600
SIC 6411 Medical insurance claim processing, contract or fee basis
Pr: Ed Wristen
Pr: Bill Thompson
VP: Lottie Kurcz
Dir IT: Dee Walters
IT Man: Jay Mathews

D-U-N-S 93-359-1562
FIRST HERITAGE CREDIT CORP
605 Crescent Blvd Ste 101, Ridgeland, MS 39157-8659
Tel (601) 952-0635 *Founded/Ownrshp* 2003
Sales NA *EMP* 150
SIC 6141 Consumer finance companies
Pr: Jim Hill
**CFO:* Bill Porter
Ex VP: Robert Crain
Ex VP: Benji Hemphill
VP: Forrest Friday

D-U-N-S 61-799-4884
FIRST HOME MORTGAGE CORP
5355 Nottingham Dr # 130, Nottingham, MD 21236-2767
Tel (877) 933-3100 *Founded/Ownrshp* 1990
Sales NA *EMP* 500
SIC 6163 Mortgage brokers arranging for loans, using money of others
CEO: David E Waters
**COO:* Cathy Smith
**CFO:* Irvin Klein
**Sr VP:* Anthony Olmert
VP Bus: Bill Heffernan

D-U-N-S 05-023-9599
▲ **FIRST HORIZON NATIONAL CORP** (TN)
165 Madison Ave Fl 10, Memphis, TN 38103-2722
Tel (901) 523-4444 *Founded/Ownrshp* 1968
Sales NA *EMP* 4,293^E
Tkr Sym FHN *Exch* NYS
SIC 6021 National commercial banks
Ch Bd: D Bryan Jordan
Pr: Michael E Kisber
CFO: William C Losch III
Chf Cred: Susan L Springfield
Ofcr: John M Daniel
Ex VP: Jeff L Fleming
Ex VP: Charles T Tuggle Jr
Board of Directors: John C Compton, Mark A Emkes, Corydon J Gilchrist, R Brad Martin, Scott M Niswonger, Vicki R Palmer, Colin V Reed, Cecelia D Stewart, Luke Yancy III

D-U-N-S 11-537-2880
FIRST HOSPITALITY GROUP INC
10275 W Higgins Rd # 300, Rosemont, IL 60018-5625
Tel (847) 299-9040 *Founded/Ownrshp* 1984
Sales 125.5MM^E *EMP* 1,500
SIC 7011 Hotels & motels
CEO: Stephen L Schwartz
**Pr:* Robert Habeeb
VP: James Stephenson
Exec: Debra Blake
Exec: Aaron Flores
Exec: Aaron Hodel
Genl Mgr: Sharon Espino
Genl Mgr: Tyler Larocca
Genl Mgr: Anthony Leitz
Genl Mgr: Jonathan Roadruck
Off Mgr: Tj Tate

FIRST INDEPENDENT BANK
See STERLING SAVINGS BANK

D-U-N-S 16-855-1484
FIRST INDUSTRIAL LP
(*Suby of* FIRST INDUSTRIAL REALTY TRUST INC) ★
311 S Wacker Dr Ste 3900, Chicago, IL 60606-6627
Tel (312) 344-4300 *Founded/Ownrshp* 1993
Sales 365.7MM *EMP* 87
SIC 6798 Real estate investment trusts
Pr: Bruce W Duncan
Genl Pt: First Industrial Realty Trust
COO: Nick Colakovic
CFO: Michael J Havalla
CFO: Scott A Musil
Ofcr: Thomas Tucci

D-U-N-S 84-936-0359
FIRST INDUSTRIAL REALTY TRUST INC
311 S Wacker Dr Ste 3900, Chicago, IL 60606-6627
Tel (312) 344-4300 *Founded/Ownrshp* 1994
Sales 365.7MM *EMP* 170
SIC 6798 Real estate investment trusts
Ch Bd: Bruce W Duncan
CFO: Scott A Musil
Chf Inves: Johannson L Yap
Ex VP: David G Harker
Ex VP: Peter O Schultz
VP: Arthur Harmon
VP: Cindy Thorson
Genl Mgr: Garry Weiss
CIO: Christopher M Schneider
IT Man: Jessica Mooney
Mktg Mgr: Kristin Nielsen
Board of Directors: Matthew S Dominski, H Patrick Hackett Jr, John Rau, L Peter Sharpe, W Ed Tyler

D-U-N-S 00-692-6851
FIRST INSURANCE CO OF HAWAII LTD (HI)
FIRST INSURANCE OF HAWAII
(*Suby of* TOKIO MARINE HOLDINGS, INC.)
1100 Ward Ave, Honolulu, HI 96814-1600
Tel (808) 527-7777 *Founded/Ownrshp* 2011
Sales NA *EMP* 330^E
SIC 6331 6411 Property damage insurance; Fire, marine & casualty insurance & carriers; Insurance agents, brokers & service
CEO: Jeffrey A Shonka
Pr: Lynn Leong
Pr: Nina Ota
Pr: April Putnam
**Pr:* Allen Bruce Uyeda
Pr: Misty Wayne
CFO: Nolan Kowano
**Sr VP:* Calvin H Hiraoka
**VP:* Antonio B Abad
VP: Ben F Bondro
**VP:* Ben F Bondroff
**VP:* Dean E Ochiai
**VP:* Darren T Okihara
**VP:* Leslie Kop Shimabuku
**VP:* Stephen J Tabussi
VP: Steve Tabussi
**VP:* Chris D Talbert
Exec: Dawn Bonak
Exec: Bruce T Matsuura

D-U-N-S 61-876-5465
■ **FIRST INSURANCE FUNDING CORP**
INFUND
(*Suby of* LAKE FOREST BANK AND TRUST CO) ★
450 Skokie Blvd Ste 1000, Northbrook, IL 60062-7917
Tel (847) 374-3000 *Founded/Ownrshp* 1986
Sales NA *EMP* 200
SIC 6159 Loan institutions, general & industrial
Pr: Frank J Burke
**Pr:* Robert G Lindeman
**Pr:* G D Wiggins
**CFO:* Michelle H Perry
Ex VP: Bob Lindeman
VP: David Abernathy
VP: Theresa Alba
VP: Eryn Brasovan
VP Opers: Jon Wicks

FIRST INSURANCE OF HAWAII
See FIRST INSURANCE CO OF HAWAII LTD

D-U-N-S 04-385-6376
FIRST INTERNATIONAL BANK AND TRUST
(*Suby of* WATFORD CITY BANCSHARES, INC.)
100 N Main St, Watford City, ND 58854-7100
Tel (701) 232-1700 *Founded/Ownrshp* 1910
Sales NA *EMP* 201
SIC 6022 State commercial banks
Pr: Glendon Olson
**Treas:* Anita Quale
Ofcr: Brad Thompson
VP: Jim Boardman
VP: Sheila Gerszewski
VP: Vicki Karpyak
VP: Terri McLean
VP: Ken Middleton
VP: Evan Ray
VP: Mark Strand
**VP:* Doug Voll

D-U-N-S 04-603-0409
■ **FIRST INTERNATIONAL EXCHANGE GROUP**
BANK ATLANTIC
(*Suby of* BB&T CORP) ★
2100 W Cypress Creek Rd, Fort Lauderdale, FL 33309-1823
Tel (954) 658-3464 *Founded/Ownrshp* 2011
Sales NA *EMP* 1,244
SIC 6035 6531 Federal savings banks; Real estate agents & managers
CEO: Jarett S Levan
**Ch Bd:* Alan B Levan
**COO:* Lloyd Devaux
**V Ch Bd:* John Abdo
**Chf Cred:* Jay C McClung
**Ofcr:* Brian Smith
**Ex VP:* Mark Manitz
**Sr VP:* Michelle Kulzer
VP: Pam Hasara
**Exec:* Doug Freeman
Dir IT: Juan Rodriguez

D-U-N-S 10-156-0431
FIRST INTERNATIONAL EXCHANGE GROUP (INC)
6632 Telegraph Rd Ste 231, Bloomfield Hills, MI 48301-3012
Tel (248) 737-9300 *Founded/Ownrshp* 1983
Sales 100.0MM *EMP* 365
SIC 8742 Management consulting services
Ch Bd: Dhafir D Dalaly
**Pr:* John Crane
**Treas:* Mary Trisini
**VP:* Glen Benoe

D-U-N-S 09-330-0853
▲ **FIRST INTERSTATE BANCSYSTEM INC**
401 N 31st St, Billings, MT 59101-1200
Tel (406) 255-5390 *Founded/Ownrshp* 1971
Sales NA *EMP* 1,742^E
Tkr Sym FIBK *Exch* NGS
SIC 6022 State commercial banks
Pr: Kevin P Riley
**Ch Bd:* James R Scott
CFO: Marcy D Mutch
Chf Cred: Stephen W Yose
Ex VP: William D Gottwals
Sr VP: Kevin J Guenthner
Board of Directors: James R Scott Jr, Steven J Corning, Jonathan R Scott, Dana L Crandall, Randall I Scott, David H Crum, Teresa A Taylor, William B Ebzery, Theodore H Williams, Charles E Hart, Peter I Wold, Charles M Heyneman, John M Heyneman Jr, David L Jahnke, Ross E Leckie

D-U-N-S 00-696-9042
■ **FIRST INTERSTATE BANK**
(*Suby of* FIRST INTERSTATE BANCSYSTEM INC) ★
401 N 31st St Bsmt, Billings, MT 59101-1296
Tel (406) 255-5000 *Founded/Ownrshp* 1971
Sales NA *EMP* 1,589
SIC 6022 State commercial banks
CEO: Lyle R Knight
Pr: Buzz Anderson
Pr: Bonnie Miller
**CFO:* Thomas W Scott
Treas: Carol Willis
Ofcr: Justin Svec
Ex VP: Bill Mitchell
Sr VP: Jack Auzqui
Sr VP: Kevin Guenthner
Sr VP: Mindy Gunther
Sr VP: Joseph Hanser
Sr VP: Glynda McConnell
VP: Diane Boyett
VP: David Dittman
VP: Kevin Eckhardt
VP: John Horner
VP: Jolyn Kanning
VP: Summers Kristi
VP: Sue Larew
VP: McCarthy Linda
VP: Cindy Lyle

D-U-N-S 00-698-3696
FIRST INVESTORS CORP (NY)
(*Suby of* FORESTERS FINANCIAL SERVICES) ★
40 Wall St Fl 10, New York, NY 10005-1343
Tel (212) 858-8000 *Founded/Ownrshp* 1935, 1968
Sales 279.8MM^E *EMP* 1,300
SIC 6282 6211 Investment advice; Brokers, security
Pr: Robert Flanagan
**CFO:* Bill Lipkus
Ofcr: Arec Ligon
Sr VP: George Karris
**VP:* Samuel Brown
**VP:* Matthew Smith
VP: Ben Zaborenko
Div Mgr: Jami Martorana

D-U-N-S 15-635-0436
FIRST MANHATTAN FUNDING LLC
261 E Broadway Ste 255, Salt Lake City, UT 84111-2446
Tel (801) 643-3022 *Founded/Ownrshp* 1999
Sales NA *EMP* 100
SIC 6162 Mortgage bankers & correspondents

D-U-N-S 07-662-4873
FIRST MARKET RESEARCH CORP
99 Needham St Apt 1305, Newton, MA 02461-1644
Tel (617) 734-7080 *Founded/Ownrshp* 1977
Sales 17.1MM^E *EMP* 1,000
Accts Kpmg Peat Marwick Llp Boston
SIC 8732 Market analysis or research
Pr: Jack Reynolds
**Pr:* James R Heiman

FIRST MED CLINIC
See GENESIS MEDICAL CENTER

D-U-N-S 12-066-9676
■ **FIRST MERCHANTS BANK**
(*Suby of* FIRST MERCHANTS CORP) ★
189 W Market St, Wabash, IN 46992-3053
Tel (260) 563-4116 *Founded/Ownrshp* 2003
Sales NA *EMP* 60
SIC 6022 State commercial banks
Pr: Bob Bell
VP: Duane Davis
VP: Michael Fisher
VP: Dennis Frieden
VP: Kris Lacy
VP: Gretchen Patterson

D-U-N-S 78-704-8367
■ **FIRST MERCHANTS BANK NATIONAL ASSOCIATION**
(*Suby of* FIRST MERCHANTS CORP) ★
200 E Jackson St, Muncie, IN 47305-2835
Tel (765) 747-1500 *Founded/Ownrshp* 1982
Sales NA *EMP* 1,000
SIC 6029 Commercial banks
Pr: Michael C Rechin
COO: Dixie Mullins
CFO: Mark K Hardwick
VP: Judy John
VP: Derek Jones
Board of Directors: Michael R Becher, F Howard Halderman

D-U-N-S 15-650-7329
▲ **FIRST MERCHANTS CORP**
200 E Jackson St, Muncie, IN 47305-2835
Tel (765) 747-1500 *Founded/Ownrshp* 1982
Sales NA *EMP* 1,529
Tkr Sym FRME *Exch* NGS
SIC 6021 6331 National commercial banks; National trust companies with deposits, commercial; Fire, marine & casualty insurance; Property damage insurance
Pr: Michael C Rechin
**Ch Bd:* Charles E Schalliol
Pr: Corrine Ganiec
COO: Mark K Hardwick
Chf Cred: John J Martin
Ofcr: Jeffrey B Lorentson
Trst Ofcr: Chuck Huffman
Trst Ofcr: Teresa Swaim
Ex VP: Michael J Stewart
Sr VP: Kimberly J Ellington

Sr VP: Stephan H Fluhler
Sr VP: Michele Kawiecki
VP: Lisa Brothers
VP: Thomas Buczek
VP: Robert Connors
VP: John B Ditmars
VP: Tom Dunson
VP: Dan Gick
VP: Gregory Gorski
VP: Lentz Gregory
VP: Leslie Holland
Board of Directors: Michael R Becher, F Howard Halderman, William L Hoy, Gary J Lehman, Patrick A Sherman, Terry L Walker, Jean L Wojtowicz

D-U-N-S 92-890-1719
FIRST MERCURY FINANCIAL CORP
(*Suby of* CRUM AND FORSTER INSURANCE) ★
26600 Telegraph Rd, Southfield, MI 48033-5300
Tel (248) 358-4010 *Founded/Ownrshp* 2011
Sales NA *EMP* 362
SIC 6331 Burglary & theft insurance; Automobile insurance
CEO: Marc Adee
Pr: Richard H Smith
CFO: John A Marazza
Ofcr: Terrance A Fleckenstein
Ex VP: E Edward Camp
Sr VP: Thomas A Greene
Sr VP: William Weaver
VP: Dick Barrett
VP: Sarah Benjamin
VP: Mark Divitto
VP: Ronald Harrell
VP: Matt Maclean
VP: Robert Wronski
Exec: Megan Champine

D-U-N-S 60-584-8514
FIRST MERCURY INSURANCE CO
(*Suby of* FIRST MERCURY FINANCIAL CORP) ★
26600 Telegraph Rd, Southfield, MI 48033-5300
Tel (248) 358-4010 *Founded/Ownrshp* 1994
Sales NA *EMP* 100
SIC 6331 Burglary & theft insurance
Pr: Richard H Smith
Treas: Jim Thomas
VP: Latrina Green
VP: Ronald P Harrell
VP: Marcia Paulsen
VP: William S Weaver
Board of Directors: Stuart Carlin, Deborah Traxinger, Timothy Traxinger

D-U-N-S 02-924-0819
▲ FIRST MIDWEST BANCORP INC
1 Pierce Pl Ste 1500w, Itasca, IL 60143-1254
Tel (630) 875-7450 *Founded/Ownrshp* 1983
Sales NA *EMP* 1,707E
Tkr Sym FMBI *Exch* NGS
SIC 6021 National commercial banks
Pr: Michael L Scudder
**Ch Bd:* Robert P O'Meara
Pr: Joan Bucaro-Lopez
Pr: Josie Pacheco
**COO:* Mark G Sander
CFO: Paul F Clemens
Treas: James P Hotchkiss
Ofcr: Brian Minnis
Ex VP: Nicholas J Chulos
VP: Sue Barreto
VP: Matt Brennan
VP: Evan Klee
VP: Julie McGrath
VP: Joe Minogue
VP: Robert Paleczny
VP: Tamra Stirn
Board of Directors: J Stephen Vanderwoude, Barbara A Boigegrain, John F Chlebowski Jr, James Gaffney, Kathryn J Hayley, Peter J Henseler, Patrick J McDonnell, Frank B Modruson, Ellen A Rudnick, Michael J Small

D-U-N-S 78-610-2876
■ FIRST MIDWEST BANK
(*Suby of* FIRST MIDWEST BANCORP INC) ★
1 Pierce Pl Ste 1500w, Itasca, IL 60143-1254
Tel (630) 875-7450 *Founded/Ownrshp* 2006
Sales NA *EMP* 55E
SIC 6021 National commercial banks
Pr: Thomas J Schwartz
Pr: David M Knapp
**COO:* Jo Ann Boylan
Ofcr: Lisa Anderson
Ofcr: James Cacioppo
Ofcr: Patti Cappa
Ofcr: Dave Clark
Ofcr: Jeanine Cozzi
Ofcr: Steve Dahlkamp
Ofcr: Zach Flahaven
Ofcr: Namrata Kanal
Ofcr: Mike Lambert
Ofcr: Louise McLaren
Ofcr: Dan Mihelich
Ofcr: Steve Olson
Ex VP: Paul Clemens
Ex VP: Robert Diedrich
**Ex VP:* Michael W Jamieson
Ex VP: Michael Kozak
**Ex VP:* Thomas M Prame
Ex VP: Stephanie Wise

D-U-N-S 04-095-4109
FIRST MORTGAGE CORP
1131 W 6th St Ste 300, Ontario, CA 91762-1118
Tel (909) 595-1996 *Founded/Ownrshp* 1975
Sales NA *EMP* 430
SIC 6162

FIRST NATIONAL BANK
See FIRST NATIONAL OF NEBRASKA INC

FIRST NATIONAL BANK
See FIRST NATIONAL OF ILLINOIS INC

D-U-N-S 00-691-6175
FIRST NATIONAL BANK
(*Suby of* FIRST NATIONAL BANK) ★
205 W Oak St, Fort Collins, CO 80521-2712
Tel (970) 482-4861 *Founded/Ownrshp* 1934, 2002
Sales NA *EMP* 400
SIC 6021 National commercial banks
Pr: Mark Driscoll
CFO: Roger Gunlickson
**CFO:* Julie D Herder
**Trst Ofcr:* Jack Wolfe
VP: Steve Boer
VP: Todd Campbell
VP: Catherine Costlow
VP: Christy A Kelderman
CIO: Brian Nienhaus
Dir IT: Greg Dickhute
IT Man: Carol Schisler

D-U-N-S 00-894-1916
FIRST NATIONAL BANK
307 E Hustan Ave, Fort Pierre, SD 57532-5201
Tel (605) 223-2521 *Founded/Ownrshp* 1979
Sales NA *EMP* 150
SIC 6021 National commercial banks
Pr: Todd Douglas
**CFO:* William Fuchs
Ofcr: Naomi Sparacello
VP: Craig Davis
VP: Gill Minski

D-U-N-S 03-632-1958
FIRST NATIONAL BANK
100 W Cano St, Edinburg, TX 78539-4507
Tel (956) 380-8587 *Founded/Ownrshp* 1981
Sales NA *EMP* 200
SIC 6021

D-U-N-S 00-690-1664
FIRST NATIONAL BANK ALASKA
101 W 36th Ave, Anchorage, AK 99503-5904
Tel (907) 777-4362 *Founded/Ownrshp* 1953
Sales NA *EMP* 738
SIC 6021 National commercial banks
Prin: Betsy Lawyer
COO: Morton V Plumb Jr
**V Ch Bd:* Lucy Mahan
Ofcr: Amy Elmore
Ofcr: Tina Graham
Sr Tst Off: Robert Tannahill
Sr VP: George Bailey
VP: Monica Barton
VP: Larry Chen
VP: Joe Gelione
VP: Lorna Gleason
VP: Dustin Hofeling
VP: Bill Inscho
VP: Doug Longacre
VP: Rich Monroe
VP: Jackie O'Neill
Board of Directors: Betsy Lawyer, Tom Tougas

D-U-N-S 00-693-8906
FIRST NATIONAL BANK AND TRUST
(*Suby of* BMO BANKCORP INC) ★
2206 W Sycamore St, Kokomo, IN 46901-4110
Tel (765) 868-3551 *Founded/Ownrshp* 2007
Sales NA *EMP* 400
SIC 6021

D-U-N-S 00-697-7417
■ FIRST NATIONAL BANK OF LONG ISLAND
(*Suby of* FIRST OF LONG ISLAND CORP) ★
10 Glen Head Rd, Glen Head, NY 11545-1411
Tel (516) 671-4900 *Founded/Ownrshp* 1927
Sales NA *EMP* 251
SIC 6021 National commercial banks
Pr: Michael Vittorio
CFO: Chris Becker
CFO: Mark D Curtis
Exec: Sallyanne K Ballweg
Genl Mgr: Donald Manfredonia
Board of Directors: Peter Quick, Eric Tveter

D-U-N-S 00-697-0172
FIRST NATIONAL BANK OF OMAHA INC
(*Suby of* FIRST NATIONAL BANK) ★
1620 Dodge St, Omaha, NE 68197-0002
Tel (402) 341-0500 *Founded/Ownrshp* 1963
Sales NA *EMP* 2,145
SIC 6021 National commercial banks
Ch Bd: Bruce R Lauritzen
**Pr:* Daniel K O'Neill
CFO: Michael A Frattone
CFO: Mike Summers
Sr Cor Off: Brian Schneider
Ofcr: Nate Brei
Ofcr: Sarah Brons
Ofcr: Stephen Seyler
Ofcr: Michael Stafford
Ofcr: Eulie Stephen
Ofcr: Arvind Thapar
Ofcr: Jeffrey C Weeks
Sr VP: David N Harger
Sr VP: David N Simmons
VP: Matt Bergmeyer
VP: Steve Eck
VP: Joseph Hutchings
VP: Melchior Janet
VP: Lori Smidt
VP: Cathy Smith
Exec: Timothy A Newkirk

D-U-N-S 00-791-1076
■ FIRST NATIONAL BANK OF PENNSYLVANIA
(*Suby of* FNB CORP) ★
166 Main St, Greenville, PA 16125-2146
Tel (724) 588-6770 *Founded/Ownrshp* 1864
Sales NA *EMP* 1,352E
SIC 6021 National commercial banks
Pr: Vincent J Delie Jr
Ch Bd: Peter Mortensen
Pr: Frank Krieder
Pr: Boyd K Pethel
Pr: John C Williams
CFO: Tito Lima
CFO: Frank Zink
Chf Mktg O: Susan B Bergen-Painter
Chf Mktg O: Richard J Steiner
Ex VP: Jonathan W Roberts
Ex VP: Barry C Robinson
Sr VP: Gardner Fredric
Sr VP: Fredric M Gardner
Sr VP: Yenner Karto
Sr VP: Rex Knisley
Sr VP: David B Yates
VP: Mauch Dale
VP: L Thomas
Exec: Michael Kozak

D-U-N-S 83-676-9331
■ FIRST NATIONAL BANK OF POLK COUNTY INC
(*Suby of* CENTERSTATE BANKS INC) ★
7722 State Road 544 Fl 1, Winter Haven, FL 33881-9570
Tel (863) 422-8990 *Founded/Ownrshp* 1999
Sales NA *EMP* 46E
SIC 6022 State commercial banks
Pr: George H Carefoot
**VP:* Lynn Briske

D-U-N-S 00-895-0727
■ FIRST NATIONAL BANK TEXAS (TX)
(*Suby of* FIRST COMMUNITY BANCSHARES INC) ★
507 N Gray St, Killeen, TX 76541-4871
Tel (254) 554-6699 *Founded/Ownrshp* 1901
Sales NA *EMP* 729E
SIC 6021 National commercial banks
V Ch Bd: P Terry Tuggle
**Pr:* James D Dreibelbis
CFO: Sylvan Gilliland
**CFO:* Jim Meredith
Ofcr: Zujey Gutierrez
Ofcr: Marietta Richard
Ofcr: Anastasha Seay
Ofcr: Wendy Wadsworth
Ex VP: Dave Epke
**Ex VP:* Bobby Hoxwrth
Sr VP: Brian Hawkins
Sr VP: Rebecca Honer
Sr VP: Bobby Maxwell
Sr VP: Nancy Mullins
Sr VP: Aimee Parker
Sr VP: Ronald J Rafay
Sr VP: George W Waggoner
Sr VP: Laurie Zimmerman
VP: Julie Arnold
VP: Carol Berger
VP: Deborah Brunson
Board of Directors: John B Plott, Major E Blair, Edgar H Rhode, John V Blankenship, T Bruce Scott, Randall O Curtis, William L Shine, William F Donahy, June Whisenhunt, James D Dreibelbis, William T Fowler, Jerold B Katz, Jack V McAdoo, Jack Morris

D-U-N-S 12-116-6771
FIRST NATIONAL INSURANCE CO OF AMERICA
(*Suby of* SAFECO CORP) ★
4333 Rootland Ave Ne, Seattle, WA 98185-0001
Tel (206) 545-5000 *Founded/Ownrshp* 1928
Sales NA *EMP* 2,000
SIC 6331 Property damage insurance; Fire, marine & casualty insurance: mutual
Treas: Stephen Bauer
Sls Mgr: Michael Yeager

D-U-N-S 82-815-3382
FIRST NATIONAL OF ILLINOIS INC
FIRST NATIONAL BANK
(*Suby of* FIRST NATIONAL BANK) ★
1620 Dodge St, Omaha, NE 68102-1593
Tel (402) 991-6131 *Founded/Ownrshp* 2008
Sales NA *EMP* 1,744E
SIC 6021 National commercial banks
Prin: Bruce Lauritzen
CFO: Sandy Kennedy
Ex VP: Rowdy Slavin
Sr VP: Tom Whitesel
VP: Chris King
VP: Jason Kremer
VP: Clifford Nostrand
VP: Jon Ripp
VP: Michelle Smithberg
Mng Dir: Craig Jones
Dir IT: Jenny Adkins

D-U-N-S 07-289-1146
FIRST NATIONAL OF NEBRASKA INC
FIRST NATIONAL BANK
1620 Dodge St, Omaha, NE 68197-0003
Tel (402) 341-0500 *Founded/Ownrshp* 1968
Sales NA *EMP* 6,571
SIC 6022 6141 7371 State commercial banks; Personal credit institutions; Computer software systems analysis & design, custom
Ch Bd: Bruce R Lauritzen
**Pr:* Daniel K O'Neill
CFO: Ken Kucera
**CFO:* Michael A Summers
**Ch:* Bruce Lauritzen
Treas: Anthony Cerasoli
Ofcr: Nicholas W Baxter
Ofcr: Noel Ginsburg
Ofcr: Matt Pyle
Ex VP: Thomas Baker
**Ex VP:* Rajive Johri
Ex VP: Scott McCormack
Ex VP: Brandon Meisinger
Ex VP: Dennis O'Neal
Ex VP: Dennis A O'Nel
Sr VP: Joseph Barry
**Sr VP:* Timothy D Hart
**Sr VP:* Jeffrey A S
Sr VP: David N Simmons
VP: Mark Baratta
VP: Cindy Blazer
Board of Directors: George J Behringer, Margaret Lauritzen Dodge, William J Henry, Michael S Mahlendorf, John T Reed

D-U-N-S 83-565-7701
■ FIRST NATIONWIDE MORTGAGE CORP
(*Suby of* CITIGROUP INC) ★
5280 Corporate Dr, Frederick, MD 21703-8502
Tel (301) 791-8108 *Founded/Ownrshp* 1994
Sales NA *EMP* 1,396
Accts Kpmg Llp Mclean Va
SIC 6163 Mortgage brokers arranging for loans, using money of others
Ch Bd: Gerald J Ford
Pr: Walter C Klein Jr
Exec: Lawrence P Washington
MIS Dir: Diana Yocke

D-U-N-S 80-676-5264
■ FIRST NBC BANK
(*Suby of* FIRST NBC BANK HOLDING CO) ★
210 Baronne St Frnt, New Orleans, LA 70112-1742
Tel (504) 566-8000 *Founded/Ownrshp* 2007
Sales NA *EMP* 20E
SIC 6022 State commercial banks
Ch Bd: Hermann Moyse III
CFO: Mary B Verdigets
**Ofcr:* Marsha S Crowle
Ex VP: Brad Calloway
Sr VP: Jean G Celestin
Sr VP: Ed Marshall
VP: Aimee Arceneaux
VP: Bill Bennett
VP: Barbara Gibbs
VP: Rena M Harris
VP: Dolly G Punch

D-U-N-S 62-013-7112
▲ FIRST NBC BANK HOLDING CO
210 Baronne St, New Orleans, LA 70112-1742
Tel (504) 566-8000 *Founded/Ownrshp* 2006
Sales NA *EMP* 565E
Tkr Sym FNBC *Exch* NGS
SIC 6022 State commercial banks
CEO: Hermann Moyse III
**Ch Bd:* Shivan Govindan
**Pr:* Ashton J Ryan Jr
COO: George L Jourdan
CFO: Albert J Richard III
**V Ch Bd:* Leon L Giorgio Jr
Chf Cred: William J Burnell
Ofcr: Marsha S Crowle
Sr VP: William M Roohi
VP: Kelly Boe
Board of Directors: William D Aaron Jr, William M Carrouche, Leander J Foley III, John F French, L Blake Jones, Louis V Lauricella, Mark G Merlo, Charles C Teamer, Joseph F Toomy

D-U-N-S 01-410-3766
■ FIRST NIAGARA BANK NATIONAL ASSOCIATION
(*Suby of* KEYCORP) ★
726 Exchange St Ste 618, Buffalo, NY 14210-1463
Tel (716) 625-7500 *Founded/Ownrshp* 2014
Sales NA *EMP* 2,392
SIC 6021 National commercial banks
Pr: Gary M Crosby
COO: Gray M Crosby
Ofcr: Charles Peterson
Assoc VP: Mary Nassoiy
Ex VP: Daniel Cantara III
Ex VP: J Lanier Little
Sr VP: G Burner
**Sr VP:* Peter Cosgrove
**Sr VP:* Jacqueline S Culliton
Sr VP: Michael Mackay
VP: Dianne Cross
VP: Holly Larsen
VP: Michael Noah
VP: Ram Shankar
VP: Deborah Syron
Board of Directors: Austin A Adams, Peter B Robinson

D-U-N-S 00-824-0843
FIRST NIAGARA FINANCIAL GROUP INC
726 Exchange St Ste 618, Buffalo, NY 14210-1463
Tel (716) 819-5500 *Founded/Ownrshp* 1998
Sales NA *EMP* 5,428E
SIC 6411

D-U-N-S 07-403-2962
■ FIRST NIAGARA RISK MANAGEMENT INC
GMAC INSURANCE
(*Suby of* FIRST NIAGARA BANK NATIONAL ASSOCIATION) ★
726 Exchange St Ste 900, Buffalo, NY 14210-1452
Tel (716) 819-5500 *Founded/Ownrshp* 1968
Sales NA *EMP* 334
SIC 6411 Insurance agents, brokers & service
CEO: Joe Tracey
**CFO:* Gretchen Deeley
Ex VP: Gary Crosby
Sr VP: Arthur Cryer
**VP:* John Hoffman
VP: Selene Kranz
VP: Bart Oddo
VP: Scott Wehrlin
Sls Dir: Matt Fair

D-U-N-S 15-650-6776
▲ FIRST OF LONG ISLAND CORP
10 Glen Head Rd, Glen Head, NY 11545-1411
Tel (516) 671-4900 *Founded/Ownrshp* 1984
Sales NA *EMP* 260E
Accts Crowe Horwath Llp New York N
Tkr Sym FLIC *Exch* NAS
SIC 6021 National commercial banks
Pr: Michael N Vittorio
CFO: Mark D Curtis
Ex VP: Christopher Becker
Ex VP: Richard Kick
Ex VP: Donald L Manfredonia
VP: Paul Daley
VP: Maria Doyle
VP: Robert Eisen
VP: Rick Hughes
VP: Laura Ierulli
VP: Jane Reed
Exec: Sallyanne K Ballweg

D-U-N-S 12-721-7078
■ FIRST PENN-PACIFIC LIFE INSURANCE CO
(*Suby of* LINCOLN NATIONAL CHINA INC) ★
1300 S Clinton St, Fort Wayne, IN 46802-3506
Tel (260) 455-6408 *Founded/Ownrshp* 1963
Sales NA *EMP* 2
SIC 6411 Insurance agents, brokers & service
Pr: John H Gotta

COO: Dede Derosa
IT Man: Tim Rodrigues

D-U-N-S 05-504-3020
FIRST PIEDMONT CORP
108 S Main St, Chatham, VA 24531-5564
Tel (434) 432-0211 Founded/Ownrshp 1969
Sales 95.7MM[E] EMP 150
SIC 4953 5084

D-U-N-S 12-788-2210
FIRST POTOMAC REALTY TRUST
7600 Wisconsin Ave # 1100, Bethesda, MD 20814-3661
Tel (301) 986-9200 Founded/Ownrshp 1997
Sales 172.8MM EMP 189[E]
Accts Kpmg Llp Mclean Virginia
SIC 6798 Real estate investment trusts
CEO: Robert Milkovich
CFO: Andrew P Blocher
Trst: Richard B Chess
Ofcr: Barry Bass
Ex VP: Samantha Sacks Gallagher
Sr VP: Tricia Moore
VP: Michael Corner
VP: Patrick Kelly
VP: Sandra P Scheuerman
VP: Mario Silva
VP: Judith Tria
VP: Matthew L Wilson
VP: Edward V Zaptin
Board of Directors: Robert H Arnold, Richard B Chess, J Roderick Heller III, R Michael McCullough, Alan G Merten, Thomas E Robinson, Terry L Stevens

FIRST PRIORITY HEALTH
See HMO OF NORTHEASTERN PENNSYLVANIA INC

D-U-N-S 01-577-2159 IMP/EXP
FIRST QUALITY BABY PRODUCTS LLC
(Suby of FIRST QUALITY ENTERPRISES INC) ★
97 Locust Rd, Lewistown, PA 17044-9340
Tel (717) 247-3516 Founded/Ownrshp 2007
Sales 161.3MM[E] EMP 800
SIC 2676 Diapers, paper (disposable): made from purchased paper
CFO: Jim Dodge

D-U-N-S 88-457-6013
FIRST QUALITY ENTERPRISES INC
80 Cuttermill Rd Ste 500, Great Neck, NY 11021-3108
Tel (516) 829-3030 Founded/Ownrshp 1992
Sales 4.6MMM[E] EMP 3,400
SIC 5149 Health foods
Ch Bd: Nader Damaghi
CFO: Jim Dodge
*Treas: Kambie Damaghi
VP: Nicholas Dottino
VP: Dan Murphy
CIO: Stephan Lemoine
CTO: Bob Kenney
Dir IT: Paul Richter
IT Man: Dan Baksa
IT Man: Amy Carmack
IT Man: Matthew Oakes

D-U-N-S 19-860-2195 IMP/EXP
FIRST QUALITY PRODUCTS INC
(Suby of FIRST QUALITY ENTERPRISES INC) ★
80 Cuttermill Rd Ste 500, Great Neck, NY 11021-3108
Tel (516) 829-4949 Founded/Ownrshp 1988
Sales 374.6MM[E] EMP 1,000
SIC 2676 Sanitary paper products
Ch Bd: Kambiz Damaghi
*Ch Bd: Nasser Damaghi
COO: Scott Shingleton
CFO: Jim Dodge
VP: Kambiz Damagh
*VP: Bob Damaghi
VP Bus Dev: Ruben Damaghi
QA Dir: Charles Smith
Dir IT: Casey Friese
Dir IT: Paul Richter
IT Man: Brian Krangel

D-U-N-S 82-764-9026 IMP
FIRST QUALITY RETAIL SERVICES LLC
(Suby of FIRST QUALITY ENTERPRISES INC) ★
601 Allendale Rd, King of Prussia, PA 19406-1417
Tel (610) 265-5000 Founded/Ownrshp 2008
Sales 342.2MM[E] EMP 1,600[E]
SIC 3822 Building services monitoring controls, automatic
CEO: Doug Strohmeir
CFO: Jim Dodge

D-U-N-S 14-353-5271 IMP
FIRST QUALITY TISSUE LLC
(Suby of FIRST QUALITY ENTERPRISES INC) ★
904 Woods Ave, Lock Haven, PA 17745-3348
Tel (570) 748-1200 Founded/Ownrshp 2002
Sales 203.9MM[E] EMP 380
SIC 2621 Tissue paper
CFO: Jim Dodge
QA Dir: Allyn Shultis
IT Man: Cary Walters
Mfg Dir: Joseph Dellaquilla
Opers Mgr: Alexander Mahfood
Prd Mgr: Dan Corbett

D-U-N-S 13-155-1848
▲ FIRST REPUBLIC BANK
111 Pine St Ste Bsmt, San Francisco, CA 94111-5628
Tel (415) 392-1400 Founded/Ownrshp 2010
Sales NA EMP 1,500
Tkr Sym FRC Exch NYS
SIC 6022 6282 6162 State commercial banks; Investment advice; Mortgage bankers
CEO: Thomas J Barrack Jr
V Ch: Katherine August-Dewilde
Pr: Kelly Johnston
COO: Jason C Bender
COO: Mike Selfridge
COO: Katherine A Wilde
CFO: Willis H Newton Jr
CFO: Michael J Roffler
CFO: Kathleen William
Chf Cred: Howard Noble
Ofcr: Alistair Christopher
Ofcr: Hafize Gaye Erkan
Ofcr: David B Lichtman
Ex VP: Edward J Dobranski
Ex VP: Nicolas Gentin
Ex VP: Brian Riley
Ex VP: Dale A Smith
Ex VP: Dianne Snedaker
Ex VP: Bill Ward
VP: Lionel Antunes
VP: Dan Bessey
Board of Directors: Reynold Levy

D-U-N-S 96-283-1520
FIRST RESERVE XII ADVISORS LLC
(Suby of CNP ASSURANCES)
1 Lafayette Pl Ste 3, Greenwich, CT 06830-5465
Tel (203) 661-6601 Founded/Ownrshp 2008
Sales 126.6MM[E] EMP 1,422[E]
SIC 6799 Investors

D-U-N-S 62-225-6543
FIRST SECURITY BANCORP
314 N Spring St, Searcy, AR 72143-7703
Tel (501) 279-3400 Founded/Ownrshp 1980
Sales NA EMP 500
SIC 6022 State commercial banks
CEO: Reynie Rutledge
*Pr: Jim Wilson
*Sr VP: James Stake
Board of Directors: Joyce Mayfield, Jeanne Rutledge

D-U-N-S 00-796-3143
FIRST SECURITY BANK
(Suby of FIRST SECURITY BANCORP) ★
314 N Spring St, Searcy, AR 72143-7703
Tel (501) 279-3400 Founded/Ownrshp 1932, 1980
Sales NA EMP 500
SIC 6022 State commercial banks
Ch Bd: Reynie Rutledge
COO: Jackie Jones
Ex VP: John Sullivan
Sr VP: Frank Faust
Sr VP: Michael Hutsell
Sr VP: Sylvia Moore
Sr VP: James Stake
VP: Gwen Anderson
VP: Alex Behel
VP: Glenda Hare
VP: Jennifer Harrison
VP: Faith Hollasch
VP: Brad McKenzie
VP: Stuart Norton
VP: Emily Shellabarger
VP: Tony Woodruff
Exec: Krystal Mathys

D-U-N-S 07-915-8318
FIRST SECURITY BENEFIT LIFE INSURANCE AND ANNUITY CO OF NEW YORK
(Suby of SECURITY BENEFIT CORP) ★
800 Westchester Ave N641, Rye Brook, NY 10573-1360
Tel (914) 697-4748 Founded/Ownrshp 2013
Sales NA EMP 4,083[E]
SIC 6411 Loss prevention services, insurance
CEO: Peg Avey

D-U-N-S 00-290-9167
FIRST SERVICE CREDIT UNION
FSCU
9621 W Sam Houston Pkwy N, Houston, TX 77064-5556
Tel (832) 688-1000 Founded/Ownrshp 2007
Sales NA EMP 57,104[E]
Accts Cliftonlarsonallen Llp Austin
SIC 6061 Federal credit unions
*Pr: David Bleazard
*COO: Mike McWethy
*CFO: Jana Heaton
*Treas: Doug Esmond
*Ofcr: John Jackson
*Ofcr: Debra E Little
VP: Barbara Kriesel
VP: Ricardo Mejia
VP: Ken Rychlik
*CIO: Frank Halstead
VP Mktg: Toby Hayes

D-U-N-S 62-164-3816
FIRST SERVICE RESIDENTIAL FLORIDA INC
SILVER PLUMBING & SEWER SVC
(Suby of FIRSTSERVICE CORPORATION)
2950 N 28th Ter, Hollywood, FL 33020-1301
Tel (954) 925-8200 Founded/Ownrshp 2002
Sales 455.8MM[E] EMP 6,500
SIC 6531 Real estate managers; Condominium manager
CEO: Timothy G O'Keefe
Pr: Gary Pyott
*Pr: Tom Roses
COO: Gail Moore
*COO: Rob Rabin
*CFO: Dan Cammarata
CFO: Robert Rabin
Sr VP: Turner Billups
VP: Rick Dingle
VP: Christopher Pappas
VP: Wendy Pennie
VP: Jennifer Potter
VP: Shelly Tygielski
VP: Debbie Youngblood

D-U-N-S 60-732-7769
FIRST SERVICES INC
(Suby of FIRSTTRANSIT) ★
600 Vine St Ste 1200, Cincinnati, OH 45202-2474
Tel (513) 241-2200 Founded/Ownrshp 2003
Sales 75.7M[E] EMP 5,008[E]
SIC 8741 7539 Management services; Automotive repair shops
Pr: Brad Thomas
*CFO: Wayne Johnson

D-U-N-S 87-437-3673
■ FIRST SIERRA FINANCIAL INC
AMERICAN EXPRESS TRAVEL
(Suby of AMERICAN EXPRESS TRAVEL RELATED SERVICES CO INC) ★
600 Travis St Ste 7050, Houston, TX 77002-3009
Tel (713) 221-8822 Founded/Ownrshp 2001
Sales NA EMP 604
SIC 6159 Travel agencies
Prin: Brad Alexander
Treas: Eroger Gebhart
Chf Mktg O: Frederick Van Etten
Ex VP: Alan Langus
Ex VP: Michael A Sabel

D-U-N-S 60-607-2429 IMP/EXP
▲ FIRST SOLAR INC
350 W Washington St # 600, Tempe, AZ 85281-1496
Tel (602) 414-9300 Founded/Ownrshp 1999
Sales 3.5MMM EMP 6,350
Tkr Sym FSLR Exch NGS
SIC 3674 3433 Solar cells; Heating equipment, except electric
CEO: James A Hughes
*Ch Bd: Michael J Ahearn
Pr: Joseph Gkishkill
Pr: Meghan Katz
COO: Philip Tymen De Jong
CFO: Mark R Widmar
Ex VP: Christopher R Bueter
Ex VP: Paul J Kaleta
Ex VP: Tim Rebhorn
Ex VP: Timothy Rebhorn
VP: Kenneth Andrews
VP: Bryan Schumaker
VP: Andrey Xavier

D-U-N-S 96-872-9348
FIRST SOURCE LLC
WYTHE WILL TZETZO
100 Pirson Pkwy, Tonawanda, NY 14150-6727
Tel (716) 877-0800 Founded/Ownrshp 2011
Sales 126.8MM[E] EMP 400
SIC 5499 2064 Gourmet food stores; Candy & other confectionery products
CEO: Keith McDaniel
Pr: Joe Conti
CFO: Rod Hogan
Ex VP: Steve Luitjens

D-U-N-S 00-792-6348
FIRST SOUTHWEST CO
325 N Saint Paul St # 800, Dallas, TX 75201-3852
Tel (214) 953-4000 Founded/Ownrshp 2003
Sales 95.2MM[E] EMP 360
SIC 6211

D-U-N-S 03-631-5463
FIRST STATE COMMUNITY BANK INC
(Suby of FIRST STATE BANCSHARES INC)
201 E Columbia St, Farmington, MO 63640-3106
Tel (573) 756-4547 Founded/Ownrshp 1983
Sales NA EMP 229
SIC 6022 State commercial banks
Ch Bd: Theresa Grindstaff
*Pr: Matthew Sebastian
Sr VP: William Baker
*VP: Greg Allen
VP: Don Gann
*VP: Beth Hoffman
VP: Keith Wade
Brnch Mgr: Bill Ramsey

D-U-N-S 79-867-3414
FIRST STATE MANAGEMENT GROUP INC
(Suby of BEAZLEY GROUP LIMITED)
141 Tremont St Ste 1200, Boston, MA 02111-1209
Tel (617) 526-7600 Founded/Ownrshp 2009
Sales NA EMP 250
SIC 6311 Life insurance
*Pr: Judy Patterson
CFO: Peg Demers
*Treas: Richard Garrett
IT Man: Fabricio Rodriguez

FIRST STEP REAL ESTATE
See FIRST STEP REALTY INC

D-U-N-S 78-653-2353
FIRST STEP REALTY INC
FIRST STEP REAL ESTATE
1620 Commonwealth Ave, Boston, MA 02135-5001
Tel (617) 264-4900 Founded/Ownrshp 2004
Sales 100.0MM EMP 150[E]
SIC 6531 Real estate brokers & agents
CEO: David Scher

D-U-N-S 78-459-6165
FIRST STUDENT INC
(Suby of FIRST GROUP OF AMERICA) ★
600 Vine St Ste 1400, Cincinnati, OH 45202-2426
Tel (513) 241-2200 Founded/Ownrshp 1983
Sales 9.0MMM[E] EMP 58,000
SIC 4151 School buses
Pr: Dennis Maple
*Sr VP: Christian Gartner
*Sr VP: Bruce Rasch
VP: Robert Lindsey
Dir Bus: Nathan Baguio
Off Mgr: Denise Ervin
IT Man: Steven Cohen
Mktg Mgr: Kathy Vask

D-U-N-S 60-604-6118
FIRST SUN MANAGEMENT CORP
WENDY'S
127 Kiowa Ln, Piedmont, SC 29673-6751
Tel (864) 654-5099 Founded/Ownrshp 1989
Sales 64.1MM[E] EMP 1,500
SIC 5812 Fast-food restaurant, chain
CEO: Joe Turner
*Pr: Kelly Durham
CFO: Durham Wk
Brnch Mgr: William Harley

D-U-N-S 00-794-6213 IMP
FIRST SUPPLY LLC (WI)
6800 Gisholt Dr, Monona, WI 53713-4803
Tel (608) 222-7799 Founded/Ownrshp 1897
Sales 467.3MM[E] EMP 600
SIC 5074 5078 5075 5712 5713 Plumbing & hydronic heating supplies; Refrigeration equipment & supplies; Warm air heating & air conditioning; Cabinets, except custom made: kitchen; Floor covering stores
CEO: Joe Poehling
*Pr: Paul Kennedy
Off Mgr: Julie Sjoblom

D-U-N-S 08-033-4433
■ FIRST TEAM AUTOMOTIVE CORP
(Suby of AUTONATION ENTERPRISES INC) ★
200 Sw 1st Ave, Fort Lauderdale, FL 33301-1875
Tel (954) 769-7000 Founded/Ownrshp 1997
Sales 105.0MM[E] EMP 100[E]
SIC 5511 New & used car dealers

D-U-N-S 08-738-7643
FIRST TEAM REAL ESTATE - ORANGE COUNTY (CA)
FIRST TEAM WALK-IN REALTY
108 Pacifica Ste 300, Irvine, CA 92618-7435
Tel (888) 236-1943 Founded/Ownrshp 1976
Sales 95.7MM[E] EMP 2,000
SIC 6531 Real estate agent, residential
CEO: Cameron Merage
Sr VP: Jeff Arcuri
VP: Todd Bruechert
Exec: Terry Leclair
Off Mgr: Mila Rodriguera
Off Admin: Blake Jones
Off Admin: Mila Sealey
Dir IT: Carlos Aguirre
Dir IT: Delia Dura
Dir IT: Timmy Ho
Tech Mgr: Marla Ferguson

FIRST TEAM WALK-IN REALTY
See FIRST TEAM REAL ESTATE - ORANGE COUNTY

D-U-N-S 09-130-0251
FIRST TECHNOLOGY FEDERAL CREDIT UNION
1335 Terra Bella Ave, Mountain View, CA 94043-1835
Tel (855) 855-8805 Founded/Ownrshp 1952
Sales NA EMP 1,178
SIC 6061 Federal credit unions
Pr: Greg A Mitchell
*Pr: Scott Jenner
*CFO: Hank Sigmon
Ex VP: Brooke Vanvleet
Sr VP: Brad Calhoun
VP: Peter Dewes
VP: Deborah Reyes
Ex Dir: Tom Gifford
Genl Mgr: Jonathan Gowins
CIO: Blanca Cuerrero
CIO: Joey Rudisill
Board of Directors: John Weidert, Tony Backes, Kathy Farmer, Tom Gifford, Greg Gillas, Jeff Hank, Dotty Hayes, Peter Horadan, Craig Nordlund, Mark Plastino

D-U-N-S 16-681-7288
FIRST TENN BROKERAGE
4990 Poplar Ave Fl 3, Memphis, TN 38117-7645
Tel (901) 818-6000 Founded/Ownrshp 1982
Sales 150.0MM EMP 40
SIC 6211 Security brokers & dealers
Pr: Paul Mann

D-U-N-S 05-023-9979 IMP
■ FIRST TENNESSEE BANK NATIONAL ASSOCIATION
(Suby of FIRST HORIZON NATIONAL CORP) ★
165 Madison Ave, Memphis, TN 38103-2723
Tel (901) 523-4444 Founded/Ownrshp 1971
Sales NA EMP 4,310[E]
SIC 6021 6162 National commercial banks; Mortgage brokers, using own money
Pr: Bryan Jordan
CFO: Joseph M Evangelisti
*CFO: Marlin L Mosby III
*CFO: Elbert L Thomas Jr
Chf Mktg O: Dan Marks
*Ex VP: Harry A Johnson III
*Sr VP: James F Keen
VP: Jaime Deal
VP: Milton A Gutellius
VP: William Humphries
VP: Ann W Roach
VP: Jamie Swisher

D-U-N-S 12-663-9462 IMP
FIRST TEXAS HOLDING CORP
1465 Henry Brennan Dr H, El Paso, TX 79936-6815
Tel (915) 633-8354 Founded/Ownrshp 1968
Sales 89.6MM[E] EMP 880
SIC 3812 Detection apparatus: electronic/magnetic field, light/heat
Pr: Tom Walsh
*CFO: Daniel Duarte

D-U-N-S 15-050-5337
FIRST TEXAS HOMES INC
GALLERY CUSTOM HOMES
500 Crescent Ct Ste 350, Dallas, TX 75201-7854
Tel (214) 613-3400 Founded/Ownrshp 1984
Sales 95.6MM[E] EMP 100
SIC 1521 New construction, single-family houses
Pr: Randall Vanwolfswinkel
Bd of Dir: Keith Hardesty
*VP: Pete Hardesty
*VP: Kathy Self
Exec: Lachelle Gilbert
Off Mgr: Megan Garnica
Sls Mgr: Karen Kuykendall
Sales Asso: Ronnie Carter
Sales Asso: Barbara Crone
Sales Asso: Michelle Hammock
Sales Asso: Sonja Hicks

D-U-N-S 08-008-6662
■ **FIRST TEXAS HOSPITAL CARROLLTON LLC**
(*Suby of* ADEPTUS HEALTH INC) ★
1401 E Trinity Mills Rd, Carrollton, TX 75006-1442
Tel (972) 810-0700 *Founded/Ownrshp* 2015
Sales 848.2M[E] *EMP* 3,172[E]
SIC 8062 General medical & surgical hospitals
CEO: Ashley Anson

D-U-N-S 07-485-7947 IMP
FIRST TEXAS PRODUCTS LLC
BOUNTY HUNTER METAL DETECTORS
(*Suby of* FIRSTTEXAS HOLDING CORP) ★
1465 Henry Brennan Dr H, El Paso, TX 79936-6815
Tel (915) 633-8354 *Founded/Ownrshp* 2007
Sales 89.6MM[E] *EMP* 800
SIC 3812

FIRST TRANSIT
See FIRSTGROUP USA INC

D-U-N-S 07-287-6915 IMP/EXP
FIRST TRANSIT INC (DE)
(*Suby of* FIRST GROUP OF AMERICA) ★
600 Vine St Ste 1400, Cincinnati, OH 45202-2426
Tel (513) 241-2200 *Founded/Ownrshp* 1969, 1999
Sales 1.2MMM[E] *EMP* 15,500
SIC 8741 7539 8742 Management services; Automotive repair shops; Transportation consultant
Pr: Brad Thomas
**CFO:* Jim Tippen
**Treas:* Christian Gartner
Sr VP: Ric Dunning
VP Mfg: Todd Hawkins
Sls Mgr: Bud Jordan

D-U-N-S 87-266-6719
FIRST TRANSIT INC
(*Suby of* FIRSTTRANSIT INC) ★
249 Wawarme Ave, Hartford, CT 06114-1509
Tel (860) 247-0050 *Founded/Ownrshp* 2014
Sales 30.4MM[E] *EMP* 1,286[E]
SIC 4111 Local & suburban transit

D-U-N-S 78-625-1561
FIRST TRUST PORTFOLIOS LP
120 E Liberty Dr Ste 400, Wheaton, IL 60187-5455
Tel (800) 621-1675 *Founded/Ownrshp* 1991
Sales 137.1MM[E] *EMP* 400
SIC 6211 Investment bankers
Mng Pt: Jim Bowen
Pt: Mark Bradley
Pr: David Pagano
Chf Cred: Jeffrey Scott
Chf Mktg O: Jeff Sedlak
Sr VP: Daniel Affetto
Sr VP: Patricia Costello
Sr VP: Mary B Dvorak
Sr VP: Ken Fincher
Sr VP: Ryan Issakainen
Sr VP: Paul McGinn
VP: Craig Anderson
VP: Steve Beatty
VP: Ash Enshiwat
VP: Dane Eppen
VP: Joe Foley
VP: Tracy Giffen
VP: Craig Pierce
VP: Nim Short
VP: Edward Sistowicz
VP: Cal Smith

FIRST UNITED BANK & TRUST CO
See FIRST UNITED BANK AND TRUST CO

FIRST UNITED BANK AND TRUST CO
See DURANT BANCORP INC

D-U-N-S 00-790-5698
FIRST UNITED BANK AND TRUST CO
FIRST UNITED BANK & TRUST CO
(*Suby of* FIRST UNITED BANK AND TRUST CO) ★
1400 W Main St, Durant, OK 74701-4906
Tel (580) 924-2211 *Founded/Ownrshp* 1980
Sales NA *EMP* 116
SIC 6022 6163 6021 State commercial banks; Loan brokers; National commercial banks
Pr: Greg Massey
COO: Mark Fish
Ofcr: Jennifer Gilbert
**Ex VP:* William Fahrendorf
**Ex VP:* Gary Forbes
Ex VP: Todd Lee
Ex VP: Stephen Phillips
Sr VP: Craig J Custer
Sr VP: Wendell Gamble
Sr VP: John Hewitt
VP: Joe P Bedwell
VP: Frank Bryan
VP: Barbara Coker
VP: Vickie Connelly
VP: Danny Flannery
VP: Joseph Garrison
VP: Russell E Johnson
**VP:* James Kahler
VP: David Keith
VP: Teresa Kirkland
VP: Janet McCollum

D-U-N-S 14-316-9386
FIRST VEHICLE SERVICES INC
(*Suby of* FIRSTTRANSIT INC) ★
600 Vine St Ste 1400, Cincinnati, OH 45202-2426
Tel (513) 241-2200 *Founded/Ownrshp* 1981
Sales 97.6MM[E] *EMP* 1,000
SIC 7549 Automotive maintenance services
Pr: Brad Thomas
**Sr VP:* Dale Domish
IT Man: Adam Silber
Board of Directors: George Emery, H L Garrett

FIRST VICTORIA NATIONAL BANK
See PROSPERITY BANK

D-U-N-S 00-793-7683
FIRST VICTORIA NATIONAL BANK (TX)
101 S Main St, Victoria, TX 77901-8154
Tel (361) 573-6321 *Founded/Ownrshp* 1867
Sales NA *EMP* 430
SIC 6021

FIRST VIRGINIA
See BUCKEYE CHECK CASHING INC

D-U-N-S 15-262-7279
FIRST WATCH OF OHIO INC
8027 Cooper Creek Blvd # 103, University Park, FL 34201-3002
Tel (941) 907-6657 *Founded/Ownrshp* 1994
Sales 53.8MM[E] *EMP* 1,350
SIC 5812 Restaurant, family: independent
Pr: Kenneth L Pendery
**COO:* Rick Akam
**CFO:* Kenneth J Cruley
CFO: Kenneth Cruleychief
CFO: Dale Lowe
**CFO:* Kenneth L Pendereo-Pres
Mktg Dir: Chris Tomasso
Mktg Dir: Cari Trimyer

D-U-N-S 00-320-2975
■ **FIRST-CITIZENS BANK & TRUST CO**
FIRST CITIZENS BANK
(*Suby of* FIRST CITIZENS BANK) ★
4300 Six Forks Rd, Raleigh, NC 27609-5718
Tel (919) 716-7000 *Founded/Ownrshp* 1898
Sales NA *EMP* 4,821
SIC 6035 Savings institutions, federally chartered
Ch Bd: Lewis Holding
**Pr:* Kenneth A Black
**Pr:* Frank B Holding Jr
**CFO:* Glenn McCoy
**V Ch Bd:* James B Hyler Jr
Assoc VP: Andrea Maier
Ex VP: Carol Yochem
Sr VP: Linda S Burwell
Sr VP: Donald Preskenis
**CIO:* Dede Ramoneda
Dir IT: Dave Park

D-U-N-S 00-742-7651
FIRSTBANK
(*Suby of* FIRSTBANK HOLDING CO) ★
10403 W Colfax Ave # 100, Lakewood, CO 80215-3811
Tel (303) 232-2000 *Founded/Ownrshp* 1963
Sales NA *EMP* 125
SIC 6021 National commercial banks
Pr: Koger Propst
**VP:* Sonja Asper
**VP:* Matt Baldner
**VP:* Chris Engen
Dir Risk M: Ebbie Denton
Dir Risk M: Katarina Gonzales

D-U-N-S 03-635-7499
■ **FIRSTBANK**
FIRST BANK, INC.
(*Suby of* FB FINANCIAL CORP) ★
211 Commerce St Ste 300, Nashville, TN 37201-1810
Tel (731) 968-4211 *Founded/Ownrshp* 1988
Sales NA *EMP* 740
SIC 6022 State commercial banks
Ch Bd: James W Ayers
**Pr:* Steve White
CFO: David Bourgeois
CFO: Renee Bunch
Sr VP: Dennis Dysart
Sr VP: Don Holsinger
Sr VP: Dave Jeffcoat
VP: Jonathan Bell
VP: Mindy Gunter
VP: Tammy Middleton
VP: Chris Staley
Dir Risk M: Clark Cummings

D-U-N-S 07-577-0016 IMP
FIRSTBANK HOLDING CO
12345 W Colfax Ave, Lakewood, CO 80215-3742
Tel (303) 232-3000 *Founded/Ownrshp* 1963
Sales NA *EMP* 1,905
SIC 6036 State savings banks, not federally chartered
Pr: John A Ikard
Ch Bd: Larry J Hauserman
Pr: Brian Ballard
Pr: Dawn Davis
Pr: Nan Hinton
Pr: Nicole Staudinger
Pr: Cleve Wortham
Co-Ch Bd: Roger L Reisher
V Ch Bd: R Kent Landmark
Ofcr: Kyle Archer
Ofcr: Nicole Ellis
Ofcr: Amber Miller
Ofcr: Kyle Wilson
Ex VP: Dave Baker
Ex VP: Buddy Douglass
Ex VP: William H Plummer
Sr VP: Sheri Barons
Sr VP: Donald Thuente
VP: Mike Brown
VP: Kelly Kaminskas
VP: Beth Klein
Board of Directors: Nancy Strohmeyer, Dennis Barrett, James A Swanson, Adam Coyle, Jack Fox, Harry H Frampton III, William Hybl, Lawrence M Kendall, Robert L Manning Jr, Margaret A Reisher, Mary S Reisher

FIRSTCARE
See SHA LLC

D-U-N-S 03-216-9471
FIRSTCAROLINACARE INSURANCE CO (NC)
(*Suby of* MOORE REGIONAL HOSPITAL) ★
42 Memorial Dr, Pinehurst, NC 28374-8707
Tel (910) 715-8100 *Founded/Ownrshp* 2000
Sales NA *EMP* 35
SIC 6324 Health maintenance organization (HMO), insurance only
Pr: Kenneth Lewis
COO: Craig Humphrey
Sls Mgr: Rebecca F Ballard
Pharmcst: Joanna McDearmon

D-U-N-S 62-613-6535
▲ **FIRSTCASH INC**
690 E Lamar Blvd Ste 400, Arlington, TX 76011-3864
Tel (817) 460-3947 *Founded/Ownrshp* 1988
Sales 704.6MM *EMP* 8,600[E]
Tkr Sym FCFS *Exch* NYS
SIC 5932 6099 Pawnshop; Check cashing agencies
CEO: Rick L Wessel
**Ch Bd:* Daniel R Feehan
Pr: T Brent Stuart
COO: Christopher Lee
CFO: R Douglas Orr
Sr VP: Sean D Moore
Sr VP: Raul R Ramos
Sr VP: Peter H Watson
Board of Directors: Daniel E Berce, Mikel D Faulkner, James H Graves, Jorge Montano, Randel G Owen

FIRSTCOMP
See ASPEN HOLDINGS INC

D-U-N-S 03-679-0806
■ **FIRSTCOMP INSURANCE CO**
(*Suby of* FIRSTCOMP) ★
222 S 15th St Ste 1500n, Omaha, NE 68102-1656
Tel (888) 500-3344 *Founded/Ownrshp* 1997
Sales NA *EMP* 500
SIC 6411 Insurance agents, brokers & service
CEO: Luke W Yeransian
**CFO:* Steve Letak
Bd of Dir: Jeff Downey
Ofcr: James P Arnold
**VP:* Robert N Phaneuf
IT Man: Steve Linbo
Sls Dir: Mark Thramer
Mktg Mgr: Chris Paulson
Sls Mgr: Cristine Giraldez
Sls Mgr: Ryan Lynch
Sls Mgr: Jim Wheeler

FIRSTENERGY
See ALLEGHENY ENERGY SERVICE CORP

FIRSTENERGY
See WEST PENN POWER CO

FIRSTENERGY
See POTOMAC EDISON CO

D-U-N-S 79-924-9461
▲ **FIRSTENERGY CORP**
76 S Main St Bsmt, Akron, OH 44308-1817
Tel (800) 736-3402 *Founded/Ownrshp* 1996
Sales 15.0MMM *EMP* 15,781
Tkr Sym FE *Exch* NYS
SIC 4911 Electric services; Distribution, electric power; Generation, electric power; Transmission, electric power
Pr: Charles E Jones
**Ch Bd:* George M Smart
Pr: James H Lash
CFO: James F Pearson
Sr VP: Dennis M Chack
VP: John Daugherty
VP: James Garanich
VP: Bob Reffner
VP: Jeffrey Steiner
VP: K Jon Taylor
IT Man: Mary Bowers
Board of Directors: Christopher D Pappas, Paul T Addison, Luis A Reyes, Michael J Anderson, Jerry Sue Thornton, William T Cottle, Robert B Heisler Jr, Julia L Johnson, Ted J Kleisner, Donald T Misheff, Thomas N Mitchell, Ernest J Novak Jr

D-U-N-S 80-045-9724
■ **FIRSTENERGY GENERATION LLC**
(*Suby of* FIRSTENERGY CORP) ★
76 S Main St, Akron, OH 44308-1812
Tel (800) 633-4766 *Founded/Ownrshp* 2000
Sales 90.7MM[E] *EMP* 150
SIC 4911 Electric services; Generation, electric power
CEO: Gary R Leidich
Bd of Dir: Michael J Anderson
Bd of Dir: Ernest Novak
Bd of Dir: Robert N Pokewaldt
Bd of Dir: Jesse T Williamson
VP: Michael Dowling
VP: Charles Lasky
VP: Ron Seeholzer

D-U-N-S 13-547-5551
■ **FIRSTENERGY NUCLEAR OPERATING CO**
(*Suby of* FIRSTENERGY CORP) ★
76 S Main St Bsmt, Akron, OH 44308-1817
Tel (800) 646-0400 *Founded/Ownrshp* 1998
Sales 7.8MMM[E] *EMP* 13,000
SIC 4911 Electric services
CEO: Anthony J Alexander
**Pr:* James H Lash
**Pr:* Garry Leidich
**COO:* Lew Myers
**Ofcr:* Samuel L Belcher
**Ex VP:* Charles E Jones
**Sr VP:* Lynn M Cavalier
**Sr VP:* Joseph Hagan
Sr VP: Marty Richey
VP: Ernest J Harkness
VP: Vito A Kaminskas
VP: Eric A Larson
VP: Kevin Ostrowski
Exec: Dennis M Chack
Exec: Rhonda S Ferguson
Exec: Trent A Smith
Exec: Steven E Strah

D-U-N-S 19-247-2751
■ **FIRSTENERGY SOLUTIONS CORP**
(*Suby of* FIRSTENERGY CORP) ★
76 S Main St Bsmt, Akron, OH 44308-1817
Tel (800) 736-3402 *Founded/Ownrshp* 1997
Sales 5.0MMM *EMP* 143[E]
SIC 4911 Electric services; Generation, electric power; Transmission, electric power
Pr: Donald R Schneider
CFO: James F Pearson
Ex VP: Richard R Grigg
Sr VP: Lynn Cavalier
Sr VP: Leila Vespoli
VP: Tony C Banks
VP: William Byrd
VP: Mark T Clark
VP: Thomas A Clark
VP: Don Moul
VP: Irene M Prezelj
VP: Ronald E Seeholzer
VP: Trent A Smith
VP: K Jon Taylor

D-U-N-S 07-090-3153
FIRSTENTERPRISES INC
FIRST FLEET
202 Heritage Park Dr, Murfreesboro, TN 37129-1556
Tel (615) 890-9229 *Founded/Ownrshp* 1995
Sales 464.9MM[E] *EMP* 3,400
Accts Dw&W Cookeville Tn
SIC 4213 Contract haulers
Pr: Gary Wilson
Opers Mgr: David Margolis

D-U-N-S 18-468-6913
FIRSTFED FINANCIAL CORP
6320 Canoga Ave, Woodland Hills, CA 91367-2526
Tel (562) 618-0573 *Founded/Ownrshp* 1987
Sales NA *EMP* 603
SIC 6021 National commercial banks
Pr: James Giraldin
Ch Bd: Brian Argrett
**Pr:* James P Giraldin
Pr: Shannon Millard
**CEO:* Babette E Heimbuch
CFO: Douglas J Goddard
Chf Cred: David W Anderson
Ofcr: Kevin Bosetti
Ofcr: Scott Gray
Ex VP: Christine D Larson
Sr VP: Matt Seaburn
Board of Directors: Nicholas C Biase, Jesse Casso Jr, Christopher M Harding, William G Ouchi, William P Rutledge, Steven L Soboroff

D-U-N-S 17-426-6494
FIRSTFLEET INC
(*Suby of* FIRST FLEET) ★
202 Heritage Park Dr, Murfreesboro, TN 37129-1556
Tel (615) 890-9229 *Founded/Ownrshp* 1986
Sales 266.5MM[E] *EMP* 2,000
SIC 4213 Contract haulers
Pr: Gary Wilson
**VP:* David Beeny
**VP:* John Hellige
**VP:* Daniel Piper
**VP:* Wayland Thompson
Brnch Mgr: John Gifford
Genl Mgr: Kelly Moore
Dir IT: David Sivils

FIRSTGROUP AMERICA
See LAIDLAW INTERNATIONAL INC

D-U-N-S 17-590-5488
FIRSTGROUP AMERICA INC
FIRST GROUP OF AMERICA
(*Suby of* FIRSTTRANSIT) ★
600 Vine St Ste 1400, Cincinnati, OH 45202-2426
Tel (513) 241-2200 *Founded/Ownrshp* 1999
Sales 10.4MMM[E] *EMP* 58,000
SIC 4151 4111 4119 4131 4141 8744 School buses; Local & suburban transit; Local passenger transportation; Intercity & rural bus transportation; Local bus charter service; Facilities support services; Base maintenance (providing personnel on continuing basis);
Pr: Dennis Maple
Pr: Brad Thomas
CFO: Mark Lawton
**Sr VP:* Christian Gartner
Sr VP: Steve Hemmerlein
**Sr VP:* Bruce Rasch
VP: Bette Norris
VP: Susan Whittaker
Brnch Mgr: James Lenway
Brnch Mgr: William Patterson
Brnch Mgr: Jim Visser
Board of Directors: Jim Andrew, Chuck Barnes, David Braun, Glenn Dinkheller, Bobbie Baker-Hartman, Jim Rude, Elvin Tobin

D-U-N-S 60-731-5392
FIRSTGROUP USA INC
FIRSTTRANSIT
(*Suby of* FIRSTGROUP PLC)
600 Vine St Ste 1400, Cincinnati, OH 45202-2426
Tel (513) 241-2200 *Founded/Ownrshp* 1999
Sales 1.3MMM *EMP* 86,000
SIC 7513 4212 4213 4225 4151 4111 Truck leasing, without drivers; Truck rental, without drivers; Local trucking, without storage; Trucking, except local; General warehousing; School buses; Local & suburban transit
CEO: Bruce Ballard
**Ch:* Tim O'Toole
Mktg Mgr: Christian Gartner

D-U-N-S 01-230-5969
FIRSTHEALTH MOORE REGIONAL MEDICAL CENTER
110 Page Rd, Pinehurst, NC 28374-8746
Tel (910) 715-1077 *Founded/Ownrshp* 2012
Sales 460.7MM *EMP* 2,500
SIC 8062 General medical & surgical hospitals
CEO: Charles Frock
Ansthlgy: Raymond R Lupkas

D-U-N-S 93-192-3072
FIRSTHEALTH OF CAROLINAS INC
MOORE REGIONAL HOSPITAL
155 Memorial Dr, Pinehurst, NC 28374-8710
Tel (910) 715-1000 *Founded/Ownrshp* 1995
Sales 695.5MM *EMP* 3,897
SIC 8062 8093 8051 8021 7991 7219 General medical & surgical hospitals; Rehabilitation center, outpatient treatment; Speech defect clinic; Family planning clinic; Skilled nursing care facilities; Dental clinic; Health club; Laundry, except power & coin-operated
CEO: Charles T Frock
Chf OB: William V Terry
Chf Rad: Lawrence K Martin
**Ch Bd:* H Edward Barnes Jr
COO: Stuart G Voelpel
CFO: Lynn De Jaco
**V Ch Bd:* David Burns
Ofcr: Michael Bollinger

Ofcr: George Bussey MD
Ofcr: Lynn Jaco
Ofcr: Stuart Voelpel
VP: Wanda Hardister
VP: S Harrington
VP: Vivian Harrington
VP: Cindy McDonald
Exec: Jerry Arnold
Exec: Wanda Cummings
Dir Inf Cn: Jane Lee
Dir Lab: Elise Forest
Dir Bus: Amy Graham
Board of Directors: C Walker Morris, Robert Bahner MD, Dr Susan Purser, Alex Bowness, Frances Reaves, David Bruton MD, Fred Ritchie, John N Ellis MD, Bruce Solomon Do, Walter S Fasolak Do, John S Stevenson MD, Russell J Hollers, David Woronoff, Ernest Hooker, Burt Place MD, John F Krahnert MD, John M May

D-U-N-S 79-666-5375
FIRSTLIGHT POWER RESOURCES SERVICES LLC
(*Suby of* GDF SUEZ ENERGY NORTH AMERICA INC) ★
200 Glastonbury Blvd # 303, Glastonbury, CT 06033-4418
Tel (860) 430-2110 *Founded/Ownrshp* 2011
Sales 84.4MM^E *EMP* 240
SIC 4911 Generation, electric power

FIRSTLINE NATIONAL INSUR CO
See HARFORD MUTUAL INSURANCE CO

D-U-N-S 79-060-4206
FIRSTMARK CAPITAL LLC
100 5th Ave Fl 3, New York, NY 10011-6903
Tel (212) 792-2200 *Founded/Ownrshp* 2007
Sales 135.1MM^E *EMP* 250^E
SIC 6282 Investment advice
Mng Pt: Lawrence Lenihan
VP: Dan Kozikowski
Mng Dir: Amish Hani
Mng Dir: Sergey D Nazarov
Mng Dir: Matt Turck
Genl Couns: Greg Raiten

D-U-N-S 00-699-8298
FIRSTMERIT BANK NATIONAL ASSOCIATION
106 S Main St Fl 5, Akron, OH 44308-1412
Tel (330) 384-7201 *Founded/Ownrshp* 1981
Sales NA *EMP* 2,836
SIC 6021

D-U-N-S 02-734-5412
FIRSTMERIT CORP
Iii Cascade Plz Fl 7, Akron, OH 44308
Tel (330) 996-6300 *Founded/Ownrshp* 1981
Sales NA *EMP* 4,112^E
SIC 6021

D-U-N-S 96-164-9121 IMP
FIRSTRONIC LLC
1655 Michigan St Ne, Grand Rapids, MI 49503-2015
Tel (616) 456-9220 *Founded/Ownrshp* 2009
Sales 104.7MM^E *EMP* 170
SIC 3559 Electronic component making machinery
Ch: Peter Barclae
**CEO:* John Sammut
CFO: Orland Baas
**VP:* Steve Fraser
**VP:* Wally Johnson

D-U-N-S 93-203-1719
FIRSTRUST CORP
909 Poydras St Ste 1700, New Orleans, LA 70112-4010
Tel (504) 584-5900 *Founded/Ownrshp* 1991
Sales NA *EMP* 312
SIC 6022 State commercial banks
Pr: Ashton J Ryan Jr
**Ch Bd:* Joseph C Canizaro
**Pr:* Michael Brown
Board of Directors: James E Livingston

D-U-N-S 05-329-3718
FIRSTRUST SAVINGS BANK
15 E Ridge Pike Ste 400, Conshohocken, PA 19428-2123
Tel (610) 941-9898 *Founded/Ownrshp* 1986
Sales NA *EMP* 400
SIC 6036 State savings banks, not federally chartered
CEO: Richard Green
**Ch Bd:* Daniel B Green
**Pr:* Timothy J Abell
Pr: Dawn Stoler
Pr: Gregory Sudell
**COO:* Margaret H Leimkuhler
CFO: Peter Nolan
Ofcr: Nancy Boland
Ofcr: Michael Poga
Ex VP: Terry Dalessandro
Sr VP: Fiorentino Carmen
Sr VP: William J Lloyd Jr
Sr VP: Kent D Nelson
VP: Rocco Biancaniello
VP: Lawrence Burns
VP: Marcey Carroll
VP: Dominic A Dimaio
VP: Nancy Gatschet
VP: Mike Okino
VP: Joseph Rago
VP: Thomas Starke

D-U-N-S 96-926-5024
FIRSTSERVICE RESIDENTIAL TEXAS INC
3102 Oak Lawn Ave Ste 202, Dallas, TX 75219-6400
Tel (214) 871-9700 *Founded/Ownrshp* 1996
Sales 165.0M^E *EMP* 10,000
SIC 8741 Management services
Pr: Cindy Huey
Treas: Darren Stanley
VP: Ashlynn Wells

D-U-N-S 94-063-5816
FIRSTSOURCE ADVANTAGE LLC
ACCOUNT SOLUTIONS GROUP
(*Suby of* FIRSTSOURCE SOLUTIONS LIMITED)
205 Bryant Woods S, Amherst, NY 14228-3609
Tel (716) 564-4400 *Founded/Ownrshp* 1995
Sales 60.5MM^E *EMP* 1,000
SIC 7322 Adjustment & collection services
Pr: Arjun Mitra
Ex VP: Santanu Nandi
VP: Jeff Markley
IT Man: Keith Delande
Opers Mgr: Charles Root

D-U-N-S 88-418-6532
FIRSTSOURCE SOLUTIONS USA INC
ACCOUNT SOLUTIONS GROUP
(*Suby of* FIRSTSOURCE SOLUTIONS LIMITED)
205 Bryant Woods S, Buffalo, NY 14228-3609
Tel (716) 564-4400 *Founded/Ownrshp* 2000
Sales 113.9MM^E *EMP* 3,000^E
SIC 8741 Management services
Ch Bd: Rajesh Subramaniam
**Pr:* Dinesh Jain
Pr: Thomas J Watters
**COO:* Stephanie Wilson
COO: Mitzi Winters
CFO: Sam Riddick
Ofcr: Virginia Marczynski
Ex VP: Gaurav Bahadur
Ex VP: Brenda Snow
Sr VP: Katie Black
Sr VP: Ganesh Iyer
Sr VP: Satwant Khalsa
VP: Jeff Markley
VP: Nancy Maze
**VP:* Arjun Mitra
Exec: Deborah Needlman

D-U-N-S 96-637-2591 IMP
FIRTH RIXSON INC
FIRTH RIXSON MONROE
(*Suby of* FIRTH RIXSON LIMITED)
181 Mckee Rd, Rochester, NY 14611-2011
Tel (585) 328-1383 *Founded/Ownrshp* 1991
Sales 125.0MM^E *EMP* 370
SIC 3462 Iron & steel forgings; Aircraft forgings, ferrous
CEO: David C Mortimer
Pr: David Hebert
CFO: Steven Clark
**Prin:* Bob Lang
Area Mgr: Zack Rush
Genl Mgr: Michael Belmont
Genl Mgr: Shawn Gould
Genl Mgr: Chris Gratton
Genl Mgr: Brian Hoover
Mfg Mgr: Wilbert Dickens

FIRTH RIXSON MONROE
See FIRTH RIXSON INC

FIS
See FIDELITY NATIONAL INFORMATION SERVICES INC

FIS
See FIDELITY INFORMATION SERVICES LLC

D-U-N-S 10-142-2731
■ **FIS DATA SYSTEMS INC**
(*Suby of* SUNGARD HOLDCO LLC) ★
200 Campus Dr, Collegeville, PA 19426-4903
Tel (484) 582-2000 *Founded/Ownrshp* 2005
Sales 2.8MMM *EMP* 13,000
SIC 7374 7372 Data processing service; Business oriented computer software
Pr: Russell P Fradin
**Ch Bd:* Glenn H Hutchins
COO: Marianne C Brown
CFO: Charles J Neral
Treas: Ralph Than
Ofcr: Patricia K Cassidy
Ex VP: Jim Heinzman
Ex VP: Brian A Traquair
Sr VP: Vince Coppola
Sr VP: Kevin J McCurry
VP: Thomas Arnold
VP: Ryan Blackwell
VP: Brian Blind
VP: Timothy Boyle
VP: Christopher Breakiron
VP: Aaron Brown
VP: Tim Cecconi
VP: David Digiacomo
VP: Ian Ferlanti
VP: Haim Glickman
VP: Jim Grogan
Board of Directors: David L Johnson, Ian K Loring, John W Marren, R Davis Noell, John I Park

D-U-N-S 15-729-3853
■ **FIS EPROCESS INTELLIGENCE LLC**
SUNGARD
(*Suby of* FIS DATA SYSTEMS INC) ★
680 E Swedesford Rd, Wayne, PA 19087-1605
Tel (888) 601-2361 *Founded/Ownrshp* 1984
Sales 210.4MM^E *EMP* 3,729
SIC 7374 5045 Data processing & preparation; Data processing service; Computer software
CEO: Mike Borman
**Pr:* Russ Fradin
**Sr VP:* Regina Brab
**Sr VP:* Anthony Calenda
**Sr VP:* Vince Coppola
**VP:* Andrew P Bronstein
**VP:* Lawrence A Gross
**VP:* George P Warren

D-U-N-S 07-149-7366
■ **FIS FINANCIAL SYSTEMS LLC**
SUNGARD
(*Suby of* FIS DATA SYSTEMS INC) ★
601 Riverside Ave, Jacksonville, FL 32204-2946
Tel (904) 438-6000 *Founded/Ownrshp* 1990
Sales 170.9MM^E *EMP* 820
SIC 7374 7372 Data processing service; Business oriented computer software
CEO: Gary Norcross
IT Man: Finbar McEvoy
Sls Mgr: Rick Seaberg

D-U-N-S 78-382-4670
■ **FIS SG LLC**
SUNGARD
(*Suby of* FIS) ★
680 E Swedesford Rd, Wayne, PA 19087-1605
Tel (484) 582-5400 *Founded/Ownrshp* 2015
Sales 2.8MMM *EMP* 13,000^E
SIC 7372 7374 Prepackaged software; Data processing & preparation
Pr: Russell P Fradin
**CFO:* Charles J Neral
**Ofcr:* Patricia K Cassidy
Sr VP: Tom Gukelberger
**Sr VP:* Victoria E Silbey
**VP:* Christopher P Breakiron
VP: Tim Carley
IT Man: Jennifer Sherman

D-U-N-S 10-720-5619 IMP
■ **FIS SYSTEMS INTERNATIONAL INC**
SUNGARD
(*Suby of* SUNGARD) ★
200 Campus Dr, Collegeville, PA 19426-4903
Tel (484) 582-2000 *Founded/Ownrshp* 1987
Sales 175.8MM^E *EMP* 700
SIC 7372 Business oriented computer software
Pr: James Ashton
**Treas:* Michael Ruane
**VP:* Thomas McDugall

D-U-N-S 07-950-3072
■ **FIS WEALTH MANAGEMENT SERVICES INC**
(*Suby of* FIS) ★
601 Riverside Ave, Jacksonville, FL 32204-2946
Tel (904) 854-5000 *Founded/Ownrshp* 2014
Sales 84.0MM^E *EMP* 310^E
SIC 7389 7374 Financial services; Computer processing services
Ch Bd: Frank R Martire
Sr VP: Maura Hunter
Sr VP: Melissa Tierney
VP: Thomas Greuling
VP: Bradford R Pineault
Mng Dir: Kay A Dunn
Mng Dir: Andrea Schussler
Sales Asso: Connor Vlahos

D-U-N-S 04-158-6855
■ **FISCAL SERVICE BUREAU OF**
(*Suby of* UNITED STATES DEPT OF TREASURY) ★
401 14th St Sw Rm 548, Washington, DC 20227-0001
Tel (202) 622-7000 *Founded/Ownrshp* 1999
Sales NA *EMP* 2,100
Accts Gene L Dorado
SIC 9311 Treasurers' office, government

D-U-N-S 03-871-9084 EXP
FISCHER HOMES INC
3940 Olympic Blvd Ste 100, Erlanger, KY 41018-1025
Tel (859) 341-4709 *Founded/Ownrshp* 1980
Sales 147.5MM^E *EMP* 352
SIC 1522 Residential construction
CEO: Bob Hawksley
**Pr:* Robert T Hawksley
**Treas:* Henry K Fischer
**VP:* Elaine Fischer
VP: Jon Jasper
**Prin:* Henry Fischer
CTO: Steve Kevill
Dir IT: John Cann
Mktg Mgr: Steve Whaley
Sls Mgr: Erin Hundley
Sls Mgr: Ann Kresky

FISCHER NUT COMPANY
See JOHN B SANFILIPPO & SON INC

FISERV
See CHECKFREE CORP

FISERV
See INFORMATION TECHNOLOGY INC

FISERV
See CHECKFREE SERVICES CORP

D-U-N-S 05-707-3744
■ **FISERV CIR INC**
(*Suby of* FISERV INC) ★
255 Fiserv Dr, Brookfield, WI 53045-5817
Tel (262) 879-5000 *Founded/Ownrshp* 1991
Sales 87.7MM^E *EMP* 1,300
SIC 7374 7372 7373 Data processing service; Application computer software; Turnkey vendors, computer systems
Pr: Jeffery W Yabuki
**Pr:* Thomas W Warsop III
**CFO:* Tom Hirsch
Treas: Brent Reeves
**Ex VP:* James Cox
**Ex VP:* Shawn Donovan
**Ex VP:* Michael P Gianoni
**Ex VP:* Rahul Gupta
**Ex VP:* Charles W Sprague

FISERV HEALTH
See HARRINGTON HEALTH SERVICES INC

D-U-N-S 12-159-4832 IMP
▲ **FISERV INC**
255 Fiserv Dr, Brookfield, WI 53045-5817
Tel (262) 879-5000 *Founded/Ownrshp* 1984
Sales 5.2MMM *EMP* 21,000
Tkr Sym FISV *Exch* NGS
SIC 7374 7371 Data processing service; Computer software development & applications
Pr: Jeffery W Yabuki
**Ch Bd:* Daniel P Kearney
Pr: Kevin P Gregoire
Pr: Rahul Gupta
Pr: Michael O'Laughlin
Pr: Kevin J Schultz
Pr: Steven Tait
Pr: Byron C Vielehr
COO: Mark A Ernst
CFO: Robert W Hau
CFO: Thomas J Hirsch
Ex VP: Cliff Skelton
VP: Cindy Albers
VP: Tracy Brewster
VP: Oscar Mireles
VP: Erik Swenson
VP: Rebekkah Wilson
Board of Directors: Alison Davis, Christopher M Flink, John Kim, Dennis F Lynch, Denis J O'leary, Glenn M Renwick, Kim M Robak, Doyle R Simons, Thomas C Wertheimer

D-U-N-S 08-926-9476
■ **FISERV SOLUTIONS LLC**
(*Suby of* FISERV INC) ★
255 Fiserv Dr, Brookfield, WI 53045-5817
Tel (262) 879-5000 *Founded/Ownrshp* 1992
Sales 529.5MM^E *EMP* 5,200
SIC 7374 2754 5084 Data processing service; Commercial printing, gravure; Industrial machinery & equipment
Pr: Jeffrey Yabuki
**Ch Bd:* Donald F Dillion
COO: Geoffrey Roach
CFO: Thomas Hirsch
Treas: Thomas J Hirsch
**Ex VP:* Shawn M Donovan
Ex VP: Lance Drummond
Ex VP: Bridie Fanning
Ex VP: Brian Fox
Ex VP: Anthony Jabbour
Ex VP: Michael Oates

D-U-N-S 06-659-8103
FISH & RICHARDSON PC
1 Marina Park Dr Ste 1700, Boston, MA 02210-1878
Tel (617) 542-5070 *Founded/Ownrshp* 1994
Sales 116.7MM^E *EMP* 525
SIC 8111 Patent solicitor
Pr: Peter J Devlin
**CFO:* Daniel Lasman
**Treas:* Dorothy P Whelan
Ex VP: Mike Mitchell
Exec: David Hosp
Comm Dir: Liz Cerasuolo
**Prin:* Gene T Barton
**Prin:* Edward A Cavazos
**Prin:* Timothy A French
Dir IT: Chuck Demille
Mktg Mgr: Megan Cianchette

D-U-N-S 83-810-3893
FISH & WILDLIFE CONSERVATION COMMISSION FLORIDA
FWC
(*Suby of* EXECUTIVE OFFICE OF GOVERNOR OF FLORIDA) ★
620 S Meridian St, Tallahassee, FL 32399-6543
Tel (850) 487-3796 *Founded/Ownrshp* 1999
Sales NA *EMP* 2,100
SIC 9512 Game & inland fish agency, government;
Ex Dir: Nick Wiley
Ofcr: Jim Moore
**Ex Dir:* Ken Haddad

D-U-N-S 92-618-1181 IMP/EXP
■ **FISH & WILDLIFE SERVICE UNITED STATES**
(*Suby of* UNITED STATES DEPARTMENT OF INTERIOR) ★
4401 Fairfax Dr Ste 325, Arlington, VA 22203-1610
Tel (703) 358-1742 *Founded/Ownrshp* 1871
Sales NA *EMP* 7,000
SIC 9512
Pr: Dale Hall
Pr: Dave Erdahl
Sr Cor Off: Thomas Gittins
Bd of Dir: Bill Cashin
Bd of Dir: Susan Miller
Ofcr: Bill Raften
Assoc Dir: Teresa R Christopher
Ex Dir: Jamie Clark
Ex Dir: Harry Dupree
Ex Dir: Jim Halpin
Ex Dir: Mike Spear

D-U-N-S 04-797-5867
FISHEL CO
FISHEL TECHNOLOGIES
1366 Dublin Rd, Columbus, OH 43215-1093
Tel (614) 274-8100 *Founded/Ownrshp* 1936
Sales 301.8MM *EMP* 1,400
Accts Crowe Horwath Llp Columbus O
SIC 1623 1731 8711 Telephone & communication line construction; Electric power line construction; Cable television line construction; Gas main construction; General electrical contractor; Engineering services
Ch: Diane F Keeler
**Pr:* John E Phillips
COO: Randy Blair
**CFO:* Paul Riewe
CFO: Paul R Riewe
**VP:* O Randy Blair
VP: Ed Evans
**VP:* Scott R Homberger
VP: Scott Homberger
**VP:* Ken E Katz
VP: Scott Keeler
**VP:* W Scott Keeler
**VP:* Vance Mauldin
**VP:* William E Pauley

FISHEL TECHNOLOGIES
See FISHEL CO

D-U-N-S 00-653-2584 IMP
FISHER & CO INC
FISHER DYNAMICS
33300 Fisher Dr, Saint Clair Shores, MI 48082
Tel (586) 746-2000 *Founded/Ownrshp* 1800
Sales 445.4MM^E *EMP* 1,260
SIC 2531 Seats, automobile
Ch: Alfred J Fisher III
**Ch:* Alfred J Fisher III
**VP:* Joseph E Blake
VP: Bill Clark
**VP:* Alfred J Fisher IV

*VP: Michael R Fisher
Ql Cn Mgr: John Olesko

FISHER & PAYKEL
See DYNAMIC COOKING SYSTEMS INC

D-U-N-S 60-743-9242 IMP
FISHER & PAYKEL APPLIANCES USA HOLDINGS INC
(Suby of FISHER & PAYKEL APPLIANCES LIMITED)
695 Town Center Dr # 180, Costa Mesa, CA 92626-1902
Tel (888) 936-7872 Founded/Ownrshp 2004
Sales 237.6MM[E] EMP 1,008
SIC 5064 Washing machines; Clothes dryers, electric & gas
CEO: Laurence Mawhinney
*VP: Linda Cooper
*CFO: Mark Richardson
Sr Cor Off: Malcolm Harris

D-U-N-S 07-586-9958
FISHER & PHILLIPS LLP
1075 Peachtree St Ne # 3500, Atlanta, GA 30309-3900
Tel (404) 231-1400 Founded/Ownrshp 1948
Sales 141.5MM[E] EMP 800
SIC 8111

D-U-N-S 02-396-5379 IMP
FISHER AUTO PARTS INC
512 Greenville Ave, Staunton, VA 24401-4755
Tel (540) 885-8901 Founded/Ownrshp 1926
Sales 702.6MM[E] EMP 1,900
SIC 5013 5531 4225 Automotive supplies & parts; Automotive parts; General warehousing
CEO: Arthur J Fisher III
*Treas: Ken Cox
*Co-Pr: Herbert L Godschalk III
*Co-Pr: Gary Shifflett
*VP: David Biery
VP: David Bluthardt
*VP: David Clymore
*VP: Larry Pavey
VP: Joe Rader
Rgnl Mgr: Norm Matton
Rgnl Mgr: Wanda Shorter

D-U-N-S 19-987-9800 IMP
■ **FISHER CLINICAL SERVICES INC**
(Suby of FISHER SCIENTIFIC INTERNATIONAL LLC) ★
7554 Schantz Rd, Allentown, PA 18106-9032
Tel (610) 391-0800 Founded/Ownrshp 2000
Sales 350.9MM[E] EMP 590
SIC 5122 Pharmaceuticals
Genl Mgr: Michael A Ivers
Sr VP: Lynne Pastir
VP: Micheal Shwartz
*Genl Mgr: Rod Stull
Dir IT: David Paul
IT Man: William Homlish
Snr PM: Brian Drozda

D-U-N-S 00-924-8816
■ **FISHER COMMUNICATIONS INC**
(Suby of SINCLAIR BROADCAST GROUP INC) ★
140 4th Ave N Ste 500, Seattle, WA 98109-4940
Tel (206) 404-7000 Founded/Ownrshp 2013
Sales 165.2MM[E] EMP 776[E]
SIC 4833 4832 Television broadcasting stations; Radio broadcasting stations
Pr: David D Smith
*Treas: Lucy Rutishauser
Sr VP: Judith A Endejan
VP: Paul Anovick
*VP: David Bochenek
VP: Glen P Christofferson
VP: James Clayton
VP: Sharon Johnston
VP: Bob Thomas
VP: Christopher G Wheeler
CTO: George Faulkner

D-U-N-S 09-549-2625 IMP/EXP
■ **FISHER CONTROLS INTERNATIONAL LLC**
FISHER FAST PARTS
(Suby of EPMCO HOLDINGS, INC.)
205 S Center St, Marshalltown, IA 50158-2891
Tel (641) 754-3011 Founded/Ownrshp 1992
Sales 1.3MMM[E] EMP 7,400
SIC 3491 3823 3625 3612 3494 Automatic regulating & control valves; Valves, automatic control; Process control regulator valves; Industrial instrmnts msrmnt display/control process variable; Relays & industrial controls; Transformers, except electric; Valves & pipe fittings
CEO: Larry W Solley
*Pr: Malcolm Burke
VP: Bill Fitzgerald
VP: David Hunter
VP: Steve Kinz
VP: Stuart Miller
Mktg Dir: Bob Findley
Sls Dir: Roger Hager
Snr PM: Joseph Hanchak

FISHER DYNAMICS
See FISHER & CO INC

FISHER FAST PARTS
See FISHER CONTROLS INTERNATIONAL LLC

D-U-N-S 83-633-1686
FISHER FINANCIAL GROUP INC
NATIONSCHOICE MORTGAGE
3303 E Baseline Rd # 113, Gilbert, AZ 85234-2738
Tel (480) 461-1111 Founded/Ownrshp 1994
Sales NA EMP 54
SIC 6162 Mortgage bankers & correspondents
Pr: Chad Fisher
*Treas: Gary Fisher
*VP: Kim Fisher

D-U-N-S 00-892-6685
FISHER FOODS MARKETING INC
4855 Frank Ave Nw, Canton, OH 44720-7425
Tel (330) 433-1180 Founded/Ownrshp 1930
Sales 120.6MM[E] EMP 700
SIC 5411 8741 Supermarkets, independent; Management services
Pr: Jeffrey A Fisher
*VP: Jack B Fisher

FISHER INDUSTRIES
See FISHER SAND & GRAVEL CO

D-U-N-S 11-508-0665
FISHER INVESTMENTS INC
PACIFIC PUBLISHING
5525 Nw Fisher Creek Dr, Camas, WA 98607-9911
Tel (888) 823-9566 Founded/Ownrshp 1973
Sales 105.9MM[E] EMP 2,000[E]
SIC 6282 Investment advisory service
*CEO: Kenneth L Fisher
*CFO: Sherrylyn Fisher
Ex VP: Bill Glaser
VP: Aaron Anderson
VP: Peter C Chizever
VP: Alan Ebright
VP: Ian Epstein
VP: Jeff Helm
VP: Lara Hoffmansa
VP: Fabrizio Ornani
VP: Kim Shickel
VP: James Smolinski
VP: Scott Stratton
VP: Farhad Teymourtash
VP: John Vertiz
VP: Paul Weinberger

FISHER RESEARCH LABORATORY
See FRL INC

D-U-N-S 03-181-0617
FISHER SAND & GRAVEL CO (ND)
FISHER INDUSTRIES
3020 Energy Dr, Dickinson, ND 58601-7184
Tel (701) 456-9184 Founded/Ownrshp 1945
Sales 314.0MM EMP 813
SIC 1442 3532 5084

D-U-N-S 00-432-1519 IMP/EXP
■ **FISHER SCIENTIFIC CO LLC**
(Suby of THERMO FISHER SCIENTIFIC INC) ★
300 Industry Dr, Pittsburgh, PA 15275-1001
Tel (412) 490-8300 Founded/Ownrshp 1991, 1998
Sales 1.6MMM[E] EMP 2,000
SIC 5049 5169 3821 3826 2869 2819 Scientific & engineering equipment & supplies; Laboratory equipment, except medical or dental; Scientific instruments; Analytical instruments; Chemicals & allied products; Laboratory equipment: fume hoods, distillation racks, etc.; Worktables, laboratory; Analytical instruments; Microscopes, electron & proton; Laboratory chemicals, organic; Industrial inorganic chemicals
Pr: Edward A Pesicka
*Pr: Joseph Bernardo
*Pr: Daniel F Pantano
CFO: Kevin P Clark
Treas: Elizabeth Suter
*Co-Pr: Jeffrey Jochims
Sr VP: Jack Ampuja
*Sr VP: Robert Forte
VP: Phil Baird
VP: Jordan Berliner
VP: Jeff Boyer
VP: Kenneth Boyle
VP: Faye Coggins
VP: Kim Decedar
VP: Jim Dellavalle
VP: Ronald Deluca
VP: Nancy Furbee
VP: Jeff Gleason
VP: Marc Hames
VP: Jeff Hecker
VP: Richard Kusmer
Board of Directors: Valerie Darville

D-U-N-S 55-744-8065 IMP/EXP
■ **FISHER SCIENTIFIC INTERNATIONAL LLC**
(Suby of THERMO FISHER SCIENTIFIC INC) ★
81 Wyman St, Waltham, MA 02451-1223
Tel (781) 622-1000 Founded/Ownrshp 1902
Sales 2.5MMM[E] EMP 19,515
SIC 2869 3821 5169 5049 Laboratory chemicals, organic; Laboratory equipment: fume hoods, distillation racks, etc.; Worktables, laboratory; Chemicals & allied products; Laboratory equipment, except medical or dental; Scientific instruments; Scientific & engineering equipment & supplies
Pr: Seth H Hoogasian
Treas: Michael E Dambach
Sr VP: Matthew R Friel
Sr VP: Shiraz Ladiwala
VP: Jeffrey Jochims
VP: Alan Malus
VP: Neil Perlman
VP: Anthony H Smith
VP: Alex Stachtiaris
Prgrm Mgr: Eric Layton
Board of Directors: J Bolduc

D-U-N-S 11-929-8979 IMP
■ **FISHER THERMO SCIENTIFIC CHEMICALS INC**
ALFA AESAR
(Suby of THERMO FISHER SCIENTIFIC INC) ★
2 Radcliff Rd, Tewksbury, MA 01876-1182
Tel (978) 521-6300 Founded/Ownrshp 2015
Sales 86.6MM[E] EMP 160[E]
SIC 5169 Industrial chemicals
Genl Mgr: Omar Bikin
IT Man: Joe Reese

D-U-N-S 55-748-0972
FISHER-BARTON INC
576 Bluemound Road 53188, Watertown, WI 53094
Tel (920) 261-0131 Founded/Ownrshp 2005
Sales 113.4MM[E] EMP 400
SIC 6719 Investment holding companies, except banks
CEO: Richard Wilkey
Pr: Darrel Turner
VP: Rick Day
VP: Jeffrey Russell
VP: Craig Smith
IT Man: Wendy McInnis
VP Opers: Andrea Loppnow

D-U-N-S 61-681-1121 IMP/EXP
■ **FISHER-PRICE INC**
(Suby of MATTEL INC) ★
636 Girard Ave, East Aurora, NY 14052-1885
Tel (716) 687-3000 Founded/Ownrshp 1994
Sales 179.7MM[E] EMP 830
SIC 5092 5945 3944 Toys & games; Vehicles, children's; Hobby, toy & game shops; Games, toys & children's vehicles
CEO: David Allmark
*Pr: Neil Friedman
Sr VP: Jerry Miller
VP: David Ciganko
VP: Jerry Drinkard
VP: Harry Mayers
VP: Dennis M Wesolowski
Dir Risk M: Paul Charland
Ex Dir: Dave Waples
Prgrm Mgr: Susan Sarro
Genl Mgr: Kevin Curran

D-U-N-S 80-821-5313 IMP
■ **FISHER-ROSEMOUNT SYSTEMS INC**
(Suby of EPMCO HOLDINGS, INC.)
1100 W Louis Henna Blvd, Round Rock, TX 78681-9921
Tel (512) 835-2190 Founded/Ownrshp 1993
Sales 369.1MM[E] EMP 1,100
SIC 3625 3621 7699 Relays & industrial controls; Motors & generators; Industrial equipment services
Pr: Tom Snead
CFO: Jerry Bragg
CFO: Harry Young
Sr VP: Joe Urbanek
VP: Duncan Schiliss
VP: Galen Wilke
Dir: David Ochoa
Prgrm Mgr: Colin Jowett
Snr Sftwr: Marina Sokolova
Netwrk Mgr: Fred Hayes
Opers Mgr: Nick Garrett

D-U-N-S 19-602-2065 IMP
FISHER-TITUS MEDICAL CENTER
272 Benedict Ave, Norwalk, OH 44857-2374
Tel (419) 668-8101 Founded/Ownrshp 1976
Sales 114.8MM EMP 850
SIC 8052 8062 Intermediate care facilities; General medical & surgical hospitals
Ch Bd: Robert Andrews
Chf Rad: Matthew Gutowicz
*Pr: Patrick J Martin
*Treas: John Payne
*V Ch Bd: Virginia Poling
*VP: Duane Woods
CIO: John Britton

D-U-N-S 02-856-5588 IMP/EXP
FISHERMANS PRIDE PROCESSORS INC
NEPTUNE FOODS
4510 S Alameda St, Vernon, CA 90058-2011
Tel (323) 232-1980 Founded/Ownrshp 1954
Sales 88.3MM[E] EMP 300
SIC 2092 Fresh or frozen packaged fish
*CEO: Howard Choi
*COO: Hector Poon
CIO: Thomas Han

FISHERY, THE
See PACIFIC SHELLFISH INC

D-U-N-S 12-795-1213 IMP
FISHIN CO
3714 Main St, Munhall, PA 15120-3234
Tel (412) 464-9000 Founded/Ownrshp 2002
Sales 185.0MM EMP 39
SIC 5146 Seafoods
Pr: Manish Kumar
VP: Brenda Sigafoos

D-U-N-S 96-167-0929 EXP
FISHING HOLDINGS LLC
RANGER BOATS
(Suby of BASS PRO GROUP LLC) ★
927 Highway 178 N, Flippin, AR 72634-9248
Tel (870) 453-2222 Founded/Ownrshp 2015
Sales 183.5MM[E] EMP 440
SIC 3732 5699 Boats, fiberglass: building & repairing; Sports apparel
Pr: Randy Hopper
*CFO: Lendl Hewis
Sr VP: Bart Schad
VP: Keith Daffron
VP: Mike Holland
IT Man: Mark Matlock
Plnt Mgr: Vernon Goodman
Advt Dir: David Sneed
Sls Mgr: Mark Zwicker

FISHMAN & TOBIN
See F&T APPAREL LLC

D-U-N-S 16-872-1012
■ **FISK ACQUISITION INC**
(Suby of TUTOR PERINI CORP) ★
111 T C Jester Blvd, Houston, TX 77007-3142
Tel (713) 868-6111 Founded/Ownrshp 2004
Sales 66.9MM[E] EMP 1,470
SIC 1731 1623 Electrical work; Cable laying construction
Pr: Kenneth J Orlowski
*CFO: Larwrence J McTague III
*Ex VP: Gregory C Thomas
VP: Orvil Anthony
VP: Norman C Clyne
VP: Tom Dinkins
VP: James E Madgett
Opers Mgr: Jeff Downing

D-U-N-S 00-842-5084 IMP/EXP
■ **FISK ELECTRIC CO**
(Suby of TUTOR PERINI CORP) ★
10855 Westview Dr, Houston, TX 77043-5047
Tel (713) 868-6111 Founded/Ownrshp 2011
Sales 374.4MM[E] EMP 1,200
Accts Deloitte & Touche Llp Los Ang
SIC 1731 General electrical contractor
Pr: Darrel Harwood
CFO: Joe Thomas
Sr VP: Gregory C Thomas
Snr PM: Winfield Haggard

D-U-N-S 07-955-3135
FISK TELECOM LLC
SDI TELECOM
1091 Yonkers Ave, Yonkers, NY 10704-3220
Tel (914) 476-2073 Founded/Ownrshp 2013
Sales 150.0MM[E] EMP 2
SIC 4813 Long distance telephone communications
*CFO: Asif Chowdhary

D-U-N-S 15-730-4239 IMP
FISKARS BRANDS INC
FISKARS GRDN & OUTDOOR LIVING
(Suby of FISKARS OYJ ABP)
7800 Discovery Dr, Middleton, WI 53562-5501
Tel (608) 259-1649 Founded/Ownrshp 1984
Sales 851.1MM[E] EMP 4,380
SIC 3052 3679 3421 3069 3423 Rubber & plastics hose & beltings; Electronic circuits; Scissors, shears, clippers, snips & similar tools; Mats or matting, rubber; Hand & edge tools
Pr: Kari Kauniskangas
*Ch Bd: Heikki Allonen
CFO: Robert Hanus
*CFO: Teemu Kangas-Karki
*Sr VP: Risto Gaggl
*Sr VP: Nina Ariluoma Hamalainen
Creative D: Dan Schallert
Mng Dir: John Grayson
CIO: John McGinley
Dir IT: Daniel Sonesson
IT Man: Dan Wendler

FISKARS GRDN & OUTDOOR LIVING
See FISKARS BRANDS INC

D-U-N-S 08-035-9371 IMP
FIT FOR LIFE LLC
GAIAM
833 W S Boulder Rd Bldg G, Louisville, CO 80027-2401
Tel (303) 222-3600 Founded/Ownrshp 2015
Sales 150.0MM EMP 100
SIC 5091 5941 Fitness equipment & supplies; Exercise equipment

D-U-N-S 82-945-4672
▲ **FITBIT INC**
405 Howard St Ste 550, San Francisco, CA 94105-2999
Tel (415) 513-1000 Founded/Ownrshp 2007
Sales 1.8MMM EMP 1,101[E]
Tkr Sym FIT Exch NYS
SIC 3829 Measuring & controlling devices
Ch Bd: James Park
COO: Hans Hartmann
COO: Hansgregory C Hartmann
CFO: William Zerella
Ofcr: Edward M Scal
Ex VP: Andy Missan
Ex VP: Timothy Roberts
VP: Tim Rosa
Snr Sftwr: Valery Karpei
*CTO: Eric N Friedman
QA Dir: Oleg Ileev
Board of Directors: Laura J Alber, Jonathan D Callaghan, Glenda Flanagan, Steven Murray, Christopher Paisley

D-U-N-S 00-391-6996
FITCH GROUP INC
FITCH RATINGS
(Suby of HEARST MAGAZINES) ★
33 Whitehall St, New York, NY 10004-2112
Tel (212) 908-0500 Founded/Ownrshp 2015
Sales 577.4MM[E] EMP 1,800
SIC 6289 Financial reporting
Pr: Paul Taylor
CFO: Theodore E Niedermayer
Ofcr: John Bonfiglio
VP: Carmen Chiappetta
VP: Bryan Erler
Dir Risk M: John Olert
Assoc Dir: Benjamin Cooper
Assoc Dir: Kerryann Rosa
Assoc Dir: Eric Rosenthal
Assoc Dir: Lydia Wong
Dir Bus: Greg Hiltebrand
Board of Directors: Stephen W Joynt

FITCH RATINGS
See FITCH GROUP INC

D-U-N-S 04-203-9480
FITCH RATINGS INC
(Suby of FITCH RATINGS) ★
33 Whitehall St, New York, NY 10004-2112
Tel (212) 612-7726 Founded/Ownrshp 1997
Sales 83.1MM EMP 277[E]
SIC 6289 Financial reporting
Pr: John Witt
CFO: Bernard De Lattre
Chf Cred: John Olert
Top Exec: Ian Linnell
Dir Bus: Julia Tell
Software D: Arlef Kaba
Software D: Parag Mathurvaishya
Netwrk Eng: Jonathan Quinones
Counsel: Kathy Russell

D-U-N-S 10-272-6692
FITE DISTRIBUTION SERVICES CO LP
1001 Donaldson Ave, San Antonio, TX 78228-5102
Tel (210) 736-3141 Founded/Ownrshp 1983
Sales 42.7MM[E] EMP 2,120
SIC 4214 4225 Local trucking with storage; General warehousing

D-U-N-S 02-089-9154
FITNESS CENTRE AT CELEBRATION HEALTH
FITNESS CENTRE AT FL HOSPITAL
400 Celebration Pl, Kissimmee, FL 34747-4970
Tel (407) 303-4400 Founded/Ownrshp 2001
Sales 3.2MMM EMP 60

SIC 7991 Physical fitness facilities
Ex Dir: Don Jones
IT Man: Claridssa Carillo
Pharmcst: Amber Bill
Pharmcst: Ruth Ann White

FITNESS CENTRE AT FL HOSPITAL
See FITNESS CENTRE AT CELEBRATION HEALTH

D-U-N-S 62-103-6057
FITNESS INTERNATIONAL LLC
LA FITNESS
3161 Michelson Dr Ste 600, Irvine, CA 92612-4406
Tel (949) 255-7200 *Founded/Ownrshp* 1996
Sales 142.0MM^E *EMP* 1,510
SIC 7991 6794 Physical fitness facilities; Franchises, selling or licensing
Pr: Jill E Greuling
CFO: Kathy Polson
Sr VP: Robert P Bryant
Sr VP: Patrick Edgerton
VP: Todd Boren
VP: Jon Hinkle
VP: Prince Jones
VP: Arie Katz
VP: Paul Norris
VP: Tamara Ruggerilo
Area Mgr: Scott Ruzycki

D-U-N-S 10-792-4490 IMP
FITTS AND GOODWIN INC
120 Corporate Blvd, West Columbia, SC 29169-4610
Tel (803) 796-4660 *Founded/Ownrshp* 1984
Sales 137.2MM^E *EMP* 39
SIC 1541 1542 Industrial buildings & warehouses; Commercial & office building contractors; Institutional building construction
Pr: John W Goodwin
Pr: Jeff Burgess
**VP:* Thomas M Fitts
Exec: Pam Sertick
Dir Bus: George Coulter

D-U-N-S 19-678-8970 IMP/EXP
FITZ AND FLOYD ENTERPRISES LLC
3 Friends Ln Ste 300, Newtown, PA 18940-3426
Tel (800) 527-9550 *Founded/Ownrshp* 2009
Sales 132.5MM^E *EMP* 130
SIC 5023 5199 5947 5719 China; Decorative home furnishings & supplies; Gifts & novelties; Christmas novelties; Gifts & novelties; China
Pr: Steve Baram
CFO: Jack Miskin

D-U-N-S 09-551-6340
FITZ VOGT & ASSOCIATES LTD
(*Suby of* TRUSTHOUSE SERVICES GROUP INC) ★
21 Armory Dr Ste L-1, Wheeling, WV 26003-6370
Tel (603) 644-0117 *Founded/Ownrshp* 2008
Sales 21.5MM^E *EMP* 1,000
SIC 5812 8742 7349 Contract food services; Food & beverage consultant; Building cleaning service
Pr: Mark Fortino
**CFO:* Charles M Swart III
VP: Kenneth Byers

D-U-N-S 02-259-3081
FITZGERALD AUTO MALL INC
FITZGERALD MAZDA
(*Suby of* J. J. F. MANAGEMENT SERVICES, INC.)
114 Baughmans Ln, Frederick, MD 21702-4011
Tel (301) 696-9200 *Founded/Ownrshp* 1991
Sales 106.1MM^E *EMP* 231
SIC 5511 Automobiles, new & used; Pickups, new & used; Vans, new & used
Ch: William Hayduk
**Owner:* Jack Fitzgerald
**Pr:* John J Fitzgerald III
**VP:* James Cash
**VP:* Dorothy M Fitzgerald
Genl Mgr: Scott Addison
Genl Mgr: Greg Lewis
Dir IT: Vincent Strosnider
IT Man: Ron Miller

D-U-N-S 09-395-2091
FITZGERALD AUTOMALL
(*Suby of* J. J. F. MANAGEMENT SERVICES, INC.)
11411 Rockville Pike, Rockville, MD 20852-5989
Tel (301) 881-4000 *Founded/Ownrshp* 1974
Sales 142.5MM^E *EMP* 923
SIC 5511 Automobiles, new & used
Pr: John J Fitzgerald
**Treas:* John Lynch
**VP:* Garry M Jenkins
Sales Asso: Christopher Watson

D-U-N-S 07-105-2948
FITZGERALD CANTOR L P
CANTOR FITZGERALD
499 Park Ave, New York, NY 10022-1240
Tel (212) 938-5000 *Founded/Ownrshp* 1992
Sales 785.0MM^E *EMP* 2,217
SIC 6211

FITZGERALD MAZDA
See FITZGERALD AUTO MALL INC

D-U-N-S 88-309-1233
FITZGERALDS GAMING CORP
301 Fremont St Fl 12, Las Vegas, NV 89101-5600
Tel (702) 388-2400 *Founded/Ownrshp* 1994
Sales 23.9MM^E *EMP* 1,498
SIC 7011 Hotels & motels; Casino hotel; Motels
Ch Bd: Don Barden
Pr: Philip D Griffith
Sec: Michael E McPherson
MIS Dir: Evelyn Robinson
Corp Couns: Cara Brown

D-U-N-S 92-932-3681
FITZGERALDS LAS VEGAS INC
(*Suby of* FITZGERALDS GAMING CORP) ★
301 Fremont St, Las Vegas, NV 89101-5600
Tel (702) 388-2224 *Founded/Ownrshp* 1992
Sales 17.2MM^E *EMP* 1,200
SIC 7011 Casino hotel
CEO: Don Bargen
**Pr:* Philip D Griffith
**CFO:* Jon Bennett

D-U-N-S 94-515-3583
FITZPATRICK COMPANIES INC
COUNTRY CURTAINS
705 Pleasant St, Lee, MA 01238-9323
Tel (413) 298-1610 *Founded/Ownrshp* 1996
Sales 97.6MM^E *EMP* 530^E
SIC 5714 5021 5023 Drapery & upholstery stores; Draperies; Curtains; Beds & bedding; Decorative home furnishings & supplies
Pr: Philip J McAvoy
**CFO:* Matthew J Heim
**Treas:* Paula S Beck
**VP:* Sandra Dignard
IT Man: Jeremy Warren

D-U-N-S 09-544-6659 IMP
▲ FIVE BELOW INC
1818 Market St Ste 2000, Philadelphia, PA 19103-3647
Tel (215) 546-7909 *Founded/Ownrshp* 2002
Sales 831.9MM *EMP* 7,600
Accts Kpmg Llp Philadelphia Pennsy
Tkr Sym FIVE *Exch* NGS
SIC 5331 5945 Variety stores; Hobby, toy & game shops
Pr: Joel D Anderson
**Ch Bd:* Thomas G Vellios
CFO: Kenneth R Bull
Ofcr: Eric M Specter
Ex VP: Michael F Romanko
VP: Bill Clark
VP: Michael Pannullo
VP: Karen Procell
VP: Douglas W Walrod
Dist Mgr: Camila Icasas
Dist Mgr: Kristin Niedringhaus
Board of Directors: Kathleen S Barclay, Catherine E Buggeln, Michael F Devine III, Daniel J Kaufman, Richard L Markee, Thomas M Ryan, Ronald L Sargent

D-U-N-S 19-538-1371
FIVE BROTHERS MORTGAGE CO SERVICES AND SECURING INC
12220 E 13 Mile Rd, Warren, MI 48093-5000
Tel (586) 772-7600 *Founded/Ownrshp* 1967
Sales NA *EMP* 700^E
SIC 6162 Mortgage companies, urban
Pr: Joseph Badalamenti
**CEO:* Nickalene Kalas
CFO: Perry Scroggie
**CFO:* Perry Scroggrie
**Sec:* Francis Badalamenti
Off Mgr: Tina Reeves
**CIO:* Bill Walsworth
CTO: William Walsworth
Mktg Dir: Leanne M Richards

D-U-N-S 09-968-8744
FIVE PRIME THERAPEUTICS INC
2 Corporate Dr, South San Francisco, CA 94080-7047
Tel (415) 365-5600 *Founded/Ownrshp* 2001
Sales 379.8MM *EMP* 157
Tkr Sym FPRX *Exch* NGM
SIC 2834 8733 Pharmaceutical preparations; Biotechnical research, noncommercial
Ch Bd: Lewis T Williams
COO: Aron M Knickerbocker
CFO: Marc L Belsky
Sr VP: Kevin Baker
Sr VP: Luis Borges
Sr VP: Robert Sikorski
Dir Sec: Francis W Sarena
Board of Directors: Franklin M Berger, Fred E Cohen, R Lee Douglas, Sheila Gujrathi, Peder K Jensen, Mark D McDade, William Ringo

D-U-N-S 00-699-4180 IMP
■ FIVE STAR BANK
(*Suby of* FINANCIAL INSTITUTIONS INC) ★
220 Liberty St, Warsaw, NY 14569-1465
Tel (585) 786-3131 *Founded/Ownrshp* 1891, 1986
Sales NA *EMP* 562
SIC 6022 State trust companies accepting deposits, commercial
Pr: Martin Birmingham
**Pr:* Martin T Griffith
Pr: Edward S Oexle
**Ch:* Robert N Latella
**Treas:* Steven Foster
Ex VP: Karl Krebs
Sr VP: Craig Burton
Sr VP: Vito Caraccio
Sr VP: Mark Debacco
**VP:* Amy Barone
**VP:* Jill Beck
**VP:* Staci Casseri

D-U-N-S 02-226-7652
FIVE STAR COOPERATIVE
1949 N Linn Ave, New Hampton, IA 50659-9406
Tel (641) 394-3052 *Founded/Ownrshp* 1916
Sales 288.5MM *EMP* 190
Accts Gardiner Thomsen Cpas Charle
SIC 5153 5191 Grains; Feed; Seeds: field, garden & flower; Fertilizer & fertilizer materials
Pr: John Eichenberger
V Ch: Leon Zeien
**Pr:* Steven Laures
**VP:* Randy Greiman
Genl Mgr: Ronald Pumhery
Genl Mgr: Ron Pumphrey
Mktg Mgr: Olin Amudson
Sls Mgr: Travis Thomas

D-U-N-S 00-970-4438
■ FIVE STAR ELECTRIC CORP
(*Suby of* GREENSTAR SERVICES CORP) ★
10132 101st St, Ozone Park, NY 11416-2616
Tel (718) 641-5000 *Founded/Ownrshp* 2008
Sales 517.3MM *EMP* 150
Accts Deloitte & Touche Llp Los Ang
SIC 1731 General electrical contractor
CEO: Gary Segal
CFO: Steven Read
Sr VP: Peter Amabile
Exec: Bob Tirella
Dept Mgr: Robert Woodland
IT Man: Jordan Bennett
Sfty Dirs: Michael Purazzo
Sls Mgr: Kenneth Benfante
Snr PM: Dominic Alois
Snr PM: Anthony A Giannico

FIVE STAR FOOD MART
See NEWCOMB OIL CO LLC

D-U-N-S 80-774-6342
FIVE STAR FOOD SERVICE INC
(*Suby of* FIVE STAR SERVICE GROUP INC) ★
6005 Century Oaks Dr # 100, Chattanooga, TN 37416-3677
Tel (423) 490-4428 *Founded/Ownrshp* 1996
Sales 151.2MM^E *EMP* 600
SIC 5962 5812 7389 Food vending machines; Cafeteria; Caterers; Contract food services; Coffee service
Pr: Alan Recher
**CFO:* Jean Bouchard
VP: Beth Conyer
VP: Bruce Garner
VP: Mike Laurer
Dir Risk M: Landon Martin
Genl Mgr: Kevin Black
Genl Mgr: Claudine Bowman
Genl Mgr: Allen Matheney
Genl Mgr: Patrick Reilly
Genl Mgr: Tim Seaton

FIVE STAR FOOD SVC DALTON DIV
See FIVE STAR HOLDING CO INC

D-U-N-S 17-683-3531
FIVE STAR HOLDING CO INC
FIVE STAR FOOD SVC DALTON DIV
248 Rollins Industrial Ct, Ringgold, GA 30736-2886
Tel (706) 937-5077 *Founded/Ownrshp* 1993
Sales 95.7MM^E *EMP* 2,000
SIC 5962 5812 5963 2099 Food vending machines; Cafeteria; Caterers; Contract food services; Direct selling establishments; Food preparations
Pr: Michael Nugent
**CFO:* Richard Dotson
**VP:* Bruce Garner
Genl Mgr: Bruce McMullen
Genl Mgr: Bob Roberts

D-U-N-S 03-136-7220
FIVE STAR INTERNATIONAL LLC (PA)
1810 S 19th St, Harrisburg, PA 17104-3205
Tel (717) 986-1500 *Founded/Ownrshp* 1974
Sales 107.0MM^E *EMP* 237
SIC 5511 7538 5013 Trucks, tractors & trailers: new & used; Truck parts & accessories; General truck repair
Ch Bd: Fred Scheler
Dir IT: Ben Varner

FIVE STAR LOGISTICS
See STCHARLES TRUCKING INC

D-U-N-S 84-474-4529
▲ FIVE STAR QUALITY CARE INC
400 Centre St, Newton, MA 02458-2094
Tel (617) 796-8387 *Founded/Ownrshp* 2000
Sales 1.3MMM *EMP* 24,800
Tkr Sym FVE *Exch* NAS
SIC 8051 8052 Skilled nursing care facilities; Intermediate care facilities
Pr: Bruce J Mackey Jr
COO: R Scott Herzig
CFO: Richard A Doyle Jr
VP: Robert Brennan
VP: Denise Kelly
VP: Katherine E Potter
Exec: Jon Cekalla
Off Mgr: Leigh Matthews
Mktg Dir: Mike Barr
Mktg Dir: Stacy J Nelson
Sls Dir: Kathy Scott
Board of Directors: Donna D Fraiche, Bruce M Gans, Barbara D Gilmore, Gerard M Martin, Barry M Portnoy

D-U-N-S 15-767-8074
FIVE STAR SERVICE GROUP INC
(*Suby of* SERVICE GROUP INVESTMENTS LLC) ★
6005 Century Oaks Dr # 100, Chattanooga, TN 37416-3677
Tel (423) 643-2600 *Founded/Ownrshp* 2007
Sales 151.2MM^E *EMP* 1,450
SIC 5963 Food services, direct sales
CEO: Steve Errico

D-U-N-S 06-741-7951
▲ FIVE9 INC
4000 Executive Pkwy # 400, San Ramon, CA 94583-4257
Tel (925) 201-2000 *Founded/Ownrshp* 2001
Sales 128.8MM *EMP* 167^E
Tkr Sym FIVN *Exch* NGM
SIC 7372 Prepackaged software
Ch Bd: Michael Burkland
CFO: Barry Zwarenstein
Ex VP: Daniel Burkland
Ex VP: Michael Crane
Ex VP: Gaurav Passi
Ex VP: Scott Welch
VP: Wendell Black
VP: Jason Yang
Prgrm Mgr: Mariel Kudic
Snr Ntwrk: Andy Branch
CTO: Ran Ezerzer
Board of Directors: Jack Acosta, Kimberly Alexy, Michael Burdiek, David Dewalt, David Welsh, Robert Zollars

FIVES CINETICS
See FIVES INC

D-U-N-S 12-417-0916 IMP
FIVES INC
FIVES CINETICS
(*Suby of* FIVES)
23400 Halsted Rd, Farmington Hills, MI 48335-2840
Tel (248) 477-0800 *Founded/Ownrshp* 1965
Sales 242.7MM^E *EMP* 585
SIC 3549 Assembly machines, including robotic
Pr: Michael Dimichelle
COO: Martin Duverne
**CFO:* Sylvain Dulude
**CFO:* Jeff Ritz
**VP:* Jerry Makuch
IT Man: Gloria Jaynes
Sftwr Eng: Brandon James
Plnt Mgr: Mark Bologna
Sls Dir: Robert Martin

D-U-N-S 61-487-1080 IMP/EXP
FIVES LANDIS CORP
(*Suby of* FIVES)
16778 Halfway Blvd, Hagerstown, MD 21740-7807
Tel (301) 797-3400 *Founded/Ownrshp* 1897
Sales 90.0MM *EMP* 260
Accts Grant Thornton Llp Southfield
SIC 3541 Grinding machines, metalworking
CEO: Dwight Myers
CFO: James F Martin
**CFO:* Rodney Peach
Bd of Dir: Michael Werick
Genl Mgr: Cindy Shank
Opers Mgr: David Tuzzolo
Ql Cn Mgr: Colin Olson
Manager: Steve Male
Sls Mgr: Thomas Hegenbarth

D-U-N-S 19-946-9300 IMP/EXP
FIVES MACHINING SYSTEMS INC
(*Suby of* FIVES)
2200 Litton Ln, Hebron, KY 41048-8435
Tel (859) 534-4600 *Founded/Ownrshp* 2005
Sales 183.7MM^E *EMP* 438
SIC 3559 Automotive related machinery
CEO: Dave Nowicki
**Pr:* Daniel Janka
**CFO:* James Martin
CFO: Jeffrey Nieuwkoop
Sr Cor Off: Jim Herrman
Sr Cor Off: Robert Wassmer
Ex VP: Detlev Penke
Exec: Jrgen Fleischer
Genl Mgr: Chip Storie
Sftwr Eng: Tony Schuck
Mfg Mgr: Craig Pilarski

D-U-N-S 00-419-9055 IMP/EXP
FIVES NORTH AMERICAN COMBUSTION INC
(*Suby of* FIVES CINETICS) ★
4455 E 71st St, Cleveland, OH 44105-5601
Tel (216) 271-6000 *Founded/Ownrshp* 2008
Sales 105.9MM^E *EMP* 334
SIC 3567 Industrial furnaces & ovens
Pr: Erik Paulhardt
**Ch Bd:* Luigi Russo
CFO: Kathy E Ruekberg
Exec: Brenda Lowe
Genl Mgr: Tom Jonozzo
CTO: Scott Neville
IT Man: Tom Robertson
VP Opers: John Newby
Ql Cn Mgr: Eric Lindhome
Sls Mgr: Ron McCuldody
Snr Mgr: Edward Orzel
Board of Directors: Martin Duverne, Wes Paisley, Frederick Sanchez

FIXTURE GALLERY, THE
See CONSOLIDATED SUPPLY CO

D-U-N-S 04-526-7002
FJ MANAGEMENT INC (UT)
FLYING J
185 S State St Ste 201, Salt Lake City, UT 84111-1561
Tel (801) 624-1000 *Founded/Ownrshp* 1982
Sales 3.5MMM^E *EMP* 15,800
SIC 5541 2911 5411 1382 6022

D-U-N-S 78-071-4853
FJC SECURITY SERVICES INC
(*Suby of* ALLIEDBARTON SECURITY SERVICES) ★
275 Jericho Tpke, Floral Park, NY 11001-2150
Tel (516) 328-6000 *Founded/Ownrshp* 2016
Sales 234.2MM^E *EMP* 5,000^E
Accts Marks Paneth & Shron Llp Wood
SIC 7381 Security guard service
CEO: Frank Califano Sr
Pr: Frank Califano Jr
COO: Mark D Coffino
CFO: Stephen B Finkel
Ofcr: Kevin Blackburn
Ofcr: Steve Cox
Ofcr: Charles Leveque
Ofcr: Stevie Martinez
Ofcr: Charles Norfleet
Ofcr: Raymond Spinella
Ofcr: Greg White
Ofcr: Douglas Willock
VP: Steven Finkel
VP: Robert Stabile
Exec: Robert Matarazzo

FJUHSD
See FULLERTON JOINT UNION HIGH SCHOOL DISTRICT EDUCATIONAL FOUNDATION

FK
See FABRI-KAL CORP

D-U-N-S 85-863-1802
FK DELLIA LLC
ALLIED OIL & GAS SERVICES
25025 North Fwy I45210, The Woodlands, TX 77380-3036
Tel (817) 546-3358 *Founded/Ownrshp* 2006
Sales 239.1MM^E *EMP* 300
SIC 1389

D-U-N-S 18-328-0973 IMP/EXP
FKA DISTRIBUTING CO LLC
HOMEDICS
3000 N Pontiac Trl, Commerce Township, MI 48390-2720
Tel (248) 863-3000 *Founded/Ownrshp* 1987
Sales 103.0MM^E *EMP* 300^E
SIC 3679 3634 Headphones, radio; Massage machines, electric, except for beauty/barber shops
Owner: Ron Ferber
**Owner:* Alon Kaufman

CFO: Bill Carroll
**CFO:* William Carroll
Ofcr: Jamie Mason
Ex VP: Alon D Kaufman
**Ex VP:* Saby Sen
VP: Barb Landry
Exec: Michelle Bain
Prgrm Mgr: Edward Clem
Dir IT: Harley Savage

FKC-LAKE SHORE
See FRONTIER-KEMPER CONSTRUCTORS INC

D-U-N-S 02-494-9414
FKG OIL CO (MO)
MOTOMART CONVENIENCE STORES
(*Suby of* MOTO, INC)
721 W Main St, Belleville, IL 62220-1553
Tel (618) 233-6754 *Founded/Ownrshp* 1954
Sales 500.0MM *EMP* 850
SIC 5541 Filling stations, gasoline
Pr: Robert Forsyth
Pr: Todd D Badgley
CFO: Tim Horan
Sec: Jeanine Eckenrod
VP: Brian Pendleton
Exec: Darlene Conner

D-U-N-S 00-145-6953 IMP/EXP
FKI INDUSTRIES INC (NY)
ACCO CHAIN & LIFTING PRODUCTS
(*Suby of* CROSBY US ACQUISITION CORP) ★
2801 Dawson Rd, Tulsa, OK 74110-5042
Tel (918) 834-4611 *Founded/Ownrshp* 1912
Sales 408.6MM[E] *EMP* 5,630
SIC 3429 3536 3535 3496 3569 3823 Furniture hardware; Hoists, cranes & monorails; Hoists; Cranes & monorail systems; Belt conveyor systems, general industrial use; Chain, welded; Baling machines, for scrap metal, paper or similar material; Industrial process control instruments; Industrial process measurement equipment; Digital displays of process variables
Ch Bd: James Slattery
**Ch Bd:* Robert G Beeston
CFO: David Dixon
**Treas:* Robert Zitnay
**VP:* Robert Miller
**VP:* Matt Nozemack
**VP:* Robert Sook

D-U-N-S 60-770-6640 IMP/EXP
FKI SECURITY GROUP LLC
FIRE KING SECURITY GROUP
101 Security Pkwy, New Albany, IN 47150-9366
Tel (812) 948-8400 *Founded/Ownrshp* 2010
Sales 162.9MM[E] *EMP* 482
SIC 2522 5044 3499 3429 Filing boxes, cabinets & cases: except wood; Vaults & safes; Safes & vaults, metal; Locks or lock sets
CEO: Mark Essig
**CFO:* Will Wolf
Ex VP: Jim Poteet
Sr VP: Debra Ayres
VP: Sam Difiglio
VP: Kimberley Field
VP: David Goffinet
VP: Burton Hillman
VP: Brenda Lally
VP: Mike McGunn
Exec: Betty Hollis

FL SMITH MINERALS
See FLSMIDTH USA INC

FLAD/LEO A DALY JOINT
See FACILITY LEADERS IN ARCHITECTURAL/ENGINEERING DESIGN PC

D-U-N-S 77-992-7982
■ **FLAG INTERMEDIATE HOLDINGS CORP**
(*Suby of* METALS USA HOLDINGS CORP) ★
2400 E Coml Blvd Ste 905, Fort Lauderdale, FL 33308
Tel (954) 202-4000 *Founded/Ownrshp* 2005
Sales 1.8MMM[E] *EMP* 2,200[E]
SIC 5051 3354 3315 Metals service centers & offices; Iron & steel (ferrous) products; Aluminum bars, rods, ingots, sheets, pipes, plates, etc.; Aluminum extruded products; Steel wire & related products
CEO: C Lourenco Goncalves
CFO: Robert C McPherson III
VP: Daniel L Henneke

FLAGLER COUNTY SCHOOL DISTRICT
See SCHOOL BOARD OF FLAGLER COUNTY

D-U-N-S 15-279-5464
FLAGLER HEALTHCARE SYSTEMS INC
FLAGLER HOSPITAL
400 Health Park Blvd, Saint Augustine, FL 32086-5784
Tel (904) 819-5155 *Founded/Ownrshp* 1984
Sales 2.0MM[E] *EMP* 1,600
Accts Dixon Hughes Goodman Llp Ashe
SIC 8062 General medical & surgical hospitals
Pr: Joseph Gordy
**COO:* Christoper Schmidt
**CFO:* Roger Carter

FLAGLER HOSPITAL
See FLAGLER HEALTHCARE SYSTEMS INC

D-U-N-S 07-323-0567
FLAGLER HOSPITAL INC
400 Health Park Blvd, Saint Augustine, FL 32086-5790
Tel (904) 819-5155 *Founded/Ownrshp* 1984
Sales 237.6MM *EMP* 1,500[E]
Accts Kpmg Llp Jacksonville Fl
SIC 8062 General medical & surgical hospitals
Pr: Joseph Gordy
CFO: Lynda Kirker
Bd of Dir: Clark Alger
Bd of Dir: Mark Bailey
Bd of Dir: Robin Burchfield
Bd of Dir: Fred Cone
Bd of Dir: Jim Wilson
Ofcr: Bill Douglas
VP: Nangela Davidson
VP: Michael Dibella
Exec: Roger Millecan
Dir Risk M: Kevin Newman
Dir Lab: Linda Andiric
Dir Lab: Yanet Pantaleon
Dir Rad: Robert Taliaferro

D-U-N-S 60-319-1701
FLAGLER SYSTEM INC
BREAKERS, THE
1 S County Rd, Palm Beach, FL 33480-4023
Tel (561) 655-6611 *Founded/Ownrshp* 1989
Sales 67.4MM[E] *EMP* 2,000[E]
SIC 7041 7997 Membership-basis organization hotels; Golf club, membership
Ch Bd: James G Kenan III
**Pr:* Paul Leone
COO: Ellen Akwa
CFO: Alex Gilmurray
VP: Kevin Walters
**VP:* John Zoller
Exec: Neeraj Mahani
Exec: Anthony Sicignano
Dir Soc: Dan Jenkins
**Prin:* Leone Paul N
Dir Sec: Arthur Birmelin

D-U-N-S 94-160-6365
FLAGSHIP CREDIT ACCEPTANCE LLC
3 Christy Dr Ste 203, Chadds Ford, PA 19317-9667
Tel (610) 717-1916 *Founded/Ownrshp* 1988
Sales 130.0MM *EMP* 986[E]
SIC 7389 Financial services
CEO: Michael C Ritter
**COO:* David Bertoncini
**CFO:* John Schwabb
**CFO:* Kenneth J Sicinski
Treas: Diana Kelly
Sr VP: Kevin Oconnell
Sr VP: Thomas R Stillman
Area Mgr: Michael Baskett
Area Mgr: Dyla Burneka
Area Mgr: Frank Hickey
Area Mgr: Kary Hooper

D-U-N-S 83-230-4625
FLAGSHIP ENTERPRISES HOLDING INC
1050 N 5th St Ste E, San Jose, CA 95112-4400
Tel (408) 977-0155 *Founded/Ownrshp* 2009
Sales 145.9MM[E] *EMP* 1,500[E]
SIC 7349 Building & office cleaning services
Pr: David M Pasek

D-U-N-S 36-169-8798
FLAGSHIP FACILITY SERVICES INC
(*Suby of* FLAGSHIP ENTERPRISES HOLDING INC) ★
1050 N 5th St Ste E, San Jose, CA 95112-4400
Tel (408) 977-0155 *Founded/Ownrshp* 1988
Sales 90.9MM[E] *EMP* 1,400
SIC 7349

D-U-N-S 07-934-2219
FLAGSHIP FOOD GROUP LLC
6455 S Yosemite St # 140, Greenwood Village, CO 80111-5139
Tel (303) 954-4979 *Founded/Ownrshp* 2012
Sales 150.4MM[E] *EMP* 700[E]
Accts Bdo Usa Llp Los Angeles Ca
SIC 2038 Ethnic foods, frozen
CFO: John Watts

D-U-N-S 80-927-3907
FLAGSHIP RESORT DEVELOPMENT CORP
60 N Maine Ave, Atlantic City, NJ 08401-5518
Tel (609) 347-3524 *Founded/Ownrshp* 1991
Sales 83.3MM[E] *EMP* 350[E]
SIC 6531 7011 Time-sharing real estate sales, leasing & rentals; Vacation lodges; Resort hotel
Pr: Bruce Kaye
**CFO:* Michael Valenti
**Sr VP:* Roxanne Passarella
**VP:* Rosemarie Grawl

D-U-N-S 06-842-1817 IMP
FLAGSTAFF MEDICAL CENTER INC
FMC
(*Suby of* NORTHERN ARIZONA HEALTHCARE CORP) ★
1200 N Beaver St, Flagstaff, AZ 86001-3118
Tel (928) 779-3366 *Founded/Ownrshp* 1936
Sales 389.9MM *EMP* 2,000
Accts Ernst & Young Us Llp Phoenix
SIC 8062 General medical & surgical hospitals
Pr: Richard Langosch
**V Ch:* James Dorman
**Pr:* William T Bradel
Sr VP: Alice Gagnaire
VP: Roger Schuler
VP: Rick Smith
Exec: Marie Merritt
Ex Dir: Doug Umlah
Dir Sec: Robert Tullis
Genl Mgr: Lisa Nelson
Secur Mgr: Bob Tulus

D-U-N-S 09-452-7165
FLAGSTAFF UNIFIED SCHOOL DISTRICT
FUSD
3285 E Sparrow Ave, Flagstaff, AZ 86004-7794
Tel (928) 527-6000 *Founded/Ownrshp* 1900
Sales 78.2MM[E] *EMP* 1,850
SIC 8211 Public combined elementary & secondary school
Top Exec: Josh B Corcoran
Top Exec: Madelyn Trillo
**Prin:* Karin Eberhard
Genl Mgr: Dan Matello
Off Mgr: Jane Gaun
Psych: Adria Curtin
Psych: Anika Divittorio
Psych: Debra Kamzelski
Psych: Dan Zanone
Snr Mgr: Leona Jarchow

D-U-N-S 87-835-7177
▲ **FLAGSTAR BANCORP INC**
5151 Corporate Dr, Troy, MI 48098-2639
Tel (248) 312-2000 *Founded/Ownrshp* 1993
Sales NA *EMP* 2,739[E]
Accts Pricewaterhousecoopers Llp De
Tkr Sym FBC *Exch* NYS
SIC 6035 Savings institutions, federally chartered; Federal savings & loan associations
Pr: Alessandro P Dinello
**Ch Bd:* John D Lewis
CFO: James K Ciroli
Ex VP: Stephen V Figliuolo
Ex VP: Patrick M McGuirk
Board of Directors: Jay J Hansen, David J Matlin, Bruce E Nyberg, James A Ovenden, Peter Schoels, David L Treadwell

D-U-N-S 17-736-0351
■ **FLAGSTAR BANK FSB**
(*Suby of* FLAGSTAR BANCORP INC) ★
5151 Corporate Dr, Troy, MI 48098-2639
Tel (248) 312-2000 *Founded/Ownrshp* 1987
Sales NA *EMP* 3,135
SIC 6035 Federal savings banks
Pr: Alessandro Dinello
Pr: Leonard Israel
COO: Steve Brooks
**COO:* Lee M Smith
CFO: Gregg Christenson
CFO: Mary McGuire
CFO: James A Ovenden
**Ch:* John D Lewis
Ofcr: Meredith Whitford
Assoc VP: Jennifer Arvo
Assoc VP: Jim Fink
**Ex VP:* Joan H Anderson
Ex VP: Salvatore J Rinaldi
Ex VP: Robert Rondeau
**Ex VP:* Mary Kay Ruedisueli
Ex VP: Michael Tierney
Sr VP: Mary F Callahan
Sr VP: Jean Garrick
Sr VP: Danielle Moseley-Tatum
Sr VP: Thomas Pitkin
**Sr VP:* Marie A Ralko
Board of Directors: William F Pickard

D-U-N-S 03-663-0509 IMP/EXP
■ **FLAGSTONE FOODS INC**
(*Suby of* TREEHOUSE FOODS INC) ★
380 Sint Pter St Ste 1000, Saint Paul, MN 55102
Tel (651) 348-4100 *Founded/Ownrshp* 2014
Sales 543.7MM[E] *EMP* 1,000
SIC 5411 2068 Grocery stores; Salted & roasted nuts & seeds
VP: Tim Larson
Sr VP: Ray Evans
Dir Bus: Pat Reardon
Opers Mgr: Russell Gallagher
Opers Mgr: Joseph Pelland
VP Sls: Josh Sowell
Sls Dir: Chris Cooke

D-U-N-S 82-532-7468
FLAHERTY & COLLINS CONSTRUCTION INC
8900 Keystone Xing # 1200, Indianapolis, IN 46240-2136
Tel (317) 816-9300 *Founded/Ownrshp* 1993
Sales 91.2MM *EMP* 40
SIC 1542 Commercial & office building contractors
CEO: David Flaherty
**Pr:* Gordon L Benner

D-U-N-S 78-316-9753 IMP/EXP
FLAKEBOARD AMERICA LIMITED
(*Suby of* FLAKEBOARD COMPANY LIMITED)
515 Rivercrossing Dr, Fort Mill, SC 29715-7900
Tel (877) 273-7680 *Founded/Ownrshp* 2006
Sales 196.4MM[E] *EMP* 650
SIC 2493 Particleboard products
Pr: Kelly Shotbolt
**CFO:* Robert Henry
**VP:* Jake Elston
**VP:* Kevin Shotbolt
Tech Mgr: Zachary Walton
Mfg Mgr: Tom Quesenberry

D-U-N-S 00-608-0840 IMP
FLAMBEAU INC (GA)
FLAMBEAU TECHNOLOGIES DIV
(*Suby of* NORDIC GROUP OF COMPANIES LTD) ★
801 Lynn Ave, Baraboo, WI 53913-2795
Tel (608) 356-5551 *Founded/Ownrshp* 1947
Sales 167.6MM[E] *EMP* 1,660
SIC 3089 3949 3944

D-U-N-S 09-341-8614
FLAMBEAU RIVER PAPER CORP
CROSS PNTE PAPER-FLAMBEAU MILL
200 1st Ave N, Park Falls, WI 54552-1260
Tel (715) 762-4612 *Founded/Ownrshp* 1978
Sales 147.5MM[E] *EMP* 535
SIC 2621 Fine paper
Pr: Butch Johnson
**VP:* Kathy Reinhard
**VP:* Scott Reinhard

D-U-N-S 78-294-9700
FLAMBEAU RIVER PAPERS LLC
200 1st Ave N, Park Falls, WI 54552-1260
Tel (715) 762-5229 *Founded/Ownrshp* 2006
Sales 175.8MM *EMP* 325
SIC 2621 Fine paper
VP: Craig Truemper
Admn Mgr: Aaron Johnson
Dir IT: Jerry Powers
Mill Mgr: Randy Stoeckel
Trfc Mgr: Renee Harvey

FLAMBEAU TECHNOLOGIES DIV
See FLAMBEAU INC

D-U-N-S 05-486-3428
FLAME ENTERPRISES INC
21500 Gledhill St, Chatsworth, CA 91311-5878
Tel (301) 668-0636 *Founded/Ownrshp* 1969
Sales 101.8MM *EMP* 57
Accts Weiser & Weiser Encino Ca
SIC 5065 5063 Electronic parts; Electrical apparatus & equipment
Pr: Michael V Epstein
**VP:* Peter Epstein
Mng Dir: Tony Nottridge
Sls Dir: Ian Parker
Sls Dir: Eric Van Ooijen
Sls Mgr: Osman Camliyar

D-U-N-S 94-145-2237 IMP/EXP
FLANDERS CORP
(*Suby of* FLANDERS HOLDINGS LLC)
531 Flanders Filter Rd, Washington, NC 27889-7805
Tel (252) 946-8081 *Founded/Ownrshp* 2016
Sales 300.0MM *EMP* 2,400
Accts Grant Thornton Charlotte Nc
SIC 3564 Filters, air: furnaces, air conditioning equipment, etc.
CEO: Peter Jones
COO: Nevin Caldwell
COO: Harry Smith
CFO: Scott Brown
CFO: Manuel Garcia
VP: Gary Chrismon
VP: Kevin Lare
Creative D: Tyler Philips
Sls Mgr: Jefferson Elwood
Sls Mgr: Brandon Houghton
Board of Directors: Joachim Gfoeller, Phil Hodges, Wesley M Measamer, David M Mock, Charlie Lee Tingen Jr

D-U-N-S 01-628-3384 IMP/EXP
FLANDERS ELECTRIC MOTOR SERVICE INC
8101 Baumgart Rd, Evansville, IN 47725-1509
Tel (812) 867-7421 *Founded/Ownrshp* 1947
Sales 139.4MM *EMP* 760
SIC 7694 5063

D-U-N-S 03-429-2268
▲ **FLANIGANS ENTERPRISES INC**
5059 Ne 18th Ave, Fort Lauderdale, FL 33334-5724
Tel (954) 377-1961 *Founded/Ownrshp* 1959
Sales 99.1MM *EMP* 1,561
Accts Marcum Llp Fort Lauderdale F
Tkr Sym BDL *Exch* ASE
SIC 5812 5921 Eating places; Liquor stores
Ch Bd: James G Flanigan
**COO:* August Bucci
**CFO:* Jeffrey D Kastner
**VP:* Christopher O'Neil
VP: Jean Picard
Board of Directors: M E Betsy Bennett, Michael B Flanigan, Patrick J Flanigan, Barbara J Kronk, Christopher J Nelms

D-U-N-S 11-891-1429 EXP
FLARE INDUSTRIES LLC
AEREON
16310 Bratton Ln Ste 350, Austin, TX 78728-2402
Tel (512) 836-9473 *Founded/Ownrshp* 2011
Sales 117.7MM *EMP* 500
SIC 3822 7359 3694 2899 1711 3569

D-U-N-S 09-338-9609
■ **FLASH FOODS LLC** (GA)
(*Suby of* CST BRANDS INC) ★
215 Pendleton St, Waycross, GA 31501-2329
Tel (912) 285-4011 *Founded/Ownrshp* 1979, 2016
Sales 503.7MM[E] *EMP* 1,300
SIC 5541 5411 Filling stations, gasoline; Convenience stores, chain
CEO: Kimberly Lubel
Off Mgr: Dina Kelsey

D-U-N-S 15-199-2732
FLASH MARKET INC
105 W Harrison Ave, West Memphis, AR 72301-4230
Tel (870) 732-2242 *Founded/Ownrshp* 1986
Sales 266.6MM[E] *EMP* 600
SIC 5541 5411 Filling stations, gasoline; Convenience stores, independent
Pr: Shane Patterson
**Sec:* Linda Patterson
**Sec:* Tj Patterson
**VP:* Jamie Patterson
**VP:* Ness Sechrest
Adm Dir: Paula Stanfield
Div Mgr: Cliff Lafitte

D-U-N-S 83-171-9773
FLAT OUT CRAZY LLC
303 W Erie St Ste 600, Chicago, IL 60654-3956
Tel (312) 284-6500 *Founded/Ownrshp* 2009
Sales 74.5MM[E] *EMP* 2,000[E]
SIC 8741 5812

D-U-N-S 00-581-6335
FLATHEAD ELECTRIC COOPERATIVE INC (MT)
2510 Us Highway 2 E, Kalispell, MT 59901-2397
Tel (406) 751-4483 *Founded/Ownrshp* 1937
Sales 107.6MM *EMP* 164
Accts Decoria Maichel & Teague Ps
SIC 4911 Distribution, electric power
Pr: Bruce Measure
**Sec:* Emery K Smith
**VP:* Douglas Grob
Exec: Wendy Price
Exec: Stephanie Wallace

D-U-N-S 78-041-8232
FLATIRON CONSTRUCTION CORP
(*Suby of* FLATIRON HOLDING INC) ★
385 Interlocken Blvd, Broomfield, CO 80021-8067
Tel (303) 485-4050 *Founded/Ownrshp* 2002
Sales 1.1MMM[E] *EMP* 743[E]
Accts Ernst & Young Llp Denver Col
SIC 1622 1629 1611 Tunnel construction; Dams, waterways, docks & other marine construction; Highway & street construction
CEO: John Diciurcio
Pr: Paul R Driscoll
Pr: Thomas J Rademacher
COO: Javier Sevilla
COO: Dale Swanberg
CFO: Donna Powell
VP: Frank Daams
VP: Elie Homsi
VP: Ed Neumann
VP: Paul Roberts
VP: Brian Stieritz
VP: Sven Stranzenbach

Exec: Christie Deluca
Exec: Adam Kuyt
Board of Directors: Adrian Franklin

D-U-N-S 18-228-4216
FLATIRON CONSTRUCTORS INC
(*Suby of* FLATIRON CONSTRUCTION CORP) ★
385 Interlocken, Broomfield, CO 80021
Tel (303) 485-4050 *Founded/Ownrshp* 1999
Sales 1.0MMM *EMP* 611
Accts Deloitte & Touche Llp Denver
SIC 1611 1622 1629 Highway & street construction; Bridge construction; Tunnel construction; Viaduct construction; Marine construction
CEO: John Diciurcio
**Pr:* Robert W French
**COO:* Javier Sevilla
**COO:* Dale Swanberg
**CFO:* Paul Driscoll
**CFO:* Lars Leitner
CFO: Donna M Powell
VP: Brian Stieritz

D-U-N-S 13-683-8831 IMP/EXP
FLATIRON HOLDING INC
(*Suby of* HOCHTIEF USA INC) ★
385 Interlocken Cres, Broomfield, CO 80021-3492
Tel (303) 485-4050 *Founded/Ownrshp* 2007
Sales 1.1MMM^E *EMP* 1,000^E
Accts Ernst & Young Llp Denver Co
SIC 1622 1629 Tunnel construction; Dams, waterways, docks & other marine construction
CEO: John Diciurcio
Pr: Paul R Driscoll
VP: Brian Stieritz
MIS Dir: Todd Walsh
Info Man: Marvin Thrall
Sftwr Eng: Steve Van Schouwen

D-U-N-S 85-936-8680
FLATIRON WEST INC
(*Suby of* FLATIRON CONSTRUCTORS INC) ★
1770 La Costa Meadows Dr, San Marcos, CA 92078-5106
Tel (760) 916-9100 *Founded/Ownrshp* 1999
Sales 201.9MM^E *EMP* 405
SIC 1622 1611 Bridge construction; General contractor, highway & street construction
Ch Bd: Thomas J Rademacher
**Pr:* Curtis E Weltz
**CEO:* John Diciurcio
**COO:* Javier Sevilla
**CFO:* Paul R Driscoll
**Ex VP:* Robert W French
**Sr VP:* Lars Leitner
**VP:* W Todd Bennett
**VP:* Frank Daams
**VP:* Richard Grabinski
**VP:* John D Nelson
**VP:* Paul C Roberts
**VP:* Robert M Schraeder
**VP:* Henry P Tolp
**VP:* Jeff Turner

FLAV-O-RICH DAIRIES
See BORDEN DAIRY CO OF KENTUCKY LLC

D-U-N-S 03-816-9467
FLAVOR 1ST GROWERS & PACKERS LLC
331 Banner Farm Rd, Mills River, NC 28759-8707
Tel (828) 890-3630 *Founded/Ownrshp* 2013
Sales 100.0MM *EMP* 200
SIC 5148 Fresh fruits & vegetables
Pr: Brian Rose
**COO:* Mitch Gaither
CFO: Nick Lyons
CFO: William Townsend
**CFO:* Jim Zuber
**Sr VP:* Kirby Johnson
**VP:* Steve Mayer
Off Mgr: Seth Grant
Opers Mgr: Chris Gach
Prd Mgr: Daniel Brittain
Prd Mgr: Tyler Gaither

D-U-N-S 07-981-2364
FLAVORS HOLDINGS INC
(*Suby of* MACANDREWS & FORBES INC) ★
35 E 62nd St, New York, NY 10065-8014
Tel (212) 572-8677 *Founded/Ownrshp* 2015
Sales 150.0MM^E *EMP* 500^E
SIC 2869 6712 Sweeteners, synthetic; Bank holding companies
CEO: David Kennedy

FLEET CAR CARRIERS
See FLEET-CAR LEASE INC

FLEET LABORATORIES
See C B FLEET CO INC

D-U-N-S 82-712-2826
FLEET LANDING
1 Fleet Landing Blvd, Atlantic Beach, FL 32233-4599
Tel (904) 246-9900 *Founded/Ownrshp* 2008
Sales 256.5MM *EMP* 34^E
SIC 8059 Nursing & personal care
Ex Dir: John S Meserve
Exec: Chris Gotschall
Dir IT: Ron Colbert
Opers Mgr: Louis Peterman
Mktg Dir: Patricia Beshel
HC Dir: Kelli Johnson
HC Dir: Carrie Turner

FLEET MANGEMENT SOLUTIONS
See TELETRAC INC

D-U-N-S 04-316-5869 IMP/EXP
FLEET WHOLESALE SUPPLY CO LLC
MILLS FLEET FARM
3035 W Wisconsin Ave, Appleton, WI 54914-1708
Tel (920) 734-8231 *Founded/Ownrshp* 1955, 1967
Sales 525.3MM^E *EMP* 300
SIC 5191 5331 5531 5211 5541 Farm supplies; Variety stores; Automotive parts; Home centers; Filling stations, gasoline
CEO: Henry C Mills II
**Pr:* Stewart C Mills Jr
**VP:* Ronald Obeidzinski

D-U-N-S 14-474-7367
FLEET-CAR LEASE INC
FLEET CAR CARRIERS
7563 Dahlia St Unit A, Commerce City, CO 80022-1553
Tel (800) 624-3256 *Founded/Ownrshp* 1984
Sales 127.2MM^E *EMP* 100
Accts Anton Collins Mitchell
SIC 4213 Automobiles, transport & delivery
CEO: Raymond J Bonanno
**Pr:* Keith Oxenreider
**Ex VP:* R James Bonanno
**VP:* Daniel Bonanno
**VP:* David Ciccarelli
**VP:* Donna Coulter
**VP:* Joel Cox
**VP:* Brian J Daly
**VP:* Ronald B Jordan
**VP:* Darren Larsen
**VP:* Dan Montanari
**VP:* Andrew Sawers
**VP:* Hyman Stallings

D-U-N-S 14-978-4837
■ **FLEET/NORSTAR EMPLOYEES BENEFIT SERVICES INC**
(*Suby of* BANK OF AMERICA CORP) ★
1 Peter Kiernan Plz, Albany, NY 12207-2758
Tel (518) 956-1007 *Founded/Ownrshp* 2004
Sales 63.6MM^E *EMP* 1,400
SIC 6282 Investment advisory service
Pr: Richard Jones
**VP:* Edward Brown
IT Man: Karen Smith

D-U-N-S 61-941-5789
▲ **FLEETCOR TECHNOLOGIES INC**
5445 Triangle Pkwy # 400, Norcross, GA 30092-2584
Tel (770) 449-0479 *Founded/Ownrshp* 1986
Sales 1.7MMM *EMP* 5,330
Tkr Sym FLT *Exch* NYS
SIC 7389 Charge account service; Credit card service
Ch Bd: Ronald F Clarke
Pt: David D Maxsimic
Pr: Kurt Adams
Pr: Andrew R Blazye
Pr: Timothy J Downs
Pr: Alexey Gavrilenya
Pr: Todd W House
Pr: Armando Netto
Pr: Gregory Secord
CFO: Eric R Dey
Ex VP: John S Coughlin
Ex VP: Charles Freund
Ex VP: Paul Holland
VP: James Howle
VP: Amit Singh
VP: Alissa Vickery

D-U-N-S 83-288-7108
■ **FLEETCOR TECHNOLOGIES OPERATING CO LLC**
(*Suby of* FLEETCOR TECHNOLOGIES INC) ★
655 Engineering Dr # 300, Norcross, GA 30092-2830
Tel (770) 449-0479 *Founded/Ownrshp* 2004
Sales 69.7MM^E *EMP* 3,428^E
SIC 7389 Personal service agents, brokers & bureaus
Pr: Ronald F Clarke

FLEETGUARD
See CUMMINS FILTRATION INC

D-U-N-S 04-525-1795 IMP
FLEETPRIDE INC
600 Las Colinas Blvd E # 400, Irving, TX 75039-5637
Tel (469) 249-7500 *Founded/Ownrshp* 1998
Sales 1.4MMM^E *EMP* 2,000^E
SIC 5531 5013 Truck equipment & parts; Truck parts & accessories; Trailer parts & accessories
CEO: Allan R Dragone
**CFO:* Amath Fall
**Chf Mktg O:* Robert Sammons
Sr VP: Chris Koshinski
**VP:* Scott Cisney
VP: Mike Deery
VP: Paul Fichiera
VP: Rick Turner
Prgrm Mgr: Vanessa Jackson
Area Mgr: Joseph Fichera
Area Mgr: Chris Sweet
Board of Directors: W M Megee

D-U-N-S 03-241-7180
FLEETWING CORP
742 S Combee Rd, Lakeland, FL 33801-6314
Tel (863) 665-7557 *Founded/Ownrshp* 1956
Sales 91.6MM *EMP* 57^E
Accts Averett Warmus Durkee Orlando
SIC 5172 5411 Petroleum products; Convenience stores, independent
Pr: C Andy Wike
**Treas:* John Kaziow
MIS Dir: Fred Buss
Sls Mgr: D Tate
Board of Directors: Cecilia McGinnis, Maryann Troiano

D-U-N-S 00-956-3131
FLEETWOOD ALUMINUM PRODUCTS INC
FLEETWOOD WINDOWS AND DOORS
1 Fleetwood Way, Corona, CA 92879-5101
Tel (800) 736-7363 *Founded/Ownrshp* 1961
Sales 113.7MM^E *EMP* 250
SIC 5031 3442

D-U-N-S 07-144-3972
FLEETWOOD AREA SCHOOL DISTRICT (PA)
801 N Richmond St, Fleetwood, PA 19522-1031
Tel (610) 944-8111 *Founded/Ownrshp* 1950
Sales 47.4MM^E *EMP* 1,035
SIC 8211 Public elementary school; Public junior high school; Public senior high school
**Prin:* Bethany Bosold
Prin: Ronald Rill
Board of Directors: Shirley Moll Heidi Orth Ja

D-U-N-S 00-194-6979
FLEETWOOD ENTERPRISES INC
1351 Pomona Rd Ste 230, Corona, CA 92882-7165
Tel (951) 354-3000 *Founded/Ownrshp* 1950
Sales 1.9MMM^E *EMP* 6,400
SIC 3799 2451 5561 Recreational vehicles; Mobile homes; Recreational vehicle parts & accessories
Pr: Nelson Potter
Ex VP: Christopher J Braun
Ex VP: Paul C Eskritt
**Ex VP:* Charley Lott
Sr VP: Todd L Inlander
VP: Ronald Brewer
**VP:* John Druheim
**VP:* Gregory Lanese
**VP:* Jon Pierce
VP: Robert N Thompson
Exec: Elsa Salazar
Board of Directors: Loren K Carroll, J Michael Hagan, Thomas B Pitcher

FLEETWOOD HOMES
See FLEETWOOD MOTOR HOMES-CALIFINC

FLEETWOOD HOMES
See FLEETWOOD RETAIL CORP

FLEETWOOD HOMES
See ALLIED RECREATION GROUP INC

D-U-N-S 83-172-2991
■ **FLEETWOOD HOMES INC**
(*Suby of* CAVCO INDUSTRIES INC) ★
1001 N Central Ave # 800, Phoenix, AZ 85004-1935
Tel (602) 256-6263 *Founded/Ownrshp* 2009
Sales 125.5MM^E *EMP* 660^E
SIC 2451 5271 Mobile homes; Mobile homes, personal or private use; Mobile homes
Pr: Charles E Lott
**VP:* Kevin M Groff
**VP:* Joseph H Stegmayer
**VP:* Daniel L Urness

FLEETWOOD LOGISTIC
See FLEETWOOD TRANSPORTATION SERVICES INC

D-U-N-S 04-876-5051 IMP
FLEETWOOD MOTOR HOMES-CALIFINC
FLEETWOOD HOMES
(*Suby of* FLEETWOOD ENTERPRISES INC) ★
3125 Myers St, Riverside, CA 92503-5527
Tel (951) 354-3000 *Founded/Ownrshp* 1976
Sales 74.4MM^E *EMP* 1,035^E
SIC 3716 Motor homes
CEO: Edward B Caudill
**Pr:* Elden L Smith
**CFO:* Boyd R Plowman
**Treas:* Lyle N Larkin
**Sr VP:* Christopher J Braun
**Sr VP:* Forrest D Theobald
Mktg Mgr: Joanna Foist

D-U-N-S 18-844-0705 IMP
■ **FLEETWOOD RETAIL CORP**
FLEETWOOD HOMES
(*Suby of* OAKWOOD HOMES) ★
2150 W 18th St Ste 300, Houston, TX 77008-1289
Tel (713) 965-0520 *Founded/Ownrshp* 2007
Sales 111.1MM^E *EMP* 1,100
SIC 5271 Mobile homes
Pr: Jack Darnall
DP Dir: John Mallinger
IT Man: Don Palmour

D-U-N-S 05-201-8157
FLEETWOOD TRANSPORTATION SERVICES INC
FLEETWOOD LOGISTIC
7632 S Us Highway 59, Burke, TX 75941-4427
Tel (936) 829-4735 *Founded/Ownrshp* 1989
Sales 110.0MM^E *EMP* 400
SIC 4213 Trucking, except local
Ch: Harry H Lynch
**Pr:* Dennis R Berryhill
**CEO:* Mark D Prowell
CFO: Gerry Powell
**CFO:* Garry Prowell
**Sec:* Ronnie L King
Off Mgr: Shannon Falagan
Sfty Dirs: Bruce Wrinkle
Opers Mgr: Lynda Garcia

FLEETWOOD WINDOWS AND DOORS
See FLEETWOOD ALUMINUM PRODUCTS INC

D-U-N-S 06-462-2863
■ **FLEISHMAN-HILLARD INC**
(*Suby of* OMNICOM GROUP INC) ★
200 N Broadway, Saint Louis, MO 63102-2730
Tel (314) 982-1700 *Founded/Ownrshp* 1997
Sales 405.0MM^E *EMP* 2,288
SIC 8743 Public relations & publicity
Pr: Dave Senay
Sr Pt: Christina Liao
Sr Pt: Eileen Marcus
Pt: Flavio D AZ
Pt: Angela Carmichael
Pt: Ruth Kim
Pt: Nicolas Ruszkowski
Pt: Dave Schad
Pt: Jerry Tolk
Pt: Jason Truesdell
V Ch: Bill Anderson
V Ch: Kurt Wehrsten
Pr: Kris Balderston
Pr: Kevin Bell
Pr: Jj Carter
Pr: Robert Dowling
Pr: Dough Michelman
**Pr:* Jack Modzelewski
Pr: Janise Murphy
Pr: Nancy Payne
**COO:* Olivier Beheydt

D-U-N-S 60-915-3887
FLEMING GANNETT INC
(*Suby of* GANNETT FLEMING AFFILIATES INC) ★
207 Senate Ave, Camp Hill, PA 17011-2316
Tel (717) 763-7211 *Founded/Ownrshp* 1989
Sales 373.2MM *EMP* 1,743
Accts Stambaugh Ness Pc Hanover P
SIC 8711 Civil engineering
CEO: William M Stout
Sr VP: Warren A Barrett
Sr VP: John A Derr
Sr VP: John V Dougherty
Sr VP: Glen L Hair
Sr VP: Gene C Koontz
Sr VP: Gene Koontz
Sr VP: John W Kovacs
Sr VP: Esther M McGinnis
Sr VP: Paul D Nowicki
Sr VP: Robert E Ragan
Sr VP: David B Thomas
VP: Martha J Averso
VP: Jeffrey Hurley
VP: John Kenny
VP: Brian W King
VP: Michael May
VP: Dennis Silbaugh
Exec: Jean Liddell

FLEMING ISLAND IMAGING CENTER
See ORANGE PARK MEDICAL CENTER

FLEMINGS-DIV
See HARTLEY CO

D-U-N-S 00-279-1866
FLETCHER ALLEN HEALTH VENTURES INC
(*Suby of* UNIVERSITY VERMONT MEDICAL CTR) ★
111 Colchester Ave, Burlington, VT 05401-1473
Tel (802) 847-5669 *Founded/Ownrshp* 1997
Sales 179.2MM^E *EMP* 6,000
SIC 8011 Medical insurance plan; Physicians' office, including specialists
Pr: Milinda Estey
**CFO:* Roger Deshaies
**Treas:* Rod Witney
Off Mgr: Maureen Leopold
Surgeon: John Lawrence
Surgeon: Kennith H Sartorelli

D-U-N-S 88-345-5354
FLETCHER HOSPITAL INC
PARK RIDGE HOSPITAL
100 Hospital Dr, Hendersonville, NC 28792-5272
Tel (828) 684-8501 *Founded/Ownrshp* 1920
Sales 146.0MM *EMP* 1,200^E
SIC 8062 General medical & surgical hospitals
Pr: Jimm Bunch
Chf Rad: Carlton Jenkins
VP: Jason Wells
Dir Rx: Barry Wood
CIO: Lee Strickland
Pathlgst: Robert Dowdswell
Nrsg Dir: Karen Owensby Rn
HC Dir: Patti Cole

D-U-N-S 00-964-7983 IMP
FLETCHER JONES LAS VEGAS INC
FLETCHER JONES TOYOTA
7300 W Sahara Ave, Las Vegas, NV 89117-2756
Tel (702) 739-9800 *Founded/Ownrshp* 1966
Sales 124.2MM^E *EMP* 430
SIC 5511 Automobiles, new & used
Pr: Fletcher Jones Jr

D-U-N-S 78-559-3005 IMP
FLETCHER JONES MOTOR CARS INC
3300 Jamboree Rd, Newport Beach, CA 92660-8528
Tel (949) 718-3000 *Founded/Ownrshp* 1991
Sales 198.7MM^E *EMP* 510^E
SIC 5511 Automobiles, new & used
Pr: Fletcher Jones Jr
**Treas:* Richard Hanki

FLETCHER JONES TOYOTA
See FLETCHER JONES LAS VEGAS INC

D-U-N-S 19-484-4874
FLETCHLINE INC
5480 Lakeview Rd, Springfield, TN 37172-6639
Tel (615) 382-0764 *Founded/Ownrshp* 1978
Sales 111.0MM^E *EMP* 185
SIC 5084 1796 Materials handling machinery; Machinery installation
Pr: Edward Fletcher Jr
**VP:* William Robert Arms Jr

FLEUR DE LAIT EAST
See ALOUETTE CHEESE USA LLC

D-U-N-S 03-375-5922 IMP
FLEX AMERICA INC
1221 N Black Branch Rd, Elizabethtown, KY 42701-4511
Tel (270) 982-3456 *Founded/Ownrshp* 2001
Sales 96.7MM *EMP* 9
SIC 5199

D-U-N-S 01-129-8072 IMP
FLEX-N-GATE CORP
1306 E University Ave, Urbana, IL 61802-2093
Tel (217) 384-6600 *Founded/Ownrshp* 1980
Sales 3.3MMM^E *EMP* 12,150
SIC 3714 Bumpers & bumperettes, motor vehicle
Pr: Shahid Khan
**Treas:* Jim Zsebok
VP: Bill Beistline
VP: Scott Quartier
Prgrm Mgr: Matt Marsh
Prgrm Mgr: Tim Williams
Genl Mgr: Paul Connolly
Genl Mgr: Chris Demerah
**CIO:* Rubina Ali
CTO: Zoran Jevdic
IT Man: Mike Dunn

D-U-N-S 87-635-4155 IMP
FLEX-N-GATE LLC
VENTRA PLASTICS
(*Suby of* FLEX-N-GATE CORP) ★
5663 E 9 Mile Rd, Warren, MI 48091-2562
Tel (800) 398-1496 *Founded/Ownrshp* 1956
Sales 159.5MM^E *EMP* 150
SIC 5162 Plastics products
Prgrm Mgr: Ian Ross
Prgrm Mgr: Jason Vernier

Prgrm Mgr: Tony Yee
Prgrm Mgr: Joe Zanutto
Sys Mgr: Aaron Boyer

D-U-N-S 10-252-5826 IMP
FLEX-N-GATE OKLAHOMA LLC
(*Suby of* FLEX-N-GATE CORP) ★
1 General St, Ada, OK 74820-2858
Tel (580) 272-6700 *Founded/Ownrshp* 2001
Sales 99.9MM[E] *EMP* 320
SIC 3714 Motor vehicle parts & accessories
IT Man: Preston Rodgers
Sfty Mgr: T Smith
Plnt Mgr: Justin Lacy
Ql Cn Mgr: Frank Taylor

D-U-N-S 82-855-8382
FLEXCARE LLC
FLEXCARE MEDICAL STAFFING
990 Reserve Dr Ste 200, Roseville, CA 95678-1391
Tel (866) 564-3589 *Founded/Ownrshp* 2007
Sales 231.8M[E] *EMP* 1,000
SIC 7363 Help supply services

FLEXCARE MEDICAL STAFFING
See FLEXCARE LLC

FLEXCO
See FLEXIBLE STEEL LACING CO INC

D-U-N-S 00-113-6035 IMP/EXP
FLEXCON CO INC
1 Flexcon Industrial Park, Spencer, MA 01562-2643
Tel (508) 885-8200 *Founded/Ownrshp* 1960
Sales 366.5MM[E] *EMP* 1,180
SIC 3081 2891 Plastic film & sheet; Adhesives
Ch Bd: Myles McDonough
**CEO:* Neil McDonough
COO: Mike Engel
COO: David Rosen
CFO: Ethan Goldman
**Treas:* C Jean McDonough
VP: Dan Twining
Dir Risk M: Brian Burgess
Telecom Ex: Audrey Bell
DP Exec: Robert Quintin
Dir IT: Eric Seaton

D-U-N-S 08-016-6590
FLEXERA HOLDINGS LP
(*Suby of* FLEXERA SOFTWARE LLC) ★
300 Park Blvd Ste 500, Itasca, IL 60143-2635
Tel (847) 466-4000 *Founded/Ownrshp* 2011
Sales 236.4MM *EMP* 90[E]
SIC 7371 7372 Computer software development; Prepackaged software

D-U-N-S 82-506-9847
FLEXERA SOFTWARE LLC
300 Park Blvd Ste 500, Itasca, IL 60143-2635
Tel (847) 466-4000 *Founded/Ownrshp* 2011
Sales 236.4MM[E] *EMP* 613
SIC 7371 7372 Computer software development; Prepackaged software
Pr: Jim Ryan
CFO: Joseph Freda
Sr VP: Randy Littleson
Sr VP: Art Middlekauff
Sr VP: Richard Northing
Sr VP: Peter Prestele
Sr VP: Dana Sacks
VP: Jim Allison
VP: Mathieu Baissac
VP: Sabine Fischer
VP: Mike Koss
VP: Elizabeth Lages
VP: Christopher Moore
VP: John Perkins

FLEXFAB DE MEXICO
See FLEXFAB LLC

D-U-N-S 00-601-9988 IMP
FLEXFAB HORIZONS INTERNATIONAL INC (MI)
FHI FAMILY OF COMPANIES
102 Cook Rd, Hastings, MI 49058-9629
Tel (269) 945-4700 *Founded/Ownrshp* 1961
Sales 128.0MM[E] *EMP* 800
SIC 3599 3052 3053 2822 Flexible metal hose, tubing & bellows; Rubber & plastics hose & beltings; Gaskets, packing & sealing devices; Synthetic rubber
CEO: Matt Decamp
**Ch Bd:* Douglas A Decamp
**CFO:* Jeffrey L Weiden
Prgrm Mgr: Bill Haywood
Mtls Mgr: Dave Anderson

D-U-N-S 12-919-3707 IMP
FLEXFAB LLC
FLEXFAB DE MEXICO
(*Suby of* FHI FAMILY OF COMPANIES) ★
1699 W M 43 Hwy, Hastings, MI 49058-9285
Tel (269) 945-2433 *Founded/Ownrshp* 1993
Sales 98.1MM[E] *EMP* 400[E]
SIC 3599 3052 2822 Flexible metal hose, tubing & bellows; Rubber & plastics hose & beltings; Synthetic rubber
CEO: Matthew De Camp
Ex VP: John Price
VP: Satish Sharma
VP: Martin Walsh
VP: Jeff Weiden
Genl Mgr: Victoria Louden
CIO: Doug Drenth
Mfg Dir: Brian Bowman
VP Mktg: David Brown
Snr Mgr: Steve Egleston
Snr Mgr: Teresa Rambin

D-U-N-S 80-634-1132 IMP
FLEXFIT LLC
350 Karin Ln Unit A, Hicksville, NY 11801-5360
Tel (516) 932-8800 *Founded/Ownrshp* 2007
Sales 97.0MM[E] *EMP* 60
SIC 2353 Hats, caps & millinery

D-U-N-S 84-769-2076
FLEXIAL CORP
(*Suby of* AMERICAN BOA INC) ★
1483 Gould Dr, Cookeville, TN 38506-4181
Tel (931) 432-1853 *Founded/Ownrshp* 2011
Sales 83.1MM[E] *EMP* 110
SIC 5088 Aeronautical equipment & supplies
Pr: Mark Harris
**CFO:* Anita Doak
VP: Roger A Colglazier
Prgrm Mgr: Stephen Bynum
Prgrm Mgr: Chris Key
Genl Mgr: Karen Brown
Genl Mgr: Dinky West
QA Dir: Tyler Fishback
IT Man: Dinky Doak
Prd Mgr: Sarah Colbaugh
Ql Cn Mgr: Gary Cummings

D-U-N-S 00-509-4230 IMP/EXP
FLEXIBLE STEEL LACING CO INC (IL)
FLEXCO
2525 Wisconsin Ave, Downers Grove, IL 60515-4200
Tel (630) 971-0150 *Founded/Ownrshp* 1907
Sales 100.3MM[E] *EMP* 420
SIC 3429

D-U-N-S 14-493-1136 IMP/EXP
FLEXIBLE TECHNOLOGIES INC
HI-TECH DURAVENT
(*Suby of* SMITHS GROUP NORTH AMERICA INC) ★
528 Carwellyn Rd, Abbeville, SC 29620-5535
Tel (864) 366-5441 *Founded/Ownrshp* 1991
Sales 172.2MM[E] *EMP* 600
SIC 3052 3089 Hose, pneumatic: rubber or rubberized fabric; Vacuum cleaner hose, rubber; Vacuum cleaner hose, plastic; Ducting, plastic
CEO: William T Smith
**CFO:* Bob Speer
VP: Harriett Simpson
IT Man: Terry L Massey
Mktg Mgr: Diane Wilson

D-U-N-S 83-937-5649 EXP
FLEXITALLIC GROUP INC
(*Suby of* FGI ACQUISITION CORP) ★
201 Kingwood Med Dr B20 Ste B 200, Houston, TX 77067
Tel (281) 604-2525 *Founded/Ownrshp* 2013
Sales 99.7MM[E] *EMP* 923[E]
SIC 3053 3533 3463 3965 Gaskets, all materials; Oil field machinery & equipment; Flange, valve or pipe fitting forgings, nonferrous; Fasteners
CEO: Jon Stokes
**CFO:* Greg English
**Sr VP:* Lee Harn
VP: Stephen Bond

FLEXMEDICAL DISPOSABLES
See CENTREX PRECISION PLASTICS

FLEXOGRAPHIC PRINTING
See AMERICAN PACKAGING CORP

FLEXON INDS DIV US WIRE CABLE
See US WIRE & CABLE CORP

FLEXPOINT FORD
See FLEXPOINT PARTNERS LLC

D-U-N-S 19-039-5314
FLEXPOINT PARTNERS LLC
FLEXPOINT FORD
676 N Michigan Ave # 3300, Chicago, IL 60611-2846
Tel (312) 327-4520 *Founded/Ownrshp* 2004
Sales 97.7MM[E] *EMP* 300[E]
SIC 5511 Automobiles, new & used
CFO: Stephen Haworth
CFO: Harris Hyman IV
VP: Christopher Ackerman
VP: Perry Ballard
VP: Jonathan Oka
Prin: Ethan A Budin
Prin: Charles E Glew
VP Opers: Steven Michienzi

D-U-N-S 04-686-9645 IMP/EXP
FLEXSOL HOLDING CORP
1531 Nw 12th Ave, Pompano Beach, FL 33069-1730
Tel (954) 941-6333 *Founded/Ownrshp* 1999
Sales 119.4MM[E] *EMP* 604[E]
SIC 2673 3082 3081 Plastic & pliofilm bags; Plastic bags: made from purchased materials; Tubes, unsupported plastic; Plastic film & sheet; Polyethylene film; Packing materials, plastic sheet
Pr: Dave Clarke
**Pr:* Brian Stevenson
**COO:* Ed Stranberg
**CIO:* Ros Poplak

D-U-N-S 03-505-4480 IMP/EXP
FLEXSOL PACKAGING CORP OF POMPANO BEACH
(*Suby of* FLEXSOL HOLDING CORP) ★
1531 Nw 12th Ave, Pompano Beach, FL 33069-1730
Tel (800) 325-7740 *Founded/Ownrshp* 1970
Sales 119.4MM[E] *EMP* 600
SIC 3089 Plastic containers, except foam
Pr: Brian Stevenson
**COO:* Ed Stranberg
**CFO:* Andrew Teo
**VP:* Grant Gamble
**Prin:* Rob Edwards
**Prin:* Irwin Friedman
**Prin:* Travis Hain
**Prin:* Aubrey Strul
**Prin:* Alfred Teo
**Prin:* Buck Warren
**CIO:* Ros Poplak

D-U-N-S 00-514-6048 IMP
▲ FLEXSTEEL INDUSTRIES INC
385 Bell St, Dubuque, IA 52001-7004
Tel (563) 556-7730 *Founded/Ownrshp* 1929
Sales 500.1MM *EMP* 1,340[E]
Accts Deloitte & Touche Llp Minneap
Tkr Sym FLXS *Exch* NGM
SIC 2512 2515 2511 Upholstered household furniture; Chairs: upholstered on wood frames; Couches, sofas & davenports: upholstered on wood frames; Recliners: upholstered on wood frames; Sofa beds (convertible sofas); Wood household furniture; Kitchen & dining room furniture; Chairs, household, except upholstered: wood; Tables, household: wood
Pr: Karel K Czanderna
**Ch Bd:* Eric S Rangen
CFO: Timothy E Hall
Sr VP: Julia K Bizzis
Sr VP: Lee David Fautsch
VP: James Gilbertson
VP: Rick Stanley
Genl Mgr: George Santiago
VP Mktg: Dan Kennedy
Board of Directors: Mary C Bottie, Lynn J Davis, Thomas M Levine, Robert J Maricich, Nancy E Uridil

D-U-N-S 83-250-5130 IMP/EXP
FLEXSTEEL PIPELINE TECHNOLOGIES INC
(*Suby of* PRIME NATURAL RESOURCES LLC) ★
1201 La St Ste 2700, Houston, TX 77002
Tel (832) 531-8555 *Founded/Ownrshp* 2009
Sales 100.3MM[E] *EMP* 111[E]
SIC 3312 Pipes, iron & steel
CEO: Thirucherai Sathyanarayanan
**Pr:* Jeff Shorter
**CFO:* Deborah Miner
Sr VP: Donald Crawford
Dir IT: Andy Ethridge

D-U-N-S 15-028-1566
FLEXTRADE SYSTEMS INC
111 Great Neck Rd Ste 314, Great Neck, NY 11021-5403
Tel (516) 627-8993 *Founded/Ownrshp* 1996
Sales 86.6MM[E] *EMP* 400
SIC 7372 Prepackaged software
Pr: Vijay Kedia
Pr: Scott Moynihan
Pr: Christopher Vandenbrande
Ofcr: James Werner
**Sr VP:* Shailendra Balani
Sr VP: Sachin Barot
**Sr VP:* Jamie Benincasa
Sr VP: John Carillo
**Sr VP:* Rajiv Kedia
Sr VP: Peter Mulieri
Sr VP: David Ullrich
VP: Frank Aquila
VP: David Chu
VP: Kapil Ghodake
VP: Karen Graham
VP: Stefan Kasabov
VP: Sharat Kumar
VP: Aaron Levine
Exec: Ariella Warner

D-U-N-S 03-037-3968 IMP
FLEXTRONICS AMERICA LLC
(*Suby of* FLEXTRONICS INTERNATIONAL USA INC) ★
6201 America Center Dr, San Jose, CA 95002-2563
Tel (408) 576-7000 *Founded/Ownrshp* 2001
Sales 995.2MM[E] *EMP* 2,785
SIC 3672 Printed circuit boards

D-U-N-S 14-424-0850 IMP
FLEXTRONICS AUTOMOTIVE USA INC
(*Suby of* FLEXTRONICS INTERNATIONAL USA INC) ★
2120 Austin Ave, Rochester Hills, MI 48309-3667
Tel (248) 853-5724 *Founded/Ownrshp* 1985
Sales 480.9MM[E] *EMP* 2,000
SIC 3625 3714 3643 Control circuit relays, industrial; Solenoid switches (industrial controls); Switches, electronic applications; Motor vehicle parts & accessories; Vacuum brakes, motor vehicle; Fuel systems & parts, motor vehicle; Oil strainers, motor vehicle; Current-carrying wiring devices
CEO: Mike McNamara
**Pr:* Franois Barbier
**Pr:* Doug Britt
**Pr:* Paul Humphries
COO: Nick Najmoihoda
**CFO:* Christopher Collier
Ofcr: Jennifer Freeborough
Ex VP: Mike De Irala
Ex VP: Nick Najmolhoda
Ex VP: Nick Najmolholda
Ex VP: Peter Scheffler
VP: David Heugh
VP: James Martin

D-U-N-S 01-601-2564 IMP
FLEXTRONICS CORP
(*Suby of* FLEXTRONICS HOLDING USA INC) ★
6201 America Center Dr, Alviso, CA 95002-2563
Tel (803) 936-5200 *Founded/Ownrshp* 2008
Sales 170.4MM[E] *EMP* 350[E]
SIC 3679 3577 3571 Electronic circuits; Computer peripheral equipment; Electronic computers
Pr: Marc A Onetto
Pr: Martin McEnroe
Sr VP: Christian Bauwens
VP: Scott Graybeal
VP: Kevin Kessel
Exec: Richard Romero
Prgrm Mgr: Rodney Chatters
Prgrm Mgr: Tina Nguyen
Prgrm Mgr: Todd Sommers
Mtls Mgr: Peter Coulter
Mtls Mgr: Teresa Lian

D-U-N-S 80-480-0266 IMP
FLEXTRONICS HOLDING USA INC
(*Suby of* FLEX LTD.)
2090 Fortune Dr, San Jose, CA 95131-1823
Tel (408) 576-7000 *Founded/Ownrshp* 2000
Sales 914.2MM[E] *EMP* 7,900
SIC 3672 3679 7371 3825 Printed circuit boards; Electronic circuits; Computer software development; Instruments to measure electricity
CEO: Ronald R Budacz
**CFO:* Robert R B Dykes
Sr VP: Ronald Budacz
**Sr VP:* Carl A Plichta
VP: Susan Hughes
**VP:* Dermott O'Flanagan
**VP:* Thomas J Smach
Dir Bus: Peter Tatley
Prgrm Mgr: Ben Attard
Prgrm Mgr: Bernard Farrales
Prgrm Mgr: Chielo Orinion

D-U-N-S 14-070-5075 IMP
FLEXTRONICS INTERNATIONAL PA INC
FLEXTRONICS INTL LATIN AMER
(*Suby of* FLEX LTD.)
847 Gibraltar Dr, Milpitas, CA 95035-6332
Tel (408) 576-7000 *Founded/Ownrshp* 1986
Sales 200.6MM[E] *EMP* 455
SIC 3444 Sheet metalwork
CEO: Michael McNamara
**Pr:* Paul Humphries
**CFO:* Bob Dykes
Bd of Dir: Stanley Needham
VP: Chris Karatsiolis
**VP:* Paul Read
Mng Dir: Paul McFarline
Prgrm Mgr: Jesus Badillo
Prgrm Mgr: Steve Langone
Genl Mgr: Christine Lee
IT Man: Robert Rosta

D-U-N-S 94-171-4834 IMP
FLEXTRONICS INTERNATIONAL USA INC
(*Suby of* FLEX LTD.)
6201 America Center Dr, San Jose, CA 95002-2563
Tel (408) 576-7000 *Founded/Ownrshp* 1987
Sales 9.5MMM[E] *EMP* 200,000
SIC 3672 Printed circuit boards
CEO: Michael McNamara
**CFO:* Christopher Collier
Ofcr: Tom Linton
Sr VP: Marylee Greene
VP: Jeff Hendrix
VP: Ted Jackson
VP: Susan Marsch
VP: Brant Miller
VP: David Moezidis
Dir Bus: Vince Casey
Prgrm Mgr: Miguel Garcia

FLEXTRONICS INTL LATIN AMER
See FLEXTRONICS INTERNATIONAL PA INC

D-U-N-S 80-149-0439
FLEXTRONICS LOGISTICS USA INC
(*Suby of* FLEXTRONICS INTERNATIONAL USA INC) ★
6201 America Center Dr, San Jose, CA 95002-2563
Tel (408) 576-7000 *Founded/Ownrshp* 2010
Sales 83.4MM[E] *EMP* 1,300
SIC 4783 Packing goods for shipping
Pr: Michael McNamara

D-U-N-S 06-498-4263
FLIGHT CENTRE TRAVEL GROUP (USA) INC
LIBERTY TRAVEL
(*Suby of* FCM TRAVEL SOLUTIONS) ★
5 Paragon Dr Ste 200, Montvale, NJ 07645-1791
Tel (201) 934-3500 *Founded/Ownrshp* 2007
Sales 468.7MM[E] *EMP* 2,100
SIC 4512 Air transportation, scheduled
Pr: Dean Smith
COO: Bernie Tessler
**CFO:* Kathryn Atwell
VP: Colette Baruth
VP: Diane Brancella
VP: Shaun Malay
Dir IT: Robert Thomas
Sales Exec: Cathy Peleaz
Advt Dir: Taleen Banelian
Sls Dir: Libert T Pines
Sls Mgr: Amanda Gesoalde

D-U-N-S 83-301-7465
FLIGHT CENTRE USA HOLDING CORP
FCM TRAVEL SOLUTIONS
(*Suby of* FLIGHT CENTRE TRAVEL GROUP LIMITED)
5 Paragon Dr Ste 200, Montvale, NJ 07645-1791
Tel (201) 312-6855 *Founded/Ownrshp* 2007
Sales 607.0MM[E] *EMP* 2,100[E]
SIC 4724 Travel agencies
Pr: Dean Smith
**VP:* Kathryn Atwell
Genl Mgr: Michael Murray
CTO: Chris Santaniello

D-U-N-S 17-682-8143
FLIGHT OPTIONS INC
26180 Curtiss Wright Pkwy, Richmond Heights, OH 44143-1453
Tel (216) 261-3880 *Founded/Ownrshp* 1998
Sales 99.4MM[E] *EMP* 1,600
SIC 4581 Aircraft maintenance & repair services
Ch: Kenneth Ricci
**Pr:* Darnell H Martens
**Pr:* Robert Pinkas
**CEO:* Michael J Silvestro
**COO:* J Chris Herzberg
**Treas:* Michael A Rossi
**Ex VP:* Matthew Doyle
**VP:* James R Dauterman
**VP:* Travis Metz
Prin: David H Davies

D-U-N-S 04-094-5177
FLIGHT SERVICES & SYSTEMS INC
5005 Rockside Rd Ste 940, Cleveland, OH 44131-6829
Tel (216) 328-0090 *Founded/Ownrshp* 1999
Sales 94.5MM[E] *EMP* 800[E]
SIC 7389 Safety inspection service
CEO: Robert Weitzel
**Ex VP:* Phil Armstrong
Dir IT: Christopher Kubala

D-U-N-S 04-617-3175
■ FLIGHTSAFETY INTERNATIONAL INC
(*Suby of* BERKSHIRE HATHAWAY INC) ★
Marine Air Terminal, Flushing, NY 11371
Tel (718) 565-4100 *Founded/Ownrshp* 1996
Sales 1.1MMM *EMP* 4,100
Accts Deloitte & Touche Llp Omaha
SIC 7363 Pilot service, aviation
Pr: Bruce N Whitman

*CFO: Ken Motschwiller
Treas: Mario D'Angelo
Ofcr: Gary Harding
*Sr VP: David Davenport
*Sr VP: Tom Eff
*Sr VP: Scott Fera
Dir Bus: Michael King
Ex Dir: Kyle Davis
Ex Dir: Chuck Gallagher
Prgrm Mgr: Tim Fincher

D-U-N-S 04-825-1552
FLIGHTSTAR AIRCRAFT SERVICES LLC (FL)
(Suby of MOELIS CAPITAL PARTNERS LLC) ★
6025 Flightline Dr, Jacksonville, FL 32221-8183
Tel (904) 741-0300 Founded/Ownrshp 1997, 2011
Sales 91.1MM EMP 425
SIC 4581 3728 Aircraft maintenance & repair services; Aircraft parts & equipment
CEO: Jerry Hernandez
*COO: Tucker Morrison
*CFO: Mark Shuman
*Ex VP: Juan Briz
VP: Tim Bergin
*VP: Steve Slusarczyk
VP: Sherman Thomas
Dir: Randy Sutterfield
Dir IT: Saikiran Kalegowda
IT Man: Eric Hopkins

D-U-N-S 06-430-1138 IMP
FLIK INTERNATIONAL CORP
(Suby of EUREST DINING SERVICES) ★
2 International Dr Fl 2, Rye Brook, NY 10573-1094
Tel (914) 935-5300 Founded/Ownrshp 1995
Sales 151.8MM^E EMP 3,300
SIC 8742 5812 Restaurant & food services consultants; Contract food services
CEO: Rick Postiglione
Pr: Scott Davis
CFO: Joseph Sargis
Ex VP: Julie A Flik
Sr VP: Neil Gardner

D-U-N-S 08-521-7701 IMP/EXP
FLINN SCIENTIFIC INC
770 N Raddant Rd, Batavia, IL 60510-4208
Tel (800) 452-1261 Founded/Ownrshp 1977
Sales 107.6MM^E EMP 243^E
SIC 3821 5049 Laboratory equipment: fume hoods, distillation racks, etc.; Laboratory equipment, except medical or dental
Ch: Margaret Flinn
*Pr: Larry Flinn
*Pr: Lawrence C Flinn III
*VP: Patrick J Flinn
IT Man: Debby Hines
Software D: Chris Green
VP Mfg: Tony Leben
Sfty Mgr: Gregg Dvorak
VP Mktg: Jim Nesbit
Sls Dir: Kevin McNulty

D-U-N-S 00-514-6329 IMP
FLINT & WALLING INC
STAR WATER SYSTEMS
(Suby of ZOELLER CO) ★
95 N Oak St, Kendallville, IN 46755-1736
Tel (260) 347-1781 Founded/Ownrshp 2000
Sales 106.8MM^E EMP 150
Accts Consolidated W/Parent Company
SIC 3561 Pumps & pumping equipment; Pumps, domestic: water or sump
Pr: Scott M Lechner
VP: Scott Wallen
Exec: Richard Conrad
Genl Mgr: Lee Jackson
MIS Dir: Leslie Hayward
Dir IT: Max Bennett
Plnt Mgr: Terry Mendenhall
Mktg Mgr: James R Baldwin
Mktg Mgr: Brett Edwards
Sls Mgr: Rita Hoover

FLINT COMMUNITY SCHOOLS
See SCHOOL DISTRICT OF CITY OF FLINT

D-U-N-S 00-692-6349
FLINT ELECTRIC MEMBERSHIP CORP
FLINT ENERGY
3 S Macon St, Reynolds, GA 31076-3104
Tel (478) 847-3415 Founded/Ownrshp 1937
Sales 195.9MM EMP 227
Accts Mcnair Mclemore Middlebrooks
SIC 4911 Distribution, electric power
CEO: Bob Ray
*CFO: Anissa Derieux
*Sr VP: Jimmy Autry
*VP: Ty Diamond
IT Man: Lori Hageman

FLINT ENERGY
See FLINT ELECTRIC MEMBERSHIP CORP

D-U-N-S 00-696-9018 IMP
■ **FLINT ENERGY SERVICES INC**
(Suby of FLINT ENERGY SERVICES LTD.)
6901 S Havana St, Centennial, CO 80112-3805
Tel (918) 294-3030 Founded/Ownrshp 1924, 1998
Sales 1.0MMM^E EMP 2,600
Accts Kpmg Llp Tulsa Oklahoma
SIC 1389 3594 1623 Servicing oil & gas wells; Oil & gas wells: building, repairing & dismantling; Roustabout service; Fluid power pumps; Oil & gas pipeline construction; Pumping station construction
VP: Lloyd Stewart
*Pr: Bryce Satter

D-U-N-S 12-884-9614
FLINT EQUIPMENT HOLDINGS INC
FLINTCO
1206 Blaylock St, Albany, GA 31705-1342
Tel (229) 888-1212 Founded/Ownrshp 2002
Sales 86.6MM^E EMP 285
SIC 5084 Industrial machinery & equipment
CEO: Thomas C Cannon
*CFO: Tony Byron Sammons

D-U-N-S 78-438-1902 IMP/EXP
FLINT GROUP NORTH AMERICA CORP
(Suby of CDR PIGMENTS & DISPERSIONS) ★
14909 N Beck Rd, Plymouth, MI 48170-2411
Tel (734) 781-4600 Founded/Ownrshp 1998
Sales 228.8MM^E EMP 1,500
SIC 2893 Printing ink
Pr: William B Miller

D-U-N-S 00-535-5854 IMP/EXP
FLINT GROUP US LLC
CDR PIGMENTS & DISPERSIONS
(Suby of CVC EUROPEAN EQUITY PARTNERS III L.P.)
14909 N Beck Rd, Plymouth, MI 48170-2411
Tel (734) 781-4600 Founded/Ownrshp 2005
Sales 3.6MMM^E EMP 8,000
SIC 2865 2893 Color pigments, organic; Printing ink
Pr: Grant Shouldice
VP: Michelle Domas
VP: Neroni Mike
VP: Wang Tan
Dir Lab: Michelle Bell
Dir Lab: Anita Payseur
Rgnl Mgr: Joe Tatosky
Genl Mgr: Mike Buystedt
Genl Mgr: Dan Hennessy
Off Mgr: Janice Smith
Netwrk Mgr: Sharon Smith

D-U-N-S 10-275-6447 IMP/EXP
FLINT HILLS RESOURCES LLC
(Suby of KOCH INDUSTRIES INC) ★
4111 E 37th St N, Wichita, KS 67220-3203
Tel (316) 828-5500 Founded/Ownrshp 2012
Sales 3.6MMM^E EMP 2,083
SIC 5169 5084 Industrial chemicals; Oil refining machinery, equipment & supplies
CEO: Bradley J Razook
*Pr: David Robertson
*CFO: Anthony Sementelli
*Treas: Wade Marquardt
VP: Jeff Cook
*VP: Phil Gaarder
VP: Randy Lenz
*VP: Mark Nichols
VP: Jamey Steinhauser
Mng Dir: Francis Murphy
Prgrm Mgr: David Sadler

D-U-N-S 05-657-6507 IMP/EXP
FLINT HILLS RESOURCES LP
FUEL WATCH
(Suby of FLINT HILLS RESOURCES LLC) ★
4111 E 37th St N, Wichita, KS 67220-3203
Tel (800) 292-3133 Founded/Ownrshp 1995
Sales 832.4MM^E EMP 1,180
SIC 5172 4612 1382 2911

FLINTCO
See FLINT EQUIPMENT HOLDINGS INC

D-U-N-S 00-790-8064
FLINTCO LLC
(Suby of AIH FLINTCO LLC) ★
1624 W 21st St, Tulsa, OK 74107-2749
Tel (918) 587-8451 Founded/Ownrshp 2013
Sales 770.8MM EMP 280
SIC 1541 1542

D-U-N-S 05-736-8151
FLIPPO CONSTRUCTION CO INC
3820 Penn Belt Pl, District Heights, MD 20747-4748
Tel (301) 967-6800 Founded/Ownrshp 1971
Sales 125.1MM^E EMP 375
SIC 1623 1622 Underground utilities contractor; Electric power line construction; Bridge construction
VP: James Wills
Pr: Jeff Flippo
Pr: Greg Mehallick
CEO: Brian Flippo
VP: Greg Mehalick
VP: John Morgan
Sfty Dirs: Gary McClanahan
Pr Mgr: Bernard Flippo

D-U-N-S 93-826-1518 IMP
■ **FLIR COMMERCIAL SYSTEMS INC**
(Suby of FLIR SYSTEMS INC) ★
6769 Hollister Ave # 100, Goleta, CA 93117-5572
Tel (805) 690-6685 Founded/Ownrshp 2004
Sales 579.3MM^E EMP 500
SIC 5065 3699 Security control equipment & systems; Security devices
CEO: Thomas A Surran
*Pr: William A Sundermeier
*CEO: Earl R Lewis
*CEO: Andrew C Teich
*Sr VP: William W Davis
*Sr VP: Anthony L Trunzo
VP: Jeff Frank
Exec: Debbie Horne
IT Man: Karen Cottriel

D-U-N-S 61-538-2210
■ **FLIR DETECTION INC**
(Suby of FLIR SYSTEMS INC) ★
1024 S Innovation Way, Stillwater, OK 74074-1508
Tel (703) 678-2111 Founded/Ownrshp 2010
Sales 222.3MM^E EMP 817
SIC 3826 Analytical optical instruments
*Pr: Dennis J Barket
*Pr: Colin Cumming
Pr: Doug Knight
*CFO: Deborah Mosier
Treas: Randahl J Finnessy
*Ofcr: Wayne Bryden
VP: Mark Bonatucci
VP: Howard Borst
Off Mgr: Monica Valdez

D-U-N-S 09-129-6244
▲ **FLIR SYSTEMS INC**
27700 Sw Parkway Ave, Wilsonville, OR 97070-8238
Tel (503) 498-3547 Founded/Ownrshp 1978
Sales 1.5MMM EMP 3,033
Tkr Sym FLIR Exch NGS

SIC 3812 3826 Search & navigation equipment; Infrared object detection equipment; Analytical instruments; Thermal analysis instruments, laboratory type; Infrared analytical instruments
Pr: Andrew C Teich
Ch Bd: Earl R Lewis
COO: Thomas A Surran
CFO: Amit Singhi
Chf Mktg O: Travis D Merrill
Sr VP: Todd M Duchene
VP: David Muessle
VP: Gary Ryker
VP: Tom Scanlon
VP: Josh Scott
VP: Tim Stevenson
VP: Detlev Suderow
VP: Steve Williams
VP: Paul Zaninovich
VP Bus Dev: Jay James
Dir Bus: Paul Czerepuszko
Dir Bus: Sue Petronio
Dir Bus: Glen Rowling
Board of Directors: John D Carter, William W Crouch, Catherine A Halligan, Angus L McDonald, Michael T Smith, Cathy A Stauffer, John W Wood Jr, Steven E Wynne

D-U-N-S 61-759-4601 IMP/EXP
■ **FLO KAY INDUSTRIES INC**
(Suby of ANDERSONS INC) ★
1919 Grand Ave, Sioux City, IA 51106-5708
Tel (712) 277-2011 Founded/Ownrshp 2015
Sales 196.4MM^E EMP 470
SIC 2873 2048 2816 Nitrogenous fertilizers; Feed supplements; Zinc pigments: zinc oxide, zinc sulfide
Pr: Bill Wolfe
*Treas: Jim Burmeister
VP: Raun Lohry

D-U-N-S 78-536-5693 IMP
FLO-TECH LLC
699 Middle St, Middletown, CT 06457-1547
Tel (860) 613-3333 Founded/Ownrshp 1991
Sales 97.0MM^E EMP 160^E
SIC 5045 3577 Printers, computer; Printers, computer
CEO: Leo Bonetti
*COO: Steve Therrien
*CFO: Arthur G Aery Jr
*VP: Mike Assunto
*VP: Scott Macgregor
VP: Nancy Marchi
IT Man: Sylvia Pagan
MIS Mgr: Joseph Miller
Sftwr Eng: Omar Rosa
Mktg Dir: Kim Prario

D-U-N-S 13-433-5947 IMP
FLODRAULIC GROUP INC
3539 N 700 W, Greenfield, IN 46140-8272
Tel (317) 890-3700 Founded/Ownrshp 2003
Sales 2.5MMM^E EMP 145
SIC 5084 Industrial machinery & equipment
Pr: Lou Laskis
*COO: Barry Stacy
CFO: Larry Gross
Sales Asso: Herman Gamez

D-U-N-S 02-636-3013 IMP/EXP
FLOOR AND DECOR OUTLETS OF AMERICA INC
F&D CORPORATE GENERAL
2233 Lake Park Dr Se # 400, Smyrna, GA 30080-8813
Tel (404) 471-1634 Founded/Ownrshp 2003
Sales 255.1MM^E EMP 500
SIC 5713 1771 Floor covering stores; Flooring contractor
CEO: Thomas Taylor
*CFO: Trevor Lang
VP: Ersan Sayman
CIO: John Adamson
IT Man: Joseph Gough

D-U-N-S 06-895-7323 IMP
FLOORS INC
CARPET ONE
200 Bank St, Southlake, TX 76092-9148
Tel (817) 421-8787 Founded/Ownrshp 1990
Sales 162.3MM^E EMP 250
SIC 5023 5713 Floor coverings; Floor covering stores
CEO: Lawrence Barr
*CEO: Randy Pack
*COO: Ron Johnson
*COO: Rocky Pack

D-U-N-S 85-858-9815
FLORAL SPECIALTIES INC
771 ROSE
20601 Aurora Rd, Cleveland, OH 44146-1001
Tel (216) 475-2302 Founded/Ownrshp 1990
Sales 93.8MM^E EMP 2,200
SIC 5992 Florists
Pr: Jeff Heinen
*Pr: Tom Heinen
CIO: Louis Penny

FLORENCE HAND NURSING HOME
See LA GRANGE TROUP COUNTY HOSPITAL AUTHORITY

D-U-N-S 00-983-4664
FLORENCE SCHOOL DISTRICT ONE
319 S Dargan St, Florence, SC 29506-2538
Tel (843) 669-4141 Founded/Ownrshp 1881
Sales 169.5MM EMP 2,250
Accts Baird & Company Cpas Llc Augu
SIC 8211 Public adult education school; Public elementary school; Public junior high school; Public senior high school
Ch: S Porter Stewart II
*CFO: Luther M Rabon
*VP: Glenn Odom

D-U-N-S 62-375-1831
FLORIDA A & M UNIVERSITY
BOARD OF GOVS STATE UNIV SYSTM
(Suby of BOARD GOVERNORS GENERAL OFFICE) ★
1601 S M L King Jr Blvd, Tallahassee, FL 32307-0001
Tel (850) 599-3000 Founded/Ownrshp 1887
Sales 199.6MM^E EMP 1,700
SIC 8221 Colleges universities & professional schools
Pr: Elmira Mangum
*Pr: Fred Gainous
Pr: Ben McCune
Pr: Kinfe K Redda
CFO: Joe Dunn
CFO: Cynthia Gaines
Bd of Dir: Jaibun Earp
Trst: Mary B Diallo
Trst: Leerie Jenkins
Ofcr: Kent Taylor
Assoc VP: Herman Brann
Ex VP: Challis Lowe
VP: Lois Bell
VP: Jerrold Gibson
*VP: Phyllis Gray-Ray
VP: Ronald Joe
VP: Jeffrey Ross
VP: Ngozi Ugochukwu
VP: Barbara Wynn
Exec: James Collins
Assoc Dir: Robert D Carroll

D-U-N-S 09-146-3414 IMP
FLORIDA A&G CO INC
ARCH MIRROR NORTH
10200 Nw 67th St, Tamarac, FL 33321-6404
Tel (800) 432-8132 Founded/Ownrshp 1989, 1998
Sales 202.7MM^E EMP 1,570
SIC 3442 5039 Metal doors; Window & door frames; Sash, door or window: metal; Store fronts, prefabricated, metal; Glass construction materials
Pr: Leon Silverstein
Dir IT: Chris Hunt

D-U-N-S 00-414-7534
FLORIDA ATLANTIC UNIVERSITY (FL)
(Suby of BOARD GOVERNORS GENERAL OFFICE) ★
777 Glades Rd, Boca Raton, FL 33431-6496
Tel (561) 297-3000 Founded/Ownrshp 1964
Sales 343.0MM^E EMP 3,053^E
SIC 8221 University
Pr: John W Kelly
Assoc VP: Carla Capeletti
Assoc VP: Charles Eugene
Assoc VP: Robert Richman
*VP: Stacy Volnick
Exec: Aldenise Oliveira
Dir Lab: Richard Mayer
Assoc Dir: J Baruch
Assoc Dir: Dominique Blanchard
Assoc Dir: Robert Davis
Assoc Dir: Reuben Ferguson
Assoc Dir: Christina Fermin
Assoc Dir: Randy Kalman
Assoc Dir: Peter Tatro

FLORIDA BLUE HMO
See HEALTH OPTIONS INC

FLORIDA CAREER COLLEGE
See EDUCATION TRAINING CORP

D-U-N-S 15-268-6143
FLORIDA CLINICAL PRACTICE ASSOCIATION INC
FCPA
1329 Sw 16th St Ste 4250, Gainesville, FL 32608-1128
Tel (352) 265-8017 Founded/Ownrshp 1976
Sales 598.1MM EMP 2
SIC 7322 Collection agency, except real estate; Adjustment bureau, except insurance
Pr: Anthony Mancuso
CFO: Christina D Williams
*Ex VP: William W Tharp
IT Man: Aaron Weldon

D-U-N-S 05-613-4406 IMP/EXP
■ **FLORIDA COCA-COLA BOTTLING CO**
(Suby of COCA-COLA REFRESHMENTS USA INC) ★
521 Lake Kathy Dr, Brandon, FL 33510-3945
Tel (813) 569-2600 Founded/Ownrshp 1926, 1988
Sales 653.8MM^E EMP 4,000
SIC 2086 Bottled & canned soft drinks
VP: Jay Ard
Snr Mgr: Christina Kerler

D-U-N-S 96-666-5932
■ **FLORIDA COMMUNITY BANK NA**
(Suby of FCB FINANCIAL HOLDINGS INC) ★
2500 Weston Rd Ste 300, Weston, FL 33331-3617
Tel (866) 764-0006 Founded/Ownrshp 2010
Sales NA EMP 140
SIC 6022 State commercial banks
CEO: Daniel Healy
*Pr: Kent Ellert
Sr VP: Ardian Zika

D-U-N-S 05-594-7154
FLORIDA CONFERENCE ASSOCIATION OF SEVENTH-DAY ADVENTISTS
655 N Wymore Rd, Winter Park, FL 32789-2867
Tel (407) 644-5000 Founded/Ownrshp 1893
Sales 59.9MM^E EMP 1,600
SIC 8661 8211 5942 6513 Seventh Day Adventist Church; Preparatory school; Books, religious; Residential hotel operation
Pr: Michael F Cauley
Treas: Elisa Rhaming
*Treas: Duane Rollins
*VP: Ken Burrill
*VP: Jim Etterson
*VP: Abel Paulin

D-U-N-S 03-142-8894 IMP
FLORIDA CRYSTALS CORP
(Suby of FANJUL CORP) ★
1 N Clematis St Ste 200, West Palm Beach, FL 33401-5551
Tel (561) 655-6303 Founded/Ownrshp 1997
Sales 530.0MM^E EMP 2,000

SIC 2061 2062 2044 4911 Raw cane sugar; Cane sugar refining; Rice milling; Electric services
Ch Bd: Alfonso Fanjul
V Ch: Jose F Fanjul Jr
*Treas: Erik J Blomqvist
VP: Van Boyette
VP: Gus Cepero
*VP: Jose Fanjul
VP: Terry Oconnor
VP: Allan Ryan
VP: Parks Shackelford
VP: Don Whittington
Exec: Maricela Torres
Dir Bus: Alejandro Londono

D-U-N-S 80-955-8919
FLORIDA DEPARTMENT OF AGRICULTURE AND CONSUMER SERVICES
(*Suby of* EXECUTIVE OFFICE OF GOVERNOR OF FLORIDA) ★
10 The Capitol, Tallahassee, FL 32399-7021
Tel (850) 617-7700 *Founded/Ownrshp* 1969
Sales NA *EMP* 3,000
SIC 9641 9611 9111 Regulation of agricultural marketing; ; Consumer protection office, government; Executive offices;

D-U-N-S 80-939-6666
FLORIDA DEPARTMENT OF CHILDREN & FAMILIES
(*Suby of* EXECUTIVE OFFICE OF GOVERNOR OF FLORIDA) ★
1317 Winewood Blvd Rm 306, Tallahassee, FL 32399-0001
Tel (850) 488-2840 *Founded/Ownrshp* 1969
Sales NA *EMP* 11,600
SIC 9441 9411 Administration of social & manpower programs; ; Administration of educational programs;
Ex Dir: David Taylor
IT Man: Rob Kenyon

D-U-N-S 80-939-6468
FLORIDA DEPARTMENT OF CORRECTIONS
(*Suby of* EXECUTIVE OFFICE OF GOVERNOR OF FLORIDA) ★
501 S Calhoun St, Tallahassee, FL 32399-6548
Tel (850) 488-7480 *Founded/Ownrshp* 1969
Sales NA *EMP* 25,000
SIC 9223 Prison, government;
*VP: Thomas A Rush
Comm Dir: Ann V Howard
IT Man: Frederick Meisiek
IT Man: Eric Mercer
Info Man: Lou Carroll
Snr Mgr: Shawn Satterfield

D-U-N-S 96-893-0664
FLORIDA DEPARTMENT OF ECONOMIC OPPORTUNITY
(*Suby of* EXECUTIVE OFFICE OF GOVERNOR OF FLORIDA) ★
107 E Madison St St120, Tallahassee, FL 32399-6545
Tel (850) 245-7362 *Founded/Ownrshp* 2011
Sales NA *EMP* 2,124
SIC 9199

D-U-N-S 80-938-5529
FLORIDA DEPARTMENT OF EDUCATION
HUMAN RESOURCES DEPARTMENT
(*Suby of* EXECUTIVE OFFICE OF GOVERNOR OF FLORIDA) ★
325 W Gaines St Ste 101, Tallahassee, FL 32399-6533
Tel (850) 245-0505 *Founded/Ownrshp* 1869
Sales NA *EMP* 2,500
SIC 9411 Administration of educational programs;
Comm Dir: Andrew Myers

D-U-N-S 80-939-6690
FLORIDA DEPARTMENT OF ENVIRONMENTAL PROTECTION
(*Suby of* EXECUTIVE OFFICE OF GOVERNOR OF FLORIDA) ★
3900 Commwl Blvd, Tallahassee, FL 32399-0001
Tel (850) 245-2112 *Founded/Ownrshp* 1993
Sales NA *EMP* 15,693
Accts Deloitte & Touche Llp
SIC 9512 Wildlife conservation agencies
Prin: Rick Scott
*Prin: Tom Beason
*Prin: Jennifer Carroll
*Prin: Candie Fuller

D-U-N-S 80-939-7458
FLORIDA DEPARTMENT OF FINANCIAL SERVICES
O F R
(*Suby of* EXECUTIVE OFFICE OF GOVERNOR OF FLORIDA) ★
200 E Gaines St, Tallahassee, FL 32399-6502
Tel (850) 413-3100 *Founded/Ownrshp* 1941
Sales NA *EMP* 1,450
Accts David W Martin Cpa Tallahas
SIC 9651 Insurance commission, government;
Treas: Tom Gallagher
*CFO: Jeff Atwater
Ofcr: Stanton Beazley
Ofcr: Bill Dubose
Ofcr: Thomas Eberhart
Ofcr: Steven E Firestone
Ofcr: Gloria Fribley-Lykes
Ofcr: Deborah D La Paz-Boxer
Ofcr: David Loy
Ofcr: Paul Sennett
Ofcr: Linda R Townsend

D-U-N-S 36-421-5061
FLORIDA DEPARTMENT OF HEALTH
(*Suby of* EXECUTIVE OFFICE OF GOVERNOR OF FLORIDA) ★
4052 Bald Cypress Way, Tallahassee, FL 32399-1700
Tel (850) 245-4500 *Founded/Ownrshp* 1997
Sales NA *EMP* 1,800^E
SIC 9431 8399 Administration of public health programs; ; Community action agency
Ex Dir: Susan Foster
IT Man: Edwin Nelson
Genl Couns: William Large

D-U-N-S 80-939-6716
FLORIDA DEPARTMENT OF HIGHWAY SAFETY AND MOTOR VEHICLES
(*Suby of* EXECUTIVE OFFICE OF GOVERNOR OF FLORIDA) ★
2900 Apalachee Pkwy, Tallahassee, FL 32399-6552
Tel (850) 617-3100 *Founded/Ownrshp* 1970
Sales NA *EMP* 3,236
SIC 9621 Aircraft regulating agencies;
Pr: Julie Jones
*Treas: Modesto W Burgos
*VP: Eduardo Gonzalez
*VP: Manuel Villamanan
*Ex Dir: David Conklin Jr

D-U-N-S 92-932-2626
FLORIDA DEPARTMENT OF JUVENILE JUSTICE
EXECUTVE OFC OF THE GOV OF FL
(*Suby of* EXECUTIVE OFFICE OF GOVERNOR OF FLORIDA) ★
2737 Centerview Dr # 1225, Tallahassee, FL 32399-0999
Tel (850) 921-3048 *Founded/Ownrshp* 1995
Sales NA *EMP* 5,000
SIC 9223 Detention center, government;
Ofcr: Jennifer Rechichi
Ex Dir: Michael Cantrell
Opers Mgr: Debra Morris

D-U-N-S 80-939-6732
FLORIDA DEPARTMENT OF LABOR AND EMPLOYMENT SECURITY
(*Suby of* EXECUTIVE OFFICE OF GOVERNOR OF FLORIDA) ★
2012 Capital Cir Se, Tallahassee, FL 32399-6583
Tel (850) 942-8341 *Founded/Ownrshp* 1969
Sales NA *EMP* 2,638
SIC 9651 9111 Labor regulatory agency; ; Executive offices;

D-U-N-S 80-939-6781
FLORIDA DEPARTMENT OF LAW ENFORCEMENT
(*Suby of* EXECUTIVE OFFICE OF GOVERNOR OF FLORIDA) ★
2331 Phillips Rd, Tallahassee, FL 32308-5333
Tel (850) 410-7000 *Founded/Ownrshp* 1967
Sales NA *EMP* 2,028
SIC 9221 Police protection;
Ofcr: Kristi Gordon
Ofcr: Belinda Murvin
Exec: Keith Kameg
Telecom Mg: Tanya Shrum

D-U-N-S 80-938-5313
FLORIDA DEPARTMENT OF LEGAL AFFAIRS
ATTORNEY GENERAL
(*Suby of* EXECUTIVE OFFICE OF GOVERNOR OF FLORIDA) ★
107 W Gaines St, Tallahassee, FL 32399-6549
Tel (850) 414-3300 *Founded/Ownrshp* 2000
Sales 51.0MM^E *EMP* 1,382
SIC 8111 9222 Legal services

D-U-N-S 80-939-6971 IMP
FLORIDA DEPARTMENT OF MILITARY
FLORIDA NATIONAL GUARD
(*Suby of* EXECUTIVE OFFICE OF GOVERNOR OF FLORIDA) ★
190 San Marco Ave, Saint Augustine, FL 32084-2765
Tel (904) 823-4748 *Founded/Ownrshp* 1845
Sales NA *EMP* 9,524^E
SIC 9711 National security;

D-U-N-S 80-939-7045
FLORIDA DEPARTMENT OF REVENUE
(*Suby of* EXECUTIVE OFFICE OF GOVERNOR OF FLORIDA) ★
2450 Oak Blvd, Tallahassee, FL 32399-0001
Tel (850) 617-8600 *Founded/Ownrshp* 1969
Sales NA *EMP* 5,000^E
SIC 9311 9111 Finance, taxation & monetary policy; ; Executive offices;
Ex Dir: Marshall Stranburg
VP: Tracy Barnes
Adm Dir: Paul Bartlett
*Ex Dir: Lisa Vickers

D-U-N-S 80-939-7102
FLORIDA DEPARTMENT OF TRANSPORTATION
FDOT
(*Suby of* EXECUTIVE OFFICE OF GOVERNOR OF FLORIDA) ★
605 Suwannee St, Tallahassee, FL 32399-6544
Tel (850) 414-4500 *Founded/Ownrshp* 1969
Sales NA *EMP* 6,000
Accts Tcba Watson Rice Llp Fort Lau
SIC 9621 Regulation, administration of transportation;
Pr Dir: Cindy Clemmons
Pr Dir: Steve Olson

D-U-N-S 93-214-2581
FLORIDA DEPARTMENT OF VETERANS AFFAIRS
FDVA
(*Suby of* EXECUTIVE OFFICE OF GOVERNOR OF FLORIDA) ★
11351 Ulmerton Rd Rm 311k, Largo, FL 33778-1629
Tel (727) 319-7427 *Founded/Ownrshp* 1989
Sales NA *EMP* 1,267^E
SIC 9451 9111 ; Executive offices;
Ex Dir: Mike Prendergast
Ex Dir: Leroy Collins
*Ex Dir: Rocky McPherson
IT Man: Walter Gilchrist
Board of Directors: Mike Prendergast

FLORIDA DETROIT DIESEL-ALLISON
See STEWART & STEVENSON FDDA LLC

D-U-N-S 60-378-4182
FLORIDA DIVISION OF ADMINISTRATIVE HEARINGS
DEPARTMENT MANAGEMENT SERVICES
(*Suby of* EXECUTIVE OFFICE OF GOVERNOR OF FLORIDA) ★
1230 Apalachee Pkwy, Tallahassee, FL 32301-3060
Tel (850) 488-9675 *Founded/Ownrshp* 1975
Sales NA *EMP* 3,376^E
SIC 9211

D-U-N-S 96-716-6260
FLORIDA EAST COAST HOLDINGS CORP
7411 Fullerton St Ste 300, Jacksonville, FL 32256-3629
Tel (800) 342-1131 *Founded/Ownrshp* 2011
Sales 317.5MM *EMP* 550^E
SIC 6719 Investment holding companies, except banks
CEO: James R Hertwig
Sr VP: Francis Chinnici

D-U-N-S 96-230-3264
FLORIDA EAST COAST INDUSTRIES LLC
2855 S Le Jeune Rd Fl 4, Coral Gables, FL 33134-6612
Tel (305) 520-2300 *Founded/Ownrshp* 2006
Sales 199.6MM^E *EMP* 220^E
SIC 6552 Land subdividers & developers, commercial
CEO: Vincent Signorello
*Pr: Jose Hevia
*Pr: Rafael Rodon
*CEO: Donald C Robinson
CFO: Jason Bewley
*CFO: M Bruce Snyder
*Treas: Juan Godoy
*Ex VP: Kolleen O P Cobb
*Ex VP: Eric D Swanson
*Ex VP: Keith A Tickell
*Sr VP: Michael A Bradish
*VP: Cobb Kolleen

D-U-N-S 00-692-3627
FLORIDA EAST COAST RAILWAY LLC
FEC
(*Suby of* FECR RAIL CORP) ★
7411 Fullerton St Ste 300, Jacksonville, FL 32256-3629
Tel (904) 538-6100 *Founded/Ownrshp* 2007
Sales 112.0MM^E *EMP* 525
SIC 4011 Railroads, line-haul operating
CEO: James R Hertwig
Pr: John Brenholt
*Ex VP: Joel Haka
*Sr VP: Fran Chinnici
Sr VP: Francis J Chinnici
*Sr VP: Andrew Westhoff
*VP: Kim Cooper
VP: Lester Hightower
VP Sls: Bradley S Hall
VP Sls: Ray Stephens
VP Sls: Peter Touesnard

D-U-N-S 08-965-7068
FLORIDA FARM BUREAU GENERAL INSURANCE CO
FARM BUREAU INSURANCE
(*Suby of* FARM BUREAU INSURANCE) ★
5700 Sw 34th St, Gainesville, FL 32608-5300
Tel (352) 378-1321 *Founded/Ownrshp* 1974
Sales NA *EMP* 249^E
SIC 6411 Insurance agents, brokers & service
CEO: William Courtney
*Pr: John Hoblick
*CFO: Mike Hill
VP: Matt Packham
Info Man: Gerald McDonough

D-U-N-S 00-692-4518 IMP
FLORIDA GAS TRANSMISSION CO LLC
PANHANDLE ENERGY
(*Suby of* CITRUS CORP) ★
1300 Main St, Houston, TX 77002-6803
Tel (713) 989-7000 *Founded/Ownrshp* 1984
Sales 337.6MM^E *EMP* 450
SIC 4923 Gas transmission & distribution
CEO: Marshall S McCrea III
COO: Eric D Herschmann
*CFO: Martin Salinas Jr
Sr VP: Steve Hotte
*VP: Michael J Doss
Dir Risk M: Paul Clayton
Dir IT: Andy Brady
IT Man: Kevin Dumas
Opers Mgr: Dave Roybal

D-U-N-S 83-447-7051
FLORIDA GULF COAST UNIVERSITY
WGCU TV
(*Suby of* BOARD GOVERNORS GENERAL OFFICE) ★
10501 Fgcu Blvd S, Fort Myers, FL 33965-6565
Tel (239) 590-1000 *Founded/Ownrshp* 1994
Sales 144.7MM^E *EMP* 1,000^E
SIC 8221 Professional schools
Pr: Wilson G Bradshaw
CFO: Gerard Carrington
Ofcr: Kim Edwards
Ofcr: Joseph Germano
Ofcr: Brian Jones
Ofcr: James Slapp
Assoc VP: Charles McBride
*VP: Steve Magiera
VP: Ronald Toll
Dir Teleco: Neal N Snyder
Assoc Dir: Tamara Tassler

D-U-N-S 01-081-4408
FLORIDA HEALTH CARE PLAN INC
(*Suby of* BLUE CROSS AND BLUE SHIELD OF FLORIDA INC) ★
1340 Ridgewood Ave, Holly Hill, FL 32117-2360
Tel (386) 615-4022 *Founded/Ownrshp* 2009
Sales NA *EMP* 800
SIC 6324 Health maintenance organization (HMO), insurance only
CEO: Edward F Simpson Jr
COO: Gary Klein
*CFO: David Schandel
Ofcr: Rob Gilliland
Software D: Dan Maxwell

Netwrk Eng: Philip Kochanski
Mktg Dir: Cindy Martinez
Doctor: Wesley Driggers
Pharmcst: Dave Fox
Counsel: Adam Dunn

D-U-N-S 00-140-9994 IMP
FLORIDA HEALTH SCIENCES CENTER INC (FL)
TAMPA GENERAL HEALTHCARE
1 Tampa General Cir, Tampa, FL 33606-3571
Tel (813) 844-7000 *Founded/Ownrshp* 1997
Sales 1.0MMM *EMP* 6,000
SIC 8062 Hospital, medical school affiliated with residency
CEO: James R Burkhart
*CEO: Jjames R Burkhart
COO: Marvin Kurtz
COO: Mary J Pennino
*CFO: Steve Short
CFO: Joanne Strobbe
Bd of Dir: Lansing Scriven
Ofcr: Kathi K Sengin
Ex VP: Calbin Gilebewell
*Ex VP: Deana L Nelson
*VP: Janet Davis
VP: Steve Durbin
*VP: Marcos F Lorenzo
*VP: Jean M Mayer
*VP: Judith M Ploszek
*VP: Joseph D Resnick
*VP: David Robbins
VP: Jon Soliz
Dir Risk M: Bonnie Conrad
Dir Risk M: Julia Kauzlarich
Dir Risk M: Sherry L Swan

D-U-N-S 83-543-8086
FLORIDA HEALTHY KIDS CORP
661 E Jefferson St # 200, Tallahassee, FL 32301-2788
Tel (850) 701-6160 *Founded/Ownrshp* 1990
Sales NA *EMP* 31
SIC 6321 Health insurance carriers
CEO: Rich Robleto
*Ch: Wendy Link
*Sec: John Benz
*VP: Lester Abberger
*Prin: David Marcus MD
Ex Dir: Pamela J Stokes
IT Man: Miles Lee
Corp Couns: Steven Malono

FLORIDA HEAT PUMP
See FHP MANUFACTURING CO

FLORIDA HOSPITAL DELAND
See MEMORIAL HOSPITAL - WEST VOLUSIA INC

FLORIDA HOSPITAL FLAGLER
See MEMORIAL HOSPITAL FLAGLER INC

D-U-N-S 00-274-0066
FLORIDA HOSPITAL HEARTLAND MEDICAL CENTER
ADVENTIST HEALTH SYSTEM SUNBEL
(*Suby of* ADVENTST HLTH SYSTM SUNBELT H) ★
4200 Sun N Lake Blvd, Sebring, FL 33872-1986
Tel (863) 314-4466 *Founded/Ownrshp* 1949
Sales 193.7MM *EMP* 1,200
SIC 8062 General medical & surgical hospitals
CEO: Brian Adams
Chf Path: Dini H Rada
*CFO: Dima Didenko

D-U-N-S 17-243-5521
FLORIDA HOSPITAL MEDICAL CENTER INC
FLORIDA HOSPITAL ORLANDO
(*Suby of* ADVENTST HLTH SYSTM SUNBELT H) ★
601 E Rollins St, Orlando, FL 32803-1273
Tel (407) 303-5600 *Founded/Ownrshp* 2015
Sales 602.5MM^E *EMP* 7,200
SIC 8062 General medical & surgical hospitals
Pr: Donald L Jernigan
Chf Mktg O: Judy Bond
Ofcr: Lisa Bowman
VP: Ed Majors
Dir Lab: Susana Savino
Dir Rad: Roland Rynos
Dir Rx: Alan Brenia
Dir Rx: Candice Morris
Adm Dir: Don Bartlett
Adm Dir: Lynn Janzen
Genl Mgr: Michelle Dolske

D-U-N-S 82-568-6504
FLORIDA HOSPITAL MEDICAL GROUP INC
FHGM
2600 Westhall Ln, Maitland, FL 32751-7102
Tel (407) 200-2700 *Founded/Ownrshp* 1993
Sales 363.6MM *EMP* 350
SIC 8011 General & family practice, physician/surgeon
Pr: Terry Owen
*Pr: Bryan Stiltz
Plas Surg: Jason Junker
Diag Rad: Josiah Bancroft
Diag Rad: Chiu-Jen P Hsu
Diag Rad: Russell N Nusynowitz
Diag Rad: Bradford R Uricchio
Diag Rad: Charles E Walbroel
Diag Rad: Wayne W Windham

FLORIDA HOSPITAL MEM MED CTR
See MEMORIAL HEALTH SYSTEMS INC

D-U-N-S 19-672-6140
FLORIDA HOSPITAL MEMORIAL FOUNDATION
305 Memorial Medical Pkwy # 212, Daytona Beach, FL 32117-5168
Tel (386) 615-4144 *Founded/Ownrshp* 2005
Sales 164.6MM *EMP* 3
SIC 7389 Fund raising organizations
Ex Dir: Juile Rand

FLORIDA HOSPITAL NEW SMYRNA
See SOUTHEAST VOLUSIA HEALTHCARE CORP

FLORIDA HOSPITAL NORTH PINELLA
See TARPON SPRINGS HOSPITAL FOUNDATION INC

FLORIDA HOSPITAL ORLANDO
See FLORIDA HOSPITAL MEDICAL CENTER INC

FLORIDA HOSPITAL TAMPA
See UNIVERSITY COMMUNITY HOSPITAL INC

D-U-N-S 79-544-5683
FLORIDA HOSPITAL WATERMAN INC
(*Suby of* ADVENTST HLTH SYSTM SUNBELT H) ★
1000 Waterman Way, Tavares, FL 32778-5266
Tel (352) 253-3333 *Founded/Ownrshp* 1992
Sales 225.1MM *EMP* 1,200
SIC 8062 General medical & surgical hospitals
CEO: David Ottati
CFO: Fran Counk
VP: Carrie Fish
VP: Edlyn Hernandez
VP: Vinay Mehindru
Dir OR: Heather Wood
Dir Lab: Wanda Rodriguez
Dir Rx: James Barnes
Dir IT: Cara Anderson
Pathlgst: Chris Kechriotis
Ansthlgy: Kenneth A Buddendorff

D-U-N-S 01-165-6414
FLORIDA HOSPITAL WESLEY CHAPEL INC
(*Suby of* ADVENTST HLTH SYSTM SUNBELT H) ★
2600 Bruce B Downs Blvd, Wesley Chapel, FL 33544-9207
Tel (813) 929-5000 *Founded/Ownrshp* 2005
Sales 165.7MM *EMP* 1[E]
SIC 8062 General medical & surgical hospitals
Pr: Jeff Bromme

D-U-N-S 55-648-0478
FLORIDA HOSPITAL ZEPHYRHILLS
37924 Medical Arts Ct, Zephyrhills, FL 33541-4323
Tel (813) 779-1900 *Founded/Ownrshp* 2005
Sales 151.0MM *EMP* 14[E]
SIC 8062 General medical & surgical hospitals
Owner: U Khin MD

D-U-N-S 13-195-4869
FLORIDA HOSPITAL ZEPHYRHILLS INC
ADVENTIST HLTH SYSTEM/SUNBELT
(*Suby of* ADVENTST HLTH SYSTM SUNBELT H) ★
7050 Gall Blvd, Zephyrhills, FL 33541-1347
Tel (813) 788-0411 *Founded/Ownrshp* 1998
Sales 133.1MM *EMP* 1,200
SIC 8062 General medical & surgical hospitals
Pr: Don Jernigan
**Pr:* Douglas Duffield
**CFO:* Donald Welch
**Ch:* Michael Schultz
VP: Sylvia Brown
Dir Lab: Ronald Uzarraga
Dir Rx: Alan Brenia
**Prin:* Scott Pittman
MIS Dir: Kelley Sasser
Cmptr Lab: Maria Roig
Dir IT: Carl Olson

D-U-N-S 17-892-9436
FLORIDA HOUSING FINANCE CORP
227 N Bronough St # 5000, Tallahassee, FL 32301-1367
Tel (850) 488-4197 *Founded/Ownrshp* 1981
Sales NA *EMP* 130
Accts Ernst & Young Llp Orlando Fl
SIC 6162 Bond & mortgage companies
Ex Dir: Stephen Auger
CFO: Barbara Goltz
DP Exec: Debbie Roberts

D-U-N-S 05-339-6669
FLORIDA INSTITUTE OF TECHNOLOGY INC
FLORIDA TECH
150 W University Blvd Ofc, Melbourne, FL 32901-6975
Tel (321) 674-8000 *Founded/Ownrshp* 1958
Sales 194.4MM *EMP* 1,100
Accts Berman Hopkins Wright & Laham
SIC 8221 4581 8299 University; Airports, flying fields & services; Flying instruction
Pr: Anthony J Catanese
CFO: Raymond Bonhomme
**Treas:* Robert E Niebuhr
Ofcr: Greg Peebles
Assoc VP: Richard Newman
**VP:* Joseph Armul
Exec: Nabil Matar
Assoc Dir: Stephanie Enstice
Assoc Dir: Curtis Robinson
**Prin:* Brenda Brown
**Prin:* Dwayne McCay

D-U-N-S 07-129-8814
FLORIDA INTERNATIONAL UNIVERSITY
BOARD OF GOVRS STATE UNIV
(*Suby of* BOARD GOVERNORS GENERAL OFFICE) ★
11200 Sw 8th St, Miami, FL 33199-2516
Tel (305) 348-2494 *Founded/Ownrshp* 1965
Sales 490.4MM *EMP* 4,000
Accts David W Martin Cpa Tallahas
SIC 8221 University
Pr: Mark Rosen
**Pr:* Mark Rosenberg
**CFO:* Kenneth Jessell
Trst: Albert E Dotson
Trst: Rosa Sugra Es
Trst: Miriam Lypez
Sr VP: Kenneth A Jessell
VP: Min Yao
Exec: Denisse V Aranda
Dir Lab: Mayra Exposito
Dir Lab: Alvaro Velandia
Assoc Dir: Sherry Carrillo
Assoc Dir: Libby Kirsch
Assoc Dir: George Philippidis

D-U-N-S 06-785-5031 EXP
FLORIDA IRRIGATION SUPPLY INC (FL)
F I S OUTDOOR
300 Central Park Dr, Sanford, FL 32771-6671
Tel (407) 425-6669 *Founded/Ownrshp* 1974
Sales 111.9MM[E] *EMP* 200
SIC 5084 Pumps & pumping equipment
Pr: Jon D Tanner
Brnch Mgr: Kevin Cox
Sales Asso: Brian McIntire

D-U-N-S 00-797-5741 IMP/EXP
FLORIDA KEYS ELECTRIC COOPERATIVE ASSOCIATION INC (FL)
91630 Overseas Hwy, Tavernier, FL 33070
Tel (305) 852-2431 *Founded/Ownrshp* 1940
Sales 85.5MM *EMP* 119
Accts Bolinger Segars Gilbert & Mo
SIC 4911 1731 1623 Distribution, electric power; Electrical work; Water, sewer & utility lines
CEO: Scott Newberry
**Pr:* David Ritz
**CFO:* Cris Beaty
**Treas:* Frank Hawkin
Bd of Dir: George Hertel
**VP:* Gretchen Holland

D-U-N-S 03-277-6163 IMP/EXP
FLORIDA LIFT SYSTEMS LLC (FL)
SOUTHERN STATES TOYOTA LIFT
115 S 78th St, Tampa, FL 33619-4220
Tel (904) 764-7662 *Founded/Ownrshp* 1954
Sales 93.9MM[E] *EMP* 152
SIC 5084 7359 7699 Lift trucks & parts; Materials handling machinery; Industrial truck rental; Customizing services
Pr: Jeffrey Fischer
**CFO:* Robert Ogilbee
Genl Mgr: David Bailey
Genl Mgr: Robert Budd
Genl Mgr: Mike Parker
DP Exec: Micheal Baldwin
Sls Mgr: Kevin Callahan

FLORIDA MED CLINIC
See FLORIDA MEDICAL CLINIC PA

D-U-N-S 80-814-8902
FLORIDA MEDICAL CLINIC PA
FLORIDA MED CLINIC
38135 Market Sq, Zephyrhills, FL 33542-7505
Tel (813) 780-8440 *Founded/Ownrshp* 1992
Sales 113.4MM[E] *EMP* 750
SIC 8011 Clinic, operated by physicians
CEO: Joe Delatorre
**Pr:* Paul E Hughes MD
CFO: Chris Alvarez
**CFO:* Colleen H Cuffe
**Treas:* Chandresh S Saraiya MD
Dir Lab: Jim Stout
Off Mgr: Beverly Thibodeau

D-U-N-S 79-832-6856
FLORIDA MUNICIPAL POWER AGENCY
8553 Commodity Cir, Orlando, FL 32819-9002
Tel (407) 355-7767 *Founded/Ownrshp* 1978
Sales 613.1MM *EMP* 67
Accts Purvis Gray And Company Llp
SIC 4911 Electric services
CEO: Nicholas P Guarriello
V Ch: Paul Kalv
**Ch:* Howard McKinnon
Ofcr: Frank Gaffney
Off Mgr: Karen Culpepper
IT Man: Steven Ruppel
Sftwr Eng: Jeff Hanson
Genl Couns: Frederick M Bryant
Counsel: Jody Finklea

FLORIDA NATIONAL GUARD
See FLORIDA DEPARTMENT OF MILITARY

FLORIDA NO - FAULT
See DIRECT GENERAL CORP

D-U-N-S 07-883-5791
FLORIDA OFFICE OF ATTORNEY GENERAL
(*Suby of* ATTORNEY GENERAL) ★
Pl-01 The Capitol, Tallahassee, FL 32399-0001
Tel (850) 414-3300 *Founded/Ownrshp* 2013
Sales NA *EMP* 1,200
SIC 9222

D-U-N-S 07-883-8551
FLORIDA PENINSULA HOLDINGS LLC
903 Nw 65th St Ste 200, Boca Raton, FL 33487-2864
Tel (561) 210-0370 *Founded/Ownrshp* 2005
Sales NA *EMP* 100
SIC 6411

D-U-N-S 00-692-2371 IMP
■ **FLORIDA POWER & LIGHT CO INC** (FL)
FPL
(*Suby of* NEXTERA ENERGY INC) ★
700 Universe Blvd, Juno Beach, FL 33408-2683
Tel (561) 694-4000 *Founded/Ownrshp* 1925
Sales 11.6MMM *EMP* 8,800
Accts Deloitte & Touche Llp Boca R
SIC 4911 Generation, electric power; Transmission, electric power; Distribution, electric power
Pr: Eric E Silagy
**Ch Bd:* James L Robo
COO: John Ketchum
**CFO:* Moray P Dewhurst
Treas: Paul I Cutler
Ex VP: Deborah H Caplan
Ex VP: Jerry Crescenti
Ex VP: Theodore Granger
Ex VP: Robert L McGrath
Ex VP: Charles E Sieving
Sr VP: Douglas Cooper
Sr VP: Anthonio Rodriguez
VP: Maria Fogarty
VP: Michael Kiley
VP: Manny Miranda

D-U-N-S 00-405-7204 IMP
FLORIDA PRODUCTION ENGINEERING INC (OH)
AUTOMOTIVE MFG & INDUS PDT
(*Suby of* EG INDUSTRIES) ★
2 E Tower Cir, Ormond Beach, FL 32174-8759
Tel (386) 677-2566 *Founded/Ownrshp* 1987
Sales 189.7MM[E] *EMP* 753
SIC 3465 3089 Moldings or trim, automobile: stamped metal; Injection molded finished plastic products; Injection molding of plastics; Automotive parts, plastic
Pr: Larry Jutte
**COO:* Derrick Redding
**Treas:* Samuel T Morgan
VP: Bill Burea
**VP:* Vinc E Ellerbrock
VP: Larry Francis
**Prin:* Brad Gotts
IT Man: Chris Hoch
IT Man: Chris Kane
Pgrm Dir: Ryan Copp

D-U-N-S 03-262-8596
■ **FLORIDA PROGRESS CORP**
PROGRESS ENERGY FLORIDA
(*Suby of* PROGRESS ENERGY INC) ★
410 S Wilmington St, Raleigh, NC 27601-1849
Tel (919) 546-6111 *Founded/Ownrshp* 2000
Sales 4.9MMM[E] *EMP* 11,000
SIC 1221 4911 4011 4449 Bituminous coal & lignite-surface mining; Generation, electric power; Railroads, line-haul operating; River transportation, except on the St. Lawrence Seaway
CEO: Richard D Keller
Bd of Dir: H W Habermeyer
**Ex VP:* William D Johnson
**Ex VP:* Robert B McGehee
**Ex VP:* Peter M Scott III

D-U-N-S 00-692-4427
■ **FLORIDA PUBLIC UTILITIES CO** (FL)
(*Suby of* CHESAPEAKE UTILITIES CORP) ★
331 W Central Ave Ste 200, Winter Haven, FL 33880-2977
Tel (352) 447-2790 *Founded/Ownrshp* 1929, 2009
Sales 219.0MM[E] *EMP* 305[E]
SIC 4911 4922 5984 Distribution, electric power; Transmission, electric power; Natural gas transmission; Propane gas, bottled
CEO: Michael P McMasters
**Pr:* Jeff Householder
**COO:* Stephen C Thompson
**CFO:* Beth W Cooper
**Treas:* Matthew M Kim
**Treas:* Thomas E Mahn
Ex VP: Drane Shelley
VP: Jeffrey S Sylvester
**VP:* Kevin J Webber
Dist Mgr: Keith Pomeroy
Genl Mgr: P Mark Cutshaw

D-U-N-S 05-977-7110
■ **FLORIDA ROCK & TANK LINES INC**
(*Suby of* PATRIOT TRANSPORTATION HOLDING INC) ★
200 W Forsyth St 7th, Jacksonville, FL 32202-4349
Tel (904) 396-5733 *Founded/Ownrshp* 1990
Sales 127.5MM *EMP* 600
SIC 4213 4212 Liquid petroleum transport, non-local; Petroleum haulage, local
Pr: Robert E Sandlin
**Treas:* Ray Van Landingham
VP: Jim Anderson
**VP:* John D Baker II
**VP:* Henry Mabbett

D-U-N-S 00-985-7855 IMP/EXP
■ **FLORIDA ROCK INDUSTRIES**
VULCAN MTLS CO VESTAVIA AL
(*Suby of* VULCAN MATERIALS CO) ★
4707 Gordon St, Jacksonville, FL 32216-4037
Tel (904) 355-1781 *Founded/Ownrshp* 2007
Sales 201.3MM[E] *EMP* 400
SIC 1422 Crushed & broken limestone; Lime rock, ground
Pr: Thompson Baker II
Pr: Hill J T
CFO: John D Milton Jr
Bd of Dir: Richard O'Brien
Bd of Dir: Donald Rice
Bd of Dir: Orin Smith
VP: Michael P Oates
VP: Wallace A Patzke Jr
Dir IT: Ross George
IT Man: Sonia Vaird
Sfty Mgr: William Walton
Board of Directors: John D Baker II

D-U-N-S 86-947-2647 IMP
■ **FLORIDA RSA 8 INC**
(*Suby of* UNITED STATES CELLULAR CORP) ★
8410 W Bryn Mawr Ave # 700, Chicago, IL 60631-3408
Tel (773) 399-8900 *Founded/Ownrshp* 1983
Sales 1.7MMM[E] *EMP* 6,100
SIC 4812 Radio telephone communication
CFO: Kenneth R Meyers
Ofcr: Alicia Dusza
Ofcr: Lori Lehnhardt
VP: Brenda Heinrich
VP: Glenn Peterson
Exec: Jordan Williams
Assoc Dir: Duygu Erdemgil
Comm Man: Chelsea Whittington
Ex Dir: Renee Erregragui
Ex Dir: Demetra King
Prgrm Mgr: Alexander Ewy

D-U-N-S 11-261-5880
FLORIDA SCHOOL CHOICE
4655 Salisbury Rd Ste 400, Jacksonville, FL 32256-0958
Tel (800) 447-1636 *Founded/Ownrshp* 2003
Sales 267.7MM *EMP* 10
SIC 8211 Private elementary & secondary schools
Prin: Michele Cuteri

D-U-N-S 06-965-3657
FLORIDA SOUTHERN COLLEGE
111 Lake Hollingsworth Dr, Lakeland, FL 33801-5698
Tel (863) 680-4111 *Founded/Ownrshp* 1934
Sales 103.5MM *EMP* 553
Accts Cliftonlarsonallen Llp Orland
SIC 8221 College, except junior
Pr: Anne Kerr
CFO: V Dennis
**VP:* Susan Conner
VP: V Terry Dennis
Dir Lab: Kathy Moss
Off Mgr: Violet McCormick
Mktg Dir: Kate Farley

D-U-N-S 08-323-7656
FLORIDA STATE COLLEGE AT JACKSONVILLE
501 W State St Ste 307, Jacksonville, FL 32202-4030
Tel (904) 632-3251 *Founded/Ownrshp* 1966
Sales 194.0MM[E] *EMP* 2,350
SIC 8221 College, except junior
Pr: Willis Holcombe
Pr: Dr Cynthia Bioteau
CFO: Cleve Warren
VP: Judith Bilsky
IT Man: Carol Kelly
IT Man: Dennis Lewis
Sftwr Eng: Mitchell Chin
Sftwr Eng: Kyle Lavalley
Opers Mgr: Richard Shierling

FLORIDA STATE COURT SYSTEM
See STATE OF FLORIDA OF JUDICIARY COURTS

D-U-N-S 07-313-5428
FLORIDA STATE UNIVERSITY (FL)
FSU
(*Suby of* BOARD GOVERNORS GENERAL OFFICE) ★
600 W College Ave, Tallahassee, FL 32306-1096
Tel (850) 644-5482 *Founded/Ownrshp* 1851
Sales 706.9MM *EMP* 13,497[E]
Accts Davie W Martin Cpa Tallahas
SIC 8221 University
Pr: Eric Barron
Pr: Jennifer Buchanan
Trst: Emily Fleming Duda
Trst: Leslie Pantin
Trst: Jayne Standley
Ofcr: Katherine Hibbard
Ofcr: Jim Smith
**Ex VP:* Lawrence Abele
**Sr VP:* John R Carnaghi
VP: Ralph Alvarez
VP: Dennis Bailey
VP: Robert Bradley
VP: Lee F Hinkle
VP: Kirby W Kemper
VP: Paul Strouts
Comm Dir: Christi Morgan
Dir Bus: David Leeka

FLORIDA TAX CREDIT SCHOLARSHIP
See STEP UP FOR STUDENTS INC

FLORIDA TECH
See FLORIDA INSTITUTE OF TECHNOLOGY INC

FLORIDA TECHNICAL COLLEGE
See INSTITUTO DE BANCA Y COMERCIO INC

FLORIDA TILE CERAMIC CENTER
See FLORIDA TILE INC

D-U-N-S 00-409-1583 IMP/EXP
FLORIDA TILE INC
FLORIDA TILE CERAMIC CENTER
998 Governors Ln Ste 300, Lexington, KY 40513-1184
Tel (859) 219-5200 *Founded/Ownrshp* 1954, 2004
Sales 148.2MM[E] *EMP* 400
SIC 3253 Wall tile, ceramic; Floor tile, ceramic
Ch: Giuliano Pini
Pr: Emilio Mussini
CEO: Michael Franceschelli
CFO: Luca Leonardi
Ex VP: Massimo Barbari
Ex VP: Bernie Schwartz
Exec: Luca Setti
Rgnl Mgr: Jason Wahl
Manager: Jon Hulshof
Sales Asso: Jacob Loudon

D-U-N-S 94-348-3016
FLORIDA TOURISM INDUSTRY MARKETING CORP
VISIT FLORIDA
2450 W Exec Ctr Cir 200, Tallahassee, FL 32301
Tel (850) 488-5607 *Founded/Ownrshp* 1996
Sales 94.9MM *EMP* 101
Accts Thomas Howell Ferguson Pa Tal
SIC 4724 8743 8742 Travel agencies; Promotion service; Management consulting services
CEO: Chris Thompson
**CFO:* Evangeline McCorvey
VP: Susannah Costello
VP: Cdme K Faulk
VP: Alfredo Gonzalez
VP: Vangie McCorvey
Off Admin: Lisa Strickland
Dir IT: Jeff Brewer
VP Sls: Eileen Forrow
Sls Mgr: Steven Bonda

D-U-N-S 07-861-0308
FLORIDA VEG INVESTMENTS LLC
MR. GREEN PRODUCE
7350 Nw 30th Ave, Miami, FL 33147-5902
Tel (305) 836-3152 *Founded/Ownrshp* 2016, 2003
Sales 125.0MM[E] *EMP* 155[E]
SIC 5148 Fresh fruits & vegetables

D-U-N-S 78-136-7359
FLORIDA VIRTUAL SCHOOL
5401 S Kirkman Rd Ste 550, Orlando, FL 32819-7932
Tel (407) 857-6588 *Founded/Ownrshp* 2006
Sales 66.1MM[E] *EMP* 1,500
SIC 8211
CEO: Ronald Blocker
Co-Ownr: Larry Banks
Owner: Julie Young
COO: William Gordon
COO: Shantana Johnson
CFO: John Pavelchak
Ex VP: Jodi Marshall
Exec: Matt Vangalis
CIO: Conrad Cross
CTO: Janet Rossi
IT Man: Randall Bronson

FLORIDA'S BLOOD CENTER
See ONEBLOOD FOUNDATION INC

D-U-N-S 01-050-7929
FLORIDAS BLOOD CENTERS INC
8669 Commodity Cir Lbby, Orlando, FL 32819-9003
Tel (407) 226-3800 *Founded/Ownrshp* 1976
Sales NA *EMP* 1,000
SIC 8099

FLORIDA'S NATURAL GROWERS
See CITRUS WORLD INC

D-U-N-S 62-076-2146 IMP
FLORIM USA INC
(*Suby of* FLORIM CERAMICHE SPA)
300 International Blvd, Clarksville, TN 37040-5307
Tel (931) 553-7548 *Founded/Ownrshp* 1901
Sales 128.1MM *EMP* 370^E
SIC 3253 Ceramic wall & floor tile
Pr: Arrigo Zapparoli
**CFO:* Giovanni Grossi
VP: Craig Lampe

D-U-N-S 00-653-9142 IMP
■ **FLORISTS TRANSWORLD DELIVERY INC**
(*Suby of* FTD COMPANIES INC) ★
3113 Woodcreek Dr, Downers Grove, IL 60515-5412
Tel (630) 719-7800 *Founded/Ownrshp* 1994
Sales 215.5MM^E *EMP* 725
SIC 5193 7389 2771 Florists' supplies; Florist telegraph service; Greeting cards
CFO: Becky Sheehan
CFO: Becky A Sheehan
Sls Dir: Carrie Mininni
Board of Directors: Kenneth M Coley, Christopher J D Ainsley, Habib Y Gorgi, Richard B Heroman, Veronica K Ho, Stephen G Kasnet, William P Phelan, Gary K Silberberg

D-U-N-S 15-999-7535 IMP
▲ **FLOTEK INDUSTRIES INC**
10603 W Sam Houston Pkwy, Houston, TX 77064-4660
Tel (713) 849-9911 *Founded/Ownrshp* 1985
Sales 334.3MM *EMP* 540
Accts Hein & Associates Llp Houston
Tkr Sym FTK *Exch* NYS
SIC 2087 2869 2899 3533 3491 Flavoring extracts & syrups; Flavors or flavoring materials, synthetic; Chemical preparations; Drilling tools for gas, oil or water wells; Gas field machinery & equipment; Industrial valves
Ch Bd: John W Chisholm
CFO: Robert M Schmitz
Ex VP: Steven A Reeves
Ex VP: Joshua A Snively Sr
Ex VP: Richard Walton
Sr VP: Robert Fielding
Sr VP: Brad Reeves
Sr VP: Beth Thibodeaux
VP: Jeff Chang
VP: Keith Dismuke
VP: Gary Flock
VP: James A Silas
VP Bus Dev: David Acker
Exec: Jerry Speer

D-U-N-S 00-425-8943 EXP
FLOTURN INC (OH)
4236 Thunderbird Ln, West Chester, OH 45014-5482
Tel (513) 860-8040 *Founded/Ownrshp* 1962, 1988
Sales 93.0MM^E *EMP* 297
SIC 3599 Machine shop, jobbing & repair
Pr: R V Glutting
**CFO:* Don Spillane
IT Man: Bill Scharinger
Sls Dir: Don Miller

D-U-N-S 78-642-1461
FLOUR CITY BAGELS INC
BRUEGGER'S BAGELS
585 Moseley Rd Ste 3, Fairport, NY 14450-3339
Tel (585) 223-0450 *Founded/Ownrshp* 1891
Sales 88.0MM^E *EMP* 654
SIC 5461 2051 Bagels; Bread, cake & related products
CEO: Claude Bergeron
**Ch Bd:* Nord Brue
**Pr:* Kenneth Greene
**COO:* Miguel Fernandez
**CFO:* Robert Parette
**Sr VP:* Donald J Ritacca
**Prin:* Jim Vinz

D-U-N-S 06-141-1120
FLOURNOY DEVELOPMENT CO
900 Brookstone Ctr Pkwy, Columbus, GA 31904-2987
Tel (706) 324-4000 *Founded/Ownrshp* 1999
Sales 88.8MM *EMP* 550
Accts Robinson Grimes & Company P
SIC 6552 1522 8741 Subdividers & developers; Apartment building construction; Condominium construction; Management services
COO: Paul Wieczorek
CFO: John R Akin
VP: Brady Blair
VP: Rod Dalson
VP: Rodney S Dawson
VP: Cathy McRae
VP: Cham Watkins
Dir IT: Scott McDavid
IT Man: Dale Wilkerson
Genl Couns: Jeremy Brewer

D-U-N-S 07-886-1552
FLOW CONTROL US HOLDING CORP
(*Suby of* PENTAIR FINANCE GROUP GMBH)
5500 Wayzata Blvd, Minneapolis, MN 55416-1241
Tel (763) 545-1730 *Founded/Ownrshp* 2012
Sales 2.8MMM^E *EMP* 4,000^E
SIC 3561 Pumps & pumping equipment
Pr: Alok Maskara
**Treas:* Michael Myer
**VP:* Angela Lageson

D-U-N-S 05-406-5057 IMP
FLOW INTERNATIONAL CORP
(*Suby of* SHAPE TECHNOLOGIES GROUP INC) ★
23500 64th Ave S, Kent, WA 98032-2618
Tel (253) 850-3500 *Founded/Ownrshp* 2014
Sales 303.7MM^E *EMP* 680
SIC 3561 Pumps & pumping equipment; Pumps, domestic: water or sump
CEO: David Savage
**Pr:* D Ick Leblanc
Pr: Dick Leblanc
**Pr:* Richard Leblanc
**CFO:* Monique Liard
**Ch:* Jerry L Calhoun
**Treas:* Allen Hsieh
Sr Cor Off: Dan Hillman
Ex VP: Tom Johnson
Sr VP: David Crewe
**VP:* Mike Arena
VP: Chip Burnham
VP: Simon Kenworthy
**VP:* Sally Lowery
VP: Rick Marshall
**VP:* Daric M Schweikart

D-U-N-S 96-226-0985
FLOW TRADERS US LLC
(*Suby of* FLOW TRADERS B.V.)
1140 Avenue Of Americas, New York, NY 10036
Tel (917) 210-5000 *Founded/Ownrshp* 2009
Sales 120.0MM *EMP* 25
SIC 6799 Investment clubs

FLOWER BASKET
See PANHANDLE COOPERATIVE ASSOCIATION

D-U-N-S 05-159-0735
FLOWER CITY PRINTING INC
1725 Mount Read Blvd, Rochester, NY 14606-2827
Tel (585) 663-9000 *Founded/Ownrshp* 1970
Sales 89.6MM^E *EMP* 300
SIC 2657 2752 Folding paperboard boxes; Commercial printing, offset
CEO: George Scharr
Ex VP: Tim Welch
VP: Carin Laniak
Dir IT: Trieu La
IT Man: Todd Haskins
Software D: Brett Mosley
Sfty Dirs: Jeremy Falkner
Sfty Mgr: JP Moulton
Plnt Mgr: Kurt Morrison
Plnt Mgr: Rich Schepler
Prd Mgr: Jim Calamia

D-U-N-S 05-647-5155 IMP/EXP
FLOWER FACTORY INC
FLOWER FACTORY SUPER STORE
5655 Whipple Ave Nw, North Canton, OH 44720-7720
Tel (330) 494-7978 *Founded/Ownrshp* 1981
Sales 140.6MM^E *EMP* 360
SIC 5199

FLOWER FACTORY SUPER STORE
See FLOWER FACTORY INC

D-U-N-S 05-416-3209
FLOWER HOSPITAL (OH)
(*Suby of* PROMEDICA HEALTH SYSTEMS INC) ★
5200 Harroun Rd, Sylvania, OH 43560-2196
Tel (419) 824-1444 *Founded/Ownrshp* 1910, 2000
Sales 222.0MM *EMP* 1,372
SIC 8062 General medical & surgical hospitals
Pr: Kevin Webb
Ofcr: Todd Smith
Ofcr: Gibian Thompson
Dir Lab: Sue Hertz
Chf Nrs Of: Erin Jaynes
QA Dir: Marilyn Lindberg
QA Dir: Rebecca Stevenson
Doctor: Daniel A Welt MD

D-U-N-S 79-608-0356 EXP
■ **FLOWERS BAKERIES LLC**
(*Suby of* FLOWERS FOODS INC) ★
1919 Flowers Cir, Thomasville, GA 31757-1137
Tel (229) 226-9110 *Founded/Ownrshp* 2000
Sales 425.6MM^E *EMP* 125
SIC 2051 2053 Bread, cake & related products; Frozen bakery products, except bread
CEO: Allen L Shiver
**Ex VP:* Bradley Alexander
**Ex VP:* Steve Avera
VP: Lynn Barton
VP: John Chasteen
VP: Robert Hancock
VP: Chuck Rich
VP: Steve Taylor
CIO: Vyto Razminas

FLOWERS BAKERY
See FRANKLIN BAKING CO LLC

FLOWERS BAKERY
See FLOWERS BAKING CO OF BRADENTON LLC

FLOWERS BAKERY
See FLOWERS BAKING CO OF VILLA RICA LLC

D-U-N-S 61-790-7845
■ **FLOWERS BAKING CO OF BRADENTON LLC**
FLOWERS BAKERY
(*Suby of* FLOWERS FOODS INC) ★
6490 Parkland Dr, Sarasota, FL 34243-4036
Tel (941) 758-5656 *Founded/Ownrshp* 1984
Sales 104.0MM^E *EMP* 300
SIC 2051 Bread, all types (white, wheat, rye, etc): fresh or frozen; Rolls, bread type: fresh or frozen
Ex VP: Marta J Turner
Genl Mgr: Nancy Cusimano
Off Mgr: Bill Steves
Sfty Mgr: Bob Brohy
Plnt Mgr: Rich Luciano

D-U-N-S 08-638-5556 IMP/EXP
■ **FLOWERS BAKING CO OF MIAMI LLC** (FL)
(*Suby of* FLOWERS FOODS) ★
17800 Nw Miami Ct, Miami, FL 33169-5092
Tel (305) 652-3416 *Founded/Ownrshp* 1977
Sales 100.0MM *EMP* 99
SIC 2051 5461 Breads, rolls & buns; Bakeries
Treas: Danna Jones
Dir IT: Dave McBride

D-U-N-S 00-810-8953
■ **FLOWERS BAKING CO OF SAN ANTONIO LLC** (TX)
BUTTER KRUST THRIFT SHOP
(*Suby of* FLOWERS FOODS INC) ★
6000 Ne Loop 410, San Antonio, TX 78218-5424
Tel (210) 661-2361 *Founded/Ownrshp* 1994
Sales 209.7MM^E *EMP* 605
SIC 2051 Bread, all types (white, wheat, rye, etc): fresh or frozen; Buns, bread type: fresh or frozen
Pr: Ryan Barrios
**Sec:* Jeff Luce
**VP:* Abel Menchaca
**VP:* Joe Richter
IT Man: Mark Poskon
Sfty Mgr: Eddie Martinez

D-U-N-S 04-285-9751 IMP/EXP
■ **FLOWERS BAKING CO OF THOMASVILLE INC** (GA)
FLOWERS FOODS
(*Suby of* FLOWERS BAKERIES LLC) ★
1919 Flowers Cir, Thomasville, GA 31757-1137
Tel (229) 226-9110 *Founded/Ownrshp* 1983, 1978
Sales 104.8MM^E *EMP* 100
SIC 2051 Bread, all types (white, wheat, rye, etc): fresh or frozen
**Treas:* Deanna Turner
**Ex VP:* Stephen R Avera
**Ex VP:* Michael A Beaty
**Ex VP:* Marta J Turner

D-U-N-S 92-982-9653 IMP
■ **FLOWERS BAKING CO OF VILLA RICA LLC**
FLOWERS BAKERY
(*Suby of* FLOWERS FOODS INC) ★
134 Doyle Mcclain Dr, Villa Rica, GA 30180-1086
Tel (770) 459-2883 *Founded/Ownrshp* 1993
Sales 154.9MM^E *EMP* 447
SIC 2051 Bakery: wholesale or wholesale/retail combined
Pr: Randy Brock
VP: Bobby Priest

FLOWERS BY BACHMAN'S
See BACHMANS INC

FLOWERS FOODS
See FLOWERS BAKING CO OF THOMASVILLE INC

D-U-N-S 00-329-4568 IMP/EXP
▲ **FLOWERS FOODS INC** (GA)
1919 Flowers Cir, Thomasville, GA 31757-1137
Tel (229) 226-9110 *Founded/Ownrshp* 1919
Sales 3.7MMM *EMP* 10,900
Tkr Sym FLO *Exch* NYS
SIC 2051 2052 Bread, cake & related products; Bread, all types (white, wheat, rye, etc): fresh or frozen; Rolls, bread type: fresh or frozen; Cakes, bakery: except frozen; Cookies & crackers
Pr: Allen L Shiver
Ch Bd: George E Deese
Pr: Robert B Hysell
Pr: Joseph G Tashie
Pr: D Keith Wheeler
COO: Bradley K Alexander
CFO: R Steve Kinsey
Treas: Kirk Tolbert
Ofcr: Robert L Benton Jr
Ofcr: Craig Parr
Ofcr: Dan W Stone
Ex VP: Stephen R Avera
Ex VP: Marta Jones Turner
Sr VP: H Mark Courtney
Sr VP: David A Hubbard
Sr VP: Mary Krier
Sr VP: Karyl H Lauder
Sr VP: Tonja Taylor
VP: Leny G Hill
VP: Jt Rieck
VP: Tonja W Taylor
Board of Directors: James T Spear, Joe E Beverly, Melvin T Stith, Franklin L Burke, C Martin Wood III, Rhonda O Gass, Benjamin H Griswold IV, Richard Lan, Margaret G Lewis, Amos R McMullian, Joseph Vincent Shields Jr, David V Singer

FLOWERS HOSPITAL
See TRIAD OF ALABAMA LLC

D-U-N-S 04-998-6144
FLOWERWOOD NURSERY INC
6470 Dauphin Island Pkwy, Mobile, AL 36605-9879
Tel (251) 443-6540 *Founded/Ownrshp* 1946
Sales 125.7MM^E *EMP* 451
SIC 0181 Nursery stock, growing of
Pr: Gregory L Smith Jr
Exec: Eric Kyser
Sales Asso: Vicky Cook
Sales Asso: Rebekah Thomas

D-U-N-S 07-844-5631
FLOWORKS INTERNATIONAL LLC
SHALE-INLAND
515 Post Oak Blvd Ste 800, Houston, TX 77027-9432
Tel (713) 839-1753 *Founded/Ownrshp* 2012
Sales 618.5MM *EMP* 1,220
Accts Pricewaterhousecoopers Llp Ho
SIC 5051 5023 Steel; Stampings, metal; Stainless steel flatware
CEO: Frank Riddick
**Pr:* Keith Barnard
**Pr:* John Higgins
**Pr:* Michael Stanwood
**CFO:* Gary Haire
**Treas:* Rick Hawthorne
**Ex VP:* Rob Broyles
**Ex VP:* Jeff Legrand
**Sr VP:* Herbert Allen
**Sr VP:* Rick Kerrigan
**VP:* Lloyd Boyd
**VP:* Michael Goldberg
VP: Gopal Nadkarni

D-U-N-S 00-424-1550 IMP
▲ **FLOWSERVE CORP** (NY)
5215 N Oconnor Blvd Connor, Irving, TX 75039
Tel (972) 443-6500 *Founded/Ownrshp* 1912
Sales 4.5MMM *EMP* 19,000^E
Tkr Sym FLS *Exch* NYS
SIC 3561 3491 3621 3494 3463 3321 Pumps & pumping equipment; Industrial valves; Pressure valves & regulators, industrial; Regulators (steam fittings); Valves, nuclear; Motors & generators; Valves & pipe fittings; Pump & compressor forgings, nonferrous; Cast iron pipe & fittings
Pr: Mark A Blinn
Pr: Thomas E Ferguson
COO: Thomas L Pajonas
CFO: Karyn F Ovelmen
Treas: Mike Dunn
Treas: John E Roueche
Ofcr: Mark D Dailey
Ofcr: Dave M Stephens
Sr VP: Keith E Gillespie
Sr VP: John H Jacko
Sr VP: Carey A O'Connor
VP: Bob Bruning
VP: Tammy Deible-Huenecke
VP: Tim Hostman
VP: Greg Jeffrey
VP: John Lenander
VP: Dale Reineke
VP: Arnold Wallace
Exec: Kevin Collins
Exec: Kari Krekorian
Board of Directors: James O Rollans, Leif E Darner, William C Rusnack, Gayla J Delly, Lynn Elsenhans, Roger L Fix, John R Friedery, Joseph E Harlan, Rick J Mills, Charles M Rampacek, David E Roberts

D-U-N-S 00-942-8822 IMP/EXP
■ **FLOWSERVE FCD CORP**
(*Suby of* FLOWSERVE CORP) ★
1350 N Mtn Spring Pkwy, Springville, UT 84663-3004
Tel (801) 489-8611 *Founded/Ownrshp* 1987
Sales 223.4MM^E *EMP* 2,000
SIC 3491 Industrial valves; Valves, automatic control
Pr: Lew Kling
**CFO:* Michael D Olsen
VP: Harvey Ghiz
Exec: Karlin Wilkes
Genl Mgr: Craig Ellsworth
CTO: Larry Simonson
Dir IT: Jerry Gorrell
Dir IT: Kevin Linderman
Software D: Nate Higbee
Sfty Mgr: Scott Folster
Sales Exec: Mike Barrera

D-U-N-S 00-535-4493 IMP
■ **FLOWSERVE FSD CORP** (MI)
(*Suby of* FLOWSERVE CORP) ★
2100 Factory St, Kalamazoo, MI 49001-4161
Tel (269) 226-3954 *Founded/Ownrshp* 1912, 1995
Sales 283.1MM^E *EMP* 1,100
SIC 3053 Gaskets, packing & sealing devices
Pr: Mark Boinn
VP: V Adams
VP: William V Adams
VP: Edwin W Carpenter
Area Mgr: Jeff Lester
QA Dir: Hiep Le
Dir IT: Mark McGrath
VP Opers: John Bowden
Mfg Mgr: Otto Castillo
Sls Mgr: Chris Groberg

D-U-N-S 15-538-9083 IMP
■ **FLOWSERVE US INC**
FCD DIVISION
(*Suby of* FLOWSERVE CORP) ★
5215 N Oconnor Blvd Ste, Irving, TX 75039
Tel (972) 443-6500 *Founded/Ownrshp* 1997
Sales 745.4MM^E *EMP* 3,300
SIC 3561 3491 Industrial pumps & parts; Valves, automatic control
CEO: Mark A Blinn
**Pr:* Michael S Staff
**Sr VP:* Mark D Dailey
**Sr VP:* Keith E Gillespie
**Sr VP:* Carey A O'Connor
**VP:* Deborah K Bethune

D-U-N-S 07-486-9967 IMP/EXP
■ **FLOWTRONEX PSI LLC**
(*Suby of* XYLEM INC) ★
10661 Newkirk St, Dallas, TX 75220-2303
Tel (469) 221-1200 *Founded/Ownrshp* 1997
Sales 93.8MM^E *EMP* 280
SIC 3561 3949 3523 3432 Pumps, domestic: water or sump; Sporting & athletic goods; Farm machinery & equipment; Plumbing fixture fittings & trim
Pr: Ken Napolitano
Treas: Robert T Butera
**Treas:* Patel Shashank

D-U-N-S 07-345-8291
FLOYD COUNTY BOARD OF EDUCATION
600 Riverside Pkwy Ne, Rome, GA 30161-2938
Tel (706) 234-1031 *Founded/Ownrshp* 1919
Sales 83.7MM^E *EMP* 1,500
SIC 8211 Public elementary & secondary schools
Ex Dir: Dennis C Abney
Admn Mgr: Mary Alcorn

D-U-N-S 07-989-3874
FLOYD COUNTY SCHOOLS
600 Riverside Pkwy Ne, Rome, GA 30161-2936
Tel (706) 234-1031 *Founded/Ownrshp* 2015
Sales 105.0MM *EMP* 1,400^E
SIC 8211 Public elementary & secondary schools
Teacher Pr: Laura Moon

D-U-N-S 10-002-7218
FLOYD COUNTY SCHOOLS
106 N Front Ave, Prestonsburg, KY 41653-7832
Tel (606) 886-2354 *Founded/Ownrshp* 1900
Sales 72.0MM^E *EMP* 1,200^E
SIC 8211 Public elementary & secondary schools

D-U-N-S 07-586-9594
FLOYD HEALTHCARE MANAGEMENT INC
FLOYD MEDICAL CENTER
304 Turner Mccall Blvd Sw, Rome, GA 30165-5621
Tel (706) 509-5000 *Founded/Ownrshp* 1990
Sales 316.3MM *EMP* 2,400
SIC 8062 General medical & surgical hospitals
Pr: Kurt Stuenkel
Ex VP: Dee B D
Netwrk Eng: Brandon Roberson

FLOYD MEDICAL CENTER
See FLOYD HEALTHCARE MANAGEMENT INC

D-U-N-S 05-682-2091
FLOYD MEMORIAL HOSPITAL AND HEALTH SERVICES
BAPTIST HEALTH FLOYD
1850 State St, New Albany, IN 47150-4990
Tel (812) 944-7701 *Founded/Ownrshp* 1951
Sales 345.0MM *EMP* 1,425
SIC 8062 Hospital, medical school affiliated with nursing & residency
Pr: Daniel Eichenberger
* *CFO:* Ted Miller
* *VP:* Sue Christopher
* *VP:* Mark Truman
Dir Lab: Linda Snelling
Ansthlgy: Arthur G Duncan
Ansthlgy: Tom Ricke
Doctor: Jack McClosky
Pgrm Dir: Christina Marietta

D-U-N-S 06-335-5986 IMP
FLOYD PETERSON CO
PETERSON CHEESE COMPANY
1102 D St Ne, Auburn, WA 98002-4015
Tel (253) 735-0313 *Founded/Ownrshp* 1975
Sales 217.0MM^E *EMP* 160
SIC 5141 5149 5143 Groceries, general line; Specialty food items; Dairy products, except dried or canned
Ch Bd: George Lyden
* *Pr:* Chuck Lyden
Pr: Michelle Stevens
Pr: Lynn Throssell
CFO: Ed Shumpert
Treas: Cub Scout
IT Man: James Brookens
Manager: Pete Pesce
Ql Cn Mgr: Shannon Hatcher
Mktg Dir: Sonia Chandwaney
Sales Asso: Pamela Branum

FLOYD WEST & COMPANY
See BURNS & WILCOX LTD

FLS AUTOMATION
See FLSMIDTH INC

D-U-N-S 01-386-5685
FLS TRANSPORTATION SERVICES INC
(*Suby of* FLS TRANSPORTATION SERVICES LIMITED)
180 N La Salle St # 2950, Chicago, IL 60601-2501
Tel (877) 744-7357 *Founded/Ownrshp* 2007
Sales 350.0MM^E *EMP* 323
SIC 8742 4731 Transportation consultant; Truck transportation brokers
Pr: Michael Flinker

D-U-N-S 78-536-9117 IMP/EXP
FLS US HOLDINGS INC
(*Suby of* FLSMIDTH A/S)
2040 Avenue C, Bethlehem, PA 18017-2118
Tel (610) 264-6011 *Founded/Ownrshp* 2001
Sales 122.7MM^E *EMP* 1,250^E
SIC 3559 3554 3549 3532 3535 Cement making machinery; Paper industries machinery; Metalworking machinery; Crushing, pulverizing & screening equipment; Conveyors & conveying equipment
Prin: Thomas Schulz
VP: David Woodruff
Genl Mgr: Ove Jepsen
S&M/VP: Kumar Rajan

FLSA
See FIRE & LIFE SAFETY AMERICA INC

D-U-N-S 00-239-0011 IMP/EXP
FLSMIDTH INC (DE)
FLS AUTOMATION
(*Suby of* FLSMIDTH A/S)
2040 Avenue C, Bethlehem, PA 18017-2118
Tel (610) 264-6011 *Founded/Ownrshp* 1928, 1965
Sales 341.4MM^E *EMP* 750
SIC 5084

D-U-N-S 03-438-0738 IMP/EXP
FLSMIDTH USA INC
FL SMITH MINERALS
(*Suby of* FLS AUTOMATION) ★
7158 S Flsmidth Dr, Midvale, UT 84047-5559
Tel (801) 871-7000 *Founded/Ownrshp* 2007
Sales 239.8MM^E *EMP* 385^E
SIC 5049 Engineers' equipment & supplies
CEO: Christian Jepsen
CFO: Ben Guren
* *Treas:* Lutz Landmesser
* *VP:* Peter J Flanagan
* *VP:* Pete Flangan
VP: Graham Lawes
* *VP:* George Robles
Off Mgr: Carol Smith
QA Dir: Ryan Radl

D-U-N-S 00-934-5979
FLUID DELIVERY SOLUTIONS LLC
6795 Corp Pkwy Ste 200, Fort Worth, TX 76126
Tel (817) 730-9761 *Founded/Ownrshp* 2010
Sales 364.9MM^E *EMP* 530^E
SIC 4941 Water supply
CEO: Dan Dunkelberg
* *Pr:* Randy Nelson
* *COO:* Lance Lammons
* *CFO:* Philip Kuntz
Off Mgr: Tambre Jones
Opers Supe: Mark Fitchett
Opers Supe: Chris Ward
Opers Mgr: Joshua Warner

Ql Cn Mgr: Rachel Trevino
Natl Sales: Matt Rutter

FLUID DYNAMICS
See PALL FILTRATION AND SEPARATIONS GROUP INC

D-U-N-S 07-830-0747 IMP
■ **FLUID HANDLING LLC**
XYLEM
(*Suby of* XYLEM INC) ★
175 Standard Pkwy, Cheektowaga, NY 14227-1233
Tel (716) 897-2800 *Founded/Ownrshp* 2011
Sales 275.2MM^E *EMP* 1,053
SIC 3561 Pumps & pumping equipment
* *Pr:* Ken Napolitano

D-U-N-S 00-545-2552 IMP/EXP
■ **FLUID MANAGEMENT INC**
FM
(*Suby of* IDEX CORP) ★
1023 Wheeling Rd, Wheeling, IL 60090-5776
Tel (847) 537-0880 *Founded/Ownrshp* 2001
Sales 83.5MM^E *EMP* 510
SIC 3559 Paint making machinery
Ch Bd: Dennis Williams
* *Pr:* Suzanne Burns
* *VP:* Jerry N Derck
* *VP:* Douglas C Lennox
* *VP:* Wayne P Sayatovic
Sftwr Eng: Don Rummelhart
Sftwr Eng: Sharon Spanogle

D-U-N-S 01-287-6241
■ **FLUID ROUTING SOLUTIONS INC**
FRS
(*Suby of* PARK-OHIO INDUSTRIES INC) ★
30000 Stephenson Hwy, Madison Heights, MI 48071-1650
Tel (248) 228-8900 *Founded/Ownrshp* 2015
Sales 236.5MM^E *EMP* 700
SIC 5013 Automotive supplies & parts
CEO: Ravi Dodaballupur
Pr: Bob Fesenmyer
Treas: Greg Robinson
VP: Gerry Darnell
Plnt Mgr: Tim Parys
Ql Cn Mgr: Frank Imes
Ql Cn Mgr: Chester Jones

D-U-N-S 10-145-0922
■ **FLUIDICS INC**
(*Suby of* EMCOR GROUP INC) ★
9815 Roosevelt Blvd Ste A, Philadelphia, PA 19114-1035
Tel (215) 671-7900 *Founded/Ownrshp* 2005
Sales 87.1MM^E *EMP* 300
SIC 1711 Mechanical contractor
CEO: Edward R Quinn
* *Pr:* Ronald M Liberati
* *CFO:* Michael J Iacobucci
CFO: Mike Iacoeucci
* *Sr VP:* Robert K Baranowski
VP: Robert Baranowski
* *VP:* Jack Dobrowolsky
VP: Dan Paulson
Exec: Jacqueline McCusker
Sales Asso: Joe Reilly

D-U-N-S 13-322-3631
▲ **FLUIDIGM CORP**
7000 Shoreline Ct Ste 100, South San Francisco, CA 94080-7603
Tel (650) 266-6000 *Founded/Ownrshp* 1999
Sales 114.7MM *EMP* 584^E
Tkr Sym FLDM *Exch* NGS
SIC 3826 Analytical instruments
CEO: S Christopher Linthwaite
* *Ch Bd:* Samuel D Colella
CFO: Vikram Jog
Ex VP: William M Smith
Ex VP: Marc Unger
VP: Jennifer L Lee
VP: Shiva Natarajan
VP: Bernhard Zimmerman
Assoc Dir: Julie Alipaz
Dir Soc: Tammy Kim
Genl Mgr: Steven C McPhail
Board of Directors: Gerhard F Burbach, Evan Jones, Patrick S Jones, John A Young

D-U-N-S 00-850-0092 IMP/EXP
FLUIDMASTER INC
30800 Rancho Viejo Rd, San Juan Capistrano, CA 92675-1564
Tel (949) 728-2000 *Founded/Ownrshp* 1957
Sales 201.3MM^E *EMP* 700
SIC 3432 3089 Plumbing fixture fittings & trim; Injection molding of plastics
CEO: Robert Anderson Schoepe
* *CFO:* Terry Bland
* *Ex VP:* Robert Connell
VP: Bill Martin
Opers Mgr: Mike Wylly
Ql Cn Mgr: April Jiang
Mktg Dir: David McFarland
Manager: Douglas Harvey
Manager: Janelle Mattern
Sls Mgr: Jeff Peterson

D-U-N-S 00-925-2065 IMP/EXP
■ **FLUKE CORP** (WA)
(*Suby of* FORTIVE CORP) ★
6920 Seaway Blvd, Everett, WA 98203-5829
Tel (425) 446-5400 *Founded/Ownrshp* 1953, 2016
Sales 1.1MMM^E *EMP* 4,159
SIC 3823 5065 7629

D-U-N-S 00-268-7614 IMP/EXP
■ **FLUKE ELECTRONICS CORP**
FLUKE NETWORKS
(*Suby of* FLUKE CORP) ★
6920 Seaway Blvd, Everett, WA 98203-5829
Tel (425) 446-5610 *Founded/Ownrshp* 1997
Sales 459.7MM^E *EMP* 1,500

SIC 3825 3823 Test equipment for electronic & electric measurement; Frequency synthesizers; Volt meters; Multimeters; Industrial process measurement equipment; Data loggers, industrial process type; Thermometers, filled system: industrial process type
Pr: Wes Pringle
* *CFO:* Monti Ackerman
VP: Jim Cavoretto
* *VP:* Paul Heydron
* *VP:* Ernie Lauber
* *VP:* Salvatore Parlatore
* *VP:* Laurence Smith
VP: James Svel
Software D: Guy Bacci
Sls Dir: Charlie Mendenhall
Mktg Mgr: Dan Klimke

D-U-N-S 08-250-4143
■ **FLUKE INTERNATIONAL CORP**
(*Suby of* FLUKE CORP) ★
6920 Seaway Blvd, Everett, WA 98203-5829
Tel (425) 347-6100 *Founded/Ownrshp* 1966
Sales 49.0MM^E *EMP* 1,150
SIC 5063 Electrical apparatus & equipment
Pr: Barbara Hulit
CFO: Monti Ackerman
Mktg Dir: Christopher Rayburn
Manager: Linda Cheever

FLUKE NETWORKS
See FLUKE ELECTRONICS CORP

D-U-N-S 00-690-7190 IMP/EXP
▲ **FLUOR CORP**
6700 Las Colinas Blvd, Irving, TX 75039-2902
Tel (469) 398-7000 *Founded/Ownrshp* 2000
Sales 18.1MMM *EMP* 38,758^E
Accts Ernst & Young Llp Dallas Tex
Tkr Sym FLR *Exch* NYS
SIC 8711 1629 1541 Engineering services; Construction & civil engineering; Structural engineering; Oil refinery construction; Industrial buildings & warehouses; Renovation, remodeling & repairs: industrial buildings; Industrial buildings, new construction; Pharmaceutical manufacturing plant construction
Ch Bd: David T Seaton
Pr: Bruce A Stanski
COO: Peter Oosterveer
CFO: Biggs C Porter
Bd of Dir: Shay Gray
Ex VP: Ray F Barnard
Ex VP: Jose-Luis Bustamante
Ex VP: Garry W Flowers
Ex VP: Glenn C Gilkey
Ex VP: Glenn Gilkey
VP: Steven Borsos
VP: Lisa Bottle
VP: Lou Del Tufo
VP: Robert Free
VP: Claus-Peter Haelsig
VP: Jose Herrero
VP: Otto Kjos
VP: Denis L Menegaz
VP: Arnold Noriega
VP: Kenneth Oscar
VP: Michael Pears
Board of Directors: Lynn C Swann, Peter K Barker, Alan M Bennett, Rosemary T Berkery, Peter J Fluor, Deborah D McWhinney, Armando J Olivera, Joseph W Prueher, Matthew K Rose, Nader H Sultan

D-U-N-S 61-542-2680
■ **FLUOR DANIEL ASIA INC**
(*Suby of* FLUOR DANIEL VENTURE GROUP INC) ★
3 Polaris Way, Aliso Viejo, CA 92656-5338
Tel (949) 349-2000 *Founded/Ownrshp* 1979
Sales 126.8MM *EMP* 4
SIC 6799 Venture capital companies
CEO: David T Seaton

D-U-N-S 04-338-3793 EXP
■ **FLUOR DANIEL CARIBBEAN INC**
(*Suby of* FLUOR DANIEL INTERCONTINENTAL) ★
Metro Office Park St2 1 # 2, Guaynabo, PR 00968
Tel (787) 783-5500 *Founded/Ownrshp* 1964
Sales 241.0MM^E *EMP* 1,200
SIC 1542 1541

D-U-N-S 80-729-0960
■ **FLUOR DANIEL CONSTRUCTION CO**
(*Suby of* FLUOR DANIEL INTERCONTINENTAL) ★
3 Polaris Way, Aliso Viejo, CA 92656-5338
Tel (949) 349-2000 *Founded/Ownrshp* 1988
Sales 3.3MM *EMP* 2,000
SIC 1622 Bridge, tunnel & elevated highway
Pr: Paul Buckham
CFO: Michael Steuert
QC Dir: Ronald Peterson

FLUOR DANIEL INTERCONTINENTAL
See FLUOR ENTERPRISES INC

D-U-N-S 61-536-5608
■ **FLUOR DANIEL VENTURE GROUP INC**
(*Suby of* FLUOR CORP) ★
1 Enterprise, Aliso Viejo, CA 92656-2606
Tel (949) 349-2000 *Founded/Ownrshp* 1968
Sales 126.8MM^E *EMP* 5
SIC 6799 Venture capital companies
Pr: Larry Fisher
* *CFO:* J Michal Conaway
CFO: Michal J Conaway
* *Treas:* Stephen F Hull

D-U-N-S 96-448-4583
FLUOR EMPLOYEE BENEFIT TRUST
6700 Las Colinas Blvd, Irving, TX 75039-2902
Tel (469) 398-7000 *Founded/Ownrshp* 2010
Sales NA *EMP* 2^E
Accts Deloitte Tax Llp Houston Tx
SIC 6411 Insurance agents, brokers & service

D-U-N-S 05-922-0392 IMP/EXP
■ **FLUOR ENTERPRISES INC**
FLUOR DANIEL INTERCONTINENTAL
(*Suby of* FLUOR CORP) ★
6700 Las Colinas Blvd, Irving, TX 75039-2902
Tel (469) 398-7000 *Founded/Ownrshp* 1971

Sales 6.1MMM^E *EMP* 34,799
SIC 1799 8711

D-U-N-S 85-843-4525
■ **FLUOR FEDERAL SERVICES INC**
(*Suby of* FLUOR DANIEL INTERCONTINENTAL) ★
100 Fluor Daniel Dr, Greenville, SC 29607-2761
Tel (864) 281-4400 *Founded/Ownrshp* 1996
Sales 86.7MM^E *EMP* 900
SIC 8711

D-U-N-S 80-809-3350 IMP
■ **FLUOR FEDERAL SOLUTIONS LLC**
(*Suby of* FLUOR CORP) ★
100 Fluor Daniel Dr, Greenville, SC 29607-2761
Tel (864) 281-4400 *Founded/Ownrshp* 2007
Sales 659.1MM^E *EMP* 2,500^E
SIC 4953 Refuse systems
Dir IT: Patrick Pickens

D-U-N-S 94-341-6610
■ **FLUOR HANFORD INC**
(*Suby of* FLUOR DANIEL INTERCONTINENTAL) ★
3160 George Wash Way, Richland, WA 99354-1659
Tel (509) 372-2000 *Founded/Ownrshp* 1995
Sales 1.1MMM^E *EMP* 3,650
SIC 4953

D-U-N-S 01-022-7788
■ **FLUOR INDUSTRIAL SERVICES INC**
(*Suby of* FLUOR DANIEL INTERCONTINENTAL) ★
1 Enterprise, Aliso Viejo, CA 92656-2606
Tel (949) 439-2000 *Founded/Ownrshp* 1986
Sales 9.6MM^E *EMP* 1,000
SIC 7349 Building maintenance services
CEO: David T Seaton

D-U-N-S 61-542-2995 IMP/EXP
■ **FLUOR INTERCONTINENTAL INC**
(*Suby of* FLUOR DANIEL INTERCONTINENTAL) ★
100 Fluor Daniel Dr, Greenville, SC 29607-2761
Tel (864) 281-4400 *Founded/Ownrshp* 1968
Sales 872.0MM^E *EMP* 3,000
SIC 1541 1542

D-U-N-S 83-263-9970
FLUOR-BWXT PORTSMOUTH LLC
1862 Shyville Rd Ste 216, Piketon, OH 45661-9749
Tel (866) 706-6992 *Founded/Ownrshp* 2009
Sales 158.5MM^E *EMP* 1,200
SIC 1795 Wrecking & demolition work
CFO: Tracy Heidelberg
Snr Mgr: Eric Wilson

D-U-N-S 01-644-0306
■ **FLUOR-LANE LLC**
(*Suby of* FLUOR CORP) ★
6315 Bren Mar Dr Ste 250, Alexandria, VA 22312-6349
Tel (571) 480-4641 *Founded/Ownrshp* 2007
Sales 320.0MM *EMP* 100
SIC 8711

D-U-N-S 00-699-2747
■ **FLUSHING BANK**
FLUSHING FINANCIAL
(*Suby of* FLUSHING FINANCIAL CORP) ★
220 Rxr Plz, Flushing, NY 11354
Tel (718) 512-2929 *Founded/Ownrshp* 1994
Sales NA *EMP* 112
SIC 6035 6163 Federal savings banks; Loan brokers
Ch: Gerard P Tully
Pr: Alex Gellerman
* *CEO:* John R Buran
* *COO:* Maria A Grasso
* *CFO:* David W Fry
Ofcr: Marilyn Salerno
Ex VP: Michael Bingold
Ex VP: Ronald Hartmann
* *Ex VP:* Francis W Korzekwinski
Sr VP: Cathy Depasquale
Sr VP: Steven Glass
Sr VP: Robert Kiraly
VP: Steven Arzt
VP: Joseph Baldasare
VP: Johanna Cava
VP: Thomas Clemens
VP: Margaret Coniglio
VP: Anil Datta
VP: Patrick Dolan
VP: Alana Domill
VP: Theodore Kalogiannis

FLUSHING FINANCIAL
See FLUSHING BANK

D-U-N-S 11-190-8752
▲ **FLUSHING FINANCIAL CORP**
220 Rxr Plz, Uniondale, NY 11556-3825
Tel (718) 961-5400 *Founded/Ownrshp* 1994
Sales NA *EMP* 442^E
Tkr Sym FFIC *Exch* NGS
SIC 6035 Federal savings banks
Pr: John R Buran
* *Ch Bd:* John E Roe Sr
COO: Maria A Grasso
CFO: Susan K Cullen
Exec: Francis W Korzekwinski

D-U-N-S 07-275-1001 IMP
FLUSHING HOSPITAL AND MEDICAL CENTER
FLUSHING HOSPITAL MEDICAL CTR
(*Suby of* JAMAICA HOSPITAL) ★
4500 Parsons Blvd, Flushing, NY 11355-2205
Tel (718) 670-5000 *Founded/Ownrshp* 1999
Sales 232.8MM *EMP* 1,568^E
Accts Cohnreznick Llp New York Ny
SIC 8062 General medical & surgical hospitals
Pr: Bruce Flanz
* *CFO:* Mounir F Doss
VP: Frederic I Weinbaum
VP: Eileen Ruggio
VP: Manzar Sassani
Assoc Dir: Stuart M Caplen
Dir Rx: Ole Ortiz
Brnch Mgr: George Vecchione
Off Mgr: Albert Dekki

CIO: Tony Gatto
CTO: Martin Hunter

FLUSHING HOSPITAL MEDICAL CTR
See FLUSHING HOSPITAL AND MEDICAL CENTER

FLY RACING
See WESTERN POWER SPORTS INC

D-U-N-S 00-648-2657
FLYERS ENERGY LLC
OLYMPIAN
2360 Lindbergh St, Auburn, CA 95602-9562
Tel (530) 885-0401 *Founded/Ownrshp* 2002
Sales 137.0MM^E *EMP* 450
SIC 5411 5541 5013 Convenience stores; Filling stations, gasoline; Pumps, oil & gas
**Pt:* David Dwelle
Genl Mgr: Jonathan Billings
Dir IT: Tom Dimercurio
Dir IT: Tom Iftiger
Dir IT: Tom Mercurio
Dir IT: Jack Rhoades
Dir IT: Stephen Traversi
IT Man: Eric Chermari
IT Man: Bill Jackson
IT Man: Brian Jones
IT Man: Bill Lasner

D-U-N-S 11-373-4420 IMP
FLYING FOOD FARE INC
FFG
212 N Sangamon St Ste 1a, Chicago, IL 60607-1722
Tel (312) 243-2122 *Founded/Ownrshp* 1983
Sales 76.8MM^E *EMP* 3,300
SIC 5812 5149 5947 Caterers; Contract food services; Sandwiches; Gift shop
Pr: Sue Ling Gin
CFO: David Cotton

D-U-N-S 00-657-5690 IMP
FLYING FOOD GROUP INC
F F G
212 N Sangamon St Ste 1a, Chicago, IL 60607-1722
Tel (312) 243-2122 *Founded/Ownrshp* 1996
Sales 176.3MM^E *EMP* 3,500
SIC 5812 Caterers
Ch Bd: Sue Ling Gin
**Pr:* Milt Liu
**CEO:* David Cotton
VP: Heather Anderson
Exec: Claude Berre
Genl Mgr: Charles Ott
Dir IT: Todd Siefert
Ql Cn Mgr: Ana Vargas
Board of Directors: David Cotton, Milt Liu

FLYING J
See FJ MANAGEMENT INC

FLYING J
See HIGHWAY SERVICE VENTURES INC

FLYING J TRAVEL PLAZA
See MG OIL CO

FLYING J TRAVEL PLAZA
See CFJ PROPERTIES LLC

D-U-N-S 04-042-2941
FLYNN ENTERPRISES LLC
2203 S Walnut St, Hopkinsville, KY 42240-4648
Tel (270) 886-0223 *Founded/Ownrshp* 1976
Sales 541.6MM^E *EMP* 150
SIC 2325 2339 2337 Dungarees: men's, youths' & boys'; Women's & misses' outerwear; Women's & misses' suits & coats
Pr: Bill R Flynn
VP Admn: Patricia Wagoner
Sls Mgr: Wes Sowards
Board of Directors: Lora Simning

D-U-N-S 79-884-2592
FLYNN PETROLEUM LLC
307 Hartford Tpke, Shrewsbury, MA 01545-4024
Tel (508) 756-7693 *Founded/Ownrshp* 1997
Sales 90.4MM *EMP* 5
Accts C Richard Piasecki Webster
SIC 5172 Petroleum products

D-U-N-S 07-931-0361
FLYNN RESTAURANT GROUP LLC
225 Bush St Ste 1800, San Francisco, CA 94104-4211
Tel (415) 835-9700 *Founded/Ownrshp* 2008
Sales 1.1MMM^E *EMP* 6,082^E
SIC 5812 Fast-food restaurant, chain
CEO: Greg Flynn
Pr: Mark Russell

FM
See FLUID MANAGEMENT INC

FM GLOBAL
See FACTORY MUTUAL INSURANCE CO

FMC
See FLAGSTAFF MEDICAL CENTER INC

D-U-N-S 00-914-6945 IMP/EXP
▲ FMC CORP
2929 Walnut St, Philadelphia, PA 19104-5054
Tel (215) 299-6000 *Founded/Ownrshp* 1928
Sales 3.2MMM *EMP* 6,000
Tkr Sym FMC *Exch* NYS
SIC 2812 2879 2869 Soda ash, sodium carbonate (anhydrous); Agricultural chemicals; Pesticides, agricultural or household; Insecticides, agricultural or household; Fungicides, herbicides; Industrial organic chemicals
Ch Bd: Pierre R Brondeau
Pr: Mark A Douglas
Pr: Eric W Norris
CFO: Paul W Graves
Treas: Thomas C Deas Jr
Ex VP: Frank Smith
Ex VP: Andrea E Utecht
VP: Ralph Alexander
VP: Gilberto Antoniazzi
VP: Michael Dornish
VP: Randy Ellis
VP: Rick Mallory
VP: Amy O'Shea
Board of Directors: Eduardo E Cordeiro, Peter D'aloia, C Scott Greer, Dirk A Kempthorne, Paul J Norris, Robert C Pallash, William H Powell, Vincent R Volpe Jr

D-U-N-S 00-617-7146 IMP/EXP
▲ FMC TECHNOLOGIES INC
5875 N Sam Houston Pkwy W, Houston, TX 77086-1497
Tel (281) 591-4000 *Founded/Ownrshp* 2000
Sales 6.3MMM *EMP* 17,400
Tkr Sym FTI *Exch* NYS
SIC 3533 Oil & gas field machinery
Ch Bd: John T Gremp
Pr: Douglas J Pferdehirt
CFO: Maryann T Mannen
CFO: Maryann T Seaman
Treas: Jay A Nutt
Ex VP: Peter Kinnear
Ex VP: Robert Potter
Ex VP: Maryann Seaman
Sr VP: Tore Halvorsen
Sr VP: Dianne B Ralston
VP: Richard G Alabaster
VP: Bradley D Beitler
VP: Euan Brown
VP: Barry Glickman
VP: Tore H Halvorsen
VP: Ryan Holmgren
VP: Nouhad Jebara
VP: Mark J Scott
VP: David Slavik
VP: Jason Williams

D-U-N-S 06-237-7486 IMP
FMH MATERIAL HANDLING SOLUTIONS INC (NV)
4105 Globeville Rd, Denver, CO 80216-4901
Tel (303) 292-5438 *Founded/Ownrshp* 2002
Sales 83.4MM^E *EMP* 170
SIC 5084 7353 5013 Materials handling machinery; Heavy construction equipment rental; Motor vehicle supplies & new parts
Pr: John L Faulkner
**CFO:* Susan Gates
Treas: Pat Faulkner
Ex VP: Bruce Murray
VP: Susan Cunningham
Mktg Dir: Maria Wagner
Sls Mgr: Matt Albrecht
Sls Mgr: Gilbert Saenz

FMI
See TOLL GLOBAL FORWARDING SCS (USA) INC

D-U-N-S 15-442-8994 IMP/EXP
FMK HOLDINGS LLC
3081 Holcom Ste H 1, Norcross, GA 30071
Tel (413) 736-4554 *Founded/Ownrshp* 2006
Sales 109.4MM^E *EMP* 757
SIC 2631 2621 2672 Pressboard; Specialty papers; Adhesive papers, labels or tapes: from purchased material
CEO: Anthony Maclaurin
Pr: Thomas G Weld
CFO: John Hanley
VP: Stephen F Pfistner

FMOL HEALTH SYSTEM
See ST FRANCIS SPECIALTY HOSPITAL INC

FMOL HEALTH SYSTEM
See OUR LADY OF LOURDES REGIONAL MEDICAL CENTER INC

FMOL HEALTH SYSTEM
See FRANCISCAN MISSIONARIES OF OUR LADY HEALTH SYSTEM INC

D-U-N-S 96-335-3581
FMR CORP
FIDELITY INVESTMENTS
82 Devonshire St, Boston, MA 02109-3605
Tel (617) 563-7000 *Founded/Ownrshp* 1977
Sales 108.5MM^E *EMP* 189^E
SIC 6211 Security brokers & dealers
Pr: James C Curvey
V Ch: Jason Deeble
Pr: Cheryl Muise
CFO: John Lunter
**Treas:* Michael B Fox
Ex VP: Abigail Johnson
Ex VP: Michelle Mayers
Ex VP: Thomas Tesauro
Sr VP: Richard Hart
Sr VP: Jay Savely
Sr VP: Kevin M Smith
Sr VP: Scott Thomas
VP: John Basile
VP: Gary Bernath
VP: Carol Bryant
VP: Mike Burke
VP: Philip Czachorowski
VP: Doris Fritz
VP: Paul Given
VP: Rick Lyman
VP: Manheim Mack

D-U-N-S 09-585-6332 IMP/EXP
FMR LLC
FIDELITY INVESTMENTS
245 Summer St, Boston, MA 02210-1133
Tel (617) 563-7000 *Founded/Ownrshp* 1946
Sales 21.5MMM^E *EMP* 41,350
SIC 6282 6211 6799 6552 6531 Investment advisory service; Brokers, security; Venture capital companies; Land subdividers & developers, commercial; Real estate managers
CEO: Abigail Johnson
Ch Bd: Edward Crosby Johnson
Pr: Charles Morrison
CFO: Stephen P Jonas
Treas: John D Crumrine
V Ch Bd: James C Curvey
Ex VP: Ted Rudich
Sr VP: Michael Askew
VP: Eileen Bird
VP: Maureen Daley
VP: Jon Erickson
VP: Rick Folk
VP: Mary Holland
VP: Robert Jameison
VP: Vincent Loporchio
VP: Philippe Mauldin
VP: Jim McAloon
VP: Steve McCarthy
VP: Matt Nash
VP: Jim Nass
VP: Samantha Oaneil

D-U-N-S 09-840-1086 IMP
FN AMERICA LLC
FNH USA
(*Suby of* FN HERSTAL SA)
7918 Jones Branch Dr # 400, Mc Lean, VA 22102-3337
Tel (703) 288-3500 *Founded/Ownrshp* 2005
Sales 83.5MM^E *EMP* 390^E
SIC 3484 Machine guns or machine gun parts, 30 mm. & below; Rifles or rifle parts, 30 mm. & below
Pr: Mark Cherpes
VP: Phyllis Andes

D-U-N-S 08-063-4595
▲ FNB CORP
1 N Shore Ctr 12 Fdral St, Pittsburgh, PA 15212
Tel (800) 555-5455 *Founded/Ownrshp* 1974
Sales NA *EMP* 3,205^E
Tkr Sym FNB *Exch* NYS
SIC 6022 6021 6162 6411 State commercial banks; National commercial banks; Mortgage bankers & correspondents; Insurance agents, brokers & service
Pr: Vincent J Delie Jr
Ch Bd: Stephen J Gurgovits
Pr: Robert Vester
CFO: Vincent J Calabrese Jr
Chf Cred: Gary L Guerrieri
Bd of Dir: Sheila Stewart
Sr VP: Timothy G Rubritz
VP: Shane Crawford
VP: Renee Laychur
VP: Elaine Mantick
Admn Mgr: Kris Cool
Board of Directors: David L Motley, William B Campbell, Gary L Nalbandian, James D Chiafullo, Heidi A Nicholas, Scott Custer, Arthur J Rooney II, Laura E Ellsworth, John S Stanik, Robert A Hormell, William J Strimbu, David J Malone, D Stephen Martz, Robert J McCarthy Jr, Frank C Mencini

D-U-N-S 11-510-8599
FNF CONSTRUCTION INC
FNF MINING DIVISION
(*Suby of* INFRASTRUCTURE HOLDINGS CO LLC) ★
115 S 48th St, Tempe, AZ 85281-2312
Tel (480) 784-2910 *Founded/Ownrshp* 1984
Sales 159.0MM *EMP* 400
Accts Mcgladrey Llp Phoenix Arizon
SIC 1611 1794 2951 General contractor, highway & street construction; Concrete construction: roads, highways, sidewalks, etc.; Excavation & grading, building construction; Asphalt & asphaltic paving mixtures (not from refineries)
Pr: Matthew W Gully
**CFO:* David Leslie James
**VP:* James Anderson Jr
**VP:* Clifford Ashcroft
**VP:* Tom Billings
**VP:* Robbert Bottcher
**VP:* William B Garrison
**VP:* Byron Hubbard
**VP:* Thomas Kennedy
**VP:* Jason Ruskey
**VP:* Shawn Sheble

FNF MINING DIVISION
See FNF CONSTRUCTION INC

FNH USA
See FN AMERICA LLC

D-U-N-S 92-616-1753
FNS INC
1545 Francisco St, Torrance, CA 90501-1330
Tel (661) 615-2300 *Founded/Ownrshp* 1995
Sales 122.4MM^E *EMP* 220
Accts Choi Kim & Park Llp Los Ang
SIC 4731 Freight forwarding
CEO: Bennett B Koo
CFO: Iris H Shin
Ex Dir: Young Cecil
Opers Mgr: Emily Lee
Mktg Mgr: Yun Bae
Mktg Mgr: Insung Park

D-U-N-S 60-503-9080 IMP/EXP
FOAM FABRICATORS INC
8722 E San Alberto Dr # 200, Scottsdale, AZ 85258-4353
Tel (480) 607-7330 *Founded/Ownrshp* 1997
Sales 85.5MM^E *EMP* 9^E
SIC 3086 Packaging & shipping materials, foamed plastic
CEO: Warren F Florkiewicz
**Pr:* James K Hughes
Exec: Tom Redd
Prin: Mary Tauscher
Dir IT: Jenise O'Rell
VP Sls: Mark Sabolcik

FOAM PAC MATERIALS COMPANY
See STOROPACK INC

D-U-N-S 83-100-5350 IMP/EXP
FOAMEX INTERNATIONAL INC
(*Suby of* FXI FOAMEX INNOVATIONS) ★
1400 N Providence Rd, Media, PA 19063-2043
Tel (610) 744-2300 *Founded/Ownrshp* 1993
Sales 161.4MM^E *EMP* 2,038
SIC 3086 Plastics foam products; Carpet & rug cushions, foamed plastic; Insulation or cushioning material, foamed plastic; Padding, foamed plastic
Pr: John G Johnson Jr
**CFO:* Harold J Earley
Ch: James B Gamache
Treas: George Karpinski
Bd of Dir: David J Lyon
**Ex VP:* Paul A Haslanger
**Ex VP:* Darrell Nance
Sr VP: Robert S Graham
Sr VP: Mark Reid
Sr VP: Fred P Rullo
**VP:* Thomas M Walsh
Board of Directors: Brandon Baer, Robert B Burke, Andrew A Campbell, Seth Charnow, Eugene I Davis, Thomas M Hudgins, Sarah Johnson, Gregory E Poling

D-U-N-S 61-997-1039 IMP
FOAMEX LP
1400 N Providence Rd # 2000, Media, PA 19063-2081
Tel (610) 565-2374 *Founded/Ownrshp* 1990
Sales 457.0MM^E *EMP* 2,668^E
SIC 3086 Plastics foam products; Carpet & rug cushions, foamed plastic; Insulation or cushioning material, foamed plastic; Padding, foamed plastic
Pt: Raymond Maybus
Pr: Gregory Ciston
VP: Thomas Sheehan
VP: Thomas Walsh
Sfty Mgr: John McLaverty

D-U-N-S 14-443-4586
FOC ACQUISITION LLC
FILET OF CHICKEN
(*Suby of* CREO CAPITAL PARTNERS LLC) ★
146 Forest Pkwy Ste B, Forest Park, GA 30297-2020
Tel (404) 361-2201 *Founded/Ownrshp* 2007
Sales 88.0MM^E *EMP* 140
SIC 5142 5421 5144 2092 Poultry, frozen: packaged; Food & freezer plans, meat; Poultry & poultry products; Fresh or frozen packaged fish
QA Dir: Dian Towns
Ql Cn Mgr: Porsche Henry
Sls Mgr: Jimmy Young

D-U-N-S 55-717-8774
FOCUS BRANDS INC
CINNABON
(*Suby of* ROARK CAPITAL GROUP INC) ★
5620 Glenridge Dr, Atlanta, GA 30342-1334
Tel (404) 255-3250 *Founded/Ownrshp* 2000
Sales 483.6MM^E *EMP* 2,479
SIC 5461 5143 6794 Pastries; Frozen dairy desserts; Franchises, selling or licensing
CEO: Steven Arndt
**Ch Bd:* Steve Romanello
Pr: Kat Cole
Pr: Paul Damico
Pr: Bill Dunn
Pr: Geoff Hill
Pr: Bruce Schroder
**CFO:* Michael Dixon
Treas: Michelle Taylor
Chf Mktg O: Gary Bales
Chf Mktg O: Thomas Bartsch
**Ofcr:* Barry Moullet
Ofcr: Martin Wehr
Sr VP: John Barberas
Sr VP: Mario Lopez-Belio
VP: Michael Borreca
VP: Rich Kamph
VP: Richard Kamph
VP: Richard Key
VP: Anissa Mandell
VP: Dean McCaskill

FOCUS COMMUNICATIONS
See FOCUS SERVICES LLC

D-U-N-S 62-236-5109
FOCUS FINANCIAL PARTNERS LLC
825 3rd Ave Fl 27, New York, NY 10022-9508
Tel (646) 519-2456 *Founded/Ownrshp* 2006
Sales 142.5MM^E *EMP* 395
SIC 6799 Investors
CEO: Ruediger Adolf
**CFO:* James Shanahan
Sr VP: Anil Abraham
Sr VP: Michael Paley
**VP:* Leonard Chang
VP: Jennifer Geoghegan
VP: Adam Karasik
**VP:* Rajini Kodialam
VP: Max Mintzer
**VP:* Linda Moore
VP: Antonia Savaria
VP: Anita Venkiteswaran
VP: Vamsi Yadlapati

FOCUS FOOD SERVICES
See FOCUS PRODUCTS GROUP INTERNATIONAL LLC

D-U-N-S 01-779-3860 IMP
FOCUS ON FAMILY
8605 Explorer Dr, Colorado Springs, CO 80920-1051
Tel (719) 531-3300 *Founded/Ownrshp* 1977
Sales 86.5MM *EMP* 750
Accts Capin Crouse Lp Colorado Spri
SIC 8322 Family service agency
CEO: Jim Daly
Pr: Faye Tharp
CFO: Mark Buzzetta
CFO: Dan Mellema
**Ch:* Patrick P Caruana
Bd of Dir: Brian Krause
Sr VP: Glenn Williams
Sr VP: Ronald Wilson
VP: Sandy Bove
**VP:* James C Dobson
VP: John Fuller
VP: Tom Minnery
VP: Kenneth Windebank
Exec: Bill Winter

D-U-N-S 94-946-5079
■ FOCUS POINT PARKING INC
(*Suby of* CENTRAL PARKING SYSTEM INC) ★
14141 W Hwy 290 Ste 700, Austin, TX 78737-9340
Tel (512) 894-3556 *Founded/Ownrshp* 2010
Sales 7.5MM^E *EMP* 1,329^E
SIC 7521 Parking lots
Pr: Clyde B Wilson Jr

D-U-N-S 07-852-8950 IMP
FOCUS PRODUCTS GROUP INTERNATIONAL LLC
FOCUS FOOD SERVICES
300 Knightsbridge Pkwy, Lincolnshire, IL 60069-3625
Tel (800) 238-2253 *Founded/Ownrshp* 2012
Sales 199.0MM[E] *EMP* 225
SIC 5023 Kitchen tools & utensils
CEO: Marc Navarre
COO: Bill Bucklew
COO: Chet Kempinski

D-U-N-S 95-866-8055
FOCUS SERVICES LLC
FOCUS COMMUNICATIONS
4102 S 1900 W, Roy, UT 84067-5600
Tel (801) 393-1635 *Founded/Ownrshp* 1995
Sales 80.9MM[E] *EMP* 1,500
SIC 7389 Telemarketing services
Pr: John Porter
**VP:* Johanna Jorgenson
**VP:* Bill Wiser
**VP Opers:* Don Markland
VP Opers: Larry Walters
**VP Sls:* Paul Liljenquist
Pr Dir: Ryan Caro

D-U-N-S 07-989-5091
■ **FOGO DE CHAO CHURRASCARIA (LOS ANGELES) LLC**
(*Suby of* FOGO DE CHAO INC) ★
14881 Quorum Dr Ste 750, Dallas, TX 75254-7051
Tel (972) 361-6200 *Founded/Ownrshp* 2014
Sales 61.6M[E] *EMP* 2,842[E]
SIC 5812 Eating places

D-U-N-S 07-986-0931
▲ **FOGO DE CHAO INC**
14881 Quorum Dr Ste 750, Dallas, TX 75254-7051
Tel (972) 960-9533 *Founded/Ownrshp* 1979
Sales 271.6MM *EMP* 2,848[E]
Tkr Sym FOGO *Exch* NGS
SIC 5812 Eating places; Steak restaurant
CEO: Lawrence J Johnson
Pr: George B McGowan
COO: Selma Oliveira
CFO: Anthony D Laday
Genl Mgr: Ryan Metcalf
Sls Dir: Kirsten Knauer
Genl Couns: Albert G McGrath

D-U-N-S 05-154-5200
FOH GROUP INC
MOVIE STAR
6255 W Sunset Blvd # 2212, Los Angeles, CA 90028-7403
Tel (323) 466-5151 *Founded/Ownrshp* 1935
Sales 86.5MM *EMP* 902[E]
SIC 2341 2342 2339 5621 5632 Women's & children's underwear; Women's & children's nightwear; Women's & children's undergarments; Bras, girdles & allied garments; Women's & misses' outerwear; Women's & misses' athletic clothing & sportswear; Jeans: women's, misses' & juniors'; Women's clothing stores; Ready-to-wear apparel, women's; Teenage apparel; Women's accessory & specialty stores; Apparel accessories; Women's dancewear, hosiery & lingerie; Handbags
Ch Bd: Thomas J Lynch
CFO: Thomas Rende
Board of Directors: Peter Cole, John Eisel, William F Harley III, Milton J Walters

D-U-N-S 12-591-4739
FOJP SERVICE CORP
28 E 28th St Fl 14, New York, NY 10016-7946
Tel (212) 891-0700 *Founded/Ownrshp* 1977
Sales 269.8MM *EMP* 120
SIC 8741

D-U-N-S 07-893-1243
FOLEY & LARDNER LLP
777 E Wisconsin Ave # 3800, Milwaukee, WI 53202-5306
Tel (414) 271-2400 *Founded/Ownrshp* 1842
Sales 421.8MM[E] *EMP* 2,250
SIC 8111 Legal services
Ch Bd: Jay Rothman
Pt: Jon W Dudas
Pt: George L Root
Mng Pt: William E Davis
Mng Pt: Jay W Freedman
Mng Pt: Michael Gay
Mng Pt: Steven H Hilfinger
Mng Pt: Kevin E Hyde
**Mng Pt:* Stanley S Jaspan
Mng Pt: Michael D Kaminski
Mng Pt: Richard W Lasater
Mng Pt: Thomas J Maida
Mng Pt: Mark L Prager
Mng Pt: Susan E Pravda
Mng Pt: Eileen R Ridley
Mng Pt: Anne E Ross
Mng Pt: Nancy J Sennett
Mng Pt: Paul A Stewart
Mng Pt: Catherine Sun
Mng Pt: Van A Tengberg
Mng Pt: Peter N Wang
Board of Directors: Richard A Weiss, Sharon R Barner, Jon M Wilson, Edmund T Baxa Jr, Mark L Prager, George L Root Jr, Jay O Rothman, Nancy J Sennett, George T Simon, Jay N Varon, Peter N Wang

D-U-N-S 03-569-9146
FOLEY CELLULOSE LLC
(*Suby of* GEORGIA-PACIFIC LLC) ★
3510 Contractors Rd, Perry, FL 32348-7738
Tel (850) 584-1121 *Founded/Ownrshp* 1992, 2013
Sales 122.9MM[E] *EMP* 558
SIC 2611 Pulp mills

D-U-N-S 00-288-5614
FOLEY CO
(*Suby of* ENERFAB INC) ★
7501 E Front St, Kansas City, MO 64120-1937
Tel (816) 241-3335 *Founded/Ownrshp* 2015
Sales 100.0MM *EMP* 286
SIC 1623 1711 1541 Pipeline construction; Plumbing contractors; Industrial buildings, new construction
CEO: Greg Purdon
**Pr:* Chris Callegari
**Sec:* Daniel Sillies
Div Mgr: Mike Gillard

D-U-N-S 00-694-4037 EXP
FOLEY EQUIPMENT CO (KS)
CATERPILLAR
(*Suby of* FOLEY TRACTOR) ★
1550 S West St, Wichita, KS 67213-1668
Tel (316) 943-4211 *Founded/Ownrshp* 1942
Sales 91.4MM[E] *EMP* 190
SIC 5084 5082 5083

D-U-N-S 07-897-2262
■ **FOLEY HOSPITAL CORP** (AL)
SOUTH BALDWIN REGIONAL MED CTR
(*Suby of* COMMUNITY HEALTH SYSTEMS INC) ★
1613 N Mckenzie St, Foley, AL 36535-2247
Tel (251) 949-3400 *Founded/Ownrshp* 1956, 2000
Sales 140.8MM *EMP* 1,300
SIC 8062 General medical & surgical hospitals
CEO: Keith Newton
Dir Vol: Mary Larue-Childre
CIO: Jeannine O Neill
Doctor: Niki Dey
HC Dir: Lounette Ingram

D-U-N-S 00-252-6994 IMP
FOLEY INC
CATERPILLAR AUTHORIZED DEALER
855 Centennial Ave, Piscataway, NJ 08854-3912
Tel (732) 885-5555 *Founded/Ownrshp* 1957
Sales 203.9MM[E] *EMP* 350
SIC 5082 7699 7353 General construction machinery & equipment; Pavers; Construction equipment repair; Heavy construction equipment rental
Ch: Kim Foley
**COO:* Susan Connolly
COO: Tom Domotorffy
CFO: George Kattak
**VP:* Ryan Foley
VP: Nicholas Kubas
VP: Norm Wagenblast
**VP:* Thomas Wagenblast
Brnch Mgr: Duarte Cardoso
IT Man: Laurie Benninger
IT Man: Jon Souliere

D-U-N-S 18-145-0453
FOLEY INDUSTRIES INC
FOLEY TRACTOR
1550 S West St, Wichita, KS 67213-1638
Tel (316) 943-4211 *Founded/Ownrshp* 1987
Sales 119.0MM[E] *EMP* 190
SIC 5082 5084 7353 6512 Construction & mining machinery; Industrial machinery & equipment; Heavy construction equipment rental; Nonresidential building operators
Ch: Paul Foley Jr
**Pr:* Ann Foley-Konecny
**CFO:* Kevin Hoops
Sls Mgr: Cllyde Wacker

D-U-N-S 00-331-0158 IMP
FOLEY PRODUCTS CO (GA)
(*Suby of* CONCRETE CO) ★
1030 1st Ave, Columbus, GA 31901-2402
Tel (706) 563-7882 *Founded/Ownrshp* 1981, 2005
Sales 87.8MM[E] *EMP* 286[E]
SIC 3272 Concrete products
CEO: Frank D Foley III
**CFO:* Timothy W Jenkins
**VP:* Eric Nix
Genl Mgr: Robert Thornton
Prd Mgr: Brian Mann

FOLEY TRACTOR
See FOLEY INDUSTRIES INC

D-U-N-S 00-427-3710 IMP
■ **FOLGER COFFEE CO** (OH)
FOLGERS
(*Suby of* J M SMUCKER CO) ★
1 Strawberry Ln, Orrville, OH 44667-1241
Tel (800) 937-9745 *Founded/Ownrshp* 1850, 1963
Sales 244.0MM[E] *EMP* 1,038
SIC 2095 Roasted coffee; Instant coffee; Coffee, ground: mixed with grain or chicory; Freeze-dried coffee
Pr: Susan E Arnold
**Pr:* Alan G Lafley
**Treas:* G W Price
**Sr VP:* Joseph H Etter
**VP:* C C Daley Jr
**VP:* David R Walker
**Prin:* J M Smucker
**Prin:* D R Walker
IT Man: E Welch
Manager: Jamie Hammond

FOLGERS
See FOLGER COFFEE CO

D-U-N-S 13-931-0510
FOLKS RESTAURANTS LTD
PO-FOLKS
508 Harmon Ave, Panama City, FL 32401-3044
Tel (850) 763-0501 *Founded/Ownrshp* 1996
Sales 24.3MM[E] *EMP* 1,132
SIC 5812 Restaurant, family: chain
Pr: Peter Sostheim

D-U-N-S 00-193-3324 EXP
FOLLETT CORP
3 Westbrook Ctr Ste 200, Westchester, IL 60154
Tel (708) 884-0000 *Founded/Ownrshp* 1923
Sales 5.7MMM[E] *EMP* 10,706
SIC 5942 5192

D-U-N-S 00-238-8445 IMP/EXP
FOLLETT CORP (PA)
801 Church Ln, Easton, PA 18040-6637
Tel (610) 252-7301 *Founded/Ownrshp* 1948
Sales 98.8MM[E] *EMP* 300[E]
SIC 3585 Ice boxes, industrial; Ice making machinery; Soda fountain & beverage dispensing equipment & parts
Ch Bd: Steven R Follett
Pr: Margaret Neuner
CFO: Peter Limone
**Ex VP:* Robert A Bryson Jr
Sr VP: Jay Amond
VP: Gary Cristofano
VP: Richard Ellspermann
Genl Mgr: Cheryl Guerro
Store Mgr: Pat Ruyak-Gullo
Tech Mgr: Phil Ingram
Tech Mgr: Christopher Omeara

D-U-N-S 06-998-8574 IMP
FOLLETT HIGHER EDUCATION GROUP INC
(*Suby of* FOLLETT CORP) ★
3 Westbrook Corp Ctr # 200, Westchester, IL 60154-5703
Tel (800) 365-5388 *Founded/Ownrshp* 1966
Sales 1.4MMM[E] *EMP* 8,877
SIC 5942 5943 5947 College book stores; School supplies; Gifts & novelties
Pr: Don Germano
COO: Michael Johnson
CFO: Robert Parrish
Treas: Timothy Henrichs
Ofcr: Roe J McFarlane
Ex VP: Tom Dillon
Ex VP: Kimberly Ellison-Taylor
Sr VP: Joseph A Hul
Sr VP: Paula Manley
Sr VP: Bill Stauffer
VP: Paul Jarra
VP: Roe McFarlane
VP: Suzanne Stegeman
VP: Patrick Usher
Exec: Clarence Mancik
Board of Directors: Timothy Henrichs, Mary Lee Schneider

D-U-N-S 19-520-1863 EXP
FOLLETT SCHOOL SOLUTIONS INC
(*Suby of* FOLLETT CORP) ★
1340 Ridgeview Dr, McHenry, IL 60050-7047
Tel (815) 759-1700 *Founded/Ownrshp* 1873
Sales 221.6MM[E] *EMP* 674
SIC 5192 Books
Pr: Todd Litzsinger
**Treas:* Timothy Henrichs

D-U-N-S 19-520-2739
FOLLETT SCHOOL SOLUTIONS INC
(*Suby of* FOLLETT CORP) ★
1433 Internationale Pkwy, Woodridge, IL 60517-4941
Tel (630) 972-5600 *Founded/Ownrshp* 1999
Sales 199.7MM[E] *EMP* 318
SIC 5192 Books
Pr: Joe Miller
Treas: Timothy Henrichs
Sales Asso: Denise L Chrisman
Board of Directors: Thomas Schenck Timothy Hen

D-U-N-S 06-311-0214
FOLSOM-CORDOVA UNIF SCH DIST (CA)
FCUSD
1965 Birkmont Dr, Rancho Cordova, CA 95742-6407
Tel (916) 294-9000 *Founded/Ownrshp* 2012
Sales 9.2MM[E] *EMP* 2,200
SIC 8221 Professional schools
Pr: Joanne Reian King
**VP:* Zak Ford
MIS Dir: Terry Kritsepis
Instr Medi: Cheryl Ramage
HC Dir: Maryann Delleney

D-U-N-S 17-479-6706 IMP
FONA INTERNATIONAL INC
1900 Averill Rd, Geneva, IL 60134-1601
Tel (630) 578-8600 *Founded/Ownrshp* 1986
Sales 89.2MM[E] *EMP* 180[E]
SIC 2087 Extracts, flavoring; Syrups, flavoring (except drink)
CEO: Joseph James Slawek
**COO:* Luke Slawek
CFO: James Evanoff
**VP:* Amy McDonald
**VP:* Tj Widuch
Exec: Toni Anthony
Exec: Barb Pugesek
IT Man: Dave Hetman
Sls Dir: Michael Patschorke

D-U-N-S 03-958-2366
FOND DU LAC RESERVATION
BLACK BEAR CASINO
1785 Highway 210, Carlton, MN 55718-8161
Tel (218) 879-4593 *Founded/Ownrshp* 1975
Sales NA *EMP* 1,007
SIC 9131 Indian reservation;
Ch Bd: Robert Peacock
**Sec:* Peter J De Foe
Bd of Dir: Nate Sandman
Genl Mgr: Maurice Ojibway
IT Man: David Finzel
Secur Mgr: Jim Urness

D-U-N-S 09-302-8843
FOND DU LAC SCHOOL DISTRICT
72 W 9th St, Fond Du Lac, WI 54935-4972
Tel (920) 929-2900 *Founded/Ownrshp* 1875
Sales 95.0MM *EMP* 900
Accts Erickson & Associates Sc A
SIC 8211 Public elementary school; Public junior high school; Public senior high school; Public special education school
Pr: Elizabeth Hayes
**VP:* Julie Nett
**Genl Mgr:* Wendy Brockert
Teacher Pr: Sharon Simmons
HC Dir: Marian Sheridan

FONTAINEBLEAU MIAMI BEACH
See FONTAINEBLUEAU FLORIDA HOTEL LLC

D-U-N-S 00-414-6841
FONTAINEBLUEAU FLORIDA HOTEL LLC
FONTAINEBLEAU MIAMI BEACH
4441 Collins Ave, Miami, FL 33140-3227
Tel (305) 538-2000 *Founded/Ownrshp* 1953, 2011
Sales 302.2MM[E] *EMP* 2,500[E]
SIC 6519 7011 5812 7991 Real property lessors; Hotels & motels; Eating places; Physical fitness facilities
Pr: Philip Goldfarb
**CFO:* John Garland
**VP:* Leo Carrillo
**VP:* Scott Flexman
**VP:* Mary Rogers
VP: Joshua Summers
Exec: Elisabeth Kinch
Exec: Marcelo Pineda
Exec: Elizabeth Romero
Exec: Ryan Wilson
Rgnl Mgr: Elaine Keller

D-U-N-S 09-474-6294 IMP
FONTANA AMERICA INC
(*Suby of* FONTANA FINANZIARIA SPA)
6125 18 Mile Rd, Sterling Heights, MI 48314-4205
Tel (586) 997-5600 *Founded/Ownrshp* 1994
Sales 1.9MMM[E] *EMP* 8,200
SIC 5085 Fasteners, industrial: nuts, bolts, screws, etc.
Pr: Giuseppe Fontana
**CEO:* Serge Zerey
Genl Mgr: Enzo Neri

D-U-N-S 07-094-0622
FONTANA UNIFIED SCHOOL DISTRICT
FUSD
9680 Citrus Ave, Fontana, CA 92335-5571
Tel (909) 357-7600 *Founded/Ownrshp* 1956
Sales 216.6MM[E] *EMP* 3,627
Accts Nigro Nigro & White Pc Temec
SIC 8211 Public elementary & secondary schools
Ex VP: Cristina Nievas
Admn Mgr: Brenda Odell
Snr Mgr: John Leyva

FONTANA WATER COMPANY
See SAN GABRIEL VALLEY WATER CO

FONTANINI ITLN MEATS SAUSAGES
See CAPITOL WHOLESALE MEATS INC

D-U-N-S 07-850-4758 IMP
FONTEM US INC
BLU ECIGS
(*Suby of* ITG BRANDS LLC) ★
1100 S Tryon St Ste 300, Charlotte, NC 28203-4297
Tel (888) 207-4588 *Founded/Ownrshp* 2012
Sales 738.9M[E] *EMP* 1,246[E]
SIC 2111 5993 Cigarettes; Cigarette store
CEO: Murray Kessler
**Pr:* Jim Raport

D-U-N-S 80-748-7665
FOOD & AGRICULTURE CALIFORNIA DEPT
(*Suby of* EXECUTIVE OFFICE OF STATE OF CALIFORNIA) ★
1220 N St Ste 365, Sacramento, CA 95814-5644
Tel (916) 654-0462 *Founded/Ownrshp* 1900
Sales NA *EMP* 2,100
SIC 9641 Regulation of agricultural marketing;
Pr: Craig McNamara
Genl Mgr: Kristi Duprey
Sls&Mrk Ex: Lisa Cooper

D-U-N-S 92-764-5523
■ **FOOD & DRUG ADMINISTRATION**
FDA- OFM
(*Suby of* UNITED STATES DEPARTMENT OF HEALTH & HUMAN SERVICES) ★
10903 Nh Ave Ste 2217, Silver Spring, MD 20903
Tel (301) 796-5000 *Founded/Ownrshp* 1907
Sales NA *EMP* 12,000
SIC 9431 Administration of public health programs;
CIO: Tim Stitely
QA Dir: Sandra J Culp
Ql Cn Mgr: Lisa P Wiley
Doctor: Sidney S Wolfe
Counsel: Howard Levine

D-U-N-S 83-818-6153
■ **FOOD & NUTRITION SERVICE**
USDA FOOD & NUTRITION SERVICE
(*Suby of* U S D A) ★
3101 Park Center Dr # 200, Alexandria, VA 22302-1500
Tel (703) 305-2060 *Founded/Ownrshp* 1969
Sales NA *EMP* 1,750[E]
SIC 9641 Regulation & inspection of agricultural products, government;
V Ch: Joshua Tashiro
CFO: Dave Burr
Ofcr: Tama Eliff
Ofcr: Rebecca Hobbs
CIO: Jacquie Butler
Nutrtnst: Eric Steiner
Nutrtnst: Judy Wilson

FOOD 4 LESS
See RALPHS GROCERY CO

FOOD 4 LESS
See PAQ INC

D-U-N-S 88-438-4744 IMP
■ **FOOD 4 LESS HOLDINGS INC**
(*Suby of* FRED MEYER INC) ★
1100 W Artesia Blvd, Compton, CA 90220-5108
Tel (310) 884-9000 *Founded/Ownrshp* 1999
Sales 139.4MM[E] *EMP* 1,343[E]
SIC 5411 Supermarkets, chain; Supermarkets, 55,000-65,000 square feet (superstore); Supermarkets, 66,000-99,000 square feet; Supermarkets, hypermarket
CEO: Donna Giordano
**CEO:* Ronald W Burkle
Ex VP: Ed Hudson
VP: Timothy Mulhall
VP: Mike Vriens
Genl Mgr: Astrid Decicco
CIO: Rick Dickson
CIO: Michael Laddon

D-U-N-S 17-704-1886
FOOD BANK OF CENTRAL & EASTERN NORTH CAROLINA INC
1924 Capital Blvd, Raleigh, NC 27604-2147
Tel (919) 875-0707 *Founded/Ownrshp* 1980
Sales 111.2MM *EMP* 70
Accts Williams Overman Pierce Llp R
SIC 8322 Individual & family services
Ch: Ed Carney
Dir Vol: Laura Brown
Dir Vol: Carter Crain
Dir Vol: Patrick Spencer
Pr: Charlie Hale
**Pr:* Peter Werbicki
**Treas:* Heather Mallard
VP: Albert Fisher
VP: Earline Middleton
VP: Allen Reep
Exec: Larry Mottler
Exec: Alvin Ragland

D-U-N-S 36-146-5651
FOOD BANK OF ROCKIES INC
WYOMING FOOD BANK OF THE ROCKI
10700 E 45th Ave, Denver, CO 80239-2906
Tel (303) 371-9250 *Founded/Ownrshp* 1978
Sales 87.4MM *EMP* 109
Accts Eks & H Llp Denver Colorado
SIC 8322 Individual & family services
CEO: Kevin D Seggelke
**CFO:* Marshall Aster
CFO: Sharon K Fiscus
CFO: Bruce Glazer
Treas: Josephine Roberson
VP: Tony Alexis
**VP:* Vincent Alexis
VP: Bill Craig
VP: DOE Kittay
Ex Dir: Willy McCrea
Nutrtnst: Lee Boteler

FOOD BAZAAR
See BOGOPA SERVICE CORP

FOOD BAZAAR
See BOGOPA ENTERPRISES INC

FOOD CARE
See ST MARYS FOOD BANK ALLIANCE

D-U-N-S 05-131-1470
FOOD CIRCUS SUPER MARKETS INC
FOODTOWN
853 State Route 35, Middletown, NJ 07748-4205
Tel (732) 671-2220 *Founded/Ownrshp* 1959
Sales 126.0MM^E *EMP* 785
SIC 5411 Supermarkets, chain
Pr: Joseph J Azzolina
**Pr:* Louis Scaduto Jr
**Treas:* Joseph Azzolina Jr
VP: Phil Scaduto
**VP:* Philip Scaduto
Exec: Nancy Fama
Store Mgr: Joe Collison
Sls Mgr: Steven Wilkens

FOOD CITY
See K-VA-T FOOD STORES INC

D-U-N-S 62-036-7888
FOOD CONCEPTS INTERNATIONAL INC
ABUELOS MEXICAN FOOD EMBASSY
4401 82nd St, Lubbock, TX 79424-3344
Tel (806) 785-8686 *Founded/Ownrshp* 1990
Sales 117.1MM^E *EMP* 3,000
SIC 5812 Chinese restaurant; Mexican restaurant
Ch: James Young
Pr: Chuck Anderson
Pr: Larry Pierson
Treas: Margaret Young
Sec: Margaret Kailee Young
VP: Greg Baker

FOOD DEPOT
See B GREEN & CO INC

FOOD DEPOT
See ALL AMERICAN QUALITY FOODS INC

FOOD EMPORIUM
See SHOPWELL INC

D-U-N-S 09-362-0347
FOOD FOLKS & FUN INC
4354 Glendale Milford Rd, Blue Ash, OH 45242-3706
Tel (513) 769-4386 *Founded/Ownrshp* 1999
Sales 21.3MM^E *EMP* 1,000
SIC 5812 Fast-food restaurant, chain
Pr: Peter Wasilezich

D-U-N-S 06-635-7369 IMP/EXP
FOOD FOR POOR INC
6401 Lyons Rd, Coconut Creek, FL 33073-3602
Tel (954) 427-2222 *Founded/Ownrshp* 1982
Sales 1.1MMM *EMP* 335
Accts Mayer Hoffman Mccann Pc Boc
SIC 8399 Community development groups
CFO: Robin G Mahfood
COO: Fred Khouri
**COO:* Frederick Khouri
**CFO:* Dennis North
**Sec:* David T Price
**Ex Dir:* Angel Aloma
**Ex Dir:* Alvaro J Pereira

D-U-N-S 14-707-0130
FOOD GIANT SUPERMARKETS INC
SUREWAY
(*Suby of* HOUCHENS MARKETS) ★
120 Industrial Dr, Sikeston, MO 63801-5216
Tel (573) 471-3500 *Founded/Ownrshp* 2004
Sales 757.8MM *EMP* 4,500
SIC 5411 Supermarkets, chain
Pr: Kevin Ladd
**Treas:* Steve Malone
**VP:* Gary Duncan
VP: Marsha Strobel
Dist Mgr: Earl Johnson
IT Man: Brent Benton

FOOD GROUP ENGINEERING
See DUBOIS CHEMICALS

FOOD IMPORT GROUP
See REMA FOODS INC

FOOD LBS/SFETY INSPTN DVSN-GMT
See HEALTH RESEARCH INC

FOOD LION
See DELHAIZE AMERICA LLC

D-U-N-S 00-344-8560 IMP
FOOD LION LLC (NC)
(*Suby of* FOOD LION) ★
2110 Executive Dr, Salisbury, NC 28147-9007
Tel (704) 633-8250 *Founded/Ownrshp* 1957, 1999
Sales 3.3MMM^E *EMP* 17,880
SIC 5411 Supermarkets, chain
Pr: Cathy Green Burns
**Pr:* Rick Anicetti
Pr: Kyle R Mitchell
COO: Joseph Hall
CFO: Stephanie Bedrick
CFO: Laura C Eagle
CFO: Susan Follas
CFO: Richard A James
CFO: Laura C Kendall
CFO: Craig Owens
CFO: Brian Woolf
VP: Shawn Beichler
VP: Michael Brooks
VP: Robert Canipe
VP: Keith Cunningham
VP: Bruce Dawson
VP: Deborah Dixson
VP: Linn Evans
VP: Gene Faller
VP: Keith Gehl
VP: Arthur Goss

D-U-N-S 07-947-3966
FOOD MANAGEMENT PARTNERS INC (TX)
120 Chula Vis, Hollywood Park, TX 78232-2234
Tel (210) 248-9340 *Founded/Ownrshp* 2004
Sales 848.5MM^E *EMP* 18,001^E
SIC 8742 Business consultant
Exec: Tracy Amass

D-U-N-S 03-318-3286 IMP
FOOD PANTRY LTD (HI)
LAMONTS GIFTS & SUNDRY
3536 Harding Ave Ste 500, Honolulu, HI 96816-2453
Tel (808) 732-5515 *Founded/Ownrshp* 1960
Sales 116.1MM^E *EMP* 600
SIC 5411 5947 Grocery stores, chain; Convenience stores, chain; Gift, novelty & souvenir shop
Pr: Thomas R Weston
**Sec:* Joanna Sullivan
VP: Darcy Takushi

FOOD PROCESSING HOLDINGS
See ALBERTVILLE QUALITY FOODS INC

D-U-N-S 00-948-1904 IMP/EXP
FOOD SERVICES OF AMERICA INC
FSA
(*Suby of* SERVICES GROUP OF AMERICA INC) ★
18100 N 71st St Ste 400, Scottsdale, AZ 85254-2227
Tel (480) 927-4000 *Founded/Ownrshp* 1931
Sales 1.6MMM^E *EMP* 1,571^E
SIC 5148 5142 5146 5141 Fruits; Vegetables; Packaged frozen goods; Fish, fresh; Groceries, general line
CEO: Doug Minert
CFO: Peter Smith
VP: Lee Clark
**VP:* Brad Parker
Dir Bus: Paul Desena
Rgnl Mgr: Jim Manske
Manager: Kevin McRae
Manager: Steve Nestor
Manager: Kim Sullivan
Sls Mgr: Tracey Jacobson
Sales Asso: Michael Hansen

FOOD TRADE
See CROSSMARK INC

D-U-N-S 19-669-6579
■ **FOODARAMA INC (DE)**
(*Suby of* SUPERVALU INC) ★
4600 Forbes Blvd Ste 1, Lanham, MD 20706-4312
Tel (301) 306-8600 *Founded/Ownrshp* 1999
Sales 85.1MM^E *EMP* 1,900
SIC 5411 Grocery stores
Ch Bd: Don Bennett
**Pr:* John Stokely

D-U-N-S 00-891-2230
FOODARAMA SUPERMARKETS INC
SHOP RITE
(*Suby of* SAKER HOLDINGS CORP) ★
922 State Route 33 Bldg 1, Freehold, NJ 07728-8499
Tel (732) 462-3120 *Founded/Ownrshp* 2006
Sales 605.9MM^E *EMP* 6,850
SIC 5411 5261 5921 Supermarkets, chain; Nurseries & garden centers; Liquor stores
Pr: Richard J Saker
Ch Bd: Joseph J Saker
CFO: Michael Shapiro
Sr VP: Joseph C Troilo
VP: Tony Popolillo
MIS Dir: Jim Connolly

D-U-N-S 19-035-4142 IMP/EXP
FOODCOMM INTERNATIONAL
THOMAS FOODS INTERNATIONAL
4260 El Camino Real, Palo Alto, CA 94306-4404
Tel (650) 813-1300 *Founded/Ownrshp* 1988
Sales 323.0MM^E *EMP* 30
Accts Moss Adams Llp Campbell Cali
SIC 5147 5142 Meats, fresh; Meat, frozen: packaged
CEO: Greg Bourke
Pr: Frank Tarantino
CFO: Tom Granndsart

FOODLAND ALBERTVILLE
See MITCHELL GROCERY CORP

D-U-N-S 00-692-6877 IMP
FOODLAND SUPER MARKET LIMITED (HI)
SACK N SAVE
3536 Harding Ave Fl 1, Honolulu, HI 96816-2453
Tel (808) 732-0791 *Founded/Ownrshp* 1948
Sales 376.5MM^E *EMP* 2,000
SIC 5411 Supermarkets, chain
Ch Bd: M Jenai Sullivan Wall
**Pr:* Abel T Porter
**CFO:* Andrew T Kawano
VP: Wendy Reeve
**VP:* Roger J Wall
VP: Kimberly Yoshimura
Dist Mgr: Ashley Houk
CIO: Robert Murphy
Dir IT: Bryan Cooper
Dir IT: Lori Honjiyo
Dir IT: Mike Walter

D-U-N-S 11-753-0436
FOODLINER INC
2099 Southpark Ct Ste 1, Dubuque, IA 52003-8095
Tel (563) 584-2670 *Founded/Ownrshp* 1982
Sales 110.1MM^E *EMP* 700
SIC 4213 Contract haulers
Pr: Robert L McCoy
**Pr:* R Michael Mc Coy
**Sec:* Robert S Mc Coy Jr
S&M/VP: Al Brillhart

D-U-N-S 04-976-5506
FOODONICS INTERNATIONAL INC
DIXIE EGG COMPANY
5139 Edgewood Ct, Jacksonville, FL 32254-3601
Tel (904) 783-0950 *Founded/Ownrshp* 1969
Sales 86.3MM^E *EMP* 200
SIC 5144

D-U-N-S 02-259-0327
FOODPRO CORP
321 E 5th St, Frederick, MD 21701-5717
Tel (301) 663-3171 *Founded/Ownrshp* 1972
Sales 122.3MM^E *EMP* 136^E
Accts Dallavalle & Co Pa Cpa S Fr
SIC 5142 5149 5148 5147 5143 5113 Packaged frozen goods; Dried or canned foods; Canned goods: fruit, vegetables, seafood, meats, etc.; Fresh fruits & vegetables; Meats, fresh; Dairy products, except dried or canned; Disposable plates, cups, napkins & eating utensils
Ch Bd: John D Brunk
**Pr:* J Edwin Furbee
**Sec:* J Dennis Easterday
Dir Soc: Kevin Putman
Genl Mgr: Jarrod Turbin
Sls&Mrk Ex: Carolyn Hetzer
VP Mktg: William Rinehart
VP Sls: Kevin McAteer
Sls Mgr: Jim Bachman
Sls Mgr: Jude Hoffman

D-U-N-S 02-211-7154
FOODS INC
DAHL'S FOODS
4343 Merle Hay Rd, Des Moines, IA 50310-1411
Tel (515) 278-1657 *Founded/Ownrshp* 1958
Sales 198.8MM^E *EMP* 1,100
SIC 5912 Drug stores
CEO: Craig Moore
**Pr:* Ross L Nixon
Genl Mgr: Cathy McDaniel
Mktg Dir: Marshal Tolly

FOODSERVICE DIVISION
See HOMER LAUGHLIN CHINA CO

D-U-N-S 80-076-5211 EXP
FOODSERVICEWAREHOUSE.COM LLC
FSW
84 Inverness Cir E, Englewood, CO 80112-5314
Tel (303) 801-0629 *Founded/Ownrshp* 2008
Sales 217.4MM^E *EMP* 246
SIC 5046

FOODTOWN
See NORKUS ENTERPRISES INC

FOODTOWN
See FOOD CIRCUS SUPER MARKETS INC

D-U-N-S 60-245-8531 IMP/EXP
▲ **FOOT LOCKER INC**
330 W 34th St, New York, NY 10001-2406
Tel (212) 720-3700 *Founded/Ownrshp* 1879
Sales 7.4MMM *EMP* 47,025
Accts Kpmg New York New York
Tkr Sym FL *Exch* NYS
SIC 5661 5941 5961 6794 Shoe stores; Footwear, athletic; Men's shoes; Women's shoes; Sporting goods & bicycle shops; Catalog & mail-order houses; Franchises, selling or licensing
Pr: Richard A Johnson
**Ch Bd:* Nicholas Dipaolo
CEO: Stephen D Jacobs
CEO: Lewis P Kimble
CFO: Lauren B Peters
Treas: John A Maurer
Treas: John Maurer
Bd of Dir: Matthew Serra
Ofcr: Paulette R Alviti
Ex VP: Robert W McHugh
Sr VP: Jeffrey L Berk
Sr VP: Giovanna Cipriano
Sr VP: Sheilagh M Clarke
Sr VP: Pawan Verma
VP: Rich Aneser
VP: Joseph Bongiorno
VP: Frank Bracken
VP: Lauren Bristow
VP: James Bulzis
VP: Lori Casavina
VP: Paul Cox
Board of Directors: Maxine Clark, Alan D Feldman, Guillermo G Marmol, Matthew M McKenna, Steven Oakland, Cheryl Nido Turpin, Kimberly K Underhill, Dona D Young

D-U-N-S 00-164-2826 IMP
■ **FOOT LOCKER RETAIL INC**
KINNEY
(*Suby of* FOOT LOCKER INC) ★
112 W 34th St Frnt 1, New York, NY 10120-0101
Tel (212) 465-9041 *Founded/Ownrshp* 1963
Sales 3.1MMM^E *EMP* 30,000
SIC 5661 5699 Shoe stores; Men's shoes; Women's shoes; Children's shoes; Sports apparel
CEO: Richard Johnson
Pr: Matthew Dserra
Ch: J Bacot
Ch: Roger Farah
**Treas:* John H Cannon
VP: Jeffrey Berk
VP: Gary Brown
Site Mgr: Omar Rivera
Board of Directors: Roger N Farah, Dale Hilbert

D-U-N-S 00-699-2457 IMP
■ **FOOT LOCKER SPECIALTY INC** (NY)
CHAMPS SPORTS
(*Suby of* FOOT LOCKER INC) ★
112 W 34th St Lbby 1, New York, NY 10120-0199
Tel (212) 720-3700 *Founded/Ownrshp* 1879
Sales 200.9MM^E *EMP* 3,100
SIC 5632 5961 7311 Apparel accessories; Costume jewelry; Catalog & mail-order houses; Fitness & sporting goods, mail order; Advertising agencies
Pr: Matt Serra
**Treas:* John H Cannon
Sr Cor Off: Bruce Hartman
**Sr VP:* Jeff Berk
IT Man: Noel Rivera

FOOTBALL FANATICS
See FANATICS INC

FOOTE HOSPITAL
See HENRY FORD ALLEGIANCE HEALTH GROUP

D-U-N-S 79-917-1020
FOOTHILL / EASTERN TRANSPORTATION CORRIDOR AGENCY
125 Pacifica Ste 100, Irvine, CA 92618-3324
Tel (949) 754-3400 *Founded/Ownrshp* 1986
Sales 175.1MM *EMP* 70
Accts Kpmg Llp Irvine Ca
SIC 1611 Highway & street construction
CEO: Michael Kraman
CFO: Amy Potter

FOOTHILL COLLEGE
See FOOTHILL-DE ANZA COMMUNITY COLLEGE DISTRICT FINANCING CORP

D-U-N-S 07-620-3421
FOOTHILL HOSPITAL-MORRIS L JOHNSTON MEMORIAL
FOOTHILL PRESBYTERIAN HOSPITAL
250 S Grand Ave, Glendora, CA 91741-4218
Tel (626) 857-3145 *Founded/Ownrshp* 1973
Sales 89.9MM *EMP* 400
SIC 8062 General medical & surgical hospitals
Pr: Robert Curry
Dir Lab: Nadia Koelliker

FOOTHILL PRESBYTERIAN HOSPITAL
See FOOTHILL HOSPITAL-MORRIS L JOHNSTON MEMORIAL

D-U-N-S 07-632-2296
FOOTHILL-DE ANZA COMMUNITY COLLEGE DISTRICT FINANCING CORP
FOOTHILL COLLEGE
12345 S El Monte Rd, Los Altos Hills, CA 94022-4504
Tel (650) 949-6100 *Founded/Ownrshp* 1957
Sales 125.7MM^E *EMP* 3,384
SIC 8222 8221 Community college; Colleges universities & professional schools
**Pr:* Betsy Bechtel
**CEO:* Kathleen Santora
Ofcr: Sarvjit Dhillon
Ofcr: Aleksandra Kuna
Ofcr: Jeffrey Stefanini
VP: Rose Myers
**VP:* Bruce Swenson
Assoc Dir: Romeo Paule
Dir IT: Sharon Luciw
Psych: Tobias Nava
Psych: Voltaire Villanueva

D-U-N-S 83-222-7946
FOOTHILLS LAND CONSERVANCY INC
373 Ellis Ave, Maryville, TN 37804-5824
Tel (865) 681-8326 *Founded/Ownrshp* 1985
Sales 237.2MM *EMP* 3
Accts Chervenak & Associates Pc Kno
SIC 8641 Environmental protection organization
Ex Dir: Bill Clabough
**Pr:* Dave Lewis

D-U-N-S 11-204-7381 IMP/EXP
■ **FOOTLOCKER.COM INC**
(*Suby of* FOOT LOCKER INC) ★
111 S 1st Ave, Wausau, WI 54401-4625
Tel (715) 842-3890 *Founded/Ownrshp* 1999
Sales 192.8MM^E *EMP* 2,000^E
SIC 5961 5661 Catalog sales; Fitness & sporting goods, mail order; Footwear, athletic
CEO: Tom Slover
VP: Patty Watsenski
Mktg Mgr: Marianne McCune

D-U-N-S 13-342-2415
FOOTPRINT ACQUISITION LLC
FOOTPRINT RETAIL SERVICES
2200 Western Ct Ste 150, Lisle, IL 60532-1843
Tel (630) 324-3400 *Founded/Ownrshp* 2015
Sales 51.0MM^E *EMP* 3,200
SIC 7389 Personal service agents, brokers & bureaus
CEO: William McKenna
Ofcr: Deborah Stevens
Adm Dir: Cathy Fenske
Adm Dir: Walter Williams
Dist Mgr: Terri Valenti
Snr Mgr: Bryant Love

FOOTPRINT RETAIL SERVICES
See FOOTPRINT ACQUISITION LLC

D-U-N-S 16-587-7531
FOR EYES OPTICAL CO OF COCONUT GROVE INC
285 W 74th Pl, Hialeah, FL 33014-5058
Tel (305) 557-9004 Founded/Ownrshp 1975
Sales 1.2MM^E EMP 1,000
SIC 3851 5995 Eyeglasses, lenses & frames; Opticians
Pr: Phillip Wolman
*VP: Robert Messa

D-U-N-S 96-834-9790
FORBES ENERGY SERVICES LTD
3000 S Business Hwy 281, Alice, TX 78332
Tel (361) 664-0549 Founded/Ownrshp 2008
Sales 244.1MM EMP 1,182^E
Accts Bdo Usa Llp Houston Texas
SIC 1389 Haulage, oil field; Oil field services; Processing service, gas
Ch Bd: John E Crisp
*COO: Charles C Forbes Jr
CFO: L Melvin Cooper
VP: Jim Maki
Prgrm Mgr: Vincent Correra
Area Mgr: Bill Friend
Off Mgr: Jeff Williams
Dir IT: Mike Tiller
Sfty Mgr: Jerry Woodall
Opers Mgr: Manny Gonzalez

D-U-N-S 14-240-5096
FORBES MANAGEMENT CO INC
499 Washington Blvd Fl 9, Jersey City, NJ 07310-2055
Tel (212) 620-2200 Founded/Ownrshp 1998
Sales 176.7MM^E EMP 700^E
SIC 6722 Management investment, open-end
Ch Bd: Malcolm S Forbes Jr
Pt: E B Gould
Pt: Gregory S Shatan
VP: Jessica Sibley
Mng Dir: Alan Griffin
Sls Dir: Mike Duffy
Sls Dir: Paul Mikhailoff
Sls Dir: Olivia Tsang
Mktg Mgr: Virginie Courtois
Sls Mgr: Olivia Gelade
Sls Mgr: Matthew Muszala

D-U-N-S 19-172-3159
FORBO AMERICA INC
(Suby of FORBO HOLDING AG)
103 Foulk Rd Ste 123, Wilmington, DE 19803-3742
Tel (302) 691-6100 Founded/Ownrshp 2000
Sales 92.9MM^E EMP 195
SIC 5023 Floor coverings
Prin: Gene Chase

D-U-N-S 17-742-3522 IMP
FORBO FLOORING INC
FORBO FLOORING SYSTEMS
(Suby of FORBO AMERICA INC) ★
8 Maplewood Dr, Hazle Township, PA 18202-9790
Tel (570) 459-0771 Founded/Ownrshp 1987
Sales 92.9MM^E EMP 142
SIC 5023 Floor coverings
Genl Mgr: Dennis Darragh
CFO: Jorg Riboni
*Sec: John Kondred
Ex VP: Matthias P Huenerwadel
Ex VP: Daniel Keist
Genl Mgr: Tim Donohue
IT Man: Peggy York

FORBO FLOORING SYSTEMS
See FORBO FLOORING INC

D-U-N-S 00-162-7504 IMP
FORBO SIEGLING LLC
(Suby of FORBO HOLDING AG)
12201 Vanstory Dr, Huntersville, NC 28078-8395
Tel (704) 948-0800 Founded/Ownrshp 1956
Sales 110.4MM^E EMP 357
SIC 3052 3535 Rubber belting; Plastic belting; Transmission belting, rubber; Conveyors & conveying equipment
Pr: Wayne E Hoffman
*CEO: This E Schneider
*CFO: Andreas Spreiter
*Ex VP: Matthias P Huenerwadel
*Ex VP: Jean-Michel Wins
*VP: Norm Nelson
CIO: Randolph Balot
Sls Mgr: Ray Kelly

D-U-N-S 55-605-4591
FORCE 3 LLC
(Suby of SIRIUS COMPUTER SOLUTIONS INC) ★
2151 Priest Bridge Dr # 7, Crofton, MD 21114-2466
Tel (301) 261-0204 Founded/Ownrshp 2016
Sales 100.4MM^E EMP 175
SIC 7373 5045 3571 Systems integration services; Computers, peripherals & software; Electronic computers
CEO: Mike Greaney
*CFO: Steve Scribner
Ofcr: Michael Greaney
Prgrm Mgr: Elizabeth Lawrence
Genl Mgr: Chris Knotts
IT Man: Rick Scott
Mktg Dir: Christy Kelley
Sls Dir: Marty Calambro
Sls Dir: Lisa Lynch
Mktg Mgr: Amy Pennington
Sls Mgr: Eric Wohl

D-U-N-S 09-788-9422 IMP
FORCE AMERICA INC
LLC, FORCE AMERICA DISTRG
501 Cliff Rd E Ste 100, Burnsville, MN 55337-1635
Tel (952) 707-1300 Founded/Ownrshp 1953
Sales 184.5MM^E EMP 235
SIC 5084 3568 Hydraulic systems equipment & supplies; Drives, chains & sprockets
*Ch Bd: Gerard Budzien
*CFO: Steve Bettendorf
*Sr VP: Michael Lynch
Mng Dir: Mike Helbig
Software D: Daniel Holland
Mfg Dir: Eric Holland
Mfg Mgr: Raymond Flynn
Opers Mgr: Jacob Hays
Opers Mgr: Antonio Pichel
Opers Mgr: Riley Wudinich
Plnt Mgr: John Rick

D-U-N-S 87-809-0687 IMP
■ FORCE PROTECTION INC
(Suby of GENERAL DYNAMICS CORP) ★
9801 Highway 78 Bldg 1, Ladson, SC 29456-3895
Tel (843) 569-8716 Founded/Ownrshp 2011
Sales 219.0MM^E EMP 1,280
SIC 3711 Military motor vehicle assembly
Ch Bd: Michael Moody
*Pr: Gary L Whited
*COO: Phillip Randall Hutcherson
*CFO: Charles A Mathis
*Treas: David H Fogg

D-U-N-S 09-183-2704 IMP
FORCE10 NETWORKS INC
DELL
350 Holger Way, San Jose, CA 95134-1362
Tel (707) 665-4400 Founded/Ownrshp 1999
Sales 144.3MM^E EMP 582
Accts Deloitte & Touche Llp San Jos
SIC 3661 Telephone & telegraph apparatus
CEO: Michael S Dell
Pr: James Hanley
Pr: Luu Nguyen
Pr: Minal Patel
Pr: Sachi Sambandan
Pr: Mark Sanders
Pr: Robert Tatnall
CFO: Karen Blasing
CFO: David Zacarias
CFO: William Zerella
Bd of Dir: Stuart Phillips
Ex VP: Ebrahim Abbasi
Sr VP: Steve Price
VP: Duane Button
VP: Mary Cole
VP: Sumit Gautam
VP: Norm Koch
VP: Bruce Miller
VP: Steve Mullaney
VP: Andrew Stewart
VP: Arun Viswanathan
Board of Directors: Howard A Bain III, B J Cassin, Keith G Daubenspeck, Dixon Doll, Dick Kramlich, Steven M Krausz, Paul Madera

D-U-N-S 08-035-7394
■ FORCEPOINT LLC
(Suby of RAYTHEON CO) ★
10900 Stonelake Blvd, Austin, TX 78759-5795
Tel (858) 320-8000 Founded/Ownrshp 2015
Sales 484.0MM^E EMP 2,000^E
SIC 7372 Prepackaged software
Chf Mktg O: Timothy A McDonough
Sr VP: John McCormick

D-U-N-S 96-244-6295
FORCHT GROUP OF KENTUCKY LLC
200 S Kentucky Ave, Corbin, KY 40701-1534
Tel (606) 528-9600 Founded/Ownrshp 2007
Sales NA EMP 2,100^E
SIC 6141 Personal credit institutions
Ofcr: David Witt
VP: Terry Forcht
Web Dev: Jason Hosler

FORD
See WW WALLWORK INC

FORD
See GABRIELLI TRUCK SALES LTD

D-U-N-S 03-514-3395
FORD ATCHLEY INC
3633 N 72nd St, Omaha, NE 68134-5197
Tel (402) 571-8801 Founded/Ownrshp 1975
Sales 89.6MM EMP 89
SIC 5511 Automobiles, new & used
Pr: Sherman Wayne Atchley
*Sec: David L Clark
*VP: Patricia Atchley
*VP: Zachary Atchley
Sls Mgr: Wesley Modin

D-U-N-S 06-543-9465
FORD AUDIO-VIDEO SYSTEMS LLC
4800 W Interstate 40, Oklahoma City, OK 73128
Tel (405) 946-9966 Founded/Ownrshp 1973
Sales 103.4MM^E EMP 278
Accts Peters & Chandler Pc Oklahoma
SIC 1731 8711 Electrical work; Designing: ship, boat, machine & product

D-U-N-S 01-581-2878
FORD BACON & DAVIS LLC
12021 Lakeland Park Blvd # 212, Baton Rouge, LA 70809-4200
Tel (225) 297-3431 Founded/Ownrshp 1998
Sales 142.5MM EMP 768
Accts Hannis T Bourgeois Llp Denh
SIC 8711 1541 1623 Construction & civil engineering; Industrial buildings & warehouses; Water, sewer & utility lines
Pr: Rick Moore
COO: Gerald Carter
CFO: Brett Hagemeier
Sr VP: Thomas E Tom Davis
*Sr VP: Ray Sherman
VP: Michael Cruse
*VP: Wrightson Jackson
VP: Walt Rachal
Sfty Dirs: Keith Sliman
VP Mktg: Tom Holtzclaw
Snr PM: Dennis Goff

D-U-N-S 02-637-1534
FORD CASA INC
5815 Montana Ave, El Paso, TX 79925-3389
Tel (915) 779-2272 Founded/Ownrshp 1969
Sales 98.7MM^E EMP 225
SIC 5511 Automobiles, new & used
Pr: Clay Lowenfield
*VP: Jerry Johnson
*VP: Justin M Lowenfield

D-U-N-S 10-807-5479
FORD FINANCIAL FUND II LP
200 Crescent Ct, Dallas, TX 75201-1834
Tel (214) 871-5151 Founded/Ownrshp 2011
Sales 140.9MM^E EMP 927^E
SIC 6282 6799 7389 Investment advice; Investors; Financial services
Prin: Kenneth Russell

D-U-N-S 80-869-5352 IMP/EXP
■ FORD FLAT ROCK ASSEMBLY PLANT
(Suby of FORD MOTOR CO) ★
1 International Dr, Flat Rock, MI 48134-9401
Tel (734) 782-7800 Founded/Ownrshp 2012
Sales 858.9MM^E EMP 2,300^E
SIC 5013 3711 Automotive supplies; Automobile assembly, including specialty automobiles
Pr: Gary A Roe

D-U-N-S 06-121-7170 IMP
FORD FOUNDATION
320 E 43rd St Fl 4, New York, NY 10017-4890
Tel (212) 573-5370 Founded/Ownrshp 1936
Sales 658.1MM EMP 556^E
SIC 6732 Charitable trust management; Educational trust management
Pr: Susan V Berresford
Pr: Rodica Mischiu
*Treas: Nicholas Gabriel
Bd of Dir: Marshall Thurgood Jr
Trst: Juliet V Garc A
Trst: Linda Charles
Ofcr: Lisa Davis
Ofcr: Roscoe G Davis
Ofcr: Wayne Fawbush
Ofcr: Luis Prez
Ofcr: Jean Ross
Ofcr: EKA E Williams
VP: Martfn Abrega
VP: Xavier D Briggs
VP: Pablo J Far As
VP: Barry Gaberman
VP: Samantha Gilbert
VP: Jacob A Gyle
VP: Dina Halpern
VP: George Harrar
VP: Forrest Hill
Board of Directors: Carl B Weisbrod, Paul A Allaire, W Richard West, Alain J P Belda, Kathryn S Fuller, Dr Juliet V Garcia, Dr Wilmot G James, Yolanda Kakabadse, Robert Kaplan, Richard Moe, Yolanda T Moses

D-U-N-S 01-051-3646 EXP
FORD GREENWAY INC
9001 E Colonial Dr, Orlando, FL 32817-4176
Tel (407) 275-3200 Founded/Ownrshp 1973
Sales 128.1MM^E EMP 300^E
SIC 5511 5012 Automobiles, new & used; Automobiles
Pr: Frank Rodriguez
*VP: Carl Atkinson

D-U-N-S 05-147-8568
FORD HABERFELDE
JIM BURKE FORD
2001 Oak St, Bakersfield, CA 93301-3010
Tel (661) 328-3600 Founded/Ownrshp 1964
Sales 114.8MM^E EMP 300^E
SIC 5511 Automobiles, new & used; Pickups, new & used
Pr: Daniel George Hay
*Sec: Beverly Burke
*Sec: Joe Hay
*VP: Michelle Hay
Off Mgr: Adriana Pena
Store Mgr: Barry Hopfe
Dir IT: Rose Charmley
Sales Exec: Chad Manning
Sls&Mrk Ex: Kyle Northway
Sls Mgr: Chris Strong
Sls Mgr: Don Summers

D-U-N-S 60-499-9664
■ FORD HOLDINGS LLC
(Suby of FORD MOTOR CO) ★
American Rd, Dearborn, MI 48121
Tel (313) 845-5338 Founded/Ownrshp 1989
Sales 3.8MMM^E EMP 31,400
SIC 6552 6512 Subdividers & developers; Commercial & industrial building operation
Ch Bd: Alex Trotman
*Pr: Kenneth A Whipple Jr
*Treas: E S Acton
*VP: Eric A Law
*VP: Malcolm S Macdonald
*VP: J M Rintamaki

D-U-N-S 00-896-0494
FORD KAYSER INC
KAYSER AUTOMOTIVE GROUP
2303 W Beltline Hwy, Madison, WI 53713-2393
Tel (608) 271-6000 Founded/Ownrshp 1925
Sales 98.5MM^E EMP 235
SIC 5511 7538 7532 7515 5521 Automobiles, new & used; General automotive repair shops; Top & body repair & paint shops; Passenger car leasing; Used car dealers
Pr: Patrick J Baxter
CFO: Linda Davis-Brown
VP: Ryan Baxter
VP: Gregg Erickson
Exec: Linda Davis
Exec: Jim Neidert
Genl Mgr: Connie Robak
IT Man: Jan Bukovich
Mktg Dir: Alfred Hall
Mktg Dir: Brad Lewis
Sls Mgr: Don Guglielmo

D-U-N-S 01-810-7912
FORD LEBANON INC
LEBANON FORD
770 Columbus Ave, Lebanon, OH 45036-1608
Tel (513) 932-1010 Founded/Ownrshp 2005
Sales 86.7MM EMP 52
SIC 5511 5521 7538 Automobiles, new & used; Pickups, new & used; Used car dealers; General automotive repair shops
Pr: Winston R Pittman Sr
CFO: Bonnie A Kasik
VP: Lisa A Cryder
Dir IT: Ian Mathews
Sales Asso: Brant Benson
Sales Asso: Danny Vanwinkle
Sales Asso: Dick Watson

D-U-N-S 00-793-2064 EXP
FORD MAC HAIK LTD (TX)
(Suby of MAC HAIK ENTERPRISES) ★
10333 Katy Fwy, Houston, TX 77024-1107
Tel (713) 932-5000 Founded/Ownrshp 2000
Sales 120.8MM^E EMP 452
SIC 5511 Automobiles, new & used; Pickups, new & used; Vans, new & used
CEO: Mac Haik
CFO: Jeff Heath
Exec: Rhonda Merritte
Genl Mgr: Bob Zweig
Off Mgr: Keith Fisher
Sls Dir: Stephanie Bennett
Sls Mgr: Lawrence Gallegos
Sls Mgr: Greg Jones
Sls Mgr: Tiffany Kearley

D-U-N-S 01-430-2830
FORD MCCAFFERTY SALES INC
MCCAFFERTY AUTO GROUP
1939 E Lincoln Hwy, Langhorne, PA 19047-3098
Tel (215) 945-8000 Founded/Ownrshp 1981
Sales 96.1MM^E EMP 201
SIC 5511 5531 7538 7514 5521 5012 Automobiles, new & used; Automotive parts; General automotive repair shops; Passenger car rental; Used car dealers; Automobiles & other motor vehicles
Pr: Fred Beans
*VP: S Elizabeth Beans
Exec: Steve Graaf
Genl Mgr: Gerald Turner
Off Mgr: Shelly James
Sls Mgr: Dave Hatalla
Sls Mgr: Richard Olive
Sls Mgr: Chris Scott
Sales Asso: William Heron
Sales Asso: Victoria Lacey
Sales Asso: Ryan Nearhood

D-U-N-S 00-514-6683 IMP/EXP
FORD METER BOX CO INC
775 Manchester Ave, Wabash, IN 46992-1420
Tel (260) 563-3171 Founded/Ownrshp 1898
Sales 93.4MM^E EMP 1,000
SIC 3494

D-U-N-S 05-363-9548
FORD MONTROSE INC
MTA LEASING
3960 Medina Rd, Fairlawn, OH 44333-2495
Tel (330) 666-0711 Founded/Ownrshp 1983
Sales 116.9MM^E EMP 440^E
SIC 5511 5521 7515 7513 7538 7532 Automobiles, new & used; Used car dealers; Passenger car leasing; Truck rental & leasing, no drivers; General automotive repair shops; Top & body repair & paint shops
Ch Bd: Michael Thompson
*CFO: Mary Lou Taylor
*VP: Chris Mills
*VP: Joseph Stefanini
Genl Mgr: Christopher Mills
Sls Mgr: Annette Bruno
Sls Mgr: Tom Mocarski

D-U-N-S 00-134-4746 IMP/EXP
▲ FORD MOTOR CO
1 American Rd, Dearborn, MI 48126-2701
Tel (313) 322-3000 Founded/Ownrshp 1919
Sales 149.5MMM EMP 199,000^E
Tkr Sym F Exch NYS
SIC 3711 3713 3714 6153 6141 7515 Automobile assembly, including specialty automobiles; Truck & bus bodies; Motor vehicle parts & accessories; Financing of dealers by motor vehicle manufacturers organ.; Buying of installment notes; Financing: automobiles, furniture, etc., not a deposit bank; Automobile loans, including insurance; Passenger car leasing
Pr: Mark Fields
Ch Bd: William Clay Ford Jr
V Ch: David Waterman
Pr: Mark Buzzell
CFO: Bob Shanks
Treas: Malcolm S Macdonald
Bd of Dir: S Cambra
Bd of Dir: Wayne Conner
Div VP: Jeffrey Gorrall
Ex VP: John Fleming
Ex VP: Valeria Fuller
Ex VP: Katherine Kjolhede
VP: Jim Bacon
VP: Raymundo Balderrama
VP: Scott Collins
VP: Keith Cooper
VP: Ed Diegel
VP: Ronald D Domas
VP: Alan Draper
VP: Felicia J Fields
VP: Elena Ford
Board of Directors: John C Lechleiter, Stephen G Butler, Ellen R Marram, Kimberly A Casiano, Gerald L Shaheen, Anthony F Earley Jr, John L Thornton, Edsel B Ford II, John S Weinberg, James P Hackett, James H Hance Jr, William W Helman IV, Jon M Huntsman Jr, William E Kennard

D-U-N-S 00-695-7419
■ FORD MOTOR CREDIT CO LLC
(Suby of FORD HOLDINGS LLC) ★
1 American Rd, Dearborn, MI 48126-2701
Tel (313) 322-3000 Founded/Ownrshp 1959

Sales NA *EMP* 6,300
SIC 6159 6141 Automobile finance leasing; Machinery & equipment finance leasing; Truck finance leasing; Automobile loans, including insurance; Consumer finance companies; Financing: automobiles, furniture, etc., not a deposit bank; Installment sales finance, other than banks
Ch Bd: Bernard B Silverstone
V Ch: Kenneth R Kent
**CFO:* Michael L Seneski
**Ofcr:* Thomas C Schneider
**Ex VP:* N Joy Falotico
**Ex VP:* Todd S Murphy
Board of Directors: Joseph R Hinrichs, Stuart J Rowley, Neil M Schloss, Robert L Shanks

D-U-N-S 06-983-4570
■ FORD MOTOR LAND DEVELOPMENT CORP
(*Suby of* FORD HOLDINGS LLC) ★
330 Town Center Dr # 1100, Dearborn, MI 48126-2711
Tel (313) 323-3100 *Founded/Ownrshp* 1989
Sales 86.6MM[E] *EMP* 800
SIC 6512 6552 Commercial & industrial building operation; Subdividers & developers
Ch: Sean Mc Court
**VP:* John Murphy

D-U-N-S 03-135-0010
FORD OLATHE SALES INC
OLATHE FORD LINCOLN
1845 E Santa Fe St, Olathe, KS 66062-1695
Tel (913) 782-0881 *Founded/Ownrshp* 1973
Sales 99.0MM[E] *EMP* 200
SIC 5511 5561 5012 Automobiles, new & used; Recreational vehicle dealers; Trucks, commercial
Pr: D F Bradley
**VP:* Don W Maddux
**Genl Mgr:* Sam Mansker
Sls Mgr: Stony Floyd
Sls Mgr: David Jones
Sls Mgr: Rob Miller
Sales Asso: Kevin Allan
Sales Asso: Marshall Barnett
Sales Asso: Steve Blew
Sales Asso: Casey Calhoun
Sales Asso: Mark Clardy

D-U-N-S 08-876-2278
FORD RESTAURANT GROUP INC
MANAGEMENT COMPANY
1514 Ranch Road 620 S, Lakeway, TX 78734-6210
Tel (512) 263-0929 *Founded/Ownrshp* 1999
Sales 47.5MM[E] *EMP* 1,100
SIC 5812 Eating places
Pr: Lynn Ford
**Pr:* Creed Ford
Off Mgr: Ginger Williams

D-U-N-S 07-101-1019
FORDHAM UNIVERSITY
441 E Fordham Rd, Bronx, NY 10458-9993
Tel (718) 817-1000 *Founded/Ownrshp* 1841
Sales 566.0MM *EMP* 4,070[E]
Accts Kpmg Llp New York Ny
SIC 8221 University
Pr: Rev Joseph M McShane Sj
Pr: Catherine Spencer
Pr: Kate Spencer
Trst: James N Loughran
Assoc VP: John Puglisi
**Sr VP:* Stephen Freedman
**Sr VP:* John J Lordan
VP: Thomas Dunne
VP: Jeffrey Gray
VP: Beverly Musgrave
VP: Shaya Phillips
VP: Joseph Quinn
VP: Joel Reidenbert
VP: Frank Sirianni
Exec: Mark Huang
Assoc Dir: Laura S Bassin
Assoc Dir: Biswa Bhowmick

D-U-N-S 00-793-6172
FORDYCE LTD (TX)
120 S Main St, Victoria, TX 77901-8147
Tel (361) 573-4309 *Founded/Ownrshp* 1929, 1943
Sales 309.6MM[E] *EMP* 136
SIC 1442

D-U-N-S 05-180-9267
FOREIGN MOTORS WEST INC
LAND ROVER METRO WEST
253 N Main St, Natick, MA 01760-1198
Tel (508) 655-5350 *Founded/Ownrshp* 1970
Sales 88.3MM[E] *EMP* 360
SIC 5511 7538 Automobiles, new & used; General automotive repair shops
Pr: Herb Chambers
**Treas:* Thomas R Mix

FOREIGN PRNT IS ALANZ AG MNCHN
See ALLIANZ GLOBAL INVESTORS OF AMERICA LP

D-U-N-S 02-104-3781
FOREMOST AFFINITY SERVICES INC (MI)
FOREMOST INSURANCE AGENCY
(*Suby of* FOREMOST CORP OF AMERICA) ★
5600 Beechtree Ln Se, Caledonia, MI 49316-9587
Tel (616) 942-3000 *Founded/Ownrshp* 1978, 1983
Sales NA *EMP* 400
SIC 6331 Fire, marine & casualty insurance
Pr: Marty Finestein
Board of Directors: Stephen J Boshoven, Robert Woudstra

D-U-N-S 05-834-0761
FOREMOST CORP OF AMERICA
(*Suby of* FARMERS INSURANCE EXCHANGE) ★
5600 Beechtree Ln Se, Caledonia, MI 49316-9587
Tel (616) 942-3000 *Founded/Ownrshp* 2000
Sales NA *EMP* 2,857
SIC 6331 Fire, marine & casualty insurance; Property damage insurance
Pr: Stephen J Leaman
COO: F Robert Woudstra
Ex VP: John J Hannigan

D-U-N-S 87-754-9923 IMP/EXP
FOREMOST FARMS USA COOPERATIVE
E10889 Penny Ln, Baraboo, WI 53913-8115
Tel (608) 355-8700 *Founded/Ownrshp* 1994
Sales 2.0MMM *EMP* 1,150
Accts Kpmg Llp Milwaukee Wi
SIC 2022 2026 2023 2021 Cheese, natural & processed; Fluid milk; Condensed milk; Evaporated whey; Powdered milk; Creamery butter
Pr: Dave Scheevel
**CFO:* Michael Doyle
**VP:* Jim Sleper
Comm Dir: Tony Simboli
VP Mfg: Doug Wilke
Natl Sales: Abigail Durso
Sls Mgr: Brent Hyden

D-U-N-S 05-593-8336
FOREMOST FINANCIAL SERVICES CORP
(*Suby of* FOREMOST CORP OF AMERICA) ★
5600 Beechtree Ln Se, Caledonia, MI 49316-9587
Tel (616) 956-3501 *Founded/Ownrshp* 1971
Sales NA *EMP* 1,700
SIC 6331 Fire, marine & casualty insurance
Pr: Bob Woudstra
Pr: Marty Feinstein
Pr: Bobby Woodstar
VP: Steve Boshoven
VP: Jack Hannigan
Board of Directors: D G Frey, S A Taylor

D-U-N-S 18-861-3517 IMP
FOREMOST GROUPS INC
FOREMOST INDUSTRIES
906 Murray Rd Ste 2, East Hanover, NJ 07936-2202
Tel (973) 428-0400 *Founded/Ownrshp* 1988
Sales 179.5MM *EMP* 150
SIC 5074 5021 Plumbing & hydronic heating supplies; Office & public building furniture; Outdoor & lawn furniture
Pr: Joe Chen
Ex VP: Bob Kermelewicz
VP: Jerry Chen
VP: Jennifer Earl
VP: Bruce Henderson
VP: Scott Kensey
VP: Kirk Travers
Genl Mgr: Allan Huang
Info Man: Berlinda Yap
Ql Cn Mgr: Alexander Ortiga
Sales Exec: James Riches

FOREMOST INDUSTRIES
See FOREMOST GROUPS INC

FOREMOST INSURANCE AGENCY
See FOREMOST AFFINITY SERVICES INC

D-U-N-S 00-695-9480
FOREMOST INSURANCE CO
FOREMOST INSURANCE GROUP
(*Suby of* FOREMOST CORP OF AMERICA) ★
5600 Beechtree Ln Se, Caledonia, MI 49316-9482
Tel (616) 942-3000 *Founded/Ownrshp* 1952
Sales NA *EMP* 1,557
SIC 6331 Fire, marine & casualty insurance
COO: F Robert Woudstra
Pr: John Gerhard
COO: Thompson Jeff
**Ex VP:* John J Hannigan
**Ex VP:* David A Heatherly
**Ex VP:* Larry J Orange
**Sr VP:* Paul D Yared
VP: Martin Brown
VP: Ron Joyner
VP: Cindy McLane
VP: Michael Pessetti
Exec: Joanna Carey
Comm Man: Amy Blue

FOREMOST INSURANCE GROUP
See FOREMOST INSURANCE CO

D-U-N-S 60-824-5197
FOREMOST LLOYDS OF TEXAS
(*Suby of* FOREMOST INSURANCE GROUP) ★
5600 Beechtree Ln Se, Caledonia, MI 49316-9587
Tel (616) 942-3000 *Founded/Ownrshp* 1982
Sales NA *EMP* 800
SIC 6331 Fire, marine & casualty insurance
Treas: Frank R Woudstra
**COO:* Robert Woudstra
VP: Cornelius Faulkner
Corp Couns: David Bearden
Corp Couns: Donald Snide

D-U-N-S 11-201-4407
FORESCOUT TECHNOLOGIES INC
190 W Tasman Dr, San Jose, CA 95134-1700
Tel (408) 213-3191 *Founded/Ownrshp* 2000
Sales 119.0MM[E] *EMP* 300[E]
SIC 7371 Computer software development
CEO: T Kent Elliott
Pr: Tom Dolan
**CFO:* Christopher Harms
Chf Mktg O: Rob Greer
**Ofcr:* Pedro Abreu
**Ofcr:* Darren Milliken
Ex VP: Brant Kennedy
Sr VP: Paul Phillips
VP: Myles Bray
VP: Rafael Brenner
VP: Louise Bulman
VP: Sam Davis
VP: Todd Debell
VP: Tom Evans
VP: Zohar Gillai
VP: Scott Gordon
VP: Niels Jensen
VP: Da-Qian Ll
VP: Rodney Toy
Dir Bus: Marty Davis
Board of Directors: James Beer, Mark Jensen, Enrique Salem

D-U-N-S 07-940-1178
▲ FORESIGHT ENERGY LP
211 N Broadway Ste 2600, Saint Louis, MO 63102-2742
Tel (314) 932-6160 *Founded/Ownrshp* 2006
Sales 984.8MM *EMP* 30[E]
Tkr Sym FELP *Exch* NYS
SIC 1221 Bituminous coal & lignite-surface mining
Pr: Robert D Moore
Genl Pt: Foresight Energy GP LLC
CFO: James T Murphy

D-U-N-S 00-805-7218
FOREST ANTHONY PRODUCTS CO
309 N Washington Ave, El Dorado, AR 71730-5614
Tel (870) 862-3414 *Founded/Ownrshp* 1986
Sales 110.7MM[E] *EMP* 470
Accts Frost Pllc Little Rock Arka
SIC 2421 2452 Sawmills & planing mills, general; Prefabricated wood buildings
Pr: Aubra H Anthony Jr
**Treas:* Ronald E Clay
**Ex VP:* Russ Anthony
**VP:* L Clary Anthony Jr
**VP:* Lynda Anthony
**VP:* Kerlin Drake
Dept Mgr: Priscilla Smith
Dir IT: Bruce White

D-U-N-S 05-394-1253 IMP
FOREST BEASLEY PRODUCTS INC (GA)
712 Uvalda Hwy, Hazlehurst, GA 31539-4808
Tel (912) 375-5174 *Founded/Ownrshp* 1997
Sales 154.2MM[E] *EMP* 275[E]
SIC 5031 Lumber, plywood & millwork
Pr: Rabun Beasley
CFO: Darrell Beasley
Exec: Gloria Brown
Sales Asso: Grant Beasley
Sales Asso: Kenny Ray

D-U-N-S 61-572-3475 EXP
FOREST BESSE PRODUCTS INC
BIRCHWOOD MANUFACTURING CO
933 N 8th St, Gladstone, MI 49837
Tel (906) 428-3113 *Founded/Ownrshp* 1966
Sales 131.0MM[E] *EMP* 502
SIC 5031 5099 Lumber, plywood & millwork; Logs, hewn ties, posts & poles
Prin: Greg Besse

D-U-N-S 07-776-6897
FOREST CITY COMMERCIAL MANAGEMENT INC
(*Suby of* FOREST CITY PROPERTIES LLC) ★
50 Public Sq Ste 1410, Cleveland, OH 44113-2202
Tel (216) 621-6060 *Founded/Ownrshp* 1966
Sales 32.9MM[E] *EMP* 1,000
SIC 6531 Real estate managers
Pr: Charles Ratner
**Ch Bd:* Samuel Miller
**Ch Bd:* Albert Ratner
**CFO:* Robert Prien

FOREST CITY ENTERPRISES, INC.
See FOREST CITY ENTERPRISES LP

D-U-N-S 00-896-5386
FOREST CITY ENTERPRISES LP
FOREST CITY ENTERPRISES, INC.
(*Suby of* FOREST CITY REALTY TRUST INC) ★
50 Public Sq Ste 1100, Cleveland, OH 44113-2267
Tel (216) 621-6060 *Founded/Ownrshp* 1920
Sales 966.0MM *EMP* 2,865
SIC 6512 6513 6552 Nonresidential building operators; Commercial & industrial building operation; Shopping center, property operation only; Apartment building operators; Subdividers & developers
Pr: David J Larue
**Ch Bd:* Charles A Ratner
CFO: Deborah J Levinson
CFO: Robert G O'Brien
Ex VP: Charles D Obert
Ex VP: Geralyn M Presti
**Ex VP:* Brian J Ratner
**Ex VP:* Deborah Ratner Salzberg
Sr VP: John R Coumoyer
Sr VP: Susan Elman
Sr VP: Denise A Gammon
Sr VP: Linda M Kane
Sr VP: Charles C Nicola
VP: Thomas G Archer
VP: Harriet Edwards-White
VP: Micheal J Evrard
VP: Larry Klein
VP: Lori L Reeves
VP: Gregory B Spivey

D-U-N-S 07-111-5638
FOREST CITY PROPERTIES LLC
(*Suby of* FOREST CITY ENTERPRISES INC) ★
50 Public Sq Ste 1360, Cleveland, OH 44113-2233
Tel (216) 621-6060 *Founded/Ownrshp* 1969
Sales 72.9MM[E] *EMP* 1,000
SIC 6512 6513 Shopping center, property operation only; Commercial & industrial building operation; Apartment hotel operation
CEO: David La Rue
**Ch Bd:* Charles Ratner
Treas: Chris Clayton
**Ex VP:* James Ratner
Sr VP: Michael R Finnegan
VP: Thomas L Ballman

D-U-N-S 07-994-0124
FOREST CITY REALTY TRUST INC
50 Public Sq, Cleveland, OH 44113-2202
Tel (216) 621-6060 *Founded/Ownrshp* 2015
Sales 978.2MM *EMP* 2,909[E]
Accts Pricewaterhousecoopers Llp Cl
SIC 6798 Real estate investment trusts
Pr: David J Larue
**Ch Bd:* Charles A Ratner
COO: Duane F Bishop
CFO: Robert G O'Brien
Sr VP: Mark Gerteis
Sr VP: Linda Kane
Sr VP: Charles D Obert
Board of Directors: Stan Ross, Arthur F Anton, Deborah Ratner Salzberg, Kenneth J Bacon, Scott S Cowen, Christine R Detrick, Michael P Esposito Jr, Deborah L Harmon, Brian J Ratner, Bruce C Ratner, Ronald A Ratner

D-U-N-S 00-422-1289 IMP
FOREST CITY TECHNOLOGIES INC (OH)
299 Clay St, Wellington, OH 44090-1128
Tel (440) 647-2115 *Founded/Ownrshp* 1955, 1978
Sales 307.7MM[E] *EMP* 1,224
SIC 3053 Gaskets & sealing devices; Gaskets, all materials
Pr: John D Cloud Sr
COO: Jeffrey R Petras
VP: Jack Deruyter
VP: Charles Schillig
**VP:* David Snowball
VP: R Gary Thomas
CTO: Spencer Flora
Opers Mgr: Anna Stanton
Ql Cn Mgr: Mike Deeks

FOREST CITY TRADING GROUP
See FCTG HOLDINGS INC

D-U-N-S 04-828-4566 IMP/EXP
FOREST CITY TRADING GROUP LLC
(*Suby of* FOREST CITY TRADING GROUP) ★
10250 Sw Greenburg Rd # 200, Portland, OR 97223-5461
Tel (503) 246-8500 *Founded/Ownrshp* 1964, 2004
Sales 864.8MM[E] *EMP* 406
SIC 5031 Lumber: rough, dressed & finished; Plywood; Particleboard
Ch Bd: John W Judy Jr
**Pr:* Craig Johnston
**CFO:* Derek Coder
Ofcr: Casey Cottrell
Dir IT: Chris McNierney
IT Man: Lance Means
VP Mktg: Scott Elston

FOREST DATACOM SERVICES
See FOREST ELECTRIC CORP

D-U-N-S 00-186-6615
■ FOREST ELECTRIC CORP (NY)
FOREST DATACOM SERVICES
(*Suby of* EMCOR GROUP INC) ★
1375 Broadway Fl 7, New York, NY 10018-0096
Tel (212) 318-1500 *Founded/Ownrshp* 1945, 1978
Sales 93.3MM[E] *EMP* 600
SIC 1731 7349 General electrical contractor; Telephone & telephone equipment installation; Computer installation; Building maintenance services
Pr: Robert Richardson
**Pr:* Harry Sassaman
**CFO:* Vincent O'Neill
**Ex VP:* Richard Lomler
VP: Terence Cain
VP: James Flaherty
**VP:* John Foley
VP: Thomas Larner
**VP:* Thomas Morris
VP: Tom Morris
VP: Tom Olsen
VP: Richard Sauer
Exec: Mitch Dreyfus

D-U-N-S 15-098-2440
FOREST HAVEN NURSING & CONVALE
315 Ingleside Ave, Baltimore, MD 21228-4423
Tel (410) 747-7425 *Founded/Ownrshp* 2004
Sales 1.3MMM *EMP* 9[E]
SIC 8051 Skilled nursing care facilities
Prin: Diana Dew
Exec: Barbara Watts

FOREST HEALTH
See FORREST GENERAL HEALTH SERVICES INC

D-U-N-S 07-744-4198
FOREST HILLS HOSPITAL
10201 66th Rd, Forest Hills, NY 11375-7624
Tel (718) 830-4000 *Founded/Ownrshp* 1968
Sales 214.1MM *EMP* 890
SIC 8062 General medical & surgical hospitals
Ex Dir: Rita Mercieca
**CEO:* Bruce J Flanz
Dir Rad: James Henglein

D-U-N-S 06-019-0477
FOREST HILLS PUBLIC SCHOOLS
6590 Cascade Rd Se, Grand Rapids, MI 49546-6497
Tel (616) 493-8800 *Founded/Ownrshp* 1956
Sales 133.4MM *EMP* 1,300
Accts Maner Costerisan Pc Lansing
SIC 8211 Public elementary & secondary schools
**CFO:* Tim Raymer
Pr Dir: Elizabeth Brink

D-U-N-S 08-970-5883
FOREST HILLS SCHOOL DISTRICT
7550 Forest Rd, Cincinnati, OH 45255-4320
Tel (513) 231-3335 *Founded/Ownrshp* 1957
Sales 91.4MM *EMP* 728
Accts Dave Yost Columbus Ohio
SIC 8211 Public elementary & secondary schools
Pr Dir: Erica Daggett
Teacher Pr: Tammy Carnahan

D-U-N-S 08-685-0138
FOREST HUNT PRODUCTS INC
401 E Reynolds Dr, Ruston, LA 71270-2818
Tel (318) 255-2245 *Founded/Ownrshp* 1977
Sales 83.8MM[E] *EMP* 350
SIC 2436 2421 Softwood veneer & plywood; Custom sawmill
Ch Bd: Alex T Hunt Jr
**Pr:* Cecil Sibley
**CFO:* James H Hough
Off Mgr: Becky Brawley

D-U-N-S 00-128-8281 IMP
FOREST LABORATORIES LLC
(*Suby of* ALLERGAN PUBLIC LIMITED COMPANY)
909 3rd Ave Fl 23, New York, NY 10022-4748
Tel (212) 421-7850 *Founded/Ownrshp* 1956, 2014
Sales 1.6MMM[E] *EMP* 6,200

SIC 2834 5122 Pharmaceutical preparations; Pharmaceuticals
Pr: R Todd Joyce
COO: Robert Stewart
Chf Mktg O: Lawrence Olanoff
Ofcr: Danielle Galanaugh
Ex VP: Michael Baker
Ex VP: Francis I Perier Jr
Ex VP: Elaine Hochberg
Ex VP: Robert Jackson
Ex VP: Bill Meury
Ex VP: Carol Reed
Ex VP: Marco Taglietti
Sr VP: John Castellana
Sr VP: Paul C Grint
Sr VP: Kevin Walsh
VP: Nancy Barnett
VP: Ian A Critchley
VP: Mark A Devlin
VP: John A Dibella
VP: Ivan Gergel
VP: C Glidewell
VP: Shashank Mahashabde

FOREST LAKE AREA SCHOOL
See INDEPENDENT SCHOOL DISTRICT 831

D-U-N-S 96-787-0929
FOREST LAKE HOSPITAL
660 N Westmoreland Rd, Lake Forest, IL 60045-1659
Tel (847) 234-5600 *Founded/Ownrshp* 2011
Sales 239.0MM *EMP* 4
Accts Crowe Horwath Llp Chicago Il
SIC 8062 General medical & surgical hospitals
Prin: Evan Laskaris
COO: Larry Shoemaker
VP: Matthew Flynn
VP: Kimberly A Nagy
VP: Marsha Oberrieder
Dir Lab: Carol Bagan
Chf Nrs Of: Karen Strathman
Off Mgr: Becky Armstrong
Off Mgr: Mari Lenartowicz
CIO: Nicole Deklotz
CIO: Christie Mills

FOREST LAWN MEMORIAL PARKS AND
See FOREST LAWN MEMORIAL-PARK ASSOCIATION

D-U-N-S 02-824-5025 IMP
FOREST LAWN MEMORIAL-PARK ASSOCIATION
FOREST LAWN MEMORIAL PARKS AND
1712 S Glendale Ave, Glendale, CA 91205-3320
Tel (323) 254-3131 *Founded/Ownrshp* 1906
Sales 129.4MM *EMP* 950
Accts Bkd Llp Tulsa Ok
SIC 5992 6553 7261 Flowers, fresh; Cemetery association; Funeral service & crematories
CEO: Darin B Drabing
**Ch Bd:* Thomas McKernan
**CEO:* John Llewellyn
**CFO:* Russel Whittenberg
**Sr VP:* Susan R Sandler
VP: Kathy Austin
**VP:* Andreea Barbu
**VP:* Larry Davis
**VP:* David Macdonald
VP: Gary Merrill
VP: Ben Sussman

D-U-N-S 01-038-4253
FOREST MANOR INC
FOREST MANOR NURSING HOME
71338 Highway 21, Covington, LA 70433-7162
Tel (985) 892-6900 *Founded/Ownrshp* 1965
Sales 801.7MM *EMP* 130
SIC 8051 Skilled nursing care facilities

FOREST MANOR NURSING HOME
See FOREST MANOR INC

FOREST MATERIAL SUPPLY
See BUILDER SUPPORT SERVICES INC

D-U-N-S 07-851-5516
FOREST PARK MEDICAL CENTER LLC
(*Suby of* VIBRANT HEALTHCARE, LLC)
11990 N Central Expy, Dallas, TX 75243-3714
Tel (972) 234-1900 *Founded/Ownrshp* 2007
Sales 202.6MM^E *EMP* 675^E
SIC 8011 Medical centers
COO: James Davis
Dir Lab: Paula Matricardi
CIO: Si Nguyen
Dir IT: Warren Ware
Nrsg Dir: Julie Camp

D-U-N-S 13-941-9675 IMP
FOREST PHARMACEUTICALS INC
(*Suby of* FOREST LABORATORIES LLC) ★
400 Interpace Pkwy Ste A1, Parsippany, NJ 07054-1119
Tel (862) 261-7000 *Founded/Ownrshp* 1984
Sales 158.7MM^E *EMP* 1,150
SIC 2834 Pharmaceutical preparations
Ch Bd: Howard Solomon
**Pr:* Kenneth Goodman
**Ex VP:* William B Sparks
VP: Doug Glidewell
VP: William J Meury
Ex Dir: Dave Boyle
Opers Mgr: Mark Rewets
Ql Cn Mgr: Tom Ferter
Ql Cn Mgr: Melissa White
Snr Mgr: Kate Jonas

D-U-N-S 17-071-5812
FOREST PRODUCTS HOLDINGS LLC
(*Suby of* MADISON DEARBORN PARTNERS IV LP) ★
1111 W Jefferson St # 300, Boise, ID 83702-5383
Tel (208) 384-6161 *Founded/Ownrshp* 2004
Sales 726.8MM^E *EMP* 10,191^E
SIC 5031 8744 Building materials, exterior; Building materials, interior; Composite board products, woodboard; Lumber: rough, dressed & finished; Facilities support services
CEO: Thomas Carlile r
**Sr VP:* Wayne Rancourt
**Sr VP:* John Sahlberg
**VP:* Kelly Hibbs

FOREST PRODUCTS SUPPLY
See MILLMAN LUMBER CO

D-U-N-S 36-356-8879
■ **FOREST RAYONIER RESOURCES LP**
RAYONIER NW FOREST RESOURCES
(*Suby of* RAYONIER INC) ★
50 N Laura St Ste 1900, Jacksonville, FL 32202-3638
Tel (904) 357-9100 *Founded/Ownrshp* 1985
Sales 102.7MM^E *EMP* 1,400
SIC 0851 Forestry services
CEO: Paul Boynton
Sr VP: Timothy Brannon

D-U-N-S 83-883-3069 IMP/EXP
■ **FOREST RIVER INC**
(*Suby of* BERKSHIRE HATHAWAY INC) ★
900 County Road 1 N, Elkhart, IN 46514-8992
Tel (574) 389-4600 *Founded/Ownrshp* 2005
Sales 2.6MMM^E *EMP* 6,000
SIC 5561 3715 Recreational vehicle dealers; Truck trailers
Pr: Peter J Liegl
**VP:* Jeff Babdock
**Prin:* Sandy Marschke
Genl Mgr: John Quake
IT Man: Gary Koontz
Mfg Dir: Rick Schraw
Ql Cn Mgr: Juan Machuca
Natl Sales: Jeff Babcock
Mktg Mgr: Mike Dolowy
Manager: John Madias
Manager: Michael Terlep

D-U-N-S 00-450-3801 EXP
FOREST SNAVELY PRODUCTS INC (PA)
600 Delwar Rd, Pittsburgh, PA 15236-1351
Tel (412) 885-4005 *Founded/Ownrshp* 1902
Sales 145.9MM *EMP* 145
SIC 5031 Lumber: rough, dressed & finished; Millwork
Ch Bd: Stephen V Snavely
**Pr:* John A Stockhausen
**CFO:* Kellie Radzik
**VP:* Susan Fitzsimmons
**VP:* Mark Spargo
**VP:* Clark Spitzer
Sales Asso: Carl Lamb
Board of Directors: William Baugh, Jay Greyson, Brent Grover

D-U-N-S 08-637-6266 IMP
FOREST SPARTANBURG PRODUCTS INC
1431 Highway 101 S, Greer, SC 29651-6731
Tel (864) 699-3100 *Founded/Ownrshp* 1978
Sales 166.5MM^E *EMP* 31
SIC 7389

D-U-N-S 96-474-8305
FOREST TOMBALL PRODUCTS INC
TOMBALL FOREST
16801 Fm 2920 Rd, Tomball, TX 77377-6018
Tel (281) 357-8196 *Founded/Ownrshp* 1999
Sales 92.1MM^E *EMP* 122^E
SIC 5083 5211 5031 Farm & garden machinery; Lumber & other building materials; Lumber, plywood & millwork
Pr: Vince Goodman
Mktg Dir: Terry Welch

D-U-N-S 78-222-6893
▲ **FORESTAR GROUP INC**
6300 Fm 2244 Rd Bldg 500, Austin, TX 78746-5833
Tel (512) 433-5200 *Founded/Ownrshp* 1955
Sales 262.4MM *EMP* 106
Accts Ernst & Young Llp Austin Te
Tkr Sym FOR *Exch* NYS
SIC 6531 1382 Real estate agents & managers; Oil & gas exploration services
CEO: Phillip J Weber
CFO: Charles D Jehl
Ofcr: Bruce F Dickson
Ofcr: David M Grimm
Ofcr: Flavious J Smith Jr
Ex VP: Tom Burleson
Ex VP: Charles Etheredge Jr
Sr VP: Anna Torma
VP: Brent Covert
VP: Randy McCuistion
VP: Sabita C Reddy
Board of Directors: Carl A Thomason, Kathleen Brown, David L Weinstein, William G Currie, Michael E Dougherty, Kenneth M Jastrow II, James A Johnson, Charles W Matthews, William C Powers Jr, James A Rubright, Richard M Smith

D-U-N-S 61-225-2718
FORESTERS EQUITY SERVICES INC
(*Suby of* INDEPENDENT ORDER OF FORESTERS, THE)
6640 Lusk Blvd Ste A202, San Diego, CA 92121-2777
Tel (858) 550-4844 *Founded/Ownrshp* 1986
Sales 110.0MM *EMP* 600
SIC 6211 Security brokers & dealers
Pr: Frank Smith
Treas: Martha Ward
Chf Mktg O: Heather Broderick
Ofcr: Mitchell Langton
VP: Laura Malechuk
**VP:* Mark McDonough
VP: Suanne Nielsen
VP: Sandy Wilson
CIO: Peter Sweers
Dir IT: Christopher Wansbrough
Mktg Mgr: Kim McCarthy

D-U-N-S 04-470-7073
FORESTERS FINANCIAL SERVICES
(*Suby of* FORESTERS SECURITIES (CANADA) INC)
40 Wall St Fl 10, New York, NY 10005-1343
Tel (212) 858-8000 *Founded/Ownrshp* 2011
Sales NA *EMP* 1,400
SIC 6036 6211 6282 6311 8742 6153 Savings & loan associations, not federally chartered; Dealers, security; Investment advisory service; Life insurance; Management consulting services; Short-term business credit
Prin: Kathryn S Head

D-U-N-S 95-795-2666
FORESTLAND GROUP LLC
1512 E Franklin St # 104, Chapel Hill, NC 27514-2816
Tel (919) 929-2497 *Founded/Ownrshp* 1995
Sales 89.6MM^E *EMP* 394
SIC 6282 Investment advice

D-U-N-S 79-235-8095
FORESTRY AND FIRE PROTECTION CALIFORNIA DEPARTMENT OF
CAL FIRE
(*Suby of* CALIFORNIA NATURAL RESOURCES AGENCY) ★
1416 9th St Ste 1535, Sacramento, CA 95814-5568
Tel (916) 653-7772 *Founded/Ownrshp* 1977
Sales NA *EMP* 3,753
SIC 9512 Land, mineral & wildlife conservation;
**Prin:* Edmund G Brown Jr
Counsel: Giny Chandler

D-U-N-S 00-950-8819
FORETHOUGHT FINANCIAL GROUP INC
(*Suby of* GLOBAL ATLANTIC FINANCIAL GROUP LIMITED)
3200 Southwest Fwy # 1300, Houston, TX 77027-7528
Tel (713) 599-0405 *Founded/Ownrshp* 2014
Sales NA *EMP* 300^E
SIC 6311 Life insurance
Pr: Michael Reardon
V Ch: John Graf
**Ex VP:* Robert Arena
**Ex VP:* Mary Cavanaugh
**Ex VP:* Paula Nelson
**Ex VP:* Eric Todd

D-U-N-S 18-826-7504
FORETHOUGHT LIFE INSURANCE CO
(*Suby of* FORETHOUGHT FINANCIAL GROUP INC) ★
1 Forethought Ctr, Batesville, IN 47006-1490
Tel (812) 934-7139 *Founded/Ownrshp* 2004
Sales NA *EMP* 200^E
SIC 6311 Life insurance carriers
Pr: Stephen R Lang
**CFO:* Charles A Russell
**Treas:* Ronald J Marek
Ex VP: Mary L Cavanaugh
**VP:* Frederick W Rockwood
CIO: Eric Todd

D-U-N-S 04-243-7293 IMP/EXP
FOREVER 21 INC
FOREVER XXI, ULC
3880 N Mission Rd, Los Angeles, CA 90031-3187
Tel (213) 741-5100 *Founded/Ownrshp* 2002
Sales 5.1MMM^E *EMP* 30,000
SIC 5632 5661 5621 Women's accessory & specialty stores; Apparel accessories; Women's shoes; Women's clothing stores
CEO: Do Won Chang
CFO: Ann Cadier Kim
Treas: Lawrence Meyer
Ex VP: Kaye Lee
Sr VP: Jong Sung Kim
VP: Brian Chung
VP: Liz Hauer
VP: Chris Lee
VP: Dee McLaughlin
Exec: Stacy Bahnsen
Exec: Maria Viola
Assoc Dir: Maria C Gasgonia

D-U-N-S 78-933-9199
FOREVER LIVING PRODUCTS US INC
7501 E Mccormick Pkwy # 105, Scottsdale, AZ 85258-3471
Tel (480) 998-8888 *Founded/Ownrshp* 1978
Sales 337.5MM^E *EMP* 2,076
SIC 5122 Cosmetics, perfumes & hair products
Pr: Rex G Maughan
**Treas:* Glen Banks
Top Exec: Gary Shreve
Sr VP: Harold Greene
Sr VP: Dave Hall
Sr VP: John S Schoppmann
Sr VP: Don Wallace
Sr VP: Carl Zander
VP: Garin Breinholt
VP: Steve Itami
VP: Rhonda Krause
VP: Lloyd Rjay
VP: Linda Ruble

FOREVER XXI, ULC
See FOREVER 21 INC

D-U-N-S 12-647-2286
FOREX CAPITAL MARKETS LLC
FXCM
55 Water St Fl 50, New York, NY 10041-3203
Tel (646) 355-0839 *Founded/Ownrshp* 1999
Sales 129.1MM^E *EMP* 400^E
Accts Ernst & Young Llp New York
SIC 6211 Security brokers & dealers
Exec: Ken Grossman
Pr: David Sassoon
VP: Henry Depaolis
VP: Michael Fazio
VP: Kenneth O'Brien
VP: Marcelo Spina
Ex Dir: Girish Rangan
MIS Mgr: Frank Lau
MIS Mgr: Steve McCabe
Software D: Andre Mermegas

D-U-N-S 13-451-0648
■ **FORFEITURE SUPPORT ASSOCIATES LLC**
FSA
(*Suby of* ENGILITY LLC) ★
20110 Ashbrook Pl Ste 220, Ashburn, VA 20147-5075
Tel (571) 291-8900 *Founded/Ownrshp* 2004
Sales 12.5MM *EMP* 1,800
Accts Thompson Greenspon Fairfax V
SIC 8111 8742 Legal services; Management consulting services
Genl Mgr: John Houck
Ofcr: Peter McCormick
Off Mgr: Paula Osheroff
IT Man: Darrance Dixon

D-U-N-S 10-793-0133
FORGE CO
1050 Thmas Jfferson St Nw, Washington, DC 20007-3837
Tel (202) 295-8100 *Founded/Ownrshp* 1977
Sales 60.8MM^E *EMP* 1,100
SIC 7521 7011 Parking garage; Parking structure; Hotels
Ch Bd: Russell Lindner
Sr Pt: Josie Crockett
Opers Mgr: Jeff Garrison

D-U-N-S 00-194-6110 IMP
FORGE INDUSTRIES INC (OH)
4450 Market St, Youngstown, OH 44512-1512
Tel (330) 782-8301 *Founded/Ownrshp* 1900, 1942
Sales 588.8MM^E *EMP* 2,000
Accts Kpmg Llp
SIC 5085 3566 3599 3531 6411 7699 Bearings; Power transmission equipment & apparatus; Gears, power transmission, except automotive; Machine shop, jobbing & repair; Road construction & maintenance machinery; Insurance brokers; Industrial equipment services
Ch Bd: William T James II
**Pr:* Carl G James
**CFO:* Dan Maisonville
**VP:* W Thomas James III

D-U-N-S 10-313-4474 IMP/EXP
■ **FORGED METALS INC**
ARCONIC FSTENING SYSTEMS RINGS
(*Suby of* ARCONIC INC) ★
10685 Beech Ave, Fontana, CA 92337-7212
Tel (909) 350-9260 *Founded/Ownrshp* 2014
Sales 160.0MM^E *EMP* 200
SIC 3353 Aluminum sheet, plate & foil
CEO: Klaus Kleinfeld
Plnt Mgr: Shawn Gould
Prd Mgr: Manny Lopez
Sls Mgr: Jody Williams

FORGED VESSEL CONNECTIONS
See AMERIFORGE GROUP INC

D-U-N-S 10-264-5462 IMP/EXP
FORGINGS FLANGES & FITTINGS LLC
(*Suby of* GLOBAL GROUP) ★
8900 Railwood Dr Unit B, Houston, TX 77078-4535
Tel (713) 695-5400 *Founded/Ownrshp* 1983
Sales 173.2MM^E *EMP* 250
SIC 5085 Industrial supplies
Pr: Danny Lee
**VP:* Stan Lee

D-U-N-S 83-221-5797 IMP
FORM HHI TECH LLC
(*Suby of* KPS CAPITAL PARTNERS LP) ★
2727 W 14 Mile Rd, Royal Oak, MI 48073-1712
Tel (248) 597-3800 *Founded/Ownrshp* 2009
Sales 147.1MM^E *EMP* 500
SIC 3462 Automotive & internal combustion engine forgings

D-U-N-S 10-822-5822 IMP
FORMAN MILLS INC
1070 Thomas Busch Mem Hwy, Pennsauken, NJ 08110-2313
Tel (856) 486-1447 *Founded/Ownrshp* 2016
Sales 402.5MM^E *EMP* 2,000
SIC 5699 Sports apparel; Leather garments
CEO: Allen Weinstein

D-U-N-S 78-638-2635
FORMATION CAPITAL LLC
3500 Lenox Rd Ne Ste 510, Atlanta, GA 30326-4229
Tel (770) 754-9660 *Founded/Ownrshp* 1999
Sales 399.2MM^E *EMP* 20,000
SIC 6211 8742 Security brokers & dealers; Financial consultant
Ch: Arnold Whitman
**Pr:* Steve Fishman
**CEO:* Brian Beckwith
CFO: Chris Sertich
Sr VP: David Russ
VP: Stephanie Hamner

D-U-N-S 96-556-5505 IMP
FORMED FIBER TECHNOLOGIES INC
CONFORM AUTOMOTIVE
125 Allied Rd, Auburn, ME 04210-7985
Tel (207) 784-1118 *Founded/Ownrshp* 2003
Sales 235.3MM^E *EMP* 900
SIC 2824 3089 2823

D-U-N-S 80-903-3236 IMP
▲ **FORMFACTOR INC**
7005 Southfront Rd, Livermore, CA 94551-8201
Tel (925) 290-4000 *Founded/Ownrshp* 1995
Sales 282.3MM *EMP* 958
Tkr Sym FORM *Exch* NGS
SIC 3674 Semiconductors & related devices; Thermoelectric devices, solid state
CEO: Michael D Slessor
**Ch Bd:* Thomas St Dennis
CFO: Michael M Ludwig
VP: Prahlad Moharir
VP: Tony Tryba
Snr Mgr: Doug Ondricek
Board of Directors: Richard Delateur, Raymond A Link, Lothar Maier, Edward Rogas Jr, Kelley Steven-Waiss, Michael W Zellner

D-U-N-S 00-425-0890 IMP
FORMICA CORP (NJ)
(*Suby of* FLETCHER BUILDING LIMITED)
10155 Reading Rd, Cincinnati, OH 45241-4805
Tel (513) 786-3400 *Founded/Ownrshp* 1913
Sales 263.8MM^E *EMP* 1,000

SIC 2541 2679 Counter & sink tops; Table or counter tops, plastic laminated; Paperboard products, converted
Pr: Frank Riddick
**Pr:* Mitchell P Quint
COO: Davod Pallas
CFO: Pamela Formica
Treas: Chris Gray
**Treas:* Lynn Younger
VP: Gerry Bollman
**VP:* R Gerard Bollman
**VP:* Edward R Case
VP: Stephen Demay
**VP:* Michael Fischer
VP: Amy Fowles
VP: Gary Garland
VP: Renee Hytry
VP: Alice Rand
VP: Bob Richards
**VP:* Raul Rosado
**VP:* Catherine Vernon
Exec: Amy Harris

D-U-N-S 10-623-8165 IMP/EXP
FORMOSA PLASTICS CORP TEXAS
(*Suby of* FPC USA) ★
201 Formosa Dr, Point Comfort, TX 77978
Tel (361) 987-7000 *Founded/Ownrshp* 1978
Sales 737.9MM[E] *EMP* 2,200
SIC 2821 Polyvinyl chloride resins (PVC)
Ch Bd: Y C Wang
Pr: Charles Cheng
**Pr:* T C Dee
**Pr:* Jason Lin
**CFO:* David Lynn
**Ch:* C T Lee
**Treas:* Robert Ho
**Ex VP:* Walter Chen
**Ex VP:* Susan Wong
VP: Rodney Moore
Sfty Mgr: Rusty Daigle

D-U-N-S 03-994-4004 IMP/EXP
FORMOSA PLASTICS CORP USA
FPC USA
9 Peach Tree Hill Rd, Livingston, NJ 07039-5702
Tel (973) 994-7674 *Founded/Ownrshp* 1978
Sales 1.3MMM[E] *EMP* 2,609
SIC 2821 2812 Polyvinyl chloride resins (PVC); Vinyl resins; Caustic soda, sodium hydroxide
Ch: C T Lee
Pr: David Lin
Pr: Jason Lin
Treas: Teh Y Liao
Ex VP: Walter Chen
VP: Bob Chou
VP: Dick Heinle
VP: I S Hwang
VP: Bob Kelley
VP: Hc Lee
VP: L Pan
VP: Paul WEI

D-U-N-S 92-778-8786 IMP
FORMOSA UTILITY VENTURE LTD
201 Formosa Dr, Point Comfort, TX 77978
Tel (361) 987-7000 *Founded/Ownrshp* 1990
Sales 228.8MM[E] *EMP* 1,500
SIC 2673 Plastic bags: made from purchased materials
Pt: Jay Su

D-U-N-S 12-167-9310 IMP/EXP
FORMS AND SURFACES INC
BERMAN GLASS
30 Pine St, Pittsburgh, PA 15223-1919
Tel (412) 781-9003 *Founded/Ownrshp* 1984
Sales 108.7MM[E] *EMP* 439
SIC 3446 Architectural metalwork
Pr: Jeffrey M Stork
**Treas:* Jim Evans
Ex VP: Tim Ellis
**VP:* Lauren S Flannery
VP: Matt Vizzini
Software D: Mike Wieczorkowski
VP Mfg: Bob Hoey
Opers Mgr: Nicole Cosnotti
Opers Mgr: Trent Gatterdam
Opers Mgr: Roberto Vasquez
VP Mktg: Karen Tullis

D-U-N-S 61-854-4928
FORNACA INC
FRANK TOYATA & SCION
2400 National City Blvd, National City, CA 91950-6628
Tel (619) 474-5573 *Founded/Ownrshp* 2014
Sales 106.6MM[E] *EMP* 230
SIC 5511 7532 5531 Automotive & home supply stores; Automotive parts; Automobiles, new & used; Top & body repair & paint shops
CEO: James Fornaca
**VP:* Gary Fenelli
**VP:* Ronald Fornaca
Off Mgr: Paulette Rettig
IT Man: Jerry Drewett

D-U-N-S 17-821-4839 EXP
FORNAZOR INTERNATIONAL INC A NEW JERSEY CORP
455 Hillsdale Ave, Hillsdale, NJ 07642-2710
Tel (201) 664-4000 *Founded/Ownrshp* 1987
Sales 125.0MM *EMP* 25[E]
SIC 0119 2034 2044 2045 2075 4449 Feeder grains; Vegetable flour, meal & powder; Rice milling; Flours & flour mixes, from purchased flour; Soybean oil, cake or meal; Intracoastal (freight) transportation
CEO: John Fornazor
**Pr:* Kevin Sinnott

D-U-N-S 00-706-6186 IMP/EXP
FORNEY INDUSTRIES INC
2057 Vermont Dr, Fort Collins, CO 80525-2913
Tel (800) 521-6038 *Founded/Ownrshp* 1932
Sales 102.9MM[E] *EMP* 250
SIC 5084

D-U-N-S 03-549-0416
■ **FORREST CITY GROCERY CO**
(*Suby of* CORE-MARK HOLDING CO INC) ★
3400 Commerce Rd, Forrest City, AR 72335-9513
Tel (870) 633-2044 *Founded/Ownrshp* 1943, 2011
Sales 111.7MM[E] *EMP* 200
SIC 5141 5993 Groceries, general line; Tobacconist
Pr: J Michael Walsh
**CFO:* Steve C Ball
**Sec:* Gregory P Antholzner
**VP:* Stacy Loretz Congdon

D-U-N-S 07-789-3386
FORREST GENERAL HEALTH SERVICES INC
PINE GROVE RECOVERY
6051 U S Highway 49, Hattiesburg, MS 39401-7200
Tel (601) 288-7000 *Founded/Ownrshp* 1952
Sales 398.6MM[E] *EMP* 4,030
SIC 8062 8063 8069 General medical & surgical hospitals; Psychiatric hospitals; Substance abuse hospitals
**CFO:* Andy Woodard

D-U-N-S 15-722-4478
FORREST GENERAL HEALTH SERVICES INC
FOREST HEALTH
(*Suby of* PINE GROVE RECOVERY) ★
6051 U S Highway 49, Hattiesburg, MS 39401-7200
Tel (601) 288-7000 *Founded/Ownrshp* 1985
Sales 398.6MM *EMP* 168
SIC 8062 General medical & surgical hospitals
CEO: Evan Dillard
**Pr:* William C Oliver
**CFO:* Ed Tucker
Exec: Kelly McDaniel
Pr Dir: Millie Swan
Doctor: Roderick Cutrer
Doctor: Bassam Mechleb MD
Doctor: Antoine Rizk
Doctor: Robert Robbins
Doctor: Bradley Secrest
Doctor: Raymond Whitehead

FORREST GENERAL HOMECARE
See FORREST GENERAL HOSPITAL

D-U-N-S 04-547-9099
FORREST GENERAL HOSPITAL
FORREST GENERAL HOMECARE
1414 S 28th Ave, Hattiesburg, MS 39402-3107
Tel (601) 288-2500 *Founded/Ownrshp* 1985
Sales 443.0MM *EMP* 30
SIC 8082 8093 Home health care services; Rehabilitation center, outpatient treatment
VP Bus: Allen Meadows
Dir Rad: Mark Laurent
Dir Env Sv: Randall Strange
Pathlgst: Timothy L Cole
Pathlgst: Leigh A Mellen
Pathlgst: Thomas G Puckett
Surgeon: Teresa Farve
Doctor: James Antinnes
Doctor: Scott C Lynn MD

D-U-N-S 17-725-9900
FORREST SOLUTIONS INC
19 W 44th St Fl 9, New York, NY 10036-6101
Tel (212) 986-3600 *Founded/Ownrshp* 1980
Sales 109.4MM[E] *EMP* 1,200[E]
SIC 7361 Employment agencies
Pr: Steve Forrest
**Owner:* Mitchell D Weiner
**Pr:* Jim Caton
Ex VP: Art Tatge
**Sr VP:* Kimberly Shephard
VP: Melanie Frost
VP: Jamie Lawless
Exec: Cassandra Novak
Mng Ofcr: Jan Powers

D-U-N-S 07-304-1451
FORREST T JONES & CO INC (MO)
3130 Brdwy Blvd, Kansas City, MO 64111
Tel (816) 756-1060 *Founded/Ownrshp* 1952
Sales NA *EMP* 228
SIC 6411 Insurance agents
Pr: Dean W Cook
**Pr:* Richard F Jones

D-U-N-S 03-571-8170 IMP
FORREST TIRE CO INC (NM)
414 S Canal St, Carlsbad, NM 88220-5676
Tel (575) 887-3567 *Founded/Ownrshp* 1971
Sales 84.7MM[E] *EMP* 200
SIC 5531 5014 Automotive tires; Automobile tires & tubes
Pr: Richard Forrest Jr
**Treas:* Robert H Forrest Jr
**VP:* Mike Forest
Store Mgr: Skipper Briggs

D-U-N-S 60-504-5848
FORRESTER CONSTRUCTION CO
12231 Parklawn Dr, Rockville, MD 20852-1723
Tel (301) 816-1700 *Founded/Ownrshp* 1988
Sales 112.9MM[E] *EMP* 150
SIC 1542 Commercial & office building contractors
Pr: David Forrester
**CFO:* Wayne Cabot
VP: John R Foeste
**VP:* D Scott Forrester
Exec: Seth Grace
Exec: William Stann
Genl Mgr: Rebecca Campbell
IT Man: Tom Gillingham
Snr PM: Jamie Hart
Snr PM: Asiad Kunaish
Snr PM: Lamarr Mayo

D-U-N-S 10-676-5928
▲ **FORRESTER RESEARCH INC**
60 Acorn Park Dr, Cambridge, MA 02140-2303
Tel (617) 613-6000 *Founded/Ownrshp* 1983
Sales 313.7MM *EMP* 1,345[E]
Tkr Sym FORR *Exch* NGS
SIC 8732 Business research service
Ch Bd: George F Colony

CFO: Michael A Doyle
Chf Mktg O: Victor Milligan
Ofcr: Steven Peltzman
Ofcr: Lucia Luce Quinn
VP: Michael Barnes
VP: Colleen Donahue-Bean
VP: Sheryl Pattek
Dir Sec: Michael Morhardt
Board of Directors: Henk W Broeders, Robert M Galford, George R Hornig, Gretchen G Teichgraeber, Michael H Welles

FORSCOM
See ARMY FORCES COMMAND UNITED STATES

D-U-N-S 09-296-6282 IMP/EXP
FORSTMANN LITTLE & CO
767 5th Ave Fl 4, New York, NY 10153-0023
Tel (212) 355-5656 *Founded/Ownrshp* 1978
Sales 123.0MM[E] *EMP* 17,034
SIC 7991 6211 Health club; Investment bankers
Ch: Julian Robertson
Genl Pt: Erskine Bowles
Genl Pt: Geoff McKay
Pt: Chris A Davis
**Pt:* Gordon A Holmes
**Pt:* Sandra Horbach
Pt: Jamie Carter Nicholls
CFO: Kathleen Broderick
VP: Kate Grant
Exec: Barb Tobias

D-U-N-S 07-844-3583
FORSYTH BALDWIN LLC
(*Suby of* FORSYTH CAPITAL INVESTORS LLC) ★
8040 Forsyth Blvd, Saint Louis, MO 63105-1707
Tel (314) 726-2152 *Founded/Ownrshp* 2008
Sales 97.9MM[E] *EMP* 512[E]
SIC 6722 Management investment, open-end

D-U-N-S 83-309-4324
FORSYTH CAPITAL INVESTORS LLC
8040 Forsyth Blvd, Saint Louis, MO 63105-1707
Tel (314) 726-2152 *Founded/Ownrshp* 2008
Sales 113.0MM[E] *EMP* 512[E]
SIC 6722 Management investment, open-end

D-U-N-S 55-675-2236
FORSYTH COUNTY BOARD OF EDUCATION
F S C
1120 Dahlonega Hwy, Cumming, GA 30040-4536
Tel (770) 887-2461 *Founded/Ownrshp* 1930
Sales 361.7MM[E] *EMP* 4,160
Accts Mauldin & Jenkins Llc Atlant
SIC 8211 School board
Ch Bd: Darla Light
COO: Mark Klingler
**CFO:* Dan Jones
Exec: Andra Cruse
Exec: Jake Grant
Schl Brd P: Nancy Roche
Board of Directors: Tom Clevland

D-U-N-S 07-979-9757
FORSYTH COUNTY SCHOOLS
1120 Dahlonega Hwy, Cumming, GA 30040-4536
Tel (770) 887-2461 *Founded/Ownrshp* 2015
Sales 60.3MM[E] *EMP* 3,701[E]
SIC 8211 Public elementary & secondary schools
COO: Rosemary Lay
Ex Dir: Charlotte Phillips
Area Mgr: Teresa Hewatt-Callaway
Dir IT: Anita Seay
IT Man: Ron McAllister
Pr Dir: Hannah Orr

FORSYTH MEDICAL CENTER
See FORSYTH MEMORIAL HOSPITAL INC

D-U-N-S 07-782-9653
FORSYTH MEDICAL CENTER FOUNDATION
(*Suby of* LAKESIDE FAMILY PHYSICIANS) ★
3333 Silas Creek Pkwy, Winston Salem, NC 27103-3013
Tel (336) 277-1120 *Founded/Ownrshp* 1964
Sales 2.4MM *EMP* 3,995
SIC 8062 General medical & surgical hospitals
CEO: Carl Armato
CFO: Dean Swindle
Ofcr: Carole Maltsby
**Ex VP:* Jacque Daniels
**Sr VP:* Herb Clegg
**Sr VP:* Paula Vincente
**Prin:* Betsy Annese
**Prin:* Edna Blanton

D-U-N-S 80-186-6278
FORSYTH MEMORIAL HOSPITAL INC
FORSYTH MEDICAL CENTER
(*Suby of* LAKESIDE FAMILY PHYSICIANS) ★
3333 Silas Creek Pkwy, Winston Salem, NC 27103-3090
Tel (336) 277-1120 *Founded/Ownrshp* 2012
Sales 1.2MMM *EMP* 47
SIC 8062 General medical & surgical hospitals
CEO: Carl Armato
Ofcr: Arnold King
**Sr VP:* Sean Sanz
VP: Andrew Griffin
VP: Bill Johnson
Dir Lab: Linda Phelps
Dir Rx: Cheryl M Ezan
Chf Nrs Of: Shirley D Matthews
Brnch Mgr: Nyda Harder
Nurse Mgr: Joy Brown
Pathlgst: Scott Kilpatrick

D-U-N-S 07-782-1718
FORSYTH TECHNICAL COMMUNITY COLLEGE INC
(*Suby of* NORTH CAROLINA COMMUNITY COLLEGE SYSTEM) ★
2100 Silas Creek Pkwy, Winston Salem, NC 27103-5150
Tel (336) 723-0371 *Founded/Ownrshp* 1964
Sales 1.1MM[E] *EMP* 1,000
Accts Cannon & Company Llp Winston
SIC 8222 9411 Community college; Administration of educational programs;

Pr: Gary Green
Ofcr: Debbra Hauser
VP: Kenneth Jarvis
Software D: Joana Themido
Psych: Kristen Bates
Psych: Jarrette Dineen
Psych: Tim Groome
Snr Mgr: Toni Beery

D-U-N-S 88-446-1757
FORSYTHE SOLUTIONS GROUP INC
(*Suby of* FORSYTHE TECHNOLOGY INC) ★
7770 Frontage Rd, Skokie, IL 60077-2634
Tel (847) 213-7000 *Founded/Ownrshp* 1984
Sales 165.2MM[E] *EMP* 520
SIC 7379 Computer related consulting services
CEO: William Brennan
Treas: Gary Lomonaco
Treas: Albert L Weiss
Sr VP: Steve Abbott
VP: Steve Avrick
VP: Robert Dvorak
VP: Richard Finecchi
VP: Mitchell Germaine
VP: Harry Manos
VP: Bill Marks
VP: Patrick Zelten
Exec: Jill Buckner

D-U-N-S 00-771-0825
FORSYTHE TECHNOLOGY INC
7770 Frontage Rd, Skokie, IL 60077-2634
Tel (847) 213-7000 *Founded/Ownrshp* 1977
Sales 3.1MMM[E] *EMP* 1,000
SIC 7377 5045 7373 Computer hardware rental or leasing, except finance leasing; Computers, peripherals & software; Computer integrated systems design; Computer-aided design (CAD) systems service
Pr: William P Brennan
CFO: Daniel Noonon
**CFO:* Albert L Weiss
Treas: Gary Lomonaco
Ex VP: Steve Abbott
Ex VP: Steve M Abbott
Sr VP: James G Bindon
**Sr VP:* Jeffrey Davies
Sr VP: Thomas R Ehmann
Sr VP: Greg P Fearing
Sr VP: Thomas R Hoffman
Sr VP: Julie Fusco Nagle
VP: Steven M Avrick
VP: Dave Buchanon
VP: John Carcone
VP: Michelle Coffield
VP: Thomas P Fahy
VP: Herb Frietsch
VP: Julie Fusco
VP: Mitchell Germaine
VP: David Gustafson

D-U-N-S 06-847-3628
FORSYTHE/MCARTHUR ASSOCIATES INC
(*Suby of* FORSYTHE TECHNOLOGY INC) ★
7770 Frontage Rd, Skokie, IL 60077-2634
Tel (847) 213-7000 *Founded/Ownrshp* 1971
Sales 3.0MMM *EMP* 173
SIC 7377 7373 5045

D-U-N-S 07-844-7584
FORT BELVOIR COMMUNITY HOSPITAL
9300 Dewitt Loop, Fort Belvoir, VA 22060-5285
Tel (703) 805-0510 *Founded/Ownrshp* 2012
Sales 100.9MM[E] *EMP* 2,218[E]
SIC 8062 General medical & surgical hospitals

D-U-N-S 07-390-5135
FORT BEND INDEPENDENT SCHOOL DISTRICT
16431 Lexington Blvd, Sugar Land, TX 77479-2308
Tel (281) 634-1000 *Founded/Ownrshp* 1959
Sales 210.1MM[E] *EMP* 9,000
SIC 8211

D-U-N-S 00-510-4930 IMP/EXP
FORT DEARBORN CO
VIRTUALCOLOR
(*Suby of* KRG CAPITAL PARTNERS LLC) ★
1530 Morse Ave, Elk Grove Village, IL 60007-5724
Tel (847) 357-9500 *Founded/Ownrshp* 1925, 2016
Sales 223.0MM[E] *EMP* 1,237
SIC 2752 2759

D-U-N-S 07-865-4712
FORT GIBSON NURSING HOME
205 E Poplar St, Fort Gibson, OK 74434-8272
Tel (918) 478-2456 *Founded/Ownrshp* 1971
Sales 280.4MM *EMP* 40
SIC 8052 Intermediate care facilities
Pt: Dale Scott
Pt: Clayton Farmer
Pt: Gilbert Green

D-U-N-S 07-286-5629
FORT HAMILTON HOSPITAL
CHARLES F KETTERING MEMORIAL H
(*Suby of* CHARLES F KETTERING MEM HOSP) ★
630 Eaton Ave, Hamilton, OH 45013-2767
Tel (513) 867-2000 *Founded/Ownrshp* 1925
Sales 121.4MM *EMP* 1,286
SIC 8062 General medical & surgical hospitals
Dir Vol: Peggy Turner
Pr: Alex Rodriguez
Dir Rad: Karen Wilson
Chf Nrs Of: Nicole Carpenter
VP Opers: Michael Mewhirter

D-U-N-S 17-559-7467
FORT HAMILTON-HUGHES HEALTHCARE CORP
630 Eaton Ave, Hamilton, OH 45013-2767
Tel (513) 867-2000 *Founded/Ownrshp* 1985
Sales 3.3MM *EMP* 1,135
SIC 8741 Management services
Pr: James A Kingsbury

D-U-N-S 07-627-4919
FORT HAYS STATE UNIVERSITY
600 Park St, Hays, KS 67601-4099
Tel (785) 628-4000 *Founded/Ownrshp* 1902

Sales 78.2MM *EMP* 1,503[E]
SIC 8221 University
Pr: Mirta Martin
Exec: Judith Getty
Off Mgr: Amy Klein
MIS Dir: Mark Bannister
VP Mktg: Kent Steward

D-U-N-S 07-383-9573
FORT HEALTHCARE INC
611 Sherman Ave E, Fort Atkinson, WI 53538-1960
Tel (920) 568-5401 *Founded/Ownrshp* 1942
Sales 128.8MM *EMP* 850
Accts Wipfli Llp Milwaukee Wi
SIC 8062 8011 General medical & surgical hospitals; Offices & clinics of medical doctors
CEO: Michael Wallace
**CFO:* James Nelson
**VP:* Renee Clark
**VP:* Kay Wipperfurth
Dir Rad: Edgardo Jiongco
Nurse Mgr: Jaime Bracken
Off Admin: Delaina Lothary
MIS Dir: Jim Dahl
Web Dev: Bob Johnston
Pathlgst: Song Zhao

D-U-N-S 04-615-6626 EXP
FORT JAMES CORP
(*Suby of* GEORGIA-PACIFIC LLC) ★
133 Peachtree St Ne, Atlanta, GA 30303-1804
Tel (404) 652-4000 *Founded/Ownrshp* 2000
Sales 1.4MMM[E] *EMP* 25,150
SIC 2621 Towels, tissues & napkins: paper & stock
Pr: James Hannan
**Ch Bd:* David L Robertson
Chf Mktg O: Douwe Bergsma

D-U-N-S 19-976-8813
FORT LAUDERDALE TRANSPORTATION INC
1330 Se 4th Ave Ste D, Fort Lauderdale, FL 33316-1958
Tel (954) 524-6500 *Founded/Ownrshp* 1980
Sales 29.6MM[E] *EMP* 1,200
SIC 7299 4789 Valet parking; Car loading
Pr: William H Bodenhamer
**VP:* Michael Solomon

D-U-N-S 18-933-8585
FORT MILL SCHOOL DISTRICT 4
YORK SCHOOL DISTRICT 4
2233 Deerfield Dr, Fort Mill, SC 29715-6941
Tel (803) 548-2527 *Founded/Ownrshp* 1923
Sales 61.1MM[E] *EMP* 1,250
SIC 8211 Public elementary & secondary schools
Teacher Pr: Liza McGarity

D-U-N-S 00-207-2148 IMP
FORT MILLER GROUP INC
(*Suby of* FORT MILLER SERVICE CORP) ★
688 Wilbur Ave, Greenwich, NY 12834-4413
Tel (518) 695-5000 *Founded/Ownrshp* 1991
Sales 126.6MM[E] *EMP* 420
SIC 3272 3441 Concrete products, precast; Fabricated structural metal
Ch Bd: John T Hedbring
**CFO:* Richard Schumaker
**Ex VP:* John Marcelle
Exec: Mary A Spiezio
Dir IT: Don McKay

D-U-N-S 79-009-7141 EXP
FORT MILLER SERVICE CORP
688 Wilbur Ave, Greenwich, NY 12834-4413
Tel (518) 695-5000 *Founded/Ownrshp* 1991
Sales 144.9MM[E] *EMP* 420
SIC 3272 3271 5211 1799 Concrete products, precast; Burial vaults, concrete or precast terrazzo; Concrete block & brick; Concrete & cinder block; Fence construction
Ch Bd: John T Hedbring
**CFO:* Richard Schumaker
**VP:* Mary Ann Spiezio

FORT MOJAVE INDIAN TRIBE
See FORT MOJAVE TRIBAL COUNCIL

D-U-N-S 07-605-9179
FORT MOJAVE TRIBAL COUNCIL
FORT MOJAVE INDIAN TRIBE
500 Merriman St, Needles, CA 92363-2299
Tel (760) 629-4591 *Founded/Ownrshp* 1957
Sales NA *EMP* 1,000
SIC 9131 Indian reservation
Ch: Timothy Williams
**V Ch:* Shan Lewis
CFO: Mike Devita
VP: Colleen Garcia
Software D: Richard Estrada
HC Dir: Elizabeth Smoka

D-U-N-S 07-130-9389
FORT PIERCE UTILITIES AUTHORITY
FPUA
206 S 6th St, Fort Pierce, FL 34950-4295
Tel (772) 466-1600 *Founded/Ownrshp* 1972
Sales 162.5MM[E] *EMP* 271
Accts Dibartolome Mcbee Hartley &
SIC 4931 4941 4924 4813 Electric & other services combined; Water supply; Natural gas distribution;
Ch: Darryl Thomas-Bey
Bd of Dir: Daniel Deiulio
Comm Man: Levette Dixon

D-U-N-S 07-490-9482
FORT SANDERS REGIONAL MEDICAL CENTER
(*Suby of* COVENANT HEALTH) ★
1901 W Clinch Ave, Knoxville, TN 37916-2307
Tel (865) 541-1111 *Founded/Ownrshp* 1983
Sales 288.3MM *EMP* 1,833
SIC 8062 Hospital, professional nursing school
Pr: Keith Altshuler
Bd of Dir: Amy Dilworth
VP: Kelly Miles
Exec: Colleen Andrews
Pharmcst: Lynette Duncan

FORT SMITH SCHOOL DISTRICT
See SPECIAL SCHOOL DISTRICT OF FORT SMITH

FORT SMITH SKILL TRAINING CTR
See BOST INC

D-U-N-S 80-226-4390
FORT WASHINGTON INVESTMENT ADVISORS INC
(*Suby of* WESTERN-SOUTHERN LIFE) ★
303 Broadway St Ste 1100, Cincinnati, OH 45202-4220
Tel (513) 361-7600 *Founded/Ownrshp* 1990
Sales 153.8MM[E] *EMP* 982
SIC 6282 Investment advisory service
Pr: Maribeth S Rahe
Pr: Larry Carone
Pr: Bunn William
Bd of Dir: Richard J Perry
VP: John Barrett
VP: Paul Cohn
VP: John Discepoli
VP: Thomas L Finn
VP: Alex Fischer
VP: John J Goetz
VP: Daniel J Kapusta
VP: Doug Kelsey
VP: Roger Lanham
VP: Jeffrey Meek
VP: Bihag N Patel
VP: David K Robinson
VP: Chuck Stutenroth
VP: Charles A Ulbricht
VP: Brendan M White
VP: Brendan White

D-U-N-S 07-430-7463
FORT WAYNE COMMUNITY SCHOOLS (IN)
1200 S Clinton St, Fort Wayne, IN 46802-3504
Tel (260) 467-2160 *Founded/Ownrshp* 1958
Sales 211.3MM[E] *EMP* 4,265
SIC 8211 Public elementary & secondary schools
**COO:* Steven M Cobb
**CFO:* Charles Cammack Jr
VP: Mark Resor
Prin: Larry Gerardot
Dir Sec: Dottie Davis
CIO: Melania Hall
MIS Dir: Jack Byrd
Teacher Pr: Kathy Carr
Psych: Elizabeth Armstrong
Psych: Scott Bojrab
HC Dir: Mary Hess
Board of Directors: Robert Armstrong, Kurt Walburn,mark Giaquint, Carl Johnson

D-U-N-S 05-604-1122 IMP
FORT WAYNE METALS RESEARCH PRODUCTS CORP
9609 Ardmore Ave, Fort Wayne, IN 46809-9625
Tel (260) 747-4154 *Founded/Ownrshp* 1970
Sales 135.4MM[E] *EMP* 520[E]
SIC 3315 Wire, steel: insulated or armored
CEO: Scott Glaze
**Pr:* Mark Michael
MIS Mgr: Brnjamin Michael
Plnt Mgr: Jerome Margraf

FORT WAYNE POOLS
See LATHAM MANUFACTURING CORP

D-U-N-S 04-283-7377
■ **FORT WAYNE POOLS**
(*Suby of* POOL CORP) ★
6930 Gettysburg Pike, Fort Wayne, IN 46804-5614
Tel (260) 459-4100 *Founded/Ownrshp* 2002
Sales 141.1MM[E] *EMP* 227
SIC 5091 3949 Swimming pools, equipment & supplies; Swimming pools, plastic
CEO: Manuel J Perez De La Mesa
**CFO:* Craig Hubbard
VP: Bill Cook
Sales Exec: Brian Follis
Mktg Mgr: Michele Zollinger

D-U-N-S 07-317-7776
FORT WORTH INDEPENDENT SCHOOL DISTRICT
FWISD
100 N University Dr, Fort Worth, TX 76107-1360
Tel (817) 871-2000 *Founded/Ownrshp* 2015
Sales 843.7MM *EMP* 10,360
Accts Weaver And Tidwell Llp Forth
SIC 8211 Public elementary school; Public junior high school; Public senior high school; Public vocational/technical school
CFO: Stephen Fortenberry
CFO: Ronald M Wilson
Ex Dir: Robert Rey
Admn Mgr: Maria Lewis
Admn Mgr: Lisa Stewart
Admn Mgr: Patricia Williams
Genl Mgr: Frank Fiallo
IT Man: Margaret Dennis

FORT WORTH STAR TELEGRAM
See STAR-TELEGRAM OPERATING LTD

D-U-N-S 02-397-7158
■ **FORTEGRA FINANCIAL CORP**
(*Suby of* CARE INVESTMENT TRUST) ★
10151 Deerwood Park Blvd # 330, Jacksonville, FL 32256-0566
Tel (866) 961-9529 *Founded/Ownrshp* 2014
Sales NA *EMP* 494[E]
SIC 6411 Insurance agents, brokers & service
Pr: Richard S Kahlbaugh
**CFO:* Walter P Mascherin
Ofcr: Craig Hart
**Ex VP:* W Dale Bullard
**Ex VP:* Robert P Emery
**Ex VP:* Joseph R McCaw
**Sr VP:* Christopher D Romaine
VP: Joe Alberti
VP: Emily Rhodin
VP: Dawn Ronan
QA Dir: Andrew Bailey

D-U-N-S 06-186-0110 IMP
FORTERRA BRICK LLC
3820 Serr Rd, Corunna, MI 48817-1146
Tel (989) 743-3444 *Founded/Ownrshp* 1958
Sales 134.3MM[E] *EMP* 1,150
SIC 3251 Brick & structural clay tile
Plnt Mgr: Tom Carr

D-U-N-S 62-198-9367 IMP
FORTERRA BRICK LLC
HANSON BRICK
(*Suby of* WESTERN ROCK PRODUCTS) ★
7400 Carmel Exec Park 2, Charlotte, NC 28226-8400
Tel (704) 341-8750 *Founded/Ownrshp* 2002
Sales 140.0MM *EMP* 234
SIC 3251 Structural brick & blocks
Pr: Jeff Bradley
**Sr VP:* Charlie Ward
Sls&Mrk Ex: Cathy Jachym

FORTERRA BUILDING PRODUCTS
See FORTERRA PIPE & PRECAST LLC

D-U-N-S 08-031-8321
■ **FORTERRA INC**
(*Suby of* FORTERRA US HOLDINGS LLC) ★
511 E John Carpenter Fwy, Irving, TX 75062-3911
Tel (469) 284-8678 *Founded/Ownrshp* 2015
Sales 228.8MM[E] *EMP* 5,565
Tkr Sym FRTA *Exch* NGS
SIC 3272 3569 Concrete products used to facilitate drainage; Cylinder pipe, prestressed or pretensioned concrete; Filters & strainers, pipeline
CEO: Jeff Bradley
**Ch Bd:* Samuel D Loughlin
**CEO:* Jeffrey Bradley
**CFO:* William Matthew Brown
**Sr VP:* Lori M Browne
**Sr VP:* Ed Sexe
**VP:* Matthew Wayman
Board of Directors: Kevin Barner, Robert Corcoran, Clint McDonnough, John McPherson, Chris Meyer, Jacques Sarrazin, Chadwick Suss, Kyle Volluz, Grant Wilbeck

D-U-N-S 04-766-3716 IMP/EXP
FORTERRA PIPE & PRECAST LLC
FORTERRA BUILDING PRODUCTS
(*Suby of* FORTERRA BUILDING PRODUCTS LIMITED)
511 E John Carpenter Fwy, Irving, TX 75062-3911
Tel (469) 458-7973 *Founded/Ownrshp* 2015
Sales 1.7MMM[E] *EMP* 4,092
SIC 3272 1771 Concrete products; Concrete work
CEO: Jeff Bradley
CFO: Matt Browne
VP: Scott Szwejbka
Genl Mgr: Pat Morrison
Genl Mgr: Rick Nash
Off Mgr: Pam Hand
Sales Exec: Daren McMorris
VP Sls: Craig Morgan
Sales Asso: Kelly Mueller

D-U-N-S 00-447-7238 IMP
FORTERRA PRESSURE PIPE INC
4416 Prairie Hill Rd, South Beloit, IL 61080-2545
Tel (815) 389-4800 *Founded/Ownrshp* 2000, 2015
Sales 92.3MM[E] *EMP* 470
SIC 3272 3317 Pressure pipe, reinforced concrete; Steel pipe & tubes
Pr: Mark Carpenter
**CFO:* Steven M Paul
Sr VP: Sam Arnaut
Sr VP: Ken Primavera
VP: Leslie D Pape
VP Sls: Gord Gajich
VP Sls: Timothy B Kennedy

D-U-N-S 08-041-7036
▲ **FORTERRA US HOLDINGS LLC**
511 E John Carpenter Fwy, Irving, TX 75062-3911
Tel (469) 284-8678 *Founded/Ownrshp* 2016
Sales 117.1MM[E] *EMP* 5,565[E]
SIC 6719 Investment holding companies, except banks
CEO: Jeffrey Bradley
Ch Bd: Samuel D Loughlin
CFO: William Matthew Brown
Sr VP: Lori M Browne
Sr VP: Ed Sexe
VP: Matthew Wayman

D-U-N-S 08-361-8467
■ **FORTH SMITH HMA LLC** (AR)
SPARKS HEALTH SYSTEM
(*Suby of* HMA) ★
1001 Towson Ave, Fort Smith, AR 72901-4921
Tel (479) 441-4000 *Founded/Ownrshp* 2000, 2009
Sales 121.3MM[E] *EMP* 2,350
SIC 8062 General medical & surgical hospitals
CEO: Dan McKay
CFO: Richard Boone
CFO: Darrel Hardy
CFO: David Rothenberger
VP: Carolyn M Moore
VP: Bruce Trahan
Prin: Katherine Irish-Clardy
Genl Mgr: Terry Hurt
Doctor: Jimmy D Acklin
Doctor: Randall Beallis
Doctor: Gary Griffin

D-U-N-S 18-613-5455
FORTHS FOODS INC
LAVALETTE FOODFAIR
3090 Woodville Dr, Huntington, WV 25701-5200
Tel (304) 525-3293 *Founded/Ownrshp* 1988
Sales 123.2MM[E] *EMP* 125
SIC 5141 5411 Groceries, general line; Grocery stores
CEO: Charles G Forth
**Pr:* Charles Forth
VP: Pat Ray

D-U-N-S 00-825-3999 IMP
FORTIFIBER CORP
300 Industrial Dr, Fernley, NV 89408-8905
Tel (800) 773-4777 *Founded/Ownrshp* 1939

Sales 92.4MM[E] *EMP* 300
SIC 2671 Paper coated or laminated for packaging; Plastic film, coated or laminated for packaging; Thermoplastic coated paper for packaging; Wrapping paper, waterproof or coated
Ch Bd: Stuart Yount
**Pr:* Carl Thoms
**CFO:* Douglas Driver
IT Man: Matthew Anderson

D-U-N-S 79-915-4534 EXP
FORTILINE INC
7025 Northwinds Dr Nw, Concord, NC 28027-3334
Tel (704) 788-9800 *Founded/Ownrshp* 1998
Sales 227.5MM[E] *EMP* 250
SIC 5085 Industrial supplies
Pr: Gene Lewis
CFO: Jason Painter
Brnch Mgr: Troy Curtis
Brnch Mgr: Todd Howell
Brnch Mgr: Efrain Mares
Brnch Mgr: Bruce Roberts
Genl Mgr: Elizabeth Rhodes
VP Opers: Ben Cagle
Opers Mgr: Alex Grippe
Opers Mgr: Quinn Kupish
Mktg Mgr: Cathy Hein

D-U-N-S 82-765-8506
FORTILINE LLC
FORTILINE WATERWORKS
(*Suby of* FORTILINE INC) ★
7025 Northwinds Dr Nw, Concord, NC 28027-3334
Tel (704) 788-9800 *Founded/Ownrshp* 1988
Sales 108.6MM[E] *EMP* 250
SIC 3317 5085 Steel pipe & tubes; Valves & fittings
Pr: Mike Swedick
VP: Frank Seymour
VP: Greg Velz
Brnch Mgr: Kevin Clark
Brnch Mgr: George Reeder
Brnch Mgr: Robert Rowley
Brnch Mgr: Pryor Tatum

FORTILINE WATERWORKS
See FORTILINE LLC

D-U-N-S 04-080-6445
▲ **FORTINET INC**
899 Kifer Rd, Sunnyvale, CA 94086-5205
Tel (408) 235-7700 *Founded/Ownrshp* 2000
Sales 1.0MMM *EMP* 4,018[E]
Tkr Sym FTNT *Exch* NGS
SIC 7372 Prepackaged software
Ch Bd: Ken Xie
Pr: Rob Atherton
**Pr:* Michael Xie
CFO: Andrew Del Matto
Ofcr: Michelle Spolver
Sr VP: Patrice Perche
VP: Pete Brant
VP: Tamir Hardof
VP: Hemant Jain
VP: Richard Kagan
VP: Scott Lewis
VP: Tyson Macaulay
VP: Dave Monery
VP: Pedro Paixao
VP: Bob Schwartz
VP: Claire Trimble
VP: Chad Whalen
VP: John Whittle
Board of Directors: Ming Hsieh, Gary Locke, William H Neukom, Christopher B Paisley, Judith Sim

D-U-N-S 13-201-3181
FORTIS CONSTRUCTION INC
1705 Sw Taylor St Ste 200, Portland, OR 97205-1922
Tel (503) 459-4477 *Founded/Ownrshp* 2003
Sales 468.9MM *EMP* 175[E]
Accts Akt Llp Lake Oswego Oregon
SIC 1542 1611 Commercial & office building, new construction; Commercial & office building contractors; General contractor, highway & street construction
Pr: James T Kilpatrick
**VP:* David Aaroe
Exec: JB Hall
Sfty Mgr: Demetra G Star

D-U-N-S 05-529-5596
■ **FORTIS INSURANCE CO**
(*Suby of* ASSURANT INC) ★
501 W Michigan St, Milwaukee, WI 53203-2700
Tel (262) 646-4633 *Founded/Ownrshp* 1978
Sales NA *EMP* 2,700
SIC 6311 6321 Life insurance; Accident insurance carriers; Health insurance carriers; Disability health insurance
Pr: Don Hamm
CFO: Howard Miller
Bd of Dir: Warren Bickford
Chf Mktg O: Steve Deraleau
Sr VP: Clark Merkley
VP: Tim Bireley
VP: Lynn Gilbertson
VP: Judy Manly
VP: Bill Ogden
VP: Kim Pollard
VP: Jeff Remsik
VP: Christine Rodriguez
Board of Directors: Robert Brian Bollock, Jon Kerry Clayton, Benjamin Maurece Cutler II

D-U-N-S 82-877-4856
FORTIS PLASTICS LLC
390 Community Dr, Henderson, KY 42420-4336
Tel (270) 827-9801 *Founded/Ownrshp* 2008
Sales 2.5MM *EMP* 1,100
SIC 5031

D-U-N-S 04-160-8311
FORTISTAR LLC
1 N Lexington Ave Ste 620, White Plains, NY 10601-1721
Tel (914) 421-4900 *Founded/Ownrshp* 1998
Sales 175.8MM[E] *EMP* 194[E]
SIC 4911 Generation, electric power
Pr: Thomas Gesicki

CFO: Scott Contino
VP: Suparna Chakladar
VP: David Comori
VP: Lee Duis
VP: Anthony Falbo
VP: Matt Macfarlane
VP: Tony Wetzel

D-U-N-S 08-019-8742
▲ FORTIVE CORP
6920 Seaway Blvd, Everett, WA 98203-5829
Tel (425) 446-5000 *Founded/Ownrshp* 2016
Sales 5.7MMM[E] *EMP* 17,065[E]
Tkr Sym FTV *Exch* NYS
SIC 3823 Industrial instrmnts msrmnt display/control process variable
Pr: Jim Lico
CFO: Charles E McLaughlin
CFO: Chuck McLaughlin
Sr VP: Pat Byrne
Sr VP: Patrick J Byrne
Sr VP: Martin Gafinowitz
Sr VP: Barbara Hulit
Sr VP: Barbara B Hulit
Sr VP: Pat Murphy
Sr VP: Patrick K Murphy
Sr VP: Wes Pringle
Sr VP: William W Pringle
Sr VP: Peter Underwood
Sr VP: Stacey Walker
VP: Raj Ratnakar
VP: Jon Schwarz

FORTNEY & WEYGANDT
See R L FORTNEY MANAGEMENT INC

D-U-N-S 09-328-2580
FORTNEY & WEYGANDT INC
(*Suby of* FORTNEY & WEYGANDT) ★
31269 Bradley Rd, North Olmsted, OH 44070-3875
Tel (440) 716-4000 *Founded/Ownrshp* 1978
Sales 89.1MM *EMP* 50
Accts Bober Markey Fedorovich & Co
SIC 1541 1542 Industrial buildings, new construction; Commercial & office building, new construction
Pr: Robert L Fortney
Sec: Greg Freeh
VP: Ruth Fortney
Exec: Hanson Mike
Off Mgr: Donna Straka

D-U-N-S 07-870-8167
FORTNEY HOSPITALITY GROUP INC (WI)
308 3rd St S, La Crosse, WI 54601-4007
Tel (608) 784-1225 *Founded/Ownrshp* 1998
Sales 15.4MM[E] *EMP* 1,000
SIC 7011 Hotels
Pr: Marc R Fortney

FORTNIGHT PRODUCTIONS
See ALLTECH INC

D-U-N-S 01-614-1967
▲ FORTRESS INVESTMENT GROUP LLC
1345 Avenue, New York, NY 10105
Tel (212) 798-6100 *Founded/Ownrshp* 1998
Sales 1.2MMM *EMP* 3,040
Tkr Sym FIG *Exch* NYS
SIC 6282 Investment advice
CEO: Randal A Nardone
Ch Bd: Peter L Briger Jr
Ch Bd: Wesley R Edens
CFO: Daniel N Bass
Ofcr: Michael Cohn
VP: Diana Bellizzi
VP: Fran Benoit
VP: David N Brooks
VP: Neil Carter
VP: Jill Chanes
VP: Robert China
VP: Scott Desiderio
VP: Dora Dragomanova
VP: Alex Gillette
VP: Susan Givens
VP: Cristina Gonzalez
VP: Jonathan Grebinar
VP: Pankaj Jain
VP: Jared Kanefsky
VP: Caroline Kim
VP: Karen Kotik
Board of Directors: David B Barry, Douglas L Jacobs, George W Wellde Jr

D-U-N-S 07-982-1557
▲ FORTRESS TRANSPORTATION AND INFRASTRUCTURE INVESTORS LLC
FORTRESS TRNSP INFRASTRUCTURE
1345 Ave Of The Americas, New York, NY 10105-2200
Tel (212) 798-6100 *Founded/Ownrshp* 2011
Sales 136.5MM *EMP* 158[E]
Tkr Sym FTAI *Exch* NYS
SIC 4789 Pipeline terminal facilities, independently operated
Ch Bd: Joseph P Adams Jr
CFO: Scott Christopher
Board of Directors: Paul R Goodwin, Kenneth J Nicholson, Ray M Robinson, Martin Tuchman

FORTRESS TRNSP INFRASTRUCTURE
See FORTRESS TRANSPORTATION AND INFRASTRUCTURE INVESTORS LLC

D-U-N-S 19-457-0776 IMP
▲ FORTUNE BRANDS HOME & SECURITY INC
520 Lake Cook Rd, Deerfield, IL 60015-5611
Tel (847) 484-4400 *Founded/Ownrshp* 1988
Sales 4.5MMM *EMP* 21,400[E]
Accts Pricewaterhousecoopers Llp Ch
Tkr Sym FBHS *Exch* NYS
SIC 2531 2599 3429 3469 Public building & related furniture; Cabinets, factory; Keys, locks & related hardware; Boxes: tool, lunch, mail, etc.: stamped metal
CEO: Christopher J Klein
Pr: Michael P Bauer
Pr: Brett E Finley
Pr: David B Lingafelter
Pr: David M Randich
CFO: E Lee Wyatt Jr
Ex VP: Samir Shah
Sr VP: Tracey Belcourt
Sr VP: Robert K Biggart
Sr VP: Sheri R Grissom
Sr VP: Nicholas I Fink
VP: Robert Biggart
VP: Scott D'Angelo
VP: Dan Luburic
Board of Directors: Ann F Hackett, Susan S Kilsby, A D David Mackay, John G Morikis, David M Thomas, Ronald V Waters III, Norman H Wesley

D-U-N-S 15-211-5643 IMP
■ FORTUNE BRANDS WINDOWS INC
SIMONTON WINDOWS
(*Suby of* PLY GEM INDUSTRIES INC) ★
3948 Townsfair Way # 200, Columbus, OH 43219-6095
Tel (614) 532-3500 *Founded/Ownrshp* 2014
Sales 92.8MM[E] *EMP* 400
SIC 1751 5211 Window & door installation & erection; Window & door (prefabricated) installation; Door & window products
Pr: Mark Savan
**Treas:* Matthew C Lenz
VP: Michael S Petersen
VP: Greg Schorr
Exec: Brenda Chapel
Exec: Beth Tucker
VP Inf Sys: Ken Cottrill
Sls Dir: Sabrina Allen-Ehle

D-U-N-S 05-440-6769 EXP
FORTUNE METAL INC OF RHODE ISLAND (RI)
2 Crow Point Rd, Lincoln, RI 02865-3259
Tel (661) 387-1100 *Founded/Ownrshp* 1998
Sales 86.4MM *EMP* 120
Accts Winnie Ng Cpa Brooklyn Ny
SIC 5093 Scrap & waste materials
CEO: Norman Ng
**VP:* Jack Mellow
Brnch Mgr: Dave Leroux

D-U-N-S 05-499-2805 IMP
FORTUNOFF FINE JEWELRY AND SILVERWARE INC
(*Suby of* HUDSONS BAY TRADING CO LP) ★
70 Charles Lindbergh Blvd, Uniondale, NY 11553-3630
Tel (516) 222-7879 *Founded/Ownrshp* 2008
Sales 71.8MM[E] *EMP* 1,800
SIC 5944 5719 Jewelry, precious stones & precious metals; Silverware; Housewares; Cutlery; Cookware, except aluminum
Pr: Helene Fortunoff
**CFO:* Michael Geraghty
**Ex VP:* Esther Fortunoff
**Ex VP:* Louis Fortunoff
Ex VP: Norman Goldberg
**Ex VP:* Leonard Tabs
VP: John A Bianco
VP: Allen Francis
VP: David Pfister
VP: Vincent Sabia
CIO: Michael Wandera

FORUM, THE
See FORUM COMMUNICATIONS CO

D-U-N-S 00-618-6944
FORUM COMMUNICATIONS CO (ND)
FORUM, THE
101 5th St N, Fargo, ND 58102-4826
Tel (701) 235-7311 *Founded/Ownrshp* 1913
Sales 27.2MM[E] *EMP* 2,200
SIC 2711 4833 4832 Newspapers, publishing & printing; Television broadcasting stations; Radio broadcasting stations
Pr: Lloyd Case
**Ch:* William C Marcil
**Sec:* Jane Marcil
VP: Marshall Johnson
VP: D Marren
Dist Mgr: Kevin Herk
Advt Dir: Aaron Becher
Advt Dir: Scott Schmeltzer
Pr Dir: Peter Miller
Sales Asso: Brent Theisen
Assoc Ed: Wendy Reuer

D-U-N-S 61-752-2482
▲ FORUM ENERGY TECHNOLOGIES INC
920 Memorial City Way # 1000, Houston, TX 77024-2653
Tel (281) 949-2500 *Founded/Ownrshp* 2005
Sales 1.0MMM *EMP* 2,663[E]
Tkr Sym FET *Exch* NYS
SIC 3533 Oil & gas field machinery; Oil field machinery & equipment; Drilling tools for gas, oil or water wells
Pr: C Christopher Gaut
Pr: Prady Iyyanki
CFO: James W Harris
Sr VP: Michael D Danford
Sr VP: James L McCulloch
VP: James Bement
VP: Mark Brookes
VP: Tom Collins
VP: Mark Dille
VP: Larry Hill
VP: A Kuruvilla
VP: Larry Maurer
VP: Sid Smith

D-U-N-S 01-735-8826
FORUM HEALTH
1350 E Market St 302, Warren, OH 44483-6608
Tel (330) 841-9011 *Founded/Ownrshp* 2010
Sales NA *EMP* 5,000
SIC 8741 8011

D-U-N-S 01-420-3840 IMP
■ FORUM US INC
(*Suby of* FET HOLDINGS LLC) ★
10344 Sam Houston Park Dr, Houston, TX 77064-4665
Tel (713) 351-7900 *Founded/Ownrshp* 2008
Sales 165.5MM[E] *EMP* 200[E]
SIC 1382 Oil & gas exploration services
CEO: C Christopher Gaut
**COO:* Prady Iyyanki
**CFO:* James W Harris
**Treas:* Tom Simms
**Sr VP:* Wendell Brooks
**Sr VP:* Michael D Danford
**Prin:* James L McCulloch

D-U-N-S 04-890-7794
▲ FORWARD AIR CORP
430 Airport Rd, Greeneville, TN 37745-1824
Tel (423) 636-7000 *Founded/Ownrshp* 1981
Sales 959.1MM *EMP* 4,536[E]
Tkr Sym FWRD *Exch* NGS
SIC 4731 Freight transportation arrangement; Freight forwarding
Ch Bd: Bruce A Campbell
Pr: Matthew J Jewell
Pr: Chris C Ruble
CFO: Rodney L Bell
CFO: Michael J Morris
Sr VP: Rodney Bell
Sr VP: Craig A Drum
VP: Jim Hoeh
VP: Gerald Kane
VP: Michael P McLean
VP: Kyle Mitchin
VP: Gavin Neilson
Board of Directors: Ronald W Allen, C Robert Campbell, R Craig Carlock, C John Langley Jr, Tracy A Leinbach, Larry D Leinweber, G Micheal Lynch, Douglas M Madden

D-U-N-S 16-658-4446 IMP
■ FORWARD AIR INC
(*Suby of* FORWARD AIR CORP) ★
430 Airport Rd, Greeneville, TN 37745-1824
Tel (423) 639-7196 *Founded/Ownrshp* 1993
Sales 752.6MM[E] *EMP* 2,400
SIC 4731 Freight transportation arrangement
Pr: Bruce Campbell
VP: Glenn A Adelaar
VP: Richard L Denhart
VP: Mark T Dunn
VP: Rene C Espinet
VP: Patrick M Fenton
VP: Michael L Hance
VP: Kevin A Hill
VP: Timothy R Osborne
VP: Jeff Taylor
VP: Joseph C Tirone
VP: Thomas S Weaver
VP: N J Woods

D-U-N-S 01-740-2991
FORWARD CORP
FORWARD DISTRIBUTING CO.
219 N Front St, Standish, MI 48658-9256
Tel (989) 846-4501 *Founded/Ownrshp* 1955
Sales 143.6MM *EMP* 600
Accts Rehmann Robson Llc Saginaw
SIC 5411 5541 5172 5812 Grocery stores; Filling stations, gasoline; Petroleum products; Eating places
Ch Bd: Terry McTaggart
**Sec:* Austin N Buttrick
**VP:* David Gould

FORWARD DISTRIBUTING CO.
See FORWARD CORP

D-U-N-S 06-366-5844 EXP
FORWARD SPACE LLC
OEC BUSINESS INTERIORS
1142 N North Branch St, Chicago, IL 60642-4211
Tel (312) 942-1100 *Founded/Ownrshp* 2014
Sales 133.1MM[E] *EMP* 150
SIC 5021 7389 Office furniture; Interior designer
Pr: Jennifer Niemann
**COO:* Thomas Worniak

D-U-N-S 96-164-6846
FOSS HOLDINGS LLC
11 Merrill Industrial Dr A1, Hampton, NH 03842-1972
Tel (603) 929-6000 *Founded/Ownrshp* 2006
Sales 121.0MM[E] *EMP* 806[E]
SIC 2297 Nonwoven fabrics
Pr: A J Nassar
Ch Bd: Frank Cougentakis
Pr: Mike Degrace
COO: Bill Cummings
Treas: Paul Koroski
VP: Don Taft

D-U-N-S 78-417-0446 IMP
FOSS MANUFACTURING CO LLC
(*Suby of* FOSS HOLDINGS LLC) ★
11 Merrill Industrial Dr A1, Hampton, NH 03842-1972
Tel (603) 929-6000 *Founded/Ownrshp* 2006
Sales 121.0MM[E] *EMP* 600[E]
SIC 2297 Nonwoven fabrics
CEO: A J Nassar
Pr: Mike De Grace
COO: Bill Cummings
CFO: Erica Rahn
Ch: Frank Cougentakis
Treas: Paul Koroski
Ex VP: Dave Rowell

D-U-N-S 06-717-2288
FOSS MARITIME CO
(*Suby of* SALTCHUK RESOURCES INC) ★
1151 Fairview Ave N, Seattle, WA 98109-4418
Tel (206) 281-4001 *Founded/Ownrshp* 1889
Sales 364.5MM[E] *EMP* 1,200
SIC 4412 4424 4492 4491 3731 4959 Deep sea foreign transportation of freight; Deep sea domestic transportation of freight; Coastwide transportation, freight; Intercoastal transportation, freight; Marine towing services; Tugboat service; Waterfront terminal operation; Shipbuilding & repairing; Environmental cleanup services
CEO: Steve Scalzo
**Pr:* Gary C Faber
**Pr:* Paul E Stevens
CFO: Kirstin L Sandaas
**Ch:* Paul Stevens
Treas: Matt Brown
**Treas:* Kirsein Sandaas
**Sr VP:* Glenn K Y Hong
**Sr VP:* Scott Merritt
**Sr VP:* Arthur J Volkle
**VP:* Joseph H Langjahr

D-U-N-S 11-864-3956 IMP
▲ FOSSIL GROUP INC
901 S Central Expy, Richardson, TX 75080-7302
Tel (972) 234-2525 *Founded/Ownrshp* 1984
Sales 3.2MMM *EMP* 15,100[E]
Tkr Sym FOSL *Exch* NGS
SIC 3873 5944 5094 5651 5632 Watches, clocks, watchcases & parts; Watches; Watches & parts; Family clothing stores; Handbags
Ch Bd: Kosta N Kartsotis
COO: John A White
CFO: Dennis R Secor
Ex VP: Eric Anderson
Ex VP: Randy C Belcher
Ex VP: Hans-Peter Gehmacher
Ex VP: Darren E Hart
Ex VP: Greg A McKelvey
Ex VP: Gregory A McKelvey
VP: Susan Harris
VP: Tom Kennedy
VP: Jayson Kim
VP: Brian McKechnie
Board of Directors: Elaine B Agather, Jeffrey N Boyer, William B Chiasson, Diane L Neal, Thomas M Nealon, Mark D Quick, James E Skinner, James M Zimmerman

D-U-N-S 93-986-2850 IMP
■ FOSSIL PARTNERS LP
FOSSIL RETRODOME
(*Suby of* FOSSIL GROUP INC) ★
901 S Central Expy, Richardson, TX 75080-7302
Tel (972) 234-2525 *Founded/Ownrshp* 1994
Sales 713.8MM[E] *EMP* 1,325
SIC 5137 2389 2339 5094 Women's & children's accessories; Apparel belts, women's & children's; Handbags; Purses; Men's miscellaneous accessories; Women's & misses' accessories; Jewelry
Pt: Kosta Kartsotis

FOSSIL RETRODOME
See FOSSIL PARTNERS LP

D-U-N-S 12-213-5148 IMP/EXP
FOSTER AND SMITH INC
DOCTORS FOSTER AND SMITH
(*Suby of* PETCO ANIMAL SUPPLIES INC) ★
2253 Air Park Rd, Rhinelander, WI 54501-8425
Tel (715) 369-3305 *Founded/Ownrshp* 2015
Sales 224.9MM[E] *EMP* 617
SIC 4813 5961

D-U-N-S 05-167-5197
FOSTER DAIRY FARMS
CRYSTAL CREAMERY
529 Kansas Ave, Modesto, CA 95351-1515
Tel (209) 576-3400 *Founded/Ownrshp* 1958
Sales 477.1MM[E] *EMP* 900
SIC 0241 Milk production
Pr: Frank Otis
**CFO:* Mark Shaw
VP: Tom Foster
**VP:* Luis Miranda
**VP:* Jeff Sussman
IT Man: Ken Stedtfeld
IT Man: Pat Ticer
VP Sls: Dennis Roberts

D-U-N-S 02-868-4363
FOSTER DAIRY PRODUCTS DISTRIBUTING
529 Kansas Ave, Modesto, CA 95351-1515
Tel (209) 576-3400 *Founded/Ownrshp* 1999
Sales 132.1MM[E] *EMP* 620
SIC 5143 2026 Dairy products, except dried or canned; Fluid milk
Pr: Jeff Foster

FOSTER FARMS
See FOSTER POULTRY FARMS

D-U-N-S 60-780-2147
FOSTER FARMS LLC
1000 Davis St, Livingston, CA 95334-1526
Tel (970) 874-7503 *Founded/Ownrshp* 1987
Sales 1.9MMM[E] *EMP* 600
SIC 0252

D-U-N-S 00-917-8856 IMP/EXP
FOSTER POULTRY FARMS
FOSTER FARMS
1000 Davis St, Livingston, CA 95334-1526
Tel (209) 394-6914 *Founded/Ownrshp* 1942
Sales 3.5MMM[E] *EMP* 12,000
SIC 0254 2015 5812 0173 5191 4212 Poultry hatcheries; Chicken hatchery; Chicken slaughtering & processing; Turkey processing & slaughtering; Chicken restaurant; Almond grove; Animal feeds; Local trucking, without storage
Pr: Ron M Foster
Pr: Donald Jackson
COO: Leslie Cardoso
**CFO:* Caryn Doyle
Treas: Regina King
Ex VP: Bob James
VP: Richie King
VP: John Landis
VP: Terry Thompson
**Prin:* George Foster
Ex Dir: Trevor Foster

D-U-N-S 96-478-8645
FOSTER WHEELER INC
(*Suby of* AMEC FOSTER WHEELER NORTH AMERICA CORP) ★
53 Frontage Rd, Hampton, NJ 08827-4031
Tel (908) 730-4000 *Founded/Ownrshp* 2001
Sales 200.8MM[E] *EMP* 36[E]
SIC 7389 Exhibit construction by industrial contractors
Ch: John Connolly
CEO: Jonathan Lewis
CFO: Ian McHoul
Ex VP: Beth Sexton
VP: Rakesh Jindal
VP: Ravi Khehar
VP: Thomas Kowalczyk

VP: Peter Kuchler
VP: Timothy Langan
VP: Richard Lively
VP: Lisa Nargi
VP: Ramon Velez
**VP:* Lisa Wood
Board of Directors: Kent Masters

D-U-N-S 00-133-9456
FOSTER WHEELER ZACK INC
(*Suby of* AMEC FOSTER WHEELER PLC)
53 Frontage Rd, Hampton, NJ 08827-4031
Tel (908) 730-4000 *Founded/Ownrshp* 1995
Sales 94.3MM[E] *EMP* 361[E]
Accts Pricewaterhousecoopers Llp Fl
SIC 8711 1629 3569 4931 Industrial engineers; Industrial plant construction; Oil refinery construction; Chemical plant & refinery construction; Generators: steam, liquid oxygen or nitrogen; Electric & other services combined
Pr: Chris Covert
**CFO:* Lee Barnett
CFO: Tony Scerbo
**Treas:* Kevin Hagan
Sr VP: Leonard F Jones
**VP:* John Paul Archambault
**VP:* Jimmy Collins
**VP:* Michelle Davies
**VP:* Rakesh Jindal
Exec: Vincent Gallo
Exec: Bill Lee

D-U-N-S 78-869-2544
FOTH & VAN DYKE LLC
2121 Innovation Ct # 100, De Pere, WI 54115-6005
Tel (920) 497-2500 *Founded/Ownrshp* 2006
Sales 133.1MM *EMP* 60
Accts Baker Tilly Virchow Kranse L
SIC 6719 Investment holding companies, except banks
Pr: Randall Homel
Treas: Howard Bornstein
VP: John Parisi
Prgrm Mgr: Jeff Roy

FOTO KEM FILM & VIDEO
See FOTO-KEM INDUSTRIES INC

D-U-N-S 02-850-0452 IMP
FOTO-KEM INDUSTRIES INC
FOTO KEM FILM & VIDEO
2801 W Alameda Ave, Burbank, CA 91505-4405
Tel (818) 846-3102 *Founded/Ownrshp* 1963
Sales 94.9MM[E] *EMP* 700
SIC 7819 Laboratory service, motion picture; Developing & printing of commercial motion picture film
CEO: William F Brodersen
COO: Robert Semmer
Bd of Dir: Melaine Diego
Sr VP: Rosanna Marino
Sr VP: Peter Santoro
**VP:* Gerald D Brodersen Jr
VP: Bill Roskilly
VP: Gerry Roskilly
VP: Tom Vice
VP: Michael Williams
Snr Sftwr: Richard Goedeken

D-U-N-S 04-383-8424 IMP
FOUGERA PHARMACEUTICALS INC
PHARMADERM
(*Suby of* SANDOZ INC) ★
60 Baylis Rd, Melville, NY 11747-3838
Tel (631) 454-7677 *Founded/Ownrshp* 1998
Sales 266.4MM[E] *EMP* 880
SIC 2834 2851 2821 3479 3829 Pharmaceutical preparations; Ointments; Paints & paint additives; Plasticizer/additive based plastic materials; Painting, coating & hot dipping; Measuring & controlling devices
CEO: Brian A Markison
**Ch Bd:* Donald Degolyer
**COO:* Jeff Bailey
**CFO:* John Golubieski
**Treas:* David Riposo
**Sr VP:* Chris Klein
VP: Iltifat Hasan
VP: George Schwab
Exec: Danielle Castellano
Assoc Dir: Ellen Gambichler
QA Dir: Gary Price
Board of Directors: Heinz W Bull, Dr Klaus Oehmichen

D-U-N-S 60-569-3126
FOULKE MANAGEMENT CORP
MT EPHRAIM DODGE
1708 Marlton Pike W, Cherry Hill, NJ 08002-3203
Tel (856) 665-9000 *Founded/Ownrshp* 1985
Sales 106.5MM[E] *EMP* 396
SIC 5511 Automobiles, new & used
Pr: Charles W Foulke
**VP:* Joseph H Mc Erlean

D-U-N-S 08-711-7156
FOULKROD ASSOCIATES
CANADA DRY OF DELAWARE VALLEY
8275 N Crescent Blvd, Pennsauken, NJ 08110-1435
Tel (856) 662-6767 *Founded/Ownrshp* 1976
Sales 92.5MM[E] *EMP* 600
SIC 3411 5149 Beverage cans, metal: except beer; Groceries & related products
Ch: Harold Honickman
VP: Earl Brown
VP: Charlie Congdon
VP: Mark Dimnik
VP: Paul Malo
VP: James McCulloch
VP: Mike Nash
VP: David Pearson
VP: Ronald Pierce
VP: David Rodych
VP: David Ryzebol

D-U-N-S 06-898-0006
FOUNDATION BUILDING MATERIALS LLC
GREAT WESTERN BUILDING MTL
2552 Walnut Ave Ste 160, Tustin, CA 92780-6992
Tel (714) 380-3127 *Founded/Ownrshp* 2011
Sales 136.3MM[E] *EMP* 137
SIC 1742 Plastering, drywall & insulation
COO: Pete Welly

D-U-N-S 08-686-3230
FOUNDATION FOR CAROLINAS
220 N Tryon St, Charlotte, NC 28202-2137
Tel (704) 973-4500 *Founded/Ownrshp* 1958
Sales 684.3MM *EMP* 40
SIC 8399 Fund raising organization, non-fee basis
Pr: Michael Marsicano
**Ex VP:* Laura Meyer Wellman
Sr VP: Judy Kerns
Sr VP: C Barton Landess
VP: Greg Beuris
VP: Wendy Gates
VP: Devire Robinson
VP: Ronald Townsend
Dir Soc: Ervin Ledbetter
Ex Dir: Aisha Strothers
Counsel: Evan Wolkofsky

D-U-N-S 07-127-6372
FOUNDATION FOR COMMUNITY BLOOD CENTER/COMMUNITY TISSUE SERVICES
349 S Main St, Dayton, OH 45402-2715
Tel (937) 461-3450 *Founded/Ownrshp* 1964
Sales 114.9MM *EMP* 520
Accts Clark Schaefer Hackett & Co M
SIC 8099 Blood bank; Organ bank
CEO: David M Smith
**COO:* Jodi L Minneman
**COO:* Diane L Wilson
**CFO:* Julia M Belden
Cmptr Lab: Kathy Paulick
Cmptr Lab: Tamara Ritz
QA Dir: Mark Martin
IT Man: Paula Baker
Mtls Mgr: Trina Pearson
Natl Sales: Scott Foor
Mktg Dir: Michael Blair

D-U-N-S 96-971-7201
■ FOUNDATION FOR MARINE ANIMAL HUSBANDRY INC
HMRH ACQUISITION CO
(*Suby of* HMRH ACQUISITION CO) ★
222 Berkeley St, Boston, MA 02116-3748
Tel (617) 351-5072 *Founded/Ownrshp* 1987
Sales 733.7M *EMP* 3,182[E]
SIC 0742 Veterinary services, specialties
Pr: Linda Zecher
**CFO:* Eric Shuman
**Treas:* Joseph Flaherty
**Ex VP:* William Bayers
**Sr VP:* Michael Dolan
Board of Directors: William Bayers, Eric Shuman, Linda Zecher

D-U-N-S 07-846-7168
FOUNDATION FOR PUBLIC SCHOOL CHILDREN OF CHARLES COUNTY INC
CCPS
(*Suby of* CHARLES COUNTY BOARD OF EDUCATION) ★
5980 Radio Station Rd, La Plata, MD 20646-3337
Tel (301) 932-6610 *Founded/Ownrshp* 2012
Sales 113.4MM[E] *EMP* 3,300
SIC 8211 Public elementary & secondary schools
Bd of Dir: Jennifer Abell
Bd of Dir: Dominic Zaccarelli
Dir Sec: Glenn Belmore
Netwrk Eng: Brian Walker
Pr Dir: Katie O Simpson
Schl Brd P: Roberta Wise
Instr Medi: Dawn Schaffer
Instr Medi: Rosemary Venable
Psych: Stacy Bateman
Psych: Scott Brain
Psych: Teresa James

FOUNDATION FOR VBMC, THE
See HEALTH QUEST

D-U-N-S 15-291-7766
▲ FOUNDATION HEALTHCARE INC
13900 N Portland Ave # 200, Oklahoma City, OK 73134-4042
Tel (405) 608-1700 *Founded/Ownrshp* 2013
Sales 126.1MM *EMP* 1,232
Tkr Sym FDNH *Exch* OTO
SIC 8062 8011 8093 General medical & surgical hospitals; Ambulatory surgical center; Specialty outpatient clinics
Ch Bd: Thomas Michaud
CEO: Stanton Nelson
CFO: Hubert King
Board of Directors: Joseph Harroz Jr, Steven L List, Robert A Moreno, Lorin E Patterson, Richard L Zahn

D-U-N-S 80-841-6841
FOUNDATION HOLDINGS INC
3311 E Old Shakopee Rd, Minneapolis, MN 55425-1361
Tel (952) 853-8100 *Founded/Ownrshp* 1997
Sales 498.8MM[E] *EMP* 9,587
SIC 8641 8721 Civic social & fraternal associations; Accounting, auditing & bookkeeping
Prin: Ralph Flees
QA Dir: Paul Jette
Snr Mgr: Rob Ross

D-U-N-S 83-296-2018
FOUNDATION MEDICAL PARTNERS IN
8 Prospect St, Nashua, NH 03060-3925
Tel (603) 577-2000 *Founded/Ownrshp* 2009
Sales 98.4MM *EMP* 15[E]
Accts Baker Newman Noyes Lc Manches
SIC 8099 Medical services organization
Pr: Susan M Desocio

D-U-N-S 96-315-1076
■ FOUNDATION MEDICINE INC
(*Suby of* ROCHE HOLDINGS INC) ★
150 2nd St, Cambridge, MA 02141-2115
Tel (617) 418-2200 *Founded/Ownrshp* 2015
Sales 93.2MM *EMP* 417
Tkr Sym FMI *Exch* NGS
SIC 8069 Cancer hospital
Pr: Michael J Pellini
**Ch Bd:* Alexis Borisy
**Pr:* Steven Kafka
**CEO:* Michael Pellini
**CFO:* Jason Ryan
**Chf Cred:* David Daly
**Chf Mktg O:* Vincent Miller
**Sr VP:* Robert Hesslein
VP: Jerry Conway
VP: Matt Franklin
VP: Lisa Ricciardi
VP: Urmi Richardson
Assoc Dir: Helena Deus
Assoc Dir: Chris Fox
Assoc Dir: Christine Vietz
Board of Directors: Michael R Dougherty, Sandra Horning, Evan Jones, Daniel O'day, David Schenkein, Michael Varney

D-U-N-S 55-692-0205
FOUNDATION OF MASSACHUSETTS EYE AND EAR INFIRMARY INC
(*Suby of* MASSACHUSETTS EYE AND EAR INFIRMARY & PHYSICIAN STAFF INC) ★
243 Charles St, Boston, MA 02114-3002
Tel (617) 523-7900 *Founded/Ownrshp* 1982
Sales 25.8MM *EMP* 1,174
SIC 8069 Eye, ear, nose & throat hospital
Ch Bd: Alexander Bernhard
**Treas:* William Darling
Top Exec: Donald J Annino Jr
Top Exec: Charles M Norris Jr
Opthamlgy: Mary L Jackson
Opthamlgy: Justin M Kanoff
Opthamlgy: Rebecca C Stacy
Nrsg Dir: Greg Donnelly

D-U-N-S 78-771-6596
FOUNDATION PROPERTY MANAGEMENT INC
F P M
911 N Studebaker Rd # 100, Long Beach, CA 90815-4980
Tel (562) 257-5100 *Founded/Ownrshp* 1981
Sales 16.5MM *EMP* 2,200[E]
Accts Cliftonlarsonallen Llp St Lo
SIC 8742 Management consulting services
CEO: Laverne R Joseph
**CFO:* Frank Rossello
**VP:* Robert Amberg
**VP:* Stuart Hartman

D-U-N-S 07-508-6421 EXP
FOUNDATION RESOLUTION CORP
CITRUS MEMORIAL HEALTH SYSTEM
502 W Highland Blvd, Inverness, FL 34452-4720
Tel (352) 726-1551 *Founded/Ownrshp* 1957
Sales 143.2MM *EMP* 1,200
SIC 8062 General medical & surgical hospitals
Pr: Ryan Beaty
**COO:* Dwight Bruining
COO: Jerrald Deloach
**CFO:* Emery Hensley
Ofcr: George Mavros
VP: Mariananda Kumar
Dir Lab: Jore Morval
Dir Rx: Craig McCurdy
Genl Mgr: Rick Evan
Dir IT: Kami Frisher
Dir IT: Nouriel Meister

D-U-N-S 07-523-5572
FOUNDERS EQUITY INC (NY)
FOUNDERS MANAGEMENT SERVICES
711 5th Ave Ste 501, New York, NY 10022-3120
Tel (212) 829-0900 *Founded/Ownrshp* 1973
Sales 361.0MM[E] *EMP* 869
SIC 6211 Investment firm, general brokerage
Pt: Michael Burnham
**Pr:* John L Teeger
CFO: Dolores Arton
Dir Bus: Steve Ewing
Prin: Robert J Strang
Off Mgr: Stephanie Litfin

D-U-N-S 12-169-1513
FOUNDERS FEDERAL CREDIT UNION
607 N Main St, Lancaster, SC 29720-2137
Tel (803) 283-5958 *Founded/Ownrshp* 1951
Sales NA *EMP* 520
SIC 6061 Federal credit unions
Pr: Bruce A Brumfield
COO: Allan Schlick
**COO:* Sam White
CFO: Tony Gilreath
Sr VP: Bob Bender
Sr VP: Resa Blackman
Sr VP: Phyllis Bunkley
Sr VP: Nicki Nash
Sr VP: Jennifer Parker
**Sr VP:* Sonny Rushing
VP: Bob Atkins
VP: Jeff Ault
VP: Barbara Tolbert

D-U-N-S 61-880-6236
FOUNDERS GROUP INC
6825 W 111th St, Worth, IL 60482-1800
Tel (708) 448-6500 *Founded/Ownrshp* 1987
Sales NA *EMP* 450
SIC 6712 Bank holding companies
Ch: Lyle C Campbell
**Pr:* Douglas Campbell
**CFO:* Randall Ytterberg
**Ex VP:* Craig Campbell
**Sr VP:* Don Beenes
**Sr VP:* Joan Meyer
IT Man: Tom Lind

D-U-N-S 00-815-2857
FOUNDERS HEALTHCARE LLC
PREFERRED HOMECARE
(*Suby of* BEECKEN PETTY OKEEFE & CO LLC) ★
4601 E Hilton Ave Ste 100, Phoenix, AZ 85034-6406
Tel (800) 636-2123 *Founded/Ownrshp* 1997
Sales 67.3MM[E] *EMP* 2,000
SIC 7352 Medical equipment rental
CEO: Robert Fahlman
**CFO:* William Keys
**Sr VP:* Tony Domenico
**VP:* Keith Crawford
VP: Kelly Landberg
VP: Kim Templeton
Dir Lab: Thomas Fleishman
Admn Mgr: Terry Jamisson
Genl Mgr: Julius Reyes
Nurse Mgr: Doris Bauer
CIO: Kevin Sauer

FOUNDERS MANAGEMENT SERVICES
See FOUNDERS EQUITY INC

FOUNTAIN GREEN ELEM SCHOOL
See HARFORD COUNTY PUBLIC SCHOOL DISTRICT

FOUNTAIN HILL MEDICAL SERVICES
See ST LUKES PHYSICIAN GROUP INC

D-U-N-S 07-360-9703
■ FOUNTAIN VALLEY REGIONAL HOSPITAL AND MEDICAL CENTER
(*Suby of* TENET HEALTHSYSTEM MEDICAL INC) ★
17100 Euclid St, Fountain Valley, CA 92708-4043
Tel (714) 966-7200 *Founded/Ownrshp* 1994
Sales 351.3MM *EMP* 1,200
SIC 8062 General medical & surgical hospitals
Prin: Joseph Badalian
Dir Recs: Kay Woinarowicz
COO: Paul Czajka
**COO:* Edward F Littlejohn
**CFO:* Ken Jordan
Dir Case M: Lewana Allen
Dir Lab: Amita Patel
Dir Rx: Ted Kim
Dir Env Sv: Nellie Stauffer
Chf Nrs Of: Mary Botticella
CIO: Edwin Delossantos

D-U-N-S 07-241-3644
FOUNTAIN VIEW MANOR INC
107 E Barclay St, Henryetta, OK 74437-5609
Tel (918) 652-7021 *Founded/Ownrshp* 1967
Sales 425.2MM *EMP* 94
SIC 8051 Skilled nursing care facilities
Pr: Sylvia Kramer
**Sec:* Thomas A Connery
**VP:* Clyde L Browers
Board of Directors: Bess Gavras

FOUNTAIN-FORT CARSON SCHOOL DI
See EL PASO COUNTY SCHOOL DISTRICT 8

D-U-N-S 06-114-4457
FOUNTAINHEAD DEVELOPMENT LLC (GA)
CHATEAU ELAN GOLF
100 Rue Charlemagne Dr, Braselton, GA 30517-2435
Tel (770) 867-0903 *Founded/Ownrshp* 2002
Sales 104.7MM[E] *EMP* 700
SIC 7992 7991 5921 5812 7011 Public golf courses; Athletic club & gymnasiums, membership; Wine; American restaurant; Resort hotel

D-U-N-S 00-777-8814
FOUR COUNTY ELECTRIC MEMBERSHIP CORP
1822 Nc Highway 53 W, Burgaw, NC 28425-4514
Tel (910) 259-2361 *Founded/Ownrshp* 1937
Sales 97.6MM *EMP* 99
Accts Dixon Hughes Goodman Llp Roan
SIC 4911 Distribution, electric power
CEO: Mitchell Keel
**Treas:* Gene Jordan
**VP:* Dan Allen
**VP:* Glenn Bradshaw
VP: Gregg Cohn

D-U-N-S 08-095-8770
FOUR COURTS INC
JEWISH HOSP ST MRYS HEALTHCARE
(*Suby of* JEWISH HOSPITAL & ST MARYS HEALTHCARE INC) ★
2100 Millvale Rd, Louisville, KY 40205-1604
Tel (502) 451-0990 *Founded/Ownrshp* 1983
Sales 26.7MM[E] *EMP* 1,551[E]
SIC 8052 Intermediate care facilities; Personal care facility
Pr: Henry C Wagner

FOUR HANDS HOME
See FOUR HANDS LLC

D-U-N-S 93-792-0130 IMP/EXP
FOUR HANDS LLC
FOUR HANDS HOME
2090 Woodward St, Austin, TX 78744-1016
Tel (512) 371-7575 *Founded/Ownrshp* 1995
Sales 115.0MM *EMP* 125
Accts Maxwell Locke & Ritter Llp Au
SIC 5023 5712 Home furnishings; Furniture stores
Pr: Matthew Briggs
**COO:* Jerome Kearns
**CFO:* Curt Welch
**Chf Mktg O:* Michael Bullock
Store Mgr: Chuck Pratz
Mktg Dir: Megan Beagle
Sls Dir: Mary Bell

D-U-N-S 36-294-5032
FOUR KEYS LLC
ROSEN NISSAN & KIA
5505 S 27th St, Milwaukee, WI 53221-4105
Tel (414) 282-9300 *Founded/Ownrshp* 2015
Sales 113.1MM[E] *EMP* 130
SIC 5511 Automobiles, new & used
Pr: Jeffrey Rosen
Bd of Dir: Kevin Berger
Exec: Donna Schuette

D-U-N-S 08-989-6737
FOUR POINTS TECHNOLOGY LLC (DC)
14900 Confrnce Ctr Dr # 100, Chantilly, VA 20151-3834
Tel (703) 657-6102 *Founded/Ownrshp* 2002, 2004
Sales 170.6MM[E] *EMP* 28
Accts Sgs Associates Llc Mclean V
SIC 5045 Computers, peripherals & software
Pr: David Gilchrist
**COO:* Joel Lipkin

*VP: Rusty Palmer
*Ex Dir: Kris Laign
Mng Dir: Jeffrey Stein
CIO: Denise Harrison
VP Sls: Mindy Palmer
Sls Dir: Jason Goldberg
Sls Mgr: Yvette Gause

D-U-N-S 01-056-8327 IMP/EXP
FOUR SEASONS PRODUCE INC
400 Wabash Rd, Ephrata, PA 17522-9100
Tel (717) 721-2800 Founded/Ownrshp 1976
Sales 255.7MM^E EMP 630
SIC 5148

FOUR SEASONS RESORT & CLUB
See US-LAS COLINAS LIMITED PARTNERSHIP

D-U-N-S 80-350-7862 IMP
FOUR SEASONS RESORT & CLUB
4150 N Macarthur Blvd, Irving, TX 75038-6417
Tel (972) 717-0700 Founded/Ownrshp 1985
Sales 38.7MM^E EMP 1,000
SIC 7011 Resort hotel
CEO: Allen Smith

D-U-N-S 08-374-6214
FOUR STAR FREIGHTLINER INC (AL)
3140 Hayneville Rd, Montgomery, AL 36108-3937
Tel (334) 263-1085 Founded/Ownrshp 1982, 2002
Sales 110.0MM EMP 175
Accts Carr Riggs & Ingram Llc Montg
SIC 5012 5531 Trucks, commercial; Truck equipment & parts
CEO: Jerry Kocan
*CFO: Gary Imdieke
Manager: Kathy Hatcher
Opers Mgr: Scott Dixon

FOUR WHEEL PARTS WHOLESALERS
See TRANSAMERICAN DISSOLUTION CO LLC

D-U-N-S 62-081-8851
FOUR WINDS INTERACTIVE LLC
FWI
1221 N Broadway, Denver, CO 80203-2179
Tel (877) 204-6679 Founded/Ownrshp 2005
Sales 128.2MM^E EMP 327^E
SIC 7372 Prepackaged software
Pr: David Levin
Exec: Faith Rose
Prgrm Mgr: Jessie McCabe
Rgnl Mgr: Jake Ellison
CTO: Dave Shapiro
QA Dir: Frank Han
IT Man: Heidi McBride
Software D: Joseph Callaghan
Sales Exec: Erika Chapman
Sales Exec: Connie Davis
Manager: Dan McRae

D-U-N-S 15-551-4904
FOURCROWN INC
WENDY'S
434 Hale Ave N Ste 160, Saint Paul, MN 55128-7568
Tel (651) 714-0030 Founded/Ownrshp 1986
Sales 38.3MM^E EMP 1,000
SIC 5812 Fast-food restaurant, chain
Pr: Mike Givens
CFO: Dan Turnquist
*VP: Don Jensen
*VP: Dan Opitz
Mktg Dir: Paul Broten

D-U-N-S 04-818-9562 IMP
FOURJAY LLC
WENDY'S FOURJAY
42 Parkstone Cir, North Little Rock, AR 72116-7086
Tel (501) 372-2000 Founded/Ownrshp 1995
Sales 28.4MM^E EMP 1,400
SIC 5812 Fast-food restaurant, chain

FOURSQUARE INTERNATIONAL
See INTERNATIONAL CHURCH OF FOURSQUARE GOSPEL

FOURTHFLOOR FASHION TALENT
See CAREER GROUP INC

D-U-N-S 06-394-0043
FOWLER FOODS INC
139 Southwest Dr, Jonesboro, AR 72401-5828
Tel (870) 935-6984 Founded/Ownrshp 1970
Sales 53.5MM^E EMP 1,500
SIC 5812 Fast-food restaurant, chain
Ch Bd: Wallace W Fowler Sr
*Pr: Chris Fowler
*CFO: Loyd McCracken
*Sec: Jama Fowler
Ex VP: Lloyd Cracken
Dir IT: Gene Brumley

D-U-N-S 00-126-5354 IMP/EXP
FOWNES BROTHERS & CO INC (NY)
16 E 34th St Fl 5, New York, NY 10016-4370
Tel (212) 683-0150 Founded/Ownrshp 1921, 1777
Sales 59.8MM^E EMP 1,600
SIC 3151 2381 5136 5137 3949 Gloves, leather: dress or semidress; Gloves, woven or knit: made from purchased materials; Gloves, men's & boys'; Gloves, women's & children's; Gloves, sport & athletic: boxing, handball, etc.
Ch Bd: Thomas Gluckman
CFO: Thomas Faivre
*Ex VP: Chris Giattino
*VP: Helmuth Dosch
*VP: Bruna Maney
*VP: Howard Samuels

FOX & HOUND ENGLISH PUB GRILLE
See FOX & HOUND RESTAURANT GROUP

D-U-N-S 16-001-5681
FOX & HOUND RESTAURANT GROUP
FOX & HOUND ENGLISH PUB GRILLE
1421 N Waterfront Pkwy, Wichita, KS 67206-6600
Tel (316) 634-0505 Founded/Ownrshp 2006
Sales NA EMP 1,029^E
SIC 5812

D-U-N-S 16-160-6314
■ **FOX BROADCASTING CO**
(Suby of FOX FILMED ENTERTAINMENT) ★
10201 W Pico Blvd, Los Angeles, CA 90064-2606
Tel (310) 369-1000 Founded/Ownrshp 1998
Sales 166.3MM^E EMP 425
SIC 4833 Television broadcasting stations
CEO: David F Devoe Jr
*Pr: Nancy Utley
*COO: Joe Earley
*CFO: Del Mayberry
Ex VP: Tracy Dolgin
Ex VP: George Greenberg
*Sr VP: Sang Gong
Sr VP: Richard Licata
VP: Robert Graziano
VP: Gary Guan
VP: Scott Hamilton
VP: Tim Krass
VP: Steve Rosenberg
VP: Roar Senstad
VP: Nina Skorus-Neely
Exec: Phillip Schenkler

D-U-N-S 06-668-6635
FOX BSB HOLDCO INC
DODGER STADIUM
(Suby of GUGGENHEIM PARTNERS LLC) ★
1000 Vin Scully Ave, Los Angeles, CA 90090-1112
Tel (323) 224-1500 Founded/Ownrshp 1971
Sales 152.0MM^E EMP 3,472^E
SIC 7941 Baseball club, professional & semi-professional
V Ch: Steve Soboroff
V Ch: Jamie McCourt
*CEO: Ron Wheeler
*COO: Dannis Mannion
Ofcr: Michael Young
Sr VP: Camille Johnston
VP: Sam Fernandez
VP: Roy Smith
VP: Danny Telford
VP: Logan White
Dir Risk M: Michelle Darringer

D-U-N-S 01-419-9174
■ **FOX BUSINESS NETWORK**
(Suby of FOX FILMED ENTERTAINMENT) ★
1211 Avenue Of The, New York, NY 10036
Tel (212) 601-7000 Founded/Ownrshp 2009
Sales 36.1MM^E EMP 1,180^E
SIC 7389 Business services
Prin: Kathryn Tuggle
Ex VP: Brian Jones
Sr VP: Tim Carry
VP: Bruce Becker

D-U-N-S 05-177-9221
FOX C-6 SCHOOL DISTRICT
CONSOLIDATED SCHOOL DST 6
745 Jeffco Blvd, Arnold, MO 63010-1432
Tel (636) 296-8000 Founded/Ownrshp 1948
Sales 102.1MM^E EMP 1,800
SIC 8211 Public elementary & secondary schools
Bd of Dir: Chris Hastings
Bd of Dir: Dawn Mullins
Bd of Dir: Sherry Poppen
VP: Steve Holloway
Adm Dir: John Ziegler
Dir Sec: Paul Burch
IT Man: Jim Boyd
IT Man: Chris Labruyere
Schl Brd P: John Laughlin
HC Dir: Decklan Fitzpatrick
HC Dir: Kim Schumscher

D-U-N-S 60-877-4381
■ **FOX CABLE NETWORK SERVICES LLC**
FCN WEST
(Suby of FOX FILMED ENTERTAINMENT) ★
10201 W Pico Blvd, Los Angeles, CA 90064-2606
Tel (310) 369-2362 Founded/Ownrshp 1996
Sales 176.5MM^E EMP 326
SIC 4841 Cable & other pay television services
CEO: Peter Rice
COO: Chase Carey
COO: James Murdoch
CFO: David Devoe
CFO: John Nallen
CFO: Cheri Vincent
Ex VP: Michael Hopkins
Ex VP: Lawrence A Jacobs
Sr VP: Mike Biard
*Sr VP: Scott Grogin
VP: Jamia Bigalow
VP: Beryl Cook
*VP: Sol Doten
VP: Teri Everett
VP: Mike Feiler
VP: Chris Killebrew
VP: Amy Manzo
VP: Reed Nolte
VP: Brian Peterson
VP: Michael Regan
VP: Melis Smith-Sattler

D-U-N-S 07-372-4262
FOX CHASE CANCER CENTER FOUNDATION
333 Cottman Ave, Philadelphia, PA 19111-2434
Tel (215) 728-6900 Founded/Ownrshp 1972
Sales 315.6MM^E EMP 1,900
Accts Pricewaterhousecoopers Llp Ph
SIC 8069 8071 8062 Cancer hospital; Medical laboratories; General medical & surgical hospitals
CEO: Michael Seiden MD
V Ch: Louis D Penna
*Pr: Michael V Seiden MD PHD
COO: Don Leedy
CFO: Tresa Laribee
Bd of Dir: James Mitchell
Bd of Dir: Thomas Tritton
Ofcr: Megan Kaminska
Ofcr: Daniel Rudolph
Ex VP: Francis J McKay
Ex VP: Francis McKay
*Sr VP: Thomas Albanesi Jr
Sr VP: Paul Engstrom
VP: Mary Daly
VP: John Gricoski
*VP: Joseph F Hediger Sr
VP: Anne Jadwin
VP: Michael Sweelney
Dir Lab: Biao Luo
Dir Rad: Sharon Shill
Dir Rx: Christine Zwickel

D-U-N-S 14-767-0608 IMP
■ **FOX ENTERTAINMENT GROUP INC**
FOX FILMED ENTERTAINMENT
(Suby of TWENTY-FIRST CENTURY FOX INC) ★
1211 Ave Of The Americas, New York, NY 10036-8701
Tel (212) 852-7000 Founded/Ownrshp 2005
Sales 1.7MMM^E EMP 12,500
SIC 7812 4841 Motion picture & video production; Cable & other pay television services
CEO: K Rupert Murdoch
*Pr: Peter Chernin
Pr: Dan Fawcett
*Pr: Peter Levinsohn
Pr: Kyle McDoniel
COO: Josh Berman
*CFO: David F Devoe
CFO: Dean Hallett
Chf Mktg O: Gary Larson
*Ofcr: Jon Miller
Ex VP: Isaacson Donna
Sr VP: Andrea Berry
Sr VP: Sean Dailey
Sr VP: Todd Daly
Sr VP: Dean Ferris
Sr VP: Chris Hannan
Sr VP: Bruce Margolis
Sr VP: Todd Rowan
Sr VP: Kathryn Tralli
VP: Gary Hall
VP: Ruthanne Herman

D-U-N-S 07-909-5776
▲ **FOX FACTORY HOLDING CORP**
915 Disc Dr, Scotts Valley, CA 95066-4543
Tel (831) 274-6500 Founded/Ownrshp 1974
Sales 366.8MM EMP 1,500^E
Tkr Sym FOXF Exch NGS
SIC 3751 Motorcycles, bicycles & parts
CEO: Larry L Enterline
*Ch Bd: Elias Sabo
CFO: Zvi Glasman
Sr VP: John Boulton
Sr VP: William Katherman
Board of Directors: Robert C Fox Jr, Joseph Hagin, Dudley Mendenhall, Carl Nichols, Ted Waitman

FOX FILMED ENTERTAINMENT
See FOX ENTERTAINMENT GROUP INC

FOX FILMS ENTERTAINMENT
See TWENTIETH CENTURY FOX FILM CORP

D-U-N-S 06-913-8774 IMP/EXP
FOX HEAD INC (CA)
FOX RACING
16752 Armstrong Ave, Irvine, CA 92606-4912
Tel (408) 776-8633 Founded/Ownrshp 1974
Sales 321.9MM^E EMP 462^E
SIC 5136 5137 5961 Sportswear, men's & boys'; Sportswear, women's & children's; Mail order house
Ch: Peter Fox
*Pr: Pete Fox
*CEO: Paul E Harrington
*VP: Geoffrey T Fox
Dir Rx: Brandon Portnoff
Genl Mgr: Ken Lockwood
Off Mgr: Kricket Atkinson
Off Mgr: Kari Hoffhaus
Mktg Mgr: Kellen Trachy
Sls Mgr: Scott Card

D-U-N-S 02-261-2775
FOX HILL HOLDINGS INC
99 Cherry Hill Rd, Parsippany, NJ 07054-1122
Tel (212) 734-1525 Founded/Ownrshp 2008
Sales NA EMP 1,832^E
SIC 6411 Insurance claim adjusters, not employed by insurance company
Ch Bd: Stephanie Spillane
VP: Robert Missus

D-U-N-S 78-046-7775 IMP
FOX HILLS AUTO INC
AIRPORT MARINA FORD
5880 W Centinela Ave, Los Angeles, CA 90045-1504
Tel (310) 649-3673 Founded/Ownrshp 1995
Sales 92.3MM^E EMP 250
SIC 5511 7538 5531 5521 Automobiles, new & used; General automotive repair shops; Automotive & home supply stores; Used car dealers
CEO: Norris J Bishton Jr
VP: Jim Canty

D-U-N-S 14-464-3384 IMP
■ **FOX INC**
HOME ENTERTAINMENT DIV
(Suby of 21ST CENTURY FOX AMERICA INC) ★
2121 Ave Of The Ste 1100, Los Angeles, CA 90067
Tel (310) 369-1000 Founded/Ownrshp 1998
Sales 950.7MM^E EMP 3,200
SIC 4833 7812 Television broadcasting stations; Motion picture production & distribution; Motion picture production & distribution, television
Ch Bd: K Rupert Murdoch
Pr: Dan Bell
*Pr: Mike Dunn
Pr: Robert Fusco
*Pr: Jay Itzkowitz
Pr: Larry Jones
Pr: Keith Schreiber
CFO: Donald Flecky
Ex VP: Marcela Martin
Ex VP: Christopher Pawlak
Sr VP: Jeff Dow
Sr VP: Michelle Garry
Sr VP: Robert Gottlieb
Sr VP: Julia Howe
Sr VP: Vincent Marcais
VP: Robert Ditzler
VP: Jon Furr
VP: Steve Harrington
VP: Doug Levy
VP: Douglas Pfaff
VP: Lance Reiss

D-U-N-S 08-021-2690
FOX MANAGEMENT INC
251 Stenton Ave, Plymouth Meeting, PA 19462-1246
Tel (610) 283-7561 Founded/Ownrshp 1982
Sales 1.0MMM^E EMP 300^E
SIC 8111 General practice attorney, lawyer

FOX NETWORK CENTER
See FOX NETWORKS GROUP INC

D-U-N-S 12-906-1938
■ **FOX NETWORKS GROUP INC**
FOX NETWORK CENTER
(Suby of FOX FILMED ENTERTAINMENT) ★
10201 W Pico Blvd 101, Los Angeles, CA 90064-2606
Tel (310) 369-9369 Founded/Ownrshp 2000
Sales 34.9MM^E EMP 1,615^E
SIC 4841 Direct broadcast satellite services (DBS)
Pr: Rupert Murdoch
Pr: Brian Sullivan
VP: Jeb Terry
Dir IT: Don Covington
Dir IT: Mona Covington
Dir IT: Raul De Quesada
Dir IT: Erin Harvego
Info Man: Tariq Khan
Info Man: Brian Willery
Software D: Joshua Johnson
Sftwr Eng: Johnathan James

FOX NEWS CHANNEL, THE
See FOX NEWS NETWORK LLC

D-U-N-S 96-380-8308
■ **FOX NEWS NETWORK LLC**
FOX NEWS CHANNEL, THE
(Suby of FOX FILMED ENTERTAINMENT) ★
1211 Avenue Of The Americ, New York, NY 10036-8799
Tel (212) 301-3000 Founded/Ownrshp 2001
Sales 110.2MM^E EMP 980
SIC 7812 Television film production
Ch Bd: Rupert Murdoch
CFO: Jack Abernethy
CFO: Mark Kranz
Ofcr: Bryan Boughton
Ex VP: Gary Hartley
Ex VP: Danny Kaye
Ex VP: Kevin Magee
Ex VP: John Moody
Sr VP: Brian Jones
Sr VP: Suzanne Scott
VP: Michael Clemente
VP: Bill Conte
VP: Mike Denby
VP: Mitchell Kweit
VP: Barbara Lafemina
VP: Richard O'Brien
VP: Douglas Pfaff
VP: Warren Vandeveer
VP: Jason Villar
VP: Paul Werner
Exec: David Clark

D-U-N-S 17-889-6127
FOX NURSING HOME CORP
(Suby of FOX MANAGEMENT INC) ★
251 Stenton Ave, Plymouth Meeting, PA 19462-1246
Tel (610) 828-2272 Founded/Ownrshp 1982
Sales 1.0MMM EMP 298^E
SIC 8051 Skilled nursing care facilities
CEO: James M Foulke
*COO: Vic Kostenko
*CFO: Ralph M Van
*VP: Joseph Murray
*VP: Joseph F Murry

D-U-N-S 17-760-7108
FOX PAINE & CO LLC
2105 Woodside Rd Ste D, Woodside, CA 94062-1153
Tel (650) 235-2075 Founded/Ownrshp 1997
Sales 107.8MM^E EMP 264^E
SIC 6211 Investment firm, general brokerage

FOX RACING
See FOX HEAD INC

D-U-N-S 79-889-2543
FOX RENT A CAR INC
5500 W Century Blvd, Los Angeles, CA 90045-5914
Tel (310) 342-5155 Founded/Ownrshp 1989
Sales 172.7MM^E EMP 1,215
SIC 7514 Passenger car rental
Pr: Allen Rezapour
COO: Sean Busking
CFO: Richard Wolff
*Treas: Mike Jaberi
VP: Jerame Jackson
*Prin: Mark Mirtorabi
*Prin: Jack Tomson
Genl Mgr: Doug Bates
IT Man: Francisco Mora
IT Man: Bhushan Shah
IT Man: Dave Stephenson

D-U-N-S 02-493-2980
■ **FOX RIVER FOODS INC** (IL)
PERFORMNCE FDSERVICE-FOX RIVER
(Suby of P F G) ★
5030 Baseline Rd, Montgomery, IL 60538-1100
Tel (630) 896-1991 Founded/Ownrshp 1947, 2012
Sales 418.7MM^E EMP 301
SIC 5142 5149 5148 5147 Packaged frozen goods; Canned goods: fruit, vegetables, seafood, meats, etc.; Fruits, fresh; Vegetables, fresh; Meats, fresh
Ch: William M Pearce
*Pr: Robert McGuigan
*CFO: Robert D Evans
*Treas: Jeffrey W Fender
*Sr VP: Kent R Berke
VP: David Watgen

D-U-N-S 02-008-0099
FOX ROTHSCHILD LLP (PA)
2000 Market St Fl 20, Philadelphia, PA 19103-3222
Tel (215) 299-2000 Founded/Ownrshp 1906, 1934
Sales 179.9MM^E EMP 843

SIC 8111

D-U-N-S 14-859-0383 IMP
■ FOX TELEVISION STATIONS LLC
KTTV-FOX 11
(*Suby of* FOX FILMED ENTERTAINMENT) ★
1999 S Bundy Dr, Los Angeles, CA 90025-5203
Tel (310) 584-2000 *Founded/Ownrshp* 1998
Sales 475.1MM[E] *EMP* 1,490
SIC 4833 7313 Television broadcasting stations; Radio, television, publisher representatives
Pr: Jim Burke
**Ch Bd:* Roger Ailes
**Pr:* Tom Herwitz
Pr: Dennis Swanson
Ex VP: Brian Lewis
**Ex VP:* Dick Slenker
Sr VP: Sharri Berg
**Sr VP:* Gerry Friedman
**Sr VP:* Jean Fuentes
Sr VP: David Keneipp
**Sr VP:* Kathy Maloney
**Sr VP:* Alec Pettersen
**Sr VP:* Betsy Swanson
VP: Annie Buranasakorn
VP: Stockton Holt
VP: Matt McLaughlin
VP: Sheila Oliver
**VP:* Molly Pauker
VP: Mike Petruzzi
VP: Connie Robinson
VP: Thomas Sheehy

FOX THEATRE
See OLYMPIA ENTERTAINMENT INC

D-U-N-S 78-662-0450
FOX VALLEY PRESS INC
495 N Commons Dr Ste 200, Aurora, IL 60504-8295
Tel (815) 439-5300 *Founded/Ownrshp* 1992
Sales NA *EMP* 1,200
SIC 2759

FOXWOODS RESORT CASINO
See MASHANTUCKET PEQUOT TRIBAL NATION

D-U-N-S 00-792-6397
FOXWORTH GALBRAITH LUMBER CO
DO IT BEST
4965 Preston Park Blvd # 400, Plano, TX 75093-5141
Tel (972) 665-2400 *Founded/Ownrshp* 1901
Sales 270.0MM *EMP* 2,500
Accts Johnson & Sheldon Pc Amari
SIC 5211 5031 2439 2431 Lumber & other building materials; Lumber, plywood & millwork; Trusses, except roof: laminated lumber; Trusses, wooden roof; Doors, wood
Pr: Jack L Foxworth
Pr: J C Galbraith III
CEO: Walter L Foxworth
CFO: Rich Perkins
Treas: Danny Mueller
VP: Grant P Foxworth
VP: Edward Galbraith
VP: Billy White
Opers Mgr: Robert Easley
Board of Directors: Karen D Raley

FP
See FRANCISCO PARTNERS LP

D-U-N-S 01-300-3962
FP HOLDINGS LP
PALMS HOTEL & RESORT, THE
(*Suby of* STATION CASINOS LLC) ★
4321 W Flamingo Rd, Las Vegas, NV 89103-3903
Tel (702) 942-7777 *Founded/Ownrshp* 2016
Sales 148.5MM[E] *EMP* 1,800
SIC 7011 Hotels & motels
VP: Mark Carlson
VP: Frank Garvey
VP: Christopher Joy
VP: Eric Saint-Marc
Ex Dir: Aaron Hartwig
Natl Sales: Stephanie Brandenburg
Natl Sales: Natika Lemon
Pr Mgr: Lindsay Feldman
Sls Mgr: Raul Daniels

FP INTERNATIONAL
See FREE-FLOW PACKAGING INTERNATIONAL INC

FP WINNER
See FREDERICK P WINNER LTD

D-U-N-S 11-157-0722
■ FPC FINANCIAL F S B
(*Suby of* DEERE & CO) ★
8402 Excelsior Dr, Madison, WI 53717-1909
Tel (608) 821-2000 *Founded/Ownrshp* 2000
Sales NA *EMP* 214
SIC 6035 Federal savings banks
Pr: Jim Meegh
Netwrk Mgr: Sean Kinsey
Mktg Mgr: Barbara Cashman

FPC USA
See FORMOSA PLASTICS CORP USA

D-U-N-S 07-378-1148
FPI MANAGEMENT INC
800 Iron Point Rd, Folsom, CA 95630-9004
Tel (916) 357-5300 *Founded/Ownrshp* 1990
Sales 73.9MM[E] *EMP* 1,400
SIC 6531 Real estate managers
Pr: Dennis Treadaway
Bd of Dir: Johnson Hill
Bd of Dir: Ellsworth House
VP: David Divine
VP: Shannon Dustin
VP: Michelle Fisher
**VP:* Gary Haugstad
VP: Kim Kisilewicz
Exec: Sheena Casey
Exec: Vanessa Dern
Exec: Renee Everett
Exec: Monica Treat

FPL
See FLORIDA POWER & LIGHT CO INC

D-U-N-S 00-329-0111 IMP/EXP
FPL FOOD LLC
1301 New Savannah Rd, Augusta, GA 30901-3843
Tel (706) 722-2694 *Founded/Ownrshp* 2004
Sales 215.8MM[E] *EMP* 800
Accts Cherry Bekaert & Holland Augu
SIC 2011 Meat packing plants
Pr: Francois Leger
Pr: Don Adams
COO: Randal Garrett
**CFO:* Cimberlie Elkins
CFO: Jerome F Sheehan
**VP:* Lee Bonecutter
**VP:* Angela Duncan
Exec: Randy Garrett
IT Man: David Steele
IT Man: Kevin Walden

FPT CLEVELAND
See FERROUS PROCESSING AND TRADING CO

FPUA
See FORT PIERCE UTILITIES AUTHORITY

D-U-N-S 96-698-2485
FQSR LLC
KBP FOODS
8900 Indian Creek Pkwy # 100, Overland Park, KS 66210-1554
Tel (913) 469-1112 *Founded/Ownrshp* 2010
Sales 105.6MM[E] *EMP* 4,500
SIC 5812 Fast-food restaurant, chain
Pr: Michael G Kulp
Mng Pt: Tim Cole
Pr: Matthew Hansen
Pr: Tony Miceli
**CFO:* Alan Salts
**Sr VP:* Barry W Dubin
VP: Anthony Gianino
**VP:* Deborah Kass

D-U-N-S 07-946-3190
FR UTILITY SERVICES
1424 4th Ave, Seattle, WA 98101-2297
Tel (425) 890-1425 *Founded/Ownrshp* 2013
Sales 243.0MM[E] *EMP* 1,600
SIC 1731 Electric power systems contractors

D-U-N-S 08-399-0937
FRAGOMEN DEL REY BERNSEN & LOEWY LLP
FDBL
7 Hanover Sq Ste 800, New York, NY 10004-2673
Tel (732) 862-5000 *Founded/Ownrshp* 1951
Sales 285.9MM[E] *EMP* 1,400
SIC 8111 General practice law office
Ch: Austin T Fragomen Jr
Mng Pt: Scott Cooper
VP: Anne-Rose V Den Bossche
VP: Colleen L Caden
Snr Sftwr: Alpana Gupta
Dir IT: Ed Yetman
IT Man: Steve Kirshon
IT Man: Harriet Obrien
Netwrk Mgr: Eon Joseph
Info Man: William Polanco
Mktg Mgr: Sheila Doerr

D-U-N-S 96-850-0111 IMP/EXP
FRAM GROUP OPERATIONS LLC
UCI-FRAM AUTOBRANDS
(*Suby of* RANK GROUP LIMITED)
1900 W Field Ct, Lake Forest, IL 60045-4828
Tel (800) 890-2075 *Founded/Ownrshp* 2011
Sales 749.8MM[E] *EMP* 2,400[E]
SIC 3694 3714 Engine electrical equipment; Motor vehicle parts & accessories
Pr: Bruce Zorich
**CFO:* George Dirado
CIO: Mark Wikingstad

D-U-N-S 14-860-3459 EXP
FRAMACO INTERNATIONAL INC
800 Westchester Ave S430, Rye Brook, NY 10573-1339
Tel (914) 633-6600 *Founded/Ownrshp* 1992
Sales 106.1MM *EMP* 28[E]
SIC 8741 Construction management
CEO: Gilles F Kacha
**Pr:* Paul Kacha
IT Man: Michael Calandrello

D-U-N-S 07-964-2321
FRAMEWORK CAPITAL PARTNERS LLC
1700 Post Oak Blvd, Houston, TX 77056-3963
Tel (713) 826-9351 *Founded/Ownrshp* 2014
Sales NA *EMP* 3,000
SIC 6719 Investment holding companies, except banks
Mng Pt: Jerry McGee

D-U-N-S 78-206-3077
FRANCES MARY ACCESSORIES INC
3732 Mt Diablo Blvd # 260, Lafayette, CA 94549-3643
Tel (925) 962-2111 *Founded/Ownrshp* 1990
Sales 4.0MM *EMP* 1,020
SIC 3171 Handbags, women's
Pr: Mary Frances Shaffer
Off Mgr: Carolyn Miller

D-U-N-S 96-353-3067
FRANCES STREITEL - SOUTH
2300 W Broadway St, Collinsville, OK 74021-1625
Tel (918) 371-2545 *Founded/Ownrshp* 2010
Sales 389.5MM *EMP* 11[E]
SIC 8051 Skilled nursing care facilities
Prin: Frances Streitel

D-U-N-S 80-565-6266
▲ FRANCESCAS HOLDINGS CORP
8760 Clay Rd, Houston, TX 77080-1859
Tel (713) 864-1358 *Founded/Ownrshp* 1999
Sales 439.3MM *EMP* 5,211
Tkr Sym FRAN *Exch* NGS
SIC 5621 5632 Women's clothing stores; Women's specialty clothing stores; Ready-to-wear apparel, women's; Women's accessory & specialty stores; Apparel accessories; Costume jewelry; Handbags
Ch Bd: Michael Barnes
**Ch Bd:* Richard Kunes
CFO: Kelly Dilts
Ofcr: Laurie Hummel
Snr Mgr: Juan Mendez
Board of Directors: Patricia Bender, Richard Emmett, Laurie Ann Goldman, Joseph O'leary, Marie Toulantis

D-U-N-S 78-046-7551
FRANCHISE TAX BOARD CALIFORNIA
CALIFRNIA GOVT OPERATIONS AGCY
(*Suby of* CALIFORNIA GOVERNMENT OPERATIONS AGENCY) ★
9646 Butterfield Way, Sacramento, CA 95827-1500
Tel (916) 845-3650 *Founded/Ownrshp* 1930
Sales NA *EMP* 6,000
SIC 9311 Taxation department, government;
Ex Ofcr: Selvi Stanislaus
**Ch Bd:* Steve Wesley
**Ex Ofcr:* Gerald H Goldberg
**Prin:* John Chaing

D-U-N-S 03-647-2371
FRANCHISEE SHIPPING CENTER CO INC
500 Bic Dr Bldg 3, Milford, CT 06461-1777
Tel (203) 301-0539 *Founded/Ownrshp* 1994
Sales 88.1MM[E] *EMP* 800
SIC 4731 5943 Agents, shipping; Stationery stores
Pr: Frederick Teluca
**VP:* Thomas Hislop
**VP:* David Worroll
**Prin:* Peter Buck
**Prin:* Mildred Shinn

D-U-N-S 09-491-7150 IMP
FRANCIS DRILLING FLUIDS LTD
(*Suby of* FDF RESOURCES HOLDINGS LLC)
240 Jasmine Rd, Crowley, LA 70526-8128
Tel (337) 783-8685 *Founded/Ownrshp* 1977
Sales 212.3MM[E] *EMP* 239
SIC 5169 1389 7353 Drilling mud; Oil field services; Oil field equipment, rental or leasing
Pr: Douglas C Chapple
VP: Jude N Gregory
Software D: Micah Willis

D-U-N-S 82-737-4203
FRANCIS E PARKER MEMORIAL HOME INC
1421 River Rd, Piscataway, NJ 08854-5800
Tel (732) 545-8330 *Founded/Ownrshp* 1996
Sales 158.3MM *EMP* 325[E]
Accts Parentebeard Llc Philadelphia
SIC 8741 Nursing & personal care facility management
Pr: Roberto Muniz
CFO: David Bridge
CFO: Michael Callan
Exec: Carol Burt
Exec: John Cerminaro
Off Mgr: Dee Carubia
QC Dir: Gloria Zayaskosky

D-U-N-S 96-865-0379
FRANCIS HOWELL SCHOOL DISTRICT
4545 Central School Rd, Saint Charles, MO 63304-7113
Tel (636) 851-4000 *Founded/Ownrshp* 2011
Sales 48.5MM[E] *EMP* 2,024[E]
SIC 8211 Public elementary & secondary schools

D-U-N-S 09-235-1733
FRANCIS HOWELL SCHOOL DISTRICT EDUCATIONAL FACILITIES AUTHORITY
4545 Central School Rd, Saint Charles, MO 63304-7113
Tel (636) 851-4000 *Founded/Ownrshp* 1950
Sales 102.6MM[E] *EMP* 2,500
Accts Kerber Eck & Braeckel Llp St
SIC 8699 Charitable organization
Pr: Marty Hodits
**CFO:* Kevin Supple
CIO: Ray Eernisse
MIS Dir: Jason Adams
Teacher Pr: Lisa Simpkins

D-U-N-S 07-199-6383
FRANCIS SAINT MEDICAL CENTER
ST. FRANCIS MEDICAL CENTER
211 Saint Francis Dr, Cape Girardeau, MO 63703-5049
Tel (573) 331-3000 *Founded/Ownrshp* 1972
Sales 424.2MM *EMP* 1,500
SIC 8062 General medical & surgical hospitals
CEO: Steven C Bjelich
**Ch Bd:* Clyde Nenninger
CFO: Edwin Bode
Bd of Dir: Jeffrey Y Chang
Bd of Dir: Patricia L Ray
Ofcr: Diane Gammon
VP: Marilyn Curtis
VP: Jeanette Fadler
VP: Rick Fehr
**VP:* Greg Pleimann
VP: Judith R Wilferth

D-U-N-S 07-430-3694 IMP
FRANCISCAN ALLIANCE INC
SAINT JAMES HOSPITAL
1515 W Dragoon Trl, Mishawaka, IN 46544-4710
Tel (574) 256-3935 *Founded/Ownrshp* 1974
Sales 2.6MMM *EMP* 19,000
Accts Lb Pricewaterhousecoopers Llp
SIC 8062 8051 General medical & surgical hospitals; Skilled nursing care facilities
Ch Bd: Jane Marie Klein
Pr: Kevin D Leahy
COO: Sam Terese
CFO: Steven Wojnicki
Treas: Ann Kathleen Magiera
Ofcr: Peter J Murphy
VP: Lisa Decker
VP: Joel Hoff
VP: Corita Last
VP: Matt Mayer
Exec: Julie Kissee
Dir Risk M: Sharon Werner
Dir Rx: Michael Olson

D-U-N-S 84-703-7868
FRANCISCAN COMMUNITIES INC
ST ANTHONY HOME
203 W Franciscan Dr, Crown Point, IN 46307-4802
Tel (219) 661-5100 *Founded/Ownrshp* 1939
Sales 111.3MM *EMP* 500
SIC 8059 Rest home, with health care
Pr: Judy Amiano
**Pr:* Linda O Neill
**Treas:* Ronald K Tinsley
Info Man: Terri Black

D-U-N-S 96-949-3514
FRANCISCAN COMMUNITIES INC
11500 Theresa Dr, Lemont, IL 60439-2727
Tel (708) 647-6500 *Founded/Ownrshp* 2011
Sales 115.2MM *EMP* 34[E]
Accts Crowe Horwath Llp Homewood I
SIC 8051 Convalescent home with continuous nursing care
Pr: Judy Amiano
**Treas:* Ronald Tinsley
Board of Directors: Judy Amiano, Annette Shoemaker

D-U-N-S 96-707-3586
FRANCISCAN HEALTH SYSTEM
ST JOSEPH MEDICAL CENTER
(*Suby of* CATHOLIC HEALTH INITIATIVES WESTERN REGION) ★
1717 S J St, Tacoma, WA 98405-4933
Tel (253) 426-4101 *Founded/Ownrshp* 1981
Sales 610.2MM *EMP* 3,183[E]
SIC 8062 General medical & surgical hospitals
Pr: Joseph W Wilczek
COO: Anne McNamara
COO: Dennis Popp
**CFO:* Mike Fitzgerald
Ofcr: Holly Stroud
Sr VP: Everett W Newcomb
VP: Meta Dooley
VP: Diann Johnston
VP: Mike Liepman
VP: Kimberly Moore
Dir Rx: Timothy W Lynch

D-U-N-S 80-453-2732
FRANCISCAN HEALTH SYSTEMS
451 Sw Sedgwick Rd, Port Orchard, WA 98367-6447
Tel (360) 874-5900 *Founded/Ownrshp* 1891
Sales 941.7MM *EMP* 4
Accts Deloitte Tax Llp Houston Tx
SIC 8011 Medical centers
Prin: Cliff Robertson

D-U-N-S 17-916-4454
FRANCISCAN HEALTH SYSTEMS OF NEW JERSEY INC
308 Willow Ave, Hoboken, NJ 07030-3808
Tel (201) 418-1000 *Founded/Ownrshp* 1985
Sales 28.9MM[E] *EMP* 1,647
SIC 8741 Hospital management; Nursing & personal care facility management
Pr: Erich Wolters
CFO: Mark Herberts
**VP:* Diann Johnston

D-U-N-S 07-920-6242
FRANCISCAN MEDICAL GROUP
1717 S J St, Tacoma, WA 98405-4933
Tel (253) 792-4365 *Founded/Ownrshp* 2013
Sales 336.6MM *EMP* 30[E]
Accts Catholic Health Initiatives E
SIC 8011 Offices & clinics of medical doctors

D-U-N-S 61-394-7738
FRANCISCAN MISSIONARIES OF OUR LADY HEALTH SYSTEM INC
FMOL HEALTH SYSTEM
4200 Essen Ln, Baton Rouge, LA 70809-2158
Tel (225) 526-4500 *Founded/Ownrshp* 1984
Sales 102.5MM *EMP* 9,000
Accts Kpmg Llp Baton Rouge La
SIC 8741 Hospital management
Ch: James W Moore Jr
**Pr:* Mr John J Finan
**CFO:* Howard Harvill
**CFO:* Bob Ramsey
**Sec:* Sr Helen Cahill
Ofcr: Elizabeth Champion
Ofcr: Philip Leblanc
**VP:* Jolee H Bollinger
VP: Jolee Bollinger
VP: Roland Funsten
**VP:* Pete Guarisco
VP: Cindy Heine
VP: Nicole Hidalgo
VP: Suzanne Schexnayder
Dir Risk M: Paula Jenkins
Dir Risk M: Harriet Percy

D-U-N-S 06-745-8174
FRANCISCAN SISTER OF CHICAGO
RELIGIOUS INSTITUTE
11500 Theresa Dr, Lemont, IL 60439-2727
Tel (708) 647-6500 *Founded/Ownrshp* 1894
Sales 51.9MM[E] *EMP* 1,754
SIC 8661 8011 Convent; General & family practice, physician/surgeon; Internal medicine practitioners
Pr: Sister Mary Francis
**Treas:* Sister Helene

D-U-N-S 60-330-7232
FRANCISCAN SISTERS OF CHRISTIAN CHARITY SPONSORED MINISTRIES INC
FSCC
1415 S Rapids Rd, Manitowoc, WI 54220-9302
Tel (920) 684-7071 *Founded/Ownrshp* 1985
Sales 67.0MM[E] *EMP* 3,000
Accts Ernst & Young Llp Milwaukee
SIC 8741 8062 Hospital management; Nursing & personal care facility management; General medical & surgical hospitals
Pr: Sister Laura Wolf
**Treas:* James Vopat
VP: Scott McConnaha

D-U-N-S 04-587-4351
FRANCISCAN UNIVERSITY OF STEUBENVILLE
1235 University Blvd, Steubenville, OH 43952-1792
Tel (740) 283-3771 Founded/Ownrshp 1946
Sales 83.5MM EMP 375E
Accts Schneider Downs & Co Inc Pitt
SIC 8221 University
Pr: Fr Sean Sheridan
COO: Matt Heaps
Ofcr: Jospeh Friona
VP: Chris Cahill
*VP: Dr Robert Filby
VP: Michael Hernon
VP: Daniel Kempton
*VP: David Skiviat
Dir Teleco: Dennis Breen
Assoc Dir: Tom Sofio
Ex Dir: Mark Joseph

D-U-N-S 14-540-0656
FRANCISCO PARTNERS LP
FP
(Suby of FRANCISCO PARTNERS MANAGEMENT LP) ★
1 Letterman Dr Bldg C, San Francisco, CA 94129-2402
Tel (415) 418-2900 Founded/Ownrshp 2000
Sales 375.5MME EMP 4,170
SIC 7373 7372 Systems integration services; Prepackaged software
Mng Pt: Dipanjan Deb
Pt: Chris Adams
Pt: Ben Ball
Pt: Peter Christodoulo
Pt: Neil Garfinkel
COO: Tom Ludwig
VP: Amir Aghdaei
VP: Alessandro Celli
VP: Brian Decker

D-U-N-S 10-911-5605
FRANCISCO PARTNERS MANAGEMENT LP
1 Letterman Dr Ste 410, San Francisco, CA 94129-1495
Tel (415) 418-2900 Founded/Ownrshp 1999
Sales 2.0MME EMP 6,405
SIC 6799 7372 Investors; Application computer software
Pt: Dipanjan Deb
Genl Pt: Neil Garfinkle
Pt: Sanford Robertson
COO: Tom Ludwig
CFO: Ann Halloran
CFO: Anne Saviano
VP: Chris Adams
VP: Patrick Brady
VP: Jason Brein
VP: Alessandro Celli
VP: Peter Christodoulo
VP: Laura Owen
VP: Adam Solomon

D-U-N-S 00-133-8110 IMP
FRANCO MANUFACTURING CO INC
555 Prospect St, Metuchen, NJ 08840-2271
Tel (732) 494-0503 Founded/Ownrshp 1952
Sales 168.6MME EMP 750
SIC 2269 2392 2211 5023 5131 Finishing plants; Printing of narrow fabrics; Towels, fabric & nonwoven: made from purchased materials; Washcloths & bath mitts: made from purchased materials; Towels, dishcloths & washcloths: cotton; Dishcloths; Washcloths; Towels & toweling, cotton; Towels; Textiles, woven; Cotton goods
Pr: Louis D Franco
*CFO: Michael Kaplan
Treas: Susan Megill
Bd of Dir: Pat Parker
*Ex VP: Jack D Franco
Ex VP: Jack Franco
*Ex VP: Morris Franco
*Sr VP: Edmund Rossi
VP: Bridget Crozier
Exec: Joseph Bianchi
CTO: Jeff Casner

D-U-N-S 01-713-7581
FRANCO-NEVADA US CORP
(Suby of FRANCO-NEVADA CORPORATION)
1745 Shea Center Dr # 310, Highlands Ranch, CO 80129-1539
Tel (303) 317-6335 Founded/Ownrshp 2007
Sales 90.7MM EMP 8
SIC 6211 Mineral royalties dealers
Pr: Steve Aaker
*CFO: Alexander Morrison

D-U-N-S 80-018-9057
FRANDELI GROUP LLC
20377 Sw Acacia St # 200, Newport Beach, CA 92660-1780
Tel (714) 450-7660 Founded/Ownrshp 2005
Sales 126.6MME EMP 400
SIC 6794 Franchises, selling or licensing
Sales Exec: Doug Pak
Snr Mgr: Angy Chin

D-U-N-S 17-671-4517
FRANDSEN CORP
5481 Saint Croix Trl # 200, North Branch, MN 55056-6130
Tel (651) 407-5700 Founded/Ownrshp 1951
Sales 274.9MME EMP 160
SIC 8742 Management consulting services
CEO: Dennis Frandsen
Ex VP: Charles Mausbach
Sr VP: Corey Cleveland
VP: James Ertz
VP: Steven Vranich
Creative D: Charlotte Wilcox
IT Man: Jim Hoffmann
VP Mktg: Amy Scheel

D-U-N-S 18-653-9623
FRANDSEN FINANCIAL CORP
(Suby of FRANDSEN CORP) ★
4388 Round Lake Rd W, Arden Hills, MN 55112-3923
Tel (651) 242-5700 Founded/Ownrshp 1983
Sales NA EMP 160
Accts Wipfli Llp St Paul Minnesot
SIC 6022 6712 State commercial banks; Bank holding companies
CEO: Richard Hoban
*Owner: Dennis Frandsen
*Pr: Charles Mauspach
*CFO: Ken Osowski
Chf Cred: Lon Kelling
Ex VP: Charles Mausbach
Ex VP: Randy Morehart
VP: Jamie Dosdall
VP: Julie Fore
VP: Nick Hinz
VP: Suzy Matschiner
VP: Randy Schroeder
VP: Todd Van Wambeke

D-U-N-S 02-845-8057 IMP
FRANK AMBROSE INC
AMBROSE INTERNATIONAL
550 Hulet Dr Ste 103, Bloomfield Hills, MI 48302-0322
Tel (248) 655-2300 Founded/Ownrshp 1974
Sales 117.5MME EMP 100
SIC 5111 Fine paper
CEO: Robert D Ambrose
*Ch Bd: Frank J Ambrose
*Pr: Chris McBride
*COO: Jeff Wagenberg
*VP: Peggy Wantuck

D-U-N-S 03-724-5818 IMP
FRANK B FUHRER HOLDINGS INC
FRANK B FUHRER WHOLESALE CO
3100 E Carson St, Pittsburgh, PA 15203-2129
Tel (412) 488-8844 Founded/Ownrshp 1970
Sales 100.4MME EMP 160
SIC 5181 Beer & other fermented malt liquors
Pr: Frank B Fuhrer III
*VP: Jack Miller

FRANK B FUHRER WHOLESALE CO
See FRANK B FUHRER HOLDINGS INC

D-U-N-S 01-250-1425 IMP
FRANK BRUNCKHORST CO LLC
BOARS HEAD
1819 Main St Ste 800, Sarasota, FL 34236-5926
Tel (941) 955-0994 Founded/Ownrshp 1993
Sales 332.9MME EMP 500
SIC 5147 Meats & meat products
Pr: Michael Martella
CFO: Blair Waldick
CIO: Mike Luczynski
Dir IT: Tim Nale
Mktg Dir: John Cannistra
Mktg Mgr: Beth Byron-Reasoner

D-U-N-S 78-706-3945
FRANK CONSOLIDATED ENTERPRISES INC
666 Garland Pl, Des Plaines, IL 60016-4725
Tel (847) 699-7000 Founded/Ownrshp 1979
Sales 121.5MME EMP 610
SIC 8742 Marketing consulting services
Pr: James S Frank
Treas: Rodd Specketer
Genl Mgr: Daniel Z Frank
QA Dir: Bridgit Glenn
IT Man: Carol Coulter
Software D: Vishal Dhar
Software D: Venu Vujjeni
Opers Mgr: Scott Brinker
VP Sls: Norman Din
Mktg Mgr: Daniel Nesbitt
Sls Mgr: Scott Edidin

FRANK D LANTERMAN REGIONAL CEN
See LOS ANGELES COUNTY DEVELOPMENTAL SERVICES FOUNDATION

D-U-N-S 00-690-4759
FRANK EDWARDS CO INC
PACIFIC POWER EQUIPMENT CO
1565 Adrian Rd, Burlingame, CA 94010-2107
Tel (650) 692-2347 Founded/Ownrshp 1915
Sales 91.5MME EMP 580
SIC 5084 5013 Engines, gasoline; Automotive supplies & parts
Pr: Robert F Edwards Jr

D-U-N-S 96-865-9052
FRANK GATES COMPANIES INC
5000 Bradenton Ave, Dublin, OH 43017-3520
Tel (614) 793-8000 Founded/Ownrshp 2011
Sales 35.9MME EMP 1,224
SIC 8742 6411 Management consulting services; Insurance agents, brokers & service
CEO: Niles C Overly
CFO: Tom Watson
Ex VP: Robert Kelly
Dist Mgr: Jane Benge
Dist Mgr: Chad Davis
VP Mktg: Brenda Proctor

D-U-N-S 07-501-0058
FRANK GATES SERVICE CO
AVIZENT
(Suby of YORK SLA) ★
5000 Bradenton Ave # 100, Dublin, OH 43017-3534
Tel (614) 793-8000 Founded/Ownrshp 2011
Sales 84.6MME EMP 1,224
SIC 8742 Management consulting services; Compensation & benefits planning consultant; Business consultant
Pr: Daniel R Sullivan
VP: John Alusio
VP: Dale Bugay
VP: Kathy Clayton-Johnson
VP: Troy Gazette
VP: Keith Johnson
VP: Brad Lipscomb
VP: Robert Missus
VP: Ron Vanhover
Exec: Julia Hall
*Prin: Frank Gates

D-U-N-S 00-737-1131 IMP
FRANK KASMIR ASSOCIATES INC
KASMIR FABRICS
3191 Commonwealth Dr, Dallas, TX 75247-6201
Tel (214) 631-8040 Founded/Ownrshp 1964
Sales 151.7MME EMP 225
SIC 5131 Drapery material, woven
Pr: Linda Kasmir
*COO: Dale Jones
*VP: Robert Bruner
*Prin: Sam Kasmir
Dir IT: Duane Suddeth
Board of Directors: Donna Flowers, Gayle Rose

D-U-N-S 00-281-2931 IMP
FRANK LIQUOR CO INC (WI)
BADGER LIQUOR-MADISON
2115 Pleasant View Rd, Middleton, WI 53562-5518
Tel (608) 836-6000 Founded/Ownrshp 1943
Sales 200.7MME EMP 475
SIC 5182 5181

D-U-N-S 01-176-0980 EXP
FRANK M GARGIULO & SON INC
GARGUILO PRODUCE
535 Sweetland Ave Ste 1, Hillside, NJ 07205-1754
Tel (908) 233-8222 Founded/Ownrshp 1932
Sales 86.9MM EMP 60
SIC 5148 Fruits, fresh; Vegetables, fresh
Pr: Michael Gargiulo

D-U-N-S 13-012-6683
FRANK RUSSELL CO
RUSSELL INVESTMENT GROUP
(Suby of TA ASSOCIATES MANAGEMENT LP) ★
1301 2nd Ave Fl 18, Seattle, WA 98101-3814
Tel (206) 505-7877 Founded/Ownrshp 2016
Sales 1.8MMME EMP 2,467
SIC 6282 6211 6722 Investment advisory service; Investment research; Security brokers & dealers; Management investment, open-end
Pr: Leonard P Brennan
CFO: Francis Sean Ryan
Treas: Jean Webber
Sr VP: Scott Hamill
VP: Brenda Ballinger
VP: Rachel Carroll
VP: Michael Davis
Assoc Dir: Rick Holloway
Comm Dir: Kate Stouffer
Mng Dir: Gregory Gilbert
Mng Dir: Victor Leverett

FRANK TOYATA & SCION
See FORNACA INC

D-U-N-S 00-285-4610
FRANK W KERR CO (MI)
43155 W 9 Mile Rd Ste 1, Novi, MI 48375-4190
Tel (248) 349-5000 Founded/Ownrshp 1951
Sales 192.9MME EMP 150
SIC 5122

D-U-N-S 00-913-7514 IMP
FRANK-LIN DISTILLERS PRODUCTS LTD (CA)
2455 Huntington Dr, Fairfield, CA 94533-9734
Tel (408) 259-8900 Founded/Ownrshp 1966
Sales 115.1MME EMP 210
SIC 5182 2085 Wine; Distilled & blended liquors
Pr: Frank J Maestri
CFO: Anthony Demaria
CFO: Anthony Demorea
*Ex VP: Mark S Pechusick
*VP: Lindley Maestri
*VP: Michael Maestri
*VP: Michael Wasteney

FRANKE CONSUMER PRODUCTS, INC.
See FRANKE KITCHEN SYSTEMS LLC

D-U-N-S 86-938-2069 EXP
FRANKE FOODSERVICE SUPPLY INC
FRANKE RESUPPLY SYSTEMS, INC.
(Suby of FRANKE USA HOLDING INC) ★
800 Aviation Pkwy, Smyrna, TN 37167-2581
Tel (615) 459-3486 Founded/Ownrshp 1994
Sales 134.8MME EMP 132E
SIC 5084 Food industry machinery
CEO: Jack S Wilson
*COO: Hans J Ott
*Treas: Dana Rosellini
Ex VP: Mike McCabe
Sr VP: Welcome Wong
VP: Oliver Bahr
VP: Jeff Watson
Exec: John Dimeglio
Ex Dir: Michael Soormann
Mng Dir: James Nicholson
CIO: Markus Bierl

D-U-N-S 96-017-5404 IMP
FRANKE KITCHEN SYSTEMS LLC
FRANKE CONSUMER PRODUCTS, INC.
(Suby of FRANKE USA HOLDING INC) ★
800 Aviation Pkwy, Smyrna, TN 37167-2581
Tel (800) 637-6485 Founded/Ownrshp 1911
Sales 135.0MME EMP 442E
SIC 3431 5074 Sinks: enameled iron, cast iron or pressed metal; Plumbing & hydronic heating supplies
Pr: Simon Davis
*Sec: Dana R Rosellini
*VP: Doris Honea

FRANKE RESUPPLY SYSTEMS, INC.
See FRANKE FOODSERVICE SUPPLY INC

D-U-N-S 83-147-9360
FRANKE SSG INC
(Suby of FRANKE USA HOLDING INC) ★
800 Aviation Pkwy, Smyrna, TN 37167-2581
Tel (615) 462-4000 Founded/Ownrshp 2004
Sales 96.4MME EMP 536
SIC 5046 Commercial cooking & food service equipment
Pr: Chris Sperka
*Treas: Dana Rosellini

D-U-N-S 86-844-4738 IMP/EXP
FRANKE USA HOLDING INC
(Suby of FRANKE HOLDING AG)
1105 N Market St Ste 1300, Wilmington, DE 19801-1241
Tel (615) 462-4000 Founded/Ownrshp 1994
Sales 462.2MME EMP 900E
SIC 3589 5023 5084 Commercial cooking & foodwarming equipment; Kitchenware; Food industry machinery
Pr: Hans J Ott
*CFO: Dana R Rosellini

FRANKENMUTH INSURANCE
See FRANKENMUTH MUTUAL INSURANCE CO INC

D-U-N-S 00-695-9373
FRANKENMUTH MUTUAL INSURANCE CO INC
FRANKENMUTH INSURANCE
1 Mutual Ave, Frankenmuth, MI 48787-0001
Tel (989) 652-6121 Founded/Ownrshp 1921
Sales NA EMP 625
SIC 6331 Fire, marine & casualty insurance: mutual; Automobile insurance; Burglary & theft insurance
*CFO: Brian S McLeod
*Sr VP: James E Wilds
VP: Tom Cannon
*VP: Frederick A Edmond
*VP: Bryan L Gilleland
VP: Bryan Gilleland
*VP: Philip J McCain
VP: Brian McLeod
VP: Suzanne Schreiner
*VP: Randall S Trinklein
CTO: John Pfister

D-U-N-S 96-617-4166 IMP/EXP
FRANKFORD CANDY LLC
9300 Ashton Rd, Philadelphia, PA 19114-3531
Tel (215) 735-5200 Founded/Ownrshp 1947
Sales 91.2MM EMP 300
SIC 2066 Chocolate & cocoa products
CEO: Stuart Selarnick
*Sr VP: Nathan Hoffman

FRANKFORT ELC & WTR PLANT BD
See ELECTRIC & WATER PLANT BOARD OF CITY OF FRANKFORT KY

D-U-N-S 00-674-4247
■ **FRANKFORT REGIONAL MEDICAL CENTER**
(Suby of HOSPITAL COPORATION OF AMERICA) ★
299 Kings Daughters Dr, Frankfort, KY 40601-4186
Tel (502) 875-5240 Founded/Ownrshp 1974
Sales 96.2MME EMP 600
SIC 8062 8011 General medical & surgical hospitals; Offices & clinics of medical doctors
Ch: Connie Gayle White
Chf Rad: George Hromyak
*CEO: Michael Mayo
COO: Nancy Simon
CFO: Osman Gruhonjic
Chf Nrs Of: Sammie Mosier
MIS Dir: Craig Willard
Doctor: Lori Ivy
Nrsg Dir: Lisa Woldridge

D-U-N-S 60-997-6543
■ **FRANKLIN ADVISERS INC**
(Suby of FRANKLIN RESOURCES INC) ★
1 Franklin Pkwy, San Mateo, CA 94403-1906
Tel (650) 312-2000 Founded/Ownrshp 1985
Sales 154.0MME EMP 1,700
SIC 6282 Investment advice
Ch Bd: Charles B Johnson

D-U-N-S 78-365-8883 EXP
FRANKLIN ALUMINUM CO INC
(Suby of JAC HOLDING CORP) ★
266 Mary Johnson Dr, Franklin, GA 30217-6399
Tel (706) 675-3341 Founded/Ownrshp 1995
Sales 111.3MME EMP 850
SIC 3354 Shapes, extruded aluminum
Pr: Jack Falcon
*COO: Mike Wood
*CFO: Robert L Dewolf Jr
*CFO: Mike Vanloonc
*VP: Dave Birchmeier
*VP: Rick Charbille
*VP: Noel Ranka
MIS Mgr: Robert Eastland
Board of Directors: George Hofman, Byron Knief

D-U-N-S 06-977-3646
FRANKLIN AND MARSHALL COLLEGE
415 Harrisburg Ave, Lancaster, PA 17603-2827
Tel (717) 291-3911 Founded/Ownrshp 1787
Sales 179.0MM EMP 800E
Accts Kpmg Llp Mc Lean Va
SIC 8221 College, except junior
Pr: Daniel Porterfield
*CFO: Eileen Austin
Trst: Richard Kneedler
Trst: Bowie Kuhn
Trst: Andrew Stefan
Assoc VP: Barry Bosley
VP: Patrick Burke
VP: Matthew Eynon
VP: Maria Mitchell
VP: Michael Murray
VP: James Pitz
VP: Kathleen Spencer
VP: Wendy Starner
VP: Beth Throne

D-U-N-S 00-319-6854 IMP
■ **FRANKLIN BAKING CO LLC** (NC)
FLOWERS BAKERY
(Suby of FLOWERS FOODS INC) ★
500 W Grantham St, Goldsboro, NC 27530-1928
Tel (919) 735-0344 Founded/Ownrshp 1939
Sales 242.6MME EMP 700
SIC 2051 Bread, all types (white, wheat, rye, etc): fresh or frozen; Rolls, bread type: fresh or frozen

Ch: ET Franklin
IT Man: Natalie Stinnett

D-U-N-S 06-697-7570
FRANKLIN BAYSTATE MEDICAL CENTER
164 High St, Greenfield, MA 01301-2613
Tel (413) 773-0211 *Founded/Ownrshp* 1895
Sales 89.8MM *EMP* 1,000
SIC 8062 General medical & surgical hospitals
Pr: Charles Gijanto
Mng Pt: Howard Trietsch
**Pr:* Cindy L Russo
**COO:* Gina Campbell
Dir OR: Beverly Pomeroy
Dir Lab: Richard Friedberg
Sfty Mgr: Jesse Hall

D-U-N-S 05-024-0126 IMP/EXP
FRANKLIN CORP
600 Franklin Dr, Houston, MS 38851-8724
Tel (662) 456-5771 *Founded/Ownrshp* 1970
Sales 254.2MM^E *EMP* 1,200
SIC 2512 Recliners: upholstered on wood frames; Couches, sofas & davenports: upholstered on wood frames; Living room furniture: upholstered on wood frames
Ch Bd: Hassell H Franklin
**Pr:* Mark Franklin
**Treas:* Jeffry M Cox
Genl Mgr: Lanny Glover
IT Man: Rodney Carter
Tech Mgr: Bart Munlin

D-U-N-S 04-643-0641
FRANKLIN COUNTY BOARD OF COMMISSIONERS
373 S High St Fl 26, Columbus, OH 43215-4591
Tel (614) 525-3322 *Founded/Ownrshp* 1803
Sales NA *EMP* 6,000
Accts Dave Yost Auditor Of State C
SIC 9111 Executive offices;
Ofcr: Zak Talarek
VP: Jane Whyde
Ex Dir: Gayle Dittmer
Ex Dir: Mitzi Kline
Off Mgr: Debbi Muncy
CIO: Adam Luckhaupt
Dir IT: Brian Evans
IT Man: Justin Nahvi
Sls&Mrk Ex: Eric Taylor

D-U-N-S 07-081-1310
FRANKLIN COUNTY BOARD OF EDUCATION
190 Kings Daughters Dr B-300, Frankfort, KY 40601-4104
Tel (502) 695-6700 *Founded/Ownrshp* 1925
Sales 49.4MM^E *EMP* 1,025
SIC 8211 School board

D-U-N-S 07-979-8736
FRANKLIN COUNTY PUBLIC SCHOOLS
25 Bernard Rd, Rocky Mount, VA 24151-6614
Tel (540) 483-5138 *Founded/Ownrshp* 2015
Sales 10.1MM^E *EMP* 1,041^E
SIC 8211 Public elementary & secondary schools

D-U-N-S 01-321-8359
FRANKLIN COUNTY SCHOOL BOARD
25 Bernard Rd, Rocky Mount, VA 24151-6614
Tel (540) 483-5138 *Founded/Ownrshp* 1880
Sales 51.6MM^E *EMP* 1,026
SIC 8211 School board
Ch Bd: G B Washburn
**VP:* Jan Mohler

D-U-N-S 11-340-2713
▲ **FRANKLIN COVEY CO**
2200 W Parkway Blvd, Salt Lake City, UT 84119-2099
Tel (801) 817-1776 *Founded/Ownrshp* 1983
Sales 200.0MM *EMP* 810^E
Tkr Sym FC *Exch* NYS
SIC 8742 8331 2741 Marketing consulting services; Job training & vocational rehabilitation services; Miscellaneous publishing
Ch Bd: Robert A Whitman
Pr: M Sean Covey
Trst Ofcr: Sandra Cordoba
Ex VP: Colleen Dom
Ex VP: Scott J Miller
Ex VP: Shawn D Moon
Ex VP: Paul S Walker
Ex VP: Paul Walker
Ex VP: Stephen D Young
VP: Breck England
Mng Dir: Sandy Rogers
Board of Directors: Clayton M Christensen, Michael Fung, Dennis G Heiner, Donald J McNamara, Joel C Peterson, E Kay Stepp

D-U-N-S 79-721-0150
FRANKLIN CREDIT HOLDING CORP
101 Hudson St Fl 25, Jersey City, NJ 07302-3984
Tel (201) 604-1800 *Founded/Ownrshp* 2008
Sales NA *EMP* 105^E
SIC 6163 6162 Loan brokers; Mortgage bankers & correspondents
Ch Bd: Thomas J Axon
CFO: Paul D Colasono
Ex VP: Kevin Gildea
Ex VP: Stephen Hague
Ex VP: Jimmy Yan

D-U-N-S 00-516-1674 IMP/EXP
▲ **FRANKLIN ELECTRIC CO INC**
9255 Coverdale Rd, Fort Wayne, IN 46809-9613
Tel (260) 824-2900 *Founded/Ownrshp* 1944
Sales 924.9MM *EMP* 4,900
Accts Deloitte & Touche Llp Chicago
Tkr Sym FELE *Exch* NGS
SIC 3621 3561 Motors, electric; Electric motor & generator auxiliary parts; Pumps & pumping equipment; Pumps, domestic: water or sump; Pumps, oil well & field
Pr: Gregg C Sengstack
CFO: Patrick Davis
CFO: John J Haines
Sr VP: Robert J Stone

VP: Steven W Aikman
VP: Daniel J Crose
VP: Julie Scheck Freigang
VP: Ken Keene
VP: Thomas J Strupp
VP: Scott Trumbull
Exec: Jeff Frank
Exec: Jeremy Hendrix
Board of Directors: David T Brown, Renee J Peterson, David A Roberts, Jennifer Sherman, Thomas R Verhage, David M Wathen

D-U-N-S 87-492-5753
FRANKLIN ENERGY SERVICES LLC
102 N Franklin St, Port Washington, WI 53074-1901
Tel (800) 598-4376 *Founded/Ownrshp* 1994
Sales 109.4MM^E *EMP* 335^E
SIC 8711 Energy conservation engineering
CEO: Paul Schueller
Pr: Mark Bowen
**Pr:* Kevin McDonough
**CFO:* Tracy C Pearson
**Ex VP:* Dan Tarrence
**Sr VP:* Tom Quasius
**Sr VP:* Tina Semotan
VP: Nels Andersen
**VP:* Ed Carroll
**VP:* Fred Dreher
VP: Kevin Lauckner

FRANKLIN FINE BEERS
See HARTFORD DISTRIBUTORS INC

D-U-N-S 06-593-1719
FRANKLIN HOSPITAL
NORTH SHORE LIJ
900 Franklin Ave, Valley Stream, NY 11580-2190
Tel (516) 256-6000 *Founded/Ownrshp* 1963
Sales 171.1MM *EMP* 1,300
SIC 8062 8051

D-U-N-S 62-661-8144 IMP
FRANKLIN PRECISION INDUSTRY INC
(*Suby of* AISAN INDUSTRY CO., LTD.)
3220 Bowling Green Rd, Franklin, KY 42134-7610
Tel (270) 598-4300 *Founded/Ownrshp* 1989
Sales 201.4MM^E *EMP* 360
SIC 3714 Motor vehicle parts & accessories
Pr: Takehiro Nakajima
**Pr:* Kenji Kasamatsu
**Sec:* Mimoru Hattori
VP: Kenji Sato
Genl Mgr: Danny Andrews
IT Man: Michael Harvey
Opers Mgr: Jon Sato
Ql Cn Mgr: Keith Scruggs
Pr Mgr: Tye Burklow

D-U-N-S 07-819-4701
FRANKLIN PUD
1411 W Clark St, Pasco, WA 99301-5469
Tel (509) 547-5591 *Founded/Ownrshp* 1947
Sales 87.6MM *EMP* 76
Accts Jan M Jutte Cpa Cgfm
SIC 4911 Distribution, electric power
CFO: Gail Funk
IT Man: Doug Gould
Genl Couns: Steve Palmer

D-U-N-S 07-188-3169
▲ **FRANKLIN RESOURCES INC**
1 Franklin Pkwy, San Mateo, CA 94403-1906
Tel (650) 312-2000 *Founded/Ownrshp* 1947
Sales 6.6MMM *EMP* 9,500^E
Tkr Sym BEN *Exch* NYS
SIC 6722 6726 Management investment, open-end; Management investment funds, closed-end
Ch Bd: Gregory E Johnson
Pr: Vijay C Advani
Pr: Jennifer M Johnson
CFO: Kenneth A Lewis
**V Ch Bd:* Rupert H Johnson Jr
Ex VP: Craig S Tyle
Board of Directors: Peter K Barker, Mariann Byerwalter, Charles E Johnson, Mark C Pigott, Laura Stein, Seth H Waugh, Geoffrey Y Yang

FRANKLIN RIDGE CARE FACILITY
See CARINGTON HEALTH SYSTEMS

D-U-N-S 00-100-4035 IMP/EXP
FRANKLIN SPORTS INC
17 Campanelli Pkwy, Stoughton, MA 02072-3703
Tel (781) 344-1111 *Founded/Ownrshp* 1945
Sales 87.4MM^E *EMP* 250
SIC 3949 Sporting & athletic goods
Pr: Larry J Franklin
Div Mgr: Seth Hochberg
VP Mktg: Chuck Quinn
Sls Dir: Bob Pacanowski
Mktg Mgr: Brendan McCarthy

D-U-N-S 06-323-4892 EXP
FRANKLIN SQUARE HOSPITAL CENTER INC
MEDSTAR FRANKLIN SQ MED CTR
(*Suby of* MEDSTAR HEALTH VNA) ★
9000 Franklin Square Dr, Baltimore, MD 21237-3901
Tel (410) 933-2777 *Founded/Ownrshp* 1901
Sales 492.8MM *EMP* 3,019
SIC 8062 8011 General medical & surgical hospitals; Offices & clinics of medical doctors
Pr: Samuel E Moskowitz
**CFO:* Robert P Lally Jr
VP: Eric Conley
**VP:* Karen Robertson-Keck
**VP:* Anthony Sclama
**VP:* Larry Strassner
Dir Teleco: Deborah Malone
Dir Inf Cn: Jackie Curry
Adm Dir: Deborah Hall
QA Dir: Jacqueline Spielman
Sfty Dirs: Kevin Knoght

D-U-N-S 94-001-5167
▲ **FRANKLIN STREET PROPERTIES CORP**
401 Edgewater Pl Ste 200, Wakefield, MA 01880-6207
Tel (781) 557-1300 *Founded/Ownrshp* 1981
Sales 243.8MM *EMP* 40^E
Tkr Sym FSP *Exch* ASE

SIC 6798 Real estate investment trusts
Ch Bd: George J Carter
Pr: Jeffery B Carter
CFO: John G Demeritt
Ex VP: Scott H Carter
VP: Leo Daley
Board of Directors: John N Burke, Brian N Hansen, Kenneth A Hoxsie, Dennis J McGillicuddy, Georgia Murray, Kathryn P O'neil

FRANKLIN TEMPLETON INVESTMENT
See FRANKLIN TEMPLETON INVESTOR SERVICES LLC

FRANKLIN TEMPLETON INVESTMENTS
See TEMPLETON WORLDWIDE INC

D-U-N-S 19-469-3503
■ **FRANKLIN TEMPLETON INVESTOR SERVICES LLC**
FRANKLIN TEMPLETON INVESTMENT
(*Suby of* FRANKLIN TEMPLETON INVESTMENTS) ★
3344 Quality Dr, Rancho Cordova, CA 95670-7361
Tel (916) 463-1500 *Founded/Ownrshp* 1981
Sales 609.3MM^E *EMP* 2,500
SIC 6211 6282 Traders, security; Investment advisory service
Pr: Greg Johnson
**Ch Bd:* Charles B Johnson
**Pr:* Basil Fox
**Sr VP:* Robert Smith

D-U-N-S 15-228-2976
■ **FRANKLIN TEMPLETON SERVICES LLC**
(*Suby of* FRANKLIN RESOURCES INC) ★
1 Franklin Pkwy, San Mateo, CA 94403-1906
Tel (650) 312-3000 *Founded/Ownrshp* 1996
Sales 209.7MM^E *EMP* 2,500
Accts Pricewater House Coopers Llp
SIC 6282 Investment advice
Pr: Martin L Flanagan
**Ch Bd:* Charles B Johnson

D-U-N-S 04-239-0601
FRANKLIN TOWNSHIP BOARD OF EDUCATION
FRANKLIN TOWNSHIP PUB SCHOOLS
1755 Amwell Rd, Somerset, NJ 08873-2793
Tel (732) 873-2400 *Founded/Ownrshp* 2011
Sales 50.0MM^E *EMP* 1,500
SIC 8211 School board
Bd of Dir: Nancy Lacorte
Dir Sec: Orvl Wilson
Sls&Mrk Ex: John Calavano
Pr Dir: Mary Clark
Teacher Pr: Brian Bonanno

FRANKLIN TOWNSHIP PUB SCHOOLS
See FRANKLIN TOWNSHIP BOARD OF EDUCATION

D-U-N-S 10-380-3235
FRANKLIN TOWNSHIP PUBLIC SCHOOL DISTRICT OF SOMERSET
1755 Amwell Rd, Somerset, NJ 08873-2746
Tel (732) 873-2400 *Founded/Ownrshp* 1900
Sales 156.7MM *EMP* 1,000
Accts Lerch Vinci & Higgins Llp F
SIC 8211 Public elementary & secondary schools
Genl Mgr: Maureen Manning

D-U-N-S 02-023-5008
FRANKLIN-PIERCE SCHOOL DISTRICT
315 129th St S, Tacoma, WA 98444-5099
Tel (253) 298-3000 *Founded/Ownrshp* 1949
Sales 51.7MM^E *EMP* 1,000
SIC 8211 Public senior high school; Public junior high school; Public elementary school; Public special education school
Off Mgr: Dana England
Dir IT: Liza Klumpar

D-U-N-S 00-288-1662
FRANKS CASING CREW & RENTAL TOOLS INC
FRANKS INTERNATIONAL
700 E Verot School Rd, Lafayette, LA 70508-2502
Tel (337) 233-0303 *Founded/Ownrshp* 1956
Sales NA *EMP* 1,250
SIC 7353 1389

FRANKS INTERNATIONAL
See FRANKS CASING CREW & RENTAL TOOLS INC

FRANKS INTERNATIONAL
See FRANKS INTERNATIONAL LLC

D-U-N-S 15-722-4155 IMP/EXP
FRANKS INTERNATIONAL LLC
FRANKS INTERNATIONAL
(*Suby of* FRANK'S INTERNATIONAL N.V.)
10260 Westheimer Rd, Houston, TX 77042-3110
Tel (281) 966-7300 *Founded/Ownrshp* 1987
Sales 653.9MM^E *EMP* 600
SIC 1382 7353 Oil & gas exploration services; Heavy construction equipment rental
Ch Bd: Donald Keith Mosing
COO: John Walker
**CFO:* Jeffrey Bird
**CFO:* Mark Margavio
VP: Burney J Latiolais
**VP:* Robert R Rader
VP Bus: Richard Rader
Mng Dir: Patrick Sibille
Area Mgr: Greg Parrish

FRANZ FAMILY BAKERY
See UNITED STATES BAKERY

FRASER PAPERS
See NEXFOR (USA) INC

FRAZIER & CO
See FRAZIER MANAGEMENT LLC

D-U-N-S 80-787-4297
FRAZIER HEALTHCARE II LP
601 Union St Ste 3200, Seattle, WA 98101-3949
Tel (206) 621-7200 *Founded/Ownrshp* 1991
Sales 117.5MM^E *EMP* 210^E

SIC 8742 Hospital & health services consultant
Pt: Dan Eckert
Pt: Alan D Frazier
Pt: Ben Magnano
Pt: Nader Naini
Dir IT: Jason Dalton

D-U-N-S 00-216-0778
FRAZIER INDUSTRIAL CO
91 Fairview Ave, Long Valley, NJ 07853-3381
Tel (908) 876-3001 *Founded/Ownrshp* 1949
Sales 204.0MM *EMP* 750
Accts Eisner Amper Llp Iselin Nj
SIC 3441 2542 Fabricated structural metal; Pallet racks: except wood
CEO: William L Mascharka
**Pr:* Carlos Oliver
**CFO:* Peter Acerra
CFO: Robert M Warren
**Ch:* Donald Frazier
VP: Dana Ansel
VP: John Goffredo
**VP:* Domenick Iellimo
VP: Lon McAllister
Sfty Mgr: David Stuard
Plnt Mgr: Ken Backer

D-U-N-S 84-915-5924
FRAZIER MANAGEMENT LLC
FRAZIER & CO
601 Union St Ste 3200, Seattle, WA 98101-3949
Tel (206) 621-7200 *Founded/Ownrshp* 1991
Sales 212.0MM^E *EMP* 1,010^E
SIC 6799 Venture capital companies
Genl Pt: Patrick Heron
Genl Pt: Richard Von Riesen
VP: Ben Magnano
Software D: Francis Lam

FRC
See FARMERS RICE COOPERATIVE

D-U-N-S 05-013-2752
FRC FOUNDERS CORP
F R C
1 Lafayette Pl Ste 3, Greenwich, CT 06830-5449
Tel (203) 661-6601 *Founded/Ownrshp* 1987
Sales 1.2MMM^E *EMP* 12,000
SIC 8741 1311 1389 8731 5084 Financial management for business; Crude petroleum & natural gas; Oil field services; Gas field services; Energy research; Petroleum industry machinery
Ch: John A Hill
CEO: William Macaulay
COO: Anne Gold
COO: Claudi S Ponsa
COO: Claudi Santiago
CFO: Jennifer Zarrilli
VP: William R Brown
VP: Lauren De Paola
VP: Michael France
VP: Bingfeng Leng
VP: Christopher Ortega
VP: Lillian Ramirez
VP: Mark Saxe
VP: Michael Scardigli
VP: Ryan Shockley
VP: DOD Wales
VP: Ryan Zafereo
Board of Directors: Edward T Bialas, Tracy Chester, Michael G France, Neil J Hartley, Neil A Wizel

D-U-N-S 00-909-2339
FRED A MORETON & CO (UT)
101 S 200 E Ste 300, Salt Lake City, UT 84111-3107
Tel (801) 531-1234 *Founded/Ownrshp* 1910
Sales NA *EMP* 175
SIC 6411 Insurance agents; Insurance brokers
Pr: William Moreton
Treas: William E Tingey
Sr VP: Gary Christensen
VP: Monte Fautin
VP: Earl F Hurst
VP: Craig L Smith
Prin: Edward B Moreton
VP Opers: David Headden
Sales Exec: Chris Didonato
Mktg Mgr: Cathy Green
Corp Couns: Carolyn Cox

D-U-N-S 07-327-4821
FRED ALGER MANAGEMENT INC
(*Suby of* FRED ALGER & COMPANY, INCORPORATED)
600 Plaza One, Jersey City, NJ 07311-4041
Tel (201) 547-3600 *Founded/Ownrshp* 1964
Sales 125.0MM *EMP* 127
SIC 6282 6211 6799 Investment advisory service; Security brokers & dealers; Investors
Pr: Daniel Chung
Sr VP: H James Blakeslee
Sr VP: Pedro Marcal
Sr VP: Lori McEvoy
VP: Dennis Hearns
VP: Ajoy Reddi
VP: Michael Young
VP: Warren Zhang

FRED BANS FORD LINCOLN MERCURY
See FRED BEANS FORD INC

D-U-N-S 07-028-2074
FRED BEANS FORD INC
FRED BANS FORD LINCOLN MERCURY
876 N Easton Rd, Doylestown, PA 18902-1095
Tel (888) 903-2085 *Founded/Ownrshp* 1970
Sales 254.6MM^E *EMP* 535
SIC 5511 7513 5521 5012 Automobiles, new & used; Truck rental & leasing, no drivers; Used car dealers; Automobiles & other motor vehicles
Pr: Fred W Beans
IT Man: Barbara Swan
Sls Mgr: Schuyler Cox

D-U-N-S 07-820-0995
FRED HUTCHINSON CANCER RESEARCH CENTER
1100 Fairview Ave N, Seattle, WA 98109-4433
Tel (206) 667-4877 *Founded/Ownrshp* 1971
Sales 615.4MM *EMP* 2,675

SIC 8733

D-U-N-S 05-060-6359
FRED LAVERY CO
LAND ROVER
(Suby of US AUTO GROUP LIMITED) ★
34602 Woodward Ave, Birmingham, MI 48009-0924
Tel (248) 645-5930 Founded/Ownrshp 1989
Sales 86.6MM EMP 54
SIC 5511 Automobiles, new & used
Pr: Frederick A Lavery Jr
Sls Mgr: Sam Shehadeh
Sales Asso: Mark Gancasz
Sales Asso: Andy Yakima

D-U-N-S 93-348-4776
FRED LOYA INSURANCE AGENCY INC
1800 N Lee Trevino Dr # 100, El Paso, TX 79936-4117
Tel (915) 595-0595 Founded/Ownrshp 1976
Sales NA EMP 545
SIC 6411 Insurance agents, brokers & service
CEO: Fred Loya Jr
Ch Bd: Chris Delazquez
*Pr: Alfredo J Loya Jr
COO: Benjamin Salazar
*CFO: Jose A Ramirez
*Prin: Flor M Loya

D-U-N-S 17-596-7991 IMP/EXP
■ **FRED MEYER INC**
(Suby of KROGER CO) ★
3800 Se 22nd Ave, Portland, OR 97202-2999
Tel (503) 232-8844 Founded/Ownrshp 1999
Sales 4.1MMM^E EMP 28,030
SIC 5411 5311 5912 5211 5731 5944 Supermarkets, chain; Supermarkets, hypermarket; Department stores; Drug stores; Home centers; Consumer electronic equipment; Jewelry stores
Pr: Micheal E Huse
*CFO: David Deatherage
Ex VP: Roger Cooke
Sr VP: Mary Loftin
Sr VP: Cheryl Perrin
VP: Beth Arkes
VP: Tony Myers
VP: Sharon Roberts
VP: Bob Shorthill
Exec: Doreen Schine
Dir Soc: Scott Bringhurst

D-U-N-S 96-284-9899
■ **FRED MEYER JEWELERS INC**
(Suby of KROGER CO) ★
3800 Se 22nd Ave, Portland, OR 97202-2999
Tel (503) 232-8844 Founded/Ownrshp 2001
Sales 577.4MM^E EMP 7,000
SIC 5944 Jewelry stores
Pr: Peter M Engel
Pr: Melinda Merrill
CFO: David W Deatherage
Ex VP: Kevin Riley
VP: Mary Loftin
VP: Molly Malone
Art Dir: Laura Mazy

D-U-N-S 62-037-0304
■ **FRED MEYER OF ALASKA INC**
(Suby of KROGER) ★
1000 E Nthrn Lights Blvd, Anchorage, AK 99508
Tel (907) 264-9600 Founded/Ownrshp 1981
Sales 68.4MM^E EMP 1,544
SIC 5311 Department stores, discount
Ch Bd: Robert G Miller
*Pr: Cyril K Green
*CFO: Kenneth Thrasher

D-U-N-S 00-790-8809 IMP
■ **FRED MEYER STORES INC** (OH)
KROGER
(Suby of KROGER CO) ★
3800 Se 22nd Ave, Portland, OR 97202-2999
Tel (503) 232-8844 Founded/Ownrshp 2003
Sales 4.5MMM^E EMP 30,000
SIC 5211 5411 5912 5731 5944 Home centers; Supermarkets, chain; Supermarkets, hypermarket; Drug stores; Consumer electronic equipment; Jewelry stores
Pr: Lynn T Gust
CFO: David Deatherage
VP: John Berglund
VP: Lou Carpio
VP: Roger Cooke
VP: Bob Currey-Wilson
VP: Rick Heffner
VP: Cheryl Lindblad
VP: Molly Malone
VP: Greg Parsons
VP: Ann Reed
VP: Carl Wojciechowski

D-U-N-S 01-758-3170 IMP
FRED OLIVIERI CONSTRUCTION CO
6315 Promway Ave Nw, North Canton, OH 44720-7695
Tel (330) 494-1007 Founded/Ownrshp 1959
Sales 97.2MM^E EMP 160
Accts Bruner-Cox Llp Cantonoh
SIC 1542 Commercial & office building, new construction
CEO: Alfred A Olivieri
*Pr: Dean L Olivieri
*Treas: Timothy L Feller
VP: Edward French
*VP: Virginia C Olivieri
Off Mgr: Craig Lonce

D-U-N-S 04-999-1292
FRED TEITELBAUM CONSTRUCTION CO
5526 N Kedzie Ave, Chicago, IL 60625-3924
Tel (954) 971-1700 Founded/Ownrshp 1953
Sales 126.0MM EMP 125
Accts Shapiro Olefsky & Company
SIC 1522 Apartment building construction; Multi-family dwelling construction
Pr: Harvey Teitelbaum
*VP: Edgar M Gettleman
Off Mgr: Deanna Reiter

D-U-N-S 00-699-8207
FRED W ALBRECHT GROCERY CO
ACME STORES
2700 Gilchrist Rd Ste A, Akron, OH 44305-4433
Tel (330) 733-2861 Founded/Ownrshp 1891, 1939
Sales 339.6MM^E EMP 2,250
SIC 5411

D-U-N-S 00-696-8713
FRED WEBER INC
2320 Creve Coeur Mill Rd, Maryland Heights, MO 63043-4207
Tel (314) 344-0070 Founded/Ownrshp 1928
Sales 304.8MM^E EMP 645
SIC 1611 1442 3272 1622 1542

FREDDIE MAC
See FEDERAL HOME LOAN MORTGAGE CORP

D-U-N-S 83-308-8292
FREDERICK COMMUNITY COLLEGE
7932 Opossumtown Pike, Frederick, MD 21702-2097
Tel (301) 846-2400 Founded/Ownrshp 2009
Sales 106.7MM^E EMP 1,400
SIC 8222 Community college
Pr: Dr Carol Eaton
Ofcr: James Markel
Assoc VP: Jerry Haynes
Ex VP: Elizabeth Zoltan
VP: Deborah Dickinson
Ex Dir: Diane Branson
Ex Dir: Gohar Farahani
Ex Dir: Sam Young
Prgrm Mgr: Beth Holmburg
Prgrm Mgr: Keri-Beth Nagel
Prgrm Mgr: Lynn Orndorff

D-U-N-S 07-962-8833
FREDERICK COUNTY PUBLIC SCHOOLS
FCPS
191 S East St, Frederick, MD 21701-5918
Tel (301) 644-5000 Founded/Ownrshp 2014
Sales 90.2MM^E EMP 5,190^E
SIC 8211 Public elementary & secondary schools
Ofcr: Diane Penn
Schl Brd P: Joy Schaefer
Art Dir: Ida Harren
Snr Mgr: Robert Kelly

D-U-N-S 10-007-9607
FREDERICK COUNTY SCHOOL DISTRICT
1415 Amherst St, Winchester, VA 22601-3009
Tel (540) 662-3888 Founded/Ownrshp 2011
Sales 139.9MM EMP 1,600
SIC 8211 Public elementary & secondary schools; Public elementary school; Public junior high school; Public senior high school
Dir IT: Judi Greathouse
IT Man: Kris Carty
IT Man: Rob Yost
Pr Dir: Steve Edwards
Teacher Pr: John Linaburg
HC Dir: Pam Unhoch

D-U-N-S 07-367-4533
FREDERICK FERRIS THOMPSON HOSPITAL
F F THOMPSON HOSPITAL
350 Parrish St, Canandaigua, NY 14424-1731
Tel (585) 396-6000 Founded/Ownrshp 1991
Sales 128.1MM EMP 1,400
SIC 8062 8011 General medical & surgical hospitals; Medical centers
Pr: Michael F Stapleton Jr
*Sr VP: Christopher Mahan
*Sr VP: Carlos R Ortiz
*Sr VP: Mark Prunoske
*VP: Kurt Koczent Rn
Off Mgr: Ed Norton
IT Man: Rob Wallace
Opers Mgr: Wendy Mulholland
Pathlgst: Scott Lapoint
Pharmcst: Brian Mosman

FREDERICK MEM HLTH CARE SYS
See FREDERICK MEMORIAL HOSPITAL INC

D-U-N-S 06-938-2398
FREDERICK MEMORIAL HOSPITAL INC (MD)
FREDERICK MEM HLTH CARE SYS
400 W 7th St, Frederick, MD 21701-4593
Tel (240) 566-3300 Founded/Ownrshp 1897
Sales 327.2MM EMP 2,600
SIC 8062 General medical & surgical hospitals
Pr: Thomas A Kleinhanzl
Chf Rad: Anthony Rowedder
Dir Vol: Sharon Hannaby
*Ch Bd: Anne Herbert Rollins
*CFO: Michelle Nahan
*Sec: Gerald Winnan
Bd of Dir: Phil Hammond
Ofcr: Cathy Casagrande
Sr VP: John Verbus
VP: Bill Rotella
VP: Don Schilling
Dir Lab: Brian Sanders
Dir Env Sv: Tony Mc Clintock

D-U-N-S 00-281-3848 IMP
FREDERICK P WINNER LTD (MD)
FP WINNER
(Suby of CHESAPEAKE BEVERAGE) ★
7001 Quad Ave, Baltimore, MD 21237-2441
Tel (410) 646-5500 Founded/Ownrshp 1925, 2014
Sales 90.5MM^E EMP 225
SIC 5181 5182 Beer & other fermented malt liquors; Liquor
*VP: Ronald L Ward
Dir IT: Adam Knepprath

FREDERICKA MANOR CARE CENTER
See FRONT PORCH COMMUNITIES AND SERVICES - CASA DE MANANA LLC

D-U-N-S 02-850-1609 IMP
FREDERICKS OF HOLLYWOOD INC
MOVIE STAR
(Suby of MOVIE STAR) ★
71 Homochitto St, Natchez, MS 39120-3966
Tel (323) 466-5151 Founded/Ownrshp 1962
Sales 86.5MM^E EMP 902
SIC 5632 5961 Women's accessory & specialty stores; Women's apparel, mail order
CEO: William Soncini
*Pr: Linda Lore
*CEO: Thomas J Lynch
*CFO: Thomas Rende

D-U-N-S 00-586-6116 IMP
▲ **FREDS INC** (TN)
4300 New Getwell Rd, Memphis, TN 38118-6801
Tel (901) 365-8880 Founded/Ownrshp 1947
Sales 2.1MMM EMP 9,336^E
Accts Bdo Usa Llp Memphis Tenness
Tkr Sym FRED Exch NGS
SIC 5331 5912 5199 6794 Variety stores; Drug stores; Variety store merchandise; Franchises, selling or licensing
CEO: Jerry A Shore
*Ch Bd: Thomas H Tashjian
Pr: Michael K Bloom
COO: Craig L Barnes
COO: Timothy A Liebmann
CFO: Rick J Hans
Ofcr: Mary Lou Gardner
Ex VP: John Foley
Ex VP: John J Foley
VP: Kevin Pitt
Board of Directors: John R Eisenman, Steven R Fitzpatrick, Michael T McMillan, B Mary McNabb, Thomas H Tashjian

D-U-N-S 18-422-5175 IMP
■ **FREDS STORES OF TENNESSEE INC**
(Suby of FREDS INC) ★
4300 New Getwell Rd, Memphis, TN 38118-6801
Tel (901) 365-8880 Founded/Ownrshp 1973
Sales 648.8MM^E EMP 7,800
SIC 5331 4731 Variety stores; Freight transportation arrangement
CEO: Michael J Hayes
VP: Joe M Carter
VP: Rick A Chambers

D-U-N-S 62-207-7253 IMP
FREE COUNTRY LTD
1071 6th Ave Fl 9, New York, NY 10018-3747
Tel (212) 719-4596 Founded/Ownrshp 1993
Sales 150.0MM^E EMP 54
SIC 5136 5137

D-U-N-S 04-485-5344 IMP
FREE-FLOW PACKAGING INTERNATIONAL INC
FP INTERNATIONAL
34175 Ardenwood Blvd, Fremont, CA 94555-3653
Tel (650) 261-5300 Founded/Ownrshp 1967
Sales 136.5MM^E EMP 350
SIC 3086 Plastics foam products; Insulation or cushioning material, foamed plastic; Packaging & shipping materials, foamed plastic
CEO: Arthur Graham Emeritus
*Pr: Joseph Nezwek
*COO: James Taylor
VP: Rex Camps
VP: Michale Keminski
IT Man: Jerry Janicki
IT Man: Huib Smeets
MIS Mgr: Warren Tang
VP Sls: Keith Lay
Mktg Dir: Jim O'Shaughnessy

D-U-N-S 14-505-4941
■ **FREEDMAN MEATS INC**
(Suby of SYSCO CORP) ★
2901 S Polk St, Dallas, TX 75224-2657
Tel (713) 229-8000 Founded/Ownrshp 1998
Sales 152.5MM^E EMP 697
SIC 5147 Meats & meat products
Pr: Ronald Boatwright
*CFO: Charles Coon
*Ex VP: Kevin Tulley
VP: Ron Boatright
VP: Kevin Broussard
*VP: Carl Mead
*VP: Dwayne Price
*VP: Korby Price
Genl Mgr: Dwayne Tadalecki
Off Mgr: Neva Meeker
Dir IT: Brian Cook

D-U-N-S 00-508-5337 IMP
FREEDMAN SEATING CO
4545 W Augusta Blvd, Chicago, IL 60651-3338
Tel (773) 524-2440 Founded/Ownrshp 1900
Sales 137.8MM^E EMP 550^E
SIC 2531 Seats, miscellaneous public conveyances; Vehicle furniture; Cabs for off-highway trucks
CEO: Gerald Freedman
*Pr: Craig Freedman
*VP: Dan Cohen
Mng Dir: Christy Nunes
IT Man: Roney Babajan
Opers Mgr: Robert Anoff
Ql Cn Mgr: Dave Klopp
Mktg Mgr: John-Paul Paonessa
Sls Mgr: Mike Beierschmitt
Sls Mgr: Tamara Hobgood
Snr Mgr: Terry Gogins

D-U-N-S 07-925-5430
FREEDOM COMMUNICATIONS HOLDINGS INC
PRESS ENTERPRISE, THE
(Suby of 2100 FREEDOM INC) ★
625 N Grand Ave, Santa Ana, CA 92701-4347
Tel (714) 796-7000 Founded/Ownrshp 2012
Sales 320.8MM^E EMP 7,600
SIC 6719 2711 4813 2721 Investment holding companies, except banks; Newspapers, publishing & printing; ; Magazines: publishing & printing
CEO: Richard E Mirman
CEO: Aaron Kushner

D-U-N-S 00-830-1764 IMP
FREEDOM COMMUNICATIONS INC
FREEDOM NEWSPAPERS
(Suby of CIVITAS MEDIA LLC) ★
625 N Grand Ave, Santa Ana, CA 92701-4347
Tel (714) 796-7000 Founded/Ownrshp 2004, 2016
Sales 5.1MM EMP 7,542
Accts Sensiba San Filippo Llp Morga
SIC 2711 2721 7313 2741 5963 Newspapers, publishing & printing; Newspapers: publishing only, not printed on site; Periodicals; Newspaper advertising representative; Miscellaneous publishing; Newspapers, home delivery, not by printers or publishers
Ch Bd: Robert Threshie
Genl Pr: Myles Robinson
Pr: Mitchell Stern
CEO: Aaron Kushner
CFO: Melissa McBride
CFO: Mark A McEachen
Ch: Robert Hardie
VP: Rachel L Sagan
VP: Richard A Wallace
Genl Mgr: Mike Little
CIO: Gina Sanders

FREEDOM DRUG
See LYNNFIELD DRUG INC

FREEDOM GRAPHIC SYSTEMS
See MBK-WI INC

FREEDOM GRAPHIC SYSTEMS
See FGS-WI LLC

FREEDOM INVESTMENTS
See OPPENHEIMER & CO INC

FREEDOM MINE
See COTEAU PROPERTIES CO

D-U-N-S 78-407-2092
FREEDOM MORTGAGE CORP
907 Pleasant Valley Ave # 3, Mount Laurel, NJ 08054-1210
Tel (866) 759-8624 Founded/Ownrshp 1990
Sales NA EMP 2,244
SIC 6162 Mortgage bankers
Pr: Stanley Middleman
*CFO: Stan Moskowitz
Chf Cred: Theresa Waring
*VP: Daniel Hefferon
VP: Audrey Shapiro

FREEDOM NEWSPAPERS
See FREEDOM COMMUNICATIONS INC

D-U-N-S 83-554-0980
FREEDOM OIL CO
814 W Chestnut St, Bloomington, IL 61701-2816
Tel (309) 828-7750 Founded/Ownrshp 1958
Sales 130.5MM EMP 250
SIC 5541 Filling stations, gasoline
Pr: Michael Owens
*CFO: Mark Stewart
*VP: Judith Owens Melcher
*VP: Suzanne Owens

FREEDOM VALU CENTER
See ERICKSON OIL PRODUCTS INC

D-U-N-S 79-915-8105
FREEDOMROADS HOLDING CO LLC
CAMPING WORLD RV SALES
250 Parkway Dr Ste 270, Lincolnshire, IL 60069-4346
Tel (847) 808-3000 Founded/Ownrshp 2003
Sales 101.2MM^E EMP 1,400
SIC 8743 Promotion service
Ofcr: Karin Bell

D-U-N-S 13-337-9854
FREEDOMROADS LLC
250 Parkway Dr Ste 270, Lincolnshire, IL 60069-4346
Tel (866) 838-5304 Founded/Ownrshp 2003
Sales 1.7MMM EMP 3,600
SIC 5561 Recreational vehicle dealers
CEO: Marcus A Lemonis
*Ex VP: Brent Moody
*Sr VP: Diana Ardelean
VP: Paul Inman
VP: Tim Wessel
VP: Brock Whinnery
Off Mgr: Samantha Martin
Mktg Dir: Robyn Barnes
Sls Mgr: David Randall
Corp Couns: Lindsey Mondo

FREEHAFER HALL ADMIN. SERVICES
See PURDUE UNIVERSITY

D-U-N-S 05-445-3329
FREEHOLD REGIONAL HIGH SCHOOL DISTRICT
11 Pine St, Englishtown, NJ 07726-1513
Tel (732) 792-7300 Founded/Ownrshp 1954
Sales 209.6MM EMP 1,400
SIC 8211 Public elementary & secondary schools
*Pr: Heshy Moses
*VP: Jennifer Sutera
Exec: Kathy Barkalow
IT Man: Patricia Smith

D-U-N-S 07-851-7506
FREEMAN DECORATING CO
1600 Viceroy Dr Ste 100, Dallas, TX 75235-2312
Tel (214) 445-1000 Founded/Ownrshp 1948
Sales 1.9MMM EMP 11^E
SIC 7389 Trade show arrangement

D-U-N-S 79-313-0139
■ **FREEMAN ENERGY CORP**
(Suby of MATERIAL SERVICE RESOURCES CORP) ★
3008 Happy Landing Dr, Springfield, IL 62711-6259
Tel (217) 698-3949 Founded/Ownrshp 1992
Sales 86.1MM^E EMP 2,088
SIC 1241 Coal mining services
Pr: Walter A Gregory

D-U-N-S 00-782-1085 IMP/EXP
FREEMAN EXPOSITIONS INC
1600 Viceroy Dr Ste 100, Dallas, TX 75235-2312
Tel (214) 445-1000 Founded/Ownrshp 2003
Sales 2.2MMM EMP 30,129
SIC 7389

D-U-N-S 10-859-7212 IMP
FREEMAN HEALTH SYSTEM
FREEMAN HOSPITAL WEST
1102 W 32nd St, Joplin, MO 64804-3503
Tel (417) 347-1111 Founded/Ownrshp 1995
Sales 501.6MM^E EMP 3,887^E
Accts Bkd Llp Springfield Mo
SIC 8062 8069 General medical & surgical hospitals; Specialty hospitals, except psychiatric
Pr: Paula Baker
V Ch: James Bracht
*CFO: Steven Graddy
*Chf Mktg O: Richard D Schooler
*Ex VP: Joseph Kirk
VP Sls: Kyle Robinson
Obsttrcn: Lee R Rice
Plas Surg: Frank Shagets
Doctor: Kathryn G Adams
Doctor: Shazia Habib
Doctor: Lee J Harwell

FREEMAN HOSPITAL WEST
See FREEMAN HEALTH SYSTEM

D-U-N-S 06-808-3344
FREEMAN MANUFACTURING & SUPPLY CO
1101 Moore Rd, Avon, OH 44011-4043
Tel (440) 934-1902 Founded/Ownrshp 1942
Sales 83.8MM^E EMP 75
SIC 5084 3087 3543 2821 Industrial machinery & equipment; Custom compound purchased resins; Industrial patterns; Plastics materials & resins
Pr: Lou Turco
Ch Bd: Gerald W Rusk
VP: Matthew Turco
Software D: Ken Mayer
Plnt Mgr: Fred Cassell
Plnt Mgr: Gene Horning
Ql Cn Mgr: Bob Ing
Sales Exec: Ian McClaskey
Sales Exec: George Wise

D-U-N-S 10-816-0003
FREEMAN SPOGLI & CO LLC
11100 Santa Monica Blvd # 1900, Los Angeles, CA 90025-0525
Tel (310) 444-1822 Founded/Ownrshp 1983
Sales 2.1MMM^E EMP 14,841
SIC 6211 Investment bankers
Genl Pt: Yining Chen
Genl Pt: Brian C Gildea
Genl Pt: Charles P Rullman
Genl Pt: J Frederick Simmons
Pr: John M Roth
CEO: Ronald P Spogli
VP: David Durbin

D-U-N-S 14-460-2000
FREEMONT RIDEOUT HEALTH GROUP
989 Plumas St, Yuba City, CA 95991-4012
Tel (530) 751-4010 Founded/Ownrshp 1907
Sales 28.2MM EMP 1,800
Accts Moss Adams Llp Stockton Ca
SIC 8062 General medical & surgical hospitals
CEO: Teresa Hamilton
CFO: L Wayne Mills
*CFO: Kevin Woodward
*Ch: Ronald M Sweeney
*Prin: John Wright
Telecom Ex: Lloyd Brown

D-U-N-S 96-796-3906
FREEPOINT COMMODITIES LLC
58 Commerce Rd, Stamford, CT 06902-4506
Tel (203) 542-6000 Founded/Ownrshp 2010
Sales 315.0MM^E EMP 285
SIC 6221 Commodity traders, contracts
CEO: David A Messer
Pr: Frank Gallipoli
Treas: Mary Yacura
Ex VP: Michael Beck
Sr VP: Godwin Joseph
VP: William Davidson
VP: Jennifer Farris
VP: Nan Swan
VP: Jeremy Weil
Mng Dir: Timothy Cannon
Mng Dir: Lou Santore

FREEPORT MCMORAN
See FREEPORT MINERALS CORP

D-U-N-S 07-456-9526
FREEPORT MEMORIAL HOSPITAL INC
FHN MEMORIAL HOSPITAL
1045 W Stephenson St, Freeport, IL 61032-4899
Tel (815) 599-0000 Founded/Ownrshp 1938
Sales 135.4MM EMP 850
SIC 8062 General medical & surgical hospitals
Pr: Dennis Hamilton
*CFO: Mike Clark
Pathlgst: Sam Roh
Surgeon: Barry Barnes
Surgeon: Rafael Castro
Obsttrcn: Farouk Isawi
Surg Cl Rc: Jeffrey Hass
Doctor: Erich Awender
Doctor: Toni Levine
Doctor: Doreen Pearson
Doctor: Howard Waitzkin

D-U-N-S 00-121-3149 IMP/EXP
■ FREEPORT MINERALS CORP
FREEPORT MCMORAN
(Suby of FREEPORT-MCMORAN INC) ★
333 N Central Ave, Phoenix, AZ 85004-2121
Tel (602) 366-8100 Founded/Ownrshp 1885, 2007
Sales 11.9MMM^E EMP 15,600
SIC 1061 1021 3312 3351 Molybdenum ores mining; Copper ore mining & preparation; Chemicals & other products derived from coking; Copper pipe
CEO: Richard C Adkerson
*Pr: Michael J Arnold
*CFO: Kathleen L Quirk
VP: J Dale Brunk
*VP: Douglas Currault II
VP: J Spencer Davis
VP: Peter J Faur
VP: Gerald Gluscic
VP: Robert G Mock
VP: Mark Mollison
VP: Stanton Rideout
VP: Gregory Stevens
VP: CD Whitmire Jr
Board of Directors: Michael Arnold

D-U-N-S 86-735-9838
FREEPORT REGIONAL HEALTH CARE FOUNDATION
FHN FOUNDATION
1045 W Stephenson St, Freeport, IL 61032-4864
Tel (815) 599-6000 Founded/Ownrshp 1984
Sales 171.6MM EMP 1,500
Accts Rsm Us Llp Rockford Illinois
SIC 8011 General & family practice, physician/surgeon
Pr: Mark Kendall
Ex VP: Michael Clark
Ex VP: Angelique Labelle
Dir Rad: Wendy Lawler
Snr Mgr: Julie Harn
Snr Mgr: Robin Hoops
Snr Mgr: Kate Janssen

D-U-N-S 08-064-8819
FREEPORT UNION FREE SCHOOL DISTRICT
235 N Ocean Ave, Freeport, NY 11520-2135
Tel (516) 867-5200 Founded/Ownrshp 1890
Sales 69.7MM^E EMP 1,096
SIC 8211 Public elementary & secondary schools
*Pr: Deborah McQuillan

D-U-N-S 18-712-2973
▲ FREEPORT-MCMORAN INC
333 N Central Ave, Phoenix, AZ 85004-2121
Tel (602) 366-8100 Founded/Ownrshp 1987
Sales 15.8MMM EMP 34,500^E
Tkr Sym FCX Exch NYS
SIC 1021 1041 1061 1044 Open pit copper ore mining; Gold ores; Molybdenum ores mining; Silver ores
Pr: Richard C Adkerson
*Ch Bd: Gerald J Ford
Pr: Harry M Conger
CFO: Kathleen L Quirk
Ofcr: Michael J Arnold
Ex VP: C H Murrish
VP: Richard McMillan
VP: Bertrand Odinet
VP: Josh Olmsted
VP: Stanton Rideout
Genl Mgr: Fred Robinson
Board of Directors: Lydia H Kennard, Andrew Langham, Jon C Madonna, Courtney Mather, Frances Fragos Townsend

D-U-N-S 79-496-6424 IMP
■ FREEPORT-MCMORAN MIAMI INC
(Suby of CYPRUS CLIMAX METALS CO) ★
333 N Central Ave, Phoenix, AZ 85004-2121
Tel (602) 366-8100 Founded/Ownrshp 1988
Sales 780.3MM^E EMP 13,000^E
SIC 1021 Underground copper ore mining; Open pit copper ore mining
Pr: Richard C Adkerson

D-U-N-S 07-886-0977
■ FREEPORT-MCMORAN OIL & GAS LLC
(Suby of FREEPORT-MCMORAN INC) ★
700 Milam St Ste 3100, Houston, TX 77002-2764
Tel (713) 579-6000 Founded/Ownrshp 2012
Sales 1.5MMM^E EMP 1,272^E
SIC 1382 Oil & gas exploration services
Ex VP: Mark Kidder
Ex VP: Mark D Kidder

D-U-N-S 17-323-9385 IMP
■ FREEPORT-MCMORAN SIERRITA INC
PHELPS DODGE
(Suby of FREEPORT MCMORAN) ★
6200 W Duval Mine Rd, Green Valley, AZ 85622
Tel (520) 648-8500 Founded/Ownrshp 1986
Sales 730.8MM^E EMP 700^E
SIC 1021 Open pit copper ore mining
Genl Mgr: Bob Wishart

D-U-N-S 96-897-2708
FREESCALE SEMICONDUCTOR HOLDINGS V INC
(Suby of NXP SEMICONDUCTORS N.V.)
6501 W William Cannon Dr, Austin, TX 78735-8523
Tel (512) 895-2000 Founded/Ownrshp 2015
Sales 4.5MMM^E EMP 8,504^E
SIC 3674 Semiconductors & related devices
Pr: Gregg A Lowe

D-U-N-S 96-757-8449
FREESCALE SEMICONDUCTOR LTD
6501 W William Cannon Dr, Austin, TX 78735-8523
Tel (512) 895-2000 Founded/Ownrshp 2003
Sales 4.6MMM EMP 17,300^E
SIC 3674
Pr: Gregg A Lowe
CFO: Daniel Durn
Sr VP: Ritu Favre
Sr VP: Jonathan A Greenberg
Sr VP: Jennifer B Wuamett
VP: Thomas Deitrich
VP: Randy Hyzak
CIO: Tarek El-Hadidi
Board of Directors: D Mark Durcan, Daniel J Heneghan, Thomas H Lister, Joanne M Maguire, John W Marren, James A Quella, Peter Smitham, Gregory L Summe, Claudius E Watts IV

D-U-N-S 07-317-7362
FREESE AND NICHOLS INC
4055 Intl Plz Ste 200, Fort Worth, TX 76109
Tel (817) 735-7491 Founded/Ownrshp 2002
Sales 117.5MM EMP 556^E
Accts Pricewaterhousecoopers Llp Da
SIC 8711 Consulting engineer
Ch Bd: Bob Herchert
*Pr: Robert F Pence
*COO: Brian Coltharp
*CFO: Cynthia P Milrany
*Sr VP: Thomas C Gooch
Sr VP: Ron M Lemons
*Sr VP: Michael Nichols
VP: Kendall King
CIO: Gary Soward

D-U-N-S 00-978-4638
FREESEN INC (IL)
(Suby of UNITED CONTRACTORS MIDWEST INC) ★
3151 Robbins Rd Ste A, Springfield, IL 62704-7410
Tel (217) 546-6192 Founded/Ownrshp 1946
Sales 107.9MM^E EMP 800
SIC 1622 1771 1629 Bridge construction; Concrete work; Blacktop (asphalt) work; Earthmoving contractor
Pr: James P Bruner
*Ch Bd: O Robert Freesen
*Ex VP: Russell Mosley
*Ex VP: Thomas Oetgen

FREESTATE ELECTRICAL SVC CO
See AES ELECTRICAL INC

FREEWAY INSURANCE
See CONFIE SEGUROS INC

D-U-N-S 19-216-6098
FREEWAY INSURANCE
SOUTH COAST AUTO INSURANCE
10801 Walker St Ste 250, Cypress, CA 90630-5044
Tel (714) 252-2500 Founded/Ownrshp 1988
Sales NA EMP 250
SIC 6411 Insurance agents
Pr: Elias Assaf
*COO: Norm Hudson
*VP: John Klaeb
Sales Exec: Barney Harris

D-U-N-S 18-122-4338
FREEWAY INSURANCE SERVICES INC
(Suby of FREEWAY INSURANCE) ★
7711 Center Ave Ste 200, Huntington Beach, CA 92647-9124
Tel (714) 252-2500 Founded/Ownrshp 1987
Sales NA EMP 565
SIC 6411 Insurance brokers
CEO: Joseph Waked
Pr: Kelly Turton
CFO: Robert Trebing
Ch: John Klaeb
Ofcr: Alex Trachtman

FREEZ WALL
See MORETRENCH AMERICAN CORP

FREEZE
See CENTRAL MILLS INC

D-U-N-S 80-678-2434
FREEZE OPERATIONS HOLDING CORP
1855 Boston Rd, Wilbraham, MA 01095-1002
Tel (413) 543-2445 Founded/Ownrshp 2007
Sales 2.5MMM^E EMP 12,800^E
SIC 5812 2024 5143 Restaurant, family: chain; Ice cream & frozen desserts; Ice cream & ices; Frozen dairy desserts
Pr: Harshavardhan V Agadi
*CFO: Steven C Sanchioni
*Sr VP: Robert K Sawyer

D-U-N-S 10-849-5540
FREIGHT ALL KINDS INC
10885 E 51st Ave, Denver, CO 80239-2507
Tel (800) 321-7182 Founded/Ownrshp 1983
Sales 113.6MM EMP 47
SIC 4731 4213 Freight transportation arrangement; Trucking, except local
CEO: Bobbye Marcove
*Pr: Sam Marcove
*CFO: Felipe Suarez
Genl Mgr: Ron Harms
Trfc Dir: Tammy Brooks
Sfty Mgr: Mike Collins
Natl Sales: Greg Bean
Natl Sales: Noam Silkoff
Sls Mgr: John Hite
Sls Mgr: Bryan Story

FREIGHT CAR DIVISION
See JOHNSTOWN AMERICA CORP

D-U-N-S 80-525-8167
FREIGHT HANDLERS INC
F H I
310 N Judd Pkwy Ne, Fuquay Varina, NC 27526-2369
Tel (919) 552-3157 Founded/Ownrshp 1991
Sales 101.0MM^E EMP 1,000
SIC 4731 7363 Freight transportation arrangement; Labor resource services
Pr: Ryan Wall
*Ch Bd: Charles W Wall
*COO: Reid Durst
*CFO: Tal Wall
Sr VP: Tyler Grange
Sr VP: Jeffrey Newton
Opers Mgr: Dave Gray

D-U-N-S 08-245-2090 IMP/EXP
▲ FREIGHTCAR AMERICA INC
2 N Rverside Plz Ste 1300, Chicago, IL 60606
Tel (800) 458-2235 Founded/Ownrshp 1901
Sales 772.8MM EMP 1,662
Tkr Sym RAIL Exch NGS
SIC 3743 Railroad equipment; Train cars & equipment, freight or passenger
Pr: Joseph E McNeely
CFO: Matthew S Kohnke
Chf Cred: Theodore W Baun
VP: Ted Baun
VP: Sean Hankinson
VP: Jeffrey Klamar
VP: Mike Macmahon
VP: Joseph Maliekel
VP: Tom McCarthy
VP: Georgia L Vlamis
Area Mgr: Gregorio Acuna
Board of Directors: James D Cirar, William D Gehl, Thomas A Madden, Malcolm F Moore, Andrew B Schmitt, S Carl Soderstrom Jr

FREIGHTLINER
See TRUCK COUNTRY OF IOWA INC

D-U-N-S 88-463-9378
FREIGHTLINER CUSTOM CHASSIS CORP
F C C C
(Suby of DAIMLER TRUCKS NORTH AMERICA LLC) ★
552 Hyatt St, Gaffney, SC 29341-2598
Tel (864) 487-1700 Founded/Ownrshp 1995
Sales 191.9MM^E EMP 900^E
SIC 3711 Truck tractors for highway use, assembly of
Pr: Robert Harvin
*Pr: Jack Conlan
IT Man: Ann Fowler
Sls Mgr: Brian Caudell

FREIGHTLINER OF BRIDGEPORT
See TRANSTECK INC

D-U-N-S 94-641-2087
FREIGHTLINER OF UTAH A LIMITED LIABILITY CO
WARNER TRUCK CENTER
2240 S 5370 W, West Valley City, UT 84120-1278
Tel (801) 978-8000 Founded/Ownrshp 1995
Sales 112.6MM^E EMP 265^E
SIC 5012 5013 7539 7538 5511 Truck tractors; Truck parts & accessories; Automotive repair shops; General automotive repair shops; New & used car dealers
Exec: Sue Brown
*Genl Mgr: Buzz Warner
Off Mgr: Dean Burrows
IT Man: Mike Shurtz
Sls Mgr: Justin Brande
Sales Asso: John McKenzie

D-U-N-S 07-900-1178
FREIGHTLINER STERLING WESTERN STAR OF ARIZONA LTD
9899 W Roosevelt St, Tolleson, AZ 85353-9272
Tel (623) 907-9900 Founded/Ownrshp 1998
Sales 90.2MM^E EMP 210^E
SIC 5013 5012 7538 Automotive supplies & parts; Trucks, commercial; Truck engine repair, except industrial
Pr: Danny Ray Cuzick
*CFO: Theril Lund
Genl Mgr: Theral Lund
Genl Mgr: Peggy Rissi
IT Man: Wes Mikkelson
Sls Mgr: James Barker
Sls Mgr: Tim Noeding

FREIGHTLINER TRUCKS
See TRUCK COUNTRY OF INDIANA INC

D-U-N-S 05-452-3241
■ FREIGHTQUOTE.COM INC
(Suby of CH ROBINSON CO INC) ★
901 Carondelet Dr, Kansas City, MO 64114-4674
Tel (913) 642-4700 Founded/Ownrshp 2015
Sales 245.8MM^E EMP 716
SIC 4731 Freight transportation arrangement
Pr: Matt Druten
VP: Pamela Thrasher
VP: Lori Wittman
Snr Sftwr: Victor Panus
*CIO: Byron Clymer

D-U-N-S 11-247-2183
FREMAR LLC
44608 273rd St, Marion, SD 57043-5465
Tel (605) 648-3941 Founded/Ownrshp 1998
Sales 95.6MM^E EMP 291
Accts Gardiner Thomsen Pc Sioux
SIC 5153 2873 Grain elevators; Plant foods, mixed: from plants making nitrog. fertilizers
*CEO: Steve Domm

D-U-N-S 00-923-6910
FREMONT BANCORPORATION
39150 Fremont Blvd, Fremont, CA 94538-1316
Tel (510) 792-2300 Founded/Ownrshp 1969
Sales NA EMP 788
SIC 6712 Bank holding companies
Ch Bd: Michael J Wallace
VP: Adarsh Sangani

D-U-N-S 07-652-6268
FREMONT BANK
(Suby of FREMONT BANCORPORATION) ★
39150 Fremont Blvd, Fremont, CA 94538-1313
Tel (510) 505-5226 Founded/Ownrshp 1964
Sales NA EMP 393
SIC 6022 State commercial banks
Ch Bd: Morris Hyman
Pr: Chris Chenoweth
Pr: Keith Fujita
Pr: Andy Mastorakis
CEO: Bradford L Anderson
COO: Patti Greenup
CFO: Ron Wagner
Ch: Michael J Wallace
V Ch Bd: Alan L Hyman
Ofcr: Bryan Horn
Ofcr: Dave Leisen
Ofcr: Rebecca Matthew
Ofcr: Rick Strand
Top Exec: Dan Morris
Ex VP: Hattie Hyman Hughes
Ex VP: Howard L Hyman
Sr VP: Kim Burdick
Sr VP: Ken Johnson
VP: Sandi Fava
VP: Gloria Villasana Fuerniss
VP: Brian Hughes

D-U-N-S 04-091-7106
FREMONT HEALTH
A J MERRICK MANOR
450 E 23rd St, Fremont, NE 68025-2387
Tel (402) 727-3795 Founded/Ownrshp 1940

Sales 137.5MM^E EMP 900^E
SIC 8062 8051 General medical & surgical hospitals; Skilled nursing care facilities
Pr: Patrick Booth
COO: Peg Kennendy
Trst: Linda McClain
Ofcr: Cindy Costanzo
*Sr VP: Brett Richmond
*VP: Peg Kennedy
*VP: Mike Sindelar
*VP: Bill Vobejda
Dir Rx: Luade Carlson
CIO: Richard Barren
Dir IT: Richard Baren

FREMONT HOTEL AND CASINO
See SAM-WILL INC

D-U-N-S 08-071-6301
FREMONT UNIFIED SCHOOL DISTRICT
FUSD
4210 Technology Dr, Fremont, CA 94538-6337
Tel (510) 657-2350 Founded/Ownrshp 1964
Sales 170.8MM^E EMP 3,500
Accts Vavrinek Trine Day & Company
SIC 8211 Public elementary & secondary schools
*Pr: Lara Calvert York
*VP: Desrie Campbell
VP: Lily K MEI
Exec: Brian Killgore
Dir Risk M: Minh Vu
Prgrm Mgr: Sue Kessler
Off Admin: Shirley Leung
Off Admin: Linda-Sue Pricer
CTO: Joseph Siam
Netwrk Mgr: Kim Youngberg
Psych: Neelam Dharod

D-U-N-S 07-968-6082
FRENCH FURNITURE ORLANDO LLC
901 Centr Flori Pkwy Unit, Orlando, FL 32824
Tel (407) 270-1111 Founded/Ownrshp 2014
Sales 1.0MMM EMP 3^E
SIC 5712 Furniture stores
Genl Mgr: Natalie Harrison

FRENCH GERLEMAN
See FRENCH-GERLEMAN ELECTRIC CO

D-U-N-S 94-936-9318
FRENCH HOLDINGS LLC
(Suby of JL FRENCH AUTO CASTINGS INC) ★
3101 S Taylor Dr, Sheboygan, WI 53081-8424
Tel (920) 458-7724 Founded/Ownrshp 2003
Sales 57.1MM^E EMP 1,250
SIC 3363 3341 8711 Aluminum die-castings; Aluminum smelting & refining (secondary); Designing: ship, boat, machine & product
CFO: Mark Burgess
*Treas: Steve Boyack

D-U-N-S 01-070-7941
FRENCH HOSPITAL MEDICAL CENTER FOUNDATION
(Suby of DIGNITY HEALTH) ★
1911 Johnson Ave, San Luis Obispo, CA 93401-4131
Tel (805) 543-5353 Founded/Ownrshp 2004
Sales 126.7MM EMP 570
Accts Kpmg Llp San Francisco Ca
SIC 8062 General medical & surgical hospitals
Ch: Jim Copeland
*Pr: Allan Iftiniuk
*CFO: Sue Anderson
Dir Risk M: Sandy Mugg
Chf Nrs Of: Julia Fogelson
MIS Dir: Cyndi Lang
Pathlgst: Ronald Rocha
Ansthlgy: Saul J David
Ansthlgy: Shawn A Fouhy
Ansthlgy: Robert J Hetzel
Ansthlgy: Scott R Smelse

FRENCH LICK RESORT
See FRENCH LICK SPRINGS RESORT INC

D-U-N-S 15-167-7283
FRENCH LICK SPRINGS RESORT INC
FRENCH LICK RESORT
8670 W State Road 56, French Lick, IN 47432-9389
Tel (888) 936-9360 Founded/Ownrshp 1991
Sales 52.0MM^E EMP 1,200
SIC 7011 Resort hotel
Pr: Luther Greg James
COO: Jamie Collins
*Sec: Shirley James
Mktg Dir: Kim Gray
Mktg Mgr: Rob Denbo
Sls Mgr: Heather Fuller

D-U-N-S 04-392-7631
FRENCH-ELLISON TRUCK CENTER LLC
4300 N Cage Blvd, Pharr, TX 78577-7518
Tel (956) 781-2401 Founded/Ownrshp 1968
Sales 121.3MM^E EMP 270
SIC 5013 5531 5511 5012 7538 Truck parts & accessories; Automotive parts; Trucks, tractors & trailers: new & used; Trucks, noncommercial; General truck repair
CFO: Doug Steinle
Genl Mgr: Danny Cuellar
Dir IT: Michael McRae
IT Man: Mike McRae

D-U-N-S 03-103-6221
FRENCH-GERLEMAN ELECTRIC CO
FRENCH GERLEMAN
2023 Westport Center Dr, Saint Louis, MO 63146-3514
Tel (314) 569-3122 Founded/Ownrshp 1923
Sales 233.3MM^E EMP 230
SIC 5063 Motor controls, starters & relays: electric; Electrical supplies
CEO: William B French
Pr: Mike Stanfill
Sr VP: Steven A Grimm
Sr VP: Don E Wagner
VP: Steve French
VP: Sean Nolan
VP: Tim Sasek
VP: Jim Wojkovich
Exec: Geli Beatty
IT Man: Mike Drone
Mktg Dir: Chris Fine

D-U-N-S 03-505-2059
FRENCHMAN VALLEY FARMERS COOPERATIVE INC
SOUTH WEST GRAIN
202 Broadway, Imperial, NE 69033-3208
Tel (308) 882-3220 Founded/Ownrshp 1968
Sales 222.3MM^E EMP 169
SIC 5153 5191 5541 Grain elevators; Feed; Fertilizer & fertilizer materials; Filling stations, gasoline
Pr: James Haarberg
*VP: Rick Taylor
Div Mgr: Dave Schneider
Genl Mgr: James Chism
Board of Directors: Dale Dueland, Richard Keiser, Steve Leibbrandt, William Tines

D-U-N-S 07-886-0797
FRENCHS FOOD CO LLC
(Suby of RECKITT BENCKISER PLC)
4 Mill Ridge Ln, Chester, NJ 07930-2486
Tel (973) 404-2600 Founded/Ownrshp 2013
Sales 173.8MM^E EMP 350
SIC 2035 Pickles, sauces & salad dressings
Snr Mgr: Chris Dempsey

FRENKEL & COMPANY
See FRENKEL BENEFITS LLC

D-U-N-S 08-860-4553
FRENKEL BENEFITS LLC
FRENKEL & COMPANY
350 Hudson St Fl 4, New York, NY 10014-4500
Tel (212) 488-0200 Founded/Ownrshp 2001
Sales NA EMP 235
SIC 6411 Insurance agents, brokers & service
Mng Pt: Scott Frenkel
Pr: Nancy Geller
Ex VP: Michael Feinstein
Ex VP: Larry Kirshner
Ex VP: Adam Okun
Sr VP: Marie Bellusci
Sr VP: Richard Delong
Sr VP: Jose Irizarry
Sr VP: Eric Labaska
Sr VP: Carol Lluch
Sr VP: Ben Polanski
Sr VP: Michael Rubin
Sr VP: Matthew Winters
VP: Ken Bonamo
VP: Michael Dischley
VP: Adam Glick
VP: Sabrina Greenman
VP: Gina Haw
VP: Richard M Jakucs
VP: Ann Jones
VP: J Kennedy

D-U-N-S 09-285-8406 IMP/EXP
FRES-CO SYSTEMS USA INC
(Suby of GOGLIO SPA)
3005 State Rd, Telford, PA 18969-1021
Tel (215) 721-4600 Founded/Ownrshp 1977
Sales 233.5MM^E EMP 360
SIC 5084 3565 2891 Packaging machinery & equipment; Packaging machinery; Adhesives & sealants
Pr: Tullio Vigano
CFO: Mark Stinson
Sr VP: Lawrence Ashton
VP: Edward Walsh
Prin: Franco Goglio
Genl Mgr: Thomas Butkus
IT Man: Kevin Hawkins
QI Cn Mgr: Raymond Olley

D-U-N-S 03-645-4056 IMP
FRESENIUS KABI USA INC
(Suby of FRESENIUS KABI AG)
3 Corporate Dr Ste 300, Lake Zurich, IL 60047-8930
Tel (847) 969-2700 Founded/Ownrshp 2008
Sales 530.3MM^E EMP 6,000^E
SIC 2834 Pharmaceutical preparations
CEO: John Ducker
Ex VP: Bruce J Wendel
Ex Dir: Dvorit Samid

D-U-N-S 01-354-7657 IMP
FRESENIUS KABI USA LLC
(Suby of FRESENIUS KABI USA INC) ★
3 Corporate Dr Ste 300, Lake Zurich, IL 60047-8930
Tel (847) 550-2300 Founded/Ownrshp 2007
Sales 530.2MM^E EMP 6,000
SIC 2834 Pharmaceutical preparations
Pr: John Ducker
*Ex VP: Steven J Adams
*Ex VP: Jack Silhavy
VP: Alexandr Gonzalez
Netwrk Eng: Jeremy Jaquet
VP Prd: David Bowman
Snr Mgr: Jack Merkel
Snr Mgr: Martha Pattillo
Snr Mgr: Thomas Schubert

FRESENIUS KIDNEY CARE
See FRESENIUS MEDICAL CARE NORTH AMERICA

FRESENIUS MEDICAL CARE
See FRESENIUS USA INC

D-U-N-S 04-940-5541 IMP/EXP
FRESENIUS MEDICAL CARE CARDIOVASCULAR RESOURCES INC
(Suby of FRESENIUS MEDICAL CARE NORTH) ★
920 Winter St Ste A, Waltham, MA 02451-1519
Tel (781) 402-9000 Founded/Ownrshp 1996
Sales 431.8MM^E EMP 18,035
SIC 8092 5047 8071 Kidney dialysis centers; Medical equipment & supplies; Medical laboratories
Pr: Susan L Crutchfield
COO: Dwight Morgan
Sr VP: Ronald Kuerbitz
Sr VP: Brian O'Connell
VP: Luca Gialdini
VP: Joseph Ruma
Dir Soc: Susan Chamberlain
*Prin: Ben J Lipps
VP Mfg: Conor Curtin
VP Mktg: Jeff Weix
VP Sls: Christina Rossi
Board of Directors: Mathias Klingler, Dr Gerd Krick, Udo Werle

D-U-N-S 95-829-1411 IMP/EXP
FRESENIUS MEDICAL CARE HOLDINGS INC
FRESENIUS MEDICAL CARE NORTH
(Suby of FRESENIUS MEDICAL CARE NORTH AMERICA HOLDINGS LIMITED PARTNERSHIP) ★
920 Winter St, Waltham, MA 02451-1521
Tel (781) 699-9000 Founded/Ownrshp 1997
Sales 10.3MMM EMP 18,500
Accts Kpmg Llp Boston Ma
SIC 3841 8092 Surgical & medical instruments; Kidney dialysis centers
CEO: Ronald Kuerbitz
Pr: Mark Costanzo
Pr: Heath Schiesser
Pr: William Valle
CFO: Angelo Moesslang
Treas: Angela Armstrong
Treas: Mark Fawcett
Sr Cor Off: Gerald Walthall
Chf Cred: David Kembel
Chf Mktg O: Frank Maddux
Ex VP: Simon Castellanos
Sr VP: Ron Castle
Sr VP: Douglas Kott
VP: Timothy Balch
VP: ARI Chompre
VP: Philip Hayden
VP: Claude Miller
Comm Man: Gwen Valenti

FRESENIUS MEDICAL CARE NORTH
See FRESENIUS MEDICAL CARE HOLDINGS INC

D-U-N-S 83-167-1982
FRESENIUS MEDICAL CARE NORTH AMERICA
FRESENIUS KIDNEY CARE
(Suby of RENEX CORP) ★
920 Winter St, Waltham, MA 02451-1521
Tel (781) 699-4404 Founded/Ownrshp 2010
Sales 11.2MMM EMP 2,027
SIC 8092 Kidney dialysis centers
Pr: Luca Chiastra
Pr: Tina Eddy
*CEO: Ron Kuerbitz
Chf Mktg O: Dave Hahn
Ofcr: Peter Connelly
Sr VP: Robert Farrell
Sr VP: Robert Sepucha
Sr VP: Brian Silva
VP: Maria Burke
VP: Bill D'Innocenzo
VP: Charles Deloach
VP: Joe Johnston
VP: Tony Lafata
VP: Claude Miller
VP: Jules J Morris
VP: Darinka Povrzenic
VP: Christian Schlaeper
VP: Tom Weider

D-U-N-S 96-927-3528
FRESENIUS MEDICAL CARE NORTH AMERICA HOLDINGS LIMITED PARTNERSHIP
(Suby of FRESENIUS MEDICAL CARE BETEILIGUNGSGES. MBH)
920 Winter St Ste A, Waltham, MA 02451-1519
Tel (781) 699-9000 Founded/Ownrshp 2006
Sales 10.3MMM^E EMP 18,500^E
SIC 3841 Surgical & medical instruments
Pr: Ronald J Kuerbitz
CFO: Peter E Gladitsch

D-U-N-S 07-659-4100 IMP
FRESENIUS USA INC (MA)
FRESENIUS MEDICAL CARE
(Suby of FRESENIUS MEDICAL CARE NORTH) ★
4040 Nelson Ave, Concord, CA 94520-1200
Tel (925) 288-4218 Founded/Ownrshp 1974, 1987
Sales 769.4MM^E EMP 1,660
SIC 2834 3841 2835 3842 2836 Intravenous solutions; Solutions, pharmaceutical; Hemodialysis apparatus; IV transfusion apparatus; Blood transfusion equipment; Blood derivative diagnostic agents; Surgical appliances & supplies; Biological products, except diagnostic
CEO: Ronald J Kuerbitz
*Pr: Mark Costanzo
*Pr: Ben Lipps
*CFO: Angelo Moesslang
*Treas: Mark Fawcett
Treas: Marc Lieberman
*Treas: Heinz Schmidt
*Sec: Douglas Kott
Sr VP: Dave Updyke
*VP: Scott Walker
Sftwr Eng: Angela McDonald

D-U-N-S 78-556-5602
FRESH & EASY NEIGHBORHOOD MARKET INC
20101 Hamilton Ave # 350, Torrance, CA 90502-1351
Tel (310) 341-1200 Founded/Ownrshp 2006
Sales 933.9M^E EMP 2,583
SIC 5411 Grocery stores, chain
CEO: Tim J R Mason
Pr: Audrey Nguyen
COO: Edward Redd
CFO: Remco Waller
Sr Cor Off: Simon Uwins
VP: Tim Ashdown
VP: Matt Edmonds
VP: Anthony Johnson
VP: Tim Lee
VP: Sam OH
VP: Odill Rodrigues
VP: Lucy Toussaint
Dir Soc: Carlos Molina

D-U-N-S 01-232-8385 IMP
FRESH ACQUISITIONS LLC
DYNAMIC FOODS
1001 E 33rd St, Lubbock, TX 79404-1816
Tel (806) 723-5600 Founded/Ownrshp 2014
Sales 97.5MM^E EMP 200
SIC 5149 5146 Bakery products; Seafoods
CEO: Allen Jones
*CFO: Jason Kemp

FRESH AND LIMITED
See FRESHWAY FOODS INC

D-U-N-S 17-584-7151
FRESH BEGINNINGS INC
ELEAD
4001 Coleman Rd N, Valdosta, GA 31602-6828
Tel (229) 242-0237 Founded/Ownrshp 1986
Sales 153.5MM^E EMP 303
SIC 5199 2052 2064 Advertising specialties; Cookies; Candy & other confectionery products
Pr: Judith S Hathcock
*CFO: David Penney
Software D: Pete Oliva

D-U-N-S 16-101-5177
FRESH CHOICE LLC
STARBUCKS
8371 Central Ave Ste A, Newark, CA 94560-3473
Tel (510) 857-1241 Founded/Ownrshp 1986
Sales 45.8MM^E EMP 1,958
SIC 5812 Eating places
Pr: Tim G O'Shea
Ch Bd: Charles A Lynch
CFO: David E Pertl
Sr VP: Tina E Freedman
Sr VP: Tina Freedman
Sr VP: Joan M Miller
Sr VP: Joan Miller
Genl Mgr: Rocio Castelaenos
Board of Directors: Charles L Boppell, Vern O Curtis, Yong Ping Duan, Carl R Hays, Barry E Krantz

D-U-N-S 84-065-1319 IMP/EXP
FRESH CONNECTION
3722 Mt Diablo Blvd, Lafayette, CA 94549-3612
Tel (925) 299-9939 Founded/Ownrshp 1993
Sales 162.5MM EMP 35
SIC 5148 Fresh fruits & vegetables
CEO: Henry H Miller
*Pr: Hank Miller

FRESH CUTS
See GET FRESH SALES INC

D-U-N-S 78-887-4274 IMP
FRESH DIRECT HOLDINGS INC
2330 Borden Ave, Long Island City, NY 11101-4515
Tel (718) 433-0982 Founded/Ownrshp 2000
Sales 378.5MM^E EMP 1,800^E
SIC 5499 4813 Gourmet food stores;
CEO: Steven Dean Furbush
*Pr: Steven Michaelson
*CFO: Jason Ackerman
*Ch: Richard Braddock
Ofcr: Andrea Fernandez
*Ex VP: Michael A Brizel
VP: Jeff Berger
VP: Larry Scott Blackmon
VP: John Boris
VP: Keith Colbourn
VP: Lisa Johnson
VP: Richard Lind
VP: Doug Needham
VP: Mike Rose
Dir Bus: Larry Pearl

FRESH ENCOUNTER
See NEEDLER ENTERPRISES INC

D-U-N-S 13-162-0114 IMP
FRESH EXPRESS INC
(Suby of CHIQUITA BRANDS LLC) ★
4757 The Grove Dr Ste 260, Windermere, FL 34786-8426
Tel (980) 636-5530 Founded/Ownrshp 1930
Sales 97.0MM^E EMP 160
SIC 0723 2099 Vegetable packing services; Food preparations
Pr: Mark Drever
Pr: Jim Lugg
VP: Rich Berry
*Prin: Tanios E Viviani
Plnt Mgr: Nanu Menon

D-U-N-S 05-378-1840
FRESH FOOD MANUFACTURING CO (PA)
(Suby of GIANT EAGLE INC) ★
101 Kappa Dr, Pittsburgh, PA 15238-2809
Tel (412) 963-6200 Founded/Ownrshp 1988
Sales 101.7MM^E EMP 2,493^E
SIC 2099 Food preparations
Pr: David S Shapira
Treas: Phillip W Oliveri
VP: Lucot John

D-U-N-S 00-446-9110 IMP/EXP
FRESH MARK INC (OH)
SUPERIOR'S BRAND MEATS
1888 Southway St Se, Massillon, OH 44646
Tel (330) 834-3669 Founded/Ownrshp 1932
Sales 521.3MM^E EMP 2,300
Accts Ernst & Young Llp Akron Oh
SIC 2013 5147 2011 Prepared beef products from purchased beef; Prepared pork products from purchased pork; Sausages & related products, from purchased meat; Meats & meat products; Meat packing plants
CEO: Neil Genshaft
*Pr: David Cochenour
*Pr: Tim Cranor
Genl Mgr: Richard Foster
Genl Mgr: Bernie Mueller
QA Dir: Greg Davis
QA Dir: Dan House
QA Dir: Debbie Seese
IT Man: Susan Caghan
Manager: Tony Lacerenza
Opers Mgr: Tom Fee

FRESH MARKET, THE
See FRESH MARKET INC

D-U-N-S 03-304-1658
FRESH MARKET INC
FRESH MARKET, THE
(Suby of POMEGRANATE HOLDINGS INC) ★
628 Green Valley Rd # 500, Greensboro, NC 27408-7791
Tel (336) 272-1338 Founded/Ownrshp 2016
Sales 1.8MMM EMP 12,400
Accts Ernst & Young Llp Charlotte
SIC 5411 Grocery stores, chain
Pr: Richard A Anicetti
V Ch: Brett Berry
VP: Marius Andersen
VP: Mark Jones
VP: Randy Kelley
VP: Ross Reynolds
Software D: Christina Helton
Software D: Armin Kalender
Genl Couns: Ashley Canupp

FRESH MERGE
See DR FRESH LLC

D-U-N-S 60-583-3458 IMP/EXP
FRESH PACIFIC FRUIT AND VEGETABLE INC
AGRO PACIFICA
7650 N Palm Ave Ste 103, Fresno, CA 93711-5793
Tel (559) 432-3500 Founded/Ownrshp 1989
Sales 169.7MM EMP 20
SIC 5148

D-U-N-S 87-758-2981 IMP
FRESH START BAKERIES INC
FRESH START BAKERIES N AMER
(Suby of ARYZTA AG)
145 S State Cckg Blvd 2 Ste 200, Brea, CA 92821
Tel (714) 256-8900 Founded/Ownrshp 2010
Sales 118.2MM^E EMP 600
SIC 2051 Bread, cake & related products
CFO: Ronan Minahan
VP: Dan Bailey
VP: Mark Flood
VP: Kim Purga
VP: William D Robles
VP: Robert Stephens
Exec: Sharon Hainey
VP Admn: Scott Oliver
VP Mfg: Mike Ward
Mfg Dir: Derek Osato

FRESH START BAKERIES N AMER
See FRESH START BAKERIES INC

FRESHBLOOMS
See DELAWARE VALLEY FLORAL GROUP INC

D-U-N-S 11-395-4270
FRESHOUSE II LLC
311 Long Meadow Dr, Salisbury, NC 28147-8200
Tel (704) 630-6950 Founded/Ownrshp 1997
Sales 86.0MM EMP 185
SIC 5148 Fresh fruits & vegetables
*Pr: Jamey M S Friedman
Genl Mgr: Mike McGinnis
Off Mgr: Donna Sloop

D-U-N-S 00-729-6820 IMP
FRESHPACK PRODUCE INC
5151 Bannock St Ste 12, Denver, CO 80216-1846
Tel (303) 412-6232 Founded/Ownrshp 2010
Sales 185.2MM^E EMP 170
SIC 5148 Fresh fruits & vegetables
CEO: Chris Wisekal
*COO: Jim Hagan
*CFO: Suzanne Sweeney
Sr VP: Tim Ray
Genl Mgr: Mike Comazzi
Opers Mgr: Shawn Dye

D-U-N-S 60-354-6172 IMP
▲ FRESHPET INC
400 Plaza Dr Fl 1, Secaucus, NJ 07094-3605
Tel (201) 520-4000 Founded/Ownrshp 2004
Sales 116.1MM EMP 190
Tkr Sym FRPT Exch NGM
SIC 2047 Dog & cat food
Pr: Scott Morris
*Ch Bd: Charles A Norris
CFO: Richard Kassar
Chf Mktg O: Amy Thompson
Ex VP: Stephen Weise
Sr VP: Thomas Farina
Sr VP: Michael Hieger
Sr VP: Stephen Macchiaverna
Sr VP: Cathal Walsh
VP: Lilliana Bolton
Board of Directors: J David Basto, Daryl G Brewster, Lawrence S Coben, Walter N George III, Christopher B Harned, Robert C King, Jonathan S Marlow, Craig D Steeneck

D-U-N-S 03-262-2268 IMP/EXP
■ FRESHPOINT CENTRAL FLORIDA INC
(Suby of FRESHPOINT INC) ★
8801 Exchange Dr, Orlando, FL 32809-7675
Tel (407) 383-8427 Founded/Ownrshp 1996
Sales 183.0MM^E EMP 300
SIC 5148 5431 Fresh fruits & vegetables; Fruit & vegetable markets
Pr: Will Fulghom
*Pr: Robert Gordon
*CFO: Elizabeth Carle
*Treas: Brian Sturgeon
VP Opers: Greg Musselwhite
Trfc Dir: George McCann
Board of Directors: Greg Prince

D-U-N-S 00-586-6033
■ FRESHPOINT DALLAS INC
AMERICAN FOOD SERVICE
(Suby of FRESHPOINT INC) ★
4721 Simonton Rd, Dallas, TX 75244-5316
Tel (972) 385-5800 Founded/Ownrshp 1917, 1993
Sales 162.7MM^E EMP 300
SIC 5148 5142 Fruits, fresh; Vegetables, fresh; Frozen fish, meat & poultry
Pr: David Hartman

D-U-N-S 11-175-2788
■ FRESHPOINT INC
(Suby of SYSCO CORP) ★
16 Forest Pkwy Bldg H, Forest Park, GA 30297-2092
Tel (404) 362-6100 Founded/Ownrshp 2001
Sales 93.7MM^E EMP 175
SIC 5148 Vegetables, fresh
Pr: Bob Massave
Pr: Kevin Naze
Exec: Nimesh Patel
*Prin: Brian Sturgeon
Dir IT: Arthur Pidgeon
Tech Mgr: John McCleskey
Site Mgr: Elizabeth Diaz
Opers Mgr: Jerrell Wilcox
VP Sls: Jon Greco
VP Sls: Joe Lafiosca

D-U-N-S 96-152-6803 EXP
■ FRESHPOINT INC
(Suby of SYSCO CORP) ★
1390 Enclave Pkwy, Houston, TX 77077-2025
Tel (281) 899-4242 Founded/Ownrshp 2000
Sales 944.4MM^E EMP 2,700
SIC 5148 Fresh fruits & vegetables
CEO: Robert Gordon
*Pr: Brian Sturgeon
Ex VP: Pete Cappiali
Ex VP: Glenn Davis
Ex VP: Thomas Lankford
*Sr VP: Richard J Dachman
VP: Cherie Brandt
VP: Luis Garcia
VP: Steve Lay
*VP: Greg Musselwhite
VP: Malcolm Robinson

D-U-N-S 00-962-6870
■ FRESHPOINT OF SOUTHERN CALIFORNIA INC
FRESHPOINT SOUTHERN CALIFORNIA
(Suby of SYSCO CORP) ★
155 N Orange Ave, City of Industry, CA 91744-3432
Tel (626) 855-1400 Founded/Ownrshp 2000
Sales 150.7MM^E EMP 208
SIC 5148 5142 Fruits, fresh; Vegetables, fresh; Packaged frozen goods
CEO: Verne L Lusby Jr
*Ex VP: Jeff Ronk
*VP: Jon Greco

D-U-N-S 19-712-8200 EXP
■ FRESHPOINT SOUTH FLORIDA INC
(Suby of FRESHPOINT INC) ★
2300 Nw 19th St, Pompano Beach, FL 33069-5227
Tel (954) 917-7272 Founded/Ownrshp 2007
Sales 120.2MM^E EMP 185^E
SIC 5148 5143 Vegetables, fresh; Dairy products, except dried or canned
Pr: John Lasko
*Ex VP: Alan Lieberman
*VP: Kevin Cook
Genl Mgr: Micah Brown
IT Man: John Zimmerman
Opers Mgr: Stefan Byles
Sls Mgr: Richard Lucas

FRESHPOINT SOUTHERN CALIFORNIA
See FRESHPOINT OF SOUTHERN CALIFORNIA INC

FRESHPRO FOOD DISTRIBUTORS
See RLB FOOD DISTRIBUTORS LP

D-U-N-S 18-390-9597
FRESHWAY FOODS INC
FRESH AND LIMITED
601 Stolle Ave, Sidney, OH 45365-8895
Tel (937) 498-4664 Founded/Ownrshp 1895
Sales 109.0MM EMP 400^E
SIC 5148 2099 Vegetables, fresh; Food preparations
Ch Bd: Frank Gilardi Jr
*Pr: Phil Gilardi
*CFO: Devon Beer
VP: Craig Cotner
VP: Don Foutty
Exec: Dan Baker
Exec: Sam Schlagetter
Sfty Mgr: Susan Davidson
Manager: David Highland

FRESHWIRE
See GMR MARKETING LLC

D-U-N-S 10-340-3754 IMP/EXP
FRESNO BEVERAGE CO INC
VALLEY WIDE BEVERAGE COMPANY
4010 E Hardy Ave, Fresno, CA 93725-2331
Tel (559) 650-1500 Founded/Ownrshp 1985
Sales 92.3MM^E EMP 180
SIC 5181 Beer & other fermented malt liquors
CEO: Louis J Amendola
VP: Dan Boitano
*VP: Todd Howerton
VP Admn: Brian Kennedy
Genl Mgr: John Amendola
Mktg Dir: Jeff Beal
Board of Directors: John Amendola, Kenny Amendola, Nick Amendola

D-U-N-S 62-781-7356
FRESNO COMMUNITY HOSPITAL AND MEDICAL CENTER
(Suby of COMMUNITY HEALTH SYSTEM) ★
2823 Fresno St, Fresno, CA 93721-1324
Tel (559) 459-6000 Founded/Ownrshp 1945
Sales 1.3MMM EMP 5,045
Accts Moss Adams Llp Stockton Ca
SIC 8062 General medical & surgical hospitals
Pr: Phillip Hinton
*CEO: Tim A Joslin
CFO: Maria Garcia
*CFO: William Grigg
*Treas: Roger Fretwell
*Sr VP: Mike Kingbury
*Sr VP: Stephen Walter
*VP: Les Abercrombie
Off Mgr: Chris Williams
Doctor: Uzair Chaudhary
Snr Mgr: Kathy Axton

D-U-N-S 07-878-8023
FRESNO COUNTY ECONOMIC OPPORTUNITIES COMMISSION (CA)
FRESNO EOC
1920 Mariposa Mall # 300, Fresno, CA 93721-2504
Tel (559) 263-1010 Founded/Ownrshp 1965
Sales 108.8MM EMP 1,300
Accts Kaku & Mersino Llp Clovis C
SIC 8322 8399 Individual & family services; Community development groups
CEO: Brian Angus
*Pr: Vongsavanh Mouanoutoua
*CFO: Salam Nalia
*Treas: Marina Magdaleno
Exec: Celiese Kai

D-U-N-S 08-720-3238
FRESNO COUNTY SUPERINTENDENT OF SCHOOLS
REGIONAL OCCUPATIONAL PROGRAM
1111 Van Ness Ave, Fresno, CA 93721-2002
Tel (559) 265-3000 Founded/Ownrshp 1971
Sales 75.1MM^E EMP 1,680
SIC 8211 Public elementary & secondary schools
Assoc Dir: Foley Dennis
Assoc Dir: Harvey Glenn
Dir IT: Raj Sra
Instr Medi: Paul Gong

FRESNO EOC
See FRESNO COUNTY ECONOMIC OPPORTUNITIES COMMISSION

D-U-N-S 00-486-8725
FRESNO TRUCK CENTER (CA)
LEE FINANCIAL SERVICES
2727 E Central Ave, Fresno, CA 93725-2425
Tel (559) 486-4310 Founded/Ownrshp 1959
Sales 161.5MM^E EMP 422
SIC 5511 5521 5531 5012 5013 6159

D-U-N-S 07-737-7836
FRESNO UNIFIED SCHOOL DISTRICT
2309 Tulare St, Fresno, CA 93721-2287
Tel (559) 457-3000 Founded/Ownrshp 1873
Sales 554.6MM^E EMP 8,400
Accts Perry Smith Sacramento Calif
SIC 8211 Public elementary school; Public junior high school; Public senior high school; Public special education school
Off Mgr: Cheryl Abrams
Off Mgr: Sheila Lay
CTO: Kurt Madden
Telecom Mg: Cheryl Mueller
Teacher Pr: John Marinovich
Instr Medi: Michael Dela Cerda
HC Dir: Gail Williams

D-U-N-S 18-565-4501
FREUDENBERG IT LP
(Suby of FREUDENBERG & CO. KG)
601 Keystone Park Dr # 600, Morrisville, NC 27560-0348
Tel (919) 321-0254 Founded/Ownrshp 2005
Sales 110.6MM^E EMP 500
SIC 7371 Computer software systems analysis & design, custom
CEO: Horst Reichardt
*Pr: Michael Heuberger
CFO: Sebastian Weiss
VP: Mohammad Ahrnmad
VP: Richard Downham
VP: Heiner Heng
VP: Jim Kunz
Snr Ntwrk: Dave Greaves
MIS Dir: Ted Lupton
Dir IT: Helge Brummer
Tech Mgr: Tj Styers

D-U-N-S 12-098-1337 IMP
FREUDENBERG MEDICAL LLC
HELIX MEDICAL
(Suby of FREUDENBERG NORTH AMERICA LIMITED PARTNERSHIP) ★
1110 Mark Ave, Carpinteria, CA 93013-2918
Tel (805) 684-3304 Founded/Ownrshp 2015
Sales 161.1MM^E EMP 400^E
SIC 3842 Prosthetic appliances
CEO: Jorg Schneewind
*Pr: Thomas Vassalo
VP: Deanna Caballero
Exec: Colleen Arabian
QC Dir: Rob Schroeder
Ql Cn Mgr: Lorena Lundeen
VP Sls: Tom Vassallo
Snr Mgr: Maggie Manzo

D-U-N-S 83-777-2631 IMP/EXP
FREUDENBERG NORTH AMERICA LIMITED PARTNERSHIP
(Suby of EXTERNA HANDELS-UND BETEILIGUNGS-GESELLSCHAFT MIT BESCHRANKTER HAFTUNG)
47774 W Anchor Ct, Plymouth, MI 48170-2456
Tel (734) 354-5505 Founded/Ownrshp 1984
Sales 1.7MMM^E EMP 6,304
SIC 2821 3714 3053 3061 Plastics materials & resins; Motor vehicle parts & accessories; Gaskets, packing & sealing devices; Mechanical rubber goods
Pr: Leesa A Smith
VP: Robert G Evans
CTO: Alex Berdichevsky
Ql Cn Mgr: Beth Miller
Sales Asso: Mark Hazel

D-U-N-S 00-108-4672 IMP
FREUDENBERG-NOK GENERAL PARTNERSHIP
F-NOK
(Suby of FREUDENBERG NORTH AMERICA LIMITED PARTNERSHIP) ★
47690 E Anchor Ct, Plymouth, MI 48170-2400
Tel (734) 451-0020 Founded/Ownrshp 1989
Sales 1.6MMM^E EMP 6,232
Accts Ernst & Young Llp
SIC 2821 3714 3053 3061 Plastics materials & resins; Motor vehicle parts & accessories; Gaskets, packing & sealing devices; Mechanical rubber goods
CEO: Mohsen M Sohi
*Pr: Brad Norton
Pr: John Rice
CFO: Ralf Krieger
*Ch: Martin Wentzler
*Sr VP: Dr Michael Heidingsfelder
*Sr VP: Yoshindo Masumoto
VP: Ted Duclos
VP: Bob Evans
*VP: Robert G Evans
*VP: Sarah A O'Hare
*VP: Leesa Smith

FREUND BAKING
See OAKHURST INDUSTRIES INC

D-U-N-S 07-997-0796
FRI HOLDING CO LLC
4170 Ashford Dunwoody Rd, Brookhaven, GA 30319-1442
Tel (404) 865-3356 Founded/Ownrshp 2015
Sales 209.1MM^E EMP 6,100^E
SIC 5812 Restaurant, family: chain

D-U-N-S 01-668-0274 IMP
FRICK SERVICES INC
3154 Depot St, Wawaka, IN 46794
Tel (260) 761-3311 Founded/Ownrshp 1920
Sales 109.4MM^E EMP 100
SIC 5191 5153 5261 4221 2048 4213 Fertilizer & fertilizer materials; Grains; Fertilizer; Farm product warehousing & storage; Prepared feeds; Trucking, except local
Ex VP: Dan Frick
*Sec: Louise R Frick

D-U-N-S 00-398-1818 IMP/EXP
■ FRICTION PRODUCTS CO
HAWK PERFORMANCE
(Suby of CBF) ★
920 Lake Rd, Medina, OH 44256-2453
Tel (330) 725-4941 Founded/Ownrshp 1989
Sales 118.6MM^E EMP 266
SIC 3728 3714 Aircraft landing assemblies & brakes; Motor vehicle brake systems & parts
CEO: Chris Disantis
*Ch: Ronald E Weinberg
VP: Don Brown
*VP: Thomas A Gilbride

D-U-N-S 06-824-8780
FRIED FRANK HARRIS SHRIVER & JACOBSON LLP
1 New York Plz Fl 27, New York, NY 10004-1980
Tel (212) 859-8000 Founded/Ownrshp 2003
Sales 504.0MM EMP 800
SIC 8111 General practice law office
Ch: Valerie Ford Jacob
Pt: Jonathan Adler
Pt: Gus Atiyah
Pt: Lawrence Barshay
Pt: John Bibona
Pt: Daniel Bursky
Pt: Nick Cherryman
Pt: Johnson L Dixie
Pt: Dan Glazer
Pt: Michelle B Gold
Pt: Peter Guryan
Pt: Jerald Howe
Pt: William Johnson
Pt: Gary L Kaplan
Pt: James Kitching
Pt: Meyer Last
Pt: Henry Lebowitz
Pt: James McCullough
Pt: Craig Miller
Pt: Robert Mollen
Pt: David Morris

D-U-N-S 18-154-9098
FRIEDKIN COMPANIES INC
AUTODIRECT SOLUTIONS
1345 Enclave Pkwy, Houston, TX 77077-2026
Tel (713) 580-3300 Founded/Ownrshp 1978
Sales 761.8MM^E EMP 1,525
SIC 5012 6211 Automobiles & other motor vehicles; Investment firm, general brokerage
Ch: Thomas Dan Friedkin
*Pr: Marcus A Watts
*COO: Michelle L McKinney
*Sec: Michael Phelps
Bd of Dir: James Lowry
VP: Tom Bittenbender
*VP: Ana Dunkel
VP: Dian O Gilvie
*VP: Kimberley A Jacobson
VP: Kimberley Jacobson
VP: Jerry Pyle
Dir Risk M: David Jarusinski

FRIEDMAN BROS. HARDWARE
See FRIEDMANS HOME IMPROVEMENT

D-U-N-S 05-167-5056 IMP
FRIEDMANS HOME IMPROVEMENT
FRIEDMAN BROS. HARDWARE
4055 Santa Rosa Ave, Santa Rosa, CA 95407-8222
Tel (707) 584-7811 Founded/Ownrshp 1998
Sales 83.4MM^E EMP 350
SIC 5251 5211 5261

FRIEDMUTTER GROUP
See BRAD HENRY FRIEDMUTTER & ASSOCIATES LTD

D-U-N-S 14-714-4356
FRIEDRICH AIR CONDITIONING CO LTD
(Suby of CORINTHIAN CAPITAL GROUP LLC) ★
10001 Reunion Pl Ste 500, San Antonio, TX 78216-4139
Tel (210) 546-0500 Founded/Ownrshp 2012
Sales 95.1MM^E EMP 90
SIC 3585 5722 Air conditioning units, complete: domestic or industrial; Household appliance stores
CEO: George Van Hoomissen
Pr: Chuck Campbell

CFO: Tracy Peterson
Natl Sales: Butch Hegeman
Sales Asso: Trey Weinand

D-U-N-S 79-933-3208 IMP/EXP
FRIEND TIRE CO
(*Suby of* YOKOHAMA TIRE) ★
11 Indl Dr, Monett, MO 65708
Tel (800) 950-8473 *Founded/Ownrshp* 1956
Sales 144.0MM *EMP* 218
SIC 5014 Automobile tires & tubes; Truck tires & tubes
Pr: Don Isbell
**VP:* Lance Isbell
**VP:* Robert Roller
Brnch Mgr: Shannon Ausburn
Brnch Mgr: Jim Budd
Brnch Mgr: Phil Jackson
Brnch Mgr: Larry Lowery
Brnch Mgr: Dave Maury

D-U-N-S 16-994-2062
FRIENDFINDER NETWORKS INC
1615 S Congress Ave # 103, Delray Beach, FL 33445-6326
Tel (561) 912-7000 *Founded/Ownrshp* 1965
Sales 314.3MM *EMP* 339
SIC 4813

D-U-N-S 01-952-0501 IMP/EXP
FRIENDLY FRUIT INC
SID WAINER & SON
2301 Purchase St Unit 1, New Bedford, MA 02746-1686
Tel (508) 999-6408 *Founded/Ownrshp* 1974
Sales 155.0MM *EMP* 450
SIC 5148 5149 Fresh fruits & vegetables; Specialty food items
Pr: Henry Wainer
**CFO:* Klaus Nygaard

FRIENDLY'S
See KESSLER FAMILY LLC

FRIENDLY'S
See J & B RESTAURANT PARTNERS OF LONG ISLAND INC

D-U-N-S 07-836-6099
FRIENDLYS ICE CREAM LLC
(*Suby of* FREEZE OPERATIONS HOLDING CORP) ★
1855 Boston Rd, Wilbraham, MA 01095-1002
Tel (413) 731-4000 *Founded/Ownrshp* 2011
Sales 2.5MMM^E *EMP* 6,385^E
SIC 2024 5812 Ice cream & ice milk; Ice cream, bulk; Eating places
CEO: John M Maguire
CFO: Todd Schwendenmann
VP: Randolph P Davis

D-U-N-S 07-883-2627
■ **FRIENDLYS MANUFACTURING AND RETAIL LLC**
(*Suby of* DEAN FOODS CO) ★
1855 Boston Rd, Wilbraham, MA 01095-1002
Tel (413) 731-4136 *Founded/Ownrshp* 2016
Sales 130.0MM^E *EMP* 400
SIC 5812 Restaurant, family: chain
Treas: Timothy Schwendenman

D-U-N-S 07-857-8398
FRIENDLYS RESTAURANTS LLC
(*Suby of* FRIENDLYS ICE CREAM LLC) ★
1855 Boston Rd, Wilbraham, MA 01095-1002
Tel (413) 731-4000 *Founded/Ownrshp* 2012
Sales 197.6MM^E *EMP* 6,350
SIC 5812 Restaurant, family: chain
Pr: James M Parrish

D-U-N-S 96-465-9325
FRIENDS & CO
1760 Reston Pkwy Ste 200, Reston, VA 20190-3358
Tel (703) 796-0333 *Founded/Ownrshp* 2010
Sales 25.6MM^E *EMP* 1,997
SIC 7361 Employment agencies
Prin: Ron Smith
**Prin:* Mark Schaul

D-U-N-S 07-615-3501
FRIENDS OF ELMBROOK MEMORIAL HOSPITAL INC
WHEATON FRANCISCAN
19333 W North Ave, Brookfield, WI 53045-4132
Tel (262) 785-2000 *Founded/Ownrshp* 1918
Sales 88.9MM^E *EMP* 900
SIC 8062 General medical & surgical hospitals
VP: Maureen Furno
Chf OB: Steven B Mc Cann
Dir Vol: April Dethloff
CFO: Kathy Peck
Ofcr: Tim Wiza
VP: Eric E Christianson
Dir Risk M: Joe Wildt
Dir Lab: Andrew Gozdowiak
Dir Soc: Gail Davis
Dir Rad: Robert Weisbecker
Dir Rx: James Fidler
Dir Env Sv: Mike Skrivseth

D-U-N-S 15-223-2609
FRIENDS OF LIBRARY FLAGLER COUNTY INC
2500 Palm Coast Pkwy Nw, Palm Coast, FL 32137-4731
Tel (386) 445-1389 *Founded/Ownrshp* 1978
Sales 70.5M *EMP* 1,400
SIC 8231 Libraries
Pr: Terry Jones
**Treas:* Ron Pokigo
**VP:* At Bryan

FRIENDS OF SINAI CHILDREN
See MOUNT SINAI HOSPITAL MEDICAL CENTER OF CHICAGO

FRIENDSHIP COMMUNITY CARE BEHA
See FRIENDSHIP COMMUNITY CARE INC

D-U-N-S 10-204-3932
FRIENDSHIP COMMUNITY CARE INC
FRIENDSHIP COMMUNITY CARE BEHA
920 University Dr, Russellville, AR 72801-4303
Tel (479) 967-2316 *Founded/Ownrshp* 1971
Sales 33.4MM *EMP* 1,100
Accts Moore And Aikman Cpas Pa Russ
SIC 8211 School for physically handicapped
CEO: Cindy Mahan
**Pr:* Charles Blanchard
Ofcr: Donovan Moore
**Ex VP:* Tom Hill
**Ex VP:* Marcia Montgomery
**Ex VP:* Angela Traweek
**VP:* Dr Finley Turner
Genl Mgr: Marcia Brown

FRIENDSHIP FOOD STORES
See BECK SUPPLIERS INC

FRIENDSHIP HOMES DIVISION
See FAIRMONT HOMES LLC

D-U-N-S 02-994-0942
FRIENDSHIP PUBLIC CHARTER SCHOOL INC
FRIENDSHIP SCHOOL
120 Q St Ne Ste 200, Washington, DC 20002-2100
Tel (202) 281-1700 *Founded/Ownrshp* 1998
Sales 87.7MM *EMP* 800^E
Accts Maner Costerisan Pc Lansing
SIC 8211 Public elementary & secondary schools
Ch: Donald L Hense
**COO:* Patricia Brantley
CFO: Erin Covington
Bd of Dir: Eric King
Dir Soc: Simone Green
Genl Couns: Ellen Dalton

FRIENDSHIP SCHOOL
See FRIENDSHIP PUBLIC CHARTER SCHOOL INC

FRIERSON BAILEY BUILDING
See BAILEY LUMBER & SUPPLY CO

D-U-N-S 03-385-3821
FRIES FARMS LLC
8816 Us Highway 301, Claxton, GA 30417-5428
Tel (912) 739-3181 *Founded/Ownrshp* 1949
Sales 366.3MM^E *EMP* 1,600
SIC 0251 2015

D-U-N-S 02-401-4461
FRINGE BENEFIT RESOURCES (MT)
1730 Alder Dr, Great Falls, MT 59404-3533
Tel (406) 268-1721 *Founded/Ownrshp* 2001
Sales NA *EMP* 12,000
SIC 6411 Insurance agents, brokers & service
Owner: Dan Oakland

D-U-N-S 04-137-0339
FRIONA INDUSTRIES LP
HI-PRO ANIMAL HEALTH
500 S Taylor St Unit 253, Amarillo, TX 79101-2447
Tel (806) 374-1811 *Founded/Ownrshp* 1986
Sales 97.2MM^E *EMP* 190
SIC 0211 Beef cattle feedlots
Pr: James E Herring
**CFO:* Dal Reid

D-U-N-S 07-399-2737
FRISBIE MEMORIAL HOSPITAL
11 Whitehall Rd, Rochester, NH 03867-3297
Tel (603) 332-5211 *Founded/Ownrshp* 1919
Sales 132.4MM *EMP* 900
Accts Berry Dunn Mcneil & Parker Ll
SIC 8062 General medical & surgical hospitals
CEO: John Marzinzik
**Ch Bd:* Greg Smith
Pr: Brooks McQuade
Ofcr: Brenda Niland
**VP:* Amy Guilfoil Dumont
VP: Corinne McDonald
VP: Timothy Sherry
**Exec:* Paula Mahoney
Dir Rx: Marcia Montminy
Ex Dir: Judy Ouellette
Off Mgr: Darlene Weiner

D-U-N-S 00-313-5936 IMP/EXP
FRISCHKORN INC
WOLSELEY INDUSTRIAL GROUP
(*Suby of* FERGUSON ENTERPRISES INC) ★
1801 Roseneath Rd, Richmond, VA 23230-4330
Tel (804) 353-0181 *Founded/Ownrshp* 1934, 2005
Sales 296.1MM^E *EMP* 275
SIC 5085 Industrial supplies; Valves & fittings
CEO: Horner Micheal W
**Pr:* Larry G Pearson
**CFO:* R Dwight Payne
**Ex VP:* S Victor Kitchen
Genl Mgr: Jan Denson
Genl Mgr: Cathy Fuller
Info Man: Mary Shlanger
Sales Asso: Mark Bliley

D-U-N-S 79-092-2363
■ **FRISCHS OHIO INC**
(*Suby of* FRISCHS RESTAURANTS INC) ★
2800 Gilbert Ave, Cincinnati, OH 45206-1206
Tel (513) 961-2660 *Founded/Ownrshp* 1962
Sales 160.0MM *EMP* 80
SIC 5812 Restaurant, family: chain
Pr: Craig F Maier
**CFO:* Donald Walker

D-U-N-S 00-699-9437
FRISCHS RESTAURANTS INC (OH)
(*Suby of* FRI HOLDING CO LLC) ★
2800 Gilbert Ave, Cincinnati, OH 45206-1206
Tel (513) 961-2660 *Founded/Ownrshp* 1905, 2015
Sales 209.1MM^E *EMP* 6,100^E
Accts Grant Thornton Llp Cincinnati
SIC 5812 Restaurant, family: chain
Pr: Aziz Hashim
VP: Stephen Hansen
Software D: Charity Worthington
Sls&Mrk Ex: Marcia Flaig
Pr Dir: Pam Morrison

D-U-N-S 00-288-1407
FRISCO INDEPENDENT SCHOOL DISTRICT
5515 Ohio Dr, Frisco, TX 75035-7002
Tel (469) 633-6000 *Founded/Ownrshp* 1890
Sales 479.0MM *EMP* 6,000
Accts Weaver And Tidwell Llp Dalla
SIC 8211 Public elementary & secondary schools; Public elementary school; Public junior high school; Public senior high school
**CFO:* Richard Bankston
Bd of Dir: Dayna Burleigh
Bd of Dir: Roger Smith
Bd of Dir: Karen Steines
Comm Dir: Shana Wortham
Pr Dir: Chris Moore
Psych: Judson Carmichael
Psych: Amy Hudspeth

D-U-N-S 12-131-0002
FRISCO MEDICAL CENTER LLP
BAYLOR MEDICAL CENTER AT FRISC
5601 Warren Pkwy, Frisco, TX 75034-4069
Tel (214) 618-2000 *Founded/Ownrshp* 2002
Sales 156.4MM *EMP* 466
SIC 8062 General medical & surgical hospitals
Pt: William A Keaton
Dir Recs: Jan Young
COO: Betty Stotts
VP: Sharn Devun
Dir Lab: Lori Grisham
Dir Rx: Bob Blanford
IT Man: Steve Seltz
Mktg Mgr: Chris Farmer

D-U-N-S 95-813-1450 IMP
■ **FRITO-LAY NORTH AMERICA INC**
PEPSICO AMERICAS FOODS
(*Suby of* PEPSICO INC) ★
7701 Legacy Dr, Plano, TX 75024-4099
Tel (972) 334-7000 *Founded/Ownrshp* 1989
Sales 8.1MMM^E *EMP* 40,000
SIC 2096 2052 2013 5812 6794 2086 Potato chips & similar snacks; Potato chips & other potato-based snacks; Tortilla chips; Corn chips & other corn-based snacks; Cookies; Snack sticks, including jerky: from purchased meat; Fast-food restaurant, chain; Chicken restaurant; Franchises, selling or licensing; Soft drinks: packaged in cans, bottles, etc.
CEO: Albert P Carey
**Pr:* Oswald Barckhahn
CFO: Hari Avula
**CFO:* Hugh F Johnston
Sr VP: Leslie Starr Keating
Sr VP: Randolph W Melville
Sr VP: Jennifer Saenz
Sr VP: Steven Williams
VP: Michael Hourihan
Dir Sec: Michael Lee
Genl Mgr: Shauneen Eagan

D-U-N-S 06-300-7314
■ **FRITZ COMPANIES INC**
U P S
(*Suby of* UPS) ★
550-1 Eccles Ave, San Francisco, CA 94101
Tel (650) 635-2693 *Founded/Ownrshp* 2001
Sales 439.4MM^E *EMP* 10,000
SIC 4731 Freight transportation arrangement
CEO: Brad Lb Mitchell

D-U-N-S 06-880-3923
FRITZ ENTERPRISES INC
F E I
1650 W Jefferson Ave, Trenton, MI 48183-2136
Tel (734) 692-4231 *Founded/Ownrshp* 1971
Sales 98.7MM^E *EMP* 169
SIC 5093 Ferrous metal scrap & waste
Pr: Leonard Fritz
**Treas:* Irma Fritz
**Ex VP:* Eric R Fritz
**VP:* Elaine M Fritz
**VP:* Raymond J Fritz
**VP:* Robert L McDonald
**VP:* Dennis J Reno
VP: Alex Sitz
**VP:* David W Splan
Exec: Kenneth Mosher
Mtls Mgr: Huron V Steel

D-U-N-S 00-732-0229 IMP/EXP
FRITZ INDUSTRIES INC (TX)
500 N Sam Houston Rd, Mesquite, TX 75149-2733
Tel (972) 285-5471 *Founded/Ownrshp* 1956
Sales 156.9MM^E *EMP* 330
SIC 2899 Chemical preparations
Pr: Dan Montgomery
Pr: Steve Laramay
**CFO:* Edward Burks
**CFO:* Mike Kovar
IT Man: Brent Duty
Software D: Dustin Baker
**VP Opers:* Eric Ulfsparre
Sls Mgr: Gabriel M Ojeda
Snr Mgr: Scott Falk

D-U-N-S 05-558-5277 IMP
FRL INC
FISHER RESEARCH LABORATORY
(*Suby of* BOUNTY HUNTER METAL DETECTORS) ★
1465 Henry Brennan Dr H, El Paso, TX 79936-6815
Tel (915) 225-0333 *Founded/Ownrshp* 1931, 2006
Sales 87.1MM^E *EMP* 800
SIC 3699 Electrical equipment & supplies
Pr: Thomas Walsh
**CFO:* Charles Schwan
Mktg Mgr: Galen Young

FROEDTERT & COMMUNITY
See FROEDTERT HEALTH INC

D-U-N-S 96-963-5056
FROEDTERT AND COMMUNITY HEALTH INC
(*Suby of* FROEDTERT HEALTH HOSPITAL) ★
9200 W Wisconsin Ave, Milwaukee, WI 53226-3522
Tel (414) 777-0960 *Founded/Ownrshp* 2011
Sales 397.5MM *EMP* 746^E
Accts Kpmg Llp Columbus Oh
SIC 8062 General medical & surgical hospitals
Ch: David J Lubar
COO: Allen Ericson
Ex VP: Joseph Hill
VP: Robert Degrand
HC Dir: Julie Haskell
Pgrm Dir: Kyle Theine

D-U-N-S 04-078-9588
FROEDTERT HEALTH HOSPITAL
9200 W Wisconsin Ave, Milwaukee, WI 53226-3522
Tel (414) 805-3000 *Founded/Ownrshp* 1965
Sales 1.1MMM *EMP* 3,459
Accts Kpmg Llp Columbus Oh
SIC 8062 General medical & surgical hospitals
Ch: P Michael Mahoney
**Pr:* Catherin Buck
**Pr:* William Petasnick
Pr: Timothy Waldoch
**Treas:* Roger Pierce
Ofcr: David Olson
Ofcr: Mary Wolbert
Ex VP: Peter Pruessing
Sr VP: Keith Allen
VP: Gary Colpaert
VP: Catherine Eastham
VP: Andrew J Norton
Exec: Pamela Mehring

D-U-N-S 83-321-9426
FROEDTERT HEALTH INC
FROEDTERT & COMMUNITY
400 Wood Prim Ste, Menomonee Falls, WI 53051
Tel (262) 251-1000 *Founded/Ownrshp* 2000
Sales 362.4MM *EMP* 9,000
Accts Kpmg Llp Columbus Oh
SIC 8062 General medical & surgical hospitals
CEO: Cathy Jacobson
**COO:* Dennis Pollard
**CFO:* Scott Hawig
**Treas:* Thomas Knoll
VP: Robert Degrand
**Prin:* Catherine Mode Eastham
Podiatrist: Robert A Mueller

D-U-N-S 00-687-0208
FROEHLING & ROBERTSON INC (VA)
3015 Dumbarton Rd, Richmond, VA 23228-5831
Tel (804) 264-2701 *Founded/Ownrshp* 1881, 1873
Sales 111.7MM^E *EMP* 488
SIC 8711 8734 Engineering services; Testing laboratories
CEO: Samuel S Proctor
**Pr:* Samuel H Kirby Jr
**CFO:* Timothy A Glynn
**CFO:* Douglas C Hensley Jr
**Ch:* Mimi S Proctor
Bd of Dir: Ginny Reed
Exec: Joyce Riggle
Dir Bus: Scott Sutton
Off Mgr: Kimberly Wright
Sfty Dirs: Curtis Childress
Opers Mgr: John Citro

D-U-N-S 01-449-5964 EXP
FROMM ELECTRIC SUPPLY CORP OF READING PENNA (PA)
2101 Centre Ave Ste 4, Reading, PA 19605-2872
Tel (610) 374-4441 *Founded/Ownrshp* 1958, 2007
Sales 213.0MM^E *EMP* 150
SIC 5063 Electrical supplies; Lighting fixtures
Ch Bd: Bernard Fromm
**Pr:* Michael Fromm
**COO:* John Hanna
VP: Barbara Fromm
VP: Trevor Martin
Brnch Mgr: Kevin Bryant
Brnch Mgr: Jared Lutz
Sales Asso: Randy Czuba
Sales Asso: John Klinges

D-U-N-S 06-122-9725
FRONT PORCH COMMUNITIES AND SERVICES - CASA DE MANANA LLC
FREDERICKA MANOR CARE CENTER
800 N Brand Blvd Fl 19, Glendale, CA 91203-1231
Tel (818) 729-8100 *Founded/Ownrshp* 1995
Sales 165.1MM *EMP* 2,500
SIC 8059 8051 Rest home, with health care; Skilled nursing care facilities
CEO: Gary Wheeler
**Pr:* Roberta Jacobsen
CFO: Bill Jennings
**CFO:* Mary Miller
CTO: Bonnie Stover

FRONTGATE CATALOG
See CINMAR LLC

FRONTIER
See CITIZENS TELECOMMUNICATIONS CO OF CALIFORNIA INC

FRONTIER
See CITIZENS TELECOMMUNICATIONS CO OF TENNESSEE LLC

FRONTIER
See CITIZENS TELECOMMUNICATIONS CO OF NEW YORK INC

D-U-N-S 79-560-2114
FRONTIER AG INC
415 W 2nd St, Oakley, KS 67748-1545
Tel (785) 462-2063 *Founded/Ownrshp* 2007
Sales 186.2MM^E *EMP* 165
SIC 5153 5191 Grains; Grain elevators; Farm supplies
CEO: Brad Cowan
**CFO:* Brian Linin
Rgnl Mgr: Ryan McLemore
Brnch Mgr: Aaron Neumann
Opers Mgr: Jim Foltz

D-U-N-S 62-398-6242
FRONTIER AIRLINES HOLDINGS INC
(*Suby of* FALCON ACQUISITION GROUP)
7001 Tower Rd, Denver, CO 80249-7312
Tel (720) 374-4200 *Founded/Ownrshp* 2013
Sales 532.3MM^E *EMP* 6,170

SIC 4512 Air transportation, scheduled; Air passenger carrier, scheduled
Pr: Barry L Biffle
Treas: Holly Nelson
Sr VP: Robert Ashcroft
Sr VP: Daniel Shurz
CIO: Amit Agarwal
Prd Mgr: Pam Armstrong

D-U-N-S 83-115-3622
FRONTIER AIRLINES INC
(*Suby of* FRONTIER AIRLINES HOLDINGS INC) ★
7001 Tower Rd, Denver, CO 80249-7312
Tel (720) 374-4200 *Founded/Ownrshp* 1994
Sales 532.2MM *EMP* 4,770
Accts Kpmg Llp Denver Colorado
SIC 4512 Air transportation, scheduled
CEO: David Siegel
V Ch: Larae B Orullian
**Pr:* Jeff S Potter
COO: Daniel McCarthy
**COO:* Bill Meehan
**CFO:* Edward Christie III
**CFO:* James Dempsey
**Treas:* Holly Nelson
**Treas:* Elissa A Potucek
Ofcr: Dan Stapleton
**Sr VP:* Ann Block
Sr VP: Christopher Collins
**Sr VP:* Howard Diamond
**Sr VP:* Paul S Tate
VP: Michael J Bowers
VP: Gary Breauninger
**VP:* Gerry Coady
VP: Dennis Crabtree
VP: Elise R Eberwein
VP: Cliff V Leuven
VP: Ronald McClellan
Board of Directors: Samuel D Addoms Chb, D Dale Browning, Rita M Cuddihy, Patricia A Engels, Robert D Taylor, James B Upchurch, Paul S Dempsey V Chb

D-U-N-S 82-538-6886
FRONTIER ALASKA
5245 Airport Indus Rd, Fairbanks, AK 99709-4468
Tel (907) 450-7250 *Founded/Ownrshp* 2008
Sales 21.4MM^E *EMP* 1,065
SIC 4512 Air transportation, scheduled
Pr: Bob Hajdukovich

D-U-N-S 00-691-4030
■ **FRONTIER CALIFORNIA INC** (CA)
VERIZON
(*Suby of* FRONTIER COMMUNICATIONS CORP) ★
140 West St, New York, NY 10007-2141
Tel (212) 395-1000 *Founded/Ownrshp* 1929, 2016
Sales 2.6MMM^E *EMP* 9,100
SIC 4813 6519 8721 5065 1731 7629 Local & long distance telephone communications; Local telephone communications; Real property lessors; Billing & bookkeeping service; Telephone & telegraphic equipment; Telephone equipment; Telephone & telephone equipment installation; Telecommunication equipment repair (except telephones); Telephone set repair
CEO: W Robert Mudge
Ex VP: William P Barr
Ex VP: Doreen A Toben
Sr VP: Dave Benson
Sr VP: William F Heitmann
VP: Lawrence T Dabbio
VP: Jeffrey Maldonado
Sales Asso: Chris Blake

D-U-N-S 79-664-6297
FRONTIER CENTRAL SCHOOL DISTRICT
5120 Orchard Ave, Hamburg, NY 14075-5657
Tel (716) 926-1710 *Founded/Ownrshp* 1951
Sales 50.6MM^E *EMP* 1,215
SIC 8211 Public elementary & secondary schools
**Treas:* Jim Pelonero
HC Dir: Richard Gray

FRONTIER COMMUNICATIONS
See COMMONWEALTH TELEPHONE CO LLC

D-U-N-S 00-691-8296 IMP
▲ **FRONTIER COMMUNICATIONS CORP** (GA)
401 Merritt 7 Ste 1, Norwalk, CT 06851-1069
Tel (203) 614-5600 *Founded/Ownrshp* 1935
Sales 5.5MMM *EMP* 19,200
Accts Kpmg Llp Stamford Connectic
Tkr Sym FTR *Exch* NGS
SIC 4813 Telephone communication, except radio; Local telephone communications; Long distance telephone communications;
Pr: Daniel J McCarthy
**Ch Bd:* Pamela D A Reeve
CFO: R Perley McBride
Ofcr: Kathleen Abernathy
Ofcr: Cecilia K McKenney
Ofcr: Kathleen Weslock
Ex VP: Jennifer Brown
Ex VP: Steve Gable
Ex VP: Peter Hayes
Ex VP: John J Lass
Ex VP: Mark D Nielsen
Ex VP: Melinda White
Sr VP: Trent Anderson
Sr VP: Craig L Collins
Sr VP: Donald W Daniels Jr
Sr VP: Michael Golob
VP: John Broughton
VP: Brian Carlo
VP: Mike Flynn
VP: Steven Jones
VP: Alan Kelsey
Board of Directors: Leroy T Barnes Jr, Peter C B Bynoe, Diana S Ferguson, Edward Fraioli, Virginia P Ruesterholz, Howard L Schrott, Mark Shapiro, Myron A Wick III

D-U-N-S 14-540-8063
■ **FRONTIER COMMUNICATIONS CORP**
CITIZENS COMMUNICATIONS-CABS
(*Suby of* FRONTIER COMMUNICATIONS CORP) ★
14450 Burnhaven Dr, Burnsville, MN 55306-4966
Tel (952) 435-3133 *Founded/Ownrshp* 1991
Sales 3.4MMM^E *EMP* 12,000
SIC 4813 Telephone cable service, land or submarine
CEO: Daniel McCarthy
Dir IT: Matt Capana

D-U-N-S 00-677-3980 IMP
■ **FRONTIER COMMUNICATIONS OF AUSABLE VALLEY INC** (NY)
(*Suby of* FRONTIER COMMUNICATIONS CORP) ★
310 Front St, Keeseville, NY 12944
Tel (518) 834-7211 *Founded/Ownrshp* 1904, 2001
Sales 111.3MM^E *EMP* 136
SIC 4813 Telephone communication, except radio
Ch Bd: Mary Agnes Wilderotter
**Pr:* Jeremiah T Carr
**Treas:* Ralph Martuci
**Treas:* Louis L Massaro
**Treas:* Martin Reinhard
**VP:* Roderick N Anstey

D-U-N-S 78-136-6273
■ **FRONTIER COMMUNICATIONS OF MINNESOTA INC**
(*Suby of* FRONTIER COMMUNICATIONS CORP) ★
1405 W 150th St, Burnsville, MN 55306-4949
Tel (952) 898-6422 *Founded/Ownrshp* 2001
Sales 145.1MM^E *EMP* 500
SIC 4813 Local telephone communications
Ch Bd: Maggie Wilderotter
Sls Mgr: Chuck Bruns

D-U-N-S 00-279-8957
■ **FRONTIER COMMUNICATIONS WEST COAST INC**
(*Suby of* VERIZON NORTHWEST INC) ★
1800 41st St, Everett, WA 98203-2355
Tel (425) 261-5321 *Founded/Ownrshp* 1964
Sales 89.5MM^E *EMP* 522
SIC 4813 Local telephone communications; Long distance telephone communications
Pr: Eilene O'Neill-Odum
**Ex VP:* John C Appel
Sr VP: Daniel O'Brien
VP: C Bercher
VP: Michael McDonough
VP: Paul Miner

D-U-N-S 09-138-7597 IMP/EXP
FRONTIER COOPERATIVE
FRONTIER COOPERATIVE HERBS
3021 78th St, Norway, IA 52318-9520
Tel (319) 227-7996 *Founded/Ownrshp* 1976
Sales 150.0MM *EMP* 505^E
SIC 5122 2099 5149 Perfumes; Spices, including grinding; Groceries & related products
CEO: Tony Bedard
**Chf Mktg O:* Clint Landis
VP: Fred Bacher
**VP:* Dave Beal
**VP:* Cole Daily
**VP:* Carla Dewalt
**VP:* Dave Karpick
**VP:* Kathy Larson
**VP:* Tracy Tunwall
CIO: Keith Barloon
CIO: Tim McCarthy

D-U-N-S 00-885-0356
FRONTIER COOPERATIVE CO (NE)
211 S Lincoln St, Brainard, NE 68626-3516
Tel (402) 545-2811 *Founded/Ownrshp* 1915
Sales 160.1MM^E *EMP* 90
SIC 5153 5191 Grain elevators; Grains; Fertilizer & fertilizer materials; Feed
Pr: Randy Robeson
Treas: Kevin Hedrichson
VP: Gale Janak
Brnch Mgr: Kevin Hevlovic

FRONTIER COOPERATIVE HERBS
See FRONTIER COOPERATIVE

D-U-N-S 78-563-4689
FRONTIER DRILLING LLC
1608 Nw Epwy Ste 102, Oklahoma City, OK 73118
Tel (405) 745-7700 *Founded/Ownrshp* 2005
Sales 87.4MM^E *EMP* 90
SIC 1381 Drilling oil & gas wells

D-U-N-S 62-150-7305 IMP
FRONTIER DRILLING USA INC
(*Suby of* PARAGON OFFSHORE DRILLING AS)
13135 Dairy Ashford Rd # 800, Sugar Land, TX 77478-3680
Tel (713) 481-7500 *Founded/Ownrshp* 2006
Sales 121.5MM^E *EMP* 700^E
SIC 1381 Directional drilling oil & gas wells
CEO: Robert Fulton
**Pr:* Dennis J Lubojacky
**Pr:* Steve Meheen
**CFO:* John E Stevenson
**VP:* Larry D Humes
**VP:* Thomas M Madden
**VP:* James R Sanislow
**VP:* Steve Souza
**VP:* Thomas R Travis

FRONTIER ELDORADO REFINING
See HOLLYFRONTIER EL DORADO REFINING LLC

FRONTIER EXPEDITERS
See ALASKA COMMERCIAL CO

D-U-N-S 00-692-4070
■ **FRONTIER FLORIDA LLC** (FL)
VERIZON
(*Suby of* FRONTIER COMMUNICATIONS CORP) ★
401 Merritt 7, Norwalk, CT 06851-1000
Tel (813) 483-2011 *Founded/Ownrshp* 1901, 2016
Sales 1.7MMM^E *EMP* 6,000
SIC 4813 6519 8721 5065 7629 Local & long distance telephone communications; Local telephone communications; Real property lessors; Billing & bookkeeping service; Telephone equipment; Telephone set repair; Telecommunication equipment repair (except telephones)
Exec: Dianne Heckemeyer
Ex Dir: Larry Radin

D-U-N-S 08-119-8830
FRONTIER HEALTH
ASSESSMENT SERVICES
1167 Spratlin Park Dr, Gray, TN 37615-6205
Tel (423) 467-3600 *Founded/Ownrshp* 1974
Sales 52.4MM *EMP* 1,000
Accts Dent K Burk Associates Pc C
SIC 8093 8322 Mental health clinic, outpatient; Rehabilitation center, outpatient treatment; Individual & family services
CEO: Teresa Kidd
**Pr:* Charles E Good
CFO: Artie Feagins
**Sr VP:* Randall E Jessee
**Sr VP:* David McKee
**Sr VP:* C Allen Musil Jr
VP: Joe Page
Ex Dir: Harry Spurling
Off Mgr: Mary Lockner
Off Mgr: Dave Smith
IT Man: Phillip White

D-U-N-S 01-819-1119
FRONTIER MANAGEMENT LLC (OR)
7420 Sw Bridgeprt Rd 10 Ste 105, Portland, OR 97224
Tel (503) 443-1818 *Founded/Ownrshp* 2000
Sales 108.3MM^E *EMP* 600
SIC 8741 Nursing & personal care facility management; Hospital management
CEO: Greg Roderick
COO: Don Harris
**CFO:* Elizabeth Comfort
CFO: Amy Landon
**VP:* Leona Ciechanowski
**VP:* Colleen Papp
**VP:* William Swearingen

FRONTIER MEAT & SUPPLY
See HASSLOCHER ENTERPRISES INC

D-U-N-S 06-839-0699
■ **FRONTIER MERGER SUB LLC**
CASH AMERICA
(*Suby of* FIRSTCASH INC) ★
1600 W 7th St, Fort Worth, TX 76102-2504
Tel (800) 223-8738 *Founded/Ownrshp* 2016
Sales 1.0MMM *EMP* 6,049
SIC 5932 6099 Pawnshop; Check cashing agencies
Pr: T Brent Stuart
CFO: Thomas A Bessant Jr
Chf Mktg O: Victor L Pepe
Ofcr: Clint D Jaynes
Ex VP: J Curtis Linscott
VP: Sandra Fulton
VP: Nina Vitagliano
Exec: Alberto Rodriguez

D-U-N-S 92-847-2794
FRONTIER PETROLEUM RESOURCES INC
6200 Savoy Dr Ste 650, Houston, TX 77036-3384
Tel (832) 242-1510 *Founded/Ownrshp* 1995
Sales 100.0MM *EMP* 50
SIC 2911 5172 Petroleum refining; Gasoline
Pr: Olatunji Odusola
CFO: Cleveland Harris

FRONTIER RADIATOR
See WELLER AUTO PARTS INC

D-U-N-S 19-965-2181 IMP
■ **FRONTIER REFINING & MARKETING LLC**
HOLLYFRONTIER
(*Suby of* HOLLYFRONTIER CORP) ★
8055 E Tufts Ave, Denver, CO 80237-2835
Tel (303) 694-0025 *Founded/Ownrshp* 1988
Sales 191.5MM^E *EMP* 650^E
SIC 2911 Petroleum refining
VP: Michael Jennings
**Treas:* Leo Hoonakker
VP: Jon Galvin
VP: Kent Olsen
**VP:* Paul Reisman
**VP:* Nancy J Zupan
Dir IT: Len Bailey
Sfty Mgr: Bill Ingraham
Mktg Mgr: Mark Plake

D-U-N-S 78-958-8936 IMP
■ **FRONTIER REFINING LLC**
(*Suby of* HOLLYFRONTIER CORP) ★
300 Morrie Ave, Cheyenne, WY 82007-1699
Tel (307) 634-3551 *Founded/Ownrshp* 2011
Sales 146.4MM^E *EMP* 306
SIC 2951 2911 Personal service agents, brokers & bureaus; Gasoline
VP: Nancy J Zupan
Sr Cor Off: James Gibbs
**Ex VP:* Doug S Aron
**Sr VP:* Denise C McWatters
**VP:* James M Stump
Sfty Mgr: Paul Drydale
Plnt Mgr: Kevin Burke

D-U-N-S 00-793-5885
■ **FRONTIER SOUTHWEST INC**
(*Suby of* FRONTIER COMMUNICATIONS CORP) ★
600 Hidden Rdg, Irving, TX 75038-3809
Tel (972) 718-5600 *Founded/Ownrshp* 1926, 2016
Sales 2.0MMM^E *EMP* 6,948
SIC 4813 Local & long distance telephone communications; Local telephone communications
Pr: Christopher M Creager
CFO: Colleen Cunniffe
Treas: Kee Chan Sin
VP: Kathleen Metzger
VP: Dulaney L Oroark III
VP: Christopher W Zorzi

D-U-N-S 96-507-2254
FRONTIER SPINNING MILLS HOLDING CORP
1823 Boone Trail Rd, Sanford, NC 27330-8662
Tel (919) 776-9940 *Founded/Ownrshp* 2013
Sales 482.8MM^E *EMP* 1,200
SIC 2281 Spinning yarn
CEO: Robin Perkins
**Ch Bd:* John L Bakane
Pr: George R Perkins III
**CFO:* Barbara Walton
Ex VP: John M Maness
Sr VP: John C Riddle
VP: John W Garris

D-U-N-S 00-995-5980 IMP/EXP
FRONTIER SPINNING MILLS INC
(*Suby of* FRONTIER SPINNING MILLS HOLDING CORP) ★
1823 Boone Trail Rd, Sanford, NC 27330-8662
Tel (919) 777-2689 *Founded/Ownrshp* 1996, 2008
Sales 481.5MM^E *EMP* 1,200
SIC 2281 Spinning yarn
CEO: George R Perkins III
**Pr:* George W Parker
**CFO:* Barbara F Walton
**Ex VP:* John M Maness
Genl Mgr: Troy Winter
CIO: Jay Langford
Plnt Mgr: Bryan Newton
Sales Exec: Robin Perkins

D-U-N-S 04-308-2283
FRONTIER TECHNOLOGY LLC
MICROAGE
8160 S Hardy Dr Ste 101, Tempe, AZ 85284-1117
Tel (480) 366-2000 *Founded/Ownrshp* 2001
Sales 108.1MM^E *EMP* 110^E
SIC 7373 Computer integrated systems design
COO: Jeffrey J McKeever
**COO:* Mark McKeever
**CFO:* Roger Rouse
VP: Marc Breckwoldt
VP: Steven W Dodenhoff
VP: James Domaz
**VP:* Tracey Hayes
VP: Bill Nanney
VP: Jeffrey S Swanson
Dir Bus: Paul Walton
Mktg Mgr: Nick Jackson

D-U-N-S 00-794-4473
■ **FRONTIER WEST VIRGINIA INC** (WV)
(*Suby of* FRONTIER COMMUNICATIONS CORP) ★
1500 Maccorkle Ave Se, Charleston, WV 25396-0002
Tel (304) 344-6409 *Founded/Ownrshp* 1916, 2009
Sales 950.0M *EMP* 1,900
SIC 4813 8721 Telephone communication, except radio; Local telephone communications; Voice telephone communications; Data telephone communications; Billing & bookkeeping service
Pr: Dennis M Bone
Treas: David R Whitehouse
Ex Dir: Pete Pizzarello

D-U-N-S 06-541-5986 IMP
■ **FRONTIER-KEMPER CONSTRUCTORS INC**
FKC-LAKE SHORE
(*Suby of* TUTOR PERINI CORP) ★
15900 Olden St, Sylmar, CA 91342-1628
Tel (818) 362-2062 *Founded/Ownrshp* 1972, 2011
Sales 266.6MM *EMP* 400
SIC 1629

D-U-N-S 05-304-3311
FROST & SULLIVAN
7550 W Ih 10 Ste 400, San Antonio, TX 78229-5825
Tel (210) 348-1000 *Founded/Ownrshp* 1961
Sales 241.1MM^E *EMP* 1,700
SIC 8732 8742

D-U-N-S 00-793-6222 IMP
■ **FROST BANK** (TX)
FROST CAPITAL GROUP, THE
(*Suby of* NEW GALVESTON CO) ★
100 W Houston St Ste 100, San Antonio, TX 78205-1400
Tel (210) 220-4011 *Founded/Ownrshp* 1899
Sales NA *EMP* 3,128
SIC 6021 National commercial banks
CEO: Richard W Evans Jr
**Pr:* Patrick Frost
Pr: Renee Sabel
COO: Charles Savino
**CFO:* Phil Green
Chf Cred: William L Perotti
Chf Inves: Tom Stringfellow
Trst Ofcr: Beverly Scott
Ex VP: Mary Beach
Ex VP: Paul Bracher
Ex VP: Bernard Conzales
Ex VP: Jim Jeffery
Ex VP: Tom McDonnell
**Ex VP:* Greg Parker
Ex VP: William Sirakos
Ex VP: Pam Thomas
Sr VP: Laura Alexander
Sr VP: Carole Arnold
Sr VP: Evans Attwell
Sr VP: Christy Bachmeyer
Sr VP: Michael S Cain

D-U-N-S 07-286-9316
FROST BROWN TODD LLC
3300 Grt Amrcn Towe 301e, Cincinnati, OH 45202
Tel (513) 651-6800 *Founded/Ownrshp* 1956
Sales 144.0MM^E *EMP* 900
SIC 8111 General practice attorney, lawyer; Labor & employment law; Environmental law; Patent, trademark & copyright law
Mng Pt: George Yund
Pt: Bernard L McKay
V Ch: Bart Greenwald
V Ch: Michael Yarbrough
COO: Jill B Burton
CFO: Frank C Szabo
Trst: Richard Moore
Ex Dir: Anne Cappel
Off Mgr: Susan Wiegert
IT Man: Paul Myers
Netwrk Eng: Ken Orr

FROST CAPITAL GROUP, THE
See FROST BANK

D-U-N-S 00-385-4619
FROST ELECTRIC SUPPLY CO
2429 Schuetz Rd, Maryland Heights, MO 63043-3314
Tel (314) 567-4004 *Founded/Ownrshp* 2004

Sales 143.1MM^E *EMP* 130
Accts Rick & Shannahan St Louis M
SIC 5063 Electrical apparatus & equipment; Wiring devices; Safety switches
Pr: John Frost
**Ex VP:* Jeff Frost
**Ex VP:* John Macarthur Jr
**VP:* Bill Freeman

D-U-N-S 83-454-0887
■ FROST INSURANCE AGENCY INC
(*Suby of* FROST CAPITAL GROUPTHE) ★
201 Lavaca St Apt 621, Austin, TX 78701-3987
Tel (512) 473-4520 *Founded/Ownrshp* 1998
Sales NA *EMP* 221
SIC 6411 Insurance agents, brokers & service
Pr: Bruce Burdett
VP: Justin Clark
VP: Lorena Contreras
VP: Lisa Foster
VP: Lori Sorg

FROST KING
See THERMWELL PRODUCTS CO INC

FROZEN BAKERY
See COTTAGE BAKERY INC

D-U-N-S 05-013-4964
FROZEN FOOD EXPRESS INDUSTRIES INC
3400 Stonewall St, Lancaster, TX 75134-1548
Tel (800) 569-9200 *Founded/Ownrshp* 1946
Sales 377.7MM *EMP* 2,183^E
SIC 4731 4213 Freight transportation arrangement; Trucking, except local
Pr: S Russell Stubbs
**COO:* John T Hickerson
**CFO:* Steve Stedman
VP: Burl G Cott
VP: David Hedgpeth
VP: Joe Jaska
VP: Jeff Kerbo
CTO: Mohit Jain
Software D: Hoke Smith
Board of Directors: Jerry T Armstrong, W Mike Baggett, Brian R Blackmarr, Barrett D Clark, Kevin Kilpatrick, T Michael O'connor, Stoney M Stubbs Jr

FRS
See FLUID ROUTING SOLUTIONS INC

D-U-N-S 36-208-7967
FRS CAPITAL CORP
1131 Sw Klickitat Way, Seattle, WA 98134-1108
Tel (206) 623-0304 *Founded/Ownrshp* 1949
Sales 1.3MMM^E *EMP* 12,002
SIC 4491 Stevedoring
VP: Larry E Donckers
Sr VP: Claude Stritmatter
**VP:* John J Aldaya
CTO: Kevin Smith
DP Dir: John Dibernardo

FRU-CON CONSTRUCTION
See BALFOUR BEATTY INFRASTRUCTURE INC

D-U-N-S 00-696-7517 IMP
FRU-CON CONSTRUCTION LLC
(*Suby of* FRU-CON CONSTRUCTION) ★
4310 Prince William Pkwy # 200, Woodbridge, VA 22192-5199
Tel (703) 586-6100 *Founded/Ownrshp* 1908, 2011
Sales 104.9MM *EMP* 150^E
Accts Deloitte & Touche Llp Dallas
SIC 1629 Waste water & sewage treatment plant construction
Pr: Thomas C James
**VP:* Michael R Fischer

D-U-N-S 00-838-4240 IMP/EXP
FRUIT GROWERS SUPPLY CO INC
27770 N Entrmt Dr Fl 3, Valencia, CA 91355
Tel (818) 986-6480 *Founded/Ownrshp* 1907
Sales 218.8MM *EMP* 300
Accts Moss Adams Llp Stockton Cali
SIC 2653 0811 5191 2448 5113 Boxes, corrugated: made from purchased materials; Timber tracts; Farm supplies; Fertilizer & fertilizer materials; Pallets, wood; Cardboard & products
CEO: Mark H Lindgren
**CFO:* Charles Boyce
**VP:* William O Knox
MIS Dir: David Rosenberg
Dir IT: Dwayne Russell
IT Man: Donna Shiver
Plnt Mgr: Reagan Foley
Mktg Mgr: Lance Freeman

D-U-N-S 03-933-6490 IMP/EXP
FRUIT OF EARTH INC
3101 High Rver Rd Ste 175, Fort Worth, TX 76155
Tel (817) 510-1600 *Founded/Ownrshp* 1980
Sales 241.4MM^E *EMP* 180
SIC 5122 2844 Cosmetics; Toilet soap; Face creams or lotions; Suntan lotions & oils; Toilet preparations
CEO: Thomas E McCurry Sr
**Pr:* Thomas E McCurry Jr
**CFO:* Leonard Shipley
Treas: Faye M Curry
**Sec:* Faye McCurry
Exec: Lisa Geiger
Exec: Sharon Vance
MIS Dir: Cynthia Wilson
Plnt Mgr: Thomas Kramka
Snr Mgr: Jim Selby

FRUIT OF THE LOOM
See UNION UNDERWEAR CO INC

D-U-N-S 11-055-3737 IMP/EXP
■ FRUIT OF LOOM INC
UNION UNDERWEARR
(*Suby of* BERKSHIRE HATHAWAY INC) ★
1 Fruit Of The Loom Dr, Bowling Green, KY 42103-7932
Tel (270) 781-6400 *Founded/Ownrshp* 1985
Sales 3.9MMM^E *EMP* 11,608
SIC 2254 2253 Knit underwear mills; Shorts, briefs, drawers (underwear), knit; Shirts & t-shirts (underwear), knit; Panties, knit; Shirts (outerwear), knit; T-shirts & tops, knit; Jogging & warm-up suits, knit
Ch Bd: Melissa Burgess-Taylor
**Pr:* Rick Medlin
**CFO:* Richard C Price
**Ex VP:* G William Newton
Sr VP: John Shivel
VP: Cameron Bailey
VP: Lis Cravens
VP: Raymond Kernea
VP: Bruce Smith
VP: Michael Spoors
IT Man: Peter Davids

D-U-N-S 02-252-8686 EXP
FRUIT PATCH SALES LLC
38773 Road 48, Dinuba, CA 93618-9718
Tel (559) 591-1170 *Founded/Ownrshp* 1999
Sales 162.5MM^E *EMP* 500
SIC 5148
**Treas:* Doug Reader

D-U-N-S 55-549-5704 IMP
FRUTH INC
FRUTH PHARMACY
4016 Ohio River Rd, Point Pleasant, WV 25550-3257
Tel (304) 675-1612 *Founded/Ownrshp* 1952
Sales 109.3MM^E *EMP* 545
Accts Crowe Horwath Llp Columbus O
SIC 5912 Drug stores
Pr: Lynne Fruth
**Ch Bd:* Donald Pullin
**Pr:* Charles Burdette
**COO:* Bob Messick
CFO: Bob Mesaith
**CFO:* Tom Willoughby
**Treas:* Lucille Cassell
VP: Laddie Burdette
VP: Eric Lambert
**VP:* Timothy Weber
MIS Dir: Tammi Commer

FRUTH PHARMACY
See FRUTH INC

D-U-N-S 00-301-5245 IMP/EXP
FRY COMMUNICATIONS INC (PA)
800 W Church Rd, Mechanicsburg, PA 17055-3198
Tel (717) 766-0211 *Founded/Ownrshp* 1934
Sales 282.1MM^E *EMP* 1,100
SIC 2752 Commercial printing, lithographic
Ch Bd: Henry Fry
**CEO:* Mike Lukas
COO: Michael Lukas
**CFO:* Mary Roberts
Off Admin: Kim Fry
Snr Sftwr: Andrew Oseghale
**CTO:* David Fry
Sys Mgr: Richard Fesler
Software D: Isaac Preston
Sfty Mgr: Rich Jones
Opers Mgr: Gary Deremer

D-U-N-S 04-977-2098
■ FRYE REGIONAL MEDICAL CENTER INC
DUKE LIFEPOINT HEALTHCARE
(*Suby of* DUKE LIFEPOINT HEALTHCARE) ★
420 N Center St Ste 20, Hickory, NC 28601-5046
Tel (828) 315-5000 *Founded/Ownrshp* 2016
Sales 219.4MM *EMP* 1,482
SIC 8062 General medical & surgical hospitals
CEO: Dennis Brunns
**Pr:* John Holland
**COO:* Craig Hume
**CFO:* Cherri Henderson
VP: Dan Meyer
VP: Douglas E Rabe
Exec: Elizabeth Elich

D-U-N-S 06-292-8361 IMP/EXP
■ FRYMASTER LLC
DEAN
(*Suby of* MANITOWOC CO INC) ★
8700 Line Ave, Shreveport, LA 71106-6800
Tel (318) 865-1711 *Founded/Ownrshp* 2009
Sales 140.8MM^E *EMP* 587^E
SIC 3589 5046 Cooking equipment, commercial; Commercial cooking & food service equipment; Restaurant equipment & supplies
Ex VP: David E Mosteller
VP: Erica Davis
Prin: Mike Kachmer
Prin: Carl Laurino
Prin: Dean Nolden
Genl Mgr: Todd Phillips
VP Mfg: Jesse Ford
Mktg Mgr: Barry Blalock

D-U-N-S 13-163-0543 IMP/EXP
FRYS ELECTRONICS INC
FRYS.COM
600 E Brokaw Rd, San Jose, CA 95112-1006
Tel (408) 350-1484 *Founded/Ownrshp* 1985
Sales 17.4MM^E *EMP* 3,698
SIC 5999 5734 5731 Telephone & communication equipment; Audio-visual equipment & supplies; Electronic parts & equipment; Computer & software stores; Video cameras, recorders & accessories
CEO: John Charles Fry
**Pr:* Randy Fry
**CFO:* David Fry
**Ex VP:* Kathryn Kolder
VP: Kathy Kolder
Dist Mgr: Shweta Trehan
Store Mgr: Paul Ardolina
Store Mgr: Eddie Ashcraft
Store Mgr: Brandon Barnes
Store Mgr: Andrew Bartlett
Store Mgr: Joe Clare

D-U-N-S 03-590-2444
■ FRYS FOOD STORES OF ARIZONA INC
SMITH'S
(*Suby of* GERBES SPRMKT / KING SOOPERS) ★
500 S 99th Ave, Tolleson, AZ 85353-9700
Tel (623) 936-2100 *Founded/Ownrshp* 1960, 1983
Sales 963.0MM^E *EMP* 10,000
SIC 5411 Supermarkets, chain
CEO: Dennis R Hood
Pr: Stephen M McKinney
Pr: Mark C Tuffin
CFO: Ron Schuster
VP: Robert Clark
VP: Kyle S McKay
Mktg Mgr: Paul Draugalis

FRYS.COM
See FRYS ELECTRONICS INC

D-U-N-S 96-762-1884
FS ENERGY AND POWER FUND
Cira Centre 2929 Arch St Cira Cent, Philadelphia, PA 19104
Tel (215) 495-1150 *Founded/Ownrshp* 2011
Sales 379.6MM *EMP* 2
SIC 6722 Management investment, open-end
Ch: Michael Forman

D-U-N-S 82-942-4519
FS INVESTMENT CORP
201 Rouse Blvd, Philadelphia, PA 19112-1902
Tel (215) 495-1150 *Founded/Ownrshp* 2009
Sales 474.8MM *EMP* 9
SIC 6726 6722 Investment offices; Management investment, open-end
Ch Bd: Michael C Forman
Pr: Gerald F Stahlecker
CFO: William Goebel
Treas: Stephen S Sypherd
**V Ch Bd:* David J Adelman
Chf Cred: James F Volk
Ex VP: Zachary Klehr
VP: Ryan Conley
Mng Dir: Sean Coleman

D-U-N-S 07-874-5029
FS INVESTMENT CORP II
Cira Centre 2929 Arch St Cira Cent, Philadelphia, PA 19104
Tel (215) 495-1150 *Founded/Ownrshp* 2013
Sales 529.4MM *EMP* 6^E
SIC 6282 Investment advice
Prin: Michael C Forman

D-U-N-S 13-943-8910 IMP/EXP
FS-ELLIOTT CO LLC
5710 Mellon Rd, Export, PA 15632-8948
Tel (724) 387-3200 *Founded/Ownrshp* 2012
Sales 108.4MM^E *EMP* 275
SIC 3563 Air & gas compressors; Air & gas compressors including vacuum pumps
CEO: Paul C Brown
**CFO:* Keith L Macurdy
**Treas:* C S Hsiao
Sys Mgr: Kevin Smedley
Info Man: Linda Miller
Sfty Mgr: Gregory Gigliotti
Mfg Mgr: Paul Carmichael
Ql Cn Mgr: Vincent Davis
Ql Cn Mgr: Mike Mohan

FSA
See FOOD SERVICES OF AMERICA INC

FSA
See FORFEITURE SUPPORT ASSOCIATES LLC

D-U-N-S 02-430-4466
FSA NETWORK INC
1545 N Park Dr Ste 101, Weston, FL 33326-3227
Tel (954) 745-2120 *Founded/Ownrshp* 2000
Sales 90.0MM^E *EMP* 400
SIC 4212 7641 Local trucking, without storage; Reupholstery & furniture repair
Pr: Charles Annett
CFO: Catherine Schwab
Genl Mgr: Jack Annett

FSA OF ECC
See ERIE COMMUNITY COLLEGE

FSC
See FARM SERVICE COOPERATIVE

D-U-N-S 04-297-8734
■ FSC CORP
(*Suby of* FINANCIAL SERVICE CORP) ★
2300 Windy Ridge Pkwy Se # 1100, Atlanta, GA 30339-5645
Tel (770) 916-6500 *Founded/Ownrshp* 1958
Sales 194.7MM^E *EMP* 200
SIC 6722 6411 8742 6211 Mutual fund sales, on own account; Life insurance agents; New business start-up consultant; Security brokers & dealers
CEO: Joby Gruber
Treas: Daniel O Williams
Chf Cred: Rick Young
Sr VP: Tim O'Rouke
Sr VP: Steve Rothstein
VP: John McGivney
VP: Thomas M Wells

D-U-N-S 08-893-6208
■ FSC SECURITIES CORP
(*Suby of* FSC CORP) ★
2300 Windy Ridge Pkwy Se # 1100, Atlanta, GA 30339-5645
Tel (770) 916-6500 *Founded/Ownrshp* 1970
Sales NA *EMP* 200
SIC 6411 6211 Insurance agents, brokers & service; Dealers, security
Pr: Jerry Murphy
Mng Pt: Robert Vogel
**COO:* Helen Praiter
**CFO:* Steve Rothstein
**Chf Mktg O:* Tom Shipley
**Ofcr:* John Dillon
Sr VP: Diane Schmidt
VP: Walter Butler
VP: Smitty Thorne
**VP:* Tom Wells
Dir IT: Jeff McKisson

FSCC
See FRANCISCAN SISTERS OF CHRISTIAN CHARITY SPONSORED MINISTRIES INC

FSCU
See FIRST SERVICE CREDIT UNION

FSG LIGHTING
See FACILITY SOLUTIONS GROUP INC

FSI
See FASTENING SOLUTIONS INC

D-U-N-S 82-546-3784
FSI DEVCO INC
(*Suby of* SALTGRASS STEAK HOUSE) ★
1510 West Loop S, Houston, TX 77027-9505
Tel (713) 850-1010 *Founded/Ownrshp* 1997
Sales 21.3MM^E *EMP* 3,000
SIC 5812 Eating places
Pr: Tilman J Fertitta
**Treas:* Paul S West

D-U-N-S 80-836-8976
FSI RESTAURANT DEVELOPMENT LIMITED
SALTGRASS STEAK HOUSE
(*Suby of* LANDRYS SEAFOOD HOUSE) ★
1510 West Loop S, Houston, TX 77027-9505
Tel (713) 386-7176 *Founded/Ownrshp* 1997
Sales 10.7MM^E *EMP* 2,241^E
SIC 5812 Steak restaurant
Prin: Kelly Roberts

FSSA
See INDIANA FAMILY AND SOCIAL SERVICES ADMINISTRATION

FST EXPRESS
See FST LOGISTICS INC

D-U-N-S 04-191-3547
FST LOGISTICS INC
FST EXPRESS
1727 Georgesville Rd, Columbus, OH 43228-3619
Tel (614) 529-7900 *Founded/Ownrshp* 2003
Sales 90.2MM^E *EMP* 240
SIC 4212 Local trucking, without storage
Pr: Arthur Decrane
**CFO:* David Kent
IT Man: Matt Cox
Opers Mgr: Clay Stanger

FSU
See FLORIDA STATE UNIVERSITY

FSW
See FOODSERVICEWAREHOUSE.COM LLC

D-U-N-S 88-443-3764 IMP
FT PRECISION INC
FTP
(*Suby of* TANAKA SEIMITSU KOGYO CO.,LTD.)
9731 Mount Gilead Rd, Fredericktown, OH 43019-9167
Tel (740) 694-1500 *Founded/Ownrshp* 1994
Sales 199.6MM^E *EMP* 512
SIC 3714 Motor vehicle parts & accessories
Pr: Tamami Nishimura
Pr: Ben Beeber
Ql Cn Mgr: James Wagner

D-U-N-S 07-990-7713
FT ZUMWALT R-II SCHOOL DISTRICT
555 E Terra Ln, O Fallon, MO 63366-2725
Tel (636) 240-2072 *Founded/Ownrshp* 1997
Sales 203.2MM *EMP* 2,800
Accts Cliftonlarsonallen St Louis
SIC 8211 Public elementary & secondary schools
Doctor: Bernard Dubray
**Pr:* Michael Price
**Pr:* Mike Swaringim
CFO: Jeffrey or
**CFO:* Jeffrey Orr
**VP:* Barbara Bryant
Prin: Alex J Tripamer
Ex Dir: Michael Neill
Pr Dir: Laura Wagner

FTC
See FARMERS TELEPHONE COOPERATIVE INC

D-U-N-S 07-920-9574
▲ FTD COMPANIES INC
3113 Woodcreek Dr, Downers Grove, IL 60515-5420
Tel (630) 719-7800 *Founded/Ownrshp* 2008
Sales 1.2MMM *EMP* 941^E
Tkr Sym FTD *Exch* NGS
SIC 5992 5947 5961 Florists; Flowers, fresh; Plants, potted; Gift, novelty & souvenir shop; Flowers, plants & bulbs: mail order
Pr: Robert S Apatoff
CFO: Becky A Sheehan
Ex VP: Scott D Levin
Ex VP: Stephen Tucker

D-U-N-S 14-953-5812 IMP
■ FTD GROUP INC
(*Suby of* FTD COMPANIES INC) ★
3113 Woodcreek Dr, Downers Grove, IL 60515-5420
Tel (630) 719-7800 *Founded/Ownrshp* 2012
Sales 591.8MM^E *EMP* 870
SIC 5193 7389 Flowers & florists' supplies; Florists' supplies; Flowers & nursery stock; Flowers, fresh; Florist telegraph service
CEO: Michael J Soenen
**Pr:* Rob Apatoff
**CFO:* Becky A Sheehan
**Ex VP:* George T Kanganis
**VP:* Jon R Burney
VP: Mark Karolich
**CTO:* Anthony M Dillon
Mktg Mgr: Jacquelyn Manetakis

D-U-N-S 87-830-4047 IMP/EXP
■ FTD INC
(*Suby of* FTD GROUP INC) ★
3113 Woodcreek Dr, Downers Grove, IL 60515-5420
Tel (630) 719-7800 *Founded/Ownrshp* 1994
Sales 342.6MM^E *EMP* 725
SIC 5193 7389 Flowers & nursery stock; Telephone services
VP: Jon R Burney
**CFO:* Becky A Sheehan
Ex VP: Frank Kern

Ex VP: Tom Moeller
VP: Jim Marshall
VP: Cheryl Michie
VP: Jandy Tomy
VP: Bryan Whitehouse
Snr Sftwr: John Hetherington
Snr Ntwrk: Greg Murphy
**CTO:* Anthony M Dillon

D-U-N-S 04-989-3410
▲ FTI CONSULTING INC
1101 K St Nw Ste B100, Washington, DC 20005-4264
Tel (202) 312-9100 *Founded/Ownrshp* 1982
Sales 1.7MMM *EMP* 4,634
Tkr Sym FCN *Exch* NYS
SIC 8742 Management consulting services; Industry specialist consultants
Pr: Steven H Gunby
**Ch Bd:* Gerard E Holthaus
CFO: Catherine M Freeman
Ofcr: Holly Paul
VP: Matthew Pachman
Exec: John Hudson
Exec: Nikolas Kristensen
Mng Dir: Richard Braun
Mng Dir: Bud Cramer
Mng Dir: Michael Ennis
Mng Dir: Dean Gaida
Board of Directors: Brenda J Bacon, Mark S Bartlett, Claudio Costamagna, Vernon Ellis, Nicholas C Fanandakis, Laureen E Seeger

D-U-N-S 61-896-9971
■ FTI LLC
(*Suby of* FTI CONSULTING INC) ★
909 Commerce Rd, Annapolis, MD 21401-2943
Tel (410) 224-8770 *Founded/Ownrshp* 2005
Sales 26.6MM^E *EMP* 1,200
SIC 8621 Health association
IT Man: Jamie McCumbie

D-U-N-S 19-217-7509
FTM CORP
BOSTON COACH
(*Suby of* FIDELITY INVESTMENTS) ★
69 Norman St Ste 13, Everett, MA 02149-1946
Tel (800) 672-7676 *Founded/Ownrshp* 1987
Sales 33.0MM^E *EMP* 1,694^E
SIC 4111 Bus line operations
Treas: John J Remondi
CFO: Mark Parr
Mktg Dir: Jeff Wdow

FTP
See FT PRECISION INC

D-U-N-S 96-891-2704
FTS INTERNATIONAL INC
777 Main St Ste 3000, Fort Worth, TX 76102-5365
Tel (682) 862-2000 *Founded/Ownrshp* 2009
Sales 1.8MMM^E *EMP* 1,501^E
SIC 1389 Hydraulic fracturing wells; Oil field services
CEO: Greg Lanham
**COO:* James Coy Randle Jr
Ex VP: Raymond Guba
Ex VP: Ross Philo
Sr VP: Chris Cummins
Sr VP: Michael Doss
Sr VP: Charles B Veazey
VP: Mark Weddington
Comm Man: Jerri Akers
Dir Sec: Jan Easterling
Off Mgr: Mary Nolan
Board of Directors: Tom Bates

D-U-N-S 96-526-0078 IMP
FTS INTERNATIONAL MANUFACTURING LLC
(*Suby of* FTS INTERNATIONAL INC) ★
777 Main St Ste 2900, Fort Worth, TX 76102-5318
Tel (817) 850-8004 *Founded/Ownrshp* 2000
Sales 250.0MM^E *EMP* 240
SIC 5082 7353 5211 Contractors' materials; Heavy construction equipment rental; Masonry materials & supplies

D-U-N-S 10-678-1326 IMP/EXP
FTS INTERNATIONAL SERVICES LLC
(*Suby of* FTS INTERNATIONAL INC) ★
777 Main St Ste 2900, Fort Worth, TX 76102-5318
Tel (817) 850-1008 *Founded/Ownrshp* 2009
Sales 167.5MM^E *EMP* 200^E
SIC 3561 8711 7353 4225 Pumps & pumping equipment; Chemical engineering; Oil field equipment, rental or leasing; General warehousing
CEO: Greg A Lanham
**COO:* Farris Wilks
CFO: Robert Darly
**CFO:* Royce Mitchell
Treas: Kevin McGlinch
Ex VP: Franklin Autry
Ex VP: Raymond Guba
Ex VP: Ross Philo
Sr VP: Chris Cummins
Sr VP: Brad Holms
Sr VP: Robert Pike
**VP:* Robert Early
VP: Donnie Golleher
VP: Sharon Hicks
VP: James Senger
Exec: Crystal Kidd

D-U-N-S 83-172-3569
FTT HOLDINGS INC
3020 Old Ranch Pkwy, Seal Beach, CA 90740-2765
Tel (562) 430-6262 *Founded/Ownrshp* 2003
Sales 230.6MM^E *EMP* 776^E
SIC 3533 Oil field machinery & equipment
Pr: Bryan Livingston
**CFO:* James Leonetti
**Ex VP:* David Haas

D-U-N-S 17-597-4948
FUCCILLO AUTOMOTIVE GROUP INC
10524 Us Route 11, Adams, NY 13605-2117
Tel (315) 232-4117 *Founded/Ownrshp* 1997
Sales 210.5MM^E *EMP* 1,500
SIC 5511 Automobiles, new & used
Ch: William B Fuccillo
Sls Mgr: Greg Lattimore

D-U-N-S 16-974-2058
FUCCILLO HYUNDAI OF GREECE INC
(*Suby of* FUCCILLO AUTOMOTIVE GROUP INC) ★
3975 W Ridge Rd, Rochester, NY 14626-3536
Tel (585) 720-9000 *Founded/Ownrshp* 2006
Sales 800.0M *EMP* 1,500
SIC 5511 5531 Automobiles, new & used; Automotive parts
Pr: William Fuccillo
**Treas:* Scott Fox

D-U-N-S 06-120-9508 IMP/EXP
FUCHS CORP
FUCHS LUBRICANTS CO
(*Suby of* FUCHS PETROLUB SE)
17050 Lathrop Ave, Harvey, IL 60426-6035
Tel (800) 323-7755 *Founded/Ownrshp* 1981
Sales 86.8MM^E *EMP* 391
Accts Kpmg Llp Chicago Il
SIC 2992 5172 2899 Lubricating oils & greases; Lubricating oils & greases; Metal treating compounds
CEO: Steven Puffpaff
CFO: Pam Watson
VP: Pamela Watson
Plnt Mgr: John Cunningham

FUCHS LUBRICANTS CO
See FUCHS CORP

FUDDRUCKERS
See KING CANNON INC

FUEL EXPRESS
See NEW DISTRIBUTING CO INC

FUEL MART
See PORTS PETROLEUM CO INC

FUEL OILS
See PETROLEUM MARKETERS INC

D-U-N-S 78-556-3680 IMP
FUEL SYSTEMS SOLUTIONS INC
(*Suby of* WESTPORT FUEL SYSTEMS INC)
780 3rd Ave Fl 25, New York, NY 10017-2024
Tel (646) 502-7170 *Founded/Ownrshp* 2016
Sales 263.4MM *EMP* 1,500^E
SIC 3714 3592 7363 Fuel systems & parts, motor vehicle; Carburetors; Engineering help service
COO: Andrea Alghisi
CFO: Pietro Bersani
Sr VP: Michael Helfand

D-U-N-S 07-993-4348
FUEL USA LLC
APPLE MKT CONVENIENCE STORES
1 Stoneglen Ct, Durham, NC 27712-8973
Tel (434) 525-1615 *Founded/Ownrshp* 2015
Sales 220.0MM *EMP* 615
SIC 5411 Convenience stores
CEO: Donald Draughon
**Pr:* J Dykstra

FUEL WATCH
See FLINT HILLS RESOURCES LP

D-U-N-S 05-062-7884 IMP
▲ FUELCELL ENERGY INC
3 Great Pasture Rd, Danbury, CT 06810-8153
Tel (203) 825-6000 *Founded/Ownrshp* 1969
Sales 163.0MM *EMP* 596
Accts Kpmg Llp Hartford Connecticu
Tkr Sym FCEL *Exch* NGM
SIC 1629 Power plant construction
Pr: Arthur A Bottone
**Ch Bd:* John A Rolls
COO: Anthony F Rauseo
CFO: Michael Bishop
Sr VP: Bruce Ludemann
Sr VP: Bruce A Ludemann
Sr VP: Daniel Samela
VP: Tony Rauseo
VP: Ben Toby
VP Bus Dev: Frank Wolak
CIO: Donna Ferenz
Board of Directors: Richard A Bromley, Paul F Browning, James Herbert England, Matthew F Hilzinger, William A Lawson, Christopher S Sotos

D-U-N-S 18-509-0503 IMP/EXP
FUGRO (USA) INC
(*Suby of* FUGRO N.V.)
6100 Hillcroft St Ste 700, Houston, TX 77081-1009
Tel (713) 772-3700 *Founded/Ownrshp* 1987
Sales 1.8MMM^E *EMP* 1,968
SIC 1389 8711 8999

D-U-N-S 04-775-2621 IMP
FUGRO CHANCE INC
(*Suby of* FUGRO (USA) INC) ★
200 Dulles Dr, Lafayette, LA 70506-3006
Tel (337) 237-1300 *Founded/Ownrshp* 1991
Sales 142.2MM^E *EMP* 1,968
SIC 8713

D-U-N-S 36-187-1759
FUGRO CONSULTANTS INC
(*Suby of* FUGRO (USA) INC) ★
6100 Hillcroft St Ste 100, Houston, TX 77081-1012
Tel (713) 369-5400 *Founded/Ownrshp* 1988
Sales 119.4MM^E *EMP* 500
SIC 8711 Engineering services
Prin: Richard K Baird Jr
**Pr:* Recep Yilmaz
**Ex VP:* G Rai Mehdiratta
VP: Nick Aschliman
IT Man: Mike Huff
Counsel: Kim R Landon
Snr PM: Tony Gray

D-U-N-S 00-460-8936 IMP
FUJI FOOD PRODUCTS INC (CA)
14420 Bloomfield Ave, Santa Fe Springs, CA 90670-5410
Tel (562) 404-2590 *Founded/Ownrshp* 1990
Sales 184.7MM^E *EMP* 700
SIC 2099 Ready-to-eat meals, salads & sandwiches
CEO: Farrell Hirsch
**CFO:* Javier Aceves
Admn Mgr: Wilma Arellano
QA Dir: Hedieh Ghazizadeh
Dir IT: Mandy Chow
Prd Mgr: Rafael Bucio
VP Mktg: David Crocker
Manager: Monica Stone

D-U-N-S 19-743-6843 IMP/EXP
FUJI VEGETABLE OIL INC
(*Suby of* FUJI OIL HOLDINGS INC.)
120 Brampton Rd, Savannah, GA 31408-2205
Tel (912) 966-5900 *Founded/Ownrshp* 1987
Sales 174.5MM^E *EMP* 105
SIC 2076 Vegetable oil mills
Ch Bd: Mikio Sakai
**Pr:* Tomoyuki Yoshida
**CEO:* Andrew Bunger
Plnt Mgr: Nick Baker

D-U-N-S 80-879-1594
FUJICOLOR PROCESSING INC
(*Suby of* FUJIFILM NORTH AMERICA CORP) ★
120 White Plains Rd # 400, Tarrytown, NY 10591-5526
Tel (914) 220-4700 *Founded/Ownrshp* 1991
Sales 99.7MM^E *EMP* 3,000
SIC 7384 Photofinishing laboratory
CEO: Hideyuki Hayashi
**Co-CEO:* Hiro Sakai

D-U-N-S 96-796-1421
FUJIFILM DIOSYNTH BIOTECHNOLOGIES USA INC
(*Suby of* FUJIFILM HOLDINGS AMERICA CORP) ★
101 J Morris Commons Ln # 300, Morrisville, NC 27560-8884
Tel (919) 337-4400 *Founded/Ownrshp* 2011
Sales 113.0MM *EMP* 432^E
SIC 2836 Biological products, except diagnostic
COO: Steve Spearman
Sr VP: John Foy
Assoc Dir: Enderass Argaw
Assoc Dir: John O'Grady
Assoc Dir: Neeraja Reddy
QA Dir: Nadia Ponder
Ql Cn Mgr: Maresa Arion
Ql Cn Mgr: Melissa Harris
Sls Mgr: Eddie McDaniel
Snr Mgr: Stephanie Kromer
Snr Mgr: Christine Vannais

D-U-N-S 19-759-6625 IMP/EXP
FUJIFILM ELECTRONIC MATERIALS USA INC
(*Suby of* FUJIFILM HOLDINGS AMERICA CORP) ★
80 Circuit Dr, North Kingstown, RI 02852-7404
Tel (401) 522-9499 *Founded/Ownrshp* 2004
Sales 173.6MM^E *EMP* 250^E
SIC 5043 5065 Photographic equipment & supplies; Magnetic recording tape; Diskettes, computer
CEO: Brian Odonnelly
Treas: Ryo Iguchi
VP: Paul Rickert
CTO: Jack Shen
IT Man: William Weber
Opers Mgr: Chuck Guilmette
Opers Mgr: John Payne
Prd Mgr: Mark Francisco

D-U-N-S 62-220-5383 IMP/EXP
FUJIFILM HOLDINGS AMERICA CORP
(*Suby of* FUJIFILM CORPORATION)
200 Summit Lake Dr Fl 2, Valhalla, NY 10595-1356
Tel (914) 789-8100 *Founded/Ownrshp* 1990
Sales 1.9MMM^E *EMP* 4,690
SIC 5043 5065 Photographic equipment & supplies; Magnetic recording tape; Diskettes, computer
Ch Bd: Kazuhito Yamamura
**Pr:* Ray Hosota
Pr: Shigeru Sano
**Sr VP:* Paul D-Andrea
Sr VP: Tadashi Sasaki
VP: Judy Melillo
VP: Go Miyazaki
**VP:* John Prendergast
VP: Joan Rutherford
Dir Rx: Yuji Igarashi
Genl Mgr: Scott Clouston

D-U-N-S 19-616-5849 IMP/EXP
FUJIFILM MANUFACTURING USA INC
(*Suby of* FUJIFILM CORPORATION)
215 Puckett Ferry Rd, Greenwood, SC 29649-7915
Tel (864) 223-2888 *Founded/Ownrshp* 1989
Sales 330.4MM^E *EMP* 1,000
SIC 2796 2752 3861 Platemaking services; Commercial printing, lithographic; Screens, projection
Pr: Todd Croker
**Ch:* Tomoyoshi Ueno
QA Dir: Gary Fincher
IT Man: Gary Pennell

D-U-N-S 04-176-7039 IMP
FUJIFILM MEDICAL SYSTEMS USA INC
(*Suby of* FUJIFILM CORPORATION)
419 West Ave, Stamford, CT 06902-6343
Tel (203) 324-2000 *Founded/Ownrshp* 1990
Sales 349.8MM^E *EMP* 449
SIC 5047 5043 3861 X-ray film & supplies; Photographic processing equipment; Photographic equipment & supplies
Pr: Naohiro Fujitani
**COO:* Johann Fernando
**Ofcr:* Diku Mandavia
**VP:* Steven C Haberlein
VP: Patrick McQuillan
**VP:* Jim Morgan
**VP:* Yujiro Nagasawa
VP: Yoshitaka Nakamura
VP: Teresa Oakley
VP: Gordon Tubbs
Exec: Sinan Batman
Exec: Valeree Quisumbing
Exec: Evelyn Toro

D-U-N-S 06-021-6165
FUJIFILM NORTH AMERICA CORP
(*Suby of* FUJIFILM HOLDINGS AMERICA CORP) ★
200 Summit Lake Dr Fl 2, Valhalla, NY 10595-1356
Tel (914) 789-8100 *Founded/Ownrshp* 1965
Sales 981.2MM^E *EMP* 3,500
SIC 7384 5043 5065 3695 2673 3861 Photofinish laboratories; Photographic equipment & supplies; Magnetic recording tape; Magnetic & optical recording media; Bags: plastic, laminated & coated; Photographic equipment & supplies; Metallic emulsion sensitized cloth or paper, photographic
Pr: Masato Yamamoto
Ch Bd: Yasuo Tanaka
Pr: Timothy W Combs
Pr: Matt Knickerbocker
Pr: Max Kurokawa
**Treas:* Suguru Enomoto
Treas: Kenji Sukeno
Div VP: William Lacy
Grp VP: Gael Lundeen
Sr VP: Hank Hayashi
VP: Stan Bauer
VP: John Bruehl
VP: Carl Gold
VP: Patrick McQuillan
VP: Dan Owens
VP: Todd Schrader
VP: Joe Visslailli
Exec: Gina Pisano
Comm Dir: Randy Nagel

D-U-N-S 01-443-8860 IMP
FUJIFILM SONOSITE INC (WA)
(*Suby of* FUJIFILM HOLDINGS CORPORATION)
21919 30th Dr Se, Bothell, WA 98021-3904
Tel (425) 951-1200 *Founded/Ownrshp* 1986
Sales 331.9MM^E *EMP* 878
Accts Kpmg Llp Seattle Washington
SIC 3845 Ultrasonic medical equipment, except cleaning
Pr: Naohiro Fujitani
Pr: Art Louncbery
Pr: Lee D Unbar
CFO: Anil Amlani
**CFO:* Michael Schuh
**CFO:* Marcus Y Smith
**Sr VP:* John S Bowers Jr
**Sr VP:* Diku Mandavia MD
Sr VP: Edison C Russell
VP: James N Branman
VP: Lee S Dunbar
VP: Andrew Dunn
VP: James M Gilmore
VP: Daina L Graham
VP: Allen W Guisinger
VP: Brian Leck
VP: Renaud Maloberti
VP: Robert L Massa
VP: Edison Russel
**VP:* Richard Salzar
VP: Rich Trayler

D-U-N-S 15-379-0233 IMP
FUJIKURA AMERICA INC
(*Suby of* AMERICA FUJIKURA LTD) ★
920 Stewart Dr Ste 150, Sunnyvale, CA 94085-3955
Tel (408) 748-6991 *Founded/Ownrshp* 2007
Sales 615.1MM^E *EMP* 2,000
SIC 5063 Power wire & cable; Electronic wire & cable; Electrical supplies
CEO: Takeaki Kitajima
**Pr:* Mitsuji Hashimoto
**Pr:* Yoichi Nagahama
**CFO:* Kitsuhiko Fukuda

FUJIREBIO AMERICA
See FUJIREBIO DIAGNOSTICS INC

D-U-N-S 04-852-4263 IMP
FUJIREBIO DIAGNOSTICS INC (PA)
FUJIREBIO AMERICA
(*Suby of* MIRACA HOLDINGS INC.)
201 Great Valley Pkwy, Malvern, PA 19355-1308
Tel (610) 240-3800 *Founded/Ownrshp* 1997, 1998
Sales 122.5MM^E *EMP* 200
SIC 5047 8011 Diagnostic equipment, medical; Offices & clinics of medical doctors
Ch Bd: Takeo Hayashi
**CEO:* Takeshi Koyama
COO: Aris Petropoulos
**CFO:* Toshio Sudo
**Sr VP:* Monte Wiltse
**VP:* Jennifer Magrowski
VP: Peter Minetti
VP: Zivjena Vucetic
Mng Dir: Christina Hall
Genl Mgr: Lola Burkenstock
Genl Mgr: Alexandra Poiesz

D-U-N-S 03-779-7453 IMP
FUJITEC AMERICA INC
(*Suby of* FUJITEC CO., LTD.)
7258 Innovation Way, Mason, OH 45040-8015
Tel (513) 755-6100 *Founded/Ownrshp* 1977
Sales 181.1MM^E *EMP* 1,100
SIC 3534 Elevators & equipment; Escalators, passenger & freight; Walkways, moving
CEO: Takakazu Uchiyama
**Pr:* Katsuji Okuda
**CFO:* Ray Gibson
VP: Kirk Feuerback
**VP:* Masashi Tsuchihata
Brnch Mgr: Joseph Smith
Dir IT: Donald Penny

D-U-N-S 01-843-1853 IMP
FUJITSU AMERICA INC
(*Suby of* FUJITSU NORTH AMERICA HOLDINGS INC) ★
1250 E Arques Ave, Sunnyvale, CA 94085-5401
Tel (408) 746-6000 *Founded/Ownrshp* 2007
Sales 1.4MMM^E *EMP* 6,225
SIC 7373 Computer integrated systems design; Systems software development services; Systems integration services
CEO: Mike Foster
Pr: Robert D Pryor
**CFO:* ARI Hovsepyan

Treas: Daniel Schembri
Ex VP: Marc Janssens
Ex VP: Bill King
Ex VP: Hiroaki Kondo
Ex VP: Steve Della Rocchetta
Ex VP: Mark Vayda
VP: Dan Callaghan
VP: Bill Erickson
VP: Erich Flynn
VP: Scott Francis
VP: Mahito Mori
VP: Michael Shpizner
Exec: Jacques Durand
Exec: George Wintner
Dir Bus: Dennis Stephenson

D-U-N-S 82-960-4172 IMP
FUJITSU COMPONENTS AMERICA INC
(*Suby of* FUJITSU COMPONENT LIMITED)
2290 N 1st St Ste 212, San Jose, CA 95131-2017
Tel (408) 745-4900 *Founded/Ownrshp* 1993
Sales 100.0MM *EMP* 38
SIC 5065 Electronic parts & equipment
Pr: Robert L Thornton
Pr: Don Cramb
Pr: Donald J Dealtry
Ch: Yasuhito Hara
Sr VP: Takashi Mori
Mktg Dir: Robert Thornton

D-U-N-S 78-773-1298 IMP
FUJITSU COMPUTER PRODUCTS OF AMERICA INC
(*Suby of* FUJITSU LIMITED)
1250 E Arques Ave, Sunnyvale, CA 94085-5401
Tel (408) 746-6000 *Founded/Ownrshp* 1991
Sales 155.3MM[E] *EMP* 600
SIC 5045 Computer peripheral equipment
Pr: Etsuro Sato
**COO:* Victor Kan
**CFO:* Motoyasu Matsuzaki
CFO: Masamichi Yamamoto
Bd of Dir: Bruce Graham
Bd of Dir: Clark Jernigan
Ofcr: Tom Duffy
Ex VP: Dennis Mull
Ex VP: Scott Francis
Sr VP: Don Klenner
VP: Bob Collins
VP: Terry Hulett
VP: Judy Kling
VP: Ram Muthaiah
VP: Glenn Wood
Exec: Bob Dickerson
Exec: Harold Fischer

D-U-N-S 79-178-0133 IMP
FUJITSU FRONTECH NORTH AMERICA INC
FFNA
(*Suby of* FUJITSU FRONTECH LIMITED)
27121 Towne Centre Dr # 100, Foothill Ranch, CA 92610-2826
Tel (949) 855-5500 *Founded/Ownrshp* 1990
Sales 126.3MM[E] *EMP* 1,400
SIC 7373 Computer systems analysis & design
Pr: Yoshihiko Masuda
**CFO:* Tatsuo Horibe
Treas: Norman Salvesen
Sr Cor Off: Anne Prine
**Sr VP:* Pat Cathey
**Sr VP:* Larry Fandel
Sr VP: Peter Kelly
**Sr VP:* Dick Zarski
**VP:* Mihaela Givulescu

D-U-N-S 08-168-0449 IMP
FUJITSU GENERAL AMERICA INC (DE)
(*Suby of* FUJITSU GENERAL LIMITED)
353 Us Highway 46, Fairfield, NJ 07004-2415
Tel (973) 575-0380 *Founded/Ownrshp* 1995
Sales 180.5MM[E] *EMP* 51
Accts Kpmg Llp New York Ny
SIC 3585 Heating & air conditioning combination units
Pr: Tedd Rozylowicz
**CFO:* Susumu Ohkawara
**Sr VP:* Roy Kuczera
VP: Nakesha Charla
VP: Jeanelle Evelina
VP: Jesse Roper
Assoc Dir: Sparkle Janey
Assoc Dir: Tifany Maile
Netwrk Eng: Florine Donella
Natl Sales: Mollie Sook
Mktg Dir: Erin Mezle

D-U-N-S 62-228-7878
FUJITSU LABORATORIES OF AMERICA INC
(*Suby of* FUJITSU LABORATORIES LTD.)
1240 E Arques Ave 345, Sunnyvale, CA 94085-5401
Tel (408) 530-4500 *Founded/Ownrshp* 1994
Sales 704.5MM[E] *EMP* 173,000
SIC 8731 Commercial physical research
Pr: Hiromu Hayashi
**Ex VP:* Nobuaki Kawato
Sr VP: Hitoshi Funatogawa
Sr VP: Nobuhiko Hara
Sr VP: Kazuhiro Matsuo
**Prin:* Masami Yamamoto

D-U-N-S 78-694-5451 IMP
FUJITSU NETWORK COMMUNICATIONS INC
(*Suby of* FUJITSU LIMITED)
2801 Telecom Pkwy, Richardson, TX 75082-3599
Tel (972) 479-6000 *Founded/Ownrshp* 2007
Sales 690.7MM *EMP* 1,400
Accts Kpmg Llp Dallas Tx
SIC 3661 3663 Fiber optics communications equipment; Cellular radio telephone
CEO: Nikito Kiname
**Pr:* Satoshi Ikeuchi
Ex VP: Barry Carter
Ex VP: Yves L Glard
Ex VP: Bill King
Ex VP: Yves Le Glard
Ex VP: Rich Marcello
Ex VP: Jack Noble
Sr VP: Bipin Badani
Sr VP: Tom Duffy
Sr VP: Rick Fiechtner
Sr VP: ARI Hovsepyan
Sr VP: Junichi Katakura
Sr VP: Joe Massery
Sr VP: Ron Mitchell
Sr VP: Andy Montrose
Sr VP: Doug Moore
Sr VP: Kenzo Nakahashi
Sr VP: Rob Taylor
Sr VP: Lynn Willenbring
VP: Paul Bresnahan

D-U-N-S 83-170-0229
FUJITSU NORTH AMERICA HOLDINGS INC
(*Suby of* FUJITSU LIMITED)
1250 E Arques Ave, Sunnyvale, CA 94085-5401
Tel (408) 737-5600 *Founded/Ownrshp* 2008
Sales 1.4MMM[E] *EMP* 6,300
SIC 7373 Computer integrated systems design; Systems software development services; Systems integration services
CEO: Robert Pryor
Pr: Hitoshi Matsumoto
**CEO:* Farhat Ali
COO: Victor Kan
CFO: Ron Choarw
Ex VP: Kazuhiko Kato
**Sr VP:* Richard Christou
Sr VP: ARI Hovsepyan
Sr VP: Kevin Wrenn
VP: William Hall
VP: Steve Rocchetta
VP: Keith Swenson

D-U-N-S 04-897-6070
FULD & CO INC
131 Oliver St Fl 3, Boston, MA 02110-2785
Tel (617) 492-5900 *Founded/Ownrshp* 1979
Sales 54.3MM[E] *EMP* 1,245[E]
SIC 8742 Industry specialist consultants
CEO: Leonard Fuld
**Pr:* Ken Sawka
**CFO:* Chuck Bartlett
Sr VP: Tarun Mehra
VP: Bill Beizer
VP: Parmelee Eastman
**VP:* C Gerber-Tomlinson
**VP:* Anthony Nagle
VP: Wayne Rosenkrans
**VP:* Michael Sandman
**VP:* Lenore Scanlon

D-U-N-S 00-645-7519
FULL CIRCLE AG (SD)
FULL CIRCLE AG - CENEX OFFICE
520 Vander Horck Ave, Britton, SD 57430
Tel (605) 448-2231 *Founded/Ownrshp* 1936
Sales 173.6MM[E] *EMP* 101
SIC 5191 5153 5541 Chemicals, agricultural; Fertilizer & fertilizer materials; Grain elevators; Filling stations, gasoline
Pr: David Andersen

FULL CIRCLE AG - CENEX OFFICE
See FULL CIRCLE AG

D-U-N-S 09-634-7851 IMP/EXP
FULL COMPASS SYSTEMS LTD (WI)
9770 Silicon Prairie Pkwy, Verona, WI 53593-8442
Tel (608) 831-7330 *Founded/Ownrshp* 1977
Sales 150.0MM[E] *EMP* 200
SIC 5999 Audio-visual equipment & supplies
CEO: Jonathan B Lipp
**Ch Bd:* Susan Lipp
**Pr:* Mark Nash
COO: Doug Carnell
**VP:* Roger Anderson
**VP:* Steven Cohan
Genl Mgr: Michelle Grabel-Komar
Tech Mgr: Erik Muchka
Tech Mgr: Jose Snabria

D-U-N-S 80-680-5636
▲ FULL HOUSE RESORTS INC
4670 S Fort Apache Rd # 190, Las Vegas, NV 89147-7961
Tel (702) 221-7800 *Founded/Ownrshp* 1987
Sales 124.5MM *EMP* 1,356
Tkr Sym FLL *Exch* NAS
SIC 7011 7993 Casino hotel; Game machines
Pr: Daniel R Lee
**Ch Bd:* Bradley M Tirpak
CFO: Lewis A Fanger
**V Ch Bd:* Carl G Braunlich
VP: Elaine L Guidroz

D-U-N-S 03-353-7374
FULL SAIL LLC
FULL SAIL REAL WORLD EDUCATION
3300 University Blvd, Winter Park, FL 32792-7435
Tel (407) 679-0100 *Founded/Ownrshp* 2010
Sales 79.3MM[E] *EMP* 1,000
SIC 8222 7389 Technical institute; Recording studio, noncommercial records
CEO: Edward E Haddock Jr
**CFO:* Debbie Magruder
VP: Matt Pengra
**VP:* Geoffrey Rogers
**Prin:* James W Heavener
**Prin:* Jon Phelps
Web Dev: Adam Bellas
Pr Dir: Kristin Weissman
Board of Directors: Joe Foglia, Jay Small, Jerry Abercrombie, Luis Garcia, Bruce Swedien, Coby Adams, Caleb A Haye, Jayme Wilkinson, David Allen, Alex Kupershmidt, Randy Birch, David Murrant, Brian Blackmore, Jan Pestinger, Henry Darnell, Craig Richards, Craig Derrick, Paul Riley, Simone Eyer, Frank Scheuring, Marc Fishman, Alfred W Schlesinger

FULL SAIL REAL WORLD EDUCATION
See FULL SAIL LLC

D-U-N-S 05-315-9484
■ FULL SPECTRUM LENDING INC
(*Suby of* COUNTRYWIDE FINANCIAL CORP) ★
35 N Lake Ave Fl 3, Pasadena, CA 91101-4192
Tel (626) 584-2220 *Founded/Ownrshp* 1996
Sales NA *EMP* 1,500
SIC 6162 6163 Mortgage bankers & correspondents; Loan brokers
Ch Bd: Greg Lumsden
**Pr:* Paul Abbamonto
COO: Thomas Boone
VP: Michelle Manzi

D-U-N-S 96-669-6577 IMP
FULLBEAUTY BRANDS INC
BRYLANE
1 New York Plz Fl 13, New York, NY 10004-1928
Tel (212) 613-9500 *Founded/Ownrshp* 2013
Sales 1.0MMM[E] *EMP* 6,500
SIC 5961 7389 5611 Women's apparel, mail order; Mail order house; Telemarketing services; Men's & boys' clothing stores
CEO: Paul Tarvin
Pr: Marten Engblom
COO: Brian Steele
Chf Mktg O: Dan Hatola
Ex VP: John Heaney
**Sr VP:* Chip Edgington
Sr VP: Robert Evans
VP: Zahir Babvani
VP: Sharon Cooperman
VP: Neal Patrick
Creative D: Peter Sotiri

D-U-N-S 10-327-4221 IMP/EXP
FULLBEAUTY BRANDS LP
BRYLANE HOME
1 New York Plz Fl 13, New York, NY 10004-1928
Tel (212) 613-9500 *Founded/Ownrshp* 2015
Sales 1.0MMM[E] *EMP* 8,000
SIC 5961 General merchandise, mail order
CEO: Paul Tarvin
CFO: Catherine Doucet
Treas: William L Thomas
Ex VP: John Heaney
VP: Jeanne Franklin
VP: Bryan Wolfe
CIO: Bob Evans
VP Opers: Mike Brown
Opers Supe: John P Martinez
Opers Supe: Kathy White
Prd Mgr: Paula J Edgcomb

D-U-N-S 60-208-9161 IMP
FULLER BRUSH CO INC
ONE FULLER WAY
1 Fuller Way, Great Bend, KS 67530-2466
Tel (620) 792-1711 *Founded/Ownrshp* 2012
Sales 112.5MM[E] *EMP* 473
SIC 2842 2844 3991 Specialty cleaning preparations; Toilet preparations; Brooms & brushes
Ch Bd: Joseph Grabowski
COO: Jerry Hickel
**CFO:* Bill McCoy
**Chf Mktg O:* Dennis Brinly
Board of Directors: Robert C Isaacs

D-U-N-S 00-968-5660 IMP
FULLER THEOLOGICAL SEMINARY
135 N Oakland Ave, Pasadena, CA 91182-0002
Tel (626) 584-5200 *Founded/Ownrshp* 1947
Sales 93.7MM *EMP* 550
Accts Capincrouse Llp Tarzana Cali
SIC 8221 Theological seminary
Pr: Mark Labberton
**Ch:* Robert M Anderson
**Ch:* David L Bere
**Treas:* Merlin W Call
**Treas:* Brian T Prinn
Trst: David L Ber
Trst: Charles W Petty
Ex VP: Bill Clark
**VP:* H Lee Merritt
VP: Doug Nason
VP: Joseph Webb
Exec: Teresa Lewis
Assoc Dir: Bert Jacklitch

D-U-N-S 03-182-4337
FULLERTON FARMERS ELEVATOR
202 Minneapolis Ave, Fullerton, ND 58441-4023
Tel (701) 375-7881 *Founded/Ownrshp* 1940
Sales 123.7MM *EMP* 24
Accts Erickson And Associates Ltd
SIC 5153 5191 Grain elevators; Farm supplies; Feed; Seeds & bulbs; Fertilizer & fertilizer materials
Genl Mgr: Andrew Hager
Genl Mgr: Andy Hagar

D-U-N-S 07-359-0804
FULLERTON JOINT UNION HIGH SCHOOL DISTRICT EDUCATIONAL FOUNDATION
FJUHSD
1051 W Bastanchury Rd, Fullerton, CA 92833-2247
Tel (714) 870-2800 *Founded/Ownrshp* 1893
Sales 145.3MM *EMP* 1,000
Accts Vavrinek Trine Day & Co Ll
SIC 8211 Secondary school
Adm Dir: Jennifer Williams
IT Man: Sunny D Garcia
Teacher Pr: Carl Erickson

D-U-N-S 00-791-2074
■ FULTON BANK NATIONAL ASSOCIATION
FULTON FINANCIAL ADVISORS
(*Suby of* FULTON FINANCIAL CORP) ★
1 Penn Sq Ste 1, Lancaster, PA 17602-2853
Tel (717) 581-3166 *Founded/Ownrshp* 1882
Sales NA *EMP* 960
SIC 6022 State commercial banks
Ch Bd: Craig A Roda
Pr: Frank Clementi
Pr: Susan Lonergan
Pr: Paul V Stahlin
CEO: R Scott Smith Jr
Treas: James E Shreiner
Ofcr: Joseph Flaim
Ofcr: Nathan S Hoover
Ofcr: C L King
Ex VP: Thomas Harrity
Ex VP: William T Kepler
Ex VP: James M Lowe
Sr VP: Jeffrey S Bankert
Sr VP: Alan Brayman
Sr VP: Sharon Hake
Sr VP: Lorance Rohlfing
VP: Laurie Eberle
VP: Jean Galliano
VP: David C Hostetter
VP: Jim Kellum
VP: Linda Long

D-U-N-S 60-319-7989
■ FULTON BANK OF NEW JERSEY
(*Suby of* FULTON FINANCIAL CORP) ★
533 Fellowship Rd Ste 250, Mount Laurel, NJ 08054-3411
Tel (856) 787-1997 *Founded/Ownrshp* 1989
Sales NA *EMP* 298
SIC 6029 6163 Commercial banks; Loan brokers
CEO: Angela Snyder
Pr: Steve Miller
Ex VP: Tom Harrity
Ex VP: Priscilla Luppke
Ex VP: Kathie Stucy
Sr VP: Stephen R Miller
Sr VP: Mary Traum
VP: Jobeth Mauriello

D-U-N-S 00-222-7247 IMP
FULTON BOILER WORKS INC
3981 Port St, Pulaski, NY 13142-4604
Tel (315) 298-5121 *Founded/Ownrshp* 1981
Sales 98.2MM[E] *EMP* 650
SIC 3443 Boilers: industrial, power, or marine
Ch Bd: Ronald B Palm
Dir IT: Scott Redden
IT Man: Fred Farnarier
IT Man: Jyri Palm
MIS Mgr: Ernie Wheeler

D-U-N-S 06-053-4443
FULTON COUNTY A R C
LEXINGTON INDUSTRIES
(*Suby of* NYSARC INC) ★
465 N Perry St, Johnstown, NY 12095-1014
Tel (518) 762-0024 *Founded/Ownrshp* 1954
Sales 59.5MM[E] *EMP* 1,450
Accts Leob & Troper Llp New York N
SIC 8331 8361 Job training services; Sheltered workshop; Residential care for the handicapped
Prin: Paul Nigra
COO: Shaloni Winston
**CFO:* Mathew Johnston

D-U-N-S 07-936-2182
FULTON COUNTY BOARD OF EDUCATION
6201 Powers Ferry Rd, Atlanta, GA 30339-2926
Tel (404) 768-3600 *Founded/Ownrshp* 1871
Sales 583.3MM[E] *EMP* 10,000
SIC 8211 School board
Pr: Linda McCain
**CFO:* Michael Russell
IT Man: Gwen Davis

D-U-N-S 07-979-8991
FULTON COUNTY SCHOOL SYSTEM
6201 Powers Ferry Rd, Atlanta, GA 30339-2926
Tel (470) 254-3600 *Founded/Ownrshp* 2015
Sales 112.2MM[E] *EMP* 10,000[E]
SIC 8211 School board

D-U-N-S 07-247-5312 IMP
FULTON DEKALB HOSPITAL AUTHORITY
GRADY HEALTH SYSTEM
191 Peachtree St Ne # 820, Atlanta, GA 30303-1740
Tel (404) 600-4097 *Founded/Ownrshp* 1945
Sales 1.0MMM[E] *EMP* 5,130
SIC 8062 General medical & surgical hospitals
CEO: John Haupert
**Ch Bd:* Pamela Stephenson
V Ch: Eduardo Mestre
COO: Joshua W Murfree Jr
**Ch:* Thomas W Dortch Jr
**Treas:* Frank Monteith
Trst: Michael R Hollis
Ofcr: Ryan Lewis
Ex VP: Phil Lanson
**Sr VP:* Timothy Jefferson
Sr VP: Craig J Tindell
VP: Ron Palmich
Dir Lab: Andrew Young
Dir Rad: Richard Smalls

FULTON FINANCIAL ADVISORS
See FULTON BANK NATIONAL ASSOCIATION

D-U-N-S 07-954-6545 IMP/EXP
▲ FULTON FINANCIAL CORP
1 Penn Sq Ste 1, Lancaster, PA 17602-2853
Tel (717) 291-2411 *Founded/Ownrshp* 1982
Sales NA *EMP* 3,460[E]
Tkr Sym FULT *Exch* NGS
SIC 6021 National commercial banks
Ch Bd: E Philip Wenger
COO: Philmer H Rohrbaugh
CFO: Patrick S Barrett
Chf Cred: Meg R Mueller
Ofcr: Shelley Armentrout
Ofcr: Rachel D Bashore
Ofcr: Amy Tritle
Trst Ofcr: Stuart Juppenlatz
VP: Chris Demko
VP: Rose Derr
VP: Angie Harcum
VP: Jim Lowe
VP: Randy Metz
VP: Jeffrey Peeling
VP: David Rorabaugh
VP: Michael Thompson
VP: Domenick Vitale
VP: Neil Wiker
Exec: Beth Ann L Chivinski
Exec: Angela M Sargent
Board of Directors: Mark F Strauss, Lisa Crutchfield, Ernest J Waters, Denise L Devine, Patrick J Freer, George W Hodges, Albert Morrison III, James R Moxley III, R Scott Smith Jr, Scott A Snyder, Ronald H Spair

FULTON MANOR
See HOLLAND HOME

D-U-N-S 94-842-5715
FUN STATION ASSOCIATES INC
FUN STATION USA
40 Rocklyn Ave, Lynbrook, NY 11563-2727
Tel (516) 599-7757 *Founded/Ownrshp* 1997
Sales 120.0MM *EMP* 1,206
SIC 7299 7999 Party planning service; Recreation equipment rental
Pr: Richard Bartlett
* *VP:* Yong SE Kim

FUN STATION USA
See FUN STATION ASSOCIATES INC

D-U-N-S 06-632-8220 EXP
■ **FUN-TEES INC**
(*Suby of* DELTA APPAREL INC) ★
4735 Corp Dr Nw Ste 100, Concord, NC 28027
Tel (704) 788-3003 *Founded/Ownrshp* 2009
Sales 114.9MM[E] *EMP* 2,000[E]
SIC 2321 2361 2331 Men's & boys' furnishings; T-shirts & tops: girls', children's & infants'; T-shirts & tops, women's: made from purchased materials
Pr: Will McGhea
* *Pr:* Lewis Reid Jr
* *Treas:* Marcus Weibel
Ofcr: Howard Hiers
* *VP:* Chris Doughlas
* *VP:* Larry Martin Jr
Off Mgr: Brendi Hensley
CIO: Keith Smith

D-U-N-S 86-718-5365
FUNDTECH CORP
30 Montgomery St Ste 501, Jersey City, NJ 07302-3821
Tel (201) 324-0203 *Founded/Ownrshp* 2011
Sales 119.1MM[E] *EMP* 438
SIC 7372 7371

FUNJET VACATIONS
See MARK TRAVEL CORP

D-U-N-S 02-400-6249 IMP
FUNKHOUSER AND CO H N (VA)
2150 S Loudoun St, Winchester, VA 22601-3615
Tel (540) 662-9000 *Founded/Ownrshp* 1967
Sales 134.1MM *EMP* 350
Accts Yount Hyde & Barbour Pc W
SIC 5461 5013 Doughnuts; Automotive supplies & parts
Pr: Robert W Claytor
* *Treas:* Rieman Royston
* *VP:* Kevin L Lafollette
* *VP:* Kenneth L Rice
Genl Mgr: Ken Rice
Plnt Mgr: Chris Greene
Sales Exec: Bob Freund

D-U-N-S 01-166-2772
FURINO & SON INC
66 Columbia Rd, Branchburg, NJ 08876-3519
Tel (908) 756-7736 *Founded/Ownrshp* 1945
Sales 127.0MM[E] *EMP* 350
SIC 1541 1542 Industrial buildings & warehouses; Nonresidential construction
CEO: Thomas Furino
* *Pr:* David Furino
* *VP:* Randy Furino
Exec: Kathleen Whitney
Sfty Dirs: Brian Ferranti

D-U-N-S 00-304-1340 IMP/EXP
FURMAN FOODS INC (PA)
FURMANO FOODS
770 Cannery Rd, Northumberland, PA 17857-8615
Tel (570) 473-3516 *Founded/Ownrshp* 1921, 1977
Sales 101.2MM[E] *EMP* 250
SIC 2033 Vegetables: packaged in cans, jars, etc.
Pr: Chad Geise
* *CEO:* David N Geise
COO: Tom Cholak
* *CFO:* Ted Hancock
* *Treas:* Ted R Hancock
VP: Franklin Furman
* *VP:* Kermit Kohl
VP: Jeff Stuck
* *VP:* Bob Vanderhook
Exec: Ralph Lambert
* *Dir Surg:* Joel Furman

FURMANITE AMERICA
See FURMANITE WORLDWIDE INC

D-U-N-S 00-517-7261 IMP
■ **FURMANITE AMERICA INC** (VA)
(*Suby of* FURMANITE AMERICA) ★
10370 Richmond Ave # 600, Houston, TX 77042-4136
Tel (713) 634-7777 *Founded/Ownrshp* 1991, 2015
Sales 97.6MM[E] *EMP* 669
SIC 7699 Industrial equipment services
CEO: Charlie Cox
* *Pr:* Joseph F Milliron
* *Pr:* Matthew Sisson
VP: Michael Funk
VP: Gary Gardner
VP: Michael Golla
* *VP:* Jay Goodyear
* *VP:* Chad Murray
* *VP:* John Tucci
Genl Mgr: Tom Cook

D-U-N-S 00-793-1868 IMP/EXP
■ **FURMANITE CORP**
(*Suby of* TEAM INC) ★
10370 Richmond Ave # 600, Houston, TX 77042-4136
Tel (713) 634-7777 *Founded/Ownrshp* 2015
Sales 529.2MM *EMP* 3,017[E]
SIC 7699 7389 Industrial equipment services; Valve repair, industrial; Pipeline & power line inspection service
Pr: Jeffery G Davis
CFO: Robert S Muff
Ex VP: Jay Goodyear
Sr VP: Mike Dills
VP: Carl Britsch
VP: Peter Casey
VP: John Norman
VP: John A Olsen
VP Bus Dev: Billy Patterson
CIO: Ross Tucker
Tech Mgr: Chuck Carmouche

D-U-N-S 78-598-1028 IMP
■ **FURMANITE WORLDWIDE INC**
FURMANITE AMERICA
(*Suby of* FURMANITE CORP) ★
10370 Richmond Ave # 600, Houston, TX 77042-4136
Tel (972) 699-4000 *Founded/Ownrshp* 1991
Sales 97.6MM[E] *EMP* 983
SIC 7699 3599 7389 Valve repair, industrial; Machine shop, jobbing & repair; Inspection & testing services
CEO: Charles R Cox
* *Pr:* C Jeffery Chick
* *COO:* Joseph E Milliron
* *Sec:* Howard C Wadsworth
* *Sr VP:* Paul E Priest
* *VP:* Louis Russo
Mng Dir: Tony Nicholls
Opers Mgr: Joyce Cordero
Opers Mgr: Kristy Daniels

FURMANO FOODS
See FURMAN FOODS INC

D-U-N-S 00-626-6738 IMP/EXP
FURNITURE BRANDS INTERNATIONAL INC
1 N Brentwood Blvd # 700, Saint Louis, MO 63105-3955
Tel (314) 863-1100 *Founded/Ownrshp* 1992
Sales 1.0MMM *EMP* 8,800
SIC 2511 2512 2515

D-U-N-S 00-787-3193 IMP
FURNITURE DISTRIBUTORS INC (NC)
KIMBRELL'S FURNITURE
4524 South Blvd, Charlotte, NC 28209-2841
Tel (704) 523-3424 *Founded/Ownrshp* 1915
Sales 136.7MM[E] *EMP* 599
SIC 5712 5713 5722

D-U-N-S 03-308-2140 IMP
FURNITURE FACTORY OUTLET LLC
FFO HOME
6500 Jenny Lind Rd Spc A, Fort Smith, AR 72908-7447
Tel (918) 427-0241 *Founded/Ownrshp* 2016
Sales 97.0MM[E] *EMP* 350
SIC 5712 2515 Furniture stores; Mattresses & bedsprings
Pr: Larry Zigerelli

D-U-N-S 17-489-0590
FURNITURE LOW LLC
1333 E 37th Ave, Denver, CO 80205-3303
Tel (303) 371-8560 *Founded/Ownrshp* 1987
Sales 110.2MM[E] *EMP* 1,200
SIC 6512 Nonresidential building operators
Rgnl Mgr: Brad Thompson
Sls Dir: Lee Marcum
Sls Mgr: Ethan Wilemon

D-U-N-S 01-298-4589
FURNITURE MARKETING GROUP INC (TX)
REGENESIS
6100 W Plano Pkwy # 1400, Plano, TX 75093-8203
Tel (214) 556-4700 *Founded/Ownrshp* 1981
Sales 181.4MM[E] *EMP* 360
SIC 5021 Office furniture
CEO: Greg Almond
* *CFO:* Robert G Bacic
* *VP:* W Cleon Almond
* *Prin:* Robert P Reece
VP Sls: Mark Reed
Mktg Dir: Judy Pantello

D-U-N-S 09-832-8180 IMP
FURNITURE MART USA INC
S.D. FURNITURE MART
140 E Hinks Ln, Sioux Falls, SD 57104-0465
Tel (605) 336-5000 *Founded/Ownrshp* 1978
Sales 138.7MM[E] *EMP* 800
Accts Eide Bailly Llp Sioux Falls
SIC 7641 5713 Reupholstery & furniture repair; Floor covering stores
Pr: Gordon J Wallenstein
* *Ch Bd:* William A Hinks
* *CFO:* Michael Sagnass
* *VP:* William B Hinks
* *VP:* Tami L Wallenstein
Store Mgr: Aaron Heaton
Sls Mgr: Chris Hines
Sales Asso: Matthew Buecksler
Sales Asso: Craig Jacquart

D-U-N-S 07-987-4532
FURNITURE OUTLETS USA INC
SOUTH DAKOTA FURNITURE MART
140 E Hinks Ln, Sioux Falls, SD 57104-0465
Tel (605) 336-5000 *Founded/Ownrshp* 1980
Sales 82.7M[E] *EMP* 1,000
SIC 5712 Furniture stores
Pr: Bill Hinks

D-U-N-S 13-158-8050
FURNITURE ROW LLC
5641 Broadway, Denver, CO 80216-1021
Tel (303) 576-0787 *Founded/Ownrshp* 1997
Sales 399.1MM[E] *EMP* 2,241[E]
SIC 5712 Furniture stores

FURNITURELAND ON MAIN
See FURNITURELAND SOUTH INC

D-U-N-S 05-348-7807 IMP/EXP
FURNITURELAND SOUTH INC (NC)
FURNITURELAND ON MAIN
5635 Riverdale Dr, Jamestown, NC 27282-9171
Tel (336) 822-3000 *Founded/Ownrshp* 1970
Sales 128.9MM[E] *EMP* 496
SIC 5712 Furniture stores
CEO: A Darrell Harris
* *Ex VP:* Jason E Harris
* *VP:* Stella Harris
CIO: Louise Sherrill
CTO: Marlon Moore
Dir IT: Todd Erickson
Mktg Dir: Leslie Frye
Sls Mgr: Dan Bly
Sls Mgr: Laurie Moore
Sls Mgr: Joel Payne
Sales Asso: McKenzie Kenny

D-U-N-S 01-166-1703
FURRION LLC
(*Suby of* FURRION LIMITED)
2612 Glenview Dr, Elkhart, IN 46514-9243
Tel (888) 354-5792 *Founded/Ownrshp* 2007
Sales 200.0MM *EMP* 15
SIC 3663 Radio & TV communications equipment

FURR'S FAMILY DINING
See BUFFET PARTNERS LP

D-U-N-S 00-514-5800 IMP
FURST-MCNESS CO
120 E Clark St, Freeport, IL 61032-3300
Tel (800) 435-5100 *Founded/Ownrshp* 1908
Sales 310.6MM *EMP* 219
Accts Baker Tilly Virchow Krause Ll
SIC 2048 5191 Feed premixes; Feed
Pr: Martha Furst
* *Ch Bd:* Frank E Furst
* *CFO:* Matt Hartman
* *Ex VP:* Kevin Gyland
* *VP:* Lawrence Feaver
* *VP:* Terry Gogel
* *VP:* Matt Heinrich
* *VP:* Jack Smit
Genl Mgr: Mark Romero
Mktg Dir: Tom Rutter
Manager: Bill Bush

D-U-N-S 17-352-6807 IMP/EXP
FURUKAWA ELECTRIC TECHNOLOGIES INC
(*Suby of* FURUKAWA ELECTRIC CO.,LTD.)
2000 Northeast Expy, Norcross, GA 30071-2932
Tel (770) 798-2082 *Founded/Ownrshp* 1988
Sales 89.6MM[E] *EMP* 800
SIC 5051 Copper products; Cable, wire
Pr: M Sakamoto
Snr Mgr: Tim Yu

D-U-N-S 78-352-3074 IMP
FURUKAWA WIRING SYSTEMS AMERICA INC
(*Suby of* FURUKAWA ELECTRIC CO.,LTD.)
950 Loma Verde Dr, El Paso, TX 79936-7899
Tel (915) 791-5579 *Founded/Ownrshp* 1987
Sales 115.1MM[E] *EMP* 1,500
SIC 2531 Public building & related furniture
Pr: Akira Matsui

FUSD
See FONTANA UNIFIED SCHOOL DISTRICT

FUSD
See FLAGSTAFF UNIFIED SCHOOL DISTRICT

FUSD
See FREMONT UNIFIED SCHOOL DISTRICT

D-U-N-S 02-789-7441
FUSION PERFORMANCE MARKETING LLC
1928 Locust St, Saint Louis, MO 63103-1612
Tel (314) 576-7500 *Founded/Ownrshp* 2004
Sales 100.0MM *EMP* 93
SIC 8742 Incentive or award program consultant; Marketing consulting services
CEO: William H Decker
* *CFO:* Michael Cox

D-U-N-S 03-780-4403
▲ **FUSION TELECOMMUNICATIONS INTERNATIONAL INC**
420 Lexington Ave Rm 1718, New York, NY 10170-1707
Tel (212) 201-2400 *Founded/Ownrshp* 1997
Sales 101.6MM *EMP* 260[E]
Tkr Sym FSNN *Exch* NAS
SIC 7372 4813 Business oriented computer software; Telephone communication, except radio;
CEO: Matthew D Rosen
* *Ch Bd:* Marvin S Rosen
Pr: Gordon Hutchins Jr
Pr: Russell P Markman
CFO: Michael R Bauer
* *Sec:* Philip D Turits
Bd of Dir: Philip Turits
Ex VP: Jan Sarro
Dir Sec: Jonathan Kaufman
Board of Directors: Larry Blum, E Alan Brumberger, Michael J Del Giudice, Paul C O'brien, Jack Rosen, William Rubin

D-U-N-S 78-466-4109
■ **FUSION-IO INC**
SANDISK
(*Suby of* WESTERN DIGITAL) ★
2855 E Cottonwood Pkwy # 200, Salt Lake City, UT 84121-7042
Tel (801) 424-5569 *Founded/Ownrshp* 2014
Sales 160.0MM[E] *EMP* 938[E]
SIC 3572 Computer storage devices
CEO: Shane Robison
* *Pr:* Lance L Smith
* *CFO:* Ted Hull
Chf Mktg O: Rick C White
Ofcr: Nancy Fazioli
Ex VP: Rich Boberg
Ex VP: Richard Boberg
* *Ex VP:* Shawn J Lindquist
* *Ex VP:* Michael Mendenhall
* *Ex VP:* Gary Smerdon
Ex VP: Ian Whiting
Ex VP: David Windley
Sr VP: David Bradford
* *Sr VP:* Pankaj Mehra
VP: Kathleen Dwyer
VP: Raj Gulati
VP: Sean Hehir
Creative D: Brett Lloyd

D-U-N-S 11-125-7957
FUSIONSTORM
ADEXIS
2 Bryant St Ste 150, San Francisco, CA 94105-1641
Tel (415) 623-2626 *Founded/Ownrshp* 1995
Sales 277.2MM[E] *EMP* 400[E]
SIC 7379 7371 7374 7376 Computer related maintenance services; Computer software systems analysis & design, custom; Data processing service; Computer facilities management
CEO: John Varel
Pr: Bill Dougherty
* *Pr:* Daniel Serpico
* *CFO:* Michael Soja
Ex VP: Eric Bieber
VP: Richard Bocchinfuso
VP: Jack Koziol
VP: Robert Linsky
VP: Lance Litchfield
VP: David Prinzing
Exec: Alan Giner

D-U-N-S 11-071-2275 IMP
FUTABA INDIANA OF AMERICA CORP
(*Suby of* FIC AMERICA CORP) ★
3320 S Keller Rd, Vincennes, IN 47591-7630
Tel (812) 895-4700 *Founded/Ownrshp* 2002
Sales 98.9MM[E] *EMP* 500
SIC 3089 3465 2396 Automotive parts, plastic; Body parts, automobile: stamped metal; Automotive & apparel trimmings
Pr: Hiroharu Murahashi
* *Treas:* Hiroshi Ishikawa
* *Prin:* Yasuyoshi Shirai
Sfty Dirs: Anthony Earnst
Ql Cn Mgr: Jamie Taylor

D-U-N-S 07-846-8537
FUTRELL & HOLT INC
2000 Enterprise Pkwy, Hampton, VA 23666-6254
Tel (757) 744-9552 *Founded/Ownrshp* 2012
Sales 20.1MM[E] *EMP* 1,300
SIC 7389 Apparel designers, commercial
CEO: Carlos Holt
* *Prin:* Darrell Futrell

D-U-N-S 06-004-5296
FUTTER GOLD MEDICAL FOUNDATION
600 Coffee Rd, Modesto, CA 95355-4201
Tel (209) 550-4724 *Founded/Ownrshp* 2002
Sales 317.3MM *EMP* 22[E]
Accts Ernst & Young Us Llp San Dieg
SIC 8011 Offices & clinics of medical doctors
CEO: James E Conforti

FUTURE ACTIVE INDUSTRIAL ELEC
See FAI ELECTRONICS CORP

D-U-N-S 14-724-5559
FUTURE CARE HEALTH AND MANAGEMENT OF HOMEWOOD INC
FUTURECARE
8028 Ritchie Hwy Ste 210b, Pasadena, MD 21122-0801
Tel (410) 766-1995 *Founded/Ownrshp* 1986
Sales 42.7MM[E] *EMP* 2,000
SIC 8741 Nursing & personal care facility management
Ch Bd: Leonard J Attman
* *CFO:* Brian Finglass
* *Sec:* Shelly A Gilden
* *V Ch Bd:* Alvin M Powers
* *VP:* Gary Attman

D-U-N-S 05-972-8071 IMP/EXP
FUTURE ELECTRONICS CORP
(*Suby of* FUTURE ELECTRONICS (CDA) LTD)
41 Main St, Bolton, MA 01740-1134
Tel (800) 444-0050 *Founded/Ownrshp* 1972
Sales 574.1MM[E] *EMP* 4,000
SIC 5065 Electronic parts; Semiconductor devices
Ch Bd: Robert G Miller
* *CFO:* Pierre Guilbault
* *Treas:* Charles Dinovo
* *Treas:* Joseph Prudente
VP: Jeffrey Halickman
* *VP:* Mario Pizzalongo
Dir IT: Ian Kearvell
IT Man: Alvaro Soares
Sls Mgr: Kelli Cain
Sls Mgr: Oscarm Medina

D-U-N-S 00-726-1415 IMP/EXP
FUTURE FOAM INC
1610 Avenue N, Council Bluffs, IA 51501-1071
Tel (712) 323-9122 *Founded/Ownrshp* 1958
Sales 424.6MM *EMP* 1,000
SIC 3086 Carpet & rug cushions, foamed plastic; Ice chests or coolers (portable), foamed plastic; Insulation or cushioning material, foamed plastic
Pr: Bruce Schneider
* *Sec:* Michael Blatt
* *VP:* Robert A Heller
Genl Mgr: Jen Smith
Genl Mgr: Marc Vitale
Off Mgr: Ronda Barclay
Off Mgr: Carol Rich
IT Man: Joni Darnell
IT Man: Russell Mosemann
Mfg Mgr: Jeff Lewis
Opers Mgr: Michael Phatipat

D-U-N-S 08-531-5539
FUTURE FOUNDATION INC
380 E Parkcenter Blvd # 230, Boise, ID 83706-3962
Tel (208) 336-0150 *Founded/Ownrshp* 1965
Sales 146.9MM[E] *EMP* 464
SIC 3354 5013 6361 Aluminum extruded products; Automotive supplies & parts; Real estate title insurance
Pr: Brent F Lloyd
* *VP:* Klara Hansberger

FUTURE GRAPHICS
See MITSUBISHI KAGAKU IMAGING CORP

D-U-N-S 96-283-2812
FUTURE TECH ENTERPRISE INC
F T E I
101 Colin Dr Unit 8, Holbrook, NY 11741-4332
Tel (631) 472-5500 *Founded/Ownrshp* 1996
Sales 175.1MM *EMP* 92
SIC 7373 Local area network (LAN) systems integrator; Value-added resellers, computer systems
Pr: Robert Venero

*CFO: Robert Johnson
*Treas: Dawn Rhodes
CTO: Ed Plitt
IT Man: Mike Rossato
Natl Sales: Dan Hickey

FUTURECARE
See FUTURE CARE HEALTH AND MANAGEMENT OF HOMEWOOD INC

D-U-N-S 61-317-4684 IMP
■ FUTUREFUEL CHEMICAL CO
(Suby of FUTUREFUEL CORP) ★
2800 Gap Rd, Batesville, AR 72501-8377
Tel (870) 698-3000 Founded/Ownrshp 2006
Sales 129.7MM^E EMP 500
SIC 2819 Industrial inorganic chemicals; Fuel propellants, solid: inorganic
Ch Bd: Paul Anthony Novelly
*CFO: Christopher Jay Schmitt
*Treas: Rose M Sparks
Bd of Dir: Donald C Bedell
*Ex VP: Paul M Flynn
VP: Rich Byers
*VP: Samuel W Dortch
Exec: Jim Hauf
*CTO: Gary McChesney
Plnt Mgr: Tony Gunderman
Snr Mgr: Vaughn Watkins

D-U-N-S 78-765-9460
▲ FUTUREFUEL CORP
8235 Forsyth Blvd 4, Saint Louis, MO 63105-1623
Tel (314) 854-8385 Founded/Ownrshp 2006
Sales 299.6MM EMP 500^E
Tkr Sym FF Exch NYS
SIC 2819 Industrial inorganic chemicals; Fuel propellants, solid: inorganic
Ch Bd: Paul A Novelly
CFO: Rose M Sparks
Ex VP: Samuel W Dortch
Ex VP: Paul M Flynn
Board of Directors: Donald C Bedell, Dale E Cole, Terrance C Z Egger, Edwin A Levy, Paul G Lorenzini, Paul M Manheim, Jeffrey L Schwartz

D-U-N-S 60-370-3799
FUTUREGEN INDUSTRIAL ALLIANCE INC
1101 Penn Ave Nw Fl 6, Washington, DC 20004-2544
Tel (202) 756-4520 Founded/Ownrshp 2005
Sales 93.8MM EMP 4
Accts Dixon Hughes Goodman Llp Tyso
SIC 8711 Pollution control engineering; Designing: ship, boat, machine & product
CEO: Kenneth K Humphreys
*CFO: Matthew Kranz
*Treas: Greg Walker
*Prin: Julian Beere
*Prin: Mick Buffier
*Prin: Phillip Cavatoni
*Prin: Sean Major
*Prin: Fredrik Palmer

D-U-N-S 93-354-9230 IMP
FUTURENET GROUP INC
12801 Auburn St, Detroit, MI 48223-3413
Tel (313) 544-7117 Founded/Ownrshp 1994
Sales 97.2MM EMP 208^E
Accts Martin Arrington Desai & Mey
SIC 1542 8748 Commercial & office building contractors; Environmental consultant
Pr: Perry Mehta
*COO: Prafulla Pande
COO: Pande Prafulla
*Treas: Dipkia Mehta
*Sr VP: Jay Mehta
*VP: Krishal Dalal
*VP: Ed Dunne
*VP: Shashi Shastri
VP: Arvind Singhal
Dir Bus: David Lakness
Dir Bus: Sukha Williams

D-U-N-S 02-197-4105 IMP
FUTUREWEI TECHNOLOGIES INC
(Suby of HUAWEI TECHNOLOGY CO.,LTD.)
5700 Tennyson Pkwy # 500, Plano, TX 75024-3583
Tel (972) 509-5599 Founded/Ownrshp 2001
Sales 304.8MM^E EMP 763
SIC 4813 Telephone communication, except radio
Pr: Wang Guc Jin
*Ex VP: Edward Lin
*Ex VP: Carl Liu
*VP: Haibo Lin
VP: Kevin Zhang
Dir IT: Andy Chen

D-U-N-S 08-033-9215
FUTURIS GLOBAL HOLDINGS LLC
(Suby of CLEARLAKE CAPITAL GROUP LP) ★
233 Wilshire Blvd Ste 800, Santa Monica, CA 90401-1207
Tel (510) 771-2333 Founded/Ownrshp 2013
Sales 500.0MM EMP 3,150
SIC 6719 Investment holding companies, except banks
CEO: Mark Gregory Dewit
*CFO: Eric Rundall
*Ch: Mervynn Dunn

D-U-N-S 01-596-0575
FUTURITY FIRST INSURANCE GROUP INC
101 Centerpoint Dr # 208, Middletown, CT 06457-7568
Tel (860) 838-4800 Founded/Ownrshp 2008
Sales NA EMP 300^E
SIC 6411 Insurance agents, brokers & service
CEO: Michael Kalen
*Pr: Edward Berube
*CFO: Peter Lahaie
Chf Cred: Michael Tanguay
Bd of Dir: Christopher Knox
Ex VP: Shelby Smith
Sr VP: Dennis E Pascarella
VP: Jon Estrellado
VP: Mark Keating
VP: Lionel Lauture
VP: Michael McGowan
Exec: Karen Matheson

D-U-N-S 07-953-9603
FUYAO GLASS AMERICA INC
(Suby of FUYAO GLASS INDUSTRY GROUP CO., LTD.)
2801 W Stroop Rd, Dayton, OH 45439
Tel (937) 626-4092 Founded/Ownrshp 2014
Sales 93.9MM^E EMP 307^E
SIC 7536 Automotive glass replacement shops
Pr: Frank Welling

FWC
See FISH & WILDLIFE CONSERVATION COMMISSION FLORIDA

D-U-N-S 00-614-2376
FWD SEAGRAVE HOLDINGS LP
SEAGRAVES FIRE APPARATUS
105 E 12th St, Clintonville, WI 54929-1518
Tel (715) 823-2141 Founded/Ownrshp 2003
Sales 137.8MM^E EMP 275
SIC 3711 Truck & tractor truck assembly; Motor trucks, except off-highway, assembly of; Snow plows (motor vehicles), assembly of; Fire department vehicles (motor vehicles), assembly of
CEO: Joseph Neiner
COO: Ulysses Parmeziani
CFO: Richard Kaelin
CFO: Aaron Smits
Plnt Mgr: John Martin

FWI
See FOUR WINDS INTERACTIVE LLC

FWISD
See FORT WORTH INDEPENDENT SCHOOL DISTRICT

D-U-N-S 84-224-1411
FX ALLIANCE INC
FXALL
(Suby of THOMCORP HOLDINGS INC.)
3 Times Sq, New York, NY 10036-6564
Tel (646) 268-9900 Founded/Ownrshp 2012
Sales 105.5MM^E EMP 239
SIC 6231 6211 Security & commodity exchanges; Security exchanges; Investment firm, general brokerage
CEO: Philip Weisberg
*CFO: John Cooley
Ofcr: Benjamin Smith
Software D: Michael Buehl
Software D: Stelian Dumitrascu
Software D: Frank Russo
Sls Dir: Francis Odonnell
*Genl Couns: James F X Sullivan
Board of Directors: Kathleen Casey, Carolyn Christie, James L Fox, Gerald D Putnam Jr, John C Rosenberg, Peter Tomozawa, Robert W Trudeau

FXALL
See FX ALLIANCE INC

FXCM
See FOREX CAPITAL MARKETS LLC

D-U-N-S 96-260-3507
▲ FXCM INC
55 Water St Fl 50, New York, NY 10041-3203
Tel (646) 432-2986 Founded/Ownrshp 2010
Sales 402.2MM EMP 804^E
Tkr Sym FXCM Exch NGM
SIC 6211 6099 Stock brokers & dealers; Foreign currency exchange
Ch Bd: Dror Niv
Pr: Josh Diamond
CEO: Brendan Callan
CEO: Ornit Niv
COO: David Sakhai
CFO: Robert Lande
Ex VP: Evan Milazzo
VP: Jaclyn Klein
VP: Alan Oliver
Mng Dir: Brad Shulman
Sls Mgr: James Munkittrick
Board of Directors: William Ahdout, James G Brown, Robin Davis, Kenneth Grossman, Arthur Gruen, Eric Legoff, Bryan Reyhani, Ryan Silverman, Eduard Yusupov

FXDD
See FXDIRECTDEALER LLC

D-U-N-S 14-228-8757
FXDIRECTDEALER LLC
FXDD
7 World Trade Ctr 32nd, New York, NY 10007-2140
Tel (212) 266-0700 Founded/Ownrshp 2002
Sales NA EMP 175
SIC 6099 Foreign currency exchange
CEO: Joseph Botkier
COO: Lubomir Kaneti
Ofcr: Dragana Bijelic
Mng Dir: James Curley
Mng Dir: Robert Slade
CIO: Shawn Dilkes
CTO: Amgad Attia
Dir IT: Stan Mashov

FXI FOAMEX INNOVATIONS
See FXI HOLDINGS INC

D-U-N-S 82-946-2535
FXI HOLDINGS INC
FXI FOAMEX INNOVATIONS
1400 N Providence Rd # 2000, Media, PA 19063-2081
Tel (610) 744-2300 Founded/Ownrshp 2009
Sales 1.3MMM^E EMP 2,038
SIC 3086 Plastics foam products; Carpet & rug cushions, foamed plastic; Insulation or cushioning material, foamed plastic; Padding, foamed plastic
Pr: John Cowles
COO: David Prilutski
CFO: Harold Earley
Sr VP: Diane Adams
Sr VP: Vincenzo Bonaddio
Sr VP: Darryl Dunn

D-U-N-S 83-144-6518 IMP/EXP
FXI INC
ROSE TREE CORPORATE CENTER II
(Suby of FXI FOAMEX INNOVATIONS) ★
1400 N Providence Rd # 2000, Media, PA 19063-2081
Tel (610) 744-2300 Founded/Ownrshp 2009
Sales 1.1MMM^E EMP 2,038
SIC 3086 Carpet & rug cushions, foamed plastic
Pr: John Cowles
COO: David J Prilutski
CFO: Harold Earley
Ex VP: Donald W Phillips
Ex VP: Kurt W Werth
Sr VP: Robert Dimartino
Sr VP: David M Minning
Sr VP: Andrew Prusky
Sr VP: John M Smail Jr
VP: Darryl Dunn
VP: Daniel Frich

D-U-N-S 79-452-1591 IMP/EXP
FYC APPAREL GROUP LLC
ALLISON TAYLOR
30 Thompson Rd, Branford, CT 06405-2842
Tel (203) 481-2420 Founded/Ownrshp 1992
Sales 95.7MM^E EMP 250
SIC 2331 2335 2337 5651 Women's & misses' blouses & shirts; Women's, juniors' & misses' dresses; Women's & misses' suits & skirts; Family clothing stores
Dir IT: Jose Ordonez

FYFFES NORTH AMERICA INC.
See TURBANA CORP

G

D-U-N-S 07-085-0607
G & C FOOD DISTRIBUTORS & BROKERS INC (NY)
PARK ST REFRIGERATED SERVICES
3407 Walters Rd, Syracuse, NY 13209-9725
Tel (315) 422-3191 Founded/Ownrshp 1976, 1988
Sales 207.9MM^E EMP 100
SIC 5147 5146 4222 Meats & meat products; Meats, fresh; Fish, fresh; Fish, frozen, unpackaged; Refrigerated warehousing & storage
Ch Bd: Dwight M Palmer
*Pr: David Lepge
Ex VP: Rich Chapman
Exec: James Emm
Dir IT: Frank Smith
VP Sls: Steven Levine

G & D INTEGRATED
See G&D INTEGRATED TRANSPORTATION INC

D-U-N-S 06-214-7871
G & G STEAM SERVICE INC
GALMOR'S
120 W 12th St, Elk City, OK 73644-6745
Tel (580) 225-4254 Founded/Ownrshp 1975
Sales 184.7MM^E EMP 185
SIC 1389 Servicing oil & gas wells; Excavating slush pits & cellars
Pr: Steve Galmor
*CFO: Jeff Klick

D-U-N-S 04-888-7046
G & J PEPSI-COLA BOTTLERS INC
9435 Waterstone Blvd # 390, Cincinnati, OH 45249-8227
Tel (513) 785-6060 Founded/Ownrshp 1968
Sales 516.5MM^E EMP 1,612
SIC 2086 Soft drinks: packaged in cans, bottles, etc.
COO: Daniel D Sweeney
V Ch: Thomas R Gross
*Pr: Sydnor I Davis
*COO: Tim Hardid
*Ch: Stanley Kaplan
*V Ch Bd: Thomas D Heekin
VP: Rick Kaplen
*Prin: George G Grubb
MIS Mgr: Con Colovos
Dir Opers: Mel Sutton
Mktg Mgr: Wanda Austin-Wingood

G & L DISTRIBUTORS
See STEW LEONARDS HOLDINGS LLC

D-U-N-S 06-258-0410
G & M OIL CO INC
16868 A Ln, Huntington Beach, CA 92647-4831
Tel (714) 375-4700 Founded/Ownrshp 1971
Sales 199.8MM^E EMP 525
SIC 5541

D-U-N-S 19-512-0324
G & R MINERAL SERVICES INC
2355 Alton Rd, Irondale, AL 35210-3701
Tel (205) 956-7300 Founded/Ownrshp 1988
Sales 49.0MM^E EMP 1,500
SIC 7349 7699 Building maintenance services; Industrial equipment services
Pr: Bobby B Rushen

D-U-N-S 00-507-6625 IMP/EXP
G & W ELECTRIC CO
305 W Crossroads Pkwy, Bolingbrook, IL 60440-4938
Tel (708) 388-5010 Founded/Ownrshp 1905
Sales 112.7MM^E EMP 740
SIC 3613 3643

D-U-N-S 00-127-1188 IMP
G & W LABORATORIES INC
111 Coolidge St, South Plainfield, NJ 07080-3801
Tel (908) 753-2000 Founded/Ownrshp 1918
Sales 258.5MM^E EMP 900
SIC 2834 Suppositories; Ointments
CEO: Ronald Greenblatt
*Pr: Jay Galeota
*Pr: Kurt Orlofski
Pr: Michael Pavlak
CFO: Glenn Vraniak
Ofcr: Jason Carter
VP: Don Bauch
VP: James Coy
VP: Michael Cutrera
VP: Philip Erickson
VP: Kevin Fennell
*VP: Aaron Greenblatt
VP: Stephen Greene
VP: Joseph Greer
VP: Edward Hazell
VP: Kumar Kantheti
VP: Scott Lamb
Exec: Gigi Gebremeskel

G 4 S
See G4S SECURE SOLUTIONS (USA) INC

G 4 S
See G4S SECURE INTEGRATION LLC

G A A
See GREENSBORO AUTO AUCTION INC

G A F
See G-I HOLDINGS INC

D-U-N-S 13-965-1384 IMP/EXP
G A M INC
(Suby of MOVIE GALLERY INC) ★
900 W Main St, Dothan, AL 36301-1410
Tel (334) 677-2108 Founded/Ownrshp 1994
Sales 260.7MM^E EMP 19,500
SIC 7841 5735 Video tape rental; Video tapes, prerecorded
Pr: Joe T Malugen
*CFO: Thomas Johnson
*VP: Harrison Parrish
*VP: Jeff Stubbs

G AND S FOODS
See GOLDBERG AND SOLOVY FOODS INC

G B C
See GENERAL BINDING CORP

G B N
See PREMIER IMAGE CORP

G B U
See GBU FINANCIAL LIFE

D-U-N-S 96-781-0776
G BRADFORD CO INC
(Suby of BRADFORD HOLDING CO INC) ★
4646 Corona Dr Ste 100, Corpus Christi, TX 78411-4383
Tel (361) 852-6392 Founded/Ownrshp 1993
Sales 50.5MM^E EMP 3,400
SIC 7363 Employee leasing service
CFO: Rick Delano

G C I
See COLLABERA INC

D-U-N-S 13-250-3371
■ G C I HOLDINGS INC
(Suby of GENERAL COMMUNICATION INC) ★
2550 Denali St Ste 1000, Anchorage, AK 99503-2751
Tel (907) 265-5600 Founded/Ownrshp 1997
Sales NA EMP 1,150
SIC 6719 Public utility holding companies
Pr: Ron Duncan
*CFO: John Lowber
*Treas: Fred Walker

G C S
See GONZALEZ CONTRACT SERVICES INC

D-U-N-S 18-002-1321 IMP
G E C O M CORP
(Suby of MITSUI MINING & SMELTING CO.,LTD.)
1025 Barachel Ln, Greensburg, IN 47240-1269
Tel (812) 663-2270 Founded/Ownrshp 1987
Sales 288.2MM^E EMP 1,100
SIC 3714 Motor vehicle body components & frame
Pr: Makoto Sakamoto
*Treas: Hidekazu Urushibara
VP: Brian Burke
*VP: Hiromasa Iwaya
*Prin: Toru Shibata
IT Man: Jeff Wright
Ql Cn Mgr: Julia Johnson
Ql Cn Mgr: Christine Pearson
Snr Mgr: Jerry Auger
Snr Mgr: Brenda Cooper

D-U-N-S 13-161-5176
■ G E COMMERCIAL FINANCE REAL ESTATE
(Suby of SECURITY CAPITAL GROUP INC) ★
292 Long Ridge Rd, Stamford, CT 06902-1627
Tel (203) 373-2211 Founded/Ownrshp 1990
Sales 108.3MM^E EMP 687^E
SIC 6798 Real estate investment trusts
Pr: Michael Pralle
Sr VP: Stephen Pierson

G E H A
See GOVERNMENT EMPLOYEES HEALTH ASSOCIATION INC

D-U-N-S 03-192-6652
G E JOHNSON CONSTRUCTION CO INC
25 N Cascade Ave Ste 400, Colorado Springs, CO 80903-1647
Tel (719) 473-5321 Founded/Ownrshp 1967
Sales 416.8MM EMP 300
Accts Martin Vejvoda And Associates
SIC 1542 Commercial & office building, new construction
Pr: James Johnson
*Ex VP: Dave Ivis
*VP: Mike Harms
*VP: Dan Starr
Exec: Kim Neuhaus
CTO: Robert Baker
IT Man: Tom Moran
Trfc Dir: Doug Ellis
Mtls Mgr: Mario Elliott
Opers Mgr: Brandon Brown
Mktg Mgr: Lori Black

G E O
See GEO CORRECTIONS HOLDINGS INC

G E REINSURANCE
See FIRST EXCESS AND REINSURANCE CORP

G E S GLOBAL EXPERIENCE
See GLOBAL EXPERIENCE SPECIALISTS INC

G F I
See GFI MANAGEMENT SERVICES INC

G H BERLIN OIL CO, THE
See BOOTH WALTZ ENTERPRISES INC

G H X INDL
See GHX INDUSTRIAL LLC

D-U-N-S 16-491-6913 IMP/EXP
G HOLDINGS INC
1 Campus Dr, Parsippany, NJ 07054-4404
Tel (973) 628-3000 *Founded/Ownrshp* 2001
Sales 2.0MMM[E] *EMP* 4,300
SIC 2869 2843 3295 Solvents, organic; Surface active agents; Roofing granules
CEO: Robert B Tafaro

D-U-N-S 87-296-9712
G I A A INC
A.G.I.A.
1155 Eugenia Pl, Carpinteria, CA 93013-2062
Tel (805) 566-9191 *Founded/Ownrshp* 1965
Sales NA *EMP* 300[E]
SIC 6411 Medical insurance claim processing, contract or fee basis
Pr: John Wigle
**CFO:* Andrew Dowen
Sr VP: Ralph Stowell
**VP:* Julie Capritto
**VP:* David McCarty
VP: Guy S Patterson
**VP:* Susan Roe
**VP:* Daglin Von Ruden
Dir IT: Fern Perusse
Netwrk Eng: Donovan Karr
Mktg Mgr: Megan Maulhardt

D-U-N-S 02-772-4293 IMP
G I JOES INC
JOE'S SPORTS, OUTDOOR & MORE
(*Suby of* GRYPHON INVESTORS INC) ★
9805 Sw Boeckman Rd, Wilsonville, OR 97070-9282
Tel (503) 682-2242 *Founded/Ownrshp* 2007
Sales 105.1MM[E] *EMP* 1,350
Accts Pricewaterhousecoopers Llp Po
SIC 5941 5699 5531 5999 Sporting goods & bicycle shops; Camping & backpacking equipment; Sports apparel; Automotive accessories; Electronic parts & equipment
Pr: Hal Smith
CFO: Phil Pepin
VP: Ron Menconi
CIO: Matt Miehers

G I L T
See GILT GROUPE HOLDINGS INC

D-U-N-S 18-884-1795 IMP
G K ENTERPRISES INC
26000 S Whiting Way Ste 2, Monee, IL 60449-8162
Tel (708) 587-2150 *Founded/Ownrshp* 1962
Sales 92.5MM[E] *EMP* 320
SIC 3743 3443 3559 3556 3536 Railroad equipment; Fabricated plate work (boiler shop); Cupolas, metal plate; Towers (bubble, cooling, fractionating, etc.): metal plate; Ladles, metal plate; Chemical machinery & equipment; Food products machinery; Hoists, cranes & monorails; Cranes, overhead traveling; Hoists
**Pr:* Kenneth Hoving
**Pr:* Jeffrey Kahn
**Treas:* Marilyn Platter
VP Sls: Greg Ciecierski

D-U-N-S 00-355-7969 IMP
G K N AEROSPACE NORTH AMERICA INC (DE)
(*Suby of* GKN PLC)
142 Js Mcdonnell Blvd, Saint Louis, MO 63135
Tel (314) 264-3000 *Founded/Ownrshp* 2000
Sales 316.1MM[E] *EMP* 1,325
SIC 3812 3728 Search & navigation equipment; Aircraft parts & equipment
CEO: Paul J Gutierrez
CFO: Peter Spears
**Treas:* Hugo Perez
VP: Bob Francis
VP: Jim Gibson
VP: Gary Kahrau
VP: Paul Westman

D-U-N-S 00-138-1649 EXP
■ **G K TECHNOLOGIES INC** (NJ)
GENERAL CABLE
(*Suby of* GENERAL CABLE CORP) ★
4 Tesseneer Dr, Highland Heights, KY 41076-9167
Tel (859) 572-8000 *Founded/Ownrshp* 1902, 1999
Sales 382.5MM[E] *EMP* 4,200
SIC 3357 3315 Building wire & cable, nonferrous; Aluminum wire & cable; Coaxial cable, nonferrous; Communication wire; Wire, steel: insulated or armored
Prin: Christopher F Virgulak
**CEO:* Gregory B Kenny

D-U-N-S 15-275-7639
G L HOMES OF FLORIDA CORP
1600 Sawgrs Corp Pkwy # 400, Sunrise, FL 33323-2890
Tel (954) 753-1730 *Founded/Ownrshp* 1985
Sales 196.7MM[E] *EMP* 450
SIC 1521 New construction, single-family houses
Pr: Itzhak Ezratti
**VP:* Alan J Fant
**VP:* N Maria Menendez
**VP:* Richard M Norwalk
IT Man: Howard Langshaw

D-U-N-S 05-371-3566
G L N INC
NICHOLS SUPER THRIFT
207 S Broadway St, Checotah, OK 74426-3807
Tel (918) 473-2369 *Founded/Ownrshp* 1971
Sales 92.3MM[E] *EMP* 700
SIC 5411 Grocery stores, independent
Pr: Gary L Nichols
**Sec:* Nora K Nichols

D-U-N-S 82-920-0968 IMP
G L SEAMAN & CO
4201 International Pkwy, Carrollton, TX 75007-1911
Tel (214) 764-6400 *Founded/Ownrshp* 2008
Sales 87.7MM[E] *EMP* 100
SIC 5021 Furniture
Pr: Rebecca Lutz
**CFO:* Ken Hartley
**VP Sls:* Mary Edwards

G L Y
See GLY CONSTRUCTION INC

D-U-N-S 60-452-1760
G M H COMMUNITIES LP
10 Campus Blvd, Newtown Square, PA 19073-3200
Tel (610) 355-8000 *Founded/Ownrshp* 2004
Sales 40.1MM[E] *EMP* 1,574[E]
SIC 6531 Real estate leasing & rentals
VP: Joseph Macchione
Sr VP: Leslie Cohn

G M S
See GYPSUM MANAGEMENT AND SUPPLY INC

G N NETCOM UNEX
See GN NETCOM INC

G P
See GEORGIA-PACIFIC BREWTON LLC

D-U-N-S 18-341-1354 IMP
G P & W INC
CENTER OIL COMPANY
600 Mason Ridge Center Dr # 2, Saint Louis, MO 63141-8571
Tel (314) 682-3500 *Founded/Ownrshp* 1986
Sales 201.7MM[E] *EMP* 52
SIC 5172 Petroleum brokers
Pr: Craig M Parker
**Ex VP:* Ronald J Kanterman

G P I
See GREENMAN-PEDERSEN INC

D-U-N-S 08-921-3268
G P JOHNSTON INC
JOHNSTON CMMNCTIONS VOICE DATA
322 Belleville Tpke, North Arlington, NJ 07031-6411
Tel (201) 991-7400 *Founded/Ownrshp* 1977
Sales 92.6MM[E] *EMP* 105
SIC 5065 Telephone equipment
Pr: Philip G Johnston
**Sr VP:* Joe Martino
**VP:* Mike Fleming

G P RESOURCES
See GENERAL PETROLEUM CORP

D-U-N-S 06-397-4430 IMP
G R B INC
TRIANGLE LABEL
6392 Gano Rd, West Chester, OH 45069-4869
Tel (800) 628-9195 *Founded/Ownrshp* 1973
Sales 118.5MM[E] *EMP* 102
SIC 5113 Shipping supplies
Pr: Roger Neiheisel
**VP:* Allen Backscheider
Exec: Linda Miller
Dir IT: Lori Neal
Opers Mgr: Gary McDougle
Sls Mgr: Todd Bonnell
Sls Mgr: Scott Kneer
Sls Mgr: Joe Sanker

D-U-N-S 04-149-4402 EXP
G ROE WM & SONS INC
NOBLE WORLDWIDE FLA CITRUS SLS
500 Avenue R Sw, Winter Haven, FL 33880-3871
Tel (863) 294-3577 *Founded/Ownrshp* 1959
Sales 98.5MM[E] *EMP* 500
SIC 2033 Fruit juices: fresh
Pr: Quentin J Roe
**CFO:* April Porter
**VP:* William G Roe II
**Prin:* Allison Lee
Mktg Dir: Darrell Genthner
Sls Dir: Danny Arnold

D-U-N-S 13-122-5302
G S & L ENTERPRISES INC
408 Highway 49 S, Jackson, MS 39218-8403
Tel (601) 939-1000 *Founded/Ownrshp* 1983
Sales 183.3MM[E] *EMP* 475
SIC 5012 5082 Trucks, commercial; General construction machinery & equipment
Pr: Gerald S Swanson
**Ch Bd:* Sherry Stribling Greener
**Ex VP:* John Lyle

G S A
See GENERAL SERVICES ADMINISTRATION US

G S C BALL
See GROCERS SPECIALTY CO

G S F
See GSF USA INC

G S I
See GO-STAFF INC

G S I
See GULF STATES INC

G S K
See GLAXOSMITHKLINE LLC

D-U-N-S 55-691-4711 IMP/EXP
G S L CORP
GREAT SALT LAKE MINERALS
765 N 10500 W, Ogden, UT 84404-9761
Tel (801) 731-3100 *Founded/Ownrshp* 1973
Sales 92.9MM[E] *EMP* 250
SIC 2819 2899 3339 Potasssium nitrate & sulfate; Salt; Magnesium refining (primary)
Pr: Angelo C Brisimitzakis
**Treas:* James D Standen
**VP:* Bob E Carter

D-U-N-S 03-799-1684
G S LONG CO INC
2517 Old Town Rd, Union Gap, WA 98903-1657
Tel (509) 575-8382 *Founded/Ownrshp* 1980
Sales 83.4MM *EMP* 100
SIC 5191

G S N
See GAME SHOW NETWORK LLC

D-U-N-S 00-107-8757 IMP
G S PRECISION INC (VT)
101 John Seitz Dr, Brattleboro, VT 05301-3642
Tel (802) 257-5200 *Founded/Ownrshp* 1958
Sales 112.4MM[E] *EMP* 410
Accts Gallagher Flynn & Co Llc Bu
SIC 3728 Aircraft assemblies, subassemblies & parts
Pr: Norman A Schneeberger
**CFO:* John Hanley
VP: John Kilburn
Mfg Mgr: Aaron Smith
Plnt Mgr: Doug Kirker
Ql Cn Mgr: John Lynde
Pgrm Dir: John Perreault
Board of Directors: Norman Schneeberger

G S S
See GOVERNMENT SCIENTIFIC SOURCE INC

G S T
See GOLDEN STAR TECHNOLOGY INC

D-U-N-S 18-527-7159 IMP
G S WIRING SYSTEMS INC
(*Suby of* G.S.ELECTECH,INC.)
1801 Production Dr, Findlay, OH 45840-5446
Tel (419) 423-7111 *Founded/Ownrshp* 1987
Sales 146.3MM[E] *EMP* 412
SIC 3714 5013 Automotive wiring harness sets; Motor vehicle supplies & new parts
Pr: George Suzuki
**Pr:* Shinichi Inagaki
**Treas:* Yukinobu Ukai
Sls Mgr: Masami Kunimi

G T A
See GEORGIA TECHNOLOGY AUTHORITY

G T C
See GEORGIA TRANSMISSION CORP

D-U-N-S 00-747-4646 IMP
G T SALES & MANUFACTURING INC
HEWITT USA
2202 S West St, Wichita, KS 67213-1114
Tel (316) 943-2171 *Founded/Ownrshp* 1946
Sales 117.5MM[E] *EMP* 177
SIC 5085 3053 3052 Industrial supplies; Rubber goods, mechanical; Hose, belting & packing; Industrial fittings; Gaskets, all materials; Hose, pneumatic: rubber or rubberized fabric
CEO: N M Onofrio Jr
VP: Rick Mullen
Dept Mgr: Gary Best
Genl Mgr: Rick Ledgerwood
Sales Asso: Anna Alexander
Sales Asso: Buddy Copelin
Sales Asso: Bill Houston
Sales Asso: Judy McGregor

D-U-N-S 00-798-5096
G W BERKHEIMER CO INC
JOHNSON CONTROLS
6000 Southport Rd, Portage, IN 46368-6405
Tel (219) 764-5200 *Founded/Ownrshp* 1919, 1961
Sales 104.8MM[E] *EMP* 300
SIC 5075 5078

D-U-N-S 03-117-6456
G W FOODS INC
HUDSON'S SUPERMARKET
2041 Railroad Ave, Willow Springs, MO 65793-9412
Tel (417) 469-4000 *Founded/Ownrshp* 1981
Sales 117.4MM[E] *EMP* 730
SIC 5411 Grocery stores, independent
Pr: Dan R Williams
**Sec:* Samuel H Grisham
**VP:* R Bruce Grisham

D-U-N-S 10-887-1096 IMP
G W PLASTICS INC
239 Pleasant St, Bethel, VT 05032-9762
Tel (802) 234-9941 *Founded/Ownrshp* 1983
Sales 190.7MM[E] *EMP* 450
SIC 3089 3544 Injection molding of plastics; Industrial molds
Pr: Brenan Riehl
Pr: Tim Holmes
**CFO:* Thomas Johansen
VP: Larry Bell
Exec: Catherine L Tempesta
Prgrm Mgr: Todd Blow
QA Dir: Joe Lembke
Dir IT: John Lemmon
VP Mfg: John Silvia
Opers Mgr: Robbie Dinkel
Plnt Mgr: Jack Courtemanche

D-U-N-S 00-696-6451 IMP
G W VAN KEPPEL CO (MO)
VAN KEPPEL LIFTRUCK
1801 N 9th St, Kansas City, KS 66101-2023
Tel (913) 281-4800 *Founded/Ownrshp* 1926
Sales 137.2MM[E] *EMP* 200
SIC 5082 7699 5084 7359 General construction machinery & equipment; Construction equipment repair; Lift trucks & parts; Equipment rental & leasing

Pr: William S Walker
**Ex VP:* Kevin L Kientz
**VP:* Brian Loderhose
Exec: Mel Williams
Brnch Mgr: Mike Brown
Brnch Mgr: Brady Romine
Genl Mgr: Glenn Henry
Genl Mgr: David Miguel
Genl Mgr: Michael Murray
IT Man: Jeff Duft
Mtls Mgr: Dave Griffin

D-U-N-S 01-794-9264
G Z K INC (OH)
ARBY'S
660 Fame Rd, Dayton, OH 45449-2356
Tel (937) 461-7500 *Founded/Ownrshp* 1960, 1989
Sales 43.6MM[E] *EMP* 1,000[E]
SIC 5812 Fast-food restaurant, chain
CEO: Neal Kaufman
**CFO:* Steven R Stanforth
**VP:* John McKeon

G&D AMERICA
See GIESECKE & DEVRIENT AMERICA INC

D-U-N-S 12-257-6374
G&D INTEGRATED TRANSPORTATION INC
G & D INTEGRATED
50 Commerce Dr, Morton, IL 61550-9196
Tel (309) 284-6700 *Founded/Ownrshp* 1984
Sales 169.2MM[E] *EMP* 590
SIC 4213 Trucking, except local
CEO: P Joseph Oneill
**Pr:* Patrick Roesler
COO: Frank McCloud
CFO: Becki Salmon
VP: Jeff Cohen
Dir Bus: Juan Arias
Genl Mgr: Cort Mills
Mtls Mgr: Dave Hasty
Mtls Mgr: Craig Mason
Opers Mgr: Isaac Aldrich
Opers Mgr: Tony Brown

D-U-N-S 02-292-7230
▲ **G&K SERVICES INC**
5995 Opus Pkwy Ste 500, Minnetonka, MN 55343-9078
Tel (952) 912-5500 *Founded/Ownrshp* 1902
Sales 978.0MM *EMP* 8,000
Tkr Sym GK *Exch* NGS
SIC 7218 7213 7219 Industrial uniform supply; Laundered mat & rug supply; Treated equipment supply: mats, rugs, mops, cloths, etc.; Work clothing supply; Apron supply; Towel supply; Uniform supply; Garment making, alteration & repair
Ch Bd: Douglas A Milroy
Pr: Kevin A Fancey
CFO: Tracy C Jokinen
Sr VP: Richard J Stutz
VP: Jeffrey L Cotter
VP: Jeffrey Cotter
VP: Ian G Davis
Brnch Mgr: Kurt Carlson
Genl Mgr: Mike Peterson
Genl Mgr: Bob De St Aubin
IT Man: Valerie Castanza
Board of Directors: John S Bronson, Lynn Crump-Caine, Wayne M Fortun, Thomas R Greco, Ernest J Mrozek, M Lenny Pippin, Alice M Richter, Lee J Schram

D-U-N-S 09-746-2824
G&L REALTY CORP LLC
439 N Bedford Dr, Beverly Hills, CA 90210-4302
Tel (310) 273-9930 *Founded/Ownrshp* 1976
Sales 266.6MM[E] *EMP* 1,010
SIC 6552 Subdividers & developers
Ch Bd: Daniel M Gottlieb
**Ch Bd:* Steven D Leibowitz
VP: Andrew Lebowitz
VP: George Nagler
**VP:* Paul Schneider

D-U-N-S 00-379-3056
G&P TRUCKING CO INC (SC)
126 Access Rd, Gaston, SC 29053-9501
Tel (803) 791-5500 *Founded/Ownrshp* 1986, 1936
Sales 168.0MM[E] *EMP* 700
Accts Grant Thornton Llp Columbia
SIC 4213 Contract haulers
Pr: G Clifton Parker
**CFO:* Billy Lynch
**Sr VP:* Steve McCourt
**Sr VP:* Richard Strobel
VP: Roger Griggs
Rgnl Mgr: Steve Dellinger
Dir IT: Mike George
Opers Mgr: David Beam
**VP Sls:* Richard Whitmire

D-U-N-S 61-681-3853 IMP/EXP
G-I HOLDINGS INC
G A F
(*Suby of* G HOLDINGS INC) ★
1361 Alps Rd, Wayne, NJ 07470-3700
Tel (973) 628-3000 *Founded/Ownrshp* 2001
Sales 1.6MMM[E] *EMP* 4,300
SIC 2869 2843 3295 Solvents, organic; Surface active agents; Roofing granules
CEO: Robert B Tafaro
**Pr:* Peter Ganz
**Pr:* Susan Yoss
COO: Richard A Nowak
CFO: John F Rebele
Treas: John Maitner
Ex VP: James Schnepper
**Ex VP:* John M Sergey
Sr VP: Tom Anderson
Sr VP: Paul Bromfield
Sr VP: Mike Kiik
VP: Joan Brown
VP: Sebastien Jossart
VP: Ted Marcopolus
Exec: Michelle Betz

D-U-N-S 60-621-3023 IMP
▲ G-III APPAREL GROUP LTD
512 7th Ave Fl 35, New York, NY 10018-0832
Tel (212) 403-0500 *Founded/Ownrshp* 1974
Sales 2.3MMM *EMP* 7,693[E]
Accts Ernst & Young Llp New York N
Tkr Sym GIII *Exch* NGS
SIC 2337 2339 2311 2329 2386 5136 Women's & misses' suits & coats; Women's & misses' outerwear; Men's & boys' suits & coats; Coats, overcoats & vests; Jackets (suede, leatherette, etc.), sport: men's & boys'; Garments, leather; Coats & jackets, leather & sheep-lined; Pants, leather; Men's & boys' clothing
Ch Bd: Morris Goldfarb
**V Ch:* Sammy Aaron
Pr: David Winn
COO: Wayne S Miller
CFO: Neal S Nackman
VP: Michael Laskau III
Dir IT: Sam Deutscher
Board of Directors: Thomas J Brosig, Alan Feller, Jeffrey Goldfarb, Jeanette Nostra, Laura Pomerantz, Allen Sirkin, Willem Van Bokhorst, Cheryl Vitali, Richard White

D-U-N-S 06-822-5002 IMP
■ G-III LEATHER FASHIONS INC (NY)
J L COLEBROOK DIVISION
(*Suby of* G-III APPAREL GROUP LTD) ★
512 Fashion Ave Fl 35, New York, NY 10018-0832
Tel (212) 403-0500 *Founded/Ownrshp* 1974
Sales 282.0MM[E] *EMP* 1,300
SIC 5199 Leather, leather goods & furs
Ch Bd: Morris Goldfarb
**Pr:* Janet Nostra-Katz
**COO:* Wayne S Miller
**CFO:* Neal S Nackman
VP: Erez Levy
CTO: Max Norman
MIS Mgr: Gary Seagobind

G/M BUSINESS INTERIORS
See GOFORTH & MARTI

D-U-N-S 79-253-4328
G2 SECURE STAFF LLC
400 Las Colinas Blvd E # 750, Irving, TX 75039-5593
Tel (972) 915-6979 *Founded/Ownrshp* 2005
Sales NA *EMP* 3,500
SIC 6411 4789 4729 Patrol services, insurance; Cargo loading & unloading services; Transportation ticket offices
Pr: Dan Norman
**Pr:* Tom Del Valle
**COO:* John Graham
**CFO:* Linda Hill
**VP:* Tim Reddell
Genl Mgr: Dobie Adam

D-U-N-S 00-943-7799
G3 ENTERPRISES INC
502 E Whitmore Ave, Modesto, CA 95358-9411
Tel (209) 341-7515 *Founded/Ownrshp* 1961
Sales 120.6MM[E] *EMP* 400
SIC 4731 Transportation agents & brokers
Pr: Robert Lubeck
**CFO:* Michael Ellis
VP: John Kalal
Exec: John Cunningham
Tech Mgr: Gordon Thomsen
Opers Mgr: Patrick Frazier
Opers Mgr: Jeff Holden
Opers Mgr: Michael Linville
Opers Mgr: Mike Riley
Prd Mgr: Cruz Flores
Ql Cn Mgr: Wesley Ayala
Board of Directors: Robert Lubeck

G4S
See RONCO CONSULTING CORP

G4S AMERICAS
See G4S TECHNOLOGY HOLDINGS (USA) INC

D-U-N-S 62-177-1229
G4S COMPLIANCE & INVESTIGATIONS INC
(*Suby of* G4S HOLDING ONE INC) ★
910 Paverstone Dr, Raleigh, NC 27615-4701
Tel (800) 927-0456 *Founded/Ownrshp* 2008
Sales NA *EMP* 450
SIC 6411 Inspection & investigation services, insurance
CEO: Michael J Malone
Pr: Carl Demarais
**Sec:* Brent Faggart
**VP:* Jodi A Darrohn
**VP:* Carl H Demarais
IT Man: Angie Dixon
Sls Mgr: Amy Wells

D-U-N-S 11-104-1401
G4S HOLDING ONE INC
(*Suby of* G4S US HOLDINGS LIMITED)
1395 University Blvd, Jupiter, FL 33458-5289
Tel (561) 622-5656 *Founded/Ownrshp* 2002
Sales 3.2MMM[E] *EMP* 68,000[E]
SIC 7381 7382 8744 8748 8742 Security guard service; Private investigator; Burglar alarm maintenance & monitoring; Facilities support services; Base maintenance (providing personnel on continuing basis); Correctional facility; Jails, privately operated; Business consulting; Training & development consultant
Pr: John Kenning
**CFO:* Susanne Jorgensen
**Treas:* Ian A Green
VP: Soren Lundsberg-Niels

D-U-N-S 11-829-4722
G4S SECURE INTEGRATION LLC
G 4 S
(*Suby of* G4S AMERICAS) ★
1299 Farnam St Ste 1300, Omaha, NE 68102-1892
Tel (402) 233-7700 *Founded/Ownrshp* 2010
Sales 320.4MM[E] *EMP* 425
SIC 1623 7382 Water, sewer & utility lines; Security systems services
CEO: Robert E Sommerfeld
CFO: Joseph Schwaderer
VP: Louie Enriquez
VP: Lee Fintel
VP: James Kawamoto
Brnch Mgr: Chris Rizzuto
MIS Dir: Terri Shindo
Dir IT: Robert Carlson
IT Man: Erika Kirchmann
IT Man: Cindy Lembke
Netwrk Eng: Eric Turney

D-U-N-S 00-190-3723
G4S SECURE SOLUTIONS (USA) INC (FL)
G 4 S
(*Suby of* G4S HOLDING ONE INC) ★
1395 University Blvd, Jupiter, FL 33458-5289
Tel (561) 622-5656 *Founded/Ownrshp* 1954, 2002
Sales 2.6MMM[E] *EMP* 38,425
SIC 7381 8744 8748 8742 Security guard service; Private investigator; Facilities support services; Base maintenance (providing personnel on continuing basis); Correctional facility; Jails, privately operated; Business consulting; Training & development consultant
Pr: John Kenning
Pr: Jeff Morrow
CFO: Tim McCormick
**CFO:* Timothy McCormick
Ofcr: Julie T Payne
Sr VP: Robert Burns
Sr VP: Donald Keens
VP: Brenda Bryant
**VP:* Ian A Green
VP: John Griffey
**VP:* Susanne Jorgensen
**VP:* Drew Levine
VP: Jayne Omalley
VP: Carl Page
VP: Marc Shapiro
VP: Chad Starwalt
**VP:* John Sumner
VP: Mark Tsuji
VP Bus Dev: Frank Finch
Exec: Wayne Beck
Board of Directors: Brian McCabe

D-U-N-S 18-823-6160
G4S SECURE SOLUTIONS INTERNATIONAL INC
(*Suby of* G4S HOLDING ONE INC) ★
1395 University Blvd, Jupiter, FL 33458-5289
Tel (561) 622-5656 *Founded/Ownrshp* 1979
Sales 47.1MM[E] *EMP* 2,184
SIC 7382 7381 Burglar alarm maintenance & monitoring; Security guard service
CEO: Grahame Gibson
**COO:* Jeff Morrow
**CFO:* Susanne Jrgensen
**Sr VP:* Julie Payne
**Sr VP:* Marc Shapiro
Dir IT: Rich Villa

D-U-N-S 96-399-8906
G4S TECHNOLOGY HOLDINGS (USA) INC
G4S AMERICAS
(*Suby of* G4S HOLDING ONE INC) ★
1395 University Blvd, Jupiter, FL 33458-5289
Tel (561) 622-5656 *Founded/Ownrshp* 2008
Sales 296.9MM[E] *EMP* 478[E]
SIC 7381 Security guard service
CEO: Grahame Gibson
Pr: Michael Janney
**COO:* Jeff Morrow
**CFO:* Susanne Jorgensen
**Sr VP:* Julie Payne
**Sr VP:* Marc Shapiro
Dir IT: Rich Villa

D-U-N-S 95-916-3064
G4S YOUTH SERVICES LLC
HASTINGS YOUTH ACADEMY
(*Suby of* G4S PLC)
6302 Benjamin Rd Ste 400, Tampa, FL 33634-5116
Tel (813) 514-6275 *Founded/Ownrshp* 1997
Sales 79.0MM[E] *EMP* 1,600
SIC 8322 Youth center
Pr: Martin J Favis
CFO: Peter Loughlin
IT Man: Dan Aderhood
VP Mktg: Chuck Kehoe

D-U-N-S 07-864-9057
G6 HOSPITALITY LLC
4001 International Pkwy, Carrollton, TX 75007-1914
Tel (972) 360-9000 *Founded/Ownrshp* 1986
Sales NA *EMP* 2,015[E]
SIC 8741

D-U-N-S 19-466-9610
G6 HOSPITALITY LLC
MOTEL 6
4001 International Pkwy, Carrollton, TX 75007-1914
Tel (972) 360-9000 *Founded/Ownrshp* 1985
Sales 365.2MM[E] *EMP* 4,418[E]
SIC 7011 Hotels & motels
CEO: Olivier Poirot
**Pr:* Jim Amorosia
**COO:* Mike Brower
**CFO:* Didier Bosc
Treas: Stephen Manthey
**Treas:* Gregg Toon
Ex VP: Patrick Ollivier
Ex VP: Jeff Palmer
**Ex VP:* Alan Rabinowitz
VP: Rick Johnson
VP: Anne Lawrence
VP: Mike McGeehan
VP: Mike Moore
VP: David Nix
VP: Perry Ping
VP: Lusk Tom
VP: Edoardo Tuccia
**VP:* John Valletta
Exec: Jacques Aferiat
Exec: Hughes Jaquier
Dir Teleco: Jason Weimer

D-U-N-S 07-321-5956 IMP
GA FOOD SERVICES OF PINELLAS COUNTY INC
G.A.FOOD SERVICE
12200 32nd Ct N, Saint Petersburg, FL 33716-1803
Tel (727) 573-2211 *Founded/Ownrshp* 1973
Sales 133.7MM[E] *EMP* 400
Accts Ernst & Young
SIC 2038 5812 Frozen specialties; Contract food services
Pr: Glenn Davenport
**COO:* John D Hale
**CFO:* Kenneth A Lobianco
**VP:* David P Karpan
Exec: Annette Henry
CTO: Andy Borgmann
Dir IT: John Forman
Dir IT: Andrew Gronek
VP Mktg: Bill Basto

D-U-N-S 08-021-2874
■ GA H IMPORTS LLC
AUTONATION HONDA COLUMBUS
(*Suby of* AUTONATION INC) ★
3000 N Lake Pkwy Ste 400, Columbus, GA 31909-2514
Tel (706) 522-2090 *Founded/Ownrshp* 2012
Sales 71.7M[E] *EMP* 1,436[E]
SIC 5511 Automobiles, new & used

GA STATE PATROL
See GEORGIA DEPARTMENT OF PUBLIC SAFETY

D-U-N-S 08-545-3806 IMP/EXP
GA TELESIS LLC
1850 Nw 49th St, Fort Lauderdale, FL 33309-3004
Tel (954) 676-3111 *Founded/Ownrshp* 2002
Sales 294.8MM[E] *EMP* 400
Accts Grant Thornton Fort Lauderdal
SIC 5088 3724 Aircraft & parts; Aircraft engines & engine parts
Pr: Abdol Moabery
Pr: Lynda Cheng
Pr: Jason Reed
**CFO:* Alvin Khoo
**CFO:* Jack Portlock
**Ex VP:* Andrew Toutt
VP: Gokhan Aydogan
VP: Nona Caroll
VP: David Ellis
**VP:* Kevin Geissler
VP: Jeffery Kramer
VP: Dean Lazarus
VP: Robert Loesch
VP: Rebecca Longo
VP: Irvin Lucas
VP: Darryl Maraj
Exec: Marion Braley

D-U-N-S 17-524-8681 IMP
GA WEST & CO INC
12526 Celeste Rd, Chunchula, AL 36521-3578
Tel (251) 679-1965 *Founded/Ownrshp* 1987
Sales 135.3MM *EMP* 1,000
Accts Wikins Miller Llc Mobile Ala
SIC 1541 Industrial buildings, new construction
Pr: Gary A West
**CFO:* J Randall Bevis
**Treas:* David Phillips
**Ex VP:* George Busby
**VP:* John Harris
**VP:* Sam Jackson
**VP:* Terry Swayne
Rgnl Mgr: Marty Friddle
Area Mgr: Roger Brown
IT Man: Darryl Wilkins
Mtls Mgr: Earl Baldwin

GAA
See GEORGIAN AMERICAN ALLOYS INC

D-U-N-S 16-799-9361 IMP
GAA HOLDINGS INC
GREAT AMERICAN SNACKS
216 8th St N, Nampa, ID 83687-3029
Tel (208) 465-5111 *Founded/Ownrshp* 2004
Sales 84.0MM[E] *EMP* 700[E]
SIC 2038

GABELLI
See GAMCO ASSET MANAGEMENT INC

D-U-N-S 08-464-2990
GABELLI & CO INC
(*Suby of* GABELLI GROUP CAP PARTNERS INC) ★
1 Corporate Ctr, Rye, NY 10580-1436
Tel (914) 921-3700 *Founded/Ownrshp* 1986
Sales 252.0MM *EMP* 30
SIC 6211 6282 Brokers, security; Dealers, security; Investment advice
Ch Bd: Daniel M Miller
CFO: John Givissis
VP: Tim Winter
MIS Dir: Arthur Lyman
Sales Asso: Bethany Steiger

GABELLI FUNDS
See GABELLI GROUP CAPITAL PARTNERS INC

D-U-N-S 79-035-7979
■ GABELLI FUNDS LLC
(*Suby of* GABELLI) ★
1 Corporate Ctr, Rye, NY 10580-1436
Tel (914) 921-5105 *Founded/Ownrshp* 1986
Sales 310.6MM[E] *EMP* 137[E]
SIC 6726 3993 Investment offices; Electric signs
VP: Brian A Campbell
**VP:* David M Goldman
VP: Chris Rainey
VP Sls: Jennifer Esposito

GABELLI GROUP CAP PARTNERS INC
See GABELLI SECURITIES INC

D-U-N-S 03-306-7497
GABELLI GROUP CAPITAL PARTNERS INC
GABELLI FUNDS
555 Theodore Fremd Ave C300, Rye, NY 10580-1455
Tel (914) 921-3700 *Founded/Ownrshp* 1981
Sales 252.0MM[E] *EMP* 359
SIC 6211 6282 Brokers, security; Dealers, security; Investment advisory service
Ch Bd: Mario J Gabelli
**Pr:* Marc Gabelli
Sr VP: Darryl S Grayson
**VP:* Raffaele Pisacane

D-U-N-S 60-264-1789
GABELLI SECURITIES INC
GABELLI GROUP CAP PARTNERS INC
(*Suby of* GABELLI FUNDS) ★
1 Corporate Ctr 401, Rye, NY 10580-1436
Tel (914) 921-3700 *Founded/Ownrshp* 1986
Sales 252.0MM[E] *EMP* 250
SIC 6211 Brokers, security; Dealers, security
Pr: Mario Gabelli
**V Ch Bd:* Salvatore F Sodano
Genl Couns: David L Fitzgerald

GABE'S
See GABRIEL BROTHERS INC

D-U-N-S 00-411-8386
GABLES ENGINEERING INC
247 Greco Ave, Coral Gables, FL 33146-1881
Tel (305) 774-4400 *Founded/Ownrshp* 1947
Sales 92.9MM[E] *EMP* 277
SIC 3679 Electronic circuits
Pr: Gary A Galimidi
VP: Charles E Rogers Jr
Dir Bus: Charlie Bibb
Genl Mgr: Rick Finale
Genl Mgr: Maritza Pedron
Genl Mgr: Rene Ramos
Genl Mgr: Raul Sanchez
DP Exec: Juan Vidal
MIS Dir: Jim Dyches
Dir IT: Maria Miranda
Dir IT: Mike Perrin

D-U-N-S 96-880-6554
GABLES REALTY LIMITED PARTNERSHIP
(*Suby of* GABLES RESIDENTIAL TRUST)
225 Ne Mizner Blvd # 400, Boca Raton, FL 33432-4078
Tel (561) 997-9700 *Founded/Ownrshp* 1994
Sales 82.7MM[E] *EMP* 1,400
SIC 6798 Real estate investment trusts
Ch Bd: Chris Wheeler
CFO: Don Stewart

D-U-N-S 80-362-7355
GABLES RESIDENTIAL SERVICES INC
(*Suby of* LION GABLES REALTY LIMITED PARTNERSHIP) ★
3399 Peachtree Rd Ne # 600, Atlanta, GA 30326-2832
Tel (404) 923-5500 *Founded/Ownrshp* 1994
Sales 88.8MM[E] *EMP* 1,200
SIC 6531 Real estate managers
CEO: Susan M Ansel
**CFO:* Dawn H Severt
VP: Chris Smurda
VP Mktg: Gigi Giannoni

D-U-N-S 01-610-6882 IMP
GABRIEL BROTHERS INC
GABE'S
(*Suby of* RUGGED WEARHOUSE) ★
55 Scott Ave, Morgantown, WV 26508-8853
Tel (304) 292-6965 *Founded/Ownrshp* 2012
Sales 522.5MM[E] *EMP* 3,500
SIC 5651 Family clothing stores
Pr: Ken Seipel
Treas: Ronald Gabriel
Treas: James Kline
VP: George Bellino

D-U-N-S 03-177-0972
■ GABRIEL COMMUNICATIONS FINANCE CO
(*Suby of* NEWSOUTH COMMUNICATIONS) ★
2 N Main St Ste 300, Greenville, SC 29601-4875
Tel (864) 672-5000 *Founded/Ownrshp* 1999
Sales 334.0MM[E] *EMP* 1,800[E]
SIC 4813 Telephone communication, except radio
CEO: James Akerhielm

GABRIEL RIDE CONTROL
See RIDE CONTROL LLC

D-U-N-S 10-112-7959
GABRIELLI TRUCK SALES LTD
FORD
15320 S Conduit Ave, Jamaica, NY 11434-4221
Tel (718) 977-7348 *Founded/Ownrshp* 1991
Sales 86.2MM[E] *EMP* 155
SIC 5511 5531 7538 Trucks, tractors & trailers: new & used; Truck equipment & parts; General truck repair
Pr: Armando Gabrielli
**VP:* Amedeo Gabrielli
Sls Mgr: Osmond Diaz
Sls Mgr: Romolo Gabrielli
Sls Mgr: J Loiacono

D-U-N-S 00-581-9438
GAC CONTRACTORS INC (FL)
4116 N Highway 231, Panama City, FL 32404-9235
Tel (850) 785-4675 *Founded/Ownrshp* 1958
Sales 99.4MM[E] *EMP* 365
SIC 1611 1629 Highway & street maintenance; Land preparation construction
Ch Bd: L Charles Hilton Jr
**Pr:* Richard M Dodd
**VP:* Carol S Atkinson
**VP:* Derwin White
Genl Mgr: Andrew Rowell
Off Mgr: Sherri Corley
IT Man: Shane Cook

GACSC
See GRAPHIC ARTS CENTER INC

D-U-N-S 07-979-9066
GADSDEN COUNTY SCHOOLS
35 Martin Luther King, Quincy, FL 32351-4411
Tel (850) 627-9651 *Founded/Ownrshp* 2015
Sales 9.3MM[E] *EMP* 1,165[E]
SIC 8211 Public elementary & secondary schools
Prin: Silvia Jackson

D-U-N-S 08-766-7267
GADSDEN INDEPENDENT SCHOOL DISTRICT
4950 Mcnutt Rd, Sunland Park, NM 88063
Tel (575) 882-6200 *Founded/Ownrshp* 1949
Sales 99.8MM^E *EMP* 2,000
Accts Griego Professional Services
SIC 8211 Public elementary & secondary schools
Pr: Jennifer Viramontes
**Pr:* Daniel Castillo
**Prin:* Craig Ford
**Prin:* Maria Saenz
Genl Mgr: Ludym Martinez
Genl Mgr: Margarita Terrazas
HC Dir: Judy Creegan

D-U-N-S 15-359-3074
■ **GADSDEN REGIONAL MEDICAL CENTER LLC**
QHG
(*Suby of* COMMUNITY HEALTH SYSTEMS INC) ★
1007 Goodyear Ave, Gadsden, AL 35903-1195
Tel (256) 494-4000 *Founded/Ownrshp* 2001
Sales 240.9MM *EMP* 1,300
SIC 8062 8082 8011 7352 General medical & surgical hospitals; Home health care services; General & family practice, physician/surgeon; Medical equipment rental
CEO: Stephen Pennington
**COO:* William Keith
**CFO:* Michael Cotton
Ofcr: Angela Tillis
Dir Risk M: Lisa Henderson
Dir Rx: Wayne Cornutt
Dir Bus: Rhonda Dehaven
Dir Sec: Mark Harper
Off Mgr: Marilyn Osborne
Nurse Mgr: Oakley Patterson
Plnt Mgr: Doug Blackwell

D-U-N-S 10-665-1540 IMP/EXP
GAF CORP
GAF MATERIALS
(*Suby of* BMCA) ★
1 Campus Dr, Parsippany, NJ 07054-4404
Tel (973) 628-3000 *Founded/Ownrshp* 1906
Sales 284.8MM^E *EMP* 525^E
SIC 3444 3634 Ducts, sheet metal; Fans, exhaust & ventilating, electric: household
Pr: Bob Tafaro
**Ex VP:* Jim Schnepper
**Sr VP:* Mike Kiik
**Sr VP:* Tim Machelski
VP: Julia Huston
VP: Larry Sterritt
IT Man: Daniel Doyle
Tech Mgr: Brandon Burton
Tech Mgr: Pete Weyrens
Netwrk Eng: John Celentano
Plnt Mgr: Nigel Abraham

GAF MATERIALS
See ELKCORP

GAF MATERIALS
See GAF CORP

D-U-N-S 00-187-0138 IMP/EXP
GAFFNEY-KROESE ELECTRICAL SUPPLY CORP (NY)
50 Randolph Rd, Somerset, NJ 08873-1240
Tel (732) 885-9000 *Founded/Ownrshp* 1931, 1946
Sales 256.3MM^E *EMP* 275
SIC 5063 5084 5085 Electronic wire & cable; Motors, electric; Generators; Materials handling machinery; Drilling equipment, excluding bits; Industrial supplies
Ch Bd: Christopher C Kroese
COO: Robert Jouas
**VP:* John S Kroese III
**Prin:* Peter Ross
Mng Dir: Mario Marchegiani
Mktg Dir: Joseph Delgiorno
Sls Mgr: Rocco Castoro
Sls Mgr: Bob O'Brien

G.A.FOOD SERVICE
See GA FOOD SERVICES OF PINELLAS COUNTY INC

D-U-N-S 10-242-1757 IMP
GAFP INC
AMERISTAR FENCE PRODUCTS
(*Suby of* ASSA ABLOY USA) ★
1555 N Mingo Rd, Tulsa, OK 74116-1506
Tel (918) 835-0898 *Founded/Ownrshp* 2013
Sales 224.3MM^E *EMP* 650
SIC 3315 Fence gates posts & fittings: steel
Pr: Johan Molin
VP: Steve Steele
Ex Dir: Ken White
Rgnl Mgr: Chris Babb
Dir IT: Steve Overacker
Sfty Mgr: Galen Sawyer
Prd Mgr: Joe Meeks
Ql Cn Mgr: Tom Ratliff
Secur Mgr: Scott Galbraith
Sales Exec: Brannon Wilson
Mktg Mgr: Chris Herold

D-U-N-S 04-721-1677
GAI CONSULTANTS INC (PA)
385 E Waterfront Dr Fl 1, Homestead, PA 15120-5070
Tel (412) 476-2000 *Founded/Ownrshp* 1958, 2003
Sales 230.1MM^E *EMP* 800
Accts Markovitz Dugan & Associates
SIC 8711 Consulting engineer
Pr: Gary Dejidas
**Pr:* Gary M Dejidas
**CFO:* Karl S Palvisak
Ex VP: Sarah Miloski
**Ex VP:* Anthony Morrocco
Ex VP: Aaron Speaks
**Sr VP:* J M Sievers
**VP:* Diane B Landers
**VP:* Anthony F Morrocco
Tech Mgr: Judson Fohr
Tech Mgr: Kenneth Jones

D-U-N-S 12-140-0063
▲ **GAIA INC**
833 W South Boulder Rd, Louisville, CO 80027-2400
Tel (303) 222-3600 *Founded/Ownrshp* 1988
Sales 188.0MM *EMP* 296
Tkr Sym GAIA *Exch* NGM
SIC 7299 7812 7999 Personal appearance services; Training motion picture production; Video production; Yoga instruction
Ch Bd: Jirka Rysavy
Pr: Brad Warkins
CFO: Paul Tarell Jr

GAIAM
See FIT FOR LIFE LLC

D-U-N-S 83-168-2146
▲ **GAIN CAPITAL HOLDINGS INC**
135 Route 202 206, Bedminster, NJ 07921
Tel (908) 731-0700 *Founded/Ownrshp* 1999
Sales 436.4MM *EMP* 772^E
Tkr Sym GCAP *Exch* NYS
SIC 6211 6221 Security brokers & dealers; Commodity contracts brokers, dealers
Pr: Glenn H Stevens
**Ch Bd:* Peter Quick
CFO: Nigel Rose
Chf Cred: Samantha Roady
Ex VP: Diego A Rotsztain
VP: Keith Ginder
VP: Nayan Patel
VP: Timothy Wzorek
Exec: Kemi Ajetunmobi
Sftwr Eng: Evgeny Trifonov
Snr Mgr: Jassim Abbasi
Board of Directors: Thomas Bevilacqua, Christopher W Calhoun, Joseph Schenk, Christopher S Sugden

GAINESVILLE REGIONAL UTILITIES
See CITY OF GAINESVILLE

D-U-N-S 08-263-5004
GAINESVILLE REGIONAL UTILITIES (INC)
GRU
301 Se 4th Ave, Gainesville, FL 32601-6857
Tel (352) 334-3400 *Founded/Ownrshp* 1912
Sales 559.8MM^E *EMP* 750
Accts Earnst & Young Llp Orlando F
SIC 4939 4941 4924 4911 Combination utilities; Water supply; Natural gas distribution;
**CFO:* Jennifer L Hunt
**CFO:* David M Richardson
VP: Patricia Kafle
VP: Lewis Walton
Exec: Sara Smith
Genl Mgr: Robert Hunzinger
Genl Mgr: Kathy E Viehe
CIO: Ronald Key
Dir IT: Susan Boyd
Dir IT: Pamela Dalziel
Dir IT: Connie Smith

GAINSCO AUTO INSURANCE
See GAINSCO INC

D-U-N-S 03-790-2590
▲ **GAINSCO INC**
GAINSCO AUTO INSURANCE
3333 Lee Pkwy Ste 1200, Dallas, TX 75219-5134
Tel (972) 629-4301 *Founded/Ownrshp* 1978
Sales NA *EMP* 395^E
Tkr Sym GANS *Exch* OTO
SIC 6331 Fire, marine & casualty insurance & carriers; Property damage insurance
V Ch Bd: James R Reis
**Ch Bd:* Robert W Stallings
Pr: Glenn Anderson
Pr: McRae B Johnston
CFO: Daniel Coots
Sr VP: Stephen L Porcelli
Sr VP: Carolyn E Ray
VP: Don Baker
VP: Brian Kirkham
Prin: Robert J Boulware
Prin: John C Goff
Board of Directors: Robert J Boulware, John C Goff, Joel C Puckett, Sam Rosen, Harden H Wiedemann, John H Williams

D-U-N-S 06-724-7072
GAL-TEX HOTEL CORP
1859 HISTORIC HOTELS
2302 Pstoffice St Ste 500, Galveston, TX 77550
Tel (409) 763-8536 *Founded/Ownrshp* 1940
Sales 79.0MM *EMP* 1,953
SIC 7011 8741

D-U-N-S 04-434-7771
GALASSOS BAKERY
10820 San Sevaine Way, Mira Loma, CA 91752-1116
Tel (951) 360-1211 *Founded/Ownrshp* 1923
Sales 117.6MM^E *EMP* 300
SIC 2051 Bakery: wholesale or wholesale/retail combined
Pr: Jeannette Galasso
**Treas:* Mark Bailey
**VP:* Rick Vargas

D-U-N-S 96-275-1967
GALATA CHEMICALS HOLDING CO LLC
464 Heritage Rd Ste 1, Southbury, CT 06488-3863
Tel (203) 236-9000 *Founded/Ownrshp* 2010
Sales 200.0MM *EMP* 120
SIC 5169 6719 Industrial chemicals; Personal holding companies, except banks
Pr: Steven McKeown
**CEO:* Erick Wisnefsky
**CFO:* Joseph Falsbury
**Treas:* Matthew Yopchick

D-U-N-S 96-275-3716 IMP
GALATA CHEMICALS LLC
(*Suby of* ARTEK SURFIN CHEMICALS LIMITED)
464 Heritage Rd Ste A1, Southbury, CT 06488-3863
Tel (203) 236-9000 *Founded/Ownrshp* 2014
Sales 134.6MM^E *EMP* 100
SIC 5169 3999 Organic chemicals, synthetic; Atomizers, toiletry; Polyvinyl chloride resins (PVC)
CEO: Luc De Temmerma
**Pr:* Steven McKeown
**CFO:* Joseph Falsbury
Treas: Matthew Yopchick
**VP:* Brian Johnson

D-U-N-S 08-193-9167
GALATI YACHT SALES LLC
CITGO
902 Bay Blvd, Anna Maria, FL 34216
Tel (941) 778-0755 *Founded/Ownrshp* 1976
Sales 83.2MM^E *EMP* 175
SIC 5551 4493 Boat dealers; Marine supplies & equipment; Marinas
**VP:* Carmine Galati
Dir IT: Chris Burkett
Mktg Dir: Randy Bright
Sales Asso: Lee Hutton
Sales Asso: Bill McCormick

GALAXY FANS & HEATERS
See LASKO PRODUCTS INC

D-U-N-S 07-997-1031
■ **GALAXY INVESTMENT HOLDINGS INC**
(*Suby of* SOFTBANK GROUP CORP.)
38 Glen Ave, Newton, MA 02459-2066
Tel (617) 928-9300 *Founded/Ownrshp* 2013
Sales 32.1MMM^E *EMP* 31,000^E
SIC 4813 4812 Local & long distance telephone communications; Data telephone communications; ; ; Cellular telephone services
Prin: Joshua O Lubov

GALCO BUILDING PRODUCTS
See SPENARD BUILDERS SUPPLY LLC

D-U-N-S 01-086-9477 EXP
GALCO INDUSTRIAL ELECTRONICS INC
(*Suby of* GII HOLDING III CORP)
26010 Pinehurst Dr, Madison Heights, MI 48071-4189
Tel (248) 542-9090 *Founded/Ownrshp* 2014
Sales 96.4MM^E *EMP* 122^E
SIC 5065 Electronic parts
Pr: Michael Conwell
**CFO:* Karen Mandarino
VP: Katie Blackburn
IT Man: David Gardner
Mfg Dir: Mark Higdon
Sales Exec: Steve Misiakowski
Mktg Dir: William Abbe
Sls Dir: Peter Maurer
Sales Asso: Carolyn Morrison

D-U-N-S 04-735-0186 IMP/EXP
GALDERMA LABORATORIES LP
(*Suby of* GALDERMA PHARMA S.A.)
14501 North Fwy, Fort Worth, TX 76177-3304
Tel (817) 961-5000 *Founded/Ownrshp* 1981
Sales 215.9MM^E *EMP* 499
SIC 2834 Dermatologicals
Pr: Todd Zavodnick
Sr VP: Phil Brown
Sr VP: Philip Brown
VP: Quintin Cassady
VP: Ken Ferrell
VP: Brian Foard
VP: Miles Harrison
VP: Kelly Huang
VP: Safia Rizvi
VP: Brant Scholfield
VP: Carol Stuckley
Exec: Donna Brunson
Exec: Michael Graeber

D-U-N-S 87-924-8201 IMP/EXP
GALE GROUP INC
27500 Drake Rd, Farmington Hills, MI 48331-3535
Tel (248) 699-4253 *Founded/Ownrshp* 2007
Sales NA *EMP* 1,232
SIC 7375

D-U-N-S 07-663-0060
GALEN HOSPITAL ALASKA INC
ALASKA REGIONAL HOSPITAL
2801 Debarr Rd, Anchorage, AK 99508-2932
Tel (907) 276-1131 *Founded/Ownrshp* 1995
Sales 226.9MM *EMP* 800
SIC 8062 General medical & surgical hospitals
CEO: Julie Taylor
**Pr:* Samuel N Hazen
**Pr:* Ernie Meier
**CEO:* Annie Holt
**COO:* Rick Davis
COO: Vic Rosenbaum
**COO:* Victor Rosenbaum
**CFO:* Lynn Kennington
CFO: Paul Morris
Exec: Marilyn Cooper
Dir Risk M: Rosemary Craig
Dir Lab: Karen Lakey

D-U-N-S 01-038-3909
■ **GALEN OF FLORIDA INC**
ST. PETERSBURG GENERAL HOSP
(*Suby of* HOSPITAL COPORATION OF AMERICA) ★
6500 38th Ave N, Saint Petersburg, FL 33710-1629
Tel (727) 341-4055 *Founded/Ownrshp* 1967
Sales 95.5MM *EMP* 600
SIC 8062 General medical & surgical hospitals
CEO: Robert B Conroy Jr
**COO:* Jack Bovender
**CFO:* Shawn Gregory
**CFO:* Stephanie McNulty
Trst: Wayne Garcia
**VP:* Ronald L Grubbs
Doctor: Robert Abady
Doctor: Abraham I Awwad
Doctor: Romeo Acosta
Doctor: Jan N Arango
Doctor: Marc S Barasch

D-U-N-S 09-934-8088
■ **GALENCARE INC**
COLUMBIA HCA
(*Suby of* HOSPITAL COPORATION OF AMERICA) ★
119 Oakfield Dr, Brandon, FL 33511-5779
Tel (813) 681-5551 *Founded/Ownrshp* 1993
Sales 350.4MM *EMP* 1,300
SIC 8062 General medical & surgical hospitals
Pr: Samuel N Hazen
V Ch: Steven Granger
**CEO:* Bland Eng
**COO:* Janice Balzano
COO: Hal Muetzel
**CFO:* Michael Terrell
**Sec:* David G Anderson
**Sr VP:* Robert T Waterman
VP: Wayne Blocker
**VP:* David Park
**VP:* Donald W Stinnett
Dir Pat Ca: Kim Fournier
Dir Risk M: Misty Milling

GALERIE AU CHOCOLAT
See ROSS ACQUISITION CO

D-U-N-S 17-471-6394 IMP/EXP
GALEY & LORD LLC
(*Suby of* PATRIARCH PARTNERS LLC) ★
670 N Main St, Society Hill, SC 29593-8502
Tel (843) 378-4511 *Founded/Ownrshp* 2003
Sales 322.2MM^E *EMP* 1,275
SIC 2211 2221 2325 2339 Broadwoven fabric mills, cotton; Denims; Broadwoven fabric mills, manmade; Polyester broadwoven fabrics; Men's & boys' dress slacks & shorts; Shorts (outerwear): women's, misses' & juniors'
CEO: John Heldrich
Genl Mgr: Carolyn Sain

D-U-N-S 80-909-0756
GALI SERVICE INDUSTRIES INC
12312 Wilkins Ave Ste 100, Rockville, MD 20852-1815
Tel (301) 986-8890 *Founded/Ownrshp* 1989
Sales 48.3MM^E *EMP* 1,350
SIC 7349 Cleaning service, industrial or commercial
CEO: Francisco Gali
**Pr:* Leroy Dock
**CFO:* Mark Terenzi

D-U-N-S 07-454-7175
GALION COMMUNITY HOSPITAL
269 Portland Way S, Galion, OH 44833-2399
Tel (419) 468-4841 *Founded/Ownrshp* 1954
Sales 101.5MM *EMP* 465
SIC 8062 8051 General medical & surgical hospitals; Skilled nursing care facilities
Pr: Lamar Wyse
COO: Bill Vandorn
**CFO:* Robert Melaragno
VP: Eric Draime
VP: Mike Senter
Dir Inf Cn: Joyce Weaver
Off Mgr: Rhonda Ridenouer
Pr Mgr: Kelby King
Obsttrcn: Eric J Hoff
Doctor: Marcia Brown

GALLAGER BASSETT SERVICES
See RISK PLACEMENT SERVICES INC

GALLAGHER & ASSOCIATES
See RJF AGENCIES INC

GALLAGHER & BURK
See OLIVER DE SILVA INC

GALLAGHER BASSETT INSUR SVCS
See GALLAGHER BASSETT SERVICES INC

D-U-N-S 14-752-5224
■ **GALLAGHER BASSETT SERVICES INC**
GALLAGHER BASSETT INSUR SVCS
(*Suby of* ARTHUR J GALLAGHER & CO) ★
2 Pierce Pl Ste 100, Itasca, IL 60143-1277
Tel (630) 773-3800 *Founded/Ownrshp* 2010
Sales NA *EMP* 3,400
SIC 6411 8741 Insurance agents & brokers; Business management
**CFO:* Jim Bond
**Treas:* Jack Lazzaro
Treas: Mark Strauch
Sr Cor Off: Jon Wawrzyniak
**Chf Mktg O:* Dave Gordon
Ofcr: Gary R Fansler
Sr VP: Gary Anderberg
Sr VP: Michael Bell
Sr VP: Srivatsan Sridharan
VP: Amy Bonita
VP: James Braniff
VP: Michael Creighton
VP: Arthur Gallagher
VP: Rex W Martin
VP: Russ Parsons
VP: Gary Wood

D-U-N-S 00-134-9914
■ **GALLAGHER BENEFIT SERVICES INC**
(*Suby of* ARTHUR J GALLAGHER & CO) ★
2 Pierce Pl, Itasca, IL 60143-1203
Tel (630) 773-3800 *Founded/Ownrshp* 1999
Sales NA *EMP* 154
SIC 6411 Insurance agents, brokers & service
Pr: James Durkin
Sr VP: John Kirkpatrick
VP: David M Ziegler
Snr Mgr: Joseph Wert

D-U-N-S 96-427-0644
GALLATIN COUNTY REST HOME
1221 Durston Rd, Bozeman, MT 59715-2725
Tel (406) 582-3300 *Founded/Ownrshp* 2010
Sales 406.4MM *EMP* 15^E
SIC 8051 Skilled nursing care facilities
Prin: Vickie West

GALLAUDET CMNTY INTERPRETING
See GALLAUDET UNIVERSITY

D-U-N-S 00-325-9439 IMP
GALLAUDET UNIVERSITY
GALLAUDET CMNTY INTERPRETING
800 Florida Ave Ne, Washington, DC 20002-3600
Tel (202) 651-5000 *Founded/Ownrshp* 1857
Sales 184.2MM *EMP* 1,200
Accts Grant Thornton Llp New York
SIC 8221 University
Pr: Dr T Alan Hurwitz
CFO: Ivey Wallace
VP: Kendall Hall

VP: Gallaudet Intramurals
**VP:* Paul Kelly
VP: Shondra Mitchell
VP Admn: Gaynelle Hayes
Ex Dir: Cynthia King
Ex Dir: Fred Weiner
IT Man: Suzy McKenzie
Pr Dir: Mercy Coogan
Board of Directors: Gary Aller Nicole Sutliffe

D-U-N-S 00-796-5346 IMP
GALLEHER CORP (DE)
9303 Greenleaf Ave, Santa Fe Springs, CA 90670-3029
Tel (562) 944-8885 *Founded/Ownrshp* 1937, 2010
Sales 175.0MM *EMP* 275
SIC 5023 Wood flooring
CEO: Jeff Hamar
Pr: Derek Hui
**Sr VP:* Rick Coates
**Sr VP:* Todd Hamar
**VP:* Ray Iodice
Brnch Mgr: Jonathan Leon
Dir IT: Rene Peregrina
Sales Asso: Denise Gonzales

D-U-N-S 01-955-1050
GALLERY AUTOMOTIVE GROUP LLC
SUZUKI GALLERY
(*Suby of* MARUBENI AUTO & CONSTRUCTION MACHINERY (AMERICA) INC) ★
918 Providence Hwy, Norwood, MA 02062
Tel (877) 201-8871 *Founded/Ownrshp* 2003
Sales 91.2MM^E *EMP* 202
SIC 5511 5012 7538 Automobiles, new & used; Automobiles; General automotive repair shops
Genl Mgr: Steven Stein
Sls Mgr: Frank McLaughlin
Sls Mgr: Kevin Misanko

GALLERY CUSTOM HOMES
See FIRST TEXAS HOMES INC

D-U-N-S 00-893-6379
GALLIKER DAIRY CO
GALLIKER'S QUALITY CHEKD
143 Donald Ln, Johnstown, PA 15904-2829
Tel (814) 266-8702 *Founded/Ownrshp* 1914
Sales 106.7MM^E *EMP* 365
SIC 2026 2086 2024 Buttermilk, cultured; Eggnog, fresh: non-alcoholic; Milk drinks, flavored; Tea, iced: packaged in cans, bottles, etc.; Ice cream & ice milk
Ch: Louis G Galliker
**Pr:* Charles Price
**Treas:* Douglas B Roberts
VP: William Livingston
**VP:* Charles D Price
Exec: Wendy Schultz
Plnt Mgr: Diane Yost
Sales Exec: Linda Campbell
VP Sls: Ray Cassidy
Mktg Dir: Ryan Sheetz
Sls Mgr: Bartolotta Ron

GALLIKER'S QUALITY CHEKD
See GALLIKER DAIRY CO

D-U-N-S 00-910-7749 IMP
GALLO GLASS CO
(*Suby of* SAN JOAQUIN VLY CONCENTRATES) ★
605 S Santa Cruz Ave, Modesto, CA 95354-4299
Tel (209) 341-3710 *Founded/Ownrshp* 1957
Sales 226.6MM^E *EMP* 1,205
SIC 3221 Glass containers
Pr: Robert J Gallo
IT Man: Craig Beck
Opers Mgr: Dean McMeechan
VP Mktg: Jere Johnson
Snr Mgr: Joshua Self

D-U-N-S 04-259-8482 IMP/EXP
GALLS LLC
1340 Russell Cave Rd, Lexington, KY 40505-3114
Tel (859) 266-7227 *Founded/Ownrshp* 2011
Sales 208.0MM^E *EMP* 600^E
SIC 5961 5399 2395 Catalog sales; Mail order house; Catalog showrooms; Pleating & stitching
CEO: Michael Wessner
Pr: Eldon Griggs
**CFO:* Michael Andrews
Top Exec: Eric Helton
**VP:* Rusty Cook
VP: Alex Marino
VP: Abe Rabiner
Prgrm Mgr: Bill Erwin
Store Mgr: Chris Parra
IT Man: Deborah Dennison
Ql Cn Mgr: Milford Jones

D-U-N-S 07-375-0192
GALLUP INC
GALLUP ORGANIZATION
901 F St Nw Ste 400, Washington, DC 20004-1419
Tel (202) 715-3030 *Founded/Ownrshp* 1958
Sales 249.1MM *EMP* 2,000
Accts Kpmg Omaha Ne
SIC 8742 Management consulting services
Ch: Jim Clifton
V Ch: Gale D Muller
V Ch: Connie Rath
COO: Jane Miller
COO: Jane E Miller
CFO: James R Krieger
Treas: Emily Nielsen
Sr VP: Annette Templeton
Exec: Jeff Bollettino
Exec: Tasha Hunt
Exec: Steve D O'Brien

GALLUP ORGANIZATION
See GALLUP INC

D-U-N-S 06-941-2153
GALLUP-MC KINLEY COUNTY PUBLIC SCHOOL DISTRICT 1 (INC) (TX)
700 Boardman Dr, Gallup, NM 87301-4707
Tel (505) 722-7711 *Founded/Ownrshp* 1958
Sales 75.4MM^E *EMP* 1,500
SIC 8211 Public elementary & secondary schools; Public junior high school; Public senior high school
Off Admin: Linda Gallegos
Off Admin: Georgia S Merrill
Off Admin: Marsha Spencer
CTO: David Oaks
IT Man: Danny John
Site Mgr: Martin Padilla
Pr Dir: Koreen Smith
Schl Brd P: Joe Menini
Schl Brd P: Titus Smith
Teacher Pr: Ron H Donkersloot
Teacher Pr: Judie Jaramillo

GALMOR'S
See G & G STEAM SERVICE INC

GALPIN FORD
See GALPIN MOTORS INC

D-U-N-S 02-945-3131 EXP
GALPIN MOTORS INC
GALPIN FORD
15505 Roscoe Blvd, North Hills, CA 91343-6598
Tel (818) 787-3800 *Founded/Ownrshp* 1964
Sales 322.6MM^E *EMP* 1,000
SIC 5511 5521 7538 7515 7514 5531 Automobiles, new & used; Used car dealers; General automotive repair shops; Passenger car leasing; Passenger car rental; Automotive & home supply stores
Pr: Herbert F Boeckman II
**Treas:* Jane Boeckmann
**VP:* Bradley M Boeckmann
VP: Laura Espino
**VP:* Alan J Skobin
VP: Rose Tapia
Exec: Carol Carlaggo
**Genl Mgr:* Phil Marshall
Genl Mgr: Steve McCord
Genl Mgr: Lilliana Munguia
MIS Dir: Frank Lucas

GALT HOUSE, THE
See AL J SCHNEIDER CO

D-U-N-S 07-939-7204 IMP
GALVESTON INDEPENDENT SCHOOL DISTRICT (TX)
3904 Avenue T, Galveston, TX 77550-8643
Tel (409) 765-2101 *Founded/Ownrshp* 1882
Sales 212.7M *EMP* 1,218
Accts B Head Maxwell & Enna P C
SIC 8211 Public elementary school; Public junior high school; Public senior high school
Trst: Beau Rawlins
Genl Mgr: David Dworsky
MIS Dir: John Mathis
Pr Dir: Dyann Polzin
HC Dir: Zia Robinson

D-U-N-S 10-363-1925
■ **GALYANS TRADING CO LLC**
(*Suby of* DICKS SPORTING GOODS INC) ★
300 Industry Dr, Pittsburgh, PA 15275-1001
Tel (724) 273-3400 *Founded/Ownrshp* 2004
Sales 193.1MM^E *EMP* 6,100
SIC 5941 5699 5661 Sporting goods & bicycle shops; Sports apparel; Footwear, athletic
CEO: Edwin J Holman
CFO: Donald P Lofe
**CFO:* Edward S Wozniak
**Chf Mktg O:* Richard Leto
**Ex VP:* C David Zoba
Sr VP: Charles Nelson
**Sr VP:* Lindsay Rice
**Sr VP:* Paul C Wagner
Sr VP: Edward Whitehead
VP: Matt Lynch

D-U-N-S 06-894-6862
GAMBLE ELIZABETH DEACONESS HOME ASSOCIATION (INC)
2139 Auburn Ave, Cincinnati, OH 45219-2906
Tel (513) 751-4224 *Founded/Ownrshp* 1888
Sales 28.6MM *EMP* 2,900
Accts Barnes Dennig & Co Ltd Cin
SIC 8062 8082 General medical & surgical hospitals; Home health care services
Ch Bd: Thomas Petry
**Pr:* Theodore H Emmerich
Bd of Dir: Thomas R Gerdes
Bd of Dir: Michael Keating

GAMBLE, JAMES MD
See TATEM BROWN FAMILY PRACTICE

D-U-N-S 15-746-7085 IMP
GAMBRINUS CO
SHINER BOCK
14800 San Pedro Ave # 310, San Antonio, TX 78232-3735
Tel (210) 483-5100 *Founded/Ownrshp* 1986
Sales 325.7MM^E *EMP* 446
SIC 5181 2082 Beer & other fermented malt liquors; Beer (alcoholic beverage)
Pr: Carlos Alvarez
**Pr:* James Bolz
CFO: Jim Bolz
**CFO:* James J O'Sullivan
**Sec:* John Horan
Exec: David Hutto
Exec: Cyndee White
Genl Mgr: Luis Alvarez
CTO: Tim Crisp
Web Prj Mg: Ron Christensen

D-U-N-S 04-109-3923
■ **GAMBRO INC**
(*Suby of* GAMBRO AB)
9540 Maroon Cir Unit 400, Englewood, CO 80112-5731
Tel (800) 525-2623 *Founded/Ownrshp* 1964, 2008
Sales 341.3MM^E *EMP* 1,950
SIC 6719 Personal holding companies, except banks
COO: Juan Bosch
VP: Frank Corbin
Web Prj Mg: Panella Todd
Sls Mgr: John M Murante

D-U-N-S 82-904-2337 IMP/EXP
■ **GAMBRO RENAL PRODUCTS INC**
(*Suby of* GAMBRO INC) ★
9540 Maroon Cir Unit 400, Englewood, CO 80112-5731
Tel (303) 222-6500 *Founded/Ownrshp* 1990
Sales 138.6MM^E *EMP* 662
SIC 3842 Surgical appliances & supplies
Pr: Nick Mendez
**CFO:* David Doerr
VP: Carla Anthony
VP: Werner Beck
**VP:* Robert Belknapp
VP: Luca Chiastra
Ex Dir: Earl Engel
Ex Dir: Frank Giese
Ex Dir: Rita Thomas
Genl Mgr: Yvonne Vigil
QA Dir: Kacey Johnson

GAMCO
See GENERAL ALUMINUM MFG CO

D-U-N-S 05-401-6118
■ **GAMCO ASSET MANAGEMENT INC** (NY)
(*Suby of* GABELLI) ★
401 Theodore Fremd Ave, Rye, NY 10580-1422
Tel (914) 921-5000 *Founded/Ownrshp* 1999
Sales 380.9MM^E *EMP* 168
SIC 6282 Investment advisory service

D-U-N-S 05-454-5202
▲ **GAMCO ASSET MANAGEMENT INC**
GABELLI
1 Corporate Ctr, Rye, NY 10580-1436
Tel (914) 921-3700 *Founded/Ownrshp* 1977
Sales 380.9MM *EMP* 168^E
Tkr Sym GBL *Exch* NYS
SIC 6282 Investment advisory service
Ch Bd: Mario J Gabelli
Pr: Douglas R Jamieson
Bd of Dir: Elisa Wilson
Ex VP: Kevin Handwerker
Board of Directors: Edwin L Artzt, Raymond C Avansino, Leslie B Daniels, Eugene R McGrath, Robert S Prather Jr, Elisa M Wilson

D-U-N-S 13-159-2755
■ **GAME SHOW NETWORK LLC**
G S N
(*Suby of* LIBERTY ENTERTAINMENT INC) ★
2150 Colorado Ave Ste 100, Santa Monica, CA 90404-5514
Tel (310) 255-6800 *Founded/Ownrshp* 2012
Sales 85.8MM^E *EMP* 202^E
SIC 4841 Cable & other pay television services
CEO: David Goldhill
Pr: Frank Cartwright
CFO: Brent Williams
**Ofcr:* Andrew Pedersen
Ex VP: Steven Brunell
VP: Tara Briganti
VP: Kam Diba
VP: Dennis K Gillespie
VP: Davin Miyoshi
VP: Jonathan Small
VP: Ryan Tredinnick
VP: Dennis Wald
Creative D: Chris Georgenes
Board of Directors: Rich Cronin, Jamie Roberts

D-U-N-S 07-940-0031
GAMECHANGE SOLAR LLC
152 W 57th St Fl 17, New York, NY 10019-3310
Tel (212) 359-0200 *Founded/Ownrshp* 2012
Sales 330.0MM *EMP* 37
SIC 5074 Heating equipment (hydronic)
CEO: Andrew Worden
**CFO:* Olga Filippova

D-U-N-S 60-245-5839 IMP/EXP
GAMESA TECHNOLOGY CORP INC
GAMESA WIND
(*Suby of* GAMESA CORPORACION TECNOLOGICA SOCIEDAD ANONIMA)
1150 Northbrook Dr # 300, Feasterville Trevose, PA 19053-8409
Tel (215) 710-3100 *Founded/Ownrshp* 2005
Sales 238.4MM^E *EMP* 800^E
SIC 6719 3621 Investment holding companies, except banks; Windmills, electric generating
CEO: Dirk Matthys

GAMESA WIND
See GAMESA TECHNOLOGY CORP INC

D-U-N-S 60-744-2428
▲ **GAMESTOP CORP**
625 Westport Pkwy, Grapevine, TX 76051-6740
Tel (817) 424-2000 *Founded/Ownrshp* 1996
Sales 9.3MMM *EMP* 20,000^E
Accts Deloitte & Touche Llp Dallas
Tkr Sym GME *Exch* NYS
SIC 5945 5734 5932 2721 Hobby, toy & game shops; Dolls & accessories; Computer & software stores; Software, computer games; Computer software & accessories; Used merchandise stores; Computers & accessories, secondhand; Magazines: publishing only, not printed on site
CEO: J Paul Raines
**Ch Bd:* Daniel A Dematteo
Pr: Michael T Buskey
COO: Tony D Bartel
CFO: Robert A Lloyd
Ex VP: Michael P Hogan
Sr VP: Steve Bain
Sr VP: Michael Cooper
Sr VP: Troy W Crawford
Sr VP: Michael K Mauler
VP: Jason Cochran
VP: Bruce Kulp
VP: Marc Summey
VP: John Watson
VP: Kevin Weimerskirch
VP: Blayne White
Board of Directors: Jerome L Davis, R Richard Fontaine, Thomas N Kelly, Shane S Kim, Steven R Koonin, Stephanie M Shern, Gerald R Szczepanski, Kathy P Vrabeck, Lawrence S Zilavy

D-U-N-S 07-884-7988
▲ **GAMING AND LEISURE PROPERTIES INC**
845 Berkshire Blvd, Wyomissing, PA 19610-1234
Tel (610) 401-2900 *Founded/Ownrshp* 2013
Sales 2.1MMM^E *EMP* 15,639^E
Tkr Sym GLPI *Exch* NGS
SIC 6519 Real property lessors
CEO: Peter M Carlino
CFO: William J Clifford
Sr VP: Curtis Magleby
Pr Mgr: Joseph N Jaffoni

D-U-N-S 13-762-9911 IMP
GAMMA CONSTRUCTION CO INC
2808 Joanel St, Houston, TX 77027-5306
Tel (713) 963-0086 *Founded/Ownrshp* 1985
Sales 101.2MM^E *EMP* 190
Accts Kurt & Associates Pc Houst
SIC 1542 Commercial & office building contractors
Pr: Keith Williams
**CFO:* Guy Windheim
**Sr VP:* Thomas R Hansen
**Sr VP:* Cecil Windsor

D-U-N-S 00-596-5363 IMP
GAMTEX INDUSTRIES LP (TX)
ASHMAN MEDALS & RECYCL COMANY
2600 Shamrock Ave, Fort Worth, TX 76107-1311
Tel (800) 749-0423 *Founded/Ownrshp* 1918
Sales 124.7MM *EMP* 90
SIC 5093 Metal scrap & waste materials
Ch: Arnold Gachman
Pr: Eric Gachman

D-U-N-S 00-850-0159 IMP
GANAHL LUMBER CO
1220 E Ball Rd, Anaheim, CA 92805-5993
Tel (714) 772-5444 *Founded/Ownrshp* 1923
Sales 310.8MM *EMP* 760
SIC 5211

D-U-N-S 96-384-8650 IMP
GANDER MOUNTAIN CO
180 5th St E Ste 1300, Saint Paul, MN 55101-1664
Tel (651) 325-4300 *Founded/Ownrshp* 2010
Sales 1.0MMM^E *EMP* 5,605
SIC 5941 Sporting goods & bicycle shops; Hunting equipment; Fishing equipment; Camping & backpacking equipment
Ch Bd: David C Pratt
**Pr:* Michael Owens
**Pr:* Derek Siddons
COO: Michael J Owens
COO: Jay Tibbets
**CFO:* Brian D Kohlbeck
**Ofcr:* Eric R Jacobsen
**Ex VP:* Lisa Schmidt
Sr VP: Jeff Csuy
Sr VP: Carissa Rollins
Sr VP: Robert J Vold
VP: Pat Mauldin
VP: Tammy Mihailidis
VP: Alan Tague
VP: Kevin Young
Board of Directors: Karen M Bohn, Marshall L Day, Richard C Dell, Gerald A Erickson, Ronald A Erickson

D-U-N-S 08-169-8342 IMP
■ **GANNETT BROADCASTING INC**
WXIA-TV
(*Suby of* TEGNA INC) ★
7950 Jones Branch Dr, Mc Lean, VA 22102-3302
Tel (703) 854-6000 *Founded/Ownrshp* 1995
Sales 401.8MM^E *EMP* 1,500^E
SIC 4833 Television broadcasting stations
Sr VP: Brooke Spectorsky
V Ch: James Johnson
**Sr VP:* Rob Mennie
Sr VP: Bob Sullivan
VP: Ellen Crooke
VP: Philip R Currie
VP: Gary Foy
VP: Dale Henn
VP: Abigail Horrigan
VP: Leslie Hurst
VP: James Jackson
VP: Kevin Lefew
VP: Lane Michaelsen
VP: Joshua Resnik
VP: Joel Rochon
Board of Directors: Douglas H Mc Corkindale

D-U-N-S 07-984-1977
▲ **GANNETT CO INC**
7950 Jones Branch Dr, Mc Lean, VA 22102-3302
Tel (703) 854-6000 *Founded/Ownrshp* 2015
Sales 6.2MMM^E *EMP* 18,700^E
Tkr Sym GCI *Exch* NYS
SIC 2711 7375 Newspapers; Information retrieval services
Pr: Robert J Dickey
Ch Bd: John Jeffry Louis
Pr: Nancy A Meyer
Pr: Chris Stegman
CFO: Alison K Engel
Chf Mktg O: Jeff Fagel
Ofcr: David Harmon
Sr VP: Daniel Bernard
VP: Kelly Andersen
VP: Michael Dickerson
VP: Chris McPherson
VP: Walter Nagel
VP: Chase Rankin
VP Bus Dev: Wayne Freedman
Board of Directors: John E Cody, Stephen W Coll, Donald E Felsinger, Lila Ibrahim, Lawrence S Kramer, Tony A Prophet, Debra A Sandler, Chloe R Sladden

D-U-N-S 02-811-9915
GANNETT FLEMING AFFILIATES INC
207 Senate Ave, Camp Hill, PA 17011-2316
Tel (717) 763-7211 *Founded/Ownrshp* 1981
Sales 331.9MM *EMP* 1,743
Accts Stambaugh Ness Pc Hanover P

SIC 8711 7374 6512 Engineering services; Data processing service; Commercial & industrial building operation
Ch Bd: William Stout
**Pr:* Robert Scaer
**Treas:* Lynn E Knepp
**Sr VP:* Robert J Dietz

D-U-N-S 00-634-2026 EXP
■ GANNETT RIVER STATES PUBLISHING CORP
ARKANSAS GAZETTE, THE
(*Suby of* GANNETT CO INC) ★
7950 Jones Branch Dr, Mc Lean, VA 22102-3302
Tel (703) 284-6000 *Founded/Ownrshp* 2015
Sales 109.8MM^E *EMP* 1,300
SIC 2711 2741 Newspapers, publishing & printing; Miscellaneous publishing
Ch Bd: William T Malone
Pr: Craig A Moon
V Ch Bd: Hugh B Patterson
VP: Donald Davis
VP: Ronald Krengel
VP: Edgar Major
VP: N Suzanne Miles

D-U-N-S 01-424-9759 IMP/EXP
■ GANNETT SATELLITE INFORMATION NETWORK LLC
USA TODAY
(*Suby of* GANNETT CO INC) ★
7950 Jones Branch Dr, Mc Lean, VA 22102-3302
Tel (703) 854-6000 *Founded/Ownrshp* 2015
Sales 514.2MM^E *EMP* 2,800
SIC 2711 Newspapers, publishing & printing
CEO: Douglas H Mc Corkindale
Pr: Tom Beusse
**Pr:* Robert J Dickey
Ch: Dave Morgan
**Treas:* Minakshi Sundaram
Ex VP: Derek Murphy
Sr VP: Craig Etheridge
Sr VP: Peter Lazarus
Sr VP: Sandra Cordova Micek
Sr VP: Michael Safran
Sr VP: Dan Thomas
VP: Maureen Consavage
VP: Laura Del Greco
VP: Lori Erdos
VP: Tony Hill
VP: Myron Maslowsky
VP: John Palmisano
VP: Scott R Singer
**VP:* Barbara W Wall

D-U-N-S 07-215-9767
GANNON UNIVERSITY
109 University Sq, Erie, PA 16541-0002
Tel (814) 871-7000 *Founded/Ownrshp* 1944
Sales 91.3MM *EMP* 600
Accts Baker Tilly Virchow Krause Ll
SIC 8221 University
Pr: Antoine Garibaldi
V Ch: Steven Ropski
Pr: Mark Jordano
VP: Gary Garnic
VP: Keith Taylor
Assoc Dir: Catherine Gillespie
Genl Mgr: Peter Mannarelli
CIO: Robert Cline
Dir IT: Gregory Duffin
Dir IT: Dan Huber
IT Man: Hamid Torab

D-U-N-S 02-041-6921 IMP/EXP
GANTRADE CORP
210 Summit Ave Ste B5, Montvale, NJ 07645-1526
Tel (201) 573-1955 *Founded/Ownrshp* 1975
Sales 126.0MM^E *EMP* 22
SIC 5169 Organic chemicals, synthetic
Pr: Mahendra Parekh
**Treas:* Joan Parekh
**VP:* Jay Moorthy
**VP:* Haron Parekh

D-U-N-S 04-862-6915 IMP/EXP
▲ GAP INC
2 Folsom St, San Francisco, CA 94105-1205
Tel (415) 427-0100 *Founded/Ownrshp* 1969
Sales 15.8MMM *EMP* 141,000
Accts Deloitte & Touche Llp San Fr
Tkr Sym GPS *Exch* NYS
SIC 5651 5641 5632 5621 5611 Family clothing stores; Jeans stores; Children's & infants' wear stores; Children's wear; Infants' wear; Women's accessory & specialty stores; Women's clothing stores; Men's & boys' clothing stores
CEO: Arthur Peck
**Ch Bd:* Robert J Fisher
Pr: Jeff Kirwan
Pr: Andi Owen
COO: Jenny Novoa
CFO: Sabrina Simmons
Chf Cred: Julie Gruber
Ex VP: Paul Chapman
Ex VP: Shawn Curran
Ex VP: Sebastian Digrande
Ex VP: Solomon Goldfarb
Ex VP: Wendi Goldman
Ex VP: Tom Keiser
Ex VP: Abinta Malik
Ex VP: Bobbi Silten
Ex VP: Sonia Syngal
Ex VP: Michael Yee
VP: Jodi Bricker
VP: Roger Chelemedos
VP: Mike Jones
VP: Joe Kambeitz
Board of Directors: Domenico De Sole, William S Fisher, Tracy Gardner, Brian Goldner, Isabella D Goren, Bob L Martin, Jorge P Montoya, Mayo A Shattuck III, Katherine Tsang

D-U-N-S 10-709-7529 IMP/EXP
GARAGE DOOR GROUP INC
AMARR GARAGE DOORS
(*Suby of* AMARR GARAGE DOORS) ★
3800 Greenway Cir, Lawrence, KS 66046-5443
Tel (800) 503-3667 *Founded/Ownrshp* 1982
Sales 102.4MM^E *EMP* 500
SIC 3442 Garage doors, overhead: metal
CEO: Richard Brenner
Genl Mgr: Andrew Claxton
Genl Mgr: Franklin Dalmida
Genl Mgr: Cory Dayton
Genl Mgr: Robert Esparragoza
Genl Mgr: Keith Laird
Genl Mgr: John Schwahn
Site Mgr: Mark Reddy
Plnt Mgr: Delbert Phlipot
Sls Mgr: Ken Wall

D-U-N-S 07-770-5200
GARAGE MANAGEMENT CO LLC
RED BALL GARAGE
770 Lexington Ave Rm 1102, New York, NY 10065-8165
Tel (212) 888-7400 *Founded/Ownrshp* 1962
Sales 214.7MM^E *EMP* 550
SIC 5511 Automobiles, new & used
Pr: Richard Chapman
MIS Mgr: Dale Reynolds

D-U-N-S 00-149-5472 IMP/EXP
■ GARAN INC (VA)
(*Suby of* BERKSHIRE HATHAWAY INC) ★
200 Madison Ave Fl 4, New York, NY 10016-3905
Tel (212) 563-1292 *Founded/Ownrshp* 1941, 2002
Sales 709.5MM^E *EMP* 4,500
SIC 2361 2369 2331 2339 2321 T-shirts & tops: girls', children's & infants'; Slacks: girls' & children's; T-shirts & tops, women's: made from purchased materials; Shirts, women's & juniors': made from purchased materials; Jeans: women's, misses' & juniors'; Men's & boys' furnishings; Sport shirts, men's & boys': from purchased materials
CEO: Seymour Lichtenstein
**Pr:* Jerald Kamiel
**CFO:* David M Fligel
Treas: Alex J Sistarenik
VP: Wayne C Cooper
VP: Kathie Fiore
**VP:* Marvin S Robinson
VP Bus Dev: Ron Dutta
Exec: Deborah Borden
Opers Mgr: Stephanie Heydt
Opers Mgr: Emily Jaffe
Board of Directors: Warren Buffett, Marc Hamburg

GARBAN INTERCAP
See ICAP SERVICES NORTH AMERICA LLC

D-U-N-S 01-920-9196
GARBER BROS INC
Kay Way Rr 139, Stoughton, MA 02072
Tel (781) 341-0800 *Founded/Ownrshp* 1947
Sales 211.0MM^E *EMP* 275
SIC 5194 5145 5141 5122 Tobacco & tobacco products; Cigarettes; Candy; Groceries, general line; Cosmetics, perfumes & hair products; Toiletries
Pr: Harold Garber
**Treas:* Amy Garber
VP Sls: John Poulakis
Mktg Dir: Ed Brown
Sls Mgr: John White

D-U-N-S 00-696-0686 EXP
GARBER MANAGEMENT GROUP INC
GARBER'S PRESTIGE AUTO SALES
999 S Washington Ave # 1, Saginaw, MI 48601-2573
Tel (989) 790-9090 *Founded/Ownrshp* 1980
Sales 377.8MM^E *EMP* 1,200
SIC 5511 Automobiles, new & used
Pr: Richard J Garber Jr
**Sec:* Patrick Hengesbach

GARBER'S PRESTIGE AUTO SALES
See GARBER MANAGEMENT GROUP INC

D-U-N-S 09-368-4694 IMP
GARCO CONSTRUCTION INC
4114 E Broadway Ave, Spokane, WA 99202-4531
Tel (509) 536-1649 *Founded/Ownrshp* 1978
Sales 134.1MM^E *EMP* 275
SIC 1541 Steel building construction
Pr: Clancy Welsh
**CFO:* James Morrison
**Ch:* James T Welsh
**Treas:* Sharon Harkrader
**VP:* Hollis E Barnett
**VP:* Frank Etter
**VP:* Jamie Welsh
**VP:* Timothy J Welsh
IT Man: Jeff Hooper
Sfty Dirs: Jay Meyers

D-U-N-S 10-303-9178
GARCOA INC
GARCOA MARKETING
26135 Mureau Rd Ste 100, Calabasas, CA 91302-3184
Tel (818) 225-0375 *Founded/Ownrshp* 1975
Sales 85.8MM^E *EMP* 1,000
SIC 7389

GARCOA MARKETING
See GARCOA INC

GARDA CASH LOGISTICS
See GARDA CL TECHNICAL SERVICES INC

D-U-N-S 79-945-5480
GARDA CL TECHNICAL SERVICES INC
GARDA CASH LOGISTICS
(*Suby of* BROOKS ARMORED CAR) ★
700 S Federal Hwy Ste 300, Boca Raton, FL 33432-6128
Tel (561) 939-7000 *Founded/Ownrshp* 1996
Sales NA *EMP* 3,000
SIC 6099 7381 Safe deposit companies; Armored car services
Pr: Stephan Cretier
V Ch: Richard Drutman
Pr: Nathalie Champlain
**Pr:* Chris W Jamroz
Ofcr: Barbara Danzi
Sr VP: Thomas P Gross
Sr VP: Michael McSpadden
VP: Jeanette Hackett
VP: Jim Purcell
VP: Sophia Sas
Assoc Dir: Twyla John

D-U-N-S 06-669-4621 IMP
GARDA CL WEST INC
GCL W
(*Suby of* GARDA CASH LOGISTICS) ★
1612 W Pico Blvd, Los Angeles, CA 90015-2410
Tel (213) 383-3611 *Founded/Ownrshp* 1947
Sales 45.3MM^E *EMP* 1,100
SIC 7381 Armored car services
Pr: Stephan Cretier
**Pr:* Chris W Jamroz

GARDAWORLD
See GW CONSULTING INC

D-U-N-S 00-694-2684
GARDEN CITY CO-OP INC
106 N 6th St, Garden City, KS 67846-5545
Tel (620) 275-6161 *Founded/Ownrshp* 1919
Sales 244.0MM^E *EMP* 66
Accts Lindburg Vogel Pierce Faris D
SIC 5153 5191 5172 Grains; Feed; Seeds: field, garden & flower; Fertilizer & fertilizer materials; Chemicals, agricultural; Petroleum products
Pr: John McClelland
**CFO:* Brent Merz
VP: Barry Brant
**VP:* Elevatorsken Jameson
Brnch Mgr: Jerald Murphy
Sfty Dirs: Kirby Bradley

D-U-N-S 07-278-4002
GARDEN CITY HOSPITAL
ADVANCE NURSING CENTER
(*Suby of* PRIME HEALTHCARE SERVICES INC) ★
6245 Inkster Rd, Garden City, MI 48135-4001
Tel (734) 458-3300 *Founded/Ownrshp* 2013
Sales 150.7MM *EMP* 1,200^E
SIC 8062 General medical & surgical hospitals
Pr: Gary R Ley
**Chf Mktg O:* H Rex Ruettinger
Exec: Lynn Giovannini
Chf Nrs Of: Karla Zarb
Cmptr Lab: Andy Mazzara
VP Opers: Art Greenlee
Surgeon: Paul Aschmetat
Surgeon: Jennifer Cook
Surgeon: Timothy J Doig
Surgeon: Fadi S Saied
Surgeon: Kevin Wong

D-U-N-S 17-734-5295
GARDEN CITY HOSPITAL FOUNDATION
6245 Inkster Rd Ste 210, Garden City, MI 48135-4001
Tel (734) 458-4421 *Founded/Ownrshp* 1986
Sales 129.3M *EMP* 2,100
SIC 8741 7389 Hospital management; Nursing & personal care facility management; Fund raising organizations
CEO: Gary Ley
Ex Dir: Darla Parsons

D-U-N-S 09-433-5320
GARDEN CITY PUBLIC SCHOOLS
1205 Fleming St, Garden City, KS 67846-4751
Tel (620) 805-7000 *Founded/Ownrshp* 1890
Sales 60.0MM *EMP* 1,100
SIC 8211 Public elementary & secondary schools; High school, junior or senior; School board
IT Man: Diana Lee
IT Man: Chris Sisk

D-U-N-S 14-473-0384
GARDEN FRESH HOLDINGS INC
SOUPPLANTATION SWEET TOMATOES
(*Suby of* SUN CAPITAL PARTNERS INC) ★
15822 Bernardo Center Dr A, San Diego, CA 92127-2362
Tel (858) 675-1600 *Founded/Ownrshp* 1978
Sales 21.0MM *EMP* 5,420
SIC 5812 Fast-food restaurant, chain
CEO: John D Morberg
**Pr:* David W Qualls
**CEO:* John Morberg
Comm Dir: Don Cowan

D-U-N-S 11-533-2637
GARDEN FRESH RESTAURANT CORP
SOUPLANTATION
(*Suby of* SOUPPLANTATION SWEET TOMATOES) ★
15822 Bernardo Center Dr A, San Diego, CA 92127-2362
Tel (858) 675-1600 *Founded/Ownrshp* 2004
Sales 21.0MM^E *EMP* 5,420
SIC 5812 Restaurant, family: chain
CEO: John D Morberg
Ch Bd: Robert A Gunst
Pr: Michael P Mack
CEO: John Morberg
CFO: David A Carr
Ofcr: Julie L Derry
Sr VP: R Gregory Keller
VP: Susan M Hoffman
VP: Kenneth J Keane
VP: Rich Thompson
Ex Dir: Carl Klein

GARDEN GROVE HOSPITAL
See KENNETH CORP

D-U-N-S 07-359-1760
GARDEN GROVE UNIFIED SCHOOL DISTRICT
10331 Stanford Ave, Garden Grove, CA 92840-6351
Tel (714) 663-6000 *Founded/Ownrshp* 1965
Sales 255.5MM^E *EMP* 5,000
SIC 8211 Public elementary & secondary schools
**Pr:* George West
**VP:* Lan Quoc Nguyen
Exec: Joli Armitage
**Prin:* Coleen Cross
Adm Dir: Norma Sifuentes
Off Admin: Dayna Burt
Off Admin: Chris Porter
Opers Mgr: Sharon Evans
Opers Mgr: Karen Landrum
Pr Dir: Abby Milone
Teacher Pr: Jason Bevacqua

D-U-N-S 12-214-7259
GARDEN HOMES INC
820 Morris Tpke Ste 301, Short Hills, NJ 07078-2619
Tel (973) 467-5000 *Founded/Ownrshp* 1955
Sales 716.2MM^E *EMP* 5,125
SIC 1531 6531 Condominium developers; Real estate agents & managers
Pr: Zygmund Wilf
Ex VP: Donald Becker
**VP:* Leonard Wilf
**Prin:* Mark Wilf

D-U-N-S 62-153-7018 IMP
GARDEN PALS INC
(*Suby of* FORMOSA TOOLS CO., LTD.)
1300 Valley Vista Dr # 209, Diamond Bar, CA 91765-3940
Tel (909) 605-0200 *Founded/Ownrshp* 1990
Sales 601.3MM^E *EMP* 20
SIC 3423 Garden & farm tools, including shovels
CEO: WEI Chun Hsu
**COO:* Robert Deal
CFO: Ivy Hsu

D-U-N-S 07-515-2090
GARDEN PROPERTIES CORP
SHORT HILLS OFFICE PLAZA
(*Suby of* GARDEN HOMES INC) ★
820 Morris Tpke, Short Hills, NJ 07078-2624
Tel (973) 467-5000 *Founded/Ownrshp* 1986
Sales 158.4MM^E *EMP* 5,000
SIC 6531 Real estate managers
Owner: Anthony Moscaritolo
**Ch Bd:* Joseph Wilf
**Pr:* Leonard Wilf
Treas: Orin Wilf
VP: Mario Dudzinski
VP: Scott T Loventhal
**VP:* Zygmund Wilf
Genl Mgr: Joseph Korn
Off Mgr: Irene Bartosh
Mktg Dir: Laura Perry

GARDEN RIDGE
See GRDG HOLDINGS LLC

D-U-N-S 79-118-3106 IMP
GARDEN RIDGE CORP
1600 E Plano Pkwy, Plano, TX 75074-8124
Tel (972) 265-6227 *Founded/Ownrshp* 1992
Sales 65.4MM^E *EMP* 3,500
SIC 5719 5999 5945 Kitchenware; Glassware; Pictures, wall; Pottery; Artificial flowers; Candle shops; Picture frames, ready made; Hobby & craft supplies; Arts & crafts supplies
CEO: Bob Demer
**CFO:* Rich Brown
Ofcr: Don Martin
Ex VP: Mark Pruitt
Sr VP: Dan Ferguson
VP: Barbara Heim
**VP:* Van Horn
**VP:* Lisa Lobble
**VP:* Jay Smith
**VP:* Linda Troy
CIO: Mark Wozny

D-U-N-S 12-580-4950
GARDEN RIDGE HOLDINGS INC
1600 E Plano Pkwy, Plano, TX 75074-8124
Tel (832) 391-7201 *Founded/Ownrshp* 1992
Sales NA *EMP* 4,000
SIC 5719 5945 5992 5947 5999

GARDEN RIDGE POTTERY
See AT HOME STORES LLC

GARDEN STATE FARMS
See PROCACCI BROS SALES CORP

GARDEN WATERING
See ROBERT BOSCH TOOL CORP

D-U-N-S 04-909-1140
GARDENA HOSPITAL LP
MEMORIAL HOSPITAL OF GARDENA
1145 W Redondo Beach Blvd, Gardena, CA 90247-3511
Tel (310) 532-4200 *Founded/Ownrshp* 1999
Sales 124.6MM *EMP* 760
SIC 8062 8322 8011 General medical & surgical hospitals; Rehabilitation services; Freestanding emergency medical center
CEO: Kathy Wojno
Pt: John N Loizeaux-Witte

GARDENSCAPE
See TRI-STATE GARDEN SUPPLY INC

D-U-N-S 06-898-0754
GARDERE WYNNE SEWELL LLP
1601 Elm St Ste 3000, Dallas, TX 75201-4761
Tel (214) 999-3000 *Founded/Ownrshp* 1920
Sales 107.4MM^E *EMP* 700
SIC 8111 General practice attorney, lawyer
Ch: Holland N O'Neil
Pt: Michael A Abbott
Pt: Val J Albright
Pt: Jose A Berlanga
Pt: Geoffrey H Bracken
Pt: Fernando C Cardona
Pt: John G Caverlee
Pt: Alexander C Chae
Pt: Merritt B Chastain III
Pt: Daniel L Cohen
Pt: James Cooper
Pt: Allen B Craig III
Pt: Jeffrey S Davis
Pt: Jerry A Devault
Pt: William D Dunn
Pt: David R Earhart
Pt: Mark Edwards
Pt: John A Eliason
Pt: Douglas K Eyberg
Pt: Richard O Faulk
Pt: John S Gray

D-U-N-S 04-662-7642
GARDINER SERVICE CO (OH)
GARDINER TRANE
31200 Bainbridge Rd Ste 1, Solon, OH 44139-2298
Tel (440) 349-5588 *Founded/Ownrshp* 1957
Sales 89.1MM^E *EMP* 160
Accts Mayer Hoffman Mccann Pc Ply
SIC 5075 1711 7623 Air conditioning & ventilation equipment & supplies; Plumbing, heating, air-conditioning contractors; Refrigeration service & repair; Air conditioning repair
CEO: William H Gardiner
**Pr:* Robert M Case
**Treas:* Michael R Reder

GARDINER TRANE
See GARDINER SERVICE CO

D-U-N-S 04-149-5490 IMP/EXP
GARDNER ASPHALT CORP
(*Suby of* GARDNER-GIBSON INC) ★
4161 E 7th Ave, Tampa, FL 33605-4601
Tel (813) 248-2441 *Founded/Ownrshp* 1973
Sales 124.7MM^E *EMP* 525
SIC 3531 Roofing equipment
Ch Bd: Raymond T Hyer
Pr: Mike Lazuk
CFO: Sean Poole
Trfc Mgr: Jennifer Martinez

GARDNER BENDER
See POWER PRODUCTS LLC

D-U-N-S 18-818-6480
GARDNER DENVER HOLDINGS INC
(*Suby of* GARDNER DENVER INC) ★
1800 Gardner Expy, Quincy, IL 62305-9364
Tel (217) 222-5400 *Founded/Ownrshp* 1992
Sales 736.1MM^E *EMP* 6,000
SIC 3564 3563 Blowers & fans; Vacuum (air extraction) systems, industrial
Pr: Winfried Kaiser
COO: Jerry Ludlum
VP: Duane Morgan
VP: Brent A Walters
Off Mgr: Paul Phillips
IT Man: John Sharp
Prd Mgr: Angelo Deriggi
Ql Cn Mgr: Brian Gaffey
Ql Cn Mgr: Dan Pfister
Sls&Mrk Ex: Gary Gillespie
Mktg Mgr: Jennifer Green

D-U-N-S 82-644-8615 IMP/EXP
GARDNER DENVER INC
(*Suby of* RENAISSANCE PARENT CORP.)
222 E Erie St Ste 500, Milwaukee, WI 53202-6062
Tel (414) 212-4700 *Founded/Ownrshp* 2013
Sales 2.1MMM^E *EMP* 6,800
SIC 3564 3561 3563 Blowers & fans; Industrial pumps & parts; Air & gas compressors including vacuum pumps
CEO: Peter Wallace
**Pr:* Barry L Pennypacker
**CFO:* Michael M Larsen
**VP:* Susan A Gunn
VP: Kevin Mineard
**VP:* Brent A Walters
IT Man: Jeff Van Dijk
Opers Mgr: Jarod Hammar
Ql Cn Mgr: Paul Brown

D-U-N-S 13-695-4497 IMP
GARDNER DENVER NASH LLC
(*Suby of* GARDNER DENVER INC) ★
2 Trefoil Dr, Trumbull, CT 06611-1330
Tel (203) 459-3923 *Founded/Ownrshp* 2004
Sales 352.6MM^E *EMP* 1,225
SIC 5084 3563 8711 3561 Compressors, except air conditioning; Air & gas compressors including vacuum pumps; Engineering services; Pumps & pumping equipment
CEO: Barry Pennypacker
**CFO:* Helen Cornell
**VP:* Armando Castorena
**VP:* T Duane Morgan
**VP:* Brent A Walters

D-U-N-S 00-637-9317 IMP/EXP
GARDNER DENVER THOMAS INC
THOMAS PRODUCTS DIVISION
(*Suby of* GARDNER DENVER INC) ★
1419 Illinois Ave, Sheboygan, WI 53081-4821
Tel (920) 457-4891 *Founded/Ownrshp* 1859
Sales 551.2MM^E *EMP* 2,467
SIC 3563 Air & gas compressors including vacuum pumps; Vacuum pumps, except laboratory
VP: Mark McElhinny
Area Mgr: Andrew Ciapetta
Dir IT: Terry Roberts
Ql Cn Mgr: John Poker
Mktg Mgr: Jennifer Schultz

D-U-N-S 03-981-4280
GARDNER EDGERTON UNIFIED SCHOOL DISTRICT 231
231 E Madison St, Gardner, KS 66030-1846
Tel (913) 856-7102 *Founded/Ownrshp* 1956
Sales 131.4MM *EMP* 800
Accts Lowenthal Singleton Webb & Wil
SIC 8211 Public elementary & secondary schools; Public elementary school; Public junior high school; Public senior high school
Treas: Andrea Allenbrand
VP: Tim Rayburn
VP: Ron Raygan
Ex Dir: Chritsty Ziegler
MIS Dir: Andy Price
Pr Dir: Leann Northway
Schl Brd P: Rob Shippy
Teacher Pr: Jody Marshall
HC Dir: Ben Booth
HC Dir: Jeremy Williams
Board of Directors: Eric Hansen

D-U-N-S 00-322-1462 IMP/EXP
GARDNER GLASS PRODUCTS INC (NC)
301 Elkin Hwy, North Wilkesboro, NC 28659-3444
Tel (336) 651-9300 *Founded/Ownrshp* 1961, 1999
Sales 101.4MM^E *EMP* 363
SIC 3231 Products of purchased glass; Mirrored glass
Pr: Tommy Huskey
**COO:* Randy Brooks
**CFO:* Melissa Lackey
**Founder:* Edd Gardner
MIS Dir: Ron Wood
Plnt Mgr: Ronnie Blevins

D-U-N-S 01-789-2803 IMP
GARDNER INC
3641 Interchange Rd, Columbus, OH 43204-1499
Tel (614) 351-1325 *Founded/Ownrshp* 1944
Sales 215.2MM^E *EMP* 300
Accts Deloitte & Touche Llp
SIC 5084 6512 Engines, gasoline; Nonresidential building operators
CEO: John F Finn
**CFO:* John T Finn
**VP:* James P Finn
VP: Ted Finn
IT Man: Chris Cooley

D-U-N-S 78-793-1070
GARDNER TRUCKING INC
(*Suby of* CRST INTERNATIONAL INC) ★
331 Premier Ct S, Franklin, TN 37067-8303
Tel (909) 563-5606 *Founded/Ownrshp* 2016
Sales 102.6MM^E *EMP* 500
SIC 4213 4212 Trucking, except local; Local trucking, without storage
Pr: Thomas J Lanting
VP: Ramona Gill
Board of Directors: Angie Caward

D-U-N-S 01-687-8670 IMP
GARDNER WHITE FURNITURE CO INC (MI)
4445 N Atlantic Blvd, Auburn Hills, MI 48326-1580
Tel (586) 774-8853 *Founded/Ownrshp* 1987
Sales 122.0MM *EMP* 425
SIC 5712 Furniture stores
Pr: Steven L Tronstein
Ex VP: Aime Fitzhugh
Ex VP: Rachel Tronstein
Ex VP: Kathy Veltri
VP: Pamela Novak-George
**VP:* Barbara Tronstein
Exec: David Gresehover
Sales Asso: Jason Groce

D-U-N-S 06-591-7817 IMP/EXP
GARDNER-GIBSON INC
4161 E 7th Ave, Tampa, FL 33605-4601
Tel (813) 248-2101 *Founded/Ownrshp* 1993
Sales 250.1MM^E *EMP* 550
SIC 2951 2851 2952

D-U-N-S 16-478-8841 IMP/EXP
GARDNER-GIBSON MANUFACTURING INC
(*Suby of* GARDNER-GIBSON INC) ★
4161 E 7th Ave, Tampa, FL 33605-4601
Tel (813) 248-2101 *Founded/Ownrshp* 2000
Sales 101.6MM^E *EMP* 225
SIC 2951 2891 2952 Asphalt paving mixtures & blocks; Adhesives & sealants; Roof cement: asphalt, fibrous or plastic
Pr: Raymond T Hyer Jr
**Sec:* Sean W Poole
MIS Dir: Neil Loftie-Eaton

D-U-N-S 00-143-0172 IMP
■ **GARELICK FARMS LLC** (MA)
(*Suby of* DEAN FOODS CO) ★
1199 W Central St Ste 1, Franklin, MA 02038-3160
Tel (508) 528-9000 *Founded/Ownrshp* 1902, 1997
Sales 350.2MM^E *EMP* 2,500
SIC 2026 Fluid milk; Buttermilk, cultured; Cottage cheese

D-U-N-S 07-312-6732
GARFF ENTERPRISES INC
KEN GARFF AUTOMOTIVE GROUP
405 S Main St Ste 1200, Salt Lake City, UT 84111-3412
Tel (801) 257-3400 *Founded/Ownrshp* 1949
Sales 576.9MM *EMP* 855
Accts Mayer Hoffman Mc Cann Pc Sal
SIC 5511 6512 Automobiles, new & used; Nonresidential building operators
Ch: Robert Garff
**Pr:* John Garff
CFO: Philip Johnson
**VP:* Rick Fulkerson
Ex Dir: Dax Derop
Ex Dir: Jason Frampton
CIO: Mark Boehlen
Sls Mgr: Michael Flaherty
Sls Mgr: Phil Green
Sls Mgr: Sam Jarvie

GARFIELDS RESTAURANT & PUB
See EATERIES INC

D-U-N-S 01-909-2477 EXP
GARGIULO INC
15000 Old Hwy 41 N, Naples, FL 34110
Tel (239) 597-3131 *Founded/Ownrshp* 1980
Sales 152.4MM^E *EMP* 400
SIC 5148 Fresh fruits & vegetables
Pr: Christian Leleu
**Pr:* Michael Sullivan
**Prin:* Jeffrey D Gargiulo
Off Mgr: Heather Didonato
IT Man: Daniel Subbert
Mktg Mgr: Robert Elliot

GARGUILO PRODUCE
See FRANK M GARGIULO & SON INC

D-U-N-S 06-615-2372
GARICH INC
THE TRISTAFF GROUP
6336 Greenwich Dr Ste A, San Diego, CA 92122-5922
Tel (858) 453-1331 *Founded/Ownrshp* 1971
Sales 40.3MM^E *EMP* 1,024
Accts Lipsey Millimaki & Co Llp
SIC 7361 8742 Employment agencies; Management consulting services
Pr: Gary O Van Eik
COO: Rick Kail
VP: Amy Moser
VP: Alex Papike
VP: Chris Papike
**VP:* Richard N Papike
VP: Thomas Tanner
Exec: Gary Eik
Exec: Erin McReynolds
Exec: Jennifer Smith
Area Mgr: Karen Van Eik

D-U-N-S 06-603-7409
GARLAND CO INC
(*Suby of* GARLAND INDUSTRIES INC) ★
3800 E 91st St, Cleveland, OH 44105-2197
Tel (216) 641-7500 *Founded/Ownrshp* 1988
Sales 163.9MM^E *EMP* 250
SIC 2952 2851

D-U-N-S 07-837-0061
GARLAND INDEPENDENT SCHOOL DISTRICT
I S D
501 S Jupiter Rd, Garland, TX 75042-7108
Tel (972) 494-8201 *Founded/Ownrshp* 1897
Sales 543.5MM *EMP* 7,307
Accts Whitley Penn Llp Houston Tex
SIC 8211 Public elementary & secondary schools; Public elementary school; Public junior high school; Public senior high school
Bd of Dir: Cliff Odenwald
Bd of Dir: Gregory Taylor
Exec: Marlene Gardner
Dir Sec: Pat Lamb
MIS Dir: Maureen Murphy
Pr Dir: Tiffany Veno
Schl Brd P: Larry Glick
Teacher Pr: Jed Reed
Instr Medi: Richelle O'Neil

D-U-N-S 19-935-4507
GARLAND INDUSTRIES INC
3800 E 91st St, Cleveland, OH 44105-2103
Tel (216) 641-7500 *Founded/Ownrshp* 1974
Sales 272.8MM^E *EMP* 500
SIC 2952 6512 8712 Roofing materials; Roofing felts, cements or coatings; Coating compounds, tar; Commercial & industrial building operation; Architectural services
Pr: David Sokol
**CFO:* Charles Ripepi
**VP:* Melvin Chrostowski
**VP:* Richard Debacco
**VP:* William Oley
**VP:* G Richard Olivier
**Sls Mgr:* Joe Orlando

GARLANDS OF BARRINGTON, THE
See BARRINGTON VENTURE HOLDING CO LLC

GARLOCK BEARINGS
See COLTEC INDUSTRIES INC

D-U-N-S 04-307-5738 IMP/EXP
■ **GARLOCK SEALING TECHNOLOGIES LLC** (NC)
(*Suby of* ENPRO INDUSTRIES INC) ★
1666 Division St, Palmyra, NY 14522-9350
Tel (315) 597-4811 *Founded/Ownrshp* 1887
Sales 332.4MM^E *EMP* 1,500
SIC 3053 3585 3714

D-U-N-S 79-128-8004 IMP/EXP
GARMIN INTERNATIONAL INC
(*Suby of* GARMIN SWITZERLAND GMBH)
1200 E 151st St, Olathe, KS 66062-3426
Tel (913) 397-8200 *Founded/Ownrshp* 2001
Sales 2.7MMM *EMP* 3,000
SIC 3812 3669 8713 Search & navigation equipment; Visual communication systems; Surveying services
CEO: Clifton Pemble
COO: Mark Stephens
**CFO:* Doug Boessen
CFO: Elle Desimone
CFO: Aimee Pearce
**Ch:* Dr Min KAO
**VP:* Andrew Etkind
Exec: Marsha Befort
Snr Sftwr: Jason Dilley
Snr Sftwr: John Estabrook
Snr Sftwr: Sharyl Godlewski

D-U-N-S 05-355-4531 IMP
GARNER ENVIRONMENTAL SERVICES INC
1717 W 13th St, Deer Park, TX 77536-2531
Tel (281) 930-1200 *Founded/Ownrshp* 1981
Sales 157.0MM^E *EMP* 250
SIC 4959 Toxic or hazardous waste cleanup; Oil spill cleanup
Pr: L D Garner
**CFO:* Cheryl Morvillo
**VP:* John Pavlicek
Brnch Mgr: Thomas Dickey
Dir IT: Mikie Sopczak
IT Man: Edgar Rotundo
Opers Mgr: Casey Anderson
Sls Mgr: Breanna Fair
Genl Couns: Bobbie Risner

D-U-N-S 07-306-2325
GARNEY COMPANIES INC (MO)
(*Suby of* GARNEY HOLDING CO) ★
1333 Nw Vivion Rd, Kansas City, MO 64118-4554
Tel (816) 741-4600 *Founded/Ownrshp* 1961
Sales 635.3MM^E *EMP* 1,100
Accts Mayer Hoffman Mccann Pc Lea
SIC 1623 1629 Sewer line construction; Water main construction; Underground utilities contractor; Waste water & sewage treatment plant construction
Pr: Mike Heitmann
**COO:* Wayne O'Brien
**COO:* Jason Seubert
**CFO:* Jeff Lacy
**VP:* Steve Ford
**VP:* Matt Foster
**VP:* Mike Gardner
**VP:* Greg Harris
**VP:* Tony Kempf
**VP:* Steve McCandless
**VP:* Scott Parrish

D-U-N-S 03-063-3663
GARNEY HOLDING CO
1333 Nw Vivion Rd, Kansas City, MO 64118-4554
Tel (816) 741-4600 *Founded/Ownrshp* 1994
Sales 633.7MM^E *EMP* 1,100
SIC 1623 1611 1629 Water main construction; Sewer line construction; Highway & street construction; Concrete construction: roads, highways, sidewalks, etc.; Waste water & sewage treatment plant construction
CEO: Mike Heitmann
**COO:* Wayne O'Brien
**COO:* Jason Seubert
**CFO:* Jeff Lacy
**Treas:* Thomas J Dahl

GARRETT ELEMENTARY SCHOOL
See HAZELWOOD SCHOOL DISTRICT

D-U-N-S 04-876-3494
GARRICK MOTORS INC
TOYOTA OF ESCONDIDO
231 E Lincoln Ave, Escondido, CA 92026-3078
Tel (760) 746-0601 *Founded/Ownrshp* 1978
Sales 100.3MM^E *EMP* 235^E
SIC 5511 Automobiles, new & used
Pr: Gary Myers
**VP:* Rick Billuni
VP Mktg: John Lovett
Mktg Dir: Damian Campos
Sls Mgr: Greg Caughey
Sls Mgr: Isaac Garcia
Sls Mgr: James Peters
Sls Mgr: Julie Whitehead

D-U-N-S 02-694-3993
GARRISON FRED OIL CO
ALL STAR FUEL
1107 Walter Griffin St, Plainview, TX 79072-5401
Tel (806) 296-6353 *Founded/Ownrshp* 1974
Sales 191.1MM *EMP* 50
SIC 5172 5541

D-U-N-S 79-653-5065
GARRISON INVESTMENT GROUP LP
1290 Avenue Of The Americ, New York, NY 10104-0008
Tel (212) 372-9500 *Founded/Ownrshp* 2007
Sales 166.4MM^E *EMP* 210
SIC 6282 Investment advisory service
Pt: Steven Stuart
Pt: Brian Chase
VP: Joshua Brandt
VP: Josh Dinstein
VP: Robert Feeney
VP: Matthew Lambert
VP: Tom McGarrity
VP: Jason Morrow
VP: Jason Reeves
Mng Dir: Ej Antonio
Mng Dir: Susan George

D-U-N-S 07-091-9159
GARRY BRADFORD MANAGEMENT CO LTD
(*Suby of* G BRADFORD CO INC) ★
4646 Corona Dr Ste 105, Corpus Christi, TX 78411-4383
Tel (361) 852-6392 *Founded/Ownrshp* 2000
Sales 26.2MM^E *EMP* 1,675^E
SIC 8741 Management services
Prin: Garry Bradford

D-U-N-S 09-722-0180
▲ **GARTNER INC**
56 Top Gallant Rd, Stamford, CT 06902-7700
Tel (203) 316-1111 *Founded/Ownrshp* 1979
Sales 2.1MMM *EMP* 7,834
Tkr Sym IT *Exch* NYS
SIC 8732 8742 8741 Commercial nonphysical research; Market analysis or research; Management consulting services; Business consultant; Management services
Ch Bd: James C Smith
CEO: Eugene A Hall
CFO: Craig W Safian
CFO: Craig Safian
Sr VP: Kendall B Davis
Sr VP: David Godfrey
Sr VP: Robin Kranch
Sr VP: Robin Kranich
Sr VP: Daniel S Peale
Sr VP: Peter Sondergaard
Sr VP: Chris Thomas
Sr VP: Per Anders Waern
VP: Moe Ali
VP: Philip Allega
VP: Robert Anderson
VP: Warren Anderson
VP: Todd Applebaum
VP: Amos Auringer
VP: Mark Bartram
VP: Alexa Bona
VP: Tiffani Bova

D-U-N-S 02-955-7733 IMP
GARTON TRACTOR INC
KUBOTA AUTHORIZED DEALER
2400 N Golden State Blvd, Turlock, CA 95382-9408
Tel (209) 632-3931 *Founded/Ownrshp* 1953
Sales 111.9MM *EMP* 205
SIC 5999 5083 Farm machinery; Farm & garden machinery
Pr: William L Garton
**Treas:* Thomas Garton
Genl Mgr: Grant Garton
Off Mgr: Jessica Martinez
Dir IT: Jeff Degraff

D-U-N-S 04-448-5860
GARVER LLC
4701 Northshore Dr, North Little Rock, AR 72118-5325
Tel (501) 376-3633 *Founded/Ownrshp* 1970
Sales 84.0MM *EMP* 285
Accts Rasco Winter Abston Moore & As
SIC 8711 Consulting engineer

CFO: Dathan Gaskill
VP: Herbert Parker
Exec: Larry Taylor
Dir IT: Matt Gross
Web Dev: Alan Watson
Snr PM: Gary Bennett
Snr PM: Scott C Leach
Snr Mgr: Scott Forbes
Board of Directors: Michael Griffin, Brock Hoskins, Stephen Jones, Frank McIllwain

GARVEY GROUP, THE
See GARVEY GROUP LLC

D-U-N-S 78-516-3119
GARVEY GROUP LLC
GARVEY GROUP, THE
7400 N Lehigh Ave, Niles, IL 60714-4024
Tel (847) 647-1900 *Founded/Ownrshp* 2001
Sales 100.0MM[E] *EMP* 320[E]
SIC 6719 Personal holding companies, except banks
**COO:* Joe Kulis
CFO: Mike Leonard
**VP:* David Nolte
Genl Mgr: Roxann Black
Dir IT: William Brady
VP Opers: Jim Oring
Plnt Mgr: Bill Grosskreuz
Prd Mgr: Bob Garcia
Prd Mgr: Charlene Pajewski
Sales Exec: Debbie Blum
Natl Sales: Eric Troyk

D-U-N-S 06-862-2455
GARY COMMUNITY SCHOOLS CORP
1988 Polk St, Gary, IN 46407-2443
Tel (219) 886-6400 *Founded/Ownrshp* 1909
Sales 186.9MM[E] *EMP* 3,278
SIC 8211 Public elementary school; Public junior high school; Public senior high school
Pr: Gregory Fleming
Treas: Frankie Goins
Ofcr: Eric Johnson
VP: Sarita Stevens
**Prin:* Dr Cheryl Pruitt
Ex Dir: Marianne Fidishin
Ex Dir: Albert Holmes
Dir IT: Lloyd Keith
Pr Dir: Charmella Greer
Schl Brd P: Antuwan Clemons
Teacher Pr: Willie Cooke

D-U-N-S 02-745-2689
GARY MERLINO CONSTRUCTION CO INC
STONEWAY CONSTRUCTION SUPPLY
9125 10th Ave S, Seattle, WA 98108-4600
Tel (206) 763-9552 *Founded/Ownrshp* 1961
Sales 168.4MM[E] *EMP* 350
SIC 1611 1623 3273 Highway & street construction; Water main construction; Sewer line construction; Ready-mixed concrete
Pr: Gary M Merlino
**Pr:* Dan Raymond
COO: Lynda Borella
**VP:* Don Merlino
**VP:* Charlie Oliver
IT Man: Cong Nguyen

GARY YEOMANS FORD
See TERRY TAYLOR FORD CO

D-U-N-S 06-348-6117
GAS BREAKER INC
17 Lee Blvd Ste D, Malvern, PA 19355-1234
Tel (610) 407-7200 *Founded/Ownrshp* 2000
Sales 100.0MM *EMP* 28
SIC 3491 Gas valves & parts, industrial
CEO: John B McGowan Jr
**Pr:* C Dean McGowan

D-U-N-S 04-154-0238
GAS CITY LTD
STEEL CITY TRUCK & AUTO
401 S Old Woodward Ave # 340, Birmingham, MI 48009-6611
Tel (815) 469-9000 *Founded/Ownrshp* 1963
Sales 92.7MM[E] *EMP* 500
SIC 5541 5411 5172

D-U-N-S 13-388-1974 IMP
■ GAS CO LLC
HAWAII GAS
(*Suby of* MACQUARIE INFRASTRUCTURE CORP) ★
745 Fort Street Mall # 1800, Honolulu, HI 96813-3818
Tel (808) 594-5530 *Founded/Ownrshp* 2006
Sales 260.3MM[E] *EMP* 317
SIC 4932 4925 5172 5984 Gas & other services combined; Gas production and/or distribution; Gases; Propane gas, bottled
CEO: Alicia Moy
**Pr:* Joseph Boivin
**Sr VP:* Joseph J Boivin Jr
VP: Stephanie C Ackerman
**VP:* Charles Mike Futrell
**VP:* Thomas K L M Young
Genl Mgr: Debra Ota
Plnt Mgr: Michael Kita
VP Mktg: Greg Toth
VP Sls: Jill Tokunaga
S&M/VP: David Uchiyama

GAS COMPANY, THE
See SOUTHERN CALIFORNIA GAS CO

D-U-N-S 79-345-2863
■ GAS CONNECTION LLC
HOMETOWN HEARTH & GRILL
(*Suby of* SUBURBAN PROPANE PARTNERS LP) ★
9801 Se 82nd Ave, Portland, OR 97086-3730
Tel (503) 771-1750 *Founded/Ownrshp* 1999
Sales 346.1MM[E] *EMP* 2,400
SIC 5984 5722 Propane gas, bottled; Gas household appliances

D-U-N-S 00-894-6733 IMP/EXP
GAS EQUIPMENT CO INC
11616 Harry Hines Blvd, Dallas, TX 75229-2203
Tel (972) 241-2333 *Founded/Ownrshp* 1937
Sales 226.1MM[E] *EMP* 550
SIC 5084 5085 3321 Instruments & control equipment; Pumps & pumping equipment; Hose, belting & packing; Valves & fittings; Ductile iron castings
Pr: Milton Ladue III
**Pr:* M J La Due III
**VP:* C K La Due
Ql Cn Mgr: Paul Trippett
Natl Sales: Lance Looper
Sls&Mrk Ex: Lori Kirk
VP Mktg: Russ Ridings

GAS MART
See SAYLE OIL CO INC

GAS MART
See DICKERSON STATIONS INC

D-U-N-S 00-282-1890
▲ GAS NATURAL INC (OH)
8470 Station St, Mentor, OH 44060-4935
Tel (440) 974-3770 *Founded/Ownrshp* 1909
Sales 112.3MM *EMP* 206[E]
Tkr Sym EGAS *Exch* ASE
SIC 4924 4911 5172 5984 Natural gas distribution; Distribution, electric power; Gases, liquefied petroleum (propane); Propane gas, bottled
Prin: Gregory J Osborne
**Ch Bd:* Michael R Winter
VP: Jed D Henthorne
Board of Directors: Michael B Bender, James P Carney, Richard K Greaves, Robert B Johnston

D-U-N-S 01-078-5681
GAS UNLIMITED INC (TX)
2277 Plaza Dr Ste 270, Sugar Land, TX 77479-6703
Tel (281) 295-5600 *Founded/Ownrshp* 1970
Sales 146.3MM[E] *EMP* 10,000
SIC 7363 Engineering help service
Pr: Leo M Glass
**CFO:* Guillermo Camargo
**Sec:* Karen T Glass
**VP:* David M Glass
IT Man: Michael Glass

D-U-N-S 01-662-0080
GASAMERICA SERVICES INC
2700 W Main St, Greenfield, IN 46140-2739
Tel (317) 468-2515 *Founded/Ownrshp* 1983
Sales 154.3MM[E] *EMP* 850
SIC 5541 5171 Filling stations, gasoline; Petroleum bulk stations
Pr: Stephanie White
**Ch:* Judy White
**Sr VP:* Keith White

D-U-N-S 06-683-8145 IMP
GASBARRE PRODUCTS INC
SINTERITE PRODUCTS DIVISION
590 Division St, Du Bois, PA 15801-2530
Tel (814) 371-3015 *Founded/Ownrshp* 1973
Sales 87.8MM[E] *EMP* 218
SIC 3542 3567 3544 Presses: forming, stamping, punching, sizing (machine tools); Industrial furnaces & ovens; Special dies, tools, jigs & fixtures
Pr: Thomas G Gasbarre
**Treas:* Carl Gasbarre
Genl Mgr: Alex Gasbarre
IT Man: Jeff Gasbarre
IT Man: Fred Gustafson
Mktg Mgr: Randy Bauer
Sls Mgr: Patrick Bowen

GASCARD
See WEST TEXAS GAS INC

D-U-N-S 00-510-9392 IMP
■ GAST MANUFACTURING INC (MI)
(*Suby of* IDEX CORP) ★
2300 M 139, Benton Harbor, MI 49022-6114
Tel (269) 926-6171 *Founded/Ownrshp* 1921
Sales 84.1MM[E] *EMP* 367
SIC 3563 3594 3621 3566 3561 Vacuum pumps, except laboratory; Air & gas compressors including vacuum pumps; Motors: hydraulic, fluid power or air; Motors & generators; Speed changers, drives & gears; Pumps & pumping equipment
Pr: Eric Ashelman
VP: Mike Fortier
VP: Fred Niemeier
VP: Del Thomas
IT Man: Jeff Wantuch
VP Sls: Lisa Walsh

D-U-N-S 78-197-5573
▲ GASTAR EXPLORATION INC
1331 Lamar St Ste 650, Houston, TX 77010-3131
Tel (713) 739-1800 *Founded/Ownrshp* 2011
Sales 107.2MM *EMP* 51[E]
Tkr Sym GST *Exch* ASE
SIC 1311 Crude petroleum & natural gas
Pr: J Russell Porter
**Ch Bd:* Jerry R Schuyler
CFO: Michael A Gerlich
VP: Henry J Hansen
Exec: Keith R Blair
Board of Directors: John H Cassels, Randolph C Coley, Stephen A Holditch, Robert D Penner

D-U-N-S 07-106-2186
GASTON COUNTY
COUNTY MANAGER OFFICE
128 W Main Ave, Gastonia, NC 28052-2306
Tel (704) 866-3100 *Founded/Ownrshp* 1846
Sales NA *EMP* 1,500
Accts Martin Starnes & Associates C
SIC 9111 County supervisors' & executives' offices; ;

D-U-N-S 19-329-4840
GASTON COUNTY SCHOOL DISTRICT
943 Osceola St, Gastonia, NC 28054-5482
Tel (704) 866-6100 *Founded/Ownrshp* 1968
Sales 241.2MM *EMP* 3,848[E]
Accts Anderson Smith & Wike Pllc Ga
SIC 8211 Public elementary & secondary schools; Public elementary school; Public junior high school; Public senior high school
Bd of Dir: Kevin Collier
Pr Dir: Todd Hagans
Teacher Pr: Resa Hoyle
Instr Medi: Grant Sparks
HC Dir: Betty Worthy

D-U-N-S 62-792-7130
GAT AIRLINE GROUND SUPPORT INC
8400 Airport Blvd, Mobile, AL 36608-9603
Tel (251) 633-3888 *Founded/Ownrshp* 1967
Sales 124.2MM[E] *EMP* 1,000
SIC 4581 Airports, flying fields & services; Airfreight loading & unloading services
CEO: Jean Raines
**Pr:* Richard Thiel
**VP:* Dian Lensch

GATE
See GIBSON APPLIED TECHNOLOGY & ENGINEERING (TEXAS) INC

GATE FUEL SERVICE
See GATE PETROLEUM CO

D-U-N-S 19-836-1698 IMP
GATE GOURMET US INC
(*Suby of* GATEGROUP US HOLDING INC) ★
1880 Campus Commons Dr # 200, Reston, VA 20191-1503
Tel (703) 964-2300 *Founded/Ownrshp* 2009
Sales 370.8MM[E] *EMP* 8,000
SIC 5812 8742 Caterers; Industry specialist consultants
CEO: Xavier Rossinyol
**Pr:* Herman Anbeek
COO: David Kuhns
CFO: Ron Lindo
CFO: Barry Oshare
**CFO:* Christoph Schmitz
**Ch:* Andreas Schmid
Genl Mgr: Greg Gasdorf
Genl Mgr: Delores Mejia
Genl Mgr: Lonnie Payne
Genl Mgr: Frank Rubal

D-U-N-S 04-239-1789
GATE PETROLEUM CO
GATE FUEL SERVICE
9540 San Jose Blvd, Jacksonville, FL 32257-5444
Tel (904) 730-3470 *Founded/Ownrshp* 1960
Sales 1.4MMM[E] *EMP* 3,200
SIC 5541 3272 5411 7997 Gasoline service stations; Prestressed concrete products; Convenience stores, chain; Country club, membership
Ch Bd: Herbert H Peyton
Treas: Jack Leuders
Treas: Jack C Lueders
VP: Donald R Davis
VP: Buzz Hoover
VP: Wayne M Levitt
VP: Joseph C Luke
VP: James McCormack
VP: Austin McCormick
VP: P Jeremy Smith Jr
VP: Tammy Woodberry
Exec: Howard Weadon
Dir Teleco: Austin McCormack

D-U-N-S 11-270-5244
GATE PRECAST CO
(*Suby of* GATE FUEL SERVICE) ★
9540 San Jose Blvd, Jacksonville, FL 32257-5432
Tel (904) 732-7668 *Founded/Ownrshp* 1989
Sales 161.1MM[E] *EMP* 1,000
SIC 3272 Concrete stuctural support & building material
CEO: Dean Gwin
**Treas:* Jack C Lueders Jr
**Sr VP:* Earl N Shimp
Opers Mgr: David Graham
Ql Cn Mgr: Conrad Filo
Mktg Dir: Brian Griffis

D-U-N-S 83-062-7209 IMP
GATEGROUP US HOLDING INC
(*Suby of* GATEGROUP FINANCIAL SERVICES SARL)
11710 Plaza America Dr # 800, Reston, VA 20190-4742
Tel (703) 964-2300 *Founded/Ownrshp* 2008
Sales 370.8MM[E] *EMP* 8,000[E]
SIC 5812 8742 Caterers; Industry specialist consultants
CEO: Andrew Gibson
**CFO:* Thomas Bucher
**Sr VP:* Jrg A Boder
**VP:* Jean-Luc Ferrazzini
**VP:* Mike Hargett
**VP:* Stein Turnert

D-U-N-S 01-347-3116 IMP
■ GATEHOUSE MEDIA LLC
(*Suby of* NEW MEDIA INVESTMENT GROUP INC) ★
175 Sullys Trl Ste 300, Pittsford, NY 14534-4560
Tel (585) 598-0030 *Founded/Ownrshp* 2013
Sales 90.6MM[E] *EMP* 70[E]
SIC 2711 7311 2759 Newspapers, publishing & printing; Advertising agencies; Commercial printing
CEO: Adam Reinebach
Pr: Rick Daniels
Pr: Peter Newton
COO: Kirk Davis
CFO: Melinda A Janik
Treas: Mark Maring
Ofcr: Keri Curtis
Sr VP: Dave Arkin
Sr VP: Bill Church
Sr VP: Brad Dennison
Sr VP: Harry Jenkins
VP: David Arkin
VP: Travis Engebretson
VP: Rick Martin
VP: Peter Meyer
VP: Wayne Pelland
VP: Polly G Sack

D-U-N-S 03-057-7337
■ GATEHOUSE MEDIA MASSACHUSETTS I INC
COMMUNITY NEWSPAPER
(*Suby of* NEW MEDIA INVESTMENT GROUP INC) ★
75 Sylvan St Ste C105, Danvers, MA 01923-2765
Tel (585) 598-0030 *Founded/Ownrshp* 2013
Sales 257.2MM[E] *EMP* 1,800
SIC 2711 Commercial printing & newspaper publishing combined
**Pr:* Kirk Davis
VP: Anne Dorsey
VP: Audrea Fulton
VP: Paul McArthur
VP: Coen Pat
VP: Rebecca Roth
Sls Mgr: Jason Taylor

D-U-N-S 05-543-3197 IMP/EXP
GATES CORP
(*Suby of* OMAHA ACQUISITION INC.)
1551 Wewatta St, Denver, CO 80202-6173
Tel (303) 744-1911 *Founded/Ownrshp* 2014
Sales 4.2MMM[E] *EMP* 13,433
SIC 3052 3089 3568 5084 4789 Rubber belting; Rubber hose; Automobile hose, rubber; V-belts, rubber; Fiber, vulcanized; Pulleys, power transmission; Water pumps (industrial); Cargo loading & unloading services
CEO: Ivo Jurek
Pr: Ken Friedman
Pr: Al Stecklein
**COO:* Walt Lifsey
**CFO:* David Naemura
CFO: J M Riess
**Ex VP:* Rasmani Bhattacharya
Ex VP: Rick Hale
**Sr VP:* Heather Dumas
**Sr VP:* Liz Huldin
Sr VP: Tom Pitstick
VP: Cheryl Avery
VP: Mark Dutell
VP: TS Khoo
VP: Harvey Mednicovy
VP: WEI Shen
VP: Julian Spence

D-U-N-S 07-965-5222
GATES GLOBAL LLC
(*Suby of* OMAHA HOLDINGS LLC) ★
1551 Wewatta St, Denver, CO 80202-6173
Tel (303) 744-1911 *Founded/Ownrshp* 2014
Sales 652.1MM[E] *EMP* 4,619[E]
SIC 1382 Aerial geophysical exploration oil & gas
CEO: Ivo Jurek
**CFO:* David Naemura

D-U-N-S 06-814-9319
GATEWAY BUILDING SYSTEMS INC (ND)
2138 Main Ave W, West Fargo, ND 58078-1346
Tel (701) 293-7202 *Founded/Ownrshp* 1958, 1977
Sales 141.1MM[E] *EMP* 250
SIC 1542 5083 Nonresidential construction; Farm building construction; Silo construction, agricultural; Agricultural machinery & equipment
Pr: Kevin Johnson
Mktg Dir: Susana Suk
Snr PM: Michael Goetz

GATEWAY CHARITABLE FOUNDATION
See GATEWAY FOUNDATION INC

D-U-N-S 02-046-1161
GATEWAY CHURCH
500 S Nolen Dr Ste 300, Southlake, TX 76092-9165
Tel (817) 328-1000 *Founded/Ownrshp* 2000
Sales 64.0MM[E] *EMP* 1,500[E]
SIC 8661 Non-denominational church
Assoc Dir: Marci Elliott

D-U-N-S 12-911-0024
GATEWAY COMMUNITY HEALTH
7457 M E Cad Blvd Ste 200, Clarkston, MI 48348-4282
Tel (313) 262-5050 *Founded/Ownrshp* 2002
Sales NA *EMP* 75
Accts Uhy Advisors Mi Inc Farmingto
SIC 6324 Hospital & medical service plans
CEO: Dr Radwan Khoury

D-U-N-S 04-088-3779
GATEWAY FOUNDATION INC
GATEWAY CHARITABLE FOUNDATION
55 E Jackson Blvd # 1500, Chicago, IL 60604-4137
Tel (312) 663-1130 *Founded/Ownrshp* 1964
Sales 90.6MM *EMP* 1,500
Accts Rsm Us Llp Chicago Illinois
SIC 8093 Substance abuse clinics (outpatient)
Ch: Victor Fonseca
Pr: Jodi Levine
**CFO:* Tomas Del Rio
**Treas:* Donal S Crossett
VP: Nike Gantes
Genl Mgr: Dawn Ruzich
Opers Supe: Winston Henry
Opers Supe: Andrea Winner
Pgrm Dir: Shannon Huggins
Snr Mgr: Yolanda Johnson

D-U-N-S 86-937-0585
GATEWAY FUNDING DIVERSIFIED MORTGAGE SERVICES LP
(*Suby of* FINANCE OF AMERICA HOLDINGS LLC)
300 Welsh Rd, Horsham, PA 19044-2248
Tel (215) 591-0222 *Founded/Ownrshp* 1994
Sales NA *EMP* 1,200
SIC 6162 Mortgage bankers; Mortgage brokers, using own money
Pt: Bruno J Pasceri
Pt: Micheal Karp
CIO: Brian McGovern

GATEWAY HEALTH CENTER
See DEACONESS HEALTH SYSTEM INC

D-U-N-S 80-443-2193
GATEWAY HEALTH PLAN INC
(*Suby of* GATEWAY HEALTH PLAN INC) ★
600 Grant St Fl 41, Pittsburgh, PA 15219-2713
Tel (412) 255-4640 *Founded/Ownrshp* 1997
Sales NA *EMP* 235
SIC 6324 Health maintenance organization (HMO), insurance only
CFO: C Eric Huss
VP Opers: Margaret Worek

D-U-N-S 80-076-9721
GATEWAY HEALTH PLAN LP
(Suby of HIGHMARK BLUE CRSS-BLUE SHIELD) ★
4 Gateway Ctr 444, Pittsburgh, PA 15222
Tel (412) 255-4640 Founded/Ownrshp 1992
Sales NA EMP 235
SIC 6324 Health maintenance organization (HMO), insurance only
Pr: Patricia J Darnley
Pt: Robert S Mirsky
Ofcr: Mary Craig
VP: Cynthia Zydel

GATEWAY HOME REALTY
See AMERICAN FINANCIAL NETWORK INC

D-U-N-S 15-207-2849 IMP
GATEWAY INC
(Suby of ACER AMERICAN HOLDINGS CORP) ★
7565 Irvine Center Dr # 150, Irvine, CA 92618-4933
Tel (949) 471-7000 Founded/Ownrshp 2007
Sales 281.6MM^E EMP 1,700
SIC 3571 3577 Personal computers (microcomputers); Computer peripheral equipment
CEO: Ed Coleman
Pr: Bradly Shaw
COO: Bryan Albrecht
COO: Peter Cohen
CFO: John Goldsberry
Treas: Craig Calle
Sr VP: Scott Bauhofer
Sr VP: Bart Brown
Sr VP: Edward R Fisher
Sr VP: Steve Phillips
Sr VP: Michael R Tyler
VP: Jack Baikie
VP: John Carson
VP: Judy Sandberg
Exec: Stacy Brown
Exec: Peter Burns
Dir Surg: Kevin Shabow
Dir Surg: Gary Thomas
Assoc Dir: Lisa Takata

D-U-N-S 12-737-6684
GATEWAY MORTGAGE GROUP LLC
244 S Gateway Pl, Jenks, OK 74037-3448
Tel (918) 712-9000 Founded/Ownrshp 2000
Sales NA EMP 600
SIC 6163 Mortgage brokers arranging for loans, using money of others
Pr: John Kevin Stitt
*Pr: Alan Ferree
*COO: Mike Goyer
*CFO: Patrick McGowan
*Ofcr: Scott Henley
Ex VP: Rob Wiggins
Sr VP: G Todd White
VP: Steve Frink
VP: Sherron Gomez
VP: Tonya Granberry
VP: John Matuszeski
VP: Kevin Osuna
VP: David Robinson

D-U-N-S 10-319-9824 IMP
GATEWAY PACKAGING CO
20 Central Industrial Dr, Granite City, IL 62040-6801
Tel (618) 451-0010 Founded/Ownrshp 1982
Sales 114.3MM^E EMP 290
SIC 2674 2679 Bags: uncoated paper & multiwall; Labels, paper: made from purchased material
Pr: Roger D Miller
*CFO: Greg Petermeyer
*VP: Rebecca J Miller
IT Man: Marshall Andersen
IT Man: Marshall Winslow
Prd Mgr: Robert Tiepelman

GATEWAY PRINTING
See ROHRER CORP

D-U-N-S 05-587-1321
GATEWAY REGION YOUNG MENS CHRISTIAN ASSOCIATION
YMCA OF GREATER SAINT LOUIS
326 S 21st St Ste 400, Saint Louis, MO 63103-2267
Tel (314) 436-1177 Founded/Ownrshp 1854
Sales 54.1MM EMP 3,750
Accts Rubinbrown Llp Saint Louis M
SIC 8641 8741 8322 Youth organizations; Management services; Individual & family services
Pr: Gary Schlansker
Pr: Dennis Argue
*COO: Karen Kocher
*CFO: Frank Ward
Sr VP: Mike Salamone
Brnch Mgr: Melinda Olds
IT Man: Mike Panagos
Pgrm Dir: Melissa Di Fiori

D-U-N-S 11-307-6186
GATEWAY SECURITY INC
604 Market St 608, Newark, NJ 07105-2911
Tel (973) 465-8006 Founded/Ownrshp 1979
Sales 87.5MM^E EMP 3,500^E
SIC 7381 Security guard service
Pr: James Dell'ermo
*Pr: James Dellermo
*CEO: Kurus Elavia
Genl Mgr: Lisa Edwards

D-U-N-S 00-336-9048 EXP
GATEWAY SUPPLY CO INC (SC)
1312 Hamrick St, Columbia, SC 29201-4517
Tel (803) 771-7160 Founded/Ownrshp 1964
Sales 116.3MM^E EMP 130
Accts Bauknight Pietras & Stormer P
SIC 5075 5074 Warm air heating & air conditioning; Plumbing & hydronic heating supplies
CEO: Sam Williams Jr
*Pr: Chris Williams
*VP: Leonard Moore Jr
VP: R Moore
Brnch Mgr: Alexandra Linton
Brnch Mgr: Lonnie McCall
Brnch Mgr: Abbie Reese
Manager: Darrell Shull
Sls Mgr: John Skeppstrom

GATEWAY TERMINAL
See WATERFRONT ENTERPRISES INC

GATEWAY TIRE & SERVICE CENTER
See DUNLAP & KYLE CO INC

D-U-N-S 78-102-3551
GATEWAY WOODSIDE INC
100 Midway Rd Ste 14, Cranston, RI 02920-5742
Tel (401) 942-2800 Founded/Ownrshp 1998
Sales 135.0MM EMP 6
SIC 6512 Shopping center, property operation only
Genl Mgr: Douglas Gordon

GATOR TIRE
See CHRISTENSEN ENTERPRISES INC

D-U-N-S 85-856-1632 EXP
■ **GATORADE CO**
(Suby of QUAKER OATS CO) ★
555 W Monroe St Fl 1, Chicago, IL 60661-3700
Tel (312) 821-1000 Founded/Ownrshp 1990
Sales 165.5MM^E EMP 1,210
SIC 2086 5149 Bottled & canned soft drinks; Beverages, except coffee & tea
Pr: Charles I Maniscalco
Treas: Juanita Theodate
VP: Carla Hassan
VP: Victoria Ingram
Comm Dir: Mary Doherty
Mktg Mgr: John Shumate
Snr Mgr: Lauren Fritts
Snr Mgr: Gina Hardy

D-U-N-S 05-448-4217
GATR OF SAUK RAPIDS INC (MN)
GATR VOLVO GMC CENTER
218 Stearns Dr, Sauk Rapids, MN 56379-2520
Tel (320) 251-7356 Founded/Ownrshp 1961
Sales 115.5MM^E EMP 240
SIC 5511 Automobiles, new & used
Pr: Robert Neitzke
*VP: Trevin Hartung
IT Man: Paula Schmitz
Sls Mgr: Jon Pearson
Sls Mgr: John Sertich
Sales Asso: Zach Campion

GATR VOLVO GMC CENTER
See GATR OF SAUK RAPIDS INC

GATSBY
See KOMODIDAD DISTRIBUTORS INC

GATTI'S PIZZA
See MR GATTIS LP

D-U-N-S 00-516-1476
▲ **GATX CORP** (NY)
222 W Adams St, Chicago, IL 60606-5312
Tel (312) 621-6200 Founded/Ownrshp 1898
Sales 1.4MMM EMP 2,253
Accts Ernst & Young Llp Chicago Il
Tkr Sym GATX Exch NYS
SIC 4741 7359 4491 Rental of railroad cars; Equipment rental & leasing; Aircraft rental; Marine cargo handling; Marine loading & unloading services
Ch Bd: Brian A Kenney
Pr: James F Earl
Pr: Thomas A Ellman
CFO: Robert C Lyons
Treas: Eric D Harkness
Ofcr: Paul F Titterton
Ofcr: Jeffery R Young
Ex VP: Deborah A Golden
Ex VP: Steven Kean
Sr VP: Niyi A Adedoyin
Sr VP: Michael T Brooks
Sr VP: James M Conniff
Sr VP: Curt F Glenn
Sr VP: William M Muckian
VP: Niyi Adedoyin
VP: Eric Harkness
VP: Stephen Yuen
Board of Directors: Diane M Aigotti, Anne L Arvia, Ernst A Haberli, James B Ream, Robert J Ritchie, David S Sutherland, Casey J Sylla, Stephen R Wilson, Paul G Yovovich

D-U-N-S 03-451-8118
GAUBERT OIL CO INC
1201 Saint Patrick St, Thibodaux, LA 70301-2541
Tel (800) 256-1250 Founded/Ownrshp 2006
Sales 167.4MM EMP 205
SIC 5172 5411

D-U-N-S 07-947-8707
GAUDENZIA INC (PA)
106 W Main St, Norristown, PA 19401-4716
Tel (610) 239-9600 Founded/Ownrshp 1968, 1969
Sales 70.6MM EMP 1,100
Accts Grant Thornton Llp Philadelph
SIC 8361 8093 Rehabilitation center, residential: health care incidental; Drug clinic, outpatient; Alcohol clinic, outpatient
Pr: Michael B Harle
*CFO: Michael Coyle
CFO: Michael R Coyle
*Treas: Charles McGeady
*VP: Michael Moyle
*Ex Dir: Robert P Kelly
Mktg Dir: Ken Dickinson

D-U-N-S 55-735-0910
GAUGHAN SOUTH LLC
SOUTH POINT HOTEL & CASINO SPA
9777 Las Vegas Blvd S, Las Vegas, NV 89183-4013
Tel (702) 796-7111 Founded/Ownrshp 2006
Sales 138.2MM^E EMP 2,400
SIC 7011 Casino hotel
VP: Dave Jensen
Exec: Sandra Hernandez
Exec: Pam Wisdom
Dir Soc: Flo Serna
Area Mgr: John Munoz
Dir IT: Deanna Thompson
IT Man: Steve Stallworth
Natl Sales: Sheryl Duits
Natl Sales: Anthony Earl
Natl Sales: Monique Kuhl
Natl Sales: Tara Wolf

D-U-N-S 00-225-4951
GAULT CHEVROLET CO INC (NY)
GAULT TOYOTA
2205 North St, Endicott, NY 13760-6124
Tel (607) 748-8244 Founded/Ownrshp 1955
Sales 127.3MM EMP 230^E
Accts Evans And Bennett Llp Certif
SIC 5511 5012 Automobiles, new & used; Automobiles & other motor vehicles; Automobiles
Pr: Bob Gault
*Ch Bd: Robert J Gault Sr
*VP: Connie Gault
Off Mgr: Carla Hamilton
Sls Mgr: Margaret Davis
Sales Asso: Tom Lavelle
Sales Asso: Thor Leighton
Sales Asso: Tim Parke
Sales Asso: Rick Sleeper

GAULT TOYOTA
See GAULT CHEVROLET CO INC

D-U-N-S 07-966-1160
GAVILON AGRICULTURE HOLDINGS CO
(Suby of MARUBENI CORPORATION)
1331 Capitol Ave, Omaha, NE 68102-1106
Tel (402) 889-4000 Founded/Ownrshp 2013
Sales 1.0MMM^E EMP 930^E
SIC 5153 5191 Grain & field beans; Fertilizers & agricultural chemicals
Pr: Jim Anderson
*CEO: John Neppl
*CFO: Kevin Lewis
*VP: Greg Konsor

D-U-N-S 07-944-4851
GAVILON AGRICULTURE INVESTMENT INC
(Suby of GAVILON AGRICULTURE HOLDINGS CO) ★
1331 Capitol Ave, Omaha, NE 68102-1106
Tel (402) 889-4000 Founded/Ownrshp 2012
Sales 1.0MMM^E EMP 500^E
SIC 5153 5191 Grain & field beans; Fertilizers & agricultural chemicals
CEO: Jim Anderson
*Pr: Brian Harlander
*COO: Greg Piper
*CFO: John Neppl
*VP: Corey Dencklau
*VP: Ed Prosser

D-U-N-S 82-748-1479
GAVILON GRAIN LLC
(Suby of GAVILON GROUP LLC) ★
1331 Capitol Ave, Omaha, NE 68102-1106
Tel (402) 889-4000 Founded/Ownrshp 2013
Sales 802.4MM^E EMP 930
SIC 6221 5153 4221 4226 Commodity contracts brokers, dealers; Grain & field beans; Farm product warehousing & storage; Special warehousing & storage
Pr: Lew Batchelder
*Pr: Corey Dencklau
*Pr: Brian Harlander

D-U-N-S 12-893-8839 IMP/EXP
GAVILON GROUP LLC
(Suby of GAVILON INTERMEDIATE HOLDINGS LLC) ★
1331 Capitol Ave, Omaha, NE 68102-1106
Tel (402) 889-4000 Founded/Ownrshp 2008
Sales 1.2MMM^E EMP 930
SIC 5153 5191 Grain & field beans; Fertilizers & agricultural chemicals
Pr: Jim Anderson
COO: Tom Ramsey
*CFO: John Neppl
VP: Shane Berrett
VP: Corey Dencklau
VP: Greg Konsor
VP: Ed Prosser
VP: Steven Zehr
VP Opers: Brian Carleton

D-U-N-S 02-095-7773
GAVILON HOLDINGS LLC
(Suby of GAVILON AGRICULTURE INVESTMENT INC) ★
1331 Capitol Ave, Omaha, NE 68102-1106
Tel (402) 889-4000 Founded/Ownrshp 2012
Sales 194.2MM^E EMP 930^E
SIC 6719 Public utility holding companies

D-U-N-S 07-912-8549
GAVILON INTERMEDIATE HOLDINGS LLC
(Suby of GAVILON HOLDINGS LLC) ★
1331 Capitol Ave, Omaha, NE 68102-1106
Tel (402) 889-4000 Founded/Ownrshp 2008
Sales 1.2MMM^E EMP 930
SIC 6722 Management investment, open-end
CEO: Jim Anderson

D-U-N-S 05-236-8206
GAYLE MANUFACTURING CO INC
1455 E Kentucky Ave, Woodland, CA 95776-6121
Tel (707) 226-9136 Founded/Ownrshp 1968
Sales 90.6MM EMP 96
SIC 3441 1541 Fabricated structural metal; Industrial buildings & warehouses
CEO: Andrew Stoll
*Pr: Gary Glenn
*CFO: James Deblasio
VP: David De Blasio
*VP: David Deblasio
*VP: Nelson Vieira
Exec: Tamara N Young
Genl Mgr: Gary Glen
IT Man: Efrain Calderon
Opers Mgr: Nelson Viera
Board of Directors: David Deblasio, Lisa Deblasio, Gary Glenn, Andrew Stoll, Nelson Vieira

GAYLORD HOTELS
See GAYLORD OPRYLAND USA INC

D-U-N-S 11-870-3529
■ **GAYLORD OPRYLAND USA INC**
GAYLORD HOTELS
(Suby of MARRIOTT INTERNATIONAL INC) ★
2800 Opryland Dr, Nashville, TN 37214-1200
Tel (615) 889-1000 Founded/Ownrshp 2012
Sales 176.4MM^E EMP 4,000
SIC 7011 Resort hotel
Ch Bd: Colin V Reed
VP: Dennis Kolodziejski
Exec: Carrie Schloss
Dir Soc: Lori Story
Comm Man: Melissa Simpson
CIO: Matt Collins
Dir IT: Lee Rotholz
Dir IT: David Sacco
Netwrk Eng: Josh Gibbar
Sales Exec: Michelle A Carter
Sales Exec: Jeff Lindeblad

D-U-N-S 00-528-4393
GAZETTE CO (IA)
GFOC HOLDINGS,
500 3rd Ave Se, Cedar Rapids, IA 52401-1608
Tel (319) 398-8211 Founded/Ownrshp 1883
Sales 119.0MM EMP 600
SIC 2711 2752 4833 Newspapers, publishing & printing; Commercial printing, lithographic; Television broadcasting stations
Pr: Chuck Peters
*CFO: Ken Slaughter
*Ch: Joe Hladky
*Treas: Scott Grasso
VP: Mary Collins

D-U-N-S 01-654-3055 IMP
GB BIOSCIENCES LLC
(Suby of SYNGENTA CORP) ★
2200 Concord Pike, Wilmington, DE 19803-2909
Tel (336) 632-6000 Founded/Ownrshp 1986, 2000
Sales 87.4MM^E EMP 320
SIC 2879 2834 2899 Pesticides, agricultural or household; Fungicides, herbicides; Pharmaceutical preparations; Druggists' preparations (pharmaceuticals); Chemical preparations
CEO: Robert Woods

D-U-N-S 80-850-0081 EXP
■ **GBC METALS LLC**
OLIN BRASS
(Suby of GLOBAL BRASS AND COPPER INC) ★
427 N Shamrock St, East Alton, IL 62024-1174
Tel (618) 258-2350 Founded/Ownrshp 2007
Sales 241.9MM^E EMP 1,900
SIC 3351 3341 3469 Brass rolling & drawing; Copper smelting & refining (secondary); Metal stampings
Pr: Bill Toler
*CEO: John Walker
*COO: John J Wasz
*CFO: Robert Michelli
*VP: John Moritz
*VP: Tom Werner
VP: Michael Wickenhauser
Mtls Mgr: Kristen Young

GBFB
See GREATER BOSTON FOOD BANK INC

D-U-N-S 96-351-0420 IMP/EXP
GBG ACCESSORIES GROUP LLC
(Suby of MAX LEATHER) ★
350 5th Ave Lbby 9, New York, NY 10118-0109
Tel (646) 839-7000 Founded/Ownrshp 2010
Sales 158.5MM^E EMP 55^E
SIC 5137 Women's & children's clothing

D-U-N-S 06-597-4644 IMP/EXP
GBG USA INC
MAX LEATHER
(Suby of GLOBAL BRANDS GROUP HOLDING LIMITED)
350 5th Ave Lbby 9, New York, NY 10118-0109
Tel (646) 839-7083 Founded/Ownrshp 1986
Sales 1.1MMM^E EMP 1,722^E
SIC 5139 5137 5136 Footwear; Sportswear, women's & children's; Sportswear, men's & boys'
CEO: Bruce Philip Rockowitz
*Pr: Dow Peter Famulak
*Pr: Jason Andrew Rabin
*CFO: Ronald Ventricelli
Sr VP: Mindi Cooke
Sr VP: Heather Mee
VP: Julie Rosen
VP: Antoinette Scarangella
*VP: Deborah Vincent
Exec: Fred Dobbs

D-U-N-S 08-012-2389
GBG WEST LLC
JOES JEANS
(Suby of MAX LEATHER) ★
350 5th Ave Fl 5, New York, NY 10118-0110
Tel (646) 839-7000 Founded/Ownrshp 2015
Sales 88.0MM EMP 140
SIC 2339 Jeans: women's, misses' & juniors'
CEO: Suzy Biszantz
*Sr VP: Elena Pickett

GBI RESEARCH
See GLOBAL DATA PUBLICATIONS INC

D-U-N-S 03-398-5557 IMP
GBK CORP
KAISER-FRANCIS OIL COMPANY
6733 S Yale Ave, Tulsa, OK 74136-3302
Tel (918) 494-0000 Founded/Ownrshp 1976
Sales 706.0MM^E EMP 2,067^E
SIC 1311 Crude petroleum production; Natural gas production
Pr: George B Kaiser
*Ex VP: James A Willis

D-U-N-S 13-447-0280
GBP MANAGEMENT INC
(Suby of GUARDIAN BUILDING PRODUCTS INC) ★
979 Batesville Rd, Greer, SC 29651-6819
Tel (864) 297-6101 Founded/Ownrshp 2002
Sales 889.1MM^E EMP 200^E

SIC 8741 Business management
Pr: Duane H Faulkner
**CFO:* David E Love
**VP:* Bruce Schneider

GBRX
See GUNDERSON LLC

GBS COMPUTER SOLUTIONS
See GBS CORP

D-U-N-S 05-466-8751 IMP
GBS CORP (OH)
GBS COMPUTER SOLUTIONS
7233 Freedom Ave Nw, North Canton, OH 44720-7123
Tel (330) 494-5330 *Founded/Ownrshp* 1971
Sales 171.7MM^E *EMP* 315
SIC 5045 5112 2675 2672 2761 2759 Computers, peripherals & software; Business forms; Folders, filing, die-cut: made from purchased materials; Labels (unprinted), gummed: made from purchased materials; Tape, pressure sensitive: made from purchased materials; Manifold business forms; Commercial printing
CEO: Eugene Calpria
**Pr:* Jeff Fusco
CFO: Michele Benson
**Ex VP:* James R Carey
VP: Robert Bathon
VP Bus Dev: Allan Greer
Dir IT: Mark Galpin
Sftwr Eng: Scott Krause
Plnt Mgr: Frank Stewart
Sales Exec: Tom Yannarell
VP Sls: Eric Moore

D-U-N-S 07-495-9834
GBU FINANCIAL LIFE
G B U
4254 Saw Mill Run Blvd, Pittsburgh, PA 15227-3394
Tel (412) 884-5100 *Founded/Ownrshp* 1892
Sales NA *EMP* 26^E
SIC 6311 Fraternal life insurance organizations
CEO: James R Stoker
**Ch Bd:* Lea Ann Hazi
**VP:* Matthew Blistan
Mktg Dir: Jim Laick
Manager: Jessica Shawley

GC ELECTRONICS
See WALDOM ELECTRONICS CORP

D-U-N-S 18-052-9323
GC SERVICES LIMITED PARTNERSHIP
6330 Gulfton St, Houston, TX 77081-1108
Tel (713) 777-4441 *Founded/Ownrshp* 2015
Sales 406.0MM^E *EMP* 9,000
Accts Ham Langston & Brezina Llp H
SIC 7322 7389 Adjustment & collection services; Telemarketing services
Pr: Frank A Taylor
CFO: Michael D Jones
Chf Cred: Brad C Batig
Ex VP: Meagan M Conway
Ex VP: Daniel R Cook
Ex VP: Gary L Hopkins
Ex VP: Mark A Schordock
Sr VP: Craig M Cappelle
Sr VP: Scott Cole
Sr VP: Linda M Spellicy
Netwrk Eng: Kola Oba

D-U-N-S 13-350-1127
GCA SERVICES GROUP INC
1350 Euclid Ave Ste 1500, Cleveland, OH 44115-1832
Tel (216) 535-4900 *Founded/Ownrshp* 2012
Sales 800.0MM *EMP* 32,000
SIC 7349 Janitorial service, contract basis
CEO: Robert Norton
**CFO:* Robert Gerber
Rgnl VP: Kevin Davis
Ex VP: Timothy H Shea
VP: Will Dunn
**VP:* Walt Griffin
VP: Neil Guliano
Dist Mgr: Ron Baker
IT Man: Jesse Villarreal
Netwrk Mgr: Dennis Pylypiak
Sls Dir: Donnie Cherry

D-U-N-S 00-147-5730
GCA SERVICES GROUP OF NORTH CAROLINA INC (NC)
ADVANTAGE STAFFING
(*Suby of* GCA SERVICES GROUP INC) ★
1 Centerview Dr Ste 109, Greensboro, NC 27407-3712
Tel (336) 294-9411 *Founded/Ownrshp* 1974
Sales 40.9MM^E *EMP* 4,000
SIC 7349 7363 Janitorial service, contract basis; Temporary help service
CEO: Robert Norton
**Pr:* Cole Leitch
**Ch:* Tom Fivgerald

GCC
See GHILOTTI CONSTRUCTION CO INC

GCCCD
See GROSSMONT-CUYAMACA COMMUNITY COLLEGE DISTRICT

D-U-N-S 00-129-3224 IMP/EXP
GCE INTERNATIONAL INC (NY)
GREAT CHINA EMPIRE
1385 Broadway Fl 21, New York, NY 10018-6022
Tel (212) 704-4800 *Founded/Ownrshp* 1920
Sales 159.2MM^E *EMP* 400
Accts Cohnreznick Llp New York New
SIC 2253 2389 2331 5137 5136 Hats & headwear, knit; Scarves & mufflers, knit; Handkerchiefs, except paper; T-shirts & tops, women's: made from purchased materials; Blouses, women's & juniors': made from purchased material; Scarves, women's & children's; Gloves, women's & children's; Scarves, men's & boys'; Gloves, men's & boys'
Ch: Peter Markson
**Pr:* Donald Oberfield
**Treas:* Martin J Kelly
Exec: Patti Disner
IT Man: Abe Anteby
IT Man: AVI Sivan
IT Man: Lisa Valdespino

D-U-N-S 09-898-3471
GCG FINANCIAL INC
3 Parkway N Ste 500, Deerfield, IL 60015-2567
Tel (847) 457-3000 *Founded/Ownrshp* 1975
Sales NA *EMP* 150
SIC 6411 8742 6211 Insurance agents; Financial consultant; Security brokers & dealers
Pr: Alan Levitz
**Ch Bd:* Robert Levitz
Ofcr: Krista Bommarito
Ofcr: Charles Melka
Ofcr: Mark Pietch
**Ex VP:* David Levitz
**Ex VP:* Rick Loudenback
**Ex VP:* Mark Pietsch
**Ex VP:* Matt Schlaepfer
**Ex VP:* Michael Smith
VP: Lauren Barnard
VP: Phillip Battin
VP: Jim Berman
VP: Brian Carlson
VP: Brian Crane
VP: Pam Davis
VP: Peter Gottstein
VP: Bob Janson
VP: Joseph Jonas
VP: Michael Kesner
VP: Mike Kesner

D-U-N-S 08-935-4695
■ **GCI INC**
ALASKA UNITED
(*Suby of* GENERAL COMMUNICATION INC) ★
2550 Denali St Ste 1000, Anchorage, AK 99503-2751
Tel (907) 868-5400 *Founded/Ownrshp* 2001
Sales 978.5MM *EMP* 7^E
Accts Grant Thornton Llp Anchorage
SIC 7389 Telemarketing services
CEO: Ronald Duncan
**Pr:* David Morris
**Sec:* John M Lowber
**Ex VP:* Gregory F Chapados
**VP:* Bruce L Broquet
**VP:* Wilson Hughes
VP: Gene Strid
Tech Mgr: Alan Caruth

D-U-N-S 79-679-8841 IMP
GCI INC
875 Battery St Fl 1, San Francisco, CA 94111-1547
Tel (415) 978-2790 *Founded/Ownrshp* 1992
Sales 159.1MM *EMP* 48
Accts Johnston Gremaux & Rossi Llp
SIC 1542 Commercial & office buildings, renovation & repair
CFO: John Lowber
Sr VP: Paul E Fearer
Sr VP: Wilson G Hughes
Sr VP: William Kelley
**VP:* Peter D Goldsmith

GCL W
See GARDA CL WEST INC

D-U-N-S 00-923-9450
GCO INC
27750 Industrial Blvd, Hayward, CA 94545-4043
Tel (510) 786-3333 *Founded/Ownrshp* 1949
Sales 132.1MM^E *EMP* 200
SIC 5074 5087 Pipe & boiler covering; Pipes & fittings, plastic; Plumbing & heating valves; Firefighting equipment; Sprinkler systems
Ch Bd: Michael H Groeniger
**Treas:* Beverly J Groeniger
**Ex VP:* Richard Alexander
**VP:* Richard Old
**VP:* James Wunsche
Brnch Mgr: Gary Spring
S&M/VP: Dick Alexander

D-U-N-S 08-011-5750
▲ **GCP APPLIED TECHNOLOGIES INC**
62 Whittemore Ave, Cambridge, MA 02140-1623
Tel (617) 876-1400 *Founded/Ownrshp* 2015
Sales 1.4MMM^E *EMP* 2,900^E
Tkr Sym GCP *Exch* NYS
SIC 2819 2899 Industrial inorganic chemicals; Chemical preparations
Pr: Gregory E Poling
Ch Bd: Ronald C Cambre
Pr: Zain Mahmood
CFO: Dean P Freeman
Ofcr: William J McCall
VP: John W Kapples
Exec: Philip Zanghi
Board of Directors: Marcia J Avedon, Marye Anne Fox, Janice K Henry, Phillip J Mason, Elizabeth Mora, Danny R Shepherd

D-U-N-S 00-194-7852
■ **GCS SYSTEMS INC**
(*Suby of* ECOLAB INC) ★
370 Wabasha St N, Saint Paul, MN 55102-1323
Tel (651) 293-2134 *Founded/Ownrshp* 1892, 2002
Sales 119.1MM^E *EMP* 1,000
SIC 5046 7699

D-U-N-S 05-324-2632 IMP/EXP
GCX CORP
3875 Cypress Dr, Petaluma, CA 94954-5635
Tel (707) 773-1100 *Founded/Ownrshp* 1998
Sales 97.2MM^E *EMP* 300^E
SIC 3429

D-U-N-S 02-432-0997 IMP
GD COPPER (USA) INC
COPPER AND COPPER TUBE
(*Suby of* GOLDEN DRAGON PRECISE COPPER TUBE GROUP INC.)
405 Gd Copper Dr, Pine Hill, AL 36769-4500
Tel (334) 637-0200 *Founded/Ownrshp* 2007
Sales 180.0MM^E *EMP* 300
SIC 3351 3999 Copper & copper alloy pipe & tube; Atomizers, toiletry
Pr: Xuhui Zhang
**Pr:* Mingxu Chen
**Prin:* Ming Xu

D-U-N-S 80-729-4541 IMP/EXP
GDB INTERNATIONAL INC
1 Home News Row, New Brunswick, NJ 08901-3601
Tel (732) 246-3001 *Founded/Ownrshp* 1993
Sales 117.6MM *EMP* 100
Accts Withumsmith&Brown Pc
SIC 2851 5162 5111 5093 Paints & allied products; Paints & paint additives; Plastics materials & basic shapes; Printing & writing paper; Plastics scrap
CEO: Sanjeev Bagaria
**Pr:* Sunil Bagaria
Ex VP: Robert Tsai
Sr VP: Mani Palani
VP: Mohammed Liaquat
Opers Mgr: Omar Morales
VP Sls: Francisco Suarez

GDC HOMES
See ACHEN-GARDNER INC

D-U-N-S 96-890-9739
GDF SUEZ ENERGY DEVELOPMENT NA INC
(*Suby of* GDF SUEZ ENERGY NORTH AMERICA INC) ★
1990 Post Oak Blvd # 1900, Houston, TX 77056-3818
Tel (713) 636-0000 *Founded/Ownrshp* 2011
Sales 85.3MM^E *EMP* 150
SIC 4911 Electric services
Pr: Herman Schopman
**CFO:* Geert Peeters
**Ex VP:* Paul J Cavicchi
Ex VP: Kelly McGrath
Ex VP: Jean Nassau
**Sr VP:* Karim Barbir
**Sr VP:* Bart Clark
**Sr VP:* Mike Thompson
**VP:* Jorge Alvarez
VP: Guy Braden
**VP:* Newton Houston

D-U-N-S 05-444-7164 IMP
GDF SUEZ ENERGY NORTH AMERICA INC
(*Suby of* ENGIE)
1990 Post Oak Blvd # 1900, Houston, TX 77056-3818
Tel (713) 636-0000 *Founded/Ownrshp* 1970
Sales 1.4MMM^E *EMP* 422
SIC 1311 8741 1629 Natural gas production; Industrial management; Power plant construction; Industrial plant construction
VP: Eric Bradley
VP: J D Burrows
VP: Ray Cunningham
VP: Reese Doggett
VP: John Funk
VP: Richard Houston
VP: Felisa Ros
VP: Mike Thompson
VP Bus Dev: Newton Houston
VP Bus Dev: Ernesto Ramirez
IT Man: Jonathan Williams

D-U-N-S 03-908-7379
GDG HOLDINGS INC
2901 E 78th St, Minneapolis, MN 55425-1501
Tel (952) 854-2044 *Founded/Ownrshp* 1975
Sales 278.0MM^E *EMP* 850^E
SIC 5084 Engines & transportation equipment
CEO: Jeff Caswell
**CEO:* Gordon D Galarneau
**Sec:* Larry Schwartz

GDGSOC
See GENERAL DYNAMICS GOVERNMENT SYSTEMS OVERSEAS CORP

D-U-N-S 10-133-7660
GDH CONSULTING INC
4200 E Skelly Dr Ste 650, Tulsa, OK 74135-3244
Tel (918) 392-1600 *Founded/Ownrshp* 2001
Sales 105.7MM^E *EMP* 787
SIC 7379 7361 7371 Computer related consulting services; Employment agencies; Computer software systems analysis & design, custom
CEO: Gerald D Hurley
Board of Directors: Charles Snell

D-U-N-S 07-930-0867
GDI FACILITY SERVICES INC
(*Suby of* GDI OMNI INC) ★
24300 Southfield Rd # 220, Southfield, MI 48075-2820
Tel (248) 483-3170 *Founded/Ownrshp* 2012
Sales 7.7MM^E *EMP* 1,007^E
SIC 7349 Building maintenance services; Janitorial service, contract basis
Pr: Claude Bigras

GDI OMNI INC.
See GDI SERVICES INC

D-U-N-S 07-948-4041
GDI SERVICES INC
780 5th Ave Ste 115, King of Prussia, PA 19406-4065
Tel (610) 584-0888 *Founded/Ownrshp* 2014
Sales 42.7MM^E *EMP* 1,700
SIC 7349 Building maintenance services; Building & office cleaning services; Janitorial service, contract basis
Pr: Peter Criville
**VP:* George Mick

D-U-N-S 07-876-5442
GDI SERVICES INC
GDI OMNI INC.
(*Suby of* 9268-4935 QUEBEC INC)
24300 Southfield Rd # 220, Southfield, MI 48075-2820
Tel (248) 483-3170 *Founded/Ownrshp* 2012
Sales 56.7MM^E *EMP* 1,150
SIC 7349 Building maintenance services; Janitorial service, contract basis
CEO: Ahmad Boomrod
VP: Michael Cadotte

GDIT
See GENERAL DYNAMICS INFORMATION TECHNOLOGY INC

GDLS
See GENERAL DYNAMICS LAND SYSTEMS INC

D-U-N-S 00-340-4308
GDT PROPERTIES INC (PA)
CNSLTD ELCTRCL DSTRIBUTOR
(*Suby of* C E D) ★
312 N 8th St, Lebanon, PA 17046-4717
Tel (717) 273-4514 *Founded/Ownrshp* 1935, 2011
Sales 170.1MM^E *EMP* 254
SIC 5063 Electrical supplies
Pr: G David Thomas
**Pr:* Mark D Bucci
**Treas:* John C Rodman
**VP:* Richard A Firth
**VP:* Stephen G Foley
**VP:* John P Hagan II
**VP:* Michael Klahr

GE
See IDX SYSTEMS CORP

GE AERO ENERGY PRODUCTS
See GE ENERGY MANUFACTURING INC

D-U-N-S 01-663-5687 IMP
■ **GE AIRCRAFT ENGINES HOLDINGS INC**
(*Suby of* GENERAL ELECTRIC CO) ★
1 Neumann Way, Cincinnati, OH 45215-1915
Tel (513) 243-8251 *Founded/Ownrshp* 1992
Sales 393.5MM^E *EMP* 1,335
SIC 7699

GE APPLIANCE DIV
See ROPER CORP

GE APPLIANCES
See HAIER US APPLIANCE SOLUTIONS INC

D-U-N-S 18-003-1908
GE ASSET MANAGEMENT INC
GE INVESTMENTS
1600 Summer St Ste 3, Stamford, CT 06905-5125
Tel (203) 326-2300 *Founded/Ownrshp* 1980
Sales 596.9MM^E *EMP* 2,200
SIC 6282

D-U-N-S 87-994-0666 IMP
■ **GE AVIATION MUSKEGON**
(*Suby of* GE AIRCRAFT ENGINES HOLDINGS INC) ★
2034 Latimer Dr, Muskegon, MI 49442-6232
Tel (231) 777-2685 *Founded/Ownrshp* 1997
Sales 152.0MM^E *EMP* 600
SIC 3724 Turbines, aircraft type
Pr: David Yacavone
Pgrm Dir: John Friedli

D-U-N-S 10-720-6559 IMP
■ **GE AVIATION SYSTEMS LLC**
(*Suby of* GENERAL ELECTRIC CO) ★
1 Neumann Way, Cincinnati, OH 45215-1915
Tel (513) 243-2000 *Founded/Ownrshp* 2006
Sales 262.3MM^E *EMP* 3,573
SIC 3812 Aircraft control systems, electronic
Pr: R F Ehr
**Pr:* J B Hines
**Ch:* Jeff Immelt
Treas: David Martin
**Ex VP:* Peter Page
VP: Charles P Blankenship Jr
VP: Ernest Marshall
Software D: Rebecca Seaberg
Mktg Mgr: Rick Eddins
Snr Mgr: Kelly Townsley

D-U-N-S 00-972-2265 IMP/EXP
■ **GE BETZ INC**
GE WATER & PROCESS TECH
(*Suby of* GENERAL ELECTRIC CO) ★
4636 Somerton Rd, Trevose, PA 19053-6742
Tel (215) 355-3300 *Founded/Ownrshp* 2002
Sales 28.5MM^E *EMP* 4,000
SIC 2899 3826 5084 3823 Water treating compounds; Water testing apparatus; Pumps & pumping equipment; Industrial instrmnts msrmnt display/control process variable
Pr: Heiner Markhoff
**CEO:* William R Cook
**Treas:* Monica A Oconnor
**Treas:* R D Voncanon
Chf Mktg O: Steve Watzeck
VP: Craig Hobkirk
IT Man: Robert Marsicano

D-U-N-S 15-995-3140
■ **GE CAPITAL INTERNATIONAL HOLDINGS CORP**
(*Suby of* GENERAL ELECTRIC CAPITAL SERVICES INC) ★
260 Long Ridge Rd, Stamford, CT 06927-1600
Tel (203) 357-4000 *Founded/Ownrshp* 1994
Sales 772.2MM^E *EMP* 10,000^E
SIC 6719

D-U-N-S 60-302-8325
■ **GE CAPITAL MONTGOMERY WARD**
(*Suby of* GENERAL ELECTRIC CAPITAL CORP) ★
3135 Easton Tpke, Stamford, CT 06927-0001
Tel (203) 357-4000 *Founded/Ownrshp* 1988
Sales NA *EMP* 2,300
SIC 6141 Consumer finance companies
Pr: Marc Sheinbaum
V Ch: Suzanne Thomas
Sr VP: Eric Dull
VP: Charles M Crabtree
VP: Maria Dipietro
VP: Mike McMahon
VP: Joanne Stewart
Dir Risk M: William Strittmatter
Mng Dir: Steve Poulin

D-U-N-S 36-154-9657
■ **GE CONSUMER FINANCE INC**
GE MONEY
(*Suby of* GENERAL ELECTRIC CO) ★
777 Long Ridge Rd, Stamford, CT 06902-1247
Tel (203) 921-1443 *Founded/Ownrshp* 1993
Sales 245.2MM^E *EMP* 11,000^E

SIC 8742 Financial consultant
Prin: Mark Begor
**Pr:* Margaret Keane
Pr: Deepak Luthra
Ofcr: Jane Wexton
VP: George Awad
VP: John Baraldi
VP: Diane Barone
VP: David Beebe
VP: Susan Bishop
VP: Dan Borchers
VP: Gautam Borooah
VP: David Caruso
VP: Donovan Goertzen
VP: Richard Kelly
VP: Bob Rendine
VP: Bart Schaller
VP: Saby Sengupta
VP: Pete Tosches
VP Bus Dev: Steve Apesos
Comm Man: Mariane Ceballo

GE CRITICAL POWER
See LINEAGE POWER HOLDINGS INC

D-U-N-S 60-387-1083 IMP/EXP
■ GE DRIVES & CONTROLS INC
(*Suby of* GENERAL ELECTRIC CO) ★
1501 Roanoke Blvd, Salem, VA 24153-6422
Tel (540) 387-7000 *Founded/Ownrshp* 1955
Sales 137.5MM[E] *EMP* 900
SIC 3612 Power transformers, electric
Pr: Steven S Roy
Genl Mgr: Richard Rafalik

GE ENERGY
See GE OIL & GAS COMPRESSION SYSTEMS LLC

GE ENERGY
See BENTLY NEVADA INC

GE ENERGY
See GE PACKAGED POWER LP

GE ENERGY CONNECTIONS
See GE ENERGY MANAGEMENT SERVICES LLC

D-U-N-S 10-283-2131 IMP
■ GE ENERGY MANAGEMENT SERVICES LLC
GE ENERGY CONNECTIONS
(*Suby of* GRID SOLUTIONS (US) LLC) ★
4200 Wildwood Pkwy, Atlanta, GA 30339-8402
Tel (678) 844-6000 *Founded/Ownrshp* 2002
Sales 2.5MMM[E] *EMP* 4,008
SIC 4911 Electric services
Pr: Russell Stokes
**Pr:* Jeffrey Immelt
Ofcr: Brian West
VP: Victor Abate
VP: Barbara A Cameron
VP: Happy R Pekins
Mng Dir: Robert Balletti
Mng Dir: Antti Kotisaari
Mng Dir: Anton Kubler
Prgrm Mgr: Brian Week
Genl Mgr: Dan Werrell

D-U-N-S 01-388-7554 IMP
■ GE ENERGY MANUFACTURING INC
GE AERO ENERGY PRODUCTS
(*Suby of* GENERAL ELECTRIC CO) ★
1333 West Loop S Ste 700, Houston, TX 77027-9117
Tel (713) 803-0900 *Founded/Ownrshp* 1998
Sales 1.5MMM[E] *EMP* 3,800
SIC 3621 3568 5084 Power generators; Power transmission equipment; Power plant machinery
Pr: Charles Blakenship
**CFO:* Richard Kasson

D-U-N-S 03-875-0035 IMP/EXP
■ GE ENERGY PARTS INC
(*Suby of* GENERAL ELECTRIC CO) ★
4200 Wildwood Pkwy, Atlanta, GA 30339-8402
Tel (678) 844-6000 *Founded/Ownrshp* 1998
Sales 282.4MM[E] *EMP* 500[E]
SIC 5065 3612 Electronic parts & equipment; Autotransformers, electric (power transformers)
Pr: Karl Fessenden
**COO:* Ann McWhorter
Treas: Charles H Coffin
**Treas:* Kristopher McBright
**VP:* Stephanie Mains
**VP:* Margaret Morton

D-U-N-S 62-385-2030 IMP
■ GE ENERGY POWER CONVERSION USA INC
CONVERTEAM
(*Suby of* GENERAL ELECTRIC CO) ★
610 Epsilon Dr, Pittsburgh, PA 15238-2808
Tel (412) 967-0765 *Founded/Ownrshp* 2011
Sales 95.5MM[E] *EMP* 325[E]
SIC 3629 Power conversion units, a.c. to d.c.: static-electric
CEO: Joe Mastrangelo
Pr: Michael Archibald
COO: Garry Rauscher
Treas: Donald Grau
Mng Dir: Jim Morrison
Snr Mgr: Ian Davies
Board of Directors: Joseph Mastrangelo Theirry

D-U-N-S 11-845-3195 IMP
■ GE ENGINE SERVICES - MCALLEN L P
MCALLEN P&RS SERVICE CENTER
(*Suby of* GE AVIATION SYSTEMS LLC) ★
6200 S 42nd St, McAllen, TX 78503-8856
Tel (956) 971-5200 *Founded/Ownrshp* 1997
Sales 92.3MM[E] *EMP* 575
SIC 3724 Aircraft engines & engine parts
Genl Mgr: Daniel Campos

D-U-N-S 01-600-4702 IMP/EXP
■ GE ENGINE SERVICES LLC
(*Suby of* GENERAL ELECTRIC CO) ★
1 Neumann Way, Cincinnati, OH 45215-1915
Tel (513) 243-2000 *Founded/Ownrshp* 1997
Sales 481.6MM[E] *EMP* 11,000
SIC 7699

D-U-N-S 03-207-0364
■ GE FINANCIAL ASSURANCE HOLDINGS INC
(*Suby of* GENERAL ELECTRIC CAPITAL SERVICES INC) ★
6604 W Broad St, Richmond, VA 23230-1702
Tel (804) 281-6000 *Founded/Ownrshp* 2001
Sales NA *EMP* 6,250
SIC 6311 Life insurance; Life insurance carriers
Ch Bd: Michael Fraizer
Sr VP: Michael S Laming
Sr VP: Kevin Schneider

GE FLEET SERVICES
See GELCO CORP

D-U-N-S 79-075-4167
GE FOUNDATION
3135 Easton Tpke, Fairfield, CT 06828-0002
Tel (203) 373-3216 *Founded/Ownrshp* 2013
Sales 132.8MM *EMP* 41[E]
SIC 6722 Management investment, open-end
Pr: Deb Elam
Dir Risk M: Derrick Ramsey
Dir Lab: Ravikanth Malladi
Admn Mgr: Andy Day
Dist Mgr: Ron Spielman
CIO: Tony Ross
CTO: Jeff Rademaekers
Dir IT: Sandesh Lal
Counsel: Joseph Noga
Counsel: Christine S Ricci
Counsel: Tony Walsh

GE GLOBAL EXCHANGE SERVICES
See GXS INC

D-U-N-S 07-986-6942
■ GE GRID SOLUTIONS LLC
(*Suby of* GENERAL ELECTRIC CO) ★
4200 Wildwood Pkwy, Atlanta, GA 30339-8402
Tel (877) 605-6777 *Founded/Ownrshp* 2015
Sales 1.0MMM *EMP* 900[E]
SIC 3612 Transformers, except electric
Pr: John Lavelle

GE HEALTHCARE
See MEDI-PHYSICS INC

D-U-N-S 01-165-8242
■ GE HEALTHCARE BIO-SCIENCES CORP
GE HEALTHCARE LIFE SCIENCES
(*Suby of* GE HEALTHCARE LIMITED)
100 Results Way, Marlborough, MA 01752-3078
Tel (800) 526-3593 *Founded/Ownrshp* 1997
Sales 739.2MM[E] *EMP* 3,955
SIC 5122 Pharmaceuticals
CEO: Joseph Hogan
**Pr:* Kieran Murphy
**CFO:* Henry Lyons
**Ex VP:* John Lynch
**Ex VP:* Mark Vachon
**VP:* Andrew Rackear

D-U-N-S 14-475-6827
■ GE HEALTHCARE FINANCIAL SERVICES INC
(*Suby of* CAPITAL ONE NATIONAL ASSOCIATION) ★
500 W Monroe St Fl 19, Chicago, IL 60661-3759
Tel (312) 697-3999 *Founded/Ownrshp* 2015
Sales NA *EMP* 900
SIC 6141 Personal credit institutions
Pr: Darren Alcus
Dir Risk M: John A Crosby
Genl Mgr: Darren Kowalske
Sftwr Eng: Sujatha Ramkumar

D-U-N-S 79-453-7043 IMP
■ GE HEALTHCARE HOLDINGS INC
(*Suby of* GE HEALTHCARE LIMITED)
3350 N Ridge Ave, Arlington Heights, IL 60004-1412
Tel (847) 398-8400 *Founded/Ownrshp* 1968
Sales 185.0MM[E] *EMP* 1,498
SIC 2835 2833 5169 5122 In vitro & in vivo diagnostic substances; Radioactive diagnostic substances; Medicinals & botanicals; Chemicals & allied products; Medicinals & botanicals
Pr: Daniel Peters
**Ex VP:* William Clarke MD
VP: Russel P Mayer
VP: J E Reller
VP: Jack Waterman
QA Dir: Lori Sekera
Dir IT: Chris Vincent
VP Mktg: Jean-Michel Cossery
Board of Directors: W M Castell, W D Davies, R E Long

D-U-N-S 05-304-6579 IMP
■ GE HEALTHCARE INC
(*Suby of* GE HEALTHCARE LIMITED)
100 Results Way, Marlborough, MA 01752-3078
Tel (800) 292-8514 *Founded/Ownrshp* 1968
Sales 1.0MMM[E] *EMP* 1,400
SIC 5122 2833 Medicinals & botanicals; Medicinals & botanicals
Pr: Jeffrey Freedman
**CFO:* Tamas Feitel
**VP:* Tom Giordano
**VP:* Vito Pulito
VP: Victor Reddick
**VP:* David Sager
**Prin:* Daniel Peters
Prgrm Mgr: Michael Passineau
Genl Mgr: Ken Shackleton
Snr Mgr: Kathleen Bove
Snr Mgr: Richard Story

GE HEALTHCARE LIFE SCIENCES
See GE HEALTHCARE BIO-SCIENCES CORP

GE HELTHCARE BSCNCE BIOPROCESS
See DATEX-OHMEDA INC

D-U-N-S 18-940-7674 EXP
■ GE INFRASTRUCTURE SENSING
GE WATER & PROCESS TECH
(*Suby of* GENERAL ELECTRIC CO) ★
4636 Somerton Rd, Feasterville Trevose, PA 19053-6742
Tel (617) 926-1749 *Founded/Ownrshp* 1968
Sales 381.1MM[E] *EMP* 2,360
SIC 3589 2086 4941 3559 2899 3823 Water purification equipment, household type; Water filters & softeners, household type; Water treatment equipment, industrial; Water, pasteurized: packaged in cans, bottles, etc.; Water supply; Desalination equipment; Water treating compounds; Water quality monitoring & control systems
Pr: John G Rice
**Pr:* Joel A Berdine
**CFO:* John J Falconi
**Treas:* Andrew J Cring
**VP:* Barbara Cameron
**VP:* Matthew G Cribbins

D-U-N-S 00-177-2060 IMP/EXP
■ GE INFRASTRUCTURE SENSING INC (OH)
GE SENSING & INSPECTION TECH
(*Suby of* GE ENERGY CONNECTIONS) ★
1100 Technology Park Dr # 100, Billerica, MA 01821-4111
Tel (978) 437-1000 *Founded/Ownrshp* 1960, 2002
Sales 277.9MM[E] *EMP* 800
SIC 3823 5084 3699 3674 3663 3625 Moisture meters, industrial process type; Industrial machinery & equipment; Electrical equipment & supplies; Semiconductors & related devices; Radio & TV communications equipment; Relays & industrial controls
Pr: Kristopher McBride
**VP:* Barbara A Cameron
Genl Mgr: Sheila Van Kuren
IT Man: Christian Brauner
IT Man: Kristin Setser
Opers Mgr: Donald Sarazen
Sls Mgr: Thomas Ballard
Sls Mgr: John Kerney
Snr Mgr: Greg Young

GE INFRASTRUCTURE WATER & PROC
See GE MOBILE WATER INC

D-U-N-S 82-465-6193 IMP/EXP
■ GE INTELLIGENT PLATFORMS INC
(*Suby of* GENERAL ELECTRIC CO) ★
2500 Austin Dr, Charlottesville, VA 22911-8319
Tel (434) 978-5000 *Founded/Ownrshp* 1986
Sales 11.0MM[E] *EMP* 1,850
SIC 3625 3674 7371 Numerical controls; Computer logic modules; Custom computer programming services
CEO: Jody Markopoulos
**CEO:* Markopoulos Jody
**CFO:* Showman Roy
**CFO:* Roy Showman
Treas: Alex Siedlecki
VP: Amy Anderson
**VP:* Bernardo Anger
**VP:* Anger Bernardo
VP: Bill Estep
**VP:* William Estep
VP: Randall Johnson
VP: Peter Thomas
VP: Erik Udstuen

GE INVESTMENTS
See GE ASSET MANAGEMENT INC

D-U-N-S 00-104-6325 IMP/EXP
■ GE IONICS INC (MA)
(*Suby of* GE WATER & PROCESS TECH) ★
3 Burlington Woods Dr # 200, Burlington, MA 01803-4531
Tel (781) 359-7000 *Founded/Ownrshp* 1948
Sales 380.9MM[E] *EMP* 2,350
SIC 3589 2086 4941 3559 2899 3823 Water purification equipment, household type; Water filters & softeners, household type; Water treatment equipment, industrial; Water, pasteurized: packaged in cans, bottles, etc.; Water supply; Desalination equipment; Water treating compounds; Water quality monitoring & control systems
Pr: David L Calhoun
**Pr:* Heinrich Markhoff
Treas: John Bergeron
Sr VP: Erik Schoepke
VP: John F Curtis
VP: Lyman B Dickerson
VP: Edward Geishecker
VP: Brian Hernon
VP: John Sabol

GE LIGHTING SYSTEMS, INC.
See GE LIGHTING SYSTEMS LLC

D-U-N-S 00-316-8374 IMP/EXP
■ GE LIGHTING SYSTEMS LLC
GE LIGHTING SYSTEMS, INC.
(*Suby of* GENERAL ELECTRIC CO) ★
3010 Spartanburg Hwy, East Flat Rock, NC 28726-2926
Tel (828) 693-2000 *Founded/Ownrshp* 1997, 1996
Sales 221.8MM[E] *EMP* 700
SIC 5063 Lighting fixtures
Pr: Paul Morse
IT Man: Daniel Lefitz

D-U-N-S 06-341-4841 EXP
■ GE MOBILE WATER INC
GE INFRASTRUCTURE WATER & PROC
(*Suby of* GE IONICS INC) ★
4545 Patent Rd, Norfolk, VA 23502-5604
Tel (757) 855-9000 *Founded/Ownrshp* 2004
Sales 98.1MM[E] *EMP* 350
SIC 3589 Water treatment equipment, industrial
Ch: Thomas Johnston
**Pr:* Heinrich Markhoff
Ofcr: Dave Meissner
**VP:* Ashim Gupta
VP: William S Miller
IT Man: Sarah Schoonover
Info Man: Jim Collister

GE MODULAR SPC/TRLR FLT SVCS
See TRANSPORT INTERNATIONAL POOL INC

GE MONEY
See GE CONSUMER FINANCE INC

GE OIL & GAS
See VETCO GRAY INC

D-U-N-S 07-944-9348
GE OIL & GAS COMPRESSION SYSTEMS LLC
GE ENERGY
16250 Port Nw, Houston, TX 77041-2667
Tel (713) 354-1900 *Founded/Ownrshp* 2016
Sales 149.4MM[E] *EMP* 200[E]
SIC 1389 Gas compressing (natural gas) at the fields
Snr Mgr: Stefano Truschi

D-U-N-S 92-833-6924 EXP
■ GE OIL & GAS LOGGING SERVICES INC
(*Suby of* GE AERO ENERGY PRODUCTS) ★
13000 Executive Dr, Sugar Land, TX 77478-4506
Tel (281) 579-9879 *Founded/Ownrshp* 2011
Sales 301.2MM[E] *EMP* 500
SIC 1389 4789 Oil field services; Cargo loading & unloading services
Pr: John Paul Jones
Pr: Marco Rossi
**CFO:* Jon Piantez
**VP:* Grant Johnston
IT Man: Diana Glaze

D-U-N-S 00-843-0456 IMP/EXP
■ GE OIL & GAS PRESSURE CONTROL LP (TX)
(*Suby of* GE AERO ENERGY PRODUCTS) ★
4424 W Sam Houston Pkwy N # 100, Houston, TX 77041-8245
Tel (281) 398-8901 *Founded/Ownrshp* 1962, 2011
Sales 521.5MM[E] *EMP* 1,500
SIC 3491 Industrial valves
CEO: Daniel C Heintzelman
Genl Pt: Scott Bender
Pt: Thomas Adams
Pt: Joel Bender
Pt: Wendell Brooks
Pt: Craig Dewees
Pt: David Landry
Pt: Kent McAllister
Pt: Brian J Small
Pr: Ian Milne
Mktg Mgr: Linda M Knight

D-U-N-S 03-017-1196
■ GE ON WING SUPPORT INC
(*Suby of* GE ENGINE SERVICES LLC) ★
3010 Red Hawk Dr Ste B, Grand Prairie, TX 75052-7713
Tel (214) 960-3322 *Founded/Ownrshp* 2010
Sales 11.5MM[E] *EMP* 1,186[E]
SIC 7699 8711 Aviation propeller & blade repair; Aviation &/or aeronautical engineering
Prin: Joel Corbitt

D-U-N-S 01-388-8503 IMP/EXP
■ GE PACKAGED POWER INC
(*Suby of* GE AERO ENERGY PRODUCTS) ★
1330 West Loop S Ste 1000, Houston, TX 77027-9102
Tel (713) 803-0900 *Founded/Ownrshp* 1997
Sales 136.4MM[E] *EMP* 600
SIC 3511 Turbines & turbine generator sets
Pr: Darryl L Wilson
**VP:* Mark E Buchanan
**VP:* Barbara A Cameron
Counsel: Bryan Kay

D-U-N-S 16-838-8846 IMP/EXP
■ GE PACKAGED POWER LP
GE ENERGY
(*Suby of* GENERAL ELECTRIC CO) ★
16415 Jacintoport Blvd, Houston, TX 77015-6589
Tel (281) 452-3610 *Founded/Ownrshp* 1997
Sales 108.4MM[E] *EMP* 375[E]
SIC 3511 Turbines & turbine generator sets
Prin: Ryan A Brown

GE PLANNING
See LKN COMMUNICATIONS INC

D-U-N-S 08-011-1410
■ GE POWER & WATER
(*Suby of* GENERAL ELECTRIC CO) ★
1 River Rd Bldg 5-419, Schenectady, NY 12345-6000
Tel (518) 385-2211 *Founded/Ownrshp* 2015
Sales 98.4MM[E] *EMP* 60,000
SIC 7382 5063 Confinement surveillance systems maintenance & monitoring; Generators
CEO: Lorraine A Bolsinger
**CEO:* Maryrose Sylvester

D-U-N-S 00-779-3297 IMP
■ GE POWER ELECTRONICS INC (NV)
(*Suby of* GE ENERGY CONNECTIONS) ★
601 Shiloh Rd, Plano, TX 75074-7210
Tel (972) 244-9288 *Founded/Ownrshp* 2000
Sales 483.4MM[E] *EMP* 1,638[E]
SIC 3661 Telephone & telegraph apparatus; Switching equipment, telephone; Telephone central office equipment, dial or manual
Pr: Jeffery Frank
**Pr:* Jeffrey P Schnitzer
**CFO:* Roxi Wen
**Treas:* Jason Garland
VP: Alexandre Franck
**VP:* Yafei Wen
Prgrm Mgr: Lauri Stapp
IT Man: Julio Gonzalez

GE RICHARDS
See GE RICHARDS GRAPHIC SUPPLIES CO INC

D-U-N-S 94-244-7764 IMP
GE RICHARDS GRAPHIC SUPPLIES CO INC
GE RICHARDS
928 Links Ave, Landisville, PA 17538-1615
Tel (717) 892-4620 *Founded/Ownrshp* 1990
Sales 165.0MM[E] *EMP* 180

SIC 5084 5045 Industrial machinery & equipment; Computers, peripherals & software
Pr: Larry Wagner
**Treas:* Judith A Wagner
**VP:* Jeffrey E Wagner
Div Mgr: Robert Schoenberger
IT Man: Horst Bernhard
IT Man: Hoyt Doyle
IT Man: Gary Houck
Sales Exec: John Hoegerl

GE SENSING & INSPECTION TECH
See GE INFRASTRUCTURE SENSING INC

GE SENSING & INSPECTION TECH
See AMPHENOL THERMOMETRICS INC

GE WATER & PROCESS TECH
See GE BETZ INC

GE WATER & PROCESS TECH
See GE INFRASTRUCTURE SENSING

D-U-N-S 11-650-5426 IMP
■ GE WIND ENERGY LLC
(*Suby of* GENERAL ELECTRIC CO) ★
13000 Jameson Rd, Tehachapi, CA 93561-8157
Tel (661) 823-6700 *Founded/Ownrshp* 2002
Sales 344.0MM[E] *EMP* 1,700
SIC 3511 Turbines & turbine generator sets
IT Man: Angeie Lentz
Snr Mgr: Jim Rostek

D-U-N-S 06-744-8241 IMP
■ GE ZENITH CONTROLS INC
(*Suby of* GENERAL ELECTRIC CO) ★
601 Shiloh Rd, Plano, TX 75074-7210
Tel (903) 436-1503 *Founded/Ownrshp* 2000
Sales 84.7MM[E] *EMP* 285
SIC 3613 Switchgear & switchgear accessories
Pr: Thomas Duffy
CFO: Jeffrey S Bornstein
VP: Robert Doherty
Prgrm Mgr: James Anderson
VP Mfg: Phillip Johnson
Plnt Mgr: David Garrison

D-U-N-S 80-033-4570 IMP/EXP
■ GE-HITACHI NUCLEAR ENERGY AMERICA LLC
(*Suby of* GENERAL ELECTRIC CO) ★
3901 Castle Hayne Rd, Wilmington, NC 28401
Tel (910) 819-5073 *Founded/Ownrshp* 2007
Sales 424.8MM[E] *EMP* 2,300
SIC 2819 Nuclear fuel & cores, inorganic
CEO: Caroline Reda
**CFO:* Craig Steven
**CFO:* Mark R Sweeney
**VP:* Christopher J Monetta
**VP:* Kevin Walsh
**Prin:* Angela Thornhill

D-U-N-S 00-692-8584 IMP/EXP
GEA FARM TECHNOLOGIES INC
(*Suby of* GEA WESTFALIA SEPARATOR INC) ★
1880 Country Farm Dr, Naperville, IL 60563-1089
Tel (630) 548-8200 *Founded/Ownrshp* 1906, 1999
Sales 199.3MM[E] *EMP* 450
SIC 5083 3523 2841 2842 Dairy machinery & equipment; Dairy equipment (farm); Detergents, synthetic organic or inorganic alkaline; Sanitation preparations
Pr: Vern Foster
**Pr:* Matt Daley
**CFO:* Patrick Ferry
Mfg Dir: Todd Finn

D-U-N-S 96-667-0171 IMP
GEA MECHANICAL EQUIPMENT US INC
GEA WESTFALIA SEPARATOR DIV
(*Suby of* METALLGESELLSCHAFT) ★
100 Fairway Ct, Northvale, NJ 07647-2401
Tel (201) 767-3900 *Founded/Ownrshp* 2010
Sales 204.6MM[E] *EMP* 530[E]
SIC 5084 7699 Industrial machinery & equipment; Industrial machinery & equipment repair
Pr: Michael Vick
CFO: Ronald Fitz
**Prin:* Clement O'Donnell
Dir IT: Dale Miller

D-U-N-S 80-762-8425 IMP/EXP
GEA NORTH AMERICA INC
METALLGESELLSCHAFT
(*Suby of* GEA GROUP AG)
9165 Rumsey Rd, Columbia, MD 21045-1929
Tel (410) 997-8700 *Founded/Ownrshp* 1998
Sales 696.9MM[E] *EMP* 530
SIC 7218 Industrial equipment launderers
CEO: Anders Wilhjelm
**Pr:* Steve Kaplan
**VP:* Robert Johnson
**VP:* William McCarter

D-U-N-S 09-181-8930
GEA PROCESS ENGINEERING INC
(*Suby of* METALLGESELLSCHAFT) ★
9165 Rumsey Rd, Columbia, MD 21045-1929
Tel (410) 772-5792 *Founded/Ownrshp* 2006
Sales 184.2MM[E] *EMP* 327
SIC 8711 Industrial engineers
Pr: Steven M Kaplan
**Treas:* Robert E Johnson Jr
Treas: Peter McGivney
**Ex VP:* Steven Lancos
**VP:* Michael Bowers
**VP:* Ronald J Matzek
VP: Ronald Matzik
**VP:* Swami Sundaram
Rgnl Mgr: Navin Lakhanpaul
IT Man: Gina De

D-U-N-S 11-350-6443 IMP/EXP
GEA PT NORTH AMERICA INC
(*Suby of* METALLGESELLSCHAFT) ★
9165 Rumsey Rd, Columbia, MD 21045-1929
Tel (410) 997-8700 *Founded/Ownrshp* 1997
Sales 83.8MM[E] *EMP* 326
SIC 8748 Business consulting
Prin: Robert E Johnson

CFO: Patrick Ferry
Ex VP: Steven Lancos
Ex VP: Ronald Matzek
VP: William McCarter
IT Man: Brian Zwart
Trfc Mgr: Ron Hazel
Manager: Josh Eagan
Manager: Jeffrey Feller
Sls Mgr: Ronald Tuckner

GEA REFRIGERATION N AMER INC
See GEA REFRIGERATION NORTH AMERICA INC

D-U-N-S 79-973-4251 IMP
GEA REFRIGERATION NORTH AMERICA INC
GEA REFRIGERATION N AMER INC
(*Suby of* GEA PT NORTH AMERICA INC) ★
3475 Board Rd, York, PA 17406-8414
Tel (717) 767-6411 *Founded/Ownrshp* 2004
Sales 83.8MM[E] *EMP* 250
SIC 3585 Refrigeration & heating equipment
CEO: John Ansbro
COO: Jim Rohrbaugh
**Treas:* Glenn A Miller
**VP:* Dennis Halsey
Web Prj Mg: Will Parshall

GEA WESTFALIA SEPARATOR DIV
See GEA MECHANICAL EQUIPMENT US INC

D-U-N-S 00-166-3012 IMP/EXP
GEA WESTFALIA SEPARATOR INC
(*Suby of* METALLGESELLSCHAFT) ★
100 Fairway Ct, Northvale, NJ 07647-2401
Tel (201) 767-3900 *Founded/Ownrshp* 1950, 1893
Sales 199.3MM[E] *EMP* 530
SIC 5083 5084 3523 Milking machinery & equipment; Industrial machinery & equipment; Dairy equipment (farm)
CEO: Michael J Vick
**Pr:* Clement O'Donnell
**VP:* Joseph Pavlosky
Sls Mgr: Constantine Tricules

D-U-N-S 09-582-1419
GEARY COUNTY UNIFIED SCHOOL DISTRICT 475
123 N Eisenhower Dr, Junction City, KS 66441-3313
Tel (785) 717-4000 *Founded/Ownrshp* 1965
Sales 78.1MM[E] *EMP* 1,200
SIC 8211 Public elementary school; Public junior high school; Public senior high school
Bd of Dir: Belle Whaley
Schl Brd P: Becky Bramlage
HC Dir: Rebekah Helget
HC Dir: Bridget Seemann

D-U-N-S 09-731-6033
GEARY LSF GROUP INC
LSF INTERACTIVE
332 Pine St Fl 6, San Francisco, CA 94104-3228
Tel (877) 616-8226 *Founded/Ownrshp* 2002
Sales 93.9MM[E] *EMP* 210
SIC 4813
Pr: Karen Kovaleski
**CFO:* Paul McKnight
**Ex VP:* Ramsay Crooks
Ex VP: Bob Rothenberg
**Ex VP:* Bob Yakominich
VP: Lauren Ferst
VP: Caroline Sherman

D-U-N-S 00-963-8198
GEARY PACIFIC CORP
GEARY PACIFIC SUPPLY
1360 N Hancock St, Anaheim, CA 92807-1921
Tel (714) 279-2950 *Founded/Ownrshp* 1961
Sales 94.2MM[E] *EMP* 128
SIC 5075

GEARY PACIFIC SUPPLY
See GEARY PACIFIC CORP

GEBBERS FARMS
See BREWSTER HEIGHTS PACKING & ORCHARDS LP

D-U-N-S 08-698-4937
GECOS INC
(*Suby of* EUROVIA)
1936 Lee Rd, Winter Park, FL 32789-7229
Tel (407) 645-5500 *Founded/Ownrshp* 1988
Sales 590.4MM[E] *EMP* 1,400
SIC 1611 2951 1623 General contractor, highway & street construction; Asphalt & asphaltic paving mixtures (not from refineries); Sewer line construction
Pr: Jean Noel Vely
Sec: P Frederick O'Dea Jr
Board of Directors: Jacques Tavernier

D-U-N-S 06-897-2199
GECU
1225 Airway Blvd, El Paso, TX 79925-3620
Tel (915) 778-9221 *Founded/Ownrshp* 1933
Sales NA *EMP* 500
SIC 6062 State credit unions, not federally chartered
CEO: Crystal Long
**CEO:* Harriet May
**CFO:* Steve Lutz
**Sr VP:* Fermin Acosta
**Sr VP:* Pierre Cardenas
VP: Martin Sena
VP: Chris Tomkins

D-U-N-S 92-959-3630
■ GEEK SQUAD INC
(*Suby of* BEST BUY CO INC) ★
1213 Washington Ave N, Minneapolis, MN 55401-1036
Tel (952) 544-0377 *Founded/Ownrshp* 2002
Sales 148.7MM[E] *EMP* 2,500
SIC 7379 Computer related consulting services
CEO: Robert Stephens

GEHL COMPANY
See MANITOU AMERICAS INC

D-U-N-S 00-608-7951 IMP/EXP
GEHL FOODS LLC (WI)
N116w15970 Main St, Germantown, WI 53022-2654
Tel (262) 251-8570 *Founded/Ownrshp* 1920, 2015
Sales 273.6MM[E] *EMP* 726
SIC 2022 5451 Natural cheese; Dairy products stores
CEO: Eric Beringause
**Pr:* Andrew Gehl
**CFO:* Tim Preuninger
**VP:* Ali Rezaei
VP: John Shaughnessy
QA Dir: Joshua Soper
Sfty Mgr: Mike Betzhold
Sfty Mgr: John Ward
Opers Mgr: Brian Dederich
Sls Mgr: Dolli Garrison
Sls Mgr: Ken Stclair

D-U-N-S 18-310-1559 IMP
GEHL POWER PRODUCTS INC
(*Suby of* GEHL CO) ★
900 Ferdig St, Yankton, SD 57078-3208
Tel (605) 665-6500 *Founded/Ownrshp* 1997
Sales 135.5MM[E] *EMP* 716
SIC 3537 3531 3535 Forklift trucks; Graders, road (construction machinery); Conveyors & conveying equipment
Pr: William D Gehl
**Treas:* Kenneth P Hahn
Mtls Mgr: Tom Bergeson
Sfty Mgr: Tony Drovdal
Plnt Mgr: David Ewald

D-U-N-S 05-782-4526
GEI CONSULTANTS INC
400 Unicorn Park Dr Ste 8, Woburn, MA 01801-3341
Tel (781) 721-4000 *Founded/Ownrshp* 1970
Sales 215.9MM[E] *EMP* 768
SIC 8711 Engineering services; Structural engineering
Pr: Raymond D Hart
COO: Ron Palmieri
Ch: Anne L Leifer
Treas: Thomas Kahl
Sr VP: Naser J Batani
Sr VP: Jim Chadwick
Sr VP: Michael Gatzow
Sr VP: Tom Keller
VP: Robert Acker
VP: Jim Ash
VP: Ronald Bourne
VP: Jesus E Gomez
VP: Dan Johnson
VP: Jeremy Pratt
VP: Billy Walton

GEICO
See GOVERNMENT EMPLOYEES INSURANCE CO INC

D-U-N-S 09-656-3747
■ GEICO CORP
(*Suby of* BERKSHIRE HATHAWAY INC) ★
1 Geico Plz, Washington, DC 20076-0005
Tel (301) 986-3000 *Founded/Ownrshp* 1978
Sales NA *EMP* 27,897
SIC 6411 Insurance agents, brokers & service
Pr: Tony Nicely
Pr: Louis A Simpson
CFO: Mike Campbell
Treas: Charles G Schara
Ex VP: Silva Franklin
Ex VP: Ron Guzinsky
Sr VP: Greg Kalinsky
Sr VP: David L Schindler
VP: John Ammendola
VP: Michelle Trindade
CIO: Harvey Demovick

D-U-N-S 80-824-3901 IMP/EXP
■ GEICO GENERAL INSURANCE CO
(*Suby of* GEICO) ★
1 Geico Plz, Washington, DC 20076-0005
Tel (301) 986-3000 *Founded/Ownrshp* 1983
Sales NA *EMP* 10,000
SIC 6411 Insurance agents, brokers & service
Pr: Olza Nicely
VP: Howard Cohen
VP: Bill Dommasch
VP: Gregory Kalinski
Prgrm Mgr: Craig Masterson
IT Man: Jim Crider
IT Man: Jeff Jacobs
IT Man: Rosalind Phillips
Plnt Mgr: Stephen J Martz
S&M/VP: Ken Allen
Counsel: Cinda Smith

D-U-N-S 00-691-9500
■ GEICO INDEMNITY CO
(*Suby of* GEICO CORP) ★
One Geico Plaza, Washington, DC 20047-0001
Tel (301) 986-3000 *Founded/Ownrshp* 1961
Sales NA *EMP* 22,889
SIC 6331 6411 Fire, marine & casualty insurance; Insurance agents, brokers & service
Pr: Olza M Nicely
Treas: Charles G Schara
VP: Shawn Burklin
VP: R Cheek
VP: Richard Van Essendelft

D-U-N-S 00-109-5686 IMP
GEIGER BROS
SUN GRAPHIX/DIV
70 Mount Hope Ave, Lewiston, ME 04240-1021
Tel (207) 755-2000 *Founded/Ownrshp* 1878
Sales 245.4MM[E] *EMP* 400
SIC 5199 3993 2752 2782 2789 Advertising specialties; Gifts & novelties; Advertising novelties; Calendars, lithographed; Periodicals, lithographed; Blankbooks & looseleaf binders; Diaries; Bookbinding & related work; Bronzing, gilding, edging & deckling: books, cards, paper
Ch Bd: Eugene G Geiger
**Ex VP:* Peter E Geiger
**Ex VP:* Ronald G Giard
**Ex VP:* Jo-An G Lantz
VP: Carrie Lautner

VP: Herb Miller
Genl Mgr: Judy Paradis
Sales Asso: Kim Corrigan

D-U-N-S 09-930-8603 IMP/EXP
■ GEIGER INTERNATIONAL INC
(*Suby of* HERMAN MILLER INC) ★
6095 Fulton Indus Blvd Sw, Atlanta, GA 30336-2806
Tel (404) 344-1100 *Founded/Ownrshp* 1999
Sales 114.0MM[E] *EMP* 522
SIC 2521 Wood office furniture
Pr: Brian C Walker
CFO: Wendell E Jacobs III
VP: Jim Clemens
MIS Dir: Charles Boden
Opers Mgr: Michael Glassford
VP Sls: Tonette Barrett
Sls Mgr: Doug Dreyer

D-U-N-S 07-916-1360
GEISINGER CLINIC
(*Suby of* GEISINGER MEDICAL CENTER) ★
100 N Academy Ave, Danville, PA 17822-9800
Tel (570) 271-6211 *Founded/Ownrshp* 1962
Sales 849.4MM *EMP* 12,000
SIC 8011 8733 Clinic, operated by physicians; Health maintenance organization; Internal medicine, physician/surgeon; Physical medicine, physician/surgeon; Medical research
CEO: Glenn D Steele Jr
Pr: David Macko
Treas: Frank J Trembulak

D-U-N-S 13-076-7890
GEISINGER HEALTH PLAN
(*Suby of* GEISINGER MEDICAL CENTER) ★
100 N Academy Ave, Danville, PA 17822-9800
Tel (570) 271-8778 *Founded/Ownrshp* 1984
Sales 1.2MMM *EMP* 900
SIC 8011 Health maintenance organization
Pr: Steve Yosu
CFO: Cinde Rouk
VP: Michael Leighow
**VP:* Frank J Trembulak
VP: Teresa Willard
Dir IT: Peter Cassidy
IT Man: Kevin Capatch

D-U-N-S 07-958-2433
GEISINGER HEALTH SYSTEM FOUNDATION
GEISINGER MEDICAL CENTER
100 N Academy Ave, Danville, PA 17822-9800
Tel (570) 271-6461 *Founded/Ownrshp* 1915
Sales 4.3MMM[E] *EMP* 13,000[E]
SIC 8741 6512 7699 Management services; Nonresidential building operators; Hospital equipment repair services
Pr: Glenn D Steele Jr
**Mng Pt:* Bruce H Hamory MD
**Ch Bd:* Frank M Henry
CEO: Robert J Weil
**COO:* Frank J Trembulak
COO: Frank Trembulak
CFO: Kevin F Brennan
Sr Cor Off: Jane Kanyock
Ofcr: Susan W Alcorn
**Ofcr:* Albert Bothe Jr
Ex VP: Howard R Grant
Ex VP: David H Ledbetter
**Ex VP:* Lynn Miller
**Ex VP:* Dominic Moffa
**Ex VP:* Ronald A Paulus
Ex VP: Steven B Pierdon
Ex VP: Susan M Robel
**Ex VP:* David Tilton
**Ex VP:* Joanne E Wade
VP: Connie Bednar
VP: Brenda Eckrote

GEISINGER MEDICAL CENTER
See GEISINGER SYSTEM SERVICES

GEISINGER MEDICAL CENTER
See GEISINGER HEALTH SYSTEM FOUNDATION

D-U-N-S 06-959-1238
GEISINGER MEDICAL CENTER
(*Suby of* GEISINGER MEDICAL CENTER) ★
100 N Academy Ave, Danville, PA 17822-0001
Tel (570) 271-6211 *Founded/Ownrshp* 1915
Sales 1.0MMM *EMP* 8,000
SIC 8062 General medical & surgical hospitals
Pr: Glenn D Steele
**Ofcr:* Rosemary Leeming
Assoc VP: Gary Kurtz
Assoc VP: John Zelonis
**Ex VP:* Albert Bothe Jr
**Ex VP:* Lynn Miller
**Ex VP:* Frank J Trembulak
**Ex VP:* Joanne E Wade
Sr VP: Thomas Sokola
VP: John R Boker
VP: Michael Leighow
Dir Lab: Robert Nowak

D-U-N-S 07-538-2077
GEISINGER SYSTEM SERVICES
GEISINGER MEDICAL CENTER
(*Suby of* GEISINGER MEDICAL CENTER) ★
100 N Academy Ave, Danville, PA 17822-9800
Tel (570) 271-6211 *Founded/Ownrshp* 1981
Sales 535.6MM *EMP* 344
SIC 8741 8082 Administrative management; Business management; Financial management for business; Personnel management; Home health care services
Pr: Glenn D Steele Jr
**Treas:* Timothy Fitzgerald
**Treas:* Frank J Trembulak
Comm Man: Scott Singer

D-U-N-S 02-795-0542
GEISINGER WYOMING VALLEY MEDICAL CENTER
(*Suby of* GEISINGER MEDICAL CENTER) ★
1000 E Mountain Dr, Wilkes Barre, PA 18711-0001
Tel (570) 808-7300 *Founded/Ownrshp* 1976
Sales 447.6MM *EMP* 15
SIC 8062 General medical & surgical hospitals

VP: Timothy Fitzgerald
Ch Bd: Glenn D Steele Jr
Treas: Frank J Trembulak
Ofcr: John Buckley
Surgeon: John A Lynott
Ansthlgy: Samuel H Plummer
Diag Rad: Mary Strickland

D-U-N-S 07-915-8812
GEISINGER-COMMUNITY MEDICAL CENTER
(*Suby of* GEISINGER MEDICAL CENTER) ★
1822 Mulberry St, Scranton, PA 18510-2369
Tel (570) 969-8000 *Founded/Ownrshp* 2012
Sales 99.6MM[E] *EMP* 1,302[E]
SIC 8062 General medical & surgical hospitals; Hospital, medical school affiliated with nursing & residency
Pr: Karl Stark
Dir Recs: Sean M Andrew
CFO: Ed Chabalowski
Treas: Felice J Freyer
Ofcr: Gina Mc Cabe
VP: Sean Mc Andrew
VP: Sean McAndrew
Dir Case M: Michelle Albright
Dir Rx: David Rowlands
Chf Nrs Of: Barbara Bossi
Sfty Dirs: Gina McCabe

D-U-N-S 01-236-4501 IMP/EXP
GEL SPICE CO INC
48 Hook Rd, Bayonne, NJ 07002-5007
Tel (201) 339-0700 *Founded/Ownrshp* 1955
Sales 125.0MM *EMP* 300
Accts Weiss & Company Llp New York
SIC 2099 5149 Spices, including grinding; Spices & seasonings
Pr: Andre Engel
**CFO:* Sam Baum
VP: Sherman Engel
VP: Leon Nisenboym
VP Sls: Joseph Mandel
S&M/VP: Mansi Trivedi
Sls Mgr: Harry Blumenfeld

D-U-N-S 96-178-5149
GEL SPICE CO LLC
48 Hook Rd, Bayonne, NJ 07002-5007
Tel (201) 339-0700 *Founded/Ownrshp* 2010
Sales 130.0MM *EMP* 250
SIC 2099 Seasonings & spices
Sr VP: Gershon Engel

D-U-N-S 00-621-2492
■ **GELCO CORP**
GE FLEET SERVICES
(*Suby of* GENERAL ELECTRIC CAPITAL CORP) ★
3 Capital Dr, Eden Prairie, MN 55344-3889
Tel (952) 828-1000 *Founded/Ownrshp* 1957, 1987
Sales NA *EMP* 2,730
SIC 6159

D-U-N-S 61-357-8335 IMP
GELITA NORTH AMERICA INC
(*Suby of* GELITA AG)
2445 Port Neal Rd, Sergeant Bluff, IA 51054-7728
Tel (712) 943-5516 *Founded/Ownrshp* 1977
Sales 225.0MM *EMP* 305
SIC 5169 2099 Gelatin; Food preparations
Pr: Robert Mayberry
VP: John Dolphin
VP: Heinrich Schmidt
Dir Lab: Jeff Abell
Genl Mgr: Pablo Silber
IT Man: Dirk Richou
Tech Mgr: Adriano Gonzales
Plnt Mgr: Gary Monk
Plnt Mgr: Tony Wise
Ql Cn Mgr: Carol Ostendorf
Sls&Mrk Ex: Lars Andersson

D-U-N-S 18-117-9953
GELLER & CO LLC
909 3rd Ave Fl 15, New York, NY 10022-4745
Tel (212) 583-6000 *Founded/Ownrshp* 1984
Sales 106.6MM[E] *EMP* 370[E]
SIC 8742 8721 Management consulting services; Certified public accountant
CEO: Martin Geller
CEO: Joe Calabrese
COO: Steve Fadem
COO: Bill Rouse
CFO: Michael Curran
CFO: Paul Kasnetz
CFO: Sue Martin
Treas: Marty Braunstein
Bd of Dir: Kerry Scaramuzza
Chf Inves: Robert Wedeking
Ofcr: Jon Persson
Exec: Eileen Gallagher

D-U-N-S 00-534-1813 IMP
■ **GELMAN SCIENCES INC** (MI)
PALL LIFE SCIENCES
(*Suby of* PALL CORP) ★
674 S Wagner Rd, Ann Arbor, MI 48103-9793
Tel (734) 665-0651 *Founded/Ownrshp* 1980, 1996
Sales 94.3MM[E] *EMP* 610
SIC 3821 3569 3564 3841 3845 3699 Laboratory apparatus, except heating & measuring; Filters, general line: industrial; Air purification equipment; Surgical instruments & apparatus; Electromedical apparatus; Insect lamps, electric
Ch Bd: Eric Krasnoff
**COO:* Don Stevens
**CFO:* Lisa McDermott
Plnt Mgr: Jeremy Surry

GELSON'S MARKETS
See ARDEN GROUP INC

D-U-N-S 02-813-5911
GELSONS MARKETS
(*Suby of* ARDEN-MAYFAIR INC) ★
13833 Freeway Dr, Santa Fe Springs, CA 90670-5701
Tel (310) 638-2842 *Founded/Ownrshp* 1966
Sales 377.6MM[E] *EMP* 2,264
SIC 5411 Supermarkets, chain
CEO: Rob McDougall
**Sr VP:* Brenda McDanile

D-U-N-S 55-549-4327 IMP
GEM INDUSTRIES INC
(*Suby of* ITR INDUSTRIES INC) ★
Hwy 123 N, Toccoa, GA 30577
Tel (706) 886-8431 *Founded/Ownrshp* 1989
Sales 93.3MM[E] *EMP* 700
SIC 3429 2531 2511 3446 2821 2515 Furniture hardware; Casket hardware; Public building & related furniture; Wood household furniture; Architectural metalwork; Plastics materials & resins; Mattresses & bedsprings
CEO: D McVeigh
**Sec:* Adrienne Rolla
VP: Al Velitizia
**Prin:* Steve Gaymor
Genl Mgr: Doug Hitchon
IT Man: Brandon Youngblood

D-U-N-S 87-806-3312
GEM REALTY CAPITAL INC
900 N Michigan Ave # 1450, Chicago, IL 60611-1542
Tel (312) 915-2900 *Founded/Ownrshp* 1994
Sales 125.4MM[E] *EMP* 666
SIC 6799 Real estate investors, except property operators
Pr: Barry Malkin
**CFO:* Michael A Elrad
**Ex VP:* Norman S Geller
VP: Barrie Bloom
Mng Dir: Denise Olson

D-U-N-S 08-046-9610
GEM-PACK BERRIES LLC
8 Corporate Park Ste 110, Irvine, CA 92606-3167
Tel (949) 861-4919 *Founded/Ownrshp* 2016
Sales 150.0MM *EMP* 4
SIC 0171 Berry crops
CFO: Nedra Joy Craig

D-U-N-S 04-988-8704 IMP/EXP
■ **GEMAIRE DISTRIBUTORS LLC**
JOHNSON CONTRLS AUTHORIZED DLR
(*Suby of* WATSCO INC) ★
2151 W Hillsboro Blvd # 400, Deerfield Beach, FL 33442-1199
Tel (954) 246-2665 *Founded/Ownrshp* 1988
Sales 137.6MM[E] *EMP* 325
SIC 5075 Air conditioning & ventilation equipment & supplies
Pr: Kenneth F Connell
**Treas:* Lina C Mori
**VP:* Barry S Logan
**VP:* Ana M Menendez
VP: Lena Mori
VP: Douglas Mullins
**VP:* Kenbian Ng
Opers Mgr: Bob Prentice
Manager: Noel Gregory

D-U-N-S 93-354-1047 IMP
GEMALTO INC
(*Suby of* GEMALTO N.V.)
9442 Capital Of, Austin, TX 78759
Tel (215) 340-2000 *Founded/Ownrshp* 1990
Sales 256.4MM[E] *EMP* 450
SIC 5045 Computers, peripherals & software
CEO: Olivier Piou
Pr: Philippe Benitez
**COO:* Philippe Vallee
**CFO:* Jacques Tierny
Treas: Pascal Chery
Treas: Christophe Pouteau
Ex VP: Philippe Cabanettes
Ex VP: Claude Dahan
Sr VP: ARI Bouzbib
Sr VP: Sebastien Cano
Sr VP: Frederic Deman
**VP:* Paul Beverly
VP: Giuseppe Colombi
VP: Benoit Jouffrey
VP: Francois Lasnier
**VP:* Martin McCourt
VP: Marc Ribas
VP: Jean-Philippe Ruault
Dir Bus: Ruault Jean-Philippe
Dir Bus: Steve Purdy

D-U-N-S 80-318-7475
GEMCRAFT HOMES GROUP INC
2205 Commerce Rd Ste A, Forest Hill, MD 21050-2576
Tel (410) 893-8458 *Founded/Ownrshp* 1993
Sales 180.0MM *EMP* 1
SIC 1522 Residential construction
Pr: Vickie Luther
**Pr:* Sharon Babcock
**VP:* Brian Fromme
Off Mgr: Sandi Duncan
Netwrk Mgr: Sean Smith

D-U-N-S 84-210-3694
GEMINI GROUP INC
175 Thompson Rd Ste A, Bad Axe, MI 48413-8274
Tel (989) 269-6272 *Founded/Ownrshp* 1996
Sales 373.3MM[E] *EMP* 480
SIC 8741 3089 Management services; Extruded finished plastic products
VP: David Hyzer
CIO: Dawn Hurlburt
Plnt Mgr: Dennis Engelhart
Plnt Mgr: Jim Stewart
Ql Cn Mgr: Wendy Barnes

GEMINI PLASTICS
See PEPRO ENTERPRISES INC

GEMOCO DIVISION
See CHROMALLOY GAS TURBINE LLC

GEMOLOGICAL INSTITUTE AMERICA
See GEMOLOGICAL INSTITUTE OF AMERICA INC

D-U-N-S 04-849-5378
GEMOLOGICAL INSTITUTE OF AMERICA INC
GEMOLOGICAL INSTITUTE AMERICA
5345 Armada Dr, Carlsbad, CA 92008-4602
Tel (760) 603-4000 *Founded/Ownrshp* 1943
Sales 321.0MM *EMP* 3,141
SIC 8249 8733 Vocational schools; Noncommercial research organizations
Pr: Susan M Jacques
COO: Allison Devlin
CFO: Carl Chilstrom
**CFO:* David Tearle
Treas: Robert Hord
Assoc VP: Susan Petrich
VP: Katherine Palmer Andrews
**VP:* Tom Moses
VP: Susan Schindelar
Exec: Rohit Tandon
Mng Dir: Kenneth Scarratt
Board of Directors: John Green Chb

GEMS SENSORS & CONTROLS
See GEMS SENSORS INC

D-U-N-S 03-315-5693 IMP
■ **GEMS SENSORS INC**
GEMS SENSORS & CONTROLS
(*Suby of* FORTIVE CORP) ★
1 Cowles Rd, Plainville, CT 06062-1107
Tel (860) 747-3000 *Founded/Ownrshp* 2016
Sales 130.6MM[E] *EMP* 400
SIC 3824 5084 3812 3625 3613 Fluid meters & counting devices; Industrial machinery & equipment; Search & navigation equipment; Relays & industrial controls; Switchgear & switchboard apparatus
Pr: Anne N De Greeg-Sasst
**Pr:* Muriel Bras-Jorge
VP: Evan Burns
IT Man: Jackie Dipietro
IT Man: Stephen Zainc
Mktg Dir: John Maurer
Sls Mgr: John Hurd
Sales Asso: Linda Collin
Sales Asso: Matt Plourd
Snr Mgr: Samuel Fabian
Snr Mgr: Carrie B Tonon

D-U-N-S 01-031-7078
GEMSTONE FOODS
412 8th Ave Ne, Decatur, AL 35601-2422
Tel (256) 686-3601 *Founded/Ownrshp* 2013
Sales 150.0MM *EMP* 700[E]
SIC 5411 2499 Grocery stores; Food handling & processing products, wood
**VP:* Jeff Power

D-U-N-S 11-533-7123
■ **GEN-PROBE INC**
(*Suby of* HOLOGIC INC) ★
10210 Genetic Center Dr, San Diego, CA 92121-4394
Tel (858) 410-8000 *Founded/Ownrshp* 2012
Sales 222.0MM[E] *EMP* 1,391
SIC 8731 Biological research
Pr: Carl W Hull
Pr: Henry L Nordhoff
**CFO:* Herm Rosenman
**Ex VP:* Daniel L Kacian PHD
**Sr VP:* R William Bowen
**Sr VP:* Diana De Walt
Sr VP: Brian B Hansen
VP: N Conway
VP: Edward Cook
VP: Dave Dunn
VP: Bruce Huebner
VP: Graham Lidgard
VP: Linda Merrill
VP: Robin Vedova
**VP:* Michael Watts
VP: Michael J Watts
Assoc Dir: Vladislav Nodelman
Assoc Dir: Ed Sanchez

D-U-N-S 07-438-1513 IMP
GENBAND US LLC
2801 Network Blvd Ste 300, Frisco, TX 75034-1881
Tel (972) 521-5800 *Founded/Ownrshp* 1999
Sales 428.3MM[E] *EMP* 1,550
SIC 3661 Telephones & telephone apparatus
Pr: David Walsh
Pr: Bg Kumar
COO: Steven Bruny
COO: Steven M Bruny
CFO: Daryl Raiford
CFO: Daryl E Raiford
Treas: Karen Leopardi
Chf Mktg O: Mehmet N Balos
Chf Mktg O: Patrick Joggerst
Ofcr: Jan E Gaulding
Ofcr: Sean Huurman
Ex VP: Brad Bush
Ex VP: Barbara Dalibard
Ex VP: Daniel R Lakey
Ex VP: Daniel Lakey
Ex VP: Keith Landau
Ex VP: John McCready
Ex VP: John McReady
Ex VP: Paul Pluschkell
Ex VP: Mark Pugerude
Ex VP: Jeff Townley

GENCO ATC
See ATC LOGISTICS & ELECTRONICS INC

GENCO ATC
See GENCO DISTRIBUTION SYSTEM INC

GENCO ATC
See I GENCO INC

D-U-N-S 79-618-5445
■ **GENCO DISTRIBUTION SYSTEM INC**
GENCO ATC
(*Suby of* FEDEX CORP) ★
100 Papercraft Park, Pittsburgh, PA 15238-3274
Tel (412) 820-3700 *Founded/Ownrshp* 2015
Sales 3.0MMM[E] *EMP* 10,000
SIC 4225 4731 General warehousing & storage; General warehousing; Freight transportation arrangement
Pr: Arthur F Smuck III
V Ch: Jim Polacheck
Pr: John McGonigle III
Pr: Mike Simpson
**Pr:* Andy Smith
Pr: Dwight Wyland
CFO: Rick Roadarmel
Chf Mktg O: Cassandra Chandler
Ex VP: John J Machota
Ex VP: Pete Rector
Ex VP: Joseph Salamunovich
**Sr VP:* Ryan Kelly
VP: Gene Bodenheimer
VP: Bob Devos
**VP:* Michael Fox
VP: Steve Hertzer
VP: Bob Karl
VP: Donnie Lockhart
VP: Bert Munnikhuis
VP: Robert Papak
**VP:* Thomas M Perry III

D-U-N-S 13-119-2767
GENCO OF LEBANON INC
100 Papercraft Park, Pittsburgh, PA 15238-3200
Tel (412) 820-3747 *Founded/Ownrshp* 1995
Sales 291.9MM[E] *EMP* 6,500
SIC 6512 Commercial & industrial building operation
Pr: Herbert Shear
COO: Dave Mabon
**CFO:* Rick Roadarmeo
Sr VP: David Gilley
**Sr VP:* Glenn Mauney
VP: Venkat Avunoori
VP: Dale Dudik
VP: Eric Fabian
**VP:* Brad Feuerbacher
VP: Jeff Gilmore
VP: Larry Katzbeck
VP: John Marx
VP: Laura Moorhead
VP: Robert Papak
**VP:* Larry Schoeneberger
Board of Directors: Eric Lange

D-U-N-S 36-321-3112
▲ **GENCO SHIPPING & TRADING LTD**
299 Park Ave Rm 1200, New York, NY 10171-3806
Tel (646) 443-8550 *Founded/Ownrshp* 2004
Sales 153.9MM *EMP* 1,609[E]
Tkr Sym GNK *Exch* NYS
SIC 4412 Deep sea foreign transportation of freight
Pr: John C Wobensmith
**Ch Bd:* Arthur L Regan
CFO: Apostolos Zafolias
Board of Directors: Eugene I Davis, James G Dolphin, Peter Kirchof, Kevin Mahony, Basil G Mavroleon

D-U-N-S 94-850-1101
■ **GENCO TRANSPORTATION MANAGEMENT LLC**
(*Suby of* GENCO ATC) ★
100 Papercraft Park, Pittsburgh, PA 15238-3200
Tel (412) 820-3700 *Founded/Ownrshp* 2003
Sales 88.7MM[E] *EMP* 1,500
SIC 4225 4111 5045 4789 General warehousing & storage; Local & suburban transit; Computers, peripherals & software; Cargo loading & unloading services
CEO: Todd R Peters
**CFO:* Rick Roadarmel
VP Sls: Dave Vehec

GENCO-ATC
See ATC TECHNOLOGY CORP

D-U-N-S 01-640-4295
GENE B GLICK CO INC
CARRAIGE HOUSE OF COLUMBIA
8801 River Crossing Blvd # 200, Indianapolis, IN 46240-2295
Tel (317) 469-0400 *Founded/Ownrshp* 1947
Sales 290.9MM[E] *EMP* 627
Accts Katz Sapper & Miller Llp In
SIC 1522 6531 6513 Multi-family dwelling construction; Real estate managers; Apartment building operators
Pr: David O Barrett
Pr: Adam Richter
**CFO:* Anita Smith
**Ex VP:* Chad Greiwe
**Sr VP:* James T Bisesi
**Sr VP:* Tom Grande
**Sr VP:* Kathy Overbey
**VP:* Dennis Edmonds
Dir IT: Curtis Taylor

D-U-N-S 05-651-4872
GENE JUAREZ SALONS LLC
3633 136th Pl Se Ste 200, Bellevue, WA 98006-1455
Tel (425) 748-1400 *Founded/Ownrshp* 2008
Sales 2.1MM[E] *EMP* 4,000
SIC 7231 Beauty shops
CEO: Scott Missaca

GENE SISKEL FILM CENTER
See ART INSTITUTE OF CHICAGO

D-U-N-S 94-082-1213
GENE WHITLEY KELLY
44439 Fish Camp Rd, New London, NC 28127-9620
Tel (704) 984-0811 *Founded/Ownrshp* 1999
Sales 328.0MM *EMP* 6
SIC 5031 Lumber: rough, dressed & finished
Owner: Kelly Gene Whitley

GENENCOR INTERNATIONAL
See DANISCO US INC

D-U-N-S 08-012-9000 IMP
■ **GENENTECH INC**
(*Suby of* ROCHE HOLDINGS INC) ★
1 Dna Way, South San Francisco, CA 94080-4990
Tel (650) 225-1000 *Founded/Ownrshp* 1986, 2009
Sales 4.2MMM[E] *EMP* 11,174
SIC 2834 Pharmaceutical preparations; Hormone preparations; Drugs acting on the cardiovascular system, except diagnostic; Drugs acting on the respiratory system
CEO: Ian Clark
COO: Myrtle S Potter
**COO:* Pascal Soriot
**CFO:* Steve Krognes
CFO: Thomas Parker
Treas: Odette Go
**Chf Mktg O:* Hal Barron
**Ofcr:* Rick Kentz

*Ofcr: Richard Scheller
*Ex VP: Stephen G Juelsgaard
Sr VP: Bruce C Cooper
Sr VP: Troy Cox
Sr VP: David A Ebersman
Sr VP: Robert L Garnick
Sr VP: Sandra J Horning
Sr VP: Paula M Jardieu
Sr VP: Ann Karlon
Sr VP: Timothy L Moore
Sr VP: John Orwin
Sr VP: Richard H Scheller
VP: Sunil Agarwal
Board of Directors: Aggie ADM Aisst, Frank J D'angelo, Frederick C Kentz III, Arthur D Levinson Phd

D-U-N-S 80-804-3678 IMP
■ GENENTECH USA INC
(Suby of GENENTECH INC) ★
1 Dna Way, South San Francisco, CA 94080-4990
Tel (650) 225-1000 Founded/Ownrshp 2007
Sales 166.8MM^E EMP 3,626^E
SIC 2834 Pharmaceutical preparations; Hormone preparations; Drugs acting on the cardiovascular system, except diagnostic; Drugs acting on the respiratory system
Prin: Ian T Clark
COO: William Young
Ex VP: David A Ebersman
Exec: Patrick Y Yang
*Prin: Leonard Kanavy
*Prin: Frederick C Kentz III
*Prin: Steve Krognes
IT Man: Michele Redhair
IT Man: Maureen Sharkey

D-U-N-S 15-871-2997
GENER8 MARITIME INC
299 Park Ave Fl 2, New York, NY 10171-0299
Tel (212) 763-5600 Founded/Ownrshp 1997
Sales 429.9MM EMP 35
Accts Deloitte & Touche Llp New Yor
Tkr Sym GNRT Exch NYS
SIC 4412 Deep sea foreign transportation of freight
Ch Bd: Peter C Georgiopoulos
COO: John P Tavlarios
CFO: Leonard J Vrondissis
IT Man: Aura C Nicolae

D-U-N-S 83-288-8155
▲ GENERAC HOLDINGS INC
S45w29290 Hwy 59, Waukesha, WI 53189-9071
Tel (262) 544-4811 Founded/Ownrshp 1959
Sales 1.4MMM EMP 3,156^E
Tkr Sym GNRC Exch NYS
SIC 3621 Motors & generators
Ch Bd: Aaron P Jagdfeld
CFO: York A Ragen
Ex VP: Terry Dolan
Ex VP: Patrick Forsythe
Ex VP: Allen D Gillette
Ex VP: Russell S Minick
Ex VP: Roger F Pascavis
Sr VP: Clement Feng
VP: Paul Cannestra
VP: Shawn Fortune
Sls&Mrk Ex: Johanna Ball
Board of Directors: Todd A Adams, John D Bowlin, Robert D Dixon, Andrew G Lampereur, Bennett Morgan, David A Ramon

D-U-N-S 00-610-3055 IMP/EXP
■ GENERAC POWER SYSTEMS INC
(Suby of GENERAC HOLDINGS INC) ★
S45w29290 Wisconsin 59 St S 45, Waukesha, WI 53189
Tel (262) 544-4811 Founded/Ownrshp 1959
Sales 684.3MM^E EMP 1,574
SIC 3621 Generator sets: gasoline, diesel or dual-fuel
Pr: Aaron Jagdfeld
*CFO: York Ragen
*Ex VP: Patrick Forsythe
Dir Lab: Jim Piquette
Opers Supe: Mary Pick
Natl Sales: Chet Larson
Manager: Brandon Bassler
Manager: Andrew Karistinos
Sls Mgr: Jude Pierson
Sales Asso: Joe Busateri

D-U-N-S 00-643-1878 EXP
GENERAC PORTABLE PRODUCTS INC
BALDOR GENERATORS
3815 Oregon St, Oshkosh, WI 54902-7100
Tel (262) 544-4811 Founded/Ownrshp 1973, 2012
Sales 885.7MM^E EMP 3,400
SIC 3621 Generators & sets, electric
Pr: Ron Tucker
*Pr: Ronald Tucker

D-U-N-S 05-122-7338
GENERAL AIR SERVICE & SUPPLY CO
1105 Zuni St, Denver, CO 80204-3399
Tel (303) 892-7003 Founded/Ownrshp 1984
Sales 84.4MM^E EMP 112^E
SIC 5169 5085 5084 5149 Industrial gases; Welding supplies; Welding machinery & equipment; Soft drinks
Pr: Gary E Armstrong
Ex VP: Brad Armstrong
*VP: Michael Owings
*VP: Art Waskey
Store Mgr: Matt Lawrenz
VP Sls: Bonnie Blakesley
Sales Asso: Chase Donald
Sales Asso: Kyle Killpack

D-U-N-S 19-433-7978
GENERAL ALUMINUM CO OF TEXAS LP
(Suby of MI WINDOWS AND DOORS INC) ★
1900 Lakeside Pkwy, Flower Mound, TX 75028-4078
Tel (972) 242-5271 Founded/Ownrshp 2001
Sales 92.6MM^E EMP 600
SIC 3442 5031 Window & door frames; Casements, aluminum; Metal doors, sash & trim
Ch Bd: Dean P Guerin
Pr: Chris Rix
COO: John Russell
CFO: Mark Swoverland

D-U-N-S 00-415-2658 IMP
■ GENERAL ALUMINUM MFG CO (OH)
GAMCO
(Suby of PARK-OHIO INDUSTRIES INC) ★
6065 Parkland Blvd, Cleveland, OH 44124-6119
Tel (440) 947-2000 Founded/Ownrshp 1981, 1944
Sales 167.2MM^E EMP 900^E
SIC 3365 3369 Aluminum & aluminum-based alloy castings; Nonferrous foundries
CEO: Edward Crawford
Pr: Bob Paulenske
Sr VP: Neil Schneider
VP: Jim Onders
Genl Mgr: Rick Steffenson
Ql Cn Mgr: Michele Bates
Corp Couns: Linda Kold

D-U-N-S 00-696-7541
■ GENERAL AMERICAN LIFE INSURANCE CO
(Suby of METLIFE INC) ★
13045 Tesson Ferry Rd, Saint Louis, MO 63128-3407
Tel (314) 843-8700 Founded/Ownrshp 1933, 1997
Sales NA EMP 1,067^E
Accts Deloitte & Touche Llp
SIC 6411 6311 Insurance agents, brokers & service; Education services, insurance; Life insurance
Ex VP: Bernard H Wolzenski
COO: Sharpe Gregory
*CFO: Steve Anderson
*CFO: Tim Klopfenstein
*Ex VP: Albert Greig Woodring
Sr VP: Jerry Mueller
VP: Karen Kotner
Dir IT: Debbie Youngs

D-U-N-S 03-686-1334
■ GENERAL AMERICAN MUTUAL HOLDING CO
(Suby of METLIFE) ★
700 Market St, Saint Louis, MO 63101-1829
Tel (314) 231-1700 Founded/Ownrshp 2000
Sales NA EMP 1,690
SIC 6311 Life insurance carriers
Pr: Richard A Liddy

D-U-N-S 03-250-4037
GENERAL ASPHALT CO INC
4850 Nw 72nd Ave, Miami, FL 33166-5642
Tel (305) 592-6005 Founded/Ownrshp 1966
Sales 103.1MM^E EMP 150
SIC 3531 Asphalt plant, including gravel-mix type
Pr: Robert A Lopez
*CFO: Curtis Simpson
*VP: Albert J Lopez
*VP: Royal Webster Jr
VP: Royal S Webter

GENERAL ASSEMBLY
See LEGISLATIVE OFFICE OF STATE OF CONNECTICUT

D-U-N-S 09-750-1357
GENERAL ATLANTIC CORP
3 Pickwick Plz Ste 200, Greenwich, CT 06830-5546
Tel (203) 629-8600 Founded/Ownrshp 1979
Sales 563.2MM^E EMP 3,298
SIC 6211 Security brokers & dealers
Pr: William Ford
VP: Steven A Denning
CTO: Richard Gionfriddo

D-U-N-S 36-126-6724
GENERAL ATLANTIC LLC
THREE PICKWICK PLAZA
600 Steamboat Rd Ste 105, Greenwich, CT 06830-7181
Tel (203) 629-8600 Founded/Ownrshp 1995
Sales 128.4MM^E EMP 536^E
SIC 6799 Investment clubs
CEO: William E Ford
*COO: J Frank Brown
*CFO: Thomas J Murphy
*Ex VP: Richard Gold
*Ex VP: Andy Papadakos
*Sr VP: David Buckley
*Sr VP: Paul Doran
Sr VP: Cory A Eaves
VP: Amit Soni
Exec: Jason Currier
Prin: Gabriel Caillaux

D-U-N-S 05-097-1340
GENERAL ATLANTIC SERVICE CO LLC
55 E 52nd St Fl 32, New York, NY 10055-0010
Tel (203) 629-8600 Founded/Ownrshp 2006
Sales 101.5MM^E EMP 962
SIC 8742 Management consulting services
CEO: William E Ford
*COO: J Frank Brown
COO: Matthew Nimetz
*CFO: Thomas J Murphy
*Ch: Steve A Denning

D-U-N-S 85-918-1984
GENERAL ATOMIC TECHNOLOGIES CORP
GENERAL ATOMICS
3550 General Atomics Ct, San Diego, CA 92121-1122
Tel (858) 455-3000 Founded/Ownrshp 1986
Sales 3.6MMM^E EMP 10,109
SIC 8731 3829 3443 7374 3499 2819 Commercial physical research; Nuclear radiation & testing apparatus; Nuclear reactors, military or industrial; Computer time-sharing; Magnets, permanent: metallic; Fuels & radioactive compounds
CEO: J Neal Blue
*Sec: John E Jones
*VP: Linden S Blue
CIO: Dave Nebo
Pr Mgr: Kimberly Kasitz

GENERAL ATOMICS
See GENERAL ATOMIC TECHNOLOGIES CORP

D-U-N-S 06-763-8957 IMP
GENERAL ATOMICS (CA)
(Suby of GENERAL ATOMICS) ★
3550 General Atomics Ct, San Diego, CA 92121-1194
Tel (858) 455-2810 Founded/Ownrshp 1955, 1986
Sales 2.2MMM^E EMP 9,000
SIC 8731 Commercial physical research; Energy research
Pr: J Neal Blue
*CFO: Liam Kelly
Treas: Karen Baldwin
Treas: Mary Cowen
Treas: Anthony Navarra
Treas: Karen Nichols
*Sr VP: Linden Blue
*Sr VP: Robert S Forney
*Sr VP: Jeffrey Quintenz
VP: David Alexander
VP: Nick Bucci
VP: L D Carter
VP: Charlotte Engstrom
VP: Scott Forney
VP: John Geriguis
VP: Gary Hopper
VP: John Metcalf
VP: David Wakayama
VP: Dane Walkes
Exec: Beverly Moore

D-U-N-S 82-468-4229 IMP/EXP
GENERAL ATOMICS AERONAUTICAL SYSTEMS INC
US GOV GA AERONAUTICAL UAV
(Suby of AERONAUTICAL SYSTEMS INC) ★
14200 Kirkham Way, Poway, CA 92064-7103
Tel (858) 312-2810 Founded/Ownrshp 1993
Sales 1.1MMM^E EMP 5,400
SIC 3721 Aircraft
Pr: Neal Blue
CFO: Max Kemp
*Treas: Tony Navarra
*VP: Brad Clark
*VP: Stacy Jakuttis
VP: John Rawls
VP: Mark Rose
Dir Bus: Carl Fisher
Dir Bus: Mike Piersante
Dir Sec: Mike Vigil
Prgrm Mgr: David Cain

D-U-N-S 00-152-7688 IMP
GENERAL BEARING CORP (DE)
(Suby of SKF MOTION TECHNOLOGIES) ★
44 High St, West Nyack, NY 10994-2702
Tel (845) 358-6000 Founded/Ownrshp 1958, 2012
Sales 126.9MM^E EMP 971
SIC 3562 Ball & roller bearings; Ball bearings & parts; Roller bearings & parts
CEO: David L Gussack
*Pr: Thomas J Uhlig
*CFO: Rocky Cambrea
VP: Joseph Hoo
VP: Jim McDonald
*VP: Corby W Self
Rgnl Mgr: Don Morris
Plnt Mgr: David Passariello
Plnt Mgr: Joe Sassano
VP Sls: Alistair G Crannis
S&M/VP: Jeffrey Williams

D-U-N-S 00-281-2949 IMP
GENERAL BEVERAGE SALES CO-MILWAUKEE (WI)
MASTER IMPORTS
6169 Mckee Rd, Fitchburg, WI 53719-5104
Tel (608) 271-1237 Founded/Ownrshp 1996
Sales 104.7MM^E EMP 124
SIC 5182 5181 Bottling wines & liquors; Beer & ale
Pr: Dan Weinstein
*Sec: Richard J Karls
Ex VP: Robert Royko
VP: Michael Gorst
*VP: Joel Minkoff
*VP: B Royko
*VP: Arvin B Weinstein
Exec: Lynn Keiser
MIS Dir: Myra Johnson
Mktg Dir: Bob Royko
Sls Mgr: Luke Bartelme

D-U-N-S 00-514-4480
GENERAL BINDING CORP (DE)
G B C
4 Corporate Dr, Lake Zurich, IL 60047-8924
Tel (847) 541-9500 Founded/Ownrshp 1947
Sales NA EMP 3,600
SIC 5044 2782 3559 3589 7629 3579

D-U-N-S 05-533-2964
GENERAL BUSINESS CREDIT
110 E 9th St Ste A1126, Los Angeles, CA 90079-2154
Tel (213) 244-9500 Founded/Ownrshp 2001
Sales NA EMP 14
SIC 6141 Financing: automobiles, furniture, etc., not a deposit bank
Pr: Daniel Ko
Off Mgr: Justin Cha

GENERAL CABLE
See G K TECHNOLOGIES INC

D-U-N-S 84-791-4173 IMP/EXP
▲ GENERAL CABLE CORP
4 Tesseneer Dr, Highland Heights, KY 41076-9136
Tel (859) 572-8000 Founded/Ownrshp 1992
Sales 4.2MMM EMP 12,000
Accts Deloitte & Touche Llp Cincinn
Tkr Sym BGC Exch NYS
SIC 3351 3357 Wire, copper & copper alloy; Communication wire; Aluminum wire & cable; Fiber optic cable (insulated)
Pr: Michael T McDonnell
CFO: Robert C Kreidler
CFO: Brian J Robinson
Chf Cred: Kurt L Drake
Bd of Dir: Charles McClure
Ofcr: Sonya Reed
Ex VP: Domingo Goenaga Campmany
Ex VP: Bob Kenny
Ex VP: Brian Robinson
Sr VP: Juan Mogollon
Sr VP: Emerson C Moser
Sr VP: Leah Stark
Sr VP: Elizabeth W Taliaferro
VP: Howard H Atkins
VP: Jay Lahman
VP: Stephen R Messinger
VP: Bob Schuermann
VP: Bill Wilson
Exec: Wendy Castillo
Dir Soc: Lisa Lawson
Board of Directors: Sallie B Bailey, Edward Childs Hall III, Gregory E Lawton, Craig P Omtvedt, Patrick M Prevost, John E Weslsh III

D-U-N-S 79-346-3209 IMP/EXP
■ GENERAL CABLE INDUSTRIES INC
(Suby of GENERAL CABLE CORP) ★
4 Tesseneer Dr, Highland Heights, KY 41076-9136
Tel (859) 572-8000 Founded/Ownrshp 1979
Sales 516.8MM^E EMP 4,200
SIC 3351 3315 3357

D-U-N-S 79-350-0448
■ GENERAL CABLETECHNOLOGIES CORP
(Suby of GENERAL CABLE CORP) ★
4 Tesseneer Dr, Highland Heights, KY 41076-9136
Tel (859) 572-8000 Founded/Ownrshp 1994
Sales 356.6MM^E EMP 3,800
SIC 3357 Building wire & cable, nonferrous; Aluminum wire & cable; Coaxial cable, nonferrous; Communication wire
Pr: Gregory B Kenny
*Treas: Brian J Robinson
*VP: Jeffrey J Whelan
CIO: Elizabeth W Taliaferro

GENERAL CHEMICAL
See CHEMTRADE CHEMICALS US LLC

D-U-N-S 60-672-1231 EXP
GENERAL CIGAR CO INC
(Suby of SWEDISH MATCH AB)
10900 Nuckols Rd Ste 100, Glen Allen, VA 23060-9277
Tel (860) 602-3500 Founded/Ownrshp 1906
Sales 44.4MM^E EMP 1,061
SIC 2121 5199 0132 Cigars; Smokers' supplies; Lighters, cigarette & cigar; Tobacco
Pr: Austin T McNamara
COO: Dan Carr
Sr VP: John Rano
VP: W Brent Currier
VP: Robert Loftus
VP: Gene Richter

D-U-N-S 19-484-8735
■ GENERAL CINEMA BEVERAGES OF OHIO INC
PEPSI BOTTLE AND GROUP
(Suby of PEPSICO) ★
1 Pepsi Way Ste 1, Somers, NY 10589-2212
Tel (914) 767-6000 Founded/Ownrshp 1989
Sales 75.2MM^E EMP 1,200
SIC 2086 Soft drinks: packaged in cans, bottles, etc.
Pr: Craig Weatherup
IT Man: Christian Luther

D-U-N-S 61-573-7822
■ GENERAL CINEMA CORP OF TEXAS
(Suby of A M C - G C T INC)
1300 Boylston St, Chestnut Hill, MA 02467-2112
Tel (617) 738-3513 Founded/Ownrshp 1994
Sales 12.5MM^E EMP 3,259^E
SIC 7832 Motion picture theaters, except drive-in
Prin: Paul Del Rossi
*Pr: Frank T Stryjewski
*Treas: G Gail Edwards
VP: Smith Robert A

D-U-N-S 17-913-5710
GENERAL COATINGS CORP
6711 Nancy Ridge Dr, San Diego, CA 92121-2231
Tel (858) 587-1277 Founded/Ownrshp 1987
Sales 106.4MM^E EMP 500
SIC 1721 1799 Painting & paper hanging; Waterproofing
CEO: Craig A Kinsman
*VP: Andrew Fluken
Info Man: Noe Moreno

D-U-N-S 01-119-9767
▲ GENERAL COMMUNICATION INC
2550 Denali St Ste 1000, Anchorage, AK 99503-2751
Tel (907) 868-5600 Founded/Ownrshp 1979
Sales 978.5MM EMP 2,370
Tkr Sym GNCMA Exch NGS
SIC 4813 4841 4812 Telephone communication, except radio; Long distance telephone communications; ; Cable & other pay television services; Radio telephone communication
Pr: Ronald A Duncan
*Ch Bd: Stephen M Brett
COO: Gregory F Chapados
CFO: Peter J Pounds
Chf Cred: Tina M Pidgeon
Ex VP: Ron Duncan
Sr VP: Paul E Landes
VP: Kelly Clouse
VP: John M Lowber
VP: Steven Starace
Prgrm Mgr: Robert Taylor

D-U-N-S 00-691-9732 IMP/EXP
GENERAL CONFERENCE OF SEVENTH-DAY ADVENTISTS
12501 Old Columbia Pike, Silver Spring, MD 20904-6601
Tel (301) 680-6000 Founded/Ownrshp 1863
Sales 227.9MM EMP 550
Accts Maner Costerisan Pc Lansing
SIC 8661 Seventh Day Adventist Church
Pr: Ted N C Wilson
*Treas: Juan Prestol-Puesan
Assoc Dir: Mario Ceballos
Assoc Dir: Joel Swanson
Ex Dir: Rajmund Dabrowski
Snr Ntwrk: Charles Mendoza

CTO: Fred Hardinge
Pr Mgr: Michelle Oetman
Genl Couns: Thomas Wetmore

D-U-N-S 08-373-7403
GENERAL CONSTRUCTION CO
(*Suby of* KIEWIT INFRASTRUCTURE WEST CO) ★
33455 6th Ave S, Federal Way, WA 98003-6335
Tel (253) 943-4200 *Founded/Ownrshp* 2002
Sales 249.9MM[E] *EMP* 1,414
Accts Kpmg Llp
SIC 1622 1629 Bridge, tunnel & elevated highway; Bridge construction; Highway construction, elevated; Dams, waterways, docks & other marine construction; Dam construction; Dock construction; Pier construction
Pr: Ronald H Morford
**Treas:* Stephen S Thomas
**Ex VP:* Ken E Riley
**Sr VP:* Parke D Ball
**Sr VP:* A T Skoro
**VP:* Jeffrey C Arviso
VP: Jeffrey Arviso
**VP:* Kent A Boden
**VP:* Paul H Guintini
**VP:* Michael J Piechoski
**VP:* Tobin A Schropp
**VP:* Phillip C Wallace
**VP:* Gregg F Woodward

D-U-N-S 17-546-5996
GENERAL DATATECH LP
999 Metro Media Pl, Dallas, TX 75247-4730
Tel (214) 857-6100 *Founded/Ownrshp* 1998
Sales 366.9MM[E] *EMP* 400
SIC 5065 Communication equipment
Genl Pt: John Roberts
Treas: Rhonda Hopper
VP: Marcia Bonner
CIO: Michael R Gilbert
IT Man: Mario Saldivar
Web Dev: Michael Roman
Netwrk Eng: Michael Crump
Mktg Dir: Darjon Bittner
Sls Dir: Brent Beasley
Sls Mgr: Jonathan Groves
Sales Asso: Johnetta Byam

D-U-N-S 04-611-3759
GENERAL DISTRIBUTING CO
5350 W Amelia Earhart Dr, Salt Lake City, UT 84116-2900
Tel (801) 531-7895 *Founded/Ownrshp* 1967
Sales 107.4MM[E] *EMP* 157
SIC 5181 Beer & other fermented malt liquors
Pr: Andrew Z Zweber
**VP:* Rebecca Ann Brennan

GENERAL DYNAMICS ADVNCED
See GENERAL DYNAMICS MISSION SYSTEMS INC

D-U-N-S 12-154-0038
GENERAL DYNAMICS C4 SYSTEMS INC
8201 E Mcdowell Rd, Scottsdale, AZ 85257-3812
Tel (480) 441-3033 *Founded/Ownrshp* 2002
Sales 1.3MMM[E] *EMP* 7,003
SIC 8711

D-U-N-S 00-138-1284 IMP
▲ GENERAL DYNAMICS CORP
2941 Frview Pk Dr Ste 100, Falls Church, VA 22042
Tel (703) 876-3000 *Founded/Ownrshp* 1952
Sales 31.4MMM *EMP* 99,900
Tkr Sym GD *Exch* NYS
SIC 3721 3731 3795 3711 3812 Aircraft; Submarines, building & repairing; Combat vessels, building & repairing; Tanks, military, including factory rebuilding; Reconnaissance cars, assembly of; Search & navigation equipment; Search & detection systems & instruments
Ch Bd: Phebe N Novakovic
CFO: Jason W Aiken
Ex VP: John P Casey
Ex VP: S Daniel Johnson
Ex VP: Mark C Roualet
Sr VP: Gregory S Gallopoulos
Sr VP: Robert W Helm
Sr VP: Walter M Oliver
VP: Mark L Burns
VP: Jeffrey S Geiger
VP: Kimberly A Kuryea
VP: Christopher Marzilli
VP: Gary L Whited
Board of Directors: William A Osborn, Mary T Barra, Laura J Schumacher, Nicholas D Chabraja, Peter A Wall, James S Crown, Rudy F Deleon, William P Fricks, John M Keane, Lester L Lyles, Mark Malcolm, James N Mattis

D-U-N-S 00-358-7024 IMP
■ GENERAL DYNAMICS DEFENSE SYSTEMS INC
(*Suby of* GENERAL DYNAMICS CORP) ★
100 Plastics Ave, Pittsfield, MA 01201-3985
Tel (413) 494-1110 *Founded/Ownrshp* 1996, 2001
Sales 180.6MM[E] *EMP* 1,900
SIC 3812 3795 3625 Search & detection systems & instruments; Tanks & tank components; Relays & industrial controls
Pr: Nicholas D Chabraja
CFO: Bob Plunkitt
MIS Dir: Charlie Banker
Pr Dir: Christine McLaughlin

GENERAL DYNAMICS ELECTRIC BOAT
See ELECTRIC BOAT CORP

D-U-N-S 04-318-9620 IMP
■ GENERAL DYNAMICS GLOBAL IMAGING TECHNOLOGIES INC
(*Suby of* GENERAL DYNAMICS GOVERNMENT SYSTEMS CORP) ★
24 Simon St, Nashua, NH 03060-3025
Tel (603) 864-6300 *Founded/Ownrshp* 1959, 2009
Sales 341.0MM[E] *EMP* 1,284
SIC 3827 3861 Optical instruments & apparatus; Aerial cameras
CEO: Stephen W Bershad
**Pr:* Scott B Conner
VP: Mark Bonney
VP: Bob McGill
Exec: Thomas Crafts
Exec: Dawn Emerson
Prgrm Mgr: Keith Spaley
Genl Mgr: G J Roe
CTO: Bill Hurst
Dir IT: Mark Gilliam
IT Man: Dudley Harris

D-U-N-S 11-618-7758
■ GENERAL DYNAMICS GOVERNMENT SYSTEMS CORP
(*Suby of* GENERAL DYNAMICS CORP) ★
2941 Fairview Park Dr, Falls Church, VA 22042-4522
Tel (703) 876-3000 *Founded/Ownrshp* 1999
Sales 1.0MMM[E] *EMP* 25,000
SIC 6719 Investment holding companies, except banks
Pr: Kenneth C Dahlberg
**VP:* Vincent Antonacci
**VP:* David Breen
**VP:* Michael Garrity
**VP:* Jim Knapp

D-U-N-S 78-495-9124
■ GENERAL DYNAMICS GOVERNMENT SYSTEMS OVERSEAS CORP
GDGSOC
(*Suby of* GENERAL DYNAMICS GOVERNMENT SYSTEMS CORP) ★
3211 Jermantown Rd, Fairfax, VA 22030-2844
Tel (703) 995-8666 *Founded/Ownrshp* 1991
Sales 5.0MM[E] *EMP* 5,000
SIC 3663 Radio & TV communications equipment
VP: Vince Antonacci

D-U-N-S 06-764-1597
■ GENERAL DYNAMICS INFORMATION TECHNOLOGY INC (VA)
GDIT
(*Suby of* GENERAL DYNAMICS GOVERNMENT SYSTEMS CORP) ★
3211 Jermantown Rd, Fairfax, VA 22030-2844
Tel (703) 995-8700 *Founded/Ownrshp* 1975, 2006
Sales 4.0MM *EMP* 24,000
SIC 7379 8711 7373 Computer related maintenance services; Professional engineer; Computer systems analysis & design; Systems engineering, computer related
Pr: S Daniel Johnson
**Treas:* David Breen
**Treas:* David H Fogg
Div VP: Jason Jones
Sr VP: Bryan Hrabosky
Sr VP: Thomas W Kirchmaier
**VP:* Vincent S Antonacci
**VP:* Marcus Collier
**VP:* Gregory S Gallopoulos
VP: Michael Garrity
VP: Spain Hall Jr
**VP:* Edward G Hudson Jr
**VP:* Thomas W Kirchmaier
VP: Catherine Schempp
**VP:* Zannie Smith
VP: Garry Waggoner
**VP:* Ray Whitehead
**VP:* Al Whitmore
Dir Bus: Robert Case
Dir Bus: Laura Jones
Board of Directors: Gerard J Demuro, Gregory S Gallopoulos, S Daniel Johnson, L Hugh Redd

D-U-N-S 13-126-6926 IMP
■ GENERAL DYNAMICS LAND SYSTEMS INC
GDLS
(*Suby of* GENERAL DYNAMICS CORP) ★
38500 Mound Rd, Sterling Heights, MI 48310-3200
Tel (586) 825-4000 *Founded/Ownrshp* 1984
Sales 2.8MMM[E] *EMP* 6,900
SIC 5088 8711 Combat vehicles; Engineering services
Pr: Gary L Whited
CFO: Evelyn Milam
**CFO:* Evelyn Milan
**Treas:* David Fogg
**VP:* Peter Keating
VP: John W Osina
VP: Anne M Regling
VP: Sue Robbins
Dir IT: Mark Cook
IT Man: Stephen Cooper
IT Man: John Milliken

D-U-N-S 17-183-7730 IMP
■ GENERAL DYNAMICS MISSION SYSTEMS INC
GENERAL DYNAMICS ADVNCED
(*Suby of* GENERAL DYNAMICS GOVERNMENT SYSTEMS CORP) ★
12450 Fair Lakes Cir # 800, Fairfax, VA 22033-3810
Tel (703) 263-2800 *Founded/Ownrshp* 2001
Sales 2.6MMM[E] *EMP* 7,991
SIC 3571 Electronic computers
CEO: Phebe N Novakovic
**CFO:* Edward Grecco
Ofcr: Wesley Gunter
**Ex VP:* John P Casey
**Ex VP:* S Daniel Johnson
**Ex VP:* Mark C Roualet
VP: Chris Brady
**Dir Surg:* Kathleen Nicodemus
Prgrm Mgr: Eugene McLaughlin
Prgrm Mgr: Jorge Rivera
Genl Mgr: Kevin Missar
Board of Directors: James Allen, Joel Birnbaum, George Hornig, James Kozlowski, Lynn Madonna, Charles Simons

D-U-N-S 12-153-8859
■ GENERAL DYNAMICS NETWORK SYSTEMS INC
GENERAL DYNAMICS WIRELESS SVCS
(*Suby of* GENERAL DYNAMICS GOVERNMENT SYSTEMS CORP) ★
101 Station Dr Apt 200, Westwood, MA 02090-2392
Tel (781) 400-7669 *Founded/Ownrshp* 2002
Sales 449.3MM[E] *EMP* 6,700
SIC 8711 Engineering services
Pr: Michael Chandler
CFO: Keith F Koon
Treas: David H Fogg
Ofcr: Ann Young
Ex VP: Raynor Reavis
VP: Brian Harrington
Admn Mgr: Steve Allington
Admn Mgr: Michael Harrison
Admn Mgr: Richard Maurer

GENERAL DYNAMICS ORDNANCE AND
See EBV EXPLOSIVES ENVIRONMENTAL CO

D-U-N-S 19-486-0813 IMP/EXP
■ GENERAL DYNAMICS ORDNANCE AND TACTICAL SYSTEMS INC
(*Suby of* GENERAL DYNAMICS CORP) ★
11399 16th Ct N Ste 200, Saint Petersburg, FL 33716-2322
Tel (727) 578-8100 *Founded/Ownrshp* 2001
Sales 506.6MM[E] *EMP* 2,277
SIC 3483 3482 2892 3489 Ammunition, except for small arms; Small arms ammunition; Explosives; Ordnance & accessories
Pr: Michael S Wilson
Bd of Dir: David D Baier
Bd of Dir: John P Casey
Bd of Dir: Randy M Collins
Bd of Dir: Gerard J Demuro
Bd of Dir: Henry C Eickelberg
Bd of Dir: Larry R Flynn
Bd of Dir: Charles M Hall
Bd of Dir: David K Heebner
Bd of Dir: Preston A Henne
Bd of Dir: Peter J Lawrence
Bd of Dir: Joseph T Lombardo
Bd of Dir: Michael J Mulligan
Bd of Dir: Phebe N Novakovic
Bd of Dir: Walter M Oliver
Bd of Dir: Alfonso Ramonet
Bd of Dir: Raynor B Reavis
Bd of Dir: William O Schmieder
Bd of Dir: John W Schwartz
Bd of Dir: John F Shipway
Bd of Dir: Michael W Toner

D-U-N-S 02-356-4888 IMP/EXP
■ GENERAL DYNAMICS SATCOM TECHNOLOGIES INC
(*Suby of* GENERAL DYNAMICS GOVERNMENT SYSTEMS CORP) ★
1700 Cable Dr Ne, Conover, NC 28613-8991
Tel (704) 462-7330 *Founded/Ownrshp* 2004
Sales 337.3MM[E] *EMP* 1,511
SIC 3663 Radio & TV communications equipment
Pr: Christopher Marzilli
Sr VP: Marvin Shoemaker
VP: Lou Dinunzio
Dir IT: Jim Barrett
Opers Mgr: Robert Featherstone
Plnt Mgr: Brian Strother

GENERAL DYNAMICS WIRELESS SVCS
See GENERAL DYNAMICS NETWORK SYSTEMS INC

D-U-N-S 16-737-7204 IMP
■ GENERAL DYNAMICS-OTS INC
(*Suby of* GENERAL DYNAMICS CORP) ★
11399 16th Ct N Ste 200, Saint Petersburg, FL 33716-2322
Tel (727) 578-8100 *Founded/Ownrshp* 1948
Sales 916.3MM[E] *EMP* 5,000
SIC 3728 3812 Military aircraft equipment & armament; Search & navigation equipment
Pr: Mike Wilson
Pr: Dan Chien
Ofcr: Bob Dunsage
Ofcr: Stephen Hetcko
**Ex VP:* Charles M Hall
VP: Catherine Luther
**VP:* Tim McAuliffe
**VP:* Mike Obrien
Exec: Garrett Dominy
**Comm Dir:* Karl Johnson
Comm Dir: Karl Johnson

GENERAL DYNMICS NASSCO-NORFOLK
See METRO MACHINE CORP

D-U-N-S 00-698-4256
■ GENERAL ELECTRIC CAPITAL CORP
(*Suby of* GENERAL ELECTRIC CO) ★
901 Main Ave, Norwalk, CT 06851-1168
Tel (203) 840-6300 *Founded/Ownrshp* 1932, 2012
Sales NA *EMP* 47,000
Accts Kpmg Llp Stamford Connecticu
Tkr Sym GEK *Exch* NYS
SIC 6159 6141 7359 Equipment & vehicle finance leasing companies; Machinery & equipment finance leasing; Financing: automobiles, furniture, etc., not a deposit bank; Installment sales finance, other than banks; Equipment rental & leasing
Ch Bd: Keith S Sherin
Pr: Thomas C Gentile
CFO: Robert C Green
Treas: Kathryn A Cassidy
Ex VP: Beverly Belcamino
Sr VP: Alex Dimitrief
Sr VP: Walter Ielusic
VP: Bruce Christensen
VP: Li Liu
Dir Risk M: Dean Debroux
Dir Risk M: Ryan A Zanin
Board of Directors: Jeffrey S Bornstein, Jeffrey R Immelt

D-U-N-S 11-618-2890
■ GENERAL ELECTRIC CAPITAL SERVICES INC
(*Suby of* GENERAL ELECTRIC CO) ★
3135 Easton Tpke, Fairfield, CT 06828-0001
Tel (203) 373-2211 *Founded/Ownrshp* 1984
Sales NA *EMP* 55,000[E]
SIC 6159 6141 7359 6162 Equipment & vehicle finance leasing companies; Machinery & equipment finance leasing; Consumer finance companies; Financing: automobiles, furniture, etc., not a deposit bank; Installment sales finance, other than banks; Equipment rental & leasing; Bond & mortgage companies
Ch Bd: Jeffrey R Immelt
Pr: Stuart D Aronson
Pr: Michael E Chen
Pr: Margaret Keane
Pr: Dmitri Stockton
CEO: Robert Stefanowski
CFO: Stewart B Koenigsberg
CFO: Trevor A Schauenberg
CFO: Keith S Sherin
Sr VP: Ray Duggins
Sr VP: Andreas Hirsemann
Sr VP: Jamie S Miller
Sr VP: John Trentos
VP: Alec Burger
VP: Kristi Colburn
VP: William Dakin Jr
VP: Sharon Garavel
VP: Tho Nghiem
VP: Mindy Squeo
VP: Joseph Turza
Board of Directors: Michael A Neal, Mark W Begor, Ronald R Pressman, Jeffrey S Bornstein, John M Samuels, William H Cary, Ryan A Zanin, Kathryn A Cassidy, Pamela Daley, Mark J Krakowiak, John Krenicki Jr, J Keith Morgan, David Nason

D-U-N-S 00-136-7960
▲ GENERAL ELECTRIC CO
41 Farnsworth St, Boston, MA 02210-1236
Tel (617) 443-3000 *Founded/Ownrshp* 1892
Sales 117.3MMM *EMP* 333,000
Tkr Sym GE *Exch* NYS
SIC 3511 3724 3632 3845 Turbines & turbine generator sets; Steam turbines; Gas turbines, mechanical drive; Aircraft engines & engine parts; Refrigerators, mechanical & absorption: household; Freezers, home & farm; Electromedical equipment; Electromedical apparatus; Magnetic resonance imaging device, nuclear
Ch Bd: Jeffrey R Immelt
Pr: Visal Leng
CFO: Jeffrey S Bornstein
Sr VP: Alexander Dimitrief
VP: Jan R Hauser
VP: Tony Mathis
VP: Jennifer Waldo
Board of Directors: Steven M Mollenkopf, W Geoffrey Beattie, James J Mulva, John J Brennan, James E Rohr, Francisco D'souza, Mary L Schapiro, Peter B Henry, James S Tisch, Susan J Hockfield, Andrea Jung, Robert W Lane, Rochelle B Lazarus, Lowell C McAdam

D-U-N-S 96-450-8043
GENERAL ELECTRIC INSURANCE PLAN TRUST
1070 High Ridge Rd, Stamford, CT 06905-1122
Tel (203) 326-2300 *Founded/Ownrshp* 2010
Sales NA *EMP* 2[E]
Accts Pricewaterhousecoopers Llp Ph
SIC 6411

D-U-N-S 06-492-3659 IMP/EXP
■ GENERAL ELECTRIC INTERNATIONAL INC
(*Suby of* GENERAL ELECTRIC CO) ★
191 Rosa Parks St, Cincinnati, OH 45202-2573
Tel (513) 813-9133 *Founded/Ownrshp* 1961
Sales 13.2MMM *EMP* 125[E]
Accts Kpmg Llp Stamford Ct
SIC 8711 Engineering services
Pr: Giuseppe Recchi
CFO: Stephen Sedita Jr
**Treas:* Michael J Geary
**VP:* Candace F Carson
**VP:* Daniel Janki
Mng Dir: Debra Hemsey
Prgrm Mgr: Mark Hachenski
Area Mgr: Luis Hernandez
Dist Mgr: Brian Fitzgerald
Genl Mgr: Chuck Elias
CIO: John Maya

D-U-N-S 94-724-4943
■ GENERAL ELECTRIC INTERNATIONAL OPERATIONS CO INC
(*Suby of* GENERAL ELECTRIC CO) ★
191 Rosa Parks St, Cincinnati, OH 45202-2573
Tel (513) 813-9133 *Founded/Ownrshp* 1976
Sales 925.0MM *EMP* 77[E]
Accts Kpmg Llp Stamford Ct
SIC 7389 Personal service agents, brokers & bureaus
Pr: Robert Smits

D-U-N-S 10-752-0769
GENERAL ELECTRIC RAILCAR SERVICES CORP
161 N Clark St Fl 7, Chicago, IL 60601-3389
Tel (312) 853-5000 *Founded/Ownrshp* 1983
Sales NA *EMP* 1,000
SIC 7359 3743 4789 3462

D-U-N-S 80-033-4430
▲ GENERAL FINANCE CORP
39 E Union St Ste 206, Pasadena, CA 91103-3929
Tel (626) 584-9722 *Founded/Ownrshp* 2007
Sales 285.8MM *EMP* 811[E]
Tkr Sym GFN *Exch* NGM
SIC 7359 5085 Shipping container leasing; Bins & containers, storage
Ch Bd: Ronald F Valenta
CFO: Charles E Barrantes
Ex VP: Jeffrey A Kluckman

VP: Christopher A Wilson
Sales Asso: Susie Osborne
Board of Directors: William H Baribault, David M Connell, Susan L Harris, Manuel Marrero, James B Roszak, Larry D Tashjian

D-U-N-S 00-317-6385 IMP/EXP
GENERAL FOAM PLASTICS CORP (VA)
GFP PLASTICS
4429 Bonney Rd Ste 500, Virginia Beach, VA 23462-3881
Tel (757) 857-0153 *Founded/Ownrshp* 1957, 1960
Sales 350.3MM[E] *EMP* 1,500
SIC 3089 Plastic processing
CEO: Jack Hall
**Pr:* George Dieffenbach
COO: Wingate Sung
**CFO:* Stan Hobbs
CFO: Bob Scott
**Ch:* Bill Fields
**Ex VP:* Sandy Caprow
VP: Eva A Austin
VP: Lamont D Kennedy II
**Prin:* Ascher Chase
Mng Dir: Tom Brandenburg

D-U-N-S 07-877-6876
▲ **GENERAL GROWTH PROPERTIES INC**
110 N Wacker Dr, Chicago, IL 60606-1526
Tel (312) 960-5000 *Founded/Ownrshp* 1986
Sales 2.4MMM *EMP* 1,700[E]
Tkr Sym GGP *Exch* NYS
SIC 6798 Real estate investment trusts
CEO: Sandeep Mathrani
Pt: Rebecca Graf
Ch Bd: J Bruce Flatt
Pr: Shobi Khan
COO: Shobi S Khan
CFO: Michael B Berman
Ex VP: Richard S Pesin
Sr VP: Tara L Marszewski
VP: Joel Bayer
VP: Lisa Bell
VP: Tom Bernier
VP: Kevin Berry
VP: Bob Bushey
VP: Bob Carlson
VP: James Cummings
VP: Dave Cuthill
VP: Kay Day
VP: Patty Hirt
VP: Joe Hope
VP: Glenn Insana
VP: Carol Jacobs
Board of Directors: Richard B Clark, Mary Lou Fiala, John K Haley, Daniel B Hurwitz, Brian W Kingston, David J Neithercut, Mark R Patterson

GENERAL HARDWARE DISTRIBUTORS
See ALASKA INDUSTRIAL HARDWARE INC

D-U-N-S 13-954-9901
GENERAL HEALTH SERVICES CORP
PRESBYTERIAN HOSPITAL DALLAS
(*Suby of* TEXAS HEALTH RESOURCES) ★
7515 Grnvlle Ave Ste 1000, Dallas, TX 75231
Tel (214) 345-8345 *Founded/Ownrshp* 1998
Sales 372.0MM[E] *EMP* 15,000
SIC 6719 Investment holding companies, except banks
Pr: Douglas Hawthorne
Opthamlgy: Gary E Fish

D-U-N-S 07-505-5160 IMP
GENERAL HEALTH SYSTEM
BATON ROUGE GENERAL
8585 Picardy Ave, Baton Rouge, LA 70809-3748
Tel (225) 387-7000 *Founded/Ownrshp* 1945
Sales 68.4MM *EMP* 3,400
Accts Postlethwaite & Netterville B
SIC 8741 6324 Hospital management; Hospital & medical service plans
CEO: Mark F Slyter
**CFO:* Kendall Johnson
**Ex VP:* Anna Cazes
**Ex VP:* Dionne E Viator
**VP:* Paul Douglas

D-U-N-S 60-920-2742
GENERAL HEALTH SYSTEM
HEART & FITNESS CENTER
(*Suby of* BATON ROUGE GENERAL) ★
5757 Corp Blvd Ste 200, Baton Rouge, LA 70808
Tel (225) 237-1500 *Founded/Ownrshp* 1983
Sales 326.8MM *EMP* 5
SIC 8071 7991 Medical laboratories; Physical fitness facilities
Prin: Dr Milton Sietman
**Pr:* Drmilton Sietman
CFO: Patricia Thomas
**CFO:* Jack Wagner

D-U-N-S 17-371-9386
GENERAL HEALTH SYSTEM MANAGEMENT INC
(*Suby of* BATON ROUGE GENERAL) ★
8585 Picardy Ave, Baton Rouge, LA 70809-3748
Tel (225) 237-1700 *Founded/Ownrshp* 1986
Sales NA *EMP* 4,000
SIC 6324 Hospital & medical service plans
VP: Don Shaw

D-U-N-S 87-634-1272
GENERAL HEALTHCARE RESOURCES INC
GHR
2250 Hickory Rd Ste 240, Plymouth Meeting, PA 19462-2225
Tel (610) 834-1122 *Founded/Ownrshp* 1993
Sales 37.8MM[E] *EMP* 1,000
SIC 8082 Home health care services
Pr: John I Quirk
**Sec:* Lawrence Palmer
Ex VP: Maury Kent

GENERAL HOSPITAL, THE
See MASSACHUSETTS GENERAL HOSPITAL

GENERAL HOSPITAL
See M G H HEALTH SERVICES CORP

D-U-N-S 18-344-6160
GENERAL HOUSING INC
2255 Industrial Blvd, Waycross, GA 31503-6969
Tel (912) 285-5068 *Founded/Ownrshp* 2005
Sales 49.1MM[E] *EMP* 1,025
SIC 2451 Mobile homes
Sec: J Wayne Roberts
VP: Tim Vinson
IT Man: Thomas Holland
Mfg Dir: Keith Graham

D-U-N-S 00-100-8986 IMP
GENERAL INSULATION CO (MA)
278 Mystic Ave Ste 209, Medford, MA 02155-6330
Tel (781) 391-2070 *Founded/Ownrshp* 1927, 1981
Sales 316.0MM[E] *EMP* 357
SIC 5033 7389 Roofing, siding & insulation;
CEO: Frank Granara
Pr: Scott Campbell
Pr: Mick Clinger
**Pr:* Rick McMullen
**Pr:* Larry Murphy
Pr: Mark Snodgrass
CFO: Jeff Gentilotti
**VP:* Lawrence D Murphy
**VP:* Mark T Oneil
**VP:* Gerry Towle
Div Mgr: Jason May

GENERAL INSURANCE, THE
See PERMANENT GENERAL COMPANIES INC

GENERAL MEDICAL SURGICAL HOSPI
See HARRISON MEDICAL CENTER

D-U-N-S 00-625-0740 IMP/EXP
▲ **GENERAL MILLS INC**
1 General Mills Blvd, Minneapolis, MN 55426-1348
Tel (763) 764-7600 *Founded/Ownrshp* 1928
Sales 16.5MMM *EMP* 42,000
Tkr Sym GIS *Exch* NYS
SIC 2099 2041 2045 2064 2024 Dessert mixes & fillings; Frosting mixes, dry: for cakes, cookies, etc.; Potatoes, dried: packaged with other ingredients; Pasta, uncooked: packaged with other ingredients; Flour; Flour mixes; Prepared flour mixes & doughs; Cake mixes, prepared: from purchased flour; Biscuit mixes, prepared: from purchased flour; Fruit & fruit peel confections; Granola & muesli, bars & clusters; Yogurt desserts, frozen
Ch Bd: Kendall J Powell
Pt: David P Homer
Pr: Kimberly A Nelson
Pr: Jon Nudi
Pr: Shawn P O'Grady
COO: Jeffrey L Harmening
COO: Christopher D O'Leary
CFO: Donal L Mulligan
Treas: Kofi Bruce
Bd of Dir: Tim Gluzsak
Ex VP: John R Church
Ex VP: Peter C Erickson
Sr VP: Richard C Allendorf
Sr VP: Jacqueline Williams-Roll
VP: Karen Anderson
VP: Mike Davis
VP: Tim Fieldhouse
VP: Michelle Helm
VP: Jeff Koenig
VP: Richard Lund
VP: Missy Mound
Board of Directors: Michael D Rose, R Kerry Clark, Robert L Ryan, David M Cordani, Eric D Sprunk, Paul Danos, Dorothy A Terrell, Alicia S Boler Davis, Jorge A Uribe, Roger W Ferguson Jr, Henrietta H Fore, Maria G Henry, Heidi G Miller, Steve Odland

D-U-N-S 03-428-6919
■ **GENERAL MILLS OPERATIONS LLC**
(*Suby of* GENERAL MILLS INC) ★
1 General Mills Blvd, Minneapolis, MN 55426-1348
Tel (763) 764-7600 *Founded/Ownrshp* 1996
Sales 193.4MM[E] *EMP* 750
SIC 4221 Grain elevator, storage only
**CEO:* Stephen Sanger
Opers Mgr: Paul Bohlsen
Mktg Mgr: Billie Norris

D-U-N-S 82-969-5910
■ **GENERAL MOTORS CHINA INC**
(*Suby of* GENERAL MOTORS LLC) ★
300 Renaissance Ctr L1, Detroit, MI 48243-1403
Tel (313) 556-5000 *Founded/Ownrshp* 2009
Sales 96.1MM[E] *EMP* 378[E]
SIC 3714 Motor vehicle parts & accessories
CEO: Lillian Orth
Ex VP: Thomas Lasorda
**Ex VP:* Matthew Tsien
Exec: Jon Centurino
Ex Dir: John Murtagh
Opers Mgr: Joe Beauchamp
Opers Mgr: Jim Vincent
Plnt Mgr: Scott Gaines
Plnt Mgr: Scott Williamson
Sls&Mrk Ex: Carolyn Landrum
VP Sls: Theodore Baun

D-U-N-S 83-244-7812
▲ **GENERAL MOTORS CO**
300 Renaissance Ctr L1, Detroit, MI 48243-1403
Tel (313) 556-5000 *Founded/Ownrshp* 1908
Sales 152.3MMM *EMP* 215,020[E]
Tkr Sym GM *Exch* NYS
SIC 3711 3714 Motor vehicles & car bodies; Motor vehicle parts & accessories
Ch Bd: Mary T Barra
Ch Bd: Theodore M Solso
Pr: Daniel Ammann
Pr: Jaime Ardila
Pr: Alan S Batey
Pr: Carel Johannes De Nysschen
Pr: Barry L Engle
Pr: Karl-Thomas Neumann
Pr: Matthew Tsien
CFO: Charles K Stevens III
Ex VP: Alicia Boler-Davis
Ex VP: James B Deluca
Ex VP: David Duckworth
Ex VP: Craig B Glidden
Ex VP: Mark L Reuss
Ex VP: Mark Weber
Sr VP: John J Quattrone
VP: Tony Cervone
VP: Thomas S Timko
Comm Man: Kelly Cusinato
Board of Directors: Carol M Stephenson, Joseph J Ashton, Linda R Gooden, Joseph Jimenez, Kathryn V Marinello, Jane L Mendillo, Michael G Mullen, James J Mulva, Patricia F Russo, Thomas M Schoewe

D-U-N-S 17-778-1390
■ **GENERAL MOTORS FINANCIAL CO INC**
AMERICREDIT
(*Suby of* GENERAL MOTORS HOLDINGS LLC) ★
801 Cherry St Ste 3500, Fort Worth, TX 76102-6854
Tel (817) 302-7000 *Founded/Ownrshp* 2010
Sales NA *EMP* 3,800
Accts Deloitte & Touche Llp Fort Wo
SIC 6141 Financing: automobiles, furniture, etc., not a deposit bank
Pr: Daniel E Berce
**Ch Bd:* Clifton H Morris Jr
Pr: Melissa Alcorn
Pr: Charles Berend
Pr: Joshua Blankenship
Pr: Elizabeth Carothers
Pr: Gary Collier
Pr: Dianne Doughty
Pr: Adriana Duran
Pr: Jeison George
Pr: Nikitas Gogos
Pr: Jeremy Greene
Pr: Chris Hammons
Pr: Tricendra Harvey
Pr: Dan Heinrich
Pr: Emily Hicks
Pr: Chris Hoke
Pr: Phillip Jeffers
Pr: David Landers
Pr: Allisen Petersen
Pr: Cindy Saunders

D-U-N-S 83-245-8033 IMP
■ **GENERAL MOTORS HOLDINGS LLC**
(*Suby of* GENERAL MOTORS CO) ★
300 Renaissance Ctr L1, Detroit, MI 48243-1403
Tel (313) 556-5000 *Founded/Ownrshp* 2009
Sales 6.4MMM[E] *EMP* 4,055[E]
SIC 3711 3714 Motor vehicles & car bodies; Motor vehicle parts & accessories
CEO: Robert A Lutz
**CFO:* Daniel Ammann
**CFO:* Ray G Young
**V Ch Bd:* Thomas G Stephens
**Ex VP:* Jaime Ardila
**Ex VP:* Mary T Barra
**Ex VP:* Michael P Millikin
**VP:* Alan Batey
VP: Ron Sobrerro

D-U-N-S 83-124-7536 EXP
■ **GENERAL MOTORS LLC**
(*Suby of* GENERAL MOTORS CO) ★
300 Renaissance Ctr L1, Detroit, MI 48243-1403
Tel (313) 556-5000 *Founded/Ownrshp* 2009
Sales 1.3MMM[E] *EMP* 1,053[E]
SIC 3711 3714 Motor vehicles & car bodies; Motor vehicle parts & accessories
CEO: Mary T Barra
**Pr:* Dan Ammann
COO: Leslie Bauer
CFO: Michael J Losh
CFO: Tom Okray
**CFO:* Ray G Young
**Ex VP:* Jaime Ardila
**VP:* Alan Batey
**VP:* Stephen J Girsky
**VP:* Melissa A Howell
**VP:* Timothy E Lee
**VP:* Daniel Nicholson
**VP:* Robert S Osborne
VP: Eric Peterson
Exec: Patricia F Bonderman
Exec: Loyd Vandagriff
Dir Rx: Cynthia Kirman

D-U-N-S 05-560-7378 IMP
GENERAL NOVELTY LTD
COACH HOUSE GIFTS
420 E 58th Ave Ste 200, Denver, CO 80216-1400
Tel (303) 292-5537 *Founded/Ownrshp* 1989
Sales NA *EMP* 1,400
SIC 5947

D-U-N-S 79-252-5615
■ **GENERAL NUTRITION CENTERS INC**
GNC
(*Suby of* GNC HOLDINGS INC) ★
300 6th Ave, Pittsburgh, PA 15222-2514
Tel (412) 288-4600 *Founded/Ownrshp* 2007
Sales 2.4MMM[E] *EMP* 13,800
SIC 5499 2023 Health & dietetic food stores; Dietary supplements, dairy & non-dairy based
Sr VP: Curt Larrimer
**Sr VP:* Michael Locke
VP: Jennifer Brinker

D-U-N-S 60-671-0960 IMP
■ **GENERAL NUTRITION COMPANIES INC**
(*Suby of* GNC INC) ★
300 6th Ave, Pittsburgh, PA 15222-2514
Tel (412) 288-4600 *Founded/Ownrshp* 2003
Sales 605.2MM[E] *EMP* 7,500
SIC 5499 Health & dietetic food stores; Health foods; Dietetic foods
Pr: Louis Mancini
**Pr:* Joseph Fortunato
**Treas:* J Kenneth Fox
**Ex VP:* Michael K Meyers
**Sr VP:* John A Dicecco
**VP:* David R Heilman
**VP:* Curtis J Larrimer
**VP:* Eileen D Scott
MIS Dir: Gerald Werner Jr
Board of Directors: Ken Fox

D-U-N-S 01-496-0165 IMP/EXP
■ **GENERAL NUTRITION CORP**
GNC
(*Suby of* GNC) ★
300 6th Ave, Pittsburgh, PA 15222-2514
Tel (412) 288-4600 *Founded/Ownrshp* 1989
Sales 1.0MMM[E] *EMP* 7,000
SIC 5499 5999 5941 5699 6794 Health & dietetic food stores; Health foods; Dietetic foods; Cosmetics; Hair care products; Exercise equipment; Sports apparel; Franchises, selling or licensing
VP: Michael Nuzzo
Pr: Amanda Skov
CFO: William E Watts
**Treas:* Mary Ellen Costa
Treas: Edwin J Kozlowski
Ex VP: Tom Dowd
Ex VP: Jeffrey Hennion
Sr VP: Anthony Phillips
Sr VP: Guru Ramanathan
Sr VP: Carl Seletz
VP: Shawn Cupples
VP: Ronald Hallock
VP: Lou Mancini
VP: Jeff Sieber

D-U-N-S 00-320-1480 IMP/EXP
■ **GENERAL PARTS INC** (NC)
CARQUEST AUTO PARTS
(*Suby of* ADVANCE AUTO PARTS INC) ★
2635 E Millbrook Rd Ste C, Raleigh, NC 27604-2989
Tel (919) 573-3000 *Founded/Ownrshp* 1960, 2014
Sales 2.2MMM[E] *EMP* 17,000
SIC 5013 5531

D-U-N-S 18-426-7248
■ **GENERAL PARTS INTERNATIONAL INC**
CARQUEST
(*Suby of* ADVANCE AUTO PARTS INC) ★
2635 E Millbrook Rd Ste B, Raleigh, NC 27604-2989
Tel (919) 573-3000 *Founded/Ownrshp* 2014
Sales 2.4MMM[E] *EMP* 18,000
SIC 5013

GENERAL PERFORMANCE PRODUCTS
See CHEMTRADE CHEMICALS CORP

D-U-N-S 00-397-0621
GENERAL PET SUPPLY INC (WI)
(*Suby of* MERCO GROUP INC) ★
7711 N 81st St, Milwaukee, WI 53223-3847
Tel (414) 365-3400 *Founded/Ownrshp* 1989
Sales 115.3MM[E] *EMP* 220
SIC 5199 Pet supplies
Pr: Bob Merar
**Treas:* Erwin Merar
**Ex VP:* David Merar
IT Man: Dan Henry
Sls Dir: B Cohn

D-U-N-S 02-934-5865 IMP
GENERAL PETROLEUM CORP
G P RESOURCES
(*Suby of* SC FUELS) ★
19501 S Santa Fe Ave, Compton, CA 90221-5913
Tel (562) 983-7300 *Founded/Ownrshp* 2006
Sales 87.6MM[E] *EMP* 225
SIC 5172 Petroleum products
CEO: James A Halsam III
**Pr:* Michael Ruehring
CFO: Scott Smith
Sr VP: Charles McDaniel
Sr VP: Charles McDaniels
**VP:* Sean Kha
Genl Mgr: Mark Mason
Genl Mgr: Kathleen Ross
CTO: Kerry Cashman
S&M/VP: Anthony Mardesich
Sls Mgr: Chris Willig

GENERAL PLASTICS
See PLASTIC SERVICES AND PRODUCTS

D-U-N-S 04-112-5402 EXP
GENERAL PLASTICS & COMPOSITES LP
GP&C
6910 E Orem Dr, Houston, TX 77075-5326
Tel (713) 644-1449 *Founded/Ownrshp* 1967
Sales 103.2MM[E] *EMP* 150
SIC 3083 Laminated plastics plate & sheet
CEO: David Walstad
**Pr:* Simon Lawrie
CFO: Rob Degeyter
VP Mfg: Jerry Retallick
VP Mfg: Ron Seifert
Mtls Mgr: Shane Sensky
Ql Cn Mgr: Mark Cox

D-U-N-S 01-108-3102
GENERAL PLUMBING SUPPLY INC
980 New Durham Rd, Edison, NJ 08817-2274
Tel (732) 248-1000 *Founded/Ownrshp* 1996
Sales 159.4MM[E] *EMP* 140
Accts Rs Kaplan & Company Woodbri
SIC 5075 5074 Warm air heating & air conditioning; Plumbing & hydronic heating supplies
Pr: Bruce Tucker
VP: Justin Freedman
**VP:* Gary Kuperstein
**VP:* Joseph Novack
VP: Joe Novak

D-U-N-S 96-357-6095 IMP
GENERAL PROCUREMENT INC
CONNECT COMPUTERS
800 E Dyer Rd, Santa Ana, CA 92705-5604
Tel (949) 679-7960 *Founded/Ownrshp* 1996
Sales 150.0MM[E] *EMP* 50[E]
Accts Jack Runke Cpa San Diego Ca
SIC 5045 Computers, peripherals & software
Pr: Imad Boukai
**VP:* Sam Boukai
Dir Bus: Janet Carmona

D-U-N-S 00-886-1379 IMP/EXP
GENERAL PRODUCE CO A CALIFORNIA LIMITED PARTNERSHIP (CA)
1330 N B St, Sacramento, CA 95811-0605
Tel (916) 441-6431 *Founded/Ownrshp* 1933
Sales 99.4MM[E] *EMP* 225
SIC 5148 Fruits, fresh; Vegetables, fresh
CEO: Tom Chan
**Pr:* Dan Chan
VP: Willard Harrison
**VP:* Don Weersing
**VP:* Sheryl Weichert
VP: Chuck Wilkinson
Genl Mgr: Jerry Sharon

D-U-N-S 00-167-3409
■ **GENERAL RE CORP**
(*Suby of* GENERAL REINSURANCE CORP) ★
120 Long Ridge Rd, Stamford, CT 06902-1839
Tel (203) 352-3000 *Founded/Ownrshp* 1921
Sales NA *EMP* 1,000[E]
SIC 6331 Fire, marine & casualty insurance
CEO: Franklin Tad Montross
**Pr:* John Cholnoky
Pr: Kathleen Crowley
Pr: Bill Guttman
Pr: Damon Vocke
CEO: Tad Montross
Treas: Eckhard A V Lkening
Ex VP: William Gasdaska Jr
Ex VP: Damon N Vocke
Sr VP: Janice Englesbe
Sr VP: Dan Lyons
**Sr VP:* Timothy Mc Caffrey
Sr VP: A Morris Tooker
VP: Amanda Aley
VP: Ralph Barbieri
VP: Kimberly Burnham
VP: Chris Callaway
VP: Anthony Clark
VP: Marc P Dahling
VP: Jolie Degrandpre
VP: Jacqueline Dimatteo
Board of Directors: Peter Lutke-Bornefeld, Salvatore R Curiale, William G Gasdaska, Winfried Heinen, Steven J Mannik, Tad Montross, Patricia H Roberts, Damon N Vocke

D-U-N-S 03-046-8565
■ **GENERAL REINSURANCE CORP**
(*Suby of* BERKSHIRE HATHAWAY INC) ★
120 Long Ridge Rd, Stamford, CT 06902-1843
Tel (203) 328-5000 *Founded/Ownrshp* 1998
Sales NA *EMP* 2,513
SIC 6331 6351 6411 6321

D-U-N-S 79-457-7015
GENERAL ROOFING SERVICES INC
(*Suby of* REPUBLIC FINANCIAL CORP) ★
3300 S Parker Rd Ste 500, Aurora, CO 80014-3522
Tel (303) 923-2200 *Founded/Ownrshp* 2004
Sales 79.5MM[E] *EMP* 1,233[E]
SIC 1761 Roofing contractor
Ch Bd: W Randal Dietrich
**Pr:* Robert Possehl
**Treas:* Ann D Hastings

D-U-N-S 00-653-5017
GENERAL RV CENTER INC (MI)
GENERAL TRAILER
25000 Assembly Park Dr, Wixom, MI 48393-0019
Tel (248) 349-0900 *Founded/Ownrshp* 1956
Sales 287.5MM[E] *EMP* 400
SIC 5561 Recreational vehicle dealers; Travel trailers: automobile, new & used; Recreational vehicle parts & accessories
Pr: Robert S Baidas
**Pr:* Loren Baidas
**CFO:* Katie Short
Opers Mgr: Grant Baidas
Sales Exec: Hal Hall
Mktg Mgr: Dennis Anderson
Sls Mgr: Bill Brown
Sls Mgr: Jason Cohen
Sls Mgr: John Dyer
Sls Mgr: Chris Miller
Sls Mgr: Bruce Terveen

D-U-N-S 00-195-4700 IMP/EXP
■ **GENERAL SERVICES ADMINISTRATION US**
G S A
(*Suby of* EXECUTIVE OFFICE OF UNITED STATES GOVERNMENT) ★
1800 F St Nw Rm 6100, Washington, DC 20405-0001
Tel (202) 501-8880 *Founded/Ownrshp* 1949
Sales NA *EMP* 13,000
SIC 9199 General government administration;
**CFO:* Kathleen M Turco
Ofcr: Richard Banach
Ofcr: Sandra Brooks
Ofcr: Bret Gist
Ofcr: Rachel Wallen
Exec: Charles Stephens
Genl Mgr: Lois Sather
Off Mgr: Gail Brush
CIO: Michael W Carleton
**CIO:* Casey Coleman
CIO: Diane Merriett

D-U-N-S 00-338-3361 IMP
GENERAL SHALE BRICK INC
(*Suby of* WIENERBERGER AG)
3015 Bristol Hwy, Johnson City, TN 37601-1511
Tel (423) 282-4661 *Founded/Ownrshp* 1928, 1999
Sales 550.3MM[E] *EMP* 1,900
SIC 5211 5031 Lumber & other building materials; Brick; Building materials, exterior; Building materials, interior
Pr: Richard L Green
COO: Berry Ron
COO: Dana Schmitt
**VP:* Mark Kinser
**VP:* Charles Smith
Dir Risk M: Brian Ogle
Dist Mgr: Marceron Bill
IT Man: Scott Clark
IT Man: Mike Downing

Info Man: Mickey Bowman
VP Opers: JB Cooper

D-U-N-S 62-080-5390
■ **GENERAL STAR INDEMNITY CO**
(*Suby of* GENERAL REINSURANCE CORP) ★
695 Main St Ste 1, Stamford, CT 06901-2141
Tel (203) 328-5000 *Founded/Ownrshp* 1971
Sales NA *EMP* 4
SIC 6321 Accident & health insurance
Pr: Patricia Roberts
**Ch Bd:* Joseph Patrick Brandon
VP: Ernest C Frohboese
VP: Gary Korsak

D-U-N-S 78-518-4206 IMP
GENERAL SUPPLY & SERVICES INC
GEXPRO
(*Suby of* REXEL HOLDINGS USA CORP) ★
1000 Bridgeport Ave 5-1, Shelton, CT 06484-4660
Tel (203) 925-2400 *Founded/Ownrshp* 2006
Sales 1.5MMM[E] *EMP* 2,077
SIC 5063 8742 Electrical apparatus & equipment; Materials mgmt. (purchasing, handling, inventory) consultant
Pr: Brian P McNally
**Ch Bd:* Christopher P Hartmann
**CEO:* Mitchell D Williams
CFO: Douglas Seymour
**CFO:* Mark Testa
**Treas:* Gary Hibbs
**VP:* Mike Burke
**VP:* Robert Casagrande
**VP:* John Gschwind
VP: William Hoyt
**VP:* Amanda Malburg
VP: Eric Packer
Exec: Jan Corbin

GENERAL SVCS ADMINISTRAITON
See GSA NATIONAL CAPITAL REGION

D-U-N-S 01-135-1681 IMP/EXP
GENERAL TRADING CO INC
455 16th St, Carlstadt, NJ 07072-1922
Tel (201) 935-7717 *Founded/Ownrshp* 1935
Sales 215.3MM[E] *EMP* 420
SIC 5141

GENERAL TRAILER
See GENERAL RV CENTER INC

GENERAL WHOLESALE BEER COMPANY
See GENERAL WHOLESALE CO

D-U-N-S 00-884-7089 IMP
GENERAL WHOLESALE CO
GENERAL WHOLESALE BEER COMPANY
1271 Tacoma Dr Nw, Atlanta, GA 30318-4145
Tel (404) 352-1041 *Founded/Ownrshp* 1982
Sales 118.0MM[E] *EMP* 350
SIC 5182 5181 Liquor; Wine; Beer & other fermented malt liquors
CEO: Jane H Young
**CFO:* William D Young Sr
**CFO:* William D Young Jr
**VP:* E Howard Young
VP: Howard E Young
Sales Exec: Dale Lowenstein

D-U-N-S 94-435-9595
GENERAL YELLOW PAGES CONSULTANTS INC
MARQUETTE GROUP
222 Ne Monroe St Ste 800, Peoria, IL 61602-1066
Tel (309) 677-0400 *Founded/Ownrshp* 1996
Sales 96.0MM[E] *EMP* 225
SIC 7311 Advertising agencies
CEO: Chris Cummings
**Pr:* Eric Webb
COO: Duane Anderson
**CFO:* Theresa Lafontaine
VP: Marti Janson
Opers Mgr: Laura Rhoades
Sls Dir: Chris Malone

GENERAL-DYNAMICS-IT
See VANGENT INC

GENERALLY YOURS GIFT SHOP
See BRYAN HEALTH WEST CAMPUS

D-U-N-S 82-744-2281
GENERIC DRUG HOLDINGS INC
(*Suby of* COURT SQUARE CAPITAL PARTNERS LP) ★
31778 Enterprise Dr, Livonia, MI 48150-1960
Tel (734) 743-6000 *Founded/Ownrshp* 2010
Sales 489.0MM[E] *EMP* 450
Accts Grant Thornton Llp Southfield
SIC 8734 5122 5047 Testing laboratories; Pharmaceuticals; Medical & hospital equipment
CEO: Terry Haas
**Pr:* Jay Levine
**CFO:* David F Liming
VP: John H Heidel

D-U-N-S 82-846-4474 IMP
GENERICS INTERNATIONAL (US) INC
QUALITEST PHARMACEUTICALS
(*Suby of* ENDO PHARMACEUTICALS INC) ★
130 Vintage Dr Ne, Huntsville, AL 35811-8216
Tel (256) 859-2575 *Founded/Ownrshp* 2010
Sales 384.3MM[E] *EMP* 1,232
SIC 2834 Pharmaceutical preparations
Pr: Rajiv De Silva
Sr VP: Blaine Davis
VP: Samba Sow
Dir Surg: Diane Servello
Genl Mgr: Darren Hall
Plnt Mgr: Aaron Ayres
Prd Mgr: Mark Riegel
Ql Cn Mgr: Kelly Key
Snr Mgr: Dewayne McDonald

D-U-N-S 00-136-7549 IMP/EXP
▲ **GENESCO INC** (TN)
JOURNEYS KIDZ
1415 Murfreesboro Pike, Nashville, TN 37217-2829
Tel (615) 367-7000 *Founded/Ownrshp* 1934
Sales 3.0MMM *EMP* 27,500
Accts Ernst & Young Llp Nashville
Tkr Sym GCO *Exch* NYS
SIC 5661 5139 5961 Shoe stores; Footwear; Catalog & mail-order houses
Ch Bd: Robert J Dennis
CFO: Mimi Eckel Vaughn
Treas: Matthew N Johnson
Sr VP: Roger G Sisson
VP: Parag Desai
VP: James Gulmi
VP: Jean Holness
VP: Kari Irons
VP: Mara Kennedy
VP: Blaine Lucas
VP: Ted Macias
VP: Alice McClellan
VP: Jeff Munzel
VP: Jeff Schenkel
VP: Scott Symington
VP: Paul D Williams
VP: Paul Williams
Board of Directors: David M Tehle, Joanna Barsh, James S Beard, Leonard L Berry, James W Bradford, Matthew C Diamond, Marty G Dickens, Thurgood Marshall Jr, Kathleen Mason, Kevin P McDermott

D-U-N-S 09-360-9113
▲ **GENESEE & WYOMING INC**
20 West Ave, Darien, CT 06820-4401
Tel (203) 202-8900 *Founded/Ownrshp* 1899
Sales 1.6MMM *EMP* 5,338[E]
Tkr Sym GWR *Exch* NYS
SIC 4011 4013 Railroads, line-haul operating; Switching & terminal services
Pr: John C Hellmann
Pr: Richard Christopher
Pr: John Kincaid
COO: David A Brown
COO: David Brown
CFO: Timothy J Gallagher
CFO: John P Lockwood
CFO: Luis Pacheco
Ofcr: Michael O Miller
Ex VP: Mark W Hastings
Sr VP: Charles W Chabot
Sr VP: Dave Ebbrecht
Sr VP: Louis Gravel
Sr VP: Bill Jasper
Sr VP: Martin D Lacombe
Sr VP: Mike Meyers
Sr VP: Dewayne Swindall
Sr VP: Paul M Victor
Sr VP: Matthew O Walsh
VP: Kenneth Charron
VP: Andy Chunko

D-U-N-S 06-394-6651
GENESEE COUNTY OF (INC)
15 Main St, Batavia, NY 14020-2136
Tel (585) 344-2550 *Founded/Ownrshp* 1802
Sales NA *EMP* 1,000
Accts Freedmaxick Cpas Pc Batavi
SIC 9111
**Treas:* Scott German
Genl Mgr: Kevin Andrews

D-U-N-S 06-982-5826
GENESEE INTERMEDIATE SCHOOL DISTRICT
ELMER A. KNOPF LEARNING CENTER
2413 W Maple Ave, Flint, MI 48507-3429
Tel (810) 591-4400 *Founded/Ownrshp* 1962
Sales 162.0MM[E] *EMP* 1,500
SIC 8211 Public combined elementary & secondary school
Treas: Cindy Gansen
VP: Jerry Ragsdale
Off Mgr: Cindy McClain
MIS Dir: Beverly Knox-Pipes
IT Man: Barbara Stewart

D-U-N-S 02-261-0718
GENESEE REGION HOME CARE ASSOCIATION INC
165 Court St, Rochester, NY 14647-0001
Tel (585) 238-4399 *Founded/Ownrshp* 2008
Sales 97.0MM *EMP* 2
SIC 8699 Membership organizations
Prin: John Biemiller

D-U-N-S 07-969-7991
GENESEE REGION HOME CARE ASSOCIATION INC (NY)
LIFETIME CARE
3111 Winton Rd S, Rochester, NY 14623-2905
Tel (585) 214-1000 *Founded/Ownrshp* 1960
Sales 97.1MM *EMP* 925
SIC 8082 Home health care services
Pr: Patricia Heffernan
**VP:* John Cauvel
**VP:* Nancy Horn
**VP:* Terrence Tehan

GENESEE ROAD COMMISSION
See COUNTY OF GENESEE

D-U-N-S 07-367-1000
GENESEE VALLEY GROUP HEALTH ASSOCIATION
LIFETIME HEALTH
800 Carter St, Rochester, NY 14621-2604
Tel (585) 338-1400 *Founded/Ownrshp* 1972
Sales 107.9MM *EMP* 576
SIC 8011 Health maintenance organization
Pr: Patricia L Bonino
CFO: Deke Duda
Telecom Ex: Chris Olsen
IT Man: James Lesure
IT Man: Brenda Rogers
Doctor: Farokh Foroozesh-Banej
Doctor: Pradip Kadakia
Doctor: David Lewin
Doctor: Steven Rich
Doctor: Edward Sassaman
Doctor: James Schuster

D-U-N-S 09-756-9136
GENESH INC
BURGER KING
8831 Long St, Lenexa, KS 66215-3586
Tel (913) 492-0007 *Founded/Ownrshp* 1999
Sales 42.5MM[E] *EMP* 1,000
SIC 5812 Fast-food restaurant, chain
Pr: Mukesh Dharod

GENESIS
See BREYUT CONVALESCENT CENTER INC

D-U-N-S 82-810-6422
GENESIS
1273 W Derrynane St, Le Center, MN 56057-4391
Tel (507) 357-6868 *Founded/Ownrshp* 2008
Sales 92.1MM *EMP* 2
Accts Carlson Highland & Co Llp
SIC 7359 Propane equipment rental
Prin: Joe Spinler

GENESIS 10
See GENESIS CORP

D-U-N-S 07-741-2331
GENESIS CORP
GENESIS 10
950 3rd Ave Ste 2702, New York, NY 10022-2874
Tel (212) 688-5522 *Founded/Ownrshp* 1999
Sales 179.7MM *EMP* 2,105
Accts Cohnreznick New York Ny
SIC 7379 8742 Computer related consulting services; Management consulting services
CEO: Harley Lippman
Mng Pt: James Heller
COO: Michael Rapken
**CFO:* Glenn Klein
Ex VP: Matt McBride
Sr VP: Mark Murphy
Ex Dir: Yav Millet
Prac Mgr: Derik Mantel
IT Man: AMI Sarnowski
Tech Mgr: William Schenck
Sales Exec: Hillary Barr

D-U-N-S 96-631-5640 IMP
■ **GENESIS CRUDE OIL LP**
(*Suby of* GENESIS ENERGY LP) ★
919 Milam St Ste 2100, Houston, TX 77002-5417
Tel (713) 860-2500 *Founded/Ownrshp* 1996
Sales 116.2MM[E] *EMP* 185
Accts Deloitte & Touche Llp Housto
SIC 4612 Crude petroleum pipelines
CEO: Grant E Sims
Pt: Mark Gorman
Pr: Steve Nathanson
CFO: Robert V Deere
Sr VP: Karen N Pape
VP: Kerry Mazoch
VP: Astanley Stanley
Sales Exec: Paul Fowler

D-U-N-S 61-031-1557
■ **GENESIS ELDER CARE REHABILATION SERVICES INC**
(*Suby of* GENESIS HEALTHCARE CORP) ★
101 E State St, Kennett Square, PA 19348-3109
Tel (610) 925-4598 *Founded/Ownrshp* 1986
Sales 32.5MM[E] *EMP* 2,100
SIC 8049 8093 Physical therapist; Rehabilitation center, outpatient treatment
Pr: George Hagger
IT Man: Maryann Kurowski

D-U-N-S 03-543-4356 IMP
■ **GENESIS ELDERCARE NATIONAL CENTERS INC** (FL)
(*Suby of* GENESIS HEALTHCARE CORP) ★
101 E State St, Kennett Square, PA 19348-3109
Tel (610) 444-6350 *Founded/Ownrshp* 1981, 2003
Sales 1.0MMM[E] *EMP* 35,000
SIC 8051 8361 Skilled nursing care facilities; Home for the aged
Pr: George V Hager
CFO: George Hagar
**Treas:* Rick Edwards
Ex VP: George V Cathey
VP: Lewis Hoch
Obsttrcn: Marc Rubinbger

D-U-N-S 96-296-5406
▲ **GENESIS ENERGY LP**
919 Milam St Ste 2100, Houston, TX 77002-5417
Tel (713) 860-2500 *Founded/Ownrshp* 1996
Sales 2.2MMM *EMP* 1,400[E]
Tkr Sym GEL *Exch* NYS
SIC 4612 5171 4212 Crude petroleum pipelines; Petroleum bulk stations & terminals; Petroleum haulage, local
Ch Bd: Grant E Sims
Genl Pt: Genesis Energy
CFO: Robert V Deere
Sr VP: Paul A Davis
VP: Richard R Alexander
VP: Jim Buford
VP: William S Goloway
VP: Karen Pape
VP: Stephen M Smith
CIO: Ed Chamras
CTO: Kenneth Farley

D-U-N-S 17-759-7564
GENESIS ENGINEERS INC
1850 Gravers Rd Ste 300, Plymouth Meeting, PA 19462-2837
Tel (610) 592-0280 *Founded/Ownrshp* 1997
Sales 98.4MM[E] *EMP* 3,100
SIC 8711 8741 Engineering services; Construction management
Pr: Bernard Friel
**Treas:* Anthony J Macchia
**VP:* Michael J Dapkunas
**VP:* Joseph W O'Donnell

D-U-N-S 10-187-0251
GENESIS HEALTH INC
BROOKS HEALTH SYSTEM
3599 University Blvd S # 1, Jacksonville, FL 32216-4259
Tel (904) 858-7600 *Founded/Ownrshp* 1982
Sales 37.3MM *EMP* 1,400
Accts Dixon Hughes Goodman Llp Ash
SIC 8069 8011 8741 Specialty hospitals, except psychiatric; Medical centers; General & family practice, physician/surgeon; Management services
Pr: Douglas M Baer
**Ch Bd:* Bruce Johnson
**Pr:* Michael R Spigel
Treas: Tim Reinschmidt
Bd of Dir: Frank Houser
Bd of Dir: Donald Wright
Sr VP: Karen Wright-Bennett
Ex Dir: Brian Fuller
Genl Mgr: Hannah Marshall
IT Man: Janet Collins
Doctor: Leif Lohrbauer

D-U-N-S 10-738-2301
GENESIS HEALTH SYSTEM
1227 E Rusholme St, Davenport, IA 52803-2459
Tel (563) 421-1000 *Founded/Ownrshp* 1994
Sales 503.8MM *EMP* 5,000
Accts Mcgladrey Llp Davenport Ia
SIC 8741 8399 7218 Hospital management; Nursing & personal care facility management; Fund raising organization, non-fee basis; Industrial launderers
CEO: Doug Cropper
Dir Recs: Betsy Tibbitts
**Pr:* Leo A Bressanelli
**COO:* Wayne Diewald
**CFO:* Mark Rogers
**Treas:* Greg Bush
**Sr VP:* Flo Spyrow
**VP:* Jackie Anhalt
**VP:* Kenneth Croken
VP: Beth Fox
**VP:* Robert Frieden
**VP:* Peter Metcalf
VP: Rob Nelson
VP: Judy Pranger
VP: Jackie A Rn-Bc
VP: Mike Sharp
VP: Florence Spyrow
VP: Robert Travis
Exec: Myron Higgins
Dir Case M: Linda Fenelly
Dir Lab: Kelly Sparks

D-U-N-S 79-337-5932
GENESIS HEALTH SYSTEMS
CROSSTOWN SQUARE
1455 Hospital Rd, Silvis, IL 61282-1834
Tel (309) 281-3270 *Founded/Ownrshp* 1991
Sales 86.9MM *EMP* 75
Accts Mcgladrey Llp Davenport Ia
SIC 8051 8059 Skilled nursing care facilities; Nursing home, except skilled & intermediate care facility

GENESIS HEALTHCARE
See FC-GEN ACQUISITION INC

D-U-N-S 13-235-4460 IMP
■ GENESIS HEALTHCARE CORP
(*Suby of* GENESIS HEALTHCARE) ★
101 E State St, Kennett Square, PA 19348-3109
Tel (610) 444-6350 *Founded/Ownrshp* 2008
Sales 6.5MMM^E *EMP* 35,000
SIC 8051 8361 Skilled nursing care facilities; Extended care facility; Home for the aged; Rehabilitation center, residential: health care incidental
Ch Bd: George V Hager Jr
Pr: Shawn Eddy
Pr: Laurence Lane
Pr: Robert Reitz
Pr: Ken Silverwood
CFO: James V McKeon
Chf Mktg O: Pat Crawford
Ofcr: Janice Rotondo
Ofcr: Mary Thomas
Ex VP: Paul Bach
Sr VP: David Bertha
Sr VP: Richard Castor
Sr VP: Eileen Coggins
Sr VP: Eileen M Coggins
Sr VP: Barbara J Hauswald
Sr VP: Wendy Labate
Sr VP: Richard Pell Jr
Sr VP: Jeanne Phillips
Sr VP: David Polakoff
Sr VP: Michael S Sherman
Sr VP: Lou A Soika

D-U-N-S 79-649-0493
▲ GENESIS HEALTHCARE INC
101 E State St, Kennett Square, PA 19348-3109
Tel (610) 444-6350 *Founded/Ownrshp* 2003
Sales 9.3MMM^E *EMP* 88,700^E
Tkr Sym GEN *Exch* NYS
SIC 8051 8052 8059 8361 Skilled nursing care facilities; Convalescent home with continuous nursing care; Extended care facility; Personal care facility; Nursing home, except skilled & intermediate care facility; Personal care home, with health care; Rehabilitation center, residential: health care incidental
CEO: George V Hager Jr
**Ch Bd:* Steven Fishman
Pr: Dan Hirschfeld
COO: Robert A Reitz
CFO: Thomas Divittorio
Ofcr: Roland G Rapp
Ex VP: Joanne Reifsnyder
Sr VP: Michael S Sherman
Board of Directors: James H Bloem, John F Depodesta, Robert H Fish, Robert Hartman, Joshua Hausman, James V McKeon, David Reis, Glenn S Schafer, Arnold Whitman

D-U-N-S 96-808-6376
■ GENESIS HEALTHCARE LLC
(*Suby of* GENESIS HEALTHCARE) ★
101 E State St, Kennett Square, PA 19348-3109
Tel (610) 444-6350 *Founded/Ownrshp* 2010
Sales 2.6MMM^E *EMP* 80,000
SIC 8051 8099 Skilled nursing care facilities; Medical services organization
**VP:* Richard Edwards
Sls&Mrk Ex: Amy Covello
Mktg Dir: Kortez Kelly
HC Dir: Sharon Glaud

D-U-N-S 12-198-8745
GENESIS HEALTHCARE SYSTEM
BETHESDA CARE
2951 Maple Ave, Zanesville, OH 43701-1406
Tel (740) 454-5000 *Founded/Ownrshp* 1800
Sales 462.0MM *EMP* 3,500
SIC 8082 Home health care services
Pr: Matthew Perry
**COO:* Al Burns
COO: Mike Deming
**CFO:* Paul Masterson
Trst: Brian Luft
Trst: Laura Wolf
Ofcr: Joanne Shumar-Jones
Trst Ofcr: Shirley Vanwye
VP: Clare McKeever
VP: Edmund J Romuto
Exec: Beth Chapman
Exec: Dianna L Leveck
Dir Risk M: Deborah Trimble
Dir Lab: Tammy Bruner
Dir Rx: Greg Hamilton

D-U-N-S 96-749-0897
GENESIS HEALTHCARE SYSTEM
2951 Maple Ave, Zanesville, OH 43701-1406
Tel (740) 454-4000 *Founded/Ownrshp* 1997
Sales 359.1MM *EMP* 2,500
SIC 8062 General medical & surgical hospitals
Pr: Tom Sieber
COO: Chuck Conner
COO: Alan Vierling
Dir Case M: Shellie Haegen
Dir Rad: Charles Muchnok
Dir Rad: Edmond Ru
Chf Nrs Of: Pat Campbell
Nurse Mgr: Barb Powell
VP Mktg: Craig Worstall

D-U-N-S 05-580-4389 IMP
GENESIS MEDICAL CENTER
FIRST MED CLINIC
(*Suby of* GENESIS HEALTH SYSTEM) ★
1227 E Rusholme St, Davenport, IA 52803-2459
Tel (563) 421-6000 *Founded/Ownrshp* 1994
Sales 266.1MM^E *EMP* 2,397
Accts Mcgladrey Llp Davenport Ia
SIC 8062 Hospital, affiliated with AMA residency
Pr: Wayne A Diewald
**Pr:* Leo A Bressanelli
**CEO:* Doug Cropper
**VP:* George Kovach
**VP:* Mike Sharp
MIS Dir: Bob Hofmann
Dir IT: Dean Hiles
Doctor: Christopher Posey

D-U-N-S 10-339-0717
GENESIS NETWORKS ENTERPRISES LLC
600 N Loop 1604 E, San Antonio, TX 78232-1268
Tel (210) 489-6600 *Founded/Ownrshp* 2001
Sales 88.9MM^E *EMP* 800
SIC 7373 Systems integration services
CEO: James Goodman
**Pr:* Sean Nelson
**Pr:* Mark Viertel
**CEO:* Todd Richard
**CFO:* Cathy Kincy
**CFO:* Perry Uhles
**Treas:* Phil Schubert
**VP:* Steve Griffith
**VP:* John Homsey
VP: John Johnson
CTO: Carsky Makarwich

D-U-N-S 83-294-2986
GENESIS PURE INC
GOYIN INTERNATIONAL
7164 Tech Dr Ste 100, Frisco, TX 75033
Tel (469) 213-2900 *Founded/Ownrshp* 2011
Sales 201.2MM^E *EMP* 90^E
SIC 5122 Vitamins & minerals; Drugs & drug proprietaries
Pr: Bobby Love
**COO:* Bill Shuler
**CFO:* Dave Bricker
**VP:* Brooks Gordon
**VP:* John Saldana
**VP:* Jinhee Woo
CIO: James Porter
Software D: Nathan Yeung

D-U-N-S 04-421-5663
GENESIS REHABILITATION HOSPITAL INC
BROOKS REHABILITATION
3599 University Blvd S # 1, Jacksonville, FL 32216-4252
Tel (904) 858-7600 *Founded/Ownrshp* 1983
Sales 86.8MM *EMP* 422
SIC 8063 8069 8051 Hospital for the mentally ill; Specialty hospitals, except psychiatric; Skilled nursing care facilities
Ex Dir: Stephen K Wilson
**Pr:* Michael Spigel
Treas: Doug Baer
Exec: Karen Gallagher
**Prin:* Stanley Carter
**Prin:* Bruce M Johnson
IT Man: Jayne Shults
IT Man: Jayne West
Web Prj Mg: Laurie Smith

D-U-N-S 04-718-2368
GENESIS SECURITY SERVICE
5900 Ave Isla Verde L, Carolina, PR 00979-5746
Tel (787) 701-2830 *Founded/Ownrshp* 2010
Sales 47.7MM^E *EMP* 4,700
SIC 7381 Detective & armored car services
CEO: Roberto Morales
**Pr:* Emilio Morales

D-U-N-S 83-158-9200 IMP
■ GENESIS SOLAR LLC
(*Suby of* NEXTERA ENERGY RESOURCES LLC) ★
700 Universe Blvd, Juno Beach, FL 33408-2657
Tel (561) 691-3062 *Founded/Ownrshp* 2011
Sales 697.1MM^E *EMP* 34^E
SIC 4911 Electric services

D-U-N-S 00-370-4830 IMP
■ GENESYS CONFERENCING INC
(*Suby of* INTERCALL)
8020 Towers Crescent Dr, Vienna, VA 22182-6224
Tel (703) 749-2500 *Founded/Ownrshp* 1996
Sales 109.6MM^E *EMP* 600
SIC 4813 Long distance telephone communications
Ch Bd: Francois Legros
**CFO:* Andrew G Lazarus
Sr VP: Steve Rust
VP: Clarissa A Peterson
VP: John D Polcari
VP: David TSO
VP: Gary G Vilardi
Dir Bus: Kurt Magdanz
Ex Dir: Joyce Finkenbiner
IT Man: Jonathan Cottingham
VP Sls: Kevin O'Brien

D-U-N-S 96-141-8878 IMP
GENESYS HEALTH SYSTEM
PEDIATRIC SPECIALTY CLINIC
(*Suby of* ASCENSION HEALTH) ★
1 Genesys Pkwy, Grand Blanc, MI 48439-8065
Tel (810) 606-5710 *Founded/Ownrshp* 1980
Sales 419.0MM^E *EMP* 5,000
SIC 8062 General medical & surgical hospitals
Ch: Roger Samuel
Chf Rad: John Morrison
**Pr:* Young S Suh
**CEO:* Elizabeth Aderholbt
**Treas:* John Boles
**Treas:* William Lovejoy
Trst: Juan Mestas
Trst: Gerald Selke
VP: Dave Caudle
VP: Curtis Clark
VP: Joy Finkenbinder
VP: Joann Herman
Dir Rad: Michelle Newman

D-U-N-S 06-982-8507
GENESYS REGIONAL MEDICAL CENTER
PEDIATRIC SPECIALTY CLINIC
(*Suby of* PEDIATRIC SPECIALTY CLINIC) ★
1 Genesys Pkwy, Grand Blanc, MI 48439-8065
Tel (810) 606-5000 *Founded/Ownrshp* 2000
Sales 403.9MM *EMP* 3,739
Accts Deloitte Tax Lp Cincinnati O
SIC 8062 General medical & surgical hospitals
Pr: Mark Taylor
**CFO:* David Carrol
Ofcr: Greg Murray
Sr VP: Denny Fischer
VP: Nicholas Evans
VP: Rick Felts
VP: Tammy Saunaitis
Dir Rx: Joy Finkenbiner
Genl Mgr: Jay Berry
Off Mgr: Chris Burns
Dir IT: Jan Capita

GENESYS TELECOM LABS
See GENESYS TELECOMMUNICATIONS LABORATORIES INC

D-U-N-S 62-228-6318
GENESYS TELECOMMUNICATIONS LABORATORIES INC
GENESYS TELECOM LABS
(*Suby of* PERMIRA ADVISERS LLP)
2001 Junipero Serra Blvd, Daly City, CA 94014-3891
Tel (650) 466-1100 *Founded/Ownrshp* 2012
Sales 923.5MM^E *EMP* 3,500
SIC 7372 Business oriented computer software
CEO: Paul Segre
**Pr:* Tom Eggemeier
COO: James W Budge
**Chf Cred:* David Sudbey
**Chf Mktg O:* Reed Henry
Ofcr: Jim Ren
Ex VP: Steve Pollock
Ex VP: David Rennyson
VP: John Carr
VP: Tracy Coti
VP: Bruce Eidsvik
VP: Eric Entzeroth
VP: Craig Farquharson
VP: Alberto Fernandez
VP: Madan Gadde
VP: Brian Hays
VP: Karl Holzthum
VP: Lisa Kost
VP: Mikhail Nekorystnov
VP: Keith Pearce
VP: Chanchal Samanta

D-U-N-S 02-144-0672
GENEVA COMMUNITY UNIT SCHOOL DISTRICT 304
227 N 4th St, Geneva, IL 60134-1307
Tel (630) 463-3000 *Founded/Ownrshp* 1953
Sales 101.9MM *EMP* 460
SIC 8211 Public elementary & secondary schools
VP: Kelly Nowak
Dir IT: Sheila Finch
Dir IT: Elizabeth Janowiak
Psych: Amy Gyllborg
Psych: Stefany Montgomery

D-U-N-S 06-602-3057
GENEVA ENTERPRISES INC
1902 Association Dr, Reston, VA 20191-1502
Tel (703) 553-4300 *Founded/Ownrshp* 1986, 1990
Sales 321.6MM^E *EMP* 1,000
SIC 5511 New & used car dealers
Ch Bd: Robert Rosenthal
**Pr:* Donald Bavely
**CFO:* Steve Farouz
**VP:* Jerry Griffin

GENEVA GENERAL HOSPITAL
See FINGER LAKES REGIONAL HEALTH SYSTEM INC

D-U-N-S 05-596-0710
GENEVA GENERAL HOSPITAL
196 North St, Geneva, NY 14456-1694
Tel (315) 787-4000 *Founded/Ownrshp* 1892
Sales 103.2MM *EMP* 870
Accts Bonadio & Co Llp Pittsford
SIC 8062 General medical & surgical hospitals
Pr: James Dooley
**CFO:* Lawrence Farnand
VP: Eileen Gage
Adm Dir: Rebecca Mack
Dir IT: Barbara Taney

D-U-N-S 09-922-8553 IMP
GENEVA HOLDINGS INC
8015 Piedmont Triad Pkwy, Greensboro, NC 27409-9407
Tel (336) 275-9936 *Founded/Ownrshp* 1979
Sales 105.7MM *EMP* 400
SIC 5084 5063

D-U-N-S 04-283-5439
GENEVA ROCK PRODUCTS INC
(*Suby of* CLYDE COMPANIES INC) ★
302 W 5400 S Ste 201, Murray, UT 84107-8237
Tel (801) 765-7800 *Founded/Ownrshp* 1954
Sales 511.2MM^E *EMP* 1,000
SIC 5032 Concrete mixtures; Asphalt mixture; Gravel
Pr: James Golding
**Treas:* Don Magee
**VP:* Carl C Clyde
**VP:* Jay Ritchie
**VP:* Nathan Schellenberg
IT Man: David Smith

GENEVA WATCH GROUP
See AWC LIQUIDATING CO

D-U-N-S 05-667-7446
GENEVE CORP
(*Suby of* GENEVE HOLDINGS INC) ★
96 Cummings Point Rd, Stamford, CT 06902-7975
Tel (203) 358-8000 *Founded/Ownrshp* 1986
Sales 279.9MM^E *EMP* 1,150
SIC 5961 3483 6282 Educational supplies & equipment, mail order; Mail order house; Ammunition components; Investment counselors
Pr: F Peter Zoch III
**Ch Bd:* Edward Netter
**Sr VP:* Robert T Keiser
**Sr VP:* Steven P Lapin
**VP:* Ronald G Strackbein

D-U-N-S 06-496-0966 IMP/EXP
GENEVE HOLDINGS INC
96 Cummings Point Rd, Stamford, CT 06902-7919
Tel (203) 358-8000 *Founded/Ownrshp* 1971
Sales 279.9MM^E *EMP* 1,750
SIC 3462 6331 Ordnance forgings, ferrous; Fire, marine & casualty insurance & carriers
Ch Bd: Edward Netter
**Pr:* F Peter Zoch II
COO: Steven B Lapin
**VP:* Robert Keiser
Doctor: Wendy Tsai

D-U-N-S 13-494-6461
GENEX COOPERATIVE INC
(*Suby of* C R I) ★
100 Mbc Dr, Shawano, WI 54166-6095
Tel (715) 526-2141 *Founded/Ownrshp* 1999
Sales 150.8MM *EMP* 777
Accts Wipfli Llp Appleton Wi
SIC 0751 5159 Artificial insemination services, livestock; Semen, bovine
CEO: Keith Heikes
**COO:* R Douglas Wilson
CFO: Joy Wyman
**VP:* Joel Amdall
**VP:* John Ruedinger
**VP:* Brown Swiss
**VP:* David Watkins
Mktg Mgr: Briana Schumacher
Sls Mgr: Greg Hoffman

D-U-N-S 09-684-3842
GENEX SERVICES LLC
(*Suby of* APAX PARTNERS LP) ★
440 E Swedesford Rd # 1000, Wayne, PA 19087-1896
Tel (610) 964-5100 *Founded/Ownrshp* 2014
Sales NA *EMP* 2,075
SIC 6411 Advisory services, insurance
Pr: Peter C Madeja
CFO: John D Keohane
Ex VP: Delphia B Frisch
Sr VP: Stanley S Jakubowski
VP: Christopher G Darrell
VP: Paul E Neff
VP: Danielle Shaw
Exec: Erik Nilson
Prgrm Mgr: Marjorie Portnoy
Brnch Mgr: Holly Andersen
Brnch Mgr: Becky Bireline

D-U-N-S 07-888-2781
GENGOTEX CORP
12301 Old Columbia Pike, Silver Spring, MD 20904-1656
Tel (240) 753-5497 *Founded/Ownrshp* 2013
Sales 100.0MM *EMP* 1
SIC 7389
CEO: Victor Igwe

GENIE, A TEREX COMPANY
See GENIE HOLDINGS INC

GENIE COMPANY, THE
See GMI HOLDINGS INC

D-U-N-S 96-955-3424
▲ GENIE ENERGY LTD
550 Broad St, Newark, NJ 07102-4531
Tel (973) 438-3500 *Founded/Ownrshp* 2011
Sales 210.1MM *EMP* 156^E
Accts Bdo Usa Llp Woodbridge New J

Tkr Sym GNE *Exch* NYS
SIC 4911 4924 4931 Electric services; Distribution, electric power; Transmission, electric power; Natural gas distribution; Electric & other services combined
Ch Bd: Howard S Jonas
Pr: Ira Greenstein
CFO: AVI Goldin
V Ch Bd: James A Courter
Ex VP: Michael Jonas
VP Bus Dev: Harold Vinegar
CTO: Alan K Burnham

D-U-N-S 12-081-4178 IMP/EXP
■ GENIE HOLDINGS INC
GENIE, A TEREX COMPANY
(*Suby of* TEREX CORP) ★
18340 Ne 76th St, Redmond, WA 98052-5020
Tel (425) 881-1800 *Founded/Ownrshp* 2002
Sales 732.6MM[E] *EMP* 2,800
SIC 3536 Hand hoists; Hoists
Pr: Ronald M Defeo
**Pr:* Tim Ford
**VP:* Kevin Bradley
**VP:* Eric I Cohen
**VP:* Robert Wylie

D-U-N-S 00-490-4041 IMP/EXP
■ GENIE INDUSTRIES INC (WA)
(*Suby of* GENIE A TEREX CO) ★
18340 Ne 76th St, Redmond, WA 98052-5020
Tel (425) 881-1800 *Founded/Ownrshp* 1966, 2002
Sales 622.4MM[E] *EMP* 1,900
SIC 3536 Hand hoists; Hoists
Pr: Matthew S Fearon
**VP:* Ward Bushnell
**VP:* Gene Dougherty
**VP:* Eric I Cohen
VP: Dave Hubbell
VP: Steve Matuschak
VP: Kevin O'Rilly
**VP:* Robert Wylie
**Prin:* Tim Ford
IT Man: Jeff Porter
Software D: Daniel Fallou

D-U-N-S 12-092-4456 IMP
■ GENIE MANUFACTURING INC
(*Suby of* GENIE A TEREX CO) ★
18340 Ne 76th St, Redmond, WA 98052-5020
Tel (425) 881-1800 *Founded/Ownrshp* 2006
Sales 82.7MM[E] *EMP* 1,800
SIC 3531 Aerial work platforms: hydraulic/elec. truck/carrier mounted
Pr: Robert Wilkerson
**Pr:* Tim Ford

D-U-N-S 17-978-0460
GENISYS SOFTWARE LTD
1345 Ave Of The Americas, New York, NY 10105-0302
Tel (732) 635-7132 *Founded/Ownrshp* 2000
Sales 40.4MM[E] *EMP* 1,270[E]
SIC 7371 7372 5734 Computer software development; Application computer software; Business oriented computer software; Computer & software stores
CEO: Ashok J Raberu
**Pr:* Lingaraj URS
**CEO:* Ashok J Rabheru
**VP:* Jaspreet Bedi

D-U-N-S 13-048-3597 IMP/EXP
GENLYTE GROUP INC
GLYT
(*Suby of* PHILIPS LIGHTING N.V.)
3000 Minuteman Rd, Andover, MA 01810-1032
Tel (781) 418-7900 *Founded/Ownrshp* 2008
Sales 420.2MM[E] *EMP* 5,000[E]
SIC 3646 3645 3648 Ceiling systems, luminous; Residential lighting fixtures; Lighting equipment
Pr: Larry K Powers
**CFO:* William G Ferko
Treas: Rene Marineau
Sr VP: Bill Wilson
VP: Mitchell Bloomberg
**VP:* Zia Eftekhar
VP: William Fabbri
VP: Ronald D Schneider
Dir Surg: Leverda Wallace
Dir Lab: Ashok Tewari
Creative D: Paul Neervoort

D-U-N-S 03-309-4678 IMP/EXP
GENLYTE THOMAS GROUP LLC
PHILIPS ENTERTAINMENT LIGHTING
(*Suby of* COLOR KINETICS) ★
200 Franklin Pk Sq Dr, Somerset, NJ 08875
Tel (800) 825-5844 *Founded/Ownrshp* 2008
Sales 421.3MM[E] *EMP* 410
SIC 3646 Commercial indusl & institutional electric lighting fixtures; Ceiling systems, luminous; Ornamental lighting fixtures, commercial; Fluorescent lighting fixtures, commercial
CFO: Bill Ferko
VP: George Preston
VP: Jeff Truax
Dir Surg: Leverda Wallace
VP Sls: Guy Petruccelli

D-U-N-S 80-534-5217
GENNX360 CAPITAL PARTNERS LP
590 Madison Ave Fl 27, New York, NY 10022-2544
Tel (212) 257-6772 *Founded/Ownrshp* 2006
Sales 123.7MM[E] *EMP* 175
SIC 6282 Investment advice
Pt: Arthur H Harper
Pt: Latasha M Akoma
Pt: Ronald Blaylock
Pt: Chuck Castine
Pt: Matthew Guenther
Pt: James Shepard
Mng Pt: Lloyd G Trotter
CFO: Glen Bushery
Prin: Matthew P Guenther

D-U-N-S 79-555-1782
GENOA A QOL HEALTHCARE CO LLC
GENOA PHARMACY
18300 Cascade Ave S, Tukwila, WA 98188-4746
Tel (253) 218-0830 *Founded/Ownrshp* 2013
Sales 520.5MM *EMP* 1,700
SIC 2834 Pharmaceutical preparations
CEO: John Figueroa
Sr VP: William Guptail

D-U-N-S 11-197-7265
GENOA HEALTHCARE LLC
(*Suby of* GENOA PHARMACY) ★
18300 Cascade Ave S # 251, Tukwila, WA 98188-4746
Tel (800) 519-1139 *Founded/Ownrshp* 2002
Sales 222.3MM[E] *EMP* 1,200
SIC 5912 Drug stores
CEO: John Figueroa
CFO: Victor Breed

GENOA PHARMACY
See GENOA A QOL HEALTHCARE CO LLC

D-U-N-S 01-883-7943
▲ GENOMIC HEALTH INC
301 Penobscot Dr, Redwood City, CA 94063-4700
Tel (650) 556-9300 *Founded/Ownrshp* 2000
Sales 287.4MM *EMP* 802[E]
Accts Ernst & Young Llp Redwood Cit
Tkr Sym GHDX *Exch* NGS
SIC 8071 8731 Medical laboratories; Biotechnical research, commercial
Ch Bd: Kimberly J Popovits
COO: G Bradley Cole
Chf Mktg O: Phillip Febbo
Ofcr: Laura Leber Kammeyer
Ofcr: Kim McEachron
Ofcr: James Vaughn
VP: Rowena Evangelista
VP: Lewis Stuart
Assoc Dir: Allison Lai
Assoc Dir: Cristina McMahon
Assoc Dir: Victoria Steiner
Board of Directors: Felix J Baker, Julian C Baker, Fred E Cohen, Henry J Fuchs, Ginger L Graham, Randall S Livingston

D-U-N-S 13-359-0328
■ GENON AMERICAS GENERATION LLC
(*Suby of* GENON AMERICAS INC) ★
211 Carnegie Ctr, Princeton, NJ 08540-6299
Tel (609) 524-4500 *Founded/Ownrshp* 1999
Sales 2.2MMM *EMP* 602[E]
Accts Kpmg Llp Philadelphia Penns
SIC 4911 Generation, electric power
Ex VP: Kirkland B Andrews
VP: Ronald B Stark

D-U-N-S 06-792-3297
■ GENON AMERICAS INC (GA)
(*Suby of* GENON ENERGY HOLDINGS INC) ★
1155 Perimeter Ctr # 100, Atlanta, GA 30338-5463
Tel (678) 579-5000 *Founded/Ownrshp* 2001
Sales 2.6MMM[E] *EMP* 1,679
SIC 4924 Natural gas distribution
CEO: J W Holden
Sr VP: Jason Few
Snr Mgr: Mark Walker

D-U-N-S 15-291-2291 IMP/EXP
■ GENON ENERGY HOLDINGS INC
(*Suby of* NRG) ★
1000 Main St, Houston, TX 77002-6336
Tel (832) 357-3000 *Founded/Ownrshp* 2010
Sales 2.6MMM[E] *EMP* 1,679
SIC 4911 Generation, electric power; ;
Pr: Edward R Muller
**CFO:* J William Holden III
Treas: Marty Holley
Bd of Dir: William L Thacker
**Sr VP:* Thomas E Legro
Sr VP: Jose P Leviste
Sr VP: William P Von Blasingame
Sr VP: Lloyd Warnock
VP: Steve Astren
VP: Mark Durow
**VP:* Angela M Nagy
VP: Terry Thompson

D-U-N-S 00-820-0680 IMP
■ GENON ENERGY INC
NRG
(*Suby of* NRG ENERGY INC) ★
804 Carnegie Ctr, Princeton, NJ 08540-6023
Tel (609) 524-4500 *Founded/Ownrshp* 2012
Sales 2.3MMM *EMP* 2,932
Accts Kpmg Llp Philadelphia Penns
SIC 4911 Electric services; Distribution, electric power; Generation, electric power; Transmission, electric power
Pr: Mauricio Gutierrez
CEO: Maria Deouca
**CFO:* Kirkland B Andrews
Sr VP: Matthew Benner
Sr VP: Karen Dyson
Sr VP: Tom Gros
Sr VP: Dan Hannon
**VP:* Ronald B Stark
VP: Walter L Stone
Prin: Heather Humalainen
CIO: Donna Benefield

D-U-N-S 13-384-3644
■ GENON ENERGY SERVICES LLC
(*Suby of* GENON AMERICAS INC) ★
211 Carnegie Ctr, Princeton, NJ 08540-6299
Tel (609) 524-4500 *Founded/Ownrshp* 2001
Sales 101.8MM[E] *EMP* 299
SIC 4911 Generation, electric power
Off Mgr: Mark Jensen
CIO: James McDonald
IT Man: Glen Pierce

D-U-N-S 11-040-2893
■ GENON MID-ATLANTIC LLC
(*Suby of* GENON NORTH AMERICA LLC) ★
211 Carnegie Ctr, Princeton, NJ 08540-6299
Tel (609) 524-4500 *Founded/Ownrshp* 2000
Sales 856.0MM *EMP* 451[E]
Accts Kpmg Llp Philadelphia Penns
SIC 4911 Distribution, electric power; Generation, electric power; Transmission, electric power
Ex VP: Kirkland B Andrews

D-U-N-S 17-719-8629 IMP
■ GENON NORTH AMERICA LLC
(*Suby of* GENON AMERICAS GENERATION LLC) ★
1155 Perimeter Ctr # 100, Atlanta, GA 30338-5463
Tel (678) 579-5000 *Founded/Ownrshp* 2000
Sales 924.9MM[E] *EMP* 798
SIC 4924 4911 6221 Natural gas distribution; Distribution, electric power; Commodity brokers, contracts
Pr: Robert E Driscoll
**Pr:* Edward R Muller
CFO: J William Holden III
**Sr VP:* Julia A Houston
VP: Angela M Nagy

D-U-N-S 78-672-2863
■ GENON POWER MIDWEST LP
(*Suby of* GENON POWER GENERATION ASSETS, LLC)
1000 Main St, Houston, TX 77002-6336
Tel (713) 497-3000 *Founded/Ownrshp* 2006
Sales 110.9MM[E] *EMP* 316[E]
SIC 4911 Electric services
Pt: David Freysinger

D-U-N-S 00-539-3103 IMP/EXP
GENOVA PRODUCTS INC (MI)
7034 E Court St, Davison, MI 48423-2504
Tel (810) 744-4500 *Founded/Ownrshp* 1962
Sales 172.3MM[E] *EMP* 570
SIC 3089 2891 2911 3494 3084 2952 Gutters (glass fiber reinforced), fiberglass or plastic; Downspouts, plastic; Fittings for pipe, plastic; Glue; Solvents; Plumbing & heating valves; Plastics pipe; Asphalt felts & coatings
Ch Bd: Robert M Williams
**Pr:* Michael S Deboer
CFO: Barry Brang
**CFO:* Nicholas S Onica
**VP:* Jeanette M Kollias
CIO: Mark Case
IT Man: Carol Scott
Mktg Mgr: Mary Berklich
Sls Mgr: Marc Maniaci
Sls Mgr: Brian Morey
Sls Mgr: Brian Stuk

D-U-N-S 12-056-0029
GENPACT
(*Suby of* GENPACT INFRASTRUCTURE (HYDERABAD) PRIVATE LIMITED)
2004 Bassett Ave Pmb 2500, El Paso, TX 79901-1923
Tel (915) 225-2500 *Founded/Ownrshp* 2006
Sales 134.3MM[E] *EMP* 2,500
SIC 7374 Data processing & preparation
Pr: Frank Freeman
VP: Tiger Tyagarajan
Snr Ntwrk: Mike Shephard
IT Man: Rodolfo Aguinaga
IT Man: Sixto Rubio
Board of Directors: Ferdinando Beccalli-Falco

D-U-N-S 07-959-7470
GENPACT INTERNATIONAL INC
(*Suby of* GENPACT LIMITED)
42 Old Ridgebury Rd Ste 1, Danbury, CT 06810-5247
Tel (203) 730-5100 *Founded/Ownrshp* 2015
Sales 183.2M[E] *EMP* 6,600
SIC 7371 Custom computer programming services
Pr: N V Tyagarajan

D-U-N-S 83-230-8352
GENPACT LIMITED
(*Suby of* GENPACT LIMITED)
1155 Avenue Of The Americ, New York, NY 10036-2711
Tel (212) 896-6600 *Founded/Ownrshp* 2007
Sales 91.6MM[E] *EMP* 325
SIC 8741 7372 Business management; Prepackaged software
CEO: NV Tiger Tyagarajan
**Ch Bd:* Robert G Scott
Sr VP: Mohit Bhatia
Sr VP: Scott McConnell
Sr VP: Anil Nanduru
VP: Christopher Acevedo
VP: Craig W Anderson
VP: Manoj Bajpai
VP: Diana L Boersma
VP: Michael Flammer
VP: David Hauser
VP: Rein Horst
VP: Brad Jolson
VP: Chetan Mehta
VP: Troy Merriman
VP: Tom Moran
VP: Doug Morehouse
VP: Jorge Moreno
VP: Umesh Pahwa
VP: Michael Plummer
VP: Michael Pommer

D-U-N-S 02-400-2549
GENPACT LLC
(*Suby of* GENPACT LIMITED)
42 Old Ridgebury Rd Ste 1, Danbury, CT 06810-5247
Tel (203) 730-5110 *Founded/Ownrshp* 1999
Sales 384.1MM *EMP* 2,300[E]
Accts Kpmg Llp Gurgaon India
SIC 8742 Management consulting services
Pr: NV Tiger Tyagarajan
Treas: Ashish Shukla
VP: Mary Hall
VP: Umacharan Iyer
VP: Holly Neumann
VP: Jeff Saye
VP: Bryan Weis
Prgrm Mgr: Prashant Menon
IT Man: Anil Nomula
Snr Mgr: Thomas La Barbera
Snr Mgr: Lloyd McKenzie

GENPAK
See GREAT PACIFIC ENTERPRISES (US) INC

D-U-N-S 05-405-4218 IMP/EXP
GENPAK LLC
(*Suby of* GENPAK) ★
68 Warren St, Glens Falls, NY 12801-4530
Tel (518) 798-9511 *Founded/Ownrshp* 1983
Sales 1.1MMM[E] *EMP* 1,850
SIC 5113 Sanitary food containers
CEO: James Allen Pattison
Pr: Kevin Kelly
Pr: Edward Rider
Sfty Mgr: Amanda Masterson
Natl Sales: Jim V Baren
Natl Sales: Jim Van Baren
Mktg Mgr: Jeff Colle
Sls Mgr: Bill Patskou

D-U-N-S 02-753-7596 IMP/EXP
GENSCO INC
4402 20th St E, Fife, WA 98424-1803
Tel (253) 620-8203 *Founded/Ownrshp* 1947
Sales 239.0MM[E] *EMP* 500
SIC 5074 3444 Heating equipment (hydronic); Sheet metalwork; Ducts, sheet metal
Ch: Charles E Walters Sr
**Pr:* Charles E Walters Jr
**Treas:* Ken R Bell
Sls Mgr: Chris McCallum
Sales Asso: Dan Peterson

D-U-N-S 17-323-4162 IMP
GENSIA SICOR INC
(*Suby of* TEVA PHARMACEUTICAL INDUSTRIES LIMITED)
19 Hughes, Irvine, CA 92618-1902
Tel (949) 455-4700 *Founded/Ownrshp* 2004
Sales 68.2MM[E] *EMP* 1,851
SIC 2834 8731 Drugs acting on the cardiovascular system, except diagnostic; Medical research, commercial
V Ch: Carlo Salvi
CTO: Frank Becker

D-U-N-S 93-330-2499
GENSTAR CAPITAL LLC
4 Embarcadero Ctr # 1900, San Francisco, CA 94111-4106
Tel (415) 834-2350 *Founded/Ownrshp* 1991
Sales 983.0MM[E] *EMP* 3,661
SIC 6799 Investors
Mng Dir: Richard Paterson
CFO: Melissa Dickerson
Ex VP: John Ryan
VP: Roman A Margolin
VP: Jean Mayer
VP: James D Nadauld
VP: Gretchen Robinson
Exec: Hugh Lytle
Exec: Raj Parikh
Exec: Neil Vangala
**Prin:* David J Golde

D-U-N-S 87-754-9097 IMP
GENTEK BUILDING PRODUCTS INC
REVERE BUILDING PRODUCTS
(*Suby of* ASSOCIATED MATERIALS LLC) ★
3773 State Rd, Cuyahoga Falls, OH 44223-2603
Tel (800) 548-4542 *Founded/Ownrshp* 2003
Sales 208.2MM[E] *EMP* 1,000
SIC 3444 3089 Siding, sheet metal; Downspouts, sheet metal; Siding, plastic
CEO: Thomas Chieffe
**Pr:* Michael Caporale
**VP:* D Keith Lavanway

D-U-N-S 07-206-4418 IMP/EXP
GENTEK INC
90 E Halsey Rd Ste 301, Parsippany, NJ 07054-3709
Tel (973) 515-0900 *Founded/Ownrshp* 1999
Sales 221.0MM[E] *EMP* 1,110
SIC 2869 2819 2844 3714 3496 Industrial organic chemicals; Industrial inorganic chemicals; Toilet preparations; Motor vehicle parts & accessories; Cable, uninsulated wire: made from purchased wire
Pr: William E Redmond Jr
**CFO:* Thomas B Testa
VP: Mark J Connor
**VP:* Douglas J Grierson
**VP:* James Imbriaco
VP: Jim Mahen
VP: Michael J Murphy
VP: Vincent J Opalewski
VP Admn: John Cowen
Sls Mgr: Lenny Andia
Board of Directors: Henry L Druker, Kathleen R Flaherty, John G Johnson Jr, John F McGovern, Richard A Rubin

D-U-N-S 04-538-9988 IMP
GENTEX CORP
324 Main St, Simpson, PA 18407-1182
Tel (570) 282-3550 *Founded/Ownrshp* 1972
Sales 162.1MM[E] *EMP* 575
SIC 3842 8731 2295 Surgical appliances & supplies; Helmets, space; Respiratory protection equipment, personal; Commercial physical research; Coated fabrics, not rubberized
Pr: L Peter Frieder Jr
CFO: Steven R Downing
Prgrm Mgr: Jon Morey
Prgrm Mgr: Greg Opalka
Ql Cn Mgr: Christine Kistler
Snr Mgr: Ken Dejonge

D-U-N-S 06-585-5363 IMP
▲ GENTEX CORP
600 N Centennial St, Zeeland, MI 49464-1374
Tel (616) 772-1800 *Founded/Ownrshp* 1974
Sales 1.5MMM *EMP* 4,757
Tkr Sym GNTX *Exch* NGS
SIC 3231 3714 3669 Mirrors, truck & automobile: made from purchased glass; Motor vehicle parts & accessories; Smoke detectors
Ch Bd: Fred Bauer
CFO: Steve Downing
Treas: Mike Hoffmann
Bd of Dir: Eric Domke
Sr VP: Mark Newton
VP: Brad Bosma

VP: Jenny Dykgraaf
VP: Ken Horner
VP: Joseph Matthews
VP: Robert Steel
Ex Dir: Matt Chiodo
Board of Directors: Gary Goode, Pete Hoekstra, James Hollars, John Mulder, Richard Schaum, Frederick Sotok, James Wallace

D-U-N-S 55-540-3690 IMP/EXP
GENTEX OPTICS INC
(*Suby of* OMEGA DALLAS) ★
183 W Main St, Dudley, MA 01571-3835
Tel (570) 282-8531 *Founded/Ownrshp* 1988
Sales 86.4MM[E] *EMP* 500
SIC 3851 3842 Lenses, ophthalmic; Goggles: sun, safety, industrial, underwater, etc.; Surgical appliances & supplies
Pr: Gerard Malledant
**CEO:* L P Frieder
**CEO:* Eric Javellaud
**CFO:* Heather M Acker
**VP:* Helene Greuzard
VP: Russell F Weymouth

D-U-N-S 07-102-3449
GENTEX POWER CORP
3701 Lake Austin Blvd, Austin, TX 78703-3503
Tel (512) 473-4084 *Founded/Ownrshp* 1998
Sales 97.2MM *EMP* 60[E]
SIC 1629 Power plant construction
Prin: Dan Kuehn
COO: Dudley Piland Jr
VP: Schwertner Ray

D-U-N-S 00-245-2758 IMP
■ **GENTHERM (TEXAS) INC** (TX)
GENTHERM TEXAS , INC.
(*Suby of* GENTHERM INC) ★
2121b Frontera Rd, Del Rio, TX 78840-8905
Tel (830) 774-3094 *Founded/Ownrshp* 1995
Sales 179.7MM[E] *EMP* 40
SIC 5013 Motor vehicle supplies & new parts
CEO: Klaus Wilhelm
**Ch Bd:* Dan Coker
**CFO:* Barry Steel

D-U-N-S 55-687-9252 IMP
▲ **GENTHERM INC**
21680 Haggerty Rd Ste 101, Northville, MI 48167-8994
Tel (248) 504-0500 *Founded/Ownrshp* 1991
Sales 856.4MM *EMP* 10,098[E]
Tkr Sym THRM *Exch* NGS
SIC 3714 Motor vehicle parts & accessories; Motor vehicle electrical equipment
Pr: Daniel R Coker
**Ch Bd:* Oscar B Marx III
CFO: Barry G Steele
CFO: Barry Steelevp
VP: Erin E Ascher
VP: Erin Ascher
VP: Dan Pace
VP: Kenneth J Phillips
VP: Kenneth Phillips
VP Bus Dev: Ryan Gaul
Genl Mgr: Dan Lock
Board of Directors: Lewis Booth, Francois J Castaing, Sophie Desormiere, Maurice E P Gunderson, Yvonne Hao, Ronald Hundzinski, Byron T Shaw II

GENTHERM TEXAS , INC.
See GENTHERM (TEXAS) INC

D-U-N-S 12-974-1026 IMP
■ **GENTIVA HEALTH SERVICES INC**
(*Suby of* KINDRED HEALTHCARE INC) ★
3350 Riverwood Pkwy Se # 1400, Atlanta, GA 30339-3314
Tel (770) 951-6450 *Founded/Ownrshp* 2015
Sales 1.7MMM *EMP* 39,200
SIC 8082 Home health care services
CEO: Tony Strange
**Pr:* David A Causby
Pr: Dean Johnson
Pr: Robert Koch
Pr: Kristen Nearhood
Pr: Richard Scrima
**CFO:* Eric R Slusser
VP: Sara Bierbaum
VP: Jacquelin Blankenship
VP: Cara Burns
VP: Pete Cavanaugh
VP: Charles Clute
VP: David Eubanks
VP: Dave Garrity
VP: Mike Grieco
VP: Chris Macinnis
VP: Herbert Mendoza
VP: John Mongelli
VP: Danny Mullins
VP: Debbi Nerstad
VP: Chris Perry

D-U-N-S 80-860-6326
GENTLE DENTAL SERVICE CORP
(*Suby of* HIG CAPITAL LLC) ★
9800 S La Cienega Blvd # 800, Inglewood, CA 90301-4440
Tel (310) 765-2400 *Founded/Ownrshp* 2007
Sales 776.8M[E] *EMP* 1,455[E]
SIC 8021 Offices & clinics of dentists
CFO: Fred Vanerden
VP Mktg: Cedric Tuck-Sherman

D-U-N-S 01-488-1627
GENUARDIS FAMILY MARKETS LP
(*Suby of* SAFEWAY INC) ★
301 E Germantown Pike, Norristown, PA 19401-6517
Tel (610) 277-6000 *Founded/Ownrshp* 1930, 2001
Sales 491.3MM[E] *EMP* 7,400
SIC 5912 5411 Drug stores; Supermarkets, independent
Genl Mgr: Don Ciotti

D-U-N-S 00-692-4948 IMP/EXP
▲ **GENUINE PARTS CO** (GA)
2999 Wildwood Pkwy, Atlanta, GA 30339-8580
Tel (770) 953-1700 *Founded/Ownrshp* 1928
Sales 15.2MMM *EMP* 39,612
Tkr Sym GPC *Exch* NYS
SIC 5013 5531 3714 5084 5085 5021 Motor vehicle supplies & new parts; Automotive & home supply stores; Automotive parts; Motor vehicle engines & parts; Industrial machine parts; Materials handling machinery; Industrial supplies; Bearings; Hose, belting & packing; Power transmission equipment & apparatus; Office furniture
Ch Bd: Thomas C Gallagher
Pr: Timothy P Breen
**Pr:* Paul D Donahue
**CFO:* Carol B Yancey
**Sr VP:* James R Neill
VP: Lee A Maher
VP: Cameron Richardson
Exec: Alex Fritsch
Exec: Scott Mosteller
Rgnl Mgr: Andy Cody
Brnch Mgr: Casey Sullivan
Board of Directors: Gary W Rollins, Mary B Bullock, E Jenner Wood III, Elizabeth W Camp, Gary P Fayard, John R Holder, Donna W Hyland, John D Johns, Robert C Loudermilk Jr, Wendy B Needham, Jerry W Nix

GENUINE PARTS DISTRIBUTORS
See TRACY INDUSTRIES INC

D-U-N-S 60-255-8202
GENWOODS HOLDCO LLC
(*Suby of* BLOUNT INTERNATIONAL INC) ★
2606 S Il Route 2, Oregon, IL 61061-9685
Tel (815) 732-2141 *Founded/Ownrshp* 2011
Sales 51.5MM[E] *EMP* 1,250
SIC 3523 Farm machinery & equipment
CFO: Mike Goldberg
VP: Greg Malicki

D-U-N-S 04-322-2160
■ **GENWORTH FINANCIAL CAPITAL INC**
(*Suby of* GENWORTH FINANCIAL INC) ★
700 Main St, Lynchburg, VA 24504-1448
Tel (434) 845-0911 *Founded/Ownrshp* 1999, 2006
Sales NA *EMP* 2,000
SIC 6411 Insurance agents, brokers & service
Pr: George Zippel

D-U-N-S 14-236-0416
▲ **GENWORTH FINANCIAL INC**
6620 W Broad St Ste 270, Richmond, VA 23230-1799
Tel (804) 281-6000 *Founded/Ownrshp* 2003
Sales NA *EMP* 4,100
Tkr Sym GNW *Exch* NYS
SIC 6311 6371 6351 Life insurance; Pensions; Mortgage guarantee insurance
Pr: Thomas J McInerney
Ch Bd: James S Riepe
Pr: Michelle Kosoi
COO: Carrie Hansen
COO: Kevin D Schneider
CFO: Kelly L Groh
Chf Inves: Daniel J Sheehan IV
Ofcr: Lori M Evangel
Ex VP: Ward E Bobitz
Ex VP: Michael S Laming
Ex VP: Scott J McKay
Sr VP: Stephen Cooke
VP: Matt Farnay
VP: Matthew D Farney
VP: Chris Jordan
VP: Matthew Matrisian
Dir Risk M: Jeremy Ashton
Dir Bus: Maggie McDonough
Board of Directors: William H Bolinder, G Kent Conrad, Melina E Higgins, David M Moffett, Thomas E Moloney, John R Nichols, James A Parke

D-U-N-S 00-794-1198
■ **GENWORTH LIFE AND ANNUITY INSURANCE CO** (VA)
(*Suby of* GENWORTH LIFE INSURANCE CO) ★
6610 W Broad St, Richmond, VA 23230-1702
Tel (804) 281-6000 *Founded/Ownrshp* 1871, 2004
Sales NA *EMP* 1,200
Accts Kpmg Llp Richmond Virginia
SIC 6311 6211 Life insurance carriers; Investment certificate sales
Ch Bd: Pamela S Schutz
V Ch: Patsy Smith
CFO: Kelly L Groh
Sr VP: Paul A Haley
Sr VP: Ronald P Joelson
Sr VP: Leon E Roday
Sr VP: Geoffrey S Stiff
VP: Jac J Amerell
VP: Pamela C Asbury
MIS Dir: Jeff Peterson

D-U-N-S 06-954-7719
■ **GENWORTH LIFE INSURANCE CO**
(*Suby of* GENWORTH FINANCIAL INC) ★
6620 W Broad St, Richmond, VA 23230-1716
Tel (804) 281-6000 *Founded/Ownrshp* 2003
Sales NA *EMP* 2,120
SIC 6311 Life insurance carriers
CEO: Thomas J McInerney
CFO: Kelly Groh
**CFO:* Martin P Klein
**CFO:* Richard McKenney
**Ex VP:* Kevin D Schneider
**Sr VP:* Leon Roday

D-U-N-S 03-751-2134
■ **GENWORTH MORTGAGE INSURANCE CORP**
(*Suby of* GENWORTH FINANCIAL INC) ★
8325 Six Forks Rd, Raleigh, NC 27615-6514
Tel (919) 846-4100 *Founded/Ownrshp* 2007
Sales NA *EMP* 1,000
SIC 6351 8741 Mortgage guarantee insurance; Management services
Ch Bd: Thomas H Mann
**CFO:* Marcia A Dal
**Sr VP:* Gerhard A Miller
**VP:* Deb Lely

D-U-N-S 14-848-3212
■ **GENWORTH NORTH AMERICA CORP**
(*Suby of* GENWORTH FINANCIAL INC) ★
6620 W Broad St Bldg 3, Richmond, VA 23230-1721
Tel (804) 281-6000 *Founded/Ownrshp* 2012
Sales NA *EMP* 5,000
SIC 6141 Personal credit institutions; Consumer finance companies; Automobile & consumer finance companies
Pr: Patrick Kelleher
**Treas:* Gary T Prizzia
**Sr VP:* Ward E Bobitz
**Sr VP:* Leon E Roday
**VP:* Scott McKay

GENYSIS BRAND SOLUTIONS
See VMI NUTRITION INC

D-U-N-S 02-532-2157 IMP
GENZYME CORP
GENZYME THERAPEUTICS DIVISION
(*Suby of* SANOFI US SERVICES INC) ★
500 Kendall St, Cambridge, MA 02142-1108
Tel (617) 252-7500 *Founded/Ownrshp* 2011
Sales 3.7MMM[E] *EMP* 12,000
SIC 2835 2834 8071 3842 2836 5122 Enzyme & isoenzyme diagnostic agents; In vitro diagnostics; Pharmaceutical preparations; Biological laboratory; Surgical appliances & supplies; Biological products, except diagnostic; Drugs & drug proprietaries
Pr: David Meeker
CFO: Philippe Sauvage
Treas: Marc Esteva
Sr VP: Wytske Kingma
Sr VP: Richard Peters
Sr VP: William Sibold
VP: Cynthia Arbeeny
VP: Debra Barngrover
VP: Paul Beninger
VP: Lilly Chai
VP: Seng Cheng
VP: Kevin Clement
VP: Cindy Conde
VP: Zoltan Csimma
VP: Barry Duke
VP: Dave Fritsche
VP: Michael J Glynn
VP: Jon Hart
VP: Darlene Jody
VP: Ellen Keith
VP: Ralph Kelly

GENZYME THERAPEUTICS DIVISION
See GENZYME CORP

D-U-N-S 00-790-1671
GEO BYERS SONS HOLDING INC
BYERS CAR RENTALS
427 S Hamilton Rd, Columbus, OH 43213-2035
Tel (614) 228-5111 *Founded/Ownrshp* 1921
Sales 187.9MM[E] *EMP* 450
SIC 5511 Automobiles, new & used; Pickups, new & used; Vans, new & used
Ch: George W Byers Jr
**Pr:* George W Byers III
**Sec:* Don Grant
**Ex VP:* Frank M Byers Jr
**VP:* Blaine Byers
**VP:* D Jay Du Rivage Jr

D-U-N-S 07-981-5117
GEO CORRECTIONS AND DETENTION LLC
(*Suby of* G E O) ★
621 Nw 53rd St Ste 700, Boca Raton, FL 33487-8242
Tel (561) 999-7490 *Founded/Ownrshp* 2012
Sales 98.4MM[E] *EMP* 10,431
SIC 8744 Correctional facility
Ch: George Zoley
CFO: Brian Evans
Treas: Shayn March
VP: James Black
VP: Ron Brack
VP: John Bulfin
VP: Louis Carrillo
VP: David Donahue
VP: Marcel Maier
VP: Amber Martin
VP: Kyle Schiller
VP: Reed Smith

D-U-N-S 07-924-2241
GEO CORRECTIONS HOLDINGS INC (FL)
G E O
(*Suby of* GEO GROUP INC) ★
1 Park Pl, Boca Raton, FL 33487-8235
Tel (432) 267-7911 *Founded/Ownrshp* 2012
Sales 376.2MM[E] *EMP* 10,432[E]
SIC 6719 Investment holding companies, except banks
CEO: George C Zoley
**Treas:* Marcel Maier
**VP:* Brian R Evans

D-U-N-S 61-270-6465
GEO GROUP INC
621 Nw 53rd St Ste 700, Boca Raton, FL 33487-8242
Tel (561) 893-0101 *Founded/Ownrshp* 1984
Sales 1.8MMM *EMP* 15,806
Accts Grant Thornton Llp Miami Flo
SIC 6798 Real estate investment trusts
Ch Bd: George C Zoley
Pr: Ann M Schlarb
CFO: Brian R Evans
Treas: Shayn P March
Sr VP: John J Bulfin
Sr VP: Stephen V Fuller
Sr VP: David J Venturella
Sr VP: Thomas M Wierdsma
VP: Ronald A Brack
VP: Philip Dugger
VP: George Gintoli
VP: Ernest Stepp
VP: J Williams
Exec: Doris Eldridge
Exec: Cynthia Gutierrez
Dir Risk M: Kathy Chiarello
Board of Directors: Clarence E Anthony, Anne N Foreman, Richard H Glanton, Christopher C Wheeler, Julie Myers Wood

D-U-N-S 79-747-0549 IMP
GEO REENTRY INC
(*Suby of* GEO GROUP INC) ★
621 Nw 53rd St Ste 700, Boca Raton, FL 33487-8242
Tel (561) 893-0101 *Founded/Ownrshp* 2010
Sales 112.7MM[E] *EMP* 4,407
SIC 8744 Correctional facility
Pr: George C Zoley
VP: Blake Barras
VP: Ronald A Brack
VP: John J Bulfin
VP: Louis Carrillo
VP: Brian R Evans
VP: Loren Grayer
VP: Marcel Maier
VP: Shayn March
VP: Laura J Sabol
VP: Laura J Shol
Board of Directors: John Bulfin, Brian Evans, Ann Schlarb, George C Zoley

D-U-N-S 80-131-4378 IMP
GEO SPECIALTY CHEMICALS INC
401 S Earl Ave Ste 3, Lafayette, IN 47904-3606
Tel (765) 448-9412 *Founded/Ownrshp* 1992
Sales 149.3MM[E] *EMP* 290
Accts Crowe Chizek & Company Oak B
SIC 2819 Industrial inorganic chemicals
CEO: Kenneth A Ghazey
VP: Dennis Grandle
Plnt Mgr: Shawn Cannon
Ql Cn Mgr: Jim Smith

D-U-N-S 00-173-0522
GEO W KISTLER INC (PA)
KISTLER-OBRIEN FIRE PROTECTION
2210 City Line Rd, Bethlehem, PA 18017-2130
Tel (610) 266-7100 *Founded/Ownrshp* 1933, 1970
Sales 87.9MM[E] *EMP* 90
SIC 5063 7382 5087 7389 Fire alarm systems; Fire alarm maintenance & monitoring; Sprinkler systems; Fire protection service other than forestry or public
Pr: George Kistler
**Pr:* Fred W Eberting
**Treas:* Thomas P Derkits
**VP:* Eric F Blasser
VP: Eric Blasser
IT Man: Irene Gutshall

D-U-N-S 17-439-4903
GEODIGM CORP
1740 Prior Ave N, Saint Paul, MN 55113-5554
Tel (952) 556-5657 *Founded/Ownrshp* 1996
Sales 102.0MM[E] *EMP* 2,038
SIC 8731 Computer (hardware) development
CEO: Andrew Hofmeister
CFO: Dave Wohlberg
**VP:* Mike Marshall
IT Man: Kerry Glewwe

D-U-N-S 09-004-2677 IMP
GEODIS LOGISTICS LLC
OHL
(*Suby of* GEODIS WILSON USA INC) ★
7101 Executive Center Dr # 333, Brentwood, TN 37027-5236
Tel (615) 401-6400 *Founded/Ownrshp* 2015
Sales 1.0MMM[E] *EMP* 2,500
SIC 4225 8742 4226 4731 General warehousing & storage; Management consulting services; Special warehousing & storage; Transportation agents & brokers
CEO: Randy Curran
Pr: Tim Lanter
Pr: David Lisiecki
Pr: Greg Sanders
Treas: Phillip Corwin
Ex VP: Matt Hoogerland
Sr VP: Derek Fain
Sr VP: Joseph Galeone
Sr VP: Lou Lambremont
Sr VP: Pal Narayanan
VP: Darren Cockrel
VP: Jim Davis
VP: Stephen Downey
VP: Steve Flamez
VP: Mike Honious
VP: Sean Kelly
VP: Penny Ricas
VP: Brian Riley
VP: Mark Usher
Exec: Donna Dillard
Dir Bus: Paul Gates
Board of Directors: Jim Martell

D-U-N-S 04-656-8283
GEODIS USA INC
BARTHCO INTERNATIONAL, INC.
(*Suby of* OHL) ★
5101 S Broad St, Philadelphia, PA 19112-1404
Tel (215) 238-8600 *Founded/Ownrshp* 2006
Sales 152.7MM[E] *EMP* 700
SIC 4731 8741 Brokers, shipping; Foreign freight forwarding; Management services
Pr: Randy Tucker
**Pr:* Patrick Moebel
**COO:* David Weiss
**CFO:* John Ercolani
CFO: John D Ercolini Jr
CFO: John J Hafferty Jr
**Treas:* Brian McLaughlin
**Sec:* Tom Wilkas
IT Man: Tony Stevenson
Sls Mgr: Tim Joyce

D-U-N-S 08-566-7327 IMP/EXP
GEODIS WILSON USA INC
(*Suby of* GEODIS WILSON HOLDING AB)
485c Us Highway 1 S # 410, Iselin, NJ 08830-3037
Tel (732) 362-0600 *Founded/Ownrshp* 1999
Sales 2.3MMM[E] *EMP* 6,000
SIC 4731 4412 4225 Freight transportation arrangement; Customhouse brokers; Foreign freight forwarding; Freight consolidation; Deep sea foreign transportation of freight; General warehousing
Pr: John Gallahan
**Sec:* Vitaliano Sicilia
**VP:* Lou Policastro

D-U-N-S 18-357-8462 IMP/EXP
GEODYNAMICS INC
10500 W Interstate 20, Millsap, TX 76066-3135
Tel (817) 341-5300 *Founded/Ownrshp* 2003
Sales 90.0MM *EMP* 240
SIC 2892 3533 Explosives; Oil & gas field machinery; Oil field machinery & equipment
CEO: David Wesson
**COO:* Nathan Clark
**CFO:* Durg Kumar
**VP:* Cameron Kirkpatrick
Rgnl Mgr: Jeff Clinton
**VP Mfg:* Robert Davis
Prd Mgr: Larry Livingston

D-U-N-S 79-788-4587
■ GEOEYE LLC
(*Suby of* DIGITALGLOBE INC) ★
2325 Dulles Corner Blvd # 1000, Herndon, VA 20171-6123
Tel (703) 480-7500 *Founded/Ownrshp* 2013
Sales 166.8MM^E *EMP* 743^E
SIC 4899 Satellite earth stations
Pt: Tara Byrnes
Pt: Shaun Callaghan
**CEO:* Matthew M O Connell
CFO: Henry E Dubois
**Sr VP:* Christopher R Tully
Sr VP: Steven P Wallach
VP: Steven R Balthazor
VP: James M Craig
VP: Dean Edmundson
VP: Chris Glanzmann
VP: Ramsey W Price
VP: Randall J Scherago

D-U-N-S 07-464-3768 IMP/EXP
GEOKINETICS INC
1500 Citywest Blvd # 800, Houston, TX 77042-2300
Tel (713) 850-7600 *Founded/Ownrshp* 1980
Sales 1.8MMM^E *EMP* 5,695^E
SIC 1382 7374 Geophysical exploration, oil & gas field; Data processing service
Pr: David J Crowley
**CFO:* Michael Muse
**Sr VP:* James W Bogardus
**Sr VP:* Richard M Cieslewicz
VP: Richard Cieslewicz
VP: Tom Lewis
VP: John Vance
Area Mgr: Tommy Miller
Genl Mgr: Francisco Gras
Genl Mgr: Donna Hainley
Tech Mgr: Dietmar Kathmann
Board of Directors: Jeff Gates, Gary Jones, Ross Solomon, Larry First

D-U-N-S 17-930-2021
GEOKINETICS MANAGEMENT INC
GRANT GEOPHYSICAL
(*Suby of* GEOKINETICS INC) ★
1500 City W Blvd Ste 800, Houston, TX 77042
Tel (281) 870-8506 *Founded/Ownrshp* 2006
Sales 178.1MM^E *EMP* 1,000
SIC 1382 Seismograph surveys
Pr: Richard F Miles

D-U-N-S 14-786-5604
GEOLOGICAL SURVEY OF ALABAMA
(*Suby of* STATE OF ALABAMA) ★
420 Hackberry Ln, Tuscaloosa, AL 35487-0001
Tel (205) 247-3592 *Founded/Ownrshp* 1848
Sales NA *EMP* 5,025^E
SIC 9199

D-U-N-S 00-719-4707 IMP/EXP
GEORG FISCHER CENTRAL PLASTICS LLC (OK)
(*Suby of* GEORG FISCHER AG)
39605 Independence St, Shawnee, OK 74804-9203
Tel (405) 273-6302 *Founded/Ownrshp* 1955, 2008
Sales 168.0MM^E *EMP* 530
SIC 3089

D-U-N-S 06-615-6001 IMP/EXP
GEORG FISCHER LLC
GEORG FISCHER PIPING
(*Suby of* GEORGE FISCHER INC) ★
9271 Jeronimo Rd, Irvine, CA 92618-1906
Tel (714) 731-8800 *Founded/Ownrshp* 1967
Sales 105.6MM^E *EMP* 115
SIC 5051 5085 Pipe & tubing, steel; Valves & fittings
COO: Yves Studer
Ex VP: Oshaben Daniel
VP: Paul Galvin
VP: Keith Jansen
VP: Thomas Sixsmith
Area Mgr: Kevin Brady
Area Mgr: Jon Cleveland
IT Man: Chris Blumer
Manager: Martin Reisacher
Sls Mgr: Max Holloway

GEORG FISCHER PIPING
See GEORG FISCHER LLC

D-U-N-S 00-248-3667
GEORGE & LYNCH INC
150 Lafferty Ln, Dover, DE 19901-7205
Tel (302) 736-3031 *Founded/Ownrshp* 1923, 1994
Sales 138.0MM^E *EMP* 300^E
SIC 1623 1611 1629 1731 Water, sewer & utility lines; Highway & street construction; Marine construction; Environmental system control installation
CEO: William B Robinson
**Pr:* Dennis J Dinger
**CFO:* Barry G Hudson
VP: Chris Baker
**VP:* Leonard Brooks
**VP:* Jeffrey I Norman
**VP:* David W McGuigan

D-U-N-S 01-424-5906 IMP/EXP
GEORGE DELALLO CO INC
DE LALLO ITALIAN FOODS
6390 Route 30, Jeannette, PA 15644-3193
Tel (724) 925-2222 *Founded/Ownrshp* 1954
Sales 174.4MM^E *EMP* 300
SIC 5149 Groceries & related products; Pasta & rice
Pr: Francis Delallo
**Pr:* Francis X Delallo
**Treas:* Philip M Polsinelli
Comm Dir: Marcy Miller

D-U-N-S 00-695-3392 IMP
GEORGE E WARREN CORP
GEWARREN
3001 Ocean Dr Ste 203, Vero Beach, FL 32963-1992
Tel (772) 778-7100 *Founded/Ownrshp* 1982
Sales 124.5MM *EMP* 35
Accts Grant Thornton Llp Orlando F
SIC 5171 Petroleum bulk stations
Pr: Thomas L Corr
**Treas:* Mike George
Ofcr: John Virtus
VP: Joseph Corr
VP: Mark Morein
VP: Darren Sylvia

D-U-N-S 04-928-2908 IMP/EXP
GEORGE FISCHER INC
(*Suby of* GEORG FISCHER AG)
3401 Aero Jet Ave, El Monte, CA 91731-2801
Tel (626) 571-2770 *Founded/Ownrshp* 1972
Sales 263.9MM^E *EMP* 1,000^E
SIC 3599 5074 3829 3559 Electrical discharge machining (EDM); Pipes & fittings, plastic; Testing equipment: abrasion, shearing strength, etc.; Foundry machinery & equipment
CEO: Chris Blumer
VP: Martin Neil
**VP:* Daniel Vaterlaus
IT Man: Tobias Auer
IT Man: Brian Iwakiri
Opers Mgr: Joe Longoria

D-U-N-S 01-075-5106
GEORGE FOX UNIVERSITY
414 N Meridian St, Newberg, OR 97132-2697
Tel (503) 538-8383 *Founded/Ownrshp* 1891
Sales 99.0MM *EMP* 450
SIC 8221 College, except junior
Pr: Robin Baker
**CFO:* G Michael Goins
VP: Brad Lau
Exec: Peggy Kilburg
Assoc Dir: Lisa Burton
Assoc Dir: Dan Schutter
Doctor: Kathy Weiss

D-U-N-S 60-270-0262
■ GEORGE G KERASOTES CORP
(*Suby of* CARMIKE CINEMAS INC) ★
1301 1st Ave, Columbus, GA 31901-2109
Tel (706) 576-3400 *Founded/Ownrshp* 2005
Sales 3.1MM^E *EMP* 1,000
SIC 7832 Exhibitors, itinerant: motion picture
Pr: Beth Kerasotes
Ex VP: Jeff Cole
Ex VP: Marge Kerasotes
Sys/Dir: Cyndi Fleck

D-U-N-S 06-252-0366
GEORGE G SHARP INC
160 Broadway, New York, NY 10038-4201
Tel (212) 732-2800 *Founded/Ownrshp* 1983
Sales 85.3MM^E *EMP* 450
SIC 3731 4225 8712 Shipbuilding & repairing; Commercial cargo ships, building & repairing; Military ships, building & repairing; General warehousing; Architectural services
Ch Bd: I Hilary Rolih
Pr: Allen Chin
COO: CHI-Cheng Yang
Treas: Al F Seneca
IT Man: Nagen Burra

D-U-N-S 02-243-6554
GEORGE J FALTER CO
3501 Benson Ave, Baltimore, MD 21227-1098
Tel (410) 646-3641 *Founded/Ownrshp* 1935
Sales 83.0MM^E *EMP* 130
SIC 5194 5145 5141 5015 Tobacco & tobacco products; Confectionery; Candy; Food brokers; Automotive supplies, used
CEO: Frank H Falter Jr
**Pr:* Frank H Falter III
Sls Mgr: Dan Pepe

D-U-N-S 00-892-8764
GEORGE J IGEL & CO INC
2040 Alum Creek Dr, Columbus, OH 43207-1714
Tel (614) 445-8421 *Founded/Ownrshp* 1911
Sales 158.5MM^E *EMP* 892
SIC 1794 1623 6552 Excavation & grading, building construction; Sewer line construction; Water main construction; Subdividers & developers
**CFO:* Jeffrey Fries
**VP:* Brian Van Deventer
**VP:* Ronald L Wallace
Sfty Dirs: Charles Cranmer
Snr Mgr: Brian Rinehart
Board of Directors: William Igel, William McCauley, Robert Werth

D-U-N-S 87-442-2749
GEORGE KAISER FAMILY FOUNDATION
7030 S Yale Ave Ste 600, Tulsa, OK 74136-5749
Tel (918) 392-1612 *Founded/Ownrshp* 1999
Sales 154.3MM *EMP* 12
SIC 8641 Civic social & fraternal associations
Prin: Stanton Doyle
Chf Inves: Robert Thomas

D-U-N-S 12-267-4526
GEORGE M LEADER FAMILY CORP
COUNTRY MEADOWS
830 Cherry Dr, Hershey, PA 17033-2007
Tel (800) 322-3441 *Founded/Ownrshp* 2001
Sales 79.9MM^E *EMP* 2,200
SIC 8051 Skilled nursing care facilities
Pr: G Michael Leader
**COO:* David C Leader
**CFO:* Ted Janeczek
VP: Randy Hanson
**VP:* Theodore R Janeczeck
Exec: Julie Steffen
Ex Dir: Kim Eichinger
Ex Dir: Dave Wagner
IT Man: Robin Gray
Sls&Mrk Ex: Tammy Sharp
Mktg Dir: Pat Hartman

D-U-N-S 07-781-7450 IMP
GEORGE MASON UNIVERSITY
4400 University Dr, Fairfax, VA 22030-4444
Tel (703) 993-1000 *Founded/Ownrshp* 1963
Sales 588.2MM^E *EMP* 5,500
SIC 8221 University
Pr: Angel Cabrera
CFO: Andrew M Bursten
Bd of Dir: Jean D Wu
Trst: Otis D Coston
Trst: Paul E Kyl
Ofcr: John Arnold
Ofcr: Christopher Ewald
Ofcr: David Green
Ofcr: Emily Ross
Assoc VP: John Blacksten
Assoc VP: Laura Gleason
**Ex VP:* S David Wu
VP: Marc Broderick
VP: Karen Petronis
Exec: Christina Lapel
Exec: Mary Levine
Exec: Carey McDaniel
Exec: Mark Stahley
Assoc Dir: Ilissa T Belanger
Assoc Dir: Amanda Meter

D-U-N-S 00-537-8013 IMP
GEORGE P JOHNSON CO (MI)
INTAGLIO ASSOCIATES IN DESIGN
(*Suby of* PROJECT WORLDWIDE INC) ★
3600 Giddings Rd, Auburn Hills, MI 48326-1515
Tel (248) 475-2500 *Founded/Ownrshp* 1914
Sales 195.2MM^E *EMP* 625
SIC 3993 7389 Signs & advertising specialties; Advertising, promotional & trade show services
CEO: Chris Meyer
Pt: Tiffany Fong
**Pr:* Denise Wong
CFO: Dave D Rews
**Treas:* Kurt Berry
Ex VP: Mike Rossi
VP: Ryan Burke
VP: John Capano
VP: Michael Cherubin
VP: Greg Gilpin
**VP:* Scott Kellner
VP: Kenny Lauer
VP: Chris Murphy
VP: Dan Patterson
VP: Rasheed Sait
VP: Jennifer Shifman
VP: Kriss Waldrum
Exec: Amy Buchanan
Exec: John Striber
Dir Soc: Tina Chavez
Dir Soc: Geng Giminski

D-U-N-S 01-466-7240 IMP
GEORGE S COYNE CHEMICAL CO INC
3015 State Rd, Croydon, PA 19021-6962
Tel (215) 785-4500 *Founded/Ownrshp* 1868
Sales 115.2MM^E *EMP* 120
SIC 5169 Chemicals, industrial & heavy
Pr: Thomas H Coyne
Treas: Don C Helwig
VP: Donald C Helwig
VP: Jack C Mair
Genl Mgr: Sherry Dugan
IT Man: Ruth Campos
Sfty Mgr: Terry Sturgis
Opers Mgr: Steve Baehser
VP Mktg: Jerry Powel
Sls Mgr: David Maugle

D-U-N-S 00-742-9111
GEORGE T SANDERS CO
GTS
10201 W 49th Ave, Wheat Ridge, CO 80033-2211
Tel (303) 423-9660 *Founded/Ownrshp* 1950
Sales 116.5MM^E *EMP* 140
SIC 5074 Plumbing fittings & supplies; Heating equipment (hydronic)
Ch: Gary Sanders
**Pr:* Scott A Horner
**CFO:* Ted Batchelder
**VP:* Beverly Sanders

D-U-N-S 01-082-5044
GEORGE W BUSH PRESIDENTIAL LIBRARY FOUNDATION
6166 N Central Expy, Dallas, TX 75206
Tel (214) 890-9943 *Founded/Ownrshp* 2009
Sales 87.3MM *EMP* 11^E
Accts Lockart Atchley & Associates
SIC 8231 Libraries
Pr: Margaret Spellings

D-U-N-S 04-814-2983
GEORGE WASHINGTON CARVER ACADEMY
45 Broadway Fl 17, New York, NY 10006-3007
Tel (404) 841-2305 *Founded/Ownrshp* 1997
Sales NA *EMP* 2,000
SIC 8299

D-U-N-S 04-399-0498
GEORGE WASHINGTON UNIVERSITY (DC)
2121 I St Nw Ste 601, Washington, DC 20052-0086
Tel (202) 242-6600 *Founded/Ownrshp* 1821
Sales 1.2MMM *EMP* 5,000
Accts Pricewaterhousecoopers Llp Mc
SIC 8221 University
Pr: Stephen Knapp
V Ch: Lydia W Thomas
Pr: Bernard Davisson
**Treas:* Louis H Katz
Trst: Nelson A Carbonell
Trst: Eugene I Lambert
Ofcr: Sanjay Rupani
Ex VP: Tyler Coffey
VP: Anne Hirshfield
VP: Roger Whitaker
VP: John F Williams
Assoc Dir: Alexandra M Gomes
Assoc Dir: Christina Huszcza

D-U-N-S 80-442-6893
GEORGE WASHINGTON UNIVERSITY HOSPITAL
900 23rd St Nw, Washington, DC 20037-2342
Tel (202) 715-4000 *Founded/Ownrshp* 1997
Sales 505.1MM *EMP* 1
SIC 8062 General medical & surgical hospitals
**CFO:* Richard Davis
Chf Nrs Of: Patricia A Winston
CIO: Mark Fehling
Pathlgst: Patricia Latham
Ansthlgy: Daniel Asay
Ansthlgy: Catherine Cleland
Ansthlgy: Kathleen Daetwyler
Ansthlgy: Genaro Gutierrez
Ansthlgy: Tanya Lutzker
Ansthlgy: Luu Nguyen
Ansthlgy: Diana Zentko

GEORGE WESTON BAKERIES
See ARNOLD FOODS CO INC

D-U-N-S 15-969-9164
GEORGECO INC
2609 Willowbrook Rd, Dallas, TX 75220-4422
Tel (214) 352-9091 *Founded/Ownrshp* 1971
Sales 141.5MM^E *EMP* 200
SIC 5032 Concrete building products
Prin: G W White
**Pr:* Jeff L Barnes
**VP:* Gary A Barnes
**VP:* Shawn White
Dir IT: Marcus Miller
Opers Mgr: David Pimm

D-U-N-S 06-531-5194
GEORGES INC
402 W Robinson Ave, Springdale, AR 72764-6359
Tel (479) 927-7000 *Founded/Ownrshp* 1939
Sales 1.3MMM^E *EMP* 4,180
SIC 2015 0254 0251 Poultry, processed; Chicken hatchery; Broiling chickens, raising of
Pr: Carl George
**Ch Bd:* Gary George
**Pr:* Charles George
CFO: Gini Driskell
CFO: Ancel McClaine
**Treas:* Angel McClane
**Ex VP:* Otto Jeck
VP: Matt Brown
Exec: Gary Clayton
Brnch Mgr: Kenny Avey
Sfty Mgr: Carla Funkhouser

GEORGE'S LIVE HAUL
See GEORGES PROCESSING INC

D-U-N-S 06-768-3557
GEORGES PROCESSING INC (AR)
GEORGE'S LIVE HAUL
(*Suby of* GEORGES INC) ★
402 W Robinson Ave, Springdale, AR 72764-6359
Tel (479) 927-7000 *Founded/Ownrshp* 1973
Sales 314.9MM^E *EMP* 4,000^E
SIC 2015 Poultry, processed
Ch: Eugene George
Pr: Monty Henderson
CEO: Gary George
Sec: Ancel McClane
Ex VP: Otto Jeck
VP: Bill Potter
Info Man: Otto Jech

D-U-N-S 10-066-9746
GEORGETOWN COUNTY SCHOOL DISTRICT
2018 Church St, Georgetown, SC 29440-2604
Tel (843) 436-7000 *Founded/Ownrshp* 1878
Sales 90.3MM^E *EMP* 1,544
Accts Mcgregor & Company Llp Columb
SIC 8211 Public elementary & secondary schools
**Ch:* Jim Dumm
Teacher Pr: Martheno Morant
HC Dir: Michael Caviris

D-U-N-S 83-315-2940
GEORGETOWN HEALTHCARE & REHAB INC
2715 South Island Rd, Georgetown, SC 29440-4415
Tel (843) 546-4123 *Founded/Ownrshp* 1994
Sales 395.2MM *EMP* 18^E
SIC 8011 Offices & clinics of medical doctors

GEORGETOWN HOSPITAL SYSTEM
See WACCAMAW COMMUNITY HOSPITAL

D-U-N-S 04-244-6765
GEORGETOWN INDEPENDENT SCHOOL DISTRICT
603 Lakeway Dr, Georgetown, TX 78628-2843
Tel (512) 943-5000 *Founded/Ownrshp* 1917
Sales 133.0MM *EMP* 1,700
Accts Maxwell & Locke & Ritter Llp
SIC 8211 Public elementary school; Public junior high school; Public senior high school
Pr: Scott Alarcon
Bd of Dir: Mark Bobinger
Bd of Dir: Sheila Carter
Bd of Dir: Mike Hewlett
Prin: Judy Johnston
Prin: Randy Weisinger
Pr Dir: Suzanne Marchman
Teacher Pr: Cheryl Hoover

D-U-N-S 06-932-9647
GEORGETOWN MEMORIAL HOSPITAL
TIDELANDS GEORGETOWN MEM HOSP
606 Black River Rd, Georgetown, SC 29440-3368
Tel (843) 626-9040 *Founded/Ownrshp* 1950
Sales 126.7MM *EMP* 1,300
SIC 8062 General medical & surgical hospitals
CEO: Jeannie Davis
V Ch: Charles A Moore
**Pr:* Bruce P Bailey
Treas: Richard Ferdon
Chf Mktg O: John Manning

Ofcr: Wanda Prevatte
VP: Pamela Maxwell
VP: Frank Scafidi
Exec: James Harper
Dir Risk M: Linda Jarels
Dir Lab: Elizabeth D Gannon
Dir Rx: Ambrose Holiday

D-U-N-S 08-040-4030
GEORGETOWN METAL PROCESSING LLC
650 Triport Rd, Georgetown, KY 40324-7800
Tel (502) 868-3450 *Founded/Ownrshp* 2016
Sales 140.0MM *EMP* 4
SIC 3317 Steel pipe & tubes

D-U-N-S 04-951-5844
GEORGETOWN UNIVERSITY
37th & O Sts Nw, Washington, DC 20057-0001
Tel (202) 687-0100 *Founded/Ownrshp* 1789
Sales 1.1MMM *EMP* 9,700
Accts Pricewaterhousecoopers Llp Mc
SIC 8221 8062 University; General medical & surgical hospitals
Pr: John J Degioia
Pr: Stacy Kerr
CFO: Paul Warda
Ofcr: Emmanuel Alignay
Ofcr: Anthony Allen
Ofcr: Clark Browne
Ofcr: David Budd
Ofcr: David Dennison
Ofcr: Larry Fowlkes
Ofcr: Paulo Freyesleben
Ofcr: Cat Glover-Bradford
Ofcr: Antony Johnson
Ofcr: Terence Mack
**Ex VP:* Howard Federoff
**Ex VP:* Robert M Groves
Sr VP: Christopher Augostini
**Sr VP:* Spiros Dimolitsas
VP: Lisette Booty
**VP:* Lisa Brown
VP: Braden Burgon
VP: Lennie Carter

D-U-N-S 80-956-1272
GEORGIA BANKERS ASSOCIATION INSURANCE TRUST INC
50 Hurt Plz Se Ste 1050, Atlanta, GA 30303-2955
Tel (404) 522-1501 *Founded/Ownrshp* 2011
Sales NA *EMP* 2^E
Accts Moore Colson & Company Pc Mar
SIC 6411 Insurance agents, brokers & service
Prin: Remer Y Brinson III

D-U-N-S 82-810-2827
GEORGIA BANKERS ASSOCIATION INSURANCE TRUST INC
50 Hurt Plz Se Ste 1050, Atlanta, GA 30303-2955
Tel (404) 522-1501 *Founded/Ownrshp* 2011
Sales NA *EMP* 2
Accts Moore Colson & Company Pc Mar
SIC 6411 Insurance agents, brokers & service
Sr VP: Dan Thomason
Sr VP: Elizabeth Chandler

D-U-N-S 07-588-3603
GEORGIA BAPTIST HEALTH CARE SYSTEM INC
100 10th St Nw Ste 700, Atlanta, GA 30309-3810
Tel (404) 814-4477 *Founded/Ownrshp* 1993
Sales 187.6MM^E *EMP* 1,300
Accts Ernst & Young Llp
SIC 8741 Hospital management; Nursing & personal care facility management
CEO: David E Harrell
**COO:* Robert Otwell
**CFO:* Ann Finlon

GEORGIA BOARD OF REGENTS
See BOARD OF REGENTS OF UNIVERSITY SYSTEM OF GEORGIA

D-U-N-S 00-586-7643 IMP/EXP
GEORGIA CROWN DISTRIBUTING CO (GA)
ALABAMA CROWN DISTRIBUTING CO
100 Georgia Crown Dr, McDonough, GA 30253-9071
Tel (770) 302-3000 *Founded/Ownrshp* 1949, 1959
Sales 200.1MM^E *EMP* 475
SIC 5182 5181 Wine & distilled beverages; Beer & ale
CEO: Donald M Leebern
**CFO:* Orlene K Bovaird
CFO: Orlene Bovaird
Ex VP: Persall Buddy
VP: Brian Hendrick
Exec: Dave Leonard
Genl Mgr: Shane Mooney
Genl Mgr: Greg Rains
IT Man: Desmond Johnson
Sls Dir: Peter Ryan
Sls Mgr: Jason Holland

D-U-N-S 80-747-9118
GEORGIA DEPARTMENT OF CORRECTIONS
(*Suby of* EXECUTIVE OFFICE OF STATE OF GEORGIA) ★
300 Patrol Rd, Forsyth, GA 31029-1868
Tel (404) 656-4593 *Founded/Ownrshp* 1943
Sales NA *EMP* 12,000
SIC 9223 Prison, government;
Ofcr: Robert Boney
Ofcr: Yeshelle Keller
Opers Mgr: Gary Bell

D-U-N-S 80-674-3159
GEORGIA DEPARTMENT OF EDUCATION
(*Suby of* EXECUTIVE OFFICE OF STATE OF GEORGIA) ★
205 Jesse Hill Jr Dr Se, Atlanta, GA 30334-9033
Tel (404) 656-2497 *Founded/Ownrshp* 1972
Sales 70.7MM^E *EMP* 1,000
SIC 8211 9411 Public elementary & secondary schools;
Prgrm Mgr: John Bridges
Off Mgr: Debbie Moss
CIO: Mike Karl

D-U-N-S 80-674-3191
GEORGIA DEPARTMENT OF HUMAN SERVICES
HUMAN RESOURCES GEORGIA DEPT
(*Suby of* EXECUTIVE OFFICE OF STATE OF GEORGIA) ★
2 Peachtree St Nw, Atlanta, GA 30303-3141
Tel (404) 651-9361 *Founded/Ownrshp* 2009
Sales NA *EMP* 9,000
SIC 9441 Administration of social & manpower programs;
CEO: Thomas Updike
Genl Mgr: Minerva Nixon
CIO: John Stewart
Software D: Douglas Simpson

D-U-N-S 00-973-5973
GEORGIA DEPARTMENT OF JUVENILE JUSTICE
(*Suby of* EXECUTIVE OFFICE OF STATE OF GEORGIA) ★
3408 Covington Hwy, Decatur, GA 30032-1513
Tel (404) 508-6500 *Founded/Ownrshp* 1996
Sales NA *EMP* 4,000
SIC 9222
Genl Mgr: Maleia Wilson
IT Man: Jack Johnson
Genl Couns: Tracy Masters

D-U-N-S 80-747-9290
GEORGIA DEPARTMENT OF LABOR
LABOR, COMMISSIONER OF
(*Suby of* EXECUTIVE OFFICE OF STATE OF GEORGIA) ★
148 Andrew Yng Intl Blvd # 100, Atlanta, GA 30303-1751
Tel (404) 232-3540 *Founded/Ownrshp* 1911
Sales NA *EMP* 1,879
SIC 9651 Labor regulatory agency;
Genl Mgr: Gregory Lane
CIO: Linda Russell
Tech Mgr: David Kilbride
Board of Directors: Andrea Harper, Brooke Lucas

D-U-N-S 14-698-5544
GEORGIA DEPARTMENT OF NATURAL RESOURCES
(*Suby of* EXECUTIVE OFFICE OF STATE OF GEORGIA) ★
2 Martin Luther King Jr, Atlanta, GA 30334-9000
Tel (404) 656-3500 *Founded/Ownrshp* 1972
Sales NA *EMP* 1,900
SIC 9512

D-U-N-S 05-124-3074
GEORGIA DEPARTMENT OF PUBLIC HEALTH
(*Suby of* HUMAN RESOURCES GEORGIA DEPT) ★
2 Peachtree St Nw Fl 15, Atlanta, GA 30303-3142
Tel (404) 657-2700 *Founded/Ownrshp* 1972
Sales NA *EMP* 6,000
SIC 9431 Administration of public health programs;
**COO:* Janie Brodnax
Dir Surg: Dafna Kanny
IT Man: Meshun Daniel
IT Man: Kathleen Robinson

D-U-N-S 80-674-3217
GEORGIA DEPARTMENT OF PUBLIC SAFETY
GA STATE PATROL
(*Suby of* EXECUTIVE OFFICE OF STATE OF GEORGIA) ★
959 E Confederate Ave Se, Atlanta, GA 30316-2531
Tel (404) 624-7739 *Founded/Ownrshp* 1937
Sales NA *EMP* 2,100
SIC 9229 Public order & safety statistics centers;

D-U-N-S 80-674-3209
GEORGIA DEPARTMENT OF REVENUE
(*Suby of* EXECUTIVE OFFICE OF STATE OF GEORGIA) ★
1800 Century Blvd Ne # 1200, Atlanta, GA 30345-3202
Tel (877) 423-6711 *Founded/Ownrshp* 1923
Sales NA *EMP* 1,439
Accts State Of Georgia Department Of
SIC 9311 Finance, taxation & monetary policy;
VP: Massah David
CTO: Wes Brooks
Netwrk Mgr: Geoffrey Catron
Netwrk Eng: Steve Weatherby

D-U-N-S 80-738-2338
GEORGIA DEPARTMENT OF TRANSPORTATION
(*Suby of* EXECUTIVE OFFICE OF STATE OF GEORGIA) ★
600 W Peachtree St Nw, Atlanta, GA 30308-3607
Tel (404) 631-1014 *Founded/Ownrshp* 1972
Sales NA *EMP* 6,400
SIC 9621 Regulation, administration of transportation;
Bd of Dir: Pamela Baughman
Bd of Dir: Elizabeth Osmon
Ofcr: Shelia Smith
Prgrm Mgr: Tony Giasi
Dir IT: Jeffrey Hill
Netwrk Eng: George Rasasombath
Snr Mgr: Sean Diehl
Snr Mgr: Gerald Ford
Snr Mgr: Michele Nystrom

D-U-N-S 17-072-9227
GEORGIA ENERGY COOPERATIVE (AN ELECTRIC MEMBERSHIP CORP)
2100 E Exch Pl Ste 300, Tucker, GA 30084
Tel (770) 270-7500 *Founded/Ownrshp* 2001
Sales 275.7MM *EMP* 15
Accts Mcnair Mclemore Middlebrooks
SIC 4911 Electric services
Pr: Glenn D Loomer
**VP:* Melissa Calzada
VP: Bill Verner
**VP:* John Winskie III
CTO: Louise Blackman
CTO: Roger Borkenhagen
CTO: Marty Williamson
DP Dir: John Broxson
Dir IT: Janet Katzenberger
Dir IT: Gary Williamson
IT Man: Ricky McGee

GEORGIA FARM BUREAU COMPANY
See GEORGIA FARM BUREAU MUTUAL INSURANCE CO

D-U-N-S 04-069-8284
GEORGIA FARM BUREAU FEDERATION INC
1620 Bass Rd, Macon, GA 31210-6503
Tel (478) 474-8411 *Founded/Ownrshp* 1937
Sales NA *EMP* 1,210
Accts Mcnair Mclemore Middlebrooks
SIC 6111 5154 8699 5191 Farmers Home Administration; Livestock; Farm bureau; Farm supplies
Pr: Vincent Duvall
**Pr:* Zippy Duvall
**Sec:* Wayne Daniel
VP: Donald Childs
**VP:* Gerald Long

D-U-N-S 05-421-4093
GEORGIA FARM BUREAU MUTUAL INSURANCE CO
GEORGIA FARM BUREAU COMPANY
(*Suby of* GEORGIA FARM BUREAU FEDERATION INC) ★
1620 Bass Rd, Macon, GA 31210-6500
Tel (478) 474-0679 *Founded/Ownrshp* 1958
Sales NA *EMP* 1,210
Accts Porter Keadle Moore Llc Atla
SIC 6411 Insurance agents, brokers & service
Pr: Vincent M Duvall
**Sec:* Carlos Wayne Daniel
Bd of Dir: Louis J Hunt
Bd of Dir: Gary H Paulk
Bd of Dir: Jimmy Perry
Bd of Dir: Marvin Ruark
Bd of Dir: Randy Ruff
Bd of Dir: James E Tate
Bd of Dir: Jeannie Tucker
Ofcr: Robert Puryear
VP: Gerald Long
Assoc Dir: Joey Kinard

D-U-N-S 06-534-8054
GEORGIA HEALTH SCIENCES FOUNDATION INC
JOINT BOARD OF FAMILY PRACTICE
(*Suby of* GEORGIA BOARD OF REGENTS) ★
1120 15th St, Augusta, GA 30912-0004
Tel (800) 869-1113 *Founded/Ownrshp* 1828
Sales 632.2MM^E *EMP* 8,500
Accts Greg S Griffin State Auditor
SIC 8062 8221 Hospital, medical school affiliation; College, except junior
Pr: Brooks A Keel
**COO:* Robert Zeyfang
CFO: William Bowes
Sr VP: Barry Goldstein
Sr VP: Douglas Miller
Sr VP: Sandra I McVcker
**VP:* Susan Barcus

D-U-N-S 00-332-1619
GEORGIA INSTITUTE OF TECHNOLOGY
GEORGIA TECH
(*Suby of* GEORGIA BOARD OF REGENTS) ★
225 North Ave Nw, Atlanta, GA 30332-0002
Tel (404) 894-2000 *Founded/Ownrshp* 1885
Sales 1.1MMM *EMP* 5,932
SIC 8221

D-U-N-S 79-321-7527
■ **GEORGIA L AMEDISYS L C**
(*Suby of* AMEDISYS INC) ★
5959 S Shrwood Frest Blvd, Baton Rouge, LA 70816
Tel (225) 292-2031 *Founded/Ownrshp* 2007
Sales 15.7MM^E *EMP* 1,167^E
SIC 8082 Home health care services
Prin: Celeste Peiffer

D-U-N-S 01-454-0928 IMP
GEORGIA L SEJONG L C
(*Suby of* SEJONG INDUSTRIAL CO., LTD.)
1641 Lukken Indl Dr W, Lagrange, GA 30240-5703
Tel (706) 845-7091 *Founded/Ownrshp* 2008
Sales 134.4MM *EMP* 180
SIC 3714 Motor vehicle parts & accessories
Pr: Sungwoo OH
CFO: Jack Kim

D-U-N-S 07-937-5556
GEORGIA MUNICIPAL ASSOCIATION INC
GMA
201 Pryor St Sw, Atlanta, GA 30303-3606
Tel (404) 688-0472 *Founded/Ownrshp* 1969
Sales 109.0MM *EMP* 96^E
Accts Crace Galvis Mcgrath Llc Ken
SIC 2711 2741 8611 Newspapers; Miscellaneous publishing; Trade associations
Ex Dir: D Lamar Norton
Pr: Kelly Shields
Ex Dir: Jim Higdon
Mng Dir: Randy Meacham
Genl Couns: Alison Earles

D-U-N-S 82-930-1493
GEORGIA PACIFIC HOLDINGS INC
(*Suby of* KOCH INDUSTRIES INC) ★
13208 Hadley St Apt 1, Whittier, CA 90601-4531
Tel (626) 926-1474 *Founded/Ownrshp* 2008
Sales 228.8MM^E *EMP* 46,275
SIC 2676 2656 2435 2821 Sanitary paper products; Sanitary food containers; Hardwood veneer & plywood; Plastics materials & resins
CEO: Jorge Arroyo

D-U-N-S 80-476-2524
GEORGIA PERIMETER COLLEGE
(*Suby of* GEORGIA BOARD OF REGENTS) ★
3251 Panthersville Rd, Decatur, GA 30034-3832
Tel (678) 891-2300 *Founded/Ownrshp* 1964
Sales 55.8MM *EMP* 2,359
SIC 8222 Community college
Pr: Rob Watts
Bd of Dir: Bonnie Martin
Ex VP: Ron Carrutch
**Ex VP:* Ron Carruth
**VP:* Vincent June
**VP:* Ronald Stark
**VP:* Jeff Tarnowski
VP: Jeffrey Tarnowski
Assoc Dir: Marian Adomakoh
Off Admin: Ganiyat Salami
Dir IT: Marisa Greenlee

GEORGIA PLANT
See MOBIS ALABAMA LLC

D-U-N-S 00-692-4989 IMP
■ **GEORGIA POWER CO** (GA)
(*Suby of* SOUTHERN CO) ★
241 Ralph Mcgill Blvd Ne, Atlanta, GA 30308-3374
Tel (404) 506-6526 *Founded/Ownrshp* 1930
Sales 8.3MMM *EMP* 7,989
Accts Deloitte & Touche Llp Atlanta
SIC 4911 Electric services; Distribution, electric power; Generation, electric power; Transmission, electric power
Ch Bd: W Paul Bowers
CFO: Thomas Fanning
CFO: W Ron Hinson
Chf Cred: Meredith Lackey
Ex VP: W Craig Barrs
Ex VP: Christopher P Cummiskey
Ex VP: James H Miller
Ex VP: Cliff Thrasher
Ex VP: Larry Westbrook
Ex VP: Anthony L Wilson
Sr VP: John L Pemberton
VP: Mark Berry
VP: Moanica Caston
VP: Lenn Chandler
VP: Jason Cuevas
VP: Sloane Evans
VP: Bryan Fletcher
VP: Oscar Harper
VP: Cherryl Harris
VP: Jeaneen Hunter
VP: Brian Ivey
Board of Directors: Robert L Brown Jr, Anna R Cablik, Stephen S Green, Doug Hertz, Jimmy C Tallent, Charles K Tarbutton, Beverly Daniel Tatum, Clyde C Tuggle, Richard W Ussery

GEORGIA PUBLIC BROADCASTING
See PUBLIC TELECOMMUNICATIONS COMMISSION GEORGIA

GEORGIA REGENTS UNIVERSITY
See AUGUSTA UNIVERSITY

D-U-N-S 06-536-1784
GEORGIA SOUTHERN UNIVERSITY
(*Suby of* GEORGIA BOARD OF REGENTS) ★
1582 Southern Dr, Statesboro, GA 30458
Tel (912) 681-5224 *Founded/Ownrshp* 1906
Sales 206.1MM *EMP* 1,700
Accts Greg S Griffin Atlanta Geor
SIC 8221 University
Pr: Brooks Keel
Comm Dir: David Thompson
Mktg Mgr: Tess Kiser

D-U-N-S 07-342-5951
GEORGIA STATE UNIVERSITY
(*Suby of* GEORGIA BOARD OF REGENTS) ★
30 Courtland St Se, Atlanta, GA 30303-3011
Tel (404) 413-2000 *Founded/Ownrshp* 1955
Sales 398.1MM *EMP* 5,500
SIC 8221

GEORGIA TECH
See GEORGIA INSTITUTE OF TECHNOLOGY

D-U-N-S 36-412-4651
GEORGIA TECH APPLIED RESEARCH CORP
OFFICE OF SPONSORED PROGRAMS
(*Suby of* OFFICE OF SPONSORED PROGRAMS) ★
505 10th St Nw, Atlanta, GA 30318-5775
Tel (404) 894-4819 *Founded/Ownrshp* 1998
Sales 358.8MM *EMP* 1,100^E
Accts Cherry Bekaert Llp Atlanta G
SIC 8731 Commercial physical research
CEO: Stephen Cross
**Pr:* G Wayne Clough
**Ch:* Leslie R Sibert
VP: Jilda D Garton

D-U-N-S 09-739-4084
GEORGIA TECH RESEARCH CORP
OFFICE OF SPONSORED PROGRAMS
505 10th St Nw, Atlanta, GA 30318-5775
Tel (404) 894-4819 *Founded/Ownrshp* 1937
Sales 653.0MM *EMP* 2,210
SIC 8732

D-U-N-S 82-561-7202
GEORGIA TECHNOLOGY AUTHORITY
GTA
(*Suby of* EXECUTIVE OFFICE OF STATE OF GEORGIA) ★
47 Trinity Ave Sw, Atlanta, GA 30334-9006
Tel (404) 463-2300 *Founded/Ownrshp* 1990
Sales 150.0MM^E *EMP* 344
SIC 4899 9199 Communication signal enhancement network system;
Ex Dir: Calvin Rhodes
**COO:* Dean Johnson
**CFO:* Kevin Stanford
Ofcr: Dale Harford
Ofcr: Steve McGinnis
Exec: Cassandra Joseph
**Prin:* Steve Nichols
Rgnl Mgr: Michael Carrick
CIO: Tom Wade
CIO: Teresa Windom
Software D: Arthur Broomes

D-U-N-S 95-862-7903 IMP
GEORGIA TRANSMISSION CORP
GTC
2100 E Exchange Pl, Tucker, GA 30084-5342
Tel (770) 270-7400 *Founded/Ownrshp* 1996

Sales 263.2MM *EMP* 285
SIC 4911 Generation, electric power; Distribution, electric power
Pr: Jerry Donovan
**CFO:* Barbara Hampton
Board of Directors: Jack E Waters

D-U-N-S 80-987-2310
■ GEORGIA WASTE SYSTEMS INC
WASTE MANAGEMENT OF ATLANTA
(*Suby of* WASTE MANAGEMENT HOLDINGS INC) ★
1001 Fannin St Ste 4000, Houston, TX 77002-6711
Tel (713) 512-6200 *Founded/Ownrshp* 1999
Sales 86.4MM^E *EMP* 335
SIC 4953 Refuse collection & disposal services
COO: James Trevathan
**CFO:* James Fish Jr

GEORGIA-PACIFIC
See COLOR-BOX LLC

D-U-N-S 80-787-1137 EXP
GEORGIA-PACIFIC BREWTON LLC
G P
(*Suby of* GEORGIA-PACIFIC LLC) ★
32224 Highway 31, Brewton, AL 36426-8191
Tel (251) 867-3622 *Founded/Ownrshp* 2007
Sales 174.7MM^E *EMP* 450
SIC 2611 2679 Pulp mills; Paper products, converted

D-U-N-S 08-022-6064
GEORGIA-PACIFIC HOLDINGS LLC
(*Suby of* KOCH INDUSTRIES INC) ★
133 Peachtree St Ne # 4810, Atlanta, GA 30303-1821
Tel (404) 652-4000 *Founded/Ownrshp* 2005
Sales 877.2MM^E *EMP* 46,270^E
SIC 6719 Investment holding companies, except banks
Pr: James Hannan

D-U-N-S 00-902-0777 IMP/EXP
GEORGIA-PACIFIC LLC (GA)
(*Suby of* GEORGIA-PACIFIC HOLDINGS LLC) ★
133 Peachtree St Ne # 4810, Atlanta, GA 30303-1821
Tel (404) 652-4000 *Founded/Ownrshp* 1927
Sales 17.1MMM^E *EMP* 46,270
SIC 2676 2656 2653 2435 2821 3275 Sanitary paper products; Sanitary food containers; Corrugated & solid fiber boxes; Hardwood veneer & plywood; Plastics materials & resins; Gypsum products
Pr: James Hannan
Pr: Sean Fallmann
Pr: Brent Paugh
Pr: Bill Sleeper
Pr: Lee M Thomas
**CFO:* Tyler Woolson
CFO: Tyler L Woolson
Chf Mktg O: Michael Dunn
Ofcr: Mark Dejean
Ofcr: William A Nahill
**Ex VP:* Christian Fischer
**Ex VP:* W Wesley Jones
Ex VP: Steve Klinger
**Ex VP:* Mark Luetters
Ex VP: Dave Paterson
**Ex VP:* Kathleen A Walters
**Sr VP:* Michael E Adams
**Sr VP:* Julie Brehm
**Sr VP:* Tye Darland
**Sr VP:* David Park
**Sr VP:* Sheila M Weidman

D-U-N-S 80-813-4006 EXP
GEORGIA-PACIFIC PACKAGING LLC
(*Suby of* GP OPERATIONS HOLDINGS LLC) ★
133 Peachtree St Ne # 4810, Atlanta, GA 30303-1821
Tel (404) 652-4000 *Founded/Ownrshp* 2006
Sales 91.5MM^E *EMP* 864
SIC 2656 Paper cups, plates, dishes & utensils

D-U-N-S 80-802-7945 EXP
GEORGIA-PACIFIC WOOD PRODUCTS SOUTH LLC
(*Suby of* GEORGIA-PACIFIC LLC) ★
133 Peachtree St Ne, Atlanta, GA 30303-1804
Tel (404) 652-4000 *Founded/Ownrshp* 2007
Sales 198.0MM^E *EMP* 2,425
SIC 2656 Paper cups, plates, dishes & utensils
Pr: Mike Rehwinkel

D-U-N-S 03-120-9304 IMP
GEORGIAN AMERICAN ALLOYS INC
GAA
200 S Biscayne Blvd # 5500, Miami, FL 33131-2333
Tel (305) 375-7560 *Founded/Ownrshp* 2012
Sales 128.6MM^E *EMP* 425
SIC 1061 Manganese ores mining
Pr: Mordechai Korf
CFO: Barry Nuss
Pr Dir: Zakaria Zalikashvili
Genl Couns: Daniela Rost
Counsel: Robert Powell

GEORGIAN MANOR APTS
See HARTMAN AND TYNER INC

D-U-N-S 08-008-7760
GEORGIAS OWN CREDIT UNION
1155 Peachtree St Ne # 400, Atlanta, GA 30309-7629
Tel (404) 874-1166 *Founded/Ownrshp* 1934
Sales NA *EMP* 211
SIC 6062 State credit unions, not federally chartered
Pr: Charlotte S Ayers
**Ch Bd:* C Edward Heath
Pr: Lorenzo Brown
**CEO:* David Preter
COO: William Lusk
CFO: Linda Finch
**CFO:* William L Lusk
**Treas:* Patrick H Casey
Chf Mktg O: Kelly Garmon
Ofcr: Cedric Horton
Sr VP: Eric Broome
VP: Greg Cook
VP: Dan Denning
VP: Adam Marlowe
VP: Barbara J Takacs

GEP
See NB VENTURES INC

GERALD CHMPN REGIONAL MED CTR
See OTERO COUNTY HOSPITAL ASSOCIATION INC

D-U-N-S 00-577-7651
GERALD H PHIPPS INC
GH PHIPPS CNSTR COMPANIES
5995 Greenwood Ste 100, Greenwood Village, CO 80111
Tel (303) 571-5377 *Founded/Ownrshp* 1952
Sales 185.1MM *EMP* 350
Accts Eks&H Lllp Fort Collins Colo
SIC 1542 3399 Commercial & office building, new construction; School building construction; Hospital construction; Laminating steel
Pr: Kurt Klanderud
Pr: Gary Constant
**CFO:* Rhonda Kay
**VP:* Rich Allison
VP: Kevin Braden
Dir Bus: Victoria Hatfield
Sls Dir: Matt Paull
Corp Couns: Danielle A Curtiss
Board of Directors: Cris Goldy, Mike Mann, Roger Treichler

D-U-N-S 07-849-1499
GERALD HOLDINGS LLC
680 Washington Blvd Fl 9, Stamford, CT 06901-3727
Tel (203) 609-8550 *Founded/Ownrshp* 2007
Sales 161.3MM^E *EMP* 550^E
SIC 6221 Commodity brokers, contracts

D-U-N-S 01-203-3635 IMP/EXP
GERALD METALS LLC
(*Suby of* GERALD HOLDINGS LLC) ★
680 Washington Blvd Fl 9, Stamford, CT 06901-3727
Tel (203) 609-8300 *Founded/Ownrshp* 1969
Sales 139.3MM^E *EMP* 550^E
SIC 5051 Nonferrous metal sheets, bars, rods, etc.
CEO: Craig Dean
Pr: Fabio Calia
CFO: Thomas Restivo
Sr VP: Eric Sugerman
VP: Kory Marks
VP: Lisa Trell
Counsel: Howard Law

D-U-N-S 09-890-0434 IMP/EXP
GERBER AGRI INTERNATIONAL LLC
(*Suby of* GERBER GOLDSCHMIDT GROUP (S A) (PTY) LTD)
1000 Parkwood Cir Se # 335, Atlanta, GA 30339-2124
Tel (770) 952-4187 *Founded/Ownrshp* 1998
Sales 111.6MM *EMP* 18^E
SIC 5144 5147

D-U-N-S 07-946-9075
GERBER GLASS (DISTRICT 1) LLC
GERBER NATIONAL GLASS SERVICES
(*Suby of* BOYD GROUP U S INC) ★
500 W Lake St, Elmhurst, IL 60126-1400
Tel (800) 826-8682 *Founded/Ownrshp* 2011
Sales 30.1MM^E *EMP* 1,200^E
SIC 7549 High performance auto repair & service
CEO: Eddie Cheskis

D-U-N-S 07-272-5716
GERBER LIFE INSURANCE CO
(*Suby of* NESTLE INFANT NUTRITION) ★
1311 Mmroneck Ave Ste 350, Fremont, MI 49412
Tel (800) 704-2180 *Founded/Ownrshp* 1967
Sales NA *EMP* 200
SIC 6311 6321 Life insurance; Accident & health insurance
**Pr:* Keith O'Reilly
VP: Tom Conde
Exec: John Craig
Mktg Mgr: Megan Sharpe
VP Legal: Robert Lodewick

GERBER NATIONAL GLASS SERVICES
See GERBER GLASS (DISTRICT 1) LLC

D-U-N-S 96-903-8558
GERBER PLUMBING FIXTURES LLC
(*Suby of* GLOBE UNION GROUP INC) ★
2500 Intrntonale Pkwy, Woodridge, IL 60517-4073
Tel (630) 679-1420 *Founded/Ownrshp* 2003
Sales 113.2MM *EMP* 53
SIC 3261 Plumbing fixtures, vitreous china
Pr: Werner Michael

D-U-N-S 00-601-9780 IMP/EXP
GERBER PRODUCTS CO
NESTLE INFANT NUTRITION
(*Suby of* NESTLE HOLDINGS INC) ★
12 Vreeland Rd Fl 2, Florham Park, NJ 07932-1521
Tel (973) 593-7500 *Founded/Ownrshp* 2007
Sales 599.1MM^E *EMP* 2,381
SIC 2023 2043 2037 2052 2086 2091 Baby formulas; Cereal breakfast foods; Fruit juices; Cookies & crackers; Pasteurized & mineral waters, bottled & canned; Canned & cured fish & seafoods
Pr: Kurt T Schmidt
Treas: Don W Gosline
VP: Kevin L Goldberg
VP: Kevin L Goldbert
VP: Craig Thompson
Dir Risk M: David Binder
Board of Directors: Dianne Jacobs, David Nieto

D-U-N-S 00-115-8195 IMP/EXP
GERBER SCIENTIFIC LLC (CT)
24 Indl Pk Rd W, Tolland, CT 06084
Tel (860) 871-8082 *Founded/Ownrshp* 1948, 2011
Sales 258.7MM *EMP* 1,950
SIC 3993 7336 3851 7372 3577 Signs & advertising specialties; Commercial art & graphic design; Lenses, ophthalmic; Prepackaged software; Magnetic ink & optical scanning devices
Pr: Michael Elia
**CFO:* John Capasso
VP: Patti Burmahl
VP: Greg Collins
VP: Peter Doscas
VP: Dhiresh Jethwa
VP: Mike Lyon
**VP:* James Martin
VP: Bud McCann
VP: Theo Ostendorf
VP: Steve H Park
VP: Johnny Wang
**VP:* Karen Watson
Exec: Paul Soderburg
Dir Risk M: Theresa Kenny

D-U-N-S 04-771-3581 IMP/EXP
GERBER TECHNOLOGY LLC
(*Suby of* AMERICAN INDUSTRIAL PARTNERS LP) ★
24 Industrial Park Rd W, Tolland, CT 06084-2806
Tel (860) 871-8082 *Founded/Ownrshp* 2016
Sales 273.8MM^E *EMP* 915
SIC 3559 7371 Foundry machinery & equipment; Custom computer programming services
CEO: Michael R Elia
Pr: Bud McCann
Pr: Jeff Rosenzweig
Pr: Paul Soderburg
**CFO:* John Capasso
**CFO:* David Kralic
**Treas:* Theresa J Kenny
**Sr VP:* Patricia L Burmahl
VP: Greg Collins
VP: Michael J Lyon
VP: Peter Morrissey
VP: Karsten Newbury
VP: Theo Ostendorf
VP: Johnny Wang

GERBES SPRMKT / KING SOOPERS
See DILLON COMPANIES INC

GERDAU AMERISTEEL
See SHEFFIELD STEEL CORP

GERDAU AMERISTEEL CORPORATION
See GERDAU AMERISTEEL CORP

D-U-N-S 78-425-3564 IMP/EXP
GERDAU AMERISTEEL CORP
GERDAU AMERISTEEL CORPORATION
(*Suby of* GERDAU S/A.)
4221 W Boy Scout Blvd # 600, Tampa, FL 33607-5760
Tel (813) 286-8383 *Founded/Ownrshp* 1956
Sales 1.4MMM^E *EMP* 7,850
SIC 3312 Blast furnaces & steel mills
Pr: Mario Longhi
**Pr:* Guilherme C Gerdau Johannpeter
**COO:* Terry Sutter
**CFO:* Barbara Smith
**VP:* Peter Campo
**VP:* Carl Czarnik
VP: Paul J Lawrence
**VP:* Robert E Lewis
VP: J Neal McCullohs III
**VP:* Rodrigo Souza
**VP:* Yuan Wang
VP: Matthew Yeatman
VP: Matthew C Yeatman

GERDAU AMERISTEEL DINWIDDIE CO
See VIRGINIA CHAPARRAL INC

D-U-N-S 14-003-8204 IMP
GERDAU AMERISTEEL SAYREVILLE INC
(*Suby of* GERDAU LONG STEEL AMERICA) ★
N Crossman Rd, Sayreville, NJ 08872
Tel (732) 721-6600 *Founded/Ownrshp* 1978
Sales 228.8MM^E *EMP* 45,000
SIC 3312 Blast furnaces & steel mills; Bars & bar shapes, steel, hot-rolled
Pr: Peter Campo
**VP:* Carl Czarnik
**VP:* Jim Kerkvliet
**VP:* Andre Pires
VP: Mark Quiring
**VP:* Rodrigo Souza
**VP:* Yuan Wang
**VP:* Matthew Yeatman

D-U-N-S 00-409-3456 IMP/EXP
GERDAU AMERISTEEL US INC (FL)
GERDAU LONG STEEL NORTH AMER
(*Suby of* GERDAU LONG STEEL AMERICA) ★
4221 W Boy Scout Blvd # 600, Tampa, FL 33607-5760
Tel (813) 286-8383 *Founded/Ownrshp* 1956, 1999
Sales 7.8MMM^E *EMP* 45,000
SIC 3312 3449 3315 Hot-rolled iron & steel products; Bars & bar shapes, steel, hot-rolled; Structural shapes & pilings, steel; Bars, concrete reinforcing: fabricated steel; Spikes, steel: wire or cut; Welded steel wire fabric; Nails, steel: wire or cut
CEO: Peter J Campo
Pr: Guilherme G Johannpeter
Treas: George Beck
Treas: Santiago Gil
Ex VP: Paulo Vasconcellos
Sr VP: T Barker
Sr VP: D Bourdon
VP: D Ballard
VP: Andr Beaudry
VP: Carl W Czarnik
VP: Andre Pires De Oliveira Dias
VP: James R Kerkvliet
VP: Expedito Luz
VP: Rodrigo Souza
VP: Yuan Wang
VP: Matthew C Yeatman
Exec: E Hendry
Board of Directors: Frederico Carlos Gerdau Jo, Andre Bier Johannpeter, Klaus Gerdau Johannpeter, Rick J Mills, Carlos Petry

D-U-N-S 19-274-0640 IMP/EXP
GERDAU AMERISTEEL US INC
(*Suby of* GERDAU LONG STEEL NORTH AMER) ★
300 Ward Rd, Midlothian, TX 76065-9646
Tel (972) 775-8241 *Founded/Ownrshp* 2007
Sales 228.8MM^E *EMP* 1,450
SIC 3312 Blast furnaces & steel mills
CEO: Mario Longhi
**CFO:* Barbara Smith
**VP:* Robert E Lewis
S&M/VP: Charles Clifton

GERDAU LONG STEEL AMERICA
See GERDAU USA INC

GERDAU LONG STEEL NORTH AMER
See GERDAU AMERISTEEL US INC

D-U-N-S 82-632-9299 IMP/EXP
GERDAU MACSTEEL INC
NITRO STEEL
(*Suby of* GRUPO GERDAU DE EMPREENDIMENTOS LTDA.)
5591 Morrill Rd, Jackson, MI 49201-7084
Tel (517) 782-0415 *Founded/Ownrshp* 2008
Sales 374.2MM^E *EMP* 1,200
SIC 3316 3312 Cold finishing of steel shapes; Bars & bar shapes, steel, cold-finished: own hot-rolled
Pr: Mark Marcucci
Sr VP: Martin H Dodd
Sr VP: Glenn Harkness
VP: Renee Arze
VP: Paul Giddens
VP: Chris Knudstrup
VP: Fernando Peredo
**VP:* Rick Szink
CIO: Frank Thomas
Plnt Mgr: Kendall Mickley
Mktg Dir: Charles Short Jr

D-U-N-S 79-046-9717
GERDAU REINFORCING STEEL
(*Suby of* GERDAU LONG STEEL NORTH AMER) ★
3880 Murphy Canyon Rd # 100, San Diego, CA 92123-4410
Tel (858) 737-7700 *Founded/Ownrshp* 2006
Sales 459.2MM^E *EMP* 1,000
SIC 1541 Steel building construction
Prin: Christopher Ervin
Treas: Steven Fellows
Dir Risk M: Jennifer Martin
Off Mgr: Kimberli Clement

D-U-N-S 19-408-1451 IMP
GERDAU USA INC
GERDAU LONG STEEL AMERICA
(*Suby of* GERDAU AMERISTEEL CORPORATION)
4221 W Boy Scout Blvd, Tampa, FL 33607-5743
Tel (813) 286-8383 *Founded/Ownrshp* 2000
Sales 8.1MMM^E *EMP* 45,000
SIC 3312 3449 3315 Blast furnaces & steel mills; Hot-rolled iron & steel products; Bars & bar shapes, steel, hot-rolled; Structural shapes & pilings, steel; Bars, concrete reinforcing: fabricated steel; Spikes, steel: wire or cut; Welded steel wire fabric; Nails, steel: wire or cut
Pr: Guilherme Johannpeter
**VP:* Peter J Campo
**VP:* Carl W Czarnik
**VP:* Rodrigo Ferreira De Souza
Info Man: Della Erickson
Ql Cn Mgr: Jim Trentadue
Board of Directors: Frederico Carlos Gerdau Jo, Andre Bier Johannpeter, Jorge Gerdau Johannpeter

GERIATRIC OTRACH CLNC/CARE MGT
See HURLEY MEDICAL CENTER

D-U-N-S 10-384-0831
GERLAND CORP
(*Suby of* 2ML REAL ESTATE INTERESTS INC) ★
3131 Pawnee St, Houston, TX 77054-3302
Tel (713) 746-3600 *Founded/Ownrshp* 2013
Sales 209.6MM^E *EMP* 1,476^E
SIC 5411 Grocery stores, chain
Pr: Kevin P Doris
**Ex VP:* Jeffrey K Reeder
**VP:* Donald Benefield
**VP:* Bill Bouquet
Sls&Mrk Ex: Alex Vonsehrwald

D-U-N-S 05-216-3342
GERMAIN TOYOTA
GERMAIN TOYOTA OF COLUMBUS
4250 Morse Xing, Columbus, OH 43219-3024
Tel (239) 592-5550 *Founded/Ownrshp* 1988
Sales 154.5MM^E *EMP* 400
SIC 5511

GERMAIN TOYOTA OF COLUMBUS
See GERMAIN TOYOTA

D-U-N-S 00-693-8849
■ GERMAN AMERICAN BANCORP
(*Suby of* GERMAN AMERICAN BANCORP INC) ★
711 Main St, Jasper, IN 47546-3042
Tel (812) 482-1314 *Founded/Ownrshp* 1910
Sales NA *EMP* 341
Accts Crowe Horwath Llp Indianapoli
SIC 6022 State commercial banks
Pr: Kenneth Sendelweck
**CFO:* Brad Rust
**Sr VP:* Chris Melton

D-U-N-S 11-974-8101
▲ GERMAN AMERICAN BANCORP INC
711 Main St, Jasper, IN 47546-3042
Tel (812) 482-1314 *Founded/Ownrshp* 1982
Sales NA *EMP* 596^E
Tkr Sym GABC *Exch* NGS
SIC 6022 State commercial banks
Ch Bd: Mark A Schroeder
Pr: Clay W Ewing
CFO: Bradley M Rust
Chf Cred: Keith A Leinenbach
Ex VP: Randall L Braun
Ex VP: D Neil Dauby
Ex VP: Brent Sternberg
VP: Clay M Barrett
Opers Mgr: Connie Goebel
Board of Directors: Raymond W Snowden, Douglas A Bawel, Michael J Voyles, Lonnie D Collins, Christina M Ernst, Marc D Fine, U Butch Klem, J David Lett, Chris A Ramsey, M Darren Root, Thomas W Seger

D-U-N-S 04-601-5194
GERMAN MOTORS CORP
BMW OF SAN FRANCISCO
1140 Harrison St, San Francisco, CA 94103-4525
Tel (415) 590-3773 *Founded/Ownrshp* 1964
Sales 90.9MM^E *EMP* 240^E

SIC 5511 7532 Automobiles, new & used; Top & body repair & paint shops
CEO: Henry Schmitt
* *Sec:* Michael Greening
* *VP:* Michele Schmitt
Exec: Evette Caceres
Off Mgr: Willis Kirk
Mktg Dir: Keith Howard
Sls Mgr: Jessy Custodio

D-U-N-S 07-940-3986
GERMANIA FARM MUTUAL INSURANCE ASSOCIATION
507 Highway 290 E, Brenham, TX 77833-5709
Tel (979) 836-5224 *Founded/Ownrshp* 1897
Sales NA *EMP* 366
SIC 6311 6331 Life insurance; Fire, marine & casualty insurance
Pr: Paul Ehlert
* *Sec:* Derrell Krebs
* *VP:* Gary Weiss
* *Prin:* David Sommer
CTO: Nancy Mahlmann
Board of Directors: William Boeer

D-U-N-S 87-650-9167
GERMANIA INSURANCE CO
(*Suby of* GERMANIA FARM MUTUAL INSURANCE ASSOCIATION) ★
507 Highway 290 E, Brenham, TX 77833-5709
Tel (979) 836-5224 *Founded/Ownrshp* 1985
Sales NA *EMP* 300
SIC 6411 Insurance agents, brokers & service
Pr: Paul Ehlert
* *Sec:* Derrell Gene Krebs
Comm Dir: Laura Popp
IT Man: Dahmann Carl

D-U-N-S 55-613-0136 IMP/EXP
GERRESHEIMER GLASS INC
537 Crystal Ave, Vineland, NJ 08360-3238
Tel (856) 692-3600 *Founded/Ownrshp* 1987
Sales 500.0MM *EMP* 1,000
SIC 3221 Medicine bottles, glass
Ch: Axel Herberg
* *CEO:* Uwe Rohrhoff
CFO: George Annen
* *CFO:* Rainer Beaujean
CFO: Chris Bouffard
CFO: Hans-Jurgen Wiecha
* *Treas:* Sanjay Dhawan
Sr VP: Roger Kurinsky
VP: Norm Angel
VP: Vincent Delfini
VP: Larry Griffith

D-U-N-S 09-873-2654
GERRITYS SUPER MARKET INC
CITY PROVISION
950 N South Rd Ste 5, Scranton, PA 18504-1430
Tel (570) 342-4144 *Founded/Ownrshp* 1971
Sales 168.8MM *EMP* 1,100
Accts Mcgrail Merkel Quinn & Associa
SIC 5411 Grocery stores, independent
Pr: Joyce A Fasula
CFO: Anna Corcoran
Exec: Doug Stark
Brnch Mgr: Jeff Smith
Genl Mgr: Jack McDonald

GERRY LANE CHEVROLET
See GERRY LANE ENTERPRISES INC

D-U-N-S 03-418-7534
GERRY LANE ENTERPRISES INC (MS)
GERRY LANE CHEVROLET
6505 Florida Blvd, Baton Rouge, LA 70806-4464
Tel (225) 926-4600 *Founded/Ownrshp* 1986, 1988
Sales 112.9MM *EMP* 250
SIC 5511

GERSHOW RECYCLING CENTERS
See GERSHOW RECYCLING CORP

D-U-N-S 04-447-6372 IMP
GERSHOW RECYCLING CORP
GERSHOW RECYCLING CENTERS
71 Peconic Ave, Medford, NY 11763-3201
Tel (631) 289-6188 *Founded/Ownrshp* 1964
Sales 122.9MM^E *EMP* 172
SIC 4953 Recycling, waste materials
CEO: Sam Gershowitz
* *Pr:* Kevin Gershowitz
* *VP:* Joseph Bertuccio
* *Prin:* Elliot Gershowitz
Info Man: Ken Assenmacher

D-U-N-S 00-890-6885 IMP/EXP
GERSON CO (MO)
STERLING
1450 S Lone Elm Rd, Olathe, KS 66061-7256
Tel (913) 262-7400 *Founded/Ownrshp* 1942
Sales 97.9MM *EMP* 302
SIC 5193 5199 5023 5094

D-U-N-S 83-196-3124
GERSON LEHRMAN GROUP INC
60 E 42nd St Fl 3, New York, NY 10165-1200
Tel (212) 223-0839 *Founded/Ownrshp* 1998
Sales 257.4MM *EMP* 300
SIC 6282 Investment research
CEO: Alexander Saint-Amand
COO: Alexander Saint-Mand
CFO: Michael Blumenstein
* *CFO:* Bart Catalane
Ofcr: Thomas Hutzel
Top Exec: Alison Chan
Sr VP: Matthew Creedon
VP: Sarah Babcock
VP: Michael Barbano
VP: Jessica Byers
VP: Jean Carrelli
VP: Robbie Chana
VP: Michael Daecher
VP: Jackie Dille
VP: Jacquelyn Dille
VP: Zecki Dossal
VP: Jack Gage
VP: Kristi Knaack
VP: Melinda Lee
VP: Kevin Legg
VP: Dana Maglio

GERSTCO DIVISION
See ARTIFLEX MANUFACTURING LLC

D-U-N-S 07-175-2414 IMP
GERTEN GREENHOUSES & GARDEN CENTER INC
5500 Blaine Ave, Inver Grove Heights, MN 55076-1206
Tel (651) 450-1501 *Founded/Ownrshp* 1952
Sales 93.8MM^E *EMP* 450^E
SIC 5261 5193 Nurseries & garden centers; Nurseries; Nursery stock, seeds & bulbs; Nursery stock
Prin: Lewis Gerten
* *Treas:* Gino Pitera
* *VP:* Glen Gerten
IT Man: Scott Fischer

D-U-N-S 00-304-2991 IMP/EXP
GERTRUDE HAWK CHOCOLATES INC (PA)
9 Keystone Industrial Par, Dunmore, PA 18512-1544
Tel (570) 342-7556 *Founded/Ownrshp* 1936
Sales 258.9MM^E *EMP* 650
SIC 2064 2066 Candy & other confectionery products; Chocolate & cocoa products
Pr: William E Auerey
* *Ch Bd:* David W Hawk
* *Pr:* William Aubrey
* *CFO:* Steve Arling

GES
See GROUNDWATER AND ENVIRONMENTAL SERVICES INC

D-U-N-S 17-121-9749 IMP
GESTAMP ALABAMA LLC
(*Suby of* GESTAMP NORTH AMERICA INC) ★
7000 Jefferson Metro Pkwy, Mc Calla, AL 35111-3956
Tel (205) 477-1412 *Founded/Ownrshp* 2012
Sales 284.6MM *EMP* 450^E
SIC 3465 Automotive stampings; Body parts, automobile: stamped metal
Pr: Francisco Riberas
Ex VP: James Barry
Dir IT: Andrew Stewart
IT Man: Josue Najera
Mtls Mgr: David Murrell
Mfg Mgr: Dan Fox

GESTAMP AUTOMOCION
See GESTAMP CHATTANOOGA LLC

D-U-N-S 83-163-2505 IMP
GESTAMP CHATTANOOGA LLC
GESTAMP AUTOMOCION
(*Suby of* GESTAMP NORTH AMERICA INC) ★
3063 Hickory Valley Rd, Chattanooga, TN 37421-1266
Tel (423) 305-6300 *Founded/Ownrshp* 2009
Sales 123.2MM *EMP* 1,000
SIC 3465 Automotive stampings
CEO: Jeffrey Wilson
* *Pr:* John Craig
* *CFO:* James Barry

D-U-N-S 16-001-6291 IMP/EXP
GESTAMP MASON LLC
(*Suby of* GESTAMP NORTH AMERICA INC) ★
200 E Kipp Rd, Mason, MI 48854-9291
Tel (517) 244-8800 *Founded/Ownrshp* 2004
Sales 191.9MM^E *EMP* 489
SIC 3398 5013 3714 3711 3465 Metal heat treating; Motor vehicle supplies & new parts; Motor vehicle parts & accessories; Motor vehicles & car bodies; Automotive stampings
CEO: Jeffrey Wilson
* *Pr:* John Craig
* *CFO:* James Barry
Ex Dir: Debra Doyle
Plnt Mgr: Walter Hill

D-U-N-S 62-366-5333 IMP
GESTAMP NORTH AMERICA INC
(*Suby of* ACEK DESARROLLO Y GESTION INDUSTRIAL SL.)
2701 Troy Center Dr # 150, Troy, MI 48084-4753
Tel (248) 743-3400 *Founded/Ownrshp* 2004
Sales 1.1MMM^E *EMP* 1,057^E
SIC 5013 Automotive supplies & parts
Pr: Jeffrey Wilson
* *CFO:* James Barry
* *VP:* John Craig
Prgrm Mgr: Dave Borkowski
Prgrm Mgr: Crystal Wiese
IT Man: Gregory Lefler
Ql Cn Mgr: Herb Mahony

D-U-N-S 78-798-0007 IMP
GESTAMP SOUTH CAROLINA LLC
(*Suby of* GESTAMP NORTH AMERICA INC) ★
1 Lsp Dr, Union, SC 29379-7785
Tel (864) 466-3960 *Founded/Ownrshp* 2009
Sales 252.7MM *EMP* 370
SIC 3465 Automotive stampings
CEO: Jeffrey Wilson
* *Pr:* John Craig
* *CFO:* James Barry

D-U-N-S 07-854-3536 IMP
GESTAMP WEST VIRGINIA LLC
(*Suby of* GESTAMP NORTH AMERICA INC) ★
3100 Maccorkle Ave Sw, South Charleston, WV 25303-1473
Tel (304) 744-4601 *Founded/Ownrshp* 2012
Sales 135.5MM *EMP* 351
SIC 3469 Stamping metal for the trade
CEO: Jeffrey Wilson
* *Pr:* John Craig
* *CFO:* James Barry

D-U-N-S 88-311-0983
GET FRESH PRODUCE INC
1441 Brewster Creek Blvd, Bartlett, IL 60103-1695
Tel (630) 837-9700 *Founded/Ownrshp* 1996
Sales 100.6MM^E *EMP* 61
SIC 5148 Fresh fruits & vegetables
Pr: Eugenio Alimondi
* *CFO:* Sharon Costabile

D-U-N-S 61-757-9149 IMP
GET FRESH SALES INC
FRESH CUTS
6745 Escondido St, Las Vegas, NV 89119-3858
Tel (702) 897-8522 *Founded/Ownrshp* 1990
Sales 209.0MM^E *EMP* 300
SIC 5148 Fresh fruits & vegetables
Pr: Dominic Caldara
* *CFO:* Scott Goldberg
Ql Cn Mgr: Karla Mendoza
Sales Exec: Chris Sanderson

D-U-N-S 00-581-7272
GET SOLD REALTY INC (VA)
BERKSHIRE HATHAWAY HOME
1171 Cntl Pk Blvd Ste 200, Fredericksburg, VA 22401
Tel (540) 371-7653 *Founded/Ownrshp* 2007
Sales 190.0MM *EMP* 12
SIC 6531 Real estate agents & managers
Pr: Dan Lesher

D-U-N-S 02-718-5121
GETYOU FOUND ONLINE MARKETING INC
301 S Elm St Ste 401, Greensboro, NC 27401-2636
Tel (336) 790-6735 *Founded/Ownrshp* 2008
Sales 284.9MM *EMP* 4
SIC 8742 Marketing consulting services
Pr: Jessamyn Bean
* *VP:* Peter Raines

D-U-N-S 05-577-8088 IMP/EXP
GETINGE USA INC
(*Suby of* GETINGE AB)
1777 E Henrietta Rd, Rochester, NY 14623-3133
Tel (585) 475-1400 *Founded/Ownrshp* 1997
Sales 115.7MM^E *EMP* 600
SIC 3842 3841 Sterilizers, hospital & surgical; Surgical & medical instruments
Pr: Charles Carrier
* *Ch Bd:* Andrew Ray
* *CFO:* Chris Dorsey
* *VP:* Terry D Cooke
VP: John Hansson
VP: Mike Kotsch
VP: Shen Lu
VP: Michael Treude
Area Mgr: Charles Dacey
CIO: Rick Alvarado
IT Man: Robert Dorsaneo

D-U-N-S 19-861-9459
GETRONICS US OPERATIONS INC
(*Suby of* GETRONICS USA INC) ★
100 Ames Pond Dr Ste 99, Tewksbury, MA 01876-1240
Tel (978) 625-5000 *Founded/Ownrshp* 2003
Sales 7.0MM^E *EMP* 1,140^E
SIC 7373 Computer integrated systems design
CEO: Kevin Roach

D-U-N-S 00-101-8167
GETRONICS USA INC (DE)
(*Suby of* COMPUCOM SYSTEMS INC) ★
290 Concord Rd, Billerica, MA 01821-3405
Tel (978) 625-5000 *Founded/Ownrshp* 1951, 2008
Sales 130.4MM^E *EMP* 2,600
SIC 7378 7373 7379 Computer & data processing equipment repair/maintenance; Local area network (LAN) systems integrator; Computer related consulting services; Computer related maintenance services
CEO: Mark Cook
* *CEO:* Andreas Ziegenhain
* *CFO:* Pom Burie
* *Treas:* William Clark
* *VP:* David Buka
MIS Dir: Roger Gilfert
Mktg Dir: Payton Chung

D-U-N-S 02-846-4894 IMP
■ **GETTY IMAGES INC**
(*Suby of* CARLYLE GROUP L P) ★
605 5th Ave S Ste 400, Seattle, WA 98104-3887
Tel (206) 925-5000 *Founded/Ownrshp* 1997
Sales 27.1MM^E *EMP* 1,300
SIC 5961
CEO: Dawn Airey
Pr: Dawn Elizabeth Airey
COO: Nicholas E Evans-Lombe
CFO: Tara Comonte
Ch: Jonathan D Klein Cha
Ex VP: Linda Ranz
Sr VP: Susan Smith Ellis
Sr VP: James C Gurke
Sr VP: Lee Martin
VP: Denise Banister
VP: Jonathan Broad
VP: Carmen Cano
VP: Jonathan Lockwood
VP: Scott Miskimens
VP: Carmin Romanelli
VP: Maged Zaher
Board of Directors: Jay Rossiter

D-U-N-S 05-773-0202
▲ **GETTY REALTY CORP**
2 Jericho Plz Ste 110, Jericho, NY 11753-1681
Tel (516) 478-5400 *Founded/Ownrshp* 1955
Sales 110.7MM *EMP* 32^E
Tkr Sym GTY *Exch* NYS
SIC 6798 Real estate investment trusts
Pr: Christopher J Constant
Ch Bd: Leo Liebowitz
COO: Mark J Olear
CFO: Danion Fielding
Sr VP: Joshua Dicker
Board of Directors: Milton Cooper, Philip E Coviello, Richard E Montag, Howard B Safenowitz

D-U-N-S 07-144-5134
GETTYSBURG COLLEGE (PA)
MAJESTIC THEATER
300 N Washington St, Gettysburg, PA 17325-1483
Tel (717) 337-6000 *Founded/Ownrshp* 1832
Sales 133.3MM *EMP* 101^E
Accts Kpmg Llp Harrisburg Pa
SIC 8221 College, except junior
Pr: Janet M Riggs
Chf Inves: Andrew Parker
Ofcr: Kevin McGuire
Ofcr: Alix Shrader
Ofcr: Samantha Wilson
Assoc VP: Michael Martys
VP: Taylor Beck
VP: Aimee Bosman
VP: Barbara Fritze
* *VP:* Daniel L Konstalid
VP: Patricia A Lawson
VP: Savannah Rose
VP: Henning Wrage
Exec: Charles Stockman
Assoc Dir: Daniel Albertson
Assoc Dir: Robert Kallin
Assoc Dir: Jill Titus
Comm Dir: Jamie Yates
Board of Directors: James Wiltgen

D-U-N-S 07-118-6118
GETTYSBURG HOSPITAL
(*Suby of* YORK HOSPITAL) ★
147 Gettys St, Gettysburg, PA 17325-2536
Tel (717) 334-2121 *Founded/Ownrshp* 2001
Sales 165.1MM *EMP* 800
Accts Ernst & Young Llp
SIC 8062 General medical & surgical hospitals
Pr: Jane Hyde
* *V Ch:* Michael Barley
Sr VP: Craig Long

D-U-N-S 10-522-4849
GETWELLNETWORK INC
7700 Old Georgetown Rd # 4, Bethesda, MD 20814-6224
Tel (240) 482-3200 *Founded/Ownrshp* 1999
Sales 83.8MM^E *EMP* 220^E
SIC 7371 Computer software development & applications
CEO: Micheal O Neal Jr
* *COO:* David D Bennett
* *CFO:* Wellford Dillard
* *CFO:* Bart Witteveen
Bd of Dir: Scott Frederick
* *Ofcr:* John George
Ex VP: Bruce Matter
Sr VP: Jim Cato
Sr VP: Stephen Hiscott
Sr VP: Sharon Kaufman
VP: Rene Barron
VP: Tony Cook
VP: Greg Essler
VP: Jeff Fallon
VP: Cheryl Gnehm
VP: Kriste J Grau
VP: Vinnie Whibbs
Board of Directors: Anthony J Principi

D-U-N-S 07-980-8813
GETYOURPERFUME.COM INC
700 Columbia St Bldg 302, Brooklyn, NY 11231-1914
Tel (888) 264-2899 *Founded/Ownrshp* 2014
Sales 170.0MM *EMP* 6
SIC 5999 Toiletries, cosmetics & perfumes
Owner: ARI Werzberger

D-U-N-S 07-466-5175
■ **GETZ BROS& CO INC**
(*Suby of* MARMON INDUSTRIAL LLC) ★
225 W Washington St # 1900, Chicago, IL 60606-2418
Tel (312) 845-5686 *Founded/Ownrshp* 1981
Sales 301.7MM^E *EMP* 1,800
SIC 5047 5031 5141 5065 5082 Medical equipment & supplies; Building materials, exterior; Building materials, interior; Groceries, general line; Electronic parts & equipment; General construction machinery & equipment; Logging & forestry machinery & equipment
CFO: Robert Lorch
MIS Mgr: Eric Mice

GEWARREN
See GEORGE E WARREN CORP

D-U-N-S 10-811-4542
■ **GEXA ENERGY LP**
(*Suby of* NEXTERA ENERGY INC) ★
20455 State Highway 249 # 200, Houston, TX 77070-2758
Tel (713) 961-9399 *Founded/Ownrshp* 2005
Sales 126.8MM^E *EMP* 300
SIC 4911 Electric services
Pr: Brian Landrum
Treas: Mark R Sorenson
VP: Larry Boisvert
VP: Jim Brown
VP: Kenny Matula
IT Man: Krystal Preston
IT Man: Jim Wohl
Opers Mgr: Nick Krause
Sls Dir: Keith Black
Sls Dir: Scott Kelly
Sls Mgr: John Winchester

GEXPRO
See GENERAL SUPPLY & SERVICES INC

D-U-N-S 92-619-8610
GF INVESTORS LLC
U.S. GREENFIBER
60 E 42nd St Rm 4510, New York, NY 10165-0012
Tel (212) 457-1138 *Founded/Ownrshp* 2013
Sales 145.3MM^E *EMP* 539^E
SIC 1742 Insulation, buildings
CEO: Michael Green
Sr VP: Ben Kramer

D-U-N-S 10-762-6434 IMP/EXP
GF MACHINING SOLUTIONS LLC
AGIE CHARMILLES
(*Suby of* GEORGE FISCHER INC) ★
560 Bond St, Lincolnshire, IL 60069-4207
Tel (847) 913-5300 *Founded/Ownrshp* 2007
Sales 90.1MM^E *EMP* 189
SIC 5084 Machine tools & metalworking machinery
Pr: Glynn Fletcher
CFO: Gregg Denig

D-U-N-S 04-939-1156
GFG MANAGEMENT LLC
5555 Glenridge Connector # 850, Atlanta, GA 30342-4810
Tel (770) 514-4871 *Founded/Ownrshp* 2010
Sales 211.0MM[E] *EMP* 2,277[E]
SIC 5461 Cookies

D-U-N-S 15-235-9092
■ GFI GROUP INC
(*Suby of* BGC PARTNERS INC) ★
55 Water St, New York, NY 10041-0004
Tel (212) 968-4100 *Founded/Ownrshp* 2015
Sales 949.8MM[E] *EMP* 2,087[E]
SIC 6211 Security brokers & dealers
CEO: Colin Heffron
**COO:* Ronald Levi
**CFO:* James A Peers
Ofcr: Suet Chong
Ofcr: Judy Leung
Ofcr: Bill Shields
Ex VP: Michael Weiser
VP: Lori Finck
VP: Melissa Mundy
VP: Douglas Steele
VP: Jason Zullin

D-U-N-S 82-465-4941
GFI MANAGEMENT SERVICES INC
G F I
50 Brdwy 140 Brdwy 41, New York, NY 10004
Tel (212) 668-1444 *Founded/Ownrshp* 1993
Sales 150.3MM[E] *EMP* 1,000[E]
SIC 6513 6512 Apartment building operators; Nonresidential building operators
CEO: Abe Eisner
**Pr:* Allen I Gross
Pr: Tice Vieira
CFO: Paul Glick
CFO: Jennifer McLean
**Sr VP:* Brian Gross
**VP:* Steven Hurwitz
VP: Daniel Lerer
VP: Amanda Pinto
VP: Jeremy Selman
VP: Randi Sherman
VP: William Watkins
**VP:* Michael Weiser

D-U-N-S 07-870-4251 IMP
GFK CUSTOM RESEARCH LLC
(*Suby of* GFK NORTH AMERICA HOLDING GMBH)
200 Liberty St Fl 4, New York, NY 10281-4111
Tel (212) 240-5300 *Founded/Ownrshp* 2014
Sales 94.3MM[E] *EMP* 900
SIC 8732 Market analysis or research; Opinion research
CEO: Matthias Hartmann
**CFO:* Pamela Knapp
Chf Cred: Thomas Finkle
Ex VP: Pat Pellegrini

GFOC HOLDINGS,
See GAZETTE CO

GFP PLASTICS
See GENERAL FOAM PLASTICS CORP

GFPS
See GREAT FALLS PUBLIC SCHOOLS DIST1

D-U-N-S 09-009-9854 IMP/EXP
GFR MEDIA LLC
EL NUEVO DIA
50 Carr 165 Ste 1, Guaynabo, PR 00968-8024
Tel (787) 641-8000 *Founded/Ownrshp* 1963
Sales 160.5MM[E] *EMP* 837[E]
SIC 4789 2711 5963 Pipeline terminal facilities, independently operated; Newspapers, publishing & printing; Newspapers, home delivery, not by printers or publishers
CEO: Maria Eugenia Ferre Rangel
**CFO:* Ana M Bonilla
VP: Gustavo A Cordova
**VP:* Jose M Espinal
VP: Antonio Ferre
VP: Elson Frontany
**VP:* Luis Gautier
**VP:* Antonio Hidalgo
**VP:* Jorge Mercado
**VP:* Carlos Nido
Genl Mgr: Agustin Meisozo

GFS
See GLOBAL FINISHING SOLUTIONS LLC

D-U-N-S 84-850-7315
GG MCGUIGGAN CORP
1085 Snelling Ave N, Saint Paul, MN 55108-2705
Tel (651) 646-4544 *Founded/Ownrshp* 1877
Sales 123.2MM[E] *EMP* 480
SIC 2679 3993 2752 Labels, paper: made from purchased material; Displays & cutouts, window & lobby; Commercial printing, offset
Pr: John P Hickey
**COO:* William J Hickey III
**CFO:* David Baumgardner

D-U-N-S 08-040-4898
GGC ACQUISITION HOLDINGS CORP
3450 E Miraloma Ave, Anaheim, CA 92806-2101
Tel (714) 414-4000 *Founded/Ownrshp* 2016
Sales 151.9MM[E] *EMP* 8,777[E]
SIC 6719 Investment holding companies, except banks
Prin: David Dominik

D-U-N-S 96-870-0554
GGC ADMINISTRATION LLC
GOLDEN GATE CAPITAL
1 Embarcadero Ctr Fl 39, San Francisco, CA 94111-3735
Tel (415) 983-2700 *Founded/Ownrshp* 2010
Sales 1.4MMM[E] *EMP* 8,590[E]
SIC 2591 Drapery hardware & blinds & shades
Pr: Stephan Scholl

D-U-N-S 05-557-6513
GGNSC HOLDINGS LLC
GOLDEN LIVING
(*Suby of* GOLDEN LIVING) ★
5220 Tennyson Pkwy # 400, Plano, TX 75024-4271
Tel (972) 372-6300 *Founded/Ownrshp* 2011
Sales 561.3MM[E] *EMP* 400[E]
SIC 8059 Rest home, with health care
VP: Michael Yao
Snr Mgr: Carla Kitts

D-U-N-S 80-863-0284
GGNSC HOLDINGS LLC
GOLDEN LIVING
(*Suby of* GOLDEN LIVING) ★
1000 Fianna Way, Fort Smith, AR 72919-9008
Tel (479) 201-2000 *Founded/Ownrshp* 2005
Sales 561.3MM[E] *EMP* 400
Accts Ernst & Young Llp Rogers Ar
SIC 8059 8051 8082 8322 Nursing home, except skilled & intermediate care facility; Skilled nursing care facilities; Home health care services; Rehabilitation services
CEO: Ronald Silva
Pr: Neil Kurtz
COO: Wendy Susienka
CFO: Ruth Ann Harmon
Treas: Shelly Henson
Treas: Ann Truitt
Ofcr: Larry Peters
Sr VP: Randy Cates
Sr VP: Michael Karicher
Sr VP: Michael Yao
VP: Nicholas Finn
VP: Jim Glensky
VP: Paul Goss
VP: Scott Norton
VP: Tricia Roberts
VP: Lisa Spears
Exec: Mickey Sellard

D-U-N-S 80-303-3943
■ GGP INC
(*Suby of* GENERAL GROWTH PROPERTIES INC) ★
110 N Wacker Dr, Chicago, IL 60606-1511
Tel (312) 960-5000 *Founded/Ownrshp* 1986
Sales 723.6MM[E] *EMP* 1,500[E]
Accts Deloitte & Touche Llp Chicago
SIC 6798 Real estate investment trusts
CEO: Sandeep Mathrani
Pt: Kate Sheehy
Pr: Gary Kahnke
Pr: Andrew Silberfein
COO: Bradley Dexter
COO: Shobi Khan
CFO: Michael B Berman
CFO: Gregory Hinton
Ex VP: Alan Barocas
Ex VP: Michael Berman
Sr VP: Sharon Palonia
Sr VP: Randy Richardson
VP: Michael McCall
VP: Thomas McCarthy
VP: Linda White
Board of Directors: Richard B Clark, Mary Lou Fiala, Bruce J Flatt, John K Haley, Cyrus Madon, David J Neithercut, Mark R Patterson, John G Schreiber

D-U-N-S 00-110-2508 IMP
■ GH BASS & CO
(*Suby of* WILSONS LEATHER OUTLET) ★
200 Madison Ave, New York, NY 10016-3903
Tel (212) 381-3900 *Founded/Ownrshp* 1987, 2013
Sales 84.8MM[E] *EMP* 4,100
SIC 3144 3143 3149 5661 Women's footwear, except athletic; Men's footwear, except athletic; Children's footwear, except athletic; Shoe stores
Pr: Bill Hutchison
Sr VP: Howard Renner

D-U-N-S 80-657-3619
GH DAIRY
GH PROCESSING
14651 Grove Ave, Ontario, CA 91762-7704
Tel (909) 606-6455 *Founded/Ownrshp* 1987
Sales 130.7MM *EMP* 225
SIC 0241 Dairy farms
Pt: Gerben Hettinga

D-U-N-S 07-969-1078
GH HOLDINGS INC
(*Suby of* GULF OIL INTERNATIONAL UK LIMITED)
Madison & Van Buren Ave, Valley Forge, PA 19482
Tel (610) 666-4000 *Founded/Ownrshp* 2012
Sales 577.5MM[E] *EMP* 1,900
SIC 2869 2992 Hydraulic fluids, synthetic base; Lubricating oils & greases
CEO: Paul De Vivo
CFO: Keller Arnold
VP: Fernanda G Clifford

GH PHIPPS CNSTR COMPANIES
See GERALD H PHIPPS INC

GH PROCESSING
See GH DAIRY

D-U-N-S 92-774-7907
GHA TECHNOLOGIES INC
8998 E Raintree Dr, Scottsdale, AZ 85260-7024
Tel (480) 951-6865 *Founded/Ownrshp* 1999
Sales 138.9MM *EMP* 165
Accts Johnson Lawdahl Plic Cpa Ph
SIC 7373 Value-added resellers, computer systems
Pr: George Hertzberg
VP: Mike Chronquist
VP: Tom Matson
**VP:* Steven Nevins
VP Sls: Roy May
VP Sls: Chris Pedersen
Manager: Jesse Abeyta
Manager: Tim Cleary
Manager: Timothy Dial
Manager: Barry Eisler
Manager: Daniel Gillespie

D-U-N-S 00-359-3030
GHAFARI ASSOCIATES LLC
17101 Michigan Ave, Dearborn, MI 48126-2736
Tel (313) 271-6280 *Founded/Ownrshp* 2000
Sales 103.0MM[E] *EMP* 385
SIC 8711 Engineering services
V Ch: Rita Dunker
COO: Ali Solaksubasi
Sr VP: Ted Oberlies
VP: Robert K Burge
VP: Robert K Burgess
VP: Richard W Butwin
VP: James Davis
VP: Bill Herrmann
VP: Dearborn MI
VP: Steven Santucci
VP: Patrick J Smithbauer
Exec: Amish Dharia
Exec: Julie Griffin
Exec: Randi Schrieber
Comm Man: Michelle Plawecki

D-U-N-S 96-159-9466 EXP
■ GHC SPECIALTY BRANDS LLC
LAB SAFETY SUPPLY
(*Suby of* WW GRAINGER INC) ★
401 S Wright Rd, Janesville, WI 53546-8729
Tel (608) 754-2345 *Founded/Ownrshp* 2010
Sales 156.5MM[E] *EMP* 1,005[E]
SIC 5961 Catalog sales
Pr: M A Pulick
Ex VP: Phil West

D-U-N-S 15-350-8080 IMP
GHD SERVICES INC
CRA SERVICES
(*Suby of* CRA HOLDINGS INC)
2055 Niagara Falls Blvd, Niagara Falls, NY 14304-5702
Tel (716) 297-6150 *Founded/Ownrshp* 1976
Sales 307.8MM[E] *EMP* 1,000
SIC 8748 Environmental consultant
Pr: Steve Quigley
**Treas:* Anthony Ying
**Ex VP:* Glenn Turchan
Snr PM: Mike Fisher
Snr PM: Judy Gilbert
Snr PM: Steven Wilsey

GHI
See GROUP HEALTH INC

D-U-N-S 00-946-9701
GHILOTTI BROS INC (CA)
525 Jacoby St, San Rafael, CA 94901-5370
Tel (415) 454-7011 *Founded/Ownrshp* 1914, 1999
Sales 112.4MM[E] *EMP* 290
SIC 1611 1794 1623 Surfacing & paving; Grading; Highway & street paving contractor; Excavation work; Water, sewer & utility lines
CEO: Dante W Ghilotti
**Pr:* Michael M Ghilotti
**CFO:* Daniel Y Chin
**VP:* Thomas G Barr
VP: Frank Palagi
Off Mgr: Kelly Mollain
Mktg Dir: Fred Smith
Snr Mgr: Kyle Jarmicki

D-U-N-S 79-404-5542
GHILOTTI CONSTRUCTION CO INC
GCC
246 Ghilotti Ave, Santa Rosa, CA 95407-8152
Tel (707) 585-1221 *Founded/Ownrshp* 1992
Sales 150.2MM[E] *EMP* 275[E]
SIC 1629 Land preparation construction
CEO: Richard W Ghilotti

D-U-N-S 60-884-1342 IMP/EXP
GHIRARDELLI CHOCOLATE CO
(*Suby of* LINDT & SPRUNGLI (USA) INC) ★
1111 139th Ave, San Leandro, CA 94578-2616
Tel (510) 483-6970 *Founded/Ownrshp* 1852
Sales 184.4MM[E] *EMP* 650
SIC 5441 2066 5812 5149 Candy, nut & confectionery stores; Chocolate; Soda fountain; Chocolate
CEO: Martin Thompson
VP: Rob Budowski
VP: John Dodge
Dir: Vellayapan Kannappen
Genl Mgr: Mike Bouchard
Dir IT: Vincent Bonnet
S&M/VP: Marty Thompson
Mktg Dir: Dan Bush
Mktg Dir: Kym Hough
Mktg Dir: Jinny Lam
Mktg Dir: Jackie Ouellette

GHJ&M
See GOLDNER HAWN JOHNSON & MORRISON INC

D-U-N-S 55-659-2426
GHM CORP
12700 Hillcrest Rd # 291, Dallas, TX 75230-2033
Tel (972) 840-1200 *Founded/Ownrshp* 1978
Sales 238.8MM[E] *EMP* 1,500
SIC 3448 1799 5999 5561 Buildings, portable: prefabricated metal; Spa or hot tub installation or construction; Swimming pools, above ground; Recreational vehicle dealers
Pr: Guy H Morgan
**Sec:* Hicks B Morgan

D-U-N-S 00-132-6131 IMP/EXP
GHP II LLC
ANCHOR HOCKING INDUS GL DIV
(*Suby of* ANCHOR HOCKING CO) ★
1115 W 5th Ave, Lancaster, OH 43130-2938
Tel (740) 687-2500 *Founded/Ownrshp* 1905
Sales 148.0MM[E] *EMP* 600
SIC 3229 3089 3411 3221 Tableware, glass or glass ceramic; Cooking utensils, glass or glass ceramic; Cups, plastic, except foam; Plates, plastic; Bottle caps, molded plastic; Bowl covers, plastic; Metal cans; Glass containers
CEO: Mark Eichorn
**CFO:* Mark Hedstrom

GHR
See GENERAL HEALTHCARE RESOURCES INC

D-U-N-S 13-029-5350 IMP
GHSP INC
CONVERGENCE TECHNOLOGIES
(*Suby of* JSJ CORP) ★
1250 S Beechtree St, Grand Haven, MI 49417-2840
Tel (248) 588-5095 *Founded/Ownrshp* 1999
Sales 222.5MM[E] *EMP* 825
SIC 3714 Motor vehicle parts & accessories
Ch: Jerry Scott
**Pr:* Paul Doyle
**Pr:* Jeff Smith
CFO: Ron Wallish
Genl Mgr: Eric Bryant
Genl Mgr: Dave Jerovsek
Genl Mgr: Rick Leffler
Snr Sftwr: Adam Bouwens
Snr Sftwr: Long Lee
Snr Sftwr: Gordon Peckham
IT Man: Jack Sischo

D-U-N-S 00-808-0756 IMP/EXP
GHX INDUSTRIAL LLC
G H X INDL
(*Suby of* UNITED DISTRIBUTORS GROUP INC) ★
3430 S Sam Houston Pkwy E, Houston, TX 77047-6531
Tel (713) 222-2231 *Founded/Ownrshp* 2007
Sales 275.0MM *EMP* 535
SIC 3053 3052 3061 Gaskets & sealing devices; Rubber hose; Oil & gas field machinery rubber goods (mechanical)
CEO: Daniel Ahuero
**Pr:* Richard Harrison
**CFO:* Dan Maddox
**VP:* Roy Torres
CIO: Cliff Nelson
Natl Sales: Jerod Griffis
Sales Asso: Kelly Broussard
Sales Asso: Ryan Lanier

D-U-N-S 80-956-3304 IMP
GIANT CEMENT HOLDING INC
(*Suby of* CEMENTOS PORTLAND VALDERRIVAS, SA)
1600 Duke St Ste 400, Alexandria, VA 22314-3421
Tel (571) 302-7150 *Founded/Ownrshp* 1999
Sales 166.1MM *EMP* 649
Accts Deloitte & Touche Llp
SIC 3241 4953 Cement, hydraulic; Recycling, waste materials
CEO: Jose A Llontop
CFO: Bratton Fennell
**VP:* F William Biddix
**VP:* Richard A Familia
Off Mgr: Angela Young
IT Man: Cathy Lehr

D-U-N-S 00-791-5713 IMP/EXP
GIANT EAGLE INC (PA)
101 Kappa Dr, Pittsburgh, PA 15238-2833
Tel (800) 362-8899 *Founded/Ownrshp* 1916, 1931
Sales 8.1MMM[E] *EMP* 36,000
SIC 5411 5141 5147 5148 5143 6794 Supermarkets, chain; Groceries, general line; Meats, fresh; Fresh fruits & vegetables; Dairy products, except dried or canned; Franchises, selling or licensing
Pr: John R Lucot
CFO: Mark J Minnaugh
Ofcr: Darin Goodwiler
Ex VP: Joseph Lucot
VP: James Bainbridge
VP: David Burnworth
VP: Raymond A Huber
VP: Jason Lapina
VP: William Parry
VP: Ian Prisuta
VP: Russ Ross
VP: John J Tedesco
VP: Gene Tommasi
Comm Man: Marion Ahlers

D-U-N-S 00-691-9757
GIANT FOOD LLC (MD)
(*Suby of* AFS) ★
8301 Profess Pl Ste 115, Hyattsville, MD 20785
Tel (301) 341-4100 *Founded/Ownrshp* 1935
Sales 2.5MMM[E] *EMP* 27,835
SIC 5411 6512 5912 Supermarkets, chain; Shopping center, property operation only; Drug stores
CEO: Richard A Baird
**CFO:* Paula A Price
Ex VP: James Astuto
**Ex VP:* Dan Currie
Ex VP: Tom Hippler
**Ex VP:* Bill Holmes
**Sr VP:* Thomas Gandolfi
**Sr VP:* Stephen Neal
**Sr VP:* Eric Weiss
VP: Mark Adamcik
VP: Susan Bowen
VP: Ira Kress
VP: Wayne Macleod
VP: Shane Sampson
Exec: James Yanger

D-U-N-S 01-393-2165 IMP
GIANT FOOD STORES LLC
MARTIN'S FOOD MARKET
(*Suby of* AFS) ★
1149 Harrisburg Pike, Carlisle, PA 17013-1667
Tel (717) 249-4000 *Founded/Ownrshp* 1981
Sales 3.0MMM[E] *EMP* 24,000
SIC 5411 Supermarkets, chain
Pr: Carl Schlicker
CFO: Rick Herring
Ex VP: John Bussenger
Ex VP: Don Gabrys
Ex VP: Jeff Martin
VP: Jodie Daubert
VP: Steve Fanion
VP: Dan Glei
VP: Steve Lamontagne
VP: Larry Stover
Dir Rx: Leigh Shirley
Board of Directors: Fritz Ahlqvist, Marshall Collins Jr, Peter Van Dun, Robert Zwartendijk

D-U-N-S 60-628-7308 IMP/EXP
■ GIANT INDUSTRIES INC
(*Suby of* WESTERN REFINING INC) ★
1250 W Washington St # 101, Tempe, AZ 85281-1794
Tel (915) 534-1400 *Founded/Ownrshp* 2007
Sales 175.1MM[E] *EMP* 881
SIC 2911 5541 5172 Petroleum refining; Gasoline service stations; Petroleum products
CEO: Jeff A Stevens
**Pr:* Morgan Gust
**Pr:* Mark J Smith
**CFO:* Mark B Cox
CFO: Gary Dalke
**Treas:* Jeffrey S Beyersdorfer
**Ex VP:* S Leland Gould
**Sr VP:* Kim H Bullerdick
**VP:* Dennis Calhoun

D-U-N-S 16-158-7548
GIANT INLAND EMPIRE RV CENTER INC
GIANT RV
9150 Benson Ave, Montclair, CA 91763-1688
Tel (909) 981-0444 *Founded/Ownrshp* 1986
Sales 97.6MM[E] *EMP* 250
SIC 5561 7538 Recreational vehicle parts & accessories; Recreational vehicle repairs
CEO: Behzad Barouti
CFO: Mark Hudson
**Treas:* Nasser Etebar
Genl Mgr: Mike Murphy
Genl Mgr: Dick Torres
Sales Exec: Jay Bensik
Sales Asso: Coleton Wirth

GIANT OF LANDOVER
See STOP & SHOP SUPERMARKET CO

GIANT RV
See GIANT INLAND EMPIRE RV CENTER INC

GIANT TRANSPORTATION DIV
See WESTERN REFINING SOUTHWEST INC

D-U-N-S 08-200-0381
GIBBS CONSTRUCTION LLC
5736 Citrus Blvd Ste 200, Harahan, LA 70123-1698
Tel (504) 733-4336 *Founded/Ownrshp* 1998
Sales 84.5MM[E] *EMP* 144[E]
SIC 1542 1541 Commercial & office building, new construction; Industrial buildings, new construction
Snr PM: Doug Bruza
Snr PM: Greg Kantak
Snr PM: Loren White

D-U-N-S 04-994-6627 IMP
GIBBS DIE CASTING CORP (KY)
(*Suby of* KOCH ENTERPRISES INC) ★
369 Community Dr, Henderson, KY 42420-4397
Tel (270) 827-1801 *Founded/Ownrshp* 1965, 1969
Sales 259.6MM[E] *EMP* 1,234
Accts Harding Shymanski And Company
SIC 3364 3363 3542 Magnesium & magnesium-base alloy die-castings; Aluminum die-castings; Die casting & extruding machines
Ch Bd: Kevin R Koch
**Pr:* Steven A Church
CFO: Angela Phaup
Ofcr: Shannon Kavanaugh
VP: John Economou
VP: Steve Link
Prgrm Mgr: Todd Sulawske
Dept Mgr: Darrell Moore
Dir IT: Chris Haire
Plnt Mgr: Robby Bealmear
Prd Mgr: Roman Bushrod
Board of Directors: Jim Butkus, Steven A Church, David Koch, James H Muehlbauer, Susan E Parsons

D-U-N-S 05-996-1847 IMP/EXP
▲ GIBRALTAR INDUSTRIES INC
3556 Lake Shore Rd # 100, Buffalo, NY 14219-1400
Tel (716) 826-6500 *Founded/Ownrshp* 1993
Sales 1.0MMM *EMP* 2,713
Tkr Sym ROCK *Exch* NGS
SIC 3499 3316 3441 3398 Strapping, metal; Cold finishing of steel shapes; Strip steel, cold-rolled: from purchased hot-rolled; Sheet, steel, cold-rolled: from purchased hot-rolled; Bars, steel, cold finished, from purchased hot-rolled; Fabricated structural metal; Metal heat treating
Pr: Frank Heard
Pr: Andy Blanchard
Pr: Paul C Soucier
CFO: Kenneth W Smith
Treas: Timothy F Murphy
Ex VP: J A Rosenecker
Ex VP: Joseph A Rosenecker
Sr VP: Paul M Murray
Sr VP: Paul Murray
Sr VP: Cherri L Syvrud
VP: Gregory Leong
VP: David A McCartney
VP: John Neil
VP: Paul Plourde
VP: Chris Smith
VP: Michael Smith
VP: John E Wagner
Comm Dir: Peter Ciotta
Board of Directors: Sharon M Brady, Jane L Corwin, Craig A Hindman, Vinod M Khilnani, William P Montague, James B Nish

D-U-N-S 01-969-6920
GIBSON APPLIED TECHNOLOGY & ENGINEERING (TEXAS) INC
GATE
16360 Park Ten Pl Ste 206, Houston, TX 77084-5048
Tel (281) 398-5781 *Founded/Ownrshp* 2000
Sales 100.0MM *EMP* 150
SIC 8711 Engineering services
Pr: Grant T Gibson
**CFO:* Brian Deleney

D-U-N-S 15-200-8538 IMP
GIBSON BRANDS INC
GIBSON USA
309 Plus Park Blvd, Nashville, TN 37217-1005
Tel (615) 871-4500 *Founded/Ownrshp* 1974
Sales 810.0MM[E] *EMP* 2,800
SIC 3931 Guitars & parts, electric & nonelectric
Ch Bd: Henry E Juszkiewicz
**Pr:* Dave Berryman
CFO: Anthony Crudele
**CFO:* Dan Krawczyk
Sr VP: Michael L Allen
Sr VP: Fred Greene
Natl Sales: Larry Urie
Mktg Dir: Reno Kling
Mktg Mgr: Jim Grundberg

GIBSON DUNN
See GIBSON DUNN & CRUTCHER LLP

D-U-N-S 07-796-3684
GIBSON DUNN & CRUTCHER LLP
GIBSON DUNN
333 S Grand Ave Ste 4600, Los Angeles, CA 90071-1512
Tel (213) 229-7000 *Founded/Ownrshp* 1880
Sales 342.1MM[E] *EMP* 1,900
SIC 8111 General practice law office
Mng Pt: Ken Doran
**Pt:* Nicholas Aleksander
**Pt:* Peter Alexiadis
**Pt:* Lisa A Alfaro
**Pt:* Terrence R Allen
Pt: Kelly Austin
**Pt:* James Barabas
**Pt:* Joseph Barbeau
**Pt:* Hatef Behnia
**Pt:* Cyrus Benson
**Pt:* Ashlie Beringer
**Pt:* Karen E Bertero
**Pt:* J Keith Biancamano
**Pt:* Robert C Bonner
**Pt:* Michael D Bopp
**Pt:* Frederick Brown
**Pt:* Thomas M Budd
**Pt:* Gregory A Campbell
**Pt:* Candice Choh
Pt: Christopher Chorba
**Pt:* Michael Collins

GIBSON ELC & TECH SOLUTIONS
See GIBSON ELECTRIC CO INC

D-U-N-S 07-023-4836
■ GIBSON ELECTRIC CO INC
GIBSON ELC & TECH SOLUTIONS
(*Suby of* EMCOR GROUP INC) ★
3100 Woodcreek Dr, Downers Grove, IL 60515-5414
Tel (630) 288-3800 *Founded/Ownrshp* 1987
Sales 99.6MM[E] *EMP* 300
SIC 1731 General electrical contractor
Pr: Daniel Fitzgibbons
CFO: Bob Springborn
Sr VP: Scott Rowe
VP: Carmen Manno
VP: Francis Sikora
Exec: Neal Medjes
Info Man: Augustine Brown
Snr PM: Benjamin Chilliro

D-U-N-S 00-792-3006
GIBSON ELECTRIC MEMBERSHIP CORP (TN)
1207 S College St, Trenton, TN 38382-3605
Tel (731) 855-4660 *Founded/Ownrshp* 1936
Sales 86.5MM *EMP* 85
Accts Alexander Thompson Arnold Pll
SIC 4911 Distribution, electric power
Pr: Dan Rodamaker
COO: Anita Jones
VP: Rita Alexander
VP: Richard Beden
VP: Emily Sullivan
CIO: Charles Philips

D-U-N-S 02-724-0811
GIBSON ENERGY MARKETING LLC
TAYLOR PROPANE GAS
3819 Towne Crossing Blvd, Mesquite, TX 75150-2799
Tel (214) 461-5600 *Founded/Ownrshp* 1998
Sales 118.7MM[E] *EMP* 150[E]
SIC 5172 5984 Butane gas; Gases, liquefied petroleum (propane); Butane gas, bottled; Propane gas, bottled
CEO: A Stewart Hanlon
**VP:* Rodney J Bantle
**VP:* Ralph Benson
**VP:* Dominic Maggiano
**VP:* Michael McGowan

D-U-N-S 09-860-7401 IMP/EXP
GIBSON OVERSEAS INC
2410 Yates Ave, Commerce, CA 90040-1918
Tel (323) 832-8900 *Founded/Ownrshp* 1979
Sales 200.5MM *EMP* 510
SIC 5023 Glassware; China; Kitchen tools & utensils
CEO: Sohail Gabbay
**COO:* Darioush Gabbay
**CFO:* Soloman Gabbay
VP: Connie Bowman
VP: Belynda Bridges
VP: Ovi Caravan
VP: Edmund Souder
VP: Robert Story
VP: Alex Wittner
Art Dir: Melissa Raney

D-U-N-S 10-261-0979
GIBSON SALES LP
DRUG EMPORIUM
2321a W Loop 281, Longview, TX 75604-2563
Tel (903) 297-0966 *Founded/Ownrshp* 1981
Sales 111.2MM *EMP* 440[E]
SIC 5912 Drug stores
Genl Pt: Glen A Gibson
Pt: Sammy Culpepper
Pt: K Elaine Gibson
Div Mgr: Billy Speer

GIBSON USA
See GIBSON BRANDS INC

GICHNER SHELTER SYSTEMS
See GICHNER SYSTEMS GROUP INC

D-U-N-S 80-803-7720
■ GICHNER SYSTEMS GROUP INC
GICHNER SHELTER SYSTEMS
(*Suby of* KRATOS UNMANNED SYSTEMS SOLUTIONS, INC)
490 E Locust St, Dallastown, PA 17313-1902
Tel (717) 246-5430 *Founded/Ownrshp* 2007
Sales 118.0MM[E] *EMP* 425[E]
SIC 3795 Specialized tank components, military
Pr: Eric M Demarco
**COO:* Richard Selvaggio
**CFO:* Deanna H Lund
**Treas:* Laura L Siegal
**VP:* Michael W Fink
**VP:* Thomas Mills
VP Sls: Scott Sarine
Mktg Mgr: Richard Smith

D-U-N-S 09-605-9134 IMP
GICON PUMPS & EQUIPMENT INC
AMERICAN W WINDMILL & SOLAR CO
1001 Texas Ave, Lubbock, TX 79401-3317
Tel (806) 401-8287 *Founded/Ownrshp* 1979
Sales 162.8MM[E] *EMP* 75
SIC 5084 5074 5039 Water pumps (industrial); Pipes & fittings, plastic; Septic tanks
VP: Robert Mark
**Ltd Pt:* Kim Ford
**Ltd Pt:* Ken Grant
**Pt:* Jerry Holton
**CFO:* Vance Grant
**Prin:* Mark Durham

D-U-N-S 07-538-1921 IMP/EXP
GIDEONS INTERNATIONAL
50 Century Blvd, Nashville, TN 37214-3672
Tel (615) 564-5000 *Founded/Ownrshp* 1963
Sales 128.7MM *EMP* 125
Accts Capin Crouse Llp Atlanta Geo
SIC 8661 5942 Religious organizations; Books, religious
Ex Dir: Craig Warner
**CFO:* Asih K Pradhan
Treas: Dennis Donnelly
Ofcr: Ronnie Kent
Ex VP: Perrin Prescott
Ex Dir: Jerry Burden
Snr Mgr: Rick Mosley

D-U-N-S 00-974-9946 IMP/EXP
GIESECKE & DEVRIENT AMERICA INC
G&D AMERICA
(*Suby of* GIESECKE & DEVRIENT GESELLSCHAFT MIT BESCHRANKTER HAFTUNG)
45925 Horseshoe Dr # 100, Dulles, VA 20166-6588
Tel (703) 480-2000 *Founded/Ownrshp* 1990
Sales 99.4MM[E] *EMP* 308
SIC 2672 5044 Coated & laminated paper; Office equipment
Pr: Scott Marquardt
**CFO:* Kevin J Fitzgerald
Sr VP: Vivek Shankar
VP: Dhananjayulu Dhaddhala
VP: Rajiv Gupta
VP: Jerome McNevitts
VP: Steve Rugen
Dir Bus: Thomas Kelly
Mng Dir: Edoardo Baumgartner
Genl Mgr: Michael Litton
Dir IT: Manjit Fervaha

D-U-N-S 07-925-5442
GIESECKE & DEVRIENT MOBILE SECURITY AMERICA INC
45925 Horseshoe Dr, Dulles, VA 20166-6588
Tel (703) 480-2100 *Founded/Ownrshp* 2016
Sales 181.0MM *EMP* 353
SIC 7382 3089 5045 7374 Protective devices, security; Plastic processing; Computers, peripherals & software; Computer graphics service
Pr: Scott Marquardt
CFO: Kevin Fitzgerald

D-U-N-S 88-352-6485
GIESEN RESTAURANT ENTERPRISES LLC
ARBY'S
10 E Belleview Way, Greenwood Village, CO 80121-1408
Tel (303) 761-7498 *Founded/Ownrshp* 1991
Sales 24.2MM[E] *EMP* 1,100
SIC 5812 Fast-food restaurant, chain

D-U-N-S 79-351-0454
GIFT COLLECTION INC
HMS HOST INTERNATIONAL
(*Suby of* HOST INTERNATIONAL INC) ★
6905 Rockledge Dr Fl 1, Bethesda, MD 20817-7826
Tel (240) 694-4100 *Founded/Ownrshp* 1988
Sales 108.7MM[E] *EMP* 2,700
SIC 6512 5812 Nonresidential building operators; Eating places
CEO: Steve Johnson
**Pr:* William W McCarten
Treas: Douglas Ribbeck
Ex VP: Mall Maalouf
Sr VP: Donald Olinger
VP: Bernard Brown
VP: Steven Johnson

GIFT SHOP
See MEMORIAL HEALTH CARE INC

GIFTS FROM THE HEART
See PHOEBE PUTNEY MEMORIAL HOSPITAL INC

GIFTS FROM THE HEART
See PHOEBE PUTNEY MEMORIAL HOSPITAL INC

GIFTS IN KIND
See GOOD360

GIGAAGE
See STEINER ELECTRIC CO

D-U-N-S 36-273-7251
▲ GIGAMON INC
3300 Olcott St, Santa Clara, CA 95054-3005
Tel (408) 831-4000 *Founded/Ownrshp* 2004
Sales 221.9MM *EMP* 482[E]
Tkr Sym GIMO *Exch* NYS
SIC 7372 3577 Prepackaged software; Computer peripheral equipment
CEO: Paul A Hooper
**Ch Bd:* Corey M Mulloy
CFO: Michael J Burns
Sr VP: Sachi Sambandan
Sr VP: Paul B Shinn
Sr VP: Helmut G Wilke
VP: Dave Cox
Snr Sftwr: Justin Ho
Snr Sftwr: Raj Mansanpally
CTO: Shehzad T Merchant
QA Dir: Gayathri Jayaraman
Board of Directors: Joan A Dempsey, Ted C Ho, John H Kispert, Paul J Milbury, Michael C Ruettgers, Robert E Switz

D-U-N-S 07-509-0910
GILA REGIONAL MEDICAL CENTER (NM)
1313 E 32nd St, Silver City, NM 88061-7251
Tel (575) 538-4000 *Founded/Ownrshp* 1937, 1960
Sales 71.3MM *EMP* 1,178
SIC 8093 8062 Rehabilitation center, outpatient treatment; General medical & surgical hospitals
CEO: Brian Cunningham
COO: Jed Rudd
CFO: David Glassburn
CFO: Omaira Heakin
CFO: Craig Stewart
Bd of Dir: Ken Foster
Bd of Dir: Richard Lawyer
Bd of Dir: Howie Morales
Bd of Dir: John P Saari
Ofcr: Ruth Pruitt
Dir Rx: Ray Goellner

GILA RIVER CASINOS
See GILA RIVER GAMING ENTERPRISES

D-U-N-S 84-920-5091
GILA RIVER GAMING ENTERPRISES
GILA RIVER CASINOS
5040 W Wildhorse Pass Blvd, Chandler, AZ 85226-5404
Tel (800) 946-4452 *Founded/Ownrshp* 1993
Sales 80.1MM[E] *EMP* 1,500
SIC 7993 5812 Slot machines; Eating places
Pr: Kenneth Manuel
Bd of Dir: Dale Enos
Exec: Eva Deherrera
Exec: Craig Horie
Dir Soc: Leslie Lau
Genl Mgr: Carolyn Thompson
Netwrk Eng: Eric Rademacher
Mktg Dir: Wendy Perez
Mktg Mgr: Lananh Tran
Sls Mgr: Deliah Rose
Snr Mgr: Pamela Johnson

D-U-N-S 09-628-7347
GILBANE BUILDING CO
MILLS GILBANE
(*Suby of* GILBANE INC) ★
7 Jackson Walkway Ste 2, Providence, RI 02903-3694
Tel (401) 456-5800 *Founded/Ownrshp* 1873
Sales 3.8MMM[E] *EMP* 2,500
Accts Mcgladrey And Pullen Llp Bost
SIC 1542 Institutional building construction
Ch Bd: Thomas F Gilbane
Pr: Michael McKelvy
CFO: Ken Alderman
Treas: Michael Costello
Treas: Richard R Roy
Ex VP: Michael R Bohn
Ex VP: Dennis Cornick
Ex VP: Daniel Mc Conaghy
Sr VP: Andrew R Faber
Sr VP: Bruce Hoffman
Sr VP: Walter McKelvey
Sr VP: Alfred K Potter II
VP: Freddie T Bustillo
VP: Thomas Comella
VP: Greg Dunkle
VP: Karen Flint
VP: John Fumosa
VP: Lori Giordano
VP: Linda Graves
VP: Mark Hill
VP: Brent Ivey

D-U-N-S 08-045-3480
GILBANE BUILDING CO / CG SCHMIDT A JOINT VENTURE
11777 W Lake Park Dr, Milwaukee, WI 53224-3047
Tel (414) 577-1177 *Founded/Ownrshp* 2014
Sales 100.0MM *EMP* 48
SIC 1542 Commercial & office building, new construction
Pt: Adam Jalen
Pt: Richard Schmidt
Snr PM: Bryce Unger

D-U-N-S 87-456-9015 IMP
GILBANE FEDERAL
(*Suby of* MILLS GILBANE) ★
1655 Grant St Fl 12, Concord, CA 94520-2445
Tel (925) 946-3100 *Founded/Ownrshp* 2010
Sales 186.7MM[E] *EMP* 500
SIC 8711 8748 Building construction consultant; Environmental consultant
CEO: Sarabjit Singh
CFO: Steve Schneider
**Sr VP:* Jon Verlinde
VP: Subhash Pantakar
IT Man: Brian Helberg
Sys Mgr: Randy Muir
VP Mktg: Dave Tenca

D-U-N-S 02-272-6165 IMP
GILBANE INC
7 Jackson Walkway, Providence, RI 02903-3638
Tel (401) 456-5800 *Founded/Ownrshp* 1908
Sales 3.8MMM[E] *EMP* 2,500

SIC 1541 1542 8741 6513 6512 Industrial buildings, new construction; Renovation, remodeling & repairs: industrial buildings; Commercial & office building, new construction; Institutional building construction; Commercial & office buildings, renovation & repair; Construction management; Residential hotel operation; Commercial & industrial building operation
**Pr:* Michael E McKelvy
**CFO:* John Ruggieri
CFO: John T Ruggieri
Ex VP: Dennis Cornick
Ex VP: Thomas Laird
**VP:* Michael R Bohn
VP: Paul Choquette
**VP:* Robert V Gilbane
**VP:* William J Gilbane Jr
VP: Steven Kononchik
VP: Marshal Lightman
VP: Jason Pelkey
VP: Michael D Smith

D-U-N-S 00-111-5245 IMP/EXP
■ GILBARCO INC (DE)
GILBARCO VEEDER-ROOT
(*Suby of* FORTIVE CORP) ★
7300 W Friendly Ave, Greensboro, NC 27410-6200
Tel (336) 547-5000 *Founded/Ownrshp* 1865, 2016
Sales 851.5MM^E *EMP* 3,600
SIC 3586

GILBARCO VEEDER-ROOT
See GILBARCO INC

D-U-N-S 02-245-3138
GILBERT FOODS LLC
HEARN-KIRKWOOD
7251 Standard Dr, Hanover, MD 21076-1322
Tel (410) 712-6000 *Founded/Ownrshp* 1974
Sales 123.0MM^E *EMP* 148
SIC 5148 5147 5146 5142 Fruits, fresh; Vegetables, fresh; Meats, fresh; Seafoods; Packaged frozen goods; Fish, frozen: packaged; Meat, frozen: packaged
Pr: Charles Gilbert
**Treas:* Patricia McCawley
Opers Mgr: Jason Hamp
Opers Mgr: Fred Taylor

D-U-N-S 83-319-3824
GILBERT GLOBAL EQUITY CAPITAL LLC
767 5th Ave Fl 15, New York, NY 10153-0028
Tel (212) 584-6200 *Founded/Ownrshp* 1997
Sales 265.1MM^E *EMP* 600^E
SIC 8741 Financial management for business
Mng Dir: Paul Wallace

D-U-N-S 87-648-0885
GILBERT HOSPITAL LLC
5656 S Power Rd Ste 133, Gilbert, AZ 85295-8490
Tel (480) 984-2000 *Founded/Ownrshp* 2003
Sales 100.0MM *EMP* 250
SIC 8062 General medical & surgical hospitals
CEO: Bryan J Hargis
**CFO:* Dennis Rutherford
**Ch:* Bradley L Newswander
Doctor: Vincent Hernandez

GILBERT TEXAS CONSTRUCTION
See KIEWIT TEXAS CONSTRUCTION LP

D-U-N-S 09-365-6569
GILBERT UNIFIED SCHOOL DISTRICT 41
140 S Gilbert Rd, Gilbert, AZ 85296-1016
Tel (480) 497-3452 *Founded/Ownrshp* 1920
Sales 250.9MM^E *EMP* 4,800
SIC 8211 Public elementary school; Public junior high school; Public senior high school
Ofcr: Jim Lockwood
MIS Dir: Joan Castelhano
Netwrk Mgr: Scott Haase
Mtls Mgr: Leonard Martinez
Pr Dir: Irene Mahoney-Paige
Psych: Amanda Marks
HC Dir: Lori Miller

D-U-N-S 06-264-0347
GILCHRIST CONSTRUCTION CO LLC
5709 New York Ave, Alexandria, LA 71302-2824
Tel (318) 448-3565 *Founded/Ownrshp* 1972, 1981
Sales 145.6MM^E *EMP* 350
SIC 1771 Concrete pumping
Pr: David R Gilchrist
**CFO:* Michael Latiolais
VP: Shane Carter
Sfty Dirs: Kevin Grage

D-U-N-S 09-622-7959 IMP
GILDAN ACTIVEWEAR (EDEN) INC (NC)
(*Suby of* GILDAN ACTIVEWEAR INC)
602 E Meadow Rd, Eden, NC 27288-3426
Tel (336) 623-9555 *Founded/Ownrshp* 1985, 1998
Sales 85.1MM^E *EMP* 160
SIC 5136 5311 Men's & boys' clothing; Department stores; Department stores, non-discount
Pr: Glenn Chamandry
**CFO:* Laurence G Sellyn
Ofcr: Mark Juba
Sr VP: Anthony Corsano
Sr VP: Dave Gardner
Sr VP: Jonathan Roiter
Sr VP: Chuck Ward
Sr VP: Linda Weiss
VP: Jason Fragapane
VP: Alfredo Silva
Genl Mgr: Charles Cole

D-U-N-S 87-906-8120 IMP
GILDAN APPAREL USA INC
ANVIL KNITWEAR, INC.
(*Suby of* ANVIL HOLDINGS INC) ★
48 W 38th St Fl 8, New York, NY 10018-0043
Tel (212) 476-0341 *Founded/Ownrshp* 1995
Sales 525.2MM^E *EMP* 5,000
SIC 2253 2331 Knit outerwear mills; Women's & misses' blouses & shirts
Ch Bd: Anthony Corsano
Ex VP: Jacob Hollander
Ex VP: Heather Stefani
VP: Chris Binnicker
VP: J Goldberg
VP: Ellen Singer

D-U-N-S 82-895-6495 IMP
GILDAN DELAWARE INC
(*Suby of* GILDAN ACTIVEWEAR INC)
3375 Joseph Martin Hwy, Martinsville, VA 24112-0495
Tel (276) 956-2305 *Founded/Ownrshp* 2008
Sales 500.0MM^E *EMP* 1,500^E
SIC 2252 2254 Socks; Underwear, knit
Pr: Michael Hoffman
Opers Mgr: Domenic Testani
Sls Dir: Tony Wilborn

D-U-N-S 78-744-7791 IMP
GILDAN USA INC
(*Suby of* GILDAN DELAWARE INC) ★
1980 Clements Ferry Rd, Charleston, SC 29492-7723
Tel (843) 849-6191 *Founded/Ownrshp* 2007
Sales 500.0MM^E *EMP* 1,500^E
SIC 2252 2254 Socks; Underwear, knit
Pr: Michael Hoffman
**VP:* Doug Leroy
VP: Shannon Preston
VP: David Voizard
Plnt Mgr: Phillip Blalock
Plnt Mgr: Steve Mauck
Sales Asso: Matthew Gillette
Sales Asso: Hannah Ross
Sales Asso: Tim Whyte

D-U-N-S 18-504-9848 IMP
▲ GILEAD SCIENCES INC
333 Lakeside Dr, Foster City, CA 94404-1147
Tel (650) 574-3000 *Founded/Ownrshp* 1987
Sales 32.6MMM *EMP* 8,000
Tkr Sym GILD *Exch* NGS
SIC 2836 Biological products, except diagnostic
Pr: John F Milligan
**Ch Bd:* John C Martin
COO: Kevin Young
CFO: Robin Washington
CFO: Robin L Washington
Ex VP: Gregg H Alton
Ex VP: Norbert W Bischofberger
Ex VP: Paul R Carter
Ex VP: Andrew Cheng
Ex VP: William A Lee
Ex VP: James R Meyers
Ex VP: Brett Pletcher
Ex VP: Hans Reiser
VP: Ron Branning
VP: Muzammil Mansuri
VP: Tobias Peschel
VP: Ann Regan
VP: John Sundy
Exec: Sheldon Okada
Assoc Dir: Marc Aquino
Assoc Dir: Scott Egler
Board of Directors: John F Cogan, Kelly A Kramer, Kevin E Lofton, John W Madigan, Nicholas G Moore, Per Wold-Olsen, Richard J Whitley, Gayle E Wilson

D-U-N-S 00-791-0417 IMP/EXP
GILES & RANSOME INC (PA)
RANSOME CAT
2975 Galloway Rd, Bensalem, PA 19020-2399
Tel (215) 639-4300 *Founded/Ownrshp* 1916, 1946
Sales 191.9MM^E *EMP* 540
SIC 5082 5084 7353

D-U-N-S 00-601-8311 IMP
GILL CORP
GRS&S
(*Suby of* GILL HOLDING CO INC) ★
706 Bond Ave Nw, Grand Rapids, MI 49503-1434
Tel (859) 625-5284 *Founded/Ownrshp* 1961
Sales 156.0MM^E *EMP* 340
SIC 3469 3312 3495 3493 3496 3465 Metal stampings; Tool & die steel; Wire springs; Steel springs, except wire; Miscellaneous fabricated wire products; Automotive stampings
Pr: James J Zawacki
**Treas:* Ted Hohman
Sls Mgr: Tom Gunn

D-U-N-S 00-831-7422 IMP/EXP
GILL CORP
4056 Easy St, El Monte, CA 91731-1054
Tel (626) 443-6094 *Founded/Ownrshp* 1945
Sales 233.3MM *EMP* 475
Accts Bdo Usa Llp Los Angeles Ca
SIC 3089 Laminating of plastic; Panels, building: plastic
Pr: Stephen E Gill
**CFO:* Bill Heinze
**VP:* Irv Freund
VP Sls: Chris Larsen
Board of Directors: Linda Gill, Nancy Gill, Phillip Gill, Stephen Gill

D-U-N-S 07-933-7831
GILL HOLDING CO INC
5271 Plainfield Ave Ne, Grand Rapids, MI 49525-1046
Tel (616) 559-2700 *Founded/Ownrshp* 2011
Sales 368.5MM^E *EMP* 1,500^E
SIC 3465 3544 Automotive stampings; Special dies & tools
CEO: Richard Perreault
**CFO:* J Timothy Gargaro

D-U-N-S 00-640-9080 IMP
GILL INDUSTRIES INC (MI)
GILL MANUFACTURING CO.
(*Suby of* GILL HOLDING CO INC) ★
5271 Plainfield Ave Ne, Grand Rapids, MI 49525-1046
Tel (616) 559-2700 *Founded/Ownrshp* 1964
Sales 212.4MM^E *EMP* 700
SIC 3465 3544 Automotive stampings; Special dies & tools
CEO: Rita Williams
**Pr:* Richard Perrault
Treas: Matthew Hale
**VP:* Joe Gill
VP: Dimitri Moustakeas
**VP:* Tom Popma
**VP:* Charles Scholfield
**VP:* Rita Woodruff
Prgrm Mgr: Craig Dedamos
Prgrm Mgr: Tony Graber
Prgrm Mgr: David-Peter Herczeg

GILL MANUFACTURING CO.
See GILL INDUSTRIES INC

D-U-N-S 15-444-4152
GILLELAND CHEVROLET CADILLAC INC
ST CLOUD COLLISION CENTER
3019 W Division St, Saint Cloud, MN 56301-3832
Tel (320) 281-4290 *Founded/Ownrshp* 1986
Sales 86.6MM *EMP* 143
SIC 5511 5531 7538

D-U-N-S 03-733-5882
GILLETTE CHILDRENS SPECIALTY HEALTHCARE
200 University Ave E, Saint Paul, MN 55101-2507
Tel (651) 291-2848 *Founded/Ownrshp* 1898
Sales 218.0MM *EMP* 623
SIC 8069 Children's hospital
Pr: Margaret Perryman
**CFO:* James Haddican
**VP:* Jon Galloway
**VP:* Christine Milbrath
**VP:* Kathryn Wardrop
IT Man: Colette Salmonowicz
Surgeon: Robert Acton
Surgeon: Arnold Leonard
Surgeon: Robert Rich
Surgeon: Daniel Saltzman
Doctor: Thomas Rieser

GILLETTE CHLDRN SPCLTY HLTH
See PEDIATRIC RHEUMATOLOGY

D-U-N-S 00-102-5931 IMP/EXP
■ GILLETTE CO
(*Suby of* P&G) ★
1 Gillette Park, Boston, MA 02127-1096
Tel (617) 421-7000 *Founded/Ownrshp* 1901
Sales 5.4MMM^E *EMP* 28,700
SIC 3421 3634 2844 3951 2899 Razor blades & razors; Electric housewares & fans; Razors, electric; Food mixers, electric: household; Toilet preparations; Cosmetic preparations; Pens & mechanical pencils; Ball point pens & parts; Fountain pens & fountain pen desk sets; Pencils & pencil parts, mechanical; Correction fluid
Pr: Edward F Degraan
**Pr:* Mark M Leckie
**Treas:* Gail Sullivan
VP: Cathleen J Chizauskas
**VP:* Terry Overbey

D-U-N-S 78-322-9677
■ GILLETTE DE MEXICO INC
(*Suby of* GILLETTE CO) ★
800 Boylston St, Boston, MA 02199-1900
Tel (617) 421-7000 *Founded/Ownrshp* 1982
Sales 9.4MM^E *EMP* 1,500
SIC 3634 Razors, electric
Pr: Edward Degaraan
Pr: Terry Overbey

D-U-N-S 06-655-7182 IMP
GILLIG LLC
(*Suby of* CC INDUSTRIES) ★
25800 Clawiter Rd, Hayward, CA 94545-3213
Tel (510) 785-1500 *Founded/Ownrshp* 2008
Sales 225.8MM^E *EMP* 700^E
SIC 3713 Truck & bus bodies
Pr: Derek Maunus
VP: Stephen Bender
VP: Jerry Sheehan
Ex Dir: Bob Birdwell
Div Mgr: Steve Davis
MIS Dir: Chuck Smith
Tech Mgr: David K Rands
VP Mfg: Steve Hasson
VP Mfg: Chris Turner
Manager: Jim Ryan
Manager: Joe Saldana

D-U-N-S 17-373-1647
GILLMAN INTERESTS INC
10595 W Sam Huston Pkwy S, Houston, TX 77099-2844
Tel (713) 776-7000 *Founded/Ownrshp* 1980
Sales 106.1MM^E *EMP* 450
SIC 5511 Automobiles, new & used; Pickups, new & used
Pr: Ramsay H Gillman
**Ofcr:* Bart Andrews

D-U-N-S 12-297-3741
GILMAN BUILDING PRODUCTS LLC
2500 Saint Marys Rd, Saint Marys, GA 31558-4141
Tel (912) 576-0300 *Founded/Ownrshp* 1999
Sales 211.2MM *EMP* 788
Accts Pricewaterhousecoopers Llp
SIC 2421 Building & structural materials, wood
Pr: Victor Garrett
**VP:* Daniel Kurtz
VP Mfg: Victor Garnett

GILSA DAIRY PRODUCTS
See LALA BRANDED PRODUCTS LLC

D-U-N-S 07-194-6966
GILSBAR INC
2100 Covington Centre, Covington, LA 70433-2981
Tel (985) 892-3520 *Founded/Ownrshp* 1959
Sales NA *EMP* 330
SIC 6411 Insurance information & consulting services; Insurance brokers
Pr: Henry J Miltenberger Jr
**Chf Mktg O:* Douglas Layman
**VP:* Shelley P Lampard
Off Mgr: Rebecca Wright
CTO: Chris Drake
IT Man: John Cueva
Mktg Dir: Wendy King
Manager: Stephen Cali
Manager: Meredith Sparrow
Sales Asso: Ashley Muller

GILSTER-MARY LEE
See MARY LEE PACKAGING CORP

D-U-N-S 05-774-4039 EXP
GILSTER-MARY LEE CORP
(*Suby of* GILSTER-MARY LEE) ★
1037 State St, Chester, IL 62233-1657
Tel (618) 826-2361 *Founded/Ownrshp* 1971
Sales 1.0MMM^E *EMP* 4,200
SIC 2043 2098 2099 2045 3089 Cereal breakfast foods; Macaroni products (e.g. alphabets, rings & shells), dry; Popcorn, packaged: except already popped; Blended flour: from purchased flour; Plastic containers, except foam
Pr: Donald E Welge
CFO: Michael Welge
**Ex VP:* Michael W Welge
**VP:* Delbert Dethrow
**VP:* Ron Tretter
**VP:* Tom Welge
Genl Mgr: Timothy Petzolt
CIO: Stephanie Siegmund
Dir IT: Alan Dell'aringa
Ql Cn Mgr: Stephanie Stull
Natl Sales: John Friedman

D-U-N-S 07-845-1336 IMP
GILT GROUPE HOLDINGS INC
G I L T
(*Suby of* HUDSON'S BAY COMPANY)
2 Park Ave Fl 4, New York, NY 10016-5602
Tel (877) 445-8692 *Founded/Ownrshp* 2016
Sales 322.2MM^E *EMP* 1,200
SIC 5611 Clothing accessories: men's & boys'
CEO: Michelle Peluso
**Pr:* Andy Page
**COO:* Tracey Weber
**CFO:* Tom Sansone
**Ex VP:* Jyothi RAO
VP: Dominique Essig
Area Mgr: Jason Flener
Snr Sftwr: Mike Chimirev
Snr Sftwr: Kevin Schultz
Software D: Robert Brazier
Sftwr Eng: Kevin He

D-U-N-S 07-882-9080 IMP/EXP
GILT GROUPE INC
GILT MAN
(*Suby of* G I L T) ★
250 Vesey St Fl 21, New York, NY 10281-1053
Tel (877) 280-0545 *Founded/Ownrshp* 2011
Sales 322.0MM^E *EMP* 1,100
SIC 5961
Ch Bd: Kevin Ryan
**Pr:* Susan Lyne
**CEO:* Michelle Peluso
**COO:* Tracey Weber
**CFO:* Tom Sansone
**Chf Mktg O:* Clay Cowan
Chf Mktg O: Lizzie Francis
**Sr VP:* Jennifer Miller
VP: Brooke Cundiff
VP: Anthony Lo Pinto
VP: Benjamin Singer
Creative D: Bradley Browder

GILT MAN
See GILT GROUPE INC

GINN
See GOSPEL OF PEACE INC

D-U-N-S 07-188-8440
GINO MORENA ENTERPRISES LLC
ONYX
111 Starlite St, South San Francisco, CA 94080-6398
Tel (800) 227-6905 *Founded/Ownrshp* 1943
Sales 51.3MM^E *EMP* 2,500
SIC 7231 Hairdressers
Area Supr: Kathy Cain
Genl Mgr: Nelson Chen
Off Mgr: Jan Vandevere
IT Man: Joan Carlson

GINSBERG FOODS
See GINSBERGS INSTITUTIONAL FOODS INC

D-U-N-S 01-274-6715
GINSBERGS INSTITUTIONAL FOODS INC
GINSBERG FOODS
29 Ginsburg Ln, Hudson, NY 12534-3431
Tel (518) 828-4004 *Founded/Ownrshp* 1909
Sales 166.5MM *EMP* 225
SIC 5148 5147 5142 5141 5143 Vegetables, fresh; Meats, fresh; Packaged frozen goods; Groceries, general line; Dairy products, except dried or canned
Pr: David Ginsberg
**CFO:* Edward M Maziejka Jr
VP: Ira Ginsberg
**VP:* Nancy Ginsberg
Mktg Mgr: Tracy Cantele
Sls Mgr: Richard Heinke
Sales Asso: Carlo Carlini
Sales Asso: Peter Clair
Sales Asso: Josie Dunbar
Sales Asso: Doug Hartnett
Sales Asso: Linda Randall

D-U-N-S 55-689-4319 IMP
GIORGIO ARMANI CORP
(*Suby of* GIORGIO ARMANI SPA)
450 W 15th St 3, New York, NY 10011-7097
Tel (212) 209-3500 *Founded/Ownrshp* 1983
Sales 440.7MM^E *EMP* 850
SIC 5136 5137 5122 5611 5621 5632 Men's & boys' clothing; Women's & children's clothing; Cosmetics, perfumes & hair products; Clothing, sportswear, men's & boys'; Clothing accessories: men's & boys'; Women's clothing stores; Apparel accessories
Ch Bd: Giorgio Armani
**Ch Bd:* Graziano De Boni
CFO: Tom Chan
Sr VP: Kirsten Peters
VP: Patrick Adent
VP: Samira Baftechi
VP: Rosana Cassano
VP: Lucinda Rosso
Creative D: Florence Lee
Dept Mgr: Ikeisha Bugg
Dept Mgr: Paula Decato

GIORGIO FOODS
See DIGIORGIO MUSHROOM CORP

D-U-N-S 00-250-9065 IMP
GIORGIO FOODS INC (PA)
(*Suby of* GIORGIO FOODS) ★
1161 Park Rd, Reading, PA 19605
Tel (610) 926-2139 *Founded/Ownrshp* 1960
Sales 92.4MM[E] *EMP* 278[E]
SIC 2033 2037 5148 2038 Mushrooms: packaged in cans, jars, etc.; Vegetables, quick frozen & cold pack, excl. potato products; Vegetables, fresh; Frozen specialties
Pr: John Majaewski
CFO: Mike Butto
CFO: Robert Erisman
CFO: Phil Impink
* *Sec:* Philip M Impink
Sr VP: Bill Litvin
Sr VP: Brian Loiseau
VP: Ron Broomhall
* *VP:* Ginaro Quaglia
QA Dir: Gary Zanecosky
IT Man: Rick Roach

D-U-N-S 96-599-7062 IMP
GIRAFFE HOLDING INC
500 Howard St, San Francisco, CA 94105-3000
Tel (415) 278-7000 *Founded/Ownrshp* 2010
Sales 1.2MMM[E] *EMP* 14,716[E]
SIC 5641 Children's & infants' wear stores
VP: Jordan Hitch

GIRARD MEDICAL CENTER
See PHILADELPHIA NORTH HEALTH SYSTEM

D-U-N-S 04-018-7895
GIRARDS GARAGE DOOR SERVICES
5962 Keystone Dr, Bath, PA 18014-8898
Tel (610) 837-4738 *Founded/Ownrshp* 1998
Sales 26.8MM[E] *EMP* 2,011[E]
SIC 7699 Garage door repair
Owner: Jim Gerard

D-U-N-S 00-698-4447
GIRL SCOUTS OF UNITED STATES OF AMERICA
GSUSA
420 5th Ave Fl 13, New York, NY 10018-2729
Tel (212) 852-8000 *Founded/Ownrshp* 1915
Sales 94.6MM *EMP* 500
Accts Grant Thornton Llp New York
SIC 8641 5137 6794 2721 Girl Scout organization; Uniforms, women's & children's; Women's & children's accessories; Copyright buying & licensing; Magazines: publishing only, not printed on site
CEO: Kathy Cloninger
* *Ch Bd:* Connie Lindsey
* *CEO:* Anna Maria Chavez
* *CFO:* Daniel Boockvar
* *CFO:* Florence Corsello
* *Ofcr:* Krista Kokjohn-Poehler
Ofcr: Joanne Rencher
Sr VP: Delphia Y Duckens
Sr VP: Courtney Q Shore
VP: Sharon H Mattews
VP: Harriet Mosatche
* *VP:* Susan Peters
* *VP:* Davia Temin

D-U-N-S 02-155-8143
GIRLING HEALTH CARE INC (TX)
(*Suby of* HARDEN HEALTHCARE SERVICES LLC) ★
1703 W 5th St Fl 7, Austin, TX 78703-4895
Tel (512) 452-5781 *Founded/Ownrshp* 1967, 2007
Sales 213.9MM[E] *EMP* 15,000
SIC 8082 Home health care services
Pr: Lew Little
Brnch Mgr: Miriam Lowery
Off Mgr: Sheila Adams

D-U-N-S 01-049-3112
GIRLING HEALTH CENTER
(*Suby of* GIRLING HEALTH CARE INC) ★
1920 Birdcreek Dr, Temple, TX 76502-1001
Tel (254) 778-4210 *Founded/Ownrshp* 1975
Sales 19.6MM[E] *EMP* 2,000
SIC 8082 Visiting nurse service
Pr: Ronda Van Meter

D-U-N-S 05-559-0582
GIT-N-GO CONVENIENCE STORES INC (IA)
2716 Indianola Ave, Des Moines, IA 50315-2377
Tel (515) 288-8565 *Founded/Ownrshp* 1972
Sales 108.3MM *EMP* 203
SIC 5411 5541 6722 Convenience stores, chain; Filling stations, gasoline; Management investment, open-end
Pr: Dennis Flora

GIUMARRA COMPANIES
See RIO VISTA VENTURES LLC

D-U-N-S 04-309-8896 EXP
GIUMARRA VINEYARDS CORP (CA)
11220 Edison Hwy, Edison, CA 93220
Tel (661) 395-7000 *Founded/Ownrshp* 1946
Sales 162.4MM *EMP* 3,000
SIC 0172 2084 2086 Grapes; Wines; Fruit drinks (less than 100% juice): packaged in cans, etc.; Tea, iced: packaged in cans, bottles, etc.
VP Sls: Randy Giumarra
CFO: William Butler
IT Man: Craig Bowers

D-U-N-S 96-335-4951
GIVAUDAN FLAVORS AND FRAGRANCES INC
(*Suby of* GIVAUDAN US) ★
1199 Edison Dr, Cincinnati, OH 45216-2265
Tel (513) 948-8000 *Founded/Ownrshp* 2004
Sales 518.9MM[E] *EMP* 2,500
SIC 2869 2087 Flavors or flavoring materials, synthetic; Perfume materials, synthetic; Flavoring extracts & syrups
CFO: Stefan Giezendanner

D-U-N-S 60-759-2920 IMP/EXP
GIVAUDAN FLAVORS CORP
(*Suby of* GIVAUDAN FLAVORS AND FRAGRANCES INC) ★
1199 Edison Dr, Cincinnati, OH 45216-2265
Tel (513) 948-8000 *Founded/Ownrshp* 2000
Sales 163.9MM[E] *EMP* 700
SIC 2869 2087

D-U-N-S 00-215-6354 IMP/EXP
GIVAUDAN FRAGRANCES CORP
(*Suby of* GIVAUDAN FLAVORS AND FRAGRANCES INC) ★
1199 Edison Dr Ste 1-2, Cincinnati, OH 45216-2265
Tel (513) 948-3428 *Founded/Ownrshp* 2000
Sales 354.9MM[E] *EMP* 1,800
SIC 2869 Perfume materials, synthetic; Flavors or flavoring materials, synthetic
CEO: Gilles Andrier
Dir IT: Peter Becker
Sls Dir: Jason Mankoo
Sls Dir: Laurie Rubaum

D-U-N-S 00-780-4680 IMP/EXP
GIVAUDAN ROURE (UNITED STATES) INC
GIVAUDAN US
(*Suby of* GIVAUDAN SA)
1199 Edison Dr, Cincinnati, OH 45216-2265
Tel (513) 948-8000 *Founded/Ownrshp* 2000
Sales 518.9MM[E] *EMP* 2,737
SIC 2869 2087 Perfume materials, synthetic; Flavors or flavoring materials, synthetic; Flavoring extracts & syrups
Pr: Michael Davis
Plnt Mgr: Koichiro Maekawa

GIVAUDAN US
See GIVAUDAN ROURE (UNITED STATES) INC

D-U-N-S 78-766-7005 IMP
GIVE SOMETHING BACK INC
GIVE SOMETHING BACK OFF SUPS
7730 Pardee Ln Ste A, Oakland, CA 94621-1555
Tel (800) 261-2619 *Founded/Ownrshp* 2004
Sales 97.9MM[E] *EMP* 90
SIC 5112 Stationery & office supplies
CEO: Sean Marx
* *Pr:* Mike Hannigan
IT Man: Verna Carter
Manager: Christian Westbrook

GIVE SOMETHING BACK OFF SUPS
See GIVE SOMETHING BACK INC

D-U-N-S 03-373-4716 IMP/EXP
GIW INDUSTRIES INC
GIW MINERALS
(*Suby of* KSB AMERICA CORP) ★
5000 Wrightsboro Rd, Grovetown, GA 30813-2842
Tel (706) 863-1011 *Founded/Ownrshp* 1996
Sales 128.4MM[E] *EMP* 499
SIC 3561 3559 Industrial pumps & parts; Foundry machinery & equipment
CEO: Wolfgang Demmler
* *CFO:* Enrico Handrick
* *VP:* Thomas Mueller
* *VP:* Robert Visintainer
Exec: Lee Whitlock
Dist Mgr: Joshua Linaman
Genl Mgr: John Love
Dir IT: Bryan Bronson
Dir IT: Matthew Bronson
IT Man: Larry Lynn
Opers Mgr: Dennis Ethington
Board of Directors: Klaus Barmann, Dr Bernd Garbe

GIW MINERALS
See GIW INDUSTRIES INC

D-U-N-S 08-580-9770
GJS HOLDING LLC
JUAREZ SALONS & SPAS
(*Suby of* EVERGREEN PACIFIC PARTNERS MANAGEMENT CO INC) ★
3633 136th Pl Se Ste 200, Bellevue, WA 98006-1455
Tel (425) 748-1400 *Founded/Ownrshp* 2006
Sales 38.6MM[E] *EMP* 1,300
SIC 7231 Beauty shops; Beauty schools
Genl Mgr: Kelli Cruz

D-U-N-S 06-183-8443
GK HOLDINGS INC
9000 Regency Pkwy Ste 500, Cary, NC 27518-8520
Tel (800) 268-7737 *Founded/Ownrshp* 2011
Sales 323.0MM *EMP* 1,314
SIC 6719 Investment holding companies, except banks
Pr: Sean Dolan
* *Treas:* Robert Kalainikas
* *Genl Couns:* Brian Holland

GKA
See GOODWILL KEYSTONE AREA

D-U-N-S 78-310-4888
GKK CORP
GKKWORKS
2355 Main St Ste 220, Irvine, CA 92614-4251
Tel (949) 250-1500 *Founded/Ownrshp* 1991
Sales 117.5MM *EMP* 210
Accts Kushner Smith Joanou & Gregson
SIC 8712 8711 Architectural engineering; Building construction consultant
Pr: Praful Kulkarni
CFO: James Staley
* *VP:* David Hunt
VP: Charles G Merrick
Genl Mgr: Vanessa Oozano
Snr Mgr: Amit Bhargava

GKKWORKS
See GKK CORP

D-U-N-S 06-765-5985 IMP
GKN AEROSPACE CHEM-TRONICS INC (CA)
CHEM-TRONICS INC. FACSIMILE
(*Suby of* GKN PLC)
1150 W Bradley Ave, El Cajon, CA 92020-1504
Tel (619) 448-2320 *Founded/Ownrshp* 1953, 2001
Sales 245.3MM[E] *EMP* 683
SIC 3724 7699 Aircraft engines & engine parts; Aircraft & heavy equipment repair services
CEO: Marcus J Bryson
* *Pr:* Michael A Beck
* *CFO:* Les Emanuel
* *VP:* Stacey Clapp
Genl Mgr: Elizabeth Alford
Genl Mgr: Priscilla Camanho
Dir IT: Sandra Candler
Sfty Mgr: Bill Robinson
Opers Mgr: Michael Worden

D-U-N-S 00-204-4162 IMP
GKN AEROSPACE MONITOR INC (NY)
(*Suby of* GKN PLC)
1000 New Horizons Blvd, Amityville, NY 11701-1138
Tel (562) 619-8558 *Founded/Ownrshp* 1947, 2006
Sales 94.7MM[E] *EMP* 275
SIC 3728 3769 Aircraft assemblies, subassemblies & parts; Guided missile & space vehicle parts & auxiliary equipment
CEO: Daniele Cagnatel
* *Ch Bd:* Kevin L Cummings
* *Pr:* Fran Novak
* *VP:* Paul Kowack
VP: Stephen Marshall
* *VP:* Patrick Powers
* *VP:* Dave Sylvain
Genl Mgr: David Maguire
MIS Mgr: Dianne Burcyk
Ql Cn Mgr: Kevin Choi

D-U-N-S 00-957-8162 IMP
GKN AEROSPACE TRANSPARENCY SYSTEMS INC
(*Suby of* GKN AMERICA CORP) ★
12122 Western Ave, Garden Grove, CA 92841-2915
Tel (714) 893-7531 *Founded/Ownrshp* 2003
Sales 86.1MM[E] *EMP* 360[E]
SIC 3089 3231 3827 3728 3081 2821 Windows, plastic; Windshields, plastic; Mirrors, truck & automobile: made from purchased glass; Optical instruments & lenses; Aircraft parts & equipment; Unsupported plastics film & sheet; Plastics materials & resins
Ch Bd: Dr John Foster
CEO: Ronald Kato
CFO: Michael Kaalund
CFO: Nick Waters
Ex VP: Mike Beck
Sr VP: Tom Battaglia
VP: Bill Beard
VP: Dave Wilmot
Prin: Kevin Cummings
Prgrm Mgr: Amy Marceau
Prgrm Mgr: Jon Szymanski
Board of Directors: Benjamin A Cosgrove, T Allan Maartor, Michael Schwabero

D-U-N-S 14-423-3608 IMP/EXP
GKN AMERICA CORP
(*Suby of* G.K.N. INDUSTRIES LIMITED)
2715 Davey Rd Ste 300, Woodridge, IL 60517-5064
Tel (630) 972-9300 *Founded/Ownrshp* 2001
Sales 779.3MM[E] *EMP* 3,000
SIC 3714 Universal joints, motor vehicle; Drive shafts, motor vehicle
Pr: Grey Denham
* *Treas:* Hugo Perez
* *VP:* John A Giannangeli

GKN AUTOMOTIVE
See GKN DRIVELINE NORTH AMERICA INC

D-U-N-S 14-735-4476 IMP/EXP
GKN DRIVELINE NEWTON LLC
(*Suby of* GKN AUTOMOTIVE) ★
1848 Gkn Way, Newton, NC 28658-9072
Tel (828) 428-1591 *Founded/Ownrshp* 2011
Sales 194.3MM[E] *EMP* 650
SIC 3462 3714 Iron & steel forgings; Gears, motor vehicle
Pr: Max Owens
CFO: Armin Laicher
Ex VP: Mike McMillan
Snr Mgr: Ibrahim Kaddouh

D-U-N-S 09-452-9401 IMP/EXP
GKN DRIVELINE NORTH AMERICA INC
GKN AUTOMOTIVE
(*Suby of* GKN AMERICA CORP) ★
2200 N Opdyke Rd, Auburn Hills, MI 48326-2389
Tel (248) 296-7000 *Founded/Ownrshp* 1977
Sales 585.5MM[E] *EMP* 1,800
SIC 3714 5013 Universal joints, motor vehicle; Drive shafts, motor vehicle; Automotive engines & engine parts
Pr: Scott Mullens
VP: Ramon Kuczera
Mng Dir: Max Owen
Counsel: Capri Pelshaw

D-U-N-S 07-175-4337
GKN NORTH AMERICA INC
(*Suby of* GKN HOLDINGS PLC)
2200 N Opdyke Rd, Auburn Hills, MI 48326-2389
Tel (248) 296-7200 *Founded/Ownrshp* 1981
Sales 228.8MM[E] *EMP* 5,580
SIC 3714 5013 7359 Motor vehicle transmissions, drive assemblies & parts; Transmissions, motor vehicle; Universal joints, motor vehicle; Drive shafts, motor vehicle; Motor vehicle supplies & new parts; Equipment rental & leasing
Pr: Robert Willig
VP: Richard Best
VP: A George
Board of Directors: Herbert Galant, David Rood

D-U-N-S 80-816-6946 IMP/EXP
GKN NORTH AMERICA SERVICES INC
(*Suby of* GKN PLC)
2715 Davey Rd Ste 300, Woodridge, IL 60517-5064
Tel (630) 972-9300 *Founded/Ownrshp* 1985
Sales 159.3MM[E] *EMP* 698
SIC 3714 5013 7359 Motor vehicle transmissions, drive assemblies & parts; Transmissions, motor vehicle; Motor vehicle supplies & new parts
Sr VP: Daniele Cagnatel
* *CEO:* Hans Buthker
* *CEO:* Kevin Cummings
* *CEO:* Mike Grunza
* *CEO:* Mike McCann

D-U-N-S 09-077-7558 IMP
GKN SINTER METALS LLC
(*Suby of* GKN PLC)
2200 N Opdyke Rd, Auburn Hills, MI 48326-2389
Tel (248) 296-7832 *Founded/Ownrshp* 1991
Sales 466.9MM[E] *EMP* 2,825
SIC 3714 3568 3369 3366 Motor vehicle engines & parts; Motor vehicle transmissions, drive assemblies & parts; Gears, motor vehicle; Bearings, motor vehicle; Power transmission equipment; Sprockets (power transmission equipment); Bearings, plain; Nonferrous foundries; Copper foundries
Pr: David J Turner
Pr: Rich McCorry
COO: Gloria Bader
Sr VP: Peter M Lgg
* *VP:* Trevor C Bonner Cbe
VP: Timothy Geiman
VP: Richard Gough
* *VP:* Rufus A Oglivie Smals
Genl Mgr: Terry Shutter
IT Man: Jason Holland
VP Mfg: John Gahrs

D-U-N-S 60-991-3538 IMP
GKN WESTLAND AEROSPACE INC
(*Suby of* GKN PLC)
3951 Al Highway 229 S, Tallassee, AL 36078-4733
Tel (334) 283-9200 *Founded/Ownrshp* 1998
Sales 231.3MM[E] *EMP* 980
SIC 3728 Aircraft body & wing assemblies & parts; Aircraft propellers & associated equipment
CEO: Kevin Cummings
* *CFO:* John Michaels
CFO: William Seeger
VP: Roger Emley
VP: John Herthum
Genl Mgr: Daniele Cagnatel
Genl Mgr: Steve Clark
Dir IT: Robert Mask
IT Man: Dianne Burcyk
IT Man: Jolene Butler
Opers Mgr: Chris Wilson

D-U-N-S 15-722-3892
GKR SYSTEMS INC
VENTURE TECHNOLOGIES
860 Centre St, Ridgeland, MS 39157-4501
Tel (601) 956-5440 *Founded/Ownrshp* 1986
Sales 139.3MM[E] *EMP* 251
Accts Horne Llp Ridgeland Mississi
SIC 5045 7373 Computers, peripherals & software; Computer systems analysis & design
CEO: Gerard R Gibert
* *COO:* Joseph Rucker
CFO: Joe Rucker
* *Sec:* Norman P Katool
Ex VP: Leonard Lane
Ex VP: Kim Ware
VP: John Bergeron
* *VP:* Mark Frye
* *VP:* Wayne Gilbert
* *CTO:* John Little
IT Man: Gary Campbell

D-U-N-S 12-337-6654
GL CAPITAL PARTNERS LLC
YORK STREET CAPITAL PARTNERS
350 Main St Ste 8, Bedminster, NJ 07921-2689
Tel (928) 526-2735 *Founded/Ownrshp* 2002
Sales NA *EMP* 12
SIC 6159 Small business investment companies
CFO: David Tahan
VP: Glenn T Kim

D-U-N-S 05-919-2914 IMP
GL GROUP INC
JAFFE BOOK SOLUTIONS
5111 Southwest Ave, Saint Louis, MO 63110-3429
Tel (314) 647-0600 *Founded/Ownrshp* 1974
Sales 227.7MM[E] *EMP* 160
SIC 5192 2789 Books; Bookbinding & related work
CEO: Gary Jaffe
* *Pr:* Sanford Jaffe
* *CFO:* Mark Rygelski
* *VP:* Donna Jaffe
* *VP:* Neil Jaffe
Creative D: Andrew Richmond
Genl Mgr: Adam Schell
Dir IT: Greg Bonebrake
IT Man: Nick Dreyer
IT Man: Scott Hankins
Mktg Mgr: Kimmy Favazza

D-U-N-S 12-543-4832
GL STAFFING SERVICES INC
1709 Banks Rd Bldg A, Margate, FL 33063-7744
Tel (954) 973-8350 *Founded/Ownrshp* 2001
Sales 30.6MM[E] *EMP* 1,000
SIC 7361 Employment agencies
Pr: Gerry Califano
* *Sec:* Lawrence J Minei
* *VP:* Robert Conde

D-U-N-S 80-100-4383
▲ GLACIER BANCORP INC
49 Commons Loop, Kalispell, MT 59901-2679
Tel (406) 756-4200 *Founded/Ownrshp* 1990
Sales NA *EMP* 2,030[E]
Accts Bkd Llp Denver Colorado
Tkr Sym GBCI *Exch* NGS
SIC 6022 State commercial banks
Pr: Michael J Blodnick
* *Ch Bd:* Dallas I Herron
Pr: Randall M Chesler
CFO: Ron J Copher
Ofcr: Don J Chery
VP: Mark Macmillan
VP: Chris Mauch
VP: Robin S Roush
VP: Michael Smith
VP: Mary Strozzi
VP: Martha Tannehill
Board of Directors: Sherry L Cladouhos, James M

English, Annie M Goodwin, Craig A Langel, Douglas J McBride, John W Murdoch, Mark J Semmens

D-U-N-S 06-555-9742

■ GLACIER BANK
(*Suby of* GLACIER BANCORP INC) ★
202 Mn St, Kalispell, MT 59901
Tel (406) 756-4200 *Founded/Ownrshp* 1990
Sales NA *EMP* 210
SIC 6022 State commercial banks
Pr: Randall M Chesler
Ofcr: Don Chery
Ofcr: Karen Hergesshiemer
Top Exec: Bob Nystuen
Ex VP: Dennis Beams
Sr VP: Duane Kechter
Sr VP: Don Lloyd
Sr VP: Jim Ness
Sr VP: Robert Taylor
VP: Jane Foley
VP: Barry Johnston
VP: Dave McNutt
VP: Gary Sparr
VP: Cheryl Zobenica

GLACIER FOODS DIVISION
See DOLE PACKAGED FOODS LLC

D-U-N-S 10-627-0861 IMP

GLACIER WATER SERVICES INC
1385 Park Center Dr, Vista, CA 92081-8338
Tel (760) 560-1111 *Founded/Ownrshp* 1983
Sales 106.2MM^E *EMP* 400^E
SIC 5962 Cold drinks vending machines
Pr: Brian H McInerney
**Ch Bd:* Charles A Norris
**COO:* Steven L Murphy
COO: Steven Murphy
**CFO:* Steve Stringer
**V Ch Bd:* Peter H Neuwirth
Ofcr: Scott Keys

D-U-N-S 14-492-7597 IMP

■ GLAD PRODUCTS CO
(*Suby of* CLOROX CO) ★
1221 Broadway Ste A, Oakland, CA 94612-1837
Tel (510) 271-7000 *Founded/Ownrshp* 1999
Sales 605.1MM^E *EMP* 4,800
SIC 3081 2673 2842 3295 Plastic film & sheet; Plastic bags: made from purchased materials; Automobile polish; Waxes for wood, leather & other materials; Cat box litter
Ch Bd: William V Stephenson
**Pr:* Thomas H Rowland
**CFO:* Donald A De Santis
**VP:* Joseph B Furey
Genl Mgr: Beth Springer
MIS Dir: Cathy Savage

D-U-N-S 08-023-6331

GLADE OPERATING LLC
110 S Main St, Moulton, TX 77975-4598
Tel (361) 596-5050 *Founded/Ownrshp* 2016
Sales 150.0MM *EMP* 3^E
SIC 1381 Drilling oil & gas wells

GLADES SUGAR HOUSE
See SUGAR CANE GROWERS COOPERATIVE OF FLORIDA

D-U-N-S 79-035-0826

GLADIATOR CORP
2882 Sand Hill Rd Ste 280, Menlo Park, CA 94025-7057
Tel (650) 233-2900 *Founded/Ownrshp* 2006
Sales 98.4MM^E *EMP* 338
SIC 7372

D-U-N-S 18-818-7298

GLADIEUX TRADING AND MARKETING CO LP
4133 New Haven Ave, Fort Wayne, IN 46803-1643
Tel (260) 423-4477 *Founded/Ownrshp* 1987
Sales 177.6MM^E *EMP* 97
SIC 5171 Petroleum terminals
Pt: James Gladieux
Pt: David Sordelet
Pt: Steven Uebelhoer
Exec: Robert Hayes

D-U-N-S 13-263-6502

▲ GLADSTONE COMMERCIAL CORP
1521 Westbranch Dr # 200, Mc Lean, VA 22102-3204
Tel (703) 287-5800 *Founded/Ownrshp* 2003
Sales 83.7MM *EMP* 5^E
Tkr Sym GOOD *Exch* NGS
SIC 6798 Real estate investment trusts
Ch Bd: David Gladstone
**V Ch:* Terry L Brubaker
Pr: Robert Cutlip
CFO: Danielle Jones
**Ex VP:* David A R Dullum
Mng Dir: Arthur Cooper

D-U-N-S 62-664-6848 IMP

GLANBIA INC
(*Suby of* GLANBIA PUBLIC LIMITED COMPANY)
121 4th Ave S, Twin Falls, ID 83301-6223
Tel (208) 733-7555 *Founded/Ownrshp* 1966
Sales 330.2MM^E *EMP* 700
SIC 2022 Natural cheese; Whey, raw or liquid
Pr: David Thomas
**CFO:* Daragh Maccabee
CFO: Mark Short
VP: Brendan Britton
VP: Mike Brown
Doctor: Geoffrey Meagher

D-U-N-S 05-099-0324 IMP/EXP

GLANBIA NUTRITIONALS (NA) INC
(*Suby of* GLANBIA PUBLIC LIMITED COMPANY)
2840 Loker Ave E Ste 100, Carlsbad, CA 92010-6677
Tel (760) 438-0089 *Founded/Ownrshp* 2006
Sales 85.0MM^E *EMP* 165^E
SIC 5169 2833 8099

D-U-N-S 92-944-4826 IMP/EXP

GLANBIA PERFORMANCE NUTRITION INC
OPTIMUM NUTRITION
(*Suby of* GLANBIA INC) ★
3500 Lacey Rd, Downers Grove, IL 60515-5422
Tel (630) 236-0097 *Founded/Ownrshp* 1999
Sales 113.5MM^E *EMP* 280
SIC 2833 5149 5122 Vitamins, natural or synthetic: bulk, uncompounded; Health foods; Vitamins & minerals
CEO: Thomas Tench
**CFO:* T J Kelly
Sr VP: Ken Strick
VP: Peter Hu
CTO: Saverio Spontella
QA Dir: Adalberto Luna
QA Dir: Chris Mendes
Opers Mgr: Vince Tornabene
Counsel: Paul Freeborn

D-U-N-S 36-080-5261

GLANT PACIFIC INC
2230 4th Ave S, Seattle, WA 98134-1515
Tel (206) 628-6222 *Founded/Ownrshp* 1987
Sales 83.8MM^E *EMP* 260^E
SIC 5949 5093 5094 5945 Knitting goods & supplies; Fabric stores piece goods; Sewing supplies; Scrap & waste materials; Precious metals; Hobby, toy & game shops
Pr: Douglas F Glant
**Ex VP:* Bruce Glant

D-U-N-S 01-203-6422 IMP

GLANTZ HOLDINGS INC
16 Court St Ste 3000, Brooklyn, NY 11241-1013
Tel (502) 271-5560 *Founded/Ownrshp* 1906
Sales 163.2MM^E *EMP* 158
SIC 5046 Neon signs
Pr: Herbert Glantz
**Ch Bd:* Joseph Hartman

GLAS-COL DIV
See TEMPLETON COAL CO INC

D-U-N-S 00-791-0979

GLASGOW INC (PA)
104 Willow Grove Ave, Glenside, PA 19038-2110
Tel (215) 884-8800 *Founded/Ownrshp* 1975
Sales 92.1MM^E *EMP* 425
SIC 2951 1611 1623 Road materials, bituminous (not from refineries); General contractor, highway & street construction; Cable laying construction; Sewer line construction; Underground utilities contractor
Pr: Bruce B Rambo
**Treas:* Lois Ann Glasgow
VP: Jim Bagley
**VP:* John Rath
Prgrm Mgr: Franklin Smith
Telecom Ex: Karen Brislin
DP Exec: Tim Call
Sales Exec: Al Fritzinger

GLASS CLASS
See VVP HOLDINGS LLC

D-U-N-S 10-656-5435 IMP

GLASS GALLERY LTD
CRYSTAL ODYSSEY
10300 Lake Bluff Dr, Saint Louis, MO 63123-7244
Tel (314) 416-4200 *Founded/Ownrshp* 1975
Sales 8.9MM *EMP* 1,100
SIC 5947 5199 Gift shop; Glassware, novelty
Pr: George Ottensmeyer
**VP:* Kirby Boyd

D-U-N-S 01-170-6504

GLASS GARDENS INC
SHOP RITE OF ROCHELLE PARK
220 W Passaic St, Rochelle Park, NJ 07662-3118
Tel (201) 843-1424 *Founded/Ownrshp* 1955
Sales 96.5MM^E *EMP* 781
SIC 5411 5921 Supermarkets, chain; Liquor stores
CEO: Jeff Brown
**VP:* Terry Glass
Exec: Lori Bettineschi

D-U-N-S 06-528-4846

GLASS MTN PUMICE INC
3400 Kauai Ct Ste 206, Reno, NV 89509-4828
Tel (775) 826-3399 *Founded/Ownrshp* 1977
Sales 350.0MM *EMP* 15
SIC 5032 Aggregate
Pr: Niilo Hyytinen
**Treas:* Elene Hyytinen

GLASSELL SCHOOL OF ART
See MUSEUM OF FINE ARTS OF HOUSTON

GLASSTEEL PARTS AND SERVICES
See PFAUDLER INC

GLATFELTER INSURANCE GROUP
See ARTHUR J GLATFELTER AGENCY INC

GLATFELTER PULP & PAPER
See GLATFELTER PULP WOOD CO INC

D-U-N-S 06-388-0355 IMP

■ GLATFELTER PULP WOOD CO INC
GLATFELTER PULP & PAPER
(*Suby of* P H GLATFELTER CO) ★
228 S Main St, Spring Grove, PA 17362-1000
Tel (717) 225-4711 *Founded/Ownrshp* 1947
Sales 1.3MMM^E *EMP* 3,545^E
SIC 5099 2411 2621 Pulpwood; Cases, carrying; Pulpwood contractors engaged in cutting; Paper mills
CEO: Dante C Parrini
**Pr:* T C Norris
**Treas:* M A Johnson II
**Sr VP:* Christopher W Astley
**Sr VP:* John P Jacunski
VP: Steve Basom
**VP:* Jonathan Bourget
VP: Barry Downing
**VP:* David C Elder
**VP:* C F Glattfelder
VP: Tim Hess
**VP:* Kent K Matsumoto
VP: Amy Wannemacher
VP: William T Yanavitch II
Board of Directors: Richard C Ill

D-U-N-S 79-022-0628 IMP

GLATT AIR TECHNIQUES INC
(*Suby of* GLATT GESELLSCHAFT MIT BESCHRANKTER HAFTUNG)
20 Spear Rd, Ramsey, NJ 07446-1288
Tel (201) 825-6308 *Founded/Ownrshp* 1973
Sales 163.2MM^E *EMP* 155
SIC 5084 Industrial machinery & equipment
CEO: Reinhard Nowak
**VP:* Richard E Davis
**VP:* Diane Lancaster
VP: Paul Portje
VP: Steve Sirabian
Board of Directors: Todd Brinberg, George Ferrito, Werner Glatt, Reinhard Nowak

D-U-N-S 04-773-8281

GLAUS PYLE SCHOMER BURNS & DEHAVEN INC
GPD GROUP
520 S Main St Ste 2531, Akron, OH 44311-1073
Tel (330) 572-2100 *Founded/Ownrshp* 1986
Sales 93.0MM *EMP* 550
Accts Bcg & Company Akron Oh
SIC 8711 8712 Consulting engineer; Architectural services
Pr: Darrin Kotecki
**Treas:* James Shives
**Sr VP:* Jeff Evans
Sr VP: Jeffrey D Evans
Exec: Amy Rienzi
Dir: MO Darwish
Dir IT: Kenny Koltas
Mktg Dir: Joe Kidder
Snr PM: Kevin Grathwol
Snr Mgr: Joseph Ciuni
Snr Mgr: Trever Powers
Board of Directors: Jeff Evans, David Martin, Mark Salopek, James Shives, Angela Wells

GLAXOSMITHKLINE BIO N AMER
See CORIXA CORP

D-U-N-S 82-892-4212 IMP/EXP

GLAXOSMITHKLINE CONSUMER HEALTHCARE LP
(*Suby of* G S K) ★
184 Libery Corner Rd, Warren, NJ 07059
Tel (251) 591-4188 *Founded/Ownrshp* 1992
Sales 1.1MMM^E *EMP* 1,700
SIC 5122 Drugs, proprietaries & sundries
Pr: Colin Mackenzie
CFO: Patrick Ansell
Sr Cor Off: Mike Amburgey
Sr Cor Off: Janet Slack
VP: Gregg R Brandyberry
VP: Jacqueline Carsanaro
VP: Raymond D Rise
Exec: John Nashette
Ex Dir: Chris Britten
Ex Dir: Joseph Kicaina
Ex Dir: Mark Levy

D-U-N-S 00-138-1342 IMP/EXP

GLAXOSMITHKLINE HOLDINGS (AMERICAS) INC (DE)
(*Suby of* GLAXOSMITHKLINE FINANCE PLC)
1105 N Market St, Wilmington, DE 19801-1216
Tel (302) 656-5280 *Founded/Ownrshp* 1830, 2009
Sales 5.7MMM^E *EMP* 24,000
SIC 2834 2836 2833 2844 8071 Cough medicines; Vaccines & other immunizing products; Vaccines; Antibiotics; Face creams or lotions; Suntan lotions & oils; Oral preparations; Toothpastes or powders, dentifrices; Medical laboratories
Pr: Deirdre Connelly
**CFO:* Julian S Heslop
Mktg Mgr: Katrina L Brown
Mktg Mgr: Isha M Williams

D-U-N-S 00-230-0077 IMP/EXP

GLAXOSMITHKLINE LLC
G S K
(*Suby of* GLAXOSMITHKLINE HOLDINGS (AMERICAS) INC) ★
5 Crescent Dr, Philadelphia, PA 19112-1001
Tel (215) 751-4000 *Founded/Ownrshp* 1967
Sales 5.5MMM^E *EMP* 11,900
SIC 2834 5122 Pharmaceutical preparations; Pharmaceuticals
CEO: Andrew Witty
Pr: Deirdre Connelly
Pr: Roger Connor
CFO: Simon Dingemans
Treas: Sarah J Chilverstainer
Ofcr: Chris Royal
Sr VP: Simon Bicknell
Sr VP: Nick Hirons
Sr VP: Bill Louv
VP: Mike Corrigan
VP: Jill G McConnell
VP: Moheb M Nasr
VP: Pascal Prigent
Exec: John Bolla
Exec: Robert Denton
Dir Lab: Robert Sanchez
Dir Bus: Charlotte Blanchard

D-U-N-S 00-385-4197 IMP

GLAZERS DISTRIBUTORS OF INDIANA LLC (IN)
OLINGER DISTRIBUTING COMPANY
(*Suby of* GLAZERS WHOLESALE DISTRIBUTORS) ★
5337 W 78th St, Indianapolis, IN 46268-4148
Tel (317) 876-1188 *Founded/Ownrshp* 1947, 1980
Sales 98.7MM^E *EMP* 200
SIC 5182 Liquor; Wine; Wine coolers, alcoholic
**Pr:* Jim Oliver
CIO: Roger Smith
VP Sls: Jim Dixon
VP Sls: Bill Stevens

GLAZERS WHOLESALE DISTRIBUTORS
See SOUTHERN GLAZERS WINE AND SPIRITS OF TEXAS LLC

D-U-N-S 00-983-0837 IMP

GLAZIER FOODS CO
(*Suby of* GORDON FOOD SERVICE INC) ★
11303 Antoine Dr, Houston, TX 77066-4429
Tel (713) 869-6411 *Founded/Ownrshp* 2014
Sales 1.0MMM^E *EMP* 550
SIC 5142 5141 Packaged frozen goods; Groceries, general line
Pr: John Miller
**VP:* Tom Dring
**VP:* Amelia A McStravick
**VP:* Judith Spring
CTO: Randy Patterson
**VP Mktg:* Troy Small
Manager: Deanne Robuck
Sls Mgr: Greg Bohnsack
Sls Mgr: Jeff Smith
Sls Mgr: Ron Vaudt

D-U-N-S 04-056-7471

GLEANER LIFE INSURANCE SOCIETY INC
5200 W Us Highway 223, Adrian, MI 49221-9461
Tel (517) 263-2244 *Founded/Ownrshp* 1894
Sales NA *EMP* 62
Accts Andrews Hooper Pavlik Plc Oke
SIC 6311 Life insurance
Pr: Ellsworth L Stout
Bd of Dir: Frank Dick
VP: Arell Chapman
VP: Jeff Patterson
Dir IT: Debra Keller

D-U-N-S 11-878-9825 IMP/EXP

GLEASON CORP
1000 University Ave, Rochester, NY 14607-1286
Tel (585) 473-1000 *Founded/Ownrshp* 2000
Sales 999.5MM^E *EMP* 2,508
SIC 3541 3829 Machine tools, metal cutting type; Gear cutting & finishing machines; Numerically controlled metal cutting machine tools; Machine tool replacement & repair parts, metal cutting types; Physical property testing equipment
Ch: James S Gleason
**Pr:* John J Perrotti
**Treas:* John W Pysnack
Sr VP: Robert P Phillips
VP: Douglas C Beerck
**VP:* Edward J Pelta
VP: Brian M Perry
VP: William J Simpson
VP: Hermann J Stadtfeld
VP: Udo Stolz
Mng Dir: Karl-Heinz K Bler

D-U-N-S 00-220-5755 IMP/EXP

GLEASON WORKS (NY)
(*Suby of* GLEASON CORP) ★
1000 University Ave, Rochester, NY 14607-1286
Tel (585) 473-1000 *Founded/Ownrshp* 1865, 1984
Sales 257.2MM^E *EMP* 926
SIC 3714 3728 3566 3541 3829 3469 Gears, motor vehicle; Gears, aircraft power transmission; Gears, power transmission, except automotive; Gear cutting & finishing machines; Numerically controlled metal cutting machine tools; Machine tool replacement & repair parts, metal cutting types; Physical property testing equipment; Metal stampings
Ch Bd: James S Gleason
**Pr:* John J Perrotti
**VP:* Nanci Malin Peck
**VP:* Edward J Pelta
**VP:* John W Pysnack

D-U-N-S 08-570-3874

GLEN BLOOMING CONTRACTORS INC
HANDWORK CONTRACTORS
901 Minsi Trl, Blooming Glen, PA 18911
Tel (215) 257-9400 *Founded/Ownrshp* 1971
Sales 84.3MM^E *EMP* 300
SIC 1611 1794 Highway & street paving contractor; Excavation work
Pr: John B Haines IV
**Sec:* John R Kibblehouse

D-U-N-S 07-336-3616

GLEN COVE HOSPITAL
101 Saint Andrews Ln, Glen Cove, NY 11542-2263
Tel (516) 674-7300 *Founded/Ownrshp* 1921
Sales 97.7MM *EMP* 1,000
SIC 8062 General medical & surgical hospitals
CEO: Michael Dowling
Surgeon: Ayal Segal
Ansthlgy: Malgorzata Adler
Ansthlgy: Katrina T Sabater

GLEN ELLYN CLINIC
See DU PAGE MEDICAL GROUP LTD

GLEN EYRIE CHRSTN CNFRENCE CTR
See NAVIGATORS

D-U-N-S 01-493-5369

GLEN GEO ENTERPRISES INC
13395 Murphy Rd, Stafford, TX 77477-4305
Tel (281) 242-6945 *Founded/Ownrshp* 1997
Sales 1.0MMM *EMP* 10
SIC 1799 5198 5084 Hydraulic equipment, installation & service; Enamels; Water pumps (industrial)
Pr: George Larry Anderson

GLEN GERY BRICK
See GLEN-GERY CORP

D-U-N-S 00-323-0158 IMP/EXP

GLEN RAVEN INC (NC)
GLENRAVEN.COM
1831 N Park Ave, Burlington, NC 27217-1137
Tel (336) 227-6211 *Founded/Ownrshp* 1880
Sales 617.3MM^E *EMP* 3,000
SIC 2221 2281 2261 2211

D-U-N-S 00-235-5857 IMP

GLEN-GERY CORP
GLEN GERY BRICK
(*Suby of* IBSTOCK BUILDING PRODUCTS LIMITED)
1166 Spring St, Reading, PA 19610-1721
Tel (610) 374-4011 *Founded/Ownrshp* 2015
Sales 190.0MM^E *EMP* 900

SIC 3251 Brick clay: common face, glazed, vitrified or hollow
Ch Bd: Steve Matsick
VP: George Robinson
VP: Ray Staub
Mktg Mgr: Tim Leese
Sls Mgr: Bill Raab

D-U-N-S 00-838-5312
GLENAIR INC
1211 Air Way, Glendale, CA 91201-2497
Tel (818) 247-6000 *Founded/Ownrshp* 1956
Sales 274.0MM^E *EMP* 1,100^E
SIC 3643 3825 3357

D-U-N-S 09-677-5358
GLENBARD TOWNSHIP HIGH SCHOOL DISTRICT 87
596 Crescent Blvd, Glen Ellyn, IL 60137-4200
Tel (630) 469-9100 *Founded/Ownrshp* 1920
Sales 47.6MM^E *EMP* 1,039
SIC 8211 Public senior high school
Teacher Pr: Josh Chambers

D-U-N-S 19-426-6870
GLENCORE LTD
(*Suby of* GLENCORE AG)
301 Tresser Blvd Fl 14, Stamford, CT 06901-3250
Tel (203) 328-4900 *Founded/Ownrshp* 1985
Sales 365.6MM^E *EMP* 215^E
SIC 6221 Commodity contracts brokers, dealers
Pr: Carlos Perezagua
**Treas:* David Porter
**VP:* Blandine Lewine
Exec: John McConaghy
Exec: Stephen Rowland
Exec: Mistakidis Telis
Dir Risk M: Vincent Digiovanni
Dir Risk M: Marisa Gianfortune
Dir Risk M: Seth Steinberg
Dept Mgr: Pam Perkins
IT Man: Don Batt

D-U-N-S 07-623-2735
GLENDALE ADVENTIST MEDICAL CENTER INC
ADVENTIST HEALTH
(*Suby of* ADVENTIST HEALTH SYSTEM/WEST) ★
1509 Wilson Ter, Glendale, CA 91206-4007
Tel (818) 409-8000 *Founded/Ownrshp* 1905
Sales 408.3MM *EMP* 2,600
Accts Ernst & Young Llp Roseville
SIC 8062 8093 8011 General medical & surgical hospitals; Mental health clinic, outpatient; Freestanding emergency medical center
Pr: Kevin A Roberts
Chf Rad: Robert McKay
**Pr:* Irene Bourdon
**COO:* Warren Tetz
CFO: John Giese
CFO: Douglas Rebok
Bd of Dir: Christine Friestad
Assoc VP: Rob Marchuk
**Sr VP:* Judy Blair
**Sr VP:* Kelly Turner
**VP:* Karen Brandt
VP: Michael S Cann
**VP:* Despina Kayichian
VP: Gwen Mathews
Exec: Nancy Cruz
Dir Lab: Cruisma Merinda
Dir Rad: Clayton Lau
Dir Rad: Tom Paw
Dir Rx: Debra Camacho

D-U-N-S 07-881-9539
GLENDALE COMMUNITY COLLEGE DIST
1500 N Verdugo Rd, Glendale, CA 91208-2894
Tel (818) 240-1000 *Founded/Ownrshp* 1927
Sales 12.5MM^E *EMP* 1,500
Accts Vavrinek Trine Day & Co Ll
SIC 8222 Community college
Pr: Dr David Viar
**Pr:* Audre Levy
**CFO:* Larry Serot
Trst: Tony Tartaglia
Ofcr: Rony Aharonian
VP: Wayne Keller
**VP:* Mary Mirch
**VP:* Ron Nakasone
VP: Arnel Pascua
VP: Lawrence Serot
**Prin:* Jim Riggs

D-U-N-S 12-280-0238
GLENDALE ELEMENTARY SCHOOL DISTRICT
7301 N 58th Ave, Glendale, AZ 85301-1893
Tel (623) 237-4000 *Founded/Ownrshp* 1913
Sales 63.8MM^E *EMP* 1,700
SIC 8211 Public elementary school
Genl Mgr: Jill Winn
MIS Dir: Tom Park
Pr Dir: Tim Cummings
Instr Medi: Janet Gironda

GLENDALE MEMORIAL CENTER
See GLENDALE MEMORIAL HEALTH CORP

D-U-N-S 06-380-2136
GLENDALE MEMORIAL HEALTH CORP
GLENDALE MEMORIAL CENTER
(*Suby of* DIGNITY HEALTH) ★
1420 S Central Ave, Glendale, CA 91204-2508
Tel (818) 502-1900 *Founded/Ownrshp* 1995
Sales 2.6MM *EMP* 1,245
SIC 8062 General medical & surgical hospitals
CEO: David S Parkin
**Pr:* Jack Ivie
**COO:* Patrick A Petre
Ofcr: Paul O'Hanian
Ofcr: Patricia Ostiller
VP: Sandra Houston
Prd Mgr: Jesus Ahedo
Pathlgst: Kenneth Frankel
Pharmcst: Anet Karamyan
Pharmcst: Young S Kim
Pharmcst: Kevin Lee

D-U-N-S 07-723-9929 IMP
GLENDALE UNIFIED SCHOOL DISTRICT
223 N Jackson St, Glendale, CA 91206-4380
Tel (818) 241-3111 *Founded/Ownrshp* 1887
Sales 194.0MM^E *EMP* 4,000
Accts Vicenti Lloyd & Stutzman Llp
SIC 8211 Public elementary & secondary schools; High school, junior or senior; Kindergarten; Specialty education
Ex VP: Henrietta Movsessian
VP: Christine Walters
Exec: Kelly Velasquez
Ex Dir: Marina Garabedyan
Ex Dir: Camille Levee
IT Man: Bruce Dalton
IT Man: Angelica Reyes
Plnt Mgr: Greg Carter
Pr Dir: Rachel Deione
Pr Dir: Steven Frasher
Psych: Annet Goodside

D-U-N-S 09-711-5539
GLENDALE UNION HIGH SCHOOL DISTRICT
GUHSD
7650 N 43rd Ave, Glendale, AZ 85301-1661
Tel (623) 435-0152 *Founded/Ownrshp* 1910
Sales 104.9MM^E *EMP* 1,800
Accts Heinfeld Meech & Co Pc P
SIC 8211 Public senior high school
Sls Mgr: Lou Wiegand

D-U-N-S 13-059-7813 IMP/EXP
GLENMARK PHARMACEUTICALS INC USA
(*Suby of* GLENMARK PHARMACEUTICALS LIMITED)
750 Corporate Dr, Mahwah, NJ 07430-2009
Tel (201) 684-8000 *Founded/Ownrshp* 2002
Sales 345.0MM^E *EMP* 91^E
Accts P Parikh & Associates Charter
SIC 5122 Pharmaceuticals
Pr: Robert Mapsuk
**CFO:* Prakash Chainani
CFO: Rajesh Desai
Sr Cor Off: Inder Arora
Sr Cor Off: Sagar Chavan
Sr Cor Off: Ajay Singh
Ofcr: Anil Bhujbal
Ofcr: Vijay Chandankar
Ofcr: Praveen Chauhan
Ofcr: Prashant Gaikwad
Ofcr: Aman Gupta
Ofcr: Rohit Kaundal
Ofcr: Amit Khairnar
Ofcr: Govind Krishnaswamy
Ofcr: Harini Kulal
Ofcr: Santosh Mali
Ofcr: Sunil Nirgude
Ofcr: Sushila Nirmal
Ofcr: Vipin Patel
Ofcr: Jitendra Patil
Ofcr: Pooja Sawant

D-U-N-S 79-180-5401
GLENMEDE CORP
1650 Market St Ste 1200, Philadelphia, PA 19103-7311
Tel (215) 419-6000 *Founded/Ownrshp* 1983
Sales 130.2MM *EMP* 250
SIC 6733 6732 Personal investment trust management; Charitable trust management
Pr: Gordon B Fowler
Pr: Huldah A Robertson
**Treas:* Laura A Williamson
Ofcr: Maria McGarry
Sr VP: Susan P Mucciarone
VP: Matthew Beardwood
**VP:* James R Belanger
VP: John Carson
VP: Matthew Cross
VP: Letitia Ewing
VP: Richard Gale
VP: Frederick Haack
VP: Margaret Kelly
VP: William Krauss
VP: Jerry Littenberg
VP: Robert Maxwell
VP: Francis Mehaffey
VP: Dennis Riley
VP: Michael Schiff
VP: Michael Serra
VP: Glenn Switzer

D-U-N-S 02-757-6420
GLENN DISTRIBUTOR INC
1301 N Wenatchee Ave, Wenatchee, WA 98801-1537
Tel (509) 663-7173 *Founded/Ownrshp* 1966
Sales 137.2MM *EMP* 19
SIC 5172 5541 7359 Fuel oil; Petroleum brokers; Filling stations, gasoline; Equipment rental & leasing
Pr: Ray Glenn
**Sec:* Pegi Glenn
**VP:* Ed Glenn

D-U-N-S 01-459-8460
GLENN O HAWBAKER INC
1952 Waddle Rd Ste 203, State College, PA 16803-1649
Tel (814) 237-1444 *Founded/Ownrshp* 1966
Sales 300.0MM *EMP* 1,200
Accts Parent Beard Llc State Colleg
SIC 2951 3281 1622 1794 1611 1422 Asphalt & asphaltic paving mixtures (not from refineries); Stone, quarrying & processing of own stone products; Bridge construction; Excavation work; Highway & street paving contractor; Crushed & broken limestone
Pr: Daniel R Hawbaker
**Treas:* Patrick G Hawbaker
**VP:* D Michael Hawbaker

D-U-N-S 05-741-1415
GLENN THURMAN INC
3180 S Belt Line Rd, Balch Springs, TX 75181-3086
Tel (972) 286-6333 *Founded/Ownrshp* 1972
Sales 120.5MM^E *EMP* 278
SIC 1611 4212 General contractor, highway & street construction; Local trucking, without storage
Pr: Glenn C Thurman
**Pr:* Gary R Maynor

D-U-N-S 07-230-6459
GLENOAKS CONVALESCENT HOSPITAL (LP)
409 W Glenoaks Blvd, Glendale, CA 91202-2916
Tel (818) 240-4300 *Founded/Ownrshp* 1984
Sales 473.1MM *EMP* 85
SIC 8062 General medical & surgical hospitals
Pt: Elaine Levine

GLENRAVEN.COM
See GLEN RAVEN INC

D-U-N-S 06-054-0382 IMP
GLENS FALLS HOSPITAL (NY)
100 Park St, Glens Falls, NY 12801-4447
Tel (518) 926-1000 *Founded/Ownrshp* 1897, 1984
Sales 316.8MM *EMP* 2,726
SIC 8011 8062 8221 Offices & clinics of medical doctors; General medical & surgical hospitals; Colleges universities & professional schools
Pr: Dianne Shugrue
**Pr:* David G Kruczlnicki
**COO:* James W Connolly
**CFO:* Mitchell J Amado III
CFO: Donna Leroux
**CFO:* D Michael Niles
Sr VP: Jeffrey Treasure Sr
VP: Douglas Barry
**VP:* Kyle Brock
VP: Cindy Gage
**VP:* Edward Hanchett
VP: James Hungerford
VP: Cindy Sherwood
VP: Celeste Steele
Exec: Joanne Detore
Dir Rad: Ed Hanchett

D-U-N-S 00-697-7441
■ **GLENS FALLS NATIONAL BANK & TRUST CO**
(*Suby of* ARROW FINANCIAL CORP) ★
250 Glen St, Glens Falls, NY 12801-3505
Tel (518) 793-4121 *Founded/Ownrshp* 1851
Sales NA *EMP* 481
SIC 6021 National commercial banks
Ch Bd: Thomas L Hoy
Pr: David S Demarco
Pr: Michael Jacobs
**Pr:* Thomas J Murphy
Pr: Martin West
CFO: Terry Goodemote
Chf Cred: David Kaiser
Ofcr: Harrison Sangster
Sr VP: Terry R Goodemote
Sr VP: Kathleen Kelleher
Sr VP: Peter Lareau
Sr VP: Charles R Petit
VP: Susan Kenneally
VP: Mary P Rabin
VP: David Riihimaki
Board of Directors: Michael B Clarke, Kenneth Hopper MD, David Kruczlnicki, Elizabeth Little, Michael F Massiano Chb, David Moynehan, Bill Owens, Richard Reisman

GLENWOOD REGIONAL MEDICAL CENT
See GLENWOOD RESOLUTION AUTHORITY INC

D-U-N-S 07-137-3625 IMP
GLENWOOD RESOLUTION AUTHORITY INC
GLENWOOD REGIONAL MEDICAL CENT
503 Mcmillan Rd, West Monroe, LA 71291-5327
Tel (318) 329-4200 *Founded/Ownrshp* 1968
Sales 777.2M *EMP* 1,156
SIC 8062 General medical & surgical hospitals
CEO: Ron Elder
**VP:* Jan Walker
CIO: Ronnie Maxwell

D-U-N-S 36-097-4906
GLENWOOD TREE EXPERTS
21457 Milwaukee Ave, Deerfield, IL 60015-5322
Tel (847) 459-0200 *Founded/Ownrshp* 1981
Sales 137.3MM^E *EMP* 351^E
SIC 0783 0782 Ornamental shrub & tree services; Lawn & garden services
Owner: Jim Sackelman

D-U-N-S 80-273-7833 IMP/EXP
GLF CONSTRUCTION CORP
(*Suby of* GRANDI LAVORI FINCOSIT SPA)
528 Nw 7th Ave, Miami, FL 33136-3102
Tel (305) 371-5228 *Founded/Ownrshp* 1993
Sales 249.4MM^E *EMP* 450
SIC 1611 1622 1542 1541 1522 Highway & street construction; Bridge, tunnel & elevated highway; Commercial & office building, new construction; Industrial buildings, new construction; Condominium construction
CEO: Francesco Senis
**COO:* Joseph M Beaird
**CFO:* Vincent L Persiani
Sr VP: Sebastian Gunningham
VP: Corrado Difabio
VP: James Gassenhemier
VP: Alejandro Gonzalez
**VP:* Ernest Howard Jr
**VP:* William E Junkin
VP: William Junkin
**VP:* Michael J Miles
VP: Susan Serrats

GLI DISTRIBUTING
See GLI INC

D-U-N-S 02-706-9889 IMP
GLI INC
GLI DISTRIBUTING
803 S Medina St, San Antonio, TX 78207-5610
Tel (210) 226-4376 *Founded/Ownrshp* 1982
Sales 1.1MMM^E *EMP* 11,040^E
SIC 5181

D-U-N-S 08-758-2107
GLICK LLC
415 W Main St, Rochester, NY 14608-1944
Tel (716) 235-1595 *Founded/Ownrshp* 2001
Sales NA *EMP* 1,200
SIC 6719 Investment holding companies, except banks
MIS Dir: Melva Boren

GLIDDEN PROFESSIONAL PAINT CTR
See AKZO NOBEL PAINTS LLC

GLIDEWELL LABORATORIES
See JAMES R GLIDEWELL DENTAL CERAMICS INC

D-U-N-S 07-502-3036
GLIMCHER REALTY TRUST (MD)
180 E Broad St Fl 20, Columbus, OH 43215-3714
Tel (614) 621-9000 *Founded/Ownrshp* 1993
Sales 381.8MM *EMP* 981^E
SIC 6512

D-U-N-S 00-402-8366 IMP
■ **GLOBAL AEROSPACE INC**
(*Suby of* GLOBAL AEROSPACE UNDERWRITING MANAGERS LIMITED)
1 Sylvan Way Ste 3, Parsippany, NJ 07054-3879
Tel (973) 490-8500 *Founded/Ownrshp* 2001
Sales NA *EMP* 271^E
SIC 6411 Insurance agents, brokers & service
CEO: Tony Medniuk
**CEO:* Nick Brown
Ofcr: Ann-Marie Friedman
Assoc VP: Eileen Cashman-Jermak
Ex VP: Jeffrey Bruno
Sr VP: Mike Falcone
Sr VP: Sharon Holahan
Sr VP: Nicholas Methven
Sr VP: Joseph Taccetta
Sr VP: Frank Turtola
VP: Sebastian Ciepiela
VP: Roger D Eveleth
VP: John Meehan
VP: David Nelson
VP: Michael Pechloff
Exec: Marilena Sharpell
Board of Directors: Nick Brown, Jeffrey Bruno, Michael Falcone, Sharon Holahan, John Kelly, Alan Tasker, Stephen Walsh

D-U-N-S 07-262-0797
GLOBAL AGGREGATE LLC
AWIZEBUY.COM
8901 E Mountain View Rd, Scottsdale, AZ 85258-4422
Tel (480) 414-9400 *Founded/Ownrshp* 1999
Sales 600.0MM *EMP* 163
SIC 6798 7389 5045 Real estate investment trusts; Financial services; Computer peripheral equipment

D-U-N-S 61-489-7440
GLOBAL AUTOMOTIVE SYSTEMS LLC
(*Suby of* DURA AUTOMOTIVE SYSTEMS LLC) ★
1780 Pond Run, Auburn Hills, MI 48326-2752
Tel (248) 299-7230 *Founded/Ownrshp* 2005
Sales 295.6MM^E *EMP* 1,000
SIC 3469 Metal stampings
CEO: Lynn Tilton
**COO:* Martin Becker
**CFO:* Jim Gregory
**Ex VP:* Franois Stouvenot
**Ex VP:* Nizar Trigui

D-U-N-S 80-564-1847
GLOBAL AVIATION HOLDINGS INC
101 World Dr, Peachtree City, GA 30269-6969
Tel (770) 632-8000 *Founded/Ownrshp* 2012
Sales NA *EMP* 2,012
SIC 4522

GLOBAL BRANDS GROUP
See GLOBAL BRANDS HOLDING GROUP LLC

D-U-N-S 07-948-8344
GLOBAL BRANDS HOLDING GROUP LLC
GLOBAL BRANDS GROUP
350 5th Ave, New York, NY 10118-0110
Tel (646) 839-7000 *Founded/Ownrshp* 2007
Sales 3.4MMM^E *EMP* 1
SIC 5136 5137 5139 Men's & boys' clothing; Women's & children's clothing; Footwear
CEO: William Fung Kwok Lun
Pr: Dow Peter Famulak
CFO: Ronald Ventricelli
CFO: Leong Kwok Yee
Ex Dir: Hau Leung Lee

D-U-N-S 80-849-9920
▲ **GLOBAL BRASS AND COPPER HOLDINGS INC**
475 N Marti Rd Ste 1050, Schaumburg, IL 60173
Tel (847) 240-4700 *Founded/Ownrshp* 2007
Sales 1.5MMM *EMP* 1,900
Tkr Sym BRSS *Exch* NYS
SIC 3351 3341 3469 Copper rolling & drawing; Brass rolling & drawing; Copper smelting & refining (secondary); Metal stampings
Pr: John J Wasz
**Ch Bd:* John H Walker
Pr: Kevin W Bense
Pr: Devin K Denner
Pr: William G Toler
CFO: Christopher J Kodosky
CFO: Robert T Micchelli

D-U-N-S 80-850-0032
■ **GLOBAL BRASS AND COPPER INC**
(*Suby of* GLOBAL BRASS AND COPPER HOLDINGS INC) ★
305 Lewis And Clark Blvd, East Alton, IL 62024-1177
Tel (618) 258-5000 *Founded/Ownrshp* 2007
Sales 1.5MMM^E *EMP* 1,900
SIC 3351 3341 3469 1542 Brass rolling & drawing; Copper smelting & refining (secondary); Metal stampings; Commercial & office building, new construction
Pr: John Wasz
**Ch Bd:* Michael Psaros
Chf Mktg O: Ann Pipkin
VP: Greg Keown
Mktg Mgr: Kon John

D-U-N-S 16-192-3149
GLOBAL BUILDING SERVICES INC
25129The Old Rd Ste 102, Stevenson Ranch, CA 91381-2287
Tel (661) 288-5733 *Founded/Ownrshp* 1986
Sales 37.3MM^E *EMP* 1,100^E
SIC 7349 Janitorial service, contract basis
Pr: Julio Belloso

D-U-N-S 80-079-2876
GLOBAL CAPITAL RESOURCES GROUP LLC
1201 Broadway Ste 608, New York, NY 10001-5405
Tel (646) 221-1898 *Founded/Ownrshp* 2007
Sales 100.0MM *EMP* 2
SIC 6722 Management investment, open-end
Pr: Benedictus D K Ayitey
Pt: Michael Megalli
VP: James E Moore

D-U-N-S 01-537-9402 IMP/EXP
GLOBAL CELLULAR INC (GA)
CELLAIRIS
6485 Shiloh Rd Ste B100, Alpharetta, GA 30005-1605
Tel (678) 513-4020 *Founded/Ownrshp* 1999
Sales 132.6MM^E *EMP* 478^E
SIC 5065 Mobile telephone equipment
CEO: Konstantine Skouras
**Pr:* Ken Taylor
**COO:* Richard Motilal
**Ofcr:* Joseph Brown
**VP:* Jason Adler
**VP:* Valerie Brunson
VP: Marty Welch
**CTO:* Rob Jackness
Sls Mgr: Ryan Mooney

GLOBAL COMMUNITIES
See COOPERATIVE HOUSING FOUNDATION CORP

D-U-N-S 01-917-7757 IMP
■ **GLOBAL COMPANIES LLC**
(*Suby of* GLOBAL OPERATING LLC) ★
800 South St Ste 500, Waltham, MA 02453-1483
Tel (800) 542-0778 *Founded/Ownrshp* 2005
Sales 558.2MM^E *EMP* 217^E
SIC 5172 5171 Fuel oil; Gasoline; Diesel fuel; Kerosene; Petroleum bulk stations & terminals
Pr: Eric Slifka
COO: Thomas J Hollister
CFO: Caroline Dorsa
Ex VP: Edward J Faneuil
Ex VP: Charles A Rudinsky
Genl Mgr: Karnig Ekizian
Mktg Mgr: Joe De Stefano

D-U-N-S 04-108-2754
GLOBAL CONSTRUCTION SERVICES LLC
934 N University Dr 453, Coral Springs, FL 33071-7029
Tel (954) 688-6255 *Founded/Ownrshp* 2010
Sales 700.0MM *EMP* 7
SIC 1522 Apartment building construction
Off Mgr: Cindy Owen

D-U-N-S 10-400-2865
GLOBAL CONTACT SERVICES LLC
118b S Main St B, Salisbury, NC 28144-4942
Tel (704) 647-9672 *Founded/Ownrshp* 2001
Sales 39.0MM^E *EMP* 1,600
SIC 7319 7389 Transit advertising services; Telemarketing services
CEO: Greg Alcorn
**COO:* Bryan Overcash
**Sr VP:* Frank Camp
VP: Bucky Cline
**VP:* Mark Petty
Dir IT: Richard Johnson

D-U-N-S 15-469-1328
■ **GLOBAL CROSSING BANDWIDTH INC**
(*Suby of* LEVEL 3 COMMUNICATIONS INC) ★
200 Meridian Centre Blvd # 130, Rochester, NY 14618-3972
Tel (212) 920-8201 *Founded/Ownrshp* 2011
Sales 150.2MM^E *EMP* 2,000
SIC 4813 7373 7374 Telephone communication, except radio; Computer integrated systems design; Data processing & preparation
Pr: David R Carey
**CFO:* John Kritzmacher
**Treas:* Mark Gottlieb
**VP:* Mitchell C Sussis

D-U-N-S 00-699-4065 IMP
■ **GLOBAL CROSSING NORTH AMERICA INC**
ROCHESTER TELEPHONE
(*Suby of* GLOBAL CROSSING NORTH AMERICAN HOLDINGS INC) ★
200 Park Ave Ste 300, Florham Park, NJ 07932-1026
Tel (973) 937-0100 *Founded/Ownrshp* 1999
Sales 177.9MM^E *EMP* 570
SIC 4813 Local & long distance telephone communications; Data telephone communications; Voice telephone communications
CEO: John J Legere
**CFO:* Jean Mandeville
**Chf Mktg O:* Anthony Christie
Ex VP: David R Caey
**Ex VP:* David R Carey
**Ex VP:* Daniel Enright
Ex VP: Matias Heinrich
**Ex VP:* John B McShane
Ex VP: John R Mulhearn
Sr VP: Paul O Brien
Sr VP: Sean Gilman
Sr VP: Derek Lister
VP: Neil Barua
VP: Mike Benjamin
VP: Ricky Chau
VP: Mike Cromwell
VP: Gabriel Holgado
VP: Dawn Kolb
VP: Paul Parente
VP: Jeremy Polster
VP: Alberto Rodriguez
Board of Directors: Mitchell Sussis

D-U-N-S 15-443-6914
■ **GLOBAL CROSSING NORTH AMERICAN HOLDINGS INC**
(*Suby of* LEVEL 3 COMMUNICATIONS INC) ★
200 Park Ave Ste 300, Florham Park, NJ 07932-1026
Tel (973) 937-0100 *Founded/Ownrshp* 2011
Sales 510.4MM^E *EMP* 3,155
SIC 4813 Telephone communication, except radio
CEO: John Legere
**Chf Mktg O:* Gary Breauninger
Sr VP: Michael Toplisek
**VP:* Mitchell C Sussis

D-U-N-S 80-788-9022
GLOBAL DATA PUBLICATIONS INC
GBI RESEARCH
441 Lexington Ave Fl 3, New York, NY 10017-3950
Tel (646) 395-5460 *Founded/Ownrshp* 2007
Sales 68.6MM^E *EMP* 1,000
SIC 7379 8732 8748 Data processing consultant; Market analysis or research; Business consulting
Pr: Ben Slattery
**CEO:* Wayne Lloyd
Sr VP: Sanford Cameron
Sr VP: Marc Elichman
Sr VP: Richard Watkins
VP: Ron Cohen
Dir Bus: Daniel Aminipour
Dir Bus: Gunit Gill
VP Mktg: Eli Caiyem
VP Sls: Janet Dresher
Sls Mgr: Thomas Boccard

GLOBAL DISTRIBUTION CENTER
See JACINTOPORT INTERNATIONAL LLC

D-U-N-S 03-973-8281 IMP
GLOBAL DIVING & SALVAGE INC
3840 W Marginal Way Sw, Seattle, WA 98106-1163
Tel (206) 623-0621 *Founded/Ownrshp* 1980
Sales 188.8MM^E *EMP* 443^E
SIC 4959 1629 7389 Oil spill cleanup; Marine construction; Divers, commercial
Pr: Devon Grennan
VP: Martin Anderson
VP: Mike Brown
VP: David Devilbiss
VP: Jennifer Jensen
**VP:* Trinity Ng-Yeung
Div Mgr: Bruce Humberstone
Off Mgr: Kathy Kaae
IT Man: Jeffery Chin
Trfc Dir: Nicole Hamilton
Mtls Mgr: Kurt Vancampen

D-U-N-S 96-730-2865
▲ **GLOBAL EAGLE ENTERTAINMENT INC**
4553 Glencoe Ave Ste 200, Marina Del Rey, CA 90292-7909
Tel (310) 437-6000 *Founded/Ownrshp* 2011
Sales 426.0MM *EMP* 1,000^E
Tkr Sym ENT *Exch* NAS
SIC 4899 7371 4813 Data communication services; Custom computer programming services; Software programming applications; ;
CEO: David M Davis
**Ch Bd:* Edward L Shapiro
CFO: Tom Severson
CFO: Michael Zemetra
Chf Cred: Wale Adepoju
Sr VP: Stephen Ballas
Sr VP: Aditya Chatterjee
VP: Zant Chapelo
VP: Alexis Steinman
CIO: Ajay Malhotra
VP Sls: Travis Peterson
Board of Directors: Jeffrey E Epstein, Stephen Hasker, Jeffrey A Leddy, Robert W Reding, Jeff Sagansky, Harry E Sloan

D-U-N-S 78-424-6790
GLOBAL EMPLOYMENT HOLDINGS INC
10375 Park Meadows Dr # 475, Littleton, CO 80124-6735
Tel (303) 216-9500 *Founded/Ownrshp* 2006
Sales 157.5MM^E *EMP* 15,000^E
SIC 7363 6719 Temporary help service; Investment holding companies, except banks
Pr: Howard Brill
**Pr:* Terry Koch
**CFO:* Wayne Cavanaugh
Ex VP: Michael Devlieger
Ex VP: John Evans
VP: Kimberly Lepre
VP: Gavin Meacham
VP: Ken Michaels
**VP:* Ashley Notthoff
Brnch Mgr: Denise Hernandez
Off Mgr: Maureen Standing

D-U-N-S 02-613-6288
■ **GLOBAL EMPLOYMENT SOLUTIONS INC**
(*Suby of* GLOBAL EMPLOYMENT HOLDINGS INC) ★
10375 Park Meadows Dr # 475, Littleton, CO 80124-6735
Tel (303) 216-9500 *Founded/Ownrshp* 2009
Sales 104.8MM^E *EMP* 2,000
SIC 7363 Temporary help service
Pr: Howard Brill
Pr: Wayne Cavanaugh
CFO: Daniel Hollenbach
Dir Pres: Tom Bodeep
Assoc VP: Rose Chu
VP: Chris Decristoforo
VP: Doug Graham
VP: Kevin Lecompte
VP: Kimberly Lepre
VP: Shawn McKinstrie
VP: Ashley Notthoff
VP: Zach Schnell
Exec: Toni Sterrett

D-U-N-S 83-140-3238
■ **GLOBAL ENERGY MARKETING LLC**
(*Suby of* GLOBAL OPERATING LLC) ★
800 South St Ste 500, Waltham, MA 02453-1439
Tel (781) 894-8800 *Founded/Ownrshp* 2009
Sales 107.5MM^E *EMP* 1,000^E
SIC 5172 4924 Fuel oil; Natural gas distribution
Pr: Eric Slifka
**COO:* Thomas J Hollister
**Ex VP:* Edward J Faneuil
**Ex VP:* Charles A Rudinsky

D-U-N-S 18-818-7710
GLOBAL ENERGY SERVICES INC
10307 Wallisville Rd, Houston, TX 77013-4117
Tel (281) 447-9000 *Founded/Ownrshp* 1996
Sales 129.9MM^E *EMP* 605
SIC 3533 Oil field machinery & equipment
CEO: Paul Deweese
**Pr:* Michael Stansberry
**CFO:* Chris Ruffner
VP Sls: Lance Vogelsang

D-U-N-S 00-147-2216 IMP/EXP
■ **GLOBAL EQUIPMENT CO INC**
GLOBAL INDUSTRIAL EQUIPMENT
(*Suby of* SYSTEMAX INC) ★
11 Harbor Park Dr, Port Washington, NY 11050-4646
Tel (516) 608-7000 *Founded/Ownrshp* 2001
Sales 205.7MM^E *EMP* 400
SIC 5085 Industrial supplies
Ch Bd: Richard Leeds
**Treas:* Steven Goldschein
**VP:* Dennis Gerard
**VP:* Bruce Leeds
VP: Natalya Mandel
Exec: Natasha Ward
Genl Mgr: Don McKenna
Genl Mgr: Chris Solomon
Off Mgr: Rachel Rick
QA Dir: Jeanette Tesoriero
Dir IT: Jason Sabshon

D-U-N-S 08-377-2749 IMP
■ **GLOBAL EXPERIENCE SPECIALISTS INC**
G E S GLOBAL EXPERIENCE
(*Suby of* VIAD CORP) ★
7000 Lindell Rd, Las Vegas, NV 89118-4702
Tel (702) 515-5500 *Founded/Ownrshp* 1976
Sales 789.1MM^E *EMP* 2,800
SIC 7389 Convention & show services
Pr: Steve Moster
**COO:* Damian Morgan
**CFO:* Dave Hall
Treas: Elyse A Newman
Ex VP: Bruce H Baum
Ex VP: Wendy Gibson
Ex VP: Chuck Grouzard
Ex VP: Shirley R Kerfoot
**Ex VP:* Eddie Newqu
Ex VP: Jason Popp
Ex VP: Vin Saia
Ex VP: Gary C Sain
Sr VP: Terry Campanaro
**Sr VP:* Chris Elam
Sr VP: Dan Hilbert
Sr VP: Paul Wedesky
VP: Scott Crawford
**VP:* Steve Gebhart
VP: John Loveless
VP: Deborah M Medrano
VP: John Osborn

D-U-N-S 80-834-4621
GLOBAL FACILITY MANAGEMENT & CONSTRUCTION INC
525 Broadhollow Rd # 100, Melville, NY 11747-3736
Tel (866) 213-2337 *Founded/Ownrshp* 2004
Sales 100.0MM *EMP* 220
SIC 8744 Facilities support services
CEO: Lauryn Blank
**Pr:* Sean Blank
**CFO:* Mike Speiller
Sr VP: Lee Mizel
VP: Chris Cucuzza
VP: Mike Russo
Sls Mgr: Lexi Pisciotto

D-U-N-S 82-823-0495
GLOBAL FINANCIAL MANAGEMENT SERVICES LLC
925 S Federal Hwy Ste 375, Boca Raton, FL 33432-6144
Tel (561) 347-5500 *Founded/Ownrshp* 2006
Sales 750.0MM^E *EMP* 14
SIC 6792 Oil leases, buying & selling on own account

D-U-N-S 13-735-2576 IMP/EXP
GLOBAL FINISHING SOLUTIONS LLC
GFS
(*Suby of* CURRAN GROUP INC) ★
12731 Norway Rd, Osseo, WI 54758-7780
Tel (715) 597-8007 *Founded/Ownrshp* 1998
Sales 94.0MM *EMP* 360
SIC 3444 Booths, spray: prefabricated sheet metal
CEO: Michael Curran
**Pr:* James Fargher
**CFO:* Joshua Eager
CTO: Scott Funk
Trfc Mgr: Wanda Vehrenkamp

D-U-N-S 80-780-2660
GLOBAL FITNESS HOLDINGS LLC
URBAN ACTIVE
1056 Wellington Way # 200, Lexington, KY 40513-2000
Tel (859) 252-5993 *Founded/Ownrshp* 2000
Sales 22.4MM^E *EMP* 1,500
SIC 7991 Athletic club & gymnasiums, membership
CFO: Denver Pratt

GLOBAL FOUNDRIES
See GLOBALFOUNDRIES US INC

D-U-N-S 80-078-6696
GLOBAL FRANCHISE GROUP LLC
PRETZEL TIME
(*Suby of* GFG MANAGEMENT LLC) ★
5555 Glenridge Connector # 850, Atlanta, GA 30342-4810
Tel (770) 514-4500 *Founded/Ownrshp* 2010
Sales 211.0MM^E *EMP* 961^E
SIC 5461 6794 Bakeries; Franchises, selling or licensing
Pr: Chris Dull
Pr: Jerry Slover
**CFO:* Lewis Loeb
**Ofcr:* John Barber
VP: Andrew Kmiec
VP Inf Sys: Gerald Brouillette
Mktg Dir: Lisa Cheatham

D-U-N-S 18-036-3611 IMP/EXP
GLOBAL GEOPHYSICAL SERVICES INC
13927 S Gessner Rd, Missouri City, TX 77489-1021
Tel (713) 972-9200 *Founded/Ownrshp* 2003
Sales 288.6MM *EMP* 1,500^E
SIC 1382 Oil & gas exploration services; Geophysical exploration, oil & gas field; Seismograph surveys
CEO: Sean M Gore
**Ch Bd:* Richard C White
COO: P Mathew Verghese
Sr VP: James E Brasher
Sr VP: Thomas J Fleure
VP: Raymond Dobrosky
VP: George Yapuncich
VP Inf Sys: Oscar Garcia
Opers Supe: Valdecir Rezende
Board of Directors: Michael S Bahorich, Michael C Forrest, Karl F Kurz, George E Matelich, Joseph P McCoy, Stanley De J Osborne

GLOBAL GROUP, THE
See GLOBAL STAINLESS SUPPLY INC

D-U-N-S 19-616-5711
GLOBAL HARNESS SYSTEMS INC
3304 Danley Rd, Philadelphia, PA 19154-1410
Tel (609) 815-2100 *Founded/Ownrshp* 2001
Sales 173.9MM^E *EMP* 845
SIC 3679

D-U-N-S 96-489-2553
GLOBAL HEALTH SOLUTIONS INC
325 Swanton Way, Decatur, GA 30030-3001
Tel (404) 592-1430 *Founded/Ownrshp* 2010
Sales 1.7MMM *EMP* 2
SIC 8099 Health & allied services
VP: T Rosenberger
VP: Thomas Rosenberger

D-U-N-S 12-487-9334
GLOBAL HEALTHCARE EXCHANGE LLC
1315 W Century Dr Ste 100, Louisville, CO 80027-9560
Tel (720) 887-7000 *Founded/Ownrshp* 2000
Sales NA *EMP* 500
SIC 6321 Health insurance carriers
CEO: Bruce Johnson
CFO: Richard Hunt
Ex VP: Kurt W Blasena
VP: John Gaither
VP: Dale Locklair
VP: Steve Woodis
Dir Bus: Sherry Jennings
Comm Man: Karen Conway
Ex Dir: Paul Manganella
Ex Dir: Debbie Sprindzunas
Genl Mgr: Nils Clausen

D-U-N-S 84-985-2389
■ **GLOBAL IMAGING SYSTEMS INC**
(*Suby of* XEROX CORP) ★
3903 Northdale Blvd 200w, Tampa, FL 33624-1854
Tel (813) 960-5508 *Founded/Ownrshp* 2007
Sales 2.4MMM^E *EMP* 5,553
SIC 5044 5045 7629 Office equipment; Computers, peripherals & software; Computer peripheral equipment; Business machine repair, electric
CEO: Thomas Salierno Jr
**Pr:* Russell Peacock
**CFO:* R Edward Bass
Ex VP: Dan Cooper
Ex VP: Daniel Robert Cooper
VP: Ed Bass
VP: Dan Brady
VP: Denny Houseman
**VP:* Roxanne Koszarycki
VP: Dawn North
VP: Ken Weilerstein
VP: Myra Wilkins
Exec: Sheila Rosenblatt
Exec: Judy Schmidt
Dir Risk M: George Achin

D-U-N-S 83-320-8528
GLOBAL INDEMNITY GROUP INC
3 Bala Plz Ste 300, Bala Cynwyd, PA 19004-3406
Tel (610) 664-1500 *Founded/Ownrshp* 2003
Sales NA *EMP* 1,080^E
SIC 6351 Surety insurance
Pr: Robert Fishman
CFO: Thomas McGeehan
VP: James Genghini
Mktg Mgr: Laura Gooding
Snr Mgr: Cindy Valko

GLOBAL INDUSTRIAL EQUIPMENT
See GLOBAL EQUIPMENT CO INC

D-U-N-S 79-252-1445 IMP/EXP
GLOBAL INDUSTRIAL TECHNOLOGIES INC
1305 Chrrington Pkwy Moon, Coraopolis, PA 15108
Tel (412) 375-6600 *Founded/Ownrshp* 2013
Sales 128.8MM^E *EMP* 599^E
SIC 3297 3255 1459 3546 3272 3589

D-U-N-S 04-990-8403 IMP
GLOBAL INDUSTRIES INC
EVOLVE FURNITURE GROUP
17 W Stow Rd, Marlton, NJ 08053-3116
Tel (856) 596-3390 *Founded/Ownrshp* 1972
Sales 142.5MM^E *EMP* 356
SIC 2522 5021 Office furniture, except wood; Furniture
Ch Bd: Joel Appel
Chf Mktg O: Michael Fishman
**Ex VP:* Jon Abraham
**Ex VP:* Jon Soll
Sls Mgr: Scott Armstrong
Sls Mgr: Don Voake
Snr Mgr: David Robinson

D-U-N-S 96-461-1578 IMP/EXP
GLOBAL INDUSTRIES INC
MFS/YORK/STORMOR
1804 E 4th St, Grand Island, NE 68801-3009
Tel (800) 247-6621 *Founded/Ownrshp* 1996
Sales 99.7MM^E *EMP* 613
SIC 7992 3589 3444 5084 5083 3535 Public golf courses; Water treatment equipment, industrial; Metal housings, enclosures, casings & other containers; Materials handling machinery; Agricultural machinery & equipment; Conveyors & conveying equipment
Pr: Jack R Henry
**CFO:* Douglas D Fargo
VP: John Haugh
VP: Randy Langen
Genl Mgr: Steve Back
Sfty Dirs: Jamie Lemburg
Manager: John Crawford
Sls Mgr: Mike Muessel
Sales Asso: Karl Sander

GLOBAL INNOVATION PARTNER
See CBRE GLOBAL INVESTORS LLC

GLOBAL INTEGRATED LOGISTICS
See AGILITY LOGISTICS CORP

D-U-N-S 94-131-9345
GLOBAL KNOWLEDGE TRAINING LLC
(*Suby of* GK HOLDINGS INC) ★
9000 Regency Pkwy Ste 400, Cary, NC 27518-8520
Tel (919) 388-1064 *Founded/Ownrshp* 1995
Sales 323.7MM *EMP* 462^E
SIC 8243 Data processing schools
Pr: Sean J Dolan
**Pr:* Brian Branson
**Treas:* Robert Kalainikas
VP: Bryan L Pickett
VP: Robert Schaffner
Exec: Priscilla Cooney
**CIO:* Satish Shetty
IT Man: Ava Hines
VP Sls: Jonathan Hensley

D-U-N-S 17-704-7677
GLOBAL MAIL INC
DHL ECOMMERCE
(*Suby of* DEUTSCHE POST AG)
2700 S Comm Pkwy Ste 300, Weston, FL 33331
Tel (800) 805-9306 *Founded/Ownrshp* 1999
Sales 91.9MM^E *EMP* 2,700
SIC 4513 Letter delivery, private air; Package delivery, private air
CEO: Lee Spratt
Ch Bd: S David Fineman
**CFO:* Terry Hilsman
**Sr VP:* Dave Loonam
**Sr VP:* Paul Tessy
VP Bus Dev: Craig Morris
Genl Mgr: Jonathan Sallaz
IT Man: Jessica Blakeney
VP Opers: Jim McAtee
Opers Supe: Kok Keng
Sls Dir: Rick Solorza

D-U-N-S 00-690-7299
GLOBAL MARINE INC (DE)
TRANSOCEAN
(*Suby of* TRANSOCEAN INC) ★
4 Greenway Plz Ste 100, Houston, TX 77046-0403
Tel (713) 232-7500 *Founded/Ownrshp* 1955, 1964
Sales 237.7MM^E *EMP* 700^E
Accts Ernst & Young Llp Houston Te
SIC 1381 1311 Drilling oil & gas wells; Crude petroleum production; Natural gas production
Pr: Gregory L Cauthen
Pr: Darrell Pelley
**CEO:* Steven L Newman
**COO:* John Stobart
**Treas:* Ramon Yi
**Ex VP:* ESA Ikheimonen
VP: Robert Herrin
VP: Keelan I Adamson
VP: Paul A King
VP: Myrtle Penelton
Dir Risk M: Ben Murrell

D-U-N-S 00-121-0616 IMP
GLOBAL MATERIAL TECHNOLOGIES INC (NY)
GMT
750 W Lake Cook Rd # 480, Buffalo Grove, IL 60089-2074
Tel (847) 495-4700 *Founded/Ownrshp* 1977
Sales 95.6MM^E *EMP* 316
SIC 3291 Steel wool
Pr: Norman Soep
**CFO:* Robert Krebs
**VP:* Alex Krupnik
**VP Admn:* Edwin Jones
Genl Mgr: Dave Colbert
VP Sls: David Colbert
Sls Mgr: Paul Bonn

D-U-N-S 78-625-1988
■ **GLOBAL OPERATING LLC**
(*Suby of* GLOBAL PARTNERS LP) ★
800 South St Ste 500, Waltham, MA 02453-1439
Tel (800) 542-0778 *Founded/Ownrshp* 2006
Sales 906.5MM^E *EMP* 869^E
SIC 4924 4911 Natural gas distribution; Electric services
Pr: Eric Slifka
**COO:* Thomas J Hollister
**Ex VP:* Edward J Faneuil
**Ex VP:* Charles A Rudinsky

D-U-N-S 13-303-2826 EXP
GLOBAL PACIFIC PRODUCE INC
11500 S Eastern Ave # 160, Henderson, NV 89052-7400
Tel (702) 898-8051 *Founded/Ownrshp* 2000
Sales 315.3MM *EMP* 250^E
SIC 5148

D-U-N-S 60-258-0867 IMP
▲ **GLOBAL PARTNERS LP**
800 South St Ste 500, Waltham, MA 02453-1483
Tel (781) 894-8800 *Founded/Ownrshp* 2005
Sales 10.3MMM *EMP* 1,890^E
Accts Ernst & Young Llp Boston Mas
Tkr Sym GLP *Exch* NYS
SIC 5172 5171 Petroleum products; Petroleum bulk stations & terminals; Petroleum terminals
Pr: Eric Slifka
Genl Pt: Global GP LLC
COO: Mark A Romaine
CFO: Daphne H Foster
Ch: Richard Slifka
Ex VP: Edward J Faneuil
Ex VP: Gregory Rudoy
Ex VP: Andrew Slifka
VP: William Davidson
VP: Joseph Destefano
VP: Jane Michalek
VP: Dylan Remley
VP: Kevin Young
Board of Directors: Daphne H Foster

D-U-N-S 00-504-7290
▲ **GLOBAL PAYMENTS INC**
GLOBALPAYMENTS
10 Glenlake Pkwy N Tower, Atlanta, GA 30328
Tel (770) 829-8000 *Founded/Ownrshp* 1967
Sales 2.9MMM *EMP* 4,438^E
Tkr Sym GPN *Exch* NYS
SIC 7389 Credit card service
CEO: Jeffrey S Sloan
**Ch Bd:* William I Jacobs
Pr: David E Mangum
CFO: Cameron M Bready
Ex VP: David L Green
Ex VP: Guido F Sacchi
Sr VP: David M Sheffield
VP: Bill Gaskin
Dir IT: Scott Ricketson
Sftwr Eng: Henry Walnut
Board of Directors: Robert H B Baldwin Jr, John G Bruno, Alex W Hart, Mitchell L Hollin, Ruth Ann Marshall, John M Partridge, Alan M Silberstein, Michael W Trapp

D-U-N-S 06-116-7842 IMP
GLOBAL PETROLEUM CORP (MA)
800 South St Ste 500, Waltham, MA 02453-1483
Tel (781) 894-6920 *Founded/Ownrshp* 1974
Sales 197.3MM^E *EMP* 210
SIC 4924 5172 4911 Natural gas distribution; ; Fuel oil; Gasoline; Diesel fuel; Kerosene;
Ch Bd: Alfred A Slifka
**CFO:* Thomas Mc Manmon
CFO: Thomas McMannon
**Treas:* Richard Slifka
Board of Directors: Richard B Slifka

D-U-N-S 83-508-8720
GLOBAL PLASTICS LP
99 Middle St Ste 1, Manchester, NH 03101-1955
Tel (800) 417-4605 *Founded/Ownrshp* 2008
Sales 137.0MM *EMP* 22^E
SIC 2821 Plastics materials & resins
Genl Pt: Chris Guimond
Genl Pt: David Guimond

D-U-N-S 01-380-1746
▲ **GLOBAL POWER EQUIPMENT GROUP INC**
400 Las Colinas Blvd E, Irving, TX 75039-5579
Tel (214) 574-2000 *Founded/Ownrshp* 1998
Sales 538.5MM *EMP* 1,244^E
Accts Bdo Usa Llp Dallas Texas
Tkr Sym GLPW *Exch* OTC
SIC 3568 1796 7699 Power transmission equipment; Power generating equipment installation; Industrial equipment services
Pr: Terence J Cryan
**Ch Bd:* Charles Macaluso
Pr: Stanley Breitweiser
Pr: Peter W Dawes
Pr: Neil Riddle
Pr: Tedd Sellers
Pr: Penny Sherrod-Campanizzi
CFO: Peggy Gaskill
CFO: Raymond K Guba
CFO: Tim Howsman
Ofcr: Keri Jolly
Ofcr: Tracy D Pagliara
Sr VP: Craig E Holmes
VP: Pj Bergkvist
VP: Gary R McCloskey
VP: Scott Snow
VP: Rich Todhunter
VP: Mark Wolfe
Exec: Kelly A Kirkconnell
Board of Directors: Carl Bartoli, David L Keller, Robert B Mills, Nelson Obus, Michael E Rescoe, Michael E Salvati, Gary J Taylor

D-U-N-S 07-101-7362
GLOBAL REINSURANCE CORP OF AMERICA
(*Suby of* WINSOR VERWALTUNGS-GMBH)
125 Broad St Lbby 5, New York, NY 10004-2440
Tel (212) 754-7500 *Founded/Ownrshp* 2007
Sales NA *EMP* 300
SIC 6321 Reinsurance carriers, accident & health
Pr: Volker Weisbrodt
Pr: Volker Wiesbrodt
CFO: Burton Henry
Sr VP: Barry Keough
Genl Couns: David Smith

D-U-N-S 02-141-3778 IMP
GLOBAL RESPONSE CORP (FL)
777 S State Road 7, Margate, FL 33068-2803
Tel (954) 973-7300 *Founded/Ownrshp* 1974
Sales 108.6MM^E *EMP* 900^E
SIC 7389

D-U-N-S 01-348-1033 IMP/EXP
GLOBAL SAFETY TEXTILES LLC
(*Suby of* GLOBAL SAFETY TEXTILES GMBH)
1556 Montgomery St, South Hill, VA 23970-3919
Tel (434) 447-7629 *Founded/Ownrshp* 2009
Sales 578.5MM^E *EMP* 2,500^E
SIC 3714 2211 3496 Motor vehicle parts & accessories; Automotive fabrics, cotton; Miscellaneous fabricated wire products
CEO: Christopher Divine
**Pr:* Frank Goehring
**COO:* Michael Ambler
CFO: Anthony Forman
VP: Rob Deutsch
VP Sls: Paul L Sullivan

GLOBAL SPORTS
See GSI COMMERCE INC

D-U-N-S 10-834-8546 IMP
GLOBAL STAINLESS SUPPLY INC
GLOBAL GROUP, THE
(*Suby of* SUMITOMO CORP OF AMERICAS) ★
8900 Railwood Dr Unit A, Houston, TX 77078-4535
Tel (713) 980-0733 *Founded/Ownrshp* 2003
Sales 185.4MM^E *EMP* 300
SIC 5051 Pipe & tubing, steel
Pr: Art Shelton

D-U-N-S 15-255-5368
GLOBAL SWITCHING INC
34 Franklin Ave Ste 220, Brooklyn, NY 11205-1221
Tel (718) 889-1100 *Founded/Ownrshp* 1999
Sales 122.2MM^E *EMP* 55
Accts Saul N Friedman & Company Br
SIC 4813 Telephone communications broker
Pr: Moses Greenfield

D-U-N-S 05-534-2690
GLOBAL TECHNOLOGY RESOURCES INC
GTRI
990 S Broadway Ste 300, Denver, CO 80209-4274
Tel (303) 455-8800 *Founded/Ownrshp* 1998
Sales 128.3MM^E *EMP* 177
Accts Mcgladrey Llp Denver Colorad
SIC 7373 Local area network (LAN) systems integrator
CEO: Greg C Byles
**Pr:* Glenn B Smith
**COO:* Steve Foster
COO: Scott Hogg
**CFO:* Eric Toler
Ex VP: Patricia Moscarelli
Sr VP: Craig Andrie
VP: Sean Mares
Assoc Dir: Carlos P Smith
CTO: Glenn Veach
Dir IT: Roman Slaybaugh

D-U-N-S 19-614-7391
GLOBAL TEL LINK CORP
(*Suby of* GTEL HOLDINGS INC) ★
2609 Cameron St, Mobile, AL 36607-3104
Tel (251) 479-4500 *Founded/Ownrshp* 2011
Sales 244.9MM^E *EMP* 835
SIC 4813 Telephone communication, except radio
CEO: Brian Oliver
Pr: Tim Eickhoff
**CFO:* Steve Yow
Ex VP: Anthony Bambocci
Sr VP: Gary Cato
Sr VP: Garth Johnson
**VP:* Robert Fragola
Exec: Margaret Phillips
VP Opers: Bob Fragola
Prd Mgr: Danny Cravey
Mktg Dir: Chris Tarbert

D-U-N-S 04-541-0110
■ **GLOBAL TELECOM & TECHNOLOGY AMERICAS INC**
(*Suby of* GTT COMMUNICATIONS INC) ★
7900 Tysons One Pl, Mc Lean, VA 22102-5971
Tel (703) 442-5500 *Founded/Ownrshp* 2005
Sales 178.1MM^E *EMP* 250
SIC 4813 Telephone communication, except radio
CEO: Richard D Calder Jr
**Ch Bd:* H Brian Thompson
**CFO:* Michael R Bauer
**CFO:* Eric A Swank
Treas: Kevin Welch
**Chf Mktg O:* Corey Eng
**Ex VP:* Layne Levine
Sr VP: Bob Burris
Sr VP: Geoffrey K Hicks
VP: Joel Eidelberg
**VP:* Andrew Goldsmith
**VP:* Gary Hale
**VP:* John G Hendler
Board of Directors: Theodore B Smith

D-U-N-S 12-765-2951 IMP/EXP
GLOBAL TRADING ENTERPRISES LLC
RASTELLI GLOBAL
504 Sharptown Rd, Swedesboro, NJ 08085-3161
Tel (856) 223-9966 *Founded/Ownrshp* 2001
Sales 111.9MM^E *EMP* 150
Accts Herbein & Company Inc Readi
SIC 5147 Meats & meat products
Pr: Anthony Rastelli
**VP:* Paul Zaun
Genl Mgr: James Haverstick

D-U-N-S 82-697-3740 IMP/EXP
GLOBAL TUBING LLC
501 County Road 493, Dayton, TX 77535-8149
Tel (713) 265-5000 *Founded/Ownrshp* 2007
Sales 121.3MM^E *EMP* 175^E
SIC 1382 Oil & gas exploration services

D-U-N-S 82-746-7866 IMP/EXP
GLOBAL TUNGSTEN & POWDERS CORP
GTP
(*Suby of* PLANSEE HOLDING AG)
1 Hawes St, Towanda, PA 18848-2134
Tel (570) 268-5000 *Founded/Ownrshp* 2008
Sales 500.0MM^E *EMP* 680
SIC 3313 3291 Tungsten carbide powder; Molybdenum silicon, not made in blast furnaces; Tungsten carbide abrasive
CEO: Andreas Lackner MD
**Pr:* Karlheinz Wax
Sls Dir: Stacy Garrity
Sales Asso: Melissa Risch
Board of Directors: Eric Rowe, Andreas Schwenninger

D-U-N-S 07-981-6100
GLOBALFOUNDRIES US 2 LLC
(*Suby of* GLOBAL FOUNDRIES) ★
2070 Route 52, Hopewell Junction, NY 12533-3507
Tel (408) 582-8140 *Founded/Ownrshp* 2015
Sales 604.1M^E *EMP* 2,800^E
SIC 3674 Semiconductors & related devices

D-U-N-S 83-041-7593 IMP
GLOBALFOUNDRIES US INC
GLOBAL FOUNDRIES
(*Suby of* MUBADALA INVESTMENT COMPANY)
2600 Great America Way, Santa Clara, CA 95054-1169
Tel (408) 462-3900 *Founded/Ownrshp* 2008
Sales 1.4MMM^E *EMP* 3,000^E
SIC 3559 3825 5065 Semiconductor manufacturing machinery; Semiconductor test equipment; Semiconductor devices
CEO: Sanjay Jha
**CFO:* Dr John Goldsberry
Ofcr: RAO Baskar
**Ofcr:* Louis Lupin
**Ex VP:* Daniel Durn
**Ex VP:* Michael Noonen
**Sr VP:* Kay Chai Ang
**Sr VP:* Gregg Bartlett
Sr VP: Kathy Borneman
**Sr VP:* Thomas Caulfield
**Sr VP:* Mojy Chian
**Sr VP:* William Davidson Jr
**Sr VP:* Ana Hunter
Sr VP: Robert Stear
**VP:* Ibrahim Ajami
VP: Kc Ang
**VP:* Norm Armour
VP: Subi Kengeri
VP: Craig Luhrmann
VP: Olivier Vatel
VP: Barbara Wesolowski

GLOBALINX
See 5LINX ENTERPRISES INC

D-U-N-S 10-169-2858
GLOBALLOGIC INC
1741 Tech Dr Ste 400, San Jose, CA 95110
Tel (408) 273-8900 *Founded/Ownrshp* 2002
Sales 424.6MM^E *EMP* 8,000
SIC 7371 7379 7373 Computer software development & applications; Computer related consulting services; Systems engineering, computer related
CEO: Shashank Samant
Pr: Glenn Rusinak
Pr: Sameer Tikoo
**COO:* Jim Dellamore
**CFO:* Doug Ahrens
**CFO:* Anna Brunelle
**CFO:* Charles Wayne Grubbs
**CFO:* Wayne Grubbs
**Ch:* Mike Daniels
**V Ch Bd:* Peter Harrison
**Chf Mktg O:* Arya Barirani
**Chf Mktg O:* Mike Devries
**Ofcr:* Bonnie Helton
**Ofcr:* Rajesh Radhakrishnan
Assoc VP: Michael Lis
Assoc VP: Rohit Nagpal
Ex VP: Sanjay Singh
Sr VP: Manoj Agarwala
**Sr VP:* Yuri Goliyad
Sr VP: Andrew Nash
VP: Roman Khmil
Board of Directors: Steve Pusey

GLOBALPAYMENTS
See GLOBAL PAYMENTS INC

D-U-N-S 14-830-1935
▲ **GLOBALSTAR INC**
300 Holiday Square Blvd # 300, Covington, LA 70433-6147
Tel (985) 335-1500 *Founded/Ownrshp* 2003
Sales 90.4MM *EMP* 325^E
Tkr Sym GSAT *Exch* ASE
SIC 4813 Voice telephone communications
Ch Bd: James Monroe III
Pr: David Kagan
CFO: Rebecca Clary
VP: L Barbee Ponder IV
VP: Jim Seese
Genl Mgr: Tom Babb
Ql Cn Mgr: Matthew Kapral
Ql Cn Mgr: Dian Ledbetter
Natl Sales: Chris Gardiner
Manager: Gary King
Board of Directors: William A Hasler, John Kneuer, James F Lynch, J Patrick McIntyre, Kenneth M Young

D-U-N-S 13-194-4493
GLOBALTRANZ ENTERPRISES INC
7350 N Dobson Rd Ste 135, Scottsdale, AZ 85256-2711
Tel (480) 339-5600 *Founded/Ownrshp* 2001
Sales 540.0MM *EMP* 454
SIC 4731 Freight transportation arrangement
CEO: Robert Farrell
Mng Pt: Thom Evans
**Ch Bd:* Andrew Leto
**Pr:* Marty Sinicrope
**CEO:* Bob Farrell
**CFO:* Renee Krug
**Ex VP:* Michael Bookout
**Ex VP:* John Hess
Sr VP: Rick Werner
VP: Brian Fisher
QA Dir: Mark Biesiada

D-U-N-S 07-828-8044
GLOBANT LLC
875 Howard St Fl 3, San Francisco, CA 94103-3027
Tel (877) 798-8104 *Founded/Ownrshp* 2003
Sales 100.0MM *EMP* 67
SIC 7371 Computer software development
CEO: Martin Migoya
Ex VP: Sandeep Chawda
**Dir Sec:* Andres Angelani

D-U-N-S 55-744-7096 EXP
GLOBE ENERGY SERVICES LLC
3204 W Highway 180, Snyder, TX 79549-7858
Tel (325) 573-1310 *Founded/Ownrshp* 2010
Sales 2.9MMM[E] *EMP* 1,900[E]
SIC 1382 Oil & gas exploration services

D-U-N-S 82-520-1697
GLOBE HOLDING CO LLC
37 Loudon Rd, Pittsfield, NH 03263-3604
Tel (603) 435-8323 *Founded/Ownrshp* 1890
Sales 88.8MM[E] *EMP* 400
SIC 6519 Real property lessors
Pr: Donald D Welch II
**VP:* George E Freese III
**VP:* Robert A Freese

D-U-N-S 00-720-4951
■ GLOBE LIFE & ACCIDENT INSURANCE CO
(*Suby of* TORCHMARK CORP) ★
204 N Robinson Ave, Oklahoma City, OK 73102-7001
Tel (972) 540-6542 *Founded/Ownrshp* 1980
Sales NA *EMP* 500
SIC 6311 6321 Life insurance carriers; Health insurance carriers
CEO: Chuck Hudson
**Treas:* Gary Coleman
**Sr VP:* Brian Mitchell
**VP:* Rosemary Montgomery
**Prin:* Mark S McAndrew
Sls&Mrk Ex: Rick Coleman

D-U-N-S 00-108-0886
GLOBE MANUFACTURING CO-OK LLC (NH)
(*Suby of* GLOBE HOLDING CO LLC) ★
37 Loudon Rd, Pittsfield, NH 03263-3604
Tel (603) 435-8323 *Founded/Ownrshp* 1887, 1890
Sales 84.5MM[E] *EMP* 375
SIC 3842 Clothing, fire resistant & protective
Pr: Donald D Welch II
**Sr VP:* George E Freese III
**Sr VP:* Robert A Freese
Dir IT: George Freese

D-U-N-S 12-168-7032 IMP/EXP
GLOBE METALLURGICAL INC
GLOBE SPECIALTY METALS
(*Suby of* GLOBE SPECIALTY METALS INC) ★
County Road 32, Waterford, OH 45786
Tel (740) 984-2361 *Founded/Ownrshp* 2006
Sales 179.7MM[E] *EMP* 440
SIC 3339 3313 2819 Silicon refining (primary, over 99% pure); Silicon, epitaxial (silicon alloy); Ferrosilicon, not made in blast furnaces; Industrial inorganic chemicals
Ch: Alan Kestenbaum
**Pr:* Jeff Bradley
**CFO:* Joe Ragan
**VP:* Marlin Perkins
VP: Jeff Watson
Genl Mgr: Eli David
Off Admin: Sarah Bonse
Sfty Mgr: Gary Obrien
Opers Mgr: Harold Odell
Plnt Mgr: Paul Lojek
Prd Mgr: Kevin Shoemaker

D-U-N-S 18-170-9775 IMP
■ GLOBE MOTORS INC
(*Suby of* ALLIED MOTION TECHNOLOGIES INC) ★
2275 Stanley Ave, Dayton, OH 45404-1226
Tel (334) 983-3542 *Founded/Ownrshp* 2013
Sales 105.7MM[E] *EMP* 418
SIC 3621 Motors & generators
CEO: Steven McHenry
**CFO:* William Gillespie

GLOBE SPECIALTY METALS
See GLOBE METALLURGICAL INC

D-U-N-S 78-284-7391
GLOBE SPECIALTY METALS INC
(*Suby of* FERROGLOBE PLC)
600 Brickell Ave Ste 3100, Miami, FL 33131-3089
Tel (786) 509-6900 *Founded/Ownrshp* 2015
Sales 800.7MM *EMP* 1,684
SIC 3339 3313 Primary nonferrous metals; Silicon refining (primary, over 99% pure); Silicon, epitaxial (silicon alloy); Ferrosilicon, not made in blast furnaces
Ch: Alan Kestenbaum
CFO: Joseph Ragan

D-U-N-S 12-463-1214 IMP/EXP
GLOBE UNION GROUP INC
(*Suby of* GLOBE UNION INDUSTRIAL CORP.)
2500 Internationale Pkwy, Woodridge, IL 60517-5090
Tel (630) 679-1420 *Founded/Ownrshp* 2002
Sales 171.0MM[E] *EMP* 233
SIC 3261 3432 7699 Plumbing fixtures, vitreous china; Plumbers' brass goods: drain cocks, faucets, spigots, etc.; General household repair services
Prin: Dennis Dugas
VP: Keith Yurko
IT Man: Julius Szabo
Natl Sales: Chris Jajko
VP Sls: Jeff Pratt
S&M/VP: Robert Perry
Mktg Dir: Michael Rosen
Sls Mgr: Ray Moulsdale

D-U-N-S 17-794-5870 IMP
GLOBECAST AMERICA INC
(*Suby of* ORANGE)
10525 Washington Blvd, Culver City, CA 90232-3311
Tel (212) 373-5140 *Founded/Ownrshp* 1993
Sales 103.8MM[E] *EMP* 400[E]
SIC 4841 Satellite master antenna systems services (SMATV)
CEO: Michele Gosetti
**CEO:* Lisa Coelho
**VP:* Batrice De Lagrevol
**VP:* Elisabeth Mazurie
Off Mgr: Sharon Dacosta
Dir IT: Shakunt Malhotra

D-U-N-S 87-891-5701 IMP/EXP
GLOBECOMM SYSTEMS INC
(*Suby of* WASSERSTEIN COSMOS CO-INVEST LP) ★
45 Oser Ave, Hauppauge, NY 11788-3808
Tel (631) 231-9800 *Founded/Ownrshp* 2013
Sales 319.6MM *EMP* 500
Accts Ernst & Young Llp Jericho Ne
SIC 3663 4813 Satellites, communications; Telephone communication, except radio
CEO: Jason Juranek
**Treas:* Catherine Cantasano
**Ofcr:* Bryan McGuirk
**Ex VP:* Julia Hanft
**Ex VP:* Dwight R Hunsicker
**Ex VP:* Michael Plourde
**Sr VP:* Michele P Scotto Di Cesare
Sr VP: Brian Morris
**Sr VP:* Paul Scardino
VP: Dov Cydulkin
**VP:* Kristen Harrison
VP: Paul Knudsen
VP: Walter Scharpf
Dir Soc: Terry Wieland

D-U-N-S 16-060-1923
GLOBENET CABOS SUBMARINOS AMERICA INC
200 E Las Olas Blvd, Fort Lauderdale, FL 33301-2299
Tel (561) 314-0500 *Founded/Ownrshp* 2003
Sales 200.0MM *EMP* 150
SIC 4813 Local & long distance telephone communications; Data telephone communications
CEO: Erick W Contag
Corp Couns: Gabriela Gonzalez

D-U-N-S 13-910-5691
▲ GLOBUS MEDICAL INC
2560 Gen Armistead Ave, Audubon, PA 19403-5214
Tel (610) 930-1800 *Founded/Ownrshp* 2003
Sales 544.7MM *EMP* 1,200
Tkr Sym GMED *Exch* NYS
SIC 3841 Surgical & medical instruments
Ch Bd: David C Paul
**Pr:* David M Demski
**Pr:* A Brett Murphy
**Pr:* Anthony L Williams
**CFO:* Daniel T Scavilla
IT Man: Jason Parrish
Mktg Dir: Scott Stanton
Manager: Chris Fell
Sales Asso: Christine Boyd
Sales Asso: Nathaniel Morris
Board of Directors: David D Davidar, Daniel T Lemaitre, Robert W Liptak, Ann D Rhoads, James R Tobin, Kurt C Wheeler

D-U-N-S 01-827-5156
GLOCKNER CHEVROLET CO
GLOCKNER CHEVY OLDS CADDY
4368 Us Route 23, Portsmouth, OH 45662
Tel (740) 353-2161 *Founded/Ownrshp* 1927
Sales 88.5MM *EMP* 181
SIC 5013 5172 5511

GLOCKNER CHEVY OLDS CADDY
See GLOCKNER CHEVROLET CO

D-U-N-S 78-402-3132
GLODYNE TECHNOSERVE INC
2700 Augustine Dr Ste 190, Santa Clara, CA 95054-2926
Tel (408) 340-5017 *Founded/Ownrshp* 2006
Sales 71.6MM[E] *EMP* 1,600[E]
SIC 7373 Computer integrated systems design
**Pr:* Haneef Sheikh
Assoc VP: Amit Jaste
Sr VP: Vijay Sonawane

D-U-N-S 01-886-8872 IMP
GLORY GLOBAL SOLUTIONS INC
(*Suby of* GLORY LTD.)
3333 Warrenville Rd # 310, Lisle, IL 60532-9831
Tel (920) 262-3300 *Founded/Ownrshp* 2012
Sales 151.9MM[E] *EMP* 267
SIC 5087 5046 5044 Service establishment equipment; Vending machines & supplies; Coin counters; Coin-operated equipment; Vending machines, coin-operated; Office equipment
Pr: Chris Reagan
**CFO:* Steve Vanzee
S&M/Dir: Joseph Ganorski

D-U-N-S 07-059-1979
GLOUCESTER COUNTY NEW JERSEY (INC) (NJ)
COURTHOUSE
2 S Broad St, Woodbury, NJ 08096-4604
Tel (856) 853-3200 *Founded/Ownrshp* 1868
Sales NA *EMP* 1,200
Accts Robert A Jones Acct & Auditor
SIC 9111
Ex Dir: William Taylor

GLOUCESTER COUNTY PUB SCHOOLS
See GLOUCESTER COUNTY SCHOOLS

D-U-N-S 15-957-4755
GLOUCESTER COUNTY SCHOOLS
GLOUCESTER COUNTY PUB SCHOOLS
6099 T C Walker Rd, Gloucester, VA 23061-4403
Tel (804) 693-5300 *Founded/Ownrshp* 1851
Sales 47.4MM[E] *EMP* 1,100
Accts Robinson Farmer Cox Associat
SIC 8211 Public elementary & secondary schools; School board
Dir Sec: Shirley Chirch
Teacher Pr: Juanita Smith

D-U-N-S 04-215-5028
GLOUCESTER TOWNSHIP BOARD OF EDUCATION
GLOUCESTER TOWNSHIP SCHOOL DST
17 Erial Rd, Blackwood, NJ 08012-3964
Tel (856) 227-1400 *Founded/Ownrshp* 1890
Sales 57.2MM[E] *EMP* 1,400
SIC 8211 Public elementary & secondary schools
IT Man: Carl Gross

D-U-N-S 07-979-9129
GLOUCESTER TOWNSHIP PUBLIC SCHOOLS
17 Erial Rd, Blackwood, NJ 08012-3964
Tel (856) 227-1400 *Founded/Ownrshp* 2015
Sales 11.5MM[E] *EMP* 1,117[E]
SIC 8211 Public elementary & secondary schools

GLOUCESTER TOWNSHIP SCHOOL DST
See GLOUCESTER TOWNSHIP BOARD OF EDUCATION

GLS
See GREAT LAKES SYNERGY CORP

D-U-N-S 13-063-1864
GLS COMPANIES
6845 Winnetka Cir, Brooklyn Park, MN 55428-1537
Tel (763) 535-7277 *Founded/Ownrshp* 1984
Sales 94.6MM[E] *EMP* 292[E]
SIC 2752 Commercial printing, offset
CEO: Gary Garner
CFO: Mike McPartland
VP: Doug Hammerseng
VP: Jeanne Haro
VP: Mike Koshiol
VP: Jayme Wisely
CIO: Frank Powell
Dir IT: Garry Calhoun
Software D: Janelle Jacobson
Software D: Dave Johnson
Sftwr Eng: Venki Kumar

D-U-N-S 07-847-7159
GLS COMPOSITES DISTIBUTION CORP (IL)
COMPOSITES ONE
(*Suby of* SYNERGY55 INC) ★
85 W Algonquin Rd Ste 600, Arlington Heights, IL 60005-4421
Tel (800) 621-8003 *Founded/Ownrshp* 1997
Sales 514.7MM[E] *EMP* 372
SIC 5169 Chemicals & allied products
Pr: Steven L Dehmlow
Sls Mgr: Mark Kirk

D-U-N-S 10-147-4505
▲ GLU MOBILE INC
500 Howard St Ste 300, San Francisco, CA 94105-3027
Tel (415) 800-6100 *Founded/Ownrshp* 2001
Sales 249.9MM *EMP* 750[E]
Tkr Sym GLUU *Exch* NGS
SIC 7371 3944 Custom computer programming services; Computer software writing services; Computer code authors; Electronic games & toys
CEO: Nick Earl
COO: Eric R Ludwig
Ch: Niccolo M De Masi
VP: Scott J Leichtner
Dir Risk M: Chris Akhavan
CTO: Tim Wilson
Sftwr Eng: Kapil Gangwar
Sftwr Eng: Swaroop Rayudu
Board of Directors: Eric R Ball, Greg Brandeau, Ann Mather, William J Miller, Benjamin R Smith IV

D-U-N-S 86-883-3851
GLUTH CONTRACT FLOORING LLC
12003 Mukilteo Speedway # 102, Mukilteo, WA 98275-5733
Tel (425) 493-9100 *Founded/Ownrshp* 2007
Sales 500.0MM *EMP* 3
SIC 1752 Floor laying & floor work

D-U-N-S 02-743-1444
GLY CONSTRUCTION INC
G L Y
200 112th Ave Ne Ste 300, Bellevue, WA 98004-5878
Tel (425) 451-8877 *Founded/Ownrshp* 2001
Sales 500.0MM *EMP* 600
Accts Berntson Porter & Company Pll
SIC 1542 Commercial & office building, new construction
Pr: Jim Karambelas
CFO: Steve Peterson
Ex VP: Ted Herb
Ex VP: Mark Kane
VP: Joni Baker
VP: Dale King
Exec: Bryce Taylor
Prin: Bill Dejarlais
Prin: Jim Elliott
Prin: Steve Hoffmann
Prin: Monty Kilcup

D-U-N-S 01-331-4952
GLYNLYON INC
300 N Mckemy Ave, Chandler, AZ 85226-2618
Tel (480) 940-0801 *Founded/Ownrshp* 2008
Sales 92.5MM[E] *EMP* 500
SIC 3999 Education aids, devices & supplies
Pr: Robert J Campbell Jr
Pr: Jen Salta
**Treas:* Beth Te Grotenhuis
VP: David Austin
VP: Brent Millon
VP: Leonor Sebastia
Snr Ntwrk: Isaac Carbajal
Sales Asso: Bruce Wallen

D-U-N-S 19-321-5704
GLYNN COUNTY BOARD OF EDUCATION
1313 Egmont St, Brunswick, GA 31520-7244
Tel (912) 267-4100 *Founded/Ownrshp* 1873
Sales 82.1MM[E] *EMP* 1,800
Accts Karp Ronning & Tindol Pc
SIC 8211 School board
Ch Bd: Hank Yeargan
HC Dir: Susan Barber

D-U-N-S 96-802-1712
GLYNN COUNTY SCHOOL SYSTEM
1313 Egmont St, Brunswick, GA 31520-7244
Tel (912) 267-4100 *Founded/Ownrshp* 2011
Sales 56.7MM[E] *EMP* 1,818[E]
SIC 8211 Public elementary & secondary schools
MIS Dir: Debbie Culpepper
Dir IT: Michael Hall
IT Man: Francis Harris
Pr Dir: Anna Hall
Pr Dir: Jim Weidhaas
HC Dir: Katrina Henley

GLYNN JOHNSON
See VON DUPRIN LLC

D-U-N-S 03-115-8397
GLYNN-BRUNSWICK MEMORIAL HOSPITAL AUTHORITY
2415 Parkwood Dr, Brunswick, GA 31520-4722
Tel (912) 466-7000 *Founded/Ownrshp* 1954
Sales 267.8MM *EMP* 1,525
SIC 8062 8011 General medical & surgical hospitals; Offices & clinics of medical doctors
CEO: Michael D Scherneck
V Ch: Eric Segerberg
V Ch: William Walls
CFO: Michael Scherneck
Sr Cor Off: Paul Trumbull
Ofcr: Tammy Gibson
Ofcr: John Nave
VP: Carlton Devooght
VP: Ellen Hamilton
VP: Marjorie Mathieu
VP: Delria Tate
Dir Lab: Loraine Boudreau
Mng Ofcr: Brendan Hunt

GLYT
See GENLYTE GROUP INC

D-U-N-S 83-123-2371 IMP
■ GM COMPONENTS HOLDINGS LLC
GMCH
(*Suby of* GENERAL MOTORS LLC) ★
300 Renaissance Ctr, Detroit, MI 48243-1402
Tel (313) 556-5000 *Founded/Ownrshp* 2009
Sales 380.6MM[E] *EMP* 1,053[E]
SIC 3711 3714 Automobile assembly, including specialty automobiles; Truck & tractor truck assembly; Military motor vehicle assembly; Motor vehicle parts & accessories
COO: Jean-Claude Ghiotti
CFO: Archie Turner
VP: John Jones
VP: Eric Peterson
**VP:* Niharika Taskar Ramdev
Exec: Ryan Kane
Dir Risk M: Rick Satawa
Assoc Dir: Mike Hegener
Prgrm Mgr: Wylie Burt
Area Mgr: Sherrell Kovach
Dist Mgr: Dick Conley

D-U-N-S 00-925-5423 IMP
GM NAMEPLATE INC
SUPERGRAPHICS
2040 15th Ave W, Seattle, WA 98119-2783
Tel (206) 284-2200 *Founded/Ownrshp* 1954
Sales 258.4MM[E] *EMP* 1,200
SIC 3479 2679 3679

GM2
See GROUP MANAGEMENT 0002 LLC

GMA
See GEORGIA MUNICIPAL ASSOCIATION INC

D-U-N-S 55-746-0623 IMP
GMA ACCESSORIES INC
CAPELLI OF NY
1 E 33rd St Fl 9, New York, NY 10016-5011
Tel (212) 684-3344 *Founded/Ownrshp* 1986
Sales 110.2MM *EMP* 250
Accts Holtz Rubenstein Reminick Llp
SIC 5137 5139 Women's & children's accessories; Shoes
Pr: George Altirs
**CFO:* Salvatore Mancino
**VP:* Masoud Altirs
Telecom Ex: Hani Afif

GMAC
See ALLY INSURANCE HOLDINGS INC

GMAC
See GRADUATE MANAGEMENT ADMISSION COUNCIL INC

GMAC INSURANCE
See MORSTAN GENERAL INSURANCE AGENCY INC

GMAC INSURANCE
See LAWLEY SERVICE INC

GMAC INSURANCE
See FIRST NIAGARA RISK MANAGEMENT INC

GMAC INSURANCE
See CHARLES L CRANE AGENCY CO

GMAC INSURANCE
See NATIONAL GENERAL MANAGEMENT CORP

D-U-N-S 13-920-6783
■ GMAC MORTGAGE GROUP LLC
(*Suby of* ALLY FINANCIAL INC) ★
4 Walnut Grove Dr, Horsham, PA 19044-2201
Tel (215) 682-1000 *Founded/Ownrshp* 2006
Sales 670.5MM[E] *EMP* 10,300
SIC 6211 Dealers, security
CEO: David M Applegate
Sales Asso: Geralyn Behring
Sales Asso: Donna Matheis

D-U-N-S 04-396-7496
■ GMAC MORTGAGE LLC
(*Suby of* GMAC MORTGAGE GROUP LLC) ★
4 Walnut Grove Dr, Horsham, PA 19044-2201
Tel (215) 682-1000 *Founded/Ownrshp* 1985

Sales NA *EMP* 7,500
Accts Pricewaterhousecoopers Llp Ne
SIC 6162 Mortgage bankers
Comm Dir: Jeannine Bruin
Area Mgr: Frank Dimaio

D-U-N-S 18-908-8768
■ GMAC MORTGAGE SECURITIES INC
(*Suby of* GMAC MORTGAGE GROUP LLC) ★
1100 Virginia Dr, Fort Washington, PA 19034-3204
Tel (215) 682-1000 *Founded/Ownrshp* 2011
Sales 92.5MM^E *EMP* 500
SIC 6211 Dealers, security
Pr: Michael O'Brien
Pr: Michael Brien
Rgnl Mgr: Scott Medrow

D-U-N-S 82-825-9239
GMACCH INVESTOR LLC
9 W 57th St, New York, NY 10019-2701
Tel (212) 750-8300 *Founded/Ownrshp* 2008
Sales 126.2MM^E *EMP* 2,003
SIC 6799 Real estate investors, except property operators

GMCH
See GM COMPONENTS HOLDINGS LLC

D-U-N-S 12-477-5359
■ GMH COMMUNITIES TRUST
(*Suby of* AMERICAN CAMPUS COMMUNITIES INC) ★
10 Campus Blvd, Newtown Square, PA 19073-3200
Tel (610) 355-8000 *Founded/Ownrshp* 2008
Sales 10.3MM^E *EMP* 1,084
SIC 6798 6513 8742 Real estate investment trusts; Apartment building operators; Real estate consultant
Ch Bd: Gary M Holloway Sr
Pr: Joseph M Coyle
Pr: John Deriggi
Pr: Bruce F Robinson
CFO: Dennis J O'Leary
Trst: James W Eastood

D-U-N-S 19-465-4422 IMP
GMI HOLDINGS INC
GENIE COMPANY, THE
(*Suby of* OVERHEAD DOOR CORP) ★
1 Door Dr, Mount Hope, OH 44660
Tel (330) 821-5360 *Founded/Ownrshp* 1994
Sales 97.0MM^E *EMP* 1,000
SIC 3699 3635 Door opening & closing devices, electrical; Household vacuum cleaners
Pr: Mike Kridel
**VP:* Craig Smith
**Prin:* Carl Adrien
VP Mfg: Tim Ikeler

GMO
See GRANTHAM MAYO VAN OTTERLOO & CO LLC

GMP METAL PRODUCTS
See WOZNIAK INDUSTRIES INC

D-U-N-S 10-672-6797
■ GMR MARKETING LLC
FRESHWIRE
(*Suby of* OMNICOM GROUP INC) ★
5000 S Towne Dr, New Berlin, WI 53151-7956
Tel (262) 786-5600 *Founded/Ownrshp* 1998
Sales 196.9MM^E *EMP* 550
SIC 8743

D-U-N-S 05-210-2555 EXP
■ GMRI INC
OLIVE GARDEN
(*Suby of* DARDEN RESTAURANTS INC) ★
1000 Darden Center Dr, Orlando, FL 32837-4032
Tel (407) 245-4000 *Founded/Ownrshp* 1995
Sales 3.7MMM^E *EMP* 112,350
SIC 5812 Seafood restaurants
Ch Bd: Joe R Lee
**Pr:* Stephen Judge
**Pr:* William R White III
COO: Richard Rivera
Ex VP: Valerie Insignares
Sr VP: Ron Bojalad
Sr VP: Gary Brown
Sr VP: Bill Holmes
Sr VP: Kathy Nahlovsky
VP: Valerie K Collins
Exec: Peter Olsacher
Board of Directors: Sherry Pears - Contrl

D-U-N-S 07-935-1774
▲ GMS INC
100 Crescent Center Pkwy, Tucker, GA 30084-7060
Tel (800) 392-4619 *Founded/Ownrshp* 1971
Sales 1.8MMM *EMP* 3,784^E
Tkr Sym GMS *Exch* NYS
SIC 3275 5031 5039 Wallboard, gypsum; Wallboard; Ceiling systems & products
Pr: G Michael Callahan Jr
Ch Bd: Richard K Mueller
CFO: H Douglas Goforth
Ofcr: Richard Alan Adams
VP: Craig D Apolinsky

GMT
See GLOBAL MATERIAL TECHNOLOGIES INC

GMT
See M T G LLC

D-U-N-S 17-381-4856 IMP
GN HEARING CARE CORP
RESOUND
(*Suby of* GN US HOLDINGS INC) ★
8001 E Bloomington Fwy, Bloomington, MN 55420-1036
Tel (800) 248-4327 *Founded/Ownrshp* 1984
Sales 225.7MM^E *EMP* 828
SIC 3842 Hearing aids
Pr: Kimberly Lody
Pr: Corrine Perritano
Pr: Melinda Sandoval
Treas: Peter Marcaccini
VP: Mike Fryar
VP: Keith Lewis
VP: Tom Woods
Opers Mgr: Shawn Timm
Opers Mgr: Brian Tsuchiya
Manager: Shaun Erdmann

D-U-N-S 15-726-9697 IMP
GN NETCOM INC
G N NETCOM UNEX
(*Suby of* GN AUDIO A/S)
900 Chelmsford St # 313, Lowell, MA 01851-8313
Tel (800) 826-4656 *Founded/Ownrshp* 1996
Sales 87.7MM^E *EMP* 540
SIC 3661 Headsets, telephone
CEO: Toon Bouten
**Pr:* Peter Fox
COO: Michael Davis
**CFO:* Dean G Kacos
**Treas:* Anna Johnson
VP: James Lucivero
VP: David Snow
**Prin:* Hanf Hendric Lund
Mng Dir: Steen Boge
Dir IT: Henric Jorgensen
VP Mktg: Stephan Petix

D-U-N-S 07-766-3271
GN US HOLDINGS INC
(*Suby of* GN HEARING A/S)
8001 E Bloomington Fwy, Minneapolis, MN 55420-1036
Tel (952) 769-8000 *Founded/Ownrshp* 1999
Sales 226.2MM^E *EMP* 870^E
Accts Kpmg Llp
SIC 3842 Hearing aids
CEO: Alan Dozier
**VP:* Bob Meekin
**VP:* Rich Swanson

GNC
See GENERAL NUTRITION CORP

GNC
See GENERAL NUTRITION CENTERS INC

D-U-N-S 79-576-9541
▲ GNC HOLDINGS INC
300 6th Ave Fl 2, Pittsburgh, PA 15222-2528
Tel (412) 288-4600 *Founded/Ownrshp* 1935
Sales 2.6MMM *EMP* 16,900^E
Tkr Sym GNC *Exch* NYS
SIC 5499 Health & dietetic food stores
CEO: Robert F Moran
**Ch Bd:* Michael F Hines
CFO: Tricia K Tolivar
Chf Mktg O: Jeffrey R Hennion
Ex VP: Michael D Dzura
Ex VP: Carmine Fortino
Ex VP: Timothy A Mantel
Sr VP: Robert M Chessen
Sr VP: Darryl Green
Sr VP: Lee Karayusuf
Sr VP: Jay R Kent
Sr VP: Robert M Kral
Sr VP: Michael Locke
Sr VP: Anthony T Phillips
Sr VP: Guru Ramanathan
VP: Shawn Cupples
VP: Amy Davis
VP: Dennis Magulick
Board of Directors: Jeffrey P Berger, Alan D Feldman, Amy B Lane, Philip E Mallott, Robert F Moran, C Scott O'hara, Richard J Wallace

D-U-N-S 15-107-6630 IMP
■ GNC INC
(*Suby of* GNC) ★
300 6th Ave Fl 2, Pittsburgh, PA 15222-2528
Tel (412) 288-4600 *Founded/Ownrshp* 1976
Sales 1.3MMM^E *EMP* 12,240
SIC 5499 Health & dietetic food stores
Ch Bd: Robert J Dinicola
**CFO:* Curtis J Larrimer
Ofcr: Gerald J Stubenhofer
**Sr VP:* Darryl Green
Sr VP: Robert M Kral

D-U-N-S 94-899-5019 IMP
GNLD INTERNATIONAL LLC
3500 Gateway Blvd, Fremont, CA 94538-6584
Tel (510) 651-0405 *Founded/Ownrshp* 2008
Sales 168.3MM^E *EMP* 441^E
SIC 5122 Vitamins & minerals
CEO: Jerry Brassfield
**Pr:* Roget Uys
**Ex VP:* George Casale
IT Man: Ryan Vo
Opers Mgr: Cecilia Balleza

D-U-N-S 05-531-1708 IMP
GNN INVESTOR LLC
(*Suby of* GEORGIA-PACIFIC LLC) ★
133 Peachtree St Ne, Atlanta, GA 30303-1804
Tel (404) 652-4000 *Founded/Ownrshp* 1990
Sales 113.6MM^E *EMP* 2,482
SIC 2621 2611 2631 2653 5111 2677 Paper mills; Business form paper; Newsprint paper; Bond paper; Kraft (sulfate) pulp; Container board; Corrugated boxes, partitions, display items, sheets & pad; Printing & writing paper; Envelopes
CEO: A D Correll
**CFO:* Danny W Huff
Ex VP: James Kelley
Board of Directors: James E Bostic Jr, William A Mamrack, Davis K Mortensen, James E Terrell

GNP COMPANY
See JFC LLC

D-U-N-S 10-867-4763
GNP CO
GOLD 'N PLUMP POULTRY
(*Suby of* MASCHHOFFS LLC) ★
4150 2nd St S Ste 200, Saint Cloud, MN 56301-3994
Tel (320) 251-3570 *Founded/Ownrshp* 2013
Sales 189.3MM^E *EMP* 1,000
SIC 2015 Chicken, processed
CEO: Michael Helgeson
**Ex VP:* Steve Jurek
**Ex VP:* Tim Wensman
QC Dir: Doug Connell
Sfty Mgr: Tim Court
Opers Mgr: Mark Page
Prd Mgr: Mike Henry
Mktg Mgr: Rory Bidinger
Sls Mgr: Wayne Krone
Sales Asso: Kelli Schuh
Snr Mgr: Ross Gunderson

GNY INSURANCE COMPANIES
See GREATER NEW YORK MUTUAL INSURANCE CO

GO AIRPORT SHUTTLE
See GO GROUP LLC

D-U-N-S 07-888-9444
■ GO DADDY OPERATING CO LLC
(*Suby of* GODADDY INC) ★
14455 N Hayden Rd Ste 219, Scottsdale, AZ 85260-6947
Tel (480) 505-8877 *Founded/Ownrshp* 2011
Sales 8.1MM^E *EMP* 4,065^E
SIC 7373 7374 Systems integration services; Computer graphics service
CEO: Blake Irving
**COO:* Scott Wagner
**Chf Mktg O:* Barb Rechterman
**Ex VP:* Phil Bienert
**Ex VP:* James Carroll
**Ex VP:* Nima Kelly
**Ex VP:* Elissa Murphy
Sr VP: Steven Aldrich
Sr VP: Jeff King
Sr VP: David Popowitz

GO FER FOOD
See MONUMENT OIL CO

D-U-N-S 05-574-6175
GO GREEN JANITORIAL SERVICES LLC
8448 Crossland Loop, Montgomery, AL 36117-0950
Tel (334) 277-5880 *Founded/Ownrshp* 2011
Sales 88.0MM *EMP* 1
SIC 7699 Cleaning services
Owner: Mekeisha T Thomas

D-U-N-S 07-951-9184
GO GROUP LLC
GO AIRPORT SHUTTLE
1200 W 35th St, Chicago, IL 60609-1305
Tel (844) 787-1670 *Founded/Ownrshp* 2014
Sales 27.5MM^E *EMP* 2,500
SIC 4111 Airport transportation

D-U-N-S 15-130-0675
GO WEST INSURANCE SERVICES INC
2386 Fair Oaks Blvd Ste 2, Sacramento, CA 95825-4741
Tel (916) 487-1102 *Founded/Ownrshp* 1998
Sales NA *EMP* 5
SIC 6411 Insurance brokers
Pr: John McNally

D-U-N-S 79-854-5356 IMP
GO WIRELESS INC
9970 W Cheyenne Ave # 100, Las Vegas, NV 89129-7700
Tel (702) 853-6200 *Founded/Ownrshp* 1994
Sales 226.5MM^E *EMP* 850
SIC 5999 Mobile telephones & equipment
Pr: Kevin Elder
Pr: John Carroll
Pr: Sean Kress
**Pr:* Rob Murray
**Treas:* Paul Huether
Area Mgr: Roque Hernandez
Dist Mgr: Thomas Martinez
Dist Mgr: Ryan Perez
Store Mgr: Marcus Cousin
Store Mgr: John Mann
Store Mgr: Michael Parker

D-U-N-S 00-586-9227
GO-MART INC (WV)
U-PAK
915 Riverside Dr, Gassaway, WV 26624-1127
Tel (304) 364-8000 *Founded/Ownrshp* 1966
Sales 188.4MM^E *EMP* 1,200
SIC 5411 5541 Convenience stores, independent; Gasoline service stations
Pr: John D Heater
**Treas:* Sam Heater
**VP:* Betty J Heater
VP: Betty Heater
Exec: Scott Gallaher
Board of Directors: Laurie O Malley

D-U-N-S 02-844-1405
GO-STAFF INC
G S I
8798 Complex Dr, San Diego, CA 92123-1402
Tel (858) 292-8562 *Founded/Ownrshp* 2001
Sales 41.2MM^E *EMP* 2,500^E
SIC 7363 8721 Temporary help service; Payroll accounting service
CEO: Scott Crumrine
**VP:* Stacey Crumrine
Div Mgr: Jacques Albarran

GOBIERNO MUNICIPAL AU
See CAROLINA MUNICIPALITY

D-U-N-S 07-942-9992
▲ GODADDY INC
14455 N Hayden Rd Ste 100, Scottsdale, AZ 85260-6947
Tel (480) 505-8800 *Founded/Ownrshp* 2014
Sales 1.6MMM *EMP* 4,761
Tkr Sym GDDY *Exch* NYS
SIC 7373 4813 Computer integrated systems design;
CEO: Blake J Irving
**Ch Bd:* Charles J Robel
Pr: Scott W Wagner
CFO: Ray Winborne
Ofcr: Auguste D Goldman
Ex VP: James M Carroll
Ex VP: Arne M Josefsberg
Ex VP: Nima J Kelly
Board of Directors: Herald Y Chen, Richard H Kimball, Gregory K Mondre, John I Park, Bob Parsons, Elizabeth S Rafael, Brian H Sharples, Lee E Wittlinger

D-U-N-S 96-776-9167
GODADDY.COM LLC
(*Suby of* YAM SPECIAL HOLDINGS INC) ★
14455 N Hayden Rd Ste 219, Scottsdale, AZ 85260-6947
Tel (480) 505-8800 *Founded/Ownrshp* 2011
Sales 448.9MM^E *EMP* 3,300
SIC 7379
CEO: Bob Parsons
**Pr:* Warren Adelman
**CFO:* Michael Zimmerman
VP: Carmelia Hackson
Snr Ntwrk: Michael Racki

D-U-N-S 00-583-3686 EXP
GODBERSEN-SMITH CONSTRUCTION CO INC
GOMACO MANUFACTURING CO
121 E State Highway 175, Ida Grove, IA 51445-1139
Tel (712) 364-3388 *Founded/Ownrshp* 1959
Sales 99.3MM *EMP* 450
SIC 3531 1622 Pavers; Finishers, concrete & bituminous: powered; Bituminous, cement & concrete related products & equipment; Bridge construction
Pr: Gary L Godbersen
**Treas:* Sharon K Godbersen
**VP:* Richard E Smith

D-U-N-S 15-063-9979
GODFATHERS PIZZA INC
2808 N 108th St, Omaha, NE 68164-3702
Tel (402) 391-1452 *Founded/Ownrshp* 1988
Sales 113.7MM^E *EMP* 2,500
SIC 5812 6794 Pizzeria, chain; Franchises, selling or licensing
Ch: Herman Cain
**Pr:* Ronald Gartlan
**CFO:* Richard W Ramm
Exec: Kathleen M Johnson
Admn Mgr: John Callaghan

D-U-N-S 04-964-4321 IMP
GODIVA CHOCOLATIER INC
(*Suby of* YILDIZ HOLDING ANONIM SIRKETI)
333 W 34th St Fl 6, New York, NY 10001-2566
Tel (212) 984-5900 *Founded/Ownrshp* 1966
Sales 586.9MM^E *EMP* 2,200
SIC 2066 5149 5441 2064 Chocolate candy, solid; Chocolate; Candy; Candy & other confectionery products
Pr: Jim Goldman
**CFO:* David Marberger
Treas: Bill Oshea
Treas: William J Shea
Treas: Sam Vulopas
Sr Cor Off: Roger Stier
Sr VP: Mike Giresi
Sr VP: Lauri Kien Kotcher
VP: Nathan Byrd
VP: Doug Caldwell
VP: Kaan Dagalti
VP: Anthony Disilvestro
VP: Rick Paschal
VP: Sunil Rege
Exec: Erica Coletta
Exec: Thierry Muret
Comm Man: Stacie Gordon
Board of Directors: Stefan Heidenreich

D-U-N-S 06-570-3670
GODSHALLS QUALITY MEATS INC
KUTZTOWN BOLOGNA
675 Mill Rd, Telford, PA 18969-2411
Tel (215) 256-8867 *Founded/Ownrshp* 1945
Sales 118.8MM^E *EMP* 200
SIC 5147 5421 Meats & meat products; Meat markets, including freezer provisioners
Pr: Mark B Godshall
**Sec:* Kendal Godshall
Ofcr: Chris Bruno
Ofcr: Leslie Poole
**VP:* Floyd Kratz
Exec: Nancy Eisenhauer
Sales Exec: Jerry Landuyt

D-U-N-S 10-915-7227
GOELLNER INC
ADVANCED MACHINE AND ENGRG
2500 Latham St, Rockford, IL 61103-3963
Tel (815) 962-6076 *Founded/Ownrshp* 1999
Sales 96.1MM^E *EMP* 450
SIC 3599 Machine & other job shop work
CEO: Willy Goellner
**Pr:* Dietmiar Goellner
**CFO:* David Leezer
Sls Dir: Dan Lapp
Manager: Randy Jacobson

GOETTLE CONSTRUCTION
See GOETTLE HOLDING CO INC

D-U-N-S 00-448-5348
GOETTLE HOLDING CO INC
GOETTLE CONSTRUCTION
12071 Hamilton Ave, Cincinnati, OH 45231-1032
Tel (513) 825-8100 *Founded/Ownrshp* 1956
Sales 83.6MM^E *EMP* 130
SIC 1799 1629 1771 1794 Shoring & underpinning work; Pile driving contractor; Foundation & footing contractor; Excavation work
Prin: Roger W Healey
**Ch Bd:* Larry P Rayburn
**Pr:* Terrence Tucker
**Sec:* Dan Baker
VP: Brent Grow
**VP:* Douglas Keller
**Prin:* Janet E Goettle
**Prin:* Richard J Goettle III

D-U-N-S 00-960-8555 IMP
GOFORTH & MARTI
G/M BUSINESS INTERIORS
110 W A St Ste 140, San Diego, CA 92101-3702
Tel (951) 684-0870 *Founded/Ownrshp* 1960
Sales 89.0MM^E *EMP* 158
SIC 5021 Office furniture
Pr: Stephen L Easley

*VP: William F Easley
Exec: Michael Lafond
Mktg Dir: Lisa McClinton

D-U-N-S 12-229-5736 IMP/EXP
GOGLANIAN BAKERIES INC
(Suby of RICH PRODUCTS CORP) ★
3401 W Segerstrom Ave, Santa Ana, CA 92704-6404
Tel (714) 549-1524 Founded/Ownrshp 2012
Sales 502.4MM^E EMP 400
SIC 5149 Bakery products
CEO: William G Gisel
CFO: Albert Altro
Plnt Mgr: Javier Avila
Sls Mgr: Eric Porat

D-U-N-S 07-887-5378
▲ GOGO INC
111 N Canal St Ste 1500, Chicago, IL 60606-7205
Tel (312) 517-5000 Founded/Ownrshp 1991
Sales 500.8MM EMP 1,073^E
Tkr Sym GOGO Exch NGS
SIC 4899 Communication signal enhancement network system
Pr: Michael J Small
*Ch Bd: Ronald T Lemay
COO: John Wade
CFO: Norman Smagley
Chf Cred: Ash A Eldifrawi
Ex VP: Anand K Chari
Ex VP: Marguerite M Elias
Snr Sftwr: Xiangliang Xia
Board of Directors: Robert L Crandall, Hugh W Jones, Michele Coleman Mayes, Robert H Mundheim, Christopher D Payne, Oakleigh Thorne, Charles C Townsend, Harris N Williams

D-U-N-S 07-950-6318
■ GOGO INTERMEDIATE HOLDINGS LLC
(Suby of GOGO INC) ★
1250 N Arlington Rd, Itasca, IL 60143
Tel (630) 647-1400 Founded/Ownrshp 2012
Sales 303.4MM^E EMP 689^E
SIC 3663 Radio & TV communications equipment

D-U-N-S 80-913-1733
■ GOGO LLC
(Suby of GOGO INTERMEDIATE HOLDINGS LLC) ★
111 N Canal St Fl 15, Chicago, IL 60606-7205
Tel (630) 647-1400 Founded/Ownrshp 2012
Sales 262.3MM^E EMP 689
SIC 3663 4812 4813 4899 Radio & TV communications equipment; Cellular radio telephone; Cellular telephone services; Telephone communication, except radio; Data communication services
Ex VP: Margee Elias
Pt: Tim Twohig
*Pr: Michael J Small
*CFO: Norman Smagley
Treas: William Sawitz
Ex VP: Anand K Chari
Ex VP: Ash A Eldifrawi
Ex VP: John Wade
Sr VP: Jonathan B Cobin
Sr VP: Marguerite M Elias
Sr VP: John B Happ
Sr VP: Mark Malosh
Sr VP: Rama Prasad
Sr VP: David Russell
VP: Jenelle T Chalmers
VP: Kelly Jackson
VP: Timothy Maxwell
VP: Joe Meszaro
VP: Clint Quanstrom
VP: Mike Syverson
VP: Arbela Takhsh
Board of Directors: Robert L Crandall, Lawrence N Lavine, Christopher Minnetian, Robert H Mundheim, Oakleigh Thorne, Charles C Townsend, Harris N Williams

D-U-N-S 00-416-2038 IMP/EXP
GOJO INDUSTRIES INC
1 Gojo Plz Ste 500, Akron, OH 44311-1085
Tel (330) 255-6000 Founded/Ownrshp 1946
Sales 305.9MM^E EMP 550
SIC 2842 3586 2844 Specialty cleaning, polishes & sanitation goods; Measuring & dispensing pumps; Toilet preparations
Pr: Mark Lerner
*Ch Bd: Joseph Kanfer
VP: Timothy Cleary
VP: Keith Dare
VP: Dan Edwards
VP: Dennis Gladin
VP: Sharon Guten
VP: Ron Hammond
VP: John Krizansky
VP: John Rogers
QA Dir: Suzanne Crossen

GOLD CIRCLE ENTERTAINMENT
See WAITT MEDIA INC

GOLD COAST BEVERAGE
See RMET HOLDINGS INC

D-U-N-S 07-963-8791
GOLD COAST BEVERAGE LLC
(Suby of REYES HOLDINGS LLC) ★
10055 Nw 12th St, Doral, FL 33172-2761
Tel (305) 591-9800 Founded/Ownrshp 2013
Sales 1.0MMM^E EMP 1,500
SIC 5181 Beer & other fermented malt liquors

D-U-N-S 03-274-2041 IMP
GOLD COAST EAGLE DISTRIBUTING LIMITED LIABILITY LIMITED PARTNERSHIP
7051 Wireless Ct, Lakewood Ranch, FL 34240-4800
Tel (941) 355-7685 Founded/Ownrshp 2002
Sales 100.0MM EMP 168
SIC 5181 Beer & other fermented malt liquors
Pt: John W Saputo
Pt: Andrea Saputo Cox
Pt: Bethany Suputo
Ofcr: Steve Macmunn
VP Sls: Pat Bruenning
Sls Mgr: Mike Rhode

D-U-N-S 14-334-9988 EXP
GOLD CREEK FOODS LLC
686 Highway 9 N, Dawsonville, GA 30534-3576
Tel (706) 216-8640 Founded/Ownrshp 2003
Sales 282.0MM^E EMP 800^E
SIC 5144 Poultry products
CFO: Craig Goodman
Off Mgr: Kellie Bearden

D-U-N-S 00-512-3211 IMP/EXP
GOLD EAGLE CO (IL)
4400 S Kildare Ave Front, Chicago, IL 60632-4372
Tel (773) 376-4400 Founded/Ownrshp 1932, 1960
Sales 89.4MM^E EMP 236^E
SIC 5013 Tools & equipment, automotive
Pr: Marc Blackman
Ch Bd: Robert F Hirsch
Pr: Howard Donnally
Pr: Randy Levy
CFO: Randall Levy
Treas: Richard M Hirsch
Bd of Dir: Don Quigley
VP: Rick Schwab
VP: Tim Stitt
Genl Mgr: Darlene Pouk
Dir IT: Rich Collins

GOLD LEAF PUBLISHERS
See NEWS AND OBSERVER PUBLISHING CO

D-U-N-S 00-140-6859
GOLD MEDAL BAKERY INC
21 Penn St, Fall River, MA 02724-1276
Tel (508) 679-8958 Founded/Ownrshp 1912
Sales 132.3MM^E EMP 500
SIC 2051 Bread, all types (white, wheat, rye, etc): fresh or frozen; Rolls, bread type: fresh or frozen
Pr: Roland S Lecomte
CFO: Claudette Torres
*Sec: Brian R Lecomte
Exec: Kevin Watters
VP Sls: Carl Culota
Mktg Dir: Meg Brien
Board of Directors: Leonidas Lecomte Family

D-U-N-S 00-423-3797 IMP/EXP
GOLD MEDAL PRODUCTS CO
GOLD MEDAL-CAROLINA
10700 Medallion Dr, Cincinnati, OH 45241-4807
Tel (513) 769-7676 Founded/Ownrshp 1931
Sales 88.6MM^E EMP 365
SIC 3556 3589 5145 3581

GOLD MEDAL-CAROLINA
See GOLD MEDAL PRODUCTS CO

D-U-N-S 10-773-2687
■ GOLD MERGER SUB LLC
(Suby of GAMING AND LEISURE PROPERTIES INC) ★
845 Berkshire Blvd # 200, Wyomissing, PA 19610-1234
Tel (610) 401-2900 Founded/Ownrshp 1938
Sales 2.0MMM^E EMP 14,738
Accts Ernst & Young Llp Las Vegas
SIC 7999 7011 Gambling establishment; Gambling machines, operation; Hotels & motels; Casino hotel

D-U-N-S 09-896-2111 EXP
GOLD METAL RECYCLERS LTD
(Suby of EMR GOLD RECYCLING LLC) ★
4305 S Lamar St, Dallas, TX 75215-4199
Tel (214) 421-0247 Founded/Ownrshp 1976
Sales 122.5MM^E EMP 150^E
SIC 5093 Metal scrap & waste materials
Pr: Kenneth Goldberg
CFO: Andrew Cooley
VP: Neil Goldberg
Dir IT: Chad Goldberg
Sfty Dirs: Eloisa Medina
Sfty Mgr: Laura Myers
Opers Mgr: Mendel Jackson

GOLD 'N PLUMP POULTRY
See GNP CO

D-U-N-S 08-038-3753
GOLD PARENT LP
11111 Santa Monica Blvd, Los Angeles, CA 90025-3333
Tel (310) 954-0444 Founded/Ownrshp 2016
Sales 819.5MM^E EMP 3,400^E
SIC 6211 Investment bankers
Prin: Jonathan D Sokoloff

D-U-N-S 61-304-0505
▲ GOLD RESOURCE CORP
2886 Carriage Manor Pt, Colorado Springs, CO 80906-3656
Tel (303) 320-7708 Founded/Ownrshp 1998
Sales 92.7MM EMP 112^E
Accts Kpmg Llp Denver Colorado
Tkr Sym GORO Exch ASE
SIC 1041 1044 Gold ores; Silver ores
Ch Bd: Bill Conrad
Pr: Jason Reid
COO: Rick Irvine
CFO: John Labate
CFO: Joe Rodriguez
Treas: David C Reid
Genl Mgr: Jesus Garcia
Corp Couns: Jessica Browne
Board of Directors: Gary C Huber, Alex G Morrison

D-U-N-S 83-016-2686
GOLD STANDARD ASSET MANAGEMENT LLC
5155 W Rosecrans Ave # 238, Hawthorne, CA 90250-6694
Tel (310) 644-3600 Founded/Ownrshp 2009
Sales 120.0MM^E EMP 20
SIC 8741 Management services

D-U-N-S 09-861-4118 IMP
GOLD STAR FOODS INC
3781 E Airport Dr, Ontario, CA 91761-1558
Tel (909) 843-9600 Founded/Ownrshp 2014
Sales 221.8MM^E EMP 210
SIC 5142 Packaged frozen goods
CEO: George Thorsen

*Pr: Leonard Amato
*COO: Cindy Yvanez
CFO: Greg Johnson
Sr VP: Larry Noble
*VP: Sean Leer

D-U-N-S 00-797-8752
GOLD STAR FS INC (IL)
101 N East St, Cambridge, IL 61238-1156
Tel (309) 937-3369 Founded/Ownrshp 1929
Sales 224.2MM EMP 120
SIC 5171 5153 5039 5191

D-U-N-S 19-705-4740 IMP
GOLDTOE MORETZ HOLDINGS CORP
(Suby of GILDAN ACTIVEWEAR INC)
2121 Heilig Rd, Salisbury, NC 28146-2316
Tel (828) 464-0751 Founded/Ownrshp 2011
Sales 101.8MM^E EMP 706
SIC 5136 5137 5699 Hosiery, men's & boys'; Children's goods; Stockings: men's, women's & children's
Pr: Steve Lineberger
*CFO: Chuck J Ward
Ofcr: John M Mortez
*VP: Greg D Huffman

D-U-N-S 09-676-3800
GOLDBELT INC
3025 Clinton Dr Ste 100, Juneau, AK 99801-7154
Tel (907) 790-4990 Founded/Ownrshp 1974
Sales 262.2MM^E EMP 800
Accts Bdo Usa Llp Anchorage Alask
SIC 4489 6512 Excursion boat operators; Commercial & industrial building operation
Ch Bd: Joseph Kahklen
*Pr: Richard Irwin
*V Ch Bd: Randy Wanamaker
Ex Dir: Dionne C Laiti
Prgrm Mgr: Bobbi Scherrer
Genl Mgr: Jim Duncan
Genl Mgr: Ron Hauck

D-U-N-S 07-229-2782
■ GOLDBERG AND SOLOVY FOODS INC
G AND S FOODS
(Suby of SYSCO CORP) ★
5925 Alcoa Ave, Vernon, CA 90058-3955
Tel (323) 581-6161 Founded/Ownrshp 2011
Sales 198.2MM^E EMP 285
SIC 5141 5149 5046 5169 Groceries, general line; Groceries & related products; Restaurant equipment & supplies; Chemicals & allied products
CEO: Paul Paget
*Pr: Earl Goldberg
QA Dir: Matt Breenan
Opers Mgr: Greg Irvine

D-U-N-S 07-506-2583
GOLDBERG LINDSAY & CO LLC
LINDSAY GOLDBERG
630 5th Ave Fl 30, New York, NY 10111-0204
Tel (212) 651-1100 Founded/Ownrshp 2001
Sales 717.9MM^E EMP 5,080
SIC 6799 8711 8712 Investors; Building construction consultant; Architectural services
Mng Pt: Alan Goldberg
CFO: Brandon Sweitzer
VP: Krishna Agrawal
Mng Dir: Ryan Miller

D-U-N-S 03-957-5261
GOLDCO LLC
BURGER KING
100 Ashford Ctr N Ste 130, Atlanta, GA 30338-4940
Tel (334) 792-1267 Founded/Ownrshp 2013
Sales 47.9MM EMP 1,700
Accts Jackson Thornton & Co Pc Dot
SIC 5812 Eating places
Exec: Sherrie Benton

D-U-N-S 08-613-0804
GOLDEN 1 CREDIT UNION
8945 Cal Center Dr, Sacramento, CA 95826-3239
Tel (916) 732-2900 Founded/Ownrshp 1933
Sales NA EMP 1,292
SIC 6062 State credit unions, not federally chartered
Pr: Teresa Halleck
Ofcr: Richard Alfaro
Ofcr: Adrianne Pitts
VP: Walter Anasovitch
VP: Greg Brown
VP: James Deas
VP: Kimberly Dyer
VP: Tom Genessy
VP: Adriana Godinez
VP: Kate Hines
VP: Amanda Holder
VP: Mary Lota
VP: Angela Popoff
VP: Michael Popp
VP: Randy Rockwell
VP: Lisa Sawnson
VP: Paul Sidhu
VP: Cyndi Simpson

D-U-N-S 03-061-8268
GOLDEN AGE NURSING HOME OF GUTHRIE INC
419 E Oklahoma Ave, Guthrie, OK 73044-3316
Tel (405) 282-6285 Founded/Ownrshp 1961
Sales 548.9MM EMP 231
SIC 8051 8361 Skilled nursing care facilities; Residential care
Pr: Holly Chappell
*VP: Mary Lou Chappell

D-U-N-S 13-791-6321 IMP/EXP
GOLDEN ALUMINUM INC
(Suby of LUPTON VENTURES INC) ★
1405 14th St, Fort Lupton, CO 80621-2718
Tel (800) 838-1004 Founded/Ownrshp 2004
Sales 101.9MM EMP 153
SIC 3353 Aluminum sheet, plate & foil
CEO: Jeffery A Frim

GOLDEN CORRAL
See INVESTORS MANAGEMENT CORP

GOLDEN CORRAL
See PLATINUM CORRAL LLC

D-U-N-S 06-178-5465
GOLDEN CORRAL CORP
(Suby of GOLDEN CORRAL) ★
5151 Glenwood Ave Ste 300, Raleigh, NC 27612-3240
Tel (919) 781-9310 Founded/Ownrshp 1973
Sales 530.2MM^E EMP 9,000
Accts Dixon Hughes Cpa By Fax On Au
SIC 5812 Restaurant, family: chain
Pr: Lance Trenary
VP: Donna Mercer
Dir Soc: Shelly Sack
Rgnl Mgr: Ian Worthington
Off Mgr: Mark Fonte
Off Mgr: Will Hodges
Board of Directors: Paul A Delacourt, John Farquharson, Wayman O Leftwich Jr, James H Maynard, John W Pope

D-U-N-S 78-144-8667
GOLDEN COUNTY FOODS INC
300 Moore Rd, Plover, WI 54467-3152
Tel (800) 489-7783 Founded/Ownrshp 1991
Sales 148.2MM^E EMP 360
SIC 2099 Food preparations
Pr: Jim Reed
*CEO: Patrick Oray
*CFO: Bob Lampo
*CFO: Douglas Reed
*VP: Marc A Gaddis
*VP: Mark Pulchinski

D-U-N-S 03-588-5367 IMP/EXP
GOLDEN EAGLE DISTRIBUTORS INC
705 E Ajo Way, Tucson, AZ 85713-5011
Tel (520) 884-5999 Founded/Ownrshp 1982
Sales 113.2MM^E EMP 300
SIC 5181 5149

D-U-N-S 00-209-5698
GOLDEN EAGLE INSURANCE CORP
(Suby of LIBERTY MUTUAL INSURANCE CO) ★
525 B St Ste 1300, San Diego, CA 92101-4421
Tel (619) 744-6000 Founded/Ownrshp 1997
Sales NA EMP 500
SIC 6331 Fire, marine & casualty insurance; Property damage insurance
CEO: J Paul Condrin III
*Pr: Frank J Kotarba
Treas: Robert Kennedy
VP: Dennis Levesque
VP: Michael Teng
Exec: Peter Wallick
Sls Mgr: Pam Derenne

D-U-N-S 00-400-8975
GOLDEN ENTERPRISES INC
(Suby of UTZ QUALITY FOODS LLC) ★
1 Golden Flake Dr, Birmingham, AL 35205-3312
Tel (205) 458-7316 Founded/Ownrshp 2016
Sales 135.8MM EMP 749^E
Accts Carr Riggs & Ingram Llc Bir
SIC 2096 Potato chips & similar snacks; Corn chips & other corn-based snacks; Tortilla chips; Cheese curls & puffs
Pr: Dylan Lissette
CFO: Todd Staub

D-U-N-S 04-842-1437
▲ GOLDEN ENTERTAINMENT INC
6595 S Jones Blvd, Las Vegas, NV 89118-3337
Tel (702) 893-7777 Founded/Ownrshp 1998
Sales 177.0MM EMP 504^E
Tkr Sym GDEN Exch NGM
SIC 7999 Gambling establishment
Ch Bd: Blake L Sartini II
COO: Stephen A Arcana
CFO: Matthew W Flandermeyer
Chf Cred: Jeffrey R Rodefer
Sr VP: Sean T Higgins
Board of Directors: Lyle A Berman, Timothy J Cope, Mark A Lipparelli, Robert L Miodunski, Neil I Sell, Terrence L Wright

D-U-N-S 09-318-0586 EXP
GOLDEN FLAKE SNACK FOODS INC
(Suby of GOLDEN ENTERPRISES INC) ★
1 Golden Flake Dr, Birmingham, AL 35205-3312
Tel (205) 323-6161 Founded/Ownrshp 1976
Sales 132.6MM^E EMP 731^E
SIC 2096 Potato chips & other potato-based snacks; Tortilla chips; Corn chips & other corn-based snacks; Pork rinds
Ch Bd: John Stein
*Pr: Mark Mc Cutcheon
*CFO: Patty Townsend

D-U-N-S 82-764-8820 IMP
GOLDEN FLEECE MANUFACTURING GROUP LLC
SOUTHWICK
(Suby of BROOKS BROTHERS GROUP INC) ★
25 Computer Dr, Haverhill, MA 01832-1236
Tel (978) 738-0855 Founded/Ownrshp 2008
Sales 126.8MM^E EMP 900
SIC 2329 Men's & boys' sportswear & athletic clothing
Pr: Claudio Del Vecchio
*CFO: Edward J Ponto
*VP: John Martynec
Sls Mgr: Craig Lickliter

GOLDEN GATE CAPITAL
See GOLDEN GATE PRIVATE EQUITY INC

GOLDEN GATE CAPITAL
See GGC ADMINISTRATION LLC

D-U-N-S 05-794-7454
GOLDEN GATE CAPITAL LP (CA)
1 Embarcadero Ctr Fl 39, San Francisco, CA 94111-3735
Tel (415) 983-2700 Founded/Ownrshp 2000
Sales 7.8MMM^E EMP 28,860
SIC 6211 Investment firm, general brokerage
*Genl Pt: Harold O Shattuck

CFO: Sue Breedlove
CFO: Patrice Prodda
Ex VP: Felix Lo
VP: Neale Attenborough
VP: Doug Ceto
VP: Brian Gornick
VP: Mike Montgomery
VP: Nick Stangl
Mng Dir: Rajeev Amara
Mng Dir: Josh Cohen

D-U-N-S 08-660-7900
GOLDEN GATE FREIGHTLINER INC
GOLDEN GATE TRUCK CENTER
(*Suby of* LEE FINANCIAL SERVICES) ★
8200 Baldwin St, Oakland, CA 94621-1910
Tel (559) 486-4310 *Founded/Ownrshp* 1983
Sales 119.3MM^E *EMP* 422
SIC 5511 5531 7538 Trucks, tractors & trailers: new & used; Truck equipment & parts; General truck repair
Pr: Gary L Howard
**CFO:* Brian Nicholson
**VP:* Doug Howard
Store Mgr: Dave Lozano

D-U-N-S 00-923-9427
GOLDEN GATE PETROLEUM CO
1340 Arnold Dr Ste 231, Martinez, CA 94553-4189
Tel (925) 335-3700 *Founded/Ownrshp* 1979
Sales 110.8MM^E *EMP* 257
SIC 5172 Gasoline; Diesel fuel; Lubricating oils & greases
Pr: Dennis M O'Keefe
**VP:* Patrick Okeefe

D-U-N-S 02-225-2022
GOLDEN GATE PRIVATE EQUITY INC
GOLDEN GATE CAPITAL
1 Embarcadero Ctr Fl 39, San Francisco, CA 94111-3735
Tel (415) 983-2706 *Founded/Ownrshp* 2000
Sales 813.9MM^E *EMP* 54,453^E
SIC 8741 5621 Management services; Ready-to-wear apparel, women's
**Mng Dir:* Prescott Ashe
**Mng Dir:* Ken Diekroeger

D-U-N-S 05-469-4245
GOLDEN GATE REGIONAL CENTER INC (CA)
1355 Market St Ste 220, San Francisco, CA 94103-1314
Tel (415) 546-9222 *Founded/Ownrshp* 1966
Sales 228.6MM *EMP* 210
Accts Lautze & Lautze San Francisco
SIC 8322 Referral service for personal & social problems; Outreach program
CEO: Ron Fell
CFO: Chris Rognier
Treas: Robert Ramirez
IT Man: Rudy Barroco
IT Man: Chris Trujillo

GOLDEN GATE TRUCK CENTER
See GOLDEN GATE FREIGHTLINER INC

D-U-N-S 13-744-2617
GOLDEN GRAIN ENERGY LLC
1822 43rd St Sw, Mason City, IA 50401-7071
Tel (641) 423-8525 *Founded/Ownrshp* 2002
Sales 221.1MM *EMP* 47
SIC 2869 Industrial organic chemicals; Ethyl alcohol, ethanol
CEO: Curtis Strong
**Ch Bd:* Dave Sovereign
COO: Chad E Kuhlers
CFO: Christine A Marchand
**V Ch Bd:* Steve Sukup
Board of Directors: Jim Boeding, Marion Cagley, Jerry Calease, Leslie M Hansen, Stanley Laures, Duane Lynch, Dave Reinhart, Roger Shaffer

D-U-N-S 19-404-3659 IMP
GOLDEN INTERNATIONAL
36720 Palmdale Rd, Rancho Mirage, CA 92270-2232
Tel (760) 568-1912 *Founded/Ownrshp* 1947
Sales 153.5MM^E *EMP* 3,000
SIC 6799 Investors
Owner: Howard Golden

GOLDEN LIVING
See GGNSC HOLDINGS LLC

GOLDEN LIVING
See PEARL SENIOR CARE LLC

GOLDEN LIVING
See GGNSC HOLDINGS LLC

GOLDEN LIVING CTRS COMMUNITIES
See GOLDEN LIVING LLC

D-U-N-S 03-927-0371 IMP
GOLDEN LIVING LLC
GOLDEN LIVING CTRS COMMUNITIES
5220 Tennyson Pkwy # 400, Plano, TX 75024-4271
Tel (972) 372-6300 *Founded/Ownrshp* 2006
Sales 1.7MMM^E *EMP* 34,298
SIC 8051 8082 8731 8093 Skilled nursing care facilities; Home health care services; Commercial physical research; Rehabilitation center, outpatient treatment
Pr: Neil Kurtz M D
Dir Vol: Amber Laney
Pr: Andrea Bennett
Pr: Don Biggs
Pr: David Stordy
**Pr:* Julianne Williams
**COO:* Cindy Susienka
CFO: Jeanne Butterworth
**CFO:* Ann Harmon
**Chf Cred:* David Friend
Chf Mktg O: Hal Price
**Ex VP:* David Beck
**Sr VP:* Michael Yao M D
VP: Gail Holland
VP: Stacey Hord
VP: John Perticone
VP: Tammy Trasti
VP: Sharon Zeigler
Board of Directors: Demetrius Freeman

D-U-N-S 08-953-5397
GOLDEN MANUFACTURING CO INC
125 Highway 366, Golden, MS 38847-9702
Tel (662) 454-3428 *Founded/Ownrshp* 1978
Sales 103.2MM^E *EMP* 400
SIC 2311 2325 2321 2326 Military uniforms, men's & youths': purchased materials; Trousers, dress (separate): men's, youths' & boys'; Uniform shirts: made from purchased materials; Jackets, overall & work
Pr: James Fennell
**Sec:* William H Thorn

D-U-N-S 08-010-1536
GOLDEN MAX LLC
12701 Directors Dr, Stafford, TX 77477-3701
Tel (832) 886-5300 *Founded/Ownrshp* 2015
Sales 108.0MM *EMP* 65
SIC 5047 Medical & hospital equipment

GOLDEN NUGGET CASINO & HOTEL
See GOLDEN NUGGET LLC

D-U-N-S 80-288-1482
■ GOLDEN NUGGET FINANCE CORP
(*Suby of* MGMRESORTS) ★
129 Fremont St, Las Vegas, NV 89101-5677
Tel (702) 385-7111 *Founded/Ownrshp* 1949
Sales 6.2MM^E *EMP* 3,387^E
SIC 7011 Casino hotel
Pr: Stephen A Wynn
**Pr:* Tilman Pergitta

GOLDEN NUGGET HOTEL AND CASINO
See GOLDEN NUGGET INC

D-U-N-S 03-875-7993
GOLDEN NUGGET INC
GOLDEN NUGGET HOTEL AND CASINO
(*Suby of* LANDRYS GAMING INC) ★
129 Fremont St, Las Vegas, NV 89101-5677
Tel (702) 385-7111 *Founded/Ownrshp* 2003
Sales 174.6MM^E *EMP* 3,145^E
SIC 5812 7011 Eating places; Casino hotel
Pr: Tilman J Fertitta
COO: Brett Kellerman
**Treas:* Rick H Liem
Ex VP: Tom Pohlman
VP: Ralph V D'Ambrosio
VP: Rj Demman
VP: Steve Devilla
VP: James Friesen
Exec: Tony Canicosa
Exec: Tige Hand
Exec: Michael Newsome
Exec: Stephanie Nguyen
Exec: Blaise Theard
Dir Soc: Korin Benmoha
Dir Soc: Christine Haberle
Dir Soc: Shelley Roberts

D-U-N-S 05-390-5325
GOLDEN NUGGET LLC
GOLDEN NUGGET CASINO & HOTEL
2550 Golden Nugget Blvd, Lake Charles, LA 70601-9031
Tel (337) 508-7777 *Founded/Ownrshp* 2014
Sales 43.3MM^E *EMP* 3,000
SIC 7011 Casino hotel

D-U-N-S 00-193-3977 IMP
GOLDEN OPTICAL CORP
SEE OPTICAL
19800 W 8 Mile Rd, Southfield, MI 48075-5730
Tel (248) 354-7100 *Founded/Ownrshp* 1945
Sales 71.0MM^E *EMP* 1,000^E
SIC 5995 6794 Eyeglasses, prescription; Contact lenses, prescription; Opticians; Franchises, selling or licensing
Ch: Donald L Golden Od
**Pr:* Richard S Golden
**CFO:* James E Lies
**VP:* Randal E Golden
VP: Catherine M Walker

D-U-N-S 04-793-0011
GOLDEN PANTRY FOOD STORES INC
1150 Wall St, Watkinsville, GA 30677-7712
Tel (800) 533-3816 *Founded/Ownrshp* 1965
Sales 103.3MM^E *EMP* 825
SIC 5411 5541

D-U-N-S 83-591-7402 EXP
GOLDEN PEANUT & TREE NUTS
HARRELL NUT COMPANY
275 Industrial Blvd, Camilla, GA 31730-3911
Tel (229) 336-7282 *Founded/Ownrshp* 1994
Sales 103.4MM^E *EMP* 250
SIC 5159 2068 Nuts & nut by-products; Salted & roasted nuts & seeds
Pr: Marty R Harrell
**CFO:* Paula Johnson

GOLDEN PEANUT AND TREE NUTS
See GOLDEN PEANUT CO LLC

D-U-N-S 16-176-5425 IMP/EXP
■ GOLDEN PEANUT CO LLC
GOLDEN PEANUT AND TREE NUTS
(*Suby of* ARCHER-DANIELS-MIDLAND CO) ★
100 N Point Ctr E Ste 400, Alpharetta, GA 30022-8262
Tel (770) 752-8160 *Founded/Ownrshp* 2011
Sales 3.4MMM^E *EMP* 1,000
SIC 0723

GOLDEN PHOENIX CENTER
See PAMPA REGIONAL MEDICAL CENTER AUXILIARY

D-U-N-S 79-472-4146
GOLDEN PUMP POULTRY INC
(*Suby of* GOLD N PLUMP POULTRY) ★
4150 2nd St S Ste 200, Saint Cloud, MN 56301-3994
Tel (320) 240-6234 *Founded/Ownrshp* 1993
Sales 68.7MM^E *EMP* 1,200
SIC 2015 0251 Chicken, processed; Broiling chickens, raising of
CEO: Michael Helgeson

D-U-N-S 05-936-0990
■ GOLDEN ROAD MOTOR INN INC
ATLANTIS CASINO RESORT
(*Suby of* MONARCH CASINO & RESORT INC) ★
3800 S Virginia St, Reno, NV 89502-6005
Tel (775) 335-4521 *Founded/Ownrshp* 1972
Sales 93.5MM^E *EMP* 1,000
SIC 7011 5812 5813 7299 Casino hotel; American restaurant; Bar (drinking places); Banquet hall facilities
Ch Bd: John Farahi
**Pr:* Bahram Farahi
**CFO:* Ronald Rowan
Treas: Michele Hayden
Ofcr: Antonio Mulei
Ofcr: Chad Padelford
Ofcr: Aaron Theis
Ex VP: Darlyne Sullivan
Dir Sec: Doug Simpson
Off Mgr: Tom Maloney
Dir IT: Zak Gulling

D-U-N-S 07-195-4291
■ GOLDEN RULE FINANCIAL CORP
(*Suby of* UNITEDHEALTH GROUP INC) ★
7440 Woodland Dr, Indianapolis, IN 46278-1720
Tel (317) 297-4123 *Founded/Ownrshp* 1964
Sales NA *EMP* 1,100
SIC 6321 6311 Accident insurance carriers; Health insurance carriers; Life insurance carriers
Pr: Larry D Jones
**Ch Bd:* Therese A Rooney
**CFO:* Patrick F Carr

D-U-N-S 07-199-4651
■ GOLDEN RULE INSURANCE CO
(*Suby of* UNITED HEALTHCARE SERVICES INC) ★
7440 Woodland Dr, Indianapolis, IN 46278-1719
Tel (317) 297-4123 *Founded/Ownrshp* 2015
Sales NA *EMP* 1,000
SIC 6321 6311 Accident insurance carriers; Health insurance carriers; Life insurance carriers
Ch Bd: Therese A Rooney
**Pr:* John M Whelan
**CFO:* Patrick F Carr
Assoc Dir: Beth Champion
Assoc Dir: Darla Galovic
Assoc Dir: Amy Gildernick
Assoc Dir: Dee Greenman
Comm Man: Dave Wilson
Mng Dir: Ashley Neice
Software D: Steven Flaugh
Netwrk Eng: Tom Cummings

GOLDEN RULE STORES
See EMERY-WATERHOUSE CO

D-U-N-S 18-647-0779
GOLDEN SPREAD ELECTRIC COOPERATIVE INC
905 S Fillmore St Ste 300, Amarillo, TX 79101-3541
Tel (806) 379-7766 *Founded/Ownrshp* 1984
Sales 292.6MM *EMP* 80
SIC 4911

D-U-N-S 88-307-3538
GOLDEN STAR RESOURCES LTD
10901 W Toller Dr Ste 300, Littleton, CO 80127-6312
Tel (303) 830-9000 *Founded/Ownrshp* 1985
Sales 550.5MM *EMP* 2,360^E
SIC 1041

D-U-N-S 15-128-0260 IMP
GOLDEN STAR TECHNOLOGY INC
G S T
12881 166th St Ste 100, Cerritos, CA 90703-2159
Tel (562) 345-8700 *Founded/Ownrshp* 1992
Sales 100.0MM^E *EMP* 98
SIC 5734 7378 5045 Computer peripheral equipment; Computer software & accessories; Computer maintenance & repair; Computers, peripherals & software
CEO: Jia Peir Wang
Pr: Alice Wang
CEO: Albert Wang
COO: Dennis Wang
Sr VP: Jeffrey Smith
VP: Larry Roelofs
Sls Dir: Kevin Patel

GOLDEN STATE CONTAINER
See VICTORY PACKAGING LP

GOLDEN STATE FENCE CO.
See FENCEWORKS INC

GOLDEN STATE FLOORING
See H - INVESTMENT CO

D-U-N-S 02-850-8703 EXP
GOLDEN STATE FOODS CORP
GSF FOUNDATION
18301 Von Karman Ave # 1100, Irvine, CA 92612-1009
Tel (949) 252-2000 *Founded/Ownrshp* 1969
Sales 277.4MM^E *EMP* 3,000
SIC 5147 2087 5142 5148 5149 Meats & meat products; Meats, cured or smoked; Syrups, drink; Packaged frozen goods; Vegetables; Vegetables, fresh; Condiments
Ch Bd: Mark Wetterau
Pr: Larry McGill
CFO: Bill Sanderson
CFO: Mike Waitukaitis
Sr Ex VP: Frank Listi
Ex VP: Neil Cracknell
Ex VP: Neil G Cracknell
Sr VP: Craig Vaxter
VP: Steve Becker
VP: John Broekhuis
VP: Philip Crane
VP: Joe Heffington
VP: John Pooley
VP: Ed Savard
VP: Jeff Steiner
VP: Scott Thomas
VP: Amy Zuborg
VP: Amy Zurborg

D-U-N-S 13-113-7481
GOLDEN STATE LUMBER INC
855 Lakeville St Ste 200, Petaluma, CA 94952-7329
Tel (707) 206-4100 *Founded/Ownrshp* 1985
Sales 235.0MM *EMP* 400
SIC 5031 5211 Lumber: rough, dressed & finished; Building materials, exterior; Building materials, interior; Lumber & other building materials
CEO: Jessica L Scerri
Pr: Rick Zaslove
COO: Paul Nobbman
COO: Rob Scerri
CFO: Christine Bean
CFO: Bob Bowler
Div Mgr: Larry Jynes
MIS Mgr: Mark Eglin

D-U-N-S 83-513-6268
GOLDEN STATE OVERNIGHT DELIVERY SERVICE INC
(*Suby of* GENERAL LOGISTICS SYSTEMS B.V.)
7901 Stnridge Dr Ste 400, Pleasanton, CA 94588
Tel (800) 322-5555 *Founded/Ownrshp* 2016
Sales 259.5MM^E *EMP* 1,900
SIC 4215

D-U-N-S 00-690-8859
■ GOLDEN STATE WATER CO
(*Suby of* AMERICAN STATES WATER CO) ★
630 E Foothill Blvd, San Dimas, CA 91773-1212
Tel (909) 394-3600 *Founded/Ownrshp* 1929
Sales 364.5MM *EMP* 700^E
Accts Pricewaterhousecoopers Llp Lo
SIC 4941 4911 Water supply; Distribution, electric power
Pr: Robert J Sprowls
CFO: James Berg
CFO: Eva G Tang
VP: Susan L Conway
VP: James Gallagher
VP: Bill Gedney
VP: Denise Kruger
VP: Diane Rentfrow
VP: Patrick Scanlon
VP: Keith Switzer
Dir Risk M: Robert Fansler
Comm Dir: Matt Puffer
Board of Directors: James L Anderson, Sarah J Anderson, Diana M Bonita, John R Fielder, Anne M Holloway, James F McNulty, Janice F Wilkins

D-U-N-S 00-286-0252
GOLDEN TRIANGLE CONSTRUCTION CO INC (PA)
8555 Old Strubenville Pik, Imperial, PA 15126
Tel (724) 828-2800 *Founded/Ownrshp* 1952
Sales 120.9MM^E *EMP* 300
SIC 1623 1611 Sewer line construction; Highway & street paving contractor
Pr: Belinda Bucci
**VP:* Charles Niederriter
**VP:* David Sciullo
Sfty Mgr: Michael Rieber

GOLDEN TROPHY STEAKS
See BRUSS CO

D-U-N-S 00-284-8588 IMP
GOLDEN VALLEY ELECTRIC ASSOCIATION INC
758 Illinois St, Fairbanks, AK 99701-2919
Tel (907) 452-1151 *Founded/Ownrshp* 1946
Sales 214.6MM *EMP* 270
Accts Bdo Usa Llp Anchorage Alask
SIC 4911 Generation, electric power; Transmission, electric power; Distribution, electric power
CEO: Cory Borgeson
V Ch: Daniel Osborne
VP: Gene Therriault
**VP:* Ron Woolff
VP: Jeff Yauney
IT Man: Koma Fenton
Sys Mgr: Paul Morgan
Sfty Mgr: Don Maynor
Sfty Mgr: Phil Newton

D-U-N-S 07-879-3486
GOLDEN VALLEY HEALTH CENTERS
737 W Childs Ave, Merced, CA 95341-6805
Tel (209) 383-1848 *Founded/Ownrshp* 1972
Sales 99.7MM *EMP* 850
SIC 8093 Specialty outpatient clinics
CEO: Tony Weber
COO: Mark A Millan
CFO: Lue Thao
Bd of Dir: Jerry Lewis
Ofcr: Lisa Swenson
Exec: Crystal Andersen
CIO: Ray Parris
Site Mgr: Brian Capizzi
Podiatrist: William Stallone
Doctor: Chris Aguilar
Doctor: Jeannette Ayala

GOLDEN VALLEY NATURAL
See INTERMOUNTAIN NATURAL LLC

D-U-N-S 07-992-8695
GOLDEN VALLEY TCA A LLC
AUDI MINNEAPOLIS
9393 Wayzata Blvd, Minneapolis, MN 55426-1862
Tel (763) 744-9393 *Founded/Ownrshp* 2012
Sales 106.5MM *EMP* 120
SIC 5511 New & used car dealers

D-U-N-S 06-415-9833
■ GOLDEN WEST FINANCIAL CORP
(*Suby of* WELLS FARGO & CO) ★
301 S College St, Charlotte, NC 28202-6000
Tel (704) 374-6565 *Founded/Ownrshp* 2008
Sales NA *EMP* 11,604
SIC 6035 Federal savings & loan associations
Ch Bd: G Kennedy Thompson
Pr: Russell W Kettell
Ex VP: Gary R Badley
Ex VP: Gary R Bradley
Sr VP: Carl M Andersen
Sr VP: William C Nunan
VP: Scott Schultz

VP: Ted Tomblison
Exec: James T Judd
Genl Mgr: Maryellen Cattani
Genl Couns: Ray W West Jr

D-U-N-S 00-482-5873
GOLDEN WEST TELECOMMUNICATIONS COOPERATIVE INC (SD)
415 Crown St, Wall, SD 57790
Tel (605) 279-2161 *Founded/Ownrshp* 1952
Sales 143.0MM^E *EMP* 340
SIC 4813 Local & long distance telephone communications
CEO: Denny Law
**CFO:* Jordy Kreut
Ofcr: Greg Goddickson
Genl Mgr: Jim Haar
Genl Mgr: Nick Rogness
Sls Mgr: James Vanloan

D-U-N-S 80-605-9606 IMP
GOLDEN WEST TRADING INC
ROYAL POULTRY
4401 S Downey Rd, Vernon, CA 90058-2518
Tel (323) 581-3663 *Founded/Ownrshp* 1992
Sales 219.8MM^E *EMP* 180
SIC 5147 5142 Meats & meat products; Meat, frozen: packaged
CEO: Erik Litmanovich
**Ch Bd:* Levi Litmanovich
**Pr:* Tony Cimolino
**Pr:* Josh Solovy
**CFO:* Richard Lunsford
**Sr VP:* Zack Levenson
IT Man: Mak Abbasi

D-U-N-S 05-687-9182
GOLDER ASSOCIATES INC
(*Suby of* GOLDER ASSOCIATES CORPORATION)
3730 Chamblee Tucker Rd, Atlanta, GA 30341-4414
Tel (770) 496-1893 *Founded/Ownrshp* 1980
Sales 262.9MM *EMP* 1,200^E
Accts Pricewaterhousecoopers Llp On
SIC 8711 Consulting engineer
Pr: Hisham Mahmoud
**CFO:* Michael J Strain
VP: Paul Jjc
VP: Stephen Wilson
Comm Man: Raaj Chandran
Rgnl Mgr: Bob Anderson
Rgnl Mgr: Kevin K Beechinor
Rgnl Mgr: Sean McFarland
Off Mgr: Michael Brown
Off Mgr: Isabel Johnson
IT Man: Mike Simpson

D-U-N-S 05-210-1185
▲ GOLDFIELD CORP DEL
1684 W Hibiscus Blvd, Melbourne, FL 32901-3082
Tel (321) 724-1700 *Founded/Ownrshp* 1906
Sales 120.5MM *EMP* 326^E
Tkr Sym GV *Exch* ASE
SIC 1623 1731 Electric power line construction; Fiber optic cable installation
Ch Bd: John H Sottile
CFO: Stephen R Wherry
Board of Directors: David P Bicks, Harvey C Eads Jr, John P Fazzini

D-U-N-S 78-322-4066
■ GOLDLEAF FINANCIAL SOLUTIONS INC
PROFITSTARS
(*Suby of* JACK HENRY & ASSOCIATES INC) ★
350 Technology Pkwy # 200, Norcross, GA 30092-2998
Tel (678) 966-0844 *Founded/Ownrshp* 1990
Sales 1.0MMM^E *EMP* 493^E
SIC 8721 8741 Billing & bookkeeping service; Financial management for business
CEO: John F Prim
**Pr:* Henry M Baroco
**Pr:* G Lynn Boggs
CFO: Scott Mayeshoff
**CFO:* Dan Owens
**CFO:* Kevin D Williams
**Ex VP:* Matthew W Pribus
**Ex VP:* W Todd Shiver
Sr VP: Rick Cusimano
Sr VP: Cheryl Schiltz
VP: Ken Bolte
VP: Ian Culling

GOLDMAN SACHS
See GOLDMAN SACHS & CO

D-U-N-S 00-698-4561
■ GOLDMAN SACHS & CO (NY)
GOLDMAN SACHS
(*Suby of* GOLDMAN SACHS GROUP INC) ★
200 West St Bldg 200, New York, NY 10282-2102
Tel (212) 346-5440 *Founded/Ownrshp* 1991
Sales 16.7MMM^E *EMP* 32,400
SIC 6211 6221 6282 6153 Security brokers & dealers; Brokers, security; Dealers, security; Underwriters, security; Commodity traders, contracts; Investment advisory service; Purchasers of accounts receivable & commercial paper
Ch Bd: Lloyd C Blankfein
**COO:* Gary D Cohn
CFO: Sam Agnew
**CFO:* Harvey M Schwartz
**CFO:* David A Viniar
Ex VP: John F Rogers
Ex VP: Kristian Vinther
Sr VP: Anthony Vitalone
VP: Irina Blokh
VP: Robert Boardman
VP: Sanjay Chojar
VP: Carmine Falco
VP: Mary Henry
VP: Magdalene Ho
VP: Kevin Joy
VP: Debbie Kemp
VP: Susan Kuller
VP: Angela Leung
VP: Bonnie S Litt
VP: Stephen McConville
VP: Michael Parekh

D-U-N-S 15-366-5067
■ GOLDMAN SACHS (ASIA) LLC
(*Suby of* GOLDMAN SACHS GROUP INC) ★
200 West St Bldg 200, New York, NY 10282-2102
Tel (212) 902-1000 *Founded/Ownrshp* 1994
Sales 262.8MM^E *EMP* 650^E
SIC 6211 6282 6722 Investment bankers; Investment advisory service; Management investment, open-end
CEO: Lloyd C Blankfein
**Pr:* Gary D Cohn
Bd of Dir: Eric S Schwartz
**Ex VP:* Alan M Cohen
**Ex VP:* Edith W Cooper
**Ex VP:* Harvey M Schwartz
VP: Richard Horn
VP: Andrea Kirk
VP: Stuart Leigh
VP: Tom Osmond
VP: Cassandra Tok
Exec: Christopher Babick
Exec: Gerhard Doetsch
Exec: David Geen
Exec: David George
Exec: Greg Mount
Exec: Michael Richman

D-U-N-S 82-938-5165
■ GOLDMAN SACHS BANK USA
(*Suby of* GOLDMAN SACHS GROUP INC) ★
200 West St, New York, NY 10282-2198
Tel (212) 902-1000 *Founded/Ownrshp* 2009
Sales NA *EMP* 11^E
SIC 6022 State commercial banks

D-U-N-S 82-758-0320
■ GOLDMAN SACHS BANK USA HOLDINGS LLC
(*Suby of* GOLDMAN SACHS GROUP INC) ★
200 West St Bldg 200, New York, NY 10282-2102
Tel (212) 357-2882 *Founded/Ownrshp* 2008
Sales NA *EMP* 6
SIC 6029 Commercial banks
V Ch: Alastair Lucas

D-U-N-S 07-872-5615
■ GOLDMAN SACHS BDC INC
(*Suby of* GOLDMAN SACHS GROUP INC) ★
200 West St Bldg 200, New York, NY 10282-2102
Tel (212) 902-1000 *Founded/Ownrshp* 2012
Sales 118.4MM *EMP* 8^E
Accts Pricewaterhousecoopers Llp Bo
SIC 6726 Investment offices
Pr: Brendan McGovern
**Ch Bd:* Ashok N Bakhru
COO: Jon Yoder
CFO: Jonathan Lamm
Ofcr: Alison Conn

D-U-N-S 96-933-5582
GOLDMAN SACHS CHARITABLE GIFT FUND
200 West St Fl 29, New York, NY 10282-2102
Tel (212) 902-4223 *Founded/Ownrshp* 2011
Sales 145.9MM *EMP* 1
Accts Pricewaterhousecoopers Llp
SIC 5947 Gift shop
CEO: Dina H Powell

D-U-N-S 78-563-9613
GOLDMAN SACHS FOUNDATION
375 Park Ave Ste 1002, New York, NY 10152-0002
Tel (212) 902-6875 *Founded/Ownrshp* 2006
Sales 314.5MM *EMP* 1
SIC 8748 Business consulting
Prin: Alastair Lucas
VP: Lloyd Ucko

D-U-N-S 05-916-4314
▲ GOLDMAN SACHS GROUP INC
200 West St Bldg 200, New York, NY 10282-2198
Tel (212) 902-1000 *Founded/Ownrshp* 1869
Sales 39.2MMM *EMP* 36,800
Tkr Sym GS *Exch* NYS
SIC 6211 6282 Security brokers & dealers; Investment advice
Ch Bd: Lloyd C Blankfein
V Ch: Michael S Sherwood
Pr: Gary D Cohn
COO: Jim Esposito
CFO: Harvey M Schwartz
Ch: Jack Levy
Bd of Dir: Mark Winkelman
Ofcr: Craig W Broderick
Ofcr: Steven Kerr
Ofcr: Stephen M Scherr
Ofcr: Barry L Zubrow
Ex VP: Alan M Cohen
Ex VP: Gregory K Palm
Ex VP: Stacy Polley
Ex VP: John F Rogers
VP: Rahul Banerjee
VP: Marcelo Barbosa
VP: Howard Epstein
VP: Jamie Love
VP: Manohar Rangineni
VP: Nan Tu

D-U-N-S 95-801-9754
■ GOLDMAN SACHS REALTY MANAGEMENT LP
ARCHON HOSPITALITY
(*Suby of* GOLDMAN SACHS GROUP INC) ★
6011 Connection Dr, Irving, TX 75039-2607
Tel (972) 368-2200 *Founded/Ownrshp* 1996
Sales 106.0MM^E *EMP* 614
SIC 8741 Financial management for business
Pt: James L Lozier Jr
Ofcr: Saleh Igal
VP: Curtis Ambrose
VP: Ron K Barger
VP: Tanya Davis
VP: Scott Gleason
VP: Curtis Harrison
VP: Brenda Higgins
VP: Milton Millman
VP: Wes Moffett
VP: Brian Nordahl
VP: Ernest Perry

VP: Becky Rice
VP: Mark Ricketts
VP: Stutz Ryan
VP: Michael Watts
VP: Mark Wolcott
VP: Chris Zertuchewong
Dir Risk M: Tom Bergstrom

D-U-N-S 78-708-2304
GOLDNER HAWN JOHNSON & MORRISON INC
GHJ&M
3700 Wells Fargo Ctr # 90, Minneapolis, MN 55402
Tel (612) 338-5912 *Founded/Ownrshp* 1989
Sales 199.9MM^E *EMP* 616
SIC 6211 Investment firm, general brokerage
Mng Dir: John L Morrison
Pr: Chad Cornell
**CFO:* Aaron J Goldstein
**VP:* Jason T Brass
**VP:* Van Zandt Hawn
**VP:* Michael E Healy
**VP:* Joseph M Heinen
**VP:* Timothy D Johnson

GOLDNER, HERMAN COMPANY
See HERMAN GOLDNER CO INC

D-U-N-S 36-061-2808
GOLDRICH & KEST INDUSTRIES LLC
5150 Overland Ave, Culver City, CA 90230-4914
Tel (310) 204-2050 *Founded/Ownrshp* 1957
Sales 243.9MM^E *EMP* 885
SIC 6552 Subdividers & developers
CFO: Warren Breslow

D-U-N-S 09-306-9797
GOLDS GYM INTERNATIONAL INC
(*Suby of* OMNI HOTELS) ★
125 E J Carpentr Fwy 13, Irving, TX 75062
Tel (972) 444-8527 *Founded/Ownrshp* 2004
Sales 146.5MM^E *EMP* 2,000
SIC 7991 6794 Physical fitness facilities; Franchises, selling or licensing
Pr: David Schnabel
**COO:* Mike Feinman
CFO: Randall R Schultz
CFO: Gene Snowden
**Chf Mktg O:* Michael Cobb
VP: Chad Benedict
VP: Dana Milkie
VP: Bill Wade
Genl Mgr: Donna Bair
Genl Mgr: Darren Snell
Genl Mgr: Alexis Vanwagoner

D-U-N-S 06-192-8505
GOLDS HOLDING CORP
4001 Maple Ave Ste 200, Dallas, TX 75219-3249
Tel (214) 574-4653 *Founded/Ownrshp* 1999
Sales 107.6MM^E *EMP* 426^E
SIC 6719 Investment holding companies, except banks
CEO: James D Caldwell
**Pr:* James Snow
**VP:* Michael Smith

GOLDSBORO MIL & GRN STOR CO
See GOLDSBORO MILLING CO

D-U-N-S 00-319-7142
GOLDSBORO MILLING CO
GOLDSBORO MIL & GRN STOR CO
938 Millers Chapel Rd, Goldsboro, NC 27534-7772
Tel (919) 778-3130 *Founded/Ownrshp* 1951
Sales 170.9MM^E *EMP* 800^E
SIC 2048 Poultry feeds; Livestock feeds
Ch Bd: J L Maxwell Jr
**Pr:* Hugh Gordon Maxwell III
**CFO:* Thomas Howell
**Sec:* J L Maxwell III
VP: Jere Pelletier
**VP:* J W Pelletier III
VP: Walter Pelletier
MIS Dir: Eric Letchworth
Dir IT: Donna Douglas
Plnt Mgr: Verl Belvin
Prd Mgr: Lorenz Falls

D-U-N-S 10-235-4115
GOLDSHIELD FIBER GLASS INC
REV GROUP
(*Suby of* FLEETWOOD ENTERPRISES INC) ★
2004 Patterson St, Decatur, IN 46733-1867
Tel (260) 728-2476 *Founded/Ownrshp* 1982
Sales 1.7MMM *EMP* 250
SIC 2221 Glass & fiberglass broadwoven fabrics
CEO: Dino Cusumano
**Pr:* Tim Sullivan
**CFO:* Dean Nolden
**Treas:* Lyle N Larkin
Sr VP: Tere Franceschi
**Sr VP:* Forrest D Theobald
**VP:* Paul Bamatter
**VP:* Stan Edme
**VP:* Larry L Mace
Genl Mgr: Pete Stevenson
QC Dir: Dave Wisel

GOLDSIGN
See CITIZENS OF HUMANITY LLC

GOLDSMITH SEEDS
See SYNGENTA CROP PROTECTION LLC

GOLF CLUB AT DESERT MOUNTAIN
See DESERT MOUNTAIN PROPERTIES LIMITED PARTNERSHIP

D-U-N-S 08-128-1636 IMP
■ GOLF GALAXY GOLFWORKS INC (OH)
(*Suby of* GOLF GALAXY INC) ★
4820 Jacksontown Rd, Newark, OH 43056-9377
Tel (740) 328-4193 *Founded/Ownrshp* 1974, 2006
Sales 83.6MM^E *EMP* 150
SIC 5091 2731 3949 5941 Golf & skiing equipment & supplies; Books: publishing only; Golf equipment; Shafts, golf club; Golf, tennis & ski shops
CEO: Mark McCormick
**CFO:* Jerry Datz

**VP:* Mark Wilson
**Prin:* Richard C Nordvoid
Genl Mgr: Jon O'Coin

D-U-N-S 96-121-5894
■ GOLF GALAXY INC
(*Suby of* DICKS SPORTING GOODS INC) ★
345 Court St, Coraopolis, PA 15108-3817
Tel (724) 273-3400 *Founded/Ownrshp* 2007
Sales 106.4MM^E *EMP* 1,460
SIC 5941 Golf goods & equipment
CEO: Edward W Stack
**Pr:* Schmidt Joseph
**COO:* Gregory B Maanum
**Treas:* Kullman Timothy
Bd of Dir: Gregg S Newmark
VP: Lee Belitsky
VP: Gregory Guentzel
**VP:* Oliver Joseph
Off Mgr: Caroleen Greenwood

GOLF VISTA ESTATES
See MHC OPERATING LIMITED PARTNERSHIP

D-U-N-S 06-641-3931 IMP
■ GOLFSMITH INTERNATIONAL HOLDINGS INC
(*Suby of* DICKS SPORTING GOODS INC) ★
11000 N Interstate 35, Austin, TX 78753-3195
Tel (512) 837-8810 *Founded/Ownrshp* 2016
Sales 217.5MM^E *EMP* 791^E
SIC 5941 5699 5661 5961 Golf goods & equipment; Sports apparel; Footwear, athletic; Catalog & mail-order houses
CEO: Martin E Hanaka
Pr: Steven Larkin
**CFO:* Dave Bushland
Bd of Dir: James A Grover
Chf Mktg O: Lisa Zoellner
**Ex VP:* Ron Hornbaker
VP: Eli Getson
VP: Andrew Spratt
Off Mgr: Charlie Davis
CTO: Larry Banken
VP Opers: Joseph J Kester

D-U-N-S 05-057-1801
■ GOLIN/HARRIS INTERNATIONAL INC
GOLINHARRIS
(*Suby of* INTERPUBLIC GROUP OF COMPANIES INC) ★
875 N Michigan Ave # 2600, Chicago, IL 60611-1821
Tel (312) 729-4000 *Founded/Ownrshp* 2005
Sales 134.1MM^E *EMP* 830
SIC 8743 Public relations & publicity
Ch Bd: Alvin Golin
**Pr:* Ellen Ryan Mardiks
**CEO:* Fred Cook
**CFO:* Brian J Beck
Sr Cor Off: Tom Harris
Ex VP: Jeffrey Burnett
Ex VP: Kathy Carliner
Ex VP: David Duschene
Ex VP: Stephen Jones
Ex VP: Wendy Simmons
Ex VP: Farah Speer
Ex VP: Tina Vennegaard
Ex VP: Tracy Weisman
Ex VP: David Zitlow
Sr VP: Kurt Markva
VP: Alicia Alfano
VP: Forrest Anderson
VP: Jennifer Baker
VP: Barret Buss
VP: Cristal Cole
VP: Karla Cutting

GOLINHARRIS
See GOLIN/HARRIS INTERNATIONAL INC

D-U-N-S 96-226-5018
▲ GOLUB CAPITAL BDC INC
150 S Wacker Dr Ste 800, Chicago, IL 60606-4102
Tel (312) 205-5050 *Founded/Ownrshp* 2007
Sales 119.9MM *EMP* 5^E
Accts Rsm Us Llp Chicago Illinois
Tkr Sym GBDC *Exch* NGS
SIC 6726 Management investment funds, closed-end
CEO: David B Golub
**Ch Bd:* Lawrence E Golub
CFO: Ross A Teune
Chf Cred: Joshua M Levinson
Mng Dir: Gregory A Robbins

D-U-N-S 00-699-4339 IMP/EXP
GOLUB CORP
PRICE CHOPPER SUPERMARKETS
461 Nott St, Schenectady, NY 12308-1812
Tel (518) 355-5000 *Founded/Ownrshp* 1930
Sales 3.4MMM *EMP* 20,434
SIC 5411 Supermarkets, chain; Convenience stores, chain
Pr: Scott Grimmett
**Ch Bd:* Neil M Golub
**CFO:* John J Endres Jr
**Treas:* Christina Maltbie
**V Ch Bd:* Jerel T Golub
**Sr VP:* Blaine R Bringhurst
Sr VP: David Golub
**Sr VP:* Dean A Little
**Sr VP:* Leo Taylor
VP: Daniela Allen
VP: Mark Bourcher
**VP:* Christine Daniels Sr
VP: Mike Davidson
**VP:* Robert Doyle
VP: Steven Duffy
**VP:* Mona J Golub
VP: Angelo Graziano
VP: Troy Johnson
VP: Michael Kenneally
VP: Dean Little
VP: Don Orlando
Board of Directors: Lee A Brathwaite and, Lita Cunningham, Mike Defabis, Edward S Dunn Jr, Robert W Schwartz

GOMACO MANUFACTURING CO
See GODBERSEN-SMITH CONSTRUCTION CO INC

D-U-N-S 00-512-0803 IMP
GONNELLA BAKING CO
1117 Wiley Rd, Schaumburg, IL 60173-4337
Tel (312) 733-2020 Founded/Ownrshp 1886
Sales 155.8MM[E] EMP 350
SIC 2051 5812 2099 2038 Bread, all types (white, wheat, rye, etc): fresh or frozen; Eating places; Food preparations; Frozen specialties
Pr: Nick Marcucci
*Treas: Thomas J Mazukelli
VP: Bob Gonnella
*VP: Robert Gonnella Jr
*VP: Daniel Herzog
*VP: Dennis Marcucci
VP: Paul Marcucci
VP: Michael Redick
VP: Bob Wolff
Genl Mgr: Steve Hanrahan
Opers Mgr: Luis Rosado
Board of Directors: Katherine Roseen

D-U-N-S 02-804-0509
GONSALVES & SANTUCCI INC
CONCO CEMENT COMPANY
5141 Commercial Cir, Concord, CA 94520-8523
Tel (925) 685-6799 Founded/Ownrshp 1961
Sales 237.0MM[E] EMP 1,000
SIC 1771 Concrete work
Ch Bd: Mathew Gonsalves
*Pr: Steven Gonsalves
*CFO: Barry Silberman
*VP: Holly Bertuccelli
*VP: Joseph Santucci
*VP: Karen Watson
*Prin: Mariah Panza Garcia

D-U-N-S 88-308-2182 IMP
GONZALES ENTERPRISES INC
AZTLAN GRAPHICS
495 Ryan Ave, Chico, CA 95973-8846
Tel (530) 343-8725 Founded/Ownrshp 1995
Sales 140.3MM[E] EMP 174
SIC 5136 Shirts, men's & boys'
CEO: Daniel Gonzales
Pr: Randy Cook
*Treas: Dawn Gonzales
VP: BJ Larossa
VP: Alec Patience
Exec: Alyssa Beltramo
Sls Mgr: Julie Arndt
Art Dir: Jimmy Richards

D-U-N-S 92-668-8102
GONZALEZ CONTRACT SERVICES INC
G C S
1670 Highwood E, Pontiac, MI 48340-1235
Tel (248) 548-6010 Founded/Ownrshp 1988
Sales 46.2MM[E] EMP 1,000
SIC 7361 Employment agencies
Pr: Gary H Gonzalez

D-U-N-S 07-972-1794
GOOD BUDDY BUDDY GOOD LLC
300 Anacostia Rd Se # 103, Washington, DC 20019-7184
Tel (240) 532-0031 Founded/Ownrshp 2015
Sales 100.0MM EMP 3
SIC 7389 Music recording producer;

D-U-N-S 82-817-2622 IMP
GOOD FOODS GROUP LLC
CHEF EARL'S
10100 88th Ave, Pleasant Prairie, WI 53158-2217
Tel (262) 465-6900 Founded/Ownrshp 2008
Sales 97.0MM[E] EMP 350
SIC 2038 5149 Frozen specialties; Breakfasts, frozen & packaged; Dinners, frozen & packaged; Lunches, frozen & packaged; Natural & organic foods
CEO: Kurt Penn
*Pr: John Fitzgerald
Opers Mgr: Charles Herrig

GOOD NEIGHBOR PHARMACY
See DON QUIJOTE (USA) CO LTD

GOOD NEIGHBOR PHARMACY
See LOUISIANA WHOLESALE DRUG CO INC

GOOD SAM
See AFFINITY GROUP HOLDING LLC

D-U-N-S 79-012-7109
GOOD SAM ENTERPRISES LLC
GSE
(Suby of GOOD SAM) ★
250 Parkway Dr Ste 270, Lincolnshire, IL 60069-4346
Tel (847) 229-6720 Founded/Ownrshp 1986
Sales 481.4MM EMP 1,704[E]
SIC 5561 7997 2721 Recreational vehicle parts & accessories; Membership sports & recreation clubs; Magazines: publishing only, not printed on site
Ch Bd: Stephen Adams
*Pr: Marcus A Lemonis
*CFO: Thomas F Wolfe
*Chf Mktg O: Tamara Ward
Ex VP: Steve Albert
*Ex VP: Matthew Baden
*Ex VP: Brent Moody
*Ex VP: John A Sirpilla
Sr VP: Michael Blumer
VP: Mark Dowis
VP: Dale Hendrix
VP: David Scifres

GOOD SAMARITAN, THE
See CHRISTIAN AID MINISTRIES

D-U-N-S 14-765-2671
GOOD SAMARITAN COMMUNITY HEALTHCARE INC
407 14th Ave Se, Puyallup, WA 98372-3770
Tel (253) 848-6661 Founded/Ownrshp 1952
Sales 418.4MM EMP 300
SIC 8062 General medical & surgical hospitals
Pr: John Long
Chf Rad: Dan Martin
Obsttrcn: Carrie Wong

D-U-N-S 93-942-8512
GOOD SAMARITAN HEALTH SERVICES FOUNDATION
259 S 4th St Fl 2, Lebanon, PA 17042-6112
Tel (717) 270-7864 Founded/Ownrshp 1987
Sales 209.9M EMP 2,000
Accts Grant Thornton Llp Philadelph
SIC 8741 7389 8721 Hospital management; Fund raising organizations; Accounting, auditing & bookkeeping
Pr: Robert J Longo
Dir Vol: Carol Seeley
*Ch: Darwin Glick
*Treas: Frederick S Wolfson

GOOD SAMARITAN HOSPITAL
See KNOX COUNTY HOSPITAL

GOOD SAMARITAN HOSPITAL
See SAMARITAN HEALTH SERVICES INC

D-U-N-S 05-238-9657 IMP
GOOD SAMARITAN HOSPITAL
1225 Wilshire Blvd, Los Angeles, CA 90017-1901
Tel (213) 977-2121 Founded/Ownrshp 1885
Sales 351.9MM EMP 1,500[E]
SIC 8062 General medical & surgical hospitals
CEO: Andrew B Leeka
Dir Recs: Marcia Stein
*Ch Bd: Charles Munger
COO: Dan McLaughlin
COO: Lynne Whaley-Welty
*CFO: Alan Ino
VP: Campbell Dean
VP: Susan Harlow
Dir Lab: Cathy Yoshimura
Dir Rad: Ralph Corbino
Dir Rx: Mark Holdych

D-U-N-S 06-194-9058
GOOD SAMARITAN HOSPITAL
600 Witmer St, Los Angeles, CA 90017-2308
Tel (213) 977-2121 Founded/Ownrshp 1887
Sales 320.8MM EMP 1
SIC 8062 General medical & surgical hospitals
Pr: Andrew Leeka
Chf OB: Stephen N Pine
CFO: Alan Ino
VP: Sammy Feuerlicht
VP: Susan Harlow
VP: Dan McLaughlin
Dir Inf Cn: Joan Finney
Dir Case M: Kelvin Matute
Dir Lab: Kathy Yoshimura
Dir Rad: Sukhvinder Puri
Dir Rx: Mark Holdych
Dir Env Sv: Jahn Butler

D-U-N-S 06-398-5261
GOOD SAMARITAN HOSPITAL
(Suby of SAMARITAN HEALTH PARTNERS) ★
2222 Philadelphia Dr, Dayton, OH 45406-1891
Tel (937) 278-2612 Founded/Ownrshp 1932
Sales 321.5MM EMP 2,000
SIC 8062 Hospital, affiliated with AMA residency
Pr: Mark S Shaker
*CFO: Scott Schelton
Dir Rad: Roger Staton
IT Man: Lisa Smith
Ansthlgy: Thaiduc T Nguyen
Doctor: Eric Fryxell
Doctor: Denise Grove
Pharmcst: Kirk Nielsen

D-U-N-S 08-250-5900
GOOD SAMARITAN HOSPITAL
(Suby of ALLENMORE HOSPITAL) ★
401 15th Ave Se, Puyallup, WA 98372-3795
Tel (253) 697-4000 Founded/Ownrshp 2006
Sales 418.4MM[E] EMP 1,600
SIC 8062 8069 General medical & surgical hospitals; Substance abuse hospitals
Pr: Diane Cecchetini
*Pr: Bishop David Wold
CFO: Tim Maurice
*VP: Marcus S Gaspard
Ex Dir: Marianne Bastin
Mktg Dir: Mike Peterson
Podiatrist: Michael J Frazier
Podiatrist: William Hahn

D-U-N-S 12-152-1665
GOOD SAMARITAN HOSPITAL
PARENT ASSISTANCE NETWORK
4503 2nd Ave Ste 209, Kearney, NE 68847-2432
Tel (308) 865-2009 Founded/Ownrshp 2002
Sales 227.7MM EMP 1
SIC 8062 General medical & surgical hospitals
Ch: Sheila Meyer
IT Man: Lesley Lafile

D-U-N-S 03-803-2756
GOOD SAMARITAN HOSPITAL AUXILIARY
1225 Wilshire Blvd, Los Angeles, CA 90017-1901
Tel (213) 977-2121 Founded/Ownrshp 2001
Sales 309.6MM EMP 1,500
Accts Deloitte Tax Llp Costa Mesa
SIC 8011 Medical centers
CEO: Andrew Leeka
COO: Claus Von Zychlin
VP: Donna Nienaber
Dir Rad: Mike Gombar

D-U-N-S 05-361-5548
GOOD SAMARITAN HOSPITAL CORVALLIS
GOOD SMARITAN REGIONAL MED CTR
3600 Nw Samaritan Dr, Corvallis, OR 97330-3700
Tel (541) 757-5111 Founded/Ownrshp 1986
Sales 356.5MM EMP 900
SIC 8062 General medical & surgical hospitals
Pr: Becky Rose
COO: Steven Jasperson
*VP: Ronald S Stevens
*Prin: Larry Mullins
Off Mgr: Don Fucillo
Dir IT: Manuel Amaez
Opers Mgr: Ron Schreiner

D-U-N-S 07-800-5824
GOOD SAMARITAN HOSPITAL KEARNEY NEBRASKA
VOLUNTEER SERVICES OF GOOD SAM
10 E 31st St, Kearney, NE 68847-2908
Tel (308) 865-7997 Founded/Ownrshp 1923
Sales 238.0MM EMP 1,300
Accts Catholic Health Initiatives E
SIC 8062 General medical & surgical hospitals
*Pr: Mike Schnieders
CFO: Bill Luke
*VP: Lisa Webb
Dir Lab: Marilyn Bicak
Comm Dir: Marsha Wilkerson
CIO: Joe Barfield
IT Man: Stacy John
Mktg Dir: Robert Smoot
Pathlgst: Steve Baker
Doctor: Beth Ernst
HC Dir: Heather Lockhart

D-U-N-S 14-754-0298
■ **GOOD SAMARITAN HOSPITAL LP**
(Suby of HOSPITAL COPORATION OF AMERICA) ★
2425 Samaritan Dr, San Jose, CA 95124-3985
Tel (408) 559-2011 Founded/Ownrshp 1996
Sales 209.6MM[E] EMP 1,800
SIC 8062 General medical & surgical hospitals
CEO: Paul Beaupre
V Ch: Sandra Hickok
COO: Jordan Herget
CFO: Lana Arad
CFO: Darrel Neuenschwander
Ofcr: Paul Deaupre
VP: Lyn Garrett
VP: Frank Hirano
VP: Jim Lamar
Chf Nrs Of: Dian Adams
Genl Mgr: Venktesh Shukla

D-U-N-S 06-801-8175
GOOD SAMARITAN HOSPITAL MEDICAL CENTER
(Suby of CATHOLIC HLTH SVCS LONG ISLAND) ★
1000 Montauk Hwy, West Islip, NY 11795-4927
Tel (631) 376-3000 Founded/Ownrshp 1997
Sales 505.1MM EMP 3,774
SIC 8062 8051 8092 General medical & surgical hospitals; Skilled nursing care facilities; Kidney dialysis centers
Ex VP: Thomas Ockers
Dir Recs: Paul Gaudio
*COO: Joseph Loiacono
*Chf Mktg O: Donald Teplitz
Ofcr: Charles Bov
*Assoc VP: Richard Bie
*Assoc VP: Ralph Corbino
*Assoc VP: Michele Dykstra
*Assoc VP: Christine Stehlik
*Sr VP: Gara Edelstein
*Sr VP: Stephen Trapan
*VP: Vincent Angeloro
*VP: Gail Donheiser

D-U-N-S 17-492-1338
GOOD SAMARITAN HOSPITAL OF CINCINNATI
CHI
(Suby of CHI) ★
375 Dixmyth Ave, Cincinnati, OH 45220-2489
Tel (513) 569-6251 Founded/Ownrshp 1852
Sales 578.9MM EMP 3,452
Accts Bkd Llp Cincinnati Oh
SIC 8062 8082 8011 General medical & surgical hospitals; Home health care services; Offices & clinics of medical doctors
Pr: John S Prout
*COO: Gerald Oliphant
*CFO: Craig Rucker
*Ch: Robert L Walker
*Sr VP: John R Robinson
Genl Mgr: Susan Murray
Obsttrcn: Jack B Basil

D-U-N-S 83-026-1173
GOOD SAMARITAN HOSPITAL OF LEBANON PENNSYLVANIA
WELLSPAN GOOD SAMARITAN HOSP
(Suby of YORK HOSPITAL) ★
252 S 4th St, Lebanon, PA 17042-6111
Tel (717) 270-7500 Founded/Ownrshp 2009
Sales 178.2MM EMP 99[E]
Accts Grant Thornton Llp Philadelph
SIC 8062 General medical & surgical hospitals
CEO: Robert J Longo
COO: Kimberly Feeman
Ex Dir: Mary Reppert
Dir Sec: Larry Phillips
CIO: Louis Eaglehouse
QA Dir: Vivian Mayopoulos
Sfty Dirs: Terrence Brandt
VP Mktg: William Mulligan
Pathlgst: Peter Phillips
Pathlgst: Jack Sees
Doctor: Daria Kovarikova

D-U-N-S 07-494-5320 IMP
GOOD SAMARITAN HOSPITAL OF MD INC
MEDSTAR HEALTH VNA
(Suby of MEDSTAR HEALTH VNA) ★
5601 Loch Raven Blvd, Baltimore, MD 21239-2945
Tel (443) 444-3780 Founded/Ownrshp 1968
Sales 325.0MM EMP 2,146
Accts Kpmg Llp Baltimore Maryland
SIC 8062 8741 General medical & surgical hospitals; Management services
Pr: Jeffrey A Matton
CFO: Deana Stout
Ch: Anthony Read
VP: Laura Odonnell
Off Mgr: Carol Grap
Off Mgr: Mary A Salango
MIS Dir: Mike Hebronk
Surgeon: Steve Petersen

GOOD SAMARITAN MEDICAL CENTER
See TENET GOOD SAMARITAN HOSPITAL INC

D-U-N-S 14-909-7821
GOOD SAMARITAN MEDICAL CENTER FOUNDATION
200 Exempla Cir, Lafayette, CO 80026-3370
Tel (303) 689-4000 Founded/Ownrshp 2004
Sales 1.0MM EMP 1,200
Accts Taylor Roth And Company Pllc
SIC 8062 General medical & surgical hospitals
CEO: Dave Ham
VP: Bert Torres
Doctor: Ellina Liptsen
HC Dir: Carol Gorman

D-U-N-S 03-071-1824
■ **GOOD SAMARITAN NURSING HOME**
(Suby of DIVERSICARE HEALTHCARE SERVICES INC) ★
403 W Main St, Cole Camp, MO 65325-1144
Tel (660) 668-4515 Founded/Ownrshp 1967
Sales 267.8MM EMP 75
SIC 8052 Intermediate care facilities
Nrsg Dir: Kyle Luetjen

D-U-N-S 06-978-1896
GOOD SAMARITAN PHYSICIAN SERVICES
HYMAN KAPLAN PAVILLION
(Suby of GOOD SAMARITAN HEALTH SERVICES FOUNDATION) ★
259 S 4th St, Lebanon, PA 17042-6112
Tel (717) 270-7500 Founded/Ownrshp 1889
Sales 171.2M[E] EMP 1,450
SIC 8062 General medical & surgical hospitals
Pr: Robert J Longo
CFO: Bill Luke
VP: Mikki Clancy
VP Bus Dev: Sammy Feuerlicht
Dir Lab: Kathy Yoshimura
Dir Sec: William Fagan
Obsttrcn: Roger Hine

D-U-N-S 79-867-5690
GOOD SAMARITAN REGIONAL HEALTH CENTER
SSM HEALTH GOOD SAMARITAN HOSP
(Suby of SSM HEALTH CARE CORP) ★
1 Good Samaritan Way, Mount Vernon, IL 62864-2402
Tel (618) 242-4600 Founded/Ownrshp 1988
Sales 132.5MM EMP 900
SIC 8062 General medical & surgical hospitals
Pr: Michael Warren
Ex VP: William Jennings
Dir Risk M: Jeralee Sargent
Dir Lab: Matt Livengood

D-U-N-S 01-562-4091
GOOD SAMARITAN REGIONAL MEDICAL CENTER
255 Lafayette Ave, Suffern, NY 10901-4812
Tel (845) 368-5000 Founded/Ownrshp 1996
Sales 286.9MM EMP 1,600
SIC 8062 General medical & surgical hospitals
CEO: Philip Patterson
*CEO: Mary Leahy
*CEO: Dominick Stanzione
CFO: Stephen Majetich
CFO: Anthony Puorro
*Sr VP: Jeff Reilly

GOOD SHEPHERD COMMUNITIES
See GOOD SHEPHERD LUTHERAN HOME OF WEST

D-U-N-S 96-254-5443
GOOD SHEPHERD HEALTH SYSTEM INC
700 E Marshall Ave, Longview, TX 75601-5580
Tel (888) 784-4747 Founded/Ownrshp 1984
Sales 170.9MM[E] EMP 2,900[E]
SIC 8062 General medical & surgical hospitals
Pr: Kenneth Cunningham
*CFO: Pat Keel
Ofcr: Christopher Thomsett
VP: Keith Creel
Dir Rx: Brad Osburg
Ex Dir: Kari Pickering
CIO: Chris Blakemore
CTO: Scott Mix
CTO: Deborah Terry
Dir IT: Kevin Covert

D-U-N-S 07-736-8967
GOOD SHEPHERD LUTHERAN HOME OF WEST
GOOD SHEPHERD COMMUNITIES
119 N Main St, Porterville, CA 93257-3713
Tel (559) 791-2000 Founded/Ownrshp 1952
Sales 15.6MM[E] EMP 1,100[E]
SIC 8361 Residential care for the handicapped
CEO: David Geske

GOOD SHEPHERD MEDICAL CENTER
See SHEPHERD GOOD HOSPITAL INC

D-U-N-S 83-591-8798
GOOD SHEPHERD REHABILITATION HOSPITAL INC
850 S 5th St, Allentown, PA 18103-3308
Tel (610) 776-3100 Founded/Ownrshp 1909
Sales 87.3MM EMP 675
Accts Baker Tilly Virchow Krause Llp
SIC 8361 8051 8093 8069 Rehabilitation center, residential: health care incidental; Skilled nursing care facilities; Specialty outpatient clinics; Specialty hospitals, except psychiatric
Pr: John Kristel
Sr VP: Anthony Bongiovanni
Exec: Jaime Broesicke
Chf Nrs Of: Samuel Miranda
Rgnl Mgr: Dennis Duerring
Site Mgr: Donna Kelley
HC Dir: Antoinette Telfort

D-U-N-S 07-327-4292
GOOD SHEPHERD SERVICES
305 7th Ave Fl 9, New York, NY 10001-6161
Tel (212) 243-7070 Founded/Ownrshp 1947
Sales 86.2MM EMP 1,200
Accts Marks Paneth Llp New York Ny
SIC 8322 General counseling services

CEO: James J Sullivan
**Pr:* Paulette Lomonaco
CFO: Greghan Fischer
**VP:* Adel Ayad
**Prin:* David A Barr
**Prin:* Denise M Kelly
**Prin:* Sheila Rule
Off Mgr: Kenya Fields
Pgrm Dir: Catherine Hodes
Pgrm Dir: Allison Micali
Pgrm Dir: Naida Pastrana

GOOD SMARITAN REGIONAL MED CTR
See GOOD SAMARITAN HOSPITAL CORVALLIS

D-U-N-S 03-655-3550
GOODTECHNOLOGY CORP
(*Suby of* BLACKBERRY LIMITED)
430 N Mary Ave Ste 200, Sunnyvale, CA 94085-2923
Tel (408) 212-7500 *Founded/Ownrshp* 2014
Sales 160.3MM *EMP* 799
SIC 7371 7382 Computer software development & applications; Custom computer programming services; Protective devices, security
Pr: Christy Wyatt
**CFO:* Ronald J Fior
Sr VP: Cheryln Chin
Sr VP: Fr D Ric ARI S
VP: Aira Cook
Mng Dir: Steve Macmillan
Snr Sftwr: Lisa Kwan
Snr Ntwrk: Jeff Newman
**CIO:* Chet Mandair
CTO: Nicholas B Van Someren
Sftwr Eng: Gautam Pulla

GOOD TIDINGS
See COMMERCE LLC

D-U-N-S 01-631-6046 IMP/EXP
GOOD TIMES USA LLC
8408 Temple Terrace Hwy, Tampa, FL 33637-5808
Tel (813) 621-8702 *Founded/Ownrshp* 2008
Sales 100.0MM *EMP* 55
Accts Warren Averett Llc Tampa Fl
SIC 5194 Tobacco & tobacco products
Pr: Joseph Tabshe
CFO: Ralph Del Rio
**VP:* Gregory Dana
Genl Mgr: Sam Saleh
VP Sls: Tim Allmond
Counsel: Tobias Tedrowe

GOOD2GO AUTO INSURANCE
See AMERICAN INDEPENDENT INSURANCE CO INC

D-U-N-S 17-423-1654
GOOD360
GIFTS IN KIND
675 N Washington St # 330, Alexandria, VA 22314-1939
Tel (703) 836-2121 *Founded/Ownrshp* 1984
Sales 314.5MM *EMP* 36[E]
Accts Bdo Usa Llp Bethesda Md
SIC 8399 Community development groups
Pr: Cindy Hallberlin
Mng Pt: Bob Schwartz
Ch Bd: Carly Fiorina
COO: Don Miller
CFO: Gerald Borenstein
CFO: David Maland
Ofcr: Elie Hollander
VP: Kevin Hagan
VP: Melissa Trumpower
Exec: Vicki Dorsey
Mktg Mgr: Morgan Greene
Board of Directors: Maria Martinez

D-U-N-S 18-973-7146
GOODE PARTNERS LLC
767 3rd Ave Fl 22, New York, NY 10017-9007
Tel (646) 722-9450 *Founded/Ownrshp* 2005
Sales 120.0MM[E] *EMP* 371[E]
SIC 6282 Investment advice
**CFO:* Paula Semelmacher
Genl Couns: Jason Berger

D-U-N-S 00-794-3996 IMP/EXP
GOODFELLOW BROS INC (WA)
1407 Walla Walla Ave, Wenatchee, WA 98801-1530
Tel (509) 667-9095 *Founded/Ownrshp* 1921
Sales 203.0MM *EMP* 1,050
Accts Moss Adams Llp Spokane Washi
SIC 1611 General contractor, highway & street construction
Pr: Chad S Goodfellow
**Treas:* Daniel Reisenauer
Ex VP: Richard Dunn
**VP:* Daniel Goodfellow

D-U-N-S 00-890-4260 IMP
GOODIN CO
2700 N 2nd St, Minneapolis, MN 55411-1679
Tel (612) 588-7811 *Founded/Ownrshp* 1937
Sales 179.3MM *EMP* 405
Accts Rsm Us Llp Minneapolis Minne
SIC 5074 5075 Pipes & fittings, plastic; Boilers, hot water heating; Radiators & parts, except electric; Furnaces, warm air; Air conditioning equipment, except room units
CEO: Greg Skagerberg
**Pr:* Steven Kelly
**CFO:* Mike Grunklee
**VP:* Joel Skagerberg
Brnch Mgr: Dale Bley
Brnch Mgr: Barry Jenson
Brnch Mgr: Bob Petersen
Brnch Mgr: Lennie Roth
Brnch Mgr: Jeff Trouten
Sls Mgr: Randy Kawczynski
Sls Mgr: Todd Killian

D-U-N-S 00-192-6922 IMP/EXP
GOODMAN DISTRIBUTION INC (NC)
(*Suby of* GOODMAN GLOBAL HOLDINGS INC) ★
1426 N 8th Ave, Ocala, FL 34470-4250
Tel (352) 620-2727 *Founded/Ownrshp* 1955
Sales 197.9MM[E] *EMP* 450
SIC 5075 Warm air heating & air conditioning
CEO: David L Swift
**CEO:* Charles Carroll
**CFO:* Larry Blackburn
**VP:* Peter Alexander

D-U-N-S 00-634-1002 IMP
GOODMAN FOOD PRODUCTS INC (CA)
DON LEE FARMS
200 E Beach Ave Fl 1, Inglewood, CA 90302-3404
Tel (310) 674-3180 *Founded/Ownrshp* 1982
Sales 89.6MM[E] *EMP* 256
SIC 2038 Frozen specialties
CEO: Donald Goodman
CFO: Barry Drinkward
Sr VP: Jean Harris
Sfty Mgr: Gerber Alvarado

D-U-N-S 13-346-8210 IMP
GOODMAN GLOBAL HOLDINGS INC
(*Suby of* GOODMAN GLOBAL INC) ★
5151 San Felipe St # 500, Houston, TX 77056-3607
Tel (713) 861-2500 *Founded/Ownrshp* 2004
Sales 717.2MM[E] *EMP* 4,401
SIC 3585 3564 Air conditioning equipment, complete; Heating equipment, complete; Heating & air conditioning combination units; Blowers & fans
Pr: Charles A Carroll
**CFO:* Lawrence M Blackburn
**Treas:* Mark M Dolan
**Ex VP:* Ben D Campbell
**Ex VP:* Donald R King

D-U-N-S 62-389-4990 IMP
GOODMAN GLOBAL INC
(*Suby of* CHILL HOLDINGS INC) ★
5151 San Felipe St # 500, Houston, TX 77056-3607
Tel (713) 861-2500 *Founded/Ownrshp* 2008
Sales 2.5MMM[E] *EMP* 8,732
SIC 3585 3564 Air conditioning equipment, complete; Heating equipment, complete; Heating & air conditioning combination units; Blowers & fans
Pr: David L Swift
**CFO:* Lawrence M Blackburn
Ex VP: Ben D Campbell
Sr VP: Terrance M Smith
Sr VP: William H Topper
VP: Richard J Baenski
IT Man: Robert Horton
Counsel: Michael Pancherz

D-U-N-S 01-080-3013 IMP/EXP
GOODMAN MANUFACTURING CO LP
(*Suby of* GOODMAN GLOBAL INC) ★
5151 San Felipe St # 500, Houston, TX 77056-3650
Tel (877) 254-4729 *Founded/Ownrshp* 2004
Sales 1.8MMM[E] *EMP* 4,000
Accts Ernst & Young Llp Houston Te
SIC 3585 Air conditioning units, complete: domestic or industrial; Heating equipment, complete; Parts for heating, cooling & refrigerating equipment
CEO: Takeshi Ebisu
**Pt:* Lawrence Blackburn
Pr: Jeffrey Ellingham
**Pr:* David Swift
CFO: Larry B Urn
VP: Dave Brown
VP: Mike Froman
VP: Bruce Kilkowski
VP: Billy Shipley
Ex Dir: Sandra Van De Walle
Ex Dir: Marc Marino

D-U-N-S 17-097-7552
GOODMAN NETWORKS INC
2801 Network Blvd Ste 300, Frisco, TX 75034-1881
Tel (972) 406-9692 *Founded/Ownrshp* 2000
Sales 1.2MMM *EMP* 3,925[E]
Accts Kpmg Llp Dallas Texas
SIC 4899 Communication signal enhancement network system; Data communication services
Pr: Ron B Hill
Pr: Cari Shyiak
COO: Ernest J Carey
CFO: Joy L Brawner
CFO: Geoffrey Miller
Ex VP: Steve Bell
Ex VP: Caren Gates
Ex VP: Jimmy Hulett
Ex VP: Ajay Ramaswami
Ex VP: Scott Willis
VP: Craig Freeman
VP: Joseph Hart
VP: Shakeeb Mir
VP: Ralf Musmann

D-U-N-S 03-588-7355
GOODMANS INC
GOODMAN'S INTERIOR STRUCTURES
1400 E Indian School Rd, Phoenix, AZ 85014-4983
Tel (602) 263-1110 *Founded/Ownrshp* 1968
Sales 86.5MM[E] *EMP* 250
SIC 5712 7389 Office furniture; Interior design services
CEO: Adam Goodman
COO: Clark REA
CFO: Jen Scrivner
VP: Tracy Pena
VP: Jaqui Sabo
Genl Mgr: Rachel Baulch
CTO: Steve Miller
Sls&Mrk Ex: Rachel Dahl

GOODMAN'S INTERIOR STRUCTURES
See GOODMANS INC

GOODRICH
See TRIUMPH ENGINE CONTROL SYSTEMS LLC

GOODRICH AEROSTRUCTURES GROUP
See ROHR INC

GOODRICH ARCFT WHEELS & BRAKES
See GOODRICH CORP

GOODRICH CORPORATION
See SIMMONDS PRECISION PRODUCTS INC

D-U-N-S 00-446-7452 IMP/EXP
■ **GOODRICH CORP** (NY)
GOODRICH ARCFT WHEELS & BRAKES
(*Suby of* UNITED TECHNOLOGIES CORP) ★
4 Coliseum Ctr 2730 W, Charlotte, NC 28217
Tel (704) 423-7000 *Founded/Ownrshp* 1912, 2012
Sales 7.9MMM[E] *EMP* 28,000
SIC 7372 3724 3728 Prepackaged software; Aircraft engines & engine parts; Aircraft parts & equipment
Pr: David Gitlin
**Pr:* Greg Watson
COO: Janet Hoskin
COO: Thann Lim
COO: Jerry Witowski
CFO: William Dries
**CFO:* Scott E Kuechle
CFO: Thomas Snead
**Treas:* Richard S Caswell
Bd of Dir: Sally O'Neil
Bd of Dir: Mike Rosado
Chf Mktg O: John Sims
Chf Mktg O: James Vieregg
**Sr VP:* Jennifer Pollino
VP: Cynthia M Egnotovich
VP: William G Stiehl
Dir Bus: John Ardussi
Dir Bus: Sebastian Pierzchlewicz
Dir Bus: Alec Searle
Dir Bus: Randy Welp

D-U-N-S 60-344-7744
■ **GOODRICH CORP**
UTC AEROSPACE SYSTEMS
(*Suby of* GOODRICH ARCFT WHEELS & BRAKES) ★
14300 Judicial Rd, Burnsville, MN 55306-4890
Tel (952) 892-4000 *Founded/Ownrshp* 1934
Sales 138.0MM[E] *EMP* 150[E]
SIC 5088

D-U-N-S 60-938-4789
GOODRICH QUALITY THEATERS INC
31 Island Way Apt 606, Clearwater Beach, FL 33767-2206
Tel (616) 698-7733 *Founded/Ownrshp* 1989
Sales 79.6MM[E] *EMP* 1,200
Accts Plante & Moran Pllc Grand Ra
SIC 7832 Motion picture theaters, except drive-in
Pr: Robert Emmett Goodrich
Mng Pt: Kevin Morgan
COO: Martin Betz
CFO: Sue Howard
**CFO:* Ross Pettinga
Area Mgr: Heath Thomas
Web Dev: Chris Rannow
Opers Mgr: Tony Knight

GOODRICH SENSORS AND INTEGRATE
See ATLANTIC INERTIAL SYSTEMS INC

GOODSPEED DISTRIBUTING
See R E GOODSPEED AND SONS DISTRIBUTING INC

D-U-N-S 15-203-1733
GOODWATER HEALTH CENTER CARE LLC
16 Jones Hill Rd, Goodwater, AL 35072-9463
Tel (256) 839-6711 *Founded/Ownrshp* 2004
Sales 196.2MM *EMP* 75
SIC 8059 Nursing & personal care

GOODWILL INDS NEW BRAUNFELS
See GOODWILL INDUSTRIES OF SAN ANTONIO

GOODWILL INDUSTRIES
See GOODWILL OF CENTRAL AND COASTAL VIRGINIA INC

D-U-N-S 06-282-3638
GOODWILL INDUSTRIES INC
EASTER SEAL MINNESOTA
553 Fairview Ave N, Saint Paul, MN 55104-3080
Tel (651) 379-5800 *Founded/Ownrshp* 1990
Sales 57.7MM *EMP* 22,000
Accts Eide Bailly Llp Minneapolis
SIC 4953 8331 8322 5932 4226 Recycling, waste materials; Job training services; Family service agency; Used merchandise stores; Special warehousing & storage
Pr: Michael Wirth-Davis
Dir Vol: Sara Triplett
CFO: Jason Seifert
Bd of Dir: John Bergstrom
Ofcr: Willen Korkowski
Ofcr: Kathryn Ross
VP: Carmen B Lemay
VP: Sheila Olson
Prgrm Mgr: Andy Sagvold
Dist Mgr: Scott Genke
Genl Mgr: Debra French

D-U-N-S 07-246-0678
GOODWILL INDUSTRIES OF CENTRAL ARIZONA FOUNDATION INC
GOODWILL OF CENTRAL ARIZONA
2626 W Beryl Ave, Phoenix, AZ 85021-1668
Tel (602) 535-4000 *Founded/Ownrshp* 1947
Sales 118.8MM *EMP* 2,100
Accts Mayer Hoffman Mccann Pc Phoe
SIC 8331 Vocational rehabilitation agency
Pr: James Teter
Pr: Tim Oneal
Pr: Richmond J Vincent
CFO: Tanya Perry
Exec: Valerie Brown
CIO: Neal Goodrich
Snr Mgr: Rhonda Brande
Board of Directors: Steve Kedzior

D-U-N-S 07-322-8728
GOODWILL INDUSTRIES OF CENTRAL FLORIDA INC
7531 S Orange Blossom Trl, Orlando, FL 32809-6901
Tel (407) 857-0659 *Founded/Ownrshp* 1959
Sales 52.9MM *EMP* 1,200
SIC 8331 8741 Skill training center; Management services
Ch Bd: Laurence Hames
**Pr:* William G Oakley
COO: Richard Coleman
**CFO:* Curtis Ramsey
**Ch:* Maximiano Brito
**Treas:* Michael Clary
Bd of Dir: Michael Smith
VP: Ken Moler
IT Man: Todd Russell
Trfc Dir: Chris Hughes
Sfty Mgr: Kate Pile

D-U-N-S 00-693-8278 IMP
GOODWILL INDUSTRIES OF CENTRAL INDIANA INC
1635 W Michigan St, Indianapolis, IN 46222-3852
Tel (317) 564-4313 *Founded/Ownrshp* 1930
Sales 128.9MM *EMP* 1,200
Accts Greenwalt Cpas Inc Indianap
SIC 5932 4783 8331 4953 Clothing, secondhand; Home furnishings, secondhand; Packing & crating; Job training services; Recycling, waste materials
Pr: James M McClelland
**Ch Bd:* Perry Griffith
**Ch Bd:* Fred C Tucker III
**Treas:* Jean Wojtowicz
VP: Betsy Delgado
VP: Ken File
VP: Kyle Lanham
**VP:* Daniel J Riley
VP: Aaron Roberts
VP: Eric Schlegel
Dir Risk M: Matthew Pearsey

D-U-N-S 08-847-5835 IMP
GOODWILL INDUSTRIES OF CENTRAL TEXAS
1015 Norwood Park Blvd, Austin, TX 78753-6608
Tel (512) 637-7100 *Founded/Ownrshp* 1958
Sales 61.8MM *EMP* 1,200
Accts Weaver And Tidwell Llp San An
SIC 8331 Vocational rehabilitation agency; Vocational training agency
Pr: Gerald L Davis
CFO: David Foster
VP: Frank Holland
VP: Roberta Schwartz
VP: Matt Williams
Dir Risk M: Charles Briscoe
Genl Mgr: Jenny Fritz
Opers Mgr: Pam Collier

D-U-N-S 05-095-7372
GOODWILL INDUSTRIES OF COLUMBIA WILLAMETTE
1943 Se 6th Ave, Portland, OR 97214-4508
Tel (503) 238-6100 *Founded/Ownrshp* 1978
Sales 135.4MM *EMP* 1,950
Accts Jarrard Seibert Pollard & Co L
SIC 8331 Sheltered workshop; Vocational training agency
Pr: John Paetel
CFO: Richard Knox
**VP:* Steve Palmer
Store Mgr: Mike White
CTO: Carl Trachenberg
Advt Mgr: Gilbert Vizon

D-U-N-S 08-195-7110
GOODWILL INDUSTRIES OF DENVER
6850 Federal Blvd, Denver, CO 80221-2628
Tel (303) 650-7700 *Founded/Ownrshp* 1918
Sales 66.3MM *EMP* 1,300
Accts Eks&H Lllp Denver Co
SIC 8399 Council for social agency
CEO: Stuart Davie
**CFO:* Mike Pritchard
**VP:* Jeff Ayers
**VP:* Randy Dohne
VP: Bob Schow
**VP:* Robert Tallmadge
**Ex Dir:* Jesse Wolff

D-U-N-S 07-853-4765 IMP
GOODWILL INDUSTRIES OF GREATER NEW YORK INC
421 27th Ave, Astoria, NY 11102-4175
Tel (718) 728-5400 *Founded/Ownrshp* 1920
Sales 115.1MM *EMP* 2,000
Accts Marks Paneth Llp New York Ny
SIC 8331 Vocational rehabilitation agency; Work experience center
CEO: William Foriester
**Treas:* Henry Gooss
Ofcr: Joan Meinking
Sr VP: Karen Means
**VP:* Gillian Attfield
VP: Linda Turner
Genl Mgr: William Staples
Pgrm Dir: Gloria Choi

D-U-N-S 06-073-6816
GOODWILL INDUSTRIES OF MIDDLE TENNESSEE INC (TN)
1015 Herman St, Nashville, TN 37208-3143
Tel (615) 742-4151 *Founded/Ownrshp* 1957
Sales 77.0MM *EMP* 2,200
SIC 8641

D-U-N-S 07-384-9044
GOODWILL INDUSTRIES OF NORTH CENTRAL WISCONSIN INC
1800 Appleton Rd, Menasha, WI 54952-1195
Tel (920) 731-6601 *Founded/Ownrshp* 1971
Sales 95.1MM *EMP* 1,400
SIC 5932 7389 8331 Used merchandise stores; Packaging & labeling services; Job training & vocational rehabilitation services
Pr: Robert A Pedersen
CIO: Nancy Coonen

D-U-N-S 07-938-3378
GOODWILL INDUSTRIES OF NORTH GEORGIA INC
2201 Lawrenceville Hwy, Decatur, GA 30033-3128
Tel (404) 420-9914 *Founded/Ownrshp* 1925
Sales 13.0MM *EMP* 1,650
SIC 8331

D-U-N-S 07-746-1432 IMP/EXP
GOODWILL INDUSTRIES OF NORTHERN NEW ENGLAND
75 Washington Ave Ste 300, Portland, ME 04101-2665
Tel (207) 774-6323 *Founded/Ownrshp* 1933
Sales 73.7MM *EMP* 1,200
Accts Berry Dunn Mcneil & Pa Ker Lc
SIC 8331 2392 Vocational rehabilitation agency; Household furnishings
CEO: Anne Roosevelt
COO: David Crossman
CFO: Steve Tselikis
Ofcr: Lynne Gaudette
VP: James Greene
Dir Case M: Larry Strout
Dir Sec: Craig Grugel
Genl Mgr: Rich Cantz
IT Man: David Wong

D-U-N-S 00-323-1784
GOODWILL INDUSTRIES OF NORTHWEST NORTH CAROLINA INC (NC)
2701 University Pkwy, Winston Salem, NC 27105-4223
Tel (336) 724-3621 *Founded/Ownrshp* 1926
Sales 83.1MM *EMP* 1,100
Accts Dixon Hughes Goodman Llp Wins
SIC 5932 8331 Used merchandise stores; Vocational rehabilitation agency
Ch: Francine Madrey
* *CEO:* Art Gibel
* *CFO:* Curtis Bland
* *Ch:* Sherry Polonsky
* *Sec:* Rip Ford
* *VP:* Dan Bradshaw
* *VP:* Sherry Carpenter
* *VP:* John Cunningham

D-U-N-S 07-815-6551
GOODWILL INDUSTRIES OF ORANGE COUNTY CALIFORNIA
410 N Fairview St, Santa Ana, CA 92703-3412
Tel (714) 547-6308 *Founded/Ownrshp* 1926
Sales 69.6MM *EMP* 1,200
Accts Kushner Smith Joanou & Gregson
SIC 5932 Used merchandise stores
CEO: Steven M Coyne
* *COO:* Kim Seebach
* *V Ch Bd:* Cheryl Barrett
* *VP:* Corrine Allen
* *VP:* Joe Burke
* *VP:* Kathy Copeland
Store Mgr: Griffin Figueroa
Sls&Mrk Ex: Marlena Jiminez

D-U-N-S 05-757-9807
GOODWILL INDUSTRIES OF SAN ANTONIO
GOODWILL INDS NEW BRAUNFELS
406 W Commerce St, San Antonio, TX 78207-3102
Tel (210) 924-8581 *Founded/Ownrshp* 1946
Sales 36.4MM *EMP* 1,024
Accts Bdo Usa Llp
SIC 8331 Vocational rehabilitation agency
Pr: Marla Jackson
COO: Jim Meehan
* *CFO:* Stephanie Parker
Bd of Dir: Laura Hernandez
VP: Patti Black
* *VP:* Lisa Brunsvold
VP: Julian Cruz
* *VP:* Greg Eads
* *VP:* Donna Lazzari
* *VP:* Mark McKeever
Comm Man: Jason Meza

D-U-N-S 07-338-7045
GOODWILL INDUSTRIES OF SAN DIEGO COUNTY
3663 Rosecrans St, San Diego, CA 92110-3226
Tel (619) 225-2200 *Founded/Ownrshp* 1929
Sales 75.9MM *EMP* 1,350
Accts Cohn Reznick Llp San Diego C
SIC 8331 Job training & vocational rehabilitation services
Ex Dir: Michael S Rowan
Dir IT: Daniel Bossert
Info Man: Mia Reed

D-U-N-S 07-699-6065 IMP/EXP
GOODWILL INDUSTRIES OF SOUTH FLORIDA INC
2121 Nw 21st St, Miami, FL 33142-7382
Tel (305) 325-9114 *Founded/Ownrshp* 1959
Sales 92.8MM *EMP* 2,600
Accts Lb Morrison Brown Argiz & Farr
SIC 8331 Work experience center
CEO: David Landsberg
* *CFO:* Beatriz Anazco
* *Ch:* Joseph Lacher
* *Treas:* Ronald Murfin
Ofcr: Gary Chilson
* *Sr VP:* Bridget Pallango
* *VP:* Sherri Scyphers Hungate
VP: Lourdes Little
* *VP:* Manny Lopez
* *VP:* Diana Valencia
* *Prin:* Dennis Pastrana

D-U-N-S 02-338-9380
GOODWILL INDUSTRIES OF SOUTHEASTERN WISCONSIN INC
5400 S 60th St, Greendale, WI 53129-1404
Tel (414) 847-4200 *Founded/Ownrshp* 1919
Sales 282.7MM *EMP* 3,391
Accts Grant Thornton Llp Appleton
SIC 8331 7349 Job training & vocational rehabilitation services; Building cleaning service
Pr: Jacqueline Hallberg
Pr: Dwight Ferguson
* *VP:* Mike Boelter
* *VP:* Pat Boelter
* *VP:* Timothy Christian
* *VP:* Dan Depies
Mktg Dir: Laura Sanders

D-U-N-S 00-958-2305 IMP
GOODWILL INDUSTRIES OF SOUTHERN CALIFORNIA
342 N San Fernando Rd, Los Angeles, CA 90031-1730
Tel (323) 223-1211 *Founded/Ownrshp* 1919
Sales 206.1MM *EMP* 2,100
Accts Grant Thornton Llp Los Angele
SIC 5331 8331 Variety stores; Vocational rehabilitation agency; Vocational training agency; Community service employment training program
Pr: Craig Smith
VP: Forrest Callahan
VP: John Dell
VP: Donna Snell
VP: Craig Stone
VP: Ray Tellez
CTO: John Quach
MIS Dir: John Grant
QI Cn Mgr: Lowena Hawes
VP Mktg: Sasha Itzikman

D-U-N-S 15-282-3662 IMP/EXP
GOODWILL INDUSTRIES OF SOUTHWEST FLORIDA INC
5100 Tice St, Fort Myers, FL 33905-5203
Tel (239) 995-2106 *Founded/Ownrshp* 1966
Sales 182.0MM[E] *EMP* 875
Accts Barton Gonzalez & Myers Pa La
SIC 5932 5087 Building materials, secondhand; Vending machines & supplies
Pr: Rick Evanchyk
V Ch: Raymond T Holland
Treas: Sharlene Dozier
* *VP:* William J Barrett
VP: Carolyn Johnson
VP: Fred Richards
VP: Jennifer Swift
Dir Bus: Michael Cloutier
Dir Bus: Pat Smith
VP Opers: John Nadeau
Pr Dir: Kirsten O'Donnell

D-U-N-S 11-432-8123
GOODWILL INDUSTRIES-MANASOTA INC
GOODWILL MANASOTA
2705 51st Ave E, Bradenton, FL 34203-3937
Tel (941) 355-2721 *Founded/Ownrshp* 1981
Sales 68.2MM *EMP* 1,000
Accts Lb Chnstophersmithleonard Etal
SIC 8331 Work experience center
CEO: Donald L Roberts
* *VP:* Amy Confer
* *VP:* Peggy Roberts
CIO: Joel Clark
VP Opers: Mary England

D-U-N-S 05-519-5176
GOODWILL INDUSTRIES-SUNCOAST INC
10596 Gandy Blvd N, Saint Petersburg, FL 33702-1427
Tel (727) 523-1512 *Founded/Ownrshp* 1954
Sales 61.3MM *EMP* 1,334
Accts Gregory Sharer & Stuart Pa Sa
SIC 5932 8093 Used merchandise stores; Rehabilitation center, outpatient treatment
Ch Bd: Marty Gladysz
* *Pr:* Deborah A Passerini
* *Pr:* R Lee Waits
* *CFO:* Gary R Hebert
* *VP:* Jacqueline R Miller
VP: Paul Norris
VP: Debbie Passerini
* *VP:* Kris A Rawson
* *VP:* James D Williams
IT Man: Lee Bice

D-U-N-S 07-869-2463
GOODWILL INDUSTRIES-SUNCOAST INC
10596 Gandy Blvd N, Saint Petersburg, FL 33702-1427
Tel (727) 523-1512 *Founded/Ownrshp* 1966
Sales 67.1MM *EMP* 1,121
SIC 7361 5932 Chauffeur registry; Used merchandise stores
Pr: Deborah Tasserini
Pr: Deborah A Passerini

D-U-N-S 07-283-8212
GOODWILL KEYSTONE AREA
GKA
1150 Goodwill Dr, Harrisburg, PA 17101-2400
Tel (610) 777-7875 *Founded/Ownrshp* 1948
Sales 60.2MM *EMP* 3,000
Accts Brown Schultz Sheridan & Fritz
SIC 8331 Work experience center
CEO: Ronald Kratofil
* *Ch:* Anthony Byrne

GOODWILL MANASOTA
See GOODWILL INDUSTRIES-MANASOTA INC

D-U-N-S 09-844-1959
GOODWILL OF CENTRAL AND COASTAL VIRGINIA INC
GOODWILL INDUSTRIES
6301 Midlothian Tpke, Richmond, VA 23225-5707
Tel (804) 745-6300 *Founded/Ownrshp* 1923
Sales 59.4MM *EMP* 1,100
Accts Keiter Certified Public Accoun
SIC 8331 Job counseling
Pr: Charles D Layman
* *VP:* William Carlson
VP: Robert Hicks
VP: Elizabeth Rountree
VP: Michael Winckler
Genl Mgr: Christina Wallace
VP Mktg: Derby Brackett

GOODWILL OF CENTRAL ARIZONA
See GOODWILL INDUSTRIES OF CENTRAL ARIZONA FOUNDATION INC

D-U-N-S 79-227-6235
GOODWILL OF NORTH GEORGIA INC
2201 Lawrenceville Hwy, Decatur, GA 30033-3128
Tel (404) 420-9900 *Founded/Ownrshp* 2007
Sales 137.5MM *EMP* 1,650[E]
Accts Grant Thornton Llp Atlanta G
SIC 5932 8331 Used merchandise stores; Job training & vocational rehabilitation services
Pr: Raymond W Bishop
* *Ch Bd:* Nicholas Hoffman
VP: Cheryl Cornett
VP: Cheryl Cornett-Earley
VP: Paul Jordan
Prgrm Mgr: Shelonda Brown
Dir IT: Kunal Vyas
IT Man: Wilson Boyce
Advt Dir: Nicole McIntosh
Mktg Dir: Courtney Eskridge
Snr Mgr: Jonathan Wilson

D-U-N-S 07-498-1721
GOODWILL OF SOUTHWESTERN PENNSYLVANIA
118 52nd St, Pittsburgh, PA 15201-2593
Tel (412) 481-9005 *Founded/Ownrshp* 1965
Sales 53.0MM *EMP* 1,250
Accts Schneider Downs & Co Inc Pitt
SIC 8331 Vocational rehabilitation agency
Pr: Michael Smith
Pr: Kathy Hrala
CFO: Suzanne Hribik
Ch: Gary Claus
Treas: John Mills
VP: Patricia Trainer
Dir Risk M: Cathy Davis
Dir IT: Kirk Selenberg
IT Man: John Obritz

D-U-N-S 60-802-2976
GOODWILL RETAIL SERVICES INC
(*Suby of* GOODWILL INDUSTRIES OF SOUTHEASTERN WISCONSIN INC) ★
5400 S 60th St, Greendale, WI 53129-1404
Tel (414) 847-4200 *Founded/Ownrshp* 2001
Sales 138.4MM *EMP* 2,129
SIC 5651 4226 Family clothing stores; Household goods, warehousing
Pr: Jacqueline L Hallberg
* *Sr VP:* Vickie Volpano
VP: Robert Schneeberg

D-U-N-S 07-360-1718
GOODWILL SOUTHERN CALIFORNIA
INLAND CAREER CENTER
8120 Palm Ln, San Bernardino, CA 92410-4961
Tel (909) 885-3831 *Founded/Ownrshp* 1928
Sales 130.3MM *EMP* 200
SIC 5932 8331 Used merchandise stores; Job training & vocational rehabilitation services
Pr: Doug Barr
VP: John Kennedy

D-U-N-S 08-506-6157
GOODWIN COLLEGE INC
1 Riverside Dr, East Hartford, CT 06118-1837
Tel (860) 895-8000 *Founded/Ownrshp* 1981
Sales 106.4MM *EMP* 115
Accts Cohnreznick Llp Hartford Ct
SIC 8221 Colleges & universities
Ch: Maria Ellis
* *CFO:* Jerry Emlet
* *Treas:* Raymond Madorin
Ofcr: Monica Carbone
* *VP:* Bryant Harrell
VP: Brooke Penders
CTO: Steven Michaud
IT Man: Katie Shutts
Mktg Dir: Philp Moore
Pgrm Dir: Michael Murphy

D-U-N-S 07-171-5676 IMP
GOODWIN PROCTER LLP
100 Northern Ave, Boston, MA 02210-1980
Tel (617) 570-1000 *Founded/Ownrshp* 1996
Sales 256.0MM[E] *EMP* 1,324
SIC 8111 Corporate, partnership & business law; Patent, trademark & copyright law; Product liability law; Real estate law
Pt: Bob Bishop
Pt: Mark J Abate
Pt: April E Abele
Pt: John D Aldock
Pt: Gina M Atwood
Pt: Gregory S Bishop
Pt: Dave Cappillo
Pt: Mitzi Chang
Pt: Derek A Cohen
Pt: Byron W Cooper
Pt: William Davisson
Pt: Kevin Dennis
Pt: Michael S Devincenzo
Pt: Amber R Dolman
Pt: John Egan
Pt: Steven A Ellis
Pt: Brian A Fairchild
Pt: Stephen C Ferruolo
Pt: Kathy Fields
Pt: Thomas F Fitzpatrick
Pt: Terry D Garnett

GOODWRENCH SERVICE CENTER
See DEMONTROND BUICK CO

D-U-N-S 00-134-0876 IMP/EXP
■ **GOODY PRODUCTS INC** (DE)
(*Suby of* NEWELL BRANDS INC) ★
3 Glenlake Pkwy, Atlanta, GA 30328-3447
Tel (770) 418-7300 *Founded/Ownrshp* 1933
Sales 142.7MM[E] *EMP* 800
SIC 3999 3089 3069 Hair & hair-based products; Barrettes; Combs, except hard rubber; Combs, plastic; Cases, plastic; Boxes, plastic; Rubber hair accessories; Curlers, hair, rubber; Combs, hard rubber; Brushes, rubber
Pr: David Klatt
Ex VP: John Creel
VP: Andrea Carter
VP Sls: Ric L Kern Jr
VP Sls: Richard L Kern

GOODYEAR
See SUMITOMO RUBBER USA LLC

GOODYEAR COML TIRE & SVC CTRS
See WINGFOOT COMMERCIAL TIRE SYSTEMS LLC

D-U-N-S 00-446-7924
▲ **GOODYEAR TIRE & RUBBER CO** (OH)
200 E Innovation Way, Akron, OH 44316-0001
Tel (330) 796-2121 *Founded/Ownrshp* 1898
Sales 16.4MMM *EMP* 66,000
Accts Pricewaterhousecoopers Llp Cl
Tkr Sym GT *Exch* NGS
SIC 3011 3052 7534 7538 7539 5013 Tires & inner tubes; Inner tubes, all types; Pneumatic tires, all types; Tire & inner tube materials & related products; Rubber & plastics hose & beltings; Automobile hose, rubber; Rubber belting; Tire retreading & repair shops; Rebuilding & retreading tires; General automotive repair shops; Truck engine repair, except industrial; Automotive repair shops; Brake services; Shock absorber replacement; Tune-up service, automotive; Motor vehicle supplies & new parts; Automotive servicing equipment; Automotive supplies & parts
Ch Bd: Richard J Kramer
Pr: Chris Delaney
CFO: Laura K Thompson
Sr VP: John D Fish
Sr VP: Paul Fitzhenry
Sr VP: John T Lucas
Sr VP: Gregory L Smith
Sr VP: Joseph Zekoski
VP: Kathleen Geier
VP: Annie Granchi
VP: Patrick Hurley
VP: Sherry Neubert
VP: Richard J Noechel
VP: Marcelo Toscani
Board of Directors: Stephanie A Streeter, William J Conaty, Thomas H Weidemeyer, James A Firestone, Michael R Wessel, Werner Geissler, Peter S Hellman, Laurette T Koellner, W Alan McCollough, John E McGlade, Michael J Morell, Roderick A Palmore

D-U-N-S 06-090-2413 IMP
■ **GOOGLE INC**
(*Suby of* ALPHABET INC) ★
1600 Amphitheatre Pkwy, Mountain View, CA 94043-1351
Tel (650) 253-0000 *Founded/Ownrshp* 1998
Sales 74.9MMM[E] *EMP* 61,814
Accts Ernst & Young Llp San Jose
SIC 4813 7375 ; Information retrieval services; Data base information retrieval; On-line data base information retrieval
CEO: Sundar Pichai
CFO: Ruth M Porat
Sr VP: Nikesh Arora

D-U-N-S 62-260-4416 EXP
■ **GOOGLE INTERNATIONAL LLC**
(*Suby of* GOOGLE INC) ★
1600 Amphitheatre Pkwy, Mountain View, CA 94043-1351
Tel (650) 253-0000 *Founded/Ownrshp* 2002
Sales 347.8MM[E] *EMP* 449[E]
SIC 4813 7375 ; ; Information retrieval services
Ch Bd: Eric Schmidt
* *CEO:* Larry Page
* *Sr VP:* David C Drummond
Sftwr Eng: Chris Hayes
Pr Mgr: Michael Mayzel
Corp Couns: Andrew McLaughlin

D-U-N-S 02-225-1367
GOOSE CREEK CONSOLIDATED INDEPENDENT SCHOOL DISTRICT
4544 Interstate 10 E, Baytown, TX 77521-8881
Tel (281) 420-4800 *Founded/Ownrshp* 1919
Sales 242.0MM *EMP* 3,000
SIC 8211

D-U-N-S 14-607-0854
▲ **GOPRO INC**
3000 Clearview Way, San Mateo, CA 94402-3710
Tel (650) 332-7600 *Founded/Ownrshp* 2004
Sales 1.6MMM *EMP* 1,539
Tkr Sym GPRO *Exch* NGS
SIC 3861 7372 Photographic equipment & supplies; Prepackaged software
Ch Bd: Nicholas Woodman
Pr: Anthony Bates
CFO: Brian McGee
Sr VP: Paul Crandell
Sr VP: Ronald Lavalley
Sr VP: Zander Lurie
VP: Brent Ayrey
VP: Colin Born
VP: Daniel Coster
VP: Charles Lafrades
Snr Sftwr: Brian Beatty
Board of Directors: Edward Gilhuly, Kenneth Goldman, Peter Gotcher, Alexander Lurie, Lauren Zalaznick

D-U-N-S 10-229-4774 IMP
GORDMANS INC
(*Suby of* SUN CAPITAL PARTNERS INC) ★
1926 S 67th St, Omaha, NE 68106-2800
Tel (402) 691-4000 *Founded/Ownrshp* 2008
Sales 660.0MM *EMP* 5,200
SIC 5311

D-U-N-S 96-612-6638 IMP
■ **GORDMANS STORES INC**
(*Suby of* SUN GORDMANS LP) ★
1926 S 67th St, Omaha, NE 68106-2800
Tel (402) 691-4000 *Founded/Ownrshp* 2008
Sales 657.8MM *EMP* 5,500[E]
Tkr Sym GMAN *Exch* NGS
SIC 5651 5963 Family clothing stores; Home related products, direct sales
Pr: Andrew T Hall
* *Ch Bd:* T Scott King
COO: Michael E Wirkkala
CFO: James B Brown
Chf Mktg O: Lisa C Evans
Sr VP: Richard H Heyman
Sr VP: Ramin Mozafari
Sr VP: Michael F Ricart
VP: Stacey M Townsend
Board of Directors: Matthew N Garff, Stewart M

Kasen, Casey C Lanza, Donald V Roach, James A Shea, Kenneth I Tuchman

D-U-N-S 18-750-1499 IMP
GORDON BIERSCH BREWING CO
10801 W Charleston Blvd # 600, Las Vegas, NV 89135-1208
Tel (702) 221-4475 *Founded/Ownrshp* 1987
Sales 99.0MM^E *EMP* 848
SIC 5813 Tavern (drinking places)
CFO: William Bullard
**CFO:* Paul Michels

GORDON BROS
See GORDON BROTHERS GROUP LLC

D-U-N-S 01-438-1995
GORDON BROTHERS GROUP LLC
GORDON BROS
800 Boylston St Ste 27, Boston, MA 02199-7016
Tel (888) 424-1903 *Founded/Ownrshp* 1998
Sales 222.1MM^E *EMP* 250
SIC 6722 Management investment, open-end
Pr: Kenneth S Frieze
Pt: Brian Cooper
Pt: Lisa F Galeota
Pt: Andrew Murphy
**Ch Bd:* Michael G Frieze
Pr: Neill J Kelly
**Pr:* Gary M Talarico
CEO: Mark T Dufton
COO: Malcolm Macaulay
**CFO:* John M Kelliher
**CFO:* Michael P Muldowney
CFO: Robert L Pagia
**CFO:* Robert Paglia
Ofcr: Don Hancock
Ofcr: Jeffrey T Lerner
VP: Andrew B Becker
VP: Michael Guelfo
VP: Jo-Ann Jackson
VP: Ronald W Liese
VP: Jim Lightburn
VP: Jan Sommers

D-U-N-S 10-835-9014
GORDON E AND BETTY I MOORE FOUNDATION
1661 Page Mill Rd, Palo Alto, CA 94304-1209
Tel (650) 213-3000 *Founded/Ownrshp* 2001
Sales 423.7MM *EMP* 75
SIC 8748 Economic consultant
Pr: Lewis W Coleman
Bd of Dir: Kathleen Justice-Moore
Bd of Dir: Kenneth F Siebel
Chf Inves: Alice A Ruth
**Chf Inves:* Denise Strack
Ofcr: William G Green
Ex Dir: Steven Moore
Genl Couns: Deb Tellier

D-U-N-S 00-640-9908 IMP/EXP
GORDON FOOD SERVICE INC
1300 Gezon Pkwy Sw, Wyoming, MI 49509-9302
Tel (888) 437-3663 *Founded/Ownrshp* 1942
Sales 2.3MMM^E *EMP* 10,600
Accts Hungerford Aldrin Nichols & Ca
SIC 5149 5142 5147 5146 5144 5143 Groceries & related products; Packaged frozen goods; Meats & meat products; Fish & seafoods; Poultry & poultry products; Dairy products, except dried or canned
Ch: Daniel A Gordon
**CEO:* James Gordon
**CFO:* Jeff Maddox
CFO: Steve Whitteberry
**Sec:* John Gordon Jr
Ex VP: Tony Grohle
VP: Gopaul Aggarwal
VP: Cheryl Carter
VP: Clif Charles
VP: Chuck Mountjoy
VP: Robert Smit
VP: Ken Vink
Comm Man: Richard Van Dyke

GORDON HOSPITAL
See ADVENTIST HEALTH SYSTEM GEORGIA INC

D-U-N-S 12-770-7227
GORDON MCCOWN CONSTRUCTION LLC
422 Admiral Blvd, Kansas City, MO 64106-1560
Tel (816) 960-1111 *Founded/Ownrshp* 1999
Sales 85.4MM^E *EMP* 150^E
SIC 1542 Commercial & office building contractors
CFO: Jeffery Placek
Off Mgr: Andrea Murdock
IT Man: Dustin Burns
Sfty Dirs: Blaine Arbuckle

D-U-N-S 06-771-5391
■ GORDON TRUCKING INC
(*Suby of* HEARTLAND EXPRESS INC) ★
151 Stewart Rd Sw, Pacific, WA 98047-2108
Tel (253) 863-7777 *Founded/Ownrshp* 2013
Sales 98.9MM^E *EMP* 2,000
SIC 4213

D-U-N-S 62-520-9460
GORES ENT HOLDINGS INC
6260 Lookout Rd, Boulder, CO 80301-3685
Tel (303) 531-3100 *Founded/Ownrshp* 2005
Sales 1.5MM *EMP* 1,150
SIC 3577 7373 3357 Computer peripheral equipment; Local area network (LAN) systems integrator; Communication wire; Coaxial cable, nonferrous; Fiber optic cable (insulated)
Pr: Donald Gruidel

D-U-N-S 13-713-7878
GORES GROUP LLC
9800 Wilshire Blvd, Beverly Hills, CA 90212-1804
Tel (310) 209-3010 *Founded/Ownrshp* 2004
Sales 6.3MMM^E *EMP* 20,120
SIC 6211 Investment firm, general brokerage
CEO: Alec Gores
**COO:* Joseph Page
**Sr VP:* Kurt Hans
**Sr VP:* Jeremy Rossen
**Sr VP:* Dewey Turner III
VP: Igor Chacartegui
VP: Kari Harmon
Mng Dir: Chris Crowell
Mng Dir: Ian Weingarten

GORES IDEA HOLDING
See IDEA INTEGRATION CORP

D-U-N-S 80-784-7020
GORES RADIO HOLDINGS LLC
(*Suby of* GORES GROUP LLC) ★
10877 Wilshire Blvd # 1805, Los Angeles, CA 90024-4341
Tel (310) 209-3010 *Founded/Ownrshp* 2007
Sales 73.1MM^E *EMP* 1,501
SIC 3699 7382 Security devices; Security systems services
Pr: Alex Gores

GORITEWAY
See RITEWAY BUS SERVICE INC

D-U-N-S 16-101-9534
GORMAN & CO INC
200 N Main St, Oregon, WI 53575-1447
Tel (608) 835-3900 *Founded/Ownrshp* 1984
Sales 116.0MM^E *EMP* 135
SIC 6552 6531 Land subdividers & developers, residential; Real estate managers
CEO: Gary Gorman

D-U-N-S 00-415-4308
▲ GORMAN-RUPP CO (OH)
600 S Airport Rd, Mansfield, OH 44903-7831
Tel (419) 755-1011 *Founded/Ownrshp* 1933
Sales 406.1MM *EMP* 1,274^E
Tkr Sym GRC *Exch* ASE
SIC 3561 3594 Pumps & pumping equipment; Industrial pumps & parts; Pumps, oil well & field; Pumps, domestic: water or sump; Fluid power pumps & motors
Pr: Jeffrey S Gorman
**Ch Bd:* James C Gorman
CFO: Wayne L Knabel
Treas: Judith L Sovine
VP: James C Kerr
Genl Mgr: Doug Renner
Sales Asso: Lynn Bond
Board of Directors: M Ann Harlan, Thomas E Hoaglin, Christopher H Lake, Kenneth R Reynolds, Rick R Taylor, W Wayne Walston

GORTITE
See DYNATECT MANUFACTURING INC

D-U-N-S 00-176-3333 IMP
GORTON SLADE & CO INC (MA)
(*Suby of* SG SEAFOOD HOLDINGS INC) ★
225 Southampton St, Boston, MA 02118-2715
Tel (617) 442-5800 *Founded/Ownrshp* 1928
Sales 166.0MM^E *EMP* 180
SIC 5146 Fish, fresh; Fish, frozen, unpackaged; Seafoods
CEO: Kimberly Gorton
**Ch Bd:* Mike Gorton Sr
**COO:* Michael Richard
CFO: James Stauffer
**CFO:* Jim Wiesen
Ex VP: Patrice Flanagan
**VP:* Ron Beane
VP: Dennis Newman
VP: Matthew Simpson
QA Dir: Bob Lafreniere
IT Man: Skye Grams

GORTONS
See GORTONS INC

D-U-N-S 05-124-2258 IMP
GORTONS INC
GORTONS
(*Suby of* NIPPON SUISAN (USA) INC) ★
128 Rogers St, Gloucester, MA 01930-5005
Tel (978) 283-3000 *Founded/Ownrshp* 1849
Sales 220.1MM^E *EMP* 975
SIC 2092 2091 Fresh or frozen packaged fish; Seafood products: packaged in cans, jars, etc.
Pr: Judson Reis
Area Mgr: Steve Malecki
Mktg Mgr: Phaedra Saltis

D-U-N-S 07-433-2388
GOSHEN COMMUNITY SCHOOLS
613 E Purl St, Goshen, IN 46526-4044
Tel (574) 533-8631 *Founded/Ownrshp* 1895
Sales 64.4MM^E *EMP* 1,300
SIC 8211 Public elementary school; Public junior high school; Public senior high school
Dir Vol: Amy Walters
Bd of Dir: Jane Devoe
Prin: Jose Boza
Prin: Don Jantzi
Prin: Sue Olinghouse
Prin: Michael Springer
Prin: Denise Tahara
Psych: Leon Bauman

GOSHEN GENERAL HOSPITAL
See GOSHEN HOSPITAL ASSOCIATION INC

D-U-N-S 96-139-9367
GOSHEN HEALTH SYSTEM INC
200 High Park Ave, Goshen, IN 46526-4810
Tel (574) 533-2141 *Founded/Ownrshp* 1995
Sales 36.1MM^E *EMP* 1,100
Accts Deloitte Tax Llp Indianapolis
SIC 5912 Drug stores
CEO: Randal E Christophel
Dir Vol: Karla Beasley
COO: Lisa Scheetz
VP: James Vancuren
VP: Alan Weldy
Dir Rx: Kent Schreck
MIS Dir: Dolph Voelker
Dir IT: Art Wager
Mtls Dir: Jessica Frye
Surgeon: Laura Morris
Obsttrcn: Martina McGowan

D-U-N-S 07-433-2453
GOSHEN HOSPITAL ASSOCIATION INC
GOSHEN GENERAL HOSPITAL
200 High Park Ave, Goshen, IN 46526-4810
Tel (574) 533-2141 *Founded/Ownrshp* 1908
Sales 228.5MM *EMP* 736
Accts Deloitte Tax Llp Indianapolis
SIC 8062 General medical & surgical hospitals
COO: Sheryl Lewis Blake
COO: Randy Cammenga
**CFO:* Amy Floria
Mtls Dir: Paul Lyons
Doctor: Eric Beachy
Doctor: Jodi Clouse
Doctor: Benjamin Nelson
Nrsg Dir: Vicki Yoder

D-U-N-S 00-790-2497 IMP/EXP
GOSIGER INC
108 Mcdonough St, Dayton, OH 45402-2267
Tel (937) 228-5174 *Founded/Ownrshp* 1922
Sales 156.2MM^E *EMP* 435
SIC 5084 Machine tools & accessories
Pr: Peter G Haley
**Mng Pt:* John Haley
**CFO:* Jerry Presell
**Ch:* Jane Haley
**Ex VP:* Jerry L Gecowets
CTO: Mark Winemiller
Mktg Dir: Mike Williams
Sls Mgr: Dave Bruestle
Sls Mgr: Michael Garver
Sls Mgr: Derek Noe
Sls Mgr: Shad O'Brien
Board of Directors: Hank Bachmann, Daniel Duvall, Charles Faruki, James Mc Swiney

D-U-N-S 05-002-0911 IMP
GOSPEL OF PEACE INC
GINN
215 Celebration Pl # 200, Kissimmee, FL 34747-5400
Tel (321) 939-4700 *Founded/Ownrshp* 1998
Sales NA *EMP* 1,400
SIC 6552

D-U-N-S 10-187-5631 IMP/EXP
GOSS INTERNATIONAL AMERICAS LLC
121 Technology Dr, Durham, NH 03824-4716
Tel (603) 749-6600 *Founded/Ownrshp* 2015
Sales 134.5MM^E *EMP* 950
SIC 7699 3555 Printing trades machinery & equipment repair; Printing presses
CEO: Mohit Uberoi
**COO:* Stan Blakney
**CFO:* Sven Doerge
Treas: Dan Dillman
VP: Thomas Clarke
VP: Pascal Orliac
VP: Torben Rasmussen
VP: Richard Schultz
VP: Jeff Upchurch

D-U-N-S 10-446-9619 IMP/EXP
GOSS INTERNATIONAL CORP
(*Suby of* SHANGHAI ELECTRIC CORP)
9018 Heritage Pkwy # 1200, Woodridge, IL 60517-5136
Tel (630) 796-7560 *Founded/Ownrshp* 2010
Sales 311.3MM^E *EMP* 2,000
SIC 3555 5084 Printing presses; Printing trades machinery, equipment & supplies
CEO: Richard Nichols
**Pr:* Jochen Meissner
Sr VP: Richard F Schultz
VP: Jacques C Navarre
Genl Mgr: Matt Sharkady
Genl Couns: Shane Lancaster

D-U-N-S 14-774-4940 EXP
GOSSEN CORP
2030 W Bender Rd, Milwaukee, WI 53209-3727
Tel (800) 558-8984 *Founded/Ownrshp* 1928
Sales 86.0MM^E *EMP* 300
SIC 2431 3089 2452 Moldings, wood: unfinished & prefinished; Molding primary plastic; Prefabricated wood buildings
Pr: Frank Butterfield Jr
CFO: John Glayson
**Ex VP:* Bob Simon
**VP:* Frank Butterfield
Brnch Mgr: Jeff Mann
IT Man: John Gleason
Opers Mgr: Fred Inlenfeld

GOSSETT MITSUBISHI
See GOSSETT MOTOR CARS INC

D-U-N-S 13-044-4961 IMP
GOSSETT MOTOR CARS INC
GOSSETT MITSUBISHI
1901 Covington Pike, Memphis, TN 38128-6980
Tel (901) 363-6556 *Founded/Ownrshp* 1985
Sales 146.0MM^E *EMP* 315
SIC 5511 5012 Automobiles, new & used; Pickups, new & used; Vans, new & used; Automobiles & other motor vehicles
Owner: Al Gossett
**Sec:* George Roser
**VP:* David Gossett
Brnch Mgr: Cathy M Millen
Genl Mgr: Kenneth Derrick
Sls Mgr: Dustin Smith
Sales Asso: Patrick Butler
Sales Asso: James Fiore
Sales Asso: Larry Perkins

D-U-N-S 00-910-1874 IMP/EXP
GOSSNER FOODS INC (UT)
1051 N 1000 W, Logan, UT 84321-6852
Tel (435) 713-6100 *Founded/Ownrshp* 1941
Sales 136.1MM^E *EMP* 360
SIC 2022 2026 2021 Natural cheese; Processed cheese; Milk, ultra-high temperature (longlife); Creamery butter
CEO: Dolores Gossner Wheeler
**Sec:* Dixie W Udy
**VP:* Greg Rowley
Plnt Mgr: Dave Larsen
Ql Cn Mgr: Rebecca Wood
Trfc Mgr: Stephen Duncan
Mktg Dir: Holly Hill

D-U-N-S 03-855-9253
GOTHAM TECHNOLOGY GROUP LLC
1 Paragon Dr Ste 200, Montvale, NJ 07645-1728
Tel (201) 802-9600 *Founded/Ownrshp* 1991
Sales 159.6MM^E *EMP* 80
SIC 5045 7361 5932 Computers, peripherals & software; Employment agencies; Computers & accessories, secondhand
CEO: Ira Silverman
Prac Mgr: David Kim
Prac Mgr: Steven Manobianco
Software D: Matthew Dallicardillo
Opers Supe: Lisa Garcia
Mktg Dir: Justin Santonastaso
Mktg Mgr: Lindsey Bohm
Mktg Mgr: Lauren Rodabaugh
Sales Asso: Audra Ireland

GOTHIC GROUND MANAGEMENT
See GOTHIC LANDSCAPING INC

D-U-N-S 11-880-1414
GOTHIC LANDSCAPING INC
GOTHIC GROUND MANAGEMENT
27502 Avenue Scott, Valencia, CA 91355-3484
Tel (661) 257-1266 *Founded/Ownrshp* 1997
Sales 144.8MM^E *EMP* 600
SIC 0782 Landscape contractors; Lawn services
Pr: Jon S Georgio
**VP:* Ronald Georgio
VP: Perry Jones
**Prin:* Mike Georgio

D-U-N-S 10-391-1418
GOTTLIEB HEALTH RESOURCES INC
701 W North Ave, Melrose Park, IL 60160-1612
Tel (708) 681-3200 *Founded/Ownrshp* 1982
Sales 135.0MM *EMP* 1,200
SIC 8741 Hospital management
CEO: John Morgan
CFO: Andy Knauff
**VP:* Brett Wakefield

D-U-N-S 07-233-4287
GOTTLIEB MEMORIAL HOSPITAL (IL)
GOTTLIEB MEMORIAL HOSPITAL HOM
701 W North Ave, Melrose Park, IL 60160-1699
Tel (708) 681-3200 *Founded/Ownrshp* 1956
Sales 129.6MM *EMP* 900
SIC 8062 General medical & surgical hospitals
Pr: Lori Price
**Pr:* John Morgan
CFO: Ellen Chin
Ofcr: Craig Mack
VP: Ellyn Chin
VP: Connie Clark
**VP:* Alan Goldberg
**VP:* Ginger Hook
Exec: Christine Palmisano
Dir Risk M: Bev Mc Adam
Dir Sec: Irwin Olef

GOTTLIEB MEMORIAL HOSPITAL HOM
See GOTTLIEB MEMORIAL HOSPITAL

D-U-N-S 05-395-0564
GOUCHER COLLEGE
1021 Dulaney Valley Rd, Baltimore, MD 21204-2780
Tel (410) 337-6000 *Founded/Ownrshp* 1885
Sales 99.0MM *EMP* 500
SIC 8221 College, except junior
Pr: Sanford J Ungar
CFO: Renae Feyer
Cmptr Lab: C Lopresto
Web Dev: Branden Kaestner

D-U-N-S 00-615-7747 IMP/EXP
GOULD ELECTRONICS INC
34929 Curtis Blvd Ste 100, Eastlake, OH 44095-4056
Tel (440) 953-5000 *Founded/Ownrshp* 1988
Sales 143.6MM^E *EMP* 2,730
SIC 3825 3497 3613 3691 3674 Instruments to measure electricity; Logic circuit testers; Oscillographs & oscilloscopes; Copper foil; Power circuit breakers; Storage batteries; Semiconductors & related devices
VP: D P Burgess
VP: Kerji Kataqiri
VP: John L Monaco

D-U-N-S 00-698-9503 IMP/EXP
GOULD PAPER CORP (NY)
(*Suby of* JAPAN PULP & PAPER (USA) CORP) ★
99 Park Ave Fl 10, New York, NY 10016-1500
Tel (212) 301-0000 *Founded/Ownrshp* 1924, 2010
Sales 1.0MMM^E *EMP* 452
SIC 5113 5111 3523 Industrial & personal service paper; Fine paper; Harvesters, fruit, vegetable, tobacco, etc.
CEO: David Berkowitz
CFO: Edward Silver
Treas: Patrick Mullen
Ex VP: Jim Costenbader
Ex VP: Takahiro Miyata
Ex VP: Joseph Ryan
Ex VP: Michael Trachtenberg
VP: Gary Bishop
VP: Robert Bunsick
VP: Dermot Burke
VP: Joseph Cali
VP: Paul Collins
VP: Warren Connor
VP: Michael Duncan
VP: Leena Etelalahti
VP: Jim Gold
VP: Robert Hartman
VP: Marion Hindenburg
VP: Steven Lubin
VP: Carl Meisel
VP: Mike Ritter

D-U-N-S 07-982-8150
GOULD PAPER CORP
(*Suby of* JAPAN PULP & PAPER (USA) CORP) ★
99 Park Ave Fl 10, New York, NY 10016-1500
Tel (212) 301-0000 *Founded/Ownrshp* 2015
Sales 1.0MMM *EMP* 500

SIC 5111 2759

D-U-N-S 00-222-5100 IMP/EXP
■ GOULDS PUMPS INC
(Suby of ITT LLC) ★
240 Fall St, Seneca Falls, NY 13148-1573
Tel (315) 568-2811 Founded/Ownrshp 1984
Sales 1.2MMM[E] EMP 4,500
SIC 3561 5084 Pumps & pumping equipment; Industrial pumps & parts; Pumps, oil well & field; Pumps, domestic: water or sump; Industrial machinery & equipment
Pr: Aris Chicles
*Ch Bd: Robert Pagano
*Pr: Ken Napolitano
Area Mgr: Richard Hill
Tech Mgr: Tom Jolly
Sales Exec: Reginald Smith
Manager: Jeff Fishel
Manager: Brian Verdehem
Sls Mgr: Steve George

GOULET SUPPLY COMPANY
See GRANITE GROUP WHOLESALERS LLC

D-U-N-S 15-751-3680 IMP/EXP
GOURMET FOODS INC
2910 E Harcourt St, Compton, CA 90221-5502
Tel (310) 632-3300 Founded/Ownrshp 1986
Sales 112.1MM[E] EMP 215[E]
SIC 5141 5812 2099 Food brokers; Eating places; Food preparations
Pr: Heinz Naef
Mng Pt: Neil Levine
*CFO: Gary David
*Sec: Ursina Naef
VP: Marcel Lagnaz
Off Mgr: Rose Wallace
CIO: Karen McCullough
IT Man: Robbie Gonzales
IT Man: Karen Smith
Plnt Mgr: Rene Fraga
Mktg Mgr: Marcel Lagnez

GOURMET FOODS INTERNATIONAL
See RUSSELL MCCALLS INC

D-U-N-S 15-095-1903
GOURMET SYSTEMS OF KANSAS INC
APPLEBEE'S
4551 W 107th St Ste 100, Shawnee Mission, KS 66207-4037
Tel (913) 967-4000 Founded/Ownrshp 2013
Sales 28.4MM[E] EMP 1,000
SIC 5812 5813 Restaurant, family: chain; Bar (drinking places)
Ch Bd: Lloyd Hill
Pt: Shelly Gagen
Ex VP: Louis A Kucic
VP: Janell Jones
VP: David R Pasley
VP: Samuel M Rothschild
VP: Rohan M St George
*VP: Robert Steinkamp
Ex Dir: Thomas Weaver
Ex Dir: Scott Zaleskin
Genl Mgr: Jill Bardeaux

GOVERNER'S OFFICE
See PUEBLO OF ISLETA

GOVERNER'S OFFICE
See EXECUTIVE OFFICE OF STATE OF WISCONSIN

GOVERNERS OFFICE, THE
See EXECUTIVE OFFICE OF STATE OF ARKANSAS

D-U-N-S 00-325-1949
■ GOVERNMENT ACCOUNTABILITY OFFICE
(Suby of CONGRESS UNITED STATES) ★
441 G St Nw, Washington, DC 20548-0001
Tel (202) 512-3000 Founded/Ownrshp 1921
Sales NA EMP 3,275
SIC 9311 Budget agency, government;
COO: Gene L Dodaro
Pr: Marlin McCrae
CFO: Richard Brown
CFO: David Fisher
VP: Tiffany Rodney
VP: Joel Willemsen
Mng Dir: Patricia A Dalton
Snr Ntwrk: Sheryl Coppenger
Snr Ntwrk: Jay Harman
CIO: Howard Williams Jr
IT Man: Renee Chase

D-U-N-S 07-627-9850
GOVERNMENT EMPLOYEES HEALTH ASSOCIATION INC (MO)
G E H A
310 Ne Mulberry St, Lees Summit, MO 64086-5861
Tel (816) 257-5500 Founded/Ownrshp 1939
Sales NA EMP 1,318
Accts Bkd Llp Kansas City Missour
SIC 6321 Health insurance carriers
Ex Dir: Julie Browne
CIO: Joseph Acosta
Dir IT: Brian Franke
IT Man: Bruce Brown
IT Man: Pat Byrne
Ql Cn Mgr: David Cook
Sales Exec: Julie Ramsey

D-U-N-S 00-691-9781
■ GOVERNMENT EMPLOYEES INSURANCE CO INC (MD)
GEICO
(Suby of GEICO CORP) ★
5260 Western Ave, Chevy Chase, MD 20815-3701
Tel (301) 986-2500 Founded/Ownrshp 1937, 1979
Sales NA EMP 10,000
SIC 6411 Insurance agents, brokers & service
Ch Bd: Olza Nicely
Pr: Bill Roberts
Pr: John Zinno
CFO: Thomas M Wells
Treas: Charles Gerard Schara
Assoc VP: Howard Dickstein
Ex VP: W Alvin Sparks Jr
Sr VP: George Rogers
VP: Pionne Corbin
*VP: Charles Davies
VP: Eve Exarhakis
VP: Richard Guertin
VP: Warren Klawitter
VP: Kirk La
VP: Luigi Lazzari
VP: Rhett Rayburn
VP: Daniel Schechter
VP: Ryan West
Board of Directors: James M Hitt, Seth Ingall, Donald Lyons, Robert Morton Miller, William Roberts, David Schindler

D-U-N-S 05-859-2122 IMP/EXP
GOVERNMENT OF DISTRICT OF COLUMBIA
OFFICE OF CONTRACTING AND PROC
441 4th St Nw, Washington, DC 20001-2714
Tel (202) 727-2277 Founded/Ownrshp 1790
Sales NA EMP 34,600
Accts Kpmg Llp Washington Dc
SIC 9111 Mayors' offices;
*CFO: Natawar Gandhi
CFO: Natwar M Gandhi
Ofcr: Ray Davidson
Ofcr: Larry McCoy
*Ofcr: George Schutter
Prgrm Mgr: Pam Taylor
CIO: Mahnaz Choobineh
CIO: Derek Sharp
Opers Mgr: Curtis Edwards
Sales Exec: Beth Brinly
Mktg Dir: Yvonne D Gilchrist

D-U-N-S 16-190-6193
▲ GOVERNMENT OF UNITED STATES
U S GOVERNMENT
1600 Pennsylvania Ave Nw, Washington, DC 20500-0003
Tel (202) 456-1414 Founded/Ownrshp 1787
Sales NA EMP 2,768,886[E]
SIC 9111
Pr: Barack H Obama
Ofcr: Karen Evans
*VP: Joseph R Biden
Exec: Jessica Carter
Exec: Betsy Hawkings
Assoc Dir: Kenneth Baer
Comm Dir: Emily Davis
Comm Dir: Marisol Garibay
Comm Dir: Brian Robinson
Ex Dir: Jim Zoia
*CTO: Megan Smith

D-U-N-S 09-114-7678
GOVERNMENT OF US VIRGIN ISLANDS
21-22 Kongens Gade, Charlotte Amalie, VI 00802
Tel (340) 774-0001 Founded/Ownrshp 1917
Sales NA EMP 2,500
SIC 9111 Governors' offices;

D-U-N-S 82-970-8408
GOVERNMENT PROPERTIES INCOME TRUST
255 Washington St Ste 300, Newton, MA 02458-1634
Tel (617) 219-1440 Founded/Ownrshp 2009
Sales 248.5MM EMP 407
SIC 6798 Real estate investment trusts
Pr: David M Blackman
Mng Trst: Barry Portnoy
CFO: Mark L Kleifges
VP: Timothy Bonang
Board of Directors: Barbara D Gilmore, John L Harrington, Adam D Portnoy, Barry M Portnoy, Jeffrey P Somers

D-U-N-S 78-580-7611
GOVERNMENT SCIENTIFIC SOURCE INC
G S S
12351 Sunrise Valley Dr, Reston, VA 20191-3415
Tel (703) 734-1805 Founded/Ownrshp 1991
Sales 196.7MM EMP 90
Accts Lydon Fetterolf Corydon Pa
SIC 5049 5047 Scientific & engineering equipment & supplies; Medical equipment & supplies
Pr: Wayne B Bardsley
Sr VP: Steve Sellentin
*VP: Smith James
VP: Mike Mendrysa
VP: James Smith
*VP: Scott Stackhouse
*VP: Sellentin Steve
Sftwr Eng: Zachariah Lingelbach
Sls Mgr: Tina Sellentin
Sales Asso: Kip Evoy
Snr Mgr: Chris Kinkaid

D-U-N-S 13-324-9941
GOVERNMENT SERVICE CENTER
315 High St Fl 10, Hamilton, OH 45011-6069
Tel (513) 887-3000 Founded/Ownrshp 2003
Sales NA EMP 1,000
SIC 9199

D-U-N-S 94-837-8567 EXP
GOVERNOR JUAN F LUIS HOSPITAL & MEDICAL CENTER
4007 Estate Diamond Ruby, Christiansted, VI 00820-4435
Tel (340) 778-6311 Founded/Ownrshp 1988
Sales 129.6MM[E] EMP 624
SIC 8062 General medical & surgical hospitals
CEO: Kendall Griffith MD
CFO: Anthony G Saul

D-U-N-S 96-858-0253
GOVERNORS ISLAND CORP
TRUST FOR GOVERNORS ISLAND, TH
10 South St Frnt Slip7, New York, NY 10004-1939
Tel (212) 440-2200 Founded/Ownrshp 2011
Sales 116.4MM EMP 12
Accts Marks Paneth Llp New York Ny
SIC 6733 Trusts
Prin: Leslie Koch

GOVERNORS OFFICE
See STATE OF UTAH

GOVERNOR'S OFFICE
See STATE OF WEST VIRGINIA

GOVERNOR'S OFFICE
See STATE OF ARIZONA

GOVERNOR'S OFFICE
See STATE OF WASHINGTON

GOVERNORS OFFICE
See EXECUTIVE OFFICE OF STATE OF COLORADO

GOVERNOR'S OFFICE, THE
See EXECUTIVE OFFICE OF COMMONWEALTH OF PENNSYLVANIA

GOVERNOR'S OFFICE
See EXECUTIVE OFFICE OF STATE OF MINNESOTA

GOVERNOR'S OFFICE
See MINNESOTA STATE COLLEGES AND UNIVERSITIES

GOVERNOR'S OFFICE
See EXECUTIVE OFFICE OF STATE OF VERMONT

D-U-N-S 80-634-8322
GOVERNORS OFFICE NEW MEXICO
(Suby of STATE OF NEW MEXICO) ★
490 Old Santa Fe Trl # 400, Santa Fe, NM 87501-2749
Tel (505) 476-2200 Founded/Ownrshp 1912
Sales NA EMP 19,423
SIC 9111 Governors' offices;
Ofcr: Nathalie Martinez
IT Man: Mark Guillen
Netwrk Mgr: Barry Hodges
Snr Mgr: Lisa Ortiz

D-U-N-S 83-540-7354
GOVERNORS OFFICE STATE OF CONNECTICUT
(Suby of STATE OF CONNECTICUT) ★
210 Capitol Ave Ste 202, Hartford, CT 06106-1535
Tel (860) 566-4840 Founded/Ownrshp 1788
Sales NA EMP 35,970
SIC 9111 Executive offices;

D-U-N-S 06-998-2130
GOVERNORS STATE UNIVERSITY
1 University Pkwy, University Park, IL 60484-3165
Tel (708) 534-5000 Founded/Ownrshp 1969
Sales 87.9MM[E] EMP 1,100
SIC 8221

D-U-N-S 00-335-5393
GOWER CORP (SC)
355 Woodruff Rd Ste 101, Greenville, SC 29607-3419
Tel (864) 458-3114 Founded/Ownrshp 1912, 1955
Sales 96.2MM[E] EMP 250
SIC 3535 5051 7373 Unit handling conveying systems; Metals service centers & offices; Computer integrated systems design
Pr: Mark Dullea
*VP: Robert Parrott
*Prin: Russell Park

D-U-N-S 09-008-3387 IMP
GOYA DE PUERTO RICO INC
Esq Calle 5 Rr 28, Bayamon, PR 00961
Tel (787) 740-4900 Founded/Ownrshp 1967
Sales 88.2MM[E] EMP 500
SIC 2032 2033 Ethnic foods: canned, jarred, etc.; Vegetables & vegetable products in cans, jars, etc.
Pr: Carlos Unaune
*VP: Jorge Unaune

D-U-N-S 00-169-4777 IMP/EXP
GOYA FOODS INC
350 County Rd, Jersey City, NJ 07307-4503
Tel (201) 348-4900 Founded/Ownrshp 1973
Sales 633.7MM[E] EMP 725
SIC 5142 Frozen vegetables & fruit products
Pr: Robert Unanue
CFO: Hilda Galimberti
*Sec: Frank Unanue
*Ex VP: Peter J Unanue
*Sr VP: Joseph F Perez
*VP: Conrad Colon
*VP: David Kinkela
VP: Rebecca Rodriguez
VP: Jorge Unanue
VP: Peter Unanue
Exec: Fernando DESA
Exec: Xiomara Florentin

GOYA FOODS OF FLORIDA
See DIANA FOODS INC

GOYIN INTERNATIONAL
See GENESIS PURE INC

D-U-N-S 80-802-8513
GP BUILDING PRODUCTS OPERATIONS LLC
GP OPERATIONS HOLDINGS LLC
(Suby of GEORGIA-PACIFIC LLC) ★
133 Peachtree St Ne, Atlanta, GA 30303-1804
Tel (404) 652-4000 Founded/Ownrshp 2007
Sales 121.3MM[E] EMP 865
SIC 2656 Paper cups, plates, dishes & utensils

D-U-N-S 13-963-8923 IMP/EXP
GP CELLULOSE LLC
(Suby of GEORGIA-PACIFIC LLC) ★
133 Peachtree St Ne # 1, Atlanta, GA 30303-1804
Tel (404) 652-6630 Founded/Ownrshp 2003
Sales 358.1MM[E] EMP 782
SIC 2611 Pulp mills
Ofcr: Wesley Jones
*Ofcr: Patrick Boushka
*Ofcr: William Frerking
*Ofcr: Richard King
*Ofcr: Cato Rodgers
*Ofcr: Marsha Seekins

D-U-N-S 60-585-1047 IMP/EXP
GP CHEMICALS EQUITY LLC
(Suby of GEORGIA-PACIFIC LLC) ★
55 Park Pl Ne, Atlanta, GA 30303-2529
Tel (404) 652-4000 Founded/Ownrshp 1984
Sales 118.7MM[E] EMP 1,300
SIC 5169 Chemicals & allied products
Ofcr: Sara Afayee
VP: Carl Wilson
IT Man: Alan Guibord

D-U-N-S 09-145-1112 EXP
GP HARMON RECYCLING LLC
(Suby of GEORGIA-PACIFIC LLC) ★
2 Jericho Plz Ste 200, Jericho, NY 11753-1681
Tel (516) 997-3400 Founded/Ownrshp 2000
Sales 184.8MM[E] EMP 185
SIC 5093 Waste paper
Pr: Marc Forman
*COO: Mark Forman
*Treas: Joyce Harvey
*VP: Vince Bonfanti
*VP: Ernst A Haverli
*VP: Dan Maddox
VP: Eric Schnell
*VP: Rick Torbeck
Genl Mgr: Ted Gloeckler

GP OPERATIONS HOLDINGS LLC
See GP BUILDING PRODUCTS OPERATIONS LLC

D-U-N-S 04-779-9267
▲ GP STRATEGIES CORP
11000 Broken Land Pkwy # 200, Columbia, MD 21044-3555
Tel (443) 367-9600 Founded/Ownrshp 1959
Sales 490.2MM EMP 3,250
Tkr Sym GPX Exch NYS
SIC 8742 8711 8748 Management consulting services; Training & development consultant; Engineering services; Environmental consultant
CEO: Scott N Greenberg
Ch Bd: Harvey P Eisen
Pr: Douglas E Sharp
CFO: Sharon Esposito-Mayer
Ex VP: Karl Baer
Ex VP: Donald R Duquette
Sr VP: Kenneth L Crawford
Sr VP: David A Gugala
Sr VP: Chuck Kooistra
Sr VP: Deborah T Ung
VP: Matt Young
Dir Bus: Paul Pearce
Board of Directors: Marshall S Geller, Laura L Gurski, Steven E Koonin, Richard C Pfenniger Jr, Samuel Robinson, A Marvin Strait

GP&C
See GENERAL PLASTICS & COMPOSITES LP

GPA
See GROUP & PENSION ADMINISTRATORS INC

D-U-N-S 11-184-8748
GPC CAPITAL CORP II
(Suby of GRAHAM PACKAGING HOLDINGS CO) ★
2401 Pleasant Valley Rd # 2, York, PA 17402-9600
Tel (717) 849-8500 Founded/Ownrshp 1998
Sales 202.5MM[E] EMP 4,100
SIC 3089 Blow molded finished plastic products; Extruded finished plastic products
Ch Bd: Philip R Yates
Pr: Roger M Prevot
CFO: Mark Buches
CFO: John E Hamilton
VP: Jay W Hereford

GPD GROUP
See GLAUS PYLE SCHOMER BURNS & DEHAVEN INC

GPHA
See GREAT PLAINS HEALTH ALLIANCE INC

D-U-N-S 94-379-0725
■ GPI HOLDINGS INC
GRAPHIC PACKAGING INTL
(Suby of GRAPHIC PACKAGING HOLDING CO) ★
1500 Riveredge Pkwy # 100, Atlanta, GA 30328-4642
Tel (770) 240-7200 Founded/Ownrshp 1995
Sales 228.8MM[E] EMP 9,000
SIC 2631 2653 2449 4922 Container, packaging & boxboard; Container board; Folding boxboard; Boxes, corrugated: made from purchased materials; Wood containers; Containers, plywood & veneer wood; Pipelines, natural gas
Pr: Stephen M Humphrey
*CFO: Daniel J Blount
*Sr VP: Wayne Juby
*Sr VP: Steven D Saucier
Sls Mgr: Juan Gil

D-U-N-S 03-371-4775
GPI LIQUIDATION INC
16 Forest Pkwy Bldg M, Forest Park, GA 30297-2001
Tel (404) 361-0215 Founded/Ownrshp 2014
Sales 134.3MM[E] EMP 230
SIC 5148

GPISD
See GRAND PRAIRIE INDEPENDENT SCHOOL DISTRICT

D-U-N-S 13-235-5574
GPM INVESTMENTS LLC
FAS MART
8565 Magellan Pkwy # 400, Richmond, VA 23227-1167
Tel (804) 266-1363 Founded/Ownrshp 2003
Sales 787.1MM[E] EMP 2,150[E]
Accts Grant Thornton Llp Raleigh
SIC 5541 5411 5172 Filling stations, gasoline; Convenience stores; Gasoline
CEO: Dave McComas
Pr: Mark Wilson
*COO: Chris Giacobone
*CFO: Mark King
VP: Barry Khrosrophanah
VP: Peter Meyer

D-U-N-S 04-329-3122
GPS HOSPITALITY LLC
2100 Riveredge Pkwy # 850, Atlanta, GA 30328-4693
Tel (770) 933-5023 Founded/Ownrshp 2012
Sales 300.0MM EMP 1,306E
SIC 5812 Fast-food restaurant, chain
CEO: Thomas A Garrett
*CFO: Scott Jasinski
*CFO: Amelia McDonald
*VP: Brian Arnold
VP: Heather Darden
*VP: Mike Kovac
*Prin: Attorney Foltz

D-U-N-S 94-950-3569
GPX CORP
300 S 4th St Ste 1100, Las Vegas, NV 89101-6028
Tel (702) 386-4789 Founded/Ownrshp 1995
Sales 23.7MME EMP 1,500
SIC 7389 Personal service agents, brokers & bureaus
Pr: Gary G Garrison

D-U-N-S 01-931-2594 IMP/EXP
GPX INTERNATIONAL TIRE CORP
124 Washington St Ste 101, Foxboro, MA 02035-1368
Tel (781) 321-3910 Founded/Ownrshp 1974
Sales 228.8MME EMP 2,500
SIC 3011 Tires & inner tubes
Pr: Craig A Steinke
*Ch Bd: Robert Sherkin
*Pr: Bryan Ganz
*Treas: Jeffrey Lucas
Off Mgr: Maureen Brooks
Board of Directors: Bryan Ganz, Eric Ganz, Neil Ganz

D-U-N-S 02-962-3329 IMP/EXP
GRABBER CONSTRUCTION PRODUCTS INC (NV)
(Suby of GRABBER HOLDINGS LLC) ★
5255 W 11000 N Ste 100, Highland, UT 84003-8955
Tel (801) 492-3880 Founded/Ownrshp 2009, 2015
Sales 97.7MME EMP 250
SIC 5072 5211

D-U-N-S 08-002-7250
GRABBER HOLDINGS LLC
(Suby of DOT FOODS INC) ★
1 Dot Way, Mount Sterling, IL 62353-1664
Tel (217) 773-4411 Founded/Ownrshp 2015
Sales 107.5MME EMP 280E
SIC 5072 5211 6719 Miscellaneous fasteners; Screws; Bolts; Rivets; Lumber & other building materials; Investment holding companies, except banks
Pr: Jospeh P Tracy

D-U-N-S 80-989-0882
GRACE HEALTH CARE
(Suby of CONSULATE HEALTH CARE CHESWICK) ★
3425 Knight Dr, Whites Creek, TN 37189-9189
Tel (615) 876-2754 Founded/Ownrshp 2003
Sales 423.5MM EMP 100
SIC 8051 Skilled nursing care facilities

D-U-N-S 80-444-2671
GRACE HOLMES INC
(Suby of JCREW) ★
770 Broadway Fl 11, New York, NY 10003-9512
Tel (212) 209-2500 Founded/Ownrshp 1997
Sales 71.8MME EMP 3,000
SIC 5611 5621 Men's & boys' clothing stores; Clothing accessories: men's & boys'; Clothing, men's & boys': everyday, except suits & sportswear; Clothing, sportswear, men's & boys'; Women's specialty clothing stores; Women's sportswear; Ready-to-wear apparel, women's; Teenage apparel
CEO: Millard Drexler
*COO: Scott Gilbertson
*CFO: Scott Rosen

D-U-N-S 80-838-3678
GRACE I W2007 LLC
85 Broad St Fl 15, New York, NY 10004-2434
Tel (212) 902-1000 Founded/Ownrshp 2007
Sales 179.6MME EMP 147
SIC 7011 Hotels & motels
COO: Ned Thompson

GRACE LIVING CENTERS
See AMITY CARE LLC

D-U-N-S 00-922-7851 IMP/EXP
GRACE PACIFIC LLC (HI)
949 Kamokila Blvd Ste 200, Kapolei, HI 96707-2046
Tel (808) 674-8383 Founded/Ownrshp 1921, 1975
Sales 163.5MME EMP 500
SIC 1611 1429 3272 Surfacing & paving; Igneous rock, crushed & broken-quarrying; Concrete products
CEO: David H Hulihee
*Sr VP: Robert M Creps
VP: Darrell Goo
VP: Robert Singlehurst
DP Exec: David Young
VP Opers: Louis Fuatagavi
Sls Mgr: James Valdez
Board of Directors: Walter Dodds, Joseph Miccio, Bill Mills, Jeffrey Watanabe, Robert Wo

D-U-N-S 12-409-3720
GRACE SINAI HOSPITAL
6701 W Outer Dr, Detroit, MI 48235
Tel (313) 966-3333 Founded/Ownrshp 2002
Sales 16.4MME EMP 5,000
SIC 8062 General medical & surgical hospitals
Pr: Paula Autry

D-U-N-S 07-807-5645
GRACELAND UNIVERSITY (IA)
1 University Pl, Lamoni, IA 50140-1699
Tel (641) 784-5000 Founded/Ownrshp 1895
Sales 114.7MM EMP 350
Accts Mcgladrey Llp Davenport Iowa
SIC 8221 College, except junior
Pr: John D Sellars
COO: David Debarthe
*VP: Janice Tiffany
CIO: Paul Davis
CIO: Kam Mahi

D-U-N-S 08-261-0648
■ **GRACENOTE INC**
(Suby of TRIBUNE MEDIA CO) ★
2000 Powell St Ste 1500, Emeryville, CA 94608-1820
Tel (510) 428-7200 Founded/Ownrshp 2014
Sales 100.0MME EMP 350E
SIC 7371 Software programming applications
Pr: Stephen White
COO: Dominique Schurman
*Sr VP: Eric Allen
*Sr VP: Tal Ball
*Sr VP: Desmond Cussen
*Sr VP: Brian Hamilton
Sr VP: Anindita Mukherjee
VP: R O Blanchard
VP: Anthony Moisant
VP: Young Yoon
Prgrm Mgr: Joe Galea

D-U-N-S 08-324-7510 IMP/EXP
■ **GRACO CHILDRENS PRODUCTS INC**
CENTURY PRODUCTS
(Suby of NEWELL BRANDS INC) ★
3 Glenlake Pkwy, Atlanta, GA 30328-3447
Tel (770) 418-7200 Founded/Ownrshp 1995
Sales 138.5MME EMP 1,420
SIC 2514 Juvenile furniture, household: metal
CEO: William A Burke
*Pr: Howard Heckes
*CFO: Ronald L Hardnock
CFO: John Jordan
MIS Mgr: Allan Rabenau

D-U-N-S 00-625-3223 IMP
▲ **GRACO INC** (MN)
88 11th Ave Ne, Minneapolis, MN 55413-1829
Tel (612) 623-6000 Founded/Ownrshp 1926
Sales 1.2MMM EMP 3,200E
Tkr Sym GGG Exch NYS
SIC 3561 3594 3563 3491 3823 3569 Pumps & pumping equipment; Fluid power pumps & motors; Motors: hydraulic, fluid power or air; Spraying outfits: metals, paints & chemicals (compressor); Industrial valves; Automatic regulating & control valves; Pressure valves & regulators, industrial; Industrial instrmnts msrmnt display/control process variable; Industrial flow & liquid measuring instruments; Fluidic devices, circuits & systems for process control; Lubricating equipment; Lubricating systems, centralized; Lubrication equipment, industrial; Lubrication machinery, automatic
Ch Bd: Lee R Mitau
Pr: Patrick J McHale
CFO: Christian E Rothe
Ex VP: David M Lowe
VP: Caroline M Chambers
VP: Mark D Eberlein
VP: Karen Park Gallivan
VP: Dale D Johnson
VP: Jeffrey P Johnson
VP: Dan Little
VP: Abigail Miller
VP: Bernard J Moreau
VP: Peter J O'Shea
VP: Jerry Powaser
VP: Charles L Rescorla
VP: Mark W Sheahan
VP: Brian J Zumbolo
Board of Directors: William J Carroll, Eric P Etchart, Jack W Eugster, Jody H Feragen, J Kevin Gilligan, Martha A Morfitt, R William Van Sant

GRACYWOODS NURSING CENTER
See HARDEN HEALTHCARE TEXAS LP

D-U-N-S 06-946-6761
GRAD INC
4001 3 Mile Rd Nw, Grand Rapids, MI 49534-1132
Tel (616) 676-5969 Founded/Ownrshp 1982
Sales 353.4MME EMP 620E
SIC 5141 5194 5145 5122 5113 5411 Groceries, general line; Tobacco & tobacco products; Candy; Drugs, proprietaries & sundries; Industrial & personal service paper; Convenience stores
Ch: Abe Abraham
*Pr: Alan Abraham
*VP: Gerald Abraham
VP: John Winkel
VP Sls: George Bennett

D-U-N-S 00-494-8191 IMP
■ **GRADALL INDUSTRIES INC**
(Suby of ALAMO GROUP INC) ★
406 Mill Ave Sw, New Philadelphia, OH 44663-3835
Tel (330) 339-2211 Founded/Ownrshp 1992, 2006
Sales 102.6MME EMP 400E
SIC 3537 3531 Industrial trucks & tractors; Construction machinery
Pr: Michael Haberman
VP: Daniel Kaltenbaugh
VP: Joseph H Keller

GRADIMAGES
See ICONIC GROUP INC

D-U-N-S 10-304-9185
GRADUATE MANAGEMENT ADMISSION COUNCIL INC
GMAC
11921 Freedom Dr Ste 300, Reston, VA 20190-5670
Tel (703) 668-9600 Founded/Ownrshp 1998
Sales 93.2MM EMP 142
Accts Lb Cliftonlarsonallen Llp Arl
SIC 8748 Testing service, educational or personnel
Ch: Dina Dommett
*Pr: Sangeet Chowfla
*Pr: David A Wilson
*COO: Shelli Arnold
*COO: Nicole Chestang
*CFO: Samuel Reimer
Bd of Dir: Ralph S Sheridan
*Chf Mktg O: Betty Su
*Ex VP: Margaret Jobst
Sr VP: Peg Fagan
VP: Alan Levine
VP: Andrew Martelli
VP: Susan Motz
VP: Ramesh Thadani
VP: Julia Tyler
Assoc Dir: Daniel Eyob
Board of Directors: James W Bradford, James M Danko, Stacey Kole, Peggy Bishop Lane, Rosemarie Mecca, Christine Poon, Ajit Rangnekar, Alfons Sauquet, Alexander Sevilla

GRADUATE SCHOOL WICHITA STATE
See WICHITA STATE UNIVERSITY

GRADY HEALTH SYSTEM
See FULTON DEKALB HOSPITAL AUTHORITY

D-U-N-S 96-161-5700
GRADY HEALTH SYSTEM
(Suby of GRADY HEALTH SYSTEM) ★
80 Jesse Hill Jr Dr Se, Atlanta, GA 30303-3050
Tel (404) 616-4360 Founded/Ownrshp 2007
Sales 1.0MMM EMP 4,500
Accts Kpmg Llp Greensboro Nc
SIC 8062 General medical & surgical hospitals
Pr: John M Haupert
V Ch: Thomas W Dortch Jr
*CFO: Mark Meyer
Chf Mktg O: Robert Rohr
*Ex VP: Timothy Jefferson
*Ex VP: Curtis Lewis
*Ex VP: Christopher R Mosley
Sr VP: Calvin Thomas IV
Off Mgr: Rebecca Daniel

D-U-N-S 05-137-0419
GRADY MEMORIAL HOSPITAL
561 W Central Ave, Delaware, OH 43015-1489
Tel (740) 615-1000 Founded/Ownrshp 1904
Sales 94.0MM EMP 348E
SIC 8062 General medical & surgical hospitals
CEO: David Blom
*Sr VP: Johnni Beckel
Nrsg Dir: Sean Troub

D-U-N-S 15-730-2324 IMP/EXP
GRAEBEL COMPANIES INC
(Suby of GRAEBEL HOLDINGS INC) ★
16346 Airport Cir, Aurora, CO 80011-1558
Tel (303) 214-6683 Founded/Ownrshp 2001
Sales 94.0MM EMP 753E
SIC 8742 Management consulting services
CEO: William Graebel
Ch Bd: David Graebel
Pr: Gene Carpenter
Pr: Amie Casias
Pr: Dale Collins
CEO: Terri Drapal
CEO: Deborah Keeton
COO: Ron Dunlap
CFO: Brad Siler
Ch: Debra Fox
Sr VP: William Borgman
Sr VP: Phil Burton
Sr VP: Mary Dymond
Sr VP: Myrla J Lance
Sr VP: Bill Nemer
Sr VP: Andy Pierce
Sr VP: Scott Snead
Sr VP: Carolyn White
VP: Pam Capecci
VP: Craig Chapman
VP: Tana C Gilmore
Board of Directors: Lars Lykke Iversen

D-U-N-S 04-146-5720
GRAEBEL HOLDINGS INC
16346 Airport Cir, Aurora, CO 80011-1558
Tel (303) 214-6683 Founded/Ownrshp 2000
Sales 94.0MM EMP 1,771
Accts Wipfli Llp
SIC 4213 4225 6719 Trucking, except local; General warehousing & storage; Investment holding companies, except banks
Ch Bd: David W Graebel
*Pr: Craig Broback
*CEO: Bill Graebel
*COO: William Graebel
*CFO: Brad Siler

D-U-N-S 04-653-4871
GRAEBEL MOVERS INC
(Suby of GRAEBEL COMPANIES INC) ★
16346 Airport Cir, Aurora, CO 80011-1558
Tel (303) 214-6683 Founded/Ownrshp 1966
Sales 91.9MME EMP 131E
SIC 4213 4214

GRAEBEL MOVING SERVICES
See GRAEBEL VANLINES HOLDINGS LLC

D-U-N-S 07-969-9003
GRAEBEL VANLINES HOLDINGS LLC
GRAEBEL MOVING SERVICES
12790 Merit Dr Bldg 9, Dallas, TX 75251-1217
Tel (972) 694-0400 Founded/Ownrshp 2014
Sales 434.8MME EMP 1,550
SIC 4213 4214 4212 Contract haulers; Household goods transport; Household goods moving & storage, local; Moving services
Pr: Brent Snyder
Ch Bd: Vasilia Peterson
CFO: David Allen

D-U-N-S 00-425-1302
GRAETERS MANUFACTURING CO (OH)
1175 Regina Graeter Way, Cincinnati, OH 45216-1998
Tel (513) 721-3323 Founded/Ownrshp 1870
Sales 110.8MME EMP 500
SIC 2024 2051 2064 2066 Ice cream, packaged: molded, on sticks, etc.; Bread, cake & related products; Candy & other confectionery products; Chocolate & cocoa products
Pr: Richard Graeter II
Treas: James Cahill
VP: Chip Graeter
*VP: Tom Kunzelman
Prin: Eric T Schulze
Off Mgr: Tacey Westerkamm
MIS Dir: Richard Grater

D-U-N-S 07-920-7220
GRAFTECH HOLDINGS INC
(Suby of GRAFTECH INTERNATIONAL LTD) ★
6100 Oak Tree Blvd # 300, Independence, OH 44131-6970
Tel (216) 676-2000 Founded/Ownrshp 1993
Sales 517.4MME EMP 1,210E
SIC 1499 3624 Graphite mining; Carbon & graphite products
CEO: Joel L Hawthorne
*VP: Erick R Asmussen
*VP: John D Moran

D-U-N-S 36-111-7534 IMP
GRAFTECH INTERNATIONAL HOLDINGS INC
UCAR CARBON
(Suby of GRAFTECH INTERNATIONAL LTD) ★
6100 Oak Tree Blvd # 300, Independence, OH 44131-6970
Tel (216) 676-2000 Founded/Ownrshp 1996
Sales 226.6MME EMP 681
SIC 3624 Carbon & graphite products; Electrodes, thermal & electrolytic uses: carbon, graphite
CEO: Joel Hawthorne
CFO: Michael Carr
VP: Mark Sullivan
Dir IT: David Hilmer
Dir IT: Julian Norley
IT Man: Joe Paris
Sys Mgr: Peter Duncanson
Ql Cn Mgr: Gary Mills

D-U-N-S 87-717-6578 IMP/EXP
GRAFTECH INTERNATIONAL LTD
(Suby of BROOKFIELD ASSET MANAGEMENT INC)
6100 Oak Tree Blvd # 300, Independence, OH 44131-6970
Tel (216) 676-2000 Founded/Ownrshp 2015
Sales 1.0MMM EMP 2,397E
SIC 3624 Carbon & graphite products
Pr: Joel L Hawthorne
*Pr: Lionel Batty
Pr: Hermanus L Pretorius
COO: Jeffrey C Dutton
*CFO: Erick R Asmussen
CFO: Quinn J Coburn
VP: Darrell Blair
*VP: John D Moran
Genl Mgr: Bill McFadden
CTO: Adrian Nuta
Dir IT: Chong Chen

D-U-N-S 13-948-0115
GRAFTON INC
GRAFTON STAFFING COMPANIES
4501 College Blvd Ste 160, Leawood, KS 66211-2337
Tel (913) 498-0701 Founded/Ownrshp 1990
Sales 8.4MM EMP 1,100
SIC 7363 7361 Help supply services; Employment agencies
CEO: Carol Carroll
*CFO: Jeffrey Hagen
*Sr VP: Richard Carroll

GRAFTON STAFFING COMPANIES
See GRAFTON INC

D-U-N-S 08-243-9191
GRAHAM ARCHITECTURAL PRODUCTS CORP
1551 Mount Rose Ave, York, PA 17403-2909
Tel (717) 849-8100 Founded/Ownrshp 1960
Sales 122.2MME EMP 330
SIC 3442 Metal doors, sash & trim
Pr: Georges Thiret
*Ch Bd: William Kerlin
*Pr: Brian Hurley
CFO: Frederick Trimmer
*Treas: Frederick R Trimmer
VP: Michael Derosa
*VP: Dennis Kelly
VP: Karen Lehr
VP Mfg: Greg Codner
Plnt Mgr: Terry Boylstein
Plnt Mgr: John Hilbert

D-U-N-S 15-744-2435
GRAHAM BROTHERS ENTERTAINMENT INC
GRAHAM COMPANIES
6999 E Business 20, Odessa, TX 79762-5483
Tel (432) 362-0401 Founded/Ownrshp 1992
Sales 178.0MME EMP 2,000
SIC 5813 Night clubs
Ch Bd: Herbert Graham
*Pr: Roger Gearhart
*CEO: Phillip Graham
*VP: Terry Graham
*Prin: W Phillip Graham
*Prin: Mehdi Shokraeifaro

GRAHAM COMPANIES
See GRAHAM BROTHERS ENTERTAINMENT INC

D-U-N-S 04-118-1447 IMP
GRAHAM COMPANIES
MIAMI LAKER
6843 Main St, Miami Lakes, FL 33014-2048
Tel (305) 821-1130 Founded/Ownrshp 1955
Sales 151.3MME EMP 650
SIC 1531 7011 0212 6552 6512 2711 Operative builders; Resort hotel; Beef cattle except feedlots; Land subdividers & developers, residential; Commercial & industrial building operation; Newspapers
Pr: Stuart S Wyllie
*Sec: Edwin E Feathers
VP: Robert Whitehead

D-U-N-S 60-342-9267
GRAHAM COMPANIES
6843 Main St, Miami Lakes, FL 33014-2048
Tel (305) 821-1130 Founded/Ownrshp 1988
Sales 441.0MME EMP 800E
SIC 6552 Land subdividers & developers, residential

D-U-N-S 11-878-4305
▲ GRAHAM CORP
20 Florence Ave, Batavia, NY 14020-3318
Tel (585) 343-2216 Founded/Ownrshp 1936
Sales 90.0MM EMP 368[E]
Accts Deloitte & Touche Llp Deloitt
Tkr Sym GHM Exch NYS
SIC 3563 3585 3443 Vacuum pumps, except laboratory; Compressors for refrigeration & air conditioning equipment; Condensers, refrigeration; Heat exchangers, condensers & components; Heat exchangers, plate type; Heat exchangers: coolers (after, inter), condensers, etc.
Pr: James R Lines
Ch Bd: James J Malvaso
CFO: Jeffrey F Glajch
VP: Alan E Smith
IT Man: Michael Brzozowski
Board of Directors: James J Barber, Alan Fortier, Gerard T Mazurkiewicz, Jonathan W Painter, Liza M Schnorr

D-U-N-S 88-495-0304
GRAHAM ENTERPRISE INC
750 Bunker Ct Ste 100, Vernon Hills, IL 60061-1864
Tel (847) 837-0777 Founded/Ownrshp 1922
Sales 662.9MM EMP 350
Accts Fgmk Llc Bannockburn Illino
SIC 5172 5411 Petroleum products; Convenience stores, independent
Pr: John C Graham
* Treas: Patrick T Graham
* VP: Eugene W Graham III

D-U-N-S 00-324-5768 IMP/EXP
▲ GRAHAM HOLDINGS CO
1300 17th St N Ste 1700, Arlington, VA 22209-3816
Tel (703) 345-6300 Founded/Ownrshp 1877
Sales 2.5MMM EMP 11,500
Accts Pricewaterhousecoopers Llp Mc
Tkr Sym GHC Exch NYS
SIC 8299 4833 4841 2721 Tutoring school; Television broadcasting stations; Cable television services; Magazines: publishing only, not printed on site
CEO: Timothy J O'Shaughnessy
* Ch Bd: Donald E Graham
CEO: Boisfeuillet Jones
CEO: David Rothkopf
COO: Hal S Jones
Treas: Daniel Lynch
Ex VP: Andrew S Rosen
Sr VP: Nicole M Maddrey
Sr VP: Ann L McDaniel
Sr VP: Gerald M Rosberg
VP: Candy Lee
Board of Directors: Katherine Weymouth, Lee C Bollinger, Christopher C Davis, Barry Diller, Thomas S Gayner, Anne M Mulcahy, Ronald L Olson, James H Shelton, Larry D Thompson, G Richard Wagoner Jr

D-U-N-S 92-775-5389
■ GRAHAM MARINE INC
(Suby of SEACOR HOLDINGS INC) ★
7910 Main St Ste 200, Houma, LA 70360-3427
Tel (985) 876-5400 Founded/Ownrshp 1995
Sales 36.8MM[E] EMP 1,500
SIC 4499 Boat rental, commercial
Pr: Milton Rose
* Treas: Lenny Dantin
* VP: Timothy Mc Keand

D-U-N-S 96-161-1642 IMP/EXP
GRAHAM PACKAGING CO EUROPE LLC
(Suby of REYNOLDS GROUP HOLDINGS LIMITED)
2401 Pleasant Valley Rd # 2, York, PA 17402-9600
Tel (717) 849-8500 Founded/Ownrshp 2011
Sales 1.7MMM[E] EMP 8,300
SIC 3089 Plastic containers, except foam
CEO: Mark S Burgess
* CFO: David W Bullock
* Treas: William E Hennessey
* Ofcr: Michael L Korniczky
* Sr VP: Peter T Lennox
Admn Mgr: Beth Knarr
Plnt Mgr: Steve Quandt
Sls Mgr: Neil Kerrod

D-U-N-S 00-744-2040 IMP
GRAHAM PACKAGING CO INC
(Suby of REYNOLDS GROUP HOLDINGS LIMITED)
700 Indian Springs Dr # 100, Lancaster, PA 17601-7801
Tel (717) 849-8500 Founded/Ownrshp 2011
Sales 3.4MMM[E] EMP 4,915[E]
SIC 5199 3089 5162 Packaging materials; Plastic containers, except foam; Plastics materials
CFO: David W Bullock
S&M/VP: Fabrice Agbassi

D-U-N-S 36-354-6698 EXP
GRAHAM PACKAGING CO LP
(Suby of GRAHAM PACKAGING CO INC) ★
700 Indian Springs Dr # 100, Lancaster, PA 17601-7801
Tel (717) 849-8500 Founded/Ownrshp 2011
Sales 1.3MMM[E] EMP 4,915
Accts Deloitte & Touche Llp Philade
SIC 3089 Plastic containers, except foam
CEO: Philip R Yates
Pr: Stacie Rampe
CEO: Mark S Burgess
COO: Roger M Prevot
Treas: Paul Wannemaher
Sr VP: Scott G Booth
Sr VP: David W Cargile Dave
Sr VP: Martin F Sauer
VP: Mark Leiden
VP: Mitch Mankosa
VP: Paul J Young

D-U-N-S 10-739-2172 IMP/EXP
GRAHAM PACKAGING HOLDINGS CO
(Suby of GRAHAM PACKAGING CO LP) ★
700 Indian Springs Dr # 100, Lancaster, PA 17601-7801
Tel (717) 849-8500 Founded/Ownrshp 2015
Sales 675.1MM[E] EMP 4,915
SIC 3089 Plastic containers, except foam
CEO: Mark S Burgess
CFO: David W Bullock
Ch: Mr Chinh E Chu
Sr VP: David W Cargile
Sr VP: George Lane
Sr VP: Peter T Lennox
Sr VP: Martin F Sauer
VP: Paul J Young
Admn Mgr: Scott Sheraw
Plnt Mgr: Pekka Sokka
Ql Cn Mgr: Robert Guyton
Board of Directors: Angelo G Acconcia, John R Chiminski, Charles E Kiernan, Gary G Michael, John R Murphy

D-U-N-S 12-181-6805
GRAHAM PACKAGING PLASTIC PRODUCTS INC
(Suby of REXAM LIMITED)
1 Seagate Ste 10, Toledo, OH 43604-1563
Tel (717) 849-8500 Founded/Ownrshp 2008
Sales 222.7MM[E] EMP 2,500
SIC 3089 Plastic containers, except foam
Ch Bd: Joseph H Lemieux

D-U-N-S 62-680-4934 IMP
GRAHAM PARTNERS INC
3811 West Chester Pike # 200, Newtown Square, PA 19073-2325
Tel (610) 408-0500 Founded/Ownrshp 1988
Sales 249.6MM[E] EMP 831
SIC 8742 6799

GRAHAM PROFESSIONAL PRODUCTS
See LITTLE RAPIDS CORP

D-U-N-S 62-154-6753
GRAIN CRAFT INC
MILNER MILLING
201 W Main St Ste 203, Chattanooga, TN 37408-1173
Tel (423) 265-2313 Founded/Ownrshp 1972
Sales 297.4MM[E] EMP 645
SIC 2041 Flour & other grain mill products
CEO: Peter Thomas Frederick
* CFO: Jonh Robert Noland
VP: Alan Koenig
VP: Kirk Stehr

D-U-N-S 92-933-2443
■ GRAIN INSPECTION PACKERS & STOCKYARDS ADMINISTRATION
(Suby of U S D A) ★
1400 Independence Ave Sw, Washington, DC 20250-0002
Tel (202) 720-0219 Founded/Ownrshp 1976
Sales NA EMP 2,000
SIC 9641 Food inspection agency, government;
* Prin: Julian Waterfield
Tech Mgr: Steven Tanner

D-U-N-S 15-382-0402 IMP/EXP
GRAIN MILLERS INC
GRAIN MILLERS SPECIALTY PDTS
10400 Viking Dr Ste 301, Eden Prairie, MN 55344-7268
Tel (952) 829-8821 Founded/Ownrshp 1975
Sales 256.9MM[E] EMP 450
SIC 2041 5084 Flour & other grain mill products; Oat flour; Dairy products manufacturing machinery
Pr: Steven J Eilertson
* Treas: Patrick Pautz
VP: Randal Baker
VP: Dan Beck
VP: Tom Giel
* VP: Christian P Kongsore
* VP: Rick L Schwein
CTO: Roger Mortenson
Software D: Brian Ecker
Sfty Mgr: Grant McCallum
Opers Mgr: Mike Lawson

GRAIN MILLERS SPECIALTY PDTS
See GRAIN MILLERS INC

D-U-N-S 19-848-4180 IMP/EXP
GRAIN PROCESSING CORP
(Suby of KENT CORP) ★
1600 Oregon St, Muscatine, IA 52761-1404
Tel (563) 264-4265 Founded/Ownrshp 1943
Sales 182.9MM[E] EMP 656[E]
SIC 2869 2085 2082 Grain alcohol, industrial; Grain alcohol for beverage purposes; Malt beverages
Pr: J C Thorpe
* Pr: Doyle Tubant
* Ch: Gage A Kent
VP: Rani Thomas
* VP: Eric Thomsen
VP: Ralph Wilkinson
VP Sls: Tom Wiesner

GRAIN SYSTEMS
See GSI GROUP LLC

D-U-N-S 05-361-8240 IMP
■ GRAINGER INTERNATIONAL INC
(Suby of WW GRAINGER INC) ★
100 Grainger Pkwy, Lake Forest, IL 60045-5202
Tel (847) 535-1000 Founded/Ownrshp 1994
Sales 238.2MM[E] EMP 271
SIC 5074 5084 5085 5072 Heating equipment (hydronic); Industrial machinery & equipment; Electric tools; Power tools & accessories
Pr: Donald G Macpherson
VP: Michael Dubose
Sfty Mgr: Michael Jolly
Pr Mgr: Laura Coy

D-U-N-S 00-742-9038
GRAINLAND COOPERATIVE
421 S Colorado Ave, Haxtun, CO 80731-2708
Tel (970) 774-6166 Founded/Ownrshp 1919, 1997
Sales 137.1MM EMP 40
SIC 5191 4221 5531 5541 Fertilizers & agricultural chemicals; Animal feeds; Seeds: field, garden & flower; Grain elevator, storage only; Automotive tires; Automotive accessories; Filling stations, gasoline
Pr: Rick Unrein
* Ch Bd: Robert Shaffer
V Ch: Gary Wernsman
VP: Jan Workman

GRAM LUMBER COMPANY
See RSG FOREST PRODUCTS INC

D-U-N-S 93-985-5565
GRAMBLING STATE UNIVERSITY
403 Main St, Grambling, LA 71245-2761
Tel (318) 274-2558 Founded/Ownrshp 1901
Sales 94.8MM[E] EMP 900
SIC 8221 9411 Service academy; Administration of educational programs;
Pr: Cynthia Warrick
Top Exec: Mahendra Singh
Assoc VP: Nettie Daniels
Assoc VP: Winfred Jones
Ex VP: Leslie Randle
VP: Rashon Carruthers
VP: Stacey Duhon
VP: Evelyn Wynn
Exec: Destinee Westmoreland
Off Mgr: Katina Crowe
DP Exec: Donyetta Davis

D-U-N-S 01-241-1977
GRAMERCY PROPERTY TRUST
521 5th Ave Fl 30, New York, NY 10175-3001
Tel (212) 297-1000 Founded/Ownrshp 2004
Sales 237.2MM EMP 100[E]
SIC 6798 Real estate investment trusts
CEO: Gordon F Dugan
* Ch Bd: Charles E Black
Pr: Benjamin P Harris
CFO: Jon W Clark
Ex VP: Edward J Matey Jr
Ex VP: Edward Matey
VP: Clifton Coffey
VP: David Corpening
VP: Christine Imming
VP: Britton Winterer
Exec: Kathy Bilotta

D-U-N-S 17-041-3319
GRAMERCY PROPERTY TRUST INC
521 5th Ave Fl 30, New York, NY 10175-3001
Tel (212) 297-1000 Founded/Ownrshp 2004
Sales 107.9MM EMP 103
SIC 6798 Real estate investment trusts
CEO: Gordon F Dugan
* Ch Bd: Allan J Baum
Pr: Benjamin P Harris
CFO: Jon W Clark
Ex VP: Edward J Matey Jr
Sr VP: Wayne Stevens
IT Man: Prudence Duke
Board of Directors: Gregory F Hughes, Jeffrey E Kelter, Charles S Laven, William H Lenehan

D-U-N-S 05-295-3783
■ GRANBURY HOSPITAL CORP (TX)
LAKE GRANBURY MEDICAL CENTER
(Suby of COMMUNITY HEALTH SYSTEMS INC) ★
1310 Paluxy Rd, Granbury, TX 76048-5655
Tel (817) 573-2273 Founded/Ownrshp 1972
Sales 121.7MM EMP 185
SIC 8062 General medical & surgical hospitals
* Owner: Di CK Carey
* Pr: Martin G Schweinhart
* CFO: W Larry Cash
* Ch: Robert Burns
* VP: T Mark Buford
* VP: James W Doucette
Mktg Dir: Amanda Maikranz
Doctor: Susan M Davis

D-U-N-S 62-164-0630
GRANCARE LLC
(Suby of MARINER HEALTHCARE MANAGEMENT) ★
1 Ravinia Dr Ste 1400, Atlanta, GA 30346-2112
Tel (770) 393-0199 Founded/Ownrshp 1997
Sales 99.7MM[E] EMP 13,800
SIC 8051 8052 8093 8071 Skilled nursing care facilities; Extended care facility; Intermediate care facilities; Rehabilitation center, outpatient treatment; Testing laboratories; Pathological laboratory
Ch Bd: Keith B Pitts
Pr: Dennis Sarcasa
VP: Ken Tabler
Board of Directors: Charles Carden, Susan Thomas Whittle

D-U-N-S 07-615-1000
GRAND AERIE OF FRATERNAL ORDER OF EAGLES
1623 Gateway Cir, Grove City, OH 43123-9309
Tel (614) 883-2200 Founded/Ownrshp 1898
Sales 11.6MM EMP 2,338
Accts Baker Tilly Virchow Krause Llp
SIC 8641 Fraternal associations
Pr: David Tice
* Ch Bd: Edgar L Bollenbacher
* Ch: Chris Lainas Jr
Treas: Bob Larsen
* Treas: Donald R Jim West

GRAND AMERICA HOTEL, THE
See GRAND AMERICA HOTELS & RESORTS INC

D-U-N-S 78-501-4858
GRAND AMERICA HOTELS & RESORTS INC
GRAND AMERICA HOTEL, THE
555 S Main St, Salt Lake City, UT 84111-4100
Tel (801) 596-5717 Founded/Ownrshp 2005
Sales 209.1MM[E] EMP 2,700[E]
SIC 7011 Hotels & motels
* VP: B T Fery
* VP: M A Sykes
Genl Mgr: Bruce Ferry
CTO: Ali Afati
Dir IT: Matt Ballif
Sls Dir: Kara Swenson
Sls Mgr: Jonathan Bakker
Sls Mgr: Laurie Cannon
Sls Mgr: Blake Carling
Sls Mgr: Danielle Palmer

D-U-N-S 06-984-1526
GRAND BLANC COMMUNITY SCHOOLS
11920 S Saginaw St, Grand Blanc, MI 48439-1402
Tel (810) 591-6000 Founded/Ownrshp 1919
Sales 85.9MM EMP 900
Accts Lewis & Knopf Pc Flint Mi
SIC 8211 Public elementary school; Public junior high school; Public senior high school

D-U-N-S 14-951-5913
▲ GRAND CANYON EDUCATION INC
3300 W Camelback Rd, Phoenix, AZ 85017-3030
Tel (602) 639-7500 Founded/Ownrshp 1949
Sales 778.2MM EMP 3,650[E]
Tkr Sym LOPE Exch NGS
SIC 8221 Colleges universities & professional schools; University
Pr: Brian E Mueller
* Ch Bd: Brent D Richardson
COO: W Stan Meyer
CFO: Daniel E Bachus
Sr VP: Brian M Roberts
VP: Mark Alexander
CIO: Joseph N Mildenhall
Board of Directors: Bradley A Casper, Sara R Dial, Jack A Henry, David J Johnson, Kevin F Warren

D-U-N-S 07-445-0750
■ GRAND CANYON UNIVERSITY INC (AZ)
(Suby of GRAND CANYON EDUCATION INC) ★
3300 W Camelback Rd, Phoenix, AZ 85017-1097
Tel (602) 639-7500 Founded/Ownrshp 1949
Sales 460.1MM[E] EMP 4
Accts Kpmg Llp Phoenix Arizona
SIC 8221 University
Pr: Gil Stafford
* Ch Bd: Brent Richardson
* Pr: Brian Mueller
* COO: Stan Meyer
* CFO: Dan Bachus
Sr VP: Sarah Boeder
Sr VP: Scott Fehrenbacher
Sr VP: Christel Mosby
Sr VP: Scott Raleigh
VP: Julie Chaney
VP: Kate Hogan
VP: Jennifer Lech
VP: Dilek Marsh
VP: Fran Roberts
VP: Kelly Sanderson
Dir Risk M: Eric Engstrom
Assoc Dir: Ryan Wilson

D-U-N-S 78-042-8900
GRAND CASINOS INC
ISLAND VIEW CASINO RESORT
3300 W Beach Blvd, Gulfport, MS 39501-1800
Tel (228) 314-2100 Founded/Ownrshp 1991
Sales 268.6MM[E] EMP 7,300[E]
SIC 7011 Casino hotel
Pt: Lindsey Inman
* Pt: Terry Green
* Pt: Rick Harder
Bd of Dir: Kim Garris
Ex VP: John Bakley
Dir Risk M: Tony Vanderslice

GRAND CIRCLE CORPORATION
See GRAND CIRCLE LLC

D-U-N-S 05-355-5256
GRAND CIRCLE LLC
GRAND CIRCLE CORPORATION
347 Congress St, Boston, MA 02210-1222
Tel (617) 350-7500 Founded/Ownrshp 1985
Sales 109.4MM[E] EMP 700[E]
SIC 4725 Tour operators
CEO: Alan E Lewis
* CFO: Sean Stover
Ex VP: Joe Cali
* VP: Andre Atemasov
VP: Thomas Cauchon
VP: Kacie Garganta
* VP: Vinod George
VP: Heather Heverling
VP: Simon Horsburgh
VP: Jeremy Loeckler
VP: Diane Rooney
VP: George Trant

D-U-N-S 10-066-5041
GRAND FORKS PUBLIC SCHOOLS
2400 47th Ave S, Grand Forks, ND 58201-3405
Tel (701) 746-2200 Founded/Ownrshp 1881
Sales 80.4MM[E] EMP 1,500
SIC 8211 Public elementary & secondary schools
Genl Mgr: Rosanne Momm

GRAND HOME FURNISHINGS
See GRAND PIANO & FURNITURE CO

GRAND HOMES
See GRAND TEXAS HOMES INC

GRAND ISLAND PUBLIC SCHOOLS
See HALL COUNTY SCHOOL DISTRICT 2

D-U-N-S 00-817-7321 IMP
GRAND ISLE SHIPYARD INC
(Suby of NANA DEVELOPMENT CORP) ★
18838 Highway 3235, Galliano, LA 70354-4038
Tel (985) 475-5238 Founded/Ownrshp 2011
Sales 812.3MM[E] EMP 1,050
SIC 1389 Oil field services
CEO: Robert C Pregeant
* Pr: Mark A Pregeant
CFO: Dan St Germaine
* Treas: Richard Pregeant
* VP: Bryan Pregeant
IT Man: Kaysee Belanger
IT Man: Buddy Toups
Snr PM: Stuart Clouatre

D-U-N-S 08-027-2576
GRAND OLE OPRY LLC
1 Gaylord Dr, Nashville, TN 37214-1207
Tel (615) 316-6180 Founded/Ownrshp 2006
Sales 1.0MM[E] EMP 1,000[E]
SIC 8741 Management services

D-U-N-S 87-915-8608
GRAND PACIFIC RESORTS INC
5900 Pasteur Ct Ste 200, Carlsbad, CA 92008-7336
Tel (760) 431-8500 *Founded/Ownrshp* 1993
Sales 206.1MM^E *EMP* 800
SIC 6531 7011 Time-sharing real estate sales, leasing & rentals; Hotels & motels
CEO: Timothy J Stripe
Pr: Sherri Weeks-Rivera
COO: Nigel Lobo
**VP:* David Brown
VP: Lisa Wanzenried
Area Mgr: Julie Daronco
Genl Mgr: Holly Ansley
Dir IT: Sabrina Lockemaston
IT Man: Dan Betbadal
IT Man: Loren Mehl
Sls&Mrk Ex: Randy Nakagawa

D-U-N-S 36-461-1822 IMP
GRAND PACKAGING INC
COMMAND PACKAGING
3840 E 26th St, Vernon, CA 90058-4107
Tel (323) 980-0918 *Founded/Ownrshp* 1989
Sales 93.9MM^E *EMP* 200
SIC 2673 Bags: plastic, laminated & coated
CEO: Pete Grande
**COO:* Albert Halimi

D-U-N-S 00-895-6823 IMP
GRAND PIANO & FURNITURE CO
GRAND HOME FURNISHINGS
4235 Electric Rd Ste 100, Roanoke, VA 24018-8445
Tel (540) 776-7000 *Founded/Ownrshp* 1946
Sales 123.0MM *EMP* 650
Accts Ja Johnson Co Pc Conyer
SIC 5712 5021 Furniture stores; Beds & bedding
CEO: George B Cartledge Jr
**Pr:* George B Cartledge III
CFO: Randy Lundy
**Treas:* Randall W Lundy
**Ex VP:* Robert G Bennett
Ex VP: Robert Bennett
VP: Alan Zeigler
Store Mgr: Paul Hurst
Store Mgr: Christopher Rhodes
VP Opers: Kenny Childs
Sls Mgr: Ray Graham

D-U-N-S 01-059-7169
GRAND PRAIRIE CITY OF (INC)
317 College St, Grand Prairie, TX 75050-5636
Tel (972) 237-8000 *Founded/Ownrshp* 1909
Sales NA *EMP* 1,000
Accts Weaver And Tidwell Llp Dalla
SIC 9111 City & town managers' offices; Mayors' offices
COO: Sholeh Karimi
CFO: Vivian Parker
Bd of Dir: Greg Giessner
Bd of Dir: Roger Lopez
Ofcr: Joshua Stelter
Exec: Diane Castillo
Exec: Susan Faulkner
Prgrm Mgr: Dane Stovall
Off Admin: Linda Townley
Dir IT: Connie J Coker
IT Man: Mike Inman

D-U-N-S 07-933-2763
GRAND PRAIRIE INDEPENDENT SCHOOL DISTRICT (TX)
GPISD
2602 S Belt Line Rd, Grand Prairie, TX 75052-5344
Tel (972) 264-6141 *Founded/Ownrshp* 1925
Sales 290.2MM *EMP* 3,500
Accts Hereford Lynch Sellars & Kir
SIC 8211 Public elementary & secondary schools; Public junior high school; Public senior high school
Bd of Dir: John Stewart
Pr Dir: Sam Buchmeyer
Instr Medi: Kathy Seybert
HC Dir: Pat Shull

D-U-N-S 01-708-4237 IMP
GRAND RAPIDS FOAM TECHNOLOGIES INC
GRFT
2788 Remico St Sw, Wyoming, MI 49519-2410
Tel (616) 726-1677 *Founded/Ownrshp* 1949
Sales 211.4MM^E *EMP* 250
SIC 5199 Foam rubber
Pr: Ben Amann

D-U-N-S 06-222-6758
GRAND RAPIDS PUBLIC SCHOOLS
1331 Franklin St Se, Grand Rapids, MI 49506-2634
Tel (616) 819-2000 *Founded/Ownrshp* 1835
Sales 258.2MM *EMP* 4,000
Accts Brickley Delong Pc Grand Rapi
SIC 8211 Elementary & secondary schools
**CFO:* Lisa Freiburger
CFO: Larry Oberst
**Ex Dir:* Mel Atkins II
Off Admin: Linda Mireles
MIS Dir: Walter Deboer
IT Man: David Vanderwall
Psych: James Gerakinis
Psych: Daniel Nelson
Psych: Dean Vernon
Pathlgst: Susan Behnke
Pathlgst: Carmelita Brown

D-U-N-S 07-426-4391 IMP
GRAND RIVER DAM AUTHORITY
GRDA
226 W Dwain Willis Ave, Vinita, OK 74301-4654
Tel (918) 256-5545 *Founded/Ownrshp* 1935
Sales 430.4MM *EMP* 468
Accts Deloitte & Touche Llp Tulsa
SIC 4911 1629 Generation, electric power; Transmission, electric power; Distribution, electric power; Dams, waterways, docks & other marine construction
CEO: Dan Sullivan
COO: Tim Brown
CFO: Carolyn Dougherty
CFO: Henry Neftzger
Ofcr: Derrick Bidleman
Ofcr: Scott Cox
Ofcr: Jason Littlefield
Dir Bus: Grant Burget
CTO: Holly Moore
Dir IT: Miya Boyken
IT Man: Ray Flaming

GRAND SIERRA RESORT AND CASINO
See MEI-GSR HOLDINGS LLC

D-U-N-S 78-225-1016
GRAND SIERRA RESORT CORP
2500 2nd St, Reno, NV 89595-1201
Tel (800) 501-2651 *Founded/Ownrshp* 2011
Sales 130.5MM^E *EMP* 1,500
SIC 7011 Resort hotel; Casino hotel
Pr: Thomas J Schrade
**CFO:* Andrew Tammen
Sr VP: Jeff Miller
VP: Corey Gene
VP: Jim Latser
Exec: Ron Pedrotti
Exec: Larry Rosborough
Ex Dir: Lisa Smith
Ex Dir: Tom Sullivan
Genl Mgr: Micheal Carsch
Genl Mgr: Edward Josimov

D-U-N-S 80-014-4128
■ **GRAND SLAM HOLDINGS LLC**
BLACKSTONE GROUP
(*Suby of* BLACKSTONE CAPITAL PARTNERS V LP) ★
345 Park Ave Bsmt Lb4, New York, NY 10154-0004
Tel (212) 583-5000 *Founded/Ownrshp* 2006
Sales 1.5MMM^E *EMP* 5,470^E
SIC 3842 Surgical appliances & supplies; Implants, surgical
CEO: Stephen A Schwarzman

GRAND STAND REGIONAL MED CTR
See GRAND STRAND REGIONAL MEDICAL CENTER LLC

D-U-N-S 60-374-8042
GRAND STRAND REGIONAL MEDICAL CENTER LLC
GRAND STAND REGIONAL MED CTR
809 82nd Pkwy, Myrtle Beach, SC 29572-4607
Tel (843) 449-4411 *Founded/Ownrshp* 2005
Sales 265.2MM *EMP* 1,000
SIC 8062 General medical & surgical hospitals
CEO: Mark Sims
Pr: Doug White
CFO: Robert Grace
Prin: Susan Satterfield
Mktg Dir: Joan Carroza
Doctor: James Brannon
Doctor: Kenneth Houghton
Doctor: Charles Tarbert

D-U-N-S 07-373-0079
GRAND STRAND WATER & SEWER AUTHORITY
GSWSA
166 Jackson Bluff Rd, Conway, SC 29526-8750
Tel (843) 443-8200 *Founded/Ownrshp* 1970
Sales 85.5MM *EMP* 310
Accts Elliott Davis Decosimo Llc C
SIC 4941 4952 Water supply; Sewerage systems
CEO: Fred R Richardson
**COO:* Irvin Wooley
**CFO:* Marguerite Carroll
**Ch:* Sidney F Thompson
**Prin:* Robert M Floyd Jr
**Prin:* Wilbur M James
**Prin:* Arnold Johnson
**Prin:* Robert Rabon
**Prin:* Richard Singleton
**Prin:* Liston Wells
Ex Dir: Fred R Ichadson

D-U-N-S 19-656-4848 IMP
GRAND SUPERCENTER INC
H MART
(*Suby of* H MART, INC.)
300 Chubb Ave, Lyndhurst, NJ 07071-3502
Tel (201) 507-9900 *Founded/Ownrshp* 2003
Sales 83.6MM^E *EMP* 200^E
Accts Choi Kim & Park Llp Irvine
SIC 5141 Groceries, general line
CEO: Ilyeon Kwon
Store Mgr: Will Wood

D-U-N-S 02-919-3661
■ **GRAND TETON LODGE CO**
JACKSON HOLE GOLF & TENNIS
(*Suby of* VAIL RESORTS INC) ★
Highway 89 5 Mls N Moran, Moran, WY 83013
Tel (307) 543-2811 *Founded/Ownrshp* 1926
Sales 12.0MM *EMP* 1,100
SIC 7011 Vacation lodges
CEO: Alex Klein
Treas: Mark Schoppet
Sr VP: Mark Bigalke

D-U-N-S 60-835-4601
GRAND TEXAS HOMES INC
GRAND HOMES
(*Suby of* GHI HOLDINGS, INC.)
15455 Dallas Pkwy # 1000, Addison, TX 75001-6772
Tel (972) 387-6000 *Founded/Ownrshp* 1986
Sales 88.1MM^E *EMP* 174
SIC 1521 New construction, single-family houses
CEO: Stephen H Brooks
CFO: David Abbott
**CFO:* Tim Litinas
VP: Beau Brooks
VP: Marsue Heffner
VP: Alan Luna
Area Mgr: Scott Houck
Div Mgr: Craig Barrow
Prd Mgr: Buzzy Broyles
Prd Mgr: Lowell Morren
Prd Mgr: Michael Pearce

GRAND THEATER, THE
See SOUTHERN THEATRES LLC

D-U-N-S 07-217-6105
GRAND TRAVERSE BAND ECONOMIC DEVELOPMENT CORP
GRAND TRAVERSE RESORT CASINOS
2331 N West Bay Shore Dr, Suttons Bay, MI 49682-9365
Tel (231) 534-8000 *Founded/Ownrshp* 1998
Sales 46.8MM^E *EMP* 1,024
SIC 7011 7993 5812 Casino hotel; Gambling establishments operating coin-operated machines; Gambling machines; Gambling machines, coin-operated; Eating places
Pr: Richard Bailey
**CFO:* Richard Andrew

D-U-N-S 10-674-8833
GRAND TRAVERSE BAND LLC
TURTLE CREEK CASINO
2605 N West Bay Shore Dr, Suttons Bay, MI 49682-9275
Tel (231) 534-7750 *Founded/Ownrshp* 1980
Sales NA *EMP* 1,100
SIC 9131 Executive & legislative combined
Ch Bd: Robert Kewaygashcum
**Ch:* Derek J Bailey
**Ch:* Sandra Witherspoon
Telecom Ex: Evans Sam

GRAND TRAVERSE RESORT CASINOS
See GRAND TRAVERSE BAND ECONOMIC DEVELOPMENT CORP

D-U-N-S 07-424-1217
GRAND TRUNK CORP
(*Suby of* COMPAGNIE DES CHEMINS DE FER NATIONAUX DU CANADA)
17641 Ashland Ave, Homewood, IL 60430-1339
Tel (708) 332-3500 *Founded/Ownrshp* 1970
Sales 155.1M *EMP* 2,000
SIC 4011 Railroads, line-haul operating
Pr: Paul M Tellier
VP: Robert A Walker

D-U-N-S 13-547-6328
GRAND TRUNK WESTERN RAILROAD CO
CN
(*Suby of* GRAND TRUNK CORP) ★
17641 Ashland Ave, Homewood, IL 60430-1339
Tel (708) 332-3500 *Founded/Ownrshp* 1992
Sales 147.3M^E *EMP* 1,900^E
SIC 4011 Railroads, line-haul operating
Pr: Claude Mongeau
**COO:* Jim Vena
**CFO:* Luc Jobin
**Ex VP:* Sean Finn
**Sr VP:* Jeff Liepelt

GRAND UNION FAMILY MARKETS
See GU MARKETS LLC

D-U-N-S 11-030-0279
GRAND UNION HEALTHCARE LLC
MONROE MANNOR
226 E Monore St, Jay, OK 74346
Tel (918) 253-4500 *Founded/Ownrshp* 2000
Sales 205.4MM *EMP* 60
SIC 8059 Nursing home, except skilled & intermediate care facility

D-U-N-S 05-969-2996
GRAND VALLEY STATE UNIVERSITY
MEADOWS GOLF CLUB , THE
1 Campus Dr, Allendale, MI 49401-9403
Tel (616) 331-5000 *Founded/Ownrshp* 1960
Sales 342.1MM *EMP* 3,428
Accts Plante & Moran Pllc Grand Ra
SIC 8221 University
Pr: Thomas J Haas
Pr: Nancy Giardina
Pr: Jeff Musser
Pr: Timothy Thimmesch
Trst: Kate P Wolters
Top Exec: Linda Masselink
Assoc VP: Julia Guevara
Ex VP: Terrell Couch
VP: Daniel Aday
**VP:* James Bachmeier
VP: Jim Bachmeier
**VP:* Jesse Bernal
**VP:* Lynn Blue
VP: Ryan Bowles
VP: Duane Clay
VP: Briand Copeland
**VP:* Gayle R Davis
VP: Gayle Davis
VP: Corinne Farleigh
**VP:* Karen Loth
VP: Jessica Macvane

GRAND VIEW HEALTH
See GRAND VIEW HOSPITAL

D-U-N-S 86-125-0868 IMP
GRAND VIEW HOSPITAL
GRAND VIEW HEALTH
700 Lawn Ave, Sellersville, PA 18960-1548
Tel (215) 453-4000 *Founded/Ownrshp* 1913
Sales 189.1MM *EMP* 1,600
Accts Crowe Horwath Llp Louisville
SIC 8062 General medical & surgical hospitals
CEO: Stuart Fine
Treas: Mitchell P Barrer
VP: Jane Ferrymd
VP: Jean Keeler
Dir Sec: Tom Hennink
Obsttrcn: Angela Boylan
Opthamlgy: Ann C Guidera
Doctor: Carl Hansen
Doctor: James Hurley
Pharmcst: Patricia Thompson

D-U-N-S 00-611-0274 IMP
GRANDE CHEESE CO
GRANDE CSTM INGREDIENTS GROUP
250 Camelot Dr, Fond Du Lac, WI 54935-8029
Tel (920) 952-7200 *Founded/Ownrshp* 1941
Sales 272.0MM^E *EMP* 760
SIC 2022 Natural cheese; Whey, raw or liquid
Pr: Wayne Matzke
**CFO:* Todd Koss
VP: Jeff Kondo

D-U-N-S 62-311-5701
GRANDE COMMUNICATIONS NETWORKS LLC
(*Suby of* RIO HOLDINGS INC) ★
401 Carlson Cir, San Marcos, TX 78666-6730
Tel (512) 878-4000 *Founded/Ownrshp* 2006
Sales 96.5MM^E *EMP* 10^E
SIC 4841 Cable & other pay television services
Sr VP: C Matthew Rohre
Treas: Douglas T Brannagan
Sr VP: W K Ferguson Jr
VP: Brady Adams
VP: Jared P Benson
VP: J Lyn Findley
**VP:* Lamar Horton
VP: Mark Machen
**VP:* Shane Schilling
VP: Kay Stroman
VP: Frank R Wink

GRANDE CSTM INGREDIENTS GROUP
See GRANDE CHEESE CO

D-U-N-S 78-826-8865
GRANDPOINT BANK
(*Suby of* GRANDPOINT CAPITAL INC) ★
355 S Grand Ave Ste 2400, Los Angeles, CA 90071-1589
Tel (213) 626-0085 *Founded/Ownrshp* 2006
Sales NA *EMP* 78
SIC 6022 State commercial banks
CEO: Don M Griffith
Pr: Ana Gomezgil
Pr: Andrew Wong
**Pr:* Dan C Yates
**Treas:* David Scarbrough
Ex VP: David Anderson
Ex VP: R Bianchini
**Ex VP:* Anthony Q Evans
Ex VP: John Nixon
**Ex VP:* David J Ross
Ex VP: Cams S Wahba
**Ex VP:* Loraine White
**Ex VP:* Anthony J Xinis
VP: Amin Eslami
VP: Hasmik Keshishyan
VP: Duane King
VP: James Moore
VP: Maria Sanchez
VP: Ctp Shaw
VP: Phil Soh
VP: Mindy Webb

D-U-N-S 80-877-3472
GRANDPOINT CAPITAL INC
333 S Grand Ave Ste 4250, Los Angeles, CA 90071-1587
Tel (213) 542-4410 *Founded/Ownrshp* 2012
Sales 168.3MM^E *EMP* 181^E
SIC 6799 Investors
CEO: Don M Griffith
**COO:* Deborah A Marsten
**CFO:* Jerro Otsuki

GRANDVIEW HOSPITAL
See STRESS CARE/BRIDGES

GRANDVIEW HOSPITAL & MED CTR
See DAYTON OSTEOPATHIC HOSPITAL

D-U-N-S 00-794-2725
GRANGE INSURANCE ASSOCIATION INC (WA)
200 Cedar St, Seattle, WA 98121-1223
Tel (206) 448-4911 *Founded/Ownrshp* 1894
Sales 141.1MM *EMP* 200
SIC 8611 Regulatory associations
Pr: Ryan M Dudley
**CFO:* Sean I McGourty
VP: Sean McGourty
**VP:* Todd C Merkley
**VP:* Steven W Stogner
**VP:* James L Van Farowe
Software D: Doug Walker
Sftwr Eng: Sathish Baskaran
Sftwr Eng: Michael Edgar
Sftwr Eng: Rachel Kerbrat
Mktg Dir: Bob Horn

GRANGE INSURANCE COMPANIES
See GRANGE MUTUAL CASUALTY CO

D-U-N-S 00-790-1861
GRANGE MUTUAL CASUALTY CO
GRANGE INSURANCE COMPANIES
671 S High St, Columbus, OH 43206-1049
Tel (614) 445-2900 *Founded/Ownrshp* 1935
Sales NA *EMP* 1,450
SIC 6331 Automobile insurance; Fire, marine & casualty insurance: mutual
CEO: Tom Welch
Pr: David Berentz
Pr: John R Delucia
Pr: Brent Lombardi
Pr: Brad Sorensen
CFO: Terri Dalenta
CFO: J Paul McCaffrey
Assoc VP: Ken Kozek
VP: Michael Basinger
VP: Tim Cunningham
VP: John Deluca
VP: Elizabeth Dinnin
VP: Sharon Hall
VP: Christopher Montgomery
VP: Doug Sharp
VP: Margaret Wildi

D-U-N-S 07-635-0230
GRANGER ASSOCIATES INC
16980 Wood Rd, Lansing, MI 48906-1044
Tel (517) 372-2800 *Founded/Ownrshp* 1974
Sales 89.4MM^E *EMP* 119
SIC 4953 1794 6552

GRANGER BUILDING SERVICES
See GRANGER CONSTRUCTION CO INC

D-U-N-S 00-385-6804
GRANGER CONSTRUCTION CO INC (MI)
GRANGER BUILDING SERVICES
6267 Aurelius Rd, Lansing, MI 48911-4296
Tel (517) 393-1670 *Founded/Ownrshp* 1960
Sales 232.1MM *EMP* 215
SIC 1542 1541

D-U-N-S 08-036-8273
GRANGES AMERICAS INC
(*Suby of* GRANGES AB)
801 Crescent Centre Dr, Franklin, TN 37067-6224
Tel (615) 778-2004 *Founded/Ownrshp* 2016
Sales 192.1MM^E *EMP* 565^E
SIC 3353 Coils, sheet aluminum

D-U-N-S 14-797-7198 IMP
GRANISER LLC
GRANISER TILE KITCHEN BATH
(*Suby of* GRANISER GRANIT SERAMIK SANAYI VE TICARET ANONIM SIRKETI)
5650 General Wash Dr, Alexandria, VA 22312-2415
Tel (703) 256-5650 *Founded/Ownrshp* 2003
Sales 103.7MM^E *EMP* 860
SIC 5032 Tile & clay products

GRANISER TILE KITCHEN BATH
See GRANISER LLC

GRANIT-BRONZ DIV
See COLD SPRING GRANITE CO INC

D-U-N-S 00-799-8933
GRANITE CITY ELECTRIC SUPPLY CO INC (MA)
19 Quincy Ave, Quincy, MA 02169-6750
Tel (617) 472-6500 *Founded/Ownrshp* 1931
Sales 286.8MM^E *EMP* 180
SIC 5063 5719 Electrical supplies; Lighting fixtures; Lamps & lamp shades; Lighting fixtures
CEO: Phyllis Papani Godwin
**Pr:* Steven Helle
**Pr:* Nicholas V Papani
**CFO:* Mark Anderson
VP: George McDonald
**Prin:* Nicholas Papani
Brnch Mgr: Ellis Cole
IT Man: Paul Knox
IT Man: Bill Raney
Manager: Jeff Hammond
Sales Asso: Bob Watson

D-U-N-S 07-632-3927 IMP
■ **GRANITE CITY FOOD & BREWERY LTD**
(*Suby of* CONCEPT DEVELOPMENT PARTNERS LLC) ★
3500 Amrcn Blvd W Ste 450, Minneapolis, MN 55431
Tel (952) 215-0660 *Founded/Ownrshp* 1997
Sales 134.1MM *EMP* 3,153^E
Accts Schechter Dokken Kanter And
Tkr Sym GCFB *Exch* OTO
SIC 5812 5813 Eating places; Drinking places
CEO: Robert J Doran
Mng Pt: Jason Adamczyk
Mng Pt: Tony Donatelle
Mng Pt: Jill Woodford
**CEO:* Phil Costner
CFO: James G Gilbertson
Ch: Fouad Z Bashour
Bd of Dir: Eric Laclair
Ofcr: Dean S Oakey
Exec: Joe Hunt
Exec: Monica Underwood

D-U-N-S 07-197-6096
■ **GRANITE CITY HOSPITAL CORP**
(*Suby of* QUORUM HEALTH CORP) ★
2100 Madison Ave, Granite City, IL 62040-4713
Tel (618) 798-3000 *Founded/Ownrshp* 2016
Sales 120.2MM *EMP* 920
SIC 8062 General medical & surgical hospitals
Pr: Michael J Culotta

D-U-N-S 00-691-4642
■ **GRANITE CONSTRUCTION CO** (CA)
(*Suby of* GRANITE CONSTRUCTION INC) ★
585 W Beach St, Watsonville, CA 95076-5123
Tel (831) 724-1011 *Founded/Ownrshp* 1922
Sales 1.2MMM^E *EMP* 1,500
Accts Pricewaterhousecoopers Llp Sa
SIC 1611 1622 Highway & street construction; General contractor, highway & street construction; Bridge construction; Tunnel construction
Pr: James H Roberts
**Ex VP:* Laurel Krzeminski
**Ex VP:* Christopher S Miller
**Sr VP:* Richard A Watts
Snr Mgr: Kathleen Schreckengost

D-U-N-S 62-282-6360
▲ **GRANITE CONSTRUCTION INC**
585 W Beach St, Watsonville, CA 95076-5123
Tel (831) 724-1011 *Founded/Ownrshp* 1922
Sales 2.3MMM *EMP* 3,200
Tkr Sym GVA *Exch* NYS
SIC 1611 1622 1629 1442 Highway & street construction; General contractor, highway & street construction; Bridge construction; Tunnel construction; Dam construction; Canal construction; Land leveling; Construction sand & gravel
Pr: James H Roberts
**Ch Bd:* William H Powell
COO: Christopher S Miller
CFO: Laurel J Krzeminski
Sr VP: Michael F Donnino
Sr VP: Martin P Matheson
Sr VP: James D Richards
Sr VP: Michael E Stoecker
Sr VP: Matt Tyler
Exec: Susan Rose
Area Mgr: Alex Rountree
Board of Directors: Claes G Bjork, James W Bradford Jr, Gary M Cusumano, William G Dorey, David H Kelsey, Michael F McNally

D-U-N-S 10-912-7378
GRANITE FALLS ENERGY LLC
15045 Highway 23 Se, Granite Falls, MN 56241-1946
Tel (320) 564-3100 *Founded/Ownrshp* 2000
Sales 231.2MM *EMP* 75^E
SIC 2869 2085 2046 Ethyl alcohol, ethanol; Distillers' dried grains & solubles & alcohol; Corn oil, refined
CEO: Steve Christensen
**Ch Bd:* Paul Enstad
CFO: Stacie Schuler
**V Ch Bd:* Rodney R Wilkison
Board of Directors: Leslie Bergquist, Dean Buesing, Kenton Johnson, Bruce Lavigne, Michael Lund, Myron D Peterson, Martin Seifert, David Thompson

D-U-N-S 00-323-9907
GRANITE GROUP WHOLESALERS LLC
6 Storrs St, Concord, NH 03301-4856
Tel (603) 224-1901 *Founded/Ownrshp* 1997
Sales 91.0MM^E *EMP* 250^E
SIC 5075 5074 Warm air heating equipment & supplies; Heating equipment (hydronic)
CFO: Russell Gagne
Off Mgr: Patrice Nogues

D-U-N-S 05-573-9577
GRANITE GROUP WHOLESALERS LLC
GOULET SUPPLY COMPANY
6 Storrs St, Concord, NH 03301-4856
Tel (603) 545-3345 *Founded/Ownrshp* 1971
Sales 206.8MM^E *EMP* 369
SIC 5074 5075 Heating equipment (hydronic); Plumbing fittings & supplies; Warm air heating equipment & supplies
CFO: Libby Stevenson
Sr VP: Tracie Sponenberg
VP: Matthew Spangler
VP: Jacob Williams
Comm Man: Dave Buck
Brnch Mgr: Joseph Ruffo
Off Mgr: Kevin Condron
Off Admin: Theresa Couture
**CIO:* Joseph Goff
IT Man: Coburn Flannery
Opers Mgr: Julie Chani

D-U-N-S 96-510-7274
GRANITE HENSEL PHELPS JV
420 6th Ave, Greeley, CO 80631-2332
Tel (970) 352-6565 *Founded/Ownrshp* 2010
Sales 650.0MM *EMP* 1,000
SIC 1541 1542 Industrial buildings & warehouses; Nonresidential construction
VP: Jon W Ball
VP: John A Franich

D-U-N-S 07-838-0655
GRANITE HOLDINGS INC
2580 28th St Sw, Grand Rapids, MI 49519-2106
Tel (616) 532-2375 *Founded/Ownrshp* 2003
Sales 132.9MM^E *EMP* 370^E
SIC 5169 Gases, compressed & liquefied
Pr: Gary Nyhuis

GRANITE MOUNTAIN QUAR NUMBER 1
See MCGEORGE CONTRACTING CO INC

D-U-N-S 00-922-1961
GRANITE ROCK CO
350 Technology Dr, Watsonville, CA 95076-2488
Tel (831) 768-2000 *Founded/Ownrshp* 1900
Sales 1.3MMM^E *EMP* 700
SIC 1442 3273 5032 2951 1611 3271 Gravel mining; Construction sand mining; Ready-mixed concrete; Sand, construction; Stone, crushed or broken; Asphalt & asphaltic paving mixtures (not from refineries); Highway & street paving contractor; Concrete block & brick
CEO: Thomas H Squeri
**V Ch:* Bruce G Woolpert
**Ch:* Mary E Woolpert
Ex VP: Rodney Jenny
VP: Shirley Ow
Area Mgr: Karl Philipovitch
Brnch Mgr: Roger Swenson
Mtls Mgr: Elden Davis
Opers Mgr: Denny Mahler
Snr Mgr: Alex Baranda

D-U-N-S 07-299-8743
GRANITE SCHOOL DISTRICT
2500 S State St, Salt Lake City, UT 84115-3164
Tel (385) 646-5000 *Founded/Ownrshp* 1904
Sales 336.2MM^E *EMP* 8,000
Accts Squire & Company Pc Orem Ut
SIC 8211 Public elementary & secondary schools
COO: Katharine Newton
Bd of Dir: Audrey Price
Bd of Dir: Carla Wonder-Mcdowell
Ofcr: Thomas Arnold
Ofcr: Janet Bell-Morley
Ofcr: Lee Dial
Ofcr: Jeremy Gilger
Ofcr: Kevin Hyde
Ofcr: Raymond Kaleel
Ofcr: Cole McAfee
Ofcr: Randall Porter
Ofcr: Kyle Rolfson
Ofcr: Allan Shinney
Ofcr: Johnny Siriprathane
Ofcr: Brett Walker
VP: Julene M Jolley
VP: Julene Oliver

D-U-N-S 19-275-2996
■ **GRANITE SERVICES INTERNATIONAL INC**
(*Suby of* GENERAL ELECTRIC CO) ★
201 N Franklin St # 1000, Tampa, FL 33602-5182
Tel (813) 242-7400 *Founded/Ownrshp* 2006
Sales 13.5MM^E *EMP* 2,000
SIC 7363 Help supply services
Pr: Randy Willis
**Treas:* Morgan Williams
**VP:* Richard T Maxstadt
IT Man: Juan Galeano

D-U-N-S 11-177-7939
GRANITE TELECOMMUNICATIONS LLC
100 Newport Avenue Ext # 1, Quincy, MA 02171-2126
Tel (617) 933-5500 *Founded/Ownrshp* 2002
Sales 865.8MM *EMP* 650
SIC 4813 Local & long distance telephone communications
CEO: Robert Hale Jr
**COO:* Rand Currier
**CFO:* Richard Wurman
VP: Sam Kline
**VP:* Paul Stutzman
Exec: Christopher Barbaro
Exec: Matthew Cotter
Exec: Judy Parsons
Dir IT: Ben McCarthy
Info Man: William Witunsky
Sftwr Eng: Varsha Talekar

D-U-N-S 10-124-8938
GRANT CADARET & CO INC
1 Lincoln Rd Fl 5, Syracuse, NY 13212-3612
Tel (315) 471-2191 *Founded/Ownrshp* 1988
Sales 153.1MM *EMP* 120
SIC 6211 Brokers, security; Dealers, security
Pr: Arthur F Grant
**CFO:* Donald J Taylor
**Sr VP:* Beda L Johnson
Sr VP: Norlyn Popo
**Sr VP:* Arnold Taylor
VP: Sherry A Deperro
VP: Kevin Makowski
Sales Asso: Grace Frost
Board of Directors: Megan Grant

GRANT GEOPHYSICAL
See GEOKINETICS MANAGEMENT INC

D-U-N-S 00-285-3240 IMP/EXP
■ **GRANT PRIDECO INC**
ATLAS BRADFORD DIVISION
(*Suby of* NOV) ★
10100 Houston Oaks Dr, Houston, TX 77064-3514
Tel (281) 878-8000 *Founded/Ownrshp* 1960, 2008
Sales 765.0MM^E *EMP* 4,857
SIC 3533 Oil & gas field machinery; Oil & gas drilling rigs & equipment; Bits, oil & gas field tools: rock; Drilling tools for gas, oil or water wells
Pr: John D Deane
Pr: David R Black
**Pr:* Jim Breihan
**CFO:* Matthew D Fitzgerald
**VP:* Greg L Boane
VP: Gary W Childress
**VP:* Philip Choyce
VP: Philip A Choyce
**VP:* Quintin V Kneen
VP: Tom McGrann
IT Man: Casey Lambright
Board of Directors: David J Butters, Eliot M Fried, Gordon T Hall, Dennis R Hendrix, Harold E Layman, Robert K Moses, Joseph E Reid, David A Trice

D-U-N-S 00-175-2971
GRANT THORNTON LLP
(*Suby of* GRANT THORNTON INTERNATIONAL LIMITED)
171 N Clark St Ste 200, Chicago, IL 60601-3370
Tel (312) 856-0200 *Founded/Ownrshp* 1924
Sales 1.1MMM^E *EMP* 4,588
SIC 8721 8742 Accounting, auditing & bookkeeping; Auditing services; Accounting services, except auditing; Management consulting services
Pt: J Michael McGuire
Pt: Jacqueline Akerblom
Pt: Paul A Beecy
Pt: Terry Bilbo
Pt: Jim Brady
Pt: Jeff Burgess
Pt: Jeffrey Burgess
Pt: Ken Cunningham
Pt: Jim Dee
Pt: Mark Edwards
Pt: Forest Frazier
Pt: Doreen Griffith
Pt: Pamela Harless
Pt: Nichole Jordan
Pt: Denise Ho Lippuner
Pt: Massimo Messina
Pt: Ben Proffitt
Pt: Randy Robason
Pt: Chris Ruckman
Pt: Srikant Sastry
Mng Pt: Jamie Fowler

D-U-N-S 08-851-6380
GRANTHAM MAYO VAN OTTERLOO & CO LLC
GMO
40 Rowes Wharf Ste 600, Boston, MA 02110-3361
Tel (617) 330-7500 *Founded/Ownrshp* 1977
Sales 357.7MM^E *EMP* 600
SIC 6282 6722 Investment counselors; Mutual fund sales, on own account
**Ch Bd:* Arjun Divecha
**CEO:* Brad Hilsabeck
CFO: Shep Burnett
**Chf Mktg O:* Ben Inker
Ofcr: Kelly Donovan
Ofcr: Carolyn Haley
Exec: Drew Tamoney
Assoc Dir: Paul Chadwick
Dir IT: Mike Patsenker
IT Man: Marc Clasby
Software D: Stefan Cegalis

GRANTS & RESEARCH DEPT.
See RELIANT MEDICAL GROUP INC

D-U-N-S 07-065-0668 IMP
GRAPEMAN FARMS LP
STEVECO
9777 Wilshire Blvd # 918, Beverly Hills, CA 90212-1910
Tel (310) 273-9540 *Founded/Ownrshp* 1974, 2011
Sales 130.3MM^E *EMP* 100^E
SIC 0172

D-U-N-S 00-353-6104
GRAPEVINE - COLLYVILLE INDEPENDENT SCHOOL DIST
VISTA ALTERNATIVE CAMPUS
3051 Ira E Woods Ave, Grapevine, TX 76051-3817
Tel (817) 251-5466 *Founded/Ownrshp* 1994
Sales 181.2MM *EMP* 11
Accts Hankins Eastup Deaton Tonn
SIC 8211 Public combined elementary & secondary school

D-U-N-S 02-032-7755
GRAPEVINE/COLLEYVILLE INDEPENDENT SCHOOL DISTRICT
3051 Ira E Woods Ave, Grapevine, TX 76051-3817
Tel (817) 251-5200 *Founded/Ownrshp* 1920, 2004
Sales 181.2MM *EMP* 1,800
Accts Hankins Eastup Deaton Tonn
SIC 8211 Public elementary & secondary schools

D-U-N-S 00-905-1665
■ **GRAPHIC ARTS CENTER INC** (DE)
GACSC
(*Suby of* CENVEO CORP) ★
2000 Nw Wilson St, Portland, OR 97209-1884
Tel (503) 224-7777 *Founded/Ownrshp* 1901, 1995
Sales 188.0MM *EMP* 450
SIC 2752 Color lithography
Pr: Frank Stammers
**Pr:* Ron Jensen
CFO: Pat Hevrdjs
VP: Fim Fetherston
VP: Keith Larson
VP: Vince Schaller
**VP:* Steven M Williamson
Board of Directors: Ron Jensen, Jerry Mahoney, Paul Riley, Rodger Willmer

D-U-N-S 05-277-1664
GRAPHIC ARTS MUTUAL INSURANCE CO INC
180 Genesee St, New Hartford, NY 13413-2200
Tel (315) 734-2000 *Founded/Ownrshp* 1914
Sales NA *EMP* 1,325
Accts Pricewaterhousecoopers Llp Bo
SIC 6331 Property damage insurance; Reciprocal interinsurance exchanges: fire, marine, casualty
Ch Bd: W Craig Heston
**Treas:* John R Zapisek
**Ex VP:* Jay Douglas Robinson

D-U-N-S 02-589-0045
GRAPHIC CENTER GROUP CORP
OFFICE GRAPHIC DESIGN
2150 Coral Way Fl 1, Coral Gables, FL 33145-2629
Tel (305) 961-1649 *Founded/Ownrshp* 2010
Sales 500.0MM *EMP* 8
SIC 7372 7336 Prepackaged software; Graphic arts & related design
CEO: Oliver Moreno

D-U-N-S 14-751-1612 IMP/EXP
■ **GRAPHIC COMMUNICATIONS HOLDINGS INC**
UWW
(*Suby of* VERITIV OPERATING CO) ★
5700 Darrow Rd Ste 110, Hudson, OH 44236-5026
Tel (330) 650-5522 *Founded/Ownrshp* 2003
Sales 263.1MM^E *EMP* 110^E
SIC 5111 7389 Fine paper; Printing broker
CEO: Mary A Laschinger
**Pr:* Matt Dawley
Pr: Mike Nash
**CEO:* Allan Dragone
**COO:* Ken Flajs
**CFO:* David Earney
**Sr VP:* Bill King
**Sr VP:* John Patneau
VP: Steven Finzer
VP: Mark Keener
VP Sls: Charlie Fetter

D-U-N-S 00-211-1896 IMP
GRAPHIC CONTROLS ACQUISITION CORP
(*Suby of* GRAPHIC CONTROLS HOLDINGS INC) ★
400 Exchange St, Buffalo, NY 14204-2064
Tel (716) 853-7500 *Founded/Ownrshp* 2004
Sales 136.6MM^E *EMP* 280
SIC 2752 2679 Tag, ticket & schedule printing: lithographic; Paper products, converted
CEO: Sam Heleba
COO: Jeffrey A Blair
**CFO:* Gary M Toomey
VP: Brandon Hoffman
VP Bus Dev: Eric Saenger
Admn Mgr: Theodore Sucher
Genl Mgr: Sam Haleba
Info Man: Gary Toomy
Sfty Mgr: Chris Talley
Mfg Mgr: Jim Freitas
Opers Mgr: Edward Eagen

D-U-N-S 08-004-9001
GRAPHIC CONTROLS HOLDINGS INC
(*Suby of* NISSHA PRINTING CO.,LTD.)
400 Exchange St, Buffalo, NY 14204-2064
Tel (716) 853-7500 *Founded/Ownrshp* 2016
Sales 136.6MM^E *EMP* 280^E
SIC 2752 2679 6719 Tag, ticket & schedule printing: lithographic; Paper products, converted; Investment holding companies, except banks
CEO: Samuel Heleba
Sec: Thomas Reardon

D-U-N-S 93-267-6484 IMP
GRAPHIC CONVERTING INC
877 N Larch Ave, Elmhurst, IL 60126-1114
Tel (630) 758-4100 *Founded/Ownrshp* 1976
Sales 91.8MM^E *EMP* 300
SIC 2675 Die-cut paper & board
Pr: John R Tinnon
**CFO:* Joe Yaney
**Prin:* Stibi Skalaski
Board of Directors: Jessica Prost

D-U-N-S 94-378-6657 IMP/EXP
▲ GRAPHIC PACKAGING HOLDING CO
1500 Riveredge Pkwy # 100, Atlanta, GA 30328-4658
Tel (770) 240-7200 *Founded/Ownrshp* 2007
Sales 4.1MMM *EMP* 12,000
Accts Ernst & Young Llp Atlanta Ge
Tkr Sym GPK *Exch* NYS
SIC 2631 2653 2671 Container, packaging & boxboard; Container board; Folding boxboard; Coated & treated board; Boxes, corrugated: made from purchased materials; Plastic film, coated or laminated for packaging
Pr: Michael P Doss
Ch Bd: David W Scheible
CFO: Stephen R Scherger
Sr VP: Carla J Chaney
Sr VP: Alan R Nichols
Sr VP: Lauren S Tashma
Sr VP: Michael S Ukropina
Sr VP: Joseph P Yost
Exec: Kelly Williams
Mtls Mgr: Juran Peters
Natl Sales: Brian Sahs
Board of Directors: G Andrea Botta, David D Campbell, Paul D Carrico, Jeffrey H Coors, Robert A Hagemann, Harold R Logan Jr, Philip R Martens, Lynn A Wentworth

D-U-N-S 79-702-4411
GRAPHIC PACKAGING INTERNATIONAL CORP
1795 Dogwood St Unit 100, Louisville, CO 80027-3131
Tel (303) 215-4600 *Founded/Ownrshp* 1992
Sales 1.0MMM *EMP* 4,200
SIC 2657 2671 2655 Folding paperboard boxes; Packaging paper & plastics film, coated & laminated; Fiber cans, drums & containers
Ch Bd: Jeffrey H Coors
**COO:* David W Scheible
COO: Gail Constancio
**CFO:* Luis E Leon
Treas: Beth Parish
CIO: Ron Bettencourt
Mill Mgr: Mark Shumate
Plnt Mgr: Roger Kuhl
Pr Dir: Paddy Broughton
Board of Directors: John D Beckett, William K Coors, Harold R Logan, James K Peterson, John Hoyt Stookey

D-U-N-S 80-883-9062 IMP/EXP
■ GRAPHIC PACKAGING INTERNATIONAL INC
(*Suby of* GRAPHIC PACKAGING HOLDING CO) ★
1500 Riveredge Pkwy # 100, Atlanta, GA 30328-4658
Tel (770) 240-7200 *Founded/Ownrshp* 1982
Sales 3.3MMM[E] *EMP* 8,896
SIC 2657 2631 7389 Folding paperboard boxes; Container, packaging & boxboard; Packaging & labeling services
CEO: Michael P Doss
**Pr:* Takashi Sugiyama
**CFO:* Daniel J Blount
Sr VP: Michael R Schmal
**Sr VP:* Lauren S Tashma
VP: Jim Barutt
VP: Walter Bowles
**VP:* Deborah R Frank
Dir Risk M: William Frye
Off Mgr: Lee Thomas
IT Man: Nathan Ducote

GRAPHIC PACKAGING INTL
See GPI HOLDINGS INC

D-U-N-S 93-354-9008 IMP
GRAPHIC PAPER INC
31 Windsor Pl, Central Islip, NY 11722-3301
Tel (631) 761-9700 *Founded/Ownrshp* 1989
Sales 100.5MM *EMP* 120
SIC 5111

D-U-N-S 02-630-6829 IMP
GRAPHIC SOLUTIONS GROUP INC (TX)
GSG
4601 Spring Valley Rd, Dallas, TX 75244-3902
Tel (214) 748-3271 *Founded/Ownrshp* 1966
Sales 104.5MM[E] *EMP* 97
SIC 5084 Printing trades machinery, equipment & supplies
Pr: Randall M Granberry
**Pr:* Mark Grandberry
**VP:* Anthony Bruckler
**VP:* Brandon Granberry
**VP:* Larry Rogers
Genl Mgr: Jason Freeman
Prd Mgr: Garry Stroup
Sls Mgr: Will Jackson
Sales Asso: John Raaser
Sales Asso: Danny Standard

D-U-N-S 08-544-0592 IMP/EXP
GRASS AMERICA INC
(*Suby of* WURTH GROUP OF NORTH AMERICA INC) ★
1202 Nc Highway 66 S, Kernersville, NC 27284-3537
Tel (336) 996-4041 *Founded/Ownrshp* 2004
Sales 102.0MM *EMP* 201
SIC 3429 Cabinet hardware
Pr: Tom Kipp
CFO: Kemenns Tollin
VP: George Domenig
Rgnl Mgr: Mike Bannister
QA Dir: Kristy Kiser
IT Man: Tom Mitchell
VP Opers: Hartmut Voght
Mtls Mgr: Larry Moore
Ql Cn Mgr: Stan Hughey
Natl Sales: Randy Pennington
Mktg Dir: Matthiaf Bulla

GRASS HOPPER COMPANY
See MORIDGE MANUFACTURING INC

D-U-N-S 12-368-1111 IMP
GRASS VALLEY INC
(*Suby of* GRASS VALLEY CANADA)
125 Crown Point Ct, Grass Valley, CA 95945-9515
Tel (530) 478-3000 *Founded/Ownrshp* 2002
Sales 131.5MM[E] *EMP* 750
SIC 3663 Radio & TV communications equipment
Pr: Marc Valentine
COO: Dave Perillo
Sr VP: Patrick Montliaud
Sr VP: Steve Ronneberg
VP: Jean-Marc Hoffer
Prgrm Mgr: Brian Kodai
CTO: Fredrick Schmidt
IT Man: Thomas Oates
VP Mfg: Lennart Hjord
VP Mktg: Michael Kronk
Pr Mgr: Denise R Williams

D-U-N-S 96-576-7945 IMP
■ GRASS VALLEY USA LLC
(*Suby of* BELDEN INC) ★
125 Crown Point Ct, Grass Valley, CA 95945-9515
Tel (800) 547-8949 *Founded/Ownrshp* 2014
Sales 182.7MM[E] *EMP* 650
SIC 3651 3661 3663 Household audio & video equipment; Television receiving sets; Radio receiving sets; Video cassette recorders/players & accessories; Telephone sets, all types except cellular radio; Radio & TV communications equipment
Pr: Marco Lopez
Sr VP: Aengus Linehan
CTO: Fredrick Schmidt
Netwrk Mgr: Thomas Oates
Sftwr Eng: Timothy Callahan

D-U-N-S 00-608-0204 IMP/EXP
GRASSLAND DAIRY PRODUCTS INC (WI)
N8790 Fairground Ave, Greenwood, WI 54437-7668
Tel (715) 267-6182 *Founded/Ownrshp* 1904
Sales 117.5MM[E] *EMP* 200[E]
SIC 2021 5143 Creamery butter; Cheese
Pr: Dallas Wuethrich
**VP:* Tayt Wuethrich
Exec: Sam Wuethrich
Dir IT: Stacy Petkovsek
Info Man: Stacy Mathis
QC Dir: Roger Mielke
Sfty Mgr: Ryan Martin
Plnt Mgr: Kevin Lucas
Plnt Mgr: Jeff Miller
Prd Mgr: Jim Heck

GRATIOT COMMUNITY HOSPITAL
See MIDMICHIGAN MEDICAL CENTER-GRATIOT

D-U-N-S 05-628-4606
GRATON ECONOMIC DEVELOPMENT AUTHORITY
(*Suby of* GRATON RESORT & CASINO) ★
915 Golf Course Dr, Rohnert Park, CA 94928-1818
Tel (707) 800-7616 *Founded/Ownrshp* 2013
Sales NA *EMP* 1,297[E]
SIC 9311 Gambling control board, government
Bd of Dir: Greg M Sarris
**Bd of Dir:* Jeannette E Anglin
**Bd of Dir:* Robert F Baguio Sr

GRATON RESORT & CASINO
See FEDERATED INDIANS OF GRATON RANCHERIA

GRAVES MENU MAKER FOODS
See MENU MAKER FOODS INC

D-U-N-S 02-205-0074
GRAVES OIL CO
RASCAL'S CONVENIENCE STORE
226 Pearson St, Batesville, MS 38606-2428
Tel (662) 563-4604 *Founded/Ownrshp* 1968
Sales 211.0MM *EMP* 146
Accts J Gary Kornegay Batesville
SIC 5171 5541 5411 Petroleum bulk stations; Filling stations, gasoline; Convenience stores, independent
Pr: C Fred Graves III
**VP:* Charlie B Graves
VP: Gary M Stiles
MIS Dir: Ben Graves

GRAVES SUPPLY
See WOMACK ELECTRIC & SUPPLY CO INC

D-U-N-S 78-498-7104
GRAVICK GROUP LLC
4985 Fm 1017, San Isidro, TX 78588-1503
Tel (956) 330-5676 *Founded/Ownrshp* 2001
Sales 1.3MM *EMP* 1,178
SIC 8742 7371 7389 Management consulting services; Computer software development & applications;

D-U-N-S 00-724-6776
■ GRAVITY FINANCIAL LLC
(*Suby of* SS&C TECHNOLOGIES HOLDINGS INC) ★
1 New Boston Dr Ste 7, Canton, MA 02021-2859
Tel (781) 828-7800 *Founded/Ownrshp* 2012
Sales 56.2MM[E] *EMP* 1,090[E]
SIC 6282 Investment advice

GRAY
See ICE BUILDERS INC

D-U-N-S 05-708-5656 IMP/EXP
■ GRAY & CO
(*Suby of* SENECA FOODS CORP) ★
3325 W Polk Rd, Hart, MI 49420-8149
Tel (231) 873-5628 *Founded/Ownrshp* 2015
Sales 87.8MM[E] *EMP* 425
SIC 2033 Maraschino cherries: packaged in cans, jars, etc.
CEO: James G Reynolds
**Ex VP:* Joshua E Reynolds
Sr VP: Jacqueline Case

D-U-N-S 00-820-5429
GRAY & CO INC
3625 N I 10 Service Rd W, Metairie, LA 70002-7029
Tel (504) 888-7790 *Founded/Ownrshp* 1948
Sales NA *EMP* 200
SIC 6331 Fire, marine & casualty insurance & carriers
Pr: Michael Gray
CFO: Robert Hughes
**VP:* Eric V Gray
**VP:* Walter Gray
**VP:* David W Pixberg

D-U-N-S 00-342-3803
GRAY & SON INC (MD)
430 W Padonia Rd, Lutherville Timonium, MD 21093-2274
Tel (410) 771-4311 *Founded/Ownrshp* 1908, 1966
Sales 110.9MM[E] *EMP* 350
Accts Jones Hall Advisors
SIC 1611 1623 1794 General contractor, highway & street construction; Water, sewer & utility lines; Excavation & grading, building construction
CEO: George V Palmer
**CEO:* Robert F Webbert
**CFO:* Rick Scheetz
**Treas:* Barbara Webbert
**VP:* Jay Hergenroeder
**VP:* Peter Placke
**VP:* Joel Stockbridge
Sfty Mgr: Nic Barone
Opers Mgr: Les Preble
Prd Mgr: Wayne Walsh

D-U-N-S 00-700-2181 IMP
GRAY CONSTRUCTION INC (KY)
(*Suby of* GRAY INC) ★
10 Quality St, Lexington, KY 40507-1450
Tel (859) 281-5000 *Founded/Ownrshp* 1960
Sales 202.2MM[E] *EMP* 300
SIC 1541 1542 8712

D-U-N-S 10-834-9234
GRAY INC
10 Quality St, Lexington, KY 40507-1443
Tel (859) 281-5000 *Founded/Ownrshp* 1960
Sales 313.2MM[E] *EMP* 450
SIC 1541 1542

D-U-N-S 08-835-1002
GRAY OIL CO INC
804 Denver Ave, Fort Lupton, CO 80621-2164
Tel (303) 857-2288 *Founded/Ownrshp* 1978
Sales 102.0MM *EMP* 60
SIC 5171 5541 5411

D-U-N-S 17-591-4456
■ GRAY TELEVISION GROUP INC
WCTV 6
(*Suby of* VOLUNTEERTV.COM) ★
4370 Peachtree Rd Ne # 500, Brookhaven, GA 30319-3056
Tel (404) 266-8333 *Founded/Ownrshp* 1996
Sales 468.8MM[E] *EMP* 2,015[E]
SIC 4833 Television broadcasting stations
CEO: Hilton H Howell Jr
**Pr:* Nick Waller
Bd of Dir: Howell Newton
Sr VP: Jason Effinger
VP: Michael Braun
VP: Kevin Latek
**VP:* Mike Smith
Snr Ntwrk: Kraig Beahn
VP Opers: Julia Campbell

D-U-N-S 04-297-3875
▲ GRAY TELEVISION INC (GA)
4370 Peachtree Rd Ne # 500, Brookhaven, GA 30319-3056
Tel (404) 504-9828 *Founded/Ownrshp* 1897
Sales 597.3MM *EMP* 3,819
Tkr Sym GTN *Exch* NYS
SIC 4833 Television broadcasting stations
Ch Bd: Hilton H Howell Jr
CFO: James C Ryan
Ex VP: Jason Effinger
Ex VP: Kevin P Latek
Ex VP: Bob Smith
Ex VP: Nick Waller
VP: Jackson S Cowart IV

D-U-N-S 08-151-5988 IMP/EXP
GRAY VESTAR INVESTORS LLC
17622 Armstrong Ave, Irvine, CA 92614-5728
Tel (949) 863-1171 *Founded/Ownrshp* 1999
Sales 509.6MM[E] *EMP* 5,860
SIC 2253 2339 2335 2337 3961 2387 Dresses, knit; Skirts, knit; Pants, slacks or trousers, knit; T-shirts & tops, knit; Sportswear, women's; Scarves, hoods, headbands, etc.: women's; Jackets, untailored: women's, misses' & juniors'; Slacks: women's, misses' & juniors'; Women's, juniors' & misses' dresses; Bridal & formal gowns; Women's & misses' suits & coats; Suits: women's, misses' & juniors'; Jackets & vests, except fur & leather: women's; Skirts, separate: women's, misses' & juniors'; Costume jewelry; Apparel belts

D-U-N-S 00-190-3202
GRAYBAR ELECTRIC CO INC (NY)
34 N Meramec Ave, Saint Louis, MO 63105-1678
Tel (314) 573-9200 *Founded/Ownrshp* 1925
Sales 6.1MMM *EMP* 8,495
SIC 5063 5065

D-U-N-S 04-957-5371
GRAYCOR INC
2 Mid America Plz Ste 400, Oakbrook Terrace, IL 60181-4714
Tel (630) 684-7110 *Founded/Ownrshp* 1996
Sales 673.4MM[E] *EMP* 1,500
SIC 1541 1542 Industrial buildings & warehouses; Commercial & office building, new construction; Hospital construction; Shopping center construction
Ch: Gray Melvin
**CFO:* Steven Gray
**Ex VP:* Matthew Gray
Exec: Todd Ostransky
VP Admn: Dave Wing
Off Mgr: Renee Delaney
Dir IT: Sergio Ruiz
Sfty Mgr: Frank Deller
Mktg Dir: Sue Traeder

D-U-N-S 00-693-0341
GRAYCOR INDUSTRIAL CONSTRUCTORS INC
(*Suby of* GRAYCOR INC) ★
2 Mid America Plz Ste 400, Oakbrook Terrace, IL 60181-4714
Tel (630) 684-7110 *Founded/Ownrshp* 1921
Sales 378.3MM[E] *EMP* 1,000
SIC 1542 1541 Commercial & office building, new construction; Industrial buildings, new construction
Ch Bd: Melvin Gray
**Pr:* Sam Potter
**CFO:* Steven Gray
**Prin:* Bradley Teckenbrock

D-U-N-S 00-518-9790 IMP/EXP
GRAYHILL INC
561 W Hillgrove Ave, La Grange, IL 60525-5997
Tel (708) 354-1040 *Founded/Ownrshp* 1940, 1976
Sales 158.8MM[E] *EMP* 800
SIC 3613 3625 3679 3643 3575 Switches, electric power except snap, push button, etc.; Switches, electric power; Switches, electronic applications; Electronic switches; Electric switches; Keyboards, computer, office machine
CEO: Gene R Hill
**Pr:* Brian May
**CFO:* Jerome J Klingenberger
**VP:* Jamie Dobravec
**VP:* Keith Hansen
**VP:* James Happel
**VP:* Michael Raleigh
Comm Man: Angie Panos
Mng Dir: Judy Williams
Snr Sftwr: Torsten Chase
Sftwr Eng: Jordan Kamm

D-U-N-S 15-769-0926
GRAYLING CORP
CHILI'S
(*Suby of* BURGER KING) ★
4220 Edison Lks Pkwy 100, Mishawaka, IN 46545
Tel (856) 384-1212 *Founded/Ownrshp* 1986
Sales 30.2MM[E] *EMP* 1,100
SIC 5812 5813 6531 Restaurant, family: chain; Bar (drinking places); Real estate agents & managers
Pr: Daniel B Fitzpatrick
**Sr VP:* James Fitzpatrick
**VP:* Christoper Collier

D-U-N-S 00-617-9774 EXP
GRAYMONT (WI) LLC (WI)
C L M
(*Suby of* GRAYMONT LIMITED)
800 Hill Ave, Superior, WI 54880-1369
Tel (715) 392-5146 *Founded/Ownrshp* 1946
Sales 216.7MM[E] *EMP* 1,500[E]
SIC 3274 Agricultural lime; Hydrated lime
Pr: William Dodge
**CFO:* Jim Hetimovich
**CFO:* Robert Kanuit
VP: David La Liberte
**VP:* Dana Stone
Sls Mgr: Terry Spooner

D-U-N-S 18-295-5120 IMP
GRAYMONT INC
301 S 700 E 3950, Salt Lake City, UT 84102-2112
Tel (801) 262-3942 *Founded/Ownrshp* 1943
Sales 234.8MM[E] *EMP* 336
SIC 1429 2951 3273 Grits mining (crushed stone); Asphalt paving mixtures & blocks; Ready-mixed concrete
CEO: Stephane Godin
**CFO:* Kenneth Lahti
**VP:* Marc Dagenais
VP: Bryan Nielson
VP: Thomas Wakefield

D-U-N-S 96-539-6427 IMP/EXP
GRAYMONT WESTERN US INC
(*Suby of* CLI HOLDINGS INC) ★
3950 S 700 E Ste 301, Salt Lake City, UT 84107-1303
Tel (801) 262-3942 *Founded/Ownrshp* 1978
Sales 221.2MM[E] *EMP* 190
SIC 1411 Limestone, dimension-quarrying
Pr: Stephane Godin
**Pr:* Gary A Poole
**CFO:* Kenneth J Lahti
**VP:* Jeff Higgs

D-U-N-S 96-546-9260
GRAYS HARBOR COMMUNITY HOSPITAL
1006 N H St, Aberdeen, WA 98520-2599
Tel (360) 532-8330 *Founded/Ownrshp* 1983
Sales 100.5MM *EMP* 99
Accts Moss Adams Llp Everett Wa
SIC 8062 General medical & surgical hospitals
Pr: Tim Kuhn
COO: Thomas Hightower
CFO: Art Tanner
**Treas:* Jim Manenica
Chf Mktg O: Brent Rowe
**VP:* Ty Palmer
IT Man: Brandon Ford

D-U-N-S 07-926-5476
GRAYS HARBOR COMMUNITY HOSPITAL FOUNDATION
GRAYS HBR CMNTY HOSP E CAMPUS
915 Anderson Dr, Aberdeen, WA 98520-1097
Tel (360) 537-5000 *Founded/Ownrshp* 1940
Sales 89.2MM *EMP* 594
SIC 8062 General medical & surgical hospitals
Pr: Sharon Schermer
VP: Marilyn Guy
Dir Rx: Tom Kloepping
Surgeon: David Parks
Surgeon: Matthew Shepherd

GRAYS HARBOR PUD
See PUBLIC UTILITY DISTRICT NO 1 OF GRAYS HARBOR COUNTY

GRAYS HBR CMNTY HOSP E CAMPUS
See GRAYS HARBOR COMMUNITY HOSPITAL FOUNDATION

D-U-N-S 00-895-3812 IMP
GRAYSON-COLLIN ELECTRIC CO-OP INC
902 N Waco St, Van Alstyne, TX 75495
Tel (903) 482-7100 Founded/Ownrshp 1937
Sales 110.3MM EMP 100
Accts Bolinger Segars Gilbert And Mo
SIC 4911 Distribution, electric power
Pr: Charles Rice
CFO: Mike Roland
*Sec: Steve Robinson
*VP: Mark Brown

D-U-N-S 00-221-1209 IMP
GRAYWOOD COMPANIES INC (NY)
JASCO CUTTING TOOLS
1390 Mount Read Blvd, Rochester, NY 14606-2820
Tel (585) 254-7000 Founded/Ownrshp 2005
Sales 102.4MM^E EMP 620
SIC 3541 3545 3544 3398 Machine tools, metal cutting type; Boring mills; Countersinking machines; Deburring machines; Machine tool accessories; Drill bits, metalworking; Taps, machine tool; Reamers, machine tool; Special dies, tools, jigs & fixtures; Metal heat treating
Ch Bd: John M Summers
*Pr: Eugene Baldino
*CFO: Diane Simon
*VP: Dave Krigeer

GRDA
See GRAND RIVER DAM AUTHORITY

D-U-N-S 96-794-6232
GRDG HOLDINGS LLC
GARDEN RIDGE
19411 Atrium Pl Ste 170, Houston, TX 77084-6024
Tel (281) 578-2334 Founded/Ownrshp 1999
Sales 107.6MM^E EMP 3,510^E
SIC 5945 Hobby & craft supplies; Arts & crafts supplies
Sftwr Eng: Jaime Gabino
Snr Mgr: Susan Wenograd

GREAT AMERCN SEAFOOD IMPORT CO
See SOUTHWIND FOODS LLC

GREAT AMERICAN
See VIDA TRIPLE-S INC

D-U-N-S 01-361-1924 IMP/EXP
GREAT AMERICAN BEAUTY INC
PALM BEACH BEAUTE
124 N Swinton Ave, Delray Beach, FL 33444-2634
Tel (561) 496-2730 Founded/Ownrshp 2001
Sales 83.0MM^E EMP 14
SIC 5122 2844 Perfumes; Perfumes & colognes
Pr: Harold Ickovics
Pr: Dyann Davis
*CFO: Paul Smith

D-U-N-S 08-482-8599
GREAT AMERICAN COOKIE CO INC
(Suby of PRETZEL TIME) ★
4685 Frederick Dr Sw, Norcross, GA 30093
Tel (877) 639-2361 Founded/Ownrshp 1984
Sales 163.2MM^E EMP 1,002^E
SIC 5461 Cookies
Pr: Steve Russo
*CFO: Sandra Buffa

D-U-N-S 01-431-4802
GREAT AMERICAN DELI
(Suby of H T HACKNEY CO) ★
5828 Main St, Ooltewah, TN 37363-8714
Tel (423) 238-5492 Founded/Ownrshp 2009
Sales 7.8MM^E EMP 1,262^E
SIC 5812

D-U-N-S 18-005-2144
■ **GREAT AMERICAN FINANCIAL RESOURCES INC**
(Suby of AMERICAN FINANCIAL GROUP INC) ★
250 E 5th St Ste 1000, Cincinnati, OH 45202-4127
Tel (513) 333-5300 Founded/Ownrshp 1987
Sales NA EMP 1,422
SIC 6371 Pension, health & welfare funds; Union welfare, benefit & health funds
Pr: S Craig Lindner
Ch Bd: Carl H Lindner
COO: Charles R Scheper
CFO: Christopher P Miliano
Assoc VP: James Niehaus
Ex VP: Ernest T Giambra
Ex VP: Keith A Jensen
Ex VP: Mark F Muething
Ex VP: David B Rich
Ex VP: Bill Thaxton
Ex VP: David Vickers
Ex VP: Brad Wolfram
Sr VP: Mathew T Dukiewicz
Sr VP: Richard L Magoteaux
Sr VP: Michael J Prager
VP: Richard E Beavers
VP: Becky Birch
VP: Paul Britzky
VP: Anne Elmore
VP: Thomas Gourlay
VP: Mike Lesar
Board of Directors: Kenneth C Ambrecht, L Thomas Hiltz, Ronald G Joseph, John T Lawrence III, William R Martin, Joseph P Tomain

D-U-N-S 07-827-2717
■ **GREAT AMERICAN HOLDING INC** (OH)
(Suby of AMERICAN FINANCIAL GROUP INC) ★
301 E 4th St, Cincinnati, OH 45202-4245
Tel (513) 369-3000 Founded/Ownrshp 2002
Sales 244.6MM^E EMP 5,100^E
SIC 6719 Investment holding companies, except banks
Pr: Carl H Lindner III

D-U-N-S 00-136-8497 IMP/EXP
GREAT AMERICAN INDUSTRIES INC (DE)
(Suby of PUBLIC LOAN CO INC) ★
300 Plaza Dr, Vestal, NY 13850-3647
Tel (607) 729-9331 Founded/Ownrshp 1928, 1985
Sales 97.8MM^E EMP 400
SIC 3086 5031 5074 3442 3069 5091 Plastics foam products; Building materials, interior; Plumbing fittings & supplies; Metal doors, sash & trim; Metal doors; Wet suits, rubber; Watersports equipment & supplies; Diving equipment & supplies
Ch Bd: Burton I Koffman
*Sr VP: Richard E Koffman

D-U-N-S 05-735-6909 IMP/EXP
■ **GREAT AMERICAN INSURANCE CO**
(Suby of AMERICAN FINANCIAL GROUP INC) ★
301 E 4th St Ste 2800, Cincinnati, OH 45202-4257
Tel (513) 369-5000 Founded/Ownrshp 2016
Sales NA EMP 4,000
SIC 6331 Fire, marine & casualty insurance; Automobile insurance; Property damage insurance; Agricultural insurance
CEO: Carl H Lindner III
Pr: Tom Allen
Pr: Scott Leone
Pr: Lisa A Pennekamp
Pr: Dennis Strickland
Pr: David L Thompson
Pr: Mark Vuono
COO: Donald D Larson
COO: Mark F Muething
CFO: Joseph E Consolino
CFO: Jennifer Meyer
CFO: David Witzgall
Div Pres: F Michael Csorba
Div Pres: Jim Muething
Div Pres: Timothy C Weber
Ofcr: William Luckman
Ex VP: Jane Kornesczuk
Ex VP: Frank Scheckton
Sr VP: Frank Ceraolo
Sr VP: Karen H Horrell
Sr VP: Aaron Latto

GREAT AMERICAN SNACKS
See GAA HOLDINGS INC

D-U-N-S 08-046-9007
GREAT AMERICAN SNACKS INC
216 8th St N, Nampa, ID 83687-3029
Tel (208) 465-5111 Founded/Ownrshp 2016
Sales 85.0MM EMP 700
SIC 2038 Frozen specialties
Genl Mgr: Daniel Horan

D-U-N-S 00-136-7366 IMP
GREAT ATLANTIC & PACIFIC TEA CO INC
A & P
2 Paragon Dr, Montvale, NJ 07645-1718
Tel (201) 573-9700 Founded/Ownrshp 1859
Sales 6.7MMM^E EMP 39,000
SIC 5411 Supermarkets, chain; Supermarkets, 55,000-65,000 square feet (superstore)
Ch Bd: Greg Mays
Owner: Douglas Palmer
Pr: Paul Hertz
CFO: David Casali
CFO: Raymond P Silcock
Ex VP: George Graham
Ex VP: Thomas O'Boyle
Sr VP: William Costantini
Sr VP: John Harlow
Sr VP: Hans Heer
VP: Victor Alessandro
VP: Garry Baskin
VP: Marina Chassap
VP: Michael Debouchel
VP: Anthony Dispaltro
VP: Aaron Florian
VP: Brenda Galgano
VP: Allan Richard
VP: Hector Rodriguez
VP: Gulsen Sanyer
VP: Dan Slavin
Board of Directors: John D Barline, Maureen Tart-Bezer, Thomas Casey, Andreas Guldin, Christian W E Haub, Dan Kourkoumelis, Edward Lewis, Gregory Rayburn, Terrence J Wallock

D-U-N-S 60-823-0736 IMP
GREAT ATLANTIC NEWS LLC
NEWS GROUP-SOUTHEAST, THE
(Suby of JIM PATTISON INDUSTRIES LTD)
1962 Highway 160 W # 102, Fort Mill, SC 29708-8057
Tel (803) 802-8630 Founded/Ownrshp 1989
Sales 303.5MM^E EMP 1,654
SIC 5192 Magazines; Periodicals; Books
Pr: Terry Moser
Exec: Rochelle Hurse
Board of Directors: Nick Desmarais, Jim Pattison Jr, John Seebach

D-U-N-S 82-874-8116
GREAT BASIN INDUSTRIAL LLC
1284 Flint Meadow Dr A, Kaysville, UT 84037-9590
Tel (801) 543-2100 Founded/Ownrshp 2007
Sales 169.4MM^E EMP 375
SIC 3443 7699 1731 Industrial vessels, tanks & containers; Tank repair & cleaning services; General electrical contractor
Pr: Dan Clegg
*CFO: James David Oldham
*Treas: Jamie Astle
*VP: Scott Kent
*VP: Jesse Memmott
*VP: Jeff Murray

D-U-N-S 04-305-4774 IMP
GREAT BAY DISTRIBUTORS INC
2750 Eagle Ave N, Saint Petersburg, FL 33716-4106
Tel (727) 584-8626 Founded/Ownrshp 1968
Sales 199.5MM^E EMP 575
SIC 5181 Beer & other fermented malt liquors
Pr: Ronald Petrini
*CFO: Craig Rubright
*VP: William Carman
*VP: Bill Carmen
*VP: Sandra Ho

D-U-N-S 03-125-0947
GREAT BEND COOPERATIVE ASSOCIATION
606 Main St, Great Bend, KS 67530-5406
Tel (620) 793-3531 Founded/Ownrshp 1959
Sales 120.8MM EMP 82
Accts Lindburg Vogel Pierce Faris H
SIC 5153 5191 5171 4221 Grains; Feed; Fertilizer & fertilizer materials; Petroleum bulk stations; Grain elevator, storage only
Pr: Frank Riedl
Treas: Rick Hiss
Board of Directors: Brian Anshutz, Eric Batman, John De Werff, Randy Fanshier, Rick Hiss, Ron Koelsch, Dale Maneth, Kevin Mauler, Robert Standish

GREAT BREWERS
See L KNIFE & SON INC

GREAT CHINA EMPIRE
See GCE INTERNATIONAL INC

GREAT DANE DIVISION OFFICE
See GREAT DANE TRAILERS INC

D-U-N-S 96-482-2860 EXP
GREAT DANE LIMITED PARTNERSHIP
GREAT DANE TRAILERS
(Suby of CC INDUSTRIES) ★
222 N Lasalle St Ste 920, Chicago, IL 60601
Tel (773) 254-5533 Founded/Ownrshp 1996
Sales 513.4MM^E EMP 1,483
SIC 3715 Truck trailers; Demountable cargo containers
Pr: William H Crown
VP: Jeff Orban
Exec: Dean Reynolds

GREAT DANE TRAILERS
See GREAT DANE LIMITED PARTNERSHIP

D-U-N-S 00-332-6840
GREAT DANE TRAILERS INC
GREAT DANE DIVISION OFFICE
(Suby of GREAT DANE TRAILERS) ★
602 E Lathrop Ave, Savannah, GA 31415-1062
Tel (912) 644-2100 Founded/Ownrshp 1985, 2007
Sales 225.5MM^E EMP 1,000^E
SIC 5013 5012 Trailer parts & accessories; Trailers for trucks, new & used
CEO: Bill Crown
Treas: Susan Nyberg
VP: Charles Fetz
VP: Jimmy Phillips
Brnch Mgr: Warren Fore
Sls Mgr: Jason Lyle

D-U-N-S 02-966-6633 IMP
GREAT ESCAPE AMUSEMENT PARK
1172 State Route 9, Queensbury, NY 12804-1372
Tel (518) 792-3500 Founded/Ownrshp 1996
Sales 47.8MM^E EMP 1,900
SIC 7996 Theme park, amusement
Pr: Six Flags
Mktg Dir: Jennifer Mance

GREAT ESCAPE OF ILLINOIS, THE
See UNIVERSAL POOL CO INC

D-U-N-S 14-797-2277
GREAT EXPRESSIONS DENTAL CENTERS PC
GREAT EXPRESSIONS DENTAL CTR
28626 Telegraph Rd, Southfield, MI 48034-1934
Tel (248) 203-2330 Founded/Ownrshp 2016
Sales 68.8MM^E EMP 1,611^E
SIC 8021 8741 Dental clinics & offices; Business management
CEO: Richard E Beckman
COO: Vito Dacchille
CFO: Greg Nodland
VP: Jack Falvo
VP Mktg: Michael Galperin

GREAT EXPRESSIONS DENTAL CTR
See GREAT EXPRESSIONS DENTAL CENTERS PC

D-U-N-S 82-531-6821
GREAT FALLS PUBLIC SCHOOLS DIST1
GFPS
1100 4th St S, Great Falls, MT 59405-4301
Tel (406) 268-6052 Founded/Ownrshp 1884
Sales 410.0M^E EMP 1,768
Accts Junkermierclarkcampanellasteve
SIC 8211 Public elementary & secondary schools
Genl Mgr: Pamela Ramsted
IT Man: Katie Allen

D-U-N-S 88-460-8147 IMP/EXP
GREAT FLOORS LLC
524 E Sherman Ave, Coeur D Alene, ID 83814-2731
Tel (208) 664-5405 Founded/Ownrshp 2000
Sales 96.9MM^E EMP 450
SIC 1752 5713 Floor laying & floor work; Carpets
Pr: Doug Chadderdon
*VP: Jim McKay
VP Opers: Will Osborne
Sales Exec: Jeff Anderson
*Mktg Dir: Teresa Gavin

D-U-N-S 61-723-0094
GREAT HEARTS ACADEMIES
GREAT HEARTS ACADEMIES - ANTHE
3102 N 56th St Ste 300, Phoenix, AZ 85018-6606
Tel (602) 438-7045 Founded/Ownrshp 2004
Sales 2.1MM EMP 1,000
Accts Fester & Chapman Pc Phoenix
SIC 8211 Public combined elementary & secondary school
*Pr: Reed Porter
Ofcr: Robert Jackson
Ofcr: Jerilyn Olson
Sr VP: Katie Cobb
*Sr VP: Lisa Handley
Sr VP: Tamika McGehee
*VP: Jessica Pacheco

GREAT HEARTS ACADEMIES - ANTHE
See GREAT HEARTS ACADEMIES

GREAT ISLAND ENERGY
See GULF OIL LIMITED PARTNERSHIP

GREAT LAKES AUTOMATION SUPPLY
See KENDALL ELECTRIC INC

GREAT LAKES BEVERAGE
See WOLPIN CO

D-U-N-S 01-821-9808 IMP/EXP
GREAT LAKES CHEESE CO INC
17825 Great Lakes Pkwy, Hiram, OH 44234-9677
Tel (440) 834-2500 Founded/Ownrshp 1958
Sales 1.4MMM^E EMP 1,700
SIC 5143 2022 Cheese; Natural cheese
Pr: Gary Vanic
CFO: Russell Mullins
*Sec: John Epprecht
VP: Kurt Epprecht
VP: Brian Gamier
Exec: Mary J Toumerit
*Prin: Marcel Dasen
*Prin: Hans Epprecht
*Prin: Albert Z Meyers
Off Mgr: Barbara Martucci
Plnt Mgr: Walt Ehret

D-U-N-S 00-521-2808 IMP/EXP
■ **GREAT LAKES CHEMICAL CORP** (DE)
(Suby of CHEMTURA CORP) ★
199 Benson Rd, Middlebury, CT 06762-3218
Tel (203) 573-2000 Founded/Ownrshp 1932
Sales 792.5MM^E EMP 3,300
SIC 2899 2842 Fire retardant chemicals; Oxidizers, inorganic; Water treating compounds; Sanitation preparations, disinfectants & deodorants; Degreasing solvent
CEO: Craig Rogerson
*Pr: Anne Noonan
VP: Eric Wisnefsky

D-U-N-S 07-968-8489
■ **GREAT LAKES COCA-COLA DISTRIBUTION LLC**
(Suby of COCA-COLA REFRESHMENTS USA INC) ★
1 Coca Cola Plz Nw, Atlanta, GA 30313-2420
Tel (404) 374-8969 Founded/Ownrshp 2015
Sales 42.2MM^E EMP 1,000
SIC 2086 Bottled & canned soft drinks

D-U-N-S 78-877-3708
GREAT LAKES DENTAL LLC
GREAT LAKES DENTAL USA
10101 W Innovation Dr # 700, Wauwatosa, WI 53226-4860
Tel (262) 966-2428 Founded/Ownrshp 2005
Sales 2.2MM EMP 1,553
SIC 8021 Dental clinics & offices

GREAT LAKES DENTAL USA
See GREAT LAKES DENTAL LLC

D-U-N-S 00-693-0358 IMP/EXP
■ **GREAT LAKES DREDGE & DOCK CO LLC**
(Suby of GREAT LAKES DREDGE & DOCK CORP) ★
2122 York Rd Ste 200, Oak Brook, IL 60523-1981
Tel (630) 574-3000 Founded/Ownrshp 1890, 2003
Sales 629.2MM EMP 500
Accts Deloitte & Touche Llp Chicago
SIC 1629 Dredging contractor; Marine construction
CEO: Jonathan W Berger
*Pr: David E Simonelli
*CFO: Mark Marinko
*Treas: Katherine M Hayes
*Sr VP: Kyle D Johnson
*Sr VP: John F Karas

D-U-N-S 36-289-9130 IMP/EXP
▲ **GREAT LAKES DREDGE & DOCK CORP**
2122 York Rd Ste 200, Oak Brook, IL 60523-1981
Tel (630) 574-3000 Founded/Ownrshp 1890
Sales 856.8MM EMP 1,858^E
Tkr Sym GLDD Exch NGS
SIC 1629 1741 Dams, waterways, docks & other marine construction; Dredging contractor; Marine construction; Foundation building
CEO: Jonathan W Berger
Pr: Christopher P Shea
Pr: David E Simonelli
COO: Kyle D Johnson
CFO: Mark W Marinko
Sr VP: Stephen E Pegg
VP: Dan Devaney
VP: Chris Gunsten
VP: William Hanson
VP: Mark Marinko
VP: Cynthia Nielsen
VP: William F Pagendarm
VP: T C Roberts
Board of Directors: Carl A Albert, Peter R Deutsch, Ryan Levenson, Robert B Uhler, Michael J Walsh

D-U-N-S 05-477-5705
GREAT LAKES ENERGY COOPERATIVE
1323 Boyne Ave, Boyne City, MI 49712-8940
Tel (231) 582-6521 Founded/Ownrshp 1938
Sales 199.7MM EMP 235
SIC 4911 Distribution, electric power
VP: Brian Wierenga
Dir IT: Missy Thenikl
VP Opers: Daniel Nelson
Sfty Dirs: Tim Hartwick
VP Mktg: Pat Anzell
Mktg Dir: Kristy Beyer
Mktg Mgr: Shari Joles

D-U-N-S 11-803-7956
GREAT LAKES FINANCIAL MANAGEMENT GROUP INC
2033 Marinette Ave, Marinette, WI 54143-3864
Tel (715) 732-9955 Founded/Ownrshp 2001
Sales 100.0MM EMP 100
SIC 6211 8742 6282 6411 Security brokers & dealers; Financial consultant; Investment advisory service; Insurance agents, brokers & service
Pr: Michael Messer

GREAT LAKES MAINTENANCE
See GREAT LAKES PETROLEUM CORP

D-U-N-S 08-030-9516
GREAT LAKES PETROLEUM CO (TN)
4500 Renaissance Pkwy, Cleveland, OH 44128-5702
Tel (216) 478-0501 Founded/Ownrshp 1997

Sales 132.2MM[E] *EMP* 100
SIC 5171 Petroleum bulk stations & terminals
CEO: Tom Arcoria
**Pr:* Anthony Arcoria
**COO:* Jeff Platko
**CFO:* Louise A Kirk
Sls Mgr: Scott Dejohn
Sls Mgr: Mike Renn

D-U-N-S 80-562-8518
GREAT LAKES PETROLEUM CORP
GREAT LAKES MAINTENANCE
6525 N Jerome Rd, Alma, MI 48801-9706
Tel (989) 463-4654 *Founded/Ownrshp* 1992
Sales 198.6MM[E] *EMP* 161
SIC 5172 Petroleum products
Pr: Jeffrey Plott
VP: Jennifer Brown

D-U-N-S 92-680-7272
GREAT LAKES REIT
823 Commerce Dr Ste 300, Oak Brook, IL 60523-8824
Tel (708) 848-5216 *Founded/Ownrshp* 1992
Sales 105.2MM *EMP* 20[E]
Accts Ernst & Young Llp Chicago Il
SIC 6798 6531 Real estate investment trusts; Real estate agents & managers
Ch Bd: Richard May
**Pr:* Patrick R Hunt
CFO: James Hicks
Chf Inves: Raymond Braun
Ex VP: Richard Rasley
Sr VP: Brett Brown
Sr VP: Kim Mills
Sr VP: Edith M Scurto
VP: Joe Gianforte

D-U-N-S 00-552-4731 IMP
GREAT LAKES SYNERGY CORP
GLS
85 W Algonquin Rd Ste 600, Arlington Heights, IL 60005-4421
Tel (847) 437-0200 *Founded/Ownrshp* 1965
Sales 89.4MM[E] *EMP* 540
SIC 5084 4226 4213

D-U-N-S 12-092-5065
GREAT LAKES UTILITIES
1323 S 7th St, Manitowoc, WI 54221
Tel (920) 686-4342 *Founded/Ownrshp* 2000
Sales 101.2MM *EMP* 11
Accts Schenck Sc Green Bay Wiscon
SIC 7539 Electrical services
Ch: Jem Brown
**Prin:* Joe Pacovsky

D-U-N-S 01-887-6789
■ **GREAT LAKES WINDOW INC**
(*Suby of* PLY GEM INDUSTRIES INC) ★
30499 Tracy Rd, Walbridge, OH 43465-9794
Tel (419) 666-5555 *Founded/Ownrshp* 2004
Sales 114.6MM[E] *EMP* 600
SIC 3089 5211 Windows, plastic; Doors, folding: plastic or plastic coated fabric; Lumber & other building materials
Pr: Lynn Morstadt
VP: Randall Booker
VP Sls: William Johnston
S&M/VP: Hans Vetter

D-U-N-S 01-685-1776 IMP
GREAT LAKES WINE & SPIRITS LLC
J. LEWIS COOPER CO.
373 Victor St, Highland Park, MI 48203-3117
Tel (313) 278-5400 *Founded/Ownrshp* 1946
Sales 379.2MM[E] *EMP* 850
SIC 5182 2084 Wine & distilled beverages; Wine coolers, alcoholic; Liquor; Wines, brandy & brandy spirits
Ch Bd: J Lewis Cooper Jr
**CEO:* Lew Cooper III
**CEO:* Syd Ross
**CFO:* John Queen
CFO: John Ricco
**Ex VP:* Ernie Almeranti
**Ex VP:* Lou Grech-Cumbo
IT Man: David Day
Info Man: Dave Long
**VP Sls:* Brad Still
Sls Dir: Matt Remillard

D-U-N-S 04-397-2199
GREAT NECK PUBLIC SCHOOLS
345 Lakeville Rd, Great Neck, NY 11020-1639
Tel (516) 441-4001 *Founded/Ownrshp* 1814
Sales 213.2MM *EMP* 1,500
SIC 8211 Public elementary & secondary schools
Treas: Carol Blach
Genl Mgr: Eleanor Demarco
Schl Brd P: Barbara Berkowitz

D-U-N-S 00-204-0277 IMP/EXP
GREAT NECK SAW MANUFACTURERS INC (NY)
BUCK BROS DIVISION
165 E 2nd St, Mineola, NY 11501-3523
Tel (800) 457-0600 *Founded/Ownrshp* 1930
Sales 232.0MM[E] *EMP* 700
SIC 5072 Hand tools
Pr: Sydney Jacoff
CFO: Rich Hollingsworth
**Ex VP:* Daniel Jacoff
Sr VP: Bob Jacoff
VP: Linc Reichhelm
Creative D: Roberta Daar
IT Man: George Brando
Manager: Sal Assenza
VP Sls: Braden Bazilus
S&M/VP: Peter Hagicostas

D-U-N-S 00-612-6742 IMP
GREAT NORTHERN CORP
395 Stroebe Rd, Appleton, WI 54914-8782
Tel (920) 739-3671 *Founded/Ownrshp* 1961
Sales 392.5MM *EMP* 1,032
Accts Grant Thornton Llp Milwaukee
SIC 2653 5199 2671 Boxes, corrugated: made from purchased materials; Plastics foam; Paper coated or laminated for packaging
CEO: John R Davis
**Ch Bd:* William Raaths
**CFO:* Terry A Abraham
Sr VP: Mike Schliesmann
Creative D: Bill Glassen
Creative D: Jim Mahnke
VP Mfg: Gary Weber
Plnt Mgr: Josh Coldiron
Plnt Mgr: Bruce Eiting
Plnt Mgr: Terry Rupell
VP Mktg: Brian Fiebig

D-U-N-S 61-929-1300
GREAT NORTHERN STAFF ADMINISTRATORS LLC
(*Suby of* AURELIUS HOLDINGS INC)
6915 Sw Mcdam Ave Ste 245, Portland, OR 97219
Tel (503) 972-1944 *Founded/Ownrshp* 1999
Sales NA *EMP* 25
SIC 6411 Insurance agents & brokers
COO: Chris Marquette
VP: Ralph Sanchez
Sales Exec: Josh Willner

D-U-N-S 09-525-3530 IMP
GREAT PACIFIC ENTERPRISES (US) INC
GENPAK
(*Suby of* GREAT PACIFIC ENTERPRISES INC)
68 Warren St, Glens Falls, NY 12801-4530
Tel (518) 761-2593 *Founded/Ownrshp* 1983
Sales 1.1MMM[E] *EMP* 2,000
SIC 3089 Plastic containers, except foam
Ch Bd: James Pattison
**CEO:* Michael Korenberg
**Ch:* James Reilly
**VP:* Nick Geer
Mktg Mgr: Michele Quirk

D-U-N-S 02-472-7336
GREAT PACIFIC NEWS CO INC
NEWS GROUP THE
(*Suby of* JIM PATTISON GROUP INC)
3995 70th Ave E Ste B, Fife, WA 98424-3616
Tel (425) 226-3250 *Founded/Ownrshp* 1997
Sales 254.4MM[E] *EMP* 1,500
SIC 5192 Books, periodicals & newspapers
Pr: Mike Cooke
**VP:* Dan McLaughlin

GREAT PACIFIC PATAGONIA
See PATAGONIA INC

GREAT PLAINS
See NORTHERN TOOL & EQUIPMENT CO INC

D-U-N-S 09-955-6359
■ **GREAT PLAINS COCA COLA BOTTLING CO**
COCA-COLA
(*Suby of* COCA-COLA REFRESHMENTS USA INC) ★
600 N May Ave, Oklahoma City, OK 73107-6324
Tel (405) 280-2000 *Founded/Ownrshp* 2011
Sales 103.5MM[E] *EMP* 297
SIC 2086 Bottled & canned soft drinks
Ch Bd: Robert F Browne
**COO:* Don Bischoff
CFO: Carie Monsey
**CFO:* Clayton Sliger
**Ex VP:* Henry W Browne Jr
VP: Bill McClure
Exec: Ron Martinez
Dist Mgr: Scott Kahmeyer
CTO: Mike Hale
Dir IT: Steve Murphy
IT Man: Jeff Hands

GREAT PLAINS ENERGY
See KANSAS CITY POWER & LIGHT CO

D-U-N-S 06-473-9076
▲ **GREAT PLAINS ENERGY INC**
1200 Main St, Kansas City, MO 64105-2122
Tel (816) 556-2200 *Founded/Ownrshp* 2001
Sales 2.5MMM *EMP* 2,899[E]
Tkr Sym GXP *Exch* NYS
SIC 4911 Electric services; Distribution, electric power; Generation, electric power; Transmission, electric power
Ch Bd: Terry Bassham
CFO: Kevin E Bryant
Ofcr: Ellen E Fairchild
Sr VP: Heather A Humphrey
VP: Steven P Busser
VP: Charles A Caisley
VP: Charles King
VP: Lori A Wright
Board of Directors: David L Bodde, Randall C Ferguson Jr, Gary D Forsee, Scott D Grimes, Thomas D Hyde, James A Mitchell, Ann D Murtlow, John J Sherman

D-U-N-S 13-019-4280
■ **GREAT PLAINS ENERGY SERVICES INC**
(*Suby of* GREAT PLAINS ENERGY INC) ★
1201 Walnut St, Kansas City, MO 64106-2149
Tel (816) 556-2200 *Founded/Ownrshp* 2003
Sales 440.4MM[E] *EMP* 395
SIC 4911 Generation, electric power; Transmission, electric power; Distribution, electric power
Pr: Mike Chesser
**Pr:* Terry Bassham
**CEO:* Michael Chesser
**Ex VP:* Scott Heidtbrink
**Sr VP:* Jim Shay
VP: Kevin Bryant
VP: William Herdegen
VP: Marvin Rollison
Dir IT: Larry Swanson
Counsel: Victoria L Schatz

GREAT PLAINS HEALTH
See NORTH PLATTE NEBRASKA HOSPITAL CORP

D-U-N-S 07-332-3586
GREAT PLAINS HEALTH ALLIANCE INC
GPHA
625 3rd St, Phillipsburg, KS 67661-2138
Tel (785) 543-2111 *Founded/Ownrshp* 1950
Sales 128.3MM[E] *EMP* 1,097
Accts Bkd Llp Wichita Ks
SIC 8742 Productivity improvement consultant
Pr: Dave Dellasega
**Pr:* Roger S John
CFO: Dennis L Fredrickson
**CFO:* Mike Hand
**Ch:* Steve Carlson
Treas: Thomas E Keller
**Sec:* Robert E Hamilton
**VP:* Beth Meyeres
VP: Brenda Olson
**VP:* Logan Sprunger
Dir IT: Lindsay Owsley

D-U-N-S 03-061-2634 EXP
GREAT PLAINS MANUFACTURING INC
LAND PRIDE
1525 E North St, Salina, KS 67401-8562
Tel (785) 823-3276 *Founded/Ownrshp* 1976
Sales 418.2MM[E] *EMP* 1,500[E]
SIC 3523 Farm machinery & equipment; Planting, haying, harvesting & processing machinery; Hulling machinery, agricultural
Pr: Roy Applequist
Pr: David Disberger
**Pr:* Daniel Rauchholz
**COO:* Linda Salem
Sr VP: Linda Otte
VP: Curt Carpenter
VP: Lana Gant
VP: Todd Haddock
Brnch Mgr: Tom Johnson
QA Dir: Dennis Teasley
Dir IT: Bob Van Ness

D-U-N-S 05-593-9203
GREAT PLAINS OILFIELD RENTAL LLC
(*Suby of* SEVENTY SEVEN OPERATING LLC) ★
777 Nw 63rd St, Oklahoma City, OK 73116-7601
Tel (405) 608-7777 *Founded/Ownrshp* 2006
Sales 119.6MM[E] *EMP* 65[E]
SIC 5084 Petroleum industry machinery
Pr: Jerome Loughridge
CEO: Jerry Winchester
COO: Karl Blanchard
CFO: Cary Baetz

GREAT PLANES MODEL DISTRS
See HOBBICO INC

D-U-N-S 04-766-4649 IMP
GREAT RIVER ENERGY
12300 Elm Creek Blvd N, Maple Grove, MN 55369-4718
Tel (763) 445-5000 *Founded/Ownrshp* 1998
Sales 983.0MM *EMP* 850
Accts Deloitte & Touche Llp Minneap
SIC 4911 Generation, electric power; Transmission, electric power
Pr: David Saggau
CFO: Larry Schmid
Ch: Michael Thorson
Treas: Clay V De Bogart
Treas: Robert Thompson
VP: Jon Breke
VP: Jim Jones
VP: Will Kaul
VP: Rick Lancaster
VP: Eric Olsen
VP: Kandance Olsen
VP: Greg Ridderbusch

D-U-N-S 10-233-2301
GREAT RIVER HEALTH SYSTEMS INC
1221 S Gear Ave, West Burlington, IA 52655-1679
Tel (319) 768-1000 *Founded/Ownrshp* 1982
Sales 1.1M *EMP* 1,170
Accts Cliftonlarsonallen Llp Minnea
SIC 8062 General medical & surgical hospitals
Pr: Mark Richardson
CFO: Todd Sladky
**VP:* Ron Halligan
VP: Tony Hayes
Doctor: Joseph Marshall
Doctor: Jonathan Snow

D-U-N-S 05-804-2961
GREAT RIVER MEDICAL CENTER
GREAT RVER HM HLTH CARE HSPICE
1221 S Gear Ave, West Burlington, IA 52655-1681
Tel (319) 768-1000 *Founded/Ownrshp* 1895
Sales 170.4MM *EMP* 1,400
SIC 8062 General medical & surgical hospitals
Pr: Mark Richardson
**Pr:* Kent Gaudian
Ofcr: Sandy Sacora
VP: Tony Hayes
Dir Lab: Nancy Mathahs
Dir Rad: Greg Fields
Dir Rad: Jay Radhakrishnan
CTO: Michael Abouassaly
Tech Mgr: Mark Brown
Sls&Mrk Ex: Craig Vouchard
Ansthlgy: Jose W Calderon

GREAT RVER HM HLTH CARE HSPICE
See GREAT RIVER MEDICAL CENTER

GREAT SALT LAKE MINERALS
See G S L CORP

D-U-N-S 60-580-0408
▲ **GREAT SOUTHERN BANCORP INC**
1451 E Battlefield St, Springfield, MO 65804-3701
Tel (417) 887-4400 *Founded/Ownrshp* 1989
Sales NA *EMP* 1,270[E]
Tkr Sym GSBC *Exch* NGS
SIC 6022 State commercial banks
Pr: Joseph W Turner
**Ch Bd:* William V Turner
CFO: Rex A Copeland
Ofcr: Stephanie Hagan
Ofcr: Steven G Mitchem
Ofcr: Laura Smith
VP: Scott Brekke
VP: Brian Fogle
VP: Cal Glasco
VP: Douglas W Marrs
VP: Linton J Thomason
Exec: Vickie Adams
Exec: Kent Lammers

D-U-N-S 07-625-3855
■ **GREAT SOUTHERN BANK**
(*Suby of* GREAT SOUTHERN BANCORP INC) ★
14309 State Highway 13, Reeds Spring, MO 65737-7529
Tel (417) 888-5880 *Founded/Ownrshp* 1989
Sales NA *EMP* 740
SIC 6021 4724 6712 National commercial banks; Travel agencies; Bank holding companies
Ch Bd: William V Turner
Pr: Joseph W Turner
VP: Teresa S Chasteen
Board of Directors: Douglas M Pitt

D-U-N-S 00-793-1421
GREAT SOUTHERN LIFE INSURANCE CO (TX)
(*Suby of* UNITED FIDELITY LIFE INSURANCE CO INC) ★
300 W 11th St, Kansas City, MO 64105-1618
Tel (816) 391-2000 *Founded/Ownrshp* 1909, 1993
Sales NA *EMP* 300
SIC 6311 Life insurance carriers
Pr: Gary Muller
**Ch Bd:* Michael A Merriman
CEO: Julie Briski
**COO:* Bill Marden

D-U-N-S 05-721-1823 IMP
GREAT SOUTHERN WOOD PRESERVING INC
1100 Us Highway 431 S, Abbeville, AL 36310-2079
Tel (334) 585-2291 *Founded/Ownrshp* 1971
Sales 367.1MM[E] *EMP* 900
SIC 2491 Structural lumber & timber, treated wood
Pr: Jimmy Rane
**COO:* Mark Callender
CFO: William Ray
Ofcr: Chris Bonner
**VP:* Michael Rane
**Prin:* Don McCullough
Genl Mgr: Scott Croft
Genl Mgr: Chuck Dickert
Genl Mgr: Bill Freeman
Dir IT: Cris Anderson
Dir IT: Godwin Chris

D-U-N-S 13-972-3357
■ **GREAT SOUTHWESTERN CONSTRUCTION INC**
(*Suby of* MYR GROUP INC) ★
1100 Topeka Way, Castle Rock, CO 80109-3105
Tel (303) 688-5816 *Founded/Ownrshp* 2000
Sales 90.4MM[E] *EMP* 184[E]
SIC 1623 Electric power line construction; Communication line & transmission tower construction
Pr: Brandon Lark
Treas: Greg Medici
**Treas:* Frank P Volpe
VP: Phil Connor
Genl Mgr: Matt McCain

D-U-N-S 01-893-5692 IMP
GREAT STATE BEVERAGES INC
BETTER BRANDS
1000 Quality Dr, Hooksett, NH 03106-2625
Tel (603) 644-2337 *Founded/Ownrshp* 1957
Sales 115.1MM[E] *EMP* 120
SIC 5181 5149 5145 Beer & other fermented malt liquors; Soft drinks; Snack foods; Fountain supplies
Pr: Robert James Koslowsky
**Ch Bd:* Robert Koslowsky Sr
**Pr:* Robert Koslowsky Jr
VP: Tom Roche
**Prin:* Michael McGinn

D-U-N-S 08-043-8122
GREAT WALL TEXTILE INC
2150 E 10th St, Los Angeles, CA 90021-2801
Tel (626) 688-0271 *Founded/Ownrshp* 2015
Sales 130.0MM *EMP* 5
SIC 5199 Fabrics, yarns & knit goods
CEO: Kewei Xie

D-U-N-S 10-995-0852
■ **GREAT WEST CASUALTY**
(*Suby of* OLD REPUBLIC INTERNATIONAL CORP) ★
1100 W 29th St, South Sioux City, NE 68776-3130
Tel (402) 494-2411 *Founded/Ownrshp* 1956
Sales NA *EMP* 708
SIC 6331 Fire, marine & casualty insurance & carriers
Pr: Al Johnson
Ex VP: P Kuehl
Ex VP: Philip Mahoney
**VP:* Mary Anderson
VP: Jim Arends
VP: Dena Cochran
VP: John Joines
VP: Terry Keime
VP: Rick Larson
VP: Randy Miller
VP: Steve Olson
VP: Eric Rosenbaum
VP: Robert Todd
VP: Rich Wright

D-U-N-S 00-749-8769
■ **GREAT WEST CASUALTY CO**
(*Suby of* GREAT WEST CASUALTY) ★
1100 W 29th St, South Sioux City, NE 68776-3130
Tel (402) 494-2411 *Founded/Ownrshp* 1956, 1985
Sales NA *EMP* 702
SIC 6331 Fire, marine & casualty insurance & carriers; Property damage insurance
Ch Bd: Scott Rager
**Pr:* Jim Jensen
**CFO:* Gaylen Tenhulzen
**Treas:* Mary Anderson

Treas: Mark Laurusevage
**VP:* Dena M Cochran

GREAT WEST FINANCIAL
See GWL&A FINANCIAL INC

D-U-N-S 07-289-9552
▲ GREAT WESTERN BANCORP INC
100 N Phillips Ave # 100, Sioux Falls, SD 57104-6715
Tel (605) 334-2548 *Founded/Ownrshp* 1968
Sales NA *EMP* 1,475
Tkr Sym GWB *Exch* NYS
SIC 6022 State commercial banks
Pr: Ken Karels
Ch Bd: Andrew Hove
Pr: Paul Thronson
CFO: Peter Chapman
Ex VP: Doug Tribble
Ex VP: Steve Ulenberg
VP: Jeff Phillips

D-U-N-S 00-894-2211
■ GREAT WESTERN BANK (SD)
(*Suby of* GREAT WESTERN BANCORP INC) ★
100 N Phillips Ave # 100, Sioux Falls, SD 57104-6725
Tel (605) 886-8401 *Founded/Ownrshp* 1935, 2003
Sales NA *EMP* 500
SIC 6022 State commercial banks
CEO: Ken Karels
Pr: Jeff Erickson
Pr: Rob Stumbaugh
COO: Bryan Kindopp
CFO: Peter Chapman
CFO: Greg Teague
Chf Cred: Ewan L Black
Ofcr: Sonya Frickenstein
Ex VP: Michael Gough
VP: John Bade
VP: Ruth Breinig
VP: Bill Fajen
VP: Pete Jardine
VP: Patrick Lefevre
VP: Jared Renken
VP: Doug Tribble

GREAT WESTERN BUILDING MTL
See FOUNDATION BUILDING MATERIALS LLC

D-U-N-S 19-270-4500
GREAT WESTERN SUPPLY INC
2626 Industrial Dr, Ogden, UT 84401-3206
Tel (801) 621-5412 *Founded/Ownrshp* 1988
Sales 107.9MM^E *EMP* 96
SIC 5074 5051 5999 1711 Plumbing fittings & supplies; Pipe & tubing, steel; Plumbing & heating supplies; Plumbing contractors
Pr: Mark Jenkins
**VP:* Glen G Jenkins
Sls Mgr: Don McFarland

GREAT WHITE ENERGY SERVICES
See ARCHER PRESSURE PUMPING LLC

GREAT WOLF LODGE
See GREAT WOLF RESORTS HOLDINGS INC

D-U-N-S 16-603-0861
GREAT WOLF RESORTS HOLDINGS INC
GREAT WOLF LODGE
525 Junction Rd Ste 6000, Madison, WI 53717-2153
Tel (608) 662-4700 *Founded/Ownrshp* 2015
Sales 396.2MM^E *EMP* 4,900
SIC 7011 Hotels & motels; Resort hotel
Ofcr: Kimberly K Schaefer
**COO:* Timothy D Black
COO: Erin Wallace
CFO: Gregory Kryder
Bd of Dir: Phil Cunningham
Ex VP: Greg Miller
Sr VP: Alexander P Lombardo
VP: Franceen Gonzales
VP: Jay Markham
VP: Scott Maupin
VP: Valerie McGee
VP: Melissa Wheeler
Exec: Christian Massey
Exec: Greg Nicolaou
Exec: McKensie Ogden
Exec: Lymont Stoutingberg
Creative D: Tristen Schill
Comm Dir: Susan L Storey

D-U-N-S 13-368-8627
GREAT-WEST FINANCIAL RETIREMENT PLAN SERVICES LLC
(*Suby of* GREAT WEST FINANCIAL) ★
11500 Outlook St, Overland Park, KS 66211-1804
Tel (847) 857-3000 *Founded/Ownrshp* 2014
Sales NA *EMP* 2,900
SIC 6411 Pension & retirement plan consultants
CEO: Robert L Reynolds

D-U-N-S 19-679-0166
GREAT-WEST LIFE & ANNUITY INSURANCE CO
(*Suby of* GREAT WEST FINANCIAL) ★
8515 E Orchard Rd, Greenwood Village, CO 80111-5002
Tel (303) 737-3000 *Founded/Ownrshp* 2014
Sales 2.7MMM *EMP* 2,362
SIC 6211 6311 Investment firm, general brokerage; Life insurance
Ch Bd: R Jeffrey Orr
Pr: Camilla Langenfeld
Pr: Edmund F Murphy
Pr: Robert L Reynolds
Pr: Robert K Shaw
Ofcr: John R Gabbert
Ex VP: Dave Johnston
Ex VP: Charles B McDevitt
Ex VP: David L Musto
Ex VP: Robert Shaw
Sr VP: Andra S Bolotin
Sr VP: Charles B Childs Jr
Sr VP: Glenn R Derback
Sr VP: Miles R Edwards
Sr VP: Ernie Friesen
Sr VP: James M Gearin
Sr VP: William S Harmon
Sr VP: Wayne T Hoffman
Sr VP: Stephen E Jenks
Sr VP: Jeffrey W Knight
Sr VP: Ron J Laeyendecker

D-U-N-S 04-235-7959
GREAT-WEST LIFE & ANNUITY INSURANCE CO OF NEW YORK
(*Suby of* GREAT-WEST LIFECO INC)
50 Main St, White Plains, NY 10606-1901
Tel (914) 682-3611 *Founded/Ownrshp* 1996, 1997
Sales NA *EMP* 1
Accts Deloitte & Touche Llp Denver
SIC 6411 Insurance agents, brokers & service
Pr: Mtg Graye
**Pr:* CP Nelson
**Ch:* RI McFeetors
**Treas:* Jh Van Harmelen
**Ofcr:* DC Aspinwall
**Ofcr:* Ba Byrne
**Ex VP:* SM Corbett
**Ex VP:* Rk Shaw
**Sr VP:* Ch Cumming
**Sr VP:* Ws Harmon
**Sr VP:* Rj Laeyendecker
**Sr VP:* Dg McLeod
**Sr VP:* RG Schultz
**Sr VP:* GE Seller

D-U-N-S 82-984-0169
GREAT-WEST LIFECO US INC
(*Suby of* POWER CORPORATION DU CANADA)
8515 E Orchard Rd, Greenwood Village, CO 80111-5002
Tel (303) 737-3000 *Founded/Ownrshp* 1998
Sales NA *EMP* 6,600^E
SIC 6311 Life insurance
Prin: Robert L Reynolds
Sr VP: David Hodge
Sr VP: Brian Schwartz
VP: Eve Hampton
Exec: Ron Laeyendecker
Snr Sftwr: John Pierce
Dir IT: Al Gonzales
Sls Dir: Adam Blitz
Sls Dir: Joe Carew
Sls Dir: Octavio Cheung
Sls Dir: Jason Fewell

D-U-N-S 61-347-8486
GREATAMERICA FINANCIAL SERVICES CORP
625 1st St Se Ste 800, Cedar Rapids, IA 52401-2031
Tel (319) 365-8000 *Founded/Ownrshp* 1992
Sales NA *EMP* 425
Accts Kpmg Llp Des Moines Ia
SIC 6159 Machinery & equipment finance leasing
CEO: Tony Golobic
V Ch: Doug Olson
**Pr:* Stanley Herkelman
**COO:* David Pohlman
**CFO:* Joe Terfler
**V Ch Bd:* Douglas Olson
Sr VP: Brian Bjella
Sr VP: Jennie Fisher
**Sr VP:* Marty Klees
Sr VP: Greg Vandewalker
Sr VP: Lane Wolbe
VP: Chris Adams
VP: Joe Andries
VP: Lindsay Bohon
VP: Jim Burns
VP: Paul Gamez
VP: Wil Meggers
VP: Terry L Robertson
VP: Lee W Rozeboom
VP: Steve Rybos
VP Bus Dev: Jon Krekelberg

D-U-N-S 03-708-0520
GREATER ALBANY PUBLIC SCHOOL DISTRICT 8 J
718 7th Ave Sw, Albany, OR 97321-2320
Tel (541) 967-4501 *Founded/Ownrshp* 1950
Sales 77.5MM^E *EMP* 1,100
SIC 8211 Public elementary & secondary schools; Public elementary school; Public junior high school; Public senior high school
Off Mgr: Jill Bush
Off Mgr: Kelli Stahr
CTO: Martha Highfill
Dir IT: Richard Thomas
Pr Dir: Jim Haggart
HC Dir: Carol A Charrier

D-U-N-S 06-487-4050 IMP
GREATER BALTIMORE MEDICAL CENTER INC
(*Suby of* GBMC HEALTHCARE, INC.)
6701 N Charles St, Baltimore, MD 21204-6808
Tel (410) 849-2000 *Founded/Ownrshp* 1986
Sales 376.6MM *EMP* 359^E
Accts Deloitte Tax Llp Mclean Va
SIC 8062 8011 Hospital, medical school affiliated with residency; Offices & clinics of medical doctors
Pr: John Chessare
CFO: Eric Melchior
Ex VP: Robert Thornton
Sr VP: John W Ellis
VP: Carolyn L Candiello
VP: Genny Selby
Exec: Renee Tankersley
Div/Sub He: George Apostolides
Ansthlgy: Brian M Block
Ansthlgy: Karen R Vail
Doctor: Tania Marcic MD

D-U-N-S 96-960-7550
GREATER BALTIMORE MEDICAL CENTER LAND CORP
6701 N Charles St, Baltimore, MD 21204-6881
Tel (443) 849-2000 *Founded/Ownrshp* 2011
Sales 413.5MM *EMP* 14
Accts Deloitte Tax Llp Mc Lean Va
SIC 8062 General medical & surgical hospitals
Pr: John Chessare
Anesthlgy: Harold Goll

D-U-N-S 16-133-1067
GREATER BOSTON FOOD BANK INC
GBFB
70 S Bay Ave, Boston, MA 02118-2704
Tel (617) 427-5200 *Founded/Ownrshp* 1981
Sales 87.2MM *EMP* 80
Accts Cohn Reznick Llp Boston Mass
SIC 8399 Antipoverty board
Pr: Catherine D'Amato
Pr: Paul G Swindlehurst
**COO:* Carol Tienken
**CFO:* David S Noymer
**Treas:* John J Wallace
Mktg Dir: Courtney Johanson
Mktg Mgr: Mekea Harvey

D-U-N-S 09-476-2572
GREATER CHICAGO FOOD DEPOSITORY
4100 W 42nd Pl, Chicago, IL 60632-3920
Tel (773) 247-3663 *Founded/Ownrshp* 1978
Sales 98.1MM *EMP* 95
Accts Plante & Moran Pllc Chicago
SIC 8322 Individual & family services
Pr: Katherine R Maehr
Dir Vol: Mark Barnfield
**COO:* Caroline Howe
CFO: Dennis James
CFO: Donald Tusek
Chf Mktg O: Joan Chow
**VP:* Bob Dolgan
**VP:* Gerry Maguire
**VP:* Steven McCullough
VP: Nicole Robinson
VP: Doug Schenkelberg
Board of Directors: Scott Davis

GREATER CHICAGOLAND CLOSEOUTS
See RICHARDS BUILDING SUPPLY CO

D-U-N-S 36-150-9375
GREATER CINCINNATI FOUNDATION
200 W 4th St Fl 1, Cincinnati, OH 45202-2775
Tel (513) 241-2880 *Founded/Ownrshp* 1963
Sales 100.1MM *EMP* 20
Accts Deloitte & Touche Llp
SIC 6732 Charitable trust management
Pr: Kathryn E Merchant
V Ch: David W Ellis III
COO: Dora Anim
**CFO:* Amy Cheney
Bd of Dir: Frank Fletcher
Ofcr: Cfre Cummings
Ofcr: Robert Killins
Ofcr: Julia Mace
Ofcr: Laura Menge
Ofcr: Norah Mock
Ofcr: Molly Robertshaw
Ofcr: Ray Watson
Ex VP: Linda Montgomery
VP: Michele Carey
VP: Amy L Cheney
VP: Beth Reiter
VP: Shiloh Turner

D-U-N-S 07-132-9338
GREATER CLARK COUNTY SCHOOLS
2112 Utica Sellersburg Rd, Jeffersonville, IN 47130-8506
Tel (812) 283-0701 *Founded/Ownrshp* 2005
Sales 90.2MM^E *EMP* 1,400
SIC 8211 Public elementary & secondary schools
Bd of Dir: Robert Valentine
Exec: Linda Dufour
MIS Dir: Mark Volgnier
Pr Dir: Erin Bojorquez

D-U-N-S 07-113-6071
GREATER CLEVELAND REGIONAL TRANSIT AUTHORITY
R T A
1240 W 6th St, Cleveland, OH 44113-1302
Tel (216) 566-5100 *Founded/Ownrshp* 1975
Sales 48.8MM *EMP* 2,700
SIC 4111

D-U-N-S 96-457-8020
GREATER HORIZONS
1055 Broadway Blvd # 130, Kansas City, MO 64105-1595
Tel (816) 842-0944 *Founded/Ownrshp* 2010
Sales 199.0MM *EMP* 28^E
Accts Bkd Llp Kansas City Mo
SIC 8399 Social services
CEO: Laura McKnight

D-U-N-S 96-639-6574
GREATER HOUSTON COMMUNITY FOUNDATION
5120 Woodway Dr Ste 6000, Houston, TX 77056-1791
Tel (713) 333-2200 *Founded/Ownrshp* 1971
Sales 225.8MM *EMP* 9
Accts Harper & Pearson Houston Tx
SIC 8733 Noncommercial research organizations
Pr: Stephen Maislin
**VP:* Emelda J Douglas
**VP:* Robert W Paddock
Ex Dir: Carol Shattuck

GREATER KANSAS CITY COMMUNITY
See COMMUNITY FOUNDATION OF WYANDOTTE COUNTY

D-U-N-S 78-271-1550
GREATER KANSAS CITY COMMUNITY FOUNDATION AND AFFILIATED TRUSTS
1055 Broadway Blvd # 130, Kansas City, MO 64105-1575
Tel (816) 842-0944 *Founded/Ownrshp* 1978
Sales 127.9MM *EMP* 46^E
Accts Bkd Llp Kansas City Mo
SIC 6732 7941 Charitable trust management; Baseball club, professional & semi-professional
CEO: Laura McKnight
V Ch: Pam Gradinger
Treas: Robert A Pearson
Bd of Dir: Carl L Chinnery
Bd of Dir: Gregory M Glore
Bd of Dir: Wallace S Hartfield
Bd of Dir: Jennifer Krizek
Bd of Dir: Linda Lenza
Bd of Dir: Lynn Mitchelson
Bd of Dir: Leisa Reid
Bd of Dir: Robin Sterneck
VP: George Bittner
VP: Jean-Paul Chaurand
VP: Brenda Chumley
VP: Randy James
VP: Roxanne Jurde
VP: Deborah L Wilkerson

D-U-N-S 07-598-4344
GREATER LAFAYETTE HEALTH SERVICES
ST ELIZABETH REGIONAL HEALTH
1501 Hartford St, Lafayette, IN 47904-2134
Tel (765) 423-6011 *Founded/Ownrshp* 1895
Sales 66.9MM^E *EMP* 2,200
SIC 8062 General medical & surgical hospitals
Pr: Terry Wilson
**VP:* Keith Lauter
Surgeon: Cathy Newman
Anstlgy: William Tilt

D-U-N-S 08-253-5274
GREATER LAFAYETTE HEALTH SERVICES INC
SAINT ELIZABETH REGIONAL HLTH
(*Suby of* SAINT JAMES HOSPITAL) ★
1501 Hartford St, Lafayette, IN 47904-2134
Tel (765) 423-6011 *Founded/Ownrshp* 1999
Sales 102.1MM^E *EMP* 2,660
SIC 8062 General medical & surgical hospitals
CEO: Terry Wilson
**CFO:* Keith Lauter
Telecom Ex: Gina Spinelli
Mktg Dir: Lisa Decker
Pharmcst: Dorianne Dunkle

D-U-N-S 05-130-8195
■ GREATER MEDIA INC
(*Suby of* BEASLEY BROADCAST GROUP INC) ★
3033 Riviera Dr Ste 200, Naples, FL 34103-2750
Tel (239) 263-5000 *Founded/Ownrshp* 2016
Sales 91.2MM^E *EMP* 864
SIC 2711 8999 4832

D-U-N-S 78-248-1550
GREATER MILWAUKEE FOUNDATION INC
101 W Pleasant St Ste 210, Milwaukee, WI 53212-3963
Tel (414) 272-5805 *Founded/Ownrshp* 1915
Sales 197.8MM *EMP* 35
SIC 8699 8733 Charitable organization; Noncommercial research organizations
Pr: Ellen Gilligan
VP: Sonja Williams
Comm Dir: Laura Mullen

D-U-N-S 00-698-4793
GREATER NEW YORK MUTUAL INSURANCE CO
GNY INSURANCE COMPANIES
200 Madison Ave Frnt 2, New York, NY 10016-3903
Tel (212) 683-9700 *Founded/Ownrshp* 1927
Sales NA *EMP* 350
SIC 6411 Property & casualty insurance agent
Ch Bd: Warren W Heck
**Pr:* Elizebeth Heck
Pr: Douglas Schelmay
VP: Margaret Klein
VP: Nancy Pearlstein
VP: John Racyzk
VP: Jeff Turisi
Mktg Mgr: Mitch Fox
Mktg Mgr: Scott Kozak

D-U-N-S 00-726-9871 EXP
GREATER OMAHA PACKING CO INC
TREX
3001 L St, Omaha, NE 68107-1409
Tel (402) 731-1700 *Founded/Ownrshp* 1952
Sales 101.4MM^E *EMP* 690
SIC 2011 5147 Meat by-products from meat slaughtered on site; Meats & meat products
Pr: Henry A Davis
**Ex VP:* Angelo Fili
**VP:* David L Davis
**VP:* Dan Jensen
VP: Kathleen Krantz
**VP:* Roy Wiggs
Exec: Kathy Cedillo
Dir IT: Lavonne Misner
IT Man: Tom Kelley
Mktg Mgr: Ryan Murphy
Sls Mgr: Eric Demar

D-U-N-S 00-132-3344
GREATER ORLANDO AVIATION AUTHORITY
ORLANDO INTERNATIONAL AIRPORT
1 Jeff Fuqua Blvd, Orlando, FL 32827-4392
Tel (407) 825-2001 *Founded/Ownrshp* 1957
Sales 430.7MM *EMP* 670
Accts Moore Stephens Lovelace Pa
SIC 4581 Airports, flying fields & services
Ch: Frank Kruppenbacher
COO: Stanley Thornton
**CFO:* Kathleen Sharman
**Treas:* Domingo Sanchez
Dir Risk M: Maury Remmers
**Ex Dir:* Phillip N Brown

D-U-N-S 96-562-7404
■ GREATER PEORIA SPECIALTY HOSPITAL LLC
KINDRED
(*Suby of* KINDRED HEALTHCARE INC) ★
500 W Romeo B Garrett Ave, Peoria, IL 61605-2301
Tel (309) 680-1500 *Founded/Ownrshp* 2010
Sales 13.8MM *EMP* 1,610^E
SIC 8062 8099 General medical & surgical hospitals; Childbirth preparation clinic
CEO: Ted Paarlberg
HC Dir: Rebecca Frakes

D-U-N-S 07-572-4245
GREATER PROVIDENCE YOUNG MENS CHRISTIAN ASSOCIATION
YMCA
371 Pine St, Providence, RI 02903-4515
Tel (401) 521-9622 *Founded/Ownrshp* 1853
Sales 23.2MM *EMP* 1,250
Accts Blum Shapiro & Company Pc Pro
SIC 8641 7991 8351 7032 8322 Youth organizations; Physical fitness facilities; Child day care services; Youth camps; Individual & family services
Pr: Karen Leslie
Pr: Carl Brown
CFO: Cheryl Bongivengo
Bd of Dir: Phil Gaeber
**VP:* Michael Fournier
Ex Dir: Joe Martino
Dir Opers: Regina Raffa
Pgrm Dir: Joelle Beyer

D-U-N-S 14-821-4489
GREATER RICHMOND BUSINESS INC
COLONIAL FORD
1833 Commerce Rd, Richmond, VA 23224-7801
Tel (804) 232-3492 *Founded/Ownrshp* 1984
Sales 102.4MM^E *EMP* 215
SIC 5511 5013 5531 7513 Automobiles, new & used; Automotive supplies & parts; Truck parts & accessories; Automotive & home supply stores; Truck leasing, without drivers
Ch Bd: George R Barkley
**Pr:* George R Barkley Jr
**Ch:* George Bob Barkely
**Sec:* Warren Schoening

D-U-N-S 10-912-2577
GREATER ROCHESTER INDEPENDENT PRACTICE ASSOCIATION INC
GREATER ROCHESTER IPA
100 Kings Hwy S Ste 2500, Rochester, NY 14617-5509
Tel (585) 922-1500 *Founded/Ownrshp* 1996
Sales 170.0MM^E *EMP* 49
SIC 8011 Offices & clinics of medical doctors
CEO: Joseph S Vasile MD
**Pr:* Gregg Coughlin
**COO:* Bill Pelino
Sr VP: Richard Gangemi
Sr VP: Hugh Thomas
VP: Jeanette Altavela
Exec: Mary Lorei
CIO: Jamie Hayslip

GREATER ROCHESTER IPA
See GREATER ROCHESTER INDEPENDENT PRACTICE ASSOCIATION INC

D-U-N-S 07-026-8800
GREATER TWIN CITIES UNITED WAY (MN)
404 S 8th St Ste 100, Minneapolis, MN 55404-1027
Tel (612) 340-7400 *Founded/Ownrshp* 1919
Sales 101.8MM *EMP* 140
Accts Lb Akins Henke And Company Sa
SIC 8322 Individual & family services
Pr: Sarah Caruso
**Ofcr:* Craig Warren
**Sr VP:* Meghan Barp
Sr VP: Barb Beard
Sr VP: Frank Forsberg
**VP:* Kevin Anderson
**VP:* Chad Brown
VP: Kittie Fahey
VP: Shaun Havis
VP: Diane Hummon
VP: Beth Jacob
VP: Bob Poferl
VP: Carol Stodieck
Exec: Bob Prestifilippo

D-U-N-S 00-585-4849
GREATER WASHINGTON EDUCATIONAL TELECOMMUNICATIONS ASSOCIATION INC
WETA TV 26
3939 Campbell Ave, Arlington, VA 22206-3440
Tel (703) 998-2600 *Founded/Ownrshp* 1953
Sales 109.6MM *EMP* 236
Accts Bdo Usa Llp Bethesda Md
SIC 4833 4832 Television broadcasting stations; Radio broadcasting stations
CEO: Sharon Percy Rockefeller
V Ch: Ann Jordan
**CFO:* James Bond
Bd of Dir: J R Heller
VP: Jeff Bieber
VP: Jim Corbley
VP: Sara Just
VP: Elaine Laughlin
VP: Sharon Rockefeller

D-U-N-S 17-435-4951
GREATER WATERBURY HEALTH NETWORK INC
64 Robbins St, Waterbury, CT 06708-2613
Tel (203) 573-6000 *Founded/Ownrshp* 1985
Sales 566.4M *EMP* 1,826^E
SIC 8741 8093 8011 Hospital management; Specialty outpatient clinics; Offices & clinics of medical doctors
Ch Bd: John Micheals
**Pr:* John H Tobin

D-U-N-S 02-046-4517
GREATER WATERTOWN COMMUNITY HEALTH FOUNDATION INC
WATERTOWN AREA HEALTH SERVICES
125 Hospital Dr, Watertown, WI 53098-3303
Tel (920) 261-4210 *Founded/Ownrshp* 1958
Sales 104.0MM *EMP* 840
SIC 8062 8011 8059 General medical & surgical hospitals; Clinic, operated by physicians; Nursing home, except skilled & intermediate care facility
CEO: Richard Keddington
**CFO:* John A Graf
VP: Jacklyn Lesniak
Ex Dir: John Bardenwerper
Opers Supe: Jennifer Boush

GREATER WICHITA YMCA
See YOUNG MENS CHRISTIAN ASSOCIATION OF WICHITA KANSAS

GREATEST SHOW ON EARTH, THE
See RNGLNG BRS BRNM & BLY COMB SHO

D-U-N-S 83-078-1584
GREATWIDE DEDICATED TRANSPORT LLC
12404 Park Central Dr # 300, Dallas, TX 75251-1803
Tel (972) 228-7344 *Founded/Ownrshp* 2008
Sales 128.7MM^E *EMP* 1,500
SIC 4213 4731

D-U-N-S 82-946-7187
GREATWIDE LOGISTICS SERVICES LLC
(*Suby of* CARDINAL LOGISTICS HOLDINGS LLC) ★
12404 Park Central Dr # 300, Dallas, TX 75251-1803
Tel (972) 228-7389 *Founded/Ownrshp* 2008
Sales 686.9MM^E *EMP* 2,800
SIC 4213 4731 Trucking, except local; Truck transportation brokers
CEO: Leo Suggs
Pr: Dave Bell
Pr: John Simone
COO: William G Doherty
Ofcr: Jeffrey Lester
Ex VP: Bob Larose
Ex VP: Rodger Mullen
Sr VP: Tyler Ellison
Sr VP: John Hove
VP: Chris Rhodes
VP: Rory S Seidens
VP: Michael Skipworth
VP Bus Dev: Kevin Wicks
Exec: Kyle Killingsworth

D-U-N-S 61-900-5382 IMP
GRECO & SONS INC
1550 Hecht Dr, Bartlett, IL 60103-1697
Tel (630) 668-1000 *Founded/Ownrshp* 1990
Sales 147.9MM^E *EMP* 200
SIC 5149 Pizza supplies
Pr: Pasquale Greco
Pr: Jeremy Sadler
CFO: Brian Barrett
CFO: Brian Barrette
Sr VP: Giancarlo Greco
**VP:* Edwardo Greco
Dir IT: Mark Sengstock
Opers Mgr: Tony Zarco
Snr Mgr: Mark Wang

D-U-N-S 00-609-7125 IMP/EXP
GREDE FOUNDRIES INC
4000 Town Ctr Ste 500, Southfield, MI 48075-1419
Tel (248) 440-9500 *Founded/Ownrshp* 1946
Sales 467.6MM^E *EMP* 4,000
SIC 3321 Gray iron castings; Ductile iron castings
Pr: Thomas F Walker Sr
**Ch Bd:* W Stewart Davis
COO: Peter E Sohlden
**CFO:* Raymond F Lowery
Grp VP: John Haas
Grp VP: Randy Priem
VP: Ed Kaczmarek
Board of Directors: Thomas Davis, Gordon Gunnlaugsson, Susan Insley, Allen Kinzer, John Mellowes, James Rulesh, Mary York

D-U-N-S 96-170-5873
■ **GREDE HOLDINGS LLC**
(*Suby of* METALDYNE PERFORMANCE GROUP INC) ★
1 Towne Sq Ste 550, Southfield, MI 48076-3710
Tel (248) 440-9500 *Founded/Ownrshp* 2014
Sales 682.5MM^E *EMP* 3,456
SIC 3321 Gray iron castings; Ductile iron castings
Pr: Douglas J Grimm
**COO:* Todd Heavin
**CFO:* Louis Lavorata
**VP:* William R Goodin
**VP:* Anthony Lovell
**VP:* Paul Suber

D-U-N-S 07-796-6950 IMP
■ **GREDE II LLC**
(*Suby of* GREDE HOLDINGS LLC) ★
4000 Town Ctr Ste 500, Southfield, MI 48075-1419
Tel (248) 522-4500 *Founded/Ownrshp* 1994
Sales 311.4MM^E *EMP* 1,600
SIC 3321 Ductile iron castings; Gray iron castings
Pr: Douglas J Grimm
**CFO:* Louis Lavorata
**VP:* Stephen Busby
DP Exec: Leonard Jennings
Opers Mgr: Stan Galyen

D-U-N-S 96-171-7886 IMP
■ **GREDE LLC**
(*Suby of* GREDE HOLDINGS LLC) ★
1 Towne Sq Ste 550, Southfield, MI 48076-3710
Tel (248) 440-9500 *Founded/Ownrshp* 2010
Sales 178.5MM^E *EMP* 750
SIC 3321 Gray iron castings; Ductile iron castings
CEO: Douglas J Grimm
**CFO:* Louis Lavorata
Mng Dir: Raul Lopez

D-U-N-S 02-972-7238 IMP
GREE USA INC
(*Suby of* GREE ELECTRIC APPLIANCES, INC. OF ZHUHAI)
20035 E Walnut Dr N, City of Industry, CA 91789-2922
Tel (909) 718-0478 *Founded/Ownrshp* 2010
Sales 154.1MM *EMP* 20
SIC 5075 Air conditioning & ventilation equipment & supplies
Pr: Charley Loh
**CFO:* Jian Chen

D-U-N-S 06-791-5991
GREECE CENTRAL SCHOOL DISTRICT
750 Maiden Ln, Rochester, NY 14615-1230
Tel (585) 966-2000 *Founded/Ownrshp* 1928
Sales 111.4MM^E *EMP* 2,073
SIC 8211 Public elementary & secondary schools
Dir Sec: Steven Chatterton

GREEHECK GROUP, THE
See GREENHECK FAN CORP

GREEK GODS
See HAIN REFRIGERATED FOODS INC

D-U-N-S 05-395-0544 IMP
GREEKTOWN CASINO LLC
OPA'S
555 E Lafayette Blvd, Detroit, MI 48226-2924
Tel (313) 223-2999 *Founded/Ownrshp* 1997
Sales 71.8MM^E *EMP* 2,200
SIC 5812 7011 Greek restaurant; Casino hotel
Pr: Michael Puggi
**COO:* Craig Ghelfi
Exec: Roger Danz
Exec: Sasha Woloch
Dir Risk M: Crystal Ford
CIO: Jason Baxter
Sftwr Eng: Jeffrey Patyk
Secur Mgr: John Autrey
VP Mktg: Jeff La France
Mktg Dir: April Aftanas
Mktg Dir: Rodney Rifenbark

D-U-N-S 96-250-9274
GREEKTOWN SUPERHOLDINGS INC
555 E Lafayette Blvd, Detroit, MI 48226-2924
Tel (313) 223-2999 *Founded/Ownrshp* 2010
Sales 331.7MM *EMP* 2
Accts Ernst & Young Llp Detroit M
SIC 6719 Investment holding companies, except banks
Prin: Tony Williams
CFO: Glen Tomaszewski
VP: Hugh Flack
Exec: Jessica Pondell
Mktg Mgr: Scott Rutledge

D-U-N-S 04-569-9949
GREELEY AND HANSEN LLC
100 S Wacker Dr Ste 1400, Chicago, IL 60606-4000
Tel (312) 558-9000 *Founded/Ownrshp* 1914
Sales 86.7MM^E *EMP* 325
SIC 8711 Consulting engineer
CEO: Andrew Richardson
**Pr:* John C Robak
CFO: Theresa Grace
VP: Val S Frenkel
Prin: Ana Dutra
Prin: Fernando Sarmiento
Prin: Nicole Spieles
Board of Directors: Ana Dutra

D-U-N-S 07-132-0456
GREEN ACQUISITION CORP (PA)
(*Suby of* CRR HOLDINGS LLC) ★
2001 Market St, Philadelphia, PA 19103-7044
Tel (215) 209-2000 *Founded/Ownrshp* 1997
Sales 239.0MM^E *EMP* 7,414
SIC 4011 Railroads, line-haul operating
Pr: Timothy T O'Toole

D-U-N-S 07-550-5768
GREEN ACRES HEALTH SYSTEMS INC
4 Ivybrook Blvd, Warminster, PA 18974-1700
Tel (215) 357-6055 *Founded/Ownrshp* 1946
Sales 26.8MM^E *EMP* 1,000
SIC 8741 8051 Nursing & personal care facility management; Skilled nursing care facilities
Pr: Allen Segal
**CFO:* Gary Segal
Board of Directors: Jane Segal

D-U-N-S 13-504-9158
GREEN APPLE LLC
APPLEBEE'S
164 Wind Chime Ct, Raleigh, NC 27615-6433
Tel (919) 846-2577 *Founded/Ownrshp* 2000
Sales 37.2MM^E *EMP* 1,000
SIC 5812 Restaurant, family: chain
CFO: John Sook
Advt Mgr: Diana Dane
Mktg Mgr: Kelsey Lawhead

GREEN ART ENTERPRISE
See OKIN-WALLACK CORP

D-U-N-S 79-121-2314
▲ **GREEN BANCORP INC**
4000 Greenbriar St, Houston, TX 77098-5204
Tel (713) 275-8220 *Founded/Ownrshp* 2006
Sales NA *EMP* 353
Tkr Sym GNBC *Exch* NGS
SIC 6021 National commercial banks
Ch Bd: Manuel J Mehos
Pr: Geoffrey D Greenwade
CFO: Elizabeth Vandervoort
**V Ch Bd:* William D Ellis
Chf Cred: Donald S Perschbacher

D-U-N-S 96-369-2673
GREEN BANK NATIONAL ASSOCIATION
4000 Greenbriar St, Houston, TX 77098-5204
Tel (713) 275-8200 *Founded/Ownrshp* 2008
Sales NA *EMP* 294^E
SIC 6029 Commercial banks
Ch Bd: Manuel J Mehos
**Pr:* Geoffrey Greenwade
Pr: Robert Stringer
**COO:* Sylvia Gonzales
**CFO:* John P Durie
Ofcr: Ermelinda Ortiz
Ex VP: David Anderson
Ex VP: Glen Bell
Ex VP: Chad Bowser
Ex VP: John Durie
Ex VP: Paco Rivera
Sr VP: Vishakha Deora
Sr VP: Walter Finger
Sr VP: Shelley Harrington
Sr VP: Ray Kembel
Sr VP: Cory Leboeuf
Sr VP: Kenneth Montag
VP: Patricia Atkinson
VP: Alesia Coffey
VP: Denise Doughtie
VP: Jaclyn Kaiser

D-U-N-S 00-338-6497
■ **GREEN BANKSHARES INC**
GREENBANK
(*Suby of* CAPITAL BANK FINANCIAL CORP) ★
100 N Main St, Greeneville, TN 37743-4920
Tel (704) 554-5901 *Founded/Ownrshp* 1985
Sales NA *EMP* 1,389
SIC 6022 State commercial banks
Ch Bd: R Eugene Taylor
Pr: Lloyd L Montgomery III
**CFO:* Christopher G Marshall
Ex VP: Adams Bill
**Ex VP:* R Bruce Singletary
Sr VP: J Robert Grubbs
VP: Michael Fowler
VP: Josh Howell
VP: Trisha Lamb
Netwrk Eng: Tim Feathers
Opers Supe: Barbara Woodard
Board of Directors: Martha M Bachman, Peter N Foss, William A Hodges, Samuel E Lynch

D-U-N-S 13-484-7177
GREEN BAY AREA PUBLIC SCHOOL DISTRICT
200 S Broadway, Green Bay, WI 54303-1516
Tel (920) 448-2101 *Founded/Ownrshp* 1847
Sales 129.6MM^E *EMP* 3,000
Accts Schenck Sc Greenbay Wisconsi
SIC 8211 Public elementary & secondary schools
**Pr:* Jean Marsch
**Pr:* Brenda Warren
Treas: Chris Wagner
Sr Cor Off: Ray Kopesh
**VP:* Katie Maloney
Exec: Jayme Blohowiak
Assoc Dir: Dara Atandare
Adm Dir: Michael Donart
CTO: Diane Doersch
Dir IT: Tony Jaworski
IT Man: Gary Wojtowski

D-U-N-S 07-751-9929 IMP
GREEN BAY CONVERTING INC
600 Packerland Dr, Green Bay, WI 54303-4822
Tel (920) 498-5100 *Founded/Ownrshp* 1999
Sales 105.1MM^E *EMP* 120^E
SIC 5113 Towels, paper; Paper tubes & cores
Pr: Gregory Santaga
**Sr VP:* Pamela Vincent
VP Sls: Cameron Moyer

D-U-N-S 05-492-7108
GREEN BAY DRESSED BEEF LLC
(*Suby of* AMERICAN FOODS GROUP LLC) ★
544 Acme St, Green Bay, WI 54302-1807
Tel (920) 436-4220 *Founded/Ownrshp* 1985
Sales 248.7MM^E *EMP* 1,400^E
SIC 2011 2013 Meat packing plants; Beef products from beef slaughtered on site; Boxed beef from meat slaughtered on site; Sausages from purchased meat; Luncheon meat from purchased meat
CFO: Doug Hagen
VP: Steve Giroux
Prd Mgr: Daniel Klaus
Ql Cn Mgr: Jackie Popowski

D-U-N-S 00-614-6997 IMP/EXP
GREEN BAY PACKAGING INC (WI)
1700 N Webster Ave, Green Bay, WI 54302-1196
Tel (920) 433-5111 *Founded/Ownrshp* 1919
Sales 741.2MM^E *EMP* 3,447
SIC 2631 2672 2653 2491

D-U-N-S 80-040-0892
▲ **GREEN BRICK PARTNERS INC**
2805 Dallas Pkwy Ste 400, Plano, TX 75093-8722
Tel (469) 573-6755 *Founded/Ownrshp* 2006
Sales 291.1MM *EMP* 200
Tkr Sym GRBK *Exch* NAS
SIC 1531 6531 Operative builders; Real estate agents & managers
CEO: James R Brickman
**Ch Bd:* David Einhorn
CFO: Richard A Costello

D-U-N-S 05-906-3107 IMP
GREEN CIRCLE GROWERS INC
51051 Us Highway 20, Oberlin, OH 44074-9637
Tel (440) 775-1411 *Founded/Ownrshp* 1972
Sales 94.5MM^E *EMP* 600^E
SIC 0181 Flowers: grown under cover (e.g. greenhouse production); Plants, potted: growing of
Pr: John Van Wingerden
**CFO:* Norman Daxter
**VP:* Dawn Van Wingerden
Exec: John O"donnell
CIO: Charles Dressler

D-U-N-S 02-205-0066
GREEN COMPANIES INC
HR GREEN DEVELOPMENT
8710 Earhart Ln Sw, Cedar Rapids, IA 52404-8947
Tel (319) 841-4000 *Founded/Ownrshp* 1953
Sales 104.5MM^E *EMP* 390
SIC 8711 8748 8713 4911 1623 Consulting engineer; Business consulting; Surveying services; Electric services; Water, sewer & utility lines
CEO: Steven R Heyer
Pr: Timothy J Hartnett
**Treas:* Michelle Byard
VP: Richard Cammarata
**VP:* David Moermond
**VP:* Jason Poppen
**VP:* Richard White
Exec: Jill Kennedy
CTO: Stacy Woodson
Plnt Mgr: William Moran
Mktg Mgr: Kimberly Sturm
Board of Directors: Steven Heyer, Patrick Hogan, David Moermond, Jason Poppen, Eliot Protsch, Richard White

D-U-N-S 00-568-8416
GREEN COUCH CORP (IL)
231 S La Salle St Fl 8, Chicago, IL 60604-1472
Tel (312) 263-1177 *Founded/Ownrshp* 2001
Sales 88.1MM^E *EMP* 300^E

SIC 7379 7371 Computer related consulting services; Custom computer programming services
Pr: Andrew Sieja
COO: Steve Robertson
Snr Sftwr: Don Frey
Snr Sftwr: Ray Ichihara
Snr Sftwr: Scott Parillo
Snr Sftwr: George Yaconi
Snr Ntwrk: Chris Stolp
QA Dir: John Boutell
QA Dir: Manjot Jassal
IT Man: Michael Markzon
IT Man: Shaun McPeck

D-U-N-S 14-485-4077
GREEN COURTE PARTNERS LLC
303 W Madison St Ste 1500, Chicago, IL 60606-3380
Tel (847) 615-1631 *Founded/Ownrshp* 2002
Sales 103.8MM^E *EMP* 294
SIC 6798 Real estate investment trusts
Ch: Randall K Rowe
**COO:* David B Lentz
Ofcr: James R Golfman
**VP:* Janna L Billips
**VP:* Chad V Gardner
**VP:* David A Hart
**VP:* Tom E Jasica
VP: David Lentz
**VP:* Matthew J Pyzyk
VP: Susi Rowe
VP: Braden L Rudolph
**VP:* Cheri M Scully
VP: Thru A Shivakumar
VP: Kian H Wagner

D-U-N-S 01-283-1553
▲ GREEN DOT CORP
3465 E Foothill Blvd # 100, Pasadena, CA 91107-6072
Tel (626) 765-2000 *Founded/Ownrshp* 1999
Sales NA *EMP* 1,012^E
Tkr Sym GDOT *Exch* NYS
SIC 6141 7389 Personal credit institutions; Credit card service
Ch Bd: Steven W Streit
Pr: Lewis B Goodwin
COO: Kuan Archer
CFO: Mark L Shifke
Sr VP: Mark Shifke
VP: John Johansen
VP: John Ricci
VP: Suzanne Rickards
VP: Christopher Strader
VP: Katherine Throop
Dir Risk M: Konstantinos Sgoutas
Board of Directors: Kenneth C Aldrich, J Chris Brewster, Mary J Dent, Saturnino Fanlo, George W Gresham, William I Jacobs, George T Shaheen

D-U-N-S 12-121-4931
GREEN DOT PUBLIC SCHOOLS CALIFORNIA
1149 S Hill St Ste 600, Los Angeles, CA 90015-2895
Tel (323) 565-1600 *Founded/Ownrshp* 1999
Sales 130.7MM *EMP* 800
Accts Vavrinek Trine Day & Co Llp R
SIC 8211
CEO: Cristina De Jesus
Pr: William Campbell
**Ofcr:* Kelly Hurley
VP: Kevin Keelen
VP: Nithya Rajan
Comm Dir: Gabriel Sanchez
Prgrm Mgr: Raquel Ventura
Genl Mgr: Chad Soleo
Off Mgr: Jesus Sandoval
Psych: Ana Delgado
Psych: Alec Fisher

D-U-N-S 02-592-4145
GREEN DOT PUBLIC SCHOOLS NATIONAL
1149 S Hill St Fl 6, Los Angeles, CA 90015-2218
Tel (323) 565-1600 *Founded/Ownrshp* 2014
Sales 136.8MM *EMP* 7
Accts Vavrinek Trine Day & Co Ll
SIC 8211
CEO: Marco Petruzzi
**COO:* Damien White
**CFO:* Sabrina Ayala
**Ofcr:* Megan Quailie
**VP:* Nithya Rajan
**VP:* Chad Soleo
**CIO:* Kevin Keelen

D-U-N-S 78-175-6267
GREEN EQUITY INVESTORS III L P
11111 Santa Monica Blvd # 2000, Los Angeles, CA 90025-3333
Tel (310) 954-0444 *Founded/Ownrshp* 1989
Sales 38.5MM^E *EMP* 1,115
SIC 6211 Investment bankers
Pt: Jonathan D Sokoloff
Genl Pt: Leonald G LP

D-U-N-S 62-408-6265
GREEN EQUITY INVESTORS IV LP
11111 Santa Monica Blvd, Los Angeles, CA 90025-3333
Tel (310) 954-0444 *Founded/Ownrshp* 2002
Sales 2.9MMM^E *EMP* 15,000^E
SIC 5941 Sporting goods & bicycle shops

D-U-N-S 94-576-5063 IMP
GREEN FARMS INC
WORLDWIDE PRODUCE
1661 Mcgarry St, Los Angeles, CA 90021-3116
Tel (213) 747-4411 *Founded/Ownrshp* 1995
Sales 230.9MM^E *EMP* 278^E
SIC 5148 Vegetables
CEO: Stuart Weisfeld
**Ofcr:* Ron Warenkiewicz
Genl Mgr: Jason Park

D-U-N-S 10-572-2854
GREEN HILLS SOFTWARE INC
30 W Sola St, Santa Barbara, CA 93101-2599
Tel (805) 965-6044 *Founded/Ownrshp* 1872
Sales 96.5MM^E *EMP* 185
SIC 5013 Motor vehicle supplies & new parts
CEO: Daniel O Dowd
Pr: Michael W Liacko
**CEO:* Daniel O'Dowd
COO: Brad Jackson
**CFO:* Jeffrey Hazarian
**Ch:* Jack Douglas
**Sr VP:* David Chandler
VP: Simon Addis
**VP:* Tim Reed
VP: David Sequino
**VP:* Christopher Smith
VP: Dom Stroud
Exec: Dan Mender
Exec: Lynn Robinson
Dir Bus: Ken Curran
Dir Bus: Gregory Rudy
Board of Directors: Daniel P Burnham

GREEN LEAF GIFT SHOP
See KISHWAUKEE COMMUNITY HOSPITAL

D-U-N-S 60-240-7103
GREEN LIGHT CAPITAL INC
140 E 45th St Fl 24, New York, NY 10017-7142
Tel (212) 922-9370 *Founded/Ownrshp* 1996
Sales 631.6MM^E *EMP* 9,300
SIC 6726 Management investment funds, closed-end
Pr: David Einhorn
Sr Cor Off: Dennis Ho
Admn Mgr: Jeff Keswin
Admn Mgr: Eric Streisand

D-U-N-S 17-687-1481 IMP
■ GREEN MOUNTAIN ENERGY CO
BEGREEN
(*Suby of* NRG ENERGY INC) ★
901 S Mo Pac Expy Ste 300, Austin, TX 78746-5883
Tel (512) 691-6100 *Founded/Ownrshp* 2010
Sales 202.8MM^E *EMP* 240
SIC 4911 ;
Pr: Paul Thomas
**Pr:* Scott Hart
**CFO:* Bryan M Decordova
**Ofcr:* Gillan Taddune
**Sr VP:* Paul N Markovich
**Sr VP:* Ron Prater
**Sr VP:* Robert P Thomas
VP: Bridgett Neely
VP: Gary Phillips
VP: Mary L Shields
VP: Mike Starck
VP: Craig Trupo
Dir Risk M: Leonard Gardner

D-U-N-S 00-793-9531 IMP
GREEN MOUNTAIN POWER CORP
(*Suby of* NORTHERN NEW ENGLAND ENERGY CORP) ★
163 Acorn Ln, Colchester, VT 05446-6611
Tel (888) 835-4672 *Founded/Ownrshp* 1893
Sales 194.8MM^E *EMP* 190
Accts Deloitte & Touche Llp Boston
SIC 4911 1623 1731 Distribution, electric power; Transmission, electric power; ; Electric power line construction; Electric power systems contractors
CEO: Mary G Powell
CFO: Dawn Bugsby
Sr VP: Brian Otley
VP: Charlotte Ancel
VP: Dawn D Bugbee
VP: Steve Costello
VP: Robert Griffin
VP: Stephen Terry
VP: Greg White
Dir IT: Mark Dincecco
Dir IT: Kelly Perry
Board of Directors: Elizabeth A Bankowski, William H Bruett, Merrill O Burns, David R Coates, Kathleen C Hoyt, Euclid A Irving, Marc A Vanderheyden

D-U-N-S 07-888-7136
■ GREEN PLAINS ATKINSON LLC
(*Suby of* GREEN PLAINS INC) ★
49131 Highway 20, Oneill, NE 68763-4693
Tel (402) 315-1658 *Founded/Ownrshp* 2013
Sales 150.0MM *EMP* 40
SIC 2869 Ethyl alcohol, ethanol

D-U-N-S 18-638-0718
▲ GREEN PLAINS INC
450 Regency Pkwy Ste 400, Omaha, NE 68114-3701
Tel (402) 884-8700 *Founded/Ownrshp* 2004
Sales 2.9MMM *EMP* 995
Tkr Sym GPRE *Exch* NGS
SIC 2869 2046 Ethyl alcohol, ethanol; Corn oil products
Pr: Todd A Becker
Ch Bd: Wayne Hoovestol
V Ch: Alain Treuer
COO: Jeffrey S Briggs
CFO: Jerry L Peters
Ex VP: Carl S Bleyl
Ex VP: Walter S Cronin
Ex VP: Mark A Hudak
Ex VP: Paul E Kolomaya
Ex VP: Michelle S Mapes
Ex VP: Michael A Metzler
Dir Risk M: George P Simpkins
Board of Directors: Jim Anderson, James Crowley, Gene Edwards, Gordon Glade, Thomas Manuel, Brian Peterson

D-U-N-S 07-925-6442 IMP
GREEN RIVER COLLEGE (WA)
12401 Se 320th St, Auburn, WA 98092-3622
Tel (253) 833-9111 *Founded/Ownrshp* 1965, 1959
Sales 5.8MM *EMP* 1,041
Accts Peterson Sullivan Llp Seattle
SIC 8222 8299 8221 Community college; Educational service, nondegree granting: continuing educ.; Colleges universities & professional schools
Pr: Eileen Ely
Pr: T I Vuong
**VP:* Deborah Casey-Powell
Off Admin: Melissa Comeau
Dir IT: Tim Mason
HC Dir: Ross Jennings

D-U-N-S 93-973-0941
GREEN THUMB PRODUCE
2648 W Ramsey St, Banning, CA 92220-3716
Tel (951) 849-4711 *Founded/Ownrshp* 1991
Sales 92.4MM^E *EMP* 250
SIC 5148 Fresh fruits & vegetables
Pr: Lonnie Saverino

D-U-N-S 18-004-2129 IMP
GREEN TOKAI CO LTD
GTC
(*Suby of* TOKAI KOGYO CO.,LTD.)
55 Robert Wright Dr, Brookville, OH 45309-1931
Tel (937) 833-5444 *Founded/Ownrshp* 1987
Sales 158.4MM^E *EMP* 825
SIC 3714 3069 Motor vehicle body components & frame; Rubber automotive products
Pr: Nobuaki Kimura
**CEO:* Fumi Kazu Hosada
VP: Dan Dowers

D-U-N-S 05-051-4496
GREEN VALLEY CORP (CA)
SWENSON, BARRY BUILDER
777 N 1st St Fl 5, San Jose, CA 95112-6350
Tel (408) 287-0246 *Founded/Ownrshp* 1961
Sales 99.4MM^E *EMP* 120
SIC 1542 1522 6512 Commercial & office building, new construction; Multi-family dwelling construction; Commercial & industrial building operation
Ch: C Barron Swenson
**Pr:* Case Swenson
**CFO:* Lee Ann Woodard
**Sr VP:* Steven W Andrews
**Sr VP:* Ronald L Cot
**Sr VP:* David A Gibbons
**VP:* Steven Andrews
**VP:* Jeffrey Current
**VP:* Jesse Nickell
**VP:* William Ryan
Off Mgr: Jennifer Cosby

GREEN VALLEY GROCERY
See MIDJIT MARKET INC

D-U-N-S 87-624-4737
GREEN VALLEY RANCH GAMING LLC
GREEN VLY RNCH RESORT & SPAS
2300 Paseo Verde Pkwy, Henderson, NV 89052-2672
Tel (702) 617-7777 *Founded/Ownrshp* 2000
Sales 54.3MM^E *EMP* 1,500
SIC 7011 Casino hotel
Genl Mgr: Bob Finch
**VP:* Joe Hasson

GREEN VLY RNCH RESORT & SPAS
See GREEN VALLEY RANCH GAMING LLC

D-U-N-S 00-696-2948
GREEN-WAY COOPERATIVE SERVICE CO
3520 E River Rd Ne, Rochester, MN 55906-5407
Tel (507) 289-4086 *Founded/Ownrshp* 1929
Sales 143.9MM *EMP* 150
SIC 5541 5171 5191

D-U-N-S 62-644-4202
■ GREENBACKS INC
ALL A DOLLAR
(*Suby of* DOLLAR TREE INC) ★
2369 W Orton Cir, Salt Lake City, UT 84119-7679
Tel (801) 977-7777 *Founded/Ownrshp* 2003
Sales 55.0MM^E *EMP* 1,600
SIC 5331 Variety stores
Pr: Brent L Bishop
VP: Terry Green
**VP:* Richard Wolfley
Art Dir: Joe Norwood

GREENBANK
See GREEN BANKSHARES INC

D-U-N-S 78-425-3382
■ GREENBANK
(*Suby of* GREENBANK) ★
100 N Main St, Greeneville, TN 37743-4920
Tel (423) 639-5111 *Founded/Ownrshp* 2002
Sales NA *EMP* 789^E
SIC 6022 State commercial banks
Pr: Stan R Puckett
VP: Telena Sizemore

D-U-N-S 00-791-9251
GREENBAX ENTERPRISES INC
884 Johnnie Dodds Blvd B, Mount Pleasant, SC 29464-3140
Tel (866) 891-1195 *Founded/Ownrshp* 1955
Sales 400.0MM *EMP* 200
Accts Ernst & Young Llp Greenville
SIC 7389 6159 6512 Trading stamp promotion & redemption; Small business investment companies; Nonresidential building operators
Pr: David Schools
Ex VP: William Edenfield
Sr VP: Robert Masche
Dept Mgr: Carey Vincent

GREENBELT TRANSPORT
See UNITED SUPPLIERS INC

D-U-N-S 94-714-6171
GREENBERG TRAURIG LLP
(*Suby of* GREENBERG TRAURIG PA) ★
200 Park Ave Fl 39, New York, NY 10166-1400
Tel (212) 801-9200 *Founded/Ownrshp* 1999
Sales 258.7MM^E *EMP* 3,500
SIC 8111 General practice attorney, lawyer
Mng Pt: Richard Rosenbaum
Sr Pt: Cliff Neimeth
Pr: Millie Badillo
Mktg Dir: Jill Perry
Corp Couns: Benjamin Adams
Corp Couns: Andrew Cosentino
Corp Couns: Jay Gordon
Corp Couns: James Leshaw
Corp Couns: Roderick Macleish
Counsel: James A Dempsey
Counsel: Kate Kalmykov

D-U-N-S 07-130-4984
GREENBERG TRAURIG PA (FL)
333 Se 2nd Ave Ste 4100, Miami, FL 33131-2207
Tel (305) 579-0500 *Founded/Ownrshp* 1969
Sales 457.3MM^E *EMP* 3,500
SIC 8111 General practice law office
CEO: Richard A Rosenbaum
Pt: Richard Melnick
**Pr:* Matthew B Gorson
**Ch:* Larry J Hoffman
Ch: Paul Schindler
**VP:* Richard G Garrett
**Prin:* David E Hirsch
IT Man: Eric Scheele

D-U-N-S 07-640-1124
GREENBERRY INDUSTRIAL LLC
(*Suby of* NAES CORP) ★
600 Se Maritime Ave # 190, Vancouver, WA 98661-8044
Tel (360) 567-0006 *Founded/Ownrshp* 2015
Sales 87.1MM^E *EMP* 350^E
SIC 1711 1541 3443 3441

D-U-N-S 01-412-1292
GREENBRIAR EQUITY GROUP LLC
555 Theodore Fremd Ave A201, Rye, NY 10580-1437
Tel (914) 925-9600 *Founded/Ownrshp* 1999
Sales 743.1MM^E *EMP* 800^E
SIC 4789 6799 Cargo loading & unloading services; Investors
Mng Pt: Reginald L Jones III
Mng Dir: Raynard D Benvenuti
Mng Dir: Jill C Raker
IT Man: Scott Parkis

D-U-N-S 02-500-4318
▲ GREENBRIER COMPANIES INC
1 Centerpointe Dr Ste 200, Lake Oswego, OR 97035-8612
Tel (503) 684-7000 *Founded/Ownrshp* 1974
Sales 2.6MMM *EMP* 10,689^E
Tkr Sym GBX *Exch* NYS
SIC 3743 4789 Railroad equipment, except locomotives; Railroad maintenance & repair services
Ch Bd: William A Furman
Pr: Alejandro Centurion
CFO: Lorie L Tekorius
Chf Cred: Martin R Baker
Ofcr: Walter T Hannan
Ex VP: Victoria McManus
Ex VP: James T Sharp
Sr VP: Adrian J Downes
VP: Chuck Garman
VP: Anne T Manning
CTO: McNeil Michael
Board of Directors: Thomas B Fargo, Graeme A Jack, Duane C McDougall, Charles J Swindells, Wendy L Teramoto, Donald A Washburn, Kelly M Williams

D-U-N-S 00-794-5520
GREENBRIER HOTEL CORP (WV)
(*Suby of* JUSTICE FAMILY GROUP LLC) ★
300 W Main St, Wht Sphr Spgs, WV 24986-2498
Tel (304) 536-1110 *Founded/Ownrshp* 1946, 2014
Sales 96.9MM^E *EMP* 1,000
SIC 7011 Resort hotel
CEO: James C Justice III
**Pr:* Jeff Kmiec
**Treas:* Michael McGovern
**Treas:* James T Miller
Exec: Monte Ortel
Exec: Bryan M Skelding
Adm Dir: Ginny Owens
Genl Mgr: Monte Hansen
Sales Exec: Hayes H Beard
Sales Exec: Josh Hardy
Mktg Dir: Erik Hastings

D-U-N-S 00-634-6254
GREENBRIER INC
TIGER FUEL COMPANY
200 Carlton Rd, Charlottesville, VA 22902-5926
Tel (434) 817-2611 *Founded/Ownrshp* 1982
Sales 275.0MM *EMP* 200
SIC 6719 Investment holding companies, except banks
Pr: David G Sutton
**CFO:* Michael Johns

D-U-N-S 61-032-2518 IMP
■ GREENBRIER INTERNATIONAL INC
DOLLAR TREE MDSG CHESAPEAKE CI
(*Suby of* DOLLAR TREE INC) ★
500 Volvo Pkwy, Chesapeake, VA 23320-1604
Tel (757) 321-5900 *Founded/Ownrshp* 2003
Sales 97.6MM^E *EMP* 200
SIC 5199 7389 Variety store merchandise; Inventory stocking service
Pr: Robert H Rudman
**VP:* Goldman Allan
**VP:* Roger Dean
**VP:* Jonathan L Elder
Genl Mgr: Mark Plowman

D-U-N-S 06-703-6159
GREENCORE US HOLDINGS
(*Suby of* GREENCORE GROUP PUBLIC LIMITED COMPANY)
222 Rosewood Dr Ste 240, Danvers, MA 01923-4520
Tel (508) 586-8418 *Founded/Ownrshp* 2014
Sales 421.5MM^E *EMP* 500^E
SIC 2043 Oatmeal: prepared as cereal breakfast food
Pr: Liam McClennon
**Treas:* Jonathan Hall
**Treas:* Paul Kenny

D-U-N-S 19-646-2220 IMP
GREENCORE USA INC
(*Suby of* GREENCORE US HOLDINGS) ★
222 Rosewood Dr Fl 4, Danvers, MA 01923-4502
Tel (978) 716-2530 *Founded/Ownrshp* 2012
Sales 164.9MM^E *EMP* 490
SIC 2099 Sandwiches, assembled & packaged: for wholesale market; Salads, fresh or refrigerated; Ready-to-eat meals, salads & sandwiches
CEO: Liam McClennon
CFO: Paul Kenny

D-U-N-S 06-894-8348
GREENE COUNTY
GREENE COUNTY GOVERNMENT
35 Greene St, Xenia, OH 45385-3101
Tel (937) 562-5006 *Founded/Ownrshp* 1850
Sales NA *EMP* 1,117
Accts Dave Yost Columbus Ohio
SIC 9111 Executive offices;
Sls&Mrk Ex: Vicki Abel

GREENE COUNTY GOVERNMENT
See GREENE COUNTY

GREENE'S ENERGY GROUP
See OLD GES INC

D-U-N-S 07-901-7414
GREENEVILLE LIGHT & POWER SYSTEM (INC) (TN)
110 N College St, Greeneville, TN 37743-5608
Tel (423) 636-6200 *Founded/Ownrshp* 1945
Sales 90.6MM^E^ *EMP* 80
SIC 4911 Distribution, electric power
Ch Bd: Willie Anderson
Genl Mgr: Bill Carroll
Genl Mgr: William M Carroll
DP Exec: John Skillman
Dir IT: Dwayne Wells
IT Man: Phil Bradley

D-U-N-S 86-825-8724
GREENEVILLE OIL & PETROLEUM INC
QUICK STOP
860 W Andrew Johnson Hwy, Greeneville, TN 37745-1293
Tel (423) 638-3145 *Founded/Ownrshp* 1994
Sales 146.9MM^E^ *EMP* 125
SIC 5172 5411 5541 Crude oil; Convenience stores, chain; Filling stations, gasoline
Pr: Allen Johnson
**CFO:* Nickie Rhoads
Dist Mgr: Paul Johnson

GREENFIELD AREA MEDICAL CENTER
See ADENA HEALTH SYSTEM

D-U-N-S 78-305-7870
GREENFIELD PLACE LLC
2575 W 5th St, Greenville, NC 27834-7813
Tel (252) 830-9100 *Founded/Ownrshp* 1999
Sales 771.4MM *EMP* 145
SIC 8051 8052 8059 Skilled nursing care facilities; Intermediate care facilities; Rest home, with health care

D-U-N-S 10-000-6071
GREENFIELD UNION SCHOOL DISTRICT
1624 Fairview Rd, Bakersfield, CA 93307-5512
Tel (661) 837-6000 *Founded/Ownrshp* 1900
Sales 69.8MM^E^ *EMP* 1,400
SIC 8211 9411 Public elementary school; Public junior high school; Administration of educational programs
Pr: Crystal Jenkins
Netwrk Mgr: Cody Bowman
Site Mgr: James Licea
Psych: Barbara Harville
Psych: Alejandro M Lopez

D-U-N-S 10-837-0524 IMP/EXP
GREENFIELD WORLD TRADE INC
LEGACY COMPANIES, THE
3355 Entp Ave Ste 160, Fort Lauderdale, FL 33331
Tel (954) 202-7419 *Founded/Ownrshp* 1999
Sales 118.7MM^E^ *EMP* 150^E^
SIC 5046 Commercial cooking & food service equipment
Pr: Oscar N Asbury
CFO: Jason Green
VP: Teresa Asbury
VP: Jonathan Vadnos
Opers Mgr: Tyler Helms
Snr Mgr: Philip Coke

D-U-N-S 00-613-6360 IMP/EXP
GREENHECK FAN CORP
GREEHECK GROUP, THE
1100 Greenheck Dr, Schofield, WI 54476-1889
Tel (715) 359-6171 *Founded/Ownrshp* 1957
Sales 786.5MM^E^ *EMP* 2,500
SIC 3564 3444 Blowers & fans; Sheet metalwork
CEO: James McIntyre
**CFO:* Gary M Stroyny
Area Mgr: Becky Gatzke
Genl Mgr: Dave Kallstrom
Genl Mgr: Ken Tokarz
Dir IT: Bob Koshalek
Mfg Dir: Jeff Lamer
Opers Mgr: Josh Holtz
Mktg Dir: Matt Spink
Sls Mgr: Chris Anderson
Snr Mgr: Brandon Jensen

D-U-N-S 14-465-6308
▲ GREENHILL & CO INC
300 Park Ave Fl 23, New York, NY 10022-7402
Tel (212) 389-1500 *Founded/Ownrshp* 1996
Sales 261.5MM *EMP* 350^E^
Tkr Sym GHL *Exch* NYS
SIC 6211 Investment bankers; Underwriters, security
CEO: Scott L Bok
**Ch Bd:* Robert F Greenhill
Pr: Kevin M Costantino
Pr: David A Wyles
COO: Harold J Rodriguez Jr
CFO: Christopher T Grubb
Mng Dir: Chris Collett
Mng Dir: Anne Eastep
Mng Dir: Michelle Jablko
Mng Dir: Richard J Lieb
Mng Dir: Brian Mooney
Board of Directors: Robert T Blakely, Steven F Goldstone, Stephen L Key, Karen P Robards

GREENLEAF
See OAKVILLE PRODUCE PARTNERS LLC

D-U-N-S 96-548-5530
GREENLEAF ADVERTISING & MEDIA INC
GREENLEAF ADVG & MEDIA INC
(*Suby of* IVIE & ASSOCIATES INC) ★
601 Silveron Ste 200, Flower Mound, TX 75028-4030
Tel (972) 899-8750 *Founded/Ownrshp* 2010
Sales 200.9MM^E^ *EMP* 12
SIC 7311 Advertising agencies
Pr: Warren C Ivie
**VP:* Jim Garrison

GREENLEAF ADVG & MEDIA INC
See GREENLEAF ADVERTISING & MEDIA INC

D-U-N-S 00-434-1335 IMP
GREENLEAF CORP (PA)
18695 Greenleaf Dr, Saegertown, PA 16433-4429
Tel (814) 763-2915 *Founded/Ownrshp* 1945, 1966
Sales 97.8MM^E^ *EMP* 450
SIC 3545 3541 Cutting tools for machine tools; Machine tools, metal cutting type
Ch Bd: Walter J Greenleaf Jr
Ch Bd: James M Greenleaf
Treas: Dave Galey
Treas: Ray Seth
Ql Cn Mgr: Elizabeth Jemetz
Mktg Mgr: Terry Olaughlin

D-U-N-S 82-884-5599
GREENLEAF HOSPITALITY GROUP INC
SYDNEY AT THE RADISSON
100 W Michigan Ave # 100, Kalamazoo, MI 49007-3963
Tel (269) 567-7691 *Founded/Ownrshp* 1999
Sales 64.1MM^E^ *EMP* 1,000^E^
SIC 7011 5813 Hotels & motels; Tavern (drinking places)
Pr: William Johnston

D-U-N-S 03-299-2778 IMP
GREENLEAF NURSERY CO
28406 Highway 82, Park Hill, OK 74451-2845
Tel (918) 457-5172 *Founded/Ownrshp* 1960
Sales 73.2MM *EMP* 1,100
Accts Moffitt Parker And Company I
SIC 0181 Nursery stock, growing of
Pr: Randy Davis
**Ch Bd:* Austin F Kenyon
**CFO:* Tom Bearer
**Co-Ch Bd:* John T Nickel
Ex VP: Richard Young
**Prin:* Harold R Nickel
**Prin:* Rebecca A Nickel
CIO: Kendra Harrison
Opers Mgr: Dominic Saether
Advt Dir: Mark Mayeske

D-U-N-S 04-418-4570
GREENLEAF WHOLESALE FLORIST INC
540 E Bridge St Ste A, Brighton, CO 80601-2171
Tel (303) 659-8000 *Founded/Ownrshp* 2003
Sales 99.0MM^E^ *EMP* 250
SIC 5193 Flowers, fresh; Flowers & nursery stock
Pr: Scott C Kitayama
**Ch Bd:* Dennis Kitayama
COO: Rob Spikol
VP: Jeff Wiltjer
Off Mgr: Jane Cimo
Dir IT: Tim Matsuno
Sls Mgr: Dana Sprayberry

D-U-N-S 00-720-2638 IMP
■ GREENLEE TEXTRON INC
(*Suby of* TEXTRON INC) ★
4455 Boeing Dr, Rockford, IL 61109-2932
Tel (815) 397-7070 *Founded/Ownrshp* 1866
Sales 256.9MM^E^ *EMP* 1,010
SIC 3549 3541 3546 Metalworking machinery; Machine tools, metal cutting type; Power-driven handtools
Pr: J Scott Hall
CFO: Jesus Guevara
VP: Scott Fenton
**VP:* Joe Mallak
VP: Mike Reynolds
**VP:* Bill Shulha
**VP:* Dan Wilkinson
**Prin:* Dzura Mike
VP Sls: Tim Vanderaa
Sls Mgr: Wayne King
Sls Mgr: Jenny Mohr

D-U-N-S 06-593-5132
GREENMAN-PEDERSEN INC
G P I
325 W Main St Bldg 1, Babylon, NY 11702-3414
Tel (631) 587-5060 *Founded/Ownrshp* 1920
Sales 140.4MM^E^ *EMP* 100^E^
SIC 8711 Civil engineering
Pr: Ralph Csogi
Treas: Michael Buoncore
VP: Thomas Gibbons
VP: Suzanne Heilpern
VP: Konrad Mayer
VP: Kirk Shields
Brnch Mgr: Lew Brode
Brnch Mgr: Paul Forte
Brnch Mgr: Gregory Johnson
Brnch Mgr: Sarah Olthof
Off Admin: Erica Muniz

D-U-N-S 78-640-3113
GREENPAGES INC
GREENPAGES TECH SOLUTIONS
33 Badgers Is W, Kittery, ME 03904-1688
Tel (207) 439-7310 *Founded/Ownrshp* 1992
Sales 130.0MM *EMP* 185
SIC 7379 Computer related maintenance services; Computer related consulting services
CEO: Ron Dupler
**Pr:* Drew Lally
**CFO:* Stephen Manero
**Ofcr:* Kevin Hall
Sr VP: Karl Pessinis
VP: Randy Becker
**VP:* Glen Jodoin
VP: Simon Johnson
Exec: John Marzi
Exec: Chris Thurber
Prgrm Mgr: Laura Lambrou

GREENPAGES TECH SOLUTIONS
See GREENPAGES INC

D-U-N-S 06-858-4662
GREENPOINT AG
3350 Players Club Pkwy, Memphis, TN 38125-8926
Tel (901) 758-1341 *Founded/Ownrshp* 2012
Sales 858.0MM^E^ *EMP* 574^E^
SIC 5191 Fertilizers & agricultural chemicals; Chemicals, agricultural; Seeds: field, garden & flower
CFO: Mark Ogletree
Off Admin: Juanita Smelser
Sls Mgr: Benny Guerrero
Sls Mgr: Gabriel Long

D-U-N-S 19-843-1496 IMP
GREENPOINT TECHNOLOGIES INC
(*Suby of* ZODIAC AEROSPACE)
4600 Carillon Pt, Kirkland, WA 98033-7344
Tel (425) 828-2777 *Founded/Ownrshp* 1987
Sales 92.0MM^E^ *EMP* 450
SIC 1799

D-U-N-S 14-867-0466
GREENSBORO AUTO AUCTION INC
G A A
3907 W Wendover Ave, Greensboro, NC 27407-1902
Tel (336) 299-7777 *Founded/Ownrshp* 1985
Sales 128.7MM^E^ *EMP* 850
SIC 5012

D-U-N-S 00-546-1627
GREENSKY LLC (GA)
5565 Glenridge Connector, Atlanta, GA 30342-4756
Tel (404) 832-4000 *Founded/Ownrshp* 2006
Sales NA *EMP* 500
SIC 6141 Consumer finance companies
CEO: David Zalik
**Pr:* Tim Kaliban
**CFO:* Robert Partlow
CIO: Marty Smith

D-U-N-S 84-793-0880 IMP
GREENSOURCE BRAND APPAREL INC
1020 Sw 34th St, Renton, WA 98057-4813
Tel (425) 656-9123 *Founded/Ownrshp* 1994
Sales 150.0MM^E^ *EMP* 30
Accts Moss Adams Llp Seattle Wash
SIC 5136 5137 Men's & boys' clothing; Women's & children's clothing
Pr: Brady Hill
**CFO:* William Gould
**Sec:* Patty Barile
**Ex VP:* John Flynn
VP Sls: Scott Lemaster

D-U-N-S 96-584-2243
GREENSPRING VILLAGE INC
7440 Spring Village Dr, Springfield, VA 22150-4446
Tel (703) 313-7800 *Founded/Ownrshp* 2010
Sales 86.9MM *EMP* 1,000
SIC 8059 Personal care home, with health care
Ex Dir: Robin Gliboff

D-U-N-S 80-629-6781
■ GREENSTAR MID-AMERICA LLC
(*Suby of* WM RECYCLE AMERICA LLC) ★
1001 Fannin St Ste 4000, Houston, TX 77002-6711
Tel (713) 512-6200 *Founded/Ownrshp* 2013
Sales 449.6MM^E^ *EMP* 600
SIC 4953 Recycling, waste materials
CEO: Marcelo Figueira
**CFO:* Lorna Conn
**Sr VP:* Eamonn Medley
**Sr VP:* Conor Roche
VP: Brian Gaughan
**VP:* Robert Pickens
VP: Rusty Waldrup
VP: Jeff Wiewiura
VP Sls: Tim Herman

D-U-N-S 82-995-4275
■ GREENSTAR SERVICES CORP
(*Suby of* TUTOR PERINI CORP) ★
30 N Macquesten Pkwy, Mount Vernon, NY 10550-1841
Tel (914) 776-8000 *Founded/Ownrshp* 2011
Sales 517.3MM^E^ *EMP* 155
SIC 1521 New construction, single-family houses
CEO: Gary Segal
CFO: Anthony Bonica

D-U-N-S 82-556-0733
■ GREENSTONE LLC
(*Suby of* PFIZER INC) ★
100 Rte 206 N, Peapack, NJ 07977
Tel (800) 447-3360 *Founded/Ownrshp* 2010
Sales 105.1MM^E^ *EMP* 1,200
SIC 5122 Pharmaceuticals
CEO: Jack Jackson
**Pr:* Gregory Schofield
**Treas:* Debra Houston
**VP:* Sheri Staak

GREENTEAM OF SAN JOSE
See WASTE CONNECTIONS OF CALIFORNIA INC

GREENUP LAWN CARE
See MASSEY SERVICES INC

D-U-N-S 62-398-6705
GREENVIEW REGIONAL HOSPITAL
1801 Ashley Cir, Bowling Green, KY 42104-3362
Tel (270) 793-1000 *Founded/Ownrshp* 2006
Sales 87.3MM *EMP* 500
SIC 8011 Offices & clinics of medical doctors
CEO: Mark Marsh
Chf Path: Donna Boden
Dir Recs: Shannon Dixon
**CEO:* Nashville Tenn
COO: Jarrett Millsaps
VP: Mary Brasseaux
Chf Nrs Of: Bill Singletary

D-U-N-S 07-987-7652
GREENVILLE COUNTY SCHOOL DISTRICT
301 E Camperdown Way, Greenville, SC 29601-2910
Tel (864) 355-3100 *Founded/Ownrshp* 2015
Sales 359.6MM^E^ *EMP* 9,600^E^
SIC 8211 Public elementary & secondary schools
Pr Dir: Oby Lyles
Teacher Pr: Lynn Gibbs
HC Dir: Catherine Storey

GREENVILLE HEALTH SYSTEM
See UPSTATE AFFILIATE ORGANIZATION

GREENVILLE NOLAND
See NOLAND CO

D-U-N-S 12-620-7224
GREENVILLE PUBLIC SCHOOLS INC
412 S Main St, Greenville, MS 38701-4747
Tel (662) 334-7000 *Founded/Ownrshp* 1890
Sales 62.4MM^E^ *EMP* 1,413
SIC 8211 9411 Public elementary & secondary schools; School board; Administration of educational programs
IT Man: Scottie Saulter
Pr Dir: Everett Chen
Schl Brd P: Betsy Alexander

D-U-N-S 07-371-4743
GREENVILLE TECHNICAL COLLEGE PUBLIC FACILITIES CORP
506 S Pleasantburg Dr, Greenville, SC 29607-2439
Tel (864) 250-8000 *Founded/Ownrshp* 1962
Sales 41.4MM^E^ *EMP* 1,200
Accts Cline Brandt Kochenower & Co
SIC 8222 8211 8221 Technical institute; Elementary & secondary schools; Colleges universities & professional schools
Pr: Thomas E Barton Jr PHD
**Pr:* Dr Keith Miller
**VP:* Jacqueline Dimaggio
VP: Lenna Young
Ex Dir: Jennie Johnson
Genl Mgr: Lee Pauly

GREENWALL PAVILION
See JEWISH HOME LIFECARE MANHATTAN

D-U-N-S 78-944-3116
GREENWASTE RECOVERY INC
625 Charles St, San Jose, CA 95112-1402
Tel (408) 283-4800 *Founded/Ownrshp* 1991
Sales 137.9MM^E^ *EMP* 170^E^
SIC 4953 Rubbish collection & disposal; Waste materials, disposal at sea
Pr: Richard Christina
**COO:* Frank Weigel
**CFO:* Don Dean
**CFO:* Dave Tilton
**Sec:* Jesse Weigel
**VP:* Murray Hall

D-U-N-S 08-758-3907
GREENWAY EQUIPMENT INC
JOHN DEERE AUTHORIZED DEALER
(*Suby of* CONMAC INVESTMENTS INC) ★
412 S Van Buren, Weiner, AR 72479-8992
Tel (870) 684-7740 *Founded/Ownrshp* 1999
Sales 95.8MM^E^ *EMP* 350^E^
SIC 5999 5082 Farm equipment & supplies; Construction & mining machinery
CEO: John L Connor
**Pr:* Marshall Stewart
**CFO:* Stephen Smith
**Sr VP:* Rick Bormann
**VP:* Chad Sandoval
**VP:* Steve Shepard

D-U-N-S 04-900-4968
GREENWAY HEALTH (GA)
(*Suby of* GREENWAY HEALTH LLC) ★
100 Greenway Blvd, Carrollton, GA 30117-4338
Tel (770) 836-3100 *Founded/Ownrshp* 1998, 2013
Sales 165.6MM^E^ *EMP* 810
SIC 7373 7371 Computer integrated systems design; Custom computer programming services
CEO: Wyche T Green III
**Pr:* Matthew Hawkins
**COO:* Gregory H Schulenburg
**CFO:* James A Cochran
CFO: James Cochran
**Chf Mktg O:* Bob Kneeley
**Ofcr:* James Ingram
VP: John Ayers
**VP:* Tim Bell
**VP:* William G Esslinger Jr
VP: Eric Grunden
VP: Tor Loege Jr
**VP:* Jonathan Samples
VP: Scott Snapp
**Dir Risk M:* David Wirta

D-U-N-S 79-079-5616
GREENWAY HEALTH LLC
100 Greenway Blvd, Carrollton, GA 30117-4338
Tel (877) 932-6301 *Founded/Ownrshp* 1977
Sales 165.6MM^E^ *EMP* 1,310
SIC 5734 Computer & software stores
CEO: Matthew J Hawkins
Pr: Eric Feibelman
Pr: Sean Murtagh
CFO: Laurens Albada
CFO: Robert R Ellis
Ex VP: Kermit Randa
Ex VP: Greg Schulenburg
Sr VP: Steven Holmquist
Sr VP: Mark Janiszewski
Sr VP: Jeremy Muench
Sr VP: Shantanu Paul
VP: Jeff Cummings
VP: Eric Grunden
VP: Sam Holliday
VP: Rob Newman
VP: Chris Riddle
VP: Lara Caldwell Stout

D-U-N-S 82-893-2710
GREENWICH AEROGROUP INC
475 Steamboat Rd Fl 2, Greenwich, CT 06830-7144
Tel (203) 618-4861 *Founded/Ownrshp* 2009

Sales 386.1MM[E] EMP 273[E]
SIC 4581 5088 7699 5085 Airports, flying fields & services; Airport terminal services; Aircraft maintenance & repair services; Airport hangar rental; Transportation equipment & supplies; Caliper, gauge & other machinists' instrument repair; Industrial supplies
Pr: Jim Ziegler
*CFO: Gene Juris
*Ex VP: Gerald A Goguen
*VP: Frank Medici
*VP Mktg: Daniel Lafrance

D-U-N-S 55-542-7954
GREENWICH HEALTH CARE SERVICES INC
5 Perryridge Rd, Greenwich, CT 06830-4608
Tel (203) 661-5330 Founded/Ownrshp 1986
Sales 1.9MM EMP 1,600[E]
Accts Ernst & Young Llp Ny Ny
SIC 8062 General medical & surgical hospitals
Pr: Frank A Corvino
*COO: Quinton Friesen
*CFO: Eugene Colucci
VP: Christine Beechner
Doctor: Maria Massimi

D-U-N-S 01-013-8097 IMP
GREENWICH HOSPITAL
(Suby of GREENWICH HEALTH CARE SERVICES INC) ★
5 Perryridge Rd, Greenwich, CT 06830-4697
Tel (203) 863-3000 Founded/Ownrshp 1986
Sales 340.7MM EMP 1,600
SIC 8062 General medical & surgical hospitals
Pr: Frank A Corvino
Treas: Chetan Vaid
*Ex VP: Brian J Doran
*Sr VP: Susan Brown
Sr VP: Brian Doran
Sr VP: Michael A Marino
*VP: Christine Beechner
*VP: Eugene Colucci
VP: Jack Mahoney
VP: Melissa Turner
Dir Soc: Patricia Babcock
Dir Rad: Ralph Sgambato
Mng Ofcr: Franklin Loria

D-U-N-S 94-834-1367
GREENWICH SCHOOL DISTRICT
GREENWICH WESTERN MIDDLE SCHL
290 Greenwich Ave, Greenwich, CT 06830-6508
Tel (203) 625-7400 Founded/Ownrshp 1962
Sales 40.6MM[E] EMP 1,982
SIC 8211 Public junior high school
*Prin: Stacey Gross
Dir Sec: Thomas Bobkowski
MIS Dir: Micheal Ting
Pr Dir: Kimberley Eves

D-U-N-S 16-162-3087 IMP
GREENWICH VILLAGE FISH CO INC
CITARELLA
2135 Broadway, New York, NY 10023-1709
Tel (631) 324-9190 Founded/Ownrshp 1980
Sales 271.0MM[E] EMP 600
SIC 5146 Fish & seafoods
Ch Bd: Gaspare Catanzaro
*Pr: Joseph R Gurrera

GREENWICH WESTERN MIDDLE SCHL
See GREENWICH SCHOOL DISTRICT

GREENWOOD COUNTY HOSPITAL
See SELF REGIONAL HEALTHCARE

D-U-N-S 13-859-2568
GREENWOOD FARMERS COOPERATIVE
MIDWEST FARMERS COOP
304 S 3rd St, Elmwood, NE 68349-6114
Tel (402) 994-2585 Founded/Ownrshp 2003
Sales 170.7MM EMP 75
SIC 5191 Farm supplies
Pr: Dale Piper

D-U-N-S 61-874-5137
GREENWOOD INC
160 Milestone Way Ste A, Greenville, SC 29615-6628
Tel (864) 288-5510 Founded/Ownrshp 1993
Sales 262.7MM[E] EMP 786
Accts Dixon Hughes Pllc Greenville
SIC 1541 7349 Industrial buildings & warehouses; Building & office cleaning services
Ch Bd: John Wood
*Pr: Brad Wood
*CFO: Chris Hemmings
*VP: Laura Lipscomb
IT Man: Kevin Crittendon

D-U-N-S 07-355-3661
GREENWOOD LEFLORE HOSPITAL
1401 River Rd, Greenwood, MS 38930-4030
Tel (662) 459-7000 Founded/Ownrshp 1950
Sales 145.8MM EMP 890
Accts Horne Llp Ridgeland Mississi
SIC 8062 General medical & surgical hospitals
Ofcr: Jim Jackson
Chf OB: Edwin M Meek Jr
*CFO: Dawne Holmes
Exec: Patsy Ruffin
Dir Inf Cn: Allison Harris
Dir Risk M: Karen B Upchurch
Dir Lab: Robert Nicholas
Assoc Dir: Jeff Curtis
Dir Rad: Monica Flowers
Dir Rx: Dean Kidd
Dir Env Sv: Mike Fleetwood

D-U-N-S 00-334-8521 IMP
GREENWOOD MILLS INC (SC)
300 Morgan Ave, Greenwood, SC 29646-4552
Tel (864) 227-2121 Founded/Ownrshp 1889
Sales 116.1MM[E] EMP 325
SIC 2211 2221 2241 2261 2262 6552 Broadwoven fabric mills, cotton; Acetate broadwoven fabrics; Poplin, manmade fiber; Twills, manmade fiber; Shirting fabrics, manmade fiber & silk; Narrow fabric mills; Dyeing cotton broadwoven fabrics; Dyeing: manmade fiber & silk broadwoven fabrics; Subdividers & developers
Pr: James C Self III
*Ex VP: Thomas J Davis
*VP: W Eddie Gaither
*VP: H Doyle Kidd
*VP: Warren L Moore
*VP: Gary Niederauer
Dir IT: Glenn Pinnel
Board of Directors: Virginia S Brennan, Sally S Harley

D-U-N-S 07-806-3203
GREENWOOD SCHOOL DISTRICT 50
1855 Calhoun Rd, Greenwood, SC 29649-9102
Tel (864) 941-5400 Founded/Ownrshp 1900
Sales 68.2MM[E] EMP 1,200
SIC 8211 Public elementary & secondary schools
V Ch: Tony Bowers
V Ch: Mark Lowe
*CFO: Henry Teague
Bd of Dir: Shell Dula
Trst: Curtis Hensley
Ofcr: Gary Moore
Info Man: Terese Grant
HC Dir: Nancy Moore

D-U-N-S 00-690-1003
GREER AUTRY & SONS INC
GREER'S
2850 W Main St, Mobile, AL 36612-2043
Tel (251) 342-7964 Founded/Ownrshp 1916
Sales 112.0MM[E] EMP 700
SIC 5411 Grocery stores
Ch Bd: J Barton Greer Jr
*Treas: Jack V Greer Jr
*VP: Robert A Greer
*VP: O M Otts III

D-U-N-S 00-446-1927
GREER INDUSTRIES INC (WV)
GREER LIMESTONE CO DIV
570 Canyon Rd, Morgantown, WV 26508-9065
Tel (304) 296-2549 Founded/Ownrshp 1920
Sales 127.8MM[E] EMP 450
SIC 3316 3272 2951 1422 3274 1446 Strip steel, cold-rolled: from purchased hot-rolled; Concrete products; Asphalt & asphaltic paving mixtures (not from refineries); Agricultural limestone, ground; Lime rock, ground; Dolomite, crushed & broken-quarrying; Lime; Industrial sand
Ch: Charles McGill
*Pr: John R Raese
*Ex VP: David A Raese
VP: James M Goff
VP: Robert A Henn
*VP: James M Troy
VP: James Troy
Admn Mgr: Dave Shaffer
Dir IT: Brad Henley
Dir IT: Matt Smith
IT Man: Dave Harmon

GREER LIMESTONE CO DIV
See GREER INDUSTRIES INC

GREER'S
See GREER AUTRY & SONS INC

D-U-N-S 01-641-1043 IMP
■ GREGG APPLIANCES INC
H.H. GREGG
(Suby of HHGREGG INC) ★
4151 E 96th St, Indianapolis, IN 46240-1442
Tel (317) 848-8710 Founded/Ownrshp 2007
Sales 485.4MM[E] EMP 2,800
SIC 5731 5722 5719 Television sets; Radios, two-way, citizens' band, weather, short-wave, etc.; Consumer electronic equipment; Electric household appliances, major; Electric household appliances, small; Bedding (sheets, blankets, spreads & pillows); Linens
CFO: Robert J Riesbeck
*Pr: Dennis L May
*COO: Troy H Risch
VP: Kelli Slavin
CIO: Stephen Nelson
Board of Directors: Lawrence P Castellani, Benjamin D Geiger, John M Roth, Charles P Rullman, Michael L Smith, Peter M Starrett

D-U-N-S 84-446-1983
GREGORY LOGISTICS INC
2844 Fair St, Poplar Bluff, MO 63901-7016
Tel (573) 785-1088 Founded/Ownrshp 1980
Sales 514.0MM EMP 100
SIC 4213 4212 Trucking, except local; Local trucking, without storage
Pr: Larry Gregory
*CFO: Carol Bounds

D-U-N-S 00-699-7241 IMP/EXP
GREGORY POOLE EQUIPMENT CO
CATERPILLAR AUTHORIZED DEALER
(Suby of PANTHER SUMMIT INDUSTRIES INC) ★
4807 Beryl Rd, Raleigh, NC 27606-1493
Tel (919) 828-0641 Founded/Ownrshp 1946
Sales 473.6MM[E] EMP 900
SIC 5082 Road construction equipment; General construction machinery & equipment
Ch Bd: J Gregory Poole III
*CFO: Kathy Morris
*Ex VP: Richard F Donnelly
Prgrm Mgr: Debby Gardner
IT Man: Joe Owen
Sales Asso: Steve Glover

D-U-N-S 03-798-0042 IMP
GREGORY PRICE INTERNATIONAL INC
PRICE GREGORY
920 Mmrial Cy Way Ste 600, Houston, TX 77024
Tel (713) 780-7500 Founded/Ownrshp 1980
Sales 428.1MM[E] EMP 1,000
SIC 1623

D-U-N-S 00-428-2661
▲ GREIF INC
425 Winter Rd, Delaware, OH 43015-8903
Tel (740) 549-6000 Founded/Ownrshp 1877
Sales 3.6MMM EMP 13,150
Accts Deloitte & Touche Llp Columbu
Tkr Sym GEF Exch NYS
SIC 2653 2449 2655 3412 3089 2674 Corrugated & solid fiber boxes; Boxes, corrugated: made from purchased materials; Shipping cases & drums, wood: wirebound & plywood; Barrels, wood: coopered; Fiber cans, drums & similar products; Drums, fiber: made from purchased material; Fiber cans, drums & containers; Drums, shipping: metal; Plastic containers, except foam; Paper bags: made from purchased materials
Pr: Peter G Watson
*Ch Bd: Michael J Gasser
CFO: Lawrence A Hilsheimer
Ex VP: Gary R Martz
Sr VP: Rob Rosenberg
Sr VP: Ivan Signorelli
VP: Wayde Heigel
VP: Vince Hlinovsky
VP: Doug Lingrel
VP: Douglas W Lingrel
VP: David C Lloyd
VP: Christopher E Luffler
VP: Jeffrey Wood
Exec: Oren Kuhn
Board of Directors: Vicki L Avril, Bruce A Edwards, Mark A Emkes, John F Finn, Daniel J Gunsett, Judith D Hook, John W McNamara, Patrick J Norton

D-U-N-S 61-727-2856 IMP
■ GREIF PACKAGING LLC
(Suby of GREIF INC) ★
366 Greif Pkwy, Delaware, OH 43015-8260
Tel (740) 549-6000 Founded/Ownrshp 2004
Sales 274.5MM[E] EMP 250[E]
SIC 3086 Packaging & shipping materials, foamed plastic
CEO: Brian Dum
*Ch: Michael J Gasser

D-U-N-S 07-995-5784
■ GREIF USA LLC
(Suby of GREIF PACKAGING LLC) ★
366 Greif Pkwy, Delaware, OH 43015-8260
Tel (740) 549-6000 Founded/Ownrshp 2005
Sales 266.9MM[E] EMP 236[E]
SIC 5093 Barrels & drums

D-U-N-S 00-426-8020 IMP
GREINER BIO-ONE NORTH AMERICA INC
GREINER-BIO-ONE
(Suby of GREINER BIO-ONE GMBH)
4238 Capital Dr, Monroe, NC 28110-7681
Tel (704) 261-7883 Founded/Ownrshp 1997
Sales 88.8MM[E] EMP 205
SIC 5047 Medical equipment & supplies
Pr: Rainer Perneker
Exec: Diane Ban
VP Mfg: Joses Sellfoser
VP Sls: Carol D'Ance
Board of Directors: Wolfgang Hock, Franz Konard

GREINER-BIO-ONE
See GREINER BIO-ONE NORTH AMERICA INC

D-U-N-S 05-880-0959 IMP
GREKA INTEGRATED INC
1700 Sinton Rd, Santa Maria, CA 93458-9708
Tel (805) 347-8700 Founded/Ownrshp 2001
Sales 107.0MM[E] EMP 145[E]
SIC 1382 Oil & gas exploration services
CEO: Randeep S Grewal
*CFO: Ken Miller
*VP: Susan Whalen

GRENADA LIVING CENTER
See COMMUNITY CARE CENTER OF GRENADA LLC

D-U-N-S 04-582-3283
GRESCO UTILITY SUPPLY INC
1135 Rumble Rd, Forsyth, GA 31029-6350
Tel (478) 315-0800 Founded/Ownrshp 1960
Sales 194.8MM EMP 130
Accts Mcnair Mclemore Middlebrooks
SIC 5063 Electrical apparatus & equipment
CEO: Steve Gramling
*CFO: Melissa Williams

D-U-N-S 03-333-3998
GRESHAM PETROLEUM CO
415 Pershing Ave, Indianola, MS 38751-3150
Tel (662) 887-2160 Founded/Ownrshp 1958
Sales 126.4MM EMP 38
SIC 5171 5984

D-U-N-S 05-915-3676
GRESHAM SMITH AND PARTNERS
GS&P
511 Union St 1400 Nashvle, Nashville, TN 37219
Tel (615) 770-8100 Founded/Ownrshp 1967
Sales 89.1MM[E] EMP 800
SIC 8712

D-U-N-S 03-839-6057
GRESHAM WOFTAM INC
(Suby of AMWINS GROUP INC) ★
1 Gresham Lndg, Stockbridge, GA 30281-6341
Tel (770) 389-1600 Founded/Ownrshp 2013
Sales NA EMP 215
SIC 6411 Insurance brokers
Ch: James V Gresham
*Pr: Tony Gresham
*Ch: George L Abernathy
*Sec: Gail S Gresham
Sr VP: Sue Altman
*Sr VP: James A Gresham
VP: Lisa Cupp
VP: Jenny Driskell
VP: Sandy Foster
VP: Art Hays
VP: Ed Hrabovsky
VP: Lil Hullinghorst
VP: Sandy McDougal-Foster
VP: Andy Packard

D-U-N-S 07-978-4773
GRESHAM-BARLOW SCHOOL DISTRICT
GRESHAM-BARLOW SCHOOL DST 10J
1331 Nw Eastman Pkwy, Gresham, OR 97030-3896
Tel (503) 618-2470 Founded/Ownrshp 1918
Sales 128.5MM EMP 1,003
Accts Pauly Rogers And Co Pc T
SIC 8211 Public elementary & secondary schools
*CFO: Jerry Jones
MIS Dir: Darrin King

GRESHAM-BARLOW SCHOOL DST 10J
See GRESHAM-BARLOW SCHOOL DISTRICT

GREY ADVERTISING
See GREY GLOBAL GROUP LLC

GREY EAGLE DISTRIBUTORS
See D & D DISTRIBUTORS LLLP

D-U-N-S 00-698-4876
GREY GLOBAL GROUP LLC
GREY ADVERTISING
(Suby of WPP PLC)
200 5th Ave Bsmt B, New York, NY 10010-3372
Tel (212) 546-2000 Founded/Ownrshp 1917, 1969
Sales 656.6MM[E] EMP 10,200
SIC 7311 Advertising agencies
Ch Bd: Jim Heekin
*V Ch: Joe Celia
V Ch: Steven G Felsher
*V Ch: Tim Mellors
Pr: Alain Groenendaal
*COO: Owen Dougherty
CFO: Piero Cantarelli
*CFO: Robert Oates
*Ofcr: Pele Cortizo-Burgess
Ofcr: Owen J Dougherty
*Ofcr: Tor Myhren
Ofcr: Ali Shabaz
Ex VP: Josh Golden
Ex VP: Robert Kaufman
*Sr VP: John A Grudzina
Sr VP: John Gurdzina
VP: Lori Bullock
VP: Mercedes Campos
VP: Courtney Jacobs
VP: Ernesto James
VP: Carl Jones

D-U-N-S 17-838-9958
GREY MOUNTAIN PARTNERS LLC
1470 Walnut St Ste 400, Boulder, CO 80302-5371
Tel (303) 449-5692 Founded/Ownrshp 2006
Sales 419.0MM[E] EMP 1,192
SIC 6726 Investment offices
VP: Brad Starkweather
Mng Dir: Jeff Vincent
Off Mgr: Tania Martin

D-U-N-S 15-119-7878 IMP
GREYHOUND LINES INC
(Suby of FIRSTGROUP PLC)
350 N Saint Paul St # 300, Dallas, TX 75201-4285
Tel (214) 849-8000 Founded/Ownrshp 1987
Sales 2.7MMM[E] EMP 8,000
SIC 4111 4215 4142

D-U-N-S 83-937-5797
GREYSTAR CORP
PENSPEN
10375 Richmond Ave # 900, Houston, TX 77042-4190
Tel (713) 953-7007 Founded/Ownrshp 1995
Sales 216.4MM[E] EMP 700
SIC 1389 Gas field services
Pr: John D Patton
*CFO: Jeff Powers
*VP: Michael Kneale
IT Man: Beejan Vessali

D-U-N-S 83-879-2158
GREYSTAR MANAGEMENT SERVICES LP
GREYSTAR MULTI-FAMILY SERVICES
750 Bering Dr Ste 300, Houston, TX 77057-2132
Tel (713) 966-5000 Founded/Ownrshp 1993
Sales 264.3MM[E] EMP 5,000
SIC 6513 6531 1522 Apartment hotel operation; Real estate brokers & agents; Remodeling, multi-family dwellings
CEO: Bob Faith
Genl Pt: Greystar Holdings
COO: Bill Maddux
CFO: Eddie Fletcher
CFO: Derek Ramsey
Ex Dir: Stacy Hunt
Ex Dir: Andrew Livingstone

GREYSTAR MULTI-FAMILY SERVICES
See GREYSTAR MANAGEMENT SERVICES LP

D-U-N-S 08-316-9735 IMP
GREYSTAR REAL ESTATE PARTNERS LLC
18 Broad St Ste 300, Charleston, SC 29401-3012
Tel (843) 579-9400 Founded/Ownrshp 2001, 1999
Sales 731.5MM[E] EMP 4,600
SIC 6531 Real estate brokers & agents
CEO: Robert Faith
*COO: Bill Maddux
*CFO: Derek Ramsey
Off Mgr: Lynn Gibson
Off Mgr: Bekah Sutter
Mktg Dir: Trisha Peters

D-U-N-S 61-415-3265
GREYSTAR RS GROUP LLC
(Suby of GREYSTAR REAL ESTATE PARTNERS LLC) ★
1201 Elm St Ste 1600, Dallas, TX 75270-2038
Tel (214) 290-7300 Founded/Ownrshp 2014
Sales 368.6MM[E] EMP 4,500[E]
SIC 8741 Management services
Pr: Terry Danner
*COO: Marysusan Wanich
*CFO: Pal Ottesen
Ex VP: Tom Daniels
Sr VP: Gail Duke
VP: Larry Kallestad

VP: Lisa Nerheim
**VP:* Gardner Rees
VP: Lynne Shirley
VP: Brian Whisnand
Dir Soc: Sarah Stotts

D-U-N-S 05-168-7130
GREYSTONE HEALTHCARE MANAGEMENT CORP
4042 Park Oaks Blvd # 300, Tampa, FL 33610-9539
Tel (813) 635-9500 *Founded/Ownrshp* 2001
Sales 228.8MM[E] *EMP* 3,000
SIC 8741 Nursing & personal care facility management
CEO: Connie Bessler
**CFO:* Ronald Swartz
Ex Dir: Mytchell Chancy

D-U-N-S 00-692-6000
GREYSTONE POWER CORP AN ELECTRIC MEMBERSHIP CORP (GA)
4040 Bankhead Hwy 78, Douglasville, GA 30134-4313
Tel (770) 942-6576 *Founded/Ownrshp* 1936
Sales 276.5MM *EMP* 260
SIC 4911 Electric services
Pr: Gary Miller
**Ch:* Calvin Earwood
**V Ch Bd:* Charles Rutland
Ofcr: Jerry Donovan
VP: Tim Williams
Board of Directors: J Calvin Earwood, Ed Haley, William Parks, W McSel Pearson, Fred E Wallace

GRFT
See GRAND RAPIDS FOAM TECHNOLOGIES INC

D-U-N-S 14-212-3202 IMP/EXP
GRI ENGINEERING & DEVELOPMENT LLC
(*Suby of* MAT-AUTOMOTIVE) ★
6700 Wildlife Way, Long Grove, IL 60047
Tel (847) 383-8478 *Founded/Ownrshp* 2003
Sales 306.0MM *EMP* 22
Accts Bdo Seidman Llp
SIC 5013 Motor vehicle supplies & new parts
CFO: Greg Purse
Treas: Heather Korsvik

D-U-N-S 07-999-7072
■ **GRID SOLUTIONS (US) LLC**
(*Suby of* GENERAL ELECTRIC CO) ★
4200 Wildwood Pkwy # 2018, Atlanta, GA 30339-8402
Tel (877) 605-6777 *Founded/Ownrshp* 2015
Sales 2.5MMM[E] *EMP* 4,060
SIC 4911 Electric services
CEO: Mark W Begor

D-U-N-S 12-352-8494
GRIDIRON CAPITAL LLC
220 Elm St Fl 2, New Canaan, CT 06840-5322
Tel (203) 972-1100 *Founded/Ownrshp* 2004
Sales 267.2MM[E] *EMP* 1,100[E]
SIC 6726 Investment offices
Mng Dir: Scott Harrison

D-U-N-S 93-160-6511
GRIDIRON TRADING MANAGEMENT CO LLC
81 Hemlock Hill Rd, New Canaan, CT 06840-3002
Tel (704) 872-5231 *Founded/Ownrshp* 1996
Sales 149.4MM[E] *EMP* 260
SIC 6221 Commodity contracts brokers, dealers

GRIFFIN FERTILIZER CO
See BEN HILL GRIFFIN INC

D-U-N-S 01-958-8672 IMP
GRIFFIN GREENHOUSE SUPPLIES INC
1619 Main St, Tewksbury, MA 01876-2047
Tel (978) 851-4346 *Founded/Ownrshp* 1967
Sales 98.9MM[E] *EMP* 220
SIC 5191 Greenhouse equipment & supplies; Seeds: field, garden & flower; Fertilizer & fertilizer materials
Pr: Richard T Hyslip
**COO:* Craig S Hyslip
**Treas:* Kenneth M Hyslip Sr
Brnch Mgr: Bill Hotz
Brnch Mgr: John Hyslip
Info Man: Alex Ho
Site Mgr: Dennis Kacewich
Opers Mgr: Guy Gallant
Opers Mgr: Jackie Tinsley
Mktg Dir: Dave Morin
Mktg Mgr: Matthew Munafo

D-U-N-S 96-542-3572
GRIFFIN HOLDINGS LLC
2121 Avenue Of The Stars, Los Angeles, CA 90067-5010
Tel (424) 245-4423 *Founded/Ownrshp* 2004
Sales 99.2MM[E] *EMP* 325[E]
SIC 8741 Business management
Prin: Dan Gabbay

D-U-N-S 07-212-8424
GRIFFIN HOSPITAL INC (CT)
MEDSOURCE
130 Division St, Derby, CT 06418-1326
Tel (203) 735-7421 *Founded/Ownrshp* 1901, 1984
Sales 142.9MM *EMP* 1,100
SIC 8062 General medical & surgical hospitals
Pr: Patrick Charmel
Pr: Georgia Jennings
**CFO:* Mark O'Neill
Treas: Robert Fox
VP: Frederick Browne
VP: James Haswell
VP: Kevin Hill
VP: Barbara Stumpo
Assoc Dir: Joseph Gnanaraj
Dir Soc: Lionel Lim
Dir Soc: Haq Nawaz

D-U-N-S 00-425-6509 IMP/EXP
■ **GRIFFIN INDUSTRIES LLC** (KY)
DAR PRO SOLUTIONS
(*Suby of* DARLING INGREDIENTS INC) ★
4221 Alexandria Pike, Cold Spring, KY 41076-1897
Tel (859) 781-2010 *Founded/Ownrshp* 1959, 2010
Sales 539.2MM[E] *EMP* 1,800
SIC 2077 Grease rendering, inedible; Tallow rendering, inedible
VP: Spike Chronowski
Off Mgr: Cindy Williams
CIO: Bill Rogers
VP Opers: Thomas Griffin

D-U-N-S 60-760-7454 EXP
GRIFFIN MANAGEMENT CO INC
LEXUS OF GREENWICH
19 Railroad Ave, Greenwich, CT 06830-6302
Tel (203) 869-6700 *Founded/Ownrshp* 1986
Sales 127.5MM[E] *EMP* 386
SIC 5511 Automobiles, new & used
Pr: Samuel R Scatterday
**Treas:* Anthony Mazza
**VP:* William J Griffin III
Genl Mgr: Eric Pagan
Store Mgr: Robert Merturi
Dir IT: Matthew Sposato
Sls Mgr: John Annunziato
Sls Mgr: Ched Gelb
Sls Mgr: John McCaffrey
Sls Mgr: Louis Rivera
Sls Mgr: Dave Sturm

D-U-N-S 05-675-8436 IMP
GRIFFIN MOTORWERKE INC
1146 6th St, Berkeley, CA 94710-1246
Tel (510) 524-7447 *Founded/Ownrshp* 1981
Sales 26.4MM[E] *EMP* 1,011
SIC 7538 5531 General automotive repair shops; Automotive parts
Pr: John Griffin

GRIFFIN OIL CO
See RIP GRIFFIN TRUCK SERVICE CENTER INC

D-U-N-S 82-604-3593 IMP
GRIFFIN PIPE PRODUCTS CO INC
10 Adams St, Lynchburg, VA 24504-1446
Tel (434) 845-8021 *Founded/Ownrshp* 2005
Sales 212.6MM[E] *EMP* 750
SIC 3317 Steel pipe & tubes
Pr: Mark S Shirely
**Treas:* D J Litwin
**VP:* M J Hower
**Prin:* Glenn E Chamberlin
CTO: John Blankenship

D-U-N-S 10-064-6132
GRIFFIN-SPALDING COUNTY SCHOOLS SYSTEM
216 S 6th St, Griffin, GA 30224-3420
Tel (770) 229-3700 *Founded/Ownrshp* 1953
Sales 108.7MM *EMP* 1,700
Accts Robinson Grimes & Company Pc
SIC 8211 Public elementary & secondary schools
Ch: James Westbury
Pr Dir: Judy Parker
Teacher Pr: Stephanie Dobbins

D-U-N-S 00-690-7380
GRIFFITH CO (CA)
3050 E Birch St, Brea, CA 92821-6248
Tel (714) 984-5500 *Founded/Ownrshp* 1922
Sales 174.8MM[E] *EMP* 194
SIC 1611 Highway & street construction
CEO: Thomas L Foss
**Ch Bd:* Jim Waltze
**COO:* Jaimie Angus
**CFO:* Gordon Csutak
VP: Dave Diaz
VP: Craig Huss
VP: Dan Muns
VP: Luke Walker
VP Bus Dev: Dan McGrew
Off Mgr: Mary McGee
Dir IT: Chris Malafa

GRIFFITH ENERGY
See SUPERIOR PLUS ENERGY SERVICES INC

D-U-N-S 00-510-5788 IMP/EXP
GRIFFITH FOODS GROUP INC (IL)
1 Griffith Ctr, Alsip, IL 60803-4701
Tel (708) 371-0900 *Founded/Ownrshp* 1919
Sales 777.1MM[E] *EMP* 2,500
SIC 2099 Seasonings: dry mixes; Spices, including grinding
Pr: D L Griffith
**CFO:* Joseph R Maslick
Treas: Nancy Rossmiller
Mng Dir: Shyam Mohan
QA Dir: Ciro Pryor

D-U-N-S 09-316-9738 IMP
GRIFFITH FOODS INC
GRIFFITH LABORATORIES USA INC
(*Suby of* GRIFFITH LABORATORIES) ★
12200 S Central Ave, Alsip, IL 60803-3408
Tel (708) 371-0900 *Founded/Ownrshp* 2016
Sales 136.4MM[E] *EMP* 440
SIC 2099 Seasonings: dry mixes; Spices, including grinding
Ch Bd: Dean L Griffith
**Pr:* Jennifer Convery
**CFO:* Joseph R Maslick

D-U-N-S 62-213-7644 IMP
GRIFFITH FOODS INTERNATIONAL INC
GRIFFITH LABORATORIES INTL
(*Suby of* GRIFFITH FOODS GROUP INC) ★
1 Griffith Ctr, Alsip, IL 60803-4701
Tel (708) 371-0900 *Founded/Ownrshp* 1978
Sales 364.6MM[E] *EMP* 2,500[E]
SIC 2099 7389 Seasonings: dry mixes; Spices, including grinding; Inspection & testing services
Pr: D L Griffith
CFO: J R Maslick
Ex VP: Herve De La Vauvre
Sr VP: William C Frost
VP: Drew M Bandusky
VP: Don Bernacchi
VP: Mike Cherry
VP: Guillermo Hernandez
VP: Paul Huebener
VP: Amy Jones
VP: Deanna Kibelkis
VP: James S Legg
VP: John McCarville
VP: Christopher Woods
Board of Directors: Lois J Griffith, Dr Ben Johnson, Dr Susan Lind, Norman H Mc Millan, Albert C Schauer

D-U-N-S 96-847-9188
GRIFFITH FOODS WORLDWIDE INC
GRIFFITH LABORATORIES
(*Suby of* GRIFFITH LABORATORIES INTL) ★
12200 S Central Ave, Alsip, IL 60803-3408
Tel (708) 371-0900 *Founded/Ownrshp* 1996
Sales 194.1MM[E] *EMP* 2,000
SIC 2099 Seasonings: dry mixes; Spices, including grinding
Pr: Herve De La Vauvre
**Ch Bd:* Dean L Griffith
Pr: Michael Plichta
Treas: Nancy Rossmiller
VP: Paul Hubner
IT Man: Dave Herring
VP Sls: Jennifer Convery

GRIFFITH LABORATORIES
See GRIFFITH FOODS WORLDWIDE INC

GRIFFITH LABORATORIES INTL
See GRIFFITH FOODS INTERNATIONAL INC

GRIFFITH LABORATORIES USA INC
See GRIFFITH FOODS INC

D-U-N-S 00-902-7491
GRIFFITH RUBBER MILLS (OR)
2625 Nw Indul St, Portland, OR 97210
Tel (503) 226-6971 *Founded/Ownrshp* 1900, 1988
Sales 103.3MM[E] *EMP* 300
SIC 3061 3069 Mechanical rubber goods; Molded rubber products
Prin: Jill Jarrett Laney
**Pr:* Jennifer Chacon
Pr: Max Gregory
**Prin:* Jennifer Laney

D-U-N-S 00-648-0875
GRIFFITHS CORP
(*Suby of* GRIFFITHS HOLDING CORP) ★
2717 Niagara Ln N, Minneapolis, MN 55447-4844
Tel (763) 557-8935 *Founded/Ownrshp* 1963
Sales 111.1MM[E] *EMP* 700
SIC 3544 3469 3444 3451 Special dies, tools, jigs & fixtures; Stamping metal for the trade; Sheet metal specialties, not stamped; Screw machine products
Ch Bd: Harold F Griffiths
**Pr:* Kenneth H Griffiths
**VP:* Keith A Griffiths
Exec: Les Fieldman

D-U-N-S 07-842-5496
GRIFFITHS HOLDING CORP
2717 Niagara Ln N, Minneapolis, MN 55447-4844
Tel (763) 557-8935 *Founded/Ownrshp* 2001
Sales 119.5MM[E] *EMP* 700
SIC 3544 3469 Special dies, tools, jigs & fixtures; Stamping metal for the trade
Ch Bd: Harold F Griffiths
**Pr:* Kenneth H Griffiths
**VP:* Keith A Griffiths
**VP:* Arthur A Hahn
Mng Dir: Paul Olson
Genl Mgr: Linda Lacy

D-U-N-S 05-059-0710 IMP/EXP
▲ **GRIFFON CORP**
712 5th Ave Fl 18, New York, NY 10019-4108
Tel (212) 957-5000 *Founded/Ownrshp* 1959
Sales 1.9MMM *EMP* 6,000
Tkr Sym GFF *Exch* NYS
SIC 3442 2431 1751 1799 3083 3663 Garage doors, overhead: metal; Garage doors, overhead: wood; Garage door, installation or erection; Home/office interiors finishing, furnishing & remodeling; Prefabricated fireplace installation; Laminated plastics plate & sheet; Laminated plastic sheets; Radio & TV communications equipment
CEO: Ronald J Kramer
**Ch Bd:* Harvey R Blau
Pr: Robert F Mehmel
CFO: Brian G Harris
Sr VP: Seth L Kaplan
VP: Michael Hansen
Genl Couns: Pamela Weinsaft

D-U-N-S 09-269-4538 IMP
GRIFOLS BIOLOGICALS INC (CA)
(*Suby of* GRIFOLS SHARED SERVICES NORTH AMERICA INC) ★
5555 Valley Blvd, Los Angeles, CA 90032-3520
Tel (323) 227-7028 *Founded/Ownrshp* 2003
Sales 133.7MM[E] *EMP* 450[E]
SIC 2836 2834 Plasmas; Pharmaceutical preparations
CEO: Greg Rich
**CFO:* Max Debrouwer
**VP:* David Bell
Assoc Dir: Lorraine Peddada
Board of Directors: Alfredo Arroyo, Tomas Daga, Thomas Glanzmann Chb, Victor Grifols, Ramon Riera, Dr Marla Salmon, Juan Ignacio Twose

D-U-N-S 14-114-9950 IMP
GRIFOLS SHARED SERVICES NORTH AMERICA INC
(*Suby of* GRIFOLS SA)
2410 Lillyvale Ave, Los Angeles, CA 90032-3514
Tel (323) 225-2221 *Founded/Ownrshp* 1987
Sales 3.6MMM[E] *EMP* 9,000[E]
SIC 5122 2834 Drugs, proprietaries & sundries; Druggists' preparations (pharmaceuticals)
CEO: Gregory Rich
**CFO:* Max Debrouwer
VP: Raul Alvarez
**VP:* David Bell
VP: Dave Dew
VP: Juan Diaz
VP: Sergio Molina
VP: Norbert Piel
VP: Wesley Shimoda
VP: Verna Shockley
Assoc Dir: Vlasta Hakes
Assoc Dir: Colleen Moreno
Board of Directors: Alfredo Arroyo, Tomas Daga, Thomas Glanzmann Chb, Victor Grifols, Ramon Riera, Dr Marla Salmon, Juan Ignacio Twose

D-U-N-S 83-973-1507 IMP
GRIFOLS THERAPEUTICS INC
(*Suby of* GRIFOLS SHARED SERVICES NORTH AMERICA INC) ★
79 Tw Alexander Dr, Durham, NC 27709-0152
Tel (919) 316-6300 *Founded/Ownrshp* 2011
Sales 820.5MM[E] *EMP* 4,763
SIC 2836 Blood derivatives
CEO: Greg Rich
**CFO:* Max Debrouwer
CFO: Debra Newman
Ex VP: John F Gaither
Sr VP: Keith Kosinski
**VP:* David Bell
Assoc Dir: Anna McSorley
QA Dir: Timothy Hamm
Dir IT: Krista Davila
Dir IT: Rose Mattiace
VP Opers: Richard Denniger
Board of Directors: Alfredo Arroyo, Tomas Daga, Thomas Glanzmann Chb, Victor Grifols, Ramon Riera, Dr Marla Salmon, Juan Ignacio Twose

D-U-N-S 04-898-7452 IMP
GRIFOLS USA LLC
(*Suby of* GRIFOLS SHARED SERVICES NORTH AMERICA INC) ★
2410 Lillyvale Ave, Los Angeles, CA 90032-3514
Tel (800) 421-0008 *Founded/Ownrshp* 2005
Sales 1.8MMM[E] *EMP* 9,000
Accts Goldman Juda & Martin Cpa S
SIC 5047 Diagnostic equipment, medical
CEO: Gregory Rich
CFO: Max Debrouwer
Treas: Montserrat Lloveras
**VP:* David Bell
VP: Max De Brouwer
Genl Mgr: Mary Hughes
Mfg Dir: Kenneth Whitlow
Sls Dir: Gary Greenstein
Sls Dir: Ken Shriner
Corp Couns: David Pierce

GRILL CONCEPTS
See GRILL ON ALLEY THE INC

D-U-N-S 17-330-4999
GRILL CONCEPTS INC
DAILY GRILL ENCINO PLACE
6300 Canoga Ave Ste 600, Woodland Hills, CA 91367-8022
Tel (818) 251-7000 *Founded/Ownrshp* 1987
Sales 78.4MM[E] *EMP* 1,470[E]
SIC 5812 Restaurant, family: independent
CEO: Bob Spivak
**Ch Bd:* Robert Spivak
**Ch Bd:* Michael Weinstock
**CFO:* Wayne Lipschitz
**Sr VP:* Louie Feinstein
**Sr VP:* John Sola
Genl Mgr: Steve Grant
Sales Exec: Grace Truong
Mktg Mgr: Juliet Mothershed

D-U-N-S 60-967-1516
GRILL CONCEPTS-DC INC
DAILY GRILL
(*Suby of* DAILY GRILL ENCINO PLACE) ★
11661 San Vicente Blvd, Los Angeles, CA 90049-5103
Tel (310) 820-5559 *Founded/Ownrshp* 1987
Sales 27.9MM[E] *EMP* 1,300
SIC 5812 Grills (eating places)
Pr: Robert Spivak
CFO: John Bayley
VP: Terri Henry

D-U-N-S 04-940-9738
GRILL ON ALLEY THE INC (CA)
GRILL CONCEPTS
11661 San Vicente Blvd # 404, Los Angeles, CA 90049-5103
Tel (310) 820-5559 *Founded/Ownrshp* 1995
Sales 26.5MM[E] *EMP* 1,300
SIC 5812 Pizzeria, chain
Pr: Robert Spivak
Pr: Thomas Kachani
Exec: John Sola

D-U-N-S 05-397-7724 IMP/EXP
GRIMCO INC (MO)
1585 Fencorp Dr, Fenton, MO 63026-2942
Tel (636) 305-0088 *Founded/Ownrshp* 1875, 1970
Sales 94.7MM[E] *EMP* 200
SIC 3469 2759 3993 3429 3312 Patterns on metal; Screen printing; Signs & advertising specialties; Manufactured hardware (general); Blast furnaces & steel mills
CEO: Robert Hummert
**Pr:* John Burkemper
**Pr:* Dale Kleinheider
Ex VP: Urse Haug
Ex VP: Michael Sparks
Exec: Melissa Graham
Rgnl Mgr: Michael Bolinger
Dist Mgr: Shaun Allen
Mktg Mgr: Emily Martin
Art Dir: Christine Jokerst

D-U-N-S 00-418-9262 IMP
■ **GRIMES AEROSPACE CO**
HONEYWELL
(*Suby of* HONEYWELL INTERNATIONAL INC) ★
550 State Route 55, Urbana, OH 43078-9482
Tel (937) 484-2000 *Founded/Ownrshp* 1923, 1997
Sales 103.3MM[E] *EMP* 1,025
SIC 3728 3647 3646 3645 3577 3571

D-U-N-S 03-356-0509 EXP
GRIMMWAY ENTERPRISES INC
GRIMMWAY FARMS
14141 Di Giorgio Rd, Arvin, CA 93203-9518
Tel (661) 854-6250 *Founded/Ownrshp* 1992

Sales 1.8MMM[E] *EMP* 4,000
SIC 0723 Vegetable packing services
Pr: Jeff Meger
* *CFO:* Steve Barnes
Ex VP: Jeff Huckaby
Genl Mgr: Steve Roodzant
Telecom Mg: Mandy Harris
Sfty Dirs: Edward Gerding
Sfty Dirs: Mark Rodriguez
Opers Mgr: Eddie Rosson
Opers Mgr: Kevin Tibbett
Plnt Mgr: Manuel Singh
Ql Cn Mgr: Luz Garcia

GRIMMWAY FARMS
See GRIMMWAY ENTERPRISES INC

GRINDING SZING LLC FORMER NAME
See PRINCE ENERGY LLC

GRINNELL FIRE PRTCTION SYSTEMS
See TYCO SIMPLEXGRINNELL

D-U-N-S 00-694-1652
GRINNELL MUTUAL REINSURANCE CO
4215 Highway 146, Grinnell, IA 50112-8110
Tel (641) 269-8000 *Founded/Ownrshp* 1909
Sales NA *EMP* 740
SIC 6411 Insurance agents, brokers & service
Pr: Larry Jansen
Pr: Jeffrey R Menary
* *CFO:* David Wingert
* *VP:* Thomas Bachmann
* *VP:* Dennis G Day
* *VP:* Shirley Linn
* *VP:* Willard McDonald
* *VP:* Mike Ward
* *CIO:* Dennis Mehmen
Board of Directors: William J Lampe, John McMahon, Paul G Stueven

D-U-N-S 04-679-9318 IMP/EXP
GRISTEDES FOODS INC
GRISTEDES SUPERMARKETS
(*Suby of* RED APPLE GROUP INC) ★
800 3rd Ave Fl 5, New York, NY 10022-7655
Tel (212) 956-5770 *Founded/Ownrshp* 1986
Sales 339.5MM *EMP* 2,180
SIC 5411 Grocery stores
Ch Bd: John Catsimatidis
* *CFO:* Mark Kassner
VP: Carmine Napolitano
Exec: Deborah Clusan
Snr Mgr: Francine Rioux

GRISTEDES SUPERMARKETS
See GRISTEDES FOODS INC

D-U-N-S 05-747-7994 IMP/EXP
GRISWOLD INDUSTRIES
CLA-VAL CO
1701 Placentia Ave, Costa Mesa, CA 92627-4416
Tel (949) 722-4800 *Founded/Ownrshp* 1975
Sales 108.4MM[E] *EMP* 410
SIC 3492 3365 3366

D-U-N-S 10-288-5035 IMP/EXP
GRIZZLY INDUSTRIAL INC
1821 Valencia St, Bellingham, WA 98229-4746
Tel (360) 676-6090 *Founded/Ownrshp* 1983
Sales 86.1MM[E] *EMP* 300
SIC 5251 Tools; Tools, power
CEO: Shiraz Balolia
* *CFO:* Colleen Lahr
* *VP:* Don Osterloh
CTO: Renee Showalter
Dir IT: Justin McCuiston
Opers Mgr: Jean Turner
Ql Cn Mgr: Bill Crofutt
Mktg Mgr: Melinda Sweet

D-U-N-S 07-407-0988 IMP/EXP
GROB SYSTEMS INC
MACHINE TOOL DIVISION
(*Suby of* GROB-WERKE BURKHART GROB E.K.)
1070 Navajo Dr, Bluffton, OH 45817-9666
Tel (419) 358-9015 *Founded/Ownrshp* 1993
Sales 151.0MM[E] *EMP* 198
SIC 3535 7699 Robotic conveyors; Industrial equipment services
CEO: Ralf Bronnenmeier
Pr: Jason Cartright
* *Pr:* Michael Hutecker
VP: William Vejnovic
IT Man: Douglas L Gesler
Sls Mgr: Darrin Lanasky
Sls Mgr: Mark Schem
Snr Mgr: David Stall

D-U-N-S 01-955-4633 IMP
GROCERS SPECIALTY CO
G S C BALL
(*Suby of* UNIFIED GROCERS INC) ★
5200 Sheila St, Commerce, CA 90040-3906
Tel (323) 264-5200 *Founded/Ownrshp* 1981
Sales 93.8MM[E] *EMP* 200
SIC 5141 Groceries, general line
Pr: Joe Falvey
* *CFO:* Rich Martin
* *Treas:* Christine Neal

D-U-N-S 02-916-1585 IMP/EXP
GROCERY OUTLET INC
CANNED FOODS GROCERY OUTLET
5650 Hollis St Ste 100, Emeryville, CA 94608-2505
Tel (510) 845-1999 *Founded/Ownrshp* 2014
Sales 155.0MM[E] *EMP* 315
SIC 5411

GROCERY SUPPLY COMPANY
See GSC ENTERPRISES INC

D-U-N-S 00-790-5748
GROENDYKE TRANSPORT INC
2510 Rock Island Blvd, Enid, OK 73701-1342
Tel (580) 234-4663 *Founded/Ownrshp* 1932
Sales 239.1MM[E] *EMP* 1,350
SIC 4213

D-U-N-S 09-719-0763 IMP
GROHE AMERICA INC
(*Suby of* GROHE NORTH AMERICA GMBH)
200 N Gary Ave Ste G, Roselle, IL 60172-1681
Tel (630) 582-7711 *Founded/Ownrshp* 1979
Sales 150.0MM *EMP* 66[E]
SIC 2499 Kitchen, bathroom & household ware: wood
CEO: Jim Griffin
* *CFO:* Alex Davidkhknian
Treas: Glen Paradise
Chf Mktg O: Michelle Helfert
VP: John P Shannon
Brnch Mgr: Patrick Hurley
Genl Mgr: Frank Profiti
Dir IT: Jason Janowiak
IT Man: Pete Rivera
IT Man: Matt Ruegge
IT Man: Armin Von Dolenga

D-U-N-S 00-284-9941
GROOT INDUSTRIES INC
2500 Landmeier Rd, Elk Grove Village, IL 60007-2627
Tel (847) 734-6400 *Founded/Ownrshp* 1970
Sales 280.4MM[E] *EMP* 300
SIC 4953 Rubbish collection & disposal; Street refuse systems
Pr: Larry Groot
* *VP:* Lee Brandsma
Sales Exec: Ted Payton

GROSS BUILDERS
See I & M J GROSS CO

D-U-N-S 06-983-7672
GROSSE POINTE PUBLIC SCHOOL SYSTEM (MI)
389 Saint Clair St, Grosse Pointe, MI 48230-1501
Tel (313) 432-3000 *Founded/Ownrshp* 1919
Sales 108.1MM *EMP* 1,200
Accts Plante & Moran Pllc Clinton
SIC 8211 Public elementary school; Public junior high school; Public senior high school
Prin: Glenn Croydon
Prin: Deborah Hubbell
Prin: Patricia J Meek
Prin: Elaine Middlekauff
Prin: Joan Robie
Prin: Jean Rusing
Prin: Kathy Satut
Prin: Ronald D Wardie
Psych: Christine Kuhl

D-U-N-S 93-156-3951
GROSSINGER AUTOPLEX INC
6900 N Mccormick Blvd # 1, Lincolnwood, IL 60712-2775
Tel (847) 674-9000 *Founded/Ownrshp* 1930
Sales 87.5MM[E] *EMP* 200[E]
SIC 5511 Automobiles, new & used
Pr: Caroline Grossinger
Genl Mgr: Al Abbas
Genl Mgr: Charlie Hanmeyer
Sls Dir: Jonathan Moscovitch
Sls Mgr: Donnie Avramov
Sls Mgr: Courtney Collins
Sales Asso: Shlomo Bogoff

D-U-N-S 03-104-2443 IMP
GROSSMAN IRON AND STEEL CO
5 N Market St, Saint Louis, MO 63102-1488
Tel (314) 231-9423 *Founded/Ownrshp* 1928
Sales 100.0MM *EMP* 90
SIC 5093 Metal scrap & waste materials; Ferrous metal scrap & waste; Nonferrous metals scrap; Wire & cable scrap
Pr: David Grossman
Sr Pt: Harry Garber
* *Ex VP:* Sidney Grossman
VP: Linus Klostermann
Exec: Cathryn Shaw
Off Mgr: Cindy Muehlhauser

D-U-N-S 07-334-1562
GROSSMONT HOSPITAL CORP
(*Suby of* SHARP REES-STEALY PHARMACY) ★
5555 Grossmont Center Dr, La Mesa, CA 91942-3077
Tel (619) 740-6000 *Founded/Ownrshp* 1953
Sales 712.6MM *EMP* 2,697
SIC 8062 General medical & surgical hospitals
CEO: Dan Gross
Chf Rad: Tere Trout
Opers Mgr: Suzie Warner
Surgeon: Steven Allsing
Doctor: Colleen Nadeau

D-U-N-S 01-052-0422
GROSSMONT HOSPITAL FOUNDATION
(*Suby of* SHARP REES-STEALY PHARMACY) ★
5555 Grossmont Center Dr, La Mesa, CA 91942-3077
Tel (619) 740-4200 *Founded/Ownrshp* 1985
Sales 673.8MM *EMP* 6
Accts Ernst & Young Us Llp San Dieg
SIC 8399 Fund raising organization, non-fee basis
Ex Dir: Elizabeth Morgante
Chf Path: Octavio Armas
Dir OR: Suzie Warner
Dir Case M: Mike Murphey
Dir Rx: Patrick Craychee
Chf Nrs Of: Janet Hanley
Pr Mgr: Sandy Pugliese

D-U-N-S 07-873-3086
GROSSMONT UNION HIGH SCHOOL DISTRICT SCHOOL FACILITIES CORP
1100 Murray Dr, El Cajon, CA 92020-5664
Tel (619) 644-8000 *Founded/Ownrshp* 1920
Sales 248.7MM *EMP* 1,887
Accts Nigro & Nigro Pc Murietta C
SIC 8211 Public elementary & secondary schools
* *Prin:* Terry Ryan
Pr Dir: Catherine Martin
HC Dir: Teresa Kemper
Board of Directors: Scott Patterson

D-U-N-S 08-000-9310
GROSSMONT-CUYAMACA COMMUNITY COLLEGE DISTRICT
GCCCD
8800 Grossmont College Dr, El Cajon, CA 92020-1765
Tel (619) 644-7010 *Founded/Ownrshp* 2015
Sales 54.0MM *EMP* 2,000[E]
SIC 8221 Colleges universities & professional schools
VP: Eddie Vasquez
Pr Dir: Lorena Ruggero

D-U-N-S 00-638-2840 IMP/EXP
GROTE INDUSTRIES INC
2600 Lanier Dr, Madison, IN 47250-1797
Tel (812) 273-2121 *Founded/Ownrshp* 1901
Sales 307.5MM[E] *EMP* 1,200
Accts Deloitte Cincinnatiohio
SIC 3231 3647 Mirrors, truck & automobile: made from purchased glass; Vehicular lighting equipment
Ch Bd: William D Grote III
* *Pr:* Dominic Grote
* *CEO:* William Dominic Grote IV
* *Treas:* Michael R Grote
* *VP:* Michael T Adams
QA Dir: Richard Ll
Dir IT: Mike Routh
Sfty Mgr: Barry Duff
Mfg Mgr: Robert Alvarez
Ql Cn Mgr: Neil Clayton
Manager: Jack Ison

D-U-N-S 08-008-9913
GROTE INDUSTRIES LLC
2600 Lanier Dr, Madison, IN 47250-1797
Tel (812) 265-8273 *Founded/Ownrshp* 1996
Sales 24.9MM[E] *EMP* 1,200
SIC 3647 3231 Vehicular lighting equipment; Mirrors, truck & automobile: made from purchased glass
Pr: William Grote IV
* *CFO:* James Braun

D-U-N-S 05-757-4097
GROTHUES BROTHERS HOLDINGS LTD
2651 Sw Military Dr, San Antonio, TX 78224-1048
Tel (830) 569-1131 *Founded/Ownrshp* 1973
Sales 274.7MM[E] *EMP* 905
SIC 5031 5211 6719 Lumber: rough, dressed & finished; Building materials, exterior; Building materials, interior; Lumber & other building materials; Millwork & lumber; Investment holding companies, except banks
Pt: Larry Grothues
CFO: Kevin Solomon
IT Man: Marvin Palacios

GROUNDSPRING
See NETWORK FOR GOOD INC

D-U-N-S 14-841-3602
GROUNDWATER AND ENVIRONMENTAL SERVICES INC
GES
1599 Rte 34 Ste 1, Wall Township, NJ 07727-3932
Tel (800) 220-3068 *Founded/Ownrshp* 1985
Sales 152.8MM[E] *EMP* 711
SIC 8748

GROUP
See UNIVERSITY OF NORTH TEXAS SYSTEM

D-U-N-S 08-271-5707
GROUP & PENSION ADMINISTRATORS INC
GPA
12770 Merit Dr Ste 200, Dallas, TX 75251-1233
Tel (972) 238-7900 *Founded/Ownrshp* 1968
Sales NA *EMP* 150
SIC 6411 Insurance information & consulting services; Pension & retirement plan consultants
Pr: Jerry Mc Peters
CFO: Tommy McDaniel
Ex VP: Kathy Enochs
VP: Edna Geer-Hudgins
VP: Neal Stanley
IT Man: Marsha Hamm
Netwrk Eng: Chaz Heed

D-U-N-S 83-967-2748 IMP
▲ GROUP 1 AUTOMOTIVE INC
800 Gessner Rd Ste 500, Houston, TX 77024-4498
Tel (713) 647-5700 *Founded/Ownrshp* 1995
Sales 10.6MMM *EMP* 12,886[E]
Tkr Sym GPI *Exch* NYS
SIC 5511 6141 7538 7532 5531 Automobiles, new & used; Automobile loans, including insurance; Engine repair; Collision shops, automotive; Automotive parts
Pr: Earl J Hesterberg
* *Ch Bd:* John L Adams
CFO: John C Rickel
Sr VP: Frank Grese Jr
VP: Darryl M Burman
VP: Peter C Delongchamps
VP: James R Druzbik
Genl Mgr: Randy Khalaf
IT Man: Michael Polley
Snr Mgr: Joe Caponigro
Board of Directors: Doyle L Arnold, Lincoln Pereira, Stephen D Quinn, J Terry Strange, Charles L Szews, Max P Watson Jr, Maryann Wright

D-U-N-S 80-801-4042
GROUP DEKKO HOLDINGS INC
(*Suby of* DEKKO ACQUISITION PARENT INC) ★
2505 Dekko Dr, Garrett, IN 46738-1886
Tel (260) 347-0700 *Founded/Ownrshp* 2006
Sales 126.0MM[E] *EMP* 1,267
SIC 3496 Miscellaneous fabricated wire products
CEO: John R May
* *Pr:* Timothy White
* *VP:* Gerald Whiteford

D-U-N-S 79-696-5168 IMP
■ GROUP DEKKO INC
(*Suby of* GRAHAM HOLDINGS CO) ★
2505 Dekko Dr, Garrett, IN 46738-1886
Tel (260) 357-3621 *Founded/Ownrshp* 2015
Sales 133.8MM[E] *EMP* 356
SIC 3479 3469 3643 3315 3089 Coating of metals & formed products; Painting of metal products; Metal stampings; Current-carrying wiring devices; Wire & fabricated wire products; Molding primary plastic
CEO: John R May
* *Pr:* Jon Jensen
VP: Larry Colestock
Prgrm Mgr: Dan Filley
CIO: Christopher Edwards
Opers Mgr: Tracy Joseph
Ql Cn Mgr: Amber Cumming
Ql Cn Mgr: Hugo Rodriguez

D-U-N-S 02-045-2850
GROUP HEALTH CO-OPERATIVE OF SOUTH CENTRAL WISCONSIN
GROUP HEALTH COOPERATIVE HMO
1265 John Q Hammons Dr # 200, Madison, WI 53717-1962
Tel (608) 251-4156 *Founded/Ownrshp* 1972
Sales NA *EMP* 500
SIC 6324

D-U-N-S 07-819-8520
GROUP HEALTH COOPERATIVE
320 Westlake Ave N # 100, Seattle, WA 98109-5233
Tel (206) 448-4141 *Founded/Ownrshp* 1945
Sales NA *EMP* 9,300
Accts Kpmg Llp Seattle Wa
SIC 6324 5999 8093 6321 Health maintenance organization (HMO), insurance only; Medical apparatus & supplies; Hearing aids; Weight loss clinic, with medical staff; Accident & health insurance
Pr: Scott Armstrong
COO: James Hereford
* *CFO:* Richard Magnuson
CFO: Rick Magnuson
Sr Cor Off: John Long
Trst: Phyllis C Best
Trst: Jerry Campbell
Trst: Ann Daley
Trst: Ira Fielding
Trst: Tracy Garland
Trst: Jennifer Joly
Trst: Bob Margulis
Trst: Changmook Sohn
Assoc VP: Chris M Taylor
Ex VP: Sue Kozik
Ex VP: Erin Leff
Ex VP: Dawn Loeliger
Ex VP: Greg Swint
Ex VP: Mark Szalwinski
* *Ex VP:* Rick Woods
Ex VP: Sally Yates

D-U-N-S 01-709-0617
GROUP HEALTH COOPERATIVE ADMINISTRATION
1265 John Q Hammons Dr # 200, Madison, WI 53717-1962
Tel (608) 251-4156 *Founded/Ownrshp* 2008
Sales 313.5MM *EMP* 50
SIC 8099 Health & allied services
Sales Exec: Al Wearing
Treas: Michael Mullee
CIO: Bruce Quade
Sales Asso: Duwayne Benzine

GROUP HEALTH COOPERATIVE HMO
See GROUP HEALTH CO-OPERATIVE OF SOUTH CENTRAL WISCONSIN

D-U-N-S 07-313-4157
GROUP HEALTH INC
GHI
(*Suby of* EMBLEMHEALTH INC) ★
441 9th Ave Frnt, New York, NY 10001-1642
Tel (212) 615-0000 *Founded/Ownrshp* 1937
Sales NA *EMP* 2,354
Accts Bdo Seidman Llp New York Ne
SIC 6324 Hospital & medical service plans
Ch Bd: John D Feerick Esq
V Ch: Stuart H Altman PHD
Pr: Frank J Branchini
Pr: Daniel P Finke
CFO: Arthur J Byrd
Bd of Dir: Gregory Floyd
Bd of Dir: Susan M Mathews
Ofcr: Mitchell Goldberg
Ex VP: Draran Ron
Sr VP: George Babitsch
Sr VP: Phillip Berman
Sr VP: Jeffrey D Chansler
VP: Mariann E Drohan
VP: Vince Hartmann
VP: Michael Palmateer
Board of Directors: Harry Nespoli, Howard Berliner, Daniel Rubino Esq, Frank J Branchini, Dennis Sullivan, Jerome S Breslaw MD, Roger Toussaint, Ethelyn A Chase, Rosa Mgill Dsw, Jay E Russ Equire, John Gerrick Esq, James F Gill Esq, Bernard Schayes Mdpc

D-U-N-S 00-189-7649 IMP
GROUP HEALTH PERMANENTE
320 Westlake Ave N # 100, Seattle, WA 98109-5233
Tel (206) 448-4491 *Founded/Ownrshp* 1998
Sales 44.2MM[E] *EMP* 1,100
SIC 8011 Offices & clinics of medical doctors
Pr: Hugh Streley MD
* *Pr:* Gary Feldbau
* *Pr:* Hugh Stralay
Pr: Edith Weller
* *CFO:* Mark West
VP: Dorothy F Teeter
Ex Dir: William L Akers
Doctor: Wendy Siu

GROUP HOSPITAL & MEDICAL SVC
See CAREFIRST INC

D-U-N-S 05-518-5862
GROUP HOSPITALIZATION AND MEDICAL SERVICES INC
CAREFIRST BLUECROSS BLUESHIELD
(*Suby of* GROUP HOSPITAL & MEDICAL SVC) ★
10455 Mill Run Cir, Owings Mills, MD 21117-4208
Tel (202) 479-8000 *Founded/Ownrshp* 1939
Sales NA *EMP* 2,000
Accts Ernst And Young Llp Baltimore

SIC 6324 Group hospitalization plans
Pr: Chet Burrell
Treas: Jeff Clasper
VP: Dawn Audia
VP: Sam Bennet
VP: Robert Quarterman
VP: Helen Struck
Dir IT: Christi C Snyder
IT Man: Ann Doyle
IT Man: Ken Fritsch
IT Man: Boenig Sandy
IT Man: Art Smith

D-U-N-S 19-972-2922
GROUP M WORLDWIDE LLC
GROUPM
(*Suby of* W P P) ★
498 7th Ave, New York, NY 10018-6798
Tel (212) 297-7000 *Founded/Ownrshp* 1999
Sales 258.6MM^E *EMP* 630^E
SIC 7319 Media buying service
Ch: Irwin Gotlieb
Sr Pt: Michael Borone
Sr Pt: Michelle Burns
Sr Pt: Sandra Chorazy
Sr Pt: Cindylynn Hermann
Sr Pt: Oksana Krynsky-Kiefer
Sr Pt: Albert Lau
Sr Pt: Anthony Miyake
Sr Pt: Brian Vaughn
Mng Pt: Scott Kruse
Mng Pt: Joanna Lyall
Mng Pt: Lyle Schwartz
Mng Pt: Denise Weimann
**Pr:* Dominic Proctor
**CEO:* Kelly Clark
CEO: Brian Lesser
**COO:* Colin Barlow
**CFO:* Stuart Diamond
Treas: Mary E Howe
Chf Inves: Rino Scanzoni

D-U-N-S 05-650-7405
GROUP MANAGEMENT 0002 LLC
GM2
1321 Upland Dr 3966, Houston, TX 77043-4718
Tel (716) 998-3386 *Founded/Ownrshp* 2010
Sales NA *EMP* 3,400
SIC 6411 Insurance information & consulting services

D-U-N-S 80-278-7937
GROUP O INC
4905 77th Ave E, Milan, IL 61264-3250
Tel (309) 736-8100 *Founded/Ownrshp* 1992
Sales 548.5MM^E *EMP* 1,520
Accts Honkamp Krueger & Co Pc Mo
SIC 8742 7389 4226 5085 Marketing consulting services; ; Special warehousing & storage; Industrial supplies
CEO: Gregg Ontiveros
CFO: Bob Marriott
**Ch:* Robert Ontiveros
Sr VP: Mike De La Cruz
VP: Mike De Cruz
VP: Kim Fox
VP: Mike Huntley
VP: Tony Lopez
VP: Kevin Mainoe
VP: Kevin Maione
**VP:* Chris Ontiveros
VP: Matt Ontiveros
Exec: Jennifer Cole

D-U-N-S 06-117-7853
GROUP RESOURCES INC
3080 Premiere Pkwy # 100, Duluth, GA 30097-8911
Tel (770) 623-8383 *Founded/Ownrshp* 1981
Sales NA *EMP* 130
SIC 6411 Insurance brokers
Pr: Tom Byrd
**Sr VP:* Andy Willoughby
VP: Sheila Autry
**VP:* Robby Kerr
IT Man: Steve Kemp
Sales Asso: Pat Lund

D-U-N-S 05-049-6447
GROUP VOYAGERS INC
AVALON WATERWAYS
5301 S Federal Cir, Littleton, CO 80123-2980
Tel (303) 703-7000 *Founded/Ownrshp* 1963
Sales 89.8MM^E *EMP* 295
SIC 4725 Tour operators
Ch Bd: Philip Gordon
**CFO:* Kevin F Ford
CIO: Ken Migaki
QA Dir: Krista McClure
IT Man: Jeff Canterbury
VP Mktg: Steven Born
Mktg Mgr: Patrice Geske
Mktg Mgr: Vanessa Parrish
Sales Asso: T J McAvoy
Sales Asso: Andrea Sirls

D-U-N-S 18-035-7795
GROUPE SEB HOLDINGS INC
(*Suby of* SEB INTERNATIONALE SAS)
1105 N Market St Ste 1142, Wilmington, DE 19801-1216
Tel (973) 736-0300 *Founded/Ownrshp* 2005
Sales 91.2MM^E *EMP* 272
SIC 5064 Electrical appliances, television & radio
Ch: Francois Duley
**Pr:* Jacques Alexandre

GROUPM
See GROUP M WORLDWIDE LLC

D-U-N-S 83-154-7612
▲ GROUPON INC
600 W Chicago Ave Ste 400, Chicago, IL 60654-2067
Tel (312) 334-1579 *Founded/Ownrshp* 2008
Sales 3.1MMM *EMP* 9,872
Tkr Sym GRPN *Exch* NGS
SIC 7311 7319 Advertising agencies; Display advertising service
CEO: Rich Williams
Pt: Mark Rose
**Ch Bd:* Eric Lefkofsky
CFO: Brian Kayman
CFO: Mike Randolfi
Ofcr: Brian Stevens
Sr VP: Vinayak Hegde
VP: Michael Scheschuk
VP: Pete Webb
VP: Andrew White
Dir Bus: Alyson Womack
Board of Directors: Peter J Barris, Robert J Bass, Daniel T Henry, Jeffrey T Housenbold, Bradley A Keywell, Theodore J Leonsis, Ann E Ziegler

D-U-N-S 07-352-3750
GROUPWARE TECHNOLOGY INC
541 Division St, Campbell, CA 95008-6934
Tel (408) 540-0090 *Founded/Ownrshp* 1992
Sales 400.0MM *EMP* 200
SIC 7373 5045 Computer-aided system services; Computers, peripherals & software; Computer software
CEO: Mike Thompson
**Ex VP:* Scott Sutter
**VP:* Josh Avila
**VP:* John Barnes
**VP:* Anthony Miley
Sales Asso: Cassidy Johnson

GROVE COLLABORATIVE
See EPANTRY LLC

D-U-N-S 01-361-7204
GROVE ELK UNIFIED SCHOOL DISTRICT
EGUSD
9510 Elk Grove Florin Rd, Elk Grove, CA 95624-1801
Tel (916) 686-5085 *Founded/Ownrshp* 1959
Sales 460.3MM^E *EMP* 5,600
Accts Perry-Smith Llp Sacramento C
SIC 8211 Public elementary & secondary schools; Public junior high school; Public senior high school; Public special education school
Dir Sec: Joe Airoso
IT Man: Kevin Williams
Pr Dir: Xanthi Pinkerton
Pr Dir: Suzanne Thibault
Teacher Pr: Evelyn Laluan
HC Dir: Don Ross

D-U-N-S 03-911-6913
GROVE INVESTORS INC
1542 Buchanan Trl E, Greencastle, PA 17225-9511
Tel (717) 597-8121 *Founded/Ownrshp* 2001
Sales 92.3MM^E *EMP* 1,300
SIC 3531 Cranes
Pr: Jeff Bust

D-U-N-S 09-470-9011
GROVE LUMBER & BUILDING SUPPLIES INC (CA)
1300 S Campus Ave, Ontario, CA 91761-4378
Tel (909) 947-0277 *Founded/Ownrshp* 1979
Sales 182.7MM^E *EMP* 240
SIC 5031 5211 Lumber, plywood & millwork; Lumber products
Pr: Raymond G Croll Jr

D-U-N-S 01-093-2713
GROVE OAK SCHOOL DISTRICT
6578 Santa Teresa Blvd, San Jose, CA 95119-1297
Tel (408) 227-8300 *Founded/Ownrshp* 1861
Sales 64.3MM^E *EMP* 1,000
Accts Vavrinek Trine Day & Co Ll
SIC 8211 Public elementary school; Public junior high school
Bd of Dir: Carolyn Bauer
**VP:* Jacquelyn Adams
VP: Dennis Hawkins
Exec: Lani Gerszewski
MIS Dir: Najeeb Qasimi

GROVE PARK INN, THE
See OMNI GROVE PARK LLC

D-U-N-S 05-438-6214
GROVE PARK INN RESORT INC
290 Macon Ave, Asheville, NC 28804-3799
Tel (828) 252-2711 *Founded/Ownrshp* 2012
Sales NA *EMP* 1,000
SIC 7011 5812 5813 7992 7991 7299

D-U-N-S 07-833-9799
GROVE SERVICES (UKRAINE) LLC (MA)
(*Suby of* GROVE SERVICES INC) ★
100 William St Ste 210, Wellesley, MA 02481-3702
Tel (617) 558-1991 *Founded/Ownrshp* 2009
Sales 350.0MM^E *EMP* 2
SIC 5144 Poultry & poultry products
Pr: Gene Spivak
**CFO:* Victor Spivak

D-U-N-S 87-777-0375 IMP/EXP
GROVE SERVICES INC
100 William St Ste 210, Wellesley, MA 02481-3702
Tel (781) 772-1187 *Founded/Ownrshp* 2001
Sales 350.0MM^E *EMP* 14
Accts Mcgladrey & Pullen Llp Burli
SIC 5141 Food brokers
Pr: Victor Spivak
**CFO:* Gene Spivak
Genl Mgr: Chaz Wilson
Sls Dir: Paulo M Trindade

D-U-N-S 18-786-9891
GROVE SHADY ADVENTIST HOSPITAL
9901 Medical Center Dr, Rockville, MD 20850-3395
Tel (240) 826-6000 *Founded/Ownrshp* 2012
Sales 306.9MM *EMP* 49
SIC 8062 General medical & surgical hospitals
Prin: David E Weigley
CFO: Victor Newinski
Bd of Dir: Philip A Besler
Bd of Dir: Robert G Brewer Jr
Bd of Dir: Peter H Plamondon
VP: Robin Toomey
Dir Lab: Rob Sanluis
Prin: Benson Klein
Ex Dir: Shelvan Arunan
Ex Dir: Frankie Blackburn
Ex Dir: Sheldon Grosberg

GROVE STONE & SAND DIVISION
See B V HEDRICK GRAVEL & SAND CO

D-U-N-S 01-971-0289 IMP/EXP
■ GROVE US LLC
MANITOWOC CRANE GROUP
(*Suby of* MANITOWOC CRANES LLC) ★
1565 Buchanan Trl E, Shady Grove, PA 17256
Tel (717) 597-8121 *Founded/Ownrshp* 1998, 2002
Sales 118.5MM^E *EMP* 78^E
SIC 3531 3537 Cranes; Platforms, cargo
Pr: Eric Etchart
**Pr:* Glen E Tellock
VP: Roger Knecht
**VP:* Larry Weyers
Prgrm Mgr: Stacy Beck
Dir IT: Jim Denig
VP Sls: Robert Hixon

D-U-N-S 05-718-7916
GROVES INDUSTRIAL SUPPLY CORP
(*Suby of* DGI SUPPLY) ★
7301 Pinemont Dr, Houston, TX 77040-6607
Tel (713) 675-4747 *Founded/Ownrshp* 1990
Sales 192.3MM^E *EMP* 144^E
SIC 5085 5084 5198 Industrial supplies; Safety equipment; Paints
Pr: David Crawford
**VP:* Timothy P Moran
**VP:* Jeff Waller
IT Man: Mike Mays
Mktg Mgr: Randi Hobson
Mktg Mgr: Grant Wilkie

GROWERS AG
See TREMONT GROUP INC

D-U-N-S 07-883-7492
GROWERS SALES AND MARKETING LLC
FARM FRESH DIRECT OF AMERICA
15 Washington St Ste 207, Monte Vista, CO 81144-1406
Tel (719) 852-2600 *Founded/Ownrshp* 2012
Sales 121.1MM *EMP* 35
SIC 5148 Fresh fruits & vegetables
CEO: James Knutzon
**CFO:* Alex Miller
Board of Directors: John Artaechevarria, Keith McGovern, Marty Myers, Jerry Smith, Virgil Valdez, Dave Warsh

D-U-N-S 00-521-3335 IMP/EXP
GROWMARK INC
1701 Towanda Ave, Bloomington, IL 61701-2057
Tel (309) 557-6000 *Founded/Ownrshp* 1962
Sales 7.0MMM *EMP* 1,036
Accts Ernst & Young Llp Chicago Il
SIC 5191 Farm supplies
Ch Bd: John Reifsteck
**CEO:* Jim Spradlin
CFO: Marshall Bohbrink
CFO: Jeff Price
**CFO:* Mike Woods
Treas: Dan Irving
**Sr VP:* Brent Ericson
**VP:* Brent Bostrom
VP: Steve Buckalew
**VP:* Kevin Carroll
VP: Tom Dowell
VP: Dennis Farmer
VP: George Key
VP: Shelly Kruse
VP: Ron Milby
**VP:* Mark Orr
**VP:* Barry Schmidt
**VP:* Gary Swango
VP: Denny Worth
Board of Directors: Ron Pierson, Chet Esther, John Reifsteck, Kim Fysh, Allen Tanner, Kevin Herink, Brad Temple, Warren Jibb, David Uhlman, Kevin Malchine, David Watt, Jack McCormick, Rick Nelson, Dennis Neuhaus, Bob Phelps

D-U-N-S 04-668-7893
GROWTH MANAGEMENT CORP
AMIGOS
3201 Pioneers Blvd # 112, Lincoln, NE 68502-5963
Tel (402) 488-8500 *Founded/Ownrshp* 1980
Sales 26.9MM^E *EMP* 1,000
SIC 5812 5411 Mexican restaurant; Convenience stores
Pr: Roger D Moore

D-U-N-S 00-386-0361
GRP INC (NC)
1823 Boone Trail Rd, Sanford, NC 27330-8662
Tel (919) 776-9940 *Founded/Ownrshp* 2010
Sales 67.5MM^E *EMP* 2,200
SIC 2281 Cotton yarn, spun

GRS&S
See GILL CORP

GRU
See GAINESVILLE REGIONAL UTILITIES (INC)

D-U-N-S 01-177-2053
GRU
301 Se 4th Ave, Gainesville, FL 32601-6857
Tel (352) 334-3434 *Founded/Ownrshp* 2010
Sales 370.4MM *EMP* 12^E
Accts Ernst & Young Llp Orlando Fl
SIC 4813

D-U-N-S 00-922-8198 IMP/EXP
GRUBB & ELLIS CO
1551 N Tustin Ave Ste 300, Santa Ana, CA 92705-8638
Tel (714) 667-8252 *Founded/Ownrshp* 2012
Sales NA *EMP* 4,500
SIC 6531 8742 6162

D-U-N-S 05-353-7234
GRUBB & ELLIS MANAGEMENT SERVICES INC
1551 N Tustin Ave Ste 300, Santa Ana, CA 92705-8638
Tel (412) 201-8200 *Founded/Ownrshp* 2000
Sales NA *EMP* 1,800
SIC 6531

D-U-N-S 05-356-4866
▲ GRUBHUB INC
111 W Washington St # 2100, Chicago, IL 60602-2783
Tel (877) 585-7878 *Founded/Ownrshp* 1999
Sales 361.8MM *EMP* 1,105^E
Tkr Sym GRUB *Exch* NYS
SIC 5961 Food, mail order
CEO: Matthew Maloney
Ch Bd: Brian McAndrews
CFO: Adam Dewitt
Chf Mktg O: Barbara Martin Coppola
Sr VP: Stanley Chia
Sr VP: Margo Drucker
Board of Directors: David Fisher, Lloyd Frink, David Habiger, Katrina Lake, Girish Lakshman, Linda Johnson Rice, Keith Richman, Justin L Sadrian, Benjamin Spero

D-U-N-S 07-996-6641
GRUDEN ACQUISITION INC
4041 Park Oaks Blvd # 200, Tampa, FL 33610-9531
Tel (800) 282-2031 *Founded/Ownrshp* 2015
Sales 36.0MM^E *EMP* 4,342
SIC 4213 Trucking, except local

D-U-N-S 03-873-5890 IMP
GRUMA CORP
MISSION FOODS
(*Suby of* GRUMA, S.A.B. DE C.V.)
5601 Executive Dr Ste 800, Irving, TX 75038-2508
Tel (972) 232-5000 *Founded/Ownrshp* 1983
Sales 2.0MMM *EMP* 7,000
SIC 0723 2096 2099 Flour milling custom services; Tortilla chips; Food preparations
Pr: Javier Velez Bautista
CFO: Javier Velez
Ch: Juan A Gonzalez Moreno
**Treas:* Dan Burke
Ex VP: Michael Crane
VP: Dave Konze
**VP:* Felipe Rubio Lamas
VP: Sam Liang
VP: Eduardo Valdes
Genl Mgr: William Buffington
CIO: Edgar Sosa
Board of Directors: Homero Huerta Moren

D-U-N-S 00-896-1047
GRUNAU CO INC
(*Suby of* API GROUP INC) ★
1100 W Anderson Ct, Oak Creek, WI 53154-1472
Tel (414) 216-6900 *Founded/Ownrshp* 2006
Sales 109.8MM *EMP* 400
Accts Kpmg Llp Minneapolis Mn
SIC 1711 Mechanical contractor; Fire sprinkler system installation
Pr: Larry Loomis
COO: Brian Knapton
CFO: Jeffrey A Hintze
Treas: Greg Keup
VP: Ted Angelo
VP: Mark Gall
Brnch Mgr: Bob Harlow

D-U-N-S 07-878-9518 IMP/EXP
GRUNDFOS PUMPS CORP
(*Suby of* GRUNDFOS HOLDING AG)
17100 W 118th Ter, Olathe, KS 66061-6599
Tel (913) 227-3400 *Founded/Ownrshp* 1973
Sales 85.8MM^E *EMP* 160
SIC 5084

D-U-N-S 00-741-3857
GRUNDY WORLDWIDE INC
400 Horsham Rd Ste 150, Horsham, PA 19044-2147
Tel (888) 647-8639 *Founded/Ownrshp* 2001
Sales NA *EMP* 5,200
SIC 6331 Automobile insurance
Pr: James Grundy
IT Man: Heather Marr
Mktg Dir: William Hoffer

D-U-N-S 09-367-1063 IMP/EXP
GRUNER + JAHR USA GROUP INC
GRUNER JAHR USA PUBLISHING DIV
1745 Broadway Fl 16, New York, NY 10019-4640
Tel (866) 323-9336 *Founded/Ownrshp* 1978
Sales 559.4MM^E *EMP* 5,058
SIC 2721 2754 Periodicals: publishing & printing; Magazines: publishing & printing; Commercial printing, gravure
Pr: Mike Amundson
**Ex VP:* Gregg Black
**Ex VP:* Larry Hawkey
**Ex VP:* Dan Nitz
VP: Yvette Miller
VP: Scott Seltz

GRUNER JAHR USA PUBLISHING DIV
See GRUNER + JAHR USA GROUP INC

D-U-N-S 18-868-6778
GRUNLEY CONSTRUCTION CO INC
15020 Shady Ste 500, Rockville, MD 20850
Tel (240) 399-2000 *Founded/Ownrshp* 1988
Sales 350.0MM *EMP* 310
Accts Baker Tilly Virchow Krause Ll
SIC 1542 Specialized public building contractors; Commercial & office buildings, renovation & repair; Commercial & office building, new construction
Pr: Kenneth M Grunley
**Pr:* Sonya Brown
Pr: Gregory M Druga
**Sr VP:* Bh Scott II
**VP:* George Rusk
**VP:* Tom Walker
IT Man: Ariel Africa

D-U-N-S 00-946-7002
GRUPE CO (CA)
3255 W March Ln Ste 400, Stockton, CA 95219-2352
Tel (209) 473-6000 *Founded/Ownrshp* 1960, 1988
Sales 91.2MM^E *EMP* 400
SIC 6531 1542 Real estate agent, residential; Real estate brokers & agents; Commercial & office building, new construction
Pr: Frank A Passadore
**Ch Bd:* Greenlaw Grupe Jr

COO: Frank Paadore
Ex VP: Nelson Bahler
VP: Chris Conklin
VP: Niem Dang
VP: Anna Depedrini
VP: Julie Dzubak
VP: Shane Hart
VP: Dan Keyser
VP: Maurice Liu
VP: Ron Reganni
VP: Ron Rugani
VP: Jeremy White

D-U-N-S 80-865-9114 IMP
GRUPO ANTOLIN KENTUCKY INC
(*Suby of* GRUPO ANTOLIN-IRAUSA SA)
208 Commerce Ct, Hopkinsville, KY 42240-6806
Tel (270) 885-2703 *Founded/Ownrshp* 1993
Sales 222.4MM *EMP* 502
Accts Uhy Llp Farmington Hills Mic
SIC 3559 2399 Automotive related machinery; Seat covers, automobile
Ch: Ernesto Antoln Arribas
**Pr:* Ken Carter
**Pr:* Max Rogers
**CEO:* Jess Pascual Santos
COO: Eric Rucker
**Sec:* Pablo Ruiz
**VP:* Ernesto Molina
**VP:* Roberto Monteros
**Prin:* Mike Sewell
IT Man: Thomas Eickhoff
Plnt Mgr: Terry Brandl

D-U-N-S 00-649-4129
GRUPO ANTOLIN NORTH AMERICA INC
(*Suby of* GRUPO ANTOLIN-IRAUSA SA)
1700 Atlantic Blvd, Auburn Hills, MI 48326-1504
Tel (248) 373-1437 *Founded/Ownrshp* 2005
Sales 903.4MM^E *EMP* 3,000
SIC 8741 8711 Management services; Engineering services
Pr: Pablo Baroja
**Pr:* Carlos Araujo
CFO: Maria Manuel
Prgrm Mgr: Brian Miscovich
IT Man: Marc Merren
IT Man: Chris Wald
IT Man: Nathan West
Ql Cn Mgr: Josh Shipp
Mktg Dir: Russell Goemaere

D-U-N-S 83-106-2018
GRUPO EDUK INC
EDUK GROUP
Marginal Rd 20 Km 2 3, Guaynabo, PR 00966
Tel (787) 982-3000 *Founded/Ownrshp* 2004
Sales 147.1MM^E *EMP* 2,000
SIC 8249 8244 8243 8222 7231 Banking school, training; Business & secretarial schools; Data processing schools; Technical institute; Cosmetology school
Pr: Guillermo Nigaglioni
Pr: Melissa Rosario

D-U-N-S 80-612-6111
GRUPO HIMA-SAN PABLO INC
HIMA SAN PABLO HOSPITAL
100 Calle Munoz Rivera, Caguas, PR 00725-3629
Tel (787) 653-3434 *Founded/Ownrshp* 2005
Sales 481.7MM *EMP* 4,200
SIC 8062 General medical & surgical hospitals
Pr: Joaquin Rodriguez Sr
VP: Francisco Medina
**VP:* Carlos Pineiro
**VP:* Dennis Tristan

GRUPO MEXICO
See ASARCO LLC

GRUPO PHOENIX
See PHOENIX PACKAGING OPERATIONS LLC

D-U-N-S 15-030-3555 IMP/EXP
GRUPO PHOENIX CORPORATE SERVICES LLC
18851 Ne 29th Ave Ste 601, Aventura, FL 33180-2844
Tel (954) 241-0023 *Founded/Ownrshp* 2004
Sales 170.5MM^E *EMP* 473
Accts Deloitte & Touche Ltda Bogo
SIC 3089 Cups, plastic, except foam
CEO: Monica Peisach
**Pr:* Alberto Peisach

D-U-N-S 96-153-8790
GRYPHON INVESTORS INC
1 Maritime Plz Ste 2300, San Francisco, CA 94111-3513
Tel (415) 217-7400 *Founded/Ownrshp* 1995
Sales 1.7MMM^E *EMP* 11,715
SIC 6799 Venture capital companies
CEO: R David Andrews
CEO: Bob Myers
Bd of Dir: Bryan Cheng
VP: Tim Bradley
Opers Mgr: Felix Park

D-U-N-S 94-220-7838
GRYPHON TECHNOLOGIES LC
80 M St Se Ste 600, Washington, DC 20003-3544
Tel (202) 617-2004 *Founded/Ownrshp* 1995
Sales 88.3MM^E *EMP* 622
SIC 8741 8711 8731 7371 Financial management for business; Engineering services; Biological research; Computer software development & applications
Pr: P J Braden
**CFO:* Palmer Marcantonio

D-U-N-S 05-606-8968 IMP
GS GLOBAL RESOURCES INC
926 Perkins Dr, Mukwonago, WI 53149-1400
Tel (262) 786-0100 *Founded/Ownrshp* 1971
Sales 83.4MM^E *EMP* 120
SIC 5084 Hydraulic systems equipment & supplies
Pr: John Thornton
**CEO:* Kishor Patel
Sls Mgr: Bill Pope
Snr Mgr: Bob Zastrow

GS&P
See GRESHAM SMITH AND PARTNERS

D-U-N-S 80-142-6839
■ GSA FEDERAL ACQUISITION SERVICE (Q)
(*Suby of* G S A) ★
2200 Crystal Dr Rm 1100, Arlington, VA 22202-3730
Tel (703) 605-5400 *Founded/Ownrshp* 2007
Sales NA *EMP* 1,273^E
SIC 9199 General government administration;

D-U-N-S 93-788-0995
■ GSA GREATER SOUTHWEST REGION OFC OF REGIONAL ADMINISTRATOR
(*Suby of* G S A) ★
819 Taylor St Rm 11a00, Fort Worth, TX 76102-6124
Tel (817) 978-2321 *Founded/Ownrshp* 2003
Sales NA *EMP* 1,200^E
SIC 9199 General government administration;
CEO: Scott Armey

D-U-N-S 12-811-2666
■ GSA MID-ATLANTIC REGION OFC OF REGIONAL ADMINISTRATOR (3A)
(*Suby of* G S A) ★
20 N 8th St, Philadelphia, PA 19107-3101
Tel (215) 446-4900 *Founded/Ownrshp* 2003
Sales NA *EMP* 1,000
SIC 9199 General government administration;
Prin: Margaret Moore

D-U-N-S 12-811-3086
■ GSA NATIONAL CAPITAL AREA REGION OF REGIONAL ADMINISTRATOR (11A)
(*Suby of* G S A) ★
7 & D St Sw Ste 7022th, Washington, DC 20407-0001
Tel (202) 708-9100 *Founded/Ownrshp* 2003
Sales NA *EMP* 1,500^E
SIC 9199

D-U-N-S 12-661-8417
■ GSA NATIONAL CAPITAL REGION
GENERAL SVCS ADMINISTRAITON
(*Suby of* GSA NATIONAL CAPITAL AREA REGION OF REGIONAL ADMINISTRATOR (11A)) ★
7 & D St Sw Rm 1065th, Washington, DC 20407-0001
Tel (202) 708-5891 *Founded/Ownrshp* 2003
Sales NA *EMP* 1,490^E
SIC 9199

D-U-N-S 05-742-4298
■ GSA OFFICE OF CHIEF FINANCIAL OFFICER
(*Suby of* G S A) ★
1800 F St Nw Rm 2140, Washington, DC 20405-0001
Tel (202) 501-1721 *Founded/Ownrshp* 2003
Sales NA *EMP* 1,000^E
SIC 9199 General government administration;
CFO: Kathleen Turko
Ofcr: Jason Bazarko
Ofcr: Carl Brown
Ofcr: Jennifer Kauffmann
Ofcr: Linda Luong
Ofcr: Regina Nally
Ofcr: Kazi Rizvi
Ofcr: Caroline Sachay
Adm Dir: Herman Clemmons
Adm Dir: Kristie Srabian
Ex Dir: Catherine Lee

D-U-N-S 12-811-2922
■ GSA PACIFIC RIM REGION OFFICE OF REGIONAL ADMINISTRATOR
(*Suby of* G S A) ★
450 Golden Gate Ave Fl 5, San Francisco, CA 94102-3405
Tel (415) 522-3001 *Founded/Ownrshp* 2005
Sales NA *EMP* 1,000^E
SIC 9199 General government administration;

D-U-N-S 02-712-1532
GSC ENTERPRISES INC
GROCERY SUPPLY COMPANY
130 Hillcrest Dr, Sulphur Springs, TX 75482
Tel (903) 885-7621 *Founded/Ownrshp* 1972
Sales 870.0MM *EMP* 575^E
SIC 5141 6099 Groceries, general line; Money order issuance
Ch Bd: Michael K McKenzie
**CEO:* Michael J Bain
**COO:* Ryan McKenzie
**CFO:* Kerry Law
VP: Larry Lane
**VP:* Janet Price
Div Mgr: Dirk Francis
Div Mgr: John Prickette
DP Dir: Larry Smith
Telecom Mg: John Bradberry
Opers Mgr: Dolly Gilliam

D-U-N-S 93-016-9789
■ GSD&M IDEA CITY LLC
(*Suby of* OMNICOM GROUP INC) ★
828 W 6th St, Austin, TX 78703-5468
Tel (512) 242-4736 *Founded/Ownrshp* 1971
Sales 97.5MM^E *EMP* 515
SIC 7311 Advertising agencies
Ch: Roy Spence
**V Ch:* Steve Gurasich
**Pr:* Marianne Malina
**CEO:* Duff M Stewart
VP: Yolanda Aquino
VP: Maureen Barry
VP: Meredith Bivens
VP: Jeanne Crockett
VP: John D'Acierno
VP: Mark Durein
VP: Bryan Edwards
VP: Jim Firestone
VP: Dorian Girard
VP: Carmen Graf
VP: Shawn Mackoff
VP: Betty McCoy
VP: Marianne Mmalina
VP: Shannon Moorman
VP: Diane Patrick
VP: Lee Pilz
VP: Coley Platt

GSE
See GOOD SAM ENTERPRISES LLC

GSE ENVIRONMENTAL
See GSE HOLDING INC

D-U-N-S 16-167-6986
GSE ENVIRONMENTAL INC
(*Suby of* GSE ENVIRONMENTAL) ★
19103 Gundle Rd, Houston, TX 77073-3515
Tel (281) 443-8564 *Founded/Ownrshp* 2004
Sales 391.7MM^E *EMP* 603^E
SIC 3081 1799 Plastic film & sheet; Protective lining installation, underground (sewage, etc.)
CEO: Charles A Sorrentino
**Ch Bd:* Daniel J Hennessy
**Pr:* Mark Arnold
**CFO:* Ernest C English Jr
Tech Mgr: Adam Maskal
Tech Mgr: Dhani B Narejo
Sls&Mrk Ex: Mohamed Abdel
VP Sls: Gary Joachim
Manager: Abhijit Khare
Sls Mgr: Manish Kushwaha
Sls Mgr: Van Thoai
Board of Directors: Michael G Evans, Marcus J George, Richard E Goodrich, Brian P Simmons

D-U-N-S 18-308-4805 IMP/EXP
GSE ENVIRONMENTAL LLC
(*Suby of* GSE ENVIRONMENTAL) ★
19103 Gundle Rd, Houston, TX 77073-3515
Tel (281) 443-8564 *Founded/Ownrshp* 2002
Sales 391.7MM^E *EMP* 603
SIC 3081 Polyethylene film
Pr: Charles A Sorrentino
**Pr:* Peter McCourt
**Pr:* Mark Whitney
CFO: Roger Klatt
Ex VP: Joellyn Champagne
**Ex VP:* Mike Kirksey
**Ex VP:* Jeffery Nigh
**Sr VP:* Daniel Storey
VP: Daniel A Daluise
VP: Gary Joachim
VP: Lee D Leggett
VP: Scott Lucas
VP: Richard S Schaefer
VP: William T Sharkey
VP: Terrance G Sheridan
**VP:* Gregg Taylor

D-U-N-S 14-797-1902 EXP
GSE HOLDING INC
GSE ENVIRONMENTAL
(*Suby of* LITTLEJOHN & CO LLC) ★
19103 Gundle Rd, Houston, TX 77073-3515
Tel (281) 443-8564 *Founded/Ownrshp* 2014
Sales 395.0MM *EMP* 608
SIC 3081 6719 Plastic film & sheet; Investment holding companies, except banks
Ch Bd: Robert Preston
**Pr:* Peter McCourt
**CFO:* Daniel C Storey
**Ex VP:* Jeffery D Nigh
**VP:* Giovanna Capra
**VP:* Steve Eckhart
**VP:* Edward Zimmel

GSF FOUNDATION
See GOLDEN STATE FOODS CORP

D-U-N-S 62-394-1853
GSF USA INC
G S F
(*Suby of* GROUPE SERVICES FRANCE)
2701 Fortune Cir E Ste D, Indianapolis, IN 46241-5519
Tel (317) 262-4958 *Founded/Ownrshp* 1987
Sales 23.9MM^E *EMP* 1,100
Accts Crowe Horwath Llp Indianapoli
SIC 7349 Janitorial service, contract basis
CEO: Regis Bernard
**Pr:* Troy Bargmann
Sales Exec: Michael Johnsen

GSG
See GRAPHIC SOLUTIONS GROUP INC

GSI
See GULFSTREAM SERVICES INC

D-U-N-S 17-818-5393 IMP
■ GSI COMMERCE INC
GLOBAL SPORTS
(*Suby of* EBAY INC) ★
935 1st Ave, King of Prussia, PA 19406-1342
Tel (610) 491-7000 *Founded/Ownrshp* 2011
Sales 1.0MMM^E *EMP* 5,848
SIC 5961 7371 7379 Catalog & mail-order houses; Computer equipment & electronics, mail order; Clothing, mail order (except women's); Cosmetics & perfumes, mail order; Custom computer programming services;
Pr: Chris Saridakis
**Pr:* Tobias Hartmann
COO: Mark Reese
CFO: Jordan Copland
CFO: Phillip Depaul
CFO: Adam Livingston
Ex VP: Dan Dobson
**Ex VP:* Jim Flanagan
**Ex VP:* Scott Hardy
**Ex VP:* Damon Mintzer
Sr VP: Gregg McNulty
VP: Mike Balik
VP: Michael R Conn
VP: Karen Fascenda
VP: Ronnie Franks
VP: Craig Hayes
VP: Mark Kirschner
VP: Mark Lavelle
Exec: David Guzman

GSI GROUP
See NOVANTA CORP

D-U-N-S 02-492-8343 IMP/EXP
■ GSI GROUP LLC
GRAIN SYSTEMS
(*Suby of* AGCO CORP) ★
1004 E Illinois St, Assumption, IL 62510-9529
Tel (217) 226-4421 *Founded/Ownrshp* 2011
Sales 1.5MMM^E *EMP* 2,029
SIC 5039

D-U-N-S 61-801-9215 EXP
■ GSI HOLDINGS CORP
(*Suby of* AGCO CORP) ★
1004 E Illinois St, Assumption, IL 62510-9529
Tel (217) 226-4421 *Founded/Ownrshp* 2011
Sales 107.8MM^E *EMP* 2,029
SIC 3523 Crop storage bins; Driers (farm): grain, hay & seed; Poultry brooders, feeders & waterers; Hog feeding, handling & watering equipment
CEO: Scott Clawson

D-U-N-S 87-982-1635 IMP
GSK CONSUMER HEALTHCARE
NOVARTIS CONSUMER HEALTH, INC.
(*Suby of* GLAXOSMITHKLINE PLC)
184 Liberty Corner Rd # 2, Warren, NJ 07059-6868
Tel (973) 503-8000 *Founded/Ownrshp* 2015
Sales 262.6MM^E *EMP* 890
SIC 2834 Pharmaceutical preparations
CEO: Joseph Jimenez
Pr: Michael Kopcha
**CFO:* John McKenna
**Treas:* Matthias Vogt
Sr VP: Christopher Fitzpatrick
VP: Kurt Furger
VP: Dianne Jacobs
VP: Robert Lodewick
VP: Kathleen Roessle
VP: Greg Tole
VP: Fred Walker
VP: Carl Ward
Exec: Craig Agrusti
Exec: Jennifer Allen
Exec: Ascension Almanza
Exec: Cassino Bruno
Exec: John Janecek
Exec: Janet McKelvey
Exec: Tracie Nunnery
Exec: Anna Porter
Exec: Steve Taber

D-U-N-S 79-095-0146
GSMA LTD
(*Suby of* GSM CONFERENCE SERVICES LIMITED)
1000 Abernathy Rd Ste 450, Atlanta, GA 30328-5623
Tel (678) 281-6600 *Founded/Ownrshp* 2006
Sales 164.0MM *EMP* 105^E
Accts Smith & Howard Pc Atlanta Ga
SIC 7389 Convention & show services
CEO: John Hoffman
**Ch Bd:* Bill Hague
**CFO:* Jeremy Sewell
Off Mgr: Cindy Elliott

D-U-N-S 60-671-0171
■ GSO CAPITAL PARTNERS LP
BLACKSTONE GROUP
(*Suby of* BLACKSTONE GROUP L P) ★
345 Park Ave Ste 1100, New York, NY 10154-1703
Tel (212) 583-5000 *Founded/Ownrshp* 2008
Sales 419.7MM^E *EMP* 900
SIC 6722 7389 Management investment, open-end; Financial services
Genl Pt: Douglas I Ostrover
**Pt:* Bennett Goodman
**Pt:* Tripp Smith
Mng Pt: Lee Shaiman
Pr: Chris Striano
COO: George Fan
Sr VP: Allan Barja
Sr VP: Amy Chen
Sr VP: Armando Gonzalez
Sr VP: Tom Iannarone
Sr VP: Nick Tassell
VP: Amit Bhatia
VP: Anthony Borreca
VP: William Dau
VP: Jana Douglas
VP: Scott Eisenberg
VP: Heiko Freitag
VP: Michael Garrow
VP: David Goldberg
VP: Andrew Jordan
VP: Valerie Kritsberg

D-U-N-S 61-032-7082 IMP/EXP
GST AUTOLEATHER INC
20 Oak Hollow St Ste 300, Southfield, MI 48033-7491
Tel (248) 436-2300 *Founded/Ownrshp* 2008
Sales 805.8MM^E *EMP* 2,100
SIC 3111 Leather tanning & finishing; Cutting of leather
Pr: Dennis E Hiller
**CFO:* Eric Evans
**Sr VP:* Cesar Hugo Escobedo
Sr VP: Cysar H Escobedo
**Sr VP:* Stephen Jeske
**VP:* Francisco Ros Jimnez
VP: Eric Kozlowski
VP Bus Dev: Francisco Jimenez
Ex Dir: Francisco R Jimynez
Ex Dir: Francisco R Jim Nez
Off Mgr: Rhonda Gasche

D-U-N-S 17-950-6829 IMP
GST AUTOMOTIVE SAFETY COMPONENTS INTERNATIONAL INC
2155 Pseo De Las Americas, San Diego, CA 92154-7907
Tel (619) 661-9347 *Founded/Ownrshp* 1994
Sales 109.5MM^E *EMP* 2,181
SIC 3714 Motor vehicle parts & accessories
Pr: Stephen B Duerk
CFO: Brian Menezes

GSUSA
See GIRL SCOUTS OF UNITED STATES OF AMERICA

D-U-N-S 60-577-9925 IMP
GSW MANUFACTURING INC
(Subyof G S WIRING SYSTEMS INC) ★
1801 Production Dr, Findlay, OH 45840-5446
Tel (419) 423-7111 Founded/Ownrshp 1989
Sales 146.3MME EMP 412
SIC 3714 3694 Automotive wiring harness sets; Engine electrical equipment
Pr: Yukinobu Ukai
CIO: William Brown
Ql Cn Mgr: Jeffrey Marok

GSWSA
See GRAND STRAND WATER & SEWER AUTHORITY

D-U-N-S 82-772-7814 IMP
GT ADVANCED TECHNOLOGIES INC
GTAT
243 Daniel Webster Hwy, Merrimack, NH 03054-4807
Tel (603) 883-5200 Founded/Ownrshp 2006
Sales 242.1MME EMP 541E
SIC 3674 Semiconductors & related devices; Photovoltaic devices, solid state
CEO: Greg Knight
*Ch Bd: Matthew E Massengill
CFO: Kanwardev Raja Singh Bal
Ofcr: Hoil Kim
Ex VP: Daniel W Squiller
VP: John Banacos
VP: Peter Bihuniak
VP: David Gray
VP: Joseph Loiselle
CTO: PS Raghavan
Netwrk Mgr: Andrew Kosko
Board of Directors: J Michal Conaway, Kathleen A Cote, Ernest L Godshalk, Richard E Newsted, John J Ray III, Robert E Switz, Noel G Watson, Thomas Wroe Jr

D-U-N-S 14-734-8346 IMP/EXP
GT TECHNOLOGIES INC
DEFIANCE GROUP THE
(Suby of GENTEK INC) ★
5859 E Executive Dr, Westland, MI 48185-1932
Tel (734) 467-8371 Founded/Ownrshp 1985
Sales 96.3MME EMP 500
SIC 8711 3714 3545 3089 Designing: ship, boat, machine & product; Motor vehicle engines & parts; Machine tool attachments & accessories; Injection molded finished plastic products
Pr: Paul Schwarzbaum
CFO: John Cattell
*Sr VP: Daniel Brinker
*Prin: William Redmond Jr
Tech Mgr: Paul Szymanski
VP Sls: Dan Brinker
Board of Directors: James E Heighway, George H Lewis III, Richard W Lock, John D Ong, Scott Roulston, Thomas H Roulston II Chb

D-U-N-S 16-993-2535 IMP
GT&S INC
5275 Tilghman St, Allentown, PA 18104-9378
Tel (610) 398-2211 Founded/Ownrshp 2004
Sales 280.4MME EMP 700
SIC 4925 5169 5084 5085 2813 5172

GTAT
See GT ADVANCED TECHNOLOGIES INC

D-U-N-S 84-985-7784 IMP
GTAT CORP
(Suby of GTAT) ★
243 Daniel Webster Hwy, Merrimack, NH 03054-4807
Tel (603) 883-5200 Founded/Ownrshp 2002
Sales 151.4MME EMP 332
Accts Ernst & Young Llp Manchester
SIC 3674 3567 Photovoltaic devices, solid state; Vacuum furnaces & ovens
*COO: Dan Squiller
*CFO: Raja Bal
*CFO: Rick Gaynor
*VP: Jeffrey J Ford
VP: Rick Tattersfield
Genl Couns: Daniel Lyman
Board of Directors: J Michal Conaway

GTC
See GREEN TOKAI CO LTD

D-U-N-S 02-272-5282
GTCR GOLDER RAUNER LLC
300 N La Salle Dr # 5600, Chicago, IL 60654-5410
Tel (312) 329-0225 Founded/Ownrshp 1998
Sales 567.7MME EMP 2,550
SIC 6726 Investment offices
VP: Stephen Jeschke
VP: Benjamin Remmert
VP: Lesly Schlender
VP: Neil Willis
*Prin: Aaron D Cohen
*Prin: Sean L Cunningham
CIO: Kevin Malover
Opers Mgr: Daniel Lornitis

D-U-N-S 01-639-5792
GTCR LLC
300 N La Salle Dr # 5600, Chicago, IL 60654-5410
Tel (312) 382-2200 Founded/Ownrshp 2009
Sales 259.6MME EMP 517E
SIC 5049 Laboratory equipment, except medical or dental
VP: Lawrence Fey
VP: Jeff Heh
VP: Travis Krueger
Exec: Aimee Broderick
Exec: Kristie Hansen-Mendez
Exec: Jeanette Lesniak
VP Admn: Silvia Flores
Mng Dir: Sean Cunningham
CIO: Jim Lott
Genl Couns: Jeffrey Wright

D-U-N-S 07-943-5151
GTCR VALOR COMPANIES INC
300 N La Salle Dr # 5600, Chicago, IL 60654-5410
Tel (312) 382-2200 Founded/Ownrshp 2014
Sales 22.0MME EMP 1,273
SIC 7389 Financial services

D-U-N-S 00-129-3950 IMP
■ GTE CORP
(Suby of VERIZON COMMUNICATIONS INC) ★
140 West St, New York, NY 10007-2141
Tel (212) 395-1000 Founded/Ownrshp 1935
Sales 11.7MMME EMP 111,285
SIC 4813 4812 3661 3663 4899 2741 Telephone communication, except radio; Local telephone communications; Local & long distance telephone communications; Voice telephone communications; Cellular telephone services; Telephones & telephone apparatus; Toll switching equipment, telephone; Data sets, telephone or telegraph; Mobile communication equipment; Airborne radio communications equipment; Satellite earth stations; Directories, telephone: publishing only, not printed on site
Ch Bd: Roy H Chestnut
*VP: David H Benson
*Prin: John W Diercksen
Board of Directors: Marianne Drost

D-U-N-S 86-132-0992
■ GTE MIDWEST INC
VERIZON MIDWEST
(Suby of GTE CORP) ★
600 Hidden Rdg, Irving, TX 75038-3809
Tel (972) 718-1856 Founded/Ownrshp 1992
Sales 56.1MME EMP 1,000
SIC 4813 Telephone communication, except radio
Pr: M Michael Foster
*Pr: Lawrence R Whitman
*VP: John C Appel

D-U-N-S 82-954-8788 IMP
■ GTE WIRELESS INC
(Suby of GTE CORP) ★
1 Verizon Way, Basking Ridge, NJ 07920-1025
Tel (908) 559-7000 Founded/Ownrshp 1981
Sales 258.1MME EMP 2,672E
SIC 4813 Telephone communication, except radio
VP: John Townsend

D-U-N-S 60-820-8286 IMP/EXP
GTECH HOLDINGS CORP
10 Memorial Blvd Ste 101, Providence, RI 02903-1125
Tel (401) 392-1000 Founded/Ownrshp 1981
Sales 156.1MME EMP 5,300
SIC 7999 7371

D-U-N-S 96-841-6219
GTEL HOLDINGS INC
2609 Cameron St, Mobile, AL 36607-3104
Tel (251) 479-4500 Founded/Ownrshp 1999
Sales 269.4MME EMP 680E
SIC 3661 7389 Telephone sets, all types except cellular radio; Telephone services

D-U-N-S 00-178-2887
GTM SERVICE INC (OH)
PARTS PRO AUTOMOTIVE WAREHOUSE
1366 Rockefeller Rd, Wickliffe, OH 44092-1973
Tel (440) 944-5099 Founded/Ownrshp 1981
Sales 87.5MME EMP 170
SIC 5013 Automotive supplies & parts
Pr: Michael McPhee
Sls Mgr: Sue Naght

G.T.M. SPORTSWEAR
See ITS GREEK TO ME INC

GTP
See GLOBAL TUNGSTEN & POWDERS CORP

GTRI
See GLOBAL TECHNOLOGY RESOURCES INC

GTS
See GEORGET SANDERS CO

D-U-N-S 09-856-0055
■ GTS DRYWALL SUPPLY CO
GTS INTERIOR SUPPLY
(Suby of G M S) ★
10819 120th Ave Ne, Kirkland, WA 98033-5024
Tel (425) 828-0608 Founded/Ownrshp 2000
Sales 116.7MME EMP 350
SIC 5032

GTS INTERIOR SUPPLY
See GTS DRYWALL SUPPLY CO

D-U-N-S 14-681-0502
GTS TECHNOLOGY SOLUTIONS INC
ARC
9211 Wterford Centre Blvd, Austin, TX 78758-7679
Tel (512) 452-0651 Founded/Ownrshp 1984
Sales 110.0MM EMP 66
Accts Maxwell Locke & Ritter Llp
SIC 5045 5112 Computer peripheral equipment; Computer & photocopying supplies
CEO: Laura Grant
*Pr: Ryan Grant
*VP: Britta Butler
*VP: Scott Sizemore
Dir IT: Nicole Bailey
Sls Mgr: Brian Norwood
Sls Mgr: Nathan Tart

GTS-WELCO
See PRAXAIR DISTRIBUTION MID-ATLANTIC LLC

D-U-N-S 08-099-6932
■ GTT COMMUNICATIONS (MP) INC
MEGAPATH
(Suby of GLOBAL TELECOM & TECHNOLOGY AMERICAS INC) ★
6800 Koll Center Pkwy # 200, Pleasanton, CA 94566-7045
Tel (925) 201-2500 Founded/Ownrshp 2015
Sales 162.1MME EMP 250
SIC 4813 7375 ; Information retrieval services
CEO: Craig Young
Pr: Dan Foster
*CFO: Paul Milley
*Co-Pr: Kurt Hoffman
Sr VP: Tony Capers
*Sr VP: Steve Chisholm
Sr VP: Arnaud Gautier
*Sr VP: David Williams
VP: Ganesh Gopal
VP: Derek Heins
VP: Matthew Hutchinson
VP: Devi Jaspal
VP: Robert McCarthy
VP: Brenda Viloria

D-U-N-S 79-077-6780
▲ GTT COMMUNICATIONS INC
7900 Tysons One Pl # 1450, Mc Lean, VA 22102-5971
Tel (703) 442-5500 Founded/Ownrshp 2005
Sales 369.2MM EMP 572E
Tkr Sym GTT Exch NYS
SIC 4813 ;
Pr: Richard D Calder Jr
*Ch Bd: H Brian Thompson
CFO: Michael Sicoli
Ex VP: Chris McKee
VP: Peter Berg
VP: Mike Fulton
VP: Rochelle Quinney
VP: Pahtkrit Sunthornvatin
Dir Risk M: Layne Levine
Sls Dir: Brian Heavener
Board of Directors: Nick Adamo, S Joseph Bruno, Rhodric C Hackman, Howard E Janzen, Elizabeth Satin, Theodore B Smith III

D-U-N-S 13-120-7271
GU MARKETS LLC
GRAND UNION FAMILY MARKETS
(Suby of C&S WHOLESALE PRODUCE) ★
4350 Middle Settlement Rd, New Hartford, NY 13413-5345
Tel (315) 793-9226 Founded/Ownrshp 2001
Sales 84.2MME EMP 1,100
SIC 5411 Grocery stores
Ch Bd: Richard B Cohen
*CFO: William Hamlin
*Ex VP: Scott Charlton

D-U-N-S 13-520-5966 IMP
GU-YOUNG TECH CO LTD
GUYOUNG TECH
(Suby of GUYOUNG TECH CO., LTD.)
26555 Evergreen Rd, Southfield, MI 48076-4206
Tel (248) 701-6663 Founded/Ownrshp 2003
Sales 86.1MM EMP 129
Accts Ahn & Han Cpas Pc Bingham F
SIC 5013 Automotive supplies & parts
Pr: Mia Kuratko

D-U-N-S 07-462-0170
GUADALUPE REGIONAL MEDICAL CENTER
1215 E Court St, Seguin, TX 78155-5129
Tel (830) 379-2411 Founded/Ownrshp 1961
Sales 91.2MM EMP 678
SIC 8062 General medical & surgical hospitals
CEO: Robert Haynes
*Ch Bd: Robert Galloway
*CEO: Deana Henk
*CFO: Penny Wallace
*VP: Fay Bennett
*VP: Lauren Carter
VP: Sheri Williams
Dir Rx: Larry Hicks
Chf Nrs Of: Daphne Blake
CIO: Steve Ratliff
Mktg Dir: Amanda Davila

D-U-N-S 00-793-0589
GUADALUPE VALLEY ELECTRIC COOPERATIVE INC (TX)
GVEC
825 E Sarah Dewitt Dr, Gonzales, TX 78629
Tel (830) 857-1200 Founded/Ownrshp 1938
Sales 224.6MM EMP 300
SIC 4911

D-U-N-S 05-631-1608
GUADALUPE-BLANCO RIVER AUTHORITY INDUSTRIAL DEVELOPMENT CORP
933 E Court St, Seguin, TX 78155-5872
Tel (361) 575-6366 Founded/Ownrshp 1935
Sales 83.8MME EMP 165
Accts Thompson Williams Biediger K
SIC 4911 4941 4952 Generation, electric power; Water supply; Sewerage systems
Pr: James L Powers
Ofcr: Jason Hamilton
Ofcr: Maribel Perkins
*VP: Tommy Mathews
VP: John P Schneider Jr
Exec: Lamarriol Smith
Exec: Todd Votteler
Div Mgr: Darel Ball
Div Mgr: Mike Urrutia
Genl Mgr: Wilfred Korth
Genl Mgr: Myrne McLeroy

D-U-N-S 00-890-8519
GUARANTEE ELECTRICAL CO
3405 Bent Ave, Saint Louis, MO 63116-2601
Tel (314) 772-5400 Founded/Ownrshp 1945
Sales 148.0MME EMP 700
Accts Uhy Llp St Louis Missouri
SIC 1731 Electrical work
CEO: Rick Oertli
Pr: Douglas Mertzlufft
CFO: Josh Voegtli
Ex VP: Doug Merzlufft
Ex VP: Roger Oertli
VP: Steve Briesacher
VP: David M Gralike
VP: Nazeeh Kiblawi
VP: Mike Minor
VP: Donald Umphryes
Sfty Mgr: Andy Fister

D-U-N-S 96-285-9778
GUARANTEE INSURANCE GROUP INC
401 E Las Olas Blvd # 1540, Fort Lauderdale, FL 33301-2210
Tel (954) 670-2900 Founded/Ownrshp 2010
Sales NA EMP 390E
SIC 6411 6331 Insurance agents, brokers & service; Workers' compensation insurance
CEO: Steven M Mariano
*Pr: John Rearer
*COO: Bob Peters
*Treas: Michael J Sluka
*Ex VP: Michael W Grandstaff
Ex VP: Christopher Pesch
Opers Supe: Tammy Watkins
Mktg Mgr: John Chisenhall

D-U-N-S 07-974-2060
GUARANTEE TRUST LIFE INSURANCE CO
1275 Milwaukee Ave # 100, Glenview, IL 60025-2489
Tel (847) 699-0600 Founded/Ownrshp 1957
Sales NA EMP 250
SIC 6321 6311 Accident insurance carriers; Health insurance carriers; Life insurance carriers
Pr: Richard S Holson III
*Treas: Barbara Taube
Sr VP: Arthur Fess
*Sr VP: Mark Stevenson
*VP: Don Abbs
*VP: Richard Affenit
VP: Glen Doering
VP: Lesley Hanslope
VP: Michael Honeysett
VP: Bobby Jann
VP Admn: Michael A Honeysett

D-U-N-S 83-966-6919
GUARANTEED RATE INC
3940 N Ravenswood Ave, Chicago, IL 60613-2420
Tel (866) 934-7283 Founded/Ownrshp 1999
Sales NA EMP 2,158
SIC 6162 Mortgage bankers
Pr: Steven B Carter
*Pr: Victor Ciardelli III
Pr: Matthew Leahy
*COO: Nikolaos Athanasiou
COO: Rob Sampson
*CFO: Ted Ahern
Ofcr: John Ruggles
Ex VP: Charles Bachtell
Ex VP: Adal Bisharat
Ex VP: Matthew Harmon
Sr VP: Ricardo H Brasil
Sr VP: Juli Rennie
VP: Carla Adona
VP: Betsy Ahern
VP: George Allen
VP: Jeff Baker
*VP: Anne Benoist
VP: Eric Burba
VP: Billy Burns
VP: Sylvia Curletto
VP: Becky Dawson

D-U-N-S 02-459-1059
GUARANTEED SUPPLY CO
1211 Rotherwood Rd, Greensboro, NC 27406-3825
Tel (336) 273-3491 Founded/Ownrshp 1965
Sales 215.6MME EMP 300
SIC 5032 5031 Brick, stone & related material; Lumber, plywood & millwork
CEO: Michael Ward
*Ch Bd: Kirby Ward
*Pr: Willie Goncharow
*Treas: Marie Grogan

D-U-N-S 15-764-2823
▲ GUARANTY BANCORP
1331 17th St Ste 200, Denver, CO 80202-1566
Tel (303) 296-9600 Founded/Ownrshp 2004
Sales NA EMP 376E
Tkr Sym GBNK Exch NGS
SIC 6022 State commercial banks
Pr: Paul W Taylor
*Ch Bd: Edward B Cordes
CFO: Christopher G Treece
Chf Cred: Cathy P Goss

D-U-N-S 00-691-5557
■ GUARANTY BANK AND TRUST CO
(Suby of GUARANTY BANCORP) ★
1331 17th St Lbby, Denver, CO 80202-5892
Tel (303) 298-6977 Founded/Ownrshp 2005
Sales NA EMP 365E
SIC 6022 State commercial banks
Ch Bd: Paul W Taylor
*Pr: Michael B Hobbs
Ex VP: Steven Mandel
*Sr VP: Amy Lovell
VP: Clint Crews
VP: Sandra Crosthwaite
*VP: Cathy Goss
VP: Michael A Justice
VP: Lee Maher
*VP: Christopher G Treece
VP: Carolyn Tyrrell

D-U-N-S 84-920-2932
GUARANTY FINANCIAL MHC
4000 W Brown Deer Rd, Milwaukee, WI 53209-1221
Tel (414) 362-4000 Founded/Ownrshp 1993
Sales NA EMP 1,933
SIC 6035 Federal savings & loan associations
CEO: John T Stuart
COO: Kevin Hanigan
CFO: Althea Bickham
CFO: Ronald D Murff
Treas: Steven Rafael
Ex VP: Scott A Almy
Board of Directors: John S Ettenheim, Milton B Ettenheim Jr, Max Gendelman, Jack Recht, Samuel D Safro, Abe A Tannenbaum

D-U-N-S 02-766-0588
GUARANTY RV INC
20 Highway 99 S, Junction City, OR 97448-9714
Tel (541) 998-2333 Founded/Ownrshp 1966
Sales 166.8MME EMP 425
SIC 5561 5511 Recreational vehicle dealers; Recreational vehicle parts & accessories; Automobiles, new & used
Pr: Herbert N Nill
*COO: Shannon Nill
*CFO: Ed Morgan
Treas: Evelyn Long
Exec: Bruce Kremis

Ex Dir: Jolene Loudon
Dir IT: Terry Creighton
Sales Exec: Bret Frost
Sls Mgr: Doug Ebner
Sales Asso: Ken Cooper

D-U-N-S 60-805-5232
■ GUARD INSURANCE GROUP INC
WESTGUARD INSURANCE COMPANY
(*Suby of* BERKSHIRE HATHAWAY INC) ★
16 S River St, Wilkes Barre, PA 18702-2494
Tel (570) 825-9900 *Founded/Ownrshp* 2012
Sales NA *EMP* 275
SIC 6331

D-U-N-S 02-274-4093
GUARD-SYSTEMS INC
1190 Monterey Pass Rd, Monterey Park, CA 91754-3615
Tel (626) 443-0031 *Founded/Ownrshp* 1961
Sales 7.9MM^E *EMP* 1,150
SIC 7381 Detective & armored car services; Guard services; Security guard service
CEO: Theodore Haas
**VP:* Leo Austin

D-U-N-S 00-532-2052 IMP
GUARDIAN AUTOMOTIVE CORP (MI)
GUARDIAN AUTOMOTIVE TRIM
(*Suby of* SRG GLOBAL INC) ★
23751 Amber Ave, Warren, MI 48089-6000
Tel (586) 757-7800 *Founded/Ownrshp* 1949, 1996
Sales 332.8MM^E *EMP* 2,500
SIC 3089 3465 Extruded finished plastic products; Molding primary plastic; Moldings or trim, automobile: stamped metal
CEO: Daniel J Davis
**Sr VP:* Kevin Myers
**VP:* Joseph Abbruzzi
**VP:* Chuck Wilson
IT Man: Chandrapal Saini
Plnt Mgr: David Serpa
Sls Mgr: Debi Owens

GUARDIAN AUTOMOTIVE TRIM
See GUARDIAN AUTOMOTIVE CORP

GUARDIAN BONDED SECURITY
See GUARDIAN GUARD SERVICES INC

GUARDIAN BUILDING PDTS DIST
See GUARDIAN BUILDING PRODUCTS DISTRIBUTION INC

D-U-N-S 82-598-5450 IMP
GUARDIAN BUILDING PRODUCTS DISTRIBUTION INC
GUARDIAN BUILDING PDTS DIST
(*Suby of* GBP MANAGEMENT INC) ★
979 Batesville Rd Ste A, Greer, SC 29651-6819
Tel (800) 569-4262 *Founded/Ownrshp* 1867
Sales 889.1MM^E *EMP* 862^E
SIC 5031 5033 5051 5032 5039 5023 Lumber, plywood & millwork; Millwork; Skylights, all materials; Roofing, siding & insulation; Roofing, asphalt & sheet metal; Insulation materials; Siding, except wood; Metals service centers & offices; Iron & steel (ferrous) products; Brick, stone & related material; Stucco; Drywall materials; Ceiling systems & products; Fireplace equipment & accessories
CEO: Thomas Highley
**CFO:* Wayne Feasby
VP: Foster Ellis
Comm Man: Michelle Lock
Brnch Mgr: Chad Mizell
Dir IT: Steve Lanzl

D-U-N-S 07-914-1333
GUARDIAN BUILDING PRODUCTS INC
(*Suby of* GUARDIAN INDUSTRIES CORP) ★
979 Batesville Rd Ste A, Greer, SC 29651-6819
Tel (864) 297-6101 *Founded/Ownrshp* 1990
Sales 889.1MM^E *EMP* 900
SIC 3296 2452 8741 Fiberglass insulation; Prefabricated wood buildings; Business management
Pr: Steven D Ziessler
Prgrm Mgr: Darrin Neitzke
IT Man: Brian Bradshaw
VP Opers: Bruce Schneider
Manager: Ron Thomas

GUARDIAN COMPLIANCE
See SEAL TECH INC

D-U-N-S 05-352-6539
GUARDIAN CORP
GUARDIAN FOOD SERVICE
3801 Sunset Ave Ste A, Rocky Mount, NC 27804-3126
Tel (252) 443-4101 *Founded/Ownrshp* 1981
Sales 40.9MM^E *EMP* 1,500
SIC 5812 Fast-food restaurant, chain
Ch Bd: Leon A Dunn Jr
**Pr:* Vincent Andracchio
**CFO:* Debra W Williams
**VP:* Martha Bridges

GUARDIAN FOOD SERVICE
See GUARDIAN CORP

D-U-N-S 08-430-0003
GUARDIAN GUARD SERVICES INC
GUARDIAN BONDED SECURITY
18000 W 8 Mile Rd, Southfield, MI 48075-4338
Tel (248) 423-1000 *Founded/Ownrshp* 2005
Sales 34.4MM^E *EMP* 1,500
SIC 7381 Security guard service
Pr: Douglas Pierce
**Treas:* Richard Pierce

GUARDIAN INDUSTRIES
See CONSOLIDATED GLASS & MIRROR CORP

D-U-N-S 05-467-1169 IMP/EXP
GUARDIAN INDUSTRIES CORP
2300 Harmon Rd, Auburn Hills, MI 48326-1714
Tel (248) 340-1800 *Founded/Ownrshp* 1989
Sales 4.9MMM^E *EMP* 19,000
SIC 3211 Flat glass
CEO: Ron Vaupel
Pt: Jerry Ray
**CFO:* Jeffrey A Knight
Treas: Ann Waichunas
VP: Bruce H Cummings
VP: Richard Johnson
VP: Paul M Rappaport
VP: Marc Talbert
VP: Scott Thomsen
VP: Donald Trofholz
VP: Rick Zoulek
Exec: Saumitra Yadav
Board of Directors: Chuck Croskey, Russell J Ebeid, Michael Filipek, David Jaffe, Anna Kalil, Mark Lacasse, Jim Moore

D-U-N-S 18-833-3702
GUARDIAN INSURANCE & ANNUITY CO INC
(*Suby of* GUARDIAN LIFE INSURANCE CO OF AMERICA) ★
7 Hanover Sq, New York, NY 10004-2616
Tel (212) 598-8000 *Founded/Ownrshp* 1970
Sales NA *EMP* 1,500
SIC 6311 6371 Life insurance carriers; Pension, health & welfare funds
Ch: Dennis Manning
Pr: Deanna Mulligan
VP: John Jennings
VP: Frank Loscalzo
VP: Jasonn D Potter
Exec: Dean Rothman

D-U-N-S 00-185-4256
GUARDIAN LIFE INSURANCE CO OF AMERICA
7 Hanover Sq Fl 14, New York, NY 10004-4025
Tel (212) 598-8000 *Founded/Ownrshp* 1860
Sales NA *EMP* 5,008
SIC 6311 6371 6324 6321 6722 6282 Life insurance carriers; Life reinsurance; Pensions; Group hospitalization plans; Dental insurance; Disability health insurance; Reinsurance carriers, accident & health; Mutual fund sales, on own account; Investment advice
CEO: Deanna Mulligan
Pr: Deon Hall-Garriques
Pr: Clay Korte
Pr: Deanna M Mulligan
Pr: James Suslavich
CFO: Marc Costantini
Treas: Barry Belfer
Chf Mktg O: Maria Umbach
Ofcr: Anthony S Marino
Ofcr: Linda Senker
Ex VP: Dong H Ahn
Ex VP: Rone Baldwin
Ex VP: Armand M De Palo
Ex VP: Gary B Lenderink
Ex VP: John P McCarthy
Ex VP: Tracy Rich
Ex VP: Tracy L Rich
Ex VP: Thomas G Sorell
Sr VP: David W Allen
Sr VP: Joseph A Caruso
Sr VP: Michael B Cefole
Board of Directors: Leo R Futia, John J Brennan, Paul B Guenther, Lloyd E Campbell, James A Kennedy, John B Caswell, Joseph D Sargent, Richard E Cavanaugh, Eric K Shinseki, Kay Knight Clarke, John A Somers, Martin J Cleary, Donald C Waite III, Nancy E Cooper, James E Daley, Deborah L Duncan

D-U-N-S 01-496-3532
GUARDIAN PROTECTION SERVICES INC
HOME SECURITY
(*Suby of* ARMSTRONG HOLDINGS INC) ★
174 Thorn Hill Rd, Warrendale, PA 15086-7528
Tel (412) 788-2580 *Founded/Ownrshp* 1991
Sales 261.5MM^E *EMP* 1,000
SIC 1731 5999 7382 Safety & security specialization; Fire detection & burglar alarm systems specialization; Alarm signal systems; Security systems services
CEO: Russell L Cersosimo
**Pr:* Joseph Colosimo
**CFO:* Richard Yobbi
**Treas:* Kirby I Campbell
Chf Mktg O: Mary L Moriarity
Ex VP: Lawrence Wargo
VP: Richard Bishop
VP: Jim Breisinger
VP: Jim Greene
VP: Kevin Santelli
**VP:* Jay L Sedwick
**VP:* Jeff Szajnecki
VP: Randall Tecza

D-U-N-S 09-750-5754
GUARDIAN SERVICE INDUSTRIES INC
161 Ave Of The Amer, New York, NY 10013-1205
Tel (212) 645-9500 *Founded/Ownrshp* 1957
Sales 76.7MM^E *EMP* 1,500^E
SIC 7349

D-U-N-S 36-066-1995
GUARDSMARK HOLDINGS INC
22 S 2nd St, Memphis, TN 38103-2695
Tel (901) 522-6000 *Founded/Ownrshp* 2002
Sales 37.0MM^E *EMP* 1,201
SIC 7363 Temporary help service
Ch Bd: Ira A Lipman
**VP:* Terri Duff
**VP:* Tommy Yarborough

D-U-N-S 00-705-5551
GUARDSMARK LLC
(*Suby of* UNIVERSAL PROTECTION SERVICE LP) ★
1551 N Tustin Ave Ste 650, Santa Ana, CA 92705-8664
Tel (714) 619-9700 *Founded/Ownrshp* 2015
Sales 281.3MM^E *EMP* 3,500^E
SIC 7381 8742 2721 Security guard service; Private investigator; Industry specialist consultants; Periodicals: publishing only
CEO: Steven S Jones
Ofcr: Michelle Craine

D-U-N-S 04-278-6392 IMP
GUCCI AMERICA INC
195 Broadway Fl 12, New York, NY 10007-4292
Tel (212) 750-5220 *Founded/Ownrshp* 1953
Sales 174.4MM^E *EMP* 1,000^E
SIC 5632 5948 5661 5611 5621 5137 Handbags; Apparel accessories; Luggage, except footlockers & trunks; Women's shoes; Men's shoes; Men's & boys' clothing stores; Ready-to-wear apparel, women's; Handbags
CEO: Christophe De Pous
Sr VP: Susan Chokachi
VP: Courtney Flint
VP: Doug McCullough
Genl Mgr: Ellen Krachman
Mktg Dir: Alison Crossen
Mktg Mgr: Joseph Facchinei
Counsel: Brooke Crescenti

D-U-N-S 04-401-0270 IMP
GUCKENHEIMER ENTERPRISES INC
1850 Gateway Dr Ste 500, San Mateo, CA 94404-4064
Tel (650) 592-3800 *Founded/Ownrshp* 1999
Sales 134.5MM^E *EMP* 2,500
SIC 5812

D-U-N-S 02-745-1731 IMP/EXP
▲ GUESS INC
1444 S Alameda St, Los Angeles, CA 90021-2433
Tel (213) 765-3100 *Founded/Ownrshp* 1993
Sales 2.2MMM *EMP* 13,500
Tkr Sym GES *Exch* NYS
SIC 2325 2339 5611 5621 5641 Men's & boys' jeans & dungarees; Women's & misses' outerwear; Clothing, sportswear, men's & boys'; Women's sportswear; Children's & infants' wear stores
CEO: Victor Herrero
**Ch Bd:* Paul Marciano
CFO: Sandeep Reddy
VP: Isaiah Kincaid
VP: Joe Toth
Mktg Dir: Maurice Marciano
Art Dir: Leslie Yoshimura
Snr Mgr: Kenny Choy
Board of Directors: Anthony Chidoni, Joseph Gromek, Kay Isaacson-Leibowitz, Maurice Marciano, Alex Yemenidjian

D-U-N-S 00-691-9807
GUEST SERVICES INC (DC)
3055 Prosperity Ave, Fairfax, VA 22031-2290
Tel (703) 849-9300 *Founded/Ownrshp* 1917
Sales 396.2MM *EMP* 3,500
Accts Pricewaterhousecoopers Llp M
SIC 5148 8741 Fresh fruits & vegetables; Management services
CEO: Gerard T Gabrys
**Pr:* Jeffrey Marquis
**CFO:* Nico Fores
CFO: Jeffrey A Mrquis
Ch: Peter S Prichard
VP: Jerry Chadwich
**VP:* Jerrold Chadwick
**VP:* Beverly Frazer
**VP:* John N Gates
**VP:* Richard Hirsch
VP: William J Hybl
**VP:* Barry Trice
VP: Barry G Trice

GUEST SUPPLY SERVICES
See SYSCO GUEST SUPPLY LLC

D-U-N-S 80-033-6344
GUGGENHEIM CAPITAL LLC
227 W Monroe St Ste 4900, Chicago, IL 60606-4900
Tel (312) 827-0100 *Founded/Ownrshp* 2001
Sales 144.0MM^E *EMP* 540
SIC 6726 Investment offices
CEO: Mark R Walter

D-U-N-S 07-832-0748
GUGGENHEIM LIFE AND ANNUITY CO
(*Suby of* GUGGENHEIM PARTNERS LLC) ★
401 Penn Pkwy Ste 300, Indianapolis, IN 46280-1385
Tel (317) 574-6213 *Founded/Ownrshp* 2010
Sales NA *EMP* 609^E
SIC 6311 Life reinsurance
Pr: Jeffrey Lange

D-U-N-S 14-260-3567
GUGGENHEIM PARTNERS LLC
330 Madison Ave Rm 201, New York, NY 10017-5045
Tel (212) 739-0700 *Founded/Ownrshp* 2006
Sales 1.5MMM^E *EMP* 10,650
SIC 8742 Business consultant
CEO: Mark R Walter
Pr: Todd L Boehly
Ch: Alan Schwartz
Top Exec: Rick McCracken
Sr VP: Kara Hansen
VP: Eoin Duane
VP: Kostadin Kolev
Prin: Thomas J Irvin
Prin: Peter O Lawson-Johnston II
Prin: B Scott Minerd
Mng Dir: Raul Elia

D-U-N-S 08-984-9400 IMP
GUHRING INC (WI)
(*Suby of* GUHRING KG)
1445 Commerce Ave, Brookfield, WI 53045-5289
Tel (262) 784-6730 *Founded/Ownrshp* 1978
Sales 87.0MM^E *EMP* 400
SIC 3545 Drills (machine tool accessories)
Ch Bd: Jorg Guhring
**Pr:* Peter Haenle
**CFO:* Craig Rotta
Rgnl Mgr: Todd Madaus
Rgnl Mgr: Israel Roman
Div Mgr: Mike Massey
Sftwr Eng: Josh Hart
Opers Mgr: Craig Zacher
Prd Mgr: Frank Balestrieri
Prd Mgr: Jonathan Sanders
Ql Cn Mgr: Tom Cerwin
Board of Directors: Peter Haenle

GUHSD
See GLENDALE UNION HIGH SCHOOL DISTRICT

D-U-N-S 01-381-4426
▲ GUIDANCE SOFTWARE INC
1055 E Colo Blvd Ste 400, Pasadena, CA 91106
Tel (626) 229-9191 *Founded/Ownrshp* 1997
Sales 107.0MM *EMP* 420
Tkr Sym GUID *Exch* NGM
SIC 7372 3572 Prepackaged software; Computer storage devices
Pr: Patrick Dennis
**Ch Bd:* Robert Van Schoonenberg
COO: Barry Plaga
Chf Mktg O: Michael Harris
Sr VP: Ken Basore
Sr VP: Alfredo Gomez
VP: David Hydorn
Dir Risk M: Daryk Rowland
Genl Mgr: Law Clerk
QA Dir: Sofia Makhlin
QA Dir: Pierre Olivier
Board of Directors: Max Carnecchia, John P Colbert, Wade Loo, Michael J McConnell

D-U-N-S 62-162-8007
■ GUIDANT PUERTO RICO BV
(*Suby of* GUIDANT/C P I) ★
12 Carr 698 Ste 171, Dorado, PR 00646-3315
Tel (787) 796-2115 *Founded/Ownrshp* 1989
Sales 153.9MM^E *EMP* 815
SIC 3845 Pacemaker, cardiac; Defibrillator
Pr: A Jay Graf
**Treas:* Zulma Suarez
**VP:* Dale Devries
**VP:* Richard R Doyle
**VP:* Jeffrey Neuenfeldt
Genl Mgr: Heriberto Diaz
Snr Ntwrk: Luis Rivera

D-U-N-S 87-726-0471
■ GUIDANT SALES LLC
GUIDANT/C P I
(*Suby of* BOSTON SCIENTIFIC CORP) ★
4100 Hamline Ave N, Saint Paul, MN 55112-5700
Tel (800) 949-9459 *Founded/Ownrshp* 2006
Sales 1.4MMM^E *EMP* 12,000
SIC 3841 3845 5047 8733 Surgical & medical instruments; Catheters; Instruments, microsurgical: except electromedical; Retractors; Electromedical equipment; Pacemaker, cardiac; Defibrillator; Medical & hospital equipment; Medical equipment & supplies; Diagnostic equipment, medical; Medical research
CEO: J Raymond Elliott
Pr: Mark C Bartell
Pr: Daniel J Brennan
Pr: Kelly Phillips
Pr: Ann Wilcox
Ch: A Jay Graf
Ofcr: Michael B Gropp
VP: Bill Charron
VP: Douglas J Cronin
VP: Beverly H Lorell MD
VP: Timothy A Pratt

GUIDANT/C P I
See GUIDANT SALES LLC

D-U-N-S 06-848-8451
GUIDEONE AMERICA INSURANCE CO
GUIDEONE AMERICA MUTL INSUR CO
(*Suby of* GUIDEONE INC) ★
1111 Ashworth Rd, West Des Moines, IA 50265-3544
Tel (515) 267-5000 *Founded/Ownrshp* 1993
Sales NA *EMP* 750
SIC 6331 Fire, marine & casualty insurance & carriers
Pr: James Wallace

GUIDEONE AMERICA MUTL INSUR CO
See GUIDEONE AMERICA INSURANCE CO

D-U-N-S 10-395-0887
GUIDEONE INC
1111 Ashworth Rd, West Des Moines, IA 50265-3544
Tel (515) 267-5000 *Founded/Ownrshp* 1983
Sales NA *EMP* 800
SIC 6311 Mutual association life insurance; Life insurance carriers
Pr: Jim Wallace

GUIDEONE INSURANCE
See GUIDEONE MUTUAL INSURANCE CO

D-U-N-S 16-145-4405
GUIDEONE MUTUAL INSURANCE CO
(*Suby of* GUIDEONE INC) ★
1111 Ashworth Rd, West Des Moines, IA 50265-3544
Tel (515) 267-5000 *Founded/Ownrshp* 1996
Sales NA *EMP* 60
SIC 6331 Fire, marine & casualty insurance & carriers
Pr: Jim Wallace
VP: Scott Redding

D-U-N-S 80-227-2307
GUIDEONE MUTUAL INSURANCE CO
GUIDEONE INSURANCE
1111 Ashworth Rd, West Des Moines, IA 50265-3544
Tel (515) 267-5000 *Founded/Ownrshp* 1947
Sales NA *EMP* 720
SIC 6411 Insurance agents, brokers & service
CEO: Jim Wallace
Pr: Gilbert Korthals
**Ex VP:* Scott Reddig
**Sr VP:* Doug Cretsinger
**VP:* Sarah Buckley
VP: Mike Faley
Dir Bus: Stacy Olson
**Prin:* Lynn Vorbrich
QA Dir: Nandhini Venkataswamy
Sls Dir: Jason Langston
**Genl Couns:* Sam Water

GUIDEWELL SOURCE
See DIVERSIFIED SERVICE OPTIONS INC

D-U-N-S 12-662-5701
▲ GUIDEWIRE SOFTWARE INC
1001 E Hillsdale Blvd # 800, Foster City, CA 94404-1643
Tel (650) 357-9100 *Founded/Ownrshp* 2001
Sales 424.4MM *EMP* 1,341[E]
Accts Kpmg Llp Santa Clara Califor
Tkr Sym GWRE *Exch* NYS
SIC 7372 Prepackaged software
Pr: Marcus S Ryu
**Ch Bd:* John Cavoores
CFO: Richard Hart
Ofcr: Priscilla Hung
Ofcr: Michael Polelle
Prgrm Mgr: Brian Lareau
Snr Sftwr: Chetana Kalahasti
Snr Sftwr: Jeff Klein
Snr Sftwr: Ivan Sabinin
CTO: Siobhan Delaney
IT Man: Eric Denton
Board of Directors: Andrew Brown, Craig Conway, Guy Dubois, Peter Gassner, Clifton Thomas Weatherford

D-U-N-S 05-571-0354
GUILD MORTGAGE CO
COMSTOCK MORTGAGE
5898 Copley Dr Fl 4, San Diego, CA 92111-7916
Tel (800) 283-8823 *Founded/Ownrshp* 1960
Sales NA *EMP* 1,000
Accts Richey May & Co Englewood C
SIC 6162 6733 Mortgage bankers; Trusts, except educational, religious, charity: management
Pr: Mary Ann McGarry
**CFO:* Terry Schmidt
Chf Mktg O: Mike Rish
Ex VP: Barry Horn
Ex VP: Aaron Nemec
Sr VP: Catherine Blocker
Sr VP: Michael Rish
Sr VP: Linda Scott
Exec: Carol Clark
Exec: Kristi Shanks
Rgnl Mgr: Bonita Mayne

D-U-N-S 02-066-4595
GUILDERLAND CENTRAL SCHOOL DISTRICT (NY)
8 School Rd, Guilderland Center, NY 12085
Tel (518) 456-6200 *Founded/Ownrshp* 1950
Sales 94.2MM *EMP* 1,100
Accts West & Company Cpas Pc Glove
SIC 8211 Public elementary & secondary schools; High school, junior or senior
**Treas:* John Rizzo
Pr Dir: Aubree Kammler

D-U-N-S 07-721-8858
GUILDERY INC
(*Suby of* MINTED LLC) ★
170 State St Ste A, Los Altos, CA 94022-2837
Tel (650) 257-0157 *Founded/Ownrshp* 2016
Sales 114.4MM[E] *EMP* 2,013[E]
SIC 5231 Wallpaper
CEO: Shane Reilly
Prin: Kelly Berger

D-U-N-S 78-547-8152
GUILDNET INC
JGB
(*Suby of* THE JEWISH GUILD FOR THE BLIND)
15 W 65th St, New York, NY 10023-6601
Tel (212) 769-6200 *Founded/Ownrshp* 1996
Sales 826.0MM *EMP* 377[E]
Accts Loeb & Troper Llp New York N
SIC 8011 Medical centers
CEO: Alan R Morse
**Ch:* James M Dubin
**Treas:* Lawrence E Goldschmidt
VP Admn: Larry Carr

D-U-N-S 05-469-9491
GUILFORD COUNTY SCHOOL SYSTEM
GUILFORD COUNTY SCHOOLS
712 N Eugene St, Greensboro, NC 27401-1622
Tel (336) 370-8100 *Founded/Ownrshp* 1898
Sales 324.1MM[E] *EMP* 10,000
SIC 8211 Public elementary & secondary schools
Ex Dir: Doris Brown
CIO: Barbara Weaver
**CIO:* Terrance Young
MIS Dir: Richard Sumner
IT Man: Phillip Henry
Teacher Pr: Steve Foster
Teacher Pr: Alyson Yates
Pgrm Dir: Dennis Cole

GUILFORD COUNTY SCHOOLS
See GUILFORD COUNTY SCHOOL SYSTEM

D-U-N-S 11-247-4023
GUILFORD HEALTH CARE CENTER INC
2041 Willow Rd, Greensboro, NC 27406-3831
Tel (336) 272-9700 *Founded/Ownrshp* 1990
Sales 877.5MM *EMP* 125
SIC 8051 Skilled nursing care facilities
Exec: Jackie Gonzales

D-U-N-S 00-323-2428 IMP/EXP
■ GUILFORD MILLS INC
(*Suby of* LEAR CORP) ★
1001 Military Cutoff Rd # 300, Wilmington, NC 28405-4376
Tel (910) 794-5810 *Founded/Ownrshp* 1946, 2012
Sales 595.1MM[E] *EMP* 2,600
SIC 2258 2399 Cloth, warp knit; Dyeing & finishing lace goods & warp knit fabric; Automotive covers, except seat & tire covers
Pr: Matt Simoncini
Pr: Chad Brooks
Pr: Shannon White
Bd of Dir: Terrence Geremski
Bd of Dir: Paul Gillease
Bd of Dir: Cheryl Jacobs
Bd of Dir: Grant Wilson
Ex VP: David Taylor
VP: Ron Houser
VP: Deborah Poole
Prd Mgr: Sandra Freeman

D-U-N-S 03-198-2796
GUIRYS INC
620 Canosa Ct, Denver, CO 80204-4108
Tel (720) 360-4840 *Founded/Ownrshp* 1962
Sales 135.9MM[E] *EMP* 105
SIC 5198 5231 5999 Paints; Wallcoverings; Paint; Wallpaper; Artists' supplies & materials
Pr: Richard L Guiry
Mktg Dir: Brandon Lilly

D-U-N-S 80-805-4774
GUITAR CENTER HOLDINGS INC
5795 Lindero Canyon Rd, Westlake Village, CA 91362-4013
Tel (818) 735-8800 *Founded/Ownrshp* 2007
Sales 2.1MMM *EMP* 10,188
SIC 5736 Musical instrument stores; Drums & related percussion instruments; Keyboard instruments
CEO: Tim Martin
Ex VP: John Bagan
Ex VP: Frank Hamlin

D-U-N-S 09-147-8008 IMP/EXP
GUITAR CENTER INC
(*Suby of* GUITAR CENTER HOLDINGS INC) ★
5795 Lindero Canyon Rd, Westlake Village, CA 91362-4013
Tel (818) 735-8800 *Founded/Ownrshp* 1996, 2007
Sales 2.1MMM[E] *EMP* 10,188
SIC 5736 Musical instrument stores; Drums & related percussion instruments; Keyboard instruments
CEO: Darrell Webb
Ch Bd: Tony Truesdale
V Ch: Greg Riggs
Pr: Ron Japinga
Pr: Sophia Lo
CFO: Tim Martin
Treas: John Unger
Chf Mktg O: Frank Hamlin
Ex VP: Michael Amkreutz
Ex VP: Dennis Haffeman
Sr VP: Flynn Chernos
VP: Gregory Barr
VP: Todd Lyche
VP: Danielle Mohn
VP: Rich Pidanick
VP: Lo Sophia
VP: Robert Stannard
VP: Victoria Wisot
Board of Directors: Norman Axelrod

D-U-N-S 18-065-3912 IMP
GUITAR CENTER STORES INC
MUSIC & ARTS CENTERS
(*Suby of* GUITAR CENTER INC) ★
5795 Lindero Canyon Rd, Westlake Village, CA 91362-4013
Tel (818) 735-8800 *Founded/Ownrshp* 2000
Sales 116.4MM[E] *EMP* 875[E]
SIC 5736 Musical instrument stores
Pr: Darrell Webb
**CFO:* Erick Mason
**Ex VP:* John Bagan
**Ex VP:* Dennis Haffeman
**Ex VP:* Tim Martin
**Sr VP:* Kevin Kazubowski
Opers Mgr: Amanda Damiano

D-U-N-S 00-911-6286 IMP/EXP
GUITTARD CHOCOLATE CO
10 Guittard Rd, Burlingame, CA 94010-2203
Tel (650) 697-4427 *Founded/Ownrshp* 1868
Sales 85.1MM[E] *EMP* 240
SIC 2066 2064 Chocolate; Cocoa & cocoa products; Candy & other confectionery products
Pr: Gary W Guittard
COO: Allen Gerry
CFO: Gerrit Dirkmaat
Exec: Brad Newcom
Dir IT: Ed Fong
VP Opers: Gerry Allen
Opers Mgr: Alvin Oey
Plnt Mgr: Eric Blickenstaff
Plnt Mgr: Kristin Wheatley
Mktg Dir: Amy Guittard
Manager: Valerie McCaffrey

GULF CAOST STABILIZED MTLS
See CAMPBELL CONCRETE & MATERIALS LP

D-U-N-S 61-362-1010
GULF COAST BANK AND TRUST CO
200 Saint Charles Ave, New Orleans, LA 70130-2903
Tel (504) 561-6100 *Founded/Ownrshp* 1990
Sales NA *EMP* 336
SIC 6022 State trust companies accepting deposits, commercial
Pr: Guy T Williams
**CFO:* Greg Hollier
Assoc VP: Joseph Spampneto

D-U-N-S 00-780-4149
GULF COAST BROADCASTING CO
KRIS TV CHANNEL SIX
(*Suby of* POST & COURIER) ★
409 S Staples St, Corpus Christi, TX 78401-3330
Tel (361) 886-6100 *Founded/Ownrshp* 1935
Sales 46.4MM[E] *EMP* 1,515
SIC 4833 5812 Television broadcasting stations; Eating places
Pr: T Frank Smith Jr
**Treas:* Susan M Hines
**VP:* T Frank Smith IV
Pgrm Dir: Joyce Applebee

D-U-N-S 87-682-0981
GULF COAST HEALTH CARE LLC
40 Palafox Pl Ste 400, Pensacola, FL 32502-5699
Tel (800) 881-9907 *Founded/Ownrshp* 2008
Sales 98.3MM[E] *EMP* 1,599[E]
SIC 8051 Skilled nursing care facilities
Prin: Barry Williams
Ofcr: Cindy Ledford
CIO: Earl Page
Dir IT: Jon Dossey
Netwrk Eng: Chris Gapske
Nrsg Dir: Lisa Gahring
Nrsg Dir: Leanne Hyatt
Nrsg Dir: Susan Rasche
HC Dir: Deidra Melton

GULF COAST HOSPITAL
See DOCTORS OSTEOPATHIC MEDICAL CENTER INC

D-U-N-S 96-865-9284
GULF COAST MEDICAL CENTRE LTD
13691 Metro Pkwy Ste 110, Fort Myers, FL 33912-4348
Tel (239) 343-1000 *Founded/Ownrshp* 1994
Sales 284.2MM *EMP* 268
SIC 8062 General medical & surgical hospitals
Prin: Jeffrey R Green

D-U-N-S 02-717-9415
GULF COAST PAPER CO INC
3705 Houston Hwy, Victoria, TX 77901-4767
Tel (361) 852-5252 *Founded/Ownrshp* 2013
Sales 255.1MM[E] *EMP* 185
Accts Roloff Hnatek & Co Llp Vic
SIC 5113 5087 Industrial & personal service paper; Janitors' supplies
Ch Bd: Speed Bancroft
**Pr:* F Speed Bancroft
**VP:* Sonny Bratz
**VP:* Clay Dibble
**VP:* Joe Morris
**VP:* Donald Wade
Brnch Mgr: Bruce Kotzur
Sales Asso: Russell Bailey
Sales Asso: Victor Godina
Sales Asso: Jeremy Graham

D-U-N-S 01-080-2080
GULF COAST REGIONAL BLOOD CENTER
BLOOD CENTER, THE
1400 La Concha Ln, Houston, TX 77054-1887
Tel (713) 790-1200 *Founded/Ownrshp* 1974
Sales 92.4MM *EMP* 634
Accts Ernst & Young Llp
SIC 8099 7371 7363 Blood bank; Custom computer programming services; Temporary help service
Pr: Brian G Gannon
**CFO:* Melissa Fisher
**Ch:* David M McClanahan
**Treas:* Greg Bernica
**Chf Mktg O:* Susan Rossmann
Adm Dir: Yvette Rubio
Rgnl Mgr: Clare Wong
CIO: McClain Doug

D-U-N-S 83-117-8020 IMP
GULF COAST SHIPYARD GROUP INC
13085 Seaway Rd, Gulfport, MS 39503-4607
Tel (228) 276-1051 *Founded/Ownrshp* 2003
Sales 165.0MM *EMP* 300[E]
SIC 3731 Shipbuilding & repairing
Pr: John Dane III
**COO:* Marvin Serna
**CFO:* Mitchell Skrmetta
Board of Directors: John Dane, Edmund Feeley, Michael Klein, Brian Michaud, William Smith

D-U-N-S 13-121-9198
GULF COAST TEACHING FAMILY SERVICES INC
2400 Edenborn Ave Ste 299, Metairie, LA 70001-1817
Tel (504) 831-6561 *Founded/Ownrshp* 1983
Sales 23.9MM *EMP* 1,150
Accts Bernard & Franks Corp Of Cp
SIC 8322 Social service center
CEO: Rick Hardie

D-U-N-S 00-809-0953 IMP
GULF COPPER & MANUFACTURING CORP
5700 Procter Ext, Port Arthur, TX 77642-0936
Tel (409) 989-0300 *Founded/Ownrshp* 1979
Sales 112.2MM[E] *EMP* 185
SIC 3731 3599 3312 3732 3498 3441 Commercial cargo ships, building & repairing; Machine shop, jobbing & repair; Blast furnaces & steel mills; Boat building & repairing; Fabricated pipe & fittings; Fabricated structural metal
Pr: Steve Hale
**Treas:* Patricia S Guillory
Treas: Pat Guilry
**VP:* Richard Vernon
Genl Mgr: Ernesto Alvarez
Genl Mgr: Carl Trent
IT Man: Jarrod Hooker
Opers Mgr: Charles Cooper
Opers Mgr: Donald Wittwer
Sales Exec: Steve Haskew
Snr Mgr: Matt Agee

GULF EAGLE SUPPLY
See GULFSIDE SUPPLY INC

GULF FIELD SERVICES
See GULF INTERSTATE ENGINEERING CO

D-U-N-S 07-262-2459
GULF HEALTH HOSPITALS INC
THOMAS HOSPITAL
(*Suby of* INFIRMARY HEALTH SYSTEM INC) ★
750 Morphy Ave, Fairhope, AL 36532-1812
Tel (251) 928-2375 *Founded/Ownrshp* 1985
Sales 11.8MM[E] *EMP* 1,200
SIC 8062 8011 General medical & surgical hospitals; Offices & clinics of medical doctors
Chf Path: Lloyd L Gardner
Chf OB: Angela R McCool
Chf Rad: Michael J Quinn
**CFO:* Patrick Murphy
Treas: Charles Earle Jr
VP: Harry Brislin
VP: Carl Craddock
VP: Doug Garner
VP: Michael L McBrearty
VP: Eddy Stephens
Dir Inf Cn: Patti Thames
Dir Lab: Art Goodson
Dir Rad: Kathy Linam

D-U-N-S 07-916-2073
GULF HEALTH HOSPITALS INC
NORTH BALDWIN INFIRMARY
1815 Hand Ave, Bay Minette, AL 36507-4110
Tel (251) 937-5521 *Founded/Ownrshp* 2013
Sales 27.0MM *EMP* 1,180
SIC 8062 General medical & surgical hospitals
CEO: Mark Nix
Dir Vol: Dorothy White
**Pr:* Ben Hansert

D-U-N-S 62-420-3824
GULF INTERNATIONAL CORP
(*Suby of* G.I. INTERNATIONAL HOLDING AMSTERDAM B.V.)
16010 Barkers Point Ln, Houston, TX 77079-4024
Tel (713) 850-3400 *Founded/Ownrshp* 1989
Sales 226.6MM[E] *EMP* 1,100
SIC 8711 Consulting engineer
**CEO:* Doug Evans
**CFO:* John Thomas
**Treas:* N R Kurtis
**Sr VP:* Rick Barnard
**Sr VP:* Criss Shipman
**Sr VP:* Bob Sprick
**VP:* David Buza

D-U-N-S 00-485-2877 EXP
GULF INTERSTATE ENGINEERING CO
GULF FIELD SERVICES
(*Suby of* GULF INTERNATIONAL CORP) ★
16010 Barkers Point Ln # 600, Houston, TX 77079-9000
Tel (713) 850-3400 *Founded/Ownrshp* 1953
Sales 124.6MM[E] *EMP* 350
SIC 8711 Petroleum, mining & chemical engineers; Consulting engineer
CEO: H Doug Evans
Pr: Bob Sprick
CFO: John D Thomas
VP: Rick Barnard
Ex Dir: Daniel Casaccia
Ql Cn Mgr: Joseph Bohinsky
Ql Cn Mgr: Joshua Brannon

D-U-N-S 13-924-0618 IMP
▲ GULF ISLAND FABRICATION INC
16225 Park Ten Pl Ste 280, Houston, TX 77084-5154
Tel (713) 714-6100 *Founded/Ownrshp* 1985
Sales 306.1MM *EMP* 1,635
Tkr Sym GIFI *Exch* NGS
SIC 3441 1389 Fabricated structural metal; Construction, repair & dismantling services; Oil field services
Pr: Kirk J Meche
**Ch Bd:* John P Laborde
COO: Todd F Ladd
Board of Directors: Murry W Burns, William E Chiles, Gregory J Cotter, Jerry D Dumas Sr, Michael A Flick, Christopher M Harding, Michael J Keeffe

D-U-N-S 14-703-7154 IMP/EXP
GULF OIL LIMITED PARTNERSHIP
GREAT ISLAND ENERGY
(*Suby of* CHELSEA PETROLEUM PRODUCTS HOLDINGS LLC) ★
80 William St Ste 400, Wellesley Hills, MA 02481-3705
Tel (339) 933-7200 *Founded/Ownrshp* 2015
Sales 736.4MM[E] *EMP* 334
SIC 5171 5172 Petroleum bulk stations & terminals; Fuel oil; Gasoline
Pr: Jerry Ashcroft
CFO: Mike Campbell
Chf Cred: Todd O'Malley
Sr VP: Walter Brickowski
Sr VP: Richard G Dery
VP: Stephanie Caldwell
VP: Michael Capparell
VP: George Christiana
VP: Eileen Farrell
VP: Cora Gangware
VP: Lawrence Kennedy
VP: Raymond Leather
VP: Maxine Mannino
VP: Geraldine Otto
VP: Mike Studley
VP: Colleen Taylor

D-U-N-S 02-690-8009 IMP/EXP
GULF PACIFIC INC
GULF PACIFIC RICE
12010 Taylor Rd, Houston, TX 77041-1239
Tel (713) 464-0606 *Founded/Ownrshp* 1994
Sales 91.8MM[E] *EMP* 89
SIC 5153 0723 Rice, unpolished; Rice drying services
CEO: Christian Brenckmann
**Pr:* Friedrich Brenckmann
**CFO:* Patrick J Casserly
**VP:* Roger Gilmore

GULF PACIFIC RICE
See GULF PACIFIC INC

D-U-N-S 00-692-3429
■ GULF POWER CO (FL)
(*Suby of* SOUTHERN CO) ★
1 Energy Pl, Pensacola, FL 32520-0001
Tel (850) 444-6111 *Founded/Ownrshp* 1925
Sales 1.4MMM *EMP* 1,391[E]
Accts Deloitte & Touche Llp Atlanta
SIC 4911 Generation, electric power; Transmission, electric power; Distribution, electric power;
Pr: S W Connally Jr
CFO: Xia Liu
Ofcr: Michael L Burroughs
VP: Bentina C Terry
Mktg Mgr: Keith Swilley
Board of Directors: Allan G Bense, Deborah H Calder, William C Cramer Jr, Julian B Macqueen, J Mort O'sullivan III, Michael T Rehwinkel, Winston E Scott

GULF SHORES DIALYSIS CENTER
See RENAL TREATMENT CENTERS-SOUTHEAST LP

D-U-N-S 03-266-1126 IMP
■ GULF SOUTH MEDICAL SUPPLY INC
(Suby of PHYSICIAN SALES & SERVICE) ★
4345 Sthpint Blvd Ste 100, Jacksonville, FL 32216
Tel (904) 332-3000 Founded/Ownrshp 1998
Sales 255.1MM^E EMP 942
SIC 5047 Medical equipment & supplies; Surgical equipment & supplies; Incontinent care products & supplies; Instruments, surgical & medical
Pr: Gary J Nutter
*VP: David Bronson
VP: Billy R Clemons
*VP: Joshua Derienzis
VP: Mark Haskins
VP: Brian Johnson
*VP: David Klarner
VP: John Piper Jr
VP: Kevin Seramur
*Prin: Gary Corless
Ex Dir: Eric Lambert

D-U-N-S 07-844-4247 IMP
■ GULF SOUTH PIPELINE CO LP
(Suby of BOARDWALK PIPELINES LP) ★
9 Greenway Plz Ste 2800, Houston, TX 77046-0926
Tel (888) 315-5005 Founded/Ownrshp 1930
Sales 467.3MM EMP 260
Accts Deloitte & Touche Llp Houston
SIC 4923 Gas transmission & distribution
Pr: Stan Horton
Sr VP: John Boone
VP: Kerry Comeaux
VP: John Early
VP: Stacy Franz
Comm Dir: Liz Johnson
Sfty Dirs: Earl Lawson
Snr Mgr: Garry Dick

D-U-N-S 06-789-6324
GULF STATES FINANCIAL SERVICES INC
SERVCO LIFE INSURANCE CO
1375 Enclave Pkwy, Houston, TX 77077-2026
Tel (713) 580-3000 Founded/Ownrshp 1982
Sales NA EMP 300
SIC 6411 Advisory services, insurance
Pr: Stephen Amos
VP: Robert Hehr
*VP: F R Mason
Dist Mgr: Scott Ray

D-U-N-S 12-874-5663
GULF STATES INC
G S I
(Suby of TIC - THE INDUSTRIAL COMPANY)
6711 E Highway 332, Freeport, TX 77541-3016
Tel (979) 233-4461 Founded/Ownrshp 2003
Sales 161.8MM^E EMP 1,600
SIC 1541 1629 Industrial buildings & warehouses; Power plant construction
CEO: Gary B McKenzie
*Pr: Richard Stoffel
*VP: James B Heath

D-U-N-S 04-890-6713
GULF STATES TOYOTA INC (TX)
(Suby of AUTODIRECT SOLUTIONS) ★
1375 Enclave Pkwy, Houston, TX 77077-2026
Tel (713) 580-3300 Founded/Ownrshp 1969
Sales 364.4MM^E EMP 1,200
SIC 5012 5013 Automotive brokers; Trucks, commercial; Automotive supplies & parts
Ch Bd: Thomas H Friedkin
*Pr: Toby N Hynes
CFO: Ed Dickinson
Ofcr: Scott Cordes
Ofcr: Bruce Stricklin
Sr VP: J C Faafino
VP: J C Sassino
*Prin: Jerry H Pyle
VP Admn: David Copeland
Telecom Ex: Wesley Wieder
CIO: Natty Gur

D-U-N-S 10-234-6764 IMP/EXP
GULF STREAM COACH INC
YELLOWSTONE RV
503 S Oakland Ave, Nappanee, IN 46550-2328
Tel (574) 773-7761 Founded/Ownrshp 1983
Sales 175.2MM^E EMP 1,200
SIC 3716 3792 3714 2451 Motor homes; Recreational van conversion (self-propelled), factory basis; Travel trailers & campers; House trailers, except as permanent dwellings; Motor vehicle parts & accessories; Mobile homes
Pr: Dan Shea
*Ch Bd: James F Shea Jr
*Pr: Brian Shea
Ex VP: Philip Sarvari
*Ex VP: Phil Savari
VP: Edward Ludwick
IT Man: Kim Miller
Sfty Mgr: Simon Timmons
Plnt Mgr: Bob Reyes
Mktg Dir: Paul Campbell
Manager: Kenny Jones
Board of Directors: Kelly Foreman

D-U-N-S 94-869-6679 IMP
GULF WINDS INTERNATIONAL INC
411 Brisbane St, Houston, TX 77061-5003
Tel (713) 747-4909 Founded/Ownrshp 1996
Sales 116.8MM EMP 71
SIC 4225 4731 General warehousing; Freight transportation arrangement
*Pr: Todd Stewart
VP: Arthur Flanagan
*VP: Ron Messner
*VP: Buddy Sexton
*VP: BJ Tarver
Exec: Veronica Pous
Sfty Mgr: Amy Ferguson
Sls Mgr: Jared Couvillon
Sls Mgr: John Scheschuk
Snr Mgr: Heather Overby

D-U-N-S 61-505-6884
■ GULFMARK ENERGY INC
(Suby of ADAMS RESOURCES & ENERGY INC) ★
17 S Briar Hollow Ln # 100, Houston, TX 77027-3155
Tel (210) 524-9725 Founded/Ownrshp 1992
Sales 618.3MM^E EMP 165
SIC 5172 Crude oil
Pr: Geoff Griffith
CFO: Richard Abshire
*Treas: Richard B Abshire
VP: Mark Thibaut

D-U-N-S 04-056-5439
▲ GULFMARK OFFSHORE INC
842 W Sam Houston Pkwy N, Houston, TX 77024-4591
Tel (713) 963-9522 Founded/Ownrshp 1996
Sales 274.8MM EMP 1,100^E
Tkr Sym GLF Exch NYS
SIC 4412 Deep sea foreign transportation of freight
Pr: Quintin V Kneen
*Ch Bd: David J Butters
CFO: James M Mitchell
Sr VP: David E Darling
Sr VP: Samuel R Rubio
Area Mgr: Mario Madalena
Board of Directors: Peter I Bijur, Brian R Ford, Sheldon S Gordon, Steven W Kohlhagen, William C Martin, Rex C Ross, Charles K Valutas

D-U-N-S 00-485-0660
▲ GULFPORT ENERGY CORP
14313 N May Ave Ste 100, Oklahoma City, OK 73134-5003
Tel (405) 848-8807 Founded/Ownrshp 1997
Sales 709.4MM EMP 230^E
Accts Grant Thornton Llp Oklahoma C
Tkr Sym GPOR Exch NGS
SIC 1311 Crude petroleum & natural gas production
Pr: Michael G Moore
*Ch Bd: David L Houston
COO: J Ross Kirtley
CFO: Aaron Gaydosik
VP: Steve R Baldwin
VP: Stuart A Maier
Mng Dir: Ty Peck
Trfc Dir: Kimberly Fowler
Mktg Dir: Dan Haynes
Board of Directors: Donald Dillingham, Craig Groeschel, C Doug Johnson, Ben T Morris, Scott E Streller

D-U-N-S 36-101-4082
GULFPORT MEMORIAL HOSPITAL EMR
4500 13th St, Gulfport, MS 39501-2515
Tel (228) 867-4000 Founded/Ownrshp 2005
Sales 45.0MM^E EMP 2,400
SIC 8062 General medical & surgical hospitals
Pr: Gary Marchand
Trst: Oney Raines

D-U-N-S 06-596-2024
GULFSIDE CASINO PARTNERSHIP DBA
WINDANCE COUNTRY CLUB
3300 W Beach Blvd, Gulfport, MS 39501-1800
Tel (228) 832-5374 Founded/Ownrshp 2006
Sales 28.5MM^E EMP 1,200
SIC 7011 Casino hotel
Genl Pt: Joel R Carter Sr
Pt: Terry Green

D-U-N-S 06-279-5893 IMP/EXP
GULFSIDE SUPPLY INC
GULF EAGLE SUPPLY
2900 E 7th Ave Ste 200, Tampa, FL 33605-4200
Tel (813) 636-9808 Founded/Ownrshp 1973
Sales 622.0MM^E EMP 850
SIC 5033 Roofing, asphalt & sheet metal
CEO: James S Resch
*Pr: Bradley James Resch
*Sec: Molly A Resch
*VP: Jill Buehler
VP: Peter Nazaretian
*VP: Stephanie Resch
Rgnl Mgr: Greg Stealey
Brnch Mgr: Corey Bryan
Brnch Mgr: Kevin Clinge
Brnch Mgr: Kelly Joyce
Brnch Mgr: Scott Peterson
Board of Directors: Jill M Buhler, Stephanie Resch, Stephanie A Rich

D-U-N-S 61-179-2912 IMP
■ GULFSTREAM AEROSPACE CORP
(Suby of GENERAL DYNAMICS CORP) ★
500 Gulfstream Rd, Savannah, GA 31408-9643
Tel (912) 965-3000 Founded/Ownrshp 2001
Sales 3.0MMM^E EMP 8,068
SIC 3721 4581 Aircraft; Aircraft maintenance & repair services
Pr: Larry R Flynn
*Pr: Larry Flynn
*CFO: Dan Clare
CFO: Dan Clear
CFO: Joseph Hartman
CFO: Michael McConnell
*Chf Mktg O: Jeannine Haas
*Ex VP: Joe Lombardo
*Sr VP: Jason Aiken
*Sr VP: Ira Berman
Sr VP: Leda Chong
*Sr VP: Dan Nale
Sr VP: Helen Roche
*Sr VP: Dennis Stuligross
VP: Mike Baker
VP: Steve Belko
VP: Stan Dixon
VP: McDonnell Douglas
VP: Richard Emery
*VP: Preston Henne
VP: Peter Jacobi

D-U-N-S 08-893-5366
■ GULFSTREAM AEROSPACE CORP (GEORGIA)
(Suby of GULFSTREAM DELAWARE CORP) ★
500 Gulfstream Rd, Savannah, GA 31408-9643
Tel (912) 965-3000 Founded/Ownrshp 1990
Sales 1.4MMM^E EMP 6,800
SIC 3721 Airplanes, fixed or rotary wing
CEO: Larry R Flynn
*CFO: Jason W Aiken
*Treas: Bill Skinner
Ex VP: Joseph T Lombardo
Sr VP: Ira Berman
*Sr VP: Preston Henne
Sr VP: Scott Neal
Sr VP: Buddy Sams
VP: Mark Burns
VP: Steve Cass
VP: Kurt Erbacher
VP: Chris Hendley
VP: Vincent J Hrenak
VP: Daniel D Nale
*VP: Mike West
Exec: Kelvin Mason
Dir Soc: Sissy Dixon

D-U-N-S 02-399-1755
■ GULFSTREAM DELAWARE CORP
(Suby of GULFSTREAM AEROSPACE CORP) ★
500 Gulfstream Rd, Savannah, GA 31408-9643
Tel (912) 965-3000 Founded/Ownrshp 1990
Sales 1.5MMM^E EMP 7,077^E
SIC 3721 5088 Aircraft; Aircraft & space vehicle supplies & parts; Aircraft & parts; Aircraft equipment & supplies
Pr: Larry Flynn
Pr: Richard Johnson
Ofcr: Tom Huff
*Sr VP: Jason Aiken
VP: Dick Johnson
*VP: Joe Lombardo
Prgrm Mgr: James Kelley
Board of Directors: Brad Kraft

D-U-N-S 07-698-5928
GULFSTREAM GOODWILL INDUSTRIES INC
1715 E Tiffany Dr, West Palm Beach, FL 33407-3224
Tel (561) 848-7200 Founded/Ownrshp 1966
Sales 46.6MM EMP 1,000
Accts Holyfield & Thomas Llc West P
SIC 8399 Fund raising organization, non-fee basis
Ch Bd: Ronald F Albano
*V Ch: Anthony Jordan
*CFO: Sherry Steff
Bd of Dir: Carl Nicola
VP: Brian Edwards
Dist Mgr: Delores Rannie
CTO: Iva Grady
IT Man: Karen Novak
Netwrk Eng: Jerome Robinson
VP Mktg: Cal Miller
Sls Mgr: Thomas Murphy

D-U-N-S 10-719-2122 IMP/EXP
GULFSTREAM SERVICES INC
GSI
103 Dickson Rd, Houma, LA 70363-7306
Tel (985) 868-0303 Founded/Ownrshp 1978
Sales 127.0MM^E EMP 140
SIC 1382 7359 Oil & gas exploration services; Equipment rental & leasing
Prin: Robert Bond Jr
*Sec: Gina Mir
*Sec: Regina Mire
VP: Mark Chauvin

GULLO TOYOTA CONROE
See TONY GULLO MOTORS I LP

D-U-N-S 78-664-3395
GUMBYS PIZZA SYSTEMS INC
3911 W Newberry Rd Ste C, Gainesville, FL 32607-2354
Tel (352) 338-7775 Founded/Ownrshp 1985
Sales 15.0MM EMP 1,300
SIC 5812 Pizzeria, chain
Pr: Jeff O'Brian
COO: Joe Obrien

GUNDAKER REALTORS BETTER HOMES
See COLDWELL BANKER GUNDAKER REAL ESTATE SCHOOL

D-U-N-S 14-816-7414 IMP
GUNDER & ASSOCIATES INC
1215 W Crosby Rd Ste 206, Carrollton, TX 75006-6920
Tel (972) 620-2801 Founded/Ownrshp 1980
Sales 85.0MM EMP 19
SIC 5075 Air conditioning equipment, except room units; Warm air heating equipment & supplies
Pr: Marshall S Gunder
VP: Pat Gunder
Manager: Robert Gunder
Sls Mgr: Charles Moates
Sales Asso: Bryan Moates

D-U-N-S 07-762-9830
GUNDERSEN CLINIC LTD
GUNDERSEN HEALTH SYSTEM
(Suby of GUNDERSON LUTHERAN MEDICAL CEN) ★
1836 South Ave, La Crosse, WI 54601-5494
Tel (608) 782-7300 Founded/Ownrshp 2010
Sales 184.9MM EMP 4,500
Accts Kpmg Llp Minneapolis Mn
SIC 8011 Clinic, operated by physicians
CEO: Jeffrey E Thompson
*VP: Julio Bird MD
VP: Jan Dehaan
Doctor: Karl Borge

GUNDERSEN HEALTH SYSTEM
See GUNDERSEN CLINIC LTD

D-U-N-S 13-746-4124
GUNDERSEN LUTHERAN ADMINISTRATIVE SERVICES INC
(Suby of GUNDERSON LUTHERAN MEDICAL CEN) ★
1900 South Ave, La Crosse, WI 54601-5467
Tel (608) 782-7300 Founded/Ownrshp 2010
Sales 652.4MM EMP 6,000
Accts Kpmg Llp Omaha Ne
SIC 8621 Health association
CEO: Jeff Thompson
*Treas: Wendy Lommen
*VP: Gregory Prairie
*VP: Wendy Williams
Genl Mgr: Liz Larsen
Prd Dir: Elaine Elliott

D-U-N-S 83-015-1739
GUNDERSEN LUTHERAN HEALTH SYSTEM INC
GUNDERSON LUTHERAN MEDICAL CEN
1900 South Ave, La Crosse, WI 54601-5467
Tel (608) 782-7300 Founded/Ownrshp 1996
Sales 980.6MM EMP 6,000^E
SIC 8062 General medical & surgical hospitals
CEO: Jeffrey E Thompson
Pr: Daniel J Lilly
CFO: Michael Allen
Ofcr: Kari Adank
Ex VP: Julio Bird
Sr VP: Jerry Arndt
Sr VP: Mark Platt
VP: Kelly Barton
VP: Jan Dehaan
VP: Bryan Erdmann
VP: Sigurd Gudersen
VP: Sigurd Gundersen
VP: Deb Rislow
Exec: Kevin Josephson

D-U-N-S 07-179-3673
GUNDERSEN LUTHERAN MEDICAL CENTER INC
LUTHERAN HOSPITAL - LA CROSSE
(Suby of GUNDERSON LUTHERAN MEDICAL CEN) ★
1900 South Ave, La Crosse, WI 54601-5467
Tel (608) 782-7300 Founded/Ownrshp 1902
Sales 894.1MM EMP 4,500
Accts Kpmg Llp Minneapolis Mn
SIC 8062 5912 General medical & surgical hospitals; Drug stores & proprietary stores
COO: Claudia Caine
CFO: Daryl Applebury
Ofcr: Mary Jafari
Ofcr: Jean Krause
Ofcr: Mary Ellen McCartney
Ex VP: Julio J Bird
Ex VP: Julio Bird
VP: Michael J Dolan
VP: Mary Gerke
VP: Sigurd B Gundersen
VP: Mary Jo Klos

GUNDERSON CLINIC
See GUNDERSON LUTHERAN INC

D-U-N-S 13-197-4057 IMP/EXP
■ GUNDERSON LLC
GBRX
(Suby of GREENBRIER COMPANIES INC) ★
4350 Nw Front Ave, Portland, OR 97210-1499
Tel (503) 972-5700 Founded/Ownrshp 1919
Sales 541.7MM^E EMP 1,300
SIC 3743 Railroad equipment; Railroad car rebuilding
Ch Bd: William A Furma
CEO: William A Furman
Genl Mgr: Mark Eitzen
Off Mgr: Tita Lin

D-U-N-S 15-326-9386
GUNDERSON LUTHERAN INC
GUNDERSON CLINIC
1836 South Ave, La Crosse, WI 54601-5429
Tel (608) 782-7300 Founded/Ownrshp 1996
Sales 11.6MM EMP 5,000
SIC 8011 Pulmonary specialist, physician/surgeon
CEO: Jeffrey E Thompson
*CFO: Michael Allen
Treas: Barb Mussman
Bd of Dir: Peg Myhre
*Ex VP: Julio Bird
*Sr VP: Kathy Klock
*Sr VP: Mark Platt
VP: Cathy Fischer
VP: Sigurd B Gundersen
VP: Scott Rathgaber
Adm Dir: Nada Ghandour

GUNDERSON LUTHERAN MEDICAL CEN
See GUNDERSEN LUTHERAN HEALTH SYSTEM INC

D-U-N-S 19-167-9393 IMP
■ GUNDERSON RAIL SERVICES LLC
YSD INDUSTRIES
(Suby of GREENBRIER COMPANIES INC) ★
1 Centerpointe Dr Ste 200, Lake Oswego, OR 97035-8612
Tel (503) 684-7000 Founded/Ownrshp 1993
Sales 301.9MM^E EMP 1,200
SIC 3743 Railroad car rebuilding
CEO: Bill Furman
*Pr: William Glenn

D-U-N-S 18-013-4355 IMP
GUNITE CORP
(Suby of TRUCK COMPONENTS INC) ★
302 Peoples Ave, Rockford, IL 61104-7092
Tel (815) 964-3301 Founded/Ownrshp 2000
Sales 306.3MM^E EMP 1,010
SIC 3714 Motor vehicle brake systems & parts; Brake drums, motor vehicle; Wheels, motor vehicle
Pr: Richard Dauch
*CEO: James Cirar
*CFO: Jeff Elmer
*VP: Omar Fakhoury
Software D: Kelly Bodway
*VP Sls: Thomas Splinter

GUNK
See RADIATOR SPECIALTY CO INC

D-U-N-S 19-993-6550 IMP
■ GUNLOCKE CO L L C
(Suby of HNI CORP) ★
1 Gunlocke Dr, Wayland, NY 14572-9515
Tel (585) 728-5111 Founded/Ownrshp 1902
Sales 131.6MM^E EMP 800^E
SIC 2521 Wood office furniture
Treas: Clarence L Burkey

VP: Timothy Costello
Genl Mgr: Diane Deleo
Mfg Dir: Michael Moffett

GUNN AUTOMOTIVE GROUP
See CURTIS C GUNN INC

D-U-N-S 18-745-9185
GUNNALLEN FINANCIAL INC
5002 W Waters Ave, Tampa, FL 33634-1313
Tel (800) 713-4046 *Founded/Ownrshp* 1986
Sales 129.1MM^E *EMP* 1,137
SIC 6211 Security brokers & dealers
CEO: Frederick O Kraus
Pr: Robert Alvarez
**Pr:* Donald Gunn
**CEO:* Richard Frueh
**COO:* Christopher Frankel
CFO: Declan Obeirne
**Chf Cred:* Andrew Butte
Sr VP: Kevin Daniels
Sr VP: James Dicesaro
VP: Frank S Dicicco
VP: Daclan O'Beirne
VP: David Ruhling

D-U-N-S 00-445-1183
GUNTON CORP
PELLA WINDOW & DOOR
26150 Richmond Rd, Cleveland, OH 44146-1438
Tel (216) 831-2420 *Founded/Ownrshp* 1954
Sales 100.2MM^E *EMP* 380
SIC 5031 Windows; Doors; Metal doors, sash & trim
Co-Ch Bd: Robert J Gunton
**Pr:* Mark Mead
COO: Bob Gunton
**Co-Ch Bd:* William E Gunton
**Treas:* Reggie Stacy
IT Man: Robert Wanamaker
Mktg Mgr: Rick Balabon
Sales Asso: Scott Berger

D-U-N-S 19-505-5785 IMP
GUNZE ELECTRONICS USA CORP
ELTECH
(*Suby of* GUNZE LIMITED)
2113 Wells Branch Pkwy # 54, Austin, TX 78728-6970
Tel (512) 990-3400 *Founded/Ownrshp* 2007
Sales 228.8MM^E *EMP* 8,000
SIC 3577 Computer peripheral equipment
Pr: Hisakazu Hiriawa
IT Man: Michael Merritt
Sales Exec: Dennis Lind
Sls Mgr: Marshall Jackson

D-U-N-S 00-555-3334
GURTZ ELECTRIC CO
GURTZ TECHNICAL SERVICES
77 W Seegers Rd, Arlington Heights, IL 60005-3916
Tel (847) 734-2400 *Founded/Ownrshp* 1958
Sales 83.5MM^E *EMP* 300
SIC 1731 Fiber optic cable installation; Voice, data & video wiring contractor; General electrical contractor
CEO: Frank Gurtz
**COO:* Paul Laskowske
**CFO:* Thomas Maimonis
Ex VP: Bohdan Gnyra
**Ex VP:* Pat Thornton
Sfty Mgr: Luis Hernandez
Snr PM: Marek Bogdanowicz
Snr PM: Brian Karlow
Snr PM: Christopher Ott

GURTZ TECHNICAL SERVICES
See GURTZ ELECTRIC CO

D-U-N-S 12-820-2798 IMP
GURU DENIM INC
TRUE RELIGION BRAND JEANS
(*Suby of* TRUE RELIGION BRAND JEANS) ★
1888 Rosecrans Ave # 1000, Manhattan Beach, CA 90266-3712
Tel (323) 266-3072 *Founded/Ownrshp* 2002
Sales 345.8MM^E *EMP* 809
SIC 5137 5611 Women's & children's clothing; Clothing accessories: men's & boys'
CEO: John Ermatinger
**CFO:* Eric Bauer
Bd of Dir: Marcello Bottoli
**Genl Couns:* Ilene Eskenazi

GURWIN JEWISH NURSING AND REHA
See ROSALIND AND JOSEPH GURWIN JEWISH GERIATRIC CENTER OF LONG ISLAND INC

D-U-N-S 00-177-8232
GUSTAVE A LARSON CO (WI)
JOHNSON CONTROLS
W233n2869 Roundy Cir W, Pewaukee, WI 53072-6285
Tel (262) 542-0200 *Founded/Ownrshp* 1936
Sales 210.0MM *EMP* 425
SIC 5075 5078 5084 5046

D-U-N-S 00-622-1808 IMP
GUSTAVUS ADOLPHUS COLLEGE
800 W College Ave, Saint Peter, MN 56082-1498
Tel (507) 933-7508 *Founded/Ownrshp* 1862
Sales 140.6MM *EMP* 700
SIC 8221 College, except junior
Pr: Rebecca Bergman
Pr: Barb Taylor
**Treas:* Ken Westpha
Ofcr: Sean Easton
VP: Eric Dugdale
VP: Tim Kennedy
VP: Brenda Moore
VP: Jones Vanhecke
VP: Kenneth Westphal
VP: Tom Young
Exec: Kirk Beyer
Exec: Paul F Tillquist
Creative D: Brian Konkol

GUSTO PACKING COMPANY
See BUTTERBALL LLC

D-U-N-S 62-387-5890
GUTHRIE & HUEBNER CO INC
5797 Dietrich Rd, San Antonio, TX 78219-3599
Tel (210) 661-4251 *Founded/Ownrshp* 2003
Sales 473.7MM *EMP* 2,500
Accts Rinaldo J Gonzalez Pc San An
SIC 1541 1629 1542 Industrial buildings, new construction; Mine loading & discharging station construction; Commercial & office building, new construction
Pr: Arthur D Huebner
**COO:* Timothy J Henning
CFO: Nita B Mc Bride
Board of Directors: Jack F Farris Chairman, Timothy S Geppert, Bruce A Jeffrey, Richard D Swartout, Robert L Urban

D-U-N-S 07-944-8475
GUTHRIE CLINIC
1 Guthrie Sq Ste B, Sayre, PA 18840-1699
Tel (570) 888-5858 *Founded/Ownrshp* 2000
Sales 700.1MM^E *EMP* 4,500^E
SIC 8011 8062 8082 Offices & clinics of medical doctors; Group health association; Health maintenance organization; Primary care medical clinic; General medical & surgical hospitals; Home health care services
Pr: Joseph Scopelliti MD
**Pr:* Francis Belardi MD Faafp
CEO: Donald Skerpon
**COO:* Staci Thompson Mha Cmpe
**COO:* Paul Vervalin MBA Facmpe
**CFO:* Richard I Bennett CPA
**Ex VP:* Paul Chacona
**Ex VP:* Marie T Droege Mha Fache
**Ex VP:* Frank Pinkosky
**Ex VP:* Michael Scalzone MD Mhcm Facog
VP: Bonnie Onofre

GUTHRIE ENTERPRISES
See TWIN TIER MANAGEMENT CORP

D-U-N-S 07-528-7599
GUTHRIE HEALTHCARE SYSTEM
GUTHRIE ROBERT PACKER HOSPITAL
1 Guthrie Sq Ste B, Sayre, PA 18840-1625
Tel (570) 888-6666 *Founded/Ownrshp* 1982
Sales NA *EMP* 2,575
SIC 8011 7352 8741

D-U-N-S 06-959-8274
GUTHRIE MEDICAL GROUP PC
(*Suby of* GUTHRIE CLINIC) ★
1 Guthrie Sq Ste B, Sayre, PA 18840-1625
Tel (570) 888-5858 *Founded/Ownrshp* 1910
Sales 228.2MM *EMP* 4,500
Accts Pricewaterhousecoopers Llp Ph
SIC 8011 Group health association
Pr: Joseph A Scopelliti
**COO:* Paul Chacona
**Ex VP:* Frank Pinkosky
**Ex VP:* Richard I Bennett
**Ex VP:* Michael Scalzone
**Ex VP:* Paul G Vervalin
VP: Minhphuong Dang
VP: Barb Pennypacker
VP: Nate Shinagawa
VP: Lynne Yaeger
Dir Risk M: Lynn Noone
Dir Rx: Jan Scott

GUTHRIE ROBERT PACKER HOSPITAL
See GUTHRIE HEALTHCARE SYSTEM

D-U-N-S 80-577-6783
GUTHY-RENKER FULFILLMENT SERVICES LLC
1845 Brevard Rd, Arden, NC 28704-9145
Tel (828) 684-4300 *Founded/Ownrshp* 2007
Sales 89.9MM^E *EMP* 600
SIC 7389 7374

D-U-N-S 60-831-5453 IMP/EXP
GUTHY-RENKER LLC
PROACTIV
100 N Sepulveda Blvd # 1600, El Segundo, CA 90245-5654
Tel (760) 773-9022 *Founded/Ownrshp* 1988
Sales 326.1MM^E *EMP* 155
SIC 5099 7812 5999 7389 Tapes & cassettes, prerecorded; Commercials, television: tape or film; Cosmetics; Telemarketing services
Pr: Greg Renker
Ex VP: Dirk Bunt
Ex VP: Kevin Knee
VP: Karen Barner
VP: Jeff Engler
**VP:* Bill Guthy
VP: Richard Herzog
VP: Margo Lane
VP: Doo Lee
VP: Kimber L Maderazzo
VP: Keith Manning
Board of Directors: Richard Woolsey

D-U-N-S 00-893-5009
GUTTMAN ENERGY INC
200 Speers Rd, Belle Vernon, PA 15012-1017
Tel (724) 489-5199 *Founded/Ownrshp* 1950
Sales 102.2MM^E *EMP* 280
SIC 8731 5172 Energy research; Lubricating oils & greases
CEO: Alan R Guttman
**Pr:* James L Guttman
**Pr:* Richard Guttman
**COO:* Scott Cargile
**Ex VP:* Raymond D Horsmon
Ex VP: Gary Smelko
Exec: Paul Schreck
QA Dir: Lindsay Farrell
Sls Mgr: George Rodgers
Sales Asso: Jodi Phillippi

D-U-N-S 03-299-1460
GUY BROWN MANAGEMENT LLC (TN)
320 Seven Springs Way # 450, Brentwood, TN 37027-4537
Tel (615) 777-1500 *Founded/Ownrshp* 1997
Sales 251.0MM *EMP* 82
SIC 5112 Office supplies
CEO: Maria Teresa Vasquez
CFO: Jay Chawan
Sr VP: Steve Creed
VP: Jack McGuire
VP: Tera Vazquez
VP: CAM Willis
Sls Dir: Cynthia Ryan

D-U-N-S 07-100-6191
■ **GUY CARPENTER & CO LLC**
(*Suby of* MARSH & MCLENNAN COMPANIES INC) ★
1166 Ave Of The Americas, New York, NY 10036-2708
Tel (917) 937-3000 *Founded/Ownrshp* 1919
Sales NA *EMP* 2,000
SIC 6411 8742 8732 Insurance information & consulting services; Financial consultant; Market analysis, business & economic research
Pr: Alex Moczarski
**Ch Bd:* Britt Newhouse
**CEO:* Andrew Marcell
CEO: Chris McKeown
**CEO:* Alex Moczarski
CFO: Eunice Adler
CFO: Ajay Junarkar
CFO: Elizabeth A Keys
**CFO:* Robert Pietrucha
Ofcr: Iain Boyer
Ofcr: Charles Higham
Ofcr: Catherine Sacks
Ex VP: Brian Johnston
Ex VP: Michael D Schnur
Ex VP: Kevin Stokes
Sr VP: Carlos Abrantes
**Sr VP:* Eric Johnson
Sr VP: Frank Johnson
Sr VP: Andy Justice
Sr VP: Daniel Meyer
**Sr VP:* Scott D Price

D-U-N-S 04-599-8445
GUY F ATKINSON CONSTRUCTION LLC
(*Suby of* CLARK CONSTRUCTION GROUP LLC) ★
350 Indiana St Ste 600, Golden, CO 80401-5098
Tel (303) 985-1660 *Founded/Ownrshp* 1999, 2000
Sales 192.2MM^E *EMP* 600
SIC 1611 Highway & street construction
Pr: John O'Keefe
**CFO:* Jeffrey Roth
VP: Jan Bohn

GUYOUNG TECH
See GU-YOUNG TECH CO LTD

GVEC
See GUADALUPE VALLEY ELECTRIC COOPERATIVE INC

D-U-N-S 14-670-7026
GVH DISTRIBUTION LTD
2601 Se Loop 289 Lubbock, Lubbock, TX 79404
Tel (806) 687-5264 *Founded/Ownrshp* 2003
Sales 85.0MM *EMP* 60
SIC 5199 Packaging materials
Pt: Joe Schmidt
Pt: Buddy Furgerson
Pt: Clay Robinett
VP: Corby Bleckert

D-U-N-S 00-311-2054 IMP
GVW GROUP LLC
GVW HOLDINGS
625 Roger Williams Ave, Highland Park, IL 60035-4807
Tel (847) 681-8417 *Founded/Ownrshp* 2005, 2006
Sales 154.3MM^E *EMP* 406
SIC 3713 Truck bodies (motor vehicles)
Ch: Andrew Taitz
**CFO:* James Maclaughlin
VP: Jim Sicking
Mng Dir: Eric Schwartz
Dir IT: Troy Henikoff
IT Man: Karen Ibele
**Genl Couns:* Jeffrey Leeb
Genl Couns: Joseph Lukas
Corp Couns: Katie Knapp

GVW HOLDINGS
See GVW GROUP LLC

D-U-N-S 14-336-7030
GW CONSULTING INC
GARDAWORLD
(*Suby of* CORPORATION DE SECURITE GARDA WORLD)
1760 Old Madow Rd Ste 400, Mc Lean, VA 22102
Tel (703) 253-8080 *Founded/Ownrshp* 2009
Sales 57.0MM^E *EMP* 2,500^E
SIC 7381 Detective services
CEO: Oliver Westmacott
**Treas:* Deborah Ray
**Sec:* Brent Wegner
**Sr VP:* Peter Dordal Jr

D-U-N-S 00-221-7834 IMP
GW LISK CO INC
2 South St, Clifton Springs, NY 14432-1118
Tel (315) 462-2611 *Founded/Ownrshp* 1953
Sales 150.6MM^E *EMP* 750
SIC 3679 4119 3492

GWALTNEY OF SMITHFIELD
See SMITHFIELD PACKING CO INC

D-U-N-S 18-989-0705
GWFS EQUITIES INC
(*Suby of* GREAT-WEST LIFE & ANNUITY INSURANCE CO) ★
8515 E Orchard Rd, Greenwood Village, CO 80111-5002
Tel (303) 737-3817 *Founded/Ownrshp* 1984
Sales 366.4MM *EMP* 16
Accts Deloitte & Touche Llp Denver
SIC 6211 Brokers, security; Dealers, security
Ch Bd: CP Nelson
Chf Cred: Ba Byrne
Ex VP: Rk Shaw
Sr VP: Ch Cumming
Sr VP: Ws Harmon
Sr VP: Rj Laeyendecker
Sr VP: GE Seller
VP: SA Bendrick
VP: C Bergeon
VP: SA Ghazaleh
VP: Judith G Gibbs
VP: SM Gile
VP: Brent Neese

D-U-N-S 05-727-2734
GWINNETT COUNTY GOVERNMENT
GWINNETT JUSTICE AND ADMINISTR
75 Langley Dr, Lawrenceville, GA 30046-6935
Tel (770) 822-8000 *Founded/Ownrshp* 1818
Sales NA *EMP* 4,000
Accts Mauldin & Jenkins Atlanta Ga
SIC 9111
Dir Risk M: Bill Swiger
Dir IT: James Waicul
IT Man: Diana Payne
Board of Directors: Charles Bannisster, Lorraine Treen-District On, Bert Nasuti-District Two, Mike Beaudreau-District th, Kevin Kenerly-District Fou

D-U-N-S 07-951-6185
GWINNETT COUNTY PUBLIC SCHOOLS
437 Old Peachtree Rd Nw, Suwanee, GA 30024-2978
Tel (678) 301-6000 *Founded/Ownrshp* 2014
Sales 1.9MMM *EMP* 20,000^E
SIC 8211 Public elementary & secondary schools
Bd of Dir: Jeff Robertson
Ex Dir: Jorge Gomez
Ex Dir: Sloan Roach
Dir Sec: Wayne Rikard
MIS Dir: Frank Elmore
IT Man: Mike Laplante
Pr Dir: Laura Nurse
Teacher Pr: Sid Camp
Psych: Jennifer Feinberg
Psych: Cari Pesavento
HC Dir: Kimberly Bennett

D-U-N-S 01-876-8684
GWINNETT HEALTH SYSTEM INC
1000 Medical Center Blvd, Lawrenceville, GA 30046-7694
Tel (678) 312-1000 *Founded/Ownrshp* 1993
Sales 698.8MM^E *EMP* 2,050^E
Accts Draffin & Tucker Llp Albany
SIC 8062 General medical & surgical hospitals
CEO: Philip R Wolfe
**Pr:* Franklin Rinker
**CFO:* Thomas Y McBride
Bd of Dir: Kelly Dunham
Ofcr: Carol Regan
VP: Wallace Brown
Dir Rx: Michael Naughton
Off Admin: Angela Hamlet
MIS Dir: Kevin Aureleo
QA Dir: Ruth T Pugh
IT Man: Emmanuel Ogidigben

D-U-N-S 07-587-7290
GWINNETT HOSPITAL SYSTEM INC
MEDCARE
(*Suby of* GWINNETT HEALTH SYSTEM INC) ★
1000 Medical Center Blvd, Lawrenceville, GA 30046-7694
Tel (678) 343-3428 *Founded/Ownrshp* 1956
Sales 698.7MM *EMP* 2,050
SIC 8062 General medical & surgical hospitals
CEO: Philip R Wolfe
**Pr:* Lea Bay
**Pr:* Jason Chandler
**Pr:* Franklin M Rinker
**COO:* Jay Dennard
**COO:* Thomas Karr
COO: Jeff Nowlin
**CFO:* Thomas Y Mc Bride III
CFO: Tommy McBride III
Ofcr: Karen Walsh
**Ex VP:* Alan Bier
**Sr VP:* Ed Brown
**Sr VP:* Patty Lavely
**VP:* Georgia P Brogdon
VP: Janet Schwalbe
Dir Risk M: Suzanne Compau
Dir Lab: Rhonda Hairston
Dir Lab: Pamela Henderson

GWINNETT JUSTICE AND ADMINISTR
See GWINNETT COUNTY GOVERNMENT

D-U-N-S 14-569-4753
GWL&A FINANCIAL INC
GREAT WEST FINANCIAL
(*Suby of* GREAT-WEST LIFECO US INC) ★
8515 E Orchard Rd, Greenwood Village, CO 80111-5002
Tel (303) 737-3000 *Founded/Ownrshp* 2014
Sales 2.7MMM *EMP* 6,600
SIC 6211 6311 Investment firm, general brokerage; Life insurance
Ch Bd: Robert Gratton
Pr: David Musto
Pr: Charles P Nelson
CEO: Robert L Reynolds
Ex VP: SM Corbett
Ex VP: Robert K Shaw
Sr VP: Miles R Edwards
Sr VP: Ernie P Friesen
Sr VP: RG Schultz
Sr VP: Jh Van Harmelen
VP: Deborah Goebel
VP: Rm Southall

D-U-N-S 06-715-4682
GWP HOLDINGS LLC
WESTERN PETERBILT
3801 Airport Way S, Seattle, WA 98108-5213
Tel (206) 624-7383 *Founded/Ownrshp* 2005
Sales 141.2MM^E *EMP* 300
SIC 5511 7513 7538 5012 Trucks, tractors & trailers: new & used; Truck leasing, without drivers; General automotive repair shops; Automobiles & other motor vehicles
CEO: Frank Anglin
**CFO:* Bill Helenberg

GWU MEDICAL FACULTY ASSOCIATES
See MEDICAL FACULTY ASSOCIATES INC

D-U-N-S 96-324-4871
GXS GROUP INC
(*Suby of* OPEN TEXT CORPORATION)
9711 Washingtonian Blvd, Gaithersburg, MD 20878-7365
Tel (301) 340-4000 *Founded/Ownrshp* 2014
Sales 90.6MM[E] *EMP* 3,000
SIC 7372 Prepackaged software
Pr: Mark J Barrenechea

D-U-N-S 03-530-2503
GXS HOLDINGS INC
100 Edison Park Dr, Gaithersburg, MD 20878-3209
Tel (301) 340-5370 *Founded/Ownrshp* 2010
Sales NA *EMP* 3,000
SIC 6719 Investment holding companies, except banks
CEO: Gary Greenfield
Pr: Michael Schwab
Ex VP: Hamid Mohyi
VP: Daniel Casco
VP: Gary Randolph
VP: George Schulze
Prgrm Mgr: Judy Lyons
Genl Mgr: Diana Howard
Snr Sftwr: Randy Burke
Snr Sftwr: Ray Chu
Snr Sftwr: Joe Dorman

D-U-N-S 92-716-6082
GXS INC
GE GLOBAL EXCHANGE SERVICES
(*Suby of* OPEN TEXT CORPORATION)
9711 Washingtonian Blvd # 5, Gaithersburg, MD 20878-7365
Tel (301) 340-4000 *Founded/Ownrshp* 2014
Sales 274.4MM[E] *EMP* 657[E]
SIC 7374 Data processing & preparation
Pr: Mark J Barrenechea
COO: Tom Thomas
**CFO:* Gregg Clevenger
Chf Mktg O: Robert E Fair
**Ex VP:* Karl Salnoske
Ex VP: Steven Scala
Ex VP: David Swanlaw
Sr VP: Clara Bart
Sr VP: Chris Beall
Sr VP: Jeff McCroskey
VP: Swanlaw David
VP: Larry De'ath
**VP:* David Goldberg
VP: Duncan Robb
VP: Pat Salmonese
VP: Karl D Salnoske
VP: Keifer Steve
VP: Jeff Stewart
VP: Raymond Teh
Exec: Mark Shooman
Dir: Steven Hillon

D-U-N-S 03-885-5029 IMP/EXP
GYMBOREE CORP
(*Suby of* GIRAFFE HOLDING INC) ★
500 Howard St Fl 2, San Francisco, CA 94105-3027
Tel (415) 278-7000 *Founded/Ownrshp* 1992
Sales 1.2MMM *EMP* 14,716
SIC 5641 Children's & infants' wear stores; Children's wear; Infants' wear
CEO: Mark Breitbard
Pr: Shelly Walsh
COO: Joelle Maher
CFO: Blair Lambert
CFO: Andrew B North
Treas: F Mario Petrocco
Treas: Mario F Petrocco
Sr VP: Kenneth F Meyers
VP: Della Berger
VP: Troy Berry
VP: Joann H Davis
VP: Deborah Nash
VP: Susan Neal
VP: Victor Spina
VP: Laura Wilkin
VP: Laura Willensky
Board of Directors: Joshua Bekenstein, Yvonne Hao, Jordan Hitch, Marko Kivisto, Lewis Klessel

D-U-N-S 19-602-5712
GYPSUM EXPRESS LTD
8280 Sixty Rd, Baldwinsville, NY 13027-1232
Tel (315) 638-2201 *Founded/Ownrshp* 1985
Sales 102.9MM[E] *EMP* 650
SIC 4212 4213 Local trucking, without storage; Trucking, except local
Ch Bd: John Wight
CFO: Janet Gmyr
**VP:* John Zink
Opers Mgr: Jerry Harris

D-U-N-S 06-273-3332 IMP
■ **GYPSUM MANAGEMENT AND SUPPLY INC**
G M S
(*Suby of* GMS INC) ★
100 Crescent Center Pkwy # 800, Tucker, GA 30084-7062
Tel (770) 939-1711 *Founded/Ownrshp* 1972
Sales 1.6MMM[E] *EMP* 3,183
SIC 5032 8742

D-U-N-S 09-780-3209
■ **GYPSUM SUPPLY CO**
ABBOTT ASSOCIATES
(*Suby of* G M S) ★
859 74th St Sw, Byron Center, MI 49315-8379
Tel (616) 583-9300 *Founded/Ownrshp* 2016
Sales 134.6MM[E] *EMP* 183
SIC 5032 Brick, stone & related material; Drywall materials
Pr: Mike Callahan

D-U-N-S 09-530-1198
GYPSUM SUPPLY CO
1125 Harrison Ave, Rockford, IL 61104-7293
Tel (815) 397-5718 *Founded/Ownrshp* 1978
Sales 139.4MM[E] *EMP* 150
SIC 5032 Plastering materials; Drywall materials
Pr: James M Gabelbauer
**Sec:* Rich Taeglow
Brnch Mgr: Doug Davenport
IT Man: Jeff Jaeger
Sfty Dirs: Ted Gill
Opers Mgr: Brandon Greetham
Opers Mgr: Bob Scott
Sls Mgr: Doug Jones

D-U-N-S 02-460-1718 IMP/EXP
GYRODATA INC (TX)
23000 Nw Lake Dr, Houston, TX 77095-5344
Tel (713) 461-3146 *Founded/Ownrshp* 1980
Sales 479.1MM[E] *EMP* 300
SIC 1389 8713 Oil field services; Surveying services
CEO: Steve Klopp
Pr: Bob McMahan
COO: Angela Lunan
CFO: Robert B Trainer Jr
Treas: Robert Trainer Jr
VP: Gary Uttecht
VP: Johnathan Wilcox
Area Mgr: Charles Hajek
Dir IT: Casey Coonce
Tech Mgr: Eric Sanchez
Software D: Eric Draper

GYRUS ACMI, INC.
See GYRUS ACMI LLC

D-U-N-S 00-719-8742 IMP
GYRUS ACMI LLC
GYRUS ACMI, INC.
(*Suby of* OLYMPUS CORP OF AMERICAS) ★
136 Turnpike Rd Ste 300, Southborough, MA 01772-2118
Tel (508) 804-2600 *Founded/Ownrshp* 2007
Sales 220.3MM[E] *EMP* 870
SIC 3841 5047 Surgical & medical instruments; Medical equipment & supplies
CEO: Roy Davis
**CFO:* Simon Shaw
CTO: James Frassica
Dir IT: Bill Forrestall
Telecom Mg: Cheri Loehr
VP Sls: Nils Ericson
Sls Dir: Jason Bening
Sls Dir: Bob Evensen
Sls Dir: Jeff Lambertz
Sls Dir: Tim Ovington
Sls Dir: Troy Prahl

D-U-N-S 00-833-8030 IMP
GYRUS ACMI LP
(*Suby of* GYRUS ACMI INC) ★
9600 Louisiana Ave N, Minneapolis, MN 55445-3280
Tel (763) 416-3000 *Founded/Ownrshp* 2007
Sales 122.6MM[E] *EMP* 867
SIC 3841 Surgical & medical instruments
Pr: Jim Hershner
VP: Laurence Hicks
VP: Albert M Juergens
VP: Gary Mell

D-U-N-S 05-345-2827
GZA GEOENVIRONMENTAL INC
(*Suby of* GZA GEOENVIRONMENTAL TECHNOLOGIES INC) ★
249 Vanderbilt Ave, Norwood, MA 02062-5033
Tel (781) 278-3700 *Founded/Ownrshp* 1989
Sales 110.1MM[E] *EMP* 380
SIC 8711 8734 Consulting engineer; Soil analysis
Pr: William R Beloff
**CFO:* Joseph P Hehir
Snr PM: Jonathan Andrews
Snr PM: Nathaniel Arai
Snr PM: John Colbert
Snr PM: Guy Dalton
Snr PM: Richard Desrosiers
Snr PM: Bernard G Fenelon
Snr PM: Christopher Frey
Snr PM: Adam Henry
Snr PM: Marc Hudock

D-U-N-S 60-266-5812
GZA GEOENVIRONMENTAL TECHNOLOGIES INC
249 Vanderbilt Ave Unit 2, Norwood, MA 02062-5033
Tel (781) 278-3700 *Founded/Ownrshp* 1964
Sales 100.1MM[E] *EMP* 455
SIC 8711 8999 1799 8744 Pollution control engineering; Building construction consultant; Geological consultant; Boring for building construction;
CEO: Bill Beloff
CFO: Joseph Hehir

H

D-U-N-S 06-109-9669 IMP
H & F GULF INC
H&F TIRE SERVICE
1834 Lincoln Hwy E, Lancaster, PA 17602-3344
Tel (717) 392-6793 *Founded/Ownrshp* 1969
Sales 111.4MM[E] *EMP* 70
SIC 5014 5531 Automobile tires & tubes; Automotive tires
Pr: Barry Lee Fitzgerald

D-U-N-S 19-217-2158
H & GL FUNDS OF NJ
700 Raymond Blvd, Newark, NJ 07105-2909
Tel (973) 589-5056 *Founded/Ownrshp* 2005
Sales 116.8MM *EMP* 10[E]
SIC 8699 Charitable organization
CFO: Hema Gandhi
Dir IT: Susie Lopes

D-U-N-S 02-075-1327
H & H AGENCY INC (CA)
20351 Sw Acacia St, Newport Beach, CA 92660-1527
Tel (949) 260-8840 *Founded/Ownrshp* 1969
Sales NA *EMP* 133[E]
SIC 6331 Automobile insurance
CEO: Michael Weinstein
Genl Couns: Helen Hayden

D-U-N-S 03-559-5925
H & M BAY INC
1800 Industrial Park Rd, Federalsburg, MD 21632-2690
Tel (410) 754-8001 *Founded/Ownrshp* 1982
Sales 135.1MM[E] *EMP* 400
Accts Orth & Kowalick Pa Dover
SIC 4731 Transportation agents & brokers
Co-Ownr: Lawrence Hayman
**Co-Ownr:* Walter Messick
**COO:* Walter Messick III
COO: Mike Ryan
Trfc Dir: Jordan Williamson

H & M COMPANY
See H AND M CONSTRUCTION CO INC

H & M CONSTRUCTORS
See MB HAYNES CORP

D-U-N-S 09-395-6311 EXP
H & M HENNES & MAURITZ LP
H&M
(*Suby of* H & M HENNES & MAURITZ HOLDING B.V.)
110 5th Ave Fl 11, New York, NY 10011-5665
Tel (212) 564-9922 *Founded/Ownrshp* 2000
Sales 757.0MM[E] *EMP* 7,500
SIC 5651 Family clothing stores
CFO: Peter Scaramelli
Dir IT: Harald Sperger
Mktg Mgr: Stacey Najman
Genl Couns: Laura Brandt

D-U-N-S 06-429-5934
H & M INTERNATIONAL TRANSPORTATION INC
485b Us Highway 1 S # 110, Iselin, NJ 08830-3068
Tel (732) 510-4640 *Founded/Ownrshp* 1968
Sales 195.2MM[E] *EMP* 1,000
SIC 4731 8741 4225 Freight forwarding; Freight consolidation; Management services; General warehousing & storage
Pr: Charles T Connors
**Pr:* Robert J Gildersleeve
Pr: Eric Witham
**CFO:* Leonard Fischetti
**Treas:* George Willmott
Ex VP: Mike Hosmer
Sr VP: Lou Ciccarelli
VP: Ray Cznadel
Genl Mgr: Tom Curry
Genl Mgr: Tim Newcomb
IT Man: James Giaquinto

H & N FISH COMPANY
See H & N FOODS INTERNATIONAL INC

H & N FOODS INTERNATIONAL
See H & N GROUP INC

D-U-N-S 05-742-5746 IMP
H & N FOODS INTERNATIONAL INC
H & N FISH COMPANY
(*Suby of* H & N FOODS INTERNATIONAL) ★
5580 S Alameda St, Vernon, CA 90058-3426
Tel (323) 586-9300 *Founded/Ownrshp* 1981
Sales 84.6MM[E] *EMP* 170
SIC 5146 Fish, fresh; Fish, frozen, unpackaged
Pr: Hua Thanh Ngo
**VP:* Bobby Ngo
**VP:* Christine Ngo
**VP:* Dat Trieu
Board of Directors: Robert Bertholf

D-U-N-S 07-834-9547
H & N GROUP INC (CA)
H & N FOODS INTERNATIONAL
5580 S Alameda St, Vernon, CA 90058-3426
Tel (323) 586-9388 *Founded/Ownrshp* 2008
Sales 104.4MM[E] *EMP* 194[E]
SIC 5146 Fish & seafoods
CEO: Hua T Ngo

D-U-N-S 00-308-3607 IMP
H & S BAKERY INC (MD)
MIGHTY GOOD
601 S Caroline St, Baltimore, MD 21231-2814
Tel (410) 558-3050 *Founded/Ownrshp* 1948, 1953
Sales 323.9MM[E] *EMP* 756
SIC 2051 Bread, cake & related products
Ch Bd: Harry Tsakalos
**Pr:* Bill Paterakis
**Treas:* Liberty Tsakalos
VP: Chuck Paterakis
Exec: Don Mann
**Prin:* John Paterakis
Info Man: Lisa Glombiak

D-U-N-S 03-191-0607
H & S CONSTRUCTORS INC (TX)
1616 Corn Product Rd, Corpus Christi, TX 78409-3017
Tel (361) 668-8674 *Founded/Ownrshp* 1982
Sales 170.4MM[E] *EMP* 750
SIC 1711 Mechanical contractor
Pr: Patrick Horn
**VP:* Michael Scott
Exec: Brian Trawick
Genl Mgr: Lea A Colwell
Opers Mgr: Ricky Mata
Opers Mgr: Charlie Westmoreland
Sls&Mrk Ex: Mark Garcia

D-U-N-S 00-691-2380 IMP
H - INVESTMENT CO
GOLDEN STATE FLOORING
6999 Southfront Rd, Livermore, CA 94551-8221
Tel (925) 245-4300 *Founded/Ownrshp* 1974
Sales 103.2MM[E] *EMP* 240
SIC 5031 Hardboard; Lumber: rough, dressed & finished; Plywood; Doors & windows
CEO: Harry S Anthony
**Pr:* Jonathan R Long
**CEO:* Matthew R Long
CFO: Michael Flener
**CFO:* Larry W Knox
Treas: Fernanda Aguiar
**VP:* Scott M Watson
Opers Mgr: Robin Salin
Plnt Mgr: Jim Bilinski
Mktg Mgr: Stephen Guenther
Board of Directors: T Nola

D-U-N-S 03-480-7313
H AND M CONSTRUCTION CO INC
H & M COMPANY
50 Security Dr, Jackson, TN 38305-3611
Tel (731) 660-3091 *Founded/Ownrshp* 1957
Sales 157.6MM[E] *EMP* 300
Accts Crowe Horwath Llp Franklin T
SIC 1541 1542 Industrial buildings & warehouses; Factory construction; Warehouse construction; Nonresidential construction
CEO: James Campbell III
**Pr:* Chris Carroll
**Sec:* Michael Farris
**Sr VP:* Roger Cook

D-U-N-S 15-735-4176 IMP
H B CHEMICAL CORP
1665 Enterprise Pkwy, Twinsburg, OH 44087-2243
Tel (330) 920-8023 *Founded/Ownrshp* 1986
Sales 110.3MM *EMP* 32[E]
SIC 5199

H B O
See HOME BOX OFFICE INC

H B O
See HBO SERVICES INC

D-U-N-S 01-156-0919 IMP/EXP
H BETTI INDUSTRIES INC
BETSON ENTERPRISES DIVISION
303 Paterson Plank Rd, Carlstadt, NJ 07072-2307
Tel (201) 438-1300 *Founded/Ownrshp* 1934
Sales 162.2MM[E] *EMP* 380
SIC 5046 5091 7699 Coin-operated equipment; Billiard equipment & supplies; Vending machine repair
CEO: Peter Betti
**Pr:* Robert Geschine
**COO:* Robert Betti
**Sec:* Steven Betti
VP: Serge Ray
VP: Nick Sarioglou
Exec: Paul Cardea
Ex Dir: Concetta Benigno
Genl Mgr: David Lerner
IT Man: Joseph Fienberg
Mktg Dir: Brian Murphy

D-U-N-S 96-824-1240
H C BOBS INC
160 Corporate Ct, Meriden, CT 06450-7177
Tel (203) 235-5775 *Founded/Ownrshp* 1990
Sales 84.9MM[E] *EMP* 3,008[E]
SIC 5651 5611 5699 5621 5641 5661 Family clothing stores; Clothing accessories: men's & boys'; Sports apparel; Women's clothing stores; Children's wear; Men's shoes
Pr: David Farrell

H C I
See HCI INC

H C I
See HURON CASTING INC

H C I
See HUNT CONSOLIDATED INC

D-U-N-S 04-790-6185
H C SCHAU & SON INC
(*Suby of* GREENCORE US HOLDINGS) ★
10350 Argonne Dr Ste 400, Woodridge, IL 60517-4999
Tel (630) 783-1000 *Founded/Ownrshp* 2012
Sales 143.9MM[E] *EMP* 200
SIC 5147 2099 Meats, fresh; Food preparations
CEO: Charles H Schau
**VP:* Randall C Schau

D-U-N-S 06-009-1956 IMP/EXP
H C STARCK INC
(*Suby of* OPUS INVESTMENT SARL)
45 Industrial Pl, Newton, MA 02461-1951
Tel (617) 630-5800 *Founded/Ownrshp* 1925
Sales 170.0MM[E] *EMP* 566
SIC 3339 3356 3313 Primary nonferrous metals; Nonferrous rolling & drawing; Electrometallurgical products
Pr: Dmitry Shashkov
COO: Mark Confroy
CFO: Paul Leblanc
CFO: Dirk Plaga
CFO: Matthias Schmitz
Treas: Richard E Howard
Ofcr: Melody Randolph
Ex VP: Andrew Towey
VP: Joe Hirt
VP: Robert K Sarafian
Genl Mgr: Lynn Brooks
Board of Directors: Dr Andreas Meier

H C T
See HEALTH CARE TEMPORARIES INC

D-U-N-S 02-726-0835 EXP
H D FOWLER CO INC
13440 Se 30th St, Bellevue, WA 98005-4439
Tel (425) 746-8400 *Founded/Ownrshp* 1947
Sales 486.0MM[E] *EMP* 424
SIC 5084 5083 5085 3321 Industrial machinery & equipment; Landscaping equipment; Industrial supplies; Valves & fittings; Water pipe, cast iron
Pr: Harold D Fowler
COO: Brian Nelson
**Treas:* James Fowler
VP: Tammi Jacobson
**VP:* David P Kirker
Mng Dir: Don Obara
Brnch Mgr: Jeff Ockerman
Brnch Mgr: Luke Short
Brnch Mgr: Dan Stucki
Genl Mgr: Kelly Allerdice
IT Man: Eric Poule

H D R
See HDR ENGINEERING INC

D-U-N-S 02-585-6899 IMP
H D SMITH LLC
SMITH MEDICAL PARTNERS DIV
3063 Fiat Ave, Springfield, IL 62703-5930
Tel (866) 232-1222 *Founded/Ownrshp* 2014
Sales 2.0MMM[E] *EMP* 500
SIC 5122 8082 Drugs & drug proprietaries; Pharmaceuticals; Proprietary (patent) medicines; Druggists' sundries; Home health care services
Ch: Henry Dale Smith
Pr: David Duross
**Pr:* J Christopher Smith
**CEO:* Henry Dale Smith Jr
**CFO:* Bill Williams
**Ex VP:* Karen Callaway
**Ex VP:* Tom Doyle
Sr VP: Joseph Conda
Sr VP: Tom Twitty
Sr VP: Scott Wilson
VP: Timothy Booth
VP: Mark De Bruin
VP: Jeff Greer
VP: Christian Herrington
VP: Chandra Prakash
VP: Harvey Tanenbaum

D-U-N-S 00-792-4756 IMP
H E BUTT GROCERY CO (TX)
H-E-B FOOD/DRUG STORES
646 S Flores St, San Antonio, TX 78204-1219
Tel (210) 938-8000 *Founded/Ownrshp* 1905
Sales 28.5MMM[E] *EMP* 85,000
Accts Ernst & Young Llp
SIC 5411 Supermarkets, chain; Co-operative food stores; Grocery stores, chain
Ch Bd: Charles C Butt
**Pr:* Craig L Boyan
**Pr:* Howard E Butt III
**CFO:* Martin H Otto
CFO: Martin Otto
Treas: Jeanine Merrill
Treas: Megan Rooney
Ex VP: Roxanne Orsak
**Ex VP:* Todd A Piland
**Sr VP:* Stephen W Butt
Sr VP: Stephen Butt
Sr VP: Todd Piland
Sr VP: Greg Souquette
VP: Bill Anderson
VP: James Aulds
VP: Mike Jarzombek
VP: Bob McCullough
VP: Craig Norman
VP: William Triplett
VP: Terry Williams
Board of Directors: Howard E Butt Jr, Eleanor Butt Crook

H. E. SARGENT
See SARGENT CORP

D-U-N-S 00-715-8363 IMP
H E WILLIAMS INC (MO)
831 W Fairview Ave, Carthage, MO 64836-3736
Tel (417) 358-4065 *Founded/Ownrshp* 1924
Sales 124.9MM[E] *EMP* 350
SIC 3646 Fluorescent lighting fixtures, commercial
Brnch Mgr: Christopher S Skillern
**Pr:* Mark Williams
**CFO:* T Paul Eckels
**Ex VP:* Danny Lambeth
Genl Mgr: Ronald Snyder
CIO: Kent Peterson
Dir IT: Phil Slinkard
Plnt Mgr: Jason Proctor
Ql Cn Mgr: Greg Sanders
Sls Mgr: John Riggan

H. ENTERPRISES
See H ENTERPRISES INTERNATIONAL INC

D-U-N-S 18-965-4304 IMP/EXP
H ENTERPRISES INTERNATIONAL INC
H. ENTERPRISES
120 S 6th St Ste 2300, Minneapolis, MN 55402-5158
Tel (612) 343-8293 *Founded/Ownrshp* 1988
Sales 138.0MM[E] *EMP* 429
SIC 5032 8611 5211 Brick, stone & related material; Concrete & cinder building products; Concrete building products; Masons' materials; Business associations; Lumber & other building materials
Pr: John E Byrne
**Ch Bd:* Richard E O'Leary
**VP:* Michael Gorman
**VP:* Susan Lewis

H F F
See HOLLIDAY FENOGLIO FOWLER LP

H F I
See HUGHES FURNITURE INDUSTRIES INC

D-U-N-S 10-763-6946
H GROUP HOLDING INC
HAWTHORN SUITES
222 W Adams St Ste 250, Chicago, IL 60606-5308
Tel (312) 750-1234 *Founded/Ownrshp* 1982
Sales 730.5MM[E] *EMP* 42,000
SIC 4512 7011 5812 5813 Air passenger carrier, scheduled; Hotel, franchised; Eating places; Drinking places
Pr: Jay A Pritzker
**Treas:* Kenneth R Posner
**VP:* Harold Handelsman
**VP:* Thomas Pritzker
VP: John Stellato

D-U-N-S 01-721-2317
H H BARNUM CO
7915 Lochlin Dr, Brighton, MI 48116-8329
Tel (800) 695-3055 *Founded/Ownrshp* 1965
Sales 96.3MM[E] *EMP* 70
SIC 5084 Controlling instruments & accessories
Pr: Kenneth M Koza Jr
**VP:* Edward M Koza
Sales Asso: Karin Richardson
Sales Asso: Scott Roland

H H I
See HOLLOWAY-HOUSTON INC

H H S
See HOSPITAL HOUSEKEEPING SYSTEMS LLC

H I M S S
See HEALTHCARE INFORMATION AND MANAGEMENT SYSTEMS SOCIETY

H I S D
See HOUSTON INDEPENDENT SCHOOL DISTRICT

D-U-N-S 00-698-0635 IMP/EXP
H J BAKER & BRO INC
2 Corporate Dr Ste 545, Shelton, CT 06484-6248
Tel (203) 682-9200 *Founded/Ownrshp* 1850, 1994
Sales 151.6MM[E] *EMP* 195
SIC 2048 5191 5052 Poultry feeds; Feed; Fertilizer & fertilizer materials; Sulfur
Ch Bd: Matthew M Smith
Pr: Edgar Devylder
**Pr:* David Smith
**CEO:* Christopher V B Smith
**CFO:* Stuart Adendorff
**Ex VP:* Jack L Williams
VP: Steve Mansfield
VP: Ken Medlock
Dir Bus: Art Bentley
IT Man: David Sith
Plnt Mgr: Mike Walsh

H J F
See HENRY M JACKSON FOUNDATION FOR ADVANCEMENT OF MILITARY MEDICINE INC

D-U-N-S 06-524-3581 IMP/EXP
■ **H J HEINZ CO LP**
HEINZ NORTH AMERICA
(*Suby of* HEINZ KRAFT FOODS CO) ★
357 6th Ave, Pittsburgh, PA 15222-2530
Tel (412) 237-5757 *Founded/Ownrshp* 2000
Sales 92.7MM[E] *EMP* 225
SIC 2038 Frozen specialties
CEO: Robert James Meier
Pr: Jeffrey P Berger
Treas: Charlie White
Ex VP: Ted Bobby
Ex VP: Brendon Buckley
Off Mgr: Julie Groetsch
Sales Exec: Dave Moran

D-U-N-S 00-512-8467
■ **H J M P CORP**
HOME JUICE CO OF MEMPHIS
(*Suby of* NATIONAL BEVERAGE CORP) ★
1930 George St Ste 2, Melrose Park, IL 60160-1501
Tel (708) 345-5370 *Founded/Ownrshp* 1946
Sales 587.3MM[E] *EMP* 1,000
SIC 2033 5149 0174 2037 Fruit juices: packaged in cans, jars, etc.; Beverages, except coffee & tea; Juices; Orange grove; Frozen fruits & vegetables
Pr: Stan Sheraton
Pr: Mike Hoeppel
**VP:* Allen Domzalski

D-U-N-S 00-978-3390
H J MARTIN & SON INC
H J MARTIN FLOORCARE
320 S Military Ave, Green Bay, WI 54303-2288
Tel (920) 494-3461 *Founded/Ownrshp* 1931
Sales 90.0MM *EMP* 3
SIC 5713 1793 1522 1542 1742 Floor covering stores; Glass & glazing work; Residential construction; Commercial & office building contractors; Drywall
Pr: Edward N Martin
Genl Mgr: Randy Krause
Telecom Ex: Terry Karasky

H J MARTIN FLOORCARE
See H J MARTIN & SON INC

D-U-N-S 00-388-2685
H J RUSSELL & CO (GA)
171 17th St Nw Ste 1600, Atlanta, GA 30363-1235
Tel (404) 330-1000 *Founded/Ownrshp* 1959
Sales 374.1MM[E] *EMP* 733
SIC 1542 8741 7389 8742 Commercial & office building, new construction; Personnel management; Brokers, contract services; Construction project management consultant
CEO: Michael B Russell
**Pr:* H Jerome Russell Jr
**CFO:* Ed Bradford
**Ch:* Herman Russell
VP: Sonia Booker
VP: Barry Compton
VP: Greg Dixon
VP: Bruce Harris
VP: James Wille
Exec: Robelyn McNair
Exec: Ed Perry

H L A
See HAROLD LEVINSON ASSOCIATES INC

D-U-N-S 02-511-6810
H LEE MOFFITT CANCER CENTER & RESEARCH INSTITUTE
12902 Usf Magnolia Dr, Tampa, FL 33612-9416
Tel (813) 745-4673 *Founded/Ownrshp* 1985
Sales 91.5MM *EMP* 100
Accts Ernst & Young Llp Tampa Fl
SIC 8062 General medical & surgical hospitals
Prin: Beth A Houghton
Bd of Dir: Thomas Brandon
VP: Lesley Harris
VP: Mark Hulse
Dir Rad: Martin Miller
Dir Rx: Viet Q Ho
Genl Mgr: John Allgeier
Netwrk Eng: Saroney Guttoh
Doctor: Melissa Alsina
Doctor: James S Barthel
Doctor: Bradford W Carter

D-U-N-S 13-930-1956
H LEE MOFFITT CANCER CENTER & RESEARCH INSTITUTE HOSPITAL INC
12902 Usf Magnolia Dr, Tampa, FL 33612-9416
Tel (813) 745-4673 *Founded/Ownrshp* 1984
Sales 951.0MM *EMP* 4,200
Accts Ernst & Young Llp
SIC 8733 Medical research
CEO: Alan F List
**Pr:* Jack Kolosky
**CFO:* Yvette Tremonti
Ex VP: Nick Potter
**Ex VP:* Thomas Sellers

D-U-N-S 84-543-6294
H LEE MOFFITT CANCER CENTER AND RESEARCH INSTITUTE INC
12902 Usf Magnolia Dr, Tampa, FL 33612-9416
Tel (813) 745-4673 *Founded/Ownrshp* 1987
Sales 951.0MM *EMP* 5,200
Accts Ernst & Young Llp Tampa Flori
SIC 8011 Physicians' office, including specialists
Pr: William Dalton
Chf Rad: Martin Silbiger
Ofcr: Karen Wartenberg
Top Exec: Kestutis P Boyev
Top Exec: Ronald C Deonti
Top Exec: Mark W El-Deiry
Top Exec: Judith C McCaffrey
Top Exec: Thomas V McCaffrey
Top Exec: Reed F Murtagh
Top Exec: Tapan A Pdhy
Top Exec: Marion B Ridley
Top Exec: Mark H Tabor
Top Exec: Tawee Tanvetyanon
Ex VP: W Pledger
VP: Yvette Tremonti
Dir Rx: Viet Q Ho

D-U-N-S 00-892-8244
H LEFF ELECTRIC CO
4700 Spring Rd, Cleveland, OH 44131-1027
Tel (216) 325-0941 *Founded/Ownrshp* 1921
Sales 155.7MM[E] *EMP* 107
Accts Bober Markey Fedorovich Akron
SIC 5063 Electrical supplies
Pr: Bruce E Leff
**Ex VP:* Sanford Leff Jr
Brnch Mgr: Randy Kellams
Genl Mgr: Tom Koberna
VP Sls: Bill Better
Sales Asso: Larry Aldridge
Sales Asso: Douglas Ruth
Sales Asso: Tyler Spencer

D-U-N-S 07-316-2067 IMP
H M DUNN CO INC
HM DUNNAIR AEROSYSTEM
(*Suby of* HM DUNN AEROSYSTEMS INC) ★
3301 House Anderson Rd, Euless, TX 76040-2001
Tel (817) 283-3722 *Founded/Ownrshp* 2011
Sales 112.8MM[E] *EMP* 564
SIC 3724 3599 3728 Aircraft engines & engine parts; Machine & other job shop work; Machine shop, jobbing & repair; Aircraft parts & equipment
CEO: Phil Milazzo
**COO:* Peter Kurto
**CFO:* Marc Szczerba
VP: Skip Steely
Prgrm Mgr: Raffi Avakian
Prgrm Mgr: Chad Johnson
Prgrm Mgr: Earl Overcash
IT Man: Danny Grounds
Prd Dir: Michael Webb
Prd Mgr: Stanley Williamson
VP Sls: Tim Roussin

H M E
See H M ELECTRONICS INC

D-U-N-S 06-311-5497 IMP
H M ELECTRONICS INC (CA)
H M E
14110 Stowe Dr, Poway, CA 92064-7147
Tel (858) 535-6000 *Founded/Ownrshp* 1971
Sales 204.9MM[E] *EMP* 539
SIC 3669 Intercommunication systems, electric
Ch Bd: Harrison Y Miyahira
**CEO:* Charles Miyahira
VP: Paul Foley
VP: Scott Hoeptner
VP: Scott Weldner
Mtls Mgr: Donnie Gilliam
Mfg Mgr: Jay Heisterkamp
Ql Cn Mgr: David Day
Ql Cn Mgr: Rich Gaboury
Ql Cn Mgr: Thomas Jordan
Mktg Dir: Daren Haas

H M G
See HOLSTON MEDICAL GROUP PC

H M T
See HMT INC

D-U-N-S 12-811-2252
H M T TANK SERVICE INC
(*Suby of* H M T) ★
24 Waterway Ave Ste 400, The Woodlands, TX 77380-3197
Tel (281) 681-7000 *Founded/Ownrshp* 1978
Sales 84.9MM[E] *EMP* 600
SIC 1799 Petroleum storage tanks, pumping & draining
Pr: Millard J Jones Jr
**VP:* Ruston P Chandler
**VP:* Lawrence W McAfee
**VP:* Scott D Spence
**VP:* Gary E Tesch
Sls Mgr: Reggie Richey
Snr Mgr: Glenn Tate

H MART
See GRAND SUPERCENTER INC

H N E
See HEALTH NEW ENGLAND INC

H O K
See HELLMUTH OBATA & KASSABAUM INC

D-U-N-S 05-666-8577 IMP/EXP
H O PENN MACHINERY CO INC (NY)
122 Noxon Rd, Poughkeepsie, NY 12603-2940
Tel (845) 452-1200 *Founded/Ownrshp* 1923, 1965
Sales 256.9MM[E] *EMP* 400
SIC 5082 5084 General construction machinery & equipment; Materials handling machinery
CEO: C E Thomas Cleveland
**Pr:* Robert W Cleveland
CFO: Gerald H Martin
**Ex VP:* Jeffrey Mitchell
VP: Michele Foriska
VP: Joel Heiporin
Genl Mgr: Anthony Bannister
Advt Mgr: Pete Cianei
Sls Mgr: Jason Scimeca
Sales Asso: Jon Hoose
Board of Directors: Sue Steffanci

D-U-N-S 00-644-2610
H O WOLDING INC (WI)
9642 Western Way, Amherst, WI 54406-9026
Tel (715) 824-5513 *Founded/Ownrshp* 1935
Sales 91.1MM[E] *EMP* 450
SIC 4213 Contract haulers
Pr: Don Wolding
**VP:* Cathy Kirsling
**VP:* Marc Wolding
CIO: Kathy Kirsling

H P G
See HEALTHTRUST PURCHASING GROUP LP

D-U-N-S 01-641-1746 IMP
H P PRODUCTS CORP
(*Suby of* FERGUSON ENTERPRISES INC) ★
4220 Saguaro Trl, Indianapolis, IN 46268-2550
Tel (317) 298-9957 *Founded/Ownrshp* 2014
Sales 351.6MM[E] *EMP* 500
SIC 5087 Janitors' supplies
Pr: Bridget Shuel-Walker
**CFO:* Mark Willoughby
IT Man: John Joray

D-U-N-S 13-882-9796
H Q GLOBAL HOLDINGS INC
(*Suby of* REGUS H)
15305 Dallas Pkwy Ste 400, Addison, TX 75001-6922
Tel (972) 361-8100 *Founded/Ownrshp* 2004
Sales 6.8MM[E] *EMP* 1,200
SIC 6519 7389 Sub-lessors of real estate; Office facilities & secretarial service rental
CEO: Peter H Harris
Ex VP: Kevin Naze
Ex VP: Kent Shoemaker
Ex VP: Brad Young
Prin: Regina Martin
Genl Mgr: Lavonia Brown
Genl Mgr: Rick Patterson
CIO: Gary Russell
MIS Dir: Gilbert Partida
IT Man: Arthur Pidgeon
MIS Mgr: Jennifer Kennedy

H Q GLOBAL WORKPLACES LLC
See HQ GLOBAL WORKPLACES INC

H R R V
See COVANTA HONOLULU RESOURCE RECOVERY VENTURE

H S A
See HEALTH SERVICES DEPARTMENT

D-U-N-S 01-761-5381
H S B C OVERSEAS CORP (DE)
(*Suby of* HSBC USA INC) ★
300 Delaware Ave Ste 1400, Wilmington, DE 19801-1650
Tel (302) 657-8400 *Founded/Ownrshp* 1987
Sales 88.2MM *EMP* 17
SIC 6722 Mutual fund sales, on own account
Pr: Richard Leigh

D-U-N-S 15-999-8632
H SCHRIER & CO INC
4901 Glenwood Rd, Brooklyn, NY 11234-1131
Tel (718) 258-7500 *Founded/Ownrshp* 1986
Sales 105.1MM[E] *EMP* 100
SIC 5141 Groceries, general line
Ch Bd: David Libertoff
**Sec:* Jonathan Libertoff
Sales Exec: Mike Serotkin

H T A
See HONDA TRADING AMERICA CORP

H T C
See HORRY TELEPHONE COOPERATIVE INC

D-U-N-S 00-792-1356 IMP/EXP
H T HACKNEY CO (TN)
502 S Gay St Ste 300, Knoxville, TN 37902-3607
Tel (865) 546-1291 *Founded/Ownrshp* 1891
Sales 22.3MM *EMP* 3,600
Accts Pugh & Company Pc Knoxville
SIC 5141 5172 2434 5084 Groceries, general line; Gasoline; Service station supplies, petroleum; Wood kitchen cabinets; Industrial machinery & equipment
Ch Bd: William B Sansom
**Pr:* Charles Shue
COO: Dean Ballinger
**CFO:* Michael D Morton
Exec: Mike Delaguaro
Exec: Arlene Kitts
Exec: Linda Martin
**VP Admn:* Leonard Robinette
Div Mgr: Scott Fitch
Opers Mgr: Rick Spears
Sls&Mrk Ex: Heather Butler

D-U-N-S 06-403-5306
■ **H T LYONS INC**
(*Suby of* TALEN ENERGY CORP) ★
7165 Ambassador Dr, Allentown, PA 18106-9255
Tel (610) 530-2600 *Founded/Ownrshp* 1998
Sales 158.5MM[E] *EMP* 350
SIC 1711 Mechanical contractor; Warm air heating & air conditioning contractor; Refrigeration contractor; Plumbing contractors
Pr: Rick Perosa
**VP:* Chris Bernecker
**VP:* Roeland F Hoeke
Genl Mgr: Buddy Kida
**Genl Mgr:* K Scott Sine
IT Man: Jason Boehm

HT PUBLISHING CO
See ROMAN CATHOLIC CHURCH OF DIOCESE OF HOUMA THIBODAUX

H T S
See HEAT TRANSFER SOLUTIONS INC

H U D
See UNITED STATES DEPT OF HOUSING AND URBAN DEVELOPMENT

H V L
See V L H INC

D-U-N-S 02-837-0617
H W HUNTER INC
HUNTER DODGE CHRYSLER JEEP RAM
1130 Auto Mall Dr, Lancaster, CA 93534-6302
Tel (661) 948-8411 *Founded/Ownrshp* 1956
Sales 84.0MM *EMP* 100
SIC 5511 7538 Automobiles, new & used; Pickups, new & used; General automotive repair shops
CEO: Timothy H Fuller
Off Mgr: Jeanie Posan
Mktg Dir: Katie Nelson

D-U-N-S 07-423-6506
H W KAUFMAN FINANCIAL GROUP INC
(*Suby of* BURNS & WILCOX) ★
30833 Northwestern Hwy, Farmington Hills, MI 48334-2551
Tel (248) 932-9000 *Founded/Ownrshp* 1969
Sales NA *EMP* 1,005
SIC 6141 6719 Installment sales finance, other than banks; Investment holding companies, except banks
**Ex VP:* Daniel T Muldowney
Sr VP: Gary Batten
Sr VP: Donald Carson
Sr VP: Harvey Goldenberg
**Sr VP:* Daniel J Kaufman
**Sr VP:* Christopher Zoidis
VP: Wayne Bates
VP: Michael Franzese
VP: Ken Laderoute
VP: Michael Maharaj
VP: Michael Paulin
VP: Kermit Shaulis

D-U-N-S 02-520-8133
H W LOCHNER INC
225 W Washington St # 1200, Chicago, IL 60606-3100
Tel (312) 372-7346 *Founded/Ownrshp* 1940, 1944
Sales 116.8MM^E *EMP* 400
SIC 8711 8742 Consulting engineer; Planning consultant
Ch: Hal Lochner
**Pr:* Larry Thomas
**CEO:* Jim Bishop
**COO:* Jeanne Cormier
**CFO:* Pieter Lesterhuis
VP: Bill Berry
**VP:* Roy Bruce
**VP:* Chuck Craycraft
VP: Carlye Sommers
VP: David Twiddy
Prin: Shelly Flores

D-U-N-S 08-422-0730
H WOLF EDWARD AND SONS INC
414 Kettle Moraine Dr S, Slinger, WI 53086-9550
Tel (262) 644-5030 *Founded/Ownrshp* 1976
Sales 281.7MM *EMP* 60
Accts Baker Tilly Virchow Krause Llp
SIC 5983 5171 Fuel oil dealers; Petroleum bulk stations
Pr: Craig Wolf
**CFO:* Steve Kreuser
**VP:* Colette Troeller

D-U-N-S 00-820-0016 IMP/EXP
▲ H&E EQUIPMENT SERVICES INC
7500 Pecue Ln, Baton Rouge, LA 70809-5107
Tel (225) 298-5200 *Founded/Ownrshp* 1961
Sales 1.0MMM *EMP* 2,045
Accts Bdo Usa Llp Dallas Texas
Tkr Sym HEES *Exch* NGS
SIC 7359 5082 Equipment rental & leasing; General construction machinery & equipment
CEO: John M Engquist
**Ch Bd:* Gary W Bagley
Pr: Bradley W Barber
CFO: Leslie S Magee
VP: Kevin Chamberlain
VP: Bill Fox
VP: Kevin Inda
VP: John Jones
VP: Melissa Samuel
VP: Bobby Slay
VP: Leonard St Germain
VP Bus Dev: Kevin Gretz
Exec: Kurt Sorensen
Board of Directors: Paul N Arnold, Bruce C Bruckmann, Patrick L Edsell, Thomas J Galligan III, Lawrence C Karlson, John T Sawyer

H&F TIRE SERVICE
See H & F GULF INC

D-U-N-S 12-653-5983
H&H CATERING LP
WOLFGANG PUCK CATERING
6801 Hollywood Blvd, Los Angeles, CA 90028-6136
Tel (323) 491-1250 *Founded/Ownrshp* 2002
Sales 14.0MM *EMP* 1,600^E
SIC 5812 Caterers
Pr: Carl Schuster
Pt: Wolfgang Puck
Exec: Christopher Jones

D-U-N-S 05-356-6669
■ H&J CAPITAL LLC
(*Suby of* UNUM GROUP) ★
8485 Goodwood Blvd, Baton Rouge, LA 70806-7878
Tel (225) 926-2888 *Founded/Ownrshp* 2010
Sales 124.0MM *EMP* 200
SIC 6719 Investment holding companies, except banks
CEO: Erich Sternberg
Pr: Deborah Sternberg
CFO: Jeff Wild

H&M
See H & M HENNES & MAURITZ LP

D-U-N-S 80-685-8614
■ H&R BLOCK BANK
(*Suby of* BLOCK FINANCIAL CORP) ★
1 H And R Block Way, Kansas City, MO 64105-1905
Tel (888) 687-4722 *Founded/Ownrshp* 2006
Sales NA *EMP* 50
SIC 6035 Federal savings banks
Pr: Kathy Barney
Dir Risk M: James M Bedsole
Comm Dir: Janine Smiley

D-U-N-S 16-530-9159
■ H&R BLOCK GROUP INC
(*Suby of* H&R BLOCK INC) ★
4400 Main St, Kansas City, MO 64111-1812
Tel (816) 854-3000 *Founded/Ownrshp* 1993
Sales 511.0MM^E *EMP* 4,581
SIC 6211 8721 8742 Security brokers & dealers; Accounting, auditing & bookkeeping; Management consulting services
CEO: Mark A Ernst
Treas: Becky Shulman
VP: Kevin Mobley
Mng Dir: Linda Murphy
Brnch Mgr: Patricia Noble
Brnch Mgr: Jeff Petty
Off Mgr: Richard Kirsch
Off Mgr: Sharon Leinhauser
Off Mgr: Lynn Miller
Off Mgr: Tammy Small
Off Mgr: Pier Vidoni

D-U-N-S 04-395-1235
▲ H&R BLOCK INC (MO)
1 H&R Block Way, Kansas City, MO 64105
Tel (816) 854-3000 *Founded/Ownrshp* 1955
Sales 3.0MMM *EMP* 97,200
Tkr Sym HRB *Exch* NYS
SIC 7291 6794 Tax return preparation services; Franchises, selling or licensing
Pr: William C Cobb
**Ch Bd:* Robert A Gerard
CFO: Tony G Bowen
Bd of Dir: Cindy Kaminski
Chf Mktg O: Kathryn M Collins
Ofcr: Thomas A Gerke
Ofcr: Jason L Houseworth
Sr VP: Alan Lowden
VP: Diane Adoma
VP: Katherine Collins
VP: Greg Floyd
VP: Kellie Logerwell
VP: Robert Moretti
VP: Walter Pirnot
VP: Steve Volmer
Board of Directors: Angela N Archon, Paul J Brown, Richard A Johnson, David Baker Lewis, Victoria J Reich, Bruce C Rohde, Tom D Seip, James F Wright

D-U-N-S 05-286-9609 IMP
■ H-C LIQUIDATING CORP
HOMECREST CABINETRY
(*Suby of* OMEGA CABINETRY) ★
1002 Eisenhower Dr N, Goshen, IN 46526-5308
Tel (574) 535-9300 *Founded/Ownrshp* 1969
Sales 95.1MM^E *EMP* 1,025
SIC 2434 Wood kitchen cabinets; Vanities, bathroom: wood
Pr: Warner R S
**Pr:* John Goebel
VP: Thomas Shmidt

H-E-B FOOD/DRUG STORES
See H E BUTT GROCERY CO

H-G A C
See HOUSTON-GALVESTON AREA COUNCIL

D-U-N-S 93-150-2764 IMP
H-HOME DIVISION HACKNEY HOME FURNISHINGS FAX O
(*Suby of* HT HACKNEY CO) ★
3036 Highway 11 S, Athens, TN 37303-6155
Tel (423) 745-9127 *Founded/Ownrshp* 2012
Sales 9.1MM^E *EMP* 1,521^E
SIC 5712 Furniture stores
Prin: Mary Hackney

H2WR / EHS SERVICES
See TOTAL SAFETY US INC

D-U-N-S 08-035-4016
■ HA 3049 UALENA STREET LLC
(*Suby of* HAWAIIAN HOLDINGS INC) ★
3375 Koapaka St Ste G350, Honolulu, HI 96819-1804
Tel (808) 835-3700 *Founded/Ownrshp* 2016
Sales 9.9MM^E *EMP* 2,494^E
SIC 4111 Airport transportation

HA ANDERSEN COMPANY
See ANDERSEN CONSTRUCTION CO

HA INTERNATIONAL
See HA-INTERNATIONAL LLC

D-U-N-S 02-881-2845 IMP
HA-INTERNATIONAL LLC
HA INTERNATIONAL
(*Suby of* DELTA-HA INC) ★
630 Oakmont Ln, Westmont, IL 60559-5548
Tel (630) 575-5700 *Founded/Ownrshp* 2001
Sales 160.8MM *EMP* 140
Accts Dugan & Lopatka Wheaton Illi
SIC 2869 Industrial organic chemicals
Pr: Douglas Sanford
CFO: Grady Collins
VP: Michael Feehan
CIO: Donna Willoughby
Plnt Mgr: Joe Ebens
Mktg Mgr: Lorena Oneill

D-U-N-S 00-608-5799
HA-USA INC
DELTA-HA, INC.
(*Suby of* HUTTENES-ALBERTUS CHEMISCHE WERKE GESELLSCHAFT MIT BESCHRANKTER HAFTUNG)
630 Oakmont Ln, Westmont, IL 60559-5548
Tel (630) 575-5700 *Founded/Ownrshp* 1933
Sales 160.8MM^E *EMP* 196^E
SIC 2869 Industrial organic chemicals
Ch Bd: Donald W Hansen
Pr: Richard Smith
CFO: Peter J Puccio

D-U-N-S 02-497-6045
HAAG FOOD SERVICE INC
HAAG FOODS AND POULTRY
300 N Haag St, Breese, IL 62230-1758
Tel (618) 526-7120 *Founded/Ownrshp* 1944
Sales 151.4MM^E *EMP* 90
SIC 5142 5144 5141

HAAG FOODS AND POULTRY
See HAAG FOOD SERVICE INC

HAAGEN-DAZS
See NESTLE DREYERS ICE CREAM CO

D-U-N-S 01-018-0267 IMP
HAAN CORP
225 Wilmington W Chester, Chadds Ford, PA 19317-9011
Tel (717) 209-7000 *Founded/Ownrshp* 2008
Sales 92.3MM^E *EMP* 380
SIC 5064 Vacuum cleaners, household
Pr: Romi Haan

HAARTZ AUTO FABRIC
See HAARTZ CORP

D-U-N-S 00-102-3084 IMP
HAARTZ CORP (MA)
HAARTZ AUTO FABRIC
87 Hayward Rd, Acton, MA 01720-3000
Tel (978) 264-2600 *Founded/Ownrshp* 1922
Sales 117.1MM^E *EMP* 400
SIC 3069 2295 Rubberized fabrics; Resin or plastic coated fabrics
Pr: John Fox
Treas: Charles Quimby
Prgrm Mgr: Jill Perry
QA Dir: Douglas Bishop
QA Dir: Gregg Kush
QA Dir: Mike Umbarger
Sftwr Eng: Thomas Laford
Ql Cn Mgr: Dominique Throop
Sls Mgr: Douglas Haartz
Sales Asso: Darren Spangler
Snr Mgr: Fiona Doskocz

D-U-N-S 12-097-4571 IMP/EXP
HAAS AUTOMATION INC
2800 Sturgis Rd, Oxnard, CA 93030-8901
Tel (805) 278-1800 *Founded/Ownrshp* 1983
Sales 212.7MM^E *EMP* 1,400^E
SIC 3541

D-U-N-S 83-863-7283
■ HAAS GROUP
(*Suby of* WESCO AIRCRAFT HOLDINGS INC) ★
1475 Phoenixville Pike, West Chester, PA 19380-1437
Tel (484) 564-4500 *Founded/Ownrshp* 2014
Sales 70.2MM^E *EMP* 1,300
SIC 8741 3369 Business management; Aerospace castings, nonferrous: except aluminum
CEO: Thaddeus J Fortin

HAAS HOP PRODUCTS
See JOHN I HAAS INC

D-U-N-S 01-161-7891 IMP/EXP
HABAND CO LLC
(*Suby of* BEDFORD FAIR APPAREL) ★
1 International Blvd # 800, Mahwah, NJ 07495-0019
Tel (570) 383-3226 *Founded/Ownrshp* 2000, 2006
Sales 115.2MM^E *EMP* 349
SIC 5961 5611 Clothing, mail order (except women's); Women's apparel, mail order; Men's & boys' clothing stores
Pr: Duke Habernickel
Ex VP: Dean Perigard
VP: Richard Elia
VP: Peter Gilman
IT Man: George Kessler
Netwrk Mgr: Steve Helms
Info Man: Jason Bankston
Opers Mgr: Micheal Fleeming
Ql Cn Mgr: Robert Kalman
VP Mktg: Steve Schlumpf
Mktg Dir: Rebecca Ackerman

D-U-N-S 04-287-6227 IMP/EXP
HABASIT AMERICA INC (GA)
(*Suby of* HABASIT HOLDING AG)
805 Satellite Blvd Nw, Suwanee, GA 30024-2879
Tel (678) 288-3600 *Founded/Ownrshp* 1967
Sales 135.8MM^E *EMP* 600
SIC 3566 Speed changers, drives & gears
CFO: Victor D'Adamio
Pr: Chris Nigon
CFO: Mike Kuba
VP: Bill Carabetta
VP: Bert Flieger
Exec: Marc Knable
Rgnl Mgr: Phil Resch
Dist Mgr: Steve Flaherty
Dist Mgr: David Moore
Dist Mgr: Edward Perz
Dist Mgr: Frank Sabatino

D-U-N-S 01-761-7036 IMP
HABEGGER CORP
JOHNSON CONTRLS AUTHORIZED DLR
4995 Winton Rd, Cincinnati, OH 45232-1504
Tel (513) 853-6644 *Founded/Ownrshp* 1952
Sales 94.4MM^E *EMP* 260
SIC 5075 Warm air heating equipment & supplies; Air conditioning & ventilation equipment & supplies
Ch Bd: Fred Habegger III
Pr: John Dor

COO: Jeff Gilley
CFO: Mike Pope
Exec: Pete Doyle
Brnch Mgr: Sean Kilbane
Brnch Mgr: John Smith
Store Mgr: Robin Dalrymple
Store Mgr: Brett Molsberry
Store Mgr: Bret Stephens
Opers Mgr: Jeff Russell

D-U-N-S 04-068-9424
HABERSHAM COUNTY BOARD OF EDUCATION
HCBOE
132 Stanford Mill Rd, Clarkesville, GA 30523
Tel (706) 754-2110 *Founded/Ownrshp* 1901
Sales 61.9MM^E *EMP* 1,000
SIC 8211 School board
Ch Bd: Robert Barron
**CFO:* Staci Newsome
**Bd of Dir:* Gilbert Barrett
**Bd of Dir:* Don Corbett
**Bd of Dir:* Pat Taylor
**Bd of Dir:* Rick Williams
HC Dir: Kathleen Clement

HABIT BURGER GRILL, THE
See HABIT RESTAURANTS LLC

HABIT BURGER GRILL
See HABIT RESTAURANTS INC

D-U-N-S 11-404-6043
▲ HABIT RESTAURANTS INC
HABIT BURGER GRILL
17320 Red Hill Ave # 140, Irvine, CA 92614-5644
Tel (949) 851-8881 *Founded/Ownrshp* 1969
Sales 230.6MM *EMP* 3,949^E
Tkr Sym HABT *Exch* NGM
SIC 5812 Hamburger stand; Sandwiches & submarines shop
Pr: Russell W Bendel
Pr: Mike Repetti
COO: Anthony Serritella
**CFO:* Ira Fils
Chf Mktg O: Matthew Hood
VP: Rob Wach
VP: Pete Whitwell
Genl Mgr: Sergio Vega
Dir IT: Brandan Bieker

D-U-N-S 02-374-3234
■ HABIT RESTAURANTS LLC
HABIT BURGER GRILL, THE
(*Suby of* HABIT BURGER GRILL) ★
17320 Red Hill Ave # 140, Irvine, CA 92614-5644
Tel (949) 851-8881 *Founded/Ownrshp* 2007
Sales 230.6MM^E *EMP* 800
SIC 5812 Hamburger stand
CEO: Russell Bendel
COO: Tony Serritella
**CFO:* Ira Fils
Chf Mktg O: Matt Hood
Dist Mgr: Ron Obando
Off Admin: Katie Lawrence
Mktg Dir: Charlotte Lucich

D-U-N-S 06-620-2052
HABITAT CO LLC
HABITAT GROUP, THE
350 W Hubbard St Ste 500, Chicago, IL 60654-5739
Tel (312) 955-0413 *Founded/Ownrshp* 1971
Sales 65.4MM^E *EMP* 1,200
SIC 6531 Real estate managers
Pr: Mark Segal
**CFO:* Barry Goldberg
**Sr VP:* Matthew Fiascone
VP: Marla Jackson
VP: Bryan Sullivan
VP: Bob Walker
Rgnl Mgr: Sarah Hankins
Rgnl Mgr: Michelle Hunt
VP Opers: Jack Devedjian
Snr PM: Cynthia Miles

D-U-N-S 09-584-9568
HABITAT FOR HUMANITY INTERNATIONAL INC
121 Habitat St, Americus, GA 31709-3498
Tel (800) 422-4828 *Founded/Ownrshp* 1989
Sales 268.2MM *EMP* 1,500
Accts Ernst & Young Us Llp Philadel
SIC 8399 8661 8322 1521 1531 Social change association; Religious organizations; Individual & family services; Single-family housing construction; Operative builders
Pr: Jonathan Reckford
CFO: Duane Bates
CFO: Ed Quibell
CFO: Robert Schmidt
Treas: Jeff Livesay
Treas: Peter Luquer
Bd of Dir: Larry Erdhardt
Bd of Dir: Daniel Fuller
Bd of Dir: Daniel C Molhoek
Bd of Dir: Laura Young
Ofcr: Sharon Grant
Ofcr: Diana Juhlin
Ofcr: Wesley Nguyen
Top Exec: Karen Lienau
Ex VP: Michael Carscaddon
Sr VP: Tony Dispigno
Sr VP: Larry Gluth
Sr VP: Robert Sayell
**VP:* Chris Clarke
VP: Gregory Foster
VP: Richard Hathaway
Board of Directors: Ted Dosch, Jessica Jackley, Steven Preston, Chuck Thiemann, Nabil Abadir, Paul Ekelschot, Carol Johnson, Larry Prible, Justin Wall, Kathleen Bader, Cary Evert, Jamie Justice, Joe Price, Ed Schreyer Paula Whiting, Joe Blomeke, Chantal Hudicourt-Ewald, Mary Kazunga, Jonathan Reckford, Sue Wilhelm, Joe Burgess, Norris Friesen, Jack Kemp, Nic Retsinas, Bob Willumstead, Elizabeth Crossman, Adam Fusselman

HABITAT GROUP, THE
See HABITAT CO LLC

D-U-N-S 13-350-7959
HAC INC
HOMELAND STORES
390 Ne 36th St, Oklahoma City, OK 73105-2508
Tel (405) 290-3000 *Founded/Ownrshp* 2011
Sales 740.0MM *EMP* 4,000
SIC 5411 Supermarkets
CEO: Marc Jones
**CFO:* Deborah A Brown
**VP:* Mark Wolowitz
VP Mktg: Phil Payment

HACC
See HARRISBURG AREA COMMUNITY COLLEGE FOUNDATION

D-U-N-S 00-528-6679 IMP/EXP
■ **HACH CO**
ELE INTERNATIONAL
(*Suby of* DANAHER CORP) ★
5600 Lindbergh Dr, Loveland, CO 80538-8842
Tel (970) 669-3050 *Founded/Ownrshp* 1999
Sales 300.1MM^E *EMP* 1,000
SIC 3826 3823 3231 2819 2869 Analytical instruments; Colorimeters (optical instruments); PH meters, except industrial process type; Turbidometers; Water quality monitoring & control systems; Medical & laboratory glassware: made from purchased glass; Chemicals, reagent grade: refined from technical grade; Laboratory chemicals, organic
Pr: Lance Reisman
Sr Cor Off: Glenn Ferguson
Ex VP: Daniel Pryor
Sr VP: Kevin Klau
VP: Lori Pegelow
**VP:* Michael Strycker
VP: Derk Walker
Genl Mgr: Glenn Cruger
IT Man: James Darby
Software D: Aaron Jarrette
VP Opers: Larry D Thompson
Board of Directors: Chris Serafin

D-U-N-S 12-817-6885 IMP
HACHETTE BOOK GROUP INC
(*Suby of* HACHETTE LIVRE)
1290 Ave Of The Americas, New York, NY 10104-0101
Tel (800) 759-0190 *Founded/Ownrshp* 2006
Sales 310.9MM^E *EMP* 970
SIC 2731 5192 Books: publishing only; Books, periodicals & newspapers
Ch Bd: David Young
**COO:* Kenneth Michaels
**CFO:* Thomas A Maciag
Sr VP: Rolf Zettersten
VP: Todd McGarity
VP: Gary Morgen
**VP:* Stephen M Mubarek
Dir Soc: Joanna Host
Creative D: Mario Pulice
Creative D: Jeffrey Shay
Creative D: Oscar Stern
Board of Directors: Arnaud Nourry

D-U-N-S 62-246-0467
HACHETTE DISTRIBUTION INC
(*Suby of* LAGARDERE NORTH AMERICA INC) ★
60 E 42nd St Ste 1940, New York, NY 10165-6201
Tel (212) 477-7373 *Founded/Ownrshp* 2004
Sales 551.5MM^E *EMP* 5,160
SIC 5192 5994 5947 Magazines; Newsstand; Magazine stand; Gift shop; Novelties
Pr: Gerry Savaria

HACIENDA MEXICAN RESTAURANTS
See HMR ACQUISITION CO INC

D-U-N-S 07-528-7854
HACIENDA-LA PUENTE UNIFIED SCHOOL DISTRICT
15959 Gale Ave, City of Industry, CA 91745-1604
Tel (626) 933-1000 *Founded/Ownrshp* 1970
Sales 122.6MM^E *EMP* 2,500
SIC 8211 Public elementary & secondary schools
Dir Sec: John Babbitt
Off Mgr: Katherine Nazaroff
Off Admin: S Rodriguez
Off Admin: Sandra Tenorio
Off Admin: Dolores Torres
Site Mgr: Wing Lane
Site Mgr: Danny Salcido
Teacher Pr: Margaret Hesselgrave
Psych: Diana Ayala
Psych: Rosanne Hoang
Psych: Jenny Tobias

D-U-N-S 07-980-6917
HACKENSACK CITY SCHOOL DISTRICT
191 2nd St, Hackensack, NJ 07601-2417
Tel (201) 646-8000 *Founded/Ownrshp* 2015
Sales 93.0MM *EMP* 800^E
SIC 8211 Public elementary & secondary schools
Schl Brd P: Veronica McKenna
Psych: Andy Cooper

D-U-N-S 61-208-4871
HACKENSACK MERIDIAN HEALTH INC
MERIDIAN HOSPITAL
(*Suby of* HACKENSACK UNIVERSITY MEDICAL CENTER) ★
343 Thornall St, Edison, NJ 08837-2206
Tel (732) 751-7500 *Founded/Ownrshp* 2016
Sales 5.9MM *EMP* 8,900
SIC 8062

D-U-N-S 07-991-4571
HACKENSACK UNIVERSITY HEALTH NETWORK INC
HACKENSACK UNIVERSITY MEDICAL
30 Prospect Ave, Hackensack, NJ 07601-1915
Tel (551) 996-2000 *Founded/Ownrshp* 1888
Sales 551.1M *EMP* 8,000
SIC 8062 General medical & surgical hospitals
Pr: Robert Charles Garrett

HACKENSACK UNIVERSITY MEDICAL
See HACKENSACK UNIVERSITY HEALTH NETWORK INC

D-U-N-S 04-279-7571
HACKENSACK UNIVERSITY MEDICAL CENTER
30 Prospect Ave Ste 1, Hackensack, NJ 07601-1915
Tel (201) 996-2000 *Founded/Ownrshp* 1888
Sales 1.3MMM *EMP* 16,075^E
SIC 8062 Hospital, medical school affiliation
Pr: Robert Charles Garrett
COO: Kenneth Bodkin
**COO:* Ketul J Patel
**CFO:* Anthony Esposito
**CFO:* Harold P Hogstron
Ch: Joseph E Parrillo
Ofcr: Tom Flynn
Ex VP: Robert L Glenning
Ex VP: Susan Pomponio
Ex VP: Ihor S Sawczuk MD
**VP:* Dr William C Black
VP: William Black
VP: Brittany Chiusolo
VP: Roderick Clemente
**VP:* Andre J Ferullo
**VP:* Antoinette Fiore
**VP:* Robert M Koller
VP: Anne Pritcheta
VP: Anne Pritchett
VP: Jackie Trobiano

D-U-N-S 80-197-1511
HACKENSACKUMC MOUNTAINSIDE
MOUNTAINSIDE HOSPITAL
(*Suby of* LHP HOSPITAL GROUP INC) ★
1 Bay Ave, Montclair, NJ 07042-4837
Tel (973) 429-6000 *Founded/Ownrshp* 1891
Sales 210.6MM *EMP* 1,200
SIC 8062 General medical & surgical hospitals
CEO: John Fromhold
Chf Rad: Richard Mattern
Chf Rad: Frank Yuppa
Pr: Marjory Langer
COO: Everett Devaney Fache
Ch: Franklyn Jenifer
Treas: Mark Drzala
Trst: Marianne Centanni
Ofcr: Timothy Murphy
Ofcr: Karen Patanella
Ofcr: E Santelmo
VP: Tony Gilberti
VP: Dusan Knezevic
Exec: Rajitha Gujja

D-U-N-S 06-518-3097
▲ **HACKETT GROUP INC**
1001 Brickell Bay Dr # 3000, Miami, FL 33131-4905
Tel (305) 375-8005 *Founded/Ownrshp* 1997
Sales 260.9MM *EMP* 904^E
Accts Bdo Usa Llp Miami Florida
Tkr Sym HCKT *Exch* NGM
SIC 8742 Management consulting services
Ch Bd: Ted A Fernandez
**COO:* David N Dungan
CFO: Robert A Ramirez
Ofcr: Ulysses S Knotts III
Ex VP: Michelle Ramirez
Sr VP: Robert C Greene
Mng Dir: Satya Bommireddy
CTO: Brad Frink
Sales Exec: Christopher Key
Snr Mgr: Gary Womack
Board of Directors: Richard N Hamlin, John R Harris, Edwin A Huston, Alan T G Wix

D-U-N-S 07-361-6930
HACKETTSTOWN COMMUNITY HOSPITAL (INC)
HACKETTSTOWN REGIONAL MED CTR
651 Willow Grove St Ste A, Hackettstown, NJ 07840-1798
Tel (908) 852-5100 *Founded/Ownrshp* 1973
Sales 84.9MM *EMP* 700^E
SIC 8062 General medical & surgical hospitals
CEO: Joseph Atrunfio
**Pr:* Gene C Milton
**CEO:* Joseph A Trunfio
COO: Rick Armstrong
**COO:* Stella Visaggio
**CFO:* Robert Peterson
Chf Mktg O: Kenneth Janowski
IT Man: Chuck Pierce
Mktg Dir: Lisa Dimiceli
Doctor: Eric Gross
Doctor: Clay Henrichs

HACKETTSTOWN REGIONAL MED CTR
See HACKETTSTOWN COMMUNITY HOSPITAL (INC)

D-U-N-S 05-585-7643 IMP
HACKLEY HOSPITAL
MERCY HEALTH PARTNERS
1700 Clinton St, Muskegon, MI 49442-5591
Tel (231) 728-4950 *Founded/Ownrshp* 1902
Sales 177.8MM *EMP* 1,500
SIC 8062 General medical & surgical hospitals
Ch Bd: Thomas E Stone
**Pr:* Gordon A Mudler
CFO: Gary Allore
**Treas:* William Eyke Jr
**V Ch Bd:* Richard Witham
Trst: Richard Wilcox
Sr VP: Shirley Lynch
VP: Michael J Ratchord
Dir Rad: Steve Rop
Chf Nrs Of: Scott Howard
Dir IT: William Stefl

D-U-N-S 96-355-0736 IMP
■ **HACKNEY LADISH INC**
(*Suby of* PCC) ★
708 S Elmira Ave, Russellville, AR 72802-9637
Tel (479) 968-7555 *Founded/Ownrshp* 1975
Sales 109.6MM^E *EMP* 330
SIC 3089 3463 Fittings for pipe, plastic; Flange, valve or pipe fitting forgings, nonferrous
CEO: Kenneth D Buck
**COO:* Brian Byrum
CFO: Ekua Ollennu
**VP:* Roger A Cooke
**VP:* Michael Maxwell
**VP:* Kirk Morgan

Genl Mgr: Ed Hagerdorn
Dir IT: Michael Bodinger
IT Man: Larry Harmeyer
IT Man: Michel Lendish
Mtls Mgr: James Keene

D-U-N-S 00-841-2512
HACKNSCK HSPTL EMPLYS FDRL CRDT UN (INC)
241 Moore St, Hackensack, NJ 07601-7533
Tel (201) 996-2000 *Founded/Ownrshp* 1979
Sales NA *EMP* 1
SIC 6061 Federal credit unions
Pr: John Ferguson

HACLA
See HOUSING AUTHORITY OF CITY OF LOS ANGELES

D-U-N-S 07-329-6535
HADASSAH MEDICAL RELIEF ASSOCIATION INC
40 Wall St, New York, NY 10005-1304
Tel (212) 355-7900 *Founded/Ownrshp* 1925
Sales 95.4MM *EMP* 330
Accts Kpmg Llp New York Ny
SIC 8322 First aid service; Temporary relief service; Refugee service
Pr: Gary Slavin
**Treas:* Ruth B Hurwitz
**VP:* Sandra Alfonsi
**VP:* Sharon Jacobson
**VP:* Sandra King
**VP:* Susan Mark
**VP:* Renee Resnik
**VP:* Natalie Silverman
**VP:* Roselle Ungar
**VP:* Theda Zuckerman

D-U-N-S 04-631-2559 IMP/EXP
■ **HADCO CORP**
(*Suby of* SANMINA CORP) ★
12a Manor Pkwy, Salem, NH 03079-2841
Tel (603) 421-3400 *Founded/Ownrshp* 2000
Sales 423.2MM^E *EMP* 7,850
SIC 3672 Printed circuit boards
Pr: Andrew E Lietz
**Ch Bd:* Horace H Irvine II
**CFO:* Timothy P Losik
Genl Mgr: Jose Carraquello

D-U-N-S 78-998-7620 IMP/EXP
HADCO METAL TRADING CO LLC
(*Suby of* SCOPE METALS GROUP LTD)
555 State Rd, Bensalem, PA 19020-7704
Tel (215) 695-2705 *Founded/Ownrshp* 2006
Sales 169.3MM^E *EMP* 160
SIC 5051 Aluminum bars, rods, ingots, sheets, pipes, plates, etc.
CEO: Gilad Fishman
CFO: Ayelet Shtaub
Prin: Ori Ben-Amotz
Brnch Mgr: Robert Worth
CTO: Itay Shtaub
Prd Mgr: Vladimir Osykin

D-U-N-S 07-047-1875
■ **HADCO SANTA CLARA INC**
(*Suby of* SANMINA CORP) ★
500 El Camino Real, Santa Clara, CA 95050-4345
Tel (408) 241-9900 *Founded/Ownrshp* 2005
Sales 64.9MM^E *EMP* 2,000^E
SIC 3672 3679 Printed circuit boards; Harness assemblies for electronic use: wire or cable
Sr VP: Chris Mastrogiacomo
VP: Jerry Bauer

HADCO SUPPLY
See AIREFCO INC

D-U-N-S 78-366-0723 IMP
HADDAD APPAREL GROUP LTD
HADDAD BRANDS
(*Suby of* HADSON REALTY DIV) ★
90 E 5th St Ste 1, Bayonne, NJ 07002-4272
Tel (201) 356-2000 *Founded/Ownrshp* 1990
Sales 155.2MM^E *EMP* 230
SIC 5137 Women's & children's clothing
Ch Bd: Edward Haddad
Ex VP: Richard Haddad
**VP:* Charles S Haddad
VP: Marc Weintraub
Mktg Dir: Fran Boller

HADDAD BRANDS
See HADDAD APPAREL GROUP LTD

D-U-N-S 07-009-5237
HADDAD ORGANIZATION LTD
HADSON REALTY DIV
90 E 5th St Ste 1, Bayonne, NJ 07002-4272
Tel (201) 339-0665 *Founded/Ownrshp* 1902
Sales 155.2MM^E *EMP* 457
SIC 6531 Real estate agents & managers
Pr: Edward Haddad
**VP:* Marc Weintraub

D-U-N-S 00-194-9916 IMP/EXP
■ **HADDON HOUSE FOOD PRODUCTS INC**
(*Suby of* UNITED NATURAL FOODS INC) ★
250 Old Marlton Pike, Medford, NJ 08055-8760
Tel (609) 654-7901 *Founded/Ownrshp* 1960, 2016
Sales 828.0MM^E *EMP* 1,300
SIC 5149 Spices & seasonings; Specialty food items
CEO: David Anderson Jr
Dir IT: Bruce Tieck
Mktg Dir: Lee Rucker

HADSON REALTY DIV
See HADDAD ORGANIZATION LTD

HAECO AMERICAS
See TIMCO AVIATION SERVICES INC

D-U-N-S 07-949-9378
HAECO USA HOLDINGS INC
(*Suby of* HONG KONG AIRCRAFT ENGINEERING COMPANY LIMITED)
623 Radar Rd, Greensboro, NC 27410-6221
Tel (336) 668-4410 *Founded/Ownrshp* 2013
Sales 768.6MM^E *EMP* 6,794^E
SIC 4581 Airports, flying fields & services
CEO: Tang Kin Wing Augustus

D-U-N-S 05-782-7420 IMP
▲ **HAEMONETICS CORP**
400 Wood Rd, Braintree, MA 02184-2486
Tel (781) 848-7100 *Founded/Ownrshp* 1971
Sales 908.8MM *EMP* 3,225
Tkr Sym HAE *Exch* NYS
SIC 3841 3845 Medical instruments & equipment, blood & bone work; Blood transfusion equipment; Electromedical equipment
Pr: Christopher Simon
**Ch Bd:* Richard J Meelia
COO: Kent Davies
CFO: William P Burke
Ofcr: Sandra L Jesse
Ex VP: Brian Burns
Ex VP: Neil Ryding
VP: Dawn Dall
VP: Dan Goldstein
VP: Walt Hauck
VP: Walter Morse
VP: Tony Pare
VP: John Perullo
VP: Howard Rosen
Board of Directors: Catherine M Burzik, Charles J Dockendorff, Susan Bartlett Foote, Ronald G Gelbman, Pedro P Granadillo, Mark W Kroll, Ronald L Merriman

D-U-N-S 09-615-7375 IMP/EXP
HAFELE AMERICA CO (NC)
(*Suby of* HAFELE GMBH & CO KG)
3901 Cheyenne Dr, Archdale, NC 27263-3157
Tel (336) 434-2322 *Founded/Ownrshp* 1973
Sales 125.7MM^E *EMP* 350
SIC 5072 Hardware; Furniture hardware
Pr: Paul K Smith
**CFO:* Gary A Crysel
**VP:* Ursula Hafele
Creative D: Laurie Hall
Genl Mgr: Brad Borne
Tech Mgr: Michael Wood
Trfc Mgr: Angela Myers
Mktg Dir: Todd Mason
Mktg Mgr: Steve Hubbard
Mktg Mgr: Jake Van Wyk
Manager: Luis Mata

D-U-N-S 04-148-8537
HAGADONE INVESTMENT CO INC
111 S 1st St, Coeur D Alene, ID 83814-2794
Tel (208) 667-3431 *Founded/Ownrshp* 1959
Sales 314.1MM^E *EMP* 2,250
SIC 2711 7011 Newspapers, publishing & printing; Motels; Hotels
Pr: Duane B Hagadone
**CFO:* Doug Magnuson
**Treas:* Art Flagan
**VP:* Brad Hagadone
**VP:* Leslie Ward

HAGEMEYER NORTH AMERICA
See HAGEMEYER PPS LTD

D-U-N-S 13-222-8862
HAGEMEYER NORTH AMERICA HOLDINGS INC
11680 Great Oaks Way, Alpharetta, GA 30022-2457
Tel (843) 745-2400 *Founded/Ownrshp* 1999
Sales 221.8MM^E *EMP* 3,400
SIC 5085

HAGEMEYER NORTH AMERICA, INC.
See VALLEN DISTRIBUTION INC

D-U-N-S 80-640-5119
HAGEMEYER PPS LTD
HAGEMEYER NORTH AMERICA
(*Suby of* SONEPAR USA HOLDINGS INC) ★
1460 Tobias Gadson Blvd, Charleston, SC 29407-4793
Tel (843) 745-2400 *Founded/Ownrshp* 1999
Sales 3.7MMM^E *EMP* 3,200
SIC 5063 Electrical apparatus & equipment
Pr: David Gabriel
**Sec:* Andros Neocleous

HAGER HINGE COMPANY
See C HAGER & SONS HINGE MANUFACTURING CO

D-U-N-S 00-693-5306 IMP
HAGERTY BROTHERS CO
INDUSTRIAL PRODUCTS DIV
1506 W Detweiller Dr, Peoria, IL 61615-1601
Tel (309) 589-0200 *Founded/Ownrshp* 1860
Sales 126.1MM^E *EMP* 275
SIC 5072 Hardware; Saw blades; Bolts; Nuts (hardware)
Pr: Randy Fellerhoff
**VP:* Tom Clark
Genl Mgr: Paul Seaman
Sls Mgr: Adam Shaw

D-U-N-S 62-627-5465
HAGERTY INSURANCE AGENCY INC
141 Rvers Edge Dr Ste 200, Traverse City, MI 49684
Tel (231) 947-6868 *Founded/Ownrshp* 1992
Sales NA *EMP* 400
SIC 6411 Insurance agents, brokers & service
Pr: McKeel Hagerty
**Pr:* Louise Hagerty
**Treas:* Fred Turcotte
Chf Mktg O: Clinton Sly
Ofcr: Penny Sweeney
VP: Dan Beutler
VP: Angie Gallo
VP: Kevin Manning
VP: Joseph Niemer
VP: Carmen Stevens
Exec: Coco Stachnik

HAGGAR CLOTHING COMPANY
See HAGGAR CORP

D-U-N-S 00-792-6645 IMP
HAGGAR CLOTHING CO (NV)
(*Suby of* HAGGAR CLOTHING CO) ★
1507 Lbj Fwy Ste 100, Farmers Branch, TX 75234-6088
Tel (214) 352-8481 *Founded/Ownrshp* 1926
Sales 622.1MM[E] *EMP* 2,200
SIC 2325 2311 2321 5611 5651 Men's & boys' trousers & slacks; Men's & boys' jeans & dungarees; Shorts (outerwear): men's, youths' & boys'; Slacks, dress: men's, youths' & boys'; Tailored suits & formal jackets; Suits, men's & boys': made from purchased materials; Tailored dress & sport coats: men's & boys'; Men's & boys' furnishings; Men's & boys' dress shirts; Sport shirts, men's & boys': from purchased materials; Flannel shirts, except work: men's, youths' & boys'; Men's & boys' clothing stores; Family clothing stores
CEO: Michael B Stitt
Pr: David Yarbrough
Treas: Robert Qualls
Chf Mktg O: Edward M Jones III
Sr VP: Steve Bernier
Sr VP: Joseph Harris
Sr VP: Rich Honiball
Sr VP: Tad Parnell
Sr VP: Sandi Stevens
Sr VP: Nanditha Zuckerman
VP: Tony Anzovino
VP: Paul Cronin
VP: Nancy Dowling
VP: Rebecca Maticko
VP: Don Schneider
VP: Linda Shirley
Dir: Kevin Oneill

D-U-N-S 16-091-1657 IMP
HAGGAR CORP
HAGGAR CLOTHING COMPANY
(*Suby of* TEXAS CLOTHING HOLDING CORP) ★
1507 Lyndon B Johnson Fwy, Farmers Branch, TX 75234-6088
Tel (214) 352-8481 *Founded/Ownrshp* 1926
Sales 631.6MM[E] *EMP* 3,200
SIC 2325 2311 2321 5611 6794 Men's & boys' trousers & slacks; Slacks, dress: men's, youths' & boys'; Jeans: men's, youths' & boys'; Shorts (outerwear): men's, youths' & boys'; Tailored suits & formal jackets; Suits, men's & boys': made from purchased materials; Tailored dress & sport coats: men's & boys'; Men's & boys' furnishings; Men's & boys' dress shirts; Sport shirts, men's & boys': from purchased materials; Flannel shirts, except work: men's, youths' & boys'; Men's & boys' clothing stores; Copyright buying & licensing
CEO: Michael B Stitt
**CFO:* Rob Adamek
Ofcr: Mary Curtis
VP: Nanditha Zuckerman
Sales Exec: Edward M Jones
Sales Exec: Barbara Switek
Mktg Mgr: Chirine Boukarroum
Mktg Mgr: Nancy Flores
Board of Directors: Rae F Evans, Donald E Godwin, Richard W Heath, Thomas G Kahn, J Neal Thomas, John C Tolleson

D-U-N-S 07-982-3517
HAGGEN ACQUISITION LLC
(*Suby of* HAGGEN OPERATIONS HOLDINGS LLC) ★
2211 Rimland Dr Ste 300, Bellingham, WA 98226-5699
Tel (360) 733-8720 *Founded/Ownrshp* 2011
Sales 919.2MM[E] *EMP* 11,676[E]
SIC 8748 Business consulting
CFO: Blake Barnett

D-U-N-S 02-726-6733
HAGGEN INC
TOP FOOD & DRUGS
(*Suby of* HAGGEN ACQUISITION LLC) ★
2211 Rimland Dr Ste 300, Bellingham, WA 98226-5699
Tel (360) 733-8720 *Founded/Ownrshp* 1962
Sales 919.2MM[E] *EMP* 3,900
Accts Moss Adams Llp
SIC 5411 5912 Supermarkets, chain; Drug stores
Pr: John Clougher
**CFO:* Blake Barnett
**CFO:* Ron Stevens
**Co-Ch Bd:* Donald Haggen
**VP:* Derrick Anderson
VP: Mike Lobaugh
**VP:* Clement Stevens
**VP:* John Turley
Genl Mgr: Jim Taylor
Mktg Mgr: Jamie Markoski

D-U-N-S 07-982-2034
HAGGEN OPERATIONS HOLDINGS LLC
2211 Rimland Dr Ste 300, Bellingham, WA 98226-5699
Tel (360) 733-8720 *Founded/Ownrshp* 2014
Sales 930.4MM[E] *EMP* 11,763[E]
SIC 8748 Business consulting

D-U-N-S 00-529-4947 IMP/EXP
HAGIE HOLDING CO (IA)
721 Central Ave W, Clarion, IA 50525-1335
Tel (515) 532-2861 *Founded/Ownrshp* 1947
Sales 167.5MM[E] *EMP* 860
SIC 3523 Sprayers & spraying machines, agricultural; Planting, haying, harvesting & processing machinery
CEO: Alan B Hagie
CFO: Melissa Hackley
Dir Soc: Carmen Rodriguez
MIS Dir: Wendy Brandt
IT Man: Lucas Boyken
Sfty Mgr: Dave Larson
Opers Mgr: Robin Tester
Prd Mgr: Nic Wycoff
Mktg Mgr: Amber Kohlhaas
Manager: Eddy Roesch
Manager: Todd Roland

D-U-N-S 01-310-9863
HAHN AUTOMOTIVE WAREHOUSE INC
ADVANTAGE AUTO STORES
415 W Main St, Rochester, NY 14608-1944
Tel (585) 235-1595 *Founded/Ownrshp* 2001
Sales 326.2MM[E] *EMP* 1,000
SIC 5013 Automotive supplies & parts
Ch Bd: Eli Futerman
**Pr:* Daniel J Chessin
CFO: Mike Piccolo
VP: Michael Kasel
**VP:* Timothy Vergo
Adm Dir: Michelle Verhay
Dist Mgr: Brian Aveyard
Genl Mgr: Keith Scott
Genl Mgr: Eddie Seagroves
Dir IT: Peter Ferrari

HAHNEMANN UNIVERSITY HOSPITAL
See TENET HEALTHSYSTEM HAHNEMANN LLC

D-U-N-S 07-999-1721
HAIER AMERICA CO LLC
(*Suby of* HAIER GROUP CORPORATION)
1800 Valley Rd, Wayne, NJ 07470-2047
Tel (973) 617-1800 *Founded/Ownrshp* 2014
Sales 500.0MM *EMP* 356[E]
SIC 5064 Ranges
CEO: Adrian Micu
CFO: Richard Cao

D-U-N-S 04-581-5722 IMP/EXP
HAIER AMERICA TRADING LLC
(*Suby of* HAIER GROUP CORPORATION)
1800 Valley Rd, Wayne, NJ 07470-2047
Tel (973) 617-1800 *Founded/Ownrshp* 1999
Sales 279.7MM[E] *EMP* 300
SIC 5064 Electrical appliances, major; Ranges; Electric household appliances
Pr: Shariff Kan
COO: Kevin Dexter
CFO: Ike Jiang
CFO: Grace Li
Sr VP: Rian Cain
Sr VP: Lintau Lu
VP: Maryjane Fanizzi
VP: Audrey Rohan
CIO: Deanna Johnston
MIS Mgr: Michael Zammit
VP Sls: Carlos Mendia

D-U-N-S 07-842-4131 IMP/EXP
HAIER US APPLIANCE SOLUTIONS INC
GE APPLIANCES
(*Suby of* QINGDAO HAIER CO., LTD.)
4000 Buechel Bank Rd, Louisville, KY 40225-0001
Tel (502) 452-4666 *Founded/Ownrshp* 2001, 2016
Sales 1.5MMM[E] *EMP* 6,000[E]
SIC 3639 Dishwashing machines, household
Pr: Pan Li
**VP:* Chunyu MA

D-U-N-S 14-927-4073 IMP
HAIFA NORTH AMERICA INC
(*Suby of* HAIFA CHEMICALS LTD.)
307 Cranes Roost Blvd, Altamonte Springs, FL 32701-3441
Tel (407) 862-6400 *Founded/Ownrshp* 2002
Sales 100.0MM *EMP* 27
SIC 5191 5169 Fertilizer & fertilizer materials; Food additives & preservatives
CEO: Marc Lebl
Ch: Natan Feldman

HAIGHT ASHBURY FREE CLINICS -
See HEALTHRIGHT 360

D-U-N-S 04-896-6654 IMP
HAIGHTS CROSS COMMUNICATIONS INC
136 Madison Ave Fl 8, New York, NY 10016-6711
Tel (212) 209-0500 *Founded/Ownrshp* 1997
Sales 99.1MM[E] *EMP* 542[E]
SIC 2731 Book publishing
CEO: Rick Noble
Pr: Kevin R Brueggeman
Pr: Rich Freese
CFO: Melissa L Linsky
Sr VP: Julie Latzer
VP: Diane Q Curtin
VP: Faiz Mohammed

D-U-N-S 82-470-0850 IMP/EXP
▲ HAIN CELESTIAL GROUP INC
1111 Marcus Ave Ste 100, New Hyde Park, NY 11042-2033
Tel (516) 587-5000 *Founded/Ownrshp* 1993
Sales 2.6MMM *EMP* 6,307
Tkr Sym HAIN *Exch* NGS
SIC 2023 2034 2096 2086 2844 Dried & powdered milk & milk products; Dried milk preparations; Dietary supplements, dairy & non-dairy based; Vegetable flour, meal & powder; Potato chips & similar snacks; Iced tea & fruit drinks, bottled & canned; Toilet preparations
Ch Bd: Irwin D Simon
COO: James R Meiers
COO: Gary W Tickle
CFO: John Carroll
CFO: Pasquale Conte
Chf Cred: Denise M Faltischek
Ex VP: Stephen Smith
Sr VP: Michael B McGuinness
VP: Tom Arcuri
VP: Helen Kor
VP: David Ziegert
Exec: Andrea Proulx
Board of Directors: Richard C Berke, Andrew R Heyer, Raymond W Kelly, Roger Meltzer, Scott M O'neil, Adrianne Shapira, Lawrence S Zilavy

D-U-N-S 96-336-8662
■ HAIN REFRIGERATED FOODS INC
GREEK GODS
(*Suby of* HAIN CELESTIAL GROUP INC) ★
21707 66th Ave W, Mountlake Terrace, WA 98043-2103
Tel (425) 485-2476 *Founded/Ownrshp* 2010
Sales 107.0MM *EMP* 18
SIC 2024 5143 Ice cream & ice milk; Yogurt
CEO: Basel Nassar
**Pr:* Irwin D Simon
**Prin:* Stephanos Margaritis

D-U-N-S 04-455-4731 IMP
HAINES & KIBBLEHOUSE INC
LOCUST RIDGE QUARRY
2052 Lucon Rd, Skippack, PA 19474
Tel (610) 584-8500 *Founded/Ownrshp* 1967
Sales 92.0MM[E] *EMP* 150
SIC 1794 1611 1422 2951 Excavation work; Surfacing & paving; Limestones, ground; Asphalt paving mixtures & blocks
Ch Bd: Scott Haines
**Pr:* John B Haines IV
**Sec:* John R Kibblehouse
Bd of Dir: John P Sivick
Top Exec: Jeff Litweiler
Off Mgr: Jeremy Huiser
Trfc Dir: Brian Hohenshilt
Sales Exec: David Potter

D-U-N-S 07-319-6867
■ HAINES CITY HEALTH MANAGEMENT ASSOCIATION INC
HMA
(*Suby of* HMA) ★
40100 Highway 27, Davenport, FL 33837-5906
Tel (863) 422-4971 *Founded/Ownrshp* 1993
Sales 173.7MM *EMP* 800
SIC 8062 General medical & surgical hospitals
CEO: Jay Finnegan
**COO:* Brent Burish
**CFO:* Tonja Mosley
**VP:* Ann Barnheart
VP: Timothy R Parry
Dir Rad: Ronald Brinsko
Dir Rx: John Dougherty
DP Dir: Louis Jones
Orthpdst: Paul Dowdy
Orthpdst: Ponnavolu Reddy
Nrsg Dir: Christine Kipt Rn

D-U-N-S 80-602-3990
HAIRSTYLISTS MANAGEMENT SYSTEMS INC
URBAN HAIR AND SPA
12700 Industrial Park Blv, Minneapolis, MN 55441-3947
Tel (763) 550-1332 *Founded/Ownrshp* 1993
Sales 15.7MM[E] *EMP* 1,000
SIC 7231 Beauty shops
Pr: Michael Kunin
**CEO:* Elliot Cohen
**CFO:* Michael Brooks
**Ch:* Daniel Kunin

D-U-N-S 00-137-9429 IMP/EXP
HAJOCA CORP
WEINSTEIN SUPPLY
127 Coulter Ave, Ardmore, PA 19003-2473
Tel (610) 649-1430 *Founded/Ownrshp* 1981
Sales 2.4MMM[E] *EMP* 3,500
SIC 5074 Plumbing fittings & supplies
Pr: Rick Fantham
**Ch Bd:* Richard J Klau
Top Exec: Snehil Mahajan
VP: Chris Pappo
**VP:* Christopher M Pappo
Exec: Eileen Urso
Brnch Mgr: Christopher Bounds
Brnch Mgr: Jack Hagan
Brnch Mgr: Eric Kelley
Brnch Mgr: Mark Price
Div Mgr: Steve Ferry

D-U-N-S 15-184-9051
HAKKASAN HOLDINGS LLC
ANGEL MANAGEMENT GROUP
6385 S Rainbow Blvd # 800, Las Vegas, NV 89118-3201
Tel (702) 212-8804 *Founded/Ownrshp* 2011
Sales 130.8MM[E] *EMP* 682[E]
SIC 8741 Hotel or motel management
Ex VP: Derek Silberstein
VP: James Algate
VP: Jason Aranas
VP: Jerome Klint
Exec: Lloyd Bansil
Exec: Brandon Grady
Exec: Rory Macdonald
Ex Dir: Omar Gutierrez
Ex Dir: Larry Murphy
Ex Dir: Tracee Nalewak
Ex Dir: Ryan Porter

D-U-N-S 80-228-3572
HAKS ENGINEERS ARCHITECTS AND LAND SURVEYORS PC
40 Wall St Fl 11, New York, NY 10005-1357
Tel (212) 747-1997 *Founded/Ownrshp* 1991
Sales 114.8MM *EMP* 595
SIC 8712 8711 8713

D-U-N-S 04-816-9056 IMP/EXP
HAL LEONARD CORP
7777 W Bluemound Rd, Milwaukee, WI 53213-3400
Tel (414) 774-3630 *Founded/Ownrshp* 1947
Sales 119.6MM[E] *EMP* 420
SIC 2741

D-U-N-S 00-922-1854
HALABI INC
DURACITE
2100 Huntington Dr, Fairfield, CA 94533-9731
Tel (707) 402-1600 *Founded/Ownrshp* 1995
Sales 119.0MM[E] *EMP* 297
SIC 3281 1799 Cut stone & stone products; Counter top installation
CEO: Fadi M Halabi
**CFO:* George Marino

D-U-N-S 04-966-8189
HALCO (MINING) INC
12 Federal St Ste 320, Pittsburgh, PA 15212-5753
Tel (412) 235-0265 *Founded/Ownrshp* 1953
Sales 292.9MM[E] *EMP* 2,400[E]
SIC 1099 Bauxite mining
Pr: Pat Fyore
**Treas:* Robert St Pierre

D-U-N-S 79-093-5170
▲ HALCON RESOURCES CORP
1000 La St Ste 6700, Houston, TX 77002
Tel (832) 538-0300 *Founded/Ownrshp* 2004
Sales 550.2MM *EMP* 323[E]
Tkr Sym HK *Exch* NYS
SIC 1311 Crude petroleum & natural gas
Ch Bd: Floyd C Wilson
Pr: Stephen W Herod
CFO: Mark J Mize
Sr VP: Quentin R Hicks
Sr VP: Leah R Kasparek
Sr VP: Tina S Obut
Sr VP: Joseph S Rinando III
Sr VP: Jon C Wright
VP: Joseph Rinando
Dir Risk M: Tim C McDonald
Corp Couns: Jason R Payne
Board of Directors: James W Christmas, Tucker S Bridwell, John W Brown, Thomas R Fuller, Kevin E Godwin, Paul P Huffard IV, David B Miller, Daniel A Rioux, Michael A Vlasic, Mark A Welsh IV

D-U-N-S 02-289-9975
HALDEMAN-HOMME INC
ANDERSON LADD
430 Industrial Blvd Ne, Minneapolis, MN 55413-2979
Tel (612) 331-4880 *Founded/Ownrshp* 1953
Sales 100.0MM *EMP* 140
SIC 5021 5211 5084 Office & public building furniture; Racks; Shelving; Flooring, wood; Materials handling machinery
Ch Bd: Ernest Stalock
**Pr:* Paul Fedji
**CEO:* Mike Propp
**Treas:* K C Gunther
**VP:* Ron Johnson
Exec: Leroy Biteler
Genl Mgr: Jason Sanborn
IT Man: Chris Betlach
IT Man: Dan Weinmeyer
Sls Mgr: Tim McGowan

D-U-N-S 10-651-3385 IMP/EXP
HALDEX BRAKE PRODUCTS CORP
(*Suby of* HALDEX PRODUCTS) ★
10930 N Pomona Ave, Kansas City, MO 64153-1256
Tel (816) 891-2470 *Founded/Ownrshp* 1998
Sales 297.0MM[E] *EMP* 500
SIC 3714 Air brakes, motor vehicle
Pr: Bo Annvik
Pr: Ulf Herlin
CFO: Stefan Johanon
Chf Mktg O: Mike Regan
**VP:* Gary Boznik
Exec: Kim Garn
Mng Dir: Magnus Bergstr
Rgnl Mgr: Dan O'Dowd
Genl Mgr: Jerry Donovan
Genl Mgr: Jim Muntean
Genl Mgr: Greg Vassmer

D-U-N-S 02-144-0151 IMP
HALDEX INC
HALDEX PRODUCTS
(*Suby of* HALDEX AB)
10930 N Pomona Ave, Kansas City, MO 64153-1256
Tel (816) 891-2470 *Founded/Ownrshp* 1973
Sales 546.3MM[E] *EMP* 3,715
SIC 3714 3594 Motor vehicle brake systems & parts; Fluid power pumps; Pumps, hydraulic power transfer
Pr: Claes Warnander
VP: Dan Debord
**VP:* Lennard Hammargren
**VP:* Charles Kleinhagen
**VP:* John Pepe
Dir IT: Doug Roof

HALDEX PRODUCTS
See HALDEX INC

HALE INDIAN RIVER GROVES
See SOUTHERN FULFILLMENT SERVICES LLC

D-U-N-S 07-366-3247 EXP
HALE TRAILER BRAKE & WHEEL INC
Cooper Rd Rr 73, Voorhees, NJ 08043
Tel (800) 232-6535 *Founded/Ownrshp* 1999
Sales 133.1MM[E] *EMP* 170
SIC 5511 7539 5531 Trucks, tractors & trailers: new & used; Trailer repair; Automobile & truck equipment & parts
Pr: Barry J Hale
VP: Thomas Weaver
Genl Mgr: Ira Eckstein
Trfc Dir: Bill Roche

D-U-N-S 04-706-7749
HALEY & ALDRICH INC
70 Blanchard Rd Ste 204, Burlington, MA 01803-5100
Tel (617) 886-7400 *Founded/Ownrshp* 1957
Sales 176.1MM[E] *EMP* 504
Accts Dicicco Gulman & Company Llp
SIC 8748 8711 Environmental consultant; Consulting engineer
Pr: Lawrence Smith
**CFO:* Robert Gabel
Bd of Dir: Eric Isacoff
Chf Mktg O: Anne Nason
Ofcr: William Fisher
Ofcr: Lisa Gray
Sr VP: Anntonette Alberti
Sr VP: Sean M Carroll
Sr VP: Marya Gorczyca
Sr VP: David Hagen
**Sr VP:* Mark X Haley
**Sr VP:* Steven R Kraemer
Sr VP: Phil Lagas
Sr VP: Bryan Sweeney
Sr VP: Paul Tornatore
VP: Doug Allen
VP: Lisa Jn Bradley
VP: Helder Costa
VP: Elie Haddad
VP: Keith Johnson
VP: Stephen Macintyre

HALEY BROS
See T M COBB CO

D-U-N-S 02-720-1219 IMP
HALF PRICE BOOKS RECORDS MAGAZINES INC
TEXAS BOOKMAN, THE
5803 E Northwest Hwy, Dallas, TX 75231-6519
Tel (214) 379-8000 *Founded/Ownrshp* 1972
Sales 254.1MM^E *EMP* 1,740^E
SIC 5942 5192 Book stores; Books
Pr: Sharon Anderson Wright
**Pr:* Kathy Doyle Thomas
CFO: Laura Beverly
**Treas:* Nando Arduini II
**Ex VP:* Jan Cornelius
Ex VP: Jan Cronelius
**Ex VP:* Tim Jernigan
Ex VP: Ellen O'Neal
VP: Bill Holland
VP: Eric James
**VP:* Charles Dee Mitchell
**VP:* Ellen O Neal
**VP:* Stephen Powers
**VP:* Robert Wilkie

D-U-N-S 05-013-1655
HALFF ASSOCIATES INC
ALBERT H HALFF ASSOCIATES
1201 N Bowser Rd, Richardson, TX 75081-2262
Tel (214) 346-6200 *Founded/Ownrshp* 1953
Sales 107.2MM^E *EMP* 532
SIC 8711 8713

D-U-N-S 10-007-9680
HALIFAX COUNTY PUBLIC SCHOOLS
1030 Mary Bethune St, Halifax, VA 24558-3213
Tel (434) 476-2171 *Founded/Ownrshp* 1900
Sales 82.4M *EMP* 1,100
SIC 8211 Public elementary & secondary schools

HALIFAX HEALTH
See HALIFAX HOME HEALTH

D-U-N-S 01-052-3041
HALIFAX HEALTH CARE SYSTEMS INC
303 N Clyde Morris Blvd, Daytona Beach, FL 32114-2709
Tel (386) 254-4000 *Founded/Ownrshp* 1928
Sales 321.4MM^E *EMP* 4,800
SIC 8062 8011 8063

D-U-N-S 79-830-0901
HALIFAX HOME HEALTH
HALIFAX HEALTH
3800 Woodbriar Trl, Port Orange, FL 32129-9626
Tel (386) 322-4700 *Founded/Ownrshp* 1987
Sales 464.9MM *EMP* 135
SIC 8082 7361 Home health care services; Nurses' registry

D-U-N-S 02-104-6429
■ HALIFAX MEDIA GROUP LLC
(*Suby of* NEW MEDIA INVESTMENT GROUP INC) ★
2339 Beville Rd, Daytona Beach, FL 32119-8720
Tel (386) 265-6700 *Founded/Ownrshp* 2015
Sales 414.4MM^E *EMP* 2,900
SIC 2711 Newspapers
CEO: Michael Redding
**COO:* Rick Martin
**Sr VP:* Bernie Szachara
Sls Mgr: Ken Workowski

D-U-N-S 01-352-6929
HALIFAX MEDIA HOLDINGS LLC
901 6th St, Daytona Beach, FL 32117-3352
Tel (386) 681-2404 *Founded/Ownrshp* 2009
Sales 305.9MM^E *EMP* 2,058^E
SIC 2711 2791 Newspapers; Newspapers, publishing & printing; Typesetting
CEO: Michael Redding

D-U-N-S 07-558-3393
HALIFAX REGIONAL MEDICAL CENTER INC
250 Smith Church Rd, Roanoke Rapids, NC 27870-4914
Tel (215) 994-4000 *Founded/Ownrshp* 1972
Sales 87.6MM *EMP* 830
Accts Dixon Hughes Goodman Llp Rale
SIC 8062 8011 General medical & surgical hospitals; Medical centers
Pr: Wil Mahone
VP: Fache Bruce
**VP:* Sherry Jensen
Dir Lab: Wanda Catts
Comm Dir: Elizabeth Huffman
Opers Mgr: Susan Ogburn

D-U-N-S 96-656-8581
HALIFAX STAFFING INC
303 N Clyde Morris Blvd, Daytona Beach, FL 32114-2709
Tel (386) 226-4560 *Founded/Ownrshp* 2011
Sales 214.0MM *EMP* 2
SIC 7363 Help supply services
Prin: Betty Holness

D-U-N-S 10-187-7884 IMP
■ HALKEY-ROBERTS CORP
(*Suby of* ATRION CORP) ★
2700 Halkey Roberts Pl N, Saint Petersburg, FL 33716-4103
Tel (727) 471-4200 *Founded/Ownrshp* 1996
Sales 100.4MM^E *EMP* 450
SIC 3842 Surgical appliances & supplies
Pr: David Battat
VP: Jim Bowling
**VP:* Alan King
**VP:* Lewis P Lecceardone
**VP:* John H Lucius
VP: Jeffery Strickland
Plng Mgr: Hanna Jasiukiewicz
CTO: Thomas Frank
IT Man: Timothy McCabe
Sfty Dirs: Mary Houle
QI Cn Mgr: Michael J Huether

HALL 2801 NETWORK ASSOC.
See HALL FINANCIAL GROUP LTD

D-U-N-S 06-599-7199
HALL AUTOMOTIVE LLC
441 Viking Dr, Virginia Beach, VA 23452-7309
Tel (757) 431-9944 *Founded/Ownrshp* 2006
Sales 342.5MM^E *EMP* 1,211
SIC 5511 Automobiles, new & used
**Pr:* William R Baker
**CEO:* Steven B Fader
CFO: William Baker
**Sec:* Christine M Champigny
**Ex VP:* Louis S Richards
**Ex VP:* Lonnie L Swiger
Dir IT: Nathan Warrior
Mktg Dir: Jean Mahon
Sales Asso: John Christian

D-U-N-S 01-024-1508
HALL CONTRACTING OF KENTUCKY INC (KY)
POWER-TEL ELECTRICAL
3800 Crittenden Dr, Louisville, KY 40209-1124
Tel (502) 367-6151 *Founded/Ownrshp* 1999
Sales 122.9MM^E *EMP* 220^E
SIC 1541 1623 1761 1731 Industrial buildings & warehouses; Underground utilities contractor; Roofing, siding & sheet metal work; Electrical work
CEO: Stephen M Priebe
**Sec:* Chris S Allen
**VP:* Mike Chism
**VP:* David Fischer
**VP:* Forrest T Roberts
**VP:* Tom Roberts Jr
**VP:* Jim Scott
**VP:* Anthony Shade
**VP:* Richard Shutt
VP Mktg: Steve Hall

D-U-N-S 06-919-0502
HALL COUNTY BOARD OF EDUCATION
711 Green St Nw Ste 100, Gainesville, GA 30501-3368
Tel (770) 534-1080 *Founded/Ownrshp* 1953
Sales 109.9MM^E *EMP* 3,600
Accts Russell W Hinton Cpa Cgfm
SIC 8211 School board
Ch: Nath Morris

HALL COUNTY GOVERNMENT
See HALL COUNTY OF GEORGIA

D-U-N-S 07-812-4617
HALL COUNTY OF GEORGIA
HALL COUNTY GOVERNMENT
2875 Browns Bridge Rd, Gainesville, GA 30504-5635
Tel (770) 535-8288 *Founded/Ownrshp* 1818
Sales NA *EMP* 1,600
Accts Bates Carter Co Llp Gainesv
SIC 9111
Ch: Richard Mecum
Ofcr: Katie Crumly
Exec: Katie Crumley
IT Man: Jessica York

D-U-N-S 07-847-3818
HALL COUNTY SCHOOL DISTRICT
711 Green St Nw Ste 100, Gainesville, GA 30501-3368
Tel (770) 534-1080 *Founded/Ownrshp* 2012
Sales 107.1MM^E *EMP* 2,744^E
SIC 8211 Public elementary & secondary schools
Bd of Dir: Todd Murrow
Adm Dir: Gary Stewart
Dir Sec: Earl Roach
Web Dev: Joseph Canada
Sls&Mrk Ex: Cindy Crow
Pr Dir: Gordon Higgins
Teacher Pr: Brad Brown
Psych: Monie Shope
HC Dir: Mamie Coker

D-U-N-S 10-060-2622
HALL COUNTY SCHOOL DISTRICT 2
GRAND ISLAND PUBLIC SCHOOLS
123 S Webb Rd, Grand Island, NE 68803-5110
Tel (308) 385-5886 *Founded/Ownrshp* 1882
Sales 89.8MM^E *EMP* 1,700
Accts Almquist Maltzahn Galloway & L
SIC 8211 9411 Elementary & secondary schools; School board; Administration of educational programs
VP: Tracy Brown
Ex Dir: Cory Gearhart
Genl Mgr: James Duff
MIS Dir: Cory Earhart
IT Man: Rose Zlomke
Pr Dir: Jack Sheard
Teacher Pr: Wayne Stelk
Psych: Mel Smith
HC Dir: Jill Foltz
HC Dir: Joanne Meyers

D-U-N-S 83-460-6543
HALL ENTERPRISES INC
LOGISTICS PLANNING SERVICES
731 Bielenberg Dr Ste 108, Woodbury, MN 55125-1701
Tel (651) 552-4905 *Founded/Ownrshp* 1987
Sales 88.3MM^E *EMP* 85
SIC 4731 Freight transportation arrangement
Ch Bd: Pamela I Hall
**Ch Bd:* Larry Hall
**Pr:* Justin Hall
**CEO:* Kirsten Hall
CFO: Mike Westland
**VP:* Nathan Hall
VP: Jason Johnson
Genl Mgr: Andrew Koval
VP Sls: Brian Mears

D-U-N-S 05-532-6110
HALL FINANCIAL GROUP LTD
HALL 2801 NETWORK ASSOC.
2323 Ross Ave Ste 200, Dallas, TX 75201-2723
Tel (972) 377-1100 *Founded/Ownrshp* 1997
Sales 101.2MM^E *EMP* 600
Accts Lane Gorman Trubitt Llp Dalla
SIC 6552 6531 Land subdividers & developers, commercial; Real estate managers
Genl Pt: Donald Braun
Pt: Craig Hall
Sr VP: Patricia Meadows

D-U-N-S 08-312-4789
HALL MANAGEMENT CORP
LAND & PERSONNEL MANAGEMENT
759 S Madera Ave, Kerman, CA 93630-1744
Tel (559) 846-7382 *Founded/Ownrshp* 2001
Sales 98.4MM^E *EMP* 2,000
Accts Gary C Simonian & Co Fresno
SIC 8741 Management services; Personnel management
Pr: Stacy Hampton
**VP:* James Randles

HALL VISION CLINIC
See THOMAS RONALD HALL OD

HALL-DALE MANOR
See NORTH COUNTRY ASSOCIATES INC

D-U-N-S 08-265-3858
▲ HALLADOR ENERGY CO
1660 Lincoln St Ste 2700, Denver, CO 80264-2701
Tel (303) 839-5504 *Founded/Ownrshp* 1949
Sales 340.1MM *EMP* 740^E
Tkr Sym HNRG *Exch* NAS
SIC 1241 1311 1382 Coal mining services; Crude petroleum & natural gas production; Oil & gas exploration services
Pr: Brent K Bilsland
**Ch Bd:* Victor P Stabio
CFO: Lawrence D Martin

D-U-N-S 00-891-5944
HALLEN CONSTRUCTION CO INC
4270 Austin Blvd, Island Park, NY 11558-1626
Tel (516) 432-8300 *Founded/Ownrshp* 1952
Sales 225.4MM *EMP* 250
Accts Albrecht Viggiano Zureck & C
SIC 1623 Water, sewer & utility lines
Ch Bd: Thomas B Poole
Pr: Ken Biondi
**Pr:* Shepard T Poole
Pr: Jim Small
**CEO:* Robert L Meschi
**Treas:* Monika Franke
**Ex VP:* Eugene J Hickey
Sr VP: Gene Hickey

D-U-N-S 00-918-5810
HALLER ENTERPRISES INC
212 Bucky Dr, Lititz, PA 17543-7695
Tel (888) 565-0546 *Founded/Ownrshp* 1983
Sales 84.6MM^E *EMP* 290
SIC 1711 1731 Plumbing contractors; Warm air heating & air conditioning contractor; General electrical contractor
Pr: Jrichard Haller
**CEO:* J Richard Haller
**CFO:* Mark Weaver
CIO: Steve Walter
Dir IT: Joshua Alonso
Dir IT: Test User
IT Man: Deana Hollister
Sales Asso: Tony Flocco
Sales Asso: Brian Suchy

HALLETT MATERIALS
See OMG MID WEST INC

D-U-N-S 96-440-9007 IMP/EXP
▲ HALLIBURTON CO
3000 N Sam Houston Pkwy E, Houston, TX 77032-3299
Tel (281) 871-2699 *Founded/Ownrshp* 1919
Sales 23.6MMM *EMP* 65,000
Tkr Sym HAL *Exch* NYS
SIC 1389 1382 1381 8711 Oil field services; Cementing oil & gas well casings; Well logging; Perforating well casings; Oil & gas exploration services; Drilling oil & gas wells; Petroleum, mining & chemical engineers
Ch Bd: David J Lesar
**Pr:* Jeffrey A Miller
CFO: Christian A Garcia
CFO: Mark McCollum
CFO: Mark A McCollum
Ex VP: Lawrence J Pope
Ex VP: Robb L Voyles
Sr VP: Christian Garcia
Sr VP: James B Renfroe
VP: James Antilley
VP: Michael Cheeseman
VP: David Field
VP: Charles E Geer Jr
VP: Larry Molnar
VP: Donald Murray
VP: Kim Stark
VP Bus Dev: David Prather
Dir Risk M: Paul Credo
Dir Risk M: Jeffrey Cregg
Dir Risk M: Paul Heuermann
Board of Directors: Debra L Reed, William E Albrecht, Alan M Bennett, James R Boyd, Milton Carroll, Murry S Gerber, Jose C Grubisich, Abdulaziz F Al Khayyal, Robert A Malone, J Landis Martin

D-U-N-S 96-464-5022 IMP
■ HALLIBURTON DELAWARE INC
(*Suby of* HALLIBURTON CO) ★
3000 Houston Ave, Houston, TX 77009-6735
Tel (713) 759-2600 *Founded/Ownrshp* 1996
Sales 20.8MMM^E *EMP* 57,300
SIC 1629 1611 1622 8711 1389 Power plant construction; Chemical plant & refinery construction; Oil refinery construction; Marine construction; Highway & street paving contractor; Bridge, tunnel & elevated highway; Bridge construction; Engineering services; Consulting engineer; Sanitary engineers; Pollution control engineering; Oil field services; Cementing oil & gas well casings; Well logging; Perforating well casings
Pr: David J Lesar
**Pr:* Lester L Colma
**Pr:* Garry H Dlaurton
**Pr:* Robert F Heinemann
**Pr:* Susan S Keith
**Pr:* Guy T Marcus
**Pr:* Gary V Mars
**Pr:* Charles Muchmore Jr
Ex VP: Albert O Cornelison
Ex VP: Christopher Gaut
Ex VP: Andy Lane
Sr VP: James B Renfroe
VP: Lyn Beaty
VP: Margaret Carriere
VP: David King
VP: Kenneth King
VP: Paul Koeller
VP: Michele Mastreen
VP: Susan Ponce
VP: Jim Renfroe
VP: Bill Sanstrom

D-U-N-S 04-329-6920 IMP/EXP
■ HALLIBURTON ENERGY SERVICES INC
(*Suby of* HALLIBURTON CO) ★
10200 Bellaire Blvd, Houston, TX 77072-5206
Tel (713) 839-3950 *Founded/Ownrshp* 1919, 1996
Sales 18.1MMM^E *EMP* 50,000^E
SIC 1389 Oil field services; Cementing oil & gas well casings; Well logging; Perforating well casings
Ch Bd: David J Lesar
**Pr:* Jeffrey Allen Miller
**CFO:* C Christopher Gaut
**CFO:* Mark A McCollum
**Treas:* Christian A Garcia
**Ex VP:* John W Gibson
**Ex VP:* Lawrence J Pope
**Sr VP:* Evelyn M Angelle
**VP:* Albert O Cornelison Jr
IT Man: Steve Matthews
IT Man: Binh Nguyen

D-U-N-S 88-309-0532
HALLMARK AVIATION SERVICES LP
(*Suby of* SWISSPORT INTERNATIONAL AG)
5757 W Century Blvd # 860, Los Angeles, CA 90045-6417
Tel (310) 215-0701 *Founded/Ownrshp* 1989
Sales 50.0MM *EMP* 1,400
SIC 7363 Help supply services
Pr: Philipp Huber
VP: Bernice James

D-U-N-S 82-677-8607
HALLMARK BUILDERS INC
520 S Main St, Middlebury, IN 46540-9701
Tel (574) 825-9850 *Founded/Ownrshp* 1992
Sales 190.0MM *EMP* 4
SIC 1521 Single-family housing construction
Pr: Cliff Miller

D-U-N-S 00-713-1113 IMP/EXP
HALLMARK CARDS INC (MO)
2501 Mcgee St, Kansas City, MO 64108-2600
Tel (816) 274-5111 *Founded/Ownrshp* 1910
Sales 7.6MMM^E *EMP* 27,000
SIC 2771

D-U-N-S 60-102-4003
▲ HALLMARK FINANCIAL SERVICES INC
777 Main St Ste 1000, Fort Worth, TX 76102-5314
Tel (817) 348-1600 *Founded/Ownrshp* 1990
Sales NA *EMP* 411^E
Accts Ernst & Young Llp Fort Worth
Tkr Sym HALL *Exch* NGM
SIC 6411 6311 Property & casualty insurance agent; Life insurance
Pr: Naveen Anand
**Ch Bd:* Mark E Schwarz
Sr VP: Jeffrey R Passmore
VP: Bill Doherty
Board of Directors: Scott T Berlin, James H Graves, Mark E Pape

D-U-N-S 11-524-7496
HALLMARK HEALTH CORP
170 Governors Ave, Medford, MA 02155-1643
Tel (781) 979-3000 *Founded/Ownrshp* 1900
Sales 6.0MM *EMP* 2,700
Accts Hallmark Health System Inc Me
SIC 8741 Management services; Nursing & personal care facility management
Chf Path: Dean Pappas
**V Ch:* Alan G Macdonald
V Ch: William F Rucci
**V Ch:* Donna West
**Treas:* John Keenan
**Treas:* James Nania
Chf Mktg O: Lori Howley
Ex VP: Matthew Paul
Dir OR: Donna Begum
Dir Lab: Mike Biskup
Ex Dir: Dawn Nee

D-U-N-S 08-337-9198
HALLMARK HEALTH SYSTEM INC
(*Suby of* HALLMARK HEALTH CORP) ★
585 Lebanon St, Melrose, MA 02176-3225
Tel (781) 979-3000 *Founded/Ownrshp* 1921
Sales 270.9MM *EMP* 2,600
SIC 8741 Hospital management
Pr: Michael V Sack
**CFO:* James Nania
**Treas:* David Drain
Ex VP: Steven Kapfhammer
VP: Maureen Hurton
Dir Pat Ca: Laurie M Cadden
Dir Rad: Elaine Gale
Off Mgr: Margaret Malenchini
CIO: Carol Dreer
Opers Mgr: Deborah Murphy
Doctor: Gamal Ragheb

D-U-N-S 04-674-8679 IMP/EXP
HALLMARK MARKETING CO LLC
(*Suby of* HALLMARK CARDS INC) ★
2501 Mcgee St, Kansas City, MO 64108-2615
Tel (816) 274-5111 *Founded/Ownrshp* 2012
Sales 2.7MMM^E *EMP* 16,200^E
SIC 5947 2542 7389 Greeting cards; Office & store showcases & display fixtures; Brokers, business: buying & selling business enterprises
V Ch: Donald J Hall
Pr: Richard Chalker

CFO: Ronald Neiger
Sr VP: Stephen D Doyal
VP: Robert Kipp
VP: Robin Younger
Dir Bus: Miller Christopher
CIO: Jason Elder
MIS Dir: Jenny Hawk
Dir IT: Danyel Bischof-Forsyth
Dir IT: Dave Caldwell

D-U-N-S 13-694-7459
HALLMARK REHABILITATION GP LLC
27442 Portola Pkwy # 200, El Toro, CA 92610-2822
Tel (949) 282-5900 *Founded/Ownrshp* 2003
Sales 21.9MM^E *EMP* 1,200
SIC 8322 Rehabilitation services

D-U-N-S 02-303-2261 IMP/EXP
HALLMARK RETAIL LLC
(*Suby of* MIX HOLDINGS INC) ★
2440 Pershing Rd Ste 200, Kansas City, MO 64108-2501
Tel (816) 274-5878 *Founded/Ownrshp* 2015
Sales 306.9MM^E *EMP* 4,000
SIC 5947 Greeting cards; Gift shop
Pr: John X Watson
IT Man: Ken Cameron

D-U-N-S 83-137-4959
HALLMARK SERVICES CORP
(*Suby of* BLUE CROSS AND BLUE SHIELD) ★
1000 E Warrenville Rd # 400, Naperville, IL 60563-2046
Tel (630) 328-4400 *Founded/Ownrshp* 2009
Sales NA *EMP* 1^E
SIC 6321 Accident & health insurance carriers
Pr: Colleen Reitan
Telecom Mg: Beth Meekma
VP Opers: Gerry Jacobus

D-U-N-S 83-052-8696
HALLWOOD FINANCIAL LIMITED
3710 Rawlins St Ste 1500, Dallas, TX 75219-4282
Tel (214) 523-1288 *Founded/Ownrshp* 2008
Sales 422.9MM^E *EMP* 479^E
SIC 5812 Pizzeria, chain
Ch Bd: Anthony J Gumbiner

D-U-N-S 07-163-0297 IMP
HALLWOOD GROUP INC
(*Suby of* HALLWOOD FINANCIAL LIMITED) ★
3710 Rawlins St Ste 1500, Dallas, TX 75219-4282
Tel (214) 528-5588 *Founded/Ownrshp* 2014
Sales 392.3MM^E *EMP* 439^E
SIC 2221 7389 Broadwoven fabric mills, manmade; Textile & apparel services
Ch Bd: Anthony J Gumbiner
Pr: William L Guzzetti
CFO: Richard Kelley
Off Mgr: Andrea Rivera
Board of Directors: Gert Lessing

D-U-N-S 11-622-7851 IMP/EXP
HALMA HOLDINGS INC
(*Suby of* HALMA INTERNATIONAL LIMITED)
11500 Northlake Dr # 306, Cincinnati, OH 45249-1658
Tel (513) 772-5501 *Founded/Ownrshp* 1979
Sales 517.3MM^E *EMP* 112
SIC 3826

D-U-N-S 12-510-2223 IMP/EXP
HALO BRANDED SOLUTIONS INC
HALO/LEE WAYNE
(*Suby of* HALO HOLDING CORP) ★
1980 Industrial Dr, Sterling, IL 61081-9064
Tel (815) 632-6988 *Founded/Ownrshp* 2003
Sales 591.3MM^E *EMP* 550
SIC 5199 Advertising specialties
Pr: Marc Simon
**CFO:* Linda Janczkowski
Ex VP: Jim Stutz
**Sr VP:* Terry McGuire

HALO CAPITAL
See HALO GROUP INC

D-U-N-S 82-474-0414
HALO GROUP INC
HALO CAPITAL
814 33rd St, Des Moines, IA 50312-3729
Tel (515) 974-6908 *Founded/Ownrshp* 2007
Sales NA *EMP* 12
SIC 6163 Mortgage brokers arranging for loans, using money of others
Pr: David Baker

D-U-N-S 13-170-6397 IMP
HALO HOLDING CORP
(*Suby of* CANDLELIGHT INVESTMENT HOLDINGS INC) ★
1980 Industrial Dr, Sterling, IL 61081-9064
Tel (815) 632-6800 *Founded/Ownrshp* 2012
Sales 591.3MM^E *EMP* 550
SIC 5199 Advertising specialties
CEO: Marc Simon

D-U-N-S 61-036-9311
HALO LLC
BASTIAN SOLUTIONS
10585 N Meridian St Fl 3, Indianapolis, IN 46290-1069
Tel (317) 575-9992 *Founded/Ownrshp* 2000
Sales 194.7MM *EMP* 450
Accts Katz Sapper & Miller
SIC 8711 3535 Engineering services; Conveyors & conveying equipment
CEO: William A Bastian II
CFO: John Smith

HALO/LEE WAYNE
See HALO BRANDED SOLUTIONS INC

D-U-N-S 02-607-7359
▲ HALOZYME THERAPEUTICS INC
11388 Sorrento Valley Rd # 200, San Diego, CA 92121-1345
Tel (858) 794-8889 *Founded/Ownrshp* 1998
Sales 135.0MM *EMP* 218^E
Tkr Sym HALO *Exch* NGM
SIC 2834 2836 Pharmaceutical preparations; Biological products, except diagnostic
Pr: Helen I Torley
**Ch Bd:* Connie L Matsui
COO: Mark J Gergen
CFO: Laurie D Stelzer
Chf Cred: Harry J Leonhardt
Chf Mktg O: Athena M Countouriotis
Sr VP: Athena Countouriotis
VP: Michael J Labarre
Board of Directors: James M Daly, Kathryn E Falberg, Jeffrey W Henderson, Kenneth J Kelley, Randal J Kirk, Matthew L Posard

HALPERNS PRVYORS STEAK SEAFOOD
See HALPERNS STEAK AND SEAFOOD CO LLC

D-U-N-S 55-608-4254 IMP/EXP
HALPERNS STEAK AND SEAFOOD CO LLC
HALPERNS PRVYORS STEAK SEAFOOD
(*Suby of* GORDON FOOD SERVICE INC) ★
4685 Welcome All Rd Sw, Atlanta, GA 30349-2541
Tel (404) 767-9229 *Founded/Ownrshp* 2015
Sales 429.8MM^E *EMP* 600^E
SIC 5147 Meats & meat products
CEO: Howard Halpern
Mng Pt: Keith Fishman
**Pr:* Ray Hicks
**CFO:* Lawrence Bayer
**Ex VP:* Ray Farmer
**Ex VP:* Kirk Halpern
VP Admn: Jody Hicks
Dir IT: Brandon Ensley
Sales Asso: Tom Neville

HALSEY FOODSERVICE
See W L HALSEY GROCERY CO INC

D-U-N-S 05-449-6682
HALVOR LINES INC (MN)
217 Grand Ave, Superior, WI 54880-1241
Tel (715) 392-8161 *Founded/Ownrshp* 1968
Sales 94.8MM^E *EMP* 350^E
SIC 4213 Trucking, except local; Contract haulers
Pr: Jon Vinje
CFO: Mark Ilikainen
**VP:* Peter Haines

D-U-N-S 07-937-5431
▲ HALYARD HEALTH INC
5405 Windward Pkwy, Alpharetta, GA 30004-3894
Tel (678) 425-9273 *Founded/Ownrshp* 2014
Sales 1.5MMM *EMP* 12,000^E
Tkr Sym HYH *Exch* NYS
SIC 3842 3841 3845 Surgical appliances & supplies; Surgical & medical instruments; Electromedical equipment; Ultrasonic scanning devices, medical
Ch Bd: Robert E Abernathy
COO: Christopher M Lowery
CFO: Steven E Voskuil
Ofcr: Rhonda D Gibby
Sr VP: Christopher G Isenberg
Sr VP: Warren J Machan
Sr VP: John W Wesley
Genl Mgr: Julie Hale
IT Man: Larhonda Cooper
Snr Mgr: Diego Amaya
Snr Mgr: Dennis Joseph
Board of Directors: Gary D Blackford, John P Byrnes, Ronald W Dollens, Heidi K Fields, William A Hawkins III, Patrick J O'leary, Maria Sainz, Julie Shimer

D-U-N-S 07-961-7666
■ HALYARD SALES LLC
(*Suby of* HALYARD HEALTH INC) ★
5405 Windward Pkwy # 100, Alpharetta, GA 30004-3894
Tel (678) 425-9273 *Founded/Ownrshp* 2014
Sales 228.8MM^E *EMP* 5,020^E
SIC 3845 3841 Electromedical equipment; Surgical & medical instruments
CEO: Robert E Abernathy
**CFO:* Steven E Voskuil

D-U-N-S 12-864-1693
HAMBLEN COUNTY BOARD OF EDUCATION
210 E Morris Blvd, Morristown, TN 37813-2341
Tel (423) 586-7700 *Founded/Ownrshp* 1960
Sales 61.3MM^E *EMP* 1,275
SIC 8211 Public elementary & secondary schools
Board of Directors: Teresa Ayers, Charles Cross, Joe Gibson, Roger Greene, James Grigsby, Janice S Haun, Pamela Jones, Clyde Kinder, Teresa Templin

D-U-N-S 07-979-9729
HAMBLEN COUNTY SCHOOL DISTRICT
210 E Morris Blvd, Morristown, TN 37813-2341
Tel (423) 586-7700 *Founded/Ownrshp* 2015
Sales 13.7MM^E *EMP* 1,140^E
SIC 8211 Public elementary & secondary schools

D-U-N-S 07-212-1304
HAMDEN TOWN OF (INC)
2750 Dixwell Ave Fl 2, Hamden, CT 06518-3320
Tel (203) 287-7100 *Founded/Ownrshp* 1786
Sales NA *EMP* 1,260
Accts Levitsky & Berney Pc Woodbri
SIC 9111
Ofcr: Holly Masi
IT Man: Salvatore Decola

D-U-N-S 11-837-3562 IMP/EXP
■ HAMILTON BEACH BRANDS INC
(*Suby of* HB PS HOLDING CO INC) ★
4421 Waterfront Dr, Glen Allen, VA 23060-3375
Tel (804) 273-9777 *Founded/Ownrshp* 1990
Sales 443.7MM^E *EMP* 500
SIC 3634 Toasters, electric: household; Ovens, portable: household; Irons, electric: household; Coffee makers, electric: household
Pr: Greg Trepp
Ch: Alfred M Rankin Jr
Treas: Denise Brown
Treas: James H Taylor
Bd of Dir: Alex Raring
VP: Eric Beam
VP: Kathleen Diller
VP: Judith B McBee
VP: Greg Salyers
Creative D: Barry Roebuck
Rgnl Mgr: Steve Izykowski
Board of Directors: Alfred M Rankin,ian M Ro, Jennifer Dickerman, Robert M Gates, Leon J Hendrix Jr, Dennis W Labarre, Richard De J Osborne, Thomas T Rankin, Britton Taplin, David F Taplin, John F Turben

D-U-N-S 07-490-9094
HAMILTON CHATTANOOGA COUNTY HOSPITAL AUTHORITY (TN)
ERLANGER HEALTH SYSTEM
975 E 3rd St, Chattanooga, TN 37403-2147
Tel (423) 778-7000 *Founded/Ownrshp* 1889
Sales 1.2MMM^E *EMP* 4,700
SIC 5912 Drug stores
CEO: Kevin Spiegel
**Pr:* James Brexler
**COO:* Charlesetta Woodard-Thompson
Trst: Russell T King Jr
Ofcr: Kim Sexton
**Sr VP:* Lynn Whisman
VP: Floyd Chasse
VP: Tanner Goodrich
VP: Blaine Morris
VP: Debra Poteet-Johnson
VP: Joseph Winick

D-U-N-S 10-761-2863
HAMILTON CITY SCHOOL DISTRICT
533 Dayton St, Hamilton, OH 45011-3455
Tel (513) 887-5000 *Founded/Ownrshp* 1900
Sales 55.1MM^E *EMP* 1,038
SIC 8211 Public senior high school; Public junior high school; Public elementary school
Dir IT: Dan Molloy
IT Man: Michael Schlereth
Pr Dir: Joni Copas

D-U-N-S 00-225-3540 IMP
HAMILTON COLLEGE
198 College Hill Rd, Clinton, NY 13323-1295
Tel (315) 859-4727 *Founded/Ownrshp* 1812
Sales 127.7MM *EMP* 650
Accts Kpmg Llp Albany Ny
SIC 8221 College, except junior
Pr: John H Stewart
**Owner:* Amy Clausen
Trst: Susannah Morgan
Ex VP: Eric R Larson
VP: Steve Bellona
VP: Julia Coash
VP: Sally Cockburn
**VP:* Karen Leach
**VP:* Richard Tantillo
VP: Richard C Tantillo
VP: Nancy Thompson
Assoc Dir: Leslie Bell
Assoc Dir: Claudet Ferrone
Assoc Dir: Amy Lindner
Assoc Dir: Laurie Russell

HAMILTON CONSTRUCTION ALASKA
See HAMILTON CONSTRUCTION CO

D-U-N-S 00-585-3932
HAMILTON CONSTRUCTION CO
HAMILTON CONSTRUCTION ALASKA
2213 S F St, Springfield, OR 97477-5207
Tel (541) 746-2426 *Founded/Ownrshp* 1995
Sales 157.7MM *EMP* 150
SIC 1622 3441

D-U-N-S 11-294-7341
HAMILTON COUNTY ECONOMIC DEVELOPMENT FOUNDATION INC
3074 Hickory Valley Rd, Chattanooga, TN 37421-1273
Tel (423) 209-8400 *Founded/Ownrshp* 1993
Sales NA *EMP* 6,137^E
SIC 9411 Administration of educational programs;

D-U-N-S 11-037-5800
HAMILTON COURT JUSTICE OFFICE
SHERIFFS DEPARTMENT
1000 Sycamore St Ste 110, Cincinnati, OH 45202-1336
Tel (513) 946-6400 *Founded/Ownrshp* 2015
Sales NA *EMP* 1,200
SIC 9229 Law enforcement statistics center, government

D-U-N-S 79-881-3432
HAMILTON HEALTH CARE SYSTEM INC
1200 Memorial Dr, Dalton, GA 30720-2529
Tel (706) 278-2105 *Founded/Ownrshp* 1983
Sales 20.4MM *EMP* 1,200^E
Accts Dixon Hughes Goodman Llp Ashe
SIC 8322 8062 Senior citizens' center or association; General medical & surgical hospitals
Pr: John Bowling
**CFO:* Gary Howard
VP: Dee Burkett Jr

D-U-N-S 02-884-4231 IMP
HAMILTON L FISHER L C
HAMILTON SCIENTIFIC
(*Suby of* OPENGATE CAPITAL LLC) ★
1716 Lawrence Dr Ste 1, De Pere, WI 54115-9108
Tel (920) 793-1121 *Founded/Ownrshp* 2012
Sales 233.9MM^E *EMP* 1,100
SIC 3821 Laboratory furniture; Laboratory equipment: fume hoods, distillation racks, etc.
Pr: Jack Roberts
**VP:* Rico Salazar

D-U-N-S 10-926-7898
HAMILTON MEDICAL CENTER INC
1200 Memorial Dr, Dalton, GA 30720-2529
Tel (706) 272-6000 *Founded/Ownrshp* 1982
Sales 216.7MM *EMP* 1,446
SIC 8062

D-U-N-S 00-699-9452
■ HAMILTON MUTUAL INSURANCE CO (IA)
(*Suby of* EMC INSURANCE COMPANIES) ★
11311 Cornell Park Dr # 500, Blue Ash, OH 45242-1891
Tel (513) 221-6010 *Founded/Ownrshp* 2005
Sales NA *EMP* 2,338
SIC 6331 Fire, marine & casualty insurance: mutual
Ch Bd: Richard Felts
**Pr:* Jeffrey Felts
**Treas:* M Brent Rouse
**Prin:* Kent A Kochheiser
Board of Directors: George W Kochheinser, John M Lockhart, Phillip Van Ekeren

HAMILTON PACIFIC
See NISCAYAH INC

D-U-N-S 17-518-9257
HAMILTON RISK MANAGEMENT CO
(*Suby of* ACADIA ACQUISITION PARTNERS, L.P.)
3155 Nw 77th Ave, Miami, FL 33122-3700
Tel (305) 716-6000 *Founded/Ownrshp* 1992
Sales NA *EMP* 198^E
SIC 6331 7323 6141 6541 6411 Fire, marine & casualty insurance; Property damage insurance; Credit reporting services; Automobile loans, including insurance; Financing: automobiles, furniture, etc., not a deposit bank; Title search companies; Insurance agents, brokers & service
Pr: Roberto Espin Jr
COO: Alberto Naon
CFO: Kevin Walton

HAMILTON SCIENTIFIC
See HAMILTON L FISHER L C

D-U-N-S 07-176-7334 IMP/EXP
■ HAMILTON SUNDSTRAND CORP
(*Suby of* UNITED TECHNOLOGIES CORP) ★
1 Hamilton Rd, Windsor Locks, CT 06096-1000
Tel (860) 654-6000 *Founded/Ownrshp* 1999
Sales 2.9MMM^E *EMP* 16,000
SIC 3621 3594 3728 3625 3823 3822 Frequency converters (electric generators); Power generators; Fluid power pumps & motors; Gears, aircraft power transmission; Actuators, industrial; Turbine flow meters, industrial process type; Auto controls regulating residntl & coml environmt & applncs
Pr: David Gitlin
Ch Bd: Ronald Mc Kenna
Pr: Michael Dumairs
Pr: Dave Gitlin
Pr: Curtis Reusser
Pr: Jeff Wiemelt
CFO: Marie Missen
CFO: David Nord
Ofcr: Joan M Davidson
VP: Dave Carter
VP: Clinton Gardiner
VP: Kevin Lindsay
VP: Steve Peery
VP: Thomas Rogan
Dir Bus: Martin Chell
Dir Bus: Bob Guirl

D-U-N-S 05-107-9937
HAMILTON SUNDSTRAND SERVICE CORP
1 Hamilton Rd, Windsor Locks, CT 06096-1000
Tel (860) 654-6000 *Founded/Ownrshp* 1999
Sales 415.5MM^E *EMP* 2,300^E
SIC 3324

D-U-N-S 14-481-7934 IMP
HAMILTON SUNDSTRAND SPACE SYSTEMS INTERNATIONAL INC
1 Hamilton Rd, Windsor Locks, CT 06096-1000
Tel (860) 654-6000 *Founded/Ownrshp* 1994
Sales 163.0MM^E *EMP* 700
SIC 3841 3826 Diagnostic apparatus, medical; Thermal analysis instruments, laboratory type
Pr: Edward Francis
Treas: Robert Deroy
**Treas:* Michael Randall
Prgrm Mgr: Nick Watling
**Genl Mgr:* Lawrence McNamara
**Oper/Dir:* Daneil Lee

HAMILTON TELECOMMUNICATIONS
See NEDELCO INC

D-U-N-S 07-550-1601
HAMILTON TOWNSHIP BOARD OF EDUCATION
90 Park Ave, Trenton, NJ 08690-2024
Tel (609) 631-4100 *Founded/Ownrshp* 1919
Sales 93.3MM^E *EMP* 1,500
SIC 8211 School board
Pr: Anthony Celentano

D-U-N-S 04-814-7300
HAMILTON TOWNSHIP SCHOOL DISTRICT
HAMILTON TWP SCHOOL DIST
1876 Dr Dennis Foreman Dr, Mays Landing, NJ 08330-2206
Tel (609) 476-6300 *Founded/Ownrshp* 1885
Sales 211.6MM *EMP* 500
Accts Hodulik & Morrison Pa Cpas
SIC 8211 Public elementary & secondary schools
Psych: Andrew Disque
HC Dir: Barbara Graf

D-U-N-S 96-264-0772
HAMILTON TOWNSHIP SCHOOL DISTRICT
90 Park Ave, Trenton, NJ 08690-2024
Tel (609) 631-4100 *Founded/Ownrshp* 2010
Sales 47.2MM^E *EMP* 1,615^E
SIC 8211 Public elementary & secondary schools
MIS Dir: Kevin Bobetich
IT Man: Erin Hill
Teacher Pr: Michael Giambelluca

HAMILTON TWP SCHOOL DIST
See HAMILTON TOWNSHIP SCHOOL DISTRICT

D-U-N-S 12-628-5415
HAMISTER GROUP LLC
10 Lafayette Sq Ste 1900, Buffalo, NY 14203-1801
Tel (716) 839-4000 *Founded/Ownrshp* 2001
Sales 180.4MM^E *EMP* 3,253
SIC 7011 8052 8741 Hotels & motels; Intermediate care facilities; Hotel or motel management
CEO: Mark E Hamister
**CFO:* W Earl McCartney
Ex VP: Earl McCartney
**Sr VP:* Cheryl Green
**Sr VP:* Daniel Hamister

**Sr VP:* David P Paul
VP: Nektaria Hamister
Genl Mgr: Janis Moeller
Genl Mgr: Teagan L Tilson
Dir IT: Joan Hudak
Web Dev: Sean Murphy

D-U-N-S 80-476-2503
HAMLET HOLDING LLC
2 Manhattanville Rd, Purchase, NY 10577-2113
Tel (914) 694-8000 *Founded/Ownrshp* 2004
Sales 438.3MM^E *EMP* 87,000^E
SIC 7011 7999 Hotels & motels; Gambling establishment; Gambling machines, operation

D-U-N-S 07-869-4155
HAMLINE UNIVERSITY
1536 Hewitt Ave, Saint Paul, MN 55104-1284
Tel (651) 523-2015 *Founded/Ownrshp* 1854
Sales 91.6MM *EMP* 563^E
Accts Clifton Larson Allen Llp Minn
SIC 8221 University
Pr: Linda N Hanson
CFO: Vicki Plaistow
Trst: Joe Graba
VP: Douglas P Anderson
VP: Mark Kondrak
Exec: Mona Freeberg
Ex Dir: Angela McCaffrey
Off Admin: Yvonne Wells-Ellis
IT Man: Danielle Brandstetter
Netwrk Mgr: Steven Dondelinger
VP Mktg: Jeffrey Rich

D-U-N-S 12-236-9411
HAMM INC
(*Suby of* SUMMIT MATERIALS CORPS I INC) ★
609 Perry Pl, Perry, KS 66073-4201
Tel (785) 597-5111 *Founded/Ownrshp* 2009
Sales 109.9MM^E *EMP* 350
SIC 1411 1771 1611 Limestone, dimension-quarrying; Blacktop (asphalt) work; Highway & street construction
Pr: Gary Hamm
VP: Bradley T Hamm
Genl Mgr: Ryan Blosser
Mtls Mgr: Dale Johnson
Sfty Mgr: Kent Miller

HAMMAKER EAST
See RUSSELL STANDARD CORP

D-U-N-S 05-831-9922
HAMMEL GREEN AND ABRAHAMSON INC (NY)
HGA ARCHITECTS AND ENGINEERS
420 N 5th St Ste 100, Minneapolis, MN 55401-2338
Tel (612) 758-4000 *Founded/Ownrshp* 1953
Sales 142.8MM *EMP* 600
Accts Boulay Pllp Minneapolis Minn
SIC 8712 8711 Architectural services; Engineering services
CEO: Daniel Avchen
**COO:* Dan Rectenwald
COO: Roger Santelman
**CFO:* Kent S Mainquist
**Treas:* Carey Bonnabeau
Assoc VP: Rich Bonnin
Assoc VP: Sean Collins
Assoc VP: Jane R Dedering
Assoc VP: John Ellingson
Assoc VP: Kevin Flynn
Assoc VP: Jennifer Klund
Assoc VP: Celine Larkin
VP: Michael Bjornberg
VP: Bill Blanski
VP: John Cook
VP: Rand Liedl
VP: Chad R Odonnell
VP: Stan Pehling
VP: Win Roney
VP: Michael Ross
VP: Steve Weir

D-U-N-S 60-807-5644
HAMMER CONSTRUCTION INC
4320 Adams Rd, Norman, OK 73069-1007
Tel (405) 310-3160 *Founded/Ownrshp* 1990
Sales 124.9MM^E *EMP* 120
SIC 1389 1794 Oil field services; Excavation & grading, building construction
Pr: Shirley Hammer
**VP:* Robby Moore
Ex Dir: Tamara Thomasson

D-U-N-S 00-221-3502 IMP
HAMMER PACKAGING CORP (NY)
200 Lucius Gordon Dr, West Henrietta, NY 14586-9685
Tel (585) 424-3880 *Founded/Ownrshp* 1912, 1980
Sales 119.2MM *EMP* 350
Accts Rizzo Digiacco Hern & Baniew
SIC 2759 Labels & seals: printing
Pr: James E Hammer
**CFO:* Christopher F Wieser
**VP:* Jason Hammer
**VP:* Marty Karpie
**VP:* Louis Lovoli
**VP:* Tom Mason
VP: Patrick Oliveto
Exec: Ann Graham
Mktg Dir: Doug Wegman
Sls Mgr: Kenneth Donohue
Sales Asso: Brian Markham

D-U-N-S 78-437-5599
HAMMERMAN & GAINER INTERNATIONAL INC
1010 Common St Ste 2600, New Orleans, LA 70112-2429
Tel (504) 681-6135 *Founded/Ownrshp* 1929
Sales 95.0MM *EMP* 250
SIC 8742 Management consulting services
Ch Bd: Larry D Oney
CFO: Terry Hightower

HAMMOND
See MILWAUKEE VALVE CO INC

D-U-N-S 00-171-2959
HAMMOND KENNEDY WHITNEY & CO INC (NY)
HKW
420 Lexington Ave Rm 402, New York, NY 10170-0499
Tel (212) 867-1010 *Founded/Ownrshp* 1903, 1965
Sales 86.2MM^E *EMP* 421
SIC 7389 Brokers, business: buying & selling business enterprises
Ch Bd: Jeffrey G Wood
**VP:* Forrest E Crisman Jr
**VP:* Glenn Scolnik

D-U-N-S 00-111-0360
HAMMOND LUMBER CO
2 Hammond Dr, Belgrade, ME 04917-4152
Tel (207) 495-3303 *Founded/Ownrshp* 1953
Sales 94.2MM^E *EMP* 415
SIC 5211 2421 5031 Lumber & other building materials; Sawmills & planing mills, general; Lumber: rough, dressed & finished
Pr: Donald C Hammond
**VP:* Michael J Hammond
Exec: Rod Bockford
Store Mgr: Al Feather
Store Mgr: Steve Hardy
Store Mgr: Bill Veilleux
Sls&Mrk Ex: Rod Wells
Sls Mgr: Andrea Hodgdon
Sls Mgr: Bill Krause
Sls Mgr: Angelica Murray
Sales Asso: Bill Burge

D-U-N-S 00-611-3450 IMP
HAMMOND POWER SOLUTIONS INC
(*Suby of* HAMMOND POWER SOLUTIONS INC)
1100 Lake St, Baraboo, WI 53913-3000
Tel (608) 356-3921 *Founded/Ownrshp* 1917
Sales 109.9MM^E *EMP* 130
SIC 5084 Industrial machinery & equipment
Ch Bd: William G Hammond
CFO: Chris Huether
**CFO:* Christopher R Huether

D-U-N-S 06-849-7189
HAMMOND PUBLIC SCHOOLS
41 Williams St, Hammond, IN 46320-1948
Tel (219) 933-2400 *Founded/Ownrshp* 1894
Sales 93.7MM^E *EMP* 1,800
SIC 8211 Public elementary & secondary schools
Bd of Dir: Cindy Murphy
**VP:* Anna Mamala
HC Dir: Sarah Ligon

D-U-N-S 00-696-8879
HAMMONS INC (MO)
COURTYARD BY MRROTT SPRNGFIELD
300 S John Q Hammons Pkwy # 900, Springfield, MO 65806-2550
Tel (417) 864-4300 *Founded/Ownrshp* 1971
Sales NA *EMP* 4,835
SIC 7011

D-U-N-S 15-428-0598 IMP
HAMON CORP
(*Suby of* HAMON & CIE (INTERNATIONAL) SA)
58 E Main St, Somerville, NJ 08876-2312
Tel (908) 333-2000 *Founded/Ownrshp* 1979
Sales 133.0MM^E *EMP* 340
SIC 1629 3564 3499 5084 Industrial plant construction; Blowers & fans; Friction material, made from powdered metal; Industrial machinery & equipment
CEO: William P Dillon
**COO:* Oliver Acheson
**Ex VP:* Don Kawecki
**Ex VP:* H James Peters
**Ex VP:* Robert Recio
VP: Neil Dahlberg
VP: Michael Lies
Rgnl Mgr: Jeremy Stegemiller
Sls Mgr: Terry King

D-U-N-S 10-630-7655
HAMOT HEALTH FOUNDATION
201 State St, Erie, PA 16550-0002
Tel (814) 877-7020 *Founded/Ownrshp* 1981
Sales 4.0MM *EMP* 2,032
Accts Parentebeard Llc Philadelphia
SIC 8741 8062 6514 Hospital management; Nursing & personal care facility management; General medical & surgical hospitals; Dwelling operators, except apartments
Pr: John T Malone
Chf Rad: Richard Williams
**Pr:* V James Fiorenzo
**CFO:* Stephen Danch
**Ch:* B Scott Kern
Treas: Ellen Patterson
Ex VP: Jim Fiorenzo
**Sr VP:* Hershey Bell
**Sr VP:* Donald Inderlied
**Sr VP:* Rochelle Krowinski
**Sr VP:* Dr Joseph McClellan
**Sr VP:* Dr James Pepicello
**Sr VP:* Lee Van Voris
**VP:* Debbie A Burbules
VP: Joe Choi
**VP:* Stephen M Danch
Dir Teleco: Brian Franz
Dir Rx: Thomas J Thompson

HAMOT MEDICAL CENTER
See UPMC HAMOT

D-U-N-S 03-061-8623
HAMPEL OIL DISTRIBUTORS INC
3727 S West St, Wichita, KS 67217-3803
Tel (316) 529-1162 *Founded/Ownrshp* 1976
Sales 110.0MM^E *EMP* 180
SIC 5171 Petroleum bulk stations
Pr: William Hampel
COO: Scott Hampel
Bd of Dir: Rick Ekum
**VP:* Ed Hampel
Brnch Mgr: Ron Brumit
Brnch Mgr: Presley Roberts
Genl Mgr: Danny Hampel
IT Man: Bob Hampel
Sfty Mgr: Steve Riney

Opers Mgr: Dustin Ruth
Sls Mgr: Lance Daniel

D-U-N-S 08-847-0802
▲ **HAMPSHIRE GROUP LIMITED**
1924 Pearman Dairy Rd A, Anderson, SC 29625-1323
Tel (212) 540-5666 *Founded/Ownrshp* 1917
Sales 91.4MM *EMP* 633^E
Tkr Sym HAMP *Exch* OTO
SIC 2339 2329 2253 Women's & misses' outerwear; Women's & misses' athletic clothing & sportswear; Women's & misses' jackets & coats, except sportswear; Sweaters & sweater jackets: men's & boys'; Men's & boys' sportswear & athletic clothing; Knit outerwear mills
Ch Bd: Paul M Buxbaum
CFO: William Drozdowski
Board of Directors: Thomas J Doyle Jr, Brett H Fialkoff, Robin Marino, Benjamin C Yogel

HAMPTON AFFILIATES
See HAMPTON INVESTMENT CO

D-U-N-S 18-435-6012
HAMPTON CITY SCHOOL DISTRICT
1 Franklin St Fl 2, Hampton, VA 23669-3570
Tel (757) 727-2000 *Founded/Ownrshp* 1994
Sales 142.9MM^E *EMP* 3,000^E
SIC 8211 Public elementary & secondary schools; School board
Ofcr: Aaron Webb
MIS Dir: John Eagle
Dir IT: Rubenia Felton
Dir IT: Aileen Girard
Dir IT: Clinton Rudd
Pr Dir: Diana Gulotta
Teacher Pr: Robbin Ruth
Psych: Edwina Simmons
HC Dir: Glory Gill

D-U-N-S 04-028-6701
HAMPTON CREEK INC
2000 Folsom St, San Francisco, CA 94110-1318
Tel (844) 423-6637 *Founded/Ownrshp* 2011
Sales 110.7MM^E *EMP* 249
SIC 2035 2052 Mayonnaise; Cookies
CEO: Joshua Tetrick
Dir Lab: John Literacki
Comm Dir: Jessica Elkus
Comm Dir: Morgan Oliveira
QA Dir: Rashmi Deshpande
VP Opers: Caroline Love

HAMPTON FARMS
See MEHERRIN AGRICULTURAL & CHEMICAL CO

HAMPTON INN
See INTERSTATE HOTELS & RESORTS INC

HAMPTON INN
See BENNETT ENTERPRISES INC

HAMPTON INN
See SUMMIT GROUP INC

HAMPTON INN
See CROSSROADS HOSPITALITY CO LLC

HAMPTON INN
See SUNSTONE HOTEL PROPERTIES INC

HAMPTON INSTITUE
See HAMPTON UNIVERSITY

D-U-N-S 10-406-5701 IMP/EXP
HAMPTON INVESTMENT CO
HAMPTON AFFILIATES
9600 Sw Barnes Rd Ste 200, Portland, OR 97225-6666
Tel (503) 297-7691 *Founded/Ownrshp* 1979
Sales 310.4MM^E *EMP* 1,300
SIC 5031 2435 2426

D-U-N-S 05-221-7106 IMP/EXP
HAMPTON LUMBER MILLS INC (OR)
WILLAMINA LUMBER COMPANY
9600 Sw Barnes Rd Ste 200, Portland, OR 97225-6666
Tel (503) 297-7691 *Founded/Ownrshp* 1942, 1983
Sales 86.1MM^E *EMP* 560
SIC 2421

D-U-N-S 79-990-8087 IMP/EXP
HAMPTON LUMBER SALES CO
(*Suby of* HAMPTON RESOURCES INC) ★
9600 Sw Barnes Rd Ste 200, Portland, OR 97225-6666
Tel (503) 297-7691 *Founded/Ownrshp* 2000
Sales 153.2MM^E *EMP* 130
SIC 5031 2421 7389 Lumber, plywood & millwork; Sawmills & planing mills, general; Log & lumber broker
Pr: Mike Phillips
**CFO:* Steve Zika
Treas: Gary Hurley
Genl Mgr: Carter Stinton
Dir IT: Matt Fellows

D-U-N-S 07-339-9362 IMP
HAMPTON PRODUCTS INTERNATIONAL CORP
50 Icon, Foothill Ranch, CA 92610-3000
Tel (949) 472-4256 *Founded/Ownrshp* 1990
Sales 138.3MM^E *EMP* 350
SIC 5072 Hardware
Pr: Hayward K Kelley III
COO: Caroline Gray
COO: Richard Tysdal
Chf Mktg O: James Hartung
Ex VP: Bob Hansen
Sr VP: Mike Kreeger
VP: Jim Bzovy
VP: Robert Gast
Genl Mgr: Michael Gianoli
MIS Dir: Howard Shen
IT Man: Bob Gast

D-U-N-S 11-267-7927 IMP/EXP
HAMPTON RESOURCES INC
9600 Sw Barnes Rd Ste 200, Portland, OR 97225-6666
Tel (503) 297-7691 *Founded/Ownrshp* 1983
Sales 153.2MM^E *EMP* 600
SIC 5031 2421 0811

D-U-N-S 07-793-2770 IMP
HAMPTON ROADS SANITATION DISTRICT (INC)
HRSD
1434 Air Rail Ave, Virginia Beach, VA 23455-3002
Tel (757) 460-2261 *Founded/Ownrshp* 1946
Sales 237.8MM *EMP* 700
Accts Kpmg Llp Norfolk Va
SIC 4952 Sewerage systems
Exec: Kristin Bauer
**CIO:* Don Corrado
CTO: Clay Wise
IT Man: Tim Marsh
IT Man: Jules Robichaud
Plnt Mgr: Brian McNamara
Mktg Dir: Jennifer L Heilman

HAMPTON ROADS TRANSIT
See TRANSPORTATION DIST COMMISION OF HAMPTON ROADS

D-U-N-S 09-959-1216
HAMPTON RUBBER CO
(*Suby of* SBP HOLDINGS) ★
1669 W Pembroke Ave, Hampton, VA 23661-1901
Tel (757) 722-9818 *Founded/Ownrshp* 1999
Sales 172.0MM^E *EMP* 286
SIC 5085 Rubber goods, mechanical; Gaskets; Hose, belting & packing; Bearings
Pr: Donald Fritzinger
**Treas:* George Dappert
**VP:* Otis A Dufrene
**VP:* Kenneth Ketterman
Brnch Mgr: Mike Brown
Genl Mgr: Wayne Dunn

D-U-N-S 00-313-5068
HAMPTON UNIVERSITY (VA)
HAMPTON INSTITUE
100 E Queen St, Hampton, VA 23668-0108
Tel (757) 727-5000 *Founded/Ownrshp* 1868
Sales 164.5MM^E *EMP* 1,050
Accts Dixon Hughes Goodman Llp Newp
SIC 8221 University
Pr: William R Harvey
Pr: Evelyn Oakley
Ofcr: Clyde Wallace
VP: Shirley Farr
Exec: Francisco Coronel
Info Man: Matthew White
Plnt Mgr: Sarita Scott
Sls&Mrk Ex: Arthur Holmes
Pr Mgr: Sylvia Rose
Genl Couns: Faye Lucas

D-U-N-S 60-738-2694
HAMPTON WOODS HEALTH & REHABILITATION CENTER
200 Hmpton Wods Cmplex Rd, Jackson, NC 27845-9503
Tel (252) 534-0131 *Founded/Ownrshp* 1990
Sales 435.3MM *EMP* 90
SIC 8051 8052 Skilled nursing care facilities; Intermediate care facilities
Nrsg Dir: Donna Tritt Rn

D-U-N-S 00-335-3448
HAMRICK MILLS INC (SC)
515 W Buford St, Gaffney, SC 29341-1703
Tel (864) 489-4731 *Founded/Ownrshp* 1900
Sales 85.8MM^E *EMP* 425
SIC 2211 2299 Sheets & sheetings, cotton; Yarns & thread, made from non-fabric materials
Pr: Carlisle Hamrick
**Ch Bd:* Wylie L Hamrick
**Sec:* Charles Hamrick
**VP:* Lyman Hamrick
IT Man: Scott Butterbaugh
Prd Mgr: Wayne Mason
Cust Svc D: Kelly Galloway

D-U-N-S 04-912-3995 IMP
HAMRICKS INC
L HAMRICK'S
742 Peachoid Rd, Gaffney, SC 29341-3499
Tel (864) 489-6095 *Founded/Ownrshp* 1945
Sales 275.9MM^E *EMP* 1,600
SIC 5651 2337 2331 2335 2339 5087

D-U-N-S 96-642-4947
HAMS RESTAURANTS INC
(*Suby of* CHELDA, INC)
3017 W Gate City Blvd # 2, Greensboro, NC 27403-3655
Tel (336) 851-4800 *Founded/Ownrshp* 1986
Sales 21.7MM^E *EMP* 1,100
SIC 5812 5813 American restaurant; Tavern (drinking places)
Pr: Charles Erwin
**Treas:* Robin Young
**VP:* Steve Stern

D-U-N-S 00-543-5896
HANCHETT PAPER CO (IL)
SHORR PACKAGING
4000 Ferry Rd, Aurora, IL 60502-9540
Tel (630) 978-1000 *Founded/Ownrshp* 1945, 1953
Sales 254.4MM^E *EMP* 230
SIC 5084 5199 Processing & packaging equipment; Packaging materials
Pr: Craig Funkhouser
**CFO:* Kevin Vrba
**Sec:* Leo A Dieter
Exec: Tim Ewalt
Brnch Mgr: Phil McKee
Brnch Mgr: Robert Taylor
Div Mgr: Mark Trainer
Dir IT: Bill Riley
Dir IT: Tom Scarborough
Dir IT: Greg Scheidt
Sls Mgr: Joe Searcy

D-U-N-S 03-345-2954 IMP
HANCOCK FABRICS INC
1 Fashion Way, Baldwyn, MS 38824-8547
Tel (662) 365-6000 *Founded/Ownrshp* 1957
Sales 283.1MM *EMP* 3,100
Accts Burr Pilger Mayer Inc San F

SIC 5949 Sewing, needlework & piece goods; Fabric stores piece goods; Notions, including trim; Patterns: sewing, knitting & needlework
Pr: Steven R Morgan
Pr: Mark Puhnaty
CFO: Rebecca I Flick
Sr VP: Dennis Lyons
Sr VP: Bob Monroe
VP: Dean Abraham
VP: Sue Arlotta
VP: Pierce Crockett
VP: Tony Gillette
VP: James Hayes
VP: Debby Hettinger
VP: Cheryl McDonald
VP: Linda G Moore
VP: Bill Sheffield
VP: Susan Zewicke
Creative D: Todd Knowlton
Board of Directors: Sam P Cortez, Steven D Scheiwe

D-U-N-S 12-269-4490
▲ HANCOCK HOLDING CO
2510 14th St, Gulfport, MS 39501-1948
Tel (228) 868-4000 *Founded/Ownrshp* 1984
Sales NA *EMP* 3,921ᴱ
Tkr Sym HBHC *Exch* NGS
SIC 6022 State commercial banks
Pr: John M Hairston
**Ch Bd:* James B Estabrook Jr
Pr: Joseph S Exnicios
COO: D Shane Loper
CFO: Michael M Achary
Chf Cred: Suzanne C Thomas
Ofcr: Samuel B Kendricks
Ofcr: Joseph S Schwertz Jr
Ex VP: Joy Lambert Phillips
VP: Brad Schild
VP: Deborah Sheridan
Board of Directors: Thomas H Olinde, Frank E Bertucci, Christine L Pickering, Hardy B Fowler, Robert W Roseberry, Terence E Hall, Joanie Teofilo, Randall W Hanna, Richard Wilkins, James H Horne, Jerry L Levens, Dean Liollio, Sonya C Little, Eric J Nickelsen

D-U-N-S 19-982-5662 IMP/EXP
HANCOCK LUMBER CO INC
4 Edes Falls Rd, Casco, ME 04015-3053
Tel (207) 627-4201 *Founded/Ownrshp* 1989
Sales 125.8MMᴱ *EMP* 550
SIC 5211 5031 Lumber & other building materials; Lumber, plywood & millwork
Pr: Kevin Hancock
**CFO:* Glenn Alby
VP: Ronald Wormwood
Opers Mgr: Jim Foster

D-U-N-S 79-786-3255
HANCOCK NATURAL RESOURCE GROUP INC
JOHN HANCOCK
(*Suby of* JOHN HANCOCK LIFE INSURANCE CO (USA)) ★
197 Clarendon St, Boston, MA 02116-5010
Tel (617) 747-1600 *Founded/Ownrshp* 2008
Sales NA *EMP* 150
SIC 6411 Insurance agents & brokers
CEO: Daniel Christensen
**Pr:* Celine Bernier
**Pr:* Bill Peressini
COO: Bruce C McKnight
CFO: Charlie Amalfi
**CFO:* Mike Morgan
**VP:* Carolyn Bailey
VP: Brett Macneil
**VP:* Suzanne Sturman
**VP:* Oliver Williams
Genl Mgr: William K McCallum

D-U-N-S 19-516-9461
HANCOCK PARK ASSOCIATES II LP
10350 Santa Monica Blvd # 295, Los Angeles, CA 90025-5074
Tel (310) 228-6900 *Founded/Ownrshp* 1986
Sales 140.5MMᴱ *EMP* 682
SIC 6552 Subdividers & developers
Genl Pt: Michael J Fourticq
Pt: Ted Fourticq
Pt: Michael F Gooch
VP: Martin Irani
Dir IT: Ekta Chopra
Genl Couns: Eric Foker

D-U-N-S 07-204-2070
HANCOCK REGIONAL HOSPITAL
801 N State St, Greenfield, IN 46140-1270
Tel (317) 462-5544 *Founded/Ownrshp* 2005
Sales 91.7MM *EMP* 1,300
SIC 8062 General medical & surgical hospitals
Ch Bd: Roy L Wilson
Chf Rad: Mary L Wolfe
**V Ch:* Linda Zimmermann PHD
**CEO:* Robert C Keen
Treas: Rick Edwards
Treas: David Willis
VP: Roberta S Dunne
VP: Michael Fletcher
VP: Sherry Gehring
VP: David Holmes
VP: Carolyn Konfirst

D-U-N-S 14-748-8266 IMP/EXP
■ HANCOR HOLDING CORP
(*Suby of* ADVANCED DRAINAGE SYSTEMS INC) ★
401 Olive St, Findlay, OH 45840-5358
Tel (419) 422-6521 *Founded/Ownrshp* 2005
Sales 173.0MMᴱ *EMP* 1,095
SIC 3084 Plastics pipe
Pr: Steven Anderson
CFO: John Haughawout
CFO: John Maag
VP: Barbara Mewhorter

D-U-N-S 05-163-3139 IMP/EXP
■ HANCOR INC
(*Suby of* HANCOR HOLDING CORP) ★
4640 Trueman Blvd, Hilliard, OH 43026-2438
Tel (614) 658-0050 *Founded/Ownrshp* 1968
Sales 173.0MMᴱ *EMP* 1,000
SIC 3084 3088 3089 3083 Plastics pipe; Plastics plumbing fixtures; Septic tanks, plastic; Laminated plastics plate & sheet
Pr: Steven A Anderson
**CFO:* John Maag
**VP:* William E Altermatt
**VP:* Pat Ferren
**VP:* Derek Kamp
Dir IT: Tim Stuart
Opers Supe: Linda Morris
Plnt Mgr: Larry Dunson
Plnt Mgr: Lark Inniger

D-U-N-S 12-067-3947 IMP/EXP
■ HAND HELD PRODUCTS INC
HONEYWELL IMAGING AND MOBILITY
(*Suby of* HONEYWELL INTERNATIONAL INC) ★
700 Visions Dr, Skaneateles Falls, NY 13153-5312
Tel (315) 554-6000 *Founded/Ownrshp* 1999
Sales 183.2MMᴱ *EMP* 770
SIC 3577 3571 3663 3578 Magnetic ink & optical scanning devices; Electronic computers; Radio & TV communications equipment; Calculating & accounting equipment
Ch Bd: John F Waldron
**CEO:* Kevin Jost
**CFO:* Joseph Hennigan
**Ch:* Darius Adamczyk
VP: Michael A Ehrhart
**VP:* David Guido
VP: Kim Ingram
Ex Dir: Paul Dickau
Software D: David Mangicaro
Mfg Mgr: Paul Puleo

D-U-N-S 00-797-9362 IMP/EXP
HAND2MIND INC (IL)
500 Greenview Ct, Vernon Hills, IL 60061-1862
Tel (847) 816-5060 *Founded/Ownrshp* 1905, 1992
Sales 118.6MMᴱ *EMP* 215
SIC 5049 5169 Laboratory equipment, except medical or dental; School supplies; Chemicals & allied products
CEO: Jim Woldenberg
**Pr:* James Woldenberg
**VP:* Dennis Goldman
VP: Barbara Plain
VP: Bill Totzke
VP Admn: Michael Grembowski

HANDEE HUGO'S
See SAMPSON-BLADEN OIL CO INC

HANDEE HUGO'S
See UNITED ENERGY INC

D-U-N-S 62-300-0192
HANDEX CONSULTING AND REMEDIATION LLC
HCR
1350 Orange Ave Ste 101, Winter Park, FL 32789-4932
Tel (352) 735-1800 *Founded/Ownrshp* 2005
Sales 92.6MMᴱ *EMP* 140
SIC 4959 Toxic or hazardous waste cleanup
Ch: Brett Fadeley
Pr: Bruce Bosserman
CEO: Robert B Case
CFO: Robert Santana
Genl Mgr: Irvin Heath
Genl Mgr: Robert Sevret
CIO: Richard Beard

D-U-N-S 11-538-1139 IMP
HANDI-FOIL CORP
135 E Hintz Rd, Wheeling, IL 60090-6059
Tel (847) 520-1000 *Founded/Ownrshp* 1984
Sales 91.6MMᴱ *EMP* 840
SIC 3497 Foil containers for bakery goods & frozen foods
Pr: Norton Sarnoff
Pr: Paj Patel
**CFO:* Peter Perkins
**VP:* Brad Sarnoff
Exec: Bob Martin
Plnt Mgr: Rich Kendzior

D-U-N-S 00-206-3915 IMP
HANDWEAR SALES INC (NY)
74 Bleecker St, Gloversville, NY 12078-2919
Tel (518) 725-8641 *Founded/Ownrshp* 1913
Sales 20.8MMᴱ *EMP* 1,200
SIC 3151 3949 2253 3021

HANDWORK CONTRACTORS
See GLEN BLOOMING CONTRACTORS INC

D-U-N-S 00-202-8876 IMP/EXP
■ HANDY & HARMAN
(*Suby of* HNH) ★
1133 Westchester Ave N-222, White Plains, NY 10604-3571
Tel (914) 461-1300 *Founded/Ownrshp* 2015
Sales 362.9MMᴱ *EMP* 1,621
SIC 3356 3399 3341 3317 3315 Precious metals; Gold & gold alloy: rolling, drawing or extruding; Silver & silver alloy: rolling, drawing or extruding; Gold & gold alloy bars, sheets, strip, etc.; Powder, metal; Flakes, metal; Silver powder; Secondary precious metals; Gold smelting & refining (secondary); Silver smelting & refining (secondary); Steel pipe & tubes; Tubing, mechanical or hypodermic sizes: cold drawn stainless; Wire products, ferrous/iron: made in wiredrawing plants; Cable, steel: insulated or armored
Pr: Jeffrey A Svoboda
**Sr VP:* Paul E Dixon
**Sr VP:* James McCabe
**VP:* Paul W Bucha
**VP:* Robert A Davidow
**VP:* Marvin L Olshan

D-U-N-S 96-792-6309
■ HANDY & HARMAN GROUP LTD
(*Suby of* HNH) ★
1133 Westchester Ave N-222, White Plains, NY 10604-3571
Tel (914) 461-1300 *Founded/Ownrshp* 2010
Sales 559.4MM *EMP* 1,925
SIC 3462 Turbine engine forgings, ferrous
Ch: Warren G Lichtenstein
**CFO:* James F McCabe

D-U-N-S 84-938-2411 EXP
■ HANDY & HARMAN LTD
HNH
(*Suby of* SPH GROUP HOLDINGS LLC) ★
1133 Westchester Ave N-222, White Plains, NY 10604-3571
Tel (914) 461-1300 *Founded/Ownrshp* 1852
Sales 649.4MM *EMP* 2,125
Tkr Sym HNH *Exch* NAS
SIC 3339 3011 3312 Precious metals; Tire & inner tube materials & related products; Wire products, steel or iron
CEO: Jack L Howard
Ch Bd: Warren G Lichtenstein
CFO: Douglas B Woodworth
Sr VP: William T Fejes Jr
Sr VP: Jeffrey A Svoboda
Board of Directors: Patrick A Demarco, Robert Frankfurt, John H McNamara Jr

HANDY ANDY
See BEXAR COUNTY MARKETS INC

D-U-N-S 02-378-8839 EXP
HANDY CO N B
65 10th St, Lynchburg, VA 24504-1621
Tel (434) 847-4495 *Founded/Ownrshp* 1891
Sales 128.0MMᴱ *EMP* 330
SIC 5051 5074 5075

D-U-N-S 02-660-0569 IMP
HANDY HARDWARE WHOLESALE INC (DE)
8300 Tewantin Dr, Houston, TX 77061-4699
Tel (713) 644-1495 *Founded/Ownrshp* 1961
Sales 197.7MMᴱ *EMP* 410
SIC 5072 5074 5063 5031 5198

HANDY HOME
See BACKYARD PRODUCTS LLC

D-U-N-S 04-378-3679
HANDY PONTIAC CADILLAC BUICK G M C INC
405 Swanton Rd, Saint Albans, VT 05478-2611
Tel (802) 524-6531 *Founded/Ownrshp* 1953
Sales 120.0MM *EMP* 25
SIC 5511 Automobiles, new & used
Pr: Lawrence Handy
**Treas:* Jeffrey Handy
**VP:* David Handy
VP: F E Handy
Sales Asso: Bud Handy
Sales Asso: Dave Reszewski

D-U-N-S 07-151-8358
HANERGY HOLDING AMERICA INC
(*Suby of* HANERGY HOLDING GROUP LIMITED)
1350 Bayshore Hwy Ste 825, Burlingame, CA 94010-1848
Tel (650) 288-3722 *Founded/Ownrshp* 2011
Sales 252.6MMᴱ *EMP* 360
SIC 4911 6719 Generation, electric power; Investment holding companies, except banks
Ch Bd: Yi Wu
**Pr:* Jeff Zhou
**COO:* Richard Gaertner
COO: Pyramyth Liu
Admn Mgr: Julie Du

D-U-N-S 13-936-2420 IMP/EXP
■ HANES COMPANIES INC
HANES INDUSTRIES
(*Suby of* LEGGETT & PLATT INC) ★
815 Buxton St, Winston Salem, NC 27101-1310
Tel (336) 747-1600 *Founded/Ownrshp* 1986
Sales 362.1MMᴱ *EMP* 805
SIC 2262 2261 2297 Dyeing: manmade fiber & silk broadwoven fabrics; Bleaching: manmade fiber & silk broadwoven fabrics; Refinishing: manmade fiber & silk broadwoven fabrics; Dyeing cotton broadwoven fabrics; Bleaching cotton broadwoven fabrics; Refinishing cotton broadwoven cloth for the trade; Nonwoven fabrics
Pr: Jerry W Greene Jr
CFO: Waller Kim Howard
Treas: J Richard Calhoun
**VP:* Earnest Jett
**VP:* Kenneth W Purser
**VP:* Michael S Walters
Brnch Mgr: Jon Sanchez
Software D: Debbie Henderson
Site Mgr: Roberta Decker
Sfty Mgr: Larry Lichvar
Ql Cn Mgr: Eric Hawn

HANES INDUSTRIES
See HANES COMPANIES INC

D-U-N-S 00-211-0492 IMP
HANES SUPPLY INC (NY)
55 James E Casey Dr, Buffalo, NY 14206-2361
Tel (716) 826-2636 *Founded/Ownrshp* 1930
Sales 97.5MMᴱ *EMP* 150
SIC 5085 5082 3496 1799 Industrial supplies; Contractors' materials; Miscellaneous fabricated wire products; Cable splicing service
Pr: William Hanes
Dir Soc: Ted Hanes
Genl Mgr: Dave Learn
Off Admin: Cheryl Edelman
IT Man: Amanda Maute
VP Mktg: Diane Morris
Sls Dir: Eric Kuras
Sls Dir: Tom Lewis
Sls Mgr: Paul Piciulo
Sales Asso: Jim Ellison
Sales Asso: Dave Holoway

D-U-N-S 78-024-5564
■ HANESBRANDS DIRECT LLC
(*Suby of* HANESBRANDS INC) ★
450 W Hanes Mill Rd, Morganton, NC 28655
Tel (336) 519-8080 *Founded/Ownrshp* 2004
Sales 98.4MMᴱ *EMP* 10,001
SIC 8742 Business consultant
Prin: Catherine Long

D-U-N-S 62-145-4722
▲ HANESBRANDS INC
1000 E Hanes Mill Rd, Winston Salem, NC 27105-1383
Tel (336) 519-8080 *Founded/Ownrshp* 1901
Sales 5.7MMM *EMP* 65,300
Tkr Sym HBI *Exch* NYS
SIC 2253 2342 2341 2322 2252 2251 T-shirts & tops, knit; Bras, girdles & allied garments; Panties: women's, misses', children's & infants'; Underwear, men's & boys': made from purchased materials; Socks; Panty hose
Ch Bd: Richard A Noll
Pr: David Bowers
**Pr:* Michael E Faircloth
Pr: John T Marsh
Pr: W Howard Upchurch
**COO:* Gerald W Evans Jr
**CFO:* Richard D Moss
CFO: Craig Peterson
Treas: Donald Cook
**Ofcr:* Elizabeth L Burger
Ex VP: Joia Johnson
VP: Jennifer Armstrong
VP: Pete Bobalik
VP: Annamarie D'Souza
VP: Annamarie Dsouza
VP: Bob Fellows
VP: Jim Flynn
VP: James Francis
VP: Matt Hall
VP: Keith Huskins
VP: Tom Kerr

D-U-N-S 07-185-8435
HANFORD COMMUNITY HOSPITAL
HANFORD COMMUNITY MEDICAL CTR
(*Suby of* ADVENTIST HEALTH SYSTEM/WEST) ★
450 Greenfield Ave, Hanford, CA 93230-3513
Tel (559) 582-9000 *Founded/Ownrshp* 1956
Sales 230.4MM *EMP* 700
SIC 8062 General medical & surgical hospitals
Ch: Scott Reiner
CFO: Eric Martinson
VP: Carrie Luyster
Dir IT: Michael Aubrey
Mktg Dir: K C Fowler
Pathlgst: Stephen M Avalos
Pathlgst: Reuben S Doggett
Pathlgst: Nicholas Rieber
Obsttrcn: Richard Ellsworth

HANFORD COMMUNITY MEDICAL CTR
See HANFORD COMMUNITY HOSPITAL

HANGER CLINIC
See HANGER INC

D-U-N-S 15-466-6218
HANGER INC
HANGER CLINIC
10910 Domain Dr Ste 300, Austin, TX 78758-7807
Tel (512) 777-3800 *Founded/Ownrshp* 1861
Sales 467.3MMᴱ *EMP* 4,886
SIC 8093 5047 3842 Specialty outpatient clinics; Artificial limbs; Orthopedic equipment & supplies; Prosthetic appliances; Braces, orthopedic; Abdominal supporters, braces & trusses
Pr: Samuel Liang
Pr: Rebecca J Hast
Pr: Kenneth W Wilson
CFO: Spencer Gordon
CFO: Thomas E Kiraly
Treas: Russell G Allen
VP: Anthony Caliguire
VP: Melissa A Debes
VP: Kimberley Deleon
VP: Thomas E Hartman
VP: John Hathaway
VP: Karyn Kessler
VP: Scott Klosterman
VP: Gilbert Mena
VP: Roger Mermelstein
VP: Jim Reichmann
Board of Directors: Christopher B Begley, Thomas P Cooper, Cynthia L Feldmann, Stephen E Hare, Cynthia L Lucchese, Richard R Pettingill, Kathryn Sullivan

D-U-N-S 02-148-6814 IMP
HANIL E HWA INTERIOR SYSTEMS GEORGIA INC
(*Suby of* SEOYON CO., LTD.)
104 Wiley Rd, Lagrange, GA 30240-5811
Tel (706) 298-9701 *Founded/Ownrshp* 2010
Sales 101.3MM *EMP* 100
SIC 3089 Automotive parts, plastic
CEO: Tae Sik Kang

D-U-N-S 07-844-8658
HANJIN SHIPPING AMERICA LLC
(*Suby of* HANJIN GROUP)
80 E State Rt 4 Ste 490, Paramus, NJ 07652-2622
Tel (201) 291-4600 *Founded/Ownrshp* 2011, 2014
Sales 203.8MMᴱ *EMP* 600
SIC 4449 Transportation (freight) on bays & sounds of the ocean
VP: Hae-Chan Park
Genl Mgr: Lawrence Burns
Genl Mgr: Yk Yun
Sls Mgr: Chalaka Herman

D-U-N-S 13-693-7658 IMP/EXP
HANJIN SHIPPING CO LTD
(*Suby of* HANJIN GROUP)
80 E Rte 4 Ste 490, Paramus, NJ 07652-2655
Tel (201) 291-4600 *Founded/Ownrshp* 2014
Sales 91.1MMᴱ *EMP* 691
SIC 4499 Steamship leasing
Ex Dir: Taisoo Suk
VP: Christian Sur
Exec: Balaam Valdez
Genl Mgr: Jay Lee
Genl Mgr: Carmine Ruggiero
Manager: John Graves
Sales Asso: Esther Hong
Sales Asso: Carol Montgomery
Sales Asso: Kris Oconnor
Sales Asso: Anita Sukala
Sales Asso: Julie Villareal

D-U-N-S 83-229-2812
■ HANKINSON RENEWABLE ENERGY LLC
(*Suby of* MURPHY USA) ★
9230 County Road 1, Hankinson, ND 58041-9484
Tel (701) 242-9420 *Founded/Ownrshp* 2009
Sales 340.0MM *EMP* 51
SIC 2869 Ethyl alcohol, ethanol
**Genl Mgr:* Wes Plummer
Genl Mgr: Linda Schiltz

D-U-N-S 04-007-4189 IMP
HANKY PANKY LTD
373 Park Ave S Fl 12, New York, NY 10016-8805
Tel (212) 725-4996 *Founded/Ownrshp* 1977
Sales 94.8MM^E *EMP* 150
SIC 5137 Women's & children's lingerie & undergarments
CEO: Lida Orzeck
**Pr:* Gale Epstein
Sr VP: Kay Legrange
Exec: Lisamarie Dominish
Ex Dir: Greg Tsirulnik
Dir IT: Scott Lee
Sales Exec: Brenda Berger
Sls Mgr: Shannerri Dechalus

D-U-N-S 06-890-1164 IMP
■ HANMI BANK (CA)
(*Suby of* HANMI FINANCIAL CORP) ★
3660 Wilshire Blvd Ph A, Los Angeles, CA 90010-2387
Tel (213) 382-2200 *Founded/Ownrshp* 1981
Sales NA *EMP* 450^E
SIC 6022 State commercial banks
Ch Bd: Joon H Lee
Pr: Susan Kim
Pr: Chong Guk Kum
Pr: Mohammad Tariq
COO: Bonita I Lee
CFO: Lonny D Robinson
CFO: Mark Yoon
CFO: Shick Yoon
Chf Cred: Randall G Ewig
Ofcr: Michael Adams
Ofcr: Ran Jung
Ofcr: Anthony Kim
Ofcr: Greg Kim
Ofcr: Katie Kwon
Ofcr: Jean Lim
Ofcr: Sharon Min
Ofcr: Joonhyok Shin
Ofcr: Peter Yang
Ex VP: Anna Chung
Ex VP: David Yang
Sr VP: Chris Cho
Board of Directors: George S Chey, John A Hall, Paul S Kim, Steve Y Oh, Joseph K Rho, William J Stolte

D-U-N-S 06-430-6132 IMP
▲ HANMI FINANCIAL CORP
3660 Wilshire Blvd Penths Ste A, Los Angeles, CA 90010
Tel (213) 382-2200 *Founded/Ownrshp* 2000
Sales NA *EMP* 622^E
Accts Kpmg Llp Los Angeles Califor
Tkr Sym HAFC *Exch* NGS
SIC 6021 National commercial banks
Pr: Chong Guk Kum
**Ch Bd:* Joseph K RHO
COO: Bonita I Lee
CFO: Romolo C Santarosa
Chf Cred: Min S Park
Ofcr: Greg D Kim
Ex VP: Jean Lim

D-U-N-S 12-164-4124 IMP
HANNA ANDERSSON LLC
(*Suby of* L CATTERTON) ★
608 Ne 19th Ave, Portland, OR 97232-2832
Tel (503) 242-0920 *Founded/Ownrshp* 2016
Sales 163.0MM *EMP* 860
SIC 5641 5621 5719 Children's & infants' wear stores; Children's wear; Infants' wear; Women's specialty clothing stores; Bedding (sheets, blankets, spreads & pillows)
Pr: Adam Stone
Plng Mgr: Marcia Satterwhite
Store Mgr: Bridget Erwin
Store Mgr: Tracy Parker
Opers Mgr: La'trina Adams
Opers Mgr: Trina Adams
Merch Mgr: Roberta Petersen

D-U-N-S 07-496-0550
HANNA HOLDINGS INC
HOWARD HANNA REAL ESTATE
1090 Freeport Rd Ste 1a, Pittsburgh, PA 15238-3166
Tel (412) 967-9000 *Founded/Ownrshp* 1957
Sales 89.0MM^E *EMP* 633
SIC 6531 6162 6361 Real estate brokers & agents; Mortgage bankers & correspondents; Title insurance
Ch Bd: Howard W Hanna Jr
**Pr:* Helen Hanna Casey
**Pr:* Howard W Hanna III
Pr: John Peluso
**CFO:* Tracy Rossettidelvaux
**Ex VP:* Annie E Hanna
**Sr VP:* Tom Ceponis
Sr VP: Barbara Reynolds
VP Mktg: Kelly Silver
Pr Dir: James Penko
Sales Asso: Priscilla Bromley

HANNAFIN, JO MD
See HOSPITAL FOR SPECIALTY SURGERY

D-U-N-S 00-694-9556 IMP
HANNAFORD BROS CO LLC (ME)
HANNAFORD SUPERMARKET & PHRM
(*Suby of* FOOD LION) ★
145 Pleasant Hill Rd, Scarborough, ME 04074-7118
Tel (207) 883-2911 *Founded/Ownrshp* 1883, 2000
Sales 5.0MMM *EMP* 25,000
SIC 5411 5912 Supermarkets; Drug stores
CEO: Dick Boer
Pr: Hugh Farrington
CFO: Paul A Fritzson
Treas: Cindy Sanborn
Ex VP: Michelle Hayes
Ex VP: Ed Tag
Sr VP: Garrett Bowne
VP: Elizabeth Campbell
VP: David Criscione
VP: Emily Dickinson
VP: Emily D Dickinson
VP: Marty Greeley
VP: Gerald Greenleaf
VP: Charles R Hurdman
VP: Blythe Mc Garvie
VP: Eric Norden
VP: Bob Schools
VP: Bradford Wise
VP: Brian Zappala
Exec: Kathy Del Giacco
Exec: Nancy Weber

D-U-N-S 02-478-1213
HANNAFORD BROTHERS CO
(*Suby of* HANNAFORD SUPERMARKET & PHRM) ★
145 Pleasant Hill Rd, Scarborough, ME 04074-9309
Tel (207) 883-2911 *Founded/Ownrshp* 2015
Sales 218.9MM *EMP* 2,700^E
SIC 5411 6519

HANNAFORD SUPERMARKET & PHRM
See HANNAFORD BROS CO LLC

HANNAH, DICK HONDA
See HANNAH MOTOR CO

D-U-N-S 02-756-3733
HANNAH MOTOR CO
HANNAH, DICK HONDA
3400 Ne Auto Mall Dr, Vancouver, WA 98662-7194
Tel (360) 944-3424 *Founded/Ownrshp* 1982
Sales 191.2MM^E *EMP* 625
SIC 5511 Automobiles, new & used
Pr: Richard Hannah
**VP:* Jason Hannah
Genl Mgr: Rachel Smith

D-U-N-S 03-018-8288
HANNAHVILLE INDIAN COMMUNITY
ISLAND RESORT AND CASINO
N14911 Hannahville Rd B 1, Wilson, MI 49896-9612
Tel (906) 466-2932 *Founded/Ownrshp* 1934
Sales NA *EMP* 1,000
SIC 9111 Executive offices
Ch Bd: Kenneth Meshigaud
**CFO:* Scott Herioux
Bd of Dir: Nicki Hardwick
Dir IT: Joe Stanchina
IT Man: Donald Kincheloe

HANNAM CHAIN SUPER 1 MARKET
See HANNAM CHAIN USA INC

D-U-N-S 18-819-1126 IMP
HANNAM CHAIN USA INC
HANNAM CHAIN SUPER 1 MARKET
2740 W Olympic Blvd, Los Angeles, CA 90006-2633
Tel (213) 382-2922 *Founded/Ownrshp* 1987
Sales 98.8MM^E *EMP* 324
SIC 5046 5411 Restaurant equipment & supplies; Supermarkets, independent
CEO: Kee W Ha

D-U-N-S 18-355-1662 IMP/EXP
HANNAS CANDLE CO
HCC BRANDS
2700 S Armstrong Ave, Fayetteville, AR 72701-7274
Tel (479) 443-5467 *Founded/Ownrshp* 1989
Sales 84.0MM^E *EMP* 500
SIC 3999 2844 5999 Potpourri; Candles; Toilet preparations; Candle shops
Pr: Burt Hanna
**VP:* Thad Hanna
**VP:* John Scott
**VP:* Joe Williams

D-U-N-S 16-479-1902
HANNIBAL REGIONAL HOSPITAL INC
HANNIBAL REGIONAL HOSPITAL OFF
6000 Hospital Dr, Hannibal, MO 63401-6887
Tel (573) 248-1300 *Founded/Ownrshp* 1901
Sales 114.4MM *EMP* 850
SIC 8062 General medical & surgical hospitals
CEO: Lynn Olson
Bd of Dir: Arvin Abueg
VP: Pranav Parikh
Exec: Amanda Wosman
Dir OR: Lori Fohey
Dir Inf Cn: Keith Griffeth
Dir Rx: Kirstin Meyer
Dir Rx: Dawn Youngblood
Dir Sec: Doug Ruble
CTO: Sandy Davis
Ansthlgy: Ryan S Easley

HANNIBAL REGIONAL HOSPITAL OFF
See HANNIBAL REGIONAL HOSPITAL INC

D-U-N-S 07-881-5873
HANON SYSTEMS USA LLC
HVCC-USA
(*Suby of* HANON SYSTEMS)
1 Village Center Dr, Van Buren Twp, MI 48111-5711
Tel (734) 710-5000 *Founded/Ownrshp* 2012
Sales 358.2MM^E *EMP* 1,000^E
SIC 3714 3585 3699 Air conditioner parts, motor vehicle; Radiators & radiator shells & cores, motor vehicle; Heaters, motor vehicle; Compressors for refrigeration & air conditioning equipment; Heat emission operating apparatus
Pr: Bob Hickson
**Mng Pt:* Robert Willing
**VP:* Kwangtaek Hong
**VP:* Jay Son

D-U-N-S 82-489-3549
HANOR CO OF WISCONSIN LLC
E4614 Us Hwy 14 And 60, Spring Green, WI 53588-9509
Tel (608) 588-9170 *Founded/Ownrshp* 1994
Sales 115.6MM^E *EMP* 670
SIC 0291 Animal specialty farm, general
CEO: Myrl Mortenson
CFO: Carl Stoner
Sr VP: Baxter Gutknecht
VP: Jim Moody

D-U-N-S 01-328-1498
HANOVER COUNTY PUBLIC SCHOOLS
200 Berkley St, Ashland, VA 23005-1302
Tel (804) 365-4500 *Founded/Ownrshp* 1850
Sales 97.6MM^E *EMP* 2,100
SIC 8211 Public elementary & secondary schools
Genl Mgr: Stephanie Koren
Psych: Megan Cox
Psych: Dorothy Heimlich
HC Dir: Terry Woody

D-U-N-S 00-698-5352 IMP
HANOVER DIRECT INC
HANOVER DIRECT OPERATING GROUP
(*Suby of* CHELSEY DIRECT LLC) ★
1200 Harbor Blvd Fl 9, Weehawken, NJ 07086-6728
Tel (201) 863-7300 *Founded/Ownrshp* 2003
Sales 525.7MM^E *EMP* 1,975
SIC 5712 5961 7389 2211 2221 Bedding & bedsprings; Catalog & mail-order houses; Telemarketing services; Pillow tubing; Comforters & quilts, manmade fiber & silk
Pr: Don Kelley
Sr VP: Ralph J Bulle
VP: Bill Kingsford
VP: Farley Nachemin
VP: Hallie Sturgill
IT Man: Pete Van Donk
Ql Cn Mgr: Al Rapella
Sales Asso: Reene Lynch

HANOVER DIRECT OPERATING GROUP
See HANOVER DIRECT INC

D-U-N-S 00-300-4439 IMP/EXP
HANOVER FOODS CORP
1486 York St, Hanover, PA 17331-7956
Tel (717) 632-6000 *Founded/Ownrshp* 1924
Sales 737.0MM^E *EMP* 2,205
SIC 2033 2032 2037 2038 2099 Canned fruits & specialties; Vegetables: packaged in cans, jars, etc.; Canned specialties; Beans & bean sprouts, canned, jarred, etc.; Macaroni: packaged in cans, jars, etc.; Frozen fruits & vegetables; Vegetables, quick frozen & cold pack, excl. potato products; Frozen specialties; Dinners, frozen & packaged; Salads, fresh or refrigerated
Pr: John A Warehime
Treas: Steven E Robertson
Ex VP: Gary Knisely
Sr VP: Alan T Young
VP: Kenneth Bartosh
VP: Pietro D Giraffa Jr
VP: Dan Schuchart
VP: Daniel E Schuchart
Genl Mgr: Joe Groves
Plnt Mgr: Roger Negley
Manager: Jerry Seidel

D-U-N-S 92-636-9497 IMP/EXP
HANOVER HEALTH CORP INC
300 Highland Ave, Hanover, PA 17331-2297
Tel (717) 637-3711 *Founded/Ownrshp* 1926
Sales 107.5M *EMP* 1,000
SIC 8062 8011 5912 General medical & surgical hospitals; Surgeon; Drug stores
Ch Bd: Michael Rice
**Pr:* William R Wald
**V Ch Bd:* C Daniel Webber
Sr VP: Marilyn Hassel
Ex Dir: Margaret Mc Kinnish
CIO: Pamela Owens
Dir IT: Greg Strevig
Opers Mgr: Stephanie Bruna
Sls Mgr: Krista Hayward
Surgeon: David L Crooks
Doctor: Young Kim

D-U-N-S 06-978-8644
HANOVER HOSPITAL INC
300 Highland Ave, Hanover, PA 17331-2297
Tel (717) 637-3711 *Founded/Ownrshp* 1924
Sales 157.5MM *EMP* 1,400
SIC 8062 General medical & surgical hospitals
CEO: James E Wissler
V Ch: Steven G McKonly
CFO: Kirby Kague
Treas: John R Schnitzer
**Ex VP:* Michael Gaskins
Sr VP: Marilyn Hassle
**VP:* Michael Ader
VP: Carol Freer
**VP:* Michael Hockenberry
Dir Rad: Barbara Renn
**Prin:* Patricia Saunders

D-U-N-S 05-292-9759
■ HANOVER INSURANCE CO
(*Suby of* OPUS INVESTMENT MANAGEMENT INC) ★
440 Lincoln St, Worcester, MA 01653-0001
Tel (508) 853-7200 *Founded/Ownrshp* 1852, 1995
Sales NA *EMP* 2,500
SIC 6331 6351 Fire, marine & casualty insurance & carriers; Property damage insurance; Liability insurance
Pr: Frederick Eppinger
Pr: Lee M Patkus
COO: Craig Rappaport
CFO: Eugene M Bullis
CFO: Edward J Parry
Ofcr: Mark J Welzenbach
Sr VP: Ann K Tripp
VP: Joseph Rovito

D-U-N-S 88-478-3739
▲ HANOVER INSURANCE GROUP INC
440 Lincoln St, Worcester, MA 01653-0001
Tel (508) 855-1000 *Founded/Ownrshp* 1852
Sales NA *EMP* 4,800^E
Tkr Sym THG *Exch* NYS
SIC 6331 6311 Automobile insurance; Property damage insurance; Workers' compensation insurance; Life insurance
Pr: Joseph M Zubretsky
Owner: Joe Green
**Ch Bd:* Michael P Angelini
Pr: Marc Cournoyer
Pr: John Kelly
Pr: Matt Mitchell
Pr: Paul Mueller
Pr: Robert Stuchbery
CFO: Eugene M Bullis
Bd of Dir: Richard A Hein
Chf Mktg O: Richard W Lavey
Ofcr: Bruce B Bartell
Ofcr: Mark L Berthiaume
Ofcr: Christine Bilotti-Peterson
Ex VP: J Kendall Huber
Ex VP: Mark L Keim
Ex VP: Andrew S Robinson
Ex VP: John C Roche
Sr VP: Andrew Robinson
VP: Michael Benadon
VP: Charles Cronin
Board of Directors: Richard H Booth, Jane D Carlin, P Kevin Condron, Cynthia L Egan, Karen C Francis, Daniel T Henry, Wendell J Knox, Joseph R Ramrath, Harriett Taggart

D-U-N-S 07-961-8434
HANRAHANMEYERS ARCHITECTS LLP
6 Maiden Ln Rm 510, New York, NY 10038-5138
Tel (212) 989-6026 *Founded/Ownrshp* 2008
Sales 179.0MM *EMP* 2
SIC 8712 Architectural engineering
Pt: Victoria Meyer
Pt: Thomas Hanrahan

HANSEN & ADKINS
See HANSEN AUTO TRANSPORT INC

D-U-N-S 94-230-7109
HANSEN AUTO TRANSPORT INC
HANSEN & ADKINS
3552 Green Ave Ste 201, Los Alamitos, CA 90720-3250
Tel (562) 430-4100 *Founded/Ownrshp* 1994
Sales 170.0MM^E *EMP* 511
SIC 4213 Automobiles, transport & delivery
CEO: Louie R Adkins
**VP:* Steve Hansen
**VP:* Mark Rumfola
**VP:* Barry Williams
Ex Dir: Juan Perez

HANSEN DISTRIBUTION GROUP
See HAWAIIAN HOUSEWARES LTD

D-U-N-S 06-087-4633
HANSEN-RICE INC
1717 E Chisholm Dr, Nampa, ID 83687-6846
Tel (208) 465-0200 *Founded/Ownrshp* 2001
Sales 90.1MM^E *EMP* 200
SIC 1541 Industrial buildings & warehouses
COO: Burke Hansen
**CFO:* John Rice

D-U-N-S 19-497-7179 IMP
■ HANSGROHE INC
(*Suby of* HANSGROHE SE)
1490 Bluegrass Lakes Pkwy, Alpharetta, GA 30004-7710
Tel (770) 360-9880 *Founded/Ownrshp* 1995
Sales 104.4MM^E *EMP* 325
SIC 3432 5074 3431 Plumbing fixture fittings & trim; Plumbing fittings & supplies; Metal sanitary ware
CEO: Erik Christensen
Ofcr: Astrid Bachmann
Exec: Sibylle Mair
Area Mgr: Joby Hardman
Opers Mgr: Roger Proffitt
Ql Cn Mgr: Erol Saracevic
Sls Dir: Claudia Mueller
Mktg Mgr: Philippe Grohe
Mktg Mgr: Angela Hoggan
Manager: Bill Nusser
Manager: Pascal Powell
Board of Directors: Erik Christensen

D-U-N-S 78-023-3151 IMP/EXP
HANSOL AMERICA INC
(*Suby of* HANSOL HOLDINGS CO., LTD.)
400 Kelby St Ste 6, Fort Lee, NJ 07024-2938
Tel (201) 461-6661 *Founded/Ownrshp* 1991
Sales 159.0MM *EMP* 22
Accts Kpmg Llp New York Ny
SIC 5113 Industrial & personal service paper
CEO: Seung R Choi
**Treas:* Sara Choi

D-U-N-S 12-824-4097
HANSON AGGREGATES EAST LLC
(*Suby of* HANSON LEHIGH INC) ★
3131 Rdu Center Dr, Morrisville, NC 27560-7687
Tel (919) 380-2500 *Founded/Ownrshp* 1998
Sales 905.4MM^E *EMP* 10,600^E
SIC 3531 5032 Asphalt plant, including gravel-mix type; Batching plants, for aggregate concrete & bulk cement; Aggregate
Pr: Jim Sprinkle
**Pr:* Dan Harrington
**Pr:* Howard Nye
CIO: Bob Dieter
IT Man: Richard Smith
Natl Sales: Don Kula
Mktg Mgr: Jeff Avant
Mktg Mgr: Rob Hatten
Mktg Mgr: Roger Hutchinson
Mktg Mgr: Raymond Liddick
Sls Mgr: Mark Odell

D-U-N-S 09-356-6040
HANSON AGGREGATES LLC
SOUTHERN STAR CONCRETE
(*Suby of* HANSON LEHIGH INC) ★
8505 Freeport Pkwy Ste 500, Irving, TX 75063
Tel (469) 417-1200 *Founded/Ownrshp* 1968
Sales 393.6MM^E *EMP* 1,000
SIC 3273 2951 5032 Ready-mixed concrete; Asphalt paving mixtures & blocks; Gravel; Sand, construction
CEO: Daniel Harrington
Pr: Martin Vogt
**CFO:* Seyda Pirinccioglu
VP: Tommy Abbott
**VP:* Michael Hyer
VP: Paul Schickler
Exec: Anna Allis
Exec: Charlotte Fitzgerald

Off Mgr: Karen Holbrooks
Dir IT: Kevin Hoople
IT Man: Norm Pitt

D-U-N-S 00-694-5414
HANSON AGGREGATES MIDWEST LLC (KY)
(*Suby of* HANSON LEHIGH INC) ★
207 Old Harrods Creek Rd, Louisville, KY 40223-2553
Tel (502) 244-7550 *Founded/Ownrshp* 1928, 2011
Sales 1.4MMM^E *EMP* 1,000
SIC 1422 1611

D-U-N-S 00-320-2272
HANSON AGGREGATES SOUTHEAST INC
(*Suby of* HANSON LEHIGH INC) ★
2310 Parklake Dr Ne # 550, Atlanta, GA 30345-2913
Tel (770) 491-2777 *Founded/Ownrshp* 1909, 1967
Sales 270.7MM^E *EMP* 860
SIC 1423 1442 Crushed & broken granite; Construction sand & gravel
VP: Justin Williams

D-U-N-S 84-975-5178
HANSON AGGREGATES WRP INC
WESTERN ROCK PRODUCTS
(*Suby of* HANSON LEHIGH INC) ★
1333 Campus Pkwy, Wall Township, NJ 07753-6815
Tel (972) 653-5500 *Founded/Ownrshp* 1987
Sales 140.0MM^E *EMP* 234
SIC 3281 3272 2951 1442 Cut stone & stone products; Concrete products; Asphalt paving mixtures & blocks; Construction sand & gravel
Pr: Alan Murray

HANSON BRICK
See FORTERRA BRICK LLC

D-U-N-S 96-734-2197 IMP/EXP
HANSON LEHIGH INC
(*Suby of* HEIDELBERGCEMENT AG)
300 E John Carpenter Fwy, Irving, TX 75062-2727
Tel (972) 653-5500 *Founded/Ownrshp* 1984
Sales 5.2MMM^E *EMP* 10,700
SIC 1442 1422 1423 3297 3273 3272 Sand mining; Gravel & pebble mining; Crushed & broken limestone; Crushed & broken granite; Cement refractories; Ready-mixed concrete; Concrete products used to facilitate drainage
CEO: Daniel Harrington
**Pr:* James K Kitzmiller
Pr: Robert Pischke
**CEO:* Jon Morrish
**CFO:* Helmut Fischer
CFO: Simon Nicholls
CFO: Leslie Russell
**Treas:* John T Berry
Sr VP: Scott Szwejbka
VP: Kelly Bennett
**VP:* Henner Bttcher
VP: Axel Conrads
VP: Mike Hyer
VP: George Lefler
VP: Gerhard Muehlbeyer
**VP:* Robert L Ross
Exec: Delia Kell

HANSON MATERIAL SERVICE
See MATERIAL SERVICE CORP

D-U-N-S 82-886-1430
HANSON PRESSURE PIPE INC
(*Suby of* FORTERRA BUILDING PRODUCTS) ★
1003 Macarthur Blvd, Grand Prairie, TX 75050-7943
Tel (972) 262-3600 *Founded/Ownrshp* 2008
Sales 185.3MM^E *EMP* 1^E
SIC 3317 3272 3999 Steel pipe & tubes; Liquid catch basins, tanks & covers: concrete; Barber & beauty shop equipment
Pr: Clifford Hahne
Prd Mgr: Charlie McAuley

D-U-N-S 02-350-9776
HANSONS WINDOWS AND SIDING OF LANSING LLC
1-800-HANSONS
977 E 14 Mile Rd, Troy, MI 48083-4519
Tel (248) 681-9202 *Founded/Ownrshp* 1998
Sales 160.7M^E *EMP* 4,000
SIC 1751 Window & door (prefabricated) installation
Pr: Brian Elias

D-U-N-S 02-984-2085 IMP/EXP
HANTOVER INC
5200 W 110th St Ste 200, Overland Park, KS 66211-1203
Tel (913) 214-4800 *Founded/Ownrshp* 1978
Sales 117.0MM^E *EMP* 160
SIC 5099 5084 Safety equipment & supplies; Food industry machinery; Materials handling machinery
Ch Bd: Bernard Huff
**Sec:* Karon Huff
Opers Mgr: Jeff Miller
Sales Exec: Tom Lamb
Sls Mgr: Larry Smith
Sales Asso: David Summerly

D-U-N-S 36-172-6008
HANTZ GROUP INC
26200 American Dr Ste 500, Southfield, MI 48034-6101
Tel (248) 304-2855 *Founded/Ownrshp* 1997
Sales 87.3MM^E *EMP* 266^E
SIC 6282 Banking & finance consultant
Pr: John Hantz
Ofcr: Johnnie Lyn Powell-Orts

D-U-N-S 18-719-7611
HANUMAN BUSINESS INC
RAMOCO FUELS
5026 Wynnefield Ave, Philadelphia, PA 19131-2531
Tel (609) 929-5146 *Founded/Ownrshp* 1987
Sales 200.0MM *EMP* 12
SIC 5541 7538 Filling stations, gasoline; General automotive repair shops
Pr: Ratnkar Patlola

D-U-N-S 04-541-8811 IMP/EXP
HANWA AMERICAN CORP
(*Suby of* HANWA CO.,LTD.)
Parker Plz 400 Kelby St F, Fort Lee, NJ 07024
Tel (201) 363-4500 *Founded/Ownrshp* 1968
Sales 500.0MM *EMP* 50
Accts Kpmg Llp New York Ny
SIC 5051 5172 5031 5084 5146 Steel; Miscellaneous nonferrous products; Fuel oil; Lumber: rough, dressed & finished; Industrial machinery & equipment; Fish & seafoods
Ch: Kozo Yamabe
Pr: Kazuyuki Ogawa
Mng Dir: Yasuo Sakai
Genl Mgr: Jai Dave

D-U-N-S 19-927-2027 IMP
HANWHA ADVANCED MATERIALS AMERICA LLC
(*Suby of* HANWHA L & C HOLDINGS USA LLC) ★
4400 N Park Dr, Opelika, AL 36801-9685
Tel (334) 741-7725 *Founded/Ownrshp* 2011
Sales 92.4MM *EMP* 70
SIC 3714 Motor vehicle parts & accessories
Plng Mgr: Tony Kim

D-U-N-S 82-693-4106 IMP
HANWHA HOLDINGS (USA) INC
(*Suby of* HANWHA CORPORATION)
300 Frank W Burr Blvd # 52, Teaneck, NJ 07666-6703
Tel (609) 655-2500 *Founded/Ownrshp* 2007
Sales 484.5MM^E *EMP* 608
SIC 5169 5013 5084 Chemicals & allied products; Automotive supplies; Industrial machinery & equipment
Pr: Tom Kim
**Treas:* Wooseok Kim

D-U-N-S 82-855-5073
HANWHA L & C HOLDINGS USA LLC
(*Suby of* HANWHA HOLDINGS (USA) INC) ★
4400 N Park Dr, Opelika, AL 36801-9685
Tel (334) 741-7725 *Founded/Ownrshp* 2008
Sales 124.4MM^E *EMP* 270^E
SIC 3083 3714 Thermoplastic laminates: rods, tubes, plates & sheet; Motor vehicle parts & accessories
CEO: Hee Chung Kim

HAPI
See HEALTH ALLIANCE WITH PHYSICIAN

HAPPY FAMILY BRANDS
See NURTURE INC

D-U-N-S 01-104-2140 IMP
■ **HAPPY HARRYS INC**
(*Suby of* WALGREENS) ★
326 Ruthar Dr, Newark, DE 19711-8017
Tel (302) 366-0335 *Founded/Ownrshp* 1962, 2006
Sales 174.0MM^E *EMP* 2,000
SIC 5912 Drug stores
Pr: Alan Levin
**Sec:* Thomas Salvatore
VP: Lois Becker
VP: Ralph Larson

D-U-N-S 03-058-9356
HAPPY HOUSE LLC (AZ)
8116 E Vista Bonita Dr, Scottsdale, AZ 85255-4281
Tel (480) 854-0788 *Founded/Ownrshp* 2011
Sales 400.0MM *EMP* 4
SIC 1521 Single-family housing construction

D-U-N-S 03-632-0992
HAPPY STATE BANK
(*Suby of* HAPPY BANCSHARES, INC)
701 S Taylor St Lb120, Amarillo, TX 79101-2405
Tel (806) 373-2265 *Founded/Ownrshp* 1970
Sales NA *EMP* 20
SIC 6022 State commercial banks
CEO: J Pat Hickman
Pr: Kyle Fuston
**Pr:* Jeffrey Peatrowsky
Pr: Craig Wells
CFO: Ronda Bartlett
Ofcr: Elaine Lee
**Ex VP:* Connie Ratliff
Sr VP: Kayla Carpenter
Sr VP: Beverly Gaines
Sr VP: Mike Jackson
Sr VP: Bryan Limmer
Sr VP: David McCullough
Sr VP: David Weiner
VP: Annette Anders
VP: Eric Barbee
**VP:* Randy Crawford
VP: Kathy McKaskle
VP: Matthew Shadid
VP: Chancy Via
VP: Rosalinda Villalon
VP: Alisa Villyard

D-U-N-S 02-141-5538
HAPPYS PIZZA CO
30201 Orchrd Lke Rd 200, Farmington Hills, MI 48334
Tel (248) 358-8888 *Founded/Ownrshp* 2005
Sales 82.4MM^E *EMP* 1,876^E
SIC 5812 Pizza restaurants
Prin: Feds Indict
**Prin:* Happy Asker

D-U-N-S 06-383-7777
HAR-BRO INC
2750 Signal Pkwy, Signal Hill, CA 90755-2207
Tel (562) 528-8000 *Founded/Ownrshp* 1956
Sales 91.7MM^E *EMP* 175
SIC 1542 1521 1522

D-U-N-S 04-036-2055 IMP
HARALAMBOS BEVERAGE CO
2300 Pellissier Pl, City of Industry, CA 90601-1500
Tel (562) 347-4300 *Founded/Ownrshp* 1976
Sales 262.6MM^E *EMP* 300^E
SIC 5181 5149 Beer & other fermented malt liquors; Beverages, except coffee & tea
CEO: H T Haralambos
**Pr:* Anthony Haralambos
CFO: Denise Conot
**VP:* Thomas Haralambos
Rgnl Mgr: Ford Poland
Dir IT: Charles Mavudzi
VP Sls: Steve Juarez
Manager: Fred Akroush
Manager: Rich Belliston
Manager: Greg Kovacic

D-U-N-S 09-447-1430
HARBERT CORP
2100 3rd Ave N Ste 600, Birmingham, AL 35203-3416
Tel (205) 987-5500 *Founded/Ownrshp* 1977
Sales 91.5MM^E *EMP* 202^E
SIC 4911 6799 Electric services; Investors
Pr: Raymond J Harbert
**Pr:* Michael D Luce
CFO: David Batwell
**Ex VP:* David A Boutwell
**Ex VP:* Charles D Miller

D-U-N-S 87-840-3914
HARBERT MANAGEMENT CORP
2100 3rd Ave N Ste 600, Birmingham, AL 35203-3416
Tel (205) 987-5500 *Founded/Ownrshp* 1993
Sales 128.3MM^E *EMP* 225
SIC 6726 6799 Investment offices; Investors
CEO: Raymond J Harbert
Mng Pt: Wayne Hunter
CFO: Sonja Keeton
Ex VP: John W McCullough
Ex VP: John W McCullough
Ex VP: Charles D Miller
Sr VP: John McCullough
VP: Michael C Bauder
VP: James Flood
VP: Raymond Harbert
VP: Thomas Hicks
VP: J Travis Pritchett

D-U-N-S 07-078-0317
HARBIN CLINIC LLC (GA)
221 Technology Pkwy Nw, Rome, GA 30165-1644
Tel (706) 295-5331 *Founded/Ownrshp* 1948
Sales 187.1MM^E *EMP* 1,200
SIC 8011 Clinic, operated by physicians
Pr: Ken Davis
Exec: Becky Wiggins
DP Exec: Michael Jones
Dir IT: David Marks
Sls&Mrk Ex: Natalie Simms
Mktg Dir: Brenda Bowen
Surgeon: Brandon D Bushnell
Surgeon: Chad M Wagner
Obsttrcn: Barry N Brass
Obsttrcn: Marc M Dean
Obsttrcn: Raymond R Jarvis

D-U-N-S 96-805-3814
■ **HARBINGER OM LLC**
(*Suby of* HRG GROUP INC) ★
450 Park Ave Fl 27, New York, NY 10022-2605
Tel (212) 906-8555 *Founded/Ownrshp* 2010
Sales 281.2MM^E *EMP* 1,285^E
SIC 6726 Investment offices
Pr: Philip Falcone
**CFO:* Francis T McCarron

D-U-N-S 79-293-2287 IMP/EXP
HARBISON CORP
15450 South Outer 40 Rd # 120, Chesterfield, MO 63017-2062
Tel (314) 727-8200 *Founded/Ownrshp* 1992
Sales 195.7MM^E *EMP* 1,200
SIC 3089 Plastic containers, except foam; Plastic processing; Closures, plastic
Pr: Keith S Harbison
**CFO:* Bob Robison
VP: Dave Winslett
CTO: Daniel Charron
Plnt Mgr: Jeff Oathout

D-U-N-S 00-802-5959 IMP/EXP
■ **HARBISON-FISCHER INC**
HARBISON-FISCHER MANUFACTURING
(*Suby of* NORRIS PRODUCTION SOLUTIONS) ★
901 N Crowley Rd, Crowley, TX 76036-3798
Tel (817) 297-2211 *Founded/Ownrshp* 1933, 2007
Sales 131.7MM^E *EMP* 450
SIC 3533 3443 Oil field machinery & equipment; Tanks, lined: metal plate
Pr: David Martin
**CFO:* Jason Taylor
**VP:* Darryl Polasek
**VP:* Jason Thompson
VP: Peter White
Ex Dir: Larry Gipson
Area Mgr: Dennis Brown
Area Mgr: Mark Lee
Dist Mgr: Jimmy Kemp
Dist Mgr: David Kruger
Telecom Mg: Sandra Bitz

HARBISON-FISCHER MANUFACTURING
See HARBISON-FISCHER INC

D-U-N-S 94-950-1522 IMP/EXP
HARBISON-WALKER REFRACTORIES CO
1305 Cherrington Pkwy, Coraopolis, PA 15108-4355
Tel (412) 375-6600 *Founded/Ownrshp* 1972
Sales 119.7MM^E *EMP* 611^E
SIC 3255 3297

D-U-N-S 78-418-7580 IMP/EXP
HARBISONWALKER INTERNATIONAL INC
1305 Cherrington Pkwy # 100, Moon Township, PA 15108-4355
Tel (412) 375-6600 *Founded/Ownrshp* 2013
Sales 880.4MM^E *EMP* 1,700
SIC 3297 3272 1459 Nonclay refractories; Solid containing units, concrete; Magnesite mining
CEO: Steven M Delo
CFO: David Bates
**CFO:* Frances Winfield
**Sr VP:* Douglas Hall
**Sr VP:* Carol Jackson
Mng Dir: Don Abrino
Mng Dir: Carl Apel
Mng Dir: Aldo Betta
Mng Dir: Bill Orlandi
Dist Mgr: Jack Bentley
Dist Mgr: Mark Curtis

D-U-N-S 00-986-8233
HARBOR CHEVROLET CORP (CA)
HARBOR CHEVROLET SALES AND SVC
3770 Cherry Ave, Long Beach, CA 90807-4321
Tel (562) 426-3341 *Founded/Ownrshp* 1923, 1956
Sales 107.5MM^E *EMP* 90
SIC 5511

HARBOR CHEVROLET SALES AND SVC
See HARBOR CHEVROLET CORP

D-U-N-S 08-837-1638
HARBOR DEVELOPMENTAL DISABILITIES FOUNDATION INC
HARBOR REGIONAL CENTER
21231 Hawthorne Blvd, Torrance, CA 90503-5501
Tel (310) 540-1711 *Founded/Ownrshp* 1977
Sales 162.3MM *EMP* 225
Accts Windes Inc Long Beach Ca
SIC 8399 Council for social agency
Prin: Patricia Del Monico
CFO: Judy Wada
Prgrm Mgr: Audrey Clurfeld
Prgrm Mgr: Liz Cohen-Zeboulon
Prgrm Mgr: Leslie Estrada
Prgrm Mgr: Steve Hankow
Prgrm Mgr: Pablo Ibanez
Prgrm Mgr: Yolanda Lopez
Prgrm Mgr: Tonantzin Martinez
Prgrm Mgr: Vincente Miles
Prgrm Mgr: Bjoern Petersen

D-U-N-S 02-803-4536 IMP
HARBOR DISTRIBUTING LLC
(*Suby of* REYES HOLDINGS LLC) ★
5901 Bolsa Ave, Huntington Beach, CA 92647-2053
Tel (714) 933-2400 *Founded/Ownrshp* 1989
Sales 120.9MM^E *EMP* 400
SIC 5181 Beer & other fermented malt liquors

D-U-N-S 61-690-8646
■ **HARBOR ELECTRIC ENERGY CO**
(*Suby of* EVERSOURCE ENERGY) ★
800 Boylston St, Boston, MA 02199-1900
Tel (617) 424-2000 *Founded/Ownrshp* 1989
Sales 352.9MM^E *EMP* 944^E
SIC 4911 Electric services
Ch Bd: Thomas J May
**Treas:* James Judge
**Genl Couns:* Doug Horan

HARBOR FREIGHT TOOLS
See CENTRAL PURCHASING LLC

D-U-N-S 00-509-6875 IMP/EXP
HARBOR FREIGHT TOOLS USA INC
26541 Agoura Rd, Calabasas, CA 91302-2093
Tel (818) 836-5000 *Founded/Ownrshp* 1993
Sales 2.3MMM^E *EMP* 10,000
SIC 5251 Tools
Pr: Eric L Smidt
Pr: Trey Feiler
COO: Robert Rene
CFO: Robert Glickman
VP: Kelly Brown
VP: Jerry Dammeir
VP: Jonathan Kendall
VP: Tony Laik
VP: Roger Sheaves
Creative D: Monique Berger
Dist Mgr: Russell Hayes

D-U-N-S 00-447-7563
HARBOR GROUP INC
INTERSTATES CONSTRUCTION SVCS
1520 N Main Ave, Sioux Center, IA 51250-2111
Tel (712) 722-1661 *Founded/Ownrshp* 1999
Sales 114.9MM *EMP* 550
Accts Eidebailly Sioux Falls Sd
SIC 1731 General electrical contractor
CEO: Larry E Den Herder
**Pr:* Scott R Peterson
CFO: Larry Herder
IT Man: Tom Schulte

D-U-N-S 11-872-6595
HARBOR GROUP INC
1115 E Broadway Ave, Norton Shores, MI 49444-2333
Tel (231) 739-7152 *Founded/Ownrshp* 1983
Sales 88.1MM^E *EMP* 130
Accts Steensma Novotny Plc Muskegon
SIC 5051 Metals service centers & offices
Pr: David F Folkert
**CFO:* Joseph Gerhardt

D-U-N-S 03-804-5063
HARBOR HOSPITAL CENTER INC
LABOUR DEPARTMENT
3001 S Hanover St, Baltimore, MD 21225-1290
Tel (410) 350-3200 *Founded/Ownrshp* 1903
Sales 209.0MM *EMP* 1,231
Accts Kpmg Llp Norfolk Va
SIC 8062 General medical & surgical hospitals
CEO: Joseph Oddis
Mtls Mgr: Nita Griffith

D-U-N-S 05-490-5930
HARBOR HOSPITAL FOUNDATION INC
(*Suby of* MEDSTAR HEALTH VNA) ★
3001 S Hanover St, Baltimore, MD 21225-1233
Tel (410) 350-2563 *Founded/Ownrshp* 1903
Sales 64.5MM^E *EMP* 1,220
Accts Kpmg Llp Norfolk Va
SIC 8062 General medical & surgical hospitals
CEO: L Barney Johnson

D-U-N-S 00-602-7536 IMP
HARBOR INDUSTRIES INC (MI)
14130 172nd Ave, Grand Haven, MI 49417-9446
Tel (616) 842-5330 *Founded/Ownrshp* 1950
Sales 174.0MM^E *EMP* 551
Accts Deloitte & Touche Llp
SIC 2541 3993 Display fixtures, wood; Signs & advertising specialties
Pr: Henry T Parker Jr
**Pr:* Timothy Parker

CFO: Roger Meyer
**VP:* Michael Detenber
**VP:* Gregory Hankamp
**VP:* Thomas Nook
**VP:* Frank Tamburello
**Prin:* Susan Wright
CTO: Rob Doremire
Plnt Mgr: Kevin Shaler
Natl Sales: Chad Ewald

D-U-N-S 18-159-1306
HARBOR MEDICAL GROUP
(*Suby of* NSMC SALEM HOSPITAL) ★
55 Highland Ave Ste 102, Salem, MA 01970-2100
Tel (978) 741-9500 *Founded/Ownrshp* 1996
Sales 31.6MM^E *EMP* 2,688^E
SIC 8011 Offices & clinics of medical doctors
Prin: North Shore Medical Center

HARBOR REGIONAL CENTER
See HARBOR DEVELOPMENTAL DISABILITIES FOUNDATION INC

D-U-N-S 04-140-5960
HARBOR STEEL AND SUPPLY CORP
(*Suby of* HARBOR GROUP INC) ★
1115 E Broadway Ave, Norton Shores, MI 49444-2333
Tel (231) 739-7152 *Founded/Ownrshp* 1985
Sales 87.9MM^E *EMP* 130
Accts Steensma Plamondon Novotny Plc
SIC 5051 Metals service centers & offices; Ferrous metals; Miscellaneous nonferrous products; Nonferrous metal sheets, bars, rods, etc.
CEO: David F Folkert
**Pr:* Stephen Heneveld
CFO: Joseph Gerhardt
DP Exec: Steve Jensen

D-U-N-S 79-210-2287
HARBOR VIEW HOLDINGS INC
433 California St Fl 7, San Francisco, CA 94104-2011
Tel (415) 982-7777 *Founded/Ownrshp* 1984
Sales 250.2MM^E *EMP* 3,500
SIC 1522 1521 6512 8741 Hotel/motel, new construction; Single-family housing construction; Nonresidential building operators; Hotel or motel management; Restaurant management
Pr: Lawrence Lui
CFO: James E Evans
VP: Tamsen McCracken

D-U-N-S 02-724-8913
HARBOR WHOLESALE GROCERY INC
3901 Hogum Bay Rd Ne, Lacey, WA 98516-3136
Tel (360) 754-4484 *Founded/Ownrshp* 1970
Sales 151.7MM^E *EMP* 300
SIC 5141 5194 5142 5122

D-U-N-S 10-095-2667
HARBOR-UCLA MEDICAL CENTER
1000 W Carson St 2, Torrance, CA 90502-2059
Tel (310) 222-2345 *Founded/Ownrshp* 1989
Sales 607.1MM *EMP* 3,000
SIC 8062 General medical & surgical hospitals
CEO: Miguel Ortiz
Doctor: Kelly Young

HARBORLITE
See IMERYS PERLITE USA INC

D-U-N-S 06-010-7240
HARBORONE BANK
770 Oak St, Brockton, MA 02301-1100
Tel (508) 895-1000 *Founded/Ownrshp* 1917
Sales NA *EMP* 373
SIC 6036 State savings banks, not federally chartered
Pr: James W Blake
**Ch Bd:* David Frenette
Pr: Maureen Wilkinson
**CFO:* Joseph Casey
Bd of Dir: Adam Cupples
Chf Mktg O: Dave Tryder
Ofcr: James Hanlon
Ofcr: Dayna Holmes
**Sr VP:* Richard W Bastiansen
**Sr VP:* Marcia G Dmitruk
**Sr VP:* Leo Donahue
**Sr VP:* Christopher K Gibbons
**Sr VP:* Leo A Macneil
Sr VP: David Reilly
Sr VP: Scott Sanborn
**Sr VP:* Patricia M Williams
VP: Murray Charron
VP: Allen Cordeiro
VP: Shirley Donahue
VP: Aguilando Fonseca
VP: Leo Macneil

D-U-N-S 07-442-0142
HARBORQUEST INC (IL)
14 E Jackson Blvd # 1210, Chicago, IL 60604-2233
Tel (312) 612-7600 *Founded/Ownrshp* 1970
Sales 4.4MM *EMP* 1,500
Accts Fgmk Llc Deerfield Il
SIC 7363 4119 7361 Temporary help service; Local passenger transportation; Employment agencies
Pr: John J Plunkett
**Pr:* Robert E Wordlaw
**Sec:* Jane Davies
**VP:* Mark Mulroe
VP: Richard S Peabody Jr
**VP:* William A Schwarz
Ex Dir: Robert Wordlaw

HARBORSIDE FINANCIAL CENTER
See IPC SYSTEMS HOLDINGS CORP

D-U-N-S 96-650-6821
■ **HARBORSIDE HEALTHCARE ADVISORS LIMITED PARTNERSHIP**
(*Suby of* KHI LLC)
101 Sun Ave Ne, Albuquerque, NM 87109-4373
Tel (505) 821-1216 *Founded/Ownrshp* 1987
Sales 29.6MM^E *EMP* 1,270^E
SIC 8051 Skilled nursing care facilities
Pr: William Mathies

D-U-N-S 13-657-8817
HARBORVIEW MEDICAL CENTER
UNIVERSITY OF WASHINGTON
(*Suby of* UNIVERSITY OF WASHINGTON INC) ★
325 9th Ave, Seattle, WA 98104-2499
Tel (206) 731-3000 *Founded/Ownrshp* 1930
Sales 858.8MM *EMP* 4,000^E
SIC 8062 General medical & surgical hospitals
Ex Dir: Eileen Whalen
COO: Claudette Cooper
COO: Scott Davies
Off Mgr: Brenda Tillery
Off Mgr: Bahaa Wanly
Web Dev: Jeff Volkman
Sftwr Eng: Lee Fouche
Opers Mgr: Ruchi Aggarwal
Pathlgst: Byung K Kim
Obsttrcn: Susan D Reed
Ansthlgy: Ian R Slade

D-U-N-S 14-706-1592 IMP/EXP
HARBOUR GROUP LTD
7701 Forsyth Blvd Ste 600, Saint Louis, MO 63105-1802
Tel (314) 727-5550 *Founded/Ownrshp* 1980
Sales 1.5MMM^E *EMP* 5,200
SIC 3823 Boiler controls: industrial, power & marine type
CEO: Jeff Fox
V Ch: Donald E Nicklson
**Pr:* Greg Fox
**Pr:* Samuel A Hamacher
**Pr:* James C Janning
**CFO:* Mike Santoni
Treas: Janelle Rickermann
**V Ch Bd:* Donald E Nickelson
**V Ch Bd:* William A Schmalz
VP: Audrey Chang
VP: Greg Meier
Board of Directors: Edward J Bock, Alfred Fleishman, Reuben Mark, John McGuckian, Julian Meyer, Stanley Rosenblum, Mahlon Rubin, Murray Weidenbaum

D-U-N-S 04-562-9656
■ **HARCO INC**
(*Suby of* RITE AID CORP) ★
30 Hunter Ln, Camp Hill, PA 17011-2400
Tel (717) 761-2633 *Founded/Ownrshp* 1997
Sales 270.0MM^E *EMP* 2,600
Accts Arthur Andersen Llp Birmingha
SIC 5912 Drug stores
Pr: Kenneth C Black
**Treas:* Matthew Schroeder
**VP:* Gerald Cardinale
**VP:* Susan Lowell
**VP:* Michael A Podgurski

D-U-N-S 13-137-1700 IMP/EXP
HARCO INDUSTRIES INC USA
333 S Van Brunt St, Englewood, NJ 07631-4610
Tel (201) 894-8941 *Founded/Ownrshp* 1985
Sales 120.0MM *EMP* 52
Accts Internal Use
SIC 5947 Gift, novelty & souvenir shop
Ch Bd: Saro Hartounian
**COO:* Nareg Hartounian
VP: Robert Kramer

D-U-N-S 10-355-9258
HARCOURT ASSESSMENT INC
CLINICAL ASSESSMENT
(*Suby of* PEARSON PLC)
19500 Bulverde Rd, San Antonio, TX 78259-3707
Tel (210) 339-5000 *Founded/Ownrshp* 2008
Sales 43.0MM^E *EMP* 1,000
SIC 8748 2741 Testing service, educational or personnel; Test development & evaluation service; Miscellaneous publishing
Ch Bd: John R Dilworth
**Ch Bd:* Michael E Hansen
**CEO:* Barry Topol
Treas: Kenneth E Fogarty
**VP:* Scott Barnes
VP: Charles P Fontaine
VP: Terry Turner
VP: Joe Wong
Dir Surg: Ray Christensen
CTO: Mickey Corona

D-U-N-S 19-412-8765 IMP/EXP
HARCROS CHEMICALS INC
5200 Speaker Rd, Kansas City, KS 66106-1048
Tel (913) 321-3131 *Founded/Ownrshp* 2001
Sales 639.4MM^E *EMP* 550
SIC 5169 2869 Industrial gases; Industrial organic chemicals
CEO: Kevin Mirner
**CFO:* Mark Loethen
VP: Nick Harden
VP: Darrell Kelley
VP: Daniel Larsen
**VP:* Martin Morgan
**VP:* Peter Radford
VP: Howard Stevenson
Exec: Dana Field
Rgnl Mgr: Rob Foley
Rgnl Mgr: Paul Spinner

D-U-N-S 10-326-8710 IMP
HARD ROCK CAFE FOUNDATION INC
(*Suby of* SEMINOLE TRIBE OF FLORIDA T V INC) ★
6100 Old Park Ln Ste 100, Orlando, FL 32835-2499
Tel (407) 445-7625 *Founded/Ownrshp* 2006
Sales 1.5MM *EMP* 3,000^E
SIC 5812 5813 7011 6794 Eating places; Bar (drinking places); Hotels & motels; Franchises, selling or licensing
Pr: Hamish Dodds
**Treas:* Chris Knipfing
**VP:* Thomas Gispanski
VP: Marie Grimm
Sls Dir: Robert Barbieri
Manager: Tara Hippensteel

D-U-N-S 80-978-9709 IMP
HARD ROCK CAFE INTERNATIONAL (USA) INC
ROCK SHOP
(*Suby of* SEMINOLE WHOLESALE DISTRS) ★
6100 Old Park Ln Ste 100, Orlando, FL 32835-2499
Tel (407) 445-7625 *Founded/Ownrshp* 2007
Sales 71.5MM^E *EMP* 1,500
SIC 5812 Eating places
Pr: Hamish Dodds
**COO:* Fred Thimm
Ex VP: Jon Lucas
Ex VP: Marco Roca
**VP:* Michael Beacham
**VP:* John Galloway
**VP:* Thomas Gispanski
VP: Duana Klein
VP: Patrick Manion
MIS Dir: Ron Ward
Sls Dir: Rohaizad Puteh

HARD ROCK HOTEL AND CASINO
See HRHH HOTEL/CASINO LLC

D-U-N-S 80-958-5974
HARD ROCK HOTEL HOLDINGS LLC
4455 Paradise Rd, Las Vegas, NV 89169-6598
Tel (702) 693-5000 *Founded/Ownrshp* 2011
Sales 28.6MM^E *EMP* 1,362^E
SIC 7011 Hotels & motels; Casino hotel
Pr: Fred J Kleisner
**VP:* Richard Szymanski

D-U-N-S 10-298-7344
HARD ROCK HOTEL INC
HARD ROCK LAS VEGAS
4455 Paradise Rd, Las Vegas, NV 89169-6598
Tel (702) 693-5000 *Founded/Ownrshp* 1993
Sales 144.1MM^E *EMP* 1,362
SIC 7011 Casino hotel
Pr: Richard Szymanski
**Ch Bd:* Peter A Morton
**CEO:* Jody Lake
**COO:* Kevin Kelley
COO: Joseph A Magliarditi
**CFO:* Dean Boswell
**CFO:* James D Bowen
CFO: James E Conley
Bd of Dir: Gilbert B Friesen
**Sr VP:* Brian D Ogaz
VP: Thomas Evans
VP: Javier De La Rosa
VP: Bob Madrigale
VP: Gary Scott

HARD ROCK LAS VEGAS
See HARD ROCK HOTEL INC

HARDAWAY CNSTR CORP TENN
See HARDAWAY CONSTRUCTION CORP

D-U-N-S 06-074-7953
HARDAWAY CONSTRUCTION CORP
HARDAWAY CNSTR CORP TENN
(*Suby of* MAIN STREET OPERATING CO INC) ★
615 Main St, Nashville, TN 37206-3617
Tel (615) 254-5461 *Founded/Ownrshp* 1924
Sales 85.6MM^E *EMP* 225
SIC 1542 1541 1522 Commercial & office building, new construction; Industrial buildings, new construction; Multi-family dwelling construction
Pr: Stan H Hardaway
**CFO:* Kerry P Sloan
**Treas:* Catherine L Hardaway
**Ex VP:* John F Sloan
VP: Ed Bullington
VP: Gary W Chesley
VP: Linda Guinn CPA
VP: Bret Obrien
Snr PM: David Dierks
Board of Directors: Susan K Goodrum, Billy D Grover, Andy Higgins, Richard M Miller, Frank Woods

D-U-N-S 13-105-6467
HARDAWAY GROUP INC
615 Main St, Nashville, TN 37206-3603
Tel (615) 254-5461 *Founded/Ownrshp* 1986
Sales 93.5MM^E *EMP* 250
SIC 1542 1541 1522 6531 Commercial & office building, new construction; Industrial buildings, new construction; Apartment building construction; Real estate managers
Ch Bd: Stan H Hardaway
VP: Linda Guinn CPA
**VP:* Kerry P Sloan

HARDE' MARTS
See CENTRAL OIL & SUPPLY CORP

HARDEE'S
See DORO INC

HARDEE'S
See BODDIE-NOELL ENTERPRISES INC

HARDEE'S
See CKE RESTAURANTS HOLDINGS INC

HARDEE'S
See DIAMOND HOSPITALITY ENTERPRISES

D-U-N-S 00-320-2900
HARDEES RESTAURANTS LLC
(*Suby of* HARDEES)
100 N Broadway Ste 1200, Saint Louis, MO 63102-2706
Tel (314) 259-6200 *Founded/Ownrshp* 1960
Sales 574.3MM^E *EMP* 16,680
SIC 5812 Fast-food restaurant, chain
Pr: Andrew F Puzder
**CFO:* Theodore Abajian
Ex VP: Michael E Murphy
Sr VP: Will Fisher
**Sr VP:* Bruce Frazer
Sr VP: James Speed
VP: Steve Lemley
Netwrk Mgr: Darry Dugger
Sales Exec: Phil Campbell
Sales Exec: Freda Davis

D-U-N-S 80-360-4839
HARDEN HEALTHCARE SERVICES LLC
3350 Riverwood Pkwy Se # 1, Atlanta, GA 30339-6401
Tel (512) 634-4965 *Founded/Ownrshp* 2007
Sales 259.8MM^E *EMP* 32,000
SIC 8082 Home health care services
CEO: Lew Little Jr
Pr: Jay Koeper
**Pr:* Kim Layton
**Pr:* Chris Roussos
**Pr:* Steve Wood
**COO:* Mike McMaude
Ofcr: Maryann Choi
**Sr VP:* Ben Hanson
VP: Brianna Braden
VP: Joyce Goss
Exec: Ken Word

D-U-N-S 83-229-2754
HARDEN HEALTHCARE TEXAS LP
GRACYWOODS NURSING CENTER
(*Suby of* HARDEN HEALTHCARE SERVICES LLC) ★
8701 N Mopac Expy, Austin, TX 78759-8376
Tel (512) 615-4965 *Founded/Ownrshp* 2001
Sales 20.0MM^E *EMP* 1,800
SIC 8059 Nursing home, except skilled & intermediate care facility
Pt: Lew Little
CFO: Scott Ellyson
CFO: Steve Wood
Sr VP: Brianna Braden
Exec: Ken Word
Genl Couns: Benjamin Hanson

D-U-N-S 80-767-9829
HARDEN HOME HEALTH LLC
AUXI HEALTH
(*Suby of* HARDEN HEALTHCARE SERVICES LLC) ★
8701 N Mopac Expy, Austin, TX 78759-8376
Tel (512) 634-4909 *Founded/Ownrshp* 2007
Sales 5.2MM^E *EMP* 3,454^E
SIC 8082 Home health care services
Prin: Lew Little Jr

D-U-N-S 04-248-3107
HARDER MECHANICAL CONTRACTORS INC
HMC
2148 Ne Mlk Blvd, Portland, OR 97212-3792
Tel (503) 281-1112 *Founded/Ownrshp* 1965
Sales 311.8MM^E *EMP* 650
SIC 1711 7389

HARDIE'S FRESH FOODS
See HARDIES FRUIT AND VEGETABLE CO LP

D-U-N-S 02-624-6959
HARDIES FRUIT AND VEGETABLE CO LP
HARDIE'S FRESH FOODS
1005 N Cockrell Hill Rd, Dallas, TX 75211-1318
Tel (214) 426-5666 *Founded/Ownrshp* 1943
Sales 126.5MM^E *EMP* 137^E
SIC 5148 Fresh fruits & vegetables
CEO: David Hardie
Genl Pt: John D Hardie
Pt: Sandra Hardie
Pr: Mark Austin
VP: Dave Allen

D-U-N-S 02-783-0264
HARDIN AUTOMOTIVE (CA)
HARDIN BUICK PONTIAC GMC
1381 S Auto Center Dr, Anaheim, CA 92806-5612
Tel (714) 533-6200 *Founded/Ownrshp* 1957
Sales 101.0MM^E *EMP* 235
SIC 5511 Automobiles, new & used
CEO: Dennis D Hardin
Genl Mgr: Roberta Bechtloff
Off Admin: Wendy Rood
IT Man: Roger Gagnon
VP Mktg: Jared Hardin
Sls Dir: Odett Keram
Sls Mgr: Dennis Leatherman

HARDIN BUICK PONTIAC GMC
See HARDIN AUTOMOTIVE

D-U-N-S 04-042-6629
HARDIN COUNTY BOARD OF EDUCATION
65 W A Jenkins Rd, Elizabethtown, KY 42701-8452
Tel (270) 369-7370 *Founded/Ownrshp* 1908
Sales 139.6MM *EMP* 2,700
Accts Stiles Carter & Associates P
SIC 8211 Public elementary & secondary schools
Off Mgr: Gloria Manis
HC Dir: Janay Sutton

D-U-N-S 03-985-0045
HARDIN MEMORIAL HOSPITAL FOUNDATION INC (KY)
913 N Dixie Ave, Elizabethtown, KY 42701-2503
Tel (270) 737-1212 *Founded/Ownrshp* 1954
Sales 215.2MM *EMP* 1,480
SIC 8062 General medical & surgical hospitals
Pr: Harry L Berry
Chf Path: Sidney Verble
Dir Recs: Ron Haulk
COO: Diane Logsdon
**CFO:* Elmer Cummings
Ofcr: Ronnie Hawks
VP: Elmer Cumming
**VP:* Dennis Johnson
Dir Rx: Kevin Sullivan
Nurse Mgr: Sandra Peace
CIO: Lisa Bennett
Board of Directors: Bill Brandenburg, Bill Hay, Gary King

D-U-N-S 06-995-4568
HARDIN SCHIFF LLP
233 S Wacker Dr Ste 6600, Chicago, IL 60606-6307
Tel (312) 258-5500 *Founded/Ownrshp* 1982
Sales 109.8MM *EMP* 630
SIC 8111 General practice law office
Genl Pt: Ronald S Safer
Pt: Michael Burnstein
Pt: Gerald Carp
Pt: W Brinkley Dickerson Jr
Pt: Peter V Fazio Jr

Pt: Aaron J Kramer
Pt: Owen Macbride
Pt: Robert H Riley
Pt: Gary Rubin
Pt: Thomas P White
Pt: Christopher J Zinski
CFO: Kevin Cowperthwaite
Board of Directors: Gary Eeves, Richard Krossee

D-U-N-S 00-447-9663
HARDIN TAYLOR SECURE MEDICAL FACILITY
(*Suby of* ALABAMA DEPT OF MENTAL HEALTH) ★
1301 Jack Warner Pkwy Ne, Tuscaloosa, AL 35404-1060
Tel (205) 556-7060 *Founded/Ownrshp* 1981
Sales 42.7MM^E *EMP* 1,000
SIC 8062 9431 General medical & surgical hospitals; Mental health agency administration, government;
Pr: Jim Reddick

D-U-N-S 18-385-5113
HARDING HOLDINGS INC
184 E 53rd Ave, Anchorage, AK 99518-1222
Tel (907) 344-1577 *Founded/Ownrshp* 1975
Sales 106.8MM *EMP* 350
SIC 1389 1542 Construction, repair & dismantling services; Commercial & office building, new construction; Commercial & office buildings, renovation & repair
Pr: James Gilbert
**CEO:* James Udelhoven
**VP:* Tim Jacques

D-U-N-S 07-566-1892
HARDING UNIVERSITY INC
915 E Market Ave, Searcy, AR 72149-5615
Tel (501) 279-4000 *Founded/Ownrshp* 1924
Sales 127.5MM *EMP* 1,445
Accts Mallory & Associates Little R
SIC 8221 University
Pr: Bruce McLarty
Bd of Dir: Milo Hadwin
VP: Keith Cronk
**VP:* Mel Sansom
Comm Man: Dan Tullos
Genl Mgr: Dutch Hoggatt
Dir IT: Judith Hart
Genl Couns: Donald Kee
Snr Mgr: Dustin Johnson

D-U-N-S 00-220-4063 IMP/EXP
▲ **HARDINGE INC** (NY)
1 Hardinge Dr, Elmira, NY 14902
Tel (607) 734-2281 *Founded/Ownrshp* 1890
Sales 315.2MM *EMP* 1,478^E
Tkr Sym HDNG *Exch* NGS
SIC 3541 3545 3553 3549 Machine tools, metal cutting type; Lathes; Grinding, polishing, buffing, lapping & honing machines; Collets (machine tool accessories); Lathes, wood turning: including accessories; Metalworking machinery
Pr: Richard L Simons
CFO: Douglas J Malone
Sr VP: James P Langa
Sr VP: Douglas C Tifft
VP: William Sepanik
Genl Mgr: Tom Mitchell
Manager: Douglas Gaulin
Sls Mgr: Brad Devon
Board of Directors: Richard R Burkhart, B Christopher Disantis, J Philip Hunter, Robert J Lepofsky, Ryan Levenson, Mitchell I Quain, Benjamin Rosenzweig, James Silver, R Tony Tripeny

D-U-N-S 18-136-1478
HARDINGS MARKET-WEST INC
211 E Bannister St Ste E, Plainwell, MI 49080-1372
Tel (269) 427-8003 *Founded/Ownrshp* 1987
Sales 120.6MM^E *EMP* 700
SIC 5411 Grocery stores, chain
Pr: Martin Hill
**VP:* Garland Smith
CIO: Brian De Vries
Sls&Mrk Ex: Curt Devries

D-U-N-S 00-619-6828
HARDRIVES INC
14475 Quiram Dr Ste 1, Rogers, MN 55374-9067
Tel (763) 428-8886 *Founded/Ownrshp* 1997
Sales 145.7MM^E *EMP* 315
SIC 1611 2951 Highway & street paving contractor; Resurfacing contractor; Asphalt paving mixtures & blocks
Pr: Steven K Hall
Ex VP: Allen Poston
**VP:* Kevin Gannon
**VP:* Donald R Hall
VP: Tony Kieger
**VP:* Sig Langerud
Sfty Mgr: Brian Kuntson
Opers Mgr: Tim Crennen

D-U-N-S 94-478-2648 IMP
HARDWARE RESOURCES INC
(*Suby of* HARBOUR GROUP LTD) ★
4319 Marlena St, Bossier City, LA 71111-7503
Tel (318) 742-0660 *Founded/Ownrshp* 2010
Sales 96.5MM^E *EMP* 166
SIC 5072 2499 Furniture hardware; Kitchen, bathroom & household ware: wood; Woodenware, kitchen & household
Pr: Gregory Gottlieb
CFO: Richard Y Yancey
Genl Mgr: Dan Young
Sftwr Eng: Charles Holbert
Sfty Mgr: Randy Grace
VP Mktg: David Tyler
Manager: Ian Bayless
Manager: Steve Pierson
Sales Asso: Jenna Cooper
Sales Asso: Brian Jones
Sales Asso: Billy Stephens

D-U-N-S 00-129-9650 IMP/EXP
HARDWARE SPECIALTY CO INC (NY)
4875 36th St, Long Island City, NY 11101-1994
Tel (718) 361-9320 *Founded/Ownrshp* 1932
Sales 104.5MM^E *EMP* 270
SIC 5063 5085 Electrical fittings & construction materials; Fasteners & fastening equipment
Pr: Edward Kaufman
CFO: Tom Moranzoni
**CFO:* Hyman Needleman
**Ex VP:* Jeffrey Kaufman
**VP:* Jeffrey Sands
Brnch Mgr: Kim Gosnell
Genl Mgr: Peter Foyto
Dir IT: Edwin Holmes
Ql Cn Mgr: Al Mueller

D-U-N-S 14-382-8882 EXP
HARDWOOD LUMBER MANUFACTURING INC
567 N Charlotte Ave, Waynesboro, VA 22980-2856
Tel (540) 946-9150 *Founded/Ownrshp* 2002
Sales 86.6MM^E *EMP* 675
SIC 2426 Hardwood dimension & flooring mills
Pr: Theodore P Rossi
CFO: Ralph Lamb
**VP:* Andrew E Becker

HARFORD CNTY GOVERNMENT TRSRY
See COUNTY OF HARFORD

D-U-N-S 06-940-2642
HARFORD COUNTY BOARD OF EDUCATION (INC)
102 S Hickory Ave, Bel Air, MD 21014-3731
Tel (410) 838-7300 *Founded/Ownrshp* 1869
Sales 522.8MM *EMP* 109^E
Accts Sb & Company Hunt Valley Mar
SIC 8211 School board
Pr: Nancy Reynolds
VP: Francis Grambo III

D-U-N-S 82-580-2986
HARFORD COUNTY PUBLIC SCHOOL DISTRICT
FOUNTAIN GREEN ELEM SCHOOL
102 S Hickory Ave, Bel Air, MD 21014-3731
Tel (410) 838-7300 *Founded/Ownrshp* 1993
Sales 131.3MM^E *EMP* 4,327
SIC 8211 Public elementary & secondary schools
Off Mgr: Kim Holthaus
Netwrk Eng: Sarah Seidl
Psych: Elizabeth Grupp
Snr Mgr: David Markland

D-U-N-S 06-939-2991
HARFORD MEMORIAL HOSPITAL INC
(*Suby of* UPPER CHESAPEAKE HEALTH FOUNDATION INC) ★
501 S Union Ave, Havre De Grace, MD 21078-3493
Tel (443) 843-5000 *Founded/Ownrshp* 1984
Sales 87.0MM *EMP* 625
SIC 8062 General medical & surgical hospitals
Pr: Lyle E Sheldon
**CFO:* Joseph Hoffman
Dir Rad: Sherry Roberts
Ex Dir: Fred Thursfield
IT Man: Joan Horner
VP Opers: Eugene Currotto

D-U-N-S 80-380-2821
HARFORD MEMORIAL HOSPITAL INC
(*Suby of* UPPER CHESAPEAKE HEALTH FOUNDATION INC) ★
501 S Union Ave, Havre De Grace, MD 21078-3493
Tel (410) 939-2400 *Founded/Ownrshp* 1911
Sales 93.7MM *EMP* 800
Accts Grant Thornton Llp Philadelph
SIC 8062 General medical & surgical hospitals
Pr: Lyle E Sheldon
VP: Craig Willig
Dir: Joy D Hoover
Dir Rx: Steve Low
Doctor: Joseph Reinhardt
Pharmcst: Ross Bouchard

D-U-N-S 00-695-0646
HARFORD MUTUAL INSURANCE CO (MD)
FIRSTLINE NATIONAL INSUR CO
200 N Main St, Bel Air, MD 21014-3544
Tel (410) 879-2360 *Founded/Ownrshp* 1842
Sales NA *EMP* 122^E
SIC 6331 Fire, marine & casualty insurance & carriers
Pr: Steven D Linkous
**Treas:* June Poole
Bd of Dir: Jeff Rink
Ofcr: David Elliott
Ex VP: F Kellner
**Ex VP:* John Spielberger
VP: Jamie Elkins
VP: Frank Keller
VP: Karen Mashinski
**VP:* Robert Ohler
**VP:* Ellen Truant

D-U-N-S 61-530-1694 IMP/EXP
HARGRAY COMMUNICATIONS GROUP INC
856 William Hilton Pkwy, Hilton Head Island, SC 29928-3423
Tel (843) 785-2166 *Founded/Ownrshp* 1986
Sales 194.9MM^E *EMP* 350
SIC 4813 Local telephone communications; Long distance telephone communications
Pr: Gloria Taggart
**Ex VP:* Leroy Harvey Jr
**VP:* Michael R Shepard
Prin: Mike Miscavage
Genl Couns: David Armistead

D-U-N-S 03-679-3149
HARGROVE AND ASSOCIATES INC
HARGROVE ENGINEERS & CONSTRS
20 S Royal St, Mobile, AL 36602-3202
Tel (251) 476-0605 *Founded/Ownrshp* 1997
Sales 203.2MM^E *EMP* 700
SIC 8711 Consulting engineer
Pr: Ralph A Hargrove
**COO:* Jim Backes
CFO: Jeb Shell
VP: Jim Backen
VP: James Backes
**VP:* Phil Hamilton
**VP:* Vicki M Studstill
**VP:* Dennis Watson
Genl Mgr: Durward Weeks
Sfty Mgr: Sonney Weaks
Snr PM: Scott Bergoon

HARGROVE ENGINEERS & CONSTRS
See HARGROVE AND ASSOCIATES INC

D-U-N-S 08-037-8697
HARIM USA LTD
(*Suby of* CASA DRUMMOND LTDA)
126 N Shipley St, Seaford, DE 19973-3100
Tel (302) 629-9136 *Founded/Ownrshp* 2011
Sales 219.7MM^E *EMP* 1,600^E
SIC 2015 Poultry, processed

D-U-N-S 12-585-1535 IMP/EXP
■ **HARKEMA SERVICES INC**
(*Suby of* UNIVERSAL CORP) ★
305 Albany Tpke, Canton, CT 06019-2528
Tel (860) 693-8378 *Founded/Ownrshp* 1946
Sales 1.7MM^E *EMP* 24,875^E
SIC 5159 Tobacco, leaf
Pr: E T Kelly
**Ch:* J Van Huystu

D-U-N-S 09-239-8189
HARKINS BUILDERS INC
2201 Warwick Way, Marriottsville, MD 21104-1600
Tel (410) 750-2600 *Founded/Ownrshp* 2002
Sales 110.5MM^E *EMP* 180
SIC 1522 1542

D-U-N-S 82-928-9813 IMP
HARLAN BAKERIES LLC
7597 E Us Highway 36, Avon, IN 46123-7171
Tel (317) 272-3600 *Founded/Ownrshp* 2007
Sales 1.3MMM^E *EMP* 1,500
SIC 5149 2051 2045 Bakery products; Bread, cake & related products; Prepared flour mixes & doughs
Pr: Hugh Harlan
**Ex VP:* Doug Harlan
Sls Mgr: Gary Coyle

D-U-N-S 14-707-5170 IMP
HARLAN BAKERIES-AVON LLC
(*Suby of* HARLAN BAKERIES LLC) ★
7597 E Us Highway 36, Avon, IN 46123-7171
Tel (317) 272-3600 *Founded/Ownrshp* 1991
Sales 101.2MM^E *EMP* 375
SIC 5149 2051 2045 Bakery products; Bread, cake & related products; Prepared flour mixes & doughs
**Ex VP:* Doug H Harlan
**Ex VP:* Paul G Hayden

D-U-N-S 18-361-6937
HARLAN CASTLE INC
150 E 58th St Fl 38, New York, NY 10155-0017
Tel (212) 644-8600 *Founded/Ownrshp* 1987
Sales 5.7MMM^E *EMP* 13,450
SIC 6726 Investment offices
Ch Bd: John K Castle
**Ch Bd:* Leonard M Harlan
V Ch: Gary Appel
**Co-Pr:* Howard Morgan
**Co-Pr:* Bill Pruellage
Ofcr: Jim Nichols
VP: Heidi Petroff
VP: William M Purellage
VP: Sylvia Rosen
Exec: Lewis Raibley
Off Mgr: Beverly Fox

D-U-N-S 02-017-6969 IMP/EXP
HARLAND CLARKE CORP
(*Suby of* HARLAND CLARKE HOLDINGS CORP) ★
15955 La Cantera Pkwy, San Antonio, TX 78256-2589
Tel (830) 609-5500 *Founded/Ownrshp* 2007
Sales 503.0MM^E *EMP* 1,301
SIC 2782 2754 7389 Blankbooks & looseleaf binders; Bank checkbooks & passbooks; Commercial printing, gravure; Telemarketing services; Advertising, promotional & trade show services
**Chf Mktg O:* Scott Hansen

D-U-N-S 09-721-6469
HARLAND CLARKE HOLDINGS CORP
(*Suby of* M & F WORLDWIDE CORP) ★
15955 La Cantera Pkwy, San Antonio, TX 78256-2589
Tel (210) 697-8888 *Founded/Ownrshp* 2005
Sales 1.7MMM^E *EMP* 9,000^E
SIC 2782 2754 7389 Blankbooks & looseleaf binders; Bank checkbooks & passbooks; Commercial printing, gravure; Telemarketing services; Advertising, promotional & trade show services
Pr: Charles T Dawson
**Pr:* Dan Singleton
**CEO:* Chuck Dawson
**CFO:* Peter A Fera Jr
**Ofcr:* Joe Filer
Sr VP: Larhesa Pollock
**VP:* Martin Wexler
VP: Bob White
CIO: Jack Jorgenson
Sftwr Eng: Alicia Banks
Counsel: Judy Norris
Board of Directors: Paul G Savas, Barry F Schwartz

D-U-N-S 02-846-3883 IMP/EXP
HARLAND M BRAUN & CO INC
BRAUN EXPORT
4010 Whiteside St, Los Angeles, CA 90063-1617
Tel (323) 263-9275 *Founded/Ownrshp* 1957
Sales 304.4MM *EMP* 30
Accts Brian Jung
SIC 5159 5199 Hides; Skins, raw; Leather & cut stock
Pr: Mike Hamilton
**VP:* Gene Beenders
**VP:* Di CK Veale
**Genl Mgr:* Roland Sebastian

D-U-N-S 03-092-0011
HARLANDALE INDEPENDENT SCHOOL DISTRICT PUBLIC FACILITIES CORP
102 Genevieve Dr, San Antonio, TX 78214-2902
Tel (210) 989-4340 *Founded/Ownrshp* 1924
Sales 170.6MM *EMP* 2,000
Accts Garza/Gonzalez & Associates S
SIC 8211 Public combined elementary & secondary school
**Pr:* Joshua J Cerna
**CFO:* Ricardo Hernandez
**VP:* David Abundis
**VP:* Christine Carrillo
**Prin:* Oscar Perez
Schl Brd P: Velma Ybarra
Teacher Pr: Diana Tudyk

D-U-N-S 07-861-3353
HARLEM CHILDRENS ZONE INC
35 E 125th St, New York, NY 10035-1816
Tel (212) 534-0700 *Founded/Ownrshp* 1974
Sales 82.7MM *EMP* 1,200
Accts Grant Thornton Llp New York
SIC 8299 Educational services
Pr: Geoffrey Canada
COO: Anne Isom
Exec: Andrew Benson
Off Mgr: Diana Borrell
Off Mgr: Keila Gonzalez
Off Admin: Angela Brown
Off Admin: Christine White
CTO: Lekeisha Eubanks
Info Man: Shanna Crowder
Pgrm Dir: Nia Dawson
Pgrm Dir: Lebaron McClary

D-U-N-S 02-990-0599
HARLEM HOSPITAL CENTER
NEW YORK CITY HEALTH AND HOSPI
(*Suby of* NEW YORK CITY HLTH & HOSPITALS) ★
506 Malcolm X Blvd, New York, NY 10037-1889
Tel (212) 939-1000 *Founded/Ownrshp* 2001
Sales 371.6MM *EMP* 62^E
SIC 8062 General medical & surgical hospitals
Prin: Stephen Shafer
Dir Risk M: Horace Felix
Dir Lab: Angus Sampath
Assoc Dir: Dilcia Ortega
Dir Rad: Donna McKenzie
Dir Rad: Beverly Nicholas
Prgrm Mgr: Monique Hedmann
Sfty Mgr: Kevin Shao

D-U-N-S 09-177-6096
HARLEM SCHOOL DISTRICT 122
8605 N 2nd St, Machesney Park, IL 61115-2003
Tel (815) 654-4500 *Founded/Ownrshp* 1994
Sales 56.3MM^E *EMP* 1,000
Accts Bdo Seldman Llp Rockford Il
SIC 8211 8741 Public elementary school; Public junior high school; Public senior high school; Management services
**Pr:* Sandi Johnson
**Treas:* Joshua Aurand
Ofcr: Gail Lanigan
Ofcr: Catherene Martin
Ofcr: Jim Nordstrom

HARLEQUIN BOOKS
See HARLEQUIN SALES CORP

D-U-N-S 13-863-7322 IMP/EXP
HARLEQUIN DISTRIBUTION CENTER
3010 Walden Ave, Depew, NY 14043-2696
Tel (716) 684-1800 *Founded/Ownrshp* 1947
Sales 92.2MM^E *EMP* 300
SIC 5192 Books
Pr: Donna Hayes
Dir IT: Karl Shoop

D-U-N-S 03-641-4001 IMP
■ **HARLEQUIN SALES CORP**
HARLEQUIN BOOKS
(*Suby of* HARLEQUIN ENTERPRISES LIMITED)
3010 Walden Ave, Depew, NY 14043-2696
Tel (716) 684-1800 *Founded/Ownrshp* 1971
Sales 124.0MM^E *EMP* 250
SIC 5192 Books
**VP:* Jim Robinson
Genl Mgr: John Reindl
Plnt Mgr: John Reindo

HARLEY ATTACHMENTS
See SWEEPSTER ATTACHMENTS LLC

D-U-N-S 04-254-2345
HARLEY MARINE SERVICES INC
PACIFIC TERMINAL SERVICES
910 Sw Spokane St, Seattle, WA 98134-1125
Tel (206) 628-0051 *Founded/Ownrshp* 1998
Sales 159.6MM^E *EMP* 400
SIC 4449 4492 Transportation (freight) on bays & sounds of the ocean; Tugboat service
Pr: Harley V Franco
**CFO:* Todd Prophet
**Sr VP:* Rod Gullickson
**VP:* Deborah Franco
**VP:* Matt Godden
**VP:* Bo Jun
**VP:* Gregg Nelsen

D-U-N-S 79-825-5584 IMP
■ **HARLEY-DAVIDSON FINANCIAL SERVICES INC**
(*Suby of* HARLEY-DAVIDSON INC) ★
222 W Adams St Ste 2000, Chicago, IL 60606-5307
Tel (312) 368-9501 *Founded/Ownrshp* 1995
Sales NA *EMP* 650
SIC 6141 6411 Automobile loans, including insurance; Insurance agents, brokers & service
Pr: Lawrence G Hund
**CFO:* Mike Sulentic
IT Man: Emile Jurgens
Sls Dir: Mark Bernoski

D-U-N-S 10-222-4623 IMP/EXP
▲ **HARLEY-DAVIDSON INC**
3700 W Juneau Ave, Milwaukee, WI 53208-2865
Tel (414) 342-4680 *Founded/Ownrshp* 1903
Sales 6.0MMM *EMP* 6,300
Tkr Sym HOG *Exch* NYS

SIC 3751 6153 6141 6411 6399 Motorcycles & related parts; Motorcycle accessories; Financing of dealers by motor vehicle manufacturers organ.; Financing: automobiles, furniture, etc., not a deposit bank; Property & casualty insurance agent; Warranty insurance, product; except automobile
Pr: Matthew S Levatich
CFO: John A Olin
Chf Cred: Paul J Jones
Bd of Dir: John Dolezal
Sr VP: Sean J Cummings
VP: Joanne M Bischmann
VP: Thomas Carl
VP: Dave Cotteleer
VP: Mike Kennedy
VP: Marc McAllister
VP: Mark H Richer
VP: Brad Rose
Board of Directors: Maryrose Sylvester, R John Anderson, Michael J Cave, George H Conrades, Donald A James, Sara L Levinson, N Thomas Linebarger, George L Miles Jr, Brian Niccol, James A Norling

D-U-N-S 00-608-0519 IMP/EXP
■ HARLEY-DAVIDSON MOTOR CO INC (WI)
(*Suby of* HARLEY-DAVIDSON INC) ★
3700 W Juneau Ave 3800, Milwaukee, WI 53208-2865
Tel (414) 343-4056 *Founded/Ownrshp* 1903, 1981
Sales 1.1MMM^E *EMP* 4,000
SIC 3751 Motorcycles, bicycles & parts
VP: Joanne M Bischmann
VP: Gail Lione
Board of Directors: R John Anderson, Richard I Beattie, Michael J Cave, George H Conrades, Donald A James, Sara L Levinson, N Thomas Linebarger, George L Miles Jr, James A Norling

D-U-N-S 10-144-8140
HARLEYSVILLE GROUP INC
(*Suby of* NATIONWIDE MUTUAL INSURANCE CO) ★
355 Maple Ave, Harleysville, PA 19438-2222
Tel (215) 256-9773 *Founded/Ownrshp* 2012
Sales NA *EMP* 1,706^E
SIC 6331 6411 Property damage insurance; Fire, marine & casualty insurance: mutual; Insurance agents, brokers & service
Pr: Stephen R Smith
**Pr:* Michael L Browne
**CFO:* Arthur E Chandler
**Treas:* Mark R Cummins
**Sr VP:* Allan R Becker
**Sr VP:* Thomas E Clark
**Sr VP:* Robert A Kauffman
**Sr VP:* Theodore A Majewski
Sr VP: Debbie Neuscheler-Fritsch
**Sr VP:* Kevin M Toth
VP: Jonathan L Griggs

D-U-N-S 00-791-1159
HARLEYSVILLE MUTUAL INSURANCE CO
355 Maple Ave, Harleysville, PA 19438-2222
Tel (215) 256-5000 *Founded/Ownrshp* 1917
Sales NA *EMP* 1,898
SIC 6311 6331 Life insurance carriers; Property damage insurance; Fire, marine & casualty insurance & carriers
CEO: Walter R Bateman II
Pr: Clinton Bothwell
Pr: Michael L Browne
Pr: William D Granato
Pr: Brandon J Hickey
Pr: Dennis J Otmaskin
CFO: Arthur Chandler
Treas: Mark Cummings
Bd of Dir: W Storts
Sr VP: Beth A Friel
Sr VP: Robert Kauffman
Sr VP: John B Keefe
Sr VP: Jenifer L Rinehart
VP: Roger Beekley
VP: James C O Neill
Board of Directors: Ellen M Dunn

D-U-N-S 06-946-3784
HARLINGEN CONSOLIDATED INDEPENDENT SCHOOL DISTRICT
407 N 77 Sunshinestrip, Harlingen, TX 78550-5820
Tel (956) 430-9500 *Founded/Ownrshp* 1900
Sales 117.9MM^E *EMP* 2,400
Accts Long Chilton Llp Harlingen
SIC 8211 Public elementary & secondary schools; Public junior high school; Public senior high school
MIS Dir: Olga Garcia
Pr Dir: Shane Strubhart
Teacher Pr: Melissa Nieto
Instr Medi: Mireya Galvan

D-U-N-S 79-691-9061
HARLINGEN MEDICAL CENTER LIMITED PARTNERSHIP
(*Suby of* PRIME HEALTHCARE SERVICES INC) ★
5501 S Expressway 77, Harlingen, TX 78550-3213
Tel (956) 365-3947 *Founded/Ownrshp* 2011
Sales 93.7MM *EMP* 528
SIC 8062 General medical & surgical hospitals
CEO: Brenda Ivory
**CFO:* David Glassburn

D-U-N-S 01-925-5041 IMP/EXP
■ HARMAN BECKER AUTOMOTIVE SYSTEMS INC
HARMAN CONSUMER GROUP
(*Suby of* HARMAN INTERNATIONAL INDUSTRIES INC) ★
30001 Cabot Dr, Novi, MI 48377-2910
Tel (248) 785-2361 *Founded/Ownrshp* 1981
Sales 764.9MM^E *EMP* 2,000
SIC 3931 3812 Autophones (organs with perforated music rolls); Navigational systems & instruments
Pr: Klaus Blickle
**Ex VP:* Herbert K Parker
**Prin:* Dinesh C Paliwal
Snr Sftwr: Dan Engel
Snr Sftwr: Dan Miller
IT Man: Jason Easter
IT Man: Mike Rosinski
Software D: Norrie Taylor
Sftwr Eng: Scott Mackay
Sales Asso: Karen Galinsky
Snr Mgr: Brent Erickson

D-U-N-S 12-897-9262
■ HARMAN CONNECTED SERVICES HOLDING CORP
(*Suby of* HARMAN INTERNATIONAL INDUSTRIES INC) ★
636 Ellis St, Mountain View, CA 94043-2207
Tel (650) 623-9400 *Founded/Ownrshp* 2015
Sales 397.8MM^E *EMP* 3,008
SIC 7373 Systems software development services
Pr: Sanjay Dhawan
Pr: Luigi Sanna
**CFO:* Pradeep Chaudhry
Assoc VP: Venkatesh Iyer
Assoc VP: Perry Teevens
**Ex VP:* Subash A K RAO
VP: Sumit Chauhan
VP: Dean Miles
VP: Mark Searle
Snr Sftwr: Prasun Banik
Snr Sftwr: Anupam Maity

HARMAN CONSUMER GROUP
See HARMAN BECKER AUTOMOTIVE SYSTEMS INC

D-U-N-S 04-765-3555
▲ HARMAN INTERNATIONAL INDUSTRIES INC
400 Atlantic St Ste 15, Stamford, CT 06901-3533
Tel (203) 328-3500 *Founded/Ownrshp* 1980
Sales 6.9MMM *EMP* 24,197^E
Accts Kpmg Llp Stamford Connectic
Tkr Sym HAR *Exch* NYS
SIC 3651 Household audio & video equipment; Household audio equipment; Audio electronic systems; Household video equipment
Ch Bd: Dinesh C Paliwal
Pr: Phillip Eyler
Pr: Michael Mauser
Pr: Mohit Parasher
CFO: Sandra E Rowland
Chf Mktg O: Ralph Santana
Ofcr: John Stacey
Ex VP: Blake Augsburger
Ex VP: Todd A Suko
Ex VP: Henry Tirri
VP: Klaus Beck
VP: Yijing H Brentano
VP: Jeffery Fay
VP: Kevin Hague
VP: Udo Huels
VP: Blake Jackson
VP: Daniel Jonas
VP: Wolfram Kohl
VP: Russel Krystolovich
VP: Carsten Olesen
VP: Jon Olson
Board of Directors: Adriane M Brown, John W Diercksen, Ann McLaughlin Korologos, Edward H Meyer, Robert Nail, Abraham N Reichental, Kenneth M Reiss, Frank S Sklarsky, Gary G Steel

D-U-N-S 08-006-1801
■ HARMAN KG HOLDING LLC
(*Suby of* HARMAN INTERNATIONAL INDUSTRIES INC) ★
400 Atlantic St Ste 1500, Stamford, CT 06901-3512
Tel (203) 328-3500 *Founded/Ownrshp* 2009
Sales 228.8MM^E *EMP* 24,197
SIC 3651 Household audio & video equipment; Household audio equipment; Audio electronic systems; Household video equipment
Ch Bd: Dinesh C Paliwal
Snr Mgr: Brad Haynes

D-U-N-S 04-978-4168
HARMAN MANAGEMENT CORP
199 1st St Ste 212, Los Altos, CA 94022-2767
Tel (650) 941-5681 *Founded/Ownrshp* 1968
Sales 244.1MM^E *EMP* 7,000
SIC 8741 5812 5046 Restaurant management; Fast-food restaurant, chain; Restaurant equipment & supplies
Pr: James Jackson
**COO:* Mr Vern Wardle
Ex VP: Alexander James
Ex VP: Doone Ray
Admn Mgr: Dwane Hanson
Admn Mgr: Chad Nicol
Admn Mgr: Craig Roberson
Off Mgr: Janet Lint
IT Man: Terri Mayoral
VP Opers: Jeremy Dimick

D-U-N-S 96-534-5940
HARMAN MEDIA LLC
WASHINGTON POST
1150 15th St Nw, Washington, DC 20071-0001
Tel (202) 334-6000 *Founded/Ownrshp* 2010
Sales 130.6MM^E *EMP* 776
SIC 2721 Magazines: publishing only, not printed on site
CEO: Sidney Harman PHD
VP: Denise Demeter
Snr Ntwrk: Milo Milovanovic

D-U-N-S 19-627-3874 IMP/EXP
■ HARMAN PROFESSIONAL INC
(*Suby of* HARMAN INTERNATIONAL INDUSTRIES INC) ★
8500 Balboa Blvd, Northridge, CA 91329-0003
Tel (818) 894-8850 *Founded/Ownrshp* 2006
Sales 135.1MM^E *EMP* 500
SIC 3651 Household audio equipment
Pr: Blake Augsburger
VP: Dennis Berry
Mktg Dir: Randy Patton
Mktg Dir: Steve Romeo
Mktg Mgr: Bose Denmark

HARMAN PROFESSIONAL SOLUTIONS
See AMX LLC

D-U-N-S 03-536-4249 IMP/EXP
HARMON CITY INC
HARMONS GROCERY
3540 S 4000 W, Salt Lake City, UT 84120-3260
Tel (801) 969-8261 *Founded/Ownrshp* 1932
Sales 429.2MM^E *EMP* 2,800
SIC 5411

D-U-N-S 02-764-7051 IMP
■ HARMON INC
HARMON SERVICE GLASS
(*Suby of* APOGEE ENTERPRISES INC) ★
7900 Xerxes Ave S # 1800, Bloomington, MN 55431-1105
Tel (952) 944-5700 *Founded/Ownrshp* 1949
Sales 231.1MM^E *EMP* 1,087
SIC 5039 Glass construction materials
VP: Dennis Pilkinton
**CEO:* Russell Huffer
**CEO:* Joseph F Puishys
VP: Beth Dienst
Genl Mgr: Jim Bald
Genl Mgr: Dave Brasch
Genl Mgr: Brian Clark
Genl Mgr: Jacob Johnson
Genl Mgr: Tim Ryals
Off Admin: Stephanie Noland
Off Admin: Renee Pettyjohn

HARMON SERVICE GLASS
See HARMON INC

D-U-N-S 11-044-1925 IMP
HARMONI INTERNATIONAL SPICE INC CALIFORNIA
HARMONY GROUP
881 S Azusa Ave, City of Industry, CA 91748-1028
Tel (626) 330-1550 *Founded/Ownrshp* 1992
Sales 152.6MM *EMP* 23
SIC 5148 5149 Fresh fruits & vegetables; Spices & seasonings
CEO: Xiao Yang Zhou
**CFO:* Rick Zhou
Admn Mgr: Jo Ann Shu
Genl Mgr: Yazhou Yan
Opers Mgr: Patrick Cruz
Opers Mgr: Betty Si

D-U-N-S 60-278-8580 IMP
▲ HARMONIC INC
4300 N 1st St, San Jose, CA 95134-1258
Tel (408) 542-2500 *Founded/Ownrshp* 1988
Sales 377.0MM *EMP* 989^E
Tkr Sym HLIT *Exch* NGS
SIC 3663 3823 Television broadcasting & communications equipment; Industrial instrmnts msrmnt display/control process variable
Pr: Patrick J Harshman
**Ch Bd:* Patrick Gallagher
CFO: Harold Covert
Sr VP: Peter Alexander
Sr VP: Nimrod Ben-Natan
Sr VP: Charles J Bonasera
Sr VP: Neven Haltmayer
Sr VP: Bart Spriester
VP: Tim Chu
Mng Dir: Gideon Leveson
Prgrm Mgr: Kevin Kerr
Board of Directors: E Floyd Kvamme, Mitzi Reaugh, William F Reddersen, Susan G Swenson, Nikos Theodosopoulos

HARMONS GROCERY
See HARMON CITY INC

D-U-N-S 09-322-3865 IMP
HARMONY FOODS CORP
SANTA CRUZ NUTRITIONALS
2200 Delaware Ave, Santa Cruz, CA 95060-5707
Tel (831) 457-3200 *Founded/Ownrshp* 2013
Sales 207.0MM^E *EMP* 400
SIC 2834 2064 Vitamin, nutrient & hematinic preparations for human use; Candy & other confectionery products
CEO: Michael Westhusing
**COO:* Randy Bridges
Ex VP: Doug Hopkinson
VP: Mark Wobken
Dir IT: Merit Herman
VP Sls: Donovan Russell
Mktg Dir: Betsy Johal

HARMONY GROUP
See HARMONI INTERNATIONAL SPICE INC CALIFORNIA

HARMONY HEALTH PLAN ILLINOIS
See HARMONY HEALTH SYSTEMS INC

D-U-N-S 94-911-6495
■ HARMONY HEALTH SYSTEMS INC
HARMONY HEALTH PLAN ILLINOIS
(*Suby of* WELL CARE HMO INC)
200 W Adams St Ste 800, Chicago, IL 60606-5220
Tel (312) 372-3471 *Founded/Ownrshp* 2004
Sales NA *EMP* 125
SIC 6324 8011 Health maintenance organization (HMO), insurance only; Offices & clinics of medical doctors
Ch Bd: Christopher Adams
**Pr:* John T Blank

D-U-N-S 08-518-7438
HARMONY PUBLIC SCHOOLS
9321 W Sam Houston Pkwy S, Houston, TX 77099-5204
Tel (281) 888-9764 *Founded/Ownrshp* 1999
Sales 265.2MM *EMP* 3,262
Accts Gomez & Company Houston Tx
SIC 8211
Pr: Oner Ulvi Celepcikay
**Treas:* Mustafa Ata Atik
VP: Laurie Bricker
**VP:* Cengizhan Keskin
**VP:* Ellen A Macdonald
**Prin:* Mehmet Basoglu
**Prin:* Serkan Kilic
Ex Dir: David Dunn
Mng Dir: Deborah S Jones

D-U-N-S 06-048-4615
HARMS OIL CO
CENTRAL STATES PETROLEUM
337 22nd Ave S, Brookings, SD 57006-2828
Tel (605) 696-5000 *Founded/Ownrshp* 1976
Sales 109.2MM^E *EMP* 80
SIC 5172 Petroleum products
Pr: Duane D Harms
**VP:* Jason Harms
Mktg Mgr: Mike Burgers
Sls Mgr: Mark Sweetman

D-U-N-S 10-371-5694
HARNETT COUNTY BOARD OF EDUCATION
HARNETT COUNTY SCHOOLS
1008 S 11th St, Lillington, NC 27546-5929
Tel (910) 893-8151 *Founded/Ownrshp* 1905
Sales 161.1MM *EMP* 2,105
Accts Dixon Hughes Goodman Llp Wins
SIC 8211 Public elementary & secondary schools

HARNETT COUNTY SCHOOLS
See HARNETT COUNTY BOARD OF EDUCATION

D-U-N-S 07-979-8915
HARNETT COUNTY SCHOOLS
(*Suby of* HARNETT COUNTY SCHOOLS) ★
1008 11th St, Lillington, NC 27546-6579
Tel (910) 893-8151 *Founded/Ownrshp* 2015
Sales 67.0MM^E *EMP* 2,032^E
SIC 8211 Public elementary & secondary schools
Bd of Dir: James Bryant
Dir Sec: Deborah Kitchens
Pr Dir: Patricia Harmon-Lewis
HC Dir: Vera Jones

D-U-N-S 07-202-3310
HARNETT HEALTH SYSTEM INC
BETSY JOHNSON REGIONAL HOSPITA
800 Tilghman Dr, Dunn, NC 28334-5510
Tel (910) 892-1000 *Founded/Ownrshp* 1935
Sales 90.6MM *EMP* 730^E
SIC 8062 General medical & surgical hospitals
Pr: Kevin Jackson
Chf Rad: Demir E Bastug
Ofcr: Doug Baer
**VP:* Vicki Allen
**VP:* Sondra Davis
**VP:* Wallace J Horne
**VP:* Mike Jones
VP: Eric Young
Dir Rx: Alice Holmes
CIO: Tim Krieger
MIS Dir: Robert Clifton

D-U-N-S 00-624-0634 IMP/EXP
HARNISH GROUP INC (WA)
17035 W Valley Hwy, Tukwila, WA 98188-5519
Tel (425) 251-9800 *Founded/Ownrshp* 1929
Sales 598.0MM^E *EMP* 1,000
SIC 5082 5013 5083 Construction & mining machinery; Tractors, construction; Front end loaders; Graders, motor; Automotive engines & engine parts; Agricultural machinery & equipment; Tractors, agricultural; Cultivating machinery & equipment; Planting machinery & equipment
Pr: John J Harnish
**VP:* Don Linn
VP: Dave Thomas
Brnch Mgr: William Ring
Brnch Mgr: Justin Shearer
Mktg Mgr: Scott Field

D-U-N-S 11-792-8155
HARO & HARO ENTERPRISES INC
115 W Walnut St Ste 4, Lodi, CA 95240-3541
Tel (209) 334-2035 *Founded/Ownrshp* 1997
Sales 12.6MM^E *EMP* 1,000
SIC 0761 Farm labor contractors
Pr: Emelia Haro
**Prin:* Jose Haro

D-U-N-S 10-766-0912
HAROLD LEVINSON ASSOCIATES INC
H L A
21 Banfi Plz N, Farmingdale, NY 11735-1544
Tel (631) 962-2400 *Founded/Ownrshp* 1980
Sales 488.9MM^E *EMP* 400^E
SIC 5194 5145 Cigarettes; Smoking tobacco; Candy
CEO: Edward Berro
**CFO:* Andrew P Defrancesco
**VP:* Rita Berro
**VP:* Barry Feldman
**VP:* Marty Glick
Dir IT: Amir Babazadeh
Dir IT: Brad Sauer

D-U-N-S 05-842-4024
HARP BUSINESS SERVICES INC
HARP INK
2725 Northwoods Pkwy A2, Peachtree Corners, GA 30071-5707
Tel (678) 482-0675 *Founded/Ownrshp* 1998
Sales 114.3MM^E *EMP* 11
SIC 2759 4225 5699 Commercial printing; General warehousing & storage; Uniforms & work clothing
CEO: Hy L Dorfman
**CFO:* Patti Dorfman

HARP INK
See HARP BUSINESS SERVICES INC

D-U-N-S 03-198-4289
HARPEL OIL CO
4204 E 105th Ave, Thornton, CO 80233-3955
Tel (303) 294-0767 *Founded/Ownrshp* 1937
Sales 106.9MM *EMP* 16^E
Accts Eks&H Lllp Denver Colorado
SIC 5171 5983 5172 Petroleum bulk stations; Fuel oil dealers; Gasoline
Pr: Doug Harpel
**VP:* Tammie Barr
Sls Mgr: James Hunter

D-U-N-S 07-189-3840
HARPER COLLEGE
HARPER COMMUNITY COLLEGE
1200 W Algonquin Rd, Palatine, IL 60067-7373
Tel (847) 925-6707 *Founded/Ownrshp* 1965
Sales 138.4MM *EMP* 1,307[E]
SIC 8221 Colleges universities & professional schools
Pr: Kenneth Ender
COO: Michael Alsup
Bd of Dir: Andy Geary
Comm Dir: Phil Burdick
Prgrm Mgr: Martha Karavitis
IT Man: Tammie Mahoney
Software D: Jennie Johns
Pr Mgr: Fredia Martin
Pgrm Dir: Kelly Hamontree
Snr Mgr: Kathy Swan

HARPER COMMUNITY COLLEGE
See HARPER COLLEGE

D-U-N-S 14-740-3638
HARPER CONSTRUCTION CO INC
2241 Kettner Blvd Ste 300, San Diego, CA 92101-1769
Tel (619) 233-7900 *Founded/Ownrshp* 1974
Sales 208.9MM[E] *EMP* 140
SIC 1542 1521 Commercial & office building contractors; Single-family housing construction
CEO: Jeffrey A Harper
**Ch:* Ron Harper
Dir Rx: Myrna Smith

HARPER GROUP
See CIRCLE INTERNATIONAL INC

D-U-N-S 04-181-4534
HARPER INDUSTRIES INC (TN)
960 N Hc Mathis Dr, Paducah, KY 42001-1771
Tel (270) 442-2753 *Founded/Ownrshp* 1980
Sales 97.6MM[E] *EMP* 250
SIC 3273 1711 1611 1542 Ready-mixed concrete; Mechanical contractor; General contractor, highway & street construction; Commercial & office building, new construction; Commercial & office buildings, renovation & repair
Pr: Billy Harper
Treas: Doug Ford

HARPER UNIVERSITY HOSPITAL
See VHS HARPER-HUTZEL HOSPITAL INC

D-U-N-S 00-163-0169 IMP
■ **HARPERCOLLINS PUBLISHERS LLC**
WILLIAM MORROW PUBLISHING
(*Suby of* NEWS CORP) ★
195 Broadway Fl 2, New York, NY 10007-3132
Tel (212) 207-7000 *Founded/Ownrshp* 1817, 2013
Sales 222.3MM[E] *EMP* 1,918
SIC 5942 2731 Book stores; Books: publishing only
CEO: Brian Murray
Pr: David Steinberger
Sr VP: Robert Zaffiris
VP: Larry Nevins
VP: Beth Silfin
Creative D: Barb Fitzsimmons
Creative D: Benjamin North
Natl Sales: Kate Walker
VP Sls: Ardy Khazaei
S&M/VP: Maggie Richards
Mktg Dir: Beth Murphy

D-U-N-S 01-453-4219
HARPETH FINANCIAL SERVICES LLC
ADVANCE FINANCIAL
100 Oceanside Dr, Nashville, TN 37204-2351
Tel (615) 341-5900 *Founded/Ownrshp* 2008
Sales NA *EMP* 1,054[E]
SIC 6162 Mortgage bankers & correspondents
CEO: Tina Hodges
CFO: Patrick Conroy
Ch: Mike Hodges
VP: Cullen Earnest
Mktg Mgr: Lisa Hendon

D-U-N-S 79-066-0067
■ **HARPOON ACQUISITION CORP**
(*Suby of* FISERV INC) ★
455 Winding Brook Dr, Glastonbury, CT 06033-4315
Tel (860) 815-5736 *Founded/Ownrshp* 2013
Sales 39.4MM[E] *EMP* 1,700
SIC 7372 7373 Business oriented computer software; Systems integration services
CEO: Louis Hernandez Jr

HARPS FOOD STORES
See HARPS FOOD STORES INC

D-U-N-S 03-564-0630 IMP
HARPS FOOD STORES INC
HARPS FOOD STORES
918 S Gutensohn Rd, Springdale, AR 72762-5165
Tel (479) 751-7601 *Founded/Ownrshp* 1925
Sales 622.8MM[E] *EMP* 3,000
SIC 5411 5122 Supermarkets, chain; Drugs, proprietaries & sundries
CEO: Roger Collins
**Pr:* Kim Eskew
**CFO:* Jim Natz
VP: Frank Ray
Dist Mgr: Boyd Tillotson
IT Man: Jim B Tackett

HARRAH'S
See CAESARS ENTERTAINMENT OPERATING CO INC

D-U-N-S 17-042-6217
■ **HARRAHS ATLANTIC CITY OPERATING CO LLC**
HARRAH'S RESORT
(*Suby of* HARRAHS) ★
777 Harrahs Blvd, Atlantic City, NJ 08401-1985
Tel (609) 441-5000 *Founded/Ownrshp* 1995
Sales 91.0MM[E] *EMP* 3,570
SIC 7011 Casino hotel
CEO: Gary W Loveman
**Ex VP:* Donald Colvin
Dir IT: Janet Miller

HARRAHS ATLANTIC CY CASINO HT
See MARINA ASSOCIATES LTD

HARRAH'S CASINO
See JAZZ CASINO CO LL C

HARRAH'S CHEROKEE
See TRIBAL CASINO GAMING ENTERPRISES

HARRAH'S CHESTER CASINO
See CHESTER DOWNS AND MARINA LLC

HARRAHS CNCIL BLUFFS CASINO HT
See HARVEYS IOWA MANAGEMENT CO INC

HARRAHS GRAND
See BL DEVELOPMENT CORP

HARRAHS LAUGHLIN CASINO & HT
See HARRAHS LAUGHLIN LLC

D-U-N-S 19-588-3004
■ **HARRAHS LAUGHLIN LLC**
HARRAHS LAUGHLIN CASINO & HT
(*Suby of* HARRAHS) ★
2900 S Casino Dr, Laughlin, NV 89029-1521
Tel (702) 298-4600 *Founded/Ownrshp* 1989
Sales 55.4MM[E] *EMP* 1,500
SIC 7011 5812 Casino hotel; Eating places
Pr: Philip G Satre
Exec: Ron Williams
Sls Mgr: Gail Strinz

D-U-N-S 95-955-5392
HARRAHS MARYLAND HEIGHTS OPERATING CO INC
HARRAH'S ST LOUIS
777 Casino Center Dr, Maryland Heights, MO 63043-4821
Tel (314) 770-8100 *Founded/Ownrshp* 2008
Sales NA *EMP* 2,200
SIC 7011 5813 5812

D-U-N-S 83-313-7610
■ **HARRAHS NORTH KANSAS CITY LLC**
(*Suby of* CAESARS ENTERTAINMENT CORP) ★
1 Riverboat Dr, North Kansas City, MO 64116-3267
Tel (816) 472-7777 *Founded/Ownrshp* 1999
Sales 30.4MM[E] *EMP* 1,200
SIC 7999 Gambling establishment

HARRAH'S RESORT
See HARRAHS ATLANTIC CITY OPERATING CO LLC

HARRAH'S ST LOUIS
See HARRAHS MARYLAND HEIGHTS OPERATING CO INC

HARREL
See DAVIS-STANDARD LLC

HARRELL NUT COMPANY
See GOLDEN PEANUT & TREE NUTS

D-U-N-S 03-241-8311 IMP/EXP
HARRELLS INC
720 Kraft Rd, Lakeland, FL 33815-3244
Tel (863) 687-2774 *Founded/Ownrshp* 2008
Sales 90.1MM[E] *EMP* 213[E]
SIC 2875 5191

D-U-N-S 80-588-0072 IMP/EXP
HARRELLS LLC
5105 New Tampa Hwy, Lakeland, FL 33815-3262
Tel (863) 687-2774 *Founded/Ownrshp* 2007
Sales 114.4MM[E] *EMP* 300[E]
SIC 2875 5191 Fertilizers, mixing only; Fertilizers & agricultural chemicals
CEO: Jack Harrell
Pr: Jeff Higgins
**Pr:* David Schermerhorn
COO: Matthew Shook
**CFO:* Gary Rust
**Sr VP:* Alex Barcia
Off Mgr: Robin Carter
Opers Mgr: George Long
Opers Mgr: Barry Mackrell
Opers Mgr: Mark Searles
Opers Mgr: Matt Shoemaker

D-U-N-S 00-274-7876
■ **HARRINGTON HEALTH SERVICES INC**
FISERV HEALTH
(*Suby of* UMR INC) ★
780 Brooksedge Plaza Dr, Westerville, OH 43081-4914
Tel (614) 212-7000 *Founded/Ownrshp* 2000, 2008
Sales NA *EMP* 900
SIC 6411 Insurance claim processing, except medical
Pr: Jeff Mills
**CFO:* Terry Moore
IT Man: Kathy Oyster

D-U-N-S 02-851-5344 EXP
HARRINGTON INDUSTRIAL PLASTICS LLC
(*Suby of* ALIAXIS SA)
14480 Yorba Ave, Chino, CA 91710-5766
Tel (909) 597-8641 *Founded/Ownrshp* 2002
Sales 210.0MM *EMP* 415
SIC 5074 Pipes & fittings, plastic; Plumbing & heating valves
Pr: Patrick Foose
**Pr:* James Swanson
CFO: Jay Rooney
VP: Jim Reid
Area Mgr: Craig Giles
Brnch Mgr: John Douglas
Brnch Mgr: Russ Goodrich
Off Mgr: Jeff Buirge
Off Mgr: Michael Cagley
Off Mgr: Casey Franzen
Off Mgr: Jeff Hojnacki

D-U-N-S 07-534-0877
HARRINGTON MEMORIAL HOSPITAL INC
100 South St Ste 1, Southbridge, MA 01550-4047
Tel (508) 765-9771 *Founded/Ownrshp* 1928, 1931
Sales 116.7MM *EMP* 1,100
SIC 8062 General medical & surgical hospitals
Pr: Edward Moore
**Ex VP:* Douglas Crapser
VP: Donald Brechner
VP: Richard Charlene
VP: Kathleen Davis
**VP:* Thomas Hijeck
VP: Charlene Richard
VP: Peg Skowron
Dir Lab: Kathryn Anestis
Dir Rad: Rola Shaheen
Dir Rx: Anthony Dubois

D-U-N-S 82-462-3003 IMP/EXP
HARRIS & FORD LLC
9307 E 56th St, Indianapolis, IN 46216-2068
Tel (317) 591-0000 *Founded/Ownrshp* 1994
Sales 210.0MM[E] *EMP* 50
SIC 5169 5085 Chemicals & allied products; Industrial supplies
Pr: Timothy M Harris
CFO: Charlie Kunkel
VP: Joseph E Ford

D-U-N-S 00-693-0416 IMP
HARRIS BMO BANK NATIONAL ASSOCIATION
(*Suby of* BMO BANKCORP INC) ★
111 W Monroe St Ste 1200, Chicago, IL 60603-4014
Tel (312) 461-2323 *Founded/Ownrshp* 1882
Sales NA *EMP* 4,319
SIC 6021 National commercial banks
Pr: David Casper
Pr: John Renzelmann
Pr: Todd Senger
Pr: Steven Zandpour
**Treas:* Stephen Lobo
Ofcr: Denise Banks
Assoc VP: Eric Lempke
Sr VP: Wes Anderson
Sr VP: Emilio Cooper
Sr VP: Jim Gallimore
Sr VP: Christy Horn
Sr VP: David Knapp
Sr VP: Greg Recker
Sr VP: Barry W Stratton
VP: Shelly Caren
VP: Stephen Dynako
VP: Chris Gessner
VP: Elizabeth Hozian
VP: Brad Isaly
VP: Derrick Johnson
VP: Kim Lahti

D-U-N-S 02-592-7625 IMP/EXP
■ **HARRIS CAPROCK COMMUNICATIONS INC** (TX)
(*Suby of* HARRIS CORP) ★
4400 S Sam Houston Pkwy E, Houston, TX 77048-5902
Tel (888) 482-0289 *Founded/Ownrshp* 1981, 2010
Sales 87.4MM[E] *EMP* 230
SIC 4813 Telephone communication, except radio
CEO: Peter Shaper
**Pr:* Tracey Haslam
Pr: Pal Jensen
Pr: Keith Johnson
**COO:* Douglas Tutt
Sr Cor Off: Jere Thompson
**Ex VP:* David Myers
**VP:* Alan Aronowitz
VP: Britt Carina Horncastle
VP: J J Thakkar
Exec: Jill M Pavlas

D-U-N-S 02-080-0595
HARRIS CENTER FOR MENTAL HEALTH AND IDD (TX)
9401 Southwest Fwy, Houston, TX 77074-1407
Tel (713) 970-7000 *Founded/Ownrshp* 1965
Sales 219.5MM *EMP* 1,500
Accts Pattillo Brown & Hill Llp
SIC 8063 Psychiatric hospitals
Ex Dir: Dr Steven B Schnee
**COO:* Dr Scott Strang
**CFO:* Alex V Lim
Prgrm Mgr: Ally Frankovich
Nurse Mgr: Yen Phan
Doctor: Linda Wittig
Pgrm Dir: Sarita Wesley
Snr Mgr: Monica Waters

D-U-N-S 10-866-4368
HARRIS CONTRACTING CO
RM THORNTON
909 Montreal Cir, Saint Paul, MN 55102-4296
Tel (651) 602-6500 *Founded/Ownrshp* 1983
Sales 207.5MM[E] *EMP* 1,100
SIC 1711 Plumbing contractors; Mechanical contractor
CEO: Greg Hosch
**Ch Bd:* Robert F Hosch
**CFO:* Tom Depauw
Genl Mgr: Vinnie Figlioli
Sfty Dirs: Daniel Kent

D-U-N-S 00-420-3337 IMP
▲ **HARRIS CORP**
1025 W Nasa Blvd, Melbourne, FL 32919-0001
Tel (321) 727-9100 *Founded/Ownrshp* 1890
Sales 7.4MMM *EMP* 21,000
Accts Ernst & Young Llp Orlando Fl
Tkr Sym HRS *Exch* NYS
SIC 3812 3663 3699 3661 3674 Search & navigation equipment; Radio & TV communications equipment; Satellites, communications; Microwave communication equipment; Receiver-transmitter units (transceiver); Security control equipment & systems; Telephones & telephone apparatus; Switching equipment, telephone; PBX equipment, manual or automatic; Integrated circuits, semiconductor networks, etc.
Ch Bd: William M Brown
Pr: Carl D D'Alessandro
Pr: William H Gattle
Pr: Christopher D Young
Pr: Edward J Zoiss
CFO: Rahul Ghai
Sr VP: Robert L Duffy
Sr VP: Sheldon J Fox
Sr VP: Dana A Mehnert
Sr VP: Scott T Mikuen
VP: Todd A Taylor
Board of Directors: James C Stoffel, James F Albaugh, Gregory T Swienton, Peter W Chiarelli, Hansel E Tookes II, Thomas A Dattilo, Roger B Fradin, Terry D Growcock, Lewis Hay III, Karen Katen, Leslie F Kenne, David B Rickard

D-U-N-S 96-787-6363
HARRIS COUNTY CLINICAL SERVICES INC
2801 Via Fortuna, Austin, TX 78746-7567
Tel (512) 899-3995 *Founded/Ownrshp* 2011
Sales 262.6MM *EMP* 4
Accts Mikeska Monahan Peckham Pc
SIC 8071 Medical laboratories
Prin: Richard Blakely

D-U-N-S 18-832-6151
HARRIS COUNTY DEPARTMENT OF EDUCATION PUBLIC FACILITY CORP
6300 Irvington Blvd, Houston, TX 77022-5618
Tel (713) 694-6300 *Founded/Ownrshp* 1889
Sales 32.6MM[E] *EMP* 1,278
SIC 8299 Educational services
**Pr:* Angela Chesnut
**CFO:* Jesus Amezqua
Bd of Dir: Marvin Morris
Bd of Dir: Ann Petty
Ofcr: John Weber
VP: Diane Trautman
Exec: Carlota Rodriguez
Dir Sec: Ecomet Burley
Prgrm Mgr: Martin Loa
IT Man: Dwayne Brooms
IT Man: Taneeka Williams

D-U-N-S 07-966-6230
HARRIS DENISE ANN TRUST
DENISE ANN HARRIS ESTATE
301 W Bay St Ste 14117, Jacksonville, FL 32202-5184
Tel (888) 504-0994 *Founded/Ownrshp* 2014
Sales 150.0MM *EMP* 1
SIC 6733 Private estate, personal investment & vacation fund trusts
Trst: Denise Cross

D-U-N-S 05-322-7708
HARRIS FARMS INC
HARRIS RANCH BEEF CO
29475 Fresno Coalinga Rd, Coalinga, CA 93210-9699
Tel (559) 884-2435 *Founded/Ownrshp* 1977
Sales 5.0MMM[E] *EMP* 1,300
SIC 0191 0211 2011 7011 5812 5541

D-U-N-S 04-433-8429 IMP/EXP
HARRIS FREEMAN & CO INC
HARRIS TEA COMPANY
3110 E Miraloma Ave, Anaheim, CA 92806-1906
Tel (714) 765-1190 *Founded/Ownrshp* 1981
Sales 267.5MM[E] *EMP* 560
SIC 5149 2099 Coffee & tea; Spices, including grinding
CEO: Anil J Shah
**Pr:* Kevin Shah
**Treas:* Meena Shah
Plnt Mgr: Sunil Vayes

D-U-N-S 08-697-6214 IMP
HARRIS HEALTH SYSTEM
SMITH CLINIC
2525 Holly Hall St, Houston, TX 77054-4124
Tel (713) 566-6400 *Founded/Ownrshp* 1965
Sales 357.4MM[E] *EMP* 5,532
SIC 8062 8011 Hospital, affiliated with AMA residency; Clinic, operated by physicians
Pr: John Guest
Dir Vol: Elizabeth Tise
Ch Bd: J Evans Attwell
CFO: Liz Alhand
CFO: Clifford Bottom
Ch: Stephen H Doncarlos
Treas: Elvin Franklin Jr
Chf Mktg O: Sue Provenzano
Ofcr: Derrick Crawford
Ofcr: Vince Temples
Sr VP: Terry Reeves
Sr VP: Alfonso Rubio
Sr VP: Robert Trenchell
VP: King Hillier
VP: Victoria Nikitin
VP: Ricci Sanchez
Dir Lab: Nabaska Richardson
Dir Rad: Cleveland Black
Dir Rx: Shahana Quadri
Board of Directors: Elvin Franklin Jr, Danny F Jackson, Jim Lemond, Mary C Spinks, E Dale Wortham

D-U-N-S 60-293-8771
■ **HARRIS IT SERVICES CORP**
(*Suby of* HARRIS CORP) ★
2235 Monroe St, Herndon, VA 20171-2824
Tel (703) 673-1400 *Founded/Ownrshp* 2008
Sales 287.4MM[E] *EMP* 3,000
SIC 8711 3663 3674 Engineering services; Radio & TV communications equipment; Semiconductors & related devices
Pr: Wayne Lucernoni
**Treas:* Charles J Greene
**VP:* John L Draheim
**VP:* Scott T Mikuen
**VP:* Lewis A Schwartz

HARRIS MEDICAL LABORATORY
See TEXAS HEALTH HARRIS METHODIST HOSPITAL FORT WORTH

HARRIS RANCH BEEF CO
See HARRIS FARMS INC

D-U-N-S 19-226-6851 EXP
HARRIS RANCH BEEF CO
(*Suby of* HARRIS RANCH BEEF CO) ★
29475 Fresno Coalinga Rd, Five Points, CA 93624
Tel (559) 884-2435 *Founded/Ownrshp* 2003
Sales 164.2MM[E] *EMP* 700
SIC 2011 2013 Meat packing plants; Sausages & other prepared meats
Ch Bd: John Harris

CFO: Robert Kettle
IT Man: Randy Dehart

D-U-N-S 13-197-2051
HARRIS SOUP CO
HARRY'S FRESH FOODS
(*Suby of* JGC FOOD CO LLC) ★
17711 Ne Riverside Pkwy, Portland, OR 97230-7370
Tel (503) 257-7687 *Founded/Ownrshp* 2013
Sales 90.4MM[E] *EMP* 200
SIC 2092 2099 Fresh or frozen fish or seafood chowders, soups & stews; Food preparations
CEO: Stan McCammon
**Pr:* Anthony Muscato
**CFO:* Claudia Pieropan
**VP:* Brian Meiners
Sls&Mrk Ex: Maureen Hotchkiss
**VP Sls:* Debra Onken
Manager: Ed Montoya
Manager: Laura Smith
Sls Mgr: Ed Brand

HARRIS TEA COMPANY
See HARRIS FREEMAN & CO INC

D-U-N-S 96-889-1499
HARRIS TECHNICAL SERVICES CORP
21000 Atl Blvd Ste 300, Dulles, VA 20166
Tel (703) 610-4200 *Founded/Ownrshp* 1987
Sales 60.1MM[E] *EMP* 2,000
SIC 7371 7379 8711 3577

D-U-N-S 04-846-3103 IMP
■ **HARRIS TEETER LLC** (NC)
(*Suby of* HARRIS TEETER SUPERMARKETS INC) ★
701 Crestdale Rd, Matthews, NC 28105-1744
Tel (704) 844-3100 *Founded/Ownrshp* 1936, 2013
Sales 3.9MMM[E] *EMP* 18,000
SIC 5411 Supermarkets, chain
Pr: Fred J Morganthall II
Treas: Douglas Stephenson
Sr VP: Daniel J Bruni
Sr VP: Karen Stout
**VP:* Rod Antolock
VP: George R Faulk Jr
VP: Mark G Hilton
VP: James M Hunter
VP: John G Hutchens Jr
VP: Luke Laperriere
VP: Jerry E Leclair
VP: Rory Mecham
VP: Dwight Moore
VP: Scott K Nations
VP: Theresa D Priore
VP: Chris Sprull
VP: Scott Wippel
Dir Risk M: Bill Richardson

D-U-N-S 04-727-9351 IMP/EXP
■ **HARRIS TEETER SUPERMARKETS INC**
(*Suby of* KROGER CO) ★
701 Crestdale Rd, Matthews, NC 28105-1744
Tel (704) 844-3100 *Founded/Ownrshp* 2014
Sales 4.0MMM[E] *EMP* 25,800
SIC 5411 Supermarkets, chain
CEO: W Rodney McMullen
**Pr:* Rod Antolock
Treas: Doug Stephenson
Sr VP: Jeff Sherman
Sr VP: Craig Stover
VP: George Faulk
VP: Bradley Graham
VP: Mark Hilton
VP: Luke Laperriere
VP: Tracey Mrozek
VP: Glenn Thomson
Exec: Vernan Moore

D-U-N-S 11-379-3996
HARRIS WILLIAM & CO INC
WILLIAM HARRIS INVESTORS
191 N Wacker Dr Ste 1500, Chicago, IL 60606-1899
Tel (312) 621-0590 *Founded/Ownrshp* 1966
Sales 126.8MM[E] *EMP* 320
SIC 6799 3317 Investment clubs; Steel pipe & tubes
CEO: Jack R Polsky
**Ch Bd:* Irving B Harris
**COO:* Adam Langsam
Treas: Ann Wolf
Dir IT: Duane Dibble
Genl Couns: David Novick

D-U-N-S 06-977-4214
HARRISBURG AREA COMMUNITY COLLEGE FOUNDATION
HACC
1 Hacc Dr, Harrisburg, PA 17110-2903
Tel (717) 780-2300 *Founded/Ownrshp* 1964
Sales 3.3MM *EMP* 1,520
Accts Smith Elliott Kearns & Company
SIC 8222 Community college
Pr: John Sygielski
Ofcr: John M Kopetchny
Sr VP: Lori Amspacker
DP Exec: Raymond Matzelle
Netwrk Mgr: Dave Shafer
Sls&Mrk Ex: Raymond Antonelli
Board of Directors: Daniel Jusco, Sue Morris, Jennifer Thompson

D-U-N-S 01-418-2471
HARRISBURG NEWS CO
CEDAR BOOK & CARD SHOP
(*Suby of* HUDSON NEWS DISTRIBUTORS LLC) ★
980 Briarsdale Rd, Harrisburg, PA 17109-5905
Tel (717) 561-8377 *Founded/Ownrshp* 2014
Sales 135.6MM[E] *EMP* 460
SIC 5192

D-U-N-S 01-058-1601
HARRISBURG SCHOOL DISTRICT INC
1601 State St, Harrisburg, PA 17103-1466
Tel (717) 703-4000 *Founded/Ownrshp* 1843
Sales 82.4MM *EMP* 1,200
SIC 8211 Public elementary & secondary schools
CFO: Peggy Morningstar
**Ofcr:* Audrey Utley
MIS Dir: Robert Hilinski
IT Man: Jodi Davis
IT Man: Bilal Hasan
IT Man: Kayla Orange
Netwrk Mgr: Greg Pankake
Teacher Pr: Samara Scott

D-U-N-S 03-449-4823
HARRISON CO LLC
4801 Viking Dr, Bossier City, LA 71111-7423
Tel (318) 747-0700 *Founded/Ownrshp* 1986
Sales 92.1MM[E] *EMP* 150[E]
SIC 5194 5145 5141 Cigarettes; Cigars; Chewing tobacco; Candy; Groceries, general line
Ex VP: Don W Bellah Jr
**Prin:* Wayne M Baquet Jr
**Prin:* John D Georges
**Prin:* Wgilbert Stroud Jr
CTO: Amy Standridge
IT Man: Pam Pickron

HARRISON COLLEGE
See EDUCATIONAL MANAGEMENT CORP

HARRISON CONSTRUCTION CO.
See APAC-ATLANTIC INC

D-U-N-S 06-974-7293
HARRISON COUNTY HOSPITAL ASSOCIATION
MARSHALL REGIONAL MEDICAL CENT
811 S Washington Ave, Marshall, TX 75670-5336
Tel (903) 927-6000 *Founded/Ownrshp* 1911
Sales 101.3MM *EMP* 600
SIC 8062 General medical & surgical hospitals
Pr: Russell J Collier
**COO:* James F Hodges
**VP:* Paula Brandon
Dir Lab: Roy Terhune
Off Mgr: Mary B Reeves
Dir Health: Linda Hickering

D-U-N-S 09-951-4275
HARRISON COUNTY SCHOOL DISTRICT
408 E B Saunders Way, Clarksburg, WV 26301-3712
Tel (304) 326-7300 *Founded/Ownrshp* 1932
Sales 81.8MM[E] *EMP* 1,400
SIC 8211 9111 Public elementary & secondary schools; County supervisors' & executives' offices
**Treas:* Sharon Haddix
IT Man: Bobbye Geopi
Netwrk Eng: Tom Fishbaugh
HC Dir: Jody Sperry

D-U-N-S 10-065-3518
HARRISON COUNTY SCHOOL DISTRICT
11072 Highway 49, Gulfport, MS 39503-4110
Tel (228) 539-5956 *Founded/Ownrshp* 1958
Sales 119.3MM *EMP* 1,800
Accts Wright Ward Hatten & Guel P
SIC 8211 Public elementary & secondary schools
Dir IT: Amy Dupree
IT Man: Amber Geiser

D-U-N-S 12-858-7685
HARRISON ELECTRICAL WORKERS TRUSTS
1220 Sw Morrison St # 300, Portland, OR 97205-2235
Tel (503) 224-0048 *Founded/Ownrshp* 1954
Sales 94.4MM *EMP* 2
SIC 6733 Trusts
Ch: Tim Gauthier

D-U-N-S 07-880-1210
HARRISON GLOBAL LLC
224 Calvary St, Waltham, MA 02453-8366
Tel (781) 863-2626 *Founded/Ownrshp* 2012
Sales 78.6MM[E] *EMP* 1,500
SIC 4119 Limousine rental, with driver

D-U-N-S 00-746-6626 IMP
HARRISON GYPSUM LLC (OK)
ALLIED CUSTOM GYPSUM
1550 Double C Dr, Norman, OK 73069-8288
Tel (405) 366-9500 *Founded/Ownrshp* 1978, 1955
Sales 228.6MM[E] *EMP* 150
SIC 1499 4213 Gypsum mining; Trucking, except local
CFO: E R Shily
Sr VP: Dan Northewitt
**VP:* Nathan Shirley
VP Opers: Kris Kinder
VP Sls: Jim Hill
Sls Mgr: Gina Russell

HARRISON MEDICAL CENTER
See HARRISON MEMORIAL HOSPITAL INC

D-U-N-S 06-714-5052
HARRISON MEDICAL CENTER
GENERAL MEDICAL SURGICAL HOSPI
2520 Cherry Ave, Bremerton, WA 98310-4229
Tel (360) 744-6510 *Founded/Ownrshp* 1943
Sales 398.0MM *EMP* 2,400[E]
SIC 8062 General medical & surgical hospitals
Pr: Scott Bosch
**Treas:* James Smalley
**Ex VP:* Adar Palis
**Sr VP:* Patty Cochrell
**Sr VP:* Forrest G Ehlinger
**Sr VP:* Mariel S Kagan
Sr VP: Jeanell Rasmussen
VP: Mariel Kagan
VP: Cynthia May
Dir Inf Cn: Cathy M Donald
Chf Nrs Of: Cindy May

D-U-N-S 07-184-4583
HARRISON MEMORIAL HOSPITAL INC
HARRISON MEDICAL CENTER
2520 Cherry Ave, Bremerton, WA 98310-4229
Tel (360) 377-3911 *Founded/Ownrshp* 1943
Sales NA *EMP* 1,725
SIC 8062

D-U-N-S 00-329-2281 EXP
HARRISON POULTRY INC (GA)
HARRISON PROPANE GAS CO
107 Star St W, Bethlehem, GA 30620-2119
Tel (770) 867-9105 *Founded/Ownrshp* 1958, 1959
Sales 181.1MM[E] *EMP* 835
SIC 0254 2015 5984 2013 2011 Chicken hatchery; Poultry slaughtering & processing; Liquefied petroleum gas, delivered to customers' premises; Sausages & other prepared meats; Meat packing plants
CEO: Sam Sloan
**Pr:* Michael Welch
**CFO:* Greg Finch
**CFO:* Jeff Megahee
Plnt Mgr: Bobby Wiley

HARRISON PROPANE GAS CO
See HARRISON POULTRY INC

D-U-N-S 09-191-1826
HARRISON SCHOOL DISTRICT TWO
1060 Harrison Rd, Colorado Springs, CO 80905-3586
Tel (719) 579-2000 *Founded/Ownrshp* 1874
Sales 90.5MM *EMP* 1,700[E]
Accts Hoelting & Company Inc Color
SIC 8211 Elementary & secondary schools
Genl Mgr: Lori Hawkins
Dir IT: Stacy Aldridge
IT Man: Alan Smith
IT Man: Dana Thomson
Teacher Pr: Karla Loria

D-U-N-S 00-517-3471 IMP
HARRISON STEEL CASTINGS CO
900 S Mound St, Attica, IN 47918-1632
Tel (765) 762-2481 *Founded/Ownrshp* 1906
Sales 145.0MM[E] *EMP* 850
SIC 3325 Steel foundries; Alloy steel castings, except investment
Pr: Wade C Harrison II
**Ch Bd:* Edward G Curtis
**Treas:* Robert S Harrison
**VP:* Geoffrey H Curtis
**VP:* Trevor H Curtis
**VP:* Wade C Harrison III
CIO: Pam Lich
Netwrk Mgr: Shane Rogers
Sfty Mgr: Ed Farrel
Sfty Mgr: John Johnson
Ql Cn Mgr: William Hollander

D-U-N-S 09-363-8729
HARRISON TRUCK CENTERS INC
3601 Adventureland Dr, Altoona, IA 50009-9589
Tel (515) 967-3500 *Founded/Ownrshp* 1997
Sales 213.2MM *EMP* 400
SIC 5511 7538 Trucks, tractors & trailers: new & used; General truck repair
Pr: Brian Harrison
Pr: Pat McKilligan
COO: Chad Harrison
CFO: Dustin Petersen

D-U-N-S 80-924-6069
HARRISON WORLDWIDE ENTERPRISES INC
WHEELCHAIR GETAWAYS
1650 Independence Dr, New Braunfels, TX 78132-3942
Tel (830) 608-9200 *Founded/Ownrshp* 1991
Sales 87.6MM[E] *EMP* 450
SIC 5571

HARRODSBURG HEALTH & REHAB CTR
See LP HARRODSBURG LLC

D-U-N-S 82-633-9611
HARRON COMMUNICATIONS LP
70 E Lancaster Ave, Malvern, PA 19355-2150
Tel (610) 644-7500 *Founded/Ownrshp* 1964
Sales 104.8MM[E] *EMP* 378[E]
SIC 8748 Business consulting
CEO: James J Bruder Jr
**Pr:* Thomas M Marturano
**CFO:* Shawn P Flannery
CFO: Thomas Marturano
Ofcr: Constance S Prince
**Ex VP:* Ryan F Pearson
Ex VP: Ryan Pearson
**VP:* Linda C Stuchell Leibert
VP: Emily Pollack
VP: Linda Stuchell
VP: Andrew Walton

D-U-N-S 14-953-1084 IMP/EXP
■ **HARRY & DAVID HOLDINGS INC**
(*Suby of* 1-800-FLOWERS.COM INC) ★
2500 S Pacific Hwy, Medford, OR 97501-8724
Tel (541) 864-2362 *Founded/Ownrshp* 2014
Sales 297.5MM[E] *EMP* 1,026
SIC 5961 1541 Catalog & mail-order houses; Food products manufacturing or packing plant construction
Pr: Craig J Johnson
Sr VP: Jackie Ardrey
Sr VP: Joseph Foley

D-U-N-S 05-352-4877 IMP
■ **HARRY AND DAVID LLC**
(*Suby of* HARRY & DAVID HOLDINGS INC) ★
2500 S Pacific Hwy, Medford, OR 97501-8724
Tel (541) 864-2500 *Founded/Ownrshp* 2004
Sales 279.2MM[E] *EMP* 1,000
SIC 5961 5947 Fruit, mail order; Gift, novelty & souvenir shop
Pr: Barbara M Hurd
CFO: Jason Phillipson
Sr VP: Jackie Ardrey
Sr VP: John Bancroft
Sr VP: Tom Forsythe
VP: Jill Borovansky
VP: Mona Cato
VP: Tony Huckabee
VP: Mark Oedekoven
Exec: Kelly Barton
Creative D: Troy Forrest

D-U-N-S 00-583-9170
HARRY GRODSKY & CO INC (MA)
33 Shaws Ln, Springfield, MA 01104-3019
Tel (413) 785-1947 *Founded/Ownrshp* 1918
Sales 99.9MM *EMP* 300
Accts Aaron & Smith Pc
SIC 1711 Plumbing contractors; Heating & air conditioning contractors; Process piping contractor
Pr: Ronald Grodsky
CFO: Scott Grodsky
Ex VP: Jeffrey Grodsky
Ex VP: Allen Sawyer
VP: Rivers Christine
VP: Richard Kelly
VP: Thomas Mahan
VP: Robert Ranahan
VP: David Streeter
VP: Brian Toomey
VP: Anthony Victor
Board of Directors: Robert G Agnoli

D-U-N-S 08-293-0645
HARRY J KLOEPPEL & ASSOCIATES INC
246 E Janata Blvd Ste 300, Lombard, IL 60148-5383
Tel (630) 206-5810 *Founded/Ownrshp* 1977
Sales 90.0MM *EMP* 12[E]
SIC 5049 Laboratory equipment, except medical or dental
Pr: Harry J Kloeppel
**Pr:* Tom Keaveney
VP: Allen Keaveney
Off Mgr: Cindy Detlof
Off Mgr: Cindy Detlos
Off Mgr: Mark Skole

D-U-N-S 04-681-8712
■ **HARRY M STEVENS INC OF NEW JERSEY**
(*Suby of* ARAMARK SERVICES INC) ★
1101 Market St, Philadelphia, PA 19107-2934
Tel (215) 238-3000 *Founded/Ownrshp* 1994
Sales 60.2MM[E] *EMP* 5,000
SIC 5812 Concessionaire
Pr: Charles Gillespie
**Treas:* Melvin Mahoney

HARRY'S FRESH FOODS
See HARRIS SOUP CO

D-U-N-S 00-300-2268 IMP/EXP
▲ **HARSCO CORP**
350 Poplar Church Rd, Camp Hill, PA 17011-2599
Tel (717) 763-7064 *Founded/Ownrshp* 1853
Sales 1.7MMM *EMP* 10,800
Accts Pricewaterhousecoopers Llp Ph
Tkr Sym HSC *Exch* NYS
SIC 7359 7353 5082 3443 3585 4789 Equipment rental & leasing; Heavy construction equipment rental; Construction & mining machinery; Scaffolding; Fuel tanks (oil, gas, etc.): metal plate; Cryogenic tanks, for liquids & gases; Cylinders, pressure: metal plate; Heat exchangers: coolers (after, inter), condensers, etc.; Evaporative condensers, heat transfer equipment; Railroad maintenance & repair services
Pr: F Nicholas Grasberger
Pr: James E Cline
Pr: James M Demitrieus
Pr: Nicholas Grasberger
Pr: William R Jacob
Pr: Richard E Lundgren
Pr: Daniel S McAtee
Pr: Eric A Reisner
COO: Gene A Iannazzo
CFO: Peter Minan
CFO: Peter F Minan
Chf Cred: Russell C Hochman
Sr VP: Tony Degregorio
Sr VP: Scott H Gerson
Sr VP: Tracey McKenzie
VP: Michael Kolinsky
VP: Stephen J Schnoor
Board of Directors: James F Earl, Kathy G Eddy, David C Everitt, Stuart E Graham, Terry D Growcock, Henry W Knueppel, Elaine La Roche, James M Loree, Phillip C Widman

D-U-N-S 07-080-8746
HARSHAW SERVICE INC
HARSHAW TRANE SERVICE
12700 Plantside Dr, Louisville, KY 40299-6387
Tel (502) 499-7000 *Founded/Ownrshp* 1976
Sales 87.2MM[E] *EMP* 156
SIC 5075 1711 5074 Air conditioning equipment, except room units; Electrical heating equipment; Warm air heating & air conditioning contractor; Plumbing & hydronic heating supplies
Pr: W Frank Harshaw
**COO:* Doug Michael
**Prin:* Kurt Barrett
IT Man: Linda Schweinhart

HARSHAW TRANE SERVICE
See HARSHAW SERVICE INC

D-U-N-S 18-214-0293 IMP
HART & COOLEY INC
(*Suby of* AIR DISTRIBUTION TECHNOLOGIES INC) ★
5030 Corp Exch Blvd Se, Grand Rapids, MI 49512
Tel (616) 656-8200 *Founded/Ownrshp* 1999
Sales 731.0MM[E] *EMP* 1,700
SIC 3446 3822 Registers (air), metal; Auto controls regulating residntl & coml environmt & applncs
Pr: Michael Winn
VP: Daniel J Disser
IT Man: Gonzalez Carlos
Mtls Mgr: Debbie Sneed
VP Mktg: Christopher J Pfaus
Manager: Tom Bauer
Manager: Brian Queensberry

D-U-N-S 07-169-3741 IMP/EXP
HART CHEMICALS INC (CA)
PACIFIC COAST CHEMICALS CO.
2424 4th St, Berkeley, CA 94710-2404
Tel (510) 549-3535 *Founded/Ownrshp* 1958, 1970
Sales 84.1MM[E] *EMP* 75
SIC 5191 5169 Farm supplies; Chemicals & allied products
CEO: Aaron K Stull
**CFO:* Don Stull
Sls Mgr: Jim Collins
Sls Mgr: Steve Shaffer

D-U-N-S 10-002-7366
HART COUNTY SCHOOLS
25 Quality St, Munfordville, KY 42765-9476
Tel (270) 524-2631 *Founded/Ownrshp* 1940

Sales 20.1MM[E] EMP 1,012
SIC 8211 Public elementary & secondary schools
*Treas: Judy Lawler

D-U-N-S 13-168-5422
HART HOTELS INC
617 Dingens St Ste 4, Buffalo, NY 14206-2474
Tel (716) 893-6551 Founded/Ownrshp 1985
Sales 80.6MM[E] EMP 1,100
SIC 7011 Hotels & motels
Ch Bd: David P Hart
*Sec: William P Hart
Brnch Mgr: Karen Piazza
Genl Mgr: Carol Bonner
Genl Mgr: Harry Falk
Genl Mgr: Heather Strauss
Off Mgr: Susan Crofts
Sales Exec: Kim Duffett
Sls Dir: Paul Klinger
Mktg Mgr: Mary Mack

D-U-N-S 55-721-4343
HART JEFFREY GROUP INC
4400 N Federal Hwy, Boca Raton, FL 33431-5187
Tel (561) 997-2238 Founded/Ownrshp 1991
Sales 110.0MM EMP 14
SIC 8732 6799 Merger, acquisition & reorganization research; Investors
Pr: Jeffrey S Obligen

D-U-N-S 13-880-2249
HART RESTAURANT MANAGEMENT INC
BURGER KING
108 N Mesquite St, Corpus Christi, TX 78401-2823
Tel (361) 882-4100 Founded/Ownrshp 1954
Sales 43.5MM[E] EMP 1,000
SIC 5812 Fast-food restaurant, chain
Pr: Robert G Hart III
IT Man: Andrew Johnson

D-U-N-S 04-701-1085 IMP/EXP
▲ HARTE HANKS INC
9601 Mcallister Fwy # 610, San Antonio, TX 78216-4632
Tel (210) 829-9000 Founded/Ownrshp 1970
Sales 495.3MM EMP 5,573
Tkr Sym HHS Exch NYS
SIC 7331 7372 Direct mail advertising services; Prepackaged software
Pr: Karen A Puckett
*Ch Bd: Christopher M Harte
Pr: Philip J Galati
COO: Shirish R Lal
CFO: Douglas C Shepard
Chf Mktg O: Frank M Grillo
Ofcr: Andrew P Harrison
Ex VP: Doug Shepard
Sr VP: Robert L R Munden
Sr VP: Joseph A Voica
VP: Carlos Alvarado
VP: Troy Bullock
VP: Amy Bybee
VP: Carolyn J Deluca
VP: Michele Fitzpatrick
VP: Jack Gaden
VP: Bill Kokos
VP: Robert Lord
VP: Aaron Ludwig
VP: Susan Pierce
VP: Michel Reid

HARTFORD, THE
See HARTFORD FINANCIAL SERVICES GROUP INC

D-U-N-S 00-691-7173
■ HARTFORD ACCIDENT & INDEMNITY CO
(Suby of HARTFORD FIRE INSURANCE CO (INC)) ★
1 Hartford Plz, Hartford, CT 06155-0001
Tel (860) 547-5000 Founded/Ownrshp 1913
Sales NA EMP 3,500
SIC 6411 Insurance agents, brokers & service
CEO: Liam E McGee
*Pr: Beth Bombara
CFO: Carol Acunto
*Ex VP: Martha Gervasi
*Ex VP: Alan J Kreczko
Ex VP: Alpa Patel
*Ex VP: Robert Rupp
Ex VP: Jack Stoddard
Sr VP: Lois Grady
Sr VP: Connie Weaver
VP: John Diehl
VP: Kate Jorens
VP: Colleen Mastroianni
Exec: Donald Aderhold
Exec: Marilyn Carey
Dir: Louise Durej

D-U-N-S 00-691-7058 IMP
■ HARTFORD CASUALTY INSURANCE CO
(Suby of HARTFORD FIRE INSURANCE CO (INC)) ★
690 Asylum Ave, Hartford, CT 06155-0002
Tel (860) 547-5000 Founded/Ownrshp 1929
Sales NA EMP 635
SIC 6411 6331 Insurance agents, brokers & service; Fire, marine & casualty insurance: mutual
Pr: Andre A Napoli
Pr: Michael Byam
*Treas: Robert W Paiano
VP: Ernest McNeill
CIO: Christina Divigard
CIO: Dana Drago
CIO: Michael Green
CIO: Jules Jodko
CIO: Brenda Pinzon
CIO: Cindy Price
CIO: Rich Reynolds

D-U-N-S 06-926-2962
HARTFORD CATHOLIC DEVELOPMENT CORP (CT)
ARCHDIOCESE OF HARTFORD, THE
134 Farmington Ave, Hartford, CT 06105-3723
Tel (860) 541-6491 Founded/Ownrshp 1837
Sales 73.0MM[E] EMP 2,000
SIC 8661 Religious organizations
Treas: Rev Charles Daly
*Pr: Henry J Mansell
*Pr: Archb Henry Manselo
*Sec: John J McCarthy

*VP: Christie A Macaluso
Ex Dir: Cori Thibodeau

HARTFORD CITY HALL
See CITY OF HARTFORD

HARTFORD COLLEGE FOR WOMEN
See UNIVERSITY OF HARTFORD

D-U-N-S 00-115-0747
■ HARTFORD COURANT CO LLC (CT)
(Suby of TRONC INC) ★
285 Broad St, Hartford, CT 06115-3785
Tel (860) 241-6200 Founded/Ownrshp 1764, 2014
Sales 173.4MM[E] EMP 750
SIC 2711 Newspapers: publishing only, not printed on site
CEO: Rick Daniels
CFO: Richard Feeney
*Treas: Thomas Brown
Sr VP: Tom Anischik
VP: Joseph Schiltz
*VP: Mary Lou Stoneburner
Admn Mgr: Louis Clayton
Brnch Mgr: Jorge Madeira
Dir IT: Bob Fancher
Dir IT: Bernie Gullotta
Dir IT: David Holub

D-U-N-S 01-864-9608
HARTFORD DISTRIBUTORS INC
FRANKLIN FINE BEERS
131 Chapel Rd, Manchester, CT 06042-1633
Tel (860) 643-2337 Founded/Ownrshp 1963
Sales 109.6MM EMP 170[E]
SIC 5181

D-U-N-S 11-836-5931
■ HARTFORD EQUITY SALES CO INC
HESCO
(Suby of HARTFORD LIFE INC) ★
200 Hopmeadow St, Weatogue, CT 06089-9793
Tel (860) 843-8213 Founded/Ownrshp 2008
Sales 160.9MM[E] EMP 2,000
SIC 6211 Brokers, security
Pr: Lowndes A Smith
Treas: J Richard Garrett
Sr VP: Jennifer Fabrizio
*Sr VP: John P Ginnetti
*Sr VP: David J McDonald
VP: Paul S Bosnyak
VP: Charles A Clinton
VP: Donald J Znamierowski
Board of Directors: Howard A York

D-U-N-S 78-708-5893
▲ HARTFORD FINANCIAL SERVICES GROUP INC
HARTFORD, THE
1 Hartford Plz, Hartford, CT 06155-0001
Tel (860) 547-5000 Founded/Ownrshp 1810
Sales NA EMP 17,400
Tkr Sym HIG Exch NYS
SIC 6331 6311 6351 6321 Fire, marine & casualty insurance; Property damage insurance; Automobile insurance; Workers' compensation insurance; Life insurance; Life insurance carriers; Life reinsurance; Surety insurance; Liability insurance; Accident & health insurance; Accident insurance carriers; Health insurance carriers
Ch Bd: Christopher J Swift
Pr: Irene Bassock
Pr: Penni Bolt
Pr: Xiangrong Cai
Pr: Cedric Delacruz
Pr: Douglas Elliot
Pr: Mike Fixer
Pr: Donna Gesualdi
Pr: Andrew Golden
Pr: Catherine Gregory
Pr: Stephen Harris
Pr: Amy T Hudson
Pr: Renee Johnson
Pr: Jason Kuselias
Pr: Greg Larsson
Pr: Bill Lombardi
Pr: Deborah A Millum
Pr: Douglas Shapiro
CFO: Beth A Bombara
Treas: Mark Ekeroth
Ofcr: Kathy Bromage
Board of Directors: H Patrick Swygert, Robert B Allardice III, Trevor Fetter, Kathryn A Mikells, Michael G Morris, Thomas A Renyi, Julie G Richardson, Teresa Wynn Roseborough, Virginia P Ruesterholz, Charles B Strauss

HARTFORD FINANCIAL SVCS GROUP
See HARTFORD INSURANCE CO OF ILLINOIS

D-U-N-S 00-691-7181
■ HARTFORD FIRE INSURANCE CO (INC)
(Suby of HARTFORD) ★
1 Hartford Plz, Hartford, CT 06115-1703
Tel (860) 547-5000 Founded/Ownrshp 1810
Sales NA EMP 18,800
SIC 6411 6311 6351 7373 Insurance agents, brokers & service; Life insurance; Surety insurance; Fidelity insurance; Systems integration services
CEO: Liam E McGee
Treas: James R Garrett
Ex VP: Brad Burdick
Ex VP: Mike Concannon
Ex VP: Srini Krishnamurthy
Sr VP: Peggy Anson
Sr VP: Jack T Crawford
Sr VP: Michael O'Halleran
Sr VP: Michael Ohalleran
Sr VP: Paul Schwartzott
VP: Patrick Greiten
VP: Tom Jones
Exec: Stephanie Dimasso
Exec: Laurie Scotti

D-U-N-S 62-458-5576
HARTFORD FOUNDATION FOR PUBLIC GIVING
10 Columbus Blvd Fl 8, Hartford, CT 06106-1976
Tel (860) 548-1888 Founded/Ownrshp 1925

Sales 113.4MM EMP 40
Accts Blum Shapiro & Company Pc
SIC 6732 8733 Charitable trust management; Noncommercial research organizations
Pr: Linda J Kelly
CFO: Virgil Blondet
Ofcr: Yvette Bello
Ofcr: Francesca Gordon
Ofcr: Dawn Grant
Ofcr: Jennyfer Holmes
Ofcr: Mary Macdonald
Ofcr: Judy McBride
Ofcr: Doug Shipman
Ofcr: Maggie Willard
Ofcr: Tom Zeleznock
VP: Christopher H All
VP: Nancy Benben
Assoc Dir: Meher Shulman

D-U-N-S 18-688-5687
HARTFORD HEALTHCARE CORP
1 State St Fl 19, Hartford, CT 06103-3102
Tel (860) 263-4100 Founded/Ownrshp 1985
Sales 2.1MMM EMP 5,100
Accts Ernst & Young Llp Hartford
SIC 8059 Personal care home, with health care
Ch Bd: Andrew Salner MD
*Pr: Elliot Joseph
CFO: John Biancamano
*CFO: Jeffrey A Flaks
*CFO: Thomas Marcoczi
*Treas: Raymond Kowalski
Ex VP: Jeffrey Flaks
Sr VP: Tracy Church
VP: Kimberly Harrison
VP: Richard Stys
Mng Dir: Richard Johnson

D-U-N-S 14-457-7959
■ HARTFORD HOLDINGS INC
(Suby of HARTFORD) ★
200 Hopmeadow St, Simsbury, CT 06070
Tel (860) 547-5000 Founded/Ownrshp 2002
Sales NA EMP 7,501
SIC 6311 Life insurance
Pr: Thomas M Marra
*Ch Bd: Ramani Ayer
VP: Lynda Godkin

D-U-N-S 06-553-3796
HARTFORD HOSPITAL
80 Seymour St, Hartford, CT 06102-8000
Tel (860) 545-5000 Founded/Ownrshp 1986
Sales 993.3MM EMP 7,500
SIC 8062 General medical & surgical hospitals
Pr: Jeffrey A Flaks
V Ch: Anthony Joyce
Pr: Barry Kriesberg
COO: Janice Giuca
CFO: Tom Marchozzi
Sr VP: Bimal Patel
Sr VP: Luis Tavares
VP: Gerry J Boisvert
VP: Jeffrey Cohen
VP: Wendy Elberth
VP: Carol Garlick
VP: Matthew Saidel
Exec: Thomas Pleva
Assoc Dir: Marcin R Dada
Assoc Dir: Charles McKay
Dir Rx: Richard Gannon
Dir Rx: Michael Rubino
Mng Ofcr: Rocco Orlando

D-U-N-S 78-695-4776
■ HARTFORD INSURANCE CO OF ILLINOIS
HARTFORD FINANCIAL SVCS GROUP
(Suby of HARTFORD FIRE INSURANCE CO (INC)) ★
690 Asylum Ave, Hartford, CT 06105-3845
Tel (860) 547-5000 Founded/Ownrshp 1979
Sales NA EMP 5,001
SIC 6411 Insurance agents, brokers & service
Pr: David K Zwiener
Pr: Jim Daley
*Pr: David K Zwiener
*CFO: Michael J Dury
CFO: Rick Ferguson
CFO: Raymond Godin
CFO: John Hess
CFO: Thomas Johnston
CFO: Christopher Swift
CFO: Marilyn Wyman
Assoc VP: Patrick Brown
Ex VP: David M Johnson
Ex VP: Alan Kreczko
Ex VP: Judith Patterson
Ex VP: Illene Whelley
Sr VP: Brenda J Furlong
Sr VP: Randall I Kiviat
Sr VP: Christine H Repasy
Sr VP: William J Smith
VP: Andrea Gardner
VP: Kevin Knull
Board of Directors: Timothy Galvin III, David P Halper, Donald J Lavalley, Debora G Westcott, Richard S Wilcox

D-U-N-S 78-695-6227
■ HARTFORD INVESTMENT MANAGEMENT CO
HIMCO
(Suby of HARTFORD) ★
1 Hartford Plz, Hartford, CT 06155-0001
Tel (860) 297-6700 Founded/Ownrshp 2008
Sales 232.3MM[E] EMP 220
SIC 6282 Investment advice
Pr: Brion Johnson
Ex VP: Joseph Darcy
Ex VP: Chris Hanlon
Ex VP: Bill Holm
Ex VP: Peter Perrotti
Ex VP: Richard E Van Steenbergen
Sr VP: Ryan Bloom
Sr VP: Paul Bukowski
Sr VP: Adriane Collimore
Sr VP: Jun Han
Sr VP: William N Holm
Sr VP: Michael Mondo
Sr VP: Kevin Nolin
Sr VP: Harry Norman

Sr VP: Chris Paolino
VP: Aadil Abbas
VP: John Cadogan
VP: Rockwell C Chris
VP: Christopher Cooper
VP: Ken Day
VP: Elizabeth Ellis

D-U-N-S 15-118-0270
■ HARTFORD LIFE AND ACCIDENT INSURANCE CO INC
(Suby of HARTFORD LIFE INC) ★
1 Hartford Plz, Hartford, CT 06115-1703
Tel (860) 547-5000 Founded/Ownrshp 1993
Sales NA EMP 5,000
SIC 6311 Life insurance
CEO: Liam E McGee
*Pr: Doug Elliot
*Pr: Thomas M Marra
*CEO: Christopher Swift
*CFO: Beth Bombara
Ex VP: Robert Rupp
VP: Gregory A Boyko
*VP: Thomas A Campbell
VP: Mary Jane Fortin
*VP: Christine H Repasy
VP: Diane Tatelman
Exec: Richard Costello
Exec: Patti Davidson
Exec: Robert Flynn

D-U-N-S 07-478-1253
■ HARTFORD LIFE AND ANNUITY INSURANCE CO
(Suby of HARTFORD LIFE INC) ★
200 Hopmeadow St, Weatogue, CT 06089-9793
Tel (860) 547-5000 Founded/Ownrshp 2008
Sales NA EMP 15
SIC 6311 6321 Life insurance carriers; Accident insurance carriers; Health insurance carriers
Ex VP: Thomas Marra
Pr: Ramani Ayer
Treas: Gregory Boyko
Off Mgr: Don Lavalley

D-U-N-S 01-720-6447
■ HARTFORD LIFE INC
(Suby of HARTFORD HOLDINGS INC) ★
200 Hopmeadow St, Simsbury, CT 06070
Tel (860) 547-5000 Founded/Ownrshp 1997
Sales NA EMP 7,500
SIC 6311 Life insurance
Ch Bd: Ramani Ayer
*CFO: Glenn Lammey
CFO: Lizabeth Zlatkus
*Ex VP: Gregory Boyko
*Ex VP: Michael Kalen
Ex VP: Sharon A Ritchey
*Sr VP: Terry Walker
Sr VP: Raymond P Welnicki
VP: Thomas Campbell
Dir Risk M: Xiangrong R Cai
CIO: Gary English

D-U-N-S 04-303-1459
■ HARTFORD LIFE INSURANCE CO
(Suby of HARTFORD LIFE INC) ★
200 Hopmeadow St, Weatogue, CT 06089-9793
Tel (860) 547-5000 Founded/Ownrshp 1902
Sales NA EMP 3[E]
Accts Deloitte & Touche Llp Hartfor
SIC 6411 Insurance agents, brokers & service
Pr: Brion S Johnson
CFO: Elisabeth Zlatkus
*Sr VP: Mark Niland
Sr VP: Peter F Sannizzaro

D-U-N-S 05-779-9637
HARTFORD PROVISION CO
HPC FOODSERVICE
625 Nutmeg Rd N, South Windsor, CT 06074-2440
Tel (860) 583-3908 Founded/Ownrshp 1908
Sales 178.5MM[E] EMP 130
SIC 5141 Groceries, general line
Pr: Barry Pearson
*Treas: Jeff Lotstein
*VP: Michael Faeth
*VP: Bob Lopena
*VP: Richard Lotstein
Sfty Mgr: Ray Corigliano

HARTFORD PUBLIC SCHOOLS
See HARTFORD SCHOOL DISTRICT

D-U-N-S 04-171-3541
HARTFORD SCHOOL DISTRICT
HARTFORD PUBLIC SCHOOLS
960 Main St Fl 9, Hartford, CT 06103-1218
Tel (860) 695-8400 Founded/Ownrshp 2002
Sales 166.2MM[E] EMP 2,797[E]
SIC 8211 Public elementary & secondary schools
*Ch: Matthew K Poland
IT Man: Christian Johnson
IT Man: Madeline Vasquez
Pr Dir: Pedro Zayas
Teacher Pr: Jill Cutler
HC Dir: Deborah Chameides
Snr Mgr: Alexander T Nardone

D-U-N-S 00-691-7223
■ HARTFORD STEAM BOILER INSPECTION AND INSURANCE CO
HSB//C
(Suby of MUNICH-AMERICAN HOLDING CORP) ★
1 State St Fl 5-12, Hartford, CT 06103-3102
Tel (860) 722-1866 Founded/Ownrshp 1866
Sales NA EMP 1,216[E]
SIC 6331 8711 7373 8742 Boiler insurance; Consulting engineer; Systems software development services; Maintenance management consultant
Pr: Gregg Barats
Pr: Edward Condon
CFO: Normand Mercier
*CFO: Peter Richter
*Treas: Ted Kmiascik
Ex VP: Anthony Trivella
Sr VP: Tony Trivella
VP: Joseph Conklin
*VP: Roberta A O'Brien

VP: Denis O'Shea
VP: J A Smith
Exec: Peter Tingus

D-U-N-S 00-281-3202 IMP
HARTLEY & PARKER LIMITED INC (CT)
100 Browning St, Stratford, CT 06615-7170
Tel (203) 375-5671 *Founded/Ownrshp* 1941
Sales 126.5MM^E *EMP* 150
SIC 5182 Liquor; Wine
Pr: Julius Rosenberg
COO: Barbara Soltis
Chf Mktg O: David Nathanson
**VP:* David Rosenberg
**VP:* Jerry Rosenberg
Sls Mgr: Frank Latorra
Sales Asso: Joe Imperia

D-U-N-S 01-756-6035
HARTLEY CO
FLEMINGS-DIV
319 Wheeling Ave, Cambridge, OH 43725-2245
Tel (740) 432-2328 *Founded/Ownrshp* 1925
Sales 174.2MM *EMP* 125
Accts Rea & Associates Inc Cambri
SIC 5541 5172 Filling stations, gasoline; Petroleum products
Ch: William H Hartley
**Pr:* Thomas C Hartley
**VP:* Joan Gross
**VP:* William H Hartley III

D-U-N-S 07-840-2948
HARTMAN AND TYNER INC (MI)
GEORGIAN MANOR APTS
24700 W 12 Mile Rd, Southfield, MI 48034-1218
Tel (248) 352-2010 *Founded/Ownrshp* 1933, 1953
Sales 36.8MM^E *EMP* 1,000
SIC 6513 6531 Apartment building operators; Real estate agents & managers
Pr: Herbert Tyner
Treas: Julie Ala
**Treas:* Ala Julie
**VP:* Daniel Adkins
Dir Risk M: Joy Frederick
Dir IT: Paul Gorman

D-U-N-S 06-641-0457
■ **HARTON JOHN W REGIONAL MEDICAL CENTER INC**
HMA
(*Suby of* HMA) ★
1801 N Jackson St, Tullahoma, TN 37388-8259
Tel (931) 393-3000 *Founded/Ownrshp* 2003
Sales 94.4MM *EMP* 500
SIC 8062 General medical & surgical hospitals
CEO: Kenneth James
**CFO:* Shaun Adams
VP: Edna High
Dir Rad: Ginger Baker
Genl Mgr: Rose Pack
Ansthlgy: Charles Padget

D-U-N-S 01-595-6162 IMP
HARTREE PARTNERS LP
HETCO
1185 Avenue Of The Americ, New York, NY 10036-2604
Tel (212) 536-8915 *Founded/Ownrshp* 1997, 2014
Sales 276.6MM^E *EMP* 200^E
SIC 6221 5172 Commodity contracts brokers, dealers; Petroleum products
Pt: Stephen Semlitz
Pt: Stephen M Hendel
Pt: Jason Lemme
VP: Lewis Chan
Snr Mgr: Eileen Merrigan

D-U-N-S 00-605-4779
HARTSON-KENNEDY CABINET TOP CO INC
522 W 22nd St, Marion, IN 46953-2926
Tel (765) 673-0451 *Founded/Ownrshp* 1948
Sales 89.7MM^E *EMP* 563
SIC 3083 Plastic finished products, laminated
Pr: William Kennedy
**VP:* Christopher L Kennedy
IT Man: Jennifer Fettig
Sales Exec: Glen Divit
Sales Exec: Joann Fiffik
Natl Sales: Doug Burkhardt

D-U-N-S 07-372-2498
HARTSVILLE LLC
CAROLINA PNES REGIONAL MED CTR
(*Suby of* RRCH HEALTHCARE PARTNERS) ★
1304 W Bobo Newsom Hwy, Hartsville, SC 29550-4710
Tel (843) 339-2100 *Founded/Ownrshp* 1995
Sales 84.9MM *EMP* 625
SIC 8011 Medical centers
CEO: Timothy Browne
**CFO:* Anthony J Seminaro
Dir Risk M: Candace Morton
Dir Rad: Steven Rogers
Surgeon: Jacqueline Mixon

D-U-N-S 06-184-7612
HARTT TRANSPORTATION SYSTEMS INC (ME)
262 Bomarc Rd, Bangor, ME 04401-2655
Tel (207) 947-1106 *Founded/Ownrshp* 1972
Sales 129.0MM *EMP* 562^E
SIC 4213

D-U-N-S 06-043-8439
HARTUNG BROTHERS INC
708 Heartland Trl # 2000, Madison, WI 53717-2172
Tel (608) 829-6000 *Founded/Ownrshp* 1975
Sales 120.0MM *EMP* 500
Accts Smith & Gesteland Llp Madiso
SIC 0161 0115 8748 Vegetables & melons; Corn; Business consulting
Pr: Dan Hartung
CFO: Daniel Layton
**VP:* Donald Hartung
VP: John Hartung
**VP:* James Noltner
**VP Bus Dev:* Larry Price
Exec: Jerry Brunner
Opers Mgr: Ryan Noltner
Board of Directors: Galen Hartung, James Hartung, John Hartung, Randy Hartung, Robert Hartung, Tara Mc Donald, Gayle Noltner

D-U-N-S 00-948-2753 IMP
HARTUNG GLASS INDUSTRIES INC
17830 W Valley Hwy, Tukwila, WA 98188-5532
Tel (425) 656-2626 *Founded/Ownrshp* 2004
Sales 150.0MM *EMP* 402
SIC 5023 Glassware
Pr: Nick Sciola
**CFO:* Richard Jamieson
Exec: Tom Moore
Genl Mgr: Todd Schulz
MIS Mgr: Carey Dyck
Opers Mgr: Bob Miller
Prd Mgr: Ken Nordyke
Manager: Sue Morton

D-U-N-S 00-828-6536 IMP
■ **HARTWELL CORP**
HASCO
(*Suby of* MCKECHNIE AEROSPACE INVESTMENTS, INC.)
900 Richfield Rd, Placentia, CA 92870-6788
Tel (714) 993-2752 *Founded/Ownrshp* 2012
Sales 148.2MM^E *EMP* 1,000
SIC 3429 Aircraft hardware
CEO: Joel Reiss
**Pr:* John Leary
**CFO:* Vicki Saugstad
VP: J Chambers
Sys/Mgr: Cinda Frye-Singer
Opers Supe: Mauricio Hernandez
Sls Mgr: Kelly Artin
Sls Mgr: Don Scott
Genl Couns: Michael Manella

D-U-N-S 12-214-7820
HARTZ GROUP INC
(*Suby of* HARTZ NORTH BERGEN) ★
667 Madison Ave Fl 24, New York, NY 10065-8099
Tel (212) 308-3336 *Founded/Ownrshp* 1984
Sales 91.6MM^E *EMP* 400
SIC 6512 6552 6531 6159 Commercial & industrial building operation; Land subdividers & developers, commercial; Land subdividers & developers, residential; Real estate agent, commercial; Real estate agent, residential; Small business investment companies
CEO: Leonard Stern
**Pr:* Edward Stern
**V Ch Bd:* Curtis B Schwartz
Ex VP: Lawrence Garb

D-U-N-S 05-810-9158 IMP/EXP
HARTZ MOUNTAIN CORP (NJ)
(*Suby of* UNICHARM CORPORATION)
400 Plaza Dr Ste 400, Secaucus, NJ 07094-3688
Tel (201) 271-4800 *Founded/Ownrshp* 1971, 2011
Sales 670.7MM^E *EMP* 1,200
SIC 5199 3999 Pet supplies; Pet supplies
Pr: Gumpei Futagami
Pr: Dan Detrolio
Chf Mktg O: Masanori Murakami
Ex VP: Peter Michelis
Ex VP: Gus Milano
Ex VP: Walter Smith
Sr VP: Vincent Rubino
VP: Matthew Brennen
VP: Anita Digiulio
VP: Joseph Hradil
VP: John Kubilus
VP: Richard Milder
VP: Frank Roscitt

D-U-N-S 06-427-8278
HARTZ MOUNTAIN INDUSTRIES INC
HARTZ NORTH BERGEN
400 Plaza Dr Ste 400, Secaucus, NJ 07094-3688
Tel (201) 348-1200 *Founded/Ownrshp* 1970
Sales 114.2MM^E *EMP* 428
SIC 6531

HARTZ NORTH BERGEN
See HARTZ MOUNTAIN INDUSTRIES INC

D-U-N-S 94-540-5116
▲ **HARVARD BIOSCIENCE INC**
84 October Hill Rd Ste 10, Holliston, MA 01746-1371
Tel (508) 893-8999 *Founded/Ownrshp* 1901
Sales 108.6MM *EMP* 437^E
Tkr Sym HBIO *Exch* NGM
SIC 3821 3826 Laboratory apparatus & furniture; Analytical instruments
Pr: Jeffrey A Duchemin
**Ch Bd:* Earl R Lewis
CFO: Robert Gagnon
Treas: Steven Friedman
VP: Yong Sun
Prd Mgr: Bill Crouss
Board of Directors: David Green, James W Green, Neal J Harte, John F Kennedy, Bertrand Loy, George Uveges

D-U-N-S 82-773-1829 IMP
HARVARD BUSINESS SCHOOL PUBLISHING CORP
HARVARD UNIVERSITY
(*Suby of* HARVARD UNIVERSITY) ★
20 Guest St Ste 700, Brighton, MA 02135-2040
Tel (617) 783-7400 *Founded/Ownrshp* 1994
Sales 207.5MM *EMP* 390^E
Accts Pricewaterhousecoopers Llp Bo
SIC 2721 2731 2741 Periodicals: publishing only; Books: publishing only; Newsletter publishing
Pr: David Wan
Pr: Patrick McManus
**COO:* Raymond Carvey
**CFO:* Paul Bills
Exec: Kathleen Mara
Exec: Mary Oloughlin
Ex Dir: John Korn
Mng Dir: Josh Macht
Dir IT: Sam O Hainer
VP Sls: Ian Fanton
Mktg Mgr: Alexandra Merceron

D-U-N-S 79-692-6546
HARVARD BUSINESS SCHOOL STUDENT ASSOCIATION INC
HBSP
Soldiers Fld, Boston, MA 02163
Tel (617) 495-6000 *Founded/Ownrshp* 1972
Sales 116.0MM^E *EMP* 1,200
SIC 8221 University
Pr: Ifunanya Maduka
Mng Pt: James Hankins
Mng Pt: Bob Higgins
Pr: Peter Hantman
**COO:* Liz Kolshak
**CFO:* Omar Muakkassa
CFO: Brenda Newkirk
Treas: Mark Young
Bd of Dir: Paul Marshall
Chf Mktg O: Brian S Kenny
VP: Sanjay Banker
VP: Shari Eberts
VP: Allen Fullerton
VP: Mike Ghaffary
VP: Barry Rudolph
VP: Nan Zheng
Exec: Renee Canning
Exec: Ellen Mahoney
Assoc Dir: Ann Carey
Assoc Dir: Eileen Chang
Assoc Dir: Maria Curcio

D-U-N-S 19-142-7277 EXP
■ **HARVARD DRUG GROUP L L C**
MAJOR PHARMACEUTICALS
(*Suby of* CARDINAL HEALTH INC) ★
17177 N Laurel Park Dr # 233, Livonia, MI 48152-3951
Tel (734) 525-8700 *Founded/Ownrshp* 2015
Sales 228.2MM^E *EMP* 450
SIC 5122 5047 8734 Pharmaceuticals; Medical & hospital equipment; Testing laboratories
CEO: Kurt Hilzinger
**Pr:* David Presper
**COO:* Doug Bowman
**CFO:* Steve Bencetic
CFO: Paul Meyers
Treas: Karen Boik
Ofcr: David Woloviec
**Sr VP:* Larry Kramer
**Sr VP:* Greg Lake
VP: Kerry Porter
VP: Scott Weaver

D-U-N-S 07-329-0728
HARVARD MAINTENANCE INC
2 S Biscayne Blvd # 3650, Miami, FL 33131-1806
Tel (305) 351-7300 *Founded/Ownrshp* 1977
Sales 247.5MM^E *EMP* 4,300
SIC 7349 Building maintenance services
Pr: Stanley K Doobin
**CFO:* Joanne C Plemenos
**Bd of Dir:* Nathalie Doobin
VP: Keith Prewitt

D-U-N-S 05-190-9448
HARVARD MANAGEMENT CO INC
(*Suby of* HARVARD UNIVERSITY) ★
600 Atlantic Ave Ste 15, Boston, MA 02210-2203
Tel (617) 720-6526 *Founded/Ownrshp* 1974
Sales 177.2MM *EMP* 179
Accts Pricewaterhousecoopers Llp Bo
SIC 8741 6722 Financial management for business; Management investment, open-end
**Pr:* Stephen Blyth
**COO:* Robert A Ettl
CFO: Kevin Shannon
Ofcr: Molly Lanzarotta
Ofcr: Sharon Wilke
Sr VP: Alec Polnarev
VP: Deborah M Baker
VP: Mary Dussault
Mng Dir: Manny Correia
Mng Dir: Robert Fletcher
Mng Dir: Kathryn I Murtagh

D-U-N-S 78-132-8513
HARVARD MEDICAL FACULTY PHYSICIANS AT BETH ISRAEL DEACONESS MEDICAL CENTER INC
HMFP
(*Suby of* BIDMC) ★
375 Longwood Ave Ste 3, Boston, MA 02215-5395
Tel (617) 632-9755 *Founded/Ownrshp* 1998
Sales 460.4MM *EMP* 800
Accts Lb Deloitte Tax Llp Jericho
SIC 8621 Medical field-related associations
CEO: Stuart A Rosenberg
**VP:* Edward L Grab

D-U-N-S 07-172-1088
HARVARD PILGRIM HEALTH CARE INC
93 Worcester St, Wellesley, MA 02481-3609
Tel (781) 263-6000 *Founded/Ownrshp* 1968
Sales NA *EMP* 1,300
SIC 6324 Health maintenance organization (HMO), insurance only
CEO: Eric H Schultz
**COO:* Roberta Herman
CFO: James W Ducharme
CFO: Charles Goheen
Treas: Steven Flood
Ofcr: Michael Comerford
**Ofcr:* Jack Lane
**Ofcr:* Laura Peabody
Sr VP: Vincent Capozzi
Sr VP: Geoffrey J Coffman
Sr VP: William J Graham
Sr VP: Pranav Mehta
Sr VP: Beth Roberts
Sr VP: Michael Sherman
VP: Michelle Clayman
VP: Vicki Coates
VP: Brenda Cole
VP: Robert Forrester
VP: Mary E Gibbs
VP: Kate McEvoy-Zdonczyk
VP: Anne Metzger

D-U-N-S 01-929-8389
HARVARD STUDENT AGENCIES INC
67 Mount Auburn St, Cambridge, MA 02138-4961
Tel (617) 495-3030 *Founded/Ownrshp* 1957
Sales 1.7MM *EMP* 1,000
SIC 7361 Employment agencies
Mng Pt: Michael Cronin
VP: Joe Molimock
Assoc Dir: Govind Bindra
Mng Dir: Jessica Li
Dir IT: Robert Bedetti
Dir IT: Calvin Tonini
Dir IT: Lukas Toth
IT Man: Brian Joseph
Opers Mgr: Jullian Duran
Mktg Mgr: Lorraine Facella
Sales Asso: Rachel Chanen

HARVARD UNIVERSITY
See PRESIDENT AND FELLOWS OF HARVARD COLLEGE

HARVARD UNIVERSITY
See HARVARD BUSINESS SCHOOL PUBLISHING CORP

HARVEST FOOD DISTRIBUTORS
See HARVEST MEAT CO INC

D-U-N-S 07-947-7130
HARVEST HILL BEVERAGE CO
1 High Ridge Park Fl 2, Stamford, CT 06905-1322
Tel (203) 914-1620 *Founded/Ownrshp* 2014
Sales 376.2MM^E *EMP* 565^E
SIC 5149 Groceries & related products
Pr: Salvatore Deprima
**CFO:* James Sheppard
**Chf Mktg O:* Ilene Bergenfeld
Sr VP: David Champlin
Sr VP: Richard Hubli

D-U-N-S 00-798-6821
HARVEST LAND CO-OP INC
1435 Nw 5th St, Richmond, IN 47374-1841
Tel (765) 962-1527 *Founded/Ownrshp* 1927
Sales 357.3MM^E *EMP* 200
Accts Blue & Co Llc Seymour In
SIC 5191 5153 Fertilizers & agricultural chemicals; Feed; Seeds: field, garden & flower; Grain elevators
Pr: Marlin Larson
**Ch:* Myron Moyer
**Treas:* Lloyd Lee

D-U-N-S 02-296-3755
HARVEST LAND COOPERATIVE
AG QUEST
711 Front St W, Morgan, MN 56266-1452
Tel (507) 249-3196 *Founded/Ownrshp* 1904
Sales 225.8MM *EMP* 150
Accts Carlson Highland & Co Llp N
SIC 5153 5191 0253 Grains; Feed; Seeds: field, garden & flower; Chemicals, agricultural; Turkeys & turkey eggs
CEO: Dave Stock
**Treas:* Tim Sullivan
**Genl Mgr:* Dennis Schreier

D-U-N-S 05-490-1912
HARVEST MANAGEMENT SUB LLC
HOLIDAY RETIREMENT
5885 Meadows Rd Ste 500, Lake Oswego, OR 97035-8646
Tel (503) 370-7070 *Founded/Ownrshp* 2007
Sales 399.0MM^E *EMP* 13,000
SIC 8361 Geriatric residential care
CEO: Edward F Lange Jr
**Pr:* Kai Hsiao
**COO:* Harvey Brownlee
**CFO:* Scott Shanaberger
**Ex VP:* Shamim Wu

D-U-N-S 87-836-0049 IMP/EXP
HARVEST MEAT CO INC
HARVEST FOOD DISTRIBUTORS
(*Suby of* SAND DOLLAR HOLDINGS INC) ★
1022 Bay Marina Dr # 106, National City, CA 91950-6327
Tel (619) 477-0185 *Founded/Ownrshp* 1994
Sales 255.8MM^E *EMP* 200
SIC 5147 Meats & meat products
CEO: John J Leavy
Pr: Kevin Leavy
CFO: Eric Doan
VP: Gary Conel
VP: Dennis Leavy
Prin: Dennis Kevin
Brnch Mgr: Darla Houston
Brnch Mgr: Bobby West
Genl Mgr: Scooter Blagg
Genl Mgr: Tim Gaskin
Genl Mgr: Mike Leavy

D-U-N-S 79-347-8293
HARVEST PARTNERS LP
280 Park Ave Fl 25w, New York, NY 10017-1231
Tel (212) 599-6300 *Founded/Ownrshp* 2009
Sales 1.2MMM^E *EMP* 12,924^E
SIC 6799 7349 Real estate investors, except property operators; Cleaning service, industrial or commercial
Mng Pt: Trevor Nelson
CFO: Debra R Kravetz
Mng Dir: Jay Wilkins

D-U-N-S 82-969-9292
HARVEST POWER INC
200 5th Ave Fl 4b, Waltham, MA 02451-8758
Tel (781) 314-9500 *Founded/Ownrshp* 2008
Sales 216.9MM^E *EMP* 350
SIC 4953 Recycling, waste materials
CEO: Christian G Kasper
Ch Bd: Paul Sellew
COO: Gary S Aguinaga
CFO: Brian Sheehan
Sr VP: Erich Bonner
Sr VP: John Eustermann
Sr VP: Jeff Knapp
Sr VP: Brian Kura
Sr VP: Steve Liffers
Sr VP: Sam Monaco
VP: Wayne Davis

VP: Thomas Kraemer
VP: Matt Mitchell
Board of Directors: Joanna Rees, Bob Simpson, Mark Weidman

D-U-N-S 07-541-5971
HARVEST SPORTING GROUP INC
SPORTSMAN'S SUPPLY
2219 Hitzert Ct, Fenton, MO 63026-2562
Tel (314) 378-8905 *Founded/Ownrshp* 2001
Sales 112.6MM^E *EMP* 60
SIC 5091 Sporting & recreation goods
Pr: Tom Siegmund
* *COO:* Eugene Horwitz
IT Man: Brad Bishop
IT Man: Eric Kauss

D-U-N-S 16-704-6432
HARVESTERS - COMMUNITY FOOD NETWORK
3801 Topping Ave, Kansas City, MO 64129-1744
Tel (816) 231-3173 *Founded/Ownrshp* 1979
Sales 85.0MM^E *EMP* 55
Accts Cbiz Mhm Llc Leawood Ks
SIC 8322 Individual & family services
Ch: Dan Weaver
* *CEO:* Karen T Haren
Dir Soc: Libby Coulter
* *Prin:* Valerie Nicholson-Watson
Genl Mgr: Steve Davis
Genl Mgr: Robin Potts
Opers Mgr: Jeff Gartin

D-U-N-S 08-722-0893
HARVEY & MADDING INC (CA)
DUBLIN HONDA
6300 Dublin Blvd, Dublin, CA 94568-7657
Tel (925) 828-9030 *Founded/Ownrshp* 1977
Sales 92.5MM *EMP* 82
SIC 5511 7538 5015 5013 Automobiles, new & used; General automotive repair shops; Motor vehicle parts, used; Motor vehicle supplies & new parts
CEO: Kenneth C Harvey
* *VP:* Brenda S Harvey
Sls Mgr: Steve Bado
Sls Mgr: Sam Samaha
Sales Asso: Wais Azizi
Sales Asso: Shah Delery
Sales Asso: Gerry Jones
Sales Asso: Marcos Varela

HARVEY BUILDING PRODUCTS
See HARVEY INDUSTRIES INC

HARVEY EXPORT
See EL HARVEY & SONS INC

D-U-N-S 16-663-8569
HARVEY FERTILIZER AND GAS CO
HARVEY GIN & COTTON
303 Bohannon Rd, Kinston, NC 28501-7434
Tel (252) 526-4150 *Founded/Ownrshp* 1871
Sales 384.9MM^E *EMP* 244
SIC 5191 2873 2875 Farm supplies; Chemicals, agricultural; Fertilizer & fertilizer materials; Nitrogenous fertilizers; Fertilizers, mixing only
Pr: Herbert Rouse
* *CFO:* Frankie Hill
* *Sec:* Llyod E Cooper
Ex VP: Gary Floyd
VP: Paul Bridgers
Sfty Dirs: Linda Huggins

HARVEY GIN & COTTON
See HARVEY FERTILIZER AND GAS CO

D-U-N-S 11-816-0597 IMP/EXP
■ **HARVEY HUBBELL CARIBE INC**
HUBELL CARIBE LIMITED
(*Suby of* HUBBELL INC) ★
Km 17 Hm 3 Rr 686, Vega Baja, PR 00693
Tel (787) 855-1075 *Founded/Ownrshp* 1984
Sales 142.9MM^E *EMP* 900
SIC 3643 Connectors & terminals for electrical devices; Plugs, electric
Pr: George Ruiz
Sfty Dirs: Mirian Candelaria

D-U-N-S 00-141-3764 IMP
HARVEY INDUSTRIES INC (MA)
HARVEY BUILDING PRODUCTS
1400 Main St Fl 3, Waltham, MA 02451-1689
Tel (781) 899-3500 *Founded/Ownrshp* 1961
Sales 1.0MMM^E *EMP* 1,610
SIC 5031 5033 3442 2431 Windows; Roofing, asphalt & sheet metal; Storm doors or windows, metal; Windows, wood
CEO: Thomas Bigony
* *Pr:* James M Barreira
* *CFO:* Scott Lassonde
* *Ch:* Erik Jarnryd
* *Sr VP:* Thomas Russell
* *Sr VP:* Vincent Walsh
VP: Randy Cail
VP: Jeffrey Ribeiro
VP: Tom Russell
Brnch Mgr: Dave Jackubowski
IT Man: Chris Zybert

D-U-N-S 80-260-6330 IMP
HARVEY INDUSTRIES LLC
3837 Mill St, Wabash, IN 46992-7838
Tel (260) 563-8371 *Founded/Ownrshp* 2007
Sales 105.3MM^E *EMP* 350
SIC 3463 3365

D-U-N-S 06-669-1130
HARVEY MUDD COLLEGE
HMC BUSINESS AFFAIRS DEPT
301 Platt Blvd, Claremont, CA 91711-5901
Tel (909) 621-8000 *Founded/Ownrshp* 1955
Sales 98.3MM *EMP* 250^E
Accts Moss Adams Llp Stockton Ca
SIC 8221 College, except junior
Pr: Maria Klawe
Pr: Timothy Hussey
Pr: Matt Leroux
Pr: Scott Martin
CFO: Robin Aspinall
* *CFO:* Andrew Dorantes
VP: Dan Macaluso
VP: Francis E Su
Off Mgr: Elizabeth Saelzler
Sys Mgr: Joe Ishikura
Mktg Dir: Neel Shah

HARVEYS CASINO HOTEL
See HARVEYS CASINO RESORTS

D-U-N-S 00-923-8965
■ **HARVEYS CASINO RESORTS**
HARVEYS CASINO HOTEL
(*Suby of* HARRAHS) ★
Hwy 50 & Stateline Ave, Stateline, NV 89449
Tel (775) 588-2411 *Founded/Ownrshp* 2001
Sales 87.1MM^E *EMP* 4,090^E
SIC 7011 Casino hotel
Ch: Phillip Satre
* *CEO:* Gary Loveman
* *CFO:* Charles Atwood
IT Man: Sam Khalifa

D-U-N-S 94-771-0141
■ **HARVEYS IOWA MANAGEMENT CO INC**
HARRAHS CNCIL BLUFFS CASINO HT
(*Suby of* HARVEYS CASINO HOTEL) ★
1 Harrahs Blvd, Council Bluffs, IA 51501-5680
Tel (712) 329-6000 *Founded/Ownrshp* 1996
Sales 32.4MM^E *EMP* 1,306
SIC 7011 Casino hotel
Pr: Gary Loveman
* *CEO:* Gaye Gullo
* *Sr VP:* Peter J Weien

HARVEY'S SUPERMARKETS
See JH HARVEY CO LLC

HARVEY'S TIRE EXCHANGE
See A & E TIRE INC

D-U-N-S 05-724-7793 IMP/EXP
HARWICK STANDARD DISTRIBUTION CORP
60 S Seiberling St, Akron, OH 44305-4217
Tel (330) 798-9300 *Founded/Ownrshp* 1971
Sales 88.9MM^E *EMP* 70
SIC 5169 Chemicals, industrial & heavy
CEO: Ernie Pouttu
* *Pr:* Jeffrey J Buda
* *CFO:* Jim Houston
* *Sr VP:* Dan Davis
VP: D R Hardesty
* *VP:* David Sultz
Creative D: Bryan Shields
* *Prin:* Richard A Chenoweth
* *Prin:* Brian Johnson
* *Prin:* Bill Knezevich
* *Prin:* Daniel G Laporte

HARWOOD, EMMA L MD
See EUGENIA CHANG MD

HASBRO CHILDREN'S HOSPITAL
See RHODE ISLAND HOSPITAL

D-U-N-S 00-120-0443 IMP/EXP
▲ **HASBRO INC**
1027 Newport Ave, Pawtucket, RI 02861-2500
Tel (401) 431-8697 *Founded/Ownrshp* 1923
Sales 4.4MMM *EMP* 5,000
Accts Kpmg Llp Providence Rhode Is
Tkr Sym HAS *Exch* NGS
SIC 3944 3942 3069 Games, toys & children's vehicles; Board games, children's & adults'; Board games, puzzles & models, except electronic; Electronic games & toys; Stuffed toys, including animals; Dolls, except stuffed toy animals; Teething rings, rubber; Baby pacifiers, rubber
Ch Bd: Brian D Goldner
CFO: Deborah M Thomas
Treas: Martin R Trueb
Chf Cred: Wiebe Tinga
Ofcr: Paul Alexander
Ofcr: Christine Meehan
Ex VP: Duncan J Billing
Ex VP: Julie Duffy
VP: Kathrin Belliveau
VP: Bob Brown
VP: Michael Green
VP: Kevin Healy
VP: Tim Hinckley
VP: David Holmes
VP: Bijay Kumar
VP: Ramesh Murthy
VP: Ben Rathbone
VP: Brian Wilk
Exec: Rafael Cancino
Board of Directors: Edward M Philip, Basil L Anderson, Richard S Stoddart, Alan R Batkin, Mary Beth West, Kenneth A Bronfin, Linda K Zecher, Michael R Burns, Hope Cochran, Crispin Davis, Lisa Gersh, Alan G Hassenfeld, Tracy A Leinbach

D-U-N-S 60-677-5153
■ **HASBRO INTERNATIONAL INC**
(*Suby of* HASBRO INC) ★
1027 Newport Ave, Pawtucket, RI 02861-2500
Tel (401) 431-8697 *Founded/Ownrshp* 1974
Sales 340.7MM^E *EMP* 4,180
SIC 3944 Games, toys & children's vehicles
Pr: Brian Coldner
CFO: David D Hargreaves
Sr VP: Wayne S Charness
Sr VP: Jackie Daya
Sr VP: Barry Nagler
VP: Paul J Alexander
VP: Kurt R Benson
VP: Nelson R Chaffee Corp
VP: Joanne Haworth
VP: Mark Monday
* *VP:* Judis A Smith
VP: Sibley Tarrant

D-U-N-S 84-808-1951
■ **HASBRO MANAGERIAL SERVICES INC**
(*Suby of* HASBRO INC) ★
1027 Newport Ave, Pawtucket, RI 02861-2500
Tel (401) 431-8697 *Founded/Ownrshp* 1923
Sales 97.2MM^E *EMP* 5,000
SIC 8741 Management services
VP: Barry Nagler

HASCO
See HARTWELL CORP

D-U-N-S 01-762-9549
HASCO MEDICAL INC
(*Suby of* MOBILITYWORKS) ★
810 Moe Dr, Akron, OH 44310-2517
Tel (214) 302-0930 *Founded/Ownrshp* 2015
Sales 91.0MM *EMP* 262^E
SIC 5999 8082 Wheelchair lifts; Home health care services
Pr: William M Koeblitz
COO: Alfredo Olivierre III
CFO: Gerhard T Schmidt
VP: Mike Dumais

D-U-N-S 10-849-1325
HASELDEN CONSTRUCTION LLC
6950 S Potomac St Ste 100, Centennial, CO 80112-4039
Tel (303) 751-1478 *Founded/Ownrshp* 1983
Sales 174.7MM^E *EMP* 279^E
SIC 1542 Commercial & office building, new construction; Hospital construction; School building construction
CEO: Ed J Haselden
* *Pr:* Byron Haselden
* *COO:* Mike Haselden
* *CFO:* Troy Schroeder
* *Ex VP:* Dave Lueders
* *VP:* Greg Conger
* *VP:* James Michael Haselden
Board of Directors: Byron Haselden

D-U-N-S 18-056-9485 IMP
HASKEL INTERNATIONAL LLC
(*Suby of* ACCUDYNE INDUSTRIES LLC) ★
100 E Graham Pl, Burbank, CA 91502-2076
Tel (818) 843-4000 *Founded/Ownrshp* 2013
Sales 102.6MM^E *EMP* 335
SIC 3561 3594 5084 5085 3699 Pumps & pumping equipment; Fluid power pumps; Hydraulic systems equipment & supplies; Hose, belting & packing; Valves, pistons & fittings; Electrical equipment & supplies
CEO: Chris Krieps
CTO: Isabelle Jolicoeur
S&M/VP: Peter Duffy

D-U-N-S 10-695-6824 EXP
HASKELL CO
111 Riverside Ave, Jacksonville, FL 32202-4950
Tel (904) 791-4500 *Founded/Ownrshp* 1999
Sales 981.0MM^E *EMP* 1,110
SIC 1541 1542 1522 1623 8712 3272

D-U-N-S 03-238-9942
HASKELL CO INC
JAX UTILITIES & WATERPROOFING
(*Suby of* HASKELL CO) ★
111 Riverside Ave, Jacksonville, FL 32202-4950
Tel (904) 791-4500 *Founded/Ownrshp* 1965
Sales 135.2MM^E *EMP* 550
SIC 1541 1542 1522 1623 8712 3272 Industrial buildings, new construction; Commercial & office building, new construction; Multi-family dwelling construction; Underground utilities contractor; Sewer line construction; Architectural engineering; Prestressed concrete products
CEO: Preston H Haskell
Pr: Steven T Halverson
CFO: Hans G Tanzler
Sr VP: John Cobb
* *Sr VP:* Greg Ferrell
Sr VP: James A Gray
Sr VP: John H Patten
Sr VP: Robert Soulby
* *Sr VP:* C Edward Vandergriff
Sys/Mgr: Clark Tucker

D-U-N-S 00-794-2147
HASKELL CORP (WA)
1001 Meador Ave, Bellingham, WA 98229-5808
Tel (360) 734-1200 *Founded/Ownrshp* 1890
Sales 161.6MM^E *EMP* 300
SIC 1542 Nonresidential construction
Pr: Fred Haskell
* *CFO:* Jeff Jenkins
* *VP:* Terrance Corrigan

D-U-N-S 12-259-2439
HASKELL LEMON CONSTRUCTION CO
3800 Sw 10th St, Oklahoma City, OK 73108-2047
Tel (405) 947-6069 *Founded/Ownrshp* 1985
Sales 85.1MM^E *EMP* 150
SIC 5032 1611 3272 2951 Paving materials; Highway & street paving contractor; Concrete products; Asphalt paving mixtures & blocks
Pr: Kent Wert
* *Sec:* Larry Lemon
* *VP:* Bob Lemon
Plnt Mgr: Brian Wolf

D-U-N-S 00-906-3512
■ **HASKINS STEEL CO INC**
(*Suby of* AMERICAN METALS CORP) ★
3613 E Main Ave, Spokane, WA 99202-4732
Tel (509) 252-9724 *Founded/Ownrshp* 2013
Sales 99.1MM^E *EMP* 95
SIC 5051 Steel
Pr: Sterling Haskins
Treas: Scott A Hskins
* *Sec:* Scott A Haskins
* *VP:* Craig Diaz
VP: Caron Munsen
Genl Mgr: David McCarrell
Sfty Mgr: Dave Kruger
Sls Mgr: Rick Pickel
Sls Mgr: Greg Whitman
Sales Asso: Dave Wright

D-U-N-S 02-703-1814
HASSLOCHER ENTERPRISES INC
FRONTIER MEAT & SUPPLY
8520 Crownhill Blvd, San Antonio, TX 78209-1119
Tel (210) 828-1493 *Founded/Ownrshp* 1946
Sales 49.5MM^E *EMP* 1,300
SIC 5812 5142 6552 Coffee shop; Meat, frozen: packaged; Subdividers & developers
Ch: Germano Hasslocher
* *Ch Bd:* Veva Hasslocher
* *Pr:* Robert C Hasslocher
* *VP:* James C Hasslocher
VP: Susan Hasslocher

HASTINGS BOOKS, MUSIC & VIDEO
See HASTINGS ENTERTAINMENT INC

D-U-N-S 04-813-3417 IMP/EXP
HASTINGS ENTERTAINMENT INC
HASTINGS BOOKS, MUSIC & VIDEO
(*Suby of* DRAW ANOTHER CIRCLE LLC) ★
3601 Plains Blvd, Amarillo, TX 79102-1098
Tel (806) 351-2300 *Founded/Ownrshp* 2014
Sales 1.1MMM^E *EMP* 5,487^E
SIC 5735 5942 7841 Video discs & tapes, prerecorded; Records, audio discs & tapes; Book stores; Video disk/tape rental to the general public
Pr: Alan Van Ongevalle
* *CEO:* Joel Weinshanker
* *CFO:* Dan Crow
* *VP:* Philip McConnell

D-U-N-S 61-163-3363
HASTINGS HEALTH SYSTEMS INC
241 North Rd, Poughkeepsie, NY 12601-1154
Tel (845) 471-2000 *Founded/Ownrshp* 1987
Sales 35.2MM^E *EMP* 1,950
SIC 8741 8062 Hospital management; General medical & surgical hospitals
Pr: Robert Savage
* *Pr:* Sister M Ann Elizabeth
* *CFO:* Marianne Muise
* *CFO:* Robert Patrick
* *Ex VP:* Donald Murphy

D-U-N-S 00-695-9688
HASTINGS MUTUAL INSURANCE CO (MI)
404 E Woodlawn Ave, Hastings, MI 49058-1091
Tel (800) 442-8277 *Founded/Ownrshp* 1885
Sales NA *EMP* 458
SIC 6411 Insurance agents & brokers
Prin: Joseph J Babiak Jr
CFO: Michael T Kinnary
Ofcr: Jane Hapway
VP: Renee Beauford
VP: Timothy Bremer
VP: Kristee Buff
VP: Bill Gregor
VP: William Gregor Jr
VP: Keith Jandahl
VP: Carl Lickley
* *VP:* Michael W Puerner
Board of Directors: John L Ward, Joseph J Babiak Jr, Douglas J Finn, Christopher J Fluke, Kellie M Haines, Frederic L Halbert, Mark A Kolanowski, Janice A Oshinski, Bruce J Osterink, James R Toburen

HASTINGS YOUTH ACADEMY
See G4S YOUTH SERVICES LLC

D-U-N-S 79-350-9241 IMP
HAT BRANDS HOLDING CORP
601 Marion Dr, Garland, TX 75042-7930
Tel (972) 494-7133 *Founded/Ownrshp* 1992
Sales 135.5MM^E *EMP* 1,700
SIC 2353 3914 3144 3143 Caps: cloth, straw & felt; Hats: cloth, straw & felt; Silversmithing; Women's footwear, except athletic; Men's footwear, except athletic
Pr: John R Tillotson
* *Ch Bd:* John R Muse
CFO: Thomas A Hough

D-U-N-S 07-150-1977
HAT LIMITED PARTNERSHIP
MANPOWER
63 Keystone Ave Ste 202, Reno, NV 89503-5570
Tel (775) 328-6020 *Founded/Ownrshp* 1979
Sales 35.9MM^E *EMP* 1,500
Accts Cupit Milligan Ogden & Willi
SIC 7363 Manpower pools
Pt: Gary Harrigan
Pt: Harrigan Enterprises
CFO: Aaron Hill
Admn Mgr: Kim Hill
Genl Mgr: Mike Harrigan
Genl Mgr: Pat Harrigan

D-U-N-S 04-037-9301
HATCH REALTY GROUP INC
1611 Lodi Ave, San Mateo, CA 94401-3644
Tel (650) 438-2444 *Founded/Ownrshp* 2013
Sales 300.0MM *EMP* 5
SIC 6531 Real estate brokers & agents
Pr: Monica Sagullo
* *Prin:* Benedict Paras

D-U-N-S 00-533-8603 EXP
HATCH STAMPING CO LLC
(*Suby of* PROPHET EQUITY LP) ★
635 E Industrial Dr, Chelsea, MI 48118-1599
Tel (734) 475-8628 *Founded/Ownrshp* 1965
Sales 129.0MM *EMP* 900
SIC 3465 3544 Automotive stampings; Special dies & tools
Pr: Daniel Craig
COO: Steve Emmert
Ex VP: Christopher A Parrott
VP: Todd Fyall
Dir Bus: Chris Craig
Prgrm Mgr: Jason Burton
CIO: Steve Rauscher
Dir IT: Steve Rocher
Opers Mgr: Valerie Houle
Plnt Mgr: Rick Botham
Plnt Mgr: Walter Wyniemko

D-U-N-S 04-461-2361
HATCHBEAUTY PRODUCTS LLC
10951 W Pico Blvd Ste 300, Los Angeles, CA 90064-2182
Tel (310) 396-7070 *Founded/Ownrshp* 2010
Sales 120.0MM^E *EMP* 84
SIC 5122 Cosmetics, perfumes & hair products
Mng Pt: Ben Bennett
**Pt:* Benjamin Bennett
**Mng Pt:* Tracy Holland
Off Mgr: Erika Beckles

D-U-N-S 00-610-6884 IMP
HATCO CORP (WI)
635 S 28th St, Milwaukee, WI 53215-1298
Tel (414) 671-6350 *Founded/Ownrshp* 1950
Sales 89.7MM^E *EMP* 360
SIC 3589 Commercial cooking & foodwarming equipment; Food warming equipment, commercial
Pr: David C Rolston
**VP:* Randall M Baumgart
**VP:* Joseph Hatchell
**VP:* Michael L Whiteley

D-U-N-S 02-660-1583
HATFIELD AND CO INC
JOHNSON CONTRLS AUTHORIZED DLR
2475 Discovery Blvd, Rockwall, TX 75032-6200
Tel (972) 288-7625 *Founded/Ownrshp* 1959
Sales 130.4MM *EMP* 102
Accts Lloyd Hughes Cpa Dallas Tex
SIC 5084 3677 5074 Industrial machinery & equipment; Filtration devices, electronic; Plumbing & heating valves
CEO: George Hatfield
**Pr:* Greg Hatfield
**CFO:* George Boles
VP: Linda Jennings
Brnch Mgr: Steve Schroder
Off Mgr: John Acton
Off Mgr: Matt Keenan
Off Mgr: Brad Lindeman
Off Mgr: Jane Warner
CIO: Harvey Sparhawk
Dir IT: Linda True

D-U-N-S 96-195-3056
HATHAWAY DINWIDDIE CONSTRUCTION CO
(*Suby of* HATHAWAY DINWIDDIE CONSTRUCTION GROUP) ★
275 Battery St Ste 300, San Francisco, CA 94111-3378
Tel (415) 986-2718 *Founded/Ownrshp* 1996
Sales 158.5MM^E *EMP* 400
SIC 1542 Commercial & office building, new construction; Commercial & office buildings, renovation & repair
CEO: Greg Cosko
**Pr:* Paul Gregory Cosko
**Ex VP:* Stephen W McCoid
**Sr VP:* Gordon D Smith
VP: Greg Burg
**VP:* Ed Conlon
Exec: Diane Cooper
CIO: Jason Warmby
Mktg Dir: Gordon Smith
Sls Dir: Scott McClure
Snr PM: Michael Niemi

D-U-N-S 96-259-9221
HATHAWAY DINWIDDIE CONSTRUCTION GROUP
275 Battery St Ste 300, San Francisco, CA 94111-3378
Tel (415) 986-2718 *Founded/Ownrshp* 1996
Sales 194.8MM^E *EMP* 400
SIC 1542 Commercial & office building contractors
CEO: Greg Cosko
**CFO:* David Miller
**Sr VP:* Stephen E Smith
**VP:* Stephen W McCoid

D-U-N-S 80-273-6251
HATTERAS FINANCIAL CORP
751 W 4th St Ste 400, Winston Salem, NC 27101-2795
Tel (336) 760-9347 *Founded/Ownrshp* 2007
Sales 379.3MM *EMP* 30^E
SIC 6798

D-U-N-S 13-166-2371
HATTERAS PRESS INC
56 Park Rd, Tinton Falls, NJ 07724-9715
Tel (732) 935-9800 *Founded/Ownrshp* 1983
Sales 88.9MM^E *EMP* 260
SIC 2752 2796 Commercial printing, lithographic; Platemaking services
Owner: Charles F Duerr
Pr: Joe Allen
**Pr:* Bill Duerr
Pr: Scott Duerr
**VP:* Tom Ayala
**VP:* Nicole Nichols
**VP:* Barbara Pistilli
VP: Phil Roura
Genl Mgr: Richard Lanza
CIO: Brent McNally
VP Opers: Sean Scanlon

D-U-N-S 09-757-1140 IMP/EXP
HATTERAS YACHTS INC
110 N Glenburnie Rd, New Bern, NC 28560-2703
Tel (252) 633-3101 *Founded/Ownrshp* 2013
Sales NA *EMP* 1,320
SIC 3732

D-U-N-S 07-790-1908
HATTIESBURG CLINIC PROFESSIONAL ASSOCIATION
415 S 28th Ave 200, Hattiesburg, MS 39401-7283
Tel (601) 264-6000 *Founded/Ownrshp* 1998
Sales 176.0MM^E *EMP* 1,693
SIC 8011 Clinic, operated by physicians
CEO: Tommy G Thornton
**Pr:* John M Fitzpatrick
**CFO:* Alex Agnew
**Sec:* Petra Schneider-Redden
**VP:* Steven W Stogner MD
Off Mgr: Jeananne Potin

Orthpdst: Brian Humpherys
Doctor: Bryan N Batso

D-U-N-S 00-698-5121
HATZEL & BUEHLER INC
(*Suby of* CONSTRUCTION MANAGEMENT SERVICES INC) ★
3600 Silverside Rd Ste A, Wilmington, DE 19810-5116
Tel (302) 478-4200 *Founded/Ownrshp* 1884
Sales 223.0MM *EMP* 700
Accts Horty & Horty Pa Wilmingto
SIC 1731 General electrical contractor
Pr: William A Goeller
**Treas:* Gerard J Herr
**VP:* Michael C Goeller
**VP Admn:* Regina Camponelli
Dir IT: Lorraine Stevens

D-U-N-S 06-596-5907
HAUPPAUGE UNION FREE SCHOOL DISTRICT
495 Hoffman Ln Ste 1, Hauppauge, NY 11788-3102
Tel (631) 265-3630 *Founded/Ownrshp* 1943
Sales 47.0MM^E *EMP* 1,151
Accts Rs Abrams & Co Llp Ronkonk
SIC 8211 Public elementary & secondary schools
Ofcr: Stephen Phelan
Dir Sec: Ed Spear
IT Man: Lisa Feliciano

D-U-N-S 05-026-8234 IMP
HAVAS HEALTH INC (NY)
HEALTH4BRANDS CATAPULT
(*Suby of* HAVAS NORTH AMERICA INC) ★
200 Madison Ave, New York, NY 10016-3903
Tel (212) 532-1000 *Founded/Ownrshp* 1980
Sales 84.1MM^E *EMP* 250
SIC 7311 Advertising agencies
**Ofcr:* Brian Robinson
Assoc VP: Stephanie Clarke
Ex VP: Noel Castro
Ex VP: Barry Goldberg
Sr VP: Meredith L Bernstein
Sr VP: Jack Englert
Sr VP: Barbara Patchefsky
Sr VP: Jess Seilheimer
Sr VP: Jarrod Walpert
VP: Crystal Clark
VP: David Groff
VP: Kellen Harris
VP: Terri Passick
VP: Kim Rostovskis
Exec: Suren Rastogi

D-U-N-S 78-206-0057
HAVAS NORTH AMERICA INC
(*Suby of* HAVAS)
200 Hudson St, New York, NY 10013-1807
Tel (212) 886-2000 *Founded/Ownrshp* 2001
Sales 421.6MM^E *EMP* 10,500
SIC 7311 5963 Advertising agencies; Direct sales, telemarketing
CEO: Yannick Bollore
Pr: Andrew Benett
Sr Cor Off: Cathy Pitegoff
**Ofcr:* Darren Moran
Exec: John REA
Creative D: Andrew Jeske
Creative D: Jon Vall
Mng Dir: Matthew Blasco
Prgrm Mgr: Michael Derosa
VP Opers: John Frantz
Art Dir: Reto Oetterli

HAVASU REGIONAL MEDICAL CENTER
See PHC-LAKE HAVASU INC

D-U-N-S 08-938-2873 IMP
HAVCO WOOD PRODUCTS LLC
3200 E Outer Rd, Scott City, MO 63780-9794
Tel (573) 334-0611 *Founded/Ownrshp* 2012
Sales 92.6MM^E *EMP* 460
SIC 2426 Flooring, hardwood; Furniture dimension stock, hardwood
VP: Chuck Bradford
Sfty Dirs: James McGhee
Sfty Dirs: Dean Walker
VP Sls: John Carr

D-U-N-S 78-725-1532
HAVEN BEHAVIORAL HEALTHCARE INC
3102 West End Ave # 1000, Nashville, TN 37203-1324
Tel (615) 393-8800 *Founded/Ownrshp* 2006
Sales 97.5MM^E *EMP* 1,000^E
SIC 8011 Psychiatrist
CEO: Michael Lindley
**Pr:* Vernon Westrich
**COO:* Al Smith
**CFO:* Rodney Cawood
**CFO:* Ken Miles
**Ofcr:* Page Barnes
Sr VP: Frank Fritsch
**Sr VP:* Kirk McConnell
**VP:* Brian Beutin
VP: Melissa Duffy
VP: Michelle Spurlock
Dir Soc: Doree Baker

D-U-N-S 03-028-9755
HAVERFORD TOWNSHIP SCHOOL DISTRICT
50 E Eagle Rd, Havertown, PA 19083-1532
Tel (610) 853-5900 *Founded/Ownrshp* 1800
Sales 98.5MM *EMP* 1,000
Accts Maillie Llp Oaks Pennsylvan
SIC 8211 Public elementary & secondary schools; High school, junior or senior
CIO: Ron Anderson
Psych: Ruta Clair
Psych: Colleen Pelton

D-U-N-S 07-827-0541 EXP
HAVERHILL CHEMICALS LLC
16800 Imperial Valley Dr # 499, Houston, TX 77060-3134
Tel (281) 885-8900 *Founded/Ownrshp* 2011
Sales 166.8MM^E *EMP* 178
SIC 2899 Chemical preparations
CEO: Alberto Spera
**CFO:* Elizabeth Labarbara

D-U-N-S 87-971-7882
■ **HAVERSTICK CONSULTING INC**
(*Suby of* KRATOS DEFENSE & SECURITY SOLUTIONS INC) ★
8770 Guion Rd Ste A, Indianapolis, IN 46268-3017
Tel (317) 218-1700 *Founded/Ownrshp* 1994
Sales 234.5MM^E *EMP* 1,420
SIC 7371 7373 Computer software development & applications; Systems integration services
Pr: Eric M Demarco
COO: Dave Carter
CFO: Deanna H Lund
Treas: Laura Siegal
VP: Phil Carrai
VP: David Carter
VP: Michael W Fink
VP: Bruce Rankin
VP Opers: Edward M Lake

D-U-N-S 08-189-2911
HAVERSTRAW STONY POINT CENTRAL SCHOOL DISTRICT INC
NORTH ROCKLAND CENTRAL SCHOOL
65 Chapel St, Garnerville, NY 10923-1238
Tel (845) 942-3053 *Founded/Ownrshp* 1957
Sales 214.3MM *EMP* 1,400
SIC 8211 Public elementary & secondary schools

D-U-N-S 00-692-5036 IMP/EXP
▲ **HAVERTY FURNITURE COMPANIES INC**
HAVERTYS
780 Johnson Ferry Rd, Atlanta, GA 30342-1434
Tel (404) 443-2900 *Founded/Ownrshp* 1885
Sales 804.8MM *EMP* 3,596^E
Accts Ernst & Young Llp Atlanta G
Tkr Sym HVT *Exch* NYS
SIC 5712 5722 5713 5021 Furniture stores; Bedding & bedsprings; Household appliance stores; Floor covering stores; Mattresses
Ch Bd: Clarence H Smith
CFO: Dennis L Fink
Treas: Jenny Hill Parker
Ofcr: Allan J Deniro
Ex VP: J Edward Clary
Ex VP: Richard D Gallagher
Sr VP: Kathleen Daly-Jennings
**Sr VP:* Rawson Haverty Jr
Sr VP: Janet E Taylor
VP: John L Gill
Board of Directors: John T Glover, L Phillip Humann, Frank S McGaughey III, Terence F McGuirk, Vicki R Palmer, Fred L Schuermann, Al Trujillo

HAVERTYS
See HAVERTY FURNITURE COMPANIES INC

D-U-N-S 86-726-9172
HAVI GLOBAL SOLUTIONS LLC
MCDONALD'S
(*Suby of* PERSECO CO DIV) ★
3500 Lacey Rd Ste 600, Downers Grove, IL 60515-5440
Tel (630) 493-7400 *Founded/Ownrshp* 1994
Sales 195.2MM^E *EMP* 500
SIC 8748 Business consulting
Pr: Daniel Musachia
**Ex VP:* Carol Cienkus
**Ex VP:* Michael Hickey
**Ex VP:* James Woods
Ex VP: Jim Woods
Sr VP: Jim Brady
**Sr VP:* David Ficken
Sr VP: Larry Mohr
VP: Rob Bauer
VP: Michele Canaday
VP: Bob Cappalli
VP: Maria Conroy
VP: Dennis Contino
VP: Ned Flanagan
VP: Tim Hagn
VP: Joe Luciano
VP: Kevin Patti
VP: Michael Richmond
VP: Scott Saddler
VP: Patricia Sullivan
Dir Bus: Mark Rafferty

D-U-N-S 60-896-8525 IMP/EXP
HAVI GROUP LIMITED PARTNERSHIP
PERSECO COMPANY DIV
3500 Lacey Rd Ste 600, Downers Grove, IL 60515-5440
Tel (630) 353-4200 *Founded/Ownrshp* 1988
Sales 5.5MMM^E *EMP* 1,000
SIC 5113 5142 5199 Disposable plates, cups, napkins & eating utensils; Napkins, paper; Packaged frozen goods; Advertising specialties
CEO: Russ Smyth
COO: Dan Musachia
CFO: Russell Doll
Ch: Theodore F Perlman
VP: Y S Kong

D-U-N-S 06-017-4364 IMP
HAVILAND ENTERPRISES INC
421 Ann St Nw, Grand Rapids, MI 49504-2019
Tel (616) 361-6691 *Founded/Ownrshp* 1936
Sales 174.0MM^E *EMP* 225
Accts Crowe Horwath Llp Grand Rapid
SIC 5169 Chemicals, industrial & heavy; Specialty cleaning & sanitation preparations; Salts, industrial; Swimming pool & spa chemicals
Prin: H Richard Garner
COO: Michael Marmo
**CFO:* Terrence J Schoen
**VP:* Arthur F Harre
**VP:* Michael J Marmo
Exec: Cindy Vand
CTO: Bob Mastbergen
Sls Mgr: Graham Torr

D-U-N-S 00-602-8492 IMP/EXP
HAVILAND PRODUCTS CO (MI)
(*Suby of* HAVILAND ENTERPRISES INC) ★
421 Ann St Nw, Grand Rapids, MI 49504-2075
Tel (616) 361-6691 *Founded/Ownrshp* 1934, 1979
Sales 120.0MM *EMP* 220
SIC 5169 2819 Chemicals, industrial & heavy; Industrial inorganic chemicals
Pr: E Bernard Haviland
CFO: Jerry Schoen
CFO: Thomas Simmons
VP: Michael Marmo
Dir Lab: Paul Nederveld
Ex Dir: Richard Nielsen
IT Man: Graham Torr
Opers Mgr: Brian Schoen
Mktg Dir: David O'Brien
Manager: Gregg Romero

HAVRE PUBLIC SCHOOLS
See HAVRE SCHOOL DISTRICT 16-A

D-U-N-S 10-004-3488
HAVRE SCHOOL DISTRICT 16-A
HAVRE PUBLIC SCHOOLS
425 6th St, Havre, MT 59501-4032
Tel (406) 265-4356 *Founded/Ownrshp* 1890
Sales 34.6MM^E *EMP* 1,000
SIC 8211 Public combined elementary & secondary school
IT Man: Alita Newton
Teacher Pr: Craig Mueller
HC Dir: Jeri Erickson

D-U-N-S 18-953-5107
HAWAI I PACIFIC HEALTH
HAWAII PACIFIC HEALTH
55 Merchant St Ste 2500, Honolulu, HI 96813-4306
Tel (808) 535-7350 *Founded/Ownrshp* 1986
Sales 159.2MM^E *EMP* 5,400
Accts Ernst & Young Us Llp Rosevill
SIC 8062 8011 General medical & surgical hospitals; Clinic, operated by physicians
Pr: Raymond Vara
**CFO:* David Okabe
**Chf Mktg O:* Kenneth B Robbins
Ofcr: David Fox
**Ex VP:* Bob Ching
**Ex VP:* Gail Lerch
**Ex VP:* Steve Robertson
VP: Maureen Flannery
VP: Earl Inouye
VP: Timothy Olderr
Assoc Dir: Ramona Clemente
Assoc Dir: Jessica Sphar

D-U-N-S 79-040-4255 IMP
HAWAII BUSINESS EQUIPMENT INC
(*Suby of* TOSHIBA AMERICA BUSINESS SOLUTIONS INC) ★
2 Musick, Irvine, CA 92618-1631
Tel (949) 462-6000 *Founded/Ownrshp* 2011
Sales 159.0MM^E *EMP* 2,700^E
SIC 5999 7629 5044 Business machines & equipment; Business machine repair, electric; Office equipment
CEO: Masahiro Yamada
**Pr:* Renee Gomes
**Pr:* Mark Mathews
**VP:* Lester Higa
**VP:* Leighann Iha
**VP:* Gregory Valen

D-U-N-S 07-251-9671
HAWAII DENTAL SERVICE
HDS
700 Bishop St Ste 700, Honolulu, HI 96813-4196
Tel (808) 521-1431 *Founded/Ownrshp* 1962
Sales NA *EMP* 90
SIC 6324 Dental insurance
Pr: Faye Kurren
**Treas:* Kelvin N Asahina
**VP:* Kathy Fay
**VP:* Cheryl Takitani
MIS Dir: Harlan Mattos
Mktg Mgr: Elaine Fujiwara

D-U-N-S 82-467-1218
HAWAII DEPARTMENT OF HUMAN RESOURCES DEVELOPMENT
(*Suby of* EXECUTIVE OFFICE OF STATE OF HAWAII) ★
235 S Beretania St # 1400, Honolulu, HI 96813-2406
Tel (808) 587-1100 *Founded/Ownrshp* 1959
Sales NA *EMP* 14,254
SIC 9199 General government administration;

D-U-N-S 82-467-1176
HAWAII DEPARTMENT OF HUMAN SERVICES
(*Suby of* EXECUTIVE OFFICE OF STATE OF HAWAII) ★
1390 Miller St Ste 209, Honolulu, HI 96813-2403
Tel (808) 586-4997 *Founded/Ownrshp* 1987
Sales NA *EMP* 1,800^E
Accts N & K Cpas Inc Honolulu Ha
SIC 9441 Administration of social & manpower programs;
Ofcr: Edwin Igrashi
Ofcr: Susan Kawamoto
IT Man: Ryan Shimamuro

D-U-N-S 82-467-1168
HAWAII DEPARTMENT OF PUBLIC SAFETY
(*Suby of* EXECUTIVE OFFICE OF STATE OF HAWAII) ★
919 Ala Moana Blvd # 407, Honolulu, HI 96814-4920
Tel (808) 587-1288 *Founded/Ownrshp* 1990
Sales NA *EMP* 2,100
SIC 9221 9229 State police; ; Public order & safety statistics centers;
Ofcr: Clifford Asato

D-U-N-S 82-467-1465
HAWAII DEPARTMENT OF TRANSPORTATION
EXECUTIVE OFFICE OF THE
(*Suby of* EXECUTIVE OFFICE OF STATE OF HAWAII) ★
869 Punchbowl St Rm 509, Honolulu, HI 96813-5003
Tel (808) 587-1830 *Founded/Ownrshp* 1959
Sales NA *EMP* 2,215^E
Accts Kobayashi Kanetoku Doi Lum

SIC 9621 Regulation, administration of transportation;

D-U-N-S 05-199-2592 IMP
■ HAWAII ELECTRIC LIGHT CO INC
(*Suby of* HAWAIIAN ELECTRIC CO INC) ★
54 Halekauila St, Hilo, HI 96720-4511
Tel (808) 935-1171 *Founded/Ownrshp* 1894
Sales 297.8MM[E] *EMP* 310
SIC 4911 Electric services
Pr: Jay M Ignacio
CFO: Paul Fujioka
* *Sr VP:* Susan A LI
* *VP:* Darcy L Endo-Omoto
* *VP:* Patsy H Nanbu
* *VP:* Tayne SY Sekimura
CTO: Chuck Strain

D-U-N-S 07-768-5147
HAWAII ENERGY RESOURCES INC
733 Bishop St Fl 28, Honolulu, HI 96813-4022
Tel (808) 547-3111 *Founded/Ownrshp* 1992
Sales 99.8MM[E] *EMP* 740
SIC 5172 2911 5171 Crude oil; Petroleum refining; Petroleum bulk stations
Pr: Henry G Neal
* *Pr:* Faye Kurren
* *VP:* Eric Lee
* *VP:* Andy Nomura
* *VP:* George Putman

D-U-N-S 03-202-8321
HAWAII FOODSERVICE ALLIANCE LLC
2720 Waiwai Loop, Honolulu, HI 96819-1940
Tel (808) 839-2004 *Founded/Ownrshp* 1997
Sales 88.7MM[E] *EMP* 83[E]
SIC 5141 5812 Food brokers; Eating places; Food services, direct sales
CEO: Andrew Chun
* *Genl Mgr:* Mark Tonini

HAWAII GAS
See GAS CO LLC

D-U-N-S 78-765-0790
HAWAII HEALTH SYSTEMS CORP
HHSC
(*Suby of* DOH) ★
3675 Kilauea Ave, Honolulu, HI 96816-2333
Tel (808) 733-4020 *Founded/Ownrshp* 1996
Sales 111.3MM[E] *EMP* 1,097
Accts Plante & Moran Pllc Grand Ra
SIC 8082 Home health care services
CEO: Alice Hall
V Ch: William F Mielcke
CEO: Derek Akiyoshi
CFO: Edward N Chu
CFO: Linda Tom
Bd of Dir: Debbie Hirano
Ofcr: Sean Sanada
Ex Dir: Lance K Segawa
CIO: Alan Ito

D-U-N-S 80-999-7203
HAWAII MEDICAL CENTER
2230 Liliha St Ste 227, Honolulu, HI 96817-1646
Tel (808) 547-6881 *Founded/Ownrshp* 2007
Sales 80.4MM[E] *EMP* 1,501
SIC 8062 General medical & surgical hospitals
CEO: Danelo Canete MD
COO: Catherine Tanaka
Doctor: Antonio Cordero
Doctor: Kent Davenport
Doctor: Jeffery Harpstrite
Doctor: Elizabeth Ignacio
Doctor: John Kristofich
Doctor: Clifford Lau
Doctor: Jeffrey Lee
Doctor: Morris Mitsunaga
Doctor: Gary Okamura

HAWAII MEDICAL CENTER W PHRM
See HAWAII MEDICAL CENTER WEST LLC

D-U-N-S 61-030-0071 IMP
HAWAII MEDICAL CENTER WEST LLC
HAWAII MEDICAL CENTER W PHRM
(*Suby of* HAWAII MEDICAL CENTER) ★
91-2141 Fort Weaver Rd, Ewa Beach, HI 96706-1993
Tel (808) 678-7000 *Founded/Ownrshp* 2007
Sales 172.5M *EMP* 1,250
SIC 8062 General medical & surgical hospitals

D-U-N-S 06-290-9809
HAWAII MEDICAL SERVICE ASSOCIATION
HMSA
818 Keeaumoku St Ste 200, Honolulu, HI 96814-2393
Tel (808) 948-6111 *Founded/Ownrshp* 2004
Sales NA *EMP* 1,500
SIC 6321 6324 Accident & health insurance; Hospital & medical service plans
Pr: Michael Gold
* *COO:* Mike Gold
CFO: Steve Van Ribbink
Sr Cor Off: Fumie Lum
* *Ofcr:* Michel Danon
Ofcr: Timothy E Johns
Ofcr: Hilton R Raethel
* *Ex VP:* Gwen S Miyasato
* *Sr VP:* Michael J Cheng
VP: Garet H Azama
VP: David Butterworth
VP: Joan M Millar

HAWAII PACIFIC HEALTH
See KAPIOLANI MEDICAL CENTER FOR WOMEN AND CHILDREN

HAWAII PACIFIC HEALTH
See HAWAI I PACIFIC HEALTH

D-U-N-S 07-249-8132
HAWAII PACIFIC UNIVERSITY
1164 Bishop St Ste 800, Honolulu, HI 96813-2817
Tel (808) 544-0200 *Founded/Ownrshp* 1965
Sales 107.4MM *EMP* 1,300
Accts Ernst & Young Us Llp San Dieg
SIC 8221 University
Pr: Geoffrey Bannister
V Ch: Justin Brown
* *CFO:* Bruce Edwards
CFO: William Kline
* *Ch:* Joachim Cox
* *Treas:* Ajello James
Ofcr: Robert Cyboron
VP: Kathleen Clark
VP: John Fleckles
Assoc Dir: Patrick Reagan
Ex Dir: Dan Brinkman

D-U-N-S 05-678-9415
HAWAII PIZZA HUT INC
(*Suby of* THEODAVIES FOOD SERVICE GROUP) ★
828 Fort Street Mall # 130, Honolulu, HI 96813-4314
Tel (808) 566-3200 *Founded/Ownrshp* 1984
Sales 36.1MM[E] *EMP* 1,800
SIC 5812 Pizzeria, chain
Pr: Henry Katsuda
* *CFO:* Kevin Kurihara
* *VP:* Rahul Agtarwal
* *VP:* Anthony Choe

D-U-N-S 10-072-7171
HAWAII SCHOOL DISTRICT
(*Suby of* OFFICE OF SUPERINTENDENT) ★
75 Aupuni St Rm 203, Hilo, HI 96720-4245
Tel (808) 974-6600 *Founded/Ownrshp* 1959
Sales 47.7MM[E] *EMP* 1,020
SIC 8211 9411 Public elementary & secondary schools;

D-U-N-S 80-993-5513
HAWAII STATE DEPARTMENT OF EDUCATION
OFFICE OF THE SUPERINTENDENT
(*Suby of* EXECUTIVE OFFICE OF STATE OF HAWAII) ★
1390 Miller St Rm 305309, Honolulu, HI 96813-2493
Tel (808) 586-3310 *Founded/Ownrshp* 1959
Sales NA *EMP* 20,000
SIC 9411 Administration of educational programs;
Ch: Lance Mizumoto
Dir Sec: Gilbert Chun
MIS Dir: Richard Asato
MIS Dir: Susan Chandler
Dir IT: Allan Stone
Pr Dir: Sandra Goya
Instr Medi: Joanna Dunn
Psych: David Randall

D-U-N-S 00-692-6901 IMP
■ HAWAIIAN AIRLINES INC
(*Suby of* HAWAIIAN HOLDINGS INC) ★
3375 Koapaka St Ste G350, Honolulu, HI 96819-1804
Tel (808) 835-3700 *Founded/Ownrshp* 2002
Sales 2.8MM *EMP* 3,039
Accts Ii Ernst & Young Llp I
SIC 4512 Air passenger carrier, scheduled; Air cargo carrier, scheduled
Pr: Mark Dunkerley
* *COO:* Jon Snook
* *CFO:* Peter R Ingram
* *CFO:* Shannon Okinaka
* *Treas:* Karen A Berry
Ex VP: Russell G Chew
Sr VP: Barb Falvey
VP: Jeff Helfrick
* *VP:* Sayle Hirashima
VP: Philip Moore
VP: Donald Sealey
Dir Surg: Richard Petersen
Board of Directors: Thomas J Trzanowski, Gregory S Anderson, William M Weisfield, Donald J Carty, Todd G Cole, Robert G Coo, Joseph P Hoar, Reno F Morella, Samson Poomaihealani, Edward Z Safady, Sharon L Soper

D-U-N-S 02-625-1010 IMP
■ HAWAIIAN COMMERCIAL & SUGAR CO
(*Suby of* ALEXANDER & BALDWIN LLC) ★
1 Hansen St, Puunene, HI 96784-2001
Tel (808) 877-0081 *Founded/Ownrshp* 2010
Sales 222.9MM[E] *EMP* 708
SIC 2061 Raw cane sugar; Sugar
Genl Mgr: Rick W Volner Jr
* *Sr VP:* Anna M Skrobecki
VP: Keith Goto
Exec: Garret Hew

D-U-N-S 12-262-7289 IMP
HAWAIIAN DREDGING CONSTRUCTION CO INC
(*Suby of* KAJIMA INTERNATIONAL INC) ★
201 Merchant St Ste 900, Honolulu, HI 96813-2999
Tel (808) 735-3211 *Founded/Ownrshp* 1992
Sales 235.0MM[E] *EMP* 500[E]
Accts Deloitte Touche Llp Honolulu
SIC 1542 1611 1522 1521 Nonresidential construction; General contractor, highway & street construction; Hotel/motel, new construction; Multi-family dwellings, new construction; New construction, single-family houses
Pr: William J Wilson
Pr: Gary M Yokoyama
* *VP:* Leonard Dempsey
* *VP:* Eric Hashizume
VP: Michael Nakashima
* *VP:* Cedric Ota
* *VP:* Paul Silen
Genl Mgr: J Majkut
Genl Mgr: Genna Yamauchi
IT Man: Miles K Yamada
QI Cn Mgr: Justin Ohara

D-U-N-S 00-692-6927 IMP
■ HAWAIIAN ELECTRIC CO INC
(*Suby of* HEI) ★
900 Richards St, Honolulu, HI 96813-2956
Tel (808) 543-7771 *Founded/Ownrshp* 1983
Sales 2.3MMM *EMP* 2,759
Accts Pricewaterhousecoopers Llp L
SIC 4911 Generation, electric power; Transmission, electric power; Distribution, electric power
Pr: Alan M Oshima
* *Ch Bd:* Constance H Lau
CFO: Tayne SY Sekimura
Ofcr: Emma Wright
Sr VP: Patricia Wong
Genl Mgr: Liuone Faagai
CIO: Steve McMenamin
Genl Couns: Lori Sunakoda
Board of Directors: Don E Carroll, Thomas B Fargo, Peggy Y Fowler, Timothy E Johns, Micah A Kane, Bert A Kobayashi Jr, Kelvin H Taketa

D-U-N-S 10-390-1773 IMP
▲ HAWAIIAN ELECTRIC INDUSTRIES INC
HEI
1001 Bishop St Ste 2900, Honolulu, HI 96813-3480
Tel (808) 543-5662 *Founded/Ownrshp* 1891
Sales 2.6MMM *EMP* 3,918
Tkr Sym HE *Exch* NYS
SIC 4911 6035 Generation, electric power; Transmission, electric power; Distribution, electric power; Federal savings banks
Pr: Constance H Lau
* *Ch Bd:* Jeffrey N Watanabe
CFO: James A Ajello
Ex VP: Jim Ajello
Ex VP: Chester A Richardson
Board of Directors: Thomas B Fargo, Peggy Y Fowler, A Maurice Myers, Keith P Russell, James K Scott, Kelvin H Taketa, Barry K Taniguchi

D-U-N-S 00-717-4191 IMP
HAWAIIAN GARDENS CASINO
21520 Pioneer Blvd # 305, Hawaiian Gardens, CA 90716-2602
Tel (562) 860-5887 *Founded/Ownrshp* 1998
Sales 63.2MM[E] *EMP* 1,000[E]
SIC 7999 Card & game services
CEO: David Moskowitz
* *Pr:* Irving Moskowitz
CFO: Jennifer Wright

D-U-N-S 12-941-3436
▲ HAWAIIAN HOLDINGS INC
3375 Koapaka St Ste G350, Honolulu, HI 96819-1804
Tel (808) 835-3700 *Founded/Ownrshp* 1929
Sales 2.3MMM *EMP* 5,548[E]
Accts Ernst & Young Llp Honolulu H
Tkr Sym HA *Exch* NGS
SIC 4512 Air transportation, scheduled
Pr: Mark B Dunkerley
* *Ch Bd:* Lawrence S Hershfield
COO: Jon Snook
COO: Jonathan Snook
CFO: Shannon L Okinaka
CFO: Scott E Topping
Ofcr: Aaron J Alter
Sr VP: Barbara D Falvey
Sr VP: AVI A Mannis
IT Man: Janette Freeman
Snr PM: Priscilla Yin

D-U-N-S 00-923-1671 IMP
HAWAIIAN HOUSEWARES LTD
HANSEN DISTRIBUTION GROUP
96-1282 Waihona St, Pearl City, HI 96782-1968
Tel (808) 453-8000 *Founded/Ownrshp* 1956
Sales 164.0MM[E] *EMP* 175
SIC 5199 5194 5141 5145 General merchandise, non-durable; Tobacco & tobacco products; Groceries, general line; Candy
Ch Bd: Diana Allen
* *Pr:* Joe Heidelmaier
* *COO:* Bob Piccinino
* *VP:* Vanoush Petrossian

D-U-N-S 80-637-3754
HAWAIIAN NATIVE CORP
900 Fort Street Mall # 1850, Honolulu, HI 96813-3721
Tel (808) 536-5500 *Founded/Ownrshp* 2004
Sales 416.8MM[E] *EMP* 25[E]
SIC 8699 Charitable organization
Pr: Christopher M Dawson
Ex Dir: Lulani Arquette

D-U-N-S 78-496-5399
■ HAWAIIAN TELCOM COMMUNICATIONS INC
(*Suby of* HAWAIIAN TELCOM HOLDCO INC) ★
1177 Bishop St, Honolulu, HI 96813-2808
Tel (808) 546-4511 *Founded/Ownrshp* 2005
Sales 611.2MM[E] *EMP* 1,400[E]
SIC 4813 4812 Telephone communication, except radio; Local & long distance telephone communications; ; Cellular telephone services
Pr: Eric K Yeaman
V Ch: James A Attwood
* *COO:* Kurt Hoffmann
* *CFO:* Robert F Reich
Sr VP: Michael Edl
Sr VP: Craig T Inouye
Sr VP: John T Komeiji
VP: Steven P Golden
VP: Francis Mukai
Snr Ntwrk: Gerry Sagucio
IT Man: Marc Hemingway
Board of Directors: James A Attwood Jr, Matthew P Boyer, Walter A Dods Jr, Stephen C Gray, William E Kennard, Raymond A Ranelli

D-U-N-S 78-496-4426
▲ HAWAIIAN TELCOM HOLDCO INC
1177 Bishop St, Honolulu, HI 96813-2837
Tel (808) 546-4511 *Founded/Ownrshp* 1883
Sales 393.4MM *EMP* 1,300[E]
Tkr Sym HCOM *Exch* NGS
SIC 4813 Telephone communication, except radio
Pr: Scott K Barber
* *Ch Bd:* Richard A Jalkut
CFO: Dan T Bessey
Ofcr: John T Komeiji
Sr VP: Kevin T Paul
VP: Amy S Aapala
VP: Gregory Chamberlain
VP: Jason K Fujita
VP: Paul G Krueger
VP: Paul Krueger
VP: Benjamin L Morgan
Board of Directors: Kurt M Cellar, Meredith J Ching, Walter A Dods Jr, N John Fontana III, Warren H Haruki, Steven C Oldham, Bernard R Phillips III, Robert B Webster, Eric K Yeaman

D-U-N-S 00-692-6943 IMP
■ HAWAIIAN TELCOM INC (HI)
(*Suby of* HAWAIIAN TELCOM COMMUNICATIONS INC) ★
1177 Bishop St, Honolulu, HI 96813-2837
Tel (808) 643-3456 *Founded/Ownrshp* 1883, 2005
Sales 605.9MM[E] *EMP* 1,400
SIC 4813 5065 7629 Local & long distance telephone communications; Local telephone communications; Telephone equipment; Telecommunication equipment repair (except telephones)
Pr: Eric K Yeaman
* *COO:* Scott K Barber
* *COO:* Kevin Nystrom
* *CFO:* Dan T Bessey
Sr VP: Meredith J Ching
* *Sr VP:* Michael Czerwinski
* *Sr VP:* John T Komeiji
VP: Michael T Brown
VP: Greg Chamberlain
VP: Lester Chu
* *VP:* William Chung
* *VP:* John Duncan
* *VP:* Michael Edl
* *VP:* Steven Golden
* *VP:* Galen Haneda
VP: Kenneth Hiraki
* *VP:* Jeffrey Hoffman
* *VP:* Rose Houser
* *VP:* Craig Inouye
* *VP:* James Leclair
* *VP:* Geoffrey Loui

D-U-N-S 88-387-7888
HAWK JIM GROUP INC
3119 S 9th St, Council Bluffs, IA 51501-7664
Tel (712) 366-2241 *Founded/Ownrshp* 1974
Sales 154.8MM[E] *EMP* 275
SIC 5012 7539 Trailers for trucks, new & used; Trailer repair
Pr: James V Hawk
* *Sec:* Lanny Goetzinger
* *VP:* Charles O'Hollearn
Genl Mgr: Richard Dunaway

HAWK PERFORMANCE
See FRICTION PRODUCTS CO

D-U-N-S 00-724-7315 IMP
■ HAWKER BEECHCRAFT GLOBAL CUSTOMER SUPPORT LLC
(*Suby of* TEXTRON AVIATION) ★
10511 E Central Ave, Wichita, KS 67206-2557
Tel (316) 676-7111 *Founded/Ownrshp* 1995
Sales 71.6MM[E] *EMP* 1,300
SIC 7699 Aircraft & heavy equipment repair services
VP: Ted Farid
* *CFO:* Sidney E Anderson
* *Treas:* George M Sellew
* *VP:* James E Knight
IT Man: Brandy Herrman

D-U-N-S 61-145-4380 IMP/EXP
■ HAWKER POWERSOURCE INC
(*Suby of* ENERSYS) ★
9404 Ooltewah Indus Blvd, Ooltewah, TN 37363-8700
Tel (423) 238-5700 *Founded/Ownrshp* 2002
Sales 94.5MM[E] *EMP* 174
SIC 5063 Batteries
Prin: Bob Aaron
* *VP:* Waseem Ahmad

D-U-N-S 07-348-5716
HAWKEYE COMMUNITY COLLEGE
1501 E Orange Rd, Waterloo, IA 50701-9014
Tel (319) 296-4201 *Founded/Ownrshp* 1966
Sales 27.6MM *EMP* 1,112
Accts Williams & Company Pc Spenc
SIC 8222 Community college; Technical institute
Pr: Linda Allen
Pr: Donna McNulty
Treas: Gisella C Baker
* *Treas:* Denise Bouska
* *VP:* Jane Bradley
* *VP:* Kathy Flynn
* *VP:* Daniel Gillen
VP: Pat Stanley
* *Prin:* Casey P McLaughlin
Ex Dir: Peg Brown
Prgrm Mgr: Jamie Bute

HAWKEYE INTERNATIONAL TRUCKS
See THOMPSON TRUCK & TRAILER INC

D-U-N-S 10-855-6333
HAWKINS ASSOCIATES INC
HAWKINS PERSONNEL GROUP
909 Ne Loop 410 Ste 104, San Antonio, TX 78209-1315
Tel (210) 349-9911 *Founded/Ownrshp* 1977
Sales 16.0MM *EMP* 4,000
SIC 7363 7361 Temporary help service; Placement agencies
Pr: Sally Hawkins
* *VP:* Jennifer Hawkins
* *VP:* William P Hawkins
Sales Exec: Elizabeth Hawkins
* *VP Sls:* Liz Hawkins

D-U-N-S 00-287-3693
HAWKINS CONSTRUCTION CO
2516 Deer Park Blvd, Omaha, NE 68105-3771
Tel (402) 342-4455 *Founded/Ownrshp* 1960
Sales 187.0MM *EMP* 400
Accts Deloitte Omaha Ne
SIC 1542 1611 1541 Farm building construction; Resurfacing contractor; Industrial buildings, new construction
CEO: Fred Hawkins Jr
* *Pr:* Kim Hawkins
* *COO:* Chris Hawkins
* *Ex VP:* James Gregory
* *Ex VP:* Matt Miller
* *Ex VP:* Dudley Rinaker
* *VP:* Robert A Bloechle
VP: Ted Butler
* *VP:* Tom Crockett
* *VP:* Jeff Fuqua
* *VP:* Chris Grojean
* *VP:* Chris Harnly

*VP: David Langenberg
*VP: Kurt Peyton

D-U-N-S 07-759-5924
HAWKINS CONSTRUCTION INC
1430 L&R Industrial Blvd, Tarpon Springs, FL 34689
Tel (727) 937-2690 Founded/Ownrshp 1975
Sales 150.0MM EMP 110
Accts Gregory Sharer & Stuart Pa
SIC 1542 Commercial & office building, new construction
Pr: John McCaugherty
*CFO: Jean Snyder
*VP: Mike Beausir
*VP: Earle Cooper
*VP: Todd Mullins
*VP: Don Ondrejcak
*Exec: Miguel Leyva
Dir Bus: Rj Walker

D-U-N-S 04-119-9639 IMP
▲ HAWKINS INC
2381 Rosegate, Roseville, MN 55113-2625
Tel (612) 331-6910 Founded/Ownrshp 1938
Sales 413.9MM EMP 636
Accts Kpmg Llp Minneapolis Minneso
Tkr Sym HWKN Exch NGS
SIC 5169 5074 2899 Chemicals & allied products; Swimming pool & spa chemicals; Industrial chemicals; Water purification equipment; Chemical preparations
Pr: Patrick H Hawkins
*Ch Bd: John S McKeon
Pr: Olivier A Guiot
CFO: Kathleen P Pepski
VP: Richard G Erstad
VP: Thomas J Keller
VP: Steven D Matthews II
VP: Theresa R Moran
VP: John R Sevenich
Brnch Mgr: Troy Blake
Plnt Mgr: Syed Hassan
Board of Directors: James A Faulconbridge, Duane M Jergenson, Mary J Schumacher, Daryl I Skaar, Daniel J Stauber, James T Thompson, Jeffrey L Wright

HAWKINS PERSONNEL GROUP
See HAWKINS ASSOCIATES INC

D-U-N-S 07-948-2306
HAWKWOOD ENERGY EAST TEXAS LLC
(Suby of HAWKWOOD ENERGY LLC) ★
1999 Bryan St Ste 900, Dallas, TX 75201-3140
Tel (303) 823-4175 Founded/Ownrshp 2014
Sales 201.5M^E EMP 7,002
SIC 1382 Oil & gas exploration services
CEO: Patrick R Oenbring
Pr: Leonard Gurule
CFO: Matthew O'Neill

D-U-N-S 07-942-6956
HAWKWOOD ENERGY LLC
4582 S Ulster St Ste 500, Denver, CO 80237-2642
Tel (303) 823-4175 Founded/Ownrshp 2012
Sales 35.0MM EMP 7,022^E
SIC 1382 Oil & gas exploration services
CEO: Patrick R Oenbring
Pr: Leonard Gurule
CFO: Matt O'Neill

D-U-N-S 07-259-5457 IMP/EXP
HAWORTH INC
(Suby of HAWORTH INTERNATIONAL LTD) ★
1 Haworth Ctr, Holland, MI 49423-8820
Tel (616) 393-3000 Founded/Ownrshp 1948
Sales 1.8MMM EMP 5,950
SIC 2522 2521 Office furniture, except wood; Wood office furniture
Pr: Franco Bianchi
Pr: Nick Haritos
*Ch: Matthew Haworth
Ofcr: Teresa Bellingar
VP: Jos Amaral
VP: Pamela W Armstrong
VP: James Johnson
VP: Michael Moon Sr
*VP: John K Mooney
VP: Paul K Smith
VP: Nancy Teutsch
Exec: Bill Altena
Exec: Victoria Barnes
Exec: Paul Hogan
Dir Bus: Cyndi King
Dir Bus: Mark Lobb
Dir Bus: Annette Plaia

D-U-N-S 07-928-2059 IMP/EXP
HAWORTH INTERNATIONAL LTD (MI)
1 Haworth Ctr, Holland, MI 49423-8820
Tel (616) 393-3000 Founded/Ownrshp 1948, 1975
Sales 1.8MMM EMP 5,950
SIC 2522 2521 Office furniture, except wood; Wood office furniture
Ch Bd: Matthew Haworth
*Pr: Frankco Bianchi
Treas: Daniel Zona
VP: John K Mooney

HAWTHORN SUITES
See H GROUP HOLDING INC

D-U-N-S 04-132-2710 IMP/EXP
HAWTHORNE MACHINERY CO
CATERPILLAR AUTHORIZED DEALER
16945 Camino San Bernardo, San Diego, CA 92127-2499
Tel (858) 674-7000 Founded/Ownrshp 1941
Sales 170.7MM^E EMP 1,000
SIC 7353 7699 5082 7359 Heavy construction equipment rental; Construction equipment repair; Construction & mining machinery; Equipment rental & leasing
Pr: Tee K Ness
COO: David Ness
CFO: Brian Verhoeven
VP: Stephen E Wittman
Brnch Mgr: Ken Emerick
Netwrk Mgr: Troy Lowe
Mtls Mgr: Craig Baker
Sfty Mgr: Steve Hollingsworth
Mktg Mgr: Zephyr Skeets
Sls Mgr: David Dean

D-U-N-S 79-767-4397 EXP
HAWTHORNE PACIFIC CORP
CATERPILLAR AUTHORIZED DEALER
(Suby of CATERPILLAR AUTHORIZED DEALER) ★
94-025 Farrington Hwy, Waipahu, HI 96797-2201
Tel (808) 676-0227 Founded/Ownrshp 2004
Sales 97.0MM^E EMP 243
SIC 5084 7353 Industrial machinery & equipment; Heavy construction equipment rental
Pr: Tee K Ness
*Pr: Stephen E Wittman
*Treas: Richard J Moss
*VP: Mike Johnson
VP: Verna Martin
VP: Kevin Tam
MIS Mgr: Roger Staehle

HAY ACQUISITION COMPANY I INC
See HAY GROUP HOLDINGS INC

D-U-N-S 62-317-7987
HAY GROUP HOLDINGS INC
HAY ACQUISITION COMPANY I INC
(Suby of HAY GROUP INVESTMENT HOLDING B.V.)
1650 Arch St Ste 2300, Philadelphia, PA 19103-2001
Tel (215) 861-2000 Founded/Ownrshp 1990
Sales 47.5M^E EMP 2,110
SIC 8742 8249 8733 Management consulting services; Business training services; Educational research agency
Ch Bd: Chris Matthews
*CEO: Stephen Kaye
*CFO: Jesse Deutsch

D-U-N-S 07-548-0350
■ HAY GROUP INC
(Suby of HAY GROUP LIMITED)
1650 Arch St Ste 2300, Philadelphia, PA 19103-2001
Tel (215) 861-2000 Founded/Ownrshp 1990
Sales 128.6MM^E EMP 432
SIC 8742

D-U-N-S 96-354-5694 IMP/EXP
HAY ISLAND HOLDING CORP
20 Thorndal Cir, Darien, CT 06820-5421
Tel (203) 656-8000 Founded/Ownrshp 1995
Sales 874.5MM^E EMP 1,600
SIC 5194 2131 Tobacco & tobacco products; Chewing tobacco; Snuff
Pr: William T Ziegler
VP: Helen Z Benjamin
*VP: Cynthia Brighton
*VP: Peter Ziegler

D-U-N-S 03-591-0202
HAYDON BUILDING CORP (AZ)
4640 E Cotton Gin Loop, Phoenix, AZ 85040-4819
Tel (602) 296-1496 Founded/Ownrshp 1995
Sales 200.6MM EMP 250
Accts Weintraub & Schanck Pc Pho
SIC 1541 1542 Industrial buildings & warehouses; Commercial & office building, new construction
Pr: Gary T Haydon
*CFO: Cynthia Lee
*VP: Mark D Eklund
*VP: Leslie H Keeble
*VP: James A Pulice Jr

HAYES BRAKE
See HB PERFORMANCE SYSTEMS INC

HAYES CHRYSLER DODGE
See HAYES CHRYSLER-DODGE-JEEP INC

D-U-N-S 05-101-1476
HAYES CHRYSLER-DODGE-JEEP INC
HAYES CHRYSLER DODGE
719 Duluth Hwy, Lawrenceville, GA 30046-4305
Tel (770) 963-5251 Founded/Ownrshp 1971
Sales 120.2MM^E EMP 380
SIC 5511 Automobiles, new & used
*Pr: Albert David Hayes
*Sec: Tim Hayes
*VP: Donald E Hayes
Exec: Travis Dixon
Exec: John Nelson
Web Prj Mg: Chris Terry
Sales Exec: Stacy Kelley
Sls Mgr: Chipper Jones

HAYES LEMMERZ INTERNATIONAL
See MAXION WHEELS

D-U-N-S 02-515-3826
HAYES MECHANICAL LLC
5959 S Harlem Ave, Chicago, IL 60638-3131
Tel (773) 784-0000 Founded/Ownrshp 2005
Sales 110.0MM^E EMP 250^E
SIC 1711 Mechanical contractor; Heating & air conditioning contractors; Ventilation & duct work contractor; Plumbing contractors
Ch Bd: Richard J Mooney
*Pr: Terry W Ancel
*COO: George Englebrecht
*CFO: Mark Tibbetts
*Sr VP: Robert Gabrysiak
Sr VP: Eric Heuser
*VP: J D Mooney
Div Mgr: Vicky Saltz
IT Man: Derick Fields
IT Man: Derrick Moore
Sfty Dirs: Bryce Pearson

D-U-N-S 00-142-0629
HAYES PUMP INC (MA)
66 Old Powder Mill Rd I, Concord, MA 01742-4696
Tel (978) 369-8800 Founded/Ownrshp 1898
Sales 116.6MM^E EMP 80
SIC 5084 3561 Pumps & pumping equipment; Pumps & pumping equipment
Pr: Eric W Zadravec
*Ch Bd: Patrick Furnari
*CFO: Scott Putman
Ex VP: Joseph Larkin
*Sr VP: Robert L Simonds
*VP Sls: J Craig Huff III
S&M/VP: Walter A Barron

D-U-N-S 04-697-9027
■ HAYES SEAY MATTERN & MATTERN INC
(Suby of AECOM) ★
10 S Jefferson St # 1600, Roanoke, VA 24011-1331
Tel (540) 857-3100 Founded/Ownrshp 2007
Sales 124.8MM^E EMP 660
SIC 8711 8712 Engineering services; Civil engineering; Architectural services
Pr: Cecil G Doyle
*COO: Steve Clinton
CFO: Roger Herald
Sr VP: Charles S Garrett
Sr VP: Glen W Pickelsimer
VP: Michael Brennan
VP: Robert Canova
VP: Edward Janney
VP: Randolph Leech
VP: James Lowe
VP: Robert J Smith

D-U-N-S 00-165-8520 IMP/EXP
■ HAYNEEDLE INC
(Suby of WALMART) ★
9394 W Dodge Rd Ste 300, Omaha, NE 68114-3319
Tel (402) 715-3000 Founded/Ownrshp 2016
Sales 217.3MM^E EMP 1,000^E
SIC 5943 5719 5945 5947 Stationery stores; Kitchenware; Lighting, lamps & accessories; Bath accessories; Hobby, toy & game shops; Gift, novelty & souvenir shop
Pr: Jon Barker
*CFO: Donn Raymond
Treas: Randy Houck
Chf Mktg O: Brian Moen
VP: Ryan Paulson
Genl Mgr: Kim Sindelar
Web Dev: Kyle Baumgartner
Web Dev: Eric Hoffman
Manager: Mike Johnson
Mktg Dir: Jeremy Podliska
Mktg Mgr: Jennifer Kross-Dorfmeyer

D-U-N-S 08-514-8146
HAYNES AND BOONE LLP
2323 Victory Ave Ste 700, Dallas, TX 75219-7673
Tel (214) 651-5000 Founded/Ownrshp 2008
Sales 192.0MM^E EMP 1,026
SIC 8111

D-U-N-S 00-895-6096 IMP/EXP
HAYNES FURNITURE CO INC
DUMP, THE
5324 Virginia Beach Blvd, Virginia Beach, VA 23462-1898
Tel (804) 276-1060 Founded/Ownrshp 1949
Sales 194.1MM^E EMP 700
SIC 5713 5712 Carpets; Furniture stores
Pr: Ellis Strelitz
*Sr VP: Bruce Breedlove
Sr VP: Joshua Mallenbaum
*Sr VP: Kurt M Rosenbach
VP: Wanda Solomon
Exec: Bill Hutchinson
Adm Dir: Randi Strelitz
Store Mgr: James Enochs
CIO: Rich Boettcher
DP Dir: Phil Joslyn
Dir IT: Rich Pocher

D-U-N-S 16-117-8660
▲ HAYNES INTERNATIONAL INC
1020 W Park Ave, Kokomo, IN 46901-6330
Tel (765) 456-6000 Founded/Ownrshp 1912
Sales 406.3MM EMP 1,147
Accts Deloitte & Touche Llp Indiana
Tkr Sym HAYN Exch NGS
SIC 3356 Nickel; Titanium
Pr: Mark M Comerford
CFO: Daniel W Maudlin
VP: Janice W Gunst
VP: Stacy Kilian
VP: Stacy Knapper
VP: Marlin Losch
VP: Jean Neel
VP: Gregory M Spalding
VP: Jeffrey L Young
Exec: Lyle Snyder
QA Dir: Debbie Denny
Board of Directors: Donald C Campion, John C Corey, Robert H Getz, Timothy J McCarthy, Michael L Shor, William P Wall

HAYNES WIRE ROPE
See HWC WIRE & CABLE CO

HAYS CISD
See HAYS CONSOLIDATED I S D

HAYS COMPANIES
See HAYS GROUP INC

D-U-N-S 10-067-2930
HAYS CONSOLIDATED I S D
HAYS CISD
21003 Interstate 35, Kyle, TX 78640-4745
Tel (512) 268-8442 Founded/Ownrshp 1967
Sales 155.8M EMP 3,000
Accts Linda Teneyuque Ito Cpa Ve Ky
SIC 8211 Public elementary & secondary schools
COO: Marty Marinez
COO: Ebell Steven
CFO: David Anderson
Trst: Marty Kanetzky
VP: Mark Jones
Exec: Marcia McClendon
Assoc Dir: Christian Huston
Assoc Dir: Anthony P Leflet
Ex Dir: Michelle Barrera
Ex Dir: Tim Persall
Admn Mgr: Judy Logan

D-U-N-S 86-702-3475
HAYS GROUP INC
HAYS COMPANIES
80 S 8th St Ste 700, Minneapolis, MN 55402-2105
Tel (612) 347-8377 Founded/Ownrshp 1994
Sales NA EMP 650
SIC 6411 Insurance agents, brokers & service
Pr: James Hays
Mng Pt: Bill Mershon
Pr: Jack Diehl
Pr: Jules Gootrad
Pr: Debbie Schmidt
*CFO: Stephen Lerum
CFO: Steve Lerum
Bd of Dir: Steve Ruben
Ex VP: Russell Berman
Ex VP: David Britt
Ex VP: Claude Campbell
Ex VP: Doug Livingston
*Ex VP: William Mershon
Ex VP: Gerald Schwalbach
Ex VP: Steve Verbeski
Ex VP: Kevin Wiskus
Ex VP: Leslie Young
*Sr VP: Michael Egan
Sr VP: George Sullivan
Sr VP: Robert Suycott
VP: Debbie Aichele

D-U-N-S 07-330-4214
HAYS MEDICAL CENTER INC
HAYSMED
2220 Canterbury Dr, Hays, KS 67601-2370
Tel (785) 623-5000 Founded/Ownrshp 1942
Sales 199.5MM EMP 1,178
Accts Wendling Noe Nelson & Johnson
SIC 8062 8051 General medical & surgical hospitals; Skilled nursing care facilities
Pr: John H Jeter MD
*COO: Bryce A Young
CFO: Bill Overbey
*CFO: William Overbey
Treas: Kenneth Beran
Ofcr: Joannah Applequist
VP: Steve Balthazor
*VP: George Harms
VP: John L Miller
VP: Christy Stahl
VP: Bruce Whittington
Dir Lab: Chardell Parke

HAYSMED
See HAYS MEDICAL CENTER INC

D-U-N-S 04-676-6895 IMP/EXP
HAYWARD BAKER INC
(Suby of KELLER FOUNDATIONS LLC) ★
7550 Teague Rd Ste 300, Hanover, MD 21076-1807
Tel (410) 551-8200 Founded/Ownrshp 1981
Sales 535.0MM^E EMP 1,200
Accts Kpmg Llp Baltimore Md
SIC 1799 Building site preparation
Pr: Eric R Drooff
CFO: Phillip Tannery
CFO: Richard N Yale
*Treas: Art D Pengelly
VP: Andy Anderson
VP: Curtis Cook
*VP: Daniel E Jordan
VP: Dan O'Neal
VP: Arthur Pengelly
*VP: Alan Ringen
*VP: John P Rubright
*VP: Steve Scherer
VP: Allen Sehn

D-U-N-S 00-245-3041 IMP/EXP
HAYWARD INDUSTRIES INC
HAYWOOD POOL PRODUCTS
620 Division St, Elizabeth, NJ 07201-2004
Tel (908) 351-5400 Founded/Ownrshp 1924
Sales 622.8MM^E EMP 1,140
SIC 3589 3561 3423 3494 3569 3089 Swimming pool filter & water conditioning systems; Pumps & pumping equipment; Pumps, domestic: water or sump; Leaf skimmers or swimming pool rakes; Valves & pipe fittings; Filters & strainers, pipeline; Plastic hardware & building products; Fittings for pipe, plastic
Pr: Robert Davis
Ch Bd: Oscar Davis
Pr: Clark Hale
CFO: Andrew Diamond
Treas: Len Brooks
Bd of Dir: Martin Krugman
VP: Adela Semonza
Dir IT: Wayne Kenworthy
IT Man: Dustin Leonard
IT Man: Glenn Levine
VP Opers: David Hawkswell

D-U-N-S 07-654-1515
HAYWARD SISTERS HOSPITAL
ST ROSE HOSPITAL
(Suby of ALECTO HEALTHCARE SERVICES LLC) ★
27200 Calaroga Ave, Hayward, CA 94545-4339
Tel (510) 264-4000 Founded/Ownrshp 2013
Sales 170.5MM EMP 850
Accts Tca Partners Llp Fresno Ca
SIC 8062 General medical & surgical hospitals
Pr: Michael Mahoney
Pr: Robert Heath
Ex Dir: Aman Dhuper
Prgrm Mgr: Rene Macias
Pharmcst: Stanley Bui
Pharmcst: Sara Jacobs
Pharmcst: Celina Li
Pharmcst: Ann Nguyen
Pharmcst: Joseph Schuetz
Cert Phar: Helene Sarwary

D-U-N-S 07-655-7883
HAYWARD UNIFIED SCHOOL DISTRICT
24411 Amador St, Hayward, CA 94544-1301
Tel (510) 784-2600 Founded/Ownrshp 1983
Sales 117.3MM^E EMP 2,400
SIC 8211 Public elementary & secondary schools; Public elementary school; Public junior high school; Public senior high school
CEO: Stan Data Dobbs
Bd of Dir: Lisa Brunner
VP: Annette Walker
*Prin: Donald Evans
Ex Dir: Yetunde Reeves
Dir Sec: Lynn Bravewomon
IT Man: Patrick Simon
Netwrk Mgr: Saleem Mahmood
Opers Supe: Mary Kerr

Opers Mgr: Tom Miller
Pr Dir: Sabrina Adanda

D-U-N-S 05-513-4423
HAYWOOD COUNTY PUBLIC SCHOOLS INC
1230 N Main St, Waynesville, NC 28786-3310
Tel (828) 456-2400 *Founded/Ownrshp* 1970
Sales 76.8MM *EMP* 1,280
SIC 8211 Public elementary & secondary schools
Ex Dir: Jenny Wood
Dir IT: Todd Trantham
IT Man: Bob Phillips
Schl Brd P: Chuck Francis
Teacher Pr: Jason Heinz
HC Dir: Mark Sheppard

HAYWOOD POOL PRODUCTS
See HAYWARD INDUSTRIES INC

D-U-N-S 07-450-6759
HAYWOOD REGIONAL MEDICAL CENTER
MIDWEST HAYWOOD
262 Leroy George Dr, Clyde, NC 28721-7430
Tel (828) 456-7311 *Founded/Ownrshp* 1927
Sales 110.4MM *EMP* 1,000
SIC 8062 General medical & surgical hospitals
CEO: Steve Heatherly
Dir Recs: Joyce Adkinson
Dir Recs: Joyce Atkinson
**Pr:* Mike Poore
**COO:* Teresa Reynolds
**CFO:* Mike McKnight
**CFO:* Gene Winters
Treas: Glenn White
**VP:* Patricia Ward
Exec: Jonathan White
Dir Risk M: Garret Neiswonger
Dir Lab: Terry Barnett
Dir Lab: Craig Toliver

HAZEL CREEK ASSISTED LIVING
See SUMMERVILLE AT HAZEL CREEK LLC

HAZEL HAWKINS MEMORIAL HOSPITA
See SAN BENITO HEALTH CARE DISTRICT

D-U-N-S 04-135-5157
HAZEL INC WILLIAM A
4305 Hazel Park Ct, Chantilly, VA 20151-2925
Tel (703) 378-8300 *Founded/Ownrshp* 1964
Sales 145.3MM[E] *EMP* 530
SIC 1623 1794

D-U-N-S 03-986-6926
HAZEL PARK PUBLIC SCHOOL DISTRICT
1620 E Elza Ave, Hazel Park, MI 48030-2358
Tel (248) 658-5217 *Founded/Ownrshp* 1883
Sales 48.4MM[E] *EMP* 1,000
SIC 8211 Public elementary & secondary schools
**CFO:* Daniel Romzek
Pr Dir: Darrin Fox

D-U-N-S 07-134-0467
HAZELDEN BETTY FORD FOUNDATION
HAZELDEN PUBG & EDUCTL SVCS
15251 Pleasant Valley Rd, Center City, MN 55012-9640
Tel (651) 213-4000 *Founded/Ownrshp* 1949
Sales 164.4MM *EMP* 651
SIC 8361 2731

HAZELDEN PUBG & EDUCTL SVCS
See HAZELDEN BETTY FORD FOUNDATION

D-U-N-S 07-195-4176
HAZELWOOD SCHOOL DISTRICT
GARRETT ELEMENTARY SCHOOL
15955 New Halls Ferry Rd, Florissant, MO 63031-1298
Tel (314) 953-5000 *Founded/Ownrshp* 1951
Sales 91.3MM[E] *EMP* 2,031
SIC 8211 Public elementary & secondary schools
Ofcr: Kevin Morganfield
Ofcr: Beverly Richards
Dir Sec: Vershaun Howze
Dir IT: David McCorkle
Teacher Pr: Kimberly McKenzie

D-U-N-S 06-496-6138 IMP
HAZEN AND SAWYER DPC
498 Fashion Ave Fl 11, New York, NY 10018-6710
Tel (212) 539-7000 *Founded/Ownrshp* 1951
Sales 270.1MM[E] *EMP* 775
SIC 8711 Consulting engineer; Designing: ship, boat, machine & product; Pollution control engineering
Pr: Charles Hocking
VP: Michael Broder
**VP:* Patrick A Davis
VP: Robert D Fiore
**VP:* Sandeep Mehrotra
**VP:* Richard Peters
VP: Paul Saurer
**VP:* Robert Taylor
**VP:* Ronald Taylor
**VP:* Peter Young
Prin: Tom McGarry

D-U-N-S 09-874-1283
HAZLETON AREA SCHOOL DISTRICT
HAZLETON ELEMENTARY/MIDDLE SCHL
1515 W 23rd St, Hazle Township, PA 18202-1647
Tel (570) 459-3111 *Founded/Ownrshp* 1966
Sales 131.9MM *EMP* 1,400
Accts Maillie Llp Oaks Pennsylvan
SIC 8211 Public junior high school
Dir Sec: Ed Harry
IT Man: Patricia Jones
Sfty Dirs: Vincent Zola

HAZLETON ELEMENTARY/MIDDLE SCHL
See HAZLETON AREA SCHOOL DISTRICT

H.B. & G BUILDING PRODUCTS INC
See HB&G BUILDING PRODUCTS INC

D-U-N-S 01-874-5430
HB COMMUNICATIONS INC (CT)
60 Dodge Ave, North Haven, CT 06473-1124
Tel (203) 747-7174 *Founded/Ownrshp* 1961
Sales 135.2MM[E] *EMP* 420
SIC 5064 5065 5731

D-U-N-S 00-615-9776 IMP/EXP
▲ HB FULLER CO (MN)
1200 Willow Lake Blvd, Saint Paul, MN 55110-5101
Tel (651) 236-5900 *Founded/Ownrshp* 1887
Sales 2.0MMM *EMP* 4,400[E]
Tkr Sym FUL *Exch* NYS
SIC 2891 2899 Adhesives & sealants; Adhesives; Adhesives, paste; Adhesives, plastic; Chemical preparations
Pr: James J Owens
CFO: James R Giertz
Sr VP: Steven Kenny
Sr VP: Patrick M Kivits
Sr VP: Patrick J Trippel
VP: Heather A Campe
VP: Elin E Gabriel
VP: Traci L Jensen
VP: Timothy J Keenan
VP: Hassan H Rmaile
Board of Directors: Thomas W Handley, Maria Teresa Hilado, J Michael Losh, Lee R Mitau, Dante C Parrini, Ann W H Simonds, John C Van Roden Jr, R William Van Sant

D-U-N-S 10-672-9627 IMP
HB PERFORMANCE SYSTEMS INC
HAYES BRAKE
5800 W Donges Bay Rd, Mequon, WI 53092-4429
Tel (262) 242-4300 *Founded/Ownrshp* 1998
Sales 84.7MM[E] *EMP* 400
SIC 3714 3751

D-U-N-S 78-318-0961
■ HB PS HOLDING CO INC
(*Suby of* NACCO INDUSTRIES INC) ★
4421 Waterfront Dr, Glen Allen, VA 23060-3375
Tel (804) 273-9777 *Founded/Ownrshp* 2011
Sales 443.7MM[E] *EMP* 484[E]
SIC 5722 Household appliance stores
Pr: Alfred M Rankin Jr
**Treas:* J C Butler
Natl Sales: Kelly Westlake
Manager: Marc Bouchard

D-U-N-S 00-793-6974 IMP
HB ZACHRY CO (TX)
(*Suby of* ZACHRY INDUSTRIAL INC) ★
527 Logwood Ave, San Antonio, TX 78221-1738
Tel (210) 475-8000 *Founded/Ownrshp* 1924, 2008
Sales 244.3MM[E] *EMP* 1,000
Accts Ernst & Young Llp San Antonio
SIC 1611 1622 1623 1629 General contractor, highway & street construction; Highway & street paving contractor; Bridge construction; Pipeline construction; Dam construction
Ch Bd: Henry B Zachry Jr
**Treas:* Gonzalo Ornelas
**Ex VP:* Charles Ebrom
**VP:* Stephen L Hoech
**VP:* Murray L Johnston Jr
**VP:* Joe J Lozano
**VP:* D Kirk McDonald

D-U-N-S 00-339-7734 IMP
HB&G BUILDING PRODUCTS INC
H.B. & G BUILDING PRODUCTS INC
(*Suby of* GRAHAM PARTNERS INC) ★
1015 S Brundidge Blvd, Troy, AL 36081-3109
Tel (334) 566-5000 *Founded/Ownrshp* 2003
Sales 171.5MM[E] *EMP* 830
SIC 2431 2421 2821 Millwork; Sawmills & planing mills, general; Plastics materials & resins
CEO: Lance Servais
COO: Brian Murray
**VP:* Paul Deal
**VP:* Mike Gibbons
Mktg Mgr: Tim Bobo

D-U-N-S 07-727-5485 IMP
HBA CORP
5310 Nw 33rd Ave Ste 211, Fort Lauderdale, FL 33309-6319
Tel (954) 731-3350 *Founded/Ownrshp* 1974
Sales 38.0MM[E] *EMP* 1,014
SIC 8051 Convalescent home with continuous nursing care
Pr: Barton D Weisman
**Sec:* Howard Lipschutz
**VP:* Dr Arthur Krosneck

D-U-N-S 07-872-9713
HBC HOLDINGS LLC
(*Suby of* WORLD AND MAIN LLC) ★
324a Half Acre Rd, Cranbury, NJ 08512-3254
Tel (609) 860-9990 *Founded/Ownrshp* 1999
Sales 236.0MM[E] *EMP* 300[E]
Accts Mayer Hoffman Mccann Cpas New
SIC 5072 5087 5074 Hardware; Shelf or light hardware; Security devices, locks; Janitors' supplies; Plumbing & hydronic heating supplies
Pr: Donald Devine
CFO: Marc Friedant
Treas: Jack Imszennik
VP: Michele Hudec
CIO: John Mitterko
QA Dir: Vincent Rotella
Natl Sales: Tim Slavicek

D-U-N-S 07-876-6887
HBC SOLUTIONS HOLDINGS LLC
10877 Wilshire Blvd Fl 18, Los Angeles, CA 90024-4373
Tel (321) 727-9100 *Founded/Ownrshp* 2013
Sales 54.9MM[E] *EMP* 1,002
SIC 3663 Radio broadcasting & communications equipment; Television broadcasting & communications equipment

D-U-N-S 18-480-8053 IMP/EXP
HBD INDUSTRIES INC
5200 Upper Metro Pl # 110, Dublin, OH 43017-5378
Tel (614) 526-7000 *Founded/Ownrshp* 1987
Sales 230.1MM *EMP* 1,534
SIC 3052 3621 3566 3564 3812

D-U-N-S 05-694-8383
HBE CORP
HOSPITAL BUILDING & EQP CO
11330 Olive Blvd, Saint Louis, MO 63141-7149
Tel (314) 567-9000 *Founded/Ownrshp* 1960
Sales 830.6MM[E] *EMP* 2,907
Accts Rubinbrown Llp Cpa Saint Lou
SIC 1542 8742 Nonresidential construction; Specialized public building contractors; Bank building construction; Hospital construction; Marketing consulting services; Financial consultant
Pr: Joseph Lehrer
**V Ch:* June Kummer
COO: Matthew Nail
CFO: Doug Adrian
CFO: Jim Phillips
Sr VP: Joe Arnold
Sr VP: Matthew T Baldy
VP: Gene Kemp
VP: Tim Rand
VP: Mike Tiffin
Dept Mgr: Andrew Hager

HBF TEXTILES
See HICKORY BUSINESS FURNITURE LLC

HBO LATIN AMERICA GROUP
See OLE HBO PARTNERS

D-U-N-S 82-564-3380
■ HBO SERVICES INC
H B O
(*Suby of* TIME WARNER CABLE ENTERPRISES LLC) ★
1100 Ave Of The Am Frnt 3, New York, NY 10036
Tel (212) 512-1000 *Founded/Ownrshp* 2003
Sales 25.9MM[E] *EMP* 2,050
SIC 7822 Distribution, exclusive of production: motion picture
CEO: Jeffrey L Bewkes

D-U-N-S 96-610-3595
■ HBR KENTUCKY LLC
(*Suby of* HARBORSIDE HEALTHCARE LIMITED PARTNERSHIP)
101 Sun Ave Ne, Albuquerque, NM 87109-4373
Tel (505) 821-3355 *Founded/Ownrshp* 2010
Sales 9.2MM[E] *EMP* 2,995[E]
SIC 8051 Skilled nursing care facilities
Prin: John Bickel
Genl Mgr: Lillian Werntz

HBSP
See HARVARD BUSINESS SCHOOL STUDENT ASSOCIATION INC

HBW GROUP
See HBW PROPERTIES INC

D-U-N-S 15-997-7693
HBW INSURANCE SERVICES LLC
(*Suby of* 2-10 HOME BUYERS WARRANTY) ★
4501 Circ 75 Pkwy Sef6200, Atlanta, GA 30339
Tel (678) 742-6300 *Founded/Ownrshp* 1999
Sales NA *EMP* 75
SIC 6411 Insurance agents, brokers & service

D-U-N-S 07-483-3336
HBW PROPERTIES INC
HBW GROUP
1055 1st St Ste 200, Rockville, MD 20850-8400
Tel (301) 424-2900 *Founded/Ownrshp* 1969
Sales 102.4MM *EMP* 85
SIC 1542 6512 6531

D-U-N-S 07-969-9597
HC COMPANIES INC
PRO CAL
(*Suby of* WINGATE PARTNERS V LP) ★
15150 Madison Rd, Middlefield, OH 44062-9495
Tel (440) 632-3333 *Founded/Ownrshp* 2015
Sales 131.1MM[E] *EMP* 570
SIC 5211 Greenhouse kits, prefabricated
Pr: Chris Koscho
**CFO:* John Landefeld

D-U-N-S 87-432-3868
▲ HC2 HOLDINGS INC
450 Park Ave Fl 30, New York, NY 10022-2637
Tel (212) 235-2690 *Founded/Ownrshp* 1994
Sales 1.1MMM *EMP* 1,970
Tkr Sym HCHC *Exch* ASE
SIC 4813 3325 8731 ; Telephone/video communications; Steel foundries; Biological research
Ch Bd: Philip A Falcone
COO: Keith M Hladek
CFO: Michael J Sena
Ofcr: Suzi Herbst
VP: Richard Ramlall
Genl Couns: Andrea L Mancuso
Board of Directors: Wayne Barr Jr, Warren H Gfeller, Lee Hillman, Robert V Leffler

HCA
See NORTHSIDE HOSPITAL

D-U-N-S 07-321-6582
■ HCA HEALTH SERVICES OF FLORIDA INC
COLUMBIA HCA
(*Suby of* HOSPITAL COPORATION OF AMERICA) ★
1 Park Plz, Nashville, TN 37203-6527
Tel (615) 344-9551 *Founded/Ownrshp* 1968
Sales 260.4MM[E] *EMP* 5,100
SIC 8062 8093 General medical & surgical hospitals; Specialty outpatient clinics
Ch: Richard M Bracken
**Pr:* Richard Bracke
**CEO:* R Milton Johnson
**Sr VP:* David G Anderson
**Sr VP:* Victor L Campbell
**Sr VP:* Jana J Davis
**Sr VP:* John M Steele

D-U-N-S 10-604-0400
HCA HEALTH SERVICES OF FLORIDA INC
OAK HILL HOSPITAL
11375 Cortez Blvd, Brooksville, FL 34613-5409
Tel (352) 597-3053 *Founded/Ownrshp* 2002
Sales 109.2MM[E] *EMP* 900
SIC 8062 General medical & surgical hospitals
CEO: Mickey Smith
CFO: David Deam
CFO: Mike Marks
VP: Diane Schneider
Dir Inf Cn: Christine Piacquaddio
Dir Lab: Don Menezes
Nurse Mgr: Nyoka Castro
CIO: Kristi Burns
CIO: Ann Karran
Dir IT: Andrew J Reck
IT Man: George Meadows

D-U-N-S 92-647-4768
■ HCA HEALTH SERVICES OF FLORIDA INC
COLUMBIA HCA
(*Suby of* HOSPITAL COPORATION OF AMERICA) ★
14000 Fivay Rd, Hudson, FL 34667-7103
Tel (727) 819-2929 *Founded/Ownrshp* 2007
Sales 37.4MM[E] *EMP* 1,000
SIC 4789 Cargo loading & unloading services
CEO: David Williams
Dir Rad: Ralph Uzzi

D-U-N-S 07-398-1417
■ HCA HEALTH SERVICES OF NEW HAMPSHIRE INC
COLUMBIA HCA
(*Suby of* HOSPITAL COPORATION OF AMERICA) ★
333 Borthwick Ave, Portsmouth, NH 03801-7128
Tel (603) 436-0600 *Founded/Ownrshp* 1994
Sales 174.0MM[E] *EMP* 1,551
SIC 8062 8063 General medical & surgical hospitals; Psychiatric hospitals
Pr: William J Schuler
**CFO:* Richard Senger
VP: Jackie Brighton
Dir OR: Kellie Drake
Dir Bus: Jeff Newberg
Dir Sec: Bill Duffy
Info Man: Robert Young
Mktg Dir: Angela Dickens
Mktg Dir: Angela Dickson
Mktg Dir: Nancy Notis
Mktg Dir: Grant Sanborn

D-U-N-S 79-769-6528
■ HCA HEALTH SERVICES OF OKLAHOMA INC
OU MEDICAL CENTER
(*Suby of* HOSPITAL COPORATION OF AMERICA) ★
700 Ne 13th St, Oklahoma City, OK 73104-5004
Tel (405) 271-6035 *Founded/Ownrshp* 1980
Sales 258.7MM[E] *EMP* 2,900
SIC 8062 General medical & surgical hospitals
CEO: Charles L Spicer Jr
**CEO:* Cole Eslyn
COO: Don Johnson
COO: Donald Whitehead
**CFO:* Watson Jim
**CFO:* James Watson
**VP:* Daniel Pryor
VP: Lance Torcom
Dir IT: Jeff Wilkins
Info Man: Ben Lewis
Psych: Kim Anderson

D-U-N-S 10-177-0519
■ HCA HEALTH SERVICES OFTENNESSEE INC
COLUMBIA HCA
(*Suby of* HOSPITAL COPORATION OF AMERICA) ★
1 Park Plz, Nashville, TN 37203-6527
Tel (615) 344-9551 *Founded/Ownrshp* 1968
Sales 305.9MM[E] *EMP* 1,550
SIC 8062 General medical & surgical hospitals
Pr: Jack Bouender
**VP:* Bettye Daugherty

D-U-N-S 17-883-6750
■ HCA HEALTH SERVICES OFTENNESSEE INC
TRISTAR SOUTHERN HILLS MED CTR
(*Suby of* COLUMBIA HCA) ★
391 Wallace Rd, Nashville, TN 37211-4851
Tel (615) 781-4000 *Founded/Ownrshp* 1978
Sales 107.1MM[E] *EMP* 1,300
SIC 8011 8062 Offices & clinics of medical doctors; General medical & surgical hospitals
CEO: R Milton Johnson
Chf Nrs Of: Mary Sharp
Dir QC: Paulette Cole
Doctor: Gina Hamrang

D-U-N-S 96-413-8275
■ HCA HEALTH SERVICES OFTENNESSEE INC
SUMMIT MEDICAL CENTER
(*Suby of* COLUMBIA HCA) ★
5655 Frist Blvd, Hermitage, TN 37076-2053
Tel (615) 316-3000 *Founded/Ownrshp* 1996
Sales 198.8MM *EMP* 1,150
SIC 8062 General medical & surgical hospitals
CEO: Jeff Whitehorn
COO: Kelly Curry
Dir Lab: Lawanda Davis
DP Dir: Rachel Tucker
MIS Dir: Joel Bain
Phys Thrpy: Holly Hill

D-U-N-S 78-763-3478
■ HCA HEALTH SERVICES OFTEXAS INC
TRISTAR HEALTH SYSTEMS
(*Suby of* HOSPITAL COPORATION OF AMERICA) ★
1 Park Plz, Nashville, TN 37203-6527
Tel (615) 344-9551 *Founded/Ownrshp* 1968
Sales 286.1MM[E] *EMP* 4,000
SIC 8062 General medical & surgical hospitals
CEO: Richard M Bracken
**Sr VP:* David G Anderson
**Sr VP:* Jana J Davis
**VP:* Michael Bray
CIO: Christopher A Young

D-U-N-S 07-792-2409
■ HCA HEALTH SERVICES OF VIRGINIA INC
HCA VIRGINIA
(*Suby of* HOSPITAL COPORATION OF AMERICA) ★
1602 Skipwith Rd, Richmond, VA 23229-5205
Tel (804) 289-4500 *Founded/Ownrshp* 1994
Sales 144.0MM^E *EMP* 1,500
SIC 8062 8093 General medical & surgical hospitals; Mental health clinic, outpatient
Pr: Samuel N Hazen
**Treas:* David C Anderson
**Sr VP:* Donald W Stinnett
**VP:* Natalie H Cline
**VP:* John M Franck II
Dir Risk M: Dana Taylor
Dir Rad: James D Wasworth
Dir Rx: Kim B Hayes
Chf Nrs Of: Sue Johnson
Dir Sec: Buddy Blanton
Phys Thrpy: Tony Santowasso

HCA THE HEALTHCARE COMPANY
See HOSPITAL CORP OF AMERICA

D-U-N-S 96-769-7686
▲ HCA HOLDINGS INC
1 Park Plz, Nashville, TN 37203-6527
Tel (615) 344-9551 *Founded/Ownrshp* 1990
Sales 39.6MMM *EMP* 233,000^E
Tkr Sym HCA *Exch* NYS
SIC 8062 General medical & surgical hospitals
Ch Bd: R Milton Johnson
Pr: Michael S Cuffe
Pr: Jon M Foster
Pr: Charles J Hall
Pr: Samuel N Hazen
Pr: A Bruce Moore Jr
CFO: William B Rutherford
Chf Mktg O: Jonathan B Perlin
Ofcr: Jane D Engelbright
Ofcr: Joseph A Sowell
Sr VP: David G Anderson
Sr VP: Ravi S Chari
Sr VP: Jana J Davis
Sr VP: Jane D Englebright
Sr VP: Sandra L Morgan
Sr VP: P Martin Paslick
Sr VP: Joseph N Steakley
Sr VP: John M Steele
Sr VP: Don Stinnett
Sr VP: Donald W Stinnett
Sr VP: Kathryn Torres
Board of Directors: John W Rowe, Robert J Dennis, Thomas F Frist III, William R Frist, Charles O Holliday Jr, Ann H Lamont, Jay O Light, Geoffrey G Meyers, Michael W Michelson, Wayne J Riley

D-U-N-S 05-810-4613
■ HCA HOSPITAL SERVICES OF SAN DIEGO
COLUMBIA HCA
(*Suby of* HOSPITAL COPORATION OF AMERICA) ★
550 N Hillside St, Wichita, KS 67214-4910
Tel (316) 962-2000 *Founded/Ownrshp* 1994
Sales 107.0MM^E *EMP* 3,080
SIC 8062 Hospital, medical school affiliated with residency
CEO: David S Nevill
CFO: David Busatti
Dir Rx: Jack Bond
Dir IT: Jeff Schauf
HC Dir: Deb Miller

D-U-N-S 19-430-3616
■ HCA INC
HOSPITAL COPORATION OF AMERICA
(*Suby of* HCA HOLDINGS INC) ★
1 Park Plz, Nashville, TN 37203-6527
Tel (615) 344-9551 *Founded/Ownrshp* 2006
Sales 23.4MMM^E *EMP* 190,000
SIC 8063 8062 8069 8093 Psychiatric hospitals; General medical & surgical hospitals; Specialty hospitals, except psychiatric; Specialty outpatient clinics
Ch Bd: Richard M Bracken
Chf Path: Dan Pankowski
Pr: Kevin Hicks
**Pr:* R Milton Johnson
Pr: Margaret G Lewis
COO: Rebecca Benoit
COO: Mathew Davis
COO: Nancy Dodson
COO: Lori Rakes Fache
COO: Troy Wood Fache
**COO:* Sam Hazen
COO: Susan Hicks
COO: Michele Meyer
COO: Matthew Sogard
CFO: Alissa Bert
CFO: Amy Chaffin
CFO: Brian Maccolley
Chf Mktg O: Jonathan Perlin
Ofcr: Sue Rachuig
Ofcr: Donald Stewart
Assoc VP: Chris Wobensmith
Board of Directors: Stephen G Pagliuca, Christopher J Birosak, Nathan C Thorne, John P Connaughton, James D Forbes, Kenneth W Freeman, Thomas F Frist III, William R Frist, Christopher R Gordon, Michael W Michelson, James C Momtazee

D-U-N-S 61-344-1609
HCA INFORMATION SERVICES INC
2555 Park Plz, Nashville, TN 37203-1512
Tel (615) 344-9551 *Founded/Ownrshp* 1987
Sales 66.4MM^E *EMP* 1,100
SIC 7374 Data processing & preparation
Pr: Noel Brown Williams

HCA MIDWEST
See BAPTIST-LUTHERAN MEDICAL CENTER

D-U-N-S 06-435-6538
■ HCA PSYCHIATRIC CO
(*Suby of* HOSPITAL COPORATION OF AMERICA) ★
1 Park Plz, Nashville, TN 37203-6527
Tel (615) 344-2390 *Founded/Ownrshp* 1997
Sales 39.2MM^E *EMP* 5,500
SIC 8063 8011 Hospital for the mentally ill; Psychiatrists & psychoanalysts
Ch: Thomas Frish Jr
**Pr:* Jack Bovender

HCA VIRGINIA
See HCA HEALTH SERVICES OF VIRGINIA INC

D-U-N-S 95-997-0971
■ HCA-HEALTHONE LLC
PRESBYTERIAN ST LUKES MED CTR
(*Suby of* HOSPITAL COPORATION OF AMERICA) ★
4900 S Monaco St Ste 380, Denver, CO 80237-3487
Tel (303) 788-2500 *Founded/Ownrshp* 1999
Sales 716.3MM^E *EMP* 4,500^E
SIC 8062 General medical & surgical hospitals
COO: Lynn Cook
Dir Recs: Colleen Simianer
CFO: David Housand
VP: Kathy Ashenfelter
VP: Linda Kanamine
Dir Lab: Diana Brown
Comm Dir: Leslie Horna
Dir Rx: Terry Farnsworth
Dir Rx: Dave Oeser
Chf Nrs Of: Jill Taylor
Dir Sec: Mike Taylor

D-U-N-S 36-257-8999
■ HCA-HOSPITAL CORP OF AMERICA
(*Suby of* HOSPITAL COPORATION OF AMERICA) ★
1 Park Plz, Nashville, TN 37203-6527
Tel (615) 344-9551 *Founded/Ownrshp* 1994
Sales 5.2MMM^E *EMP* 134,000
SIC 8062 8063 General medical & surgical hospitals; Psychiatric hospitals
Ch Bd: Thomas F Frist Jr
Board of Directors: Robert J Dennis, John W Rowe

HCBOE
See HOUSTON COUNTY BOARD OF EDUCATION

HCBOE
See HABERSHAM COUNTY BOARD OF EDUCATION

HCC BRANDS
See HANNAS CANDLE CO

D-U-N-S 05-644-4060
■ HCC INDUSTRIES INC
(*Suby of* AMETEK SENSOR TECHNOLOGY BUS) ★
4232 Temple City Blvd, Rosemead, CA 91770-1552
Tel (626) 443-8933 *Founded/Ownrshp* 2005
Sales 170.9MM^E *EMP* 800
SIC 3679 Hermetic seals for electronic equipment
Pr: Richard Ferraid

D-U-N-S 78-112-0100
HCC INSURANCE HOLDINGS INC
TOKIO MARINE HCC
13403 Northwest Fwy, Houston, TX 77040-6006
Tel (713) 690-7300 *Founded/Ownrshp* 2015
Sales NA *EMP* 1,983^E
SIC 6311 6321 6331 Life insurance; Accident & health insurance; Fire, marine & casualty insurance
CEO: Christopher J B Williams
**Pr:* William N Burke Jr
Pr: Melissa Elliott
Pr: Nathan Harris
COO: Kendall Jones
**CFO:* Brad T Irick
Ex VP: Pamela J Penny
Ex VP: Pamela Penny
Sr VP: Brad Breau
Sr VP: Randy D Rinicella
Sr VP: Brian Steele
VP: Mark Adams
VP: Dave Boatman
VP: Sharon Brock
VP: Brenda Bull
VP: Charlie Carlson
VP: Nicky Davis
VP: Christopher Day
VP: Mike Hausmann
VP: Jackie Kellems
VP: Robin Lang
Board of Directors: Ian Brimecome, Akira Harashima, Ichiro Ishii

D-U-N-S 17-812-0689
HCC LIFE INSURANCE CO
(*Suby of* TOKIO MARINE HCC) ★
225 Townpark Dr Nw # 145, Kennesaw, GA 30144-5885
Tel (770) 973-9851 *Founded/Ownrshp* 1987
Sales NA *EMP* 278
SIC 6411 Insurance brokers
Pr: Craig J Kelbel Jr
**COO:* Daniel Strusz
**CFO:* Mark Sanderford
Bd of Dir: Mark Carney
**Sr VP:* David Grider
Sr VP: Stephen Guglielmo
**Sr VP:* Larry Stewart
VP: Edward H Ellis Jr
VP: Tom Matchinsky
VP: Jay Ritchie
Rgnl Mgr: Paul Dito

HCC SURETY GROUP
See AMERICAN CONTRACTORS INDEMNITY CO

HCCAO
See HIGHLAND COUNTY COMMUNITY ACTION ORGANIZATION INC

D-U-N-S 07-756-1538
HCF MANAGEMENT INC
HEALTH CARE FACILITIES
1100 Shawnee Rd, Lima, OH 45805-3583
Tel (419) 999-2010 *Founded/Ownrshp* 1968
Sales 121.4MM^E *EMP* 3,100
SIC 8051 6513 Skilled nursing care facilities; Apartment building operators
Pr: Jim Unverferth
**CEO:* Robert Wilson
Ex VP: Steve Wilder
VP: Michael Hohl
**VP:* Robert Noft
**VP:* Fred J Rinehart
VP: David Seitz
VP: Richard A Unverferth
**VP:* Michalynn Wilson
Dir Risk M: Ryan Stechschulte
Rgnl Mgr: Dave Walsh

HCGH HOWARD COUNTY GEN HOSP
See HOWARD COUNTY GENERAL HOSPITAL INC

D-U-N-S 01-022-1574
▲ HCI GROUP INC (FL)
5300 W Cypress St Ste 100, Tampa, FL 33607-1712
Tel (813) 849-9500 *Founded/Ownrshp* 2007
Sales NA *EMP* 310
Tkr Sym HCI *Exch* NYS
SIC 6331 6411 Fire, marine & casualty insurance; Property & casualty insurance agent
Ch Bd: Paresh Patel
CFO: Richard R Allen
Sr VP: Mark Harmsworth
VP: Andrew L Graham
Board of Directors: George Apostolou, Wayne Burks, James Macchiarola, Sanjay Madhu, Gregory Politis, Anthony Saravanos, Martin A Traber

D-U-N-S 05-374-0353 IMP/EXP
HCI INC (CA)
H C I
(*Suby of* LOMBARDY HOLDINGS INC) ★
3166 Hrseless Carriage Rd, Norco, CA 92860-3612
Tel (951) 520-4202 *Founded/Ownrshp* 1981
Sales 85.0MM^E *EMP* 400
SIC 1623 Communication line & transmission tower construction
Pr: Steven G Silagi
CFO: Stephen Young
Bd of Dir: Rakesh Garach
VP: Brian Clarke
Dept Mgr: Tom Canfield
Genl Mgr: Bob Warwick

D-U-N-S 19-729-8524
HCL AMERICA INC
(*Suby of* HCL TECHNOLOGIES LIMITED)
330 Potrero Ave, Sunnyvale, CA 94085-4194
Tel (408) 733-0480 *Founded/Ownrshp* 1995
Sales 2.8MMM *EMP* 7,000
Accts Sr Batliboi & Co Llp Hary
SIC 7376 7371 8741 Computer facilities management; Computer software development; Management services
Ch: Shiv Nadar
V Ch: Vineet Nayar
**Pr:* Saurav Adhikari
**CEO:* Manish Anand
**CEO:* Roshni Nadar Malhotra
**CFO:* Pawan K Danwar
**Chf Mktg O:* Sundararajan M Sundar
Assoc VP: Srinivas Ajjarapu
Ex VP: Ian Greenhalgh
Ex VP: Darren Oberst
Sr VP: Andrew Jornod
VP: Sunil Aggarwal
VP: Wynn Baum
VP: Alfred Corrieri
VP: Sivakumar Gopalakrishnan
VP: Bharath Krishnaswamy
VP: Richard Mizuno
VP: Ayut Patel
VP: Srivatchan Rajaraman
VP: Richard Seel
VP: Sadagopan S Singam

HCL AXON
See AXON SOLUTIONS INC

D-U-N-S 36-299-7889
HCL GLOBAL SYSTEMS INC
24543 Indoplex Cir # 220, Farmington Hills, MI 48335-2529
Tel (248) 473-0720 *Founded/Ownrshp* 2005
Sales 78.7MM *EMP* 11,000
Accts Farquharson Pointon & Lepsetz
SIC 7379 7371 Computer related consulting services; Software programming applications
Pr: Durga Prassad Gadde

D-U-N-S 11-342-4154 IMP
HCL LIQUIDATION LTD
HUSSEY FABRICATED PRODUCTS
100 Washington St, Leetsdale, PA 15056-1000
Tel (724) 251-4200 *Founded/Ownrshp* 1984
Sales 116.3MM^E *EMP* 697
SIC 3351 Rails, copper & copper alloy
CFO: Joseph Criptko
VP: R L Peterson
Exec: Brian McNamara
Exec: Ron Pynos
MIS Dir: James Zanotti
VP Mktg: R A Stragand
Sls Dir: Mary Graff
Sls Dir: Richard Kyle
Mktg Mgr: Dan Borkowski
Sls Mgr: Joe Collins
Sls Mgr: Dave Ziolkowski

D-U-N-S 05-801-2022
HCO HOLDING I CORP
(*Suby of* HNC PARENT INC) ★
999 N Sepulveda Blvd, El Segundo, CA 90245-2714
Tel (323) 583-5000 *Founded/Ownrshp* 2012
Sales 250.7MM^E *EMP* 560
SIC 6719 Investment holding companies, except banks
CEO: Mike Kenny
**CEO:* Brian C Strauss
CFO: Jason Peel
**CFO:* Dori M Reap
**Sr VP:* Robert D Armstrong
**Sr VP:* James F Barry
**Sr VP:* Christopher J Brink
**Sr VP:* Alan K Davenport
Sr VP: Estevan Fairfax
**Sr VP:* Kirk R Kandler
VP: Mark Adams
VP: Mark R Adams
VP: Bob Armstrong
VP: Inigo Bang
VP: Craig T Carter
VP: Alok Gupta
VP: Donald Lenaker
VP: Ariel Lender

D-U-N-S 14-745-2494
▲ HCP INC
1920 Main St Ste 1200, Irvine, CA 92614-7230
Tel (949) 407-0700 *Founded/Ownrshp* 1985
Sales 2.5MMM *EMP* 187^E
Tkr Sym HCP *Exch* NYS
SIC 6798 Real estate investment trusts
Pr: Lauralee E Martin
CFO: Timothy M Schoen
Ex VP: Scott A Anderson
Ex VP: Jonathan Bergschneider
Ex VP: Thomas D Kirby
Ex VP: Thomas M Klaritch
Ex VP: Troy E McHenry
Ex VP: Kendall Young
Sr VP: Darren A Kowalske
VP: Matthew Harrison
VP: Tom Hulme
VP: Ellie McNichols
VP: Angela Playle
VP: Tracy Porter
VP: Patrick Strangle
Board of Directors: Brian G Cartwright, Christine N Garvey, David B Henry, James P Hoffmann, Michael D McKee, Peter L Rhein, Joseph P Sullivan

HCPSS
See HOWARD COUNTY PUBLIC SCHOOL SYSTEM

HCR
See HANDEX CONSULTING AND REMEDIATION LLC

D-U-N-S 07-932-0794
■ HCR MANOR CARE INC
(*Suby of* MANOR CARE INC) ★
333 N Summit St Ste 103, Toledo, OH 43604-2617
Tel (419) 252-5743 *Founded/Ownrshp* 2005
Sales 582.8MM^E *EMP* 56,063^E
SIC 8051 Skilled nursing care facilities
Prin: David Lanning

D-U-N-S 04-831-4108
■ HCR MANORCARE MEDICAL SERVICES OF FLORIDA LLC
MANOR CARE
(*Suby of* MANOR CARE OF AMERICA INC) ★
333 N Summit St Ste 100, Toledo, OH 43604-2617
Tel (419) 252-5500 *Founded/Ownrshp* 1996
Sales 88.4MM^E *EMP* 520
SIC 8051 Convalescent home with continuous nursing care
Ch Bd: Paul Ormond
COO: Stephen L Guillard
**COO:* Keith Weikel
CFO: Steven M Cardnavgn
**CFO:* Steve Cavannough
**Treas:* Douglas G Haag
**VP:* R Jeffrey Bixler
Off Mgr: Alice Brandon
Mktg Dir: Traci Roberts

HCSC
See HEALTH CARE SERVICE CORP ILLINOIS STATE PAC NFP

D-U-N-S 14-438-5346
HCSC INSURANCE SERVICES CO
(*Suby of* BLUE CROSS AND BLUE SHIELD) ★
300 E Randolph St, Chicago, IL 60601-5014
Tel (312) 653-6000 *Founded/Ownrshp* 2005
Sales NA *EMP* 1^E
SIC 6311 Life insurance
Pr: Raymond F McCaskey
Ex VP: Martin G Foster
Sr VP: Deborah D Rodriguez
CIO: Maria Suarez
Mktg Dir: Cynthia Jania
Mktg Dir: William Jeffries
Mktg Dir: Jen Kruse
Mktg Dir: Phil Pitt

D-U-N-S 19-807-1529
■ HCSG SUPPLY INC
(*Suby of* HEALTHCARE SERVICES GROUP INC) ★
45 Runway Dr Ste H, Levittown, PA 19057-4737
Tel (215) 269-0988 *Founded/Ownrshp* 2005
Sales 116.2MM^E *EMP* 5,005^E
SIC 5099 Durable goods
Prin: Daniel Mc Cartney

D-U-N-S 02-857-8187
HCTEC PARTNERS LLC
7105 S Springs Dr Ste 208, Franklin, TN 37067-1712
Tel (615) 577-4030 *Founded/Ownrshp* 2010
Sales 120.0MM *EMP* 110
SIC 8741 Management services
CEO: William Bartholomew
**COO:* Steve Schott
**CFO:* Lance Fusacchia
**Ch:* Campbell Langdon
**VP:* Ben Bernecker
**VP:* Ryan Roth
CTO: James Oleksa
Dir IT: Bob Craig
Dir Health: Teresa Carter

D-U-N-S 05-045-8975 EXP
HD AMERICAN ROAD LLC
ORLANDO HARLEY DAVIDSON
3770 37th St, Orlando, FL 32805-6617
Tel (407) 423-0346 *Founded/Ownrshp* 2000
Sales 91.7MM^E *EMP* 250
SIC 5571 Motorcycle dealers; Motorcycles
CFO: Rob Ferrentino
Genl Mgr: Ghizlane Aguenegou
IT Man: Scott Buxton
Sls Mgr: Chris Skinner

D-U-N-S 79-317-2250 IMP
■ HD BUILDER SOLUTIONS GROUP LLC
(*Suby of* HD SUPPLY HOLDINGS LLC) ★
2455 Paces Ferry Rd Se C9, Atlanta, GA 30339-1834
Tel (770) 443-8211 *Founded/Ownrshp* 2007
Sales 550.0MM^E *EMP* 1,631^E

SIC 5023 1752 1799 Floor coverings; Floor laying & floor work; Drapery track installation
Pr: Tom Lazzaro

D-U-N-S 78-099-1233 IMP
■ HD SUPPLY CONSTRUCTION SUPPLY GROUP INC
(*Suby of* HD SUPPLY HOLDINGS LLC) ★
3100 Cumberland Blvd Se, Atlanta, GA 30339-5940
Tel (770) 852-9000 *Founded/Ownrshp* 1996
Sales 3.3MMM^E *EMP* 3,740^E
SIC 5072 5039 5031 Hardware; Air ducts, sheet metal; Joists; Soil erosion control fabrics; Lumber, plywood & millwork
CEO: Joseph J Deangelo
Pr: Greg Roth
CFO: Alan Sollenberger
VP: Tim Klei

D-U-N-S 19-251-0290 IMP/EXP
■ HD SUPPLY CONSTRUCTION SUPPLY LTD
(*Suby of* HD SUPPLY CONSTRUCTION SUPPLY GROUP INC) ★
3100 Cumberland Blvd Se # 1700, Atlanta, GA 30339-5939
Tel (770) 852-9000 *Founded/Ownrshp* 2005
Sales 1.6MMM^E *EMP* 3,740^E
SIC 5031 5039 5072 Lumber, plywood & millwork; Air ducts, sheet metal; Joists; Soil erosion control fabrics; Hardware
CEO: Joseph J Deangelo
Pr: John Stegeman
VP: Ricardo Nunez
Sales Asso: Shawn Harrell
Sales Asso: Robert Shenk

D-U-N-S 78-444-9485 IMP/EXP
HD SUPPLY DISTRIBUTION SERVICES LLC
CROWN BOLT
26940 Aliso Viejo Pkwy, Aliso Viejo, CA 92656-2622
Tel (949) 643-4700 *Founded/Ownrshp* 2005
Sales NA *EMP* 1,078
SIC 5072

D-U-N-S 79-146-4022
HD SUPPLY FACILITIES MAINTENANCE GROUP INC
3100 Cumberland Blvd Se, Atlanta, GA 30339-5940
Tel (770) 852-9000 *Founded/Ownrshp* 2007
Sales 3.8MMM^E *EMP* 3,976^E
SIC 5087

D-U-N-S 17-121-8949 IMP
■ HD SUPPLY FACILITIES MAINTENANCE LTD
USABLUEBOOK
(*Suby of* HD SUPPLY GP & MANAGEMENT, INC.)
3100 Cumberland Blvd Se # 1700, Atlanta, GA 30339-5940
Tel (770) 852-9000 *Founded/Ownrshp* 2004
Sales 5.1MMM^E *EMP* 3,967^E
SIC 5087 Cleaning & maintenance equipment & supplies
Pr: Joseph J Deangelo
**CFO:* Evan Levitt
CFO: Ronald F Turk
VP: Kevin Peters
Area Mgr: Milton Deputy
Natl Sales: Thomas Enneking
Pr Mgr: Donna Taliercio
Mktg Mgr: Lauree D McGrady
Mktg Mgr: Bruce Prevo
Manager: Jennifer Smyrniotis
Sales Asso: Jennifer Swisher

HD SUPPLY GLOBAL SUPPORT CENTER
See HD SUPPLY INC

D-U-N-S 82-584-0593
▲ HD SUPPLY HOLDINGS INC
3100 Cumberland Blvd Se # 1480, Atlanta, GA 30339-5939
Tel (770) 852-9000 *Founded/Ownrshp* 2007
Sales 7.3MMM *EMP* 15,000^E
Tkr Sym HDS *Exch* NGS
SIC 5087 5072 5085 Cleaning & maintenance equipment & supplies; Hardware; Industrial supplies
Pr: Joseph J Deangelo
**Ch Bd:* James G Berges
COO: Steven Margolius
**CFO:* Evan Levitt
CFO: Evan J Levitt
**Ex VP:* John Stegeman
**Sr VP:* Ronald J Domanico
**Sr VP:* Margaret Newman
Sr VP: Margaret M Newman
**Sr VP:* Ricardo J Nunez
Sr VP: William P Stengel
VP: Jim Maddox

D-U-N-S 61-357-1038
■ HD SUPPLY HOLDINGS LLC
(*Suby of* HD SUPPLY GLOBAL SUPPORT CENTER) ★
3100 Cumberland Blvd Se # 1700, Atlanta, GA 30339-5939
Tel (770) 852-9000 *Founded/Ownrshp* 2004
Sales 11.5MMM^E *EMP* 14,999
SIC 5051 5074 5084 5099 Cast iron pipe; Pipes & fittings, plastic; Plumbing & heating valves; Meters, consumption registering; Safety equipment & supplies
Pr: Anesa Chaibi
Pr: Rich Feichter
Pr: Frank Garcia
Pr: Tom Lazzaro
COO: Steve Leclair
CFO: Mark T Jamieson
Sr VP: Vidya Chauhan
Sr VP: Paul Iaderosa

HD SUPPLY HOME IMPRV SOLUTIONS
See HD SUPPLY REPAIR & REMODEL LLC

D-U-N-S 02-912-7586 IMP
■ HD SUPPLY INC
HD SUPPLY GLOBAL SUPPORT CENTER
(*Suby of* HDS HOLDING CORP) ★
3100 Cumberland Blvd Se # 1700, Atlanta, GA 30339-5939
Tel (770) 852-9000 *Founded/Ownrshp* 2007
Sales 7.3MMM *EMP* 15,000
Accts Pricewaterhousecoopers Llp At
SIC 5031 5033 Building materials, exterior; Building materials, interior; Doors & windows; Roofing, siding & insulation
Pr: Joseph J Deangelo
**Ch Bd:* James G Berges
Pr: Mark Foster
Pr: Jim Maddox
Pr: Rob Vicini
CFO: Evan J Levitt
CFO: Rich Schaefer
Sr VP: Mark Fabere
Sr VP: Joseph Izganics
Sr VP: Margaret Newman
Sr VP: Ricardo Nunez
VP: Lester Jenkins
VP: Michael Kemp
VP: Michael Vitale
Exec: John Stegeman
Board of Directors: Brian A Bernasek, Paul B Edgerley, Mitchell Jacobson, Lew Klessel, Nathan K Sleeper, Stephen M Zide

HD SUPPLY INTERIOR SOLUTIONS
See ISI DESIGN AND INSTALLATION SOLUTIONS INC

D-U-N-S 79-204-7545
■ HD SUPPLY POWER SOLUTIONS GROUP INC
(*Suby of* HD SUPPLY HOLDINGS LLC) ★
501 W Church St Ste 100, Orlando, FL 32805-2270
Tel (407) 841-4755 *Founded/Ownrshp* 2004
Sales 221.8MM^E *EMP* 847
SIC 5063 Electrical apparatus & equipment
Pr: Joseph J Deangelo
**VP:* Marc Gonzalez
VP: Jason Herin
**VP:* Evan Levitt
**VP:* Ricardo Nunez

D-U-N-S 60-301-3256 IMP
■ HD SUPPLY REPAIR & REMODEL LLC
HD SUPPLY HOME IMPRV SOLUTIONS
(*Suby of* HD SUPPLY GP & MANAGEMENT, INC.)
1695 Eureka Rd, Roseville, CA 95661-3027
Tel (916) 751-2300 *Founded/Ownrshp* 2007
Sales 156.3MM^E *EMP* 800
SIC 5211 Home centers
Pr: Rich Fiechter
CFO: Jody Porter

D-U-N-S 00-331-5934 IMP
■ HD SUPPLY WATERWORKS GROUP INC
(*Suby of* HD SUPPLY HOLDINGS LLC) ★
501 W Church St Ste 100, Orlando, FL 32805-2270
Tel (407) 841-4755 *Founded/Ownrshp* 2004
Sales 2.0MMM^E *EMP* 2,966^E
SIC 5051 5074 5084 5099 Cast iron pipe; Pipes & fittings, plastic; Plumbing & heating valves; Meters, consumption registering; Safety equipment & supplies
CEO: Joseph J Deangelo
**Pr:* Anesa Chaibi
**Pr:* Rich Fiechter
**Pr:* Frank Garcia
**Pr:* Tom Lazzaro
**Pr:* Steve Margolius
**Pr:* Rick McClure
**Pr:* Mike Stanwood
**Pr:* Jerry Webb
**COO:* Steve Leclair
**CFO:* Mark T Jamieson
**Sr VP:* Vidya Chauhan
**Sr VP:* Paul Iaderosa
**Sr VP:* Michele Markham
**Sr VP:* Meg Newman
**Sr VP:* Ricardo Nunez

D-U-N-S 62-756-4029 IMP/EXP
■ HD SUPPLY WATERWORKS LTD
(*Suby of* HD SUPPLY WATERWORKS GROUP INC) ★
3100 Cumberland Blvd Se, Atlanta, GA 30339-5940
Tel (770) 852-9000 *Founded/Ownrshp* 2004
Sales 1.2MMM^E *EMP* 2,600
SIC 5074 Plumbing & hydronic heating supplies
Pr: Stephen O Leclair
CFO: Don Clayton
Dir IT: Neil Brinson
Dir IT: Paul Conry
Dir IT: Kay Kirkland
VP Opers: Paul Iaderosa
Sales Asso: Kenneth Jensen

D-U-N-S 02-353-6088 IMP
HDC DISTRIBUTING LTD
7100 High Life Dr, Houston, TX 77066-3713
Tel (281) 880-2730 *Founded/Ownrshp* 2009
Sales 203.7MM *EMP* 2
Accts Tiller & Company Baytown Tex
SIC 5199 Nondurable goods

HDI
See HYDRAQUIP INC

D-U-N-S 03-512-2456
HDR ARCHITECTURE INC
(*Suby of* HDR INC) ★
8404 Indian Hills Dr, Omaha, NE 68114-4098
Tel (402) 399-1000 *Founded/Ownrshp* 1996
Sales 241.5MM *EMP* 1,426
Accts Ernst & Young Llp Omaha Ne
SIC 8711 Designing: ship, boat, machine & product
CEO: George A Little
**Pr:* Eric L Keen
**Pr:* Douglas Wignall
**CFO:* Terence C Cox
**Treas:* Chad Hartnett

D-U-N-S 18-729-4624
HDR ENGINEERING INC
H D R
(*Suby of* HDR INC) ★
8404 Indian Hills Dr, Omaha, NE 68114-4098
Tel (402) 399-1000 *Founded/Ownrshp* 1996
Sales 1.2MMM *EMP* 6,111
Accts Ernst & Young Llp Omaha Ne
SIC 8742 8711 Management consulting services; Engineering services
CEO: George A Little
Pr: Eric L Keen
COO: George Little
CFO: Terence C Cox
Treas: Chad M Hartnett
Ex VP: Terry Cox
VP: Laurence D Bory
VP: Bill Burgel
CIO: Mike Geppert
Tech Mgr: Doug Wilson
Info Man: Mark Graff

D-U-N-S 06-866-8805
HDR INC
8404 Indian Hills Dr, Omaha, NE 68114-4098
Tel (402) 399-1000 *Founded/Ownrshp* 1996
Sales 2.0MMM^E *EMP* 9,633
Accts Ernst & Young Llp Omaha Ne
SIC 8712 8711 8742 8748 4789 Architectural services; Engineering services; Management consulting services; Industry specialist consultants; Systems analysis & engineering consulting services; Passenger train services
Ch Bd: George A Little
V Ch: Ronald L Harrisformer
Pr: Doug Wignall
CFO: Terance C Cox
CFO: Terrence C Cox
CFO: Terry Cox
Treas: Wendy L Lacey
Bd of Dir: Merle Bachman
Bd of Dir: Eddie Bumbaugh
Assoc VP: Diane Hamlin
Assoc VP: Chris Sklavounakis
Ex VP: Gary L Bleeker
Ex VP: Tim Connolly
Ex VP: Elwin Larson
Ex VP: Charles O'Reilly
Sr VP: Rex Fisher
Sr VP: Roger Parkins
VP: Rob Berman
VP: Lynne Bonge
VP: James Chapman
VP: Shannon D'Agostino
Board of Directors: Richard R Bell

HDS
See HAWAII DENTAL SERVICE

D-U-N-S 82-587-9104
■ HDS HOLDING CORP
(*Suby of* HD SUPPLY HOLDINGS INC) ★
3100 Cumberland Blvd Se, Atlanta, GA 30339-5940
Tel (770) 852-9000 *Founded/Ownrshp* 2007
Sales 7.3MMM^E *EMP* 15,000^E
SIC 5087 5072 5085 Cleaning & maintenance equipment & supplies; Hardware; Industrial supplies
CEO: Joseph J Deangelo
Corp Couns: Jim Brumsey

D-U-N-S 18-443-0627 IMP
HDS RETAIL NORTH AMERICA LP
LS TRAVEL RETAIL NORTH AMERICA
(*Suby of* HACHETTE DISTRIBUTION INC) ★
60 E 42nd St Rm 3410, New York, NY 10165-3410
Tel (212) 477-7373 *Founded/Ownrshp* 1988
Sales 550.0MM^E *EMP* 4,506^E
SIC 5994 News dealers & newsstands
Pt: Gerry Savaria
**Pt:* Craig Liden
**Pt:* Vadim Motlik
VP: Karen Hardy
Area Mgr: Stephanie Hatch
Snr PM: Doug Harrington

HDT ENGINEERED TECHNOLOGIES
See HUNTER DEFENSE TECHNOLOGIES INC

D-U-N-S 80-060-7454
HDT GLOBAL INC
30500 Aurora Rd Ste 100, Solon, OH 44139-2776
Tel (216) 438-6111 *Founded/Ownrshp* 2014
Sales 369.3MM^E *EMP* 650
SIC 8711

HEAD PENN RACQUET SPORTS
See HEAD USA INC

HEAD START SCHOOL
See MISSISSIPPI ACTION FOR PROGRESS INC

HEAD TYROLIA WINTER SPORTS
See HTM USA HOLDINGS INC

D-U-N-S 15-466-6341 IMP
HEAD USA INC
HEAD PENN RACQUET SPORTS
(*Suby of* HEAD TYROLIA WINTER SPORTS) ★
3125 Sterling Cir Ste 101, Boulder, CO 80301-2394
Tel (800) 874-3235 *Founded/Ownrshp* 1996
Sales 100.0MM *EMP* 109
SIC 5091 Diving equipment & supplies; Skiing equipment; Racquet sports equipment & supplies
Ch Bd: Johan Eliasch
**CEO:* Kevin Kempin
**COO:* Rose Mary Traynor
**Treas:* Gunter Hagspiel
Comm Man: Allison Barnett

D-U-N-S 00-176-2137
HEADCO INDUSTRIES INC (IL)
BEARING HEADQUARTERS CO
2601 Parkes Dr, Broadview, IL 60155-4517
Tel (708) 681-4400 *Founded/Ownrshp* 1939, 1968
Sales 132.4MM^E *EMP* 275
SIC 5085 3599 5084

D-U-N-S 11-203-6939
HEADSTRONG CORP
(*Suby of* GENPACT LLC) ★
11921 Freedom Dr Ste 550, Reston, VA 20190-5635
Tel (703) 272-6761 *Founded/Ownrshp* 2011
Sales 146.0MM^E *EMP* 2,300
SIC 7379 8999 Computer related consulting services; Communication services
Pr: Sandeep Sahai
**CFO:* Adarsh Mehra
Ex VP: Lalit Bajaj
VP: Michael Barrett
VP: Ben Levy
Exec: Sameer Srivastava
Snr Sftwr: Ruhi Shukla
Snr Sftwr: Dhivya Thiruvengadam
QA Dir: Melvin Lontoc
Tech Mgr: Prabhu Damodharan
Tech Mgr: Surajit Dutta

D-U-N-S 78-619-5701 IMP/EXP
▲ HEADWATERS INC
10701 S River Front Pkwy # 300, South Jordan, UT 84095-3524
Tel (801) 984-9400 *Founded/Ownrshp* 1987
Sales 895.3MM *EMP* 2,831
Tkr Sym HW *Exch* NYS
SIC 3272 3271 3281 2952 Concrete products; Siding, precast stone; Concrete block & brick; Building stone products; Asphalt felts & coatings
Ch Bd: Kirk A Benson
Pr: William H Gehrmann III
Pr: Murphy K Lents
Pr: Brent A Spann
Pr: Bobby L Whisnant
CFO: Donald P Newman
VP: Harlan M Hatfield
VP: David Marshall

D-U-N-S 03-089-0953 IMP/EXP
■ HEADWATERS RESOURCES INC
ISG RESOURCES
(*Suby of* HEADWATERS INC) ★
10701 S River Front Pkwy # 300, South Jordan, UT 84095-3524
Tel (801) 984-9400 *Founded/Ownrshp* 2002
Sales 126.3MM^E *EMP* 1,000
SIC 5032 4953 8711 Cement; Masons' materials; Refuse systems; Engineering services
Pr: William H Gehrmann
**Pr:* Kurt Benson
**CFO:* Don Newman
**Treas:* Scott Jackson
**Treas:* Steven G Stewart
**VP:* Harlan M Hatfield
VP: Brandon Trask
Sls&Mrk Ex: John Ward

D-U-N-S 08-865-3576 IMP
HEADWAY TECHNOLOGIES INC
(*Suby of* TDK CORPORATION)
682 S Hillview Dr, Milpitas, CA 95035-5457
Tel (408) 934-5300 *Founded/Ownrshp* 1994
Sales 253.3MM^E *EMP* 3,139
SIC 3572 Magnetic storage devices, computer
Pr: Mao-Min Chen
CFO: Thomas Surran
VP: Moris Dovek
**VP:* Gary Pester
Snr Ntwrk: David Stoeckle
CTO: Jinsong Wang
VP Opers: David Wagner
Snr Mgr: Yuhui Tang

D-U-N-S 83-311-8164
HEALD CAPITAL LLC
(*Suby of* CORINTHIAN COLLEGES, INC.)
601 Montgomery St Fl 14, San Francisco, CA 94111-2618
Tel (415) 808-1400 *Founded/Ownrshp* 2010
Sales 83.8MM^E *EMP* 801^E
SIC 6719 Investment holding companies, except banks
Pr: Larry Barton
IT Man: Gerald Reddick

D-U-N-S 83-763-1142
HEALOGICS INC
5220 Belfort Rd Ste 130, Jacksonville, FL 32256-6018
Tel (904) 296-6526 *Founded/Ownrshp* 1995
Sales 257.0M^E *EMP* 2,455
SIC 8093 Specialty outpatient clinics
Ch: Edgar Otto
**CEO:* James E Patrick
**CFO:* James M Tyler
VP: Leanne Odonnell
IT Man: David Berens
Pgrm Dir: Geraldine Zimmerman

D-U-N-S 07-951-5003
HEALTH & EDUCATION SERVICES INC
199 Rosewood Dr Ste 250, Danvers, MA 01923-1684
Tel (978) 921-1293 *Founded/Ownrshp* 1971
Sales 28.2MM^E *EMP* 1,000
Accts Deloitte Taxllp Boston Ma
SIC 8093 Mental health clinic, outpatient
Pr: Paul O'Shea
**Ch:* Michael Shea
**Treas:* Janice Preston
**Prin:* Kevin Norton

D-U-N-S 92-704-9767
HEALTH & FAMILY SERVICES KENTUCKY CABINET FOR
(*Suby of* EXECUTIVE OFFICE OF COMMONWEALTH OF KENTUCKY) ★
275 E Main St B, Frankfort, KY 40601-2321
Tel (502) 564-5497 *Founded/Ownrshp* 1996
Sales NA *EMP* 8,300
SIC 9431 Administration of public health programs;
Prin: Mark D Birdwhistell
Ofcr: Audrey Haynes
IT Man: Denise Purvis
IT Man: Donna Temple

D-U-N-S 05-295-2058
HEALTH & HOSPITAL CORP OF MARION COUNTY
DIVISION OF PUBLIC HEALTH
3838 N Rural St Fl 8, Indianapolis, IN 46205-2930
Tel (317) 221-2000 *Founded/Ownrshp* 1951
Sales 505.0MM^E *EMP* 3,982
SIC 8062 General medical & surgical hospitals
Pr: Mack Gutwein
CFO: Marjorie Olaughlin
Treas: Marjorie Laughlin
**Treas:* Daniel Sellers
**VP:* Greg Porter
Comm Dir: Kate McGaffery
Ex Dir: Catherine Parker
Prgrm Mgr: Jason Doerflein
Brnch Mgr: Michael Brune
Brnch Mgr: Davod Jackson
Genl Mgr: Donna Laake

HEALTH ACCESS NETWORK
See CROZER-KEYSTONE HEALTH NETWORK

D-U-N-S 07-578-7333
HEALTH ACQUISITION CORP
ALLEN HEALTH CARE SERVICES
(*Suby of* NATIONAL HOME HEALTH CARE CORP) ★
7000 Austin St Ste 2, Forest Hills, NY 11375-4739
Tel (718) 657-2966 *Founded/Ownrshp* 1987
Sales 16.4MM^E *EMP* 1,500
SIC 8082 Home health care services
Pr: Ian Rowe
**CFO:* Robert P Heller

D-U-N-S 83-169-8431
HEALTH ALLIANCE INC
HEALTHALLIANCE OF HUDSON VLY
741 Grant Ave, Lake Katrine, NY 12449-5350
Tel (845) 334-3151 *Founded/Ownrshp* 2007
Sales 3.8MM *EMP* 2,100^E
Accts Charles A Barragato & Co Llp
SIC 8062 General medical & surgical hospitals
Pr: David Scarpino
**CFO:* Steven Haas
Sr VP: Margo McGilvrey
Chf Nrs Of: Kathy Luney
Genl Mgr: Leslie Dawson
QA Dir: Joseph Marsciovete

D-U-N-S 17-482-2775
HEALTH ALLIANCE MEDICAL PLANS INC
(*Suby of* CARLE HOLDING CO INC) ★
301 S Vine St, Urbana, IL 61801-7429
Tel (217) 337-8000 *Founded/Ownrshp* 1989
Sales NA *EMP* 540^E
Accts Kpmg Llp Chicago Illinois
SIC 6321 6324 Accident & health insurance; Health maintenance organization (HMO), insurance only
CEO: Jeff Ingrum
**CFO:* Gordon W Salm
Ofcr: Wyatt Scheiding
VP: Theresa Radosevich
VP: Patti Thornton
Dir IT: Larry Russell
IT Man: Jim Obrien
Sales Exec: Mary Tournoux
Mktg Dir: Lori Rund
Mktg Mgr: Janet Ward

D-U-N-S 09-382-3185
HEALTH ALLIANCE PLAN OF MICHIGAN
(*Suby of* HENRY FORD HOSPITAL) ★
2850 W Grand Blvd, Detroit, MI 48202-2692
Tel (313) 872-8100 *Founded/Ownrshp* 1973
Sales NA *EMP* 1,174
Accts Lb Deloitte Tax Llp Detroit
SIC 6324 8011 8099 Hospital & medical service plans; Health maintenance organization; Group health association; Medical services organization
Pr: Timothy Sullivan
COO: Matthew Walsh
CFO: Ronald Berry
Assoc VP: Marc Vanderburg
Ex VP: Dianna Ronan
Sr VP: Maurice McMurray
VP: Derick Adams
VP: Joel Keiper
VP: Don Kiefiuk
VP: Alice Macdermott
VP: Annette Marcath
Assoc Dir: Sachin Varma

D-U-N-S 11-338-0849
HEALTH ALLIANCE WITH PHYSICIAN
HAPI
60 Hospital Rd, Leominster, MA 01453-2205
Tel (978) 466-2000 *Founded/Ownrshp* 1997
Sales NA *EMP* 25
SIC 6411 Medical insurance claim processing, contract or fee basis
Ex Dir: John Minizhiello

HEALTH AND DENTAL PLAN
See W W GRAINGER INC GROUP BENEFIT TRUST I

D-U-N-S 80-678-1373
HEALTH AND HUMAN SERVICES COMMISSION TEXAS
(*Suby of* EXECUTIVE OFFICE OF STATE OF TEXAS) ★
4900 N Lamar Blvd, Austin, TX 78751-2316
Tel (512) 424-6500 *Founded/Ownrshp* 1991
Sales NA *EMP* 12,000
SIC 9441 9431 Administration of social & manpower programs; ; Administration of public health programs;
**CFO:* Tracy Henderson
CFO: William Lowrey
Ofcr: Joseph Chicola
VP: Arturo Loera
VP: Cecile Ward
Off Mgr: Randy Hale
Off Mgr: Kimberlee Ulery
Dir IT: Edward Medina
Dir IT: Hope Morgan
Web Dev: Donna Herrin
Genl Couns: Carey Smith

HEALTH AND WELFARE DEPT OF THE
See LABORERS PENSION & WELFARE FUNDS

HEALTH AT HOME
See CSLCS LLC

D-U-N-S 07-912-4053
HEALTH CARE AUTHORITY OF CITY OF HUNTSVILLE
HUNTSVILLE HOSP WOMEN CHILDREN
101 Sivley Rd Sw, Huntsville, AL 35801-4421
Tel (256) 265-1000 *Founded/Ownrshp* 1986
Sales 6.0MM^E *EMP* 8,000
SIC 8011 8062 Offices & clinics of medical doctors; General medical & surgical hospitals
CEO: David Spillers
Chf Rad: Timothy Baker
**CFO:* Kelly Towers
VP: Michael W D
Pharmcst: Melissa O'Neill

D-U-N-S 60-288-7726
HEALTH CARE AUTHORITY OF CULLMAN COUNTY
CULLMAN EMERGENCY MEDICAL SERV
1912 Al Highway 157, Cullman, AL 35058-0609
Tel (256) 737-2000 *Founded/Ownrshp* 1984
Sales 96.5MM *EMP* 1,000^E
Accts Draffin & Tucker Llp Albany
SIC 8062 General medical & surgical hospitals
CEO: James D Weidner
**COO:* Jete Edmisson
**Treas:* Debbie Mickle

D-U-N-S 07-545-7283
HEALTH CARE AUTHORITY OF LAUDERDALE COUNTY AND CITY OF FLORENCE
COFFEE HEALTH GROUP
205 Marengo St, Florence, AL 35630-6033
Tel (256) 768-9191 *Founded/Ownrshp* 1943
Sales 69.4MM^E *EMP* 1,475^E
SIC 8051 8062 Skilled nursing care facilities; General medical & surgical hospitals
Pr: Russell Pigd
**Pr:* Carl Bailey
Dir Case M: Neida Fuqua
Dir Rx: Jarod Ott
Chf Nrs Of: Barbara Murphy
Dir Pat Ac: Dave Davis
Psych: Connie Fleming
Doctor: Michael L Brummitt

D-U-N-S 07-898-3939
HEALTH CARE AUTHORITY OF MORGAN COUNTY - CITY OF DECATUR
DECATUR MORGAN HOSPITAL
1201 7th St Se, Decatur, AL 35601-3337
Tel (256) 355-0370 *Founded/Ownrshp* 1915
Sales 152.8MM^E *EMP* 1,500
SIC 8062 Hospital, AMA approved residency
Pr: Nat Richardson
**CFO:* Danny Crowe
**VP:* Jason Lockette
VP: Allen Tsai
Cert Phar: Mac Hazel
Cert Phar: Sharmalita Hines
Cert Phar: Heather Stewart

HEALTH CARE CAPITAL CNSLD
See HEALTH CARE CAPITAL INC

D-U-N-S 80-831-5725
HEALTH CARE CAPITAL INC
HEALTH CARE CAPITAL CNSLD
2 Ravinia Dr Ste 1350, Atlanta, GA 30346-2116
Tel (770) 393-3355 *Founded/Ownrshp* 1993
Sales NA *EMP* 1,532
Accts Deloitte & Touche Llp
SIC 6162 8051 8741 Mortgage bankers & correspondents; Skilled nursing care facilities; Management services
Pr: Michael S Brown
**COO:* Richard Greer
**CFO:* Bryan F Sodel
**Treas:* Wayne Moorhead
**VP:* Bill Nida
**VP:* Matt Robinson

HEALTH CARE FACILITIES
See HCF MANAGEMENT INC

D-U-N-S 06-266-9478
HEALTH CARE FOUNDATION OF WILSON
WILSON MEDICAL CENTER
2505a Nash St Nw, Wilson, NC 27896-1311
Tel (252) 281-2105 *Founded/Ownrshp* 1964
Sales 117.2MM *EMP* 1,100
SIC 8062 General medical & surgical hospitals
CEO: William E Caldwell
COO: Bert Beard
CFO: Lynn Lambert
CFO: Melissa Packer
Chf Mktg O: Ronald Stahl
VP: Rick Guarino
VP: Denise O'Hara
Off Mgr: Barbara Stancil

HEALTH CARE GROUP
See HEALTH CARE INDUSTRIES CORP

D-U-N-S 14-747-4886
HEALTH CARE INC
PROMISE REGIONAL MEDICAL CENTE
1701 E 23rd Ave, Hutchinson, KS 67502-1105
Tel (620) 665-2000 *Founded/Ownrshp* 1983
Sales 127.4MM *EMP* 1,300
Accts Bkd Llp Wichita Ks
SIC 8062 7352 6512 General medical & surgical hospitals; Medical equipment rental; Nonresidential building operators
**Pr:* Kevin Miller
**CFO:* David Busatti
**Prin:* Joyce Radke

D-U-N-S 04-432-5272
HEALTH CARE INDUSTRIES CORP (OH)
HEALTH CARE GROUP
4195 Sugarcreek Dr, Bellbrook, OH 45305-1328
Tel (937) 848-2973 *Founded/Ownrshp* 1980
Sales 34.7MM^E *EMP* 1,025
SIC 8051 8052 Skilled nursing care facilities; Intermediate care facilities
Pr: Rosalyn B Semelsburger

D-U-N-S 17-709-0248
HEALTH CARE MANAGEMENT ADMINISTRATORS INC
HEALTHCARE MGT ADMINISTRATORS
(*Suby of* REGENCECARE) ★
220 120th Ave Ne, Bellevue, WA 98005-3040
Tel (425) 462-1000 *Founded/Ownrshp* 1986
Sales NA *EMP* 121^E
SIC 6411 Insurance claim adjusters, not employed by insurance company
CEO: David Snodgrass
**VP:* Clay Ellis

HEALTH CARE MGT COUNSELORS
See KURT SALMON US LLC

HEALTH CARE SERVICE
See DENTAL NETWORK OF AMERICA LLC

D-U-N-S 03-089-0891
HEALTH CARE SERVICE CORP A MUTUAL LEGAL RESERVE CO
BLUE CROSS AND BLUE SHIELD
300 E Randolph St Fl 4, Chicago, IL 60601-7302
Tel (312) 653-6000 *Founded/Ownrshp* 1936
Sales NA *EMP* 14,264
Accts Ernst & Young Llp Chicago Il
SIC 6324 6321 6411 Hospital & medical service plans; Dental insurance; Health maintenance organization (HMO), insurance only; Health insurance carriers; Medical insurance claim processing, contract or fee basis
CEO: Patricia Hemingway Hall
**Pr:* Karen Atwood
**Pr:* M Ted Haynes
**Pr:* Bert Marshall
**Pr:* Mark Owen
**Pr:* Kurt Shipley
**Pr:* Jeffery Tikkanen
COO: Colleen F Reitan
COO: Patricia Williams
**CFO:* Kenneth Avner
CFO: Denise A Bujck
**CFO:* Eric Feldstein
**Treas:* Gerard Mallen
Chf Mktg O: Theresa Arias
Ofcr: Linda Seman
**Ex VP:* John Cannon
**Ex VP:* Martin Foster
Ex VP: Tara D Gurber
**Ex VP:* Colleen Reitan
**Ex VP:* Paula Steiner
**Sr VP:* Gary Brantz
Board of Directors: Marlin Ray Perryman, Timothy Burke, Waneta Tuttle, Milton Carroll, Robert Clarke, Michelle Collins, James Corrigan, Dennis Gannon, Dianne Gasbarra, Patricia Heminway Hall, Thomas Hix

D-U-N-S 07-860-4947
HEALTH CARE SERVICE CORP ILLINOIS STATE PAC NFP
HCSC
300 E Randolph St Fl 4, Chicago, IL 60601-7302
Tel (312) 653-6000 *Founded/Ownrshp* 2002
Sales NA *EMP* 304^E
SIC 6321 Accident & health insurance
COO: Colleen Reitan
VP: Austin Waldron
IT Man: Harry Preste

D-U-N-S 01-428-7171
HEALTH CARE TEMPORARIES INC
H C T
8926 Sherbourne St Ste D, Houston, TX 77016-4900
Tel (713) 631-7106 *Founded/Ownrshp* 1980
Sales 16.5MM^E *EMP* 1,100
SIC 8082 1542 1522 1081 5082 Home health care services; Commercial & office building contractors; Remodeling, multi-family dwellings; Metal mining services; General construction machinery & equipment
Pr: Arthur Woods
**Sec:* D'Anne Woods
**VP:* Bonita Woods

D-U-N-S 62-099-9706
HEALTH CARE UNLIMITED INC
CENTURY MEDICAL
1100 E Laurel Ave, McAllen, TX 78501-5722
Tel (956) 994-9911 *Founded/Ownrshp* 1990
Sales 88.0MM^E *EMP* 500
SIC 5047 8082 Medical equipment & supplies; Home health care services
Pr: Joseph Ramon III
Dir Bus: Jorge Sanchez

HEALTH CENRAL
See WEST ORANGE HEALTHCARE DISTRICT INC

HEALTH CENTRAL
See WEST ORANGE MEMORIAL HOSPITAL TAX DISTRICT

D-U-N-S 07-261-9542
HEALTH CHOICE ARIZONA INC
(*Suby of* IASIS INVESTMENT LLC) ★
410 N 44th St Ste 900, Phoenix, AZ 85008-6522
Tel (480) 968-6866 *Founded/Ownrshp* 1990
Sales NA *EMP* 200
SIC 6321 6411 Accident & health insurance; Insurance agents, brokers & service
Pr: Carolyn Rose
Dir IT: Melissa Small
Netwrk Mgr: Forad Matti

HEALTH CTR AT HRRISON MEM HOSP
See TRILOGY REHAB SERVICES LLC

D-U-N-S 11-125-3712
HEALTH DEPARTMENT OKLAHOMA STATE
(*Suby of* EXECUTIVE OFFICE OF STATE OF OKLAHOMA) ★
1000 Ne 10th St, Oklahoma City, OK 73117-1207
Tel (405) 271-5600 *Founded/Ownrshp* 1970
Sales NA *EMP* 2,200^E
SIC 9431 Administration of public health programs;
Bd of Dir: Jana Winfree
Ofcr: Dick Gunn
IT Man: Patsy Leisering
Genl Couns: Don Maisch
Pgrm Dir: Janet Love
Art Dir: William A Stegall
Snr Mgr: Pam Archer

D-U-N-S 01-455-2258
HEALTH DIAGNOSTIC LABORATORY INC
INNOVATIVE DIAGNOSTIC LAB
(*Suby of* TRUE HEALTH DIAGNOSTICS LLC) ★
4401 Dominion Blvd, Glen Allen, VA 23060-3379
Tel (804) 343-2718 *Founded/Ownrshp* 2014
Sales 314.0MM *EMP* 511^E
SIC 8734 Testing laboratories
CEO: Joseph McConnell
**Chf Mktg O:* Tara Dall
**Ex VP:* Douglas L Sbertoli
Sr VP: Dan Dunham
Sr VP: Mark A Herzog
VP: Scott Blackwell
VP: Connie Chao-Shern
VP: Maciek Sasinowski
**Dir Sec:* G Russell Warnick
**CTO:* Michael Woodard
QA Dir: Sandra Miller

D-U-N-S 13-754-4552
HEALTH E SYSTEMS LLC
HEALTHESYSTEMS
5100 W Lemon St Ste 311, Tampa, FL 33609-1129
Tel (813) 463-1235 *Founded/Ownrshp* 2002
Sales NA *EMP* 412
SIC 6411 Insurance information & consulting services
Pr: Matt Collins
Sr VP: Robert Goldberg
VP: Michael McCord
Off Mgr: Stephanie Narvades
Snr Sftwr: Deepa Ramaiyer
Snr Ntwrk: Dave Kievets
QA Dir: Elizabeth Acosta
QA Dir: Lorna Mithra
QA Dir: Prasanth Nair
Dir IT: Craig Hoss
VP Sls: Todd Pisciotti

HEALTH EAST WOODWINDS
See WOODWINDS HEALTH CAMPUS

D-U-N-S 36-293-5173
HEALTH FACILITIES MANAGEMENT CORP
(*Suby of* CIRCLE B ENTERPRISES HOLDING CO INC) ★
731 N Main St, Sikeston, MO 63801-2151
Tel (573) 471-1276 *Founded/Ownrshp* 1984
Sales 39.6MM^E *EMP* 2,800
SIC 6531 Real estate managers
Pr: Don C Bedell
**Treas:* Lonnie Hasty
**VP:* William C Mitchell

HEALTH FIRST
See SENIOR HEALTH PARTNERS INC

HEALTH FIRST
See HF MANAGEMENT SERVICES LLC

HEALTH FIRST HEALTH PLANS
See CAPE CANAVERAL HOSPITAL INC

HEALTH FIRST HEALTH PLANS
See HOLMES REGIONAL MEDICAL CENTER INC

HEALTH FIRST HEALTH PLANS
See HEALTH FIRST INC

D-U-N-S 94-718-7423
HEALTH FIRST HEALTH PLANS INC
(*Suby of* HEALTH FIRST HEALTH PLANS) ★
6450 Us Highway 1, Rockledge, FL 32955-5747
Tel (321) 434-5600 *Founded/Ownrshp* 1997
Sales NA *EMP* 155
Accts Ernst & Young Orlando Fl
SIC 6324 Health maintenance organization (HMO), insurance only
Pr: Jerry Senne
**Ch Bd:* William Brennan
**Treas:* Robert Galloway
**VP:* Larry Garrison

D-U-N-S 80-704-9655
HEALTH FIRST INC
HEALTH FIRST HEALTH PLANS
6450 Us Highway 1, Rockledge, FL 32955-5747
Tel (321) 434-4300 *Founded/Ownrshp* 1995
Sales 1.2MMM *EMP* 7,400
Accts Ernst & Young Llp Orlando Fl
SIC 8062 8011 8082 8069 7991 6324 General medical & surgical hospitals; Medical centers; Home health care services; Chronic disease hospital; Health club; Health maintenance organization (HMO), insurance only
Pr: Steve Johnson
Ch Bd: James Shaw
V Ch: Albert Francis
Pr: Christine Rushnell
COO: Larry F Garrison
COO: Jo Powell
CFO: Robert C Galloway
V Ch Bd: Russell E Fischer
Bd of Dir: Timothy Laird
VP: Nicki Andersen
VP: Joseph L Collins
VP: Sally Forsberg
VP: David Mathias
VP: Judy Smith
VP: Roberta B Stoner
Exec: Rodney Moore
Exec: John Pcolka
Exec: Dan Tesenair
Exec: Mitch Williams
Dir Rx: Katherine Goldman

D-U-N-S 18-319-6138
HEALTH FITNESS CORP
(*Suby of* TRUSTMARK COMPANIES) ★
1700 W 82nd St Ste 200, Minneapolis, MN 55431-1465
Tel (800) 639-7913 *Founded/Ownrshp* 2010
Sales 157.3MM^E *EMP* 5,500^E
SIC 8099 7991 Health screening service; Physical fitness facilities
Pr: Paul Lotharius
**COO:* Brian Gagne
**CFO:* Karen Preusker
**Chf Mktg O:* James O Reynolds MD
**Chf Mktg O:* Dennis Richling
**Ofcr:* Tatiana Shnaiden
Sr VP: J Mark McConnell
VP: Brian Harrigan
VP: Arch Hasler
VP: Kathy Machak
VP: Sean McManamy
VP: Kelly Merriman
VP: Dana Park
VP: Greg Siedschlag
VP Bus Dev: Nancy Cashon
VP Bus Dev: Scott Kinzer
Board of Directors: David F Durenberger, K James Ehlen MD, Wendy D Lynch, Robert J Marzec, John C Penn, Curtis M Selquist, Mark W Sheffert, Linda Hall Whitman, Rodney A Young

HEALTH INSUR PLAN ADMNSTRATORS
See HIP ADMINISTRATORS OF FLORIDA INC

D-U-N-S 01-679-6499
▲ HEALTH INSURANCE INNOVATIONS INC
15438 N Florida Ave # 201, Tampa, FL 33613-1223
Tel (877) 376-5831 *Founded/Ownrshp* 2008
Sales NA *EMP* 192^E
Tkr Sym HIIQ *Exch* NGM
SIC 6411 Insurance agents, brokers & service
CEO: Gavin Southwell
**Ch Bd:* Michael W Kosloske
Pr: Sue Rogerio
COO: Josef Denother
CFO: Michael D Hershberger
Ofcr: Heidi Hanstein
Sr VP: Lori Kosloske
CTO: Sheldon Wang

D-U-N-S 62-316-8457
HEALTH INVESTMENT CORP
14642 Newport Ave Ste 388, Tustin, CA 92780-6059
Tel (714) 669-2085 *Founded/Ownrshp* 1991
Sales 136.2MM^E *EMP* 1,700
SIC 8062 General medical & surgical hospitals
CEO: George Houpf
**CFO:* Michael White
Genl Couns: Sharyn Alcaraz

D-U-N-S 08-619-0493
■ HEALTH MANAGEMENT ASSOCIATES INC
HMA
(*Suby of* COMMUNITY HEALTH SYSTEMS INC) ★
5811 Pelican Bay Blvd # 500, Naples, FL 34108-2711
Tel (239) 598-3131 *Founded/Ownrshp* 2014
Sales 5.3MMM^E *EMP* 40,400
SIC 8062 General medical & surgical hospitals
Pr: John M Starcher Jr
Chf Rad: Jim Barnes
**Ch Bd:* William J Schoen
Pr: C Campbell
COO: Cindi Butcher
COO: Daniel J Knell
COO: Phil Minden
COO: Christopher Rakunas
COO: Joshua Self
COO: Christian Stroucken
COO: Patrice Tavernier
COO: Joseph Webb
CFO: Cassie Ball
CFO: Thomas Brook
**CFO:* Kelly E Curry
CFO: Bob Farnham
CFO: Kyle Johnson
CFO: Arthur Koszalinski
CFO: Gregory Pearson
Ex VP: Kelly Curry
**Ex VP:* Kerrin E Gillespie

D-U-N-S 07-526-6346
■ HEALTH MANAGEMENT SYSTEMS INC
HMS BUSINESS SERVICES
(*Suby of* HMS HOLDINGS CORP) ★
5615 High Point Dr # 100, Irving, TX 75038-2434
Tel (214) 453-3000 *Founded/Ownrshp* 1974
Sales 198.8MM^E *EMP* 1,125
SIC 7374 7372 Data processing & preparation; Application computer software; Business oriented computer software
Pr: William C Lucia
Pr: Carrie Cunningham
Pr: Christopher Frey
Pr: Arika Pierce
CFO: Pam Baffoni
**CFO:* Walter Hosp
Sr VP: Kimberly Glenn
Sr VP: Joe Joy
**Sr VP:* Joseph Joy
**Sr VP:* Donna Price
**Sr VP:* Stephen Vaccaro
**VP:* Thomas A Baggett Jr
VP: Peter Demy
VP: Peter Fleischman
VP: Lawrence Friedman
**VP:* Michael Hostetler
VP: Susan Jeffries
VP: Dave Viestenz

D-U-N-S 80-939-9892
HEALTH MISSISSIPPI ORGANIZATION INC
FINANCE AND ACCOUNTS
(*Suby of* EXECUTIVE OFFICE OF STATE OF MISSISSIPPI) ★
570 E Woodrow Wilson Ave, Jackson, MS 39216-4538
Tel (601) 576-7400 *Founded/Ownrshp* 1877
Sales 104.9MM^E *EMP* 2,000
SIC 8099 Physical examination service, insurance
**Ch Bd:* Lucius Lampton
Ofcr: Mitchell Adcock
Ofcr: Paul Byers
Ofcr: Thomas Dobbs
Ofcr: Scottie Martin
Ofcr: Dena Pope IV
Dir Lab: Wanda Ingersoll
Dir Lab: Sammie Malone
Dir Lab: Daphne Ware
Prgrm Mgr: Steven Quilter
Sfty Mgr: Regina Derstine

D-U-N-S 84-800-3661
■ HEALTH NET FEDERAL SERVICES LLC
(*Suby of* HEALTH NET OF CALIFORNIA INC) ★
2025 Aerojet Rd, Rancho Cordova, CA 95742-6418
Tel (916) 935-5000 *Founded/Ownrshp* 1997
Sales NA *EMP* 1,000
SIC 6324 Hospital & medical service plans
Pr: Thomas F Carrato
Chf Mktg O: Jay L Siverstein

D-U-N-S 09-848-9776
■ HEALTH NET HEALTH PLAN OF OREGON INC
(*Suby of* HEALTH NET INC) ★
13221 Sw 68th Pkwy Ste 20, Tigard, OR 97223-8328
Tel (503) 213-5000 *Founded/Ownrshp* 1997
Sales NA *EMP* 250
SIC 6324 8011 Hospital & medical service plans; Offices & clinics of medical doctors
Ch Bd: C E Skeeters MD
**Pr:* Chris Ellertson
**CEO:* Martin A Preizler
**CFO:* Pat Isaac
**Ofcr:* Brenda Bruns
VP: Ted Falk
VP: Kevin McCartin
VP: Ron Morgan
VP: Louise Walczak
Ex Dir: Judy Irving

D-U-N-S 79-833-0908
■ HEALTH NET INC
(*Suby of* CENTENE CORP) ★
21650 Oxnard St Fl 25, Woodland Hills, CA 91367-7829
Tel (818) 676-6000 *Founded/Ownrshp* 2015
Sales NA *EMP* 8,014
Accts Deloitte & Touche Llp Los Ang
SIC 6324 6311 Hospital & medical service plans; Life insurance carriers
Pr: Jay M Gellert
Pr: Thomas F Carrato
Pr: Steven H Nelson
COO: James E Woys
Treas: Kevin Low
Ofcr: Rich Hall
Ofcr: Juanell Hefner
Ex VP: Marvin Rich
Ex VP: Gary Smith
Sr VP: Angelee F Bouchard
Sr VP: Gerald V Coil
VP: Sharon Almany
VP: Lou Desorbo
VP: Alida Dodd
VP: Jeff Flynn
VP: Jody Giordano
VP: Ed Jackson
VP: Herb Kan
VP: Dave Meadows
VP: Steve Miller
VP: Marie Montgomery

D-U-N-S 80-984-5167
■ HEALTH NET OF ARIZONA INC
(*Suby of* HEALTH NET INC) ★
1230 W Washington St # 401, Tempe, AZ 85281-1250
Tel (602) 286-9242 *Founded/Ownrshp* 1997
Sales NA *EMP* 700
SIC 6324 Hospital & medical service plans
Pr: Rose Megian
Ofcr: Sharon Bottrill

D-U-N-S 11-520-5437
■ HEALTH NET OF CALIFORNIA INC
(*Suby of* HEALTH NET INC) ★
21281 Burbank Blvd Fl 4, Woodland Hills, CA 91367-7073
Tel (818) 676-6775 *Founded/Ownrshp* 1997
Sales NA *EMP* 1,075
SIC 6324 8062 6311 6321 6331 5912 Hospital & medical service plans; General medical & surgical hospitals; Life insurance carriers; Disability health insurance; Accident & health insurance carriers; Workers' compensation insurance; Drug stores & proprietary stores
Ch Bd: Jay Gellert
Chf Cred: Patricia Clarey
Bd of Dir: Bruce Willison
Ex VP: Joseph Capezza
VP: Juanell Hefner
VP: Dorothy Lucas
VP: Gary Neiman
VP: Dan Tyler
Exec: Barbara Armstrong
Exec: George Spencer
Prgrm Mgr: Yuliya Andreyeva

D-U-N-S 15-242-7324
HEALTH NEW ENGLAND INC
H N E
(*Suby of* BAYSTATE MEDICAL CENTER) ★
1 Monarch Pl Ste 1500, Springfield, MA 01144-1500
Tel (413) 787-4000 *Founded/Ownrshp* 1985
Sales NA *EMP* 222
SIC 6324 Health maintenance organization (HMO), insurance only
Ch: Michael J Daly
**Pr:* Peter Straley
**CEO:* Maura McCaffrey
**CFO:* Michael Marrone
**Treas:* Dennis Chalke
**Chf Mktg O:* Laurie E Gianturco
Ofcr: Patrick O'Shea
VP: Ashley Allen
**VP:* David Boss
**VP:* James M Kessler
**VP:* Philip M Lacombe
**VP:* Bruce M Ruder

HEALTH ONE
See ROSE MEDICAL GROUP

D-U-N-S 13-931-2565
HEALTH OPTIONS INC
FLORIDA BLUE HMO
4800 Deerwood Campus Pkwy, Jacksonville, FL 32246-6498
Tel (904) 564-5700 *Founded/Ownrshp* 1984
Sales NA *EMP* 450
Accts Price Waterhouse Coopers Llp
SIC 6324 Group hospitalization plans; Health maintenance organization (HMO), insurance only
Pr: Joyce Kramzer
CFO: Robert Chris
**Treas:* William Coats
**VP:* Charles Richards
**Prin:* Robert Lufrano

HEALTH PARTNERS
See TENNESSEE WEST HEALTHCARE INC

D-U-N-S 94-822-2021
HEALTH PARTNERS INC
HEALTH PARTNERS ORGANIZATION
8170 33rd Ave S, Minneapolis, MN 55425-1614
Tel (952) 883-6000 *Founded/Ownrshp* 1984
Sales 884.4MM^E *EMP* 18,000
SIC 8062 General medical & surgical hospitals
Pr: Mary Brainerd
Mng Pt: Bradley E Cooper
V Ch: Margaret A Lund
Pr: Laura Oberst
Sr VP: Doug Smith
VP: Donna Zimmerman
Ex Dir: Eliot Seide
Nurse Mgr: Linda Brunsgaard
Web Dev: Michael Fluto
Software D: Richena Rogers
Opers Mgr: Amy Murphy

HEALTH PARTNERS ORGANIZATION
See HEALTH PARTNERS INC

D-U-N-S 18-696-0332
HEALTH PARTNERS PLANS INC
901 Market St Ste 500, Philadelphia, PA 19107-4496
Tel (215) 849-9606 *Founded/Ownrshp* 1985
Sales 1.5MMM *EMP* 620^E
Accts Kpmg Llp Philadelphia Pennsy
SIC 8011 Health maintenance organization
Pr: William S George
**COO:* Elaine Markezin
**CFO:* Martin J Brill
**Treas:* Karen Armtrong
**Sr VP:* Don Daddario
**Sr VP:* Judy B Harrington
**Sr VP:* Debra Kircher
**Sr VP:* Vicki Sessoms
VP: Johnna Baker
VP: Joe Brand
VP: Rebecca Kohl
VP: Caroline Russell
Exec: Theresa Ritchie

D-U-N-S 10-572-2623
■ HEALTH PLAN OF NEVADA INC
(*Suby of* UNITED HEALTHCARE) ★
2720 N Tenaya Way, Las Vegas, NV 89128-0424
Tel (702) 242-7300 *Founded/Ownrshp* 1981
Sales 1.3MMM *EMP* 250
SIC 8011 Health maintenance organization
Pr: Jon Bunker
Chf Mktg O: Steven Evans
Sr VP: A P Smith Jr
VP: A Smith

D-U-N-S 92-983-9777
HEALTH PLAN OF SAN JOAQUIN
7751 S Manthey Rd, French Camp, CA 95231-9802
Tel (209) 942-6300 *Founded/Ownrshp* 1994
Sales NA *EMP* 120
Accts Deloitte & Touche Llp
SIC 6324 Health maintenance organization (HMO), insurance only
CEO: Amy Shinn
CIO: Sanjay Vail
Dir IT: Katherine Kutz
Info Man: Jerry Sonderman
Mktg Dir: David Hurst

D-U-N-S 09-420-8816
HEALTH PLAN OF UPPER OHIO VALLEY INC (WV)
52160 National Rd E, Saint Clairsville, OH 43950-9306
Tel (740) 695-3585 *Founded/Ownrshp* 1979
Sales NA *EMP* 400
Accts Ernst & Young Us Llp Indianap
SIC 6324 8082 Health maintenance organization (HMO), insurance only; Home health care services
Pr: Phillip D Wright
**Ch Bd:* James Newton
**CFO:* John J Yeager
VP: Patti Fass
Dir IT: Scott Kreitzer
Mktg Dir: Patti Fast
Genl Couns: Robert Kota

D-U-N-S 00-514-6840
HEALTH PLANS INC
(*Suby of* HARVARD PILGRIM HEALTH CARE INC) ★
1500 W Park Dr Ste 330, Westborough, MA 01581-3912
Tel (508) 752-2480 *Founded/Ownrshp* 2005
Sales NA *EMP* 222
SIC 6411 Insurance agents, brokers & service
Pr: William R Breidenbach
**VP:* Deborah Hodges
VP: Christopher Parr
Exec: Kathy Sasena
Sls&Mrk Ex: Deborah Hovagimian
Manager: Peter Connolly
Manager: John Webber

D-U-N-S 07-748-4280
■ HEALTH PLUS PREPAID HEALTH SERVICES PLAN INC
(*Suby of* AMERIGROUP CORP) ★
9 Pine St Fl 14, New York, NY 10005-4702
Tel (718) 532-1011 *Founded/Ownrshp* 2011
Sales NA *EMP* 800
SIC 6321 6324 8741 Accident & health insurance; Hospital & medical service plans; Management services
CEO: Thomas Early
Ex Dir: Berry Volin

D-U-N-S 06-870-8999
HEALTH PRODUCTS RESEARCH INC
ADVANCE INSIGHTS
(*Suby of* INVENTIV HEALTH INC) ★
500 Atrium Dr Ste 100, Somerset, NJ 08873-4161
Tel (908) 534-4148 *Founded/Ownrshp* 1999
Sales 98.4MM^E *EMP* 2,810
SIC 8742 8732 Marketing consulting services; Sales (including sales management) consultant; Commercial nonphysical research
Pr: Norman Stalsberg
VP: Ashish Kathuria
IT Man: Eric Langman

D-U-N-S 61-929-1052
HEALTH QUEST
FOUNDATION FOR VBMC, THE
(*Suby of* HEALTH QUEST SYSTEMS INC) ★
45 Reade Pl, Poughkeepsie, NY 12601-3947
Tel (845) 454-8500 *Founded/Ownrshp* 2006
Sales 156.3MM *EMP* 11
Accts Pricewaterhousecoopers Llp N
SIC 8099 Medical services organization
CEO: Adil Ameer
**CFO:* Donna M McGregor
Ofcr: Florie Munroe
VP: Disanto Benjamin
VP: Mark Kochanowski
VP: David Ping
Exec: Ronald Tatelbaum
Exec: Rosemary Wieting
Assoc Dir: Thomas Diaz
Dir Rad: Scott Berger
Dir Rx: William Silta

D-U-N-S 61-716-3977
HEALTH QUEST SYSTEMS INC
1351 Route 55 Ste 200, Lagrangeville, NY 12540-5144
Tel (845) 475-9500 *Founded/Ownrshp* 1985
Sales 870.8MM *EMP* 2,000
Accts Pricewaterhousecoopers Llp N
SIC 8741 Hospital management
CEO: Denise George
Dir Vol: Michelle Piazza
**CFO:* Yann Kepple
Bd of Dir: Drayton Grant
**Sr VP:* Ann Armater
Sr VP: Michael Holzhueter
Sr VP: Timmian Massie
**Sr VP:* David Ping
**Sr VP:* Ron Tatelbaumm
**VP:* Mary Ann Keppel
Off Mgr: Heather Brown

D-U-N-S 00-243-6061
HEALTH RESEARCH INC (NY)
FOOD LBS/SFETY INSPTN DVSN-GMT
150 Broadway Ste 560, Menands, NY 12204-2726
Tel (518) 431-1200 *Founded/Ownrshp* 1953
Sales 677.8MM *EMP* 1,400
Accts Bonadio & Co Llp Albany Ne
SIC 8733 Noncommercial research organizations
Ex Dir: Barbara Ryan
Assoc Dir: Charles Cummins
Adm Dir: Tony Watson
**Ex Dir:* Cheryl Mattox
Brnch Mgr: Cheryl A Mattox
Dir IT: John Bintz

D-U-N-S 04-400-7990
■ HEALTH RESOURCES & SERVICES ADMINISTRATION
HRSA
(*Suby of* UNITED STATES DEPARTMENT OF HEALTH & HUMAN SERVICES) ★
5600 Fishers Ln, Rockville, MD 20852-1750
Tel (301) 443-5460 *Founded/Ownrshp* 1997
Sales NA *EMP* 1,860
SIC 9431 Administration of public health programs;
Prin: Ernia Hughes
Pr: Mylandar Davis
Ofcr: Anthony Anyanwu
Ofcr: Renetta Boyd
Ofcr: Tom Flavin
Ofcr: Mary Kenney
Ofcr: Lara Purkey
Ofcr: Nawraz Shawir
Ofcr: Scott Snyder
Ofcr: Anne Stephan
Ofcr: Stacy B Stryer
Ofcr: Melinda Tinsley
Ofcr: Sherese Warren
VP: Christine Lim

D-U-N-S 06-757-1174
HEALTH SCHOLARSHIPS INC
1005 Boulder Dr, Gray, GA 31032-6141
Tel (478) 742-6569 *Founded/Ownrshp* 1988
Sales 198.8MM *EMP* 1
Accts Mcnair Mclemore Middlebrooks
SIC 6732 Trusts: educational, religious, etc.
Pr: Joe Wall

HEALTH SCIENCES CENTER
See TTU HSC RESEARCH & GRADUATE SCHOOL

HEALTH SCIENCES DIVISION
See TRUSTEES OF COLUMBIA UNIVERSITY IN CITY OF NEW YORK

D-U-N-S 01-970-4037
HEALTH SCIENCES SOUTH CAROLINA (SC)
1320 Main St Ste 625, Columbia, SC 29201-3286
Tel (803) 544-4772 *Founded/Ownrshp* 2004
Sales 83.4MM *EMP* 10

Accts Bdo Usa Llp Atlanta Ga
SIC 8731 Biological research
Pr: Helga Rippen
Assoc VP: Windsor Sherrill
VP: Michelle Dodenhoff

HEALTH SEMINARS
See EPI PRINTERS INC

D-U-N-S 80-474-5420
HEALTH SERVICES DEPARTMENT
H S A
(*Suby of* EXECUTIVE OFFICE OF STATE OF ARIZONA) ★
150 N 18th Ave Ste 163, Phoenix, AZ 85007-3237
Tel (602) 542-1025 *Founded/Ownrshp* 1912
Sales NA *EMP* 3,486
SIC 9431 Administration of public health programs;
CFO: David Reese
Ofcr: Teresa Ehnert
Ofcr: Kathy McCanna
Ofcr: Ruth Penn
Ofcr: Richard Young
Exec: Stephanie Bishop
Prgrm Mgr: Hong Chartrand
Prgrm Mgr: Virginia James
Prgrm Mgr: Lisa Rasmussen
Prgrm Mgr: Isaac Robert
Admn Mgr: Steven Gonzales
Board of Directors: Catherine Eden

D-U-N-S 87-642-4654
HEALTH SERVICES FOR CHILDREN WITH SPECIAL NEEDS INC
1101 Vermont Ave Nw # 1002, Washington, DC 20005-3560
Tel (202) 467-2737 *Founded/Ownrshp* 1994
Sales 154.8MM *EMP* 100
Accts Cohen Rutherford Knight Pc Be
SIC 8322 Social services for the handicapped
CEO: Thomas Chapman
**COO:* Bruce Goldman
Off Mgr: Phyllis Montgomery

D-U-N-S 02-804-4481
HEALTH SERVICES MANAGEMENT INC
206 Fortress Blvd, Murfreesboro, TN 37128-5269
Tel (615) 896-1191 *Founded/Ownrshp* 2009
Sales 156.1MM *EMP* 3
Accts Matlock Clements Pc Murfreesb
SIC 8741 Hospital management; Nursing & personal care facility management
Prin: Preston Sweeney

D-U-N-S 79-660-9857
HEALTH SERVICES OF FOX CHASE CANCER CENTER
(*Suby of* FOX CHASE CANCER CENTER FOUNDATION) ★
333 Cottman Ave, Philadelphia, PA 19111-2434
Tel (215) 728-6900 *Founded/Ownrshp* 1985
Sales 228.3M *EMP* 1,800
SIC 8011 8062 8733 Offices & clinics of medical doctors; General medical & surgical hospitals; Medical research
Pr: Robert C Young MD
**COO:* R Donald Leedy
**CFO:* Tresa Laribee
**Treas:* Joseph Hediger

D-U-N-S 08-890-7514
HEALTH SERVICES OF VIRGINIAS INC
500 Cherry St, Bluefield, WV 24701-3306
Tel (304) 327-1100 *Founded/Ownrshp* 1976
Sales 317.4M *EMP* 1,040ᴱ
Accts Brown Edwards & Company Ll
SIC 8062 General medical & surgical hospitals
Pr: Robert Perkinson
CFO: Richard Cox
**CFO:* Patti Gusler
**Ch:* Chandler Wote
Treas: Janet Cole
**Sec:* Bill Albert
**VP:* Jack Brewster
VP: Sandee Cheynet
Dir Lab: Lori Christian
Dir Rad: Kay Cooper
Opers Mgr: Terri Kosinar

D-U-N-S 03-293-6281
HEALTH SHARE OF OREGON (OR)
2121 Sw Broadway Ste 200, Portland, OR 97201-3181
Tel (503) 416-2172 *Founded/Ownrshp* 2013
Sales 663.2MMᴱ *EMP* 3
Accts Moss Adams Llp Portland Or
SIC 8099 Health & allied services
Comm Man: Beth Sorensen
Off Mgr: Corey Kirk
CIO: John Sanders
QA Dir: Mike Holmes
Snr PM: Paul Bollinger
Snr PM: Sandra Clark

D-U-N-S 96-489-6968
HEALTH SYSTEMS FACILITIES INC
1005 Boulder Dr, Gray, GA 31032-6141
Tel (478) 621-2100 *Founded/Ownrshp* 2010
Sales 102.1MM *EMP* 1
Accts Mcnair Mclemore Middlebrooks &
SIC 7389 Business services
CEO: Kay F Gray

D-U-N-S 02-329-7240
HEALTH SYSTEMS INC
1220 N Main St, Sikeston, MO 63801-4827
Tel (573) 481-9625 *Founded/Ownrshp* 1998
Sales NA *EMP* 948
SIC 6321 8011 8322 Health insurance carriers; Internal medicine, physician/surgeon; Referral service for personal & social problems
Pr: Jim Lincoln
VP: Tara Smith
**Prin:* Marty Beuke
**Prin:* Tracey Smith

HEALTH SYSTEMS MINNESOTA
See PARK NICOLLET HEALTH SERVICES

HEALTH TEXAS PROVIDE NETWORK
See FAMILY MEDICAL CENTER AT ROCKWALL

HEALTH4BRANDS CATAPULT
See HAVAS HEALTH INC

D-U-N-S 06-054-8005
HEALTHALLIANCE HOSPITAL BROADWAY CAMPUS
(*Suby of* HEALTHALLIANCE OF HUDSON VLY) ★
396 Broadway, Kingston, NY 12401-4626
Tel (845) 331-3131 *Founded/Ownrshp* 1891
Sales 110.0MM *EMP* 800
Accts Charles A Barragato & Co Llp
SIC 8062 General medical & surgical hospitals
Pr: David Scarpino
Dir Vol: Amy McAden
**COO:* Joseph C Marsicovete
**CFO:* Patricia Gavis
**Chf Mktg O:* Paul Llobet
**Ofcr:* Joshua Ratner
Ofcr: Robert Seidman
VP: Joseph Bailey
VP: Margo McGilvrey
Dir Rx: Priti Shah
Ex Dir: John Ritchie

D-U-N-S 06-052-8064
HEALTHALLIANCE HOSPITAL MARYS AVENUE CAMPUS
(*Suby of* HEALTHALLIANCE OF HUDSON VLY) ★
105 Marys Ave, Kingston, NY 12401-5848
Tel (845) 338-2500 *Founded/Ownrshp* 1903
Sales 60.9MM *EMP* 2,100
SIC 8062 8051

D-U-N-S 06-992-0916
HEALTHALLIANCE HOSPITALS INC
60 Hospital Rd, Leominster, MA 01453-2205
Tel (978) 466-2000 *Founded/Ownrshp* 1993
Sales 159.9MM *EMP* 1,350
SIC 8062 Hospital, affiliated with AMA residency
Pr: Deborah Weymouth
Dir Recs: Debbie Borkowski
**CFO:* Michael Cofone
Obsttrcn: Bettyann Cirillo

HEALTHALLIANCE OF HUDSON VLY
See HEALTH ALLIANCE INC

HEALTHCARE AUTH FOR BPTST HLTH
See BAPTIST HEALTH

D-U-N-S 14-457-9646
HEALTHCARE AUTHORITY FOR BAPTIST HEALTH AND AFFILIATE OF UAB HEALTH SYSTEM
BAPTIST MEDICAL CENTER SOUTH
2105 E South Blvd, Montgomery, AL 36116-2409
Tel (334) 286-2987 *Founded/Ownrshp* 1963
Sales 543.8MM *EMP* 1,500ᴱ
SIC 8062 General medical & surgical hospitals
CEO: Russell Tyner
**COO:* Robin Barca
**CFO:* Katrina Belt
CFO: Guy Laprad
**VP:* Ben F Kelley Jr
Dir Rad: Jackie Davis
Dir Rad: Jeffrey Hicks
Dir Rx: Gary Mount
Dir IT: Walt Haywood
Dir IT: Rob Sumter
Pr Dir: Tom M Kinnon
Board of Directors: Ben Kelly

D-U-N-S 80-907-9064 IMP
HEALTHCARE INFORMATION AND MANAGEMENT SYSTEMS SOCIETY
H I M S S
33 W Monroe St Ste 1700, Chicago, IL 60603-5616
Tel (312) 664-4467 *Founded/Ownrshp* 1993
Sales 87.7MM *EMP* 500ᴱ
Accts Mcgladrey Llp Chicago Il
SIC 8099 Blood related health services
Ch Bd: Scott Maclean
**Pr:* H Stephen Lieber
**COO:* J Norris Orms
COO: R N Orms
**CFO:* Dennis R James
Bd of Dir: Steven J Fox
Bd of Dir: John Hansmann
Bd of Dir: Anna M Harris
Bd of Dir: Daniel Herman
Bd of Dir: Joy Keeler
Bd of Dir: Sunny Sanyal
Bd of Dir: Tricia Spellman
**Ex VP:* Jeremy Bonfini
**Ex VP:* John Hoyt
Ex VP: John P Hoyt
Ex VP: R Orms
**Ex VP:* Steve Rosenfield
VP: Rosemary Brandt
VP: Susan Farrell
VP: John Hoyt
VP: Liz Johnson

HEALTHCARE MGT ADMINISTRATORS
See HEALTH CARE MANAGEMENT ADMINISTRATORS INC

D-U-N-S 55-736-2618
HEALTHCARE PARTNERS INVESTMENTS LLC
HPI
14024 Quail Pointe Dr, Oklahoma City, OK 73134-1006
Tel (405) 424-6677 *Founded/Ownrshp* 2004
Sales 59.7MMᴱ *EMP* 1,000
SIC 8093 Specialty outpatient clinics
CEO: Ed Gray
**Ch Bd:* C Robert Steves
**CFO:* Carl Mikesh
VP: Thomas Fondren
VP: Donald Grunden
VP: Ashley White
CIO: Tamatha Smith
VP Mktg: Ken Talton

D-U-N-S 94-497-5622
■ **HEALTHCARE PARTNERS LLC**
HEALTHCARE PARTNERS MED GROUP
(*Suby of* DAVITA INC) ★
2175 Park Pl, El Segundo, CA 90245-4705
Tel (310) 354-4200 *Founded/Ownrshp* 2012
Sales 320.9MMᴱ *EMP* 3,700
SIC 8011 Group health association
CEO: Robert J Margolis
Pr: Marianne Garrity
COO: Dennis L Kogod
CFO: Ted Halkias
Bd of Dir: Gary Standke
Ofcr: Chan Chuang
Ofcr: Hugo Ruiz
Ofcr: Melayne Yokum
**Ex VP:* Matthew Mazdyasni
Sr VP: Mary Evans
VP: Merlin Aalborg
VP: Paula De Almeida
VP: Evelyn Kimball
VP: Jamie Phillips
VP: Dan Reynolds
Dir Rad: Ravi Sookdeo

HEALTHCARE PARTNERS MED GROUP
See HEALTHCARE PARTNERS LLC

D-U-N-S 02-763-2659
HEALTHCARE PARTNERS NEVADA LLC
700 E Warm Springs Rd # 230, Las Vegas, NV 89119-4324
Tel (702) 932-8500 *Founded/Ownrshp* 2009
Sales 83.1MMᴱ *EMP* 1,000ᴱ
SIC 8011 Medical centers
Pr: Sherif Abdou
Sr VP: Bard Coats
Sr VP: Todd Lefkowitz
Ex Dir: Michelle Ross
Prac Mgr: Candace Fisher

D-U-N-S 80-872-0007
HEALTHCARE REALTY TRUST INC
3310 West End Ave Ste 700, Nashville, TN 37203-1097
Tel (615) 269-8175 *Founded/Ownrshp* 1992
Sales 388.4MM *EMP* 236ᴱ
SIC 6798 Real estate investment trusts
Ch Bd: David R Emery
COO: JD Steele
CFO: J Christopher Douglas
Ex VP: John M Bryant Jr
Ex VP: Todd J Meredith
Ex VP: B Douglas Whitman II
VP: Amanda Callaway
VP: Stephen Cox
VP: Robert Dillard
VP: Julie Ferrell
VP: Rob Hull
VP: Jessica King
VP: Richard Langreck
VP: Revell Lester
VP: Andrew Loope
VP: Revell Michael
VP: Rebecca T Oberlander
VP: Sushil Puria
VP: Kimberly Sullivan
Board of Directors: Nancy H Agee, Charles Raymond Fernandez, Peter F Lyle, Edwin B Morris III, John Knox Singleton, Bruce D Sullivan, Dan S Wilford

D-U-N-S 94-195-2657
HEALTHCARE RESOURCE GROUP INC
12610 E Mirabeau Pkwy # 900, Spokane Valley, WA 99216-1534
Tel (509) 209-2000 *Founded/Ownrshp* 1994
Sales NA *EMP* 208
SIC 6411 7322 8742 8721 Medical insurance claim processing, contract or fee basis; Adjustment & collection services; Management consulting services; Accounting, auditing & bookkeeping
CEO: Steven McCoy
**COO:* Gregory West
**CFO:* Kristina English
**VP:* Richard Lewis
Dir Bus: Judy Griffith
Ex Dir: Jason Coffin
Rgnl Mgr: Nash Castle
Software D: Dustin Crossley

D-U-N-S 15-331-5429
■ **HEALTHCARE RESOURCES CORP**
HOMESTEAD NURSING HOME
(*Suby of* GENESIS HEALTHCARE CORP) ★
1113 Easton Rd, Willow Grove, PA 19090-1901
Tel (215) 659-3060 *Founded/Ownrshp* 1982
Sales 1.5MMM *EMP* 240
SIC 8059 8361 Nursing home, except skilled & intermediate care facility; Rehabilitation center, residential: health care incidental
Ch Bd: Michael Walker
**Pr:* David C Barr
CFO: George V Hager Jr
Treas: Barbara J Hauswald
Sr VP: James Wankmiller
Off Mgr: Sharon Adams
Nrsg Dir: Charles Hall
Board of Directors: Richard R Howard

HEALTHCARE SERVICES
See SAN JOAQUIN HOSPITAL

D-U-N-S 08-419-2111
▲ **HEALTHCARE SERVICES GROUP INC** (PA)
3220 Tillman Dr Ste 300, Bensalem, PA 19020-2028
Tel (215) 639-4274 *Founded/Ownrshp* 1976
Sales 1.4MMM *EMP* 45,900
Tkr Sym HCSG *Exch* NGS
SIC 8059 7349 8049 Nursing home, except skilled & intermediate care facility; Hospital housekeeping; Dietician
Pr: Theodore Wahl
**Ch Bd:* Daniel P McCartney
CFO: John C Shea
Chf Cred: Jason J Bundick
**Ex VP:* Michael E McBryan
Ex VP: Bryan D McCartney
VP: Bryan Foy
VP: Ryan Viets
Rgnl Mgr: Chris Fleenor
Rgnl Mgr: Mike Irrizarry
Rgnl Mgr: Bill Kauffman
Board of Directors: John M Briggs, Diane S Casey, Robert L Frome, John J McFadden, Robert J Moss, Dino D Ottaviano, Jude Visconto

D-U-N-S 08-489-1985
HEALTHCARE SERVICES OF OZARKS INC (MO)
OXFORD HEALTHCARE
3660 S National Ave, Springfield, MO 65807-7311
Tel (417) 882-4170 *Founded/Ownrshp* 1974
Sales 22.3MM *EMP* 1,400
Accts Bkd Llp Springfield Mo
SIC 7363 8082 Temporary help service; Home health care services
Pr: Karen R Thomas
Pr: Debbie Garner
CFO: Rick McGge
**VP:* Steve Edwards
Ex Dir: Jennifer Twombly
Dir IT: Phil Desai

D-U-N-S 96-216-0839
■ **HEALTHCARE SOLUTIONS INC**
(*Suby of* OPTUM RX) ★
2736 Meadow Church Rd # 300, Duluth, GA 30097-5236
Tel (866) 810-4332 *Founded/Ownrshp* 2015
Sales 116.5MM *EMP* 400
SIC 8742 Compensation & benefits planning consultant
Pr: Joe Boures
Pr: Brian Keeton
**CFO:* Tom Oram
**Ex VP:* Jim Andrews
**Ex VP:* Joe Favazzo
**Ex VP:* Joe Pagano
**Ex VP:* Eileen Ramallo
**Ex VP:* Dennis Sponer
Sr VP: Brian Carpenter
Sr VP: Nancy Hamlet
Sr VP: Elaine Vega
Sr VP: Chris Wicker
VP: Dean Castaldo
VP: Matthew Depew
VP: Dieter Pinner
VP: Tamara Webb

HEALTHCARE SYTEMS
See SOUTH COUNTY HOSPITAL HEALTHCARE SYSTEM ENDOWMENT AND AFFILIATES

D-U-N-S 82-737-1928
HEALTHCARE TECHNOLOGY INTERMEDIATE HOLDINGS INC
(*Suby of* HEALTHCARE TECHNOLOGY INTERMEDIATE INC) ★
301 Commerce St Ste 3300, Fort Worth, TX 76102-4133
Tel (817) 871-4000 *Founded/Ownrshp* 2009
Sales 2.6MMMᴱ *EMP* 7,300ᴱ
SIC 8732 Market analysis or research; Business research service

D-U-N-S 07-944-6230
■ **HEALTHCARE TECHNOLOGY INTERMEDIATE INC**
(*Suby of* QUINTILES IMS HOLDINGS INC) ★
83 Wooster Hts, Danbury, CT 06810-7548
Tel (203) 448-4600 *Founded/Ownrshp* 2016
Sales 2.6MMMᴱ *EMP* 7,290ᴱ
SIC 8742 8732 Business consultant; Market analysis or research; Business research service
CEO: Thomas Pike
COO: Kevin Gordon
CFO: Michael McDonnel
Ex VP: James Erlinger

D-U-N-S 07-940-2799
HEALTHCARE TRUST INC (MD)
405 Park Ave Fl 15, New York, NY 10022-9406
Tel (215) 449-3638 *Founded/Ownrshp* 2014
Sales 247.4MM *EMP* 3ᴱ
Accts Kpmg Llp Chicago Illinois
SIC 6798 Real estate investment trusts
CEO: Todd Jensen
**CFO:* Cathy Kurtz

D-U-N-S 83-017-0010
HEALTHCARE TRUST OF AMERICA INC
16435 N Scottsdale Rd, Scottsdale, AZ 85254-1533
Tel (480) 998-3478 *Founded/Ownrshp* 2006
Sales 403.8MM *EMP* 170ᴱ
Accts Deloitte & Touche Llp Phoenix
SIC 6798 Real estate investment trusts
Ch Bd: Scott D Peters
CFO: Robert A Milligan
Ex VP: Mark D Engstrom
Ex VP: Amanda L Houghton
Ex VP: Dan Klein
Genl Mgr: Brenda Michael
VP Opers: Judy Klein
Mktg Mgr: Jason Lance
Board of Directors: W Bradley Blair II, Maurice J Dewald, Warren D Fix, Peter N Foss, Larry L Mathis, Steve W Patterson, Gary T Wescombe

D-U-N-S 79-053-4341
HEALTHEAST CARE INC
HEALTHEAST CARE SYSTEMS
(*Suby of* HEALTHEAST CORPORATE) ★
559 Capitol Blvd, Saint Paul, MN 55103-2101
Tel (651) 232-2300 *Founded/Ownrshp* 1990
Sales 69.2MMᴱ *EMP* 1,000
SIC 8741 8721 Hospital management; Accounting, auditing & bookkeeping
CEO: Timothy Hanson
**COO:* Ann Schrader
**CFO:* Bob Gill
Dir IT: Darlene Mc Donough
Mktg Dir: Lia Christiansen
Pharmcst: Jessica T Liu
Pharmcst: Andrew Riehle

D-U-N-S 17-439-7265
HEALTHEAST CARE SYSTEM
HEALTHEAST CORPORATE
1700 University Ave W # 5, Saint Paul, MN 55104-3727
Tel (651) 232-5353 *Founded/Ownrshp* 1986
Sales 943.5MM *EMP* 5,500
SIC 8741 8062 7389 Hospital management; General medical & surgical hospitals; Document storage service
Pr: Timothy H Hanson
**Pr:* Kathryn Correia
COO: Anne Schrader
Sr VP: Paul Torgerson
**VP:* Dr Robert Beck
**VP:* Gary French
**VP:* Roger Green
VP: Steve Kolar
VP: Martin Paul
**VP:* Ann Schrader
**VP:* Steven Sprint
VP: Ginny Sullivan
Dir Bus: Len Kaiser
Board of Directors: Tim Marx, Heidi Wilson

HEALTHEAST CARE SYSTEMS
See HEALTHEAST CARE INC

D-U-N-S 04-355-0037
HEALTHEAST COMPANIES INC
(*Suby of* HEALTHEAST CORPORATE) ★
1700 University Ave W, Saint Paul, MN 55104-3727
Tel (651) 232-2300 *Founded/Ownrshp* 1979, 1980
Sales 35.1MM^E *EMP* 1,508
SIC 8082 8051 8011 Home health care services; Skilled nursing care facilities; Offices & clinics of medical doctors
Pr: Timothy H Hanson
**VP:* Roger Green

HEALTHEAST CORPORATE
See BETHESDA HEALTHEAST HOSPITAL

HEALTHEAST CORPORATE
See HEALTHEAST ST JOHNS HOSPITAL

HEALTHEAST CORPORATE
See HEALTHEAST CARE SYSTEM

D-U-N-S 15-758-0002
HEALTHEAST ST JOHNS HOSPITAL
HEALTHEAST CORPORATE
(*Suby of* HEALTHEAST CORPORATE) ★
1575 Beam Ave, Saint Paul, MN 55109-1126
Tel (651) 232-7000 *Founded/Ownrshp* 2001
Sales 127.0MM^E *EMP* 713
SIC 8062 General medical & surgical hospitals
Pr: Kathryn Correia
Exec: Jill Gillispie
CTO: Jack Jackson
Pathlgst: Carl McGary

D-U-N-S 78-451-2527
HEALTHEAST ST JOSEPHS HOSPITAL
ST. JOSEPH'S HOSPITAL
45 10th St W, Saint Paul, MN 55102-1062
Tel (651) 232-3000 *Founded/Ownrshp* 1987
Sales 270.4MM *EMP* 1,164
SIC 8062 General medical & surgical hospitals
Pr: Timothy Hanson
Dir Risk M: Carol Beehler
Doctor: Karen McConville

D-U-N-S 79-350-6390
▲ HEALTHEQUITY INC
15 W Scenic Pointe Dr # 100, Draper, UT 84020-6120
Tel (801) 727-1000 *Founded/Ownrshp* 2002
Sales 126.7MM *EMP* 636^E
Tkr Sym HQY *Exch* NGS
SIC 8399 6371 6036 6321 6282 Health systems agency; Pension, health & welfare funds; Savings institutions, not federally chartered; Accident & health insurance; Investment advice
Pr: Jon Kessler
**Ch Bd:* Robert W Selander
CFO: Darcy Mott
**V Ch Bd:* Stephen D Neeleman
Ex VP: Ashley Dreier
Ex VP: Frode Jensen
Ex VP: Jon Soldan
Ex VP: Matthew Sydney
Board of Directors: Frank A Corvino, Adrian T Dillon, Adrian T Dillon, Evelyn Dilsaver, Michael O Leavitt, Frank T Medici, Manu Rana, Ian Sacks

HEALTHESYSTEMS
See HEALTH E SYSTEMS LLC

D-U-N-S 80-809-8094
HEALTHFIRST HEALTH PLAN OF NEW JERSEY INC
25 Broadway Fl 9, New York, NY 10004-1058
Tel (212) 801-6000 *Founded/Ownrshp* 2007
Sales NA *EMP* 1
SIC 6321 Health insurance carriers
Pr: Paul Dickstein

D-U-N-S 80-809-7021
HEALTHFIRST PHSP INC
(*Suby of* HEALTHFIRST, INC.)
100 Church St Fl 17, New York, NY 10007-2607
Tel (212) 801-6000 *Founded/Ownrshp* 1994
Sales NA *EMP* 11
SIC 6321 Health insurance carriers
Pr: Pat Wang

D-U-N-S 06-690-5357
■ HEALTHLAND INC
RYCAN
(*Suby of* CPSI) ★
1600 Utica Ave S Ste 300, Minneapolis, MN 55416-1468
Tel (612) 787-3120 *Founded/Ownrshp* 2016
Sales 90.0MM^E *EMP* 488^E
SIC 7373 5045 Turnkey vendors, computer systems; Computers
CEO: Chris Bauleke
Pr: Angie Franks
CFO: Todd Laddusaw
CFO: Patrick Spangler
Ex VP: Julie Weber-Kramer
Ex VP: Thomas Ziel
Sr VP: James D Anderson
Sr VP: Mark Middendorf
Sr VP: Tracey Schroeder
Sr VP: Bob Zdon
VP: Julie Kramer
VP: John Savage
Board of Directors: Jack A Kane, Carl Witonsky

HEALTHLINK
See LRGHEALTHCARE

HEALTHMARK/ATG
See FCB WORLDWIDE INC

D-U-N-S 13-955-2087
HEALTHMARKETS INC
HEALTHMARKETS INSURANCE AGENCY
9151 Blvd 256, North Richland Hills, TX 76180
Tel (817) 255-3100 *Founded/Ownrshp* 1984
Sales NA *EMP* 1,370
Accts Kpmg Llp Dallas Texas
SIC 6311 6321 Life insurance; Health insurance carriers
Pr: Kenneth J Fasola
**COO:* Darrick A Duke
**CFO:* R Scott Donovan
Ex VP: Derrick Duke
**Ex VP:* Richard Fiedotin
**Ex VP:* Brian Poger
**Ex VP:* Mark H Smith
VP: Denise Cotter
VP: Susan E Dew
VP: Jack Heller
VP: Consuelo Palacios
VP: Amy Porteous
VP: Alan Tracy

HEALTHMARKETS INSURANCE AGENCY
See HEALTHMARKETS INC

D-U-N-S 96-311-5857
HEALTHMARKETS LLC
(*Suby of* HEALTHMARKETS INSURANCE AGENCY) ★
9151 Boulevard 26, North Richland Hills, TX 76180-5600
Tel (817) 255-3100 *Founded/Ownrshp* 2006
Sales NA *EMP* 700^E
SIC 6311 6321 Life insurance; Health insurance carriers
CFO: Donna Bruskie

D-U-N-S 02-778-1348
HEALTHNOTES LLC
COLUMBIA AURORA MIDWIVES
1501 S Potomac St, Aurora, CO 80012-5411
Tel (303) 695-2600 *Founded/Ownrshp* 1960
Sales 130.4MM^E *EMP* 1,500^E
SIC 8062 General medical & surgical hospitals
COO: Dan Miller
Pr: Elyse Gellerman
COO: Ryan Simpson
CFO: Bill Voloch
Ofcr: John Sanchez
VP: Kathy Yeager
Dir Lab: Lucy Tyler
Dir Rad: Terry Hurlbert
Dir IT: Lea Kurlinski
Anesthlgy: Sena M Jensen
Anesthlgy: Cynthia V Kruger

D-U-N-S 01-347-0133
HEALTHNOW NEW YORK INC
BLUE CROSS BLUE SHIELD WSTN NY
257 W Genesee St, Buffalo, NY 14202-2657
Tel (716) 887-6900 *Founded/Ownrshp* 1940
Sales NA *EMP* 2,200
SIC 6324 6411 Group hospitalization plans; Insurance agents, brokers & service
Ex VP: Cheryl Howe
CEO: Alphonso O'Neil-White
COO: Bob Hoover
CFO: Chrisopher Leardini
CFO: Stephen Swift
Bd of Dir: Dena Owens
Ex VP: Steve Swift
VP: Gloria J Beczkowski
VP: Pauline E Cataldi
VP: Gretchen Fierle
VP: Ellen Grant
VP: Gary Kerl
VP: Gerald Klopfer
VP: Lisa Meyers
VP: Raghu Ram
VP: Melissa Tucker

D-U-N-S 79-705-3212
HEALTHPARTNERS INC
8170 33rd Ave S, Bloomington, MN 55425-4516
Tel (952) 883-6000 *Founded/Ownrshp* 1984
Sales 1.1MMM^E *EMP* 9,000
Accts Kpmg Llp Minneapolis Mn
SIC 8011 Offices & clinics of medical doctors
Pr: Mary Brainerd
**CFO:* David A Dziuk
Bd of Dir: John E Gherty
Bd of Dir: Eliot A Seide
**Ofcr:* Andrea Walsh
Sr VP: Calvin Allen
Sr VP: David Gesko
Sr VP: Scott Schnuckle
VP: Charles Abrahamson
VP: David Bergh
VP: Don Daddario
VP: Tricia Dege
VP: Tammie Lindquist
VP: Nico Pronk
VP: Nicolaas P Pronk
VP: Vicki Sessoms
VP: Mary Stom
VP: Barbara Tretheway
VP: Ted Wise

D-U-N-S 02-894-8573
HEALTHPLAN HOLDINGS INC
(*Suby of* WIPRO LIMITED)
3501 E Frontage Rd, Tampa, FL 33607-1704
Tel (813) 289-1000 *Founded/Ownrshp* 2016
Sales NA *EMP* 1,051
Accts Pricewaterhousecoopers Llp Ta
SIC 6399 Deposit insurance
CEO: Jeff W Bak
CFO: Stephen M Saft
Chf Mktg O: Anne Marie Faria
VP: Susan Murray
VP: Kim Warner
Snr Ntwrk: Yury Shmerlis
CIO: James Vertino
Dir IT: Dave Hemke
Tech Mgr: Alan Goldsmith
Software D: Jon Ranes
Sales Asso: Rosemary Menendez

D-U-N-S 18-822-7268
HEALTHPLAN SERVICES INC
(*Suby of* HEALTHPLAN HOLDINGS INC) ★
3501 E Frontage Rd # 125, Tampa, FL 33607-1704
Tel (813) 289-1000 *Founded/Ownrshp* 2001
Sales 300.0MM^E *EMP* 1,051
SIC 8741 Hospital management; Nursing & personal care facility management
Pr: Jeffery W Bak
COO: Kristin Baca
CFO: Thomas Chadwick
CFO: Stephen M Saft
Ex VP: Michael Buda
Ex VP: Arthur T Schultz
Sr VP: Mark Andrews
Sr VP: Todd Cowan
Sr VP: Gregory C Fisher
Sr VP: Terri Gonzalez
Sr VP: Jay McLauchlin
Sr VP: Dennis Prysner
VP: Phillip Coldiron
VP: Gregory T Fisher
VP: Lori Gonzalez
VP: Trent King
VP: Barbara Mathey
VP: Karen Mulroe
VP: Steven Strobl
VP: Delana Traugott
VP: Ronald Walters

D-U-N-S 13-089-6392
HEALTHPLEX INC
333 Earle Ovington Blvd # 300, Uniondale, NY 11553-3608
Tel (516) 542-2200 *Founded/Ownrshp* 1977
Sales NA *EMP* 620
SIC 6324 Dental insurance
Ch Bd: Stephen J Cuchel
COO: Christopher Schmidt
CFO: Vignola Valerie
CFO: Valerie Vignola
Treas: George Kane
Ex VP: Martin Kane
VP: Valerie Foster
VP: Jerry Gallo
VP: Joni Howe
VP: Philip J Rizzuto
Mng Dir: Jun Chen

D-U-N-S 96-333-2312
HEALTHPLUS INSURANCE CO
2050 S Linden Rd, Flint, MI 48532-4159
Tel (810) 230-2000 *Founded/Ownrshp* 2010
Sales NA *EMP* 2
SIC 6321 Health insurance carriers
Prin: Bea Raymond

D-U-N-S 09-540-0909
HEALTHPLUS OF MICHIGAN INC
HEALTHPLUS PARTNERS
2050 S Linden Rd, Flint, MI 48532-4159
Tel (810) 230-2000 *Founded/Ownrshp* 1979
Sales NA *EMP* 400
SIC 6324

HEALTHPLUS PARTNERS
See HEALTHPLUS OF MICHIGAN INC

D-U-N-S 96-750-2167
HEALTHPLUS PARTNERS INC
(*Suby of* HEALTH ALLIANCE PLAN OF MICHIGAN) ★
2050 S Linden Rd, Flint, MI 48532-4159
Tel (810) 230-2192 *Founded/Ownrshp* 2002
Sales 299.7MM *EMP* 145^E
SIC 8748 Business consulting
Pr: Michael Genord MD

HEALTHPORT
See CIOX HEALTH LLC

D-U-N-S 15-255-3228
HEALTHPORT INC
925 North Point Pkwy # 350, Alpharetta, GA 30005-5214
Tel (770) 360-1700 *Founded/Ownrshp* 2008
Sales NA *EMP* 3,875
SIC 6324 7373 7374 Hospital & medical service plans; Turnkey vendors, computer systems; Data processing & preparation
Pr: Michael J Labedz
**COO:* Steve Roberts
**CFO:* Brian M Grazzini
**Ch:* Pat Haynes
Ofcr: Rita K Bowen
**Sr VP:* Jonathan Arkin
Sr VP: Kerry De Vallette
Sr VP: Bill Garvis
**Sr VP:* Bill Matits
VP: Rasheed Allen
VP: Larry Arnold
VP: Paul Gue
VP: Craig F Klein
**VP:* Deryl Metze
**VP:* Matt Rohs

HEALTHRIDER
See ICON HEALTH & FITNESS INC

D-U-N-S 06-014-2130
HEALTHRIGHT 360
HAIGHT ASHBURY FREE CLINICS -
1735 Mission St Ste 2050, San Francisco, CA 94103-2417
Tel (415) 762-3700 *Founded/Ownrshp* 1966
Sales 96.1MM *EMP* 450
Accts Armanino Llp San Ramon Ca
SIC 8093 8011 Detoxification center, outpatient; Clinic, operated by physicians; Psychiatric clinic
CEO: Vitka Eisen
V Ch: Maria Mangini
CFO: Pamela Banks
**CFO:* David Crawford
CFO: Carl Gill
**VP:* Wayne Garcia
**VP:* Mardell Gavriel
VP: Denise Williams

D-U-N-S 15-193-5749
HEALTHSHARE INC
CHILD DEVELOPMENT CENTER
416 Connable Ave, Petoskey, MI 49770-2212
Tel (231) 487-4803 *Founded/Ownrshp* 1982
Sales 226.9MM *EMP* 150^E
Accts Ernst & Young Llp Grand Rapid
SIC 8741 8062 Hospital management; Nursing & personal care facility management; General medical & surgical hospitals
Pr: Jeffrey Wendling
**Ch Bd:* Lawrence D Buhl
**Treas:* Richard Lent
**V Ch Bd:* Thomas N Fairbairn

D-U-N-S 06-382-8842
HEALTHSMART PACIFIC INC
LONG BEACH PAIN CENTER
20377 Sw Acacia St # 110, Newport Beach, CA 92660-0781
Tel (562) 595-1911 *Founded/Ownrshp* 1996
Sales 148.3MM^E *EMP* 1,200
Accts Statewide Health Planning & De
SIC 8062 General medical & surgical hospitals
CEO: Michael Ddrobot
**CEO:* Michael D Drobot
Dir Case M: Patricia Bussey
Dir Sec: Robert Vance
CTO: Javier Chavez
Pharmcst: Arleioh Williams
Phys Thrpy: Heidi Endert
Board of Directors: Randolph Taylor

D-U-N-S 95-744-6289
HEALTHSMART PREFERRED CARE II LP
2002 W Loop 289 Ste 103, Lubbock, TX 79407-7701
Tel (806) 473-2500 *Founded/Ownrshp* 1994
Sales NA *EMP* 314
SIC 6324 Hospital & medical service plans
Ch Bd: Ted L Parker
**Pr:* David Adams
Treas: Mike Hedlund
**VP:* Jane Williamson Rn
VP Mktg: Lynda Woods

D-U-N-S 14-732-4128 EXP
HEALTHSOURCE DISTRIBUTORS LLC
SAVEBIG RX
7200 Rutherford Rd # 150, Baltimore, MD 21244-2717
Tel (410) 653-1113 *Founded/Ownrshp* 2003
Sales 226.8MM *EMP* 60
Accts Weil Akman Baylin & Coleman
SIC 5122 Pharmaceuticals
Pr: Jerry Wolasky
VP Sls: Marc Loeb

D-U-N-S 14-426-1724
■ HEALTHSOURCE INC
(*Suby of* CIGNA HEALTH CORP) ★
2 College Park Dr, Hooksett, NH 03106-1636
Tel (603) 268-7000 *Founded/Ownrshp* 1997
Sales NA *EMP* 4,100
SIC 6324 8741 8011 Hospital & medical service plans; Administrative management; Health maintenance organization
Pr: H Edward Hanway
CFO: Robert C Williams
Treas: Bach MAI Tai
VP: Ann Duscoll

D-U-N-S 11-430-2219 IMP
▲ HEALTHSOUTH CORP
3660 Grandview Pkwy # 200, Birmingham, AL 35243-3332
Tel (205) 967-7116 *Founded/Ownrshp* 1984
Sales 3.1MMM *EMP* 27,110
Tkr Sym HLS *Exch* NYS
SIC 8069 8051 Specialty hospitals, except psychiatric; Extended care facility
Pr: Jay Grinney
**Ch Bd:* Leo I Higdon Jr
Pr: April Anthony
COO: Mark J Tarr
CFO: Douglas E Coltharp
Treas: Edmund M Fay
Ofcr: Elissa J Charbonneau
Ofcr: Cheryl B Levy
Ex VP: Patrick Darby
VP: Crissy Carlisle
VP: Murray Meadows
Dir Inf Cn: Janet Rossi
Board of Directors: John W Chidsey, Donald L Correll, Yvonne M Curl, Charles M Elson, Joan E Herman, John E Maupin Jr, L Edward Shaw Jr

D-U-N-S 07-967-9121
■ HEALTHSOUTH HOME HEALTH CORP
(*Suby of* HEALTHSOUTH HOME HEALTH HOLDINGS INC) ★
3660 Grandview Pkwy, Birmingham, AL 35243-3330
Tel (205) 967-7116 *Founded/Ownrshp* 2014
Sales 4.5MM^E *EMP* 3,800^E
SIC 8082 8099 Home health care services; Medical services organization
Pr: Jay Grinney

D-U-N-S 07-967-9204
■ HEALTHSOUTH HOME HEALTH HOLDINGS INC
(*Suby of* HEALTHSOUTH CORP) ★
3660 Grandview Pkwy, Birmingham, AL 35243-3330
Tel (205) 967-7116 *Founded/Ownrshp* 2014
Sales 4.5MM^E *EMP* 3,800^E
SIC 8099 8082 6719 Medical services organization; Home health care services; Personal holding companies, except banks
Pr: Jay Grinney

D-U-N-S 60-487-1038
■ HEALTHSOUTH REHABILITATION HOSPITAL OF CYPRESS LLC
(Suby of HEALTHSOUTH CORP) ★
3660 Grandview Pkwy, Birmingham, AL 35243-3330
Tel (205) 967-7116 Founded/Ownrshp 1998
Sales 28.3MM^E EMP 1,000
SIC 8093 Specialty outpatient clinics
Ch Bd: Richard Scrushy

D-U-N-S 14-719-9533
HEALTHSPAN INTEGRATED CARE
(Suby of MERCY HEALTH) ★
1001 Lakeside Ave E # 1200, Cleveland, OH 44114-1158
Tel (216) 621-5600 Founded/Ownrshp 2013
Sales 435.0MM EMP 1,240
Accts Bkd Llp Cincinnati Oh
SIC 8011 Health maintenance organization
CEO: Kenneth Page
*Pr: Patricia D Kennedy-Scott
*CEO: George Halverson
*CFO: Thomas Revis
Counsel: Paula Ohliger

D-U-N-S 08-831-8618
■ HEALTHSPRING INC
(Suby of CIGNA) ★
530 Great Circle Rd, Nashville, TN 37228-1309
Tel (615) 291-7000 Founded/Ownrshp 2012
Sales NA EMP 3,200^E
SIC 6324 Hospital & medical service plans; Group hospitalization plans; Health maintenance organization (HMO), insurance only
CEO: Herbert A Fritch
*Pr: Michael G Mirt
*COO: Mark A Tulloch
*CFO: Karey L Witty
Ch: Gerald Coil
*Ex VP: Sharad Mansukani
*Sr VP: J Gentry Barden
VP: Jeff Brown
VP: Kelly Christopher
VP: Claudia Douds
VP: Robyn Leland
VP: Louise McCagg
VP: Ron Minson
VP: Allen Perez
VP: Sandee Safer
VP: Dirk Wales
Comm Dir: Desiree Dankowski

D-U-N-S 01-230-3297
■ HEALTHSPRING USA LLC
(Suby of HEALTHSPRING INC) ★
44 Vantage Way Ste 300, Nashville, TN 37228-1550
Tel (615) 291-7000 Founded/Ownrshp 2006
Sales NA EMP 31^E
SIC 6324 Hospital & medical service plans; Group hospitalization plans; Health maintenance organization (HMO), insurance only
Pr: Shawn Morris
Pr: Kyle Duke
Pr: Victor Wesolowski
COO: Greg Allen
CFO: Cynthia Williams
Sr VP: Gentry Barden
Sr VP: Lyle Hill
VP: Gary Bailey
VP: Kenneth Nunez
VP: Heather Peterson
Dir IT: Andy Laman

D-U-N-S 18-170-2804 IMP
HEALTHSTAR COMMUNICATIONS INC
1000 Wyckoff Ave Ste 202, Mahwah, NJ 07430-3164
Tel (201) 560-5370 Founded/Ownrshp 1987
Sales 84.7MM^E EMP 620
SIC 7372 7311 6719 Prepackaged software; Advertising agencies; Personal holding companies, except banks
CEO: Jerry Brager
*Pr: John Corcoran
*Pr: Myron Holubiak
COO: Leigh Paeschke
*CFO: Jim Sivori
*Ex VP: Peter Cossman
Ex VP: Ken Dutcher
Ex VP: Joseph Mastracchio
Ex VP: Kimberly Romagnola
*Sr VP: Patricia Brock
Sr VP: Mike McCauley
Sr VP: Cira Montreys
VP: Lewis Campanaro
VP: Jim King
VP: Jeanine Kober
VP: Shannon Sweeney
Assoc Dir: Michele Giordano
Creative D: Jeff Lipman

D-U-N-S 62-588-8748
▲ HEALTHSTREAM INC
209 10th Ave S Ste 450, Nashville, TN 37203-0788
Tel (615) 301-3100 Founded/Ownrshp 1999
Sales 209.0MM EMP 972^E
Tkr Sym HSTM Exch NGS
SIC 7372 7371 Prepackaged software; Custom computer programming services
Ch Bd: Robert A Frist Jr
COO: J Edward Pearson
CFO: Gerard M Hayden Jr
Sr VP: Jeffrey S Doster
Sr VP: Thomas Schultz
Sr VP: Michael Sousa
Exec: Susanne Lipscomb
Sls&Mrk Ex: Healthstreams Australia
Sls Dir: Tom Emberson
Sls Dir: Holly Woods
Mktg Mgr: Kira Lindquist
Board of Directors: Thompson S Dent, Frank Gordon, C Martin Harris, Jeffrey L McLaren, Dale Polley, Linda Rebrovick, Michael Shmerling, William W Stead, Deborah Taylor Tate

D-U-N-S 96-159-2222
HEALTHTECH HOLDINGS INC
3102 West End Ave Ste 400, Nashville, TN 37203-1623
Tel (615) 383-7300 Founded/Ownrshp 2009
Sales 106.1MM^E EMP 419^E
SIC 7372 Prepackaged software
CEO: Thomas M Stephenson
VP: Eric Anderton
VP: Stan Gilbreath
*CIO: Geoff Roten
*CTO: Alan Maclamroc
VP Mktg: Tom Mitchell

D-U-N-S 83-695-4099
HEALTHTEXAS PROVIDER NETWORK
(Suby of BHCS) ★
8080 N Cntrl Expy Ste 600, Dallas, TX 75206-3794
Tel (972) 860-8600 Founded/Ownrshp 1994
Sales 206.8MM EMP 350
SIC 8011 Offices & clinics of medical doctors
Pr: Gary Brock
*Pr: William Roberts
*Treas: Sarah Gahm

D-U-N-S 16-198-6757
HEALTHTRAX INC
WORK FIT
2345 Main St, Glastonbury, CT 06033-2211
Tel (860) 633-5572 Founded/Ownrshp 1986
Sales 44.5MM^E EMP 1,000
SIC 7991 7997 Health club; Racquetball club, membership
Pr: Kenneth F Navarro
*COO: Robert E Stauble Jr
*CFO: Pat Donnelly
Ofcr: Patsy Eagleson
VP: Mike Vanamberg
Pgrm Dir: Linda Roy

D-U-N-S 80-862-3636
HEALTHTRAX INTERNATIONAL INC
2345 Main St, Glastonbury, CT 06033-2211
Tel (860) 633-5572 Founded/Ownrshp 1984
Sales 8.1MM EMP 1,400
SIC 7991 Physical fitness facilities
Prin: Robert E Stauble Jr

D-U-N-S 95-908-1746 IMP
HEALTHTRONICS INC
(Suby of HT INTERMEDIATE CO LLC) ★
9825 Spectrum Dr Bldg 3, Austin, TX 78717-4930
Tel (512) 328-2892 Founded/Ownrshp 2015
Sales 187.4MM^E EMP 588^E
SIC 3845 Lithotripters
CEO: Russel Newman
Sr VP: Clint Davis
VP: Clint Davis
VP: Gary Kozen
VP: James Maguire
VP: Mark Rooney
Off Admin: Hope Buck
Ql Cn Mgr: Thuy Tran
Genl Couns: Anthony Mustillo

D-U-N-S 02-214-7063
HEALTHTRONICS SERVICE CENTER LLC
9825 Spectrum Dr Bldg 3, Austin, TX 78717-4930
Tel (512) 328-2892 Founded/Ownrshp 1992
Sales 165.9MM EMP 400
SIC 1389

D-U-N-S 06-840-6763
HEALTHTRUST PURCHASING GROUP LP
H P G
155 Franklin Rd Ste 400, Brentwood, TN 37027-4693
Tel (615) 377-1294 Founded/Ownrshp 1999
Sales 88.8MM^E EMP 200^E
SIC 7389 Purchasing service
CEO: Ed Jones
Pr: Netta Collins
Pr: Mark Dumond
Pr: Susan Mojaverian
Pr: Belinda Vanatta
CFO: John Paul
Treas: Samuel Howard
Ex VP: Michael Berryhill
VP: Bob Davis
VP: Bill Francis
VP: Mark Holroyd
VP: Patrick Lowry
VP: Tarkington Steve
VP: Doug Swanson
VP: Darrel Weatherford
VP: Shelly Workman

HEALTHWAY
See MAKERS OF KAL INC

D-U-N-S 05-995-1988
▲ HEALTHWAYS INC
701 Cool Springs Blvd, Franklin, TN 37067-2697
Tel (615) 614-4929 Founded/Ownrshp 1981
Sales 770.6MM EMP 2,400
Tkr Sym HWAY Exch NGS
SIC 8082 8099 Home health care services; Health screening service
CEO: Donato J Tramuto
*Ch Bd: Kevin G Wills
CFO: Glenn Hargreaves
Bd of Dir: Mary J England
VP: Mike Davis
VP: Colleen Kemp
VP: Heidi Kim
VP: Richard Olson
Ex Dir: Jon Werger
Mktg Mgr: Jennifer Hadley
Genl Couns: Mary Flipse
Board of Directors: Mary Jane England, Robert J Greczyn Jr, Peter Hudson, Bradley S Karro, Paul H Keckley, Conan J Laughlin, Lee A Shapiro

D-U-N-S 78-734-1853
HEALTHWELL FOUNDATION
9801 Washingtonian Blvd # 900, Gaithersburg, MD 20878-5356
Tel (800) 675-8416 Founded/Ownrshp 2006
Sales 89.2MM EMP 1
Accts Raffa Pc Washington Dc
SIC 8082 Home health care services
Pr: Krista Zodet

HEALTHWORKS
See LUTHER HOSPITAL

HEALTHWRKS WELLNESS FITNES CTR
See CORNING HOSPITAL

D-U-N-S 02-475-8743
HEALTHY START COALITION OF PALM BEACH COUNTY IN
2300 High Ridge Rd, Boynton Beach, FL 33426-8747
Tel (561) 374-7613 Founded/Ownrshp 2009
Sales 87.8MM EMP 2
Accts Keefe Mccullough & Co Ft L
SIC 8351 Child day care services
Prin: Triste Brooks
CFO: Bill Cosgrove
CFO: Jennifer Diehl

HEARN-KIRKWOOD
See GILBERT FOODS LLC

D-U-N-S 02-906-2072
HEARST BUSINESS MEDIA CORP
(Suby of HEARST MAGAZINES) ★
2620 Barrett Rd, Gainesville, GA 30507-7901
Tel (770) 532-4111 Founded/Ownrshp 1980
Sales 92.1MM^E EMP 75
SIC 2721 Magazines: publishing only, not printed on site
Pr: Richard P Malloch
*Treas: Robert D Wilbanks
*VP: Thomas D Cross
*VP: Peter Rowlinson

D-U-N-S 00-920-4371 IMP
HEARST COMMUNICATIONS INC
SAN FRANCISCO CHRONICLE
901 Mission St, San Francisco, CA 94103-3052
Tel (415) 777-1111 Founded/Ownrshp 1996
Sales 419.4MM^E EMP 1,700
SIC 2711 Newspapers, publishing & printing
Pr: Frank J Vega
CFO: Jerretta Avery
CFO: Elizabeth Cain
Bd of Dir: John Nejedly
Ex VP: Gary Anderson
VP: James Artz
VP: Fred Broi
VP: Peter Negulescu
VP: Hernan Ponce
Exec: Darien Dumanis
Exec: Barbara Wright
Assoc Dir: Danielle Cumbo
Board of Directors: Carlos Gutierrez

D-U-N-S 00-152-7241 IMP
HEARST CORP
HEARST MAGAZINES
300 W 57th St Fl 42, New York, NY 10019-3790
Tel (212) 649-2000 Founded/Ownrshp 1887
Sales 5.3MMM^E EMP 20,589
SIC 2721 2731 2711 4832 4833 7383 Magazines: publishing only, not printed on site; Books: publishing only; Newspapers, publishing & printing; Newspapers: publishing only, not printed on site; Radio broadcasting stations; Television broadcasting stations; News feature syndicate
Pr: Steven R Swartz
Pr: Mark E Aldam
Pr: Nick Brien
Pr: John McKeon
Pr: David A Schirmer
COO: Susan Pape
CFO: Mitchell Scherzer
Ch: William R Hearst III
Treas: Carlton J Charles
Chf Cred: Neeraj Khemlani
Bd of Dir: Lisa Hagerman
Chf Inves: Roger P Paschke
Ofcr: Wendy Wilk
Ex VP: Michael A Clinton
Ex VP: Rob Cravaritis
Ex VP: Tom Cross
Ex VP: Steven A Hobbs
Ex VP: Michael C Labonia
Ex VP: Lincoln Millstein
Sr VP: James M Asher
Sr VP: Eve Burton

D-U-N-S 13-592-8922 IMP
HEARST HOLDINGS INC
(Suby of HEARST MAGAZINES) ★
300 W 57th St, New York, NY 10019-3741
Tel (212) 649-2000 Founded/Ownrshp 1996
Sales 580.5MM^E EMP 15,000
SIC 2721 4841 Magazines: publishing only, not printed on site; Cable television services
Ch Bd: George R Hearst Jr
*CFO: Ronald J Doerfler
Treas: Jon D Smith Jr
*Ofcr: James M Asher
*Sr VP: Cathleen P Black
*Sr VP: John G Conomikes
*Sr VP: George B Irish
*Sr VP: Raymond E Joslin
Art Dir: Ron Gabriel

HEARST MAGAZINES
See HEARST CORP

D-U-N-S 02-959-5878
HEARST NEWSPAPERS LLC
HOUSTON CHRONICLE
4747 Southwest Fwy, Houston, TX 77027-6901
Tel (713) 220-7171 Founded/Ownrshp 2007
Sales 292.2MM^E EMP 1,320^E
SIC 2711 Newspapers
Ch: Jack Sweeney
*Pr: John T O'Loughlin
Treas: James Smith
*Ex VP: Jeff Cohen
Ex VP: Robert D Cravaritis
VP: Mario Barson
VP: Linda Schaible
Exec: Fonnie Ray Davis
Exec: Andrea Mooney
Exec: Elizabeth Scott
Ex Dir: Divya Visentini

D-U-N-S 87-774-9861
HEARST TELEVISION INC
(Suby of HEARST MAGAZINES) ★
300 W 57th St, New York, NY 10019-3741
Tel (212) 887-6800 Founded/Ownrshp 2013
Sales 584.1MM^E EMP 3,324
SIC 4833 Television broadcasting stations
Ch Bd: David J Barrett
Ch Bd: Frank A Bennack Jr
Pr: Glenn Haygood
Pr: Jordan Wertlieb
Ex VP: Terry Mackin
Ex VP: Anthony J Vinciquerra
Sr VP: Frank C Biancuzzo
Sr VP: Roger Keating
Sr VP: Philip M Stolz
VP: Emerson Coleman
VP: Caroline Scollard-Taplett
Board of Directors: John G Conomikes, Ken J Elkins, George R Hearst Jr, William R Hearst III, Bob Marbut, Gilbert C Maurer, David Pulver, Caroline L Williams

HEART & FITNESS CENTER
See GENERAL HEALTH SYSTEM

D-U-N-S 87-629-1175
HEART HOSPITAL OF SOUTH DAKOTA LLC
AVERA HEART HOPSITAL SD
4500 W 69th St, Sioux Falls, SD 57108-8148
Tel (605) 977-7000 Founded/Ownrshp 1999
Sales 101.1MM EMP 400
SIC 8062 3842 General medical & surgical hospitals; Sterilizers, hospital & surgical
CEO: Jon Soderholm
COO: Shelia Orr
*CFO: Jean White
Ofcr: Peggy Goos
VP: Becky Smith
Exec: Vicki Tencate
Dir Pat Ca: Jana Sorlie
Dir Rx: Kathy Vanhove
Genl Mgr: Josh Merkley
Dir IT: Dan Marnach
Sfty Dirs: Steve Lee

D-U-N-S 15-103-8544
HEART OF AMERICA MANAGEMENT LLC
1501 River Dr, Moline, IL 61265-1315
Tel (309) 797-9300 Founded/Ownrshp 1978
Sales 93.8MM^E EMP 1,500
SIC 8741 5812 7011 Business management; Eating places; Hotels & motels
Ex VP: Kim Whalen
Sr VP: Damen Trebilcock
VP: Melinda Kuehne
VP: John Schulz
Genl Mgr: Cathy Lenzi

D-U-N-S 80-977-8566
HEART TO HEART INTERNATIONAL INC
13250 W 98th St, Lenexa, KS 66215-1359
Tel (913) 764-5200 Founded/Ownrshp 1992
Sales 99.5MM EMP 30
Accts Keller & Owens Llc Overland
SIC 8399 Health systems agency
Pr: Gary Morsch
*Ch Bd: Jim Kerr
*CEO: Jim Mitchum
*CFO: Bud Jeffress
VP: Pete Brumbaugh
Assoc Dir: Brian McDonell
Comm Dir: Dan Weinbaum
Pgrm Dir: Carla Orner

D-U-N-S 96-283-1095 IMP
■ HEARTH & HOME TECHNOLOGIES LLC
HEATILATOR
(Suby of HNI CORP) ★
7571 215th St W, Lakeville, MN 55044-9887
Tel (952) 985-6000 Founded/Ownrshp 1981
Sales 535.0MM^E EMP 2,800
SIC 3429 4925 Fireplace equipment, hardware: andirons, grates, screens; Gas production and/or distribution
Pr: Brad D Determan
Pr: Bob Hawkinson
*VP: Michael Ramsay
VP: Ed Ray
Rgnl Mgr: Ed Ricklick
Store Mgr: Faye Schimke
Dir IT: Eugene Schutte
Sls&Mrk Ex: Shannon Quinn
Pr Dir: Mike Fukatsu

D-U-N-S 96-868-2526 IMP
■ HEARTHMARK LLC
JARDEN BRANDS CONSUMABLES
(Suby of NEWELL BRANDS) ★
9999 E 121st St, Fishers, IN 46037-9727
Tel (765) 557-3000 Founded/Ownrshp 2003
Sales 708.4MM^E EMP 1,400
SIC 3221 Food containers, glass
Pr: Chris Scherzinger
Treas: Ian G H Ashken
VP: Stanley Ng
VP: Robert P Totte
CIO: Jason Eskew
IT Man: Augustus Griffith
Ql Cn Mgr: Michael Walters
Natl Sales: Michele Alanen
VP Sls: Moira Menninga
Mktg Mgr: Steve Hungsberg
Mktg Mgr: Brett Westerman

D-U-N-S 83-035-3103 EXP
HEARTHSIDE FOOD SOLUTIONS LLC
3250 Lacey Rd Ste 200, Downers Grove, IL 60515-8384
Tel (630) 967-3600 Founded/Ownrshp 2009
Sales 2.3MMM^E EMP 7,850
SIC 2043 2038 Cereal breakfast foods; Snacks, including onion rings, cheese sticks, etc.
CEO: Richard Sealise
CFO: Scott Edgcomb
*CFO: Fred Jasse
CFO: James Jorasky
Sr VP: Ronald Hink
*VP: Bob Scalia
VP: John Weller

Exec: Patricia Richards
Area Supr: Diane Phipps
QA Dir: Jason Eastman
QA Dir: Donna Eversole

HEARTHSONG
See PLOW & HEARTH LLC

D-U-N-S 18-617-3860 IMP
HEARTLAND AUTOMOTIVE INC
300 S Warren Dr, Greencastle, IN 46135-7573
Tel (765) 653-4263 *Founded/Ownrshp* 1997
Sales 228.8MM^E *EMP* 600
SIC 3714 Motor vehicle parts & accessories
QC Dir: Patrick Garrison
VP Mktg: Terry Tekegaua
Mktg Mgr: Tatsushi T Okane

D-U-N-S 08-209-5761
HEARTLAND BANK AND TRUST
(*Suby of* HEARTLAND BANCORP INC)
401 N Hershey Rd, Bloomington, IL 61704-3742
Tel (309) 662-4444 *Founded/Ownrshp* 1971
Sales NA *EMP* 125
SIC 6022 State commercial banks
CEO: Fred L Drake
* *Pr:* Patrick F Busch
COO: Martin Dudley
* *CFO:* Matt Doherty
Trst Ofcr: Brian Massey
* *Ex VP:* Lance Carter
* *Ex VP:* Diane Lanier

HEARTLAND BUSINESS SYSTEMS
See HEARTLAND LABEL PRINTERS LLC

D-U-N-S 92-929-2712
HEARTLAND CATFISH CO INC
55001 Highway 82 W, Itta Bena, MS 38941-9613
Tel (662) 254-7100 *Founded/Ownrshp* 1995
Sales 84.6MM^E *EMP* 415
SIC 2092 Fresh or frozen packaged fish
CEO: Danny Walker
* *Pr:* William Tackett
* *Pr:* Joseph A Walker
* *Sec:* Brian L Crawford
* *VP:* Jimmy Killies Tackett
VP: Marty Tackett
VP Opers: Tim Millwood
Manager: Don Davis

D-U-N-S 00-798-7563
HEARTLAND CO-OP
2829 Westown Pkwy Ste 350, West Des Moines, IA 50266-1340
Tel (515) 225-1334 *Founded/Ownrshp* 1907
Sales 854.4MM *EMP* 678
Accts Bergan Paulsen & Company Pc
SIC 5153 0762 2048 Grains; Farm management services; Livestock feeds
Pr: Arthur L Churchill
Dir IT: Dave Cunitz
IT Man: Mike Thronson

D-U-N-S 07-997-1647
■ **HEARTLAND EMPLOYMENT SERVICES LLC**
(*Suby of* HCR MANOR CARE INC) ★
333 N Summit St, Toledo, OH 43604-1531
Tel (419) 252-5743 *Founded/Ownrshp* 2004
Sales 98.4MM^E *EMP* 55,000
SIC 7361 Nurses' registry

D-U-N-S 15-512-1668
▲ **HEARTLAND EXPRESS INC**
901 N Kansas Ave, North Liberty, IA 52317-4726
Tel (319) 626-3600 *Founded/Ownrshp* 1978
Sales 736.3MM *EMP* 4,200^E
Tkr Sym HTLD *Exch* NGS
SIC 4213 Trucking, except local; Contract haulers
Ch Bd: Michael Gerdin
CFO: John P Cosaert
VP: Christopher A Strain
VP: Todd A Trimble
VP Sls: Kent D Rigdon
Board of Directors: Benjamin J Allen, Lawrence D Crouse, Larry D Gordon, James G Pratt

D-U-N-S 00-986-5684
■ **HEARTLAND EXPRESS INC OF IOWA**
(*Suby of* HEARTLAND EXPRESS INC) ★
901 N Kansas Ave, North Liberty, IA 52317-4726
Tel (319) 626-3600 *Founded/Ownrshp* 1978
Sales 528.6MM *EMP* 2,862
SIC 4213 Contract haulers
Pr: Michael Gerdin
* *CFO:* John Cosaert
* *Ex VP:* Rich Meehan
* *VP:* Todd Trimble
* *VP:* Dennis Wilkinson

D-U-N-S 80-784-4170
▲ **HEARTLAND FINANCIAL USA INC**
1398 Central Ave, Dubuque, IA 52001-5021
Tel (563) 589-2000 *Founded/Ownrshp* 1981
Sales NA *EMP* 1,799^E
Tkr Sym HTLF *Exch* NGS
SIC 6022 State commercial banks
Ch Bd: Lynn B Fuller
Pr: Bruce K Lee
Pr: Jack Lloyd
COO: Bruce C Rehmke
CFO: Bryan R McKeag
* *V Ch Bd:* Mark C Falb
* *V Ch Bd:* Thomas L Flynn
Chf Cred: Kenneth J Erickson
Ofcr: Janet M Quick
Ofcr: Rodney L Sloan
Ex VP: Steve Braden
Ex VP: Michael J Coyle
Ex VP: Brian J Fox
Ex VP: David L Horstmann
Ex VP: Douglas J Horstmann
Ex VP: Kelly J Johnson
Ex VP: Mark G Murtha
Ex VP: Frank E Walter
VP: Mark Erickson
Board of Directors: James F Conlan, John W Cox Jr, R Michael McCoy, Kurt M Saylor, John K Schmidt, Duane E White

HEARTLAND FOOD PRODUCTS GROUP
See TC HEARTLAND LLC

D-U-N-S 18-120-1773
HEARTLAND HEALTH
5325 Faraon St, Saint Joseph, MO 64506-3488
Tel (816) 271-6000 *Founded/Ownrshp* 1984
Sales 584.3MM *EMP* 32,000
Accts Bkd Llp Kansas City Missouri
SIC 8062 7322 8721 General medical & surgical hospitals; Adjustment & collection services; Billing & bookkeeping service
CEO: Mark Laney MD
V Ch: Sheri Spader
* *Pr:* Lowell Kruse
Pr: Christine Rattin
* *COO:* Cut Kretzinger
CFO: David Warmerdam
* *CFO:* John Wilson
* *Ch:* Alfred L Purcell
* *Ch:* David Solanski
Bd of Dir: Becky Davison
* *Chf Mktg O:* Robert Permet
Ofcr: Chuck Tozer
VP: Charles Mullican

D-U-N-S 83-443-6875
■ **HEARTLAND HEALTHCARE SERVICES LLC**
(*Suby of* OMNICARE INC) ★
4755 South Ave, Toledo, OH 43615-6422
Tel (419) 535-8435 *Founded/Ownrshp* 1994
Sales 204.4MM *EMP* 200
Accts Ernst & Young Llp Toledo Oh
SIC 8011 Offices & clinics of medical doctors
CFO: Jeffrey Cremean
CFO: Dorothy Kuhl
Exec: Jodi Lenic
Genl Mgr: Jerry Krbec
Info Man: Craig C Varner
Sfty Dirs: Cheryl Paxton
Opers Mgr: Paula Johnson
Pharmcst: Daniel Feyes Jr
Pharmcst: Mary Garcia
Pharmcst: Joseph McKown
Pharmcst: Theresa Senyo

HEARTLAND HM HALTHCARE HOSPICE
See IN HOME HEALTH LLC

D-U-N-S 14-579-1625
HEARTLAND HOME FOODS INC
BURGER KING
1400 Opus Pl Ste 900, Downers Grove, IL 60515-5762
Tel (800) 492-5592 *Founded/Ownrshp* 2007
Sales 71.8MM^E *EMP* 4,000
SIC 5812 8741

D-U-N-S 78-739-5151
HEARTLAND IMAGING COMPANIES INC
LAWRENCE PHOTO-GRAPHIC
1211 W Cambridge Cir Dr, Kansas City, KS 66103-1313
Tel (913) 621-1211 *Founded/Ownrshp* 1981
Sales 141.0MM *EMP* 373
Accts Baird Kurtz & Dobson
SIC 5043 Photographic equipment & supplies; Printing apparatus, photographic
Ch: Robert J Gourley
* *Treas:* Thomas M Prater
VP: Walter Stolarski
* *VP:* Vernon Vogel
Brnch Mgr: Tom Kelly
Genl Mgr: Ty Roth

HEARTLAND INDUSTRIES
See BACKYARD STORAGE SOLUTIONS LLC

D-U-N-S 61-502-9352 EXP
HEARTLAND LABEL PRINTERS LLC
HEARTLAND BUSINESS SYSTEMS
1700 Stephen St, Little Chute, WI 54140-2550
Tel (920) 788-7720 *Founded/Ownrshp* 1994
Sales 196.7MM *EMP* 130
Accts Schenck Sc Appleton Wisconsi
SIC 5065 2672 Modems, computer; Adhesive papers, labels or tapes: from purchased material
CEO: Peter Helander
Pr: Joe Zoeller
* *VP:* Bud Nackers
Mng Dir: Ben Turner
Off Mgr: Mary Kasten
Snr Ntwrk: Paul Fandrey
IT Man: Renee Miller
IT Man: Josh Streich
IT Man: Amy Toporski
Netwrk Eng: Mike Biese
Mktg Mgr: Jim Check

HEARTLAND PAPER
See CHRIS CAM CORP

D-U-N-S 01-083-9657
■ **HEARTLAND PAYMENT SYSTEMS LLC**
(*Suby of* GLOBALPAYMENTS) ★
300 Carnegie Ctr Ste 300, Princeton, NJ 08540-6255
Tel (609) 683-3831 *Founded/Ownrshp* 2015
Sales 2.6MMM *EMP* 3,734^E
Accts Deloitte & Touche Llp Philade
SIC 7389 8721 Credit card service; Payroll accounting service
CEO: Robert O Carr
* *COO:* Conan Lane
* *CFO:* Samir Zabaneh
* *Co-Pr:* David Gilbert
* *Co-Pr:* Michael A Lawler
VP: Peter Drew
VP: Jeff Zander
Exec: Steven Gamary
* *Dir Sec:* Marty Moretti
* *Dir Sec:* John R South
Area Mgr: Tom Riley

D-U-N-S 07-953-9855
■ **HEARTLAND PET FOODS MANUFACTURING INC**
(*Suby of* BLUE BUFFALO CO LTD) ★
8101 E 32nd St, Joplin, MO 64804-7966
Tel (417) 952-1400 *Founded/Ownrshp* 2012
Sales 200.0MM *EMP* 150
SIC 2048 Dry pet food (except dog & cat)
Pr: William Bishop Jr

D-U-N-S 14-333-8056
■ **HEARTLAND RECREATIONAL VEHICLES LLC**
HEARTLAND RV
(*Suby of* THOR INDUSTRIES INC) ★
2831 Dexter Dr, Elkhart, IN 46514-8225
Tel (574) 266-8726 *Founded/Ownrshp* 2003
Sales 247.0MM^E *EMP* 700^E
SIC 3799 Recreational vehicles
CEO: Timothy M Hoffman

D-U-N-S 01-064-5919
HEARTLAND REGIONAL MEDICAL CENTER
(*Suby of* HEARTLAND HEALTH) ★
5325 Faraon St, Saint Joseph, MO 64506-3488
Tel (816) 271-6000 *Founded/Ownrshp* 1898
Sales 562.8MM *EMP* 2,600
Accts Bld Llp Kansas City Missour
SIC 8062 General medical & surgical hospitals
Ch: Alfred L Purcell
* *CEO:* Mark Laney
CFO: Spencer Klaasen
Bd of Dir: David Berger
VP: Rattin Christine
VP: Steve Wenger
Dir Risk M: Becky Kanjirathinkou
Dir Case M: Linda Bahrke
Pathlgst: David Halbach

HEARTLAND REGIONAL MEDICAL CTR
See MARION HOSPITAL CORP

HEARTLAND RV
See HEARTLAND RECREATIONAL VEHICLES LLC

D-U-N-S 96-352-5493
■ **HEARTLAND-WASHINGTON MANOR OF KENOSHA WI LLC**
MANORCARE HLTH SRVCES- KENOSHA
(*Suby of* HCR MANOR CARE INC) ★
3100 Washington Rd, Kenosha, WI 53144-1604
Tel (262) 658-4622 *Founded/Ownrshp* 1985
Sales 341.0MM *EMP* 1^E
SIC 8051 Skilled nursing care facilities

D-U-N-S 80-186-2772
HEARTSHARE HUMAN SERVICES OF NY ROMAN CATHOLIC DIOCESE OF BROOKLYN
12 Metrotech Ctr Fl 29, Brooklyn, NY 11201-3858
Tel (718) 422-4200 *Founded/Ownrshp* 1914
Sales 91.9MM *EMP* 1,200^E
Accts Loeb & Troper Llp New York N
SIC 8322 Individual & family services
Pr: William R Guarinello
* *Treas:* Michael Abatemarco
* *Ex VP:* Mia Higgins
* *Ex VP:* Linda Tempel
* *Sr VP:* Evelyn Alvarez
* *Sr VP:* Anthony F Bianca
* *Sr VP:* George Cincotta Jr
* *Sr VP:* Carol Smith-Njiiri
* *VP:* Robert C Golden
* *VP:* John T Sharkey
* *VP:* Ralph A Subbiondo

D-U-N-S 83-043-5702
HEARTWARE INTERNATIONAL INC
(*Suby of* MEDTRONIC INC) ★
500 Old Connecticut Path, Framingham, MA 01701-4574
Tel (508) 739-0950 *Founded/Ownrshp* 2016
Sales 276.8MM *EMP* 600^E
SIC 3841 Surgical instruments & apparatus
Pr: Douglas Godshall
CFO: Peter F McAree
Ofcr: Jeffrey Larose
Ofcr: Katrin Leadley MD
Sr VP: Larry Knopf
Sr VP: James Schuermann
Sr VP: Mark Strong

HEARUSA
See AUDIOLOGY DISTRIBUTION LLC

D-U-N-S 00-911-8407 IMP/EXP
HEAT AND CONTROL INC (CA)
21121 Cabot Blvd, Hayward, CA 94545-1132
Tel (510) 259-0500 *Founded/Ownrshp* 1950
Sales 269.4MM^E *EMP* 1,200
SIC 3556 7699

HEAT TRANSFER PRODUCTS
See HTP INC

D-U-N-S 13-700-6933 EXP
HEAT TRANSFER PRODUCTS GROUP LLC
WITT HEAT TRANSFER PRODUCTS
(*Suby of* RHEEM MANUFACTURING CO INC) ★
201 Thomas French Dr, Scottsboro, AL 35769-7405
Tel (256) 259-7400 *Founded/Ownrshp* 2013
Sales 207.8MM^E *EMP* 200
SIC 5084 Heat exchange equipment, industrial

D-U-N-S 01-116-8775
HEAT TRANSFER SOLUTIONS INC
H T S
(*Suby of* HTS ENGINEERING LTD)
3350 Yale St, Houston, TX 77018-7741
Tel (832) 328-1010 *Founded/Ownrshp* 2000
Sales 125.1MM^E *EMP* 100
SIC 5075 Air conditioning & ventilation equipment & supplies
Pr: Derek Gordon
* *CFO:* David Kviring
VP: David Warner
* *Prin:* Mike Donovan
* *Prin:* Grant Yaney
Off Mgr: Melinda Barry
Trfc Dir: Tara Woodin
Sls Mgr: Kimberly Thompson

D-U-N-S 14-540-4112 IMP
■ **HEATCRAFT REFRIGERATION PRODUCTS LLC**
HEATCRAFT WORLDWIDE RFRGN PDTS
(*Suby of* LENNOX INTERNATIONAL INC) ★
2175 W Park Place Blvd, Stone Mountain, GA 30087-3535
Tel (770) 465-5600 *Founded/Ownrshp* 2000
Sales 381.4MM^E *EMP* 1,100
SIC 3585 Refrigeration equipment, complete
VP Opers: Michael Vincent
Bus Dev Di: Kevin Chunn

HEATCRAFT WORLDWIDE RFRGN PDTS
See HEATCRAFT REFRIGERATION PRODUCTS LLC

D-U-N-S 00-106-0656 IMP
HEATH CONSULTANTS INC
TEX SOL
9030 W Monroe Rd, Houston, TX 77061-5212
Tel (713) 844-1300 *Founded/Ownrshp* 1933
Sales 137.8MM^E *EMP* 460
SIC 8711 3826 3812 Engineering services; Consulting engineer; Analytical instruments; Water testing apparatus; Gas analyzing equipment; Environmental testing equipment; Search & navigation equipment
Ch Bd: Milton W Heath Jr
* *Pr:* Carolyn Heath Haag
* *Prin:* Graham G Midgley
Info Man: Alan Kenfield
Mktg Mgr: Vivian Marinelli

D-U-N-S 15-037-8748 IMP/EXP
HEATH TECNA INC
ZODIAC ARLN CABIN & INTR WASH
(*Suby of* ZODIAC AEROSPACE)
3225 Woburn St, Bellingham, WA 98226-5656
Tel (360) 738-2005 *Founded/Ownrshp* 2000
Sales 163.8MM^E *EMP* 660^E
SIC 3728 5088 Aircraft parts & equipment; Aircraft & space vehicle supplies & parts
VP: David Flemming
VP: Derick Neumann
VP: Cindy Schiller

HEATILATOR
See HEARTH & HOME TECHNOLOGIES LLC

D-U-N-S 00-882-5267
HEATING AND PLUMBING ENGINEERS INC
HPE
407 Fillmore Pl, Colorado Springs, CO 80907-6049
Tel (719) 633-5571 *Founded/Ownrshp* 1985
Sales 91.5MM^E *EMP* 400
SIC 1711 Mechanical contractor
Pr: William Eustace
COO: Kelly Eustace
Dir Risk M: Gary Leak
Div Mgr: Dennis Schroeder
Dir IT: Shane Ritchard
IT Man: Dani Howling
Sfty Dirs: Gary W Leak

D-U-N-S 01-270-2320 IMP
HEATRON INC (MO)
(*Suby of* NIBE INDUSTRIER AB)
3000 Wilson Ave, Leavenworth, KS 66048-4637
Tel (913) 651-4420 *Founded/Ownrshp* 1976, 2016
Sales 87.3MM^E *EMP* 240
SIC 3567 3634 Heating units & devices, industrial: electric; Electric housewares & fans
Pr: H B Turner
CFO: Boyd Laurie
VP: Bob Martter
IT Man: Starla Jones
Sfty Mgr: John Burch
Sls Mgr: David Simpson

D-U-N-S 00-637-1272 IMP/EXP
HEAVEN HILL DISTILLERIES INC
1064 Loretto Rd, Bardstown, KY 40004-2229
Tel (502) 348-3921 *Founded/Ownrshp* 1942
Sales 185.6MM^E *EMP* 505
SIC 2085 Bourbon whiskey
Pr: Max L Shapira
Bd of Dir: Gwen Simpson
* *Ex VP:* Harry J Shapira
* *VP:* Craig Beam
VP: Parker Bean
* *VP:* Joseph L Fraser
* *VP:* Debbie Morris
* *VP:* H Mark Pulliam
S&M/VP: Ed Shapira
Mktg Dir: Carmen Galea
Mktg Mgr: Brittany Blevins

HEAVENER NURSING CENTER
See K & C LLC

D-U-N-S 06-080-1529
HEAVY & GENERAL CONSTRUCTION LABORERS UNION LOCAL NO 472
LABORS LOCAL NO 472
700 Raymond Blvd, Newark, NJ 07105-2909
Tel (973) 589-5050 *Founded/Ownrshp* 1946
Sales 116.8MM *EMP* 14
Accts Hulse & Associates Pc Fairfie
SIC 8631 Labor union
Pr: John Hibbs
* *Prin:* Eugene Grambo

D-U-N-S 02-488-1091
HEAVY & GENERAL LABORERS LOCAL 472 & 172 FUNDS OF NJ
604 Us Highway 206, Trenton, NJ 08610-4314
Tel (609) 291-9197 *Founded/Ownrshp* 2001
Sales 105.2MM *EMP* 4
Accts Schultheis & Panettieri Llp H
SIC 8631 Labor unions & similar labor organizations

D-U-N-S 12-210-0555
HEAVY CONSTRUCTORS INC
EXCAVATING SPECIALISTS
4101 Deadwood Ave, Rapid City, SD 57702-9692
Tel (605) 342-3144 *Founded/Ownrshp* 1983
Sales 92.1MM^E *EMP* 300

SIC 1542 1794 1623 1611 Commercial & office building, new construction; Excavation & grading, building construction; Underground utilities contractor; Highway & street construction
Pr: David Gustafson
**Treas:* Wayne D Gustafson
**VP:* Terry Larson

D-U-N-S 05-569-2321 IMP/EXP
HEAVY MACHINES INC
HMI ELECTRIC DIVISION
3926 E Raines Rd, Memphis, TN 38118-6936
Tel (901) 260-2200 *Founded/Ownrshp* 1971
Sales 87.7MM[E] *EMP* 141
SIC 5082 7699 7353 3531 5063 Construction & mining machinery; Mining machinery & equipment, except petroleum; Cranes, construction; Forestry equipment; Industrial machinery & equipment repair; Heavy construction equipment rental; Forestry related equipment; Motors, electric
Pr: Richard O Wilson Jr
**CFO:* Ted Bailey
VP: Eric Hinshaw
VP: Michael Moseley
VP: James A Nelson
Dir IT: Cozy Sykes
Sales Exec: Phillip Burton
Sls Dir: Tony Grubbs

HEAVY STRUCTURES
See BLUESCOPE CONSTRUCTION INC

D-U-N-S 80-990-1036
HEAVY VEHICLE ELECTRONIC LICENSE PLATE INC
101 N 1st Ave Ste 2275, Phoenix, AZ 85003-1906
Tel (602) 412-2240 *Founded/Ownrshp* 1993
Sales 88.7MM *EMP* 5
Accts Mcgladrey Llp Phoenix Az
SIC 7538 General automotive repair shops
Pr: Karen Rasmussen
Genl Mgr: Jeff Christian
IT Man: Peter Monn

HEAVYQUIP
See ITR NORTH AMERICA LLC

D-U-N-S 80-864-8245 IMP
HEB GROCERY CO LP
BROADWAY CENTRAL MARKET
(*Suby of* H-E-B FOOD/DRUG STORES) ★
646 S Flores St, San Antonio, TX 78204-1219
Tel (210) 938-8000 *Founded/Ownrshp* 2001
Sales 96.2MM[E] *EMP* 41[E]
SIC 5411 Supermarkets, chain
Pt: Charles Butt
Pt: Charlene Curry
CFO: Martin Otto
VP: Winell Herron
VP: Robert Loeffler
Ex Dir: John Archer
Ex Dir: Max Campbell
Ex Dir: Gus Kroos
Store Dir: Ryan Wilson
Admn Mgr: Felix Perez
Sls&Mrk Ex: Katrina Wilgus

HEB ISD
See HURST-EULESS-BEDFORD INDEPENDENT SCHOOL DISTRICT

D-U-N-S 01-997-7664
HEBCO PETROLEUM DISTRIBUTORS INC (TX)
(*Suby of* H-E-B FOOD/DRUG STORES) ★
646 S Main Ave, San Antonio, TX 78204-1210
Tel (210) 938-8419 *Founded/Ownrshp* 1998
Sales 84.1MM[E] *EMP* 80
SIC 5172 Petroleum products
Pr: Charles C Butt

D-U-N-S 07-325-7008
HEBREW HOME FOR AGED AT RIVERDALE
5901 Palisade Ave, Bronx, NY 10471-1205
Tel (718) 581-1000 *Founded/Ownrshp* 1917
Sales 72.6MM *EMP* 1,200
SIC 8059 Rest home, with health care
Pr: Daniel A Reingold
CFO: Fred German
**CFO:* Luz Liebeskind
**Ch:* Jeffrey S Maurer
**Treas:* Joseph Wygoda
**Ex VP:* Daniel Reingold
Genl Mgr: Melissa Cohen
Genl Mgr: Patricia Greaney
CIO: David Finkelstein
Doctor: Ernesto A Espana
Doctor: Roupa Sadana

D-U-N-S 07-091-4155
HEBREW HOME OF GREATER WASHINGTON (MD)
CHARLES EAST LIFE COMMUNITY
6121 Montrose Rd, Rockville, MD 20852-4803
Tel (301) 881-0300 *Founded/Ownrshp* 1910
Sales 72.3MM *EMP* 1,000
Accts Schiavi Wallace & Rowe Pc Lut
SIC 8051 Skilled nursing care facilities
CEO: Warren R Slavin
**Ch:* Marc F Solomon
**Treas:* Harry A Harrison
**Sr VP:* Pat Carter
**Sr VP:* Karen Rosenthal
Sr VP: Terri Tanner-Hill
**VP:* Stephanie Baker
VP: Edward Coutren
VP: Beth Deluceney
VP: Barry Eisenberg
VP: Abbey Fagin
**VP:* Tom Keefe
**VP:* Nicholas Simmonds
**VP:* Edward Van Coutren
**VP:* Carol Cohen Wolfe
Exec: Gale Deitch

D-U-N-S 03-083-2075
HEBREW REHABILITATION CENTER
HEBREW SENIOR LIFE
1200 Centre St, Boston, MA 02131-1011
Tel (617) 363-8000 *Founded/Ownrshp* 1903
Sales 119.8MM *EMP* 2,500
Accts Dixon Hughes Goodman Llp Gree
SIC 8069 Chronic disease hospital
Pr: Louis J Woolf
Dir Vol: Sara Smolover
CFO: James D Hart
Ch: Hinda Marcus
Treas: Leo R Breitman
Bd of Dir: Steven Levy
Ofcr: Marsha Slotnick
Assoc VP: Ruth Stark
Ex VP: Patricia Leddy
VP: Kimberly Brooks
VP: Alan Jones
VP: Lewis Lipsitz
VP: Lewis A Lipsitz MD
VP: John Matulis
VP: Katelyn Quynn
Exec: Robert Kass
Dir Case M: Patricia Stinson
Dir Bus: Dana Kern

HEBREW SENIOR LIFE
See HEBREW REHABILITATION CENTER

D-U-N-S 00-692-7610
▲ HECLA MINING CO
6500 N Mineral Dr Ste 200, Coeur D Alene, ID 83815-9408
Tel (208) 769-4100 *Founded/Ownrshp* 1891
Sales 443.5MM *EMP* 1,404
Accts Bdo Usa Llp Spokane Washing
Tkr Sym HL *Exch* NYS
SIC 1041 1044 1031 1081 Gold ores; Silver ores; Lead & zinc ores; Exploration, metal mining
Pr: Phillips S Baker Jr
**Ch Bd:* Ted Crumley
CFO: Lindsay Hall
Treas: Judy Cloos
Sr VP: Dean WA McDonald
Sr VP: Lawrence P Radford
VP: Clayr Alexander
VP: Alain Grenier
VP: Scott Hartman
VP: Luke Russell
VP: David C Sienko
Board of Directors: George R Johnson, George R Nethercutt Jr, Stephen F Ralbovsky, Terry V Rogers, Charles B Stanley, Anthony P Taylor

D-U-N-S 87-816-8459
HECNY TRANSPORTATION INC
1416 Francisco St, Torrance, CA 90501-1313
Tel (310) 347-3400 *Founded/Ownrshp* 1995
Sales 100.0MM *EMP* 20
SIC 4731 Freight transportation arrangement
Pr: Tony Lee

D-U-N-S 09-138-8090
HEDGES ASSOCIATES INC (IA)
COLDWELL BANKER
5408 Blairs Forest Way Ne, Cedar Rapids, IA 52402-8802
Tel (319) 378-8760 *Founded/Ownrshp* 1950
Sales 235.0MM *EMP* 80
SIC 6531 Real estate agent, residential
Pr: Carl Esker
**Sec:* Carol Esker

D-U-N-S 08-166-2769
HEDRICK BROTHERS CONSTRUCTION CO INC
2200 Centre Park West Dr # 100, West Palm Beach, FL 33409-6473
Tel (561) 689-8880 *Founded/Ownrshp* 1979
Sales 99.3MM *EMP* 100
Accts Templeton & Company Llp West
SIC 1542 Commercial & office building, new construction; Commercial & office buildings, renovation & repair
Pr: Dale Hedrick
**CFO:* Eric Engstrom
**Ex VP:* Gene Parker
VP: Jack Ullrich
Dir IT: David Wilson
**Genl Couns:* Patrick Painter
Snr PM: Rick Ricalton

HEDSTROM FITNESS
See BALL BOUNCE AND SPORT INC

D-U-N-S 03-353-2094 EXP
HEELY-BROWN CO
1280 Chattahoochee Ave Nw, Atlanta, GA 30318-3683
Tel (404) 352-0022 *Founded/Ownrshp* 1947
Sales 113.8MM[E] *EMP* 92
SIC 5033 Roofing & siding materials
CFO: John Comiskey
**Pr:* William H Brown
**Treas:* Mike Spencer
Off Mgr: Greg Crosby
MIS Dir: Jeffrey Karl
Board of Directors: Mary M Brown, Jeffrey Karl

D-U-N-S 04-581-1809
HEERY INTERNATIONAL INC
(*Suby of* BALFOUR BEATTY LLC) ★
999 Peachtree St Ne # 300, Atlanta, GA 30309-4426
Tel (404) 881-9880 *Founded/Ownrshp* 1986
Sales 168.9MM *EMP* 700
SIC 8712 8711 8742 Architectural services; Engineering services; Management consulting services
Pr: Richard B Driggs
**CEO:* Theodor Sak
**COO:* Glenn Jardine
**CFO:* Theodore E Sak
Sr VP: Gregory H Peirce
VP: Su Cunningham
VP: Douglas Graham
VP: Michael Holleman
VP: Dennis Lagatta
VP: Jim Peterkin
VP: Robert Power
VP: Gordon Smith
VP: Daniel Wise
Exec: Stewart Skubel

D-U-N-S 04-001-9770
HEFFERNAN INSURANCE BROKERS
1350 Carlback Ave, Walnut Creek, CA 94596-7299
Tel (925) 934-8500 *Founded/Ownrshp* 1988
Sales NA *EMP* 430
SIC 6411

D-U-N-S 00-829-4332 IMP
HEHR INTERNATIONAL INC
HEHR INTERNATIONAL POLYMERS
3333 Casitas Ave, Los Angeles, CA 90039-2207
Tel (323) 663-1261 *Founded/Ownrshp* 1946
Sales 167.9MM[E] *EMP* 750
SIC 3442 Window & door frames
CEO: Mary G Utick
Board of Directors: Warren Jones

HEHR INTERNATIONAL POLYMERS
See HEHR INTERNATIONAL INC

HEI
See HAWAIIAN ELECTRIC INDUSTRIES INC

D-U-N-S 13-333-8256
HEI HOSPITALITY LLC
HEI HOTELS & RESORTS
101 Merritt 7 Corp, Norwalk, CT 06851
Tel (203) 849-8844 *Founded/Ownrshp* 2002
Sales 238.5MM[E] *EMP* 3,250
SIC 7011 Hotels & motels
CEO: Anthony Rutledge
Ch Bd: Gary Mendell
CEO: Ted Darnall
CEO: Anthony R Rutledge
CFO: Clark W Hanrattie
VP: Gerald Barrack
VP: Stephen L Chan
VP: Roger Clark
VP: Charles Colletta
VP: W J Maciver
VP: Brian Mayer
VP: Karl Murphy
VP: Dave Nussear
VP: Steen Petri
VP: George Rendell
VP: Brian Russo
VP: Pam Siegler
VP: Dan Walworth
VP: Tory Waterman

HEI HOTELS & RESORTS
See HEI HOSPITALITY LLC

D-U-N-S 04-411-7455 IMP
■ HEICO AEROSPACE CORP
(*Suby of* HEICO AEROSPACE HOLDINGS CORP) ★
3000 Taft St, Hollywood, FL 33021-4441
Tel (954) 987-6101 *Founded/Ownrshp* 1993
Sales 134.4MM[E] *EMP* 311
SIC 3724 3812 Aircraft engines & engine parts; Search & navigation equipment
Pr: Luis J Morell
**CEO:* Eric A Mendelson
**Treas:* Thomas S Irwin
**Treas:* Carlos L Macau
Sr VP: Mike Siegel
VP: Vladimir Cervera
Dir Lab: Jay Bankemper
Genl Couns: Ross Baron

D-U-N-S 02-795-3590 IMP
■ HEICO AEROSPACE HOLDINGS CORP
(*Suby of* HEICO CORP) ★
3000 Taft St, Hollywood, FL 33021-4441
Tel (954) 987-4000 *Founded/Ownrshp* 1997
Sales 305.3MM[E] *EMP* 1,011
SIC 3724 Aircraft engines & engine parts
**CEO:* Eric Mendelson
**Treas:* Thomas S Irwin
**Ex VP:* James R Reum
VP: Pat Markham

D-U-N-S 78-653-3117 IMP/EXP
HEICO COMPANIES L L C
5600 Three First Nat Plz, Chicago, IL 60602
Tel (312) 419-8220 *Founded/Ownrshp* 1988
Sales 1.7MMM[E] *EMP* 2,300
SIC 3315 3589 3448 3531 1731 3663 Wire, ferrous/iron; Wire products, ferrous/iron: made in wiredrawing plants; Sewage & water treatment equipment; Sewer cleaning equipment, power; Shredders, industrial & commercial; Prefabricated metal buildings; Prefabricated metal buildings; Construction machinery; Cranes; Logging equipment; Cranes, locomotive; Electrical work; Radio & television switching equipment
Ch: Emily Heisley Stoeckel
**Pr:* E A Roskovensky
CFO: Terence R Rogers
**CFO:* L G Wolski
VP: Kathy Watts

D-U-N-S 80-957-0781 IMP
▲ HEICO CORP
3000 Taft St, Hollywood, FL 33021-4441
Tel (954) 987-4000 *Founded/Ownrshp* 1993
Sales 1.1MMM *EMP* 4,675[E]
Accts Deloitte & Touche Llp Miami
Tkr Sym HEI *Exch* NYS
SIC 3724 3728 7699 Aircraft engines & engine parts; Aircraft training equipment; Aircraft & heavy equipment repair services; Aircraft flight instrument repair
Ch Bd: Laurans A Mendelson
Pr: Eric A Mendelson
COO: John Hunter
CFO: Carlos L Macau Jr
Sr Ex VP: Thomas S Irwin
Sr VP: Tom Moorefield
VP: Paul Belisle
VP: Adam Bentkover
VP: Mike Garcia
Prgrm Mgr: Alex Ledesma
QA Dir: Nestor Rodriguez
Board of Directors: Thomas M Culligan, Adolfo Henriques, Samuel L Higginbottom, Mark H Hildebrandt, Wolfgang Mayrhuber, Julie Neitzel, Alan Schriesheim, Frank J Schwitter

HEICO ELECTRONIC TECH GROUP
See HEICO ELECTRONIC TECHNOLOGIES CORP

D-U-N-S 07-104-1797
■ HEICO ELECTRONIC TECHNOLOGIES CORP
HEICO ELECTRONIC TECH GROUP
(*Suby of* HEICO CORP) ★
3000 Taft St, Hollywood, FL 33021-4441
Tel (954) 987-6101 *Founded/Ownrshp* 1996
Sales 151.1MM[E] *EMP* 1,415
SIC 3728 Aircraft parts & equipment
Pr: Laurans Mendelson
**Prin:* Thomas Irwin

D-U-N-S 00-514-6592
HEICO HOLDING INC
27501 Bella Vista Pkwy, Warrenville, IL 60555-1609
Tel (630) 353-5000 *Founded/Ownrshp* 2000
Sales 1.3MMM[E] *EMP* 6,800
SIC 6719 Investment holding companies, except banks
Pr: Michael E Heisley
**Ex VP:* E A Roskovensky
Board of Directors: Michael E Heisley Jr, Emily Heisley Stoeckel

D-U-N-S 80-472-7568 IMP/EXP
HEIDELBERG AMERICAS INC
(*Suby of* HEIDELBERGER DRUCKMASCHINEN AG)
1000 Gutenberg Dr Nw, Kennesaw, GA 30144-7028
Tel (770) 419-6500 *Founded/Ownrshp* 1983
Sales 460.4MM[E] *EMP* 3,000
SIC 5084 Printing trades machinery, equipment & supplies
Pr: James P Dunn

HEIDELBERG DISTRIBUTING DIV
See DAYTON HEIDELBERG DISTRIBUTING CO

D-U-N-S 05-317-1617 IMP/EXP
HEIDELBERG USA INC
(*Suby of* HEIDELBERG AMERICAS INC) ★
1000 Gutenberg Dr Nw, Kennesaw, GA 30144-7028
Tel (770) 419-6500 *Founded/Ownrshp* 1993
Sales 476.6MM[E] *EMP* 1,000
SIC 5084 3555 Printing trades machinery, equipment & supplies; Printing trades machinery
Pr: Harald Weimer
CFO: Thomas Topp
Sr VP: Ulrich Koehler
Sr VP: James Martin
Sr VP: Susan P Nofi
VP: Brian Chapin
VP: Ralph Pasquariello
Mng Dir: Andy V Jensen
Genl Mgr: Guenther Keppler
Genl Mgr: Jason Ong
Dir IT: Marc Herbig

D-U-N-S 01-793-9083
HEIDMAN INC
MCDONALD'S
500 Grant St, Akron, OH 44311-1121
Tel (330) 535-8400 *Founded/Ownrshp* 1959
Sales 31.9MM[E] *EMP* 1,000
SIC 5812 Fast-food restaurant, chain
Pr: John Blickle
**Prin:* Charles Booth

D-U-N-S 83-026-3427
HEIDMAR INC
20 Glover Ave Ste 14, Norwalk, CT 06850-1236
Tel (203) 662-2600 *Founded/Ownrshp* 2000
Sales 122.4MM[E] *EMP* 168[E]
SIC 1389 Oil field services
CEO: Hans Van Der Zijde
**Pr:* Olaf Halvorssen
**COO:* Ben Ognibene
**CFO:* Kathleen Haines
**Treas:* Charles N Tammara
**Ex VP:* Per Heilmann
Genl Couns: John Greenwood
Board of Directors: John A Shapiro

D-U-N-S 00-552-5159
▲ HEIDRICK & STRUGGLES INTERNATIONAL INC (DE)
233 S Wacker Dr Ste 4900, Chicago, IL 60606-6372
Tel (312) 496-1200 *Founded/Ownrshp* 1953
Sales 548.3MM *EMP* 1,659[E]
Tkr Sym HSII *Exch* NGS
SIC 7361 Employment agencies; Executive placement
Pr: Tracy R Wolstencroft
Sr Pt: Lauren Doliva
Pt: Lori Perella
Pt: Chris Pierce-Cooke
Pt: Guy Sava
Pt: Bill Trau
Mng Pt: Torrey Foster
Mng Pt: Robbie Knight
Mng Pt: Gareth McIlroy
Mng Pt: Stephen Miles
Mng Pt: Todd Monti
Mng Pt: Steve Mullinjer
Mng Pt: Christine Stimpel
V Ch: Theodore Jadick
V Ch: Nathaniel Sutton
V Ch: John Wood
CEO: Anne Lim O'Brien
CFO: Richard W Pehlke
Ofcr: Richard W Greene
Ex VP: Stephen W Beard
Ex VP: Richard Caldera
Board of Directors: V Paul Unruh, Elizabeth L Axelrod, Richard I Beattie, Clare M Chapman, John A Fazio, Mark Foster, Gary E Knell, Lyle Logan, Jill Kanin-Lovers, Willem Mesdag

HEIDTMAN STEEL PRODUCTS
See CENTAUR INC

D-U-N-S 00-292-9610 IMP
HEIDTMAN STEEL PRODUCTS INC (OH)
(Suby of HEIDTMAN STEEL PRODUCTS) ★
2401 Front St, Toledo, OH 43605-1199
Tel (419) 691-4646 Founded/Ownrshp 1962, 1984
Sales 264.3MM^E EMP 1,000
SIC 3316 3312 Strip steel, cold-rolled: from purchased hot-rolled; Sheet or strip, steel, hot-rolled
CEO: John C Bates
Pr: Tim Berra
CFO: Mark Ridenour
Prin: F Wm Heidtman
Prin: Margery Heidtman
MIS Dir: Jim Hill

HEIFER INTERNATIONAL
See HEIFER PROJECT INTERNATIONAL INC

D-U-N-S 07-739-9780
HEIFER PROJECT INTERNATIONAL INC
HEIFER INTERNATIONAL
1 World Ave, Little Rock, AR 72202-3825
Tel (501) 907-2600 Founded/Ownrshp 1989
Sales 125.2MM EMP 304
Accts Deloitte & Touche Llp Little
SIC 8399 6732 9532 Social change association; Trusts: educational, religious, etc.; Community & rural development
CEO: Pierre Ferrari
*COO: Steve Denne
*CFO: Robert Bob Bloom
CFO: Ken Harrison
Ofcr: Rebecca Alderfer
Ofcr: Ingrid Arinez
Ofcr: Dilip Bhandari
Ofcr: Jennifer Jameson
Ofcr: Maria Schrader
VP: Sahr Lebbie
VP: Christopher Lu
Board of Directors: Charles Stewart

D-U-N-S 03-260-7820
HEIGHTS OF TYLER
(Suby of TOUCHSTONE COMMUNITIES INC) ★
2650 Elkton Trl, Tyler, TX 75703-0580
Tel (903) 266-7200 Founded/Ownrshp 2010
Sales 652.3M^E EMP 2,454^E
SIC 8322 Rehabilitation services

D-U-N-S 00-609-7398 IMP
■ **HEIL CO**
HEIL ENVIRONMENTAL
(Suby of DOVER ENGINEERED SYSTEMS INC) ★
2030 Hamilton Place Blvd # 200, Chattanooga, TN 37421-6040
Tel (866) 367-4345 Founded/Ownrshp 1993
Sales 629.9MM^E EMP 2,000
SIC 3715 Trailer bodies
Pr: Pat Carroll
*CFO: Darren Bird
VP: Bob McMackins
VP: Yassir Shanghai
*VP: Tom Vatter
VP: Alex Waddell
Dir IT: Sean Neimarlija
Plnt Mgr: John Kalson
Snr Mgr: Randy Wells

HEIL ENVIRONMENTAL
See HEIL CO

D-U-N-S 06-661-2698 IMP
HEILIND ELECTRONICS INC
MAVERICK ELECTRONICS
58 Jonspin Rd, Wilmington, MA 01887-1068
Tel (978) 658-7000 Founded/Ownrshp 1974
Sales 741.7MM^E EMP 705
SIC 5065 3679 5063 Electronic parts & equipment; Harness assemblies for electronic use: wire or cable; Hanging & fastening devices, electrical
CEO: Robert W Clapp
Opers Mgr: Elizabeth Steele
Sales Exec: Sharon Benjamin
Sales Asso: Doreen Valdez

HEIMARK DISTRIBUTING
See TRIANGLE DISTRIBUTING CO

D-U-N-S 00-892-1215 IMP
HEINEKEN USA INC
(Suby of HEINEKEN BROUWERIJEN B.V.)
360 Hamilton Ave Ste 1103, White Plains, NY 10601-1882
Tel (914) 681-4100 Founded/Ownrshp 1946
Sales 301.0MM^E EMP 400
SIC 5181 Beer & other fermented malt liquors
Ch Bd: Rudolf Gs Van Den Brink
*Pr: Frans Van Der Minne
*CFO: Gabriele Giudici
*CFO: Dan Sullivan
Chf Mktg O: Monisha Abraham
*Sr VP: Scott Blazek
*Sr VP: Dirk De Vos
VP: Jeffrey Colbert
VP: Allyson Cruz
VP: Brian Fried
VP: Oscar Garcia
VP: Peter Hall
*VP: Julie Kinch
*VP: Amy Nenner
VP: Ward Steve
*VP: T Daniel Tearno
*VP: Daniel Walsh
VP: Colin Westcott-Pitt
VP: Meri Wick
VP: Rick Wright
Exec: Patricia Click

D-U-N-S 00-699-8611 IMP
HEINENS INC
4540 Richmond Rd, Warrensville Heights, OH 44128-5757
Tel (216) 475-2300 Founded/Ownrshp 1929
Sales 357.6MM^E EMP 2,350
Accts Hill & Stonestreet
SIC 5411 Supermarkets, hypermarket
CEO: J Jeffrey Heinen
*Pr: Thomas J Heinen
*CFO: Maryanne Correnti

D-U-N-S 08-967-2463
HEINZ ENDOWMENTS
625 Liberty Ave Fl 30, Pittsburgh, PA 15222-3110
Tel (412) 281-5777 Founded/Ownrshp 1995
Sales 112.8MM EMP 32
SIC 6732 Charitable trust management; Educational trust management
Pr: Grant Oliphant
*CFO: Jack Kim
Ofcr: Melanie R Brown
Ofcr: Carmen Lee
Ex VP: Mallory Walker
Dir Surg: John M Ellis
Ex Dir: Barbara Robinson
Ex Dir: William REA
Ex Dir: Konrad Weis

D-U-N-S 04-526-3092 EXP
■ **HEINZ FROZEN FOOD CO**
(Suby of HEINZ KRAFT FOODS CO) ★
357 6th Ave, Pittsburgh, PA 15222-2539
Tel (412) 237-5700 Founded/Ownrshp 1993
Sales 228.8MM^E EMP 2,602
SIC 2038 2037 8741 Frozen specialties; Potato products, quick frozen & cold pack; Vegetables, quick frozen & cold pack, excl. potato products; Management services
CEO: William R Johnson
*Pr: Neil Harrison
CFO: Art Winkleblack
*Treas: John C Crowe
Chf Mktg O: Brian Hansberry
VP: Brendan Foley
*VP: Charles C White
Plnt Mgr: Jim Kirton

D-U-N-S 00-431-8846 IMP/EXP
■ **HEINZ KRAFT FOODS CO**
(Suby of KRAFT HEINZ CO) ★
1 Ppg Pl Ste 3200, Pittsburgh, PA 15222-5415
Tel (412) 456-5700 Founded/Ownrshp 2013
Sales 9.9MMM^E EMP 24,000
SIC 2033 2038 2032 2098 Tomato sauce: packaged in cans, jars, etc.; Frozen specialties; Baby foods, including meats: packaged in cans, jars, etc.; Bean sprouts: packaged in cans, jars, etc.; Soups, except seafood: packaged in cans, jars, etc.; Macaroni & spaghetti
CEO: Bernardo Hees
Pr: Brendan Foley
Pr: Matt Hill
Pr: Emin Mammadov
Pr: Jane S Miller
Pr: Michael D Milone
Pr: Dave Moran
Pr: Scott Ohara
COO: Mike Nolan
CFO: Paulo Basilio
CFO: Arthur Winkelblack
Ofcr: Stephen S Clark
Ofcr: Edward Smyth
Ex VP: Theodore N Bobby
Ex VP: Joe Jiminez
Ex VP: David Moran
Ex VP: Eduardo Pelleissone
Ex VP: Dave Woodward
Sr VP: Edward J McMenamin
VP: John C Crowe
VP: Jeffrey Fisher
Board of Directors: Thomas J Usher, Charles E Bunch, Michael F Weinstein, Leonard S Coleman Jr, John G Drosdick, Edith E Holiday, Candace Kendle, Dean R O'hare, Nelson Peltz, Dennis H Reilley, Lynn C Swann

HEINZ NORTH AMERICA
See H J HEINZ CO LP

D-U-N-S 84-207-8750 EXP
HEINZEL IMPORT & EXPORT INC
(Suby of WILFRIED HEINZEL AKTIENGE-SELLSCHAFT)
220 E 42nd St Rm 3010, New York, NY 10017-5816
Tel (212) 953-3200 Founded/Ownrshp 1980
Sales 221.0MM^E EMP 10
Accts Mcgladrey Llp New York New Y
SIC 5111 Printing & writing paper
Pr: Andrew Paul
*COO: Moncef Reisner
*CFO: Dietmar Geigl
*Ex VP: Claire Fraser

D-U-N-S 94-950-0292 IMP
HELEN OF TROY LP
(Suby of HELEN OF TROY TEXAS CORP) ★
1 Helen Of Troy Plz, El Paso, TX 79912-1150
Tel (915) 225-8000 Founded/Ownrshp 1996
Sales 145.3MM^E EMP 504^E
SIC 3999 3634 Hair & hair-based products; Combs, except hard rubber; Hair, dressing of, for the trade; Personal electrical appliances; Hair dryers, electric; Curling irons, electric; Razors, electric
CEO: Julien Mininberg
CFO: Thomas J Benson
VP: Vincent D Carson

D-U-N-S 04-612-0994 IMP/EXP
HELEN OF TROY TEXAS CORP
(Suby of HELEN OF TROY LIMITED)
1 Helen Of Troy Plz, El Paso, TX 79912-1148
Tel (915) 225-8000 Founded/Ownrshp 1994
Sales 244.4MM^E EMP 815^E
SIC 3999 Hair driers, designed for beauty parlors
CEO: Julien Mininberg
*CFO: Thomas J Benson
*Treas: Deanna Nasser
*Ex VP: Arthur August
*Ex VP: Michael Cafaro
*Sr VP: Robert D Spear
Dir IT: Frank Gonzalez

D-U-N-S 00-703-6759 IMP
HELENA CHEMICAL CO
(Suby of MARUBENI AMERICA CORP) ★
255 Schilling Blvd # 200, Collierville, TN 38017-2279
Tel (901) 761-0050 Founded/Ownrshp 1957
Sales 3.8MMM^E EMP 4,000
Accts Ernst & Young Llp Memphis Tn
SIC 5191 2819 Fertilizers & agricultural chemicals; Seeds & bulbs; Chemicals, high purity: refined from technical grade
CEO: Mike McCarty
CFO: Troy D Traxler Jr
Treas: Roger Lewis
VP: Milton Allen
Software D: Ying Zhang

D-U-N-S 61-193-0418
HELENA INDUSTRIES INC
(Suby of HELENA CHEMICAL CO) ★
225 Schilling Blvd # 400, Collierville, TN 38017-7177
Tel (901) 820-5700 Founded/Ownrshp 2005
Sales 104.1MM^E EMP 300
Accts Cannon & Company Memphis Ten
SIC 2879 Agricultural chemicals
Pr: Phil Hollis
*Sec: Byron Phillips
Opers Mgr: Josh Branch

D-U-N-S 07-939-6131 IMP
HELENA LABORATORIES CORP
1530 Lindbergh Dr, Beaumont, TX 77707-4131
Tel (409) 842-3714 Founded/Ownrshp 1966
Sales 232.7MM^E EMP 1,000
SIC 3841 3826 Medical instruments & equipment, blood & bone work; Electrophoresis equipment
Ch: Tipton L Golias
Pr: Joe Golias
Treas: Ann Golias
VP: Noel Bartlett
VP: David Mayes
VP: Ovay H Mayes
VP: John O'Keefe
VP: Eric Petersen
CTO: Anthony Weber
MIS Dir: Kathy McAnulty
IT Man: Kyle Petersen

D-U-N-S 08-422-8915 IMP/EXP
HELGESEN INDUSTRIES INC
7261 State Road 60, Hartford, WI 53027-9222
Tel (262) 709-4444 Founded/Ownrshp 1977
Sales 112.8MM^E EMP 400
SIC 3443 Tanks, standard or custom fabricated: metal plate; Weldments
Pr: Ronald S Marshall
*VP: Thomas C Marshall
VP: Paul Vanderkin
IT Man: David Urbaniak
*VP Mfg: Nathaniel L Marshall
Sfty Dirs: Johnathan Friess
Snr Mgr: Kyle Johnson

D-U-N-S 14-492-1343 IMP/EXP
■ **HELICOPTER SUPPORT INC**
SIKORSKY COMMERCIAL
(Suby of SIKORSKY AIRCRAFT CORP) ★
124 Quarry Rd, Trumbull, CT 06611-4816
Tel (203) 416-4000 Founded/Ownrshp 1998
Sales 143.4MM^E EMP 270
SIC 5088 4581 3728 Helicopter parts; Aircraft maintenance & repair services; Aircraft parts & equipment; Aircraft body & wing assemblies & parts
Pr: David Adler
*Treas: Rajeev Bhalla
*Treas: Richard S Caswell
*Ex VP: John Chimini
*VP: Christopher Bogan
Prgrm Mgr: Donn Cornell
IT Man: Kayle Frost
Software D: John Whalen
QC Dir: Edward Smith
Sfty Mgr: John Bourett
QI Cn Mgr: Lisa Grondin

D-U-N-S 07-858-6145
HELIGEAR ACQUISITION CO
NORTHSTAR AEROSPACE CHICAGO
6006 W 73rd St, Bedford Park, IL 60638-6106
Tel (708) 728-2000 Founded/Ownrshp 2012
Sales 267.3MM EMP 780
SIC 3724 7699 Aircraft engines & engine parts; Aircraft flight instrument repair
CEO: David McConnaughey
*CFO: Robert Burkhardt
*CFO: Aaron Tam
VP: Brian Cheek
*VP: Greg Harper
*VP: Jason Young
Sls&Mrk Ex: Sarah Weeks
*Genl Couns: David Anderson
Snr Mgr: James Friske
Board of Directors: Aaron Tam

D-U-N-S 18-385-0031
HELIOS
(Suby of PROGRESSIVE ENTERPRISES HOLDINGS INC) ★
250 Progressive Way, Westerville, OH 43082-9615
Tel (614) 794-3300 Founded/Ownrshp 2010
Sales NA EMP 530^E
SIC 6411

D-U-N-S 07-967-3050
HELIX ACQUISITION HOLDINGS INC
MW INDUSTRIES
9501 Tech Blvd Ste 401, Rosemont, IL 60018
Tel (847) 349-5760 Founded/Ownrshp 2011
Sales 104.9MM^E EMP 1,055^E
SIC 6719 Investment holding companies, except banks
CEO: William Marcum

D-U-N-S 14-854-9512
HELIX ELECTRIC INC
6795 Flanders Dr, San Diego, CA 92121-2903
Tel (858) 535-0505 Founded/Ownrshp 1985
Sales 367.7MM^E EMP 1,500
SIC 1731

D-U-N-S 09-838-5404 IMP/EXP
▲ **HELIX ENERGY SOLUTIONS GROUP INC**
3505 W Sam Houston Pkwy N, Houston, TX 77043-1252
Tel (281) 618-0400 Founded/Ownrshp 1979
Sales 695.8MM EMP 1,445
Tkr Sym HLX Exch NYS
SIC 1629 1389 1311 Marine construction; Well logging; Crude petroleum production; Natural gas production
Ch Bd: Owen Kratz
COO: Scott A Sparks
*CFO: Anthony Tripodo
Treas: Clifford H Buster
Ofcr: Joshua Cordle
Ofcr: Jay Norwood
Ex VP: Johnny Edwards
Ex VP: Alisa B Johnson
Ex VP: Scotty Sparks
Sr VP: Michael V Ambrose
Sr VP: Lloyd Hajdik
VP: Sharon Adams
VP: Hin Chiu
VP: Chuck McGregor
VP Bus Dev: David Carr
Exec: Regina Roat
Board of Directors: John V Lovoi, T William Porter, Nancy K Quinn, Jan Rask, William L Transier, James A Watt

HELIX MEDICAL
See FREUDENBERG MEDICAL LLC

D-U-N-S 09-375-9298 IMP/EXP
HELLA CORPORATE CENTER USA INC
HELLA NORTH AMERICA, INC.
(Suby of HELLA HOLDING INTERNATIONAL GMBH)
43811 Plymouth Oaks Blvd, Plymouth, MI 48170-2539
Tel (586) 232-4788 Founded/Ownrshp 1978
Sales 182.9MM^E EMP 680
Accts Gray Hunter Stenn Llp
SIC 3625 5013 5088 3822 3585 3429 Industrial electrical relays & switches; Automotive supplies & parts; Marine supplies; Auto controls regulating residntl & coml environmt & applncs; Refrigeration & heating equipment; Manufactured hardware (general)
CEO: Joseph V Borruso
*Pr: Steve Lietaert
*CFO: Edward L Macek
*Treas: C Elaine Wylie
CIO: Luis Gomezdelcampo
VP Mktg: Alfredo De La Vega
VP Sls: Richard Bloomfield
S&M/VP: Julie Martin

D-U-N-S 11-904-5300 IMP
HELLA ELECTRONICS CORP
(Suby of HELLA NORTH AMERICA INC) ★
43811 Plymouth Oaks Blvd, Plymouth, MI 48170-2539
Tel (734) 414-0900 Founded/Ownrshp 1983
Sales 141.3MM^E EMP 640
SIC 3625 3714 Industrial electrical relays & switches; Motor vehicle parts & accessories
CEO: Joseph V Borruso
Pr: Steve Hubble
CEO: Marc Rosenmayr
CFO: Peter Martin
Treas: Kye Hemphill
Treas: Frank Mueller
Ex VP: Steve Profeta
VP: Mark Brainard
Mng Dir: Ramashankar Pandey
Prgrm Mgr: Randall Bushong
Prgrm Mgr: Michael Dwyer

HELLA NORTH AMERICA, INC.
See HELLA CORPORATE CENTER USA INC

D-U-N-S 14-601-8887 IMP
HELLAS CONSTRUCTION INC
12710 Res Blvd Ste 240, Austin, TX 78759
Tel (512) 250-2910 Founded/Ownrshp 2003
Sales 146.3MM EMP 320
Accts Ha&W Llp Atlanta Ga
SIC 1629 Athletic & recreation facilities construction; Athletic field construction; Golf course construction; Tennis court construction
CEO: Reed J Seaton
CFO: Frank Petrini
VP: Robert G Allison
VP: Matt Schnitzler
Snr PM: Josh Davidson
Board of Directors: Dan Schlopakohl

D-U-N-S 05-716-4014 IMP
HELLERMANNTYTON CORP
(Suby of HELLERMANNTYTON BETA SARL)
7930 N Faulkner Rd, Milwaukee, WI 53224-3423
Tel (414) 355-1130 Founded/Ownrshp 2006
Sales 102.6MM^E EMP 320
SIC 3089 2891 Injection molded finished plastic products; Extruded finished plastic products; Adhesives
Pr: James R Campion
*Sec: Peter D Jonas
VP: Mike Kennard
*VP: Terry Turtle
Dir IT: Eric Schilder
Sales Exec: Thomas Jacomet
VP Mktg: Terri Tuttle
Mktg Mgr: Todd Fries

HELLIER
See ACUREN INSPECTION INC

D-U-N-S 88-368-9051
HELLMAN & FRIEDMAN LLC
1 Maritime Plz Fl 12, San Francisco, CA 94111-3502
Tel (415) 788-5111 Founded/Ownrshp 1993
Sales 2.4MMM EMP 8,703
SIC 6726 Investment offices
CFO: Lee Georgia
Mng Dir: Stefan Goetz
Mng Dir: Jeffrey Goldstein
*Mng Dir: Patrick Healy
Mng Dir: Goldstein Jeffrey
Mng Dir: Anupam Mishra
Mng Dir: Erik Ragatz
Mng Dir: Thomas Steyer
Mng Dir: Allen Thorpe
Mng Dir: Tarim Wasim
Off Mgr: Mary Shen

D-U-N-S 18-307-7684 IMP/EXP
HELLMANN WORLDWIDE LOGISTICS INC
(*Suby of* HELLMANN WORLDWIDE LOGISTICS GMBH & CO. KG)
10450 Doral Blvd, Doral, FL 33178-2372
Tel (305) 406-4500 *Founded/Ownrshp* 1997
Sales 322.0MM^E *EMP* 700
SIC 4731 Freight forwarding
Pr: Christopher Dale
**CFO:* Julian Riches
Sr VP: Anthony Colucci
VP: Peter George
**VP:* Chris Sims
Dir Bus: Carmen Brown
Dir Bus: James Cassidy
Dir Bus: Mari Dominguez
Area Mgr: Robert Meadows
Admn Mgr: Ambre Gine
Brnch Mgr: Ben Luijckx

D-U-N-S 80-634-5203
HELLMUTH OBATA & KASSABAUM INC
H O K
(*Suby of* HOK INC) ★
1 Bush St Ste 200, San Francisco, CA 94104-4404
Tel (415) 243-0555 *Founded/Ownrshp* 1995
Sales 30.9MM^E *EMP* 1,808
SIC 8712 8711 8742 7389 0781 Architectural services; Engineering services; Management consulting services; Interior design services; Landscape architects
CEO: Patrick Macleamy
**Pr:* William Hellmuth
**Treas:* Lisa Green
**Ofcr:* Thomas Robson
Sr VP: Dave Troup
VP: David Crotty
MIS Dir: Kenneth Young
IT Man: Donny Russel

D-U-N-S 05-070-1176 IMP/EXP
HELLY HANSEN (US) INC (WA)
(*Suby of* HELLY HANSEN AS)
14218 Stewart Rd Ste 100a, Sumner, WA 98390-5500
Tel (800) 435-5901 *Founded/Ownrshp* 1980, 1997
Sales 510.0MM *EMP* 150
SIC 5137 5699 2339 2329 Women's & children's dresses, suits, skirts & blouses; Apparel belts, women's & children's; Work clothing; Marine apparel; Raincoats; Ski jackets & pants: women's, misses' & juniors'; Down-filled coats, jackets & vests: women's & misses'; Ski & snow clothing: men's & boys'; Men's & boys' leather, wool & down-filled outerwear
Genl Mgr: Filip Fracke
VP Sls: Brent Turner

D-U-N-S 10-168-9693 IMP/EXP
HELM AMERICA CORP
(*Suby of* HELM AG)
1110 Centennial Ave Ste 2, Piscataway, NJ 08854-4169
Tel (732) 981-1160 *Founded/Ownrshp* 1982
Sales 871.5MM^E *EMP* 100
SIC 5169 5122 5191 4231 4226 Chemicals & allied products; Pharmaceuticals; Fertilizer & fertilizer materials; Trucking terminal facilities; Special warehousing & storage
Pr: Andreas Weimann
**Treas:* William Vanfossen
Bd of Dir: Hans-Christian Sievers

D-U-N-S 14-841-7348 IMP
HELM FERTILIZER CORP (FLORIDA)
(*Suby of* HELM AMERICA CORP) ★
401 E Jackson St Ste 1400, Tampa, FL 33602-5264
Tel (813) 621-8846 *Founded/Ownrshp* 1986
Sales 767.3MM^E *EMP* 14
Accts Israeloff Trattner & Co Pc
SIC 5191 6221 Fertilizer & fertilizer materials; Commodity traders, contracts
Pr: Dale Miller
**Treas:* Mike Mohatt

D-U-N-S 02-143-1333
HELM GROUP INC
2283 Business Us 20 E, Freeport, IL 61032
Tel (815) 235-2244 *Founded/Ownrshp* 1979
Sales 153.7MM^E *EMP* 200
SIC 1611 1622 1629

D-U-N-S 09-928-5504 IMP/EXP
HELM US CORP
(*Suby of* HELM AMERICA CORP) ★
1110 Centennial Ave Ste 2, Piscataway, NJ 08854-4169
Tel (732) 981-1116 *Founded/Ownrshp* 1984
Sales 83.7MM^E *EMP* 20
SIC 5169 Chemicals, industrial & heavy
VP: Soeren Beck
**CFO:* William V Fossen
Sls Mgr: Kevin Kiplinger

D-U-N-S 00-722-3100
▲ HELMERICH & PAYNE INC
1437 S Boulder Ave # 1400, Tulsa, OK 74119-3623
Tel (918) 742-5531 *Founded/Ownrshp* 1920
Sales 1.6MMM *EMP* 6,738
Tkr Sym HP *Exch* NYS
SIC 1381 1389 6512 Drilling oil & gas wells; Gas field services; Nonresidential building operators; Commercial & industrial building operation; Shopping center, property operation only
CEO: John W Lindsay
**Ch Bd:* Hans Helmerich
CFO: Juan Pablo Tardio
Chf Cred: Cara M Hair
Sr VP: Jeffrey L Flaherty
Sr VP: Robert L Stauder
VP: John R Bell
VP: Scott Murry
Dir IT: Vic Alonci
IT Man: Lloyd Wheeler
IT Man: Rick Wozencraft
Board of Directors: Randy A Foutch, Paula Marshall, Thomas A Petrie, Donald F Robillard Jr, Francis Rooney, Edward B Rust Jr, John D Zeglis

D-U-N-S 04-150-0018 IMP
■ HELMERICH & PAYNE INTERNATIONAL DRILLING CO INC
(*Suby of* HELMERICH & PAYNE INC) ★
1437 S Boulder Ave # 1400, Tulsa, OK 74119-3623
Tel (918) 742-5531 *Founded/Ownrshp* 1967
Sales 1.5MMM^E *EMP* 6,574
Accts Ernst & Young Llp Tulsa Okla
SIC 1381 Drilling oil & gas wells; Directional drilling oil & gas wells
CEO: Hans Helmerich
**Ex VP:* John Lindsay
VP: James W Bishop
VP: Jeffrey L Flaherty
VP: Ronald D Fullerton
VP: Warren G Hubler
VP: David W Moyer
**VP:* Rob Stauder
VP: Robert L Stauder
VP: Clint Whisenhunt
Exec: M A Orr

D-U-N-S 05-829-2699
HELMSLEY ENTERPRISES INC
HELMSLEY ORGANIZATION
230 Park Ave Rm 659, New York, NY 10169-0698
Tel (212) 679-3600 *Founded/Ownrshp* 1970
Sales 230.8MM^E *EMP* 2,500
SIC 6513 8742 1522 Residential hotel operation; Apartment hotel operation; Real estate consultant; Residential construction
Ch Bd: John Codey
**CFO:* Abe Wolf
Ofcr: Ryan Kelsey
Off Mgr: Carol Astle
Pgrm Dir: Jim O'Sullivan

HELMSLEY ORGANIZATION
See HELMSLEY ENTERPRISES INC

D-U-N-S 04-415-5869
HELMSLEY-NOYES CO LLC
(*Suby of* HELMSLEY ORGANIZATION) ★
230 Park Ave Rm 659, New York, NY 10169-0698
Tel (212) 679-6772 *Founded/Ownrshp* 1898
Sales 216.6MM^E *EMP* 10
SIC 6531 Real estate brokers & agents; Real estate managers

D-U-N-S 16-184-4378
HELMSMAN MANAGEMENT SERVICES LLC
LIBERTY MUTUAL
(*Suby of* LIBERTY MUTUAL INSURANCE CO) ★
175 Berkeley St, Boston, MA 02116-5066
Tel (857) 224-1970 *Founded/Ownrshp* 1983
Sales NA *EMP* 400
SIC 6331 Fire, marine & casualty insurance
Pr: Douglas Nelson
Treas: Larry Yahia
**VP:* Peter Clas
Mng Dir: Mark Siciliano

D-U-N-S 60-229-9794
HELP AT HOME LLC
OXFORD HEALTHCARE
1 N State St Ste 800, Chicago, IL 60602-3312
Tel (312) 762-9999 *Founded/Ownrshp* 1975
Sales 47.2MM^E *EMP* 1,000
SIC 8082 Home health care services
CEO: Ron Ford
**COO:* Joel Davis
COO: Amy White
VP: Mary Boyd
Dir Risk M: Michelle Wersching
Brnch Mgr: Todd Patterson
Off Mgr: Alicia Copeland
Off Mgr: Ruo Han
Off Mgr: Hee Tai
QA Dir: Jason Ford
Dir QC: Sue Simmons
Board of Directors: Joel Davis, Ron Ford

D-U-N-S 82-723-3685
HELP USA INC
115 E 13th St, New York, NY 10003-5305
Tel (212) 400-7000 *Founded/Ownrshp* 1986
Sales 98.7MM^E *EMP* 800
SIC 6513 8322 Apartment building operators; Individual & family services
Pr: Tom Hameline
**Pr:* Laurence Belinsky
CFO: Joseph A Gallo
Ofcr: Thomas Mauro
VP: Pedro Fragoso
Ex Dir: Craig Galati
Plnt Mgr: Pat Gray

D-U-N-S 96-587-1663
HELP USA INC AND AFFILIATES
115 E 13th St, New York, NY 10003-5305
Tel (212) 400-7000 *Founded/Ownrshp* 2010
Sales 86.8MM *EMP* 2^E
Accts Loeb & Troper Llp New York N
SIC 8322 Social service center

D-U-N-S 17-221-0007 IMP
HELP/SYSTEMS LLC
6455 City West Pkwy, Eden Prairie, MN 55344-3246
Tel (952) 933-0609 *Founded/Ownrshp* 2015
Sales 87.8MM^E *EMP* 300
SIC 7372 Business oriented computer software
CEO: Chris Heim
Pr: Jim Cassens
**CFO:* Dan Mayleben
VP: Tom Huntington
Tech Mgr: Jill Martin
VP Mktg: Mike Devine
Sls Dir: Nick Elder

HELZBERG DIAMONDS
See HELZBERGS DIAMOND SHOPS INC

D-U-N-S 00-696-5735
■ HELZBERGS DIAMOND SHOPS INC
HELZBERG DIAMONDS
(*Suby of* BERKSHIRE HATHAWAY INC) ★
1825 Swift Ave, Kansas City, MO 64116-3644
Tel (816) 842-7780 *Founded/Ownrshp* 1995
Sales 341.7MM^E *EMP* 2,500
SIC 5944 Jewelry stores
CEO: Beryl Raff
Chf Mktg O: Becky Higgins
VP: Mitch Maggart
VP: Jeff Rohr
**VP:* Randall Swain
Exec: Kevin Fitzpatrick
Dir: Bill Simms
Ex Dir: William Simms
Store Mgr: Bill Miller
Netwrk Mgr: Bob Barrentine
Mktg Dir: Cory M Gordon

D-U-N-S 03-950-3776
HEMET UNIFIED SCHOOL DISTRICT
HEMETUSD
1791 W Acacia Ave, Hemet, CA 92545-3797
Tel (951) 765-5100 *Founded/Ownrshp* 1964
Sales 3.9MM *EMP* 1,346
Accts Vavrinektrinedey & Co Llp Ran
SIC 8211 Public elementary & secondary schools; Elementary school; Public adult education school
Exec: Sid Cottrell
Exec: Maria Leyva
**Prin:* Dr Lafaye Platter
Dir IT: Emil Basilio
Dir IT: Emil Desilio
Pr Dir: Alexandrea Cass
Schl Brd P: Paul Bakkurn
Schl Brd P: Ross Valenzuela
Psych: Terri Foster
HC Dir: Tracy Piper

HEMET VALLEY MEDICAL CENTER
See PHYSICIANS FOR HEALTHY HOSPITALS INC

D-U-N-S 07-249-6912
HEMET VALLEY MEDICAL CENTER-EDUCATION
1117 E Devonshire Ave, Hemet, CA 92543-3083
Tel (951) 652-2811 *Founded/Ownrshp* 2009
Sales 90.5MM^E *EMP* 1,200
SIC 8062 General medical & surgical hospitals
CEO: Kali Chaudhuri
Chf Path: Mildred Ramos
Chf OB: Syed Rizvi
Chf Rad: Frederick E Whit
CFO: Kathy Cain
Treas: Lorraine Augustine
Dir Rx: Steve Kelso
**Prin:* Girdhari Purohit
Dir Sec: Kathy Spoon
CIO: Mike Dozier
IT Man: Steve Shaw

HEMETUSD
See HEMET UNIFIED SCHOOL DISTRICT

D-U-N-S 07-881-4566
▲ HEMISPHERE MEDIA GROUP INC
4000 Ponce De Leon Blvd # 650, Coral Gables, FL 33146-1431
Tel (305) 421-6364 *Founded/Ownrshp* 2013
Sales 129.7MM *EMP* 300^E
Tkr Sym HMTV *Exch* NGM
SIC 4841 Cable & other pay television services
Pr: Alan J Sokol
**Ch Bd:* Peter M Kern
Pr: Jose E Ramos
CFO: Craig D Fischer
**V Ch Bd:* James M McNamara
Ex VP: Lucia Ballas-Traynor
Ex VP: Vicky Bathija
Ex VP: Alex J Tolston
Sr VP: Leonardo Guevara
Board of Directors: Gabriel Brener, John Engelman, Andrew Frey, Ernesto Vargas Guajardo, Leo Hindery Jr, Eric C Neuman, Vincent L Sadusky, Eric Zinterhofer

HEMLOCK SEMICONDUCTOR GROUP
See HEMLOCK SEMICONDUCTOR OPERATIONS LLC

D-U-N-S 09-539-5216 IMP
■ HEMLOCK SEMICONDUCTOR OPERATIONS LLC
HEMLOCK SEMICONDUCTOR GROUP
(*Suby of* DOW CORNING CORP) ★
12334 Geddes Rd, Hemlock, MI 48626-9409
Tel (989) 642-5201 *Founded/Ownrshp* 1959
Sales 169.4MM^E *EMP* 400
SIC 3295 Silicon, ultra high purity: treated
Pr: Richard Doorndos
VP: Marie N Eckstein
Tech Mgr: Andrew Togashi

D-U-N-S 00-128-3944 IMP/EXP
HEMPEL (USA) INC (TX)
(*Suby of* HEMPEL A/S)
600 Conroe Park North Dr, Conroe, TX 77303-2207
Tel (936) 523-6000 *Founded/Ownrshp* 1950
Sales 119.8MM^E *EMP* 188
SIC 2851 Marine paints; Paints & paint additives; Lacquers, varnishes, enamels & other coatings
Pr: Jeff Powell
**VP:* Eric Massey
Opers Mgr: Janie Castaneda

D-U-N-S 07-215-0394
HEMPFIELD AREA SCHOOL DISTRICT
4347 State Route 136, Greensburg, PA 15601-6411
Tel (724) 834-2590 *Founded/Ownrshp* 1960
Sales 87.0MM *EMP* 845
SIC 8211 Public elementary & secondary schools; High school, junior or senior
**Pr:* Sonya Brajdic
**Pr:* John Henry
**VP:* Diane Caibattoni
Teacher Pr: Robert Reger
Teacher Pr: Patricia Strickengloss

D-U-N-S 04-775-4098
HEMPHILL CONSTRUCTION CO INC
1858 Highway 49 S, Florence, MS 39073-9427
Tel (601) 932-2060 *Founded/Ownrshp* 1963
Sales 106.4MM^E *EMP* 285
SIC 1623 1542 Water & sewer line construction; Commercial & office building, new construction
CEO: Richard Rula
**CFO:* Diarin Granthan
**Ex VP:* Lynn Guthrie
VP: Ricky Eiland
Sfty Dirs: Dwayne Toombs

D-U-N-S 04-559-0809
HEMPSTEAD UNION FREE SCHOOL DISTRICT
185 Peninsula Blvd, Hempstead, NY 11550-4900
Tel (516) 292-7001 *Founded/Ownrshp* 1847
Sales 188.2MM *EMP* 1,200
Accts Nawrocki Smith Llp Melville
SIC 8211 Public elementary & secondary schools
Bd of Dir: Dianne Hamilton
Dir Sec: Andrew Hardwick
MIS Dir: Daniel Espina
IT Man: David Lasker

D-U-N-S 00-302-5285
HEMPT BROS INC (PA)
205 Creek Rd, Camp Hill, PA 17011-7499
Tel (717) 774-2911 *Founded/Ownrshp* 1925
Sales 106.5MM^E *EMP* 250
SIC 1611 3273 2951 1442 0212 General contractor, highway & street construction; Ready-mixed concrete; Paving mixtures; Construction sand mining; Gravel mining; Beef cattle except feedlots
Pr: Max J Hempt
**Treas:* Joseph L Theurer
**Sec:* Gerald L Hempt
**VP:* Joseph R Nokovich
VP: Albert Tompkins
Dir IT: Christine Murphy
Sfty Dirs: Tyler Boudreau
Sls&Mrk Ex: Terri Anavitarte
Sls Mgr: Michael Snoke
Sls Mgr: Jeff Yost

D-U-N-S 60-815-7046
HENDERSON & PHILLIPS INC
USI INSURANCE SERVICES
(*Suby of* USI INSURANCE SERVICES) ★
101 W Main St Ste 900, Norfolk, VA 23510-1653
Tel (757) 625-1800 *Founded/Ownrshp* 1996
Sales NA *EMP* 125
SIC 6411 Insurance agents, brokers & service; Insurance brokers
CEO: Dudley Fulton
Pr: Jeff Snyder
CEO: Steve Deal
CFO: Robert Schneider
Treas: Dave Hess

HENDERSON COUNTY BOARD OF EDUC
See HENDERSON COUNTY SCHOOL DISTRICT

D-U-N-S 12-462-9528
HENDERSON COUNTY BOARD OF PUBLIC EDUCATION
HENDERSON COUNTY PUB SCHOOLS
414 4th Ave W, Hendersonville, NC 28739-4325
Tel (828) 697-4510 *Founded/Ownrshp* 1840
Sales 75.8MM^E *EMP* 1,850
SIC 8211 Public elementary & secondary schools
**CFO:* Kerry Shannon
Dir IT: Jarod Pace

D-U-N-S 07-451-2559
HENDERSON COUNTY HOSPITAL CORP
MARGARET R PARDEE MEMORIAL HOS
800 N Justice St, Hendersonville, NC 28791-3410
Tel (828) 698-7191 *Founded/Ownrshp* 1953
Sales 190.4MM *EMP* 1,300
SIC 8062 8051 8082 General medical & surgical hospitals; Skilled nursing care facilities; Home health care services
CEO: Robert P Goodwin
**CEO:* James Kirby
**CFO:* Pamela Booher

HENDERSON COUNTY PUB SCHOOLS
See HENDERSON COUNTY BOARD OF PUBLIC EDUCATION

D-U-N-S 92-799-0879
HENDERSON COUNTY SCHOOL DISTRICT
HENDERSON COUNTY BOARD OF EDUC
1805 2nd St, Henderson, KY 42420-3367
Tel (270) 831-5000 *Founded/Ownrshp* 1976
Sales 73.1MM *EMP* 1,130
Accts Crafton & Wilson & Co
SIC 8211 Public elementary & secondary schools
**CFO:* Walt Spencer
Pr Dir: Julie Wischer
Teacher Pr: Jinger Carter
Teacher Pr: Adrienne Cruse
Instr Medi: Kris Gordon

D-U-N-S 07-979-8806
HENDERSON COUNTY SCHOOLS
414 4th Ave W, Hendersonville, NC 28739-4254
Tel (828) 697-4733 *Founded/Ownrshp* 2015
Sales 16.9MM^E *EMP* 1,781^E
SIC 8211 Public elementary & secondary schools
CFO: Bernard Sochia
Exec: Molly Gorsuch
Teacher Pr: Scott Rhodes

HENDERSON MANUFACTURING
See HENDERSON PRODUCTS INC

D-U-N-S 06-840-7266
■ HENDERSON PRODUCTS INC
HENDERSON MANUFACTURING
(*Suby of* HENDERSON ENTERPRISES GROUP, INC.)
1085 S 3rd St, Manchester, IA 52057-2003
Tel (563) 927-2828 *Founded/Ownrshp* 2009
Sales 83.0MM^E *EMP* 250
SIC 3537 Industrial trucks & tractors
Pr: Mart E Ward

*CFO: Steve Hoeger
VP: Glennt Beck
VP: Jeff Coldert
VP: Robert McKinley
VP: Bruce Scott

D-U-N-S 17-355-5988 EXP
HENDRICK AUTOMOTIVE GROUP
6000 Monroe Rd Ste 100, Charlotte, NC 28212-6178
Tel (704) 568-5550 Founded/Ownrshp 1986
Sales 1.3MMM^E EMP 5,000
SIC 5511

D-U-N-S 06-838-2050
HENDRICK MEDICAL CENTER
1900 Pine St, Abilene, TX 79601-2432
Tel (325) 670-2000 Founded/Ownrshp 1923
Sales 325.2MM EMP 2,900
Accts Condley And Company Llp Abile
SIC 8062 General medical & surgical hospitals
CEO: Tim Lancaster
*CFO: Jeremy Walker
*Sr VP: Joe Pearson
*VP: Norm Archibald
*VP: Stephen T Faehnle
VP: Susan Wade
Dir Risk M: Carol Kramer
Nurse Mgr: Marla Panzer
Dir QC: Gaye Hay
Dir IT: Duane Donaway
Anesthlgy: Trent Emmett

D-U-N-S 07-929-2930
HENDRICKS COUNTY HOSPITAL
HENDRICKS REGIONAL HEALTH
1000 E Main St, Danville, IN 46122-1991
Tel (317) 745-4451 Founded/Ownrshp 1962
Sales 235.3MM EMP 99^E
SIC 8062 8051 General medical & surgical hospitals; Skilled nursing care facilities
CEO: Kevin P Speer JD
CFO: Isadore Revas
*CFO: Isadora Rivas
VP: Dennis Barger
VP: Yvonne Culpepper
VP: Gary Everling
Dir Risk M: David Petrous
Dir Rad: Stan Metzger
Dir Rx: Mark Roy
Ex Dir: Deborah Case
Prgrm Mgr: Judy Spelz

D-U-N-S 00-693-6702
HENDRICKS COUNTY RURAL ELECTRIC MEMBERSHIP CORP
HENDRICKS POWER COOPERATIVE
86 N County Road 500 E, Avon, IN 46123-9481
Tel (317) 745-5473 Founded/Ownrshp 1936
Sales 86.7MM EMP 75
SIC 4911 Distribution, electric power
CEO: Donnis Mizelle
Pr: Matthew Hession

D-U-N-S 60-195-1218
HENDRICKS HOLDING CO INC
690 3rd St Ste 300, Beloit, WI 53511-6219
Tel (608) 362-8981 Founded/Ownrshp 2000
Sales 115.7MM^E EMP 512
SIC 6726 Investment offices; Management investment funds, closed-end
CEO: Brent Fox
*Pr: Rob Gerbitz
*CFO: Mark Koziol
Treas: Carla Swain
*Sr VP: Larry Evinger
*Sr VP: Kevin Rogers
*Sr VP: Jacquie Seymour
VP: Karl Leo
Mng Dir: Jon Coulter
Pr Dir: Kim Bliss

HENDRICKS POWER COOPERATIVE
See HENDRICKS COUNTY RURAL ELECTRIC MEMBERSHIP CORP

HENDRICKS REGIONAL HEALTH
See HENDRICKS COUNTY HOSPITAL

D-U-N-S 15-060-8644 IMP
HENDRICKS REGIONAL HEALTH GUILD INC
1000 E Mn St, Danville, IN 46122
Tel (317) 745-4451 Founded/Ownrshp 1962
Sales 129.0M EMP 1,600^E
SIC 8062 General medical & surgical hospitals
CEO: Kevin Speer
*Pr: Bonnie Walton
COO: Mark Roy
CFO: John Komenda
*Treas: Mary Kay Hood
Ofcr: Tammy Vukusich
VP: John Sparzo
Dir Rad: Stan Metzeger
CIO: Larry Westrich
CTO: Tonya Prentice
Cmptr Lab: Anita Dickman

HENDRICKSON TRUCK SUSPENSION
See HENDRICKSON USA LLC

D-U-N-S 78-707-2151
HENDRICKSON USA LLC
(Suby of BOLER CO) ★
500 Park Blvd Ste 450, Itasca, IL 60143-3153
Tel (630) 874-9700 Founded/Ownrshp 2005
Sales 98.8MM^E EMP 334^E
SIC 3537 Industrial trucks & tractors
CFO: Warren Kelleher
VP: Jim Colley
VP: Rick Johnson
VP: Mike Keeler
VP Admn: Nancy Coons
CIO: Matthew Boler

D-U-N-S 79-012-6143 IMP
HENDRICKSON USA LLC
HENDRICKSON TRUCK SUSPENSION
(Suby of BOLER CO) ★
800 S Frontage Rd, Woodridge, IL 60517-4900
Tel (630) 910-2844 Founded/Ownrshp 1913
Sales 824.4MM^E EMP 2,400^E
SIC 5012 Trucks, commercial
VP: Rick Johnson
Exec: Jerome Cortez
Exec: Matt Joy
Exec: Suresh Mehta
Exec: Jerry Reynolds
Mng Dir: Mark Page
Genl Mgr: Paul Pschouwstra
QA Dir: Jacob Harper
Opers Mgr: Jay Underwood
Plnt Mgr: John Harrell
Plnt Mgr: Devin Reynolds

D-U-N-S 07-563-5094
HENDRIX COLLEGE (AR)
1600 Washington Ave, Conway, AR 72032-3080
Tel (501) 329-6811 Founded/Ownrshp 1884
Sales 105.1MM EMP 336
SIC 8221 University
Pr: William Tsutsui
V Ch: Kevin Krajcir
Pr: W E Arnold
Trst: Johnnie Amonette
Trst: Joseph Bates
Trst: David Knight
VP: Pamela Owen
VP: Robert G Young
Assoc Dir: Molly Bradney
*Prin: J Timmothy Cloyd
Dir IT: Jerry Blackburn
Board of Directors: Lydia McDonald

D-U-N-S 10-001-2848
HENDRY COUNTY SCHOOL DISTRICT
DISTRICT SCHOOL BOARD OF HENDR
25 E Hickpochee Ave, Labelle, FL 33935-5015
Tel (863) 674-4642 Founded/Ownrshp 1925
Sales 54.0MM^E EMP 1,000
SIC 8211 Public elementary & secondary schools
*Ch Bd: Ray Clinard
Schl Brd P: Dwayne Brown
Schl Brd P: Patrick Langford
HC Dir: Jeff Caulkins
HC Dir: Lucinda Kelley

D-U-N-S 18-723-4179 IMP/EXP
HENGST OF NORTH AMERICA INC
(Suby of HENGST SE & CO. KG)
29 Hengst Blvd, Camden, SC 29020-7796
Tel (803) 432-5992 Founded/Ownrshp 2005
Sales 96.0MM EMP 270
Accts Bauknight Pietras Stormer Pa
SIC 3714 Filters: oil, fuel & air, motor vehicle
Pr: Robert Junker
*Sec: Ingo Van De Kamp
*VP: Carsten Schnese
Genl Mgr: Martin Wachenfeld
Ql Cn Mgr: Jorg Hemsing
Ql Cn Mgr: James Houser

D-U-N-S 12-940-9996 IMP
HENGST USA INC
(Suby of HENGST SE & CO. KG)
29 Hengst Blvd, Camden, SC 29020-7796
Tel (803) 432-5992 Founded/Ownrshp 2004
Sales 164.0MM EMP 239
SIC 3714 Filters: oil, fuel & air, motor vehicle
Pr: Jens Roettgering
CFO: Hans Gruenhag
Genl Mgr: Martin Wachenfeld

D-U-N-S 06-929-9381
HENIFF TRANSPORTATION SYSTEMS LLC
2015 Spring Rd SE 780, Oak Brook, IL 60523-3941
Tel (630) 230-2100 Founded/Ownrshp 2007
Sales 113.9MM^E EMP 450
SIC 4213 Trucking, except local
*VP: Scott Templeman

D-U-N-S 60-588-4449 IMP/EXP
HENKEL CONSUMER GOODS INC
(Suby of SCHWARZOPF) ★
7201 E Henkel Way, Scottsdale, AZ 85255-9678
Tel (860) 571-5100 Founded/Ownrshp 2004
Sales 2.4MMM^E EMP 2,900
SIC 2841 Soap & other detergents
Pr: Norbert Koll
Pr: Derek Bufkin
Pr: Raymond Wong
Treas: Todd Gatzulis
*Treas: Raphaela Lessmann
*VP: Brad A Gazaway
VP: Jason Lohrey
VP: Bill Tyree
Creative D: George Polowyk
Prgrm Mgr: Matt Taha
Prgrm Mgr: Shane Turner

D-U-N-S 05-144-1731 IMP
HENKEL CORP
SCHWARZOPF
(Suby of HENKEL OF AMERICA INC) ★
1 Henkel Way, Rocky Hill, CT 06067-3581
Tel (860) 571-5100 Founded/Ownrshp 1970
Sales 2.5MMM^E EMP 4,542
SIC 2843 2821 2833 2899 2891 Surface active agents; Plastics materials & resins; Thermoplastic materials; Medicinals & botanicals; Vitamins, natural or synthetic: bulk, uncompounded; Chemical preparations; Adhesives
CEO: Hans Van Bylen
Ch Bd: Dr Jochen Krautter
Pr: Jeffrey C Piccolomini
CFO: Michael Desalvio
CFO: Michael Grimaud
Treas: Raphaela Dohm
Ex VP: Carsten Knobel
Ex VP: Kathrin Menges
Sr VP: Jerry Perkins
VP: Martin Andree
VP: Paul Berry
VP: Michael Biondolillo
VP: Angela Cackovich
VP: Renata Casaro
VP: Cindy Demers
VP: Andy N Garcia
VP: Dan Langer
VP: Michael Olosky
VP: Michael Rauch
VP: Gary Raykovitz
VP: Steffen Ruebke

D-U-N-S 05-474-4784 IMP
HENKEL OF AMERICA INC
(Suby of HENKEL AG & CO. KGAA)
1 Henkel Way, Rocky Hill, CT 06067-3581
Tel (860) 571-5100 Founded/Ownrshp 1979
Sales 2.5MMM^E EMP 5,342
SIC 2869 2843 2821 2833 2899 2891 Industrial organic chemicals; Fatty acid esters, aminos, etc.; Surface active agents; Plastics materials & resins; Thermoplastic materials; Medicinals & botanicals; Vitamins, natural or synthetic: bulk, uncompounded; Chemical preparations; Adhesives
Pr: Jeffrey C Piccolomini
*Ch Bd: Dr Lothar Steinebach
*Treas: Raphaela Dohm
*Sr VP: William B Read III
VP: Frederic Chupin
*VP: Raphaela Lessmann
VP: Scot Miller
VP: Dan Wohletz
VP Sls: Bobby Santulli

D-U-N-S 08-019-8735
HENKELS & MCCOY GROUP INC
985 Jolly Rd, Blue Bell, PA 19422-1958
Tel (215) 283-7600 Founded/Ownrshp 2015
Sales 1.3MMM^E EMP 5,000
SIC 1623 Water, sewer & utility lines; Oil & gas pipeline construction; Telephone & communication line construction; Electric power line construction
CEO: T Roderick Henkels
Treas: Joseph C Paulits IV

D-U-N-S 00-893-7815 IMP
HENKELS & MCCOY INC
(Suby of HENKELS & MCCOY GROUP INC) ★
985 Jolly Rd, Blue Bell, PA 19422-1958
Tel (215) 283-7600 Founded/Ownrshp 1923
Sales 1.3MMM EMP 4,718
SIC 1623

D-U-N-S 03-717-6518
HENLEY MANAGEMENT CO
555 Skokie Blvd Ste 555, Northbrook, IL 60062-2854
Tel (847) 480-4690 Founded/Ownrshp 1979
Sales 130.5MM^E EMP 689^E
SIC 6719 Investment holding companies, except banks
Pr: Richard W Colburn

D-U-N-S 00-423-2062
■ **HENNEGAN CO** (KY)
(Suby of CONSOLIDATED GRAPHICS INC) ★
7455 Empire Dr, Florence, KY 41042-2923
Tel (859) 282-3600 Founded/Ownrshp 1886, 2007
Sales 86.3MM^E EMP 370
SIC 2752 2789 Commercial printing, lithographic; Color lithography; Bookbinding & related work
Pr: Gary Greis
Pr: Robert B Ott Jr
Treas: Donald C Fleck
Treas: Alex McDermott
VP: Jeff Beiting
VP: Michael D Butler
VP: Michael Fleury
VP: Roger Helms
VP: Dennis J Purcell
VP: Greg Trachsel
VP: Mike Vandenburg

D-U-N-S 06-815-8369
HENNEPIN COUNTY
300 S 6th St, Minneapolis, MN 55487-0999
Tel (612) 348-3000 Founded/Ownrshp 1852
Sales NA EMP 10,246
SIC 9111 County supervisors' & executives' offices
Bd of Dir: Saundra Dawson
Bd of Dir: Pam Flenniken
Bd of Dir: Lorraine Lutgen
Ofcr: Gerri Baumgartner
Ofcr: Nicole Fernandez
Ofcr: Angela Kaiser
Ofcr: Brian McInerney
Ofcr: Shirley Qual
Ofcr: Pam Teske
Comm Man: Coleen Brady
Comm Man: Michael Freeman
Board of Directors: Gail Dorfman, Randy Johnson, Linda Koblick, Peter McLaughlin, Mike Opat, Penny Steele, Mark Stenglein

HENNEPIN COUNTY MEDICAL CENTER
See HENNEPIN HEALTHCARE SYSTEM INC

D-U-N-S 12-001-9070
HENNEPIN HEALTHCARE SYSTEM INC
HENNEPIN COUNTY MEDICAL CENTER
(Suby of HENNEPIN COUNTY) ★
701 Park Ave, Minneapolis, MN 55415-1623
Tel (612) 873-3000 Founded/Ownrshp 2007
Sales 771.1MM EMP 5,000
SIC 8062 5912 General medical & surgical hospitals; Drug stores & proprietary stores
CEO: Jon Pryor
CIO: Brita Hansen
Nrsg Dir: John Gray
Nrsg Dir: Jen Pierce
HC Dir: Lynn Weber
Pgrm Dir: Benita Dieperink

D-U-N-S 03-353-2326
HENNESSY CADILLAC INC
LANDROVER NORTHPOINT
3040 Piedmont Rd Ne, Atlanta, GA 30305-2636
Tel (404) 261-5700 Founded/Ownrshp 1986
Sales 109.6MM^E EMP 325
SIC 5511 Automobiles, new & used
CEO: Mark W Hennessy
*Sec: Devers Hayes
*VP: Steve Hennessy
Exec: Kelly Collins
Genl Mgr: Brad Selz
Store Mgr: Tony Hendrix
Sls Mgr: Mike Johnson
Sales Asso: John Allen
Sales Asso: Larry Bass
Sales Asso: Bob Beers
Sales Asso: Steven Crawford

D-U-N-S 00-554-9159 IMP/EXP
■ **HENNESSY INDUSTRIES INC**
(Suby of FORTIVE CORP) ★
1601 Jp Hennessy Dr, La Vergne, TN 37086-3524
Tel (615) 641-7533 Founded/Ownrshp 1961, 2016
Sales 97.8MM^E EMP 438
SIC 3714 5013 Motor vehicle parts & accessories; Automotive hardware
Pr: Sanjay Chowbey
Pr: Howard Hagan
Ql Cn Mgr: Phil Bourassa

D-U-N-S 80-913-3775
HENNIGES AUTOMOTIVE HOLDINGS INC
HENNIGS AUTOMOBILES
(Suby of AVIC AUTOMOTIVE SYSTEMS HOLDING CO.,LTD)
2750 High Meadow Cir, Auburn Hills, MI 48326-2796
Tel (248) 340-4100 Founded/Ownrshp 2007
Sales 1.0MMM^E EMP 7,000
SIC 3069 2891 3714 Rubber automotive products; Adhesives & sealants; Motor vehicle electrical equipment
CEO: Douglas Delgrosso
CFO: Larry Williams
VP: Ann Budin
VP: Geri Gasperut
VP: Boris Gavric
VP: Larry Rollins
VP: Peter Soto

D-U-N-S 00-997-1289
HENNIGES AUTOMOTIVE IOWA INC
(Suby of SCHLEGEL CORP) ★
3200 Main St, Keokuk, IA 52632-2259
Tel (319) 524-4560 Founded/Ownrshp 1951
Sales 121.3MM^E EMP 500
SIC 3069 3442 3429 2295 Rubber automotive products; Metal doors, sash & trim; Manufactured hardware (general); Sealing or insulating tape for pipe: coated fiberglass
Prin: Larry Williams

D-U-N-S 17-678-4585 IMP/EXP
HENNIGES AUTOMOTIVE SEALING SYSTEMS NORTH AMERICA INC
METZELER AUTO PROFILE SYSTEMS
(Suby of HENNIGS AUTOMOBILES) ★
2750 High Meadow Cir, Auburn Hills, MI 48326-2796
Tel (248) 340-4100 Founded/Ownrshp 2008
Sales 124.1MM EMP 750
SIC 3053 2891 3714 Gaskets, packing & sealing devices; Adhesives & sealants; Motor vehicle parts & accessories
Pr: Lorenze Williams
*CEO: Rob Depierre
*CFO: Larry Williams

HENNIGS AUTOMOBILES
See HENNIGES AUTOMOTIVE HOLDINGS INC

D-U-N-S 00-425-6814 IMP/EXP
HENNY PENNY CORP
1219 Us Route 35, Eaton, OH 45320-8621
Tel (937) 456-8400 Founded/Ownrshp 1986
Sales 168.6MM^E EMP 631
SIC 3589 Cooking equipment, commercial; Food warming equipment, commercial
CEO: Steve Cobb
*Pr: Rob Connelly
CFO: Brian Brooks
CFO: Art Harlan
Off Mgr: Judy Phillips
Dir IT: Sam Stewart
Opers Mgr: John Olsen

D-U-N-S 04-252-6749 EXP
HENRICKSEN & CO INC
1101 W Thorndale Ave, Itasca, IL 60143-1366
Tel (630) 250-9090 Founded/Ownrshp 1968
Sales 152.4MM EMP 210
Accts Sikich Llp Naperville Illino
SIC 5021 7389 Office furniture; Interior designer
Pr: Michael D Assell
*CFO: Tim Osborn
*Ch: Stephen E McPartlin
*Ex VP: Richard D Failla
*Ex VP: Russell Frees
*VP: Dick Nash
Dir Bus: Emily Keon
Snr PM: Dominick Sanginito

D-U-N-S 08-812-1421
HENRICO COUNTY PUBLIC SCHOOLS
3820 Nine Mile Rd Ste A, Richmond, VA 23223-4831
Tel (804) 652-3717 Founded/Ownrshp 1960
Sales 228.7MM^E EMP 5,600^E
SIC 8211 Public elementary & secondary schools
Ch Bd: Beverly L Cocke
Ex Dir: Kevin G Adams

D-U-N-S 11-283-2865
HENRICO DOCTORS HOSPITAL
1602 Skipwith Rd, Richmond, VA 23229-5298
Tel (804) 289-4500 Founded/Ownrshp 2002
Sales 428.3MM EMP 63^E
SIC 8069 Cancer hospital
CFO: Chris Benton
VP: Teresa Bailey
VP: Richard Stauffer
*Prin: Patrick Farell
Mktg Dir: Patty Campbell
Doctor: Stephen W Cross MD

D-U-N-S 06-790-6941
HENRIETTA BUILDING SUPPLIES INC
ENERGY INSULATION SYSTEMS
1 Riverton Way, West Henrietta, NY 14586-9754
Tel (585) 334-2365 Founded/Ownrshp 1974
Sales 85.8MM^E EMP 100
SIC 5031 Building materials, exterior
Ch: Richard Szustakowski
CFO: Ronald Cedruly

D-U-N-S 07-174-1995
HENRIETTA D GOODALL HOSPITAL INC
25 June St, Sanford, ME 04073-2621
Tel (207) 324-4310 *Founded/Ownrshp* 1928
Sales 91.6MM *EMP* 1,016
SIC 8062

D-U-N-S 00-694-6131
HENRY A PETTER SUPPLY CO LLC
5110 Charter Oak Dr, Paducah, KY 42001-5209
Tel (270) 575-6922 *Founded/Ownrshp* 1890
Sales 120.4MM^E *EMP* 209
SIC 5085 Industrial supplies
**Pr:* Bruce Austin
**Pr:* John Sircy
**Ch:* Bob Petter
Exec: Patsy Hayden
Genl Mgr: Bruce Wilcox
IT Man: Ron Overton

D-U-N-S 02-814-0234 IMP
HENRY AVOCADO CORP
2355 E Lincoln Ave, Escondido, CA 92027-1298
Tel (760) 745-6632 *Founded/Ownrshp* 1924
Sales 180.2MM *EMP* 88
Accts White Nelson Diehl Evans Llp
SIC 0179 4213 Avocado orchard; Trucking, except local
Pr: Philip Henry
CFO: Jerry Miller
VP: Betty Guerrero
VP: Rick Opel
Off Mgr: Lori Deaver
Off Mgr: Yolanda Herrera
Opers Mgr: Uziel Gonzales
Sls Mgr: Chris Varvel

D-U-N-S 07-853-3815
HENRY CO LLC
999 N Sepulveda Blvd, El Segundo, CA 90245-2714
Tel (310) 955-9200 *Founded/Ownrshp* 2016
Sales 222.2MM^E *EMP* 560
SIC 2952 2821 2891 Roof cement: asphalt, fibrous or plastic; Polyurethane resins; Sealants
Pr: Frank Ready
CFO: Jason Peel
Sr VP: Mark R Adams
Sr VP: Alan K Davenport
Sr VP: John Dobson
Sr VP: Kirk R Kandler
Sr VP: Kurt Leibel
VP: Matt O'Hanlon
Manager: Mike Wahba

D-U-N-S 10-001-3879
HENRY COUNTY BOARD OF EDUCATION
33 N Zack Hinton Pkwy, McDonough, GA 30253-2344
Tel (770) 957-6601 *Founded/Ownrshp* 1935
Sales 261.0MM^E *EMP* 5,200
SIC 8211 School board
Ch Bd: Pam Nutt
Ofcr: Greg Benton
Ofcr: Joseph Chambers
Ofcr: Earl Parker
Pr Dir: John D Hardin

HENRY COUNTY PUBLIC SCHOOLS
See HENRY COUNTY SCHOOL DISTRICT

D-U-N-S 19-352-6209
HENRY COUNTY SCHOOL DISTRICT
HENRY COUNTY PUBLIC SCHOOLS
3300 Kings Mountain Rd, Collinsville, VA 24078
Tel (276) 634-4700 *Founded/Ownrshp* 1995
Sales 51.5MM^E *EMP* 1,200
SIC 8211 Public elementary & secondary schools
Exec: Robert Vogler
MIS Dir: Teh-Way Lee
Pr Dir: Monica Hatchett

D-U-N-S 07-989-4371
HENRY COUNTY SCHOOLS
33 N Zack Hinton Pkwy, McDonough, GA 30253-2344
Tel (770) 957-6601 *Founded/Ownrshp* 2015
Sales 196.1MM^E *EMP* 4,239^E
SIC 8211 Public elementary & secondary schools
Exec: Kent Morrow
Ex Dir: Valerie Suessmith
Pr Dir: John D Hardin
Psych: Misty Bert
HC Dir: April Brown

D-U-N-S 07-439-4263 IMP
HENRY CROWN AND CO
CC INDUSTRIES
222 N La Salle St # 2000, Chicago, IL 60601-1120
Tel (312) 236-6300 *Founded/Ownrshp* 1973
Sales 1.3MMM^E *EMP* 1,483
SIC 2514 Lawn furniture: metal
Pr: James S Crown
Genl Pt: Richard Goodman

D-U-N-S 96-952-7600
HENRY E HUNTINGTON LIBRARY AND ART GALLERY
1151 Oxford Rd, San Marino, CA 91108-1218
Tel (626) 405-2100 *Founded/Ownrshp* 2011
Sales 90.0MM *EMP* 3
Accts Singerlewak Llp Los Angeles
SIC 8231 Libraries

D-U-N-S 01-392-6779 IMP
HENRY F TEICHMANN INC
HFT
3009 Washington Rd, Mc Murray, PA 15317-3202
Tel (724) 941-9550 *Founded/Ownrshp* 1947
Sales 201.6MM^E *EMP* 400
SIC 1541 8711 8742 Industrial buildings, new construction; Engineering services; Construction project management consultant
Pr: Arch McIntyre
**Ch Bd:* Newton N Teichmann Sr
Pr: Daniel L Chen
**Pr:* Mark F Piedmonte
**VP:* Kenneth E Lemasters Jr
Sys Mgr: Jim Workmaster
VP Opers: Gordon Jungquist
VP Opers: Mark Piedmonte

HENRY FORD ALLEGIANCE HEALTH
See W A FOOTE MEMORIAL HOSPITAL

D-U-N-S 60-285-0166
HENRY FORD ALLEGIANCE HEALTH GROUP
FOOTE HOSPITAL
205 N East Ave, Jackson, MI 49201-1753
Tel (517) 788-4800 *Founded/Ownrshp* 1983
Sales 91.6MM^E *EMP* 3,000
SIC 8741 8721 Hospital management; Nursing & personal care facility management; Accounting, auditing & bookkeeping
Ch: Larry Schultz
**Pr:* Georgia Fojtasek
**Pr:* Tim Levy
**CFO:* Jeanne Hettinger
CFO: Charlie Johnson
CFO: Jeanne M Wickens
VP: Alan Thompkins
VP: Jay Warren
**Prin:* John Nally

D-U-N-S 07-313-4603 IMP
HENRY FORD HEALTH SYSTEM
HENRY FORD HOSPITAL
1 Ford Pl, Detroit, MI 48202-3450
Tel (313) 916-2600 *Founded/Ownrshp* 1989
Sales 1.5MMM *EMP* 23,000
SIC 8062 General medical & surgical hospitals
CEO: Nancy Schlichting
Dir Recs: Theresa Dean
Dir Recs: Erica Jordan
**Pr:* Gail L Warden
COO: Gary Beaulac
**COO:* Robert Riney
**CFO:* James M Connelly
Bd of Dir: Paul Edwards
Ofcr: Meredith Phillips
Ofcr: Karen Schmidt
**Ex VP:* Mark A Kelley MD
Sr VP: Gary E Roundig
VP: Matt Acosta
VP: Noel Baril
VP: John Carey
VP: Jon Fitzgerald
VP: Scott M Geiger
VP: Veeresh Jankauskas
VP: Peter Johnson
VP: Dan Kus
VP: Ruben Munoz

D-U-N-S 96-459-0777
HENRY FORD HEALTH SYSTEM
HENRY FORD HOSPITAL
(*Suby of* HENRY FORD HOSPITAL) ★
1 Ford Pl 5f, Detroit, MI 48202-3450
Tel (313) 876-1031 *Founded/Ownrshp* 2010
Sales 2.3MMM *EMP* 308^E
SIC 8699

HENRY FORD HOSPITAL
See HENRY FORD HEALTH SYSTEM

HENRY FORD HOSPITAL
See HENRY FORD HEALTH SYSTEM

D-U-N-S 07-839-6058
HENRY FORD MACOMB HOSPITAL CORP
ST JOSEPH MERCY OF MACOMB
(*Suby of* HENRY FORD HOSPITAL) ★
15855 19 Mile Rd, Clinton Township, MI 48038-3504
Tel (586) 263-2300 *Founded/Ownrshp* 1990
Sales NA *EMP* 3,400
SIC 8062 General medical & surgical hospitals
CEO: Barbara Rossmann
CFO: Terry Goodbalian
Chf Mktg O: Joseph Naoum
**Ex VP:* Gary Beaulac
Sr VP: Barbara Rossman
VP: Terry Goodbalian
**VP:* Michael Markel Jr
Dir Rad: Deep G Bai
Dir Rad: Joseph Blechinger
Dir Rx: Richard Jennings
Chf Nrs Of: Karen Standfest

D-U-N-S 00-547-0750
HENRY FORD MACOMB HOSPITALS
(*Suby of* HENRY FORD HOSPITAL) ★
215 North Ave, Mount Clemens, MI 48043-1716
Tel (586) 466-9310 *Founded/Ownrshp* 2008
Sales 411.0MM *EMP* 1,043^E
SIC 8062 General medical & surgical hospitals
Pr: Stephen J Hathaway
Ex Dir: Sheila Sperti
DP Exec: Robert Jones

D-U-N-S 01-891-8894
HENRY FORD MEDICAL CENTER
(*Suby of* HENRY FORD HOSPITAL) ★
39450 W 12 Mile Rd, Novi, MI 48377-3600
Tel (248) 661-7393 *Founded/Ownrshp* 2009
Sales 39.3MM^E *EMP* 1,813^E
SIC 8011 Offices & clinics of medical doctors
Prin: Daniel Kus
Mktg Mgr: Jody Bott

D-U-N-S 06-098-3871 IMP
HENRY FORD WYANDOTTE HOSPITAL
(*Suby of* HENRY FORD HOSPITAL) ★
2333 Biddle Ave, Wyandotte, MI 48192-4668
Tel (734) 246-6000 *Founded/Ownrshp* 1999
Sales 267.9MM *EMP* 1,600
SIC 8062 General medical & surgical hospitals
CEO: Denise Brooks-Williams
**Pr:* Annette S Phillips
**CEO:* Nancy M Schlichting
Off Mgr: Jane Cain
Surgeon: Fadi F Baidoun

D-U-N-S 07-534-2279
HENRY HEYWOOD MEMORIAL HOSPITAL
HEYWOOD HOSPITAL
(*Suby of* HEYWOOD HEALTHCARE INC) ★
242 Green St, Gardner, MA 01440-1336
Tel (978) 632-3420 *Founded/Ownrshp* 1907
Sales 99.1MM *EMP* 850
SIC 8062

D-U-N-S 14-467-6566
HENRY M JACKSON FOUNDATION FOR ADVANCEMENT OF MILITARY MEDICINE INC
H J F
6720a Rockledge Dr # 100, Bethesda, MD 20817-1888
Tel (240) 694-2000 *Founded/Ownrshp* 1983
Sales 414.2MM *EMP* 2,200
Accts Bdo Usa Llp Bethesda Md
SIC 8099 Medical services organization
Pr: John W Lowe
**CFO:* Craig Anderson
**VP:* Elizabeth Folk
**VP:* Arthur W Hapner
Assoc Dir: Ann Borlo
Dir IT: P J Clark
IT Man: Richard Burris

D-U-N-S 08-540-5439
HENRY MAYO NEWHALL HOSPITAL
23845 Mcbean Pkwy, Valencia, CA 91355-2083
Tel (661) 253-8000 *Founded/Ownrshp* 1972
Sales 307.4MM *EMP* 1,600^E
SIC 8062 General medical & surgical hospitals
Pr: Roger E Seaver
Ch Bd: Elizabeth Hopp
Treas: James Hickens
Ofcr: Kingman Ho
Sr VP: C R Hudson
VP: Marlee Lauffer
VP: John Schleif
VP: Fredy Shen
VP: Terry Stone
VP: Bob Yerby
Dir Lab: Cindy Martin
Dir Lab: Rashida Soni

D-U-N-S 87-436-1608
HENRY MAYO NEWHALL MEMORIAL HEALTH FOUNDATION INC
HENRYMAYO NEWHALL MEM HOSP
23845 Mcbean Pkwy, Valencia, CA 91355-2001
Tel (661) 253-8000 *Founded/Ownrshp* 1972
Sales 251.8MM *EMP* 1,500
SIC 8062 General medical & surgical hospitals
Pr: Roger Seaver
Obsttrcn: Nicholas J Tuso

D-U-N-S 03-610-4799
HENRY MAYO NEWHALL MEMORIAL HOSPITAL
23845 Mcbean Pkwy, Valencia, CA 91355-2001
Tel (661) 253-8112 *Founded/Ownrshp* 2013
Sales 245.5MM *EMP* 94^E
SIC 8011

D-U-N-S 00-891-9961 IMP
HENRY MODELL & CO INC
MODELL'S SPORTING GOODS
498 7th Ave Fl 20, New York, NY 10018-6704
Tel (212) 822-1000 *Founded/Ownrshp* 1946
Sales 731.7MM^E *EMP* 5,430
Accts Bdo Usa Llp New York Ny
SIC 5941 5661 5611 5621 5641 5961 Sporting goods & bicycle shops; Footwear, athletic; Clothing, sportswear, men's & boys'; Women's sportswear; Children's & infants' wear stores; Catalog & mail-order houses
Ch Bd: Mitchell B Modell
Pr: Joe Paltenstein
Ex VP: Lawrence Brustein
Ex VP: Cary Deleo
VP: Ron Brunette
VP: Joseph Conley
VP: Dave Fletcher
VP: Hans Kantor
VP: Willy Kaplan
VP: Tami Mohney
Exec: Richard Schneider
Exec: Onnik Tateossian

D-U-N-S 60-416-7338 IMP
■ **HENRY PRATT CO LLC**
(*Suby of* MUELLER CO LLC) ★
401 S Highland Ave, Aurora, IL 60506-5580
Tel (630) 844-4000 *Founded/Ownrshp* 1901
Sales 90.5MM^E *EMP* 420
SIC 3491 Industrial valves; Water works valves; Valves, nuclear
Pr: Dale B Smith
**CFO:* Darrell Jean
VP: Jan Babush
**VP:* Randy Berger
**VP:* Steve Sharp
MIS Dir: Sarada Mohapatra
Sfty Mgr: Ryan Kline
Opers Mgr: John Howard
Plnt Mgr: Allen Olson
Natl Sales: Tom Hoban
VP Sls: Bernard Haviland

HENRY SCHEIN ANIMAL HEALTH
See BUTLER ANIMAL HEALTH SUPPLY LLC

D-U-N-S 01-243-0880 IMP/EXP
▲ **HENRY SCHEIN INC**
135 Duryea Rd, Melville, NY 11747-3834
Tel (631) 843-5500 *Founded/Ownrshp* 1932
Sales 10.6MMM *EMP* 19,000
Tkr Sym HSIC *Exch* NGS
SIC 5047 5122 7372 Dental equipment & supplies; Medical equipment & supplies; Veterinarians' equipment & supplies; Pharmaceuticals; Business oriented computer software
Ch Bd: Stanley M Bergman
**Pr:* James P Breslawski
Pr: Peter McCarthy
Pr: Lonnie Shoff
**CFO:* Steven Paladino
Treas: Keith Dreyer
Treas: Joel Geliebter
Treas: Ferdinand Jahnel
**Ofcr:* Gerald A Benjamin
Ofcr: David C McKinley
**Ofcr:* Mark E Mlotek
Sr VP: James A Harding
Sr VP: Michael Racioppi
Sr VP: Paul Rose
**Sr VP:* Walter Siegel
Sr VP: Michael P Zack
VP: Patrick Allen
VP: Scott Becker
VP: Ravi Bhir
VP: Joseph Buckshaw
VP: John Chatham
Board of Directors: Bradley T Sheares, Barry J Alperin, Lawrence S Bacow, Paul Brons, Joseph L Herring, Donald J Kabat, Kurt P Kuehn, Philip A Laskawy, Carol Raphael, E Dianne Rekow

HENRY TECH INC INTL SLS CO
See HENRY TECHNOLOGIES INC

D-U-N-S 00-507-1741 IMP/EXP
HENRY TECHNOLOGIES INC (IL)
HENRY TECH INC INTL SLS CO
(*Suby of* HENDRICKS HOLDING CO INC) ★
701 S Main St, Chatham, IL 62629-1655
Tel (217) 483-2406 *Founded/Ownrshp* 1914
Sales 86.5MM^E *EMP* 500
SIC 3491 3585 3567 3564 3545 3494 Gas valves & parts, industrial; Automatic regulating & control valves; Regulators (steam fittings); Refrigeration equipment, complete; Evaporative condensers, heat transfer equipment; Industrial furnaces & ovens; Blowers & fans; Machine tool accessories; Valves & pipe fittings
Pr: Michael Giordano
Genl Mgr: Sandy Macdonald
Sls Mgr: Ron Ceminsky
Sls Mgr: Jim Funk
Sls Mgr: Kenny Price

D-U-N-S 00-714-8042
HENRY WURST INC (MO)
NORTH KANSAS CITY
1331 Saline St, North Kansas City, MO 64116-4400
Tel (816) 701-0825 *Founded/Ownrshp* 1937
Sales 129.2MM^E *EMP* 320
SIC 2752 7331 Commercial printing, lithographic; Mailing service
Ch: John C Wurst
**Pr:* Mark Hanf
**CEO:* Michael S Wurst
**CFO:* Kate Stewart
VP: John Kulias
Plnt Mgr: Howard Stamper
Prd Mgr: Sherri Meyer
Sales Exec: Mark Gearon

HENRYMAYO NEWHALL MEM HOSP
See HENRY MAYO NEWHALL MEMORIAL HEALTH FOUNDATION INC

D-U-N-S 02-296-4340
HENRYS FOODS INC
234 Mckay Ave N, Alexandria, MN 56308-8550
Tel (320) 763-3194 *Founded/Ownrshp* 1929
Sales 155.1MM^E *EMP* 150
SIC 5194 5145 5111 5113 5141 Tobacco & tobacco products; Confectionery; Industrial & personal service paper; Groceries, general line
CEO: H Thomas Eidsvold
**VP:* Jim Eidsvold
Genl Mgr: Dale Erickson
Off Mgr: Karren Janachovsky
IT Man: Meduna Daniel
IT Man: Daniel Meduna
Sls Dir: Terry Loeffler
Sls Dir: Mike Loge
Sls Mgr: Duane Anderson

D-U-N-S 04-438-0350 EXP
HENRYS TACKLE LLC
(*Suby of* BIG ROCK SPORTS MARKETING) ★
158 Little Nine Rd, Morehead City, NC 28557-8482
Tel (252) 726-6186 *Founded/Ownrshp* 1996
Sales 136.6MM^E *EMP* 350
SIC 5091 Sporting & recreation goods; Fishing tackle

D-U-N-S 06-332-2085 IMP/EXP
HENSEL PHELPS CONSTRUCTION CO
420 6th Ave, Greeley, CO 80631-2332
Tel (970) 352-6565 *Founded/Ownrshp* 1960
Sales 3.1MMM *EMP* 2,000
Accts Kpmg Llp Denver Co
SIC 1542 1521 1771 1522 1541 1622 Nonresidential construction; Single-family housing construction; Concrete work; Residential construction; Industrial buildings & warehouses; Bridge, tunnel & elevated highway
Pr: Jeffrey Wenaas
CFO: Stephen J Carrico
Ex VP: Jon W Ball
Ex VP: Michael J Choutka
Ex VP: Wayne S Lindholm
Ex VP: Richard G Tucker
VP: Leonard J Arnold
VP: Allan J Bliesmer
VP: Rashad Friday
VP: Steve M Grauer
VP: Kirk J Hazen
VP: Bradley A Jeanneret
VP: Robert P Majerus
VP: Cuyler R McGinley
VP: James R Pappas Jr
VP: Jason Spencer
VP: William A Thompson
VP: Jose Vasquez
VP: Eric L Wilson
VP: Brad D Winans
VP: Quincy Yaw

D-U-N-S 96-779-4533
HENSEL PHELPS GRANITE HANGAR JOINT VENTURE
18850 Von Kamon 100, Irvine, CA 92612
Tel (949) 852-0111 *Founded/Ownrshp* 2011
Sales 300.0MM *EMP* 200
SIC 1542 1629 Nonresidential construction; Heavy construction
VP: Cuyler R McGinley
VP: John A Franich

D-U-N-S 07-847-5336
HENSEL PHELPS SERVICES LLC
(*Suby of* HENSEL PHELPS CONSTRUCTION CO) ★
4437 Brookfield Corp 20 Ste 207, Chantilly, VA 20151
Tel (703) 828-3200 *Founded/Ownrshp* 2012
Sales 250.0MM *EMP* 5
SIC 1522 8744 1521 1541 1623 1611 Residential construction; Facilities support services; Single-family housing construction; Industrial buildings & warehouses; Water, sewer & utility lines; Highway & street construction
Ex VP: Michael J Choutka
Pr: Edwin Glenn Miller

D-U-N-S 83-162-9238
HENSEL PHELPS SOLTEK JV
(*Suby of* HENSEL PHELPS CONSTRUCTION CO) ★
420 6th Ave, Greeley, CO 80631-2332
Tel (970) 352-6565 *Founded/Ownrshp* 2009
Sales 100.0MM *EMP* 4E
SIC 1542 1541 Nonresidential construction; Industrial buildings & warehouses
Mng Pt: Edwin Calhoun

D-U-N-S 96-181-4295
HENSEL PHELPS-GRANITE JV
420 6th Ave, Greeley, CO 80631-2332
Tel (970) 352-6565 *Founded/Ownrshp* 2010
Sales 100.0MM *EMP* 40
SIC 1541 1542 1629 1611 Industrial buildings & warehouses; Nonresidential construction; Heavy construction; Highway & street construction
VP: Jon Ball
Pr: William G Dorey

D-U-N-S 06-288-7237 IMP/EXP
HENSLEY INDUSTRIES INC
(*Suby of* KOMATSU AMERICA CORP) ★
2108 Joe Field Rd, Dallas, TX 75229-3255
Tel (972) 241-2321 *Founded/Ownrshp* 1980
Sales 141.7MME *EMP* 500
SIC 3325 Alloy steel castings, except investment
Ch: H Shinozuka
**Pr:* Hidekichi Kuribayashi
**CFO:* John Fielder
**VP:* Ralph Huebner
VP: Laura Merry
**VP:* K Tatsumikawa

D-U-N-S 11-599-3297
HEPACO LLC
2711 Burch Dr, Charlotte, NC 28269-4476
Tel (704) 598-9787 *Founded/Ownrshp* 1984
Sales 333.9MME *EMP* 550
SIC 4959 Oil spill cleanup
Pr: Ron L Horton Jr
**Pr:* Ronald L Horton Sr
**CFO:* Ron Dwyer
**Treas:* Richard G Horton
Ex VP: Richard Lutz
Ex VP: Rhonda Pope
**VP:* Neville W Anderson
VP: Vonda Hall
**VP:* Ronald L Horton Jr
Exec: Chris Carmichael
Exec: Pat Lazaroski

D-U-N-S 61-823-1281
HEPHAESTUS HOLDINGS INC
(*Suby of* KPS CAPITAL PARTNERS LP) ★
39475 W 13 Mile Rd # 105, Novi, MI 48377-2359
Tel (248) 479-2700 *Founded/Ownrshp* 2005
Sales 154.6MME *EMP* 1,000
SIC 3462 3463 Iron & steel forgings; Nonferrous forgings
CEO: George Thanopolous

HERAEUS EELCTRO
See HERAEUS ELECTRO-NITE CO LLC

D-U-N-S 15-728-8721 IMP
HERAEUS ELECTRO-NITE CO LLC
HERAEUS EELCTRO
(*Suby of* HERAEUS PRECIOUS METALS MGT) ★
770 Township Line Rd # 300, Yardley, PA 19067-4232
Tel (215) 944-9000 *Founded/Ownrshp* 1851
Sales 98.4MME *EMP* 401
SIC 3812 3823 Search & navigation equipment; Primary elements for process flow measurement
Pr: Michael G Midash
Genl Mgr: Alex Lee
MIS Mgr: Mike Saracino
Ql Cn Mgr: Wiebke Kuharic
Ql Cn Mgr: James Ledama
Mktg Mgr: Christian Pels
Sls Mgr: Shawn Growe
Sls Mgr: Frank Meier

D-U-N-S 00-126-4563 IMP
HERAEUS INC HIC
HERAEUS PRECIOUS METALS MGT
(*Suby of* HERAEUS HOLDING GESELLSCHAFT MIT BESCHRANKTER HAFTUNG)
770 Township Line Rd, Yardley, PA 19067-4219
Tel (212) 752-2180 *Founded/Ownrshp* 1851
Sales 598.4MME *EMP* 1,981
SIC 3399 3823 3339 3469 Paste, metal; Temperature measurement instruments, industrial; Precious metals; Machine parts, stamped or pressed metal
Pr: Maike Schuh Klaeren
**Treas:* Thomas Lyons
Off Mgr: Angrina Sthely
Off Mgr: Mary Yerkes

D-U-N-S 00-244-9262 IMP/EXP
HERAEUS METALS NEW YORK LLC
(*Suby of* HERAEUS PRECIOUS METALS MGT) ★
540 Madison Ave, New York, NY 10022-3213
Tel (212) 752-2181 *Founded/Ownrshp* 1989
Sales 155.1MME *EMP* 1,800
SIC 5094 Precious metals
**VP:* Artin Janian
Genl Mgr: Gerry Dawson

HERAEUS PRECIOUS METALS MGT
See HERAEUS INC HIC

D-U-N-S 05-667-7503 IMP
HERAEUS PRECIOUS METALS NORTH AMERICA LLC
(*Suby of* HERAEUS DEUTSCHLAND GMBH & CO. KG)
15524 Carmenita Rd, Santa Fe Springs, CA 90670-5610
Tel (562) 921-7464 *Founded/Ownrshp* 2000
Sales 89.3MME *EMP* 414
SIC 3341 2899 Gold smelting & refining (secondary); Silver smelting & refining (secondary); Platinum group metals, smelting & refining (secondary); Chemical preparations; Salt
Prd Mgr: Gustavo Covarrubias
Prd Mgr: Larry Rogers

HERALD JOURNAL, THE
See HERALD NEWSPAPERS CO INC

D-U-N-S 83-443-9010
HERALD MEDIA HOLDINGS INC
70 Fargo St Ste 600, Boston, MA 02210-2131
Tel (617) 423-4545 *Founded/Ownrshp* 1994
Sales 135.7MME *EMP* 1,800
SIC 2711 Commercial printing & newspaper publishing combined
Pr: Patrick J Purcell

D-U-N-S 00-223-6636
HERALD NEWSPAPERS CO INC
HERALD JOURNAL, THE
(*Suby of* ADVANCE PUBLICATIONS, INC.)
220 S Warren St, Syracuse, NY 13202-1676
Tel (315) 470-0011 *Founded/Ownrshp* 1960
Sales 378.8MME *EMP* 3,496
SIC 2711 Newspapers, publishing & printing
Ch: Stephen A Rogers
**Pr:* Tim Kennedy
**Treas:* Donald E Newhouse
Prd Dir: Patricia McAluney
Sales Exec: Patrice David
Advt Dir: Bill Allison

D-U-N-S 05-347-4896
HERB CHAMBERS I-93 INC
CHAMBERS MOTOR CARS OF BOSTON
259 Mcgrath Hwy, Somerville, MA 02143-3417
Tel (617) 666-4100 *Founded/Ownrshp* 1992
Sales 482.7MME *EMP* 1,800
SIC 5511 Automobiles, new & used
CFO: James Duchesneau
CFO: Bruce H Spatz
Treas: Herbert G Chambers
VP: James L Xaros
Genl Mgr: Scott Birtles
Genl Mgr: Jay Gubala
CIO: Brad Gomez
MIS Dir: Brad Gomes
Sls Mgr: Pranav Gill
Sls Mgr: Shannon Smith
Sales Asso: Ted Bouchard

D-U-N-S 82-944-6108 IMP/EXP
HERBALIFE INTERNATIONAL INC
(*Suby of* HERBALIFE LTD INC) ★
990 W 190th St, Torrance, CA 90502-1014
Tel (310) 410-9600 *Founded/Ownrshp* 2010
Sales 91.5MME *EMP* 359E
SIC 5499 Spices & herbs
CEO: Michael O Johnson

D-U-N-S 87-303-5968 IMP
HERBALIFE INTERNATIONAL OF AMERICA INC
(*Suby of* HERBALIFE LTD INC) ★
800 W Olympic Blvd # 406, Los Angeles, CA 90015-1360
Tel (310) 410-9600 *Founded/Ownrshp* 1984
Sales 1.2MMME *EMP* 2,000
SIC 5122 Vitamins & minerals
CEO: Michael O Johnson
**Pr:* Des Walsh
**COO:* Rich Goudis
**CFO:* John De Simone
**Treas:* Richard Yamashita
Sr VP: Eric Zepeda
VP: Mark Schissel
IT Man: Dan Moran
IT Man: Georgio Sorani

D-U-N-S 03-702-7554 IMP/EXP
HERBALIFE LTD INC
(*Suby of* WH INTERMEDIATE HOLDINGS LTD)
800 W Olympic Blvd # 406, Los Angeles, CA 90015-1360
Tel (310) 410-9600 *Founded/Ownrshp* 2002
Sales 1.3MMME *EMP* 3,000
SIC 2833 Medicinals & botanicals
Ch Bd: Michael O Johnson
Pr: Carol Hannah
Pr: Gregory Probert
Treas: William D Lowe
Bd of Dir: Ken Diekroeger
Ex VP: Alan L Hoffman
Sr VP: Stacy Brovitz
Sr VP: Pamela Jones Harbour
Sr VP: William M Rahn
VP: Angela Arboleda
VP: Tyrone D Bland
VP: Jean Marie Cacciatore
VP: Bosco Chiu
VP: Michele Crocker
VP: Steven Dentali
VP: Sue Egstrand
VP: Robert Engelbrecht
VP: Jamie Hardenbergh
VP: Jenny Hienrich
VP: Judith Kanoskie
VP: Jack Kavulich
Board of Directors: Carole Black, Lawrence Higby, Michael J Levitt

D-U-N-S 96-452-8900
HERBERT H LEHMAN COLLEGE
AFFIRMATIVE ACTION/EEO DEPARTM
(*Suby of* AFFIRMATIVE ACTION/EEO DEPT) ★
250 Bedford Park Blvd W, Bronx, NY 10468-1527
Tel (718) 960-8261 *Founded/Ownrshp* 2010
Sales 1.3MM *EMP* 1,000
Accts Deans Archer & Co Cpa S Vall
SIC 8221 Colleges universities & professional schools
Pr: Ricardo R Fernandez
Exec: Susan Kleiman

D-U-N-S 07-268-1208
HERBERT J THOMAS MEMORIAL HOSPITAL ASSOCIATION
ST. FRANCIS HOSPITAL OF CHARLE
(*Suby of* ST FRANCIS HOSPITAL OF CHARLE) ★
4605 Maccorkle Ave Sw, Charleston, WV 25309-1311
Tel (304) 766-3600 *Founded/Ownrshp* 1946
Sales 154.6MM *EMP* 1,244
Accts Arnett Carbis Toothman Llp Ch
SIC 8062 General medical & surgical hospitals
Pr: Stephen P Dexter
COO: Daniel Lauffer
**Treas:* Charles O Covert
Ofcr: Drema Pierson
**VP:* Cynthia Barnette
Dir Rx: Mitch Vickers
Adm Dir: Melissa Layne
Dir Pat Ac: Deonna Diamond
Nurse Mgr: Kelly Hughes
IT Man: Matt Barnes
Psych: Holly Danner

D-U-N-S 00-961-6780 IMP
HERBERT MALARKEY ROOFING CO
MALARKEY ROOFING PRODUCTS
3131 N Columbia Blvd, Portland, OR 97217-7472
Tel (503) 283-1191 *Founded/Ownrshp* 1956
Sales 158.7MME *EMP* 490
SIC 2952 Roofing materials
Pr: James Fagan
**Sr VP:* Gregory B Malarkey
VP: John Cruba
CTO: Jesse Nelson
Sls Mgr: Aaron Wood

D-U-N-S 07-258-6043
HERBRUCK POULTRY RANCH INC
6425 Grand River Ave, Saranac, MI 48881-9669
Tel (616) 642-9421 *Founded/Ownrshp* 1958
Sales 85.6MME *EMP* 400
SIC 0252 Chicken eggs
Pr: Stephen Herbruck
**Ch Bd:* Marilyn Herbruck
**VP:* Gregory Herbruck
**VP:* Terry Herbruck
VP Sls: Doug Diekema

D-U-N-S 61-488-6062 IMP
▲ HERC HOLDINGS INC
27500 Riverview Ctr Blvd, Bonita Springs, FL 34134-4325
Tel (239) 301-1000 *Founded/Ownrshp* 1918
Sales 13.0MMME *EMP* 4,600
Tkr Sym HRI *Exch* NYS
SIC 7359 Equipment rental & leasing
Pr: Lawrence H Silber
**Ch Bd:* Herbert L Henkel
COO: James Bruce Dressel
CFO: Barbara L Brasier
Ofcr: Christian J Cunningham
Sr VP: Richard F Marani
VP: Nancy Merola

D-U-N-S 00-556-9314 EXP
■ HERC RENTALS INC
(*Suby of* HERC HOLDINGS INC) ★
27500 Rverview Ctr Bldg 7, Bonita Springs, FL 34134
Tel (239) 301-1001 *Founded/Ownrshp* 1965
Sales 587.2MME *EMP* 550
SIC 7359 Equipment rental & leasing
Pr: Lawrence H Silber
**COO:* Bruce Dressel
CFO: Bob Goffredo
**CFO:* Paul J Siracusa
**Ch:* Christian Cunningham
**Ch:* Herbert L Henkel
Ex VP: Brian Kennedy
VP: Carlo Cavecchi
VP: Elizabeth M Higashi
Brnch Mgr: Barry Roth
**CIO:* Richard Marani
Board of Directors: Carl T Berquist, Frank B Bilotta, George W Tamke, Henry C Wold

D-U-N-S 14-353-3532
▲ HERCULES CAPITAL INC
400 Hamilton Ave Ste 310, Palo Alto, CA 94301-1805
Tel (650) 289-3060 *Founded/Ownrshp* 2004
Sales 157.1MM *EMP* 63E
Tkr Sym HTGC *Exch* NYS
SIC 6799 Venture capital companies
Ch Bd: Manuel A Henriquez
CFO: Mark R Harris
Chf Cred: Melanie Grace
CIO: Scott Bluestein
Board of Directors: Robert P Badavas, Thomas J Fallon, Rodney A Ferguson, Doreen Woo Ho, Joseph F Hoffman, Susanne D Lyons, Allyn C Woodward Jr

D-U-N-S 14-341-4186
■ HERCULES DRILLING CO LLC
HERCULES INTERNATIONAL DRLG
(*Suby of* HERCULES OFFSHORE INC) ★
9 Greenway Plz Ste 2200, Houston, TX 77046-0931
Tel (713) 350-5100 *Founded/Ownrshp* 2004
Sales 98.4MME *EMP* 1,800
SIC 8741 Management services
**Ex VP:* Stephen M Butz
**Ex VP:* James W Noe
**Sr VP:* Terry L Carr
**Sr VP:* Troy L Carson
Sr VP: T O'Keefe
**VP:* Richard E McClaine
**VP:* Craig M Muirhead
IT Man: Robert Aultman
VP Opers: Mike Kelley

D-U-N-S 07-978-5688
HERCULES FILMS LLC
12600 Cardinal Mdw, Sugar Land, TX 77478-6195
Tel (920) 284-0796 *Founded/Ownrshp* 2014
Sales 110.0MME *EMP* 25
SIC 3081 5199 Unsupported plastics film & sheet; Packaging materials

D-U-N-S 78-866-1358
HERCULES HOLDING II LLC
1 Park Plz, Nashville, TN 37203-6527
Tel (615) 344-9551 *Founded/Ownrshp* 2013
Sales 2.0MMME *EMP* 199,000
SIC 8062 8063 8069 8093 General medical & surgical hospitals; Psychiatric hospitals; Specialty hospitals, except psychiatric; Specialty outpatient clinics
Prin: Jack Bovender

D-U-N-S 00-131-5647 IMP/EXP
■ HERCULES INC
(*Suby of* ASHLAND LLC) ★
500 Hercules Rd, Wilmington, DE 19808-1513
Tel (302) 594-5000 *Founded/Ownrshp* 1912, 2008
Sales 1.3MMME *EMP* 4,660
SIC 2869 2891 Olefins; Adhesives
CEO: Allen A Spizzo
**Treas:* Stuart C Shears
Treas: Stuart Shears
Bd of Dir: Allan Cohen
Ex VP: David Hausrath
VP: Ray Fisher
VP: Scott Gregg
VP: Dale Macdonald
VP: Karen Murphy
VP: Paul C Raymond
VP: Vincent M Romano
VP: John T Rynd
VP: Anne Schumann
Board of Directors: Allan H Cohen

HERCULES INTERNATIONAL DRLG
See HERCULES DRILLING CO LLC

D-U-N-S 60-540-2887 IMP/EXP
▲ HERCULES OFFSHORE INC
9 Greenway Plz Ste 2200, Houston, TX 77046-0931
Tel (713) 350-5100 *Founded/Ownrshp* 2004
Sales 98.4MME *EMP* 1,000E
Tkr Sym HEROQ *Exch* OTO
SIC 1381 1389 Drilling oil & gas wells; Construction, repair & dismantling services; Derrick building, repairing & dismantling
Pr: John T Rynd
**Ch Bd:* Lawrence Dickerson
Pr: Claus E Feyling
CFO: Troy L Carson
Sr VP: Todd A Pellegrin
Sr VP: Beau M Thompson
VP Bus Dev: Blair Heines
Dir Risk M: Cyndi Featherston
Dir Bus: Coleman McDonough
Genl Couns: William Gordon
Board of Directors: David Brown, Jon Cole, Eugene Davis, Gary Hanna

D-U-N-S 07-388-9842
HERD ENTERPRISES INC
BROWARD FACTORY SERVICE
3500 N 28th Ter, Hollywood, FL 33020-1104
Tel (954) 920-9774 *Founded/Ownrshp* 1973
Sales NA *EMP* 186
SIC 6351 Warranty insurance, home
Pr: Crockett Herd
**VP:* Christine Walton
Brnch Mgr: Rusty Herd
Off Mgr: Lisa Insinger
Board of Directors: Judith Herd

D-U-N-S 18-852-7162
HERE HOLDING CORP
(*Suby of* NOKIA OYJ)
425 W Randolph St, Chicago, IL 60606-1530
Tel (312) 894-7000 *Founded/Ownrshp* 1987
Sales 612.0MME *EMP* 3,364
SIC 7379 Disk & diskette conversion service
Pr: Denise Doyle
V Ch: Judson C Green
Pr: Amir Rakha
CFO: Steve Collins
**Treas:* Robert Burns
Ex VP: John K Macleod
Ex VP: Jeffrey L Mize
Ex VP: Amreesh Modi
Sr VP: Clifford I Fox
Sr VP: Winston V Guillory
VP: Lonnie Arima
VP: Mary Hardwick
VP: Jim Murphy
Dir Bus: Koon Ng

D-U-N-S 14-822-7317
HERE NORTH AMERICA LLC
(*Suby of* HERE HOLDING CORP) ★
425 W Randolph St, Chicago, IL 60606-1530
Tel (312) 894-7000 *Founded/Ownrshp* 1987
Sales 98.4MME *EMP* 850
SIC 7371 Computer software development
CEO: Sean Fernback
Pt: Marc Naddell
VP: Clifford I Fox
VP: Richard E Shuman

D-U-N-S 13-958-1276 IMP
HERFF JONES LLC
CAMERA ART
(*Suby of* VARSITY SPIRIT FASHIONS) ★
4501 W 62nd St, Indianapolis, IN 46268-2569
Tel (800) 837-4235 *Founded/Ownrshp* 1985
Sales 747.2MME *EMP* 2,050
SIC 3911 2721 2741 Rings, finger: precious metal; Periodicals; Yearbooks: publishing & printing
CEO: Jeffrey Webb
Pr: Adam Blumenfeld
Pr: David A Burkert
Pr: Kenneth G Langlois
Treas: David S Homeier
Ex VP: Barbara Zahm
Sr VP: Maggie Waples
VP: Donald J Agin
VP: Bruce Alfreds
VP: Christine L Bachmann
VP: Bernard R Crandall
VP: Bernard Crandall
VP: Rex Crandall

VP: Mark D Dillman
VP: Celeste Guernsey
VP: Larry Hill
VP: Larry T Hill
VP: K Kirk
VP: Megan McQuire
VP: Michael S Parrett
VP: Ginger D Plexico

HERITAGE APPAREL
See TSG SKI & GOLF LLC

HERITAGE AUCTION GALLERIES
See HERITAGE CAPITAL CORP

D-U-N-S 06-412-0017 IMP
HERITAGE BAG CO
NOVOLEX
501 Gateway Pkwy, Roanoke, TX 76262-3481
Tel (972) 241-5525 *Founded/Ownrshp* 1973
Sales 153.9MM^E *EMP* 650
SIC 2673

HERITAGE BANK
See HERITAGE GROUP INC

D-U-N-S 07-663-1209
■ HERITAGE BANK
(*Suby of* HERITAGE FINANCIAL CORP) ★
201 5th Ave Sw Ste 101, Olympia, WA 98501-1063
Tel (360) 943-1500 *Founded/Ownrshp* 1993
Sales NA *EMP* 242
SIC 6022 State commercial banks
Pr: Jeffrey J Deuel
CFO: Ed Cameron
Ch: Donald V Rhodes
Treas: Don Hinson
Ofcr: Susan Derenzo
Ofcr: Wendy Macgregor
Ofcr: Angela Martin
Ex VP: Thomas Henning
Ex VP: Donald J Hinson
Ex VP: Cindy M Huntley
Ex VP: Greg Patjens
Sr VP: Lynn Eerkes
Sr VP: Charles M Folsom
Sr VP: James Hastings
Sr VP: Jim Liming
Sr VP: Beth Meidinger
Sr VP: John Parry
Sr VP: Lauren Pool
Sr VP: Lisa Welander
VP: Lori Bellingar
VP: Sean Eckton

D-U-N-S 05-312-6322 IMP
HERITAGE CAPITAL CORP (TX)
HERITAGE AUCTION GALLERIES
3500 Maple Ave Ste 1700, Dallas, TX 75219-3941
Tel (214) 528-3500 *Founded/Ownrshp* 1972
Sales 143.4MM^E *EMP* 300^E
SIC 5094 Coins
Pr: Greg Rohan
**Ch Bd:* R Steve Ivy
**Pr:* Todd Imhof
**COO:* Paul Minshull
**CFO:* Michael Haynes
**Co-Ch Bd:* James L Halperin
Sr VP: Michael Moline
VP: Rob Rosen
VP: Brian Shipman
Mng Dir: Erin Patzewitsch
Genl Mgr: Kathleen Guzman

D-U-N-S 00-635-4500
HERITAGE CO INC (AR)
HERITAGE TELEMARKETING
2402 Wildwood Ave Ste 500, North Little Rock, AR 72120-5094
Tel (501) 835-9111 *Founded/Ownrshp* 1958
Sales 41.9MM^E *EMP* 1,000
SIC 7389 2721 Telemarketing services; Periodicals: publishing only
Pr: John C Braune
**Pr:* John Braune
**Pr:* Marilyn Michie Zornik
**CEO:* Sandra Franecke
**COO:* Mike Land
**CFO:* Glenda Keenihan
**Ex VP:* Chip Miller
VP Sls: Rhonda Ward

D-U-N-S 04-234-2076
▲ HERITAGE COMMERCE CORP
150 Almaden Blvd Lbby, San Jose, CA 95113-2019
Tel (408) 947-6900 *Founded/Ownrshp* 1997
Sales NA *EMP* 193^E
Accts Crowe Horwath Llp Sacramento
Tkr Sym HTBK *Exch* NGS
SIC 6022 State commercial banks
Pr: Walter T Kaczmarek
Ch Bd: Jack W Conner
COO: Keith A Wilton
CFO: Lawrence D McGovern
Chf Cred: Margaret Incandela Evp
Ofcr: Celine Benzon
Ofcr: Trisha Parnell
Ofcr: David E Porter
Ofcr: Serena Ruan
Ex VP: Michael E Benito
Ex VP: Robert P Gionfriddo
Ex VP: Teresa Powell
Ex VP: Deborah K Reuter
Sr VP: Bill Davis
Sr VP: John O Fox
Sr VP: Michael Hansen
Sr VP: Jeffrey Javier
Sr VP: Janice Miyatake
Sr VP: Jeffrey Perkins
Sr VP: Roxanne S Vane
VP: Ruth Brown

D-U-N-S 83-180-5143
HERITAGE COOPERATIVE INC
11177 Township Road 133, West Mansfield, OH 43358-9709
Tel (419) 294-2371 *Founded/Ownrshp* 2009
Sales 686.0MM^E *EMP* 270^E
SIC 5153 5261 4925 4932 Grains; Fertilizer; Liquefied petroleum gas, distribution through mains; Gas & other services combined
CEO: Eric N Parthemore
**COO:* John T Dunbar
**CFO:* Lyle Gottfried
VP: Ed Nienaber
Area Mgr: Derek Fauber
Brnch Mgr: Chuck Gentis
Brnch Mgr: John Luellen
Brnch Mgr: Mike Maginn
Off Mgr: Lisa Warne
Dir IT: Brad Kummerer
Opers Mgr: Wade Bahan

D-U-N-S 05-994-6756
HERITAGE ENTERPRISES INC
HERITAGE HEALTH
115 W Jefferson St # 401, Bloomington, IL 61701-3937
Tel (309) 828-4361 *Founded/Ownrshp* 1990
Sales 167.1MM^E *EMP* 2,500
SIC 8051 Skilled nursing care facilities
CEO: Benjamin Hart
Pr: Jenny Clyatt
COO: Cheryl Lowney
CFO: Craig Ater
Ch: Steve Wannemacher
Sec: Craig Hart
Sr VP: Connie Hoselton
Sr VP: David Underwood
Plnt Mgr: Steve Luttrell

D-U-N-S 07-837-4967
HERITAGE ENVIRONMENTAL SERVICES INC
7901 W Morris St, Indianapolis, IN 46231-3301
Tel (317) 243-0811 *Founded/Ownrshp* 1970
Sales 265.0MM^E *EMP* 590
SIC 5093 4213 8731 7389 1799 8711 Oil, waste; Contract haulers; Commercial physical research; Brokers' services; Exterior cleaning, including sandblasting; Engineering services
CEO: Kenneth S Price
**Treas:* John P Vercruysse
VP: Jim Copien
MIS Dir: Krisann Wampler
Dir IT: Bryan Bailey
Dir IT: Brad Hudson
S&M/VP: John Renkes

D-U-N-S 13-081-4528 IMP
HERITAGE ENVIRONMENTAL SERVICES LLC
SOLID OAK
(*Suby of* HERITAGE ENVIRONMENTAL SERVICES INC) ★
7901 W Morris St, Indianapolis, IN 46231-1366
Tel (317) 243-0811 *Founded/Ownrshp* 1989
Sales 265.0MM^E *EMP* 590
SIC 5093 4213 8731 7389 1799 8711 Oil, waste; Contract haulers; Commercial physical research; Brokers' services; Exterior cleaning, including sandblasting; Engineering services
VP: David Franz
Dir IT: Bryan Bailey
Telecom Mg: Jim Wampler
Opers Mgr: Tanya Cotten

D-U-N-S 82-482-8966
▲ HERITAGE FINANCIAL CORP
201 5th Ave Sw, Olympia, WA 98501-1063
Tel (360) 943-1500 *Founded/Ownrshp* 1997
Sales NA *EMP* 748^E
Accts Crowe Horwath Llp Sacramento
Tkr Sym HFWA *Exch* NGS
SIC 6036 Savings institutions, not federally chartered; Savings & loan associations, not federally chartered
Pr: Brian L Vance
**Ch Bd:* Anthony B Pickering
CFO: Donald J Hinson
**V Ch Bd:* Brian S Charneski
Chf Cred: David A Spurling
Ex VP: Jeffrey J Deuel

D-U-N-S 18-130-9381
HERITAGE FINANCIAL GROUP INC
721 N Westover Blvd, Albany, GA 31707-1401
Tel (229) 420-0000 *Founded/Ownrshp* 2010
Sales NA *EMP* 426^E
SIC 6035

D-U-N-S 18-548-1751 IMP/EXP
HERITAGE FOOD SERVICE GROUP INC
5130 Executive Blvd, Fort Wayne, IN 46808-1149
Tel (260) 482-1444 *Founded/Ownrshp* 2011
Sales 100.0MM^E *EMP* 233^E
SIC 5087 Restaurant supplies
Pr: John McDonough
**CEO:* R Bruce Dye
**Treas:* Peter Suffredini
Ex VP: Dave Morris
**VP:* Michael Denvir
CIO: Mike Sajdak
Sls&Mrk Ex: Mac Routen
Sls Mgr: Linda Maynard

D-U-N-S 07-484-2063
HERITAGE FOUNDATION
214 Msschstts Ave Ne Bsmt, Washington, DC 20002
Tel (202) 546-4400 *Founded/Ownrshp* 1973
Sales 96.9MM *EMP* 270
Accts Mcgladrey Llp Gaithersburg M
SIC 8733 Noncommercial research organizations
Pr: Edwin J Feulner
Treas: John A Vonkannon
Trst: Phillip Truluck
**VP:* Stuart M Butler
VP: Stuart Butler
VP: Becky N Dulop
**VP:* Becky Norton Dunlop
**VP:* John P Fogarty
**VP:* Michael G Franc
**VP:* Michael M Gonzalez
**VP:* Kim Holmes
VP: John Kannon
**VP:* Edwin Meese III
VP: Derrick Morgan
**VP:* Ted E Schelenski
**VP:* Michael A Spiller
**VP:* John Von Kannon
**VP:* Genevieve Wood
Exec: Lori McNicoll
Assoc Dir: Miguel Leonardo
Assoc Dir: Ryan Nichols

HERITAGE GOLF GROUP, INC.
See HERITAGE GOLF GROUP LLC

D-U-N-S 12-568-5771 IMP
HERITAGE GOLF GROUP LLC
HERITAGE GOLF GROUP, INC.
(*Suby of* GTCR GOLDER RAUNER LLC) ★
12750 High Bluff Dr # 400, San Diego, CA 92130-2230
Tel (858) 720-0694 *Founded/Ownrshp* 1999
Sales 80.6MM^E *EMP* 1,200
SIC 7992 Public golf courses
CEO: James A Husband
COO: John Hungerford
**CFO:* Angela Kasten
**Ex VP:* Gary L Dee
Exec: Denise Hungerford
Exec: Robin Irwin
Genl Mgr: Brady Boyd
Genl Mgr: Mark Knowles
Genl Mgr: Ron Parris
Genl Mgr: Randy Shannon
CIO: Rich Canale

D-U-N-S 61-630-9279
HERITAGE GROUP INC
HERITAGE BANK
1101 12th St, Aurora, NE 68818-2005
Tel (402) 694-3136 *Founded/Ownrshp* 2000
Sales NA *EMP* 149
SIC 6029 Commercial banks
VP: Kevin Henderson
Trst Ofcr: Steve Arnett
Opers Mgr: Robert Morris
Mktg Dir: Katie Leff

HERITAGE HEALTH
See HERITAGE ENTERPRISES INC

D-U-N-S 07-921-5662
HERITAGE HOME GROUP LLC
THOMASVILLE FURNITURE
1925 Eastchester Dr, High Point, NC 27265-1404
Tel (314) 863-1100 *Founded/Ownrshp* 2013
Sales 1.3MMM^E *EMP* 4,324
SIC 2511 2512 2515 Wood bedroom furniture; Kitchen & dining room furniture; Dining room furniture: wood; Desks, household: wood; Wood upholstered chairs & couches; Chairs: upholstered on wood frames; Couches, sofas & davenports: upholstered on wood frames; Recliners: upholstered on wood frames; Sofa beds (convertible sofas)
CEO: Pierre De Villemejane
CFO: Daniel Harrington
Chf Mktg O: Regan Iglesia
Sr VP: Blair Hawley
Sr VP: Paul Peters
Sr VP: Lynda Scott
Sr VP: Mark E Stephens
VP: Richard Isaak
VP: Todd Sessa
CTO: Tod Phelps

HERITAGE HOUSE
See WESLEYLIFE

D-U-N-S 80-312-2576
HERITAGE HOUSE NURSING CENTER
3103 Wisconsin Ave, Vicksburg, MS 39180-4825
Tel (601) 883-9911 *Founded/Ownrshp* 2007
Sales 318.8MM *EMP* 2^E
SIC 8049 Nurses, registered & practical
Exec: Robert Greer

D-U-N-S 07-940-4956
▲ HERITAGE INSURANCE HOLDINGS INC
2600 Mccormick Dr Ste 300, Clearwater, FL 33759-1071
Tel (727) 362-7200 *Founded/Ownrshp* 2012
Sales NA *EMP* 247^E
Tkr Sym HRTG *Exch* NYS
SIC 6331 Fire, marine & casualty insurance
Ch Bd: Bruce Lucas
**Pr:* Richard Widdicombe
COO: Ernie Garateix
CFO: Steven Martindale
Ex VP: Sharon Binnun
Ex VP: Arlene Luis
Ex VP: Mel Russell
VP: Paul Neilson
VP: Joseph Peiso
Board of Directors: Pete Apostolou, James Masiello, Nicholas Pappas, Joseph Vattamattam

D-U-N-S 07-915-2214
HERITAGE INTERESTS LLC
4300 Jetway Ct, North Highlands, CA 95660-5702
Tel (916) 481-5030 *Founded/Ownrshp* 2011
Sales 89.5MM^E *EMP* 252
SIC 1751 5031 2431 Cabinet & finish carpentry; Finish & trim carpentry; Lumber, plywood & millwork; Windows & window parts & trim, wood; Louver windows, glass, wood frame
Pr: Edward Zuckerman
**CFO:* Dennis Gardemeyer
**VP:* Charlie Gardemeyer

D-U-N-S 96-157-6139
HERITAGE MANAGEMENT GROUP INC
(*Suby of* ASPHALT MATERIALS INC) ★
2384 Glebe St, Carmel, IN 46032-7272
Tel (317) 569-0877 *Founded/Ownrshp* 1993
Sales 176.8MM^E *EMP* 241
SIC 7389 Fund raising organizations
Pr: Charles S Frick
Sec: Nancy Frick

HERITAGE MANOR NURSING HOME
See PLANTATION MANAGEMENT CO LLC

HERITAGE OF GERING
See VETTER HEALTH SERVICES INC

D-U-N-S 01-571-1591
■ HERITAGE OPERATING LP
HERITAGE PROPANE
(*Suby of* AMERIGAS PARTNERS LP) ★
754 River Rock Dr, Helena, MT 59602-0240
Tel (406) 442-9759 *Founded/Ownrshp* 2012
Sales 381.7M^E *EMP* 2,521
SIC 5984 5172 Propane gas, bottled; Petroleum products
Pr: James E Bertelsmeyer
**Pt:* Michael Krimbill
**Pr:* Robert Paul Grady
VP: C S Sheffield
Dist Mgr: Peter Dawson
Genl Mgr: Lacy Silvan

D-U-N-S 19-644-7353 IMP
HERITAGE PRODUCTS INC
(*Suby of* HIRUTA KOGYO CO., LTD.)
2000 Smith Ave, Crawfordsville, IN 47933-1055
Tel (765) 364-9002 *Founded/Ownrshp* 1988
Sales 93.7MM^E *EMP* 216
SIC 3465 Automotive stampings
Pr: Takaharu Miyake
**Treas:* Tatsunori Shigeta
**Prin:* Bryan Y Funai

HERITAGE PROPANE
See HERITAGE OPERATING LP

HERITAGE PROPANE
See TITAN PROPANE LLC

D-U-N-S 10-568-7859
HERITAGE SPORTSWEAR INC
VIRGINIA T'S
102 Reliance Dr, Hebron, OH 43025-9204
Tel (740) 928-7771 *Founded/Ownrshp* 1986
Sales 189.6MM^E *EMP* 75^E
SIC 5136 5137 Sportswear, men's & boys'; Sportswear, women's & children's
Pr: Gerald T Jurden

HERITAGE TELEMARKETING
See HERITAGE CO INC

HERITAGE VALLEY HEALTH SYSTEM
See VALLEY MEDICAL FACILITIES INC

D-U-N-S 12-168-6976
HERITAGE VALLEY HEALTH SYSTEM INC
(*Suby of* HERITAGE VALLEY HEALTH SYSTEM) ★
2580 Constitution Blvd, Beaver Falls, PA 15010-1294
Tel (724) 728-7000 *Founded/Ownrshp* 1983
Sales 5.1MM *EMP* 4,291
Accts Arnett Carbis Toothman Llp Pi
SIC 8741 8062 Management services; General medical & surgical hospitals
Pr: Norman F Mitry
**Ch Bd:* Timothy Merrill
V Ch: Laura A Vassamillet
**COO:* Rose Mary Nalan
Treas: Frank Papa
Ofcr: Rosemary Nolan
VP: Rick Beaver
**VP:* Daniel Brooks
**VP:* David Carleton
**VP:* John T Cinicola
**VP:* Bruce Edwards
VP: Anne Hitchak
VP: Laura Wagner
Dir Lab: Sue Bitcko

D-U-N-S 82-591-0420
▲ HERITAGE-CRYSTAL CLEAN INC
2175 Point Blvd Ste 375, Elgin, IL 60123-9211
Tel (847) 836-5670 *Founded/Ownrshp* 1980
Sales 350.0MM *EMP* 1,251
Tkr Sym HCCI *Exch* NGM
SIC 7699 8734 Waste cleaning services; Hazardous waste testing
Pr: Joseph Chalhoub
COO: Gregory Ray
CFO: Mark Devita
Sr VP: John Lucks
VP: Ellie Bruce
VP: Tom Hillstrom
Brnch Mgr: Jerry Rittmann
Brnch Mgr: Phil Tiberi
IT Man: Carla Sipe
Sfty Mgr: Bruce Daniels
Mktg Dir: Tom Nadolski

D-U-N-S 00-999-0065 IMP
■ HERITAGE-CRYSTAL CLEAN LLC
(*Suby of* HERITAGE-CRYSTAL CLEAN INC) ★
2175 Point Blvd Ste 375, Elgin, IL 60123-9211
Tel (847) 836-5670 *Founded/Ownrshp* 1999
Sales 337.1MM^E *EMP* 540
SIC 4953 Hazardous waste collection & disposal

D-U-N-S 00-241-7004
HERLEY INDUSTRIES INC
ULTRA ELECTRONICS HERLEY
(*Suby of* ULTRA ELECTRONICS DEFENSE INC) ★
3061 Industry Dr, Lancaster, PA 17603-4092
Tel (717) 397-2777 *Founded/Ownrshp* 1965, 2015
Sales 145.3MM^E *EMP* 1,022^E
SIC 7382 Security systems services
CEO: Rakesh Sharma
**COO:* Carlos Santiago
VP: Adam Bottenfield
Genl Mgr: Howard Eckstein
Genl Mgr: Ed Weatherwax
Ql Cn Mgr: John Decker
Mktg Dir: Joseph Napolitano
Manager: Art Caggiano
Sls Mgr: Ray Umbarger

D-U-N-S 07-117-9246
HERLEY-CTI INC (DE)
ULTRA ELECTRONICS HERLEY
(*Suby of* ULTRA ELECTRONICS HERLEY) ★
9 Whippany Rd, Whippany, NJ 07981-1540
Tel (973) 884-2580 *Founded/Ownrshp* 1973, 2004
Sales 95.5MM^E *EMP* 900
SIC 3679 Microwave components; Oscillators
Pr: Eric Demarco
**CEO:* Deanna Lund

*Treas: Laura Siegal
VP: Dottie Day
*VP: Michael Fink
VP: Charles L Pourciau Jr
Div Mgr: Terence Ede
Genl Mgr: Edward Weatherwax
MIS Dir: Alan Kobb
QA Dir: Alexander Art
QC Dir: Arthur Alexander

D-U-N-S 00-893-7765
HERMAN GOLDNER CO INC
GOLDNER, HERMAN COMPANY
7777 Brewster Ave, Philadelphia, PA 19153-3298
Tel (215) 365-5400 Founded/Ownrshp 1887
Sales 103.6MM EMP 275
Accts Kreischer Miller Horsham Pen
SIC 1711 7699 Mechanical contractor; Plumbing contractors; Warm air heating & air conditioning contractor; Boiler & heating repair services
Ch Bd: Gerard C Goldner
*Pr: Stephen Williams
*CEO: Herman W Goldner
*CFO: John D Goldner
*Ex VP: Thomas H Graziano
*VP: Len Ditullio
VP: Keith Gottlieb
*VP: Steve Leonardo
CIO: Kevin Sherin
DP Exec: Miriam Demattei
Sales Exec: Rob Scanlan

D-U-N-S 00-601-2801 IMP/EXP
▲ **HERMAN MILLER INC** (MI)
855 E Main Ave, Zeeland, MI 49464-1372
Tel (616) 654-3000 Founded/Ownrshp 1905
Sales 2.2MMM EMP 7,510^E
Tkr Sym MLHR Exch NGS
SIC 2521 2522 2541 2542 2531 Wood office furniture; Office furniture, except wood; Wood partitions & fixtures; Partitions & fixtures, except wood; Public building & related furniture
Pr: Brian C Walker
*Ch Bd: Michael A Volkema
Pr: Steven C Gane
Pr: Louise McDonald
Pr: John McPhee
CEO: John Edelman
CFO: Jeffrey M Stutz
Treas: Kevin Veltman
Ex VP: John G Edelman
Ex VP: Andrew J Lock
Ex VP: John J McPhee
Sr VP: Malisa Bryant
Sr VP: H Timothy Lopez
Sr VP: Michael F Ramirez
VP: Jeffrey L Kurburski
Board of Directors: David O Ulrich, Mary Vermeer Andringa, David A Brandon, Brenda Freeman, Douglas D French, J Barry Griswell, John R Hoke III, Lisa A Kro, Heidi Manheimer, Dorothy A Terrell

D-U-N-S 04-440-5686
HERMAN WEISSKER INC (CA)
(Suby of MERUELO ENTERPRISES INC) ★
1645 Brown Ave, Riverside, CA 92509-1859
Tel (951) 826-8800 Founded/Ownrshp 1959, 1999
Sales 129.8MM^E EMP 500^E
SIC 1623 8711 1731 Water, sewer & utility lines; Engineering services; Electrical work
CEO: Luis Alberto Armona
*Pr: Ron Politte
*CFO: Marty Mayeda
Off Mgr: Kieth Nelson

D-U-N-S 04-350-1196 IMP/EXP
HERMANN COMPANIES INC (MO)
7701 Forsyth Blvd # 1000, Saint Louis, MO 63105-1818
Tel (314) 863-9200 Founded/Ownrshp 1956
Sales 175.5MM^E EMP 600
SIC 3086 Packaging & shipping materials, foamed plastic
Ch Bd: Robert R Hermann
*Pr: Dolores M Frank

D-U-N-S 02-747-6506
HERMANSON CO LLP (WA)
1221 2nd Ave N, Kent, WA 98032-2945
Tel (206) 575-9700 Founded/Ownrshp 1979
Sales 103.6MM EMP 270
Accts Berntson Porter & Company Pll
SIC 1711 Heating & air conditioning contractors; Ventilation & duct work contractor
Pr: Rick Hermanson
Pt: James Macdonald
COO: Dan Brock
Genl Mgr: Gerald D Hermanson
Sfty Dirs: Brian Sorensen

D-U-N-S 60-645-8479 IMP
HERMISTON FOODS INC
(Suby of NORPAC FOODS INC) ★
2250 S Highway 395, Hermiston, OR 97838-9466
Tel (541) 567-8448 Founded/Ownrshp 1988
Sales 228.8MM^E EMP 4,000
SIC 2037 Frozen fruits & vegetables; Vegetables, quick frozen & cold pack, excl. potato products; Potato products, quick frozen & cold pack
Pr: Erik Jacobson
*VP: George Smith
Ql Cn Mgr: Manuel Aviles

HERMITAGE AT CEDAR FIELD
See VIRGINIA UNITED METHODIST HOMES INC

HERNANDO HEALTHCARE
See HERNANDO HMA INC

D-U-N-S 02-562-4321
■ **HERNANDO HEALTHCARE INC** (FL)
BROOKSVILLE REGIONAL HOSPITAL
(Suby of HMA) ★
17240 Cortez Blvd, Brooksville, FL 34601-8921
Tel (352) 796-5111 Founded/Ownrshp 1982
Sales 145.5MM EMP 131
SIC 8062 General medical & surgical hospitals
CEO: Kathy Burke
Chf OB: Imad Jandali
Chf Rad: Lana Bellon
Dir Recs: Linda Sanchez
Dir Inf Cn: Debbie Sonnier
Dir Lab: Asghar Shaikh
Dir Rad: Sheryl Clemente
Dir Rad: Amy Moore
CIO: Lee Burch
Ansthlgy: Christopher J Lombardi

D-U-N-S 03-645-0521
■ **HERNANDO HMA INC**
HERNANDO HEALTHCARE
(Suby of HMA) ★
17240 Cortez Blvd, Brooksville, FL 34601-8921
Tel (352) 796-5111 Founded/Ownrshp 2005
Sales 181.1MM EMP 600
SIC 8062 General medical & surgical hospitals
CEO: Ken Wicker
*COO: Bayode Omosaiye
*CFO: Matthew Seagroves
*Ex Dir: Thomas D Barb
Doctor: Mowaffak Atfeh
Doctor: Adel Eldin
Doctor: Rajiva Goyal
Doctor: Jared Salinsky
Doctor: Imad Tarabishy

D-U-N-S 08-009-7712
■ **HERNDON AEROSPACE & DEFENSE LLC**
(Suby of KLX INC) ★
3801 Lloyd King Dr, O Fallon, MO 63368-2224
Tel (314) 739-7400 Founded/Ownrshp 2016
Sales 122.1MM^E EMP 145^E
SIC 5088 Aircraft & parts
Mng Dir: Scott Herndon
*CFO: Gerry Modglin
*Genl Mgr: Daniel Rodriguez

D-U-N-S 13-434-5169 IMP/EXP
■ **HERNDON PRODUCTS LLC**
(Suby of HERNDON AEROSPACE & DEFENSE LLC) ★
3801 Lloyd King Dr, O Fallon, MO 63368-2224
Tel (314) 739-7400 Founded/Ownrshp 2015
Sales 104.0MM EMP 120
SIC 5088 Aircraft & parts
Pr: Scott Herndon
*COO: Daniel Rodrigues
*CFO: Gerard Modglin
Prgrm Mgr: Paul Rice
Genl Mgr: Michelle Schilly
Genl Mgr: Wayne Swaim
Pgrm Dir: Peter Harris

D-U-N-S 16-046-4017
HERON LAKE BIOENERGY LLC
(Suby of PROJECT VIKING LLC) ★
91246 390th Ave, Heron Lake, MN 56137-3175
Tel (507) 793-0077 Founded/Ownrshp 2013
Sales 115.6MM EMP 37
SIC 1321 2869 Ethane (natural) production; Ethyl alcohol, ethanol
CEO: Steve Christensen
*Ch Bd: Paul Enstad
CFO: Stacie Schuler
*V Ch Bd: Rodney R Wilkison
VP: Doug Schmitz
Genl Mgr: Bob Ferguson
Advt Mgr: Kim Henrickson
Board of Directors: Leslie Bergquist, Dean Buesing, Robert Ferguson, Kenton Johnson, Michael Kunerth, Milton McKeown, Doug Schmitz, Marty Seifert, David Woestehoff

D-U-N-S 00-237-8784 IMP/EXP
HERR FOODS INC (PA)
20 Herr Dr, Nottingham, PA 19362-9788
Tel (610) 932-9330 Founded/Ownrshp 1946
Sales 496.1MM^E EMP 1,500
SIC 2096 Potato chips & similar snacks; Potato chips & other potato-based snacks
Ch Bd: James M Herr
*Pr: Edwin Herr
*CFO: Gerry Kluis
VP: Randy Longo
VP: Jim Rock
Brnch Mgr: Jeff Dietz
Brnch Mgr: Paul Jova
Brnch Mgr: Patrick Sifer
Genl Mgr: Joy Wolfe
Opers Mgr: Jim Abshire
Sales Exec: Scott Carmean

D-U-N-S 79-150-5253
HERRERA PETROLEUM CORP
5209 Nw 74th Ave Ste 279, Miami, FL 33166-4800
Tel (786) 267-5467 Founded/Ownrshp 2006
Sales 71.8MM^E EMP 3,000
SIC 5983 Fuel oil dealers
Pr: Raul Herrera
*CEO: Rafael Herrera
*Ofcr: Edwin Cardona
*VP: Victor Nasim

D-U-N-S 02-919-8025 IMP
HERRERO BUILDERS INC
2100 Oakdale Ave, San Francisco, CA 94124-1516
Tel (415) 824-7675 Founded/Ownrshp 1955
Sales 84.0MM^E EMP 130
SIC 1541 Industrial buildings, new construction
Ch Bd: Mark D Herrero
*Pr: Rick Herrero
CFO: James Totoritis
Ofcr: Stephanie Roberson
Exec: Saptarshi Desai
Exec: Sonia Menjivar
Opers Mgr: Kathleen Carroll
Opers Mgr: Robert Purcell

D-U-N-S 00-913-7126 IMP
HERRICK CORP
STOCKTON STEEL DIVISION
3003 E Hammer Ln, Stockton, CA 95212-2801
Tel (209) 956-4751 Founded/Ownrshp 1988
Sales 302.1MM^E EMP 900
SIC 3441 Fabricated structural metal
CEO: David H Dornsife
*Pr: Doug Griffin
*CFO: Peter Abila
IT Man: Patrick Lynch
Snr PM: Lee Becker

HERRICKS UFSD
See HERRICKS UNION FREE SCHOOL DISTRICT

D-U-N-S 03-815-9836
HERRICKS UNION FREE SCHOOL DISTRICT
HERRICKS UFSD
999 Herricks Rd Ste B, New Hyde Park, NY 11040-1353
Tel (516) 305-8903 Founded/Ownrshp 1898
Sales 112.0MM EMP 373
SIC 8211 Public elementary & secondary schools
Genl Mgr: Sufia Yasmin
Schl Brd P: Nancy Feinstein

D-U-N-S 02-970-0283 IMP
HERSCHEND ENTERTAINMENT CO LLC
SILVER DOLLAR CITY
5445 Triangle Pkwy # 200, Norcross, GA 30092-2584
Tel (770) 441-1940 Founded/Ownrshp 1950
Sales 191.4MM^E EMP 2,500
Accts Bkd Llp Springfield Mo
SIC 7999 5947 5812 Tourist attraction, commercial; Cave operation; Gift shop; Novelties; Eating places
Prin: Andrew Wexler
VP: Ned Stancliff
IT Man: Brandon Kenney
Sys Mgr: Jimmy Dean

D-U-N-S 07-143-7560
HERSCHER SCHOOL DISTRICT 2
501 N Main St, Herscher, IL 60941-9595
Tel (815) 426-2162 Founded/Ownrshp 1949
Sales 37.5MM^E EMP 1,020
SIC 8211 Public elementary school; Public junior high school; Public senior high school; School board
Pr: Marcie Kolberg
Genl Mgr: Heather Crane

D-U-N-S 09-225-8099
HERSHA HOSPITALITY MANAGEMENT LP
44 Hersha Dr Fl 1, Harrisburg, PA 17102-2241
Tel (717) 412-5500 Founded/Ownrshp 1998
Sales 177.4MM^E EMP 1,681
SIC 7011 Hotels & motels
Pt: Jay H Shah
Pt: David Desfor
Pt: Kanti D Patel
Pt: Thomas D Reese
Pt: Hasu Shah
COO: Michael Murray
COO: Neil H Shah
CFO: Ashish Parikh
Ex VP: Gregory Ade
Ex VP: Sal Shahriar
Sr VP: Simon J Little
VP: Foiz Ahmed
VP: Stephanie Esposito
VP: Robert C Hazard III
VP: Joann Weber

D-U-N-S 02-382-8945
HERSHA HOSPITALITY TRUST
44 Hersha Dr, Harrisburg, PA 17102-2241
Tel (717) 236-4400 Founded/Ownrshp 1998
Sales 470.3MM EMP 48^E
Accts Kpmg Llp Philadelphia Pennsy
SIC 6798 Real estate investment trusts
CEO: Jay H Shah
*Ch Bd: Hasu P Shah
Pr: Neil H Shah
COO: Michael Murray
CFO: Ashish R Paikh
CFO: Ashish R Parikh
CFO: Ashish Parikh
Treas: David L Desfor
Treas: David Desfor
Ex VP: Greg Ade
Sr VP: Dani Elhachem
VP: Keith Black
VP: Sandra Cardona
VP: Jay Linsey
VP: Charles Paloux
VP: Bennett Thomas
VP: William J Walsh
VP: Lily Yu
Exec: Iliana Alvarez
Board of Directors: Thomas J Hutchison III, Donald J Landry, Michael A Leven, Dianna F Morgan, John M Sabin

D-U-N-S 00-300-2052 IMP/EXP
▲ **HERSHEY CO**
100 Crystal A Dr, Hershey, PA 17033-9524
Tel (717) 534-4200 Founded/Ownrshp 1894
Sales 7.3MMM EMP 20,713
Tkr Sym HSY Exch NYS
SIC 2066 2064 2099 Chocolate & cocoa products; Chocolate bars, solid; Chocolate candy, solid; Chocolate coatings & syrup; Candy & other confectionery products; Candy bars, including chocolate covered bars; Chocolate candy, except solid chocolate; Licorice candy; Baking powder & soda, yeast & other leavening agents; Dessert mixes & fillings
Pr: John P Bilbrey
Pr: Michele G Buck
*COO: Michele Buck
*CFO: Patricia A Little
*Chf Mktg O: Peter Horst
Ofcr: Kevin R Walling
*Sr VP: Terence O'Day
Sr VP: Terence L O'Day
*Sr VP: William Papa
*Sr VP: Leslie M Turner
Sr VP: Leslie Turner
*Sr VP: Kevin Walling
*Sr VP: D Michael Wege
Sr VP: Waheed Zaman
VP: Joe Beck
VP: David Tacka
VP: Mike Wege

D-U-N-S 00-301-0022
HERSHEY CREAMERY CO
HERSHEY'S ICE CREAM
301 S Cameron St, Harrisburg, PA 17101-2815
Tel (717) 238-8134 Founded/Ownrshp 1894, 1927
Sales 163.2MM^E EMP 450
SIC 2024 Ice cream & ice milk; Sherbets, dairy based
Pr: George H Holder
*Treas: Thomas Holder
VP: Joe Gostomski
*VP: Walter Holder
VP: Neil Patrick
*VP: Thomas J Ryan III
Brnch Mgr: Brian Howard
Brnch Mgr: David Tracy
IT Man: Carrie Williams
Sls&Mrk Ex: Mark Scharlow

D-U-N-S 00-791-1571
HERSHEY ENTERTAINMENT & RESORTS CO (PA)
HERSHEY LODGE & CONVENTION CTR
27 W Chocolate Ave # 100, Hershey, PA 17033-1672
Tel (717) 534-3131 Founded/Ownrshp 1893, 1927
Sales 476.8MM^E EMP 7,100
SIC 7011 7996 Hotels; Amusement parks
Pr: William R Simpson
*Treas: Wendy L McClintock
*VP: Nate Douty
*VP: David P Lavery
VP: John Lawn
*VP: Franklin A Miles Jr
*VP: James Miles
*VP: Kimberly Schaller
*VP: William F Simpson Jr
Exec: Ken Gladysz
Exec: Steven Turchin

HERSHEY LODGE & CONVENTION CTR
See HERSHEY ENTERTAINMENT & RESORTS CO

HERSHEY'S ICE CREAM
See HERSHEY CREAMERY CO

HERTZ
See OVERLAND WEST INC

D-U-N-S 00-698-5196 EXP
■ **HERTZ CORP**
(Suby of HERTZ INVESTORS INC) ★
8501 Williams Rd, Estero, FL 33928-3325
Tel (239) 301-7000 Founded/Ownrshp 1918, 1967
Sales 10.5MMM EMP 33,000
Accts Pricewaterhousecoopers Llp Mi
SIC 7514 7515 7513 7359 5521 6794 Rent-a-car service; Passenger car leasing; Truck rental, without drivers; Truck leasing, without drivers; Equipment rental & leasing; Automobiles, used cars only; Trucks, tractors & trailers: used; Franchises, selling or licensing
Pr: John P Tague
CFO: Elyse B Douglas
CFO: Thomas C Kennedy
Ofcr: Heather Hartman
Ofcr: Annette Mailhiot
Ofcr: Ryan McNichol
Ofcr: Priscilla Wood
Ex VP: Tyler A Best
Ex VP: John A Thomas
Sr VP: Robert J Bailey
Sr VP: Robin C Kramer
Sr VP: Dave Myrick
Sr VP: Harold E Rolfe
Sr VP: Donald F Steele
VP: Tony Bedalov
VP: Frank E Camacho
Exec: Jeffrey T Foland
Exec: Thomas Sabatino
Board of Directors: Carl T Berquist, Michael J Durham, Carolyn Everson, Vincent J Intrieri, Henry R Keizer, Michael F Koehler, Linda Fayne Levinson, Samuel Merksamer, Daniel A Ninivaggi

D-U-N-S 08-023-4851
HERTZ GLOBAL HOLDINGS INC
8501 Williams Rd Fl 3, Estero, FL 33928-3325
Tel (239) 301-7000 Founded/Ownrshp 2015
Sales 100.9M^E EMP 4,600
Tkr Sym HTZ Exch NYS
SIC 7515 7514 Passenger car leasing; Passenger car rental
Pr: Lawrence H Silber
*Ch Bd: Herbert L Henkel
COO: James Bruce Dressel
CFO: Barbara L Brasier
CFO: Thomas C Kennedy
Ofcr: Christian J Cunningham
Ex VP: Tyler A Best
Ex VP: Matthew Jauchius
Ex VP: Alexandria P Marren
Ex VP: Robert J Stuart
Ex VP: Eliana Zem
Sr VP: Richard F Marani
VP: Nancy Merola
Board of Directors: James H Browning, Patrick D Campbell, Michael A Kelly, Courtney Mather, Stephen A Mongillo, Louis J Pastor, Mary Pat Salomone

D-U-N-S 00-698-5188 IMP
■ **HERTZ INTERNATIONAL LTD**
(Suby of HERTZ CORP) ★
225 Brae Blvd, Park Ridge, NJ 07656-1870
Tel (201) 307-2000 Founded/Ownrshp 1957
Sales 422.7MM^E EMP 5,470
SIC 7514 7515 7513 Rent-a-car service; Passenger car leasing; Truck rental, without drivers; Truck leasing, without drivers
CEO: John Pague
Pr: Brian Kennedy
*Pr: Craig Kroch
*Treas: Robert Rillings
Ex VP: Paul Siracusa
VP: Linda Pitzenberger
*VP: William Sider
VP: Leslie Westover
Site Mgr: Allen Grensteiner
Manager: Lamar Berry
Sls Mgr: Aaron Frame

D-U-N-S 78-319-3639
■ **HERTZ INVESTORS INC**
(Suby of HERC HOLDINGS INC) ★
225 Brae Blvd, Park Ridge, NJ 07656-1870
Tel (201) 307-2000 Founded/Ownrshp 2005
Sales 10.5MMM^E EMP 4,000

SIC 7514 7515 7513 7359 5521 6794 Rent-a-car service; Passenger car leasing; Truck rental, without drivers; Truck leasing, without drivers; Equipment rental & leasing; Automobiles, used cars only; Trucks, tractors & trailers: used; Franchises, selling or licensing
Prin: George Tamke
VP: Simon Ellis

D-U-N-S 17-602-2929
■ HERTZ LOCAL EDITION CORP
(*Suby of* HERTZ CORP) ★
225 Brae Blvd, Park Ridge, NJ 07656-1870
Tel (201) 307-2000 *Founded/Ownrshp* 1980
Sales 162.7MM^E *EMP* 2,735^E
SIC 7514 Rent-a-car service
Prin: Kherri Gomez

D-U-N-S 78-157-7028 IMP
■ HERTZ TECHNOLOGIES INC
WARR ACRES
(*Suby of* HERTZ CORP) ★
5601 Nw Expressway, Warr Acres, OK 73132-5232
Tel (405) 280-4983 *Founded/Ownrshp* 1991
Sales 95.7MM^E *EMP* 1,009
SIC 7514 Rent-a-car service
Pr: Gary Orrell
Treas: Robert H Rillings
Ex VP: Mark Holzwart
VP: Robert Moore
IT Man: Troy Withey
Opers Mgr: Lance Highfill

D-U-N-S 00-522-8721 IMP
HERTZBERG-NEW METHOD INC (IL)
PERMA-BOUND
617 E Vandalia Rd, South Jacksonville, IL 62650-3544
Tel (217) 243-5451 *Founded/Ownrshp* 1954
Sales 285.7MM^E *EMP* 600
SIC 5192 Books
Pr: James Q Orr
**Sec:* Todd Young
Dir Rx: Victor Ramirez
Dept Mgr: Steven Henson
Mktg Dir: Brett Hoffman
Manager: Kit Carson
Manager: Brian Smith
Sls Mgr: Dan Willis
Sales Asso: Kathy Pratt

D-U-N-S 04-674-1187 IMP/EXP
HERZOG CONTRACTING CORP
600 S Riverside Rd, Saint Joseph, MO 64507-9775
Tel (816) 233-9001 *Founded/Ownrshp* 1969
Sales 487.9MM^E *EMP* 950
SIC 1629 1611 4953

HESCO
See HARTFORD EQUITY SALES CO INC

D-U-N-S 60-363-1326 IMP
▲ HESKA CORP
3760 Rocky Mountain Ave, Loveland, CO 80538-7084
Tel (970) 493-7272 *Founded/Ownrshp* 1988
Sales 104.6MM *EMP* 310^E
Tkr Sym HSKA *Exch* NAS
SIC 2834 5122 Veterinary pharmaceutical preparations; Animal medicines
Pr: Kevin S Wilson
**Ch Bd:* Sharon L Riley
COO: Jason A Napolitano
CFO: John McMahon
Ex VP: Steven M Eyl
Ex VP: Nancy Wisnewski
Board of Directors: G Irwin Gordon, David E Sveen, Bonnie J Trowbridge, Carol A Wrenn

D-U-N-S 08-444-6202
HESPERIA UNIFIED SCHOOL DISTRICT
15576 Main St, Hesperia, CA 92345-3482
Tel (760) 244-4411 *Founded/Ownrshp* 1880
Sales 137.6MM^E *EMP* 2,500
Accts Nigro Nigro & White
SIC 8211 Public combined elementary & secondary school
VP: Cody Gregg
VP: Ella Rogers
Dir Sec: Debra Quinones
Genl Mgr: Kortney Grimm
Genl Mgr: Steven Rollins
Dir IT: Lori Mente
Dir IT: Michael Tepner
IT Man: Patty Torres
Sys Mgr: Harvey Miller
Pr Dir: David Olney
Teacher Pr: Larry Porras

D-U-N-S 00-697-9785
▲ HESS CORP
1185 Ave Of The Americas, New York, NY 10036-2601
Tel (212) 997-8500 *Founded/Ownrshp* 1920
Sales 6.5MMM *EMP* 2,770
Tkr Sym HES *Exch* NYS
SIC 1311 2911 5171 5541 4911 Crude petroleum production; Natural gas production; Petroleum refining; Petroleum bulk stations; Petroleum terminals; Filling stations, gasoline; Transmission, electric power
CEO: John B Hess
**Ch Bd:* James Quigley
Pr: Gerald A Jamin
COO: Gregory P Hill
CFO: John P Rielly
Treas: Robert M Biglin
Ex VP: Curtis Carpenter
Ex VP: Eloise Castillo
Ex VP: David Chaimengyew
Ex VP: Abhay Shah
Sr VP: Christopher Baldwin
Sr VP: Gary Boubel
Sr VP: William Drennen
Sr VP: John A Gartman
Sr VP: Zhanna Golodryga
Sr VP: Timothy B Goodell
Sr VP: Barbara Lowery-Yilmaz
Sr VP: Lawrence H Ornstein
Sr VP: John J Scelfo
Sr VP: John V Simon
Sr VP: Brian D Truelove

Board of Directors: Rodney F Chase, Terrence J Checki, Edith E Holiday, David McManus, Kevin O Meyers, John H Mullin III, Frederic G Reynolds, William G Schrader

D-U-N-S 07-885-2704
■ HESS OIL VIRGIN ISLAND CORP
(*Suby of* HESS CORP) ★
1185 Ave Of The Amer 39, New York, NY 10036-2603
Tel (212) 997-8500 *Founded/Ownrshp* 1973
Sales 228.8MM^E *EMP* 3,000
SIC 2911 Petroleum refining
Ch Bd: John Hess
Top Exec: Justin Mayer
Ex VP: Eloise Castillo
Ex VP: Doris Moore
Sr VP: Howard Paver
VP: William Hanna
VP: Stuart Lake
VP: Richard Lawlor
VP: Bob Spinieo
Comm Dir: Steve Hess
Genl Mgr: Carol Beal

D-U-N-S 07-870-2574 IMP
■ HESS TRADING CORP
(*Suby of* HESS CORP) ★
1185 Ave Of The Americas, New York, NY 10036-2601
Tel (212) 997-8500 *Founded/Ownrshp* 2012, 2016
Sales 177.8MM^E *EMP* 154^E
SIC 5199 Art goods & supplies
Prin: Steven A Villas
**Pr:* Gregory P Hill
**CEO:* John B Hess
**Sr VP:* Gary Boubel
**Sr VP:* Zhanna Golodryga
**Sr VP:* Richard Lynch

HETCO
See HARTREE PARTNERS LP

HEWITT USA
See G T SALES & MANUFACTURING INC

HEWLETT FOUNDATION
See HEWLETT WILLIAM AND FLORA FOUNDATION (INC)

HEWLETT PACKARD
See INDIGO AMERICA INC

D-U-N-S 07-874-3996
HEWLETT PACKARD
3000 Hanover St, Palo Alto, CA 94304-1185
Tel (650) 857-1501 *Founded/Ownrshp* 2013
Sales 98.4MM^E *EMP* 1,835^E
SIC 7371

D-U-N-S 07-983-4910
▲ HEWLETT PACKARD ENTERPRISE CO
3000 Hanover St, Palo Alto, CA 94304-1185
Tel (650) 857-5817 *Founded/Ownrshp* 2015
Sales 50.1MMM *EMP* 241,100^E
Tkr Sym HPE *Exch* NYS
SIC 7372 7379 3572 Prepackaged software; Computer related maintenance services; Computer storage devices
Ch Bd: Patricia F Russo
Pr: Margaret C Whitman
COO: Christopher P Hsu
CFO: Timothy C Stonesifer
Treas: Kirt P Karros
Chf Mktg O: Henry Gomez
Ex VP: Rick Hanson
Ex VP: Alan May
Ex VP: Michael G Nefkens
Ex VP: Antonio Neri
Ex VP: John F Schultz
Ex VP: Robert Youngjohns
Sr VP: Jeff T Ricci
VP: Matteo Del Vecchio
Board of Directors: Gary M Reiner, Dan Ammann, Mary Agnes Wilderotter, Marc L Andreessen, Michael J Angelakis, Leslie A Brun, Pamela L Carter, Klaus Kleinfeld, Raymond J Lane, Ann M Livermore, Raymond E Ozzie

HEWLETT PACKARD ENTERPRISE DEV
See HEWLETT-PACKARD ENTERPRISES LLC

D-U-N-S 05-133-9257
HEWLETT WILLIAM AND FLORA FOUNDATION (INC)
HEWLETT FOUNDATION
2121 Sand Hill Rd, Menlo Park, CA 94025-6909
Tel (650) 234-4500 *Founded/Ownrshp* 1966
Sales 624.6MM *EMP* 60
SIC 8699 Charitable organization
Pr: Paul Brest
CFO: Charlene Cooper
Treas: William F Nichols
Treas: Luisa Smith
Ofcr: Jean Bordewich
Ofcr: Christine Clark
Ofcr: Sabrina Coleman
Ofcr: Lori Grange
Ofcr: Reuben Roqueni
Ofcr: Pat Scheid
Ofcr: Sarah Staats
Ofcr: Eli Sugarman

D-U-N-S 83-127-6311 IMP
■ HEWLETT-PACKARD ENTERPRISES LLC
HEWLETT PACKARD ENTERPRISE DEV
(*Suby of* HP INC) ★
3000 Hanover St, Palo Alto, CA 94304-1185
Tel (650) 857-1501 *Founded/Ownrshp* 2012
Sales 770.6MM^E *EMP* 977^E
SIC 3571 Electronic computers
Ch: Meg Whitman
Sftwr Eng: Abraham Lui

D-U-N-S 09-075-4292
■ HEWLETT-PACKARD FINANCIAL SERVICES CO
(*Suby of* HEWLETT PACKARD ENTERPRISE CO) ★
200 Connell Dr Ste 5000, Berkeley Heights, NJ 07922-2816
Tel (908) 288-9315 *Founded/Ownrshp* 2015

Sales NA *EMP* 1,800
SIC 6159 7389 Equipment & vehicle finance leasing companies; Financial services
CEO: Irving H Hoffman
VP: G McCarthy
**CTO:* Gary Thome
IT Man: Lorraine Miller

D-U-N-S 02-614-6535 IMP
HEXAGON METROLOGY INC
(*Suby of* HEXAGON AB)
250 Circuit Dr, North Kingstown, RI 02852-7441
Tel (401) 886-2000 *Founded/Ownrshp* 2001
Sales 477.6MM^E *EMP* 1,900
SIC 3823 3545 Industrial instrmnts msrmnt display/control process variable; Precision measuring tools
Pr: Norbert Hanke
V Ch: Robert Chisholm
**Pr:* Angus Taylor
CFO: Pamela Beaulieu
**CFO:* Mark Delaney
VP: Mark Dellaney
VP: Bernard Haeberlin
VP: Duncan Redgewell
Snr Sftwr: Ryan Gundry
Snr Sftwr: Robert Jurca
Snr Sftwr: Michael Monsen

D-U-N-S 82-836-9678
HEXAWARE TECHNOLOGIES INC
CALIBER POINT
(*Suby of* HEXAWARE TECHNOLOGIES LIMITED)
101 Wood Ave S Ste 600, Iselin, NJ 08830-2767
Tel (609) 409-6950 *Founded/Ownrshp* 2001
Sales 328.1MM *EMP* 700
Accts Deloitte Haskins & Sells Llp
SIC 7379 Computer related consulting services
CEO: Ramakarthikeyan Srikrishna
COO: Manab Sen
Bd of Dir: Mark F Dzialga
Ofcr: Deependra Chumble
Sr VP: Yogendra Shah
**VP:* Kalpesh Bhatt
VP: Dhruv Patel
VP: Michael Rennell
VP: Narendra Sharma
Exec: Hanumant Karangutkar
Exec: Pradeep Katkade
Exec: Tamanna Kulal
Exec: Leena Likhite
Exec: Anand Parulekar
Exec: Meena Pasupathy
Exec: Santosh Peddaram
Exec: Priyanka Tripathi
Exec: Irfan Zia
Board of Directors: P R Chandrasekar, Ravi Vaidyanathan

D-U-N-S 00-911-8563 EXP
▲ HEXCEL CORP
281 Tresser Blvd Ste 1503, Stamford, CT 06901-3261
Tel (203) 969-0666 *Founded/Ownrshp* 1946
Sales 1.8MMM *EMP* 5,897
Tkr Sym HXL *Exch* NYS
SIC 2821 3728 3089 3624 2891 3489 Plastics materials & resins; Epoxy resins; Polyurethane resins; Elastomers, nonvulcanizable (plastics); Aircraft parts & equipment; Fiberglass doors; Fibers, carbon & graphite; Adhesives; Epoxy adhesives; Sealants; Honeycombed metal
Ch Bd: Nick L Stanage
CFO: Wayne C Pensky
Sr VP: Robert G Hennemuth
Sr VP: Ira J Krakower
VP: John Gildenstern
VP: Kimberly Hendricks
VP Bus Dev: Timothy Swords
CTO: Nanci Pickrell
DP Exec: Kevin Martin
QA Dir: John Owens
Ql Cn Mgr: Ana Aktoprak

D-U-N-S 08-031-7420
■ HEXION HOLDINGS LLC
(*Suby of* APOLLO GLOBAL MANAGEMENT LLC) ★
180 E Broad St, Columbus, OH 43215-3707
Tel (614) 225-4000 *Founded/Ownrshp* 2010
Sales 4.1MMM *EMP* 4,131^E
SIC 6719 Investment holding companies, except banks
Ch Bd: Craig O Morrison
**CFO:* George Knight
**Ex VP:* Joseph P Bevilaqua
**Ex VP:* Dale N Plante

D-U-N-S 00-133-8797
■ HEXION INC
(*Suby of* HEXION LLC) ★
180 E Broad St Fl 26, Columbus, OH 43215-3707
Tel (614) 225-4000 *Founded/Ownrshp* 1899
Sales 4.1MMM *EMP* 5,100^E
SIC 2821 Thermosetting materials; Acrylic resins; Epoxy resins; Melamine resins, melamine-formaldehyde
Ch Bd: Craig O Morrison
Pr: Joseph P Bevilaqua
Pr: Dale N Plante
CFO: George F Knight
Ex VP: Marcello Boldrini
Ex VP: Nathan E Fisher
Ex VP: Anthony B Greene
Ex VP: Douglas A Johns
Ex VP: Karen E Koster
Ex VP: Kevin W McGuire
Ex VP: Judith A Sonnett
VP: Jim Cowie
VP: Karen Schuttenberg
VP: Timothy Wise
Board of Directors: William H Joyce, Scott M Kleinman, Geoffrey A Manna, Robert Kalsow-Ramos, Jonathan D Rich, David B Sambur, Marvin O Schlanger

D-U-N-S 16-649-5924 IMP/EXP
■ HEXION LLC
(*Suby of* HEXION HOLDINGS LLC) ★
180 E Broad St Fl 26, Columbus, OH 43215-3707
Tel (614) 225-4000 *Founded/Ownrshp* 2010

Sales 4.1MMM^E *EMP* 5,100
SIC 2821 2899 Thermosetting materials; Chemical preparations
CEO: Craig O Morrison
**Treas:* George Knight
**Ex VP:* William H Carter

D-U-N-S 15-322-1663 IMP
HEXPOL COMPOUNDING LLC
HEXPOL POLYMERS
(*Suby of* HEXPOL HOLDING INC) ★
14330 Kinsman Rd, Burton, OH 44021-9648
Tel (440) 834-4644 *Founded/Ownrshp* 2010
Sales 469.5MM^E *EMP* 800
SIC 3087 2821 Custom compound purchased resins; Thermoplastic materials
CEO: Tracy Garrison
VP: Rakshit Lamba
VP: Leonard McClean
VP: Marc Pignataro
Genl Mgr: Stephen W Chase
Genl Mgr: Peter Mollett
Genl Mgr: Glenn Thurman
CIO: Steven Lubowicz
Mtls Mgr: Don Rogers
Sales Exec: Andrew Wallace
Sls Mgr: Scott Lieberman

D-U-N-S 15-292-1862 IMP/EXP
HEXPOL COMPOUNDING NC INC
(*Suby of* HEXPOL HOLDING INC) ★
280 Crawford Rd, Statesville, NC 28625-8541
Tel (704) 872-1585 *Founded/Ownrshp* 2004
Sales 228.8MM^E *EMP* 3,100
SIC 3069 3087 2891 Rubber automotive products; Custom compound purchased resins; Adhesives & sealants
Prin: Tracy Garrison
**Pr:* Georg Brunstam
**Pr:* Shannon Smith
CFO: Karin Gunnarsson
**CFO:* Urban Ottosson
Dir IT: Scott Bleistein

D-U-N-S 08-022-8454
HEXPOL HOLDING INC
(*Suby of* HEXPOL AB)
14330 Kinsman Rd, Burton, OH 44021-9648
Tel (440) 834-4644 *Founded/Ownrshp* 2012
Sales 135.3MM^E *EMP* 4,490
SIC 6719 Investment holding companies, except banks
Pr: Georg Brunstam

HEXPOL POLYMERS
See HEXPOL COMPOUNDING LLC

D-U-N-S 96-281-6836
HEYCO PRODUCTS INC
(*Suby of* PENN ENGINEERING & MANUFACTURING CORP) ★
1800 Industrial Way, Toms River, NJ 08755-4809
Tel (732) 286-4336 *Founded/Ownrshp* 2016
Sales 90.0MM^E *EMP* 200
SIC 3351 3679 Copper rolling & drawing; Commutators, electronic
Treas: Richard Cardone

D-U-N-S 62-253-5979
HEYWOOD HEALTHCARE INC
242 Green St, Gardner, MA 01440-1336
Tel (978) 632-3420 *Founded/Ownrshp* 1986
Sales 5.2M *EMP* 2,500^E
SIC 8741 Hospital management
Pr: Winfield Brown
**Ch Bd:* Kenneth Pierce
Netwrk Eng: Bob Bronson
Netwrk Eng: John Demalia

HEYWOOD HOSPITAL
See HENRY HEYWOOD MEMORIAL HOSPITAL

D-U-N-S 62-737-4452
HF GROUP LLC
8844 Mayfield Rd, Chesterland, OH 44026-2632
Tel (440) 729-2445 *Founded/Ownrshp* 2006
Sales 28.0MM *EMP* 1,516
SIC 2732 Books: printing & binding
COO: Paul Parisi
VP: Jim Bratton
**VP:* Steve Eisenberg
VP: Mark Melahn
Mng Dir: Jim Heckman
Genl Mgr: Lori Johnson
Plnt Mgr: Tim Baker

D-U-N-S 78-489-2742
HF HOLDINGS INC
(*Suby of* BAIN CAPITAL LP) ★
1500 S 1000 W, Logan, UT 84321-8206
Tel (435) 750-5000 *Founded/Ownrshp* 1999
Sales 94.9MM^E *EMP* 3,263
SIC 3949 3088 Treadmills; Exercising cycles; Gymnasium equipment; Trampolines & equipment; Hot tubs, plastic or fiberglass
CEO: Robert C Gay

D-U-N-S 12-650-7073 IMP
HF MANAGEMENT SERVICES LLC
HEALTH FIRST
100 Church St Fl 18, New York, NY 10007-2601
Tel (212) 801-6000 *Founded/Ownrshp* 1999
Sales 733.7MM^E *EMP* 1,850
Accts Ernst & Young Llp New York
SIC 8741 Management services
CEO: Daniel McCarthy
COO: Jim Boothe
COO: James Both
COO: Mary Hood
CFO: Dan Phillips
**Treas:* David Falk
Bd of Dir: Tom Tyree
**Chf Mktg O:* Jay Schectman
Ofcr: Sonya Henderson
VP: Robert Allen
VP: Christie Bowes
VP: Robert Branchini
VP: Sharon Gardner
VP: Scott Greene

VP: Dave Gutwald
VP: Stewart Hamilton
VP: George Hulse
VP: David Kleinhanzl
VP: Michael Lauto
VP: Nemesio Ortiz
VP: Norbert Scharff

D-U-N-S 79-662-1449 IMP/EXP
HFA INC
135 E Hintz Rd, Wheeling, IL 60090-6035
Tel (847) 520-1000 *Founded/Ownrshp* 1991
Sales 228.8MM^E *EMP* 700
SIC 3497 Foil containers for bakery goods & frozen foods
Pr: Norton Sarnoff
**CFO:* Peter Perkins
**VP:* Brad Sarnoff
**VP:* David Sarnoff

HFC
See HOUSEHOLD FINANCE CORP

D-U-N-S 08-020-1471
■ **HFC PRESTIGE INTERNATIONAL US LLC**
(*Suby of* P&G) ★
350 5th Ave, New York, NY 10118-0110
Tel (212) 389-7800 *Founded/Ownrshp* 2015
Sales 30.0MM *EMP* 3,000
SIC 2844 2676 3421 2842 2841 Toilet preparations; Towels, napkins & tissue paper products; Razor blades & razors; Specialty cleaning preparations; Soap: granulated, liquid, cake, flaked or chip

D-U-N-S 78-656-5544
HFF HOLDINGS LLC
HOLIDAY FENOGLIO FOWLER
1 Oxford Ctr, Pittsburgh, PA 15219-1400
Tel (412) 281-8714 *Founded/Ownrshp* 2003
Sales NA *EMP* 3
SIC 6162 Mortgage bankers & correspondents; Loan correspondents; Bond & mortgage companies
CEO: John H Pelusi Jr
**CFO:* Gregory Conley
Off Mgr: Carol Colby

D-U-N-S 79-880-0749
▲ **HFF INC**
301 Grant St Ste 1100, Pittsburgh, PA 15219-1419
Tel (412) 281-8714 *Founded/Ownrshp* 1982
Sales NA *EMP* 810
Tkr Sym HF *Exch* NYS
SIC 6162 Real property lessors; Mortgage bankers & correspondents; Loan correspondents
CEO: Mark D Gibson
**Pr:* Joe B Thornton Jr
COO: Nancy O Goodson
CFO: Gregory R Conley
Mng Dir: Phil Mahler

D-U-N-S 10-692-7585
HFI ENTERPRISES INC
HINTZSCHE OIL
2s181 County Line Rd, Maple Park, IL 60151-8815
Tel (630) 557-2406 *Founded/Ownrshp* 1962
Sales 117.0MM^E *EMP* 125
SIC 5172 5191 Diesel fuel; Gasoline; Fuel oil; Chemicals, agricultural; Fertilizer & fertilizer materials; Feed
Pr: David Hintzsche
**Treas:* Matt Gadow
**VP:* Ronald Hintzsche

D-U-N-S 00-429-3478 IMP/EXP
HFI LLC
59 Gender Rd, Canal Winchester, OH 43110-9733
Tel (614) 491-0700 *Founded/Ownrshp* 1969, 1993
Sales 240.0MM *EMP* 4,000
SIC 2396 2821 3714 3429 3086 Automotive trimmings, fabric; Polyurethane resins; Motor vehicle parts & accessories; Manufactured hardware (general); Plastics foam products
CEO: Walter Dennis Jr
COO: Larry Barth
**CFO:* Neil Fillman
VP: Robert S Chapell
**VP:* Takao Okamoto
**VP:* Todd Sousa
**VP:* Kurt Stuckenbrock
Genl Mgr: Brad Myers
Genl Mgr: Rene Rios
CIO: Eric Zimmer
VP Opers: Jorge Veloz

D-U-N-S 08-507-4052 IMP/EXP
HFI WIND DOWN INC
DREXEL HERITAGE FURNITURE
1925 Eastchester Dr, High Point, NC 27265-1404
Tel (336) 888-4800 *Founded/Ownrshp* 2001
Sales 511.7MM^E *EMP* 3,300
SIC 2511 2512 Wood bedroom furniture; Dining room furniture: wood; Couches, sofas & davenports: upholstered on wood frames; Chairs: upholstered on wood frames
Pr: Dan Bradley
**Pr:* Lenwood Rich
**Sec:* Jon Botsford
Sls Mgr: Phil Miller

D-U-N-S 10-677-7667
HFS HOLDING CORP
HOSPITAL FORMS & SYSTEMS
8900 Ambassador Row, Dallas, TX 75247-4510
Tel (214) 634-8600 *Founded/Ownrshp* 1982
Sales 121.3MM^E *EMP* 550
SIC 2679 5112 2675 Labels, paper: made from purchased material; Business forms; Die-cut paper & board
Pr: Peter A Pyhrr
VP Mfg: Tom Helenbrook
Manager: Melissa Whitehead

HFT
See HENRY F TEICHMANN INC

HG BUYING
See HOMEGOODS INC

HGA
See HUNT GUILLOT & ASSOCIATES LLC

HGA ARCHITECTS AND ENGINEERS
See HAMMEL GREEN AND ABRAHAMSON INC

D-U-N-S 01-179-3958
HGGC LLC
1950 University Ave # 350, East Palo Alto, CA 94303-2286
Tel (650) 321-4910 *Founded/Ownrshp* 2007
Sales 351.0MM^E *EMP* 553
SIC 6799 Investors
CEO: Rich Lawson
Mng Pr: Gary Crittenden
Pr: Jay Tabu
**CFO:* Les Brown
Ofcr: Gregory Benson
Sr VP: Lee Story
Sr VP: Neil White
VP: Jared Archibald
VP: Jacob Hodgman
VP: Paul C Huntsman
VP: Paul Huntsman
VP: Steven Leistner
VP: Phil Sampognaro
VP: Hudson Smith
VP: Steven P Smith
VP: Ryan Stratton
VP: Jay J Tabu
VP: Neil H White
Exec: Jeremiah Jewkes

D-U-N-S 06-742-1347 EXP
HGS (USA) LLC
(*Suby of* HINDUJA VENTURES LIMITED)
1901 E War Memorial Dr, Peoria, IL 61614-7807
Tel (309) 679-4281 *Founded/Ownrshp* 2004
Sales 193.8MM^E *EMP* 2,500
SIC 7389
Pr: Kathy Hamburger
CFO: Steve Czirjack
Bd of Dir: Jennifer Dorothy
Ofcr: Jeff Macdonald
Ex VP: Anthony Joseph
Ex VP: Sanjay Sinha
VP: Jack Biersdorfer
VP: Lester Hnelson III
VP: Jaime Nunez
MIS Dir: Steven Nelson
Dir IT: Brett Stoller

D-U-N-S 12-609-6838 IMP
■ **HGST INC**
(*Suby of* WD) ★
3403 Yerba Buena Rd, San Jose, CA 95135-1500
Tel (800) 801-4618 *Founded/Ownrshp* 2002
Sales 953.6MM^E *EMP* 2,303^E
SIC 3572 Computer storage devices
CEO: John Coyne
**Pr:* Stephen Milligan
**COO:* Douglas A Gross
CFO: Tom Constantino
**CFO:* Michael A Murray
Sr VP: Dennis Brown
Sr VP: Mark Grace
Sr VP: Jerry Kagele
VP: Brendan Collins
VP: Steven Craig
VP: Kevin Haughey
VP: Ken Higgins
VP: George Horvath
VP: Adele McLean
VP: Owen Melroy
VP: Tsutomu Numata
VP: Mark Rochlin
VP: Mike Yousef

HGT
See HUB GROUP TRUCKING INC

D-U-N-S 00-166-3962
HH BENFIELD ELECTRIC SUPPLY CO INC
25 Lafayette Ave, White Plains, NY 10603-1613
Tel (914) 948-6660 *Founded/Ownrshp* 1951
Sales 253.3MM^E *EMP* 200
Accts O Conner Davies Munns & Dobbin
SIC 5063 Electrical apparatus & equipment; Electrical supplies
Ch Bd: Dan McLaughlin
**Pr:* Daniel J McLaughlin
**CFO:* William G Roloff
VP: Joe Mauriello
Sls Mgr: Adam Kohli

D-U-N-S 00-112-7976 IMP
■ **HH BROWN SHOE CO INC**
COVE SHOE COMPANY DIVISION
(*Suby of* B H SHOE HOLDINGS INC) ★
124 W Putnam Ave Ste 1a, Greenwich, CT 06830-5317
Tel (203) 661-2424 *Founded/Ownrshp* 1992
Sales 250.6MM^E *EMP* 1,200
SIC 3143 3144 Work shoes, men's; Boots, dress or casual: men's; Women's footwear, except athletic
Ch Bd: Francis C Rooney Jr
Pr: James Issler
CEO: J E Issler
Ex VP: J Scott Bohling
VP: Keith Duplain
VP: Mark McGranahan
VP: Jason Reed
VP: Robert Skorvanek
Genl Mgr: David Issler
Dir IT: Sharon Jones
Web Dev: Beth Martin
Board of Directors: Warren E Buffett

D-U-N-S 01-976-7645
HH GLOBAL USA INC
(*Suby of* HH GLOBAL LIMITED)
175 E Hawthorn Pkwy # 325, Vernon Hills, IL 60061-1460
Tel (847) 816-6303 *Founded/Ownrshp* 2011
Sales 200.0MM *EMP* 90
SIC 8742 Marketing consulting services
CEO: Robert Macmillan
**Ch Bd:* Stuart Wallis
**CFO:* Edward Parsons
VP: Lee Goudie

H.H. GREGG
See GREGG APPLIANCES INC

D-U-N-S 08-007-7510
HH HEALTH SYSTEM - SHOALS LLC (AL)
1300 S Mongomery Ave, Sheffield, AL 35660
Tel (256) 386-4673 *Founded/Ownrshp* 2014
Sales 2.7MM^E *EMP* 1,500
SIC 8062 General medical & surgical hospitals

D-U-N-S 02-669-1444
HH LIQUIDATING CORP
ZINC CORPORATION AMERICA DIV
110 E 59th St Fl 34, New York, NY 10022-1308
Tel (646) 282-2500 *Founded/Ownrshp* 1981
Sales 86.0MM^E *EMP* 843
SIC 3624 2999 3356 3339 Carbon & graphite products; Electrodes, thermal & electrolytic uses: carbon, graphite; Carbon specialties for electrical use; Coke, calcined petroleum: made from purchased materials; Coke (not from refineries), petroleum; Lead & zinc; Zinc refining (primary), including slabs & dust
Ch Bd: William E Flaherty
VP: Robert D Scherich

D-U-N-S 96-939-5982
HH MEDSTAR HEALTH INC
5565 Sterrett Pl Ste 500, Columbia, MD 21044-2679
Tel (410) 772-6500 *Founded/Ownrshp* 2011
Sales 282.3MM *EMP* 8^E
Accts Kpmg Llp Mc Lean Va
SIC 8082 Home health care services
Pr: Kenneth A Samet

D-U-N-S 01-183-8619
HHC FOUNDATION OF NEW YORK CITY INC
160 Water St Fl 10, New York, NY 10038-5037
Tel (646) 458-2810 *Founded/Ownrshp* 2008
Sales NA *EMP* 35,000
Accts Kpmg Llp New York Ny
SIC 6321 Fraternal accident & health insurance organizations
Ch Bd: Michael Stocker

D-U-N-S 07-489-2076
■ **HHC INC**
(*Suby of* HOUSECALL HOME HEALTH) ★
6501 Deane Hill Dr, Knoxville, TN 37919-6006
Tel (865) 292-6000 *Founded/Ownrshp* 1994
Sales 25.0MM^E *EMP* 2,000
SIC 8082 Home health care services
Pr: Ladonna Dolomantino
**Pr:* Greg Davis

D-U-N-S 80-691-9515
▲ **HHGREGG INC**
4151 E 96th St, Indianapolis, IN 46240-1414
Tel (317) 848-8710 *Founded/Ownrshp* 1955
Sales 1.9MMM *EMP* 5,100
Accts Kpmg Llp Indianapolis Indian
Tkr Sym HGG *Exch* NYS
SIC 5731 5722 5712 Radio, television & electronic stores; Household appliance stores; Furniture stores
Pr: Robert Riesbeck
**Ch Bd:* Catherine A Langham
CFO: Kevin J Kovacs
CFO: Kevin Kovacs
Chf Mktg O: Keith M Zimmerman
Ofcr: Sam Johnson
Sr VP: Matt Phillips
Sr VP: Andrew Terry
VP: Mabelle Lim
VP: Diane Lutz
Genl Mgr: Zachary Dugger
Board of Directors: Michael Andretti, Gregory M Bettinelli, William P Carmichael, Lawrence P Castellani, Benjamin D Geiger, Kenneth J Kocher, John M Roth, Peter M Starrett, Kathleen C Tierney

D-U-N-S 01-004-4865
HHHUNT CORP (VA)
800 Hethwood Blvd, Blacksburg, VA 24060-4207
Tel (540) 552-3515 *Founded/Ownrshp* 1972
Sales 63.0MM^E *EMP* 1,500
SIC 6513 Apartment building operators
CEO: Harry Hunt IV
Ch Bd: Harry H Hunt III
COO: Daniel Schmitt
Ex VP: David Crowder
Sr VP: James Nicholson
VP: Stephen Jones
VP: James R King
VP: David E Tuggle
S&M/VP: Larry Mills

D-U-N-S 15-449-7523
HHHUNT PROPERTY MANAGEMENT INC
800 Hethwood Blvd, Blacksburg, VA 24060-4207
Tel (540) 552-3515 *Founded/Ownrshp* 1983
Sales 24.5MM^E *EMP* 1,000
SIC 6513 Apartment building operators
Pr: David E Reem Snyder
**Ch:* Harry H Hunt III
**VP:* Jim King
**VP:* Janet Riddlebarger
**VP:* David Tuggle
VP Bus: James Nicholson

D-U-N-S 07-867-1135
■ **HHI FORGING LLC**
(*Suby of* HHI GROUP HOLDINGS LLC) ★
2727 W 14 Mile Rd, Royal Oak, MI 48073-1712
Tel (248) 284-2900 *Founded/Ownrshp* 2005
Sales 105.7MM^E *EMP* 500^E
SIC 3462 Automotive forgings, ferrous: crankshaft, engine, axle, etc.

D-U-N-S 19-045-4988 IMP
HHI FORMTECH INDUSTRIES LLC
2727 W 14 Mile Rd, Royal Oak, MI 48073-1712
Tel (248) 597-3800 *Founded/Ownrshp* 2006
Sales 166.2MM^E *EMP* 600
SIC 3463 Automotive forgings, nonferrous
Ex VP: Richard J Larkin
**COO:* R Harris
**CFO:* Charles Moore
CFO: Chip Moore
Ofcr: Chris Jones
Admn Mgr: Linda Jarbo
Admn Mgr: Tim Welbaum

Ql Cn Mgr: Anna Pachut
Mktg Mgr: Harding Fears

D-U-N-S 96-219-6577
■ **HHI GROUP HOLDINGS LLC**
(*Suby of* METALDYNE PERFORMANCE GROUP INC) ★
2727 W 14 Mile Rd, Royal Oak, MI 48073-1712
Tel (248) 284-2900 *Founded/Ownrshp* 2012
Sales 105.7MM^E *EMP* 500^E
SIC 7549 Automotive maintenance services
CEO: George Thanopoulos

D-U-N-S 60-856-6717
HHJ HOLDINGS LIMITED
1957 Crooks Rd A, Troy, MI 48084-5504
Tel (248) 652-9716 *Founded/Ownrshp* 1998
Sales 151.4MM^E *EMP* 950
SIC 1611 2951 Highway & street paving contractor; Asphalt & asphaltic paving mixtures (not from refineries)

HHM
See 44 NEW ENGLAND MANAGEMENT CO

HHSC
See HAWAII HEALTH SYSTEMS CORP

D-U-N-S 05-128-6706
HI DEVELOPMENT CORP
111 W Fortune St, Tampa, FL 33602-3206
Tel (813) 229-6686 *Founded/Ownrshp* 1959
Sales 60.5MM^E *EMP* 1,000
SIC 8741 Hotel or motel management
Pr: Andre Callen
**VP:* Claire Callen
**VP:* David H Callen
**VP:* Tarquin Callen
VP: David Clement
**Prin:* Robinson Callen
Off Mgr: Victoria Schrock

HI TECH CONSULTANTS
See HTC GLOBAL SERVICES INC

D-U-N-S 83-716-5021 IMP
▲ **HI-CRUSH PARTNERS LP**
3 Riverway Ste 1350, Houston, TX 77056-1982
Tel (713) 960-4777 *Founded/Ownrshp* 2012
Sales 339.6MM *EMP* 290^E
Tkr Sym HCLP *Exch* NYS
SIC 1442 1481 Sand mining; Mine & quarry services, nonmetallic minerals; Mine exploration, nonmetallic minerals
CEO: Robert E Rasmus
Genl Pt: Hi-Crush GP LLC
COO: Jefferies V Alston III
VP: William Barker

D-U-N-S 02-089-0059 IMP
HI-LEX AMERICA INC
(*Suby of* TSK OF AMERICA INC) ★
5200 Wayne Rd, Battle Creek, MI 49037-7392
Tel (269) 968-0781 *Founded/Ownrshp* 1975
Sales 166.3MM *EMP* 1,100
SIC 3496 3357 Cable, uninsulated wire: made from purchased wire; Nonferrous wiredrawing & insulating
Ch Bd: Katsuaki Shima
**Pr:* Tom Strictland
IT Man: Dave Cubic
Snr Mgr: John Wyllie
Board of Directors: K Tokuhiro, Thomas G Welsh

HI-LIFT OF MICHIGAN COMPANY
See MORRISON INDUSTRIES INC

HI-PRO ANIMAL HEALTH
See FRIONA INDUSTRIES LP

D-U-N-S 02-115-8892
HI-PRO FEEDS INC
(*Suby of* HI-PRO FEEDS LP)
1201 E 11th St, Friona, TX 79035-1410
Tel (806) 250-2791 *Founded/Ownrshp* 2006, 2012
Sales 151.4MM^E *EMP* 425^E
SIC 2048 Prepared feeds
CEO: Dean Prevost
**Sr VP:* Daren Kennett
VP: Mark Knief
Plnt Mgr: Lonnie Holland
Plnt Mgr: Robert Kruger
Plnt Mgr: Mark Osborne
Sls Mgr: Jim Langelaan
Sales Asso: Kody Kimbrough

D-U-N-S 00-828-8938 IMP
HI-SHEAR CORP
(*Suby of* LISI AEROSPACE)
2600 Skypark Dr, Torrance, CA 90505-5373
Tel (310) 784-4025 *Founded/Ownrshp* 1996
Sales 252.5MM^E *EMP* 1,070
SIC 3452 3429 Bolts, nuts, rivets & washers; Aircraft hardware
CEO: Christian Darville
CFO: Jean S Micheletti
VP: Edmond Balassanian
VP: Jack Smith
CTO: Paul Maddox

HI-TECH DURAVENT
See FLEXIBLE TECHNOLOGIES INC

HI-TECH PHARMACAL - AN AKORN
See HI-TECH PHARMACAL CO INC

D-U-N-S 10-119-6749 IMP
■ **HI-TECH PHARMACAL CO INC**
HI-TECH PHARMACAL - AN AKORN
(*Suby of* AKORN INC) ★
369 Bayview Ave, Amityville, NY 11701-2801
Tel (631) 789-8228 *Founded/Ownrshp* 2014
Sales 103.3MM^E *EMP* 448^E
SIC 2834 Pharmaceutical preparations
Pr: David S Seltzer
Pr: Gary M April
**CFO:* William Peters
**Ex VP:* Kamel Egbaria
VP: Chris Losardo
VP: Joseph Matajy

*VP: Margaret Santorufo
Admn Mgr: Ellen Solomon
Dir IT: Tom Fitch
*VP Opers: Eyal Mares
Sfty Dirs: William Kemptner

HI-TECH PLASTICS
See ROYAL TECHNOLOGIES CORP

HIALEAH HOSPITAL
See TENET HIALEAH HEALTHSYSTEM INC

D-U-N-S 06-504-1386
HIBBARD NURSING HOME INC
1037 W Main St, Dover Foxcroft, ME 04426-3752
Tel (207) 564-8129 Founded/Ownrshp 1964
Sales 627.5MM EMP 135
SIC 8052 8051 Intermediate care facilities; Skilled nursing care facilities
Pr: Jane Hibbard-Merrill

D-U-N-S 00-236-7761
HIBBERT CO
400 Pennington Ave, Trenton, NJ 08618-3105
Tel (609) 392-0478 Founded/Ownrshp 1933
Sales 92.5MM[E] EMP 446
SIC 7331 7389 Direct mail advertising services; Printers' services: folding, collating
CEO: Timothy J Moonan
*Ch Bd: Joan Moonan
*Sr VP: Ron Arellano
*Sr VP: Mario Devincenzi
*Sr VP: Rosemary M Hober
*Sr VP: Kenneth J Swiatkowski
*Sr VP: Paul Zukowski
VP: Mario De Vincenzi
VP: George Dowbnia
Software D: Sambabu Chellappa
Mktg Dir: Jennifer Gonzalez

D-U-N-S 79-741-1964 IMP
■ **HIBBETT SPORTING GOODS INC**
HIBBETT SPORTS
(Suby of HIBBETT SPORTS INC) ★
2700 Milan Ct, Birmingham, AL 35211-6919
Tel (205) 942-4292 Founded/Ownrshp 1992
Sales 943.0MM EMP 8,900
SIC 5941 5661 5699 Sporting goods & bicycle shops; Team sports equipment; Footwear, athletic; Sports apparel
CEO: Jeffry O Rosenthal
*Sr VP: Scott Bowman
*Sr VP: Ared Briskin
*Sr VP: Cathy E Pryor
VP: Jeff Gray
VP: Alicia Kahn
VP: Chris Thomsen
Exec: Derrick Ross
Dir IT: Rick Hubbard
Dir IT: Terry Mayfield
Sls&Mrk Ex: Rebecca Jones

HIBBETT SPORTS
See HIBBETT SPORTING GOODS INC

D-U-N-S 79-273-9000 IMP
▲ **HIBBETT SPORTS INC**
2700 Milan Ct, Birmingham, AL 35211-6919
Tel (205) 942-4292 Founded/Ownrshp 1945
Sales 943.1MM EMP 8,900[E]
Tkr Sym HIBB Exch NGS
SIC 5941 5661 5699 Sporting goods & bicycle shops; Team sports equipment; Footwear, athletic; Sports apparel
Pr: Jeffry O Rosenthal
*Ch Bd: Michael J Newsome
CFO: Scott J Bowman
Sr VP: Jared S Briskin
Sr VP: Cathy E Pryor
VP: William Quinn
Board of Directors: Jane F Aggers, Anthony F Crudele, Karen S Etzkorn, Terrance G Finley, Albert C Johnson, Carl Kirkland, Ralph T Parks, Thomas A Saunders II, Alton E Yother

D-U-N-S 06-654-2952 IMP
HIBBING TACONITE CO (A JOINT VENTURE)
200 Public Sq Ste 3300, Cleveland, OH 44114-2315
Tel (216) 694-5700 Founded/Ownrshp 1973
Sales 1.1MMM[E] EMP 1,560
SIC 1011 Iron ore mining; Iron ore pelletizing; Iron ore beneficiating
CEO: Joseph A Carrabba
Ex VP: Laurie Brlas
Ex VP: Donald Gallagher

D-U-N-S 01-217-8831 IMP/EXP
HIBU INC
(Suby of HIBU (UK) LIMITED)
90 Merrick Ave Ste 530, East Meadow, NY 11554-1575
Tel (516) 730-1900 Founded/Ownrshp 2001
Sales 1.8MMM[E] EMP 7,000
SIC 2741 Directories: publishing & printing
CEO: Mike Pocock
Genl Pt: Mark Boudreau
*Ch Bd: John Condron
*Pr: Joseph Walsh
*COO: Mark Payne
*CFO: Tony Bates
*CFO: Jim Haddad
*Ch: Bob Wigley
Sr Cor Off: Stephen Wolf
Ofcr: Patrick J Marshall
Ex VP: Jerry Kingkade
Sr VP: Victoria Sharrar
VP: John Butler
VP: Thomas Cody
VP: John Davis
VP: Russ Michels
VP: Michael Voucas
Exec: Todd Minnier

D-U-N-S 06-794-7507
HICKMAN MILLS C-1 SCHOOL DISTRICT
9000 Old Santa Fe Rd, Kansas City, MO 64138-3913
Tel (816) 316-7000 Founded/Ownrshp 1902
Sales 80.1MM[E] EMP 1,500
SIC 8211 Public elementary & secondary schools; School board

D-U-N-S 00-699-9460 IMP
HICKMAN WILLIAMS & CO
250 E 5th St Ste 300, Cincinnati, OH 45202-4198
Tel (513) 621-1946 Founded/Ownrshp 1890, 1922
Sales 195.8MM EMP 92
Accts Grant Thornton Llp Cincinnat
SIC 5051 5052 5169 5085 5084 Metals service centers & offices; Ferroalloys; Pig iron; Coal & other minerals & ores; Coke; Coal; Chemicals & allied products; Abrasives; Industrial machinery & equipment
Pr: David H Gelwicks
*COO: Robert J Gray
*COO: Terry L Meadors
*Treas: Pamela J Evans
*VP: Robert E Davis
*VP: Steven W Stark
CIO: Terrence Gaither

D-U-N-S 12-804-5148 IMP
■ **HICKORY BUSINESS FURNITURE LLC**
HBF TEXTILES
(Suby of HNI CORP) ★
900 12th Street Dr Nw, Hickory, NC 28601-4763
Tel (828) 322-1169 Founded/Ownrshp 1979
Sales 137.7MM[E] EMP 650
SIC 2521 2299 Wood office furniture; Batting, wadding, padding & fillings
Pr: Stan A Askren
*CFO: Kurt A Tjaden
CFO: Karen Wilson
*Ex VP: Don Mead
*VP: Steven M Bradford
VP: Jill Vandersleet-Scott
Exec: Steve Taranto
Mktg Mgr: Joyce Lail
Sales Asso: Alison Dimola

D-U-N-S 00-321-6850 IMP/EXP
HICKORY SPRINGS MANUFACTURING CO (NC)
HSM SOLUTIONS
235 2nd Ave Nw, Hickory, NC 28601-4950
Tel (828) 328-2201 Founded/Ownrshp 1944
Sales 756.4MM[E] EMP 2,500
SIC 3069 3495 2514 5072 2399

D-U-N-S 62-279-0405
HICKS HOLDINGS LLC
2200 Ross Ave Ste 5000, Dallas, TX 75201-7902
Tel (214) 615-2300 Founded/Ownrshp 2004
Sales 184.3MM[E] EMP 2,033
SIC 3679 Liquid crystal displays (LCD)
COO: Casey Shilts
VP: Curt Crofford
Exec: Mack Hicks
Mng Dir: Rick Neuman

D-U-N-S 03-705-6413
HICKSVILLE UNION FREE SCHOOL DISTRICT (INC)
200 Division Ave, Hicksville, NY 11801-4827
Tel (516) 733-6600 Founded/Ownrshp 1901
Sales 104.3MM EMP 590
SIC 8211 Public elementary school; Public junior high school; Public senior high school
*Treas: Sharon Denueo
Schl Brd P: Phil Heckler
Pgrm Dir: Robin Throne

D-U-N-S 55-628-8280 IMP
HID GLOBAL CORP
(Suby of ASSA ABLOY USA) ★
611 Center Ridge Dr, Austin, TX 78753-1013
Tel (800) 237-7769 Founded/Ownrshp 2000
Sales 409.5MM[E] EMP 997
SIC 3825 1731 8741 Radio frequency measuring equipment; Access control systems specialization; Management services
Pr: Denis Hebert
*Sr VP: Rodney Glass
*Sr VP: Tam Hulusi
*VP: Marc Bielmann
*VP: Bridget Burke
VP: Chris Kirby
*VP: Mary Procykv
VP: Phil Scarfo
VP: Debra Spitler
Exec: Sheila Farris
IT Man: Steven Roman

HIDALGO COUNTY WELFARE DEPT
See COUNTY OF HIDALGO

HIDDEN VILLA RANCH
See LUBERSKI INC

HIDDEN VILLA RANCH
See LUBERSKI INC

D-U-N-S 94-140-1192
HIE HOLDINGS INC
2839 Mokumoa St, Honolulu, HI 96819-4402
Tel (808) 833-2244 Founded/Ownrshp 1981
Sales 109.0MM[E] EMP 501[E]
SIC 2095 7993 Roasted coffee; Coin-operated amusement devices
Pr: Michael Boulware
*Treas: Karen Erwin
*Sr VP: Steven Boulware
VP: Sidney Bouleware
*VP: Glenn Boulware
Sls&Mrk Ex: Eloise Kim

HIG CAPITAL
See HIG CAPITAL PARTNERS III LP

D-U-N-S 14-845-7620
HIG CAPITAL INC
1450 Brickell Ave # 3100, Miami, FL 33131-3460
Tel (305) 379-2322 Founded/Ownrshp 1998
Sales 624.4MM[E] EMP 2,519
SIC 8742 6211 Management consulting services; Investment firm, general brokerage
Pr: Sami Mnaymneh
*Pr: Anthony Tamer

D-U-N-S 13-462-2534 IMP
HIG CAPITAL LLC
1450 Brickell Ave Fl 31, Miami, FL 33131-3460
Tel (305) 379-2322 Founded/Ownrshp 1998
Sales 2.4MMM[E] EMP 6,181[E]
SIC 6211 Investment firm, general brokerage
CFO: Bret Wiener
VP: Mike Gallagher
VP: Enoch Kariuki
VP: Dan Katz
VP: Robert Milam
VP: Arjun Mohan
VP: Joseph Pagliuca
VP: Chris Paldino
VP: Matthew Robinson
VP: Luis Suarez
VP: Benjamin Taylor

D-U-N-S 82-489-1477
HIG CAPITAL MANAGEMENT INC
1450 Brickell Ave Fl 31, Miami, FL 33131-3460
Tel (305) 379-2322 Founded/Ownrshp 1993
Sales 3.7MMM[E] EMP 7,423
SIC 6211 Investment firm, general brokerage
Pr: Sami Mnaymneh
CFO: Ruth Brophy
Ofcr: David Dungan
*VP: Anthony Tamer
Prin: J Rn-Marc Vogler
*Mng Dir: Doug Berman
*Mng Dir: John Black
*Mng Dir: John Bolduc
Mng Dir: Thibaud Caulier
Mng Dir: George Creel
*Mng Dir: Charles Hanemann

D-U-N-S 15-322-5631
HIG CAPITAL PARTNERS III LP
HIG CAPITAL
(Suby of HIG CAPITAL MANAGEMENT INC) ★
1450 Brickell Ave # 3100, Miami, FL 33131-3444
Tel (305) 379-2322 Founded/Ownrshp 2002
Sales 87.0MM[E] EMP 530
SIC 6211 5084 7352 7699 8748 3842 Security brokers & dealers; Safety equipment; Medical equipment rental; Medical equipment repair, non-electric; Safety training service; Surgical appliances & supplies
CEO: Sami Mnaymneh
VP: Seth Goldberg

D-U-N-S 07-858-8116 IMP
HIG MIDDLE MARKET LLC
1 Market Spear Tower 18f, San Francisco, CA 94105
Tel (415) 439-5500 Founded/Ownrshp 2008
Sales 116.4MM[E] EMP 1,800[E]
SIC 8021 Dentists' office
Co-CEO: Sami Mnaymneh
Co-CEO: Tony Tamer

D-U-N-S 08-037-5651
▲ **HIG SURGERY CENTERS LLC**
1450 Brickell Ave Fl 31, Miami, FL 33131-3460
Tel (305) 379-2322 Founded/Ownrshp 2009
Sales 959.8MM[E] EMP 5,100[E]
SIC 8062 3851 General medical & surgical hospitals; Ophthalmic goods

D-U-N-S 82-527-8968
HIG TRANSPORT HOLDINGS INC
(Suby of HIG CAPITAL LLC) ★
1450 Brickell Ave Fl 31, Miami, FL 33131-3460
Tel (305) 379-2322 Founded/Ownrshp 2007
Sales 20.8MM[E] EMP 1,258
SIC 8742 Management consulting services
Pr: Anthony Tamer

D-U-N-S 02-032-2418
HIGGINBOTHAM INSURANCE AGENCY MCKINNEY INC
500 W 13th St Ste 200, Fort Worth, TX 76102-4659
Tel (817) 336-2377 Founded/Ownrshp 2004
Sales NA EMP 240
SIC 6411 Insurance agents & brokers
CEO: James R Reid
*CFO: James Krause
VP: Paul Harrison
*VP: James Hubbard
*VP: R Morgan Woodruff

D-U-N-S 12-512-7618
HIGGINBOTHAM INSURANCE GROUP INC
500 W 13th St Ste 200, Fort Worth, TX 76102-4659
Tel (800) 728-2374 Founded/Ownrshp 2004
Sales NA EMP 257[E]
SIC 6411 Insurance agents, brokers & service
Pr: Rusty Reid
*CFO: Jim Krause
Ex VP: Dana Jones
Ex VP: Jason Littlejohn
Sr VP: Michael Hermes
VP: Becky Brooks
VP: Stephen Hoffman
VP: Parker Holt
VP: Andrea Silva
Dir Risk M: Kevin Springer
Mng Dir: Ed Coker

D-U-N-S 17-072-9896 IMP
HIGH CONCRETE GROUP LLC
HIGH CONCRETE STRUCTURES
(Suby of HIGH INDUSTRIES INC) ★
125 Denver Rd, Denver, PA 17517-9315
Tel (717) 336-9300 Founded/Ownrshp 2006
Sales 128.5MM[E] EMP 900
Accts Kpmg Llp Harrisburg Pa
SIC 1791 3272 Precast concrete structural framing or panels, placing of; Prestressed concrete products
CEO: Michael F Shirk
*Pr: John J Seroky
*COO: Jeffrey L Sterner
*CFO: Michael W Van Belle
*Treas: Terrence A Warco
Ex VP: Lance Lorah
Ex VP: Ned Schneider
*VP: Dean M Glick
*VP: Daniel R Pietropola
*VP: David B Schneider
VP: Chuck Weyland

HIGH CONCRETE STRUCTURES
See HIGH CONCRETE GROUP LLC

D-U-N-S 82-973-7415
HIGH FALLS OPERATING CO LLC
(Suby of NORTHAMERICAN BREWERIES) ★
445 Saint Paul St, Rochester, NY 14605-1726
Tel (585) 546-1030 Founded/Ownrshp 2008
Sales 109.0MM[E] EMP 800
SIC 2082 Malt beverage products

D-U-N-S 00-253-4568 IMP
HIGH GRADE BEVERAGE
891 Georges Rd, Monmouth Junction, NJ 08852-3057
Tel (732) 821-7600 Founded/Ownrshp 1935
Sales 127.1MM[E] EMP 300
SIC 5181 Beer & other fermented malt liquors
Ch Bd: Joseph De Marco
*Pr: Anthony De Marco
*Sec: Elizabeth De Marco
*Ex VP: George Policastro
*VP: Herbert Schloss

D-U-N-S 08-487-7505
HIGH INDUSTRIES INC
1853 William Penn Way, Lancaster, PA 17601-6713
Tel (717) 293-4444 Founded/Ownrshp 2006
Sales 397.0MM[E] EMP 2,107
Accts Kpmg Llp Harrisburg Pa
SIC 1791 3272 5051 3441 Structural steel erection; Prestressed concrete products; Steel; Fabricated structural metal
CEO: Michael F Shirk
*Ch Bd: S Dale High
Pr: Jeffrey L Sterner
CFO: Michael W Van Belle
CFO: Mike Vanbelle
Treas: James E Tritch
Treas: John Vozzella
Treas: Terrence A Warco
Ex VP: Mark C Fitzgerald
Sr VP: Darryl Gordon
Sr VP: Bob Shannon
VP: Michael Belle
VP: Karen A Biondolillo
VP: Thomas R Esposito
VP: Lisa Fulginiti
VP: Tina Ginnis
VP: Dean M Glick
VP: Michael Klatt
VP: Constantinos Kondos
VP: Bernd Laudorn
VP: Allon Lefever
Board of Directors: Paula R Crowley, Gregory A High, Steven D High, W Thomas Kennedy III, Richard G King, Daniel R Langdon, Scott Newkam

D-U-N-S 00-111-0055 IMP/EXP
HIGH LINER FOODS (USA) INC
(Suby of HIGH LINER FOODS INCORPORATED)
1 Highliner Ave, Portsmouth, NH 03801-7140
Tel (603) 431-6865 Founded/Ownrshp 1957
Sales 532.1MM[E] EMP 1,100[E]
SIC 2092 Seafoods, frozen: prepared
CEO: Henry Demone
*Pr: Keith Decker
*Treas: Kelvin Nelson
Sr VP: Chris Mulder
VP: Jeff Donde
Opers Mgr: Sean Rudd

D-U-N-S 83-213-3388
HIGH PERFORMANCE INDUSTRIES HOLDINGS INC
HOLLEY
1801 Russellville Rd, Bowling Green, KY 42101-3542
Tel (270) 782-2900 Founded/Ownrshp 2011
Sales 87.4MM[E] EMP 605
SIC 3592 3714 Carburetors; Fuel pumps, motor vehicle
Pr: Tom Tomlinson
*VP: Terrill M Rutledge
*VP: Stephen Trussell
*VP: Trevor Wiggins

D-U-N-S 05-223-0406
HIGH PLAINS BAPTIST HOSPITAL INC
1600 Wallace Blvd, Amarillo, TX 79106-1789
Tel (806) 358-5800 Founded/Ownrshp 1995
Sales 37.3MM[E] EMP 2,000
SIC 8062 6513 8051 General medical & surgical hospitals; Retirement hotel operation; Skilled nursing care facilities
CEO: John Hicks
*COO: David Kilarski
*CFO: Phyllis Cowling

D-U-N-S 96-791-8942
HIGH PLAINS CHRISTIAN MINISTRIES FDN
701 Park Place Ave Fl 2, Amarillo, TX 79101-4064
Tel (806) 337-5292 Founded/Ownrshp 2011
Sales 200.8MM EMP 2
Accts Connor Mcmillon Mitchell & She
SIC 8699 Membership organizations
Pr: T H Holloway

D-U-N-S 03-131-9973
HIGH PLAINS PIZZA INC
PIZZA HUT
7 W Parkway Blvd, Liberal, KS 67901-2081
Tel (620) 624-5638 Founded/Ownrshp 1965
Sales 39.8MM[E] EMP 1,100
SIC 5812 Pizzeria, chain
Pr: William K Colvin
*Sec: Virginia Colvin
*VP: Kent Colvin
IT Man: Bobbi Banning

D-U-N-S 01-427-1543
HIGH PLAINS POWER INC
1775 E Monroe, Riverton, WY 82501
Tel (800) 826-3446 Founded/Ownrshp 1997
Sales 97.0MM EMP 53
Accts Schmidt & Company Llc Lees Su
SIC 4911 Transmission, electric power
CEO: Marlene Morss
*Pr: Mark Park
*CFO: Jon Mayes

Treas: Jim Miller
VP: Matt Brown
Genl Mgr: Jeffrey Hohn

D-U-N-S 07-784-7952
HIGH POINT REGIONAL HEALTH
RADIATION THERAPY
(*Suby of* UNC HOSPITALS) ★
601 N Elm St, High Point, NC 27262-4331
Tel (336) 878-6000 *Founded/Ownrshp* 2013
Sales 224.9MM *EMP* 2,338
SIC 8062 General medical & surgical hospitals
Pr: Ernie Bovio
Dir Vol: Bobbi Watkins
*COO: Greg Taylor
*CFO: Kimberly Crews
*Chf Mktg O: Dale Williams
Ofcr: Wil Elder
*VP: Katherine Burns
*VP: Denise Potter
Dir Lab: Sherrie Livecchi
Dir Rad: Tara Eisenberg
Dir Rx: Mark Haltom

D-U-N-S 14-287-7179
HIGH POINT SAFETY AND INSURANCE MANAGEMENT CORP
(*Suby of* PALISADES SAFETY INSURANCE AGENCY INC) ★
331 Newman Springs Rd # 304, Red Bank, NJ 07701-5692
Tel (732) 978-6000 *Founded/Ownrshp* 2003
Sales NA *EMP* 585
SIC 6411 Insurance agents, brokers & service
Pr: James A Tignanelli
*Prin: Linda Schwabenbauer

HIGH POINT SCHOOL
See WASHTENAW INTERMEDIATE SCHOOL DISTRICT

D-U-N-S 95-844-1594
HIGH POINT SOLUTIONS INC
5 Gail Ct, Sparta, NJ 07871-3438
Tel (973) 940-0040 *Founded/Ownrshp* 1996
Sales 145.8MM *EMP* 50
Accts Kpmg Llp Short Hills Nj
SIC 5045 7373 Computers, peripherals & software; Computer integrated systems design
Pr: Michael Mendiburu
*CFO: Sandra Curran
*VP: Tim Hennessey
*VP: Tom Mendiburu
*VP: Kurt Vandermark

D-U-N-S 06-743-9976
HIGH POINT UNIVERSITY
1 University Pkwy, High Point, NC 27268-4260
Tel (336) 841-9000 *Founded/Ownrshp* 1924
Sales 161.6MM *EMP* 680
Accts Smith Leonard Pllc High Poin
SIC 8221 Colleges & universities
Pr: Dr Nido R Qubein
Assoc VP: Roger Clodfelter
*VP: Ms Deborah Butt
IT Man: Matthew Brown
Netwrk Mgr: Phillip Chadwell
Opers Mgr: Don Moore

D-U-N-S 07-928-7175
HIGH RIDGE WIND LLC
15445 Innovation Dr, San Diego, CA 92128-3432
Tel (888) 903-6926 *Founded/Ownrshp* 2013
Sales 258.5MM[E] *EMP* 826
SIC 4911 Electric services
Pr: Tristan Grimbert
Sec: Robert Miller
VP: Ryan Pfaff

D-U-N-S 61-533-2280
■ **HIGH SIERRA ENERGY LP**
(*Suby of* NGL ENERGY PARTNERS LP) ★
3773 Cherry Creek N Dr St, Denver, CO 80209-3804
Tel (303) 815-1010 *Founded/Ownrshp* 2012
Sales 134.4MM[E] *EMP* 130
SIC 5172 Petroleum products
Pt: James Burke
Pt: Nicholas Aretakis
Pt: Stephen Creamer
Pt: Marjorie A Hargrove
Pt: David Kehoe
Sr VP: Jack Eberhardt
Sr VP: Bill Laughlin
VP: Douglas White
VP: James Winter

D-U-N-S 05-166-1622
HIGH SIERRA POOLS INC
2704 Columbia Pike, Arlington, VA 22204-4440
Tel (703) 920-1750 *Founded/Ownrshp* 2001
Sales 87.3MM[E] *EMP* 1,250
Accts Michael Meyer And Associates
SIC 8741 7389 Business management; Swimming pool & hot tub service & maintenance
Pr: Stephen Lavery
*VP: Radoslaw Kaczor
*VP: Viktor Nekoranec
Sales Exec: Radek Kaczor

D-U-N-S 80-621-7910
HIGH STEEL STRUCTURES LLC
(*Suby of* HIGH INDUSTRIES INC) ★
1915 Old Philadelphia Pike, Lancaster, PA 17602-3410
Tel (717) 299-5211 *Founded/Ownrshp* 1970
Sales 166.2MM *EMP* 600
Accts Kpmg Llp Harrisburg Pa
SIC 1541 Steel building construction
CEO: Michael F Shirk
*Pr: Brian Laborde
*CFO: Michael W Van Belle
*Treas: Terrence A Warco
*Sr VP: Steven M Bussanmas
*VP: Dean M Glick
*VP: Paul A Lipinsky
*VP: Ronald D Medlock
*VP: Craig D Thompson

D-U-N-S 06-431-9838
HIGH-TECH INSTITUTE HOLDINGS INC
ANTHEM EDUCATION GROUP
3383 N State Road 7, Lauderdale Lakes, FL 33319-5617
Tel (602) 328-2800 *Founded/Ownrshp* 2012
Sales 146.3MM[E] *EMP* 1,000[E]
SIC 6719

D-U-N-S 02-165-7622
HIGH-TECH INSTITUTE INC
BRYMAN SCHOOL
2250 W Peoria Ave A100, Phoenix, AZ 85029-4923
Tel (602) 274-4300 *Founded/Ownrshp* 1982
Sales 61.2MM[E] *EMP* 1,000
SIC 8221

D-U-N-S 55-711-1093 IMP
■ **HIGHBRIDGE CAPITAL MANAGEMENT LLC**
(*Suby of* J P MORGAN ASSET MANAGEMENT INC) ★
40 W 57th St Fl 33, New York, NY 10019-4001
Tel (212) 287-5496 *Founded/Ownrshp* 1989
Sales 101.0MM[E] *EMP* 135[E]
SIC 6211 Brokers, security
Mng Pt: Scott Kapnick
Mng Pt: Martin Astengo
Mng Pt: Glenn Dubin
Pr: Todd Builione
COO: Todd C Builione
Sr VP: Eric Colandrea
Sr VP: Jonathan Dorfman
Sr VP: Daniel Jackson
Sr VP: Irina Mirkin
Sr VP: Patricia Morrissey
Sr VP: Blair Salveson
Sr VP: Susan Soh
Sr VP: Ryan Spayde
VP: Eiler Andrew
VP: Alex Chudner
VP: Jamie Donsky
VP: Andrew Eiler
VP: Prem Itharat
VP: Vipul Kaushal
VP: Anthony Landy
VP: Mike Marcucilli

D-U-N-S 17-935-3370
HIGHCREST INVESTORS LLC
(*Suby of* BUFFALO INVESTORS CORP) ★
Icahn Associates Corp 767, New York, NY 10153
Tel (212) 702-4323 *Founded/Ownrshp* 1993
Sales 1.4MMM[E] *EMP* 3,750
SIC 3743 4741 4789 4813 Freight cars & equipment; Rental of railroad cars; Railroad car repair; Local telephone communications; Long distance telephone communications;
Ch Bd: Carl C Icahn

D-U-N-S 96-234-2254
HIGHER ONE HOLDINGS INC
(*Suby of* WINCHESTER ACQUISITION HOLDINGS CORP) ★
115 Munson St, New Haven, CT 06511-3540
Tel (203) 776-7776 *Founded/Ownrshp* 2016
Sales 157.9MM *EMP* 1,300[E]
SIC 7389 Financial services
CEO: Marc Sheinbaum
CFO: Christopher Wolf
Chf Mktg O: Lutz Braum
Ofcr: Mark Archer
Ofcr: Robert Reach
Sr VP: Matt Dorf
VP: Andrew M Crawford
VP: Thomas Kavanaugh
VP: Jennifer Sanders
VP: Whitney Stewart
VP: Sean Townsend

D-U-N-S 86-757-9752
HIGHER ONE INC
(*Suby of* HIGHER ONE HOLDINGS INC) ★
115 Munson St, New Haven, CT 06511-3540
Tel (203) 776-7776 *Founded/Ownrshp* 2000
Sales 99.6MM[E] *EMP* 450[E]
SIC 7389 Financial services
Ex VP: Miles Lasater
*COO: Casey McGuane
*CFO: Christopher Wolf
*Chf Cred: Richard J Howells
Bd of Dir: John Bado
Bd of Dir: Paul Biddelman
*Ofcr: Mark Archer
*Ofcr: Suzanne Cafferty Ross
*Sr VP: Rob Reach
*VP: Tom Anderson
VP: David Bernier
VP: Wayne Christian
VP: Jack Debaar
VP: Paul Dickson
VP: Matt Dorf
VP: Doug Fraser
VP: Kati Kennedy
VP: Nora Lee
VP: Kelcey Reed
VP: Whitney Stewart
VP: Laurensia Sturgis
Board of Directors: Robert Hartheimer

HIGHGATE HOLDINGS
See HIGHGATE HOTELS INC

D-U-N-S 19-520-3922
HIGHGATE HOTELS INC
HIGHGATE HOLDINGS
545 E J Carpentr Fwy 14, Irving, TX 75062
Tel (972) 444-9700 *Founded/Ownrshp* 1976
Sales 142.7MM[E] *EMP* 968
SIC 8741 Hotel or motel management
Pr: Mahmood Khimji
COO: Steve Barick
*Treas: Mehdi Khimji
Ex VP: William Geiler
Ex VP: Brian A Winston
Sr VP: David H Snell
Sr VP: Rick Whitworth
*VP: Jaffer Khimji
VP: Jeff Toscano

VP: Jason Vlacich
Off Mgr: Amanda Kusek

D-U-N-S 10-224-9158
HIGHJUMP SOFTWARE INC
(*Suby of* ACCELLOS INC) ★
5600 W 83rd St Ste 600, Minneapolis, MN 55437-1065
Tel (952) 947-4088 *Founded/Ownrshp* 2014
Sales 146.5MM[E] *EMP* 771
SIC 7371 Computer software development & applications
CEO: Michael Cornell
*CFO: Flint Seaton
*Chf Mktg O: Chad Collins
*Ex VP: Ross Elliott
Sr VP: Joe Couto
Sr VP: David Grosvenor
VP: Leeann Belski
VP: Joanne Gulnac
VP: David McMahon
VP: Scott Mills
Genl Mgr: Bill Ashburn

D-U-N-S 15-209-4850
HIGHLAND BAKING CO INC
2301 Shermer Rd, Northbrook, IL 60062-6721
Tel (847) 677-2789 *Founded/Ownrshp* 1984
Sales 137.5MM[E] *EMP* 635
SIC 5149 2051 Bakery products; Bread, cake & related products
Pr: James Rosen
VP: Michael Galenson
VP: John Updegraff
IT Man: Liana Fishel
VP Sls: Ira Keeshin
Sls Mgr: Peter Wroblewski

D-U-N-S 01-023-7977
■ **HIGHLAND CAPITAL BROKERAGE INC**
(*Suby of* LADENBURG THALMANN FINANCIAL SERVICES INC) ★
3535 Grandview Pkwy Ste 6, Birmingham, AL 35243-1945
Tel (205) 263-4400 *Founded/Ownrshp* 2000, 2016
Sales NA *EMP* 267
SIC 6411 Insurance agents, brokers & service
CEO: Jim Gelder
*CFO: Drew Lawrence
Sr VP: Mike McGlothlin
*VP: Keith A Miller
Prin: Paul M Harrington

D-U-N-S 06-252-3548
HIGHLAND CAPITAL HOLDING CORP
(*Suby of* NFP ADVISORS) ★
3535 Grandview Pkwy # 600, Birmingham, AL 35243-1945
Tel (205) 263-4400 *Founded/Ownrshp* 1997
Sales NA *EMP* 550
SIC 6411 Insurance agents, brokers & service
CEO: John L Robinson Jr
*COO: J Forrest Collier
*CFO: Keith D Duke
*Ex VP: W Todd Carlisle
*VP: Rhonda Padgett
Prin: Richard F Biborosch
Prin: Paul M Pistilli
Prin: Kenneth D Savino
VP Mktg: Tony Catrini
VP Mktg: Tracy McGrath
VP Sls: Kevin Donnelly

D-U-N-S 05-832-9769 IMP
HIGHLAND CAPITAL MANAGEMENT LP
300 Crescent Ct Ste 700, Dallas, TX 75201-7849
Tel (972) 628-4100 *Founded/Ownrshp* 1993
Sales 230.3MM[E] *EMP* 170
SIC 6211 Investment firm, general brokerage
Pr: James Dondero
*Pt: Mark Okada
Pt: Jack Yang
Pt: Terry Jones
Exec: Melissa Schroth
Assoc Dir: Candice Griffith
Dir Bus: Nikki Gill
Mng Dir: Philip Braner
Mng Dir: Ted Dameris
Mng Dir: Stephen Dedyo
Mng Dir: Carla Martin

D-U-N-S 78-741-1255
HIGHLAND CONTAINERS INC
(*Suby of* ADVANCE DESIGN & PACKAGING) ★
3520 Dillon Rd, Jamestown, NC 27282-9802
Tel (336) 887-5400 *Founded/Ownrshp* 1992
Sales 108.5MM[E] *EMP* 450
SIC 2653 Boxes, corrugated: made from purchased materials
Pr: Doug Johnston
Genl Mgr: Steve Barnett
Genl Mgr: Rodney Benson

D-U-N-S 13-104-2640
HIGHLAND CORP
FAST STOP FOOD MARKETS
108 Mill Ave, Hohenwald, TN 38462-1533
Tel (800) 924-8514 *Founded/Ownrshp* 1974
Sales 118.3MM *EMP* 150
Accts Bdo Usa Llp Memphis Tn
SIC 5171 5411 Petroleum bulk stations; Petroleum terminals; Convenience stores, independent
Pr: David M Adcox
*CFO: Tammie Haskins
*Sec: Connie Adcox
VP: Scott Lindley

D-U-N-S 09-281-4201
HIGHLAND COUNTY COMMUNITY ACTION ORGANIZATION INC
HCCAO
1487 N High St Ste 500, Hillsboro, OH 45133-6812
Tel (937) 393-3060 *Founded/Ownrshp* 1965
Sales 5.4MM *EMP* 1,381
SIC 8322 Individual & family services
Pr: Fred Berry
*Sec: Richard Graves
*VP: Greg Barr
*Ex Dir: Julia Wise
Ex Dir: Julie Wise

D-U-N-S 15-153-3726
HIGHLAND HOMES LTD
HIGHLAND HOMES OF DALLAS
5601 Democracy Dr Ste 300, Plano, TX 75024-3674
Tel (972) 789-3500 *Founded/Ownrshp* 1985
Sales 285.4MM[E] *EMP* 400
SIC 1521 1531 New construction, single-family houses; Speculative builder, single-family houses
Pt: Rodger Sanders
Pt: Jean Ann Brock
VP: Mike Moore
VP: Gonzalo Romero
Div Mgr: Garon Bruce
Opers Mgr: Shane Anthony
Opers Mgr: Amy Kinney
Sales Exec: Jeff Cook
Mktg Mgr: Erin Barton
Sales Asso: Brooke Kavieff
Sales Asso: Kelley Porter

HIGHLAND HOMES OF DALLAS
See HIGHLAND HOMES LTD

D-U-N-S 05-364-9430
HIGHLAND HOSPITAL OF ROCHESTER
(*Suby of* UNIVERSITY OF ROCHESTER) ★
1000 South Ave, Rochester, NY 14620-2782
Tel (585) 473-2200 *Founded/Ownrshp* 1889
Sales 312.7MM *EMP* 2,500
Accts Pricewaterhousecoopers Llp Ph
SIC 8062 General medical & surgical hospitals
Pr: Steven I Goldstein
*CFO: Adam Anolik
*CFO: Leonard J Shute
*VP: Kathy Parrinello R N
Mtls Mgr: Eric Grayeski
Mktg Dir: Kristin Olaughlin
Doctor: Sidney S Weinstein MD

HIGHLAND HOUSE
See CENTURY FURNITURE LLC

D-U-N-S 18-566-1329 IMP
HIGHLAND INDUSTRIES INC
(*Suby of* TAKATA) ★
1350 Bridgeport Dr Ste 1, Kernersville, NC 27284-3794
Tel (336) 992-7500 *Founded/Ownrshp* 1987
Sales 264.3MM[E] *EMP* 590
SIC 2221 Automotive fabrics, manmade fiber
Pr: David Jackson
Treas: Shunkichi Shimizu
*VP: Todd McCurry
VP: Bruce Thames
Exec: Jenny Fisher

D-U-N-S 08-921-2591
HIGHLAND LAKES COUNTRY CLUB & COMMUNITY ASSOCIATION
2240 Lakeside Dr W, Highland Lakes, NJ 07422-1857
Tel (973) 764-4366 *Founded/Ownrshp* 1936
Sales 2.9MM *EMP* 2,000
SIC 7997 Country club, membership
Pr: Steve Hastie
*Treas: Jeanne Jameson

D-U-N-S 07-673-4920
HIGHLAND PARK INDEPENDENT SCHOOL DISTRICT
7015 Westchester Dr, Dallas, TX 75205-1061
Tel (214) 780-3000 *Founded/Ownrshp* 1914
Sales 151.8MM *EMP* 700
Accts Weaver And Tidwell Llp Dalla
SIC 8211 Public elementary & secondary schools; High school, junior or senior
Teacher Pr: Brenda West
Instr Medi: Jill Bellomy

D-U-N-S 16-607-9249
HIGHLANDER PARTNERS LP
300 Crescent Ct Ste 550, Dallas, TX 75201-1817
Tel (214) 245-5000 *Founded/Ownrshp* 2004
Sales NA *EMP* 643
SIC 6159 Small business investment companies
Mng Pt: Jeff L Hull
Genl Pt: Highlander P GP
Pt: Alex L Guiva
Pt: Robert A Sussman
Pr: Michael R Nicolais
VP: Charles Thomas
Off Mgr: Rachael Giloini

D-U-N-S 07-979-8986
HIGHLANDS COUNTY SCHOOLS
426 School St, Sebring, FL 33870-4048
Tel (863) 471-5564 *Founded/Ownrshp* 2015
Sales 16.4MM[E] *EMP* 1,751[E]
SIC 8211 Public elementary & secondary schools

D-U-N-S 01-901-0529 IMP
HIGHLANDS FUEL DELIVERY LLC (ME)
IRVING ENERGY DIST & MKTG
(*Suby of* OCEAN INVESTMENTS CORP) ★
190 Commerce Way, Portsmouth, NH 03801-3242
Tel (603) 559-8700 *Founded/Ownrshp* 1986, 1954
Sales 872.8MM[E] *EMP* 900
SIC 5172 5541 1389 Gasoline; Filling stations, gasoline; Construction, repair & dismantling services
Pr: Darren Gillis
*Treas: James Sepanski
Ex Dir: Stephanie Pines
Genl Mgr: Tara Frost
CIO: Jessica Diffin
Sls Mgr: Kathy Ellis

D-U-N-S 80-670-0266
HIGHLANDS INSURANCE GROUP INC
10370 Richmond Ave, Houston, TX 77042-4141
Tel (713) 952-0665 *Founded/Ownrshp* 1990
Sales NA *EMP* 629
SIC 6331 6351 Fire, marine & casualty insurance; Workers' compensation insurance; Fire, marine & casualty insurance & carriers; Assessment associations: fire, marine & casualty insurance; Surety insurance
Pr: John W Cowley
CFO: Albert J Marino
*Sec: Stephen L Kibblehouse

HIGHLGHTS FOR CHILDREN PUBLSHR
See HIGHLIGHTS FOR CHILDREN INC

D-U-N-S 00-449-5115 IMP
HIGHLIGHTS FOR CHILDREN INC (OH)
HIGHLGHTS FOR CHILDREN PUBLSHR
1800 Watermark Dr, Columbus, OH 43215-1035
Tel (614) 486-0631 *Founded/Ownrshp* 1946
Sales 196.7MM[E] *EMP* 737
SIC 2721

D-U-N-S 07-927-2761
HIGHLINE MEDICAL CENTER
16251 Sylvester Rd Sw, Burien, WA 98166-3017
Tel (206) 244-9970 *Founded/Ownrshp* 1958
Sales 180.9MM *EMP* 1,253
Accts Catholic Health Initiatives E
SIC 8062 8051 General medical & surgical hospitals; Skilled nursing care facilities
Ch: Larry Bjork
**Pr:* Tony McLean
**Pr:* Sue O'Brien
COO: Karen Lautermilch
**CFO:* Lloyd Musselman
**Treas:* Mark Benedum
Trst: Uli CHI
Trst: Harry Pierce
Chf Mktg O: James Andrew
VP: Jeff Frankel
VP: Byron Kaersner
Exec: Beth Bautista
Dir Rx: Thuy Vo
Board of Directors: Lori Anderson, Michael Dehaan, Scott Enck, Byron Kaersner, Steve Odachowski, Buddy Orr, Earl Wiitala

D-U-N-S 18-930-1518
HIGHLINE MEDICAL SERVICES INC
16255 Sylvester Rd Sw # 202, Burien, WA 98166-3017
Tel (206) 431-5304 *Founded/Ownrshp* 1985
Sales 102.6MM *EMP* 6
SIC 8011 Dispensary, operated by physicians

D-U-N-S 07-821-4947
HIGHLINE PUBLIC SCHOOLS
15675 Ambaum Blvd Sw, Burien, WA 98166-2523
Tel (206) 631-3000 *Founded/Ownrshp* 1941
Sales 221.9MM *EMP* 2,000[E]
Accts Troy Kelley King County Wash
SIC 8211 Public elementary school; Public junior high school; Public senior high school; Public vocational/technical school
Pr: Julie Burr- Spani
**CFO:* Duggan Harman
Prin: Kyle Minaglia
Prin: Tom Symons
Ex Dir: Erma Sechrist
Pr Dir: Catherine C Carbone-Rogers
Teacher Pr: Steve Grubb
HC Dir: Nancy Boldt

HIGHMARK BLUE CROSS BLUE SHELD
See HIGHMARKS INC

D-U-N-S 07-217-9633
HIGHMARK BLUE CROSS BLUE SHIELD WEST VIRGINIA
HIGHMARK INC., PITTSBURGH, PA
(*Suby of* HIGHMARK BLUE CRSS-BLUE SHIELD) ★
614 Market St, Parkersburg, WV 26101-5146
Tel (304) 424-7700 *Founded/Ownrshp* 1937
Sales NA *EMP* 560
Accts Pricewaterhousecoopers Llp Ph
SIC 6321 Accident & health insurance carriers
Pr: J Fred Earley
**Treas:* Karen Hanlon
VP: James Miller
Mktg Dir: Fred Earley
Doctor: Stephen Campbell
Doctor: Houman Khosrovi
Doctor: Steven Miller

HIGHMARK BLUE CRSS-BLUE SHIELD
See HIGHMARK INC

D-U-N-S 06-709-6644
HIGHMARK INC
HIGHMARK BLUE CRSS-BLUE SHIELD
120 5th Ave, Pittsburgh, PA 15222-3000
Tel (412) 544-7000 *Founded/Ownrshp* 1996
Sales NA *EMP* 35,000
SIC 6321 6324 6411 6512 Accident & health insurance; Group hospitalization plans; Dental insurance; Health maintenance organization (HMO), insurance only; Medical insurance claim processing, contract or fee basis; Nonresidential building operators
Ch: J Robert Baum
**Pr:* William Winkenwerder
**CEO:* John S Brouse
CFO: Nanette P Nan Deturk
CFO: Domenic Palmieri
**Treas:* Nanette P Deturk
Ofcr: Elizabeth Farbacher
**Ofcr:* Jayanth Godla
Ofcr: Maryann Neely
Ofcr: Douglas Renshaw
Ofcr: Lidia Wielechowski
Ex VP: Tyrone S Alexander
Ex VP: Virginia Calega
Ex VP: Mary Anne Darragh
Ex VP: Daniel Lebish
Ex VP: Fg Merkel
Ex VP: David O'Brien
Sr VP: Pete Dzimiera
Sr VP: Donald R Fischer
Sr VP: Steven C Nelson
VP: Matthew Childs
Board of Directors: Terrence W Cavanaugh, Louis Civitarese

HIGHMARK INC., PITTSBURGH, PA
See HIGHMARK BLUE CROSS BLUE SHIELD WEST VIRGINIA

D-U-N-S 00-248-8542
HIGHMARKS INC
HIGHMARK BLUE CROSS BLUE SHELD
800 Delaware Ave Ste 900, Wilmington, DE 19801-1368
Tel (302) 421-3000 *Founded/Ownrshp* 1935
Sales NA *EMP* 650
Accts Ernst & Young Llp Baltimore
SIC 6321 Health insurance carriers
Pr: Timothy J Constantine
CFO: Mark G Chaney
**Assoc VP:* Phillip A Carter
VP: Paul Brown
VP: Kalpesh Doshi
VP: Peg Eitl
Dir Risk M: Philip Carter
CIO: Bill Jones
Dir QC: Deb Sweeney
Sales Exec: Mary Knapp
Mktg Mgr: John Reed
Board of Directors: Thomas Archie, Max S Bell Jr, Bernard Daney, Garrett B Lyons, Robert F Rider, Frances West

D-U-N-S 80-626-3633
HIGHMOUNT EXPLORATION & PRODUCTION LLC
(*Suby of* ENERVEST LTD) ★
16945 Northchase Dr # 1750, Houston, TX 77060-2151
Tel (281) 873-1500 *Founded/Ownrshp* 2014
Sales 200.7MM[E] *EMP* 300
SIC 1382 Oil & gas exploration services
CEO: Steven B Hinchman
Pr: Malcolm Johns
**CFO:* Dennis G Millet

D-U-N-S 80-835-2202
HIGHPOINT GLOBAL LLC
300 N Meridian St Ste 190, Indianapolis, IN 46204-1779
Tel (317) 576-4500 *Founded/Ownrshp* 2006
Sales 98.3MM *EMP* 192
SIC 8742 Management consulting services
CEO: Benjamin Lanius
**Pr:* Rachel Lanius
CFO: Stephen Niemeier
VP: Tom Miller
Dir IT: Charles Hammett
IT Man: Chad Pryor
Snr PM: Neil Pabst

D-U-N-S 78-627-5813
HIGHPOINT SOLUTIONS LLC
301 E Germantown Pike # 1, East Norriton, PA 19401-6517
Tel (610) 233-2700 *Founded/Ownrshp* 2006
Sales 153.4MM[E] *EMP* 515
Accts Grant Thornton Philadelphia
SIC 7371 Computer software systems analysis & design, custom
CEO: John P Seitz
**Pr:* Thomas Clancy
**CFO:* James Dandy
Bd of Dir: Steve Brock
Sr VP: Jeff Dibartolomeo
Sr VP: James Slubowski
VP: Chris Colapietro
VP: Mike Cram
VP: Mike Germain
VP: Diana Howard
VP: Lior Keet
VP: Eric Letts
VP: Robert Lorence
VP: Ralph Lynn
VP: Bret Piano
VP: Sam Schmitt
Assoc Dir: Mayank Srivastava
Board of Directors: Kayne Anderson

HIGH'S
See NEW RIDGE ASSOCIATES INC

D-U-N-S 19-722-8737
HIGHTOWERS PETROLEUM CO INC
3577 Commerce Dr, Middletown, OH 45005-5232
Tel (513) 423-4272 *Founded/Ownrshp* 1985
Sales 308.0MM *EMP* 50
SIC 5172 Diesel fuel; Gasoline
CEO: Steve Hightower Sr
**CFO:* Gary Visher
**VP:* Yudell Hightower
Pr Mgr: Tracey Bunch

D-U-N-S 87-275-9803
HIGHWATER ETHANOL LLC
24500 Us Highway 14, Lamberton, MN 56152-1179
Tel (507) 752-6160 *Founded/Ownrshp* 2009
Sales 110.2MM *EMP* 40
SIC 2869 Ethyl alcohol, ethanol
CEO: Brian Kletscher
**Ch Bd:* David G Moldan
CFO: Lucas Schneider
**Treas:* Luke Spalj
**V Ch Bd:* Timothy J Vanderwal
Exec: Tom Streifel
Opers Mgr: Chad Altermatt
Board of Directors: Russell J Derickson, William Garth, George M Goblish, Ronald E Jorgenson, Michael Landuyt

HIGHWAY
See LOUISE PARIS LTD

HIGHWAY DEPARTMENT
See TOWN OF LORRAINE

HIGHWAY PARTOL
See TENNESSEE DEPARTMENT OF SAFETY

HIGHWAY PATROL
See OKLAHOMA DEPT OF PUBLIC SAFETY

D-U-N-S 87-888-3107
HIGHWAY PATROL CALIFORNIA
(*Suby of* BUSINESS TRANSPORTATION & HOUSING AGENCY STATE OF CALIFORNIA) ★
601 N 7th St, Sacramento, CA 95811-0208
Tel (916) 376-3256 *Founded/Ownrshp* 1947
Sales NA *EMP* 7,541[E]
SIC 9221 State highway patrol;
Exec: Dan Jacowitz
Admn Mgr: Kelly Young
Genl Mgr: Robert Jones
IT Man: Bob Brown
Sys Mgr: Julie Green

D-U-N-S 00-114-8428 EXP
HIGHWAY SAFETY CORP
CONNECTICUT GALVANIZING
239 Commerce St Ste C, Glastonbury, CT 06033-2448
Tel (860) 659-4330 *Founded/Ownrshp* 1980
Sales 108.3MM *EMP* 115
Accts Cohn Reznick Llp Hartford Co
SIC 3444 3479 Guard rails, highway: sheet metal; Galvanizing of iron, steel or end-formed products
CEO: W Patric Gregory
**Pr:* Frank Luszcz
**CFO:* Robert West
Trfc Mgr: Alex Callis
S&M/VP: Roy Riedl

D-U-N-S 14-420-5010
HIGHWAY SERVICE VENTURES INC
FLYING J
100 Arbor Oak Dr Ste 305, Ashland, VA 23005-2266
Tel (804) 752-4966 *Founded/Ownrshp* 1984
Sales 97.9MM[E] *EMP* 450
Accts Kpmg Llp East Cary Street Ri
SIC 5541 5411 5812 Truck stops; Convenience stores; Restaurant, family: chain
Pr: Roger Cole
**CFO:* William Carter Dages
IT Man: Wes Moore
Counsel: Albert Lilly

HIGHWAY TECHNOLOGIES GROUP
See HTS ACQUISITION INC

D-U-N-S 60-698-2049
HIGHWAY TECHNOLOGIES INC
6811 Dixie Dr, Houston, TX 77087-5134
Tel (713) 845-1800 *Founded/Ownrshp* 2007
Sales NA *EMP* 1,000
SIC 1622 7359

D-U-N-S 03-455-3610
HIGHWAYS INC
PAVING DIVISION
1623 Galleria Blvd, Brentwood, TN 37027-2926
Tel (615) 373-5445 *Founded/Ownrshp* 1981
Sales 108.5MM[E] *EMP* 250
SIC 1611 Highway & street paving contractor
Pr: Allen Linder
**Sec:* Linda Vaughn
**VP:* Mark Odom

D-U-N-S 09-512-1760
▲ HIGHWOODS PROPERTIES INC
3100 Smoketree Ct Ste 600, Raleigh, NC 27604-1050
Tel (919) 872-4924 *Founded/Ownrshp* 1978
Sales 604.6MM *EMP* 447
Tkr Sym HIW *Exch* NYS
SIC 6798 Real estate investment trusts
Pr: Edward J Fritsch
**Ch Bd:* O Temple Sloan Jr
COO: Theodore J Klinck
CFO: Mark F Mulhern
Sr VP: Jeffrey D Miller
Sr VP: Kevin E Penn
VP: Daniel L Clemmens
VP: Steve Guinn
VP: Thomas Hill
VP: Mack Pridgen
Mktg Dir: Vicki Norris
Board of Directors: Charles A Anderson, Gene H Anderson, Carlos E Evans, David J Hartzell, Sherry A Kellett

D-U-N-S 80-826-4290
■ HIGHWOODS REALTY LIMITED PARTNERSHIP
(*Suby of* HIGHWOODS PROPERTIES INC) ★
3100 Smoketree Ct Ste 600, Raleigh, NC 27604-1050
Tel (919) 872-4924 *Founded/Ownrshp* 1994
Sales 604.6MM *EMP* 432[E]
SIC 6519 6531 6798 Real property lessors; Real estate managers; Real estate investment trusts
Pr: Edward J Fritsch
Genl Pt: Highwoods Properties
CFO: Mark F Mulhern

HIIG
See HOUSTON INTERNATIONAL INSURANCE GROUP LTD

HILAND DAIRY FOOD
See ROBERTS DAIRY CO LLC

D-U-N-S 03-113-7391
HILAND DAIRY FOODS CO LLC (IL)
1133 E Kearney St, Springfield, MO 65803-3435
Tel (417) 862-9311 *Founded/Ownrshp* 1938, 1979
Sales 805.9MM[E] *EMP* 1,350
Accts Bkd Llp Springfield Mo
SIC 2026 2024 2037 5143 Fluid milk; Cream, sour; Dips, sour cream based; Cottage cheese; Ice cream & frozen desserts; Fruit juices; Dairy products, except dried or canned
Exec: Janis Jennings
**Prin:* Woody Rogers
Brnch Mgr: Gabe Andes
Brnch Mgr: Tom Bombardier
Genl Mgr: Barry Beaman
QA Dir: Wayman Stipp
Sfty Mgr: Karl Farris
Plnt Mgr: Jaime Menchaca
Ql Cn Mgr: Eric Werther
Sls Mgr: Michael Dorrian

D-U-N-S 07-871-9042
HILB GROUP LLC
8720 Stony Point Pkwy # 125, Richmond, VA 23235-1990
Tel (804) 414-6501 *Founded/Ownrshp* 2009
Sales NA *EMP* 520[E]
SIC 6411 Insurance brokers
CEO: Robert J Hilb
Pr: David Hobbs
CFO: Bill Widhelm
Chf Mktg O: Jason Angus
Sr VP: Robert Blanton

HILBERS CONTRACTORS & ENGRG
See HILBERS INC

D-U-N-S 07-155-7813
HILBERS INC
HILBERS CONTRACTORS & ENGRG
1210 Stabler Ln, Yuba City, CA 95993-2620
Tel (530) 673-2947 *Founded/Ownrshp* 1988
Sales 110.6MM *EMP* 75
Accts Kcoe Isom Llp Yuba City Cal
SIC 1542 1541 Commercial & office building contractors; Industrial buildings, new construction
Pr: Kurt G Hilbers
**Treas:* Glenn Hilbers
VP: Susan P Growney
**VP:* Larry E Hilbers
**VP:* Tom Jones
Sfty Dirs: Jason Whipple
Board of Directors: Mike Cagley

D-U-N-S 79-308-2660
HILCO INC
HILCO TRADING
5 Revere Dr Ste 430, Northbrook, IL 60062-1583
Tel (847) 714-1288 *Founded/Ownrshp* 1990
Sales 83.4MM[E] *EMP* 500
SIC 7389 6531 Merchandise liquidators; Real estate brokers & agents
CEO: Neil R Aaronson
**Pr:* Gregory S Apter
**Pr:* Jeffrey B Hecktman
**Pr:* Michael Keefe
COO: Ernie Deyle
COO: Jeffrey Paronto
**CFO:* John P Chen
CFO: David Zwick
Chf Mktg O: Gary Epstein
Ex VP: Jack Butler
Ex VP: Cory Lipoff
**Ex VP:* Benjamin L Nortman
**Ex VP:* Edward J Siskin
Sr VP: Daniel Arnold
Sr VP: Len Berliner
Sr VP: Andrew Chused
Sr VP: Tom Davidson
Sr VP: Adam Evans
**Sr VP:* David Kirshenbaum
Sr VP: Mike Mahler
**Sr VP:* Navin Nagrani

HILCO TRADING
See HILCO INC

D-U-N-S 07-840-0654
HILCORP ALASKA LLC
3800 Centerpoint Dr, Anchorage, AK 99503-5825
Tel (907) 777-8300 *Founded/Ownrshp* 2011
Sales 83.6MM[E] *EMP* 6[E]
SIC 1382 Aerial geophysical exploration oil & gas

D-U-N-S 60-641-0538 IMP
HILCORP ENERGY CO
1111 Travis St, Houston, TX 77002-5924
Tel (713) 209-2400 *Founded/Ownrshp* 1988
Sales 57.2MM[E] *EMP* 1,350
SIC 1311 1382 Crude petroleum production; Oil & gas exploration services
CEO: Jeffrey D Hildebrand
**Pr:* Greg R Lalicker
Treas: Melinda Weilenger
VP: Kimberly Doupe
VP: Bill Schroeter
Dir IT: Stefano Giani
Dir IT: Sandy Higgins
Dir IT: David Horn
Dir IT: Rene Lorenzo
Dir IT: Jim Noot
Dir IT: Tulsi Zeidman

HILDEBRAND CARE CENTER
See SHADOW MOUNTAIN MANAGEMENT CORP

D-U-N-S 14-161-1496 IMP/EXP
HILEX POLY CO LLC
NOVOLEX
(*Suby of* NOVOLEX HOLDINGS INC) ★
101 E Carolina Ave, Hartsville, SC 29550-4213
Tel (843) 857-4800 *Founded/Ownrshp* 2003
Sales 2.0MMM[E] *EMP* 4,200
SIC 2673 2674 Plastic bags: made from purchased materials; Paper bags: made from purchased materials
CEO: Stanley B Bikulege
Pr: Paul Ebbert
COO: David Bocher
**COO:* Ben Mascarello
CFO: Marv Liebman
**CFO:* Paul Palmisano
VP: Mike McGuiness
Exec: Mike Cole
VP Opers: Jim Lassiter
Plnt Mgr: Patrick Hover
Sls Mgr: Legis Lation

D-U-N-S 17-410-8092
HILITE INDUSTRIES INC
(*Suby of* HILITE INTERNATIONAL INC) ★
1671 S Broadway St, Carrollton, TX 75006-7496
Tel (972) 242-2116 *Founded/Ownrshp* 2002
Sales 144.0MM[E] *EMP* 1,000
SIC 6719 Investment holding companies, except banks
CEO: Karl Hammer
**COO:* Jrg Feuring
**CFO:* Stefan Eck
**CFO:* Michael T Kestner
**Ch:* Craig Stinson
**Treas:* Ronald G Campbell
VP: Tim Bowes
VP: Richard Smith
Ql Cn Mgr: Paul Llamas
S&M/VP: William Person
Sls Mgr: Bill Innis

D-U-N-S 11-829-1009 IMP
HILITE INTERNATIONAL INC
1671 S Broadway St, Carrollton, TX 75006-7496
Tel (972) 242-2116 Founded/Ownrshp 1999
Sales 400.2MM^E EMP 1,000
SIC 5531 Automotive parts
Pr: Karl Hammer
*COO: Joerge Feuring
COO: Jorg Feuring
*CFO: Stefan Eck
CTO: Jason Chester

D-U-N-S 01-361-6594
HILL & MARKES INC (NY)
1997 State Highway 5s, Amsterdam, NY 12010-8177
Tel (518) 842-2410 Founded/Ownrshp 1906, 1937
Sales 128.6MM^E EMP 141
SIC 5087 5113 Restaurant supplies; Janitors' supplies; Industrial & personal service paper
Pr: Jeffrey Finkle
Pr: Kristeen Jaracz
*CEO: Neal Packer
VP: Richard Michaud
*VP: Andrea Packer
*VP: Kelvin W Scharf
Exec: Jim Izzano
Sls Mgr: Jason Packer
Sls Mgr: Michael Shoemaker
Sales Asso: Bob Fagle

D-U-N-S 04-268-6048
HILL & WILKINSON CONSTRUCTION GROUP LTD
HILL & WILKINSON GEN CONTRS
2703 Telecom Pkwy Ste 120, Richardson, TX 75082-3555
Tel (214) 299-4300 Founded/Ownrshp 1968
Sales 450.0MM EMP 240
SIC 1541 1542

HILL & WILKINSON GEN CONTRS
See HILL & WILKINSON CONSTRUCTION GROUP LTD

D-U-N-S 04-123-7058 IMP
HILL AND KNOWLTON STRATEGIES LLC
(Suby of W P P) ★
466 Lexington Ave Frnt 4, New York, NY 10017-3173
Tel (212) 885-0300 Founded/Ownrshp 1987
Sales 243.3MM^E EMP 2,400
SIC 8743 8748 Public relations & publicity; Business consulting
Pr: Paul Stasiulis
*Ch Bd: Jack Martin
Pr: Alfonso Cuellar
COO: Vivian Lines
*COO: Mark Thorne
CFO: Marcelo Quiroga
*Treas: Tom Lobene
Bd of Dir: Elaine Cruikshanks
Ex VP: Alison Eyles-Owen
Ex VP: Claire Koeneman
Ex VP: Joshua Reynolds
Sr VP: Brendan Hodgson
Sr VP: Joshua Lamel
Sr VP: Peggy O'Neill
VP: Annie Armbrust
VP: Brent Curry
VP: Fran Ois Ducharme
VP: Sarah Fox
VP: Paola Gants
VP: Steve Getzug
VP: Brian Grancagnolo

D-U-N-S 05-659-9178 IMP
HILL BROTHERS CHEMICAL CO
1675 N Main St, Orange, CA 92867-3499
Tel (714) 998-8800 Founded/Ownrshp 1923
Sales 123.2MM^E EMP 155^E
Accts Mcgladrey & Pullen
SIC 5169 2819 Acids; Calcium chloride & hypochlorite; Magnesium compounds or salts, inorganic
Pr: Ronald R Hill
*CFO: Thomas F James
*Sec: Kathryn J Waters
Ofcr: Shane Burkhart
*Ex VP: Matthew Thorne
VP: Bob Roth
Sales Exec: William Stark
VP Mktg: Rusty Mosher

D-U-N-S 08-954-3797
HILL BROTHERS CONSTRUCTION CO INC
20831 Highway 15, Falkner, MS 38629-9123
Tel (662) 837-3041 Founded/Ownrshp 1978
Sales 92.0MM^E EMP 500^E
SIC 1611 1622 1541 1542 General contractor, highway & street construction; Bridge, tunnel & elevated highway; Bridge construction; Highway construction, elevated; Tunnel construction; Industrial buildings & warehouses; Nonresidential construction
CEO: Kenneth W Hill Jr
*Pr: Gerald C Hill
*Treas: Kenneth W Drewery
*VP: Sterling Akers
*VP: Clyde R Robertson
Mktg Mgr: Becky Lindsey

D-U-N-S 02-642-7935
HILL COUNTRY BAKERY LLC
122 Stribling, San Antonio, TX 78204-1915
Tel (210) 475-9981 Founded/Ownrshp 1998
Sales 221.8MM^E EMP 600
SIC 5149 5461 Bakery products; Bakeries
*Mng Pt: Steve O'Donnell
*CFO: Phil J Butrum
Exec: Rickelia Wright
Ex Dir: Henry Egeolu
QA Dir: Marce Hernandez
IT Man: Anthony Perez
Mfg Dir: Juan Ancira
Ql Cn Mgr: Jennifer Hoppe

D-U-N-S 02-885-7147 IMP
■ **HILL COUNTRY ELECTRIC SUPPLY LP**
(Suby of WESCO DISTRIBUTION INC) ★
4801 Freidrich Ln Ste 200, Austin, TX 78744-2701
Tel (512) 428-9300 Founded/Ownrshp 2015
Sales 132.1MM^E EMP 110
SIC 5063 Electrical apparatus & equipment
Pt: Scott Schieffer
Pt: Wayne Blasingame
Pt: David Inman
Rgnl Mgr: Joe Conaway
IT Man: Darrell Jones
Opers Mgr: David Stockton
Sales Asso: Chris Aguilar
Sales Asso: Abe Rhodes
Snr Mgr: David Hall

D-U-N-S 12-337-4352
HILL COUNTRY FURNITURE PARTNERS LTD
ASHLEY FURNITURE HOMESTORE
1431 Fm 1101, New Braunfels, TX 78130-2622
Tel (830) 515-1400 Founded/Ownrshp 2002
Sales 102.5MM EMP 400
SIC 5712 Furniture stores
Pt: Gary Seals
CFO: Travis Williams
IT Man: Jeff Venglar
VP Mktg: Tom Steele

D-U-N-S 02-575-2961
HILL COUNTRY HOLDINGS LLC
1431 Fm 1101, New Braunfels, TX 78130-2622
Tel (830) 515-1400 Founded/Ownrshp 2008
Sales 84.8MM^E EMP 278^E
SIC 6719 Investment holding companies, except banks
VP: Shawn Seals
IT Man: Eric Ruelas

HILL GROUP, THE
See HILL MECHANICAL CORP

HILL HOLLIDAY
See INDEPENDENT ADVERTISING INC

D-U-N-S 08-080-4701
▲ **HILL INTERNATIONAL INC**
2005 Market St Fl 17, Philadelphia, PA 19103-7042
Tel (215) 309-7700 Founded/Ownrshp 2004
Sales 720.6MM EMP 4,759
Tkr Sym HIL Exch NYS
SIC 8742 8741 Construction project management consultant; Construction management
CEO: David L Richter
Ch Bd: Craig L Martin
Pr: Raouf S Ghali
CFO: John Fanelli III
Ch: Irvin E Richter
Ofcr: Catherine H Emma
Ex VP: William H Dengler Jr
Sr VP: Mark Dixon
Sr VP: Ronald F Emma
Sr VP: J Charles Levergood
Sr VP: Paul Roberts
Board of Directors: Camille S Andrews, Brian W Clymer, Steven R Curts, Alan S Fellheimer, Steven M Kramer, Craig L Martin, Gary F Mazzucco

D-U-N-S 01-800-3806 EXP
HILL INTERNATIONAL TRUCKS NA LLC (OH)
47866 Y And O Rd, East Liverpool, OH 43920-8724
Tel (330) 386-6440 Founded/Ownrshp 1890
Sales 86.1MM^E EMP 195
SIC 5511 5531 7538 Trucks, tractors & trailers: new & used; Truck equipment & parts; General automotive repair shops
VP Opers: Michael Barber
Opers Mgr: Jared Williams
Sales Exec: Fred Biscella
VP Sls: Jeff Mundy
Mktg Mgr: Travis Biscella

D-U-N-S 04-999-3207
HILL MECHANICAL CORP
HILL GROUP, THE
11045 Gage Ave, Franklin Park, IL 60131-1437
Tel (847) 451-5000 Founded/Ownrshp 1936
Sales 125.1MM^E EMP 500
SIC 1711

D-U-N-S 88-335-7436 IMP/EXP
■ **HILL PHOENIX INC**
(Suby of DOVER RFRGN & FD EQP INC) ★
2016 Gees Mill Rd Ne, Conyers, GA 30013-1301
Tel (770) 285-3264 Founded/Ownrshp 1887
Sales 1.0MMM^E EMP 3,500
SIC 3632 Household refrigerators & freezers
Pr: Bill Johnson
*CFO: Al Alden
VP: Lynn Brenton

D-U-N-S 80-968-8885
■ **HILL-ROM CO INC**
(Suby of HILL-ROM INC) ★
1069 State Road 46 E, Batesville, IN 47006-9167
Tel (812) 934-7777 Founded/Ownrshp 1981
Sales 95.3MM^E EMP 910
SIC 7352 Medical equipment rental
Pr: John J Greisch
*CFO: Mark Guinan
*Sr VP: Andreas G Frank
*Sr VP: Scott Jeffers
VP: Mark Baron
VP: Bertha Hazelwood
*VP: Richard G Keller
VP: Daniel Longoria
VP: Perry Stuckey
VP: Greg Tucholski
Snr Sftwr: James Allen

D-U-N-S 05-065-6982
▲ **HILL-ROM HOLDINGS INC**
2 Prudential Plz Ste 4100, Chicago, IL 60601
Tel (312) 819-7200 Founded/Ownrshp 1969
Sales 2.6MMM EMP 10,000
Tkr Sym HRC Exch NYS
SIC 3841 7352 Surgical & medical instruments; Medical equipment rental
Pr: John J Greisch
*Ch Bd: Rolf A Classon
Pr: Carlos Alonso
Pr: Alton Shader
Pr: Taylor Smith
COO: Carlyn D Solomon
CFO: Steven J Strobel
Ofcr: Kenneth Meyers
Sr VP: Andreas Frank
VP: Richard Keller
VP: Jason Richardson
Board of Directors: William G Dempsey, James R Giertz, Charles E Golden, William H Kucheman, Ronald A Malone, Eduardo R Menasce, Stacy Enxing Seng

D-U-N-S 00-424-5668 IMP/EXP
■ **HILL-ROM INC**
(Suby of HILL-ROM HOLDINGS INC) ★
1069 State Route 46 E, Batesville, IN 47006-9167
Tel (812) 934-7777 Founded/Ownrshp 1969
Sales 1.0MMM^E EMP 6,000
SIC 7352 2599

D-U-N-S 07-201-8278
HILLCO LTD
ROBERT HILL CONSTRUCTION CO
1435 Hwy 258 N, Kinston, NC 28504-7208
Tel (252) 523-9094 Founded/Ownrshp 1952
Sales 155.7MM^E EMP 7,000
SIC 8051 8059 5047 5122 Skilled nursing care facilities; Rest home, with health care; Medical equipment & supplies; Pharmaceuticals
Pr: Steven Hill
Treas: Pete Eimen
*Sec: Lucy Hill
VP: Catherine Emma
*VP: Greg Hill
*VP: Robert Hill Jr
Dir IT: Aaron Frizzell

D-U-N-S 92-641-8799
HILLCREST BANCSHARES INC
HILLCREST BANK
11111 W 95th St, Shawnee Mission, KS 66214-1824
Tel (913) 492-7500 Founded/Ownrshp 1975
Sales NA EMP 200
SIC 6022 State commercial banks
Pr: Tom Davies
COO: Lucy Jones
CFO: Dick Degen
Ofcr: Carol Sevy
Ex VP: Kevin Kramer
VP: Dave Freeland
VP: Lois Stewart

HILLCREST BANK
See HILLCREST BANCSHARES INC

D-U-N-S 07-511-9024
HILLCREST BAPTIST MEDICAL CENTER (TX)
BRAZOS VALLEY HEALTH NETWORK
100 Hillcrest Med Blvd, Waco, TX 76712
Tel (254) 202-8675 Founded/Ownrshp 1920
Sales 251.5MM EMP 2,200
Accts Bkd Llp Houston Tx
SIC 8062 Hospital, medical school affiliated with nursing & residency
Pr: Glenn A Robinson
*CFO: Richard W Perkins
Treas: Peter Eimen
Ex VP: Richard Perkins
Dir Lab: Kele Crouch
Off Mgr: Debbie Muerer
CIO: James Gillian
CIO: Richard Warren
MIS Dir: Gina Roberts
Dir IT: Darlene Gorham
Telecom Mg: Ray Bell

HILLCREST CENTER
See CRESTVIEW CONVALESCENT HOME INC

D-U-N-S 06-888-2091
HILLCREST EGG & CHEESE CO (OH)
HILLCREST FOOD SERVICE
2735 E 40th St, Cleveland, OH 44115-3510
Tel (216) 361-4625 Founded/Ownrshp 1974
Sales 122.4MM^E EMP 105
SIC 5143 5142 5147 5144 5149 5148 Dairy products, except dried or canned; Packaged frozen goods; Meats, fresh; Eggs; Canned goods: fruit, vegetables, seafood, meats, etc.; Fruits, fresh; Vegetables, fresh
Pr: Armin Abraham
CFO: James Romano
*Treas: Galina Yakobovitch
*VP: David Abraham
IT Man: Lloyd Langham

HILLCREST FOOD SERVICE
See HILLCREST EGG & CHEESE CO

HILLCREST HOSPITAL CLAREMORE
See AHS CLAREMORE REGIONAL HOSPITAL LLC

HILLCREST HOSPITAL SOUTH
See AHS SOUTHCREST HOSPITAL LLC

HILLCREST REHAB HLTH CARE CTR
See BEVERLY ENTERPRISES - MINNESOTA LLC

D-U-N-S 00-684-8568 IMP/EXP
HILLDRUP COMPANIES INC
HILLDRUP MOVING & STORAGE
4022 Jefferson Davis Hwy, Stafford, VA 22554-4827
Tel (703) 221-7155 Founded/Ownrshp 1976
Sales 95.4MM EMP 450
SIC 4212

HILLDRUP MOVING & STORAGE
See HILLDRUP COMPANIES INC

D-U-N-S 82-516-5132
▲ **HILLENBRAND INC**
1 Batesville Blvd, Batesville, IN 47006-7756
Tel (812) 934-7500 Founded/Ownrshp 2007
Sales 1.5MMM EMP 6,000^E
Accts Pricewaterhousecoopers Llp In
Tkr Sym HI Exch NYS
SIC 3535 3995 Conveyors & conveying equipment; Bulk handling conveyor systems; Burial caskets; Burial vaults, fiberglass
Pr: Joe A Raver
Ch Bd: F Joseph Loughrey
Pr: Kimberly K Ryan
Pr: Christopher H Trainor
CFO: Kristina A Cerniglia
CFO: Cynthia L Lucchese
Ofcr: Diane R Bohman
Sr VP: William A Canady
Sr VP: Scott P George
VP: Nicholas R Farrell
VP: Jan M Santerre
VP: Eric M Teegarden
Board of Directors: Edward B Cloues II, Gary L Collar, Helen W Cornell, Mark C Deluzio, Joy M Greenway, Thomas H Johnson, Eduardo R Menasce, Neil S Novich, Stuart A Taylor II

D-U-N-S 03-440-2966 IMP
HILLER COMPANIES INC
(Suby of PON NORTH AMERICA INC) ★
3751 Joy Springs Dr, Mobile, AL 36693-5134
Tel (251) 661-1275 Founded/Ownrshp 1983
Sales 159.4MM^E EMP 604
SIC 1731 5084 5088 Fire detection & burglar alarm systems specialization; Safety equipment; Marine supplies
CEO: Patrick Lynch
CFO: James T Garner
CFO: Eric Savadra
*CFO: Claude Warren
VP: Johnny Williams
Exec: Laurie Craver
Exec: Amy Lacey
Sls Mgr: Dixie Pellegrino
Board of Directors: L Duncan Greenwood

D-U-N-S 10-647-2418
HILLIARD CITY SCHOOL DISTRICT
2140 Atlas St, Columbus, OH 43228-9647
Tel (614) 921-7000 Founded/Ownrshp 1887
Sales 211.4MM EMP 1,700
Accts Dave Yost Columbus Ohio
SIC 8211 Public elementary & secondary schools
*Treas: Brian W Wilson
*Prin: Dale A McVey
MIS Dir: Chris Lewis
Teacher Pr: Roy Walker
HC Dir: Vicky Clark

D-U-N-S 00-220-6530 IMP
HILLIARD CORP (NY)
100 W 4th St, Elmira, NY 14901-2190
Tel (607) 733-7121 Founded/Ownrshp 1905
Sales 106.5MM EMP 610^E
Accts Mengel Metzer Barr & Co Llp
SIC 3564 3569 3823 Purification & dust collection equipment; Filters; Industrial instrmnts msrmnt display/control process variable
Ch Bd: Arie J Van Den Blink
*Pr: Gene A Ebbrecht
CFO: Lark Hilliard
*CFO: Gordon J Webster
*Ex VP: Steven J Chesebro
VP: Lindsey Canfield
*VP: Michael V Cantando
*VP: David Ochab
*VP: Juan G Parra
*VP: Jon L Williams
Genl Mgr: Laura Blew

HILLIARD LYONS
See J J B HILLIARD W L LYONS LLC

HILLIARD LYONS
See HILLIARD-LYONS INC

D-U-N-S 80-483-1105
HILLIARD-LYONS INC
HILLIARD LYONS
(Suby of HOUCHENS INDUSTRIES INC) ★
500 W Jefferson St # 700, Louisville, KY 40202-2861
Tel (502) 588-8400 Founded/Ownrshp 2008
Sales 25.3MM^E EMP 1,100
SIC 7389 Financial services
CEO: James R Allen
*VP: Chambers Moore
VP Opers: Sherri Heun

D-U-N-S 16-094-6992 IMP/EXP
HILLMAN COMPANIES INC
(Suby of HMAN INTERMEDIATE II HOLDINGS CORP) ★
10590 Hamilton Ave, Cincinnati, OH 45231-1764
Tel (513) 851-4900 Founded/Ownrshp 2010
Sales 786.9MM EMP 2,605
SIC 5072 7699 Hardware; Miscellaneous fasteners; Bolts, nuts & screws; Key duplicating shop
Ch Bd: Douglas J Cahill
CFO: Anthony A Vasconcellos
CFO: Jim Waters
Ofcr: Jessa Klippel
Sr VP: Terry R Owe
Sr VP: Terry Rowe
VP: Katie Durant
VP: George Huelsmann
VP: Dianne Lowry
VP: Bill Moreland
Prin: Mandy Holmes
Board of Directors: Max W Hillman Jr, Aaron P Jagdfeld, Jonathan R Lynch, Kevin M Mailender, Joseph Scharfenberger, Tyler Wolfram, Philip K Woodlief, Richard F Zannino

D-U-N-S 08-289-7922 IMP
HILLMAN GROUP INC
(Suby of HILLMAN COMPANIES INC) ★
10590 Hamilton Ave, Cincinnati, OH 45231-1764
Tel (513) 851-4900 Founded/Ownrshp 1998
Sales 221.8MM^E EMP 1,900
SIC 5072 Hardware
Ch: Douglas J Cahill
CEO: Gregory J Gluchowski Jr
CEO: James P Waters
CFO: Jeffrey S Leonard
CFO: Mike Schaeper
CFO: Anthony Vasconcellos
Sr VP: Ali Fartaj
Sr VP: John Glass
Sr VP: Todd Spangler
VP: Gary L Seeds
Prin: Doug Roberts

D-U-N-S 15-426-3644 IMP
HILLMAN GROUP INC
(*Suby of* HILLMAN COMPANIES INC) ★
8990 S Kyrene Rd, Tempe, AZ 85284-2907
Tel (800) 800-4900 *Founded/Ownrshp* 2000
Sales 55.0MM *EMP* 1,700
SIC 3429 5162 3599 Keys & key blanks; Plastics materials; Custom machinery
CEO: Max W Hillman
**Pr:* Richard P Hillman
**Pr:* Stephen W Miller
**CEO:* Greg Gluchowski
**COO:* Debbie Genna
**Treas:* David Brown
**VP:* George Heredia
**VP:* Michael Mueller
**VP:* David M Richards
IT Man: Dan Henderson
**VP Mfg:* Mark Yeary

D-U-N-S 10-737-1494
▲ HILLS BANCORPORATION
131 Main St, Hills, IA 52235-7777
Tel (319) 679-2291 *Founded/Ownrshp* 1982
Sales NA *EMP* 421
Tkr Sym HBIA *Exch* OTO
SIC 6022 State commercial banks
Pr: Dwight O Seegmilleer
COO: Keith Jones
CFO: Shari J Demaris
Trst Ofcr: Aaron Schaefer
**VP:* Theodore H Pacha
VP: Peter Sorensen
VP: Tracy Stotler
Genl Mgr: Jeff Riley
Board of Directors: Michael S Donovan, Thomas J Gill, Michael E Hodge, Emily A Hughes, James A Nowak, John W Phelan, Ann Marie Rhodes, Thomas R Wiele, Sheldon E Yoder

D-U-N-S 00-531-3846
■ HILLS BANK AND TRUST CO (IA)
(*Suby of* HILLS BANCORPORATION) ★
131 Main St, Hills, IA 52235-7777
Tel (319) 679-2291 *Founded/Ownrshp* 1904
Sales NA *EMP* 250
SIC 6022 State commercial banks
Pr: Dwight Seegmiller
Ofcr: Jace Bailey
Ofcr: Shaun Barry
Ofcr: Molly E Brown
Ofcr: Sarah Gould
Ofcr: Kenzie Hein
Ofcr: Holly Huggins
Ofcr: Peggy Keele
Ofcr: Brandon Keese
Ofcr: Bob Lamkins
Ofcr: Terry McAllister
Ofcr: Todd Nelson
Ofcr: Matthew Olson
Ofcr: Holly Randall
Ofcr: Kim Snyder
Ofcr: Teresa Walker
Trst Ofcr: Dale Farland
Trst Ofcr: Erin Grabe
Sr VP: Thomas Cilek
Sr VP: Brad Langguth
Sr VP: James Pratt

D-U-N-S 06-877-5311 IMP/EXP
■ HILLS PET NUTRITION INC
(*Suby of* COLGATE-PALMOLIVE CO) ★
400 Sw 8th Ave Ste 101, Topeka, KS 66603-3925
Tel (785) 354-8523 *Founded/Ownrshp* 1987
Sales 1.5MMM^E *EMP* 2,700
SIC 5149 2048 2047 Pet foods; Prepared feeds; Dog & cat food
CEO: Neil Thompson
Bd of Dir: Brady Sisk
VP: Richard Hawkins
VP: Sara Scrittore
Exec: Blake Hawley
Exec: Hein Meyer
Assoc Dir: Jason Murphy
Assoc Dir: Jim Walsh
Assoc Dir: Craig Wetnight
Comm Dir: Patricia Evans
Opers Mgr: Susan Brown

HILLSBORO REHABILITATI
See MIDAMERICA CARE FOUNDATION INC

D-U-N-S 03-078-5760
HILLSBORO SCHOOL DISTRICT 1J
3083 Ne 49th Pl, Hillsboro, OR 97124-6006
Tel (503) 640-8403 *Founded/Ownrshp* 1914
Sales 183.1MM^E *EMP* 3,500
Accts Pauly Rogers And Co PcT
SIC 8211 Public senior high school; Public junior high school
Dir Vol: Coleen Garrett
CFO: Diane Blaricom
VP: Walt Hellman
Off Mgr: Linda Cady
Pr Dir: Nicole Kaufman
Schl Brd P: Kim Strelchun
Teacher Pr: Kona Lew-Williams

D-U-N-S 06-591-5209
HILLSBOROUGH COMMUNITY COLLEGE INC
DISTRICT BRD TRUSTEES HILLSBOR
39 Columbia Dr, Tampa, FL 33606-3584
Tel (813) 253-7000 *Founded/Ownrshp* 1968
Sales 64.9MM^E *EMP* 1,025
SIC 8222 Community college
Pr: Ken Atwater
Pr: Pat Dix
Pr: Paul Nagy
**CFO:* Al Erdman
CFO: Barbara Larson
Exec: Kimberly Mathew
Nrsg Dir: Alma I Vega

D-U-N-S 07-979-9075
HILLSBOROUGH COUNTY PUBLIC SCHOOLS
901 E Kennedy Blvd, Tampa, FL 33602-3502
Tel (813) 272-4050 *Founded/Ownrshp* 2015
Sales 3.0MMM *EMP* 26,000^E
SIC 8211 Public elementary & secondary schools
Prgrm Mgr: Clara Reynolds
Dir IT: Charles Fuhrmeister
Psych: Elmer Booth

D-U-N-S 04-247-1060
HILLSBOROUGH COUNTY SCHOOL DISTRICT
MIDDLE SCHOOLS EDUCATION OFF
901 E Kennedy Blvd, Tampa, FL 33602-3502
Tel (813) 272-4000 *Founded/Ownrshp* 1934
Sales 2.0MMM *EMP* 25,000
Accts Kpmg Llp Tampa Fl
SIC 8211 Public elementary & secondary schools
Ch: April Griffin
Bd of Dir: Christopher Jargo
Bd of Dir: Francine Lawson
VP: Steven Nguyen
Dir Risk M: Xiomara Fuentes
Dir Risk M: Holly Sloop
Comm Man: Paula Romano
Dir Sec: John R Newman
CIO: Barrington Williamson
MIS Dir: Pansy Houghton
Prd Mgr: Denise Castillo

D-U-N-S 05-238-9244
HILLSBOROUGH TOWNSHIP BOARD OF EDUCATION
379 S Branch Rd, Hillsborough, NJ 08844-4489
Tel (908) 431-6600 *Founded/Ownrshp* 2004
Sales 125.0MM *EMP* 1,100
Accts Timothy M Vrabel/Chris W Hwa
SIC 8211 School board
Pr: Thomas Kinst
HC Dir: Lorraine Borek

D-U-N-S 79-119-0395
HILLSBOROUGH TOWNSHIP SCHOOL DISTRICT
379 S Branch Rd, Hillsborough, NJ 08844-4489
Tel (908) 431-6600 *Founded/Ownrshp* 2007
Sales 24.2MM^E *EMP* 1,200^E
SIC 8211 Public elementary school
Treas: Thomas Bittle
MIS Dir: Joel Handler
Pr Dir: Kia Bergman
Teacher Pr: Michael Volpe

D-U-N-S 04-878-1561
HILLSDALE COLLEGE
HILLSDALE COLLEGE BOOK STORE
33 E College St, Hillsdale, MI 49242-1298
Tel (517) 437-7341 *Founded/Ownrshp* 1844
Sales 200.3MM *EMP* 504
Accts Plante & Moran Pllc Portage
SIC 8221 8211 College, except junior; Academy; Private elementary school; Private senior high school
Pr: Larry P Arnn
VP: Jack Oxenrider
Genl Mgr: Kevin Kirwan
Psych: Iona Kopp
Doctor: Rein Zeller
Snr Mgr: Victoria Fassett

HILLSDALE COLLEGE BOOK STORE
See HILLSDALE COLLEGE

D-U-N-S 00-521-3962 EXP
■ HILLSHIRE BRANDS CO
SARA LEE FOOD & BEVERAGE
(*Suby of* TYSON FOODS INC) ★
400 S Jefferson St Fl 1, Chicago, IL 60607-3812
Tel (312) 614-6000 *Founded/Ownrshp* 1942, 2014
Sales 3.6MMM^E *EMP* 9,100^E
SIC 2013 2051 2053 Sausages & other prepared meats; Breads, rolls & buns; Frozen bakery products, except bread
Pr: Sean M Connolly
**CFO:* Maria Henry
CFO: Dennis Leatherby
Sr Cor Off: Thao Dekool
Ofcr: Jon Harris
Ofcr: Tony Reece
**Ex VP:* Andrew P Callahan
**Ex VP:* Kent B Magill
Ex VP: Judith Sprieser
Ex VP: David L Van Bebber
Sr VP: Brian Davison
Sr VP: James G Ruehlmann
VP: Greg Appleton
VP: Sara Bakery
VP: Bill Crosby
VP: Rick Elmore
VP: Ernie Hanington
VP: Thomas Hayes
VP: Kristen Holleman
VP: Stephen Kincanon
VP: Sheila Moore

D-U-N-S 07-970-0878
HILLSIDE FAMILY OF AGENCIES
1183 Monroe Ave, Rochester, NY 14620-1662
Tel (585) 256-7500 *Founded/Ownrshp* 1837
Sales 143.3MM *EMP* 2,300
Accts Dopkins & Company Llp Buffal
SIC 8361 8322 8093 Children's home; Individual & family services; Specialty outpatient clinics
Pr: Dennis Richardson
**CFO:* Paul Perrotto
Treas: Eileen Semmler
Ofcr: Kimberly Benson
Ex Dir: Wayne O'Connor
Prgrm Mgr: Jean Burdick
Info Man: Caroyln Kenny
Sls&Mrk Ex: John Barr
Sls Mgr: Matthew Burgdorf
Sls Mgr: Meredith Feary
Doctor: James W Cotter

D-U-N-S 62-053-0147
HILLSIDE FAMILY OF AGENCIES
(*Suby of* HILLSIDE FAMILY OF AGENCIES) ★
1183 Monroe Ave, Rochester, NY 14620-1662
Tel (585) 256-7500 *Founded/Ownrshp* 1995
Sales 100.1MM *EMP* 1^E
SIC 8322 Family service agency
Pr: Dennis Richardson

HILLSIDE MANOR
See BEAVER DAM COMMUNITY HOSPITALS INC

D-U-N-S 10-542-3599
HILLSIDES CHILDRENS CENTER
HILLSIDE'S COMMUNITY SERVICE P
24 Liberty St, Bath, NY 14810-1507
Tel (607) 776-7480 *Founded/Ownrshp* 2002
Sales 100.0MM *EMP* 2
SIC 8322 Social service center
Prin: Dennis M Richardson

HILLSIDE'S COMMUNITY SERVICE P
See HILLSIDES CHILDRENS CENTER

D-U-N-S 08-351-3960
HILLSTONE RESTAURANT GROUP INC
BANDERA
147 S Beverly Dr, Beverly Hills, CA 90212-3002
Tel (310) 385-7343 *Founded/Ownrshp* 1977
Sales 151.4MM^E *EMP* 4,500
SIC 5812 5813 Restaurant, family: chain; Cocktail lounge
Pr: George W Biel
**COO:* James V Branstetter
**CFO:* Scott Ashby
Genl Mgr: Tim Landrey
IT Man: John Reynolds
VP Opers: Tino Ciambriello

D-U-N-S 00-424-5353
HILLTOP BASIC RESOURCES INC
HILLTOP CONCRETE
1 W 4th St Ste 1100, Cincinnati, OH 45202-3610
Tel (513) 651-5000 *Founded/Ownrshp* 1930
Sales 135.0MM^E *EMP* 190
SIC 1442 3273 Construction sand mining; Gravel mining; Ready-mixed concrete
CEO: John F Steele Jr
**Pr:* Kevin M Sheehan
**CFO:* Paul Hennekes
**VP:* Brad Slabaugh
Genl Mgr: Mike Marchioni
MIS Dir: Sabriana Ferree
Opers Mgr: Roger Thayer

HILLTOP CONCRETE
See HILLTOP BASIC RESOURCES INC

D-U-N-S 04-837-0071
▲ HILLTOP HOLDINGS INC
200 Crescent Ct Ste 1330, Dallas, TX 75201-6920
Tel (214) 855-2177 *Founded/Ownrshp* 1998
Sales NA *EMP* 5,300
Tkr Sym HTH *Exch* NYS
SIC 6022 7389 State commercial banks; Financial services
Pr: Jeremy B Ford
**Ch Bd:* Gerald J Ford
CFO: William B Furr
**V Ch Bd:* Alan B White
Ofcr: Darren Parmenter
Ex VP: Corey G Prestidge

D-U-N-S 07-967-9560
■ HILLTOP SECURITIES HOLDINGS LLC
(*Suby of* HILLTOP HOLDINGS INC) ★
200 Crescent Ct Ste 1330, Dallas, TX 75201-6920
Tel (214) 855-2177 *Founded/Ownrshp* 2014
Sales 236.5MM^E *EMP* 892^E
SIC 6211 Brokers, security
Pr: Jeremy B Ford
**CFO:* Darren E Parmenter

D-U-N-S 05-866-8138
■ HILLTOP SECURITIES INC
QUINN/SOUTHWEST
(*Suby of* HILLTOP SECURITIES HOLDINGS LLC) ★
1201 Elm St Ste 3500, Dallas, TX 75270-2108
Tel (214) 859-1800 *Founded/Ownrshp* 1984
Sales 183.3MM^E *EMP* 360^E
SIC 6211 Brokers, security; Dealers, security; Bond dealers & brokers
Pr: Robert W Peterson
Ch Bd: William D Felder IV
Pr: Joseph Freeze
CFO: Stacy M Hodges
Treas: Laura Leventhal
Ofcr: Dagmara Frankowska
Ex VP: Miles Benickes
Ex VP: David Frieden
Ex VP: Kevin D Kott
Ex VP: Daniel R Leland
Ex VP: Richard H Litton
Ex VP: Holly Peritz
Ex VP: Mark Sachse
Ex VP: Jeffrey J Singer
Ex VP: Larry G Tate
Ex VP: Michael Urman
Sr VP: Jeff Bohnsack
Sr VP: Rick Crews
Sr VP: Maryrose Dombrowski
Sr VP: Joe Gendell
Sr VP: Kyle Grossart

D-U-N-S 80-163-9647
HILLTOPPER HOLDING CORP
303 Perimeter Ctr N # 500, Atlanta, GA 30346-3401
Tel (770) 698-9040 *Founded/Ownrshp* 2000
Sales 257.7MM^E *EMP* 10,000
SIC 8051 8741 Skilled nursing care facilities; Management services
CEO: Kent Fosha

D-U-N-S 19-681-8488
HILLWOOD DEVELOPMENT CORP
3090 Olive St Ste 300, Dallas, TX 75219-7640
Tel (214) 303-5535 *Founded/Ownrshp* 1985
Sales 165.4MM^E *EMP* 150
SIC 6552 6531 Subdividers & developers; Real estate agent, commercial
Pr: David A Newsom
**Ch Bd:* H Ross Perot Jr
**CFO:* James C Swaim
**Treas:* M Thomas Mason
**Treas:* Tom Mason
Ofcr: Fred Balda
Ex VP: Robert Vicente
VP: Shelby Bush
VP: Doug Dureau
VP: Timothy Kinnear
VP: Angie Mastrocola
**VP:* Todd L Platt
VP: Don Reid
VP: Perry Wallace
VP: Jake Walter

D-U-N-S 00-696-6865
HILLYARD INC
302 N 4th St, Saint Joseph, MO 64501-1720
Tel (816) 233-1321 *Founded/Ownrshp* 1907
Sales 463.9MM^E *EMP* 800
SIC 5169 5087 Industrial chemicals; Cleaning & maintenance equipment & supplies
Pr: Robert Roth
CFO: Neil Ambrose
CFO: Lance Woodall
**Ex VP:* Scott Hillyard
Ex VP: Jim Roth
VP: Marc George
VP: Doug Holland
VP: Jon Martin
VP: Steven Stumpf
Dir Risk M: Bob Vey
Area Mgr: Greer Heindel

D-U-N-S 13-160-2112 IMP/EXP
HILMAR CHEESE CO INC
HILMAR INGREDIENTS
8901 Lander Ave, Hilmar, CA 95324-9327
Tel (209) 667-6076 *Founded/Ownrshp* 1984
Sales 220.1MM^E *EMP* 600^E
SIC 2022 Natural cheese
Pr: John J Jeter
CFO: Donald Jay Hicks
Sls Mgr: James Shriver

HILMAR INGREDIENTS
See HILMAR CHEESE CO INC

HILO FISH COMPANY
See CMU & ASSOCIATES INC

HILO HATTIE
See POMARE LTD

D-U-N-S 05-964-0362
HILO MEDICAL CENTER
1190 Waianuenue Ave, Hilo, HI 96720-2094
Tel (808) 932-3000 *Founded/Ownrshp* 2008
Sales 150.6MM *EMP* 1,310
SIC 8011 Medical centers
CEO: Dan Brinkman
Chf Rad: Ming Peng
**CFO:* Money Atwal
Sls&Mrk Ex: Elena Cabatu
Dir Health: Carol Kelley-Rimozsky

D-U-N-S 80-004-0206
■ HILSTAR INSURANCE CO
INFINITY NATIONAL INSURANCE CO
(*Suby of* INFINITY PROPERTY AND CASUALTY CORP) ★
2201 4th Ave N, Birmingham, AL 35203-3863
Tel (205) 870-4000 *Founded/Ownrshp* 1992
Sales NA *EMP* 450
SIC 6331 Automobile insurance
Pr: Glen N Godwin
**VP:* Roger Prestridge
**VP:* Sheila H Williams

D-U-N-S 00-117-3525 IMP/EXP
HILTI INC
(*Suby of* HILTI OF AMERICA INC) ★
7250 Dallas Pkwy Ste 1000, Plano, TX 75024-4998
Tel (800) 879-8000 *Founded/Ownrshp* 1981
Sales 357.5MM^E *EMP* 800
SIC 5072 Hand tools
Pr: Cary Evert
**CFO:* Eugene Hodel
Ex VP: Bo Risberg
VP: Pat Ahmad
**VP:* Kelly Beaver
VP: John Guttery
VP: Bertrand Pallud
VP: Marty Schofield
Dir Bus: Thomas Allen
Dir Bus: Terri Hendricks
Rgnl Mgr: Kent Cook

D-U-N-S 13-105-8364 IMP/EXP
HILTI OF AMERICA INC
(*Suby of* HILTI AKTIENGESELLSCHAFT)
7250 Dallas Pkwy Ste 1000, Plano, TX 75024-4998
Tel (800) 879-8000 *Founded/Ownrshp* 1976
Sales 409.8MM^E *EMP* 800^E
SIC 5084 3546 3825 Drilling equipment, excluding bits; Drills & drilling tools; Standards & calibration equipment for electrical measuring
Pr: Cary Evert

HILTON
See PARK HOTELS & RESORTS INC

HILTON
See DEZURIK INC

D-U-N-S 07-922-5174
■ HILTON GARDEN INNS MANAGEMENT LLC
(*Suby of* HILTON) ★
7930 Jones Branch Dr, Mc Lean, VA 22102-3388
Tel (703) 448-6100 *Founded/Ownrshp* 2013
Sales 30.2MM^E *EMP* 2,785^E
SIC 7011 Hotels & motels; Inns
VP: W Steven Standefer

D-U-N-S 07-919-1779
HILTON GLOBAL HOLDINGS LLC
(*Suby of* HILTON WORLDWIDE) ★
7930 Jones Branch Dr # 1100, Mc Lean, VA 22102-3388
Tel (703) 883-1000 *Founded/Ownrshp* 2010
Sales 359.4M^E *EMP* 7,491^E
SIC 6794 7011 Franchises, selling or licensing; Hotels

D-U-N-S 18-995-1247
■ HILTON GRAND VACATIONS CO LLC
(*Suby of* HILTON) ★
5323 Millenia Lakes Blvd # 400, Orlando, FL 32839-3395
Tel (407) 722-3100 *Founded/Ownrshp* 2001
Sales 315.6MM^E *EMP* 611
SIC 6552 Subdividers & developers
Treas: Stuart Zais
Ex VP: Sarah Kramer
Ex VP: Michael Shader
**Sr VP:* Johann Murray
**Sr VP:* Mark Wang
VP: David Desforges
VP: Dave Hager
VP: Barbara Hollkamp
VP: Anthony Picciano
VP: Gus Riera
VP: Marie Sarno
**VP:* Rebecca Sloan
VP: Casa Ybel

D-U-N-S 07-922-6805
■ HILTON HAWAII CORP
HILTON WORLDWIDE HOLDINGS
(*Suby of* HILTON WORLDWIDE HOLDINGS INC) ★
7930 Jones Branch Dr, Mc Lean, VA 22102-3388
Tel (703) 883-1000 *Founded/Ownrshp* 2013
Sales 10.2MM^E *EMP* 5,009^E
SIC 7011 Hotels & motels
Prin: Hilda Hilton
Ex VP: Matt Schuyler
Sls Mgr: Brittany Aanestad
Sls Mgr: Jessica Jankowski
Sls Mgr: Georgette Lake
Sls Mgr: Brittani Libring
Sls Mgr: Ava Setzer
Sls Mgr: Tammy Wade

D-U-N-S 00-787-3268
■ HILTON HAWAIIAN VILLAGE LLC (HI)
(*Suby of* HILTON) ★
2005 Kalia Rd, Honolulu, HI 96815-1917
Tel (808) 949-4321 *Founded/Ownrshp* 1961, 1998
Sales 82.9MM^E *EMP* 1,725
SIC 7011 5812 5813

D-U-N-S 06-932-4689
■ HILTON HEAD HEALTH SYSTEM LP
HILTON HEAD HOSPITAL AND CLINICS
(*Suby of* TENET HEALTHCARE CORP) ★
25 Hospital Cntr Blvrd, Hilton Head Island, SC 29926
Tel (843) 681-6122 *Founded/Ownrshp* 1994
Sales 137.3MM *EMP* 425
SIC 8062 General medical & surgical hospitals
Genl Pt: Tenet Health System
COO: Brad Moore
COO: Tom Neal

HILTON HEAD HOSPITAL AND CLINICS
See HILTON HEAD HEALTH SYSTEM LP

D-U-N-S 86-140-6163
HILTON HEAD HOSPITAL REHAB
35 Bill Fries Dr Bldg D, Hilton Head Island, SC 29926-2731
Tel (843) 681-4088 *Founded/Ownrshp* 1994
Sales 94.3MM *EMP* 2
SIC 8049 Occupational therapist
Owner: R S Jones

D-U-N-S 80-816-2098
HILTON HOTELS HOLDINGS CORP
345 Park Ave, New York, NY 10154-0004
Tel (212) 583-5000 *Founded/Ownrshp* 2007
Sales NA *EMP* 7,140
SIC 7011 6794

D-U-N-S 96-557-7872
■ HILTON HOTELS HOLDINGS LLC
(*Suby of* HILTON WORLDWIDE HOLDINGS INC) ★
7930 Jones Branch Dr, Mc Lean, VA 22102-3388
Tel (703) 883-1000 *Founded/Ownrshp* 2010
Sales 172.7MM^E *EMP* 7,150^E
SIC 7011 Hotels & motels

D-U-N-S 07-922-5234
■ HILTON ILLINOIS HOLDINGS LLC
(*Suby of* HILTON WORLDWIDE HOLDINGS INC) ★
7930 Jones Branch Dr, Mc Lean, VA 22102-3388
Tel (703) 883-1000 *Founded/Ownrshp* 2013
Sales 6.5MM^E *EMP* 5,005^E
SIC 7011 Hotels & motels

D-U-N-S 07-530-2570
■ HILTON INNS INC
(*Suby of* HILTON) ★
9336 Civic Center Dr, Beverly Hills, CA 90210-3604
Tel (310) 278-4321 *Founded/Ownrshp* 1965
Sales 188.3MM^E *EMP* 3,479^E
SIC 7011 Hotels & motels
Ch Bd: Stephen F Bollenbach
Pr: Linda Bain
**Pr:* Dieter H Huckestein
**CFO:* Matthew J Hart
**Ex VP:* Thomas L Keltner
Sr VP: Phil Cordell
Sr VP: Habib Enayetullah
Sr VP: Molly McKenzie-Swartz
Sr VP: Patrick B Terwilliger
VP: Francisco Alvarenga
VP: Craig Armstrong
VP: Dawn Beghi
VP: Bill Brooks
VP: Damien Dean
VP: David Depkon
VP: William Fortier
VP: Dianne Jaskulske
VP: Linda Matthies
VP: Mary B Parks
VP: David Thompson
Comm Dir: Jeanne Rice

D-U-N-S 01-206-2642
HILTON INTERNATIONAL CO
(*Suby of* HILTON INTERNATIONAL HOTELS (UK) LIMITED)
5201 Blue Lagoon Dr # 600, Miami, FL 33126-2075
Tel (305) 444-3444 *Founded/Ownrshp* 1987
Sales 370.0MM^E *EMP* 49,690
SIC 7011 5812 Hotels & motels; Eating places
Prin: Christopher J Nassetta
**Pr:* Joe Berger
**VP:* Jeff Diskin
**VP:* William G Margaritis
VP: Chris Marshall
**VP:* Matthew W Schuyler
Mng Dir: Ron Yariv
Genl Mgr: Christian Riof
Dir IT: Luis De Avila
Sls Mgr: Jenifer Winters
Snr Mgr: Gwen Forbes

D-U-N-S 79-869-2539
■ HILTON NEW YORK
HILTON NEW YORK AND TOWERS
(*Suby of* HILTON) ★
1335 Ave Of The Americas, New York, NY 10019-6012
Tel (212) 586-7000 *Founded/Ownrshp* 2001
Sales 54.5MM^E *EMP* 1,400
SIC 6512 Commercial & industrial building operation
Genl Mgr: Mark Lauer
Bd of Dir: Conrad Wangeman
MIS Dir: Israel Deleon

HILTON NEW YORK AND TOWERS
See HILTON NEW YORK

D-U-N-S 03-167-6307
■ HILTON RESERVATIONS WORLDWIDE LLC
(*Suby of* HILTON) ★
2050 Chenault Dr, Carrollton, TX 75006-5096
Tel (972) 770-6100 *Founded/Ownrshp* 1997
Sales 106.5MM^E *EMP* 2,000
SIC 7011 Hotels & motels
CEO: Christopher J Nassetta
**Pr:* Joe Berger
**Ex VP:* Kathryn Beiser
**Ex VP:* Kristin Campbell
**Ex VP:* Jeff Diskin
VP: Bryan Thomason
IT Man: Doug Weidler

D-U-N-S 04-442-8506 IMP
■ HILTON SUPPLY MANAGEMENT LLC
(*Suby of* HILTON) ★
7930 Jones Branch Dr # 400, Mc Lean, VA 22102-3388
Tel (703) 883-1000 *Founded/Ownrshp* 1967
Sales 240.3MM^E *EMP* 330
SIC 5046 5021 Hotel equipment & supplies; Furniture
Pr: Chris Nassetta
IT Man: Victoria Graham

HILTON WORLDWIDE
See BH HOTELS HOLDCO LLC

HILTON WORLDWIDE HOLDINGS
See HILTON HAWAII CORP

D-U-N-S 07-913-2993
▲ HILTON WORLDWIDE HOLDINGS INC
7930 Jones Branch Dr # 100, Mc Lean, VA 22102-3389
Tel (703) 883-1000 *Founded/Ownrshp* 1919
Sales 11.2MMM *EMP* 164,000
Tkr Sym HLT *Exch* NYS
SIC 7011 6794 Hotels & motels; Resort hotel; Franchises, selling or licensing
Pr: Christopher J Nassetta
**Ch Bd:* Jonathan D Gray
CFO: Kevin J Jacobs
Chf Cred: Christopher W Silcock
Ofcr: Matthew W Schuyler
Ex VP: Kristin A Campbell
Ex VP: Ian R Carter
Ex VP: James E Holthouser
Ex VP: Mark D Wang
Sr VP: Katie Beirne Fallon
Board of Directors: Jon M Huntsman Jr, Judith A McHale, John G Schreiber, Elizabeth A Smith, Douglas M Steenland, William J Stein

HILTON WORLDWIDE, INC.
See PARK HOTELS & RESORTS INC

HIMA SAN PABLO HOSPITAL
See GRUPO HIMA-SAN PABLO INC

D-U-N-S 83-194-9545
HIMAGINE SOLUTIONS INC
600 Emerson Rd Ste 225, Saint Louis, MO 63141-6725
Tel (314) 627-5135 *Founded/Ownrshp* 2014
Sales 100.0MM *EMP* 1,000
SIC 8741 7361 Hospital management; Nursing & personal care facility management; Employment agencies
**CFO:* Mark D Rowland
Exec: Michelle Martin
Dir IT: Don Sloan

HIMCO
See HARTFORD INVESTMENT MANAGEMENT CO

D-U-N-S 10-752-1189 IMP
HINCKLEY & SCHMITT INC
HINCKLEY SPRINGS
(*Suby of* SUNTORY INTERNATIONAL CORP) ★
6055 S Harlem Ave, Chicago, IL 60638-3985
Tel (773) 586-8600 *Founded/Ownrshp* 1996
Sales 147.2MM^E *EMP* 2,190
SIC 2086 5149 7359 Water, pasteurized: packaged in cans, bottles, etc.; Water, distilled; Mineral or spring water bottling; Equipment rental & leasing
Pr: David A Krishcok
Ql Cn Mgr: Tiffany Miller

HINCKLEY COMPANY, THE
See TALARIA CO LLC

HINCKLEY SPRINGS
See HINCKLEY & SCHMITT INC

D-U-N-S 07-507-1399
HINDS COMMUNITY COLLEGE DISTRICT PUBLIC IMPROVEMENT CORP
501 E Main St, Raymond, MS 39154-9700
Tel (601) 857-5261 *Founded/Ownrshp* 1916
Sales 24.3MM^E *EMP* 1,000
SIC 8222 8221 Community college; Colleges universities & professional schools
CEO: Robert Smith
**Pr:* Clayde Muse

D-U-N-S 19-732-9089 IMP
HINES CORP
1218 E Pontaluna Rd Ste B, Norton Shores, MI 49456-9634
Tel (231) 799-6240 *Founded/Ownrshp* 1987
Sales 240.4MM^E *EMP* 650
SIC 3443 3823 3589 3531 3535 5082 Boilers: industrial, power, or marine; Fluidic devices, circuits & systems for process control; Floor washing & polishing machines, commercial; Construction machinery; Roofing equipment; Conveyors & conveying equipment; General construction machinery & equipment
Pr: Larry Hines
CFO: Greg Longcore
VP: Michele Buckley
VP: Mark Hefty
VP: Jeffrey McCauley
VP: Tom Thompson
Software D: Ginger Smith

D-U-N-S 83-147-5285
HINES GLOBAL REIT INC
2800 Post Oak Blvd # 5000, Houston, TX 77056-6100
Tel (888) 220-6121 *Founded/Ownrshp* 2008
Sales 476.8MM *EMP* 27^E
Accts Deloitte & Touche Llp Houston
SIC 6798 Real estate investment trusts
CEO: Sherri Shugart
**CFO:* Ryan T Sims
**Treas:* J Shea Morgenroth
**Chf Inves:* Edmund A Donaldson
Mng Dir: Young Lim

D-U-N-S 61-925-0665 IMP
HINES HORTICULTURE INC
HINES NURSERIES
12621 Jeffrey Rd, Irvine, CA 92620
Tel (949) 559-4444 *Founded/Ownrshp* 2008
Sales 1.8MMM^E *EMP* 2,100
SIC 0181 5261

D-U-N-S 00-793-1645 IMP
HINES INTERESTS LIMITED PARTNERSHIP
2800 Post Oak Blvd # 4800, Houston, TX 77056-6118
Tel (713) 621-8000 *Founded/Ownrshp* 1957, 1990
Sales 2.0MMM^E *EMP* 3,200
Accts Ernst & Young Llp Houston Tx
SIC 6552 Land subdividers & developers, commercial
Pt: Gerald D Hines
Pt: Jeffrey C Hines
CFO: Charles M Baughn
Chf Inves: Edmund Donaldson
Ex VP: Jim Buie
Ex VP: Ken Hubbard
Ex VP: Louis Sklar
Sr VP: Jesse Carrillo
Sr VP: Thomas Danilek
Sr VP: Daniel Rashin
VP: Michael Allen
VP: Ty Bennion
VP: David Braaten
VP: Jerry L Brown
VP: Michael Chiat
VP: David Congdon
VP: Mark Cummings
VP: James Curry
VP: Thomas D'Arcy
VP: Tom Darcy
VP: Michael Desguin
Board of Directors: Sherri W Schugart

HINES NURSERIES
See HINES HORTICULTURE INC

D-U-N-S 96-992-7375 IMP
HINES PRECISION INC
5680 Old Highway 54, Philpot, KY 42366-9645
Tel (270) 729-4242 *Founded/Ownrshp* 1999
Sales 172.9MM^E *EMP* 1,283
SIC 3469 3444 Metal stampings; Sheet metalwork
Pr: Kevin Booth
CFO: Bill Young
**VP:* Joseph Acquisto
VP: Mark Osborne
**VP:* Steven Shultz
Info Man: Henry Waldschmidt
VP Mfg: Ray Goodman
Opers Mgr: David Parsley

D-U-N-S 82-603-4717
HINES REAL ESTATE INVESTMENT TRUST INC
2800 Post Oak Blvd # 4800, Houston, TX 77056-6100
Tel (713) 621-8000 *Founded/Ownrshp* 2004
Sales 218.7MM *EMP* 5^E
Accts Deloitte & Touche Llp Houston
SIC 6798 Real estate investment trusts
Prin: Jeffrey Hines

D-U-N-S 07-470-6896
HINKLE CONTRACTING CORP
(*Suby of* SUMMIT MATERIALS LLC) ★
395 N Middletown Rd, Paris, KY 40361-2138
Tel (859) 987-3670 *Founded/Ownrshp* 2010
Sales 291.7MM^E *EMP* 850
SIC 1611 1422 3273 3272 3271 2951 Highway & street paving contractor; Grading; Crushed & broken limestone; Ready-mixed concrete; Concrete products; Concrete block & brick; Asphalt paving mixtures & blocks
CEO: Thomas Hinkle
**Pr:* Henry Hinkle
**Treas:* Thomas M Brannock
**Ex VP:* William Cress
VP: Willie Griffith
VP: Tom Hainkle

VP: Chris Keller
VP: Jeffrey Mingus
VP: Tom Ralston
**VP:* Gordon Wilson
Area Mgr: Greg Howard

D-U-N-S 88-490-4624 IMP/EXP
HINO MOTORS MANUFACTURING USA INC
(*Suby of* HINO MOTORS, LTD.)
37777 Interchange Dr, Farmington Hills, MI 48335-1030
Tel (248) 442-9077 *Founded/Ownrshp* 1994
Sales 105.8MM^E *EMP* 64
SIC 5013 Truck parts & accessories
Pr: Hideyuki Omata
**CEO:* Kazuhiro Somiya
**VP:* Hiroyuri Kobayashi
Admn Mgr: Lora Sorek
Sales Asso: Kim Shaieb
Snr Mgr: Jennifer Presher

D-U-N-S 06-947-8352
HINSHAW & CULBERTSON LLP
222 N La Salle St Ste 300, Chicago, IL 60601-1081
Tel (312) 704-3000 *Founded/Ownrshp* 1934
Sales 200.0MM *EMP* 1,010
SIC 8111 General practice law office
Mng Pt: J William Roberts
Pt: Kevin Joseph Burke
Pt: Donald L Mrozek
COO: Evan Brown
CFO: Robert Johnson
CFO: Ed Oconnell
Bd of Dir: Peter E Pederson
VP: Jennifer Friedman
Exec: Jennifer Soria
Exec: Terry Wand
Off Mgr: Cheryl Coates

HINTZSCHE OIL
See HFI ENTERPRISES INC

D-U-N-S 03-841-4004
HIP ADMINISTRATORS OF FLORIDA INC
HEALTH INSUR PLAN ADMNSTRATORS
(*Suby of* EMBLEMHEALTH INC) ★
3251 Hollywood Blvd # 401, Hollywood, FL 33021-6947
Tel (954) 893-6400 *Founded/Ownrshp* 1994
Sales NA *EMP* 500
SIC 6324 Hospital & medical service plans
CEO: Anthony Watson
**VP:* James Grenidge

D-U-N-S 07-966-1552
HIRAIN TECHNOLOGIES USA INC
(*Suby of* BEIJING JINGWEI HIRAIN TECHNOLOGIES CO., LTD.)
37632 Hills Tech Dr, Farmington Hills, MI 48331-5727
Tel (248) 839-1309 *Founded/Ownrshp* 2009
Sales 100.0MM *EMP* 6
SIC 5013 8711 Automotive supplies & parts; Engineering services
CEO: Yong Deng

D-U-N-S 03-376-4283 IMP/EXP
HIRATA CORP OF AMERICA
(*Suby of* HIRATA CORPORATION)
5625 Decatur Blvd, Indianapolis, IN 46241-9509
Tel (317) 856-8600 *Founded/Ownrshp* 1980
Sales 150.0MM *EMP* 100
Accts Pricewaterhousecoopers Llp
SIC 3535 3537 8711 Conveyors & conveying equipment; Industrial trucks & tractors; Engineering services
Pr: Biagio Longo
**Ex VP:* Kenichiro Otomaru
Snr PM: Joseph Rizk

D-U-N-S 10-673-8339
HIRE THINKING INC
ADVANTAGE XPO
(*Suby of* ADVANTAGE STAFFING) ★
220 Norwood Park S Ste 1, Norwood, MA 02062-4690
Tel (781) 251-8000 *Founded/Ownrshp* 2004
Sales 27.8MM^E *EMP* 1,250
SIC 7363 Temporary help service
Pr: Karen Browne
**Treas:* Daniel A Lasman
VP Sls: Matt Stager

HIRERIGHT
See CORPORATE RISK HOLDINGS III INC

D-U-N-S 79-234-8021
HIRERIGHT LLC
(*Suby of* CORPORATE RISK HOLDINGS LLC) ★
3349 Michelson Dr Ste 150, Irvine, CA 92612-8881
Tel (949) 428-5800 *Founded/Ownrshp* 2013
Sales 287.3MM^E *EMP* 407^E
SIC 7375 7374 Data base information retrieval; Data verification service
CEO: John Fennelly
COO: Brian Pierson
CFO: Richard Little
CFO: Thomas Spaeth
Ofcr: Jim Weber
VP: Catherine Aldrich
VP: Robin Allen
VP: Jeana Campbell
VP: Gregg Freeman
VP: Dante Jones
VP: Susan Kirton
VP: Tony Magro
VP: Marc Maloy
VP: Megan Mayer
VP: Mary O'Loughlin
Exec: Michele Dominguez

HIRESTRATEGY
See ADDISON PROFESSIONAL FINANCIAL SEARCH LLC

D-U-N-S 36-072-9693 IMP/EXP
HIROTEC AMERICA INC
(*Suby of* HIROTEC CORPORATION)
3000 High Meadow Cir, Auburn Hills, MI 48326-2837
Tel (248) 836-5100 *Founded/Ownrshp* 1988

Sales 107.0MM^E *EMP* 600
Accts Plante & Moran Pllc Auburn H
SIC 3569 Assembly machines, non-metalworking
CEO: Katsutoshi Uno
**Pr:* Jim Toeniskoetter
**CFO:* Brian McGinnity
**Ex VP:* Paul Demarco
**VP:* Scott Abbate
**VP:* Sharon Beetham
**VP:* Brian Hopkins
**VP:* Gary Krus

D-U-N-S 00-796-5460 EXP
HIRSCH PIPE & SUPPLY CO INC (CA)
15025 Oxnard St Ste 100, Van Nuys, CA 91411-2640
Tel (818) 756-0900 *Founded/Ownrshp* 1934, 1946
Sales 167.3MM^E *EMP* 265
SIC 5074 Plumbing & hydronic heating supplies
Pr: William D Glockner Jr
**Ch Bd:* Daniel J Mariscal
CFO: Bradley A Enstein
**CFO:* Joseph R King
**Treas:* Greg Mariscal
Brnch Mgr: Gonzalo Chanto
IT Man: Bill Glockner
IT Man: Jeremiah Owen

D-U-N-S 82-843-5870 EXP
HIRSCHFELD HOLDINGS LP
HIRSCHFELD INDUSTRIES
112 W 29th St, San Angelo, TX 76903-2553
Tel (325) 486-4201 *Founded/Ownrshp* 1926
Sales 171.7MM^E *EMP* 800^E
SIC 1622 3441 Bridge construction; Fabricated structural metal
Pt: Dennis Hirschfeld
**CFO:* Rodney L Goodwill
CFO: Brandon Moore
**Ex VP:* John O Quinn
**Sr VP:* Jacob Balderas
VP: Doug Ames
VP: Wendall Hirschfeld
VP: Gary Scherf
Genl Mgr: Brian Patton
Trfc Dir: Dana Keesee
Sfty Mgr: Kim Coats

HIRSCHFELD INDUSTRIES
See HIRSCHFELD STEEL GROUP LP

HIRSCHFELD INDUSTRIES
See HIRSCHFELD HOLDINGS LP

D-U-N-S 10-729-9851
HIRSCHFELD STEEL GROUP LP
HIRSCHFELD INDUSTRIES
(*Suby of* INSIGHT EQUITY LP) ★
112 W 29th St, San Angelo, TX 76903-2553
Tel (325) 486-4201 *Founded/Ownrshp* 2006
Sales 90.3MM^E *EMP* 400
SIC 3441 Fabricated structural metal
CEO: Dennis Hirschfeld
Pr: Richard W Phillips
CFO: Mide Depopus
CFO: Rodney L Goodwill
Ofcr: Jeff Jost
Ex VP: Jacob Balderas

D-U-N-S 00-528-0078 IMP
HIRSH INDUSTRIES INC (IA)
3636 Westown Pkwy Ste 100, West Des Moines, IA 50266-6713
Tel (515) 299-3200 *Founded/Ownrshp* 1986
Sales 163.1MM^E *EMP* 620
SIC 2522 2541 Filing boxes, cabinets & cases: except wood; Wood partitions & fixtures
Pr: G Wayne Stewart
**Sec:* Howard Cook
DP Exec: Joe Antonelli
VP Opers: Tom Apostolico
VP Opers: Joe Smith
Natl Sales: Roger Pettit
Sls&Mrk Ex: Meagan Patterson
VP Sls: Dave Jensen
VP Sls: Jeff Stanton

D-U-N-S 00-622-2186 IMP
HIRSHFIELDS INC (MN)
LATHROP PAINT
725 2nd Ave N Ste 1, Minneapolis, MN 55405-1600
Tel (612) 377-3910 *Founded/Ownrshp* 1967
Sales 254.2MM^E *EMP* 305
SIC 5198 5231 2851 Wallcoverings; Paints; Varnishes; Paint brushes, rollers, sprayers; Wallpaper; Paint; Paint brushes, rollers, sprayers & other supplies; Paints & paint additives
CEO: Frank Hirshfield
VP: Charles Gimon

D-U-N-S 05-248-4961 IMP/EXP
HIS CO INC
HISCO
6650 Concord Park Dr, Houston, TX 77040-4098
Tel (713) 934-1600 *Founded/Ownrshp* 1940
Sales 182.8MM^E *EMP* 288^E
SIC 5065 5063 Electronic parts & equipment; Electronic wire & cable; Insulators, electrical
CEO: Robert Dill
**CFO:* Mark Linville
**Ex VP:* Paul Gill
**VP:* Jim Caprile
**VP:* Bill Doshier
**VP:* Mark Joslyn
VP: Tom McElroy
VP: Brian Murphy
**VP:* Tommy O'Connor
VP: Nelson Picard
VP: Jeffrey Plath
**VP:* Paul Seaback
**VP:* Thor Skonnord
**VP:* Scott Stover
**VP:* Merle O Tanner

D-U-N-S 80-373-8236 IMP/EXP
HIS INTERNATIONAL CORP
NO KIDDING
34 W 33rd St Fl 2, New York, NY 10001-3304
Tel (212) 594-4250 *Founded/Ownrshp* 1993
Sales 102.2MM *EMP* 40
SIC 5137 Infants' wear
Pr: Stephen Rahmey
**CFO:* Eli Hamui
Ex VP: Ralph Zirdok

D-U-N-S 96-576-8075 IMP
HIS INTERNATIONAL GROUP LLC
(*Suby of* BENTEX GROUP, INC.)
34 W 33rd St Fl 2, New York, NY 10001-3304
Tel (212) 967-3990 *Founded/Ownrshp* 2009
Sales 113.0MM *EMP* 35
SIC 5136 Women's & children's clothing
VP: George Saade

HISAL
See HITACHI SOLUTIONS AMERICA LTD

D-U-N-S 01-320-0824
HISAMITSU PHARMACEUTICAL CO INC
(*Suby of* HISAMITSU PHARMACEUTICAL CO., INC.)
2730 Loker Ave W, Carlsbad, CA 92010-6603
Tel (760) 931-1756 *Founded/Ownrshp* 1998
Sales 137.2MM^E *EMP* 626
SIC 8733 Medical research
CEO: Nakatomi Hirotaka

HISCO
See HIS CO INC

D-U-N-S 79-047-0392
HISCOX INC
(*Suby of* HISCOX LTD)
520 Madison Ave Rm 3200, New York, NY 10022-4324
Tel (914) 273-7400 *Founded/Ownrshp* 2005
Sales NA *EMP* 150^E
SIC 6411 Fire insurance underwriters' laboratories; Insurance agents & brokers
Pr: Ben Walter
**Ch Bd:* Robert S Childs
**COO:* Eric Pruss
**CFO:* Gavin Watson
VP: Brigitte Anninos
VP: Irma Edel
VP: Louis Panas
VP: Stephen Scialdone
Mktg Mgr: Caitlin Florance

D-U-N-S 01-676-3662 IMP/EXP
HISENSE USA CORP
(*Suby of* HISENSE GROUP CO., LTD.)
7310 Mcginnis Ferry Rd, Suwanee, GA 30024-1281
Tel (678) 318-9060 *Founded/Ownrshp* 2007
Sales 358.4MM^E *EMP* 50
SIC 7622 Radio & television repair; Television repair shop
CEO: Lan Lin
**CFO:* Sophie Chen
VP: Steven Cohen
VP: Zhan Jiajin
VP: Lin Lan
Opers Mgr: Simon Xia
Sls Mgr: Sonny Ming

HISPANIC OUTREACH SERVICES
See ROMAN CATHOLIC DIOCESE OF ALBANY INC

HISSHO SUSHI
See LWIN FAMILY CO

D-U-N-S 14-722-1006 IMP/EXP
■ **HISTORIC AOL LLC**
(*Suby of* AOL INC) ★
22000 Aol Way, Dulles, VA 20166-9302
Tel (703) 265-1000 *Founded/Ownrshp* 2001
Sales 1.0MMM^E *EMP* 4,450
SIC 4813 7299 ; Information services, consumer
CEO: Timothy M Armstrong
**Ch Bd:* J Michael Kelly
V Ch: K J Nova
Pr: Brad Garlinghouse
**Pr:* Ron Grant
**Pr:* Lisa Hook
Pr: Jeff Levick
**Pr:* Joe Redling
**Pr:* Joanna Shields
**Pr:* Neil Smit
**CFO:* Arthur Minson
**V Ch Bd:* Ted Leonsis
**V Ch Bd:* Joseph A Ripp
**Chf Mktg O:* John Burbank
Top Exec: Bob Venezia
Ex VP: Peter Ashkin
Ex VP: Randall Boe
Ex VP: Ted Cahall
Ex VP: Joel Davidson
Ex VP: Chuck Gafvert
Ex VP: Dave Hermon

D-U-N-S 05-310-8895
■ **HISTORIC LIFEPOINT HOSPITALS INC**
(*Suby of* LIFEPOINT HEALTH INC) ★
330 Seven Springs Way, Brentwood, TN 37027-5098
Tel (615) 372-8500 *Founded/Ownrshp* 1999, 2005
Sales 1.1MMM^E *EMP* 9,900
SIC 8062 General medical & surgical hospitals
CEO: William F Carpenter III
**COO:* William M Gracey
**CFO:* Leif M Murphy
**Sr VP:* Neil D Hemphill
IT Man: Greg Hostettler
IT Man: Mace Morgan
IT Man: David Wright
VP Mktg: Mary Shipp

D-U-N-S 06-462-5205
HISTORIC RESTORATION INC
812 Gravier St Apt 200, New Orleans, LA 70112-1467
Tel (504) 493-6129 *Founded/Ownrshp* 1982
Sales 168.3MM^E *EMP* 530
SIC 6552 Land subdividers & developers, residential; Land subdividers & developers, commercial
**Sec:* Ray T Spadafora
VP: Sidney Barthelemy
VP: Josh Collen
DP Exec: Chad Penny
VP Opers: Fernando Portillo

D-U-N-S 95-846-6278 IMP
■ **HISTORIC TW INC**
(*Suby of* TIME WARNER INC) ★
75 Rockefeller Plz, New York, NY 10019-6908
Tel (212) 484-8000 *Founded/Ownrshp* 1996
Sales 2.2MMM^E *EMP* 9,830^E
SIC 3652 6794 2741 7812 4841 2721 Compact laser discs, prerecorded; Magnetic tape (audio): prerecorded; Music licensing to radio stations; Performance rights, publishing & licensing; Music royalties, sheet & record; Music, sheet: publishing only, not printed on site; Music books: publishing only, not printed on site; Motion picture production & distribution; Television film production; Motion picture production & distribution, television; Video tape production; Cable television services; Magazines: publishing only, not printed on site
V Ch Bd: R E Turner
**Pr:* Richard D Parsons
**CFO:* Joseph Ripp
**Ex VP:* Christopher P Bogart
**VP:* Carl F Dill Jr
**CTO:* Michael Dunn

D-U-N-S 10-184-7804 IMP/EXP
HIT PROMOTIONAL PRODUCTS INC
7150 Bryan Dairy Rd, Largo, FL 33777-1501
Tel (727) 541-5561 *Founded/Ownrshp* 1981
Sales 215.1MM^E *EMP* 525^E
SIC 2759 3993 Promotional printing; Signs & advertising specialties
VP: Arthur W Schmidt
COO: Eric Shonebarger
Chf Mktg O: Stacy Zumwalt
VP: Jake Gaines
VP: Steve Hettrich
VP: Melissa Mezerowski
Exec: James Walsh
**Prin:* Elizabeth Schmidt
Rgnl Mgr: Tom Levin
MIS Dir: Anne Maass
MIS Dir: Lou Maggio

D-U-N-S 05-156-2908 IMP/EXP
HITACHI AMERICA LTD
(*Suby of* HITACHI, LTD.)
50 Prospect Ave, Tarrytown, NY 10591-4698
Tel (914) 332-5800 *Founded/Ownrshp* 1959
Sales 3.4MMM^E *EMP* 15,537
SIC 5084 5065 3577 5063 5045 3651

HITACHI AUTOMOTIVE PRODUCTS
See HITACHI AUTOMOTIVE SYSTEMS AMERICAS INC

D-U-N-S 13-035-8682 IMP/EXP
HITACHI AUTOMOTIVE SYSTEMS AMERICAS INC
HITACHI AUTOMOTIVE PRODUCTS
(*Suby of* HITACHI AMERICA LTD) ★
955 Warwick Rd, Harrodsburg, KY 40330-1067
Tel (859) 734-9451 *Founded/Ownrshp* 1985
Sales 888.9MM^E *EMP* 3,000
SIC 3694 3714 3699 3625 Alternators, automotive; Ignition systems, high frequency; Motor vehicle parts & accessories; Electrical equipment & supplies; Relays & industrial controls
Pr: Masaaki Fujisawa
**COO:* Shigetoshi Nashimoto
**CFO:* Hiroyuki Okada
**Treas:* H Utsunomiya
Ex VP: Rex L Carter
VP: Steven King
**VP:* Scott McBroom
VP: Ann Riley
Exec: Kevin Henson
Prgrm Mgr: Ed Abernethy
Prgrm Mgr: Andy Z Zachar

D-U-N-S 15-400-8312 IMP
HITACHI CABLE AMERICA INC
(*Suby of* HITACHI METALS AMERICA LTD) ★
2 Manhattanville Rd # 301, Purchase, NY 10577-2118
Tel (914) 694-9200 *Founded/Ownrshp* 2014
Sales 165.1MM^E *EMP* 613
SIC 3052 Rubber & plastics hose & beltings
CEO: Toro Aoki
CFO: David Zinsner
**Sec:* Tatsuo Kinoshita
Sr VP: John Gibson
VP: Katsura Ishikawa
Genl Mgr: Kenny Crecelius
Manager: Jon Taylor

D-U-N-S 02-126-4114 IMP
HITACHI CHEMICAL CO AMERICA LTD
(*Suby of* HITACHI CHEMICAL COMPANY, LTD.)
2150 N 1st St Ste 350, San Jose, CA 95131-2061
Tel (408) 873-2200 *Founded/Ownrshp* 1975
Sales 131.4MM *EMP* 72
Accts Armanino Mckenna Llp Cpas Sa
SIC 5063 5065 Wiring devices; Circuit breakers; Semiconductor devices; Capacitors, electronic
Pr: Toshinari Itakura
**CFO:* Tomoe Kalnay

D-U-N-S 60-289-8603 IMP
HITACHI COMPUTER PRODUCTS (AMERICA) INC
(*Suby of* HITACHI DATA SYSTEMS CORP) ★
1800 E Imhoff Rd, Norman, OK 73071-1200
Tel (405) 360-5500 *Founded/Ownrshp* 1986
Sales 97.1MM^E *EMP* 600
SIC 3577 3572 7379 Computer peripheral equipment; Computer storage devices; Computer related consulting services
Pr: George Wilson
**Treas:* Randy Reynolds
Ex VP: Michiharu Nakamura
Sr VP: Stephen Gomersall
Sr VP: Kazuaki Masamoto
Mgr Info S: Robin Woodard
Opers Mgr: Melissa Ashley
Plnt Mgr: Alan Albert

D-U-N-S 00-459-5661 IMP
HITACHI CONSULTING CORP
(*Suby of* HITACHI, LTD.)
14643 Dallas Pkwy Ste 800, Dallas, TX 75254-8870
Tel (214) 665-7000 *Founded/Ownrshp* 2000
Sales 691.7MM^E *EMP* 4,500
SIC 7379 7374 ; Data processing & preparation
Pr: Philip R Parr
CFO: Bruce V Ballengee
**CFO:* Barry Honea
Ex VP: Charles Cochran
Ex VP: Larry Deboever
Ex VP: Patrik Sj Stedt
VP: John Allen
VP: William Boucher
VP: Gary Brown
VP: Chris Buri
VP: Greg Carter
VP: Steve Crosnoe
VP: Bob Davis
VP: Stephen Engel
VP: Rob Farris
VP: Willi Graef
VP: Randy Green
VP: Kevin Greenan
VP: Brad Hairston
VP: Peter Halis
VP: John Head

D-U-N-S 62-182-4911
HITACHI CONSULTING SOFTWARE SERVICES INC
(*Suby of* HITACHI CONSULTING CORP) ★
8000 Jarvis Ave Ste 130, Newark, CA 94560-1155
Tel (510) 742-4100 *Founded/Ownrshp* 2011
Sales 26.2MM^E *EMP* 2,000
SIC 7299 7371 Information services, consumer; Computer software development
CEO: Philip R Parr
**CFO:* Robert Hersh
**Ex VP:* Douglas Allen
**Ex VP:* Ismael Fernandez De La Mata
**Ex VP:* GK Murthy
**Ex VP:* John O'Brien
Sr VP: Allen Deary
VP: Phil Hodsdon
VP: Gopala Krishna
VP: Feroze Mohammed
VP: Sudheer Reddy
VP: Nick Simanteris
VP: Xiaomin Zheng

D-U-N-S 09-853-3599 IMP
HITACHI DATA SYSTEMS CORP
(*Suby of* HITACHI DATA SYSTEMS HOLDING CORP) ★
2845 Lafayette St, Santa Clara, CA 95050-2642
Tel (408) 970-1000 *Founded/Ownrshp* 1979, 1989
Sales 2.3MMM^E *EMP* 3,287
SIC 5045 7378 7379 5734 4225 3571 Computers; Computer & data processing equipment repair/maintenance; Computer related maintenance services; Computer & software stores; Modems, monitors, terminals & disk drives: computers; General warehousing & storage; Mainframe computers
Pr: Jack Domme
**Ch Bd:* Minoru Kosuge
**CFO:* Susan Lynch
Ofcr: Miklos Sandorfi
Ex VP: Greg Coplans
**Ex VP:* Randy Demont
Ex VP: Mark Mickelson
Ex VP: Yoshinori Okami
Ex VP: Frans Van Rijn
Ex VP: Michael Vath
Ex VP: Marlene Woodworth
Sr VP: Hicham Abdessamad
**Sr VP:* Rex Carter
Sr VP: Michael Cremen
Sr VP: Kevin Eggleston
Sr VP: Jeff Henry
Sr VP: Mark Kay
Sr VP: Michael V Th
Sr VP: Michael Walkey
Sr VP: Michael D Walkey
VP: Sean Moser

D-U-N-S 06-599-9646
HITACHI DATA SYSTEMS HOLDING CORP
(*Suby of* HITACHI, LTD.)
2845 Lafayette St, Santa Clara, CA 95050-2642
Tel (408) 970-1000 *Founded/Ownrshp* 1989
Sales 2.3MMM^E *EMP* 3,600
SIC 7299 Personal item care & storage services
CEO: Jack Domme
**CFO:* Susan Lynch
Ofcr: Cheryl Davenport
Ex VP: Marlene Woodworth
VP: Keigo Iechika
VP: Atsushi Ugajin

D-U-N-S 10-565-0860 IMP
HITACHI HIGH TECHNOLOGIES AMERICA INC
(*Suby of* HITACHI HIGH-TECHNOLOGIES CORPORATION)
10 N Martingale Rd # 500, Schaumburg, IL 60173-2099
Tel (847) 273-4141 *Founded/Ownrshp* 2002
Sales 179.1MM^E *EMP* 519
SIC 5065 Electronic parts & equipment
CEO: Craig Kerkove
**CFO:* Masahito Hashimoto
Ex VP: Stephen Snoke
**Sr VP:* Andrew Gelb
**Sr VP:* Mamoru Harada
**VP:* Phil Bryson
**VP:* Brian Buckingham
**VP:* Brian Cunningham
**VP:* Karen Folliard
VP: Kenji Osaki
Sls Mgr: John Chick

D-U-N-S 01-361-7840 IMP
HITACHI KOKI USA LTD
HITACHI POWER TOOL USA
(*Suby of* HITACHI KOKI CO., LTD.)
1111 Broadway Ave, Braselton, GA 30517-2900
Tel (770) 925-1774 *Founded/Ownrshp* 1995

Sales 95.6MM^E *EMP* 175
SIC 5084 Industrial machinery & equipment
CEO: Shoji Matsushima
VP: Steve Karaga
VP: Hiro Yumoto
Genl Mgr: Benjie Hopkins
CIO: Jason Saur
Sls Dir: Jason Trucchi

D-U-N-S 60-315-6043 IMP
HITACHI MEDICAL SYSTEMS AMERICA INC
(*Suby of* HITACHI HEALTH CARE MANUFACTURING, K.K.)
1959 Summit Commerce Park, Twinsburg, OH 44087-2371
Tel (330) 425-1313 *Founded/Ownrshp* 1989
Sales 221.8MM^E *EMP* 370
SIC 5047 Diagnostic equipment, medical
Pr: Donald Broomfield
COO: Steve Stofiel
* *Treas:* Richard Kurz
VP: Bill Bishop
* *VP:* William Bishop
VP: Xiaodong Che
* *VP:* James Confer
VP: Jim R Confer
VP: John Hahn
* *VP:* Richard Katz
VP: Richard Kurtz
* *VP:* Robert McCarthy
* *VP:* Sheldon Schaffer
VP: Sheldon Shaffer

D-U-N-S 07-057-2482 IMP/EXP
HITACHI METALS AMERICA LTD
(*Suby of* HITACHI METALS, LTD.)
2 Manhattanville Rd # 301, Purchase, NY 10577-2103
Tel (914) 694-9200 *Founded/Ownrshp* 1965, 2016
Sales 897.1MM^E *EMP* 7,919
SIC 3264 3577 3365 5051 3321 3559 Magnets, permanent: ceramic or ferrite; Computer peripheral equipment; Aluminum & aluminum-based alloy castings; Steel; Castings, rough: iron or steel; Ductile iron castings; Gray iron castings; Automotive related machinery
CEO: Hideaki Takahashi
* *Ch Bd:* Tomoyasu Kubota
* *Pr:* Tomoyuki Hatano
* *Pr:* Hiroaki Nakanishi
* *CFO:* Toshiki Aoki

D-U-N-S 05-939-2535 IMP
HITACHI METALS AUTOMOTIVE COMPONENTS USA LLC
HMAC
18986 Route 287, Tioga, PA 16946-8815
Tel (217) 347-0600 *Founded/Ownrshp* 2016
Sales 89.6MM^E *EMP* 522
SIC 3465 3321 3559

D-U-N-S 07-852-4489
HITACHI METALS FOUNDRY AMERICA INC
1955 Brunner Dr, Waupaca, WI 54981-8866
Tel (715) 258-6600 *Founded/Ownrshp* 2014
Sales 567.3MM^E *EMP* 5,320
SIC 3321

HITACHI POWER TOOL USA
See HITACHI KOKI USA LTD

D-U-N-S 79-347-1509 IMP
HITACHI SOLUTIONS AMERICA LTD
HISAL
(*Suby of* HITACHI SOLUTIONS, LTD.)
851 Traeger Ave Ste 200, San Bruno, CA 94066-3037
Tel (650) 615-7600 *Founded/Ownrshp* 1990
Sales 88.8MM^E *EMP* 300
SIC 5045 7372 7373 Computer software; Prepackaged software
CEO: Keiho Akiyama
COO: Tom Galambos
Sr VP: Scott Millwood
VP: Craig Burbidge
VP: Gord Smith
Dir Bus: John Koontz
CIO: Mark Veronda
Mktg Dir: Tamara Schoder
Mktg Mgr: Kacee Roberts

D-U-N-S 79-347-7865 IMP/EXP
HITCHCOCK INDUSTRIES INC
CONSOLIDATED PRECISION PDTS
(*Suby of* CPP POMONA) ★
8701 Harriet Ave S, Minneapolis, MN 55420-2787
Tel (952) 881-1000 *Founded/Ownrshp* 2006
Sales 97.1MM^E *EMP* 375
SIC 3365 3364 3544 3369 Aluminum & aluminum-based alloy castings; Magnesium & magnesium-base alloy die-castings; Special dies, tools, jigs & fixtures; Nonferrous foundries
VP: Mike McLaughlin
VP: James M Meath
QA Dir: Kim Barsness
VP Sls: Chris Fillmore
Board of Directors: Robert A Buch, Carleton G Hitchcock, Jonathan T Hitchcock, Colleen M Swedberg

D-U-N-S 00-107-8682 IMP/EXP
HITCHINER MANUFACTURING CO INC
594 Elm St, Milford, NH 03055-4306
Tel (603) 673-1100 *Founded/Ownrshp* 1949
Sales 226.8MM *EMP* 1,580
Accts Grant Thornton Llp Boston Ma
SIC 3324 Steel investment foundries
Ch: John H Morison III
* *COO:* Mark Damien
* *VP:* Scott Biederman
* *VP:* Jorge Campillo
VP: Amy Demmons
* *VP:* Randal J Donovan
* *VP:* Michael Foster
* *VP:* Brian Hoover
VP: Scott McDonald
* *VP:* Ken Miller
* *VP:* Michel Petit
* *VP:* John Sexton
* *VP:* Timothy Sullivan
Exec: Dave Cashon
Exec: Michael Hayes

HITCHLAND GRAIN CO
See ATTEBURY GRAIN LLC

D-U-N-S 00-450-8750
HITE CO (PA)
3101 Beale Ave, Altoona, PA 16601-1509
Tel (814) 944-6121 *Founded/Ownrshp* 1949
Sales 139.4MM^E *EMP* 230
SIC 5063 Electrical fittings & construction materials
CEO: R Lee Hite
* *Pr:* T Scott Lawhead
* *COO:* Ronald R Eberhart
* *CFO:* Ronald Muffie
Ex VP: Ron Eberhart
VP: John Hatch
Brnch Mgr: Andy Miller
Store Mgr: Mike Belmont
Store Mgr: Bill Hertrich
Store Mgr: Christopher Trahan
CTO: Katherine Hite-Brouse

D-U-N-S 96-240-4849 EXP
HITOUCH BUSINESS SERVICES LLC
74 Kenny Pl, Saddle Brook, NJ 07663-5916
Tel (201) 636-9900 *Founded/Ownrshp* 2010
Sales 698.8MM^E *EMP* 379^E
SIC 5112 5021 5149 Stationery & office supplies; Computer & photocopying supplies; Office & public building furniture; Groceries & related products
Pr: Michael Brown
* *CEO:* Howard L Brown
* *COO:* Michael J Palmer
* *CFO:* Anthony Cavalieri

D-U-N-S 00-325-8746 IMP
HITT CONTRACTING INC (VA)
2900 Fairview Park Dr # 300, Falls Church, VA 22042-4513
Tel (703) 846-9000 *Founded/Ownrshp* 1943
Sales 1.0MMM *EMP* 775
Accts Deloitte & Touche Llp Mclean
SIC 1542 Commercial & office buildings, renovation & repair
Ch Bd: Russell A Hitt
* *CFO:* Michael McGrae
* *Co-Pr:* Brett Hitt
* *Co-Pr:* James E Millar
Ex VP: Thomas Boogher
* *Ex VP:* John M Britt
Ex VP: John W Kane
Ex VP: Yogen Patel
Sr VP: David R Kane
Sr VP: Carson P Knizevski
Sr VP: Brian S Kriz
Sr VP: Joseph P Lafonte Jr
Sr VP: Peter T Lanfranchi
Sr VP: David R Michaelson
Sr VP: Kevin L Ott
Sr VP: John Planz
Sr VP: Nick D Raico
VP: Sue Alexander
* *VP:* Jeremy S Bardin
VP: Jeremy Bardin
VP: Michael Bellusci

D-U-N-S 13-166-9293
■ **HITTITE MICROWAVE LLC**
(*Suby of* ANALOG DEVICES INC) ★
2 Elizabeth Dr, Chelmsford, MA 01824-4112
Tel (978) 250-3343 *Founded/Ownrshp* 2014
Sales 145.1MM^E *EMP* 506^E
SIC 3674 Integrated circuits, semiconductor networks, etc.; Modules, solid state
Pr: Rick D Hess
CFO: William W Boecke
VP: Everett Cole III
VP: Susan J Dicecco
VP: William D Hannabach
VP: John McCullar
VP: Larry W Ward
Dir IT: George Papamitrou

D-U-N-S 03-561-7679 IMP
HIXSON LUMBER SALES INC
310 S Tennessee St, Pine Bluff, AR 71601-4453
Tel (870) 535-1436 *Founded/Ownrshp* 1959
Sales 200.0MM *EMP* 275
SIC 2421 5031

D-U-N-S 12-473-2186
HK DESIGNS INC
MY DIAMOND STORY
535 5th Ave Fl 18, New York, NY 10017-3685
Tel (212) 201-0755 *Founded/Ownrshp* 1999
Sales 84.0MM *EMP* 22
SIC 5094 Jewelry; Diamonds (gems)
Ch Bd: Hasmukh H Dholakiya
Genl Mgr: David Narkar

D-U-N-S 08-109-1126 IMP
HKF INC
THERM PACIFIC
5983 Smithway St, Commerce, CA 90040-1607
Tel (323) 225-1318 *Founded/Ownrshp* 1990
Sales 92.0MM^E *EMP* 450
SIC 5075 3873 5064 3567 3643 Warm air heating & air conditioning; Watches, clocks, watchcases & parts; Electrical appliances, television & radio; Industrial furnaces & ovens; Current-carrying wiring devices
Pr: James P Hartfield

D-U-N-S 96-964-0791
HKI SUPPORT INC
352 Park Ave S, New York, NY 10010-1709
Tel (212) 532-0544 *Founded/Ownrshp* 2011
Sales 162.5MM *EMP* 2^E
SIC 8699 Charitable organization

HKS ARCHITECTS
See HKS INC

D-U-N-S 05-084-7490
HKS INC
HKS ARCHITECTS
350 N Saint Paul St # 100, Dallas, TX 75201-4240
Tel (214) 969-5599 *Founded/Ownrshp* 1980
Sales 368.1MM *EMP* 1,400^E
SIC 8712 Architectural engineering
Pr: Dan H Noble
COO: J Mark Jones
COO: Mark J Ones
CFO: Larry D Lemaster
Ex VP: Craig Beale
* *Ex VP:* Nunzio Desantis
Ex VP: Nunzio M Desantis
Ex VP: Robert Marlineck
Ex VP: Robert Piatek
Ex VP: Jeff Stouffer
* *Ex VP:* Jeffrey Stouffer
* *Ex VP:* Bryan Trubey
Ex VP: Mark Voorl
Ex VP: Laurie Waggener
Sr VP: Noel Barrick
Sr VP: Joseph Buskuhl
Sr VP: Lorenzo Castillo
Sr VP: Davis E Chauvir
Sr VP: Jesse R Corigan Jr
Sr VP: Ernest W Hanchey Jr
Sr VP: Thomas E Harvy
Board of Directors: Francis Gallagher, William Hinton, Shannon Kraus, Kirk Teske

HKW
See HAMMOND KENNEDY WHITNEY & CO INC

D-U-N-S 01-727-3375
HL FINANCIAL SERVICES LLC
500 W Jefferson St, Louisville, KY 40202-2823
Tel (502) 588-8400 *Founded/Ownrshp* 2008
Sales 360.1MM^E *EMP* 1,155^E
SIC 7389 Financial services
VP: Allen Duffin

D-U-N-S 19-670-4092 IMP
HL-A CO
HONDA LOCK OF AMERICA
(*Suby of* HONDA MOTOR CO., LTD.)
101 Thomas B Mur Ind Blvd, Bremen, GA 30110
Tel (678) 309-2000 *Founded/Ownrshp* 1988
Sales 123.9MM^E *EMP* 504^E
Accts Ernst & Young Llp
SIC 3429 3714 Locks or lock sets; Keys & key blanks; Motor vehicle body components & frame
CEO: Tsugiaki Umeda
VP: Roger Tinsley
VP: Sandra M Wilkinson
Exec: Sharon Chamberlain
MIS Dir: Ben Tolbert
QA Dir: Hiroyuki Watanabe
Plnt Mgr: Greg Phillips
Ql Cn Mgr: Billy Baker

D-U-N-S 96-857-8000
HLSS MANAGEMENT LLC
(*Suby of* HLSS HOLDINGS, LLC)
2002 Summit Blvd Fl 6, Brookhaven, GA 30319-1560
Tel (561) 682-7561 *Founded/Ownrshp* 2011
Sales NA *EMP* 1
SIC 6162 Mortgage bankers

D-U-N-S 07-922-8005
■ **HLT ESP INTERNATIONAL FRANCHISE LLC**
(*Suby of* HILTON WORLDWIDE HOLDINGS INC) ★
7930 Jones Branch Dr, Mc Lean, VA 22102-3388
Tel (703) 883-1000 *Founded/Ownrshp* 2013
Sales 3.1MM^E *EMP* 5,004^E
SIC 7011 Hotels & motels

D-U-N-S 07-940-4329
HM DUNN AEROSYSTEMS INC
3301 House Anderson Rd, Euless, TX 76040-2001
Tel (817) 283-3722 *Founded/Ownrshp* 2013
Sales 124.0MM *EMP* 620
SIC 3724 Aircraft engines & engine parts
CEO: Philip Milazzo
* *CFO:* Marc Szczerba
Genl Mgr: Chris Dunn

HM DUNNAIR AEROSYSTEM
See H M DUNN CO INC

D-U-N-S 07-126-0375
HM HEALTH SOLUTIONS INC
AHN - ALLEGHENY HEALTH NETWORK
(*Suby of* HIGHMARK BLUE CRSS-BLUE SHIELD) ★
120 5th Ave, Pittsburgh, PA 15222-3000
Tel (412) 544-7226 *Founded/Ownrshp* 2013
Sales 1.1MMM^E *EMP* 35,000^E
SIC 8099 6321 Organ bank; Health insurance carriers
Pr: David L Holmberg
* *CFO:* Karen Hanlon
* *Treas:* Nanette P Deturk
Ex VP: Melissa Anderson
Sr VP: David Carter

D-U-N-S 78-816-4358
HM INSURANCE GROUP INC
(*Suby of* HIGHMARK BLUE CRSS-BLUE SHIELD) ★
120 5th Ave, Pittsburgh, PA 15222-3000
Tel (412) 544-1000 *Founded/Ownrshp* 1990
Sales NA *EMP* 750
Accts Pricewaterhousecoopers Llp Ph
SIC 6311 6371 Life insurance; Pension, health & welfare funds
CEO: Michael W Sullivan
* *Pr:* Matt Rhenish
* *Treas:* Daniel I Wright
Ofcr: Robert Frew
* *Sr VP:* Cathy Blanchard
Sr VP: Mark Nave
* *Sr VP:* Gene Susi
VP: Pamela Brown
VP: Dan Cloyd
VP: David Daley
VP: Donald Direso
VP: Mark Lancellotti
VP: Tony Lopez
VP: Matthew Ornelas
VP: Domenic Palmieri
VP: Matt Piroch
VP: Eugene Susi
Board of Directors: Jim Burgess

D-U-N-S 60-274-3150 IMP
HM PUBLISHING CORP
(*Suby of* HOUGHTON MIFFLIN HOLDINGS INC) ★
222 Berkeley St, Boston, MA 02116-3748
Tel (617) 251-5000 *Founded/Ownrshp* 2003
Sales 126.4MM^E *EMP* 3,546^E
SIC 2731 Book publishing; Textbooks: publishing only, not printed on site
Ex VP: Stephen Richards
Sr VP: Gerald Hughes
Sr VP: Paul Weaver
Board of Directors: Michael Ward, David Blitzer, Charlese Brizius, Robert Friedman, Steve Gandy, Seth Lawry, James Levy, Mark Nunnelly, Michael Perik, Scott Sperling

D-U-N-S 17-679-7918 IMP/EXP
HM RICHARDS INC
120 H M Richards Way, Guntown, MS 38849-4001
Tel (662) 365-9485 *Founded/Ownrshp* 1997
Sales 131.0MM *EMP* 838
SIC 2512 Living room furniture: upholstered on wood frames
CEO: William A Quirk
CFO: Michael E McCaulla
* *Ch:* Jeffrey Seaman
VP: Joe Tarrant
* *VP:* Joey Torrent
* *VP Mfg:* Thomas Wells

HMA
See POPLAR BLUFF REGIONAL MEDICAL CENTER

HMA
See HARTON JOHN W REGIONAL MEDICAL CENTER INC

HMA
See HAINES CITY HEALTH MANAGEMENT ASSOCIATION INC

HMA
See HEALTH MANAGEMENT ASSOCIATES INC

HMA
See PEACE RIVER REGIONAL MEDICAL CENTER

HMA
See SPACE COAST HEALTH FOUNDATION INC

HMA
See PHYSICIANS REGIONAL MEDICAL CENTER

HMA
See HONDA MANUFACTURING OF ALABAMA LLC

D-U-N-S 10-734-6934
HMA INC
HOLMES MURPHY
3001 Westown Pkwy Stop 1, West Des Moines, IA 50266-1328
Tel (515) 223-6800 *Founded/Ownrshp* 1984
Sales NA *EMP* 344
SIC 6411 6321 8742 Insurance agents; Health insurance carriers; Disability health insurance; Reinsurance carriers, accident & health; Management consulting services
Ch Bd: J Douglas Reichardt
Pr: Nickolas J Henderson
COO: Dave Shipley
Sr VP: Craig E Hansen
Sr VP: Lori Wiederin
VP: Luanne Longo
VP: Lori McMurray
VP: Gail Steffen
VP: James S Swift
VP: Mark Vanbuskirk
Dir IT: Darcy Janssen

HMAC
See HITACHI METALS AUTOMOTIVE COMPONENTS USA LLC

D-U-N-S 07-947-8958
HMAN GROUP HOLDINGS INC
10590 Hamilton Ave, Cincinnati, OH 45231-1764
Tel (513) 851-4900 *Founded/Ownrshp* 2014
Sales 360.2MM^E *EMP* 2,605^E
SIC 6719 5072 7699 Investment holding companies, except banks; Hardware; Miscellaneous fasteners; Bolts, nuts & screws; Key duplicating shop
Prin: Steve Murray

D-U-N-S 07-947-8956
HMAN INTERMEDIATE HOLDINGS CORP
(*Suby of* HMAN GROUP HOLDINGS INC) ★
245 Park Ave Fl 16, New York, NY 10167-2402
Tel (513) 851-4900 *Founded/Ownrshp* 2014
Sales 278.5MM^E *EMP* 2,605^E
SIC 6719 5072 7699 Investment holding companies, except banks; Hardware; Miscellaneous fasteners; Bolts, nuts & screws; Key duplicating shop
Prin: Steve Murray

D-U-N-S 07-936-4173
HMAN INTERMEDIATE II HOLDINGS CORP
(*Suby of* HMAN INTERMEDIATE HOLDINGS CORP) ★
10590 Hamilton Ave, Cincinnati, OH 45231-1764
Tel (513) 851-4900 *Founded/Ownrshp* 2014
Sales 786.9MM^E *EMP* 2,605^E
SIC 5072 7699 Hardware; Miscellaneous fasteners; Bolts, nuts & screws; Key duplicating shop
CEO: James P Waters

HMC
See HARDER MECHANICAL CONTRACTORS INC

HMC BUSINESS AFFAIRS DEPT
See HARVEY MUDD COLLEGE

D-U-N-S 00-690-9634 IMP/EXP
HMCLAUSE INC (CA)
(*Suby of* GROUPE LIMAGRAIN HOLDING)
260 Cousteau Pl Ste 210, Modesto, CA 95357
Tel (530) 747-3700 *Founded/Ownrshp* 1856, 1969
Sales 87.1MM^E *EMP* 300
SIC 0181 Seeds, vegetable: growing of
Pr: Matthew M Johnston
* *VP:* Andre Cariou
VP: Agnes Mistretta

Dir IT: Gerry Hawkins
VP Sls: Andr Cariou

HMFP
See HARVARD MEDICAL FACULTY PHYSICIANS AT BETH ISRAEL DEACONESS MEDICAL CENTER INC

D-U-N-S 08-028-2092
HMG HOLDING CORP
(*Suby of* HOSPITLIST MEDICINE PHYSICIANS) ★
920 Winter St, Waltham, MA 02451-1521
Tel (781) 699-9000 *Founded/Ownrshp* 2010
Sales 89.4MM^E *EMP* 560^E
SIC 8741 6719 Hospital management; Investment holding companies, except banks
CEO: Ronald Kuerbitz

HMH
See HOUGHTON MIFFLIN HARCOURT CO

D-U-N-S 07-848-0903
■ **HMH PUBLISHERS LLC**
HMRH ACQUISITION CO
(*Suby of* HOUGHTON MIFFLIN HARCOURT PUBLISHERS INC) ★
222 Berkeley St, Boston, MA 02116-3748
Tel (617) 351-5000 *Founded/Ownrshp* 2012
Sales 13.0MM^E *EMP* 3,295^E
SIC 2731 Book publishing
Pr: Linda Zecher
**CFO:* Eric Shuman
**Treas:* Joseph Flaherty
**Ex VP:* William Bayers
**Sr VP:* Michael Dolan

HMI ELECTRIC DIVISION
See HEAVY MACHINES INC

HMMA
See HYUNDAI MOTOR MANUFACTURING ALABAMA LLC

HMO BLUE
See HORIZON HEALTHCARE PLAN HOLDING

D-U-N-S 07-272-6581
HMO MINNESOTA (MN)
BLUE PLUS
3535 Blue Cross Rd, Saint Paul, MN 55122-1154
Tel (952) 456-8434 *Founded/Ownrshp* 1974
Sales 850.9MM *EMP* 40
SIC 8011 Health maintenance organization
CEO: Andrew Czajkowski
**Ch Bd:* Jonathon Killmer
**CFO:* Tim Peterson
Board of Directors: Gerald Etesse, Lonnie Nichols, Patricia Riley

D-U-N-S 96-003-9022
HMO OF LOUISIANA INC
(*Suby of* BLUE CROSS) ★
5525 Reitz Ave, Baton Rouge, LA 70809-3802
Tel (225) 295-3307 *Founded/Ownrshp* 1985
Sales NA *EMP* 10
SIC 6324 Health maintenance organization (HMO), insurance only
Pr: Gery Barry
CFO: Carl Kennedy

D-U-N-S 16-099-7037
HMO OF NORTHEASTERN PENNSYLVANIA INC
FIRST PRIORITY HEALTH
19 N Main St, Wilkes Barre, PA 18711-0302
Tel (570) 200-4300 *Founded/Ownrshp* 2015
Sales NA *EMP* 148
Accts Pricewaterhousecoopers Llp Ph
SIC 6324 Group hospitalization plans
Pr: Denise Cesare
COO: William Reed
VP: Kent Davidson

D-U-N-S 00-516-3456 IMP/EXP
HMP SERVICES HOLDING INC
721 Union Blvd, Totowa, NJ 07512-2207
Tel (973) 812-0400 *Founded/Ownrshp* 1906, 1910
Sales 102.4MM^E *EMP* 550
SIC 5084 5199

D-U-N-S 19-467-7423
HMR ACQUISITION CO INC
HACIENDA MEXICAN RESTAURANTS
1501 N Ironwood Dr, South Bend, IN 46635-1841
Tel (574) 272-5922 *Founded/Ownrshp* 1996
Sales 50.0MM *EMP* 13,000
SIC 5812 5813 Mexican restaurant; Cocktail lounge
Pr: Vicki Farmwald
**Pr:* Dean Goodwin
**CEO:* Robert Kill
**CFO:* Tammy Boetsma
Exec: Shelly Daly
Genl Mgr: Alex Fisher
Genl Mgr: Gloria Marietta
Genl Mgr: Linda Zirkelbach
Mktg Mgr: Jonathan Fizer

D-U-N-S 80-719-7454
HMR ADVANTAGE HEALTH SYSTEMS INC
101 Grace Dr, Easley, SC 29640-9088
Tel (864) 269-3725 *Founded/Ownrshp* 1993
Sales 1.3MMM^E *EMP* 253
SIC 8741 Nursing & personal care facility management
Pr: Michael H Mc Bride
**Pr:* Michael H McBride
**Sec:* John O'Brien
Ex Dir: Wayne Adams
Ex Dir: Todd Griggs
IT Man: Jeff Vassay
Nrsg Dir: Julius Shayo
HC Dir: Karey Kelley

HMRH ACQUISITION CO
See HMH PUBLISHERS LLC

HMRH ACQUISITION CO
See FOUNDATION FOR MARINE ANIMAL HUSBANDRY INC

HMS BUSINESS SERVICES
See HEALTH MANAGEMENT SYSTEMS INC

D-U-N-S 12-907-7280
▲ **HMS HOLDINGS CORP**
5615 High Point Dr # 100, Irving, TX 75038-2434
Tel (214) 453-3000 *Founded/Ownrshp* 2003
Sales 474.2MM *EMP* 2,316^E
Tkr Sym HMSY *Exch* NGS
SIC 7322 Collection agency, except real estate
Ch Bd: William C Lucia
Pr: Joel Portice
Pr: Douglas M Williams
CFO: Jeffrey S Sherman
Ofcr: Cynthia Nustad
Ofcr: Scott Pettigrew
Ex VP: Meredith W Bjorck
Ex VP: Gene Defelice
Ex VP: Semone Neuman
Ex VP: Semone Wagner
VP: Mark Olson
Board of Directors: Alex Michael Azar II, Robert Becker, Craig R Callen, William F Miller III, Ellen A Rudnick, Bart M Schwartz, Richard H Stowe, Cora M Tellez

HMS HOST INTERNATIONAL
See GIFT COLLECTION INC

HMSA
See HAWAII MEDICAL SERVICE ASSOCIATION

D-U-N-S 83-922-3898 IMP
HMSHOST CORP
(*Suby of* AUTOGRILL SPA)
6905 Rockledge Dr Fl 1, Bethesda, MD 20817-7826
Tel (240) 694-4100 *Founded/Ownrshp* 1999
Sales 1.0MMM^E *EMP* 27,900
SIC 5812 5813 5994 5947 Grills (eating places); Concessionaire; Cocktail lounge; Newsstand; Gift shop
Pr: Steve Johnson
Treas: Joy Butler
**Treas:* Mark T Ratych
Sr VP: Mike Hasenzahl
VP: Kevin Erickson
Dir Soc: Arden Shutt
Prgrm Mgr: Michaela Lamarchesino
Genl Mgr: Stephen Hackshall
Genl Mgr: Asghar Pourhadi
Dir IT: Michele Adkins
MIS Mgr: Oakley Bright

D-U-N-S 09-599-5429 IMP/EXP
HMT INC
H M T
24 Waterway Ave Ste 400, The Woodlands, TX 77380-3197
Tel (281) 681-7000 *Founded/Ownrshp* 1978
Sales 107.2MM^E *EMP* 600
SIC 7699 3443 7389 1791 Tank repair; Fuel tanks (oil, gas, etc.): metal plate; Industrial & commercial equipment inspection service; Storage tanks, metal: erection
CEO: Millard H Jones
**Pr:* Gary E Tesch
**CEO:* S Kent Rockwell
**Treas:* J Wayne Jean
Treas: Nichole Wheeler
Ex VP: Tom Hoyer
**VP:* Scott D Spence
Area Mgr: Fausto Estrada
Area Mgr: Art Velasco
Genl Mgr: John Carnew
Genl Mgr: Wayne Jones

D-U-N-S 83-122-9492
HMX LLC
HMX OPERATING CO
125 Park Ave Fl 7, New York, NY 10017-5627
Tel (212) 682-9073 *Founded/Ownrshp* 2009
Sales 206.8MM^E *EMP* 870^E
SIC 2211 Apparel & outerwear fabrics, cotton

HMX OPERATING CO
See HMX LLC

HN PRECISION-NY
See NATIONWIDE PRECISION PRODUCTS CORP

D-U-N-S 07-853-4945
HNC PARENT INC
999 N Sepulveda Blvd, El Segundo, CA 90245-2714
Tel (310) 955-9200 *Founded/Ownrshp* 2012
Sales 250.7MM^E *EMP* 560
SIC 2952 2821 2891 Roof cement: asphalt, fibrous or plastic; Polyurethane resins; Sealants
Prin: Rob Newbold

HNH
See HANDY & HARMAN LTD

D-U-N-S 00-526-9709 EXP
▲ **HNI CORP** (IA)
408 E 2nd St, Muscatine, IA 52761-4140
Tel (563) 272-7400 *Founded/Ownrshp* 1944
Sales 2.3MMM *EMP* 10,400
Tkr Sym HNI *Exch* NYS
SIC 2522 2542 2521 2541 3433 3429 Office furniture, except wood; Filing boxes, cabinets & cases: except wood; Desks, office: except wood; Chairs, office: padded or plain, except wood; Partitions for floor attachment, prefabricated: except wood; Wood office furniture; Filing cabinets (boxes), office: wood; Desks, office: wood; Chairs, office: padded, upholstered or plain: wood; Partitions for floor attachment, prefabricated: wood; Room heaters, except electric; Stoves, wood & coal burning; Manufactured hardware (general)
Ch Bd: Stan A Askren
Pr: Jerry Dittmer
Pr: Jeff Lorenger
CFO: Kurt A Tjaden
Treas: Ellsworth Mc
Treas: William F Snydacker
Ex VP: Bradley D Determan
Ex VP: Eric K Jungbluth
Ex VP: Phillip M Martineau
VP: Steven M Bradford
VP: David Crimmins
VP: Tamara Feldman
VP: Richard Johnson
VP: Donna D Meade
Board of Directors: Brian E Stern, Mary H Bell, Ronald V Waters III, Miguel M Calado, Cheryl A Francis, John R Hartnett, James R Jenkins, Mary K W Jones, Dennis J Martin, Larry B Porcellato, Abbie J Smith

HNMC
See HOUSTON NORTHWEST MEDICAL CENTER EDUCATION FOUNDATION INC

D-U-N-S 03-623-7571
HNRC DISSOLUTION CO
AEI RESOURCES HOLDING
201 E Main St 100, Lexington, KY 40507-2003
Tel (606) 327-5450 *Founded/Ownrshp* 2007
Sales 405.9MM^E *EMP* 3,991
SIC 1222

D-U-N-S 04-160-1790
HNTB CORP
(*Suby of* HNTB HOLDINGS LTD) ★
715 Kirk Dr, Kansas City, MO 64105-1310
Tel (816) 472-1201 *Founded/Ownrshp* 2003
Sales 900.0MM *EMP* 3,800
SIC 8711 8712 Consulting engineer; Architectural services
CEO: Robert Slimp
Pr: Art Hadnett
Pr: Dan Papiernik
COO: Jim Anglin
CFO: Terry Campbell
CFO: Terry M Campbell
Ch: Harvey Hammond
Ch: Michael Wright
Ch: Paul Yarossi
Assoc VP: Anthony Bartello
Assoc VP: Christian Brown
Assoc VP: Kuan S Go
Assoc VP: Tarek Hatab
Assoc VP: Christine Hoagland
Assoc VP: Antonio Lagala
Assoc VP: Beth Larkin
Assoc VP: Aj Piechnik
Assoc VP: Raymond Sandiford
Assoc VP: Wendy Taylor
Assoc VP: Narayana Velaga
Assoc VP: Gary W Walsh

D-U-N-S 16-787-6478
HNTB HOLDINGS LTD
715 Kirk Dr, Kansas City, MO 64105-1310
Tel (816) 472-1201 *Founded/Ownrshp* 2003
Sales 907.8MM^E *EMP* 3,800
SIC 8712 8711 Architectural services; Consulting engineer
Ch: Harvey Hammond
**Pr:* Paul A Yarossi
Assoc VP: Laurie Cullen
Assoc VP: Michael Inabinet
Assoc VP: Lawrence Meeker
**Ex VP:* Kenneth Graham
Ex VP: Joel Sorenson
**Ex VP:* Edward Spedon
VP: Charles Dulic
VP: James D Fisher
VP: Roland A Lavallee
VP: Scott M Smith
Exec: Deborah Caponetto
Dir Bus: Mary A Simons

HO-CHUNK CASINO
See HO-CHUNK NATION

D-U-N-S 88-455-5756
HO-CHUNK INC
(*Suby of* WINNEBAGO TRIBE OF NEBRASKA) ★
1 Mission Dr, Winnebago, NE 68071-4900
Tel (402) 878-4135 *Founded/Ownrshp* 1995
Sales 155.9MM^E *EMP* 310
Accts Mcgladrey & Pullen Llp Omaha
SIC 5172 Petroleum products
CEO: Lance Morgan
COO: Jan King
**CFO:* Dennis Johnson
**VP:* Annette Hamilton
Dir IT: Joe Stoos
Board of Directors: Lauren Buchanan, Ann Downes, Kenny Mallory

D-U-N-S 11-842-8267
HO-CHUNK NATION
HO-CHUNK CASINO
W9814 Airport Rd, Black River Falls, WI 54615-5406
Tel (800) 280-2843 *Founded/Ownrshp* 1963
Sales NA *EMP* 3,300
SIC 9131 Indian reservation
Pr: Wilfrid Cleveland
**Pr:* Wade Blackdeer
Ofcr: Kristin W Eagle
Ofcr: Diane M Rave
Ex Dir: Tracy Thundercloud
Mktg Mgr: Rob Reider

D-U-N-S 82-588-8311
HOAG MEMORIAL HOSPITAL PRESBYTERIAN
1 Hoag Dr, Newport Beach, CA 92663-4162
Tel (949) 764-4624 *Founded/Ownrshp* 1944
Sales 822.4MM *EMP* 3,800
SIC 8062 General medical & surgical hospitals
CEO: Robert Braithwaite
CFO: Tim Paulson
Sr VP: Flynn A Andrizzi
VP: John Baker
VP: Trish Bartel
VP: Andrew Guarni
VP: Kris Iyer
VP: Bret Kelsey
VP: Timothy C Moore
VP: Jim Rice
VP: Nina B Robinson
VP: Langston Trigg
VP: Joanne Tucker
Dir OR: Carole Metcalf
Dir Inf Cn: Rosalie Desantis
Dir Lab: Sue Beaty

D-U-N-S 02-858-0143
HOAG ORTHOPEDIC INSTITUTE LLC (CA)
16250 Sand Canyon Ave, Irvine, CA 92618-3714
Tel (855) 999-4641 *Founded/Ownrshp* 2008
Sales 91.2MM *EMP* 42^E
SIC 8011

D-U-N-S 78-956-1342
HOAK MEDIA LLC
3963 Maple Ave Ste 450, Dallas, TX 75219-3236
Tel (972) 960-4840 *Founded/Ownrshp* 2003
Sales 129.2MM^E *EMP* 580
SIC 4833 Television broadcasting stations
Pr: Eric D Van Den Branden
**Ch:* Jim Hoak
**Ex VP:* Rich Adams
**VP:* Jeff Rutan

D-U-N-S 19-432-5056
HOAR CONSTRUCTION LLC
2 Metroplex Dr Ste 400, Birmingham, AL 35209-6877
Tel (205) 803-2121 *Founded/Ownrshp* 1972
Sales 442.0MM *EMP* 600
SIC 1541

D-U-N-S 79-607-8426
■ **HOB ENTERTAINMENT LLC**
HOUSE OF BLUES
(*Suby of* LIVE NATION WORLDWIDE INC) ★
7060 Hollywood Blvd, Los Angeles, CA 90028-6014
Tel (323) 769-4600 *Founded/Ownrshp* 2006
Sales 78.6MM^E *EMP* 3,000
SIC 7929 Entertainers & entertainment groups
CEO: Michael Rapino
**Pr:* Joseph C Kaczorowski
**Sr VP:* Peter Cyffka
VP: Todd Miller
VP: Paul Sewell
VP: Eric Stenta
Mktg Mgr: Ritch Wilder
Counsel: Nancy Lee
Snr Mgr: Laura Cancro

D-U-N-S 83-553-9248 IMP
HOB-LOB LTD
HOBBY LOBBY CREATIVE CENTERS
7707 Sw 44th St, Oklahoma City, OK 73179-4808
Tel (405) 745-1100 *Founded/Ownrshp* 1994
Sales 71.8MM^E *EMP* 13,000
SIC 5945 5999 5949 5947 Arts & crafts supplies; Hobbies; Picture frames, ready made; Sewing & needlework; Gift, novelty & souvenir shop
Pr: David Green
CFO: Jon Cargil
CFO: John Cargill
Ex VP: Steve Green
VP: Brian Jones
VP: Steve Seay
Exec: Don Winslow
IT Man: Bill Adkerson
Opers Mgr: Richard Price
VP Mktg: Steve Stringer
VP Legal: Peter Dobelbower

D-U-N-S 07-968-0203
HOBART AND WILLIAM SMITH COLLEGES
300 Pulteney St, Geneva, NY 14456-3304
Tel (315) 781-3337 *Founded/Ownrshp* 1822
Sales 106.4MM *EMP* 337^E
Accts Kpmg Llp Albany Ny
SIC 8221 College, except junior
Pr: Mark D Gearan
Bd of Dir: Stina Bridgeman
VP: Fred Damiano
VP: Robb Flowers
VP: Bob Murphy
VP: Jeff Vanlone
Assoc Dir: Caitlin Connelly
Off Mgr: Terri Travis
Off Admin: Carol McCormack

D-U-N-S 96-968-1654
HOBART AND WILLIAM SMITH COLLEGES
327 Pulteney St, Geneva, NY 14456-3301
Tel (315) 781-3337 *Founded/Ownrshp* 2011
Sales 161.7MM *EMP* 140
Accts Pricewaterhousecoopers Llp
SIC 8221 Colleges universities & professional schools

D-U-N-S 00-427-9337 IMP/EXP
■ **HOBART BROTHERS CO** (OH)
ITW HOBART BROTHERS
(*Suby of* ILLINOIS TOOL WORKS INC) ★
101 Trade Sq E, Troy, OH 45373-2488
Tel (937) 332-5439 *Founded/Ownrshp* 1917, 1996
Sales 340.5MM^E *EMP* 1,447
SIC 3548 3537 Welding apparatus; Industrial trucks & tractors
VP: Sundaram Nagarajan
CFO: Scott Koizumi
**VP:* Grant Harvey
**Prin:* W H Hobart Et Al
**Prin:* S E Hobart
Dist Mgr: Darren Stane
Genl Mgr: Dan Jackson
Genl Mgr: Mark Thibeault
Dir IT: Jim Stammen
Opers Mgr: Tina Duncan
Opers Mgr: Don Koester

D-U-N-S 62-343-7951 IMP
■ **HOBART CORP**
(*Suby of* ILLINOIS TOOL WORKS INC) ★
701 S Ridge Ave, Troy, OH 45374-0005
Tel (937) 332-3000 *Founded/Ownrshp* 1992
Sales 296.1MM^E *EMP* 2,700
SIC 3589 3556 3596 3585 3321

HOBART SERVICE
See ITW FOOD EQUIPMENT GROUP LLC

D-U-N-S 06-233-1244 IMP/EXP
HOBBICO INC (IL)
GREAT PLANES MODEL DISTRS
1608 Interstate Dr, Champaign, IL 61822-1000
Tel (217) 398-3630 *Founded/Ownrshp* 1971, 1984
Sales 142.8MM^E *EMP* 700

SIC 5092 5961

D-U-N-S 10-204-3320
HOBBS & CURRY FAMILY LIMITED PARTNERSHIP LLLP
4119 Massard Rd, Fort Smith, AR 72903-6223
Tel (479) 785-0844 *Founded/Ownrshp* 1995
Sales 109.0MM^E *EMP* 570
SIC 1542 Commercial & office building contractors
Genl Pt: C David Curry
Pt: Janice Hobbs Powell

D-U-N-S 08-029-7998
HOBBS BONDED FIBERS LLC
200 Commerce Dr, Waco, TX 76710-6975
Tel (254) 741-0040 *Founded/Ownrshp* 2015
Sales 110.2MM^E *EMP* 440^E
SIC 2297 2299 Bonded-fiber fabrics, except felt; Apparel filling: cotton waste, kapok & related material; Batts & batting: cotton mill waste & related material
Pr: Larry Hobbs
Exec: Norman Conner
VP Admn: Norman Brings
Dir IT: Danny Natividad
Manager: Steve Watson
Trfc Mgr: Odis Webster

D-U-N-S 00-801-0761 IMP/EXP
HOBBS BONDED FIBERS NA LLC
(*Suby of* HOBBS BONDED FIBERS LLC) ★
200 Commerce Dr, Waco, TX 76710-6975
Tel (254) 741-0040 *Founded/Ownrshp* 1953
Sales 110.2MM^E *EMP* 250^E
SIC 2297 2299 Bonded-fiber fabrics, except felt; Apparel filling: cotton waste, kapok & related material; Batts & batting: cotton mill waste & related material
Pr: Larry Hobbs
**CFO:* Jim Freeman
Sales Exec: Andy Hobbs

D-U-N-S 06-897-3627
HOBBS MUNICIPAL SCHOOLS
1515 E Sanger St, Hobbs, NM 88240-4713
Tel (575) 433-0100 *Founded/Ownrshp* 1918
Sales 59.0MM^E *EMP* 1,050
Accts Accounting & Consulting Group
SIC 8211 Public elementary & secondary schools
Ex Dir: James Johns

HOBBY LOBBY CREATIVE CENTERS
See HOB-LOB LTD

D-U-N-S 06-103-8741 IMP/EXP
HOBBY LOBBY STORES INC
7707 Sw 44th St, Oklahoma City, OK 73179-4899
Tel (855) 329-7060 *Founded/Ownrshp* 1977
Sales 4.4MMM^E *EMP* 30,218^E
SIC 5945 Hobby & craft supplies
CEO: David Green
Pr: David Adney
**Pr:* Steven T Green
Pr: Bob Mackey
Pr: Becky Robinson
**CFO:* Jon Cargill
Ex VP: Stan Lett
VP: Thornton Casey
VP: Bill Darrow
VP: Peter Dobelbower
VP: Darsee Green-Lett
VP: Ken Haywood
VP: Timothy Mattingly
VP: Richelle D McKinley
VP: Steve Seay
VP: Bill Woody
VP: Tammecca Youngblood

HOBO PANTRY FOOD STORES
See HOME OIL CO INC

D-U-N-S 07-987-3842
HOBOKEN UNIVERSITY MEDICAL CENTER
(*Suby of* CAREPOINT HEALTH MANAGEMENT ASSOCIATES LLC) ★
308 Willow Ave, Hoboken, NJ 07030-3808
Tel (201) 418-1000 *Founded/Ownrshp* 2015
Sales 188.4MM *EMP* 41^E
SIC 8062 General medical & surgical hospitals

HOBOKEN UNIVERSITY MEDICAL CTR
See HUDSON HEALTHCARE INC

HOBOKEN UNIVERSITY MEDICAL CTR
See HUMC OPCO LLC

D-U-N-S 82-641-3924
HOBSONS INC
(*Suby of* DAILY MAIL AND GENERAL TRUST P L C)
50 E Business Way Ste 300, Cincinnati, OH 45241-2398
Tel (513) 891-5444 *Founded/Ownrshp* 1993
Sales 86.0MM^E *EMP* 550
SIC 8741 Administrative management
Pr: Craig Heldman
Pr: Todd Jibby
**CFO:* Lee Wall
VP: Scott Frost
VP: Monica Morrell
VP: Kathy Ovans
VP: John Shin
VP Opers: Dan Conrad
Mktg Dir: Nahid Sabti
Mktg Mgr: Kristen Auguste
Pgrm Dir: Jennifer Beyer

D-U-N-S 02-341-3444
HOC HOLDINGS INC
7310 Pacific Ave, Pleasant Grove, CA 95668-9708
Tel (916) 921-8950 *Founded/Ownrshp* 2008
Sales 465.7MM^E *EMP* 697^E
SIC 5082 5084 5083 7359 Construction & mining machinery; Tractors, construction; Materials handling machinery; Agricultural machinery; Equipment rental & leasing
Pr: Kenneth Monroe

D-U-N-S 12-860-4506 IMP
HOCHTIEF USA INC
(*Suby of* HOCHTIEF AMERICAS GMBH)
375 Hudson St Fl 6, New York, NY 10014-7462
Tel (212) 229-6000 *Founded/Ownrshp* 1996
Sales 11.6MMM^E *EMP* 6,000
SIC 1542 1541 1522 8741 8742 6799 Nonresidential construction; Commercial & office building, new construction; Design & erection, combined: non-residential; Specialized public building contractors; Industrial buildings & warehouses; Industrial buildings, new construction; Factory construction; Hotel/motel, new construction; Condominium construction; Construction management; Construction project management consultant; Real estate investors, except property operators
Prin: Marcelino Fernndez Verdes
Genl Couns: Hartmut Paulsen

D-U-N-S 10-759-8344 IMP
HOCKENBERGS EQUIPMENT AND SUPPLY CO INC
CHEF'S WAREHOUSE
7002 F St, Omaha, NE 68117-1013
Tel (402) 339-8900 *Founded/Ownrshp* 1983
Sales 156.4MM^E *EMP* 213
SIC 5046 Restaurant equipment & supplies
Pr: Thomas D Schrack Jr
**Ch Bd:* Tom Schrack Sr

HOCKING COLLEGE
See HOCKING TECHNICAL COLLEGE

D-U-N-S 07-164-8950
HOCKING TECHNICAL COLLEGE
HOCKING COLLEGE
3301 Hocking Pkwy, Nelsonville, OH 45764-9588
Tel (740) 753-3591 *Founded/Ownrshp* 1966
Sales 29.3MM *EMP* 1,021
Accts Millhuff-Stang Cpa Inc Por
SIC 8222 8249 8221 Technical institute; Vocational schools; Colleges universities & professional schools
Pr: Ron Erickson
**CFO:* John Light PHD
**Treas:* J William Hill

HODES LIVER & PANCREAS CENTER
See LIVER AND PANCREAS CENTER UNIVERSITY OF MARYLAND ST JOSEPH MEDICAL CENTER

D-U-N-S 00-151-9107 IMP/EXP
HOEGANAES CORP
(*Suby of* GKN NORTH AMERICA SERVICES INC) ★
1001 Taylors Ln, Cinnaminson, NJ 08077-2034
Tel (856) 303-0366 *Founded/Ownrshp* 2002
Sales 131.3MM^E *EMP* 523^E
SIC 3312 3399 Blast furnaces & steel mills; Metal powders, pastes & flakes
VP: Kalathur Narasimhan
VP: Joel Feit
VP: Dennis Jackson
VP: Wilson Jeff
VP: Mike Mattingly
VP: William Michael
VP: Sim Narahan
**VP:* Peter Saitis
VP: Jeffery Wilson
QA Dir: Dave Stojakovich
Dir IT: Herbert Shaw

D-U-N-S 07-335-7527
HOEHN MOTORS INC
HOEHN PORSCHE-MERCEDES-AUDI
5475 Car Country Dr, Carlsbad, CA 92008-4311
Tel (760) 438-4454 *Founded/Ownrshp* 1975
Sales 90.0MM^E *EMP* 200
SIC 5511 Automobiles, new & used
Pr: Theodore Hoehn III
**VP:* Robert Hoehn
Genl Mgr: Vas Chohan
Genl Mgr: Kris Truman
Opers Mgr: Steven Kuehl
Sales Exec: Charles Eder
Sls Mgr: Josh Beesemyer
Sls Mgr: Ron Edwards
Sales Asso: Heick Moussavian

HOEHN PORSCHE-MERCEDES-AUDI
See HOEHN MOTORS INC

D-U-N-S 14-464-6569 IMP
HOERBIGER COMPRESSION TECHNOLOGY AMERICA HOLDING INC
(*Suby of* HOERBIGER HOLDING AG)
3350 Gateway Dr, Pompano Beach, FL 33069-4841
Tel (954) 974-5700 *Founded/Ownrshp* 1999
Sales 164.8MM^E *EMP* 591
SIC 3494 7699 Valves & pipe fittings; Valve repair, industrial
Pr: Franz Gruber
**Sec:* Peter Laube

D-U-N-S 00-179-4049 IMP
HOERBIGER CORP OF AMERICA INC (FL)
(*Suby of* HOERBIGER COMPRESSION TECHNOLOGY AMERICA HOLDING INC) ★
3350 Gateway Dr, Pompano Beach, FL 33069-4841
Tel (954) 974-5700 *Founded/Ownrshp* 1963
Sales 91.8MM^E *EMP* 350
Accts Deloitte Tax Llp Miami Flori
SIC 3491 Industrial valves
Pr: Don York
Treas: Heather Henderson
**Sec:* Thomas Rabil
**Ex VP:* Hannes Hunschosky
Sr VP: Josef Leitner
VP: Tim Bremner
**VP:* Bruce Driggett
**VP:* Christean Kapp
**VP:* Donald York
Exec: Babak Farrokhzad
Mng Dir: Franz Soffa

D-U-N-S 00-521-6221 IMP/EXP
HOFFER PLASTICS CORP (DE)
500 N Collins St, South Elgin, IL 60177-1195
Tel (847) 741-5740 *Founded/Ownrshp* 1953
Sales 130.9MM^E *EMP* 375
SIC 3089 Injection molding of plastics
Pr: William A Hoffer
**Treas:* Mary Eagin
**VP:* Jack Shedd
QA Dir: Melanie Nelson
Plnt Mgr: George Brewer
Plnt Mgr: Bob Fowler
Plnt Mgr: Les McMichael
Ql Cn Mgr: Linda Clarke
VP Sls: William Hoffer
Mktg Dir: Charlotte Canning

D-U-N-S 07-156-8745
HOFFMAN & HOFFMAN INC (GA)
HOFFMAN BUILDING TECHNOLOGIES
3816 Patterson St, Greensboro, NC 27407-3238
Tel (336) 292-8777 *Founded/Ownrshp* 1947
Sales 85.0MM^E *EMP* 225
SIC 5075

HOFFMAN BUILDING TECHNOLOGIES
See HOFFMAN & HOFFMAN INC

D-U-N-S 11-267-7810 IMP
HOFFMAN CORP
805 Sw Broadway Ste 2100, Portland, OR 97205-3361
Tel (503) 221-8811 *Founded/Ownrshp* 1983
Sales 98.1MM^E *EMP* 750
Accts Kpmg Llp Portland Or
SIC 8741 1541 1542 1623 1629 Management services; Industrial buildings, new construction; Renovation, remodeling & repairs: industrial buildings; Commercial & office building, new construction; Water main construction; Waste water & sewage treatment plant construction
Pr: Wayne A Drinkward
**CFO:* Mario Nudo
Ex VP: Ken Hoffman
**Ex VP:* Richard L Silliman
VP: Samantha Bartfield
VP: Darcy Doyle
VP: David Hoffman
VP Bus Dev: Barton Eberwein
Genl Mgr: Murl Ferguson
Genl Mgr: Ryan Thrush
MIS Mgr: Pat Gorrell

D-U-N-S 13-073-2274 IMP/EXP
HOFFMAN ENCLOSURES INC
PENTAIR TECHNICAL PRODUCTS
(*Suby of* PENTAIR PUBLIC LIMITED COMPANY)
2100 Hoffman Way, Anoka, MN 55303-1745
Tel (763) 421-2240 *Founded/Ownrshp* 1988
Sales 789.9MM^E *EMP* 1,500^E
SIC 3444 3699 3613 3469 3053 Housings for business machines, sheet metal; Electrical equipment & supplies; Switchgear & switchboard apparatus; Metal stampings; Gaskets, packing & sealing devices
Pr: Alok Maskara
Treas: Mark Borin
Exec: Trent Jones
Exec: Mike Roskosch
IT Man: Kelly Adkins
Sfty Mgr: Joe Friederichs
Sfty Mgr: Joel Pettit
Opers Mgr: Tom Erickson
Opers Mgr: Dean Willey
Advt Dir: Bob Kalivoda
Sales Asso: Dan Bahr

HOFFMAN ENTERPRISES
See JETOBRA INC

D-U-N-S 00-219-1211 IMP/EXP
■ **HOFFMANN-LA ROCHE INC** (NJ)
(*Suby of* ROCHE HOLDINGS INC) ★
340 Kingsland St, Nutley, NJ 07110-1199
Tel (973) 235-5000 *Founded/Ownrshp* 1905
Sales 1.1MMM^E *EMP* 5,027
SIC 2834 8733 Pharmaceutical preparations; Medical research
Pr: George B Abercrombie
Pr: Kurt Seiler
**CFO:* Ivor Macleod
Treas: William L Hennrich
Bd of Dir: Lance Willsey
Sr VP: Alain Gscheidle
Sr VP: Maryjo Zaborowski
VP: Carl J Accettura
**VP:* Frederick C Kentz III
**VP:* Tom Lyon
VP: Steven C Sembler
VP: Barbara Senich
Exec: Peter Borgulya
Exec: Susan Gabra
Exec: Maria Rivas
Assoc Dir: Hans Bitter
Comm Dir: Odeta Rimkeviciute
Dir Bus: Guido Kaiser

HOFFMAN'S CHOCOLATES
See BFC FINANCIAL CORP

D-U-N-S 04-314-7412 IMP/EXP
HOFFMASTER GROUP INC (DE)
(*Suby of* WELLSPRING CAPITAL MANAGEMENT LLC) ★
2920 N Main St, Oshkosh, WI 54901-1221
Tel (920) 235-9330 *Founded/Ownrshp* 2005, 2016
Sales 426.0MM^E *EMP* 809
SIC 2676 Towels, napkins & tissue paper products; Napkins, paper: made from purchased paper
CEO: Rory Leyden
Pr: William Mullenix
Pr: Mike Narquardt
Pr: Russsell Snow
CFO: David L Walkowski
VP: Jeff Cunningham
Exec: Fabricio Biscardi
Sfty Mgr: Mike Gonzales
Opers Mgr: Tim Allen
Natl Sales: Robert Alexander
VP Mktg: Cindy Herbert

HOFS HUT LCLLES SMOKEHOUSE BBQ
See HOFS HUT RESTAURANT INC

D-U-N-S 05-291-5580
HOFS HUT RESTAURANT INC
HOFS HUT LCLLES SMOKEHOUSE BBQ
2601 E Willow St, Signal Hill, CA 90755-2214
Tel (310) 406-6340 *Founded/Ownrshp* 2010
Sales 142.0MM *EMP* 2,986
SIC 5812 Barbecue restaurant; American restaurant
Pr: Craig Hofman
Exec: Chris Ferrell
Genl Mgr: Allen Cameron
VP Opers: Paul Williamson
Opers Supe: Jorge Angulo
Opers Supe: Chris Gorman

HOF'S HUT RESTAURANTS AND BKY
See HOFS HUT RESTAURANTS INC

D-U-N-S 02-841-6196
HOFS HUT RESTAURANTS INC
HOF'S HUT RESTAURANTS AND BKY
2601 E Willow St, Signal Hill, CA 90755-2214
Tel (562) 596-0200 *Founded/Ownrshp* 1951
Sales 58.8MM^E *EMP* 1,345
SIC 5812 Restaurant, family: chain
Pr: Craig Hoffman
**Pr:* Paul Bowman
CFO: Dennis Jones
Genl Mgr: Carl Tierney
Dir IT: Dana Gonzalez
IT Man: Rebekah Gonzalez
IT Man: Curtis Yamashiro

D-U-N-S 06-593-1800
HOFSTRA UNIVERSITY
100 Hofstra University, Hempstead, NY 11549-4000
Tel (516) 463-6600 *Founded/Ownrshp* 1935
Sales 397.4MM *EMP* 2,000
Accts Kpmg Llp New York Ny
SIC 8221 University
Pr: Stuart Rabinowitz
CFO: Joshua Robinson
Treas: Grant Saff
VP: Melissa Cefalu
VP: Jessica Eads
Dir Soc: Andrew Cohen
Dir IT: Kathleen Dwyer
Mktg Dir: Debbi Honorof

D-U-N-S 05-441-5021 IMP/EXP
HOG SLAT INC (NC)
206 Fayetteville St, Newton Grove, NC 28366-9071
Tel (866) 464-7528 *Founded/Ownrshp* 1970
Sales 715.1MM^E *EMP* 600
SIC 1542 3272 3523 0213 Farm building construction; Floor slabs & tiles, precast concrete; Hog feeding, handling & watering equipment; Hogs
Ch Bd: William T Herring Sr
Pr: William T Herring Jr
Sec: Magalene Herring
VP: David D Herring
Exec: Tommy Herring
Area Mgr: Pat Williams
Genl Mgr: Rick Rouse
Store Mgr: Lance Heuser
CTO: Denise Holland
Site Mgr: Ron Maassen
Site Mgr: Mike Thode

HOGAN ADMINISTRATIVE CENTER
See SCHOOL DISTRICT OF LACROSSE

D-U-N-S 07-265-9238
HOGAN LOVELLS US LLP
555 13th St Nw, Washington, DC 20004-1109
Tel (202) 637-5600 *Founded/Ownrshp* 1994
Sales 453.0MM^E *EMP* 2,500
SIC 8111 Corporate, partnership & business law; Patent, trademark & copyright law; Securities law
Mng Pt: Emily Yinger
Pt: Jeanne S Archibald
Pt: Barton S Aronson
Pt: A C Arumi
Pt: Raymond J Batla
Pt: David H Ben-Meir
Pt: Barbara Bennett
Pt: Christopher D Berry
Pt: Dirk Besse
Pt: Arlene L Chow
Pt: Alexander D Cobey
Pt: Colin W Craik
Pt: Celine J Crowson
Pt: Alice V Curran
Pt: Daniel M Davidson
Pt: Agnes P Dover
Pt: Alexander E Dreier
Pt: David R Dunn
Pt: Prentiss E Feagles
Pt: Adam S Feuerstein
Pt: Amy B Freed

D-U-N-S 00-633-5251
HOK GROUP INC (GA)
10 S Broadway Ste 200, Saint Louis, MO 63102-1729
Tel (314) 421-2000 *Founded/Ownrshp* 1955, 1980
Sales 347.4MM^E *EMP* 1,839
SIC 8711 8712 8742 Engineering services; Architectural services; Planning consultant
CEO: Patrick Macleamy
**Pr:* William Hellmuth
**Treas:* James Beittenmiller
Sr VP: Jim Fair
Sr VP: Bill O'Dell
VP: Javier Espinosa
VP: Todd Osborne
VP: Andy Singletary
**Prin:* Carl Galioto
IT Man: Donny Russell
Mktg Mgr: Kathie Dunn
Board of Directors: Carl Galioto, William Hellmuth, Patrick Macleamy, Richard Mascia, Thomas Robson

D-U-N-S 96-987-1560
HOK INC
(*Suby of* HOK GROUP INC) ★
10 S Broadway Ste 200, Saint Louis, MO 63102-1729
Tel (314) 421-2000 *Founded/Ownrshp* 1999
Sales 66.1MM^E *EMP* 1,808
SIC 0781 8712 8711 Landscape planning services; Architectural services; Engineering services
Pr: William Hellmuth
Pr: Andrew Gayer
Sr VP: Randy Kray
VP: Randy Buescher
VP: Steven Crang
VP: Jeffrey Davis
VP: Debra Handy
VP: Hans Hecker
VP: Herman Howard
VP: Cheryl Jefferies
VP: Michael Nolan

VP: Joseph Ostafi IV
VP: Misty Yanko
Dir Bus: Kristen Harrison
Dir Bus: Mandy Weitknecht
Board of Directors: Daniel Hajjar, Sandra Paret, James Beittenmiller, Nancy Hamilton, Tom Polucci, Duncan Broyd, Jan Harmon, Thomas Robson, Robert Chicas, William Hellmuth, Paul Strohm, Ernest Cirangle, Susan Williams Klumpp, Jay Tatum, Kenneth Drucker, Richard Macia, Paul Woolford, Chris Fannin, Patrick Macleamy, Carl Galioto, Lawrence Malcic, Jeff Goodale, Rebecca Nolan, Lisa Green, William O'dell

D-U-N-S 78-215-9321
HOL-DAV INC
JOHNSON LEXUS OF RALEIGH
5839 Capital Blvd, Raleigh, NC 27616-2937
Tel (888) 240-7435 *Founded/Ownrshp* 1990
Sales 85.6MM^E *EMP* 220
SIC 5511 5012 Automobiles, new & used; Automobiles & other motor vehicles
Pr: C David Johnson Jr
Sr VP: Charlie Bratton
Genl Mgr: Brett Smith
CTO: Bob Humphrey
Sales Exec: Jeremy Bridges
Sls Mgr: Jeffrey Ketcham
Sls Mgr: Stan Muecke
Sls Mgr: Jay Tetreault
Sales Asso: Godfrey Akenabor
Sales Asso: Sean Alazraki
Sales Asso: Jay Huh

D-U-N-S 00-283-7508
HOLADAY-PARKS-FABRICATORS INC
4600 S 134th Pl, Tukwila, WA 98168-3241
Tel (206) 248-9700 *Founded/Ownrshp* 1952
Sales 84.0MM *EMP* 350
SIC 1711 Mechanical contractor
Co-Pr: Dave Beck
**Co-Pr:* Dan Connell
**Co-Pr:* Bijit Giri
**VP:* Jerry Freel
**VP:* Grace Pizzey
VP: Eric Veen
Genl Mgr: Ron Kiel
Genl Mgr: Erin Villeneuve
Dir IT: June Nailon
Dir IT: Eric Der Veen
IT Man: Erik Frederickson

D-U-N-S 60-896-3674 IMP
HOLCIM (US) INC
HOLCIM USA
(*Suby of* LAFARGEHOLCIM LTD)
6211 N Ann Arbor Rd, Dundee, MI 48131-9527
Tel (734) 529-4278 *Founded/Ownrshp* 1981
Sales 739.7MM^E *EMP* 1,800
SIC 3241 3272 Portland cement; Concrete products
Pr: Filiberto Ruiz
Sr VP: GA Tan Jacques
**Sr VP:* Norman L Jagger
**Sr VP:* Alyse Martinelli
**Sr VP:* Jeff Ouhl
**VP:* David Loomes
VP: Chrysanth Silva
Exec: Brian Carter
Prgrm Mgr: Jodie Earle
Brnch Mgr: Bill Tooman
Dir IT: James Jones

HOLCIM USA
See HOLCIM (US) INC

D-U-N-S 04-463-3142
■ **HOLDCO LLC**
(*Suby of* TIME WARNER CABLE ENTERPRISES LLC) ★
13820 Sunrise Valley Dr, Herndon, VA 20171-4659
Tel (703) 345-2400 *Founded/Ownrshp* 2001
Sales 113.1MM^E *EMP* 480
SIC 4813
VP: Clay Carney
VP: Raj Kumar
VP Mktg: Chip Snyder
Mktg Dir: Margie Locke
Mktg Dir: Wendy Wilson

D-U-N-S 16-708-0667 IMP/EXP
HOLDEN INDUSTRIES INC
500 Lake Cook Rd Ste 400, Deerfield, IL 60015-5269
Tel (847) 940-1500 *Founded/Ownrshp* 2004
Sales 284.4MM^E *EMP* 1,091
SIC 2752 2672 3545 3589 3541 3441 Commercial printing, lithographic; Adhesive papers, labels or tapes: from purchased material; Machine tool accessories; Sewage & water treatment equipment; Sewer cleaning equipment, power; Machine tools, metal cutting type; Fabricated structural metal
Ch Bd: Joseph S Haas
**CFO:* Gregory R Hamilton
CFO: Donald Hotz
Ofcr: Joe Walsh
**Ex VP:* Arthur R Miller

HOLDER CONSTRUCTION
See HOLDER CORP

D-U-N-S 82-833-8488
HOLDER CONSTRUCTION CO
3333 Riverwood Pkwy Se # 400, Atlanta, GA 30339-3304
Tel (770) 988-3000 *Founded/Ownrshp* 1997
Sales 600.9MM^E *EMP* 785^E
SIC 1542 Commercial & office building, new construction
CEO: Thomas M Holder
**CFO:* Dave O'Haren
Ex VP: Doug Hunter
Ex VP: Lee Johnston
Ex VP: Jesse Pendrey
Sr VP: Wayne Wadsworth
VP: Gavin Kalley
VP: Michael Kenig
VP: Chad Martin
VP: Rick Morgan
VP: Ray Riddle
VP: William Turpin

D-U-N-S 11-029-2471 IMP
HOLDER CONSTRUCTION GROUP LLC
3333 Riverwood Pkwy Se # 400, Atlanta, GA 30339-3304
Tel (770) 988-3000 *Founded/Ownrshp* 2011
Sales 158.5MM^E *EMP* 450
SIC 1542 Commercial & office building, new construction
**Pr:* Dave W Miller
**Pr:* John Redmond
**Pr:* Thomas Shumaker
**Pr:* Drew Yantis
**VP:* John Thomas

D-U-N-S 00-332-0850
HOLDER CORP
HOLDER CONSTRUCTION
3300 Cumberland Blvd Se # 400, Atlanta, GA 30339-8103
Tel (770) 988-3000 *Founded/Ownrshp* 1984
Sales 111.7MM^E *EMP* 470
SIC 6552 1542 Subdividers & developers; Commercial & office building, new construction
Ch Bd: John Holder
V Ch: Michael E Kenig
**CFO:* Lori Pisarcik
**V Ch Bd:* Thomas M Holder
**Ex VP:* J C Pendrey Jr
**Sr VP:* Jeff Mixson
Sr VP: Rick Morgan
**Sr VP:* Chris Smith
**VP:* Henry Petree
Site Mgr: Jason Rollins
Pr Mgr: Helen M Henley

D-U-N-S 79-668-2859
HOLDING CO OF VILLAGES INC
VILLAGES, THE
1000 Lake Sumter Lndg, The Villages, FL 32162-2693
Tel (352) 753-2270 *Founded/Ownrshp* 1959
Sales 239.1MM^E *EMP* 2,000^E
SIC 6531 Real estate agent, commercial
CEO: H Gary Morse
Pr: Jennifer Parr
**Treas:* W Thomas Brooks
VP: Tracy Mathews
VP: John Parker
**VP:* John F Wife
Genl Mgr: Ingo Fockler
Genl Mgr: Greg Hightman
Opers Mgr: Robert Hoopfer
Sls&Mrk Ex: David Ortwein

D-U-N-S 13-196-1161
HOLIDAY BUILDERS INC
2293 W Eau Gallie Blvd, Melbourne, FL 32935-3184
Tel (321) 610-5156 *Founded/Ownrshp* 1983
Sales 84.1MM^E *EMP* 101
Accts Berman Hopkins Wright & Laham
SIC 1521 New construction, single-family houses
CEO: Bruce Assam
**CFO:* Richard Fadil
VP Bus Dev: Michelle Smallwood
Sales Asso: Joseph Fortun

D-U-N-S 80-778-2750
HOLIDAY COMPANIES
4567 American Blvd W, Bloomington, MN 55437-1123
Tel (952) 830-8700 *Founded/Ownrshp* 1992
Sales 1.0MMM^E *EMP* 4,500
SIC 5541 5411 5172

HOLIDAY FENOGLIO FOWLER
See HFF HOLDINGS LLC

HOLIDAY INN
See MIDAMERICA HOTELS CORP

HOLIDAY INN
See ATRIUM HOTELS INC

HOLIDAY MAZDA
See MIKE SHANNON AUTOMOTIVE INC

HOLIDAY QUALITY FOODS
See NORTH STATE GROCERY INC

HOLIDAY RETIREMENT
See HARVEST MANAGEMENT SUB LLC

HOLIDAY STATION STORES
See LYNDALE TERMINAL CO

D-U-N-S 04-596-5258
HOLIDAY STATIONSTORES INC
(*Suby of* HOLIDAY COMPANIES) ★
4567 American Blvd W, Bloomington, MN 55437-1123
Tel (952) 830-8700 *Founded/Ownrshp* 1964
Sales 1.0MMM^E *EMP* 3,993
SIC 5541 5411

HOLIDAY VALLEY RESORT
See WIN-SUM SKI CORP

D-U-N-S 02-361-4100 IMP
HOLIDAY WHOLESALE INC
225 Pioneer Dr, Wisconsin Dells, WI 53965-8397
Tel (608) 253-0404 *Founded/Ownrshp* 1951
Sales 188.4MM^E *EMP* 250
SIC 5194 5145 5113 5199 Tobacco & tobacco products; Candy; Industrial & personal service paper; General merchandise, non-durable
Pr: Joseph B Gussel
**Pr:* Bernard Gussel Jr
**Treas:* Angela Myer
Chf Mktg O: Dixie Marquardt
**VP:* Patrick Jagoe
IT Man: Ben Wrist
Sls Mgr: Edward Wojnicz

D-U-N-S 80-915-7175
HOLIEN INC
ANZA
312 9th Ave Se Ste B, Watertown, SD 57201-4853
Tel (605) 886-3889 *Founded/Ownrshp* 1993
Sales 154.6MM^E *EMP* 2,300^E
SIC 3612 3672 3993 Specialty transformers; Circuit boards, television & radio printed; Electric signs; Signs, not made in custom sign painting shops
Pr: Dennis D Holien

CFO: Greg Kulefa
CFO: Greg Kulesa

D-U-N-S 04-320-0344
HOLLADAY CORP (VA)
3400 Idaho Ave Nw Ste 400, Washington, DC 20016-3050
Tel (202) 362-2400 *Founded/Ownrshp* 1952
Sales 288.4MM^E *EMP* 770
SIC 1522 6531 Apartment building construction; Real estate managers
Pr: Wallace F Holladay
**Sec:* Helga Carter
Sr VP: S L Weber
**VP:* John T Phair

D-U-N-S 01-062-0755
HOLLAND & HART LLP
555 17th St Ste 3200, Denver, CO 80202-3921
Tel (303) 295-8000 *Founded/Ownrshp* 1947
Sales 180.3MM^E *EMP* 904
SIC 8111 General practice law office
Mng Pt: Thomas O'Donnell
**Pt:* John Husband
Pt: Ronald Martin
Pr: Colleen Jasper
Pr: Judy A Johnson
Pr: Wendy Shanks
Pr: Julie J Winkler
VP: Carolyn Gilroy
Dir IT: Yevgeniy Kolmanovich
Dir IT: Bill Maywhort
Counsel: Robert Bassett

D-U-N-S 07-758-3318
HOLLAND & KNIGHT LLP
524 Grand Regency Blvd, Brandon, FL 33510-3931
Tel (813) 901-4200 *Founded/Ownrshp* 1968
Sales 529.2MM^E *EMP* 2,500
SIC 8111 General practice law office
Mng Pt: Steven Sonberg
Pt: Alfred B Adams
Pt: Jim Davis
Pt: Ralph T Lepore
Pt: Howell W Melton
Pt: George Mencio
Pt: Michael D Rechtin
CFO: Michael Marget
VP: Tracy Nichols
Exec: Kelly-Ann G Cartwright
Exec: William Honan
Exec: Brad Kimbro
Exec: Nicholas G Milano
Exec: Steven Wright

HOLLAND AMERCN LINES-WESTOURS
See HOLLAND AMERICA LINE INC

D-U-N-S 10-133-5172
■ **HOLLAND AMERICA LINE INC**
HOLLAND AMERCN LINES-WESTOURS
(*Suby of* CARNIVAL CORP) ★
300 Elliott Ave W Ste 100, Seattle, WA 98119-4122
Tel (206) 281-3535 *Founded/Ownrshp* 1989
Sales 256.6MM^E *EMP* 1,410
SIC 4725 Tour operators
CEO: Stein Kruse
**Treas:* Todd Kimmel
Ex VP: Charlie Ball
**Ex VP:* David Giersdorf
Ex VP: Paul Goodwin
Ex VP: Tim Howie
Ex VP: Keith A Taylor
Sr VP: Larry D Calkins
**Sr VP:* Dan Grausz
**Sr VP:* Richard Meadows
VP: Eva Andreson
VP: Patricia Bothwell
**VP:* Larry Calkins
VP: Mark Kammerer
VP: Ares M Michaelides
VP: William J Morani
VP: Matthew Sams
VP: Brendan Vierra

D-U-N-S 07-998-0401
HOLLAND AMERICA LINE NV DBA HOLLAND AMERICA LINE NV LLC
300 Elliott Ave W Ste 100, Seattle, WA 98119-4122
Tel (206) 281-3535 *Founded/Ownrshp* 1996
Sales 165.6MM^E *EMP* 1,500
SIC 4489 Excursion boat operators

D-U-N-S 07-257-7877
HOLLAND COMMUNITY HOSPITAL AUXILIARY INC (MI)
HOLLAND HOSPITAL
602 Michigan Ave, Holland, MI 49423-4918
Tel (616) 748-9346 *Founded/Ownrshp* 1917
Sales 230.2MM *EMP* 1,500
Accts Plante & Moran Pllc Traverse
SIC 8062 General medical & surgical hospitals
Pr: Dale Sowders
**VP:* Chuck Kohlruss
**VP:* Michael Matthews
**VP:* Mark Pawlak
VP: Bill Vanderyliet
**VP:* Patti Vandort
Exec: Carolyn Schaefer
Dir: Mike Parker
Dir Rx: Bill Brackenridge
Ex Dir: Judy Rozendal
Telecom Ex: Darrell Speinke

D-U-N-S 06-020-1696
HOLLAND HOME (MI)
FULTON MANOR
2100 Raybrook St Se # 300, Grand Rapids, MI 49546-5783
Tel (616) 235-5000 *Founded/Ownrshp* 1892
Sales 62.4MM *EMP* 1,300
SIC 8361 8051 Home for the aged; Skilled nursing care facilities
CEO: H David Claus
Ex Dir: Carolyn Flietstra
Ex Dir: Scott Halquist
Ex Dir: Steve Velzen
Ex Dir: Kitty Vydareny
Ex Dir: Rene Wheaton

Nurse Mgr: Jessica Troyer
VP Mktg: Chris Micely
Board of Directors: Hermina Breuker

HOLLAND HOSPITAL
See HOLLAND COMMUNITY HOSPITAL AUXILIARY INC

D-U-N-S 02-756-4012
HOLLAND INC
BURGERVILLE USA
109 W 17th St, Vancouver, WA 98660-2932
Tel (360) 694-1521 *Founded/Ownrshp* 1992
Sales 136.3MM^E *EMP* 1,600
SIC 8741 Restaurant management
CEO: Jeff Harvey
COO: Janice Williams
**VP:* Beth Brewer
Genl Mgr: John Crutchfield
Site Mgr: Irma Quintana
Snr Mgr: James Anderson

D-U-N-S 04-422-3139 IMP/EXP
HOLLAND LP
HOLLAND SPECIALTY VEHICLES
(*Suby of* CURRAN GROUP INC) ★
1000 Holland Dr, Crete, IL 60417-2120
Tel (708) 672-2300 *Founded/Ownrshp* 1974
Sales 276.7MM^E *EMP* 820
SIC 2899 3743 Fluxes: brazing, soldering, galvanizing & welding; Railroad equipment
Pr: Philip C Moeller
**Treas:* Frank J Francis
VP: Kevin Flaherty
Genl Mgr: Robert Norby
Genl Mgr: Andrew Smith
QA Dir: Jyll Boudreau
Dir IT: James Tieri
Software D: Wayne T Dodgen
Software D: Andrea Ellis
Software D: David Haffner
Software D: James Jackson

D-U-N-S 01-747-9825
HOLLAND OIL CO
1485 Marion Ave, Akron, OH 44313-7625
Tel (330) 835-1815 *Founded/Ownrshp* 1954
Sales 179.2MM *EMP* 625
Accts Bober Markey Fedorovich & Co
SIC 5541 5172 5411 Gasoline service stations; Gasoline; Service station supplies, petroleum; Convenience stores
Pr: Lisa M Holland-Toth
**Ex VP:* Lynn Gorman
**Sr VP:* Michael J Toth
MIS Dir: Joe Ryan
**VP Opers:* Carl Hummel
**VP Merchng:* John Ballard

HOLLAND PARTNERS GROUP
See HOLLAND PARTNERS ROCK CREEK LANDING LLC

D-U-N-S 13-203-1035
HOLLAND PARTNERS ROCK CREEK LANDING LLC
HOLLAND PARTNERS GROUP
1111 Main St Ste 700, Vancouver, WA 98660-2970
Tel (360) 694-7888 *Founded/Ownrshp* 2000
Sales 92.3MM^E *EMP* 752
SIC 6531 Real estate agents & managers
CEO: Clyde P Holland Jr
Pr: Jeff Dickerson
Pr: Thomas B Parsons
COO: Bob Coppess
COO: Robbie Dodd
COO: Eli Hanacek
VP: Julie Schuh
VP: Lydia Thompson
VP: Michael Voorhees
Snr PM: Jake Stone

D-U-N-S 16-745-9580
HOLLAND RESIDENTIAL LLC
(*Suby of* HOLLAND PARTNERS GROUP) ★
1111 Main St Ste 700, Vancouver, WA 98660-2970
Tel (360) 694-7888 *Founded/Ownrshp* 2003
Sales 84.4MM^E *EMP* 500^E
SIC 6513 8741 Apartment building operators; Management services
**CFO:* Robbie Dodd
Sr VP: Jeff Dickerson

HOLLAND SPECIALTY VEHICLES
See HOLLAND LP

D-U-N-S 07-889-0564
HOLLANDER HOME FASHIONS HOLDINGS LLC
6501 Congress Ave Ste 300, Boca Raton, FL 33487-2840
Tel (561) 997-6900 *Founded/Ownrshp* 1953
Sales 163.0MM *EMP* 924
SIC 2392 Cushions & pillows

D-U-N-S 00-215-2817 IMP/EXP
HOLLANDER SLEEP PRODUCTS LLC
(*Suby of* HOLLANDER HOME FASHIONS HOLDINGS LLC) ★
6501 Congress Ave Ste 300, Boca Raton, FL 33487-2840
Tel (561) 997-6900 *Founded/Ownrshp* 2014
Sales 141.1MM^E *EMP* 800
SIC 2392 2221 5719

HOLLEY
See HIGH PERFORMANCE INDUSTRIES HOLDINGS INC

D-U-N-S 04-214-3714 IMP
HOLLEY PERFORMANCE PRODUCTS INC
(*Suby of* HOLLEY) ★
1801 Russellville Rd, Bowling Green, KY 42101-3542
Tel (270) 782-2900 *Founded/Ownrshp* 1996
Sales 87.4MM^E *EMP* 605^E
SIC 3714 3592 Fuel pumps, motor vehicle; Carburetors
Pr: Tom Tomlinson
**VP:* Terrill M Rutledge

*VP: Stephen Trussell
Netwrk Mgr: John Law
VP Opers: Tom Flynn
Opers Mgr: Randy Chisholm
Plnt Mgr: Bill Christopher

D-U-N-S 01-963-0016
■ HOLLIDAY FENOGLIO FOWLER LP
H F F
(*Suby of* HFF INC) ★
9 Greenway Plz Ste 700, Houston, TX 77046-0914
Tel (713) 852-3500 *Founded/Ownrshp* 2003
Sales NA *EMP* 198^E
SIC 6162 Mortgage bankers & correspondents
Pt: John H Pelusi Jr
Dir Surg: Jeff Hollinden
Assoc Dir: Corbin Chaffin
Assoc Dir: Bryan J Clark
Assoc Dir: Brian Torp
Mng Dir: Davis Adams
Mng Dir: Walter Coker
Mng Dir: James M Dockerty
Mng Dir: James M Fowler
Mng Dir: Robert A Rizzi
Mng Dir: Ralph Smalley

D-U-N-S 00-100-6360 IMP/EXP
HOLLINGSWORTH & VOSE CO (MA)
112 Washington St, East Walpole, MA 02032-1098
Tel (508) 850-2000 *Founded/Ownrshp* 1892
Sales 776.8MM^E *EMP* 1,700
SIC 2621 3053 2297 2499 Filter paper; Gasket materials; Nonwoven fabrics; Battery separators, wood
Pr: Val Hollingsworth
CFO: Jeff Sherer
CFO: Joseph Sherer
Treas: William Crowe
VP: Josh Ayer
VP: John Fitzgerald
VP: Jochem Hofstetter
VP: Jean Fran Ois
VP: Kevin Porter
VP: David Von Loesecke
Genl Mgr: Daryl Ives
Board of Directors: Arthur Hollingsworth, Schuyler Hollingsworth Jr, Daniel T V Huntoon III, William Smart

D-U-N-S 84-980-3572
HOLLINGSWORTH LOGISTICS MANAGEMENT LLC
EXOS PROMAT SYSTEMS
(*Suby of* LOGISTICS HOLLINGSWORTH GROUP LLC) ★
14225 W Warren Ave, Dearborn, MI 48126-1456
Tel (313) 768-1400 *Founded/Ownrshp* 1993
Sales 99.3MM *EMP* 700
SIC 4225 4783 General warehousing & storage; Packing & crating
CEO: Stephen S Barr

D-U-N-S 03-489-6712
HOLLINGSWORTH OIL CO INC
1503 Memorial Blvd Ste B, Springfield, TN 37172-3269
Tel (615) 242-8466 *Founded/Ownrshp* 1980
Sales 547.4MM *EMP* 300
Accts Robinson Hughes & Christopher
SIC 5171 Petroleum bulk stations
Ch Bd: Glenn Hollingsworth
**Pr:* Ronnie H Hollingsworth
**VP:* Jennifer Johnston
Mktg Mgr: Tammy Palmore

D-U-N-S 94-676-3695
HOLLIS TELEPHONE CO INC
TDS
515 Junction Rd, Madison, WI 53717-2151
Tel (608) 831-1000 *Founded/Ownrshp* 1984
Sales 853.0MM *EMP* 2,700
SIC 4813 Telephone communication, except radio
Pr: David Wittwer

D-U-N-S 00-552-7098 IMP/EXP
HOLLISTER INC (IL)
2000 Hollister Dr, Libertyville, IL 60048-3781
Tel (847) 680-1000 *Founded/Ownrshp* 1959, 1968
Sales 713.2MM^E *EMP* 2,400
SIC 3841 3842 Surgical & medical instruments; Surgical appliances & supplies
Pr: George Maliekel
**CFO:* Sam Brilliant
**VP:* Denis R Chevaleau
VP: Holly Crandell
**VP:* Robert A Crowe
VP: Robert C Crowe
VP: Christian Fadier
VP: Monika W Jacobi
VP: Daniel Mackin
VP: John McCarthy
VP: David McFaul
VP: Riley A Murray
VP: Shekhar Nevgi
VP: Michael Sorkin
VP: Jim Stupar
Dir Bus: Ken Kolakowski

HOLLISTER-STIER LABORATORIES
See JUBILANT HOLLISTERSTIER LLC

D-U-N-S 00-628-2214 IMP/EXP
HOLLISTER-WHITNEY ELEVATOR CORP (IL)
2603 N 24th St, Quincy, IL 62305-1215
Tel (217) 222-0466 *Founded/Ownrshp* 1900, 1959
Sales 103.1MM^E *EMP* 250
SIC 3534 Elevators & moving stairways
VP: Herbert W Glaser
**VP:* Frank H Musholt
Admn Mgr: Brian Musholt
Genl Mgr: Michael Gash
CIO: Bill Schuering
Dir IT: Bill Schuring
Info Man: William Schuering

D-U-N-S 04-162-2598
HOLLOMAN CORP
333 N Sam Houston Pkwy E, Houston, TX 77060-2414
Tel (281) 878-2600 *Founded/Ownrshp* 2002
Sales 1.0MMM^E *EMP* 1,500
SIC 1541 1623 1389 Industrial buildings & warehouses; Oil & gas pipeline construction; Roustabout service
Ch Bd: Sam E Holloman
**Pr:* Mark Stevenson
**COO:* Bryce Harrell
CFO: James Ebeling
**CFO:* Jim Ebeling
**VP:* Eric Prim
**VP:* Colin Young
Dir Bus: Wayne Stewart
Div Mgr: Matthew Fitzen
Div Mgr: Bill Tullos
IT Man: Lupe Cortez

D-U-N-S 61-937-4374
HOLLOWAY DISTRIBUTING INC
210 E Owen Ave, Puxico, MO 63960-9160
Tel (573) 222-6255 *Founded/Ownrshp* 1982
Sales 103.6MM *EMP* 90
Accts Maloney Wright & Robbins Far
SIC 5145 5194 5149 Candy; Tobacco & tobacco products; Groceries & related products
Pr: Terry Holloway
**Sec:* Debbie Holloway
IT Man: Sherry Thompson
Opers Mgr: Ron Carr

D-U-N-S 00-426-0097 IMP/EXP
HOLLOWAY SPORTSWEAR INC
(*Suby of* AUGUSTA SPORTSWEAR INC) ★
2633 Campbell Rd, Sidney, OH 45365-8863
Tel (937) 497-7575 *Founded/Ownrshp* 2006, 1946
Sales 97.7MM^E *EMP* 700
SIC 2329 2339 2392

D-U-N-S 02-660-4280 IMP/EXP
HOLLOWAY-HOUSTON INC
H H I
5833 Armour Dr, Houston, TX 77020-8195
Tel (713) 674-5631 *Founded/Ownrshp* 1960
Sales 146.2MM^E *EMP* 215
SIC 5072 Hardware
**Treas:* Eileen Dutton
Mktg Dir: Ezequiel Ortuno
Mktg Mgr: Bob Knight
Sales Asso: Robert Dill
Sales Asso: Jordan Hamilton
Sales Asso: Kyle Macy

D-U-N-S 14-481-8395
■ HOLLY ENERGY PARTNERS LP
(*Suby of* HOLLYFRONTIER CORP) ★
2828 N Harwood St # 1300, Dallas, TX 75201-2174
Tel (214) 871-3555 *Founded/Ownrshp* 2004
Sales 358.8MM *EMP* 245^E
Tkr Sym HEP *Exch* NYS
SIC 4612 4613 5171 Crude petroleum pipelines; Refined petroleum pipelines; Petroleum terminals
CEO: Michael C Jennings
Genl Pt: Holly Logistic Services
Pr: Mark A Plake
CFO: Richard L Voliva III
Bd of Dir: Charles Darling
Ex VP: Douglas S Aron
Sr VP: Mark T Cunningham
Sr VP: Denise C McWatters
VP: Neale M Hickerson
VP Bus Dev: Mark Plake

D-U-N-S 78-334-6257
HOLLY HILL HOUSE INC
HOLLY HILL NURSING & REHAB
100 Kingston Rd, Sulphur, LA 70663-4016
Tel (337) 625-5843 *Founded/Ownrshp* 1963
Sales 480.3MM *EMP* 40
SIC 8051 Skilled nursing care facilities
CEO: Charles Fellows
**Pr:* Beth Fellows
**VP:* Hugh D Fellows

HOLLY HILL NURSING & REHAB
See HOLLY HILL HOUSE INC

D-U-N-S 06-747-0443 IMP/EXP
■ HOLLY HUNT ENTERPRISES INC
HOLLY HUNT STUDIO
(*Suby of* KNOLL INC) ★
801 W Adams St Ste 700, Chicago, IL 60607-3068
Tel (312) 329-5999 *Founded/Ownrshp* 2014
Sales 173.2MM^E *EMP* 400
SIC 5021 Office & public building furniture
CEO: Holly Hunt
**Pr:* David Schutte
CFO: Mary Kelly
Exec: Sarah Talsma
Genl Mgr: Victoria Lopez
Off Mgr: Lisa Esposito
IT Man: Justin Latta
Merch Mgr: Hunt Tackbary
Sls Mgr: Mark Hemphill
Sales Asso: Hillary Maurer
Sales Asso: Emily Strup

HOLLY HUNT STUDIO
See HOLLY HUNT ENTERPRISES INC

D-U-N-S 00-309-9777
HOLLY POULTRY INC
2221 Berlin St, Baltimore, MD 21230-1637
Tel (410) 727-6210 *Founded/Ownrshp* 1992
Sales 159.6MM^E *EMP* 195
SIC 5144 5147 Poultry products; Meats & meat products
Pr: Mike Fine
**CFO:* Roy Tarash
IT Man: Tim Cheche
Sls Mgr: Chris Desmarais
Sls Mgr: John Finnegan

HOLLYFRONTIER
See FRONTIER REFINING & MARKETING LLC

D-U-N-S 00-896-5808 EXP
▲ HOLLYFRONTIER CORP
2828 N Harwood St # 1300, Dallas, TX 75201-2174
Tel (214) 871-3555 *Founded/Ownrshp* 1947
Sales 13.2MMM *EMP* 2,704^E
Accts Ernst & Young Llp Dallas Tex
Tkr Sym HFC *Exch* NYS
SIC 2911 4613 Petroleum refining; Gasoline; Jet fuels; Diesel fuels; Refined petroleum pipelines
Ch Bd: Michael C Jennings
**Pr:* George J Damiris
CFO: Douglas S Aron
Sr VP: Denise C McWatters
Sr VP: James M Stump
VP: Mike Achacoso
VP: Mark T Cunningham
VP: Neale Hickerson
VP: Conrad Jenson
VP: Marie Perry
VP: James E Resinger
VP: Mark Williams
Board of Directors: Douglas Y Bech, R Kevin Hardage, Robert J Kostelnik, James H Lee, Franklin Myers, Michael E Rose, Tommy A Valenta

D-U-N-S 07-632-0253 IMP
■ HOLLYFRONTIER EL DORADO REFINING LLC
FRONTIER ELDORADO REFINING
(*Suby of* HOLLYFRONTIER) ★
1401 Douglas Rd, El Dorado, KS 67042-3674
Tel (316) 321-2200 *Founded/Ownrshp* 1999
Sales 191.1MM^E *EMP* 400
SIC 2911 Petroleum refining
CEO: Michael C Jennings
Telecom Ex: Jan Ridgeray
IT Man: Craig Long
Sfty Dirs: Mark Malinauskas
Opers Mgr: Allan Engraf

D-U-N-S 04-891-8817
■ HOLLYFRONTIER NAVAJO REFINING LLC
NAVAJO REFINING COMPANY LLC
(*Suby of* HOLLYFRONTIER CORP) ★
501 E Main St, Artesia, NM 88210-9606
Tel (575) 748-3311 *Founded/Ownrshp* 1969
Sales 152.7MM^E *EMP* 500
SIC 2911 2951 Light distillates; Gasoline blending plants; Jet fuels; Diesel fuels; Asphalt paving mixtures & blocks
Ch: Michael C Jennings
**CEO:* George J Damiris
**VP:* Doug S Aron
**VP:* Denise C McWatters
VP: Jeff Schmidlen
**VP:* James M Stump
Genl Mgr: Bob O'Brien

D-U-N-S 83-066-7726
■ HOLLYFRONTIER REFINING & MARKETING LLC
(*Suby of* HOLLYFRONTIER CORP) ★
2828 N Harwood St # 1300, Dallas, TX 75201-1518
Tel (214) 871-3555 *Founded/Ownrshp* 2009
Sales 194.1MM^E *EMP* 2,625^E
SIC 2911 4612 Petroleum refining; Gasoline; Jet fuels; Diesel fuels; Crude petroleum pipelines
Ch Bd: Michael C Jennings
**CFO:* Bruce R Shaw
Ofcr: Matthew Clifton
**Sr VP:* George J Damiris
**Sr VP:* Denise C McWatters
**Sr VP:* James M Stump
VP: Nancy Hartmann
VP: Marie Perry
**VP:* P Dean Ridenour
VP: Henry Teichholz

HOLLYWOOD CASINO
See INDIANA GAMING CO LP

HOLLYWOOD CASINO
See MOUNTAINVIEW THOROUGHBRED RACING ASSOCIATION LLC

D-U-N-S 80-101-5199 IMP
■ HOLLYWOOD CASINO CORP
(*Suby of* PENN NATIONAL GAMING INC) ★
825 Berkshire Blvd # 200, Reading, PA 19610-1247
Tel (610) 373-2400 *Founded/Ownrshp* 2003
Sales 31.8MM^E *EMP* 3,000
SIC 7011 8741 Hotels; Casino hotel; Hotel or motel management
Pr: Edward Pratt III
**Pr:* Robert D Sheldon
**CFO:* Paul C Yates
**VP:* Walter E Evans
**VP:* Charles F Lafrano III
VP: Donald A Shapiro
VP: Walter E Vans

HOLLYWOOD CASINO JOLIET
See EMPRESS CASINO JOLIET CORP

HOLLYWOOD CASINO ST LOUIS
See ST LOUIS GAMING VENTURES LLC

D-U-N-S 07-602-2136
HOLLYWOOD CITY OF (INC)
2600 Hollywood Blvd Ste B, Hollywood, FL 33020-4800
Tel (954) 921-3231 *Founded/Ownrshp* 1925
Sales NA *EMP* 1,294
Accts Mcgladrey Llp Fort Lauderdal
SIC 9111 City & town managers' offices;
CIO: Kenneth R Fields
CTO: John Moss

D-U-N-S 19-610-2438
HOLLYWOOD ENTERTAINMENT CORP
HOLLYWOOD VIDEO
(*Suby of* MOVIE GALLERY INC) ★
9275 Sw Peyton Ln, Wilsonville, OR 97070-9200
Tel (503) 214-4600 *Founded/Ownrshp* 2005
Sales 313.6MM^E *EMP* 19,000
SIC 7841 Video disk/tape rental to the general public
Pr: Joe Malugen
COO: Lawrence Plotnick
Bd of Dir: S Todd
Ofcr: Lynn Fletcher
Sr VP: Richard Maicki
Sr VP: Michael D Robinson
VP: John Scales
Rgnl Mgr: Brett Baker
Brnch Mgr: Lana Hudnut
Dist Mgr: Joe Elizondo
Dist Mgr: Bob Peters

D-U-N-S 01-735-1446
HOLLYWOOD HOLDING CO LLC
HOLLYWOOD SUPER MARKET
2670 W Maple Rd, Troy, MI 48084-7133
Tel (248) 643-0309 *Founded/Ownrshp* 1950, 2011
Sales 106.3MM^E *EMP* 600^E
SIC 5921 5141 5411 Beer (packaged); Wine; Groceries, general line; Supermarkets, chain
Pr: William D Welch
VP: Kim Welch Harlan
VP: Tom Welch

D-U-N-S 05-882-8760
HOLLYWOOD MEDICAL CENTER LP
HOLLYWOOD PRESBYTERIAN MED CTR
(*Suby of* CHA RENETATIVE MEDICINE) ★
1300 N Vermont Ave, Los Angeles, CA 90027-6098
Tel (213) 413-3000 *Founded/Ownrshp* 2005
Sales 281.2MM *EMP* 1,250
SIC 8062 General medical & surgical hospitals
Pt: Jeff Nelson

HOLLYWOOD PRESBYTERIAN MED CTR
See HOLLYWOOD MEDICAL CENTER LP

HOLLYWOOD PRESBYTERIAN MED CTR
See CHA HOLLYWOOD MEDICAL CENTER LP

HOLLYWOOD SUPER MARKET
See HOLLYWOOD HOLDING CO LLC

HOLLYWOOD THEATERS
See WALLACE THEATER HOLDINGS INC

HOLLYWOOD VIDEO
See HOLLYWOOD ENTERTAINMENT CORP

HOLM INDUSTRIES
See ILPEA INDUSTRIES INC

D-U-N-S 96-164-5574
HOLMAN AUTOMOTIVE GROUP INC
(*Suby of* HOLMAN FORD) ★
244 E Kings Hwy, Maple Shade, NJ 08052-3400
Tel (856) 663-5200 *Founded/Ownrshp* 2001
Sales 962.2MM^E *EMP* 3,000^E
SIC 5511 New & used car dealers
**Ch Bd:* Melinda K Holman
Pr: Bill Cariss
Pr: Chris Conroy
**CEO:* Carl A Ortell
**COO:* Brian R Bates
**Ch:* Joseph S Holman
Sr VP: Bill Kwelty
VP: Frank Beideman
VP: Jim Creighton
VP: Rick Deeck
VP: Glenn Gardner

D-U-N-S 03-227-2643 EXP
HOLMAN AUTOMOTIVE INC
SOUTH FLORIDA LEASING & RENTAL
(*Suby of* HOLMAN FORD) ★
12 E Sunrise Blvd, Fort Lauderdale, FL 33304-1951
Tel (954) 779-2000 *Founded/Ownrshp* 1955
Sales 83.4MM^E *EMP* 234
SIC 5511 5531 Automobiles, new & used; Automotive parts
Pr: Melinda K Holman
**Ch Bd:* Joseph S Holman
**CFO:* Brian R Bates
Treas: Gaye Rankin
VP: Frank Beideman
**VP:* Robert R Campbell
**VP:* William J Cariss
**VP:* Angelo J Nori
Genl Mgr: Peter Brandt
Genl Mgr: Larry Oden
Mktg Mgr: Matthew McGowan

D-U-N-S 06-570-2847 IMP/EXP
HOLMAN ENTERPRISES INC
HOLMAN FORD
244 E Kings Hwy, Maple Shade, NJ 08052-3400
Tel (856) 662-1042 *Founded/Ownrshp* 1946
Sales 1.5MMM^E *EMP* 3,751
SIC 5511 New & used car dealers
Pr: Mindy Holman
Ch Bd: Joseph S Holman
Pr: M K Holman
COO: Melinda Homan
Exec: John McKeon
Sls Mgr: Henry Tomassini

HOLMAN FORD
See HOLMAN ENTERPRISES INC

D-U-N-S 00-690-7562
■ HOLMES & NARVER INC
(*Suby of* AECOM) ★
999 W Town And Country Rd, Orange, CA 92868-4713
Tel (714) 567-2400 *Founded/Ownrshp* 1933, 1972
Sales 85.1MM^E *EMP* 450
SIC 8711 8742 8741 1542 Engineering services; Training & development consultant; Construction management; Nonresidential construction
CEO: Danny Seal
**Pr:* Raymond Landy
**CFO:* Dennis Deslatte
VP: William Autrey
VP: Michel Flynn
VP: Jeryl Jalsin
**Prin:* Tina Clugston

HOLMES DISTRIBUTORS
See HORIZON SOLUTIONS LLC

HOLMES MURPHY
See HMA INC

D-U-N-S 07-347-4389
HOLMES MURPHY AND ASSOCIATES LLC
(*Suby of* HOLMES MURPHY) ★
3001 Westown Pkwy, West Des Moines, IA 50266-1395
Tel (800) 247-7756 *Founded/Ownrshp* 1971
Sales NA *EMP* 300
SIC 6411 Insurance agents

CEO: Daniel T Keough
Pr: Pam McCoige
**COO:* Nickolas J Henderson
Chf Mktg O: Scott Conard
Sr VP: Steve McManus
**VP:* Clifford Augspurger
VP: Eric Bolduc
**VP:* Chris Boyd
**VP:* Steve Flood
**VP:* Laure Guisinger
VP: Steve Gwinn
**VP:* John A Hurley II
VP: Doug Muth
VP: Preston Pomykal
VP: Kurt Ratzlaff
VP: Amber Shaddox
VP: Jeffrey Shald
VP: Greg Stitts
Comm Dir: Mark Fitzgibbons
Board of Directors: Mike Foley, Wally Gomaa

D-U-N-S 09-892-8898
HOLMES REGIONAL MEDICAL CENTER INC
HEALTH FIRST HEALTH PLANS
(*Suby of* HEALTH FIRST HEALTH PLANS) ★
1350 Hickory St, Melbourne, FL 32901-3224
Tel (321) 434-7000 *Founded/Ownrshp* 1937
Sales 412.4MM *EMP* 2,778
SIC 8062 General medical & surgical hospitals
CEO: Steve Johnson
Chf Rad: Jose Ramos
Pr: Jerry Senne
CFO: Robert C Galloway
Treas: William C Potter
VP: Kent Brown
VP: Joseph G Felkner
VP: James S Mitchell III
Mktg Dir: Keith Lunquist
Psych: Michael J Foley
Psych: Cory Lawler

D-U-N-S 15-362-3137
▲ HOLOGIC INC
250 Campus Dr, Marlborough, MA 01752-3020
Tel (508) 263-2900 *Founded/Ownrshp* 1985
Sales 2.8MMM *EMP* 5,290^E
Tkr Sym HOLX *Exch* NGS
SIC 3845 3844 3841 Ultrasonic medical equipment, except cleaning; Electrotherapeutic apparatus; X-ray apparatus & tubes; Medical instruments & equipment, blood & bone work
Ch Bd: Stephen P Macmillan
COO: Eric B Compton
CFO: Robert W McMahon
Sr VP: Mark D Myslinski
Sr VP: Jay A Stein
VP: David Brady
VP: Joe Ywuc
Prgrm Mgr: Jack McCrorey
CIO: David Rudzinsky
VP Opers: Pete Rowden
Manager: Don Nedbalsky
Board of Directors: Christopher J Coughlin, Sally W Crawford, Scott T Garrett, Nancy L Leaming, Lawrence M Levy, Christiana Stamoulis, Elaine S Ullian, Amy Wendell

D-U-N-S 60-364-0251 IMP/EXP
■ HOLOPHANE CORP
(*Suby of* ACUITY BRANDS INC) ★
3825 Columbus Rd Bldg A, Granville, OH 43023-8604
Tel (866) 759-1577 *Founded/Ownrshp* 1989
Sales 215.8MM^E *EMP* 2,050^E
SIC 3646 3648 Commercial indusl & institutional electric lighting fixtures; Outdoor lighting equipment
CEO: Vernon J Nagel
VP: Daren Cox
IT Man: Jean Gartside
Mtls Mgr: Todd Collins
S&M/VP: Randy Crothers
Sls Mgr: John Schneider

D-U-N-S 03-469-7276 IMP
HOLSTON GASES INC
545 W Baxter Ave, Knoxville, TN 37921-6846
Tel (865) 573-1917 *Founded/Ownrshp* 1958
Sales 123.5MM^E *EMP* 184
SIC 5169 5084 2813 Gases, compressed & liquefied; Oxygen; Acetylene; Welding machinery & equipment; Industrial gases
CEO: Bill Baxter
**Pr:* Robert Anders
VP: Phil Kirby
DP Dir: Steve Bowyer
Opers Mgr: Robert Parsons
Sls Dir: Dave Korte

D-U-N-S 78-243-6067
HOLSTON MEDICAL GROUP PC
H M G
2323 N John B Dennis Hwy, Kingsport, TN 37660-4771
Tel (423) 857-2000 *Founded/Ownrshp* 1987
Sales 106.0MM^E *EMP* 955^E
SIC 8011 General & family practice, physician/surgeon
Pr: Jerry L Miller MD
Off Mgr: Beth Medlin
Off Mgr: Sue Watts
IT Man: Bonnie Drew
Netwrk Mgr: Gary Rowland
Software D: Scott Rose
Netwrk Eng: Tim Parsons
Doctor: Chris Mitchell

D-U-N-S 00-839-6426 IMP/EXP
■ HOLSUM BAKERY INC (AZ)
(*Suby of* FLOWERS FOODS INC) ★
2322 W Lincoln St, Phoenix, AZ 85009-5827
Tel (602) 252-2351 *Founded/Ownrshp* 1881, 2008
Sales 201.0MM^E *EMP* 580
SIC 2051

D-U-N-S 06-102-1312 IMP/EXP
HOLSUM DE PUERTO RICO INC
CARIBE BAKERS
Carr 2 Km 20 1 Bo Cndlria St Ca, TOA Baja, PR 00949
Tel (787) 798-8282 *Founded/Ownrshp* 1998
Sales 101.2MM *EMP* 900
SIC 2051 Bread, cake & related products
Pr: Ramon Calderon
**Treas:* Raul Buso
**Ex VP:* Julio Vigoreaux
VP: Consuelo Abries

D-U-N-S 02-164-1121
HOLSUM OF FORT WAYNE INC
(*Suby of* LEWIS BROTHERS BAKERIES INC) ★
136 Murray St, Fort Wayne, IN 46803-2333
Tel (260) 456-2130 *Founded/Ownrshp* 1977
Sales 209.3MM^E *EMP* 2,500
SIC 2051 Bread, all types (white, wheat, rye, etc): fresh or frozen
Pr: Lewis Jr Jack
**Treas:* Jeffery J Sankovitch
**VP:* Rodger Lesh
Off Mgr: Chris Davidson

HOLT CA
See HOLT OF CALIFORNIA

HOLT CAT
See HOLT TEXAS LTD

D-U-N-S 07-871-8707
HOLT CONSTRUCTION CORP
50 E Washington Ave, Pearl River, NY 10965-2308
Tel (845) 735-4054 *Founded/Ownrshp* 1919
Sales 208.6MM *EMP* 180
Accts Anchin Block & Anchin Llp N
SIC 1541 8742 Industrial buildings & warehouses; Industrial buildings, new construction; Construction project management consultant
CEO: Jack Holt
**Pr:* Christopher Asaro
**COO:* Phil Stiller
**CFO:* Matthew Anselmi
**VP:* Robert Bryan
**VP:* Jay Holt
Genl Mgr: John Coppinger
Genl Mgr: Walter Smyth
Off Mgr: Jen Cogliano
Mktg Mgr: Amanda Holt
Snr PM: Bruce Messina

D-U-N-S 08-179-9194
HOLT EQUIPMENT CO LLC
4508 River Rd, Louisville, KY 40222-6113
Tel (502) 899-7513 *Founded/Ownrshp* 1999
Sales 106.4MM^E *EMP* 500
SIC 5082 General construction machinery & equipment

D-U-N-S 02-865-9787 IMP
HOLT OF CALIFORNIA
HOLT CA
(*Suby of* HOC HOLDINGS INC) ★
7310 Pacific Ave, Pleasant Grove, CA 95668-9708
Tel (916) 991-8200 *Founded/Ownrshp* 1999
Sales 465.7MM^E *EMP* 734
SIC 5082 5084 5083 7359 Construction & mining machinery; Tractors, construction; Materials handling machinery; Agricultural machinery; Equipment rental & leasing
Ch Bd: Victor Wykoff Jr
**Pr:* Kenneth Monroe
**CFO:* Daniel Johns
**V Ch Bd:* Gordon Beatie
**Ex VP:* Ronald Monroe
VP: Cary Roulet
Sls Mgr: Julian Ramirez

D-U-N-S 02-266-5731
HOLT PAPER AND CHEMICAL CO INC
31375 John Deere Dr, Salisbury, MD 21804-1412
Tel (410) 742-7577 *Founded/Ownrshp* 1961
Sales 94.8MM^E *EMP* 90
SIC 5142 5087 5113 5147 Packaged frozen goods; Janitors' supplies; Industrial & personal service paper; Cups, disposable plastic & paper; Towels, paper; Meats & meat products
Ch Bd: John T Holt III
**Treas:* Scott Booth
Sls Mgr: Alicha Toms
Sales Asso: Phil Malta

D-U-N-S 00-813-4959 IMP/EXP
HOLT TEXAS LTD
HOLT CAT
5665 Se Loop 410, San Antonio, TX 78222-3903
Tel (210) 648-1111 *Founded/Ownrshp* 1987
Sales 544.6MM^E *EMP* 1,700
SIC 3531 5082 7353 7699 Dozers, tractor mounted: material moving; Road construction & maintenance machinery; Excavating machinery & equipment; Heavy construction equipment rental; Construction equipment repair
CEO: Peter M Holt
**Pr:* Allyn Archer
**CFO:* Paul Hensley
**Ch:* Benjamin D Holt
VP: Bob Harwood
VP: Chuck Strickland
Prd Mgr: Charlie Duff
Mktg Dir: Matt Cook

D-U-N-S 17-553-7810 IMP/EXP
HOLTEC INTERNATIONAL
1001 N Us Highway 1, Jupiter, FL 33477-4482
Tel (561) 745-7772 *Founded/Ownrshp* 2006
Sales 305.3MM^E *EMP* 800
SIC 2819 8711 Nuclear fuel scrap, reprocessing; Engineering services
Pr: Kris Singh
CFO: Robert R Galvin
CFO: Alan Soler
Sr VP: Pankaj Chaudry
Sr VP: Pierre Paul Oneid
Genl Couns: Andrew R Ryan
Board of Directors: Frank Bongrazio, Eduardo Glandt, James Miller, George Norcross, Jim Saxton, Martha Singh

D-U-N-S 01-439-0582
HOLTZBRINCK PUBLISHERS LLC
MACMILLAN
(*Suby of* M P S) ★
175 5th Ave, New York, NY 10010-7703
Tel (646) 307-5151 *Founded/Ownrshp* 1998
Sales 201.6MM^E *EMP* 1,446
SIC 2731

D-U-N-S 00-895-8563
HOLTZINGER FRUIT CO INC
1312 N 6th Ave, Yakima, WA 98902-1420
Tel (509) 457-5115 *Founded/Ownrshp* 1955
Sales 109.7MM^E *EMP* 500
SIC 5148 4222 Fruits, fresh; Warehousing, cold storage or refrigerated
Pr: Charles Holtzinger
Sls Mgr: Steve Black
Sales Asso: Mary Neal

HOLTZMAN EQUIPMENT & CNSTR DIV
See HOLTZMAN OIL CORP

D-U-N-S 05-917-0829
HOLTZMAN OIL CORP
HOLTZMAN EQUIPMENT & CNSTR DIV
5534 Main St, Mount Jackson, VA 22842-9508
Tel (540) 477-3131 *Founded/Ownrshp* 1972
Sales 293.4MM *EMP* 110
SIC 5172 Petroleum products
Pr: Bill Holtzman
**VP:* Richard Koontz

D-U-N-S 00-477-5599
HOLY CROSS ELECTRIC ASSOCIATION INC
HOLY CROSS ENERGY
3799 Highway 82, Glenwood Springs, CO 81601-9309
Tel (970) 945-5491 *Founded/Ownrshp* 1939
Sales 121.1MM *EMP* 155
Accts Dreyer & Kelso Pc Pa Kansas C
SIC 4911 Distribution, electric power
Pr: Michael Glass
**Treas:* Robert Gardner
Treas: Dave Munk
Bd of Dir: Hal Clark
**VP:* Megan Gilman
Mng Dir: Steve Casey
IT Man: Rick Arnhold
IT Man: Ted Jessup

HOLY CROSS ENERGY
See HOLY CROSS ELECTRIC ASSOCIATION INC

D-U-N-S 07-429-6930
HOLY CROSS HEALTH INC
CATHOLIC HEALTH EAST
(*Suby of* CATHOLIC HEALTH EAST) ★
1500 Forest Glen Rd, Silver Spring, MD 20910-1460
Tel (301) 754-7000 *Founded/Ownrshp* 1978
Sales 413.8MM *EMP* 3,270
SIC 8062 General medical & surgical hospitals
Pr: Kevin Sexton
Chf Path: R Snyder
Chf Path: Robert Snyder
Pr: Abdul Abbasi
COO: Khoury Bernie
CFO: Stephen Bush
**CFO:* Anne Dgillis
Sr VP: Judith Fruiterman
**VP:* Eileen Cahill
VP: Annice Cody
**VP:* Patrick Connely
VP: Wendy Friar
VP: Manuel Ocasio
VP: Matthew Picard
Assoc Dir: Lola Gbadamosi
Dir Rad: Mike Hanbury

D-U-N-S 01-059-1055
HOLY CROSS HOSPITAL
2701 W 68th St, Silver Spring, MD 20910
Tel (301) 754-7000 *Founded/Ownrshp* 1928
Sales 111.6MM *EMP* 1,600
SIC 8062 8011 General medical & surgical hospitals; Offices & clinics of medical doctors
Pr: Mark Clement
CFO: Rene' Suntay
VP: Neil Murphy
Dir Risk M: Georgiana Barley
Dir Rx: Nosakhare Osayamwen
Dir Rx: Victor Plenys
CIO: Demetrio Lovato
CIO: Ken Soewkowski
Dir IT: Jeff Smith
IT Man: Judy Flexman
Mktg Dir: Ted Lally

D-U-N-S 07-222-8851
HOLY CROSS HOSPITAL INC
(*Suby of* CATHOLIC HEALTH EAST) ★
4725 N Federal Hwy, Fort Lauderdale, FL 33308-4668
Tel (954) 771-8000 *Founded/Ownrshp* 1998
Sales 20.9MM^E *EMP* 2,300
Accts Deloitte Tax Llp Cincinnati
SIC 8062 General medical & surgical hospitals
CEO: Patrick Taylor
Dir Recs: Jay Schatz
Dir Vol: Abbie Klaits
**COO:* Richard Brown
**CFO:* Linda Wilford
Ofcr: Janice Schuck
VP: Ivan Delevic
VP: Rita Levasseur
Dir Lab: Valerie Conigilio
Dir Lab: Bart Musial
Dir Rad: Cindy Siegel

HOLY FAMILY HOSPITAL & MED CTR
See TAS-CHFH

D-U-N-S 06-831-9755
HOLY FAMILY MEMORIAL INC (WI)
WOODLAND CLINIC
2300 Western Ave, Manitowoc, WI 54220-3712
Tel (920) 320-2011 *Founded/Ownrshp* 1890
Sales 123.9MM *EMP* 1,300
SIC 8062 General medical & surgical hospitals
CEO: Mark Herzog
Pr: Charles Laham
**Ch:* William Casey
**Treas:* Donald Brisch
Ofcr: Mary Maurer
**VP:* Pat Brandel
VP: Brett Norell
Dir Rx: Greg Unertl
MIS Dir: Tara Crabb
IT Man: William Hampton
Sfty Dirs: Dan Linsmeier

HOLY FAMILY REG SCH-S CAMPUS
See ARCHDIOCESE OF DETROIT ED OFF

D-U-N-S 07-544-0149 EXP
HOLY NAME MEDICAL CENTER INC
718 Teaneck Rd, Teaneck, NJ 07666-4245
Tel (201) 833-3000 *Founded/Ownrshp* 1925
Sales 320.4MM *EMP* 1,800^E
Accts Withumsmithbrown Pc Morristow
SIC 8062 General medical & surgical hospitals; Hospital, professional nursing school
Pr: Michael Maron
Chf Rad: Jacquelin Brunetti
V Ch: Salvatore Laraia
**CFO:* Gregory Adams
Sr VP: Sheryl Slonim
VP: Cynthia Kaufhold
VP: Judy Kutzleb
VP: April Rodgers
VP: Beverly Sanborn
Exec: Karen Chapman
Prac Mgr: Juliana Avalo

D-U-N-S 15-091-3234
HOLY REDEEMER HEALTH SYSTEM INC
667 Welsh Rd Ste 300, Huntingdon Valley, PA 19006-6308
Tel (215) 938-0180 *Founded/Ownrshp* 1985
Sales 287.2MM *EMP* 3,800
SIC 8082 Visiting nurse service
Pr: Michael B Laign
COO: Mark Jones
COO: Lawrence Roth
CFO: John Morozin
**CFO:* Russell Wagnes
**Sr VP:* Denise Collins
Sr VP: Patrick Kennedy
VP: Teresa Giannetti
VP: Nancy Mandes
VP: Joseph Thompson
Dir: Barbara Tantum
Dir Rx: Randie Oberlender

D-U-N-S 15-091-2517
HOLY REDEEMER HEALTHCARE SYSTEM
(*Suby of* HOLY REDEEMER HEALTH SYSTEM INC) ★
667 Welsh Rd Ste 300, Huntingdon Valley, PA 19006-6308
Tel (215) 938-0180 *Founded/Ownrshp* 1999
Sales 36.2MM^E *EMP* 2,000
SIC 8099 Blood related health services
Pr: Michael Laign
COO: Mark Jones

D-U-N-S 07-119-5630
HOLY SPIRIT HOSPITAL OF SISTERS OF CHRISTIAN CHARITY
503 N 21st St, Camp Hill, PA 17011-2288
Tel (717) 763-2100 *Founded/Ownrshp* 1956
Sales 289.8MM *EMP* 2,698
SIC 8062 General medical & surgical hospitals
Pr: Romaine Niemeyer
COO: Richard A Schaffner
Chf Mktg O: Scott Dugan
Ofcr: Amy Cook
Ofcr: AMI Zumkhawala-Cook
Exec: Chelsea Smith
Dir Risk M: Ellen Feidt
Dir Lab: Jeff Seiple
Prin: Fred Kireta
Adm Dir: Meg Gallager-Molina
Prac Mgr: Deb Slopey
Board of Directors: Sara Brooks

HOLYOKE FINE HOMES
See LEWIS LEASE CRUTCHERWA LLC

D-U-N-S 06-697-5657
HOLYOKE MEDICAL CENTER INC
(*Suby of* VALLEY HEALTH SYSTEMS INC) ★
575 Beech St, Holyoke, MA 01040-2223
Tel (413) 534-2554 *Founded/Ownrshp* 1984
Sales 132.8MM^E *EMP* 1,250
Accts Pricewaterhousecoopers Llp Ha
SIC 8062 General medical & surgical hospitals
Pr: Spiridon E Hatiras
**Pr:* Hank J Porten
CFO: Brad Klinkowski
**Treas:* Antonio Correia
Sr VP: Tony Correia
VP: Michael A Zwirko
Dir Inf Cn: Carol Wojnarowski
Genl Mgr: Gina Lucchesi
CIO: Carl Cameron
DP Dir: Debbie Lajoie
MIS Dir: Todd McDermott

D-U-N-S 10-003-1863
HOLYOKE PUBLIC SCHOOLS
57 Suffolk St Ste 101, Holyoke, MA 01040-5015
Tel (413) 534-2000 *Founded/Ownrshp* 1983
Sales 11.7MM^E *EMP* 1,581^E
SIC 8211 Public elementary & secondary schools
Assoc Dir: Stacey Funston
**Prin:* Eduardo Carballo
Teacher Pr: Jennifer Boulias

D-U-N-S 02-325-7363
HOLZ MOTORS INC
5961 S 108th Pl, Hales Corners, WI 53130-2501
Tel (414) 425-2400 *Founded/Ownrshp* 1949
Sales 100.0MM *EMP* 190
SIC 5511 New & used car dealers
Owner: Jerome J Holz
**VP:* Douglas Nalbert
Sls Mgr: Mark Fleischmann

D-U-N-S 06-493-4081
HOLZER CONSOLIDATED HEALTH SYSTEMS INC
100 Jackson Pike, Gallipolis, OH 45631-1560
Tel (740) 446-5060 *Founded/Ownrshp* 1985
Sales 175.9MM *EMP* 1,500
Accts Plante & Moran Pllc Columbus
SIC 8062 General medical & surgical hospitals
Pr: Brent Saundrs

D-U-N-S 08-633-9720
HOLZER HEALTH SYSTEM
100 Jackson Pike, Gallipolis, OH 45631-1560
Tel (740) 446-5000 *Founded/Ownrshp* 2015
Sales 149.5MM *EMP* 614E
Accts Plante & Moran Pllc Columbus
SIC 8062 General medical & surgical hospitals
CEO: Michael Canady
Surgeon: Ronn A Grandia
Diag Rad: Kevin M McCann

D-U-N-S 04-964-5104
HOLZER HOSPITAL FOUNDATION INC
HOLZER MEDICAL CENTER
100 Jackson Pike, Gallipolis, OH 45631-1560
Tel (740) 446-5000 *Founded/Ownrshp* 1929
Sales 161.3MM *EMP* 1,000
Accts Plante & Moran Pllc Columbus
SIC 8062 General medical & surgical hospitals
Ch Bd: Brent A Saunders
**CEO:* Christopher T Meyer
**Chf Mktg O:* Michael R Canady
Ex VP: John Cunningham
Exec: Lisa Adkins
Exec: Ralph Fisher
Dir OR: Sue Gilliam
Dir Teleco: Kevin Waller
Ex Dir: Troy D Miller
Software D: Susan King
Doctor: Joseph Crum

HOLZER MEDICAL CENTER
See HOLZER HOSPITAL FOUNDATION INC

D-U-N-S 01-042-2897 IMP
HOM FURNITURE INC
JC IMPORTS
10301 Woodcrest Dr Nw, Minneapolis, MN 55433-6519
Tel (763) 767-3600 *Founded/Ownrshp* 1973
Sales 216.7MME *EMP* 950
SIC 5712 Furniture stores
Ch Bd: Wayne Johansen
**Pr:* Rodney Johansen
Store Dir: Greg Bailey
Genl Mgr: Carl Nyberg
Store Mgr: Ken Coyne
QA Dir: Stacy Czapiewski
Info Man: Will Strootman
Merch Mgr: Kyle Johansen
Sls Mgr: Brenda Becker
Sls Mgr: Brian Gaspard
Sls Mgr: John Nelson

D-U-N-S 14-181-8919
▲ HOME BANCSHARES INC
719 Harkrider St Ste 100, Conway, AR 72032-5619
Tel (501) 339-2929 *Founded/Ownrshp* 1989
Sales NA *EMP* 1,424E
Accts Bkd Llp Little Rock Arkansa
Tkr Sym HOMB *Exch* NGS
SIC 6022 State commercial banks
Pr: C Randall Sims
**Ch Bd:* John W Allison
COO: J Stephen Tipton
**CFO:* Brian S Davis
**V Ch Bd:* Robert H Adcock Jr
Exec: Donna J Townsell

D-U-N-S 13-824-4731 IMP
■ HOME BOX OFFICE INC
H B O
(*Suby of* WARNER COMMUNICATIONS INC) ★
1100 Avenue Of The Americ, New York, NY 10036-6712
Tel (212) 512-1000 *Founded/Ownrshp* 2003
Sales 602.0MME *EMP* 2,000
SIC 4841 7812

D-U-N-S 84-173-7455 IMP
HOME BREW MART INC
BALLAST PT BREWING & SPIRITS
9045 Carroll Way, San Diego, CA 92121-2405
Tel (858) 790-6900 *Founded/Ownrshp* 1992
Sales 189.3MME *EMP* 425
SIC 2082 5999 Ale (alcoholic beverage); Alcoholic beverage making equipment & supplies
CEO: Jim Buechler
**CEO:* Jack White
**COO:* Yuseff Cherney
**CFO:* Rick Morgan
VP: Colby Chandler
Board of Directors: James Buechler, Jack White Jr

D-U-N-S 05-549-3902
HOME BUYERS WARRANTY CORP
2-10 HOME BUYERS WARRANTY
10375 E Harvard Ave # 100, Denver, CO 80231-3966
Tel (720) 747-6000 *Founded/Ownrshp* 2002
Sales NA *EMP* 600
SIC 6351 1531 Warranty insurance, home; Speculative builder, single-family houses
CFO: Mark Lewis
Treas: I L Likes
VP: Henry B Allen
VP: Mike Bartosch
VP: Maurice Edney
VP: Dave Johnson
VP: Carl Knighten
VP: Charles Nail Jr
VP: James W Prather
VP: Bart Wares
CIO: Mark Stockford

D-U-N-S 17-124-3603
HOME CARE OF CENTRAL CAROLINA INC
ADVANCED HOME CARE
4001 Piedmont Pkwy, High Point, NC 27265-9402
Tel (336) 878-8822 *Founded/Ownrshp* 1984
Sales 108.9MM *EMP* 400
SIC 8082 Home health care services
Pr: Joel C Mills
**CFO:* James P Hogan

D-U-N-S 15-075-5007
HOME CARE PRODUCTS & PHARMACY
(*Suby of* EVANGELICAL COMMUNITY HOSPITAL) ★
1 Hospital Dr, Lewisburg, PA 17837-9350
Tel (570) 522-2000 *Founded/Ownrshp* 1985
Sales 104.5MM *EMP* 1,000
Accts Parenterandolph Llc Pa
SIC 5912 7352 5999 Drug stores & proprietary stores; Medical equipment rental; Medical apparatus & supplies
Pr: Michael Okeef
**Pr:* Michael Ikeef

HOME CARE TEAM, THE
See MEDICAL TEAM INC

D-U-N-S 00-426-1913
HOME CITY ICE CO
6045 Bridgetown Rd Ste 1, Cincinnati, OH 45248-3047
Tel (513) 574-1800 *Founded/Ownrshp* 1956
Sales 289.5MME *EMP* 1,225
SIC 2097 Ice cubes
Prin: Joseph H Head
**Pr:* Thomas E Sedler
**COO:* Edward T Sedler
CFO: Jay Stautberg
CFO: James Stautburg
**Treas:* Thomas F Sedler
Software D: Michael Gillum
Sfty Dirs: Kathy Winters
Opers Mgr: Andrew Medberry
Plnt Mgr: Robert Eberly
Plnt Mgr: William Fletcher

HOME DEPOT, THE
See HOME DEPOT INTERNATIONAL INC

HOME DEPOT, THE
See HOME DEPOT USA INC

D-U-N-S 07-227-1711
▲ HOME DEPOT INC
HOME DEPOT, THE
2455 Paces Ferry Rd Se, Atlanta, GA 30339-1834
Tel (770) 433-8211 *Founded/Ownrshp* 1978
Sales 88.5MMM *EMP* 385,000
Accts Kpmg Llp Atlanta Georgia
Tkr Sym HD *Exch* NYS
SIC 5261 5211 5231 5251 1751 1752 Nurseries & garden centers; Lawn & garden equipment; Lawn & garden supplies; Lumber & other building materials; Lumber products; Door & window products; Masonry materials & supplies; Paint, glass & wallpaper; Glass; Paint & painting supplies; Wallcoverings; Hardware; Tools; Window & door installation & erection; Floor laying & floor work
Ch Bd: Craig A Menear
CFO: Carol B Tome
Ex VP: Matthew A Carey
Ex VP: Timothy M Crow
Ex VP: Edward P Decker
Ex VP: Ted Decker
Ex VP: Marvin Ellison
Ex VP: Mark Q Holifield
Ex VP: William G Lennie
Ex VP: Teresa Wynn Roseborough
Sr VP: Lyne Castonguay
VP: Derek Bottoms
VP: Giles Bowerman
VP: Roberta Hoptry
VP: Dwaine Kimmet
VP: Kerri McKechnie
VP: Thomas Spahr
VP: Scott Spata
VP: Mike Zizak
Exec: Chance Beeler
Board of Directors: Wayne M Hewett, Gerard J Arpey, Karen L Katen, Ari Bousbib, Mark Vadon, Jeff Boyd, Gregory D Brenneman, J Frank Brown, Albert P Carey, Armando Codina, Helena B Foulkes, Linda R Gooden

D-U-N-S 62-424-2293 IMP/EXP
■ HOME DEPOT INTERNATIONAL INC
HOME DEPOT, THE
(*Suby of* HOME DEPOT THE) ★
2455 Paces Ferry Rd Se, Atlanta, GA 30339-1834
Tel (770) 384-3889 *Founded/Ownrshp* 1989
Sales 51.2MMME *EMP* 300,000E
SIC 5211 Home centers
Pr: Kelly Caffarelli
**Treas:* Marshall Day
**VP:* Paul Gaffney
**VP:* Daniel J Paris
**VP:* Lawrence A Smith
**VP:* Carol Tome

HOME DEPOT, THE
See HOME DEPOT INC

D-U-N-S 78-326-6950 IMP/EXP
■ HOME DEPOT USA INC
HOME DEPOT, THE
(*Suby of* HOME DEPOT) ★
2455 Paces Ferry Rd Se, Atlanta, GA 30339-1834
Tel (770) 433-8211 *Founded/Ownrshp* 1989
Sales 51.2MMME *EMP* 300,000
SIC 5023 5999 Home furnishings; Plumbing & heating supplies
CEO: Francis S Blake
Pr: Lyne Castonguay
Pr: Craig A Menear
CFO: Carol B Tome
Sr VP: Giles Bowman
VP: Matt Carey
VP: Christopher Duffy
Corp Couns: Jill U Edmondson

D-U-N-S 79-698-0071
HOME DIALYSIS OF MUHLENBERG COUNTY INC
(*Suby of* FRESENIUS MEDICAL CARE CARDIOVASCULAR RESOURCES INC) ★
95 Hayden Ave, Lexington, MA 02421-7942
Tel (781) 402-9000
Sales 23.7MME *EMP* 1,248E
SIC 7389 Business services
Prin: Jim McCammon

HOME EMERGENCY SOLUTIONS
See HOMESERVE USA CORP

HOME ENTERTAINMENT DIV
See FOX INC

D-U-N-S 94-478-6375
■ HOME HEALTH CARE AFFILIATES INC
(*Suby of* GENTIVA HEALTH SERVICES INC) ★
106 Riverview Dr, Flowood, MS 39232-8908
Tel (601) 362-7801 *Founded/Ownrshp* 2008
Sales 14.1MME *EMP* 1,000
SIC 8082 Home health care services
Pr: Steven J Bell
**CFO:* Brent W Jorgeson

HOME HEALTH RANDOLPH HOSPITAL
See RANDOLPH HOSPITAL INC

HOME JUICE CO OF MEMPHIS
See H J M P CORP

D-U-N-S 01-926-5073
HOME MARKET FOODS INC
140 Morgan Dr Ste 100, Norwood, MA 02062-5076
Tel (781) 948-1500 *Founded/Ownrshp* 1996
Sales 409.8MME *EMP* 1,716
SIC 2013 Frozen meats from purchased meat
Pr: Douglas K Atamian
**Pr:* Wesley L Atamian
**VP:* Rocky Schroeder
VP: Mike Weiermiller
QA Dir: John Peck
Mfg Dir: Rick Manda
Opers Mgr: Patty Carr
Ql Cn Mgr: Chitsanzo Kachaje
Sls Dir: Dana Geremonte
Sls Dir: Scott Lubow
Mktg Mgr: Liz Ammon

HOME NEWS & TRIBUNE
See ASBURY PARK PRESS INC

D-U-N-S 03-148-1294
HOME OIL CO INC (AL)
HOBO PANTRY FOOD STORES
5744 E Us Highway 84, Cowarts, AL 36321-9085
Tel (334) 793-1544 *Founded/Ownrshp* 1966
Sales 102.7MM *EMP* 200
Accts Carpenter Wiggins Jordan Th
SIC 5171 5411 5541 5172 Petroleum bulk stations; Convenience stores, chain; Filling stations, gasoline; Petroleum products
Pr: Tim Shirley
**Ch Bd:* Thomas A Shirley
**CFO:* Jeff D Groover
**VP:* Christopher A Shirley

D-U-N-S 00-506-3532 IMP/EXP
HOME PRODUCTS INTERNATIONAL - NORTH AMERICA INC
(*Suby of* HPI) ★
4501 W 47th St, Chicago, IL 60632-4407
Tel (773) 890-1010 *Founded/Ownrshp* 1952, 1987
Sales 207.6MME *EMP* 400
SIC 3089 3499 Boxes, plastic; Organizers for closets, drawers, etc.: plastic; Ironing boards, metal
CEO: George Hamilton
**CFO:* Dennis Doheny
**Sr VP:* Kathy Evans
**Sr VP:* Grant Fagan
**VP:* John Pugh

D-U-N-S 15-293-5193
HOME PRODUCTS INTERNATIONAL INC
HPI
4501 W 47th St, Chicago, IL 60632-4407
Tel (773) 890-1010 *Founded/Ownrshp* 1997
Sales 376.7MME *EMP* 600
SIC 6719 Investment holding companies, except banks; Personal holding companies, except banks
CEO: George Hamilton
Pr: Randy Chambers
COO: Richard A Hssert
**CFO:* Dennis Doheny
VP: Jose Cabanin
**VP:* Chris Henry
**VP:* Joseph Lacambra
VP: Charles Veselits

D-U-N-S 86-101-6046
HOME PROPERTIES INC
(*Suby of* LONE STAR FUNDS) ★
300 Clinton Sq, Rochester, NY 14604-1795
Tel (585) 546-4900 *Founded/Ownrshp* 2015
Sales 671.9MM *EMP* 1,200
SIC 6798 Real estate investment trusts
Pr: Edward J Pettinella
**CFO:* David P Gardner
**Ofcr:* Robert J Luken
Ex VP: David Gardner
**Ex VP:* Ann M McCormick
Ex VP: Ann McCormick
Sr VP: Janine Schue
**Sr VP:* John E Smith
VP: Cynthia Burrell
VP: Scott Doyle
VP: Donald R Hague
VP: Gerald Korn
VP: Robert Luken
VP: Paul H O'Leary
VP: Kimberly Pepe
VP: Biography Photo
VP: John Smith
VP: Michele Wilson
VP: Jodi Wyatt

D-U-N-S 87-441-8106
HOME PROPERTIES LIMITED PARTNERSHIP
(*Suby of* HOME PROPERTIES INC) ★
850 Clinton Sq, Rochester, NY 14604-1730
Tel (585) 546-4900 *Founded/Ownrshp* 1993
Sales 11.5MME *EMP* 1,000
SIC 6513 Apartment building operators
CFO: David P Gardner

HOME SECURITY
See GUARDIAN PROTECTION SERVICES INC

HOME-STYLE INDUSTRIES
See LIPPERT COMPONENTS INC

D-U-N-S 18-951-8033
HOMEAWAY INC
1011 W 5th St Ste 300, Austin, TX 78703-5363
Tel (512) 684-1100 *Founded/Ownrshp* 2004
Sales 446.7MM *EMP* 1,780
SIC 6531 7389 7375 Real estate listing services; Real estate leasing & rentals; Accomodation locating services; On-line data base information retrieval
Pr: Brian H Sharples
Pt: Martin Slagter
COO: Thomas E Hale
CFO: Lynn Atchison
Chf Mktg O: Mariano Dima
VP: William Bowles
VP: Jeff Hurst
VP: Michael Osborn
VP: Venu Venugopal
CTO: Ross A Buhrdorf
Sftwr Eng: Bryan Harclerode
Board of Directors: Lanny Baker, Simon Breakwell, Jeffrey D Brody, Kevin Krone, Simon Lehmann, Woody Marshall, Tina Sharkey

D-U-N-S 82-639-9305
HOMEBRIDGE FINANCIAL SERVICES INC
194 Wood Ave S Fl 9, Iselin, NJ 08830-2761
Tel (201) 498-9300 *Founded/Ownrshp* 1991
Sales NA *EMP* 1,250E
SIC 6162 Mortgage bankers
Pr: Douglas Rotella
Ofcr: Tia Holloway
VP: Mark Ross
**VP:* Dorothy Tracy
Exec: Al Ragin
**Prin:* Gianni Cerretani
Area Mgr: Joe Greiner
Brnch Mgr: Edward Bocchino
Brnch Mgr: Ruby Guimbard
IT Man: Ian Orevillo
Tech Mgr: Chris Frescki

HOMECARE NURSING SERVICE
See UNLIMITED CARE INC

D-U-N-S 04-322-8324
HOMECARE PREFERRED CHOICE INC
BEVERLY HEALTHCARE
(*Suby of* GOLDEN LIVING) ★
1000 Fianna Way, Fort Smith, AR 72919-9008
Tel (479) 201-2000 *Founded/Ownrshp* 2008
Sales 36.7MME *EMP* 1,200
SIC 8082 Home health care services
Pr: Cindy H Susienka
**VP:* Bob Donovan

HOMECREST
See MASTERBRAND CABINETS INC

HOMECREST CABINETRY
See H-C LIQUIDATING CORP

HOMEDICS
See FKA DISTRIBUTING CO LLC

D-U-N-S 80-591-0650 IMP/EXP
■ HOMEGOODS INC
HG BUYING
(*Suby of* TJ MAXX) ★
770 Cochituate Rd, Framingham, MA 01701-4666
Tel (508) 390-3199 *Founded/Ownrshp* 1992
Sales 357.3MME *EMP* 1,500
SIC 5719 Kitchenware
Pr: Ken Canestrari
Treas: Jamie Lowell
Treas: Mary B Reynolds
Sr VP: Robert Cataldo
Sr VP: Richard Sherr
VP: Alfred Appel
VP: Jeffrey Naylor

D-U-N-S 01-417-7548
HOMELAND ENERGY SOLUTIONS LLC
2779 Highway 24, Lawler, IA 52154
Tel (563) 238-5555 *Founded/Ownrshp* 2005
Sales 269.9MM *EMP* 46
SIC 2869 2085 2046 Ethyl alcohol, ethanol; Distillers' dried grains & solubles & alcohol; Corn oil products
Ch Bd: Patrick Boyle
CFO: David A Finke
**V Ch Bd:* Maurice Hyde
VP: Stan Wubbena
Board of Directors: Randy Bruess, Mathew Driscoll, Keith Eastman, Stephen Eastman, Leslie Hansen, Edward Hatten, Chad Kuhlers

HOMELAND STORES
See HAC INC

D-U-N-S 08-695-9157 IMP/EXP
HOMELITE CONSUMER PRODUCTS INC
(*Suby of* TTI) ★
1428 Pearman Dairy Rd, Anderson, SC 29625-2000
Tel (864) 226-6511 *Founded/Ownrshp* 2003
Sales 279.5MME *EMP* 1,300
SIC 5083 Lawn machinery & equipment
Pr: Lee Sowell
CFO: Philippe Duisson
**CFO:* Ken Faith
**Treas:* Bette Ann Braeutigam
VP Mktg: Mike Sarrah

D-U-N-S 04-986-0505
■ HOMEQ SERVICING CORP
(*Suby of* OCWEN LOAN SERVICING LLC) ★
4837 Watt Ave, North Highlands, CA 95660-5108
Tel (916) 339-6192 *Founded/Ownrshp* 2010
Sales NA *EMP* 1,200
SIC 6162 6163 6111 6159 Mortgage bankers; Agents, farm or business loan; Student Loan Marketing Association; Automobile finance leasing
Pr: Arthur Lyon
**COO:* Keith G Becher
Treas: John A Hollstien

D-U-N-S 00-432-3481 IMP/EXP
HOMER LAUGHLIN CHINA CO (DE)
FOODSERVICE DIVISION
672 Fiesta Dr, Newell, WV 26050-1299
Tel (304) 387-1300 *Founded/Ownrshp* 1927
Sales 76.9MM^E *EMP* 1,000^E
SIC 3262 5719

D-U-N-S 16-662-4655
HOMESERVE USA CORP
HOME EMERGENCY SOLUTIONS
(*Suby of* HOMESERVE PLC)
601 Merritt 7 Fl 6, Norwalk, CT 06851-1174
Tel (203) 351-4924 *Founded/Ownrshp* 2003
Sales 300.0MM *EMP* 700
SIC 8741 1521 Administrative management; Single-family home remodeling, additions & repairs
Pr: Thomas Rusin
**CFO:* Rich Gannon
**Treas:* Chris Miller
VP: Jason Barnes
**VP:* Neil Grant
Creative D: Marie Davis
**CIO:* Dave Berry
Board of Directors: Mike Frosch, Betty Montgomery

D-U-N-S 07-692-9699
■ **HOMESERVICES OF AMERICA INC**
(*Suby of* BERKSHIRE HATHAWAY ENERGY CO) ★
333 S 7th St Fl 27, Minneapolis, MN 55402-2438
Tel (612) 336-5900 *Founded/Ownrshp* 1998
Sales NA *EMP* 2,252
SIC 6351 6361 Warranty insurance, home; Real estate title insurance
CEO: Ronald Peltier
**Pr:* R Michael Knapp
**Pr:* Robert Moline
Pr: J P Peltier
**Sr VP:* Dana Strandmo
**Sr VP:* Micheal Warmka
**Sr VP:* Mike Warmka
**VP:* Jim Lamphere
VP: John Mullarky
**VP:* Patty Smejkal
Off Mgr: Jeffrey A Long

D-U-N-S 06-947-3163
■ **HOMESERVICES OF ILLINOIS LLC**
BERKSHIRE HATHAWAY HOME
(*Suby of* HOMESERVICES OF AMERICA INC) ★
1370 Meadow Rd, Skokie, IL 60076
Tel (847) 853-5000 *Founded/Ownrshp* 2009
Sales NA *EMP* 510
SIC 6162 Mortgage bankers & correspondents
Pr: Nancy Agy
COO: Bob Harroun
VP: Suzanne Boose
VP: Michael Mazzei
VP: George H Moloney III
VP: George Moloney
Off Mgr: Becky Hauser
Sls&Mrk Ex: Donna August
VP Sls: Shirley Amico
S&M/VP: Connie Atterbury

D-U-N-S 05-335-1230
HOMESITE GROUP INC
HOMESITE INSURANCE
(*Suby of* AMERICAN FAMILY INSURANCE) ★
1 Federal St Ste 400, Boston, MA 02110-2003
Tel (617) 832-1300 *Founded/Ownrshp* 2014
Sales NA *EMP* 41
SIC 6411 Property & casualty insurance agent
Pr: Fabian J Fondriest
COO: Douglas Batting
Ofcr: Maureen Fidler
Sr VP: Anthony Scavongelli
VP: Chris Conti
VP: Alex Cunningham
**VP:* Randall Dyen
VP: Chuck Giovanniello
VP: Jim Morahan
VP: Peter Settel
VP: Stephen Stayton
Exec: Monique Bartolo

HOMESITE INSURANCE
See HOMESITE GROUP INC

D-U-N-S 07-984-3765
HOMESTEAD HOSPITAL INC
(*Suby of* BAPTIST HEALTH SOUTH FLORIDA INC) ★
975 Baptist Way, Homestead, FL 33033-7600
Tel (786) 243-8000 *Founded/Ownrshp* 1940
Sales 175.9MM *EMP* 1^E
Accts Deloitte & Touche Llp
SIC 8062 General medical & surgical hospitals
CEO: William M Duquette
VP: Ken Spell
Ansthlgy: Gabriel J Perez

HOMESTEAD NURSING HOME
See HEALTHCARE RESOURCES CORP

D-U-N-S 00-694-1207
HOMESTEADERS LIFE CO
5700 Westown Pkwy Ofc, West Des Moines, IA 50266-8214
Tel (515) 440-7777 *Founded/Ownrshp* 1906
Sales NA *EMP* 170
SIC 6311 Legal reserve life insurance
CEO: Stephen Lang
**Ch Bd:* Graham Cook
Ex VP: Marla Lacey
Ex VP: Lyndon Peterson
Ex VP: Judy Ralston
**Ex VP:* Judy Ralston-Hansen
VP: Will Bischoff
**VP:* Glen Hare
VP: Tom Heuer
VP: James Koher
VP: Kevin Kubik

D-U-N-S 15-146-8873
■ **HOMESTREET BANK**
(*Suby of* HOMESTREET INC) ★
601 Union St Ste 2000, Seattle, WA 98101-2326
Tel (206) 623-3050 *Founded/Ownrshp* 1985
Sales NA *EMP* 495
SIC 6036 State savings banks, not federally chartered
CEO: Mark K Mason
Ch Bd: Bruce Williams
V Ch: Brian Dempsey
Pr: Ansar Khalil
Pr: Edward C Schultz
CFO: Debra L Johnson
Ofcr: Nancy Dennehy
Ofcr: Godfrey Evans
Ofcr: Amanda Finnegan
Ofcr: Jay Huber
Ofcr: Gina Lewis
Ofcr: Steve Morgensen
Ex VP: Howard Bell
Ex VP: Robert Saito
Ex VP: Martin A Steele
Sr VP: Randy Daniels
Sr VP: Rose Marie David
VP: Richard Bennion
VP: Steve Kirsop
VP: Patricia A Leach
VP: Paulette Lemon
Board of Directors: Thomas E King, Donald R Voss

D-U-N-S 07-924-7268
▲ **HOMESTREET INC** (WA)
601 Union St Ste 2000, Seattle, WA 98101-1378
Tel (206) 623-3050 *Founded/Ownrshp* 1921
Sales NA *EMP* 2,139
Tkr Sym HMST *Exch* NGM
SIC 6036 6022

D-U-N-S 04-556-4861
HOMESTYLE DINING LLC
BENNIGAN'S
3701 W Plano Pkwy Ste 200, Plano, TX 75075-7837
Tel (972) 244-8900 *Founded/Ownrshp* 1993
Sales 413.7MM^E *EMP* 10,525
SIC 5812 6794 Restaurant, family: chain; Franchises, selling or licensing
COO: Howard Finkelstein
VP: Kathy McGee
VP: Scott Neice

HOMETEAM ENVIRONMENTAL SVCS
See HOMETEAM PEST DEFENSE INC

D-U-N-S 95-727-9011
■ **HOMETEAM PEST DEFENSE INC**
HOMETEAM ENVIRONMENTAL SVCS
(*Suby of* ROLLINS INC) ★
3100 Mckinnon St Ste 120, Dallas, TX 75201-1111
Tel (214) 665-8700 *Founded/Ownrshp* 2008
Sales 64.0MM^E *EMP* 1,400
SIC 7342 Disinfecting & pest control services
Pr: Jerry Gahlhoff
Pr: Dennis Cone
Pr: Mike Johnson
**CFO:* Kevin Wolf
**Sr VP:* Craig Innes
**VP:* Julie Bimmerman
**VP:* Brady Camp
Genl Mgr: Duane Alewine
Genl Mgr: Jim Blaney
Genl Mgr: Justin Burlingame
Genl Mgr: Tim Carey

D-U-N-S 02-340-6759
HOMETOWN AMERICA LLC
HOMETOWN AMERICA MANAGEMENT
150 N Wacker Dr Ste 2800, Chicago, IL 60606-1610
Tel (312) 604-7500 *Founded/Ownrshp* 1997
Sales 49.2MM^E *EMP* 1,000
SIC 6512 Nonresidential building operators
CEO: Richard Cline
Exec: Pat Kerber

HOMETOWN AMERICA MANAGEMENT
See HOMETOWN AMERICA LLC

D-U-N-S 01-963-3523
HOMETOWN AMERICA MANAGEMENT CORP
(*Suby of* HOMETOWN AMERICA MANAGEMENT) ★
150 N Wacker Dr Ste 2800, Chicago, IL 60606-1610
Tel (312) 604-7500 *Founded/Ownrshp* 2002
Sales 17.5MM^E *EMP* 1,000
SIC 6515 Mobile home site operators
CEO: Richard Cline
**COO:* Greg Oberry

D-U-N-S 02-577-3693
HOMETOWN AUTO RETAILERS INC
1230 Main St, Watertown, CT 06795-3128
Tel (203) 756-8908 *Founded/Ownrshp* 1997
Sales 233.0MM *EMP* 297
SIC 5511 Automobiles, new & used
Pr: Corey Shaker
CFO: Charles F Schwartz
Bd of Dir: Bernard J Dzinski
**VP:* William C Muller Jr
**VP:* Joseph Shaker
Board of Directors: Bernard J Dzinski Jr, Steven A Fournier, Timothy C Moynahan

D-U-N-S 55-644-3711
HOMETOWN BUFFET INC
OLD COUNTRY BUFFET
(*Suby of* OLD COUNTRY BUFFET RESTAURANTS) ★
120 Chula Vis, San Antonio, TX 78232-2234
Tel (651) 994-8608 *Founded/Ownrshp* 1998
Sales 166.2MM^E *EMP* 5,364
SIC 5812 Buffet (eating places); Steak restaurant
Pr: Peter Donbavand
**CFO:* A Keith Wall
**VP:* Paul Holovnia

D-U-N-S 19-498-8965
HOMETOWN CONVENIENCE LLC
DOUBLE KWIK
51 Highway 2034, Whitesburg, KY 41858-7686
Tel (606) 633-2525 *Founded/Ownrshp* 2002
Sales 84.2MM^E *EMP* 700
SIC 5172 Gasoline

D-U-N-S 05-617-7413
HOMETOWN ENTERPRISES INC
KFC
18815 139th Ave Ne Ste C, Woodinville, WA 98072-3565
Tel (425) 486-6336 *Founded/Ownrshp* 1994
Sales 40.6MM^E *EMP* 1,000
SIC 5812 Fast-food restaurant, chain
CEO: Sam Sibert

HOMETOWN HEARTH & GRILL
See GAS CONNECTION LLC

D-U-N-S 13-724-2322
HOMETOWN URGENT CARE
2400 Corp Exchange Dr # 102, Columbus, OH 43231-7605
Tel (614) 505-7633 *Founded/Ownrshp* 2000
Sales 66.5MM^E *EMP* 1,905^E
SIC 8062 General medical & surgical hospitals

D-U-N-S 07-916-9938
▲ **HOMETRUST BANCSHARES INC**
10 Woodfin St, Asheville, NC 28801-3022
Tel (828) 259-3939 *Founded/Ownrshp* 2012
Sales NA *EMP* 505^E
Tkr Sym HTBI *Exch* NGS
SIC 6035 Federal savings banks
Ch Bd: Dana L Stonestreet
CFO: Tony J Vuncannon
Chf Cred: Keith Houghton
Ofcr: Parrish Little
Ofcr: Teresa White
Ex VP: Thomas R Goins
Ex VP: Howard L Sellinger
Ex VP: C Hunter Westbrook
Sr VP: David Carpenter
VP: Amy Lowman
Exec: Thomas Goins

D-U-N-S 00-507-0339
■ **HOMETTE CORP**
SKYLINE MAINSFIELD
(*Suby of* SKYLINE CORP) ★
2520 Bypass Rd, Elkhart, IN 46514-1518
Tel (574) 294-6521 *Founded/Ownrshp* 1962
Sales 114.7MM^E *EMP* 650
SIC 2452 3792 Modular homes, prefabricated, wood; Travel trailers & campers
Ch Bd: Thomas Deranek
**CFO:* John Pilarski

D-U-N-S 83-652-9920
■ **HOMEWARD RESIDENTIAL HOLDINGS INC**
(*Suby of* OCWEN FINANCIAL CORP) ★
1525 S Belt Line Rd, Coppell, TX 75019-4913
Tel (877) 304-3100 *Founded/Ownrshp* 2012
Sales 106.3MM^E *EMP* 1,706^E
SIC 7389 Financial services
Pr: Ronald M Faris
**VP:* Mark Zeidman

D-U-N-S 82-531-1231
■ **HOMEWARD RESIDENTIAL INC**
(*Suby of* HOMEWARD RESIDENTIAL HOLDINGS INC) ★
16675 Addison Rd, Addison, TX 75001-5116
Tel (877) 304-3100 *Founded/Ownrshp* 2008
Sales NA *EMP* 3,400
SIC 6162 Mortgage bankers & correspondents
Pr: David M Applegate
**CFO:* John V Britti
**Treas:* Ellen Coleman
**Sr VP:* Joel Gendron
**VP:* Barry J Bier
**VP:* Mark Zeidman

D-U-N-S 06-490-3974
HOMEWOOD RETIREMENT CENTERS OF UNITED CHURCH OF CHRIST INC (MD)
16107 Elliott Pkwy, Williamsport, MD 21795-4084
Tel (301) 582-1626 *Founded/Ownrshp* 1932
Sales 3.8MM *EMP* 1,075
Accts Smith Elliott Kearns & Company
SIC 8051 8361 Skilled nursing care facilities; Home for the aged
Pr: Ernest W Angell
**VP:* George Mc Cullough Jr
MIS Dir: Gary Recher
Board of Directors: Lisa Bethel

HOMEWOOD SUITES
See PROMUS HOTELS LLC

D-U-N-S 14-781-4735 IMP/EXP
■ **HON CO LLC**
(*Suby of* HNI CORP) ★
200 Oak St, Muscatine, IA 52761-4341
Tel (563) 272-7100 *Founded/Ownrshp* 1999
Sales 847.4MM^E *EMP* 4,000
SIC 2521 Wood office furniture
Pr: Jerry Dittmer
VP: Jerry L Vande Kieft
VP: Tim Rethlake
VP: Jean Reynolds
Dir Bus: Greg Berkebile
IT Man: Don Hirsch
IT Man: Shawn Rininger
Plnt Mgr: Kory Schreiner
Ql Cn Mgr: John Hayes
Sls Mgr: Ben Brewster
Sls Mgr: Heidi Fields

D-U-N-S 78-532-8167 IMP/EXP
HONDA AIRCRAFT CO INC
HONDAJET
(*Suby of* HONDA MOTOR CO., LTD.)
6430 Ballinger Rd, Greensboro, NC 27410-9063
Tel (336) 662-0246 *Founded/Ownrshp* 2011
Sales 221.1MM^E *EMP* 450
SIC 3728 Aircraft parts & equipment
Exec: Claire Anderson
Dir IT: Mark Rector
IT Man: Steve Johnston
IT Man: Sassan Khoubyari
Opers Mgr: William Kluepfel
Opers Mgr: Tom Watson
Ql Cn Mgr: Steven Shipley
S&M/VP: Douglas Danuser
Snr Mgr: Josef Fila
Snr Mgr: Junichi Kondo
Snr Mgr: Ronald Simon

HONDA DE SAN JUAN
See BELLA INTERNATIONAL CORP

D-U-N-S 80-849-6574 IMP
HONDA ENGINEERING NORTH AMERICA INC
(*Suby of* HONDA ENGINEERING CO.,LTD.)
24000 Honda Pkwy, Marysville, OH 43040-9251
Tel (937) 642-5000 *Founded/Ownrshp* 1982
Sales 176.6MM^E *EMP* 350
SIC 3544 Special dies & tools; Industrial molds
Pr: Akira Takeshita
Div Mgr: Bob Brizendine

HONDA FINANCIAL SERVICES
See AMERICAN HONDA FINANCE CORP

HONDA LOCK OF AMERICA
See HL-A CO

D-U-N-S 07-984-6360
HONDA LOGISTICS NORTH AMERICA INC
(*Suby of* HONDA LOGISTICS INC.)
11590 Township Road 298, East Liberty, OH 43319-9487
Tel (937) 642-0335 *Founded/Ownrshp* 2013
Sales 175.6MM^E *EMP* 1,245
SIC 4226 Special warehousing & storage
Pr: Tamaki Hashimoto

D-U-N-S 82-796-1264 EXP
HONDA MANUFACTURING OF ALABAMA LLC
HMA
(*Suby of* AMERICAN HONDA MOTOR CO INC) ★
1800 Honda Dr, Lincoln, AL 35096-5107
Tel (205) 355-5000 *Founded/Ownrshp* 1999
Sales 71.8MM^E *EMP* 2,300
SIC 5511 Automobiles, new & used
Pr: Jeff Tomko

D-U-N-S 79-205-0838 IMP/EXP
HONDA MANUFACTURING OF INDIANA LLC
(*Suby of* AMERICAN HONDA MOTOR CO INC) ★
2755 N Michigan Ave, Greensburg, IN 47240-9341
Tel (812) 222-6000 *Founded/Ownrshp* 2007
Sales 228.8MM^E *EMP* 2,000
SIC 3711 Automobile assembly, including specialty automobiles
Pr: Bob Nelson
**VP:* Kiyoshi Ikeyama
Dir IT: Sam Labarbara
IT Man: Jeremy Stallsmith

HONDA NORTH
See INTERNATIONAL CARS LTD INC

D-U-N-S 18-770-0604
HONDA NORTH AMERICA INC
(*Suby of* HONDA MOTOR CO., LTD.)
700 Van Ness Ave, Torrance, CA 90501-1486
Tel (310) 781-4961 *Founded/Ownrshp* 1987
Sales 5.0MMM^E *EMP* 40,000
SIC 3711 8748 Automobile assembly, including specialty automobiles; Business consulting
Pr: Takuji Yamada
Pr: Tetsuo Iwamura
Ofcr: Nichole Whitley
Ex VP: Takashi Sekiguchi
Sr VP: Gary Mabrey
Sr VP: Tsutomu Morimoto
VP: Charlie Baker
VP: Hiroshi Soda
Dir Teleco: Roger Cope
Genl Mgr: Bob Fegan
Netwrk Eng: Alan Cruz

D-U-N-S 09-216-2643 IMP/EXP
HONDA OF AMERICA MFG INC
MARYSVILLE AUTO PLANT
(*Suby of* AMERICAN HONDA MOTOR CO INC) ★
24000 Honda Pkwy, Marysville, OH 43040-9251
Tel (937) 642-5000 *Founded/Ownrshp* 1978
Sales 3.0MMM^E *EMP* 13,500
SIC 3711 Automobile assembly, including specialty automobiles
Pr: Akio Hamada
Pr: Bill Easdale
**CEO:* Tomomi Kosaka
COO: Steve Mortimer
VP: James Wehrman
**Prin:* John Adams
VP Admn: Tim Garrett
Mng Dir: Satoshi Aoki
Prgrm Mgr: Jose Banaag
Admn Mgr: Dave Reed
Dept Mgr: Donald Moore

D-U-N-S 01-216-5564 IMP/EXP
HONDA OF SOUTH CAROLINA MFG INC
(*Suby of* AMERICAN HONDA MOTOR CO INC) ★
1111 Honda Way, Timmonsville, SC 29161-9421
Tel (843) 346-8000 *Founded/Ownrshp* 1998
Sales 228.8MM^E *EMP* 600
SIC 3799 All terrain vehicles (ATV)
Pr: Katsumi Fujimoto
Pr: Kenichi Inoue
Sr VP: Dane Espenschied
**VP:* Brian Newman
Info Man: Jason Grimsley
Plnt Mgr: Jeff Helton
Sales Exec: Holly Baker

D-U-N-S 10-789-3067 IMP/EXP
HONDA POWER EQUIPMENT MFG INC
(*Suby of* AMERICAN HONDA MOTOR CO INC) ★
3721 Nc Hwy 119, Swepsonville, NC 27359
Tel (336) 578-5300 *Founded/Ownrshp* 1984
Sales 111.6MM^E *EMP* 335^E
SIC 3524 Lawn & garden mowers & accessories
Pr: Yoshi Toyozumi

**Treas:* Taku Kitamura
Sls Dir: Chris Farmer

D-U-N-S 19-855-0605 IMP/EXP
HONDA PRECISION PARTS OF GEORGIA LLC
(*Suby of* AMERICAN HONDA MOTOR CO INC) ★
550 Honda Pkwy, Tallapoosa, GA 30176-4344
Tel (770) 574-3400 *Founded/Ownrshp* 2005
Sales 136.7MM^E *EMP* 500
SIC 3089 Automotive parts, plastic
IT Man: Greg Smith
Netwrk Eng: Matthew Lail

D-U-N-S 15-750-9696 IMP
HONDA R&D AMERICAS INC
(*Suby of* HONDA R&D CO.,LTD.)
1900 Harpers Way, Torrance, CA 90501-1521
Tel (310) 781-5500 *Founded/Ownrshp* 2015
Sales 787.1MM^E *EMP* 1,537
SIC 5511 Automobiles, new & used
CEO: Frank Paluch
CFO: Michael Ryan
CFO: Ravi Sud
VP: Charles Allen
Genl Mgr: Morishi Horiuchi
Dir IT: Ed Dimayuga
IT Man: C Perry
Software D: Chris Sible
Snr Mgr: Anthony Arcuri

D-U-N-S 06-458-9773 IMP/EXP
HONDA TRADING AMERICA CORP
H T A
(*Suby of* HONDA TRADING CORPORATION)
19210 Van Ness Ave, Torrance, CA 90501-1102
Tel (310) 787-5000 *Founded/Ownrshp* 2000
Sales 266.0MM^E *EMP* 200
SIC 5013 Automotive supplies & parts
Pr: Nobuhiko Shiozaki
**Treas:* Naoki Kominami
**Sr VP:* Greg Norval

D-U-N-S 02-244-2727 IMP
HONDA TRANSMISSION MANUFACTURING OF AMERICA INC
(*Suby of* AMERICAN HONDA MOTOR CO INC) ★
6964 State Route 235 N, Russells Point, OH 43348-9703
Tel (937) 843-5555 *Founded/Ownrshp* 1981
Sales 228.8MM^E *EMP* 1,200
SIC 3714 Motor vehicle parts & accessories; Wheels, motor vehicle; Frames, motor vehicle; Exhaust systems & parts, motor vehicle
Pr: Yuji Takahashi
**Pr:* Masanori Kato
**COO:* Steve Mortimer
**VP:* Gary Hand
Exec: Michael Snyder
MIS Dir: Joseph Berner
IT Man: David Burgess
Sfty Dirs: Jerry Cline
Ql Cn Mgr: Rob Kress
Snr Mgr: Mitsuru Onishi

HONDAJET
See HONDA AIRCRAFT CO INC

D-U-N-S 96-996-2757 IMP
HONEST CO INC
12130 Millennium Ste 500, Playa Vista, CA 90094-2946
Tel (310) 917-9199 *Founded/Ownrshp* 2011
Sales 89.5MM^E *EMP* 304
SIC 2341 2833 Panties: women's, misses', children's & infants'; Vitamins, natural or synthetic: bulk, uncompounded
CEO: Brian Lee
**Pr:* Jessica Alba
**COO:* David Parker
**Ofcr:* Christopher Gavigan
**Prin:* Sean Kane
Rgnl Mgr: Queenie Hilfer
CTO: Oleg Pylnev
Web Dev: Camile Orillaneda
Ql Cn Mgr: Colleen Maguire
Mktg Dir: Jennifer Rosenberg
Sls Dir: Sonja Bjornsen

D-U-N-S 06-259-4536
HONEY BAKED HAM CO LLC (GA)
3875 Mansell Rd Ste 100, Alpharetta, GA 30022-1531
Tel (678) 966-3100 *Founded/Ownrshp* 1973
Sales 300.0MM *EMP* 900
SIC 5421 Meat markets, including freezer provisioners
CEO: Paul Roth
CFO: Phillip Eakins
**Sr VP:* Pete Stanca
VP: Leon Denning
VP: Lawrence Garon
VP: Leon Golding
VP: Nancy Luginbill
Store Mgr: Paul Meadows
IT Man: Paul Ritter
Mktg Dir: Robin Bayless

HONEY ROCK CAMP
See TRUSTEES OF WHEATON COLLEGE

HONEYBUCKETS
See NORTHWEST CASCADE INC

HONEYVILLE FOOD PRODUCTS
See HONEYVILLE INC

D-U-N-S 05-242-5246 IMP
HONEYVILLE INC
HONEYVILLE FOOD PRODUCTS
1080 N Main St Ste 101, Brigham City, UT 84302-1470
Tel (435) 494-4193 *Founded/Ownrshp* 1951
Sales 217.9MM^E *EMP* 200
SIC 5153 Wheat; Corn
Ch Bd: Lowell Sherrat
**Pr:* Robert W Anderson
**Treas:* Steven T Christensen
**VP:* Tyler Christensen

HONEYWELL
See GRIMES AEROSPACE CO

HONEYWELL
See METROLOGIC INSTRUMENTS INC

D-U-N-S 07-988-7593
■ **HONEYWELL AEROSPACE INC**
(*Suby of* HONEYWELL INTERNATIONAL INC) ★
1944 E Sky Harbor Cir N, Phoenix, AZ 85034-3442
Tel (602) 365-3099 *Founded/Ownrshp* 2015
Sales 132.7MM^E *EMP* 959^E
SIC 3812 7363 7699 Aircraft/aerospace flight instruments & guidance systems; Pilot service, aviation; Aviation propeller & blade repair
CEO: Timothy O Mahoney
**Pr:* Paolo Carmassi
**Pr:* Briand Greer
**Pr:* Garrett Mikita
**Pr:* Rob Wilson

D-U-N-S 06-862-3032 IMP
■ **HONEYWELL ANALYTICS INC**
(*Suby of* HONEYWELL INTERNATIONAL INC) ★
405 Barclay Blvd, Lincolnshire, IL 60069-3609
Tel (847) 955-8200 *Founded/Ownrshp* 2005
Sales 178.6MM^E *EMP* 1,045
SIC 3491 3829 Process control regulator valves; Gas detectors
Pr: Carl Johnson
**Treas:* John J Tus
Sr VP: Patrick Hogan
**VP:* Paul H Brownstein
**VP:* John Hakanson
CTO: Jerry Evans
IT Man: Arnold Bowman
Sftwr Eng: Michael Grady
VP Mktg: Ron Walczak
Mktg Mgr: Nelson Rivera

D-U-N-S 60-701-7449 IMP
■ **HONEYWELL ELECTRONIC MATERIALS INC**
(*Suby of* HONEYWELL INTERNATIONAL INC) ★
15128 E Euclid Ave, Spokane Valley, WA 99216-1801
Tel (509) 252-2200 *Founded/Ownrshp* 1999
Sales 255.6MM^E *EMP* 1,100
SIC 3679 3674 3643 Electronic circuits; Semiconductors & related devices; Current-carrying wiring devices
Pr: David Diggs
Treas: John J Tus
VP: James M Di Stefano
VP: Ezra Eckhardt
IT Man: Srinivas Chada
IT Man: Fred Hidden
IT Man: Fukuyama Ken
IT Man: Mike Piotrowski
IT Man: Brent Wilcox
QC Dir: Tom Herrington
QC Dir: Catheryn Watson

HONEYWELL FIRST RESPONDER PDTS
See MORNING PRIDE MFG LLC

HONEYWELL IMAGING AND MOBILITY
See HAND HELD PRODUCTS INC

D-U-N-S 00-132-5240 IMP/EXP
■ **HONEYWELL INC**
(*Suby of* HONEYWELL INTERNATIONAL INC) ★
115 Tabor Rd, Morris Plains, NJ 07950-2546
Tel (973) 455-2000 *Founded/Ownrshp* 1927
Sales 9.9MMM^E *EMP* 50,143^E
SIC 3823 3812 3669 3491 3699 3822 Industrial instrmnts msrmnt display/control process variable; Temperature instruments: industrial process type; Controllers for process variables, all types; Programmers, process type; Aircraft control systems, electronic; Aircraft/aerospace flight instruments & guidance systems; Space vehicle guidance systems & equipment; Fire alarm apparatus, electric; Gas valves & parts, industrial; Security control equipment & systems; Auto controls regulating residntl & coml environmt & applncs; Energy cutoff controls, residential or commercial types; Thermostats, except built-in; Humidistats: wall, duct & skeleton
Ch Bd: Michael R Bonsignore
V Ch: David Larson
Pr: Nance Katherine Dicciani
Pr: Jeff Laufatte
CFO: Daniel Darazsdi
CFO: Richard Wallman
Sr VP: James T Porter
VP: Karen O Bachman
VP: Richard Diemer
VP: Jeff Donnell
VP: Barry Ford
VP: Edward D Grayson
VP: Emil Hensle
VP: Stephen Hirshfeld
VP: Allen C Riess
VP: Dale Wallis
VP: Arnie Weimerskirch
VP: Jo Whidmayer
VP: Lloyd Wilky
VP: Greg Wischstadt

D-U-N-S 13-969-1877 IMP/EXP
▲ **HONEYWELL INTERNATIONAL INC**
115 Tabor Rd, Morris Plains, NJ 07950-2546
Tel (973) 455-2000 *Founded/Ownrshp* 1920
Sales 38.5MMM *EMP* 129,029
Tkr Sym HON *Exch* NYS
SIC 3724 3812 3585 2824 2821 3714 Aircraft engines & engine parts; Turbines, aircraft type; Research & development on aircraft engines & parts; Aircraft control systems, electronic; Cabin environment indicators; Radar systems & equipment; Aircraft flight instruments; Air conditioning equipment, complete; Heating equipment, complete; Humidifiers & dehumidifiers; Nylon fibers; Polyester fibers; Polyethylene resins; Motor vehicle parts & accessories; Filters: oil, fuel & air, motor vehicle; Motor vehicle brake systems & parts; PVC valves
Ch Bd: David M Cote
Pr: Darius Adamczyk
Pr: Alexandre Ismail
Pr: Timothy O Mahoney
CFO: Thomas A Szlosek
Ofcr: Kevin Walker
Sr VP: Katherine L Adams
Sr VP: Mark R James
Sr VP: Krishna Mikkilineni
VP: Robert Andersen
VP: Rhonda G Germany
VP: Don Gress
VP: Rebecca Liebert
VP: Anthony Schultz
Board of Directors: Bradley T Sheares, William S Ayer, Robin L Washington, Kevin Burke, D Scott Davis, Linnet F Deily, Judd Gregg, Clive Hollick, Grace D Lieblein, Jaime Chico Pardo, George Paz

HONEYWELL SAFETY PRODUCTS
See SPERIAN PROTECTION USA INC

HONEYWELL SAFETY PRODUCTS
See NORCROSS SAFETY PRODUCTS LLC

D-U-N-S 07-924-5827 EXP
■ **HONEYWELL SAFETY PRODUCTS USA INC**
(*Suby of* HONEYWELL INTERNATIONAL INC) ★
2711 Centerville Rd, Wilmington, DE 19808-1660
Tel (302) 636-5401 *Founded/Ownrshp* 2010
Sales 426.4MM^E *EMP* 2,733^E
SIC 5099 Lifesaving & survival equipment (non-medical)
CEO: David M Cote
**Pr:* Roger Fradin
**Pr:* Terrence Hahn
**Pr:* Alex Ismail
**Pr:* Andreas Kramvis
**Pr:* Tim Mahoney

D-U-N-S 62-306-4300 EXP
■ **HONEYWELL SPECIALTY WAX & ADDITIVES INC**
(*Suby of* HONEYWELL INTERNATIONAL INC) ★
101 Columbia Rd, Morristown, NJ 07960-4640
Tel (973) 455-2000 *Founded/Ownrshp* 1997
Sales 114.2MM^E *EMP* 1,200^E
SIC 2999 5169 Waxes, petroleum: not produced in petroleum refineries; Waxes, except petroleum
CEO: David Cote
**Pr:* John Gottshall
Bd of Dir: D S Davis
Bd of Dir: George Paz
VP: Elena Doom
VP: Paul Vasington
Snr Ntwrk: Jack Stanley
VP Sls: Matt Herlevic

HONEYWELL UOP
See UOP LLC

D-U-N-S 02-009-3779
HONIGMAN MILLER SCHWARTZ AND COHN LLP
660 Woodward Ave Ste 2290, Detroit, MI 48226-3583
Tel (313) 465-7000 *Founded/Ownrshp* 1948
Sales 91.0MM^E *EMP* 500
SIC 8111 General practice law office
CEO: David Foltyn
Pt: Joscelyn C Boucher
Pt: Amy M Brooks
Pt: Noel E Day
Pt: Andrew Doctoroff
Pt: Andrew Gerdes
Pt: William Hammond
Pt: Wayne D Hillyard
Pt: Kelly T Murphy
Pt: Jonathan P O'Brien
Pt: Richard W Paige
Pt: Kathryn D Soulier
Pt: Michelle Epstein Taigman
Pt: Phillip D Torrence
Pt: Andrew N Weber
Pt: Thomas A Wootton
Pt: Lisa Budyk Zimmer
COO: Pamela Mullen
**V Ch Bd:* Alan Stuart Schwartz
Chf Mktg O: Frederick Morsches
Board of Directors: William O Hochkammer, Alan Stuart Schwartz V Ch

D-U-N-S 03-193-8079
HONNEN EQUIPMENT CO
JOHN DEERE AUTHORIZED DEALER
5055 E 72nd Ave, Commerce City, CO 80022-1513
Tel (303) 287-7506 *Founded/Ownrshp* 1963
Sales 89.2MM^E *EMP* 280
SIC 5082 5084 Construction & mining machinery; Industrial machinery & equipment
Pr: Mark Honnen
**CFO:* Scott Long
CFO: Mike Martin
**VP:* Jon Asbury
Sls Mgr: Marty Hlawati

D-U-N-S 18-389-2579
HONOLULU SCHOOL DISTRICT
(*Suby of* OFFICE OF SUPERINTENDENT) ★
4967 Kilauea Ave, Honolulu, HI 96816-5731
Tel (808) 733-4950 *Founded/Ownrshp* 1967
Sales 47.7MM^E *EMP* 1,530
SIC 8211 Public elementary & secondary schools;
Board of Directors: Pauline Kokubun

HONOLULU STAR ADVERTISER
See OAHU PUBLICATIONS INC

D-U-N-S 05-472-3697 IMP
HONOR HOLDINGS INC (PA)
(*Suby of* BURRIS RETAIL LOGISTICS) ★
1801 N 5th St, Philadelphia, PA 19122-2198
Tel (215) 236-1700 *Founded/Ownrshp* 1946
Sales 146.5MM^E *EMP* 110
SIC 5141 5142 Groceries, general line; Packaged frozen goods
Pr: Richard J Singer
VP: Greg Cyganiewicz
Dir IT: Joe Windfelder
VP Sls: Joe Adams
VP Sls: Marjorie Rossiter
Manager: Gene Overcash
Sls Mgr: Keith Blake
Sales Asso: Bruce Banning
Sales Asso: Ronnie Bortnicker
Sales Asso: Julie Singer

HONORHEALTH
See SCOTTSDALE HEALTHCARE HOSPITALS

D-U-N-S 07-768-9974
HONPA HONGWANJI HAWAII BETSUIN
1727 Pali Hwy, Honolulu, HI 96813-1612
Tel (808) 536-7044 *Founded/Ownrshp* 1923
Sales 14.7MM^E *EMP* 1,700
SIC 8661 Buddhist Temple
Pr: Alan Goto

D-U-N-S 78-581-0222 IMP
HONSADOR LUMBER LLC
91-151 Malakole St, Kapolei, HI 96707-1893
Tel (808) 479-3071 *Founded/Ownrshp* 2004
Sales 124.1MM^E *EMP* 250
SIC 5031 5211 Lumber, plywood & millwork; Lumber & other building materials
CEO: Carl Liliequist
Pr: Terris Inglett
Treas: Brian Moore
Sr VP: Errol Nii
VP: Wayne Lincoln

D-U-N-S 00-852-0967
HOOBER INC
KUBOTA
3452 Old Philadelphia Pike, Intercourse, PA 17534-7005
Tel (717) 768-8231 *Founded/Ownrshp* 1965
Sales 94.0MM^E *EMP* 224
SIC 5999 7699 5083

D-U-N-S 83-047-9478 IMP/EXP
HOOD COMPANIES INC
623 N Main St Ste 300, Hattiesburg, MS 39401-3464
Tel (601) 582-1545 *Founded/Ownrshp* 1998
Sales 789.9MM^E *EMP* 1,350^E
SIC 3086 2952 6719 Insulation or cushioning material, foamed plastic; Roofing materials; Investment holding companies, except banks
Pr: Warren Hood
**CFO:* Larry D Davis

D-U-N-S 07-855-6251
HOOD CONTAINER CORP
(*Suby of* HOOD COMPANIES INC) ★
623 N Main St Ste 100, Hattiesburg, MS 39401-3464
Tel (601) 582-1545 *Founded/Ownrshp* 2012
Sales 117.1MM^E *EMP* 250^E
SIC 2673 Bags: plastic, laminated & coated
Pr: Warren A Hood Jr
**CFO:* John A Johnson
VP Sls: Ron Zimbelman

D-U-N-S 96-270-6151
HOOD CONTAINER OF LOUISIANA LLC
(*Suby of* HOOD CONTAINER CORP) ★
2105 Highway 964, Saint Francisville, LA 70775-7473
Tel (225) 336-2530 *Founded/Ownrshp* 2010
Sales 117.1MM^E *EMP* 250
SIC 2621 Paper mills
VP: Wayne Morgan

D-U-N-S 80-389-9397
HOOD DISTRIBUTION INC
(*Suby of* MCEWEN LUMBER CO) ★
15 Professional Pkwy # 8, Hattiesburg, MS 39402-2647
Tel (601) 264-2962 *Founded/Ownrshp* 2008
Sales 130.0MM *EMP* 196
SIC 8741 Business management
Pr: Chris Norris
Plnt Mgr: Jim Benefield
Plnt Mgr: Stan Majure
Plnt Mgr: Larry Stephens
Sales Asso: John Cahill

D-U-N-S 03-307-5284 IMP/EXP
HOOD INDUSTRIES INC (MS)
MCEWEN LUMBER CO
15 Professional Pkwy # 8, Hattiesburg, MS 39402-2647
Tel (601) 264-2962 *Founded/Ownrshp* 1983
Sales 368.0MM^E *EMP* 1,150
SIC 2436 2421 5031 Panels, softwood plywood; Resawing lumber into smaller dimensions; Kiln drying of lumber; Lumber, plywood & millwork; Paneling, wood
Pr: Donald Grimm
Treas: Warren Hood Jr
VP: John Hammack
VP: John Johnson
VP: Bill Wislocki
Mng Dir: Chris Norris
Genl Mgr: Kevin Evans
Sales Exec: Tim Cochran
Sls Mgr: Carolyn Ryals

D-U-N-S 09-210-4470 IMP
HOOD PACKAGING CORP
(*Suby of* HOOD COMPANIES INC) ★
25 Woodgreen Pl, Madison, MS 39110-9531
Tel (601) 853-7260 *Founded/Ownrshp* 1976
Sales 245.6MM^E *EMP* 750
SIC 2674 Bags: uncoated paper & multiwall
Pr: Robert Morris
**Treas:* Warren A Hood Jr
**VP:* John Johnson
Genl Mgr: Matthew Hegstrom
Genl Mgr: Greg Sheppard
Genl Mgr: Michael Vidler

D-U-N-S 00-312-0748 IMP/EXP
▲ **HOOKER FURNITURE CORP** (VA)
440 Commonwealth Blvd E, Martinsville, VA 24112-2040
Tel (276) 632-2133 *Founded/Ownrshp* 1924
Sales 247.0MM *EMP* 645^E
Tkr Sym HOFT *Exch* NGS
SIC 2511 2512 2517 2521 Wood household furniture; Wood bedroom furniture; Wood desks, bookcases & magazine racks; End tables: wood; Upholstered household furniture; Home entertainment unit cabinets, wood; Wood office furniture
Ch Bd: Paul B Toms Jr
Pr: Michael W Delgatti Jr
Pr: George Revington

CFO: Paul A Huckfeldt
Ex VP: Steve Lush
Sr VP: Anne M Jacobsen
Board of Directors: W Christopher Beeler Jr, John L Gregory III, E Larry Ryder, David G Sweet, Ellen C Taaffe, Henry G Williamson Jr

D-U-N-S 00-192-6971
HOOPER CORP
2030 Pennsylvania Ave, Madison, WI 53704-4746
Tel (608) 249-0451 *Founded/Ownrshp* 1959
Sales 220.7MM *EMP* 350
Accts Mcgladrey Llp Madison Wiscon
SIC 1623 1711 Electric power line construction; Pipe laying construction; Mechanical contractor
Pr: G Frederick Davie
CFO: Bob Schaller
*CFO: Robert Schaller
Sr VP: Eddee Alvarez
*VP: Jerry A Diebling
*VP: Keith J Judenis
*VP: Steven Lindley
*VP: Dave P Miller
*VP: David Orr
Genl Mgr: Steven Millman

HOOSIER ELECTRONICS FINCL SVCS
See CADILLAC PRODUCTS INC

D-U-N-S 06-280-2574 IMP
HOOSIER ENERGY RURAL ELECTRIC COOPERATIVE INC
CO-OP COMFORT CREDIT
2501 S Cooperative Way, Bloomington, IN 47403-5175
Tel (812) 876-2021 *Founded/Ownrshp* 1935
Sales 667.9MM^E *EMP* 475
Accts Deloitte & Touche Llp Indian
SIC 4911 Electric services; Transmission, electric power; Distribution, electric power
Ch Bd: Charlie Meier
*Pr: James S Weimer
*CEO: J Steven Smith
CFO: Jeff Retseck
CFO: Donna L Snyder
VP: Rob Horton
VP: David W Sandefur
Comm Man: Claire Gregory
Genl Mgr: Bill Harding
MIS Dir: Barbara Myers
Dir IT: Ed Karas
Board of Directors: Robert D Stroup, Harry Althoff, Vaughn Tucker, August A Bauer, Dale Walther, Donald Braun, James Weimer, Darin Duncan, Herbert C Haggard, Jerry C Jackle, Emil Page, Larry Peters, Jerry Pheifer

HOOSIER PARK CASINO
See HOOSIER PARK LLC

D-U-N-S 83-441-9772
HOOSIER PARK LLC
HOOSIER PARK CASINO
(*Suby of* CENTAUR LLC) ★
4500 Dan Patch Cir Xxx, Anderson, IN 46013-3161
Tel (765) 642-7223 *Founded/Ownrshp* 2007
Sales 220.0MM *EMP* 1,112^E
SIC 7948 Racing, including track operation
Pt: Roderick Ratcliff
CFO: Kurt Wilson
Exec: Brenda Bowling
Exec: Ginger Shaw
Genl Mgr: James Brown
Genl Mgr: Emily Gaskin
Sales Exec: Zach Wilson
Pr Dir: Grant Scharton
Advt Mgr: Kiersten Sadzewicz
Pgrm Dir: Larry Kauffman
Pgrm Dir: Larry Kaufmann
Board of Directors: Ralph Brown, Gene Ciscell, Rudy McMillan, Jeff Smith

HOOTERS
See CORNETT HOSPITALITY LLC

HOOTERS
See RMD CORP

HOOTERS
See TEXAS WINGS INC

D-U-N-S 12-094-6041
HOOTERS OF AMERICA LLC
1815 The Exchange Se, Atlanta, GA 30339-2027
Tel (770) 951-2040 *Founded/Ownrshp* 2011
Sales 315.7MM^E *EMP* 5,600
SIC 5812 6794 American restaurant; Franchises, selling or licensing
Pr: Coby Brooks
*COO: Jim Parrish
CFO: Rodney Foster
*Ofcr: Claudia Levitas
Rgnl Mgr: Gretchen Drury
Rgnl Mgr: Mike Thomas
Genl Mgr: Phillip Ali
Genl Mgr: Claude Contoif
Genl Mgr: Steve Marshall
Genl Mgr: Ryan Rayburn
Genl Mgr: Cedric Solland

D-U-N-S 61-347-7652
HOOVER CITY SCHOOL DISTRICT
HOOVER CITY SCHOOLS
2810 Metropolitan Way, Hoover, AL 35216
Tel (205) 439-1000 *Founded/Ownrshp* 1987
Sales 83.8MM^E *EMP* 1,500
SIC 8211 Public elementary & secondary schools
*Pr: Earl Cooper
Pr: William Veitch
Bd of Dir: Josh Lynch
Adm Dir: James Knichredom
Dir IT: Brian Fancher
IT Man: Troy McCraw
Schl Brd P: Donna Frazier
Teacher Pr: Mary Veal

HOOVER CITY SCHOOLS
See HOOVER CITY SCHOOL DISTRICT

HOOVER CONTAINER GROUP
See HOOVER GROUP INC

HOOVER CONTAINER SOLUTIONS
See HOOVER MATERIALS HANDLING GROUP INC

D-U-N-S 14-815-0212 IMP/EXP
HOOVER GROUP INC
HOOVER CONTAINER GROUP
2135 Highway 6 S, Houston, TX 77077-4319
Tel (800) 844-8683 *Founded/Ownrshp* 1985
Sales 110.9MM^E *EMP* 230
Accts Habif Arogeti & Wyne Llp
SIC 3496 3412 3443 3089 7359 3411 Miscellaneous fabricated wire products; Metal barrels, drums & pails; Industrial vessels, tanks & containers; Tanks, lined: metal plate; Tanks, standard or custom fabricated: metal plate; Plastic containers, except foam; Plastic & fiberglass tanks; Equipment rental & leasing; Metal cans
Prin: Donald W Young
Pr: Paul Lewis
VP: Scott T Meints
VP: Johan Wramsby
Netwrk Mgr: Travis Conley

D-U-N-S 00-446-2131 IMP
HOOVER INC
TTI FLOORCARE
(*Suby of* TECHTRONIC INDUSTRIES COMPANY LIMITED)
7005 Cochran Rd, Solon, OH 44139-4303
Tel (330) 499-9200 *Founded/Ownrshp* 2007
Sales 316.2MM^E *EMP* 600
SIC 5064 Vacuum cleaners, household
Pr: Chris Gurreri
*Pr: Dan Gregory
*CFO: Matt Shene
VP: D A Gault
VP: Frank Wittman
VP: Thomas Yu
VP Admn: Lynn Dragomier
IT Man: Keith Minton
Opers Mgr: Skip Lawton
Sls&Mrk Ex: Peter McCormick
Pr Mgr: Claudia Chiquillo

D-U-N-S 96-283-2796 IMP/EXP
HOOVER MATERIALS HANDLING GROUP INC
HOOVER CONTAINER SOLUTIONS
(*Suby of* HOOVER CONTAINER GROUP) ★
2135 Highway 6 S, Houston, TX 77077-4319
Tel (800) 844-8683 *Founded/Ownrshp* 1992
Sales 103.4MM^E *EMP* 102
SIC 5113 3089 Containers, paper & disposable plastic; Plastic containers, except foam
Ch Bd: Donald W Young
Pr: Paul Lewis
CFO: Joseph Levy
VP: Conrad A Arnold
VP: Scott T Meints
VP: Scott Meints
IT Man: Sharif Taha
Software D: Barry Bucher
Advt Dir: Bill Terry
Manager: David Boom
Sls Mgr: John Ashcorn

D-U-N-S 61-034-0705 IMP
HOOVER PRECISION PRODUCTS INC
(*Suby of* TSUBAKI NAKASHIMA CO.,LTD.)
2200 Pendley Rd, Cumming, GA 30041-6448
Tel (770) 889-9223 *Founded/Ownrshp* 1990
Sales 166.7MM^E *EMP* 1,300
SIC 3399 Steel balls
CEO: Kenji Yamada
*Pr: Eric Sturdy
*CEO: Takanori Kondo
COO: Takashige Suehiro
*CFO: James W Brandon Jr
*CFO: Gary Duran
VP: Brian Jennings
VP: Lois Labarreare
Netwrk Eng: Richard Mishoe
Plnt Mgr: Tom Williams

D-U-N-S 00-537-9425 IMP
HOOVER UNIVERSAL INC
JOHNSON CONTROLS BATTLE
(*Suby of* JOHNSON CONTROLS INC) ★
49200 Halyard Dr, Plymouth, MI 48170-2481
Tel (734) 454-0994 *Founded/Ownrshp* 1985
Sales 741.8MM^E *EMP* 2,000
SIC 2531 Seats, automobile
Pr: Keith E Wandell
*Treas: Thomas Jeppson
*VP: Jeffrey S Edwards
*VP: William J Kohler
*VP: John David Major
*VP: Jerome D Okarma
*VP: Clare Renshaw
*VP: Stephen Allen Roell

D-U-N-S 96-268-3038
HOP ENERGY HOLDINGS INC
4 W Red Oak Ln Ste 310, White Plains, NY 10604-3606
Tel (914) 304-1300 *Founded/Ownrshp* 2006
Sales 182.5MM^E *EMP* 867
SIC 5983 Fuel oil dealers
CEO: Richard Nota
Treas: Fred Lord
*Prin: Michael Anton
*Prin: Steve Zambito

D-U-N-S 83-712-2753
HOP ENERGY LLC
KEYSER ENERGY
(*Suby of* HOP ENERGY HOLDINGS INC) ★
4 W Red Oak Ln Ste 310, White Plains, NY 10604-3606
Tel (914) 304-1300 *Founded/Ownrshp* 2006
Sales 182.5MM^E *EMP* 865
SIC 5983 Fuel oil dealers
Pr: Michael Anton
*CFO: Richard Nota
Treas: Fred Lord
*Sr VP: Laura Cicchelli
*Sr VP: Steve Loizeaux
*Sr VP: Matthew J Ryan
VP: John Kuebler
VP: Elaine Sheldon
Admn Mgr: Cindie Gagnon

IT Man: Gloria Martos
IT Man: Jose Mondia

D-U-N-S 13-856-8956 IMP
▲ HOPE BANCORP INC
3731 Wilshire Blvd, Los Angeles, CA 90010-2830
Tel (213) 639-1700 *Founded/Ownrshp* 2002
Sales NA *EMP* 938^E
Tkr Sym HOPE *Exch* NGS
SIC 6021 National commercial banks
Ch Bd: Kevin S Kim
Pr: Kyu S Kim
CFO: Douglas J Goddard
Ofcr: Mark H Lee
Ofcr: Brian E Van Dyk
Ex VP: Daniel H Kim

D-U-N-S 13-512-7277
HOPE CHRISTIAN COMMUNITY FOUNDATION
4515 Poplar Ave Ste 324, Memphis, TN 38117-7507
Tel (901) 682-6201 *Founded/Ownrshp* 1998
Sales 88.7MM *EMP* 4
Accts Fouts & Morgan Cpas Memphis
SIC 8661 Religious organizations
VP Opers: Brian Cochrane

D-U-N-S 05-094-7084
HOPE COLLEGE
141 E 12th St, Holland, MI 49423-3663
Tel (616) 395-7000 *Founded/Ownrshp* 1866
Sales 111.0MM *EMP* 650^E
Accts Plante & Moran Pllc Grand Ra
SIC 8221 Colleges universities & professional schools
Pr: Dr John C Knapp
*Pr: James Bultman
*CFO: Thomas Bylsma
Trst: David Myers
*VP: Tom Bylsma
*VP: Richard Frost
*VP: William C Vanderbilt
*VP: Dave Vanderwel
VP: Scott Wolterink
Dir Lab: Abe Anaya
Assoc Dir: Chris Bohle

HOPE GLOBAL DIV
See NFA CORP

D-U-N-S 01-025-6881
HOPE HAVEN AREA DEVELOPMENT CENTER CORP (IA)
828 N 7th St Ste 1, Burlington, IA 52601-4921
Tel (319) 752-0110 *Founded/Ownrshp* 1970
Sales 10.7MMM *EMP* 60
Accts Cpa Associates Pc Burlington
SIC 8361 Rehabilitation center, residential: health care incidental
Ex Dir: Bob Bartles
Genl Mgr: Cheryl Enger

D-U-N-S 08-368-9315
HOPE NETWORK
COMMUNITY PARTNERSHIP CENTER
3075 Orchard Vista Dr Se # 100, Grand Rapids, MI 49546-7069
Tel (616) 301-8000 *Founded/Ownrshp* 2000
Sales 123.6MM *EMP* 2,162
Accts Beene Garter Llp Grand Rapids
SIC 8331 Vocational rehabilitation agency; Sheltered workshop
Pr: Phill W Weaver
Pr: Phil Hickmon
CFO: Richard Fabbrini
*CFO: Marc Kole
Ex VP: Patricia Howe
Exec: Shane Klotz
Ex Dir: David Smith
Prgrm Mgr: Laurie Binkley
Prgrm Mgr: Jerri Bozeman
Prgrm Mgr: Laura Britting
Prgrm Mgr: Virginia Luedtke

HOPKINS ALTERNATIVE PROGRAM IN
See INDEPENDENT SCHOOL DISTRICT 270

D-U-N-S 08-025-0980
HOPKINS COUNTY SCHOOL DISTRICT
320 S Seminary St, Madisonville, KY 42431-2424
Tel (270) 825-6000 *Founded/Ownrshp* 2016
Sales 7.8MM^E *EMP* 1,050^E
SIC 8211 Public elementary & secondary schools

D-U-N-S 06-939-0037
HOPKINS JOHNS MEDICAL SERVICES CORP (MD)
WYMAN PARK MEDICAL CTR
(*Suby of* JOHNS HOPKINS HEALTH SYS CORP) ★
3100 Wyman Park Dr, Baltimore, MD 21211-2803
Tel (410) 338-3071 *Founded/Ownrshp* 1941, 1981
Sales 92.2MM^E *EMP* 1,487
SIC 8011 8741 Health maintenance organization; Management services
COO: Barbara Cook MD
*Pr: Steven Kravet MD
COO: Linda Gilligan
MIS Dir: Cathy Zager

D-U-N-S 00-711-8318 IMP/EXP
HOPKINS MANUFACTURING CORP
428 Peyton St, Emporia, KS 66801-3722
Tel (620) 342-7320 *Founded/Ownrshp* 2011
Sales 225.0MM^E *EMP* 650
SIC 3714 Motor vehicle parts & accessories
Pr: Brad Kraft
Pr: Mary Volland
*CFO: Jim Daniels
Chf Mktg O: Michael S Williams
*Sr VP: David Moore
VP: Jim Garton
VP: Sue Wyda
Dir IT: Brian Curtis
Dir IT: Brian Curtiss
Dir IT: Brad Krest
VP Opers: Randy Kuntz

D-U-N-S 61-862-8689
HOPS GRILL & BAR INC
HOPS GRILL & BREWERY
(*Suby of* DON PABLOS) ★
Hancock At Washington St, Madison, GA 30650
Tel (706) 342-4552 *Founded/Ownrshp* 2009
Sales 139.0MM^E *EMP* 3,500
SIC 5813 5812 Bar (drinking places); Eating places
CEO: Tom E Dupree
VP: Tim Ligon
VP Opers: Duncan McLean

HOPS GRILL & BREWERY
See HOPS GRILL & BAR INC

D-U-N-S 02-359-1845
HOPSON OIL CO INC
MARQUARDT HEATING
1225 Whiterock Ave, Waukesha, WI 53186-3711
Tel (262) 542-5343 *Founded/Ownrshp* 1960
Sales 135.0MM *EMP* 35
SIC 5171 5983 1711 Petroleum bulk stations; Fuel oil dealers; Heating systems repair & maintenance
Pr: Terry Nagel
*VP: Clint Wendet

D-U-N-S 07-831-3394 IMP
HOPUNION LLC
203 Division St, Yakima, WA 98902-4622
Tel (509) 453-4792 *Founded/Ownrshp* 2006
Sales 140.0MM *EMP* 154
SIC 5181 Beer & ale

HORACE GREELEY HIGH SCHOOL
See CHAPPAQUA CENTRAL SCHOOL DISTRICT INC

D-U-N-S 06-234-2324
▲ HORACE MANN EDUCATORS CORP
1 Horace Mann Plz, Springfield, IL 62715-0001
Tel (217) 789-2500 *Founded/Ownrshp* 1945
Sales NA *EMP* 1,396^E
Accts Kpmg Llp Chicago Illinois
Tkr Sym HMN *Exch* NYS
SIC 6311 6331 6411 Life insurance; Property damage insurance; Property & casualty insurance agent; Pension & retirement plan consultants
Pr: Marita Zuraitis
*Ch Bd: Gabriel L Shaheen
CFO: Dwayne D Hallman
Chf Cred: Ann M Caparros
Ofcr: John P McCarthy
Ex VP: William J Caldwell
Ex VP: Matthew P Sharpe
Sr VP: Bret A Conklin
Sr VP: Sandra L Figurski
Sr VP: Kelly J Stacy
Genl Couns: Donald M Carley
Board of Directors: Daniel A Domenech, Stephen J Hasenmiller, Ronald J Helow, Beverley J McClure, H Wade Reece, Robert Stricker, Steven O Swyers

D-U-N-S 07-561-0402
■ HORACE MANN LIFE INSURANCE CO
(*Suby of* HORACE MANN EDUCATORS CORP) ★
1 Horace Mann Plz, Springfield, IL 62715-0001
Tel (217) 789-2500 *Founded/Ownrshp* 2016
Sales NA *EMP* 1^E
SIC 6411 Insurance agents, brokers & service
Pr: Louis G Lower II
*CFO: Peter H Heckman
Chf Mktg O: Dan Jensen
VP: Richard Atkinson
VP: Kelvin Hubbard
*VP: George J Zock

D-U-N-S 61-103-2751
■ HORACE MANN PROPERTY & CASUALTY INSURANCE CO
(*Suby of* HORACE MANN EDUCATORS CORP) ★
1 Horace Mann Plz, Springfield, IL 62715-0001
Tel (217) 789-2500 *Founded/Ownrshp* 2005
Sales NA *EMP* 10
SIC 6331 Fire, marine & casualty insurance
Pr: Louis G Lower II
Ex VP: Stephen P Cardinal
Ex VP: Doug W Reynolds
Sr VP: Bret A Conklin
IT Man: Fred Baskett

D-U-N-S 07-142-6837
■ HORACE MANN SERVICE CORP
(*Suby of* HORACE MANN EDUCATORS CORP) ★
1 Horace Mann Plz, Springfield, IL 62715-0001
Tel (217) 789-2500 *Founded/Ownrshp* 1989
Sales NA *EMP* 350
SIC 6411 Insurance agents, brokers & service; Insurance adjusters
Ch Bd: Lou Lower
*Pr: Peter H Heckman
Assoc VP: Jack Dickinson
Sr VP: Dewayne D Hallman
VP: Rhonda Armstead
*VP: Ann Mary Caparros
VP: Dick Madden
VP: Margo Smith
VP: Jim Strebler
VP: Sheila Wortham
CIO: Mark Hansen

D-U-N-S 06-221-8859 IMP
HORIBA INTERNATIONAL CORP
(*Suby of* HORIBA,LTD.)
9755 Research Dr, Irvine, CA 92618-4626
Tel (949) 250-4811 *Founded/Ownrshp* 1998
Sales 152.8MM^E *EMP* 930^E
SIC 3829 Measuring & controlling devices
Ch Bd: Atsushi Horiba
*Pr: Masayuki Adachi
*CEO: Jai Hakhu
*VP: Richard Marting

D-U-N-S 01-189-2510
■ HORIZON AIR INDUSTRIES INC
(*Suby of* ALASKA AIR GROUP INC) ★
19521 International Blvd, Seatac, WA 98188-5402
Tel (206) 241-6757 *Founded/Ownrshp* 1986
Sales 281.5MM^E *EMP* 3,900

SIC 4512 4522 Air passenger carrier, scheduled; Air cargo carrier, scheduled; Flying charter service
CEO: David Campbell
Treas: John F Schaefer Jr
* *Treas:* Rudi H Schmidt
* *Sr VP:* Thomas M Gerharter
Sr VP: Eugene Hahn
* *Sr VP:* Andrea L Schneider
VP: Yvonne Daverin
* *VP:* Eugene C Hahn
* *VP:* Jean Hahn
VP: Dan Russo
VP: Daniel Scott
* *VP:* Diana Shaw
* *VP:* Arthur E Thomas

D-U-N-S 11-974-7624
▲ HORIZON BANCORP
515 Franklin St, Michigan City, IN 46360-3328
Tel (219) 879-0211 *Founded/Ownrshp* 1983
Sales NA *EMP* 558^E
Tkr Sym HBNC *Exch* NGM
SIC 6021 National commercial banks
Ch Bd: Craig M Dwight
CFO: Mark E Secor
Ex Ofcr: Kathie A Deruiter

D-U-N-S 00-693-9326
■ HORIZON BANK NATIONAL ASSOCIATION
(*Suby of* HORIZON BANCORP) ★
515 Franklin St, Michigan City, IN 46360-3328
Tel (219) 873-2640 *Founded/Ownrshp* 1872
Sales NA *EMP* 370
SIC 6021 National commercial banks
Ch Bd: Craig M Dwight
* *Pr:* Thomas H Edwards
* *CFO:* Mark Secor
Ofcr: Stammy Ellinger
Sr VP: Carla Kanney
Sr VP: Rachel Saxon
VP: Barb Bialko
VP: David Bly
VP: John Crandle
VP: Becky Doperalski
VP: Sandy Moffett
* *VP:* James Neff Sr
VP: Mark Ritzi
VP: Keene Taylor
Exec: Steve Kring
Exec: Bruce Piekarski

D-U-N-S 80-041-6864
■ HORIZON BAY MANAGEMENT LLC
HORIZON BAY SENIOR COMMUNITIES
(*Suby of* BROOKDALE SENIOR LIVING) ★
5426 Bay Center Dr # 600, Tampa, FL 33609-3440
Tel (813) 287-3900 *Founded/Ownrshp* 2011
Sales 108.5MM^E *EMP* 3,500
SIC 8611 6531 1522 Community affairs & services; Real estate agents & managers; Residential construction
VP: Dotty J Bollinger
VP: Mary Sue Patchet
Ex Dir: Shannon East

HORIZON BAY SENIOR COMMUNITIES
See HORIZON BAY MANAGEMENT LLC

D-U-N-S 00-695-3558 IMP
HORIZON BEVERAGE CO INC (MA)
PREMIUM BEVERAGE CO
45 Commerce Way, Norton, MA 02766-3313
Tel (508) 587-1110 *Founded/Ownrshp* 1932
Sales 164.1MM^E *EMP* 310
SIC 5181 5182 Beer & other fermented malt liquors; Wine; Liquor
CEO: Robert L Epstein
* *CFO:* James L Rubenstein
Area Mgr: Dave Castro

HORIZON BLUE CROSS BLUE SHIELD
See HORIZON NJ HEALTH

HORIZON BLUE CROSS BLUE SHLD
See HORIZON HEALTHCARE SERVICES INC

D-U-N-S 07-862-2398
HORIZON COACH LINES
17810 Meeting House Rd # 200, Sandy Spring, MD 20860-1002
Tel (301) 260-2060 *Founded/Ownrshp* 2011
Sales 112.9MM^E *EMP* 2,500^E
SIC 4141 Local bus charter service
CEO: Francis Sherman

D-U-N-S 13-022-8625
HORIZON CONSTRUCTION GROUP INC
5201 E Terrace Dr Ste 300, Madison, WI 53718-8362
Tel (608) 354-0900 *Founded/Ownrshp* 1996
Sales 145.3MM *EMP* 44
Accts Sva Cpas Sc
SIC 1542 1522 Commercial & office building contractors; Residential construction
CEO: John Faust
* *Pr:* Daniel Fitzgerald

D-U-N-S 02-866-4472 IMP
■ HORIZON DISTRIBUTORS INC
(*Suby of* POOL CORP) ★
5214 S 30th St, Phoenix, AZ 85040-3730
Tel (480) 337-6700 *Founded/Ownrshp* 2005
Sales 265.5MM^E *EMP* 427
SIC 4971 5083 Irrigation systems; Farm & garden machinery; Irrigation equipment
Pr: James W Ross
* *Treas:* Terry Speth
* *VP:* Mark W Joslin
* *VP:* Manuel J Perez De La Mesa
* *VP:* Stephen C Nelson
Genl Mgr: Colleen Knoll
Sls Mgr: Chris Husband
Sls Mgr: Scott Jones
Sales Asso: Jeff Bauer
Board of Directors: Manuel J Perez De La Mesa

D-U-N-S 04-460-1899
HORIZON ENERGY SERVICES LLC
203 E 80th St, Stillwater, OK 74074-8368
Tel (405) 533-4800 *Founded/Ownrshp* 2011
Sales 223.7MM^E *EMP* 350
Accts Wilsey Meyer Eatmon Tate Pllc
SIC 1381 Drilling oil & gas wells

D-U-N-S 12-210-0829
HORIZON FOOD SERVICE INC
BURGER KING
6101 S 58th St Ste B, Lincoln, NE 68516-3652
Tel (402) 421-6400 *Founded/Ownrshp* 1983
Sales 36.7MM^E *EMP* 1,200
SIC 5812 Fast-food restaurant, chain
Pr: Dennis Erickson
* *VP:* Dave Schmidt

D-U-N-S 07-980-1125
▲ HORIZON GLOBAL CORP
2600 W Big Beaver Rd # 555, Troy, MI 48084-3323
Tel (248) 593-8820 *Founded/Ownrshp* 2015
Sales 575.5MM *EMP* 2,700^E
Tkr Sym HZN *Exch* NYS
SIC 3714 3711 5531 Trailer hitches, motor vehicle; Motor vehicle electrical equipment; Wreckers (tow truck), assembly of; Automobile & truck equipment & parts
Ch Bd: A Mark Zeffiro
Ch Bd: Samuel Valenti III
Pr: John Aleva
Pr: Carl Bizon
CFO: David Rice
Sr VP: Paul Caruso
VP: Maria Duey
VP: Jay Goldbaum
Board of Directors: David C Dauch, Richard L Devore, Denise Ilitch, Richard D Siebert

D-U-N-S 02-915-8008 IMP
HORIZON GROUP USA INC (NJ)
45 Technology Dr, Warren, NJ 07059-5184
Tel (908) 810-1111 *Founded/Ownrshp* 2000
Sales 220.2MM^E *EMP* 404
SIC 5092 Toys & hobby goods & supplies
Pr: James H Cash
Pr: Evan Buzzerio
CFO: Holli Gabler
Ex VP: Cara A Costa
Ex VP: Lawrence Fine
VP: Connie Greene
VP: Roshan Wijerama
VP Mktg: Hiu Lee
Art Dir: John Shammas
Snr Mgr: Dusti Gecz

D-U-N-S 60-859-0105
■ HORIZON HEALTH CORP
(*Suby of* PSYCHIATRIC SOLUTIONS INC) ★
1965 Lakepointe Dr # 100, Lewisville, TX 75057-6424
Tel (972) 420-8200 *Founded/Ownrshp* 2007
Sales 166.7MM^E *EMP* 2,914
SIC 8093 8069 Rehabilitation center, outpatient treatment; Alcoholism rehabilitation hospital; Drug addiction rehabilitation hospital
Pr: Joey A Jacobs
Pr: Jack Devaney
CFO: Jack E Polson
Chf Mktg O: Bill Mulcahy
VP: Steven T Davidson
* *VP:* Christopher L Howard
VP: Joyce Keegan
VP: Matthew Lisagor
VP: Brent Turner
VP: Anthony J Vadella
IT Man: James Bass

D-U-N-S 15-413-1924
HORIZON HEALTHCARE PLAN HOLDING
HMO BLUE
(*Suby of* HORIZON BLUE CROSS BLUE SHLD) ★
3 Penn Plz E Ste 15-D, Newark, NJ 07105-2258
Tel (973) 466-4000 *Founded/Ownrshp* 1984
Sales 1.1MMM *EMP* 575
SIC 8011 Health maintenance organization
* *Pr:* Christy Bell
* *Treas:* Robert Pures
IT Man: Mitchell Slade

D-U-N-S 00-256-9564
HORIZON HEALTHCARE SERVICES INC
HORIZON BLUE CROSS BLUE SHLD
3 Penn Plz E Ste 1, Newark, NJ 07105-2200
Tel (973) 466-4000 *Founded/Ownrshp* 1932
Sales NA *EMP* 4,700
SIC 6324 6411 6321 Hospital & medical service plans; Health maintenance organization (HMO), insurance only; Group hospitalization plans; Dental insurance; Insurance agents, brokers & service; Accident & health insurance
CEO: Robert A Marino
* *COO:* Kevin P Conlin
* *CFO:* Robert J Pures
* *Ex VP:* Christy W Bell
Ex VP: Christy Bell
Ex VP: Kevin Conlin
* *Sr VP:* Mark Barnard
* *Sr VP:* Douglas E Blackwell
* *Sr VP:* Margaret Coons
* *Sr VP:* Christopher M Lepre
* *Sr VP:* Linda A Willett
VP: Joseph Albano
VP: Charlie Bowles
VP: Donna Celestini
VP: Michael Considine
VP: William Frantel
VP: Patrick Geraghty
VP: Tim Hahn
VP: Dave Huber
VP: Gary Lin
VP: Robert Meehan

D-U-N-S 14-432-4571 IMP/EXP
HORIZON HOBBY LLC
4105 Fieldstone Rd, Champaign, IL 61822-8800
Tel (217) 352-1913 *Founded/Ownrshp* 1985
Sales 213.0MM^E *EMP* 700
SIC 5092 Hobby goods
CEO: Joe Ambrose
* *CFO:* Roger Rhodes
CFO: Jason Trybom
* *Ch:* Rick L Stephens
* *Ex VP:* Kurt Bock
* *Ex VP:* Janet Ottmers
VP: Ed Delaporte
VP: John Easley
* *VP:* Steve Hall
Dir Risk M: Brian Reinhart
Off Mgr: Terri Kirby

D-U-N-S 08-296-4847
HORIZON HOLDINGS INC (NE)
6101 S 58th St Ste B, Lincoln, NE 68516-3652
Tel (402) 421-6400 *Founded/Ownrshp* 1985
Sales 24.4MM^E *EMP* 1,000
SIC 5812 Fast-food restaurant, chain
Pr: Dennis Ericson

D-U-N-S 62-510-8956
HORIZON HOLDINGS LLC
1 Bush St Ste 650, San Francisco, CA 94104-4412
Tel (415) 788-2000 *Founded/Ownrshp* 1989
Sales 86.4MM^E *EMP* 515
SIC 6799 2053 Investment clubs; Cakes, bakery: frozen

D-U-N-S 07-146-1362
HORIZON HOUSE INC
120 S 30th St, Philadelphia, PA 19104-3403
Tel (215) 386-3838 *Founded/Ownrshp* 1952
Sales 11.7MM *EMP* 1,200
Accts Bdo Usa Llp Philadelphia Pa
SIC 8361 6512 8322 8093 Rehabilitation center, residential: health care incidental; Commercial & industrial building operation; Individual & family services; Specialty outpatient clinics
Ch: Gabriel Ross
* *Ch Bd:* Gregory O Bruce
* *Pr:* Jeffrey W J Wilush
* *CFO:* Jeff Wilush
* *Sr VP:* Gerald F Skillings
* *VP:* Thomas L Bailey
* *VP:* David C Dunbeck
Exec: Denise Bernier
MIS Dir: Kariemah White-Mack
IT Man: Erv Martin
Pgrm Dir: Theresa Murphy

D-U-N-S 19-330-5187
■ HORIZON LINES HOLDING CORP
(*Suby of* MATSON ALASKA INC) ★
2550 W Tyvola Rd Ste 530, Charlotte, NC 28217-0158
Tel (704) 973-7000 *Founded/Ownrshp* 2008
Sales 76.6MM^E *EMP* 1,598
SIC 4731 6512 Freight transportation arrangement; Nonresidential building operators
CFO: M Mark Urbania
Pr: Richard Rodriguez
* *COO:* John V Keenan
* *Ex VP:* Michael T Avara
* *Ex VP:* Michael F Zendan II
* *Sr VP:* William A Hamlin
* *VP:* Marion Davis
VP: Greg Hohm
VP: Gabriel M Serra
* *VP:* Robert S Zuckerman
IT Man: Ryan Schnell

D-U-N-S 12-064-0508 IMP/EXP
HORIZON LINES LLC
2550 W Tyvola Rd Ste 530, Charlotte, NC 28217-0158
Tel (877) 678-7447 *Founded/Ownrshp* 1998
Sales 193.0MM^E *EMP* 1,020
SIC 4424 4783 4731 4412

D-U-N-S 60-471-9690
HORIZON MEDIA INC
75 Varick St Ste 1404, New York, NY 10013-1917
Tel (212) 220-5000 *Founded/Ownrshp* 1988
Sales 161.5MM^E *EMP* 630
SIC 7319 Media buying service
Pr: William A Koenigsberg
Pt: Sarah Baehr
* *COO:* Vincent O'Toole
* *Ofcr:* Taylor Valentine
* *Ofcr:* Rick Watrall
* *Ex VP:* Serena Duff
* *Ex VP:* Marianne Gambelli
* *Ex VP:* Eva Kantrowitz
* *Ex VP:* Rich Simms
Sr VP: Charlotte Cochrane
Sr VP: Michael O'Connor
* *Sr VP:* Jake Phillips
VP: Sarah Bachman
VP: Cherie Calingasan
VP: Tom Closs
VP: Larry Curran
VP: Greg Depalma
VP: Heather Giudice
VP: Michelle Gordon
VP: Jared Gruner
VP: Joe Hadari

D-U-N-S 83-469-0075
HORIZON NJ HEALTH
HORIZON BLUE CROSS BLUE SHIELD
(*Suby of* HORIZON BLUE CROSS BLUE SHLD) ★
210 Silvia St, Ewing, NJ 08628-3242
Tel (609) 718-9001 *Founded/Ownrshp* 1994
Sales NA *EMP* 275
SIC 6321 Mutual accident & health associations
Pr: Karen L Clark
CFO: James Valessio
* *Chf Mktg O:* Mark Calderon
Ex VP: Christy Bell
VP: Jim Albano
VP: Phil Bonaparte
VP: Peggy Coons
VP: Jai Pillai
Dir Rx: Sam Currie
Mktg Dir: Leonard Kudgis
Pharmcst: Jennifer Garmise

D-U-N-S 96-461-3413
HORIZON PHARMA INC
150 Saunders Rd Ste 130, Lake Forest, IL 60045-2585
Tel (224) 383-3000 *Founded/Ownrshp* 2014
Sales 296.9MM *EMP* 304^E
SIC 2834 Pharmaceutical preparations
Pr: Timothy P Walbert
* *CFO:* Paul W Hoelscher
* *Ex VP:* Robert F Carey
Ex VP: Robert Carey
Ex VP: Paul Hoelscher
Ex VP: David Kelly
* *Ex VP:* Barry J Moze
Ex VP: Barry Moze
* *Ex VP:* Jeffrey W Sherman
Ex VP: John Thomas
VP: Brian Anderson
VP: Ken Baker
VP: Brian Beeler
VP: John Devane
VP: Amy Grahn
VP: Ingrid Hoos
VP: Vikram Karani
VP: Jeffrey Kent
VP: Mary Martin
VP: Gerry McCluskey
Assoc Dir: Jon Eller

D-U-N-S 00-892-6255
HORIZON RESOURCES (ND)
317 2nd St W, Williston, ND 58801-5903
Tel (701) 572-2171 *Founded/Ownrshp* 1929
Sales 470.9MM *EMP* 150
Accts Junkermier Clark Campanella
SIC 5172 5541 5411 5191 Petroleum products; Filling stations, gasoline; Convenience stores; Farm supplies; Fertilizers & agricultural chemicals
CEO: Jeff Wagner
* *Ch Bd:* Wagner Harmon
* *Ch Bd:* Dennis Stromme
* *CFO:* James Radtke
* *Sec:* Myron Lee
* *VP:* Les Bean

D-U-N-S 80-898-5204
HORIZON RETAIL CONSTRUCTION
1500 Horizon Dr, Sturtevant, WI 53177-2066
Tel (262) 638-6000 *Founded/Ownrshp* 2005
Sales 161.5MM^E *EMP* 195^E
SIC 1542 Commercial & office building contractors
Pr: Patrick Christensen
COO: Stefanie Martinez
* *VP:* Daniel Siudak
Snr PM: Brent Whiteside

D-U-N-S 79-604-4410
HORIZON SERVICES INC
320 Century Blvd, Wilmington, DE 19808-6270
Tel (302) 762-1200 *Founded/Ownrshp* 1997
Sales 84.4MM^E *EMP* 199
SIC 1711 Plumbing, heating, air-conditioning contractors
Pr: David Geiger
* *VP:* Mark Aitken
Sls Mgr: John Cameron

D-U-N-S 80-461-5438 IMP
HORIZON SOLUTIONS LLC
HOLMES DISTRIBUTORS
175 Josons Dr, Rochester, NY 14623-3440
Tel (585) 274-8235 *Founded/Ownrshp* 2007
Sales 238.5MM^E *EMP* 280
SIC 5063 5085 Electrical apparatus & equipment; Industrial supplies
Pr: Jim Newton
* *Ch Bd:* J Richard Wilson
* *Sec:* Michael C Herrmann
* *Sr VP:* Karen Baker
* *Sr VP:* Kathy Biesecker
* *Sr VP:* Don Harrington
VP: Tim Bridge
* *VP:* Peter B Roby
Area Mgr: Gregg Schorr
IT Man: Denise Baker
Sales Asso: Ed Marcoux

D-U-N-S 93-358-1456
HORIZON TELCOM INC
68 E Main St, Chillicothe, OH 45601-2503
Tel (740) 772-8200 *Founded/Ownrshp* 1995
Sales 109.7MM^E *EMP* 285
SIC 4813 Local telephone communications
Ch Bd: Robert Mc Kell
* *Pr:* Thomas Mc Kell
* *CFO:* Jack Thompson
VP: Joey Holibaugh
Exec: Peter Holland
Genl Mgr: Narty Forde
Netwrk Mgr: Dave Morgan
VP Opers: Joe Corbin

D-U-N-S 80-713-0500
HORIZON THERAPEUTICS INC
RAVICTI
(*Suby of* HORIZON PHARMA INC) ★
150 Saunders Rd Ste 150, Lake Forest, IL 60045-2523
Tel (224) 383-3000 *Founded/Ownrshp* 2015
Sales 113.5MM *EMP* 54
SIC 2834 Pharmaceutical preparations
Pr: Timothy P Walbert
* *CFO:* Paul W Hoelscher
Sr VP: Ashley Gould
VP: Jitendra Ganju
VP: Sylvia Wheeler
Exec: Lissa Quirino
Assoc Dir: Marzena Jurek
Board of Directors: Bo Jesper Hansen, Jake R Nunn, Theodore Schroeder, Daniel G Welch

D-U-N-S 07-609-0232
HORIZON WEST HEALTHCARE INC
(*Suby of* HORIZON WEST INC) ★
4020 Sierra College Blvd # 190, Rocklin, CA 95677-3906
Tel (916) 624-6230 *Founded/Ownrshp* 1977
Sales 47.8MM^E *EMP* 1,810^E
SIC 8051 Convalescent home with continuous nursing care
CEO: Martine D Harmon
Dir Recs: Jeffrey Graine
Dir Recs: Mandy Johnson
* *Sec:* Dennis Roccaforte
Ofcr: Linda Lutz
* *VP:* Bernice Schrabeck
Dir Soc: Vickie Amerson

Dir Soc: Stephanie Barnes
Dir Soc: Jessica Dunn
Dir Soc: Kathryn Galuppo
Dir Soc: Dorothy Lyon
Dir Soc: Debby McFarland

D-U-N-S 60-515-1737
HORIZON WEST INC
4020 Sierra College Blvd, Rocklin, CA 95677-3906
Tel (916) 624-6230 *Founded/Ownrshp* 1987
Sales 99.0MM^E *EMP* 2,500
SIC 8051 Skilled nursing care facilities
Pr: Ken McGuire
**CFO:* Alan MA
Nrsg Dir: Aletta Prinsloo

D-U-N-S 14-478-0996 IMP/EXP
HORIZONS HOLDINGS LLC
HORIZONS WINDOW FASHIONS
(*Suby of* SPRINGS WINDOW FASHIONS LLC) ★
1705 S Waukegan Rd, Waukegan, IL 60085-6700
Tel (800) 858-2352 *Founded/Ownrshp* 2013
Sales 168.5MM^E *EMP* 221
SIC 5023 Window shades; Floor cushion & padding; Resilient floor coverings: tile or sheet
Pr: Russ Voelz
Mktg Dir: Tom Perkowitz

HORIZONS WINDOW FASHIONS
See HORIZONS HOLDINGS LLC

D-U-N-S 00-614-7383
▲ HORMEL FOODS CORP
1 Hormel Pl, Austin, MN 55912-3680
Tel (507) 437-5611 *Founded/Ownrshp* 1891
Sales 9.2MMM *EMP* 20,700
Accts Ernst & Young Llp Minneapolis
Tkr Sym HRL *Exch* NYS
SIC 2011 2013 2032 Meat packing plants; Sausages from meat slaughtered on site; Hams & picnics from meat slaughtered on site; Frankfurters from meat slaughtered on site; Canned meats (except baby food) from purchased meat; Beef stew from purchased meat; Corned beef from purchased meat; Spreads, sandwich: meat from purchased meat; Chili with or without meat: packaged in cans, jars, etc.
Pr: James Snee
Genl Pt: David Goettsch
**Ch Bd:* Jeffrey M Ettinger
V Ch: Kim Bruggeman
Pr: Steven G Binder
Pr: Deanna T Brady
COO: Michael J Guanella
**CFO:* Jody H Feragen
**CFO:* James N Sheehan
**Treas:* Roland G Gentzler
Treas: Eldon Quam
Ex VP: Ronald Fielding
Grp VP: Glenn R Leitch
Grp VP: Larry L Vorpahl
Sr VP: Bryan D Farnsworth
Sr VP: Lawrence C Lyons
**Sr VP:* Lori J Marco
Sr VP: Kevin L Myers
VP: Steve Althaus
VP: Brett Asleson
VP: Jeffrey R Baker

D-U-N-S 60-838-9115
■ HORMEL FOODS CORPORATE SERVICES LLC
(*Suby of* HORMEL FOODS CORP) ★
1 Hormel Pl, Austin, MN 55912-3680
Tel (507) 437-5611 *Founded/Ownrshp* 2004
Sales 112.2MM^E *EMP* 500
SIC 5147 Meats & meat products
VP Mktg: Whitney Velasco-Aznar
Corp Couns: Sarah Nelsen

D-U-N-S 00-725-7603 IMP/EXP
HORNADY MANUFACTURING CO
3625 W Old Potash Hwy, Grand Island, NE 68803-4905
Tel (308) 382-1390 *Founded/Ownrshp* 1949
Sales 139.8MM^E *EMP* 260
SIC 3482 3559 3483 Small arms ammunition; Ammunition & explosives, loading machinery; Ammunition, except for small arms; Ammunition loading & assembling plant
Pr: Steve Hornady
COO: Steve Hordy
CFO: Mark Kroeker
**VP:* Jason Hornady
Genl Mgr: Scott Catlett
Genl Mgr: Scott Javins
Genl Mgr: Lance Zobel
Sfty Mgr: Matt Spencer
Sfty Mgr: Doug Wilkinson

D-U-N-S 94-729-9590
▲ HORNBECK OFFSHORE SERVICES INC
103 Northpark Blvd # 300, Covington, LA 70433-6111
Tel (985) 727-2000 *Founded/Ownrshp* 1997
Sales 476.0MM *EMP* 1,233
Tkr Sym HOS *Exch* NYS
SIC 4499 Boat & ship rental & leasing, except pleasure; Chartering of commercial boats
Ch Bd: Todd M Hornbeck
COO: Carl G Annessa
CFO: James O Harp Jr
Ex VP: John S Cook
Ex VP: Samuel A Giberga
VP Bus Dev: Larry Francios
CIO: Eduardo Alfaro
Counsel: Michael J Nicaud
Board of Directors: Larry D Hornbeck, Bruce W Hunt, Steven W Krablin, Patricia B Melcher, Kevin M Meyers, John T Rynd, Bernie W Stewart, Nicholas L Swyka Jr

D-U-N-S 02-604-7410 EXP
■ HORNBECK OFFSHORE SERVICES LLC
HOS
(*Suby of* HORNBECK OFFSHORE SERVICES INC) ★
103 Northpark Blvd # 300, Covington, LA 70433-6111
Tel (985) 727-2000 *Founded/Ownrshp* 1996
Sales 115.5MM^E *EMP* 700^E
SIC 1382 Oil & gas exploration services
Pr: Todd M Hornbeck
**Treas:* Mark S Myrtue
**Ex VP:* Carl G Annessa
**Ex VP:* John S Cook
**Ex VP:* Samuel A Giberga
**Ex VP:* James O Harp Jr

HORNBLOWER CRUISES & EVENT
See HORNBLOWER YACHTS LLC

D-U-N-S 06-656-9823
HORNBLOWER YACHTS LLC
HORNBLOWER CRUISES & EVENT
On The Embarcadero Pier 3 St Pier, San Francisco, CA 94111
Tel (415) 788-8866 *Founded/Ownrshp* 1980
Sales 115.1MM^E *EMP* 1,000
Accts Rina Accountacy Corporation C
SIC 4489 Excursion boat operators
CEO: Terry Macrae
COO: Michael Burke
VP: Cindee Beechwood
VP: Cameron Clark
VP: Scott Thornton
VP: Jim Unger
Genl Mgr: Jill Benson
Genl Mgr: Kevin Lorton
Natl Sales: Joy Liu
S&M/VP: Annabella Stagner
Sls Mgr: Monica Antola

D-U-N-S 07-507-1546
HORNE LLP
HORNE WEALTH ADVISORS
1020 Highland Colony Pkwy # 400, Ridgeland, MS 39157-2129
Tel (601) 948-0940 *Founded/Ownrshp* 2003
Sales 91.0MM^E *EMP* 479
SIC 8721 8742 Certified public accountant; Financial consultant
Pt: Hugh J Parker
**Pt:* Wendy F Eversole
COO: Terry Traylor
Snr Mgr: Thomas W Prewitt

HORNE WEALTH ADVISORS
See HORNE LLP

D-U-N-S 04-602-9518 IMP/EXP
HORNERXPRESS INC
5755 Powerline Rd, Fort Lauderdale, FL 33309-2001
Tel (954) 772-6966 *Founded/Ownrshp* 1969
Sales 119.7MM^E *EMP* 200^E
SIC 5091 3949 3561 Swimming pools, equipment & supplies; Spa equipment & supplies; Sporting & athletic goods; Pumps & pumping equipment
Pr: William A Kent
COO: Ross Champion
**Treas:* Gary Chisling
Genl Mgr: Chuck Schilling
CTO: William Ken

D-U-N-S 04-085-4601 IMP/EXP
HORNERXPRESS-SOUTH FLORIDA INC
AUTO PILOT
5755 Powerline Rd, Fort Lauderdale, FL 33309-2001
Tel (800) 432-6966 *Founded/Ownrshp* 1969
Sales 232.9MM^E *EMP* 400
SIC 5091 Swimming pools, equipment & supplies
COO: Sean Assam
**VP:* Don Detwiler
VP: Mike Dooley
**VP:* Darren Goldstein
**VP:* Eric Levine

D-U-N-S 11-313-3953
HORNOR TOWNSEND & KENT INC
(*Suby of* PENN MUTUAL LIFE INSURANCE CO) ★
600 Dresher Rd, Horsham, PA 19044-2204
Tel (215) 957-7300 *Founded/Ownrshp* 1969
Sales 84.9MM^E *EMP* 1,100
SIC 6211 Security brokers & dealers
Pr: Michelle A Barry
**Treas:* Stacey N Polakowski
Ex VP: Joseph Radovic
VP: Greg Driscoll
VP: Rob Lazarus
**VP:* Nancy S Rush
IT Man: Ravi Patel
Sls Mgr: Michael Sidoti

D-U-N-S 06-221-5777
HORRY COUNTY SCHOOL DISTRICT
335 Four Mile Rd, Conway, SC 29526-4506
Tel (843) 488-6700 *Founded/Ownrshp* 1952
Sales 472.8MM *EMP* 5,000
Accts Mcgregor & Company Llp Colum
SIC 8211 Public elementary & secondary schools
Ofcr: William Latham
Ex Dir: Sandra Cannon
Ex Dir: Donna Gramstad
Ex Dir: Arlene Ray
Ex Dir: Melissa Schamel
Ex Dir: Denise Vereen
Off Mgr: Katie Bomyea
IT Man: David Knight
Pr Dir: Teal Harding
Teacher Pr: Mary Anderson

D-U-N-S 00-978-8811
HORRY TELEPHONE COOPERATIVE INC
H T C
3480 Highway 701 N, Conway, SC 29526-5702
Tel (843) 365-2151 *Founded/Ownrshp* 1952
Sales 161.0MM *EMP* 690
SIC 4813 4841 7382 ; Local & long distance telephone communications; Cable & other pay television services; Security systems services
Ch Bd: Charles Whaoey
**Ch Bd:* Charles Whaley
**CEO:* Mike Hagg
**CFO:* Duane Carlton Lewis Jr
**Treas:* Cynthia Cannon
**VP:* Delain Stevens
Telecom Ex: Nicole Clark
CIO: Sid Blackwelder
Dir IT: Jim Forbes
IT Man: Jennifer Anderson
IT Man: Norma Carvalho

D-U-N-S 60-907-4703 IMP/EXP
HORSEHEAD CORP
(*Suby of* HORSEHEAD HOLDING CORP) ★
4955 Steubenville Pike, Pittsburgh, PA 15205-9604
Tel (724) 774-1020 *Founded/Ownrshp* 2004
Sales 303.1MM^E *EMP* 418^E
SIC 3339 3629 Zinc smelting (primary), including zinc residue; Mercury arc rectifiers (electrical apparatus)
Pr: James M Hensler
**Pr:* James Hensler
**Sr VP:* Greg Belland
VP: William Flatley
VP: Richard Krablin
**VP:* Robert Scherich
Genl Mgr: Charles Brehm
Dir IT: Mark Drobka
Dir IT: John Pusateri
VP Opers: Bob Elwell
Opers Supe: Jim Allen

D-U-N-S 80-708-0077
HORSEHEAD HOLDING CORP
4955 Steubenville Pike, Pittsburgh, PA 15205-9604
Tel (724) 774-1020 *Founded/Ownrshp* 2003
Sales 414.9MM *EMP* 747
SIC 3339 Primary nonferrous metals; Zinc refining (primary), including slabs & dust; Zinc smelting (primary), including zinc residue; Nickel refining (primary)
Ch Bd: James M Hensler
Ofcr: Timothy D Boates
Sr VP: Ali Alavi
VP: Lee Burkett
VP: Ryan J Hutchison
VP: Ryan Hutchison
VP: Gary R Whitaker
Exec: Bruce Morgan
VP Sls: James A Totera

HORSESHOE BOSSIER CITY
See HORSESHOE ENTERTAINMENT

HORSESHOE CASINO HOTEL
See CAESARS RIVERBOAT CASINO LLC

D-U-N-S 82-524-8073
■ HORSESHOE ENTERTAINMENT
HORSESHOE BOSSIER CITY
(*Suby of* CAESARS ENTERTAINMENT CORP) ★
711 Horseshoe Blvd, Bossier City, LA 71111-4472
Tel (318) 742-0711 *Founded/Ownrshp* 2004
Sales 71.5MM^E *EMP* 2,532
SIC 7011 Casino hotel
Genl Pt: Harriahs Ent
CFO: David Eisendrath
IT Man: Jamie Fretwell
IT Man: John Rohrer
Secur Mgr: Greg Jackson
Mktg Dir: Scott Harris

D-U-N-S 84-313-6821 IMP
■ HORSESHOE HAMMOND LLC
(*Suby of* CAESARS ENTERTAINMENT CORP) ★
777 Casino Center Dr, Hammond, IN 46320-1003
Tel (866) 711-7463 *Founded/Ownrshp* 1992
Sales 43.5MM^E *EMP* 1,700
SIC 7999 5947 5812 Gambling establishment; Gift, novelty & souvenir shop; Eating places
**Pr:* Gary Loveman
**VP:* Thomas Lambrecht

D-U-N-S 09-873-1318
HORST GROUP INC
320 Granite Run Dr, Lancaster, PA 17601-6806
Tel (717) 560-1919 *Founded/Ownrshp* 1979
Sales 153.5MM^E *EMP* 360
SIC 1542 1541 6531 Commercial & office building, new construction; Industrial buildings, new construction; Real estate agents & managers
Pr: Randall L Horst
**VP:* Richard A Watson Jr
Mng Dir: Shirlee Barlow
CIO: Dale Frankhouser

D-U-N-S 03-034-3689 IMP/EXP
HORTIFRUT IMPORTS INC
(*Suby of* HORTIFRUT S.A.)
9450 Corkscrew Palms Cir, Estero, FL 33928-6422
Tel (239) 552-4453 *Founded/Ownrshp* 2010
Sales 123.4MM *EMP* 35^E
Accts Davidson & Nick Cpas Naples
SIC 5148 Fruits, fresh
Ch: Victor Moller
**Pr:* Gonzalo Canessa
**VP:* Aribel Aguirre-Beck
VP: Aribel Beck

D-U-N-S 02-406-4040 IMP
HORTON FRUIT CO INC (KY)
4701 Jennings Ln, Louisville, KY 40218-2967
Tel (502) 969-1371 *Founded/Ownrshp* 1940
Sales 94.3MM^E *EMP* 175
SIC 5148 Fruits, fresh; Vegetables, fresh
Pr: Albert C Horton
**Treas:* Steve Edelen
**VP:* William R Benoit
Exec: Bill Benoit
Exec: Norma Wood
Plnt Mgr: John Belcher

D-U-N-S 08-587-2497
HORTON GROUP INC
HORTON INSURANCE AGENCY
10320 Orland Pkwy, Orland Park, IL 60467-5658
Tel (708) 845-3000 *Founded/Ownrshp* 1971
Sales NA *EMP* 350
SIC 6411 6331 6321 6311 Insurance agents, brokers & service; Fire, marine & casualty insurance; Accident & health insurance; Life insurance
Prin: Ronald R Assise
Mng Pt: Andy Baskel
Pr: Tom Cassady
Pr: Tim Graham
**Pr:* Glenn M Horton
Pr: Rob McIntyre
**Pr:* Steven J Topel
**COO:* George Daly
**CFO:* Jim Farmer
CFO: Tim Scott
Ex VP: Rae Beaudry
Sr VP: Bob Dechene
Sr VP: Paul Johnson
Sr VP: Jeff Kaminski
Sr VP: Luis Paz
Sr VP: Paul Shaheen
Sr VP: Ken Tidwell
Sr VP: Mike Wojcik
Sr VP: Edward Young
VP: Gary Fitzgerald
VP: Tony Hopkins

D-U-N-S 15-336-9228
HORTON INDUSTRIES INC
101 Industrial Blvd, Eatonton, GA 31024-7254
Tel (706) 485-8506 *Founded/Ownrshp* 1984
Sales 172.2MM^E *EMP* 1,481^E
SIC 2451 5271 Mobile homes; Mobile homes
Pr: N Dudley Horton Jr
**Sec:* Maude H Hicks
**VP:* Steve Sinclair
Sls Mgr: Dan Haley

HORTON INSURANCE AGENCY
See HORTON GROUP INC

D-U-N-S 04-894-5005
HORTON VANS INC (GA)
(*Suby of* HORTON INDUSTRIES INC) ★
130 Coleman Dr, Eatonton, GA 31024-6703
Tel (706) 923-2900 *Founded/Ownrshp* 1998, 1987
Sales 136.8MM^E *EMP* 1,450
SIC 3713 3792 Car carrier bodies; Travel trailers & campers
Pr: N Dudley Horton Jr

D-U-N-S 96-903-9846
HORTONWORKS INC
5470 Great America Pkwy, Santa Clara, CA 95054-3644
Tel (408) 916-4121 *Founded/Ownrshp* 2011
Sales 121.9MM *EMP* 850
Tkr Sym HDP *Exch* NGS
SIC 7372 Prepackaged software
Ch Bd: Robert Bearden
Pr: Herbert Cunitz
Pr: Steven Dean
Pr: Jamie Engesser
Pr: Brian Marshall
Pr: Ferguson Mitch
CFO: Scott Davidson
Ofcr: ARI Zilka
VP: Kamal Brar
VP: Shaun Connolly
VP: Tim Hall
VP: Bob Page
VP: Christopher Prophett
VP: Scott Reasoner
VP: Ulf Sandberg
Board of Directors: Peter Fenton, Martin Fink, Kevin Klausmeyer, Jay Rossiter, Michelangelo Volpi

HOS
See HORNBECK OFFSHORE SERVICES LLC

D-U-N-S 00-283-6013
HOS BROTHERS CONSTRUCTION INC
7733 W Bostian Rd, Woodinville, WA 98072-9787
Tel (425) 481-5569 *Founded/Ownrshp* 1955, 1982
Sales 84.9MM^E *EMP* 400
SIC 1611 1629 Grading; Earthmoving contractor
Pr: John Caunt
**VP:* Branston J Weyer
Sfty Dirs: Kate Wicks

D-U-N-S 06-158-6129 IMP/EXP
HOSHIZAKI AMERICA INC
(*Suby of* HOSHIZAKI CORPORATION)
618 Highway 74 S, Peachtree City, GA 30269-3016
Tel (770) 487-2331 *Founded/Ownrshp* 1981
Sales 175.9MM^E *EMP* 550
SIC 3585 5078 Ice making machinery; Ice boxes, industrial; Refrigeration equipment & supplies
Pr: Chris Leader
CEO: Tetsuya Yamamoto
Sec: Tatsuya Hirano
Sr VP: Carter Davis
VP: Bill Anderson
VP: Katsutoshi Matsushima
VP: Bob McFarland
Dir Bus: Jon O'Hern
Dist Mgr: Bill Crider
Sls Mgr: Louis Irizarry

D-U-N-S 02-919-9858 IMP
HOSKIN & MUIR INC
CARDINAL SHOWER ENCLOSURES
6611 Preston Ave Ste C, Livermore, CA 94551-5108
Tel (925) 373-1135 *Founded/Ownrshp* 1972
Sales 85.8MM^E *EMP* 240
SIC 5031 Molding, all materials
Pr: Don Ross
**VP:* Mikel Kinser

D-U-N-S 14-463-5182 IMP/EXP
HOSOKAWA MICRON INTERNATIONAL INC
HOSOKAWA MICRON POWDER SYSTEMS
(*Suby of* HOSOKAWA MICRON CORPORATION)
10 Chatham Rd, Summit, NJ 07901-1310
Tel (908) 273-6360 *Founded/Ownrshp* 1986
Sales 45.9MM^E *EMP* 1,500
SIC 3559 Chemical machinery & equipment; Plastics working machinery
Pr: Isao Sato
Pr: Rob Boorhees
Ex VP: Yoshio Hosokawa
Ex VP: Holger Niemeier
Rgnl Mgr: Steve Craig

HOSOKAWA MICRON POWDER SYSTEMS
See HOSOKAWA MICRON INTERNATIONAL INC

D-U-N-S 18-563-5757
HOSPICE ADVANTAGE LLC
(*Suby of* CLOVERLEAF PARTNERS) ★
401 Center Ave Ste 130, Bay City, MI 48708-5939
Tel (989) 891-2200 *Founded/Ownrshp* 2015
Sales 66.9MM^E *EMP* 1,900

SIC 8052 8082 Personal care facility; Home health care services
Pr: Rodney A Hildebrant
Dir Vol: Kris Beatty
Dir Vol: Laynie Humphrey
Dir Vol: Rachel Mayer
Dir Vol: Christine McIntosh
Dir Vol: Jessica Sapp
Dir Vol: Amy Slone
**CFO:* Douglas McGuire
Ex VP: Jeff Lang
VP: Jeremy Bolling
Exec: Julie Wheelock

HOSPICE HM HLTH OLATHE MED CTR
See OLATHE MEDICAL CENTER INC

D-U-N-S 03-989-8978
HOSPICE OF FLORIDA SUNCOAST
SUNCOAST HOSPICE
5771 Roosevelt Blvd # 400, Clearwater, FL 33760-3415
Tel (727) 527-4483 *Founded/Ownrshp* 1977
Sales 102.4MM *EMP* 1,400
Accts Crowe Horwath Llp South Bend
SIC 8399 Health systems agency
Pr: Rafael Sciullo
**CFO:* Anne Hochsprung
**Ch:* Kelli E Hanley Crabb
**Treas:* Charles Whetstone
Trst: Hugh Parker
VP: Lynne Craver
VP: Scott Kistler
VP: Becky McDonald
Exec: Dee Touhey
Ex Dir: William Harper
Netwrk Mgr: Jonathan Boid

D-U-N-S 10-768-7022
HOSPICE OF PALM BEACH COUNTY INC
5300 East Ave, West Palm Beach, FL 33407-2270
Tel (561) 848-5200 *Founded/Ownrshp* 1978
Sales 89.8MM *EMP* 864
Accts Crowe Horwarth Llp South Bend
SIC 8059 Personal care home, with health care
Pr: David Fielding
**COO:* Randy Prange
**CFO:* Richard Calcote
CFO: Gregory M Kiel
**VP:* Fred Watson
Dir Soc: Lauren Barry
Dir Bus: Bob Burwen
Prgrm Mgr: Kathleen Crum
Genl Mgr: Eileen Coursen
CIO: Bivek Pathak
Dir IT: Vicki Rautbord

D-U-N-S 14-876-8732
HOSPICE OF VALLEY
1510 E Flower St, Phoenix, AZ 85014-5698
Tel (602) 530-6900 *Founded/Ownrshp* 1977
Sales 74.7MM^E *EMP* 1,600
Accts Ernst & Young Us Llp Phoenix
SIC 8082 Home health care services
CEO: Susan Levine
Dir Vol: Joy Pesuti
COO: Vicki Hochstetler
Ofcr: Sharon Jones
**Sr VP:* Gregory K Mayer
**Sr VP:* Debbie Shumway
VP: Carol Crockett
VP: Rita Meiser
Exec: Jerry Smithson
Dir Bus: Pattie Palmer
Off Mgr: Jennifer Leslie

D-U-N-S 16-749-1489
HOSPICE OF WESTERN RESERVE INC
17876 Saint Clair Ave, Cleveland, OH 44110-2602
Tel (216) 383-2222 *Founded/Ownrshp* 1978
Sales 88.9MM *EMP* 800
SIC 8059 Personal care home, with health care
CEO: William E Finn
V Ch: James L Hambrick
**CFO:* John E Harvan Jr
Dir: Shareefah Sabur
Sls&Mrk Ex: Jane Van Bergen
Pr Mgr: Kimberly Tutolo
Pharmcst: Wayne Grant
Snr Mgr: Leslie Griffith

D-U-N-S 01-122-3265
HOSPICE TREASURE CHEST
COMMUNITY HOSPICE N E FLORIDA
4266 Sunbeam Rd Ste 100, Jacksonville, FL 32257-2426
Tel (904) 596-6278 *Founded/Ownrshp* 2004
Sales 96.1MM *EMP* 2
SIC 5932 Used merchandise stores

D-U-N-S 14-158-8017 IMP/EXP
■ HOSPIRA INC
(*Suby of* PFIZER INC) ★
275 N Field Dr, Lake Forest, IL 60045-2510
Tel (224) 212-2000 *Founded/Ownrshp* 2015
Sales 4.4MMM *EMP* 19,000
SIC 2834 3841 Pharmaceutical preparations; Proprietary drug products; Tablets, pharmaceutical; Diagnostic apparatus, medical; Medical instruments & equipment, blood & bone work; IV transfusion apparatus
CEO: F Michael Ball
**CFO:* Thomas E Werner
Treas: Karen Hoehne
Ofcr: Serap Erisken
**Sr VP:* Royce R Bedward
Sr VP: Richard Davies
Sr VP: John B Elliot
Sr VP: Sumant Ramachandra
VP: Roger Beglin
VP: Kelly Glivar
VP: Joshua Gordon
VP: Sean Odonnell
VP: Pamela Puryear
VP: Lisa Skeens
VP: Ron Squarer
VP: Leah Taylor
VP: Rohit Vishnoi

D-U-N-S 07-925-8644
HOSPITAL ACQUISITION LLC
5340 Legacy Dr Ste 150, Plano, TX 75024-3131
Tel (469) 241-2100 *Founded/Ownrshp* 2012
Sales 450.6MM^E *EMP* 7,800^E
SIC 8069 8051 Specialty hospitals, except psychiatric; Skilled nursing care facilities
CEO: Kevin Cooper
**Prin:* Twila Loudder

D-U-N-S 07-247-3812
HOSPITAL AUTHORITY OF COLQUITT COUNTY (GA)
COLQUITT REGIONAL MEDICAL CTR
3131 S Main St, Moultrie, GA 31768-6925
Tel (229) 985-3420 *Founded/Ownrshp* 1939
Sales 110.3MM *EMP* 725^E
Accts Draffin & Tucker Llp Albany
SIC 8062 General medical & surgical hospitals
Pr: James R Lowry
V Ch: James Jeter
COO: Robert Howe
COO: Lorene Wallace
CFO: Larry Simms
**CFO:* Larry W Sims
**VP:* Greg K Johnson
**VP:* Shamb Purohit
VP: T Scott Romanowski
VP: Madis Spires
**VP:* Dena Zinker
Dir Lab: Cary Cardwell
Dir Lab: Anthony Moser
Dir Rad: Matthew Paine
Dir Rx: Matthew Clifton
Dir Rx: Wayne Evans

D-U-N-S 07-587-7076
HOSPITAL AUTHORITY OF VALDOSTA AND LOWNDES COUNTY GEORGIA
SOUTH GEORGIA MEDICAL CENTER
2501 N Patterson St, Valdosta, GA 31602-1735
Tel (229) 333-1000 *Founded/Ownrshp* 1955
Sales 310.3MM *EMP* 3,000
SIC 8062 General medical & surgical hospitals
CEO: Randy Sauls
Chf OB: T Hank Moseley
Chf Rad: W Cameron Wright
Treas: Paula Carter
Ofcr: Carolyn Blanton
Netwrk Mgr: Charles Marshburn
Pathlgst: Will Hansen
Obsttrcn: Jerthitia S Taylor Grate
Opthamlgy: Scott Petermann
Doctor: Brook Bearden
Doctor: Wiley Don

HOSPITAL BUILDING & EQP CO
See HBE CORP

D-U-N-S 06-856-9953
HOSPITAL CENTRAL SERVICES INC
2171 28th St Sw, Allentown, PA 18103-7093
Tel (610) 791-2222 *Founded/Ownrshp* 1970
Sales 103.4MM *EMP* 1,200
SIC 8741 Management services
CEO: Peter J Castagna Jr
Pr: J Michael Lee
CFO: Thomas D Fenstermacher
Ex VP: Timothy Crimmins
CIO: Ray D Kehler

D-U-N-S 07-168-4559
HOSPITAL COMMITTEE FOR LIVERMORE-PLEASANTON AREAS
VALLEY CARE HEALTH SYSTEM, THE
(*Suby of* STANFORD LINEAR ACCELERATOR CE) ★
5555 W Las Positas Blvd, Pleasanton, CA 94588-4000
Tel (925) 847-3000 *Founded/Ownrshp* 2015
Sales 171.4MM^E *EMP* 1,200
SIC 8062 8741 General medical & surgical hospitals; Hospital management
CEO: Scott Gregerson
Mng Pt: Michael Ranahan
Trst: Ryan Chance
Ofcr: Felicia Ziomek
VP: Vern Brown
VP: Jessica Jordan
VP: Doreen Maples
VP: Ken Mercer
VP: Cindy Noonan
Exec: Karen Moundsbury
Exec: Magda Ursu
Dir Rx: Dennis Ong

D-U-N-S 85-998-5129
HOSPITAL COMMITTEE FOR LIVERMORE-PLEASANTON AREAS
VALLEYCARE HEALTH SYSTEM
1111 E Stanley Blvd, Livermore, CA 94550-4115
Tel (925) 447-7000 *Founded/Ownrshp* 1994
Sales 269.2MM^E *EMP* 1,000
SIC 8741 Administrative management; Hospital management
CEO: Marcelina L Feit

HOSPITAL COPORATION OF AMERICA
See HCA INC

D-U-N-S 05-066-8656
■ HOSPITAL CORP OF AMERICA
HCA THE HEALTHCARE COMPANY
(*Suby of* HOSPITAL COPORATION OF AMERICA) ★
1 Park Plz, Nashville, TN 37203-6527
Tel (615) 344-9551 *Founded/Ownrshp* 1989
Sales 99.2MM^E *EMP* 800
Accts Ernst & Young Nashville Tn
SIC 8062 8063 General medical & surgical hospitals; Psychiatric hospitals
CEO: R Milton Johnson
**Ch Bd:* Thomas F Frist Jr
**COO:* Jack O Bovender Jr
**Ch:* Richard M Bracken
Sr VP: Thomas H Cato
**Sr VP:* John O Colton
**Sr VP:* Joseph L Di Lorenzo
**Sr VP:* Donald W Fish
Sr VP: Eugene C Fleming
**Sr VP:* Paul J McKnight Jr
Sr VP: Joseph D Moore
Sr VP: Philip R Patton
**VP:* Donald J Israel
Board of Directors: Charles T Harris III, Carl E Reichardt, Frank S Royal, John L Thornton

D-U-N-S 18-985-6404
HOSPITAL DAMAS INC
(*Suby of* DAMAS FOUNDATION, INC)
2213 Ponce Byp, Ponce, PR 00717-1313
Tel (787) 840-8686 *Founded/Ownrshp* 1987
Sales 53.3MM^E *EMP* 1,000
SIC 8062 General medical & surgical hospitals
Pr: Mariano McConnie Angel
**VP:* Dr Felix Colon

D-U-N-S 07-539-4080
HOSPITAL DANBURY INC
24 Hospital Ave, Danbury, CT 06810-6077
Tel (203) 739-7000 *Founded/Ownrshp* 1885
Sales 622.7MM *EMP* 3,000
SIC 8062 Hospital, medical school affiliated with residency
Ch Bd: John M Murphy
**Ch Bd:* James Kennedy
**Ch Bd:* Ervin Shames
**COO:* Michael Daglio
COO: Mike Daglio
Ofcr: Francis Flaherty
**Sr VP:* Moreen O Donahue
**Sr VP:* Matthew A Miller
**Sr VP:* Phyllis F Zappala
Dir Rx: Kathleen Haddy
Dir Rx: Mark Zonenshine

D-U-N-S 10-797-4540
HOSPITAL ESPANOL AUXILIO MUTUO DE PUERTO RICO INC
SOCIEDAD ESPANOLA DE AUXILIO
(*Suby of* SOCIEDAD ESPAOLA DE AUXILIO MUTUO Y BENEFICENCIA DE PUERTO RICO) ★
Ave Ponce De Leon, San Juan, PR 00918-1000
Tel (787) 758-2000 *Founded/Ownrshp* 1992
Sales NA *EMP* 2,000
SIC 6324 Hospital & medical service plans
Pr: Enrique Fierres
**Pr:* Angel Cocero
**Treas:* Luis Cid
**VP:* Amador Perdido
**VP:* Angel Sanchez
**VP:* Donato Vigil
Dir Risk M: Maria Mejias
Prin: Myriam Colon

D-U-N-S 08-333-7360
HOSPITAL FOR SPECIAL CARE
(*Suby of* CENTER OF SPECIAL CARE, INC.)
2150 Corbin Ave, New Britain, CT 06053-2298
Tel (860) 827-4924 *Founded/Ownrshp* 1960
Sales 152.6MM *EMP* 25
Accts Blum Shapiro & Company Pc Cpas
SIC 8069 Chronic disease hospital
Pr: Jhon J Votto
Dir Vol: Lyn Robinson
**Pr:* David Crandall
Pr: Felicia Dedominicis
CFO: Lori Whelen
VP: Carl Ficks
VP: Victoria Golab
VP: George Olt
VP: Jankowski Stan
Exec: Michael Boutot
Dir Risk M: Donna Reinholdt
Dir Rx: Kevin Gatland

HOSPITAL FOR SPECIAL SURGERY
See NEW YORK SOCIETY FOR RELIEF OF RUPTURED AND CRIPPLED MAINTAINING HOSPITAL FOR

D-U-N-S 10-167-7065
HOSPITAL FOR SPECIALTY SURGERY
HANNAFIN, JO MD
535 E 70th St Fl 6, New York, NY 10021-4898
Tel (212) 606-1469 *Founded/Ownrshp* 1992
Sales 750.9MM *EMP* 3
SIC 8011 8062 Offices & clinics of medical doctors; General medical & surgical hospitals
Owner: Jo Hannafin MD

HOSPITAL FORMS & SYSTEMS
See HFS HOLDING CORP

D-U-N-S 80-640-2397
HOSPITAL HIMA SAN PABLO CAGUAS
100 Ave Luis Munoz Marin, Caguas, PR 00725-6184
Tel (787) 653-3434 *Founded/Ownrshp* 2007
Sales 199.1MM *EMP* 1
SIC 8062 General medical & surgical hospitals
Prin: Aixa Rodriguez

D-U-N-S 09-511-1274
HOSPITAL HOUSEKEEPING SYSTEMS INC
811 Barton Springs Rd # 300, Austin, TX 78704-8702
Tel (512) 478-1888 *Founded/Ownrshp* 1975
Sales 64.7MM^E *EMP* 3,200
SIC 7349 Janitorial service, contract basis
CEO: Tom Spry
**COO:* Roy Thorton
**CFO:* Craig Holmes
VP: Bill Rose

D-U-N-S 10-537-5799
HOSPITAL HOUSEKEEPING SYSTEMS LLC
H H S
216 E 4th St, Austin, TX 78701-3610
Tel (512) 478-1888 *Founded/Ownrshp* 2000
Sales 98.4MM^E *EMP* 4,500
SIC 7349 Cleaning service, industrial or commercial
CEO: Joe Terry
Pr: Bruce Moore
CEO: Ryan Williams
COO: Bobby Floyd
CFO: Jared Hughes
CFO: Gary Link
Sr VP: Clay Huntsman
VP: Scott Alexander
VP: Vincent Bartges
VP: Jonathan Beveridge
VP: Dan Franklin
VP: Pat Gaines
VP: Dan Montoya
VP: Ted Peters
VP: Boyd Schultz
VP: Jim Sturman
VP: Brian Weed
Dir Bus: Brad Fellers
Dir Bus: Amy Fritzer
Dir Bus: Zach Hjornevik

HOSPITAL INTERAMERICANO
See CENTRO MEDICO DEL TURABO INC

HOSPITAL METROPOLITANO
See METROPADIA HEALTH SYSTEM INC

D-U-N-S 06-925-5172
HOSPITAL OF CENTRAL CONNECTICUT
(*Suby of* CENTRAL CONNECTICUT HEALTH ALLIANCE INC) ★
100 Grand St, New Britain, CT 06052-2016
Tel (860) 224-5011 *Founded/Ownrshp* 1983
Sales 338.1MM *EMP* 2,500
SIC 8062 General medical & surgical hospitals
Pr: Clarence J Silvia
Chf Rad: Sidney Ulreich
**CFO:* Ralph Becker
Ofcr: Sabrin Gregrich
Ofcr: Matteo J Lopreiato
Ofcr: Debra A Muscio
VP: Pat Hamel
VP: Brian A Rogoz
VP: Bridget A Wheeler
Dir Rad: Kevin W Dickey MD
Dir Rad: Edward Lombardo

D-U-N-S 07-540-6579 IMP
HOSPITAL OF ST RAPHAEL PHYSICIANS IPA II INC (CT)
YALE-NEW HAVEN HOSPITAL SAINT
1450 Chapel St, New Haven, CT 06511-4405
Tel (203) 789-3000 *Founded/Ownrshp* 1907
Sales 198.3MM^E *EMP* 3,426
SIC 8062 8011 Hospital, affiliated with AMA residency; Health maintenance organization
Ch Bd: Sister Barbara Conroy
**Pr:* David Benfer
Ofcr: Nancy Havill
Surgeon: Alfredo Axtmayer
Diag Rad: Jayson Vittori

D-U-N-S 07-873-2894
HOSPITAL OF UNIVERSITY OF PENNSYLVANIA
(*Suby of* CLINICAL PRACTICES OFT) ★
3400 Spruce St Ofc, Philadelphia, PA 19104-4208
Tel (215) 301-3776 *Founded/Ownrshp* 2012
Sales 2.1MMM *EMP* 25^E
SIC 8062 General medical & surgical hospitals
V Ch: Larry Kricka
Assoc Dir: John McCabe
Mng Dir: Colleen Robbins
Prac Mgr: Regina Howard
Prac Mgr: Judith Venuto
Off Mgr: Carol Lockman
Web Dev: Ying Xing
Opers Mgr: Stacie Watkins
Doctor: Dimitry Baranov
Doctor: Lee Goldberg
Doctor: Matthew Levine

D-U-N-S 00-981-5499
HOSPITAL SERVICE DISTRICT 1 INC
WEST JEFFERSON MEDICAL CENTER
1101 Medical Center Blvd, Marrero, LA 70072-3147
Tel (504) 347-5511 *Founded/Ownrshp* 1956
Sales 200.9MM *EMP* 2,000
Accts Bkd Llp Dallas Texas
SIC 8062 General medical & surgical hospitals
CEO: Nancy R Cassagne
CFO: Nancy Bassagne
VP: Theresa Anderson
VP: James Callaghan
VP: Frank Martinez
Exec: Kenneth Coignet
Exec: Scott Goodstal
Dir Surg: Ron Bailey
Dir Sec: Charles Credow
Nurse Mgr: Kristy Bromley
CIO: David Graser

D-U-N-S 06-953-6381
HOSPITAL SERVICE DISTRICT 3 LAFOURCHE PARISH (LA)
THIBODAUX REGIONAL MEDICAL CTR
602 N Acadia Rd, Thibodaux, LA 70301-4823
Tel (985) 493-4740 *Founded/Ownrshp* 1967
Sales 162.6MM *EMP* 800
SIC 8062 8051 8082 General medical & surgical hospitals; Skilled nursing care facilities; Home health care services
**CEO:* Greg Stock
CFO: Steven C Gaubert
Bd of Dir: Jake Giardina
Ofcr: Oliver Bourgeois
Ofcr: Dana Rodrigue
Dir Lab: Anne Guidry
Dir Rx: Monica Sanchez
Prgrm Mgr: Pamela Bledsoe
Off Mgr: Robyn Toups
Nurse Mgr: Ellen Matthews
IT Man: Chris Ford

D-U-N-S 11-742-3277
HOSPITAL SERVICE DISTRICT NO 1
TERREBONNE GENERAL MEDICAL CTR
8166 Main St, Houma, LA 70360-3404
Tel (985) 873-4141 *Founded/Ownrshp* 1954
Sales 189.3MM^E *EMP* 1,400
SIC 8062 General medical & surgical hospitals
Pr: Phyllis Peoples
**VP:* Kevin Ghirardi
**VP:* Sid Hutchinson
VP: Sidney Hutchinson
**VP:* Teresita McNabb
**VP:* Mary Miller
Exec: Rose Cuneo
Dir Lab: Cathy Kohmann
Dir Rad: Michael Muntz

Dir Rx: Cindy Duet
Dir Sec: Dean Marcel

D-U-N-S 07-944-7561
HOSPITAL SERVICE DISTRICT NO 1 OF TANGIPAHOA PARISH
NORTH OAKS HEALTH SYSTEM
15770 Paul Vega Md Dr, Hammond, LA 70403-1475
Tel (985) 230-6934 *Founded/Ownrshp* 1960
Sales 292.7MM *EMP* 1,825
SIC 8062

HOSPITAL SHARED SERVICES
See HSS INC

HOSPITAL SIS OF THE 3RD ORDER
See ST MARYS HOSPITAL

D-U-N-S 05-800-6537
HOSPITAL SISTERS HEALTH SYSTEM
4936 Laverna Rd, Springfield, IL 62707-9797
Tel (217) 523-4747 *Founded/Ownrshp* 1978
Sales 166.7MM *EMP* 1,501
Accts Crowe Horwath Llp Chicago Il
SIC 8082 Home health care services
CEO: Mary Starmann-Perharrison
Chf Rad: Shawn Shekar
Dir Recs: Cathy Moroney
**Pr:* Sister J Trstensky
**COO:* Larry Schumacher
CFO: Patricia Huettl
Treas: James Pawlak
**Sec:* Lisa Rusciolelli
Ofcr: Terri Hernandez
Ofcr: Jay Justice
VP: Lois Klay
VP: Monica Laws
VP: Daniel McCormack
VP: Mark Novak
VP: Brian Reardon
Dir Risk M: Denny Taylor
Dir Lab: Lynn Jelenc
Dir Rad: Steve Sabo
Dir Rx: Michael Murbarger

D-U-N-S 06-873-4466
HOSPITAL UNIONTOWN INC
500 W Berkeley St, Uniontown, PA 15401-5596
Tel (724) 430-5000 *Founded/Ownrshp* 1965
Sales 129.1MM *EMP* 1,100[E]
Accts Bkd Llp Springfield Mo
SIC 8062 General medical & surgical hospitals
CEO: Steve Handy
VP: Dan Glover
Dir Rx: Bill Johnson
Chf Nrs Of: Rebecca Amberosini
Adm Dir: Elaine Bell
Ex Dir: Betty Rock
CIO: Tricia Tomich
CTO: Jeffrey Frye
Mktg Dir: Karen Deicas
Pr Dir: Karen Deicaf
Nrsg Dir: Sue A Milsom

HOSPITAL-NORTH MISS MED CTR
See NORTH MISSISSIPPI HEALTH SERVICES INC

D-U-N-S 80-804-1045
HOSPITALISTS MANAGEMENT GROUP LLC
COGENT-HMG
(*Suby of* HMG HOLDING CORP) ★
4535 Dressler Rd Nw, Canton, OH 44718-2545
Tel (866) 464-7497 *Founded/Ownrshp* 2011
Sales 89.4MM[E] *EMP* 560[E]
SIC 8741 Hospital management
**CFO:* Susan Brownie
Chf Mktg O: Ronnie Jacobs MD
Chf Mktg O: M F Maida MD
Ofcr: Michael Friedlander MD
Ofcr: Ronald Greeno
Ofcr: Russell L Holman
Ofcr: Julia Wright MD
VP: Andrea Funk
**VP:* David Hess
VP: Elizabeth Yanko

D-U-N-S 61-136-5479
HOSPITALITY INVESTMENTS LIMITED PARTNERSHIP
3808 N Sullivan Rd # 34, Spokane Valley, WA 99216-1608
Tel (509) 928-3736 *Founded/Ownrshp* 1989
Sales 57.7MM[E] *EMP* 1,200
SIC 6799 Real estate investors, except property operators
Genl Pt: Terry Wynia

D-U-N-S 92-687-8810
▲ HOSPITALITY PROPERTIES TRUST
255 Washington St Ste 300, Newton, MA 02458-1634
Tel (617) 964-8389 *Founded/Ownrshp* 1995
Sales 1.9MMM *EMP* 400
Tkr Sym HPT *Exch* NGS
SIC 6798 Real estate investment trusts
Pr: John G Murray
Mng Trst: Adam Portnoy
CFO: Mark L Kleifges
Trst: Bruce Gans
Trst: John Harrington
Sr VP: Ethan S Bornstein
VP: Timothy Bonang
VP: Ethan Bornstein
Prin: David Lepore
Genl Mgr: Lou Gatti
DP Exec: Richard Hamm

HOSPITALITY SHOP
See KENT COUNTY MEMORIAL HOSPITAL

D-U-N-S 03-557-5724
HOSPITALITY WEST LLC
PIZZA HUT
745 S Garfield Ave Ste A, Traverse City, MI 49686-3479
Tel (231) 941-5052 *Founded/Ownrshp* 1998
Sales 20.4MM *EMP* 1,800
SIC 5812 Pizzeria, chain

HOSPITALS PRVIDENCE MEM CAMPUS
See TENET HOSPITALS LIMITED

HOSPITLIST MEDICINE PHYSICIANS
See SOUND INPATIENT PHYSICIANS INC

HOSS
See VOSS AUTO NETWORK INC

D-U-N-S 94-386-7507
HOSSS STEAK & SEA HOUSE INC
170 Patchway Rd, Duncansville, PA 16635-8431
Tel (814) 695-7600 *Founded/Ownrshp* 1995
Sales 128.9MM[E] *EMP* 3,000
SIC 5812 5146 5046 Steak restaurant; Seafood restaurants; Fish & seafoods; Restaurant equipment & supplies
Pr: William Bullock
**CEO:* Willard E Campbell
**CFO:* Carl Raup
**VP:* Bob Pleva
VP: Mark Spinazzola
VP Bus Dev: Bill Bratton
Genl Mgr: Bill Glacken
Genl Mgr: Dan Isenberg
Dir IT: Carl Swope
Opers Mgr: Rob Billet
Opers Mgr: Chip Gapshes

D-U-N-S 00-691-9872 EXP
▲ HOST HOTELS & RESORTS INC
6903 Rockledge Dr # 1500, Bethesda, MD 20817-1818
Tel (240) 744-1000 *Founded/Ownrshp* 1929
Sales 5.3MMM *EMP* 240
Tkr Sym HST *Exch* NYS
SIC 6798 7011 Real estate investment trusts; Hotels & motels
Pr: W Edward Walter
**Ch Bd:* Richard E Marriott
CFO: Gregory J Larson
Ex VP: Elizabeth A Abdoo
Sr VP: Christopher Ford
Sr VP: Brian G Macnamara
Sr VP: Alastair McPhail
VP: Marlo Goldstein
VP: Karen Grubber
VP: Carmen Hui
VP: Brian Macnamara
VP: Gus Napoli
VP: Matthew Richardson
VP: Rogerio Souza
VP: Rick Werber
Board of Directors: Mary L Baglivo, Sheila C Bair, Terence C Golden, Ann McLaughlin Korologos, John B Morse Jr, Walter C Rakowich, Gordon H Smith

D-U-N-S 08-072-8152 IMP/EXP
■ HOST HOTELS & RESORTS LP
(*Suby of* HOST HOTELS & RESORTS INC) ★
6903 Rockledge Dr # 1500, Bethesda, MD 20817-1818
Tel (240) 744-1000 *Founded/Ownrshp* 1998
Sales 5.3MMM *EMP* 251
Accts Kpmg Llp Mclean Virginia
SIC 6798 7011 Real estate investment trusts; Hotels
Pr: W Edward Walter
Genl Pt: Host Hotels Resorts
CFO: Gregory J Larson
Sr VP: Jeffrey Clark
Sr VP: Doug Henry
VP: Matthew Ahrens
VP: Kerry Gaber
VP: Doug Link
VP: Larry Oleck
VP: Michael Rock
Exec: Elisa Gois

D-U-N-S 00-690-7646 IMP
HOST INTERNATIONAL INC
(*Suby of* HMSHOST CORP) ★
6905 Rockledge Dr Fl 1, Bethesda, MD 20817-7826
Tel (240) 694-4100 *Founded/Ownrshp* 1914, 1995
Sales 831.9MM[E] *EMP* 23,000
SIC 5812 5813 5994 5947 Snack bar; Fast-food restaurant, chain; Cafeteria; American restaurant; Cocktail lounge; Newsstand; Gift shop
CEO: Tom Fricke
**Pr:* Joe P Martin
**Treas:* Mark T Ratych
VP: Shyam S Dua
Genl Mgr: Larry Jenkins
Snr Mgr: Matt McGill

HOST LANE
See DOTSTER INC

D-U-N-S 93-875-1310
HOST MARRIOTT SERVICES INC
(*Suby of* HMSHOST CORP) ★
6711 Democracy Blvd, Bethesda, MD 20817-1128
Tel (240) 344-1000 *Founded/Ownrshp* 1995
Sales 203.2MM[E] *EMP* 23,000
SIC 7011 Hotels & motels
Pr: William W McCarten

HOSTESS BRANDS
See OLD HB INC

D-U-N-S 07-994-5048
▲ HOSTESS BRANDS INC
1 E Armour Blvd, Kansas City, MO 64111-1201
Tel (816) 701-4600 *Founded/Ownrshp* 2015
Sales 425.3MM[E] *EMP* 2,305[E]
Tkr Sym TWNK *Exch* NAS
SIC 2051 5461 Bread, cake & related products; Cakes; Cookies; Doughnuts; Pastries
Pr: William Toler
**Ch Bd:* C Dean Metropoulos
COO: Stuart Wilcox
CFO: Thomas Peterson
Chf Mktg O: Burke Raine
Ofcr: Michael Cramer
Ofcr: Andrew Jacobs
Sr VP: Jolyn Sebree

D-U-N-S 07-879-7211
■ HOSTESS BRANDS LLC
(*Suby of* HOSTESS BRANDS INC) ★
1 E Armour Blvd, Kansas City, MO 64111-1201
Tel (816) 701-4600 *Founded/Ownrshp* 2013, 2016
Sales 425.1MM[E] *EMP* 1,130
SIC 2051 Bread, cake & related products
Pr: William Toler
**COO:* Stuart Wilcox
**CFO:* Thomas Peterson
**Chf Mktg O:* Burke Raine
**Ex VP:* Michael Cramer
**Sr VP:* Andrew Jacobs
**Sr VP:* Jolyn Sebree

D-U-N-S 07-912-5215
■ HOSTESS HOLDINGS LP
(*Suby of* HOSTESS BRANDS INC) ★
1 E Armour Blvd, Kansas City, MO 64111-1201
Tel (816) 701-4600 *Founded/Ownrshp* 2013
Sales 154.0M[E] *EMP* 1,169[E]
SIC 5461 Cakes

D-U-N-S 06-950-2693
HOSTING.COM INC
900 Suth Broadway Ste 400, Denver, CO 80209
Tel (720) 389-3800 *Founded/Ownrshp* 1997
Sales 110.3MM[E] *EMP* 335[E]
SIC 7379 Computer related consulting services
CEO: Art Zeile
**COO:* Joel Daly
**CFO:* Chris Wheeler
**Ex VP:* Don Barlow
**Ex VP:* Bill Santos
IT Man: Michael Musgrove
Software D: Dan Miller
Mktg Mgr: Jennifer Waymire

D-U-N-S 78-529-2681
HOSTMARK INVESTORS LIMITED PARTNERSHIP
HOSTMARK MANAGEMENT GROUP, THE
1300 E Wdfield Rd Ste 400, Schaumburg, IL 60173
Tel (847) 517-9100 *Founded/Ownrshp* 1994
Sales 122.9MM[E] *EMP* 1,800
SIC 8741 Hotel or motel management
Ex VP: Charles A Gavzer

HOSTMARK MANAGEMENT GROUP, THE
See HOSTMARK INVESTORS LIMITED PARTNERSHIP

D-U-N-S 01-901-1373
HOSTWAY CORP
(*Suby of* LITTLEJOHN & CO LLC) ★
100 N Riverside Plz # 800, Chicago, IL 60606-1564
Tel (312) 238-0125 *Founded/Ownrshp* 1998
Sales 166.2MM[E] *EMP* 347
SIC 4813
CEO: Robert Boles
COO: Bart H De Maertelaere
**COO:* John Martis
CFO: Steven J Armond
**Ex VP:* John Hanjoo
Sr VP: John Enright
**VP:* Todd Benjamin
VP: John Lee
VP: David Newton
**VP:* Mike Robski
VP: Tony Savoy

HOT DOG ON A STICK
See BOHICA LIQUIDATION INC

D-U-N-S 18-055-8207
HOT LINE CONSTRUCTION INC
9020 Brentwood Blvd Ste H, Brentwood, CA 94513-4049
Tel (925) 634-9333 *Founded/Ownrshp* 1986
Sales 224.5MM *EMP* 425
Accts Wayne Long & Co Bakersfield
SIC 1731 1799 Electric power systems contractors; Cable splicing service
Pr: Carol Bade
**CFO:* Kelly G Kutchera
**VP:* Troy Myers
Off Mgr: Cruz Munos

HOT SPOT
See R L JORDAN OIL CO OF NORTH CAROLINA INC

D-U-N-S 87-724-5639
HOT SPRINGS NATIONAL PARK HOSPITAL HOLDINGS LLC
NATIONAL PARK MEDICAL CENTER
(*Suby of* RRCH HEALTHCARE PARTNERS) ★
1910 Malvern Ave, Hot Springs, AR 71901-7752
Tel (501) 321-1000 *Founded/Ownrshp* 2008
Sales 91.5MM[E] *EMP* 900[E]
SIC 8062 General medical & surgical hospitals
CEO: Jerry Mabry
CFO: Robbie Pettey
Dir Rx: William Reeves
Doctor: Ferrell D Hass
Doctor: John R Pace
Doctor: Brenda Powell
Doctor: Gregory Whorton
HC Dir: Tonya Clark

HOT STUFF FOODS
See ORION FOOD SYSTEMS LLC

D-U-N-S 60-322-6986 IMP
HOT TOPIC INC
TORRID
(*Suby of* 212F HOLDINGS LLC)
18305 San Jose Ave, City of Industry, CA 91748-1237
Tel (626) 839-4681 *Founded/Ownrshp* 2013
Sales 3.1MMM[E] *EMP* 5,000
SIC 2326 5632 5699 Men's & boys' work clothing; Apparel accessories; Designers, apparel
CEO: Lisa Harper
CFO: James J McGinty
**CFO:* George Wehlitz
Treas: Brenda Morris
Sr VP: Jeff Allison
Sr VP: Robin Elledge
VP: Cindy Boden
VP: Denise Corey
VP: Hank Henderson
VP: Tricia Higgins
VP: Jerome Kahn
VP: Alain Krakirian
VP: Sue McPherson-Spissu
VP: Sue Spiss
VP: Pam Wallace
Board of Directors: Steven Becker, Evelyn Dan, Matthew Drapkin, Terri Funk Graham, W Scott Hedrick, John Kyees, Andrew Schuon, Thomas Vellios

D-U-N-S 83-247-9419
HOTEL ACQUISITION CO LLC
THAYER LODGING GROUP
1997 Annapolis Exch Pkwy, Annapolis, MD 21401-3271
Tel (410) 268-0515 *Founded/Ownrshp* 2009
Sales 1.7MMM[E] *EMP* 19,100
SIC 8741 7011 Hotel or motel management; Hotels

D-U-N-S 92-780-2868
HOTEL CLEANING SERVICES INC
9609 N 22nd Ave, Phoenix, AZ 85021-1806
Tel (602) 588-0864 *Founded/Ownrshp* 1994
Sales 30.0MM *EMP* 1,500
SIC 7349 Building maintenance services; Building & office cleaning services
Pr: John Knoepker
**CEO:* Debra Knoepker
**VP:* Tim Bottoms
Area Mgr: Sheila Adams
Area Mgr: Manny Cordova

HOTEL DISCOUNT
See HOTELS.COM LP

D-U-N-S 80-563-8272
HOTEL EQUITIES INC
41 Perimeter Ctr E # 510, Atlanta, GA 30346-1910
Tel (770) 934-2170 *Founded/Ownrshp* 2004
Sales 131.7MM[E] *EMP* 700
SIC 6799 8741 Investors; Hotel or motel management
CEO: Frederick W Cerrone
CFO: Alan Bennett
Chf Inves: Dennis Meroney
VP: Chuck Powell
Exec: Algernon Smith
Dir Bus: Garfield Campbell
Dir Bus: Bob Keating
Genl Mgr: Lauren Cato
Genl Mgr: Glynn Knight
Genl Mgr: Andrew Peterson
VP Opers: Rob Cote

HOTEL GROUP, THE
See HOTEL GROUP INC

D-U-N-S 18-864-1849
HOTEL GROUP INC
HOTEL GROUP, THE
201 5th Ave S Ste 200, Edmonds, WA 98020-3481
Tel (425) 771-1788 *Founded/Ownrshp* 1984
Sales 119.7MM[E] *EMP* 1,500
SIC 7011 Hotels & motels
CEO: Douglas N Dreher
Pr: Molly Bruder
**Ex VP:* Lara R Latture
**VP:* Robert E Lee
**Prin:* Edmond A Lee
Rgnl Mgr: Nancy Mark
Brnch Mgr: John Hepner
Genl Mgr: Amanda Anderson
Genl Mgr: Diane Bates
Genl Mgr: Jerry Beach
Genl Mgr: Leonard Clifton

HOTELS & HOSPITALITY GROUP
See JONES LANG LASALLE AMERICAS INC

D-U-N-S 10-729-5169
■ HOTELS.COM LP
HOTEL DISCOUNT
(*Suby of* EXPEDIA INC) ★
5400 Lyndon B Johnson Fwy # 500, Dallas, TX 75240-1019
Tel (214) 361-7311 *Founded/Ownrshp* 2005
Sales 100.3MM[E] *EMP* 1,150
SIC 7389 7375 Reservation services; Hotel & motel reservation service; Information retrieval services
CEO: David Litman
Pr: Scott Booker
CFO: Mel Robinson
Sr VP: Jack Richards
Dir Soc: Becky Williamson
QA Dir: Allison Faucett
Software D: Matt Brown
Mktg Mgr: Brandi Taylor
Sls Mgr: Steven Voisinet
Snr PM: Chase Pleming
Snr Mgr: Lee Nestlerode

D-U-N-S 95-983-4917
HOTH INC
RAVN AIR GROUP
4700 Old Intl Airport Rd, Anchorage, AK 99502-1020
Tel (907) 266-8300 *Founded/Ownrshp* 2015
Sales 91.0MM[E] *EMP* 520[E]
SIC 4522 4512 Flying charter service; Air transportation, scheduled
Pr: Robert Hajdukovich
**Sec:* Michael Hageland

D-U-N-S 16-787-3855 IMP
HOTWIRE COMMUNICATIONS LLC
1 Belmont Ave Ste 1100, Bala Cynwyd, PA 19004-1614
Tel (800) 355-5668 *Founded/Ownrshp* 2005
Sales 105.0MM[E] *EMP* 300[E]
SIC 4813 Telephone communication, except radio
Genl Pt: Kristin Johnson
Rgnl Mgr: Eddie Miranda
Genl Mgr: Marty Mohr
Genl Mgr: Laurie Murphy
Dir IT: Nick Fuhs
Dir IT: Chris Rios
Netwrk Eng: Victor Cooper
VP Sls: Tom Horne
Sls Mgr: Carl Lender

D-U-N-S 00-694-4565 IMP/EXP
HOUCHENS FOOD GROUP INC (KY)
HOUCHENS MARKETS
(*Suby of* HOUCHENS INDUSTRIES INC) ★
700 Church St, Bowling Green, KY 42101-1816
Tel (270) 843-3252 *Founded/Ownrshp* 1918, 1988
Sales 2.2MMM *EMP* 10,335
SIC 5411 5541 5093

D-U-N-S 78-620-4722
HOUCHENS INDUSTRIES INC
700 Church St, Bowling Green, KY 42101-1816
Tel (270) 843-3252 Founded/Ownrshp 1988
Sales 3.2MMM EMP 16,000
Accts Bkd Llp Bowling Green Kentu
SIC 6719 Investment holding companies, except banks; Grocery stores, chain
CEO: James P Gipson
CFO: Gordon Minter
*Treas: Mike Givens
Top Exec: David Burnett
VP: Don Sidwell
Rgnl Mgr: Donnie Gipson
Rgnl Mgr: Jeff Grinstead
Brnch Mgr: Joe Skaggs
Dist Mgr: Keith Sherley
Div Mgr: Alan Walker
Dir IT: David Puvkett
Board of Directors: Chester Gregory, Sarah Glenn Grise, W Ruel Houchens, Peter Mahurin

HOUCHENS MARKETS
See HOUCHENS FOOD GROUP INC

D-U-N-S 00-539-6973 IMP/EXP
HOUGEN MANUFACTURING INC (MI)
3001 Hougen Dr, Swartz Creek, MI 48473-7935
Tel (810) 635-7111 Founded/Ownrshp 1959
Sales 99.9MM^E EMP 130
SIC 5084 3545 3546 3541 Machine tools & metalworking machinery; Drill bits, metalworking; Broaches (machine tool accessories); Power-driven handtools; Machine tools, metal cutting type
CEO: Randall Hougen
*Pr: Gregory Phillips
CFO: Bob Maguffee
*Treas: Therese Y Hougen
*VP: Victor Hougen
Genl Mgr: Mary Chrastek
CTO: Jeffrey Gill
IT Man: Sarah Starkel
Mtls Mgr: Steven Tift
Plnt Mgr: Dan Piggott

D-U-N-S 00-226-1535 IMP/EXP
HOUGHTON INTERNATIONAL INC (PA)
(Suby of GH HOLDINGS INC) ★
945 Madison Ave, Norristown, PA 19403-2306
Tel (610) 666-4000 Founded/Ownrshp 1910, 2012
Sales 577.5MM^E EMP 1,600
SIC 2869 2992 Hydraulic fluids, synthetic base; Lubricating oils & greases
Pr: Paul Devivo
*CFO: Keller Arnold
*Ex VP: Michael J Shannon
*Sr VP: Richard R Lovely
*Sr VP: Dave Slinkman
VP: Bruce R Richards
VP: Charles E Santangelo
VP: Michael Shannon
VP: David Slinkman
VP: Steve M Taylor
Rgnl Mgr: Joe O'Malley

HOUGHTON LAKE HEALTH PARK
See MIDMICHIGAN HEALTH SERVICES

HOUGHTON MIFFLIN HARCOURT
See HOUGHTON MIFFLIN HOLDING CO INC

D-U-N-S 07-848-0960
▲ HOUGHTON MIFFLIN HARCOURT CO
HMH
222 Berkeley St Fl 1-11, Boston, MA 02116-3788
Tel (617) 351-5000 Founded/Ownrshp 2006
Sales 1.4MMM EMP 4,500^E
Tkr Sym HMHC Exch NGS
SIC 3999 2731 Education aids, devices & supplies; Book publishing
Pr: L Gordon Crovitz
*Ch Bd: Lawrence K Fish
Pr: Ellen Archer
CFO: Joseph P Abbott Jr
Chf Mktg O: John K Dragoon
Ofcr: Mary J Cullinane
Ofcr: Bridgett P Paradise
Ex VP: William F Bayers
Ex VP: William Bayers
Ex VP: Timothy L Cannon
Ex VP: Brook M Colangelo
Ex VP: Martin Davy
Ex VP: Rose Else-Mitchell
Ex VP: Margery Mayer
Ex VP: Lee R Ramsayer
Sr VP: Bob Sheridan
VP: Stephen Birnie
VP: Cheryl Cramer
VP: Catherine Crowe-Lile
VP: Paul Donovan
VP: Greg Dumont
Board of Directors: Jill A Greenthal, John F Killian, John R McKernan Jr, Brian Napack, E Rogers Novak Jr, Tracey D Weber

D-U-N-S 96-828-5903
■ HOUGHTON MIFFLIN HARCOURT PUBLISHERS INC
(Suby of HMH) ★
222 Berkeley St Fl 1-11, Boston, MA 02116-3788
Tel (617) 351-5000 Founded/Ownrshp 2013
Sales 1.0MMM^E EMP 3,300^E
SIC 2731 Textbooks: publishing & printing
Pr: Linda Zecher
*CFO: Eric Shuman
*Treas: Joseph Flaherty
*Ex VP: William Bayers
*Sr VP: Michael Dolan

D-U-N-S 00-101-5924 IMP
■ HOUGHTON MIFFLIN HARCOURT PUBLISHING CO
HOUGHTON MIFFLIN PUBLISHING
(Suby of HMH) ★
222 Berkeley St, Boston, MA 02116-3748
Tel (617) 351-5000 Founded/Ownrshp 2002
Sales 1.0MMM^E EMP 3,300
SIC 2731 Books: publishing only; Textbooks: publishing only, not printed on site
Pr: Linda K Zecher
*Pr: Gary Gentel
*Pr: James G Nicholson
*Pr: Lesa Scott
*Treas: Joseph Flaherty
Treas: William Kesler
*Chf Cred: Mary Cullinane
*Chf Mktg O: John K Dragoon
Ex VP: Bill Bayers
*Ex VP: William Bayers
*Ex VP: Tim Cannon
*Ex VP: Joanne Karimi
Sr VP: Lance Benzley
*Sr VP: Brook Colangelo
Sr VP: Catherine Crowelile
*Sr VP: Michael Dolan
Sr VP: James Oneill
*Sr VP: Mark Short
Sr VP: Steve Zukowski
VP: Stephen Birnie
VP: Charlie Christina
Board of Directors: Eric Shuman, Linda Zecher

D-U-N-S 78-709-0096
HOUGHTON MIFFLIN HOLDING CO INC
HOUGHTON MIFFLIN HARCOURT
222 Berkeley St Fl 1-11, Boston, MA 02116-3788
Tel (617) 351-5000 Founded/Ownrshp 2009
Sales NA EMP 3,550
SIC 2731

D-U-N-S 13-202-2513 IMP
HOUGHTON MIFFLIN HOLDINGS INC
222 Berkeley St Fl 1-11, Boston, MA 02116-3788
Tel (617) 351-5000 Founded/Ownrshp 2002
Sales 631.5MM^E EMP 3,550
SIC 2731 Book publishing; Textbooks: publishing only, not printed on site
Ex VP: Stephen Richards
VP: Paul Donovan
VP: Debbie Engel
VP: Donna Ritchie
VP: Ciara Smyth
Assoc Dir: Carla Gray
Sales Exec: Wendy Wooldridge
Mktg Dir: Sue Cowden
Sls Mgr: Kathy Busby
Snr Mgr: Scott Olson

HOUGHTON MIFFLIN PUBLISHING
See HOUGHTON MIFFLIN HARCOURT PUBLISHING CO

D-U-N-S 07-189-4554
▲ HOULIHAN LOKEY INC
10250 Constellation Blvd # 5, Los Angeles, CA 90067-6200
Tel (310) 553-8871 Founded/Ownrshp 1972
Sales 693.7MM EMP 981
Tkr Sym HLI Exch NYS
SIC 6211 6282 Security brokers & dealers; Investment bankers; Investment advice
CEO: Scott L Beiser
*Ch Bd: Irwin N Gold
*Pr: Scott J Adelson
*Pr: David A Preiser
CFO: J Lindsey Alley
VP: Oscar Aarts
VP: Jonathan Adams
VP: Laurent Benshimon
VP: Hector Calzada
VP: Nathan Court
VP: Carey Douglas
VP: Cedric Fontenit
VP: Christopher Glad
VP: Ryan Goldenberg
VP: Juan Guzman
VP: Cory Hebenstreit
VP: James Holmes
VP: Deirdre Johnson
VP: Mark Johnson
VP: Paul Mallarkey
VP: Brian Miller
Board of Directors: Ron K Barger, Jacqueline Kosecoff, Robert J B Lenhardt, Robert A Schriesheim, Bennet Van De Bunt, Paul E Wilson

D-U-N-S 04-509-2277
HOULIHANS RESTAURANTS INC
8700 State Line Rd # 100, Leawood, KS 66206-1572
Tel (913) 901-2500 Founded/Ownrshp 1972
Sales 206.2MM^E EMP 4,200
SIC 5812 5813 Restaurant, family: chain; Cocktail lounge
CEO: Robert Hartnett
*Pr: Brian Dailey
*CFO: Robert Ellis
Exec: Kristina Driver
Dir IT: Jason Clark
VP Mktg: Jen Gulvik
Mktg Mgr: Amanda Stone
Mktg Mgr: Chris Wirt

D-U-N-S 80-842-7327
■ HOURGLASS HOLDINGS LLC
(Suby of US SILICA HOLDINGS INC) ★
8490 Progress Dr Ste 300, Frederick, MD 21701-4996
Tel (301) 682-0600 Founded/Ownrshp 2007
Sales 452.5MM^E EMP 701
SIC 1446 Silica sand mining
CEO: Bryan Shinn
*Treas: Michael Thompson
*Sec: Christine Marshall

HOUSE OF BLUES
See HOB ENTERTAINMENT LLC

D-U-N-S 02-951-9725
HOUSE OF FABRICS INC
FABRICLAND
(Suby of JO-ANN FABRICS & CRAFTS) ★
5555 Darrow Rd, Hudson, OH 44236-4011
Tel (330) 656-2600 Founded/Ownrshp 1998
Sales 69.5MM^E EMP 3,000
SIC 5949 5945 5722 Fabric stores piece goods; Sewing supplies; Notions, including trim; Arts & crafts supplies; Sewing machines
Ch Bd: Alan Rosskamm
V Ch: Robert Norton
*Treas: James Kerr
Sr VP: Anthony C Dissinger
Sr VP: Fred Johnson
*Sr VP: Betty Rosskamm
Sr VP: Justin Zimmerman
VP: David Bolen
*VP: Brian Carney
VP: Peter El Ginol
VP: John Stec
*VP: Donald Tomoff
Comm Dir: Thomas E Connors

D-U-N-S 03-945-6348
HOUSE OF LA ROSE CLEVELAND INC (OH)
6745 Southpointe Pkwy, Brecksville, OH 44141-3267
Tel (440) 746-7500 Founded/Ownrshp 1979
Sales 116.7MM^E EMP 210
SIC 5181 Beer & other fermented malt liquors
Ch Bd: Thomas A La Rose
*Pr: James P La Rose
*V Ch Bd: Joseph F La Rose
*VP: Peter C La Rose
Exec: Al Scott
Dir IT: Dan Brinegar
IT Man: Fred Stewart
Sls Mgr: Mike Graves
Sls Mgr: Dave Mansky

D-U-N-S 00-319-9346 IMP/EXP
HOUSE OF RAEFORD FARMS INC
(Suby of NASH JOHNSON & SONS FARMS INC) ★
1000 E Central Ave, Raeford, NC 28376-3039
Tel (910) 289-6900 Founded/Ownrshp 1958, 1925
Sales 1.0MMM^E EMP 6,000
Accts Morre Stephens Frost Cpa
SIC 2015 Turkey, slaughtered & dressed; Turkey, processed: frozen; Chicken, slaughtered & dressed; Chicken, processed: frozen
Pr: Donald Taber
*CEO: Robert Johnson
CFO: Mike McLeod
*CFO: Ken Qualls
*Ch: Marvin Johnson
Treas: Doug Senogles
VP: Steve Dunn
Genl Mgr: Steve Stefanick
IT Man: Andy Spivey
Plnt Mgr: Greg Steamblock
Ql Cn Mgr: Terry Conroy

D-U-N-S 00-761-0843 IMP/EXP
HOUSE OF RAEFORD FARMS OF LOUISIANA LLC
(Suby of NASH JOHNSON & SONS FARMS INC) ★
3867 2nd St, Arcadia, LA 71001-5376
Tel (318) 263-9004 Founded/Ownrshp 1997
Sales 116.6MM^E EMP 700
SIC 0251 2015 Broiling chickens, raising of; Chicken, slaughtered & dressed; Chicken, processed: fresh
COO: Don Tabor
Off Mgr: Christy Jackson
Plnt Mgr: Darrell McBroom
Sls Mgr: Kenneth Brasher

D-U-N-S 61-845-5265
HOUSE OF REPRESENTATIVES PENNSYLVANIA
(Suby of LEGISLATIVE OFFICE OF COMMONWEALTH OF PENNSYLVANIA) ★
Main Capitol Bldg Rm 132, Harrisburg, PA 17120-0001
Tel (717) 787-3607 Founded/Ownrshp 1776
Sales NA EMP 2,000
SIC 9121 Legislative bodies, state & local;
Genl Mgr: Rep Samuel Smith
*Genl Mgr: Representative Samuel Smith
MIS Dir: Kathy Sullivan

D-U-N-S 80-719-7744
HOUSE OF REPRESENTATIVES TEXAS
(Suby of LEGISLATIVE OFFICE TEXAS) ★
105 W 15th St, Austin, TX 78701-1933
Tel (512) 463-0865 Founded/Ownrshp 1845
Sales NA EMP 1,000
SIC 9121 Legislative bodies, state & local;
Prin: Joe Straus

D-U-N-S 93-335-1660
■ HOUSE OF REPRESENTATIVES UNITED STATES
(Suby of CONGRESS UNITED STATES) ★
The Capitol, Washington, DC 20515-0001
Tel (202) 224-3121 Founded/Ownrshp 1787
Sales NA EMP 10,000
Accts Cotton & Company Llp/Matthew
SIC 9121 Congress;
Prin: John A Boehner
*Ofcr: Daniel Beard
Ofcr: James Eagen
Comm Dir: Michael Hartigan
Comm Dir: Richard Rapoza
*Prin: Karen Lehman Haas
*Prin: Dan Strodell
Admn Mgr: Robert Thorsen
IT Man: Demetrice Brown
Opers Mgr: Greg Bias
Counsel: Tom Rust

D-U-N-S 05-641-4584 IMP
HOUSE OF SPICES (INDIA) INC
12740 Willets Point Blvd, Flushing, NY 11368-1506
Tel (718) 507-4900 Founded/Ownrshp 1970
Sales 125.6MM^E EMP 230
SIC 5149 2099 5153 2033 2024 Pasta & rice; Food preparations; Grain & field beans; Vegetable pastes: packaged in cans, jars, etc.; Ice cream & frozen desserts
Ch: Gordhandas L Soni
*Pr: Niel Soni
CFO: Chetan Soni

D-U-N-S 02-978-6472
HOUSE OF TOOLS AND ENGINEERING INC
HTE TECHNOLOGIES
2021 Congressional Dr, Saint Louis, MO 63146-4103
Tel (314) 731-4444 Founded/Ownrshp 1959
Sales 98.5MM^E EMP 95
SIC 5084 Pneumatic tools & equipment; Hydraulic systems equipment & supplies
Pr: R K Shearburn
VP: Dave Alexander
VP: Tom Bielicki
*VP: Jean M Shearburn
VP: Marion Strickland
Sfty Mgr: Jim Grace
VP Sls: Lupe Rohrer

D-U-N-S 00-792-1372 EXP
HOUSE-HASSON HARDWARE CO (TN)
3125 Water Plant Rd, Knoxville, TN 37914-6640
Tel (800) 333-0520 Founded/Ownrshp 1906
Sales 335.2MM^E EMP 375
Accts Pugh & Company Pc Knoxville
SIC 5072 5031 Hardware; Lumber, plywood & millwork
*VP: David Helfenberger
*VP: Steve Henry
*VP: Don M McLean
*VP: Mike Woolf
Rgnl Mgr: David Baumberger
Rgnl Mgr: Pat McCutcheon
CIO: Larry Fennell
Dir IT: Dennis Quilliams
Manager: Michael C Brady
Sls Mgr: Joel Barker
Sls Mgr: Reed Seabrook

HOUSECALL HOME HEALTH
See HOUSECALL MEDICAL RESOURCES INC

D-U-N-S 84-996-7518
■ HOUSECALL MEDICAL RESOURCES INC
HOUSECALL HOME HEALTH
(Suby of AMEDISYS INC) ★
1400 Cntrpint Blvd St 100, Knoxville, TN 37932
Tel (865) 689-7123 Founded/Ownrshp 2005
Sales 25.0MM^E EMP 2,000
SIC 8082 8741 5999 Home health care services; Nursing & personal care facility management; Medical apparatus & supplies
CEO: John Heller
VP: Michael Hall

D-U-N-S 00-693-0598
HOUSEHOLD FINANCE CORP
HFC
(Suby of HSBC FINANCE CORP) ★
2700 Sanders Rd, Prospect Heights, IL 60070-2701
Tel (847) 790-1590 Founded/Ownrshp 1925
Sales NA EMP 109^E
SIC 6141 6162 6351 6153 6159 6311 Consumer finance companies; Installment sales finance, other than banks; Mortgage bankers; Credit & other financial responsibility insurance; Mercantile financing; Equipment & vehicle finance leasing companies; Life insurance carriers
Ch Bd: David A Schoenholz
*Pr: Tomothey M Detelich
*CEO: W F Aldinger
*CFO: S C Penney
Sr VP: Bruce A Fletcher
Sr VP: Richard Klesse
*VP: Colin Kelly

D-U-N-S 55-630-1638
HOUSEHOLD REALTY CORP
(Suby of HSBC FINANCE CORP) ★
2700 Sanders Rd Fl 1, Prospect Heights, IL 60070-2701
Tel (847) 790-1590 Founded/Ownrshp 1999
Sales NA EMP 1,500
SIC 6141 Consumer finance companies
Pr: Gary Gilmer
*Sr VP: B A Crittenden
*Sr VP: R M Jakubowicz
*Sr VP: E A Kerkow
*Sr VP: P A Miller
*Sr VP: S J Reading
*Sr VP: D D Wesseling

D-U-N-S 18-671-4085 IMP
■ HOUSEWARES HOLDING CO INC
(Suby of NACCO INDUSTRIES INC) ★
14785 Preston Rd Ste 1100, Dallas, TX 75254-6823
Tel (440) 449-9600 Founded/Ownrshp 1988
Sales 2.6MMM^E EMP 5,500
SIC 3634 5719 Toasters, electric: household; Kitchenware
CEO: Alfred M Rankin Jr
Treas: J Butler Jr

D-U-N-S 07-723-3732
HOUSING AUTHORITY OF CITY OF LOS ANGELES
HACLA
2600 Wilshire Blvd Fl 2, Los Angeles, CA 90057-3400
Tel (213) 252-2500 Founded/Ownrshp 1938
Sales NA EMP 1,184
SIC 9531

D-U-N-S 03-349-1911
HOUSING AUTHORITY OF CITY OF NEWARK
500 Broad St, Newark, NJ 07102-3112
Tel (973) 273-6000 Founded/Ownrshp 1938
Sales NA EMP 1,922
SIC 9531 Housing authority, non-operating: government
Ex Dir: Keith Kinard
VP: Larry Howell
Adm Dir: Domingo Senande
Rgnl Mgr: Marcella Holmes
Opers Supe: Andre McNair
Genl Couns: Ellen Harris

D-U-N-S 07-911-9448
HOUSING AUTHORITY OF COUNTY OF SANTA CLARA
505 W Julian St, San Jose, CA 95110-2300
Tel (408) 275-8770 Founded/Ownrshp 2013
Sales 315.9MM EMP 4
SIC 6531 Housing authority operator
Ex Dir: Alex Sanchez

HOUSING AUTHORITY OF THE CITY
See CITY OF RIVERSIDE

D-U-N-S 01-080-3559
HOUSTON BAPTIST UNIVERSITY
7502 Fondren Rd, Houston, TX 77074-3298
Tel (281) 649-3000 *Founded/Ownrshp* 1960
Sales 104.0MM *EMP* 250
Accts Fitts Roberts & Co Pc Houston
SIC 8221 8661 University; Religious organizations
Pr: Robert B Sloan Jr
Ofcr: Phillip Rhodes
VP: Charles Bacarisse
VP: Don Looser
VP: James Steen
Assoc Dir: Janet Feng
Genl Mgr: Lacie Hinkle
HC Dir: Eduardo Borges

D-U-N-S 10-766-2280
HOUSTON CASUALTY CO
TOKIO MARINE HCC
(*Suby of* TOKIO MARINE HCC) ★
13403 Northwest Fwy, Houston, TX 77040-6006
Tel (713) 462-1000 *Founded/Ownrshp* 1988
Sales NA *EMP* 169
SIC 6331 Property damage insurance; Fire, marine & casualty insurance & carriers
CEO: Frank J Bramanti
**Ch Bd:* Stephen Way
**Pr:* Thomas Kaiser
**Ex VP:* Frank Bramanti
Sr VP: Barry Aframe
Sr VP: James L Bechter
Sr VP: Shelly Iacobell
Sr VP: Richard Ruffee
VP: Steve Hansen
VP: Stephen Macdonough
VP: Laura Pantelides
VP: Todd Ruyak

HOUSTON CHRONICLE
See HEARST NEWSPAPERS LLC

D-U-N-S 07-416-2462
HOUSTON COMMUNITY COLLEGE INC
3100 Main St Ste Mc1148, Houston, TX 77002-9331
Tel (713) 718-5001 *Founded/Ownrshp* 1967
Sales 99.8MM *EMP* 5,000
SIC 8222 Community college
V Ch: Neeta Sane
Treas: Debbie Husmann
Trst: Bruce A Austin
Trst: Diane O Guzm N
Trst: Richard M Schechter
Trst: Robert M Worsham
Ofcr: William J Fenley
Ofcr: Wilma Perkins
Ofcr: Alfred Postel
Exec: Chris Bourne
Ex Dir: Martha Oburn

HOUSTON COMMUNITY NEWSPAPER
See ASP WESTWARD LP

D-U-N-S 03-949-7011
HOUSTON COUNTY BOARD OF EDUCATION
HCBOE
1100 Main St, Perry, GA 31069-3531
Tel (478) 988-6200 *Founded/Ownrshp* 1925
Sales 292.5MM *EMP* 3,856
Accts Greg S Griffin State Auditor
SIC 8211 School board
Ch Bd: Fred Wilson
Ofcr: Gary Copa
Admn Mgr: David Carpenter
Admn Mgr: Rodney Champion
Admn Mgr: Patsy Hutto
Admn Mgr: Peggy Jackson
Admn Mgr: Pat Witt

D-U-N-S 07-911-1423
HOUSTON COUNTY HEALTHCARE AUTHORITY
SOUTHEAST ALABAMA MEDICAL CTR
1108 Ross Clark Cir, Dothan, AL 36301-3022
Tel (334) 793-8111 *Founded/Ownrshp* 1957
Sales 311.8MM *EMP* 2,500
Accts Draffin & Tucker Llp Atlanta
SIC 8062 General medical & surgical hospitals
Pr: Rick Sutton
Chf Path: Mark E Shertzer
**COO:* Charlie Brannon
**CFO:* Derek Miller
CFO: Terri Parsons
CFO: David Pike
Chf Mktg O: Trenace Debreuil
Ofcr: Cheryl Rodgers
Ofcr: Larry Walker
**VP:* Diane Buntyn
**VP:* Ronnie Dean
VP: Peggy S Fair
VP: Karen Loftin
VP: Peggy Sease-Fair
VP: Rick Smith
VP: Rich Temple
VP: Kenneth B Tucker
VP Bus Dev: Amy Bamett
Dir Rad: Mike Williams
Dir Rx: Philip Atkinson

D-U-N-S 36-154-7412
HOUSTON COUNTY SCHOOL SYSTEM
1100 Main St, Perry, GA 31069-3531
Tel (478) 988-6200 *Founded/Ownrshp* 2009
Sales 6.1MM[E] *EMP* 3,856[E]
SIC 8211 Public elementary & secondary schools
Bd of Dir: Gillis Dawkins
VP: Walt Downing
Prin: Shakira Shamel
Pr Dir: Beth McLaughlin
Teacher Pr: Sharon Moore
Psych: Amanda Coker
Occ Thrpy: Diane Phillips

D-U-N-S 05-247-5027 IMP/EXP
HOUSTON FOAM PLASTICS INC
2019 Brooks St, Houston, TX 77026-7297
Tel (713) 224-3484 *Founded/Ownrshp* 1970
Sales 85.9MM[E] *EMP* 300
SIC 3086 Insulation or cushioning material, foamed plastic; Packaging & shipping materials, foamed plastic
Pr: K E Kurtz II
**Treas:* Patty Harrington
**VP:* Robert Kurtz
Exec: Rene Gonzalez

D-U-N-S 16-484-5869
HOUSTON FOOD BANK
535 Portwall St, Houston, TX 77029-1332
Tel (713) 223-3700 *Founded/Ownrshp* 1981
Sales 155.4MM *EMP* 208[E]
Accts Lb Blazek & Vetterling Housto
SIC 8399 Community action agency
Pr: Brian Greene
Dir Vol: Oleg Jolic
**COO:* Stan Edde
**CFO:* Klaudia Brace
CFO: Beth Tanner
**Treas:* Louise Duble
**Treas:* Janet Matura
Ofcr: Jennifer Reeves
Exec: Glenda Bates
Comm Dir: Adele Brady
Comm Man: Adele Jordan

D-U-N-S 83-148-3834
HOUSTON FOODS INC
BURGER KING
4415 Highway 6, Sugar Land, TX 77478-4476
Tel (281) 201-2700 *Founded/Ownrshp* 1993
Sales 37.0MM[E] *EMP* 1,198[E]
SIC 5812 Fast-food restaurant, chain
Pr: Shoukat Dhanani

D-U-N-S 07-248-2375
HOUSTON HEALTHCARE SYSTEM INC
1601 Watson Blvd, Warner Robins, GA 31093-3431
Tel (478) 922-4281 *Founded/Ownrshp* 2008
Sales 235.9MM[E] *EMP* 2,000
SIC 8062 General medical & surgical hospitals
CEO: Cary Martin
V Ch: Kent McBride
**CFO:* Mike Fowler
CFO: Sean Whilden
Bd of Dir: Fred Graham
Bd of Dir: Jack Ragland
Bd of Dir: Tommy Stalnaker
Bd of Dir: Sonny Watson
Ofcr: Audra Cabiness
Ofcr: Heather Stewart
**Sr VP:* Skip Philips
VP: Mike Ohara
Dir OR: Diane Taylor

D-U-N-S 03-264-0486
HOUSTON HOSPITALS INC
1601 Watson Blvd, Warner Robins, GA 31093-3431
Tel (478) 929-9544 *Founded/Ownrshp* 2008
Sales 233.0MM *EMP* 32[E]
Accts Pershing Yoakley Knoxville T
SIC 8062 General medical & surgical hospitals
CEO: Cary W Martin
**CFO:* Sean Whilden

HOUSTON HOTEL
See STERLING HOSPITALITY INC

D-U-N-S 06-129-2124
HOUSTON INDEPENDENT SCHOOL DISTRICT (TX)
H I S D
4400 W 18th St, Houston, TX 77092-8501
Tel (713) 556-6005 *Founded/Ownrshp* 1923
Sales 2.3MM *EMP* 22,440
Accts Deloitte & Touche Llp Houston
SIC 8211 Public elementary & secondary schools
Pr: Michael Lunceford
**CFO:* Melinda Garrett
**Sec:* Diana Davila
Exec: Jackie Cayton
Exec: Andrew Monzon
Exec: Alice Reuter
Exec: Daniel Serenil
Exec: Larry Trout
Ex Dir: Randy Tullos
Dir IT: Lori Nichols
Dir IT: Ben Willson

D-U-N-S 83-174-9671
HOUSTON INTERNATIONAL INSURANCE GROUP LTD
HIIG
(*Suby of* WESTAIM HIIG LIMITED PARTNERSHIP)
800 Gessner Rd Ste 600, Houston, TX 77024-4538
Tel (713) 935-4800 *Founded/Ownrshp* 2014
Sales NA *EMP* 92[E]
SIC 6331 Fire, marine & casualty insurance
CEO: Stephen L Way
**CFO:* Rhonda Kemp
**CFO:* Peter Presperin
Treas: Cindy Casale
**Ex VP:* Ed Ellis
Sr VP: Kirby Hill
Sr VP: Ahmad Mian
Sr VP: Mark Rattner
**Sr VP:* Michael Schmidt
Sr VP: L Byron Way
VP: Janet Yienger

D-U-N-S 09-248-7172 IMP/EXP
HOUSTON LBC L P
(*Suby of* LBC BELGIUM HOLDING NV)
11666 Port Rd, Seabrook, TX 77586-1603
Tel (281) 474-4433 *Founded/Ownrshp* 1998
Sales 142.0MM[E] *EMP* 130
SIC 5171 Petroleum bulk stations; Petroleum terminals
Pt: Rory Moran
Pt: David Knowles
Pt: Michael S McKinney
IT Man: Marian Esther
Opers Supe: Brett Rushton
Sls Mgr: Paulo Leal

D-U-N-S 07-844-2175
HOUSTON LIVESTOCK SHOW AND RODEO EDUCATIONAL FUND
8334 Nrg Park Fl 2, Houston, TX 77054-2930
Tel (832) 667-1000 *Founded/Ownrshp* 1932
Sales 23.4MM *EMP* 1,200
Accts Pricewaterhousecoopers Llp H
SIC 7999 Rodeo operation
CEO: Joel Cowley
**Pr:* R H Stevens
**COO:* Leroy Shafer
**CFO:* Jennifer Hazelton
**VP:* Andrew Sloan
**Prin:* Paul G Somerville

D-U-N-S 96-684-9684
HOUSTON LIVESTOCK SHOW AND RODEO INC
8334 Nrg Park, Houston, TX 77054-2930
Tel (832) 667-1000 *Founded/Ownrshp* 1932
Sales 122.5MM *EMP* 2
Accts Pricewaterhousecoopers Llp Ho
SIC 7313 Radio, television, publisher representatives
Ch Bd: Rh Stevens Jr

HOUSTON METRO TRNST AUTH
See METROPOLITAN TRANSIT AUTHORITY OF HARRIS COUNTY

D-U-N-S 05-445-6546
■ **HOUSTON NORTH POLE LINE**
(*Suby of* QUANTA SERVICES INC) ★
1608 Margaret St, Houston, TX 77093-4010
Tel (713) 691-3616 *Founded/Ownrshp* 2001
Sales 733.3MM[E] *EMP* 2,373
SIC 1623 Electric power line construction
Pr: Earl C Austin Jr
**Pr:* Elton G Sackett
CFO: Leslie Shackett
**VP:* Martha K Austin
VP: Derrell Isenberg
**VP:* Bryan Michalsky
IT Man: Brad Clanton

D-U-N-S 10-268-2150
■ **HOUSTON NORTH WEST MEDICAL CENTER INC**
HOUSTON NORTHWEST MEDICAL CTR
(*Suby of* TENET HEALTHCARE FOUNDATION) ★
710 Cypress Creek Pkwy # 34, Houston, TX 77090-3402
Tel (281) 440-1000 *Founded/Ownrshp* 1974
Sales 140.8MM[E] *EMP* 1,600
SIC 8062 General medical & surgical hospitals
CEO: Tim Puthoff
**Pr:* Louis Garcia
CFO: Ron Watson
Ofcr: Melba Bright

D-U-N-S 61-275-5801
■ **HOUSTON NORTHWEST MEDICAL CENTER EDUCATION FOUNDATION INC**
HNMC
(*Suby of* TENET HEALTHCARE CORP) ★
710 Cypress Station Dr # 340, Houston, TX 77090-1506
Tel (281) 440-1000 *Founded/Ownrshp* 1997
Sales 211.2MM[E] *EMP* 2,100
SIC 8062 General medical & surgical hospitals
CEO: Tim Puthoff C
COO: Allyn Glenn
COO: Susan Jadlouski
CFO: Sean Gallager
CFO: Mark Runyon
Dir Rad: Madan Kulkarni
Dir Rad: Hai Nguyen
Dir Rad: Ralph Norton
Mng Dir: Susan J Dewitt
Nurse Mgr: Claudia M Neil
CIO: Lisa Andersonwilliam

HOUSTON NORTHWEST MEDICAL CTR
See HOUSTON NORTH WEST MEDICAL CENTER INC

D-U-N-S 00-478-8188
■ **HOUSTON PIPE LINE CO LP**
(*Suby of* ENERGY TRANSFER PARTNERS LP) ★
800 E Sonterra Blvd, San Antonio, TX 78258-3940
Tel (713) 222-0414 *Founded/Ownrshp* 1925
Sales 172.9MM[E] *EMP* 266
SIC 4922 Pipelines, natural gas
Pt: Kelcy L Warren
Pr: Marshall S McCrea
CFO: Martin Salinas
Treas: Jeff Z Weiler
Sr VP: Thomas P Mason
VP: Lana Hillebrand
Exec: Nick Moshou
Sls Dir: Lee Papayoti

D-U-N-S 07-417-9896
HOUSTON SAM STATE UNIVERSITY
SHSU
(*Suby of* TEXAS STATE UNIVERSITY SYSTEM) ★
1806 Ave J, Huntsville, TX 77340
Tel (936) 294-1111 *Founded/Ownrshp* 1879
Sales 183.6MM *EMP* 2,200[E]
SIC 8221 University
Pr: Dana Hoyt
CFO: Vaf Ddk
Assoc VP: Roy Adams
Assoc VP: David Hammonds
VP: Shirin Edwin
VP: Dana Gibson
VP: Melva Gomez
**VP:* Jaimie Hebert
VP: Jamie L Hebert
**VP:* Frank R Holmes
VP: Frank Holmes
**VP:* Al Hooten
VP: Kristina Kaskel-Ruiz
VP: Seth Lecompte
VP: David McKinney
**VP:* Frank Parker
VP: Randall Powell
VP: Edwina Reece
VP: William Robinson
**VP:* Heather Thielemann
Exec: Psy Ajb

D-U-N-S 19-436-1986
HOUSTON SERIES OF LOCKTON COMPANIES LLC
(*Suby of* LOCKTON COMPANIES) ★
5847 San Felipe St # 320, Houston, TX 77057-3000
Tel (713) 458-5200 *Founded/Ownrshp* 1986
Sales NA *EMP* 600
SIC 6411 Insurance agents & brokers
COO: Bob Bobo
**Pr:* David Lockton
Assoc VP: Jeff Estrada
Ex VP: Anthony Scott Convery
Ex VP: Kenneth Gould
Ex VP: Stacy Seaberg
Sr VP: Robert Bruce
Sr VP: Albert Martin
Sr VP: Rachel Walker
Sr VP: Thomas Wronski
VP: Clay Brooks
VP: John S Canter
VP: Roy M Tristan

HOUSTON STAFFORD ELECTRICAL
See IES RESIDENTIAL INC

D-U-N-S 00-842-6439 IMP
■ **HOUSTON SYSCO INC**
(*Suby of* SYSCO CORP) ★
10710 Grens Crossing Blvd, Houston, TX 77038
Tel (713) 672-8080 *Founded/Ownrshp* 1953, 1970
Sales 533.5MM[E] *EMP* 750
SIC 5149 5142 5046 5141 2099 Canned goods: fruit, vegetables, seafood, meats, etc.; Packaged frozen goods; Commercial cooking & food service equipment; Groceries, general line; Food preparations
CEO: Bill Delaney
**Pr:* David Devane
**Pr:* Michael W Green
**COO:* Thomas E Lankford
**CFO:* Scott Klienver
**Sr VP:* Greg Bertrand
**Sr VP:* Scott Charlton
VP: Mike Stith
Exec: Leonard Bryan
CIO: Twila M Day
MIS Dir: Kelly Russell

D-U-N-S 05-361-8782
HOUSTON TRIBOLOGY SALES & MARKETING OFFICE
A L S
10450 Stncliff Rd Ste 210, Houston, TX 77099
Tel (281) 599-1242 *Founded/Ownrshp* 2010
Sales 98.4MM[E] *EMP* 11,000
SIC 8742 Marketing consulting services
IT Man: Fran Christopher

D-U-N-S 05-869-5743 IMP
HOUSTON TUBULARS INC
13600 Hatfield Rd, Pearland, TX 77581-2729
Tel (281) 485-4014 *Founded/Ownrshp* 1981
Sales 88.4MM[E] *EMP* 150
SIC 1389 Pipe testing, oil field service
Pr: Dennis J Hayden
**VP:* Kathy Hayden
**Opers Mgr:* Claudio Cruz

D-U-N-S 01-079-1390 IMP/EXP
▲ **HOUSTON WIRE & CABLE CO INC**
10201 North Loop E, Houston, TX 77029-1415
Tel (713) 609-2100 *Founded/Ownrshp* 1975
Sales 308.1MM *EMP* 397[E]
Tkr Sym HWCC *Exch* NGS
SIC 5063 Electronic wire & cable
Pr: James L Pokluda III
CFO: Nicol G Graham
Rgnl Mgr: Eric Jacques
Rgnl Mgr: John Schrader
Sls Mgr: Gregory Crary
Sls Mgr: Craig Zei
Board of Directors: Michael T Campbell, I Stewart Farwell, Mark A Ruelle, William H Sheffield, G Gary Yetman

D-U-N-S 07-218-8840
HOUSTON-GALVESTON AREA COUNCIL
H-G A C
3555 Timmons Ln Ste 120, Houston, TX 77027-6466
Tel (713) 627-3200 *Founded/Ownrshp* 1966
Sales NA *EMP* 200
Accts Whitley Penn Llp Houston Tex
SIC 6035 Federal savings & loan associations
CEO: Jack Steele
**CFO:* Nancy Haussler
Ex Dir: Nydia Delagarza
Ex Dir: Nydia De La Garza
Prgrm Mgr: Mike Temple
Sales Asso: Mario Osio

D-U-N-S 94-938-3780 IMP
HOUWELING NURSERIES OXNARD INC
HOUWELING'S TOMATOES
645 Laguna Rd, Camarillo, CA 93012-8523
Tel (805) 488-8832 *Founded/Ownrshp* 1996
Sales 221.8MM[E] *EMP* 450
Accts Kpmg Llp Burnaby Canada
SIC 5141 Groceries, general line
Pr: Casey Houweling
**CFO:* Christopher Brocklesby
**VP Sls:* William Wilber

HOUWELING'S TOMATOES
See HOUWELING NURSERIES OXNARD INC

D-U-N-S 96-524-3129
HOV SERVICES INC
(*Suby of* SOURCEHOV LLC) ★
2701 E Grauwyler Rd, Irving, TX 75061-3414
Tel (248) 837-7100 *Founded/Ownrshp* 2011
Sales 90.7MM[E] *EMP* 1,945[E]
SIC 7374 7334 7389 2752 7331 7379 Data processing & preparation; Photocopying & duplicating services; Microfilm recording & developing service; Decals, lithographed; Mailing service; Data processing consultant

Pr: Suresh Yannamani
* *CFO:* James G Reynolds
* *Ex VP:* Kenneth L Shaw
Sr VP: Mark Trivette
VP: Susan Stallings
Opers Mgr: Patricia C Watson
Sales Exec: Jesse Singh
Snr PM: Chris Barker

D-U-N-S 04-742-6569 IMP/EXP
HOVENSA LLC
1 Estate Hope, Christiansted, VI 00820
Tel (340) 692-3000 *Founded/Ownrshp* 1999
Sales 57.6MM^E *EMP* 1,300
SIC 1382

D-U-N-S 78-900-3365 IMP
HOVEROUND CORP
6010 Cattleridge Dr, Sarasota, FL 34232-6060
Tel (941) 739-6200 *Founded/Ownrshp* 1992
Sales 90.6MM^E *EMP* 437
SIC 3842 Wheelchairs
Pr: Thomas E Kruse
COO: Joyce Boyle
* *CFO:* George W Kruse
CFO: Robert Munch
* *Treas:* Lisa W Ondrula
VP: Margaret A Hollowy
* *VP:* Gordon L Nelson
VP: Shani Reardon
VP: Don Shapiro
Exec: Joyce Norris
Dir IT: Jan Vandalen

D-U-N-S 04-665-0388
▲ HOVNANIAN ENTERPRISES INC
K HOVNANIAN
110 W Front St, Red Bank, NJ 07701-5997
Tel (732) 747-7800 *Founded/Ownrshp* 1959
Sales 2.1MMM *EMP* 2,078^E
Accts Deloitte & Touche Llp New Yor
Tkr Sym HOV *Exch* NYS
SIC 1521 1531 1522 6162 6361 Single-family housing construction; Condominium developers; Townhouse developers; Speculative builder, single-family houses; Residential construction; Mortgage bankers; Title insurance
Ch Bd: ARA K Hovnanian
COO: Thomas J Pellerito
COO: Lucian T Smith III
* *CFO:* J Larry Sorsby
Treas: David L Bachstetter
VP: John Cummins
VP: Martinez Emilio
VP: David Friend
VP: Mark Hodge
VP: ARA Hovnanin
VP: Paul Marabella
VP: Bill Moore
VP: Brad G O'Connor
VP: Joseph F Riggs
VP: Nicholas Tappas
VP: David Valiaveedan
Exec: Charmane Spahr
Board of Directors: Robert B Coutts, Edward A Kangas, Joseph A Marengi, Vincent Pagano Jr, Stephen D Weinroth

D-U-N-S 07-206-5816
HOWARD COMMUNITY HOSPITAL
HOWARD REGIONAL HEALTH SYSTEMS
3500 S Lafountain St, Kokomo, IN 46902-3800
Tel (765) 453-0702 *Founded/Ownrshp* 1958
Sales 299.9M *EMP* 1,050
Accts Caskey & Daily Pc Indianapoli
SIC 8062 8063 General medical & surgical hospitals; Psychiatric hospitals
Pr: James P Alender
Chf Path: Douglas Eglen
Chf Rad: Shamin Dada
CFO: Brain Regen
Dir Rad: Connie Boling
Dir Rx: John Davidson
Dir Rx: George Spinning
Off Mgr: Cassie Gardner
IT Man: Keith Kelly
IT Man: Karen Thomson
Pathlgst: Douglas E Egland

D-U-N-S 03-033-4544
HOWARD COUNTY GENERAL HOSPITAL INC
HCGH HOWARD COUNTY GEN HOSP
(*Suby of* JOHNS HOPKINS HEALTH SYS CORP) ★
5755 Cedar Ln, Columbia, MD 21044-2999
Tel (410) 740-7935 *Founded/Ownrshp* 1969
Sales 236.0MM *EMP* 1,800^E
Accts Pricewaterhousecoopers Llp B
SIC 8062 General medical & surgical hospitals
Pr: Vic Broccolino
V Ch: Gary Blechman
* *CFO:* James E Young
Chf Mktg O: Michael Macon
Ofcr: Linda Holley
Sr VP: Carl Humphreys
* *VP:* Eric Aldrich
VP: Mark Applestein
VP: Lynn Bell
* *VP:* Jay H Blackman
Dir Risk M: Digna Wheatley

D-U-N-S 18-069-3335
HOWARD COUNTY OF MARYLAND (INC)
3430 Court House Dr # 100, Ellicott City, MD 21043-4300
Tel (410) 313-2195 *Founded/Ownrshp* 1800
Sales NA *EMP* 3,463
Accts Cohn Reznick Llp Baltimore
SIC 9111 Executive offices;
Exec: Ken Ulman
Dir Vol: Elissa Reineck
Pr: Mark Miller
* *Ofcr:* Raquel Sanodo
Ofcr: Darryl Thomas
Netwrk Eng: James Cox

D-U-N-S 07-962-8849
HOWARD COUNTY PUBLIC SCHOOL SYSTEM
HCPSS
10910 State Route 108, Ellicott City, MD 21042-6106
Tel (410) 313-6600 *Founded/Ownrshp* 2014
Sales 206.0MM^E *EMP* 8,084^E
SIC 8211 School board
Bd of Dir: David Bruzga
Bd of Dir: Kathleen Hanks
Bd of Dir: Joy Menkemeir
Adm Dir: Daniel Michaels
Adm Dir: Marion Miller
Ex Dir: Anne Yenchko
Dir Sec: Terry Street
MIS Dir: Sherrill Tart
Software D: Ken Mason
Netwrk Eng: Linwood Brown
Pr Dir: John White

HOWARD ENERGY PARTNERS
See HOWARD MIDSTREAM ENERGY PARTNERS LLC

D-U-N-S 14-603-1146
HOWARD G BUFFETT FOUNDATION
145 N Merchant St Apt 1, Decatur, IL 62523-1216
Tel (217) 429-3988 *Founded/Ownrshp* 2007
Sales 152.7MM *EMP* 1
SIC 7389 Fund raising organizations
Prin: Howard G Buffett

HOWARD HANNA REAL ESTATE
See HANNA HOLDINGS INC

D-U-N-S 00-807-6879
■ HOWARD HUGHES CORP
(*Suby of* HOWARD HUGHES REALTY) ★
13355 Noel Rd Fl 22, Dallas, TX 75240-6602
Tel (702) 791-4000 *Founded/Ownrshp* 1980
Sales 133.2MM^E *EMP* 25
SIC 6552 6512 7992 Land subdividers & developers, commercial; Commercial & industrial building operation; Public golf courses
CEO: David R Weinreb
Pr: Grant Herlitz
Treas: Kevin T Orrock
Bd of Dir: David Tripp
Sr VP: Aaron Haas
VP: Julie Cleaver
VP: Jeff Geen
VP: Randy Kostroske
VP: Chuck Kubat
Corp Couns: Sandra Turner

D-U-N-S 96-561-4626
▲ HOWARD HUGHES CORP
13355 Noel Rd Fl 22, Dallas, TX 75240-6602
Tel (214) 741-7744 *Founded/Ownrshp* 2010
Sales 797.0MM *EMP* 1,000^E
Tkr Sym HHC *Exch* NYS
SIC 6798 Real estate investment trusts
CEO: David Weinreb
Ch Bd: William A Ackman
Pr: Grant Herlitz
CFO: Andrew Richardson
Bd of Dir: Philip Fruge
Sr VP: Peter Riley
Sr VP: Steven Robinson
VP: Nick Vanderboom
Exec: Christopher Curry
Board of Directors: Adam Flatto, Jeffrey Furber, Allen Model, R Scot Sellers, Steven Shepsman, Burton M Tansky, Mary Ann Tighe

D-U-N-S 07-386-2773
HOWARD HUGHES MEDICAL INSTITUTE INC
4000 Jones Bridge Rd, Chevy Chase, MD 20815-6720
Tel (301) 215-8500 *Founded/Ownrshp* 1953
Sales 2.7MMM *EMP* 3,000
SIC 8733

HOWARD HUGHES REALTY
See HUGHES CORP

HOWARD JOHNSON
See RESORT HOSPITALITY ENTERPRISES LTD

D-U-N-S 87-753-7097
HOWARD MIDSTREAM ENERGY PARTNERS LLC
HOWARD ENERGY PARTNERS
(*Suby of* ALINDA CAPITAL PARTNERS LLC) ★
17806 W Ih 10 Ste 210, San Antonio, TX 78257-8222
Tel (210) 298-2222 *Founded/Ownrshp* 2013
Sales 114.6MM^E *EMP* 130^E
SIC 5085 Pipeline wrappings, anti-corrosive
CEO: Mike Howard
Pr: Brad Bynum
CFO: Scott Archer
Sr VP: Mark Helmke
Sr VP: Mike Spears
Sr VP: Josh Weber
VP: Steve Cruse
VP Opers: Brandon Burch

HOWARD MILLER CLOCK COMPANY
See HOWARD MILLER CO

D-U-N-S 00-601-1316 IMP/EXP
HOWARD MILLER CO (MI)
HOWARD MILLER CLOCK COMPANY
860 E Main Ave, Zeeland, MI 49464-1365
Tel (616) 772-9131 *Founded/Ownrshp* 1946
Sales 95.4MM^E *EMP* 500
SIC 3873 3829 3823 Clocks, except timeclocks; Measuring & controlling devices; Industrial instrmnts msrmnt display/control process variable
Ch Bd: Philip Miller
* *Pr:* Howard C Miller
* *VP:* Dennis Palasek
Web Dev: Pat V Hulst
Sls Mgr: Bill Papoosha

HOWARD REGIONAL HEALTH SYSTEMS
See HOWARD COMMUNITY HOSPITAL

D-U-N-S 15-538-5867 IMP
HOWARD SUPPLY CO LLC
CLIFTON SUPPLY COMPANY
4100 Intl Plz Ste 850, Fort Worth, TX 76109
Tel (817) 529-9950 *Founded/Ownrshp* 1985
Sales 103.3MM^E *EMP* 125
SIC 5084 5082 Oil well machinery, equipment & supplies; Oil field equipment
Pr: Michael R Barber
Pr: Wayne Moody
COO: Juergen Baron Lukas
CFO: Michael Taylor
Store Mgr: Matt Beddoe
Store Mgr: Timothy Bender
Store Mgr: Luis Lopez
Store Mgr: Zed Nelson
Store Mgr: Sid Shepard
Store Mgr: Mike Smith
Store Mgr: Brian Wilson

D-U-N-S 00-980-7652
HOWARD TERNES PACKAGING CO
35275 Industrial Rd, Livonia, MI 48150-1231
Tel (734) 793-4130 *Founded/Ownrshp* 1948
Sales 98.8MM^E *EMP* 450
SIC 4783 6512 6552 Packing goods for shipping; Commercial & industrial building operation; Land subdividers & developers, commercial; Land subdividers & developers, residential
Ch Bd: Howard A Ternes Jr
* *Pr:* Charles E Ross
COO: Bill Bejin
* *VP:* Richard Everhart
Prgrm Mgr: Lauren Turner
Dir IT: Tony Beddow
Telecom Mg: Dennis Davis
Plnt Mgr: Robert Kidd

D-U-N-S 05-628-2296 EXP
HOWARD UNIVERSITY
2400 6th St Nw, Washington, DC 20059-0002
Tel (202) 806-6100 *Founded/Ownrshp* 1867
Sales 398.9MM *EMP* 5,600
SIC 8221 University
Pr: Dwayne Frederick
COO: Agnes Day
CFO: Rufus Blackwell
CFO: John Grish
Trst: John J Howard
Ofcr: Sheryl Wesley
Sr VP: Carol Winston
VP: Jeanette Gibbs
VP: Donald Rickford
VP: Harry Robinson
Dir IT: Miriam Ahmed

D-U-N-S 19-847-3282 IMP
HOWARD UNIVERSITY HOSPITAL
CARDIOLOGY DEPT
2041 Georgia Ave Nw, Washington, DC 20060-0002
Tel (202) 865-6100 *Founded/Ownrshp* 1974
Sales 162.6MM *EMP* 8
SIC 8062 General medical & surgical hospitals
COO: Oliver Crump
CFO: Joseph Huber
VP: Craig Washington
Exec: Ricardo Caldera
Exec: Glenda Hodges
Dir Lab: Tammy Naab
Dir Sec: Marvin Cooper
Dir Pat Ac: Veronica Brown-Mayo
* *Genl Mgr:* Buirdell Bennis
Telecom Ex: Rose Reed
Cmptr Lab: Diana Davis

D-U-N-S 79-410-7099
HOWARD UNIVERSITY HOSPITAL
DEPARTMENT OF SURGERY
2041 Georgia Ave Nw, Washington, DC 20060-0002
Tel (202) 865-1441 *Founded/Ownrshp* 2007
Sales 166.9MM^E *EMP* 2,000
SIC 8062

D-U-N-S 17-089-0172
HOWARDCENTER INC
208 Flynn Ave Ste 3j, Burlington, VT 05401-5420
Tel (802) 488-6900 *Founded/Ownrshp* 1884
Sales 80.2MM *EMP* 1,128
Accts Kittell Branagan & Sargent Cpa
SIC 8322 Individual & family services
CEO: Todd Centybear
* *Pr:* Karen Oniel
* *CFO:* Charles Stringer
* *Treas:* John Mc Soley
VP: Hal Colston
* *VP:* Peter McCarthy
Exec: Barbara Graf

HOWCO GROUP
See HOWCO METALS MANAGEMENT LLC

D-U-N-S 94-221-8116 IMP/EXP
HOWCO METALS MANAGEMENT LLC
HOWCO GROUP
9611 Telge Rd, Houston, TX 77095-5114
Tel (281) 649-8800 *Founded/Ownrshp* 2002
Sales 97.2MM^E *EMP* 150
Accts Ernst & Young Glasgow Scotla
SIC 5051 3999 8741 Steel; Barber & beauty shop equipment; Business management
Pr: John Ferguson
COO: Dave Davidson
* *Sec:* Kenneth Ness
Sr VP: Douglas Ferguson
* *VP:* Keith Itzel
VP: Joe Klumpyan
* *VP:* David Meyer
Mng Dir: David Birch
Mng Dir: Ian Blackburn
Mng Dir: M N Howat
Genl Mgr: Glenn Bilanoski

D-U-N-S 05-484-3438 IMP/EXP
■ HOWDEN NORTH AMERICA INC (MI)
HOWDENS
(*Suby of* ANDERSON GROUP INC) ★
2475 George Urban Blvd # 100, Depew, NY 14043-2022
Tel (803) 741-2700 *Founded/Ownrshp* 1980
Sales 287.5MM^E *EMP* 566
SIC 3564 3568 Exhaust fans: industrial or commercial; Couplings, shaft: rigid, flexible, universal joint, etc.
CEO: Matthew Ingle
* *Pr:* Karl Kimmerling
* *Ch:* Will Samuel
VP: Grahame Gurney
IT Man: Tara Vannorman
Plnt Mgr: David Smith
Manager: Chuck Bailey
Manager: George Junor
Manager: Tom Snare

HOWDENS
See HOWDEN NORTH AMERICA INC

D-U-N-S 05-489-0397
HOWE-OTTO INC (IL)
951 E 3300 North Rd, Farmer City, IL 61842-7027
Tel (309) 928-9730 *Founded/Ownrshp* 1979
Sales 650.0MM *EMP* 5
SIC 0116 0115 7389 Soybeans; Corn;
Pr: Dona Mae Howe
* *COO:* Joseph Howe
* *Treas:* Tyler Roth
* *VP:* Bret Fogal

D-U-N-S 07-784-3308
HOWELL CHILD CARE CENTER INC
3738 Howell Day Care Rd, La Grange, NC 28551-6808
Tel (252) 566-9011 *Founded/Ownrshp* 1970
Sales 1.1MM *EMP* 1,400
SIC 8361 8052 Children's home; Intermediate care facilities
Pr: Sandra Hedrick
* *VP:* Jim Panton

D-U-N-S 08-774-9313
HOWELL PUBLIC SCHOOLS (MI)
HOWELL PUBLIC SCHOOLS DISTRICT
411 N Highlander Way, Howell, MI 48843-1021
Tel (517) 548-6200 *Founded/Ownrshp* 1853
Sales 66.5MM^E *EMP* 1,740
SIC 8211 Public elementary & secondary schools
Bd of Dir: Mark Leahy
Exec: John Tiefenbach
IT Man: Glenna Macdonald
IT Man: Paul Pominville
Psych: Catherine Deschenes
Psych: Caroline Grabowski

HOWELL PUBLIC SCHOOLS DISTRICT
See HOWELL PUBLIC SCHOOLS

D-U-N-S 05-425-4602
HOWELL TOWNSHIP BOARD OF EDUCATION
HOWELL TWP PUBLIC SCHOOLS
200 Sqnkum Yellowbrook Rd, Howell, NJ 07731
Tel (732) 751-2480 *Founded/Ownrshp* 1890
Sales 50.1MM^E *EMP* 1,000
Accts Robert A Hulsart And Company
SIC 8211 Public elementary school; Public senior high school

HOWELL TWP PUBLIC SCHOOLS
See HOWELL TOWNSHIP BOARD OF EDUCATION

D-U-N-S 05-831-1945 IMP
■ HOWMEDICA OSTEONICS CORP
STRYKER ORTHOPAEDICS
(*Suby of* STRYKER CORP) ★
325 Corporate Dr, Mahwah, NJ 07430-2006
Tel (201) 831-5000 *Founded/Ownrshp* 1998
Sales 697.0MM^E *EMP* 3,950^E
SIC 3842 5047 Surgical appliances & supplies; Orthopedic equipment & supplies
Pr: Kevin A Lobo
* *CFO:* William R Jellison
* *Treas:* Jeanne M Blondia
Ofcr: Peter Lauk
* *VP:* Yin C Becker
* *VP:* Steven P Benscoter
* *VP:* Dean H Bergy
* *VP:* William E Berry Jr
Comm Man: Alicia Sovart
Genl Mgr: John Murray
Board of Directors: Stephen P Macmillan

D-U-N-S 01-476-8660
■ HOWMET CASTINGS & SERVICES INC
(*Suby of* ALCOA POWER & PROPULSION) ★
1616 Harvard Ave, Newburgh Heights, OH 44105-3040
Tel (216) 641-4400 *Founded/Ownrshp* 2004
Sales 531.2MM^E *EMP* 3,954^E
SIC 3324 Commercial investment castings, ferrous
Pr: Eric M Brzostek
VP: Natalie Schilling

D-U-N-S 02-090-0049 IMP/EXP
■ HOWMET CORP
ALCOA POWER & PROPULSION
(*Suby of* HOWMET HOLDINGS CORP) ★
1616 Harvard Ave, Newburgh Heights, OH 44105-3040
Tel (800) 242-9898 *Founded/Ownrshp* 1975
Sales 1.5MMM^E *EMP* 10,000
SIC 3324 3542 5051 3479 Commercial investment castings, ferrous; Machine tools, metal forming type; Ferroalloys; Ingots; Coating of metals & formed products
Pr: David L Squier
* *Sr VP:* Marklin Lasker
* *Sr VP:* James R Stanley
* *VP:* Roland A Paul
* *VP Mfg:* B Dennis Albrechtsen

D-U-N-S 00-657-5799 IMP
■ HOWMET HOLDINGS CORP
(*Suby of* ARCONIC INC) ★
1 Misco Dr, Whitehall, MI 49461-1799
Tel (231) 894-5686 *Founded/Ownrshp* 1970
Sales 1.5MMM^E *EMP* 10,000

SIC 3324 3542 5051 3479 Commercial investment castings, ferrous; Machine tools, metal forming type; Ferroalloys; Ingots; Coating of metals & formed products
CEO: Mario Longhi
**Pr:* Raymond B Mitchell
**VP:* James R Stanley

D-U-N-S 07-480-1598
HOWREY LLP
1299 Pennsylvania Ave Nw, Washington, DC 20004-2400
Tel (202) 783-0800 *Founded/Ownrshp* 2000
Sales 53.9MM^E *EMP* 1,540
SIC 8111

D-U-N-S 07-622-4179 IMP/EXP
HOWROYD-WRIGHT EMPLOYMENT AGENCY INC
APPLE ONE EMPLOYMENT
(*Suby of* AGILE 1) ★
327 W Broadway, Glendale, CA 91204-1301
Tel (818) 240-8688 *Founded/Ownrshp* 1964
Sales 134.9MM^E *EMP* 1,300
SIC 7361 Labor contractors (employment agency); Executive placement
CEO: Janice Bryant Howroyd
**Pr:* Bernard Howroyd
**CFO:* Michael Hoyal
Div VP: Bill Lindsay
VP: Rachel Borowski
**VP:* Brett Howroyd
VP: Michael A Howroyd
VP: Michael Nisenson
Dir Bus: Robert Junious
Brnch Mgr: Diana Felix
Brnch Mgr: Lynni Gard

D-U-N-S 10-730-0246 IMP
HOYA CORP
HOYA VISION CARE
(*Suby of* HOYA CORPORATION)
651 E Corporate Dr, Lewisville, TX 75057-6403
Tel (972) 221-4141 *Founded/Ownrshp* 1981
Sales 107.4MM^E *EMP* 560
SIC 3851 Ophthalmic goods
CFO: Mark Evett
VP: Gregg Fowler
VP: Rick Tinson
Netwrk Eng: Monty Weaver
VP Opers: Sandy Morgan
VP Mktg: Mike Elton
VP Sls: Rich Montag
Sls Dir: Steve Scialabba
Mktg Mgr: Jennifer MA
Mktg Mgr: Heather Padgett
Manager: John Aguero

D-U-N-S 61-982-1978 IMP
HOYA HOLDINGS INC
(*Suby of* HOYA CORPORATION)
680 N Mccarthy Blvd # 120, Milpitas, CA 95035-5120
Tel (408) 654-2300 *Founded/Ownrshp* 1973
Sales 113.0MM^E *EMP* 600
SIC 3861 3825 3827 Photographic sensitized goods; Test equipment for electronic & electric measurement; Optical instruments & lenses
CEO: Hiroshi Suzuki
**COO:* Eiichiro Ikeda
**CFO:* Ryo Hirooka
MIS Dir: Andy Wong
IT Man: Cedric Yiu

HOYA VISION CARE
See HOYA CORP

D-U-N-S 09-060-9483
HP COMMUNICATIONS INC (CA)
13341 Temescal Canyon Rd, Corona, CA 92883-4980
Tel (951) 572-1200 *Founded/Ownrshp* 1998
Sales 158.5MM^E *EMP* 240
Accts Steven A Flores Placentia C
SIC 1623 Communication line & transmission tower construction
Pr: Nicholas Goldman
**Ex VP:* Ahmad Olomi
**VP:* Chris Price
Dir Bus: Hank Goldmann
Netwrk Eng: Adela Corona

D-U-N-S 04-666-7523
■ **HP ENTERPRISE SERVICES LLC**
ELECTRONIC DATA SYSTEMS
(*Suby of* HEWLETT PACKARD ENTERPRISE CO) ★
5400 Legacy Dr, Plano, TX 75024-3105
Tel (972) 604-6000 *Founded/Ownrshp* 2015
Sales 21.4MMM^E *EMP* 139,500
SIC 7374 7371 8742 Data processing service; Custom computer programming services; Marketing consulting services; Business planning & organizing services; Management engineering; Materials mgmt. (purchasing, handling, inventory) consultant
Pr: Ronald A Rittenmeyer
**CFO:* Catherine A Lesjak
**CFO:* Ronald P Vargo
**Treas:* James T Murrin
**Ex VP:* Storrow M Gordon
Sr VP: Pete Karolczak
Sr VP: Sean Kenny
**Sr VP:* Tina M Sivinski
VP: Michael Boustridge
VP: Raymond E Cline Jr
VP: Christopher Dergane
VP: Allen Hammond
VP: Ian Miller
**VP:* Cherri Musser
VP: Ken Quaglio
VP: Michael Spooner
Comm Man: Bob Pena

D-U-N-S 00-100-8697 IMP/EXP
HP HOOD LLC
6 Kimball Ln Ste 400, Lynnfield, MA 01940-2685
Tel (617) 887-8441 *Founded/Ownrshp* 1846
Sales 1.9MMM *EMP* 4,500
Accts Pricewaterhousecoopers Llp Bo
SIC 2026 2024 2022 Fluid milk; Cream, sweet; Yogurt; Ice cream & frozen desserts; Processed cheese
CFO: Gary R Kaneb
Ex VP: James F Walsh
VP: Sorin Hilgen
Creative D: Esan Sivalingam
Rgnl Mgr: Dave Solmen
Area Mgr: Chuck Arnone
Area Mgr: Mark Burford
Genl Mgr: Andy Macdonald
MIS Dir: Jerry Fougere
Mtls Mgr: Wandette Chin
Plnt Mgr: John Marchildon

D-U-N-S 00-912-2532
▲ **HP INC**
1501 Page Mill Rd, Palo Alto, CA 94304-1126
Tel (650) 857-1501 *Founded/Ownrshp* 1939
Sales 48.2MMM *EMP* 287,000
Tkr Sym HPQ *Exch* NYS
SIC 3571 7372 3861 3577 3572 3575 Personal computers (microcomputers); Minicomputers; Prepackaged software; Cameras, still & motion picture (all types); Diazotype (whiteprint) reproduction machines & equipment; Printers, computer; Optical scanning devices; Computer storage devices; Computer terminals
Pr: Dion Weisler
Pr: Van Munoz
COO: Jon Flaxman
CFO: Catherine A Lesjak
Bd of Dir: Laurel Krieger
Bd of Dir: Yogesh Kumar
Ofcr: Tracy S Keogh
Ofcr: Stuart C Pann
Ex VP: John M Hinshaw
Ex VP: Abdo George Kadifa
Ex VP: Mike Koehler
Ex VP: Michael G Nefkens
VP: Joe Ayers
VP: Paul Barker
VP: Ashim Bose
VP: Vincent Brissot
VP: Luciana Broggi
VP: Dominic Brown
VP: Christopher Carey
VP: Rob Chapple
VP: Vivek Chopra
Board of Directors: Aida A Alvarez, Carl Bass, Robert R Bennett, Charles V Bergh, Stephanie A Burns, Mary Anne Citrino, Stacey Mobley, Stacy Brown-Philpot

D-U-N-S 92-980-0118 IMP
HP PELZER AUTOMOTIVE SYSTEMS INC
(*Suby of* HP PELZER HOLDING GMBH)
1175 Crooks Rd, Troy, MI 48084-7136
Tel (248) 280-1010 *Founded/Ownrshp* 1995
Sales 220.0MM^E *EMP* 900
SIC 3061 2273 Automotive rubber goods (mechanical); Carpets & rugs
CEO: John Pendleton
**COO:* Stuart McRobbie
**CFO:* Wayne Robinson
Prgrm Mgr: Antonio Salinas
Sys Mgr: Lori Murdick
Mtls Mgr: Ginger Fryberger
Mtls Mgr: Lori Post
Plnt Mgr: Daniel Benenati
Plnt Mgr: Mike Jenkins
Ql Cn Mgr: Al Damron
Ql Cn Mgr: Tracy Jeffcoat

HPC FOODSERVICE
See HARTFORD PROVISION CO

D-U-N-S 96-869-3502
■ **HPC HOLDINGS LLC**
COMPOSITE GROUP, THE
(*Suby of* BULK MOLDING COMPOUNDS INC) ★
3637 Ridgewood Rd, Fairlawn, OH 44333-3123
Tel (330) 666-3751 *Founded/Ownrshp* 2014
Sales 144.9MM^E *EMP* 690^E
SIC 2821 2655 Molding compounds, plastics; Cans, composite: foil-fiber & other: from purchased fiber
CEO: Terry Morgan
**CFO:* Tom Meola

D-U-N-S 12-624-5872
HPC LLC
HPC SPECIALTY PHARMACY
63 S Royal St Ste 800, Mobile, AL 36602-3235
Tel (251) 441-1990 *Founded/Ownrshp* 2002
Sales 85.0MM *EMP* 90
SIC 5122 Pharmaceuticals
Pr: Todd Vereen
Dir Rx: Cory Wiggins
Sls Dir: Philip Epstein
Nrsg Dir: Jan Wheeler

HPC SPECIALTY PHARMACY
See HPC LLC

HPE
See HEATING AND PLUMBING ENGINEERS INC

HPI
See HOME PRODUCTS INTERNATIONAL INC

HPI
See HEALTHCARE PARTNERS INVESTMENTS LLC

D-U-N-S 07-929-2847
■ **HPL HOUSTON PIPE LINE CO LLC**
(*Suby of* ENERGY TRANSFER EQUITY LP) ★
800 E Sonterra Blvd, San Antonio, TX 78258-3940
Tel (713) 222-0414 *Founded/Ownrshp* 2014
Sales 9.1MM^E *EMP* 1,988^E
SIC 4922 Pipelines, natural gas
Pr: Michael S McConnell

D-U-N-S 07-851-7870
HPM CONSTRUCTION LLC
(*Suby of* HENSEL PHELPS CONSTRUCTION CO) ★
17911 Mitchell S, Irvine, CA 92614-6015
Tel (949) 474-9170 *Founded/Ownrshp* 2012
Sales 300.0MM *EMP* 100
SIC 1542 Nonresidential construction
Pr: Karen Price
Sec: Cuyler McGinley
VP: Cindy McMackin

D-U-N-S 08-676-8814
HPR PARTNERS LLC
801 Warrenville Rd # 550, Lisle, IL 60532-1396
Tel (630) 737-0788 *Founded/Ownrshp* 1998
Sales 131.9MM^E *EMP* 2,000
SIC 5141 Food brokers
CEO: Phillip J Mason

D-U-N-S 01-712-2193
HPS LLC
3275 N M 37 Hwy, Middleville, MI 49333-9126
Tel (269) 795-3308 *Founded/Ownrshp* 1949
Sales 1.0MMM *EMP* 38
Accts Meyaard Tolman & Venlet Pc Z
SIC 7389 Purchasing service
**CFO:* Thomas J La Pres
**Treas:* Dwith Gascho
**Treas:* Joseph Schodde
VP: Thomas Lapres
VP: Mike Sandy
IT Man: Brian McKinley
Mktg Mgr: Kendra Tossava
Manager: Preston Fouts
Manager: Emley Navarro
Manager: Brian Smith
Board of Directors: Marvin Baird

HPSA
See MITSUBISHI HITACHI POWER SYSTEMS AMERICA-ENERGY AND ENVIRONMENT LTD

D-U-N-S 07-945-0246
■ **HPT TRS IHG-2 INC**
(*Suby of* HOSPITALITY PROPERTIES TRUST) ★
255 Washington St Ste 300, Newton, MA 02458-1634
Tel (617) 964-8389 *Founded/Ownrshp* 2005
Sales 138.3MM^E *EMP* 2,812^E
SIC 7011 Hotels & motels
COO: John Murray

D-U-N-S 13-883-8904
HQ GLOBAL WORKPLACES INC
H Q GLOBAL WORKPLACES LLC
(*Suby of* REGUS CORP) ★
15305 Dallas Pkwy Ste 400, Addison, TX 75001-6922
Tel (972) 361-8100 *Founded/Ownrshp* 2004
Sales 46.4MM^E *EMP* 1,190
SIC 6519 7389 Sub-lessors of real estate; Office facilities & secretarial service rental; Telephone answering service; Mailbox rental & related service

HR CAPITAL MANAGEMENT
See PAY STAFF

HR GREEN DEVELOPMENT
See GREEN COMPANIES INC

D-U-N-S 83-199-3501
HR SOLUTIONS LLC
47632 Loweland Ter, Sterling, VA 20165-5143
Tel (703) 493-0084 *Founded/Ownrshp* 2006
Sales 10.0MM *EMP* 5,000
SIC 8742 Human resource consulting services
CEO: Paul Sandhu

HR STRATEGIES
See ALLSTAFF MANAGEMENT INC

D-U-N-S 00-793-3328
▲ **HRG GROUP INC**
450 Park Ave Fl 29, New York, NY 10022-2640
Tel (212) 906-8555 *Founded/Ownrshp* 1954
Sales 5.2MMM *EMP* 15,922
Tkr Sym HRG *Exch* NYS
SIC 3691 3634 3999 6311 Storage batteries; Batteries, rechargeable; Electric household cooking appliances; Pet supplies; Life insurance
Pr: Omar M Asali
**Ch Bd:* Joseph S Steinberg
CFO: George Nicholson
**Ex VP:* David M Maura

D-U-N-S 00-421-2908 IMP/EXP
HRH DOOR CORP
WAYNE DALTON
1 Door Dr, Mount Hope, OH 44660
Tel (850) 208-3400 *Founded/Ownrshp* 2009
Sales 669.3MM^E *EMP* 2,500
SIC 3442 2431 Garage doors, overhead: metal; Garage doors, overhead: wood
CEO: Willis Mullet
**Pr:* Thomas B Bennett III
CFO: Joseph Selogy
Exec: Theresa Rivelli
**Prin:* E E Muller
**Prin:* Alma Mullet
**Prin:* W C Pyers
Genl Mgr: Theresa Labute
Sls Mgr: Kyle Paris

D-U-N-S 07-452-1675
■ **HRH OF NC INC**
(*Suby of* DUKE LIFEPOINT HEALTHCARE) ★
68 Hospital Rd, Sylva, NC 28779-2722
Tel (828) 586-7000 *Founded/Ownrshp* 2014
Sales 184.3MM^E *EMP* 1,144^E
SIC 8062 General medical & surgical hospitals
CEO: William F Carpenter III
Dir OR: Tim Bell
Dept Mgr: Daren Carley
Sfty Dirs: Garnett Coke
Doctor: Rachel Downey

D-U-N-S 07-861-0822
HRHH GAMING SENIOR MEZZ LLC
(*Suby of* HARD ROCK HOTEL HOLDINGS LLC) ★
4455 Paradise Rd, Las Vegas, NV 89169-6574
Tel (702) 693-5026 *Founded/Ownrshp* 2012
Sales 2.7MM^E *EMP* 1,338^E
SIC 7999 Gambling establishment

D-U-N-S 93-094-3951
HRHH HOTEL/CASINO LLC
HARD ROCK HOTEL AND CASINO
(*Suby of* BREF HR LLC) ★
4455 Paradise Rd, Las Vegas, NV 89169-6574
Tel (702) 693-5000 *Founded/Ownrshp* 2011
Sales 200.4MM *EMP* 1,363
SIC 7011 Hotels
CEO: Dean Boswell
**Ch Bd:* Peter A Morton
**Pr:* Frederick Kleisner
CFO: Jody Lake
**Sr VP:* Brian D Ogaz
Genl Mgr: Servando Daniels
Genl Mgr: Cindy Faraci
Natl Sales: Brad Hayden
Natl Sales: Mike Roth
Pr Mgr: Lauren Sasso
Snr Mgr: Robin Young

D-U-N-S 07-718-9541
HRI INC
(*Suby of* COLAS INC) ★
1750 W College Ave, State College, PA 16801-2719
Tel (814) 238-5071 *Founded/Ownrshp* 1998
Sales 316.1MM^E *EMP* 700
SIC 1611 Highway & street construction
Pr: Jeff Lamb
**VP:* Kent Wible
Assoc Dir: Roger Diehl
Area Mgr: Ron Barger
Div Mgr: Travis Boyd
Genl Mgr: Jim Andrews
IT Man: Mike Gampp
IT Man: Mike Sharp
Sfty Dirs: Chris McHugh
Opers Mgr: Jason Lamire
Plnt Mgr: Shawn McFarland

HRSA
See HEALTH RESOURCES & SERVICES ADMINISTRATION

HRSD
See HAMPTON ROADS SANITATION DISTRICT (INC)

HSAA
See HWASEUNG AUTOMOTIVE ALABAMA LLC

HSAA
See HWASEUNG AUTOMOTIVE AMERICA HOLDINGS INC

D-U-N-S 01-661-2660
■ **HSB GROUP INC**
(*Suby of* MUNICH-AMERICAN HOLDING CORP) ★
1 State St, Hartford, CT 06102-8900
Tel (860) 722-1866 *Founded/Ownrshp* 2009
Sales NA *EMP* 2,428^E
SIC 6331 6411 6799 8711 8742 Fire, marine & casualty insurance; Insurance agents, brokers & service; Investors; Engineering services; Management consulting services
CEO: Gregory Barats
Pr: Michelle Kilroy
Pr: Denis M O'Shea
Chf Inves: James C Rowan
Ex VP: Nancy Onken
VP: Susan Ahrens
VP: Roger Royer
VP: J A Smith
Exec: Richard H Booth
Web Dev: Al Tremblay
VP Mktg: Pamela Gorajek
Board of Directors: Theodore Kmiecik, Roberta O'brien, Nancy Onken, Peter Richter

HSB INDUSTRIAL RISK INSURERS
See WESTPORT INSURANCE CORP

HSBC ARENA
See CROSSROADS ARENA LLC

D-U-N-S 13-168-2015 IMP/EXP
HSBC BANK USA
(*Suby of* HSBC USA INC) ★
300 Delaware Ave Ste 1400, Wilmington, DE 19801-1650
Tel (302) 778-0169 *Founded/Ownrshp* 1999
Sales NA *EMP* 6,500
SIC 6022 State commercial banks
Pr: Irene Dorner
Pr: David Goeden
Pr: Andy Ireland
CFO: Robert M Butcher
Sr VP: Irene Grant
Sr VP: Vincent J Mancuso
Sr VP: Daniel A Nissenbaum
VP: Mohamed Mansour
VP: Richard Martin
Exec: Janet L Burak
Exec: George T Wendler

D-U-N-S 82-587-1820
HSBC BANK USA NATIONAL ASSOCIATION
(*Suby of* HSBC USA INC) ★
1800 Tysons Blvd Ste 50, Mc Lean, VA 22102-4267
Tel (800) 975-4722 *Founded/Ownrshp* 1990
Sales NA *EMP* 17^E
SIC 6021 National commercial banks
Pr: Irene Dorner
Sr VP: Lori Vetters

D-U-N-S 05-555-7276
HSBC FINANCE CORP
(*Suby of* HSBC INVESTMENTS (NORTH AMERICA) INC) ★
1421 W Shure Dr Ste 100, Arlington Heights, IL 60004-7818
Tel (224) 880-7000 *Founded/Ownrshp* 1878, 1981
Sales NA *EMP* 1,600^E
SIC 6141 Consumer finance companies
CEO: Kathryn G Madison
**Ch Bd:* Patrick J Burke
CEO: Kathryn Madison
COO: Vittorio Severino
CFO: Michael A Reeves
Ex VP: Julie A Davenport
Ex VP: Loren C Klug
Ex VP: Stephen R Nesbitt
Ex VP: Richard E O'Brien
Ex VP: Karen P Pisarczyk
Sr VP: Jeff Barden
VP: Mark Burnstine
VP: Jaime Saucedo
VP: Mark Seter
Exec: Rhydian H Cox

Board of Directors: Phillip D Ameen, Barry F Kroeger, Samuel Minzberg, Thomas K Whitford

D-U-N-S 62-311-2914
HSBC INVESTMENTS (NORTH AMERICA) INC
(*Suby of* HSBC NORTH AMERICA HOLDINGS INC) ★
2700 Sanders Rd, Prospect Heights, IL 60070-2701
Tel (847) 564-5000 *Founded/Ownrshp* 2003
Sales NA *EMP* 15,650
SIC 6141 7389 6351 6159 6162 6311 Consumer finance companies; Credit card service; Credit & other financial responsibility insurance; Machinery & equipment finance leasing; Mortgage bankers; Life insurance carriers
Ch Bd: William F Aldinger
V Ch: Sandra Derickson
COO: Brendan McDonagh
Assoc VP: Adrian Martinez
Ex VP: Terri Pearce
VP: Thomas Arduino
VP: Thomas P Richardson
Assoc Dir: Barry Caveney
Comm Man: Tony Burkhart
IT Man: Doug Sepanik
Sls&Mrk Ex: James Coyne

D-U-N-S 14-666-8061
HSBC NORTH AMERICA HOLDINGS INC
(*Suby of* HSBC HOLDINGS PLC)
452 5th Ave 7, Lake Forest, IL 60045
Tel (224) 544-4400 *Founded/Ownrshp* 1980
Sales NA *EMP* 25,151[E]
SIC 6351 Credit & other financial responsibility insurance
CEO: Irene Dorner
CEO: Joseph W Hoff
CFO: Edgar D Ancona
Ofcr: Kunal Patel
Ex VP: Thomas M Kimble
Ex VP: Beverley A Sibblies
Sr VP: Bruce A Fletcher
VP: James Strange
Exec: Stephen Bottomley
Exec: Thomas M Detelich
Genl Couns: Kenneth H Robin
Board of Directors: William R P Dalton, Anthea Disney, Robert K Herdman, Louis Hernandez Jr, Richard A Jalkut, George A Lorch, Samuel Minzberg, Beatriz R Perez, John L Thornton

D-U-N-S 07-279-6535
HSBC NORTH AMERICA INC
(*Suby of* HSBC INVESTMENTS (NORTH AMERICA) INC) ★
1 Hsbc Ctr Ste 1, Buffalo, NY 14203-2842
Tel (716) 841-2424 *Founded/Ownrshp* 1999
Sales NA *EMP* 15,650
SIC 6021 6035 6221 6091 6211 National commercial banks; Federal savings banks; Commodity brokers, contracts; Nondeposit trust facilities; Security brokers & dealers
Ch Bd: Irene M Dorner
**COO:* Stephen P Fitzmaurice Rpa
**CFO:* Gerard Mattia
VP: Daniel Komanski

D-U-N-S 05-046-8156
HSBC SECURITIES (USA) INC
(*Suby of* HSBC NORTH AMERICA HOLDINGS INC) ★
107 Iris Glen Dr Se, Conyers, GA 30013-1675
Tel (212) 525-5000 *Founded/Ownrshp* 2005
Sales 192.4MM[E] *EMP* 813
SIC 6211 Security brokers & dealers
Ch Bd: Patrick Nolan
**Pr:* Mark Bucknall
CFO: Karen Almquist
Sr Cor Off: Michael Reeves
Ex VP: Sumeet Chabria
Ex VP: Josh Neyer
Sr VP: Vince Ferrentino
Sr VP: Shane Lovell
Sr VP: Sharyn Malone
Sr VP: Wolfgang Peck
Sr VP: Douglas Yorke
VP: James Carlone
Exec: Steve Carlson
Exec: Scott Jackson

D-U-N-S 00-697-6732
HSBC USA INC
(*Suby of* HSBC NORTH AMERICA INC) ★
107 Iris Glen Dr Se, Conyers, GA 30013-1675
Tel (212) 525-5000 *Founded/Ownrshp* 1973
Sales NA *EMP* 6,500
Accts Pricewaterhousecoopers Llp N
SIC 6021 National commercial banks
Ch Bd: Irene M Dorner
COO: Martyn T Brush
COO: Timothy Hinsdale
**COO:* Gregory T Zeeman
COO: Gregory Zeeman
CFO: Cian Burke
**CFO:* Eric K Ferren
CFO: John T McGinnis
Top Exec: Mario Romaldini
Sr Ex VP: Steven A Bottomley
Sr Ex VP: Patrick A Cozza
Sr Ex VP: Steven G Ekert
Sr Ex VP: Mark A Hershey
Sr Ex VP: Patrick M Nolan
Sr Ex VP: Gary E Peterson
Ex VP: Mary E Bilbrey
Ex VP: Loren C Klug
**Ex VP:* Patrick D Schwartz
Ex VP: Lisa M Sodeika
Ex VP: Suzanne Brienza
Sr VP: John Murray
Board of Directors: Philip Ameen, Jeffrey A Bader, Kevin M Blakely, William R P Dalton, Anthea Disney, Robert K Herdman, Richard A Jalkut, Samuel Minzberg, Nancy G Mistretta

HSBIIC
See HARTFORD STEAM BOILER INSPECTION AND INSURANCE CO

D-U-N-S 12-375-6574
HSCB FOUNDATION INC
450 Clarkson Ave, Brooklyn, NY 11203-2012
Tel (718) 270-3041 *Founded/Ownrshp* 2002
Sales 94.1MM *EMP* 1
SIC 8699 Charitable organization
Pr: Ivan Lintiver
**Pr:* Ivan Lisntziver
**Treas:* Frederick Hammond

D-U-N-S 15-606-5393
HSG RESOURCES INC
(*Suby of* LIST & CLARK COMPANY)
9660 Legler Rd, Shawnee Mission, KS 66219-1291
Tel (913) 492-5920 *Founded/Ownrshp* 1983
Sales 103.8MM[E] *EMP* 115
SIC 1442

D-U-N-S 96-543-0734
HSHS MEDICAL GROUP INC
3051 Hollis Dr 200, Springfield, IL 62704-7450
Tel (217) 492-9696 *Founded/Ownrshp* 2008
Sales 112.4MM *EMP* 600
Accts Crowe Horwath Llp Chicago Il
SIC 8011 Medical centers
CEO: Richard Rolston

HSHS SAINT MARY'S HOSPITAL
See ST MARYS HOSPITAL DECATUR OF HOSPITAL SISTERS OF THIRD ORDER OF ST FRANCIS

HSM SOLUTIONS
See HICKORY SPRINGS MANUFACTURING CO

D-U-N-S 13-043-3407 IMP/EXP
■ HSN IMPROVEMENTS LLC
(*Suby of* CORNERSTONE BRANDS INC) ★
16501 Rockside Rd, Maple Heights, OH 44137-4323
Tel (216) 662-6553 *Founded/Ownrshp* 2001
Sales 111.3MM[E] *EMP* 1,500[E]
SIC 5961 Catalog sales

D-U-N-S 82-818-3140 IMP/EXP
▲ HSN INC
1 Hsn Dr, Saint Petersburg, FL 33729-0001
Tel (727) 872-1000 *Founded/Ownrshp* 1981
Sales 3.6MMM *EMP* 6,600[E]
Tkr Sym HSNI *Exch* NGS
SIC 5961 5331 5712 Catalog & mail-order houses; Variety stores; Furniture stores
CEO: Mindy Grossman
Sr Pt: Christy McGraw
**Ch Bd:* Arthur C Martinez
COO: Judy A Schmeling
Chf Mktg O: William C Brand
Ofcr: Maria Martinez
Ex VP: Steve Armstrong
Ex VP: John Aylward
Ex VP: Brian Bradley
Ex VP: Julie Campbell
Ex VP: Lisa Letizio
Ex VP: Ryan Ross
Ex VP: Rob Solomon
Sr VP: Michael Attinella
Sr VP: Robert Monti
VP: Gregory Baker
VP: Sean Bunner
VP: Bryon Colby
VP: Sandy Conrad
VP: Erick Cortes
VP: Jane Dyer
Board of Directors: William Costello, Fiona Dias, James M Follo, Stephanie Kugelman, Thomas J McInerney, John B Morse Jr, Matthew E Rubel, Ann Sarnoff

D-U-N-S 07-690-2113 IMP
■ HSN LLC
(*Suby of* HSN INC) ★
1 Hsn Dr, Saint Petersburg, FL 33729-0001
Tel (727) 872-1000 *Founded/Ownrshp* 1986
Sales 725.4MM[E] *EMP* 3,650
SIC 5961 General merchandise, mail order; Mail order house
CEO: Mindy F Grossman
Pt: Jeff Beck
**Pr:* Bill Brand
COO: Mark Ethier
**COO:* Judy Schmeling
**CFO:* Michael Attinella
Ex VP: Mary Ellen Pollin
Sr VP: Jay Herratti
VP: Kris Kulesza
VP: Lisa Letizio
VP: Jane Smith
VP: Roderick White

D-U-N-S 10-429-9628 IMP/EXP
■ HSNI LLC
(*Suby of* HSN INC) ★
1 Hsn Dr, Saint Petersburg, FL 33729-0001
Tel (727) 872-1000 *Founded/Ownrshp* 1998
Sales 55.6MM[E] *EMP* 2,100
SIC 5961 Television, home shopping
CEO: Mindy Grossman
COO: Judy Schmeling
CFO: Michael J Attinella
Ex VP: Robert Monti
Ex VP: Rob Solomon
VP: Arthur Martinez

D-U-N-S 07-884-1917
HSP EPI ACQUISITION LLC
ENTERTAINMENT
1401 Crooks Rd Ste 150, Troy, MI 48084-7106
Tel (248) 404-1520 *Founded/Ownrshp* 2012
Sales 213.8MM[E] *EMP* 488[E]
SIC 2731 Books: publishing only

D-U-N-S 07-341-5267
HSS INC
HOSPITAL SHARED SERVICES
900 S Broadway Ste 100, Denver, CO 80209-4269
Tel (303) 603-3000 *Founded/Ownrshp* 1967
Sales 119.8MM *EMP* 2,600
Accts Hein & Associates Llp Denver
SIC 8082 7381 7382 Home health care services; Security guard service; Protective devices, security
Pr: Wayne Schell
COO: Tony W York
**CFO:* Mike Ratkiewicz
Ofcr: Tevita Mahe
Ofcr: Samir Singh
IT Man: Ken Greenwald
Opers Mgr: Nate Brown
Opers Mgr: Glenn Spies

D-U-N-S 05-759-8729
HSS LLC
VALUEPOINT MATERIAL SOLUTIONS
5310 Hampton Pl Ste B, Saginaw, MI 48604-8202
Tel (989) 777-2983 *Founded/Ownrshp* 1999
Sales 129.6MM[E] *EMP* 139
SIC 8741 8742 7389 Management services; Materials mgmt. (purchasing, handling, inventory) consultant; Purchasing service
CEO: Eric Larson
**Prin:* Phil Shaltz
**Prin:* Scott Shively

D-U-N-S 01-925-3160
■ HST LESSEE BOSTON LLC
SHERATON BOSTON
(*Suby of* STARWOOD HOTELS & RESORTS WORLDWIDE LLC) ★
39 Dalton St, Boston, MA 02199-3901
Tel (617) 236-2000 *Founded/Ownrshp* 1965
Sales 68.8MM[E] *EMP* 1,140
SIC 7011 5812 7299 5813 Hotels & motels; Eating places; Banquet hall facilities; Drinking places
Treas: Gregory Larson
VP: Lloyd Macneil
VP: Susan McDonnell
Mng Dir: Colleen Keating

D-U-N-S 07-929-1995 IMP
HT INTERMEDIATE CO LLC
9825 Spectrum Dr Bldg 3, Austin, TX 78717-4930
Tel (512) 328-2892 *Founded/Ownrshp* 2014
Sales 187.4MM[E] *EMP* 658[E]
SIC 3845 Lithotripters

D-U-N-S 80-109-5696
HTC GLOBAL SERVICES INC
HI TECH CONSULTANTS
3270 W Big Beaver Rd # 100, Troy, MI 48084-2901
Tel (248) 786-2500 *Founded/Ownrshp* 1990
Sales 187.5MM[E] *EMP* 1,200
SIC 7379 Computer related consulting services
CEO: Madhava Reddy
Ex VP: Shami Khorana
**Ex VP:* Chary Mudumby
Sr VP: Greg Fisher
**VP:* Girish Arora
**VP:* Fredric Hagelton
**VP:* James Joseph
VP: Krishnan Prasad
VP: Sutbir Randhawa
**VP:* Narayan Renga
VP Bus Dev: Rolf Carlson
Dir Bus: Karan Panwar
Board of Directors: Sunil Jacob- Dir Laurie Ma

HTE TECHNOLOGIES
See HOUSE OF TOOLS AND ENGINEERING INC

D-U-N-S 08-455-6661
HTH CORP (HI)
1668 S King St Fl 2, Honolulu, HI 96826-2074
Tel (808) 469-4111 *Founded/Ownrshp* 1975, 2004
Sales 76.4MM[E] *EMP* 1,250
SIC 7011 5812 6512 Resort hotel; Eating places; Commercial & industrial building operation
CEO: Corine Watanabe
**Pr:* John Hayashi
**CFO:* Lauralei Taraka
**VP:* Robert Minicola
Dir IT: Frederic Chau
Board of Directors: Corine Hayashi

D-U-N-S 11-849-2768
HTI LTD
HUNTON TRANE
10555 Westpark Dr, Houston, TX 77042-5232
Tel (713) 266-3900 *Founded/Ownrshp* 1999
Sales 265.4MM[E] *EMP* 450
SIC 5075 Air conditioning equipment, except room units; Warm air heating equipment & supplies
Pr: Richard Hunton
Pr: Craig Becker
COO: Richard O Hunton Jr
CFO: Bruce Seher
Sr VP: Brad Lacy
VP: Larry Bower
VP: Albert Mireles
VP: Kevin Murphy
VP: Ron Shepherd
VP: Robert Tyler
MIS Dir: Louis Bergh

D-U-N-S 06-713-4502
■ HTI MEMORIAL HOSPITAL CORP (TN)
COLUMBIA HCA
(*Suby of* HOSPITAL COPORATION OF AMERICA) ★
3441 Dickerson Pike, Nashville, TN 37207-2539
Tel (615) 769-2000 *Founded/Ownrshp* 1959, 1995
Sales 246.2MM *EMP* 1,250
SIC 8062 General medical & surgical hospitals
Pr: Steve Otto
Snr Mgr: Melissa Osesek

D-U-N-S 82-553-2088 IMP
HTM USA HOLDINGS INC
HEAD TYROLIA WINTER SPORTS
(*Suby of* HEAD SPORT GMBH)
3125 Sterling Cir Ste 101, Boulder, CO 80301-2394
Tel (800) 874-3235 *Founded/Ownrshp* 1993
Sales 147.8MM[E] *EMP* 600
SIC 5091 5139 3949 Racquet sports equipment & supplies; Golf equipment; Diving equipment & supplies; Skiing equipment; Footwear, athletic; Sporting & athletic goods
Pr: David Haggerty
**Treas:* Ralf Bernhart
**VP:* Klaus Hotter
**VP Sls:* Robert Langlois

D-U-N-S 08-480-5860 IMP
HTP INC
HEAT TRANSFER PRODUCTS
272 Duchaine Blvd, New Bedford, MA 02745-1222
Tel (508) 763-8071 *Founded/Ownrshp* 1983
Sales 172.7MM[E] *EMP* 200
SIC 5084 3443 Heat exchange equipment, industrial; Heat exchangers, condensers & components
CEO: David B Davis
**Pr:* David R Martin
Natl Sales: Brad Monaghan
VP Sls: Todd Romig
Art Dir: Tony Rennick

D-U-N-S 79-150-5626
HTS ACQUISITION INC
HIGHWAY TECHNOLOGIES GROUP
915 Harger Rd, Oak Brook, IL 60523-1497
Tel (630) 368-0920 *Founded/Ownrshp* 2007
Sales NA *EMP* 1,500
SIC 3646 3229 3645

D-U-N-S 00-508-5972 IMP
HU-FRIEDY MFG CO LLC (IL)
AMERICAN DENTAL
3232 N Rockwell St, Chicago, IL 60618-5935
Tel (773) 975-3975 *Founded/Ownrshp* 1908
Sales 116.0MM[E] *EMP* 625[E]
SIC 3843 Dental hand instruments
Ch Bd: Ron Saslow
**Pr:* Ken Serota
**Ch:* Dick Saslow
Exec: Sandy Youngren
Genl Mgr: Dolly Ayala
IT Man: Richard Shapiro
Mktg Dir: Patrick Bernardi

D-U-N-S 84-891-4016
HUALALAI INVESTORS LLC
100 Kaupulehu Dr, Kailua Kona, HI 96740-5699
Tel (808) 325-8400 *Founded/Ownrshp* 2006
Sales 231.1MM[E] *EMP* 758[E]
SIC 6552 Land subdividers & developers, commercial

D-U-N-S 07-828-4967 IMP
HUAWEI DEVICE USA INC
(*Suby of* HUAWEI INVESTMENT & HOLDINGS CO., LTD.)
5700 Tennyson Pkwy # 600, Plano, TX 75024-3583
Tel (214) 919-6688 *Founded/Ownrshp* 2010
Sales 153.0MM[E] *EMP* 500[E]
SIC 3663 Cellular radio telephone
Pr: Zhiqiang Xu
**Treas:* Ailing Lin
**Prin:* Jiangao Cui

D-U-N-S 05-848-1986
HUAWEI TECHNOLOGIES USA INC
(*Suby of* HUAWEI TECHNOLOGY CO.,LTD.)
5700 Tennyson Pkwy # 500, Plano, TX 75024-7157
Tel (214) 545-3700 *Founded/Ownrshp* 2011
Sales 124.4MM[E] *EMP* 860[E]
SIC 8748 Telecommunications consultant
Pr: Ming He
**Pr:* Charles Ding
Top Exec: Suresh Vaidyanathan
Sr VP: George Reed
VP: Jerry Prestinario
Mng Dir: Zhan Bo
VP Sls: Bill Gerski
Mktg Dir: Joy Tan
Pr Mgr: Sing Wang

D-U-N-S 02-883-0115 IMP
HUB DISTRIBUTING INC
ANCHOR BLUE
(*Suby of* SUN CAPITAL PARTNERS INC) ★
1260 Corona Pointe Ct, Corona, CA 92879-5013
Tel (951) 340-3149 *Founded/Ownrshp* 2003
Sales 231.1MM[E] *EMP* 3,000
SIC 5611 5621 5632 5137 5136 5094 Men's & boys' clothing stores; Women's clothing stores; Apparel accessories; Women's & children's clothing; Men's & boys' clothing; Jewelry & precious stones
CEO: Thomas Sands
Treas: Scott Rosner
**Treas:* Thomas Shaw
VP: Andrew Boada
VP Mktg: Erik Forsell

D-U-N-S 00-102-3613 IMP
HUB FOLDING BOX CO INC (MA)
PLASTIC TECHNOLOGY DIVISION
774 Norfolk St, Mansfield, MA 02048-1826
Tel (508) 339-0005 *Founded/Ownrshp* 1921, 1955
Sales 138.4MM[E] *EMP* 315
SIC 2657 Folding paperboard boxes
Pr: Alfred Dirico
CFO: Hal Wilmot
**VP:* Anthony H Dirico
Creative D: Zane Peterson
Off Mgr: Pat Silvia
QA Dir: Craig Stoetzel
Dir IT: Carl Schneider
Mfg Mgr: Bryon Brandow
Plnt Mgr: Rich Kline
Prd Mgr: Art Todd
Ql Cn Mgr: John Proterra

D-U-N-S 15-514-3480
▲ HUB GROUP INC
2000 Clearwater Dr, Oak Brook, IL 60523-8809
Tel (630) 271-3600 *Founded/Ownrshp* 1971
Sales 3.5MMM *EMP* 2,633
Tkr Sym HUBG *Exch* NGS
SIC 4731 Transportation agents & brokers; Brokers, shipping; Truck transportation brokers; Freight forwarding
Ch Bd: David P Yeager
V Ch: Mark Yeager
Pr: Brian D Alexander
Pr: James J Damman
Pr: Brandi P Kelly
**Pr:* Donald G Maltby
Pr: Bob Ramey
Pr: John C Vesco
CFO: Joseph Hyde

CFO: Terri A Pizzuto
Chf Mktg O: Christopher Kravas
Ex VP: James B Gaw
Ex VP: Vincent C Paperiello
Ex VP: Phillip D Yeager
VP: Douglas G Beck
VP: Richard Onken
Board of Directors: Gary D Eppen, James C Kenny, Charles R Reaves, Martin P Slark, Jonathan P Ward

D-U-N-S 10-180-2072
■ HUB GROUP TRUCKING INC
HGT
(*Suby of* HUB CITY TERMINALS, INC.)
2000 Clearwater Dr, Oak Brook, IL 60523-8809
Tel (630) 271-3600 *Founded/Ownrshp* 2006
Sales 81.3MM^E *EMP* 1,435
SIC 4212 Draying, local: without storage
**VP:* Bob Rhodes

D-U-N-S 06-120-4012
HUB INTERNATIONAL GROUP NORTHEAST INC
HUB INTERNATIONAL NE
(*Suby of* HUB INTERNATIONAL LIMITED) ★
5 Bryant Park Fl 4, New York, NY 10018
Tel (212) 338-2000 *Founded/Ownrshp* 2013
Sales NA *EMP* 346
SIC 6411 Insurance brokers
CEO: Mark Cohen
Bd of Dir: Martin Hughes
**Sr VP:* James E Hutchinson
Sr VP: Robert Shcolnik
VP: Robert Fiorito
VP: Rachel Romero
**VP:* Lucille Feldman Warner

D-U-N-S 60-965-7056
HUB INTERNATIONAL INSURANCE SERVICES INC
PETERSON MILANEY INSUR ASSOC
(*Suby of* HUB INTERNATIONAL LIMITED) ★
3390 University Ave # 300, Riverside, CA 92501-3314
Tel (951) 788-8500 *Founded/Ownrshp* 1988
Sales NA *EMP* 1,163
SIC 6411 Insurance agents, brokers & service
CEO: Roy H Taylor
**Pr:* Kirk Christ
**Ex VP:* Travis McElvany
**Exec:* Andrew Forchelli

D-U-N-S 78-436-8586
HUB INTERNATIONAL LIMITED
(*Suby of* HELLMAN & FRIEDMAN LLC) ★
300 N La Salle Dr Ste 17, Chicago, IL 60654-3406
Tel (312) 596-7522 *Founded/Ownrshp* 2013
Sales NA *EMP* 8,055
SIC 6411 Insurance agents, brokers & service; Property & casualty insurance agent
Ch Bd: Martin Hughes
Pr: Richard Gulliver
CFO: Joseph Hyde

D-U-N-S 09-594-2371
HUB INTERNATIONAL MIDWEST LTD
(*Suby of* HUB INTERNATIONAL LIMITED) ★
55 E Jackson Blvd 1400a, Chicago, IL 60604-4102
Tel (312) 922-5000 *Founded/Ownrshp* 2006
Sales NA *EMP* 717
SIC 6411 Insurance agents; Life insurance agents
Pr: Neil Hughes
**Ex VP:* Rick Havron
**Ex VP:* Bobby Simms
**Ex VP:* Steve Simms
**VP:* Philip Adler
**VP:* Jason Romick
IT Man: Michael Farley

HUB INTERNATIONAL NE
See HUB INTERNATIONAL GROUP NORTHEAST INC

D-U-N-S 07-414-7232
HUB INTERNATIONAL OF CALIFORNIA INC
(*Suby of* HUB INTERNATIONAL LIMITED) ★
6701 Center Dr W Ste 1500, Los Angeles, CA 90045-1561
Tel (310) 568-5900 *Founded/Ownrshp* 2002
Sales NA *EMP* 158^E
SIC 6411 Insurance brokers
Pr: Frank C Hayes
Sr VP: Antonio Casabat
Sr VP: Shanning Vanoni
**VP:* Kathy Quintana

D-U-N-S 06-849-8625
HUB INTERNATIONAL OF ILLINOIS LIMITED
MACK AND PARKER
(*Suby of* HUB INTERNATIONAL LIMITED) ★
300 N Lslle St Fl 17, Chicago, IL 60654
Tel (312) 922-5000 *Founded/Ownrshp* 2006
Sales NA *EMP* 500
SIC 6411 Insurance brokers
Pr: Mike Ahlert
**Pr:* Richard A Gulliver
**CFO:* Tom Musson
**Ch:* Martin P Hughes
**Sr VP:* Sam Valeo
**VP:* Richard Babb
**VP:* Kenneth Rosinski

D-U-N-S 00-696-1932
HUBBARD BROADCASTING INC
3415 University Ave W, Saint Paul, MN 55114-2099
Tel (651) 642-4656 *Founded/Ownrshp* 1921
Sales 330.7MM^E *EMP* 1,200
SIC 4833 7812 4832

D-U-N-S 00-692-3197 EXP
HUBBARD CONSTRUCTION CO (FL)
MID-FLORIDA MATERIALS DIVISION
(*Suby of* HUBBARD GROUP INC) ★
1936 Lee Rd Ste 101, Winter Park, FL 32789-7201
Tel (407) 645-5500 *Founded/Ownrshp* 1920
Sales 381.1MM^E *EMP* 712
Accts Deloitte & Touche Llp Tampa
SIC 1611 2951 1623 General contractor, highway & street construction; Highway & street paving contractor; Asphalt & asphaltic paving mixtures (not from refineries); Sewer line construction
Prin: Patrick Sulliot
**CEO:* Alan M Cahill
**CFO:* P Frederick O DEA Jr
**Ch:* Pierre Anjolras
VP: Phil Anderson
VP: Paul Giles
Div Mgr: Joe Kanaday

D-U-N-S 36-111-4861
HUBBARD GROUP INC
(*Suby of* GECOS INC) ★
1936 Lee Rd Ste 101, Winter Park, FL 32789-7201
Tel (407) 645-5500 *Founded/Ownrshp* 1988
Sales 590.4MM^E *EMP* 900
Accts Deloitte & Touche Llp Tampa
SIC 1611 2951 1623 General contractor, highway & street construction; Asphalt & asphaltic paving mixtures (not from refineries); Sewer line construction
Pr: William J Capehart
COO: Kurt Klinect
CFO: P Frederick Odea Jr
Sec: P Frederick O'Dea Jr
VP: Bill Capehart
Exec: John Hubbard
Div Mgr: Tony Geach

HUBBELL GLOBAL OPERATIONS
See HUBBELL LIGHTING INC

D-U-N-S 00-118-1858 IMP
▲ HUBBELL INC
40 Waterview Dr, Shelton, CT 06484-4300
Tel (475) 882-4000 *Founded/Ownrshp* 1888
Sales 3.3MMM *EMP* 16,200
Accts Pricewaterhousecoopers Llp Ha
Tkr Sym HUBB *Exch* NYS
SIC 3643 Current-carrying wiring devices
Ch Bd: David G Nord
Pr: Gerben W Bakker
Pr: Kevin A Poyck
Pr: Rodd R Ruland
Pr: Darrin S Wegman
CFO: William R Sperry
Treas: Maria R Lee
Sr VP: An-Ping Hsieh
Sr VP: William T Tolley
VP: Joseph A Capozzoli
VP: John Carr
VP: Mac Criswell
VP: Kevin P Ryan
Board of Directors: Carlos M Cardoso, Anthony J Guzzi, Neal J Keating, John F Malloy, Judith F Marks, John G Russell, Steven R Shawley, Richard J Swift

D-U-N-S 00-510-5994 IMP
■ HUBBELL INC (DELAWARE)
HUBBELL RACO DIVISION
(*Suby of* HUBBELL INC) ★
3902 W Sample St, South Bend, IN 46619-2933
Tel (574) 234-7151 *Founded/Ownrshp* 1933, 1981
Sales 278.5MM^E *EMP* 2,300
SIC 3644 3699 3613 Outlet boxes (electric wiring devices); Electrical equipment & supplies; Switchgear & switchboard apparatus
Pr: Timothy H Powers
**Pr:* Gary N Amato
CFO: Bob Bates
**Treas:* James H Biggart
VP: Wesson M Brown
Natl Sales: Joseph Dani
Mktg Mgr: Wanda Korcz

D-U-N-S 18-817-6499 IMP/EXP
■ HUBBELL INDUSTRIAL CONTROLS INC
FEMCO RADIO CONTROLS
(*Suby of* HUBBELL INC) ★
4301 Cheyenne Dr, Archdale, NC 27263-3246
Tel (336) 434-2800 *Founded/Ownrshp* 1985
Sales 92.5MM^E *EMP* 350
SIC 3625 Motor controls, electric
Ch Bd: Timothy H Powers
**CEO:* David G Nord
**CFO:* William Tolley
**Treas:* James H Biggart Jr
**VP:* Gary N Amato
**VP:* Gerben W Bakker
Snr Sftwr: Jonathan King
Opers Mgr: D King
Sls Mgr: R C Roll

D-U-N-S 80-453-8817 IMP/EXP
■ HUBBELL LIGHTING INC
HUBBELL GLOBAL OPERATIONS
(*Suby of* HUBBELL INC) ★
701 Millennium Blvd, Greenville, SC 29607-5251
Tel (864) 678-1000 *Founded/Ownrshp* 1985
Sales 1.0MMM^E *EMP* 1,215
SIC 3648 Lighting equipment; Outdoor lighting equipment
Pr: Scott H Muse
Pr: Paul Ross
**Treas:* James H Biggart
Ofcr: Nicole Hill
VP: Tom Benton
**VP:* Wayne A Cable
**VP:* Richard W Davies
VP: Ron Newbold
VP: Kenneth Page
VP: William Sperry
VP: Chris Stockton
VP: Kent Welke

D-U-N-S 04-826-5974 IMP/EXP
■ HUBBELL POWER SYSTEMS INC
(*Suby of* HUBBELL INC) ★
200 Center Point Cir # 200, Columbia, SC 29210-5894
Tel (803) 216-2600 *Founded/Ownrshp* 1994
Sales 411.2MM^E *EMP* 1,200
SIC 3643 Current-carrying wiring devices
Pr: William Tolley
Pr: Patrick Clemente
VP: Mike Estes
**VP:* Kevin Potts
VP: Brian Serati
IT Man: Mark Admar
Mktg Mgr: Richard Hesson
Sls Mgr: Brian Johannssen

HUBBELL RACO DIVISION
See HUBBELL INC (DELAWARE)

HUBELL CARIBE LIMITED
See HARVEY HUBBELL CARIBE INC

D-U-N-S 15-531-7522 IMP
HUBER + SUHNER INC
(*Suby of* HUBER + SUHNER (USA) CORPORATION)
8530 Steele Creek Place D, Charlotte, NC 28273-4277
Tel (704) 790-7300 *Founded/Ownrshp* 1986
Sales 120.0MM *EMP* 75
SIC 3679 3678 3357 5065 Microwave components; Electronic connectors; Nonferrous wiredrawing & insulating; Electronic parts & equipment
Pr: Andy Hollywood
COO: URS Ryffel
CFO: Bernhard Schwarzer
CFO: Ivo Wechsler
**Treas:* Sean Thomas
Ofcr: Peter Schmid
VP: Stephan Hofstetter
VP: Drew Nixon
Genl Mgr: Mike Canfield
CTO: Peter Baumann
IT Man: Sam Higgins

D-U-N-S 15-129-4696 EXP
HUBER ENGINEERED WOODS LLC
(*Suby of* JM HUBER CORP) ★
10925 David Taylor Dr, Charlotte, NC 28262-1040
Tel (704) 547-0671 *Founded/Ownrshp* 2003
Sales 159.9MM^E *EMP* 515
SIC 2493 Reconstituted wood products
Pr: Albert Landers
IT Man: Ben Bynoe
IT Man: Todd Hair
Plnt Mgr: Mike Walker
Manager: Heath Walker
Genl Couns: Michael Ditano

D-U-N-S 00-427-0997 IMP/EXP
HUBERT CO LLC
(*Suby of* FRANZ HANIEL & CIE. GMBH)
9555 Dry Fork Rd, Harrison, OH 45030-1994
Tel (513) 367-8600 *Founded/Ownrshp* 1946, 2000
Sales 208.0MM^E *EMP* 309
SIC 5046 Store fixtures; Store equipment; Display equipment, except refrigerated
Pr: Bert Kohler
CFO: Robert Pickering
VP: Charles Dennis
VP: Mark Rudy
VP: Brad Sherman
Exec: Lisa Sant
Exec: Lisa Van Sant
Genl Mgr: Chris Lewis
Off Mgr: Liz Oneill
IT Man: Cheryl Meiser
IT Man: Amy Pettit

D-U-N-S 00-531-5233
▲ HUBSPOT INC
25 1st St Ste 200, Cambridge, MA 02141-1814
Tel (888) 482-7768 *Founded/Ownrshp* 2005
Sales 181.9MM *EMP* 1,157
Accts Deloitte & Touche Llp Boston
Tkr Sym HUBS *Exch* NYS
SIC 7372 Prepackaged software; Business oriented computer software
Ch Bd: Brian Halligan
Pr: J D Sherman
COO: JD Sherman
CFO: John Kinzer
Chf Mktg O: Kipp Bodnar
Ofcr: Mark Roberge
VP: Katie Burke
VP: Alison Elworthy
VP: Cindy Goodrich
VP: Nataly Kelly
VP: David McNeil
VP: Yoav Shapira
Board of Directors: Larry Bohn, Ron Gill, Julie Herendeen, Lorrie Norrington, Michael Simon, David Skok

D-U-N-S 00-535-4436 IMP
■ HUCK INTERNATIONAL INC
ALCOA FASTENING SYSTEMS RINGS
(*Suby of* ARCONIC FSTENING SYSTEMS RINGS) ★
3724 E Columbia St, Tucson, AZ 85714-3410
Tel (520) 519-7400 *Founded/Ownrshp* 1940, 1991
Sales 268.1MM^E *EMP* 1,600
SIC 3429 3452 Aircraft hardware; Metal fasteners; Nuts, metal
Pr: Olivier Jarrault
**Treas:* Peter Hong
VP Sls: Terry Keenaghan

HUCKLEBERRY'S FRESH MARKETS
See ROSAUERS SUPERMARKETS INC

HUCK'S
See MARTIN & BAYLEY INC

HUDD TRANSPORATION
See DAMCO DISTRIBUTION SERVICES INC

D-U-N-S 05-915-4968
HUDSON CITY BANCORP INC
W80 Century Rd, Paramus, NJ 07652
Tel (201) 967-1900 *Founded/Ownrshp* 1999
Sales NA *EMP* 1,581^E
SIC 6035

D-U-N-S 07-514-1309
HUDSON CITY SAVINGS BANK
80 W Century Rd, Paramus, NJ 07652-1478
Tel (201) 967-1900 *Founded/Ownrshp* 1999
Sales NA *EMP* 1,260
SIC 6035 6163

D-U-N-S 00-350-1640 EXP
HUDSON CONSTRUCTION CO (TN)
JAMES C HUDSON CONSTRUCTION CO
1615 Sholar Ave, Chattanooga, TN 37406-2800
Tel (423) 624-2631 *Founded/Ownrshp* 1956, 1963
Sales 119.6MM^E *EMP* 60
Accts Johnson Hickey Murchison Chat
SIC 1542 Commercial & office building, new construction
Pr: Steven T Hudson
Treas: William Hines
**Sec:* Wanda Padgett
**VP:* Stanley Hendon
Mng Dir: Ralph Maddux
Admn Mgr: Larry Mason
Site Mgr: Leslee Edwards-Moore
Sfty Mgr: Sandy Cantrell

HUDSON COUNTY CORRECTIONAL CTR
See COUNTY OF HUDSON

HUDSON GARDENS
See AAH HUDSON LP

D-U-N-S 12-913-3463
▲ HUDSON GLOBAL INC
1325 Avenue Of The Americ, New York, NY 10019-6071
Tel (212) 351-7300 *Founded/Ownrshp* 2003
Sales 463.2MM *EMP* 1,600^E
Tkr Sym HSON *Exch* NGS
SIC 7361 7363 Employment agencies; Executive placement; Help supply services; Temporary help service
CEO: Stephen A Nolan
**Ch Bd:* Jeffrey E Eberwein
CFO: Patrick Lyons
Sr VP: David F Kirby
Board of Directors: Alan L Bazaar, Richard K Coleman Jr, Jeffrey E Eberwein, Ian V Nash

D-U-N-S 96-879-0811 IMP
HUDSON GROUP (HG) INC
(*Suby of* DUFRY AG)
1 Meadowlands Plz, East Rutherford, NJ 07073-2150
Tel (201) 939-5050 *Founded/Ownrshp* 2007
Sales 1.2MMM^E *EMP* 5,000^E
SIC 2731 Book publishing
Pr: Joseph Didomizio
Pt: Courtney Thornton
Pr: Brian Berkner
**COO:* Roger Fordyce
CFO: Catherine Oberg
**Treas:* William Wolf
Chf Mktg O: Michael Levy
**Ex VP:* Michael Mullaney
Sr VP: Doug Martino
Sr VP: Mike Petersen
Sr VP: Andy Rattner
Sr VP: Bobby Watson
Sr VP: Bill Wolf Sr
VP: Laura P Alphran
VP: Ray Bowen
VP: Mark Rickoff
VP: Laura Samuels
VP: Gary Schwartz
Creative D: Steve Goulbourne

D-U-N-S 16-162-4853
HUDSON HEALTH PLAN INC
MVP HEALTH CARE
303 S Broadway Ste 321, Tarrytown, NY 10591-5455
Tel (800) 339-4557 *Founded/Ownrshp* 1985
Sales NA *EMP* 225
SIC 6321

D-U-N-S 06-580-7059
HUDSON HEALTHCARE INC
HOBOKEN UNIVERSITY MEDICAL CTR
308 Willow Ave, Hoboken, NJ 07030-3808
Tel (201) 418-1000 *Founded/Ownrshp* 2011
Sales NA *EMP* 1,125
SIC 8062

D-U-N-S 07-854-1051
HUDSON HOSPITAL OPCO LLC
CHRIST HOSPITAL
176 Palisade Ave, Jersey City, NJ 07306-1121
Tel (201) 795-8200 *Founded/Ownrshp* 2012
Sales 125.2MM *EMP* 1,350
SIC 8062 General medical & surgical hospitals
CEO: Peter Kelly
Pr: Doreen Wilde
CFO: George Popco
**CFO:* Patrick Ryan
Ofcr: Margaret Casey
**VP:* William Atkinson
**VP:* Nizar Kifaieh
**VP:* Allyson Miller
Pharmcst: Lisette Acevedo

D-U-N-S 82-673-8051
HUDSON HOTEL BAR
356 W 58th St, New York, NY 10019-1804
Tel (212) 554-6000 *Founded/Ownrshp* 2008
Sales 72.9MM^E *EMP* 5,000
SIC 7011 Hotels & motels
CEO: Michael Gross
Board of Directors: Michael Gross

D-U-N-S 61-476-7713
HUDSON HOTELS CORP
400 Linden Oaks Ste 120, Rochester, NY 14625-2818
Tel (585) 419-4000 *Founded/Ownrshp* 1996
Sales 7.0MM^E *EMP* 1,500
SIC 7011 8741 Hotels; Hotel or motel management
Pr: Thomas W Blank

D-U-N-S 80-622-6960
HUDSON INSURANCE CO
(*Suby of* ODYSSEY RE HOLDINGS CORP) ★
100 William St Fl 5, New York, NY 10038-5044
Tel (212) 978-2800 *Founded/Ownrshp* 2007
Sales NA *EMP* 125
SIC 6311 Life insurance
Pr: Christopher Gallagher

D-U-N-S 06-534-7044
HUDSON LEASECO LLC
356 W 58th St, New York, NY 10019-1804
Tel (212) 247-2353 *Founded/Ownrshp* 2000
Sales 150.0MM *EMP* 535
SIC 6719 Investment holding companies, except banks
Chf Mktg O: Laura Turk

D-U-N-S 00-385-5715
HUDSON NEWS DISTRIBUTORS LLC
(*Suby of* DUFRY AG)
701 Jefferson Rd, Parsippany, NJ 07054-3718
Tel (201) 867-3600 *Founded/Ownrshp* 1960
Sales 1.3MMM^E *EMP* 1,606^E
SIC 5192 Magazines; Books; Newspapers
Ch Bd: James S Cohen
**COO:* Ronald Clark
Ofcr: Ryan Scanlan
Dir IT: Harsha Mahadav

D-U-N-S 96-360-8265
▲ HUDSON PACIFIC PROPERTIES INC
11601 Wilshire Blvd Fl 6, Los Angeles, CA 90025-0509
Tel (310) 445-5700 *Founded/Ownrshp* 2009
Sales 520.8MM *EMP* 234^E
Tkr Sym HPP *Exch* NYS
SIC 6798 Real estate investment trusts
Ch Bd: Victor J Coleman
Pr: Jim Soutter
COO: Mark T Lammas
Chf Inves: Alexander Vouvalides
Ofcr: Steven M Jaffe
Ex VP: Christopher J Barton
Ex VP: Joshua Hatfield
Ex VP: Dale Shimoda
Ex VP: Arthur X Suazo
Ex VP: Kay L Tidwell
Sr VP: Drew Gordon
Sr VP: Gary Hansel
Sr VP: David Tye
Board of Directors: Theodore R Antenucci, Frank Cohen, Richard B Fried, Jonathan M Glaser, Robert L Harris II, Mark D Linehan, Robert M Moran Jr, Michael Nash, Barry A Porter

HUDSON POINTE AT RIVERDALE CEN
See RIVERDALE CENTER FOR NURSING AND REHABILITATION LLC

D-U-N-S 02-660-6863 IMP/EXP
HUDSON PRODUCTS CORP
(*Suby of* HUDSON PRODUCTS HOLDINGS INC) ★
9660 Grunwald Rd, Beasley, TX 77417-8600
Tel (281) 396-8195 *Founded/Ownrshp* 1967
Sales 161.0MM^E *EMP* 505
SIC 3443 Heat exchangers, condensers & components
Pr: Grady Walker
CFO: Steve Brewer
**VP:* Darrell Zahn
IT Man: Robert J Giammaruti

D-U-N-S 82-826-0146
HUDSON PRODUCTS HOLDINGS INC
9660 Grunwald Rd, Beasley, TX 77417-8600
Tel (281) 396-8100 *Founded/Ownrshp* 2006
Sales 184.6MM^E *EMP* 727
SIC 3443 Air coolers, metal plate
CEO: Grady Walker
Pr: Sam Chapple
COO: Terry Brown
VP: Bob Giammaruti
Dept Mgr: Lynn Bennett
Genl Mgr: Robert Mitchell
CIO: Howard Okabayashi
Sfty Dirs: Jo Admire
Sls Mgr: Sam George
Genl Couns: Dwayne Youngberg

HUDSON RIVER COMMUNITY HEALTH
See HUDSON RIVER HEALTHCARE INC

D-U-N-S 01-095-0624
HUDSON RIVER HEALTHCARE INC
HUDSON RIVER COMMUNITY HEALTH
1200 Brown St Ste 12, Peekskill, NY 10566-3622
Tel (914) 734-8800 *Founded/Ownrshp* 1975
Sales 133.8MM *EMP* 713
Accts Cohnreznick Llp New York New
SIC 8011 Medical centers
CEO: Anne Nolon
**COO:* Allison Dubois
**CFO:* Thomas Sexton
**Ex VP:* Paul Kaye
**Ex VP:* Jeanette Phillips
**Ex VP:* James D Sinkoff

D-U-N-S 06-106-6569
HUDSON UNITED BANK (NJ)
(*Suby of* TD BANK US HOLDING CO) ★
1000 Macarthur Blvd, Mahwah, NJ 07430-2035
Tel (201) 236-2600 *Founded/Ownrshp* 1890, 2004
Sales NA *EMP* 1,280
SIC 6141 6022 Personal credit institutions; State commercial banks
Pr: Kenneth T Neilson
Ex VP: James Mayo
Ex VP: James W Nall

D-U-N-S 03-048-3531
HUDSON VALLEY BANK
21 Scarsdale Rd, Yonkers, NY 10707-3204
Tel (914) 961-6100 *Founded/Ownrshp* 1972
Sales NA *EMP* 418
SIC 6029

D-U-N-S 02-066-3415
HUDSON VALLEY COMMUNITY COLLEGE
SUNY ADMINISTRATION
(*Suby of* SUNY ADMINISTRATION) ★
80 Vandenburgh Ave Ste 1, Troy, NY 12180-6096
Tel (518) 629-4822 *Founded/Ownrshp* 1953
Sales 36.8MM *EMP* 1,200^E
Accts Uhy Llp Albany New York
SIC 8222 9411 Community college; Administration of educational programs;
Pr: Andrew J Matonak
Ofcr: Ronald Hall
Ofcr: Muhammad Khan
Ofcr: Michael Winnie

D-U-N-S 18-173-6547
HUDSON VALLEY FEDERAL CREDIT UNION
137 Boardman Rd, Poughkeepsie, NY 12603-4821
Tel (845) 463-3011 *Founded/Ownrshp* 1963
Sales NA *EMP* 875^E
SIC 6061 Federal credit unions
Pr: Mary D Madden
VP: Diane Allenbaugh
VP: Tony Rohrmeier
VP: Herb White
Brnch Mgr: Julie Barr
Brnch Mgr: Kimberly Brennan
Brnch Mgr: Virginia Bromsey
Brnch Mgr: Robyn Williams
IT Man: Janet Giannetta
IT Man: Martin Gilmore
Netwrk Mgr: John Brozycki

D-U-N-S 11-279-0803
HUDSON VALLEY HOLDING CORP
21 Scarsdale Rd, Yonkers, NY 10707-3204
Tel (914) 961-6100 *Founded/Ownrshp* 1982
Sales NA *EMP* 421^E
SIC 6022

D-U-N-S 07-667-4787
HUDSON VALLEY HOSPITAL CENTER
(*Suby of* NEWYORK-PRESBYTERIAN HOSPITAL) ★
1980 Crompond Rd, Cortlandt Manor, NY 10567-4182
Tel (914) 737-9000 *Founded/Ownrshp* 1889
Sales 166.1MM *EMP* 527^E
SIC 8062 General medical & surgical hospitals
Ch Bd: Edward Macdonald
**Pr:* John C Federspiel
**V Ch Bd:* Minerva Benjamin Abramson
VP: Bob Palumberi
Adm Dir: Sue Hyatt
Dir Sec: Kevin McConville
IT Man: Kevin Murphy
Doctor: David Horgan
Pharmcst: Dominick Corbi

HUDSON- SHARP MACHINE COMPANY
See THIELE TECHNOLOGIES INC

D-U-N-S 78-878-1362
HUDSON-RPM DISTRIBUTORS LLC
150 Blackstone River Rd # 6, Worcester, MA 01607-1482
Tel (617) 328-9500 *Founded/Ownrshp* 1999
Sales 173.7MM^E *EMP* 700
SIC 5192 Magazines
VP: John A Cirrone
Opers Mgr: Dave Dwelly
Sls Dir: Patricia Hurwitz

D-U-N-S 78-598-9109
HUDSONS BAY TRADING CO LP
3 Manhattanville Rd, Purchase, NY 10577-2116
Tel (914) 694-4444 *Founded/Ownrshp* 2009
Sales 620.2MM^E *EMP* 9,000^E
SIC 5311 Department stores, non-discount
Mng Pt: Richard Baker
Pt: Robert Baker
Pt: Francis Casale
Pt: Donald Hutchison
Pt: Christina Johnson
Pt: William Mack
Pt: Lee Neibart
Pt: Brian Pall
Pt: Donald Watros
Board of Directors: Donald Watros

HUDSON'S SUPERMARKET
See G W FOODS INC

D-U-N-S 10-585-2925
HUEN ELECTRIC INC
1801 W 16th St, Broadview, IL 60155-3955
Tel (708) 343-5511 *Founded/Ownrshp* 1993
Sales 90.7MM^E *EMP* 500
SIC 1731

D-U-N-S 92-764-4294 IMP
HUF NORTH AMERICA AUTOMOTIVE PARTS MANUFACTURING CORP
(*Suby of* HUF HULSBECK & FURST GMBH & CO. KG)
9020 W Dean Rd, Milwaukee, WI 53224-2853
Tel (414) 365-4950 *Founded/Ownrshp* 1995
Sales 114.7MM *EMP* 450
SIC 3714 Motor vehicle parts & accessories
Pr: George Haeussler
**CFO:* Leslie Carbine
MIS Dir: Patrick Dickey
QC Dir: Ken Youker
Plnt Mgr: John Brown
Ql Cn Mgr: Mass Carella
Sls Dir: Christopher Buchanan
Sales Asso: Pam Williams

D-U-N-S 00-606-9223 IMP/EXP
HUFCOR INC (WI)
2101 Kennedy Rd, Janesville, WI 53545-0824
Tel (608) 756-1241 *Founded/Ownrshp* 1901, 1978
Sales 149.1MM^E *EMP* 600
SIC 2542 3442

D-U-N-S 00-232-0331 EXP
HUFF PAPER CO (PA)
HUFF UNITED
10 Crk Pky Namns Crk Ctr Namns Crk Cntr, Boothwyn, PA 19061
Tel (610) 497-5100 *Founded/Ownrshp* 1922, 1977
Sales 85.7MM^E *EMP* 75
SIC 5113 Industrial & personal service paper; Bags, paper & disposable plastic; Paper & products, wrapping or coarse
Ch Bd: W Lloyd Snyder III
**Pr:* Paul Burns
**Ex VP:* Fred Hilbert
**VP:* Robert E Ward

HUFF UNITED
See HUFF PAPER CO

D-U-N-S 05-196-1589 IMP
HUGG AND HALL EQUIPMENT CO (AR)
7201 Scott Hamilton Dr, Little Rock, AR 72209-3147
Tel (501) 562-1262 *Founded/Ownrshp* 1970
Sales 256.5MM^E *EMP* 348
Accts Ferguson Cobb & Associates P
SIC 5084 5082 7353 7699 5083 3531 Industrial machinery & equipment; Lift trucks & parts; Materials handling machinery; Road construction equipment; General construction machinery & equipment; Heavy construction equipment rental; Industrial machinery & equipment repair; Construction equipment repair; Landscaping equipment; Backhoes, tractors, cranes, plows & similar equipment
Ch: John C Hugg
**Pr:* Robert M Hall
**Treas:* John Hugg
**VP:* Mike Clark
VP: Jim Hancock
VP: Tim Waychoff
Admn Mgr: Michelle Morris
Brnch Mgr: Jim Greenlee
Genl Mgr: Jonathan Brown
IT Man: Dan Bowlin
Sales Asso: Jason Henson

HUGH CHATHAM MEM HOSP NURSING
See HUGH CHATHAM MEMORIAL HOSPITAL INC

D-U-N-S 06-744-1436
HUGH CHATHAM MEMORIAL HOSPITAL INC
HUGH CHATHAM MEM HOSP NURSING
180 Parkwood Dr, Elkin, NC 28621-2430
Tel (336) 835-3722 *Founded/Ownrshp* 1929
Sales 102.9MM *EMP* 750
SIC 8062 8051 8361 General medical & surgical hospitals; Convalescent home with continuous nursing care; Geriatric residential care
CEO: Paul H Hammes
CFO: Mary Greene
Bd of Dir: Judy Snyder
Dir Lab: Diane Rocotta
Dir Rx: Greg Holcomb
Chf Nrs Of: Donna Parsons
Nurse Mgr: Lynn Kennedy
QC Dir: Charlotte Lawson
Pharmcst: James Hobeck
Pharmcst: Eugenia Key
Phys Thrpy: Marc Womeldorf

D-U-N-S 94-591-2756
HUGH DUNCAN & ASSOCIATES INC
26908 Mlibu Cove Colny Dr, Malibu, CA 90265-4321
Tel (310) 457-7432 *Founded/Ownrshp* 1995
Sales 150.0MM *EMP* 50
SIC 7311 Advertising consultant
CEO: Hugh Duncan
**Pr:* Bobby Wentworth

D-U-N-S 11-745-3514
HUGH M CUNNINGHAM INC
2029 Westgate Dr Ste 120, Carrollton, TX 75006-6474
Tel (972) 888-3833 *Founded/Ownrshp* 1948
Sales 114.5MM^E *EMP* 85
SIC 5074 5085 5083 5199 Plumbing fittings & supplies; Industrial supplies; Irrigation equipment; Architects' supplies (non-durable)
Pr: David A Cunningham
COO: Hal Haas
VP: William Allen
VP: Brad Feldman
VP: Mathieu Mark
VP: Dan Townsend
DP Exec: Debbie Dingess
Opers Mgr: Drey Hayford
Mktg Mgr: Jonathan Bunch
Sales Asso: Patricia Cozart

D-U-N-S 60-612-2138
■ HUGHES COMMUNICATIONS INC
(*Suby of* ECHOSTAR SATELLITE SERVICES LLC) ★
11717 Exploration Ln, Germantown, MD 20876-2711
Tel (301) 428-5500 *Founded/Ownrshp* 2011
Sales 1.3MM *EMP* 2,254
SIC 4813 4899 3663 Telephone communication, except radio; Data telephone communications; ; Satellite earth stations; Satellites, communications; Space satellite communications equipment
Pr: Pradman P Kaul
**CFO:* Grant A Barber
**Treas:* Deepak V Dutt
Treas: Ren Lapidario
Ex VP: Grant A Brber
**Ex VP:* T Paul Gaske
**Ex VP:* Adrian Morris
**Ex VP:* Bahram Pourmand
Sr VP: Bob Buschman
Sr VP: John Corrigan
Sr VP: Dan Fraley
**Sr VP:* Dean A Manson
Sr VP: John McEwan
Sr VP: Dave Zatloukal
VP: Edward Fitzpatrick
VP: Steven Kee
Exec: Hiep Pham

D-U-N-S 01-858-3922
■ HUGHES CORP
HOWARD HUGHES REALTY
(*Suby of* ROUSE CO LP) ★
10801 W Charleston Blvd # 300, Las Vegas, NV 89135-1200
Tel (702) 791-4000 *Founded/Ownrshp* 1996
Sales 191.7MM *EMP* 70
SIC 6552 Subdividers & developers
Pr: Kevin T Orrock
Assoc VP: Jeff Geen
Ex VP: W S Gibbons
Sr VP: Sherveen Baftechi
Sr VP: Peggy Chandler
Sr VP: John Dewolf
Sr VP: Andrew Schwartz
Sr VP: Nicholas D Vanderboom
VP: Robert Carroll
VP: Rob Centra
VP: Chuck Kubat
VP: John Potts
Comm Man: Michael Fredericks
Board of Directors: John Goolsby, William R Lummis, E R Vacchina, Milton H West Jr

D-U-N-S 60-623-1363 IMP/EXP
HUGHES FURNITURE INDUSTRIES INC
H F I
952 S Stout Rd, Randleman, NC 27317-7638
Tel (336) 498-8700 *Founded/Ownrshp* 2002
Sales 92.0MM^E *EMP* 337
SIC 2512 7641 2426 Living room furniture: upholstered on wood frames; Upholstery work; Furniture stock & parts, hardwood
VP: Bruce Hughes
**Prin:* Rita Spencer
DP Dir: Jim Crawford
Sales Exec: Dean Hoover

D-U-N-S 07-327-4185
HUGHES HUBBARD & REED LLP
(*Suby of* HUGUES HUBBARD ET REED)
1 Battery Park, New York, NY 10004-1438
Tel (212) 837-6000 *Founded/Ownrshp* 1925
Sales 141.5MM^E *EMP* 766
SIC 8111 General practice attorney, lawyer
Pt: Charles H Scherer
Pt: William L Allinder
Pt: Ned H Bassen
Pt: Candace Beinecke
Pt: George A Davidson
Pt: Merrikay S Hall
Pt: John K Hoyns
Pt: Norman C Kleinberg
Pt: Theodore H Latty
Pt: Kenneth A Lefkowitz
Pt: William R Maguire
Pt: Theodore V H Mayer
Pt: Timothy J McCarthy
Pt: James Modlin
Pt: Yasuo Okamoto
Pt: William R Stein
Pt: Nick Swerdloff
COO: Gerard F Cruse
CFO: Renee Selitto

HUGHES KITCHEN & BATH COLLECTN
See HUGHES SUPPLY INC

D-U-N-S 05-688-6380 IMP/EXP
■ HUGHES NETWORK SYSTEMS LLC
(*Suby of* HUGHES COMMUNICATIONS INC) ★
11717 Exploration Ln, Germantown, MD 20876-2799
Tel (301) 428-5500 *Founded/Ownrshp* 2004
Sales 37.3MM^E *EMP* 1,924
SIC 4899 Data communication services
Pr: Pradman P Kaul
COO: Bill Humes
COO: Chuck McClain
COO: Sylvia McLaughlin
CFO: Ilya Alter
**CFO:* Grant A Barber
CFO: James Lucchese
**Treas:* Deepak V Dutt
Assoc VP: Ashok D Mehta
Ex VP: Grant A Brber
Ex VP: T P Gaske
Ex VP: Adrian Morris
Sr VP: Sandi Kerentoff
**Sr VP:* Dean A Manson
**Sr VP:* Thomas J McElroy
VP: Bob Buschman
VP: John Corrigan
VP: Robert O Feierbach
VP: Kamran Givpoor
VP: Michael Gorsuch
VP: Peter Gulla
Board of Directors: Andrew D Africk, Jeffrey A Leddy, Aaron J Stone

D-U-N-S 07-835-6154
HUGHES SATELLITE SYSTEMS CORP
100 Inverness Ter E, Englewood, CO 80112-5308
Tel (303) 706-4000 *Founded/Ownrshp* 2012
Sales 1.8MMM *EMP* 2
Accts Kpmg Llp Denver Colorado
SIC 4813
CEO: Michael T Dugan

D-U-N-S 00-692-3205 EXP
HUGHES SUPPLY INC
HUGHES KITCHEN & BATH COLLECTN
(*Suby of* WEINSTEIN SUPPLY) ★
2920 Ford St, Fort Myers, FL 33916-5533
Tel (239) 334-2205 *Founded/Ownrshp* 2011
Sales 221.8MM^E *EMP* 3,500
SIC 5063 5074 5075 5085 1711 Electrical apparatus & equipment; Building wire & cable; Plumbing & hydronic heating supplies; Pipes & fittings, plastic; Plumbing & heating valves; Warm air heating & air conditioning; Industrial supplies; Plumbing contractors
CEO: Thomas I Morgan
**CFO:* David Bearman
**Ch:* David H Hughes
Ofcr: David English
Sales Asso: Edwards Cristina
Sales Asso: Kenneth Ferrell

D-U-N-S 19-717-5862 IMP/EXP
HUGO BOSS USA INC
(*Suby of* HUGO BOSS AG)
55 Water St Fl 48, New York, NY 10041-3204
Tel (212) 940-0600 *Founded/Ownrshp* 2002
Sales 242.9MM^E *EMP* 900
SIC 2311 2325 2337 5136 5611 6794 Men's & boys' suits & coats; Men's & boys' trousers & slacks; Women's & misses' suits & coats; Suits: women's, misses' & juniors'; Skirts, separate: women's, misses' & juniors'; Jackets & vests, except fur & leather: women's; Men's & boys' suits & trousers; Men's & boys' sportswear & work clothing; Men's & boys' outerwear; Men's & boys' clothing stores; Franchises, selling or licensing
Pr: Anthony Lucia
**Pr:* Gretchen Ruoillard
**CEO:* Andre Maeder
COO: William Scott
CFO: Dr Karsten Koelsch
Sr VP: Karine Schnapp
VP: Kennie Anderson
VP: Mike Heagy
Creative D: Jason Wu

**Mng Dir:* Mark Brashear
Mng Dir: Gareth Incledon

HUGULEY MEMORIAL MEDICAL CTR
See ADVENTIST HEALTH SYSTEMS/ SUN BELT

D-U-N-S 10-661-7074 IMP
HUHTAMAKI AMERICAS INC
(*Suby of* HUHTAMAKI BEHEER V B.V.)
9201 Packaging Dr, De Soto, KS 66018-8600
Tel (913) 583-3025 *Founded/Ownrshp* 2000
Sales 151.1MM[E] *EMP* 400
SIC 3089 Plastic containers, except foam
CEO: Jukka Moisio
Ofcr: Hannu Tikkanen
**Ex VP:* Clay Dunn
**Ex VP:* Suresh Gupta
**Ex VP:* Olli Koponen
**Ex VP:* Shashank Sinha
**Sr VP:* Sari Lindholm
**Prin:* Norman Botwinik
**Prin:* Steve Lyons

D-U-N-S 08-671-4149 IMP/EXP
HUHTAMAKI FILMS INC
(*Suby of* HUHTAMAKI OYJ)
9201 Packaging Dr, De Soto, KS 66018-8600
Tel (913) 583-3025 *Founded/Ownrshp* 2002
Sales 132.0MM[E] *EMP* 647
SIC 3089 Plastic containers, except foam
CEO: Clay Dunn
**Treas:* Earlene A Sells
**VP:* John Odea
Genl Mgr: Athos Ikonomous

D-U-N-S 04-114-3850 IMP/EXP
HUHTAMAKI INC
(*Suby of* HUHTAMAKI OYJ)
9201 Packaging Dr, De Soto, KS 66018-8600
Tel (913) 583-3025 *Founded/Ownrshp* 2000
Sales 1.0MMM[E] *EMP* 3,000
SIC 2656 3565 Sanitary food containers; Ice cream containers: made from purchased material; Labeling machines, industrial
CEO: Jukka Moisio
**Pr:* Clay Dunn
Treas: Earlene Seales
Bd of Dir: Anthony Simon
Ofcr: Jennifer Young
Ex VP: Olli Koponen
VP: Fred Betzen
**VP:* John O'Dea
Mng Dir: Ulf Wienboker
Rgnl Mgr: Jim Snyder
Genl Mgr: Jeffrey Benton

D-U-N-S 05-397-1644
HULCHER SERVICES INC
(*Suby of* FIRST FINANCIAL RESOURCES INC) ★
611 Kimberly Dr, Denton, TX 76208-6300
Tel (940) 387-0099 *Founded/Ownrshp* 1978
Sales 411.2MM[E] *EMP* 650
SIC 4953 4789 Hazardous waste collection & disposal; Railroad maintenance & repair services
Pr: Frank Given
**CEO:* Greg Bristow
**Treas:* Curry Vogelsang
**Ex VP:* Ron Ewing
Sr VP: Hillen Robert
VP: Brett Siedelmann
VP: Rick Turner
Exec: Peter Tilton
VP Admn: Robert Brown
Genl Mgr: Robert Doherty
Dir IT: Dean Blanchone

D-U-N-S 07-602-1252
■ **HULL & CO INC**
(*Suby of* BROWN & BROWN INC) ★
1815 Griffin Rd Ste 300, Dania Beach, FL 33004-2252
Tel (954) 920-6790 *Founded/Ownrshp* 2005
Sales NA *EMP* 465
SIC 6411 Insurance brokers
Pr: Anthony T Strianese
**CFO:* William N Simons
Treas: Joseph S Failla Jr
**VP:* Cory T Walker
**Exec:* Edwin Calabrese
**Prin:* Richard Hull
Brnch Mgr: Patti Argo
Mktg Dir: Bob Briggs
Mktg Dir: Casey Pechin

D-U-N-S 80-853-4163
HULU LLC
2500 Broadway Fl 2, Santa Monica, CA 90404-3065
Tel (310) 571-4700 *Founded/Ownrshp* 2007
Sales 656.1MM[E] *EMP* 1,000[E]
SIC 4833 4813 Television translator station;
CEO: Mike Hopkins
**CEO:* Jason Kilar
VP: Tiffany Bollin
VP: Chad Ho
VP: Jim O'Donnell
VP: Jim O'Gorman
VP: Eugene WEI
Assoc Dir: Angie Kang
Creative D: Tom Walker
Prgrm Mgr: Alex Gutarin
Prgrm Mgr: Shae Ryan

HUMAN CAPITAL
See METROPOLITAN NASHVILLE PUBLIC SCHOOLS

D-U-N-S 10-821-7654
HUMAN FACTORS APPLICATIONS INC
(*Suby of* TERRANEAR PMC, LLC)
1000 Burr Ridge Pkwy, Burr Ridge, IL 60527-0849
Tel (630) 850-6900 *Founded/Ownrshp* 2010
Sales 11.3MM[E] *EMP* 1,000
SIC 7363 8748 Engineering help service; Business consulting
Pr: Amar Raval
**Treas:* Theresa Doyle
**Ex VP:* Kenneth Fillman

D-U-N-S 79-705-7437
HUMAN GENOME SCIENCES INC
(*Suby of* GLAXOSMITHKLINE PLC)
14200 Shady Grove Rd, Rockville, MD 20850-7464
Tel (301) 309-8504 *Founded/Ownrshp* 2012
Sales 90.0MM[E] *EMP* 1,100
SIC 8731 2834 Biotechnical research, commercial; Medical research, commercial; Pharmaceutical preparations
Pr: H Thomas Watkins
CFO: David P Southwell
Bd of Dir: Ngoc T Ha
Ex VP: James H Davis PHD
Sr VP: Susan D Bateson
Sr VP: Perry Karsen
Sr VP: Craig C Parker
Sr VP: Curran M Simpson
VP: Robert Benson
VP: Alain D Cappeluti
VP: Michael R Fannon
VP: Margery B Fischbein
VP: Vincent Gogh
VP: Daniel Gold
VP: Art Mandell
VP: Kevin P McRaith
VP: Tuomo Patsi
VP: Tuomo P Tsi
VP: Michele M Wales
Dir Surg: Bill Hannon
Assoc Dir: Stephen Currier
Board of Directors: Allan Baxter Phd, Richard J Danzig, Colin Goddard Phd, Maxine Gowen Phd, John L Lamattina Phd, Augustine Lawlor, George J Morrow, Gregory Norden, Robert C Young

HUMAN RESOURCES DEPARTMENT
See FLORIDA DEPARTMENT OF EDUCATION

HUMAN RESOURCES GEORGIA DEPT
See GEORGIA DEPARTMENT OF HUMAN SERVICES

HUMAN SERVICES, DEPARTMENT OF
See SOUTH DAKOTA DEPARTMENT OF HUMAN SERVICES

HUMANA
See HUMCO INC

D-U-N-S 80-534-9198
■ **HUMANA GOVERNMENT BUSINESS INC**
(*Suby of* HUMANA INC) ★
305 N Hurstbourne Pkwy 1b, Louisville, KY 40222-8533
Tel (502) 318-0935 *Founded/Ownrshp* 1993
Sales NA *EMP* 19,000
SIC 6321 Health insurance carriers
CEO: Tim McClain
**Pr:* Orie Mullen
**CFO:* David Lewis
Rgnl Mgr: Michelle Treadaway
Sales Asso: Sonia Sieler

D-U-N-S 08-246-3647
■ **HUMANA HEALTH PLAN INC**
(*Suby of* HUMANA INC) ★
8431 Fredericksburg Rd # 340, San Antonio, TX 78229-3455
Tel (210) 615-5100 *Founded/Ownrshp* 1981
Sales NA *EMP* 1,247
SIC 6324 6321 8011 Health maintenance organization (HMO), insurance only; Accident & health insurance; Offices & clinics of medical doctors
CEO: Michael B McCallister
COO: Greg Wolf
Prgrm Mgr: Dave Schmelz
Dir IT: Niel Berman
Dir IT: Zhong Liu
Info Man: Molly Freeman
Sales Exec: Christina M Candler

D-U-N-S 78-793-4397
■ **HUMANA HEALTH PLAN OF KANSAS INC**
(*Suby of* HUMANA INC) ★
500 W Main St Ste 300, Louisville, KY 40202-4268
Tel (502) 580-1000 *Founded/Ownrshp* 1982
Sales NA *EMP* 1,800
SIC 6324 6321 Health maintenance organization (HMO), insurance only; Health insurance carriers
CFO: James E Murray
COO: Charlie Boston
CFO: Scott Johnson
**Treas:* James W Doucette
VP: Marsden Connolly
VP: Mark Iorio
VP: Jaewon Ryu
Mktg Dir: David Gabbard
Pharmcst: Mike Kuratko
Snr Mgr: Mary Barnes
Snr Mgr: Kathleen Mahoney

D-U-N-S 04-994-4143
▲ **HUMANA INC**
500 W Main St Ste 300, Louisville, KY 40202-4268
Tel (502) 580-1000 *Founded/Ownrshp* 1961
Sales NA *EMP* 51,700
Tkr Sym HUM *Exch* NYS
SIC 6324 6321 6411 Hospital & medical service plans; Health maintenance organization (HMO), insurance only; Health insurance carriers; Medical insurance claim processing, contract or fee basis
Pr: Bruce D Broussard
Dir Recs: Tammy Ney
**Ch Bd:* Kurt J Hilzinger
COO: James E Murray
CFO: Brian A Kane
Ofcr: Roy A Beveridge
Ofcr: Jody L Bilney
Ofcr: Christopher H Hunter
Ofcr: Timothy S Huval
Ofcr: Christopher Kay
Sr VP: Brian P Leclaire
Sr VP: Heidi S Margulis
Sr VP: Christopher M Todoroff
VP: Dale Aggen
VP: John E Barger
VP: Beth Bierbower
VP: Linda Bowers
VP: Steve Chick
VP: Alisa Coppock
VP: Roger Cude
VP: Tracie Fahy
Board of Directors: Frank A D'amelio, W Roy Dunbar, David A Jones Jr, William J McDonald, William E Mitchell, David B Nash, James J O'brien, Marissa T Peterson

D-U-N-S 08-618-1922
■ **HUMANA INSURANCE CO**
(*Suby of* HUMANA INC) ★
1100 Employers Blvd, Green Bay, WI 54344-0002
Tel (502) 580-1000 *Founded/Ownrshp* 1986
Sales NA *EMP* 2,200
SIC 6311 6321 Life insurance carriers; Health insurance carriers; Accident insurance carriers
CEO: Bruce D Broussard
**Pr:* Michael McAllister
**Ex VP:* James E Murray
**Sr VP:* Roy A Beveridge
**Sr VP:* Jody L Bilney
**Sr VP:* Christopher H Hunter
**VP:* Ronald Edward Van Thiel
VP: Mark Wernicke
**VP:* Tod James Zacharias
**VP Admn:* David Blair Pietenpol
Dir IT: Brian Jansen

D-U-N-S 78-793-5162
■ **HUMANA INSURANCE CO OF KENTUCKY**
(*Suby of* HUMANA INC) ★
500 W Main St Ste 300, Louisville, KY 40202-4268
Tel (502) 580-1000 *Founded/Ownrshp* 1985
Sales NA *EMP* 1,500
SIC 6321 8741 Health insurance carriers; Management services
Pr: Michael B McCallister
**Treas:* James H Bloem
VP: George Bauernfeind
Board of Directors: James E Murray

HUMANE SOCIETY INTERNATIONAL
See HUMANE SOCIETY OF UNITED STATES

D-U-N-S 07-265-5970
HUMANE SOCIETY OF UNITED STATES
HUMANE SOCIETY INTERNATIONAL
1255 23rd St Nw Ste 800, Washington, DC 20037-1595
Tel (202) 452-1100 *Founded/Ownrshp* 1954
Sales 194.2MM *EMP* 600[E]
Accts Mcgladrey Llp Gaithersburg M
SIC 8699 Animal humane society
CEO: Wayne Pacelle
**COO:* Laura Maloney
**CFO:* G Thomas Waite III
**Ex VP:* Patricia A Forkan
Sr VP: Jonathan Lovvorn
Sr VP: Heidi Prescott
VP: Michaelen Barsness
VP: Kitty Block
VP: Michelle Cho
**VP:* Michael Markarian
Dir Soc: Heather Main

D-U-N-S 06-880-2045 IMP
HUMANETICS II LTD (TX)
(*Suby of* C H INDUSTRIES INC) ★
1700 Columbian Club Dr, Carrollton, TX 75006-5534
Tel (972) 416-1304 *Founded/Ownrshp* 1992
Sales 87.5MM[E] *EMP* 337
SIC 3444 3599 Sheet metalwork; Custom machinery
CEO: Art Holbrook
Pr: Robert Hasty
CFO: Danny Goodwin
VP: Laurie Hasty
Dir Bus: Shane Thornton
Prd Mgr: Saul Cervantes

D-U-N-S 15-350-0434 IMP/EXP
HUMANSCALE CORP
11 E 26th St Fl 8, New York, NY 10010-1425
Tel (212) 725-4749 *Founded/Ownrshp* 1981
Sales 171.4MM[E] *EMP* 400
Accts Lawrence B Goodman & Co Pa Fa
SIC 3577 2521 Computer peripheral equipment; Wood office furniture
CEO: Robert King
**Pr:* Heather Fennimore
**Pr:* Paul Levy
Ofcr: Jane Abernethy
**VP:* Michele Gerards
VP: Nancy Pedrick
Exec: Marie Le
Mng Dir: Tony Hendrick
Dist Mgr: Steve McManama
Off Mgr: Sharonda Chavis
Off Mgr: Claire Lee

D-U-N-S 02-235-6737
HUMBLE INDEPENDENT SCHOOL DISTRICT
HUMBLE ISD
20200 Eastway Village Dr, Humble, TX 77338-2405
Tel (281) 641-1000 *Founded/Ownrshp* 1919
Sales 397.0MM *EMP* 5,000
Accts Whitley Penn Llp Houston Tex
SIC 8211 Public elementary & secondary schools; Public elementary school; Public junior high school; Public senior high school
CFO: Elizabeth Lynn
Bd of Dir: Dave Martin
Dir Sec: Cheryl Vitale
Genl Mgr: Jerri Monbaron
MIS Dir: Arthur Allen
Pr Dir: Robin McAdams
Pr Dir: Jamie Mount
Schl Brd P: Robert Sitton
Psych: Carol Reiner
Psych: Denise Toro

HUMBLE ISD
See HUMBLE INDEPENDENT SCHOOL DISTRICT

D-U-N-S 07-875-9348
HUMC HOLDCO LLC
308 Willow Ave, Hoboken, NJ 07030-3808
Tel (201) 418-1000 *Founded/Ownrshp* 2010
Sales 247.7MM[E] *EMP* 1,139[E]
SIC 6211 Investment firm, general brokerage
Prin: Yasmine Thomas

D-U-N-S 07-831-1985
HUMC OPCO LLC
HOBOKEN UNIVERSITY MEDICAL CTR
(*Suby of* HUMC HOLDCO LLC) ★
308 Willow Ave, Hoboken, NJ 07030-3808
Tel (201) 418-1000 *Founded/Ownrshp* 2011
Sales 170.1MM *EMP* 1,125
Accts Bdo Usa Llp
SIC 8062 General medical & surgical hospitals
**CEO:* Philip Schaengold
**VP:* Vincent Riccitelli

D-U-N-S 86-763-2234
■ **HUMCO INC**
HUMANA
(*Suby of* HUMANA INC) ★
500 W Main St Ste 300, Louisville, KY 40202-2943
Tel (502) 580-1000 *Founded/Ownrshp* 2008
Sales NA *EMP* 200
SIC 6321 Accident & health insurance
Pr: Michael Mc Callister
Prgrm Mgr: Brenda Renier
Sales Exec: Nick Kompara

D-U-N-S 11-516-8010
HUMPHREY COMPANIES LLC
2851 Prairie St Sw, Grandville, MI 49418-2179
Tel (616) 530-1717 *Founded/Ownrshp* 1984
Sales 146.4MM[E] *EMP* 695
SIC 3537 3714 3089 5023 5162 Industrial trucks & tractors; Motor vehicle parts & accessories; Molding primary plastic; Home furnishings; Plastics sheets & rods
CEO: James A Humphrey
**CFO:* James D Green
**Ch:* John W Humphrey

D-U-N-S 05-085-5618
HUMPHRIES AND CO LLC
4581 S Cobb Dr Se Ste 200, Smyrna, GA 30080-6906
Tel (770) 434-1890 *Founded/Ownrshp* 2007
Sales 133.0MM *EMP* 90
SIC 1542 Commercial & office buildings, renovation & repair; Store front construction
VP: P Scott Moore
Mng Pt: Kirk J Thompson
COO: Jimmy Humpries
**Sec:* Mike Kiblinger
Ofcr: William G Snider
**VP:* Paul M King Jr
**VP:* Charles R Sharitz
**VP:* J Kirk Thompson Jr
**Genl Couns:* Garth Snider
Snr PM: Steve Little
Snr PM: John Tomlinson

D-U-N-S 00-800-1349 IMP
HUNT BUILDING CO LTD (TX)
(*Suby of* HUNT COMPANIES INC) ★
4401 N Mesa St Ste 201, El Paso, TX 79902-1150
Tel (915) 533-1122 *Founded/Ownrshp* 1947, 1971
Sales 199.8MM[E] *EMP* 416
SIC 1522 6531 1542 7389 Multi-family dwellings, new construction; Real estate managers; Shopping center construction; Financial services
Ch Bd: W L Hunt
**Genl Pt:* Hbc Construction Managers
**Ltd Pt:* Hunt Building Corporation
**Pr:* M L Hunt
**Pr:* William Kell
CFO: Steve De Bara
**CFO:* William C Sanders CPA
**Treas:* James C Hunt
Ex VP: Vahe Gabriel
**Ex VP:* Gary B Sapp
**Sr VP:* Robert R Cabello
**Sr VP:* Steve Colon
Sr VP: Christopher Lawton-Smith
**Sr VP:* Richard J Marshall
**Sr VP:* Johnny E McFarlin
**Sr VP:* John T Philley
**Sr VP:* Robin G Vaughn CPA
**Sr VP:* Ken Wall
**Sr VP:* David K Wray
**Sr VP:* K Douglas Wright
**VP:* Alfredo Aguayo
Board of Directors: Brion Georges, Richard Gleichauf, Matt Myllykangas

D-U-N-S 13-611-5255
HUNT COMPANIES INC
4401 N Mesa St, El Paso, TX 79902-1150
Tel (915) 533-1122 *Founded/Ownrshp* 1977
Sales 371.7MM[E] *EMP* 680[E]
SIC 1522 6531 1542 Multi-family dwellings, new construction; Real estate managers; Shopping center construction
Pr: Chris Hunt
Pr: Steve Coln
**Pr:* M L Hunt
Pr: Gary Sapp
COO: Paul Kopsky Jr
CFO: William Kell
CFO: Clay Parker
**Chf Inves:* James C Hunt
Ex VP: William C Sanders
Ex VP: David Wray
Sr VP: Clarence Ansley
Sr VP: Karl Becker
Sr VP: Brenda Christman
Sr VP: Anne Scharm
Sr VP: Ken Wall
VP: Jeff Cole
VP: Richard Coomber
VP: Brion Georges
VP: Elena Montero
VP: Kay Riley
VP: Karl Schosser

D-U-N-S 10-399-4109
HUNT CONSOLIDATED INC
H C I
(*Suby of* RRH CORP) ★
1900 N Akard St, Dallas, TX 75201-2300
Tel (214) 978-8000 *Founded/Ownrshp* 1980
Sales 9.8MMM[E] *EMP* 2,571

SIC 6799 1311 2911 1382 0212

D-U-N-S 00-693-8179
■ HUNT CONSTRUCTION GROUP INC
(Suby of AECOM) ★
7720 N 16th St Ste 100, Phoenix, AZ 85020-4493
Tel (480) 368-4700 Founded/Ownrshp 1944, 2014
Sales 132.4MM^E EMP 700^E
SIC 8741 Construction management
CEO: Robert G Hunt
*Pr: Michael Fratianni
*Treas: David Smith
Treas: David B Smith
*Ex VP: Stephen W Atkins
*Ex VP: Robert S Aylesworth
Ex VP: Mike Fratianni
Ex VP: Michael J Gausden
*Ex VP: Robert Hart
Ex VP: Robert F Hart
*Ex VP: William Hornbake
*Ex VP: Kenneth Johnson
Ex VP: Kenneth L Johnson
*Ex VP: Mark E Lavoy
*Ex VP: William Morthland
Ex VP: William G Morthland
*Ex VP: Jose M Pienknagura
*VP: Matthew Barnes
*VP: Scott Blanchard
*VP: Belinda Burke
VP: Belinda D Burke

D-U-N-S 07-957-1683
■ HUNT CORP
(Suby of AECOM TECHNICAL SERVICES INC) ★
6720 N Scottsdale Rd # 300, Scottsdale, AZ 85253-4460
Tel (480) 368-4755 Founded/Ownrshp 2014
Sales 206.2MM^E EMP 550
SIC 1541 6531 6552 Industrial buildings & warehouses; Real estate agents & managers; Real estate managers; Subdividers & developers
Pr: Michael Fratianni
*Treas: David Smith
*Ex VP: Stephen Atkins
Ex VP: Robert M Decker
*Ex VP: Jose Pienknagura
VP: Peter Clark
VP: Richard Dejean
VP: Michael Gausden
VP: Troy Hoberg
VP: Randall Ket
VP: Mark Lavoy
VP: William D Mott
*VP: Lucinda S New
VP: William Palmer
VP: Warner Peck
VP: Jack E Sovern
VP: Monte J Thurmond
VP: Ronald Wildermuth
VP: Robert B Woods

D-U-N-S 16-091-1848
HUNT DOMINION CORP
1601 Elm St Ste 3900, Dallas, TX 75201-4708
Tel (214) 880-8400 Founded/Ownrshp 2000
Sales 175.4MM^E EMP 175
SIC 1311 1382 1241 Crude petroleum production; Natural gas production; Oil & gas exploration services; Coal mining services
Pr: Bruce Hunt
VP: Tom Nelson
Board of Directors: D H Hunt

D-U-N-S 02-303-8482
HUNT ELECTRIC CORP
MIDWAY TECHNOLOGY SOLUTIONS
7900 Chicago Ave S, Minneapolis, MN 55420-1324
Tel (651) 646-2911 Founded/Ownrshp 1965
Sales 191.5MM^E EMP 600
Accts Mcgladrey
SIC 1731 General electrical contractor
Pr: Michael Hanson
*VP: James J Basara
*VP: Lamont Herman
*VP: Timothy Holmberg
*VP: Curtis Southward
VP: Jeff Tyllia
Div Mgr: Dick Jenniges
Off Mgr: Stella Hendricks
QA Dir: Roger Beckermann
IT Man: Ron Somerville
Sfty Dirs: Diana Nelson

D-U-N-S 05-703-3516
HUNT ELECTRIC SUPPLY CO
1213 Maple Ave, Burlington, NC 27215-6958
Tel (336) 229-5351 Founded/Ownrshp 1971
Sales 97.6MM^E EMP 85
SIC 5063 5211 Electrical apparatus & equipment; Electrical construction materials
CEO: R Sam Hunt III
*Pr: R Samuel Hunt IV
*Pr: Vicky S Hunt
*VP: Rodney Sharpe
IT Man: Sharon Parrish

HUNT FOODS COMPANY
See CONAGRA GROCERY PRODUCTS CO LLC

D-U-N-S 01-283-6610 EXP
HUNT GUILLOT & ASSOCIATES LLC
HGA
603 E Reynolds Dr, Ruston, LA 71270-2822
Tel (318) 255-6825 Founded/Ownrshp 1997
Sales 100.1MM^E EMP 375
SIC 8711 Engineering services
CFO: Glen Mitchell
VP: Jay Guillot
VP: Don Olson
Genl Mgr: Keith Cranford
Genl Mgr: Don Plumber
Dir IT: John Estes
Mktg Mgr: Fredrick Moore
Sls Mgr: Mike Causey
Snr Mgr: John McBride

D-U-N-S 07-487-8968 IMP
HUNT MEMORIAL HOSPITAL DISTRICT
HUNT REGIONAL MEDICAL CENTER
4215 Joe Ramsey Blvd E, Greenville, TX 75401-7852
Tel (903) 408-5000 Founded/Ownrshp 1960
Sales 122.8MM EMP 900
Accts Bkd Llp Dallas Texas
SIC 8062 8071 8082 General medical & surgical hospitals; Medical laboratories; Home health care services
CEO: Richard Carter
COO: John Heatherly
*CFO: Jerii Rich
Off Mgr: Tammy Ballard
CTO: Kelli Caldwell
Netwrk Mgr: Steven Jones
Psych: Wade Barker
Psych: Matthew Barrow
Psych: Pairoj Pratumrat
Psych: Michael Sills
Psych: Michel Stephan

D-U-N-S 09-923-9634
HUNT MIDWEST ENTERPRISES INC
8300 Ne Underground Dr # 100, Kansas City, MO 64161-9767
Tel (816) 455-2500 Founded/Ownrshp 1979
Sales 91.2MM^E EMP 310^E
SIC 6552 1422 6211 Subdividers & developers; Lime rock, ground; Investment firm, general brokerage
Ch Bd: Jim Holland
*Pr: Lee A Derrough
*Pr: Ora Reynolds
*CFO: Don Hagan
*Ch: Jack W Steadman
*VP: Lamar Hunt
Dir: Aaron Schmidt
Genl Mgr: Mike Bell
Genl Mgr: Brenner Holland
Off Mgr: Sarah Jones
Sls Mgr: Ryan Tompkins

D-U-N-S 00-735-3402
HUNT OIL USA INC
(Suby of H C I) ★
1900 N Akard St, Dallas, TX 75201-2300
Tel (214) 978-8000 Founded/Ownrshp 1934
Sales 9.8MMM^E EMP 2,074
SIC 1311 1382 2911

HUNT REGIONAL MEDICAL CENTER
See HUNT MEMORIAL HOSPITAL DISTRICT

D-U-N-S 82-491-6126 IMP
HUNTAIR INC
(Suby of NORTEK AIR SOLUTIONS LLC) ★
19855 Sw 124th Ave, Tualatin, OR 97062-8007
Tel (503) 639-0113 Founded/Ownrshp 2006
Sales 137.5MM^E EMP 300
SIC 3585 Refrigeration & heating equipment
Pr: Dave E Benson
*Ch Bd: Ed Hunt
QA Dir: Jason Wilkinson
IT Man: Jim Hoekema
IT Man: Allen Mills
Opers Mgr: Mark Andersen
Opers Mgr: Mark Anderson
Prd Mgr: Scott Ness
Natl Sales: John Hobson

HUNTER BUILDINGS & MFG
See HUNTER BUILDINGS LLC

D-U-N-S 60-254-9094 IMP
HUNTER BUILDINGS LLC
HUNTER BUILDINGS & MFG
14935 Jacintoport Blvd, Houston, TX 77015-6523
Tel (281) 452-9800 Founded/Ownrshp 2006
Sales 141.6MM^E EMP 120
SIC 1542 Commercial & office building contractors
Mng Pt: Michael Leblanc
VP: Buddy Tucker
VP: Glenn Whitlock
Genl Mgr: Lynn Efferson
Mtls Mgr: Nathan Conrad
VP Sls: Alisha Nash
Manager: Shane Bruce
Manager: Bucky Crowson
Manager: Stephanie Wilder
Sales Asso: Rebecca Bergeron
Snr PM: Joey Dawson

D-U-N-S 00-582-9601
HUNTER CONTRACTING CO (AZ)
701 N Cooper Rd, Gilbert, AZ 85233-3703
Tel (480) 892-0521 Founded/Ownrshp 1961
Sales 193.6MM^E EMP 620
SIC 1611 1629 1622 General contractor, highway & street construction; Dams, waterways, docks & other marine construction; Waste water & sewage treatment plant construction; Bridge, tunnel & elevated highway
Ch Bd: Max Taddei
*Pr: Rob Padilla
*CFO: Samuel J Napolitano
*Sr VP: Allen Andrews
*VP: Bob Carlson
*VP: Chuck English
Off Mgr: Karl Schmidt

D-U-N-S 80-779-4206 EXP
HUNTER DEFENSE TECHNOLOGIES INC
HDT ENGINEERED TECHNOLOGIES
(Suby of HDT GLOBAL INC) ★
30500 Aurora Rd Ste 100, Solon, OH 44139-2776
Tel (216) 438-6111 Founded/Ownrshp 2009
Sales 289.3MM^E EMP 650
SIC 3433 3569 3822 8331 8711 3549 Room & wall heaters, including radiators; Filters; Auto controls regulating residntl & coml environmt & applncs; Sheltered workshop; Engineering services; Assembly machines, including robotic
CEO: R Andrew Hove
Pr: Gaylord Seemann
Pr: Mike Stolarz
*CFO: Anthony Dilucente
CFO: Tony Dilucente
CFO: George Rascati

Ex VP: Robin Carney
*Sr VP: Prabha Gopinath
*Sr VP: Greg Miller
*Sr VP: Carl Pates
VP: Rita Thomas

HUNTER DODGE CHRYSLER JEEP RAM
See H W HUNTER INC

D-U-N-S 04-618-8165 IMP/EXP
HUNTER DOUGLAS INC
(Suby of HUNTER DOUGLAS N.V.)
1 Blue Hill Plz Ste 1569, Pearl River, NY 10965-6101
Tel (845) 664-7000 Founded/Ownrshp 1976
Sales 2.1MMM^E EMP 8,625
SIC 2591 3444 5084 Window blinds; Window shades; Venetian blinds; Sheet metalwork; Industrial machinery & equipment
Pr: Marvin B Hopkins
*Ch Bd: Ralph Sonnenberg
*Pr: David H Sonnenberg
*CFO: Leen Reijtenbagh
CFO: Craig Smith
*Ex VP: Ajit Mehra
VP: Dilip Joglekar
Exec: Lori Rubino
Adm Dir: Mary Lonergan
Genl Mgr: Bryan Clabeaux
Dir IT: Paul Sherman

D-U-N-S 15-807-1766 IMP/EXP
HUNTER DOUGLAS WINDOW FASHIONS INC
(Suby of HUNTER DOUGLAS INC) ★
1 Duette Way, Broomfield, CO 80020-1090
Tel (303) 466-1848 Founded/Ownrshp 1998
Sales 200.6MM^E EMP 950^E
SIC 2591 Drapery hardware & blinds & shades
Pr: Marv Hopkins
*Ex VP: Ajit Mehra
VP: Dilip Joglekar
VP: Richard Pellett
VP: Dennis Szostek
Dir Bus: Ken Witherell
Mng Dir: Bonnie Earl
IT Man: Brian Hobbs
IT Man: Robert Werner
Mtls Mgr: Linda Fields
Opers Mgr: Troy Daley

D-U-N-S 00-628-8203 IMP/EXP
HUNTER ENGINEERING CO INC (MO)
11250 Hunter Dr, Bridgeton, MO 63044-2391
Tel (314) 731-3020 Founded/Ownrshp 1948, 1933
Sales 172.0MM^E EMP 700
SIC 3559

D-U-N-S 15-724-2132 IMP/EXP
HUNTER FAN CO
CASABLANCA FAN COMPANY
(Suby of MIDOCEAN PARTNERS) ★
7130 Goodlett Farms Pkwy Ste 400, Memphis, TN 38103
Tel (901) 743-1360 Founded/Ownrshp 1986
Sales 138.9MM^E EMP 350
SIC 5064 3634 3645 Fans, household: electric; Ceiling fans; Residential lighting fixtures
CEO: John Alexander
Pr: Tom Breeden
*CFO: Charles Turner
Sr VP: Joe Deering
VP: James Barrett
*VP: Thomas Blackwell
VP: Kenneth Garvey
VP: Tammy Judd
VP: Alan Walter
Genl Mgr: Kyle P Brown
Dir IT: Raymond Curry

D-U-N-S 86-874-7247 IMP/EXP
HUNTER INDUSTRIES INC
1940 Diamond St, San Marcos, CA 92078-5190
Tel (800) 383-4747 Founded/Ownrshp 1993
Sales 672.3MM^E EMP 1,300^E
SIC 5087 3084 Sprinkler systems; Plastics pipe
Pr: Gregory Hunter
Pr: Arne Pike
*Treas: Kari Pelters
Dist Mgr: Craig Berlin
VP Mktg: Gene Smith
Sls Mgr: Tony Newton

D-U-N-S 03-858-0064 EXP
HUNTER INDUSTRIES L P
1940 Diamond St, San Marcos, CA 92078-5190
Tel (760) 744-5240 Founded/Ownrshp 1981
Sales 124.5MM^E EMP 800^E
SIC 1629 Irrigation system construction; Earthmoving contractor
Pt: Richard E Hunter
Pt: Ann K Hunter-Welborn

D-U-N-S 06-643-4648 IMP
HUNTER INDUSTRIES LTD
COLORADO MATERIALS
5080 Fm 2439, New Braunfels, TX 78132
Tel (512) 353-7757 Founded/Ownrshp 1997
Sales 245.1MM^E EMP 500
SIC 1611 2951 1442 General contractor, highway & street construction; Asphalt & asphaltic paving mixtures (not from refineries); Gravel mining
Ch Bd: John R Weisman
COO: Gregory Hunter
*Treas: Walter Ulbricht
*VP: Ronnie Jones
*VP: Mark D Reininger
Prgrm Mgr: Mary Barraclough

D-U-N-S 00-887-1365
■ HUNTER PANELS LLC
(Suby of CARLISLE SYNTEC) ★
15 Franklin St Ste B2, Portland, ME 04101-7119
Tel (888) 746-1114 Founded/Ownrshp 1975
Sales 88.1MM^E EMP 250
SIC 3086 Insulation or cushioning material, foamed plastic
*VP: Jim Whitton
Sls Mgr: Matt Peterson

D-U-N-S 18-904-7975
HUNTER ROBERTS CONSTRUCTION GROUP LLC
55 Water St Fl 51, New York, NY 10041-3201
Tel (212) 321-6800 Founded/Ownrshp 2005
Sales 1.0MMM^E EMP 260
Accts Grassi & Co Jericho New Yor
SIC 8742 1542 Construction project management consultant; Commercial & office building contractors
Pr: James C McKenna
COO: Austin Dimech
*Ex VP: Paul Andersen
Ex VP: Paul Anderson
Ex VP: Bobby Ferguson
*Sr VP: John Alicandri
VP: Bill Allan
*VP: Kevin Barrett
*VP: Alex Craig
*VP: Tim Dillon
*VP: Dan Dirscherl
VP: Eric Hook
*VP: Mark Lamble
VP: K Lindsey
VP: Robert Masucci
*VP: Chuck Petrusky
*Exec: Brian Aronne
Exec: Thomas Ascher
Exec: Marie Cahill
Exec: Robert Fee
Exec: Michelle Fisher

D-U-N-S 01-405-6014 EXP
HUNTER TRUCK SALES & SERVICE INC
480 Pittsburgh Rd, Butler, PA 16002-7654
Tel (724) 586-5770 Founded/Ownrshp 1938
Sales 141.7MM^E EMP 233
SIC 5511 5531 7538 Trucks, tractors & trailers: new & used; Truck equipment & parts; General truck repair
Pr: Homer Hunter
CEO: Jeffrey Hunter
CFO: Raff Fischer
Sec: William Hunter
VP: Harry Hunter
Genl Mgr: Dick Mong

HUNTERDON HEALTH CARE
See HUNTERDON MEDICAL CENTER (INC)

D-U-N-S 06-988-6216
HUNTERDON MEDICAL CENTER (INC) (NJ)
HUNTERDON HEALTH CARE
2100 Wescott Dr, Flemington, NJ 08822-4604
Tel (908) 788-6100 Founded/Ownrshp 1948
Sales 267.7MM EMP 2,200
SIC 8062 General medical & surgical hospitals
CEO: Robert P Wise
Chf Path: Steven Diamond
Dir Vol: Joy Stump
*COO: Lawrence Grand
COO: Don Pinner
*CFO: Gail Kosyla
Trst: Carla Jardim
Trst: Hugh Prentice
*VP: Deborah Hoskins
VP: Patricia Steingall
Exec: Ross Miller
Dir OR: Donna Cole
Dir Teleco: Deirdre Meade
Dir Risk M: Stephanie Dougherty
Dir Rx: David Adelman
Board of Directors: William Atwater

D-U-N-S 80-851-4517 IMP
HUNTING ENERGY SERVICES INC
HUNTING OILFIELD SERVICES.
(Suby of HUNTING PLC)
2 Northpoint Dr Ste 400, Houston, TX 77060-3233
Tel (281) 820-3838 Founded/Ownrshp 1993
Sales 347.8MM^E EMP 577
SIC 1389 8741 Oil field services; Management services
CEO: Dennis L Proctor
Assoc VP: Gene McBride
VP: Will Oliver
Ex Dir: Jim Johnson
QI Cn Mgr: German Rivero

D-U-N-S 61-028-0307 IMP
HUNTING INNOVA INC
INNOVA ELECTRONICS
(Suby of HUNTING PLC)
8383 N Sam Houston Pkwy W, Houston, TX 77064-3452
Tel (281) 653-5500 Founded/Ownrshp 1989
Sales 102.8MM^E EMP 350
SIC 3672 3613 8711 Printed circuit boards; Power switching equipment; Engineering services
CEO: Dennis Proctor
Pr: Leon Chenn
CFO: Robert Snider
Prd Mgr: Mary Leamons

HUNTING OILFIELD SERVICES.
See HUNTING ENERGY SERVICES INC

D-U-N-S 07-682-6015 IMP/EXP
■ HUNTINGTON ALLOYS CORP
PART OF SPECIAL METALS
(Suby of PCC) ★
3200 Riverside Dr, Huntington, WV 25705-1764
Tel (304) 526-5100 Founded/Ownrshp 1928
Sales 325.8MM^E EMP 1,000
SIC 3356 Nickel & nickel alloy: rolling, drawing or extruding
Pr: Kenneth D Buck
Sr VP: Steve Tassen
*VP: Roger P Becker
*VP: Darrin Bird
VP: Max Bleiler
VP: Shailesh J Patel
*VP: Steve Zylstra
Exec: Nona Rimmer
Genl Mgr: John Pierotti
*Genl Mgr: Kent Semelroth
Dir IT: Bob Shields

D-U-N-S 04-643-1227
▲ HUNTINGTON BANCSHARES INC
41 S High St, Columbus, OH 43215-6170
Tel (614) 480-8300 *Founded/Ownrshp* 1966
Sales NA *EMP* 12,243ᴱ
Tkr Sym HBAN *Exch* NGS
SIC 6021 National commercial banks
Ch Bd: Stephen D Steinour
Pr: Amy Beck
Pr: Jessica Burnett
Pr: Wes Haberman
Pr: Shantel Hampton
Pr: Susan Lelonek
Pr: Dave Nash
Pr: Chay Rankin
Pr: Jill Tubaugh
Pr: Erich Voss
CFO: Howell D McCullough II
Treas: Seth McDonald
Chf Inves: Randy Bateman
Ofcr: Helga S Houston
Ofcr: Daniel J Neumeyer
Assoc VP: Larry Slivon
Ex VP: David S Anderson
Ex VP: Barbara Benham
Ex VP: Richard A Cheap
Ex VP: Donald Kimble
Ex VP: Steven Short
Board of Directors: John C Inglis, Lizabeth Ardisana, Peter J Kight, Ann B Crane, Jonathan A Levy, Robert S Cubbin, Eddie R Munson, Robert S Cubbin, Richard W Neu, Steven G Elliott, David L Porteous, Michael J Endres, Kathleen H Ransier, Gina D France, Gina D France, John B Gerlach Jr

D-U-N-S 07-954-5703
HUNTINGTON BEACH UNION HIGH SCHOOL DISTRICT
5832 Bolsa Ave, Huntington Beach, CA 92649-1181
Tel (714) 903-7000 *Founded/Ownrshp* 1991
Sales 108.1MMᴱ *EMP* 1,552
SIC 8211 Public elementary & secondary schools
**Pr:* Bonnie Castrey
Bd of Dir: Matthew Harper
**VP:* Kathleen Iverson
Adm Dir: John Klungreseter
Genl Mgr: Kevin Smith
Schl Brd P: Susan Henry
Instr Medi: Shirley Bowen
Psych: Claudia Gomez
Board of Directors: Bonnie Bruce, Bonnie Castrey, Sallie Dashiell, Matthew Harper, Michael Simons

D-U-N-S 07-268-4152
HUNTINGTON CABELL HOSPITAL INC
CABELL HOME HEALTH SERVICES
1340 Hal Greer Blvd, Huntington, WV 25701-0195
Tel (304) 526-2000 *Founded/Ownrshp* 1955
Sales 473.1MM *EMP* 2,300ᴱ
SIC 8062 Hospital, professional nursing school with AMA residency
Pr: Brent A Marsteller
Chf Rad: Peter Chirico
**Treas:* Floyd Eharlow Jr
VP: Bradley Burck
**VP:* David Graley
VP: Dennis Lee
Ex Dir: Michele Conley
Prgrm Mgr: Christi Kuhner
QA Dir: Valerie Hopkins-Smith
Tech Mgr: Garry Atkins
Doctor: Betts Carpenter

D-U-N-S 07-891-5303
HUNTINGTON COUNTY COMMUNITY SCHOOL CORP
2485 Waterworks Rd, Huntington, IN 46750-4145
Tel (260) 356-8312 *Founded/Ownrshp* 1966
Sales 61.3MMᴱ *EMP* 1,000
SIC 8211 Public combined elementary & secondary school
**Treas:* Sheila Hall
MIS Dir: Nick Vickrey
Dir IT: Tom Ashley

D-U-N-S 06-911-6521
HUNTINGTON HOSPITAL
100 W California Blvd, Pasadena, CA 91105-3010
Tel (626) 397-5000 *Founded/Ownrshp* 2011
Sales 551.9MM *EMP* 213ᴱ
SIC 8062 General medical & surgical hospitals
Prin: Peter W Corrigan
Pr: Linda Jackson
VP: Jim Noble
VP: Paula Verette
Telecom Ex: Sonia Houston
Snr Ntwrk: Thomas Hart
CTO: Sheryl Rudie
IT Man: Weldon Clark
IT Man: Larry Murphy
Netwrk Mgr: Joe Tabor
Surgeon: Magdi Alexander

D-U-N-S 04-919-0598
HUNTINGTON HOSPITAL AUXILIARY
270 Park Ave, Huntington, NY 11743-2799
Tel (631) 351-2257 *Founded/Ownrshp* 1917
Sales 325.5MM *EMP* 6
SIC 5947 5499 8322 Gift shop; Coffee; Social service center
Pr: Barbara Mawra
**Pr:* Kathy Dyckes

D-U-N-S 06-802-0726
HUNTINGTON HOSPITAL DOLAN FAMILY HEALTH CENTER INC
270 Park Ave, Huntington, NY 11743-2799
Tel (631) 351-2000 *Founded/Ownrshp* 1915
Sales 302.9MM *EMP* 2,000
SIC 8062 General medical & surgical hospitals
Pr: Michael J Dowling
Dir Recs: Robert Coehlo
Dir Recs: Robert Coelho
**Ch Bd:* Irving Klein
**CEO:* Kevin Lawlor
**Treas:* Gordon Hargraves
Bd of Dir: Robert Zingale
Top Exec: Joseph G Gavin Jr
**VP:* Michael J Alesandro
VP: Cynthia Hoey
VP: Robert Mottola
VP: Emily Patterson
VP: Michael Quartier
Exec: Sue Schmeising
Dir Rx: Mateyunas Jack

D-U-N-S 00-130-7495 IMP
■ HUNTINGTON INGALLS INC
(*Suby of* HUNTINGTON INGALLS INDUSTRIES INC) ★
4101 Washington Ave, Newport News, VA 23607-2734
Tel (757) 380-2000 *Founded/Ownrshp* 2011
Sales 3.5MMMᴱ *EMP* 19,000ᴱ
SIC 3731 Shipbuilding & repairing; Submarines, building & repairing; Military ships, building & repairing; Tankers, building & repairing
Pr: Matt Mulherin
**Treas:* D R Wyatt
VP: Dwayne Blake
VP: William Ermatinger
VP: Douglass Fontaine
**VP:* Alene Kaufman
**VP:* Barbara A Niland
Genl Mgr: Janet Barker
Genl Mgr: Jim Kaltenschnee
MIS Dir: Bobby Tolbert
IT Man: Richard Clabbers
Board of Directors: Ken Mahler

D-U-N-S 96-736-2331
▲ HUNTINGTON INGALLS INDUSTRIES INC
4101 Washington Ave, Newport News, VA 23607-2734
Tel (757) 380-2000 *Founded/Ownrshp* 1886
Sales 7.0MMM *EMP* 36,000ᴱ
Accts Deloitte & Touche Llp Richmon
Tkr Sym HII *Exch* NYS
SIC 3731 Military ships, building & repairing
Pr: C Michael Petters
CFO: Barbara A Niland
CFO: Thomas Stiehle
Treas: D R Wyatt
Ofcr: William R Ermatinger
Ofcr: Chavis Harris
Ex VP: Christopher D Kastner
Ex VP: Mitchell B Waldman
Ex VP: Kellye L Walker
VP: Carolyn E Apostolou
VP: Daniel L Arczynski
VP: Ray Bagley
VP: Bill Bell
VP: Dwayne B Blake
VP: Gerald Boyd
VP: Greg Bury
VP: Mary Cullen
VP: Jerri Fuller Dickseski
VP: John Donnelly
VP: Jennifer Dunn
VP: William Ebbs
Board of Directors: Stephen R Wilson, Robert F Bruner, Augustus Leon Collins, Thomas B Fargo, Victoria D Harker, Anastasia D Kelly, Paul D Miller, Thomas C Schievelbein, Karl M Von Der Heyden, John K Welch

D-U-N-S 78-101-1999
■ HUNTINGTON INGALLS INDUSTRIES INTERNATIONAL SHIPBUILDING INC
(*Suby of* HUNTINGTON INGALLS INC) ★
1000 Access Rd, Pascagoula, MS 39567-4485
Tel (228) 935-1122 *Founded/Ownrshp* 2011
Sales 185.3MMᴱ *EMP* 1ᴱ
SIC 3731 Combat vessels, building & repairing
Pr: Philip Teek
**Treas:* James L Sanford
VP: Lori Harper
VP: Richard Schenk

D-U-N-S 00-541-7522
■ HUNTINGTON INSURANCE INC
(*Suby of* HUNTINGTON NATIONAL BANK) ★
519 Madison Ave, Toledo, OH 43604-1206
Tel (419) 720-7900 *Founded/Ownrshp* 1898
Sales NA *EMP* 189
SIC 6411 Insurance agents
Pr: Paul Baldwin
Pr: Mary Beth Sullivan
CFO: Dennis Raab
Treas: Pamela M Alspach
Sr VP: Robert C Hawker Cpcu Arm
Sr VP: Ralph Burkley
Sr VP: William N Fether
Sr VP: Robert C Hawker
Sr VP: Ronald L Murray
Sr VP: Leslie Talkington
VP: A D Story

HUNTINGTON LEARNING CENTER
See HUNTINGTON LEARNING CORP

D-U-N-S 08-975-0780
HUNTINGTON LEARNING CORP
HUNTINGTON LEARNING CENTER
496 Kinderkamack Rd G01, Oradell, NJ 07649-1512
Tel (201) 261-8400 *Founded/Ownrshp* 1977, 1986
Sales 152.3MMᴱ *EMP* 1,200
SIC 8299 Tutoring school
Ch: Raymond J Huntington
**VP:* Eileen C Huntington

HUNTINGTON MEMORIAL HOSPITAL
See PASADENA HOSPITAL ASSOCIATION LTD

D-U-N-S 09-972-8669 IMP
■ HUNTINGTON NATIONAL BANK
(*Suby of* HUNTINGTON BANCSHARES INC) ★
17 S High St Fl 1, Columbus, OH 43215-3413
Tel (614) 480-4293 *Founded/Ownrshp* 1979
Sales NA *EMP* 11,873
SIC 6029 Commercial banks
Pr: Stephen D Steinour
Pr: Renee Csuhran
Pr: Sadhana Mohan
Pr: William C Shivers
**COO:* Paul Heller
CFO: Steve Franzel
**CFO:* Howell D McCullough III
CFO: Tonya Spires
Assoc VP: Timothy Bender
**Ex VP:* Richard A Cheap
Ex VP: David Ring
Sr VP: William R Adon
Sr VP: Jennifer Clark
Sr VP: Laurens J De Kort
Sr VP: Diane L Dougherty
Sr VP: Joe Flannery
Sr VP: Molly Glaser
Sr VP: Kim E Lyttle
Sr VP: Richard Machinski
**Sr VP:* Mary W Navarro
Sr VP: Joseph M Petite
Board of Directors: David L Porteous, Dave Anderson, Kathleen H Ransier, Don M Casto III, Ann B Crane, Steven G Elliott, Michael J Endres, John B Gerlach Jr, Peter J Kight, Jonathan A Levy, Richard W Neu

HUNTINGTON TOWN HALL
See TOWN OF HUNTINGTON

D-U-N-S 06-321-9607
HUNTLEIGH USA CORP
545 E John Carpenter Fwy, Irving, TX 75062-3931
Tel (972) 719-9180 *Founded/Ownrshp* 2011
Sales 123.5MMᴱ *EMP* 2,300
SIC 4581

D-U-N-S 07-475-1827 IMP
HUNTON & WILLIAMS LLP
Riverfront Plz E Towe 951, Richmond, VA 23219
Tel (804) 788-8200 *Founded/Ownrshp* 1901
Sales 356.5MMᴱ *EMP* 1,541
SIC 8111 General practice law office
Mng Pt: Walfrido Martinez
Pt: W Christopher Arbery
Pt: Steven H Becker
Pt: Ken Bell
Pt: Stephen Bennett
Pt: Lawrence J Bracken II
Pt: Emerson V Briggs
Pt: Tyler P Brown
Pt: Christopher Graffiin Browning
Pt: Eric R Burner
Pt: Terence G Connor
Pt: Cyane Crump
Pt: J Mark Debord
Pt: Robert H Edwards Jr
**Pt:* Juan Enjamio
Pt: Edward J Fuhr
Pt: Robert J Grey Jr
Pt: Robert J Hahn
Pt: Doug Heffner
Pt: Matthew C Henry
Pt: Louanna O Heuhsen
Board of Directors: William Brownell

HUNTON TRANE
See HTI LTD

D-U-N-S 15-926-0202 IMP/EXP
■ HUNTSMAN ADVANCED MATERIALS AMERICAS LLC
(*Suby of* HUNTSMAN ADVANCED MATERIALS LLC) ★
10003 Woodloch Forest Dr # 260, The Woodlands, TX 77380-1955
Tel (281) 719-6000 *Founded/Ownrshp* 2003
Sales 91.4MMᴱ *EMP* 490
SIC 2899 Chemical preparations
Bd of Dir: Michael K Young
Ofcr: Gary Perez
Ex VP: Robert Haight
VP: Curtis Dowd
VP: Tom Fisher
Admn Mgr: Carol Hollinshead
Sfty Mgr: Leyton Brown
Opers Mgr: Dennis Ivins
Plnt Mgr: Bannie Cockerham

D-U-N-S 14-145-8583 EXP
■ HUNTSMAN ADVANCED MATERIALS LLC
(*Suby of* HUNTSMAN CORP) ★
500 S Huntsman Way, Salt Lake City, UT 84108-1235
Tel (801) 584-5700 *Founded/Ownrshp* 2008
Sales 91.4MMᴱ *EMP* 491
SIC 2821 2891 3087 Plastics materials & resins; Adhesives & sealants; Custom compound purchased resins
VP: Maria Csiba-Womersley
VP: Kevin Hardman

D-U-N-S 18-257-5584 IMP
▲ HUNTSMAN CORP
10003 Woodloch Forest Dr # 260, The Woodlands, TX 77380-1955
Tel (281) 719-6000 *Founded/Ownrshp* 1970
Sales 10.3MMM *EMP* 15,000
Accts Deloitte & Touche Llp Houston
Tkr Sym HUN *Exch* NYS
SIC 2821 3081 2869 2816 2865 Polystyrene resins; Polyethylene film; Ethylene; Propylene, butylene; Titanium dioxide, anatase or rutile (pigments); Dyes & pigments
Pr: Peter R Huntsman
**Ch Bd:* Jon M Huntsman
CEO: Anthony P Hankins
CFO: J Kimo Esplin
Treas: John R Heskett
Div Pres: Monte G Edlund
Div Pres: Paul G Hulme
Div Pres: James H Huntsman
Div Pres: Simon Turner
**V Ch Bd:* Nolan D Archibald
Bd of Dir: Patrick Harker
Ex VP: David Stryker
Ex VP: David M Stryker
Ex VP: Twila I Everett
Sr VP: Ronald W Gerrard
Sr VP: Brian V Ridd
Sr VP: R Wade Rogers
Sr VP: Russ R Stolle
VP: Patricia Albisser
VP: Ron D Brown
VP: Maria Csiba-Womersley

D-U-N-S 13-162-8534 IMP/EXP
■ HUNTSMAN HOLDINGS LLC
(*Suby of* HUNTSMAN CORP) ★
500 S Huntsman Way, Salt Lake City, UT 84108-1235
Tel (801) 584-5700 *Founded/Ownrshp* 2005
Sales 332.1MMᴱ *EMP* 11,595
SIC 2821 2911 3081 2869 Polystyrene resins; Petroleum refining; Polyethylene film; Ethylene; Propylene, butylene
CEO: Peter R Huntsman
CFO: J Kimo Esplin
Ch: Jon M Huntsman
Ex VP: Samuel D Scruggs

D-U-N-S 08-737-6146 IMP/EXP
■ HUNTSMAN INTERNATIONAL LLC
(*Suby of* HUNTSMAN CORP) ★
1003 Woodloch Forest Dr, The Woodlands, TX 77380
Tel (281) 719-6000 *Founded/Ownrshp* 1999
Sales 10.3MMM *EMP* 15,000
SIC 2821 3081 2869 2816 2865 Polystyrene resins; Polyethylene film; Ethylene; Propylene, butylene; Titanium dioxide, anatase or rutile (pigments); Dyes & pigments
Pr: Peter R Huntsman
**Ch Bd:* Jon M Huntsman
**CFO:* J Kimo Esplin
Ex VP: David M Stryker
VP: Randy W Wright
Info Man: Karl Schosser

D-U-N-S 92-605-7969 IMP/EXP
■ HUNTSMAN INTERNATIONAL TRADING CORP
(*Suby of* HUNTSMAN PETROCHEMICAL LLC) ★
10003 Woodloch Forest Dr # 260, The Woodlands, TX 77380-1955
Tel (281) 719-6000 *Founded/Ownrshp* 1994
Sales 539.5MMᴱ *EMP* 300
SIC 5169 Chemicals & allied products
CEO: Peter R Huntsman
**Ch:* Jon M Huntsman
**VP:* Sean Douglas
**VP:* J Kimo Esplin
**VP:* Kevin C Hardman
**VP:* John R Heskett
VP: James H Huntsman
VP: Steve Jorgensen
VP: Stu Monteith
Exec: Van Cockerham
Exec: Becky Rieger

D-U-N-S 14-717-3017 IMP/EXP
■ HUNTSMAN PETROCHEMICAL LLC
(*Suby of* HUNTSMAN INTERNATIONAL LLC) ★
500 S Huntsman Way, Salt Lake City, UT 84108-1235
Tel (801) 584-5700 *Founded/Ownrshp* 1994
Sales 492.3MMᴱ *EMP* 1,500
SIC 2911 Petroleum refining
Pr: Peter R Huntsman
CFO: J Kimo Esplin
Treas: Jena Howland
Ex VP: James R Moore
VP: Kevin C Hardman
VP: L Russell Healy
VP: Karen Huntsman

D-U-N-S 07-835-4818 IMP/EXP
■ HUNTSMAN-COOPER LLC (UT)
(*Suby of* HUNTSMAN INTERNATIONAL LLC) ★
500 S Huntsman Way, Salt Lake City, UT 84108-1235
Tel (801) 584-5700 *Founded/Ownrshp* 1982
Sales 121.1MMᴱ *EMP* 1,000
SIC 2821 Polystyrene resins
VP: Curt Ogdon

D-U-N-S 07-765-3269
HUNTSVILLE CITY BOARD OF EDUCATION
200 White St Se, Huntsville, AL 35801-4104
Tel (256) 428-6800 *Founded/Ownrshp* 1890
Sales 265.3MMᴱ *EMP* 3,000
SIC 8211 School board
Pr: Laurie McCaulley
Exec: Kenneth Carpenter
Schl Brd P: Topper Birney
Psych: Rhea Zerr

D-U-N-S 07-846-3427
HUNTSVILLE CITY SCHOOLS
200 White St Se, Huntsville, AL 35801-4104
Tel (256) 428-6800 *Founded/Ownrshp* 2012
Sales 45.7MMᴱ *EMP* 2,942ᴱ
SIC 8211 Elementary & secondary schools
Dir Sec: Al Lankford
MIS Dir: Sandra Simmons
Pr Dir: Rena Anderson
Teacher Pr: Micah Fisher
HC Dir: Deborah Berry

HUNTSVILLE DIVISION
See BENCHMARK ELECTRONICS HUNTSVILLE INC

HUNTSVILLE HOSP WOMEN CHILDREN
See HEALTH CARE AUTHORITY OF CITY OF HUNTSVILLE

D-U-N-S 00-548-5577
HUNTSVILLE HOSPITAL
101 Sivley Rd Sw, Huntsville, AL 35801-4470
Tel (256) 265-1000 *Founded/Ownrshp* 2009
Sales 799.3MM *EMP* 2,363ᴱ
SIC 8062 General medical & surgical hospitals
CEO: David Spillers

D-U-N-S 09-938-6146
HUNTSVILLE INDEPENDENT SCHOOL DISTRICT
ADMINSTRATION OFFICE
441 Fm 2821 Rd E, Huntsville, TX 77320-9223
Tel (936) 435-6300 *Founded/Ownrshp* 1875
Sales 54.2MMᴱ *EMP* 1,000
Accts Kenneth C Davis & Company Hu
SIC 8211 Public elementary & secondary schools
Exec: Emily Demilliano
Exec: Shannon Duncan
Pr Dir: Emily Demilliani
HC Dir: Debora Homann

D-U-N-S 07-417-9300
HUNTSVILLE MEMORIAL HOSPITAL AUXILIARY
110 Memorial Hospital Dr, Huntsville, TX 77340-4940
Tel (936) 291-3411 *Founded/Ownrshp* 1927
Sales 84.2MM *EMP* 600
Accts Bkd Llp Houston Texas
SIC 8062 General medical & surgical hospitals
CEO: Ralph Beaty
CFO: Dorothy Nevill
Dir Bus: Lisa Moody
Ex Dir: Dawn Lawrence
Opers Mgr: Liz McGinty

HUNTSVILLE UTILITIES
See CITY OF HUNTSVILLE ELECTRIC SYSTEMS

D-U-N-S 00-720-5065
HUNZICKER BROTHERS INC (OK)
501 N Virginia Ave, Oklahoma City, OK 73106-2638
Tel (405) 239-7771 *Founded/Ownrshp* 1920, 1989
Sales 133.1MM^E *EMP* 145
SIC 5063 Electrical supplies
CEO: Myers Lockard
Mng Pt: Julie Edmondson
**Ex VP:* John D Henderson
VP: Mike Bell
VP: Steve Evans
Off Mgr: Barb Parsons
Opers Mgr: Evan Smith
**VP Sls:* Jerry Young
Mktg Dir: Richard Dean
Mktg Mgr: Brandi Guethle
Sales Asso: Gregory Helton

D-U-N-S 04-458-1734
▲ HURCO COMPANIES INC
1 Technology Way, Indianapolis, IN 46268-5106
Tel (317) 293-5309 *Founded/Ownrshp* 1968
Sales 219.3MM *EMP* 769^E
Tkr Sym HURC *Exch* NGS
SIC 3823 7372 Computer interface equipment for industrial process control; Prepackaged software
Ch Bd: Michael Doar
Pr: Gregory S Volovic
COO: Chad Back
CFO: Sonja K McClelland
Bd of Dir: Andrew Lewis
Ex VP: John P Donlon
VP: Himat Patel
Genl Mgr: Philippe Chevalier
Dir IT: Kris Hayes
IT Man: Eric Hamm
Software D: Wiaam Suleiman
Board of Directors: Thomas A Aaro, Robert W Cruickshank, Jay C Longbottom, Andrew Niner, Ronald Strackbein

HURD WINDOWS & DOORS
See HWD ACQUISITION INC

D-U-N-S 09-870-8352 IMP/EXP
■ HURLEY INTERNATIONAL LLC
(*Suby of* NIKE INC) ★
1945 Placentia Ave, Costa Mesa, CA 92627-3420
Tel (949) 548-9375 *Founded/Ownrshp* 2001
Sales 89.2MM^E *EMP* 201
SIC 2329 5137 Knickers, dress (separate): men's & boys'; Women's & children's clothing
CEO: Robert M Hurley
VP: Brett Bjorkman
VP: Dwight Dunn
VP: Courtney Skiba
Dir: Sherilyn Miller
Creative D: Brandon Bale
Creative D: Ryan Clemens
Genl Mgr: Jason Haynes
Prd Mgr: Shivani Bhardwaj
Sls Dir: Ron Morelos
Mktg Mgr: Ryan Fosegan

D-U-N-S 07-423-2273
HURLEY MEDICAL CENTER
GERIATRIC OTRACH CLNC/CARE MGT
1 Hurley Plz, Flint, MI 48503-5902
Tel (810) 257-9000 *Founded/Ownrshp* 1905
Sales 378.4MM *EMP* 2,884
SIC 8062 Hospital, professional nursing school with AMA residency
CEO: Melanie Devalac
Chf Path: Cathy Blight
Chf Rad: Apparao Mukkamala
**CFO:* Kevin Murphy
Treas: Thomas James
Treas: Maryann Turouske
Bd of Dir: Michael Marulli
VP: Melanie Gavulic
VP: Karen Lopez
Dir Lab: Beth Friedt
Dir Rad: Dawn Hiller
Dir Rad: Dawn Sturk
Board of Directors: James Wheeler, Delores Ennis, Anthony Whittbrodt, Chris Flores, Thomas James, Joel Kleiner, Thomas Landall, Pamela Loving, Ira Rutherford, Judy Samelson, Ernest Vahala

D-U-N-S 04-086-8049
HURLEY OF AMERICA INC
(*Suby of* HURLEY CORP)
803 Linden Ave Ste 3, Rochester, NY 14625-2723
Tel (781) 438-7830 *Founded/Ownrshp* 1998
Sales 14.1MM^E *EMP* 1,200^E
SIC 7349 7382 Janitorial service, contract basis; Security systems services
Pr: Barton L Munro Jr
Dir Bus: Ronald O'Brien

D-U-N-S 08-221-2721 IMP
HURON CASTING INC
H C I
7050 Hartley St, Pigeon, MI 48755-5190
Tel (989) 453-3933 *Founded/Ownrshp* 1976
Sales 96.3MM^E *EMP* 450^E
SIC 3325 3369 Alloy steel castings, except investment; Nonferrous foundries
Pr: Leroy Wurst
**CFO:* Matt Davis
**VP:* Devere Sturm
Off Mgr: Terry Waitt
IT Man: Jim Lapratt
Plnt Mgr: Chris Wurst
Trfc Mgr: Linda Wolfram

D-U-N-S 14-897-0184
▲ HURON CONSULTING GROUP INC
550 W Van Buren St # 1600, Chicago, IL 60607-3827
Tel (312) 583-8700 *Founded/Ownrshp* 2002
Sales 769.0MM *EMP* 2,821^E
Tkr Sym HURN *Exch* NGS
SIC 8742 8748 Hospital & health services consultant; Financial consultant; School, college, university consultant; Educational consultant
Pr: James H Roth
**Ch Bd:* John F McCartney
COO: C Mark Hussey
**V Ch Bd:* George E Massaro
Ex VP: Diane E Ratekin
VP: Mark Dogadalski
VP: Phil Hausken
Mng Dir: John Bodine
Mng Dir: Peter Eschenbach
Mng Dir: Paul Johnson
Mng Dir: Mark Linver
Board of Directors: James D Edwards, H Eugene Lockhart, John S Moody, Debra Zumwalt

D-U-N-S 11-136-7897
■ HURON CONSULTING SERVICES LLC
(*Suby of* HURON CONSULTING GROUP INC) ★
550 W Van Buren St # 1600, Chicago, IL 60607-3827
Tel (312) 583-8700 *Founded/Ownrshp* 2002
Sales 107.2MM^E *EMP* 1,757
SIC 8748 Business consulting
CEO: James H Roth
Pr: Natalia Delgado
**Pr:* Mary Sawall
**Ex VP:* C Mark Hussey
**VP:* John D Kelly
**VP:* Diane E Ratekin
Mng Dir: Terry Lloyd

D-U-N-S 11-928-2978
HURON HEALTH CARE CENTER INC
ADMIRALS PNTE NRSING RHBLTTION
1920 Cleveland Rd W, Huron, OH 44839-1211
Tel (419) 433-4990 *Founded/Ownrshp* 1993
Sales 584.9MM *EMP* 125
SIC 8051 Skilled nursing care facilities
Mktg Dir: Jody Corsillas

D-U-N-S 06-984-3852
HURON VALLEY BOARD OF EDUCATION
2390 S Milford Rd, Highland, MI 48357-4934
Tel (248) 684-8000 *Founded/Ownrshp* 1946
Sales 113.5MM *EMP* 1,400
Accts Plante & Moran Pllc Auburn Hi
SIC 8211 Public elementary school; Public junior high school; Public senior high school; School board
Pr: Lindsay Cotter
Prin: Peg Sell

D-U-N-S 07-982-7308
HURON VALLEY SCHOOLS
2390 S Milford Rd, Highland, MI 48357-4934
Tel (248) 684-8000 *Founded/Ownrshp* 2015
Sales 118.3MM *EMP* 1,899^E
Accts Plante & Moran Pllc Auburn H
SIC 8211 Public elementary & secondary schools
Netwrk Eng: Stephanie Anderson
Teacher Pr: Scott Lindberg
Psych: Beverly Groth
Psych: Gina Pryor

D-U-N-S 00-533-7332 IMP/EXP
HURON VALLEY STEEL CORP (MI)
1650 W Jefferson Ave, Trenton, MI 48183-2136
Tel (734) 479-3500 *Founded/Ownrshp* 1961
Sales 132.3MM^E *EMP* 260
Accts Baker Tilly Verchow Krause Llp
SIC 5093 3341 3559 Nonferrous metals scrap; Zinc smelting & refining (secondary); Aluminum smelting & refining (secondary); Recycling machinery
Pr: Eric R Fritz
**Pr:* Ronald Dalton
COO: Richard Wolanski
CFO: Dick Anderson
Sr VP: Ron Dalton
Sr VP: David Wallace
**VP:* Mark Gaffney

HURON-CLINTON METROPARKS
See HURON-CLINTON METROPOLITAN AUTHORITY

D-U-N-S 07-423-3917
HURON-CLINTON METROPOLITAN AUTHORITY
HURON-CLINTON METROPARKS
13000 Highridge Dr, Brighton, MI 48114-9058
Tel (810) 227-2757 *Founded/Ownrshp* 1939
Sales NA *EMP* 1,000
Accts Rehmann Robson Troy Mi
SIC 9512 Recreational program administration, government;
CEO: Anthony V Marrocco
**Treas:* John P McCulloch
Mktg Mgr: Kassie Kretzschmar

D-U-N-S 05-900-4614 IMP/EXP
■ HURST JAWS OF LIFE INC
(*Suby of* IDEX CORP) ★
711 N Post Rd, Shelby, NC 28150-4246
Tel (704) 487-6961 *Founded/Ownrshp* 1994
Sales 91.5MM^E *EMP* 700
SIC 3569 3561 3594 Firefighting apparatus; Industrial pumps & parts; Fluid power pumps & motors
VP: Bruce Lear
VP: Ken Bostwick
VP: David D Hart
VP: Dean Perry
VP: Mark Schaub
CIO: Divakar Kamath
Mktg Mgr: Linda Roothame

HURST MANUFACTURING DIVISION
See NIDEC MOTOR CORP

D-U-N-S 07-316-2935
HURST-EULESS-BEDFORD INDEPENDENT SCHOOL DISTRICT
HEB ISD
1849 Central Dr, Bedford, TX 76022-6017
Tel (817) 267-3311 *Founded/Ownrshp* 1955
Sales 226.9MM *EMP* 2,322
Accts Weaver And Tidwell Llp Forth
SIC 8211 Public elementary & secondary schools
Ofcr: Tanya Hassell
Schl Brd P: Ellen Jones
Teacher Pr: Jodie Hawkins

D-U-N-S 82-543-9651
HUSCH BLACKWELL LLP
4801 Main St Ste 1000, Kansas City, MO 64112-2551
Tel (816) 983-8000 *Founded/Ownrshp* 2008
Sales 261.4MM^E *EMP* 1,390
SIC 8111 General practice law office
Mng Pt: Gregory Smith
Pt: Lisa J Berns
Pt: James Borthwick
Pt: Caroline G Chicoine
Pt: Joseph Conran
Pt: Joseph W Cornelison
Pt: Samuel Digirolamo
Pt: Joyce Dixon
Pt: Bradley Hiles
Pt: Ralph Kalish
Pt: Benjamin Mann
Pt: John R Phillips
Pt: Ronald Schowalter
Pt: James Warden
Pt: Maurice Watson
Pt: Ralph G Wrobley
Mng Pt: Robert J Tomaso

D-U-N-S 14-774-3983 IMP/EXP
HUSCO INTERNATIONAL INC
2239 Pewaukee Rd, Waukesha, WI 53188-1638
Tel (262) 513-4200 *Founded/Ownrshp* 1983
Sales 288.8MM^E *EMP* 1,200
SIC 3492 Control valves, fluid power: hydraulic & pneumatic
Pr: Austin Ramirez
**CFO:* Todd Hoytink
Ex VP: Michael Grebe
VP: Jason Schuetz
VP: Rick Sievert
VP: Gary Strand
Dir: Ken Pooch
Mng Dir: Todd Zakreski
IT Man: Terry Balsewicz
Opers Mgr: David Connolly
Plnt Mgr: Chris Elliott

D-U-N-S 02-254-6639
HUSKER AG LLC
54048 Highway 20, Plainview, NE 68769-4072
Tel (402) 582-4446 *Founded/Ownrshp* 2000
Sales 149.2MM *EMP* 52^E
Accts Eide Bailly Llp Minneapolis
SIC 2869 Ethanolamines; Ethyl alcohol, ethanol
Ch Bd: Robert Brummels
**Treas:* Scott Carpenter

D-U-N-S 07-930-9874
HUSKER AG MARKETING INC
(*Suby of* HUSKER AG LLC) ★
54048 Highway 20, Plainview, NE 68769-4072
Tel (402) 582-4446 *Founded/Ownrshp* 2014
Sales 108.9MM *EMP* 5
SIC 8742 Marketing consulting services
Pr: Robert Brummels
**Treas:* Scott Carpenter
**VP:* Bernie Wrede

HUSKY HARDWOOD FLOORS
See LUMBER LIQUIDATORS INC

D-U-N-S 10-126-4414 IMP/EXP
HUSKY INJECTION MOLDING SYSTEMS INC
(*Suby of* HUSKY INJECTION MOLDING SYSTEMS LTD)
288 North Rd, Milton, VT 05468-3072
Tel (905) 951-5000 *Founded/Ownrshp* 1964
Sales 229.9MM^E *EMP* 668
SIC 5084 7699 Plastic products machinery; Industrial equipment services
Ch Bd: Michael McKendry
**Pr:* George Haltsis
**CEO:* John Galt
**CFO:* Daniel Gagnon
VP: David Cook
**VP:* Dirk Schlimm
**VP:* Richard Sieradzki
Mng Dir: Michael Kirschnick
Genl Couns: Micael McKendry

HUSQVARNA CONSMR OUTDOOR PDTS
See HUSQVARNA OUTDOOR PRODUCTS INC

D-U-N-S 55-547-0798 IMP/EXP
HUSQVARNA CONSTRUCTION PRODUCTS NORTH AMERICA INC
DIMAS DIVISION
(*Suby of* HUSQVARNA HOLDING AB)
17400 W 119th St, Olathe, KS 66061-7740
Tel (913) 928-1000 *Founded/Ownrshp* 2007
Sales 138.0MM^E *EMP* 570
SIC 3541 3291 5085 5082 3425 2951 Saws & sawing machines; Abrasive products; Abrasives; Contractors' materials; Saw blades & handsaws; Asphalt paving mixtures & blocks
Pr: Anders Strobe
IT Man: Peggy Hastings

D-U-N-S 61-802-7424 EXP
HUSQVARNA CONSUMER OUTDOOR PRODUCTS NA INC
(*Suby of* HUSQVARNA AB)
9335 Harris Corners Pkwy P, Charlotte, NC 28269-3818
Tel (704) 597-5000 *Founded/Ownrshp* 2006
Sales 2.3MMM^E *EMP* 6,000
SIC 3524 Lawn & garden tractors & equipment
CEO: Alan Shaw
CFO: Fredric Ostman
CFO: Robert Tish
Treas: Ted D Parks
Manager: Pete Love

D-U-N-S 62-644-9636 IMP/EXP
HUSQVARNA OUTDOOR PRODUCTS INC
HUSQVARNA CONSMR OUTDOOR PDTS
(*Suby of* HUSQVARNA CONSUMER OUTDOOR PRODUCTS NA INC) ★
1 Poulan Dr, Nashville, AR 71852-3305
Tel (870) 845-1234 *Founded/Ownrshp* 2005
Sales 207.8MM^E *EMP* 810^E
SIC 3524 Lawn & garden equipment
Prin: Richey Lagrone
Genl Mgr: Tony Cochran
Sfty Mgr: Dakota Fowler
Natl Sales: Chris Cole
Natl Sales: Bill White
Manager: Brian Hanes
Sls Mgr: Austin Brock

D-U-N-S 13-619-4789 IMP
HUSQVARNA US HOLDING INC
(*Suby of* HUSQVARNA AB)
20445 Emerald Pkwy, Cleveland, OH 44135-6009
Tel (216) 898-1800 *Founded/Ownrshp* 2001
Sales 133.7MM^E *EMP* 1,400
SIC 3582 Dryers, laundry: commercial, including coin-operated
CFO: George Weigand
**Treas:* Marie-Louise Wingard
**Sr VP:* Richard Pietch
**Sr VP:* Ronald Zajaczkowski

HUSSEY COPPER
See LIBERTAS COPPER LLC

HUSSEY FABRICATED PRODUCTS
See HCL LIQUIDATION LTD

D-U-N-S 00-696-7731 IMP
HUSSMANN CORP
HUSSMANN REFRIGERATION
(*Suby of* PANASONIC CORPORATION)
12999 St Charles Rock Rd, Bridgeton, MO 63044-2483
Tel (314) 291-2000 *Founded/Ownrshp* 2016
Sales 433.5MM^E *EMP* 900
SIC 3585 Refrigeration & heating equipment; Refrigeration equipment, complete; Lockers, refrigerated; Counters & counter display cases, refrigerated
CEO: Dennis Gibson
CFO: Tom Cordy
CFO: Steve Hagler
VP: Dennis Gipson
VP: Tom Ryan
Exec: Jackie Bascio
Exec: John Bear
Dir IT: Steve Bochenek
IT Man: Larry Leonard
Web Dev: Carman Merritt

D-U-N-S 13-614-7027 IMP/EXP
HUSSMANN INTERNATIONAL INC
(*Suby of* PANASONIC CORPORATION)
12999 St Charles Rock Rd, Bridgeton, MO 63044-2419
Tel (314) 291-2000 *Founded/Ownrshp* 2016
Sales 228.8MM^E *EMP* 9,100
SIC 3585 5963 Refrigeration equipment, complete; Food services, direct sales
CEO: Dennis Gipson
Pr: D G Gipson
Pr: L R Rauzon
COO: John Gialouris
CFO: Tim Figge
Treas: P Hong
VP: J A Cutillo
VP: Steve Douglas
VP: Brian J Hostetler
VP: P Nachtigal
VP: M C Schaefer
VP: G E Swimmer

HUSSMANN REFRIGERATION
See HUSSMANN CORP

D-U-N-S 04-395-0807 IMP
HUTCHENS INDUSTRIES INC
215 N Patterson Ave, Springfield, MO 65802-2296
Tel (417) 862-5012 *Founded/Ownrshp* 1950
Sales 113.0MM^E *EMP* 700
SIC 3714 Shock absorbers, motor vehicle
Pr: Jeffrey C Hutchens
VP: Jim Cantrell
VP: J Detherage

D-U-N-S 79-990-8066 IMP/EXP
HUTCHINGS AUTOMOTIVE PRODUCTS INC
2041 Nw 15th Ave, Pompano Beach, FL 33069-1405
Tel (954) 958-9866 *Founded/Ownrshp* 1998
Sales 72.8MM *EMP* 1,000
SIC 3465 Body parts, automobile: stamped metal
CEO: James L Hutchings
**Pr:* Donald J Hutchings
**VP:* William O Hood
VP: William Hood
Ql Cn Mgr: Franco Seravalli
VP Sls: Mike Federle

D-U-N-S 01-898-0235
HUTCHINS MOTORS INC (ME)
O'CONNOR MOTRO COMPANY
187 Riverside Dr, Augusta, ME 04330-4133
Tel (207) 622-3191 *Founded/Ownrshp* 1947, 2005
Sales 88.6MM^E *EMP* 200^E
SIC 5511 5012 Automobiles, new & used; Trucks, commercial
CEO: Randall Hutchins
**CFO:* Troy Knowlan
Exec: Anna Starrett

D-U-N-S 00-102-3704 IMP
■ HUTCHINSON AEROSPACE & INDUSTRY INC
(*Suby of* HUTCHINSON CORP) ★
82 South St, Hopkinton, MA 01748-2205
Tel (508) 417-7000 *Founded/Ownrshp* 1943, 2000
Sales 96.0MM^E *EMP* 421

SIC 3714 3061 3724 Shock absorbers, motor vehicle; Mechanical rubber goods; Aircraft engines & engine parts
CEO: Cedric Duclos
CFO: Laurent Godbillot
Treas: Shano Cristilli
VP: Paul Stupinski
Prin: Grant Hintze
Admn Mgr: Brenda Tomlinson
Genl Mgr: Donovan Deal
Genl Mgr: Tom Foley
Genl Mgr: Tim Russell
VP Opers: Scott Pollock

D-U-N-S 00-601-5382 IMP
■ HUTCHINSON ANTIVIBRATION SYSTEMS INC (MI)
HUTCHINSON AUTOMOTIVE
(*Suby of* HUTCHINSON CORP) ★
460 Fuller Ave Ne, Grand Rapids, MI 49503-1912
Tel (616) 459-4541 *Founded/Ownrshp* 1986, 1988
Sales 146.7MM^E *EMP* 673
SIC 3069 3061 Molded rubber products; Mechanical rubber goods
CEO: Jacques Maign
Pr: Jim Todoroff
MIS Dir: Doug Mauk
IT Man: Thomas Stickroe
VP Sls: Bruce Aittama

HUTCHINSON AUTOMOTIVE
See HUTCHINSON ANTIVIBRATION SYSTEMS INC

D-U-N-S 08-108-7892 EXP
■ HUTCHINSON CORP
(*Suby of* HUTCHINSON)
460 Fuller Ave Ne, Grand Rapids, MI 49503-1912
Tel (616) 459-4541 *Founded/Ownrshp* 2006
Sales 981.0MM^E *EMP* 3,175
SIC 3069 3011 Molded rubber products; Mittens, rubber; Tires, cushion or solid rubber
Ch Bd: Yves Rene Manot
**Pr:* Gerard Gehin
Pr: Franck Larmande
**Treas:* Thomas Popma
Plnt Mgr: Jim Johnston
Mktg Mgr: Walt Jenkins
Pgrm Dir: Shawn Munger

D-U-N-S 36-108-1623 IMP
■ HUTCHINSON FTS INC
(*Suby of* HUTCHINSON CORP) ★
1060 Centre Rd, Auburn Hills, MI 48326-2600
Tel (248) 589-7710 *Founded/Ownrshp* 1996
Sales 273.8MM^E *EMP* 1,075
SIC 3714 3061 3567 3492 3443 3429 Air conditioner parts, motor vehicle; Mechanical rubber goods; Industrial furnaces & ovens; Fluid power valves & hose fittings; Fabricated plate work (boiler shop); Manufactured hardware (general)
CEO: Paul H Campbell
**VP:* Sean Canty
Plnt Mgr: Paul Macdonald

D-U-N-S 83-013-3794
HUTCHINSON HEALTH CARE
1095 Highway 15 S, Hutchinson, MN 55350-5000
Tel (320) 234-5000 *Founded/Ownrshp* 2006
Sales 93.9MM *EMP* 99
SIC 8082 Home health care services
Pr: Steve Mulder

HUTCHINSON HEART
See HUTCHINSON REGIONAL MEDICAL CENTER INC

D-U-N-S 19-860-4852 IMP/EXP
■ HUTCHINSON INDUSTRIES INC
(*Suby of* HUTCHINSON CORP) ★
460 Southard St, Trenton, NJ 08638-4224
Tel (609) 394-1010 *Founded/Ownrshp* 1988
Sales 156.4MM^E *EMP* 450
SIC 3069 Rubber automotive products
Pr: Pascal Seraderian
Off Admin: Harriet H Zipper
QI Cn Mgr: Timothy Rancourt

D-U-N-S 04-940-2753
HUTCHINSON OIL CO INC
HUTCHIS
515 S Main St, Elk City, OK 73644-6700
Tel (580) 225-0301 *Founded/Ownrshp* 1969
Sales 123.4MM^E *EMP* 150
SIC 5171 5541 Petroleum bulk stations; Filling stations, gasoline
Pr: David Hutchinson
**Treas:* Linda Hutchinson

D-U-N-S 07-626-2955
HUTCHINSON REGIONAL MEDICAL CENTER INC
HUTCHINSON HEART
(*Suby of* PROMISE REGIONAL MEDICAL CENTE) ★
1701 E 23rd Ave, Hutchinson, KS 67502-1105
Tel (620) 665-2000 *Founded/Ownrshp* 1967
Sales 27.8MM^E *EMP* 1,000
Accts Wendling Noe Nelson & Johnson
SIC 8062 General medical & surgical hospitals
CFO: Cassandra Dolen
Pr: Michael Krach
**CEO:* Kendall Johnson
COO: Mike Connell
VP: Robyn Chadwick
VP: Todd Laffoon
VP: Dan Stafford
Exec: Rita Blackburn
Exec: Carl Caton
Exec: Gary Holderman
Dir Teleco: Randy Miller

HUTCHINSON SALES
See HUTCHINSON SEALING SYSTEMS INC

D-U-N-S 08-558-2505 IMP
■ HUTCHINSON SEALING SYSTEMS INC
HUTCHINSON SALES
(*Suby of* HUTCHINSON CORP) ★
1060 Centre Rd, Auburn Hills, MI 48326-2600
Tel (248) 375-3720 *Founded/Ownrshp* 1999
Sales 238.3MM^E *EMP* 1,075
SIC 3069 Rubber automotive products
Pr: Robert C Hanson
**Treas:* John Attard
VP Sls: Bob Hanson
Sls Dir: Wayne Hodges

D-U-N-S 00-645-6768 IMP
HUTCHINSON TECHNOLOGY INC (MN)
(*Suby of* HEADWAY TECHNOLOGIES INC) ★
40 W Highland Park Dr Ne, Hutchinson, MN 55350-9300
Tel (320) 587-3797 *Founded/Ownrshp* 1965, 2016
Sales 252.8MM *EMP* 2,489^E
SIC 3679 8731 Electronic circuits; Electronic research
Pr: Richard J Penn
**Ch Bd:* Wayne M Fortun
COO: Wendy Wick
CFO: David P Radloff
VP: Nancy Fischer
VP: Beatrice Graczyk
VP: Peter Ickert
VP: Mark Jelkin
VP: Dale M Ruzicka
VP: Schaefer Scott
VP Bus Dev: Rich Myers
Exec: John Farmerie
Exec: Matthew Lang
Exec: Paul Pesavento
Exec: Karen Raske
Exec: Randy Seifert
Board of Directors: Martha Goldberg Aronson, Russell Huffer, Frank P Russomanno, Phil E Soran, Thomas R Verhage

HUTCHIS
See HUTCHINSON OIL CO INC

D-U-N-S 82-871-2232
HUTCO INC
114 Park Center Dr, Broussard, LA 70518-3605
Tel (337) 837-5594 *Founded/Ownrshp* 1986
Sales 49.5MM^E *EMP* 1,300
SIC 7363 Help supply services
Pr: James M Hutchison Jr
CFO: Bernard J Barilleaux
**Sec:* Bernard Barilleaux
**VP:* Scott Hutchison

D-U-N-S 06-674-7346
HUTTER CONSTRUCTION CORP
HUTTER HOMES
810 Turnpike Rd, New Ipswich, NH 03071-3845
Tel (603) 878-2300 *Founded/Ownrshp* 1973
Sales 90.0MM *EMP* 150
SIC 1541 1542 Industrial buildings & warehouses; Nonresidential construction
Pr: Lars A Traffie
CFO: Rich Upsall
**CFO:* Richard Upsall
**Treas:* James J Traffie
**VP:* Gary Bertram
**VP:* Quentin Jones
Sales Exec: Diane Cooper
Sls Mgr: Nels Traffie

HUTTER HOMES
See HUTTER CONSTRUCTION CORP

D-U-N-S 00-630-6740 IMP/EXP
▲ HUTTIG BUILDING PRODUCTS INC
HUTTIG SASH & DOOR CO
555 Maryville University, Saint Louis, MO 63141-5805
Tel (314) 216-2600 *Founded/Ownrshp* 1885
Sales 659.6MM *EMP* 1,000
Accts Kpmg Llp St Louis Missouri
Tkr Sym HBP *Exch* NAS
SIC 5031 5033 Millwork; Door frames, all materials; Doors, combination, screen-storm; Doors; Roofing & siding materials; Insulation materials
Pr: Jon P Vrabely
Ch Bd: Delbert H Tanner
CFO: Oscar A Martinez
VP: Gregory W Gurley
VP: Brian D Robinson
VP: Brian Robinson
Genl Mgr: Scott Wisser
Off Mgr: Kim Marques
Sls Mgr: Jordan Post
Sales Asso: Stephanie Cunningham
Sales Asso: Melissa Ollmetzer
Board of Directors: Donald L Glass, James F Hibberd, Gina G Hoagland, Patrick L Larmon, J Keith Matheney

HUTTIG SASH & DOOR CO
See HUTTIG BUILDING PRODUCTS INC

D-U-N-S 78-846-0509
HUTTON CONSTRUCTION CORP
2229 S West St, Wichita, KS 67213-1113
Tel (316) 942-8855 *Founded/Ownrshp* 1992
Sales 96.5MM^E *EMP* 185^E
SIC 1542 Commercial & office building, new construction; Commercial & office buildings, renovation & repair
Pr: Ben Hutton
**CFO:* Peggy West
**Ofcr:* Jim Keusler
**VP:* Josh Herrman

D-U-N-S 07-639-2331
HUTZEL HOSPITAL
WOMENS CENTER
3980 John R St, Detroit, MI 48201-2018
Tel (313) 745-7555 *Founded/Ownrshp* 1985
Sales 44.1MM^E *EMP* 1,884
SIC 8062 General medical & surgical hospitals
CEO: Mike Duggin
Mtls Mgr: Butch Johnson

D-U-N-S 17-905-7674
HVAC DISTRIBUTORS INC
2 Old Market St, Mount Joy, PA 17552-1320
Tel (717) 653-6674 *Founded/Ownrshp* 1987
Sales 147.5MM^E *EMP* 98
Accts Hatter Harris & Beittel Llp
SIC 5075 Warm air heating & air conditioning
Pr: David W McIlwaine
CFO: Rollie McSherry
**Sec:* William B McIlwaine
Brnch Mgr: Dennis Fitzmaurice
Mktg Mgr: Bridget Hudacs
Mktg Mgr: Heather Seitz
Sls Mgr: Eric Rodenhauser
Sales Asso: Eric Germer

D-U-N-S 04-475-6844
HVB AMERICA INC
(*Suby of* UNICREDIT BANK AG)
150 E 42nd St Fl 29, New York, NY 10017-5632
Tel (212) 672-6000 *Founded/Ownrshp* 1996
Sales NA *EMP* 600
SIC 6082 Foreign trade & international banking institutions
COO: Christopher Wrenn
Top Exec: Mark Bowles
IT Man: Harm Bandholz

HVCC-USA
See HANON SYSTEMS USA LLC

D-U-N-S 04-109-5555
HVH TRANSPORTATION INC
181 E 56th Ave Ste 200, Denver, CO 80216-1748
Tel (303) 292-3656 *Founded/Ownrshp* 1956
Sales 94.9MM^E *EMP* 540
Accts Marrs Sevier & Company Llc
SIC 4213 Trucking, except local; Less-than-truckload (LTL) transport
Ch Bd: Robert L Holder
**Pr:* Bruce Holder
CFO: John Lundein
**Treas:* Wayne Holder
VP: David Felton
Genl Mgr: Jim Pirano
DP Exec: Harold Hajoway
Trfc Mgr: Larry Wolf
Mktg Dir: Dave Antonio

D-U-N-S 16-010-4873
HVHC INC
(*Suby of* HIGHMARK BLUE CRSS-BLUE SHIELD) ★
175 E Houston St, San Antonio, TX 78205-2255
Tel (210) 340-3531 *Founded/Ownrshp* 1996
Sales NA *EMP* 6,350
SIC 6324 Hospital & medical service plans
Pr: Walter F Froh
**Ch Bd:* Robert C Gray
**CFO:* Michael Kincaid
**CFO:* Douglas C Shepard
Sr VP: Bob Cox
VP: Cheryl Grobelny
Snr Mgr: Michael Thibdeau

D-U-N-S 18-959-3275
■ HVM LLC
EXTENDED STAY HOTELS
(*Suby of* ESA MANAGEMENT LLC) ★
11525 N Community House, Charlotte, NC 28277-3609
Tel (980) 345-1600 *Founded/Ownrshp* 2013
Sales 395.2MM *EMP* 9,300
SIC 7011 Hotels & motels
CEO: James L Donald
Ex VP: Hugh Wall
VP: Mark D Mahoney

D-U-N-S 09-133-1835
HW HOLDCO LLC
BUILDER MAGAZINE
1 Thomas Cir Nw Ste 600, Washington, DC 20005-5803
Tel (202) 452-0800 *Founded/Ownrshp* 1976
Sales 196.8MM^E *EMP* 630
SIC 2721 7389 Trade journals: publishing only, not printed on site; Trade show arrangement
CEO: Peter Goldstone
**CFO:* Matthew Flynn
Sr VP: Maryjo Lindholm
**VP:* Michael Bender
VP: Julie James
VP: Neal Kielar
VP: Bill McGrath
VP: Bob Powers
VP: Sharon Stearns
VP: Sarah Welcome
VP: Nelson Wischovit
VP: Nelson Wischovitch
VP: Nelson Wiscovitch
Assoc Dir: Amie Gilmore
Dir Soc: Kristina Reardon
Dir Soc: Bryan Rippeon

D-U-N-S 07-983-3496 IMP
HWASEUNG AUTOMOTIVE ALABAMA LLC
HSAA
(*Suby of* HSAA) ★
100 Sonata Dr, Enterprise, AL 36330-7338
Tel (334) 348-9516 *Founded/Ownrshp* 2015
Sales 138.0MM *EMP* 600
Accts Warren Averett Llc Montgomer
SIC 3714 3069 Air conditioner parts, motor vehicle; Weather strip, sponge rubber
Pr: Hyeong Jin Kim
CFO: Kang Chan Park

D-U-N-S 15-196-4025 IMP
HWASEUNG AUTOMOTIVE AMERICA HOLDINGS INC
HSAA
(*Suby of* HS R&A CO.,LTD)
100 Sonata Dr, Enterprise, AL 36330-7338
Tel (334) 348-9516 *Founded/Ownrshp* 2003
Sales 192.5MM *EMP* 600
Accts Warren Averett Llc Montgomer
SIC 3069 5085 Weather strip, sponge rubber; Hose, belting & packing
Pr: Harry Kim
CFO: Paul Park
Admn Mgr: David Kim
Prd Mgr: James Hwang
Snr Mgr: Chuck Patterson

D-U-N-S 07-983-3491
HWASEUNG AUTOMOTIVE USA LLC
(*Suby of* HSAA) ★
101 Development Ln, Enterprise, AL 36330-7381
Tel (334) 348-9516 *Founded/Ownrshp* 2015
Sales 104.9MM *EMP* 43^E
SIC 3714 Air conditioner parts, motor vehicle
Pr: Hyeong Jin Kim
**CFO:* Kang Chan Park

D-U-N-S 14-508-4849 IMP
HWASHIN AMERICA CORP
(*Suby of* HWASHIN CO., LTD.)
661 Montgomery Hwy, Greenville, AL 36037-3527
Tel (334) 382-1100 *Founded/Ownrshp* 2003
Sales 368.0MM *EMP* 470
SIC 5531 Automotive parts
Ch: Ho Jeong
**Pr:* Seojin Jeong
**Pr:* Hyun Park
**CFO:* Milton Park
Plnt Mgr: Gary Malak

D-U-N-S 78-082-0580 IMP
■ HWC WIRE & CABLE CO
HAYNES WIRE ROPE
(*Suby of* HOUSTON WIRE & CABLE CO INC) ★
10201 North Loop E, Houston, TX 77029-1415
Tel (713) 609-2160 *Founded/Ownrshp* 1985
Sales 123.7MM^E *EMP* 282^E
SIC 5063 Electrical apparatus & equipment; Transformers & transmission equipment
CEO: James L Pokluda III
**CFO:* Nicol G Graham
**VP:* John Marchiando
Admn Mgr: Lynda Danna
Snr Ntwrk: Alex Rigsby

D-U-N-S 62-486-8568 EXP
HWD ACQUISITION INC
HURD WINDOWS & DOORS
(*Suby of* SIERRA PACIFIC INDUSTRIES) ★
575 S Whelen Ave, Medford, WI 54451-1738
Tel (800) 433-4873 *Founded/Ownrshp* 2014
Sales 121.6MM^E *EMP* 500
SIC 2431 Window frames, wood
Pr: Dominic Truniger
**CFO:* Dave Roland
VP: David Kochendorfer
**CTO:* Bill Schultz
QI Cn Mgr: Mike Czerniak

D-U-N-S 14-465-8478
HWRT OIL CO LLC
1 Piasa Ln, Hartford, IL 62048-1504
Tel (618) 254-2855 *Founded/Ownrshp* 2004
Sales 2.8MMM *EMP* 22
Accts Uhy Llc St Louis Missouri
SIC 5172 Petroleum products
Pr: Matthew Schrimpf
**Treas:* Susan Hatfield
**VP:* Bryan Hatfield
Area Mgr: Russell Andrews

D-U-N-S 15-776-8214
HWZ DISTRIBUTION GROUP LLC
NEXGEN BUILDING SUPPLY
(*Suby of* NEXGEN BUILDING SUPPLY) ★
40 W Crescentville Rd, West Chester, OH 45246-1215
Tel (513) 618-0300 *Founded/Ownrshp* 1920
Sales 129.3MM^E *EMP* 135
SIC 5032 Drywall materials
CEO: Robert Hoge
**Pr:* Richard Wolgemuth
**CFO:* Bruce Fhaey

D-U-N-S 02-332-0005 IMP
HY CITE ENTERPRISES LLC
ROYAL PRESTIGE
333 Holtzman Rd, Madison, WI 53713-2109
Tel (608) 273-3373 *Founded/Ownrshp* 1963
Sales 94.8MM^E *EMP* 350
SIC 5023 Home furnishings; Stainless steel flatware; Decorative home furnishings & supplies; Glassware
Pr: Erik Johnson
**COO:* Peter Johnson Jr
**VP:* Arin Brost
VP: Angella Gordillo
VP: Erick Jostad
**VP:* James Martin
**VP:* Larry Schauff
**VP:* Anna Stebbins
VP: Dave Zimmerman
Mktg Mgr: Ruben Santiago

D-U-N-S 09-310-0238
HY-LINE NORTH AMERICA LLC
(*Suby of* EW GROUP GMBH)
1755 West Lakes Pkwy A, West Des Moines, IA 50266-8227
Tel (515) 225-6030 *Founded/Ownrshp* 1978
Sales 115.1MM^E *EMP* 700
SIC 0254 Chicken hatchery
Pt: Dennis Casey
**Pr:* Harold Block
**CFO:* Charles Bingman
Dir IT: Gerald Fitzgerald
Sales Asso: Petek Settar

HY-MILER
See DISTRICT PETROLEUM PRODUCTS INC

HY-POWER
See HYPOWER INC

D-U-N-S 05-136-8439 IMP/EXP
HY-TEK MATERIAL HANDLING INC
2222 Rickenbacker Pkwy W, Columbus, OH 43217-5002
Tel (614) 497-2500 *Founded/Ownrshp* 1989
Sales 90.4MM^E *EMP* 130

SIC 5084 5013 7538 7513 1796 Materials handling machinery; Conveyor systems; Lift trucks & parts; Truck parts & accessories; Truck engine repair, except industrial; Truck rental, without drivers; Machinery installation
Pr: Samuel Grooms
**CFO:* David Tumbas
**VP:* Mark Bruner
**VP:* Donnie Johnson
VP: Tony Murray
VP: David Price
Dir Bus: Al Marchionda
Dir IT: Tim Stewart
IT Man: Susan Wright
Mktg Dir: Claire Rigot
Sls Mgr: Scott Moe

D-U-N-S 96-488-9641
HY-VEE AND AFFILIATES BENEFIT PLAN AND TRUST
5820 Westown Pkwy, West Des Moines, IA 50266-8223
Tel (515) 267-2800 *Founded/Ownrshp* 2010
Sales NA *EMP* 2[E]
Accts Rsm Mcgladrey Inc Des Moine
SIC 6411 Pension & retirement plan consultants
Prin: Charlie Bridges

D-U-N-S 00-692-5671 IMP/EXP
HY-VEE INC
5820 Westown Pkwy, West Des Moines, IA 50266-8223
Tel (515) 267-2800 *Founded/Ownrshp* 1930
Sales 9.8MMM *EMP* 84,000
SIC 5411 5912 5921 Supermarkets, chain; Convenience stores, chain; Drug stores; Liquor stores
CEO: Randy Edeker
**V Ch:* Andy McCann
Pr: Mark Brauer
Pr: Rob Douglas
Pr: Pat Hensley
Pr: Mark Millsap
Pr: Lisa Stowater
Pr: Donna Tweeten
**CFO:* Mike Skokan
**Ofcr:* Jay Marshall
Ex VP: Darren Baty
Ex VP: Brett Bremser
**Ex VP:* Sheila Laing
Ex VP: Jon S Wendel
Sr VP: Charles M Bell
Sr VP: Laura Fulton
VP: Dennis A Ausenhus
VP: Jane Esbeck
VP: Tod Hockenson
VP: Freddie L Housman
VP: Jane B Knaack-Esbeck

D-U-N-S 12-004-0683
HYATT AUTOMOTIVE LLC
HYUNDAI - ISUZU
1887 Highway 501, Myrtle Beach, SC 29577-9768
Tel (843) 626-3657 *Founded/Ownrshp* 1999
Sales 180.0MM *EMP* 110
SIC 5511 Automobiles, new & used
Pt: Charles F Hyatt

HYATT CENTER
See HYATT CORP

HYATT CENTER
See DORADO BEACH HOTEL CORP

D-U-N-S 00-690-4783
■ HYATT CORP
HYATT CENTER
(*Suby of* HYATT EQUITIES LLC) ★
150 N Riverside Plz, Chicago, IL 60606
Tel (312) 750-1234 *Founded/Ownrshp* 1967, 1979
Sales 3.3MMM[E] *EMP* 35,700
SIC 7011 Hotels & motels
Ch Bd: Thomas J Pritzker
Pr: Dan Azark
Pr: Eric Fish
**Pr:* Doug Geoga
**Pr:* Mark S Hoplamazian
Pr: Bill Lumpkin
Pr: Katie Meyer
CFO: Harmit J Singh
Chf Mktg O: Angela Perry
Sr VP: Jim Chu
**Sr VP:* Harold Handelsman
Sr VP: Patrick McCudden
Sr VP: Rob Schnitz
Sr VP: Susan T Smith
VP: Bill Bernahl
VP: Chris Brogan
VP: Mark Chase
VP: Mike Daley
VP: Paul Daly
VP: Chris Dobbins
VP: Jeffrey Hansen

D-U-N-S 03-760-3297
■ HYATT EQUITIES LLC
(*Suby of* HYATT HOTELS CORP) ★
71 S Wacker Dr Fl 14, Chicago, IL 60606-4637
Tel (312) 750-1234 *Founded/Ownrshp* 2004
Sales 3.5MMM[E] *EMP* 36,760
SIC 7011 Hotels
Ch Bd: Thomas J Pritzker
**CFO:* Gebhard F Rainer
Exec: Laura Kasik

HYATT HOTEL
See HYATT INTERNATIONAL CORP

HYATT HOTEL
See CLASSIC RIVERDALE INC

HYATT HOTEL
See CC-NAPLES INC

D-U-N-S 60-249-5579
▲ HYATT HOTELS CORP
71 S Wacker Dr Ste 1000, Chicago, IL 60606-4716
Tel (312) 750-1234 *Founded/Ownrshp* 1957
Sales 4.3MMM *EMP* 45,000[E]
Tkr Sym H *Exch* NYS
SIC 7011 6794 Hotels & motels; Franchises, selling or licensing
Pr: Mark S Hoplamazian
**Ch Bd:* Thomas J Pritzker
Pr: H Charles Floyd
Pr: Peter Fulton
Pr: Peter J Sears
Pr: David Udell
CFO: Atish Shah
Chf Mktg O: Maryam Banikarim
Ofcr: Robert W K Webb
Ex VP: Stephen G Haggerty
Ex VP: Rena Hozore Reiss
VP: Jen Acerra
VP: Heather Geisler
Board of Directors: William Wrigley Jr, Richard A Friedman, Susan D Kronick, Mackey J McDonald, Cary D McMillan, Pamela M Nicholson, Jason Pritzker, Michael A Rocca, Richard C Tuttle, James H Wooten Jr

D-U-N-S 11-416-4197 IMP/EXP
■ HYATT HOTELS MANAGEMENT CORP
(*Suby of* HYATT CENTER) ★
71 S Wacker Dr Ste 1000, Chicago, IL 60606-4716
Tel (312) 750-1234 *Founded/Ownrshp* 1977
Sales 1.1MMM[E] *EMP* 35,700
SIC 7011 Hotels & motels
Pr: Chuck Floyd
Sr Cor Off: Frank Orc
Ex VP: Labelle Van
**Sr VP:* Frank Borg
Sr VP: David Tarr
VP: Linda R Olson
Exec: Tracy Gainer

D-U-N-S 14-771-0644
■ HYATT HOTELS OF FLORIDA INC
HYATT REGENCY ORLANDO
(*Suby of* HYATT HOTELS CORP) ★
9801 International Dr, Orlando, FL 32819-8104
Tel (407) 284-1234 *Founded/Ownrshp* 2013
Sales 173.1MM[E] *EMP* 1,800
SIC 7011 5812 5813

D-U-N-S 04-739-1206 IMP
■ HYATT INTERNATIONAL CORP
HYATT HOTEL
(*Suby of* HYATT HOTELS CORP) ★
71 S Wacker Dr 12, Chicago, IL 60606-4637
Tel (312) 750-1234 *Founded/Ownrshp* 1957
Sales 2.9MMM[E] *EMP* 30,996
SIC 7011 Hotels & motels
Pr: Bernd Chorengel
**Pr:* Mark S Hoplamazian
CFO: Ken Posner
CFO: Gary Smith
Sr VP: Louis Chun
Sr VP: Chuck Floyd
Sr VP: Michelle Kincaid
**VP:* Michael Evanoff
VP: Gebhard Rainer
VP: Robert V Schnitz
VP: Len Stoga

HYATT PLACE SAN JOSE HOTEL
See WEST SAN CARLOS HOTEL PARTNERS LLC

HYATT REGENCY CHICAGO
See KATO KAGAKU CO LTD

HYATT REGENCY MCCORMICK PLACE
See METROPOLITAN PIER AND EXPOSITION AUTHORITY

HYATT REGENCY ORLANDO
See HYATT HOTELS OF FLORIDA INC

HYATT SELECT HOTELS GROUP
See SELECT HOTELS GROUP LLC

HYBRID APPAREL
See HYBRID PROMOTIONS LLC

D-U-N-S 12-967-1165 IMP/EXP
HYBRID PROMOTIONS LLC
HYBRID APPAREL
10711 Walker St, Cypress, CA 90630-4750
Tel (714) 952-3866 *Founded/Ownrshp* 1999
Sales 658.8MM[E] *EMP* 400[E]
Accts Richardson Kontogouris Emerson
SIC 5136 5137 5611 Men's & boys' clothing; Women's & children's clothing; Men's & boys' clothing stores
COO: David Lederman
VP Opers: Etienne Capgras

HYCLONE BIOPROCESSES CONT DIV
See HYCLONE LABORATORIES INC

D-U-N-S 08-183-2461 IMP/EXP
■ HYCLONE LABORATORIES INC
HYCLONE BIOPROCESSES CONT DIV
(*Suby of* GENERAL ELECTRIC CO) ★
925 W 1800 S, Logan, UT 84321-6241
Tel (435) 792-8000 *Founded/Ownrshp* 2014
Sales 142.0MM[E] *EMP* 636
SIC 2836 8071

D-U-N-S 80-002-3991
HYCROFT MINING CORP
ALLIED NEVADA GOLD
9790 Gateway Dr Ste 200, Reno, NV 89521-8923
Tel (775) 358-4455 *Founded/Ownrshp* 2007
Sales 310.4MM *EMP* 428[E]
SIC 1041 1044 Gold ores; Silver ores
Pr: Randy E Buffington
**Ch Bd:* Robert M Buchan
CFO: Stephen M Jones
VP: Brian Christie
VP: Garry Keizer
VP: Michael Moran
VP: Tracey Thom
Dir IT: Todd Sylvester
Board of Directors: John W Ivany, Stephen A Lang, Cameron A Mingay, Terry M Palmer, Carl A Pescio, A Murray Sinclair, Robert G Wardell

D-U-N-S 07-916-8191 IMP
HYDAC TECHNOLOGY CORP
2260 City Line Rd 2280, Bethlehem, PA 18017-2130
Tel (205) 520-1220 *Founded/Ownrshp* 1975
Sales 137.5MM[E] *EMP* 500
SIC 3492 Fluid power valves & hose fittings
Pr: Matthias Mueller
**Pr:* Werner Dieter
CFO: Ted Dikeman
**VP:* Ilek Ozsoy
Area Mgr: Mark Haake
Area Mgr: Bud Lavigne
Area Mgr: Patrick Powers
Area Mgr: Ken Rosenbecker
Div Mgr: Eric Ramseyer
Div Mgr: John Welch
Genl Mgr: Eric Ringholm

HYDRA POOLS
See PI INC

D-U-N-S 19-520-0212 IMP
HYDRADYNE LLC
15050 Faa Blvd, Fort Worth, TX 76155-2215
Tel (817) 391-1547 *Founded/Ownrshp* 2003
Sales 459.6MM[E] *EMP* 590
SIC 5084 Hydraulic systems equipment & supplies
Pr: David Parks
Exec: Donna Breaux
Genl Mgr: Parker Cook
Genl Mgr: Chris Raschke
Genl Mgr: Danny Rogers
Sfty Mgr: Jeff O'Connor
Opers Mgr: Mae Johnson
Opers Mgr: Kasha Paepke

D-U-N-S 13-120-1493 IMP
HYDRAFORCE INC
500 Barclay Blvd, Lincolnshire, IL 60069-4314
Tel (847) 793-2300 *Founded/Ownrshp* 1987
Sales 198.6MM[E] *EMP* 850[E]
SIC 3492 Control valves, fluid power: hydraulic & pneumatic
Pr: James Brizzolara
VP: Greg Balog
VP: Bernhard Biederma
VP: Arthur Smith
Mng Dir: Chuck Kloser
Rgnl Mgr: Craig Sinnott
Prd Mgr: Bob Little
Ql Cn Mgr: Tony Dimarcantonio
Ql Cn Mgr: Gerald K Heitmann
Ql Cn Mgr: Robert Karm
Sls&Mrk Ex: Amanda Wilkins
Board of Directors: John Pepe

D-U-N-S 05-923-1126 IMP/EXP
HYDRANAUTICS
(*Suby of* PERMACEL AUTOMOTIVE) ★
401 Jones Rd, Oceanside, CA 92058-1216
Tel (760) 901-2597 *Founded/Ownrshp* 1987
Sales 133.5MM *EMP* 450
SIC 2899 3589 Chemical preparations; Water treatment equipment, industrial
CEO: Brett Andrews
**COO:* Upen Bharwada
Bd of Dir: Ben Freeman
VP: Jannies Burlingame
**VP:* Ellen Class
**VP:* Michael Concannon
**VP:* Norio Ikeyama
**VP:* Karin Stink
**VP:* Randolph Truby
**VP:* Marek Wilf
IT Man: Ibrahim Abdul

D-U-N-S 02-068-0331 IMP
HYDRAPOWER INTERNATIONAL INC
950 N Collier Blvd # 202, Marco Island, FL 34145-2725
Tel (239) 642-5379 *Founded/Ownrshp* 1973
Sales 96.5MM[E] *EMP* 1,100
SIC 3542 Shearing machines, power; Press brakes; Presses: hydraulic & pneumatic, mechanical & manual
Pr: Robin F Wissing

HYDRAQUIP
See EMPLOYEE OWNED HOLDINGS INC

D-U-N-S 00-389-7949 IMP
HYDRAQUIP INC (TX)
HDI
(*Suby of* HYDRAQUIP) ★
16330 Central Green Blvd # 200, Houston, TX 77032-5151
Tel (713) 680-1951 *Founded/Ownrshp* 1951
Sales 186.8MM[E] *EMP* 117
SIC 5084 Hydraulic systems equipment & supplies; Pneumatic tools & equipment
Pr: Tim Nichols
CFO: Matt Weisser
Treas: David Tyler Jr
**Ex VP:* Gordon Shellhaaf
**VP:* Scott Nelson
**Prin:* Richard Neels
Brnch Mgr: Bill Cross
Brnch Mgr: Dalton Hamilton
Brnch Mgr: Jake Rackley
CIO: Chad Ferreira
Sls&Mrk Ex: Ruth Robinson

HYDRAULIC SUPPLY CO
See AERO HARDWARE & SUPPLY INC

D-U-N-S 04-037-0249 IMP/EXP
HYDRAULICS INTERNATIONAL INC
9201 Independence Ave, Chatsworth, CA 91311-5905
Tel (818) 998-1231 *Founded/Ownrshp* 1975
Sales 90.3MM *EMP* 360[E]
Accts Roschke & Wall Agoura Hills
SIC 3728 Aircraft parts & equipment
**CEO:* Nicky Ghaemmaghami
**CFO:* Shah Banifazl
**VP:* Linda Ghaemmaghami

HYDREL
See KILPATRICK TOWNSEND & STOCKTON LLP

D-U-N-S 96-582-6774 IMP
HYDRIL CO
TENARIS HYDRIL
(*Suby of* TENARIS) ★
302 Mccarty St, Houston, TX 77029-1140
Tel (713) 670-3500 *Founded/Ownrshp* 2006
Sales 98.9MM[E] *EMP* 747
SIC 3533 Oil & gas field machinery
Pr: Brad Lowe
Mng Dir: Alberto Agostini
Board of Directors: Chris North

HYDRIL PRESSURE CONTROL
See HYDRIL USA DISTRIBUTION LLC

D-U-N-S 06-205-6288 IMP/EXP
■ HYDRIL USA DISTRIBUTION LLC
HYDRIL PRESSURE CONTROL
(*Suby of* GE AERO ENERGY PRODUCTS) ★
3300 N Sam Houston Pkwy E, Houston, TX 77032-3411
Tel (281) 449-2000 *Founded/Ownrshp* 2008
Sales 492.4MM[E] *EMP* 1,700
SIC 3533 Oil & gas field machinery
Pr: Charles Chauvier
**VP:* Chuck Chauviere
**Genl Mgr:* Mat R Castaneda
IT Man: Michael Seghers
Snr Mgr: Frank Emerich

D-U-N-S 82-896-4341 IMP/EXP
HYDRIL USA MANUFACTURING LLC
3300 N Sam Houston Pkwy E, Houston, TX 77032-3411
Tel (281) 449-2000 *Founded/Ownrshp* 2008
Sales 205.9MM[E] *EMP* 1,000
SIC 3069

D-U-N-S 00-643-5887 IMP/EXP
HYDRITE CHEMICAL CO (WI)
300 N Patrick Blvd Fl 2, Brookfield, WI 53045-5816
Tel (262) 792-1450 *Founded/Ownrshp* 1929
Sales 532.5MM *EMP* 800
SIC 5169 2819 2841 2869

D-U-N-S 96-413-2864 IMP
■ HYDRO-AIRE INC
(*Suby of* CRANE AEROSPACE INC) ★
3000 Winona Ave, Burbank, CA 91504-2540
Tel (818) 526-2600 *Founded/Ownrshp* 1999
Sales 113.5MM[E] *EMP* 602[E]
SIC 3728 Aircraft parts & equipment
CEO: Brendan J Curran
**Treas:* Tazewell Rowe
VP: Mike Brady
Ex Dir: Stuart Johnson
Sftwr Eng: Herman Yih

D-U-N-S 62-157-7188 IMP
HYDRO-GEAR INC
(*Suby of* DANFOSS A/S)
1411 S Hamilton St, Sullivan, IL 61951-2264
Tel (217) 728-2581 *Founded/Ownrshp* 1975
Sales 84.7MM[E] *EMP* 350[E]
SIC 3594 Hydrostatic drives (transmissions)
Pr: Ray Hauser
Pt: Agri Fab
Pt: Ronald D Harshman
Pr: Gary Harvey
Pt: Jack Obiala
QA Dir: Jason Shoemaker
Info Man: Todd Westjohn
Prd Mgr: Dave Pratt
Ql Cn Mgr: Justin Adcock
Ql Cn Mgr: Curt Allen
Ql Cn Mgr: Shawn Fagin

D-U-N-S 16-872-5054
HYDROCARBON EXCHANGE CORP
5910 N Cntrl Expy # 1380, Dallas, TX 75206-5126
Tel (214) 987-0257 *Founded/Ownrshp* 2004
Sales 340.2MM *EMP* 8
Accts Bdo Usa Llp Dallas Texas
SIC 4924 Natural gas distribution
Pr: R Scott Hopkins

D-U-N-S 10-267-3886
HYDROCHEM LLC
(*Suby of* AZZ WSI) ★
900 Georgia Ave, Deer Park, TX 77536-2518
Tel (713) 393-5600 *Founded/Ownrshp* 2007
Sales 440.0MM[E] *EMP* 2,086
SIC 7349 Cleaning service, industrial or commercial
CEO: Gary Noto
**Pr:* Gregory G Rice
CFO: Judy Shields
Div VP: Jj Daniel
Div VP: Chip Gunter
VP: Roger Raney
Brnch Mgr: Earl Lewis
Brnch Mgr: Jim Swantner
Genl Mgr: Stephanie Celaya
VP Opers: Christopher Bourg
Sfty Dirs: Sam Adame

D-U-N-S 09-673-2706 IMP
HYDROMAT INC (MO)
11600 Adie Rd, Maryland Heights, MO 63043-3510
Tel (314) 432-0070 *Founded/Ownrshp* 1979
Sales 85.4MM *EMP* 187
Accts Deloitte & Touche Llp
SIC 5084 Metalworking machinery
Pr: Bruno Schmitter
Pr: Rich Vales
**CFO:* Bruce Falconer
CIO: Scott Frisby
Plnt Mgr: Rudy Bieri
Manager: Bill Nuetzel

D-U-N-S 00-416-3390 IMP/EXP
HYGENIC CORP
(*Suby of* CORTEC GROUP) ★
1245 Home Ave, Akron, OH 44310-2575
Tel (330) 633-8460 *Founded/Ownrshp* 2000
Sales 85.3MM[E] *EMP* 324
SIC 3069 3061 Medical & laboratory rubber sundries & related products; Mechanical rubber goods
Pr: Marshall Dahneke
**CFO:* Niels Lichti
Sr VP: Kathy Yoder
**VP:* Ralph Buster
VP: Dwayne Hofstatter
VP: Bob Poirier
IT Man: Bob Crabbs
Web Dev: Greg Sloane

Ql Cn Mgr: Nevin Gerber
Ql Cn Mgr: Antonio Gonzalez
Ql Cn Mgr: Tim Green

D-U-N-S 84-847-5328
HYLA INC
HYLA MOBILE
Prk W 1 & 2 1507 Lbj Fwy, Farmers Branch, TX 75234
Tel (972) 573-0300 *Founded/Ownrshp* 2010
Sales 83.1MM^E *EMP* 125
SIC 5084 Recycling machinery & equipment
Ch: Ronald T Lemay
**Pr:* Biju Nair
**Treas:* Shad Spears
Ofcr: Jim Fredericks

HYLA MOBILE
See HYLA INC

D-U-N-S 09-990-4435 IMP
HYLAND HILLS PARK & RECREATION DISTRICT
HYLAND HLLS GOLF CRS/WTER WRLD
8801 Pecos St, Denver, CO 80260-5038
Tel (303) 427-7873 *Founded/Ownrshp* 1955
Sales 50.4MM *EMP* 1,600
SIC 7999 Recreation services
Pr: Donald Cciancio II
**Pr:* Donald C Ciancio II
**Treas:* Sarah Heil
**VP:* Nicholas J McCoy
**Ex Dir:* Greg Mastriona

HYLAND HLLS GOLF CRS/WTER WRLD
See HYLAND HILLS PARK & RECREATION DISTRICT

D-U-N-S 78-751-5550
HYLAND SOFTWARE INC
(*Suby of* TCB) ★
28500 Clemens Rd, Westlake, OH 44145-1145
Tel (440) 788-5000 *Founded/Ownrshp* 2007
Sales 590.3MM^E *EMP* 1,680
SIC 7372 Application computer software
CEO: Bill Priemer
**Ch Bd:* Christopher J Hyland
Ex VP: Miguel A Zubizarreta
**Sr VP:* Noreen Kilbane
**Sr VP:* Brenda Kirk
VP: Drew Chapin
VP: Mark Davis
VP: Bill Filion
VP: Ken Malone
VP: Ed McQuiston
**VP:* Timothy Pembridge
VP: John Phelan
VP: Bill Premier
VP: Daniel Wilson
VP: Alfonso Zubizarreta
Exec: Paul Davis
Creative D: Mike Discenzo

D-U-N-S 80-829-1236
HYLANT GROUP
8 Cadillac Dr Ste 230, Brentwood, TN 37027-5392
Tel (615) 732-6500 *Founded/Ownrshp* 2007
Sales NA *EMP* 600
SIC 6361 Title insurance
Prin: Kimberly Riley

D-U-N-S 06-809-5702
HYLANT GROUP INC
811 Madison Ave Fl 11, Toledo, OH 43604-5626
Tel (419) 255-1020 *Founded/Ownrshp* 1998
Sales NA *EMP* 610
SIC 6411 Insurance agents
CEO: Michael Hylant
**Ch Bd:* Patrick Hylant
Pr: Todd Belden
**Pr:* William F Buckley
**Pr:* John W Chaney
Pr: Scott Dillabaugh
Pr: Tony Evans
Pr: Michael Gilbert
Pr: Chris Godley
Pr: Richard Hylant
Pr: Clay Jennings
Pr: Thomas O'Connell
**Pr:* William P Pridgeon
Pr: Kim Riley
Pr: Kimberly L Riley
Pr: Frank Treco
Pr: Michael Yon
COO: Christine Mahboob
COO: Morrie Sanderson
COO: Patrick Savage
CFO: Bill Pridgeon

HYMAN KAPLAN PAVILLION
See GOOD SAMARITAN PHYSICIAN SERVICES

D-U-N-S 07-866-9398 IMP
HYOSUNG HOLDINGS USA INC
(*Suby of* HYOSUNG CORPORATION)
15801 Prixham Hll Ave 5 Ste 575, Charlotte, NC 28277
Tel (704) 790-6100 *Founded/Ownrshp* 2009
Sales 550.0MM^E *EMP* 508
SIC 2299 2296 Fabrics: linen, jute, hemp, ramie; Tire cord & fabrics
CEO: Terry Swanner
**Pr:* Keiho Lee
**CFO:* Hyeong Seob Jeong

D-U-N-S 18-320-8727 IMP/EXP
HYOSUNG USA INC
(*Suby of* HYOSUNG HOLDINGS USA INC) ★
15801 Brixham Hill Ave # 575, Charlotte, NC 28277-4795
Tel (704) 790-6136 *Founded/Ownrshp* 1993
Sales 550.0MM *EMP* 250
Accts Kpmg Llp New York Ny
SIC 2221 2296 5199 Broadwoven fabric mills, manmade; Cord for reinforcing rubber tires; Fabrics, yarns & knit goods
CEO: Terry Swanner
**CFO:* Hyeong Seob Jeong
Adm Dir: J Walker

HYPAC
See BOMAG AMERICAS INC

HYPERACTIVE
See E & J LAWRENCE CORP

D-U-N-S 18-179-2714 IMP
■ **HYPERCOM CORP**
HYPERCOM NETWORK SYSTEMS
(*Suby of* VERIFONE SYSTEMS INC) ★
8888 E Raintree Dr # 300, Scottsdale, AZ 85260-3951
Tel (480) 642-5000 *Founded/Ownrshp* 2011
Sales 105.0MM^E *EMP* 1,431
SIC 3578 7372 7299 5065 Point-of-sale devices; Automatic teller machines (ATM); Application computer software; Information services, consumer; Electronic parts
CEO: Philippe Tartavull
Pr: Heidi R Goff
CFO: Grant Lyon
CFO: Robert M Vreeland
Ch: Norman Stout
Ofcr: Irina Delapaz
Ex VP: Jennifer Miles
Sr VP: John H Andrews
Sr VP: O B Rawls
Sr VP: Ob Rawls IV
Sr VP: Douglas J Reich
Sr VP: Ronald R Rhodes
Sr VP: William Rossiter
Sr VP: Scott Tsujita
VP: Lloyd Baylard
VP: Tk Cheung
VP: Kathy Crumley
VP: Chris Dismukes
VP: Gary Franza
VP: Chris Henry
VP: Ulf Hnick
Board of Directors: Daniel D Diethelm, Johann J Dreyer, Keith B Geeslin, Thomas Ludwig, Ian K Marsh, Phillip J Riese, Norman Stout

HYPERCOM NETWORK SYSTEMS
See HYPERCOM CORP

D-U-N-S 05-632-9527 IMP/EXP
HYPERTHERM INC
21 Great Hollow Rd, Hanover, NH 03755-3124
Tel (603) 643-3441 *Founded/Ownrshp* 1971
Sales 490.4MM^E *EMP* 1,350
SIC 3541 Machine tools, metal cutting type
Ch Bd: Richard W Couch Jr
**Pr:* Evan Smith
**CFO:* Cary Chan
Treas: Carolyn Maloney
Ofcr: Codie Rockwood
**VP:* Barbara Couch
**VP:* Jeffrey Deckrow
VP: Dave Laprade
VP: Gordon Rice
**VP:* Peter Vickers
Dist Mgr: Tommy Hanchette

D-U-N-S 09-457-2005
■ **HYPONEX CORP** (DE)
SCOTTS- HYPONEX
(*Suby of* SCOTTS MIRACLE-GRO PRODUCTS) ★
14111 Scottslawn Rd, Marysville, OH 43040-7800
Tel (937) 644-0011 *Founded/Ownrshp* 1980, 1988
Sales 488.5MM^E *EMP* 3,000
SIC 2873 2875 Fertilizers: natural (organic), except compost; Plant foods, mixed: from plants making nitrog. fertilizers; Fertilizers, mixing only; Potting soil, mixed
Pr: James Hagedorn
**CFO:* David C Evans
**Ex VP:* David M Brockman
**Ex VP:* Christopher Nagel

D-U-N-S 36-171-1542
HYPOWER INC
HY-POWER
5913 Nw 31st Ave, Fort Lauderdale, FL 33309-2207
Tel (954) 978-9300 *Founded/Ownrshp* 1991
Sales 152.8MM^E *EMP* 250
Accts Mcgladrey & Pullen Llp Fort L
SIC 1623 1731 Pipe laying construction; Electrical work
Pr: Bernard Paul-Hus
**CFO:* Stephen Cassetta
**Ex VP:* Eric Paul-Hus
VP: Raymond McCorkel
Sys Mgr: Edwin Mierisch
VP Opers: Luis Morejon
Sls Mgr: Millie Magli
Snr PM: Zack Caratozzolo

D-U-N-S 05-026-4621 IMP
HYPRO INC
600 S Jefferson St, Waterford, WI 53185-4218
Tel (608) 348-4810 *Founded/Ownrshp* 1969
Sales 365.2MM^E *EMP* 1,000
SIC 3599 Machine shop, jobbing & repair
Pr: Robert Schildt
CFO: Michelle Burgess
**Sec:* Dorothy Schildt
**VP:* Gary Schildt
VP: Kirk Schildt
QA Dir: Brenda Funk
IT Man: Roy Nelson
QC Dir: Ron Ruebensam
Plnt Mgr: Rick Brey
Plnt Mgr: Chad Lueder
Ql Cn Mgr: Tim Schumacher

D-U-N-S 04-364-7130 IMP/EXP
HYSPAN PRECISION PRODUCTS INC
1685 Brandywine Ave, Chula Vista, CA 91911-6097
Tel (619) 421-1355 *Founded/Ownrshp* 1968
Sales 95.4MM^E *EMP* 450
SIC 3568 3496 3441 Ball joints, except aircraft & automotive; Woven wire products; Expansion joints (structural shapes), iron or steel
Pr: Donald R Heye
**CFO:* Eric Barnes
**CFO:* Phillip Ensz

HYSTER AND YALE
See NMHG HOLDING CO

HYSTER COMPANY
See HYSTER-YALE GROUP INC

D-U-N-S 00-902-1429 IMP/EXP
■ **HYSTER-YALE GROUP INC**
HYSTER COMPANY
(*Suby of* HYSTER-YALE MATERIALS HANDLING INC) ★
1400 Sullivan Dr, Greenville, NC 27834-9007
Tel (252) 931-5100 *Founded/Ownrshp* 1993
Sales 1.9MMM^E *EMP* 5,100
SIC 3537 Lift trucks, industrial: fork, platform, straddle, etc.; Trucks, tractors, loaders, carriers & similar equipment
Ch Bd: Alfred Mrankin
**Pr:* Charles A Bittenbender
**Pr:* Gregory J Breier
**Pr:* Brian K Frentzko
**Pr:* Colin Wilson
Ofcr: Sharon Clark
VP: Rajiv Prasad
IT Man: Gidu Sriram
Sftwr Eng: Tyler Conboy
Opers Mgr: Andy Street
Natl Sales: Joey Bishop

D-U-N-S 60-247-2573
▲ **HYSTER-YALE MATERIALS HANDLING INC**
5875 Landerbrook Dr # 300, Cleveland, OH 44124-6511
Tel (440) 449-9600 *Founded/Ownrshp* 1989
Sales 2.5MMM *EMP* 5,500
Tkr Sym HY *Exch* NYS
SIC 3537 Lift trucks, industrial: fork, platform, straddle, etc.
Ch Bd: Alfred M Rankin Jr
CFO: Kenneth C Schilling
Treas: Brian K Frentzko
Treas: Brian Frentzko
Chf Mktg O: Lauren E Miller
Sr VP: Charles A Bittenbender
Sr VP: Rajiv K Prasad
VP: Jennifer M Langer
Board of Directors: J C Butler Jr, Carolyn Corvi, John P Jumper, Dennis W Labarre, F Joseph Loughrey, Claiborne R Rankin, John M Stropki, Britton T Taplin, Eugene Wong

HYUNDAI - ISUZU
See HYATT AUTOMOTIVE LLC

D-U-N-S 60-739-7783
HYUNDAI CAPITAL AMERICA
HYUNDAI FINANCE
(*Suby of* HYUNDAI MOTOR AMERICA) ★
3161 Michelson Dr # 1900, Irvine, CA 92612-4418
Tel (714) 965-3000 *Founded/Ownrshp* 1989
Sales NA *EMP* 540^E
SIC 6141 Automobile loans, including insurance
CEO: Sam Sanghyuk Suh
**Pr:* Sukjoon Won
**CEO:* Jwa Jin Cho
COO: Daniel Kwon
**CFO:* Minsok Randy Park
VP: Kwansun Ahn
VP: Katherine Cassidy
VP: Hristo Malchev
VP: Karen Moon
VP: Pierric Senay
VP: Adem Yilmaz

HYUNDAI FINANCE
See HYUNDAI CAPITAL AMERICA

D-U-N-S 61-471-1760
HYUNDAI MERCHANT MARINE (AMERICA) INC
(*Suby of* HYUNDAI MERCHANT MARINE CO., LTD.)
222 Las Colinas Blvd W, Irving, TX 75039-5421
Tel (972) 501-1100 *Founded/Ownrshp* 1982
Sales 97.9MM^E *EMP* 520
Accts Kpmg Llp Los Angeles Ca
SIC 4731 Agents, shipping
CEO: Seock Dong Lee
VP: Lamont Petersen
Sls Mgr: C W Lee
Board of Directors: Jae Lee

D-U-N-S 13-193-6494 IMP/EXP
HYUNDAI MOTOR AMERICA
(*Suby of* HYUNDAI MOTOR COMPANY)
10550 Talbert Ave, Fountain Valley, CA 92708-6032
Tel (714) 965-3000 *Founded/Ownrshp* 1985
Sales 471.9MM^E *EMP* 600
Accts Kpmg Llp Los Angeles Califor
SIC 5511 6141 6153 Automobiles, new & used; Automobile & consumer finance companies; Short-term business credit
CEO: B H Lee
CEO: Gail Lee
CFO: J Suh
CFO: Sukjoon Won
Ex VP: Frank Ferrara
Ex VP: Jerry Flannary
VP: Wee Chie
VP: Derrick Hatami
Ex Dir: Chung Cho
Ex Dir: Ruth Eisen
Ex Dir: Ron Haughey
Board of Directors: J K Choi, M K Chung, N M Kim, K A Lee

D-U-N-S 11-001-2890 IMP/EXP
HYUNDAI MOTOR MANUFACTURING ALABAMA LLC
HMMA
(*Suby of* HYUNDAI MOTOR COMPANY)
700 Hyundai Blvd, Montgomery, AL 36105-9626
Tel (334) 387-8000 *Founded/Ownrshp* 2002
Sales 71.8MM *EMP* 3,300
SIC 5511 Automobiles, new & used
Pr: Young Deuk Lim
VP: John Kalson
VP: Jang Kim
Exec: Nicholas Burbage
Genl Mgr: Franklin Odrobina
IT Man: Khang Martin
Ql Cn Mgr: Paul Kim
Ql Cn Mgr: Yvette Shuford
Secur Mgr: Larry Pugh

Sls Mgr: Phrede Espinosa
Sales Asso: Kevin Ohnemus

D-U-N-S 13-583-1811
HYUNDAI OF NEW PORT RICHEY LLC
3936 Us Highway 19, New Port Richey, FL 34652-6152
Tel (727) 569-0999 *Founded/Ownrshp* 2002
Sales 239.0MM *EMP* 85
SIC 5511 7549 Automobiles, new & used; Automotive maintenance services
**CFO:* Michael R Macarthur
CFO: Michael Mullins
Sls Mgr: Warren Blackburn

D-U-N-S 61-453-1622 IMP
HYUNDAI TRANSLEAD
(*Suby of* HYUNDAI MOTOR COMPANY)
8880 Rio San Diego Dr # 600, San Diego, CA 92108-1634
Tel (619) 574-1500 *Founded/Ownrshp* 1989
Sales 850.2MM^E *EMP* 2,092
SIC 3443 3715 3412 Industrial vessels, tanks & containers; Semitrailers for truck tractors; Metal barrels, drums & pails
CEO: KS Lee
COO: Moon S Chung
**COO:* Glen Harney
CFO: Steve Choi
**CFO:* Sb Yoon
Genl Mgr: Jim Tratnik
IT Man: Rodolfo Bravo
IT Man: Carlos Carrillo
Opers Mgr: Karen Gutierrez
VP Mktg: Brett Bartel
VP Sls: Stuart James

D-U-N-S 07-969-4382
■ **HYVE SOLUTIONS CORP**
(*Suby of* SYNNEX CORP) ★
44201 Nobel Dr, Fremont, CA 94538-3178
Tel (864) 349-4415 *Founded/Ownrshp* 2012
Sales 2.0MM^E *EMP* 5,000
SIC 7374 Data processing & preparation
CEO: Kevin Murai
**Pr:* Peter Larocque
Prgrm Mgr: Pam Searl
Trfc Mgr: Terry Coker
Sales Exec: Triet Pham
Sls Mgr: Nicole Lin

I

I & G BELLEVUE
See LASALLE INCOME & GROWTH FUND IV

I & K DISTRIBUTORS
See COUNTRYSIDE FOODS LLC

D-U-N-S 06-890-5272
I & M J GROSS CO
GROSS BUILDERS
14300 Ridge Rd Ste 100, Cleveland, OH 44133-4936
Tel (440) 237-1681 *Founded/Ownrshp* 1916
Sales 104.5MM^E *EMP* 200
SIC 1522 Multi-family dwellings, new construction
Pr: Gary Gross
**VP:* Harley Gross
Genl Mgr: Dick Devaney
Off Mgr: Debbie Baran
Sls&Mrk Ex: Kris Kutz
Mktg Dir: Beth Bakker

D-U-N-S 11-987-9729
I & S ACQUISITION CORP
(*Suby of* INGLETT & STUBBS INTERNATIONAL HOLDINGS PTY LIMITED)
5200 Riverview Rd Se, Mableton, GA 30126-2953
Tel (404) 881-1199 *Founded/Ownrshp* 2005
Sales 163.1MM^E *EMP* 1,455^E
SIC 1731 General electrical contractor
Pr: Jeffrey Giglio
**CFO:* Kimberly Warren
**VP:* J Terry Frierson

I A C
See INDUSTRIAL ACOUSTICS CO INC

I A C
See IRVINE APARTMENT COMMUNITIES LP

I A I
See INTERNATIONAL ASSEMBLY INC

I A P
See INTEGRATED AGRIBUSINESS PROFESSIONALS COOPERATIVE INC

I A S
See INTEGRATED ARCHIVE SYSTEMS INC

I B B
See INTERNATIONAL BULLION AND METAL BROKERS (USA) INC

I B S
See IRWIN BUILDERS SUPPLY CORP

I B T
See INTERNATIONAL BROTHERHOOD OF TEAMSTERS

I C
See I C SYSTEM INC

I C A
See INFRASTRUCTURE CORP OF AMERICA

I C A NN
See INTERNET CORP FOR ASSIGNED NAMES AND NUMBERS

I C C
See ILLINOIS CENTRAL COLLEGE

D-U-N-S 14-717-9717 IMP
I C CLASS COMPONENTS CORP
CLASSIC
23605 Telo Ave, Torrance, CA 90505-4028
Tel (310) 539-5500 *Founded/Ownrshp* 1985
Sales 87.9MM^E *EMP* 250

SIC 5065 Electronic parts & equipment
Pr: Jeffrey Klein
**COO:* Chris Klein
**COO:* Kris Klein
CFO: Nasser Shamsian
**Sec:* Emma Klein
VP: Joseph Jareck
**VP:* Perry Klein
**VP:* Ray Liston
**VP:* Mike Thomas
Brnch Mgr: Carlos Ismerio
IT Man: Al C Camacho

I C I
See INTERVEST CONSTRUCTION OF ORLANDO INC

I C I
See INTERNATIONAL CRANKSHAFT INC

D-U-N-S 07-135-1985
I C SYSTEM INC
I C
444 Highway 96 E, Saint Paul, MN 55127-2557
Tel (651) 483-8201 *Founded/Ownrshp* 1941
Sales 84.9MM^E *EMP* 1,000
SIC 7322

I C W
See INSURANCE CO OF WEST

D-U-N-S 11-441-8119 IMP
I CYPRESS CO
PEBBLE BEACH COMPANY
1700 17 Mile Dr, Pebble Beach, CA 93953
Tel (831) 647-7500 *Founded/Ownrshp* 1992
Sales 160.2MM^E *EMP* 2,500^E
SIC 7011 Hotels & motels
CEO: Bill Perocchi
Pr: Cody Plott
CFO: David Heuck
Ex VP: Mark Stilwell
Dir Soc: Matthew Barksdale
CTO: Allison Sandlin
VP Sls: Tim Ryan

I D C
See IDC RESEARCH INC

I D G
See INDUSTRIAL DISTRIBUTION GROUP INC

I D L
See RYAN DIRECTIONAL SERVICES INC

I D T
See INTEGRATED DEVICE TECHNOLOGY INC

I D T
See INTEGRATED DNA TECHNOLOGIES INC

I E A
See INFRASTRUCTURE AND ENERGY ALTERNATIVES LLC

I E I
See INTERCONTINENTAL EXPORT IMPORT INC

I F A
See INTERMOUNTAIN FARMERS ASSOCIATION

I F C O SYSTEMS
See IFCO SYSTEMS NORTH AMERICA LLC

I G BURTON IMPORTS
See IG BURTON & CO INC

I G I
See INTERNATIONAL GROUP INC

I G T
See INTERNATIONAL GAME TECHNOLOGY INC

D-U-N-S 94-851-2116
■ I GENCO INC
GENCO ATC
(*Suby of* GENCO ATC) ★
100 Papercraft Park, Pittsburgh, PA 15238-3200
Tel (800) 677-3110 *Founded/Ownrshp* 1995
Sales 267.7MM^E *EMP* 1,000
SIC 4225 4111 5045 General warehousing & storage; Local & suburban transit; Computers, peripherals & software
Ch: Herb Shear
**Pr:* David Mabon
Pr: John Marx
**Pr:* Joseph Salamunovich
**CEO:* Arthur Smuck
**COO:* Art Smuck
**CFO:* Michael Fox
**CFO:* Rick Roadarmel
**CFO:* Andy Smith
**Ex VP:* Pete Rector
**VP:* Thomas M Perry III
**VP:* Marc Sherman

I H C
See INTERSTATE HIGHWAY CONSTRUCTION INC

I H G
See SIX CONTINENTS HOTELS INC

I I D
See IMPERIAL IRRIGATION DISTRICT

I I E
See INSTITUTE OF INTERNATIONAL EDUCATION INC

I I T
See ILLINOIS INSTITUTE OF TECHNOLOGY

D-U-N-S 61-638-8976
I KESTREL ACQUISITION CORP
1035 Swabia Ct, Durham, NC 27703-8462
Tel (919) 990-7500 *Founded/Ownrshp* 2005
Sales 366.4MM^E *EMP* 1,567
SIC 2821 2822 2869 2899 2891 2851 Plastics materials & resins; Epoxy resins; Acrylic resins; Polyurethane resins; Butadiene-acrylonitrile, nitrile rubbers, NBR; Vinyl acetate; Rosin sizes; Adhesives; Paints & allied products
Ch Bd: John S Gaither
**COO:* Douglas E Frey
**CFO:* Roger L Willis
VP: Bethy Cassidy

I L B
See INTERNATIONAL LINE BUILDERS INC

I L C
See ILC INDUSTRIES LLC

I L S
See SUPPLY TECHNOLOGIES LLC

I M A
See IMA DAIRY & FOOD USA INC

I M A
See INTEGRATED MANUFACTURING & ASSEMBLY LLC

I M E A
See ILLINOIS MUNICIPAL ELECTRIC AGENCY

I M I
See IRVING MATERIALS INC

I M S
See INTEGREON MANAGED SOLUTIONS INC

I O
See IO DATA CENTERS LLC

D-U-N-S 17-828-5599 IMP
I O INTERCONNECT LTD
I/O INTERCONNECT
1202 E Wakeham Ave, Santa Ana, CA 92705-4145
Tel (714) 564-1111 *Founded/Ownrshp* 1986
Sales 234.7MM^E *EMP* 1,500
SIC 3678 3679 Electronic connectors; Harness assemblies for electronic use: wire or cable
CEO: Gary Kung

I P A
See INTERMOUNTAIN POWER AGENCY

I P G
See INTERTAPE POLYMER CORP

D-U-N-S 15-693-1248 IMP
I P R PHARMACEUTICAL INC
(*Suby of* ASTRAZENECA PLC)
San Isdro Indus Park Lot, Canovanas, PR 00729
Tel (787) 957-1400 *Founded/Ownrshp* 1985
Sales 125.7MM^E *EMP* 800
SIC 2834 Tablets, pharmaceutical
Pr: Ruben Freyre
CFO: James Lovell

I P S
See INTEGRATED POWER SERVICES LLC

I R
See INFINEON TECHNOLOGIES AMERICAS CORP

I R S
See INTERNAL REVENUE SERVICE

I R T
See INTERACTIVE RESPONSE TECHNOLOGIES INC

I R T C
See INTUITIVE RESEARCH AND TECHNOLOGY CORP

I S C
See ISC CONSTRUCTORS LLC

I S C O
See ISCO INDUSTRIES INC

I S D
See GARLAND INDEPENDENT SCHOOL DISTRICT

I S D 181 COMMUNITY EDUCATION
See BRAINERD PUBLIC SCHOOLS

I S O
See ISO SERVICES INC

D-U-N-S 60-643-6959
I S O INDUSTRIES INC
5353 E Princess Anne Rd F, Norfolk, VA 23502-1861
Tel (757) 855-0900 *Founded/Ownrshp* 2004
Sales 171.0MM *EMP* 15
Accts Goodman & Company Norfolk Vi
SIC 5172 Fuel oil
Pr: Robert G Powell
Genl Mgr: Kathy Wright
Off Mgr: Mike Sano

I S S
See INTELLIGENT SOFTWARE SOLUTIONS USA LLC

D-U-N-S 00-884-7782
I SUPPLY CO (OH)
1255 Spangler Rd, Fairborn, OH 45324-9768
Tel (937) 878-5240 *Founded/Ownrshp* 1974
Sales 207.1MM^E *EMP* 175
SIC 5087 5113 Janitors' supplies; Containers, paper & disposable plastic
CEO: Jerry Parisi
**Pr:* Gerald Parisi
**Treas:* Anita Boshears
Ofcr: Dan Woolery
**VP:* Tim Detrick
VP: Paul Droullard
VP: Tim Fery
**VP:* Joseph Parisi
**VP:* Gene Shepard
**VP:* Dan Strawn
Mktg Dir: Paul Slagle

IT G
See ITG HOLDINGS INC

IT V
See INTERNATIONAL TIMBER AND VENEER LLC

I W C
See INSTITUTIONAL WHOLESALE CO INC

I-57 SERVICE CENTER
See JBS PACKERLAND INC

I-69 TRAILER CENTER
See NOVAE CORP

I-90 NISSAN
See MD AUTO GROUP LLC

D-U-N-S 17-510-1625
■ I-FLOW CORP
(*Suby of* KIMBERLY-CLARK CORP) ★
43 Discovery Ste 100, Irvine, CA 92618-3773
Tel (800) 448-3569 *Founded/Ownrshp* 2009
Sales 69.8MM^E *EMP* 1,100^E
SIC 3841 Surgical instruments & apparatus
Pr: Donald Earhart
**COO:* James J Dal Porto
**CFO:* James R Talevich
VP: Roger Massenger
VP: Brock Thompson
Sls Mgr: Donna Arruda
Sls Mgr: Tom McMurtry

D-U-N-S 18-290-3625 IMP
I/N TEK LP
(*Suby of* ARCELORMITTAL USA LLC) ★
30755 Edison Rd, New Carlisle, IN 46552-9695
Tel (574) 654-1000 *Founded/Ownrshp* 2002
Sales 111.5MM^E *EMP* 250
SIC 3316 Strip steel, cold-rolled: from purchased hot-rolled
Sfty Mgr: David Lisak

I/O INTERCONNECT
See I O INTERCONNECT LTD

D-U-N-S 01-284-3235 IMP
I2 ASIA LLC
21983 W 83rd St, Shawnee, KS 66227-3133
Tel (913) 422-1600 *Founded/Ownrshp* 2007
Sales 110.0MM *EMP* 10
SIC 5084 Industrial machinery & equipment

D-U-N-S 62-232-6684
I2 TECHNOLOGIES INC
(*Suby of* JDA SOFTWARE GROUP INC) ★
11701 Luna Rd, Dallas, TX 75234-6072
Tel (469) 357-1000 *Founded/Ownrshp* 2010
Sales 79.8MM^E *EMP* 1,280^E
SIC 7372 Business oriented computer software
CEO: Jackson L Wilson Jr
Pr: Raymond B Greer
CFO: Michael J Berry
Bd of Dir: Berry Cash
Bd of Dir: James D Maikranz
Ex VP: Hiten D Varia
Sr VP: John Harvey
Sr VP: Nancy J Litzler
Sr VP: Graham C Newland
Sr VP: Surku Sinnadurai
Sr VP: Aditya Srivastava
Sr VP: M Miriam Wardak
VP: Ken Coulter
VP: Chris Dorr
VP: Steven Minisini
Board of Directors: Stephen P Bradley Phd, J Coley Clark, Richard L Clemmer, Richard Hunter, Michael J Simmons, Lloyd G Waterhouse

D-U-N-S 00-379-5551
I2C INC
1300 Island Dr Ste 105, Redwood City, CA 94065-5170
Tel (650) 480-5222 *Founded/Ownrshp* 2000
Sales 157.1MM^E *EMP* 400
SIC 5045 Computers, peripherals & software
CEO: Amir Wain
Pr: Usman Baig
**CFO:* Charlie Noreen
Chf Mktg O: Marc Winitz
**Sr VP:* Jim Ackerson
Sr VP: Cathy Iannuzzelli
**Sr VP:* Stephan Koukis
**Sr VP:* Jon Round
**VP:* Maryann Allison
VP: Nancy Baunis
VP: Chris Craver
**VP:* Steve Diamond
VP: Henry Gage Jr
**VP:* Khalid Hameed
**VP:* Ed Kelly
**VP:* Zohair Mustafeez
VP: Zahir Pervaiz
VP: John Sommerfield
VP: Lori Thomas

D-U-N-S 07-918-3701
I3 ELECTRONICS INC (NY)
100 Eldredge St, Binghamton, NY 13901-2631
Tel (607) 238-7077 *Founded/Ownrshp* 2013
Sales 105.6MM^E *EMP* 420^E
SIC 3672 Printed circuit boards
Pr: Jim Matthews Jr
Ofcr: Michelle Eldred
Sr VP: Voya Markovich
Pgrm Dir: Neal Driver

D-U-N-S 87-801-6443
I3 GROUP INC
INTERIOR INVESTMENTS
550 Bond St, Lincolnshire, IL 60069-4207
Tel (847) 325-1000 *Founded/Ownrshp* 1994
Sales 113.4MM^E *EMP* 120
Accts Miller Cooper & Co Ltd
SIC 5021 1799 Office & public building furniture; Office furniture installation
Pr: Don Shannon
**VP:* Michael Greenberg

IA
See INTERIOR ARCHITECTS INC

D-U-N-S 00-233-3136
IA CONSTRUCTION CORP (PA)
(*Suby of* BARRETT INDUSTRIES CORP) ★
24 Gibb Rd, Franklin, PA 16323-6225
Tel (814) 432-3184 *Founded/Ownrshp* 1924
Sales 91.5MM^E *EMP* 250
SIC 1611 2951 1622 1623 General contractor, highway & street construction; Road materials, bituminous (not from refineries); Bridge construction; Highway construction, elevated; Water main construction; Sewer line construction
Pr: Robert Doucet
**Treas:* Fred Shelton
VP: Randy Eller
VP: Robert S Field
**VP:* Donald Rosenbarger
**VP:* Dennis States
Sfty Dirs: Larry Hirchak
Board of Directors: Dominique J Leveille

IAAI
See INSURANCE AUTO AUCTIONS INC

IAC GROUP
See INTERNATIONAL AUTOMOTIVE COMPONENTS GROUP NORTH AMERICA INC

D-U-N-S 84-474-9127
■ IAC SEARCH & MEDIA INC
ASK.COM
(*Suby of* IAC/INTERACTIVECORP) ★
555 12th St Ste 500, Oakland, CA 94607-3699
Tel (510) 985-7400 *Founded/Ownrshp* 2005
Sales 148.9MM^E *EMP* 506
SIC 7375 Information retrieval services
CEO: Doug Leeds
Pr: George S Lichter
**COO:* Shane McGilloway
**CFO:* Dominic Butera
**CFO:* Steven J Sordello
Ofcr: Steven Pickering
**Ex VP:* Tuoc Luong
**Ex VP:* Brett M Robertson
VP: Valerie Combs
VP: Scott Garrell
VP: Kirk Lawrence
VP: Dirk Regel
VP Bus Dev: Oliver Hill

D-U-N-S 17-518-0819
▲ IAC/INTERACTIVECORP
555 W 18th St, New York, NY 10011-2822
Tel (212) 314-7300 *Founded/Ownrshp* 1986
Sales 3.2MMM *EMP* 5,000
Tkr Sym IAC *Exch* NGS
SIC 7372 7375 5961 Prepackaged software; Information retrieval services; On-line data base information retrieval; Catalog & mail-order houses
Exec: Barry Diller
Pr: Jon Miller
CEO: Mandy Ginsberg
CEO: Joseph Levin
CEO: Sean Moriarty
CEO: Sam Yagan
CFO: Glenn H Schiffman
V Ch Bd: Victor A Kaufman
Ex VP: Chuck Geiger
Ex VP: Mark Stein
Sr VP: Mary Osako
Sr VP: Mark J Stein
Sr VP: Gregg Winiarski
VP: Michael Daruty
VP: Peter McArthur
VP: Michael Schwerdtman
Exec: Rich Platt
Assoc Dir: Zachary Roseman

D-U-N-S 00-424-3184 IMP
IAMS CO
(*Suby of* MARS INC) ★
8700 S Masn Montgomery Rd, Mason, OH 45040-9760
Tel (800) 675-3849 *Founded/Ownrshp* 2014
Sales 193.1MM^E *EMP* 1,000
SIC 2047 2048 Dog food; Cat food; Prepared feeds
CEO: AG Losley
**CFO:* Brian Robson

D-U-N-S 07-949-2183
IAP GLOBAL SERVICES LLC
7315 N Atlantic Ave, Cape Canaveral, FL 32920-3721
Tel (321) 784-7100 *Founded/Ownrshp* 2014
Sales 546.7MM^E *EMP* 1,659^E
SIC 6726 Investment offices
CFO: Terrance Derosa
**Sr VP:* Rochelle Cooper
**VP:* Barbara Jerich

D-U-N-S 01-081-6486
IAP WORLD SERVICES INC
(*Suby of* WATER WORKS PLUMBING HEATING) ★
7315 N Atlantic Ave, Cape Canaveral, FL 32920-3721
Tel (321) 784-7100 *Founded/Ownrshp* 2005
Sales 247.6MM^E *EMP* 835^E
SIC 4731 4581 8744 4911 1541 4813 Freight transportation arrangement; Airports, flying fields & services; Airport control tower operation, except government; Facilities support services; Transmission, electric power; ; ; Industrial buildings & warehouses; Wire telephone
Pr: Douglas Kitani
**Treas:* Ann Gonzalez
**VP:* Rochelle L Cooper
Genl Couns: David Craig Jr
Board of Directors: Barbara Jerich

D-U-N-S 78-433-0677
IAP WORLDWIDE SERVICES INC
WATER WORKS PLUMBING HEATING
(*Suby of* IAP GLOBAL SERVICES LLC) ★
7315 N Atlantic Ave, Cape Canaveral, FL 32920-3721
Tel (973) 633-5115 *Founded/Ownrshp* 2004
Sales 546.7MM *EMP* 1,647
Accts Rsm Us Llp Mclean Virginia
SIC 4731 4581 8744 4911 Freight transportation arrangement; Airports, flying fields & services; Facilities support services; ; Transmission, electric power; Distribution, electric power
CEO: Douglas Kitani
**CFO:* Terry Derosa
Ofcr: Rick Bastien
**Sr VP:* Rochelle Cooper
VP: Pascal Budge
**VP:* Barbara Jerich
VP: Daniel Russell
Dir Bus: Bob Hammerle
Prgrm Mgr: William Taylor
Genl Mgr: Larry Autry
CTO: Mark Hoyt

IAS ADMINISTRATION
See CHURCH OF SCIENTOLOGY INTERNATIONAL

IASAIR
See INTEGRATED AIRLINE SERVICES INC

D-U-N-S 96-589-6140
IASIS GLENWOOD REGIONAL MEDICAL CENTER LP
(*Suby of* IASIS HEALTHCARE LLC) ★
503 Mcmillan Rd, West Monroe, LA 71291-5327
Tel (318) 329-4200 *Founded/Ownrshp* 2010
Sales 38.4MM[E] *EMP* 3,702[E]
SIC 8011 Medical centers
CEO: Ron Elder
Chf Nrs Of: Jeremy Tinnerello
QC Dir: Cheryl Faulkenberry

D-U-N-S 04-381-1228
IASIS HEALTHCARE CORP
(*Suby of* IASIS INVESTMENT LLC) ★
117 Seaboard Ln Bldg E, Franklin, TN 37067-2855
Tel (615) 844-2747 *Founded/Ownrshp* 1994
Sales 3.9MMM[E] *EMP* 12,395[E]
SIC 8062 General medical & surgical hospitals
CEO: David R White
Pr: Sandra McRee
Pr: W Carl Whitmer
COO: Phillip J Mazzuca
CFO: John M Doyle
Ofcr: Julie Heath
Ofcr: Greg Jahn
Sr VP: Jorge Munoz
VP: Joey Abney
VP: Irene Hudson
VP: Kyle R Manzeck
VP: Bob Reinhardt
VP: Jack Sanderlin
VP: William Stephens
VP: Sean Tussey
Dir Lab: Judy Barnes
Dir Lab: Kevin Brown
Dir Lab: Scott Croft
Dir Lab: Jim McBride
Dir Rx: Lydia Nesemann
Board of Directors: Thomas C Geiser

D-U-N-S 82-775-6078
IASIS HEALTHCARE LLC
(*Suby of* IASIS HEALTHCARE CORP) ★
117 Seaboard Ln Bldg E, Franklin, TN 37067-2855
Tel (615) 844-2747 *Founded/Ownrshp* 2004
Sales 2.7MMM *EMP* 12,395[E]
SIC 8062 General medical & surgical hospitals
Pr: W Carl Whitmer
**COO:* Phillip J Mazzuca
**COO:* Sandra K McRee
**CFO:* John M Doyle
Sr VP: James Hoffman
VP: Russ Follis
VP: Michele M Peden
CTO: Chris Dahl
IT Man: Robert Morland

D-U-N-S 15-202-8325
IASIS INVESTMENT LLC
113 Seaboard Ln Ste 200a, Franklin, TN 37067-4830
Tel (615) 844-2747 *Founded/Ownrshp* 2004
Sales 4.1MMM[E] *EMP* 12,396[E]
Accts Ernst & Young Llp Nashville
SIC 8062 General medical & surgical hospitals
Tech Mgr: Beverly McKenzie

D-U-N-S 16-892-0499 IMP
IAT INTERNATIONAL INC
555 E Main St Ste 1101, Norfolk, VA 23510-2232
Tel (757) 622-7239 *Founded/Ownrshp* 1997
Sales 90.0MM[E] *EMP* 6
SIC 5088 Railroad equipment & supplies
Pr: Avraham Ashkenazi
**Sec:* Patricia Ashkenazi

D-U-N-S 79-029-0915
IATSE NATIONAL HEALTH AND WELFARE FUND
55 W 39th St Fl 5, New York, NY 10018-3850
Tel (212) 580-9092 *Founded/Ownrshp* 2007
Sales 177.7MM *EMP* 4
Accts Schultheis & Panettieri Llp H
SIC 8011 Offices & clinics of medical doctors
Ch: Steven Rapaport

IB AMERICAS
See INTERNATIONAL BACCALAUREATE ORGANIZATION INC

IB TECHNOLOGY SOLUTIONS
See INCEDO INC

D-U-N-S 05-317-8823 IMP
IBAHN CORP
SUITE TECHNOLOGY
126 W 10000 S Ste 100, Sandy, UT 84070
Tel (801) 952-2000 *Founded/Ownrshp* 1999
Sales 91.6MM[E] *EMP* 200
SIC 4813

D-U-N-S 11-171-4812
IBASIS INC
(*Suby of* KONINKLIJKE KPN N.V.)
10 Maguire Rd Ste 300, Lexington, MA 02421-3120
Tel (781) 505-7500 *Founded/Ownrshp* 1996
Sales 168.3MM[E] *EMP* 372
SIC 4813 Long distance telephone communications; Telephone communications broker
CEO: Feddo Hazewindus
Pr: Michael Hughes
CFO: Jorg De Graaf
Bd of Dir: Izhar Armony
Ofcr: Mark Flynn
Sr VP: Edwin Van
VP: Oubay Atassi
VP: Julia Frevold
VP: Brad Guth
VP: Gert Huizer
VP: Jayesh Patel
VP: Tamah Solomon Rosker
VP: Mark Saponar
VP: Mark Sapornar
VP: Ellen Schmidt
VP: Tim Walsh
Dir Bus: Mark Fuller
Dir Bus: Jay Riley
Board of Directors: Robert H Brumley, Charles N Corfield, W Frank King Phd

IBC BANK
See INTERNATIONAL BANK OF COMMERCE

IBERDROLA RENEWABLES, LLC
See AVANGRID RENEWABLES LLC

D-U-N-S 14-241-9964
■ **IBERDROLA USA MANAGEMENT CORP**
(*Suby of* AVANGRID INC) ★
52 Farm View Dr, New Gloucester, ME 04260-5100
Tel (207) 688-6300 *Founded/Ownrshp* 2003
Sales 199.7MM[E] *EMP* 450
SIC 5063 Power transmission equipment, electric
CEO: Robert D Kump
Pr: Thorn Dickinson
Pr: Mary Smith
**COO:* Kevin Walker
**CFO:* Jose Maria Torres
VP: Steven R Adams
**VP:* Sheri Lamoureux
Comm Dir: John Carroll
IT Man: Scott Mahoney
Software D: Elaine Willey
Netwrk Eng: Donald Holling

IBERIA FINANCIAL SERVICES
See IBERIABANK

D-U-N-S 07-945-2934
IBERIA PARISH SCHOOL DISTRICT
1500 Jane St, New Iberia, LA 70563-1544
Tel (337) 685-4395 *Founded/Ownrshp* 1879
Sales 95.5MM[E] *EMP* 2,000
Accts Kolder Champagne Slaven & Co
SIC 8211 Public elementary & secondary schools
MIS Dir: Gwen Migues
Teacher Pr: Jacklene Jones

D-U-N-S 09-269-0288
■ **IBERIABANK**
IBERIA FINANCIAL SERVICES
(*Suby of* IBERIABANK CORP) ★
200 W Congress St, Lafayette, LA 70501-6873
Tel (800) 682-3231 *Founded/Ownrshp* 1995
Sales NA *EMP* 798
SIC 6036 6163 Savings & loan associations, not federally chartered; Loan brokers
Pr: Daryl G Byrd
Pr: Gregory A King
Pr: Kevin P Rafferty
COO: Sally Adami
COO: Michael J Brown
CFO: Marilyn W Burch
Ch: William H Fenstermaker
Ofcr: Kucera Dennis
Ex VP: Elizabeth A Ardoin
Ex VP: George J Becker III
Ex VP: J Randolph Bryan
Ex VP: John Davis
Ex VP: John R Davis
Ex VP: Donna Kasmiersky
Ex VP: Michael Naquin
Ex VP: David Shutley
Sr VP: Gerald Abshire
Sr VP: Michelle Fracchia
Sr VP: Fred Malzahn
Sr VP: Kathaleen Parks
Sr VP: Anthony J Restel

D-U-N-S 92-725-8202
▲ **IBERIABANK CORP**
200 W Congress St, Lafayette, LA 70501-6873
Tel (337) 521-4003 *Founded/Ownrshp* 1994
Sales NA *EMP* 3,216[E]
Tkr Sym IBKC *Exch* NGS
SIC 6022 State commercial banks
Pr: Daryl G Byrd
**Ch Bd:* William H Fenstermaker
Pr: Chuck Cosby
Pr: Samuel L Erwin
Pr: Rhonda Prosser
COO: Michael J Brown
CFO: Anthony J Restel
Treas: Eric Movassaghi
**V Ch Bd:* E Stewart Shea III
Chf Cred: H Spurgeon Mackie Jr
Ofcr: J Randolph Bryan
Ofcr: Carrie F Curet
Ex VP: Beth Ardoin
Ex VP: George Becker
Ex VP: Robert M Kottler
Ex VP: Barry Mulroy
Ex VP: Barry Rocky
Ex VP: Robert B Worley Jr
VP: Paula Allred
VP: Mike B Barnes
VP: Martin B Brown
Board of Directors: Elaine D Abell, Harry V Barton Jr, Ernest P Breaux Jr, John N Casbon, Angus R Cooper II, John E Koerner III, Rick E Maples, David H Welch

D-U-N-S 00-799-8230
IBERVILLE INSULATIONS LLC (LA)
11621 Sun Belt Ct, Baton Rouge, LA 70809-4209
Tel (225) 752-2194 *Founded/Ownrshp* 1981
Sales 83.4MM *EMP* 200
Accts Daigrepont & Brian Baton Roug
SIC 1799 Insulation of pipes & boilers
Area Mgr: Ben Felterman
Opers Mgr: Jeff T Starkey

IBEW
See INTERNATIONAL BROTHERHOOD OF ELECTRICAL WORKERS

D-U-N-S 16-726-7756
IBEW LOCAL 18
4189 W 2nd St, Los Angeles, CA 90004-4340
Tel (213) 387-8274 *Founded/Ownrshp* 1947
Sales 96.1MM *EMP* 18
Accts Miller Kaplan Arase Llp North
SIC 8631 Labor unions & similar labor organizations
Pr: Frank Miramontes

IBEX GLOBAL
See TRG CUSTOMER SOLUTIONS INC

D-U-N-S 07-016-8039
■ **IBG LLC** (CT)
(*Suby of* INTERACTIVE BROKERS GROUP INC) ★
1 Pickwick Plz, Greenwich, CT 06830-5551
Tel (203) 618-5800 *Founded/Ownrshp* 1994, 2007
Sales 2.0MMM *EMP* 421[E]
Accts Deloitte & Touche Llp New Yor
SIC 6211 8732 Dealers, security; Commercial nonphysical research
**CFO:* Paul Brody
CFO: Bill Cavagnaro

D-U-N-S 62-690-2316 IMP
IBL LIMITED LLC
4001 International Pkwy, Carrollton, TX 75007-1914
Tel (972) 360-9000 *Founded/Ownrshp* 1990
Sales NA *EMP* 17,800
SIC 7011

IBM
See INTERNATIONAL BUSINESS MACHINES CORP

IBM
See KENEXA CORP

D-U-N-S 03-751-8412
■ **IBM CREDIT LLC**
(*Suby of* IBM) ★
1 North Castle Dr, Armonk, NY 10504-1725
Tel (914) 765-1900 *Founded/Ownrshp* 1981
Sales NA *EMP* 1,500
SIC 6153 6159 Installment paper; Equipment & vehicle finance leasing companies
Pr: Joseph C Lane
**Pr:* Mark Loughridge
**Treas:* Michael Cromar
**Treas:* Daniel Zuchelli
**VP:* James W Boyken
**VP:* Jesse J Greene
**VP:* John J Shay Jr
**VP:* Paula L Summa
Board of Directors: Robert F Woods

D-U-N-S 00-169-7945
■ **IBM WORLD TRADE CORP**
(*Suby of* IBM) ★
1 New Orchard Rd Ste 1, Armonk, NY 10504-1722
Tel (914) 765-1900 *Founded/Ownrshp* 1923
Sales 39.2MMM[E] *EMP* 113,000
SIC 3571 3577 7377 7379 Electronic computers; Computer peripheral equipment; Computer rental & leasing; Computer related maintenance services
CEO: Virginia M Rometty
Pt: Asif Samad
V Ch: Samuel Prabhakar
**CFO:* Mark Loughridge
**Treas:* Martin J Schroeter
Sr VP: Steven A Mills
VP: Larry Bowden
VP: Michael Daniels
VP: Raj Desai
VP: Jan Janick
**VP:* David L Johnson
VP: Abby Kohnstamm
VP: Paul Ledak
VP: Farid Metwaly
VP: Tim Ravey
VP: Walker Royce
VP: Bob Sutor
VP: Eric Tsou
VP: Anthony Yu
Exec: John Maciver

D-U-N-S 07-991-1503
IBP CORP HOLDINGS INC
495 S High St Ste 50, Columbus, OH 43215-5689
Tel (614) 692-6360 *Founded/Ownrshp* 2015
Sales 51.3MM[E] *EMP* 2,000[E]
SIC 1742 6719 Insulation, buildings; Investment holding companies, except banks
Pr: William Jenkins

IBS
See INTEGRATED BAGGING SYSTEMS CORP

D-U-N-S 78-376-4434 EXP
IBS PARTNERS LTD
1 N University Dr Ut400a, Plantation, FL 33324-2038
Tel (954) 581-0922 *Founded/Ownrshp* 1985
Sales 352.4MM[E] *EMP* 1,600
SIC 2086 Soft drinks: packaged in cans, bottles, etc.
Genl Pt: Nick A Caporella
Ex VP: Edward Knecht
Ex Dir: Raymond Notarantonio

D-U-N-S 00-385-4437 IMP/EXP
IBT INC (MO)
9400 W 55th St, Shawnee Mission, KS 66203-2042
Tel (913) 677-3151 *Founded/Ownrshp* 1949, 1962
Sales 161.5MM *EMP* 320
SIC 5085 5084

IBUYPOWER
See AMERICAN FUTURE TECHNOLOGY CORP

D-U-N-S 02-134-4700
■ **IC BUS LLC**
(*Suby of* NAVISTAR INC) ★
600 Bayford Dr, Conway, AR 72034
Tel (501) 327-7761 *Founded/Ownrshp* 1995
Sales NA *EMP* 1,100
SIC 3713 3711 Bus bodies (motor vehicles); Chassis, motor vehicle
VP: Raymond Allen
VP: Don Ferran
VP: Debbie Isaacs

D-U-N-S 00-203-3988
■ **IC BUS OF OKLAHOMA LLC**
(*Suby of* IC BUS LLC) ★
2322 N Mingo Rd, Tulsa, OK 74116-1218
Tel (918) 833-4000 *Founded/Ownrshp* 2000
Sales 228.8MM[E] *EMP* 1,000
SIC 3711 3713 Motor vehicles & car bodies; Truck & bus bodies
Pr: Grant Tick
**VP:* Michael Cancelliere

D-U-N-S 17-608-1537
IC COMPLIANCE LLC
TALENTWAVE
1065 E Hillsdale Blvd # 300, Foster City, CA 94404-1613
Tel (650) 378-4150 *Founded/Ownrshp* 2015
Sales 258.7MM[E] *EMP* 5,500
SIC 7371 8721 Computer software development & applications; Payroll accounting service
CEO: Teresa Creech
CFO: Keith Corbin
CIO: Lynn Dunn

IC GROUP
See INTERNATIONAL AUTOMOTIVE COMPONENTS GROUP NORTH AMERICA HOLDINGS INC

ICAHN
See IEH FM HOLDINGS LLC

D-U-N-S 18-580-7088
■ **ICAHN ENTERPRISES HOLDINGS LP**
(*Suby of* ICAHN ENTERPRISES LP) ★
767 5th Ave Fl 17, New York, NY 10153-0028
Tel (212) 702-4300 *Founded/Ownrshp* 1987
Sales 19.1MMM *EMP* 59,559
SIC 6512 5719 6211 5093 Nonresidential building operators; Beddings & linens; Security brokers & dealers; Security brokers & dealers; Scrap & waste materials
Ch Bd: Carl C Icahn
CFO: Andrew Skobe

D-U-N-S 55-589-7164 IMP
▲ **ICAHN ENTERPRISES LP**
767 5th Ave Ste 4700, New York, NY 10153-0108
Tel (212) 702-4300 *Founded/Ownrshp* 1987
Sales 19.1MMM *EMP* 88,191
Tkr Sym IEP *Exch* NGS
SIC 6722 3714 7999 3743 5093 6531 Management investment, open-end; Motor vehicle parts & accessories; Gambling establishment; Railroad equipment; Ferrous metal scrap & waste; Real estate leasing & rentals
Pr: Keith Cozza
CFO: Sunghwan Cho
Treas: John Saldarelli
Ofcr: Peter Reck
VP: Gail Golden
Genl Couns: Mark Weitzen
Counsel: Felicia Buebel

D-U-N-S 07-886-1598 IMP
ICAHN SCHOOL OF MEDICINE AT MOUNT SINAI (NY)
MOUNT SINAI HOSPITAL, THE
(*Suby of* MOUNT SINAI HOSPITAL) ★
1 Gustave L Levy Pl, New York, NY 10029-6504
Tel (212) 241-6500 *Founded/Ownrshp* 1968
Sales 1.7MMM *EMP* 7,000
Accts Ernst & Young Llp New York N
SIC 8249 Medical training services
CEO: Ken Davis
**CFO:* Stephen Harvey
Bd of Dir: Sergio Lira
VP: Teri Willey
Dir Lab: Gomathi Jayaraman
Assoc Dir: Alan Krissoff
Assoc Dir: Abby Livingston
Adm Dir: Shinolia Brown
Genl Mgr: James Godbold
Netwrk Mgr: Carl Thompson
Tech Mgr: Andrew Pizzimenti

ICAI
See ITOCHU CHEMICALS AMERICA INC

D-U-N-S 01-346-2120
ICAN BENEFIT GROUP LLC
5300 Broken Sound Blvd Nw, Boca Raton, FL 33487-3520
Tel (800) 530-4226 *Founded/Ownrshp* 2005
Sales NA *EMP* 150[E]
SIC 6411 Insurance information & consulting services
**Pr:* Sam Shatz
Ex VP: Victor Scavo

D-U-N-S 05-359-1566
ICAP CAPITAL MARKETS LLC
(*Suby of* ICAP PLC)
1100 Plaza Five, Jersey City, NJ 07311-4003
Tel (212) 732-6900 *Founded/Ownrshp* 2007
Sales NA *EMP* 600[E]
SIC 6099 Deposit brokers; Foreign currency exchange

D-U-N-S 18-614-9964
ICAP ENERGY LLC
(*Suby of* ICAP PLC)
9931 Corporate Campus Dr, Louisville, KY 40223-4035
Tel (502) 327-1400 *Founded/Ownrshp* 2001
Sales 96.3MM[E] *EMP* 78[E]
SIC 5172 Crude oil
CFO: Dan Godbey
VP: Gary Burton
Comm Dir: Ivette Collazo
Mng Dir: Paul Newman
Snr Sftwr: Alex Zaytsev
CIO: Arthur D'Arcy
Info Man: Scott Boucher
Sftwr Eng: Hemalben Patel
Genl Couns: Joe Wright

D-U-N-S 07-887-5465
ICAP SERVICES NORTH AMERICA LLC
GARBAN INTERCAP
(*Suby of* ICAP PLC)
1100 Plaza Five Fl 12, Jersey City, NJ 07311-4003
Tel (212) 341-9900 *Founded/Ownrshp* 1998
Sales 305.8MM[E] *EMP* 804
SIC 6211 Brokers, security
CEO: Michael Spencer
**COO:* Ken Pigaga
CFO: Philip Currpy
Sr VP: Kevin Doherty
VP: Mike Accolla

VP: Christopher Balzotti
VP: Grant Morrow
Exec: Lisa Wiegandt
Prgrm Mgr: Kim Grable-Stanton
Snr Sftwr: Andrew Bobrowski
Snr Sftwr: Dmitri Rasnitsyn

D-U-N-S 19-281-3111 EXP
ICC CHEMICAL CORP
PRIOR CHEMICAL
(*Suby of* ICC INDUSTRIES INC) ★
460 Park Ave Fl 7, New York, NY 10022-1841
Tel (212) 521-1700 *Founded/Ownrshp* 2007
Sales 232.2MM^E *EMP* 50
SIC 5169 5122 5162 Chemicals & allied products; Pharmaceuticals; Plastics materials & basic shapes
Ch: Naveen Chandra
Ch Bd: John J Farber
Pr: William R Brunger
Treas: Susan Aibinder

D-U-N-S 04-617-7341 IMP/EXP
ICC INDUSTRIES INC
460 Park Ave Fl 7, New York, NY 10022-1841
Tel (212) 521-1700 *Founded/Ownrshp* 1950
Sales 856.7MM^E *EMP* 2,528
SIC 2821 2869 2911 2899 3081 2834

ICC NEXERGY
See INVENTUS POWER INC

ICD
See INDEPENDENCE CONTRACT DRILLING INC

ICE
See INTERCONTINENTAL EXCHANGE INC

ICE
See INTERCONTINENTAL EXCHANGE INC

D-U-N-S 18-064-8115
ICE BUILDERS INC
GRAY
(*Suby of* GRAY INC) ★
421 E Cerritos Ave, Anaheim, CA 92805-6320
Tel (714) 491-1317 *Founded/Ownrshp* 2001
Sales 84.8MM^E *EMP* 180
SIC 1541

D-U-N-S 00-627-8428 EXP
ICE CREAM SPECIALTIES INC (MO)
NORTH STAR DISTRIBUTING
(*Suby of* PRAIRIE FARMS DAIRY INC) ★
8419 Hanley Industrial Ct, Saint Louis, MO 63144-1917
Tel (314) 962-2550 *Founded/Ownrshp* 1957
Sales 99.2MM^E *EMP* 412
SIC 2024 Ice cream & frozen desserts
Pr: Leonard Southwell
Sales Exec: Bob Apple

ICE GALLERY
See INTERNATIONAL CRUISE & EXCURSION GALLERY INC

D-U-N-S 61-078-1051 IMP
ICE INDUSTRIES INC
3810 Herr Rd, Sylvania, OH 43560-8925
Tel (419) 842-3612 *Founded/Ownrshp* 2002
Sales 244.6MM^E *EMP* 450
SIC 3469 Metal stampings
**COO:* Paul Bishop
**Ex VP:* Jeff Boger
Exec: Stan Pryba
Genl Mgr: Gene Swick

D-U-N-S 07-595-5575
ICE MILLER LLP
1 American Sq Ste 2900, Indianapolis, IN 46282-0019
Tel (317) 236-2100 *Founded/Ownrshp* 1910
Sales 93.8MM^E *EMP* 600
SIC 8111 Legal services
Pt: Phillip Bayt
Pt: Steven Humke
Pt: Byron Myers
Pt: Phillip Scaletta
Pt: Myra Selby
Pt: Richard Thrapp
Mng Pt: Judy S Okenfuss
COO: Mitchell Hopwell
COO: Mitchell E Hopwood
CFO: John Daniels
CIO: Tim Eckenrode

ICE-O-MATIC
See MILE HIGH EQUIPMENT LLC

ICEC
See OXBOW SULPHUR INC

D-U-N-S 04-742-6747 IMP
■ ICEE CO
(*Suby of* J & J SNACK FOODS CORP) ★
1205 S Dupont Ave, Ontario, CA 91761-1536
Tel (800) 426-4233 *Founded/Ownrshp* 1967
Sales 192.4MM^E *EMP* 700
SIC 2038 5145 3559 2087 Frozen specialties; Popcorn & supplies; Plastics working machinery; Flavoring extracts & syrups
Pr: Gerald B Shreiber
**Pr:* Dan Fachner
**CFO:* Kent Galloway
**VP:* Rodney N Sexton
Sftwr Eng: Daniel Penner
Trfc Dir: Carol Lopez
Opers Mgr: Bob Whitis
Sls Mgr: Tim Hughes

D-U-N-S 07-618-3909
■ ICF CONSULTING GROUP INC
(*Suby of* ICF INTERNATIONAL INC) ★
9300 Lee Hwy, Fairfax, VA 22031-6050
Tel (703) 934-3000 *Founded/Ownrshp* 1969
Sales 949.3MM *EMP* 4,000
SIC 8742 Management consulting services
CEO: Sudhakar Kesavan
CFO: James C Morgan
Treas: Terrance Mc Govern
Sr VP: Sal Fazzolari
Sr VP: Abyd Karmali
VP: Gray F Michael
VP: Paul Weeks
Prin: Troy Barker
Prin: Rinaldo A Campana

D-U-N-S 07-264-8579
■ ICF INC LLC
(*Suby of* ICF CONSULTING GROUP INC) ★
9300 Lee Hwy Ste 200, Fairfax, VA 22031-6051
Tel (703) 934-3000 *Founded/Ownrshp* 1985, 1969
Sales 165.4MM^E *EMP* 2,470
SIC 8742 8748 Management consulting services; Business consulting
Ch Bd: Sudhakar Kesavan
Pr: John Wasson
CFO: James C Morgan
Treas: Terrance Mc Govern
Sr VP: Douglas Beck
Sr VP: James E Daniel
Sr VP: Barbara Rudin

D-U-N-S 13-900-1544
▲ ICF INTERNATIONAL INC
9300 Lee Hwy Ste 200, Fairfax, VA 22031-6051
Tel (703) 934-3000 *Founded/Ownrshp* 1969
Sales 1.1MMM *EMP* 6,400
Accts Grant Thornton Llp Mclean Vi
Tkr Sym ICFI *Exch* NGS
SIC 8742 8748 Management consulting services; Business consulting
Ch Bd: Sudhakar Kesavan
Pr: John Wasson
CFO: James C Morgan
Ofcr: Colette Laforce
Ex VP: Louise Clements
Ex VP: Ellen Glover
Ex VP: Cheryl W Gris
Ex VP: Sanjay Gupta
Sr VP: John T Guda
Sr VP: Jim Lawler
Sr VP: Terrence McGovern
Sr VP: Sergio Ostria
Sr VP: Samuel Visner
VP: Carol Babb
VP: Dean Bakeris
VP: Frances Heilig
VP: Ricki Henschel
VP: Robert Kwartin
VP: Larry Luskin
VP: Asif Mahmud
VP: Todd Pantezzi
Board of Directors: Eileen O'shea Auen, Edward H Bersoff, Cheryl W Grise, Sanjay Gupta, Peter M Schulte

D-U-N-S 61-484-4590
■ ICG LLC
(*Suby of* INTERNATIONAL COAL GROUP INC) ★
114 Smiley Dr, Saint Albans, WV 25177-1504
Tel (304) 760-2400 *Founded/Ownrshp* 2004
Sales 151.0MM^E *EMP* 3,500
SIC 1241 Coal mining services
Pr: Bennett K Hatfield

D-U-N-S 83-253-6796 IMP
ICHOR SYSTEMS INC
(*Suby of* FP) ★
9660 Sw Herman Rd, Tualatin, OR 97062-7905
Tel (503) 625-2251 *Founded/Ownrshp* 2009
Sales 371.3MM *EMP* 426
Accts Kpmg Llp Portland Oregon
SIC 3559 5984 Semiconductor manufacturing machinery; Liquefied petroleum gas dealers
Prin: Andrew Kowal
**Pr:* Maurice Carson
Pr: Peter English
**Pr:* Mark Hutson
**CEO:* Thomas M Rohrs
COO: David Savage
**Sr VP:* Phil R Barros
**Sr VP:* Mark A Thomas
Snr Sftwr: Kelly Pustejovsky
IT Man: Huey Burke
VP Opers: Kim McGuire

D-U-N-S 79-786-5540 IMP/EXP
ICI AMERICA INC
(*Suby of* PERMABOND AMERICAS) ★
10 Finderne Ave, Bridgewater, NJ 08807-3365
Tel (908) 203-2800 *Founded/Ownrshp* 1966
Sales 99.5MM^E *EMP* 3,000
SIC 2821 3081 2869 2843 2865 Acrylic resins; Polyurethane resins; Unsupported plastics film & sheet; Industrial organic chemicals; Surface active agents; Cyclic crudes & intermediates
Ch Bd: William H Power
CFO: Tim Brownlee
**CFO:* R J Forrest
**Treas:* R Timothy Brownlee
**VP:* Clive A Grannum
Mng Dir: Ken Dowling
Genl Mgr: Guha Rajasekaran

D-U-N-S 79-867-2218 IMP
ICI AMERICAN HOLDINGS LLC
PERMABOND AMERICAS
(*Suby of* IMPERIAL CHEMICAL INDUSTRIES LIMITED)
10 Finderne Ave, Bridgewater, NJ 08807-3365
Tel (908) 203-2800 *Founded/Ownrshp* 1992
Sales 614.8MM^E *EMP* 14,800
SIC 2851 2821 3081 2869 2843 2865 Paints & allied products; Paints: oil or alkyd vehicle or water thinned; Enamels; Lacquer: bases, dopes, thinner; Acrylic resins; Polyurethane resins; Unsupported plastics film & sheet; Industrial organic chemicals; Surface active agents; Cyclic crudes & intermediates
VP: Stephen Bradford

D-U-N-S 06-114-4291 EXP
ICI CONSTRUCTION INC
24715 W Hardy Rd, Spring, TX 77373-5764
Tel (281) 355-5151 *Founded/Ownrshp* 1982
Sales 175.1MM *EMP* 102
Accts Karlins Ramey & Tompkins Llc
SIC 1542 Commercial & office building, new construction; School building construction; Commercial & office buildings, renovation & repair
Pr: Russell Cobb
**Treas:* Tom Cobb
**Sr VP:* Chris Sidwa
**VP:* B J Cobb
VP: Chris Graves
**VP:* Steve Williams
Exec: Amanda Crimm
Snr PM: Ron Armistead
Snr PM: Mitch Manning
Snr PM: Deen Rilauddeen

D-U-N-S 00-948-4908 IMP/EXP
ICICLE SEAFOODS INC
SEWARD FISHERIES
(*Suby of* COOKE SEAFOOD USA INC) ★
4019 21st Ave W Ste 300, Seattle, WA 98199-1299
Tel (206) 282-0988 *Founded/Ownrshp* 2016
Sales 231.4MM^E *EMP* 500
SIC 2092 2091 Shellfish, frozen: prepared; Fish, frozen: prepared; Salmon: packaged in cans, jars, etc.
Pr: Chris Ruettgers
Pr: Christopher Ruettgers
COO: Tony Jolley
CFO: Ladon Johnson
Ex VP: John Woodruff
VP: Shinichi Ode
Genl Mgr: Chris Pugmire
Genl Mgr: Rob Rogers
Sfty Mgr: Rexanne Stafford
VP Sls: Bob Jansing
Mktg Mgr: Frank Zennan

ICL
See INSTITUTE FOR COMMUNITY LIVING INC

D-U-N-S 07-835-7916 IMP
■ ICL HOLDING CO INC
LCI HOLDING COMPANY, INC.
(*Suby of* CARLYLE PARTNERS IV LP) ★
5340 Legacy Dr Bldg 4150, Plano, TX 75024-3178
Tel (469) 241-2100 *Founded/Ownrshp* 2005
Sales 71.9MM^E *EMP* 14,400^E
SIC 8069 8051 Specialty hospitals, except psychiatric; Skilled nursing care facilities
CEO: Neil Douglas

D-U-N-S 96-226-5885 IMP/EXP
ICL NORTH AMERICA INC
(*Suby of* ISRAEL CHEMICALS LTD.)
622 Emerson Rd Ste 500, Saint Louis, MO 63141-6742
Tel (314) 983-7500 *Founded/Ownrshp* 2010
Sales 149.7MM^E *EMP* 550^E
SIC 2819 Chemicals, high purity: refined from technical grade
CEO: Charles M Weidhas
**VP:* Anantha Desikan
**VP:* Paul M Schlessman
Genl Mgr: Ariana Cohen

D-U-N-S 08-527-1638 IMP/EXP
ICL PERFORMANCE PRODUCTS LP
(*Suby of* ISRAEL CHEMICALS LTD.)
622 Emerson Rd Ste 500, Saint Louis, MO 63141-6742
Tel (314) 983-7500 *Founded/Ownrshp* 2005
Sales 296.5MM^E *EMP* 550
SIC 2819 Chemicals, high purity: refined from technical grade
CEO: Mark Volmer
Pr: Thomas York
CFO: Paul Schlessman
VP: Michael Bork
VP: Bruene Cremer
VP: Heather Luther
VP: Deborah Tallo
VP: Terry Zerr
Dir Rx: Edward Goldberg
CIO: Christy M Barker
Plnt Mgr: Bret Graham

D-U-N-S 83-468-3369
ICM INC
310 N 1st St, Colwich, KS 67030-9655
Tel (316) 796-0900 *Founded/Ownrshp* 1995
Sales 169.6MM^E *EMP* 440^E
SIC 8748 8711 Energy conservation consultant; Consulting engineer; Construction & civil engineering
CEO: David Vander Griend
CFO: Andy Bulloch
VP: Brock Beach
Exec: Carleen Stearns
Dir Lab: Jackie Lissolo
Off Mgr: Reva Carlson
IT Man: Mike Spellman
VP Opers: Tom Ranallo
Trfc Mgr: Dave Hemmen
VP Mktg: Chris Mitchell
Genl Couns: Brian Burris

ICMA RETIREMENT
See INTERNATIONAL CITY MANAGEMENT ASSOCIATION RETIREMENT CORP

D-U-N-S 07-079-6743 IMP/EXP
■ ICO - SCHULMAN LLC
(*Suby of* A SCHULMAN INC) ★
24624 Interstate 45, Spring, TX 77386-4084
Tel (832) 663-3131 *Founded/Ownrshp* 2010
Sales 328.8MM^E *EMP* 3,000^E
SIC 2821 Plastics materials & resins
Pr: Joseph Gingo
Pr: David J Phillips
Treas: Joseph J Levanduski
Bd of Dir: Charles T McCord
VP: Paul Giddens
VP: Andy Ubhi

D-U-N-S 17-930-8267
ICON CENTRAL LABORATORIES INC
(*Suby of* ICON PUBLIC LIMITED COMPANY)
123 Smith St, Farmingdale, NY 11735-1004
Tel (631) 777-8833 *Founded/Ownrshp* 1994
Sales 179.8MM^E *EMP* 8,500
SIC 8071 8734 Medical laboratories; Testing laboratories
CEO: Ciaran Murray
**Pr:* Robert Scott Edwards
VP: Gail Fowler
VP: Eimear Kenny
**VP:* Dr Nuala Murphy
VP: Jim Wagner
Dir Lab: Kristi C Leggett
Genl Mgr: Clare Osullivan
Snr Mgr: Karen Colicci

ICON CLINICAL RESEARCH
See ICON DEVELOPMENT SOLUTIONS LLC

D-U-N-S 87-288-5173
ICON CLINICAL RESEARCH LLC
ICON DEVELOPMENT SOLUTIONS
(*Suby of* ICON CLINICAL RESEARCH LIMITED)
2100 Pennbrook Pkwy, North Wales, PA 19454-4105
Tel (215) 616-3000 *Founded/Ownrshp* 1992
Sales 151.6MM^E *EMP* 654
SIC 8731 Commercial physical research
CEO: Bill Taaffe
**Pr:* William Taaffe
COO: Malcolm Burgess
**COO:* John W Hubbard
**Treas:* David Peters
Sr VP: Jody Fleisig
VP: John Allinson
VP: David Bartholomew
VP: Todd Czajka
VP: Scott Neff
VP: Kate Tranotti
VP: Marcin Wlodarczyk
Exec: Sharon Walters
Exec: Maria Wetzel
Assoc Dir: Darlene Cantrelle
Assoc Dir: Eloise Harris
Assoc Dir: Cynthia Holt
Assoc Dir: Lynn Leech
Assoc Dir: Tom McCloskey
Assoc Dir: June Polonsky

ICON DEVELOPMENT SOLUTIONS
See ICON CLINICAL RESEARCH LLC

D-U-N-S 83-041-8658
ICON DEVELOPMENT SOLUTIONS LLC
ICON CLINICAL RESEARCH
(*Suby of* ICON PUBLIC LIMITED COMPANY)
820 W Diamond Ave Ste 100, Gaithersburg, MD 20878-1419
Tel (301) 944-6810 *Founded/Ownrshp* 1997
Sales 15.0MM *EMP* 10,000
SIC 8733 Noncommercial research organizations
CEO: Ciaran Murray
Ch: Thomas Lynch
Sr VP: Stuart Madden
VP: Ralf Brueckner
VP: Adrian Pencak
Mng Dir: Timothy J Myers
IT Man: Candy Dehn
VP Sls: Daniel Smith

D-U-N-S 80-817-7661 IMP
ICON EYEWEAR INC
5 Empire Blvd, South Hackensack, NJ 07606-1805
Tel (201) 330-9333 *Founded/Ownrshp* 1993
Sales 130.2MM^E *EMP* 130^E
Accts Josephson Luxenberg Kance And
SIC 5099 Sunglasses
Ch Bd: Michael Chang
**Pr:* Bruce Bartley
Pr: Karen Goh
Pr: George Hanley
Pr: Jack Woods
**Ex VP:* Julie Chang
**Ex VP:* Joe Massa
**VP:* Mike Cotton
VP Opers: Charlie Destifano
Sls Dir: Jack Hanlon

D-U-N-S 08-392-2229 EXP
ICON HEALTH & FITNESS INC
HEALTHRIDER
1500 S 1000 W, Logan, UT 84321-8206
Tel (435) 750-5000 *Founded/Ownrshp* 2006
Sales 1.2MMM^E *EMP* 3,263
SIC 3949 Treadmills; Exercising cycles; Gymnasium equipment
Ch Bd: Scott R Watterson
Pr: Greg Law
**Pr:* David J Watterson
COO: Duane Harvey
**CFO:* S Fred Beck
CFO: Debra Moore
Treas: Shelly Underwood
**V Ch Bd:* Robert C Gay
Chf Mktg O: David Watterson
VP: Bob Allen
VP: Kurt Facer
VP: Blake Watterson
VP Bus Dev: Lynn Brenchley
Exec: Alan Lawrence
Comm Man: Melanie Jensen
Board of Directors: W Steve Albrecht, Greg Benson, Alan H Freudenstein, Robert C Gay, Lester W B Moore, Charles W Robbins, Gary E Stevenson, David J Watterson, Scott R Watterson Chb

D-U-N-S 15-030-4855
■ ICON HOLDING CORP
ICON INTERNATIONAL
(*Suby of* OMNICOM GROUP INC) ★
107 Elm St Fl 15, Stamford, CT 06902-3834
Tel (203) 328-2300 *Founded/Ownrshp* 2000
Sales 797.3MM^E *EMP* 200
SIC 7389 7319 Barter exchange; Media buying service
Pr: John P Kramer
**CFO:* Clarence V Lee III
Chf Cred: Christopher Levy

D-U-N-S 00-511-9714
ICON IDENTITY SOLUTIONS INC (IL)
1418 Elmhurst Rd, Elk Grove Village, IL 60007-6417
Tel (847) 364-2250 *Founded/Ownrshp* 1925, 1997
Sales 107.6MM *EMP* 450
Accts Mcgladrey Llp Chicago Il
SIC 3993 Signs & advertising specialties; Neon signs
Pr: Kurt Ripkey
**CFO:* John Callan
**Ex VP:* Tom Hunt
**Ex VP:* Melanee Jech
Ex VP: Douglas Long
Ex VP: John Noonan
Sr VP: Evan Wollak

VP: Matt Czyl
VP: Pat Doak
Prgrm Mgr: Michelle Daniels

ICON INTERNATIONAL
See ICON HOLDING CORP

D-U-N-S 13-175-7304
■ ICON INTERNATIONAL INC
(*Suby of* ICON INTERNATIONAL) ★
4 Stamford Plz 15th, Stamford, CT 06902-3834
Tel (203) 328-2300 *Founded/Ownrshp* 1985
Sales 797.3MM *EMP* 200
SIC 7389 7319 Barter exchange; Media buying service
CEO: John P Kramer
Treas: Joanne Cancro
Chf Cred: Christopher Levy
**Ex VP:* Clarence V Lee III
VP: Tom Bartholomew
VP: Paul Florio
VP: Anita Garrison
VP: Leslie Moses
VP: Debbie Nieves
VP: Jerry Padilla
**VP:* Gary Perlman
VP: John Stofka
VP: Jim Tully
VP: Maureen Walsh
VP: Thomas Worms
VP Bus Dev: Daniel Barutio
VP Bus Dev: Brian Connally
Assoc Dir: Marie Weissert

ICONECTIV
See TELCORDIA TECHNOLOGIES INC

D-U-N-S 08-027-4444
ICONEX LLC (GA)
INTERACTIVE PRINTER SOLUTIONS
(*Suby of* ATLAS HOLDINGS LLC) ★
3097 Satellite Blvd, Duluth, GA 30096-1242
Tel (917) 282-0861 *Founded/Ownrshp* 2015, 2016
Sales 162.0MM[E] *EMP* 45
SIC 5111 2621 Printing & writing paper; Printing paper
CEO: Eddie Noel
CFO: James Andrews
VP: Jonathan Collier
VP: Jim Griffiths
VP: Pam Hill
VP: Dahn Nilsen
VP Sls: Charles M Gonzalez

D-U-N-S 02-307-0298
ICONIC GROUP INC
GRADIMAGES
3490 Martin Hurst Rd, Tallahassee, FL 32312-1702
Tel (800) 628-4509 *Founded/Ownrshp* 1976
Sales 100.0MM *EMP* 200
SIC 7335 Commercial photography
CEO: Paul Rasmussen
**CFO:* John Kampschroeder
Manager: Laura Moran

D-U-N-S 09-482-5262
▲ ICONIX BRAND GROUP INC
1450 Broadway Fl 3, New York, NY 10018-2232
Tel (212) 730-0030 *Founded/Ownrshp* 1978
Sales 379.2MM *EMP* 137[E]
Tkr Sym ICON *Exch* NGS
SIC 6794 3143 3144 Patent buying, licensing, leasing; Men's footwear, except athletic; Women's footwear, except athletic
Pr: John Haugh
**Ch Bd:* F Peter Cuneo
CFO: David Jones
Ex VP: David Blumberg
Ex VP: Jason Schaefer
VP: Federico De Bellegarde
Board of Directors: Drew Cohen, Barry Emanuel, Mark Friedman, Sue Gove, Sanjay Khosla, James A Marcum, Kristen O'hara

D-U-N-S 00-649-3691
ICONMA LLC (OR)
850 Stephenson Hwy, Troy, MI 48083-1127
Tel (248) 583-1930 *Founded/Ownrshp* 2000
Sales 131.2MM[E] *EMP* 1,556
SIC 7363 Help supply services; Temporary help service
CEO: Claudine S George
**VP:* William Pelletier
**VP:* Sat Yalaman
Opers Mgr: Deepak Kumar

ICP
See ISLAND COMPUTER PRODUCTS INC

ICP
See PCB GROUP INC

D-U-N-S 00-722-3964 IMP/EXP
ICREST INTERNATIONAL LLC
JCP
(*Suby of* ITOCHU CORPORATION)
725 S Figueroa St # 3050, Los Angeles, CA 90017-5454
Tel (213) 488-8303 *Founded/Ownrshp* 2000
Sales 458.9MM *EMP* 33
Accts Deloitte & Touche Llp Los An
SIC 5148 5147 Fresh fruits & vegetables; Meats & meat products
CEO: Takeshi Yagubhi
Sls Mgr: Ken Park

D-U-N-S 11-444-2648
ICROSSING INC
(*Suby of* HEARST MAGAZINES) ★
300 W 57th St Fl 20f, New York, NY 10019-3741
Tel (212) 649-3900 *Founded/Ownrshp* 2011
Sales 100.9MM[E] *EMP* 900
SIC 8742 7311 Marketing consulting services; Advertising consultant
Pr: Brian Powley
Pr: Mark Mulhern
Pr: Mike Parker
**CFO:* Michael J Jackson
**Chf Cred:* Dave Johnson
**Ofcr:* Brian Haven
**Ofcr:* David Santos
**Ex VP:* Rod Lenniger
**Sr VP:* Darren Prock
**Sr VP:* Paramjeet Sanghera
Sr VP: Gary Stein
Sr VP: Shoshana Winter
VP: Christopher Andrew
VP: Andrew Schmeling
VP: Steven Shay
Assoc Dir: Matt Kischer
Assoc Dir: Harry Lee
Assoc Dir: Andrea Nelson
Creative D: Craig Sosonko
Creative D: Craig Wong

D-U-N-S 62-535-0371
ICS CONTRACT SERVICES LLC
1251 Marietta Blvd Nw, Atlanta, GA 30318-4140
Tel (404) 367-8286 *Founded/Ownrshp* 2005
Sales 19.0MM[E] *EMP* 1,000
SIC 7349 Janitorial service, contract basis
Genl Mgr: Ken Barrett
Off Mgr: Colleen Fowler

D-U-N-S 11-838-0146 IMP
▲ ICU MEDICAL INC
951 Calle Amanecer, San Clemente, CA 92673-6212
Tel (949) 366-2183 *Founded/Ownrshp* 1984
Sales 341.6MM *EMP* 2,446[E]
Tkr Sym ICUI *Exch* NGS
SIC 3841 3845 IV transfusion apparatus; Catheters; Pacemaker, cardiac
Ch Bd: Vivek Jain
CFO: Scott E Lamb
VP: Alison D Burcar
VP: Clay Fradd
VP: Tom McCall
VP: Steven C Riggs
VP: Dan Wait
Dir IT: Ben Sousa
Sftwr Eng: Gary Kephart
Opers Mgr: Mike Hisey
Ql Cn Mgr: Don Waits
Board of Directors: Elisha W Finney, David C Greenberg, George A Lopez, Joseph R Saucedo, Richard H Sherman, Robert S Swinney

D-U-N-S 05-874-4512
ICV PARTNERS
810 7th Ave Ste 3501, New York, NY 10019-5842
Tel (212) 455-9600 *Founded/Ownrshp* 1998
Sales 84.2MM[E] *EMP* 484[E]
SIC 6282 6211 Investment advisory service; Investment firm, general brokerage
Pr: Willie Woods
CFO: Gregory Nolff
Ofcr: David Maue
VP: Zeena H RAO
VP: Ashley Smith
VP: Jermaine Warren

D-U-N-S 09-148-9716
ICW GROUP HOLDINGS INC
11455 El Camino Real, San Diego, CA 92130-2088
Tel (858) 350-2400 *Founded/Ownrshp* 1981
Sales NA *EMP* 550[E]
SIC 6331 6411 Fire, marine & casualty insurance & carriers; Insurance brokers
CEO: Kevin M Prior
**Ch Bd:* Ernest Rady
**Treas:* Sariborz Rostamian
VP: John Gustafson
VP: James Senior

IDA
See NOVA MUD INC

D-U-N-S 13-118-8419
IDA TOWER
1010 12th St, Altoona, PA 16601-3411
Tel (814) 944-4055 *Founded/Ownrshp* 1974
Sales 41.9MM[E] *EMP* 3,900
SIC 6513 Apartment building operators
Pt: Roger Bunnell
Board of Directors: Michelle Peterson

D-U-N-S 03-545-0571
▲ IDACORP INC (ID)
1221 W Idaho St, Boise, ID 83702-5627
Tel (208) 388-2200 *Founded/Ownrshp* 1998
Sales 1.2MMM *EMP* 2,002[E]
Tkr Sym IDA *Exch* NYS
SIC 4911 Electric services; Distribution, electric power; Generation, electric power; Transmission, electric power
Pr: Darrel T Anderson
**Ch Bd:* Robert A Tinstman
CFO: Steven R Keen
VP: Brian R Buckham
VP: Kenneth W Petersen
Board of Directors: Thomas Carlile, Richard J Dahl, Ronald W Jibson, Judith A Johansen, Dennis L Johnson, J Lamont Keen, Christine King, Richard Navarro

D-U-N-S 82-520-1486
IDAHO DEPARTMENT OF HEALTH AND WELFARE
(*Suby of* EXECUTIVE OFFICE OF STATE OF IDAHO) ★
450 W State St Fl 9, Boise, ID 83702-6056
Tel (208) 334-5500 *Founded/Ownrshp* 1972
Sales NA *EMP* 3,100[E]
SIC 9431 Administration of public health programs;

D-U-N-S 82-501-7395
IDAHO DEPARTMENT OF TRANSPORTATION
EXECUTIVE OFFICE OF THE STATE
(*Suby of* EXECUTIVE OFFICE OF STATE OF IDAHO) ★
3311 W State St, Boise, ID 83703-5879
Tel (208) 334-8000 *Founded/Ownrshp* 1974
Sales NA *EMP* 2,650[E]
SIC 9621 Regulation, administration of transportation;
Ch: Darrell Manning
**V Ch:* Gary Blick
Ofcr: Jon Pope
Rgnl Mgr: Aaron Bauges
Rgnl Mgr: Mike Ebright
Rgnl Mgr: Nestor Fernandez
IT Man: Shannon Barnes
IT Man: Craig Schumacher
Sfty Mgr: Steve Spoor

IDAHO DISTRIBUTING
See C STEIN INC

D-U-N-S 02-964-2717
IDAHO FALLS SCHOOL DISTRICT NO 91 EDUCATION FOUNDATION INC
690 John Adams Pkwy, Idaho Falls, ID 83401-4073
Tel (208) 525-7500 *Founded/Ownrshp* 1992
Sales 73.6MM *EMP* 1,100
Accts Wipfli Llp Cpas And Consultan
SIC 8211 Public elementary & secondary schools; School board
Exec: Carrie Smith
Dir IT: Nancy Baumgart
IT Man: Marlene Gardner
Pr Dir: Margaret Wimborne

D-U-N-S 02-191-6034 EXP
IDAHO FOREST GROUP LLC
687 W Cnfield Ave Ste 100, Coeur D Alene, ID 83815
Tel (208) 255-3200 *Founded/Ownrshp* 2008
Sales 131.4MM[E] *EMP* 800
SIC 5211 Lumber products
CFO: Kevin Esser
VP: Erol Deren
Mill Mgr: Mike Henley
Mill Mgr: Chris Pease
Natl Sales: Ken Koenig

D-U-N-S 82-847-5264
IDAHO FOREST GROUP LLC
4447 E Chilco Rd, Athol, ID 83801-8477
Tel (208) 255-3200 *Founded/Ownrshp* 2008
Sales 164.4MM[E] *EMP* 750
SIC 2421 Sawmills & planing mills, general
Pr: Scott Atkison
**Ch Bd:* Marc A Brinkmeyer
**CFO:* Kevin Esser
**VP:* Beti Becker
**VP:* Erol Deren
Genl Mgr: Carmen Ruffes

D-U-N-S 09-880-3265
IDAHO PACIFIC LUMBER CO INC
1770 S Spanish Sun Way, Meridian, ID 83642-8024
Tel (208) 375-8052 *Founded/Ownrshp* 1979
Sales 181.1MM *EMP* 70
Accts Eide Bailly Llp Boise Idaho
SIC 5031 Lumber: rough, dressed & finished
Pr: Eric D Grandeen
CFO: Sharon Jensen
**CFO:* Patrick J Sullivan
**Treas:* Tori Shields
Exec: Mark Hutchinson
Off Mgr: Niki Robin
IT Man: Ron Meeuf

D-U-N-S 07-842-8810
IDAHO POTATO PACKERS CORP (ID)
(*Suby of* NONPAREIL CORP) ★
40 N 400 W, Blackfoot, ID 83221-5632
Tel (208) 785-3030 *Founded/Ownrshp* 1944, 1973
Sales 99.3MM[E] *EMP* 300
SIC 5148 Potatoes, fresh
CEO: Harold M Abend
**CFO:* John Fullmer
**Treas:* Eileen Abend
**VP:* Howard Phillips

D-U-N-S 00-692-7271
■ IDAHO POWER CO (ID)
(*Suby of* IDACORP INC) ★
1221 W Idaho St, Boise, ID 83702-5627
Tel (208) 388-2200 *Founded/Ownrshp* 1989, 1998
Sales 1.2MMM *EMP* 2,029[E]
Accts Deloitte & Touche Llp Boise
SIC 4911 Electric services; Transmission, electric power; Generation, electric power; Distribution, electric power
Pr: Darrel T Anderson
**Ch Bd:* Robert A Tinstman
COO: Lon Van Wyck
**CFO:* Steven R Keen
Bd of Dir: Lana Skouras
Bd of Dir: Dawn Thompson
**Sr VP:* Rex Blackburn
VP: Randy Allphin
VP: Jim Burdick
VP: Steve Keen
**VP:* Lonnie Krawl
VP: Tracie Metcalf
VP: Ken W Petersen
VP: Tonja Phetmisay
VP: Naomi Shankel
VP: Lori D Smith
Board of Directors: Robert A Tinstman, C Stephen Allred, Thomas J Wilford, Richard J Dahl, Ronald W Jibson, Judith A Johansen, Dennis L Johnson, J Lamont Keen, Christine King, Jan B Packwood, Joan H Smith

D-U-N-S 07-834-1468
IDAHO STATE UNIVERSITY
FINANCE AND ADMINISTRATION
921 S 8th Ave, Pocatello, ID 83209-0001
Tel (208) 282-0211 *Founded/Ownrshp* 1901
Sales 141.2MM *EMP* 1,900
Accts Moss-Adams Llp Eugene Oregon
SIC 8221 University
Pr: Arthur C Vilas
Dir Vol: Linda Burke
Pr: Debbie Henrickson
Pr: V L Mitchell
Ofcr: John R Gregory
Ofcr: Chad Harball
VP: Barbara Adamcik
VP: Jameson Bastow
VP: Roy Dunker
VP: Melanie Fischel
VP: James A Fletcher
VP: Selena Grace
VP: Devin Mock
VP: Robert Pearce
VP: Scott Scholes
VP: Cornelis Der Schyf
VP: Patricia Terrell
VP: Pauline Thiros
VP: Kent Tingey
VP: Angie Wojcik
Exec: Chris Gilliam

D-U-N-S 16-918-9396
IDAHO STATE UNIVERSITY
AIRCRAFT TECHNOLOGY
1455 Flightline, Pocatello, ID 83204-7550
Tel (208) 232-8485 *Founded/Ownrshp* 1936
Sales 130.5MM *EMP* 3
Accts Moss Adams Llp Eugene Oregon
SIC 8249 Vocational schools
Pr: Richard Bowen
Ex Dir: Veronica Hapgood

D-U-N-S 09-467-7994 IMP/EXP
■ IDAHO TIMBER LLC
(*Suby of* LEUCADIA NATIONAL CORP) ★
3540 E Longwing Ln # 270, Meridian, ID 83646-1104
Tel (208) 377-3000 *Founded/Ownrshp* 2005
Sales 141.5MM[E] *EMP* 450
SIC 0831 Forest products
CEO: Ted Ellis
**CFO:* Scott Beechie
**VP:* Brock Lenon
**VP:* Dave Taugher

D-U-N-S 18-121-8660
■ IDAHO-PACIFIC CORP
(*Suby of* OTTER TAIL CORP) ★
4723 E 100 N, Rigby, ID 83442-5811
Tel (208) 538-6971 *Founded/Ownrshp* 1987
Sales 299.4MM[E] *EMP* 250
SIC 2034

D-U-N-S 80-680-5441 IMP/EXP
IDAHOAN FOODS LLC
357 Constitution Way, Idaho Falls, ID 83402-3538
Tel (208) 542-3700 *Founded/Ownrshp* 2009
Sales 350.0MM *EMP* 700
SIC 2034 Potato products, dried & dehydrated
VP: Glen Walter
Exec: David Macfarlane
MIS Dir: Dustin Thueson
Dir IT: Steve Simmons
IT Man: Rich Powell
Netwrk Eng: Jim Bramlette
Sfty Mgr: Steve Fox
Plnt Mgr: Kenny Kniep
Prd Mgr: Shane Williams
Natl Sales: Richard Scott
Mktg Mgr: Jared Miller

IDB BANK OF NEW YORK
See ISRAEL DISCOUNT BANK OF NEW YORK

D-U-N-S 62-527-5706 IMP
IDB HOLDINGS INC
(*Suby of* ORNUA FOODS UK LIMITED)
601 S Rockefeller Ave, Ontario, CA 91761-7871
Tel (909) 390-5624 *Founded/Ownrshp* 1989
Sales 1.1MMM[E] *EMP* 1,500
SIC 5143 2022 Dairy products, except dried or canned; Cheese; Processed cheese
CEO: Jim Dekeyser
**Sec:* Peter Dolan
Dir IT: Elizabeth Ocasio
IT Man: Greg Jensen
Opers Mgr: Sam Lopez

D-U-N-S 11-082-9926
IDC CONSTRUCTION MANAGEMENT INC
(*Suby of* CH2M HILL ENGINEERS INC) ★
2020 Sw 4th Ave Ste 300, Portland, OR 97201-4973
Tel (503) 224-6040 *Founded/Ownrshp* 2008
Sales 228.0MM *EMP* 250
SIC 8741 Construction management
Pr: Kenneth Durant

D-U-N-S 00-176-5395
IDC RESEARCH INC (MA)
I D C
(*Suby of* EXECUTRAIN) ★
5 Speen St, Framingham, MA 01701-4674
Tel (508) 872-8200 *Founded/Ownrshp* 1964
Sales 156.2MM[E] *EMP* 1,700
SIC 8732 Market analysis or research
Pr: Kirk Campbell
COO: Michelle Kloss
COO: Lindsey Vangulden
**CFO:* Mark Sullivan
**Ch:* Patrick J McGovern
Assoc VP: Jozef Gemela
Assoc VP: Kevin Robock
**Ex VP:* Crawford Del Prete
**Sr VP:* Frank Gens
Sr VP: Alexa McCloughan
**VP:* Debra Bernardi
VP: Bill Casey
VP: Bradley Christenson
VP: Scott Langdoc
VP: Heather Levinson
VP: Rebecca Levitt
VP: Rick Nicholson
Exec: Jonathan Arber
Exec: Lionel Lamy
Exec: Laurentiu Popescu
**Dir Risk M:* John Gantz

D-U-N-S 84-219-3216
IDEA INTEGRATION CORP
GORES IDEA HOLDING
(*Suby of* ASTADIA CONSULTING UK LIMITED)
12724 Gran Bay Pkwy W, Jacksonville, FL 32258-9485
Tel (877) 727-8234 *Founded/Ownrshp* 2012
Sales 87.3MM *EMP* 669
SIC 7373 Computer integrated systems design
CEO: Paul Cooley
VP: Mel Castleberry
Off Mgr: Jan Brushwood
Dir IT: Robert Hitchins

IDEA NUOVA GLOBAL
See IDEA NUOVA INC

D-U-N-S 17-724-6337 IMP
IDEA NUOVA INC
IDEA NUOVA GLOBAL
302 5th Ave Fl 5, New York, NY 10001-3604
Tel (212) 643-0680 *Founded/Ownrshp* 1987
Sales 143.2MM *EMP* 150
Accts Mayer Hoffman Mccann Cpas New
SIC 5021 Beds & bedding
Pr: Nathan Accad
CFO: Issac Ades
VP: Benjamin Accad

D-U-N-S 00-304-1915
IDEA PUBLIC SCHOOLS (TX)
505 Angelita Dr Ste 9, Weslaco, TX 78599-8694
Tel (956) 377-8000 *Founded/Ownrshp* 2000
Sales 208.2MM *EMP* 2,381
Accts Padgett Stratemann & Co Ll
SIC 8211 Private elementary school; Private junior high school
Ch: Mike Rhodes
**Pr:* Thomas E Torkelson
COO: Joann Gonzales
**CFO:* Wyatt Truscheit
**Treas:* Bill Carrera
Sr Cor Off: Matthew Randazzo
**VP:* Carlo Hershberger
VP: Efren Montenegro
VP: Bethany Solis
Dir IT: Jorge G Martinez
Software D: Edison Coronado

D-U-N-S 08-883-4288
IDEA TRAVEL CO
13145 Byrd Ln Ste 101, Los Altos Hills, CA 94022-3211
Tel (650) 948-0207 *Founded/Ownrshp* 1973
Sales 86.1MM[E] *EMP* 1,100
SIC 4724 Travel agencies
CEO: Michael Schoendorf
CTO: Ram Bodapati
Software D: Beverly Hoh

D-U-N-S 00-704-0348 IMP
IDEAL CHEMICAL AND SUPPLY CO
4025 Air Park St, Memphis, TN 38118-9036
Tel (901) 363-7720 *Founded/Ownrshp* 1932
Sales 96.7MM[E] *EMP* 104
SIC 5169 7389 Industrial chemicals; Laundry soap chips & powder; Packaging & labeling services
CEO: Sam Block Jr
**CFO:* Terri Vaugh
**VP:* Jeffrey Block
**VP:* Kelly McCabe
IT Man: Bob Kavner

D-U-N-S 05-379-5241 IMP
IDEAL CLAMP PRODUCTS INC
8100 Tridon Dr, Smyrna, TN 37167-6603
Tel (615) 459-5800 *Founded/Ownrshp* 2011
Sales 211.0MM[E] *EMP* 800
SIC 3429 Clamps, metal
Pr: Mike Reese
VP: Thomas Reeve
Off Mgr: Lara Kilpatrick
Telecom Ex: Joe Wilkerson
Opers Mgr: Jorge Alvarez
Plnt Mgr: Mike Priddy
Natl Sales: Mark Moffitt

D-U-N-S 01-365-9076
IDEAL CONCEPTS INC
667 Union Blvd, Allentown, PA 18109-3249
Tel (610) 740-0000 *Founded/Ownrshp* 2007
Sales 97.0MM *EMP* 33
SIC 8742 Marketing consulting services
Prin: John Pequeno
Sls Mgr: Michael Papuc

D-U-N-S 01-429-6052
IDEAL CONTRACTING LLC
2525 Clark St, Detroit, MI 48209-1337
Tel (313) 843-8000 *Founded/Ownrshp* 1998
Sales 238.5MM *EMP* 50
SIC 1542 1742 1771 1791 Nonresidential construction; Plastering, drywall & insulation; Concrete work; Structural steel erection
Pr: Loren Venegas
CFO: Rachael Morton
**VP:* Robert Kohut P E
**VP:* Kevin Foucher
VP: Jon Hautau
VP Opers: Greg Sorrentino

IDEAL DOOR
See CLOPAY BUILDING PRODUCTS CO INC

D-U-N-S 00-509-4685 IMP/EXP
IDEAL INDUSTRIES INC
1375 Park Ave, Sycamore, IL 60178-2429
Tel (815) 895-5181 *Founded/Ownrshp* 1916
Sales 357.4MM[E] *EMP* 1,225
SIC 3825 3643 Electrical power measuring equipment; Current-carrying wiring devices
Pr: Jim James
**Ch Bd:* David W Juday
CFO: Jim Faltonower
**CFO:* Cannelle Giblin
CFO: Pfotenhauer James
**VP:* Vicki Slomka
Exec: Clark Tim
Genl Mgr: Nick Shkordoff
Dir IT: Tim Clark
IT Man: Dave Aubert
IT Man: Bruce Shaver
Board of Directors: Christopher Baldwin, Peter Dorsman

D-U-N-S 94-124-9930 IMP
IDEALAB
(*Suby of* IDEALAB HOLDINGS LLC) ★
130 W Union St, Pasadena, CA 91103-3628
Tel (626) 356-3654 *Founded/Ownrshp* 2006
Sales 180.3MM[E] *EMP* 650
SIC 5511 6726 New & used car dealers; Investment offices
Ch Bd: Bill Gross
V Ch: Larry Gross
**Pr:* Marcia Goodstein
**CFO:* Craig Chrisney
Bd of Dir: Allen Morgan
**VP:* Teresa Bridwell
**VP:* Kristen Ding
CTO: Jerome Budzik
CTO: Idealab Hostmaster
Web Dev: Douglas Tally
Board of Directors: Benjamin M Rosen, Jon F Welch Jr

D-U-N-S 02-231-8245
IDEALAB HOLDINGS LLC
130 W Union St, Pasadena, CA 91103-3628
Tel (626) 585-6900 *Founded/Ownrshp* 1996
Sales 184.8MM[E] *EMP* 825
SIC 6799 5045 5734 Venture capital companies; Computer software; Computer software & accessories
CEO: Bill Gross
**Pr:* Marcia Goodstein
**CFO:* Craig Chrisney
Bd of Dir: Allen Morgan
**VP:* Kristen Ding
**VP:* Wes Ferrari

IDEASPHERE
See TWINLAB HOLDINGS INC

D-U-N-S 12-425-9503 IMP
IDEAVILLAGE PRODUCTS CORP
155 Route 46 W Fl 4, Wayne, NJ 07470-6831
Tel (973) 826-8400 *Founded/Ownrshp* 2002
Sales 162.0MM[E] *EMP* 38
SIC 5961 General merchandise, mail order
Pr: Anand Khubani
Pr: Loriann Lombardo
**CFO:* David M Epstein
CFO: Tracy Wertz
Sys Mgr: Alfredo Sanoguel
VP Mktg: Robin Bonnema
VP Sls: Christina Black
VP Sls: Mike Govindani

D-U-N-S 78-575-0373 IMP/EXP
IDEMITSU LUBRICANTS AMERICA CORP
(*Suby of* APOLLO IDEMITSU CORP) ★
701 Port Rd, Jeffersonville, IN 47130-8425
Tel (812) 284-3300 *Founded/Ownrshp* 1992
Sales 206.6MM *EMP* 85
Accts Deloitte & Touche Llp Detroit
SIC 2992 Lubricating oils & greases
Pr: Shoichi Tominaga
**Pr:* Masashi Yokomura
**VP Admn:* Shinji Otsubo
Genl Mgr: Heather Couch
IT Man: Jacob Apperson
**VP Mfg:* Tammi Walts
Sfty Dirs: Sandra Vargas
Mtls Mgr: Kristi Hunter
Natl Sales: Ryan Stanton
**VP Sls:* Shukichi Shimoda
Snr Mgr: Tony Kosicki

IDENTITY GROUP
See IDENTITY HOLDING CO LLC

D-U-N-S 07-874-5534
IDENTITY GROUP HOLDINGS CORP
1480 Gould Dr, Cookeville, TN 38506-4152
Tel (931) 432-4000 *Founded/Ownrshp* 2014
Sales 219.3MM[E] *EMP* 940
SIC 3089 3086 3993 3953 Injection molding of plastics; Plastics foam products; Signs & advertising specialties; Marking devices
CEO: Brad Wolf
**CFO:* Brian Mogensen

D-U-N-S 07-874-5506
IDENTITY GROUP HOLDINGS LLC
(*Suby of* IDENTITY GROUP HOLDINGS CORP) ★
1480 Gould Dr, Cookeville, TN 38506-4152
Tel (931) 432-4000 *Founded/Ownrshp* 2007
Sales 91.5MM[E] *EMP* 615
SIC 3953 Marking devices
CEO: Brad Wolf
**CFO:* Brian Mogensen

D-U-N-S 80-076-9551 IMP/EXP
IDENTITY HOLDING CO LLC
IDENTITY GROUP
1480 Gould Dr, Cookeville, TN 38506-4152
Tel (931) 432-4000 *Founded/Ownrshp* 2007
Sales 135.1MM[E] *EMP* 600
SIC 3953 2672 Marking devices; Labels (unprinted), gummed: made from purchased materials
Pr: Brad Wolf
**CFO:* Brian Mogensen
**VP:* Lee Brantley
**VP:* David Durfee
VP: Charles Horsley
VP: Ron Jarvis
**VP:* Warren Soltis
Exec: Chris Thompson

D-U-N-S 01-145-5446
IDERA INC
POINTSECURE
2950 North Loop W Ste 700, Houston, TX 77092-8806
Tel (713) 523-4433 *Founded/Ownrshp* 2014
Sales 137.1MM[E] *EMP* 405[E]
SIC 7371 7372 Computer software development & applications; Software programming applications; Application computer software
CEO: Randy Jacops
**COO:* Chris Smith
CFO: Trey Chambers
**CFO:* York Richards
VP: Josh Stephens
Dir Soc: Rhonda Phelan
Dir IT: Benjamin Jolly
Software D: Saurabh Kapoor
Software D: Robert Wilkinson
Sftwr Eng: Mark Slavens
Sales Exec: Darin Galloway

D-U-N-S 18-358-0844
▲ IDEX CORP
1925 W Field Ct Ste 200, Lake Forest, IL 60045-4862
Tel (847) 498-7070 *Founded/Ownrshp* 1987
Sales 2.0MMM *EMP* 6,801[E]
Tkr Sym IEX *Exch* NYS
SIC 3561 3563 3594 Industrial pumps & parts; Air & gas compressors; Fluid power pumps & motors
CEO: Andrew K Silvernail
COO: Eric D Ashleman
CFO: Heath A Mitts
Chf Mktg O: Walter Aranton
Ofcr: Jeffrey D Bucklew
Ofcr: Michael J Yates
Ex VP: Jeff Krautkramer
Sr VP: Denise R Cade
VP: Mark Dilliplaine
VP: Turan Erdogan
VP: Abhishek Khandelwal
VP: Andy Kiss
VP: Azam Owaisi
VP: Gary Wood

D-U-N-S 07-393-1891 IMP
■ IDEX HEALTH & SCIENCE LLC
(*Suby of* IDEX CORP) ★
600 Park Ct, Rohnert Park, CA 94928-7906
Tel (707) 588-2000 *Founded/Ownrshp* 2002
Sales 137.3MM[E] *EMP* 781
SIC 3821 3829 3826 3823 3494 Laboratory apparatus & furniture; Measuring & controlling devices; Analytical instruments; Industrial instrmnts msrmnt display/control process variable; Valves & pipe fittings
Pr: Jeff Cannon
VP: Heath A Mitts
VP: Dominic A Romeo
VP: Daniel J Salliotte
VP: Lisa Walsh
Sls Dir: Marty McCoy
Mktg Mgr: Bev Newton

D-U-N-S 10-818-3757
▲ IDEXX LABORATORIES INC
1 Idexx Dr, Westbrook, ME 04092-2041
Tel (207) 556-0300 *Founded/Ownrshp* 1983
Sales 1.6MMM *EMP* 6,800
Tkr Sym IDXX *Exch* NGS
SIC 3826 2834 5047 Blood testing apparatus; Electrolytic conductivity instruments; Water testing apparatus; Veterinary pharmaceutical preparations; Instruments, surgical & medical
Ch Bd: Jonathan W Ayers
CFO: Brian P McKeon
Chf Mktg O: Pat Venters
Ex VP: Jay Mazelsky
Ex VP: Michael J Williams
VP: Rick Cotta
VP: Jeff Dixon
VP: George Fennell
VP: Scott Hamilton
VP: Dan Meyaard
VP: Jacqueline L Studer
VP: Giovani Twigge
Board of Directors: Bruce L Claflin, Thomas Craig, William T End, Rebecca M Henderson, Barry C Johnson, Daniel M Junius, Lawrence D Kingsley, M Anne Szostak, Sophie V Vandebroek

IDG CHARLOTTE
See IDG USA LLC

D-U-N-S 15-779-0791
IDG COMMUNICATIONS INC
INFOWORLD PUBLISHING COMPANY
(*Suby of* EXECUTRAIN) ★
5 Speen St, Framingham, MA 01701-4674
Tel (508) 875-5000 *Founded/Ownrshp* 1987
Sales 92.2MM[E] *EMP* 1,200
SIC 2721 2731 Trade journals: publishing only, not printed on site; Magazines: publishing & printing; Books: publishing & printing
CEO: Michael Friedenberg
**Pr:* David Hill
Pr: Bob Melk
CEO: Matthew Yorke
**Treas:* Edward B Bloom
Sr VP: Pam Stenson
VP: Joel Martin
VP: Eric Owen
VP: Mike Romoff

D-U-N-S 00-192-2681 IMP
IDG USA LLC
IDG CHARLOTTE
2100 The Oaks Pkwy, Belmont, NC 28012
Tel (704) 398-6600 *Founded/Ownrshp* 2016
Sales 662.3MM[E] *EMP* 1,200
SIC 5085 5084

D-U-N-S 80-702-2483
IDHASOFT INC
SEMAFOR TECHNOLOGIES USA
(*Suby of* IDHASOFT LIMITED)
6 Concourse Pkwy Ste 500, Atlanta, GA 30328-5360
Tel (770) 248-2999 *Founded/Ownrshp* 2007
Sales 148.8MM[E] *EMP* 1,200
SIC 7379 Computer related consulting services
CEO: Alok Pathak
CFO: Murali Anantharaman
**CFO:* Purnima Kaddi
Ex VP: Ashish Dayal
Ex VP: Hiren Shah
Ex VP: Jim Waites
**Sr VP:* Roger Cunningham
VP: Dermot Barry
VP: Philip Brennan
VP: Nagesh Doddaka
Exec: Rohan Bhoir
Dir Bus: Shefali Pathak

IDI
See INDUSTRIAL DIELECTRICS HOLDINGS INC

IDI DISTRIBUTORS
See INSULATION DISTRIBUTORS INC

IDIRECT TECHNOLOGIES
See VT IDIRECT INC

D-U-N-S 00-433-3738 IMP
■ IDL WORLDWIDE INC (PA)
(*Suby of* MATTHEWS INTERNATIONAL CORP) ★
6515 Penn Ave, Pittsburgh, PA 15206-4407
Tel (412) 965-3954 *Founded/Ownrshp* 1937, 2004
Sales 144.5MM[E] *EMP* 753
SIC 3993 2752

D-U-N-S 07-926-9855
■ IDQ ACQUISITION CORP
(*Suby of* ARMORED AUTOGROUP PARENT INC) ★
2901 W Kingsley Rd, Garland, TX 75041-2312
Tel (214) 778-4600 *Founded/Ownrshp* 2014
Sales 112.0MM[E] *EMP* 1,324[E]
SIC 3585 Air conditioning equipment, complete
CEO: Michael Klein

IDS
See INTEGRATED DEICING SERVICES LLC

D-U-N-S 80-609-5217 IMP
■ IDSC HOLDINGS LLC
SNAP-ON INDUSTRIAL
(*Suby of* SNAP-ON TOOLS) ★
2801 80th St, Kenosha, WI 53143-5656
Tel (262) 656-5200 *Founded/Ownrshp* 1920
Sales 449.7MM[E] *EMP* 4,010
SIC 3423 3559 7372 6794 5013 3546 Mechanics' hand tools; Automotive maintenance equipment; Prepackaged software; Patent owners & lessors; Motor vehicle supplies & new parts; Power-driven handtools
Pr: Nick Pinchuk
Pr: Anthony Roberts
CFO: Martin M Ellen
Sr VP: Aldo Pagliari
Rgnl Mgr: Christophe Bodard
Genl Mgr: Andrea Ehlert
Off Admin: Joanne Valentini

D-U-N-S 80-903-9910 IMP
▲ IDT CORP
550 Broad St, Newark, NJ 07102-4531
Tel (973) 438-1000 *Founded/Ownrshp* 1990
Sales 1.5MMM *EMP* 1,250
Tkr Sym IDT *Exch* NYS
SIC 4813 Telephone communication, except radio; Local & long distance telephone communications;
CEO: Shmuel Jonas
Ch Bd: Howard S Jonas
Ofcr: Marcelo Fischer
Ofcr: Barbara Krekstein
Ex VP: Menachem Ash
Ex VP: Joyce J Mason
Sr VP: Anthony S Davidson
VP: Eli Korn
VP: Bill McGlinn
VP: Richard McGonnigal
VP: Alfredo O'Hagan
VP: Geoff Rochwarger
VP: Terrence Stronz
VP: Julie Wilson
Board of Directors: Michael Chenkin, Eric F Cosentino, Bill Pereira, Judah Schorr

D-U-N-S 80-286-4061
■ IDT DOMESTIC TELECOM INC
(*Suby of* IDT CORP) ★
520 Broad St, Newark, NJ 07102-3121
Tel (973) 438-1000 *Founded/Ownrshp* 2001
Sales 240.7MM[E] *EMP* 1,200
SIC 4813 Telephone communication, except radio
CEO: Bill Pereira
Ex VP: Sab Ventola
Exec: Theodore Tewksbury

IDVA
See ILLINOIS DEPARTMENT OF VETERANS AFFAIRS

D-U-N-S 12-442-4826 IMP
IDX CORP
TRIANGLE SYSTEMS
1 Rider Trail Plaza Dr, Earth City, MO 63045-1313
Tel (314) 739-4120 *Founded/Ownrshp* 2001
Sales 425.3MM[E] *EMP* 1,045
SIC 2542 Office & store showcases & display fixtures
CEO: Terry Schultz
Pr: Bill Delaney
Pr: Bruce Moco
Pr: Tony Volpe
**CFO:* Fritz Baumgartner
**Ex VP:* Bob Heditsian
**Ex VP:* Scott Norvell
**Ex VP:* Mark Pritchard
VP: Gordon Bjorkman
VP: Jim Comarata
**VP:* William Delaney
VP: John Morehead
VP: Mike Watts

D-U-N-S 02-066-6681
■ IDX SYSTEMS CORP
GE
(*Suby of* GENERAL ELECTRIC CO) ★
40 Idx Dr, South Burlington, VT 05403-7771
Tel (802) 658-2664 *Founded/Ownrshp* 1969, 2006
Sales 98.4MM[E] *EMP* 2,409
SIC 7371 Computer software systems analysis & design, custom
Pr: John Dineen
VP: Nan O'Leary
IT Man: Bruce Hoversland
Sftwr Eng: David Banks
Sftwr Eng: Alex Fong
Sftwr Eng: Praveen Kysetti
Mktg Mgr: Ramiro Roman
Manager: Don Mainardi

D-U-N-S 09-302-6672
IEA RENEWABLE ENERGY INC (WI)
RESIDUAL MANAGEMENT TECHNOLOGY
(*Suby of* I E A) ★
2647 Wtrfrnt Pw E Dr # 100, Indianapolis, IN 46214-2060
Tel (765) 832-8526 *Founded/Ownrshp* 1977, 2013
Sales 179.0MM[E] *EMP* 562
SIC 8711 8748 Engineering services; Environmental consultant
Pr: John Paul Roehm
**CFO:* Tracy Pearson
VP: Steve Johannsen
**VP:* Kenneth Knecht

D-U-N-S 00-246-3305
▲ IEC ELECTRONICS CORP
105 Norton St, Newark, NY 14513-1298
Tel (315) 331-7742 *Founded/Ownrshp* 1966
Sales 127.0MM *EMP* 798[E]
Tkr Sym IEC *Exch* ASE
SIC 3672 3679 Printed circuit boards; Electronic circuits
Ch Bd: Jeffery T Schlarbaum
CFO: Michael T Williams
Ofcr: Matt Smith
Sr VP: Jens Hauvn
Sftwr Eng: Nathaniel Pearson
Opers Mgr: Justin Whitlow
Pgrm Dir: Barbara Reifsteck
Board of Directors: Keith M Butler, Charles P Hadeed, Lynn J Hartrick, Andrew M Laurence, Jeremy R Nowak, Eric Singer

D-U-N-S 82-744-3552
■ IEH FM HOLDINGS LLC
ICAHN
(*Suby of* ICAHN ENTERPRISES HOLDINGS LP) ★
767 5th Ave Ste 4700, New York, NY 10153-0108
Tel (212) 702-4300 *Founded/Ownrshp* 2008
Sales 7.4MMM[E] *EMP* 59,559[E]
SIC 3462 3559 3694 3812 3674 Automotive & internal combustion engine forgings; Railroad, construction & mining forgings; Degreasing machines, automotive & industrial; Automotive electrical equipment; Acceleration indicators & systems components, aerospace; Computer logic modules

IEHP
See INLAND EMPIRE HEALTH PLAN

IEPA
See ILLINOIS ENVIRONMENTAL PROTECTION AGENCY

IES
See INTERNATIONAL EQUIPMENT SOLUTIONS LLC

IES ABROAD
See INSTITUTE FOR INTERNATIONAL EDUCATION OF STUDENTS

D-U-N-S 05-241-7230
■ IES COMMERCIAL INC
(*Suby of* INTEGRATED ELECTRICAL SERVICES INC) ★
5433 Westheimer Rd # 500, Houston, TX 77056-5399
Tel (713) 860-1500 *Founded/Ownrshp* 2007
Sales 578.8MM[E] *EMP* 2,583[E]
SIC 1731 Electrical work
VP: William Albright
VP: Robert Callahan
Mktg Dir: Lisa Marshall

D-U-N-S 07-420-7655 EXP
■ IES RESIDENTIAL INC
HOUSTON STAFFORD ELECTRICAL
(*Suby of* INTEGRATED ELECTRICAL SERVICES INC) ★
10203 Mula Cir, Stafford, TX 77477-3326
Tel (281) 498-2212 *Founded/Ownrshp* 1998
Sales 224.0MM[E] *EMP* 1,000
SIC 1731 Electrical work
Pr: Richard Nix
VP: Robert Callahan
Sfty Dirs: Randall Alten

D-U-N-S 06-370-5635
IESI MD CORP
PROGRESSIVE WASTE SOLUTIONS
(*Suby of* PROGRESSIVE WASTE SOLUTIONS LTD) ★
2911 52nd Ave Ste A, Hyattsville, MD 20781-1134
Tel (410) 768-1900 *Founded/Ownrshp* 2011
Sales 200.5MM[E] *EMP* 320[E]
SIC 4953 4212 Refuse collection & disposal services; Garbage collection & transport, no disposal
CEO: Joseph Quarin

D-U-N-S 02-660-9367 IMP
IESI NY CORP
(*Suby of* PROGRESSIVE WASTE SOLUTIONS LTD) ★
99 Wood Ave S Ste 1001, Iselin, NJ 08830-2713
Tel (201) 443-3000 *Founded/Ownrshp* 1997
Sales 252.8MM[E] *EMP* 520
SIC 4953 Refuse systems
VP: Stephen T Moody
**CFO:* Thomas J Cowee
**VP:* Edward L Apuzzi
**VP:* Thomas L Brown
MIS Dir: Raymond Digioia
Plnt Mgr: Joe Loverde
Board of Directors: Jeffrey J Keenan

D-U-N-S 04-201-4977 IMP
IEWC CORP (WI)
INDUSTRIAL ELECTRIC WIRE CABLE
5001 S Towne Dr, New Berlin, WI 53151-7956
Tel (262) 782-2255 *Founded/Ownrshp* 1961
Sales 177.2MM[E] *EMP* 196
SIC 5063 Wire & cable
Pr: David Nestingen
Ex VP: Paul Bryant
Ex VP: Kyle Spader
Exec: Michelle Osman
Rgnl Mgr: Carole Kelly

D-U-N-S 83-023-3321
IF MUSIC INC
401 Orange St, Palm Harbor, FL 34683-5449
Tel (727) 515-3004 *Founded/Ownrshp* 2008
Sales 38.5MM[E] *EMP* 2,000
SIC 2741
CEO: Kent White
**Pr:* Michael A Boyd

D-U-N-S 03-684-5329
IF&P FOODS INC
INDIANAPOLIS FRUIT COMPANY
4501 Massachusetts Ave, Indianapolis, IN 46218-3160
Tel (317) 546-2425 *Founded/Ownrshp* 1987, 1997
Sales 203.2MM[E] *EMP* 380
SIC 5148 Fruits
Pr: Mike Mascari
**Sec:* Greg Corsaro
**VP:* Danny Corsaro
**VP:* Chris Mascari
**VP:* Christopher Mascari
**VP:* Peter Piazza
Area Mgr: Marc Jones
IT Man: Christopher Bradley
Prd Mgr: Rebecca Contreras
Sls Dir: John Cunningham
Mktg Mgr: Antonia Mascari

IFB SOLUTIONS
See WINSTON-SALEM INDUSTRIES FOR BLIND INC

D-U-N-S 96-860-6970 IMP/EXP
IFCO SYSTEMS NORTH AMERICA LLC
I F C O SYSTEMS
13100 Nw Fwy Ste 625, Houston, TX 77040-6340
Tel (888) 714-2430 *Founded/Ownrshp* 2011
Sales 813.8MM[E] *EMP* 277[E]
SIC 2448

D-U-N-S 62-678-0977
IFES INC
2011 Crystal Dr Fl 10, Arlington, VA 22202-3732
Tel (202) 350-6750 *Founded/Ownrshp* 1987
Sales 87.7MM *EMP* 300
Accts Argy Wiltse & Robinson Pc
SIC 8733 Research institute
Pr: William Sweeney
COO: Wyatt A Stewart III
Prgrm Mgr: Homeyra Mokhtarzada

IFF
See INTERNATIONAL FLAVORS & FRAGRANCES INC

IFG COMPANIES
See FIRST FINANCIAL INSURANCE CO INC

IFIC
See INTERNATIONAL FIDELITY INSURANCE CO

D-U-N-S 07-986-5905
IFM GLOBAL INFRASTRUCTURE FUND
114 W 47th St Fl 26, New York, NY 10036-1511
Tel (212) 784-2260 *Founded/Ownrshp* 2015
Sales 107.1MM[E] *EMP* 398[E]
SIC 6799 1623 Investors; Water, sewer & utility lines
CEO: Brett Himbury
Bd of Dir: Michael Migro
**Ofcr:* Joshua Lim
VP: Neil Doherty
VP: May Soh
VP: Olivier Sueur
Assoc Dir: Simon Tung
Assoc Dir: Nick Zannis
Ex Dir: Tom Osborne

IFPRI
See INTERNATIONAL FOOD POLICY RESEARCH INSTITUTE

D-U-N-S 96-349-3734
IFR SYSTEMS INC
(*Suby of* AEROFLEX INC) ★
10200 W York St, Wichita, KS 67215-8935
Tel (316) 522-4981 *Founded/Ownrshp* 1998
Sales 87.5MM[E] *EMP* 500[E]
SIC 4581 Aircraft servicing & repairing
Pr: Jeffrey A Bloomer
CFO: Dan Kelly
VP: Fred Arnold
VP: Kevin Lewis
Tech Mgr: Lyndon Zielke

D-U-N-S 95-746-7848
IFS NORTH AMERICA INC
(*Suby of* INDUSTRIAL AND FINANCIAL SYSTEMS, IFS AB)
300 Park Blvd Ste 555, Itasca, IL 60143-2635
Tel (888) 437-4968 *Founded/Ownrshp* 1995
Sales 83.1MM[E] *EMP* 250
SIC 7372 7379 8243 Prepackaged software; Data processing consultant; Software training, computer
CEO: Cindy Jaudon
CFO: Mitch Dwight
Bd of Dir: William Aranha
VP: Jan Brunaes
VP: Ronny Frey
Dir Bus: Len Iseldyke
Dir Bus: Stephanie Pusey
CIO: Bjorn Wetterlin
Manager: Bruce Cotter
Manager: Marcus Novy

D-U-N-S 08-419-3580
IG BURTON & CO INC
I G BURTON IMPORTS
793 Bay Rd, Milford, DE 19963-6122
Tel (302) 422-3041 *Founded/Ownrshp* 1960
Sales 225.0MM *EMP* 245
SIC 5511 7538 Automobiles, new & used; Pickups, new & used; Trucks, tractors & trailers: new & used; General automotive repair shops
Pr: Charles Burton
**VP:* Irwin G Burton III

D-U-N-S 96-979-0281
IG STAFFING HOLDINGS LLC
4170 Ashford Dnwody Rd Ne, Brookhaven, GA 30319-1442
Tel (404) 257-7900 *Founded/Ownrshp* 2007
Sales 188.6MM[E] *EMP* 1,000
SIC 7361 Employment agencies
CEO: Rich Lingle

IGA
See BUEHLER FOODS INC

IGA
See KIRBY FOODS INC

IGA
See ADAMS & SULLIVAN LLC

IGA
See SKOGENS FOODLINER INC

D-U-N-S 06-659-9101
IGATE AMERICAS INC
1 Broadway Fl 13, Cambridge, MA 02142-1100
Tel (617) 914-8000 *Founded/Ownrshp* 2011
Sales NA *EMP* 2,300
SIC 7371 7373

D-U-N-S 18-175-9119
IGATE CORP
(*Suby of* CAPGEMINI CONSULTING) ★
100 Somerset Corp Blvd # 5000, Bridgewater, NJ 08807-2842
Tel (908) 219-8050 *Founded/Ownrshp* 2015
Sales 1.5MMM[E] *EMP* 33,484[E]
SIC 7371 7374 7389 Computer software development; Data processing service; Process serving service
Pr: Ashok Vemuri
Pr: Rajaram Lanka
CFO: Sujit Sircar
Assoc VP: Mehool Kakabalia
Ex VP: Derek Kemp
Ex VP: Sanjay Tugnait
Sr VP: Srikanth Iyengar
VP: Frank Kuyan
VP: Shashank Tayal
Snr Sftwr: Sheik Athil
IT Man: Poornima Chockiah

D-U-N-S 05-435-6303
IGATE INC
(*Suby of* IGATE CORP) ★
1305 Cherrington Pkwy, Moon Township, PA 15108-4355
Tel (412) 787-2100 *Founded/Ownrshp* 1999, 1986
Sales 98.4MM[E] *EMP* 5,000
SIC 7373 Computer integrated systems design
Pr: Ashok Vemuri
**Ch Bd:* Ashok Trivedi
**Treas:* Ram S Prasad
**VP:* Sujit Sircar
Assoc Dir: Anu Bhaskaran
Assoc Dir: Abhay Chaudhari
Assoc Dir: Mark McKeithen
Prgrm Mgr: Santosh Kinikar
Snr Sftwr: Jeriel Gladson
Snr Sftwr: Saurabh Shah
IT Man: R Ganeshkumar

D-U-N-S 14-872-8368 IMP
IGATE TECHNOLOGIES INC
(*Suby of* IGATE CORP) ★
100 Somerset Corp Blvd # 5000, Bridgewater, NJ 08807-2842
Tel (908) 219-8050 *Founded/Ownrshp* 2000
Sales 215.2MM[E] *EMP* 3,000
SIC 7371 Custom computer programming services
CEO: Ashok Vemuri
**CFO:* Sujit Sircar
Treas: Suresh Nair
**Ex VP:* Srinivas Kandula
**Ex VP:* Derek Kemp
**Ex VP:* Sanjay Tugnait
Exec: Arjun Nandi
Prgrm Mgr: Subramaniam Vaikuntam
Snr Sftwr: Yamunadevi Sekhar
Snr Sftwr: Rajitha Yada
Sftwr Eng: Enoch Satyam

IGC
See INTERMOUNTAIN GAS CO

D-U-N-S 09-106-9856
IGLESIA EPISCOPAL PUERTORRIQUENA INC
COLEGIO SAN JUSTO
Carr 848 Km 1 1 Bo Sait J St Ca, Trujillo Alto, PR 00978
Tel (787) 761-9800 *Founded/Ownrshp* 1971
Sales 17.7MM[E] *EMP* 1,350
SIC 8661 Episcopal Church
Pr: Bishop David Alvarez
**Treas:* Darling Martinez
Treas: Eileen Rosado

D-U-N-S 96-457-2726
IGLOO HOLDINGS CORP
32 Crosby Dr, Bedford, MA 01730-1448
Tel (781) 687-8500 *Founded/Ownrshp* 2010
Sales 423.0MM[E] *EMP* 2,600[E]
SIC 6289 7375 Financial reporting; Information retrieval services
Prin: Mason Slaine

D-U-N-S 96-457-2791
IGLOO INTERMEDIATE CORP
(*Suby of* IGLOO HOLDINGS CORP) ★
32 Crosby Dr, Bedford, MA 01730-1448
Tel (781) 687-8500 *Founded/Ownrshp* 2010
Sales 106.2MM[E] *EMP* 2,600
SIC 6289 7375 Financial reporting; Information retrieval services

D-U-N-S 06-211-8427 IMP/EXP
IGLOO PRODUCTS CORP
777 Igloo Rd, Katy, TX 77494-2972
Tel (281) 394-6800 *Founded/Ownrshp* 2014
Sales 350.0MM *EMP* 1,050
SIC 3086 Ice chests or coolers (portable), foamed plastic
Pr: Mark Parrish
**CFO:* Laura Snyder
**Ex VP:* Tony Carfagno
**Sr VP:* Fred Lewis
**VP:* Angela Sizemore
**VP:* Candi Whitsel
Off Mgr: Janette Martinez
Opers Mgr: Kevin Mingus
Opers Mgr: Jose Ortega
Opers Mgr: Emma Tobar

IGM
See INTERSTATE GAS MARKETING INC

D-U-N-S 78-824-5681 IMP
▲ IGNITE RESTAURANT GROUP INC
10555 Richmond Ave # 100, Houston, TX 77042-5054
Tel (713) 366-7500 *Founded/Ownrshp* 1991
Sales 492.0MM *EMP* 8,800
Tkr Sym IRG *Exch* NGS
SIC 5812 6794 Eating places; Franchises, selling or licensing
CEO: Robert S Merritt
**Ch Bd:* Paul R Vigano
COO: Debra Eybers
CFO: Brad A Leist
Dir Sec: Ellen Clarry
VP Mktg: Lou Anne Banks
Board of Directors: F Philip Handy, Ann Iverson, Joseph N Stein

D-U-N-S 08-717-7338
IGNITED LLC
2150 Park Pl Ste 100, El Segundo, CA 90245-4714
Tel (310) 773-3100 *Founded/Ownrshp* 1999
Sales 180.0MM *EMP* 126
SIC 7311 Advertising agencies
CEO: Eric Johnson
COO: Bill Rosenthal
**COO:* William Rosenthal
CFO: Whitney Stephenson
Art Dir: Brandon Levin

D-U-N-S 07-849-8871
IGNITIONONE INC
200 Park Ave Fl 27, New York, NY 10166-0005
Tel (888) 744-6483 *Founded/Ownrshp* 2013
Sales 150.0MM *EMP* 450
SIC 7319 Display advertising service; Media buying service
Pr: Roger Barnette
CEO: Will Margiloff
COO: Mark Ambrose
COO: Jonathan Ragals
CFO: Scott Levine
Sr VP: Eric Carlyle
Sr VP: Barry Schnur
VP: Mitch Berg
CTO: Craig Pohan
QA Dir: Harold Cuebas
QA Dir: Bridget Liszewski

IGOV.COM
See MA FEDERAL INC

IGP
See INTERNATIONAL GARDEN PRODUCTS INC

D-U-N-S 02-066-6256
IGP INDUSTRIES LLC
INDUSTRIAL GROWTH PARTNERS
101 Mission St Ste 1500, San Francisco, CA 94105-1731
Tel (415) 882-4550 *Founded/Ownrshp* 1997
Sales 128.3MM[E] *EMP* 383
SIC 7389 Brokers, business: buying & selling business enterprises
VP: Daniel Delaney
VP: Karen Greaves
Mng Dir: Jeffrey M Webb

D-U-N-S 08-935-4583 IMP/EXP
IGT GLOBAL SOLUTIONS CORP
(*Suby of* INTERNATIONAL GAME TECHNOLOGY PLC)
10 Memorial Blvd, Providence, RI 02903-1160
Tel (401) 392-1000 *Founded/Ownrshp* 1980
Sales 509.5MM[E] *EMP* 4,920
SIC 7999 3575 7372 7378 2752 7374

D-U-N-S 04-755-7145
IH SERVICES INC
127 Tanner Rd, Greenville, SC 29607-5918
Tel (864) 297-3748 *Founded/Ownrshp* 1955
Sales 66.0MM[E] *EMP* 2,700
SIC 7349 5014 7217 Janitorial service, contract basis; Tires & tubes; Carpet & rug cleaning plant
CEO: Ryan Hendley
**Ch Bd:* Dickson L Hendley
**Pr:* Taylor M Bruce
**CFO:* Michael G Putnam
**Sec:* Lucille Hendley
VP: Todd Hendley
VP: Jim Legates
VP: Edwin White
Dir Bus: Seth Bruce
Brnch Mgr: James Clary
Dist Mgr: Duane Norman

IHA
See INTEGRATED HEALTH ASSOCIATES INC

D-U-N-S 07-927-7688
IHA HEALTH SERVICES CORP
ANN ARBOR NEUROLOGY
24 Frank Lloyd Wright Dr, Ann Arbor, MI 48105-9484
Tel (734) 747-6766 *Founded/Ownrshp* 2010
Sales 207.8MM *EMP* 3
SIC 8011 Obstetrician
Pr: William J Fileti
**VP:* Richard Duffy
**VP:* Chris Holda
**VP:* Linda Macellven
**VP:* Martin Murray

IHC HEALTH SERVICES
See INTERMOUNTAIN HEALTH CARE INC

D-U-N-S 18-362-1390
IHC HEALTH SERVICES INC
DIXIE MEDICAL CENTER
(*Suby of* IHC HEALTH SERVICES) ★
1380 E Medical Center Dr, St George, UT 84790-2123
Tel (801) 442-5000 *Founded/Ownrshp* 1972
Sales 394.0MM *EMP* 4,000
SIC 8062 8011 8322 8049 8093 8069 General medical & surgical hospitals; Offices & clinics of medical doctors; Pathologist; Individual & family services; Speech specialist; Substance abuse clinics (outpatient); Specialty hospitals, except psychiatric
Pr: William Nelson
**Pr:* Charles Sorenson
**CFO:* Bert Zimmerli
Dir Risk M: Teri Chase-Dunn
Dir Sec: Scot Newbrough
Cmptr Lab: Dave Loughmiller
Sls&Mrk Ex: Craig Skousen
Orthpdst: Zachary Leitze

D-U-N-S 06-945-6655 IMP
■ IHEARTCOMMUNICATIONS INC
(*Suby of* IHEARTMEDIA CAPITAL I LLC) ★
200 E Basse Rd, San Antonio, TX 78209-4489
Tel (210) 822-2828 *Founded/Ownrshp* 1974, 2008
Sales 6.2MMM *EMP* 19,200
Accts Ernst & Young Llp San Antonio
SIC 4832 4833 7312 Radio broadcasting stations; Television broadcasting stations; Outdoor advertising services
Ch Bd: Robert W Pittman
**Pr:* Richard J Bressler
Treas: Crystal Duncan
Bd of Dir: Brian Jay
Bd of Dir: Gary Sullivan
Ex VP: Steven Cutler
Ex VP: John Partilla
Ex VP: Alissa Pollack
Ex VP: Robert H Walls Jr
Sr VP: Brian Glicklich
Sr VP: Scott D Hamilton
Sr VP: Kenneth E Wyker
VP: Larry Brown
VP: Trisha Dall
VP: Cal Hall
VP: Bill Hurley
VP: Ronald Kruczynski
VP: Julio Manso
VP: Mark Marino
VP: Sara McClure
VP: Adrienne Pabst

D-U-N-S 07-851-1866
■ IHEARTMEDIA CAPITAL I LLC
(*Suby of* IHEARTMEDIA CAPITAL II LLC) ★
200 E Basse Rd, San Antonio, TX 78209-4489
Tel (210) 822-2828 *Founded/Ownrshp* 2008
Sales 6.2MMM *EMP* 10,400^E
SIC 4813 4899 Telephone communication, except radio; Data communication services; Communication signal enhancement network system
Ch Bd: Robert W Pittman
Pr: Richard J Bressler
Sr VP: Scott D Hamilton

D-U-N-S 96-813-8813
■ IHEARTMEDIA CAPITAL II LLC
(*Suby of* IHEARTMEDIA INC) ★
200 E Basse Rd, San Antonio, TX 78209-4489
Tel (210) 822-2828 *Founded/Ownrshp* 2008
Sales 6.7MMM^E *EMP* 20,800^E
SIC 4899 4813 Communication signal enhancement network system; Telephone communication, except radio
Ch Bd: Robert W Pittman
**Pr:* Richard J Bressler
**CEO:* Scott R Wells
**Ch:* Christopher William Eccleshare

D-U-N-S 82-776-1300
▲ IHEARTMEDIA INC
200 E Basse Rd Ste 100, San Antonio, TX 78209-4490
Tel (210) 822-2828 *Founded/Ownrshp* 2007
Sales 6.2MMM *EMP* 18,700
Tkr Sym IHRT *Exch* OTO
SIC 4832 7312 Radio broadcasting stations; Outdoor advertising services; Billboard advertising; Poster advertising, outdoor
Ch Bd: Robert W Pittman
Ch Bd: C William Eccleshare
Pr: Richard J Bressler
CEO: Scott R Wells
Treas: Brian Coleman
Ex VP: Joe Robinson
Ex VP: Radha Subramanyam
Ex VP: Robert H Walls Jr
Sr VP: Scott D Hamilton
Sr VP: John Hogan
Sr VP: Steven J Macri
VP: George Allen
VP: Fernando Bauermeister
VP: Claudia Bays
VP: Trisha Dall
VP: Kristen Delaney
VP: William Feehan
VP: Marlon George
VP: Damon Gunkel
VP: Tim Hager
VP: Earl Jones

IHG
See INTER-CONTINENTAL HOTELS CORP

D-U-N-S 07-861-0098 IMP
IHI E&C INTERNATIONAL CORP
(*Suby of* IHI INC) ★
1080 Eldridge Pkwy, Houston, TX 77077-2575
Tel (713) 270-3100 *Founded/Ownrshp* 2012
Sales 353.6MM *EMP* 450^E
Accts Grossman Yanak & Ford Llp Pit
SIC 8711 Engineering services
Pr: Glyn Rodgers
**COO:* Rod McCracken
**CFO:* Sean Johnston
**Ofcr:* Chris Celano
VP: Eric Balkom
VP: John Coffin
VP: Kamal Shah

D-U-N-S 10-111-3975 IMP
IHI INC
(*Suby of* IHI CORPORATION)
150 E 52nd St Fl 24, New York, NY 10022-6246
Tel (212) 599-8100 *Founded/Ownrshp* 1977
Sales 367.8MM^E *EMP* 500
Accts Ernst & Young Llp New York N
SIC 5099 8732 8711 5084 Firearms & ammunition, except sporting; Market analysis, business & economic research; Engineering services; Industrial machinery & equipment
Pr: Kazuaki Kama
**Pr:* Tsutomu Yoshida
**Ex VP:* Ichiro Hashimoto
**Ex VP:* Yuji Hiruma
**Ex VP:* Tamotsu Saito

IHMS
See INTERNATIONAL HOTEL MANAGEMENT SERVICES INC

IHOP
See SUNSHINE RESTAURANT MERGER SUB LLC

D-U-N-S 03-443-7795
■ IHP I OWNER JV LLC
(*Suby of* N-STAR) ★
399 Park Ave, New York, NY 10022-4614
Tel (212) 547-2640 *Founded/Ownrshp* 2014
Sales 49.7MM^E *EMP* 1,524^E
SIC 8741 Hotel or motel management
CEO: David Hamamoto
CFO: Debra Hess
Ex VP: Ronald Lieberman

D-U-N-S 83-012-6178 IMP
IHP OPERATIONS LLC
INNOVATIVE HEARTH PRODUCTS
(*Suby of* INNOVATIVE HEARTH PRODUCTS IHP) ★
2701 S Harbor Blvd, Santa Ana, CA 92704-5803
Tel (714) 549-7782 *Founded/Ownrshp* 2012
Sales 139.3MM^E *EMP* 347
SIC 3433 Heating equipment, except electric
CEO: Mark Klein
**CFO:* Linda Pahl
VP: Gerardo Lozano
Rgnl Mgr: Pilar Garcia
CIO: Andreas Fellner
Dir IT: Amy Cho
Plnt Mgr: Mike Feist
Plnt Mgr: Sam Scarbrough
Plnt Mgr: Albert Talamantes
Prd Mgr: Ansel Garcia
Manager: Brent Weber

D-U-N-S 00-353-6755
IHS DIALYSIS INC (FL)
6001 Broken Sound Pkwy Nw, Boca Raton, FL 33487-2765
Tel (561) 443-0743 *Founded/Ownrshp* 2005
Sales 61.9MM^E *EMP* 5,000^E
SIC 8092 Kidney dialysis centers
CEO: Nelson R Shaller
**Pr:* Kathleen McDonnell

D-U-N-S 62-036-5023
IHS GLOBAL INC
(*Suby of* IHS HOLDING INC) ★
15 Inverness Way E, Englewood, CO 80112-5710
Tel (303) 790-0600 *Founded/Ownrshp* 1987
Sales 180.0MM^E *EMP* 2,060
SIC 7299 8732 8748 7375 7373 Information services, consumer; Market analysis, business & economic research; Business analysis; Business consulting; Information retrieval services; Systems software development services; Systems integration services
CEO: Jerre Stead
**Pr:* Scott Key
**Ex VP:* Jonathan Gear
**Ex VP:* Steve Green
**Ex VP:* Anurag Gupta
**Sr VP:* David Cooke
Sls Dir: Laura Lamb

D-U-N-S 19-733-1002
IHS HOLDING INC
(*Suby of* IHS INC) ★
15 Inverness Way E, Englewood, CO 80112-5710
Tel (303) 790-0600 *Founded/Ownrshp* 1992
Sales 180.0MM^E *EMP* 2,300
SIC 7299 8732 8748 7375 Information services, consumer; Market analysis, business & economic research; Business analysis; Business consulting; Information retrieval services
CEO: Richard G Walker
COO: Robert Carpenter
COO: Bob Lockwood
Co-COO: Jeff Tarr
Sr VP: Ernesto Ramirez
VP: Paul Everson
VP: Steve Foreman
VP: Jonathan Gear
**VP:* Stephen Green
VP: George Guo
VP: Todd Hyatt
VP: Scott Key
VP: Jo Labbienti
VP: Don Lesem
VP: Thomas Littman
VP: Ed Mattix
VP: Randal Meske
VP: George Nagy
VP: Mike Neal
VP: John Oechsle
VP: Philip Pete

D-U-N-S 19-822-4532
IHS INC
(*Suby of* MARKIT LTD)
15 Inverness Way E, Englewood, CO 80112-5710
Tel (303) 790-0600 *Founded/Ownrshp* 2016
Sales 2.1MMM *EMP* 8,600^E
SIC 7299 8732 8748 7375 Information services, consumer; Market analysis, business & economic research; Business analysis; Business consulting; Information retrieval services
CEO: Jerre L Stead
V Ch: Daniel Yergin
Pr: Lance Uggla
CFO: Todd Hyatt
Ex VP: Shane Akeroyd
Ex VP: Jane Okun Bomba
Ex VP: Jonathan Gear
Ex VP: Sari Granat
Ex VP: Randy Harvey
Ex VP: Adam Kansler
Ex VP: Murray Mercier
Ex VP: Yaacov Mutnikas
Ex VP: Jeff Sisson
Ex VP: Michele Trogni
Sr VP: David Cooke
VP: Peter Augustini
VP: Don Bari
VP: Blake Bartlett
VP: Tom Biracree
VP: Jane Bomba
VP: Eric Boyer

II
See INSULATIONS INC

D-U-N-S 15-192-8512 IMP
II STANLEY CO INC
(*Suby of* STANLEY ELECTRIC CO.,LTD.)
1500 Hill Brady Rd, Battle Creek, MI 49037-7320
Tel (269) 660-7777 *Founded/Ownrshp* 1985
Sales 304.6MM^E *EMP* 800
SIC 5063 4911 Electrical fittings & construction materials; Distribution, electric power
Pr: Satoshi Nakamura
CFO: Jerry Hammond
**CFO:* Glenn Kirk
**Sec:* Shoji Ichikawa
**Ex VP:* Mike Isham
Ex VP: Zygadlo Rich
Dir Rx: Ashish Stefano
Dept Mgr: Setsu Okubo
IT Man: Susan Cummings
Sls Mgr: Eiicha Hirroka

D-U-N-S 05-552-9333 IMP
▲ II-VI INC (PA)
375 Saxonburg Blvd, Saxonburg, PA 16056-9499
Tel (724) 352-4455 *Founded/Ownrshp* 1971
Sales 827.2MM *EMP* 8,490
Accts Ernst & Young Llp Pittsburgh
Tkr Sym IIVI *Exch* NGS
SIC 3827 3229 3674 3699 Optical instruments & lenses; Optical elements & assemblies, except ophthalmic; Optical glass; Fiber optics strands; Semiconductors & related devices; Laser welding, drilling & cutting equipment
Ch Bd: Francis J Kramer
**Pr:* Vincent D Mattera Jr
COO: Gary Alan Kapusta
CFO: Mary Jane Raymond
Dir Bus: Evan Lundstedt
CTO: Giovanni Barbarossa
Dir IT: Gary Ruland
Opers Mgr: Ejiro Emorhokpor
Sls Mgr: Laura Logan
Sales Asso: Jon Loadman
Snr Mgr: Ryan Brolley
Board of Directors: Joseph J Corasanti, Wendy F Dicicco, Thomas E Mistler, Marc Y E Pelaez, William A Schromm, Howard H Xia

IIMAK
See INTERNATIONAL IMAGING MATERIALS INC

D-U-N-S 07-914-1418
IJKG LLC
BAYONNE MEDICAL CENTER
714 Bergen Ave, Jersey City, NJ 07306-4802
Tel (201) 858-5000 *Founded/Ownrshp* 2007
Sales 168.3MM^E *EMP* 1,058
SIC 8741 Hospital management
Chf Path: Raoul Rudelli
Ex Dir: Rita Poss
Pathlgst: Jyoti Deshpande
Surgeon: Zbigniew Moszczynski

D-U-N-S 82-528-0352
IJKG OPCO LLC
BAYONNE MEDICAL CENTER
(*Suby of* BAYONNE MEDICAL CENTER) ★
714 Bergen Ave, Jersey City, NJ 07306-4802
Tel (201) 858-5000 *Founded/Ownrshp* 2007
Sales 168.3MM *EMP* 1,058
SIC 8741 Hospital management
**Pr:* Dr Mark Spektor Dl
**CFO:* Patrick Ryan
Chf Nrs Of: Rita Poss
Opers Mgr: Veronica S Maria
Doctor: Gregory Anselmi
Doctor: Barry Elkind MD
Doctor: Raul Rudelli
Pharmcst: Tony Fazio

D-U-N-S 03-025-2949 IMP
IJOT DEVELOPMENT INC
1300 Clay St Ste 600, Oakland, CA 94612-1427
Tel (925) 258-9909 *Founded/Ownrshp* 1982
Sales 122.6MM^E *EMP* 1,600
SIC 2531 2599 Public building & related furniture; Work benches, factory
Pr: Michael Gompertz

D-U-N-S 02-985-3015
IKASYSTEMS CORP
134 Turnpike Rd Ste 200, Southborough, MA 01772-2136
Tel (508) 251-3182 *Founded/Ownrshp* 2003
Sales 157.6MM^E *EMP* 142^E
SIC 5045 Computer software
CEO: Joe Marabito
**Ch Bd:* Ravi Ika
**COO:* Alisha Bloom
**CFO:* Bradley T Miller
**CFO:* John Rogers
**Sr VP:* Brian Kim
Sr VP: Madu Narahari
Sr VP: Raghu Ramaya
Sr VP: Carl Ricker
**Sr VP:* Philip J Spinelli
VP: Jeff Rimpas

D-U-N-S 04-933-8858
IKE GAMING INC
EL CORTEZ HOTEL
600 Fremont St, Las Vegas, NV 89101-5614
Tel (702) 385-5200 *Founded/Ownrshp* 1962
Sales 76.4MM^E *EMP* 1,400
SIC 7011 Casino hotel
Pr: Ike Lawrence Epstein
**Pr:* John D Gaughan
CFO: Joe Woody
**Sec:* Alan J Woody
**VP:* Kenneth Espstien
**VP:* Brady Exber
**VP:* Wayne Starker
Genl Mgr: Tomg Kiminski
Genl Mgr: Jack Thalgott
Dir IT: Randy Grijalva

D-U-N-S 11-847-0939 IMP/EXP
IKEA HOLDING US INC
(*Suby of* INGKA HOLDING OVERSEAS B.V.)
1105 N Market St Ste 1044, Wilmington, DE 19801-1216
Tel (302) 655-4126 *Founded/Ownrshp* 1984
Sales 1.3MMM^E *EMP* 13,000
SIC 5021 5712

D-U-N-S 79-307-5920
IKEA NORTH AMERICA SERVICES LLC
(*Suby of* IKEA HOLDING US INC) ★
420 Alan Wood Rd, Conshohocken, PA 19428-1141
Tel (610) 834-0180 *Founded/Ownrshp* 1989
Sales 299.6MM^E *EMP* 350^E
SIC 6794 5712 Franchises, selling or licensing; Furniture stores
Pr: Mike Ward
Pr: Odd Friis
COO: Hans Ljungberg
COO: Rick Wilson
CFO: Soren Hansen
Treas: Jim Quinn
**Treas:* John Robinson
Prin: Antoine Jackson
Area Mgr: Jan Andersson
Admn Mgr: Grace Gu
Store Mgr: Jim Anastos

IKEC
See INDIANA-KENTUCKY ELECTRIC CORP

D-U-N-S 03-442-0455 IMP
IL FORNAIO (AMERICA) CORP
(*Suby of* ROARK CAPITAL GROUP INC) ★
770 Tamalpais Dr Ste 400, Corte Madera, CA 94925-1795
Tel (415) 945-0500 *Founded/Ownrshp* 2012
Sales 292.2MM^E *EMP* 6,600
SIC 5812 5813 5149 5461 2051 Italian restaurant; Drinking places; Bakery products; Bakeries; Bread, cake & related products
CEO: Michael Hislop
Mng Pt: Dalton Archie
**Pr:* Michael J Beatrice
**CFO:* Sean K Maloney
Sr VP: Maurizio Mazzon
VP: Demetri Gill
VP: Mario Lombardo
Assoc Dir: Sergio Lopez
Creative D: Paul Kellerhals
Genl Mgr: Maria Dauria
Genl Mgr: Chamal Perera

ILB
See INTERNATIONAL LINE BUILDERS INC

D-U-N-S 18-726-6259 IMP
ILC DOVER LP
(*Suby of* NEW ILC DOVER INC) ★
1 Moonwalker Rd, Frederica, DE 19946-2080
Tel (302) 335-3911 *Founded/Ownrshp* 2011
Sales 90.6MM^E *EMP* 475
SIC 3842 3721 7389 Personal safety equipment; Space suits; Balloons, hot air (aircraft); Design services
Genl Pt: William Wallach
Pt: Dan Herring
Software D: Greg Burns
VP Sls: Rhonda Haller
Manager: Darren Newsome
Sls Mgr: Chris Rombach

D-U-N-S 07-971-2025
■ ILC HOLDINGS INC
(*Suby of* TRANSDIGM GROUP INC) ★
105 Wilbur Pl, Bohemia, NY 11716-2426
Tel (631) 567-5600 *Founded/Ownrshp* 1966, 2016
Sales 144.4MM^E *EMP* 354^E
SIC 3674 Semiconductors & related devices
CEO: Clifford P Lane

D-U-N-S 00-250-1005 IMP
■ ILC INDUSTRIES LLC (NY)
I L C
(*Suby of* ILC HOLDINGS INC) ★
105 Wilbur Pl, Bohemia, NY 11716-2426
Tel (631) 567-5600 *Founded/Ownrshp* 2010, 2008
Sales 144.7MM^E *EMP* 354^E
SIC 3674 Semiconductors & related devices
CEO: Clifford P Lane
CFO: Ken Sheedy
Exec: S Millman
Exec: A W Trapani
Pdt Mgr: Jerry Kessler

ILC RESOURCES
See IOWA LIMESTONE CO

D-U-N-S 78-764-8054 IMP
ILCO UNICAN HOLDING CORP
400 Jeffreys Rd, Rocky Mount, NC 27804-6624
Tel (252) 446-3321 *Founded/Ownrshp* 1988
Sales 108.1MM^E *EMP* 1,000
SIC 3429 Keys, locks & related hardware; Keys & key blanks; Locks or lock sets
Ch Bd: Aaron M Fish

D-U-N-S 82-818-6291
▲ ILG
6262 Sunset Dr, South Miami, FL 33143-4843
Tel (305) 666-1861 *Founded/Ownrshp* 1976
Sales 697.4MM *EMP* 5,600^E
Tkr Sym ILG *Exch* NGS
SIC 8699 Travel club; Hotels & motels
Ch Bd: Craig M Nash
Pr: Kelvin M Bloom
Pr: John Burlingame
Pr: David C Gilbert
CEO: Sergio D Rivera
COO: Jeanette E Marbert
CFO: William L Harvey
Treas: John A Galea
Ex VP: Annie Welsh
Sr VP: Victoria J Kincke
Board of Directors: Thomas O Ryder, David Flowers, Victoria L Freed, Chad Hollingsworth, Lewis J Korman, Thomas J Kuhn, Thomas J McInerney, Thomas P Murphy Jr, Stephen R Quazzo, Sergio D Rivera

D-U-N-S 78-854-7784
ILITCH HOLDINGS INC
LITTLE CAESAR'S
2211 Woodward Ave, Detroit, MI 48201-3467
Tel (313) 983-6000 *Founded/Ownrshp* 1997
Sales 482.8MM[E] *EMP* 6,828
SIC 7941 7922 5812 Sports clubs, managers & promoters; Theatrical producers & services; Eating places
Ch Bd: Michael Ilitch
Pr: Christopher Ilitch
CFO: Scott Fisher
CFO: Todd Seroka
V Ch Bd: Malina Ilitch
Ex VP: Craig Turnbull
VP: Stanford P Berenbaum
VP: Richard Fenton
VP: John Kotlar
VP: Doug Kuiper
VP: Steve Marquardt
VP: Joan Rivard

D-U-N-S 04-657-5494
■ **ILLIANA DISPOSAL SERVICE INC**
ALLIED WASTE SERVICES NW IND
(*Suby of* ALLIED WASTE INDUSTRIES INC) ★
865 Wheeler St, Crown Point, IN 46307-2766
Tel (219) 662-8600 *Founded/Ownrshp* 1991
Sales 98.9MM[E] *EMP* 400
SIC 4953 Refuse collection & disposal services; Recycling, waste materials
Pr: Dave Schutt
**VP:* Doug Rosenbum

D-U-N-S 06-740-8856
ILLINOIS AGRICULTURAL ASSOCIATION
ILLINOIS FARM BUREAU
1701 Towanda Ave, Bloomington, IL 61701-2050
Tel (309) 557-2111 *Founded/Ownrshp* 1919
Sales 50.3MM *EMP* 5,050
SIC 8611 6722 8742 6311 7514

ILLINOIS AUTO CENTRAL
See ILLINOIS AUTO ELECTRIC CO

D-U-N-S 00-693-0648 IMP
ILLINOIS AUTO ELECTRIC CO
ILLINOIS AUTO CENTRAL
700 Enterprise St, Aurora, IL 60504-8148
Tel (630) 862-3300 *Founded/Ownrshp* 1915
Sales 110.5MM *EMP* 240
SIC 5084 5013 5083 5078 7699 3519

D-U-N-S 00-693-0655
■ **ILLINOIS BELL TELEPHONE CO**
AT&T ILLINOIS
(*Suby of* AT&T MIDWEST) ★
225 W Randolph St Fl Li, Chicago, IL 60606-1839
Tel (618) 344-9077 *Founded/Ownrshp* 1881, 1984
Sales 2.3MMM[E] *EMP* 14,929
SIC 4813 8721 6512 Local & long distance telephone communications; Local telephone communications; Voice telephone communications; Data telephone communications; Billing & bookkeeping service; Commercial & industrial building operation
Pr: Carrie Hightman
IT Man: Mike Brown

D-U-N-S 78-726-8853
ILLINOIS BONE & JOINT INSTITUTE
LAKE SHORE ORTHOPEDICS
350 S Greenleaf St # 405, Gurnee, IL 60031-5709
Tel (847) 336-2344 *Founded/Ownrshp* 1985
Sales 85.0MM *EMP* 800
SIC 8011 Offices & clinics of medical doctors
Prin: Edward Hamming
**Prin:* Robert Dugan MD
**Prin:* Bruce Hamming MD
**Prin:* Edward Logue MD
**Prin:* Bruce Summerville MD
Orthpdst: Edward G Hammin
Orthpdst: Bruce A Hmming

D-U-N-S 78-973-3029
ILLINOIS BONE AND JOINT INSTITUTE LLC
900 Rand Rd Ste 200, Des Plaines, IL 60016-2359
Tel (847) 375-3000 *Founded/Ownrshp* 1991
Sales 139.3MM[E] *EMP* 700
SIC 8011 Orthopedic physician
Pr: Wayne M Goldstein MD
Off Admin: Amy Illarde
Surgeon: David Garelick
Doctor: Michael Kornblatt
Doctor: Christ Pavlatos

ILLINOIS BRICK COMPANY
See SOUTHFIELD CORP

D-U-N-S 04-192-9217
ILLINOIS CENTRAL COLLEGE
I C C
1 College Dr, Peoria, IL 61635-0002
Tel (309) 694-5011 *Founded/Ownrshp* 1966
Sales 53.9MM[E] *EMP* 1,800
SIC 8222 Community college
Pr: John S Erwin
**VP:* Rita Ali
**VP:* Bruce Budde
VP: David Cook
VP: Tracy Morris
VP: Margaret Swanson
Store Mgr: Carla Greer
Netwrk Mgr: Dan Robinson

D-U-N-S 05-944-7961 IMP/EXP
ILLINOIS CENTRAL RAILROAD CO
CANADIAN NATIONAL ILL CENTL RR
(*Suby of* COMPAGNIE DES CHEMINS DE FER NATIONAUX DU CANADA)
17641 Ashland Ave, Homewood, IL 60430-1339
Tel (708) 332-3500 *Founded/Ownrshp* 1989
Sales 445.5MM[E] *EMP* 3,600
SIC 4011 Railroads, line-haul operating
Pr: Luc Jobin
**Pr:* Mike Cory
**CEO:* Ghislain Houle
CFO: Dale W Phillips
Sr VP: Donald Skelton
**VP:* Sean Finn

D-U-N-S 17-207-1818
ILLINOIS CENTRAL SCHOOL BUS LLC
MINNESOTA CENTRAL SCHOOL BUS
78 N Chicago St 2, Joliet, IL 60432-4421
Tel (815) 744-4800 *Founded/Ownrshp* 2004
Sales 200.0MM[E] *EMP* 1,500[E]
SIC 4151 School buses
**CFO:* Scott Cheshareck
Exec: Jen Varner

ILLINOIS COMMUNITY COLLEGE BD
See ILLINOIS COMMUNITY COLLEGE SYSTEM

D-U-N-S 00-920-1943
ILLINOIS COMMUNITY COLLEGE SYSTEM
ILLINOIS COMMUNITY COLLEGE BD
(*Suby of* ISBE) ★
401 E Capitol Ave, Springfield, IL 62701-1706
Tel (217) 528-2858 *Founded/Ownrshp* 1965
Sales 270.9MM[E] *EMP* 1,300
SIC 8221 9411 Colleges universities & professional schools; Administration of educational programs
Pr: Geoffrey Obrzut
**VP:* Elaine S Johnson
Assoc Dir: Brittany Boston
Assoc Dir: Robert Brice
Assoc Dir: Jana Ferguson
Assoc Dir: Whitney Hagy
Assoc Dir: Mackenzie Montgomery
Assoc Dir: Sarah Robinson
Off Admin: Marie Nolden

ILLINOIS CONSOLIDATED TELE CO
See CONSOLIDATED COMMUNICATIONS OF ILLINOIS CO

D-U-N-S 01-022-1109
ILLINOIS CONSTRUCTORS CORP
39w866 Fabyan Pkwy, Elburn, IL 60119-9801
Tel (630) 232-7280 *Founded/Ownrshp* 1975
Sales 25.4MM[E] *EMP* 1,500
SIC 1611 Concrete construction: roads, highways, sidewalks, etc.
Pr: John Mackanin Pe
Treas: Larry Slad
Genl Mgr: Rusy Mitcheff

D-U-N-S 96-166-6257
■ **ILLINOIS CORN PROCESSING LLC**
(*Suby of* SEACOR HOLDINGS INC) ★
1301 S Front St, Pekin, IL 61554-4065
Tel (309) 353-3990 *Founded/Ownrshp* 2009
Sales 200.0MM *EMP* 75
SIC 2085 Grain alcohol for beverage purposes
Pr: Donald Oldham
**Pr:* Randy Schrick
Ql Cn Mgr: Doug Leathers

D-U-N-S 80-671-5603
ILLINOIS DEPARTMENT OF HUMAN SERVICES
(*Suby of* EXECUTIVE OFFICE OF GOVERNOR) ★
401 S Clinton St, Chicago, IL 60607-3800
Tel (312) 793-1547 *Founded/Ownrshp* 1974
Sales NA *EMP* 2,800
SIC 9431 Mental health agency administration, government;
CFO: Carol Kraus
CIO: Doug Kasa
MIS Dir: Gene Hagerman

D-U-N-S 80-632-8373
ILLINOIS DEPARTMENT OF MILITARY AFFAIRS
ILLINOIS MILITARY AFFAIRS
(*Suby of* EXECUTIVE OFFICE OF GOVERNOR) ★
1301 N Macarthur Blvd, Springfield, IL 62702-2317
Tel (217) 761-3910 *Founded/Ownrshp* 1818
Sales NA *EMP* 1,265
SIC 9711 National Guard;

D-U-N-S 80-681-0313
ILLINOIS DEPARTMENT OF NATURAL RESOURCES
(*Suby of* EXECUTIVE OFFICE OF GOVERNOR) ★
1 Natural Resources Way # 100, Springfield, IL 62702-1290
Tel (217) 782-6302 *Founded/Ownrshp* 1913
Sales NA *EMP* 2,000
SIC 9512 9111 Land, mineral & wildlife conservation; ; Executive offices;

D-U-N-S 80-666-0296
ILLINOIS DEPARTMENT OF PUBLIC HEALTH
(*Suby of* EXECUTIVE OFFICE OF GOVERNOR) ★
535 W Jefferson St Lbby, Springfield, IL 62702-5058
Tel (217) 785-4302 *Founded/Ownrshp* 1877
Sales NA *EMP* 6,406
SIC 9431 Administration of public health programs;
CEO: Lamar Hasbrouck
**CFO:* Gary T Robinson
**Prin:* Tayseer Rehan

D-U-N-S 80-681-2467
ILLINOIS DEPARTMENT OF TRANSPORTATION
(*Suby of* EXECUTIVE OFFICE OF GOVERNOR) ★
2300 S Dirksen Pkwy, Springfield, IL 62764-0001
Tel (217) 782-7820 *Founded/Ownrshp* 1972
Sales NA *EMP* 22,852[E]
SIC 9621 Regulation, administration of transportation;
**Ch Bd:* David Vaught
Genl Couns: Roma Larson
Snr Mgr: Roger Driskell
Snr Mgr: Mike Healy

D-U-N-S 80-681-2582
ILLINOIS DEPARTMENT OF VETERANS AFFAIRS
IDVA
(*Suby of* EXECUTIVE OFFICE OF GOVERNOR) ★
833 S Spring St, Springfield, IL 62704-2617
Tel (217) 782-6641 *Founded/Ownrshp* 1970
Sales NA *EMP* 1,200
SIC 9451 Administration of veterans' affairs
Ex Dir: Dan Grant
**CFO:* Deborah Miller
Assoc Dir: Michelle Dufour
Comm Dir: Chris Wills
CIO: Steven Depooter
Genl Couns: Daniel Kelber

D-U-N-S 87-932-4861
ILLINOIS ENVIRONMENTAL PROTECTION AGENCY
IEPA
(*Suby of* EXECUTIVE OFFICE OF GOVERNOR) ★
1021 North Grand Ave E, Springfield, IL 62702-4059
Tel (217) 782-3397 *Founded/Ownrshp* 1970
Sales NA *EMP* 1,487
SIC 9511 Air, water & solid waste management
Ex Dir: Douglas Scott
**VP:* William Child

ILLINOIS FARM BUREAU
See ILLINOIS AGRICULTURAL ASSOCIATION

D-U-N-S 04-208-4434
ILLINOIS INSTITUTE OF TECHNOLOGY (IL)
I I T
10 W 35th St, Chicago, IL 60616-3717
Tel (312) 567-3000 *Founded/Ownrshp* 1891
Sales 276.8MM *EMP* 1,662
Accts Kpmg Llp Chicago Il
SIC 8221 University
Pr: John L Anderson
Recvr: Maurice Barnette
**Ch:* Robert Pritzker
Assoc VP: Ronald Staudt
VP: David Baker
VP: Jean Bingham
VP: Alan W Cramb
VP: Mary Dawson
VP: Sidney Guralnick
VP: Elizabeth Hughes
VP: Patricia Laughlin
VP: Michael McGibbon
VP: Antoinette Murril
VP: Susan Wallace
VP: Darsh Wasan
VP: Bruce Watts
Assoc Dir: Faye Bulaclac
Assoc Dir: Pamela Dallas
Assoc Dir: Ryan Nelson
Assoc Dir: Mazin Safar
Comm Man: Vince Laconte

D-U-N-S 96-969-0515
ILLINOIS MASONIC CHARITIES FUND
2866 Via Verde St, Springfield, IL 62703-4388
Tel (217) 529-8900 *Founded/Ownrshp* 2011
Sales 132.9MM *EMP* 2
Accts Eck Schafer & Punke Llp Sprin
SIC 8322 Individual & family services
Ch: James D Williams

D-U-N-S 05-786-4449
ILLINOIS MASONIC MEDICAL CENTER
SIX CORNERS MEDICAL CENTER
(*Suby of* ADVOCATE HEALTH CARE NETWORK) ★
836 W Wellington Ave, Chicago, IL 60657-5147
Tel (773) 975-1600 *Founded/Ownrshp* 1909
Sales 220.5MM[E] *EMP* 3,460
SIC 8062 General medical & surgical hospitals
CEO: Susan Nordstrom Lopez
**VP:* Dr William Wener
Off Mgr: Maryann Wasner
Doctor: Edwin Feldman MD
Doctor: Kamala A Ghey MD
Doctor: John P Kirby MD
Doctor: Sunil N Patel MD
Pharmcst: Grazyna Niemczura

ILLINOIS MILITARY AFFAIRS
See ILLINOIS DEPARTMENT OF MILITARY AFFAIRS

D-U-N-S 12-231-9072
ILLINOIS MUNICIPAL ELECTRIC AGENCY
I M E A
3400 Conifer Dr, Springfield, IL 62711-8301
Tel (217) 789-4632 *Founded/Ownrshp* 1984
Sales 327.1MM *EMP* 28
Accts Baker Tilly Virchow Krause Ll
SIC 4911 Distribution, electric power
Pr: Kevin M Gaden
CFO: Bob Chidres
**CFO:* Bob Childers
**Sr VP:* Phillip Doc Mueller
**VP:* Troy Fodor
**VP:* Kevin Wagner
Secur Mgr: Alice M Schum

D-U-N-S 09-317-2104
ILLINOIS MUNICIPAL RETIREMENT FUND
IMRF
2211 York Rd Ste 500, Oak Brook, IL 60523-2337
Tel (630) 368-1010 *Founded/Ownrshp* 1939
Sales NA *EMP* 186
SIC 6371

D-U-N-S 00-693-5324
ILLINOIS MUTUAL LIFE INSURANCE CO
300 Sw Adams St, Peoria, IL 61634-0002
Tel (309) 674-8255 *Founded/Ownrshp* 1910
Sales NA *EMP* 212
SIC 6321 6311 Disability health insurance; Life insurance carriers
Pr: Katy McCord
**Ch Bd:* Michel A Mc Cord
Pr: Mary Gensel
Pr: Ellen Gorman
Pr: Scott Reed
Treas: Sheryl Baker
Bd of Dir: Robert D Bollegar
Bd of Dir: Cindy Walls
**Ex VP:* W E Palmatier
VP: J W Marshall
VP: Lawrence P Smith
VP: Lawrence Smith
Exec: Judith McCord

D-U-N-S 02-110-4786
■ **ILLINOIS POWER GENERATING CO**
(*Suby of* NEW AMEREN ENERGY RESOURCES) ★
601 Travis St Ste 1400, Houston, TX 77002-3253
Tel (713) 507-6400 *Founded/Ownrshp* 2013
Sales 534.0MM *EMP* 384[E]
Accts Ernst & Young Llp Houston Te
SIC 4911 Generation, electric power
Pr: Robert C Flexon
**Ch Bd:* Kevin Howell
CFO: Clint C Freeland
VP: J Clinton Walden

ILLINOIS POWER HOLDINGS, LLC
See IPH LLC

D-U-N-S 15-300-5306
■ **ILLINOIS POWER RESOURCES LLC**
NEW AMEREN ENERGY RESOURCES
(*Suby of* ILLINOIS POWER HOLDINGS LLC) ★
1901 Chouteau Ave, Saint Louis, MO 63103-3003
Tel (314) 554-4110 *Founded/Ownrshp* 2013
Sales 544.9MM[E] *EMP* 421[E]
SIC 4911 Electric services
**Pr:* Daniel F Cole
**CEO:* Thomas R Voss
**CFO:* Martin J Lyons Jr
**Sr VP:* Gregory L Nelson
**VP:* Jerre E Birdsong

D-U-N-S 80-681-2558
ILLINOIS STATE BOARD OF EDUCATION
ISBE
(*Suby of* EXECUTIVE OFFICE OF GOVERNOR) ★
100 N 1st St Ste 1, Springfield, IL 62702-5011
Tel (217) 782-4321 *Founded/Ownrshp* 1975
Sales NA *EMP* 1,300
SIC 9411
Pr Dir: Matthew Vanover
Snr Mgr: Brian Houser

D-U-N-S 07-704-2869
ILLINOIS STATE MEDICAL SOCIETY
20 N Michigan Ave Ste 700, Chicago, IL 60602-4890
Tel (312) 782-2749 *Founded/Ownrshp* 1850
Sales 189.9MM[E] *EMP* 226
SIC 8621 Medical field-related associations
CEO: Alexander Lerner
CIO: Suzanne Nelson

D-U-N-S 80-681-0164
ILLINOIS STATE OF STATE POLICE
(*Suby of* EXECUTIVE OFFICE OF GOVERNOR) ★
801 S 7th St, Springfield, IL 62703-2487
Tel (217) 782-7263 *Founded/Ownrshp* 1941
Sales NA *EMP* 2,800
SIC 9221 State police;
Bd of Dir: Jan Bowsher
Bd of Dir: Ralph Caldwell
Ofcr: Michael Kindhart
Exec: Rick Hector
Dir Lab: Jan Johnson
Genl Mgr: Matthew Buchanan
Genl Mgr: Fran Schnorf
Off Mgr: Cathy Gullo
CTO: Carol Gibbs
IT Man: Matthew Burger

D-U-N-S 07-233-2430
ILLINOIS STATE OF TOLL HIGHWAY AUTHORITY
(*Suby of* EXECUTIVE OFFICE OF GOVERNOR) ★
2700 Ogden Ave, Downers Grove, IL 60515-1703
Tel (630) 241-6800 *Founded/Ownrshp* 1953
Sales NA *EMP* 1,750
Accts Mcgladrey & Pullen Llp Schau
SIC 9621 Regulation, administration of transportation;
Pr: John Mitola
COO: Karen Burke
**CFO:* Mike Colsch
Ex Dir: Jeffrey S Dailey
Ex Dir: Jack Hartman
IT Man: Christine Benn
IT Man: Wendy Maka
Genl Couns: Tom Bamonte
Snr Mgr: Joseph Gomez

D-U-N-S 00-514-6428
▲ **ILLINOIS TOOL WORKS INC**
155 Harlem Ave, Glenview, IL 60025-4075
Tel (847) 724-7500 *Founded/Ownrshp* 1912
Sales 13.4MMM *EMP* 48,025
Accts Deloitte & Touche Llp Chicag
Tkr Sym ITW *Exch* NYS
SIC 3089 3965 3499 2891 3585 Injection molded finished plastic products; Closures, plastic; Synthetic resin finished products; Fasteners; Strapping, metal; Adhesives & sealants; Refrigeration & heating equipment
Ch Bd: E Scott Santi
CFO: Michael M Larsen
Treas: Michael Robinson
Ofcr: Mary K Lawler
Ex VP: Roland M Martel
Ex VP: Michael R Zimmerman
Sr VP: Mary Lawler
VP: John Brooklier
VP: Dennis Martin
VP: Randall J Scheuneman
VP: Randall Scheuneman
VP: James H Wooten
Exec: Michael Klear

ILLINOIS VALLEY COMMUNITY HOSP
See IV HEALTHCORP INC

D-U-N-S 03-055-2913
ILLINOIS VALLEY COMMUNITY HOSPITAL INC
925 West St, Peru, IL 61354-2757
Tel (815) 223-3300 *Founded/Ownrshp* 1986
Sales 84.7MM *EMP* 650

SIC 8062 General medical & surgical hospitals
CEO: Tommy Hobbs
**Pr:* Kris Paul
**CFO:* Steve Davis
**VP:* James Loveland
**VP:* Bobby Smith
Snr Mgr: Christine Fivek

D-U-N-S 00-693-5407
■ ILLINOIS-AMERICAN WATER CO
(*Suby of* AMERICAN WATER WORKS CO INC) ★
300 N Water Works Dr, Belleville, IL 62223-8601
Tel (618) 236-1181 *Founded/Ownrshp* 1946
Sales 151.8MM^E *EMP* 430
SIC 4941 Water supply
Pr: Karla Olson Teasley
**Treas:* Charles Overath
**VP:* Mark Johnson
**VP:* R D Michem
VP: Frederick Ruckman
VP Opers: Mike Smyth
VP Opers: Barry Suits

D-U-N-S 03-330-5264 IMP
▲ ILLUMINA INC
5200 Illumina Way, San Diego, CA 92122-4616
Tel (858) 202-4500 *Founded/Ownrshp* 1998
Sales 2.2MMM *EMP* 4,600^E
Tkr Sym ILMN *Exch* NGS
SIC 3826 3821 Analytical instruments; Clinical laboratory instruments, except medical & dental
Ch Bd: Jay T Flatley
**Pr:* Francis A Desouza
CFO: Marc A Stapley
Ofcr: Christian O Henry
Ex VP: Tristan B Orpin
Sr VP: Paul L Bianchi
Sr VP: Charles Dadswell
Sr VP: Paula Dowdy
Sr VP: Nicholas J Naclerio
Sr VP: Mostafa Ronaghi
VP: Mya Thomae
Board of Directors: Frances Arnold, A Blaine Bowman, Daniel M Bradbury, Karin Eastham, Robert S Epstein, Philip W Schiller, Roy A Whitefield

D-U-N-S 94-584-5048 IMP
ILLUMINATIONS.COM INC
1736 Corporate Cir, Petaluma, CA 94954-6924
Tel (707) 776-2000 *Founded/Ownrshp* 2004
Sales 57.6MM^E *EMP* 1,049
SIC 5961 5947 Mail order house; Novelties
Pr: Wallis D Arnold

D-U-N-S 19-845-3953
ILONA FINANCIAL GROUP INC
1807 S Washington St, Naperville, IL 60565-2446
Tel (630) 699-6147 *Founded/Ownrshp* 2003
Sales NA *EMP* 150^E
SIC 6311 Life insurance carriers
Pr: Peter Fitzpatrick
**Treas:* Norman Fair

D-U-N-S 09-327-0262 IMP
ILPEA INDUSTRIES INC
HOLM INDUSTRIES
745 S Gardner St, Scottsburg, IN 47170-2178
Tel (812) 837-6616 *Founded/Ownrshp* 1989
Sales 181.7MM^E *EMP* 700
SIC 3053 3089 Gaskets, all materials; Window frames & sash, plastic
Pr: Wayne Heverly
**VP:* Ken Chenoweth
Dir IT: Bill Abbott
Plnt Mgr: Jim Arndt

D-U-N-S 83-115-7651
ILPEA INDUSTRIES INC
745 S Gardner St, Scottsburg, IN 47170-2178
Tel (812) 752-2526 *Founded/Ownrshp* 2009
Sales 325.9MM^E *EMP* 700^E
SIC 5085 Gaskets
Pr: Wayne Heverly
**VP:* Paul Schiefley
Natl Sales: Bert Decapite
Natl Sales: Steve Pandur

ILSCO
See BARDES CORP

D-U-N-S 00-424-9843 IMP
ILSCO CORP (OH)
UTILCO DIV
(*Suby of* ILSCO) ★
4730 Madison Rd, Cincinnati, OH 45227-1426
Tel (513) 533-6200 *Founded/Ownrshp* 1894
Sales 109.9MM^E *EMP* 470
SIC 3643 3369 3451 3678 3544 3469

D-U-N-S 80-446-5115 IMP/EXP
ILUKA RESOURCES INC
(*Suby of* ILUKA RESOURCES LIMITED)
12472 St John Church Rd, Stony Creek, VA 23882-3239
Tel (434) 348-4300 *Founded/Ownrshp* 2007
Sales 193.9MM^E *EMP* 493^E
SIC 1481 Nonmetallic mineral services
Prin: Matthew B Blackwell
Genl Mgr: Shane Tilka

D-U-N-S 96-959-1226
ILWU-PMA WELFARE TRUST
1188 Franklin St Ste 101, San Francisco, CA 94109-6852
Tel (415) 673-8500 *Founded/Ownrshp* 2011
Sales 676.2MM *EMP* 2^E
Accts Pricewaterhousecoopers Llp Ph
SIC 8699 Charitable organization
Prin: Michael Ouchida

D-U-N-S 61-735-5990 IMP
■ IM FLASH TECHNOLOGIES LLC
(*Suby of* MICRON TECHNOLOGY INC) ★
4000 N Flash Dr, Lehi, UT 84043-5148
Tel (801) 767-4000 *Founded/Ownrshp* 2005
Sales 225.9MM^E *EMP* 450
SIC 3674 Integrated circuits, semiconductor networks, etc.
Pr: Amy Rawlinson
**Ex Ofcr:* Keyvan Esfarjani
Snr Sftwr: Mike Burgess
Netwrk Mgr: Rod Keyes
Sftwr Eng: Bing Wang
Opers Mgr: Jade Bennett

I.M.A.
See INTERCHURCH MEDICAL ASSISTANCE INC

D-U-N-S 07-992-4104
IMA DAIRY & FOOD USA INC
I M A
(*Suby of* I.M.A. SPA)
7 New Lancaster Rd, Leominster, MA 01453-5224
Tel (732) 343-7600 *Founded/Ownrshp* 1961
Sales 221.8MM^E *EMP* 4,600
SIC 5083 Dairy machinery & equipment

D-U-N-S 12-862-2409
IMAGE ONE MARKETING GROUP INC
11956 Bernardo Plaza Dr # 525, San Diego, CA 92128-2538
Tel (858) 673-8299 *Founded/Ownrshp* 2002
Sales 910.4MM *EMP* 3
SIC 7311 5199 Advertising consultant; Advertising specialties
Pr: Stephen Gregory Carmichael

D-U-N-S 84-913-8508
■ IMAGE SOLUTIONS INC
CSC REGULATORY SERVICE GROUP
(*Suby of* CSC) ★
100 S Jefferson Rd # 300, Whippany, NJ 07981-1055
Tel (973) 560-0404 *Founded/Ownrshp* 2011
Sales 86.9MM^E *EMP* 500^E
SIC 7374 Computer processing services
Pr: Jinsoo Kim
**COO:* Paul Chung
**CFO:* Peter Kim

IMAGEWEAR
See WALMAN OPTICAL CO

D-U-N-S 07-876-4119
IMAGINE COMMUNICATIONS CORP
(*Suby of* GORES GROUP LLC) ★
3001 Dallas Pkwy Ste 300, Frisco, TX 75034-8639
Tel (469) 803-4900 *Founded/Ownrshp* 2012, 1995
Sales 464.4MM^E *EMP* 1,400
SIC 4899 3663 Data communication services; Radio broadcasting & communications equipment; Television broadcasting & communications equipment
CEO: Charlie Vogt
Pr: Steve Foreman
Pr: Pablo Gargiulo
**Ex VP:* Jeff Liening
VP: Ron Gutman
VP: Ajay Kapoor
VP: John McNamara
Prgrm Mgr: Patty Miller
CIO: John Borthayre
CTO: Pat McCoy
Software D: Bill Willett

D-U-N-S 18-750-7660 IMP
IMAGINE PRINT SOLUTIONS INC
1000 Valley Park Dr, Shakopee, MN 55379-1879
Tel (952) 903-4400 *Founded/Ownrshp* 1988
Sales 380.2MM^E *EMP* 1,240
Accts Larson Allen Llp Minneapolis
SIC 2759 Promotional printing
CEO: Robert J Lothenbach
VP Sls: Tony Hoholik

D-U-N-S 96-321-6259
IMAGINE SCHOOLS NON-PROFIT INC
1005 N Glebe Rd Ste 610, Arlington, VA 22201-5758
Tel (703) 527-2600 *Founded/Ownrshp* 2004
Sales 93.7MM *EMP* 3,500^E
SIC 8299 Educational services
Pr: Dennis Bakke
**VP:* Eileen Bakke
VP: James McFadden

D-U-N-S 12-030-3438
IMAGINE SCHOOLS OF DELAWARE INC
(*Suby of* IMAGINE SCHOOLS ON BROADWAY) ★
8071 Nw 54th St, Doral, FL 33166-4004
Tel (305) 648-5962 *Founded/Ownrshp* 2004
Sales 112.1M^E *EMP* 1,700
SIC 8211 Private combined elementary & secondary school
Ch: Octavio J Visiedo
**Pr:* Wade Dyke
**CFO:* Javier Montiel

D-U-N-S 14-911-0806
IMAGINE SCHOOLS ON BROADWAY
1005 N Glebe Rd Ste 610, Arlington, VA 22201-5758
Tel (703) 527-2600 *Founded/Ownrshp* 2003
Sales 1.4MM *EMP* 3,600
Accts Berman Hopkins Wright Laham Cp
SIC 8211 Elementary & secondary schools
Pr: Dennis W Bakke
CFO: Rob Huey
VP: Jennifer Butzow
Off Mgr: Barbara Mecca
Off Admin: Lisa Bukke
Dir IT: Thomas Henderson
Snr Mgr: Tammy Schubel

D-U-N-S 80-882-8222
IMAGING CENTER OF N CENTRAL INDIANA
2201 W Boulevard, Kokomo, IN 46902-6070
Tel (765) 452-0808 *Founded/Ownrshp* 1993
Sales 122.1MM *EMP* 19
Accts Bucheri Mccarty & Metz Llp Ko
SIC 8071 X-ray laboratory, including dental

IMAGING SCIENCES INTERNATIONAL
See DENTAL IMAGING TECHNOLOGIES CORP

IMAGINIT TECHNOLOGIES
See RAND WORLDWIDE SUBSIDIARY INC

D-U-N-S 93-358-8691
▲ IMATION CORP
1099 Helmo Ave N Ste 250, Oakdale, MN 55128-3414
Tel (651) 704-4000 *Founded/Ownrshp* 1996
Sales 529.2MM *EMP* 600^E
Tkr Sym IMN *Exch* NYS
SIC 3695 3572 Magnetic & optical recording media; Computer software tape & disks: blank, rigid & floppy; Optical disks & tape, blank; Video recording tape, blank; Computer storage devices; Computer tape drives & components; Disk drives, computer; Magnetic storage devices, computer
CEO: Robert B Fernander
**Ch Bd:* Joseph A De Perio
CFO: Danny Zheng
**Dir Risk M:* Barry L Kasoff
CTO: Geoff S Barrall
Board of Directors: Tracy McKibben, Donald H Putnam, Robert Searing, Alex Spiro

D-U-N-S 15-972-1794 IMP/EXP
■ IMATION ENTERPRISES CORP
(*Suby of* IMATION CORP) ★
1099 Helmo Ave N Ste 250, Saint Paul, MN 55128-3414
Tel (651) 704-4000 *Founded/Ownrshp* 1996
Sales 66.5MM^E *EMP* 1,115
SIC 3695 3845 5112 Magnetic disks & drums; Magnetic tape; Electromedical equipment; Data processing supplies
CEO: Mark E Lucas
CFO: Paul R Zeller
Sr VP: Gregory J Bosler
Sr VP: John L Sullivan
VP: John P Breedlove
VP: Randy J Christofferson
VP: Patricia Hamm
VP: Nobuyoshi Kawasaki
VP: Subodh K Kulkarni
VP: Brian J Plummer
Board of Directors: Lawrence E Eaton, Michael S Fields, William W George, Linda W Hart, Ronald T Lemay, Marvin L Mann, Glen Taylor, Daryl J White

IMB
See INTERNATIONAL MISSION BOARD OF SOUTHERN BAPTIST CONVENTION

IMC
See INTERAMERICAN MOTOR CORP

IMC FINANCIALS MARKET
See IMC-CHICAGO LLC

D-U-N-S 19-826-6277
IMC-CHICAGO LLC
IMC FINANCIALS MARKET
233 S Wacker Dr Ste 4300, Chicago, IL 60606-6377
Tel (312) 244-3300 *Founded/Ownrshp* 2000
Sales 141.8MM^E *EMP* 131
SIC 6231 Stock exchanges
Mng Dir: Scott Knudsen
CTO: Henk Kamphuis
Dir IT: Will Edelmuth
Sftwr Eng: Nandan Ghosale

D-U-N-S 83-270-2976 IMP/EXP
IMC-METALSAMERICA LLC
(*Suby of* PMR) ★
135 Old Boiling Sprng Rd, Shelby, NC 28152-0648
Tel (704) 482-8200 *Founded/Ownrshp* 2009
Sales 125.0MM *EMP* 75
SIC 3331 Primary copper; Primary copper smelter products; Bars (primary), copper; Slabs (primary), copper
Pr: Bernard C Shilberg

D-U-N-S 08-333-1249 IMP
IMCD US LLC
(*Suby of* IMCD N.V.)
14725 Detroit Ave Ste 300, Lakewood, OH 44107-4124
Tel (216) 228-8900 *Founded/Ownrshp* 2015
Sales 177.1MM^E *EMP* 90
SIC 5169 Chemicals & allied products
Pr: John L Mastrantoni
**CFO:* Bruce D Jarosz
VP: Alison M Azar
Mktg Mgr: Mark Walter
Manager: Alison Azar
Manager: Kevin Trainor
Sls Mgr: Rebecca Bergman
Sls Mgr: Janeen Dolinar
Sls Mgr: Jeanine Hill-Jacob

D-U-N-S 13-134-5761 IMP/EXP
■ IMCLONE SYSTEMS LLC
(*Suby of* ELI LILLY AND CO) ★
440 Us Highway 22, Bridgewater, NJ 08807-2477
Tel (908) 541-8000 *Founded/Ownrshp* 2008
Sales 272.6MM^E *EMP* 1,128
SIC 2836 2834 Biological products, except diagnostic; Pharmaceutical preparations
CEO: John H Johnson
Dir Vol: Jenny Greda
**Ch Bd:* Carl C Icahn
CFO: Ana I Stancc
CFO: Harlan W Mdcoo
**CFO:* Kenneth J Zuerblis
Bd of Dir: Ronald Martell
Bd of Dir: Larry Witte
**Sr VP:* Richard Crowley
Sr VP: Ronald A Mrtell
Sr VP: Sjoseph Tarnowski
VP: Michael Barry
VP: Paul A Goldstein
**VP:* Gregory T Mayes
Assoc Dir: Scott Stachowski
Assoc Dir: Bill Strong

D-U-N-S 08-993-6686 IMP/EXP
IMCO GENERAL CONSTRUCTION INC (WA)
2116 Buchanan Loop, Ferndale, WA 98248-9801
Tel (360) 671-3936 *Founded/Ownrshp* 1978
Sales 115.1MM^E *EMP* 180^E
SIC 1541 1629 1542 Industrial buildings, new construction; Waste water & sewage treatment plant construction; Nonresidential construction
Ch: Frank Imhof
**Treas:* Tyler Kimberley
**VP:* Patti Imhof
Dir IT: Brian Lawrence
Dir IT: Brian Smith
IT Man: Dan Brunner
Sfty Mgr: Lisa Young
Mktg Dir: Ashley Kimberley
Snr PM: Mark Rocha

IMCOR
See INTERSTATE MECHANICAL CORP

IME
See INTERMOUNTAIN ELECTRIC INC

D-U-N-S 13-658-2108
IMEDX INC
3560 Lenox Rd Ne Ste 3000, Atlanta, GA 30326-4287
Tel (404) 418-0096 *Founded/Ownrshp* 2009
Sales 65.4MM^E *EMP* 3,000
SIC 7338 Secretarial & typing service
CEO: Christopher Foley
CFO: Bob Attanasio
**CFO:* Jon Tropsa
Sr VP: Jim Banghart
VP: Taylor Duderstadt
VP: Earl Flannery
CTO: Patti Clements
Mktg Mgr: Herini Betha
Manager: Pat Mahoney

D-U-N-S 79-501-0792 IMP/EXP
IMERYS FILTRATION MINERALS INC
(*Suby of* IMERYS USA INC) ★
1732 N 1st St Ste 450, San Jose, CA 95112-4579
Tel (805) 562-0200 *Founded/Ownrshp* 2005
Sales 848.1MM^E *EMP* 1,499
SIC 1499 Diatomaceous earth mining
CEO: Douglas A Smith
**Pr:* John Oskan
CFO: Leslie Zimmer
**Treas:* Fred Weber
**V Ch Bd:* Paul Woodberry
Genl Mgr: George Christoferson

D-U-N-S 78-056-5636 EXP
IMERYS MINERALS CALIFORNIA INC
(*Suby of* IMERYS FILTRATION MINERALS INC) ★
2500 San Miguelito Rd, Lompoc, CA 93436-9743
Tel (805) 736-1221 *Founded/Ownrshp* 1991
Sales 711.7MM^E *EMP* 1,145
SIC 1499 3295 Diatomaceous earth mining; Minerals, ground or treated
Pr: Douglas A Smith
**CEO:* John Oskam
**CFO:* John Leichty
VP: Jack Murray
VP: Bruno Van Herpen
MIS Dir: Bill Kinman

D-U-N-S 00-954-1780 IMP/EXP
IMERYS PERLITE USA INC
HARBORLITE
(*Suby of* IMERYS FILTRATION MINERALS INC) ★
1732 N 1st St Ste 450, San Jose, CA 95112-4579
Tel (408) 643-0215 *Founded/Ownrshp* 1992
Sales 146.9MM^E *EMP* 173
SIC 1499 Perlite mining
CFO: John Liechty
Off Mgr: Paul Sowards

D-U-N-S 79-052-2791 EXP
IMERYS TALC AMERICA INC
(*Suby of* IMERYS)
1732 N 1st St Ste 450, San Jose, CA 95112-4579
Tel (805) 562-0260 *Founded/Ownrshp* 1992
Sales 155.2MM^E *EMP* 562^E
SIC 3295 1499 Talc, ground or otherwise treated; Talc mining
Pr: Brian Hanrahan

D-U-N-S 06-149-0140 IMP/EXP
IMERYS USA INC (GA)
(*Suby of* IMERYS)
100 Mansell Ct E Ste 300, Roswell, GA 30076-4860
Tel (770) 645-3300 *Founded/Ownrshp* 1990
Sales 1.1MMM^E *EMP* 4,069
SIC 1455 1459 1429 1422 2819 Kaolin mining; Clays (common) quarrying; Marble, crushed & broken-quarrying; Lime rock, ground; Calcium carbide
CEO: Denis Musson
CFO: Jeffrey C Hicks
Ofcr: Merilee Long
VP: Damien Caby
VP: Phil Jones
VP: Daniel Moncino
Exec: Anna Kucherenko
Exec: Joan Malit
Rgnl Mgr: Ray Hall
Dir IT: Tony Lyons
Dir IT: Kathryn Simpson

D-U-N-S 19-418-8645
IMG
DEMO DELUXE
4560 Dorinda Rd, Yorba Linda, CA 92887-1800
Tel (714) 974-1700 *Founded/Ownrshp* 1983
Sales 76.8MM^E *EMP* 4,000
SIC 7389 Demonstration service
Pt: Jim Smith
IT Man: Pat Stamatelatos

D-U-N-S 18-877-0416 IMP/EXP
IMI AMERICAS INC
(*Suby of* IMI PLC)
5400 S Delaware St, Littleton, CO 80120-1663
Tel (763) 488-5400 *Founded/Ownrshp* 1981
Sales 669.4MM^E *EMP* 4,000
SIC 2542 Partitions & fixtures, except wood
Pr: Robert Guerra
**Pr:* Greg Croydon
**Treas:* Jim Etter
VP: Pat Burgoyne
Off Mgr: Pam Brown

IMI PRECISION ENGINEERING
See NORGREN INC

IMI SENSORS
See PCB PIEZOTRONICS INC

D-U-N-S 00-638-1537
IMI SOUTH LLC
IRVING MATERIALS
(*Suby of* I M I) ★
1440 Selinda Ave, Louisville, KY 40213-1954
Tel (502) 456-6930 *Founded/Ownrshp* 2000
Sales 90.7MM^E *EMP* 510
SIC 3273 Ready-mixed concrete

IMIC HOTELS
See INTERSTATE MANAGEMENT & INVESTMENT CORP

D-U-N-S 01-403-5752
IMLERS POULTRY LP
IMLERS POULTRY TRANSPORTATION
1887 Route 764, Duncansville, PA 16635-7952
Tel (814) 943-5563 *Founded/Ownrshp* 1968
Sales 100.0MM *EMP* 170
SIC 5144 5147 5141 5142 Poultry: live, dressed or frozen (unpackaged); Meats & meat products; Groceries, general line; Packaged frozen goods
CFO: Melissa Lovrich
**Pt:* Brian Imler
**Pt:* Fred Imler Jr
QA Dir: Randy Fenske
Dir IT: Chris Pechtold

IMLERS POULTRY TRANSPORTATION
See IMLERS POULTRY LP

D-U-N-S 01-855-7605
■ **IMMEDIATE CLINIC HEALTHCARE INC**
(*Suby of* ENDURA HEALTHCARE) ★
27101 Puerta Real Ste 450, Mission Viejo, CA 92691-8566
Tel (949) 487-9500 *Founded/Ownrshp* 2012
Sales 434.3M^E *EMP* 1,009^E
SIC 8082 Home health care services
Pr: Mike Dalton
**Treas:* Soon Burnam

IMMI
See INDIANA MILLS & MANUFACTURING INC

D-U-N-S 15-980-3972
■ **IMMIXGROUP INC**
(*Suby of* ARROW ELECTRONICS INC) ★
8444 Westpark Dr Ste 200, Mc Lean, VA 22102-5112
Tel (703) 752-0610 *Founded/Ownrshp* 2015
Sales 435.1MM^E *EMP* 201^E
SIC 7371 7379 Custom computer programming services; Computer hardware requirements analysis
Pr: Art Richer
**CFO:* Noel N Samuel
Ofcr: Don Logan Jr
**Ex VP:* Stephen Charles
VP: Erinn Connor
VP: Andrew Cox
VP: Tierra White
Mng Dir: Steve Michael
VP Sls: Craig Harper
Sls Dir: John Severino
Sls Mgr: Anthony Bracewell
Board of Directors: Nelson Carbonell, Thomas B Newell

D-U-N-S 09-869-2374
■ **IMMIXTECHNOLOGY INC**
(*Suby of* IMMIXGROUP INC) ★
8444 Westpark Dr Ste 200, Mc Lean, VA 22102-5112
Tel (703) 752-0610 *Founded/Ownrshp* 1997
Sales 221.8MM^E *EMP* 201
SIC 5045 Computers, peripherals & software
CEO: Art Richer
**CFO:* Noel Samuel
**Ex VP:* Steve Charles
**VP:* Bill Bottoms
**VP:* Skip Liesegang
**VP:* Phill Magaro
VP Mktg: Lou A Brossman
Snr Mgr: Jennifer Taylor

D-U-N-S 06-144-6282 IMP/EXP
IMMUCOR INC
(*Suby of* IVD INTERMEDIATE HOLDINGS B INC) ★
3130 Gateway Dr, Peachtree Corners, GA 30071-1189
Tel (770) 441-2051 *Founded/Ownrshp* 2011
Sales 379.9MM *EMP* 1,090^E
SIC 2835 In vitro & in vivo diagnostic substances; Blood derivative diagnostic agents; In vitro diagnostics; In vivo diagnostics
Pr: Jeffrey R Binder
CFO: R Deible
**CFO:* Dominique Petitgenet
VP: Dave Campbell
VP: Richard Kirkendall
VP: Michael C Poynter
VP: Daniel L Ruckman
VP: Dan Swaine
CTO: Andy Patterson
MIS Dir: Casey Brost
Web Dev: Winnie Tsui
Board of Directors: Jeffrey K Rhodes, Todd B Sisitsky

D-U-N-S 02-813-4799
■ **IMMUNEX CORP**
(*Suby of* AMGEN INC) ★
51 University St, Seattle, WA 98101-3614
Tel (206) 551-5169 *Founded/Ownrshp* 2002
Sales 88.4MM^E *EMP* 700
SIC 2834 8731 2836 Pharmaceutical preparations; Drugs affecting parasitic & infective diseases; Biotechnical research, commercial; Biological products, except diagnostic
Pr: Roger Pearlmutter
Pr: Michael Mumford
Pr: Douglas E Williams
COO: Bruce Phillips
COO: Peggy V Phillips
CFO: Michael Aguir
Sr Cor Off: Scott Bailey
Ex VP: Gail Kerber
VP: Valoree E Dowll
VP: Steven Gillis
VP: David A Mann
VP: Kendall Mohler
**VP:* Steve M Odre
VP: D Sassenfeld
Assoc Dir: Douglas Hostler

D-U-N-S 00-122-5275 IMP
■ **IMO INDUSTRIES INC**
COLFAX FLUID HANDLING
(*Suby of* COLFAX CORP) ★
1710 Airport Rd, Monroe, NC 28110-7394
Tel (704) 289-6511 *Founded/Ownrshp* 1997, 1998
Sales 139.4MM^E *EMP* 479^E
SIC 3561 3714 3829 Pumps & pumping equipment; Motor vehicle parts & accessories; Motor vehicle transmissions, drive assemblies & parts; Aircraft & motor vehicle measurement equipment; Pressure transducers
CEO: Darryl Mayhorn
**Pr:* Brannan Charles Scott
**CFO:* Christopher Doulware
**VP:* Pryor Daniel Alexis
VP: Mark Bowie
**VP:* Lehman Mark Paul
**VP:* Flexon William Walter
IT Man: Peggy Lee
Netwrk Mgr: John Howie

D-U-N-S 96-784-5467
IMOBILE LLC
207 Terminal Dr, Plainview, NY 11803-2301
Tel (516) 433-9300 *Founded/Ownrshp* 2006
Sales 76.0MM^E *EMP* 5,000^E
SIC 5999 Mobile telephones & equipment
CEO: Sarabjit Lamba
Pr: Chetan Sharma

IMPA
See INDIANA MUNICIPAL POWER AGENCY

D-U-N-S 16-001-1516
■ **IMPAC GROUP INC**
(*Suby of* WESTROCK MWV LLC) ★
1950 N Ruby St, Melrose Park, IL 60160-1110
Tel (708) 344-9100 *Founded/Ownrshp* 2002
Sales 63.4MM^E *EMP* 1,526
SIC 2657 Folding paperboard boxes
Pr: Richard Block

D-U-N-S 93-774-8440
▲ **IMPAC MORTGAGE HOLDINGS INC**
19500 Jamboree Rd, Irvine, CA 92612-2401
Tel (949) 475-3600 *Founded/Ownrshp* 1995
Sales 166.9MM *EMP* 564^E
Tkr Sym IMH *Exch* ASE
SIC 6798 Real estate investment trusts
Ch Bd: Joseph R Tomkinson
Pr: William S Ashmore
CFO: Todd R Taylor
Ex VP: Ronald M Morrison
VP: Charles Evans
VP: Justin Moisio
Board of Directors: Leigh J Abrams, Frank P Filipps, Stephan R Peers, James Walsh

D-U-N-S 05-227-7008
IMPACT CHEMICAL TECHNOLOGIES INC
PRODUCTION CHEMICALS
10501 E Hwy 80, Midland, TX 79706
Tel (432) 458-3500 *Founded/Ownrshp* 1994
Sales 90.5MM^E *EMP* 152
SIC 5169 Chemicals & allied products
Pr: Autry C Stephens
**VP:* Brandon Martin

D-U-N-S 62-110-5936
IMPACT FORGE GROUP LLC
(*Suby of* HEPHAESTUS HOLDINGS INC) ★
2805 Norcross Dr, Columbus, IN 47201-4911
Tel (812) 342-4437 *Founded/Ownrshp* 2006
Sales 142.4MM^E *EMP* 500
SIC 3462 3463 Iron & steel forgings; Nonferrous forgings
CEO: George Thanopolous
**VP:* Dennis Potter
Genl Mgr: Walter Powers
Dir IT: Terry McInerney
Dir IT: Francis Walker
QC Dir: John Williamson
Prd Mgr: Andy Larrison
Ql Cn Mgr: Jeff Cornn
Ql Cn Mgr: Joe Keeley

D-U-N-S 00-505-2360 IMP
■ **IMPACT PRODUCTS LLC**
(*Suby of* S P RICHARDS CO) ★
2840 Centennial Rd, Toledo, OH 43617-1898
Tel (419) 841-2891 *Founded/Ownrshp* 2001, 2014
Sales 100.8MM^E *EMP* 151
SIC 5084 5087 2392 3089 Safety equipment; Janitors' supplies; Mops, floor & dust; Buckets, plastic; Tissue dispensers, plastic
CEO: Terry Neal
Pr: John Irwin
**CFO:* Jeff Beery
VP: James Kenchtges
Exec: Catherine U Hague
Dir IT: Brian Byczynski
QC Dir: Todd Frendt
Natl Sales: Adam Siegel
Sls&Mrk Ex: Robert Armbruster
VP Mktg: Jeannie McCarthy
VP Sls: Duane Carey

IMPACT RESOURCE GROUP
See WERE READY TO ASSEMBLE INC

D-U-N-S 05-844-4719
IMPACT TELECOM LLC
(*Suby of* GARRISON INVESTMENT GROUP LP) ★
9000 E Nichols Ave # 230, Centennial, CO 80112-3475
Tel (866) 557-8919 *Founded/Ownrshp* 2005
Sales 133.5MM^E *EMP* 280^E
SIC 7389 Telephone services
Pr: Robert Beaty
Pr: Jason McKesson
COO: Chuck Griffin
Treas: Douglas Funsch
Ex VP: Nermin Selimic

IMPARK
See IMPERIAL PARKING CORP

IMPARK
See IMPERIAL PARKING (US) LLC

IMPAX
See WILSON TOOL INTERNATIONAL INC

D-U-N-S 00-259-5734
▲ **IMPAX LABORATORIES INC**
30831 Huntwood Ave, Hayward, CA 94544-7003
Tel (510) 240-6000 *Founded/Ownrshp* 1993
Sales 860.4MM *EMP* 1,290
Tkr Sym IPXL *Exch* NGS
SIC 2834 Pharmaceutical preparations
Pr: G Frederick Wilkinson
**Ch Bd:* Robert L Burr
CFO: Bryan M Reasons
Chf Cred: Deborah M Penza
Sr VP: Mark Fitch
Sr VP: Mark A Schlossberg
Board of Directors: Leslie Z Benet, Richard A Bierly, Allen Chao, Michael Markbreiter, Mary K Pendergast, Peter R Terreri, Janet S Vergis, Nigel Ten Fleming

D-U-N-S 09-463-3120 IMP/EXP
IMPCO TECHNOLOGIES INC
(*Suby of* FUEL SYSTEMS SOLUTIONS INC) ★
3030 S Susan St, Santa Ana, CA 92704-6435
Tel (714) 656-1200 *Founded/Ownrshp* 2006
Sales 121.7MM^E *EMP* 540
SIC 3714 3592 7363 Fuel systems & parts, motor vehicle; Carburetors; Engineering help service
Genl Mgr: Massimo Fracchia
Pr: Brian Olson
COO: Brad E Garner
Sr Cor Off: Richard Baverstock
Genl Mgr: Linda Berger
VP Sls: Jim Vasilenko

IMPERIAL - SAVANNAH
See IMPERIAL SUGAR CO

D-U-N-S 13-797-7224 IMP/EXP
IMPERIAL BAG & PAPER CO LLC
255 Us Highway 1 And 9, Jersey City, NJ 07306-6727
Tel (201) 437-7440 *Founded/Ownrshp* 2006
Sales 1.2MMM^E *EMP* 318
SIC 5087 Janitors' supplies
CEO: Robert Tillis
**Pr:* Jason Tillis
**CFO:* Paul Cervino
CFO: Robert De Gregorio
CFO: Robert Degregorio
Ex VP: William Needham
**Sr VP:* Jeffery Burdick
**VP Sls:* Chris Freeman
Sls Mgr: Joseph F Murray

IMPERIAL BEVERAGE
See CKL CORP

D-U-N-S 00-184-3127 EXP
IMPERIAL DISTRIBUTORS INC
33 Sword St, Auburn, MA 01501-2146
Tel (508) 756-5156 *Founded/Ownrshp* 1939
Sales 799.7MM^E *EMP* 750
Accts Rsm Us Llp Boston Massachus
SIC 5122 Toiletries
CFO: Herb Daitch
CFO: Joyce Martin
VP: Ralph Cruz
VP: Joe Kirby
VP: Sandra Noonan
VP: Don Polsi
VP: Tammy Remillard
CTO: Mike Cashman
Dir IT: Dovid Kashnow
IT Man: Mike Leblanc
Opers Mgr: Derek Potter

IMPERIAL FABRICS
See ASCOT ENTERPRISES INC

D-U-N-S 07-910-2043
IMPERIAL GROUP MANUFACTURING INC
4545 Airport Rd, Denton, TX 76207-3927
Tel (940) 565-8505 *Founded/Ownrshp* 2013
Sales 651.7MM^E *EMP* 1,892
SIC 3715 Truck trailers; Trailer bodies; Truck trailer chassis
Pr: Brian Crumbaugh
**VP:* John Hatherly
**VP:* Ian Kirson

D-U-N-S 60-989-5248
IMPERIAL GUARD AND DETECTIVE SERVICES INC
IMPERIAL GUARD SERVICE
2555 Poplar Ave, Memphis, TN 38112-3822
Tel (866) 840-2066 *Founded/Ownrshp* 1968
Sales 41.7MM^E *EMP* 2,000
SIC 7381 Security guard service
Pr: R O Brewer
CFO: Mike Tardy
**Sec:* Robin Todd
**VP:* William Brinson
VP: Randy Ford
IT Man: John Purifoy
MIS Mgr: Jack Tardy
Secur Mgr: Seth Miller

IMPERIAL GUARD SERVICE
See IMPERIAL GUARD AND DETECTIVE SERVICES INC

D-U-N-S 00-958-4624 IMP
IMPERIAL IRRIGATION DISTRICT
I I D
333 E Barioni Blvd, Imperial, CA 92251-1773
Tel (800) 303-7756 *Founded/Ownrshp* 1911
Sales 995.5MM^E *EMP* 1,300
SIC 4911 4971 4931 ; Water distribution or supply systems for irrigation; Electric & other services combined
Pr: Stephen Benson
**Pr:* Anthony Sanchez
**CEO:* Keven Kelly
Ofcr: Raquel Lopez
Ofcr: Belen Valenzuela
**VP:* Mike Abatti
**VP:* Norma Sierra Galindo
**VP:* Stella Mendoza
Genl Mgr: Olivia Ramirez
CIO: Samuel E Singh
Dir IT: Carl Stills

D-U-N-S 04-910-9734
IMPERIAL MANAGEMENT CORP
(*Suby of* SOUTHPORT LANE MANAGEMENT LLC) ★
4670 I 49 N Service Rd, Opelousas, LA 70570-0882
Tel (337) 942-5691 *Founded/Ownrshp* 2013
Sales NA *EMP* 190^E
SIC 6331 Fire, marine & casualty insurance & carriers
CEO: H Marcus Carter Jr
**Pr:* Je Brignac
**CFO:* Dirk Boudreaux

IMPERIAL PALACE HOTEL & CASINO
See IMPERIAL PALACE OF MISSISSIPPI LLC

D-U-N-S 93-947-6370
IMPERIAL PALACE OF MISSISSIPPI LLC
IMPERIAL PALACE HOTEL & CASINO
850 Bayview Ave, Biloxi, MS 39530-1701
Tel (228) 432-3243 *Founded/Ownrshp* 1997
Sales NA *EMP* 2,300^E
SIC 7011 5812 5813 7832

D-U-N-S 60-413-6192 EXP
IMPERIAL PARKING (US) LLC
IMPARK
900 Haddon Ave Ste 333, Collingswood, NJ 08108-2101
Tel (856) 854-7111 *Founded/Ownrshp* 2011
Sales 448.7MM^E *EMP* 4,620
SIC 7521 Parking structure; Parking lots
Pr: Allan Copping
**Treas:* Bradley Yen

D-U-N-S 08-032-3019
IMPERIAL PARKING CORP
IMPARK
(*Suby of* IMPERIAL PARKING CANADA CORPORATION)
900 Haddon Ave Ste 333, Collingswood, NJ 08108-2101
Tel (856) 854-7111 *Founded/Ownrshp* 2004
Sales 41.7MM^E *EMP* 9,000^E
SIC 7521 Parking structure; Parking lots
Pr: Allan C Copping

IMPERIAL PIPE & SUPPLY
See BAKERSFIELD PIPE AND SUPPLY INC

D-U-N-S 04-596-0218 IMP
IMPERIAL PLASTICS INC
21320 Hamburg Ave, Lakeville, MN 55044-9032
Tel (952) 469-4951 *Founded/Ownrshp* 1996
Sales 156.4MM^E *EMP* 570^E
SIC 3089

D-U-N-S 00-808-6472 IMP/EXP
IMPERIAL SUGAR CO
IMPERIAL - SAVANNAH
(*Suby of* LOUIS DREYFUS CO NORFOLK) ★
3 Sugar Creek Center Blvd # 500, Sugar Land, TX 77478-2210
Tel (281) 491-9181 *Founded/Ownrshp* 1905, 2016
Sales 437.4MM^E *EMP* 530
SIC 2062 5149 Cane sugar refining; Granulated cane sugar from purchased raw sugar or syrup; Powdered cane sugar from purchased raw sugar or syrup; Sugar, refined
Pr: Michael Gorrell
**CEO:* John C Sheptor
**CFO:* H P Mechler
**Treas:* J Eric Story
**Sr VP:* Louis T Bolognini
**VP:* George Muller
**VP:* Jeffrey Zanchelli

D-U-N-S 04-933-7249 IMP/EXP
IMPERIAL TOY LLC
16641 Roscoe Pl, North Hills, CA 91343-6104
Tel (818) 536-6500 *Founded/Ownrshp* 2006
Sales 207.4MM^E *EMP* 800
SIC 3944 Games, toys & children's vehicles
CFO: Mark Milner
Ex VP: Bobby Ivanic
Sr VP: Lee Loetz
VP: Heidi Dianaty
VP: Judy Tambourine
Mng Dir: Steve Handelsman
Genl Mgr: Curtis Millican
IT Man: Leone Zion
VP Opers: Lisa Castanon
Natl Sales: Susan Vigil
VP Sls: David Opell

D-U-N-S 60-733-3221 IMP
IMPERIAL TRADING CO LLC
701 Edwards Ave, Harahan, LA 70123-3167
Tel (504) 733-1400 *Founded/Ownrshp* 1916
Sales 163.7MM^E *EMP* 230^E
SIC 5194 5141 5145 Cigarettes; Groceries, general line; Candy
Prin: John D Georges
Pr: Emile Cantrell
COO: Willie Green
COO: Bill Kearney IV
CFO: Gerald Pelias
CFO: Gil Stroud Jr
Exec: Cheryl Analla
Exec: John Georges
Dir IT: Suzanne Wyman
VP Opers: Richard Duhon
Sls Mgr: Larry Bruce

IMPERIAL TURF PRODUCTS
See JAMES MORIEL

D-U-N-S 04-659-2515 EXP
IMPERIAL WESTERN PRODUCTS INC
BIOTANE PUMPING
86600 Avenue 54, Coachella, CA 92236-3812
Tel (760) 398-0815 *Founded/Ownrshp* 1966
Sales 167.5MM^E *EMP* 289
SIC 5159 2841 2869

D-U-N-S 14-077-9922
▲ IMPERVA INC
3400 Bridge Pkwy Ste 200, Redwood City, CA 94065-1195
Tel (650) 345-9000 *Founded/Ownrshp* 2002
Sales 234.3MM *EMP* 923[E]
Tkr Sym IMPV *Exch* NYS
SIC 7371 Computer software development & applications
Ch Bd: Anthony J Bettencourt
CFO: Terrence J Schmid
Ofcr: Michael D Mooney
Sr VP: Meg Bear
Sr VP: Merav Davidson
Sr VP: Jason Forget
Sr VP: Brett Hooper
Sr VP: Mark Kraynak
Sr VP: Tram T PHI
VP: Jason Huey
VP: Gary Pfeiffer
VP: Karl Soderlund
VP: Henk Spanjaard
VP Bus Dev: Sharon Besser
Board of Directors: Geraldine Elliott, Charles Giancarlo, Albert A Pimentel, Randall Spratt, Allan Tessler, James R Tolonen

D-U-N-S 36-153-1585 IMP/EXP
IMPLUS FOOTCARE LLC
2001 Tw Alexander Dr, Durham, NC 27709-0184
Tel (919) 544-7900 *Founded/Ownrshp* 1989
Sales 138.3MM[E] *EMP* 371
SIC 5139 Shoe accessories
CEO: Seth Richards
Pr: Steve Couder
**Pr:* Todd Vore
COO: Sam Prestipino
**CFO:* Bill Alfano
CFO: Rodney Bullock
**Ex VP:* Steve Head
Web Dev: Genevieve Kuczewski
VP Opers: Andrew Louis
VP Prd: Merrick Jones
Natl Sales: Tommy Nason

IMPORT DIRECT
See E & S INTERNATIONAL ENTERPRISES INC

D-U-N-S 14-657-4673 IMP
IMPREMEDIA LLC
LA RAZA
(*Suby of* US HISPANIC MEDIA INC) ★
1 Metrotech Ctr Fl 18, Brooklyn, NY 11201-3949
Tel (212) 807-4785 *Founded/Ownrshp* 2012
Sales 103.5MM[E] *EMP* 566
SIC 2711 Newspapers: publishing only, not printed on site
VP: Olga Casabona

D-U-N-S 06-458-0129
IMPRESA AEROSPACE LLC
344 W 157th St, Gardena, CA 90248-2135
Tel (310) 354-1200 *Founded/Ownrshp* 1987
Sales 88.0MM[E] *EMP* 275
SIC 3728 3444 Aircraft parts & equipment; Sheet metalwork
CEO: Scott Smith
VP: Dennis Fitzgerald
**VP:* David Hirsch
Genl Mgr: Jose Banuelos
Genl Mgr: Paul Duff
Genl Mgr: Eric Haworth
Ql Cn Mgr: Ernest Florez

D-U-N-S 02-136-6930 IMP/EXP
▲ IMPRESO INC
TSTIMPRESO
652 Southwestern Blvd, Coppell, TX 75019-4419
Tel (972) 462-0100 *Founded/Ownrshp* 2000
Sales 83.3MM *EMP* 170
Tkr Sym ZCOM *Exch* OTO
SIC 2761 2679 2086 Manifold business forms; Telegraph, teletype & adding machine paper; Paper products, converted; Water, pasteurized: packaged in cans, bottles, etc.
Ch Bd: Marshall D Sorokwasz
**VP:* Susan M Atkins
**VP:* Jeff Boren
**VP:* John L Graves
Manager: Adam Smith

D-U-N-S 10-539-4956
IMPRIVATA INC
(*Suby of* IMPRIVATA INTERMEDIATE HOLDINGS, INC.)
10 Maguire Rd Ste 125, Lexington, MA 02421-3110
Tel (781) 674-2700 *Founded/Ownrshp* 2001
Sales 119.1MM *EMP* 452[E]
SIC 7372 7382 Prepackaged software; Application computer software; Business oriented computer software; Security systems services
Pr: Gus Malezis
CFO: Jeffrey Kalowski
Chf Mktg O: Clay Ritchey
Ofcr: Sean Kelly
Ofcr: Kelliann McCabe
Sr VP: Geoff Hogan
Sr VP: Christopher Shaw
VP: Barbara Dumery
VP: John Milton
VP: Aaron Miri
VP: Chris Woodham

D-U-N-S 00-997-1727
■ IMPSAT FIBER NETWORKS INC
(*Suby of* LEVEL 3 GC LIMITED)
2040 N Dixie Hwy, Wilton Manors, FL 33305-2255
Tel (954) 779-7171 *Founded/Ownrshp* 2007
Sales 111.2MM[E] *EMP* 1,352
SIC 4899 Communication signal enhancement network system
Ch Bd: Ricardo Verdagaer
COO: Hector Alonzo
CFO: Hector Alonso
Ex VP: Marcelo Girotti
Ex VP: Mariano Torre Gomez
Sr VP: Guillermo V Pardo
Sr VP: Jose Torres
VP: Laurinda Pang

IMRF
See ILLINOIS MUNICIPAL RETIREMENT FUND

IMS
See INTERNATIONAL MEDICATION SYSTEMS LTD

IMS
See INTERNATIONAL MILL SERVICE INC

IMS
See INTEGRATED MEDICAL SYSTEMS INTERNATIONAL INC

D-U-N-S 17-786-0801 EXP
IMS COMPANIES LLC
1 Innovation Dr, Des Plaines, IL 60016-3161
Tel (847) 391-8100 *Founded/Ownrshp* 2002
Sales 675.0MM[E] *EMP* 1,316[E]
SIC 3469 8711 3679 3714 3444 Metal stampings; Engineering services; Harness assemblies for electronic use: wire or cable; Gears, motor vehicle; Sheet metal specialties, not stamped
CEO: Mark Simanton
**COO:* James Talarek
**VP:* Steve Szczech

D-U-N-S 02-302-0097
IMS HEALTH INC
(*Suby of* HEALTHCARE TECHNOLOGY INTERMEDIATE HOLDINGS INC) ★
100 Ims Dr, Parsippany, NJ 07054-2957
Tel (203) 448-4600 *Founded/Ownrshp* 2010
Sales 2.6MMM *EMP* 7,275
SIC 7379 Computer related maintenance services
CEO: ARI Bousbib
**Treas:* Jeffrey Ford
**Sr VP:* Harvey A Ashman
VP: Tom Kinsley
VP: Andrei Stoica
VP: Emanuele Triggiano
VP: Robert Wahl
Dir IT: Jim Hundemer
Tech Mgr: John Villalon
VP Sls: Steve Jennings
Snr PM: Pierre Botros
Board of Directors: Karen Katen

IMSCO
See INTERNATIONAL MANAGEMENT SERVICES CO INC

IMT GROUP
See IMT INSURANCE CO

D-U-N-S 06-962-7883
IMT INSURANCE CO
IMT GROUP
4445 Corporate Dr Ste 100, West Des Moines, IA 50266-5999
Tel (515) 327-2777 *Founded/Ownrshp* 1883
Sales NA *EMP* 189
SIC 6331 7374 Property damage insurance; Fire, marine & casualty insurance & carriers; Data processing service
VP: Sean Kennedy
**Treas:* Gregory J Blythe
Sr VP: Jodi Bybee
**Sr VP:* Dennis Patterson
**VP:* Brad Buchanan
**VP:* Chris Owenson
**VP:* Mark Vasey
Dir IT: Tom Minger
Dir IT: Anne West
IT Man: Terry Staton
Opers Mgr: Jeff Wilson
Board of Directors: Sharon K Heaton, Wilmer D Honnold, Richard M Willis

IMTT
See INTERNATIONAL-MATEX TANK TERMINALS

D-U-N-S 83-174-0464
■ IN HOME HEALTH LLC
HEARTLAND HM HALTHCARE HOSPICE
(*Suby of* MANOR CARE OF AMERICA INC) ★
333 N Summit St, Toledo, OH 43604-1531
Tel (419) 252-5500 *Founded/Ownrshp* 2010
Sales 25.8MM[E] *EMP* 1,807[E]
SIC 8082 Home health care services

D-U-N-S 10-203-3461 IMP
IN TOUCH MINISTRIES INC
INTOUCH MINISTRY
3836 Dekalb Tec Pkwy, Atlanta, GA 30340-3604
Tel (770) 451-1001 *Founded/Ownrshp* 1982
Sales 88.5MM *EMP* 200
Accts Lb Habif Arogeti & Wynne Llp
SIC 7922 Television program, including commercial producers; Radio producers
CEO: Phillip Bowen
**Pr:* Charles F Stanley
COO: Brad Cornell
CFO: Anita Clift
**CFO:* Mitch Crowe
Sr VP: Van Mylar
Ex Dir: Wayne Odom
Dir IT: Caleb Santos
IT Man: Holly Vaughn
Prd Mgr: Gary Longenecker
Trfc Mgr: Michael Hudson

IN VENTIVE COMMERCIAL SERVICES
See VENTIV HEALTH INC

D-U-N-S 02-914-4821
IN-N-OUT BURGERS
4199 Campus Dr Ste 900, Irvine, CA 92612-8604
Tel (949) 509-6200 *Founded/Ownrshp* 1963
Sales 365.4MM[E] *EMP* 10,000
SIC 5812 Fast-food restaurant, chain
Pr: Lynsi Martinez
CFO: Roger Kotch
**Treas:* Tom Martin
**Ex VP:* Darrell Chambliss
**Ex VP:* Ken Iriart
**Sr VP:* Kenneth Rose
VP: Keith Brazeau
**VP:* Jim Little
VP: Arnold M Wensinger
Dir Risk M: Michael Leavins
Dir Soc: Jennifer Knox
Dir Soc: Monique Macalinao
Dir Soc: Jordan Visu

D-U-N-S 01-525-2468 IMP
INA CHUBB HOLDINGS INC
(FORMERLY ACE INA HOLDINGS, INC.)
(*Suby of* CHUBB GROUP HOLDINGS INC) ★
436 Walnut St, Philadelphia, PA 19106-3703
Tel (215) 640-1000 *Founded/Ownrshp* 1998
Sales NA *EMP* 3,471
SIC 6411 Insurance agents, brokers & service
CEO: Dominic Frederico
Pr: John Moore
**Pr:* Susan Rivera
**Ex VP:* Bruce L Kessler
Sr VP: Craig Hanrahan
Sr VP: Robert Omrod
Sr VP: Alexander Wells
VP: Mike Driscoll
VP: Diane Herkness
**VP:* Steven Reiss
Exec: Rosmary Hernandez
Exec: Steven Roth

D-U-N-S 04-470-1894
INA CORP
(*Suby of* INA CHUBB HOLDINGS INC) ★
1601 Chestnut St Ste 1, Philadelphia, PA 19192-0004
Tel (215) 761-1000 *Founded/Ownrshp* 1983
Sales NA *EMP* 3,200
SIC 6331 Property damage insurance; Fire, marine & casualty insurance & carriers
Pr: Gerald A Isom
Treas: Robert K Gross
Sr VP: Robert P Irvan
VP: Paul Bergsternsson
VP: Robert Bradley
VP: Harry E Hoyt
VP: Robert A Kingsley Jr
VP: John A Murphy Jr
VP: Paul H Rohrkemper
VP: James A Sears
Div/Sub He: Caleb Fowler

D-U-N-S 16-189-3557 IMP/EXP
INALFA ROOF SYSTEMS INC
INALFA-HOLLANDIA
(*Suby of* INALFA ROOF SYSTEMS GROUP B.V.)
1370 Pacific Dr, Auburn Hills, MI 48326-1569
Tel (248) 371-3060 *Founded/Ownrshp* 2011
Sales 359.4MM[E] *EMP* 630
SIC 3714 Sun roofs, motor vehicle
Pr: Ton Hougen
CFO: Wim Das
**CFO:* Mary S Drexler
**Ex VP:* Mike Smith
Tech Mgr: Steve Schornak
Plnt Mgr: Mario Diaz

INALFA-HOLLANDIA
See INALFA ROOF SYSTEMS INC

D-U-N-S 10-749-4960
INAMAR LTD
(*Suby of* ACE US HOLDINGS INC) ★
1601 Chestnut St, Philadelphia, PA 19192-0003
Tel (215) 640-1000 *Founded/Ownrshp* 1977
Sales NA *EMP* 1,000
SIC 6321 Accident & health insurance
CEO: Bryan Dowd
VP: M T Lebo

D-U-N-S 19-609-4283
■ INC AEROJET ROCKETDYNE OF DE
(*Suby of* AEROJET ROCKETDYNE HOLDINGS INC) ★
8900 De Soto Ave, Canoga Park, CA 91304-1967
Tel (818) 586-1000 *Founded/Ownrshp* 2013
Sales 708.4MM[E] *EMP* 2,000[E]
SIC 2869 3724 Rocket engine fuel, organic; Aircraft engines & engine parts
CEO: Eileen P Drake
Sr VP: Paul Meyer
**VP:* Pete Gleszer
Genl Mgr: Yvette Velasquez
CIO: Steven Miller
IT Man: Timothy Durand
IT Man: Dennis Gerik

INC CSE W-INDUSTRIES
See W CSE INDUSTRIES INC

D-U-N-S 07-959-3183
▲ INC RESEARCH HOLDINGS INC
3201 Beechleaf Ct Ste 600, Raleigh, NC 27604-1500
Tel (919) 876-9300 *Founded/Ownrshp* 1998
Sales 1.4MMM *EMP* 6,400[E]
Tkr Sym INCR *Exch* NGS
SIC 8731 Commercial physical research; Biological research
CEO: D Jamie Macdonald
Pr: Tara Fitzgerald
Pr: Michael Gibertini
Pr: Alistair Macdonald
CFO: Gregory S Rush
Ofcr: Christopher L Gaenzle

D-U-N-S 96-362-1776
■ INC RESEARCH LLC
(*Suby of* INC RESEARCH HOLDINGS INC) ★
3201 Beechleaf Ct Ste 600, Raleigh, NC 27604-1500
Tel (919) 876-9300 *Founded/Ownrshp* 2010
Sales 1.0MMM[E] *EMP* 5,119
SIC 8731 Medical research, commercial
CEO: Jamie Macdonald
**Pr:* John Potthoff
**CEO:* James T Ogle
**COO:* Alistair Macdonald
**CFO:* David Gill
CFO: Dan Harnett
CFO: Gregory S Rush
CFO: Jim Stelten
Treas: Thomas Zajkowski
Ofcr: Michael L Corrado
Ex VP: John Barker
**Ex VP:* Neil Ferguson
Ex VP: Nicholas Kenny
Ex VP: Mark Roseman
Sr VP: Richard Mark
Sr VP: Chris Smyth
Sr VP: Manfred Weiler
Sr VP: Tom Zoda
VP: Paula Bain
VP: Kevin Brandenburg
VP: Tim Dietlin

D-U-N-S 07-838-8867
INCEDO INC
IBTECHNOLOGY SOLUTIONS
2350 Mission College Blvd, Santa Clara, CA 95054-1532
Tel (408) 531-6040 *Founded/Ownrshp* 2012
Sales 25.5MM *EMP* 1,200[E]
SIC 7379 Computer related consulting services
CEO: Ashish Choudhary
Pr: Arun Ubale
Ofcr: Yelena Kharisova
VP: Sanjeev Sardana
Exec: Pawneet Kaur
Prgrm Mgr: Vishakha Agarwal
Snr Sftwr: Gautam Acharya
Snr Sftwr: Divya Agarwal
Snr Sftwr: Ashish Kapoor

D-U-N-S 08-045-8340
INCEPTION PARENT INC
9 W 57th St Fl 43, New York, NY 10019-2700
Tel (212) 515-3200 *Founded/Ownrshp* 2016
Sales 2.0MMM[E] *EMP* 6,189[E]
SIC 6726 Management investment funds, closed-end
CEO: Leon Black

INCOMM
See INTERACTIVE COMMUNICATIONS INTERNATIONAL INC

D-U-N-S 13-182-5510
INCOMM HOLDINGS INC
250 Williams St Nw Fl 5, Atlanta, GA 30303-1032
Tel (770) 240-6100 *Founded/Ownrshp* 1992
Sales NA *EMP* 884
SIC 6099 Clearinghouse associations, bank or check
CEO: M Brooks Smith
**Pr:* Phil Graves
**CFO:* Scott Meyerhoff
CFO: Ken Taylor
Treas: Kirk Callwood
**Ex VP:* Brian Parlotto
Ex VP: Robert Skiba
Ex VP: Frank Squill
Off Mgr: Dasha Lackey

D-U-N-S 05-810-0772
INCONTACT INC
UCN
(*Suby of* NICE LTD)
75 W Towne Ridge Pkwy # 1, Sandy, UT 84070-5522
Tel (801) 320-3200 *Founded/Ownrshp* 2016
Sales 221.9MM *EMP* 1,015[E]
SIC 7372 4813 Prepackaged software; Application computer software; Local & long distance telephone communications
CEO: Paul Jarman
CFO: Gregory S Ayers
Chf Mktg O: Randy Littleson
Ofcr: Trent Savage
Ofcr: Rajeev Shrivastava
Ex VP: William Robinson
Sr VP: Jeff Canter
VP: Rusty Jensen
Mng Dir: Mitch Galutera
Snr Sftwr: Clark Vantussenbrook
QA Dir: Karson Butterfield

D-U-N-S 55-696-7347
▲ INCYTE CORP
1801 Augustine Cut Off, Wilmington, DE 19803-4404
Tel (302) 498-6700 *Founded/Ownrshp* 1991
Sales 753.7MM *EMP* 692[E]
Tkr Sym INCY *Exch* NGS
SIC 2834 Pharmaceutical preparations
Ch Bd: Herve Hoppenot
CFO: David W Gryska
Ofcr: David Stollman
Ex VP: Reid M Huber
Ex VP: Eric H Siegel
Ex VP: Paula J Swain
Ex VP: Wenqing Yao
VP: Pamela M Murphy
VP: Jayant Shukla
VP: Matthew Spear
VP: William Williams
VP Bus Dev: Erin Hugger
Assoc Dir: Maryanne Covington
Assoc Dir: Trupti Sheth
Assoc Dir: Tim Young
Board of Directors: Julian C Baker, Paul A Brooke, Paul J Clancy, Wendy L Dixon, Paul A Friedman

D-U-N-S 07-026-1144
IND SCHOOL DIST 621
MOUNDS VIEW SCHOOL DISTRICT 62
350 Highway 96 W, Saint Paul, MN 55126-1951
Tel (651) 621-6000 *Founded/Ownrshp* 1952
Sales 168.4MM *EMP* 1,450
Accts Malloy Montague Karnowski R
SIC 8211 8742 Public senior high school; Public special education school; Public junior high school; Public elementary school; Management consulting services
Bd of Dir: Sager Marre
Schl Brd P: Amy Jones

D-U-N-S 13-120-3945
INDECK ENERGY SERVICES INC
600 N Buffalo Grove Rd # 300, Buffalo Grove, IL 60089-2432
Tel (847) 520-3212 *Founded/Ownrshp* 1985
Sales 296.8MM[E] *EMP* 301
SIC 4911 Distribution, electric power; Generation, electric power
Pr: Lawrence A Lagowski
Pr: David Hicks
CFO: Thomas M Capone
Sr VP: Lawrence A Lgowski
VP: Michael Dubois
VP: William R Garth
VP: David N Hicks
VP: Joseph M Oskorep
VP Bus Dev: Kathleen Heffley

VP Opers: John E Har
Plnt Mgr: Kris Zimmermann

D-U-N-S 02-566-2586 EXP
INDECK POWER EQUIPMENT CO
1111 Willis Ave, Wheeling, IL 60090-5841
Tel (847) 541-8300 *Founded/Ownrshp* 1985
Sales 87.0MM[E] *EMP* 93[E]
Accts Bdo Seidman Llp Chicago Ill
SIC 5084 5074 7359 Power plant machinery; Engines & parts, diesel; Boilers, power (industrial); Equipment rental & leasing
Pr: Marsha Forsythe Fournier
Ch Bd: Gerald Forsythe
**CFO:* Lawrence A Lagowski
CFO: Lawrence A Lgowski

D-U-N-S 00-233-8713 IMP/EXP
INDEL INC
(*Suby of* ROWAN TECHNOLOGIES, INC.)
10 Indel Ave, Rancocas, NJ 08073
Tel (609) 267-9000 *Founded/Ownrshp* 1956
Sales 495.3MM[E] *EMP* 4,000[E]
SIC 3567 3548 3822 3541 3563

D-U-N-S 07-951-0482
INDEPENDENCE BLUE CROSS LLC
(*Suby of* INDEPENDENCE HEALTH GROUP INC) ★
1901 Market St Fl 32, Philadelphia, PA 19103-1465
Tel (215) 241-2400 *Founded/Ownrshp* 2016
Sales NA *EMP* 7,691[E]
SIC 6324 6411 8748 Hospital & medical service plans; Medical insurance claim processing, contract or fee basis; Employee programs administration
**Pr:* Daniel J Hilferty
**COO:* Yvette D Bright
**CFO:* Alan Krigstein
Sr VP: Richard Neeson
Sr VP: Richard Snyder
Sr VP: Steven I Udvarhelyi
CIO: Michael Green
Dir IT: Chuck Stefanosky
Prd Mgr: Carlos Smith
Sls&Mrk Ex: Koleen Cavanaugh
VP Mktg: Scott Post

D-U-N-S 10-225-5416
INDEPENDENCE CARE SYSTEMS INC
257 Park Ave S Fl 2, New York, NY 10010-7381
Tel (212) 584-2500 *Founded/Ownrshp* 2002
Sales 266.9MM *EMP* 1[E]
Accts Baker Tilly Virchow Krause Llp
SIC 8322 6324 Social services for the handicapped; Hospital & medical service plans
Pr: Rick Surpin
VP: Ann Berson
VP: John Caticchio
VP: Kathryn Haslanger
Exec: Regina Estela
QA Dir: Adell Kraivanger
Dir IT: Kerri O Lopez
Pr Dir: Loreen Loonie

INDEPENDENCE CITY HALL
See CITY OF INDEPENDENCE

INDEPENDENCE CONSTRUCTION MTLS
See ALLAN MYERS LP

D-U-N-S 07-841-8792
INDEPENDENCE CONTRACT DRILLING INC
ICD
11601 N Galayda St, Houston, TX 77086-3617
Tel (281) 598-1230 *Founded/Ownrshp* 2012
Sales 88.4MM *EMP* 305
Tkr Sym ICD *Exch* NYS
SIC 1381 Drilling oil & gas wells
Pr: Byron A Dunn
**Ch Bd:* Thomas R Bates Jr
CFO: Philip A Choyce
Sr VP: David C Brown
Sr VP: J Scott Thompson
VP: Christopher K Menefee
VP: Aaron W Mueller
VP Opers: Philip A Dalrymple
Board of Directors: James Crandell, Arthur Einav, Matthew D Fitzgerald, Daniel F McNease

D-U-N-S 00-452-5580 IMP
INDEPENDENCE EXCAVATING INC (OH)
5720 E Schaaf Rd, Independence, OH 44131-1396
Tel (216) 524-1700 *Founded/Ownrshp* 1956, 1962
Sales 152.4MM *EMP* 350
Accts Ciuni & Panichi Cleveland Oh
SIC 1629 1794 1611 1771 1795 Land preparation construction; Excavation work; General contractor, highway & street construction; Concrete repair; Demolition, buildings & other structures
CEO: Victor Digeronimo Sr
**Pr:* Victor Digeronimo Jr
Ofcr: Tom Steblinski
**VP:* Rick Digeronimo
CTO: Jeff Wisniewski

D-U-N-S 07-950-4061
INDEPENDENCE HEALTH GROUP INC
1901 Market St, Philadelphia, PA 19103-1480
Tel (215) 241-2400 *Founded/Ownrshp* 2014
Sales NA *EMP* 9,500[E]
SIC 6321 Accident & health insurance
Pr: Daniel J Hilferty
**CFO:* Alan Krigstein
**Ex VP:* Christopher Cashman
**Ex VP:* Richard J Neeson
**Ex VP:* Paul A Tufano
**Ex VP:* I Steven Udvarhelyi
**VP:* Yvette D Bright

D-U-N-S 02-660-3407
■ **INDEPENDENCE HOLDING CO**
(*Suby of* GENEVE HOLDINGS INC) ★
96 Cummings Point Rd, Stamford, CT 06902-7919
Tel (203) 358-8000 *Founded/Ownrshp* 1980
Sales NA *EMP* 600[E]
Tkr Sym IHC *Exch* NYS
SIC 6311 6321 Life insurance; Accident & health insurance
Ch Bd: Roy T K Thung
**COO:* David T Kettig
**CFO:* Teresa A Herbert
**Sr VP:* Larry R Graber

D-U-N-S 00-173-5091
INDEPENDENCE HOSPITAL INDEMNITY PLAN INC
BLUE CROSS
(*Suby of* INDEPENDENCE BLUE CROSS LLC) ★
1901 Market St, Philadelphia, PA 19103-1480
Tel (215) 241-2400 *Founded/Ownrshp* 1938
Sales NA *EMP* 9,500
SIC 6321 Accident & health insurance
Pr: Daniel J Hilferty
Pr: Brett A Mayfield
**COO:* Christopher D Butler
COO: Michele Petrone
**CFO:* Alan Krigstein
**Ch:* Robert H Young
Treas: Gene Brown
Ofcr: Karen Lessin
**Ex VP:* Yvette Bright
Ex VP: Richard J Neeson
Sr VP: Yvette D Bright
Sr VP: Stephen P Fera
Sr VP: Kathryn A Galarneau
Sr VP: Mucheal A Green
Sr VP: John Janney
Sr VP: John R Janney
Sr VP: Brian Lobley
Sr VP: Carolyn W Luther
**Sr VP:* Daniel Lyons
Sr VP: Kathleen A McEndy
**Sr VP:* Donna O Moore

INDEPENDENCE MEDICAL
See RGH ENTERPRISES INC

D-U-N-S 01-583-6974 IMP
■ **INDEPENDENCE OILFIELD CHEMICALS LLC**
(*Suby of* INNOSPEC INC) ★
1450 Lake Robbins Dr # 400, The Woodlands, TX 77380-3263
Tel (713) 936-4340 *Founded/Ownrshp* 2012
Sales 109.0MM[E] *EMP* 200
SIC 2899 5169 Chemical preparations; Chemicals & allied products
Pr: Jeff Hibbeler
**CFO:* Corbin Barnes
**Ex VP:* Jaime De Los Santos
**Sr VP:* Jeff Dawson
Sr VP: Clark Emrich
**Sr VP:* Butch Gothard
Sr VP: Larry Hodnett
VP: Rya Dhana
Sls Mgr: Tina Sonnier

D-U-N-S 96-727-8057
INDEPENDENCE REALTY TRUST INC
2929 Arch St Ste 1650, Philadelphia, PA 19104-2864
Tel (215) 243-9000 *Founded/Ownrshp* 2011
Sales 109.5MM *EMP* 300[E]
Accts Kpmg Llp Philadelphia Pennsy
SIC 6798 Real estate investment trusts
Ch Bd: Scott F Schaeffer
Pr: Farrell M Ender
CFO: James J Sebra

D-U-N-S 07-626-0082
INDEPENDENCE SCHOOL BOARD OF EDUCATION
201 N Forest Ave, Independence, MO 64050-2696
Tel (816) 521-5300 *Founded/Ownrshp* 1866
Sales 182.8MM *EMP* 1,800
SIC 8211 School board
Pr: Ann Franklin
**Treas:* Jill Esry
Top Exec: Carl Stafford
Genl Mgr: Dan Sherman
Dir IT: Brent Catlett
Pr Dir: Jana Corrie
Pr Dir: Sherry Potter
Teacher Pr: Linda G Gray Smith
Psych: Yvonne Rito

D-U-N-S 07-998-8284
INDEPENDENCE SCHOOL DISTRICT
201 N Forest Ave Ste 30, Independence, MO 64050-2697
Tel (816) 521-5300 *Founded/Ownrshp* 2015
Sales 18.3MM[E] *EMP* 1,800[E]
SIC 8211 Public elementary & secondary schools

D-U-N-S 06-337-5086
INDEPENDENCE TITLE CO
ITCOA
5900 Sheph Mount Cove Bld, Austin, TX 78730
Tel (512) 372-8455 *Founded/Ownrshp* 2006
Sales NA *EMP* 130[E]
SIC 6361 Title insurance
CEO: Jay Southworth
**COO:* Brian Pitman
Ofcr: Phyllis Anderson
**Sr VP:* Chad Decker
**Sr VP:* Terri Morrison
**Sr VP:* Judith Sullings
VP: Denise Holmes
VP: Dan Phares
Area Mgr: Jason L Bragg

D-U-N-S 04-943-2446
■ **INDEPENDENT ADVERTISING INC**
HILL HOLLIDAY
(*Suby of* INTERPUBLIC GROUP OF COMPANIES INC) ★
53 State St, Boston, MA 02109-2820
Tel (617) 437-1600 *Founded/Ownrshp* 1998
Sales 103.5MM[E] *EMP* 767
SIC 7311 7331 7389 8732 Advertising agencies; Direct mail advertising services; Promoters of shows & exhibitions; Market analysis or research
CEO: Mike Sheehan
**Pr:* Karen Kaplan
**CFO:* Steve Andrews
**Treas:* Ellen Johnson
**V Ch Bd:* Richard Pantano
**Ofcr:* Dirk Herbert
Ex VP: Graham Ritchie
Sr VP: Mariusz Pisarek
Sr VP: Kim Portrate
VP: Rowena Alston
VP: Liz Brown
VP: Michael Burns
VP: Adam Cahill
VP: Summer Dembek
VP: Wilma Epstein
VP: Mary Gallagher
VP: Karen Gardiner
VP: Dan Gardner
VP: Holly Gross
VP: Lauren Herman
VP: Luke Higgins

D-U-N-S 05-585-7395
■ **INDEPENDENT BANK CORP**
(*Suby of* INDEPENDENT BANK CORP) ★
230 W Main St, Ionia, MI 48846-1655
Tel (616) 527-2400 *Founded/Ownrshp* 1974
Sales NA *EMP* 896[E]
Accts Crowe Horwath Llp Grand Rapi
SIC 6022 State commercial banks
Pr: William B Kessel
**Pr:* William J Boer
CFO: William R Kohls
Ofcr: Bernie Marvin
Ofcr: Tamara Pearson
Assoc VP: Coni Burns
Ex VP: Stefanie M Kimball
Ex VP: A Perry
Sr VP: Martha Blandford
Sr VP: Charles Schadler
VP: Larry Arendt
VP: Lisa Brown
VP: Sherry Conklin
VP: Jordan Glassco
VP: Melissa Hewlett
VP: Pamela Martin
VP: Cheryl McKellar
VP: Brian Oathout
VP: Kevin Pierce
VP: Trevor Tooker
VP: David Verkeyn
Board of Directors: William J Boer

D-U-N-S 06-586-9216
▲ **INDEPENDENT BANK CORP** (MI)
4200 E Beltline Ave Ne, Grand Rapids, MI 49525-9783
Tel (616) 527-5820 *Founded/Ownrshp* 1973
Sales NA *EMP* 831[E]
Tkr Sym IBCP *Exch* NGS
SIC 6022 State commercial banks
Pr: William B Kessel
**Ch Bd:* Michael M Magee Jr
CFO: Robert N Shuster
Ofcr: Dennis J Mack
Ex VP: Mark L Collins
Ex VP: Stefanie M Kimball
Ex VP: David C Reglin
Sr VP: Richard E Butler
Sr VP: Peter R Graves
Sr VP: James J Twarozynski
Board of Directors: William J Boer, Joan A Budden, Stephen L Gulis Jr, Terry L Haske, Christina Keller, James E McCarty, Matthew J Missad, Charles C Van Loan

D-U-N-S 15-216-0768
▲ **INDEPENDENT BANK CORP**
2036 Washington St, Hanover, MA 02339-1617
Tel (781) 878-6100 *Founded/Ownrshp* 1985
Sales NA *EMP* 2,321
Tkr Sym INDB *Exch* NGS
SIC 6022 State commercial banks
Pr: Christopher Oddleifson
**Ch Bd:* Donna L Abelli
Pr: Bruce Bumpus
COO: Denis Sheahan
CFO: Robert Cozzone
Ofcr: Jeremy Kimbrell
Ex VP: Jane L Lundquist
Sr VP: Robert D Cozzone
VP: Thomas Banks
VP: John Barron
VP: Nanette Davidson
VP: Scott Ewing
VP: Raymond Fuerschbach
VP: Jeffrey Guimond
VP: Pasqual Kioumejian
VP: Elizabeth Lynch
VP: Tracey Scalata
VP: Richard Weir
VP: William Zawacki
Board of Directors: Frederick Taw, William P Bissonnette, Brian S Tedeschi, Kevin J Jones, Thomas R Venables, Mary L Lentz, Eileen C Miskell, John J Morrissey, Daniel F O'brien, Carl Ribeiro, John H Spurr Jr, Maurice H Sullivan Jr

D-U-N-S 83-005-0170
▲ **INDEPENDENT BANK GROUP INC**
1600 Redbud Blvd Ste 400, McKinney, TX 75069-3258
Tel (972) 548-9004 *Founded/Ownrshp* 2002
Sales NA *EMP* 587
Tkr Sym IBTX *Exch* NGM
SIC 6021 National commercial banks
Ch Bd: David R Brooks
COO: James C White
CFO: Michelle S Hickox
**V Ch Bd:* Daniel W Brooks
Mktg Dir: Peggy Smolen

D-U-N-S 13-039-4521
INDEPENDENT BANKERS FINANCIAL CORP
11701 Luna Rd, Farmers Branch, TX 75234-6026
Tel (972) 650-6000 *Founded/Ownrshp* 1983
Sales NA *EMP* 626
SIC 6712 Bank holding companies
Pr: Michael O'Rourke
CFO: Terry Hoover
**Sec:* Patricia Blackshear
Sr VP: Barry Musgrove
Sr VP: Deborah Nelson
Sr VP: Gregary Todd

INDEPENDENT BANKERSBANK THE
See TIB - INDEPENDENT BANKERSBANK

D-U-N-S 01-954-8368
INDEPENDENT BREWERS UNITED CORP
MAGIC HAT BREWING COMPANY
(*Suby of* NORTHAMERICAN BREWERIES) ★
431 Pine St Ste G12, Burlington, VT 05401-5093
Tel (802) 862-6114 *Founded/Ownrshp* 2010
Sales 85.3MM[E] *EMP* 573[E]
SIC 2082 2084 Malt beverages; Wines
Pr: Martin R Kelly
Treas: Eric Peterson
**VP:* Steve Hood

D-U-N-S 79-545-4834
INDEPENDENT ELECTRIC SUPPLY CORP
41 Innerbelt Rd, Somerville, MA 02143-4417
Tel (617) 625-5155 *Founded/Ownrshp* 1992
Sales 85.1MM[E] *EMP* 70
Accts Markovitz Dugan & Associates
SIC 5063 Electrical apparatus & equipment
Pr: Daniel H Gray
**CEO:* William L Gray
**Treas:* Bruce Gray
VP: Marc Reisfelt
Brnch Mgr: Dave Paolicelli

D-U-N-S 06-912-8924
INDEPENDENT ELECTRIC SUPPLY INC (CA)
(*Suby of* SONEPAR USA) ★
2001 Marina Blvd, San Leandro, CA 94577-3204
Tel (520) 908-7900 *Founded/Ownrshp* 1973
Sales 601.4MM[E] *EMP* 525[E]
SIC 5063 Electrical apparatus & equipment; Wiring devices; Electrical construction materials; Cable conduit
Pr: Doug Walo
CFO: Greg Adrian
Prin: Timothy Birky
Brnch Mgr: Kevin Horn
Sls Mgr: Bob Sitzman
Sales Asso: Noe Garcia
Sales Asso: Ed Little
Sales Asso: Alonzo Pangilinan
Sales Asso: Brian Smartt
Sales Asso: Vanessa Williams

D-U-N-S 09-933-0227
INDEPENDENT HEALTH ASSOCIATION INC
511 Farber Lakes Dr Ste 2, Williamsville, NY 14221-8272
Tel (716) 631-3001 *Founded/Ownrshp* 1980
Sales NA *EMP* 1,050
Accts Deloitte & Touche Llp Buffalo
SIC 6324 Health maintenance organization (HMO), insurance only
Pr: Michael C D
**CFO:* Mark Johnson

D-U-N-S 12-849-1706
INDEPENDENT HEALTH CORP
(*Suby of* INDEPENDENT HEALTH ASSOCIATION INC) ★
511 Farber Lakes Dr Ste 2, Buffalo, NY 14221-8272
Tel (716) 631-3001 *Founded/Ownrshp* 1984
Sales NA *EMP* 900[E]
Accts Deloitte Tax Llp Detroit Mi
SIC 6324 Hospital & medical service plans
CEO: Michael C D
**CFO:* Mark Johnson
Bd of Dir: Jim Pokoj
Ofcr: Amy McDonald
Ex VP: Jill Syracuse
Sr VP: Ann Pentkowski
VP: Kathy Glieco
VP: Melissa Hayes
VP: Pamela Menard
VP: Frank Sava
VP: Robert Tracy
Exec: Gord Cumming

D-U-N-S 79-097-6588
INDEPENDENT INSURANCE INVESTMENTS INC
(*Suby of* INVERNESS MANAGEMENT LLC) ★
1000 River Rd Ste 300, Conshohocken, PA 19428-2440
Tel (610) 832-4940 *Founded/Ownrshp* 2005
Sales NA *EMP* 820
SIC 6331 6411 Automobile insurance; Property damage insurance; Insurance agents, brokers & service
CEO: William Lockhorn

D-U-N-S 10-849-2638
INDEPENDENT ORDER OF ODD FELLOWS
PIKES PEAK LODGE 38
575 S Union Blvd, Colorado Springs, CO 80910-3458
Tel (719) 633-2002 *Founded/Ownrshp* 1880
Sales 514.7MM[E] *EMP* 171[E]
SIC 8641 Fraternal associations
Sales Exec: George Epperson
**Prin:* Craig Highland

D-U-N-S 17-788-3816
INDEPENDENT PHARMACY COOPERATIVE
1550 Columbus St, Sun Prairie, WI 53590-3901
Tel (608) 825-9556 *Founded/Ownrshp* 1984
Sales 1.0MMM *EMP* 65
Accts Grant Thornton Llp Appleton
SIC 5122 7299 Drugs & drug proprietaries; Buyers' club
Pr: Don Anderson
VP: Robert Tinsley
Exec: Michelle R Johnson
Trfc Mgr: Janet Spellbring
Sales Exec: Dean Slaugenhoup
Mktg Dir: Mindy Herrmann
Sls Dir: Tim Knight
Sls Dir: Mike Mitchell
Sls Dir: Stacy Tuschen
Manager: Jeff Haag
Sales Asso: Lisa Hawkins

D-U-N-S 00-176-5932 IMP
INDEPENDENT PIPE & SUPPLY BUSINESS TRUST
6 Whitman Rd, Canton, MA 02021-2706
Tel (781) 828-8500 *Founded/Ownrshp* 1930
Sales 93.8MM[E] *EMP* 100

SIC 5074 Heating equipment (hydronic); Plumbing fittings & supplies; Pipes & fittings, plastic; Plumbing & heating valves
CEO: Jeffrey Nierman
**Ch Bd:* Edward J Nierman
**Ch Bd:* Sheldon Nierman
COO: Larry Pengel
Treas: Sharon Norton
**Ex VP:* Alan H Mirson
VP: Eric Kessler
Sls Mgr: Chris Andersen
Sls Mgr: Ronald Belliveau
Sls Mgr: George Niemiec
Sales Asso: Dan Dockham

D-U-N-S 62-344-0591 EXP
INDEPENDENT PROCUREMENT ALLIANCE PROGRAM LLC
IPAP
1650 Tri Park Way Ste B, Appleton, WI 54914-1698
Tel (920) 832-1100 *Founded/Ownrshp* 1998
Sales 425.0MM *EMP* 25
SIC 5143 Dairy products, except dried or canned
Pr: Scott Eithun
IT Man: Brian Zoromski
Sls Mgr: Liz Bunker

D-U-N-S 05-433-1868 IMP
■ INDEPENDENT PROPANE CO LLC
(*Suby of* INERGY PROPANE LLC) ★
2591 Dallas Pkwy Ste 105, Frisco, TX 75034-8543
Tel (972) 731-5454 *Founded/Ownrshp* 1996
Sales 124.1MM^E *EMP* 1,008
SIC 5984 5172 Propane gas, bottled; Gases, liquefied petroleum (propane)
Pr: William R Moler
**Ch:* John J Sherman

INDEPENDENT PUBLISHERS GROUP
See CHICAGO REVIEW PRESS INC

D-U-N-S 95-992-1529
INDEPENDENT PURCHASING COOPERATIVE INC
9200 S Dadeland Blvd # 800, Miami, FL 33156-2758
Tel (305) 670-0041 *Founded/Ownrshp* 1996
Sales 171.9MM^E *EMP* 100^E
Accts Bdo Usa Llp Miami Florida
SIC 7389 Purchasing service
Pr: Jan Risi
Pr: Dennis Clabby
**CFO:* Ceoroger Trombino
Bd of Dir: Bill Cornelius
VP: Roger Trombino
Comm Dir: Robert Hopkins
Prgrm Mgr: Don Purser
Genl Mgr: Robert Yanno
Snr Sftwr: Ariel Alonso
Dir IT: James A Esposito
Dir IT: Fernando Mejia

INDEPENDENT PWR SYSTEMS & LGE
See LGE ELECTRICAL SALES INC

D-U-N-S 07-175-3248
INDEPENDENT SCHOOL DIST 625
ST. PAUL PUBLIC SCHOOLS
360 Colborne St, Saint Paul, MN 55102-3228
Tel (651) 767-8100 *Founded/Ownrshp* 1856
Sales 156.1MM^E *EMP* 6,500
Accts Kpmg Llp Minneapolis Mn
SIC 8299 Educational services
Pr: Kate Wilcox-Harris
Bd of Dir: John Brodrick
Dir Sec: Laura Olson
Prgrm Mgr: Faye Norton
CIO: Julie Huppertz
DP Exec: Steve Fox
IT Man: Nancy Demars-Wolfe
IT Man: Mary Engel
IT Man: Susan Hollingsworth
IT Man: Millard Neymark
IT Man: Greg Renner

D-U-N-S 07-177-6108
INDEPENDENT SCHOOL DISTRICT #535
ROCHESTER PUBLIC SCHOOLS
615 7th St Sw, Rochester, MN 55902-2052
Tel (507) 328-3000 *Founded/Ownrshp* 1859
Sales 228.7MM *EMP* 2,500
Accts Cliftonlarsonallen Llp Austi
SIC 8211 Public combined elementary & secondary school; Public special education school
**Treas:* John Carlson
Ex Dir: Brooke Bass
Off Mgr: Sandra Gibson
Dir IT: Cynthia Martenson

D-U-N-S 07-239-6823
INDEPENDENT SCHOOL DISTRICT 1 OF TULSA COUNTY
TULSA PUBLIC SCHOOLS
3027 S New Haven Ave, Tulsa, OK 74114-6131
Tel (918) 746-6800 *Founded/Ownrshp* 1907
Sales 365.8MM^E *EMP* 6,115
SIC 8211 Public elementary & secondary schools
Pr: Mr Gary Percefull
Dir Vol: Valerie Vanhoose
Treas: Mark A Poole
**Treas:* Joe Stoeptelwerth
Bd of Dir: Oma Copeland
Bd of Dir: Charles Greenough
Bd of Dir: David G Page
Bd of Dir: Barry L Steichen
**VP:* Ms Anna America
Mng Dir: Lincoln Cochran
Dir Sec: Gary Rudick

D-U-N-S 07-176-6745
INDEPENDENT SCHOOL DISTRICT 181
804 Oak St, Brainerd, MN 56401-3755
Tel (218) 454-6900 *Founded/Ownrshp* 1920
Sales 84.6MM *EMP* 700
Accts Clifton Larson Allen Llp Bra
SIC 8211 Public elementary & secondary schools
Comm Man: Jill Neumann
Schl Brd P: Tom Haglin
Schl Brd P: Ruth Nelson
Psych: Jeffrey Johnson
Snr Mgr: Amynda Hadfield

D-U-N-S 05-277-9287
INDEPENDENT SCHOOL DISTRICT 270
HOPKINS ALTERNATIVE PROGRAM IN
1001 Highway 7, Hopkins, MN 55305-4737
Tel (952) 988-4000 *Founded/Ownrshp* 1900
Sales 129.3MM *EMP* 1,334
Accts Cliftonlarsonallen Llp Minnea
SIC 8211 Public elementary & secondary schools
Ch: Wendy Donovan
Dir IT: Kathy Israel
IT Man: John Wetter
Nutrtnst: Yolanda Conley
Board of Directors: Curt Wallman

D-U-N-S 07-148-9827
INDEPENDENT SCHOOL DISTRICT 271
BLOOMINGTON PUB SCHL DST 271
1350 W 106th St, Bloomington, MN 55431-4152
Tel (952) 681-6400 *Founded/Ownrshp* 1918
Sales 98.9MM^E *EMP* 2,200
Accts Kern Dewenter Viere Ltd B
SIC 8211 Public elementary & secondary schools; Public elementary school; Public junior high school; Public senior high school
Ex Dir: David Heistad
Dir Sec: Michael Oxerough
Genl Mgr: Kim Agate
MIS Dir: John Weisser
IT Man: Emily Lambrecht
Schl Brd P: Dick Bergstrom
Teacher Pr: Mary Burroughs
Psych: Gretchen Johnson
Psych: Lauri Munoz
Psych: Nathan Schoch
Psych: Annie Stroup

D-U-N-S 09-391-6252
INDEPENDENT SCHOOL DISTRICT 273
EDINA PUBLIC SCHOOLS
5701 Normandale Rd, Minneapolis, MN 55424-2401
Tel (952) 848-3900 *Founded/Ownrshp* 1949
Sales 74.6MM^E *EMP* 1,200
Accts Malloy Montague Karnowski R
SIC 8211 Public elementary & secondary schools
Prin: Carol Meyer
HC Dir: Mary Heiman

D-U-N-S 07-175-7397
INDEPENDENT SCHOOL DISTRICT 279
OSSEO AREA PUBLIC SCHOOLS
11200 93rd Ave N, Maple Grove, MN 55369-3669
Tel (763) 391-7000 *Founded/Ownrshp* 1952
Sales 319.6MM *EMP* 2,700
Accts Maloy Montague Karnowski Ra
SIC 8211 Public elementary & secondary schools
**Ch:* Dean G Henke
Teacher Pr: Judy McDonald

D-U-N-S 07-649-2578
INDEPENDENT SCHOOL DISTRICT 281
ROBBINSDALE AREA SCHOOL DST
4148 Winnetka Ave N, Minneapolis, MN 55427-1210
Tel (763) 504-8000 *Founded/Ownrshp* 1915
Sales 129.5MM^E *EMP* 2,000
Accts Larsonallen Llp Minneapolis
SIC 8211 Public senior high school; Public junior high school
Ofcr: Alex Weber
**Ex Dir:* Stephanie Crosby
**Ex Dir:* Al Ickler
**Ex Dir:* Jeff Priess
**Ex Dir:* Lori Simon
Prgrm Mgr: Cynthia Smith
Pr Dir: Latisha Gray
Psych: Amie Wold
Psych: Dan Woodbury
Pgrm Dir: Kerry Froehlich
Pgrm Dir: Aviva Hillenbrand

D-U-N-S 03-798-9860
INDEPENDENT SCHOOL DISTRICT 52
7217 Se 15th St, Oklahoma City, OK 73110-5235
Tel (405) 737-4461 *Founded/Ownrshp* 1942
Sales 22.4MM^E *EMP* 1,350
SIC 8211 Public elementary & secondary schools

D-U-N-S 03-001-6422
INDEPENDENT SCHOOL DISTRICT 622 (MN)
2520 12th Ave E, Saint Paul, MN 55109-2420
Tel (651) 748-7622 *Founded/Ownrshp* 1942
Sales 58.9MM^E *EMP* 1,458
SIC 8211 Public elementary & secondary schools
Ex Dir: Theresa Auge
Ex Dir: Scott Duddeck
Genl Mgr: Ed McCarthy

D-U-N-S 10-225-0867
INDEPENDENT SCHOOL DISTRICT 623 (INC)
ROSEVILLE AREA SCHOOLS
1251 County Road B2 W, Saint Paul, MN 55113-3299
Tel (651) 635-1600 *Founded/Ownrshp* 1949
Sales 109.8MM *EMP* 962
Accts Cliftonlarsonallen Llp Minnea
SIC 8211 Public elementary & secondary schools
**CFO:* Barbara Anderson
Mktg Dir: Carrie Smith
Snr Mgr: Heather Brian

D-U-N-S 01-034-7839
INDEPENDENT SCHOOL DISTRICT 624 (INC)
WHITE BEAR LAKE AREA SCHOOLS
4855 Bloom Ave, White Bear Lake, MN 55110-5418
Tel (651) 407-7500 *Founded/Ownrshp* 1957
Sales 113.5MM *EMP* 1,000
Accts Malloy Montague Karnowski R
SIC 8211 Public elementary & secondary schools
Ex Dir: Pete Willcoxon Sr
IT Man: Steve Allen
Teacher Pr: Linda Goers

D-U-N-S 07-150-1092
INDEPENDENT SCHOOL DISTRICT 709
DULUTH PUBLIC SCHOOLS
215 N 1st Ave E, Duluth, MN 55802-2058
Tel (218) 336-8700 *Founded/Ownrshp* 1908
Sales 133.9MM *EMP* 2,300
Accts Wipfli Llp Duluth Minnesota
SIC 8211 Elementary school; Secondary school
Genl Mgr: Peggy Blalock
Schl Brd P: Judy Seliga-Punyko
Teacher Pr: Tim Sworsky
HC Dir: Jason Crane

D-U-N-S 07-651-0304
INDEPENDENT SCHOOL DISTRICT 831
FOREST LAKE AREA SCHOOL
6100 210th St N, Forest Lake, MN 55025-9617
Tel (651) 982-8100 *Founded/Ownrshp* 1918
Sales 86.3MM *EMP* 1,100
Accts Malloy Montague Karnowski R
SIC 8211 Public elementary school; Public junior high school; Public senior high school
Teacher Pr: Donna Friedmann

D-U-N-S 07-178-3930
INDEPENDENT SCHOOL DISTRICT 834
STILLWATER AREA SCHOOL DST
1875 Greeley St S, Stillwater, MN 55082-6079
Tel (651) 351-8340 *Founded/Ownrshp* 1955
Sales 57.0MM^E *EMP* 1,000
SIC 8211 Public elementary & secondary schools
Bd of Dir: Becky Webb
Ex Dir: Malinda Lansfeldt
Ex Dir: Robert McDowell
Teacher Pr: Cathy Moen
Psych: Kristina King
Psych: Liz Nelson

D-U-N-S 07-864-5561
INDEPENDENT SCHOOL DISTRICT 9 TULSA COUNTY OK
UNION SCHOOL DISTRICT
8506 E 61st St, Tulsa, OK 74133-1926
Tel (918) 357-4321 *Founded/Ownrshp* 1923
Sales 136.9MM *EMP* 1,250
Accts Rsm Us Llp Oklahoma City Okl
SIC 8211 Public elementary & secondary schools
CEO: Ed Payton
Off Mgr: Diane Smith
CTO: Joshua Starks
Pr Dir: Gretchen H Bethell

D-U-N-S 02-071-1842
INDEPENDENT SCHOOL DISTRICT I-29
NORMAN PUBLIC SCHOOLS
131 S Flood Ave, Norman, OK 73069-5463
Tel (405) 364-1339 *Founded/Ownrshp* 1891
Sales 139.2MM *EMP* 1,889
Accts Eide Bailly Llp Oklahoma Cit
SIC 8211 Public elementary school; Public junior high school; Public senior high school
**CFO:* Brenda R Burkett
**Treas:* Janine Warren
Ex Dir: Jenny Dakil
Off Admin: Dawn Denton
Off Admin: Celina Lautzenheiser
Off Admin: Roberta White
IT Man: Lyndon Berglan
Pr Dir: Alesha Leemaster
Psych: Robyn Weiser
HC Dir: Beth Roberson

D-U-N-S 96-210-0660
INDEPENDENT SCHOOL DISTRICT NO 271
1350 W 106th St, Minneapolis, MN 55431-4152
Tel (952) 681-6400 *Founded/Ownrshp* 2010
Sales 146.6MM *EMP* 6^E
Accts Kern Dewenter Viere Ltd Blo
SIC 8211 Elementary & secondary schools
Prin: Jennifer Hazel

D-U-N-S 07-134-0830
INDEPENDENT SCHOOL DISTRICT NO 77
MANKATO AREA PUBLIC SCHOOL
10 Civic Center Plz, Mankato, MN 56001-7794
Tel (507) 387-3167 *Founded/Ownrshp* 1874
Sales 101.9MM *EMP* 1,200
Accts Cliftonlarsonallen Llp Austi
SIC 8211 Public elementary & secondary schools
**CFO:* Jerry Kolander
Dir IT: Jared Kegler
Pr Dir: Shelly Schultz
Schl Brd P: Ann Hendricks

D-U-N-S 12-274-0046
INDEPENDENT SCHOOL DISTRICT OF BOISE CITY
BOISE SCHOOL DISTRICT
8169 W Victory Rd, Boise, ID 83709-4164
Tel (208) 854-4000 *Founded/Ownrshp* 1881
Sales 234.4MM *EMP* 3,025
Accts Eide Bailly Llp Boise Idaho
SIC 8211 Public elementary & secondary schools
Trst: Aj Balukoff

D-U-N-S 08-562-5200 EXP
INDEPENDENT STATIONERS INC
IS.GROUP
250 E 96th St Ste 510, Indianapolis, IN 46240-3730
Tel (317) 845-9155 *Founded/Ownrshp* 1977
Sales 202.0MM^E *EMP* 36
Accts Greenwalt Cpas Inc Indianap
SIC 5021 5112 Office furniture; Stationery & office supplies
Pr: Michael Gentile
**CFO:* Bruce A Campbell
**Ch:* Kenny Sayes
**Treas:* Bryan Kristenson
**Ex VP:* Charles Forman
**VP:* Kevin France
VP: France Kevin
Admn Mgr: Cora Lienemann
Mktg Dir: Janet Eshenour

INDEPENDENT STAVE COMPANY
See ISCO HOLDING CO INC

D-U-N-S 00-626-8494 IMP/EXP
INDEPENDENT STAVE CO LLC (MO)
LEBANON SUPPLY COMPANY
(*Suby of* INDEPENDENT STAVE CO) ★
1078 S Jefferson Ave, Lebanon, MO 65536-3601
Tel (417) 588-4151 *Founded/Ownrshp* 1945, 1983
Sales 311.2MM^E *EMP* 1,000
SIC 2449 5947 2499 Barrels, wood: coopered; Gift shop; Kitchen, bathroom & household ware: wood
CEO: John Joseph Boswell
**Pr:* Brad Boswell
**Sec:* W Paul Walker
IT Man: James Ledbetter

D-U-N-S 60-261-2681
INDEPENDENT TRANSPORTERS OF HANDICAPPED INC
221 N Sunrise Service Rd, Manorville, NY 11949-9604
Tel (631) 878-9270 *Founded/Ownrshp* 1978
Sales 64.2MM^E *EMP* 1,300
Accts Grant Thornton Llp New York
SIC 8361 4729 Home for the mentally handicapped; Carpool/vanpool arrangement
CEO: Walter W Stockton
**CFO:* Mary Beth Maag
**Treas:* Bruce Fuhrmann
Dir Surg: Tom Traklval

INDEPNDNCE HOSP INDEMNITY PLAN
See COMPSERVICES INC

INDIA INK
See ZWD PRODUCTS CORP

INDIAN CREEK HYDRO
See LVDE CORP

D-U-N-S 00-636-8815 IMP/EXP
■ INDIAN INDUSTRIES INC (IN)
ESCALADE SPORTS
(*Suby of* ESCALADE INC) ★
817 Maxwell Ave, Evansville, IN 47711-3870
Tel (812) 467-1200 *Founded/Ownrshp* 1927, 1972
Sales 112.1MM^E *EMP* 466
SIC 3949 Ping-pong tables; Archery equipment, general; Billiard & pool equipment & supplies, general; Basketball equipment & supplies, general
VP: James Allshouse
IT Man: Jason Borg
Natl Sales: Doug Hunter
Mktg Dir: Patrick Griffin
Mktg Dir: Ken Young
Sls Dir: Jack Bowman
Sls Dir: Craig Stawiarski
Board of Directors: B E Matthews Jr, A Graves Williams Jr

INDIAN NATION WHOLESALE
See STEPHENSON WHOLESALE CO INC

INDIAN OAKS LIVING CENTER
See PM MANAGEMENT - KILLEEN II NC LLC

D-U-N-S 06-860-8983
INDIAN PRAIRIE COMMUNITY UNIT SCHOOL DISTRICT
INDIAN PRAIRIE SCHOOL DISTRICT
780 Shoreline Dr, Aurora, IL 60504-6192
Tel (630) 375-3000 *Founded/Ownrshp* 1972
Sales 124.5MM^E *EMP* 3,000
SIC 8211 Public elementary school; Public combined elementary & secondary school; Public senior high school
CIO: David Zoner
Plnt Mgr: Adrienne Morgan
Pr Dir: Jason Altenbern
Board of Directors: Kathleen H Baldwin, Jeannette A Clark, Deanne M Harzinski, Mark Metzger, Pete Neumeister, Judith S Sotir, Owen Wavrinek

INDIAN PRAIRIE SCHOOL DISTRICT
See INDIAN PRAIRIE COMMUNITY UNIT SCHOOL DISTRICT

D-U-N-S 07-920-8989
INDIAN RIVER COUNTY
1800 27th St Bldg B, Vero Beach, FL 32960-0310
Tel (772) 567-8000 *Founded/Ownrshp* 1926
Sales NA *EMP* 1,500
Accts Rehmann Robson Llc Vero Beach
SIC 9111 Executive offices;
Ex Dir: John King
Telecom Mg: Terry Smith

D-U-N-S 61-171-0427
INDIAN RIVER MEMORIAL HOSPITAL INC
1000 36th St, Vero Beach, FL 32960-6592
Tel (772) 567-4311 *Founded/Ownrshp* 1984
Sales 203.9MM *EMP* 1,400
SIC 8062 8011 General medical & surgical hospitals; Offices & clinics of medical doctors
Ch Bd: Thomas Segura
Dir Vol: Mary Jane Stewart
Ch Bd: Charles Sheehan
CEO: Jeffrey L Susi
CFO: Gregory Gardner
Treas: Jack Pastor
Treas: Jack Weisbaum
Brnch Mgr: Dee Boshaw
Psych: Mariamma Pyngolil
Obsttrcn: Donna Fabean

D-U-N-S 87-807-1638
INDIAN RIVER SCHOOL DISTRICT
31 Hosier St, Selbyville, DE 19975-9300
Tel (302) 436-1000 *Founded/Ownrshp* 1969
Sales 67.5MM^E *EMP* 1,650^E
SIC 8211 Public elementary & secondary schools
Dir Sec: Preston Lewis
MIS Dir: Davis Maull

D-U-N-S 07-222-0825
INDIAN RIVER STATE COLLEGE FOUNDATION INC
3209 Virginia Ave, Fort Pierce, FL 34981-5596
Tel (772) 462-7340 *Founded/Ownrshp* 1960
Sales 10.5MM *EMP* 5,000
Accts Berger Toombs Elam Gaines &
SIC 8222 Community college

*Ex Dir: Ann L Decker

D-U-N-S 05-302-4758
INDIAN RIVER TRANSPORT CO
2580 Executive Rd, Winter Haven, FL 33884-0929
Tel (863) 324-2430 Founded/Ownrshp 1993
Sales 107.5MM^E EMP 500^E
SIC 4213 Refrigerated products transport
Ch: John J Harned
*Pr: Marguerite Harned
Dir IT: Matt Hurst
Sfty Dirs: Anthony Black
Sfty Dirs: Mark Gresset
Opers Mgr: William Wolven

D-U-N-S 06-587-7888 IMP/EXP
INDIAN SUMMER COOPERATIVE INC
3958 W Chauvez Rd Ste 1, Ludington, MI 49431-8200
Tel (231) 845-6248 Founded/Ownrshp 1973
Sales 86.3MM^E EMP 400
SIC 2033 0723 4213 2035 Apple sauce: packaged in cans, jars, etc.; Fruit juices: packaged in cans, jars, etc.; Fruits: packaged in cans, jars, etc.; Fruit (fresh) packing services; Trucking, except local; Contract haulers; Pickles, sauces & salad dressings
Pr: Roy D Hackert
*Sec: Steven Hull
Opers Mgr: Doyle Fenner

INDIANA AMERICAN WATER
See INDIANA-AMERICAN WATER CO INC

D-U-N-S 14-039-2650
INDIANA ANNUAL UNITED METHODIST CHURCH
301 Pennsylvania Pkwy, Indianapolis, IN 46280-1397
Tel (317) 924-1321 Founded/Ownrshp 2003
Sales 13.8MM^E EMP 1,100
SIC 8661 Methodist Church
*Ex Dir: Nick Yarde

D-U-N-S 12-720-2989 IMP
INDIANA ARCELORMITTAL HARBOR LLC
ARCELORMITTAL INDIANA HARBOR W
(Suby of ARCELORMITTAL USA LLC) ★
3210 Watling St, East Chicago, IN 46312-1716
Tel (219) 399-1200 Founded/Ownrshp 2002
Sales 228.8MM^E EMP 900
SIC 3312 Blast furnaces & steel mills
CEO: Rodney B Mott
Prin: Louis Schorsch
Genl Mgr: Richard Morris
Opers Supe: David Bixenman

D-U-N-S 94-695-5648 IMP
INDIANA AUTOMOTIVE FASTENERS INC
(Suby of AOYAMA SEISAKUSHO CO.,LTD.)
1300 Anderson Blvd, Greenfield, IN 46140-7934
Tel (317) 467-0100 Founded/Ownrshp 1996
Sales 110.5MM^E EMP 401
SIC 3452 3714 Bolts, nuts, rivets & washers; Motor vehicle parts & accessories
Pr: Heisaburo Hidaka
*VP: Pete Murray
Plnt Mgr: Randall Shepherd
Snr Mgr: Lecia Huckeby
Snr Mgr: Michael Lee

D-U-N-S 82-479-9381
INDIANA DEPARTMENT OF NATURAL RESOURCES
(Suby of EXECUTIVE OFFICE OF STATE OF INDIANA) ★
402 W Washington St W299, Indianapolis, IN 46204-2739
Tel (317) 232-4020 Founded/Ownrshp 1938
Sales NA EMP 1,510
SIC 9512 Land, mineral & wildlife conservation;
Brnch Mgr: Steve Lucas

D-U-N-S 82-479-9555
INDIANA DEPARTMENT OF TRANSPORTATION
(Suby of EXECUTIVE OFFICE OF STATE OF INDIANA) ★
100 N Senate Ave Rm N758, Indianapolis, IN 46204-2219
Tel (317) 232-3166 Founded/Ownrshp 1989
Sales NA EMP 3,600
SIC 9621 Regulation, administration of transportation;
Prin: Karl Browning
*CFO: Dan Brassard
*Prin: Mitchell E Daniels Jr

D-U-N-S 80-989-6780
INDIANA DEPT OF CORRECTION
(Suby of EXECUTIVE OFFICE OF STATE OF INDIANA) ★
302 W Washington St E334, Indianapolis, IN 46204-4701
Tel (317) 232-2430 Founded/Ownrshp 1958
Sales NA EMP 6,000
SIC 9223 Prison, government;
CEO: Randy Koester
*Ch: Christopher Meloi
Ofcr: Debbie Abram
Ofcr: Jerry Ammon
Ex Dir: Aaron Garner
CIO: Doug Garrison
Pgrm Dir: Jayne Grimes
Pgrm Dir: Randy Short

D-U-N-S 82-479-9613
INDIANA DEPT OF WORKFORCE DEVELOPMENT
(Suby of EXECUTIVE OFFICE OF STATE OF INDIANA) ★
10 N Senate Ave, Indianapolis, IN 46204-2277
Tel (317) 233-5661 Founded/Ownrshp 1991
Sales NA EMP 1,650
SIC 9111
CFO: Randy Gillespie

D-U-N-S 82-479-9225
INDIANA FAMILY AND SOCIAL SERVICES ADMINISTRATION
FSSA
(Suby of EXECUTIVE OFFICE OF STATE OF INDIANA) ★
402 W Washington St W461, Indianapolis, IN 46204-2243
Tel (317) 233-4454 Founded/Ownrshp 1991
Sales NA EMP 9,700
SIC 9441
CEO: Debra Minott
Genl Mgr: Gregory Jinks
Web Dev: Angela Chaffee

INDIANA FARM BUREAU
See UNITED FARM FAMILY MUTUAL INSURANCE CO

D-U-N-S 07-957-0479
INDIANA FARM BUREAU INC
225 S East St, Indianapolis, IN 46202-4002
Tel (317) 692-7851 Founded/Ownrshp 1919
Sales NA EMP 1,200^E
SIC 6411 Insurance agents, brokers & service
Pr: Donald Villwock
*VP: Isabella Chism
*VP: Randy L Kron
VP: Randy Spurlock
IT Man: Kim Bray
Software D: Leslie Thompson
Netwrk Eng: Debbie Katterhenry

D-U-N-S 55-547-1838 IMP
INDIANA FCC INC
(Suby of F.C.C. CO., LTD.)
555 Industrial Dr, Portland, IN 47371-9399
Tel (260) 726-8023 Founded/Ownrshp 1988
Sales 228.8MM^E EMP 450
SIC 3714 Clutches, motor vehicle
Pr: Yoshitaka Saito
VP Admn: Jeff Bailey
Prd Mgr: John McShane
Snr Mgr: Todd Muhlenkamp
Snr Mgr: Mike Shepherd

D-U-N-S 01-592-2552
■ **INDIANA GAMING CO LP**
HOLLYWOOD CASINO
(Suby of PENN NATIONAL GAMING INC) ★
777 Hollywood Blvd, Lawrenceburg, IN 47025-2503
Tel (812) 539-8000 Founded/Ownrshp 2008
Sales 78.9MM^E EMP 1,700
SIC 7011 Casino hotel
Genl Pt: G Argosy

D-U-N-S 00-693-8211
■ **INDIANA GAS CO INC**
VECTREN
(Suby of VECTREN UTILITY HOLDINGS INC) ★
20 Nw 4th St, Evansville, IN 47708-1724
Tel (812) 491-4000 Founded/Ownrshp 1945
Sales 307.3MM^E EMP 875^E
SIC 4924 Natural gas distribution
Ch Bd: Neil C Ellerbrook
Ch Bd: James Street
*CEO: Carl Chapman
*CFO: Jerome A Benkert Jr
Sr VP: John Little
VP: Elizabeth I Witte
VP: Robert Goocher
*VP: M Susan Hardwick
VP: Tim Hewitt
VP: Ellis Redd
VP: Rick Schach
Exec: April Johnson
Exec: Christine R Morgan
Board of Directors: Ronald E Christian, William S Duty

INDIANA GRAND
See CENTAUR ACQUISITION LLC

D-U-N-S 05-330-3889
INDIANA HARBOR BELT RAILROAD CO
2721 161st St, Hammond, IN 46323-1099
Tel (219) 989-4703 Founded/Ownrshp 1896
Sales 100.6MM^E EMP 750^E
Accts Mcgladrey Llp Chicago Illino
SIC 4013 4011 Switching & terminal services; Railroads, line-haul operating
CEO: Jim Roots
*Pr: Cindy Sanborn
*CFO: Derek Smith
Ex Dir: Mark Manion
Genl Mgr: Chuck Allen
Genl Mgr: Pat Daly
Sls Dir: Leo Pauwels
Genl Couns: R Serpe

D-U-N-S 85-846-9067
INDIANA HEALTHCARE CORP
835 Hospital Rd, Indiana, PA 15701-3629
Tel (724) 357-7000 Founded/Ownrshp 1987
Sales 32.7M EMP 1,100
Accts Ernst & Young Llp Pittsburgh
SIC 8741 Hospital management
CEO: Steven Wolf
*CFO: Larry Marshall
*Prin: Robert Parker
Board of Directors: Mrs Susan Delaney, Robert D Duggan, Robert G Goldstrohm MD, Herbert L Hanna MD, Alan Holsinger, Robert T Jack, James Miller

D-U-N-S 96-381-6397
INDIANA HOSPITAL
823 Hospital Rd, Indiana, PA 15701-3629
Tel (724) 357-7125 Founded/Ownrshp 2010
Sales 107.1MM^E EMP 3
SIC 8741 Hospital management
Prin: Ali Tunio
Doctor: Durre S Ahmed MD

INDIANA INDUSTRIAL CONTRACTORS
See INDUSTRIAL CONTRACTORS SKANSKA INC

D-U-N-S 04-533-7771
INDIANA INSTITUTE OF TECHNOLOGY INC
INDIANA TECH
1600 E Washington Blvd, Fort Wayne, IN 46803-1297
Tel (260) 422-5561 Founded/Ownrshp 1930
Sales 84.6MM EMP 450
Accts Bkd Llp Fort Wayne In
SIC 8221 College, except junior
CEO: Arthur E Snyder
Ofcr: Lisa Green
VP: John Shannon
Board of Directors: A Nineteen Member Board

D-U-N-S 00-693-8229
INDIANA INSURANCE CO
(Suby of LIBERTY MUTUAL INSURANCE CO) ★
6281 Tri Ridge Blvd # 1, Loveland, OH 45140-8345
Tel (816) 216-5313 Founded/Ownrshp 1851
Sales NA EMP 750
SIC 6331 Fire, marine & casualty insurance
Pr: Richard Bell
Snr Mgr: Joan Grade
Snr Mgr: Celeste Sanford

D-U-N-S 07-977-0307
INDIANA LABORERS WELFARE FUND
413 Swan St, Terre Haute, IN 47807-4224
Tel (812) 238-2551 Founded/Ownrshp 2014
Sales NA EMP 3^E
Accts Lm Henderson & Company Llp In
SIC 6371 Pension, health & welfare funds

D-U-N-S 11-072-4122 IMP
INDIANA LLC ADVICS MANUFACTURING
ABI
(Suby of ADVICS NORTH AMERICA INC) ★
10550 James Adams St, Terre Haute, IN 47802-9294
Tel (812) 298-1617 Founded/Ownrshp 2010
Sales 113.0MM^E EMP 400
SIC 3714 Air brakes, motor vehicle
*Pr: Atsushi Takenaga
*Treas: Kazuza Tsukamoto

D-U-N-S 00-698-5584
■ **INDIANA MICHIGAN POWER CO**
AEP
(Suby of AEP) ★
1 Riverside Plz, Columbus, OH 43215-2355
Tel (614) 716-1000 Founded/Ownrshp 1907
Sales 2.1MMM EMP 2,551^E
SIC 4911 Electric services; Distribution, electric power; Generation, electric power; Transmission, electric power
Ch Bd: Nicholas K Akins
*Pr: Paul Chodak III
*CFO: Brian X Tierney
*VP: Thomas A Kratt
VP: Mark Peifer
Mktg Mgr: Ron Kalie
Board of Directors: Lisa M Barton, Marc E Lewis, Mark C McCullough, Robert P Power, Carla E Simpson, Barry O Wiard

D-U-N-S 00-606-3101 IMP/EXP
INDIANA MILLS & MANUFACTURING INC
IMMI
18881 Immi Way, Westfield, IN 46074-3001
Tel (317) 896-9531 Founded/Ownrshp 1961
Sales 203.0MM^E EMP 1,000
SIC 3714 Motor vehicle parts & accessories
CEO: Larry Gray
*Pr: James R Anthony
CFO: Kevin Boen
Prgrm Mgr: Dan Crowe
MIS Dir: Randy Norman
IT Man: Lisa Chaffin
Sls Dir: Tim Catherine

D-U-N-S 83-112-8231 IMP
INDIANA MULTIMATIC MFG INC
(Suby of MULTIMATIC INC)
201 Re Jones Rd, Butler, IN 46721-9570
Tel (260) 868-1000 Founded/Ownrshp 2009
Sales 101.8MM^E EMP 200
SIC 3465 Body parts, automobile: stamped metal
Pr: Peter Czapka
*VP: Martin Bressel
Prgrm Mgr: Marc Willwerth

D-U-N-S 05-721-4579
INDIANA MUNICIPAL POWER AGENCY
IMPA
11610 N College Ave, Carmel, IN 46032-5602
Tel (317) 573-9955 Founded/Ownrshp 1983
Sales 456.5MM EMP 84^E
SIC 4911 Distribution, electric power; Generation, electric power
CEO: Raj RAO
CFO: Chris Rettig
Ex VP: David C Forward
Sr VP: Jack Alvey
VP: Bev Matthews
VP: Peter Prettyman
VP: Frank Smardo
VP: Kerry Vincent
Secur Mgr: John R Lloyd

D-U-N-S 00-603-7436
■ **INDIANA NEWSPAPERS LLC** (IN)
INDIANAPOLIS STAR, THE
(Suby of GANNETT CO INC) ★
130 S Meridian St, Indianapolis, IN 46225-1046
Tel (317) 444-4000 Founded/Ownrshp 1998, 2015
Sales 193.5MM^E EMP 1,300
SIC 2711 2752 Newspapers, publishing & printing; Commercial printing, lithographic
Pr: Karen Crotchfelt
*Treas: Michael A Hart
VP: Dawn Fisher-Polomski
*VP: Gracia C Martore
VP: Peter Ricker
MIS Dir: Glen Berryman
IT Man: Steve Walker
Board of Directors: Robert J Dickey

D-U-N-S 80-989-5717
INDIANA OFFICE OF ADJUTANT GENERAL
ADJUTANT GENERAL'S OFFICE
(Suby of EXECUTIVE OFFICE OF STATE OF INDIANA) ★
2002 S Holt Rd, Indianapolis, IN 46241-4804
Tel (317) 247-3559 Founded/Ownrshp 1816
Sales NA EMP 1,992
SIC 9711
Genl Pt: R Martin Umbarger

D-U-N-S 83-037-4695
INDIANA ORTHOPAEDIC HOSPITAL LLC
8450 Northwest Blvd, Indianapolis, IN 46278-1381
Tel (317) 956-1000 Founded/Ownrshp 2002
Sales 145.7MM EMP 200^E
SIC 8069 Orthopedic hospital
CEO: Jane Keller
CFO: Anthony Gioia
Dir Inf Cn: Heather Hohenberger
Dir Risk M: Tiffini White
Dir Lab: Tiffany Moody
Ansthlgy: Joseph Lafnitzegger
Doctor: David M Kaehr
Doctor: Michael L Kramer

D-U-N-S 61-396-3131 IMP/EXP
INDIANA PACKERS CORP
(Suby of MITSUBISHI CORPORATION)
Hwy 421 S & Cr 100 N, Delphi, IN 46923
Tel (765) 564-3680 Founded/Ownrshp 1994
Sales 368.4MM^E EMP 1,540
SIC 2011 2013 Pork products from pork slaughtered on site; Bacon, slab & sliced from meat slaughtered on site; Sausages & other prepared meats
Pr: Russ Yearwood
*Pr: Edward J Nelson
*CEO: Masao Watanabe
*VP: James Hardison
*VP: Randy Toleman

D-U-N-S 82-479-9597
INDIANA POLICE STATE
(Suby of EXECUTIVE OFFICE OF STATE OF INDIANA) ★
100 N Senate Ave Rm N340, Indianapolis, IN 46204-2213
Tel (317) 232-8241 Founded/Ownrshp 1933
Sales NA EMP 1,900
SIC 9221 State police;
Dir Lab: Brad Scully
Prgrm Mgr: Gayle Hicks
IT Man: Irv Goldblatt
Pr Dir: Robert Dittmer
Pgrm Dir: Michael Cales
Pgrm Dir: Bertha Herron
Pgrm Dir: Duane Long
Snr Mgr: Max Michael

D-U-N-S 07-496-1061
INDIANA REGIONAL MEDICAL CENTER
835 Hospital Rd, Indiana, PA 15701-3629
Tel (724) 357-7000 Founded/Ownrshp 1913
Sales 139.7MM EMP 1,100
SIC 8062 8011 General medical & surgical hospitals; Offices & clinics of medical doctors
Pr: Stephen A Wolfe
*CFO: Larry Marshall
*Ch: Todd Brice
*Ch: Beverly Gazza
*Treas: Joseph Geary
Exec: Suzanne Redman
Dir: Larry Sedlemeyer
Dir Sec: Danny Sacco
Off Mgr: Dawn Landis
Pathlgst: Stanley Geyer
Surgeon: John W Hsu

D-U-N-S 01-123-4267
INDIANA SECONDARY MARKET FOR EDUCATION LOANS INC
11595 N Meridian St # 200, Carmel, IN 46032-6924
Tel (317) 715-9000 Founded/Ownrshp 1980
Sales NA EMP 120
SIC 6111 Student Loan Marketing Association
Pr: Stephen W Clinton
*Ch Bd: Robert Macgille
*CFO: Joseph Wood

D-U-N-S 82-479-9407
INDIANA STATE DEPARTMENT OF HEALTH
(Suby of EXECUTIVE OFFICE OF STATE OF INDIANA) ★
2 N Meridian St Ste 1, Indianapolis, IN 46204-3010
Tel (317) 233-1325 Founded/Ownrshp 1991
Sales NA EMP 2,217
SIC 9431 Administration of public health programs;
VP: Jennifer Dunlap
Genl Mgr: Howard Cundif
Genl Mgr: Kimberly Diller
Pgrm Dir: Deana McMurray
Pgrm Dir: Tasha Smith

D-U-N-S 07-595-3448
INDIANA STATE UNIVERSITY
200 N 7th St, Terre Haute, IN 47809-1902
Tel (800) 468-6478 Founded/Ownrshp 1865
Sales 128.6MM EMP 1,700
Accts Paul D Joyce Cpa-State Of In
SIC 8221 University
Pr: Daniel J Bradley
*Pr: Lyod Benjamins
*Treas: Dianne McKee
Bd of Dir: Leslie Ballard
Bd of Dir: Stanley Henderson
VP: Mark Green
VP: Jeffrey Jacso
Assoc Dir: Carol A Reed
Ex Dir: Robert Jefferson
Ex Dir: John Sanders
CIO: Lisa Spence

D-U-N-S 00-174-7609 IMP
INDIANA SUGARS INC
911 Virginia St, Gary, IN 46402-2705
Tel (219) 886-9151 Founded/Ownrshp 1983
Sales 422.7MM^E EMP 170

SIC 5149 Groceries & related products; Sugar, refined; Salt, edible; Flavourings & fragrances
Ch Bd: Ronald Yonover
**Treas:* John Yonover
VP: Vito Jasinevicius
VP: James Oconnell
IT Man: John Witt
Trfc Dir: Sonia Rodriguez
Opers Mgr: John Tritt
VP Sls: Scott Sievers

INDIANA TECH
See INDIANA INSTITUTE OF TECHNOLOGY INC

INDIANA TOLL ROAD
See ITR CONCESSION CO LLC

INDIANA TOOL & DIE
See JASPER ENGINE EXCHANGE INC

D-U-N-S 01-639-3092
INDIANA UNIVERSITY FOUNDATION INC
1500 N State Road 46 Byp, Bloomington, IN 47408
Tel (812) 855-8311 *Founded/Ownrshp* 1936
Sales 294.5MM *EMP* 240
Accts Deloitte & Touche Llp Indiana
SIC 8299 Educational services
Pr: Gene Tempel
**CFO:* James Perin
Off Mgr: Beth Gillespie

D-U-N-S 07-597-4899
INDIANA UNIVERSITY HEALTH BALL MEMORIAL HOSPITAL INC
IU HEALTH ALBANY PHARMACY
(*Suby of* INDIANA UNIVERSITY HOSPITAL) ★
2401 W University Ave, Muncie, IN 47303-3428
Tel (765) 751-1449 *Founded/Ownrshp* 1929
Sales 395.1MM *EMP* 3,000
SIC 8062 Hospital, medical school affiliated with nursing & residency
**Pr:* Michael Haley
COO: Jeff Bird
CFO: Carol Fields
Chf Nrs Of: Karla Cox
CIO: Rod Evans
Dir QC: Claire Lee
Opers Mgr: Kim Koss
Plnt Mgr: Andy Raih
Pr Dir: Will Henderson
Pathlgst: Thomas Kocoshis
Pharmcst: Robert Adler

D-U-N-S 07-205-2137
INDIANA UNIVERSITY HEALTH BLOOMINGTON INC
IU HEALTH BLOOMINGTON HOSPITAL
601 W 2nd St, Bloomington, IN 47403-2317
Tel (812) 353-5252 *Founded/Ownrshp* 1905
Sales 359.8MM *EMP* 3,200
SIC 8062 General medical & surgical hospitals
Pr: Mark E Moore
CFO: David Massengale
**CFO:* Jim Myers
Dir Rad: Bruce N Monson
Dir IT: Adam Endwright
IT Man: Karen Neal
Info Man: Mike Bruce
Orthpdst: Thomas S Vinje
Ansthlgy: Nader Rezvan
Doctor: John R Thompson
Nrsg Dir: Pam Adams

D-U-N-S 96-524-8321
INDIANA UNIVERSITY HEALTH INC
INDIANA UNIVERSITY HOSPITAL
1701 Senate Blvd, Indianapolis, IN 46202-1239
Tel (317) 962-2000 *Founded/Ownrshp* 2010
Sales 1.6MMM^E *EMP* 17,242
Accts Ernst & Young Llp Indianapoli
SIC 8062 6324 General medical & surgical hospitals; Health maintenance organization (HMO), insurance only
Pr: Daniel F Evans Jr
COO: Al W Gatmaitan
Chf Mktg O: Richard Graffis MD
Ofcr: Karlene Kerfoot
Ex VP: Linda Everett
Ex VP: Jonathan E Gottlieb
Ex VP: Ryan C Kitchell
Sr VP: Mark Lantzy
VP: Michelle Altobella
VP: Jo Brooks
VP: Tory C Castor
VP: Linda Chase
VP: Brian Donnelly
VP: Brian Kremer
VP: Anita J McVay
VP: Catherine Cooper - Weidner
VP Bus Dev: Scott Black
Exec: Michelle Janney
Dir Risk M: Cindy Debord
Board of Directors: V William Hunt, Sara E Barker, James E Lingeman MD, Myles Brand, Angela B McBride, D Craig Brater MD, Thomas W Chapman, Bishop Michael J Coyner, Stephen L Ferguson, Charles E Golden, David W Goodrich, Adam Herbert Jr

INDIANA UNIVERSITY HOSPITAL
See INDIANA UNIVERSITY HEALTH INC

D-U-N-S 07-313-0049
INDIANA UNIVERSITY OF PENNSYLVANIA
STATE SYSTM OF HIGHER EDUC OF
(*Suby of* STATE SYSTEM HIGHER EDUCATN PA) ★
1011 S Dr Room 201 Sutton, Indiana, PA 15705-0001
Tel (724) 357-2200 *Founded/Ownrshp* 1875
Sales 133.0MM^E *EMP* 1,846
Accts Cliftonlarsonallen Llp Plymou
SIC 8221 9411 University; Administration of educational programs;
Pr: Michael Driscoll
**VP:* James Begany
VP: Evan Bohnen
**VP:* Gerald Intemann
**VP:* Rhonda Luckey
**VP:* William Speidel
**VP:* Cornelius Wooten

D-U-N-S 07-207-8199
INDIANA WESLEYAN UNIVERSITY
4201 S Washington St, Marion, IN 46953-4974
Tel (765) 674-6901 *Founded/Ownrshp* 1919
Sales 228.7MM *EMP* 1,000
Accts Bkd Lp Fort Wayne In
SIC 8221 Colleges & universities
Pr: David Wright
Assoc VP: Diane McDaniel
Ex VP: Keith Newman
VP: John Jones
**VP:* Duane Kilty
VP: Mandy Ogunnowo
VP: Thomas E Phillippe Sr
VP: Elvin Weinmann
**Prin:* Henry Smith
Ex Dir: Mark Pederson
CTO: Katie Wampler
Board of Directors: Tiffany Lewis

D-U-N-S 00-693-8930
■ **INDIANA-AMERICAN WATER CO INC**
INDIANA AMERICAN WATER
(*Suby of* AMERICAN WATER WORKS CO INC) ★
555 E County Line Rd # 201, Greenwood, IN 46143-1064
Tel (800) 492-8373 *Founded/Ownrshp* 1872
Sales 128.1MM^E *EMP* 363
SIC 4941 Water supply
Pr: Alan Deboy

D-U-N-S 00-777-7915
INDIANA-KENTUCKY ELECTRIC CORP
IKEC
(*Suby of* OVEC) ★
3932 Us Rte 23, Piketon, OH 45661
Tel (740) 289-7200 *Founded/Ownrshp* 1952
Sales 104.5MM *EMP* 320
SIC 4911 Generation, electric power; Transmission, electric power
Pr: Nicholos Akins
**COO:* Mark Peifer
**CFO:* John Brodt

D-U-N-S 06-281-1757
INDIANAPOLIS AIRPORT AUTHORITY
7800 Col Weircook Dr # 100, Indianapolis, IN 46241-8009
Tel (317) 487-9594 *Founded/Ownrshp* 1962
Sales 87.2MM^E *EMP* 480
Accts Bkd Llp Indianapolis In
SIC 4581 Airports, flying fields & services
Pr: Mike Wells
**Treas:* Stu Grauel
**Treas:* Robert Thomson
**VP:* Kelly Flynn

INDIANAPOLIS FRUIT COMPANY
See IF&P FOODS INC

D-U-N-S 00-693-8310
■ **INDIANAPOLIS POWER & LIGHT CO**
(*Suby of* AES) ★
1 Monument Cir, Indianapolis, IN 46204-2901
Tel (317) 261-8261 *Founded/Ownrshp* 1926
Sales 882.1MM^E *EMP* 1,250
SIC 4911 Generation, electric power
CEO: Ken Zagzebski
Pr: Kelly M Huntington
Pr: Sandi Vasel
COO: Ronald E Talbot
Treas: Anita M Hill
VP: William Henley
VP: Jim Sadtler
IT Man: Erick Jones

D-U-N-S 07-596-7992
INDIANAPOLIS PUBLIC SCHOOLS
IPS
120 E Walnut St, Indianapolis, IN 46204-1389
Tel (317) 226-4000 *Founded/Ownrshp* 1835
Sales 403.3MM^E *EMP* 8,000
SIC 8211 Public elementary & secondary schools
Pr Dir: Tosha Baskin
Teacher Pr: Mindy Schlegal

INDIANAPOLIS STAR, THE
See INDIANA NEWSPAPERS LLC

INDIANHEAD CASH & CARRY
See INDIANHEAD FOODSERVICE DISTRIBUTOR INC

D-U-N-S 01-916-8970
INDIANHEAD COMMUNITY ACTION AGENCY INC
1000 College Ave W, Ladysmith, WI 54848-2118
Tel (715) 532-4222 *Founded/Ownrshp* 1966
Sales 12.9MM *EMP* 1,200^E
Accts Wipfli Llp Madison Wisconsin
SIC 8399 Community action agency
CEO: Brett Gerber
**Ex Dir:* Jerome Drahos
Dir IT: Bob Carter

D-U-N-S 02-321-2079
INDIANHEAD FOODSERVICE DISTRIBUTOR INC
INDIANHEAD CASH & CARRY
313 N Hastings Pl, Eau Claire, WI 54703-3440
Tel (715) 834-2777 *Founded/Ownrshp* 1976
Sales 142.0MM^E *EMP* 90
SIC 5142 5141 5147 5143 Packaged frozen goods; Groceries, general line; Meats, fresh; Dairy products, except dried or canned
Pr: Thomas Gillett
**Treas:* Elizabeth Gillett
Sls Mgr: Mark Danielson

D-U-N-S 82-463-1873 IMP/EXP
■ **INDIGO AMERICA INC**
HEWLETT PACKARD
(*Suby of* HP INC) ★
165 Dascomb Rd 1, Andover, MA 01810-5886
Tel (978) 474-2000 *Founded/Ownrshp* 2001
Sales 243.4MM^E *EMP* 420
SIC 5049 Scientific & engineering equipment & supplies
Pr: Catherine Lesjak
CFO: Alon Bar-Shany
**Treas:* Charles N Charnas
Sr Cor Off: Franc Gentili
**VP:* Ann O Baskins
VP: Jane Shea Seitz
**Ex Dir:* Todd Cromwell
Rgnl Mgr: Mike Daly
Rgnl Mgr: Brett Rowley
Rgnl Mgr: Emile Tabassi
IT Man: James Jandreau

D-U-N-S 00-222-7296 IMP
INDIUM CORP OF AMERICA (NY)
34 Robinson Rd, Clinton, NY 13323-1419
Tel (800) 446-3486 *Founded/Ownrshp* 1934
Sales 203.3MM^E *EMP* 780
SIC 3356 Solder: wire, bar, acid core, & rosin core
Ch Bd: William N Macartney III
**Pr:* Gregory P Evans
CFO: Leslie E Schenk
VP: James A Slattery
Genl Mgr: Paul Gassensmith
IT Man: Thomas Pearson
Mktg Mgr: Ploessl Robert

D-U-N-S 79-740-8549
INDIVIOR INC
(*Suby of* INDIVIOR PLC)
10710 Midlothian Turnpik Ste 430, Richmond, VA 23235
Tel (804) 379-1090 *Founded/Ownrshp* 2014
Sales 258.9MM^E *EMP* 330
SIC 5122 Pharmaceuticals
CEO: Shaun Thaxter
**CFO:* Cary Claiborne
**Ch:* Howard Pien
Dir Bus: Rolley E Johnson
**Prin:* Richard Simkin
**Ex Dir:* Daniel Tass

D-U-N-S 05-494-6025 IMP/EXP
INDOFF INC
11816 Lackland Rd Ste 200, Saint Louis, MO 63146-4248
Tel (314) 997-1122 *Founded/Ownrshp* 1971
Sales 272.5MM^E *EMP* 450
SIC 5021 5044 5084 Office furniture; Office equipment; Materials handling machinery
Pr: Jim Malkus
Pt: Annette Martin
**Ch Bd:* Dennis Mourning
**CFO:* Julie Frank
**Ch:* John S Ross
VP: Colin Faulkingham
**VP:* Pam Hake
VP: Marilyn Melcher
**VP:* Robin Migdal
VP: Robin Migdoff
VP: Marsha Olinghouse
VP: Jo Warfield

D-U-N-S 00-151-9230 IMP
INDOPCO INC
NATIONAL STARCH AND CHEMICAL
(*Suby of* PERMABOND AMERICAS) ★
10 Finderne Ave Ste A, Bridgewater, NJ 08807-3365
Tel (908) 685-5000 *Founded/Ownrshp* 1997
Sales 510.6MM^E *EMP* 9,748^E
SIC 2891 2046 2821 2869 2899 2099 Adhesives; Sealants; Industrial starch; Edible starch; Plastics materials & resins; Industrial organic chemicals; Perfume materials, synthetic; Flavors or flavoring materials, synthetic; Fatty acid esters, aminos, etc.; Chemical preparations; Food preparations
Ch Bd: John McAdam
Pr: Rama Chandran
CFO: R J Forrest
VP: Christine B Gibson
VP: Peter C Maloff
VP: Peter A Salis
IT Man: Tom Merritt

D-U-N-S 08-021-0887
INDORAMA VENTURES XYLENES & PTA LLC
1401 Finley Island Rd, Decatur, AL 35601-7910
Tel (256) 340-5200 *Founded/Ownrshp* 2015
Sales 225.0MM^E *EMP* 425
SIC 2911 Aromatic chemical products
**Pr:* S N Mohta

INDRAMAT DIV
See BOSCH REXROTH CORP

D-U-N-S 19-720-4290 IMP/EXP
■ **INDSPEC CHEMICAL CORP**
(*Suby of* OCCIDENTAL PETROLEUM CORP) ★
133 Main St, Petrolia, PA 16050-9717
Tel (724) 756-2370 *Founded/Ownrshp* 1996
Sales 91.7MM^E *EMP* 300
SIC 2865 2819 Resorcinol; Sodium & potassium compounds, exc. bleaches, alkalies, alum.; Sodium sulfate, glauber's salt, salt cake; Sodium sulfides
Pr: Mark Koppel
IT Man: Al Wourst
Plnt Mgr: Dave Dorko

D-U-N-S 78-959-1302
INDUS ENTERPRISES INC
TEXAS JASMINE WHOLESALE
7051 Southwest Fwy, Houston, TX 77074-2007
Tel (713) 784-4335 *Founded/Ownrshp* 1992
Sales 113.9MM *EMP* 98
SIC 5149 5194 5912 Groceries & related products; Tobacco & tobacco products; Proprietary (non-prescription medicine) stores
Pr: Zulfiqar A Momin
**VP:* Khowaja Barkat A
**VP:* Barkat A Khowaja
**Prin:* Jamshed Momin

D-U-N-S 00-130-6547 IMP/EXP
INDUSTRIAL ACOUSTICS CO INC (NY)
I A C
233 S 13th St Ste 1100, Lincoln, NE 68508-2003
Tel (718) 931-8000 *Founded/Ownrshp* 1949, 1998
Sales 122.8MM^E *EMP* 600
SIC 3448 1742 Prefabricated metal buildings; Acoustical & ceiling work
Pr: Kenneth Delasho
VP: Mike Walsh

D-U-N-S 17-136-8553 IMP/EXP
INDUSTRIAL AIR TOOL
INDUSTRIAL AIR TOOL, L.P.
(*Suby of* PORTA LATHE) ★
1305 W Jackson Ave, Pasadena, TX 77506-1709
Tel (713) 477-3144 *Founded/Ownrshp* 2004
Sales 111.6MM^E *EMP* 108
SIC 5084 Industrial machinery & equipment
Pr: Andy Gessner
Pt: William Pinkley
Sales Asso: Gabriel Arredondo
Sales Asso: Rolando Rodriguez
Sales Asso: Harold Schmidt

INDUSTRIAL AIR TOOL, L.P.
See INDUSTRIAL AIR TOOL

D-U-N-S 00-386-8650
INDUSTRIAL BUILDERS INC
1307 County Road 17 N, West Fargo, ND 58078-3818
Tel (701) 282-4977 *Founded/Ownrshp* 1953
Sales 102.5MM^E *EMP* 318
SIC 1629 1622 1542 1611 1623 Dam construction; Bridge construction; Commercial & office building, new construction; Commercial & office buildings, renovation & repair; School building construction; Institutional building construction; Resurfacing contractor; Pipeline construction
Pr: Paul W Diederich
**Ex VP:* Donn O Diederich
**VP:* Roger Haberman
**VP:* Ron Mack
Genl Mgr: Kent Sand

D-U-N-S 05-097-8329 IMP
INDUSTRIAL CHEMICALS INC
2042 Montreat Dr Ste A, Vestavia, AL 35216-4040
Tel (205) 823-7330 *Founded/Ownrshp* 1970
Sales 99.5MM *EMP* 130
Accts Warren Averett Llc Birmingha
SIC 5169 Chemicals, industrial & heavy
Pr: William L Welch
**VP:* L B Welch
IT Man: Mark Jeter

D-U-N-S 11-202-5445 IMP
INDUSTRIAL CONTAINER SERVICES - FL LLC
(*Suby of* INDUSTRIAL CONTAINER SERVICES LLC) ★
2400 Maitland Ctr, Zellwood, FL 32798
Tel (407) 930-4182 *Founded/Ownrshp* 2001
Sales 214.0MM *EMP* 100
SIC 5085 Drums, new or reconditioned
**Pr:* Charles Veniez
**CFO:* Kevin Breheny
Exec: Kim Williams
IT Man: Pam Graham
Manager: Dan Bartley
Manager: Scott Russell

D-U-N-S 03-991-3699 IMP
INDUSTRIAL CONTAINER SERVICES LLC
(*Suby of* AURORA CAPITAL GROUP) ★
2400 Maitland Center Pkwy, Maitland, FL 32751-4127
Tel (800) 273-3786 *Founded/Ownrshp* 2001
Sales 353.1MM^E *EMP* 130
SIC 3443 3411 3412 Fabricated plate work (boiler shop); Metal cans; Metal barrels, drums & pails
Pr: Charles Veniez
**COO:* Gerald Butler
CFO: Kevin Breheny
Opers Mgr: Moses Kingsbury

D-U-N-S 00-700-9889 IMP/EXP
INDUSTRIAL CONTRACTORS SKANSKA INC
INDIANA INDUSTRIAL CONTRACTORS
(*Suby of* SKANSKA USA INC) ★
401 Nw 1st St, Evansville, IN 47708-1001
Tel (812) 423-7832 *Founded/Ownrshp* 2013
Sales 416.7MM^E *EMP* 1,000
SIC 1541 1542

D-U-N-S 08-095-4308
INDUSTRIAL CONTROLS DISTRIBUTORS LLC
JOHNSON CONTRLS AUTHORIZED DLR
(*Suby of* ERIKS N.V.)
17 Christopher Way, Eatontown, NJ 07724-3325
Tel (732) 918-9000 *Founded/Ownrshp* 1976
Sales 90.0MM *EMP* 250
SIC 5075 5074 Air conditioning equipment, except room units; Heating equipment (hydronic)
Pr: Tom Comstock
CFO: Pat Larosa
VP: John Perry
Dept Mgr: Paul Rector
Genl Mgr: Rebecca Clarke
VP Mktg: Paul Barsa
Sales Asso: Michael Barnwell
Sales Asso: Tony Biondi
Sales Asso: David Cohen
Sales Asso: Stephen Guyon
Sales Asso: John Marinko

D-U-N-S 36-461-8777
INDUSTRIAL DEVELOPMENTS INTERNATIONAL LLC
INDUSTRIAL DEVELOPMENTS INTL
1100 Peachtree S, Atlanta, GA 30309
Tel (404) 479-4000 *Founded/Ownrshp* 2012
Sales 176.8MM^E *EMP* 167
SIC 6552 6531 Land subdividers & developers, commercial; Real estate managers
CEO: Timothy J Gunter
**Pr:* Henry D Gregroy Jr
COO: David Birdwell
**CFO:* Linda Booker
Ex VP: Karl Knauff
Ex VP: Matt O'Sullivan
Sr VP: Bert Calvert
**VP:* David R Birdwell
VP: Kelli Delozier

VP: Scott Helms
VP: Jon Kelly
VP: David Laibstain
**VP:* Matthew C O'Sullivan
VP: Paul Pontius
VP: Michael Salisbury
VP: Rita Skaggs
VP: Bob Tardy
Exec: Lisa Roberts

INDUSTRIAL DEVELOPMENTS INTL
See INDUSTRIAL DEVELOPMENTS INTERNATIONAL LLC

D-U-N-S 00-493-9229 IMP/EXP
INDUSTRIAL DIELECTRICS HOLDINGS INC
IDI
407 S 7th St, Noblesville, IN 46060-2708
Tel (317) 773-1766 *Founded/Ownrshp* 1966
Sales 187.6MM^E *EMP* 630
SIC 3644 Insulators & insulation materials, electrical
Pr: Thomas K Merrell
**VP:* John D Merrell

D-U-N-S 02-987-0664 IMP/EXP
INDUSTRIAL DISTRIBUTION GROUP INC
I D G
2100 The Oaks Pkwy, Belmont, NC 28012
Tel (704) 398-5600 *Founded/Ownrshp* 2016
Sales 737.1MM^E *EMP* 932
SIC 5084 7699

INDUSTRIAL ELECTRIC WIRE CABLE
See IEWC CORP

INDUSTRIAL ELEMENTARY SCHOOL E
See INDUSTRIAL INDEPENDENT SCHOOL DISTRICT

D-U-N-S 87-718-2865 IMP/EXP
INDUSTRIAL FABRICATORS INC
4328 York Hwy, Gastonia, NC 28052-6801
Tel (704) 864-5026 *Founded/Ownrshp* 1994
Sales 117.1MM^E *EMP* 210
Accts Miller Sherrill Blake Eagle Cp
SIC 3441 Fabricated structural metal
Pr: Roger Bingham
CFO: Tim Davis
**VP:* Pat Bingham
Opers Mgr: Robin Craig

D-U-N-S 02-762-9476 IMP
INDUSTRIAL FINISHES & SYSTEMS INC
SOUTHERN ABRASIVES
3455 W 1st Ave, Eugene, OR 97402-5449
Tel (541) 485-1503 *Founded/Ownrshp* 1958
Sales 115.7MM *EMP* 160
Accts Moss Adams Llp Cpa S
SIC 5085 5198 Abrasives; Paints, varnishes & supplies
Pr: Glenn Duckworth
**Ch:* Stuart W Barr
VP Mktg: Fred Hood

INDUSTRIAL FOOD INGREDIENTS
See SCOULAR CO

INDUSTRIAL GROWTH PARTNERS
See IGP INDUSTRIES LLC

D-U-N-S 83-133-1165
INDUSTRIAL INCOME TRUST INC
518 17th St Ste 17, Denver, CO 80202-4130
Tel (303) 228-2200 *Founded/Ownrshp* 2009
Sales NA *EMP* 30^E
SIC 6091

D-U-N-S 02-081-5114
INDUSTRIAL INDEPENDENT SCHOOL DISTRICT
INDUSTRIAL ELEMENTARY SCHOOL E
511 5th St, Vanderbilt, TX 77991-5000
Tel (361) 284-3226 *Founded/Ownrshp* 1947
Sales 12.0MM *EMP* 25,144
Accts Sliva & Reed Pc Bay City
SIC 8211 Public elementary school; Public senior high school; Public junior high school
VP: Amy Hessler
Schl Brd P: Dale Allen

D-U-N-S 94-987-8722 IMP
INDUSTRIAL LAMINATES/NORPLEX INC
(*Suby of* IDI) ★
665 Lybrand St, Postville, IA 52162-7792
Tel (563) 864-7321 *Founded/Ownrshp* 2002
Sales 85.0MM^E *EMP* 180
SIC 3089 3081 Laminating of plastic; Unsupported plastics film & sheet
Pr: Thomas K Merrell
**Sec:* Terrence M Doll
**Sec:* Lawrence Henss
**VP:* Jay Merrell
Mktg Dir: Robert O Smail

D-U-N-S 00-235-0593 IMP/EXP
INDUSTRIAL MANUFACTURING CO LLC
(*Suby of* SUMMA HOLDINGS INC) ★
8223 Brecksville Rd Ste 1, Brecksville, OH 44141-1367
Tel (440) 838-4700 *Founded/Ownrshp* 1979, 2000
Sales 594.4MM^E *EMP* 1,600
SIC 2542 3728 3566 Lockers (not refrigerated): except wood; Cabinets: show, display or storage: except wood; Shelving, office & store: except wood; Aircraft body & wing assemblies & parts; Aircraft assemblies, subassemblies & parts; Speed changers, drives & gears
CEO: James Benenson Jr
**Pt:* Clement Benenson
**Pr:* James Benenson III
**CFO:* John E Cvetic

INDUSTRIAL MECHANICAL COMPANY
See CCC GROUP INC

INDUSTRIAL METAL SUPPLY CO
See NORMAN INDUSTRIAL MATERIALS INC

D-U-N-S 00-378-1127 IMP
INDUSTRIAL PIPING INC
(*Suby of* IPI ACQUISITION, LLC)
212 S Tryon St Ste 1050, Charlotte, NC 28281-0003
Tel (704) 588-1100 *Founded/Ownrshp* 1952
Sales 97.5MM^E *EMP* 650
Accts Cherry Bekaert Llp Charlotte
SIC 3599 3569 Machine shop, jobbing & repair; Sprinkler systems, fire: automatic
CEO: Stephen Boord
**COO:* Kevin Walsh
**CFO:* Robert Coston
Chf Mktg O: Matt Ryan
**VP:* David Brakefield
VP: Bill McClung
CIO: Jeff Wolverton

D-U-N-S 16-143-4576 IMP/EXP
INDUSTRIAL PIPING SPECIALISTS INC
IPS
606 N 145th East Ave, Tulsa, OK 74116-2111
Tel (918) 437-9100 *Founded/Ownrshp* 1986
Sales 86.0MM^E *EMP* 184
SIC 5051 5085

INDUSTRIAL PRODUCTS
See BEHLEN MFG CO

INDUSTRIAL PRODUCTS DIV
See HAGERTY BROTHERS CO

D-U-N-S 00-895-4661 IMP/EXP
INDUSTRIAL SUPPLY CO INC
1635 S 300 W, Salt Lake City, UT 84115-5107
Tel (801) 484-8644 *Founded/Ownrshp* 1927
Sales 99.0MM^E *EMP* 130
SIC 5084 5085 Safety equipment; Machine tools & accessories; Welding machinery & equipment; Abrasives; Fasteners, industrial: nuts, bolts, screws, etc.; Rubber goods, mechanical
CEO: Chris Bateman
**Pr:* Randy Y Evans
**Ch:* Phil Thompson
Chf Mktg O: Jeff Mattson
**VP:* Shawn Newell
**VP:* Jessica Polychronis
VP: Jessica Yurgaitis
Brnch Mgr: Brian Cowden
IT Man: Tony Kittere
Sls Mgr: Dan Dedman
Sls Mgr: Shawn Holmes

INDUSTRIAL TIMBER & LUMBER CO
See ITL CORP

INDUSTRIAS LANCERMEX SA DE CV
See LANCER CORP

INDUSTRY SOURCE , THE
See TNG WORLDWIDE INC

D-U-N-S 82-847-4630 IMP
INDY EQUIPMENT INDEPENDENCE RECYCLING INC
6220 E Schaaf Rd, Independence, OH 44131-1332
Tel (216) 524-0999 *Founded/Ownrshp* 2008
Sales 250.0MM *EMP* 250
SIC 3531 Construction machinery
Pr: Victor Digeronimo
Off Mgr: Ronald Brocco
VP Mktg: Shannon Carlisle

D-U-N-S 16-190-9049
INDYNE INC
11800 Sunrise Valley Dr # 250, Reston, VA 20191-5302
Tel (703) 903-6900 *Founded/Ownrshp* 1999
Sales 311.5MM^E *EMP* 1,700
Accts Argy Wiltse & Robinson Pc M
SIC 8744 8748 7382 Base maintenance (providing personnel on continuing basis); Communications consulting; Security systems services
Pr: C Donald Bishop
**Pr:* Mr Donyer Miller
**COO:* Jeffrey Riemer
VP: Gayle Kall
Prgrm Mgr: Victoria Velez
Dir IT: Robert Trujillo
Netwrk Mgr: Kevin Andres
Software D: Arnel Capacio

D-U-N-S 00-398-3483 IMP/EXP
INEOS AMERICAS LLC
INEOS TECHNOLOGIES
(*Suby of* INEOS GROUP AG)
2600 S Shore Blvd Ste 500, League City, TX 77573-2944
Tel (281) 535-6600 *Founded/Ownrshp* 1965
Sales 1.0MMM^E *EMP* 2,600
SIC 2873 2869 Nitrogenous fertilizers; Industrial organic chemicals
Mng Pt: Daniel Moore
COO: Michael Szanyi
CFO: William Bernard
VP: Greg Musler
Dir Rx: Joe Walton
Dir IT: Joachim Pieper
IT Man: Chris Dow
IT Man: Vincent Gauthier
IT Man: Brian Harley
IT Man: Peter Moore
Tech Mgr: Cameron Robinson

D-U-N-S 00-818-8117 IMP/EXP
INEOS AMERICAS LLC
(*Suby of* INEOS HOLDINGS LIMITED)
7770 Rangeline Rd, Theodore, AL 36582-5212
Tel (251) 443-3000 *Founded/Ownrshp* 2003
Sales 188.5MM^E *EMP* 520
SIC 2869 2865 Acetone, synthetic; Phenol, alkylated & cumene
COO: Ron Deakins
CFO: Beverley Hoyle
IT Man: Stuart Buchman
VP Mktg: Ben Smith

D-U-N-S 83-881-2449
INEOS NITRILES USA LLC
(*Suby of* INEOS TECHNOLOGIES) ★
2600 S Shore Blvd Ste 250, League City, TX 77573-3091
Tel (281) 535-6600 *Founded/Ownrshp* 2015
Sales 107.2MM^E *EMP* 700^E
SIC 2821 Plastics materials & resins
Prin: Jim Ratcliffe

D-U-N-S 60-316-5379 IMP/EXP
INEOS STYROLUTION AMERICA LLC
(*Suby of* INEOS STYROLUTION GROUP GMBH)
4245 Meridian Pkwy # 151, Aurora, IL 60504-8018
Tel (630) 820-9500 *Founded/Ownrshp* 2011
Sales 180.0MM^E *EMP* 125^E
SIC 2869 Industrial organic chemicals
Pr: Alexander Gluck
**CEO:* Kevin McQuade
**CFO:* Chris De La Camp
Sfty Mgr: Craig Kotowski

INEOS TECHNOLOGIES
See INEOS AMERICAS LLC

D-U-N-S 62-380-4809 IMP/EXP
INEOS USA LLC
(*Suby of* INEOS GROUP AG)
2600 S Shore Blvd Ste 500, League City, TX 77573-2944
Tel (281) 535-6600 *Founded/Ownrshp* 2005
Sales 1.1MMM^E *EMP* 2,449
SIC 2821 3999 Plastics materials & resins; Atomizers, toiletry
CEO: Robert Learman
COO: Frederick Rulander
CFO: Robert Sokol
Ch: Jim Ratcliffe
VP: Scott Jackson
VP: Gary Wallace
Dir Lab: Kirk McFarlane
IT Man: Steve Vice
Site Mgr: Denver Drake
Sfty Mgr: Tony Matchett
Sfty Mgr: Malcolm McGregor

D-U-N-S 12-528-5150 IMP
INERGY AUTOMOTIVE SYSTEMS (USA) LLC
(*Suby of* INERGY AUTOMOTIVE SYSTEMS)
2710 Bellingham Dr # 400, Troy, MI 48083-2045
Tel (248) 743-5700 *Founded/Ownrshp* 2000
Sales 1.0MMM^E *EMP* 4,000
SIC 3714 Fuel systems & parts, motor vehicle
VP: Paul Wouters
CIO: D A Stevens
VP Sls: John Dick

D-U-N-S 18-245-4681
INERGY HOLDINGS LP
2 Brush Creek Blvd # 200, Kansas City, MO 64112-1712
Tel (816) 842-8181 *Founded/Ownrshp* 1996
Sales 221.8MM^E *EMP* 2,910
SIC 5172 6719 Petroleum products; Gases, liquefied petroleum (propane); Investment holding companies, except banks
Pr: John J Sherman
Pr: Phillip L Elbert
CFO: R Brooks Sherman Jr
Ex VP: Phillip Elbert
Sr VP: Williambill Moler
Sr VP: Laura L Ozenberger
VP: Michael Campbell
Counsel: Michael Post
Board of Directors: Warren H Gfeller, Arthur B Krause, Richard T O'brien

D-U-N-S 12-576-5680
■ INERGY PROPANE LLC
(*Suby of* SUBURBAN PROPANE PARTNERS LP) ★
2 Brush Creek Blvd # 200, Kansas City, MO 64112-1712
Tel (816) 842-8181 *Founded/Ownrshp* 2012
Sales 152.8MM^E *EMP* 1,008
SIC 5984 5172 Propane gas, bottled; Gases, liquefied petroleum (propane)
Pr: Phillip L Elbert
VP: Kent Blackford
VP: Barry Cigich
VP: Don Krider
VP: Jason Reeves
VP: R B Sherman
VP: Barry Wall

D-U-N-S 82-905-7814 IMP
■ INFASTECH DECORAH LLC
(*Suby of* STANLEY BLACK & DECKER INC) ★
1304 Kerr Dr, Decorah, IA 52101-2406
Tel (563) 382-4216 *Founded/Ownrshp* 2011
Sales 96.8MM^E *EMP* 475^E
SIC 3452 3965 Bolts, metal; Fasteners
COO: Kevin V Fernando
Genl Mgr: Nick McIntyre

D-U-N-S 05-055-2082 IMP
INFICON INC
(*Suby of* INFICON HOLDING AG)
2 Technology Pl, East Syracuse, NY 13057-9714
Tel (315) 434-1149 *Founded/Ownrshp* 1970, 2000
Sales 137.3MM^E *EMP* 810
SIC 3823 3812 Industrial process control instruments; Search & navigation equipment
Pr: Peter Maier
CFO: Matthias Troendle
VP: Hoang Cao
VP: Stephen Chabot
VP: Terry Perkins
VP: URS Waelchli
VP: Jerry Wander
Prgrm Mgr: Kenneth Rosys
Off Admin: Sandy Conner
CIO: Thomas Good
Dir IT: John Neidig

D-U-N-S 17-721-2305 IMP/EXP
INFILTRATOR WATER TECHNOLOGIES LLC
CHAMPION POLYMERS RECYCLING
(*Suby of* ONTARIO TEACHERS' PENSION PLAN BOARD)
4 Business Park Rd, Old Saybrook, CT 06475-4238
Tel (860) 577-7000 *Founded/Ownrshp* 2015
Sales 103.5MM^E *EMP* 300
SIC 3089

INFINEON TECHNOLOGIES AG
See INFINEON TECHNOLOGIES US HOLDCO INC

D-U-N-S 04-167-4912 IMP
INFINEON TECHNOLOGIES AMERICAS CORP
I R
(*Suby of* INFINEON TECHNOLOGIES AG)
101 N Sepulveda Blvd, El Segundo, CA 90245-4318
Tel (310) 726-8000 *Founded/Ownrshp* 2015
Sales 665.9MM^E *EMP* 3,500
SIC 3674 Semiconductors & related devices
CEO: Oleg Khaykin
COO: Gary Tanner
**CFO:* Ilan Daskal
Ex VP: Petra Nagel
VP: Tim Bixler
VP: John Burgess
VP: Fred Farris
VP: Henry Gao
VP: Henning Hauenstein
VP: Tim McDonald
VP: Jerry McKinney
VP: Phil Ockelmann
VP: James Tu
Exec: Nazanin Amani
Exec: Jeremy Limjuco
Exec: Rick Sivan
Dir Risk M: Phil Bahng

D-U-N-S 10-323-1692 IMP
INFINEON TECHNOLOGIES NORTH AMERICA CORP
640 N Mccarthy Blvd, Milpitas, CA 95035-5113
Tel (866) 951-9519 *Founded/Ownrshp* 2015
Sales 475.1MM^E *EMP* 1,200
SIC 3674

D-U-N-S 07-969-9553
INFINEON TECHNOLOGIES US HOLDCO INC
INFINEON TECHNOLOGIES AG
(*Suby of* INFINEON TECHNOLOGIES AG)
640 N Mccarthy Blvd, Milpitas, CA 95035-5113
Tel (408) 956-8960 *Founded/Ownrshp* 2014
Sales 101.1MM^E *EMP* 972^E
SIC 3674 Integrated circuits, semiconductor networks, etc.
CEO: David Lewis
Pr: Ken Ostrom
CFO: Dominik Asam
**CFO:* Andrew Prillwitz
VP: Weng Tan
Exec: Chris Gillert
Dir IT: Trung Le
Dir IT: Klaudia Seiling
IT Man: Jorg Domaschke
IT Man: Wesley Swail
VP Opers: Kurt Gruber
Board of Directors: David Lewis, Andrew Prillwitz, Michelle Thomas

D-U-N-S 02-133-1686 EXP
▲ INFINERA CORP
140 Caspian Ct, Sunnyvale, CA 94089-1000
Tel (408) 572-5200 *Founded/Ownrshp* 2000
Sales 886.7MM *EMP* 2,056
Tkr Sym INFN *Exch* NGS
SIC 3661 7372 Fiber optics communications equipment; Prepackaged software
CEO: Thomas J Fallon
**Ch Bd:* Kambiz Y Hooshmand
**Pr:* David F Welch
CFO: Brad Feller
Sr VP: Robert J Jandro
Sr VP: James L Laufman
VP: Matthew Mitchell
Sftwr Eng: Chetan Balasubramanya
Snr PM: Brian Buckley
Snr Mgr: Tom Castillo
Snr Mgr: Carol Cook
Board of Directors: John P Daane, Marcel Gani, Paul J Milbury, Mark A Wegleitner

D-U-N-S 03-210-5889 IMP/EXP
INFINEUM USA LP
(*Suby of* INFINEUM INTERNATIONAL LIMITED)
1900 E Linden Ave, Linden, NJ 07036-1133
Tel (908) 474-0100 *Founded/Ownrshp* 1998
Sales 1.3MMM^E *EMP* 600
SIC 5169 Oil additives; Chemical additives
Pr: Mark Struglinski
Exec: Steven Haffner
Exec: Trevor Russell
Mng Dir: Garrett Doherty
Sys Mgr: Leonid Moreyn
Opers Mgr: Bryan Boyle
Plnt Mgr: John Englishman
Sls Dir: Ken Kalisky
Mktg Mgr: Ahmad Zareh
Counsel: Carl Howard
Counsel: Annette Poblete

D-U-N-S 01-106-6144 IMP
INFINITE COMPUTER SOLUTIONS INC
(*Suby of* INFINITE COMPUTER SOLUTIONS (INDIA) LIMITED)
15201 Diamondback Dr # 125, Rockville, MD 20850-3312
Tel (301) 355-7760 *Founded/Ownrshp* 2001
Sales 278.7MM *EMP* 650
SIC 7379 7371 Computer related consulting services; Custom computer programming services
Ch Bd: Sanjay Govil
**CEO:* Upinder Zutshi
**Ex VP:* Sanjeev Gulati
**Ex VP:* K S RAO
Ex VP: Amit Srivastav
Sr VP: Vamsee Chepur

*Sr VP: Sheppard Lyngdoh
Sr VP: Ravi Nimmagadda
*Sr VP: Ashoka Tankala
VP: Jay Fahey
Exec: Kamal Kumar
Exec: Anita Tomar
Dir Bus: Senthil Arumugam

D-U-N-S 96-364-0557
INFINITE ENERGY HOLDINGS INC
7001 Sw 24th Ave, Gainesville, FL 32607-3704
Tel (352) 240-4121 Founded/Ownrshp 2010
Sales 154.1MM^E EMP 250
SIC 4911 4924 Distribution, electric power; Natural gas distribution
Pr: Darin Cook
*CEO: Richard S Blaser
*CFO: Robert Scott Thomas
*Genl Couns: Jeffrey Traynham

D-U-N-S 96-878-6749
INFINITE ENERGY INC
INTELLIGENT ENERGY
(Suby of INFINITE ENERGY HOLDINGS INC) ★
7001 Sw 24th Ave, Gainesville, FL 32607-3704
Tel (352) 331-1654 Founded/Ownrshp 1994
Sales 152.8MM^E EMP 10
SIC 4924 Natural gas distribution
CEO: Darin Cook
*Pr: Richard Blaser
Chf Mktg O: Brad Gamble
VP: Becky Patrick
Dir IT: Jennifer L Mueller
IT Man: Delmiro Campelo
IT Man: Sajid Hudson
Software D: Srinivas Jonnalagadda
Software D: Sonia Kulkarni
VP Mktg: Bill Kinneary
Sls Mgr: Justin Bishop

D-U-N-S 03-813-8625
INFINITE RF HOLDINGS INC
17802 Fitch, Irvine, CA 92614-6002
Tel (949) 261-1920 Founded/Ownrshp 2016
Sales 155.0MM^E EMP 436^E
SIC 5999 6719 Electronic parts & equipment; Investment holding companies, except banks
Pr: Terry Jarnigan

INFINITI FINANCIAL SERVICE
See NISSAN MOTOR ACCEPTANCE CORP

D-U-N-S 03-003-2155
■ INFINITY CASUALTY INSURANCE CO
(Suby of INFINITY INSURANCE CO) ★
2201 4th Ave N, Birmingham, AL 35203-3863
Tel (205) 870-4000 Founded/Ownrshp 1972, 2005
Sales NA EMP 1,000
SIC 6331 Automobile insurance
Pr: Jim Gober
*Treas: J Thomas Brooks
*VP: Thomas B Freeland
*VP: M F Washburne
Sftwr Eng: Jay Zimmerman

D-U-N-S 80-074-5762 IMP
INFINITY CLASSICS INTERNATIONAL INC
INFINITY HOSIERY
1368 38th St, Brooklyn, NY 11218-3612
Tel (718) 851-2577 Founded/Ownrshp 1995
Sales 98.8MM^E EMP 351
SIC 5139 Footwear
Ch Bd: Joe Steinberg

D-U-N-S 17-577-1570
INFINITY CONSTRUCTION SERVICES LP
INFINITY GROUP, THE
(Suby of PROSAFE) ★
926 Brazosport Blvd S, Clute, TX 77531-5715
Tel (979) 388-8579 Founded/Ownrshp 2003
Sales 162.9MM^E EMP 1,100
SIC 1629 1542 Chemical plant & refinery construction; Institutional building construction
Pr: Harold E Monical
VP: Jerry Monical
VP: Mark Monical
Dir IT: Chad Funk

INFINITY GROUP, THE
See INFINITY CONSTRUCTION SERVICES LP

D-U-N-S 61-476-6392
■ INFINITY GROUP INC
(Suby of INFINITY INSURANCE CO) ★
2201 4th Ave N, Birmingham, AL 35203-3863
Tel (205) 870-4000 Founded/Ownrshp 1992
Sales NA EMP 2,000
SIC 6331 Automobile insurance
CEO: James R Gober
*Treas: Roger Prestridge
Dir Bus: Yolanda Perez
Snr Mgr: Carl Walker

INFINITY HOSIERY
See INFINITY CLASSICS INTERNATIONAL INC

D-U-N-S 06-453-3557
■ INFINITY INSURANCE AGENCY INC
(Suby of INFINITY INSURANCE CO) ★
2201 4th Ave N, Birmingham, AL 35203-3863
Tel (205) 870-4000 Founded/Ownrshp 2005
Sales NA EMP 1,000
SIC 6411 Insurance agents & brokers
Pr: Edward Stevens
*Treas: David M Schaffer
*Ex VP: John P Kimsey
*VP: Larry M Glover

D-U-N-S 19-389-5885
■ INFINITY INSURANCE CO
(Suby of INFINITY PROPERTY AND CASUALTY CORP) ★
2201 4th Ave N, Birmingham, AL 35203-3863
Tel (205) 870-4000 Founded/Ownrshp 1979
Sales NA EMP 2,300
SIC 6331 Fire, marine & casualty insurance
CEO: James R Gober
*Pr: Glen N Godwin
*CFO: Robert Bateman
Sr VP: Ralph Gravelle
VP: Jim Orrison
Dir Bus: Jim Dougherty
Rgnl Mgr: Kyle Berthiaume
Brnch Mgr: Stephen Bloor
Brnch Mgr: John Burg
Snr Sftwr: Dustin Duncan
Snr Sftwr: Christy Spink

INFINITY NATIONAL INSURANCE CO
See HILSTAR INSURANCE CO

D-U-N-S 03-250-7836
INFINITY OILFIELD SERVICES LLC
1 Eye Center Dr, Muncy, PA 17756-9200
Tel (570) 567-7027 Founded/Ownrshp 2009
Sales 90.8MM^E EMP 200
SIC 5172 Crude oil

D-U-N-S 83-938-7966
▲ INFINITY PHARMACEUTICALS INC
784 Memorial Dr, Cambridge, MA 02139-4613
Tel (617) 453-1000 Founded/Ownrshp 1995
Sales 109.0MM EMP 222^E
Tkr Sym INFI Exch NGS
SIC 2834 8731 Pharmaceutical preparations; Commercial physical research
Ch Bd: Adelene Q Perkins
CFO: Lawrence E Bloch
Treas: Christopher M Lindblom
Ex VP: William C Bertrand Jr
Ex VP: Sujay Kango
Board of Directors: Jose Baselga, Jeffrey Berkowitz, Anthony B Evnin, Eric S Lander, Norman C Selby, Ian F Smith, Michael C Venuti

D-U-N-S 12-182-2287
▲ INFINITY PROPERTY AND CASUALTY CORP
3700 Colonnade Pkwy # 600, Birmingham, AL 35243-3216
Tel (205) 870-4000 Founded/Ownrshp 2002
Sales NA EMP 2,300
Tkr Sym IPCC Exch NGS
SIC 6331 Automobile insurance
Ch Bd: James R Gober
CFO: Robert H Bateman
Ex VP: Samuel J Simon
Sr VP: Glen N Godwin
Sr VP: Scott C Pitrone
IT Man: Marvis Owen
Board of Directors: Victor T Adamo, Richard J Bielen, Teresa A Canida, Angela Brock-Kyle, Harold E Layman, E Robert Meaney, William Stancil Starnes, James L Weidner, Samuel J Weinhoff

D-U-N-S 00-219-4509 IMP
INFINITY RESOURCES INC (IL)
CRITICS' CHOICE VIDEO & DVD
900 N Rohlwing Rd, Itasca, IL 60143-1161
Tel (630) 735-1000 Founded/Ownrshp 1994
Sales 86.2MM^E EMP 600
SIC 5961 Record &/or tape (music or video) club, mail order
CEO: Dennis E Abboud
*COO: Jack Datz
*CFO: Russ Huggins
*VP: Gary Rowlings
*VP: Jim Shriver
CTO: Anthony Giovingo
IT Man: Randy S Miguel

D-U-N-S 78-375-0078
■ INFINITY STANDARD INSURANCE CO
(Suby of INFINITY INSURANCE CO) ★
2201 4th Ave N, Birmingham, AL 35203-3863
Tel (205) 870-4000 Founded/Ownrshp 2016
Sales NA EMP 1,150
SIC 6331 Automobile insurance
Ch: Michael D Krause
*VP: Keith Hefner

D-U-N-S 12-091-3801
INFIRMARY HEALTH SYSTEM INC
5 Mobile Infirmary Cir, Mobile, AL 36607-3513
Tel (251) 435-3030 Founded/Ownrshp 1982
Sales 58.3MM EMP 5,000
SIC 8062 6512 1542 7322 5047 7389 General medical & surgical hospitals; Nonresidential building operators; Nonresidential construction; Collection agency, except real estate; Medical equipment & supplies; Fund raising organizations
CEO: D Mark Nix
*Pr: E Chandler Bramlett
Ex VP: Joe Denton
Ex VP: Alan Whaley
VP: Harry Brislin
VP: Howard H Fache
VP: Danny Harrison
VP: Eddy Stephens
Exec: Tom Crout
Dir Rad: Anthony Mosley
Dir Rx: Jim Easter

INFLUENT
See PCCW TELESERVICES (US) INC

D-U-N-S 12-600-0301 IMP
INFOBLOX INC
(Suby of DELTA HOLDCO, LLC)
3111 Coronado Dr, Santa Clara, CA 95054-3206
Tel (408) 986-4000 Founded/Ownrshp 2016
Sales 358.2MM EMP 25^E
Accts Ernst & Young Llp San Jose C
SIC 7374 7371 7379 Data processing & preparation; Data processing service; Custom computer programming services; Computer software development & applications; Software programming applications; Computer related consulting services
Pr: Jesper Andersen
CFO: Janesh Moorjani
Chf Mktg O: Ashish Gupta
Ex VP: Scott J Fulton
Ex VP: Atul Garg
Ex VP: David Gee
Ex VP: Norma Lane
Ex VP: Bill McCarthy
Ex VP: Stepehn Yu
VP: Sonya Andreae
VP: Liza Burns
VP: Sara Lamarch

D-U-N-S 11-813-5995
INFOCISION MANAGEMENT CORP
325 Springside Dr, Akron, OH 44333-4504
Tel (330) 668-1400 Founded/Ownrshp 1982
Sales 323.1MM^E EMP 2,783
SIC 7389 Telemarketing services
CEO: Craig Taylor
Ch Bd: Gary Taylor
Pr: Steve Boyazis
CFO: Dave Hamrick
Ofcr: Michael Van Scyoc
Ex VP: Mike Langenfeld
Sr VP: Steve Brubaker
Sr VP: Ken Dawson
VP: Michael Vanscyoc
CTO: Michael White
QA Dir: Julie Oddo

D-U-N-S 19-752-2659
INFOCROSSING INC
(Suby of WIPRO LIMITED)
2 Christie Hts, Leonia, NJ 07605-2233
Tel (201) 840-4700 Founded/Ownrshp 1999
Sales 151.8MM^E EMP 882
SIC 7374 Data processing service
CEO: Pinaki Kar
V Ch: Robert B Wallach
CFO: Shiva Kumar
*CFO: Yogesh Patel
Ex VP: Bridget Malone
*Sr VP: Nicholas J Letizia
Sr VP: Nicholas Letizia
VP: Richard Divosevic
VP: Stephen Fangman
VP: John Hammack
*VP: Garry Lazarewicz
VP: Howard Liebman
*VP: Dan Martino
VP: Jim Turner
VP Bus Dev: Rick Hulbert

D-U-N-S 79-164-7092
INFOGAIN CORP
485 Alberto Way Ste 100, Los Gatos, CA 95032-5476
Tel (408) 355-6000 Founded/Ownrshp 1990
Sales 85.2MM EMP 597
SIC 7379 7373 8742 8748 7374 1731 Computer related consulting services; Computer integrated systems design; Management information systems consultant; Systems engineering consultant, ex. computer or professional; Data processing & preparation; Electrical work
CEO: Sunil Bhatia
*Pr: Kapil K Nanda
Pr: Brian Rogan
CFO: Aloke Ghosh
*CFO: Phil Johnson
*CFO: Dean Wohlwend
Sr VP: Ray Allen
Sr VP: Mark De La Vega
Sr VP: Nishith Mathur
VP: Laki Balaji
VP: Girish Kannalli
VP: Manoj Mittal
VP: Hari Pendyla
Exec: Lokesh Joshi
Exec: Shashi Tekade
Dir Bus: Neha Kapoor

D-U-N-S 06-865-1702 IMP
INFOGROUP INC
YESMAIL
1020 E 1st St, Papillion, NE 68046-7611
Tel (402) 836-4500 Founded/Ownrshp 2010
Sales 433.9MM^E EMP 2,100
SIC 7331 Direct mail advertising services
Ch Bd: Michael Iaccarino
Pr: Larry Buchweitz
Pr: Mike Fisher
Pr: Robert Hylkema
Pr: Mark Litvinoff
Pr: Pankaj Mathur
Pr: Don Patrick
COO: Jim Scott
CFO: Stormy L Dean
*CFO: Richard Hanks
*CFO: John Hofman
Chf Mktg O: Slade Kobran
Sr VP: Vivian Ayuso
*Sr VP: Prunda Das
Sr VP: Nicholas Dayan
*Sr VP: Lisa Greene
Sr VP: Andrea Haldeman
Sr VP: Ann Kennedy
Sr VP: Cary Zackman
VP: Darren Amato
VP: Tom Claire
Board of Directors: Jim Sturm

D-U-N-S 19-342-5923 IMP
INFONET SERVICES CORP
BT INFONET
(Suby of BRITISH TELECOMMUNICATIONS PUBLIC LIMITED COMPANY)
2160 E Grand Ave, El Segundo, CA 90245-5024
Tel (310) 335-2859 Founded/Ownrshp 2005
Sales 218.6MM^E EMP 1,085
SIC 4813 7373 7375 Data telephone communications; Computer integrated systems design; Information retrieval services
CEO: David Andrew
*Pr: Jose A Collazo
*COO: Pete Sweers
*CFO: Akbar H Firdosy
Sr Cor Off: John Martinez
Ofcr: Nigel Perks
Ex VP: John Boltes
*Ex VP: John C Hoffman
*Ex VP: Michael J Timmins
*Sr VP: Paul Galleberg
Sr VP: Don Niven
VP: James Ashmore
VP: John Hoffman
Exec: Janis Harwell

INFOPRINT
See RICOH PRODUCTION PRINT SOLUTIONS LLC

D-U-N-S 11-146-6152
INFOR (US) INC
LILLY SOFTWARE ASSOCIATES
(Suby of LUX BOND CO) ★
13560 Morris Rd Ste 4100, Alpharetta, GA 30004-8995
Tel (678) 319-8000 Founded/Ownrshp 2002
Sales 1.5MMM^E EMP 3,980
SIC 7372 Prepackaged software
CEO: Charles Phillips
*Ch Bd: Carl James Schaper
Pr: Ronald Andris
Pr: Duncan Angove
Pr: Greg Corgan
*Pr: Stephan Scholl
*COO: Pam Murphy
CFO: Jeff Laborde
*CFO: Kevin Samuelson
CFO: Maureen Thomas
Ex VP: Paul Z Carreiro
Ex VP: Sean E Feeney
Ex VP: John Flavin
Ex VP: Soma Somasundaram
*Sr VP: Jim Byrnes
Sr VP: Chip Coyle
Sr VP: Thibault De Clisson
*Sr VP: Gregory Giangiordano
Sr VP: Tim Moylan
*Sr VP: Bruce Richardson
VP: Bob Benstead

D-U-N-S 07-847-2182
INFOR INC
LUX BOND CO
(Suby of INFOR LUX BOND CO) ★
641 Ave Of The Americas # 4, New York, NY 10011-2038
Tel (646) 336-1700 Founded/Ownrshp 2009
Sales 2.6MMM EMP 12,817
SIC 7371 7372 Custom computer programming services; Computer software development & applications; Business oriented computer software
CEO: Charles Phillips
*Ch Bd: Jim Schaper
Pr: Duncan Angove
Pr: Stephan Scholl
*COO: Pam Murphy
*CFO: Jeffrey Laborde
*Sr VP: Jay Hopkins
VP: Jay Dunbar
VP: Robert McKee
VP: Jason Taylor
Snr Sftwr: Ron Monroe
Board of Directors: Prescott Ashe, Stewart Bloom, David Dominik, C J Fitzgerald

D-U-N-S 07-952-9385
INFOR LUX BOND CO
641 Ave Of The Americas, New York, NY 10011-2014
Tel (646) 336-1700 Founded/Ownrshp 2014
Sales 2.6MMM^E EMP 12,920^E
SIC 7371 7372 8748 Custom computer programming services; Computer software development & applications; Business oriented computer software; Business consulting
CEO: Charles Phillips

D-U-N-S 14-314-7762
INFORELIANCE CORP
4050 Legato Rd Ste 700, Fairfax, VA 22033-2897
Tel (703) 246-9360 Founded/Ownrshp 2000
Sales 87.1MM^E EMP 330^E
SIC 7371 Computer software development
Pr: Andrew J Butler
*Ch Bd: William T Williams
*Pr: Andrew Butler
COO: Marshall Thames
CFO: Chrissy Bristow
VP: John Sankovich
Exec: Matthew Toloczko
Creative D: Shab Nassirpour
Dir Bus: Aaron Faulkner
Prgrm Mgr: Joanne Morris
Prgrm Mgr: Kristie O'Shea

D-U-N-S 82-532-0344
INFORMATICA LLC
(Suby of ITHACA HOLDCO 2 LLC)
2100 Seaport Blvd, Redwood City, CA 94063-5596
Tel (650) 385-5000 Founded/Ownrshp 2015
Sales 1.0MMM EMP 3,664^E
SIC 7372 Prepackaged software
CEO: Anil Chakravarthy
COO: Charles Hardison
*Ofcr: Sally Jenkins
*Ofcr: Jo Stoner
Ex VP: Paul J Hoffman
Ex VP: Girish Pancha
*Ex VP: Charles Race
*Ex VP: Ansa Sekharan
*Ex VP: Amit Walia
Sr VP: Graham C Burrows
Sr VP: Bart Foster
Sr VP: Jeff Moses
Sr VP: Barr Shriver
Sr VP: Graeme Thompson
VP: Franz Aman
VP: Pankaj Anand
VP: Michael Benson
VP: Sachin Chawla
VP: Brad Cook
VP: Darren Cunningham
VP: Candy Desantis

D-U-N-S 07-885-1615
INFORMATION BUILDERS INC (NY)
2 Penn Plz Fl 28, New York, NY 10121-2898
Tel (212) 736-4433 Founded/Ownrshp 1975
Sales 531.5MM^E EMP 1,500
SIC 7373 6794 Computer systems analysis & design; Patent buying, licensing, leasing
Pr: Gerald D Cohen
CFO: Harry Lerner
*Sr VP: Michael Corcoran
*Sr VP: Harry J Lerner
*Sr VP: Peter Mittelman
Sr VP: Sylvain Pavlowski
Sr VP: David Sandel
Sr VP: David Small
VP: Jos M Garc A-Soto
VP: Dennis Bartels

VP: Jon Deutsch
VP: Jake Freivald
VP: Jos M Garcia-Soto
VP: Michael Harchik
VP: Brian Joynt
VP: Rees Langston
VP: Marc Luvshis
VP: Terry Purcell
**VP:* Martin B Slagowitz
VP: Brian Suter
VP: Tom Villani

D-U-N-S 04-366-9030
INFORMATION INNOVATORS INC
(*Suby of* TRIPLE-I HOLDINGS LLC) ★
7400 Fullerton Rd Ste 210, Springfield, VA 22153-2830
Tel (703) 635-7088 *Founded/Ownrshp* 2002
Sales 149.3MM[E] *EMP* 574
SIC 7379 Computer related consulting services
CEO: Steven C Ikirt
Pr: Junji Takahashi
**Pr:* Franco Tao
COO: Edward Meagher
**CFO:* Denise Wilder
Sr VP: Daniel Matthews
VP: Rodney Caswell
VP: Brian Hall
**VP:* Mark Harrington
VP: Mark Muller
VP: Karen Triplett
Dir Soc: Angela Jackson
Dir Bus: Ken York

D-U-N-S 05-529-5026
■ **INFORMATION NETWORK SYSTEMS INC**
(*Suby of* LEIDOS HOLDINGS INC) ★
700 N Frederick Ave, Gaithersburg, MD 20879-3328
Tel (301) 240-7000 *Founded/Ownrshp* 2016
Sales 40.7MM[E] *EMP* 1,000
SIC 7373 7363 Systems engineering, computer related; Help supply services
Pr: June Shrewsbury
**Treas:* Kenneth Possenriede

D-U-N-S 16-950-1694
INFORMATION PROVIDERS INC
33 10th Ave S Ste 301, Hopkins, MN 55343-1309
Tel (952) 938-1400 *Founded/Ownrshp* 1996
Sales NA *EMP* 430
SIC 6411 Insurance agents, brokers & service
Pr: Frederick Peters
Sales Exec: Troy Novicky

D-U-N-S 09-473-8267
INFORMATION RESOURCES INC
INFOSCAN
150 N Clinton St, Chicago, IL 60661-1402
Tel (312) 726-1221 *Founded/Ownrshp* 2011
Sales 685.3MM[E] *EMP* 3,600
SIC 7372 Prepackaged software
Ch Bd: Rick Lenny
Pt: Nagi Jonnalagadda
Pt: Ed See
**Pr:* Andrew Appel
**Pr:* Lawrence Benjamin
**Pr:* Beverly A Grant
**Pr:* Nigel Howlett
Pr: John Lawlor
**Pr:* Bernhard Nann
Pr: Mark Parise
Pr: Thomas E Peterson
Pr: Robert I Tomei
**Pr:* Mark Tims
Pr: Derek Wiszniewski
COO: Jean Cooney
**CFO:* Mike Duffey
Div Pres: Rick Kurz
Div Pres: Marks S Parise
**Chf Mktg O:* Andrew A Salzman
Chf Mktg O: Stephen Webster
Ofcr: Robert C Blattberg
Board of Directors: Jeffrey P Ansell, Matt Ebbel, Raj Gupta, Lawrence Jackson, Steven Klinsky, Mathew J Lori, Don W McGeorge

D-U-N-S 79-880-9211
▲ **INFORMATION SERVICES GROUP INC**
281 Tresser Blvd Ste 901, Stamford, CT 06901-3246
Tel (203) 517-3100 *Founded/Ownrshp* 2006
Sales 209.2MM *EMP* 1,134[E]
Tkr Sym III *Exch* NGM
SIC 8742 7379 Management consulting services; Computer related consulting services
Ch Bd: Michael P Connors
CFO: David E Berger
CFO: David Berger
Ex VP: R James Cravens
VP: Tim Leonard
Board of Directors: Neil G Budnick, Gerald S Hobbs, Christine Putur, Donald C Waite III

D-U-N-S 08-956-3498
■ **INFORMATION TECHNOLOGY INC**
FISERV
(*Suby of* FISERV INC) ★
1345 Old Cheney Rd, Lincoln, NE 68512-1266
Tel (402) 423-2682 *Founded/Ownrshp* 1995
Sales 125.8MM[E] *EMP* 1,200
SIC 5045 7373 7374 7371 Computer peripheral equipment; Systems software development services; Data processing & preparation; Custom computer programming services
Pr: Thomas M Cypher
Sr VP: Dave Carden
Sr VP: Jim McLoughlin
Sr VP: Erik Wichita
Prgrm Mgr: Jon Burmeister
Snr Ntwrk: Andrew Malone

D-U-N-S 82-604-6703
■ **INFORMEDRX INC**
(*Suby of* OPTUM RX) ★
4805 E Thistle Landing Dr # 100, Phoenix, AZ 85044-6478
Tel (800) 282-3232 *Founded/Ownrshp* 2000
Sales 115.3MM[E] *EMP* 495
SIC 8742 Management consulting services
Prin: Mark Thierer

**VP:* Jeffrey Park
**Prin:* Gordon S Glenn

INFOSCAN
See INFORMATION RESOURCES INC

D-U-N-S 18-485-0097
INFOSYS MCCAMISH SYSTEMS LLC
(*Suby of* INFOSYS LIMITED)
6425 Powers Ferry Rd, Atlanta, GA 30339-2908
Tel (770) 690-1500 *Founded/Ownrshp* 1985
Sales NA *EMP* 320
SIC 6399 7373 Warranty insurance, product; except automobile; Computer integrated systems design
Pr: J Gordon Beckham Jr
**COO:* Rishi Kumar Jain
**Sr VP:* Mark Dephillips
VP: Samuel Sam
VP Admn: Lisa Johnson
Sftwr Eng: Mike Dyer
Sftwr Eng: Michael Lake
Board of Directors: Ravi Kumar S, Richard Magner

D-U-N-S 96-718-8702
INFOSYS PUBLIC SERVICES INC
(*Suby of* INFOSYS LIMITED)
800 King Farm Blvd # 505, Rockville, MD 20850-5979
Tel (301) 354-8600 *Founded/Ownrshp* 2009
Sales 98.4MM[E] *EMP* 2,000
SIC 7371 7374 8742 Custom computer programming services; Computer software systems analysis & design, custom; Computer software development & applications; Optical scanning data service; Management engineering
CEO: Eric Paternoster
**Ch Bd:* Jefferey Lehman
**VP:* Jim Havelka

D-U-N-S 14-883-0594
INFOTELECOM HOLDINGS LLC
BROADVOX
75 Erieview Plz Fl 4, Cleveland, OH 44114-1839
Tel (216) 373-4811 *Founded/Ownrshp* 2001
Sales 166.4MM[E] *EMP* 400
SIC 4813 7373 ; ; Computer system selling services

D-U-N-S 95-812-0552
INFOVISION INC
800 E Campbell Rd Ste 388, Richardson, TX 75081-1841
Tel (972) 234-0058 *Founded/Ownrshp* 1995
Sales 95.5MM[E] *EMP* 600
Accts Perkins Dexter Sinopoli & Ha
SIC 8711 7371 Consulting engineer; Computer software systems analysis & design, custom
Pr: Sean Yalamanchi
Mng Pt: Lisa Annis
**VP:* Raman Kovelamudi
Admn Mgr: Lina Lim
Off Mgr: Katie Uebele
IT Man: Brian Ray
Board of Directors: Sean Yalamanchi

INFOWORLD PUBLISHING COMPANY
See IDG COMMUNICATIONS INC

D-U-N-S 06-783-6641
■ **INFRA SOURCE INC**
(*Suby of* QUANTA SERVICES INC) ★
2311 Green Rd Ste D, Ann Arbor, MI 48105-2965
Tel (734) 434-2000 *Founded/Ownrshp* 2012
Sales 618.0MM[E] *EMP* 2,000
SIC 1521 General remodeling, single-family houses
Prin: Jack Webb

D-U-N-S 15-190-9637 IMP/EXP
■ **INFRA-METALS CO**
(*Suby of* RELIANCE STEEL & ALUMINUM CO) ★
580 Middletown Blvd D100, Langhorne, PA 19047-1877
Tel (215) 741-1000 *Founded/Ownrshp* 2006
Sales 354.4MM[E] *EMP* 514
SIC 5051 Steel
CEO: Gregg J Mollins
Pr: Mark Haight
CFO: Herb Dubrow
CFO: Christopher Moreton
Treas: Robert J Joubran
Prin: Tom Gores
IT Man: Michael Diamond
IT Man: William Stoner
Opers Mgr: Don Everett
Sls Mgr: Randy Frevert
Sales Asso: Aaron Gentilucci

D-U-N-S 07-966-5657
INFRAREIT INC (MD)
1807 Ross Ave Fl 4, Dallas, TX 75201-8002
Tel (214) 855-6700 *Founded/Ownrshp* 2001
Sales 151.2MM *EMP* 3
SIC 6798 Real estate investment trusts
Pr: David A Campbell
**Ch Bd:* W Kirk Baker
CFO: Brant Meleski
Sr VP: Stacey H Dore

D-U-N-S 02-995-0339
■ **INFRASOURCE LLC**
(*Suby of* QUANTA SERVICES INC) ★
2936 S 166th St, New Berlin, WI 53151-3506
Tel (713) 629-7600 *Founded/Ownrshp* 2000
Sales 772.5MM[E] *EMP* 2,500
SIC 1623 1542 Water, sewer & utility lines; Nonresidential construction

INFRASOURCE SERVICES, INC.
See QUANTA FIBER NETWORKS INC

D-U-N-S 96-978-1165
INFRASTRUCTURE AND ENERGY ALTERNATIVES LLC
I E A
3900 White Ave, Clinton, IN 47842-1160
Tel (708) 397-4200 *Founded/Ownrshp* 2011
Sales 280.9MM *EMP* 882
SIC 8731 1731 Energy research; Energy management controls
CEO: Paul M Daily

D-U-N-S 01-070-4695
INFRASTRUCTURE CORP OF AMERICA
I C A
(*Suby of* HDR INC) ★
750 Old Hickory Blvd # 200, Brentwood, TN 37027-4567
Tel (615) 377-4730 *Founded/Ownrshp* 2015
Sales 132.7MM[E] *EMP* 700
SIC 8742 8711 8741 Management consulting services; Engineering services; Financial management for business
Pr: Howard Eley
COO: Mark Acuff
**Ex VP:* David Rader
Off Mgr: Melondy Crain
IT Man: Stan King

D-U-N-S 83-165-3063
INFRASTRUCTURE HOLDINGS CO LLC
(*Suby of* J H WHITNEY & CO) ★
115 S 48th St, Tempe, AZ 85281-2312
Tel (480) 784-2910 *Founded/Ownrshp* 2008
Sales 164.1MM *EMP* 850[E]
Accts Mcgladrey & Pullen Llp Phoen
SIC 1611 1794 2591 General contractor, highway & street construction; Concrete construction: roads, highways, sidewalks, etc.; Excavation & grading, building construction; Blinds vertical
CFO: David James

D-U-N-S 87-711-9214
INFRATECH CORP
2036 Baker Ct Nw, Kennesaw, GA 30144-6423
Tel (770) 792-8700 *Founded/Ownrshp* 1994
Sales 125.0MM[E] *EMP* 300
SIC 1623 Electric power line construction
CEO: Christopher Prangley
**COO:* Derek Lee
**CFO:* James Dunn
**VP:* Jerry Wilson
Genl Mgr: Steve Mitchell

D-U-N-S 00-607-7150 IMP
INFRATROL MANUFACTURING CORP
INNOVATIVE MODERN COATERS
2500 S 162nd St, New Berlin, WI 53151-2808
Tel (262) 797-8140 *Founded/Ownrshp* 1997
Sales 600.0MM *EMP* 43
SIC 3567

INFUND
See FIRST INSURANCE FUNDING CORP

D-U-N-S 13-806-3016
INFUSION SOFTWARE INC
INFUSIONSOFT
1260 S Spectrum Blvd, Chandler, AZ 85286-8415
Tel (480) 807-0644 *Founded/Ownrshp* 2007
Sales 164.3MM[E] *EMP* 361[E]
SIC 7379 7371 Computer related consulting services; Computer software development
CEO: Clate Mask
**CFO:* Curtis Smith
**CFO:* Brent Stumme
**Sr VP:* Hal Halladay
Sr VP: Elizabeth Pitt
**VP:* Marc Chesley
VP: Anita Grantham
VP: Roy Kelly
VP: Dave Lee
**VP:* Scott Martineau
VP: Jo Anne Ravielli
VP: Adam Ross
**VP:* Kathy Sacks
VP: Scott Stagg
**VP:* Aaron Stead
Exec: Kristina Rueling

INFUSIONSOFT
See INFUSION SOFTWARE INC

D-U-N-S 87-775-1698
■ **ING BANK FSB**
ING DIRECT
(*Suby of* CAPITAL ONE FINANCIAL CORP) ★
802 Delaware Ave, Wilmington, DE 19801-1377
Tel (302) 658-2200 *Founded/Ownrshp* 2000
Sales NA *EMP* 749[E]
SIC 6035 6211 Savings institutions, federally chartered; Security brokers & dealers
CEO: Ralph Hamers
**COO:* Jim Kelly
**COO:* Roel Louwhoff
**CFO:* Pg Flynn
**CFO:* Patrick Flynn
Ex VP: Brian Myres
Dir IT: Lynda Baker
IT Man: Berak Thomas
Software D: Dennis Brennan
Opers Mgr: Frederick West
Genl Couns: Deneen Stewart

ING DIRECT
See ING BANK FSB

D-U-N-S 12-443-2134 IMP
ING USA HOLDING CORP
1 S Orange St, Wilmington, DE 19801-5006
Tel (302) 658-2200 *Founded/Ownrshp* 1999
Sales NA *EMP* 1,171
SIC 6035

D-U-N-S 14-835-6033
INGALLS HEALTH SYSTEM
INGALLS MEMORIAL HOSPITAL
1 Ingalls Dr, Harvey, IL 60426-3558
Tel (708) 333-2333 *Founded/Ownrshp* 1981
Sales 285.4MM *EMP* 2,963
Accts Crowe Horwath Llp Chicago Il
SIC 8062 General medical & surgical hospitals
Pr: Kurt E Johnson
Pr: Scott Strausser
**CFO:* Vincent Pryoor
Bd of Dir: Robert Harris
Bd of Dir: Mitchell Krawczyk
VP: Siva Schulman
Dir Bus: Heidi Ruhe
Adm Dir: Jack Branding
Ex Dir: Aaron Bontrager

Genl Mgr: Fred Saviano
Sls&Mrk Ex: Renata Cichowicz

INGALLS MEMORIAL HOSPITAL
See INGALLS HEALTH SYSTEM

D-U-N-S 06-744-4927
INGALLS MEMORIAL HOSPITAL
1 Ingalls Dr, Harvey, IL 60426-3558
Tel (708) 333-2300 *Founded/Ownrshp* 1922
Sales 285.4MM *EMP* 2,296
SIC 8062 General medical & surgical hospitals
Pr: Kurt Johnson
**CFO:* Vince Pryor
Opers Mgr: Maia Thiagarajan
Ansthlgy: Robert S Tumacder
Doctor: William Baker
Doctor: Shaun Grannis
Doctor: Sarah Halleran
Doctor: Steven Hugenberg
Doctor: William Kessler
Doctor: Suthat Liangpunsakul
Doctor: Veronica Mesquida

D-U-N-S 14-847-9173 IMP
INGENICO CORP (DELAWARE)
INGENICO NORTH AMERICA
(*Suby of* INGENICO PREPAID SERVICES FRANCE SAS)
3025 Windward Plz Ste 600, Alpharetta, GA 30005-8734
Tel (678) 456-1200 *Founded/Ownrshp* 1983
Sales 118.8MM[E] *EMP* 378
SIC 3577 Magnetic ink recognition devices
CEO: Philip Lazare
**Pr:* Jelss Dowin
CFO: Michael Wasserfuhr
Ex VP: Rick Centeno
Ex VP: Michel Leger
Sr VP: Deborah Dixson
Sr VP: Scott Tubbs
VP: Gregory Boardman
VP: Rhonda Boardman
VP: Alan Forgione
VP: Rod Hometh
VP: Charles K Kovach
VP: Deb McAteer
VP: Mark Treco
VP: Marty Widmann

INGENICO NORTH AMERICA
See INGENICO CORP (DELAWARE)

INGENUITY MEDIA GROUP
See MARTIN AGENCY INC

D-U-N-S 00-136-8026 IMP/EXP
INGERSOLL-RAND CO
(*Suby of* INGERSOLL-RAND PUBLIC LIMITED COMPANY)
800 Beaty St Ste B, Davidson, NC 28036-6924
Tel (704) 655-4000 *Founded/Ownrshp* 1871
Sales 8.9MMM[E] *EMP* 35,560
SIC 3561 3429 3546 3563 3531 Pumps & pumping equipment; Furniture builders' & other household hardware; Keys, locks & related hardware; Power-driven handtools; Air & gas compressors including vacuum pumps; Winches
Ch Bd: Michael W Lamach
Pr: Michael D Radcliff
CFO: Susan K Carter
Sr VP: Marcia J Avedon
Sr VP: Paul Camuti
Sr VP: Maria Green
Sr VP: Robert L Katz
Sr VP: Gary Michel
Sr VP: Don H Rice
VP: Kevin Deane
VP: Douglass Dickinson
VP: Wb Gould
VP: Sean McBride
VP: Keith Sultana
VP: Josh Van Dyke
Dir Bus: Joshua Weidman
Board of Directors: Tony L White, Ann C Berzin, John Bruton, Jared L Cohon, Gary D Forsee, Edward E Hagenlocker, Constance Horner, Theodore E Martin, John P Surma, Richard J Swift

D-U-N-S 96-330-6712 IMP/EXP
INGERSOLL-RAND US TRANE HOLDINGS CORP
(*Suby of* INGERSOLL-RAND PUBLIC LIMITED COMPANY)
1 Centennial Ave Ste 101, Piscataway, NJ 08854-3921
Tel (732) 652-7100 *Founded/Ownrshp* 2008
Sales 9.0MMM[E] *EMP* 29,000[E]
SIC 3585 Refrigeration & heating equipment
CEO: Michael W Lamach
**CFO:* Steven R Shawley
VP: Xiangjun Yu

D-U-N-S 07-992-9405 EXP
▲ **INGEVITY CORP**
5255 Virginia Ave, North Charleston, SC 29406-3615
Tel (843) 740-2300 *Founded/Ownrshp* 2016
Sales 1.1MMM[E] *EMP* 1,500[E]
Tkr Sym NGVT *Exch* NYS
SIC 2819 Industrial inorganic chemicals
Pr: Michael Wilson
CFO: John C Fortson
Ex VP: Edward Arthur Rose III
Sr VP: Michael P Smith
Exec: Ed Woodcock

D-U-N-S 60-367-8512
■ **INGEVITY SOUTH CAROLINA LLC**
(*Suby of* INGEVITY CORP) ★
5255 Virginia Ave, North Charleston, SC 29406-3615
Tel (843) 740-2300 *Founded/Ownrshp* 2003
Sales 162.2MM[E] *EMP* 700[E]
SIC 2611 Kraft (sulfate) pulp; Pulp mills, chemical & semichemical processing
Exec: Awilda Quinones

D-U-N-S 80-123-5508
INGHAM REGIONAL MEDICAL CENTER
MCLAREN GREATER LANSING
(*Suby of* MCLAREN HEALTH CARE CORP) ★
401 W Greenlawn Ave, Lansing, MI 48910-0899
Tel (517) 975-7800 *Founded/Ownrshp* 1992
Sales 312.9MM *EMP* 2,500
SIC 8062 General medical & surgical hospitals
CEO: Philip Incarnati
Dir Vol: Donna Gardner
**Pr:* Dennis Litos
**CFO:* DaleThompson
CFO: Robert Wright
VP Opers: Leah Searcy
Orthpdst: Kelly Coffey
Orthpdst: Floyd Goodman
Orthpdst: Erich Hornbach
Obsttrcn: Andrea Dionne
Obsttrcn: Erin Grey

D-U-N-S 02-441-8584 IMP/EXP
▲ INGLES MARKETS INC (NC)
2913 Us Highway 70, Black Mountain, NC 28711-9103
Tel (828) 669-2941 *Founded/Ownrshp* 1965
Sales 3.8MMM *EMP* 25,000
Tkr Sym IMKTA *Exch* NGS
SIC 5411 5912 5541 2026 6512 Supermarkets, chain; Drug stores & proprietary stores; Gasoline service stations; Fluid milk; Shopping center, property operation only
Pr: James W Lanning
**Ch Bd:* Robert P Ingle II
**CFO:* Ronald B Freeman
Board of Directors: Fred D Ayers, L Keith Collins, Ernest E Ferguson, Laura Ingle Sharp, Brenda S Tudor

D-U-N-S 00-388-2313
INGLETT & STUBBS LLC (GA)
(*Suby of* I & S ACQUISITION CORP) ★
5200 Riverview Rd Se, Mableton, GA 30126-2953
Tel (404) 881-1199 *Founded/Ownrshp* 1953, 2005
Sales 135.0MM *EMP* 850
SIC 1731

INGLEWOOD HIGH SCHOOL
See INGLEWOOD UNIFIED SCHOOL DISTRICT

D-U-N-S 10-064-4343
INGLEWOOD UNIFIED SCHOOL DISTRICT
INGLEWOOD HIGH SCHOOL
401 S Inglewood Ave, Inglewood, CA 90301-2599
Tel (310) 419-2500 *Founded/Ownrshp* 1953
Sales 6.8MM *EMP* 1,600
Accts Vavrinek Trine Day & Co Ll
SIC 8211 Public senior high school
**Pr:* Dr Carliss McGhee
Ofcr: Leslie Gaulden
**VP:* Ms La Deirdre Wilson
**Prin:* Ofelia Lariviere
Teacher Pr: Sharrel Carter
Teacher Pr: Mona Hasson

D-U-N-S 07-318-3642 IMP/EXP
INGOMAR PACKING CO LLC
9950 S Ingomar Grade, Los Banos, CA 93635
Tel (209) 826-9494 *Founded/Ownrshp* 1982
Sales 87.2MM^E *EMP* 251
SIC 2033 Tomato paste: packaged in cans, jars, etc.
Pr: Gregory Pruett
**VP:* William B Cahill Jr
Sls Dir: Mark Stegeman

D-U-N-S 13-104-4299
INGRAM BARGE CO
(*Suby of* INGRAM INDUSTRIES INC) ★
4400 Harding Pike, Nashville, TN 37205-2204
Tel (615) 298-8200 *Founded/Ownrshp* 1984
Sales 176.4MM^E *EMP* 2,500
SIC 4449 River transportation, except on the St. Lawrence Seaway
CEO: Orrin H Ingram
Pr: Kaj Shah
COO: David G Sehrt
Chf Cred: Dan Martin
Bd of Dir: Chip Lacy
Ofcr: Dan Mecklenborg Sr
Ex VP: Eleanor McDonald
Sr VP: Kim Nowell
Sr VP: Crystal Taylor
VP: Chuck Arnold
VP: Keith Aulson
VP: Tom Vorholt
Exec: Jim Blackmon
Dir Risk M: Angela Angrick
Board of Directors: John R Ingram, Orrin Ingram, Eleanor McDonald

INGRAM BOOK COMPANY
See INGRAM BOOK GROUP INC

D-U-N-S 12-157-3724 IMP/EXP
INGRAM BOOK GROUP INC
INGRAM BOOK COMPANY
(*Suby of* INGRAM INDUSTRIES INC) ★
1 Ingram Blvd, La Vergne, TN 37086-3629
Tel (615) 213-5000 *Founded/Ownrshp* 1995
Sales 2.8MMM^E *EMP* 2,050
SIC 5192 Books, periodicals & newspapers
Pr: Shawn Morin
**Ch Bd:* John Ingram
**CFO:* Brian Dauphin
VP: Marcos Farrow
VP: Andrew Gatlin
VP: Eric Hawkins
VP: Phil Ollila
VP: Steve Pait
VP: Steve Pate
VP: Pamela Smith
VP: George Tattersfield
VP: Gerard Viveiros
Dir Teleco: Phil Watson

D-U-N-S 11-300-4696 IMP/EXP
INGRAM ENTERTAINMENT HOLDINGS INC
2 Ingram Blvd, La Vergne, TN 37089-2000
Tel (615) 287-4000 *Founded/Ownrshp* 1999
Sales 606.0MM^E *EMP* 1,000
SIC 5065 5045 Tapes, audio & video recording; Computers & accessories, personal & home entertainment
CEO: Claire W Tucker
**Pr:* David B Ingram
**Treas:* Jeffrey D Skinner
**Treas:* Wade L Smith
**Sr VP:* W Donnie Daniel

D-U-N-S 60-235-2676 IMP/EXP
INGRAM ENTERTAINMENT INC
(*Suby of* INGRAM ENTERTAINMENT HOLDINGS INC) ★
2 Ingram Blvd, La Vergne, TN 37089-2000
Tel (615) 287-4000 *Founded/Ownrshp* 1997
Sales 606.0MM^E *EMP* 410
SIC 5065 5092 5099 Diskettes, computer; Video games; Video & audio equipment
Pr: David B Ingram
V Ch: W Donnie Daniel
Pr: Robert W Webb
CFO: Donnie Daniel
Ex VP: Robert A Geistman
Sr VP: John J Fletcher
Sr VP: Bob Geistman
VP: Greg Patry
Exec: James Ellis
Brnch Mgr: Jessie Wagley
Web Dev: Boris Stoev

D-U-N-S 00-894-3839 IMP/EXP
INGRAM INDUSTRIES INC (TN)
4400 Harding Pike Ste 310, Nashville, TN 37205-2314
Tel (615) 298-8200 *Founded/Ownrshp* 1962, 1978
Sales 3.3MMM^E *EMP* 5,015
SIC 5192 4449

D-U-N-S 00-491-9486 IMP/EXP
■ INGRAM MICRO INC
(*Suby of* TIANJIN TIANHAI INVESTMENT CO., LTD.)
3351 Michelson Dr Ste 100, Irvine, CA 92612-0697
Tel (714) 566-1000 *Founded/Ownrshp* 1979, 2016
Sales 43.0MMM *EMP* 27,700
Tkr Sym IM *Exch* NYS
SIC 5045 Computers, peripherals & software; Computer peripheral equipment; Computers; Computer software
CEO: Alain Monie
CFO: Gina Mastantuono
Ex VP: Augusto Aragone Coppola

INGRAM MICRO MOBILITY
See TOUCHSTONE WIRELESS REPAIR AND LOGISTICS LP

D-U-N-S 04-975-1670
INGRAM READYMIX INC
3580 Farm Market 482, New Braunfels, TX 78132
Tel (830) 625-9156 *Founded/Ownrshp* 1957
Sales 94.3MM^E *EMP* 480
SIC 3273

D-U-N-S 00-481-1423 IMP/EXP
▲ INGREDION INC
5 Westbrook Corporate Ctr # 500, Westchester, IL 60154-5795
Tel (708) 551-2600 *Founded/Ownrshp* 1906
Sales 5.6MMM *EMP* 11,000
Tkr Sym INGR *Exch* NYS
SIC 2046 Wet corn milling; Corn starch; Corn oil products; Corn sugars & syrups
Ch Bd: Ilene S Gordon
CFO: Jack C Fortnum
Chf Cred: Christine M Castellano
Sr VP: Anthony P Delio
VP: George Bisoglio
VP: Neal R Christian
VP: Ron Deis
VP: Matt Galvanoni
VP: Matthew R Galvanoni
VP: Neil Grimwood
VP: Rick Kyle
VP: Jim Low
VP: Ron McCrimmond
VP: Manish Shah
VP: Craig Shirley
VP: Kevin Wilson
Dir Rx: Paul Bratley

INHALATION TOXICOLOGY RES INST
See LOVELACE BIOMEDICAL & ENVIRONMENTAL RESEARCH INSTITUTE

INITIAL AIRPORT SERVICES
See INITIAL CONTRACT SERVICES INC

D-U-N-S 17-442-7575
INITIAL CONTRACT SERVICES INC
INITIAL AIRPORT SERVICES
(*Suby of* RENTOKIL INITIAL UK LTD)
1780 Corporate Dr Ste 440, Norcross, GA 30093-2958
Tel (678) 812-3079 *Founded/Ownrshp* 1986
Sales 27.9MM^E *EMP* 2,500
SIC 7349 Janitorial service, contract basis
Pr: Edward S Fleury
**CFO:* Barry Collins
CFO: Deborah Hubbard

INITIATIVE MEDIA
See MEDIABRANDS WORLDWIDE INC

D-U-N-S 80-016-4956 IMP/EXP
INKCYCLE INC
TONERCYCLE
11100 W 82nd St, Lenexa, KS 66214-1502
Tel (913) 894-8387 *Founded/Ownrshp* 1992
Sales 86.9MM^E *EMP* 490
SIC 3955 7699 7378 5045 8249 5734 Print cartridges for laser & other computer printers; Printing trades machinery & equipment repair; Computer peripheral equipment repair & maintenance; Computer peripheral equipment; Printers, computer; Computers; Business training services; Printers & plotters: computers; Personal computers
Pr: Rick Krska
**COO:* Tom Cunningham
**CFO:* Cathy Lynch
**Ex VP:* Brad Roderick
**VP:* Bob Ehlers
**VP:* Joy James
**VP:* Carl Little
VP: Inkcycle Names
**VP:* Keith Riley
**CTO:* Tom Ashley

D-U-N-S 01-075-8667
INKTEL HOLDINGS CORP
13975 Nw 58th Ct, Miami Lakes, FL 33014-3114
Tel (305) 523-1100 *Founded/Ownrshp* 1997
Sales 85.2MM^E *EMP* 420
SIC 7389 Telemarketing services
**COO:* Summer Dennis
**CFO:* Manuel Hernandez
**CFO:* Albert Llodra
Top Exec: Abigail Auslander
**Ex VP:* Dan Arriola
**Sr VP:* Dave Drayton
**VP:* Robert J Ballwanz
**VP:* Chris Chinni
**VP:* Tim Sanchez
VP: Kyla Starks
CIO: Ken Mark

D-U-N-S 60-293-4239
INLAND BANCORP INC
2805 Butterfield Rd # 370, Oak Brook, IL 60523-1168
Tel (630) 218-8000 *Founded/Ownrshp* 2005
Sales 85.3MM *EMP* 112^E
SIC 6719 Investment holding companies, except banks
CEO: Daniel Goodwin
Sr Pt: Lawrence Aaron
**Pr:* Howard Jaffe
**VP:* Cheri Andersen

INLAND CAREER CENTER
See GOODWILL SOUTHERN CALIFORNIA

D-U-N-S 08-117-6356
INLAND COUNTIES REGIONAL CENTER INC
INLAND REGIONAL CENTER
1365 S Waterman Ave, San Bernardino, CA 92408-2804
Tel (909) 890-3000 *Founded/Ownrshp* 1971
Sales 378.4MM *EMP* 586^E
Accts Windes Inc Long Beach Ca
SIC 8741 Management services
CEO: Carol A Fitzgibbons
**Ex Dir:* Carol Fitzgibbons
Prgrm Mgr: Lawana Blair
Prgrm Mgr: Mia Gurri
Off Admin: Stephen Hughes
Psych: Beth Adelman
Psych: Martha Barragan
Psych: Susannah Bernard
Psych: Sara Burchfield
Psych: Rafael Cendejas
Psych: Jaime Cruz

D-U-N-S 07-937-0518
INLAND CRUDE PURCHASING LLC
727 N Waco Ave Ste 400, Wichita, KS 67203-3900
Tel (316) 263-3201 *Founded/Ownrshp* 2012
Sales 175.0MM *EMP* 3
SIC 5172 Crude oil

D-U-N-S 83-270-6712
INLAND DIVERSIFIED REAL ESTATE TRUST INC
2901 Butterfield Rd, Oak Brook, IL 60523-1190
Tel (630) 218-8000 *Founded/Ownrshp* 2008
Sales 185.8MM *EMP* 4^E
Accts Kpmg Llp Chicago Illinois
SIC 6798 Real estate investment trusts
Pr: Barry Lazarus
**CFO:* Steven T Hippel

D-U-N-S 93-355-2804
INLAND EMPIRE HEALTH PLAN
IEHP
10801 6th St Ste 120, Rancho Cucamonga, CA 91730-5987
Tel (909) 890-2000 *Founded/Ownrshp* 1994
Sales NA *EMP* 855
Accts Moss Adams Llp Irvine Califo
SIC 6321 6324 Accident & health insurance; Health maintenance organization (HMO), insurance only
CEO: Brad Gilbert
COO: Phillip W Branstetter
**CFO:* Chet Uma
**Ch:* Bob Buster
Dir IT: Terry Terr
IT Man: Nicole Hall
Board of Directors: Bob Buster, Jerry Eaves, Dr Ernest Garcia, Dennis Hansburger, Tom Mullin, Tex Ritter, Drew Williams

D-U-N-S 04-365-6206
INLAND EMPIRE UTILITIES AGENCY A MUNICIPAL WATER DISTRICT (INC)
6075 Kimball Ave, Chino, CA 91708-9174
Tel (909) 993-1600 *Founded/Ownrshp* 1950
Sales 290.9MM^E *EMP* 308
Accts Mayer Hoffman Mccann Pc Irv
SIC 4941 Water supply
Pr: Terry Catlin
**Pr:* John Anderson
COO: Jon Florio
CFO: Christina Valencia
**Sec:* Ging Cookman
**Sec:* Steve Elie
**Bd of Dir:* Michael Camacho
Ofcr: Bonita Fan
Ofcr: Jason Gu
VP: Angel Santiago
**VP:* Wyatt Troxel
Exec: Martha Davis

D-U-N-S 08-936-1620 IMP
INLAND FRESH SEAFOOD CORP OF AMERICA INC
INLAND SEAFOOD
1651 Montreal Cir, Tucker, GA 30084-6933
Tel (404) 350-5850 *Founded/Ownrshp* 1976
Sales 292.0MM *EMP* 650
SIC 5146 5144 5147 Fish & seafoods; Seafoods; Poultry & poultry products; Meats & meat products
CEO: Demmond Bill
Pr: Chris Rosenberger
CFO: Sussman Eric
Founder: Joel Knox
VP: Micharl Robins
Genl Mgr: Robert Pidgeon
Dir IT: Dale Borney

INLAND GROUP
See INLAND REAL ESTATE GROUP OF COMPANIES

D-U-N-S 00-690-7679 EXP
INLAND KENWORTH (US) INC (CA)
(*Suby of* INLAND INDUSTRIES LTD)
9730 Cherry Ave, Fontana, CA 92335-5257
Tel (909) 823-9955 *Founded/Ownrshp* 1934, 1989
Sales 143.4MM^E *EMP* 417
SIC 5012 7538 5013 7513 Trucks, commercial; Diesel engine repair: automotive; Truck parts & accessories; Truck rental & leasing, no drivers
Ch: Leigh Parker
**Pr:* Jim Beidrwieden
**CEO:* William Currie
**CFO:* Les Ziegler

D-U-N-S 00-620-5298 IMP
INLAND LABEL AND MARKETING SERVICES LLC
2009 West Ave S, La Crosse, WI 54601-6207
Tel (608) 788-5800 *Founded/Ownrshp* 1945
Sales 109.0MM *EMP* 400
SIC 2754 2752

D-U-N-S 00-605-4100
INLAND PAPERBOARD AND PACKAGING INC
1300 S Mo Pac Expy Fl 3, Austin, TX 78746-6933
Tel (512) 234-5001 *Founded/Ownrshp* 1978, 1984
Sales 1.1MMM^E *EMP* 9,387
Accts Ernst & Young Llp Austin Tex
SIC 2653 2631 3086 2679 2657 Corrugated boxes, partitions, display items, sheets & pad; Solid fiber boxes, partitions, display items & sheets; Linerboard; Packaging & shipping materials, foamed plastic; Corrugated paper: made from purchased material; Folding paperboard boxes
Ch Bd: William B Howes
**Pr:* Dale E Stahl
**CFO:* Michael H Sullivan
**Treas:* David Terpin
Treas: Joseph Tomlinson
**Ex VP:* Bart J Doney
**Ex VP:* James C Foxworthy
**Ex VP:* J Patrick Malley III
**VP:* Steve Householder
**VP:* M Richard Warner
VP: Edwin L Wilson
Board of Directors: David Dolben, Clifford J Grum, Kenneth Jastrow II, Harold Maxwell, Joseph E Turk

D-U-N-S 10-319-0062
INLAND REAL ESTATE GROUP OF COMPANIES
INLAND GROUP
2901 Butterfield Rd, Oak Brook, IL 60523-1190
Tel (630) 218-8000 *Founded/Ownrshp* 1967
Sales 299.4MM^E *EMP* 1,114
SIC 6513 6512 6162 6282 1522 1542 Apartment building operators; Commercial & industrial building operation; Mortgage bankers; Investment advice; Multi-family dwelling construction; Commercial & office building, new construction
**CFO:* Alan Kremin
**Ch:* Robert D Parks
**Treas:* Alan F Kremin
Ex VP: Robert H Baum
**Sr VP:* Sharon Anderson-Cox
Sr VP: Karen Kautz
VP: Robert Barg
VP: Maureen Denard
**VP:* Janice J Fox
VP: Gail Gress
VP: Frances Panico
VP: Sunder Pappu
**VP:* Matthew Tice
Board of Directors: Joann M Armenta, Catherine L Lynch

D-U-N-S 11-820-2753
INLAND REAL ESTATE INVESTMENT CORP
(*Suby of* INLAND GROUP) ★
2901 Butterfield Rd, Oak Brook, IL 60523-1190
Tel (630) 218-8000 *Founded/Ownrshp* 1987
Sales 238.4MM^E *EMP* 59
SIC 6211 6798 Security brokers & dealers; Real estate investment trusts
CEO: Mitchell A Sabshon
**Ch Bd:* Robert D Parks
**Pr:* Brenda G Gujral
Treas: Catherine L Ynch
**Sec:* Catherine L Lynch
Ex VP: Brett A Brown
**Sr VP:* Patricia Challenger
Sr VP: Janet Heintz
Sr VP: Elliot Kamenear
**Sr VP:* Roberta S Matlin
Sr VP: Rahul Sehgal
VP: Sharon Anderson-Cox
VP: Ravi Bansal
VP: Robert Barg
VP: Lev Dean
VP: Bob Edmiston
VP: Kim Karas
VP: Michael Podboy
VP: Eric Spiess
VP: Nicole Spreck
VP: Matthew Tice

INLAND REGIONAL CENTER
See INLAND COUNTIES REGIONAL CENTER INC

INLAND SEAFOOD
See INLAND FRESH SEAFOOD CORP OF AMERICA INC

D-U-N-S 12-127-3023
INLAND SECURITIES CORP
(*Suby of* INLAND REAL ESTATE INVESTMENT CORP) ★
2901 Butterfield Rd, Oak Brook, IL 60523-1190
Tel (630) 218-8000 *Founded/Ownrshp* 1998
Sales 238.1MM *EMP* 45
Accts Kpmg Llp Chicago Il
SIC 6211 Brokers, security
CEO: Michael T Ezzell II
Treas: Catherine Lynch
Chf Cred: Suzanne L Bond
Ex VP: Colin Cosgrove
Sr VP: Denise Faber
Sr VP: Shawn Vaughan
VP: James Anderson
VP: Ronald Cole
VP: Rod Curtis
VP: Drew Dedelow
VP: Peter Fisher
VP: Jeff Hertz
VP: Roberta S Matlin
VP: Kathleen A Pelletier
VP: Jeff Spah
VP: Robert Speidel
VP: Michael Vozella

D-U-N-S 02-290-5400
INLAND TRUCK PARTS CO INC
4400 College Blvd Ste 145, Overland Park, KS 66211-2326
Tel (913) 345-9664 *Founded/Ownrshp* 1967
Sales 166.2MM[E] *EMP* 525
SIC 5013 7538

INLAND VALLEY DAILY BULLETIN
See CALIFORNIA NEWSPAPERS LIMITED PARTNERSHIP

D-U-N-S 14-794-5968
INMAN HOLDING CO INC
INMAN MILLS
300 Park Rd, Inman, SC 29349-1754
Tel (864) 472-2121 *Founded/Ownrshp* 1985
Sales 200.7MM[E] *EMP* 659[E]
SIC 2211 2221 Broadwoven fabric mills, cotton; Broadwoven fabric mills, manmade
CEO: Robert H Chapman III
**Pr:* Norman H Chapman
**CFO:* James C Pace Jr
**VP:* William P Bowan
**VP:* Ben Truslow
**VP Mfg:* George Abbott

INMAN MILLS
See INMAN HOLDING CO INC

D-U-N-S 00-334-8471 IMP
INMAN MILLS (SC)
(*Suby of* INMAN MILLS) ★
300 Park Rd, Inman, SC 29349-1754
Tel (864) 472-2121 *Founded/Ownrshp* 1901
Sales 200.7MM[E] *EMP* 625
SIC 2281 Yarn spinning mills
CEO: Rober H Chapman III
**Pr:* Norman H Chapman
COO: George Abbott
CFO: Matt Ezell
**CFO:* James C Pace Jr
VP: William E Bowen Jr
Plnt Mgr: George A Abbott
Plnt Mgr: Brandon Crowe
Plnt Mgr: Bill Hightower

D-U-N-S 14-499-8200 EXP
INMAR INC
INMAR PROMOTION SERVICES
635 Vine St, Winston Salem, NC 27101-4186
Tel (800) 765-1277 *Founded/Ownrshp* 2014
Sales 1.0MMM[E] *EMP* 4,524
SIC 7389 Inventory computing service
CEO: L David Mounts
**Pr:* Bob Carter
**Pr:* Steve Dollase
**Pr:* Jeff Pepperworth
**Pr:* John Ross
**CFO:* Drew Dixon
**Chf Mktg O:* Travis Lewis
**Ex VP:* Fred Jorgenson
Ex VP: Sharon Joyner-Payne
**Ex VP:* Mark Wright
VP: Michael Cole
VP: Delinah L Collins
VP: David Evans
Exec: Sylvia Hutchens

INMAR PROMOTION SERVICES
See INMAR INC

D-U-N-S 03-285-2613
INMARSAT INC
(*Suby of* INMARSAT PLC)
1101 Conn Ave Nw Ste 1200, Washington, DC 20036-4344
Tel (202) 248-5150 *Founded/Ownrshp* 1998
Sales 136.6MM[E] *EMP* 1,400
SIC 3663 Satellites, communications
VP: Louise Billingsley
Genl Mgr: Mike Carew
VP Mktg: Alena Koci

D-U-N-S 07-877-3463 IMP
INMUSIC BRANDS INC
(*Suby of* NUMARK INDUSTRIES LP) ★
200 Scenic View Dr, Cumberland, RI 02864-1847
Tel (401) 658-3131 *Founded/Ownrshp* 2012
Sales 300.0MM *EMP* 66[E]
SIC 5736 Musical instrument stores
Pr: John E Odonnell
COO: Paul Antrop
**CFO:* Paul Stansky
QA Dir: Aaron Hachen
IT Man: Kyle Mello
Tech Mgr: Robert Griffith
Sls Mgr: Keith Stewart

INN AT CHATEAU ELAN
See ELAN CHATEAU RESORTS LLC

INN MAID PRODUCTS
See T MARZETTI CO

D-U-N-S 17-597-0644
INN OF MOUNTAIN GODS RESORT AND CASINO
CASINO APACHE TRAVEL CENTER
287 Carrizo Canyon Rd, Mescalero, NM 88340-9641
Tel (575) 464-7777 *Founded/Ownrshp* 2004
Sales 59.4MM[E] *EMP* 1,251[E]
SIC 7999 7011 Gambling establishment; Casino hotel
Ch Bd: Carleton Naiche-Palmer PHD
**COO:* Elizabeth Foster-Anderson
CFO: Lance Kintz
**Treas:* Hazel Botella-Spottedbird
Treas: Karen Braswell
Ofcr: Debra Gonzales
**VP:* Jackie Blaylock
Exec: James Muldowney
Exec: Mike Schoen
**Prin:* R Miles Ledgerwood
**Prin:* Manuel Lujan Jr
Board of Directors: R Miles Ledgerwood, Manuel Lujan Jr

D-U-N-S 10-135-4012
▲ INNERWORKINGS INC
600 W Chicago Ave Ste 850, Chicago, IL 60654-2529
Tel (312) 642-3700 *Founded/Ownrshp* 2002
Sales 1.0MMM *EMP* 1,600
Accts Ernst & Young Llp Chicago Il
Tkr Sym INWK *Exch* NGS
SIC 2752 7374 7372 Commercial printing, lithographic; Data processing & preparation; Publishers' computer software
Pr: Eric D Belcher
**Ch Bd:* Jack M Greenberg
CFO: Jeffrey P Pritchett
Chf Cred: Peter Thompson
Sr VP: John Calzaretta
Sr VP: Ryan K Spohn
VP: Jo Epkes
VP: Brian Finnerty
VP: Londy Furlo
VP: Brian Gillespie
VP: Glenn Hammer
VP: Seth Kessler
VP: Dan Lubinski
VP: Bryan Miller
VP: Jan Sevcik
VP: Doug Watanabe
VP Bus Dev: Harris Atkins
VP Bus Dev: Sarah Hirsch
VP Bus Dev: Francine Pepitone
Dir Bus: John Cunningham
Board of Directors: Charles K Bobrinskoy, David Fisher, J Patrick Gallagher Jr, Julie M Howard, Linda S Wolf

D-U-N-S 78-331-4776
INNISFREE HOTELS INC
113 Bay Bridge Dr, Gulf Breeze, FL 32561-4470
Tel (850) 934-3609 *Founded/Ownrshp* 1985
Sales 100.0MM *EMP* 2,000
SIC 7011 Hotels & motels
CEO: Julian B Macqueen
**Pr:* Harlan Butler
Pr: Jill Miller
**CFO:* Brooks Moore
Ofcr: Al Parker
**VP:* Michael Nixon
**VP:* Carol Ruben
Sls Dir: Ivana Coteat

D-U-N-S 02-142-0677
INNOCO TECHNOLOGY GROUP INC
1608 Nw 84th Ave, Doral, FL 33126-1032
Tel (305) 477-8117 *Founded/Ownrshp* 2007
Sales 161.5MM *EMP* 22
Accts Prats Fernandez & Co Coral G
SIC 5065 Communication equipment
Pr: Ramaseshan Sethuraman
**CFO:* Suresh Ranganathan
**Mng Dir:* Diego Mazar

D-U-N-S 79-649-0584
INNOCOR FOAM TECHNOLOGIES LLC
(*Suby of* SLEEP INNOVATIONS) ★
200 Schulz Dr Ste 2, Red Bank, NJ 07701-6745
Tel (732) 263-0800 *Founded/Ownrshp* 2009
Sales 180.0MM[E] *EMP* 408[E]
SIC 3086 Plastics foam products; Carpet & rug cushions, foamed plastic; Insulation or cushioning material, foamed plastic; Padding, foamed plastic
CEO: Carol S Eicher
VP: Judy Kelman
Board of Directors: Carol S Eicher

D-U-N-S 78-855-7015 IMP/EXP
INNOCOR INC
SLEEP INNOVATIONS
(*Suby of* COMFORT INTERMEDIATE HOLDING, LLC)
200 Schulz Dr Ste 2, Red Bank, NJ 07701-6745
Tel (844) 824-9348 *Founded/Ownrshp* 2012
Sales 665.5MM[E] *EMP* 1,685
SIC 2515 2392 3069 Mattresses & foundations; Cushions & pillows; Bathmats, rubber
CEO: Carol S Eicher
**CFO:* Doug Vaughan
VP: Lisa Cohen
Sls Dir: James Harris
Board of Directors: Carol S Eicher, Donald C Mueller, Bruce Roberson

D-U-N-S 19-516-0908
▲ INNODATA INC
3 University Plz, Hackensack, NJ 07601-6208
Tel (201) 371-8000 *Founded/Ownrshp* 1988
Sales 58.5MM *EMP* 5,090[E]
Tkr Sym INOD *Exch* NGM
SIC 7374 Data processing & preparation; Data entry service
Ch Bd: Jack S Abuhoff
COO: Ashok Mishra
CFO: O'Neil Nalavadi
Board of Directors: Haig S Bagerdjian, Louise C Forlenza, Stewart R Massey, Michael J Opat, Anthea C Stratigos

D-U-N-S 11-932-0781
INNOMARK COMMUNICATIONS LLC
3005 W Tech Blvd, Miamisburg, OH 45342-0824
Tel (513) 285-1040 *Founded/Ownrshp* 2000
Sales 126.2MM *EMP* 500
SIC 7319 Display advertising service
Plnt Mgr: Kent Johncox
VP Sls: Kathryn Newell
Mktg Dir: Melissa Molyneaux

D-U-N-S 61-090-3960
▲ INNOPHOS HOLDINGS INC
259 Prospect Plains Rd A, Cranbury, NJ 08512-3706
Tel (609) 495-2495 *Founded/Ownrshp* 2004
Sales 789.1MM *EMP* 1,387[E]
Tkr Sym IPHS *Exch* NGS
SIC 2874 2819 Phosphatic fertilizers; Industrial inorganic chemicals
Pr: Kim Ann Mink
CFO: Hermanus Kieftenbeld
Ofcr: Sherry Duff
Sr VP: Joseph Golowski
Sr VP: Jean Marie Mainente
Sr VP: Yasef Murat
VP: Charles Brodheim
Comm Man: Jo Sterenberg
Ql Cn Mgr: Eric McGregor
Sls Dir: Marco Coen
Sls Mgr: Jesse Davidson
Board of Directors: Gary Cappeline, Linda Myrick, Karen Osar, John Steitz, Peter T Thomas, James Zallie, Robert J Zatta

D-U-N-S 15-553-2257 IMP/EXP
■ INNOPHOS INC
(*Suby of* INNOPHOS INVESTMENTS II INC) ★
259 Prospect Plains Rd A, Cranbury, NJ 08512-3706
Tel (609) 495-2495 *Founded/Ownrshp* 2004
Sales 335.8MM[E] *EMP* 990
SIC 2819 Industrial inorganic chemicals
Pr: Randolph Gress
CFO: Neil Salmon
VP: Thomas Benner
VP: Louis Calvarin PHD
VP: William Farran
VP: Jose Gonzalez
VP: Amy Hartzell
VP: Karen Kennedy
CTO: Fernando Birman
QA Dir: Jane Murphy
Dir IT: Walter Matchim
Board of Directors: Gary Cappeline, Amado Cavazos, Linda Myrick, Karen Osar, John Steitz, Stephen Zide

D-U-N-S 07-950-7424
■ INNOPHOS INVESTMENTS II INC
(*Suby of* INNOPHOS INVESTMENTS HOLDINGS, INC.)
259 Prospect Plains Rd, Cranbury, NJ 08512-3706
Tel (609) 495-2495 *Founded/Ownrshp* 2012
Sales 335.8MM[E] *EMP* 990[E]
SIC 2874 2819 Phosphates; Industrial inorganic chemicals
Ch Bd: Randolph Gress
CFO: Mark Feuerbach
VP: Iris Alvarado
VP: Charles Brodheim
VP: William Farran

D-U-N-S 04-200-6515 IMP
▲ INNOSPEC INC
8310 S Valley Hwy Ste 350, Englewood, CO 80112-5931
Tel (303) 792-5554 *Founded/Ownrshp* 1938
Sales 1.0MMM *EMP* 1,300
Tkr Sym IOSP *Exch* NGS
SIC 2911 2869 Fuel additives; Perfumes, flavorings & food additives
Pr: Patrick S Williams
COO: Philip J Boon
CFO: Ian P Cleminson
Chf Cred: David E Williams
Sr VP: Catherine Hessner
Sr VP: Ian M McRobbie
VP: Bruce McDonald
VP: John Tayler
VP: Jim Vrzak
VP: Brian R Watt
Mfg Dir: Trey Griffin

INNOVA ELECTRONICS
See HUNTING INNOVA INC

D-U-N-S 60-594-4870
INNOVACARE SERVICES CO LLC
173 Bridge Plz N, Fort Lee, NJ 07024-7575
Tel (201) 969-2300 *Founded/Ownrshp* 2012
Sales NA *EMP* 1,304
SIC 6324 8011 8741 8742 Group hospitalization plans; Health maintenance organization; Management services; Marketing consulting services
Pr: Rick Shinto
**Ch Bd:* Daniel E Straus
Pr: Stacy Mays
**Pr:* Timothy J O'Donnell
Pr: Timothy P O'Rourke
Pr: Raul F Montalvo Orsini
COO: Marcia Anderson
**COO:* Penelope Kokkinides
**COO:* Jess Parks
CFO: Kim Bressen
**CFO:* Douglas Malton
**Chf Cred:* Nancy Waltermire
Chf Mktg O: Rod St Clair
**Ex VP:* John S Brittain Jr
**Ex VP:* Robert G Torricelli
**Sr VP:* Eugene Huang
**VP:* Mark Cary
VP: Carol Hairston
**VP:* Howard Kamins
**VP:* Samir Mistry
VP: Samir K Mistry

INNOVAGE
See TOTAL LONGTERM CARE INC

D-U-N-S 05-371-9188
INNOVASIAN CUISINE ENTERPRISES INC
18251 Cascade Ave S, Tukwila, WA 98188-4700
Tel (425) 251-3706 *Founded/Ownrshp* 1999
Sales 86.5MM *EMP* 37
SIC 5149 Specialty food items
CEO: Joe Zalke

D-U-N-S 07-954-4160
■ INNOVATION HEALTH PLAN INC (VA)
(*Suby of* AETNA LIFE INSURANCE CO INC) ★
3130 Fairview Park Dr # 300, Falls Church, VA 22042-4529
Tel (703) 914-2925 *Founded/Ownrshp* 2012
Sales NA *EMP* 3,205[E]
SIC 6324 Hospital & medical service plans
Ex Dir: Amy Turner

D-U-N-S 02-718-4489
INNOVATION INSTITUTE LLC
1 Centerpointe Dr Ste 200, La Palma, CA 90623-2529
Tel (714) 735-3750 *Founded/Ownrshp* 2011
Sales 150.0MM *EMP* 40[E]
SIC 8099 Medical services organization
Pr: Joseph Randolph
**CFO:* Ed Wong
**Ex VP:* Larry Stofko
Ex Dir: Lloyd Comeau
Dir IT: Alfonso Barragan

D-U-N-S 16-941-7735
INNOVATION VENTURES LLC
LIVING ESSENTIALS
38955 Hills Tech Dr Ste 1, Farmington Hills, MI 48331-3431
Tel (248) 960-1700 *Founded/Ownrshp* 2000
Sales 125.3MM[E] *EMP* 100
SIC 5149 Groceries & related products
CEO: Manoj Bhargava
Natl Sales: Garrett Dempsey

INNOVATIONS BY VP SUPPLY
See V P SUPPLY CORP

D-U-N-S 61-496-7300
INNOVATIVE AG SERVICES CO
2010 S Main St, Monticello, IA 52310-7707
Tel (319) 465-3501 *Founded/Ownrshp* 2005
Sales 657.0MM *EMP* 500
Accts Meriwether Wilson And Company
SIC 5999 Feed & farm supply
CEO: Rick Vaughan
**Pr:* Randy Blake
**CFO:* Brenda Hoefler
VP: Ron Barkema
**VP:* Paul Cook
VP Opers: Brian Kramer
VP Sls: Michael Duncomb

D-U-N-S 00-596-5756 IMP
INNOVATIVE COMMUNICATIONS CORP
INNOVATIVE TELEPHONES
4611 Tutu Park Mall # 200, St Thomas, VI 00802-1735
Tel (340) 777-7700 *Founded/Ownrshp* 1997
Sales 151.7MM[E] *EMP* 500[E]
SIC 4813 4841 Telephone communication, except radio; Local & long distance telephone communications; ; Data telephone communications; Cable television services
CEO: Seth Davis
**Pr:* Shawn O-Donnell
Trst: Adrian Labennett
VP: Beverly Chongasing
VP: Emiel Michiels
Genl Mgr: Brent Butler
IT Man: Rene Henry
Advt Mgr: Elaine Angert

INNOVATIVE DIAGNOSTIC LAB
See HEALTH DIAGNOSTIC LABORATORY INC

D-U-N-S 02-575-2093
INNOVATIVE EMPLOYEE SOLUTIONS INC
9665 Gran Rdge Dr Ste 420, San Diego, CA 92123
Tel (858) 715-5100 *Founded/Ownrshp* 1987
Sales 82.9MM[E] *EMP* 1,500
SIC 8721 Payroll accounting service
CEO: Karla Hertzog
**CFO:* Peter Limone
**VP:* Darlene Bruder
**VP:* Tania Fiero
**VP:* Trevor Foster
Off Mgr: Chris Jahn
Sales Exec: Jae Cazimero
Board of Directors: Karla Hertzog

D-U-N-S 80-714-2778
INNOVATIVE ENERGY SERVICES INC
16600 Park Row, Houston, TX 77084-5019
Tel (281) 392-5199 *Founded/Ownrshp* 1988
Sales 119.7MM[E] *EMP* 107
SIC 5084 Oil well machinery, equipment & supplies
Pr: Rick Adams
**Pr:* Doug Gaither
**Sr VP:* William Clayton
VP: Eddie Rodarte

D-U-N-S 07-865-6004
INNOVATIVE HEARTH HOLDINGS LLC
INNOVATIVE HEARTH PRODUCTS IHP
1508 Elm Hill Pike # 108, Nashville, TN 37210-3637
Tel (714) 549-7782 *Founded/Ownrshp* 1971
Sales 139.3MM[E] *EMP* 580
SIC 3433 Wall heaters, except electric
CEO: Mark Klein
**CFO:* Linda Pahl

INNOVATIVE HEARTH PRODUCTS
See IHP OPERATIONS LLC

INNOVATIVE HEARTH PRODUCTS IHP
See INNOVATIVE HEARTH HOLDINGS LLC

D-U-N-S 05-479-4466 IMP
INNOVATIVE HEARTH PRODUCTS LLC
LENNOX
1508 Elm Hill Pike # 108, Nashville, TN 37210-3637
Tel (615) 925-3417 *Founded/Ownrshp* 2010, 2012
Sales 145.7MM[E] *EMP* 349

SIC 3634 3433 Heating units, electric (radiant heat): baseboard or wall; Heating equipment, except electric
Pr: Mark Klein
**CFO:* Linda Pahl

D-U-N-S 13-494-2718
INNOVATIVE IDM LLC
AUTOMATION CONTROLS DIRECT
1625 Wallace Dr Ste 110, Carrollton, TX 75006-6654
Tel (214) 574-9500 *Founded/Ownrshp* 2000
Sales 105.5MM^E *EMP* 95
SIC 5063 7622 3699 Electrical apparatus & equipment; Antenna repair & installation; Electrical equipment & supplies
Pr: Eugene Gray
**VP:* Timothy W Mueller II
IT Man: Todd Mueller
MIS Mgr: Kenneth Skillett
VP Sls: Chad Kauffman

D-U-N-S 83-318-5130
INNOVATIVE MATTRESS SOLUTIONS LLC
MATTRESS WHSE SLEEP OUTFITTERS
11060 Winfield Rd, Winfield, WV 25213-7934
Tel (304) 586-2863 *Founded/Ownrshp* 2002
Sales 92.3MM^E *EMP* 450
SIC 8741 Management services
CEO: Kimberly Knopf
CFO: Nathen McBrayer

INNOVATIVE MODERN COATERS
See INFRATROL MANUFACTURING CORP

D-U-N-S 05-124-0872
INNOVATIVE OFFICE SOLUTIONS LLC
151 Cliff Rd E Ste 40, Burnsville, MN 55337-1586
Tel (952) 808-9900 *Founded/Ownrshp* 2001
Sales 431.9MM^E *EMP* 225
SIC 5112 5021 Office supplies; Office furniture
CFO: Brooks Smith
Exec: John Townsend
**CIO:* Jason Player

D-U-N-S 60-502-1948
INNOVATIVE RESOURCE GROUP LLC
APS HEALTHCARE
(*Suby of* PARTNERS HEALTHCARE SOLUTIONS, INC.)
44 S Broadway Ste 1200, White Plains, NY 10601-4458
Tel (800) 305-3720 *Founded/Ownrshp* 2007
Sales 5.2MM^E *EMP* 1,018
SIC 8099 Health screening service

D-U-N-S 96-911-1210
INNOVATIVE SERVICE TECHNOLOGY MANAGEMENT SERVICES INC
IST MANAGEMENT SERVICES
934 Glenwood Ave Se # 250, Atlanta, GA 30316-1875
Tel (404) 582-8850 *Founded/Ownrshp* 1997
Sales 98.4MM^E *EMP* 1,500
SIC 8744 Facilities support services
CEO: Hal Blackman
Pr: Daniel Blechinger
Pr: Chris Eckl
Pr: Ashleigh Fiora
CFO: Dale McKee
Sr VP: Craig Hamel
VP: Jason Jeray
VP Admn: Lori Mitchum
Off Mgr: Anthony Jones
Software D: Dennis Flanagan
Software D: Page Gedney

D-U-N-S 00-681-5158
INNOVATIVE STAFFING INC (UT)
859 W South Jordan Pkwy # 77, South Jordan, UT 84095-5601
Tel (801) 984-0252 *Founded/Ownrshp* 2000
Sales 33.8MM^E *EMP* 1,100
SIC 7363 Employee leasing service
Pr: Michelyn Farnsworth
**VP:* John Farnsworth
VP: Ronald Messenheimer

INNOVATIVE STORAGE SYSTEMS
See INNOVATIVE STORE SYSTEMS INC

D-U-N-S 06-751-1266
INNOVATIVE STORE SYSTEMS INC
INNOVATIVE STORAGE SYSTEMS
1351 S Beach Blvd Ste L, La Habra, CA 90631-1126
Tel (562) 947-4101 *Founded/Ownrshp* 1989
Sales 3.2MM^E *EMP* 2,019
SIC 2542 Partitions & fixtures, except wood
Pr: Ronald Benudiz
**CFO:* Natalie Benudiz

INNOVATIVE TELEPHONES
See INNOVATIVE COMMUNICATIONS CORP

D-U-N-S 07-954-9065
INNOVATIVE XCESSORIES & SERVICES LLC
1862 Sparkman Dr Nw, Huntsville, AL 35816-1122
Tel (877) 330-1331 *Founded/Ownrshp* 2012, 2014
Sales 106.4MM^E *EMP* 1,500
SIC 5012 3711 Automobiles & other motor vehicles; Automobile assembly, including specialty automobiles
CEO: Kevin Heronimus
**Pr:* Jim Scott
**CFO:* Tim Garner
Ex VP: Mike Boyko
Ex VP: Paul Desmet
Ex VP: Omer Gursoy
Ex VP: George Lezon
Ex VP: Joe Olivastri
VP: Steve Decker
VP: Ben Dollar
VP: Brent Kwapisz
VP: Michael Magnuson
VP: Terry Pe

D-U-N-S 04-194-9520
■ **INNOVEL SOLUTIONS INC**
(*Suby of* SEARS ROEBUCK AND CO) ★
3333 Beverly Rd, Hoffman Estates, IL 60179-0001
Tel (847) 286-2500 *Founded/Ownrshp* 1940
Sales 774.2MM^E *EMP* 8,000
SIC 4731 8741 8742 Agents, shipping; Management services; Management consulting services
Pr: Jeffrey A Starecheski
**Treas:* Jim Krise
**VP:* Richard Mc Laughlin
**VP:* Roger Will
Genl Mgr: Laura Matus
Opers Mgr: Georgia Majors

D-U-N-S 62-623-8117
■ **INNOVEX INC**
(*Suby of* QUINTILES TRANSNATIONAL CORP) ★
10 Waterview Blvd Ste 100, Parsippany, NJ 07054-7605
Tel (973) 257-4500 *Founded/Ownrshp* 1999
Sales 73.4MM^E *EMP* 1,500
SIC 8734 8999 7374 Testing laboratories; Communication services; Data processing & preparation
Pr: Anthony Yost
VP: Edward F Heimers
IT Man: Walter Smalty
VP Mktg: Theresa Borgia
VP Mktg: Matt Carey

D-U-N-S 82-746-0341
INNOVIS HEALTH LLC
ESSENTIA HEALTH
(*Suby of* ESSENTIA HEALTH) ★
1702 University Dr S, Fargo, ND 58103-4940
Tel (701) 364-8000 *Founded/Ownrshp* 2007
Sales 333.8MM^E *EMP* 99
SIC 8093 Specialty outpatient clinics
COO: Tim Sayler

D-U-N-S 14-476-2668
INNVISION HOSPITALITY INC
504 Carver Rd, Griffin, GA 30224-3936
Tel (888) 875-6202 *Founded/Ownrshp* 2004
Sales 97.0MM^E *EMP* 80
SIC 5131 5021 7389 Textiles, woven; Furniture; Interior design services
Ch: Walter Jones Jr
**Pr:* Chris Parker
Sls Mgr: Emille Aboona

D-U-N-S 15-137-3891 IMP
INOAC USA INC
(*Suby of* DIA SEIKO CO., LTD.)
1515 Equity Dr Ste 200, Troy, MI 48084-7129
Tel (248) 619-7031 *Founded/Ownrshp* 1926
Sales 193.4MM^E *EMP* 20,000
SIC 3085 3714 Plastics bottles; Motor vehicle parts & accessories
CEO: Toyohiko Okina
**Pr:* Charles Little
**Pr:* Carl D Malz
**CFO:* Ed Yeaste
**Ch:* Soichi Inoue
VP: Andy Dargavell
**VP:* Yasutaka Haruta
**VP:* Noriyoshi Suzuki
Dir IT: Mark Bell

D-U-N-S 13-672-9634 IMP/EXP
▲ **INOGEN INC**
326 Bollay Dr, Goleta, CA 93117-5550
Tel (805) 562-0500 *Founded/Ownrshp* 2001
Sales 159.0MM *EMP* 547
Tkr Sym INGN *Exch* NGS
SIC 3841 3842 Surgical & medical instruments; Surgical appliances & supplies
CEO: Raymond Huggenberger
**Ch Bd:* Heath Lukatch
Pr: Scott Wilkinson
CFO: Alison Bauerlein
Ex VP: Matthew Scribner
Ex VP: Brenton Taylor
IT Man: Eric Dahlke
VP Mktg: Byron Myers
Snr Mgr: Liza Favela
Board of Directors: R Scott Greer, Loren McFarland, Benjamin Anderson-Ray, Heather Rider

D-U-N-S 79-808-5890
INOLA HEALTH CARE CENTER INC
400 N Broadway, Inola, OK 74036-9424
Tel (918) 543-8800 *Founded/Ownrshp* 1988
Sales 300.9MM *EMP* 50
SIC 8011 Medical centers
Pr: Howard Childers
Nrsg Dir: Pam Childers
HC Dir: Rory Childers

D-U-N-S 18-835-4831 IMP
INOVA DIAGNOSTICS INC
(*Suby of* WERFENLIFE SA.)
9900 Old Grove Rd, San Diego, CA 92131-1638
Tel (858) 586-9900 *Founded/Ownrshp* 2008
Sales 113.6MM^E *EMP* 570
SIC 2835 8731 In vitro & in vivo diagnostic substances; In vitro diagnostics; In vivo diagnostics; Medical research, commercial
CEO: Roger Ingles
**CFO:* Pere Solagagles
VP: Abdul Chohan
VP: Ronda Elliott
VP: Michael Mahler
Exec: Valerie Brouillette
Mfg Mgr: Wendy Eads
Ql Cn Mgr: Catherine Riturban
Ql Cn Mgr: Rhonda Sundberg
Sls Dir: Rita Grueter
Sls Mgr: Carl Schroder

INOVA FAIRFAX HOSPITAL
See INOVA HEALTH CARE SERVICES

INOVA FAIRFAX HOSPITAL
See LOUDOUN HOSPITAL CENTER

D-U-N-S 05-442-7455
INOVA HEALTH CARE SERVICES (VA)
INOVA FAIRFAX HOSPITAL
(*Suby of* INOVA HEALTH SYSTEM) ★
8110 Gatehouse Rd 200e, Falls Church, VA 22042-1217
Tel (703) 289-2000 *Founded/Ownrshp* 1956
Sales 2.1MMM *EMP* 13,000
SIC 8062 8093 General medical & surgical hospitals; Specialty outpatient clinics
Ch: Nicholas Carosi
Pr: Maggie Cornett
Pr: Jennifer Siciliano
**Pr:* John Knox Singleton
Treas: Peggy Harris
**Treas:* Lydia Thomas
Ofcr: Rachna Krishnan
**VP:* James Hughes
**VP:* Richard C Magenheimer
VP: Denise Osborne
VP: Heather Russell
**VP:* H Patrick Walters
Exec: Kylanne Green
Dir Risk M: Maureen Burke
Dir Risk M: Diane Carey
Dir Risk M: Heidi Harrison

D-U-N-S 19-201-8141
INOVA HEALTH SYSTEM
8110 Gatehouse Rd 200e, Falls Church, VA 22042-1217
Tel (703) 289-2069 *Founded/Ownrshp* 1977
Sales 2.3MMM^E *EMP* 16,000
SIC 8741 8011 8062 8049 8059 8051 Hospital management; Offices & clinics of medical doctors; General medical & surgical hospitals; Physical therapist; Nutrition specialist; Speech specialist; Nurses & other medical assistants; Convalescent home; Nursing home, except skilled & intermediate care facility; Skilled nursing care facilities
CEO: John Knox Singleton
Pr: Lori Brown
Pr: Paul Casillas
COO: Daniel Jackson Fache
**COO:* Mark Stauder
COO: Keith Turner
**CFO:* Richard Magenheimer
**Ch:* Stephen Cumbie
**Ex VP:* Loring Flint
**Ex VP:* Marshall Ruffin
VP: John Fay
VP: John Gaul
VP: Nancy Gosnell
Exec: Thomas Graves
Dir Risk M: Diane Dickerson
Dir Rx: Shirin Byrd

D-U-N-S 80-435-1476
INOVA HEALTH SYSTEM SERVICES
(*Suby of* INOVA HEALTH SYSTEM) ★
8110 Gatehouse Rd 200e, Falls Church, VA 22042-1217
Tel (703) 289-2000 *Founded/Ownrshp* 1987
Sales 69.7MM^E *EMP* 1,000^E
SIC 8062

INOVA LOUDOUN HOSPITAL
See LOUDOUN HEALTHCARE INC

D-U-N-S 82-947-9877
INOVA WOODBURN SURGERY CENTER LLC
(*Suby of* INOVA FAIRFAX HOSPITAL) ★
3289 Woodburn Rd Ste 100, Annandale, VA 22003-7343
Tel (703) 226-2640 *Founded/Ownrshp* 2008
Sales 47.1MM^E *EMP* 1,748^E
SIC 8011 Offices & clinics of medical doctors
Prin: Vannette Poole

D-U-N-S 07-851-0797
▲ **INOVALON HOLDINGS INC**
4321 Collington Rd # 100, Bowie, MD 20716-2646
Tel (301) 809-4000 *Founded/Ownrshp* 1998
Sales 437.2MM *EMP* 3,323^E
Tkr Sym INOV *Exch* NGS
SIC 7371 7374 7372 Custom computer programming services; Data processing & preparation; Prepackaged software
Ch Bd: Keith R Dunleavy
Pr: Robert A Wychulis
CFO: Thomas R Kloster
CTO: Joseph R Rostock

D-U-N-S 80-636-8390
INOVALON INC
4321 Collington Rd # 100, Bowie, MD 20716-2646
Tel (301) 262-3848 *Founded/Ownrshp* 2006
Sales 227.5MM^E *EMP* 900
SIC 8733 ; Computer software systems analysis & design, custom
Pr: Keith R Dunleavy
Pr: Dan Mendelson
Pr: Robert A Wychulis
COO: Christopher Greiner
CFO: Thomas Kloster
Sr VP: Stephen Decherney
Sr VP: Luis Gutierrez
VP: Daniel J Holohan III
CTO: Joe Rostock
Dir IT: Mohammad R Chowdhury
Dir IT: Nicole Gray
Board of Directors: Denise K Fletcher, Lee D Roberts, William J Teuber Jr

D-U-N-S 04-104-9169
▲ **INPHI CORP**
2953 Bunker Hill Ln # 300, Santa Clara, CA 95054-1131
Tel (408) 217-7300 *Founded/Ownrshp* 2000
Sales 246.6MM *EMP* 472
Tkr Sym IPHI *Exch* NYS
SIC 3674 Semiconductors & related devices; Integrated circuits, semiconductor networks, etc.
Pr: Ford Tamer
Ch Bd: Diosdado P Banatao
CFO: John Edmunds
Sr VP: Ron Torten
VP: Charles Roach
VP: Hojjat Salemi
VP: Mona Taylor
VP: Norman K Yeung
CTO: Lawrence TSE

VP Mktg: Loi Nguyen
Genl Couns: Richard Ogawa
Board of Directors: Nicholas E Brathwaite, David Liddle, Bruce McWilliams, Elissa Murphy, Sam S Srinivasan

INPO
See INSTITUTE OF NUCLEAR POWER OPERATIONS

D-U-N-S 10-672-2606 IMP/EXP
INPRO CORP
FIRELINE 520
S80w18766 Apollo Dr, Muskego, WI 53150-9219
Tel (262) 679-9010 *Founded/Ownrshp* 1993
Sales 136.4MM^E *EMP* 420
SIC 3081 Unsupported plastics film & sheet
CEO: Stephen J Ziegler
Pr: Steve Baumgautner
**CEO:* Philip J Ziegler
**COO:* Glenn Kennedy
**CFO:* Andy Ciesielski
Sr VP: Mark Ala
**VP:* Mark Alan
VP: Steve Baumgardner
VP: Steve Baumgarnter
VP: Steve Baumgartner
**VP:* Matt Bennett
**VP:* Steve Bumgartner
**VP:* Michael R Sekula
Exec: William Kraus

D-U-N-S 62-671-8154
INRIX INC
10210 Ne Pints Dr Ste 400, Kirkland, WA 98033
Tel (425) 284-3800 *Founded/Ownrshp* 2004
Sales 176.7MM^E *EMP* 1,023^E
SIC 3651 Household audio & video equipment
Pr: Bryan Mistele
CFO: Jeff Decillia
**CFO:* Saul Gates
**Chf Mktg O:* Steve Banfield
**Ofcr:* Rafay Khan
Sr VP: Don Butler
**Sr VP:* Mark Daymond
**Sr VP:* Alex Meyer
VP: Mike Arcuri
**VP:* Scott Baker
VP: Ryan Glancy
VP: Chris Handley
VP: Andreas Hecht
VP: Jonathan Maron
VP: Rick Schuman
VP: Nick Simmons
VP: David Weld
VP: Danny Woolard
Exec: Lynne Partridge

D-U-N-S 02-703-4644 IMP
INSCO DISTRIBUTING INC
12501 Network Blvd, San Antonio, TX 78249-3306
Tel (210) 690-8400 *Founded/Ownrshp* 1958
Sales 123.5MM^E *EMP* 272
SIC 5078 5075 Commercial refrigeration equipment; Air conditioning equipment, except room units; Warm air heating equipment & supplies
Pr: Rudy Trevino
**CFO:* James McCann
**VP:* Jeannie T Horky
VP: Ryder Horky
VP: A Trevino
**VP:* B G Trevino
Rgnl Mgr: Kay Ford
Dir IT: Mark Lehman
IT Man: Julio E Ruiz
Sls Mgr: Christine Degeorge

D-U-N-S 01-131-0018
INSERRA SUPERMARKETS INC
SHOP-RITE
20 Ridge Rd Ste 1, Mahwah, NJ 07430-2328
Tel (201) 529-5900 *Founded/Ownrshp* 1933
Sales 472.2MM^E *EMP* 4,000
SIC 5411 5735 Supermarkets, chain; Video tapes, prerecorded
CEO: Lawrence R Inserra
**Treas:* Theresa Inserra
**Ex VP:* Steve Chalas
VP: Marie Inserra
Dir Rx: Cary Lampert
CTO: Nelson Ota

INSERV
See WILLBROS DOWNSTREAM LLC

D-U-N-S 62-128-8562
INSIDE SOURCE INC
INSIDE SOURCE/YOUNG
985 Industrial Rd Ste 101, San Carlos, CA 94070-4157
Tel (650) 508-9101 *Founded/Ownrshp* 1990
Sales 90.1MM^E *EMP* 140
SIC 5021 Office & public building furniture
Pr: David Denny
COO: Kristen Haren
Sr VP: Gary Young
VP: Tina Fong
VP: Nancy Kusich
VP: David Lombardi
IT Man: Wendy Joos
VP Sls: Anne Wagner
Sales Asso: Stacy Robinson

INSIDE SOURCE/YOUNG
See INSIDE SOURCE INC

D-U-N-S 18-925-6212
INSIDEVIEW TECHNOLOGIES INC
444 De Haro St Ste 210, San Francisco, CA 94107-2398
Tel (415) 728-9309 *Founded/Ownrshp* 2005
Sales 89.3MM^E *EMP* 150
SIC 5045 Computers, peripherals & software
CEO: Umberto Milletti
COO: James Desser
Chf Mktg O: Tracy Eiler
Chf Mktg O: Brian Kelly
Chf Mktg O: Rand Schulman
Chf Inves: John Hawie
Ex VP: Joseba Trullos
Sr VP: Mike Delaat
VP: Mike Aguillard

VP: Joe Andrews
VP: Karen Burr
VP: Christian Dunster
VP: Carl Longhofer
VP: Rob Pannoni
VP: Paul Rhodes
VP: Kenneth Wanless
Dir Risk M: John Kelly
Board of Directors: Jim Simons

D-U-N-S 07-153-8925
■ INSIGHT COMMUNICATIONS CO INC
INSIGHT MIDWEST HOLDINGS
(*Suby of* TIME WARNER) ★
810 7th Ave, New York, NY 10019-5818
Tel (917) 286-2300 *Founded/Ownrshp* 2012
Sales 609.9MM^E *EMP* 4,035
SIC 4841 4813 Cable television services; Telephone communication, except radio;
Pr: Michael S Willner
**Ch Bd:* Sidney R Knafel
**Pr:* Dinni Jain
**Ex VP:* John F Abbot
Ex VP: Chris Slattery
Sr VP: Mike Page
VP: Charlie Barnes
**Prin:* Satish Adige

D-U-N-S 14-799-8280
INSIGHT COMMUNICATIONS OF KENTUCKY LP
810 7th Ave Fl 28, New York, NY 10019-9000
Tel (917) 286-2300 *Founded/Ownrshp* 1985
Sales NA *EMP* 1,000
SIC 4841

D-U-N-S 15-755-2118
■ INSIGHT DIRECT USA INC
(*Suby of* PC WHOLESALE) ★
201 N Central Ave, Phoenix, AZ 85004-0073
Tel (480) 333-3000 *Founded/Ownrshp* 1986
Sales 7.7MMM^E *EMP* 4,000
SIC 5045 3571 Computers, peripherals & software; Personal computers (microcomputers)
CEO: Kenneth T Lamneck
**Pr:* Steven Dodenhoff
**CFO:* Glynis Bryan
**Treas:* Helen Johnson
**VP:* Mark N Rogers
VP: Michael Schelbert
CIO: Rick Goddard
CIO: David Rice
CIO: James Webster
Sls Mgr: Nicki Macdonald

D-U-N-S 87-638-3589
▲ INSIGHT ENTERPRISES INC
201 N Central Ave, Phoenix, AZ 85004-0073
Tel (480) 333-3000 *Founded/Ownrshp* 1988
Sales 5.3MMM *EMP* 5,406^E
Accts Kpmg Llp Phoenix Arizona
Tkr Sym NSIT *Exch* NGS
SIC 5045 7379 5065 Computers, peripherals & software; Computer peripheral equipment; Computer software; Disk drives; Computer related consulting services; Modems, computer; Communication equipment
Pr: Kenneth T Lamneck
Ch Bd: Timothy A Crown
CFO: Glynis A Bryan
Treas: Helen K Johnson
Ofcr: Steven Andrews
VP: John Carnahan
VP: Carolyn Haas
VP: Brian Hickie
VP: Dana A Leighty
VP: Carole Sowers
VP: Jeffrey Warner
Board of Directors: Richard E Allen, Bruce Armstrong, Catherine Courage, Bennett Dorrance, Michael M Fisher, Larry A Gunning, Anthony A Ibarguen, Kathleen S Pushor

D-U-N-S 17-589-8936
INSIGHT EQUITY A P X L P
VISION-EASE LENS
1400 Civic Pl Ste 250, Southlake, TX 76092-7647
Tel (817) 488-7775 *Founded/Ownrshp* 2004
Sales 76.7MM^E *EMP* 1,200^E
SIC 6722 3441 3443 3556 3714 5171 Management investment, open-end; Bridge sections, prefabricated highway; Tanks, lined: metal plate; Food products machinery; Motor vehicle parts & accessories; Petroleum terminals

D-U-N-S 12-846-2509 IMP/EXP
INSIGHT EQUITY ACQUISITION CO LLC
(*Suby of* INSIGHT EQUITY HOLDINGS LLC) ★
1400 Civic Pl Ste 250, Southlake, TX 76092-7647
Tel (817) 354-2715 *Founded/Ownrshp* 2003
Sales 193.7MM^E *EMP* 800
SIC 2911 6722 3851 3441 Petroleum refining; Management investment, open-end; Lenses, ophthalmic; Bridge sections, prefabricated highway
CFO: Scott Lambert

D-U-N-S 62-045-7296
INSIGHT EQUITY HOLDINGS LLC
1400 Civic Pl Ste 250, Southlake, TX 76092-7647
Tel (817) 488-7775 *Founded/Ownrshp* 2000
Sales 1.5MMM *EMP* 4,000
SIC 6726 3851 2911 3441 Investment offices; Lenses, ophthalmic; Petroleum refining; Bridge sections, prefabricated highway
VP: Brad Buser
**VP:* Jack Waterstreet

D-U-N-S 19-039-7401
INSIGHT EQUITY LP
(*Suby of* INSIGHT EQUITY HOLDINGS LLC) ★
1400 Civic Pl Ste 250, Southlake, TX 76092-7647
Tel (817) 488-7775 *Founded/Ownrshp* 2002
Sales 602.2MM^E *EMP* 2,402
SIC 6722 3441 3443 3556 3714 5171 Management investment, open-end; Bridge sections, prefabricated highway; Tanks, lined: metal plate; Food products machinery; Motor vehicle parts & accessories; Petroleum terminals; Petroleum bulk stations
Mng Pt: Ted Beneski
**Pt:* Warren Bonham
**Pt:* Eliot Kerlin
**Pt:* Victor L Vescovo
**Sr VP:* Andrew Boisseau
**Sr VP:* Jack Waterstreet
**VP:* Brad Buser
**VP:* James Jackson
**VP:* Dan Lenahan
VP: Jack Nadal
**VP:* Ben Stolbach

D-U-N-S 96-192-8400
INSIGHT GLOBAL LLC
(*Suby of* IG STAFFING HOLDINGS LLC) ★
4170 Ashford Dunwoody 250, Brookhaven, GA 30319-1457
Tel (404) 257-7900 *Founded/Ownrshp* 2001
Sales 207.4MM^E *EMP* 650
SIC 7361 Employment agencies
CEO: Glenn Johnson
**CEO:* Rich Lingle
**CFO:* Mike Lewis
Treas: John Harris
VP: Bert Bean
VP: Rebecca Grandy
Software D: Michael Knowlin
Software D: Peri Levengood
Netwrk Eng: John Alexander
Natl Sales: Joel Givan
Mktg Mgr: Katie Catalogna

D-U-N-S 13-022-5811
INSIGHT HEALTH SERVICES HOLDINGS CORP
26250 Entp Ct Ste 100, Lake Forest, CA 92630
Tel (949) 282-6000 *Founded/Ownrshp* 2010
Sales 237.6MM^E *EMP* 1,490^E
Accts Pricewaterhousecoopers Llp Or
SIC 8071 Testing laboratories
Pr: Louis E Hallman III
**CEO:* Robert V Baumgartner
**COO:* Bernard J O'Rourke
**CFO:* Keith S Kelson
**Ex VP:* Patricia R Blank
Ex VP: Patricia Blank
**Sr VP:* Michael C Jones
**Sr VP:* Scott A McKee
Opers Mgr: Jeffrey Hammett
Counsel: Maria Eridondo
Board of Directors: Eugene Linden, Wayne B Lowell, Richard Nevins, James A Ovenden, Keith E Rechner, Steven G Segal

D-U-N-S 96-774-5527
INSIGHT INVESTMENTS CORP
611 Anton Blvd Ste 700, Costa Mesa, CA 92626-7050
Tel (714) 939-2300 *Founded/Ownrshp* 1987
Sales 169.7MM^E *EMP* 266
SIC 7377 5045 Computer peripheral equipment rental & leasing; Computer peripheral equipment
CEO: John Ford
**Pr:* Richard Heard
VP: Carol Boldt

D-U-N-S 18-385-3795
INSIGHT INVESTMENTS LLC
INSIGHT SYSTEMS EXCHANGE
(*Suby of* INSIGHT INVESTMENTS CORP) ★
611 Anton Blvd Ste 700, Costa Mesa, CA 92626-7050
Tel (714) 939-2300 *Founded/Ownrshp* 1987
Sales 169.7MM^E *EMP* 264^E
SIC 7377 5045 Computer peripheral equipment rental & leasing; Computer peripheral equipment
CEO: John W Ford
**Pr:* Richard Heard
**CFO:* Christopher Czaja
VP: Carol Boldt

INSIGHT MIDWEST HOLDINGS
See INSIGHT COMMUNICATIONS CO INC

D-U-N-S 00-833-3408
■ INSIGHT MIDWEST LP
(*Suby of* TIME WARNER) ★
810 7th Ave Fl 28, New York, NY 10019-9000
Tel (917) 286-2300 *Founded/Ownrshp* 1999
Sales 82.6MM^E *EMP* 3,900
SIC 4841 Cable television services
Ch Bd: Michael S Willner
Pr: Dinni Jain
COO: William Osbourne Jr
CFO: John Abbot
Ex VP: Hamid Heidary
Sr VP: Elliot Brecher
VP: Bam Liem

D-U-N-S 09-473-3862 IMP
■ INSIGHT NORTH AMERICA INC
PC WHOLESALE
(*Suby of* INSIGHT ENTERPRISES INC) ★
444 Scott Dr, Bloomingdale, IL 60108-3111
Tel (630) 924-6700 *Founded/Ownrshp* 2002
Sales 7.7MMM^E *EMP* 4,500
SIC 5045

INSIGHT OPTICAL MANUFACTURING
See OPTICAL FOR EYES CO

D-U-N-S 88-434-7568 IMP
■ INSIGHT PUBLIC SECTOR INC
(*Suby of* INSIGHT ENTERPRISES INC) ★
2250 W Pinehurst Blvd # 200, Addison, IL 60101-6100
Tel (630) 924-6801 *Founded/Ownrshp* 2002
Sales 149.0MM^E *EMP* 150
SIC 5045 Computers
Pr: Kenneth Lamneck
**CFO:* Glynis Bryan
**Sr VP:* Helen K Johnson
**VP:* Dana A Leighty

INSIGHT SYSTEMS EXCHANGE
See INSIGHT INVESTMENTS LLC

D-U-N-S 80-453-0632
■ INSIGNIA/ESG HOTEL PARTNERS INC
(*Suby of* CB RICHARD ELLIS REAL ESTATE SERVICES LLC) ★
11150 Santa Monica Blvd # 220, Los Angeles, CA 90025-3380
Tel (310) 765-2600 *Founded/Ownrshp* 1998
Sales 71.0MM^E *EMP* 5,800
SIC 6512 Property operation, retail establishment
CEO: Mary Ann Tighe
Pr: John Powers
IT Man: Mike Taylor
Board of Directors: Andrew L Farkas

D-U-N-S 87-816-4086
■ INSITU INC
(*Suby of* BOEING CO) ★
118 Columbia River Way, Bingen, WA 98605-9086
Tel (509) 493-8600 *Founded/Ownrshp* 1994
Sales 84.3MM^E *EMP* 167
SIC 8711 3999 Aviation &/or aeronautical engineering; Airplane models, except toy
Pr: Ryan Hartman
Pr: Steve Norlund
**Treas:* Lra Schey
Ofcr: Tina Sicilia
**VP:* Heidi Capozzi
VP: Bill Clark
**VP:* Charlie Guthrie
VP: Kenneth Liu
VP: Bobby L Lo
VP: Paul McDuffee
**VP:* Gary Viviani
VP Bus Dev: Suzanne McNamara

D-U-N-S 03-940-6616 IMP
■ INSITUFORM TECHNOLOGIES LLC
(*Suby of* AEGION CORP) ★
17988 Edison Ave, Chesterfield, MO 63005-3700
Tel (636) 530-8000 *Founded/Ownrshp* 1980
Sales 705.5MM^E *EMP* 3,280
SIC 1623 Pipeline construction; Underground utilities contractor
CEO: Charles R Gordon
**CFO:* David A Martin
**Treas:* Kenneth L Young
Ofcr: Charles Butler
**Ofcr:* David F Morris
**Sr VP:* Brian J Clarke
**Sr VP:* Dorwin E Hawn
VP: Chuck Delaney
VP: Ken Foster
VP: John Reeser
**VP:* Laura Villa
VP: Kenneth Young
Board of Directors: Stephen P Cortinovis, Stephanie A Cuskley, John P Dubinsky, Charles R Gordon, Juanita H Hinshaw, M Richard Smith, Alfred L Woods

D-U-N-S 96-550-6678
INSOURCE PERFORMANCE SOLUTIONS LLC
5601 77 Center Dr Ste 240, Charlotte, NC 28217-0735
Tel (704) 643-3232 *Founded/Ownrshp* 2003
Sales 76.6MM^E *EMP* 2,000
SIC 7363 Help supply services
Pr: Jeff Larkin
Pr: Kevin Clark
Pr: Ken Southerland
Opers Mgr: Dan Lovett

INSPECTION OILFIELD SERVICES
See IOS/PCI LLC

D-U-N-S 07-101-7438 IMP/EXP
INSPECTORATE AMERICA CORP
(*Suby of* BSI INSPECTORATE AMERICA) ★
12000 Aerospace Ave # 200, Houston, TX 77034-5587
Tel (713) 944-2000 *Founded/Ownrshp* 1980
Sales 242.1MM^E *EMP* 764^E
SIC 7389 8734 8731 Petroleum refinery inspection service; Inspection & testing services; Testing laboratories; Product testing laboratory, safety or performance; Agricultural research
Pr: Kevin Somers
**CFO:* Barry Benton
VP: Brad Cook
**VP:* Carlos Yamamoto
Dir Lab: Hector Fimbres
Dir Lab: Stephen Hughes
Admn Mgr: Scott Arntzen
Div Mgr: Marq Montano
Genl Mgr: Michael Ducharme
Cmptr Lab: Kerry Sanphy
Sls Mgr: Robert Mallon

D-U-N-S 79-434-2758
INSPECTORATE AMERICA HOLDING INC
BSI INSPECTORATE AMERICA
(*Suby of* INSPECTORATE HOLDINGS PLC)
12000 Aerospace Ave # 200, Houston, TX 77034-5587
Tel (713) 944-2000 *Founded/Ownrshp* 1991
Sales 242.1MM^E *EMP* 764
SIC 7389 8734 Inspection & testing services; Testing laboratories
Pr: Neil Hopkins
**CFO:* Barry Benton
CFO: James Davis
VP: Alan Aronowitz
VP: Mark Esselman
VP: Brit Horncastle
VP: Randy Neck
VP: Aldo Rodriguez

D-U-N-S 11-317-3269
■ INSPERITY HOLDINGS INC
ADMINISTAFF OF TEXAS, INC.
(*Suby of* INSPERITY INC) ★
19001 Crescent Springs Dr, Kingwood, TX 77339-3802
Tel (281) 358-8986 *Founded/Ownrshp* 1986
Sales 1.6MMM^E *EMP* 1,316^E
SIC 7363 Help supply services
Pr: Paul J Sarvadi

D-U-N-S 18-126-2080
▲ INSPERITY INC
19001 Crescent Springs Dr, Kingwood, TX 77339-3802
Tel (281) 358-8986 *Founded/Ownrshp* 1986
Sales 2.6MMM *EMP* 2,400
Tkr Sym NSP *Exch* NYS
SIC 8742 7363 7361 6311 Human resource consulting services; Employee leasing service; Employment agencies; Life insurance
Ch Bd: Paul J Sarvadi
**Pr:* Richard G Rawson
COO: A Steve Arizpe
CFO: Douglas S Sharp
Ex VP: Jay E Mincks
VP: Michael Berger
Dist Mgr: Howard Brenner
Dist Mgr: Robert Haight
Dist Mgr: Ryan Shapiro
Sls Dir: Dana Atteberry
Sls Mgr: Hal Hardin
Board of Directors: Michael W Brown, Timothy Clifford, Michelle McKenna-Doyle, Peter A Feld, Carol R Kaufman, John M Morphy, Norman R Sorensen, Austin P Young

D-U-N-S 01-880-9974
INSPHERE INSURANCE SOLUTIONS INC
(*Suby of* HEALTHMARKETS LLC) ★
9151 Boulevard 26, North Richland Hills, TX 76180-5600
Tel (817) 255-3100 *Founded/Ownrshp* 2009
Sales NA *EMP* 277^E
SIC 6411 Insurance agents, brokers & service
CEO: Kenneth J Fasola
**Ex VP:* R Scott Donovan
**Ex VP:* Derrick A Duke
**Sr VP:* N Lee Bedford
**Sr VP:* Michael Burson
Sr VP: Jack Heller
VP: Dallas Richins
Sls Mgr: Robert Newman
Sls Mgr: Chris Roughen
Snr Mgr: George Canova
Snr Mgr: Karen Degeurin

INSPIRA HEALTH CTR BRIDGETON
See INSPIRA MEDICAL CENTERS INC

D-U-N-S 78-875-6927
INSPIRA HEALTH NETWORK INC
2950 College Dr Ste 2d, Vineland, NJ 08360-6933
Tel (856) 641-8680 *Founded/Ownrshp* 1983
Sales 415.1MM *EMP* 3,063
SIC 8741 8062 Hospital management; General medical & surgical hospitals
Pr: John A Diangelo
**Pr:* Chester Kaletkowski
**Ex VP:* Eileen Cardile
**Sr VP:* Erich Florentine
VP: Carolyn Heckman
VP: Steven Linn
Dir Bus: Joseph Alessanvrini
Mktg Mgr: Robin Priggemeier
Obsttrcn: Peter S Konchak
Ansthlgy: Tamer A Attia
Ansthlgy: Aboulnasr Hamada

D-U-N-S 06-989-0911
INSPIRA MEDICAL CENTERS INC
INSPIRA HEALTH CTR BRIDGETON
(*Suby of* INSPIRA HEALTH NETWORK INC) ★
333 Irving Ave, Bridgeton, NJ 08302-2123
Tel (856) 575-4500 *Founded/Ownrshp* 2010
Sales 412.1MM *EMP* 3,063
Accts Withumsmithbrown Pc Morristow
SIC 8062 General medical & surgical hospitals
Pr: John D'Angelo
Pr: Colleen M Bodhuin
COO: Kristin Mullen
**COO:* Wayne Schiffner
CFO: Tom Baldosaro
Treas: Herb Deininger
Sr VP: Dawn Jenkins
VP: Dave Murray
Comm Dir: Linda Macdonald
Dir Rad: Glenda Smith
Dir Rx: Joe Alessandrini

D-U-N-S 07-981-3907
INSPIRA MEDICAL CENTERS INC
INSPIRA MEDICAL CTR WOODBURY
(*Suby of* INSPIRA HEALTH CTR BRIDGETON) ★
509 N Broad St, Woodbury, NJ 08096-1617
Tel (856) 845-0100 *Founded/Ownrshp* 1966
Sales 174.4MM *EMP* 1^E
Accts Withumsmithbrown Pc Morristow
SIC 8062 General medical & surgical hospitals
**Pr:* John A Diangelo
Exec: Elizabeth Hatfield
CIO: Robert Mizia

INSPIRA MEDICAL CTR WOODBURY
See INSPIRA MEDICAL CENTERS INC

D-U-N-S 07-928-8110
▲ INSTALLED BUILDING PRODUCTS INC
495 S High St Ste 50, Columbus, OH 43215-5689
Tel (614) 221-3399 *Founded/Ownrshp* 1977
Sales 662.7MM *EMP* 4,526^E
Tkr Sym IBP *Exch* NYS
SIC 1522 5033 5211 Residential construction; Insulation materials; Insulation material, building
Ch Bd: Jeffrey W Edwards
Pr: W Jeffrey Hire
Pr: R Scott Jenkins
Pr: Matthew J Momper
Pr: Warren W Pearce
Pr: Brad A Wheeler
Pr: Randall S Williamson
COO: Jay P Elliott
CFO: Michael T Miller
Treas: Todd R Fry
Sr VP: William W Jenkins
Sr VP: Jason R Niswonger
Board of Directors: Margot L Carter, Lawrence A Hilsheimer, Janet E Jackson, J Michael Nixon, Steven G Raich, Robert H Schottenstein, Michael H Thomas

D-U-N-S 05-285-6622
■ INSTALLED BUILDING PRODUCTS LLC
(*Suby of* INSTALLED BUILDING PRODUCTS INC) ★
495 S High St Ste 50, Columbus, OH 43215-5689
Tel (614) 221-3399 *Founded/Ownrshp* 1954, 2002
Sales 500.0MM *EMP* 2,800

SIC 1742 5211 1761

D-U-N-S 12-284-7507
■ INSTALLED BUILDING PRODUCTS LLC
BUILDERS INSULATION NH
(*Suby of* INSTALLED BUILDING PRODUCTS LLC) ★
62 King St, Auburn, NH 03032-3973
Tel (603) 645-1604 *Founded/Ownrshp* 2001
Sales 24.9MM^E *EMP* 1,559^E
SIC 1761 5021 5719 2515 Gutter & downspout contractor; Shelving; Fireplace equipment & accessories; Foundations & platforms
Genl Mgr: Kyle Niemela

INSTALLOY
See TEXAS PIPE AND SUPPLY CO LTD

D-U-N-S 04-816-6672
INSTANT WEB LLC
IWCO DIRECT
7951 Powers Blvd, Chanhassen, MN 55317-9326
Tel (952) 474-0961 *Founded/Ownrshp* 1968
Sales 296.5M^E *EMP* 2,200
SIC 7331 Direct mail advertising services
CEO: Jim Andersen
**CFO:* Joe Morrision
**Chf Mktg O:* Patrick Deck
VP: Don Brady
VP: Jill Burg
VP: Rick Eggers
**VP:* Debora Haskel
VP: Jeffrey Jurick
VP: Jerry Montella
VP: Alan Sherman
IT Man: Len Johnson

D-U-N-S 07-935-9891
INSTANT WEB LLC
IWCO DIRECT
7951 Powers Blvd, Chanhassen, MN 55317-9326
Tel (952) 474-0961 *Founded/Ownrshp* 2014
Sales 140.0MM^E *EMP* 2,200
SIC 7331 Direct mail advertising services
CEO: Jim Andersen
Chf Mktg O: Patrick Deck
Ex VP: Joe Morrison
Sr VP: Stephen Pasi
VP: Brian Anderson
VP: Jill Burg
VP: Mike Ertel
VP: Mary Hyland
VP: Ged Maguire
Mng Dir: Deanne Sheeley
Prgrm Mgr: Minh Nguyen

D-U-N-S 00-322-0225 IMP/EXP
▲ INSTEEL INDUSTRIES INC (NC)
1373 Boggs Dr, Mount Airy, NC 27030-2145
Tel (336) 786-2141 *Founded/Ownrshp* 1958
Sales 418.5MM *EMP* 790^E
Tkr Sym IIIN *Exch* NGS
SIC 3315 Wire & fabricated wire products; Welded steel wire fabric; Wire, steel: insulated or armored
Pr: H O Woltz III
CFO: Michael C Gazmarian
VP: Richard T Wagner
Exec: Trish Draughn
VP Admn: James F Petelle
Genl Mgr: Greg Mills
Genl Mgr: Dale Olp
Genl Mgr: Chad Swavey
IT Man: Christi Smiley
Software D: Julia Terry
Sls Mgr: Calvin Chandler
Board of Directors: Charles B Newsome, Gary L Pechota, W Allen Rogers II, Jon M Ruth, Joseph A Rutkowski

D-U-N-S 18-329-9502 IMP/EXP
■ INSTEEL WIRE PRODUCTS CO
(*Suby of* INSTEEL INDUSTRIES INC) ★
1373 Boggs Dr, Mount Airy, NC 27030-2145
Tel (336) 719-9000 *Founded/Ownrshp* 1981
Sales 216.2MM^E *EMP* 685^E
SIC 3315 Welded steel wire fabric
Pr: H O Woltz III
CFO: Michael C Gazmarian
VP: Lyle Bullington
VP: James F Petelle
VP: Chris Stauffer
VP: Richard Wagner
Sfty Mgr: Anthony Shannon
Sales Exec: Tammy Mosley
Sls Mgr: Jim Hoenig
Sales Asso: Kathy McMillian
Sales Asso: Ashley Morton

D-U-N-S 14-485-1409
INSTINET CORP
(*Suby of* INSTINET GROUP INC) ★
1095 Avenue Of The, New York, NY 10036
Tel (212) 310-9500 *Founded/Ownrshp* 1968
Sales 134.2MM^E *EMP* 600
SIC 6211 7379 Brokers, security; Computer related maintenance services
CEO: Fumiki Kondo
Ch Bd: Ed Nicoll
CEO: Glenn Lesko
COO: Frank M Freitas
CFO: Jacob Asbury
CFO: Nathalie Leroy
Co-CEO: Anthony Abenante
Ex VP: Alex Goor
CTO: Chris Rogers

INSTINET GROUP INCORPORATED
See INSTINET GROUP LLC

D-U-N-S 02-162-3777
INSTINET GROUP LLC
INSTINET GROUP INCORPORATED
(*Suby of* NOMURA SECURITIES INTERNATIONAL INC) ★
Worldwide Plz 309 W 49th, New York, NY 10019
Tel (212) 310-9500 *Founded/Ownrshp* 2007
Sales 163.5MM^E *EMP* 600
SIC 6231 Stock exchanges
CEO: Fumiki Kondo
Ch Bd: Ian Strachan
COO: Frank M Freitas
CFO: Jacob Asbury
CFO: John F Fay
Sr VP: Jay McEntire
Sr VP: Gerry Milligan
VP: Jeff Axelrod
VP: Lauren Bradley
VP: Eric Chaney
VP: Wadood Chaudhary
VP: Jesse Forster
VP: Steven Gero
VP: John Lafrance
VP: Dillon McNiven
VP: Brian Shannon
VP: Daniel Siry
VP: Jeffrey Soule
VP: Stephen Stern
VP: Geoff Von Wiegen
Dir Surg: Thomas H Glocer

D-U-N-S 96-163-0063
INSTITUCION EDUCATIVA NETS INC
Urb Sierra Bayamn, Bayamon, PR 00961
Tel (787) 785-5511 *Founded/Ownrshp* 1995
Sales 20.9MM^E *EMP* 3,000
SIC 8299 8322 Educational services; General counseling services
Pr: Jose A Llorens
**Ex VP:* Brenda Rivera
**VP:* Gilbert Arrreaga

D-U-N-S 17-330-6457
INSTITUTE FOR COMMUNITY LIVING INC
ICL
125 Broad St, New York, NY 10004-2400
Tel (212) 385-3030 *Founded/Ownrshp* 1986
Sales 88.5MM *EMP* 1,200
Accts Grassi & Co Cpas Pc Jericho
SIC 8052 Home for the mentally retarded, with health care
Pr: David Woodlock
**COO:* Chris Copeland
**COO:* Stella Pappas
**CFO:* Dewey Howard
**Treas:* Michael V Balistreri
Bd of Dir: Lisa Delduke
Bd of Dir: Alden Haffner
**Ex VP:* Gina Jacobson
**Sr VP:* Pamela Tindall-Obrien
VP: Gregory Kramer
VP: Pat Valerio

D-U-N-S 07-484-9589
INSTITUTE FOR DEFENSE ANALYSES INC
4850 Mark Center Dr, Alexandria, VA 22311-1882
Tel (703) 845-2000 *Founded/Ownrshp* 1956
Sales 223.9MM *EMP* 1,500
Accts Pricewaterhousecoopers Llp M
SIC 8733 Research institute
CEO: David Chu
Mng Pt: Edward R Jayne II
**Ch:* Suzanne H Woolsey
**Treas:* Dean Graves Jr
Bd of Dir: William H Press
Ofcr: Marco Quiroga
VP: Dale Lichtblau
Adm Dir: Bruce Angier
IT Man: Brad Gernand
IT Man: Chris Murphy
Netwrk Mgr: Brian Greene

D-U-N-S 08-166-5374
INSTITUTE FOR FAMILY HEALTH
INSTITUTE FOR URBAN FMLY HLTH
2006 Madison Ave, New York, NY 10035-1217
Tel (212) 633-0800 *Founded/Ownrshp* 1985
Sales 104.1MM *EMP* 603
Accts O Connor Davies Llp Harrison
SIC 8011 Ambulatory surgical center; General & family practice, physician/surgeon
Pr: Neil Calman
COO: Peter A Grisafi
CFO: Gail Shamilov
**Sr VP:* Maxine Golub
**Sr VP:* Virna Little
**Sr VP:* Nicole Nurse
Sr VP: Robert Schiller
VP: Steve Carter
VP: Brian Flynn
**VP:* Edward Fried
VP: Kathleen McGovern-Kearns
Comm Man: Robin Lally

D-U-N-S 07-231-7324
INSTITUTE FOR INTERNATIONAL EDUCATION OF STUDENTS
IES ABROAD
33 W Monroe St Ste 2300, Chicago, IL 60603-5405
Tel (312) 944-1750 *Founded/Ownrshp* 1950
Sales 86.7MM *EMP* 150
Accts Lb Crowe Horwath Llp Chicago
SIC 8299 Student exchange program
Pr: Mary Dwyer
COO: Richard Ellis
**CFO:* William Martens
Sr VP: Bob Meghji
VP: Bill Martens
VP: Roger Sheffield
**VP:* Michael Steinberg
CIO: Ian Ellis
Dir IT: Keith Scehen

INSTITUTE FOR LGSLATIVE ACTION
See NATIONAL RIFLE ASSOCIATION OF AMERICA

D-U-N-S 07-417-3873
INSTITUTE FOR REHABILITATION & RESEARCH (TX)
MEMORIAL HERMANN MEMORIAL CITY
(*Suby of* MEMORIAL HERMANN MEM CY HOSP) ★
1333 Moursund St, Houston, TX 77030-3405
Tel (713) 799-5000 *Founded/Ownrshp* 1959, 2006
Sales 112.8MM *EMP* 90
SIC 8062 General medical & surgical hospitals
Ex VP: Dale St Arnold
CFO: David Strickler
**VP:* Carrol Aulbaugh
Dir Risk M: Rodgie Mann

D-U-N-S 79-198-1202
INSTITUTE FOR TRANSFUSION MEDICINE
5 Parkway Ctr 875, Pittsburgh, PA 15220-3608
Tel (412) 209-7316 *Founded/Ownrshp* 1987
Sales 1.7MM *EMP* 1,200
Accts Ernst & Young Us Llp Pittsbur
SIC 8099 Blood bank
CEO: James P Covert
**COO:* Jim Fitzgerald
VP: Linda Hahn
VP: Andrea Hassett
**VP:* Darrell J Triulzi
Ex Dir: Daniel Rock
Ex Dir: Joan Sevcik
Prgrm Mgr: Mary Wiegel
Software D: Melissa Hopkins

INSTITUTE FOR URBAN FMLY HLTH
See INSTITUTE FOR FAMILY HEALTH

D-U-N-S 04-768-4758
INSTITUTE OF ELECTRICAL AND ELECTRONICS ENGINEERS INC
3 Park Ave Fl 17, New York, NY 10016-5902
Tel (212) 419-7900 *Founded/Ownrshp* 1963
Sales 189.6MM^E *EMP* 1,068
SIC 8621 Engineering association
Pr: Roberto De Marca
**Pr:* Peter W Staecker
**CFO:* Thomas Siegert
**Ch:* Shu Ping Chang
Trst: Jaime Aguirre
Chf Inves: Sandeep Pandya
Ex VP: Didier Ryelandt
VP: Richard D Beach
VP: Trevor Clarkson
VP: Zac Clingaman
VP: Richard Higgins
VP: David Nam
VP: Sid Sachdev
Exec: James Dumser
Exec: Lawrence Hamerman
Exec: Charles Herget
Exec: Teck Low
Exec: Levent Onural
Exec: Cary Yang

D-U-N-S 07-103-2973 EXP
INSTITUTE OF INTERNATIONAL EDUCATION INC (NY)
I I E
809 United Nations Plz, New York, NY 10017-3503
Tel (212) 883-8200 *Founded/Ownrshp* 1919
Sales 586.6MM *EMP* 450
Accts Pricewaterhousecoopers Llp Ne
SIC 8299 Educational services
Ch: Thomas Johnson
Pt: Saul T Caisman
V Ch: Diane J Paton
**Pr:* Allan Goodman
**COO:* Peggy Blumenthal
CFO: Nancy Khan
Ofcr: Candice Homan
Ofcr: Zehra Mirza
Ofcr: Daaimah Muhammad
Ex Dir: Nancy Overholt
Prgrm Mgr: Lina Aleryani

D-U-N-S 09-857-8834
INSTITUTE OF NUCLEAR POWER OPERATIONS
INPO
700 Galleria Pkwy Se # 100, Atlanta, GA 30339-5943
Tel (770) 644-8000 *Founded/Ownrshp* 1979
Sales 114.4MM *EMP* 365
Accts Bennett Thrasher Llp Atlanta
SIC 8999 Nuclear consultant
Pr: Robert F Willard
**Pr:* Jim Ellis
**CFO:* Kris Straw
VP: William Webster
Exec: Richard Larosa
**VP Admn:* James R Morris
Prgrm Mgr: Tim A Chapin
Prgrm Mgr: Bob Wood
Genl Mgr: Kris Rogers
CIO: Alison Collop
Dir IT: Ruth E Todd

D-U-N-S 02-462-4298 IMP
■ INSTITUTION FOOD HOUSE INC (NC)
PERFORMNCE FOODSERVICE-HICKORY
(*Suby of* P F G) ★
543 12th Street Dr Nw, Hickory, NC 28601-4754
Tel (800) 800-0434 *Founded/Ownrshp* 1965, 2012
Sales 487.8MM^E *EMP* 622
SIC 5141 5142 Groceries, general line; Packaged frozen goods
Pr: Gerald Davis
**Ch Bd:* Boyd L George
CFO: Michael J Highland
**Sec:* Ron W Knedlik
Sr VP: Jeff Sykes
**VP:* Thomas Dooley
**Prin:* Moses George
Rgnl Mgr: Tim Jones
MIS Dir: Jay Schwarz
Netwrk Mgr: Ellen Beck
Opers Mgr: Johnny Duncan

D-U-N-S 03-460-8091
INSTITUTIONAL WHOLESALE CO INC (TN)
I W C
535 Dry Valley Rd, Cookeville, TN 38506-4937
Tel (931) 537-4000 *Founded/Ownrshp* 1958
Sales 210.4MM^E *EMP* 175
SIC 5141 5142 Groceries, general line; Packaged frozen goods
Owner: Jimmy W Mackie
**Sec:* John M Mackie
**VP:* James Robert Mackie

D-U-N-S 09-059-6503
INSTITUTO DE BANCA Y COMERCIO INC
FLORIDA TECHNICAL COLLEGE
(*Suby of* EDUK GROUP) ★
56 Carr 20, Guaynabo, PR 00966-3300
Tel (787) 982-3000 *Founded/Ownrshp* 2007
Sales 91.3MM *EMP* 2,000
Accts Kevane Grant Thornton Llp San
SIC 8249 8244 8243 8222 7231 Banking school, training; Business & secretarial schools; Data processing schools; Technical institute; Cosmetology school
Pr: Guillermo Nigaglioni
Pr: Melissa Rosario
**Pr:* Ebbesen Samuel
**CFO:* Jose Cordorva
**Ch:* Fidel Alonso Valls
**VP:* Rafael Jimenez

D-U-N-S 79-246-9868 IMP
■ INSTRUMENT & VALVE SERVICES CO
(*Suby of* FISHER FAST PARTS) ★
205 S Center St, Marshalltown, IA 50158-2823
Tel (641) 754-3011 *Founded/Ownrshp* 1991
Sales 129.6MM^E *EMP* 350
SIC 3494 3825 7699 Valves & pipe fittings; Instruments to measure electricity; Valve repair, industrial
Pr: Gary Major
**Pr:* Denny Cahill
**Treas:* Phil Stafford

D-U-N-S 01-081-5926 IMP
■ INSTRUMENT TRANSFORMERS LLC
(*Suby of* GENERAL ELECTRIC CAPITAL CORP) ★
1907 Calumet St, Clearwater, FL 33765-1190
Tel (727) 461-9413 *Founded/Ownrshp* 2015
Sales 208.8MM^E *EMP* 500
SIC 3612 Instrument transformers (except portable)
**Pr:* James M Koepsell
**VP:* William Booth
Sales Exec: Koepsell Jim

D-U-N-S 55-722-3252 IMP
INSTRUMENTATION LABORATORY CO
(*Suby of* INSTRUMENTATION LABORATORY SPA)
180 Hartwell Rd, Bedford, MA 01730-2443
Tel (800) 955-9525 *Founded/Ownrshp* 1991
Sales 535.9MM^E *EMP* 1,100
SIC 3841 2819 8731 2835 Diagnostic apparatus, medical; Chemicals, reagent grade: refined from technical grade; Commercial physical research; In vitro & in vivo diagnostic substances
Pr: Ramon E Benet
**CFO:* Javier Gomez
CFO: Jose Guererro
Treas: Thomas H Conway
Sr VP: Ramon Benet
Sr VP: Ramone Benet
**VP:* Jose Luis Martin
VP: Jose Martin
VP: Giovanni Russi
VP: Stephen Trotta
Dist Mgr: IL Andersen

INSULATED TRANSPORT PRODUCTS
See SIGNODE INDUSTRIAL GROUP LLC

D-U-N-S 09-827-7759
INSULATION DISTRIBUTORS INC
IDI DISTRIBUTORS
8303 Audubon Rd, Chanhassen, MN 55317-9494
Tel (952) 279-6400 *Founded/Ownrshp* 1979
Sales 264.0MM^E *EMP* 230
SIC 5033 Insulation materials
CEO: Joseph Novogratz
VP: Christopher Novogratz
Genl Mgr: Thomas Bird
IT Man: Jackie Nuebauer

D-U-N-S 06-265-8729 IMP/EXP
INSULATIONS INC (LA)
II
1101 Edwards Ave, Harahan, LA 70123-2227
Tel (504) 733-5033 *Founded/Ownrshp* 1970
Sales 152.1MM^E *EMP* 1,000
SIC 1799 1761 1741

D-U-N-S 00-965-7891 IMP
INSULECTRO
20362 Windrow Dr Ste 100, Lake Forest, CA 92630-8140
Tel (949) 587-3200 *Founded/Ownrshp* 1991
Sales 131.2MM^E *EMP* 120
SIC 5065 Electronic parts
CEO: Timothy P Redfern
**Pr:* Patrick Redfern
**CFO:* Brad Biddle
**VP:* Kevin M Miller
VP: Ken Parent
**VP:* Kenneth Parent
IT Man: Kenny Chao
Opers Mgr: Jim McKay
Opers Mgr: Ricardo Soto
Sls Mgr: Lorrie Stearns

D-U-N-S 05-133-4402 IMP
▲ INSULET CORP
600 Technology Park Dr # 200, Billerica, MA 01821-4150
Tel (978) 600-7000 *Founded/Ownrshp* 2000
Sales 324.2MM *EMP* 647^E
Tkr Sym PODD *Exch* NGS
SIC 3841 Surgical & medical instruments
Ch Bd: Patrick J Sullivan
Pr: Daniel Levangie
Pr: Shacey Petrovic
CFO: Michael L Levitz
Ex VP: Brad Thomas
Sr VP: Aiman Abdel-Malek
Sr VP: Charles Alpuche
Sr VP: David Colleran
Sr VP: Michael Spears
VP: Jason Ng
VP: Daniel Trodden
Board of Directors: Sally Crawford, John A Fallon, Jessica Hopfield, David Lemoine, Timothy J Scannell, Steven Sobieski, Regina Sommer, Joseph Zakrzewski

D-U-N-S 12-273-9428 EXP
■ INSURANCE AUTO AUCTIONS INC
IAAI
(*Suby of* KAR AUCTION SERVICES INC) ★
2 Westbrook Corporate Ctr # 1000, Westchester, IL 60154-5722
Tel (708) 492-7000 *Founded/Ownrshp* 2007
Sales 267.0MM^E *EMP* 1,089

SIC 5012 Automobile auction; Automobiles
Pr: John Kett
**COO:* David R Montgomery
COO: David Montgomery
**Sr VP:* Donald J Hermanek
VP: Peter Doder
**VP:* Sidney L Kerley
VP: Dan Oscarson
VP: Anna Sension
VP: Mark Walsh
VP: Patrick Walsh
Brnch Mgr: Chet Bourdeau

INSURANCE BROKER
See PARKER SMITH & FEEK INC

D-U-N-S 83-317-3334
INSURANCE CLAIMS MANAGEMENT INC
404 S Barstow St, Eau Claire, WI 54701-3667
Tel (715) 830-6000 *Founded/Ownrshp* 2003
Sales NA *EMP* 300E
SIC 6411 Insurance claim processing, except medical
CEO: Paul Gross
**CFO:* Travis Wiemer
**Exec:* Michael Anderson
Genl Mgr: Steven Ashby
CTO: Hal Brown

D-U-N-S 05-926-8409
INSURANCE CO OF WEST
ICW
(*Suby of* ICW GROUP HOLDINGS INC) ★
15025 Innovation Dr, San Diego, CA 92128-3455
Tel (858) 350-2400 *Founded/Ownrshp* 1974
Sales NA *EMP* 309E
SIC 6331 Fire, marine & casualty insurance; Property damage insurance
Pr: Kevin Prior
**Ch Bd:* Ernest Rady
Pr: Stacey McAdam
**Treas:* H Michael Freet
Treas: Michael H Freet
Sr VP: Doug Browne
VP: Krikor Derderian
VP: Paul Zamora
Dir Risk M: Tom Jolliff
Brnch Mgr: Gina Douglas
Snr Sftwr: Ramya Tata

INSURANCE COMMISSIONER
See CALIFORNIA DEPARTMENT OF INSURANCE

D-U-N-S 07-862-8989
INSURANCE FUND NEW YORK STATE
NYSIF
(*Suby of* EXECUTIVE OFFICE OF STATE OF NEW YORK) ★
199 Church St Fl 13, New York, NY 10007-1100
Tel (212) 587-7390 *Founded/Ownrshp* 1914
Sales NA *EMP* 2,400E
SIC 9199
CEO: Dennis Hayes
Ofcr: Harold Bachman
Brnch Mgr: Suzan Kornblush

D-U-N-S 04-760-3444
INSURANCE HOUSE INC
1904 Leland Dr Se, Marietta, GA 30067-6102
Tel (770) 952-0080 *Founded/Ownrshp* 1964
Sales NA *EMP* 310E
SIC 6331 6411 6141 Property damage insurance; Fire, marine & casualty insurance & carriers; Insurance brokers; Licensed loan companies, small
CEO: Jill K Jinks
**Pr:* John Gordon Jinks Jr
COO: Jacqueline M Schaendorf
CFO: Kerry Buchan
Treas: Roy Little
Manager: Joe Carter

D-U-N-S 18-930-5592
INSURANCE OFFICE OF AMERICA INC
1855 W State Road 434, Longwood, FL 32750-5036
Tel (407) 788-3000 *Founded/Ownrshp* 1988
Sales NA *EMP* 757
SIC 6411 Insurance agents
CEO: Heath Ritenour
**Pr:* Jeff Lagos
**COO:* Mary Lawless
CFO: Greg Evans
**CFO:* Jay Grevers
**Ch:* John Ritenour
Ex VP: Scott Kuzmic
Ex VP: Nan Macgruer
Ex VP: Woody Power
**Ex VP:* Jon Thurman
**Sr VP:* Danny Anderson
Sr VP: Sherry Barrett
Sr VP: Robert Motley
VP: Jennifer Botting
VP: John Burkart
VP: Daniel L Caudill
VP: Randy Christopher
VP: Ray Dorsey
VP: Bob Hamilton
VP: Ty Harris
VP: John Harrold
Board of Directors: Wesley Scovanner

INSURANCE RESOURCES
See REGIONS INSURANCE GROUP

D-U-N-S 05-665-9725
■ **INSURANCE SERVICES OFFICE INC**
VERISK ANALYTICS
(*Suby of* VERISK ANALYTICS INC) ★
545 Washington Blvd Fl 12, Jersey City, NJ 07310-1613
Tel (201) 469-2000 *Founded/Ownrshp* 1997
Sales 964.8MME *EMP* 6,495
SIC 7375 Information retrieval services
CEO: Scott Stephenson
Pr: Michael D'Amico
Pr: Shawn Deane
Pr: John J Kollar
COO: Scott G Stephenson
Treas: Eva F Huston
Sr Cor Off: Wagner Sunday
Ofcr: Neil Spector
Ex VP: Mark V Anquillare
Ex VP: Carole J Banfield
Sr VP: Vincent P McCarthy
Sr VP: Kevin B Thompson
VP: Karthi Balakrishnan
VP: Kyle G Caswell
VP: Christopher Cpcu
VP: Bill Foster
VP: Vince McCarthy
VP: Christopher H Perini
VP: Mark Popolizio
VP: Carl Smith
VP: John Swedo

INSURENOW DIRECT
See CRUMP LIFE INSURANCE SERVICES INC

D-U-N-S 02-071-7203
INSURICA (OK)
INSURICA, INC.
(*Suby of* NORTH AMERICAN GROUP) ★
5100 N Classen Blvd # 300, Oklahoma City, OK 73118-5263
Tel (405) 556-2205 *Founded/Ownrshp* 1959
Sales NA *EMP* 290
SIC 6411 Insurance agents
Ch Bd: Bill Durrett
**Pr:* Mike Ross
**CFO:* Ed Young
**Ex VP:* Gary Jarmon
**Sr VP:* John Hester
VP: Tim McFall
**VP:* Jeff Nickles
**VP:* Kevin Wellfare
Dir Risk M: Michael Whitson
Opers Mgr: Lettie Tovar
Prd Mgr: Keith McCombs

INSURICA, INC.
See INSURICA

D-U-N-S 07-870-3731
INSURITY INC
170 Huyshope Ave, Hartford, CT 06106-2817
Tel (866) 476-2606 *Founded/Ownrshp* 2011
Sales 44.2MME *EMP* 1,000E
SIC 7374 Data processing service
CEO: Jeffrey Glazer
**Ch Bd:* Danny Daniel Sr
Pr: Sylvester Mathis
**COO:* Bob Larew
**CFO:* Rick Sorensen
CFO: Rick S Sorensen
**Sr VP:* Lani Cathey
**Sr VP:* Kenny Lebleu
VP: Jim Hatch
VP: Christine Kasson
VP: Ajay Kelshiker
VP: Clyde Owen
VP: Sergio Oyola
**VP:* Ken Safft
VP: Krista Weaver

D-U-N-S 92-903-3959 EXP
▲ **INSYS THERAPEUTICS INC**
1333 S Spectrum Blvd, Chandler, AZ 85286-8458
Tel (480) 500-3127 *Founded/Ownrshp* 1990
Sales 330.8MM *EMP* 510
Tkr Sym INSY *Exch* NGM
SIC 2836 2834 Biological products, except diagnostic; Pharmaceutical preparations; Druggists' preparations (pharmaceuticals)
Ch Bd: John N Kapoor
COO: Daniel Brennan
CFO: Darryl S Baker
VP: Steve Sherman
Sls Mgr: Kevin Flynn
Sls Mgr: Josh Knox

INTAGLIO ASSOCIATES IN DESIGN
See GEORGE P JOHNSON CO

D-U-N-S 05-731-6531 IMP/EXP
■ **INTALCO ALUMINUM LLC**
ALCOA INTALCO WORKS
(*Suby of* ALCOA CORP) ★
4050 Mountain View Rd, Ferndale, WA 98248-9683
Tel (360) 384-7061 *Founded/Ownrshp* 2016
Sales NA *EMP* 1,180
SIC 3334 Primary aluminum; Ingots (primary), aluminum
Pr: Barry S Hullett
Treas: Peter Hong
VP: Christie Breves
VP: Margaret Cosentino
VP: John Kenna
VP: A Sue Zemba
Exec: Mike Rousseau
Ql Cn Mgr: Corinne Baresich
Ql Cn Mgr: Vincent Mulroe
Ql Cn Mgr: Dennis Slagle
Sls Mgr: Chad Sandy

D-U-N-S 19-160-0303 IMP
INTAT PRECISION INC
(*Suby of* AISIN TAKAOKA CO.,LTD.)
2148 N State Road 3, Rushville, IN 46173-9302
Tel (765) 932-5323 *Founded/Ownrshp* 1988
Sales 211.2MME *EMP* 400
SIC 3321 Ductile iron castings
Pr: Donald Carson
Genl Mgr: Sandeep Deshpande
CTO: Dave Payne

INTCOMEX
See SOFTWARE BROKERS OF AMERICA INC

D-U-N-S 60-321-5513 IMP/EXP
■ **INTCOMEX INC**
(*Suby of* CVCI INTCOMEX INVESTMENT, L.P.)
3505 Nw 107th Ave Ste 1, Doral, FL 33178-9800
Tel (305) 477-6230 *Founded/Ownrshp* 2004
Sales 250.0MME *EMP* 204E
SIC 7371 5045 Computer software development & applications; Computers
Ch Bd: Anthony Shalom
Pr: Michael Shalom
COO: Leopoldo Coronado
CFO: Bert Lopez
CFO: Humberto Lopez
CFO: Russell A Olson
Treas: Eloy Fernandez
VP: Yali Luna
Exec: Elio Rotondo
Mng Dir: Matthew Deleon
Prgrm Mgr: Johanna Rodriguez
Board of Directors: Enrique Bascur, Adolfo Henriques, Thomas A Madden, Juan Pablo Pallordet

D-U-N-S 00-506-7004 IMP
INTEC GROUP INC
666 S Vermont St, Palatine, IL 60067-6950
Tel (847) 358-0088 *Founded/Ownrshp* 1953
Sales 120.6MME *EMP* 425
SIC 3089 Molding primary plastic; Injection molding of plastics
Pr: Steven M Perlman
VP: Michael Gaines
Dir Bus: Craig Richards
Genl Mgr: John Martin
Off Mgr: Char Kovac
Ql Cn Mgr: Rena Drewes
Board of Directors: Stanley M Perlman, Gary C White

D-U-N-S 15-379-5554
INTECH CONSTRUCTION LLC
3020 Market St Fl 2, Philadelphia, PA 19104-2999
Tel (215) 243-2000 *Founded/Ownrshp* 1986
Sales 135.0MME *EMP* 170
SIC 8741 Construction management
**VP:* David Maguire
Dir Bus: Matthew Morgan
Dir IT: Scott Force
Sfty Dirs: James Ryan
Snr PM: Peter Hricko
Snr PM: Andrew O'Donnell
Snr PM: Darrin Reazor

D-U-N-S 80-852-4920
■ **INTEGER GROUP L L C**
(*Suby of* OMNICOM GROUP INC) ★
7245 W Alaska Dr, Lakewood, CO 80226-3228
Tel (303) 393-3000 *Founded/Ownrshp* 1993
Sales 114.1MME *EMP* 805
SIC 7311 8742 8743 Advertising agencies; Marketing consulting services; Promotion service
Ch Bd: Jeremy Pagden
**CEO:* Mike Sweeney
**COO:* Frank Maher
**CFO:* Chris Stoeber
Ex VP: Morgan McAlenney
Ex VP: Scott Richards
Sr VP: Reyna Alishio
Sr VP: Todd Brandes
Sr VP: Craig Elston
Sr VP: Bryce McTavish
VP: Michele Crowley
VP: Kevin Hall
VP: Nick Hoadley
VP: Kiel Huhn
VP: Meg Kinney
VP: Julie Landy
VP: In Lee
VP: Dave Vanchina
Creative D: Shannon Ball
Creative D: Juan Cabrera
Creative D: Shannan Garrison

D-U-N-S 17-874-4632 IMP
▲ **INTEGER HOLDINGS CORP**
2595 Dallas Pkwy Ste 310, Frisco, TX 75034-8530
Tel (716) 759-5600 *Founded/Ownrshp* 1970
Sales 800.4MM *EMP* 9,559
Tkr Sym ITGR *Exch* NYS
SIC 3675 3692 3691 Electronic capacitors; Primary batteries, dry & wet; Storage batteries
Pr: Thomas J Hook
Ch Bd: Bill R Sanford
Pr: Jennifer M Bolt
Pr: Jeremy Friedman
Pr: Antonio Gonzalez
Pr: Declan Smyth
CFO: Michael Dinkins
Ofcr: Kristin Trecker
Sr VP: Timothy G McEvoy
VP: Dave Bolton
VP: George Cintra
Board of Directors: Pamela G Bailey, Joseph W Dziedzic, Jean Hobby, M Craig Maxwell, Filippo Passerini, Peter H Soderberg, Donald Spence, William B Summers Jr

D-U-N-S 08-317-1244
■ **INTEGRA LIFESCIENCES CORP** (DE)
JARIT
(*Suby of* INTEGRA LIFESCIENCES HOLDINGS CORP) ★
311 Enterprise Dr, Plainsboro, NJ 08536-3344
Tel (609) 275-2700 *Founded/Ownrshp* 1994
Sales 369.8MME *EMP* 887
SIC 3841 Surgical & medical instruments
CEO: Peter Arduini
**Pr:* Stuart M Essig
Pr: Ray Petersen
**CFO:* Glenn G Coleman
Bd of Dir: Raymond Murphy
Ofcr: Kevin Breeden
Ex VP: Jerry Backe
Sr VP: Richard Gorelick
VP: Simon Archibald
**VP:* Mark Augusti
**VP:* Kenneth Burhop
**VP:* Robert T Davis Jr
VP: Joanne Harla
**VP:* John B Henneman
VP: Tim Mikac
VP: Ray Peterson
VP: Peter Silvis
VP: Joseph Vinhais

D-U-N-S 79-016-8090 EXP
▲ **INTEGRA LIFESCIENCES HOLDINGS CORP**
311 Enterprise Dr, Plainsboro, NJ 08536-3344
Tel (609) 275-0500 *Founded/Ownrshp* 1989
Sales 882.7MM *EMP* 3,500
Tkr Sym IART *Exch* NGS
SIC 3841 2836 3842 Surgical & medical instruments; Biological products, except diagnostic; Surgical appliances & supplies; Implants, surgical
Pr: Peter J Arduini
**Ch Bd:* Stuart M Essig
Pr: Robert T Davis Jr
CFO: Glenn G Coleman
Ofcr: Lisa Evoli
VP: Kenneth Burhop
VP: Richard D Gorelick
Ex Dir: Scott Heidler
Prgrm Mgr: Priyanka Shah
Opers Mgr: Cyril Choukroun
Ql Cn Mgr: Nathan Thomas
Board of Directors: Keith Bradley, Richard E Caruso, Barbara B Hill, Lloyd W Howell Jr, Donald E Morel Jr, Raymond G Murphy, Christian S Schade, James M Sullivan

D-U-N-S 14-897-5076
INTEGRA LOGISTICS LLC
4400 Alexander Dr 1w, Alpharetta, GA 30022-3753
Tel (678) 775-5140 *Founded/Ownrshp* 2005
Sales 90.0MME *EMP* 60
SIC 4731 Freight transportation arrangement
CFO: Tony Johnson
VP: Lane Woodard

INTEGRA TELECOM
See ELECTRIC LIGHTWAVE HOLDINGS INC

INTEGRA TELECOM
See ELECTRIC LIGHTWAVE LLC

D-U-N-S 05-505-5573
INTEGRA US MARKETING LLC
(*Suby of* INTEGRA PETROCHEMICALS PTE. LTD.)
5075 Westheimer Rd # 790, Houston, TX 77056-5643
Tel (713) 224-2044 *Founded/Ownrshp* 2002
Sales 90.0MME *EMP* 4
SIC 8742 Marketing consulting services

D-U-N-S 83-128-2772
INTEGRACARE HOLDINGS INC
2559 Sw Grapevine Pkwy, Grapevine, TX 76051-1000
Tel (817) 310-4999 *Founded/Ownrshp* 2009
Sales 561.9MME *EMP* 5,604E
SIC 6719 Investment holding companies, except banks
Pr: Benjamin A Breier
**CFO:* David Hagey
**Sr VP:* Donald H Robinson
VP: Larry Birkhead
**VP:* James T Flowers
**VP:* Christopher T Gearad
**VP:* Jeffrey P Stodghill
Sls Mgr: Steve Allen

INTEGRACOLOR GROUP
See INTEGRACOLOR LLC

D-U-N-S 00-732-6358 IMP/EXP
INTEGRACOLOR LLC
INTEGRACOLOR GROUP
(*Suby of* ORORA LIMITED)
3210 Innovative Way, Mesquite, TX 75149-2756
Tel (972) 289-0705 *Founded/Ownrshp* 2015
Sales 108.5MME *EMP* 450
SIC 2752 2754 Commercial printing, lithographic; Commercial printing, gravure
Pr: Larry King
CFO: Tony Mendoza
DP Exec: Ryan Riley
Board of Directors: Lorn Davis, Bill Yost

D-U-N-S 78-798-3543
INTEGRAL GROUP LLC
191 Peachtree St Ne # 4100, Atlanta, GA 30303-1748
Tel (404) 224-1860 *Founded/Ownrshp* 1993
Sales 299.5MME *EMP* 310
Accts Fraizer & Deeter Llc Atlanta
SIC 6552 8748 6798 6799 6722 Subdividers & developers; Business consulting; Real estate investment trusts; Real estate investors, except property operators; Management investment, open-end
CEO: Egbert L J Perry
COO: Kenneth Chestnut
COO: Valerie Edwards
CFO: Mitchell Powell
VP: Daryl Jones
VP: Judi J Jones
VP: Eric Pinckney
Exec: Tyrone Williams
Dir IT: Neal Mitchell
VP Opers: Kevin Owens
Sls Dir: Jamie Lee

D-U-N-S 01-852-9181
INTEGRAL HEALTH PLAN INC
INTEGRITY QUALITY CARE
4631 Woodland Corp Blvd, Tampa, FL 33614
Tel (866) 258-4326 *Founded/Ownrshp* 2011
Sales 94.2MM *EMP* 12E
Accts Kpmg Llp Greensboro Nc
SIC 8099 Blood related health services
CEO: James Young

INTEGRAL SOLUTIONS GROUP
See J M SMITH CORP

D-U-N-S 10-192-5139
■ **INTEGRAL SYSTEMS INC**
(*Suby of* KRATOS DEFENSE & SECURITY SOLUTIONS INC) ★
4820 Estgate Mall Ste 200, San Diego, CA 92121
Tel (443) 539-5330 *Founded/Ownrshp* 2011
Sales 113.9MME *EMP* 690E
SIC 7373 Computer systems analysis & design; Systems integration services
Pr: Paul G Casner
CFO: Bill Bambarger
CFO: William M Bambarger
CFO: Deanna Lund
CFO: Christopher Roberts
Treas: Thomas Hyman
Ex VP: R Miller Adams
Ex VP: Stuart C Daughtridge
Sr VP: Sandee Carter
Sr VP: James B Kramer
Sr VP: Don Patrick
Sr VP: John Schladweiler
VP: David Bryant
VP: Craig Dempster
VP: Joan Grewe
VP: Kathryn J Herr

VP: Roger Hiyama
VP: Ron Johnson
VP: Eric Kirby
VP: Donald Mack
VP: Levi A Royster

D-U-N-S 15-143-9767
INTEGRAMED AMERICA INC
(Suby of INTEGRAMED HOLDING CORP) ★
2 Manhattanville Rd, Purchase, NY 10577-2113
Tel (914) 253-8000 Founded/Ownrshp 2012
Sales 137.1MM^E EMP 1,534
SIC 8093 Specialty outpatient clinics
Ch Bd: Jay Higham
Pr: Dan P Doman
*Pr: Daniel P Doman
Pr: Joseph Travia
COO: Lawrence Friedman
CFO: Eugene R Curcio
CFO: John W Hlywak
*CFO: Timothy P Sheehan
CFO: Timothy Sheehan
*Ex VP: Scott Soifer
*VP: Jeffrey Futterman
*VP: Claude E White
Exec: Mary K Caricato

D-U-N-S 07-862-3992
INTEGRAMED HOLDING CORP
(Suby of SAGARD CAPITAL PARTNERS LP) ★
2 Manhattanville Rd, Purchase, NY 10577-2113
Tel (914) 253-8000 Founded/Ownrshp 2012
Sales 232.5MM^E EMP 1,534^E
SIC 6719 Investment holding companies, except banks
Pr: Jay Higham
Chf Mktg O: Shannon Delage
VP: Brad Senstra
VP: Gail Thakarar

D-U-N-S 78-822-6751 IMP
INTEGRATED AGRIBUSINESS PROFESSIONALS COOPERATIVE INC
I A P
7108 N Fresno St Ste 150, Fresno, CA 93720-2960
Tel (559) 440-1980 Founded/Ownrshp 1991
Sales 154.5MM EMP 8
Accts Horg & Gray Cpa S Fresno Ca
SIC 5191 Chemicals, agricultural; Fertilizer & fertilizer materials
Ch Bd: Dean Miller
*Pr: Bob Higby
*VP: Melissa McQueen
*VP: Patrick Menagh

D-U-N-S 11-882-3798
INTEGRATED AIRLINE SERVICES INC
IASAIR
(Suby of CONSOLIDATED AVIATION SERVICES) ★
1639 W 23rd St Ste 240, Jamaica, NY 11430
Tel (718) 880-3453 Founded/Ownrshp 2013
Sales 181.0MM^E EMP 1,500
SIC 4581 Air freight handling at airports
Pr: Tom Wheeling
COO: Stephen Navin
*CFO: Michael Labarbera
Treas: Harry B Combs
*Sr VP: Ray Jetha
*Sr VP: Liane Kelly
*VP: Julio Feliciano
IT Man: Mike Cornell
IT Man: Andrew Oldham
VP Sls: Glen Avila
S&M/VP: Ken Katchen

D-U-N-S 92-646-6475
INTEGRATED ARCHIVE SYSTEMS INC
I A S
1121 San Antonio Rd D100, Palo Alto, CA 94303-4311
Tel (650) 390-9995 Founded/Ownrshp 1994
Sales 170.0MM EMP 61
SIC 8742 5045 Management information systems consultant; Computer software
CEO: Amy Joyce RAO
*CFO: Anna Borden
*VP: Karin Napier
VP: John Woodall
CIO: Linda Lagarejos
Sales Asso: Julia Nash
Sales Asso: Vy Pham
Sales Asso: Scott Reynolds
Sales Asso: Brian Warren

INTEGRATED BAGGING SYSTEMS
See INTEPLAST GROUP CORP

D-U-N-S 79-024-6771 IMP
INTEGRATED BAGGING SYSTEMS CORP
IBS
(Suby of INTEGRATED BAGGING SYSTEMS) ★
101 Interplast Blvd, Lolita, TX 77971-4115
Tel (361) 874-3000 Founded/Ownrshp 1992
Sales 111.9MM^E EMP 1,100^E
SIC 3081 Packing materials, plastic sheet
Pr: Dr John Young
*Pr: Joe Chen
CIO: Lambert Wang

D-U-N-S 13-789-8362
INTEGRATED DEICING SERVICES LLC
IDS
175 Ammon Dr, Manchester, NH 03103-3311
Tel (603) 647-1717 Founded/Ownrshp 2008
Sales 138.8MM^E EMP 550
SIC 3728 4581 Deicing equipment, aircraft; Aircraft servicing & repairing
Pr: Salvatore Calvino
VP: Linda Langsten
Mng Dir: Gil Schuckman
Genl Mgr: Scott Cummings
Genl Mgr: Mike Doroshenko
Genl Mgr: Bill Downing
Genl Mgr: Al Greene
Genl Mgr: Kirk Hannah
Genl Mgr: Andrew Hook
Genl Mgr: Ray Kristinsson
Genl Mgr: Matt Ohmann
Board of Directors: Geoffrey Baldwin, John Bragg, George Caines, David Hoffman, Roger Langille, Matthew Maclellan, Mike McAloon, Jeff McDowall

D-U-N-S 03-814-2600 IMP
▲ INTEGRATED DEVICE TECHNOLOGY INC
I D T
6024 Silver Creek Vly Rd, San Jose, CA 95138-1011
Tel (408) 284-8200 Founded/Ownrshp 1980
Sales 697.3MM EMP 1,767^E
Accts Pricewaterhousecoopers Llp Sa
Tkr Sym IDTI Exch NGS
SIC 3674 Semiconductors & related devices
Pr: Gregory L Waters
Ch Bd: John Schofield
CFO: Brian C White
Ex VP: Bill Pereira
VP: Matthew D Brandalise
VP: Sailesh Chittipeddi
VP: Jimmy Lee
VP: Mario Montana
Exec: Shanelle Robinson
Info Man: Raymond Lee
Mfg Mgr: Kathy Lower
Board of Directors: Ken Kannappan, Selena Loh Lacroix, Gordon Parnell, Robert Rango, Norman Taffe

D-U-N-S 17-846-1687
INTEGRATED DNA TECHNOLOGIES INC
I D T
1710 Commercial Park, Coralville, IA 52241-2760
Tel (319) 626-8400 Founded/Ownrshp 1987
Sales 164.7MM^E EMP 725
SIC 8733 5047 Research institute; Diagnostic equipment, medical
Pr: Joseph Walder
Pr: Greg Fender
*COO: Trey Martin
*CFO: Allen Siegal
*VP: Mark Campbell
VP: Patrick J Marschall
*VP: Aaron Warner
QA Dir: Bill Jones
Web Dev: Jason Hambright
Web Dev: Karl Ungs
Web Dev: Karl Zumdome

D-U-N-S 96-828-5481
▲ INTEGRATED DRILLING EQUIPMENT HOLDINGS CORP
25311 I 45 N Bldg 6, Spring, TX 77380
Tel (281) 465-9393 Founded/Ownrshp 1981
Sales 87.2MM EMP 270
Accts Whitley Penn Llp Houston Tex
Tkr Sym IRIG Exch OTO
SIC 3533 7539 5084 Drilling tools for gas, oil or water wells; Electrical services; Drilling equipment, excluding bits
CEO: Jim Terry
*Ch Bd: James N Mills
CFO: N Michael Dion
*V Ch Bd: Stephen Cope

D-U-N-S 83-983-2631 IMP/EXP
▲ INTEGRATED ELECTRICAL SERVICES INC
5433 Westheimer Rd # 500, Houston, TX 77056-5339
Tel (713) 860-1500 Founded/Ownrshp 1997
Sales 695.9MM EMP 3,106
Accts Ernst & Young Llp Houston Te
Tkr Sym IESC Exch NGM
SIC 1731 Electrical work
Pr: Robert W Lewey
Ch Bd: Jeffrey L Gendell
CFO: Tracy A McLauchlin
Sr VP: Bob Callahan
Sr VP: Margery M Harris
Sr VP: Gail D Makode
Sr VP: Danniel Petro
Sr VP: Bobby Stalvey
Sr VP: Jim Thurman
Sr VP: Peter Van Nort
VP: William Albright
VP: Richard China
VP: Terry Freeman
VP: Christopher Haas
VP: Gail Makode
VP: Richard A Nix
VP: James A Robertson

INTEGRATED GENETICS
See ESOTERIX GENETIC LABORATORIES LLC

D-U-N-S 92-866-9027
INTEGRATED HEALTH ASSOCIATES INC
IHA
24 Frank Lloyd Wright Dr, Ann Arbor, MI 48105-9484
Tel (734) 747-6766 Founded/Ownrshp 1994
Sales 148.1MM^E EMP 800
SIC 8011 Offices & clinics of medical doctors
Pr: William J Fileti
*Ch Bd: Robert Breakey MD
*CFO: Lowell Sprague
*Treas: James L Marley
*VP: Linda Macellven
*VP: Martin Murray
Dir IT: Chris Holda
Sales Exec: Amy Middleton

D-U-N-S 12-176-0243
INTEGRATED HEALTHCARE SYSTEMS INC
3311 E Murdock St, Wichita, KS 67208-3054
Tel (316) 689-9111 Founded/Ownrshp 1982
Sales 60.6MM^E EMP 1,000
SIC 7359 Equipment rental & leasing

D-U-N-S 94-877-4492 IMP
INTEGRATED MANUFACTURING & ASSEMBLY LLC
I M A
6501 E Nevada St, Detroit, MI 48234-2833
Tel (734) 530-5600 Founded/Ownrshp 1996
Sales 198.6MM^E EMP 600
SIC 2531 Seats, automobile
Owner: James Comer
VP Opers: Leonard Fox
Plnt Mgr: Kerry Kirsch

D-U-N-S 78-580-3404 IMP
INTEGRATED MEDICAL SYSTEMS INTERNATIONAL INC
IMS
(Suby of STERIS CORP) ★
3316 2nd Ave N, Birmingham, AL 35222-1214
Tel (205) 879-3840 Founded/Ownrshp 2001
Sales 117.9MM EMP 1,100
Accts Barfield Murphy Shank & Smit
SIC 3841 7699 Surgical & medical instruments; Professional instrument repair services
CEO: Gene Robinson
*CFO: David Strevy
Ex VP: James Boyette
Ex VP: Lenny Jordan
VP: Andy Edwards
VP: Victor Graffeo
VP: Brian Jones
VP: Art Klebba
Dir Soc: Terry Clunie
*Prin: Debra Robinson
Adm Dir: Kim Morris

D-U-N-S 62-249-7188
■ INTEGRATED PAYMENT SYSTEMS INC
(Suby of FIRST DATA CORP) ★
6200 S Quebec St Ste 320b, Greenwood Village, CO 80111-4750
Tel (402) 951-7008 Founded/Ownrshp 1992
Sales NA EMP 751
SIC 6099 Money order issuance
Pr: Charles T Fote
VP: Ron Darnall
VP: George Zirkel

D-U-N-S 80-057-4167 IMP
INTEGRATED POWER SERVICES LLC
I P S
3 Independence Pt Ste 100, Greenville, SC 29615-4543
Tel (864) 451-5600 Founded/Ownrshp 2012
Sales 200.0MM^E EMP 900
SIC 7694 Motor repair services
CEO: John Zuleger
CFO: Jason Martin
Sr VP: John Covington
Sr VP: Greg Lewis
Sr VP: Jason McDonald
Sr VP: Tom Reid

D-U-N-S 94-778-3122 IMP/EXP
INTEGRATED PROCUREMENT TECHNOLOGIES INC
IPT
7230 Hollister Ave, Goleta, CA 93117-2807
Tel (805) 682-0842 Founded/Ownrshp 1996
Sales 99.2MM^E EMP 48
SIC 5088 5065 Aircraft & parts; Navigation equipment & supplies; Communication equipment
CEO: Etty Yenni
*COO: Ken Krutenat
*CFO: Scott Heinz
Dir Bus: Tay Lai
Manager: Cathy Price

D-U-N-S 78-871-6954
■ INTEGRATED PRODUCTION SERVICES INC
(Suby of COMPLETE PRODUCTION SERVICES INC) ★
16800 Greenspt Pk Dr 200s, Houston, TX 77060-2300
Tel (281) 774-6700 Founded/Ownrshp 2007
Sales 200.9MM^E EMP 270
SIC 1389 3599 Construction, repair & dismantling services; Custom machinery
Pr: Jeff Kaufmann
Pr: Jose Bayardo
COO: Clinton Coldren
*Treas: Robert S Taylor
VP: Robert Copeland
*VP: John Graham
VP: Richard Guerra
*VP: Brian K Moore
VP: Scott Ritter
IT Man: John Finuken
Sls&Mrk Ex: Steve Mayo

D-U-N-S 07-915-2135
INTEGRATED SERVICE MANAGEMENT LLC
12312 Wilkins Ave, Rockville, MD 20852-1846
Tel (703) 480-2671 Founded/Ownrshp 2012
Sales 28.9MM^E EMP 3,000
SIC 7349 Building & office cleaning services
Ch: Fran Gali

D-U-N-S 60-820-8245 IMP
INTEGRATED SILICON SOLUTION INC
1623 Buckeye Dr, Milpitas, CA 95035-7423
Tel (408) 969-6600 Founded/Ownrshp 2015
Sales 328.9MM EMP 590^E
SIC 3674 Semiconductors & related devices
CEO: Jimmy Lee
Pr: Scott Howarth
Sr VP: Sanjiv Asthana
VP: John M Cobb
VP: Shou-Kong Fan
Sls Dir: Ray Stella
Sls Mgr: Carrie Tsai

D-U-N-S 05-436-6463 IMP/EXP
INTEGRATED SUPPLY NETWORK LLC (FL)
ISN
2727 Interstate Dr, Lakeland, FL 33805-2304
Tel (863) 603-0777 Founded/Ownrshp 1985, 1984
Sales 209.6MM^E EMP 275
SIC 5013 5072 Tools & equipment, automotive; Power handtools
Pr: Bruce Weber
*CFO: William Driscoll
*VP: Peter D Weber

D-U-N-S 05-065-4651
INTEGREON MANAGED SOLUTIONS INC
I M S
(Suby of INTEGREON MANAGED SOLUTIONS (INDIA) PRIVATE LIMITED)
2011 Crystal Dr Ste 200, Arlington, VA 22202-3779
Tel (201) 213-6107 Founded/Ownrshp 1998
Sales 104.8MM EMP 1,612
Accts Sr Batliboi & Associates Llp
SIC 8111 Legal services
CEO: Robert Gogel
*CFO: Kenneth Stelzer
Sr VP: Michael Dorsam
VP: Vicky Brown
VP: Marcia Goldenberg
VP: Mark Jewell
VP: Tara Lamy
VP: Michelle Richard
*VP: Benjamin Romualdez
VP: Mark Ross
*VP: Andrew Sims

D-U-N-S 96-941-2456
INTEGRIS AMBULATORY CARE CORP
5300 N Independence Ave, Oklahoma City, OK 73112-5556
Tel (405) 949-6026 Founded/Ownrshp 2011
Sales 152.6MM EMP 9^E
Accts Kpmg Llp Oklahoma City Ok
SIC 8062 General medical & surgical hospitals
Prin: Barton H Dawson

D-U-N-S 08-699-5966
INTEGRIS BAPTIST MEDICAL CENTER INC (OK)
BAPTIST MEDICAL CENTER OKLA
(Suby of INTEGRIS HEALTH INC) ★
3300 Nw Expressway, Oklahoma City, OK 73112-4418
Tel (405) 949-3011 Founded/Ownrshp 1950, 1983
Sales 582.8MM EMP 2,700
SIC 8062 General medical & surgical hospitals
Pr: Chris Hammes
*CFO: Wentz J Miller
Bd of Dir: William C Goad
VP: William Hood
CIO: Mark Hargrove
Opers Mgr: Jake Brownlow
Mktg Dir: Maggie Wolff
Surgeon: Lori M Kautzman
Obsttrcn: Lynn Horton
Doctor: Jeffrey Thompson
Doctor: Brian C Williams

D-U-N-S 12-195-6734
INTEGRIS HEALTH INC
3300 Nw Expwy Bldg C32, Oklahoma City, OK 73112-4418
Tel (405) 949-6066 Founded/Ownrshp 1983
Sales 1.3MMM EMP 9,500
SIC 8062 General medical & surgical hospitals
CEO: Bruce Lawrence
Pr: Avilla Williams
*COO: Chris Hammes
COO: Murali Krishna
*CFO: David Hadley
Bd of Dir: David Kallenberger
VP: Jeff Brown
VP: Kathie Calbone
VP: Susan Dragoo
VP: Jerry Gardner
VP: Phil Lance
VP: Paul Szymanski
VP: Jason Thompson
VP: Hardy Watkins
VP: Keith Wilton
Assoc Dir: William Green
Assoc Dir: Vivek Kohli

D-U-N-S 96-967-9773
INTEGRIS HEALTH INC
5300 N Independence Ave # 280, Oklahoma City, OK 73112-5555
Tel (405) 949-6026 Founded/Ownrshp 2011
Sales 253.5MM EMP 17^E
Accts Kpmg Llp Oklahoma City Ok
SIC 8099 Health & allied services

D-U-N-S 16-655-8614
■ INTEGRIS METALS CORP
(Suby of JOSEPH T RYERSON & SON INC) ★
455 85th Ave Nw, Minneapolis, MN 55433-6026
Tel (763) 717-9000 Founded/Ownrshp 2006
Sales 250.7M^E EMP 2,400
SIC 5051 Metals service centers & offices; Iron & steel (ferrous) products; Copper products; Miscellaneous nonferrous products
CEO: Neil Lovage
Treas: Everett P Chesley
*VP: Mark Irwin
VP: Terrance Rogers
CIO: Michael Pionk
Dir IT: Jim Chorosevic
Dir IT: John Jassava
*VP Sls: Robert Bell
Mktg Mgr: Valarie Enkhaus

D-U-N-S 82-980-0825
INTEGRIS PHYSICIANS SERVICES INC
5300 N Independence Ave # 260, Oklahoma City, OK 73112-5556
Tel (405) 951-2529 Founded/Ownrshp 1995
Sales 110.2MM EMP 3
SIC 8742 Management consulting services
CEO: Stan Hupfeld
*Pr: Lisa Anderson

D-U-N-S 08-256-5755
INTEGRIS RURAL HEALTHCARE OF OKLAHOMA INC
INTEGRIS RURAL HEALTHCARE OKLA
3300 Nw Expwy, Oklahoma City, OK 73112-4418
Tel (405) 951-2277 Founded/Ownrshp 1994
Sales 131.5MM^E EMP 1,896
SIC 8062 6513 General medical & surgical hospitals; Retirement hotel operation
CEO: Stan Hupfeld
*Pr: Bruce Lawrence
*COO: Tim Johnsen
Doctor: Rajesh Kanagala
Doctor: Paul Maton
Doctor: Robert Rankin
Doctor: Danny Smith
Doctor: Clinton Wallis

INTEGRIS RURAL HEALTHCARE OKLA
See INTEGRIS RURAL HEALTHCARE OF OKLAHOMA INC

D-U-N-S 08-321-3228
INTEGRITY BUSINESS SOLUTIONS LLC
4740 Talon Ct Se Ste 8, Grand Rapids, MI 49512-5462
Tel (616) 656-6010 *Founded/Ownrshp* 2001
Sales 107.6MM[E] *EMP* 85
SIC 5112 Office supplies
Genl Mgr: Kevin Knolll

D-U-N-S 06-197-7484
INTEGRITY LIFE INSURANCE CO
(*Suby of* WESTERN-SOUTHERN LIFE) ★
400 Broadway St, Cincinnati, OH 45202-3312
Tel (513) 362-8000 *Founded/Ownrshp* 2000
Sales NA *EMP* 1[E]
SIC 6311 Life insurance
Pr: John R Lindholm
**CFO:* Don Cummings
**Treas:* Jim Vance
Sr VP: John F O'Connell
**VP:* Ed Babbitt
**VP:* Dennis L Carr
VP: Charles White

INTEGRITY NUTRACEUTICALS INTL
See FHG CORP

INTEGRITY QUALITY CARE
See INTEGRAL HEALTH PLAN INC

D-U-N-S 92-847-3024
INTEGRITY SOLUTION SERVICES INC
NARS
20 Corporate Hills Dr, Saint Charles, MO 63301-3749
Tel (636) 530-7985 *Founded/Ownrshp* 1993
Sales 283.9MM[E] *EMP* 3,300
SIC 8748 7322 Business consulting; Collection agency, except real estate
CEO: Tim Bauer
**Pr:* Harry Jackson

D-U-N-S 17-602-5096
INTEGRITY STAFFING SOLUTIONS INC
700 Prides Xing 300, Newark, DE 19713-6102
Tel (302) 661-8770 *Founded/Ownrshp* 1997
Sales 591.6MM[E] *EMP* 26,000
SIC 7363 Temporary help service
Pr: Todd B Bavol
**CFO:* Sean Montgomery
VP: Deborah Pierce
Rgnl Mgr: Brandon Blanton
Sfty Mgr: Nichole Wheeler
Snr Mgr: Jason Lockwood

INTEGRITY TRANSITIONAL HOSP
See DENTON TRANSITIONAL LTCH LP

D-U-N-S 07-031-4053
■ **INTEGRITY URGENT CARE CLINICS INC**
(*Suby of* IMMEDIATE CLINIC HEALTHCARE INC) ★
4323 Integrity Center Pt, Colorado Springs, CO 80917-1683
Tel (719) 591-2558 *Founded/Ownrshp* 2014
Sales 292.1M[E] *EMP* 1,001[E]
SIC 8082 8011 8051 Home health care services; Offices & clinics of medical doctors; Skilled nursing care facilities
Pr: Mike Dalton
**Treas:* Soon Burnam

INTEGRO INSURANCE BROKERS
See INTEGRO LTD

D-U-N-S 61-164-9430
INTEGRO LTD
INTEGRO INSURANCE BROKERS
1 State St Fl 9, New York, NY 10004-1817
Tel (212) 295-8000 *Founded/Ownrshp* 2015
Sales NA *EMP* 468
SIC 6411 Insurance brokers
Pr: Peter Garvey
Mng Pt: Leslie Dewald
**CFO:* Andrew Behrends
Sr VP: Darryl Abbey
Sr VP: Annacarin Jansson
Sr VP: John Salvucci
Sr VP: Mark Santoleri
Sr VP: Neal Wallace
VP: Patty Boylan
VP: Jarrod Hitt
VP: Ed Mascher
VP: Renae Parent
VP: Olivia Peniston
Dir Risk M: Norma Pierson
Dir Bus: Matthew Clemo

D-U-N-S 36-334-3232
INTEGRO USA INC
(*Suby of* INTEGRO INSURANCE BROKERS) ★
1 State St Fl 9, New York, NY 10004-1817
Tel (212) 295-8000 *Founded/Ownrshp* 2005
Sales NA *EMP* 350[E]
SIC 6411 Insurance agents & brokers
Pr: Marc Kunney
**Ch Bd:* Robert Clements
**Pr:* Peter Garvey
**CEO:* Roger Egan Sr
**CFO:* Joe Salerno
Treas: Joe Meyer
Bd of Dir: Jack Byrne

D-U-N-S 87-771-9260
INTEGRYS ENERGY GROUP INC
200 E Randolph St # 2200, Chicago, IL 60601-6433
Tel (312) 228-5400 *Founded/Ownrshp* 1993
Sales 4.1MMM *EMP* 4,888[E]
SIC 4931 5172 4911

D-U-N-S 07-989-5916
■ **INTEGRYS HOLDING INC** (WI)
(FOMERLY: GET ACQUISITION CORP)
(*Suby of* WEC ENERGY GROUP INC) ★
231 W Michigan St, Milwaukee, WI 53201
Tel (414) 221-2345 *Founded/Ownrshp* 1993, 2015
Sales 1.4MMM[E] *EMP* 1,337[E]
SIC 4931 Electric & other services combined
Ch Bd: Gale E Klappa
**Pr:* Allen L Leverett
**CFO:* J Patrick Keyes
VP: Stephen P Dickson

D-U-N-S 04-789-7855 IMP/EXP
▲ **INTEL CORP**
2200 Mission College Blvd, Santa Clara, CA 95054-1549
Tel (408) 765-8080 *Founded/Ownrshp* 1968
Sales 55.3MMM *EMP* 107,300[E]
Accts Ernst & Young Llp San Jose C
Tkr Sym INTC *Exch* NGS
SIC 3674 3577 7372 Semiconductors & related devices; Microprocessors; Microcircuits, integrated (semiconductor); Memories, solid state; Computer peripheral equipment; Prepackaged software; Application computer software
Ch Bd: Andy D Bryant
Pt: Doug Parker
V Ch: Lalitha Immaneni
Pr: Leslie L Vadasz
Pr: Howard Wright
CEO: Brian M Krzanich
CFO: Stacy J Smith
Treas: Jacqueline Tan
Ex VP: William M Holt
Ex VP: William Holt
Ex VP: Gadi Oren
Ex VP: Paul S Otellini
Sr VP: Anand Chandrasekher
Sr VP: Robert B Crooke
Sr VP: Douglas L Davis
Sr VP: Amir Faintuch
Sr VP: Gregory R Pearson
Sr VP: Joshua M Walden
Sr VP: Christopher Young
VP: Catherine Ahaus
VP: Niraj Anand

D-U-N-S 05-421-5186 IMP
■ **INTEL MASSACHUSETTS INC**
(*Suby of* INTEL CORP) ★
75 Reed Rd, Hudson, MA 01749-2895
Tel (978) 553-4000 *Founded/Ownrshp* 1997
Sales 128.8MM[E] *EMP* 900
SIC 3674 Integrated circuits, semiconductor networks, etc.
Pr: Arvind Sodhani
Brnch Mgr: Ed Caldwell
Dir IT: Amit Gupta
IT Man: Gary Reinking
IT Man: Kelly Stinson
Tech Mgr: Tony Piscopo
Opers Mgr: Sue Strittmatter
Mktg Mgr: Kristen Hardeman

D-U-N-S 13-892-6998
▲ **INTELIQUENT INC**
550 W Adams St Fl 9, Chicago, IL 60661-3636
Tel (312) 384-8000 *Founded/Ownrshp* 2004
Sales 248.6MM *EMP* 177
Tkr Sym IQNT *Exch* NGS
SIC 4813
Pr: Matthew J Carter Jr
**Ch Bd:* James P Hynes
CFO: Kurt J Abkemeier
Chf Mktg O: John M Schoder
Ex VP: John T Bullock
Ex VP: Brett A Scorza
Sr VP: Richard L Monto
VP: Charlie Drexler
VP: Ed Emberson
Board of Directors: Joseph A Beatty, Edward M Greenberg, Lawrence M Ingeneri, Timothy A Samples, Rian J Wren, Lauren F Wright

D-U-N-S 01-174-7982
INTELLECTUAL VENTURES LLC
3150 139th Ave Se Ste 500, Bellevue, WA 98005-4046
Tel (425) 467-2300 *Founded/Ownrshp* 1999
Sales 149.2MM[E] *EMP* 500[E]
SIC 7379
Pr: Adriane Brown
**Ex VP:* Chris Alliegro
**Ex VP:* Andy Elder
Ex VP: Masanobu Katoh
**Ex VP:* David Kris
**Ex VP:* Casey T Tegreene
Ex VP: Loria Yeadon
Sr VP: Mona Locke
VP: Kirk Muzzy
VP: Eric Nagel
VP: Maurizio Vecchione
Exec: Camilla McMillan
Assoc Dir: John S Foster Jr
Dir Bus: Russell Hannigan

INTELLICLAIM, CLAIMSLINK
See CEI GROUP INC

INTELLIGENCER, THE
See OGDEN NEWSPAPERS INC

INTELLIGENCER/RECORD THE
See CALKINS MEDIA INC

D-U-N-S 06-896-9984
INTELLIGENT CONSUMER HOLDINGS LLC (GA)
ALL CONNECT
980 Hammond Dr Ste 1000, Atlanta, GA 30328-8187
Tel (404) 260-2200 *Founded/Ownrshp* 1996
Sales 195.0MM[E] *EMP* 830
SIC 7299 Information services, consumer
Sr VP: Ron Carpinella
VP Mktg: Jagdish N Sheth

D-U-N-S 61-856-3720
INTELLIGENT DECISIONS INC
21445 Beaumeade Cir, Ashburn, VA 20147-6036
Tel (703) 554-1600 *Founded/Ownrshp* 1988
Sales 186.2MM[E] *EMP* 400
SIC 3571 5045

INTELLIGENT ENERGY
See INFINITE ENERGY INC

D-U-N-S 07-940-5385
INTELLIGENT INVESTMENTS LLC (SC)
1010 Park Dr, Myrtle Beach, SC 29577-4362
Tel (980) 989-4016 *Founded/Ownrshp* 2011
Sales 765.0MM *EMP* 10
SIC 6726 7389 Investment offices;
CEO: Antonio Johnson

COO: Demarko Terrell Lee
COO: Jose Pastrana

D-U-N-S 96-351-9939
INTELLIGENT SOFTWARE SOLUTIONS USA LLC
I S S
5450 Tech Center Dr # 400, Colorado Springs, CO 80919-2341
Tel (719) 452-7000 *Founded/Ownrshp* 1997
Sales 117.2MM *EMP* 525
SIC 7371 Computer software development
Pr: Jay Jesse
CFO: Nikki Herman
VP: Lisa Jesse
VP: Dennis Linn
VP: Jesse Miller
Prgrm Mgr: Brad Carman
Prgrm Mgr: Rollin Cogburn
Prgrm Mgr: Kevin Light
Snr Sftwr: Dave Hoffer
Snr Sftwr: Guy Pascarella
Snr Sftwr: Kevin Schnake

D-U-N-S 07-853-2184 IMP
INTELLIGRATED INC
7901 Innovation Way, Mason, OH 45040-9498
Tel (866) 936-7300 *Founded/Ownrshp* 2001
Sales 18.4MM[E] *EMP* 2,800
SIC 3535 Conveyors & conveying equipment
CEO: Chris Cole
Pr: Jim McCarthy
CFO: Edward Puisis
Ex VP: Jim Sharp
Sr VP: Bill Harton
Sr VP: Jim McDonald
VP: Mike Blough
VP: Crawford Cyril
VP: William Harton
VP: Bryan Jones
VP: Mike Roach
VP: Tom Schulte
VP: Ken Thouvenot

D-U-N-S 08-328-1845
■ **INTELLIGRATED SYSTEMS INC**
(*Suby of* HONEYWELL INC) ★
7901 Innovation Way, Mason, OH 45040-9498
Tel (866) 936-7300 *Founded/Ownrshp* 1996, 2016
Sales 800.0MM *EMP* 3,200
SIC 3535 5084 7371 Conveyors & conveying equipment; Industrial machinery & equipment; Computer software development
CEO: Chris Cole
Pr: Jim McCarthy
CFO: Ed Puisis
Bd of Dir: Robert Forlenza
Ex VP: Gregory Cronin
Ex VP: Kevin V Roach
Ex VP: Jim Sharp
Sr VP: John Cullen
Sr VP: John Sorensen
VP: Dick Braatz
VP: Cyril Crawford
VP: Crawford Cyril
VP: Michael Hession
VP: Eric Palotas
Dir Bus: Bill Natsch

D-U-N-S 06-468-1054
■ **INTELLIGRATED SYSTEMS LLC**
(*Suby of* INTELLIGRATED SYSTEMS INC) ★
7901 Innovation Way, Mason, OH 45040-9498
Tel (513) 701-7300 *Founded/Ownrshp* 2001
Sales 228.8MM[E] *EMP* 2,300
SIC 3535 5084 7371 Conveyors & conveying equipment; Materials handling machinery; Computer software development
CEO: Chris Cole
**Pr:* Jim McCarthy
**CFO:* Ed Puisis
Ex VP: James Sharp
**Sr VP:* Jim McKnight
**VP:* Bryan Jones
Prgrm Mgr: Robert McKnight
Genl Mgr: Amy Ball
Snr Sftwr: Jeffrey Hanna
VP Mfg: Lee Yarberry
Sales Exec: Richard Scheiring

D-U-N-S 00-626-6001 IMP/EXP
■ **INTELLIGRATED SYSTEMS OF OHIO LLC** (DE)
(*Suby of* INTELLIGRATED SYSTEMS INC) ★
7901 Innovation Way, Mason, OH 45040-9498
Tel (513) 701-7300 *Founded/Ownrshp* 2010, 2009
Sales 196.5MM[E] *EMP* 2,800
SIC 3535 5084 3537 Conveyors & conveying equipment; Industrial machinery & equipment; Palletizers & depalletizers
Pr: Jim McCarthy
Pr: Dennis Gates
**Ex VP:* Stephen Ackerman
Ex VP: Chuck Waddle
**VP:* Stephen Causey
VP: Wes Goode
VP: Rick Osen
VP: Frank Pellegrino
VP: Tom Schulte
VP: Royal Smith
CTO: Raymond Neiser

D-U-N-S 14-460-7160
■ **INTELLINEX LLC**
ACS LEARNING SERVICES
(*Suby of* XEROX BUSINESS SERVICES LLC) ★
6000 Fredom Sq Dr Ste 100, Independence, OH 44131
Tel (216) 685-6000 *Founded/Ownrshp* 2006
Sales 125.0MM[E] *EMP* 325
SIC 4813
Mng Dir: Richard Klingshirn
VP Opers: Leo Blankenship

D-U-N-S 03-159-2467
INTELLIRISK MANAGEMENT CORP
(*Suby of* IQOR US INC) ★
335 Madison Ave Fl 27, New York, NY 10017-4653
Tel (646) 274-3030 *Founded/Ownrshp* 1998

Sales 89.9MM[E] *EMP* 6,000
SIC 7322 Adjustment & collection services
Ex VP: Norm Meritt
**CFO:* Paul Clark
**Ex VP:* Christopher Dorval
**Ex VP:* Barry Grant
**Ex VP:* Greg Harmer
**Ex VP:* Gary Praznik
**Ex VP:* Graeme Stirrett
**Sr VP:* James Wallace
VP: Judah Kaplan

D-U-N-S 09-033-8422
INTELLISOURCE LLC
1899 Wynkoop St Ste 900, Denver, CO 80202-1093
Tel (303) 692-1100 *Founded/Ownrshp* 1999
Sales 90.0MM *EMP* 7,500
SIC 8742 Management consulting services
CEO: Robyn Donahue
**COO:* Ajay Bagal
**Sr VP:* Matt Pollard
Off Mgr: Jennifer Rogers

D-U-N-S 10-672-4235
INTELLISWIFT SOFTWARE INC
MAGAGNINI
2201 Walnut Ave Ste 180, Fremont, CA 94538-2334
Tel (510) 490-9240 *Founded/Ownrshp* 2001
Sales 96.0MM[E] *EMP* 325
SIC 7379 Computer related consulting services
CEO: Parag Patel
VP: John Magagnini
**Prin:* Bob Patel
Sls&Mrk Ex: Tiffany Tran

D-U-N-S 83-980-9159 IMP
INTELSAT CORP
(*Suby of* INTELSAT JACKSON HOLDINGS SA)
7900 Tysons One Pl, Mc Lean, VA 22102-5971
Tel (703) 559-6800 *Founded/Ownrshp* 2006
Sales 409.6MM[E] *EMP* 1,111
SIC 4841 Direct broadcast satellite services (DBS)
Ch Bd: David McGlade
**Pr:* Stephen Spengler
**CFO:* Michael McDonnell
**Treas:* Hank Courson
Treas: Kevin Watson
**Ex VP:* Michelle Bryan
**Ex VP:* Thierry Guillemin
Ex VP: Tony Trujillo Jr
Sr VP: Bruce A Haymes
Sr VP: Michael S Liebow
**Sr VP:* Kurt Riegelman
**VP:* Sajid Ajmeri
**VP:* Stephen Chernow
**VP:* Angela Galyean
**VP:* Michael Green
VP: Jay Yass
Exec: Chris Nibecker
Dir Teleco: Amy Voorhees

D-U-N-S 06-485-7527 IMP
INTELSAT GLOBAL SERVICE LLC
(*Suby of* INTELSAT CORP) ★
7900 Tysons One Pl, Mc Lean, VA 22102-5971
Tel (703) 559-7129 *Founded/Ownrshp* 2013
Sales 277.7MM[E] *EMP* 873
SIC 4899 Data communication services
Ch Bd: Thierry Guillemin
VP: Conny L Kuman

D-U-N-S 17-589-5452 IMP
INTELSAT HOLDING CORP
(*Suby of* INTELSAT INVESTMENTS SA)
7900 Tysons One Pl Fl 14, Mc Lean, VA 22102-5972
Tel (202) 703-5599 *Founded/Ownrshp* 2006
Sales 392.9MM[E] *EMP* 1,112
SIC 4899 Satellite earth stations
CEO: Stephen Spengler
**COO:* James B Frownfelter
**CFO:* Jeffrey Freimark
**Ex VP:* Michael Antonovich
**Ex VP:* James W Cuminale
**Ex VP:* Phillip Spector

D-U-N-S 12-719-0002 IMP
INTELSAT USA SALES CORP
(*Suby of* INTELSAT GLOBAL SALES & MARKETING LTD.)
7900 Tysons One Pl, Mc Lean, VA 22102-5971
Tel (703) 559-6800 *Founded/Ownrshp* 2001
Sales 364.6MM[E] *EMP* 1,300
SIC 4899 Data communication services
CEO: David McGlade
**CFO:* Patricia Casey
**Ex VP:* Michael McDonnell
**Ex VP:* Phillip L Spector
**Ex VP:* Stephen Spengler
**Sr VP:* Thierry Guillemin
**Sr VP:* Kurt Riegelman

D-U-N-S 78-694-1427 IMP
INTEPLAST GROUP CORP
INTEGRATED BAGGING SYSTEMS
9 Peach Tree Hill Rd, Livingston, NJ 07039-5702
Tel (973) 994-8000 *Founded/Ownrshp* 1991
Sales 3.2MM *EMP* 7,400
SIC 2673 Bags: plastic, laminated & coated
Ch Bd: John Young
Pr: Homer Shieh
CFO: Robert Wang

D-U-N-S 14-804-5701
■ **INTER AMERICAN PRODUCTS INC**
KENLAKE FOODS
(*Suby of* KROGER CO) ★
1240 State Ave, Cincinnati, OH 45204-1728
Tel (800) 645-2233 *Founded/Ownrshp* 1989
Sales 259.5MM[E] *EMP* 3,000[E]
SIC 2095 2099 2033 2079 2087 2022 Roasted coffee; Spices, including grinding; Jellies, edible, including imitation: in cans, jars, etc.; Preserves, including imitation: in cans, jars, etc.; Salad oils, except corn: vegetable refined; Concentrates, drink; Processed cheese; Natural cheese
CEO: David B Dillon
**Pr:* Rodney McMullen
**Genl Mgr:* Bill Lucia

INTER COMMUNITY HOSPITAL
See CITRUS VALLEY HEALTH PARTNERS INC

D-U-N-S 06-744-8142
INTER LOCAL PENSION FUND INC
455 Kehoe Blvd Ste 100, Carol Stream, IL 60188-5203
Tel (630) 752-8400 Founded/Ownrshp 1950
Sales NA EMP 5
SIC 6371 Pension funds
Ex Dir: Elizabeth Jacobs

D-U-N-S 16-113-5447 IMP
▲ INTER PARFUMS INC
551 5th Ave, New York, NY 10176-0001
Tel (212) 983-2640 Founded/Ownrshp 1985
Sales 468.5MM EMP 311E
Tkr Sym IPAR Exch NGS
SIC 2844 Toilet preparations; Perfumes & colognes; Cosmetic preparations
Ch Bd: Jean Madar
*Pr: Philippe Benacin
*CFO: Russell Greenberg
VP: Alex Canavan
Exec: Michelle Habert
VP Mktg: Marina Mamakos
Board of Directors: Robert Bensoussan, Patrick Choel, Michel Dyens Francois Heil, Jean Levy

D-U-N-S 00-325-4513 IMP
INTER-AMERICAN DEVELOPMENT BANK
BANCO INTERAMERICANO DE DESAR
1300 New York Ave Nw, Washington, DC 20577-0001
Tel (202) 623-1000 Founded/Ownrshp 1952
Sales NA EMP 2,000E
Accts Kpmg Llp Washington Dc
SIC 6082 Foreign trade & international banking institutions
Pr: Luis A Moreno
V Ch: Robert J Deal Jr
COO: Julie T Katzman
*CFO: Gustavo De Rosa
Treas: Otto Gutierrez
Treas: Charles O Sethness
Bd of Dir: Jose Cartas
Bd of Dir: Alan Gill
Ofcr: Gustavo Olmedo
VP: Santiago Levy Algazi
VP: K B Dillon
VP: Joaquim Levy
VP: Levy Santiago
VP: Jaime Sujoy
Exec: Juan Bonilla

INTER-CHEM
See INTERNATIONAL CHEMICAL CO

D-U-N-S 01-207-1643
INTER-CITY TIRE & AUTO CENTER INC
UNDERCARE
777 Dowd Ave, Elizabeth, NJ 07201-2118
Tel (908) 354-5533 Founded/Ownrshp 1980
Sales 83.1MME EMP 200
SIC 5531 5013 7538 Automotive tires; Automotive supplies & parts; Automotive servicing equipment; General automotive repair shops
Pr: Morris Erbesh
CFO: Agnes Feltz
Board of Directors: Agnes Seltez

D-U-N-S 07-619-2475
INTER-CON SECURITY SYSTEMS INC
210 S De Lacey Ave # 200, Pasadena, CA 91105-2048
Tel (626) 535-2200 Founded/Ownrshp 1973
Sales 506.2MME EMP 25,000
SIC 7381 Guard services; Protective services, guard; Security guard service
Ch Bd: Enrique Hernandez
*Pr: Neil Martau
COO: Lance Mueller
CFO: Paul Miller
CFO: Robin Simpson
Ofcr: Melvin Allen
Ofcr: Daniel Desenna
VP: Enzo Giancaspero
*VP: Roland A Hernandez
VP: Jerry Neville
VP: Franklin Rodriguez
VP: Rebecca Rowland
VP: Dane Shepard
VP: Richard Stack
VP: Robert Williams
Exec: Mariela Gonzalez

D-U-N-S 14-297-5080
INTER-CONTINENTAL HOTELS CORP
IHG
(Suby of IHC INTER-CONTINENTAL (HOLDINGS) CORP)
3 Ravinia Dr Ste 100, Atlanta, GA 30346-2121
Tel (770) 604-5000 Founded/Ownrshp 1946
Sales 61.0MME EMP 1,806E
SIC 7011 Hotels & motels
CEO: Kirk Kinsell
*CFO: Robert J Chitty
*CFO: Robert Gunkel
Sr VP: Laura Miller
VP: Paul Huang
Comm Dir: Giles Deards
*Prin: Stevan Porter
Rgnl Mgr: Marlena Norris
Genl Mgr: Debbie Mahone
Genl Mgr: Jerome Qiu
Genl Mgr: Oscar Rodriguez

D-U-N-S 01-337-8807 IMP
INTER-COUNTY BAKERS INC
INTER-COUNTY BAKERY SUPPLY
1095 Long Island Ave A, Deer Park, NY 11729-3800
Tel (631) 957-1350 Founded/Ownrshp 1995
Sales 85.0MM EMP 91
SIC 5142 Bakery products, frozen
CEO: Theodore P Heim Jr
*Pr: Theodore P Heim Sr
CFO: Laura Mulligan
Sales Exec: Andrew Hislop

INTER-COUNTY BAKERY SUPPLY
See INTER-COUNTY BAKERS INC

D-U-N-S 60-471-2828
INTER-TEL TECHNOLOGIES INC
(Suby of MITEL (DELAWARE) INC) ★
1146 N Alma School Rd, Mesa, AZ 85201-3000
Tel (480) 858-9600 Founded/Ownrshp 1977
Sales 300.0MM EMP 118
SIC 5999 1731 5065 3661 3577 Telephone equipment & systems; Telephone & telephone equipment installation; Electronic parts & equipment; Telephone & telegraph apparatus; Computer peripheral equipment
Pr: Craig W Rauchle

D-U-N-S 12-087-1090
INTER-VALLEY HEALTH PLAN INC
300 S Park Ave Ste 300, Pomona, CA 91766-1546
Tel (909) 623-6333 Founded/Ownrshp 1979
Sales NA EMP 70
Accts Ernst & Young Us Llp Irvine
SIC 6324 8011 Hospital & medical service plans; Offices & clinics of medical doctors
CEO: Ronald Bolding
*CFO: Michael Nelson
Sls Mgr: Kathleen Cade
Surgeon: Vinod K Garg
Obsttrcn: Stephanie J Cropper
Obsttrcn: Simmi P Dhaliwal
Opthamlgy: Boban Joseph
Genl Couns: Gail Blackrock

D-U-N-S 05-730-3372 IMP/EXP
INTER-WIRE PRODUCTS INC
INTERWIRE GROUP
355 Main St Ste 2, Armonk, NY 10504-1844
Tel (914) 273-6633 Founded/Ownrshp 1981
Sales 96.8MME EMP 147
Accts Bdo Usa Llp Valhalla Ny
SIC 5051 Metal wires, ties, cables & screening
Pr: Frank Cardile Jr
*V Ch Bd: Deborah Cardile
VP: Lanny Wright
Genl Mgr: Susan Cook
Dir IT: Bob Chellis
Sales Asso: Laura L Peterson
Sales Asso: Stephanie Ramey

INTERA INTERNATIONAL
See INTERRA GROUP INC

D-U-N-S 79-892-9902
▲ INTERACTIVE BROKERS GROUP INC
1 Pickwick Plz, Greenwich, CT 06830-5551
Tel (203) 618-5800 Founded/Ownrshp 1977
Sales 1.2MMM EMP 1,087E
Accts Deloitte & Touche Llp New Yor
Tkr Sym IBKR Exch NGS
SIC 6211 Security brokers & dealers
Ch Bd: Thomas Peterffy
*Pr: Milan Galik
*CFO: Paul J Brody
*V Ch Bd: Earl H Nemser
Ex VP: Thomas A Frank
Sr VP: Steve Sanders

D-U-N-S 94-087-2591
■ INTERACTIVE BROKERS LLC
(Suby of IBG LLC) ★
2 Pickwick Plz Ste 210, Greenwich, CT 06830-5576
Tel (203) 618-5700 Founded/Ownrshp 1998
Sales 104.6MME EMP 139E
SIC 6211 Security brokers & dealers
CFO: Paul Brody
Ofcr: Arnold J Feist
VP: David Battan
VP: Susan Cramer
VP: Bradford Jacobowitz
Mng Dir: David Friedland
Mng Dir: Steve Kelsey
Mng Dir: William McGowan
Mng Dir: Richard Roman
Mng Dir: Steve Sanders
Off Mgr: Steven Donahue

D-U-N-S 80-189-6200
INTERACTIVE COMMUNICATIONS INTERNATIONAL INC
INCOMM
(Suby of INCOMM HOLDINGS INC) ★
250 Williams St Nw # 5000, Atlanta, GA 30303-1032
Tel (770) 240-6100 Founded/Ownrshp 1992
Sales NA EMP 600E
SIC 6099 Clearinghouse associations, bank or check
Pr: M Brooks Smith
COO: Daniel Kahrs
COO: Daniel Pree
*CFO: Scott Meyerhoff
Sr VP: Jeff Lewis
VP: Jerry Cutler
VP: Anne Gillman
Genl Mgr: Reece Fish
Snr Sftwr: Vijay Koirala
Snr Sftwr: Tanmaya Malik
Snr Sftwr: Scott McCall

D-U-N-S 79-283-0184
■ INTERACTIVE DATA CORP
(Suby of ICE) ★
32 Crosby Dr, Bedford, MA 01730-1448
Tel (781) 687-8500 Founded/Ownrshp 1992
Sales 939.2MM EMP 2,600
SIC 6289 7375 Financial reporting; Information retrieval services
Pr: Stephen C Daffron
COO: Jay S Nadler
CFO: Vincent Chippari
CFO: Vincent A Chippari
Sr Cor Off: Andrew Koven
Ex VP: Tim Noble
Ex VP: Bob Skea
Sr VP: Lou J Gehring
VP: Lorin Beatty
VP: Bill Burns
VP: William Burns
VP: Bill Chambers
VP: Julie Craig
VP: Scott Feagans
VP: Lou Gehring
VP: Lydia Klein
VP: Philippe Rasborn
VP: Carol Sweeney
Exec: Neil Rudden

D-U-N-S 11-985-1215
■ INTERACTIVE DATA PRICING AND REFERENCE DATA LLC
(Suby of INTERACTIVE DATA CORP) ★
32 Crosby Dr, Bedford, MA 01730-1448
Tel (781) 687-8800 Founded/Ownrshp 1974
Sales NA EMP 1,765E
SIC 6022 State commercial banks
CEO: Stephen C Daffron
*Pr: Steven Crane
*COO: John King
*CFO: Vincent A Chippari
*VP: Lori Hannay
Mng Dir: James Farrer
Snr Sftwr: Niral Shukla
Snr Ntwrk: Stanley Chua
Snr Ntwrk: Stephen Hew
CTO: Jinping Shi
IT Man: Kaushal Amin

D-U-N-S 08-001-2237
INTERACTIVE HEALTH HOLDINGS CORP
(Suby of FRIEDMAN FLEISCHER & LOWE, LLC)
1700 E Golf Rd Ste 900, Schaumburg, IL 60173-5816
Tel (847) 590-0200 Founded/Ownrshp 2015
Sales 676.0MME EMP 1,977E
SIC 8099 Physical examination & testing services; Health screening service; Physical examination service, insurance
Pr: Cathy Kenworthy

D-U-N-S 80-898-3696
INTERACTIVE HEALTH SOLUTIONS INC
(Suby of INTERACTIVE HEALTH HOLDINGS CORP) ★
1700 E Golf Rd Ste 900, Schaumburg, IL 60173-5816
Tel (866) 279-1636 Founded/Ownrshp 2011
Sales 25.6MME EMP 1,972
SIC 8099 Physical examination & testing services; Health screening service; Physical examination service, insurance
Pr: Cathy Kenworthy
Ex VP: Charlie Estey
*VP: Richard Bi
*VP: Aaron Money
Dir Bus: Elizabeth Lynch
Rgnl Mgr: Alison Furlin
IT Man: Ken Stiple
Sls Mgr: Cathlene Lambert
Snr Mgr: Courtney Schroeder

D-U-N-S 07-829-8647
INTERACTIVE INTELLIGENCE GROUP INC
7601 Interactive Way, Indianapolis, IN 46278-2727
Tel (317) 872-3000 Founded/Ownrshp 2016
Sales 341.3MM EMP 2,309E
SIC 7372 Application computer software
Ch Bd: Donald E Brown
COO: William J Gildea III
CFO: Ashley A Vukovits
Ofcr: Gary R Blough
Ofcr: Thomas J Fisher
Ofcr: Jeff M Platon
Ofcr: Paul F Weber

D-U-N-S 94-114-5153
■ INTERACTIVE INTELLIGENCE INC
(Suby of INTERACTIVE INTELLIGENCE GROUP INC) ★
7601 Interactive Way, Indianapolis, IN 46278-2727
Tel (800) 267-1364 Founded/Ownrshp 1994
Sales 125.4MME EMP 849E
SIC 7372 7371 Application computer software; Custom computer programming services
Ch Bd: Donald E Brown MD
Pr: Bill Gildea
*CFO: Stephen R Head
CFO: Steve Head
*Chf Mktg O: Joseph A Staples
*Ex VP: Gary R Blough
VP: Joe Adams
VP: Gary Blough
*VP: Pamela J Hynes
VP: Pamela Hynes
VP: Douglas T Shinsato
VP: Jeff Swartz
Board of Directors: Richard G Halperin, Edward L Hamburg Phd, Michael C Heim, Mark E Hill, Richard A Reck

INTERACTIVE PRINTER SOLUTIONS
See ICONEX LLC

D-U-N-S 83-812-2950
INTERACTIVE RESPONSE TECHNOLOGIES INC
I R T
(Suby of CYBER CITY TELESERVICES MARKETING INC) ★
895 Sw 30th Ave Ste 201, Pompano Beach, FL 33069-4887
Tel (954) 484-4973 Founded/Ownrshp 2010
Sales 82.7MME EMP 2,700
SIC 7389 Telephone services
Pr: Richard Eychner
CFO: James M Pelky
*Ex VP: Martin J Lehtio II
*Sr VP: Sandra Gobbo
Dir IT: Terry Scott
Web Dev: Ian Jory
Genl Couns: Stephen Ferber

D-U-N-S 00-968-1586 IMP/EXP
■ INTERAMERICAN MOTOR CORP (CA)
IMC
(Suby of AUTOZONE INC) ★
8901 Canoga Ave, Canoga Park, CA 91304-1512
Tel (818) 678-6571 Founded/Ownrshp 1962, 2014
Sales 290.7MME EMP 250
SIC 5013 5599 Automotive supplies & parts; Dune buggies
CEO: John Mosunic
*Treas: Hanns Hederer
*Ex VP: Winfred Baur
VP: John Taillon
Area Mgr: James Loushin
Admn Mgr: Sieclinde Pelaez
Manager: Walt Drechsler

D-U-N-S 04-333-7401 IMP/EXP
INTERBAKE FOODS LLC
NORSE DAIRY SYSTEMS
(Suby of GEORGE WESTON LIMITED)
3951 Westerre Pkwy # 200, Henrico, VA 23233-1312
Tel (804) 755-7107 Founded/Ownrshp 1972
Sales 263.3MME EMP 1,031
SIC 2052 2051 Cookies; Crackers, dry; Bread, cake & related products; Breads, rolls & buns; Cakes, pies & pastries
Pr: Raymond Baxter
VP: Rick Lee
Genl Mgr: Annie Cicinelli
IT Man: Gunther Brinkman
QC Dir: Denise Bullock
Opers Mgr: Will Schleuss
Mktg Mgr: Annie Owens

D-U-N-S 03-635-3530
INTERBANK INC
(Suby of OLNEY BANCSHARES OF TEXAS INC)
4921 N May Ave, Oklahoma City, OK 73112-6041
Tel (580) 928-5511 Founded/Ownrshp 1901, 1976
Sales NA EMP 400
SIC 6712 Bank holding companies
Ch Bd: John T French
Pr: C H Wyatt
CFO: Brad Stieben
Ex VP: Brad Maddoux
Ex VP: Keith Schwandt
Sr VP: Darla Hoffman
VP: Scott Keeney
Genl Mgr: Stephanie Craig

D-U-N-S 00-497-8656 IMP/EXP
INTERBOND CORP OF AMERICA (FL)
BRANDSMART USA
3200 Sw 42nd St, Hollywood, FL 33020
Tel (954) 797-4000 Founded/Ownrshp 1980
Sales 506.9MME EMP 2,400
Accts Kaufman Rossin & Co Pa Miam
SIC 5731 5722 Consumer electronic equipment; High fidelity stereo equipment; Television sets; Video cameras & accessories; Electric household appliances, major
CEO: Robert Perlman
*Pr: Michael Perlman
*Treas: Eric Beazley
Sr VP: Vincent Visco
VP: Eydie Bowe
*VP: Bobby Johnson
*VP: Lary Sinewitz
VP: Ellen Stevens
VP Sls: Neil Anello
Mktg Dir: Lara Aronoff

D-U-N-S 17-333-7445 IMP/EXP
INTERBOND HOLDING CORP
BRANDSMART U.S.A.
3200 Sw 42nd St, Fort Lauderdale, FL 33312-6813
Tel (954) 797-4000 Founded/Ownrshp 1990
Sales 567.0MME EMP 2,100
Accts Kaufman Rossin And Co
SIC 7629 3699 5722 Electrical repair shops; Appliance cords for household electrical equipment; Electric household appliances
Pr: Michael Pearlman

D-U-N-S 07-841-7659
INTERBORO MANAGEMENT INC
155 Mineola Blvd, Mineola, NY 11501-3920
Tel (516) 213-0286 Founded/Ownrshp 2011
Sales NA EMP 135E
SIC 6411 Insurance agents, brokers & service
Pr: David Nichols

D-U-N-S 07-525-6552
■ INTERBRAND CORP
(Suby of OMNICOM GROUP INC) ★
130 5th Ave Fl 4, New York, NY 10011-4305
Tel (212) 798-7500 Founded/Ownrshp 1962
Sales 105.8MME EMP 800
SIC 8742 7336 Marketing consulting services; Package design
CEO: Jez Frampton
*Pr: David Martin
CEO: Josh Feldmeth
CEO: Beth Viner
*CFO: James Bruce
*CFO: Kelly Gall
CFO: Patrice Quemoun
Ofcr: Leslie Butterfield
Ofcr: Andy Payne
*VP: Pawel Tulin
Creative D: Steve Leder
Creative D: Andreas Rotzler

D-U-N-S 61-137-2681
■ INTERCEPT INC
INTERCEPT PAYMENT SOLUTIONS
(Suby of FIS) ★
3150 Holcomb Bridge Rd, Norcross, GA 30071-1330
Tel (770) 248-9600 Founded/Ownrshp 2006
Sales NA EMP 1,600
SIC 6099 7374 Electronic funds transfer network, including switching; Data processing & preparation
Ch Bd: William P Foley II
*CFO: Al Stinson
VP Opers: Charlie Honaker

INTERCEPT PAYMENT SOLUTIONS
See INTERCEPT INC

D-U-N-S 09-972-0724 IMP
INTERCERAMIC INC
INTERCRAMIC TILE STONE GALLERY
(Suby of INTERNACIONAL DE CERAMICA, S.A.B. DE C.V.)
2333 S Jupiter Rd, Garland, TX 75041-6007
Tel (214) 503-4967 Founded/Ownrshp 1995
Sales 174.5MME EMP 650
SIC 3253 5032 Ceramic wall & floor tile; Tile, structural clay
CEO: Victor Almeida
*Ex VP: Steve Belken

**Ex VP:* Humberto Maese
**Sr VP:* Edmeerto Maese
Dir IT: Manuel Ic-Rada
Opers Mgr: Frank Gomez
Opers Mgr: Todd Wilkinson
S&M/VP: Kory Bowling
Sls Mgr: Elizabeth Ballesteros
Sls Mgr: Kevin Deaton
Sls Mgr: Deanna Ellington

D-U-N-S 07-521-9113
INTERCHURCH MEDICAL ASSISTANCE INC (MD)
I.M.A.
1730 M St Nw Ste 1100, Washington, DC 20036-4500
Tel (202) 888-6200 *Founded/Ownrshp* 1960
Sales 162.9MM^E *EMP* 150
Accts Raffa Pc Washington Dc
SIC 8661 Religious organizations
Ch: Lisa Rothenberger
**CEO:* Richard Santos
**CFO:* Tracey Stevens
**Treas:* William C Clarke
Ofcr: Sarah Craciunoiu
Ofcr: Ramatou Hassane
Assoc Dir: Christopher Glass

D-U-N-S 92-885-0759
INTERCOASTAL HEALTH SYSTEMS INC
1309 N Flagler Dr, West Palm Beach, FL 33401-3406
Tel (561) 650-6272 *Founded/Ownrshp* 2001
Sales 190.1M *EMP* 3,100
SIC 8741 8069 Hospital management; Nursing & personal care facility management; Specialty hospitals, except psychiatric
CEO: Robert Freymuller
CFO: Oscar Fernandez

INTERCOMMUNITY HEALTH NETWORK
See INTERCOMMUNITY HEALTH PLANS INC

D-U-N-S 04-904-2398
INTERCOMMUNITY HEALTH PLANS INC
INTERCOMMUNITY HEALTH NETWORK
3600 Nw Samaritan Dr, Corvallis, OR 97330-3737
Tel (541) 757-5111 *Founded/Ownrshp* 1993
Sales 256.2MM *EMP* 10
Accts Kpmg Llp
SIC 8099 Medical services organization
Pr: Kelly Kaiser

D-U-N-S 12-159-1358
INTERCON CONSTRUCTION INC
INTERCON ENERGY SERVICES
5512 State Rd 19 & 113, Waunakee, WI 53597-9530
Tel (608) 850-4820 *Founded/Ownrshp* 1984
Sales 165.2MM *EMP* 625
Accts Sva Certified Public Accountan
SIC 1623 Oil & gas line & compressor station construction; Oil & gas pipeline construction; Communication line & transmission tower construction; Cable laying construction
Pr: Anna Hillebrandt
Pr: Chris Wozniak
**Treas:* Jamie De Bruin
VP: Jamie Debruin
**VP:* Jeff Hillebrandt
Sfty Dirs: Tim Knaup
VP Mktg: Steve Allen
Board of Directors: Jamie De Bruin, Gail Deveau

INTERCON ENERGY SERVICES
See INTERCON CONSTRUCTION INC

INTERCONTINENTAL CELLULOSE SLS
See EKMAN & CO INC

D-U-N-S 07-887-0113
▲ INTERCONTINENTAL EXCHANGE INC
ICE
5660 New Northside Dr # 300, Atlanta, GA 30328-5823
Tel (770) 857-4700 *Founded/Ownrshp* 2000
Sales 3.3MMM *EMP* 5,549
Tkr Sym ICE *Exch* NYS
SIC 6231 Security & commodity exchanges
Ch Bd: Jeffrey C Sprecher
Pr: Charles A Vice
CFO: Scott A Hill
Dir Sec: David S Goone
Board of Directors: Charles R Crisp, William J Hague, Fred W Hatfield, Thomas E Noonan, Frederic V Salerno, Judith A Sprieser, Vincent Tese

D-U-N-S 83-569-1841
■ INTERCONTINENTAL EXCHANGE INC
ICE
(*Suby of* ICE) ★
1415 Moonstone, Brea, CA 92821-2832
Tel (770) 857-4700 *Founded/Ownrshp* 2000
Sales 3.0MMM *EMP* 2,902
SIC 6231 Security & commodity exchanges
Ch Bd: Jeffrey C Sprecher
Pr: Ben Jackson
Pr: Bruce Tupper
Pr: Brad Vannan
Pr: Charles A Vice
CFO: Scott A Hill
Sr VP: Edwin D Marcial
Sr VP: Jonathan H Short
Prin: Charles R Crisp
Prin: Jean-Marc Forneri
Prin: Judd A Gregg

D-U-N-S 60-236-2931 IMP/EXP
INTERCONTINENTAL EXPORT IMPORT INC
I E I
8815 Centre Park Dr # 400, Columbia, MD 21045-2282
Tel (410) 674-5600 *Founded/Ownrshp* 1984
Sales 135.6MM^E *EMP* 70
SIC 5162 Plastics products
CEO: Saurabh Naik
**CFO:* Srinath Dharmapadam
**VP:* Rajiv Naik
Software D: Vinit Dedhia
Snr Mgr: Saureen Desai

D-U-N-S 12-598-7318 IMP
INTERCONTINENTAL HOTELS GROUP RESOURCES INC
(*Suby of* INTERCONTINENTAL HOTELS LIMITED)
3 Ravinia Dr Ste 100, Atlanta, GA 30346-2121
Tel (770) 604-5000 *Founded/Ownrshp* 1997
Sales 3.6MMM^E *EMP* 60,000
SIC 7011 8741 6794 Hotels & motels; Business management; Financial management for business; Hotel or motel management; Franchises, selling or licensing
CEO: Kirk Kinsell
Pr: Mindy Cohen
**CFO:* Robert Gunkel
Ofcr: Damali Stansbury
VP: Michael Torres
Exec: Joe Buentello
Exec: Rene Oskam
Comm Dir: Emma Corcoran
Prgrm Mgr: Amy Takahashi
Area Mgr: Lisa Britton
Genl Mgr: Chandra Badola

D-U-N-S 01-358-2069
INTERCOUNTY APPLIANCE CORP
10 National Blvd, Medford, NY 11763-2253
Tel (631) 543-6900 *Founded/Ownrshp* 1956
Sales 94.4MM^E *EMP* 85
SIC 5064 Electric household appliances
Pr: Vito Blandi
**VP:* Robert Stevens
Board of Directors: Richard Merhige

INTERCRAMIC TILE STONE GALLERY
See INTERCERAMIC INC

D-U-N-S 17-842-7910
INTERDENT INC
SMILE KEEPERS
(*Suby of* HIG MIDDLE MARKET LLC) ★
9800 S La Cienega Blvd # 800, Inglewood, CA 90301-4442
Tel (310) 765-2400 *Founded/Ownrshp* 2012
Sales 116.3MM^E *EMP* 1,800
SIC 8021 Dentists' office
Pr: Ivar S Chhina
COO: Scott Bremen
**CFO:* Robert W Hill
CFO: Scott R McCloud
VP: Judy Dunbar
VP: Karen Feldman
Rgnl Mgr: Cathy Lee
**CIO:* Lee Rouman
Counsel: Megan Wallace

D-U-N-S 79-210-1024
INTERDENT SERVICE CORP
(*Suby of* SMILE KEEPERS) ★
9800 S La Cienega Blvd # 800, Inglewood, CA 90301-4442
Tel (310) 765-2400 *Founded/Ownrshp* 1999
Sales 60.6MM^E *EMP* 1,700
SIC 8021 Dental clinics & offices
CEO: Marshal Salomon
**CFO:* Jeff Hertzig
Sr VP: Kevin Webb

D-U-N-S 07-112-6072 IMP/EXP
INTERDESIGN INC (OH)
SWISSTECH PRODUCTS
30725 Solon Indus Pkwy, Solon, OH 44139-4380
Tel (440) 248-0136 *Founded/Ownrshp* 1974
Sales 183.2MM^E *EMP* 280
SIC 5023 Home furnishings
Pr: Robert Immerman
Ex VP: Chris Banning
Sr VP: Joyce Libman
VP: Ross Neaffer
VP: Jason Shefrin
**VP:* Robert Woolnough
Exec: Moore Marjie
IT Man: Lesli Kelley
IT Man: Debi Sapolin
Natl Sales: Sarah Kutz
VP Sls: Dave Savchuk

D-U-N-S 80-632-9855
▲ INTERDIGITAL INC
200 Bellevue Pkwy Ste 300, Wilmington, DE 19809-3727
Tel (302) 281-3600 *Founded/Ownrshp* 1972
Sales 441.4MM *EMP* 330^E
Tkr Sym IDCC *Exch* NGS
SIC 3663 5999 6794 Mobile communication equipment; Mobile telephones & equipment; Patent owners & lessors
Pr: William J Merritt
**Ch Bd:* S Douglas Hutcheson
CFO: Richard J Brezski
Ex VP: Jannie K Lau
Ex VP: James J Nolan
Exec: Scott A McQuilkin
Exec: Lawrence F Shay

D-U-N-S 87-432-2860 IMP
■ INTERFACE AMERICAS INC
(*Suby of* INTERFACE INC) ★
2859 Pcs Frry St 2000, Atlanta, GA 30339
Tel (770) 437-6800 *Founded/Ownrshp* 2000
Sales 335.9MM^E *EMP* 1,800
SIC 2273 Carpets & rugs
Pr: John R Wells
**CFO:* Patrick C Lynch
**Treas:* Keith Wright
IT Man: Brian Moran
Mktg Dir: Kristy Sherlund

D-U-N-S 82-641-9280
INTERFACE FLOORING SYSTEMS INC
2859 Paces Ferry Rd Se, Atlanta, GA 30339-5701
Tel (800) 336-0225 *Founded/Ownrshp* 1987
Sales 602.2M^E *EMP* 1,000
SIC 3272 1771 3999 Floor slabs & tiles, precast concrete; Flooring contractor; Atomizers, toiletry
CEO: John R Wells
**CFO:* Patrick C Lynch

D-U-N-S 06-453-9372 IMP/EXP
▲ INTERFACE INC
2859 Paces Ferry Rd Se # 2000, Atlanta, GA 30339-6216
Tel (770) 437-6800 *Founded/Ownrshp* 1973
Sales 1.0MMM *EMP* 3,346
Tkr Sym TILE *Exch* NGS
SIC 2273 Carpets & rugs
Ch Bd: Daniel T Hendrix
**Pr:* Jay D Gould
CFO: Patrick C Lynch
Chf Mktg O: Jo Ann Herold
Ofcr: Matthew J Miller
Ofcr: Kathleen R Owen
Ofcr: Nigel Stansfield
Sr VP: Robert Boogaard
Sr VP: Robert A Coombs
Sr VP: Raymond S Willoch
VP: Sanjay Lall
Board of Directors: John P Burke, Andrew B Cogan, Carl I Gable, Christopher G Kennedy, K David Kohler, James B Miller Jr, Sheryl D Palmer

D-U-N-S 92-608-1712 EXP
INTERFACE PERFORMANCE MATERIALS INC
216 Wohlsen Way, Lancaster, PA 17603-4043
Tel (717) 390-1886 *Founded/Ownrshp* 2012
Sales 176.1MM^E *EMP* 400
SIC 3053 Gasket materials
Pr: Victor Swint
CFO: Bob Rathsam
Ex VP: Louis J Dannibale
Genl Mgr: Bill Cassidy
Dir IT: Jeff Barrall
Plnt Mgr: Lee Ketterman

D-U-N-S 14-706-2681
INTERFACE SECURITY SYSTEMS LLC
3773 Corporate Centre Dr, Earth City, MO 63045-1130
Tel (314) 595-0100 *Founded/Ownrshp* 1998
Sales 246.7MM^E *EMP* 538
SIC 4813
CEO: Michael Shaw
**COO:* Michael McLeod
**CFO:* Ken Obermeyer
**Ex VP:* Chuck Moeling
**Ex VP:* Matt Stopa
CTO: Beverly Henson
Natl Sales: Kathie Milton
Mktg Mgr: Don Meadows
Sls Mgr: Jimmy Bordelon
Sls Mgr: Mike Sawyer
Sales Asso: Dave Schafer

D-U-N-S 60-663-3907 IMP/EXP
■ INTERFACEFLOR LLC
(*Suby of* INTERFACE INC) ★
1503 Orchard Hill Rd, Lagrange, GA 30240-5709
Tel (706) 882-1891 *Founded/Ownrshp* 1981
Sales 367.0MM *EMP* 1,500
SIC 2273 Finishers of tufted carpets & rugs
VP: Cindi Oakey
Exec: Shannon Deluca
Exec: Mike Gutierrez
Exec: Joan Holda
CTO: Him Logan
IT Man: Brian Moran
IT Man: Gary Skinner
IT Man: Tony Smart
MIS Mgr: Dimitri Sergeev
VP Mktg: Kristy Sherlund

D-U-N-S 07-616-0449
INTERFAITH MEDICAL CENTER
1545 Atlantic Ave, Brooklyn, NY 11213-1122
Tel (718) 613-4000 *Founded/Ownrshp* 1982
Sales 147.2MM *EMP* 1,550
SIC 8062 General medical & surgical hospitals
CEO: Venra Glicpsman
COO: Amini McIntosh
CFO: Gregory Dixon
VP: Gwendolyn Lewis
**Prin:* Gregory Dickson
**Prin:* Edward Glicpsman
CIO: Sarooq Ajmal
Mtls Mgr: Peter Wong
Ansthlgy: Samir S Bassily
Pharmcst: Chihong Lin
Pharmcst: Joseph Pipiton

D-U-N-S 05-421-8938
■ INTERFINANCIAL INC
(*Suby of* ASSURANT INC) ★
28 Liberty St Fl 41, New York, NY 10005-1449
Tel (212) 859-7000 *Founded/Ownrshp* 1980
Sales 199.4MM^E *EMP* 4,100
SIC 6719 Investment holding companies, except banks
CEO: Kerry Clayton
IT Man: William Henson

INTERFINISH
See CHICAGO METALLIC CORP

D-U-N-S 07-850-3454
INTERFOOD INC
(*Suby of* INTERFOOD HOLDING B.V.)
777 Brickell Ave Ste 702, Miami, FL 33131-2866
Tel (786) 953-8320 *Founded/Ownrshp* 2006
Sales 238.6MM *EMP* 25
SIC 5143 Butter
Ch Bd: Frank Van Stipdonk
**Pr:* Jason Medcalf
**V Ch Bd:* F C G M Van Stipdonk
**VP:* Johannes Van De Hueval

D-U-N-S 11-519-1322
INTERFOODS OF AMERICA INC
9500 S Dadeland Blvd # 800, Miami, FL 33156-2852
Tel (305) 670-0746 *Founded/Ownrshp* 1996
Sales 117.6MM^E *EMP* 3,576
SIC 5812 6794 Fast-food restaurant, chain; Chicken restaurant; Franchises, selling or licensing
Ch Bd: Robert S Berg
**COO:* Steven M Wemple
**CFO:* Francis X Maloney
Exec: Robert Sanford
Area Mgr: Gavert Bucknor

Area Supr: Sharon Mann
Dist Mgr: Richard Thomason
Dir IT: Bryan McKinney
Sls&Mrk Ex: Mark Reineri

D-U-N-S 16-725-4486 IMP/EXP
INTERFOR US INC
(*Suby of* INTERFOR CORPORATION)
2211 Rimland Dr Ste 220, Bellingham, WA 98226-8654
Tel (360) 788-2299 *Founded/Ownrshp* 2004
Sales 586.3MM^E *EMP* 3,400
SIC 0811 2421 5031 Timber tracts; Lumber: rough, sawed or planed; Lumber, plywood & millwork; Lumber: rough, dressed & finished
Pr: Duncan K Davies
**Treas:* Norm Chow
**Sr VP:* John A Horning
**VP:* J Steven Hofer
**VP:* Otto F Schulte
**VP:* Richard J Slaco
**VP:* Mark Stock

D-U-N-S 05-515-7903
INTERGRAPH CORP
INTERGRAPH PROCESS POWER & MAR
(*Suby of* HEXAGON AB)
305 Intergraph Way, Madison, AL 35758-7567
Tel (256) 730-2000 *Founded/Ownrshp* 1969, 2010
Sales 937.1MM^E *EMP* 4,000
SIC 7372 7373 7379 Application computer software; Computer integrated systems design; Computer related consulting services
CEO: Ola Rollen
**Pr:* Gerhard Sallinger
COO: Scott Moore
**CFO:* Steven Cost
Ex VP: Melanie Eakes
Ex VP: Charles Evans
Ex VP: Patrick Holcomb
Ex VP: John Ilhoite
VP: Swanner Christie
VP: Ron Davis
VP: Glen Gilkey
VP: Horst Harbauer
VP: Bart Hoogenraad
VP: Steve Marz
VP: Rob Mott
VP: Robert Mott
VP: Brad Robbins
VP: Daniel Siwko
VP: Dave Stinson
VP: Bryan Urquhart
Exec: David Hill

INTERGRAPH PROCESS POWER & MAR
See INTERGRAPH CORP

D-U-N-S 06-510-6460
INTERHEALTH CORP
PIH HEALTH
12401 Washington Blvd, Whittier, CA 90602-1006
Tel (562) 698-0811 *Founded/Ownrshp* 1959
Sales 15.0MM *EMP* 1,400
Accts Deloitte Tax Llp San Diego C
SIC 8062 8011 General medical & surgical hospitals; Offices & clinics of medical doctors
Ch Bd: Jane Dicus
**V Ch:* Richard Atwood
**Treas:* Kenton Woods
**VP:* Ronald Yoshihara
CIO: Jim Pelgrin

D-U-N-S 61-465-4804
INTERIM HEALTHCARE INC
INTERIM SERVICES
(*Suby of* THE HALIFAX GROUP LLC)
1601 Swgrs Corp Pkwy # 100, Sunrise, FL 33323-2827
Tel (800) 338-7786 *Founded/Ownrshp* 2012
Sales 509.6MM^E *EMP* 2,548^E
SIC 6794 7363 8082 Franchises, selling or licensing; Medical help service; Home health care services
Pr: Kathleen Gilmartin
CFO: Bill Bologna
**Sec:* Michael Slupecki
**V Ch Bd:* Allan C Sorensen
Sr VP: Jane Hinton
VP: Paula Bergman
VP: Kelli Coursey
**VP:* Max Hahnen
VP: David Haslup
**VP:* Barbara Mc Cann
VP: Michael Moran
**VP:* Satish Movva
VP: Charyl Schroeder
VP: Phyllis Sholar
VP: Steven Turner
VP: Ray Umansky
VP: Keith Walsh
Exec: Kristy Brown
Dir Risk M: Dwight E Garner
Dir Bus: Joette Springle
Dir Bus: Sara Watson

D-U-N-S 19-672-8075
INTERIM HOME HEALTHCARE CO
INTERIM SERVICES
2526 Ward Blvd, Wilson, NC 27893-1600
Tel (252) 243-7808 *Founded/Ownrshp* 1988
Sales 56.1MM^E *EMP* 3,000
SIC 8082 Home health care services
Pr: John Morris
**Sec:* June Piper
**VP:* Lisa Morris

INTERIM SERVICES
See SALO INC

INTERIM SERVICES
See INTERIM HOME HEALTHCARE CO

INTERIM SERVICES
See INTERIM HEALTHCARE INC

D-U-N-S 13-051-7766
INTERIOR ARCHITECTS INC
IA
500 Sansome St Ste 8th, San Francisco, CA 94111-3211
Tel (415) 434-3305 *Founded/Ownrshp* 1984
Sales 96.7MM *EMP* 500

SIC 8712

INTERIOR EXTERIOR BUILDING SUP
See INTERIOR/EXTERIOR BUILDING SUPPLY LIMITED PARTNERSHIP

INTERIOR INVESTMENTS
See I3 GROUP INC

D-U-N-S 08-042-8640
INTERIOR LOGIC GROUP INC (GA)
3050 Peachtree Rd Nw, Atlanta, GA 30305-2212
Tel (770) 560-7186 Founded/Ownrshp 2014
Sales 6.7MM[E] EMP 1,000
SIC 7389 Interior design services
CFO: Lee Robinson
*CEO: Mark Fikse

D-U-N-S 10-317-2961 IMP
INTERIOR SPECIALISTS INC
(Suby of FARADAY HOLDINGS LLC)
1630 Faraday Ave, Carlsbad, CA 92008-7313
Tel (760) 929-6700 Founded/Ownrshp 2014
Sales 449.4MM[E] EMP 2,639
SIC 1752 1799 Carpet laying; Drapery track installation
Pr: Alan Davenport
Pr: Brian Reed
Pr: Lee Singer
Pr: Joe Terrana
Pr: Tom Tidmore
*CFO: Robert Hess
*Sr VP: Randy Bafus
*Sr VP: Dennis Crowley
*Sr VP: Pat Crowley
VP: John McMillen
Exec: Holly Newland

D-U-N-S 03-440-8617
INTERIOR/EXTERIOR BUILDING SUPPLY LIMITED PARTNERSHIP
INTERIOR EXTERIOR BUILDING SUP
727 S Cortez St, New Orleans, LA 70119-6908
Tel (504) 488-1998 Founded/Ownrshp 1965
Sales 173.8MM[E] EMP 130
SIC 5031 Building materials, exterior; Building materials, interior
Pt: James Geary
Brnch Mgr: Scott Broussard
Brnch Mgr: Tim Landry
DP Exec: Shannon Hill
Sales Asso: Greg Pitcher

D-U-N-S 61-873-6557
INTERLAKE HOLDING CO
1 Landmark Sq Ste 710, Stamford, CT 06901-2670
Tel (203) 977-8900 Founded/Ownrshp 1987
Sales 118.4MM EMP 25
Accts Grant Thornton Llp Cleveland
SIC 4449 4499 Intracoastal (freight) transportation; Boat & ship rental & leasing, except pleasure
Ch Bd: Paul R Tregurtha
Pr: James R Barker
VP: Robert F Dorn
VP: John Hopkins

D-U-N-S 12-101-7771 IMP/EXP
INTERLAKE MECALUX INC
(Suby of MECALUX, SA)
1600 N 25th Ave, Melrose Park, IL 60160-1868
Tel (708) 344-9999 Founded/Ownrshp 2000
Sales 419.8MM[E] EMP 650
SIC 5084 2542 Industrial machinery & equipment; Partitions & fixtures, except wood
Pr: Angel De Arriba
CFO: Susan Elizabeth
VP: Javier Carrillo
VP: Vinnie Depaola
VP: Kyle Middleton
Genl Mgr: Daniel Joly
Genl Mgr: Tim Kelleher
CTO: Vinod Rodrigo
Dir IT: Pete Deckert
Dir IT: Kryzsztof Zygulski
IT Man: John Meile

D-U-N-S 06-889-0011
INTERLAKE STEAMSHIP CO
(Suby of INTERLAKE HOLDING CO) ★
7300 Engle Rd, Middleburg Heights, OH 44130-3429
Tel (440) 260-6900 Founded/Ownrshp 1913
Sales 118.4MM EMP 25
SIC 4432 Freight transportation on the Great Lakes
Ch: James R Barker
*Pr: Mark W Barker
*CFO: Andrew Langlois
CFO: William Thornton
*V Ch Bd: Paul R Tregurtha
Ofcr: Kevin Czekanski
*Sr VP: Robert F Dorn
Opers Mgr: Chad Kidder
Opers Mgr: Phil Moore

D-U-N-S 61-193-7053
INTERLEMO USA INC
(Suby of LEMO S.A.)
635 Park Ct, Rohnert Park, CA 94928-7940
Tel (707) 578-8811 Founded/Ownrshp 1986
Sales 85.8MM[E] EMP 101
SIC 5065 Connectors, electronic
Genl Mgr: Peter Mueller
Mktg Dir: Joachim Vobis

D-U-N-S 08-079-2989 IMP
■ **INTERLINE BRANDS INC**
SUPPLY WORKS
(Suby of INTERLINE BRANDS INC) ★
801 W Bay St, Jacksonville, FL 32204-1605
Tel (904) 421-1400 Founded/Ownrshp 2000
Sales 2.3MMM[E] EMP 4,000[E]
SIC 5074 5063 5072 Plumbing fittings & supplies; Electrical fittings & construction materials; Hardware
Ch Bd: Michael J Grebe
Pr: Fred Odell
*CEO: Kenneth D Sweder
*CFO: Federico Pensotti
*CFO: Tom Tossavainen
*Treas: John Ebner
*Sr VP: Kevin O'Meara
*Sr VP: William R Pray
VP: Michael Agliata
*VP: Laurence W Howard
VP: Jay Polekoff
VP: Per E Sorensen
VP: Jim Spahn
Board of Directors: Gideon Argov, Michael E Dedomenico, John J Gavin, Barry J Goldstein, Ernest K Jacquet, Christopher W Santoro, Drew T Sawyer

D-U-N-S 36-111-2936 IMP/EXP
■ **INTERLINE BRANDS INC**
(Suby of HOME DEPOT THE) ★
701 San Marco Blvd, Jacksonville, FL 32207-8175
Tel (904) 421-1400 Founded/Ownrshp 2015
Sales 2.5MMM[E] EMP 1,001
SIC 5074 5063 5072 Plumbing fittings & supplies; Electrical fittings & construction materials; Hardware
Pr: Kenneth D Sweder
COO: Kenneth Sweder
CFO: Federico Pensotti
Chf Mktg O: Jonathan S Bennett
VP: Michael Agliata
VP: D J Christensen
VP: Chad Kluko
VP: Annette A Ricciuti
Genl Mgr: Ran Garver
Genl Mgr: Julie Kobliska
Snr Sftwr: Jarrel Cobb

D-U-N-S 10-213-4178 IMP/EXP
INTERLOCK INDUSTRIES INC
545 S 3rd St Ste 310, Louisville, KY 40202-1936
Tel (502) 569-2007 Founded/Ownrshp 1982
Sales 359.4MM[E] EMP 1,000
SIC 3341 4121 3444 3354 2653

D-U-N-S 00-521-4077 IMP
INTERMATIC INC
7777 Winn Rd, Spring Grove, IL 60081-9698
Tel (815) 675-2321 Founded/Ownrshp 1891
Sales 236.1MM[E] EMP 795
SIC 3612 3645 Line voltage regulators; Residential lighting fixtures
Pr: David Schroeder
*Ch Bd: Douglas M Kinney Sr
COO: Daniel Dallemolle
Ex VP: Lenay Tenburn
VP: James R Bohn
VP: Linnea T Bruin
VP: Oscar Ibarra
VP: Gary Koetters
VP: William Sommers
Exec: David Hawthorne
Exec: Connie Kinsch
Exec: Jennifer Reed
Exec: Paul Surczyn

D-U-N-S 79-924-6558 IMP
■ **INTERMEC INC**
(Suby of HONEYWELL INTERNATIONAL INC) ★
16201 25th Ave W, Lynnwood, WA 98087-2520
Tel (425) 348-2600 Founded/Ownrshp 2013
Sales 798.6MM[E] EMP 2,312
SIC 3577 Computer peripheral equipment; Bar code (magnetic ink) printers; Optical scanning devices
Ch Bd: Allen J Lauer
CFO: Robert J Driessnack
CFO: Lanny H Michael
Sr VP: Yukio Morikubo
Sr VP: Earl R Thompson
VP: Timothy Breidenbaugh
VP: Larry N Colson
VP: David W Danjczek
VP: Peter Fausel
VP: Larry Klimczyk
VP: John Orourke
VP: Ian Snadden

D-U-N-S 00-490-8729 IMP
■ **INTERMEC TECHNOLOGIES CORP** (WA)
(Suby of INTERMEC INC) ★
16201 25th Ave W, Lynnwood, WA 98087-2520
Tel (425) 348-2600 Founded/Ownrshp 1966, 1997
Sales 675.3MM[E] EMP 1,745
SIC 3577 2759 Computer peripheral equipment; Printers, computer; Optical scanning devices; Readers, sorters or inscribers, magnetic ink; Labels & seals: printing
Pr: John Waldron
*Treas: John J Tus
VP: Scott Anderson
*VP: Michael Colwell
VP: Bob Driessnack
VP: Earl Thompson
VP: David Yung
Prin: Gene Shultice
Rgnl Mgr: Tracey Jones IV
Snr Sftwr: Tony Carter
Sftwr Eng: Peter Girodat
Board of Directors: Michael Keane

D-U-N-S 17-507-1398
■ **INTERMEDIA COMMUNICATIONS INC**
(Suby of VERIZON BUSINESS GLOBAL LLC) ★
3608 Queen Palm Dr, Tampa, FL 33619-1317
Tel (800) 940-0011 Founded/Ownrshp 2006
Sales 413.4MM[E] EMP 5,073
SIC 4813 Local & long distance telephone communications; Voice telephone communications; Data telephone communications;
Pr: David C Ruberg
Pr: James M Walters
Pr: Jeanne M Walters
CFO: Robert M Manning
Sr VP: Richard J Buyens
Sr VP: James F Geiger
VP: Particia A Kurlin
VP: Dick Marchant
VP: Mark Tubb
CIO: Ruben Lopez
VP Pub Rls: Barbara L Samson

D-U-N-S 80-940-9647
INTERMEDIX CORP
6451 N Federal Hwy # 1000, Fort Lauderdale, FL 33308-1424
Tel (954) 308-8700 Founded/Ownrshp 2005
Sales 275.0MM[E] EMP 2,000
SIC 7372 Business oriented computer software
CEO: Joel Portice
Pr: Mike McHale
Pr: Brad Pond
*COO: Ken Cooke
COO: Kenneth Cooke
*CFO: Michael Wallace
Ex VP: Randy Keller
Ex VP: Dave Poole
Ex VP: David Poole
Sr VP: Michael Brook
Sr VP: Jack Donahue
Sr VP: Bryan Kaplan
Sr VP: Pamela Krop
Sr VP: Dan Pope
Sr VP: Calvin Rogers
VP: Karen Alford
VP: B J Guillot
VP: Darryl Hartung
VP: Pamela Olkowski
VP: Omar Perez
VP: William Ryan
Board of Directors: Thomas H Lee

D-U-N-S 12-091-9766 IMP
INTERMET CORP
301 Commerce St Ste 2901, Fort Worth, TX 76102-4122
Tel (817) 348-9190 Founded/Ownrshp 2005
Sales 341.4MM[E] EMP 2,337
SIC 3321 3714 3462 3365 3364 Ductile iron castings; Motor vehicle parts & accessories; Automotive forgings, ferrous: crankshaft, engine, axle, etc.; Aluminum & aluminum-based alloy castings; Magnesium & magnesium-base alloy die-castings
Pr: Jeff Mihalic
Pr: Robert Axe
Pr: Troy Jonas
Pr: Eric Showalter
CFO: William H Whalen
Ofcr: Bob Flaherty
Sls Dir: Kyle Klein
Counsel: Alan J Miller

D-U-N-S 00-303-2752 IMP/EXP
INTERMETRO INDUSTRIES CORP
(Suby of ALI GROUP NORTH AMERICA CORP) ★
651 N Washington St, Wilkes Barre, PA 18705-1799
Tel (570) 825-2741 Founded/Ownrshp 1998, 2015
Sales 560.5MM[E] EMP 1,500
SIC 3496 2542 3537 3411 3315 2441 Miscellaneous fabricated wire products; Shelving, made from purchased wire; Grocery carts, made from purchased wire; Cabinets: show, display or storage: except wood; Dollies (hand or power trucks), industrial except mining; Metal cans; Steel wire & related products; Nailed wood boxes & shook
Pr: John Nackley
Treas: Don McAlonan
VP: Tom Uells
VP: Tom Youells
Dir IT: James Kilgallon
QC Dir: Wayne Scott
Mktg Mgr: Dave Salus

D-U-N-S 17-063-2405
INTERMOOR INC
101 Youngswood Rd, Morgan City, LA 70380-2276
Tel (985) 385-3083 Founded/Ownrshp 2004
Sales 236.2MM[E] EMP 120[E]
SIC 1381 Drilling oil & gas wells
Pr: Thomas Fulton
*Pr: Chuck Minton
*VP: Larry Puckett
*VP: Scott Thomas
IT Man: Ramus Martin
Ql Cn Mgr: Amy Clemons

D-U-N-S 00-880-1797
■ **INTERMOUNTAIN ELECTRIC INC**
IME
(Suby of QUANTA SERVICES INC) ★
5050 Osage St Ste 500, Denver, CO 80221-7822
Tel (303) 733-7248 Founded/Ownrshp 1946, 1999
Sales 123.6MM[E] EMP 400
SIC 1542 8742 3671 Commercial & office building contractors; Construction project management consultant; Cathode ray tubes, including rebuilt
Pr: Tom Allen
Ex VP: Lee Brown
*VP: Jason Clay
*VP: David Hoyt
VP: Steve Miller
*VP: Tom Pourchot
Exec: Terri Duran
Dir IT: Fritz Fruend

D-U-N-S 17-795-0441 IMP/EXP
INTERMOUNTAIN ELECTRONICS INC OF PRICE UTAH
1511 S Highway 6, Price, UT 84501-7408
Tel (435) 637-7160 Founded/Ownrshp 1985
Sales 86.0MM EMP 143
SIC 3699 5063

D-U-N-S 00-895-4380 IMP
INTERMOUNTAIN FARMERS ASSOCIATION
I F A
1147 W 2100 S, South Salt Lake, UT 84119-1563
Tel (801) 972-2122 Founded/Ownrshp 1915
Sales 214.0MM EMP 400[E]
SIC 5999 5191

D-U-N-S 18-191-2262
■ **INTERMOUNTAIN GAS CO**
IGC
(Suby of MDU RESOURCES GROUP INC) ★
555 S Cole Rd, Boise, ID 83709-0940
Tel (208) 377-6000 Founded/Ownrshp 2008
Sales 101.3MM[E] EMP 210[E]
SIC 4924 Natural gas distribution
Ch Bd: Richard Hokin
*Pr: William C Glynn
*CEO: Nicole A Kivisto
*Ex VP: Scott Madison
*VP: Mark Chiles
VP: Diane Petersen
Dir Risk M: Gary Panter
Genl Mgr: Mike McGrath
IT Man: Fred Leakeas
Sfty Mgr: Robert Peterson
Opers Mgr: Charles Haszier

D-U-N-S 02-203-9596
INTERMOUNTAIN HEALTH CARE HEALTH SERVICES
INTERMOUNTAIN MEDICAL CENTER
5121 S Cottonwood St, Murray, UT 84107-5701
Tel (801) 507-5358 Founded/Ownrshp 2007
Sales 2.1MMM[E] EMP 30,000
SIC 8011

D-U-N-S 07-295-5503
INTERMOUNTAIN HEALTH CARE INC
IHC HEALTH SERVICES
36 S State St Ste 1600, Salt Lake City, UT 84111-1441
Tel (801) 442-2000 Founded/Ownrshp 1975
Sales 6.0MMM EMP 36,000
Accts Kpmg Llp Salt Lake City Ut
SIC 8062 General medical & surgical hospitals
Pr: Marc Harrison
*Ch Bd: Scott Anderson
COO: Keith Alexander
*COO: Laura S Kaiser
COO: Gary Pherson
CFO: Brian Hickenlooper
CFO: Ron Jensen
CFO: Jeremiah Radandt
*V Ch Bd: Bruce Reese
Trst: Penny S Brooke
Trst: Clark D Ivory
Trst: Edward G Kleyn
Trst: Joann B Seghini
Ofcr: Dean Lin
VP: Phyliss Domm
*VP: Douglas J Hammer
VP: Larry D Hancock
VP: Kim Henrichsen
VP: Terri Kane
VP: Mikelle Moore
VP: John Rich
Board of Directors: Merrill Gappmayer, F Ann Millner Ph D, Scott Anderson, Robert H Garff, Joann B Seghini Ph D, Teresa Beck, Elizabeth Hammond MD, Richard R Price MD, Douglas C Black, Randy Horiuchi, Bruce T Reese, Mark R Briesacher MD, Rebecca Chavez-Houck, Marc R Udall MD, Penny S Brooke, Clark Ivory, Jane Carule, Linda C Leckman MD, Daniel W Davis MD, Lawrence S Lewin, Spencer F Eccles, Kent H Murdock, Irene S Fisher, Robert Parsons

D-U-N-S 09-932-5060
INTERMOUNTAIN INDUSTRIES INC
555 S Cole Rd, Boise, ID 83709-0940
Tel (208) 377-6000 Founded/Ownrshp 1984
Sales 147.9MM[E] EMP 450
SIC 4924 Natural gas distribution
Ch Bd: Richard Hokin
Pr: William C Glynn
Ofcr: Linda Murray

INTERMOUNTAIN MEDICAL CENTER
See INTERMOUNTAIN HEALTH CARE HEALTH SERVICES

D-U-N-S 02-252-0311 IMP
INTERMOUNTAIN NATURAL LLC
GOLDEN VALLEY NATURAL
1740 S Yellowstone Hwy, Idaho Falls, ID 83402-4328
Tel (208) 227-9000 Founded/Ownrshp 1997
Sales 221.8MM[E] EMP 650
SIC 5147 2013 Meats, cured or smoked; Snack sticks, including jerky: from purchased meat
CEO: Bryce Esplin
Manager: Roger Ball

D-U-N-S 84-927-0694
INTERMOUNTAIN PLASTIC DISTRIBUTION INC
2300 S Decker Lake Blvd B, Salt Lake City, UT 84119-2022
Tel (801) 201-1212 Founded/Ownrshp 2000
Sales 138.0MM EMP 3
SIC 5162 Plastics materials & basic shapes
*Pr: Talley Goodson
*CFO: Wynn Clayton

D-U-N-S 06-980-5455
INTERMOUNTAIN POWER AGENCY
I P A
10653 S River Front Pkwy # 120, South Jordan, UT 84095-3531
Tel (801) 938-1333 Founded/Ownrshp 1970
Sales 698.0MM EMP 500
SIC 4911

D-U-N-S 12-121-4985
INTERMOUNTAIN POWER SERVICE CORP
ITSC
850 W Brush Wellman Rd, Delta, UT 84624-9522
Tel (435) 864-4414 Founded/Ownrshp 1982
Sales 351.8MM[E] EMP 485
SIC 4911 Generation, electric power
Pr: Jon A Finlinson
*Sec: Roger Stowell
*VP: Jon P Christensen
IT Man: Lance Johnson
IT Man: Brook Pace
Sfty Dirs: Lewis Rawlinson
Opers Supe: Lloyd Leavitt

D-U-N-S 00-686-5273 IMP
INTERMOUNTAIN RURAL ELECTRIC ASSOCIATION
IREA
5496 N Us Highway 85, Sedalia, CO 80135-8600
Tel (303) 688-3100 Founded/Ownrshp 1938
Sales 279.9MM EMP 176
SIC 4911 Electric services
Pr: Timothy White
Chf Mktg O: Richard Stith
*VP: Bruff Shea
Exec: Gerry Hacker
Genl Mgr: Stan Lewandowski
Genl Mgr: Martha Lord
IT Man: David Jones
IT Man: Anne Thomas

IT Man: Robert Youngquist
Snr PM: Mark Jurgemeyer

D-U-N-S 18-216-4707
INTERMOUNTAIN WEST COMMUNICATIONS CO
701 S 9th St, Las Vegas, NV 89101-7068
Tel (702) 642-3333 *Founded/Ownrshp* 1983
Sales 204.9MM^E *EMP* 650
SIC 4833 Television broadcasting stations
Ch Bd: James E Rogers

D-U-N-S 15-312-5625
INTERNAL MEDICINE GROUP FREMONT
ST JOHNS CLINIC
1965 S Fremont Ave # 350, Springfield, MO 65804-2201
Tel (417) 820-3128 *Founded/Ownrshp* 2004
Sales 464.3MM *EMP* 30
SIC 8011 Internal medicine practitioners
Obsttrcn: Barbara E Wotherspoon

D-U-N-S 04-053-9587
■ INTERNAL REVENUE SERVICE
I R S
(*Suby of* UNITED STATES DEPT OF TREASURY) ★
1111 Constitution Ave Nw, Washington, DC 20224-0002
Tel (202) 803-9000 *Founded/Ownrshp* 1862
Sales NA *EMP* 92,800
SIC 9311 Taxation department, government;
CFO: Robin Canady
Ofcr: Daniel Bennett
Ofcr: Carol Campbell
Ofcr: Andrew Dyer
Ofcr: John M Robinson
Ofcr: Maryann Smith
VP: Stephen Blanton
VP: Tonia Gilmore
Exec: Michele Hamilton
Exec: Elerine McMurry
Prgrm Mgr: Elizabeth Solino

D-U-N-S 94-291-6578
▲ INTERNAP CORP
1 Ravinia Dr Ste 1300, Atlanta, GA 30346-2128
Tel (404) 302-9700 *Founded/Ownrshp* 1996
Sales 318.2MM *EMP* 650
Tkr Sym INAP *Exch* NGS
SIC 7373 7375 Computer integrated systems design; Information retrieval services
Pr: Peter Aquino
Mng Pt: Brian Hammond
COO: Michel Vent
CFO: Kevin M Dotts
Bd of Dir: Jeffrey Enebrad
Sr VP: Pete Bell
Sr VP: Peter G Bell
Sr VP: Peter M Evans
Sr VP: Satish Hemachandran
Sr VP: Michael Higgins
Sr VP: Mike Higgins
Sr VP: Mandira Mehra
Sr VP: Steven A Orchard
Sr VP: Christian Primeau
VP: John Maggard
VP: Patricia Watkins
Exec: Steve Francis
Board of Directors: Charles B Coe, Patricia L Higgins, Gary M Pfeiffer, Daniel C Stanzione, Debora J Wilson

D-U-N-S 83-472-1649
INTERNATIONAL AIRMOTIVE HOLDING CO INC
(*Suby of* BBA AVIATION PLC)
900 Nolen Dr Ste 100, Grapevine, TX 76051-8641
Tel (214) 956-3000 *Founded/Ownrshp* 1998
Sales 15.3MM^E *EMP* 1,571^E
SIC 7699 3724 Aircraft & heavy equipment repair services; Aircraft engines & engine parts
Pr: Hugh McElory
**CFO:* Douglas Meador

D-U-N-S 95-937-7995
INTERNATIONAL ASSEMBLY INC
I A I
750 E Los Ebanos Blvd A, Brownsville, TX 78520-4865
Tel (956) 499-7933 *Founded/Ownrshp* 1992
Sales 145.6MM^E *EMP* 750^E
SIC 5162 Plastics materials & basic shapes
Pr: Robert Katusak

D-U-N-S 15-191-7101 IMP
INTERNATIONAL AUTO PROCESSING INC
1 Joe Frank Harris Blvd, Brunswick, GA 31523-7802
Tel (912) 554-8432 *Founded/Ownrshp* 1988
Sales 179.4MM^E *EMP* 350
SIC 5012 7542 7538 7532 Automobiles & other motor vehicles; Carwashes; General automotive repair shops; Top & body repair & paint shops
Pr: James M Showalter
**CEO:* Robert Miller
**CFO:* Masahisa Kobayashi
Ex Dir: Jack McConnell

D-U-N-S 96-808-8687
INTERNATIONAL AUTOMOTIVE COMPONENTS GROUP NORTH AMERICA HOLDINGS INC
IC GROUP
(*Suby of* INTERNATIONAL AUTOMOTIVE COMPONENTS GROUP SA)
28333 Telegraph Rd, Southfield, MI 48034-1953
Tel (248) 455-7000 *Founded/Ownrshp* 2006
Sales 5.4MMM^E *EMP* 15,000
SIC 5013 Motor vehicle supplies & new parts
Pr: Robert S Miller
**COO:* Brian K Pour
**CFO:* Dennis E Richardville
**Ex VP:* Janis N Acosta
**Sr VP:* Robbie Bryan
Dir IT: Les Tolley
Tech Mgr: Steve Molino
Mtls Mgr: Patti Stewart
Plnt Mgr: Richard Lee
Board of Directors: Patrick Machir

D-U-N-S 79-319-6341 IMP/EXP
INTERNATIONAL AUTOMOTIVE COMPONENTS GROUP NORTH AMERICA INC
IAC GROUP
(*Suby of* INTERNATIONAL AUTOMOTIVE COMPONENTS GROUP SA)
28333 Telegraph Rd, Southfield, MI 48034-1953
Tel (248) 455-7000 *Founded/Ownrshp* 2007
Sales 9.7MMM^E *EMP* 28,425
SIC 3089 5013 Automotive parts, plastic; Automotive supplies & parts
Pr: Robert Steven Miller
**Ch Bd:* Wilbur L Ross Jr
**CFO:* Dennis E Richardville
CFO: Dennis Richardville
**Ex VP:* Janis N Acosta
Ex VP: Kathleen Sheehan
**Sr VP:* Brian K Pour
VP: Sam Moody
VP: Jargen Moschini
VP: Maurice Sessel
Dir IT: Jerry Martin

D-U-N-S 04-638-1281
INTERNATIONAL BACCALAUREATE ORGANIZATION INC
IB AMERICAS
(*Suby of* ORGANISATION DU BACCALAUREAT INTERNATIONAL (OBI))
7501 Wisconsin Ave # 200, Bethesda, MD 20814-6519
Tel (301) 202-3000 *Founded/Ownrshp* 1975
Sales 166.2MM^E *EMP* 130
Accts Ernst & Young Us Llp Indianap
SIC 8299 Educational service, nondegree granting: continuing educ.
Prin: Siva Kumari
**Prin:* Bradley Richardson

D-U-N-S 11-982-2534 IMP
▲ INTERNATIONAL BANCSHARES CORP
1200 San Bernardo Ave, Laredo, TX 78040-6301
Tel (956) 722-7611 *Founded/Ownrshp* 1979
Sales NA *EMP* 3,218^E
Tkr Sym IBOC *Exch* NGS
SIC 6022 State commercial banks
Ch Bd: Dennis E Nixon
**Treas:* Imelda Navarro
**VP:* R David Guerra
Board of Directors: Javier De Anda, Irving Greenblum, Douglas B Howland, Peggy J Newman, Larry A Norton, Roberto R Resendez, Leonardo Salinas, Antonio R Sanchez Jr

D-U-N-S 06-202-4112
INTERNATIONAL BANK FOR RECONSTRUCTION & DEVELOPMENT (INC)
WORLD BANK, THE
1818 H St Nw, Washington, DC 20433-0001
Tel (202) 473-1000 *Founded/Ownrshp* 1945
Sales NA *EMP* 15,000
SIC 6082 Foreign trade & international banking institutions
Pr: Jim Yong Kim
COO: SRI Mulyani Indrawati
CFO: Joaquim Levy
Ofcr: Arif Abdul
Ofcr: Bali Adawal
Ofcr: Santiago Afanador
Ofcr: Rajan Bhardvaj
Ofcr: Abdol Chenari
Ofcr: Jose Delcour
Ofcr: Renee Desclaux
Ofcr: Weijen Din
Ofcr: Mubashir Farooqi
Ofcr: Virginia Foley
Ofcr: Raul Gochez
Ofcr: Joseph Gonzalez
Ofcr: Andrew Hatleberg
Ofcr: Rashid Jamal
Ofcr: Andrea James
Ofcr: Prabhakar Joshi
Ofcr: Sanjeev Katti
Ofcr: Askandar Khan

D-U-N-S 04-147-0519 IMP
■ INTERNATIONAL BANK OF COMMERCE
IBC BANK
(*Suby of* INTERNATIONAL BANCSHARES CORP) ★
1200 San Bernardo Ave, Laredo, TX 78040-6301
Tel (956) 722-7611 *Founded/Ownrshp* 1979
Sales NA *EMP* 1,622
SIC 6022 State commercial banks
Pr: Dennis Nixon
Treas: Michael Saenz
Bd of Dir: Guillermo Trevino
Ofcr: Gabriela Carriedo
Ex VP: Richard Capps
Ex VP: William Cuellar
Ex VP: Carlos Martinez
**Ex VP:* Dalia Martinez
Ex VP: J Jorge Verduzco
Sr VP: Eddie Aldrete
Sr VP: Shannon Galloway
Sr VP: Yvette Gonzalez
Sr VP: Delores Hansen
Sr VP: Ron A Lalonde
Sr VP: Chris Loeher
**Sr VP:* Imelda Navarro
Sr VP: Rosie Ramirex
Sr VP: John A Villarreal
Sr VP: Chris Weller
Sr VP: Dustin Wells
Sr VP: Terri Yaklin

D-U-N-S 60-606-9607 IMP
INTERNATIONAL BRAKE INDUSTRIES INC
CARLSON QUALITY BRAKE
(*Suby of* QUALITOR INC) ★
4300 Quality Dr, South Bend, IN 46628-9665
Tel (419) 905-7468 *Founded/Ownrshp* 1967
Sales 83.6MM^E *EMP* 862
SIC 3713 3714 Truck & bus bodies; Motor vehicle brake systems & parts
Pr: Greg Andes
**Treas:* Scott Gibaratz

D-U-N-S 01-184-2841
■ INTERNATIONAL BROADCASTING BUREAU
(*Suby of* UNITED STATES DEPT OF STATE) ★
3919 Voa Site B Rd, Grimesland, NC 27837-8977
Tel (252) 758-2171 *Founded/Ownrshp* 1950
Sales NA *EMP* 5,128
SIC 9199 Civil service commission, government;

D-U-N-S 06-927-5980
INTERNATIONAL BROTHERHOOD OF ELECTRICAL WORKERS
IBEW
900 7th St Nw Bsmt 1, Washington, DC 20001-4089
Tel (202) 833-7000 *Founded/Ownrshp* 1955
Sales 160.0MM *EMP* 970
Accts Lb Calibre Cpa Group Pllc Bet
SIC 8631 Labor unions & similar labor organizations
Pr: Edwin D Hill
CFO: Jeff Miller
**Sec:* Salvatore J Chilia
VP: Curtis Henke
VP: John O'Rourke
Exec: Melinda Brent
DP Exec: Kirk Groenendaal
Software D: Bing Ye

D-U-N-S 96-480-6710
INTERNATIONAL BROTHERHOOD OF ELECTRICAL WORKERS - PENSION BENEFIT FUND
900 7th St Nw, Washington, DC 20001-3886
Tel (202) 728-6200 *Founded/Ownrshp* 2010
Sales 171.7MM *EMP* 26^E
Accts Calibre Cpa Group Pllc Washin
SIC 8631 Trade union
Prin: Ed Hill
Treas: Richard Shereda
VP: Joseph Davis
Dir IT: Victor Evans
Opers Mgr: John Greene

D-U-N-S 05-628-6222
INTERNATIONAL BROTHERHOOD OF TEAMSTERS
I B T
25 Louisiana Ave Nw, Washington, DC 20001-2130
Tel (202) 624-6800 *Founded/Ownrshp* 1903
Sales 167.8MM *EMP* 649^E
Accts Novak Francella Llc Bala Cynw
SIC 8631 Labor union
Pr: James P Hoffa
Treas: Ken Hall
Ofcr: Beatrice Newbury
VP: Charlie Andrew
VP: David Cabral
VP: Jonathan Gardner
VP: Richard K Hall
VP: Ron Herrera
VP: Chuck Mack
VP: John Murphy
VP: Myron Sharp
VP: David Yoders

D-U-N-S 78-494-5172
INTERNATIONAL BUILDING MATERIALS LLC
INTERNATIONAL WOOD PRODUCTS
14421 Se 98th Ct, Clackamas, OR 97015-9626
Tel (503) 650-9663 *Founded/Ownrshp* 1996
Sales 100.0MM *EMP* 55
SIC 5031 Lumber: rough, dressed & finished; Plywood
Pr: Dave Stelle
**CEO:* Doug Hart
**CFO:* Terry D Watson
VP Sls: Stelle Dave

D-U-N-S 09-506-8003 IMP
INTERNATIONAL BULLION AND METAL BROKERS (USA) INC
I B B
14051 Nw 14th St Ste 3, Sunrise, FL 33323-2885
Tel (954) 660-6900 *Founded/Ownrshp* 2003
Sales 105.6MM^E *EMP* 100^E
SIC 5094 Jewelry
Pr: Gavin M Kovacs
**Pr:* Stephen Kovacs

D-U-N-S 00-136-8083 IMP/EXP
▲ INTERNATIONAL BUSINESS MACHINES CORP (NY)
IBM
1 New Orchard Rd Ste 1, Armonk, NY 10504-1722
Tel (914) 499-1900 *Founded/Ownrshp* 1910
Sales 81.7MMM *EMP* 377,757
Tkr Sym IBM *Exch* NYS
SIC 7379 7371 3571 3572 3674 Computer related consulting services; Computer software development; Software programming applications; Minicomputers; Mainframe computers; Personal computers (microcomputers); Computer storage devices; Disk drives, computer; Tape storage units, computer; Semiconductors & related devices; Microcircuits, integrated (semiconductor)
Ch Bd: Virginia M Rometty
Pt: Tom Flanagan
V Ch: Al Strong
CFO: Martin J Schroeter
Treas: Lillian Hanson
Bd of Dir: Pam Borgen
Bd of Dir: Amy Reinhardt
Bd of Dir: Joan Spero
Ex VP: Kari Barbar
Ex VP: Nicholas M Donofrio
Sr VP: Michelle H Browdy
Sr VP: Diane J Gherson
VP: Carla Berryann
VP: Staunton Brooks
VP: Jack Brown
VP: Winn Brown
VP: Morgan Clark
VP: John Fitzgerald
VP: Phil Francisco
VP: Anne Gray
VP: Mark Hennessy
Board of Directors: Joan E Spero, Kenneth I Chenault, Sidney Taurel, Michael L Eskew, Peter R Voser, David N Farr, Mark Fields, Alex Gorsky, Shirley Ann Jackson, Andrew N Liveris, W James McNerney Jr, James W Owens

D-U-N-S 07-953-2065
INTERNATIONAL CARS LTD INC (MA)
HONDA NORTH
382 Newbury St, Danvers, MA 01923-1060
Tel (800) 514-1627 *Founded/Ownrshp* 1974, 1989
Sales 113.0MM^E *EMP* 260
SIC 5511 5521 Automobiles, new & used; Used car dealers
CEO: Marshall Jespersen
CFO: Dave Dubois
**CFO:* David Dubois
Genl Mgr: Richard Collins
Genl Mgr: Joe Dettrey
IT Man: Devin Sullivan
Sls Mgr: Steve Collins
Sls Mgr: Rui Moreira
Sales Asso: Jim Godbout
Sales Asso: Jerome Ravenell
Sales Asso: Gary Thigpen

D-U-N-S 07-986-3232
INTERNATIONAL CENTRE FOR DISPUTE RESOLUTION
AMERICAN ARBITRATION ASSN
120 Brdwy Fl 21, New York, NY 10271
Tel (212) 484-4181 *Founded/Ownrshp* 2015
Sales 36.9MM^E *EMP* 1,000
SIC 7389 Arbitration & conciliation service

D-U-N-S 07-003-8104 IMP/EXP
INTERNATIONAL CHEMICAL CO (OK)
INTER-CHEM
1887 E 71st St, Tulsa, OK 74136-3922
Tel (918) 496-7711 *Founded/Ownrshp* 1976
Sales 755.0MM^E *EMP* 42
SIC 5191 Fertilizers & agricultural chemicals
Ch Bd: John R Arend
**CEO:* Brad Thomas
**CFO:* Eugene B Graves
**Ex VP:* Albert A Colby Jr
Sr VP: Gene Graves
VP: Aaron C Choquette
VP: Martha Starr
**Prin:* B P Abney
**Prin:* Tricia Arend
CTO: Wally Wells
Opers Mgr: Denny Arend

D-U-N-S 04-115-7397
INTERNATIONAL CHURCH OF FOURSQUARE GOSPEL
FOURSQUARE INTERNATIONAL
1910 W Sunset Blvd # 200, Los Angeles, CA 90026-3275
Tel (213) 989-4234 *Founded/Ownrshp* 1921
Sales 206.2MM^E *EMP* 5,000
SIC 8661 6512 7032 8211 8221 Miscellaneous denomination church; Nonresidential building operators; Sporting & recreational camps; Elementary & secondary schools; Colleges universities & professional schools
Pr: Glenn C Burris Jr
**CFO:* Ron Thigpenn
**Treas:* Brent Morgan
**VP:* Sterling Brackett
**VP:* Tammy Dunahoo
**VP:* Jared Roth
**VP:* James C Scott Jr
**Prin:* Paul Risser
Snr Sftwr: Adrian Bakula

D-U-N-S 02-187-6420
INTERNATIONAL CITY MANAGEMENT ASSOCIATION RETIREMENT CORP
ICMA RETIREMENT
777 N Capitol St Ne # 600, Washington, DC 20002-4239
Tel (202) 962-4600 *Founded/Ownrshp* 1972
Sales 222.8MM *EMP* 850
SIC 7389 6722 Financial services; Management investment, open-end
Pr: Robert Schultze
CFO: Michael Guarasci
Sr VP: Angela Montez
VP: Jerry Backenstoe
VP: Tammy Berger
VP: Gary Helm
VP: Steven Janssen
VP: David Tanguay
Board of Directors: Eric Anderson, Collette Chilton, Eric McKissack, David Mora, Robert O'neill

D-U-N-S 61-484-3881
■ INTERNATIONAL COAL GROUP INC
(*Suby of* ARCH COAL INC) ★
114 Smiley Dr, Saint Albans, WV 25177-1504
Tel (304) 760-2400 *Founded/Ownrshp* 2011
Sales 190.8MM^E *EMP* 4,266^E
SIC 1222 1221 Bituminous coal-underground mining; Bituminous coal & lignite-surface mining
Pr: Bennett K Hatfield
**CFO:* Bradley W Harris
**Sr VP:* Phillip M Hardesty
Sr VP: Oren Eugene Kitts
**Sr VP:* Roger L Nicholson
Sr VP: William Scott Perkins
MIS Dir: Steve Horton
IT Man: Jim Friderick
IT Man: David Schweigert
Plnt Mgr: Joe N Tussey
VP Mktg: Merritt Marc

D-U-N-S 05-531-7320 IMP
INTERNATIONAL COFFEE & TEA LLC
COFFEE BEAN & TEA LEAF, THE
5700 Wilshire Blvd # 120, Los Angeles, CA 90036-3659
Tel (310) 237-2326 *Founded/Ownrshp* 1998
Sales 192.8MM^E *EMP* 2,850
Accts Deloitte & Touche Los Angeles
SIC 5812 5499 6794 Coffee shop; Coffee; Tea; Franchises, selling or licensing
Pr: John Fuller

COO: Eric Foo Kok Cheng
CFO: Melvin Allias
CFO: Karen Cate
**CFO:* Jeff Harris
Treas: John Garrow
Sr VP: Andrew Nathan
Sr VP: Adam Tabachnikoff
VP: Michael R Beck
VP: Coralie C Lewis
VP: Lacy Novell Morris

D-U-N-S 61-692-0104 IMP
INTERNATIONAL COMMERCE & MARKETING CORP
POSTAL PRODUCTS UNLIMITED
500 W Oklahoma Ave, Milwaukee, WI 53207-2649
Tel (414) 290-1500 *Founded/Ownrshp* 1988
Sales 122.2MM^E *EMP* 140
SIC 5085 5961 Industrial supplies; Mail order house
Pr: Brian P Nelson
**CFO:* James Hess
Ex Dir: Victor Frangopoulous
Web Dev: Andrew Otoo
Sls&Mrk Ex: John Ludwig
Mktg Dir: Sean Buyeske

D-U-N-S 01-810-2264
INTERNATIONAL COMMUNICATIONS EXCHANGE CORP (OH)
4033 Ellery Ave, Moraine, OH 45439-2133
Tel (937) 296-9605 *Founded/Ownrshp* 1990
Sales 100.0MM *EMP* 12
SIC 8748 7379 Telecommunications consultant; Computer related consulting services
Pr: Alan Doll

D-U-N-S 07-969-3872
INTERNATIONAL CONSORTIUM FOR ADVANCED MANUFACTURING RESEARCH INC
3 Courthouse Sq Fl 2, Kissimmee, FL 34741-5440
Tel (407) 742-4252 *Founded/Ownrshp* 2014
Sales 120.0MM *EMP* 9
SIC 8731 Commercial physical research
Pr: Dave Saathoff
**Ex Dir:* Dan Holladay

D-U-N-S 16-587-5928 IMP
INTERNATIONAL COSMETICS & PERFUMES
30 W 21st St Fl 7, New York, NY 10010-6959
Tel (212) 643-0011 *Founded/Ownrshp* 1996
Sales 90.4MM^E *EMP* 300^E
SIC 5122 Cosmetics, perfumes & hair products
Pr: Emmanuel Lajugie-Saujet
**Pr:* Thomas Saujet
VP: Adam Brecht
VP: Vanessa Dabich
VP: Dina Rosenbloom
Mktg Mgr: Clementine Grenot

D-U-N-S 62-162-6597 IMP
INTERNATIONAL CRANKSHAFT INC
I C I
(*Suby of* NIPPON STEEL & SUMITOMO METAL CORPORATION)
101 Carley Ct, Georgetown, KY 40324-9303
Tel (502) 868-0003 *Founded/Ownrshp* 2012
Sales 164.4MM *EMP* 260
Accts Deloitte & Touche Llp Louisvi
SIC 3714 Crankshaft assemblies, motor vehicle
Pr: Nobuaki Masuda
**Sec:* Kozo Matsumoto
**VP:* William McCurley

D-U-N-S 00-206-2052
INTERNATIONAL CRUISE & EXCURSION GALLERY INC
ICE GALLERY
15501 N Dial Blvd, Scottsdale, AZ 85260-1615
Tel (602) 395-1995 *Founded/Ownrshp* 1996
Sales 1.2MMM^E *EMP* 15,000
Accts Deloitte & Touche Llp
SIC 4724 Travel agencies
Pr: John Rowley
COO: Glenn Nadel
COO: Glenn A Nadell
VP: Rendy Buness
**Prin:* Marcia Rowley
Ex Dir: Patrick Ryan
Mng Dir: Kevin Sharp
Mktg Dir: Michelle Spatafore

D-U-N-S 02-290-5608 IMP/EXP
■ **INTERNATIONAL DAIRY QUEEN INC**
(*Suby of* BERKSHIRE HATHAWAY INC) ★
7505 Metro Blvd Ste 500, Minneapolis, MN 55439-3018
Tel (952) 830-0200 *Founded/Ownrshp* 1998
Sales 91.4MM^E *EMP* 450
SIC 5812 Ice cream stands or dairy bars
Pr: Charles W Mooty
CFO: James S Simpson
VP: Lee Banbury
VP: Tim Hawley
VP: Michael D Keller
VP: Judy Munoz
VP: Ann Stone
Genl Mgr: Edward Alexander
Genl Mgr: Edward Baldwin
Genl Mgr: Edward Bernardino
Genl Mgr: Edward Berube

D-U-N-S 08-156-8040 IMP/EXP
INTERNATIONAL DATA GROUP INC
EXECUTRAIN
1 Exeter Plz Fl 15, Boston, MA 02116-2856
Tel (617) 534-1200 *Founded/Ownrshp* 1964
Sales 3.5MMM *EMP* 13,450
SIC 2721 8732 7389 Trade journals: publishing only, not printed on site; Market analysis or research; Trade show arrangement
CEO: Patrick J McGovern
**CFO:* Edward B Bloom
CFO: Ted Bloom
VP: Bill Laberis
VP: Nancy Percival
QA Dir: Iris Whalen
Info Man: Glenn Mosesso
Web Dev: Mark Savery
Sls Mgr: Cheryl Giangregorio
Genl Couns: Leigh Mills

D-U-N-S 15-709-7411
■ **INTERNATIONAL DEVELOPMENT UNITED STATES AGENCY FOR**
USAID
(*Suby of* EXECUTIVE OFFICE OF UNITED STATES GOVERNMENT) ★
1300 Penn Ave Nw 848, Washington, DC 20004-3002
Tel (202) 712-0000 *Founded/Ownrshp* 1963
Sales NA *EMP* 9,000
SIC 9611 Economic development agency, government;
**CFO:* David Ostermeyer
Ofcr: Amanda Boachie
Ofcr: Caryle Cammisa
Ofcr: Walter Lee
Ofcr: Peggy Manthe
Ofcr: Tiana Martin
Ofcr: Benjamin Phelps
Ofcr: Pat Fn'piere
Ofcr: Roy Plucknett
Ofcr: Greg Raney
Ofcr: Susan Werner
Board of Directors: Paula Kohler

D-U-N-S 02-460-4352
INTERNATIONAL EDUCATION CORP
16485 Laguna Canyon Rd # 300, Irvine, CA 92618-3840
Tel (949) 272-7200 *Founded/Ownrshp* 1996, 1989
Sales 134.0MM^E *EMP* 1,000
Accts Almich & Associates Irvine C
SIC 8249 Vocational schools
Pr: Fardad Fateri
Pr: Joseph Bartolome
Pr: William Murtagh Jr
**Pr:* Shoukry Tiab
**COO:* Joseph W Fox
**COO:* Janis Paulson
**CFO:* George P Harbison
**CFO:* Sanjay Sardana
**Ex VP:* Sandra N Lockwood
**Sr VP:* Aaron J Mortensen
**VP:* Joanna Gut-Vargas

D-U-N-S 07-828-7874
INTERNATIONAL EQUIPMENT SOLUTIONS LLC
IES
(*Suby of* KPS CAPITAL PARTNERS LP) ★
2211 York Rd Ste 320, Oak Brook, IL 60523-4030
Tel (630) 570-6880 *Founded/Ownrshp* 2011
Sales 572.6MM^E *EMP* 1,732^E
SIC 3531 Cabs, for construction machinery
CEO: Steve Andrews

D-U-N-S 78-610-5197
INTERNATIONAL FELLOWSHIP OF CHRISTIANS & JEWS INC
30 N La Salle St Ste 2600, Chicago, IL 60602-3356
Tel (312) 641-7200 *Founded/Ownrshp* 1983
Sales 129.3MM *EMP* 42
Accts Mcgladrey Llp Chicago Il
SIC 8661 Religious organizations
Pr: Rabbi Yechiel Eckstein
COO: David Wolfard
**VP:* Yael Eckstein
Comm Dir: Michael Stoltz
Web Dev: James Dalton
Mktg Dir: Ronda Henna

D-U-N-S 00-256-9754
INTERNATIONAL FIDELITY INSURANCE CO
IFIC
1111 Raymond Blvd Fl 20, Newark, NJ 07102-5206
Tel (973) 286-7911 *Founded/Ownrshp* 1904, 1964
Sales NA *EMP* 240
SIC 6351 Fidelity or surety bonding
Pr: Fred Mitterhoff
Pr: George Rettig
**COO:* Robert Minister
**Treas:* Maria Costa
Treas: Charlotte S WEI
Ofcr: Charlotte Weiss
Ex VP: George James
**Sr VP:* Jerry Watson
VP: Anna Dime
**VP:* Norman R Konvitz
**VP:* Daniel Mitterhoff
VP: Bruce Monahan
VP: Dorothy O'Connor
**VP:* Beatriz Sampedro
VP: Beatrib Sanpedro
Board of Directors: George F Brenner

D-U-N-S 05-628-1876 IMP
INTERNATIONAL FINANCE CORP
WORLD BANK, THE
1818 H St Nw, Washington, DC 20433-0001
Tel (202) 458-2454 *Founded/Ownrshp* 1956
Sales NA *EMP* 2,100^E
SIC 6082 Foreign trade & international banking institutions
CEO: Jin-Yong Cai
**Pr:* Robert Zoellick
Chf Cred: Robin Glantz
Chf Cred: Vivek Pathak
Chf Inves: Denis Clarke
Chf Inves: Nina Zegger
Ofcr: Desmond Andrades
Ofcr: Zafar Azhar
Ofcr: Sabin Basnyat
Ofcr: Masud Cader
Ofcr: Patrick Chen
Ofcr: Bud Childs
Ofcr: Richard Davis
Ofcr: Chisako Fukuda
Ofcr: Maxine Garvey
Ofcr: Siriam Gopalakrishnan
Ofcr: Luis Guerrero
Ofcr: Aichin Jones
Ofcr: Davit Karapetyan
Ofcr: Adrienne Kennedy
Ofcr: Bernard Lauwers

D-U-N-S 10-011-2478
INTERNATIONAL FINANCIAL GROUP INC
ISG COMPANIES
238 International Rd, Burlington, NC 27215-5129
Tel (336) 586-2500 *Founded/Ownrshp* 1993
Sales NA *EMP* 300
SIC 6331 Fire, marine & casualty insurance & carriers
Pr: Robert Linton
Dir IT: Wade Staunton

D-U-N-S 00-153-4833 IMP/EXP
▲ **INTERNATIONAL FLAVORS & FRAGRANCES INC** (NY)
IFF
521 W 57th St, New York, NY 10019-2929
Tel (212) 765-5500 *Founded/Ownrshp* 1909
Sales 3.0MMM *EMP* 6,820
Accts Pricewaterhousecoopers Llp Ne
Tkr Sym IFF *Exch* NYS
SIC 2869 2844 2087 Flavors or flavoring materials, synthetic; Perfume materials, synthetic; Toilet preparations; Flavoring extracts & syrups
Ch Bd: Andreas Fibig
CFO: Roger Blanken
CFO: Alison A Cornell
CFO: Richard O'Leary
Treas: Kim Crawford
Treas: Chad Weller
Ex VP: Ahmet Baydar
Ex VP: Julian W Boyden
Ex VP: Angelica T Cantlon
Ex VP: Anne Chwat
Ex VP: Beth E Ford
Ex VP: Francisco Fortanet
Ex VP: Wayne Howard
Ex VP: Gregory Yep
Sr VP: Dennis M Meany
VP: Bob Anderson
VP: Mark Dewis
VP: Dionisio Ferenc
VP: David Gerics
VP: John Grywalski
VP: Todd Hand
Board of Directors: Dale F Morrison, Marcello V Bottoli, Linda B Buck, Michael Ducker, David R Epstein, Roger W Ferguson Jr, John F Ferraro, Christina Gold, Henry W Howell Jr, Katherine M Hudson

D-U-N-S 02-031-3540 IMP
INTERNATIONAL FOOD POLICY RESEARCH INSTITUTE
IFPRI
2033 K St Nw Ste 400, Washington, DC 20006-1018
Tel (202) 862-5600 *Founded/Ownrshp* 1975
Sales 169.2MM^E *EMP* 200
Accts Kpmg Llp Mc Lean Va
SIC 8731 8733 Commercial physical research; Noncommercial research organizations
Exec: Graterol Eduardo
Pgrm Dir: Howarth Bouis

D-U-N-S 07-950-4031 IMP/EXP
INTERNATIONAL FOREST PRODUCTS LLC
1 Patriot Pl, Foxboro, MA 02035-1374
Tel (508) 698-4600 *Founded/Ownrshp* 1972
Sales 99.6MM^E *EMP* 100
SIC 0831 Forest products
Ch: Robert K Kraft
Pr: Jim Cobery
Pr: Daniel Kraft
COO: Jonathan A Kraft
COO: Daniel Moore
CFO: Michael Quattromani
VP: Larry Burton
VP: Terry Maceachen
VP: Eduardo Porta
VP: Rob Shepard
Genl Mgr: Terry McNally

D-U-N-S 78-744-6962 IMP/EXP
INTERNATIONAL GAME TECHNOLOGY
(*Suby of* I G T) ★
9295 Prototype Dr, Reno, NV 89521-8986
Tel (775) 448-7777 *Founded/Ownrshp* 1980
Sales 259.9MM^E *EMP* 740^E
SIC 3999 5099 Slot machines; Game machines, coin-operated
CEO: G Thomas Baker
Pr: Renato Ascoli
Treas: Claudio Demolli
Ex VP: Robert Bittman
Ex VP: Joe Kaminkow
Ex VP: Paul Mathews
Sr VP: Sarah Beth Brown
Sr VP: Ward Chilton
Sr VP: Anthony Ciorciari
Sr VP: Rich Pennington
VP: Randy Kirner
VP: Matt Wilkerson
Exec: Andrew Wood

D-U-N-S 06-502-0216 IMP
INTERNATIONAL GAME TECHNOLOGY INC
I G T
(*Suby of* INTERNATIONAL GAME TECHNOLOGY PLC)
7900 W Sunset Rd, Las Vegas, NV 89113-2188
Tel (702) 669-7777 *Founded/Ownrshp* 2015
Sales 500.6MM^E *EMP* 4,400
SIC 7999 Gambling & lottery services; Lottery operation; Lottery tickets, sale of
CEO: Renato Ascoli
**CFO:* Alberto Fornaro
**Co-CEO:* Walter Bugno
**Co-CEO:* Michael Chambrello
Sr VP: Ken Bossingham
Sr VP: Ward Chilton
VP: Craig Churchill
Sftwr Eng: Steven Morris

D-U-N-S 15-782-6843 IMP/EXP
INTERNATIONAL GARDEN PRODUCTS INC
IGP
30590 Se Kelso Rd, Boring, OR 97009-6016
Tel (503) 663-1698 *Founded/Ownrshp* 1997
Sales 28.3MM^E *EMP* 1,000
SIC 0181 Nursery stock, growing of
Pr: Jay Hulbert
**CFO:* Ron Ridout

D-U-N-S 13-643-1848 IMP/EXP
INTERNATIONAL GREETINGS USA INC
(*Suby of* IG DESIGN GROUP PLC)
338 Industrial Blvd, Midway, GA 31320-5214
Tel (912) 884-9727 *Founded/Ownrshp* 1990
Sales 99.7MM^E *EMP* 225
SIC 2679 Gift wrap, paper: made from purchased material
CEO: Paul Fineman
**CEO:* Lawrence Louis
**CFO:* Anthony Lawrinson
**Ch:* John Charlton
Ex VP: Rich Eckman
**VP:* Wain Yarber
Software D: Tim Crean
Opers Mgr: Otis Cloud
Sls Mgr: Sara Motes

D-U-N-S 12-228-0092 IMP/EXP
INTERNATIONAL GROUP INC
I G I
(*Suby of* INTERNATIONAL GROUP INC, THE)
1007 E Spring St, Titusville, PA 16354-7826
Tel (814) 827-4900 *Founded/Ownrshp* 1943
Sales 158.0MM^E *EMP* 500
SIC 5169 2911 Waxes, except petroleum; Oils, lubricating; Petrolatums, nonmedicinal; Paraffin wax
**Pr:* Kenneth Reucassel
CFO: David Imrie

D-U-N-S 83-079-5543
INTERNATIONAL HOTEL MANAGEMENT SERVICES INC
IHMS
(*Suby of* THE INDIAN HOTELS COMPANY LIMITED)
2 E 61st St, New York, NY 10065-8401
Tel (212) 838-8000 *Founded/Ownrshp* 1986
Sales 107.3MM^E *EMP* 700
SIC 7011 Hotels & motels
Pr: Raymond Bickson
**CFO:* Anil P Goel
**VP:* Deepa Misra Harris
**VP:* Jodi Leblanc
Dir: Uday Narain
Board of Directors: Anil P Goel, Jodi Le Balnc, Rajesh K Parekh

INTERNATIONAL HOUSE
See UNIVERSITY OF CHICAGO

D-U-N-S 10-861-8745 IMP/EXP
INTERNATIONAL IMAGING MATERIALS INC
IIMAK
310 Commerce Dr, Amherst, NY 14228-2396
Tel (716) 691-6333 *Founded/Ownrshp* 1926
Sales 145.9MM^E *EMP* 587
SIC 3955 3555 Ribbons, inked: typewriter, adding machine, register, etc.; Printing trades machinery
Ch Bd: Richard Marshall
**CEO:* Douglas Wagner
**CFO:* Joe Perna
**Sr VP:* Susan R Stamp
Prgrm Mgr: John Edick
Board of Directors: David Jaffe, William Mantoague, John Paxton, Robert Scribner, Eric Wilnes

D-U-N-S 19-059-1016
INTERNATIONAL INDUSTRIES INC
210 Larry Joe Harless Dr, Gilbert, WV 25621
Tel (304) 664-3227 *Founded/Ownrshp* 1987
Sales 114.0MM^E *EMP* 1,104
SIC 6211 Investment bankers
Ch Bd: James Harless
**Pr:* Gary G White
**Treas:* Raymond McKinney
**VP:* C Fred Shewey

D-U-N-S 06-622-5574
INTERNATIONAL LEASE FINANCE CORP
(*Suby of* AERCAP US GLOBAL AVIATION LLC) ★
10250 Constellation Blvd, Los Angeles, CA 90067-6200
Tel (310) 788-1999 *Founded/Ownrshp* 2014
Sales 85.9MM^E *EMP* 564^E
SIC 7359 8741 5599 Aircraft rental; Business management; Aircraft dealers
CEO: Henri Courpron
CFO: Elias Habayeb
Treas: Pamela Hendry
Sr VP: Kurt H Schwarz
Sr VP: Philip Scruggs
VP: Spiro Farougias
VP: Joey Johnsen
VP: Richard Lee
VP: Philipe Renault
CTO: Thomas Harrison
IT Man: Erin O'Gorman

D-U-N-S 12-238-2849
■ **INTERNATIONAL LINE BUILDERS INC**
I L B
(*Suby of* MDU RESOURCES GROUP INC) ★
19020 Sw Cipole Rd Ste A, Tualatin, OR 97062-8362
Tel (503) 692-0193 *Founded/Ownrshp* 1997
Sales 144.7MM^E *EMP* 300
SIC 1623 Electric power line construction
CEO: Ronald Tipton
**Pr:* Michael A Bass
**Pr:* Charles R Griffin
VP: Lee Brown
**VP:* Antonio Y De Ocampo
VP Admn: Marla Jordan
Div Mgr: Kevin Nelsen
Dir IT: John Paiste

D-U-N-S 60-334-8236
■ **INTERNATIONAL LINE BUILDERS INC**
ILB
(*Suby of* MDU RESOURCES GROUP INC) ★
2520 Rubidoux Blvd, Riverside, CA 92509-2147
Tel (951) 682-2962 *Founded/Ownrshp* 1989
Sales 86.8MM^E *EMP* 180
SIC 1731 Electrical work
CEO: Jeffrey S Thiede

*Pr: Mike Bass
*Sr VP: Don McNair

D-U-N-S 07-112-7153 IMP/EXP
INTERNATIONAL MANAGEMENT GROUP (OVERSEAS) LLC
1360 E 9th St Ste 100, Cleveland, OH 44114-1782
Tel (216) 522-1200 Founded/Ownrshp 2014
Sales 435.9M EMP 1,708
Accts Mai Wealth Advisors Llc Cleve
SIC 7941 7999 7922 Manager of individual professional athletes; Sports instruction, schools & camps; Theatrical producers & services
Treas: William Prip
*Pr: Ian Todd
*CFO: Arthur J La Fave Jr
CFO: Chip McCarthy
Treas: Carolyn Sweeney
Ofcr: Tony Crispino
Sr VP: David Abrutyn
Sr VP: Ivan Bart
Sr VP: Jeremy Cole
Sr VP: Mindy Coppin
Sr VP: Diarmuid Crowley
Sr VP: Graham Fry
*Sr VP: Neil Graff
Sr VP: Martin Jolly
*Sr VP: Peter Kuhn
*Sr VP: Kevin Lavan
Sr VP: James Leitz
Sr VP: Rob Mason
Sr VP: Gary Pluchino
Sr VP: Bobby Sharma
Sr VP: Mark Steinberg

D-U-N-S 11-303-6755
INTERNATIONAL MANAGEMENT SERVICES CO INC
IMSCO
3633 Wheeler Rd Ste 350, Augusta, GA 30909-6545
Tel (706) 855-1014 Founded/Ownrshp 1993
Sales 224.1MM^E EMP 1,500^E
SIC 8742 Materials mgmt. (purchasing, handling, inventory) consultant
Ch: Nancy C Hall
*Pr: David W Bowles
*Treas: Tammy A Bridgers
*Sr VP: Robert Prugar

D-U-N-S 07-957-0830
INTERNATIONAL MARKET CENTERS INC
(Suby of INTERNATIONAL MARKET CENTERS LP) ★
475 S Grand Central Pkwy, Las Vegas, NV 89106-4552
Tel (702) 599-9621 Founded/Ownrshp 2011
Sales 162.8MM EMP 206
SIC 6798 Real estate investment trusts
Ch Bd: Robert J Maricich
Pr: Dorothy Belshaw
COO: Pedro Zapata
CFO: William F Lacey
Ex VP: Scott Eckman
Sr VP: Carolyn Conley
Snr PM: Dennis Cole
Board of Directors: Ryan Cotton, Scott Graves, James P Hoffmann, Philip Loughlin, Kimberly McCaslin, Eric S Rangen

D-U-N-S 96-842-8800
INTERNATIONAL MARKET CENTERS LP
495 S Grand Central Pkwy, Las Vegas, NV 89106-4555
Tel (702) 599-9621 Founded/Ownrshp 2011
Sales 162.8MM^E EMP 206^E
SIC 8741 Management services
CEO: Robert Naricich
CFO: William Lacey
VP: Dana Andrew
Genl Couns: Kim A Rieck

D-U-N-S 18-637-5218
INTERNATIONAL MEDICAL CORPS
12400 Wilshire Blvd # 1500, Los Angeles, CA 90025-1030
Tel (310) 826-7800 Founded/Ownrshp 1984
Sales 232.6MM EMP 63^E
SIC 8322 Disaster service
Ch: Robert Simon
*Pr: Nancy Aossey
Trst: Sarah Ahrens
Ofcr: Elizabeth Apopo
Ofcr: John Gayflor
Ofcr: Sara Hoffman
Ofcr: Martha Houle
Ofcr: Ahmad Jaran
Ofcr: Maki Justin
Ofcr: Joe Martinez
Ofcr: Tatiana Megale
Ofcr: Andrew Mina
Ofcr: Jennifer Naiboka
Ofcr: Boi B Robin
Ofcr: EMI Samata
Ofcr: Heidi Saravia
Ofcr: Natalie Sarles
Ofcr: LI Zhou
VP: David Giron
VP: Rebecca Milner
VP: William Sundblad

D-U-N-S 05-575-0020
■ **INTERNATIONAL MEDICATION SYSTEMS LTD**
IMS
(Suby of AMPHASTAR PHARMACEUTICALS INC) ★
1886 Santa Anita Ave, South El Monte, CA 91733-3414
Tel (626) 442-6757 Founded/Ownrshp 1998
Sales 226.3MM^E EMP 720
SIC 2834 2833 3841 Drugs acting on the central nervous system & sense organs; Anesthetics, in bulk form; Surgical & medical instruments
Pr: Jack Zhang
COO: Mary Luo
*COO: Mary Luo Zhang
CIO: Carmen Rueda
MIS Dir: Tony Kwan
IT Man: Bernard Chu
VP Opers: Paul Yu

INTERNATIONAL MERCHANTS
See REQ/JQH HOLDINGS INC

D-U-N-S 06-435-2529
INTERNATIONAL MILL SERVICE INC
IMS
(Suby of MILL SERVICES CORP) ★
1155 Bus Ctr Dr Ste 200, Horsham, PA 19044
Tel (215) 956-5500 Founded/Ownrshp 2007
Sales 108.5MM^E EMP 1,100
SIC 3295 3341 1422 8742 Slag, crushed or ground; Secondary nonferrous metals; Cement rock, crushed & broken-quarrying; Public utilities consultant
Pr: Raymond S Kalouche
*Treas: Daniel E Rosati
VP: Aarne Anderson
CIO: Michael McGraw
IT Man: Steve Helbig
Opers Mgr: Brad Brentin

D-U-N-S 06-235-1499
INTERNATIONAL MISSION BOARD OF SOUTHERN BAPTIST CONVENTION
IMB
3806 Monument Ave, Richmond, VA 23230-3932
Tel (804) 353-0151 Founded/Ownrshp 1845
Sales 93.5MM^E EMP 4,686
Accts Clifton Gunderson Llp Glen A
SIC 8661 2731 7812 Baptist Church; Pamphlets: publishing & printing; Audio-visual program production
Pr: Tom Elliff
*Ch Bd: Jimmy Perichard
*CFO: David A Steverson
*V Ch Bd: O Tim Locher
*Ex VP: Claude A Meador
VP: Tom Williams
VP: Ken Winter
Mng Dir: Brenda Helms
Mng Dir: Barbara Smith
CIO: Sherry Stence
CTO: Mark Grigg

D-U-N-S 06-927-5188
INTERNATIONAL MONETARY FUND
700 19th St Nw, Washington, DC 20431-0002
Tel (202) 623-7000 Founded/Ownrshp 1944
Sales NA EMP 2,700
SIC 6082 Foreign trade & international banking institutions
Mng Dir: Christine Lagarde
Treas: G M Fitzpatrick
Ofcr: Justin J Ayres
Ofcr: Naly De Carvalho
Ofcr: Sheila Edmund
Ofcr: Tom A Ferris
Ofcr: Graham Newman
Ofcr: Sharon Slattery
Ofcr: Yuri Starostine
Ofcr: Duncan Whitcher
Top Exec: Valeria Fichera
Top Exec: Mark Lewis
Exec: George Brookings
Exec: Ydahlia Metzgen
Dir Soc: Marie Swerdlow

D-U-N-S 07-779-3206
INTERNATIONAL MOTOR CARS INC
PASSPORT AUTOMOTIVE GROUP
5000 Auth Way, Suitland, MD 20746-4205
Tel (301) 423-8400 Founded/Ownrshp 1975
Sales 97.7MM^E EMP 225
SIC 5511 7538 5521 New & used car dealers; General automotive repair shops; Used car dealers
Pr: Everett A Hellmuth III
*VP: Bruce Dunigan
Genl Mgr: Jay McLean
Sls Mgr: Joe Long

D-U-N-S 00-625-9931 IMP/EXP
■ **INTERNATIONAL MULTIFOODS CORP**
J M SMUCKER
(Suby of J M SMUCKER CO) ★
1 Strawberry Ln, Orrville, OH 44667-1241
Tel (330) 682-3000 Founded/Ownrshp 2000, 2004
Sales 205.3MM^E EMP 1,450
SIC 5145 5149 5143 2048 2041 Candy; Snack foods; Chewing gum; Coffee, green or roasted; Tea bagging; Baking supplies; Pizza supplies; Cheese; Livestock feeds; Pizza dough, prepared; Flour; Flour mixes
CEO: Gary Costley PHD
*Pr: Dan C Swander
*CFO: John E Byom
*Sr VP: Frank W Bonvino
VP: Ralph P Hargrow
VP: Dennis R Johnson
Prd Mgr: Aaron Koehn
Mktg Dir: Joe Stanziano

D-U-N-S 96-404-4825
INTERNATIONAL OPERATING ENGINEERS UNION 49 HEALTH AND WELFARE FUND
3001 Metro Dr Ste 500, Bloomington, MN 55425-1617
Tel (952) 854-0795 Founded/Ownrshp 2010
Sales 141.0MM EMP 11^E
Accts Legacy Professionals Llp Minn
SIC 8631 Labor unions & similar labor organizations
Prin: William Addleman

D-U-N-S 00-119-8829 IMP/EXP
INTERNATIONAL PACKAGING CORP
INTERPAK
517 Mineral Spring Ave, Pawtucket, RI 02860-3408
Tel (401) 724-1600 Founded/Ownrshp 1957
Sales 93.5MM^E EMP 600
SIC 3499 3089

D-U-N-S 00-638-2253 IMP/EXP
INTERNATIONAL PAINT LLC
(Suby of AKZONOBEL) ★
6001 Antoine Dr, Houston, TX 77091-3503
Tel (713) 682-1711 Founded/Ownrshp 1921, 1987
Sales 160.8MM^E EMP 400
SIC 2851 Enamels; Lacquer: bases, dopes, thinner; Varnishes
Rgnl Mgr: Roger Bain
QA Dir: Steve Vento
Dir IT: Henry Vasterling
IT Man: Gunawan Thofandi
Tech Mgr: Mike Royer
Tech Mgr: Mike Winter
Mktg Mgr: Jo A Plsek
Sls Mgr: Kevin Perego

D-U-N-S 00-131-6561 IMP/EXP
▲ **INTERNATIONAL PAPER CO** (NY)
6400 Poplar Ave, Memphis, TN 38197-0198
Tel (901) 419-9000 Founded/Ownrshp 1898
Sales 22.3MMM EMP 56,000
Accts Deloitte & Touche Llp Memphi
Tkr Sym IP Exch NYS
SIC 2621 2653 2656 2631 2611 Paper mills; Printing paper; Text paper; Bristols; Boxes, corrugated: made from purchased materials; Food containers (liquid tight), including milk cartons; Cartons, milk: made from purchased material; Container, packaging & boxboard; Container board; Packaging board; Pulp mills
Ch Bd: Mark S Sutton
Pr: Glenn R Landau
Pr: Jean-Michel Ribieras
CFO: Carol L Roberts
Sr VP: W Michael Amick Jr
Sr VP: C Cato Ealy
Sr VP: William P Hoel
Sr VP: Tommy S Joseph
Sr VP: Thomas G Kadien
Sr VP: Timothy S Nicholls
Sr VP: Sharon R Ryan
Sr VP: Chris Werner
VP: Paul Karee
VP: Brian McDonald
Dir Bus: Danny R Long
Comm Man: Claudia Brand
Board of Directors: Ray G Young, David J Bronczek, Ahmet C Dorduncu, Ilene S Gordon, Jay L Johnson, Stacey J Mobley, Joan E Spero, John L Townsend III, William G Walter, J Steven Whisler

D-U-N-S 07-940-8566
INTERNATIONAL PAPER CORP
6400 Poplar Ave, Memphis, TN 38197-0198
Tel (901) 818-5598 Founded/Ownrshp 2014
Sales 98.4MM^E EMP 4,000
SIC 7389

D-U-N-S 06-077-8842
INTERNATIONAL PENTECOSTAL HOLINESS CHURCH
EMMANUEL COLLEGE
7300 Nw 39th Expy, Bethany, OK 73008-2340
Tel (405) 787-7110 Founded/Ownrshp 1911
Sales 73.9MM^E EMP 4,650
SIC 8661 Pentecostal Church
Prin: James Leggett
COO: Michael Gray
Sr VP: Douglas Compton
VP: Doc Ron Carpenter
*Ex Dir: Doug Beacham

INTERNATIONAL PLUS
See NOS COMMUNICATIONS INC

D-U-N-S 12-231-7498 IMP
INTERNATIONAL PRECISION COMPONENTS CORP
I.P.C.C.
28468 N Ballard Dr, Lake Forest, IL 60045-4508
Tel (847) 247-2050 Founded/Ownrshp 1984
Sales 107.5MM^E EMP 320
SIC 3089 Injection molding of plastics
Pr: Michael D Stolzman
COO: Rocky Scalzo
CFO: Robert Istok
*VP: Karen M Stolzman
Plnt Mgr: Mirek Szczesny
Plnt Mgr: Virgis Valeika

INTERNATIONAL PRODUCE EXCHANGE
See BALDOR SPECIALTY FOODS INC

INTERNATIONAL RAM ASSOCIATES
See AIR SERV SECURITY INC

D-U-N-S 04-780-2223 EXP
INTERNATIONAL RELIEF AND DEVELOPMENT INC
IRD
1621 N Kent St Ste 400, Arlington, VA 22209-2119
Tel (703) 247-3068 Founded/Ownrshp 1998
Sales 249.7MM EMP 313
Accts Raffa Pc Washington Dc
SIC 8322 Individual & family services
CEO: Kris Manos
*Pr: Arthur B Keys Jr
*CFO: Beverly Morris-Armstrong
*CFO: Elsie Tama
Ofcr: Ingrid Fitzgerald
Ofcr: Matthew Law
VP: Tamara Jack

D-U-N-S 07-885-4940
INTERNATIONAL RESCUE COMMITTEE INC
IRC AND PARTNERS
122 E 42nd St Fl 12, New York, NY 10168-1299
Tel (212) 551-3000 Founded/Ownrshp 1933
Sales 688.9MM EMP 8,000
SIC 8322 Social service center
Pr: David Miliband
Ofcr: Esther Ahn
Ofcr: Jasmin Farmer
Ofcr: Kimberly Gildersleeve
Ofcr: Oasis Pena
Ofcr: Ellyson Perkins
Ofcr: Sara Rowbottom
Ofcr: Anjuli Shivshanker
Ofcr: Zoran Sredojevic
Sr VP: Carrie Welch
VP: Ciaran Donnelly
VP: Bob Kitchen
Board of Directors: Merryl H Tisch

INTERNATIONAL REST MGT GROUP
See INTERNATIONAL RESTAURANT MANAGEMENT GROUP INC

D-U-N-S 11-125-0031 EXP
INTERNATIONAL RESTAURANT MANAGEMENT GROUP INC
INTERNATIONAL REST MGT GROUP
4531 Pnc De Leon Blvd 3 Ste 300, Miami, FL 33146
Tel (305) 476-1611 Founded/Ownrshp 1992
Sales 59.1MM^E EMP 2,000
SIC 5812 Lunchrooms & cafeterias
Pr: Hoi Sang Yeung
*VP: Ying Ho
*VP: Nita Y Yeung
*VP: Sing-Yan S Yeung
CIO: Raymond Wong
IT Man: Yeung Hoi
Sales Exec: Edwin Samuel
Mktg Dir: Johanna Wade

D-U-N-S 87-690-5654 IMP/EXP
INTERNATIONAL RESTAURANT SERVICES INC
CHILI'S
Amelia Dist Ctr 23 Ema St, Guaynabo, PR 00968
Tel (787) 273-3131 Founded/Ownrshp 1994
Sales 81.6MM^E EMP 1,200
Accts Kevane Grant Thornton Llp San
SIC 5813 5812 Bars & lounges; Eating places
Pr: Arthur Jotic
*VP: Ramon Leal

INTERNATIONAL RISK CONSULTANTS
See IRC INC

D-U-N-S 02-307-7154
■ **INTERNATIONAL SECURITIES EXCHANGE HOLDINGS INC**
(Suby of NASDAQ INC) ★
60 Broad St Fl 26, New York, NY 10004-4138
Tel (212) 943-2400 Founded/Ownrshp 2016
Sales 126.0MM^E EMP 224^E
SIC 6231 Stock option exchanges
CEO: Robert Greifeld
V Ch: Frank Jones
Pr: Adena Friedman
Pr: Hans-Ole Jochumsen
CFO: Michael Ptasznik
Ex VP: Salil Donde
Ex VP: Nelson Griggs
Ex VP: Edward Knight
Ex VP: Lars Ottersgrd
Ex VP: Brad Peterson
Ex VP: Thomas Wittman

D-U-N-S 83-157-9177
INTERNATIONAL SECURITIES EXCHANGE LLC
(Suby of INTERNATIONAL SECURITIES EXCHANGE HOLDINGS INC) ★
60 Broad St Fl 26, New York, NY 10004-2349
Tel (212) 943-2400 Founded/Ownrshp 2004
Sales 139.6MM^E EMP 224
SIC 6231 Stock option exchanges
CFO: Bruce Cooperman
CTO: Lawrence P Cambell
Corp Couns: Joseph Ferraro

D-U-N-S 78-491-7064
INTERNATIONAL SERVICES INC
1250 Barclay Blvd, Buffalo Grove, IL 60089-4500
Tel (847) 808-5590 Founded/Ownrshp 1991
Sales 60.8MM^E EMP 1,200
SIC 8742

D-U-N-S 09-491-5493
INTERNATIONAL SHIPHOLDING CORP
29000 Us Highway 98 C201, Daphne, AL 36526-7272
Tel (251) 243-9100 Founded/Ownrshp 1978
Sales 259.4MM EMP 458^E
SIC 4412 4424 Deep sea foreign transportation of freight; Deep sea domestic transportation of freight
Ch Bd: Erik L Johnsen
CFO: Manuel G Estrada
Ex VP: Peter M Johnston
VP: Sheila Dean-Rosenbohm
Tech Mgr: Regis Burkhardt
Board of Directors: Kenneth H Beer, Niels M Johnsen, H Merritt Lane III, Edwin A Lupberger, James J McNamara, Harris V Morrissette, T Lee Robinson Jr

D-U-N-S 09-000-5059
INTERNATIONAL SHIPPING AGENCY INC
INTERSHIP
500 Paseo Monaco Apt 55, Bayamon, PR 00956-9776
Tel (787) 778-2355 Founded/Ownrshp 1960
Sales 69.7MM^E EMP 1,500
SIC 4491 4731 Stevedoring; Docks, piers & terminals; Agents, shipping
Pr: David R Segarra Jr
*CFO: Maria Caraballo
*Treas: Pablo Jose Alvarez
*VP: Salustino Alvarez
VP: Jose Garcia

D-U-N-S 62-128-7564 IMP/EXP
■ **INTERNATIONAL SNUBBING SERVICES LLC**
(Suby of SESI LLC) ★
190 Industries Ln, Arnaudville, LA 70512-6331
Tel (337) 754-7233 Founded/Ownrshp 2000
Sales 180.0MM^E EMP 300
SIC 1389 7353 Oil field services; Oil field equipment, rental or leasing
Pr: Mark Hardy
CFO: Jamie Kartsimas
Sr VP: Steven Courville
Sr VP: Dave Hardy
VP Opers: John Hardy
VP Opers: Tony Sanders
Opers Mgr: Kelvin Brereton
Opers Mgr: Gregorio Loginow

D-U-N-S 96-437-8459 IMP/EXP
■ **INTERNATIONAL SPECIALTY PRODUCTS INC**
ASHLAND
(*Suby of* ASHLAND LLC) ★
1361 Alps Rd, Wayne, NJ 07470-3700
Tel (859) 815-3333 *Founded/Ownrshp* 2011
Sales 437.0MM[E] *EMP* 2,800
SIC 2869 2821 2843 2842 2899 Amines, acids, salts, esters; Plastics materials & resins; Surface active agents; Specialty cleaning, polishes & sanitation goods; Chemical preparations
CEO: Sunil Kumar
**CFO:* Douglas Vaughan
**Treas:* Susan B Yoss
VP: Jon Stern
Genl Mgr: Melvin W Martin
IT Man: Justin Dunlap
Software D: Sanath Kalutota
Sls&Mrk Ex: Steven Olsen
Sls Mgr: Mark Dailey

D-U-N-S 04-796-6643 IMP
▲ **INTERNATIONAL SPEEDWAY CORP**
1 Daytona Blvd, Daytona Beach, FL 32114-1252
Tel (386) 254-2700 *Founded/Ownrshp* 1953
Sales 645.3MM *EMP* 807[E]
Accts Ernst & Young Llp Tampa Flo
Tkr Sym ISCA *Exch* NGS
SIC 7948 Automotive race track operation; Stock car racing; Motorcycle racing; Race track operation
CEO: Lesa France Kennedy
**Ch Bd:* James C France
Pr: John R Saunders
COO: Joel S Chitwood III
CFO: Daniel W Houser
Chf Mktg O: Daryl Q Wolfe
Ofcr: Brett Scharback
Ex VP: Craig A Neeb
Sr VP: W Garrett Crotty
Sr VP: W Grant Lynch Jr
Sr VP: Roger R Vandersnick
VP: Douglas Bolas
VP: Laura Jackson
VP: Brian Wilson
Board of Directors: Larry Aiello Jr, J Hyatt Brown, Brian Z France, Wiliam P Graves, Sonia M Green, Christy F Harris, Larry D Woodard

INTERNATIONAL SUPPLIERS
See KERZNER INTERNATIONAL NORTH AMERICA INC

D-U-N-S 04-987-1288
INTERNATIONAL TECHNIDYNE CORP
ACCRIVA DIAGNOSTICS
(*Suby of* ACCRIVA DIAGNOSTICS HOLDINGS, INC.)
6260 Sequence Dr, San Diego, CA 92121-4358
Tel (858) 263-2300 *Founded/Ownrshp* 2015
Sales 92.3MM[E] *EMP* 400
SIC 3841 3829 Diagnostic apparatus, medical; Medical diagnostic systems, nuclear
Pr: Scott Cramer
**COO:* Tom Whalen
**CFO:* Greg Tibbitts
**Sr VP:* Matt Bastardi
**VP:* Kimberly Ballard
VP: Lesley Traver
Rgnl Mgr: Joel Payne
Sls Mgr: Bill Eno
Sls Mgr: Brian Maley
Sls Mgr: Regine Voegele

D-U-N-S 82-519-8484 IMP
INTERNATIONAL TEXTILE GROUP INC
804 Green Valley Rd # 300, Greensboro, NC 27408-7000
Tel (336) 379-6299 *Founded/Ownrshp* 2006
Sales 610.4MM *EMP* 4,750
SIC 3714 3496 2211 2231 2221 2273 Fabrics, woven wire; Denims; Draperies & drapery fabrics, cotton; Upholstery fabrics, cotton; Tickings; Worsted fabrics, broadwoven; Upholstery fabrics, wool; Polyester broadwoven fabrics; Draperies & drapery fabrics, manmade fiber & silk; Upholstery fabrics, manmade fiber & silk; Carpets & rugs
Pr: Kenneth T Kunberger
CFO: Gail A Kuczkowski
Treas: Craig J Hart
Ex VP: Gary Kernaghan
VP: Pete Baumann
VP: Nelson Bebo
VP: Robert Fariole
VP: Robert E Garren
VP: Neil W Koonce
VP: Kara Nicholas

D-U-N-S 96-719-5231
INTERNATIONAL TIMBER AND VENEER LLC
ITV
(*Suby of* INTERNATIONAL VENEER COMPANY, INC.)
75 Mcquiston Dr, Jackson Center, PA 16133-1635
Tel (724) 662-0880 *Founded/Ownrshp* 1996
Sales 121.4MM[E] *EMP* 170
SIC 2435 5031 Veneer stock, hardwood; Composite board products, woodboard
Ex VP: Bo Edwards
**Treas:* H Tyler Howerton
**VP:* Mike Rastatter

D-U-N-S 92-995-6225
■ **INTERNATIONAL TRADE ADMINISTRATION**
(*Suby of* US DOC) ★
14th /Constitution Ave Nw, Washington, DC 20230-0001
Tel (202) 482-2000 *Founded/Ownrshp* 1980
Sales NA *EMP* 2,400
SIC 9611 Trade commission, government;
CFO: Mary Pleffner
IT Man: Laura Merchant

D-U-N-S 12-892-5539
INTERNATIONAL TRANSMISSION CO
ITC TRANSMISSION
(*Suby of* ITC HOLDINGS CORP) ★
27175 Energy Way, Novi, MI 48377-3639
Tel (248) 374-7100 *Founded/Ownrshp* 2002
Sales 90.4MM[E] *EMP* 100
SIC 4911 Transmission, electric power
Pr: Joseph L Welch
**CFO:* Edward Rahill
**VP:* Linda H Blair
**VP:* Cameron M Bready
**VP:* Jon E Jipping
**VP:* Daniel J Oginsky
VP: Thomas W Vitez

D-U-N-S 00-373-4018
INTERNATIONAL TRUCK AND ENGINE CORP
6125 Urbana Rd, Springfield, OH 45502-9279
Tel (937) 390-4045 *Founded/Ownrshp* 1999
Sales 79.8MM[E] *EMP* 1,500
SIC 4212 Local trucking, without storage
Prin: Bob Baker
**Ch Bd:* Mr Daniel Ustian
**CEO:* John R Horne
**CFO:* Robert C Lannert
**Sr VP:* Robert A Boardman
VP: Donald Kohs
Exec: Dorothy Crump
Dir IT: Brian Powell
Mtls Mgr: Daren Martin

D-U-N-S 05-868-8318
INTERNATIONAL TRUCKS OF HOUSTON LLC
TEXAS TRUCK CENTERS OF HOUSTON
8900 North Loop E, Houston, TX 77029-1218
Tel (713) 674-3444 *Founded/Ownrshp* 1988
Sales 118.6MM[E] *EMP* 250
SIC 5511 5531 Trucks, tractors & trailers: new & used; Truck equipment & parts

D-U-N-S 62-198-8302
INTERNATIONAL TURF INVESTMENT CO INC
3001 Street Rd, Bensalem, PA 19020-2006
Tel (215) 639-9000 *Founded/Ownrshp* 1990
Sales 59.6MM[E] *EMP* 2,486
SIC 7948 Horse race track operation; Racehorse training; Stables, racing; Thoroughbred horse racing
**VP:* William Hogwood

D-U-N-S 06-777-8209
INTERNATIONAL UNION OF OPERATING ENGINEERS
1121 L St Ste 401, Sacramento, CA 95814-3969
Tel (916) 444-6880 *Founded/Ownrshp* 1939
Sales 53.4MM[E] *EMP* 1,350
SIC 8631 Labor union

D-U-N-S 02-040-6815
INTERNATIONAL UNION OF OPERATING ENGINEERS LOCAL 30 (DC)
INTERNTIONAL UN OPER ENGINEERS
11506 Myrtle Ave, Richmond Hill, NY 11418-1717
Tel (718) 847-8484 *Founded/Ownrshp* 1959
Sales 5.7MM *EMP* 1,000
Accts Schultheis & Panettien Llp Ha
SIC 8631 6512 Collective bargaining unit; Nonresidential building operators
IT Man: Ralph Pascarella

INTERNATIONAL UNION UAW
See UAW PUBLIC RELATIONS

D-U-N-S 07-313-2227
INTERNATIONAL UNION UNITED AUTOMOBILE AEROSPACE AND AGRICULTURAL IMPLEMENT WORKERS OF AM
U A W
8000 E Jefferson Ave, Detroit, MI 48214-3963
Tel (313) 926-5000 *Founded/Ownrshp* 1935
Sales 171.4MM[E] *EMP* 3,000
SIC 8631 Labor union
Pr: Dennis Williams
VP: James Settles
MIS Dir: Stanley Thornton
IT Man: Andrew Dunn

INTERNATIONAL UNN OF OPRTNG EN
See OPERATING ENGINEERS LOCAL 49

D-U-N-S 96-159-4343 IMP/EXP
INTERNATIONAL VITAMIN CORP
IVC
500 Halls Mill Rd, Freehold, NJ 07728-8811
Tel (951) 361-1120 *Founded/Ownrshp* 2009
Sales 530.0MM *EMP* 860
SIC 2834 5149 8099 Vitamin preparations; Organic & diet foods; Nutrition services
Pr: Steven Dai
COO: Glenn Davis
Treas: Eva Pinto
Ex VP: Mike Richtmyer
Sr VP: Thomas E Bocchino
Sr VP: Michael Durso
Sr VP: Dan Tannenbaum
VP: Diane Dottavio
VP: Stephen Rosenman
VP: Bart Smith
VP: John Yonkin

D-U-N-S 55-683-2710
INTERNATIONAL WAXES INC
(*Suby of* IGI THE INTERNATIONAL GROUP, INC.)
45 Route 446, Smethport, PA 16749-5413
Tel (814) 887-5501 *Founded/Ownrshp* 1990
Sales 141.2MM[E] *EMP* 200
SIC 5169 Waxes, except petroleum
Pr: William R Reucassel
**CFO:* David Imrie
**Treas:* James Gelly
**Treas:* John J Tus
**VP:* Kenneth Reucassel

INTERNATIONAL WIRE GROUP
See CAMDEN WIRE CO INC

D-U-N-S 05-491-0935
INTERNATIONAL WIRE GROUP
12 Masonic Ave, Camden, NY 13316-1202
Tel (315) 245-3800 *Founded/Ownrshp* 2011
Sales 442.1MM[E] *EMP* 1,615[E]
SIC 3351 Wire, copper & copper alloy
CEO: Rodney Kent
**CFO:* Donald Dekay

D-U-N-S 88-349-8446 IMP
INTERNATIONAL WIRE GROUP INC
BARE WIRE DIVISION
(*Suby of* INTERNATIONAL WIRE GROUP) ★
12 Masonic Ave, Camden, NY 13316-1202
Tel (315) 245-2000 *Founded/Ownrshp* 2004
Sales 442.1MM[E] *EMP* 1,600
SIC 3357 Nonferrous wiredrawing & insulating
Ch Bd: Rodney D Kent
V Ch: William L Pennington
**CFO:* Glenn J Holler
**VP:* Geoff Kent
VP: Charles Lovenguth
VP: James Mills
IT Man: Zbig Crula

INTERNATIONAL WOOD PRODUCTS
See INTERNATIONAL BUILDING MATERIALS LLC

D-U-N-S 01-038-5979
■ **INTERNATIONAL-MATEX TANK TERMINALS**
IMTT
(*Suby of* MACQUARIE INFRASTRUCTURE CORP) ★
321 Saint Charles Ave, New Orleans, LA 70130-3145
Tel (504) 586-8300 *Founded/Ownrshp* 2014
Sales 258.0MM[E] *EMP* 1,000
SIC 4226 1799 Petroleum & chemical bulk stations & terminals for hire; Petroleum storage tank installation, underground; Petroleum storage tanks, pumping & draining; Dock equipment installation, industrial
Pr: Richard D Courtney
CFO: James May
VP: David Hart
VP: James E Miles III
VP: Jim Papernik
Admn Mgr: Rhonda Yelverton
Mktg Dir: Rene Gurdian

D-U-N-S 04-441-8221
INTERNET BRANDS INC
909 N Sepulveda Blvd # 11, El Segundo, CA 90245-2727
Tel (310) 280-4000 *Founded/Ownrshp* 1998, 2014
Sales 275.5MM[E] *EMP* 649[E]
SIC 7374 Computer graphics service
CEO: Robert N Brisco
**Pr:* Gregory T Perrier
**COO:* Lisa Morita
COO: Lisa Vila
**CFO:* Scott Friedman
**Chf Mktg O:* Chuck Hoover
Ex VP: Eugene Schutt
**Ex VP:* B Lynn Walsh
Sr VP: Mark Miller
VP: Chris Braun
VP: Neal Sainani
VP: Rod Stoddard

D-U-N-S 04-551-1487
INTERNET CORP FOR ASSIGNED NAMES AND NUMBERS
I C A NN
12025 Waterfront Dr # 300, Los Angeles, CA 90094-3220
Tel (310) 823-9358 *Founded/Ownrshp* 1998
Sales 219.5MM *EMP* 160[E]
Accts Ernst & Young Us Llp Playa Vi
SIC 7373 Systems software development services
Ch Bd: Steve Crocker
CFO: Xavier Calvez
**Bd of Dir:* Cherine Chalaby
**Bd of Dir:* Ron Da Silva
**Bd of Dir:* Rinalia Abdul Rahim
VP: Duncan Burns
VP: Jamie Hedlund
VP: Rodrigo De La Parra
VP: Christopher Mondini
VP: Becky Nash
VP: Paul Verhoef
Exec: Ted Bartles
Exec: Gabriella Schittek

D-U-N-S 95-743-9946 IMP
INTERNET PIPELINE INC
IPIPELINE
222 Valley Creek Blvd # 300, Exton, PA 19341-2385
Tel (484) 348-6555 *Founded/Ownrshp* 2015
Sales 107.6MM *EMP* 413
SIC 7372 Prepackaged software
CEO: Timothy Wallace
**Pr:* Andrew Damico
**Pr:* Paul Melchiorre
**COO:* Lawrence Berran
**CFO:* Larry Berran
**Chf Mktg O:* Michael Persiano
Assoc VP: Maura Kane
Ex VP: Kevin Kemmerer
**Dir Sec:* Bill Atlee
Off Mgr: Ginger Rosen
**CTO:* Brian Siedman

INTERNTIONAL UN OPER ENGINEERS
See INTERNATIONAL UNION OF OPERATING ENGINEERS LOCAL 30

INTERNTNAL RHBLTTION ASSOC INC
See CIGNA HEALTH MANAGEMENT INC

INTERNTNAL WRLDWIDE INVSTMENTS
See TREMAYNE ANTONIO WILLIAMS GLOBAL ESTATE ENTRUST TRUST

D-U-N-S 18-055-7811
INTERPACIFIC GROUP INC
576 Beale St, San Francisco, CA 94105-2019
Tel (415) 442-0711 *Founded/Ownrshp* 1986
Sales 56.2MM[E] *EMP* 1,306
SIC 8721 Accounting, auditing & bookkeeping
Pr: Dave Smith

INTERPAK
See INTERNATIONAL PACKAGING CORP

D-U-N-S 00-615-1336 IMP
INTERPLASTIC CORP (MN)
MOLDING PRODUCTS
1225 Willow Lake Blvd, Saint Paul, MN 55110-5145
Tel (651) 481-6860 *Founded/Ownrshp* 1959
Sales 324.4MM[E] *EMP* 600
SIC 2821 Plastics materials & resins; Polyesters
CEO: James D Wallenfelsz
**CFO:* Steven Dittel
**Treas:* David Engelsgaard
**Sr VP:* Bob Deroma
**VP:* Mark Brost
VP: Mark J Brost
**VP:* James Cecere
**VP:* Ivan Levy
**VP:* Terry Pendy
**VP:* Reagan Stephens
Sfty Mgr: Tracy Baysinger

D-U-N-S 14-413-0259 IMP
INTERPLEX INDUSTRIES INC
(*Suby of* INTERPLEX HOLDINGS PTE. LTD.)
1434 110th St Ste 301, College Point, NY 11356-1448
Tel (718) 961-6212 *Founded/Ownrshp* 2014
Sales 132.5MM[E] *EMP* 10[E]
SIC 3471 3825 3674 3469 Electroplating of metals or formed products; Instruments to measure electricity; Semiconductor circuit networks; Stamping metal for the trade
Ch Bd: Jack Seidler
**CFO:* Belinda Lin Zijun
Chf Mktg O: Sanjiv Chhahira
Opers Mgr: Peter Salvas

INTERPOINT
See CRANE ELECTRONICS INC

INTERPUBLIC GROUP OF COMPANIES
See JACK MORTON WORLDWIDE INC

INTERPUBLIC GROUP OF COMPANIES
See DEUTSCH INC

INTERPUBLIC GROUP OF COMPANIES
See R/GA MEDIA GROUP INC

D-U-N-S 00-698-5790
▲ **INTERPUBLIC GROUP OF COMPANIES INC**
909 3rd Ave Fl 7, New York, NY 10022-4764
Tel (212) 704-1200 *Founded/Ownrshp* 1902
Sales 7.6MMM *EMP* 49,200
Tkr Sym IPG *Exch* NYS
SIC 7311 8742 Advertising agencies; Marketing consulting services
Ch Bd: Michael I Roth
CEO: Sean Finnegan
CFO: Frank Mergenthaler
Chf Mktg O: Tony Bombacino
Ex VP: Richard Doomany
Ex VP: Philippe Krakowsky
Sr VP: Andrew Bonzani
Sr VP: Christopher F Carroll
Sr VP: Julie M Connors
Sr VP: John Halper
Sr VP: Peter Leinroth
VP: Simon Bond
VP: David J Weiss
Board of Directors: Deborah G Ellinger, H John Greeniaus, Mary J Steele Guilfoile, Dawn Hudson, William T Kerr, Henry S Miller, Jocelyn Carter-Miller, Jonathan F Miller, David M Thomas

D-U-N-S 12-580-7094 IMP/EXP
INTERRA GROUP INC
INTERA INTERNATIONAL
400 Interstate N Pkwy Ste, Atlanta, GA 30339-5017
Tel (770) 612-8101 *Founded/Ownrshp* 2000
Sales 142.0MM[E] *EMP* 130
SIC 5141 6719 Food brokers; Investment holding companies, except banks
**Ex VP:* Michael Crump
**VP:* Claudia Membreno

D-U-N-S 12-772-0899
INTERSECTION MEDIA HOLDINGS INC
10 Hudson Yards Fl 26, New York, NY 10001-2159
Tel (212) 644-6200 *Founded/Ownrshp* 2003
Sales 300.0MM *EMP* 460
SIC 7312 6719 Outdoor advertising services; Investment holding companies, except banks
CEO: Al Kelly
**Pr:* Scott Goldsmith
**CFO:* Craig Abolt
Ch: Dan Doctoroff
Sr VP: Heather McGuire
Prgrm Mgr: Svetlana Shafirovich
IT Man: Cindy McNally
Netwrk Eng: Gregory Neilson

D-U-N-S 09-414-2846
▲ **INTERSECTIONS INC**
3901 Stonecroft Blvd, Chantilly, VA 20151-1032
Tel (703) 488-6100 *Founded/Ownrshp* 1996
Sales 203.8MM[E] *EMP* 448
Tkr Sym INTX *Exch* NGM
SIC 7323 Credit bureau & agency
Ch Bd: Michael R Stanfield
COO: Johan Roets
CFO: Ronald L Barden
VP: Alain Kouyate
Dir IT: Brad Missal
Mktg Mgr: Gracel Kirk
Board of Directors: John M Albertine, Thomas G Amato, H Stephen Bartlett, Thomas L Kempner, Bruce L Lev, John H Lewis, David A McGough

INTERSHIP
See INTERNATIONAL SHIPPING AGENCY INC

D-U-N-S 08-028-3083 IMP/EXP
■ **INTERSIL COMMUNICATIONS LLC**
(*Suby of* INTERSIL CORP) ★
1001 Murphy Ranch Rd, Milpitas, CA 95035-7912
Tel (408) 432-8888 *Founded/Ownrshp* 1999
Sales 126.1MM[E] *EMP* 1,017
SIC 3674 Semiconductors & related devices
Pr: Necip Sayiner
**CFO:* Rick Crowley
Treas: Lisi John

*Sr VP: Andrew Cowell
*Sr VP: Thomas C Tokos
Dir IT: Terry Brophy
IT Man: Steven Smith
Sftwr Eng: Chris Korbut

D-U-N-S 12-485-1549 IMP
▲ INTERSIL CORP
1001 Murphy Ranch Rd, Milpitas, CA 95035-7912
Tel (408) 432-8888 Founded/Ownrshp 1967
Sales 521.6MM EMP 1,027E
Tkr Sym ISIL Exch NGS
SIC 3674 3679 Semiconductors & related devices; Integrated circuits, semiconductor networks, etc.; Electronic circuits
Pr: Necip Sayiner
*Ch Bd: Donald Macleod
CFO: Richard Crowley
Treas: John Lisi
Bd of Dir: Malcolm Cambra
Sr VP: Susan J Herdman
Sr VP: Roger Wendelken
VP: Carlos Garcia
VP: Sunny Gupta
VP: Clifton Ho
VP: Lan Tran
VP: Masayuki Wajima
Board of Directors: Mercedes Johnson, Gregory Lang, Ernest Maddock, Forrest E Norrod

D-U-N-S 07-883-8762 IMP/EXP
INTERSTATE BATTERIES INC
(Suby of INTERSTATE BATTERY SYSTEM INTERNATIONAL INC) ★
12770 Merit Dr Ste 400, Dallas, TX 75251-1296
Tel (972) 991-1444 Founded/Ownrshp 2013
Sales 220.1MME EMP 712E
SIC 5531 3694 Batteries, automotive & truck; Battery charging alternators & generators
Ch: Norm Miller
*Pr: Scott Miller
VP: Mary Kincheloe
Dir Soc: Pam Hinkle
Rgnl Mgr: Brian Michalski
*Genl Mgr: Dale Herold
*Genl Mgr: Walt Holmes
*Genl Mgr: Tyler Reeves
CIO: Onyeka Nchege
IT Man: Jennifer Youngblood
Opers Mgr: Jason Mills

D-U-N-S 96-552-6197 IMP
INTERSTATE BATTERY SYSTEM INTERNATIONAL INC
12770 Merit Dr Ste 1000, Dallas, TX 75251-1245
Tel (972) 991-1444 Founded/Ownrshp 1991
Sales 552.8MME EMP 1,350
SIC 5531 Batteries, automotive & truck
VP: Jeff Haddock
VP: Chris Antoniou
VP: Grant Dismore
VP: Walt Holmes
VP: Walter Holmes
VP: Scott Miller
VP: Billy Norris
VP: Billy M Norris
VP: William Norris
IT Man: Stacey Carpenter
IT Man: Rebecca Esgro

D-U-N-S 07-352-1536
INTERSTATE BLOOD BANK INC
5700 Pleasant View Rd, Memphis, TN 38134-5028
Tel (901) 384-6200 Founded/Ownrshp 1950
Sales 34.2MME EMP 1,250
SIC 8099 Blood related health services; Blood bank; Plasmapherous center
Pr: Larry A Moss
*Treas: Matt Moss
Genl Mgr: Randy Hirsh

D-U-N-S 04-431-3443 IMP
INTERSTATE CHEMICAL CO INC
UNITED-ERIE DIVISION
2797 Freedland Rd, Hermitage, PA 16148-9099
Tel (724) 981-3771 Founded/Ownrshp 1968
Sales 392.7MME EMP 335
SIC 5169 2819 Chemicals & allied products; Industrial inorganic chemicals
Pr: Albert R Puntureri
Ex VP: Paul R Cirillo
Ex VP: Lou Razzano
VP: Meg Grober
*VP: Joseph S Puntureri
VP Opers: Trey Soates
Plnt Mgr: Joseph Mikolic
Natl Sales: Jack Verigood
VP Mktg: Rich Sirillo
Mktg Dir: Rich Cirillo
Manager: Thomas Fargo

D-U-N-S 12-259-8279
INTERSTATE CLEANING CORP
1566 N Warson Rd, Saint Louis, MO 63132-1106
Tel (314) 428-0566 Founded/Ownrshp 1984
Sales 53.5MME EMP 1,300E
SIC 7349 Janitorial service, contract basis
Pr: John E Brauch Jr
*Ex VP: Michael P Brauch
*Ex VP: Philip R Gaudy

D-U-N-S 60-251-7229
INTERSTATE COMPANIES INC
INTERSTATE POWER SYSTEMS
(Suby of GDG HOLDINGS INC) ★
2501 American Blvd E, Minneapolis, MN 55425-1319
Tel (952) 854-2044 Founded/Ownrshp 1975
Sales 277.8MME EMP 60
SIC 7538 8711 5085 Diesel engine repair: automotive; Engineering services; Power transmission equipment & apparatus
Ch Bd: Gordon D Galarneau
*CEO: Travis Penrod
*CFO: Larry Schwartz
*Ex VP: Michael Masters
VP: Chris Decus
VP: Keith Yingling
Brnch Mgr: Gary Berger
Genl Mgr: Dave Walch

IT Man: Seliskar Becca
VP Opers: Robert Woodward
Sales Exec: Bryan Swanson

D-U-N-S 00-452-1613 IMP
INTERSTATE DIESEL SERVICE INC (OH)
INTERSTATE-MCBEE
5300 Lakeside Ave E, Cleveland, OH 44114-3916
Tel (216) 881-0015 Founded/Ownrshp 1947, 1953
Sales 84.0MME EMP 325
SIC 5013 3714 Automotive engines & engine parts; Fuel systems & parts, motor vehicle; Fuel pumps, motor vehicle
CEO: Alfred J Buescher
*Pr: Ann Buescher
*COO: Brad Buescher

D-U-N-S 05-549-8216
INTERSTATE DISTRIBUTOR CO
(Suby of SALTCHUK RESOURCES INC) ★
11707 21st Avenue Ct S, Tacoma, WA 98444-1236
Tel (253) 537-9455 Founded/Ownrshp 2011
Sales 369.5MME EMP 3,760
SIC 4213 Trucking, except local
Pr: Marc Rogers
*Treas: Rodney A Mc Lean
VP: Todd Bailey
*VP: Jo Borden
VP: Cathy Canonica
*VP: Terry S Mc Lean
VP: Tim Nelson
Dir Risk M: Dana Grandey
Genl Mgr: Ethel Dungey
IT Man: Nettie Reed
Opers Mgr: Jennifer Ford

D-U-N-S 01-914-3163
INTERSTATE ELECTRICAL SERVICES CORP
70 Treble Cove Rd, North Billerica, MA 01862-2208
Tel (978) 667-5200 Founded/Ownrshp 1966
Sales 92.2MM EMP 600
Accts Mcgladrey Llp Boston Massach
SIC 1731 Electronic controls installation; Communications specialization
Pr: Jim P Alibrandi
CFO: Thomas O'Toole
CFO: Thom Otoole
*Treas: Pasquale A Alibrandi
*Ex VP: Carl Brand
VP: Brian Lewis
*VP: John Sloane
Comm Man: Mark Trabucco
Sfty Dirs: Erik Richman

D-U-N-S 00-828-9043
■ INTERSTATE ELECTRONICS CORP
L-3 INTERSTATE ELECTRONICS
(Suby of L-3 COMMUNICATIONS CORP) ★
602 E Vermont Ave, Anaheim, CA 92805-5607
Tel (714) 758-0500 Founded/Ownrshp 1955
Sales 115.2MME EMP 1,102
SIC 3825 3812 3679 Test equipment for electronic & electric measurement; Navigational systems & instruments; Liquid crystal displays (LCD)
Pr: Thomas L Walsh
*VP: Carol Grogg
Genl Mgr: Nancy Sturmer

D-U-N-S 17-732-8291
INTERSTATE GAS MARKETING INC
IGM
2018 S 6th St, Indiana, PA 15701-6012
Tel (724) 465-7958 Founded/Ownrshp 1987
Sales 135.1MME EMP 230
SIC 4925 5172 Gas: mixed, natural & manufactured; Gases
Pr: Michael Melnick
*Treas: John Pisarsik
*VP: William Gregg

D-U-N-S 62-605-8655
INTERSTATE GAS SUPPLY INC
6100 Emerald Pkwy, Dublin, OH 43016-3248
Tel (614) 659-5000 Founded/Ownrshp 1989
Sales 1.4MMM EMP 190E
SIC 1311 Natural gas production
Pr: Scott White
*COO: Jim Baich
*Chf Mktg O: Nicole Ringle
*Ex VP: Doug Austin
VP: Mike Gatt
VP: Jason Moore
VP: Patrick Smith
QA Dir: Matthew Olms
IT Man: Ty Montag
Mktg Mgr: Kraig Lotter
Manager: Evan Bollie

D-U-N-S 00-779-7657 IMP
INTERSTATE HIGHWAY CONSTRUCTION INC
I H C
7135 S Tucson Way, Centennial, CO 80112-3987
Tel (303) 790-7132 Founded/Ownrshp 1956
Sales 1.3MMM EMP 400
SIC 1611 Concrete construction: roads, highways, sidewalks, etc.; Highway & street paving contractor; General contractor, highway & street construction; Airport runway construction
CEO: J Kenyon Schaeffer
*Pr: James Randall
*Treas: Jeffrey C Littman
*VP: John L Edwards
*VP: John Medberry
*VP: Calvin Thomas
Ql Cn Mgr: Hassan Barzegar

D-U-N-S 03-550-8816
INTERSTATE HOTELS & RESORTS INC
HAMPTON INN
(Suby of THAYER LODGING GROUP) ★
4501 Fairfax Dr Ste 500, Arlington, VA 22203-1668
Tel (703) 387-3100 Founded/Ownrshp 1998, 2010
Sales 1.7MMME EMP 19,060
SIC 7011 Hotels & motels
CEO: Thomas F Hewitt
*Ch Bd: Jim Abrahamson
Pr: Samuel E Knighton

CFO: Carrie McIntyre
CFO: Bruce A Riggins
Ofcr: Jane Blake
Ex VP: C Anderson
Ex VP: Christopher L Bennett
Ex VP: Edward Blum
Ex VP: Erica H Hageman
Ex VP: Erica Hageman
Sr VP: Patrick Beron
Sr VP: George J Brennan
Sr VP: Emily Lynn
Sr VP: Michael Miner
Sr VP: Michele Reing
Sr VP: Sherry Serio
VP: David Altobello
VP: Bill Deller
VP: Laura E Fitzrandolph
VP: Dawn Gallagher

D-U-N-S 04-177-2195
INTERSTATE MANAGEMENT & INVESTMENT CORP
IMIC HOTELS
1 Surrey Ct, Columbia, SC 29212-3100
Tel (803) 772-2629 Founded/Ownrshp 1981
Sales 63.0MME EMP 1,400
SIC 7011 Hotels & motels
CEO: E L Pooser Jr
*Pr: Bert Pooser III
*VP: Jeff Buchko
*VP: Kathy Rabune
*VP: Rick Rabune

D-U-N-S 96-801-4865
INTERSTATE MANAGEMENT CO LLC
(Suby of HAMPTON INN) ★
4501 Fairfax Dr Ste 500, Arlington, VA 22203-1668
Tel (703) 387-3100 Founded/Ownrshp 1998
Sales 98.4MM EMP 11,000
SIC 8741 Hotel or motel management

D-U-N-S 92-897-2520 IMP
INTERSTATE MEAT & PROVISION
STERLING PACIFIC MEAT COMPANY
6114 Scott Way, Commerce, CA 90040-3518
Tel (323) 838-9400 Founded/Ownrshp 1995
Sales 85.9MME EMP 100
SIC 5142 5147 Packaged frozen goods; Meat brokers
CEO: Jim Asher

D-U-N-S 10-280-5546
INTERSTATE MECHANICAL CORP
IMCOR
1841 E Washington St, Phoenix, AZ 85034-1230
Tel (800) 628-0211 Founded/Ownrshp 1983
Sales 143.9MME EMP 380
SIC 1711 Mechanical contractor
Ch Bd: Merle M Karber
CFO: Sterling Smith
*Treas: Susan Baxter
*VP: Rick Karber
Exec: Lori Hareza
Dir Bus: Jeremy Ettesvold
Genl Mgr: Wendy Cuthbertson
Mktg Mgr: Tim McVey

INTERSTATE MFG & SUPPLY DIV
See SPS COMPANIES INC

INTERSTATE MNROE MCHY SUPS DIV
See STATCO ENGINEERING & FABRICATORS INC

D-U-N-S 80-433-6709
INTERSTATE NATIONAL DEALER SERVICES INC
6120 Powers Ferry Rd S, Atlanta, GA 30339-2996
Tel (678) 894-3500 Founded/Ownrshp 2003
Sales NA EMP 140
SIC 6399 6221 Warranty insurance, automobile; Commodity contracts brokers, dealers
Pr: Mark H Mishler
Sr Pt: Richard Ocallaghan
COO: Christine Bianco
*CFO: Geoffrey Tirone
Ofcr: Stephanie Gueye
*Ex VP: Lawrence J Altman
*Ex VP: Sansone Dominic
VP: Nicole Aiello
VP: Dave Pakula
*VP: Gerry Thanner
IT Man: Robert Kollar

D-U-N-S 06-692-8623 EXP
INTERSTATE PAPER LLC
(Suby of INTERSTATE RESOURCES INC) ★
2366 Interstate Rd Ste 1, Riceboro, GA 31323-3934
Tel (912) 884-3371 Founded/Ownrshp 1982
Sales 150.0MME EMP 240
SIC 2631 Kraft linerboard
CEO: Antoine N Frem
Pr: Charles Feghali
Sec: Ramez G Skaff
Sfty Dirs: Ronnie Moore

D-U-N-S 09-726-1036
INTERSTATE PERSONNEL SERVICES INC
PASCHALL TRUCK LINES
3443 Us Highway 641 S, Murray, KY 42071-7112
Tel (270) 753-1717 Founded/Ownrshp 1973
Sales 178.6MME EMP 1,176E
Accts Katz Sapper & Miller Llp In
SIC 4213 Trucking, except local
Pr: Randall A Waller Sr
*Treas: Judy Ingersoll
*Treas: Anthony Waller Jr
*VP: Hal T Bishop
*VP: Thomas J Stephens
*VP: Luther G Waller

INTERSTATE PLASTICS
See DONGALEN ENTERPRISES INC

D-U-N-S 00-694-0522 IMP
■ INTERSTATE POWER AND LIGHT CO (IA)
(Suby of ALLIANT ENERGY CORP) ★
200 1st St Se, Cedar Rapids, IA 52401-1409
Tel (319) 398-4411 Founded/Ownrshp 1882
Sales 1.7MMM EMP 1,766
SIC 4911 4924 4961

INTERSTATE POWER SYSTEMS
See INTERSTATE COMPANIES INC

D-U-N-S 36-199-7740
INTERSTATE POWER SYSTEMS INC
(Suby of INTERSTATE POWER SYSTEMS) ★
2901 E 78th St, Minneapolis, MN 55425-1501
Tel (952) 854-2044 Founded/Ownrshp 2005
Sales 147.3MME EMP 60E
SIC 5084 Trucks, industrial
CEO: Jeff Gaswell
*CEO: Travis Penrod
*CFO: Larry Schwartz
*Ch: Gordan Galarneau
VP: Vince Story
Genl Mgr: Mike Creamer
Dir IT: Tom McHenry
IT Man: Shane Sargent
VP Opers: Mike Severson

INTERSTATE POWERCARE
See POWERCARE AND SERVICE SOLUTIONS INC

D-U-N-S 07-548-3412
INTERSTATE REALTY MANAGEMENT CO INC (NJ)
3 E Stow Rd, Marlton, NJ 08053-3188
Tel (856) 596-0500 Founded/Ownrshp 1973
Sales 99.3MME EMP 1,300
SIC 6531 6513 Real estate managers; Condominium manager; Rental agent, real estate; Apartment hotel operation
Ch Bd: Michael J Levitt
*Pr: Mark Morgan
*Treas: Jim Bleiler
VP: Michael Boettger
Mng Dir: David L Anderson
VP Opers: Paul Sassani

D-U-N-S 05-651-4524 IMP/EXP
INTERSTATE RESOURCES INC
(Suby of INDEVCO SAL)
1300 Wilson Blvd Ste 1075, Arlington, VA 22209-2330
Tel (703) 243-3355 Founded/Ownrshp 1988
Sales 334.5MME EMP 930
SIC 2631 2653 7389 Kraft linerboard; Boxes, corrugated: made from purchased materials; Purchasing service
CEO: Neetmat Frem
COO: James Morgan
CFO: Pierre Khattar
CFO: Pierre Khatter
VP: Roger Malone
VP: Dave Stauffer
VP: David Stauffer
Rgnl Mgr: Laurie Maggio
Genl Mgr: Pete Bugas
Genl Mgr: Al Cantrell
Genl Mgr: Doug McKee

D-U-N-S 04-709-7410 IMP
INTERSTATE RESTORATION LLC
3401 Quorum Dr Ste 300, Fort Worth, TX 76137-3621
Tel (817) 293-0035 Founded/Ownrshp 2007
Sales 163.0MME EMP 160
SIC 1542 1522 7349 Commercial & office buildings, renovation & repair; Remodeling, multi-family dwellings; Building maintenance services
Ex VP: Clay Mazur
Exec: Chris Wiggins
Genl Mgr: Samuel Jack
Sls&Mrk Ex: Brenda Pereda
Snr PM: Darrin Dewitt

D-U-N-S 15-209-5006 IMP
INTERSTATE WAREHOUSING OF VIRGINIA LLC
(Suby of TIPPMANN PROPERTIES INC) ★
9009 Coldwater Rd Ste 300, Fort Wayne, IN 46825-2072
Tel (260) 490-3000 Founded/Ownrshp 1997
Sales 116.5MME EMP 539
SIC 4222 Warehousing, cold storage or refrigerated
Ch: John Tippmann
*Pr: Charles Tippmann
*VP: Joseph Greco
*VP: Steven Tippmann
Rgnl Mgr: Andrew Jackson
Off Mgr: Christina Hall
Opers Supe: Robert Elhart
Opers Supe: Doug Romba
Opers Mgr: Jarad Gerardot
Sls Dir: David Hastings

INTERSTATE-MCBEE
See INTERSTATE DIESEL SERVICE INC

D-U-N-S 04-258-2577
INTERSTATES CONSTRUCTION SERVICES INC
(Suby of INTERSTATES CONSTRUCTION SVCS) ★
1520 N Main Ave, Sioux Center, IA 51250-2111
Tel (712) 722-1662 Founded/Ownrshp 1999
Sales 110.4MM EMP 325
Accts Eide Bailly Llp Sioux Falls
SIC 1731 3629 Electrical work; Computerized controls installation; Electronic generation equipment
CEO: Scott Peterson
*Ch Bd: Larry E Den Herder
*Pr: David A Crumrine
*COO: Catherine Bloom
*VP: Dave Los
*VP: Wayne McDaniel
*VP: Lowell Reith
*VP: Randy Van Vorst
Software D: Patrick Brausey

INTERSTATES CONSTRUCTION SVCS
See HARBOR GROUP INC

D-U-N-S 10-885-1353
INTERSYSTEMS CORP
1 Memorial Dr Ste 6, Cambridge, MA 02142-1356
Tel (617) 621-0600 Founded/Ownrshp 1978
Sales 500.0MM EMP 1,400
SIC 7371 Computer software development & applications
Pr: Phillip T Ragon
CFO: Ryan Brenneman

CFO: Jack Macheras
VP: Jerry Bartlett
VP: Christine Chapman
**VP:* Richard Currier
**VP:* Joe Desantis
VP: Steve Garrington
VP: Paul Grabscheid
**VP:* Paul Grabsheid
VP: Boris Mamkin
**VP:* Robert Nagle
**VP:* Matthew Nee
VP: RB Omo
VP: John F Paladino
**VP:* Susan Ragon
VP: Jim Rose
VP: Larry Roth
VP: Ray Vrtiska

D-U-N-S 10-569-4947 IMP
INTERTAPE POLYMER CORP
I P G
(*Suby of* IPG (US) INC) ★
100 Paramount Dr Ste 300, Sarasota, FL 34232-6051
Tel (941) 727-5788 *Founded/Ownrshp* 1995
Sales 293.8MM^E *EMP* 600
SIC 2672 Tape, pressure sensitive: made from purchased materials
Pr: Gregory A Yull
**CFO:* Eric Johnson
**VP:* Jim B Carpenter
**VP:* Bernard J Pitz

INTERTAPE POLYMER GROUP
See IPG (US) HOLDINGS INC

D-U-N-S 15-451-8278 IMP
INTERTEC SYSTEMS LLC
(*Suby of* ADIENT US LLC) ★
45000 Helm St Ste 200, Plymouth, MI 48170-6040
Tel (734) 254-3268 *Founded/Ownrshp* 2016
Sales 89.3MM^E *EMP* 516
SIC 3714 Motor vehicle parts & accessories; Instrument board assemblies, motor vehicle

D-U-N-S 00-172-2722
INTERTECH CI (PA)
(*Suby of* INTERTECH SECURITY GROUP LLC) ★
1501 Preble Ave, Pittsburgh, PA 15233-2248
Tel (412) 246-1200 *Founded/Ownrshp* 1999
Sales 159.3MM^E *EMP* 180
SIC 5065 Security control equipment & systems
CEO: Ronald Petnuch
CFO: Bart Huchel
**Ex VP:* Christopher J Wetzel
VP: Michael Devinney
**VP:* Matthew Petnuch
Tech Mgr: Ben Campbell
Sls Mgr: Keith Robbins

D-U-N-S 10-912-3406 IMP/EXP
INTERTECH GROUP INC
4838 Jenkins Ave, North Charleston, SC 29405-4816
Tel (843) 744-5174 *Founded/Ownrshp* 1982
Sales 1.6MMM^E *EMP* 15,832
SIC 3949 Fishing equipment
CEO: Anita G Zucker
COO: Jay Tiedemann
Ex VP: Robert Johnston
Ex VP: Brice Sweatt
Sr VP: Sarah Van Mosel
VP: Jan Clark
VP: Tom Platte
IT Man: Jerry Zucker
Counsel: Jeffrey Winkler

D-U-N-S 80-832-0050
INTERTECH SECURITY GROUP LLC
1501 Preble Ave Ste 6, Pittsburgh, PA 15233-2248
Tel (724) 742-4900 *Founded/Ownrshp* 2005
Sales 178.7MM^E *EMP* 180
SIC 7382 Security systems services; Burglar alarm maintenance & monitoring; Protective devices, security
CFO: Bart Huchel

D-U-N-S 62-736-3877
INTERTEK
545 E Algonquin Rd Ste F, Arlington Heights, IL 60005-4376
Tel (847) 871-1020 *Founded/Ownrshp* 2006
Sales 604.6MM^E *EMP* 2,564^E
SIC 8748 Business consulting
CEO: Wolfhart Hauser
**Pr:* Greg Tieman

INTERTEK AUTOMOTIVE RESEARCH
See INTERTEK USA INC

INTERTEK ETL SEMKO
See INTERTEK TESTING SERVICES NA INC

D-U-N-S 03-769-0302 IMP
INTERTEK TESTING SERVICES NA INC
INTERTEK ETL SEMKO
(*Suby of* INTERTEK GROUP PLC)
3933 Us Route 11, Cortland, NY 13045-9715
Tel (607) 753-6711 *Founded/Ownrshp* 1996
Sales 298.5MM^E *EMP* 1,400
SIC 8734 Testing laboratories; Product testing laboratory, safety or performance
CEO: Wolfhart Hauser
**Pr:* Gregg Tiemann
**CFO:* Lloyd Pitchford
**Treas:* Tim Courossi
**Ex VP:* Stefan Butz
**VP:* Nimer Hafi
VP: Todd Little
**VP:* Derwyn Reuber
VP: Patrick Sweeney
**VP:* Jeff Turcotte
Dir Lab: Mickey Moore

D-U-N-S 07-415-9310 IMP
INTERTEK USA INC
INTERTEK AUTOMOTIVE RESEARCH
(*Suby of* INTERTEK UK HOLDINGS LIMITED)
2 Riverway Ste 500, Houston, TX 77056-2083
Tel (713) 543-3600 *Founded/Ownrshp* 1988
Sales 1.0MMM^E *EMP* 4,000
SIC 4785 8734 Surveyors, marine cargo; Inspection services connected with transportation; Calibration & certification
Pr: Jay Gutierrez
VP: Rick Huntley
**VP:* Graham Lees
**VP:* Mark Vise
Dir Bus: Lori Payne
Brnch Mgr: Kevin Gilbert
Dir IT: William Quilindo
IT Man: Tom Drink
IT Man: Sheida Sadrai
Sls Dir: Justin McAdams

INTERTHERM
See NORTEK GLOBAL HVAC LLC

D-U-N-S 83-729-3943
■ **INTERVAL ACQUISITION CORP**
INTERVAL INTERNATIONAL
(*Suby of* INTERVAL INTERNATIONAL INC) ★
6262 Sunset Dr Ste 400, South Miami, FL 33143-4843
Tel (954) 431-0060 *Founded/Ownrshp* 2008
Sales 46.3MM^E *EMP* 1,700
SIC 4724 Travel agencies
Pr: Craig M Nash
**COO:* Paul Rishell
**CFO:* William Carl Drew
**Treas:* Eduardo Fernandez
**Ex VP:* Jeanette E Marbert

D-U-N-S 13-211-7024
■ **INTERVAL HOLDING CO INC**
(*Suby of* INTERVAL INTERNATIONAL) ★
6262 Sunset Dr Fl 6, South Miami, FL 33143-4843
Tel (305) 666-1861 *Founded/Ownrshp* 2002
Sales 6.3MM^E *EMP* 1,700
SIC 8699 8721 6531 Travel club; Billing & bookkeeping service; Escrow agent, real estate
Prin: Jeanette Marbert

INTERVAL INTERNATIONAL
See INTERVAL ACQUISITION CORP

D-U-N-S 08-359-9936 EXP
■ **INTERVAL INTERNATIONAL INC**
(*Suby of* ILG) ★
6262 Sunset Dr Ste 400, South Miami, FL 33143-4843
Tel (305) 666-1861 *Founded/Ownrshp* 2008
Sales 179.3MM *EMP* 2,080
SIC 8699 Travel club
CEO: Craig M Nash
**COO:* Jeanette E Marbert
**CFO:* William Carl Drew
Bd of Dir: Robert Healey
Ex VP: Marcos Agostini
Sr VP: Sharon Freed
Sr VP: Marie Lee
VP: Janice Anderson
VP: Bryan T Broek
VP: Larry Dettelis
VP: Raul Estrada
VP: David Gilbert
VP: Edrea Kaiser
VP: Katy Keusch
VP: Estrada Raul
VP: Lori C Rrp
VP: David Valdez

D-U-N-S 06-348-8522 IMP
INTERVARSITY CHRISTIAN FELLOWSHIP/USA
TWENTY ONE HUNDRED PRODUCTIONS
635 Science Dr, Madison, WI 53711-1099
Tel (608) 274-9001 *Founded/Ownrshp* 1941
Sales 105.7MM *EMP* 1,613
Accts Capin Crouse Llp Greenwood
SIC 8661 2731 7032 Religious organizations; Books: publishing & printing; Bible camp
Pr: Alexander Hill
**Ch:* Rudy Hernandez
**Treas:* Mark Felton
VP: A Fryling
**VP:* Robert Fryling
**VP:* Andrew Ginsberg
**VP:* Tom Lin
**VP:* James Lundgren
**VP:* Karon Morton
**VP:* Kim Porter
**VP:* Paul Tokonaga
Exec: Scott Wilson
Assoc Dir: Roy Stephen
Comm Dir: Anna Gissing

INTERVENTIONAL ASSOCIATES OF M
See UT MEDICAL GROUP INC

D-U-N-S 17-409-1686
INTERVEST CONSTRUCTION OF ORLANDO INC
I C I
2379 Beville Rd, Daytona Beach, FL 32119-8720
Tel (386) 788-0820 *Founded/Ownrshp* 1980
Sales 127.6MM^E *EMP* 249
SIC 1522 1521 Multi-family dwelling construction; New construction, single-family houses
Pr: Morteza Hosseini-Kargar
CFO: Tom McCall
CFO: Jean Trinder
VP: Dick Smith
VP: Sherrie Williams
Exec: Robert Fortier

D-U-N-S 03-767-8216 IMP
■ **INTERVET INC**
(*Suby of* MERCK & CO INC) ★
29160 Intervet Ln, Millsboro, DE 19966-4217
Tel (302) 934-4341 *Founded/Ownrshp* 2007
Sales 86.2MM^E *EMP* 800
SIC 2836 Veterinary biological products
Pr: Christopher Ragland
VP: Stephen Collins
Assoc Dir: Joyce Woods
Ql Cn Mgr: Arthur Bowden
Natl Sales: Clayton Coder
Natl Sales: Graham Welch
Natl Sales: Craig Wheeler

D-U-N-S 11-743-9273
■ **INTERVOICE LLC**
(*Suby of* CONVERGYS CORP) ★
17787 Waterview Pkwy, Dallas, TX 75252-8027
Tel (972) 454-8000 *Founded/Ownrshp* 2011
Sales 125.7MM^E *EMP* 736^E
SIC 3661 Telephone & telegraph apparatus; PBX equipment, manual or automatic
V Ch: David Bradenberg
V Ch: Stanley Brannan
Pr: Jeffrey Daly
Ex VP: Ray Naeini
Ex VP: Bob Ritchey
Ex VP: Donald R Walsh
Sr VP: Dwain H Ammond
Sr VP: Gordon H Givens
Sr VP: Kenneth Goldberg
Sr VP: Dwain H Hammond
Sr VP: Mark Haris
Sr VP: Richard Herrmann
Sr VP: Marie A Jackson
Sr VP: Francis G Sherlock
VP: Marc Gardner
VP: Manuel James
VP: Walt Mirkowicz
VP: Phil Osborn
VP: Greg Smith
VP: Steve Wind
VP: Carol Wingard

D-U-N-S 09-952-8531
INTERWEST INSURANCE SERVICES INC
KEMPER INSURANCE
3636 American River Dr # 2, Sacramento, CA 95864-5952
Tel (916) 488-3100 *Founded/Ownrshp* 1992
Sales NA *EMP* 315
SIC 6411 Insurance brokers
Ch: Tom Williams
Pr: Thomas Williams
CEO: Keith Schuler
COO: Nancy Luttenbacher
CFO: Donald Pollard
Ex VP: Steve Azevedo
Ex VP: William O'Keefe
VP: Greg Clauser
VP: Jim Foley
VP: Craig Houck
VP: Tom Hughes
VP: Valerie Lyons
VP: Greg Scoville
VP: Phil Watkins
VP: Cari Zieske
Exec: Denise Brown
Exec: Sam Wlasiuk
Assoc Dir: Ann Quinn

INTERWIRE GROUP
See INTER-WIRE PRODUCTS INC

D-U-N-S 95-607-8919
■ **INTERWOVEN INC**
AUTONOMY INTERWOVEN
(*Suby of* HEWLETT PACKARD ENTERPRISE CO) ★
1140 Enterprise Way, Sunnyvale, CA 94089-1412
Tel (312) 580-9100 *Founded/Ownrshp* 2015
Sales 112.6MM^E *EMP* 888
SIC 7372 Business oriented computer software
CEO: Anthony Bettencourt
**CFO:* John E Calonico Jr
**Chf Mktg O:* Benjamin E Kiker Jr
**Ex VP:* Shams Rashid
Sr VP: Jeff Kissling
Sr VP: Steven J Martello
VP: Brian Bauer
VP: John Graham
VP: Jack Jia
VP: Jeff Reid
VP: Rex Thexton

D-U-N-S 80-786-9362 IMP/EXP
INTEVA PRODUCTS LLC
(*Suby of* RENCO GROUP INC) ★
1401 Crooks Rd, Troy, MI 48084-7106
Tel (248) 655-8886 *Founded/Ownrshp* 2007
Sales 3.8MMM^E *EMP* 11,500
SIC 3714 5085 Motor vehicle parts & accessories; Industrial supplies
Pr: Lon Offenbacher
CFO: William Dircks
VP: Floranne Dunford
VP: Steven Galle
VP: Jan Griffiths
VP: William Hanna
VP: Michael Maddelein
Mng Dir: Reed Zhang
Prgrm Mgr: Mark Bade
Prgrm Mgr: Aurelia Marin
Rgnl Mgr: Carolyn Bohlken

D-U-N-S 09-862-6062 IMP/EXP
INTEX RECREATION CORP
4001 Via Oro Ave Ste 210, Long Beach, CA 90810-1400
Tel (310) 549-5400 *Founded/Ownrshp* 1970
Sales 173.5MM^E *EMP* 679^E
SIC 5091 5092 5021 3081 Watersports equipment & supplies; Toys; Waterbeds; Vinyl film & sheet; Polyethylene film
Pr: Tien P Zee
Exec: Tom Lindahl
Info Man: Wayne Farmer
Sls Dir: Steve DOE

INTIER AUTOMOTIVE SEATING
See MAGNA SEATING OF AMERICA INC

D-U-N-S 96-784-0369
■ **INTIMATE BRANDS HOLDING LLC**
(*Suby of* INTIMATE BRANDS INC) ★
3 Limited Pkwy, Columbus, OH 43230-1467
Tel (614) 415-7000 *Founded/Ownrshp* 2011
Sales 458.9MM^E *EMP* 228^E
SIC 5632 Lingerie (outerwear)
V Ch: Kenneth B Gilman
Sls Mgr: Jill Granoff

D-U-N-S 15-061-4829
■ **INTIMATE BRANDS INC**
(*Suby of* L BRANDS) ★
3 Limited Pkwy, Columbus, OH 43230-1467
Tel (614) 415-7000 *Founded/Ownrshp* 1993
Sales 457.4MM^E *EMP* 228^E
SIC 5632 Lingerie (outerwear)
CFO: Stuart Burgdoerfer

D-U-N-S 62-079-3877
▲ **INTL FCSTONE INC**
708 3rd Ave Rm 1500, New York, NY 10017-4108
Tel (212) 485-3500 *Founded/Ownrshp* 1924
Sales 14.7MMM *EMP* 1,200
Tkr Sym INTL *Exch* NGS
SIC 6282 6211 6289 Investment advice; Security brokers & dealers; Mineral, oil & gas leasing & royalty dealers; Security & commodity clearinghouses
Pr: Sean M O'Connor
Ch Bd: John Radziwill
COO: Xuong Nguyen
CFO: William J Dunaway
Ofcr: Josh Cruce
VP: Albert Barbella
VP: Joseph Cassidy
VP: Michelle Dorea
VP: Nancey McMurtry
VP: Thiago Vieira
VP: Chris Weinberg
VP: Michael Wiseman
Dir Risk M: Tricia Harrod
Dir Risk M: Brian Spears

INTOUCH MINISTRY
See IN TOUCH MINISTRIES INC

D-U-N-S 09-012-1661
INTOUCH SOLUTIONS INC (KS)
7045 College Blvd Ste 300, Overland Park, KS 66211-1529
Tel (913) 317-9700 *Founded/Ownrshp* 1999
Sales 108.0MM^E *EMP* 500
SIC 8742 Marketing consulting services
CEO: Faruk Capan
**Ex VP:* Wendy Blackburn
Ex VP: Boris Kushkuley
**Ex VP:* Angela Tenuta
**Ex VP:* David Windhausen
**Sr VP:* Megan O'Connor
Sr VP: Paul Pierce
Sr VP: Eric Vollmuth
VP: Jill Groebl
**VP:* Pat McNerney
**VP:* Connie Mullinix
VP: Greg Schutta
Exec: Connie Millinix
Dir: Joe Abella
Creative D: Charley Aldridge
Creative D: Chris Boyer
Creative D: Erin Cwiakala
Creative D: Joanna Friel
Creative D: Kit Hunnell
Creative D: Craig Johnston
Creative D: Jeff Macfarland

D-U-N-S 79-682-3511
INTOWN HOLDING CO LLC
2727 Paces Fery Rd 2 1200, Atlanta, GA 30339
Tel (770) 799-5000 *Founded/Ownrshp* 1997
Sales NA *EMP* 0^E
Accts Deloitte & Touche Llp Atlanta
SIC 6712 Bank holding companies

D-U-N-S 82-865-3225
INTOWN HOSPITALITY INVESTORS LP
INTOWN SUITES
980 Hammond Dr Ste 1400, Atlanta, GA 30328-8144
Tel (770) 799-5000 *Founded/Ownrshp* 2007
Sales 48.9MM^E *EMP* 1,100
SIC 7011 Motel, franchised
CFO: Dennis M Cassel

INTOWN SUITES
See INTOWN HOSPITALITY INVESTORS LP

D-U-N-S 09-617-3950 IMP
INTRA AMERICAN METALS INC
INTRAMETCO
14297 Bergen Blvd Ste 200, Noblesville, IN 46060-3383
Tel (317) 219-4444 *Founded/Ownrshp* 1979
Sales 118.0MM^E *EMP* 11
SIC 5093 Nonferrous metals scrap
Off Mgr: Saundra Jackson

INTRADECO APPAREL
See INTRADECO INC

D-U-N-S 14-070-5653 IMP/EXP
INTRADECO APPAREL INC
(*Suby of* INTRADECO APPAREL) ★
9500 Nw 108th Ave, Medley, FL 33178-2517
Tel (305) 264-8888 *Founded/Ownrshp* 2001
Sales 325.0MM *EMP* 180^E
Accts Kabat Schertzer De La Torre
SIC 2389 Men's miscellaneous accessories
CEO: Felix J Siman
**CFO:* Jose E Siman
VP: Martha Dugan
Off Mgr: Manuel Moreno
IT Man: Leonor Sagovia
Opers Mgr: Edgar Aguirre
S&M/VP: Hector Gutierrez

D-U-N-S 10-833-6066 IMP/EXP
INTRADECO INC
INTRADECO APPAREL
9500 Nw 108th Ave, Medley, FL 33178-2517
Tel (305) 264-6022 *Founded/Ownrshp* 2013
Sales 335.7MM^E *EMP* 180^E
SIC 5136 5199 5065 Men's & boys' clothing; Cotton yarns; Electronic parts
Pr: Jose E Siman
**VP:* Felix J Siman
**Prin:* Rolando Calsa
IT Man: Rafael Olivares
IT Man: Leonor Segovia

D-U-N-S 18-970-5820 IMP
INTRAHEALTH INTERNATIONAL INC
6340 Quadrangle Dr # 200, Chapel Hill, NC 27517-7891
Tel (919) 313-9100 *Founded/Ownrshp* 2005
Sales 90.4MM *EMP* 154ᴱ
Accts Gelman Rosenberg & Freedman B
SIC 8011 Health maintenance organization
Pr: Pape Amadou Gaye
Ofcr: Jennifer Gloc
Sr VP: Rebecca Kohler
VP: Maureen Corbett
VP: Scott Sherman Edd
Prgrm Mgr: Laura Hurley
Prgrm Mgr: Kate Stratten
Software D: Carl Leitner
Snr PM: Nick Ford
Snr Mgr: Corinne Mahoney
Board of Directors: Todd Wohler, Walter Davenport, Joseph P Davis III, Marilyn Deluca, Sheila Leatherman, Josh Nesbit, Charles Ok Pannenborg, Nilda Peragallo, Carlos Correcha-Price, Beverly Rubin

D-U-N-S 80-323-7697
▲ INTRALINKS HOLDINGS INC
150 E 42nd St Fl 8, New York, NY 10017-5626
Tel (212) 543-7700 *Founded/Ownrshp* 1996
Sales 276.1MM *EMP* 930ᴱ
Tkr Sym IL *Exch* NYS
SIC 7372 7382 Prepackaged software; Security systems services
Pr: Ronald W Hovsepian
**Ch Bd:* Patrick J Wack Jr
CFO: Christopher J Lafond
Chf Mktg O: Jay Muelhoefer
Ex VP: Scott N Semel
VP: Jorge Mira
Board of Directors: Brian J Conway, Peter Gyenes, Thomas Hale, Habib Kairouz, Robert C McBride, Harsha Ramalingam, J Chris Scalet, Jim Steele

D-U-N-S 94-885-4443 IMP/EXP
■ INTRALINKS INC
(*Suby of* INTRALINKS HOLDINGS INC) ★
150 E 42nd St Fl 8, New York, NY 10017-5626
Tel (212) 543-7700 *Founded/Ownrshp* 2007
Sales 240.8MMᴱ *EMP* 380
SIC 4899 7375 Data communication services; Information retrieval services
Pr: Ronald W Hovsepian
CFO: Derek Irwin
**CFO:* Anthony Plesner
Ex VP: Julian Henkin
Ex VP: Scott N Semel
**Ex VP:* Fahim Siddiqui
Sr VP: Wasif Awan
Sr VP: David Barbero
Sr VP: Frank Brunetti
Sr VP: Douglas Gordon
**Sr VP:* Gary Hirsch
Sr VP: Dave Roy
VP: Michael Baldwin
VP: Christopher Ford
VP: Seminaro Frank
VP: Rob Piane
VP: Allan Robertson
VP: Martha Stuart
VP: George Waidell
Dir Bus: Charles Roberts
Board of Directors: Brian J Conway, Habib Kairouz, Harry D Taylor

D-U-N-S 09-198-3275
INTRALOT INC
INTRALOT USA
(*Suby of* INTRALOT S.A.)
11360 Technology Cir, Duluth, GA 30097-1502
Tel (678) 473-7200 *Founded/Ownrshp* 2001
Sales 94.7MMᴱ *EMP* 240
SIC 7379
Pr: Thomas F Little
**Ch Bd:* Socrates Kokkalis
Pr: Lynn Becker
**CEO:* Constantinos Antonopoulos
**COO:* Andreas Papoulias
**CFO:* Toula Argentis
VP: Byron Boothe
Dir IT: Stegios Binopoulos
Opers Mgr: Dennis Karras
VP Sls: John Pittman

INTRALOT USA
See INTRALOT INC

D-U-N-S 06-546-7052 IMP/EXP
INTRALOX LLC
(*Suby of* LAITRAM LLC) ★
301 Plantation Rd, Harahan, LA 70123-5326
Tel (504) 733-6739 *Founded/Ownrshp* 1990
Sales 233.1MMᴱ *EMP* 608
SIC 3535 Conveyors & conveying equipment
Sfty Dirs: Zhinong Yan

INTRAMETCO
See INTRA AMERICAN METALS INC

D-U-N-S 09-229-6524
INTRANSIT INC
UTI TRANSPORT SOLUTIONS
(*Suby of* UTI UNITED STATES INC) ★
3525 Excel Dr, Medford, OR 97504-9798
Tel (541) 773-3993 *Founded/Ownrshp* 2006
Sales 99.1MMᴱ *EMP* 110
SIC 4731 Brokers, shipping
Pr: Donald R Farthing
VP: Suellen Rowe
VP: Pat Walden

D-U-N-S 07-870-5231
INTRAPAC (PLATTSBURGH) INC
(*Suby of* INTRAPAC INTERNATIONAL CORP) ★
4 Plant St, Plattsburgh, NY 12901-3771
Tel (518) 561-2030 *Founded/Ownrshp* 2000
Sales 104.9MMᴱ *EMP* 693ᴱ
SIC 5199 3565 Packaging materials; Packaging machinery

D-U-N-S 07-866-0879
INTRAPAC INTERNATIONAL CORP
136 Fairview Rd Ste 320, Mooresville, NC 28117-9519
Tel (704) 360-8910 *Founded/Ownrshp* 2012
Sales 120.0MM *EMP* 900
SIC 3085 3221 Plastics bottles; Glass containers
CEO: Ray Grupinski

D-U-N-S 07-921-4173
▲ INTRAWEST RESORTS HOLDINGS INC
1621 18th St Ste 300, Denver, CO 80202-5905
Tel (303) 749-8200 *Founded/Ownrshp* 2007
Sales 570.9MM *EMP* 5,350ᴱ
Accts Kpmg Llp Denver Colorado
Tkr Sym SNOW *Exch* NYS
SIC 7011 7999 6531 Ski lodge; Resort hotel; Ski instruction; Ski rental concession; Real estate agents & managers
CEO: Thomas F Marano
**Ch Bd:* Wesley R Edens
COO: Sky Foulkes
CFO: Travis Mayer
Sr VP: Karen Sanford

D-U-N-S 36-155-8182 IMP
INTREN INC
TRENCH-IT
18202 W Union Rd, Union, IL 60180-9710
Tel (815) 923-2300 *Founded/Ownrshp* 1991
Sales 204.9MMᴱ *EMP* 300ᴱ
SIC 1623 Underground utilities contractor
Pr: Lance Rosenmayer
Pr: Jason Combs
**CFO:* Mike McArthy
Ex VP: Michael Sandberg
**VP:* Rob Wiggs
Genl Mgr: Amanda Glissman
Off Mgr: Patty Cassens
IT Man: Kyle Juno
Snr Mgr: Mike Schoon

D-U-N-S 01-273-2421
■ INTREPID HEALTHCARE SERVICES INC
(*Suby of* TEAMHEALTH) ★
4605 Lankershim Blvd, North Hollywood, CA 91602-1818
Tel (888) 447-2362 *Founded/Ownrshp* 2015
Sales 693.9MM *EMP* 2,841ᴱ
SIC 8011 Physicians' office, including specialists
CEO: Adam D Singer
Pr: R Jeffrey Taylor
CFO: Richard H Kline III
Chf Mktg O: Kerry E Weiner
Ex VP: Richard G Russell
Sr VP: Glenn Appelbaum
Sr VP: Beth Hawley
Sr VP: Fernando J Sarria
Sr VP: Jeffrey Winter
VP: Felix Aguirre
VP: Mark C Citron
VP: Jamie S Glazer
VP: Patrick Holmes
VP: Timothy Lary
VP: Kathleen Loya
VP: Marcie Matthews
VP: Robert Roig
VP: Cary Rosoff

D-U-N-S 82-588-6638
▲ INTREPID POTASH INC
707 17th St Ste 4200, Denver, CO 80202-3432
Tel (303) 296-3006 *Founded/Ownrshp* 2007
Sales 287.1MM *EMP* 893ᴱ
Accts Kpmg Llp Denver Colorado
Tkr Sym IPI *Exch* NYS
SIC 1474 Potash mining
Ch Bd: Robert P Jornayvaz III
**V Ch:* Hugh E Harvey Jr
Ex VP: David Honeyfield
Ex VP: James N Whyte
Sr VP: Brian D Frantz
Sr VP: John G Mansanti
VP: Kelvin Feist
VP: Ken Heisel
VP: Gary Kohn
VP: Margaret E McCandless
Genl Mgr: Robert Baldridge
Board of Directors: Terry Considine, Chris A Elliott, J Landis Martin, Barth E Whitham

D-U-N-S 14-451-6205 IMP
■ INTREPID POTASH-NEW MEXICO LLC
(*Suby of* INTREPID POTASH INC) ★
1996 Potash Mines Rd, Carlsbad, NM 88220-8965
Tel (575) 887-5591 *Founded/Ownrshp* 2004
Sales 201.9MMᴱ *EMP* 628ᴱ
SIC 1474 Potash, soda & borate minerals
Pr: David W Honeyfield
**Pr:* Hugh Harvey
**Sr VP:* Kelvin G Feist
**Sr VP:* John G Mansanti
**VP:* Rod Gloss
**VP:* Robert Jornayvaz
Sfty Mgr: Dale Janway

INTREPID USA HEALTHCARE SVCS
See INTREPID USA INC

D-U-N-S 09-182-8587
INTREPID USA INC
INTREPID USA HEALTHCARE SVCS
(*Suby of* PATRIARCH PARTNERS LLC) ★
4055 Valley View Ln # 500, Dallas, TX 75244-5048
Tel (214) 445-3750 *Founded/Ownrshp* 1999
Sales 152.3MMᴱ *EMP* 2,500
SIC 7363 8082 Medical help service; Home health care services
CEO: Charles Sweet
**CFO:* Andrew Kerr
Genl Mgr: Kyle Chandler
Off Mgr: Sara Ayers
Off Mgr: Sonja Carter
IT Man: Rachel Barrientez

D-U-N-S 19-102-7528
▲ INTREXON CORP
20374 Seneca Meadows Pkwy, Germantown, MD 20876-7004
Tel (301) 556-9900 *Founded/Ownrshp* 1998
Sales 173.6MM *EMP* 734
Tkr Sym XON *Exch* NYS
SIC 8731 Biotechnical research, commercial
Ch Bd: Randal J Kirk
Owner: Jeffrey Perez
Pr: Geno J Germano
COO: Andrew J Last
CFO: Rick L Sterling
Sr VP: Ena Chan Cratsenberg
Sr VP: Corey L Huck
Sr VP: Joel Liffmann
Sr VP: Nir Nimrodi
Sr VP: Joseph L Vaillancourt
Sr VP: Robert F Walsh III

D-U-N-S 00-694-4029 IMP
INTRUST BANK NA
(*Suby of* INTRUST FINANCIAL CORP) ★
105 N Main St, Wichita, KS 67202-1401
Tel (316) 383-1111 *Founded/Ownrshp* 1876
Sales NA *EMP* 939
SIC 6021 National trust companies with deposits, commercial
Ch Bd: C Q Chandler IV
V Ch: J Lentell
**Pr:* Jay Smith
**CFO:* Brian Heinrichs
**Chf Cred:* Rick Beach
Ofcr: Jim Betts
Ofcr: Cathy Cowley
Ofcr: Molly Darrenkamp
Ofcr: Lisa Elliott
Ofcr: Lisa Vance
Ex VP: Anna Anderson
Ex VP: Steve L Hipp
Ex VP: Bruce A Long
Ex VP: Julius Madas
Ex VP: Janeen Smalley
Sr VP: Rhonda Disney
Sr VP: Roger Eastwood
Sr VP: Joe Eaton
Sr VP: John Goff
Sr VP: Gail Johnson
Sr VP: Troy Jordan
Board of Directors: Richard M Kerschen, C Robert Buford, Thomas D Kitch, Frank Carney, Eric T Knorr, Richard G Chance, Charles Koch, C Q Chandler III, William B Moore, George T Chandler, Paul Seymour Jr, Stephen L Clark, Kenneth Shannon, R L Darmon, Donald Slawson, Charles Dieker, John Stewart III, Martin Eby Jr, Jeffrey Turner

D-U-N-S 12-176-8790
INTRUST FINANCIAL CORP
105 N Main St, Wichita, KS 67202-1412
Tel (316) 383-1111 *Founded/Ownrshp* 1971
Sales NA *EMP* 950
Accts Bkd Llp Kansas City Mo
SIC 6712 6022 Bank holding companies; State commercial banks
CEO: Charles Q Chandler III
Ch Bd: C Q Chandler III
Pr: C Q Chandler IV
COO: Rick L Beach
CFO: Jay L Smith
Chf Cred: Alicia M Guagliardo
Ofcr: Graty Bolier
Ofcr: Douglas Gaumer
Ofcr: Gina Ireland
Ofcr: Mark Maier
Ex VP: Roger Eastwood
Ex VP: Steve L Hipp
Sr VP: T R Goeing
VP: Deanna Boyles
VP: Blaine Carnprobst
VP: Joseph Eaton
VP: Dan Eilert
VP: Sandra Jasnoski
VP: Greg Scafe
VP: Don Wilson

D-U-N-S 96-617-1837 IMP/EXP
INTSEL STEEL DISTRIBUTORS LLC
INTSEL STEEL WEST
(*Suby of* TRIPLE-S STEEL HOLDINGS INC) ★
11310 W Little York Rd, Houston, TX 77041-4917
Tel (713) 937-9500 *Founded/Ownrshp* 1960
Sales 184.8MMᴱ *EMP* 200
SIC 5051 3312 3444 Iron & steel (ferrous) products; Blast furnaces & steel mills; Sheet metal specialties, not stamped
VP: Troy Arceneaux
Genl Mgr: Craig Peterson
Opers Mgr: Austin Shirley

INTSEL STEEL WEST
See INTSEL STEEL DISTRIBUTORS LLC

INTUIT FINANCIAL SERVICES
See DIGITAL INSIGHT CORP

D-U-N-S 11-329-0969
▲ INTUIT INC
2700 Coast Ave, Mountain View, CA 94043-1140
Tel (650) 944-6000 *Founded/Ownrshp* 1983
Sales 4.6MMM *EMP* 7,900
Accts Ernst & Young Llp San Jose C
Tkr Sym INTU *Exch* NGS
SIC 7372 Business oriented computer software
Ch Bd: Brad D Smith
CFO: R Neil Williams
Ch: Scott D Cook
Ex VP: Caroline F Donahue
Ex VP: Laura A Fennell
Ex VP: Sasan K Goodarzi
Ex VP: Cece Morken
Ex VP: H Tayloe Stansbury
Sr VP: Eric Dunn
VP: David Cole
VP: Mark J Flournoy
VP: Gail Houston
VP: Jeff Langston
VP: Holger Wenzky
VP: Dan Wernikoff
Board of Directors: Eve Burton, Scott D Cook, Richard Dalzell, Diane B Greene, Suzanne Nora Johnson, Dennis D Powell, Raul Vazquez, Jeff Weiner

D-U-N-S 08-294-8303
INTUITIVE RESEARCH AND TECHNOLOGY CORP
I R T C
5030 Bradford Dr Nw # 205, Huntsville, AL 35805-1923
Tel (256) 922-9300 *Founded/Ownrshp* 1999
Sales 247.0MMᴱ *EMP* 287
SIC 8711 8748 Engineering services; Systems engineering consultant, ex. computer or professional
CEO: Angel R Almodovar
**Pr:* Harold Brewer
VP: Albert Killen
VP: Tommie Newberry

D-U-N-S 93-864-7021 IMP
▲ INTUITIVE SURGICAL INC
1020 Kifer Rd, Sunnyvale, CA 94086-5301
Tel (408) 523-2100 *Founded/Ownrshp* 1995
Sales 2.3MMM *EMP* 3,211
Accts Ernst & Young Llp San Francis
Tkr Sym ISRG *Exch* NGS
SIC 3841 Surgical & medical instruments
Pr: Gary S Guthart
**Ch Bd:* Lonnie M Smith
CFO: Marshall L Mohr
Chf Mktg O: Myriam J Curet
Ex VP: Jerry McNamara
Ex VP: David J Rosa
Sr VP: Mark J Meltzer
Sr VP: Colin Morales
VP: Adam Clark
VP: Mark Johnson
VP: Jade Kondo
VP: Jamie E Samath
VP: David Stoffel
Board of Directors: Craig H Barratt, Michael A Friedman, Amal M Johnson, Keith R Leonard Jr, Alan J Levy, Mark J Rubash, Lonnie M Smith, George Stalk Jr

D-U-N-S 07-691-6246 IMP/EXP
▲ INVACARE CORP
1 Invacare Way, Elyria, OH 44035-4190
Tel (440) 329-6000 *Founded/Ownrshp* 1971
Sales 1.1MMM *EMP* 4,700
Tkr Sym IVC *Exch* NYS
SIC 3842 2514 2813 Surgical appliances & supplies; Wheelchairs; Personal safety equipment; Beds, including folding & cabinet, household: metal; Industrial gases; Oxygen, compressed or liquefied
Ch Bd: Matthew E Monaghan
**CFO:* Robert K Gudbranson
**Sr VP:* Dean J Childers
**Sr VP:* Anthony C Laplaca
**Sr VP:* Patricia A Stumpp
**Sr VP:* Gordon Sutherland
VP: Doug Uelmen
Prgrm Mgr: Tim Lis
Opers Mgr: Junior Gonzalez
Sls&Mrk Ex: John Dmytriw
Manager: Brian Murphy
Board of Directors: Susan H Alexander, Michael F Delaney, Marc M Gibeley, C Martin Harris, James L Jones, Dale C Laporte, Michael J Merriman, Clifford D Nastas

D-U-N-S 15-736-4295 IMP/EXP
INVACARE CORP (TW)
39400 Taylor Pkwy, North Ridgeville, OH 44035-6270
Tel (440) 329-6000 *Founded/Ownrshp* 2004
Sales 1.6MMMᴱ *EMP* 45
SIC 3842 Surgical appliances & supplies
Pr: A Malachi Mixon III

D-U-N-S 16-510-4469 IMP
INVAGEN PHARMACEUTICALS INC
(*Suby of* CIPLA (EU) LIMITED)
7 Oser Ave Ste 4, Hauppauge, NY 11788-3811
Tel (631) 231-3233 *Founded/Ownrshp* 2016
Sales 129.0MM *EMP* 370
Accts Christopher E Gargiulo Cpa
SIC 2834 5122 Pharmaceutical preparations; Pharmaceuticals
Pr: Sudhakar Vidiyala
COO: Madhava U Reddy
Ofcr: Sumit Markanday
Dir Lab: Ajay Vemula

D-U-N-S 10-797-1306
INVENERGY LLC
1 S Wacker Dr Ste 1800, Chicago, IL 60606-4630
Tel (312) 224-1400 *Founded/Ownrshp* 2001
Sales 98.5MMᴱ *EMP* 140ᴱ
SIC 8711 Energy conservation engineering
Pr: Michael Polsky
**COO:* Jim Murphy
**Ex VP:* James Murphy
**Ex VP:* Jim Shield
**Sr VP:* Joe Condo
Sr VP: Amy Francetic
**Sr VP:* Alex George
**Sr VP:* Bryan Schueler
Sr VP: Paul Turner
VP: Dan Ewan
VP: Eric Fiste
VP: Joel Link
VP: Steve Ryder
VP: Kris Zadlo
Dir Bus: Brett Oakleaf

D-U-N-S 18-793-6138 IMP
▲ INVENSENSE INC
1745 Tech Dr Ste 200, San Jose, CA 95110
Tel (408) 501-2200 *Founded/Ownrshp* 2003
Sales 418.4MM *EMP* 632ᴱ
Accts Deloitte & Touche Llp San Jo
Tkr Sym INVN *Exch* NYS
SIC 3812 Gyroscopes
Pr: Behrooz Abdi
**Ch Bd:* Amit Shah
CFO: Mark Dentinger
VP: Daniel Goehl
VP: MO Maghsoudnia
VP: Eitan Medina
Off Mgr: Sarah Carmichael
Sls Mgr: Mike Daneman
Board of Directors: Jon Olson, Eric Stang

D-U-N-S 07-858-1518
INVENSIS INC
(Suby of INVENSIS TECHNOLOGY PRIVATE LIMITED)
1000 N West St Ste 1200, Wilmington, DE 19801-1058
Tel (302) 351-3509 Founded/Ownrshp 2010
Sales 22.0MM^E EMP 1,200
SIC 7374 Data processing & preparation
Pr: Vara Prasad Rongala

INVENSYS ENVIRONMENTAL CONTRLS
See SCHNEIDER ELECTRIC BUILDINGS LLC

INVENSYS PROCESS SYSTEMS
See INVENSYS PROCESSS SYSTEMS INC

D-U-N-S 15-420-9639 IMP
INVENSYS PROCESSS SYSTEMS INC
INVENSYS PROCESS SYSTEMS
(Suby of SCHNEIDER ELECTRIC SE)
10900 Equity Dr, Houston, TX 77041-8226
Tel (713) 329-1600 Founded/Ownrshp 1965
Sales 1.3MMM^E EMP 8,000
SIC 3822 Temperature controls, automatic; Refrigeration controls (pressure); Refrigeration/air-conditioning defrost controls; Humidity controls, air-conditioning types
Pr: Michael J Caliel
CFO: Jack Spencer
Sr VP: Raja Macha
VP: Silji Abraham
VP: James Bachmann
VP: Rick Bilberry
VP: Robert E Cook
VP: Jason Dietrich
*VP: Jay S Ehle
*VP: Gary Frebjeger
VP: Bob Jones
*VP: Victoria Jule
*VP: Peter Kent
VP: Bruce Larson
VP: Vinay Moorthy
VP: Ron Pariseau
Dir Bus: Bill Schiel

INVENSYS RAIL
See SIEMENS RAIL AUTOMATION CORP

D-U-N-S 00-101-3994 IMP
INVENSYS SYSTEMS INC
SCHNEIDER ELECTRIC
(Suby of INVENSYS LIMITED)
10900 Equity Dr, Houston, TX 77041-8226
Tel (713) 329-1600 Founded/Ownrshp 1914
Sales 238.5MM^E EMP 531^E
SIC 3823 8711 8741 Industrial instrmnts msrmnt display/control process variable; Flow instruments, industrial process type; Pressure measurement instruments, industrial; Liquid level instruments, industrial process type; Industrial engineers; Management services
Pr: Gary Freburger
*CFO: Brian Dibenedetto
*Sr VP: Karen Hamilton
*Sr VP: Peter Kent
VP: Mike Caliel
VP: Stephen Halsey
Dir IT: Jill Ret
IT Man: Dave Atkins
IT Man: Judy Faulk
IT Man: Stefano Oliveri
IT Man: Townwell Robin

D-U-N-S 96-400-0835
INVENTIV GROUP HOLDINGS INC
(Suby of DOUBLE EAGLE PARENT INC) ★
1 Van De Graaff Dr, Burlington, MA 01803-5188
Tel (609) 951-6800 Founded/Ownrshp 2016
Sales 2.3MMM^E EMP 7,112^E
SIC 8742 8731 Marketing consulting services; Medical research, commercial; Commercial physical research
CEO: R Blane Walter

D-U-N-S 08-572-6037
INVENTIV HEALTH CLINICAL INC
(Suby of INVENTIV HEALTH INC) ★
504 Carnegie Ctr, Princeton, NJ 08540-6241
Tel (609) 514-9400 Founded/Ownrshp 2011
Sales 274.9MM^E EMP 2,300
SIC 8731 Commercial physical research
Pr: Riaz Bandali
COO: Patricia Coleman
*COO: Gregg Dearhammer
CFO: George A McMillan
CFO: Thomas J Newman
*CFO: Richard Shimota
*Chf Mktg O: Jeffrey Freitag
Ex VP: George Butler
Ex VP: Bengt Danielsson
Ex VP: Mike Ivers
Sr VP: James P Burns
*Sr VP: Mj Carino
*Sr VP: Joseph A Fortunato
Sr VP: Steven Leventer
Sr VP: Valerie Palumbo
VP: Brandon Eldredge
VP: St Phane Marin
VP: Kevin McKay
VP: George Scott
VP: Roger Taft
Exec: Philippe Chahinian

D-U-N-S 07-869-8514
INVENTIV HEALTH CLINICAL SRE LLC
(Suby of INVENTIV HEALTH INC) ★
1 Van De Graaff Dr, Burlington, MA 01803-5188
Tel (800) 416-0555 Founded/Ownrshp 2004
Sales 179.7MM^E EMP 126^E
SIC 5122 Pharmaceuticals

D-U-N-S 11-479-4493 IMP
INVENTIV HEALTH INC
(Suby of INVENTIV GROUP HOLDINGS INC) ★
1 Van De Graaff Dr, Burlington, MA 01803-5188
Tel (800) 416-0555 Founded/Ownrshp 2010
Sales 2.3MMM EMP 7,111
Accts Deloitte & Touche Llp Boston
SIC 8731 Commercial physical research
CEO: Michael Bell
Pr: Michael McKelvey
Pr: Tom Sebok
Pr: Eric Sirota
Pr: Jeffrey Thomas
Pr: Jeffrey Wilks
COO: Mike Bell
*COO: Gregg Dearhammer
*CFO: Jonathan E Bicknell
CFO: Richard Shimota
Ofcr: William L Holden
Ex VP: Ryan Deshazer
Ex VP: Frederick Finnegan
Ex VP: Rick Finnegan
*Ex VP: Michael A Griffith
Ex VP: Raymond Hill
*Ex VP: Michael J McKelvey
Ex VP: Chuck Shea
Ex VP: Valerie Sullivan
VP: Ernie Bendinelli
VP: Gene Black

D-U-N-S 62-411-7805
INVENTRUST PROPERTIES CORP
2809 Butterfield Rd, Oak Brook, IL 60523-1151
Tel (855) 377-0510 Founded/Ownrshp 2004
Sales 450.0MM EMP 362^E
SIC 6798 Real estate investment trusts
Ch Bd: J Michael Borden
Pr: Thomas P McGuinness
Pr: Jonathan T Roberts
CFO: Michael E Podboy
Ofcr: Adam M Jaworski
Ex VP: David F Collins
VP: Christy L David
Board of Directors: Scott A Nelson, Michael A Stein

D-U-N-S 83-733-0679 IMP/EXP
▲ INVENTURE FOODS INC
5415 E High St Ste 350, Phoenix, AZ 85054-5484
Tel (623) 932-6200 Founded/Ownrshp 1995
Sales 282.5MM EMP 1,100^E
Tkr Sym SNAK Exch NGM
SIC 2096 2037 Potato chips & similar snacks; Fruits, quick frozen & cold pack (frozen)
CEO: Terry McDaniel
*Ch Bd: David L Meyers
CFO: Steve Weinberger
Sr VP: E Brian Foster
Sr VP: Daniel W Hammer
Sr VP: Steven Sklar
VP: Sandip Parikh
Off Admin: Whitney Hunsaker
IT Man: Malissa McGivern
Sfty Dirs: Krista Himes
Sls Dir: Robert Delgado
Board of Directors: Ashton D Asensio, Timothy A Cole, Macon Bryce Edmonson, Harold S Edwards, Paul J Lapadat

D-U-N-S 96-797-0968 IMP
INVENTUS POWER INC
ICC NEXERGY
1200 Internationale Pkwy, Woodridge, IL 60517-4975
Tel (630) 410-7900 Founded/Ownrshp 2014
Sales 565.2MM^E EMP 1,595
SIC 3629 Battery chargers, rectifying or nonrotating
CEO: Patrick Trippel
*Pr: Stephen McClure
*CFO: Kevin Oconnor
*CFO: Kenneth J Wroblewski
Ofcr: Sean Harrigan
*Ex VP: John Gatti
*VP: Anson Martin
*VP: Chris Turner
*VP: Like Xie
Off Mgr: Debbie Panzica
IT Man: Chris Hogrefe

D-U-N-S 80-526-7036
INVERNESS MANAGEMENT LLC
21 Locust Ave Ste 1d, New Canaan, CT 06840-4735
Tel (203) 966-4177 Founded/Ownrshp 1997
Sales 203.9MM^E EMP 820
SIC 6799 Investors
Co-Founder: W McComb Dunwoody
Mng Pt: James Comis

D-U-N-S 82-905-9398
INVESCO AGENCY SECURITIES INC
1360 Peachtree St Ne # 600, Atlanta, GA 30309-3283
Tel (404) 892-0896 Founded/Ownrshp 2008
Sales 132.8MM EMP 2
SIC 6798 Real estate investment trusts
CFO: Donald Ramon

D-U-N-S 08-149-8818
■ INVESCO AIM ADVISORS INC
AIM BLUE CHIP FUNDS
(Suby of INVESCO LTD) ★
11 Greenway Plz Ste 2500, Houston, TX 77046-1188
Tel (713) 626-1919 Founded/Ownrshp 1976, 2007
Sales 232.8MM^E EMP 2,000
SIC 6722 Management investment, open-end
Ch: Martin L Flanagan
Pr: Jay McCraw
Pr: Philip A Taylor
Ofcr: Jesse Dean
Ofcr: Richard Sproll
Ofcr: Shannon Vasquez
Ex VP: Lisa Brinkley
Sr VP: Karen Dunn Kelley
Sr VP: Leslie A Schmidt
VP: Clay King
VP: Heather Lindsey
VP: Jim Russell
Exec: Nancy Patterson
Dir Soc: Nancy Beckdeane
Dir Soc: Yottis Wilson

D-U-N-S 08-893-3622
▲ INVESCO LTD
1555 Peachtree St Ne 18, Atlanta, GA 30309-2460
Tel (404) 892-0896 Founded/Ownrshp 1935
Sales 5.1MMM EMP 6,490
Tkr Sym IVZ Exch NYS
SIC 6282 Investment advice; Investment advisory service
Pr: Martin L Flanagan
*Ch Bd: Ben F Johnson III
Pr: Pat Pacchiarotti
CFO: Loren M Starr
Ofcr: Colin D Meadows
VP: Theo Heldman
VP: Peter Hubbard
VP: Kevin Marsh
VP: Tom Rocco
VP: Andrew Stevenson
VP: Ivo Turkedjiev
VP: Jeannie Underwood
Board of Directors: Joseph R Canion, C Robert Henrikson, Denis Kessler, Edward P Lawrence, Nigel Sheinwald, G Richard Wagoner Jr, Phoebe A Wood

D-U-N-S 83-086-2939
INVESCO MORTGAGE CAPITAL INC
1555 Peachtree St Ne, Atlanta, GA 30309-2460
Tel (404) 892-0896 Founded/Ownrshp 2008
Sales 437.5MM EMP 4
Accts Grant Thornton Llp Iselin Ne
Tkr Sym IVR Exch NYS
SIC 6798 Real estate investment trusts
Pr: Richard J King
COO: Robson J Kuster
CFO: Richard Lee Phegley Jr
Chf Inves: John M Anzalone
VP: Betsy Warrick

D-U-N-S 07-282-0343
INVEST WEST FINANCIAL CORP
1933 Cliff Dr Ste 1, Santa Barbara, CA 93109-1502
Tel (805) 957-0095 Founded/Ownrshp 1970
Sales 154.9MM^E EMP 845
SIC 6726 6513 Investment offices; Apartment hotel operation
Ch: Dale Marquis
Pr: Matt Marquis
CEO: Dale J Marquis
VP: Thomas Gamble
Brnch Mgr: Michael Vidal
CTO: Jennifer Mertz
IT Man: Helen Mercer

D-U-N-S 80-198-0140
INVESTCORP INTERNATIONAL HOLDINGS INC
(Suby of INVESTCORP, S. A.)
280 Park Ave Fl 36, New York, NY 10017-1285
Tel (212) 599-4700 Founded/Ownrshp 2005
Sales 320.8MM^E EMP 676^E
SIC 6282 Investment advisory service
Pr: Christopher O'Brian
VP: James Christopoulos
VP: Brian Streko
Mng Dir: Prashant Kolluri
Mng Dir: Herb Myers
CIO: Lionel Erdely

D-U-N-S 11-632-3838
INVESTCORP INTERNATIONAL INC
(Suby of INVESTCORP INTERNATIONAL HOLDINGS INC) ★
280 Park Ave Fl 36, New York, NY 10017-1285
Tel (212) 599-4700 Founded/Ownrshp 1986
Sales 176.6MM^E EMP 429^E
SIC 6531 Real estate agents & managers
CEO: Nemir A Kirdar
Chf Inves: Lionel Erdely
Top Exec: Brian Murphy
Assoc VP: Feras A Majed
VP: Gupta Amit
VP: Jesse Brundige
VP: Sandeep Jain
VP: Michael Moriarty
VP: Justin Patnode
VP: Nirav Shah
VP: Priya Singh
VP: Gayan Wijesinha
VP: Ali Zainal

D-U-N-S 15-399-0635
INVESTCORP SERVICES INC
(Suby of INVESTCORP INTERNATIONAL HOLDINGS INC) ★
280 Park Ave Fl 36, New York, NY 10017-1285
Tel (212) 599-4700 Founded/Ownrshp 1982
Sales 125.5MM^E EMP 429
SIC 6282 Investment advisory service
CEO: Nemir Kirdar
*Pr: Christopher O'Brian
*Treas: Mayme Tong
*VP: Victor Okoth

D-U-N-S 06-654-1442
INVESTMENT RARITIES INC
7850 Metro Pkwy Ste 121, Minneapolis, MN 55425-1530
Tel (952) 853-0700 Founded/Ownrshp 1973
Sales 147.9MM EMP 60
SIC 5999 Coins; Numismatist shops
Pr: James R Cook
Bd of Dir: Thomas Dillon
Bd of Dir: Harry Meltz

D-U-N-S 79-100-4807
▲ INVESTMENT TECHNOLOGY GROUP INC
ITG
165 Broadway, New York, NY 10006-1404
Tel (212) 588-4000 Founded/Ownrshp 1983
Sales 634.8MM EMP 1,037^E
Tkr Sym ITG Exch NYS
SIC 6211 Brokers, security; Dealers, security
Pr: Francis J Troise
*Ch Bd: Minder Cheng
Pr: Prem Balasubramanian
Pr: Mahalakshmi Gobalakrishna
Pr: Marisa Napoli
Pr: Christopher Ross
Pr: Gunjan Sharma
Pr: Sean Whyte
CEO: Robert J Boardman
CEO: Michael Corcoran
CEO: Etienne Phaneuf
CEO: Alasdair Thomson
CFO: Steven R Vigliotti
Treas: Philip Pearson
Chf Mktg O: Heather Evans
VP: Laura Broussard
VP: Phil Chevalier
VP: Chad Dale
VP: Anthony Gaglio
VP: Joe Gentile
VP: Jennifer Goldstein
Board of Directors: Brian G Cartwright, Timothy L Jones, R Jarrett Lilien, Kevin J Lynch, T Kelley Millet, Lee M Shavel, Steven S Wood

D-U-N-S 60-744-1172
▲ INVESTORS BANCORP INC
101 Jfk Pkwy Ste 3, Short Hills, NJ 07078-2793
Tel (973) 924-5100 Founded/Ownrshp 2015
Sales NA EMP 1,597
Tkr Sym ISBC Exch NGS
SIC 6035 Savings institutions, federally chartered
Pr: Kevin Cummings
COO: Domenick A Cama
CFO: Sean Burke
Ofcr: Richard S Spengler
Ex VP: Paul Kalamaras
VP: Sergio Alonso
VP: Jawad Chaudhry
VP: William Cosgrove
VP: Mary Ward
Brnch Mgr: Lisa Bernardo
Brnch Mgr: Michael Blinder
Board of Directors: Robert C Albanese, Dennis M Bone, Doreen R Byrnes, Domenick A Cama, William V Cosgrove, Brian D Dittenhafer, James J Garibaldi, Michele N Siekerka, James H Ward III

D-U-N-S 60-584-4609
INVESTORS BANCORP MHC
101 Jfk Pkwy Ste 3, Short Hills, NJ 07078-2793
Tel (973) 376-5100 Founded/Ownrshp 1997
Sales NA EMP 1,942
SIC 6036 Savings institutions, not federally chartered
Pr: Robert Cashill

D-U-N-S 07-516-0978
■ INVESTORS BANK
(Suby of INVESTORS BANCORP INC) ★
101 John F Kennedy Pkwy # 3, Short Hills, NJ 07078-2793
Tel (973) 376-5100 Founded/Ownrshp 1926, 1997
Sales NA EMP 875
SIC 6036 State savings banks, not federally chartered
Pr: Kevin Cummings
Pr: Sharon Lingswiler
COO: Domenick A Cama
Ofcr: Elias A Djecki
Ex VP: Paul Kalamaras
Ex VP: Richard S Spengler
Sr VP: Mark Balsam
Sr VP: Dennis Budinich
Sr VP: Sean Burke
Sr VP: William Cosgrove
Sr VP: Catherine Cossa
Sr VP: Andrew Markey
Sr VP: Jeanette Muldoon
Sr VP: Elaine Rizzo
Sr VP: Thomas F Splaine
VP: Scott Agnoli
VP: Jessica Ballew
VP: James Brown
VP: Emma Cartier
VP: Alex Chiarella
VP: Robert Dempsey

D-U-N-S 92-884-9926
INVESTORS CAPITAL HOLDINGS LLC
(Suby of ARETEC GROUP INC) ★
6 Kimball Ln Ste 150, Lynnfield, MA 01940-2684
Tel (781) 246-7982 Founded/Ownrshp 2014
Sales 93.6MM EMP 59^E
SIC 6211 6282 Security brokers & dealers; Investment advisory service
COO: James Wallace
CFO: Kathleen L Donnelly
Chf Cred: John G Cataldo
Web Dev: Keith Zerfas

D-U-N-S 08-605-2297
■ INVESTORS FIDUCIARY TRUST CO
STATE STREET KANSAS CITY
(Suby of STATE STREET CORP) ★
801 Pennsylvania Ave, Kansas City, MO 64105-1307
Tel (816) 871-4100 Founded/Ownrshp 1995
Sales 122.5MM^E EMP 1,100
SIC 6722 6733 6282 Money market mutual funds; Trusts, except educational, religious, charity: management; Investment advice
Pr: W Andrew Fry
*CFO: Stephen Hilliard
*CFO: Allen Strain
VP: Kenneth Ducharme
*VP: Robert Novellano
*VP: Marvin Rau
VP: Rudolf Vanderschoot
*VP: Michelle Warner
Telecom Mg: Scott McNair
IT Man: John Vanbuskirk

D-U-N-S 03-402-6112
INVESTORS MANAGEMENT CORP
GOLDEN CORRAL
801 N West St, Raleigh, NC 27603-1137
Tel (919) 653-7499 Founded/Ownrshp 1971
Sales 533.8MM^E EMP 9,000
SIC 5812 8741 Restaurant, family: chain; Management services
VP: Ann Perez
VP: Sam Starling
Mng Dir: Jim Hyler

D-U-N-S 07-867-5345
INVESTORS REAL ESTATE TRUST
1400 31st Ave Sw Ste 60, Minot, ND 58701-6965
Tel (701) 837-4738 Founded/Ownrshp 1970
Sales 188.3MM EMP 445
SIC 6798 Real estate investment trusts
CEO: Timothy P Mihalick
*Ch Bd: Jeffrey L Miller
*V Ch: John D Stewart
Pr: Mark Decker Jr
COO: Diane K Bryantt
CFO: Ted E Holmes
Ex VP: Michael A Bosh
Sr VP: Andrew Martin
VP: Charles Greenberg

Creative D: Joshua Gagne
Sls&Mrk Ex: Shawna Myers
Board of Directors: Jeffrey P Caira, Linda J Hall, Terrance P Maxwell, Pamela J Moret, Stephen L Stenehjem, Jeffrey K Woodbury

D-U-N-S 02-201-1316
▲ INVESTORS TITLE CO
121 N Columbia St, Chapel Hill, NC 27514-3502
Tel (919) 968-2200 *Founded/Ownrshp* 1972
Sales NA *EMP* 265^E
Tkr Sym ITIC *Exch* NGM
SIC 6361 6351 Real estate title insurance; Surety insurance
Ch Bd: J Allen Fine
**Pr:* James A Fine Jr
**Ex VP:* W Morris Fine
VP: Elizabeth Bryan
VP: Drew Foley
VP: Jenna Geigerman
VP: Carol Hayden
VP: Andrew Mercaldo
Board of Directors: David L Francis, Richard M Hutson II, R Horace Johnson, H Joe King Jr, James R Morton, James H Speed Jr

D-U-N-S 05-745-2948
■ INVESTORS TITLE INSURANCE CO
(*Suby of* INVESTORS TITLE CO) ★
121 N Columbia St, Chapel Hill, NC 27514-3502
Tel (919) 968-2200 *Founded/Ownrshp* 1972
Sales NA *EMP* 200
SIC 6361 Real estate title insurance
Pr: W Morris Fine
CFO: James A Fine Jr
VP: David A Bennington
VP: Elizabeth P Bryan
VP: Doug Kubel

D-U-N-S 14-105-7807 IMP
INVISTA CAPITAL MANAGEMENT LLC
(*Suby of* KOCH INDUSTRIES INC) ★
2801 Centerville Rd, Wilmington, DE 19808-1609
Tel (302) 683-3000 *Founded/Ownrshp* 2004
Sales 2.3MMM^E *EMP* 11,000
SIC 2869 Laboratory chemicals, organic
Pr: Steve R McCracken
**CFO:* William C Pickett
**VP:* Morris L Cranor
Off Mgr: Carla Norwood

D-U-N-S 60-179-6084
INVIVA INC
434 Hudson St Apt 2, New York, NY 10014-3937
Tel (212) 741-9322 *Founded/Ownrshp* 2000
Sales NA *EMP* 3,719
SIC 6411 Insurance agents & brokers
Ch Bd: David Smilow
**CFO:* Tim Rogers
CFO: Mark Singleton
**V Ch Bd:* Laurence P Greenberg
Off Mgr: John Knox
CIO: Michael Girouard

D-U-N-S 18-870-5818 IMP/EXP
INX GROUP LTD
(*Suby of* SAKATA INX CORPORATION)
150 N Martingale Rd # 700, Schaumburg, IL 60173-2408
Tel (630) 382-1800 *Founded/Ownrshp* 1988
Sales 300.9MM^E *EMP* 1,275
SIC 2893 Printing ink
Pr: Kotaro Morita
**Ch Bd:* Hiroshi Ota
**Pr:* Richard Clendenning
**COO:* Greg Polasik
**Treas:* Akio Miyata

D-U-N-S 00-510-3528 IMP/EXP
INX INTERNATIONAL INK CO
(*Suby of* INX GROUP LTD) ★
150 N Martingale Rd # 700, Schaumburg, IL 60173-2009
Tel (630) 382-1800 *Founded/Ownrshp* 1992
Sales 298.8MM^E *EMP* 1,100
SIC 2893 Printing ink
Pr: Rick Clendenning
**Ch Bd:* Kotaro Morita
COO: John Hrdlick
**CFO:* Bryce Kristo
Sr VP: Michael J Tennis
VP: Michael Brice
VP: Bill Giczkowski
VP: James Kochanny
**VP:* Matthew Mason
IT Man: Andrew Davidson
Sls Dir: Vimal Mehra

D-U-N-S 03-956-4741 IMP
INZI DISPLAY AMERICA INC
(*Suby of* INZI DISPLAY CO., LTD.)
7880 Airway Rd Ste B6e, San Diego, CA 92154-8308
Tel (619) 929-3501 *Founded/Ownrshp* 2010
Sales 106.0MM *EMP* 4
SIC 3651 Television receiving sets
Pr: Yoonhyoung Cho
CFO: Yang Myung Kwon

D-U-N-S 82-985-8070
IO DATA CENTERS LLC
I O
615 N 48th St, Phoenix, AZ 85008-6608
Tel (480) 513-8500 *Founded/Ownrshp* 2008
Sales 99.4MM^E *EMP* 200^E
SIC 7379 Computer related consulting services
CEO: George Slessman
Pr: Anthony Wanger
COO: David Shaw
CFO: Michael Berry
CFO: Jonathan F Mauck
Chf Cred: Bob Olson
Chf Mktg O: Anthony J D'Ambrosi
Ofcr: J Parker Lapp
Ex VP: Jim Kleeman
Ex VP: Brent Wouters
Sr VP: Adil Attlassy
Sr VP: Elizabeth Kubycheck
Sr VP: Alan McIntosh
Sr VP: Aaron Peterson
Sr VP: Anne Wolf
Sr VP: Ronald Yaggi
VP: Bob Butler
VP: Rick Crutchley
VP: Peter Goh
VP: Kathy Kim
VP: Steve Langley

IOCHPE HOLDINGS, LLC
See IOCHPE HOLDINGS LLC

D-U-N-S 07-841-1372
IOCHPE HOLDINGS LLC
IOCHPE HOLDINGS, LLC
(*Suby of* IOCHPE HOLDINGS AUSTRIA GMBH)
39500 Orchard Hill Pl # 500, Novi, MI 48375-5370
Tel (734) 737-5000 *Founded/Ownrshp* 2000
Sales 2.0MMM^E *EMP* 8,000
SIC 3714 Motor vehicle parts & accessories
CEO: Dan Ioschpe
**Treas:* Eric Moraw
**VP:* Steve Esau
**VP:* John Salvette

D-U-N-S 79-065-9978
IOD INC
1030 Ontario Rd, Green Bay, WI 54311-8014
Tel (920) 469-5000 *Founded/Ownrshp* 2006
Sales 171.2MM^E *EMP* 1,220^E
SIC 7375 Remote data base information retrieval; On-line data base information retrieval
Ch Bd: Michael P Wickman
Pr: Tonya Lovelace
Pr: Christine Magee
Pr: Matthew Zastoupil
CEO: George Abatjoglou
CFO: Kevin Rukamp
Ofcr: Amy Derlink
Ex VP: Frank Mamone
Sr VP: Robert Donnelly
VP: Scot Nemchik
Area Mgr: Ryan Allen

D-U-N-S 06-975-2475
IOM HEALTH SYSTEM LP
LUTHERAN HOSPITAL OF INDIANA
7950 W Jefferson Blvd, Fort Wayne, IN 46804-4140
Tel (260) 435-7001 *Founded/Ownrshp* 1903
Sales 240.0MM^E *EMP* 2,000^E
SIC 8062 General medical & surgical hospitals; Hospital, medical school affiliation
Pr: William L Anderson
CFO: Mike Makola
**VP:* Jerry Beasley
**VP:* Jan Dax
Dir Lab: Mike Saalfrank
Dir Rx: Kelley Thornton
Ex Dir: Carmen D Bruce
Dir Sec: Tim Davie
Dir Pat Ac: Chiquita Collins
Off Mgr: Kay Faulkner
QA Dir: Mary Brill

D-U-N-S 02-428-3928 IMP/EXP
ION AUDIO LLC
(*Suby of* INMUSIC BRANDS INC) ★
200 Scenic View Dr, Cumberland, RI 02864-1847
Tel (401) 658-3743 *Founded/Ownrshp* 2003
Sales 107.9MM *EMP* 40
SIC 5999 Audio-visual equipment & supplies
CFO: Paul Stansky

D-U-N-S 04-908-1441 IMP/EXP
▲ ION GEOPHYSICAL CORP
2105 Citywest Blvd # 900, Houston, TX 77042-2837
Tel (281) 933-3339 *Founded/Ownrshp* 1968
Sales 221.5MM *EMP* 560
Tkr Sym IO *Exch* NYS
SIC 7372 3829 Application computer software; Geophysical & meteorological testing equipment; Seismographs; Seismometers; Seismoscopes
Pr: R Brian Hanson
**Ch Bd:* James M Lapeyre Jr
COO: Ken Williamson
COO: Kenneth G Williamson
CFO: Steven A Bate
Ofcr: Christopher T Usher
Ex VP: Colin T Hulme
Ex VP: Jamey S Seely
Sr VP: Steve Bate
VP: Des Flynn
VP: Scott P Schwausch
VP: Scott Schwausch
Board of Directors: David H Barr, Michael C Jennings, Franklin Myers, S James Nelson Jr, John N Seitz

D-U-N-S 10-649-9791 IMP
ION LABS INC
5355 115th Ave N, Clearwater, FL 33760-4840
Tel (727) 527-1072 *Founded/Ownrshp* 2012
Sales 97.6MM^E *EMP* 116
SIC 5122 2834 Vitamins & minerals; Vitamin, nutrient & hematinic preparations for human use
CEO: Clayton Desjardine
Treas: Dawn Carrell
VP: Allan Toole
Exec: Leslie Boggs
Ql Cn Mgr: Sue Millar
Sls Dir: Victoria Travers

D-U-N-S 55-687-4980
ION MEDIA NETWORKS INC
ION TELEVISION
601 Clearwater Park Rd, West Palm Beach, FL 33401-6233
Tel (561) 659-4122 *Founded/Ownrshp* 2009
Sales 246.4MM^E *EMP* 508
SIC 4833 Television broadcasting stations
Pr: R Brandon Burgess
Pr: John Ford
Pr: Steve Friedman
Pr: Douglas Holloway
**CFO:* Gordon Lavalette
**Chf Cred:* Jeff Quinn
Ex VP: Leslie Glenn Chesloff
Ex VP: Marc Zand
Sr VP: John Heffron
VP: Mark Barrington
VP: Kendra Cleary
VP: Hayes Fountain
VP: Michael Hubner
VP: Robert Marino
VP: William O'Shea
VP: Blaine Rominger
VP: Robert Russo
VP: Carole Smith
VP: A Tek
VP: Sharon Wildto
VP Bus Dev: John Lawson

ION TELEVISION
See ION MEDIA NETWORKS INC

D-U-N-S 07-870-8914
IONA COLLEGE (INC)
715 North Ave, New Rochelle, NY 10801-1890
Tel (914) 633-2000 *Founded/Ownrshp* 1940
Sales 151.4MM *EMP* 750
Accts Bdo Usa Llp New Rochelle Ny
SIC 8221 College, except junior
Pr: Joseph E Nyre
Ofcr: Anne Giannone
VP: Mary Durkin
VP: Justine Erickson
VP: Antony Halaris
VP: Jeanne Salvatore
VP: Joan Steel
Off Mgr: Margaret Bohan
Off Mgr: Audrey Emaus
Off Admin: Theresa Battiato
MIS Dir: John Mallozzi
Board of Directors: Matt Rizzetta

D-U-N-S 87-757-3550 IMP
IONBOND LLC
(*Suby of* IHI IONBOND AG)
1823 E Whitcomb Ave, Madison Heights, MI 48071-1413
Tel (248) 398-9100 *Founded/Ownrshp* 1994
Sales 90.4MM^E *EMP* 500
SIC 3398 3479 Metal heat treating; Bonderizing of metal or metal products
CEO: Joe Haggerty
**Pr:* Ton Hurkmans
CFO: Gary Elwood
**CFO:* Lukas Haldimann
**CFO:* Antonie Polumba
**VP:* Walter N Kreil Jr
Genl Mgr: Debbie Degraaf
QC Dir: Pat Betz
Ql Cn Mgr: SRI Kondapaneni

D-U-N-S 36-194-9092
▲ IONIS PHARMACEUTICALS INC
2855 Gazelle Ct, Carlsbad, CA 92010-6670
Tel (760) 931-9200 *Founded/Ownrshp* 1989
Sales 283.7MM *EMP* 428^E
Tkr Sym IONS *Exch* NGS
SIC 2834 8731 3845 Pharmaceutical preparations; Medical research, commercial; Electromedical equipment
Ch Bd: Stanley T Crooke
**COO:* B Lynne Parshall
CFO: Elizabeth L Hougen
Sr VP: C Frank Bennett
Sr VP: Richard S Geary
Sr VP: Brett P Monia
Sr VP: Patrick R O'Neil
VP: Frank Bennet
Exec: Lori Cooper
Assoc Dir: Chris Coffin
Ex Dir: WEI Cheng
Board of Directors: Spencer R Berthelsen, Joseph Klein III, Joseph Loscalzo, Frederick T Muto, Joseph H Wender

D-U-N-S 80-230-9922
■ IOS/PCI LLC
INSPECTION OILFIELD SERVICES
(*Suby of* LBFOSTER) ★
652 N Sam Houston Pkwy E, Houston, TX 77060-5900
Tel (281) 310-5357 *Founded/Ownrshp* 2015
Sales 192.0MM^E *EMP* 200
SIC 1389 7389 Oil field services; Pipeline & power line inspection service; Safety inspection service
CFO: Jody Arceneaux
**COO:* Franklin P McLaughlin
VP: Jimmy Clark
VP: Justin Jarski
VP: Bobby Lopez

D-U-N-S 13-837-6103 IMP
IOWA 80 GROUP INC
515 Sterling Dr, Walcott, IA 52773-8573
Tel (563) 468-5500 *Founded/Ownrshp* 1965
Sales 324.5MM^E *EMP* 1,000
SIC 5541 5399 7542 5812 Truck stops; Country general stores; Truck wash; Restaurant, family: independent
Pr: William I Moon III
**Ch Bd:* Carolyn Moon
**Pr:* William I Moon III
**CFO:* James L Tillotson
**VP:* Jack Horan
**VP:* Rodney Pugh
Netwrk Mgr: Burke Strand

D-U-N-S 02-235-6000
IOWA 80 TRUCKSTOP INC
(*Suby of* IOWA 80 GROUP INC) ★
755 W Iowa 80 Rd I-80, Walcott, IA 52773-8572
Tel (563) 284-6961 *Founded/Ownrshp* 1965
Sales 125.8MM^E *EMP* 300
SIC 5541 5399 7542 5812 Truck stops; Country general stores; Truck wash; Restaurant, family: independent
Pr: William I Moon III
**Ch Bd:* Carolyn Moon
**CFO:* James L Tillotson
**VP:* Jack Horan
**VP:* Delia Moon Meier

D-U-N-S 96-635-0964
IOWA BANKERS BENEFIT PLAN
8800 Nw 62nd Ave, Johnston, IA 50131-2849
Tel (515) 286-4300 *Founded/Ownrshp* 2011
Sales NA *EMP* 2
Accts Deloitte Tax Lp Minneapolis
SIC 6411 Pension & retirement plan consultants
Pr: Becki Rogers Neese

D-U-N-S 08-348-7173
IOWA CITY COMMUNITY SCHOOL DISTRICT (IA)
1725 N Dodge St, Iowa City, IA 52245-9589
Tel (319) 688-1000 *Founded/Ownrshp* 1900
Sales 779.2M *EMP* 1,600
Accts Lb Stan Miller Coralville Ia
SIC 8211 Public elementary & secondary schools
COO: Pat Witinok
**CFO:* Craig Hansel
Treas: Bennett Bork
Exec: Celeste Shoppa
IT Man: Kelly Nelson

D-U-N-S 80-834-8668
IOWA DEPARTMENT OF CORRECTIONS
(*Suby of* IOWA DEPARTMENT OF EXECUTIVE OFFICE) ★
510 E 12th St Rm 4, Des Moines, IA 50319-9025
Tel (515) 725-5701 *Founded/Ownrshp* 1983
Sales NA *EMP* 1,729
SIC 9223 Prison, government;
Comm Dir: Staci Ballard

D-U-N-S 80-834-1499
IOWA DEPARTMENT OF EXECUTIVE OFFICE
(*Suby of* STATE OF IOWA) ★
State Capital, Des Moines, IA 50319
Tel (515) 281-5211 *Founded/Ownrshp* 1846
Sales NA *EMP* 1,730
SIC 9111 Governors' offices;
Pr: Troy Price
Comm Dir: Phil Roeder

D-U-N-S 80-834-8841
IOWA DEPARTMENT OF HUMAN SERVICES
(*Suby of* IOWA DEPARTMENT OF EXECUTIVE OFFICE) ★
1305 E Walnut St Rm 114, Des Moines, IA 50319-0106
Tel (515) 281-5454 *Founded/Ownrshp* 1978
Sales NA *EMP* 1,730
SIC 9441 Administration of social & manpower programs;
CFO: Jan Clausen
**Ex Dir:* Eugene I Gessow
Off Mgr: Linda Miller
Snr Mgr: Lorrie Tritch

D-U-N-S 80-834-9088
IOWA DEPARTMENT OF PUBLIC DEFENSE
(*Suby of* IOWA DEPARTMENT OF EXECUTIVE OFFICE) ★
7105 Nw 70th Ave, Johnston, IA 50131-1824
Tel (515) 252-4211 *Founded/Ownrshp* 1846
Sales NA *EMP* 1,700^E
SIC 9711 National security;
Ex Dir: Maj Ron Dardis

D-U-N-S 80-834-9047
IOWA DEPARTMENT OF TRANSPORTATION
(*Suby of* IOWA DEPARTMENT OF EXECUTIVE OFFICE) ★
800 Lincoln Way, Ames, IA 50010-6915
Tel (515) 239-1111 *Founded/Ownrshp* 1975
Sales NA *EMP* 1,720^E
SIC 9621 Regulation, administration of transportation;
CEO: Nancy Richardson
Prgrm Mgr: Mary Stahlhut

D-U-N-S 07-347-6590
IOWA FARM BUREAU FEDERATION
5400 University Ave, West Des Moines, IA 50266-5950
Tel (515) 225-5400 *Founded/Ownrshp* 1921
Sales 85.9MM *EMP* 1,866^E
Accts Meriwether Wilson And Company
SIC 8699 5154 6311 6321 6411 Farm bureau; Cattle; Life insurance carriers; Health insurance carriers; Insurance agents, brokers & service
Pr: Craig D Hill
**Sec:* Dennis J Presnall

D-U-N-S 61-482-3722
IOWA FINANCE AUTHORITY
2015 Grand Ave Ste 200, Des Moines, IA 50312-4903
Tel (515) 725-4900 *Founded/Ownrshp* 1975
Sales NA *EMP* 89
Accts Kpmg Llp Des Moines Ia
SIC 6163 Loan brokers
CEO: David Jamison
**COO:* Steven Harvey
Ofcr: Jennifer Amodeo
Ofcr: Lisa Strait
Genl Mgr: Carolann Jensen
IT Man: Cindy Harris
Genl Couns: Mark Thompson
Genl Couns: Joanna Wilson

D-U-N-S 04-475-6625
IOWA FIRE PROTECTION INC
735 Robins Rd, Hiawatha, IA 52233-1317
Tel (319) 378-0820 *Founded/Ownrshp* 1967
Sales 3.0MMM *EMP* 19
SIC 1711 Fire sprinkler system installation
Pr: William Heck

IOWA HEALTH PHYSICIANS
See IOWA PHYSICIANS CLINIC MEDICAL FOUNDATION

D-U-N-S 83-620-4271
IOWA HEALTH SYSTEM
UNITYPOINT HEALTH
1776 West Lakes Pkwy # 400, West Des Moines, IA 50266-8378
Tel (515) 241-6161 *Founded/Ownrshp* 1994
Sales 2.8MMM *EMP* 18,923
Accts Bkd Llp Kansas City Mo
SIC 8062 8721 8741 General medical & surgical hospitals; Accounting, auditing & bookkeeping; Hospital management
Pr: Bill Leaver
Pt: David Williams

Pr: Katherine Pearson
Pr: Scott Whitson
COO: Tammy Stapp
**CFO:* Mark Johnson
**Treas:* Mike Stone
Ofcr: Heidi Goodman
**Ex VP:* Kevin Vermeer
Sr VP: Alan Kaplan
VP: Pam Askew
VP: Matt Behrens
**VP:* Denny Drake
VP: Joy M Grosser
VP: Mary E Hagen
VP: Joyce McDanel
VP: Jim Mormann
VP: Rob Quin
VP Bus Dev: Sid Ramsey
Dir Risk M: Barb Earles

IOWA LASER TECHNOLOGY
See ONEAL STEEL INC

D-U-N-S 00-527-6738
IOWA LIMESTONE CO (IA)
ILC RESOURCES
3301 106th Cir, Urbandale, IA 50322-3740
Tel (515) 243-3160 *Founded/Ownrshp* 1913
Sales 89.3MM^E *EMP* 101
SIC 1422 5191 Limestones, ground; Phosphate rock, ground
Pr: Franklin Goode
**Pr:* Carl Lamberti
**CEO:* Richard W Witt
**Sec:* Linda E Morris-Dowie
VP: Linda Dowie
**VP:* Mike Tjarks
**VP:* Jim Tompt
IT Man: Ben Caplan
Mktg Dir: Dick Witt

D-U-N-S 00-528-6539 IMP/EXP
■ **IOWA MOLD TOOLING CO INC**
(*Suby of* OSHKOSH CORP) ★
500 W Us Highway 18, Garner, IA 50438-1090
Tel (641) 923-3711 *Founded/Ownrshp* 2000
Sales 111.1MM^E *EMP* 375
SIC 3531 3713 3563 Cranes; Truck bodies (motor vehicles); Air & gas compressors including vacuum pumps
Prin: Bradley M Nelson
COO: Richard Long
Plnt Mgr: Jerry Douglas
VP Sls: Eric Neitzke
Mktg Mgr: Axel Cadena

D-U-N-S 18-682-5956 IMP
IOWA NETWORK SERVICES INC
AUREON NETWORK SERVICES
7760 Office Plaza Dr S, West Des Moines, IA 50266-5998
Tel (515) 830-0110 *Founded/Ownrshp* 1984
Sales 657.1MM *EMP* 490
SIC 4813 Long distance telephone communications; Voice telephone communications
CEO: Richard M Vohs
**VP:* Dennis M Creveling
VP: Howard Juul
Exec: Beth Ellis
IT Man: Mike Czizal
Software D: Adam Sanford
VP Sls: Thomas Beem
Mktg Mgr: Kristi Petersen
Sls Mgr: Marty Ouverson
Snr Mgr: Mike Czizek

D-U-N-S 10-238-5650
IOWA PACIFIC HOLDINGS LLC
PERMIAN BASIN RAILWAYS
118 S Clinton St Ste 400, Chicago, IL 60661-5772
Tel (312) 466-0900 *Founded/Ownrshp* 2006
Sales 107.6MM^E *EMP* 200
SIC 4011 Railroads, line-haul operating
CEO: Edwin Ellis
Pr: Steve Hill
**Pr:* H Michael McConville
Ex VP: Mike McConville
VP: Todd Cecil
VP: Howard W Clark III
VP: Edward Pajor
**Prin:* Clark E Johnson Jr
**VP Opers:* Mike McCondille
VP Mktg: Steve Gregory
VP Sls: Jack Dapkus

D-U-N-S 82-562-6245
IOWA PHYSICIANS CLINIC MEDICAL FOUNDATION
IOWA HEALTH PHYSICIANS
1221 Pleasant St Ste 200, Des Moines, IA 50309-1424
Tel (515) 241-6212 *Founded/Ownrshp* 1993
Sales 376.3MM *EMP* 1,000
SIC 8011 Medical centers
CEO: C Eric Crowell
**CFO:* Robin McNichols
VP: Wayne Schellhammer
Genl Mgr: Jean Duncan

D-U-N-S 80-467-0255
IOWA SELECT FARMS LLP
811 S Oak St, Iowa Falls, IA 50126-9501
Tel (641) 648-4479 *Founded/Ownrshp* 1993
Sales 283.8MM^E *EMP* 850
SIC 0213 Hog feedlot
Genl Pt: Jeff Hansen
COO: Clint Hoversten
CFO: William Foley
Ofcr: Keith Kratchmer
Prd Dir: Tony Thies
Sfty Mgr: Eric Wiechmann

IOWA STATE JUDICIAL BRANCH
See JUDICIARY COURTS OF STATE OF IOWA

D-U-N-S 60-547-0905
IOWA STATE UNIVERSITY FOUNDATION
ISU FOUNDATION
2505 University Blvd, Ames, IA 50010-8622
Tel (515) 294-4607 *Founded/Ownrshp* 1950
Sales 133.0MM *EMP* 103
Accts Kpmg Llp Omaha Ne
SIC 8399 Fund raising organization, non-fee basis
Pr: Roger Neuhaus
**Pr:* Dan Saftig
Treas: Joan Piscitello
VP: Rich Bundy
**VP:* Lisa Eslinger
Assoc Dir: Aimee Wesley
Adm Dir: Amy Pilcher

D-U-N-S 00-530-9844
IOWA STATE UNIVERSITY OF SCIENCE AND TECHNOLOGY
1350 Beardshear Hall, Ames, IA 50011-2025
Tel (515) 294-6162 *Founded/Ownrshp* 1987
Sales 858.9MM *EMP* 5,800^E
Accts Mary Mosiman Cpa-Warren G Je
SIC 8221 University
Pr: Gregory Geoffroy
Pr: Pam Cain
**Pr:* Elizabeth Hoffman
**Pr:* Steven Leath
COO: Lisa Sebring
Treas: Brad Dye
Ofcr: Brooke Langlitz
VP: Martino Harmon
**VP:* Thomas Hill
**VP:* Warren Madden
Comm Dir: Rob Schweers

D-U-N-S 05-534-2679
IOWA STUDENT LOAN LIQUIDITY CORP
6775 Vista Dr, West Des Moines, IA 50266-9305
Tel (515) 243-5626 *Founded/Ownrshp* 1979
Sales NA *EMP* 214
Accts Kpmg Llp Des Moines Iowa
SIC 6111 6141 Student Loan Marketing Association; Personal credit institutions
Pr: Steven W McCullough
CFO: Walter Witthoff
**Treas:* Erin Lacey
Exec: Suzanne Lowman
Ex Dir: Tracy Wilson
Software D: Jason Flogel
Opers Mgr: Ron Foresman

IOWA TURKEY GROWERS COOP
See WEST LIBERTY FOODS LLC

D-U-N-S 10-222-8590
■ **IPALCO ENTERPRISES INC**
AES
(*Suby of* AES CORP) ★
1 Monument Cir, Indianapolis, IN 46204-2901
Tel (317) 261-8261 *Founded/Ownrshp* 1983
Sales 1.2MMM *EMP* 1,401^E
Accts Ernst & Young Llp Indianapoli
SIC 4911 Electric services; Distribution, electric power; Generation, electric power; Transmission, electric power
Pr: Kenneth J Zagzebski
**Ch Bd:* Thomas M O'Flynn
**CFO:* Craig L Jackson
Board of Directors: Renaud Faucher, Paul L Freedman, Andrew J Horrocks, Michael S Mizell, Olivier Renault, Richard A Sturges, Margaret E Tigre

IPAP
See INDEPENDENT PROCUREMENT ALLIANCE PROGRAM LLC

D-U-N-S 79-649-1418
IPAYMENT HOLDINGS INC
(*Suby of* IPAYMENT INVESTORS INC) ★
30721 Russell Ranch Rd # 200, Westlake Village, CA 91362-7383
Tel (310) 436-5294 *Founded/Ownrshp* 2001
Sales 666.8MM *EMP* 427^E
SIC 7389 Personal service agents, brokers & bureaus
Pr: Ob Rawls IV
**COO:* Greg Cohen
**CFO:* Robert Purcell

D-U-N-S 05-874-7945
IPAYMENT INC
(*Suby of* IPAYMENT HOLDINGS INC) ★
30721 Russell Ranch Rd # 200, Westlake Village, CA 91362-7383
Tel (212) 802-7200 *Founded/Ownrshp* 2006
Sales 666.8MM *EMP* 422^E
SIC 7389 Credit card service
CFO: Mark C Monaco
Ex VP: Barnett Sutton
Ex VP: Afshin M Yazdian
Sr VP: Philip J Ragona
VP: Dale Kennedy
VP: Pat Sauder
VP Sls: Christian Murray
VP Sls: Jayanne Nase
Ansthlgy: Francis Copeland
Ansthlgy: Philip Johnson
Ansthlgy: Kathleen Leavy

D-U-N-S 79-645-2873
IPAYMENT INVESTORS INC
40 Burton Hills Blvd, Nashville, TN 37215-6199
Tel (615) 665-1858 *Founded/Ownrshp* 2001
Sales 666.8MM^E *EMP* 853^E
SIC 7389 Credit card service
Genl Couns: Philip Ragona
CFO: Teresa Sparks
VP Sls: Christa Shook

D-U-N-S 14-829-8396
IPC (USA) INC
(*Suby of* ITOCHU CORPORATION)
4 Hutton Cntre Dr Ste 700, Santa Ana, CA 92707
Tel (949) 648-5600 *Founded/Ownrshp* 2012
Sales 303.4MM^E *EMP* 96
SIC 5172 Aircraft fueling services; Diesel fuel; Gasoline
CEO: Hiroki Okinaga
**CFO:* James Takeuchi
**VP:* Randy Jones

IPC INFORMATION SYSTEMS
See IPC SYSTEMS INC

D-U-N-S 09-717-6135
IPC INTERNATIONAL CORP
10255 W Higgi, Rosemont, IL 60018
Tel (847) 444-2000 *Founded/Ownrshp* 2013
Sales 124.3MM^E *EMP* 5,800
SIC 7381 8742 2389 3199

D-U-N-S 83-313-8253 IMP/EXP
IPC SYSTEMS HOLDINGS CORP
HARBORSIDE FINANCIAL CENTER
(*Suby of* SILVER LAKE PARTNERS II LP) ★
1500 Plaza Ten Fl 15, Jersey City, NJ 07311-4050
Tel (201) 253-2000 *Founded/Ownrshp* 2010
Sales 220.6MM^E *EMP* 1,630^E
SIC 5045 4813 Computers, peripherals & software;
Pr: Greg Kenepp
COO: Charles Auster
Sr VP: Michael Speranza
**Prin:* Lance Boxer
Mng Dir: Ritske Clewits
Off Mgr: Donna Palumbo
CIO: Richard Bozzuto
Software D: Sergey Polyakov
Netwrk Eng: Greg Brady
Sales Exec: Andrew Matlak
Sls Dir: Mike Tavares

D-U-N-S 07-844-8961 IMP
IPC SYSTEMS INC
IPC INFORMATION SYSTEMS
Harborside Fincl 2nd St, Jersey City, NJ 07311
Tel (201) 253-2000 *Founded/Ownrshp* 2015
Sales 694.2MM^E *EMP* 1,500
SIC 3661 Telephone & telegraph apparatus
CEO: Neil Barua
**CFO:* Ben Chrnelich
Sr VP: Don C Bell
**Sr VP:* David Brown
**Sr VP:* Lionel Grosclaude
**Sr VP:* Don Henderson
Sr VP: Pete Simms
VP: Gary Everett
VP: Neil Gray
VP: Lois Liebowitz
Dir IT: Frank Tanski

D-U-N-S 07-841-2524
IPC/RAZOR LLC
277 Park Ave Fl 39, New York, NY 10172-2901
Tel (212) 551-4500 *Founded/Ownrshp* 2010
Sales 88.3MM^E *EMP* 2,000
SIC 3541 Machine tools, metal cutting type

I.P.C.C.
See INTERNATIONAL PRECISION COMPONENTS CORP

D-U-N-S 15-762-1830 IMP
IPEG INC
CONAIR
(*Suby of* SEWICKLEY CAPITAL INC) ★
200 W Kensinger Dr # 100, Cranberry Township, PA 16066-3428
Tel (724) 584-5500 *Founded/Ownrshp* 1950
Sales 124.9MM^E *EMP* 631
SIC 3559

IPFS CORPORATION
See FINANCIAL HOLDING CORP

D-U-N-S 07-682-9084
IPFS CORP
(*Suby of* CAPITAL PAYMENT PLAN) ★
101 Hudson St Fl 33, Jersey City, NJ 07302-3905
Tel (201) 557-4625 *Founded/Ownrshp* 2010
Sales NA *EMP* 300
SIC 6311 Life insurance carriers
Pr: Paul Zarookian
CFO: Jason Stuart
**CFO:* Michael Vogen
Treas: Steven J Bensinger
**Ex VP:* Kevin Olsen
**Ex VP:* James Williamson
**Sr VP:* Claude Graham
VP: James Donaldson

D-U-N-S 09-582-5634
IPFS CORP
CAPITAL PAYMENT PLAN
1055 Broadway Blvd Fl 11, Kansas City, MO 64105-1575
Tel (816) 627-0500 *Founded/Ownrshp* 1974
Sales NA *EMP* 520
SIC 6153 Buying of installment notes
Pr: Michael Gallagher
Pr: Skip Fisher
**COO:* Paul Zarookian
**CFO:* Bryan Andres
**Sr VP:* Jim Bennett
**Sr VP:* Herb Chirico
**Sr VP:* Ted Koeth
**Sr VP:* J Kevin Olsen
IT Man: Dave Bruner
Mktg Mgr: Chad Creamer

D-U-N-S 11-292-7095 IMP/EXP
IPG (US) HOLDINGS INC
INTERTAPE POLYMER GROUP
(*Suby of* INTERTAPE POLYMER GROUP INC) ★
100 Paramount Dr Ste 300, Sarasota, FL 34232-6051
Tel (941) 727-5788 *Founded/Ownrshp* 1997
Sales 333.9MM^E *EMP* 2,003
SIC 2672 3953 Tape, pressure sensitive: made from purchased materials; Stencils, painting & marking
Pr: Greg Yull
Pr: Jim Bob Carpenter
Pr: Burgess Hildreth
Pr: Gregary Yull
Sls Dir: Dave Griffith

D-U-N-S 11-291-9001
IPG (US) INC
(*Suby of* INTERTAPE POLYMER GROUP) ★
100 Paramount Dr Ste 300, Sarasota, FL 34232-6051
Tel (941) 727-5788 *Founded/Ownrshp* 1997
Sales 322.9MM^E *EMP* 1,008
SIC 2672 3953 Tape, pressure sensitive: made from purchased materials; Stencils, painting & marking
Pr: Dale Mc Sween
**VP:* Burgess Hildreth

D-U-N-S 04-702-7433 IMP
▲ **IPG PHOTONICS CORP**
50 Old Webster Rd, Oxford, MA 01540-2706
Tel (508) 373-1100 *Founded/Ownrshp* 1990
Sales 901.2MM *EMP* 3,740^E
Tkr Sym IPGP *Exch* NGS
SIC 3699 3229 3674 Laser systems & equipment; Fiber optics strands; Semiconductor diodes & rectifiers
Ch Bd: Valentin P Gapontsev
CFO: Timothy P V Mammen
Sr VP: Angelo P Lopresti
Sr VP: Trevor D Ness
Sr VP: Alexander Ovtchinnikov
Sr VP: Felix Stukalin
VP: Trevor Ness
VP: Jack Ward
Mng Dir: Eugene Scherbakov
Genl Mgr: Heinrich Endert
**CTO:* Igor Samartsev
Board of Directors: Michael C Child, Henry E Gauthier, William S Hurley, Catherine P Lego, Eric Meurice, John R Peeler, Eugene Scherbakov, Thomas J Seifert

D-U-N-S 06-879-5795
■ **IPH II LLC**
(*Suby of* DYNEGY INC) ★
601 Travis St Ste 1400, Houston, TX 77002-3253
Tel (713) 507-6400 *Founded/Ownrshp* 2013
Sales 805.9MM^E *EMP* 923^E
SIC 4939 Combination utilities
CEO: Robert C Flexon
CFO: Clint C Freeland

D-U-N-S 07-923-8300
■ **IPH LLC**
ILLINOIS POWER HOLDINGS, LLC
(*Suby of* IPH II LLC) ★
601 Travis St Ste 1400, Houston, TX 77002-3253
Tel (713) 507-6400 *Founded/Ownrshp* 2013
Sales 740.1MM^E *EMP* 477^E
SIC 4911 Electric services; Generation, electric power

IPIPELINE
See INTERNET PIPELINE INC

D-U-N-S 79-120-3719
IPREO HOLDINGS LLC
1359 Broadway Fl 2, New York, NY 10018-7123
Tel (212) 849-5000 *Founded/Ownrshp* 2014
Sales 136.1MM^E *EMP* 600^E
SIC 8748 Business consulting
**CFO:* Brian Dockray
Treas: Anne Montana
Ex VP: Neil Hyman
Ex VP: Agnies Watson
Ex VP: Ronnie West
**Ex VP:* Charlie Young
VP: Pete Bentson
VP: James Kellum
VP: David Miranda
VP: Amber Seidel
VP: Jason Tuthill
VP: Karen West
Exec: Anthony Lansizero
Assoc Dir: Colin Williams

D-U-N-S 79-957-9623
IPREO LLC
IPREO PRIVATE CAPITAL MARKETS
(*Suby of* IPREO HOLDINGS LLC) ★
1359 Broadway Fl 2, New York, NY 10018-7123
Tel (212) 849-5000 *Founded/Ownrshp* 2000
Sales 138.5MM^E *EMP* 450^E
SIC 8748 Business consulting
CEO: Scott C Ganeles
**Pr:* Kevin Marcus
COO: David Miranda
**CFO:* Brian Dockray
Ex VP: Bill Sherman
Ex VP: Chris Taylor
**Ex VP:* Allen Williams
VP: Karen West
Assoc Dir: John Bauer
Assoc Dir: Tim Carr
Mng Dir: Brett Suchor

IPREO PRIVATE CAPITAL MARKETS
See IPREO LLC

D-U-N-S 02-757-5242
IPROSPECT.COM INC
(*Suby of* DENTSU AEGIS NETWORK LTD.)
1 South Sta Ste 300, Boston, MA 02110-2212
Tel (617) 449-4300 *Founded/Ownrshp* 1998
Sales 35.9MM^E *EMP* 2,500^E
SIC 8742 Marketing consulting services
Pr: Jeremy Cornfeldt
COO: Carlos Estrada
Sr VP: Kim Sivillo
VP: Vic Drabicky
VP: Ashwini Karandikar
Dir Bus: Emmaclare Huntriss
Genl Mgr: Shayne Garcia
Mktg Mgr: Katie Getz
Sls Mgr: Jordan Hiser
Snr Mgr: Greg Wright

IPS
See INDIANAPOLIS PUBLIC SCHOOLS

IPS
See INDUSTRIAL PIPING SPECIALISTS INC

D-U-N-S 00-839-1815 IMP/EXP
IPS CORP
WELD-ON ADHESIVES
(*Suby of* NAUTIC PARTNERS LLC) ★
455 W Victoria St, Compton, CA 90220-6064
Tel (310) 898-3300 *Founded/Ownrshp* 1953, 2015
Sales 229.2MM^E *EMP* 400
SIC 2891 Adhesives, plastic; Cement, except linoleum & tile
CEO: Thomas Tracy Bilbrough
Pr: Greg Paquin
CFO: William Barton

Bd of Dir: Chad Gomez
Ex VP: Larry Birch
VP: Dave Doering
VP: Edwin Gutierrez
VP: Richard Larson
VP: Andreas Schneider
CIO: Stephen M Gardiner
VP Mktg: Gary Clarke

D-U-N-S 62-041-0613 IMP
IPSCO KOPPEL TUBULARS LLC
TMK-IPSCO
(Suby of TMK IPSCO) ★
6403 6th Ave, Koppel, PA 16136
Tel (724) 847-6389 *Founded/Ownrshp* 2008
Sales 226.5MM^E *EMP* 950
SIC 3312 Pipes & tubes
Ch: Piotr Galitzine
**Pr:* David Mitch
**Sr VP:* Scott Barnes
**VP:* Prasenjit Adhikari
Genl Mgr: Michaell Penceri

D-U-N-S 80-855-4141
IPSCO TUBULARS INC
TMK IPSCO
(Suby of TMK IPSCO INC) ★
10120 Houston Oaks Dr, Houston, TX 77064-3514
Tel (281) 949-1023 *Founded/Ownrshp* 2015
Sales 411.2MM^E *EMP* 1,154
SIC 3498 Fabricated pipe & fittings
Ch: Piotr Galitzine
**Pr:* David Mitch
**COO:* Joel Mastervich
**COO:* Joel C Mastervich
**CFO:* Adrian Cobb
**CFO:* Evgeny Makarov
**VP:* Scott Barnes
Comm Dir: Roger Bentley
Genl Mgr: Bert Wingrove
Ql Cn Mgr: Larry Bush
Sls Mgr: Anthony Cargo

D-U-N-S 01-492-5486
IPSOFT INC
17 State St Fl 14, New York, NY 10004-1501
Tel (888) 477-6388 *Founded/Ownrshp* 1999
Sales 167.6MM^E *EMP* 423
SIC 7376 7363 7374 8742 Computer facilities management; Employee leasing service; Data processing service; Management consulting services
Ch Bd: Chetan Dube
Pr: Christopher Vercelli
CEO: Jeya Kumar
VP: Eray Ekici
VP: Morgan Gebhardt
VP: Mike Ghicas
VP: Mike Hicas
VP: Meeta Pandy
VP: Peter J Sajewski
Dir Bus: Susan Ascolese
Dir Bus: Robert Kirk

D-U-N-S 01-985-3592
IPSOS AMERICA INC
(Suby of IPSOS)
1271 Ave Of The, New York, NY 10020
Tel (212) 265-3200 *Founded/Ownrshp* 1998
Sales 270.8MM^E *EMP* 3,015^E
SIC 8742 Management consulting services
CEO: James T Smith
**CFO:* Debra S Mason
Sr VP: Thomas Aw Miller
VP: Fred Church
VP: Richard Lim
VP: David Nemiah

D-U-N-S 04-658-3027
IPSOS PUBLIC AFFAIRS INC
(Suby of IPSOS AMERICA INC) ★
222 S Rverside Plz Fl 4, Chicago, IL 60606
Tel (312) 526-4000 *Founded/Ownrshp* 1966
Sales 109.3MM^E *EMP* 1,500
SIC 8732 8731 Market analysis or research; Commercial physical research
Pr: Robert Philpott
CFO: Rick Carbone
CFO: Tony Solarz
**Ex VP:* Ignacio Galceran
**Ex VP:* Barbara Goff
**Ex VP:* Lawrence Levin
**Ex VP:* Nan Martin
**Ex VP:* Robert Skolnick
**Ex VP:* Mark Turim
Sr VP: Tom Mularz
Sr VP: Laura Quinn
VP: George Schaumann
Dir Teleco: Christina McCormack

D-U-N-S 55-737-5391
IPSWITCH INC
WHATSUP GOLD
83 Hartwell Ave, Lexington, MA 02421-3116
Tel (781) 676-5700 *Founded/Ownrshp* 1991
Sales 104.0MM^E *EMP* 300
SIC 5045 Computer software
CEO: Joe Krivickas
Pr: Rich Kennelly
Pr: Warren Neuburger
CFO: David Stott
Chf Mktg O: Jeanne Hopkins
Ofcr: Austin Omalley
Ex VP: Diane Albano
Ex VP: Ennio Carboni
Ex VP: Michael Grossi
Ex VP: Richard Welch
VP: Richard Allen
VP: Frank Kenney
VP: L Frank Kenney
VP: Mary-Katherine McCarey
Board of Directors: Patrick Melampy, Robert A Steinkrauss

IPT
See INTEGRATED PROCUREMENT TECHNOLOGIES INC

D-U-N-S 15-605-8237
IQNAVIGATOR INC
6465 Greenwood Plaza Blvd, Greenwood Village, CO 80111-4905
Tel (303) 563-1500 *Founded/Ownrshp* 1999
Sales 120.5MM^E *EMP* 320^E
SIC 7371 7361 Computer software development; Labor contractors (employment agency)
Pr: Joseph Juliano
**CFO:* Barry Capoot
Ex VP: Kieran Brady
Ex VP: Graden Gerig
Ex VP: Jagan Reddy
Ex VP: Eric Riddle
Ex VP: Jeffrey Varon
VP: Taylor Allis
VP: Dianna Anderson
VP: Lonnie Byxbe
VP: Christine Calandrella
VP: Victor Chayet
VP: Suzette Fulton-Fike
VP: Michelle Hudson
VP: Matt Katz
VP: Kevin Poll
VP: Nicholas Pollard
VP: Lexy S Spikes
VP: Norman Weeks
VP: Alan Winegar
VP: Byron Wittenberg

IQOR AFTERMARKET SERVICES
See IQOR GLOBAL SERVICES LLC

D-U-N-S 92-985-0147
IQOR GLOBAL SERVICES LLC
IQOR AFTERMARKET SERVICES
(Suby of IQOR HOLDINGS INC) ★
1 Progress Plz Ste 7, Saint Petersburg, FL 33701-4553
Tel (727) 369-0878 *Founded/Ownrshp* 2014
Sales NA *EMP* 19,000
SIC 8748 4731 Telecommunications consultant; Freight transportation arrangement
Pr: Daniel Montenaro
**Pr:* Hartmut Liebel
**COO:* Bryan Maguire
**VP:* Grant Newmyer

D-U-N-S 96-599-5553
IQOR HOLDINGS INC
1 Progress Plz, New York, NY 10017
Tel (866) 657-2057 *Founded/Ownrshp* 2007
Sales 514.7MM *EMP* 32,000^E
Accts Grant Thornton Llp New York
SIC 7374 Data processing & preparation
Pr: Hartmut Liebel
**COO:* Bryan Maguire
**COO:* Gary Praznik
**CFO:* Margaret M Cowherd
**Ofcr:* Mason Argiropoulos
**Ofcr:* Daniel L Montenaro
**Ex VP:* Gary Cole
**Ex VP:* Dick Eychner
**Sr VP:* David Mahoney
**VP:* Erik Carlson
**VP:* Mark Underhill

D-U-N-S 14-420-0511
IQOR US INC
(Suby of IQOR HOLDINGS INC) ★
1 Progress Plz Ste 170, Saint Petersburg, FL 33701-4335
Tel (866) 657-2057 *Founded/Ownrshp* 1998
Sales 273.4MM^E *EMP* 17,000
SIC 7322 Adjustment & collection services
Ch Bd: Randy L Christofferson
Pr: Patrick Burwell
Pr: Mike Frappollo
Pr: Saladin Glanton
Pr: Chris Karounos
Pr: Deb McEldowney
**Pr:* Norm Merritt
Pr: Jamie Welsh
**COO:* Rakesh Kumar
**CFO:* Margaret M Cowherd
CFO: John Hunts
**Chf Cred:* Dan Montenaro
Sr VP: Cindy Arnberg
Sr VP: Russ Jakubowski
Sr VP: Sumit Malhotra
Sr VP: David Wright
VP: Bobby Anderson
VP: Carmen Bruno
VP: Vinh Ho
VP: Kristin Husby
VP: Ed Makela

IQORE
See RECEIVABLE MANAGEMENT SERVICES CORP

D-U-N-S 61-265-5274 IMP/EXP
IQUIQUE US LLC
2320 W Commodore Way # 200, Seattle, WA 98199-1287
Tel (206) 286-1661 *Founded/Ownrshp* 1988
Sales 98.9MM^E *EMP* 200
SIC 0921 Fishing preserves
Off Mgr: Michelle Berger

D-U-N-S 03-361-0858
IRA HIGDON GROCERY CO
150 Iga Way, Cairo, GA 39828
Tel (229) 377-1272 *Founded/Ownrshp* 1909
Sales 96.0MM *EMP* 85
Accts Guy & Johnson Pc Thomasvil
SIC 5141 5147 5142 5143 2111 5194 Groceries, general line; Meats, fresh; Meat, frozen: packaged; Dairy products, except dried or canned; Cigarettes; Tobacco & tobacco products
CEO: L I Higdon
VP: Matt Higdon

IRAS MOUNIR ABANNI
See AMERICAN CENTURY INVESTMENT MANAGEMENT INC

D-U-N-S 04-039-4657
IRB MEDICAL EQUIPMENT LLC
1000 Health Park Blvd B, Grand Blanc, MI 48439-7324
Tel (810) 953-0760 *Founded/Ownrshp* 1994
Sales 147.2MM^E *EMP* 287
SIC 5047 7389 Medical equipment & supplies;
Genl Mgr: Allen Hunt

D-U-N-S 00-785-1207
■ **IRBY CONSTRUCTION CO** (MS)
(Suby of QUANTA SERVICES INC) ★
318 Old Highway 49 S, Richland, MS 39218-9449
Tel (601) 709-4729 *Founded/Ownrshp* 1946, 2000
Sales 216.3MM^E *EMP* 700
Accts Haddock Reid Eubank Betts Pllc
SIC 1623 1731 Electric power line construction; Transmitting tower (telecommunication) construction; Fiber optic cable installation
Prin: Lee Jones
**CFO:* Robert A Croft Sr
**VP:* Gary Bodam
**VP:* David D Brittain
**VP:* James H Haddox
**VP:* Mike Leech
**VP:* Eddie Moak
**VP:* Tana L Pool
VP: Argyle Scott
**VP:* Doug Walo
**VP:* Mike Wigton

IRBY ELECTRICAL DISTRIBUTORS
See STUART C IRBY CO

IRC AND PARTNERS
See INTERNATIONAL RESCUE COMMITTEE INC

D-U-N-S 61-149-2661
IRC INC
INTERNATIONAL RISK CONSULTANTS
(Suby of NFP ADVISORS) ★
1 Corporation Way Ste 230, Peabody, MA 01960-7925
Tel (781) 581-9800 *Founded/Ownrshp* 1990
Sales 65.1MM^E *EMP* 1,450
SIC 8742 Financial consultant
VP: Stephen Bloomberg

D-U-N-S 01-699-0074
IRC RETAIL CENTERS LLC
(Suby of D R A) ★
814 Commerce Dr Ste 300, Oak Brook, IL 60523-8823
Tel (877) 206-5656 *Founded/Ownrshp* 1994
Sales 203.9MM *EMP* 129^E
Accts Kpmg Llp Chicago Illinois
SIC 6798 Real estate investment trusts
CEO: Mark E Zalatoris
**CFO:* Brett A Brown
**Chf Cred:* Carol Adams
**Ex VP:* D Scott Carr
Sr VP: William W Anderson
**Sr VP:* Beth Sprecher Brooks
VP: Fred Fisher
VP: Judy Fu
VP: Philip Menolascina
VP: Matt Swanson
VP: Mary J Wenmouth
Exec: Paul Montes
Board of Directors: Thomas P D'arcy, Daniel L Goodwin, Joel G Herter, Heidi N Lawton, Thomas H McAuley, Thomas R McWilliams, Meredith Wise Mendes, Joel D Simmons

IRD
See INTERNATIONAL RELIEF AND DEVELOPMENT INC

IREA
See INTERMOUNTAIN RURAL ELECTRIC ASSOCIATION

IREDELL HEALTH SYSTEM
See IREDELL MEMORIAL HOSPITAL INC

D-U-N-S 07-449-8064
IREDELL MEMORIAL HOSPITAL INC
IREDELL HEALTH SYSTEM
557 Brookdale Dr, Statesville, NC 28677-4100
Tel (704) 873-5661 *Founded/Ownrshp* 1954
Sales 152.5MM *EMP* 1,448
SIC 8062 8051 General medical & surgical hospitals; Skilled nursing care facilities
Pr: Ed Rush
COO: David Myers
**VP:* Fred Karnap
**Prin:* Skip Smith
IT Man: Keith Williams
Opers Mgr: Cindy Miller
Doctor: Naim E Bouhussein MD
Nrsg Dir: Connie Cook
Pharmcst: Donna Gibson

D-U-N-S 07-105-7160
IREDELL-STATESVILLE SCHOOLS (NC)
549 N Race St, Statesville, NC 28677-3915
Tel (704) 872-8931 *Founded/Ownrshp* 1910
Sales 163.0MM *EMP* 3,300
Accts Mccannon Rogers Driscoll & A
SIC 8211 Public elementary & secondary schools; Public senior high school; Public junior high school; Public elementary school
**CFO:* Melissa Wike
Genl Mgr: Kara Steele
Dir IT: David Blattner
Dir IT: Darryll Corpening
Info Man: Karen Cutler
Pr Dir: Susie Wiberg
Teacher Pr: Bill Long
HC Dir: Kelly Marcy

D-U-N-S 04-751-2959
IREX CORP
(Suby of NORTH LIME HOLDINGS CORP) ★
120 N Lime St, Lancaster, PA 17602-2923
Tel (717) 397-3633 *Founded/Ownrshp* 2006
Sales 246.7MM^E *EMP* 1,734
Accts Baker Tilly Virchow Krause Llp
SIC 1799 Coating, caulking & weather, water & fireproofing; Asbestos removal & encapsulation
Pr: W K Liddell
**Sec:* Lori Pickell
VP: Gale Blefko
**VP:* James Hipolit
Exec: Linda Taylor
Dir IT: Michael Kelly

D-U-N-S 82-945-2569
▲ **IRIDIUM COMMUNICATIONS INC**
1750 Tysons Blvd Ste 1400, Mc Lean, VA 22102-4244
Tel (703) 287-7400 *Founded/Ownrshp* 2000
Sales 411.3MM *EMP* 244^E
Tkr Sym IRDM *Exch* NGS
SIC 4899 Data communication services
CEO: Matthew J Desch
**Ch Bd:* Robert H Niehaus
CEO: Donald L Thoma
**COO:* S Scott Smith
**Ofcr:* Thomas J Fitzpatrick
Ex VP: Bryan J Hartin
Ex VP: Scott T Scheimreif
VP: Richard P Nyren
Board of Directors: Thomas C Canfield, Jane L Harman, Alvin B Krongard, Eric T Olson, Steven B Pfeiffer, Parker W Rush, Henrik O Schliemann, Barry J West

D-U-N-S 78-866-5958 IMP/EXP
IRIS USA INC
(Suby of IRIS OHYAMA INC.)
11111 80th Ave, Pleasant Prairie, WI 53158-2910
Tel (262) 612-1000 *Founded/Ownrshp* 1985
Sales 130.9MM^E *EMP* 310
SIC 3089 Cases, plastic
CEO: Akihiro Ohyama
**Pr:* Kentaro Ohayama
CFO: Linda Kupper
VP: Bernadette Gaubert
VP: Justin Johnson
VP: Dick Konsinowski
VP: Hideo Ohyama
VP: Tom Thompson
Ex Dir: Hiromi Rozell
Genl Mgr: Al Muto
Sfty Mgr: Sharon Emerson

D-U-N-S 80-738-0951
▲ **IROBOT CORP**
8 Crosby Dr, Bedford, MA 01730-1402
Tel (781) 430-3000 *Founded/Ownrshp* 1990
Sales 616.7MM *EMP* 622^E
Tkr Sym IRBT *Exch* NGS
SIC 3569 3731 Robots, assembly line: industrial & commercial; Submersible marine robots, manned or unmanned
Ch Bd: Colin M Angle
COO: John Billingsley
COO: Christian Cerda
CFO: Alison Dean
Ex VP: Russell J Campanello
VP: Richard E Campbell
VP: Mario Munich
VP: Youssef Saleh
Exec: Kelly Needham
Exec: Marie Papas
Exec: Chris Ritchie
Exec: Carl Vonnegut
Exec: Marcus Williams
Dir Bus: Anders Bialek
Board of Directors: Michael Bell, Ronald Chwang, Gail Deegan, Deborah G Ellinger, Andrea Geisser, michelle V, Andrew Miller

D-U-N-S 61-038-3317
IRON AGE HOLDINGS CORP
(Suby of FENWAY PARTNERS LLC) ★
3 Robinson Plz Ste 300, Pittsburgh, PA 15205-1018
Tel (412) 788-0888 *Founded/Ownrshp* 1997
Sales 100.0MM *EMP* 745
SIC 5139 5661 3143 3144 Shoes; Shoe stores; Men's footwear, except athletic; Women's footwear, except athletic
Pr: David Eckert
CFO: Gary Lortye
Bd of Dir: Peter Lamm
Bd of Dir: James McKitrick
VP: Sean M Cubie
VP: Andrea Geisser
VP: William Mills
VP: Willie Taafe
S&M/VP: Richard Kusmer

D-U-N-S 96-841-5781
IRON BOW HOLDINGS INC
4800 Westfields Blvd # 300, Chantilly, VA 20151-4247
Tel (703) 279-3000 *Founded/Ownrshp* 2011
Sales 301.6MM^E *EMP* 310
SIC 7379 7373 Computer related consulting services; Value-added resellers, computer systems
Pr: Rene B Lavigne
**CFO:* Charles Curran
**Sr VP:* Lance J Lerman
**Sr VP:* Marc Mercilliott
**Sr VP:* Stuart Strang
Board of Directors: Rene Lavigne

D-U-N-S 82-771-4507 IMP
IRON BOW TECHNOLOGIES LLC
(Suby of IRON BOW HOLDINGS INC) ★
4800 Westfields Blvd # 300, Chantilly, VA 20151-4247
Tel (703) 279-3000 *Founded/Ownrshp* 1983
Sales 301.6MM^E *EMP* 310
Accts Grant Thornton Mclean Va
SIC 3571 Electronic computers
Pr: Rene Lavigne
**CFO:* Charles L Curran
**Sr VP:* Lance Lerman
**Sr VP:* Stu Strang
**VP:* Mark Monticelli
Genl Mgr: Lisa Esteppe
Genl Mgr: John Meier
Genl Mgr: Andrew Sabonis
Off Mgr: Jennifer McConkey
Snr Sftwr: Kyle Richardson
Dir IT: Ray Harris

D-U-N-S 62-253-5417
▲ **IRON MOUNTAIN INC**
1 Federal St Fl 7, Boston, MA 02110-2003
Tel (617) 535-4766 *Founded/Ownrshp* 1951
Sales 3.0MMM *EMP* 20,000
Tkr Sym IRM *Exch* NYS
SIC 4226 8741 7375 6798 Document & office records storage; Management services; Information retrieval services; Real estate investment trusts
Pr: William L Meaney

Ch Bd: Alfred J Verrecchia
CFO: Stuart B Brown
CFO: Roderick Day
Chf Mktg O: Theodore Maclean
Ofcr: Deirdre J Evens
Ex VP: Ernest W Cloutier
Ex VP: John J Connors
Ex VP: Annie Drapeau
Ex VP: Patrick J Keddy
Ex VP: Anastasios Tsolakis
Ex VP: Wallace Tsolakis
Sr VP: Barry Payne
VP: Ned Bicks
VP: Jen Doherty
VP: Mackenzie Fribance
VP: Stephen Haggett
VP: Todd Koopersmith
VP: Steve Kowalkoski
VP: Michael J Lewis
VP: Melissa Marsden
Board of Directors: Jennifer M Allerton, Ted R Antenucci, Pamela M Arway, Clarke H Bailey, Kent P Dauten, Paul F Deninger, Walter C Rakowich

D-U-N-S 62-141-7633
■ IRON MOUNTAIN INFORMATION MANAGEMENT LLC
(*Suby of* IRON MOUNTAIN INC) ★
1 Federal St, Boston, MA 02110-2012
Tel (617) 357-4455 *Founded/Ownrshp* 1996
Sales 2.6MMM[E] *EMP* 17,280
SIC 4226 Document & office records storage
Pr: C Richard Reese
Pr: William Meaney
CFO: Jeff Lawrence
CFO: Brian McKeon
Opers Mgr: Craig Homenko

D-U-N-S 05-979-7472
■ IRON MOUNTAIN/PACIFIC RECORDS MANAGEMENT INC
(*Suby of* IRON MOUNTAIN INFORMATION MANAGEMENT LLC) ★
1 Federal St, Boston, MA 02110-2012
Tel (617) 357-4455 *Founded/Ownrshp* 1998
Sales 185.6MM[E] *EMP* 9,000
SIC 7382 Protective devices, security
Ch Bd: Clark Bailey
**Treas:* Jeff Lawrence

D-U-N-S 96-386-2003
IRON WORK 40 361 & 417 HLTH FND
451 Park Ave S, New York, NY 10016-7390
Tel (212) 684-1586 *Founded/Ownrshp* 2011
Sales 101.0MM *EMP* 3[E]
SIC 1791 Iron work, structural
Prin: Kevin Orourke

D-U-N-S 07-886-9753 IMP
IRONGATE ENERGY SERVICES LLC
ALLIS CHALMERS
19500 State Highway 249 # 600, Houston, TX 77070-3065
Tel (832) 678-8585 *Founded/Ownrshp* 2013
Sales 168.0MM[E] *EMP* 276[E]
SIC 1389 Servicing oil & gas wells
CEO: Terry Keane
**VP:* Dwight Gross
**VP:* Monty Johnston

IRONPLANET.
See IRONPLANET INC

D-U-N-S 12-471-5546 IMP/EXP
IRONPLANET INC
IRONPLANET.
3825 Hopyard Rd Ste 250, Pleasanton, CA 94588-2787
Tel (925) 225-8600 *Founded/Ownrshp* 1999
Sales 166.6MM[E] *EMP* 316
SIC 7389 Auction, appraisal & exchange services
CEO: Gregory J Owens
Pr: James J Jeter
CFO: Debbie Schleicher
Chf Mktg O: Matt Ackley
Chf Mktg O: Susan Stillings
Sr VP: Randall E Berry
Sr VP: Douglas P Feick
Sr VP: Mike Groves
Sr VP: Michael J O'Donnell
VP: Jeffrey L Barca-Hall
VP: Paul C Blalock
VP: Paul Blalock
VP: Matthew J Bousky
VP: Douglas Feick
VP: Jeff Holmes
VP: Randy Johnston
VP: H Andrew Pyron

D-U-N-S 83-158-0977
IRONSHORE SERVICES INC
IRONSHORE SPECIALTY INSURANCE
(*Suby of* IRONSHORE INSURANCE LTD)
1 State St Fl 8, New York, NY 10004-1506
Tel (646) 826-6600 *Founded/Ownrshp* 2007
Sales NA *EMP* 319[E]
SIC 6411 Property & casualty insurance agent
CEO: Kevin H Kelley
**Ch Bd:* Domenic Serratore
**Pr:* Shaun E Kelly
**CEO:* Kevin Kelley
**COO:* Mitchell E Blaser
CFO: William Gleason
Ofcr: Alyssa Turkovitz
Ex VP: Pierre Samson
Sr VP: Andrew Archambault
Sr VP: Alice Johansson
Sr VP: Daniel Owen
Sr VP: Rick Paladino
Sr VP: Matthew Wasta
VP: Alicia Bromfield
VP: Tim Delaney
VP: Dawn Krigstin
VP: Valerie Onderka
VP: Nick Wills

IRONSHORE SPECIALTY INSURANCE
See IRONSHORE SERVICES INC

D-U-N-S 03-946-7360
IRONSHORE SPECIALTY INSURANCE CO
(*Suby of* TIG INSURANCE CO) ★
2850 Lake Vista Dr # 150, Lewisville, TX 75067-4228
Tel (646) 826-6600 *Founded/Ownrshp* 1952
Sales NA *EMP* 700
SIC 6331 Automobile insurance
CEO: Michael Mitrovic
Pr: Richard Scott Donovan
Treas: Nicolas Arizaga
Treas: Michael Sluka
VP: Cynthia Crandall

D-U-N-S 05-445-1401
▲ IRONWOOD PHARMACEUTICALS INC
301 Binney St, Cambridge, MA 02142-1030
Tel (617) 621-7722 *Founded/Ownrshp* 1998
Sales 149.5MM *EMP* 474[E]
Tkr Sym IRWD *Exch* NGS
SIC 2834 8731 Pharmaceutical preparations; Commercial physical research
CEO: Peter M Hecht
**Ch Bd:* Terrance G McGuire
Chf Cred: Thomas A McCourt
Sr VP: Brian M Cali
Sr VP: Mark G Currie
Sr VP: Thomas Graney
Sr VP: Michael Hall
VP: Gina Consylman
Exec: Jonathan Rosin
Assoc Dir: Anjeza Gjino
Assoc Dir: Elizabeth Shea
Comm Man: Holly John
Board of Directors: Andrew Dreyfus, Marsha H Fanucci, Julie H McHugh, Lawrence S Olanoff, Edward P Owens, Christopher T Walsh, Douglas Williams

D-U-N-S 60-395-5949 IMP
IROQUOIS GAS TRANSMISSION SYSTEM LP
1 Corporate Dr Ste 600, Shelton, CT 06484-6260
Tel (203) 925-7200 *Founded/Ownrshp* 1989
Sales 201.1MM *EMP* 105
SIC 4922

D-U-N-S 01-373-3613 IMP
IRR SUPPLY CENTERS INC (NY)
NORTHRUP SUPPLY
908 Niagara Falls Blvd # 125, North Tonawanda, NY 14120-2085
Tel (716) 692-1600 *Founded/Ownrshp* 1965
Sales 208.9MM[E] *EMP* 360
SIC 5074 Plumbing & hydronic heating supplies
Ch Bd: William R Irr
**Pr:* Michael P Duffy
**Pr:* Michael Stetter
Brnch Mgr: Jim Adamski
Genl Mgr: Dave Baldwin
Genl Mgr: Robert Hendricks
Web Prj Mg: Kevin Saky
Sales Asso: Mathew Sanscrainte
Sales Asso: Renee Weiser

D-U-N-S 14-912-6752 IMP
IRVIN AUTOMOTIVE PRODUCTS INC
(*Suby of* PISTON GROUP) ★
2600 Centerpoint Pkwy, Pontiac, MI 48341-3172
Tel (248) 451-4100 *Founded/Ownrshp* 2016
Sales 305.7MM[E] *EMP* 7[E]
SIC 3429 2396 Manufactured hardware (general); Automotive trimmings, fabric
Pr: Joseph Finn
VP: Timothy Mann
VP: Justin Szerlong
CIO: Jason Kennedy

D-U-N-S 82-554-1998
IRVINE APARTMENT COMMUNITIES LP
I A C
(*Suby of* IRVINE CO LLC) ★
110 Innovation Dr, Irvine, CA 92617-3040
Tel (949) 720-5600 *Founded/Ownrshp* 1993
Sales 51.3MM[E] *EMP* 1,500
SIC 6513 6552 6798 Apartment building operators; Subdividers & developers; Real estate investment trusts
V Ch: Raymond Watson
Ex VP: Mike Ellis
VP: Mark Henningan
Mktg Dir: Lisa Cappel

D-U-N-S 00-496-6313
IRVINE CO LLC
550 Newport Center Dr # 160, Newport Beach, CA 92660-7027
Tel (949) 720-2000 *Founded/Ownrshp* 1977
Sales 2.0MMM[E] *EMP* 2,000
SIC 6552 6531 0174 0191 4841 Subdividers & developers; Land subdividers & developers, commercial; Land subdividers & developers, residential; Real estate managers; Rental agent, real estate; Citrus fruits; General farms, primarily crop; Cable television services
Ch Bd: Donald L Bren
**Pr:* Doug Holte
COO: Jon Webber
**CFO:* Chip Fedalen Jr
CFO: Mark Lay
Ex VP: Steve Case
Ex VP: Ron Keith
**Sr VP:* Mark Henigan
VP: Gino Bianchini
VP: Rex V Conde
VP: Nicole Conniff
VP: Bradley Engelland
VP: Steven Kellenberg
VP: Derek Knudsen
VP: Peter Moersch
VP: Shawn Monterastelli
VP: James Mullen
VP: Jon Paynter
Exec: Steve Mandzik

IRVINE COMPANY OFFICE PROPERTY
See IRVINE EASTGATE OFFICE II LLC

D-U-N-S 36-125-3680
IRVINE EASTGATE OFFICE II LLC
IRVINE COMPANY OFFICE PROPERTY
550 Newport Center Dr, Newport Beach, CA 92660-7011
Tel (949) 720-2000 *Founded/Ownrshp* 2013
Sales 329.0MM[E] *EMP* 3,000
SIC 6798 Real estate investment trusts
VP: Pam Van Nort

D-U-N-S 05-927-0884
IRVINE RANCH WATER DISTRICT INC
15600 Sand Canyon Ave, Irvine, CA 92618-3102
Tel (949) 453-5300 *Founded/Ownrshp* 1961
Sales 124.4MM *EMP* 315
SIC 4941 4952 Water supply; Sewerage systems
Genl Mgr: Paul Jones
**Treas:* Robert Jacobson
Board of Directors: Brian Brady, Mary Aileen Matheis, E Darryl Miller, John Withers

D-U-N-S 06-615-1853
IRVINE UNIFIED SCHOOL DISTICT
IRVINE UNIFIED SCHOOL DISTRICT
5050 Barranca Pkwy, Irvine, CA 92604-4698
Tel (949) 936-5000 *Founded/Ownrshp* 1972
Sales 159.9MM[E] *EMP* 2,212
Accts Vavrinek Trine Day & Co Ll
SIC 8211 Public elementary & secondary schools; Public elementary school; Public junior high school; Public senior high school
**CEO:* Michael B Regele
Treas: Hilda Rahmann
CTO: Brianne Ford
Schl Brd P: Lauren Brooks
Psych: Susan Rashap
Psych: Angelique Strausheim

IRVINE UNIFIED SCHOOL DISTRICT
See IRVINE UNIFIED SCHOOL DISTICT

D-U-N-S 02-624-5076
IRVING BRAKEBUSH INC
TRINITY VALLEY FOODS
(*Suby of* BRAKEBUSH BROTHERS INC) ★
2230 E Union Bower Rd, Irving, TX 75061-8814
Tel (972) 554-0590 *Founded/Ownrshp* 2013
Sales 213.6MM[E] *EMP* 375
SIC 5144 Poultry & poultry products
CEO: Carl Brakebush
**VP:* Dennis Jameson
Manager: Johan Delport

D-U-N-S 94-885-1175 IMP
IRVING CONSUMER PRODUCTS INC
IRVING TISSUE DIV
(*Suby of* IRVING CONSUMER PRODUCTS LIMITED)
1 Eddy St, Fort Edward, NY 12828-1711
Tel (518) 747-4151 *Founded/Ownrshp* 1996
Sales 98.4MM[E] *EMP* 310
SIC 2621 Towels, tissues & napkins: paper & stock
Prin: J K Irving
**VP:* Arthur L Irving
VP: Bo B Lam
VP: Rachel Roy
VP: Bernice Wall

IRVING ENERGY DIST & MKTG
See HIGHLANDS FUEL DELIVERY LLC

D-U-N-S 07-670-0988
IRVING INDEPENDENT SCHOOL DISTRICT INC
IRVING INDEPENDENT SCHOOL DST
2621 W Airport Fwy, Irving, TX 75062-6020
Tel (972) 600-5000 *Founded/Ownrshp* 1946
Sales 232.8MM[E] *EMP* 3,934
Accts Weaver And Tidwell Llp Dalla
SIC 8211 Public elementary & secondary schools
**Pr:* Larry Stipes
**CFO:* Gary Micinski
Bd of Dir: Jerry Christian
Bd of Dir: Ronda Huffstetler
Bd of Dir: Steven Jones
**VP:* Randy Randal
Dir Sec: Terry Zettle
Prgrm Mgr: Delia Watley
DP Exec: Diana Jauregui
MIS Dir: Bonnie Russell
Dir IT: John Mynatt
Board of Directors: Barbara Cardwell, Rhonda Huffstetler, Mike Junstadt, Terry Waldrun

IRVING INDEPENDENT SCHOOL DST
See IRVING INDEPENDENT SCHOOL DISTRICT INC

IRVING MATERIALS
See IMI SOUTH LLC

D-U-N-S 00-604-1917
IRVING MATERIALS INC
I M I
8032 N State Road 9, Greenfield, IN 46140-9097
Tel (317) 326-3101 *Founded/Ownrshp* 1967
Sales 794.8MM[E] *EMP* 2,200
SIC 3273 3271 5032 2951 Ready-mixed concrete; Concrete block & brick; Sand, construction; Gravel; Stone, crushed or broken; Asphalt paving blocks (not from refineries)
Pr: Earl G Brinker
CFO: Earl Brinker
**Ch:* Pete Irving
VP: Brad Kosiba
Dir IT: Billy Carroll
IT Man: Brent Neufelder
Trfc Dir: Gideon Brown
Trfc Dir: Shane Deal
Plnt Mgr: Wayne Carter
Plnt Mgr: Jerry Cyr
Plnt Mgr: Jeremy Geary
Board of Directors: Allen Rosenberg Sr, Tom Thomas

D-U-N-S 02-234-8226
IRVING MCDAVID HONDA LP
MCDAVID, DAVID HONDA
3700 W Airport Fwy, Irving, TX 75062-5903
Tel (972) 790-2000 *Founded/Ownrshp* 1998
Sales 100.0MM *EMP* 120
SIC 5511 Automobiles, new & used
Pr: B David McDavid Sr

IRVING MICHAELS & COMPANY
See MICHAELS ENTERPRISES INC

D-U-N-S 18-999-1701 IMP/EXP
IRVING OIL TERMINALS INC
190 Commerce Way, Portsmouth, NH 03801-3281
Tel (603) 559-8736 *Founded/Ownrshp* 1998
Sales 402.8MM[E] *EMP* 99[E]
SIC 5171 Petroleum terminals
**Pr:* Mike Ashar
**CFO:* Kevin Dumaresque
**Ofcr:* Darren Gillis
Genl Mgr: Kevin Boyle
VP Mktg: Arthur Irving
Mktg Mgr: Leann Wright

D-U-N-S 82-881-2672
IRVING PLACE CAPITAL LLC
745 5th Ave Fl 7, New York, NY 10151-0802
Tel (212) 551-4500 *Founded/Ownrshp* 2002
Sales 1.6MMM[E] *EMP* 10,120[E]
SIC 5999 5099 Pets & pet supplies; Firearms & ammunition, except sporting
VP: Bret Bowerman
VP: Brad Jacobsen
Mng Dir: Phil Carpenter

IRVING TISSUE DIV
See IRVING CONSUMER PRODUCTS INC

D-U-N-S 03-939-1834
IRVINGTON PUBLIC SCHOOLS
1 University Pl Fl 4, Irvington, NJ 07111-2627
Tel (973) 399-6800 *Founded/Ownrshp* 1898
Sales 77.9MM[E] *EMP* 1,250
SIC 8211 Public elementary & secondary schools
Bd of Dir: Renee Burgess
Ofcr: Roger Monel
Web Dev: Carol Coleman
Web Dev: Rochelle Lipsky
Software D: Christiana Amadi
Software D: Valerie Benn
Software D: Wesly Ertulien
Software D: Kerline Moreau
Software D: Caren Pozniak
Software D: Christina Rishiy
Software D: Roslyn Turner-Ince

D-U-N-S 01-424-2275
IRWIN BUILDERS SUPPLY CORP
I B S
10249 Garnet Ln, Irwin, PA 15642-3874
Tel (724) 863-5200 *Founded/Ownrshp* 1960
Sales 88.8MM[E] *EMP* 70[E]
SIC 5031 5211 Building materials, exterior; Building materials, interior; Lumber & other building materials
Pr: Daniel J Paulone
**Treas:* Marie Paulone
**VP:* Patrice L Paulone
Opers Mgr: Dave George

IRWIN CONSTRUCTION ACCESSORIES
See IRWIN INDUSTRIAL TOOL CO

D-U-N-S 15-064-3468 IMP/EXP
■ IRWIN INDUSTRIAL TOOL CO
IRWIN CONSTRUCTION ACCESSORIES
(*Suby of* NEWELL BRANDS INC) ★
8935 N Pointe Exec Pk Dr, Huntersville, NC 28078-4857
Tel (704) 987-4555 *Founded/Ownrshp* 2002
Sales 833.8MM[E] *EMP* 4,166
SIC 3423 3545 3421 Screw drivers, pliers, chisels, etc. (hand tools); Wrenches, hand tools; Mechanics' hand tools; Drill bits, metalworking; Snips, tinners'
CEO: Michael B Polk
**Pr:* Neil R Eibeler
**Pr:* Robert Hudson
**Pr:* Ross Poter
VP: Adam Mack
VP: Christopher Tesmer
Exec: Amanda Busch
CTO: Tom Hamilton
VP Opers: Isaac Read
Plnt Mgr: David Finch
VP Sls: William Shine

D-U-N-S 02-841-7079
IRWIN INDUSTRIES INC
(*Suby of* PARK CORP) ★
1580 W Carson St, Long Beach, CA 90810-1455
Tel (310) 233-3000 *Founded/Ownrshp* 1922
Sales 300.0MM[E] *EMP* 710
Accts Meaden & Moore Ltd Cpa S
SIC 1629 1731 1796 7353 1542 Power plant construction; Electric power systems contractors; Power generating equipment installation; Heavy construction equipment rental; Nonresidential construction
CEO: Ricardo B Teamor
CFO: Al Storer
Off Mgr: Rhonda Smith
Counsel: Carly Drake

D-U-N-S 03-446-2671 EXP
IRWIN INTERNATIONAL INC
AIRCRAFT SPRUCE
225 Airport Cir, Corona, CA 92880-2527
Tel (951) 372-9555 *Founded/Ownrshp* 1980
Sales 91.1MM[E] *EMP* 160
SIC 5599 5088 Aircraft instruments, equipment or parts; Aircraft & parts
Pr: James J Irwin
**VP:* Elizabeth Irwin
Exec: Jerry Aquilar
Mktg Dir: Desiree Czaplinski
Sls Mgr: Tom Glaze
Sls Mgr: Jack Samuels
Sales Asso: Amanda Cox
Sales Asso: Amy Dukes
Sales Asso: James Mason

D-U-N-S 00-601-5424 IMP/EXP
IRWIN SEATING CO
COUNTRY ROADS
(*Suby of* IRWIN SEATING HOLDING CO) ★
3251 Fruit Ridge Ave Nw, Grand Rapids, MI 49544-9748
Tel (616) 784-2621 *Founded/Ownrshp* 1999
Sales 130.4MM^E *EMP* 600^E
SIC 2531 Public building & related furniture
Pr: Win Irwin
**Pr:* Earle S Irwin
**CFO:* Ray Vander Kooi
**Sr VP:* Bruce J Cohen
**Sr VP:* Dale I Tanis
**Sr VP:* John Eichinger
**Sr VP:* John Fynewever
**Sr VP:* Robert E Weakley
Exec: Wayne Berens
Dir Bus: Bill Macleod
CIO: Bernie Stevens

D-U-N-S 10-463-4212 IMP/EXP
IRWIN SEATING HOLDING CO
3251 Fruit Ridge Ave Nw, Grand Rapids, MI 49544-9748
Tel (616) 574-7400 *Founded/Ownrshp* 1999
Sales 130.4MM^E *EMP* 725
SIC 2531 7641 Public building & related furniture; School furniture; Stadium seating; Furniture repair & maintenance; Furniture refinishing; Antique furniture repair & restoration
Pr: Earle S Irwin
**Sr VP:* Dale I Tanis

ISAAC E CRARY JUNIOR HIGH SCHL
See WATERFORD SCHOOL DISTRICT

D-U-N-S 02-205-1291
■ ISAAC FAIR CORP
(*Suby of* FAIR ISAAC SOFTWARE HOLDINGS LIMITED)
3550 Engrg Dr Ste 200, Norcross, GA 30092
Tel (770) 810-8000 *Founded/Ownrshp* 1996
Sales 70.3MM^E *EMP* 3,000
SIC 7371 Software programming applications
VP: Chris Anderson
COO: Tom Duvall
VP: Rachel Carawan
VP: Charles M Osborne

D-U-N-S 08-896-1180 IMP
ISABELLA GERIATRIC CENTER INC
515 Audubon Ave, New York, NY 10040-3403
Tel (212) 342-9200 *Founded/Ownrshp* 1970
Sales 97.4MM *EMP* 1,050
Accts Oconnor Davies Llp Harrison
SIC 8051 Skilled nursing care facilities
CEO: Mark J Kator
Dir Vol: Rosa Pascual
**Ch:* Mark Lipton
Bd of Dir: Gregory Fortin
Bd of Dir: John Green
**VP:* John Zeiss
Dir Soc: Ann McDermott
Dir Sec: Laverne Collins
IT Man: Jean Bienaime
IT Man: Renato Leonel
Info Man: Debbie Alvarado

D-U-N-S 03-701-8207 IMP
ISACO INTERNATIONAL CORP (FL)
5980 Miami Lakes Dr E, Miami Lakes, FL 33014-2404
Tel (305) 594-4455 *Founded/Ownrshp* 1980
Sales 162.6MM^E *EMP* 250
SIC 5136 Men's & boys' clothing
Pr: Isaac Zelcer
VP: Robert Weaver
VP: Alan Zelcer

D-U-N-S 14-479-8480 IMP/EXP
ISAGENIX INTERNATIONAL LLC
155 E Rivulon Blvd, Gilbert, AZ 85297-0002
Tel (480) 889-5747 *Founded/Ownrshp* 2002
Sales 126.7MM^E *EMP* 350^E
SIC 2834 Vitamin, nutrient & hematinic preparations for human use
Treas: Jack Spitzer
Chf Mktg O: Kevin Adams
VP: Travis Garza
VP: Justin Powell
Dir Soc: Jessica Leadingham
**Prin:* James Pierce
Snr Sftwr: David Rinehart
CIO: Darren Fujii
QA Dir: Kyla Boudreau
QA Dir: Anthony Yeatropoulos
Software D: Matthew Ellison

ISBE
See ILLINOIS STATE BOARD OF EDUCATION

D-U-N-S 96-820-0639
ISC ACQUISITION CORP
ISC BUILDING MATERIALS
7645 Railhead Ln, Houston, TX 77086-3201
Tel (281) 590-6000 *Founded/Ownrshp* 2011
Sales 97.8MM^E *EMP* 100
SIC 5032 5031 Drywall materials; Wallboard; Enameled tileboard
Pr: Narciso Flores
**VP:* Michael Flores

ISC BUILDING MATERIALS
See ISC ACQUISITION CORP

D-U-N-S 60-948-0686
ISC CONSTRUCTORS LLC
ISC
(*Suby of* ISC GROUP L L C) ★
20480 Highland Rd, Baton Rouge, LA 70817-7347
Tel (225) 756-8001 *Founded/Ownrshp* 1989
Sales 224.6MM^E *EMP* 1,000
SIC 1731 Electrical work
Ch Bd: Edward L Rispone
VP: Steve Derouen
Exec: Lauren Read
Area Mgr: Chad Potier
Off Mgr: Susann Boudreaux
QA Dir: Forrest Skiver
Dir IT: Luke Dicharry
Dir IT: Brooke Lyons
IT Man: Brook Loin
IT Man: Brook Lyon
Sls Mgr: Bill Jones

D-U-N-S 11-125-8448
ISC GROUP L L C
20480 Highland Rd, Baton Rouge, LA 70817-7347
Tel (225) 756-8001 *Founded/Ownrshp* 1989
Sales 224.6MM^E *EMP* 1,700
SIC 1731 Electrical work
Pr: Gerard L Rispone
Ex VP: Glen R Redd

D-U-N-S 05-412-5190 IMP
■ ISCAR METALS INC
(*Suby of* BERKSHIRE HATHAWAY INC) ★
300 Westway Pl, Arlington, TX 76018-1021
Tel (817) 258-3200 *Founded/Ownrshp* 2008
Sales 134.9MM^E *EMP* 383
Accts Pricewaterhousecoopers Llp Ha
SIC 5084 Tool holders (chucks, turrets)
Pr: Jacob Harpaz
Pr: Sarah Tidwell
**Ex VP:* Reggie Lowder
VP: Rod Zimmerman
IT Man: Rames Gantanant
Opers Mgr: Eitan Ganor
Manager: Randall Wilson
Sls Mgr: Stephan Hardesty
Sales Asso: Shawn Kalinec
Sales Asso: Robert Swanson

D-U-N-S 13-942-7561 IMP/EXP
ISCO HOLDING CO INC
INDEPENDENT STAVE COMPANY
1078 S Jefferson Ave, Lebanon, MO 65536-3601
Tel (417) 588-4151 *Founded/Ownrshp* 1983
Sales 311.2MM^E *EMP* 1,150
SIC 2449 Barrels, wood: coopered
Ch Bd: John J Boswell
S&M/VP: Aime B Dewane

D-U-N-S 00-700-3999 IMP/EXP
ISCO INDUSTRIES INC (KY)
I S C O
100 Witherspoon St, Louisville, KY 40202-1396
Tel (502) 318-6626 *Founded/Ownrshp* 2012
Sales 450.0MM *EMP* 330
SIC 5085 5083 Valves & fittings; Irrigation equipment
CEO: Jimmy Kirchdorfer Jr
**Pr:* Mark T Kirchdorfer
**CFO:* Christopher Feger
Sys/Dir: Mike Grosse
Web Dev: Wes Merkamp
Manager: Garry Bouvet
Manager: Malcolm Collins
Sls Mgr: Mark Chittick
Sls Mgr: Jim Fletcher
Sls Mgr: Josh Hill

ISD 12
See EDMOND PUBLIC SCHOOLS

D-U-N-S 82-537-9576
ISD HOLDINGS INC
4715 Frederick Dr Sw, Atlanta, GA 30336-1809
Tel (404) 691-7400 *Founded/Ownrshp* 1999
Sales 123.5MM^E *EMP* 400^E
SIC 7389 2542 2759 2752 Design services; Fixtures, store: except wood; Screen printing; Commercial printing, offset
CEO: Harmon B Miller IV
**Pr:* Paul R Papantonis
**CFO:* David D Seem

D-U-N-S 02-484-1802
■ ISD PLAINFIELD LLC
PLAINFIELD RENAL CENTER
(*Suby of* DAVITA INC) ★
8110 Network Dr, Plainfield, IN 46168-9024
Tel (317) 838-8089 *Founded/Ownrshp* 2008
Sales 301.0MM *EMP* 99
SIC 8092 Kidney dialysis centers
Prin: Jim Hilger

D-U-N-S 80-866-8235
■ ISD RENAL INC
(*Suby of* DAVITA INC) ★
424 Church St Ste 1900, Nashville, TN 37219-2387
Tel (615) 777-8200 *Founded/Ownrshp* 2005
Sales 48.8MM^E *EMP* 2,200^E
SIC 8069 8092 8742 Cancer hospital; Kidney dialysis centers; Management consulting services
Pr: Dennis L Kogod
**CFO:* James K Hilger
**VP:* David R Finn
**VP:* Chetan P Mehta
**VP:* Javier J Rodriguez
**VP:* Steven I Grieger
**VP:* Thomas O Usilton

D-U-N-S 05-872-6696 IMP
ISEC INC
6000 Greenwood Plaza Blvd # 200, Greenwood Village, CO 80111-4818
Tel (410) 381-6049 *Founded/Ownrshp* 1967
Sales 295.9MM *EMP* 1,150
Accts Martin Vejvoda And Associates
SIC 1751 Cabinet & finish carpentry
Pr: Dusty Morgan
**CFO:* Charlie Dietrich
**Sr VP:* Tim McCoy
**Sr VP:* Brent Paden
**Sr VP:* Michael Polanchyck
**Sr VP:* Greg Timmerman
**VP:* Branden Derks
**VP:* David Herzel
**VP:* Kelly Martin
VP: Sara Milchman
**VP:* Joan Norblom
**VP:* Mike Polanchyck
**VP:* Chris Stoudt
**VP:* Jeff Walker

D-U-N-S 00-482-8687
ISEMOTO CONTRACTING CO LTD (HI)
648 Piilani St, Hilo, HI 96720-4691
Tel (808) 935-7194 *Founded/Ownrshp* 1926
Sales 132.0MM^E *EMP* 400
Accts Deloitte & Touche Llp Honolul
SIC 1629 1542 1541 Land preparation construction; Commercial & office building contractors; Industrial buildings, new construction
Pr: Leslie K Isemoto
**Pr:* Leslie Isemoto
**VP:* Jerry Egami
**VP:* Lester Sakamoto
**VP:* Bryan Tomiyoshi
Genl Mgr: Loren Tsugawa

ISG COMPANIES
See INTERNATIONAL FINANCIAL GROUP INC

D-U-N-S 78-330-6327
■ ISG INFORMATION SERVICES GROUP AMERICAS INC
T P I
(*Suby of* INFORMATION SERVICES GROUP INC) ★
25025 N I 45 Ste 225, The Woodlands, TX 77380
Tel (281) 465-5700 *Founded/Ownrshp* 2007
Sales 86.5MM^E *EMP* 600
Accts Pricewaterhousecoopers Housto
SIC 7379 Computer related consulting services
Pr: David Berger
**Mng Pt:* Mitt Salvaggio
Pr: William Cantor
**Ex VP:* Harry Somerdyk
VP: Warren Clark
**VP:* Michael P Connors
VP: Kathy Welch
Exec: Tanaka Suzanne
IT Man: Michael Desorcie
IT Man: Greg Moore

ISG RESOURCES
See HEADWATERS RESOURCES INC

IS.GROUP
See INDEPENDENT STATIONERS INC

D-U-N-S 18-119-9837 IMP/EXP
ISHAN INTERNATIONAL INC
TABAN CO
500 Smith St, Farmingdale, NY 11735-1115
Tel (631) 618-3000 *Founded/Ownrshp* 1983
Sales 141.0MM *EMP* 6
Accts Marks Paneth Llp New York Ny
SIC 5065 Electronic parts & equipment
Pr: Abdulrahman S Khwaja

ISHARES
See BLACKROCK INSTITUTIONAL TRUST CO NATIONAL ASSOCIATION

D-U-N-S 12-170-8010
ISI DESIGN AND INSTALLATION SOLUTIONS INC
HD SUPPLY INTERIOR SOLUTIONS
(*Suby of* INTERIOR SPECIALISTS INC) ★
6321 Emperor Dr Ste 201, Orlando, FL 32809-5513
Tel (407) 872-1865 *Founded/Ownrshp* 2016
Sales 132.6MM^E *EMP* 1,000^E
SIC 7389 1752 1799 1751 Interior design services; Floor laying & floor work; Drapery track installation; Cabinet building & installation
Pr: Joseph Izganics
CFO: Evan Levitt
VP: Marc Gonzalez
VP: Dan S Mc Devitt

D-U-N-S 02-215-3294
ISI HR INC
859 W South Jordan Pkwy # 77, South Jordan, UT 84095-3509
Tel (801) 984-0252 *Founded/Ownrshp* 2011
Sales 155.0MM *EMP* 27
SIC 7361 Employment agencies
Pr: Michelyn Farnsworth

ISI RESEARCHSOFT
See THOMSON REUTERS (SCIENTIFIC) INC

D-U-N-S 83-203-8462 EXP
ISLAND APPAREL
135 Renfrew Dr, Athens, GA 30606-3936
Tel (706) 548-3420 *Founded/Ownrshp* 2001
Sales 53.1MM^E *EMP* 1,400
SIC 2325 Men's & boys' trousers & slacks
Pr: Fritz Felchlin

D-U-N-S 15-506-8950
ISLAND COMPUTER PRODUCTS INC
ICP
20 Clifton Ave, Staten Island, NY 10305-4912
Tel (718) 556-6700 *Founded/Ownrshp* 1989
Sales 334.7MM^E *EMP* 205
Accts Del Rey & Company Llp Cpa S
SIC 5045 7373 7379 7378 Computers, peripherals & software; Computer integrated systems design; Computer related consulting services; Computer maintenance & repair
Pr: Michele Fabozzi
COO: Joe Sullivan
CFO: Laura Andersen
**CFO:* Annette Fabozzi
VP: Leonard Dicostanzo
VP: Louis Esposito
Dir Bus: Paul Fabozzi
**CIO:* Paul S Fabozzi

D-U-N-S 88-444-3599
ISLAND HOLDINGS INC
NATIONAL MORTGAGE & FINANCE CO
1022 Bethel St Fl 4, Honolulu, HI 96813-4302
Tel (808) 531-1311 *Founded/Ownrshp* 1990
Sales 247.0MM^E *EMP* 450
SIC 6512 Insurance building operation
Pr: Colbert M Matsumoto
**CFO:* Nolan N Kawano
CFO: Nolan Kawano
VP: Wayne Hikida
VP: Keith Kogachi
VP: Todd Yamanaka
VP: Todd Yamanka
Exec: Shirley MA

ISLAND HOSPITAL
See SKAGIT COUNTY PUBLIC HOSPITAL DISTRICT 2

D-U-N-S 09-383-1530
ISLAND HOSPITALITY MANAGEMENT LLC
222 Lakeview Ave Ste 200, West Palm Beach, FL 33401-6146
Tel (561) 832-6132 *Founded/Ownrshp* 2007
Sales 697.9MM^E *EMP* 4,000
SIC 8741 Hotel or motel management
Pr: Tim Walker
**CFO:* Dennis Craven
**Sr VP:* Barbara A Bachman
**Sr VP:* Phillip M Cohen
**Sr VP:* Michele Mainelli
**Sr VP:* Roger Pollak
**Sr VP:* Jeffrey Waldt
**VP:* Rob Auerbach

D-U-N-S 07-766-4522
ISLAND INSURANCE CO LIMITED
CLAIMS CENTER
(*Suby of* NATIONAL MORTGAGE & FINANCE CO) ★
1022 Bethel St, Honolulu, HI 96813-4302
Tel (808) 564-8200 *Founded/Ownrshp* 1939
Sales NA *EMP* 386
SIC 6331 6411 Property damage insurance; Fire, marine & casualty insurance & carriers; Insurance agents, brokers & service
CEO: John Schapperle
Ch: Colbert Matsumoto
Sr VP: Beverly Ament
Sr VP: Nolan Kawano
VP: Jeff Fabry
VP: Riki Fujitani
VP: Paul Iijima
VP: Sharon Lee
VP: Glenn Motogawa
VP: Leila Tamashiro
VP: Pamela Watanabe

ISLAND MINI MART
See ALOHA PETROLEUM LTD

D-U-N-S 78-471-2122
ISLAND OAKS LIVING CENTER LLC
3647 Maybank Hwy, Johns Island, SC 29455-4825
Tel (843) 559-5888 *Founded/Ownrshp* 2006
Sales 742.7MM *EMP* 99
SIC 8051 Skilled nursing care facilities
Prin: John Swift

D-U-N-S 15-362-1446 IMP/EXP
ISLAND OASIS FROZEN COCKTAIL CO INC
(*Suby of* KERRY GROUP PUBLIC LIMITED COMPANY)
141 Norfolk St, Walpole, MA 02081-1703
Tel (508) 660-1177 *Founded/Ownrshp* 2015
Sales 156.6MM^E *EMP* 210
Accts Kpmg Peat Marwick Llp
SIC 5142 Fruit juices, frozen
CEO: J Michael Herbert
**CFO:* Scott A Kumf
Sr VP: Jeff Lombardo
VP: Barry Boehme
Genl Mgr: Joe Keaney
IT Man: Joshua Wexler
Opers Mgr: Randy Mackenzie
Opers Mgr: Thomas Powell
Plnt Mgr: John Kasinecz
VP Sls: Mike Walsh
Manager: Michael Adams

D-U-N-S 07-323-4056
ISLAND ONE INC
ISLAND ONE RESORTS
7345 Greenbriar Pkwy, Orlando, FL 32819-8935
Tel (407) 859-8900 *Founded/Ownrshp* 1981
Sales 177.7MM^E *EMP* 900
SIC 1522 Residential construction
CEO: Deborah A Linden
Sr VP: Karen S Holbrook
VP: Nancy L Ogden
Exec: Cathy White

ISLAND ONE RESORTS
See ISLAND ONE INC

D-U-N-S 17-370-9148
ISLAND OPERATING CO INC
108 Zachary Dr, Scott, LA 70583-5332
Tel (337) 262-0620 *Founded/Ownrshp* 1986
Sales 411.7MM^E *EMP* 1,300
SIC 1389 Oil field services
Pr: Gregg H Falgout
CFO: Kaoen Deen
Ex VP: Kimberly Falgout
VP: Christine Falgout
VP: Ray Williams
Software D: Roy Miller
Mktg Mgr: Darrel Mouton
Sls Mgr: Sadi Hulin

D-U-N-S 16-824-2068
ISLAND PALM COMMUNITIES LLC
215 Duck Rd Bldg 950, Schofield Barracks, HI 96857
Tel (808) 275-3100 *Founded/Ownrshp* 2012
Sales 170.0MM^E *EMP* 250
SIC 6531 Real estate leasing & rentals

ISLAND RESORT AND CASINO
See HANNAHVILLE INDIAN COMMUNITY

D-U-N-S 05-062-4428
■ ISLAND TELEPHONE CO (MI)
TDS
(*Suby of* TDS TELECOMMUNICATIONS CORP) ★
37940 King Hwy, Beaver Island, MI 49782
Tel (608) 831-1000 *Founded/Ownrshp* 1957, 1991
Sales 867.0MM *EMP* 2,700
SIC 4813 Local telephone communications
Pr: David A Witter

ISLAND VIEW CASINO RESORT
See GRAND CASINOS INC

ISLANDS FINE BURGER & DRINKS
See ISLANDS RESTAURANTS LP

D-U-N-S 78-688-8305
ISLANDS RESTAURANTS LP
ISLANDS FINE BURGER & DRINKS
5750 Fleet St Ste 120, Carlsbad, CA 92008-4709
Tel (760) 268-1800 *Founded/Ownrshp* 1982
Sales 123.0MM^E *EMP* 2,500
SIC 5812 Hamburger stand
Sr VP: Ben Schwartz
Pt: Tony Deguazier
COO: Jeff Brackey
CFO: Rob Richards
VP: Lewis Jackson
VP: Tim Perreira
Genl Mgr: Val Parez
Genl Mgr: Carmen Valentino
Off Mgr: Scott Blakeman
IT Man: Chris Wdowiak
Mktg Mgr: Jessica Swart

ISLE OF CAPRI BILOXI
See RIVERBOAT CORP OF MISSISSIPPI

D-U-N-S 79-536-8232
▲ ISLE OF CAPRI CASINOS INC
600 Emerson Rd Ste 300, Saint Louis, MO 63141-6762
Tel (314) 813-9200 *Founded/Ownrshp* 1990
Sales 978.5MM *EMP* 6,600^E
Accts Ernst & Young Llp St Louis
Tkr Sym ISLE *Exch* NGS
SIC 7011 7948 Hotels & motels; Racing, including track operation
CEO: Eric L Hausler
**Ch Bd:* Robert S Goldstein
Pr: Arnold L Block
CFO: Michael A Hart
Ofcr: Donn R Mitchell II
Sr VP: Stacy Dewalt
Board of Directors: Bonnie Biumi, Alan J Glazer, Jeffrey D Goldstein, Richard A Goldstein, Gregory J Kozicz, Lee S Wielansky

D-U-N-S 08-757-3130
■ ISLE OF CAPRI LAKE CHARLES
(*Suby of* ISLE OF CAPRI CASINOS INC) ★
100 Westlake Ave, Westlake, LA 70669-5716
Tel (337) 430-2400 *Founded/Ownrshp* 1994
Sales 40.6MM^E *EMP* 2,021
SIC 7011 Casino hotel
CEO: Bernard Goldstein
**Pr:* John M Gallaway
**Pr:* Allan B Solomon
**CFO:* Rexford Yeisley

D-U-N-S 11-368-7164
ISMIE MUTUAL INSURANCE CO
(*Suby of* ILLINOIS STATE MEDICAL SOCIETY) ★
20 N Michigan Ave Ste 700, Chicago, IL 60602-4822
Tel (312) 782-2749 *Founded/Ownrshp* 1976
Sales NA *EMP* 225^E
SIC 6351 Liability insurance
CEO: Alexander R Lerner
**Pr:* Harold L Jersen MD
CFO: Dave Wichmann
**Sec:* Walter Whisler MD
VP: Cheryl Koos
VP: Steve Maes
VP: Audrey Vanagunas
Snr PM: Ed Thiemann

ISN
See INTEGRATED SUPPLY NETWORK LLC

D-U-N-S 78-814-2123
ISO NEW ENGLAND INC
1 Sullivan Rd, Holyoke, MA 01040-2841
Tel (413) 535-4000 *Founded/Ownrshp* 1997
Sales 163.1MM *EMP* 610
SIC 8611 Public utility association
Pr: Gordon Van Welie
**COO:* Vamsi Chadalavada
**CFO:* Robert C Ludlow
Treas: Norman Sproehnle
**VP:* Jamshid Afnan
VP: Jamshid A Afnan
VP: Kevin A Kirby
VP: Jeff McDonald
VP: Stephen Rourke
Dir IT: Debi Smith
IT Man: Steve Bonasoni
Board of Directors: Kathleen Abernathy, Roberta S Brown, Roberto Denis, Ray Hill, Paul Levy, Barney Rush, Philip Shapiro, Vickie Vanzandt, Christopher Wilson

D-U-N-S 10-540-5091
ISO SERVICES INC
I S O
545 Washington Blvd Fl 12, Jersey City, NJ 07310-1613
Tel (201) 469-2000 *Founded/Ownrshp* 2002
Sales 114.0MM^E *EMP* 3,000^E
SIC 7375 Data base information retrieval
CEO: Scott G Stephenson
**Ex VP:* Mark V Anquillare
**Ex VP:* Kenneth E Thompson
**Sr VP:* Vince McCarthy
**Sr VP:* Perry F Rotella
VP: Tom Befi
VP: Phil Hatfield
Div/Sub He: Anne M Connell
Genl Mgr: Karen Smith
IT Man: Sam Halas
Sftwr Eng: Angela Jones

D-U-N-S 08-043-1615 IMP/EXP
ISOCHEM NORTH AMERICA INC (NY)
6800 Jericho Tpke 120w, Syosset, NY 11791-4436
Tel (516) 393-5915 *Founded/Ownrshp* 2016
Sales 120.0MM *EMP* 100
SIC 5169 Chemicals & allied products
CEO: Alireza Ehsani

ISOLA GROUP S.A.R.L.
See ISOLA USA CORP

D-U-N-S 19-139-7702 IMP
ISOLA USA CORP
ISOLA GROUP S.A.R.L.
(*Suby of* TPG GROWTH) ★
3100 W Ray Rd Ste 301, Chandler, AZ 85226-2527
Tel (480) 893-6527 *Founded/Ownrshp* 2005
Sales 197.1MM^E *EMP* 500
SIC 3083 Plastic finished products, laminated
Pr: Raymond Sharpe
Pr: Robert Chaney
**Pr:* Matt Laront
**CFO:* Gordon Bitter
**Ex VP:* Tarun Amla
VP: Mike Behling
**VP:* Lambert Calvert
**VP:* Richard Caron
VP: Chuck Englebert
**VP:* Nina Haralambidis
VP: Tim McCloskey
VP: Alan R Potte

D-U-N-S 13-541-2869 IMP/EXP
ISP CHEMICALS INC
1361 Alps Rd, Wayne, NJ 07470-3700
Tel (973) 628-4000 *Founded/Ownrshp* 2001
Sales 188.8MM^E *EMP* 1,500^E
SIC 2869

D-U-N-S 00-218-8894 IMP/EXP
■ ISP CHEMICALS LLC
(*Suby of* ASHLAND LLC) ★
455 N Main St, Calvert City, KY 42029-8942
Tel (270) 395-4165 *Founded/Ownrshp* 2001, 2011
Sales 133.7MM^E *EMP* 600^E
SIC 2869 Industrial organic chemicals

D-U-N-S 02-731-9338
ISRAEL BIRTHRIGHT FOUNDATION
33 E 33rd St Fl 7, New York, NY 10016-5354
Tel (212) 457-0036 *Founded/Ownrshp* 1999
Sales 123.5MM *EMP* 35
Accts Grant Thornton Llp New York
SIC 8641 Civic social & fraternal associations
Pr: Robert Aronson
**COO:* Maxyne Finkelstein
**CFO:* David Shapiro

D-U-N-S 07-646-2324
ISRAEL DISCOUNT BANK OF NEW YORK
IDB BANK OF NEW YORK
(*Suby of* ISRAEL DISCOUNT BANK LIMITED)
511 5th Ave, New York, NY 10017-4997
Tel (212) 551-8500 *Founded/Ownrshp* 1949
Sales NA *EMP* 500
SIC 6022 State commercial banks
Pr: Arie Sheer
**Ch Bd:* Jacob Berman
Pr: Nomi Clarke
Pr: Rafael Cohen
Pr: Glenn Corrales
Pr: Patrick Egan
Pr: Golan Kochanovsky
Pr: Grisel Mendez
Pr: Lance Reisch
Pr: Ilya Teplitskiy
Pr: Enio Torres
Pr: Rowena Yan
Pr: Li Zhou
**COO:* David Cohen
CFO: Tom Kehrer
Ofcr: Debra Angulo
Top Exec: Howard Weinberg
**Ex VP:* Haim Bar-Ziv
Ex VP: Adam Barsky
Ex VP: Christopher Camuglia
**Ex VP:* Edmond Eskenazi

D-U-N-S 09-511-1217
ISS FACILITY SERVICES HOLDING INC
(*Suby of* ISS HOLDING INC) ★
1019 Central Pkwy N # 100, San Antonio, TX 78232-5078
Tel (210) 495-6021 *Founded/Ownrshp* 1978
Sales 590.4MM^E *EMP* 15,000
SIC 7349 Building maintenance services
CEO: Jennifer Bonilla
**COO:* Mauro Scigliano
**CFO:* Fergus Oconnrll
Sr VP: Katie Holloway
VP: Arrish Bautista
VP: Billy Tenardhi
VP: Michael Trolley

D-U-N-S 80-142-6128
ISS FACILITY SERVICES INC
(*Suby of* ISS FACILITY SERVICES HOLDING INC) ★
1019 Central Pkwy N # 100, San Antonio, TX 78232-5078
Tel (210) 495-6021 *Founded/Ownrshp* 2007
Sales 386.9MM^E *EMP* 4,000^E
SIC 7699 Cleaning services
CFO: Fergus O'Connell
COO: Mauro Scigliano
**Ex VP:* Kelli Cubeta
**Ex VP:* Jon Love
**Ex VP:* Beth Phalen
Sr VP: Katie Holloway
**Sr VP:* Mike Kopp
Dir Bus: Wade Shelton
Genl Mgr: Trent Harr
Genl Mgr: Randy Jordan
CIO: Anthony Lackey

D-U-N-S 96-346-8454
ISS HOLDING INC
(*Suby of* ISS A/S)
1019 Central Pkwy N # 100, San Antonio, TX 78232-5078
Tel (210) 495-6021 *Founded/Ownrshp* 2007
Sales 590.4MM^E *EMP* 15,000^E
SIC 7349 Building maintenance services
CEO: Jennifer Bonilla
Sr VP: Katie Holloway

D-U-N-S 12-436-6928
ISS MANAGEMENT & FINANCE CO INC
(*Suby of* ISS FACILITY SERVICES HOLDING INC) ★
1019 Central Pkwy N Ste 1, San Antonio, TX 78232-5078
Tel (210) 495-6021 *Founded/Ownrshp* 1999
Sales 156.8MM^E *EMP* 5,004^E
SIC 7381 Security guard service
Prin: Darrell Glover

D-U-N-S 05-127-3266
ISS TMC SERVICES INC
(*Suby of* ISS FACILITY SERVICES INC) ★
81 Dorsa Ave, Livingston, NJ 07039-1002
Tel (973) 740-0032 *Founded/Ownrshp* 1964
Sales 72.6MM^E *EMP* 2,500
SIC 6512 7349 7699 Nonresidential building operators; Janitorial service, contract basis; Building maintenance, except repairs; Cleaning services
CEO: Philip Caprio
**VP:* Joseph C Caprio
**VP:* Philip W Caprio Jr

D-U-N-S 15-423-2920
ISS WORLDWIDE
B G SERVICE SOLUTIONS
1225 E 18th St, Kansas City, MO 64108-1605
Tel (816) 421-8088 *Founded/Ownrshp* 1972
Sales 48.4MM^E *EMP* 3,425
SIC 7349 7381 Building maintenance, except repairs; Janitorial service, contract basis; Security guard service
Ch: Ronald Baker
**Pr:* Sonny Price
**VP:* Judy Brown
VP Opers: Dennis Dean

D-U-N-S 07-183-8924
ISSAQUAH SCHOOL DISTRICT 411
565 Nw Holly St, Issaquah, WA 98027-2899
Tel (425) 837-7000 *Founded/Ownrshp* 1889
Sales 246.4MM^E *EMP* 1,700
SIC 8211 9411 Public elementary school; Public junior high school; Public senior high school; Administration of educational programs
**CFO:* Jacob Kuper
Bd of Dir: Connie Fletcher
Exec: Thomas Mullins
Genl Mgr: William Joslin
Web Dev: Brian Ruedi
Pr Dir: L Michelle
Teacher Pr: Lisa Hechtman
Psych: Kristina Ashby
Psych: Kirkpatrick Terry

D-U-N-S 10-288-6215 IMP
ISSC INC
SEAPORT STEEL
3660 E Marginal Way S, Seattle, WA 98134-1130
Tel (206) 343-0700 *Founded/Ownrshp* 1983
Sales 111.2MM^E *EMP* 95
SIC 5051 Structural shapes, iron or steel; Plates, metal; Steel
Pr: Rory James
**Ch Bd:* Mary McCullough
COO: Rodger Parr
**CFO:* Nathaniel Highlander
**Sec:* Joseph Brotherton
Ofcr: Nelson Reeves
Prgrm Mgr: Mike Ridgley
Opers Mgr: Todd Raymond
Prd Mgr: Jennifer Cresap
Board of Directors: Joseph Brotherton, Nancy Pleas Chair Emeritu, Lawrence James, Mary McCullough Chb, Ryan Pleas, Colleen Raymond

ISSD
See PERFORMANCE CONTRACTING INC

IST MANAGEMENT SERVICES
See INNOVATIVE SERVICE TECHNOLOGY MANAGEMENT SERVICES INC

D-U-N-S 02-811-6122
▲ ISTAR INC
1114 Ave Of The Americas, New York, NY 10036-7703
Tel (212) 930-9400 *Founded/Ownrshp* 1993
Sales 514.5MM *EMP* 188^E
Tkr Sym STAR *Exch* NYS
SIC 6798 Real estate investment trusts
Ch Bd: Jay Sugarman
COO: Geoffrey G Jervis
CFO: David Distaso
Ex VP: Karl Frey
Ex VP: Steven P Magee
Ex VP: Vernon Schwartz
Sr VP: Chase S Curtis Jr
VP: Phil Burke
Board of Directors: Clifford De Souza, Robert W Holman Jr, Robin Josephs, John G McDonald, Dale Anne Reiss, Barry W Ridings

D-U-N-S 16-960-9687
ISTATE TRUCK INC
(*Suby of* INTERSTATE POWER SYSTEMS) ★
2601 American Blvd E, Bloomington, MN 55425-1321
Tel (952) 854-2044 *Founded/Ownrshp* 2002
Sales 130.2MM^E *EMP* 60^E
SIC 5084 Industrial machinery & equipment
CEO: Gordon D Galarneau
**Pr:* Jim Williams
**CEO:* Jeff Caswell
Genl Mgr: Travis Sandau
Genl Mgr: Jeff Webber
Mktg Mgr: Carl Brown

ISU FOUNDATION
See IOWA STATE UNIVERSITY FOUNDATION

D-U-N-S 07-840-7418 IMP
ISUZU NORTH AMERICA CORP
(*Suby of* ISUZU MOTORS LIMITED)
1400 S Douglass Rd # 100, Anaheim, CA 92806-6906
Tel (714) 935-9300 *Founded/Ownrshp* 1975
Sales 255.7MM^E *EMP* 600
SIC 5511 5084 5013 5015 Automobiles, new & used; Engines & parts, diesel; Automotive supplies & parts; Motor vehicle parts, used
CEO: Masayuki Fujimori
**Pr:* Yoshihumi Komura
**CEO:* Makoto Kawahara
VP: Dave Barnaich
Ex Dir: Edward Crawford
Sls Mgr: Ed Fischer

ISUZU OF MADISON
See ZIMBRICK INC

D-U-N-S 07-691-9211
IT CONVERGENCE
5370 Kietzke Ln Ste 200, Reno, NV 89511-2059
Tel (415) 675-7935 *Founded/Ownrshp* 1998
Sales 90.3MM^E *EMP* 605
Accts Hood & Strong Llp
SIC 8742 Management consulting services
Pr: Patrick Krause
**Pt:* Andrew Meinnert
**COO:* Jake Van Der Vort
**CFO:* Joseph Long
**Ex VP:* Dean Welch
**VP:* Bryan Koh
Software D: Ricardo Moreno
Snr Mgr: Jim HEI

IT SAVVY
See B2B COMPUTER PRODUCTS LLC

D-U-N-S 14-183-3587
IT1 SOURCE LLC
1860 W University Dr # 100, Tempe, AZ 85281-3247
Tel (480) 777-5995 *Founded/Ownrshp* 2003
Sales 90.0MM *EMP* 85
SIC 5734 Computer & software stores
Sales Exec: Justin Heninger
Sales Exec: Robb Knutson
Sales Exec: Richard Parrill

D-U-N-S 04-349-0986
ITA GROUP INC
4600 Westown Pkwy Ste 100, West Des Moines, IA 50266-1042
Tel (515) 326-3400 *Founded/Ownrshp* 1963
Sales 155.0MM^E *EMP* 550
Accts Mcgladrey Llp Des Moines Ia
SIC 8742 4724 Incentive or award program consultant; Travel agencies
CEO: Thomas J Mahoney
**CFO:* Brent V Waal
**Sr VP:* John McCabe
VP: Phil Brewster
**VP:* CJ McKoy
**VP:* John Rose
**VP:* Kent Schlawin
**Prin:* Mary Z Bussone
Prgrm Mgr: Ellen Darcy
Prgrm Mgr: Ellen Duwelius
Prgrm Mgr: Jen Easter

ITALCEMENTI GROUP
See ESSROC CEMENT CORP

D-U-N-S 09-595-8724 IMP
ITALGRANI USA INC
7900 Van Buren St, Saint Louis, MO 63111-3611
Tel (314) 638-1447 *Founded/Ownrshp* 1987
Sales 275.4MM^E *EMP* 95
SIC 2041 5153 Flour & other grain mill products; Grain & field beans
Pr: James Meyer
**Ex VP:* Hank Thilmony
Genl Mgr: Sharon Connelly
S&M/VP: Patrick Jacoby
Mktg Mgr: Patrick Beem

ITALIAN CONCEPTS
See NAJARIAN FURNITURE CO INC

D-U-N-S 06-774-2969
ITALIAN RESTAURANT
(*Suby of* BREAKERS) ★
1 S County Rd, Palm Beach, FL 33480-4023
Tel (561) 655-6611 *Founded/Ownrshp* 2013
Sales 166.1M^E *EMP* 1,705^E
SIC 5812 Eating places

ITC DELTA COMMUNICATIONS
See ITC DELTACOM INC

D-U-N-S 10-691-6554
ITC DELTACOM INC
ITC DELTA COMMUNICATIONS
7037 Old Madison Pike Nw, Huntsville, AL 35806-2107
Tel (256) 382-5900 *Founded/Ownrshp* 2010
Sales 440.3MM *EMP* 3,030
SIC 4813 4899

D-U-N-S 12-907-1630
ITC HOLDINGS CORP
(*Suby of* ITC INVESTMENT HOLDINGS, INC.)
27175 Energy Way, Novi, MI 48377-3639
Tel (248) 946-3000 *Founded/Ownrshp* 2016
Sales 1.0MMM *EMP* 637^E
SIC 4911 Transmission, electric power
Pr: Joseph L Welch
COO: Jon E Jipping
CFO: Rejji P Hayes
Treas: Gretchen Holloway
Ofcr: Matthew Dills
Ofcr: Wendy A McIntyre
Ofcr: Daniel Oginsky
Ex VP: Linda H Blair
Sr VP: Christine Mason Sonera
VP: Joseph F Bennett III
VP: Matthew Carstens
VP: Terry S Harvill
VP: Ron Hinsley
VP: Fred G Stibor
VP: Thomas W Vitez
Board of Directors: Robert A Elliott

ITC TRANSMISSION
See INTERNATIONAL TRANSMISSION CO

ITCOA
See INDEPENDENCE TITLE CO

D-U-N-S 80-030-7253
ITELLIGENCE INC
(*Suby of* ITELLIGENCE AG)
10856 Reed Hartman Hwy, Cincinnati, OH 45242-2820
Tel (513) 956-2000 *Founded/Ownrshp* 1995
Sales 105.0MM^E *EMP* 410^E
SIC 7379 Computer related consulting services
CEO: Herbert Vogel
**Pr:* Steven Niesman
**CFO:* Tim Breen
**CFO:* Norbert Rotter
**Ex VP:* Uwe Bohnhorst
Ex VP: Dave Noonan
Ex VP: Birgit Wittenbreder
VP: Joe Belluso
VP: Gene Climer
**VP:* Robert Fiorillo
VP: Andrea Jensen
**VP:* Mark Mueller
VP: Jenny Roach
VP: Darshan Shah
**VP:* Steve Short
Exec: Stefan Hoffmann

D-U-N-S 11-396-2864
ITEX DEVELOPMENT CORP
6633 N Lincoln Ave, Lincolnwood, IL 60712-3605
Tel (847) 674-2383 *Founded/Ownrshp* 1994
Sales 50.2MM^E *EMP* 1,500
SIC 8742 Hospital & health services consultant
Pt: Jack Raychenbach
**Pt:* Robert Hartman
**Pt:* Bernard Hollander

ITG
See INVESTMENT TECHNOLOGY GROUP INC

D-U-N-S 05-455-4373
ITG BRANDS LLC (TX)
(*Suby of* IMPERIAL BRANDS PLC)
714 Green Valley Rd, Greensboro, NC 27408-7018
Tel (336) 335-7000 *Founded/Ownrshp* 2012
Sales 5.1MMM^E *EMP* 2,900^E
SIC 2111

D-U-N-S 14-981-1510 IMP/EXP
ITG HOLDINGS INC
IT G
(*Suby of* INTERNATIONAL TEXTILE GROUP INC) ★
804 Green Valley Rd # 300, Greensboro, NC 27408-7039
Tel (336) 379-6220 *Founded/Ownrshp* 2003
Sales 450.0MM^E *EMP* 4,000^E
SIC 2211 2231 2221 2273 2262 2261 Denims; Draperies & drapery fabrics, cotton; Upholstery fabrics, cotton; Tickings; Worsted fabrics, broadwoven; Upholstery fabrics, wool; Polyester broadwoven fabrics; Draperies & drapery fabrics, manmade fiber & silk; Upholstery fabrics, manmade fiber & silk; Carpets & rugs; Finishing plants, manmade fiber & silk fabrics; Finishing plants, cotton
CEO: Joseph L Gorga
Ex VP: Gary Kernaghan
VP Sls: Nelson Bebo

D-U-N-S 82-997-2863
■ **ITG INC**
(*Suby of* ITG) ★
1 Liberty Plz Fl 4, New York, NY 10006-1426
Tel (212) 588-4000 *Founded/Ownrshp* 1978
Sales 399.2MM^E *EMP* 900
SIC 6211 Brokers, security
Prin: Francis J Troise
**CEO:* Maureen Ohara
**CFO:* Howard C Naphtali
Top Exec: David B Drossman
Sr VP: Sujal Bharucha
Sr VP: Stephen Killian
VP: Scott Bauer
VP: Allison Cassidy
Dir Bus: Will Kennedy
Mng Dir: Doug Clark
Mng Dir: Will Geyer
Board of Directors: Kevin J Lynch

D-U-N-S 10-005-5789
ITHACA CITY SCHOOL DISTRICT
400 Lake St, Ithaca, NY 14850-2132
Tel (607) 274-2201 *Founded/Ownrshp* 1870
Sales 52.4MM^E *EMP* 1,200
SIC 8211 Public elementary school; Public junior high school; Public senior high school
Netwrk Eng: Mary Gottlieb
Netwrk Eng: Les McCormick
Netwrk Eng: Dale Perry
Psych: Gillian Devenpeck
Psych: Jesse Dillon
Psych: Cornelia McCrary
Psych: Jill Tripp
HC Dir: Judy Hoffman

D-U-N-S 04-134-0159
ITHACA COLLEGE
953 Danby Rd, Ithaca, NY 14850-7002
Tel (607) 274-3011 *Founded/Ownrshp* 1892
Sales 330.9MM *EMP* 1,350
SIC 8221

D-U-N-S 94-224-3445
ITHAKA HARBORS INC
2 Rector St Fl 18, New York, NY 10006-1852
Tel (212) 500-2600 *Founded/Ownrshp* 1995
Sales 85.7MM *EMP* 214
Accts Eisneramper Llp New York Ny
SIC 7379 Computer related maintenance services
Pr: Kevin Guthrie
Trst: Eugene Lowe
Assoc VP: Alex Humphreys
**Ex VP:* Laura Brown
**Ex VP:* Eileen Fenton
**Ex VP:* Michael Spinella
**VP:* Gerard Aurigemma
**VP:* Bruce Heterick
**VP:* Heidi McGregor
VP: Dale Myers
VP: Jabin White
Assoc Dir: Brian Larsen
Dir Rx: Deirdre Ryan

D-U-N-S 00-420-8906 IMP/EXP
ITL CORP (DE)
INDUSTRIAL TIMBER & LUMBER CO
(*Suby of* NORTHWEST HARDWOODS INC) ★
23925 Commerce Park, Cleveland, OH 44122-5821
Tel (216) 831-3140 *Founded/Ownrshp* 1957, 2015
Sales 86.8MM^E *EMP* 171
SIC 2421 2426 Kiln drying of lumber; Custom sawmill; Hardwood dimension & flooring mills
Pr: Larry Evans
Sales Exec: Dave Allegretto

D-U-N-S 17-514-4989 IMP/EXP
ITOCHU CHEMICALS AMERICA INC
ICAI
(*Suby of* ITOCHU INTERNATIONAL INC) ★
360 Hamilton Ave Fl 6, White Plains, NY 10601-1811
Tel (914) 333-7800 *Founded/Ownrshp* 1987
Sales 87.5MM^E *EMP* 51
SIC 5169 Chemicals & allied products
Pr: Yasuyuki Harada
**Ch Bd:* Hideo Ohori
**Pr:* Hiroaki Yamashita
**CFO:* Mamoru Seki
**Sr VP:* Naohiko Yoshikawa
VP: Yoshikazu Kaho
VP: Alex Tabaco
Sls Mgr: Jim Lawler

D-U-N-S 00-698-5956 IMP/EXP
ITOCHU INTERNATIONAL INC
(*Suby of* ITOCHU CORPORATION)
1251 Avenue Of The Americ, New York, NY 10020-1104
Tel (212) 818-8000 *Founded/Ownrshp* 1952
Sales 3.7MMM^E *EMP* 6,000
Accts Deloitte & Touche Llp New Yor
SIC 5131 5084 5065 5051 5153 5141 Textiles, woven; Industrial machinery & equipment; Electronic parts & equipment; Communication equipment; Ferrous metals; Grains; Groceries, general line
Pr: Tomofumi Yoshida
**CFO:* Satoshi Watanabe
Ex VP: Kotaro Suzuki
**Sr VP:* Tatsushi Shingsu
**Sr VP:* Hidefumi Suzuki
VP: Michael Mimnaugh
VP: Jason Rosenberg
VP: Nobuyuki Tabata
Dir Risk M: Charles Mead
Genl Mgr: Kazuki Iwakiri
IT Man: George Sprance

D-U-N-S 78-680-2947 IMP
ITOCHU PROMINENT USA LLC
(*Suby of* ITOCHU INTERNATIONAL INC) ★
1411 Broadway Fl 7, New York, NY 10018-3566
Tel (212) 827-5707 *Founded/Ownrshp* 1993
Sales 200.0MM *EMP* 200
SIC 5199 Bags, textile
**CEO:* Takeshi Ogura

D-U-N-S 96-872-5668
ITP RAIL ASSOCIATES INC
35 E Main St Ste 415, Avon, CT 06001-3845
Tel (860) 693-6120 *Founded/Ownrshp* 2010
Sales 151.7MM *EMP* 3
SIC 8742 Sales (including sales management) consultant
CEO: Asa Briggs
Prin: Erik Frenzel

D-U-N-S 78-036-5487
ITR CONCESSION CO HOLDINGS LLC
8801 S Anthony Ave, Chicago, IL 60617-3056
Tel (312) 552-7100 *Founded/Ownrshp* 2006
Sales 153.0MM *EMP* 500
SIC 4785 6719 Toll road operation; Investment holding companies, except banks
CFO: Gusyeung Yeung

D-U-N-S 78-278-7290
ITR CONCESSION CO LLC
INDIANA TOLL ROAD
(*Suby of* IFM GLOBAL INFRASTRUCTURE FUND) ★
52551 Ash Rd, Granger, IN 46530-7226
Tel (574) 674-8836 *Founded/Ownrshp* 2015
Sales 97.3MM^E *EMP* 390
SIC 1611 Highway & street maintenance
CEO: Ken Daley
**COO:* Rick Fedder
CFO: Sally Erhardt
**CFO:* Gus Yeung
**CIO:* Juan Ignacio Gomez Lobo
IT Man: Dan Kompare
Sfty Mgr: Ray Hoover

D-U-N-S 15-556-5435 IMP
ITR INDUSTRIES INC
441 Saw Mill River Rd, Yonkers, NY 10701-4913
Tel (914) 964-7063 *Founded/Ownrshp* 2010
Sales 170.1MM^E *EMP* 700
SIC 3431 3429 3446 3088 Shower stalls, metal; Manufactured hardware (general); Architectural metalwork; Shower stalls, fiberglass & plastic
Ch Bd: Mario F Rolla
**Pr:* Adrienne Rola
**Pr:* Peter M Rolla

D-U-N-S 62-238-4936 IMP/EXP
ITR NORTH AMERICA LLC
HEAVYQUIP
6301 Northwind Pkwy, Hobart, IN 46342-2495
Tel (219) 947-8230 *Founded/Ownrshp* 2006
Sales 88.6MM^E *EMP* 250
SIC 5084 Industrial machine parts
Pr: Brett Clemens
CFO: Chris Gilleo
VP: Jim Delaney

D-U-N-S 00-521-5729
ITRIA LLC
333 7th Ave Fl 18, New York, NY 10001-5086
Tel (212) 644-4555 *Founded/Ownrshp* 2007
Sales 221.1MM *EMP* 2^E
SIC 6531 Real estate agent, residential
Prin: Sameer Deshmukh

D-U-N-S 00-129-4651 IMP
■ **ITRON ELECTRICITY METERING INC**
(*Suby of* ITRON INC) ★
313 N Highway 11, West Union, SC 29696-2706
Tel (864) 638-8300 *Founded/Ownrshp* 1892, 2004
Sales 222.7MM^E *EMP* 750
SIC 3825 3823 3824 3679 3829 3612 Watt-hour meters, electrical; Time cycle & program controllers, industrial process type; Speedometers; Mechanical measuring meters; Attenuators; Measuring & controlling devices; Transformers, except electric
CEO: Michael Higgins
**CEO:* Malcolm Unsworth
CFO: Ambory Ken
IT Man: Ken Elrod

D-U-N-S 09-364-9895
▲ **ITRON INC**
2111 N Molter Rd, Liberty Lake, WA 99019-9469
Tel (509) 924-9900 *Founded/Ownrshp* 1977
Sales 1.8MMM *EMP* 8,000
Tkr Sym ITRI *Exch* NGS
SIC 3829 7371 Measuring & controlling devices; Computer software development & applications
Pr: Philip C Mezey
**Ch Bd:* Jon E Eliassen
V Ch: Lynda L Ziegler
COO: Tom Deitrich
CFO: W Mark Schmitz
Bd of Dir: Joan Stephens
Ex VP: Jafar K Aqeel
Ex VP: Julie Carfora
Ex VP: John Shaub
Sr VP: Michel C Cadieux
Sr VP: Bruce Douglas
VP: Rusty Agi
VP: Phyllis Batchelder
VP: Kris Bradley
VP: Mark Champagne
VP: Lynn Collins
VP: Frederic Droin
VP: Deloris Duquette
VP: Christophe Fontaine
VP: Derek Gibbs
VP: Greg Harrington
Board of Directors: Lynda L Ziegler, Kirby A Dyess, Charles H Gaylord Jr, Thomas S Glanville, Frank M Jaehnert, Timothy M Leyden, Sharon L Nelson, Daniel S Pelino, Gary E Pruitt, Diana D Tremblay

D-U-N-S 18-246-0790 IMP
ITS GREEK TO ME INC
G.T.M. SPORTSWEAR
520 Mccall Rd Ste A, Manhattan, KS 66502-7098
Tel (785) 537-8822 *Founded/Ownrshp* 1992
Sales 361.8MM^E *EMP* 900^E
SIC 5136 5699 5137 5947 2759 Sportswear, men's & boys'; Sports apparel; Sportswear, women's & children's; Gift shop; Screen printing
CEO: David Dreiling
**Pr:* John Strawn
**CFO:* Rob Berard
Dir IT: Ford Brethour
Advt Mgr: Carrie Rich

D-U-N-S 00-137-9804 IMP
ITS LOGISTICS LLC (NV)
620 Spice Islands Dr, Reno, NV 89501
Tel (775) 358-5300 *Founded/Ownrshp* 1998
Sales 91.1MM^E *EMP* 375
SIC 4731 4225 Freight forwarding; Brokers, shipping; General warehousing
Pr: Jeffrey Lynch
**Treas:* Darryl Bader
**VP:* Daniel Allen
Plng Mgr: Chad Watnes
CIO: Chad Harden
Dir IT: David Espinosa
Sfty Dirs: Roxie Holben
Opers Mgr: Robert Heaton
Sls Dir: Jim Roy
Board of Directors: Daniel Allen, Darryl Bader, Jeffrey Lynch

D-U-N-S 12-756-3984
ITS TECHNOLOGIES & LOGISTICS LLC
(*Suby of* ITS TECHNOLOGIES & LOGISTICS LLC) ★
8200 185th St Ste A, Tinley Park, IL 60487-9244
Tel (708) 225-2400 *Founded/Ownrshp* 2008
Sales 316.5MM^E *EMP* 1,500
SIC 4789 Cargo loading & unloading services

D-U-N-S 96-172-0443
ITS TECHNOLOGIES & LOGISTICS LLC
8200 185th St Ste A, Tinley Park, IL 60487-9244
Tel (708) 225-2400 *Founded/Ownrshp* 2006
Sales 316.5MM^E *EMP* 1,502^E
SIC 4789 Cargo loading & unloading services
CFO: Mary Vankoevering

ITSC
See INTERMOUNTAIN POWER SERVICE CORP

D-U-N-S 12-653-8649
ITSQUEST INC
4505 82nd St Ste 3, Lubbock, TX 79424-3219
Tel (806) 785-9100 *Founded/Ownrshp* 2003
Sales 7.7MM *EMP* 2,000
SIC 7361 Employment agencies
Pr: Jeff Reagan
**VP:* Sarah Reagan
Area Mgr: Carol Everly
Area Mgr: Santiago Soto
IT Man: Sean Finkbone
Opers Mgr: Joshua Weldy
Mktg Mgr: Nick Merton

D-U-N-S 05-255-4441
■ **ITT CORP**
EXELIS
(*Suby of* ITT LLC) ★
77 River Rd, Clifton, NJ 07014-2000
Tel (973) 284-0123 *Founded/Ownrshp* 2005
Sales 228.8MM^E *EMP* 9,609
SIC 3812 Search & navigation equipment
Pr: Chris Bernhardt

D-U-N-S 80-103-9371
■ **ITT DEFENSE & ELECTRONICS INC**
(*Suby of* ITT LLC) ★
1650 Tysons Blvd Ste 1700, Mc Lean, VA 22102-4827
Tel (703) 790-6300 *Founded/Ownrshp* 1995
Sales 101.0MM^E *EMP* 1,148
SIC 3679 3678 3674 3769 3489 Electronic circuits; Electronic connectors; Semiconductors & related devices; Guided missile & space vehicle parts & auxiliary equipment; Ordnance & accessories
Pr: Henry Driese
**CEO:* Marvin R Sambur
CFO: Heidi Kunz
**CFO:* Mark Lang
Bd of Dir: Markos Tambakeras
VP: Kelvin Coppock
VP: Robert Ferrante
**VP:* Jack Murrel
VP: James O Murrell
VP: Ann Reese
VP: Billy Thomas
VP: Edward Williams
VP Bus Dev: Judy Smith

D-U-N-S 05-470-1560
ITT EDUCATIONAL SERVICES INC
CENTER FOR PROFESSIONAL DEV
13000 N Meridian St, Carmel, IN 46032-1455
Tel (317) 706-9200 *Founded/Ownrshp* 1946
Sales 849.8MM *EMP* 8,400
SIC 8221

D-U-N-S 04-983-1704 IMP
■ **ITT ENIDINE INC**
ENIVATE - AEROSPACE DIVISION
(*Suby of* ITT LLC) ★
7 Centre Dr, Orchard Park, NY 14127-2281
Tel (716) 662-1900 *Founded/Ownrshp* 1995
Sales 123.4MM^E *EMP* 650
SIC 3724 3714 3593 Aircraft engines & engine parts; Motor vehicle parts & accessories; Fluid power cylinders & actuators
Ch Bd: Munish Nanda
**Pr:* Dennis Schully
**CEO:* Dennise Ramos
VP: Christophe Lee
VP: Mike Semo
Plnt Mgr: Dan Claycomb
Ql Cn Mgr: Joe Konieczny
Natl Sales: Gregory Herman
Mktg Dir: Brian Plecas
Sls Dir: William Wilk
Sales Asso: Fran Zandi

D-U-N-S 80-019-8905 IMP/EXP
ITT FLUID TECHNOLOGY CORP
1133 Westcstr Ave N100 Ste N, White Plains, NY 10604
Tel (914) 641-2000 *Founded/Ownrshp* 1986
Sales 1.1MMM^E *EMP* 9,000
SIC 3494 3594 3561

D-U-N-S 08-040-5592
■ **ITT GOULDS PUMPS INC**
(*Suby of* ITT INC) ★
240 Fall St, Seneca Falls, NY 13148-1573
Tel (914) 641-2129 *Founded/Ownrshp* 2004
Sales 1.1MMM^E *EMP* 4,500
SIC 3561 5084 Pumps & pumping equipment; Industrial machinery & equipment
Prin: Michael J Savinelli

D-U-N-S 08-026-7418
▲ **ITT INC**
1133 Westchester Ave N-100, White Plains, NY 10604-3543
Tel (914) 641-2000 *Founded/Ownrshp* 1920
Sales 2.4MMM *EMP* 9,700^E
Tkr Sym ITT *Exch* NYS
SIC 3594 3625 3823 3812 Fluid power pumps & motors; Control equipment, electric; Fluidic devices, circuits & systems for process control; Radar systems & equipment
Pr: Denise L Ramos
**Ch Bd:* Frank T Macinnis
Pr: Farrokh Batliwala
CFO: Thomas M Scalera
Chf Cred: Mary Beth Gustafsson
Ofcr: Victoria Creamer
Sr VP: Victoria L Creamer
VP: Steven C Giuliano

D-U-N-S 00-121-6845 IMP/EXP
■ **ITT LLC** (IN)
(*Suby of* ITT INC) ★
1133 Westchester Ave N-100, White Plains, NY 10604-3543
Tel (914) 641-2000 *Founded/Ownrshp* 1920, 2016
Sales 4.8MMM^E *EMP* 9,700
SIC 3594 3625 3823 3812 Fluid power pumps & motors; Control equipment, electric; Fluidic devices, circuits & systems for process control; Radar systems & equipment
Pr: Denise L Ramos
Pr: Farrokh Batliwala
Pr: Aris C Chicles
Pr: Luca Savi
Pr: Neil W Yeargin
CFO: Thomas M Scalera
Chf Cred: Mary Beth Gustafsson
Ex VP: Aris Chicles
VP: Steven C Giuliano
Exec: Pooja Mukundan
Prgrm Mgr: Derek Bach
Board of Directors: Orlando D Ashford, G Peter D'aloia, Donald Defosset Jr, Christina A Gold, Richard P Lavin, Rebecca A McDonald, Timothy H Powers

D-U-N-S 00-240-6106 IMP
■ **ITT WATER & WASTEWATER USA INC**
(*Suby of* XYLEM INC) ★
1 Greenwich Pl Ste 2, Shelton, CT 06484-7603
Tel (203) 712-8999 *Founded/Ownrshp* 1957, 1980
Sales 87.2MM^E *EMP* 456
SIC 5084 Pumps & pumping equipment
Pr: Ron Port
**VP:* Frank Oliveira

*VP: Jonny Sandstedt
Rgnl Mgr: Robert Wright
Area Mgr: Christer Helmerius
Plnt Mgr: Tobias Hahn

D-U-N-S 07-954-1784
ITUTOR GROUP INC
3945 Freedom Cir Ste 500, Santa Clara, CA 95054-1225
Tel (408) 982-9401 Founded/Ownrshp 2014
Sales 13.0MM^E EMP 1,300
SIC 8299 Tutoring school
CEO: Eric Yang
*COO: Franz Chen
*COO: Jerry Huang
*CFO: Arthur Shen
*CTO: Jing Chang

D-U-N-S 00-102-4355 IMP
■ **ITW ARK-LES CORP**
(Suby of ILLINOIS TOOL WORKS INC) ★
95 Mill St, Stoughton, MA 02072-1422
Tel (781) 297-6000 Founded/Ownrshp 1937
Sales 98.4MM^E EMP 1,295
SIC 3643 3644

ITW FLTER PDTS TRNSM FLTRATION
See FILTERTEK INC

D-U-N-S 80-789-6261 IMP/EXP
■ **ITW FOOD EQUIPMENT GROUP LLC**
HOBART SERVICE
(Suby of ILLINOIS TOOL WORKS INC) ★
701 S Ridge Ave, Troy, OH 45374-0001
Tel (937) 332-3000 Founded/Ownrshp 1995
Sales 436.3MM^E EMP 1,300
SIC 5046 3556 Restaurant equipment & supplies; Food products machinery
*Pr: Tom Szafranski
*Ex VP: Chris O Herlihy
CIO: Norm Dykes
Netwrk Eng: Matthew French
Plnt Mgr: Gary Duench

ITW HOBART BROTHERS
See HOBART BROTHERS CO

IU HEALTH ALBANY PHARMACY
See INDIANA UNIVERSITY HEALTH BALL MEMORIAL HOSPITAL INC

IU HEALTH BLOOMINGTON HOSPITAL
See INDIANA UNIVERSITY HEALTH BLOOMINGTON INC

D-U-N-S 02-270-0290
IU HEALTH WEST HOSPITAL
1111 Ronald Reagan Pkwy # 223, Avon, IN 46123-7085
Tel (317) 217-3000 Founded/Ownrshp 1990
Sales 191.4MM EMP 931^E
SIC 8062 General medical & surgical hospitals
Owner: Daniel Weed

D-U-N-S 07-891-8976
IUHLP LIQUIDATION INC
LA PORTE HOSPITAL & HLTH SVCS
1007 Lincolnway, La Porte, IN 46350-3201
Tel (219) 326-1234 Founded/Ownrshp 1966
Sales 648.0MM EMP 1,500
SIC 8062 General medical & surgical hospitals
CEO: Thor Thordarson
*CFO: Mark Rafalski
CFO: Mark Rasalski
CFO: Jerry Wasserstein
Ex VP: Maria Fruth
Dir Sec: Robin Ortt
Dir Sec: Michael Strubel
Mktg Dir: Neil Mangus
Ansthlgy: John Murphy
Doctor: Joseph Arulandu
Doctor: Allan Fischer

D-U-N-S 13-174-3895
IUPAT DISTRICT COUNCIL 78
JATF
1300 Sw 12th Ave, Pompano Beach, FL 33069-4619
Tel (954) 946-9311 Founded/Ownrshp 2003
Sales 347.5MM EMP 65
SIC 8631 Labor unions & similar labor organizations
Sec: Tim Maitland

D-U-N-S 18-904-8143
IV HEALTHCORP INC
ILLINOIS VALLEY COMMUNITY HOSP
925 West St, Peru, IL 61354-2757
Tel (815) 223-3300 Founded/Ownrshp 1918
Sales 93.6MM^E EMP 745
SIC 8062 8741 5912 General medical & surgical hospitals; Hospital management; Drug stores & proprietary stores
Pr: Steven A Hayes
*Pr: Kris Paul
*CFO: Stephen Davis
*Ch: Harry Debo
*VP: James Loveland
Off Mgr: Dawn Moutray

D-U-N-S 83-549-9302 IMP
IVAN SMITH FURNITURE CO LLC
IVAN SMITH FURNITURE WINNFIELD
5434 Technology Dr, Shreveport, LA 71129-2682
Tel (318) 688-1335 Founded/Ownrshp 1997
Sales 118.4MM^E EMP 600
SIC 5712 Furniture stores
*Prin: Ivan I Smith III

IVAN SMITH FURNITURE WINNFIELD
See IVAN SMITH FURNITURE CO LLC

IVANS INSURANCE SOLUTIONS
See APPLIED SYSTEMS INC

D-U-N-S 18-415-0258 IMP
IVAX CORP
(Suby of TEVA PHARMACEUTICAL INDUSTRIES LIMITED)
4400 Biscayne Blvd, Miami, FL 33137-3212
Tel (305) 329-3795 Founded/Ownrshp 2006
Sales 697.1MM^E EMP 10,100
SIC 2834 Pharmaceutical preparations; Drugs acting on the cardiovascular system, except diagnostic; Drugs acting on the central nervous system & sense organs; Drugs acting on the respiratory system
Ch Bd: Phillip Frost MD
V Ch: Jane Hsaio
*Pr: Neil W Flanzraich
*Pr: William Marth
*CFO: Thomas Beier
CFO: Richard Friedman
*V Ch Bd: Jane Hsiao PHD
*Sr VP: Rafick G Henein PHD
*Sr VP: Clifford Montgomery
Sr VP: Steve Rubin
*Sr VP: Ronald Schultz
VP: Michael Fetell
VP: Edmond Fry
*VP: Deborah Griffin
VP: Stephen Sheriff

D-U-N-S 88-407-5235 IMP
IVAX PHARMACEUTICALS LLC
(Suby of IVAX CORP) ★
74 Nw 176th St, Miami, FL 33169-5043
Tel (305) 575-6000 Founded/Ownrshp 1995
Sales 69.8MM^E EMP 1,500
SIC 2834 Pharmaceutical preparations

IVC
See INTERNATIONAL VITAMIN CORP

D-U-N-S 96-897-2427
IVD HOLDINGS INC
3130 Gateway Dr, Peachtree Corners, GA 30071-1106
Tel (770) 441-2051 Founded/Ownrshp 2011
Sales 379.9MM^E EMP 1,090^E
SIC 2835 Blood derivative diagnostic agents; In vitro diagnostics; In vivo diagnostics
Prin: Jeffrey R Binder

D-U-N-S 07-920-4246 IMP
IVD INTERMEDIATE HOLDINGS B INC
(Suby of IVD HOLDINGS INC) ★
3130 Gateway Dr, Peachtree Corners, GA 30071-1106
Tel (770) 441-2051 Founded/Ownrshp 2011
Sales 379.9MM^E EMP 1,090^E
SIC 2835 In vitro diagnostics; In vivo diagnostics

D-U-N-S 12-772-3323
IVEY MECHANICAL CO LLC
514 N Wells St, Kosciusko, MS 39090-3200
Tel (662) 289-8601 Founded/Ownrshp 1972
Sales 129.5MM EMP 790
Accts Carr Riggs & Ingram Ridgeland
SIC 1711 Plumbing, heating, air-conditioning contractors
Ch Bd: Larry Terrell
*Pr: Denny Terrell
*CFO: Randy Dew
VP: Robert P Arnold
*VP: Bob Cooper
VP: Edward J Lamprecht
VP: David Landrum
Div Mgr: Mike Young
Off Mgr: Lynda Parker
IT Man: Donald Thurman
Sfty Mgr: Bo Harrel

D-U-N-S 80-976-6397
IVIE & ASSOCIATES INC
601 Silveron Ste 200, Flower Mound, TX 75028-4030
Tel (972) 899-5000 Founded/Ownrshp 1993
Sales 259.5MM EMP 242
SIC 7311 Advertising agencies
Pr: Warren Ivie
Pr: Brandon Ivie
Treas: Sharon Renee Rawlings
Ex VP: Kay Ivie
Sr VP: Gibran Mahmud
Sr VP: Buddy Martensen
VP: David Bailey
VP: Bob Epping
VP: Sharon Kay Ivie
VP: Garrison Jim
VP: Gary Long
VP: Jodi D Marsh
VP: Osye Pritchett
VP: Renee Rawlings
Creative D: Darrell Basgall
Creative D: Chad Revelle
Creative D: Anthony Woolridge

D-U-N-S 17-693-5203
IVOCLAR VIVADENT INC
IVOCLAR WILLIAMS
(Suby of IVOCLAR VIVADENT AKTIENGESELLSCHAFT)
175 Pineview Dr, Amherst, NY 14228-2286
Tel (716) 691-0010 Founded/Ownrshp 1986
Sales 105.7MM^E EMP 233
SIC 5047 8021 Dental equipment & supplies; Dental laboratory equipment; Dentists' professional supplies; Offices & clinics of dentists
Ch Bd: Robert A Ganley
Sr Cor Off: John Stack
VP: Sarah Anders
VP: Michael Gaglio
VP: Thomas Kingston
VP: Deborah Lamond
VP: Patrick M Segnere
VP: George Tysowsky
Exec: Ashley Frischkorn
Area Mgr: Jarg Brenn
Genl Mgr: Ulises Merino

IVOCLAR WILLIAMS
See IVOCLAR VIVADENT INC

D-U-N-S 96-997-1014
IVOX SOLUTIONS LLC
4485 Sw Port Way, Palm City, FL 34990-5586
Tel (772) 286-8183 Founded/Ownrshp 2007
Sales 125.5MM^E EMP 450
SIC 5065 4812 Mobile telephone equipment; Cellular telephone services
CEO: Rob Newton
CFO: Christopher Stapleton

IVY TECH CENTRAL OFFICE
See IVY TECH COMMUNITY COLLEGE OF INDIANA

D-U-N-S 07-206-6681
IVY TECH COMMUNITY COLLEGE OF INDIANA
IVY TECH CENTRAL OFFICE
50 W Fall Creek Pkwy N Dr, Indianapolis, IN 46208-5752
Tel (317) 921-4882 Founded/Ownrshp 1963
Sales 424.3MM^E EMP 8,553
SIC 8221 College, except junior
Pr: Sue Ellspermann
CFO: Chris Ruhl
VP: Steve Tinscher
Mktg Dir: Karen Henderson
HC Dir: Christine Rethlake

IVYWOOD INTERIORS
See WOODSIDE GROUP INC

IWCO DIRECT
See INSTANT WEB LLC

IWCO DIRECT
See INSTANT WEB LLC

IWIF
See CHESAPEAKE EMPLOYERS INSURANCE CO

D-U-N-S 01-865-1778 IMP
IWKA HOLDING CORP
6600 Center Dr, Sterling Heights, MI 48312-2666
Tel (586) 795-2000 Founded/Ownrshp 1998
Sales 87.0MM^E EMP 792
SIC 3549 5084 7371 8711

D-U-N-S 17-941-5773
▲ **IXIA**
26601 Agoura Rd, Calabasas, CA 91302-1959
Tel (818) 871-1800 Founded/Ownrshp 1997
Sales 516.9MM EMP 1,727^E
Tkr Sym XXIA Exch NGS
SIC 3825 7371 Network analyzers; Custom computer programming services; Software programming applications
Pr: Bethany Mayer
*Ch Bd: Errol Ginsberg
COO: Alexander J Pepe
CFO: Brent T Novak
Chf Mktg O: Marie Hattar
Ofcr: Dennis J Cox
Sr VP: Matthew S Alexander
Sr VP: Walker H Colston II
Sr VP: Hans-Peter Klaey
Sr VP: Alex Pepe
Sr VP: Christopher L Williams
VP: Deepesh Arora
VP: Curt Crosby
VP: Raymond Graaf
VP: Bob Shaw
Board of Directors: Laurent Asscher, Ilan Daskal, Jonathan Fram, Gail Hamilton

D-U-N-S 02-036-2635
IXONOS USA LIMITED
(Suby of IXONOS OYJ)
85 2nd St, San Francisco, CA 94105-3459
Tel (949) 278-1354 Founded/Ownrshp 2010
Sales 50.1MM^E EMP 1,000
SIC 7373 8731 Systems software development services; Computer (hardware) development
VP: Jo Javier

D-U-N-S 10-302-7843
▲ **IXYS CORP**
1590 Buckeye Dr, Milpitas, CA 95035-7418
Tel (408) 457-9000 Founded/Ownrshp 1983
Sales 317.2MM EMP 958^E
Tkr Sym IXYS Exch NGS
SIC 3674 Semiconductors & related devices; Integrated circuits, semiconductor networks, etc.; Modules, solid state; Rectifiers, solid state
Ch Bd: Nathan Zommer
*CEO: Uzi Sasson
Ofcr: Kent Loose
VP: Mark F Heisig
VP: Clifford Knudsen
VP: Kent Paris
Genl Mgr: Thea Kern
Dir IT: Mohan Raswant
Board of Directors: Donald L Feucht, Samuel Kory, S Joon Lee, Timothy A Richardson, James M Thorburn, Kenneth D Wong

D-U-N-S 96-831-2178
IYPAD INTERNATIONAL INC NFP
419 S East Ave, Oak Park, IL 60302-3969
Tel (773) 654-7141 Founded/Ownrshp 2011
Sales NA EMP 4,000
SIC 9441 Administration of social & manpower programs
Pr: Diane Urban

IZZY
See JSJ FURNITURE CORP

J

D-U-N-S 94-823-1774
J & B GROUP INC
13200 43rd St N, Saint Michael, MN 55376-8420
Tel (763) 497-3913 Founded/Ownrshp 1995
Sales 133.2MM^E EMP 340^E
SIC 6719 5963 Investment holding companies, except banks; Food services, direct sales
Ch Bd: Robert Hageman
*Pr: Michael Hageman
VP: Gary Hageman
CTO: Barb Bartlett
Plnt Mgr: Brad Karels

D-U-N-S 05-796-7390 IMP/EXP
J & B IMPORTERS INC
J & B NORTHEAST
11925 Sw 128th St, Miami, FL 33186-5209
Tel (305) 238-1866 Founded/Ownrshp 1971
Sales 100.0MM EMP 400
SIC 5091 Bicycle parts & accessories
Pr: Ben Joannou Sr
CEO: Mitchell Gurdjian
CEO: Ben Joannou Jr
Treas: Barry Silvers
Ex VP: Jacques Gurdjian
VP: Harreit Margolesky
VP: Bill Tannen
Exec: Lourdes Barsky
Exec: Lisa Macia
Genl Mgr: Eric Larson
IT Man: George Philotas

J & B MATERIALS
See PACIFIC GYPSUM SUPPLY INC

J & B NORTHEAST
See J & B IMPORTERS INC

D-U-N-S 93-243-7783
J & B RESTAURANT PARTNERS OF LONG ISLAND INC
FRIENDLY'S
(Suby of J & B RESTAURANT PARTNERS OF LONG ISLAND LLC) ★
3385 Vtrans Mem Hwy Ste A, Ronkonkoma, NY 11779-7660
Tel (631) 218-9067 Founded/Ownrshp 1997
Sales 38.8MM^E EMP 1,210
SIC 5812 Restaurant, family: chain
Pr: Joseph Vitrano

D-U-N-S 13-224-5007
J & B RESTAURANT PARTNERS OF LONG ISLAND LLC
4000 Veterans Memorial Hw, Bohemia, NY 11716-1040
Tel (631) 218-9067 Founded/Ownrshp 2000
Sales 51.9MM^E EMP 1,400^E
SIC 5812 Restaurant, family: chain
Pr: Joseph P Vitrano
CFO: Jerry Snearly

D-U-N-S 00-812-0750 IMP
J & B SAUSAGE CO INC
J BAR B FOODS
100 Main, Waelder, TX 78959-5329
Tel (830) 788-7661 Founded/Ownrshp 1969
Sales 104.1MM^E EMP 340
SIC 2011 5147 2013 Sausages from meat slaughtered on site; Meats & meat products; Sausages & other prepared meats
CEO: Danny Janecka
*Sec: Noreen Janecka
*VP: Lyndell Bisbee
VP: Leslie Clifton
*VP: Danny Janecka II
IT Man: Marcus Cruz
VP Sls: Brian Pirkle
Sls Mgr: Gilbert Velasquez

D-U-N-S 09-709-6093 IMP/EXP
J & B WHOLESALE DISTRIBUTING INC
(Suby of J & B GROUP INC) ★
13200 43rd St Ne, Saint Michael, MN 55376-8420
Tel (763) 497-3913 Founded/Ownrshp 1979
Sales 500.0MM EMP 340
SIC 5147 5144 5142 5143 5148 Meats, fresh; Meats, cured or smoked; Poultry: live, dressed or frozen (unpackaged); Fish, frozen: packaged; Cheese; Vegetables, fresh
CEO: Robert Hageman
*Pr: Michael Hageman
*CFO: James Chapa
CIO: Chuck Ballard

D-U-N-S 19-517-2531 IMP
J & D PRODUCE INC
7310 N Expressway 281, Edinburg, TX 78542-1232
Tel (956) 380-0353 Founded/Ownrshp 1979
Sales 105.7MM^E EMP 420
SIC 5148 Fresh fruits & vegetables
Pr: James V Bassetti Jr
*VP: Diane Bassetti
Opers Mgr: Edgardo Garcia
Mktg Mgr: Jeff Brechler
Board of Directors: Shawn M Allen, Yvonne Benavidez

D-U-N-S 02-980-8208
J & D RESTAURANT GROUP LLC
JACK IN THE BOX
1301 Solana Blvd Ste 2300, Roanoke, TX 76262-1676
Tel (817) 693-5119 Founded/Ownrshp 2009
Sales 42.2MM^E EMP 1,128^E
SIC 5812 Fast-food restaurant, chain

D-U-N-S 07-259-3692
J & H OIL CO
SERVICE OIL
2696 Chicago Dr Sw, Grand Rapids, MI 49519-1628
Tel (616) 534-2181 Founded/Ownrshp 1970
Sales 373.8MM EMP 70
Accts Uhy Llp Sterling Heights Mic
SIC 5172 5013 Petroleum products; Automotive supplies & parts
Pr: Jerry Hop
CFO: Joe Albers
*VP: Sandra Arrasmith
*VP: Craig Hoppen
Mktg Dir: Abby Albers
Sls Mgr: Leonard Kern
Sales Asso: Julie Smith

J & J DISTR CO
See ALLIED BEVERAGE GROUP LLC

D-U-N-S 00-157-6099 IMP
J & J FARMS CREAMERY INC (NY)
5748 49th St Ste 1, Maspeth, NY 11378-2191
Tel (718) 821-1200 Founded/Ownrshp 1968
Sales 165.0MM EMP 40^E
Accts Schwartz & Company New York
SIC 5143 5149 Dairy products, except dried or canned; Juices
Pr: Simon Friedman
*Treas: Morris Schlager
VP Sls: Morris Glauber

D-U-N-S 00-333-6971 IMP/EXP
J & J INDUSTRIES INC (GA)
J&J/INVISION
818 J And J Dr, Dalton, GA 30721-3647
Tel (706) 529-2100 *Founded/Ownrshp* 1957
Sales 202.8MM^E *EMP* 765
SIC 2273 Carpets, hand & machine made
CEO: David Jolly
V Ch: James Bethel
CFO: Maria Chavarria
**CFO:* Tom Pendley
VP: Marc Cormier
**VP:* Bill Crosley
VP: Terry Davis
**VP:* Louis Fordham
VP: Gregg Hayes
VP: Ross Leaonard
**VP:* Doug Schneller
**VP:* Brad Townsend

D-U-N-S 05-512-4077
J & J MAINTENANCE INC (TX)
J & J WORLDWIDE SERVICES
7710 Rialto Blvd Unit 200, Austin, TX 78735-8575
Tel (512) 444-7271 *Founded/Ownrshp* 1970
Sales 356.4MM^E *EMP* 1,500
SIC 1799 Post-disaster renovations
Pr: Mike Voudouris
**Ch Bd:* John L Voudouris
**CFO:* Terry Reynolds
**Sec:* Sharron A Voudouris
**VP:* Tim Ferry
**VP:* Steve Kelley
**VP:* Duke Malvaney

D-U-N-S 11-860-3331 IMP/EXP
J & J PRODUCE INC
J&J FAMILY OF FARMS
(*Suby of* J&J PRODUCE HOLDINGS, INC.)
4003 Seminole Pratt, Loxahatchee, FL 33470-3754
Tel (561) 422-9777 *Founded/Ownrshp* 1981
Sales 100.0MM *EMP* 150
SIC 5148 0161 Fresh fruits & vegetables; Cucumber farm; Pepper farm, sweet & hot (vegetables); Squash farm
Pr: Chris Erneston III
Recvr: Damien Kearse
Recvr: Marco Trejo
Recvr: Greg Waldon
**CFO:* Mark Campbell
**VP:* Tj Bauer
**VP:* David Beecher
**VP:* Michael Bentel
**VP:* Brian Rayfield
**VP Sls:* Kohl Brown
Board of Directors: John Leavitt

D-U-N-S 93-895-8113
■ J & J SANITATION INC
WASTE CONNECTIONS OF NEBRASKA
(*Suby of* WASTE CONNECTIONS US INC) ★
87181 494th Ave, Oneill, NE 68763-5388
Tel (402) 336-3011 *Founded/Ownrshp* 1987
Sales 2.0MMM *EMP* 22
SIC 4953 Refuse collection & disposal services; Recycling, waste materials
Pr: Ronald J Mittelstaedt
**Treas:* Michael R Foos
Off Mgr: Amy Strong

D-U-N-S 05-473-2839
▲ J & J SNACK FOODS CORP
6000 Central Hwy, Pennsauken, NJ 08109-4672
Tel (856) 665-9533 *Founded/Ownrshp* 1971
Sales 992.7MM *EMP* 3,400
Tkr Sym JJSF *Exch* NGS
SIC 2053 2087 2086 2024 2052 2051 Frozen bakery products, except bread; Doughnuts, frozen; Syrups, drink; Mineral water, carbonated: packaged in cans, bottles, etc.; Ices, flavored (frozen dessert); Juice pops, frozen; Cookies; Bread, cake & related products
Ch Bd: Gerald B Shreiber
Pr: Daniel Fachner
COO: Robert M Radano
**CFO:* Dennis G Moore
Sr VP: Gerard G Law
VP: Juventino Torres
Genl Mgr: Phil Rosile
Genl Mgr: Terry Shepard
Manager: Josh Bohannon
Manager: James Bonlie
Manager: Scott Bossler
Board of Directors: Sidney R Brown, Vincent Melchiorre, Peter G Stanley

D-U-N-S 12-088-1974 IMP
■ J & J SNACK FOODS CORP OF CALIFORNIA
(*Suby of* J & J SNACK FOODS CORP) ★
5353 S Downey Rd, Vernon, CA 90058-3725
Tel (323) 581-0171 *Founded/Ownrshp* 1978
Sales 119.1MM^E *EMP* 380^E
SIC 2052 5149 Pretzels; Cookies
CEO: Gerald B Shreiber
**VP:* Dennis Moore
VP Inf Sys: John Griffith
QA Dir: Bennett Taracena
Trfc Mgr: Sheena Hughes

J & J WORLDWIDE SERVICES
See J & J MAINTENANCE INC

D-U-N-S 08-031-9972
J & K EXPRESS INC
5046 N Conway Ave, Mission, TX 78573-3941
Tel (956) 584-3130 *Founded/Ownrshp* 2015
Sales 16.6MM^E *EMP* 3,130
SIC 7389

J & L INDUSTRIES
See ALLIANCE MACHINE SYSTEMS INTERNATIONAL LLC

D-U-N-S 12-464-8697 IMP
J & M SALES INC
FALLAS DISCOUNT STORES
15001 S Figueroa St, Gardena, CA 90248-1721
Tel (310) 324-9962 *Founded/Ownrshp* 1993
Sales 71.8MM^E *EMP* 2,500
SIC 5651 6531 5311 5611 5621 Unisex clothing stores; Real estate listing services; Department stores, discount; Men's & boys' clothing stores; Women's clothing stores
Pr: Michael Fallas
**VP:* Duane Huesers

D-U-N-S 62-777-4615
J & R ASSOCIATES
WINDSOR CONSTRUCTION
14803 Holland Rd, Brookpark, OH 44142-3065
Tel (440) 250-4080 *Founded/Ownrshp* 1987
Sales 53.3MM^E *EMP* 1,000
SIC 1542 8361 6514 Institutional building construction; Home for the aged; Dwelling operators, except apartments
Pr: John Coury Sr

D-U-N-S 00-986-6807
J & R SCHUGEL TRUCKING INC
2026 N Broadway St, New Ulm, MN 56073-1030
Tel (800) 359-2900 *Founded/Ownrshp* 2012
Sales 123.4MM^E *EMP* 500
SIC 4213 Trucking, except local; Contract haulers
Genl Mgr: Dan Denhol
Ql Cn Mgr: Kala Hannay
Sls Mgr: Jim Elness

D-U-N-S 06-119-3194
J A M T LEYDEN ENTERPRISES INC (RI)
BIG JOHN'S TREE FARM
179 Plain Meeting Hse Rd, West Greenwich, RI 02817-2049
Tel (401) 258-9246 *Founded/Ownrshp* 1987
Sales 100.1MM *EMP* 10
SIC 0811 Timber tracts
Pr: John Leyden

D-U-N-S 07-960-1171
J ALEXANDERS HOLDINGS INC
3401 West End Ave Ste 260, Nashville, TN 37203-6862
Tel (615) 250-1602 *Founded/Ownrshp* 1975
Sales 217.9MM *EMP* 3,400
Tkr Sym JAX *Exch* NYS
SIC 5812 Eating places; American restaurant; Steak & barbecue restaurants; Steak restaurant
Pr: Lonnie J Stout II
**Ch Bd:* Frank R Martire
COO: J Michael Moore
CFO: Mark A Parkey
VP: Jessica H Root
Board of Directors: Douglas K Ammerman, Timothy T Janszen, Ronald B Maggard Sr, Raymond R Quirk

D-U-N-S 05-649-6953
■ J ALEXANDERS LLC (TX)
(*Suby of* FIDELITY NATIONAL FINANCIAL INC) ★
3401 West End Ave Ste 260, Nashville, TN 37203-6862
Tel (615) 269-1900 *Founded/Ownrshp* 1971, 2012
Sales 454.1MM^E *EMP* 2,720^E
SIC 5812 Fast-food restaurant, chain; Restaurant, family: chain
Pr: Lonnie J Stout II
**CFO:* Gregory Lewis
**CFO:* R Gregory Lewis
**CFO:* Jeffrey Rice
**VP:* Mark A Parkey
Exec: Jason Waters
Genl Mgr: Jeff Heflin
Genl Mgr: Ryan Kavanaugh
IT Man: Jeanne Larose

D-U-N-S 18-974-8023
J AMBROGI FOOD DISTRIBUTION INC
1400 Metropolitan Ave, Thorofare, NJ 08086
Tel (856) 845-0377 *Founded/Ownrshp* 1987
Sales 115.1MM^E *EMP* 175
SIC 5141 Food brokers
Pr: John G Ambrogi
**Treas:* Kristy K Ambrogi

D-U-N-S 06-639-0951
J AND L HOLDING CO INC
12235 Robin Blvd, Houston, TX 77045-4826
Tel (713) 434-7600 *Founded/Ownrshp* 1990
Sales 138.6MM^E *EMP* 55
SIC 5171 Petroleum bulk stations
Pr: L L Leach III

D-U-N-S 06-215-3176 IMP
■ J B HUNT TRANSPORT INC
(*Suby of* JB HUNT TRANSPORT SERVICES INC) ★
615 J B Hunt Corporate Dr, Lowell, AR 72745-9143
Tel (479) 820-0000 *Founded/Ownrshp* 1969
Sales 3.1MMM^E *EMP* 14,171
SIC 4213 Trucking, except local
Ch: Kirk Thompson
**Pr:* John Roberts
**Pr:* John N Roberts III
**CFO:* Jerry W Walton
**Treas:* David N Chelette
Ex VP: Paul R Bergant
Ex VP: Kay J Palmer
Ex VP: Bob D Ralston
**VP:* David G Mee
Exec: David Martin
Genl Mgr: James Labarge

D-U-N-S 15-428-0655 IMP/EXP
J B POINDEXTER & CO INC
600 Travis St Ste 200, Houston, TX 77002-2995
Tel (713) 655-9800 *Founded/Ownrshp* 1983
Sales 1.0MMM^E *EMP* 3,072
SIC 3713

D-U-N-S 04-139-1822 IMP
J B SULLIVAN INC
SULLIVAN'S FOODS
425 1st St Ste 1, Savanna, IL 61074-1519
Tel (815) 273-4511 *Founded/Ownrshp* 1976
Sales 174.3MM^E *EMP* 1,450
SIC 5411 Grocery stores
CEO: John B Sullivan
**Pr:* Scott Sullivan
**Sec:* June A Sullivan

J BAR B FOODS
See J & B SAUSAGE CO INC

D-U-N-S 05-617-9021 IMP/EXP
J BAXTER BRINKMANN INTERNATIONAL CORP
BRIKMANN J BAXTER INTL
4099 Mcewen Rd Ste 375, Dallas, TX 75244-5009
Tel (972) 387-4939 *Founded/Ownrshp* 1981
Sales 182.1MM^E *EMP* 800
SIC 3648 3631 Spotlights; Barbecues, grills & braziers (outdoor cooking)
Pr: J Baxter Brinkmann

D-U-N-S 10-206-3521 IMP/EXP
▲ J C PENNEY CO INC
6501 Legacy Dr, Plano, TX 75024-3698
Tel (972) 431-1000 *Founded/Ownrshp* 1902
Sales 12.6MMM *EMP* 105,000
Accts Kpmg Llp Dallas Texas
Tkr Sym JCP *Exch* NYS
SIC 5311 5961 Department stores, non-discount; Catalog & mail-order houses; Catalog sales
CEO: Marvin R Ellison
**Ch Bd:* Myron E Ullman III
Pr: Rebecca McComb
CFO: Edward J Record
Ofcr: Mary Beth West
Ex VP: Brynn L Evanson
Ex VP: Janet M Link
Ex VP: Therace M Risch
Ex VP: Elizabeth Sweney
Sr VP: Siiri Dougherty
Sr VP: Andrew S Drexler
Sr VP: Jan Hodges
Sr VP: Jodie Johnson
Sr VP: Dennis P Miller
Sr VP: David Plummer
Sr VP: James Starke
Sr VP: Angela Swanner
Sr VP: John J Tighe
VP: Eric Blackwood
VP: Shannon Broussard
VP: Angelina Dryden
Board of Directors: Ronald W Tysoe, Colleen C Barrett, Paul Brown, Thomas J Engibous, Amanda Ginsberg, Craig Owens, Leonard H Roberts, Stephen I Sadove, Javier G Teruel, R Gerald Turner

D-U-N-S 18-759-7646 IMP/EXP
■ J C PENNEY EUROPE INC
JC PENNEY
(*Suby of* JC PENNEY) ★
6501 Legacy Dr, Plano, TX 75024-3698
Tel (972) 431-1000 *Founded/Ownrshp* 1969
Sales 544.9MM^E *EMP* 560
SIC 5137 5136 5023 Women's & children's clothing; Men's & boys' clothing; Home furnishings
CEO: Mike Ullman
Ch Bd: Pat Hampton
**Pr:* Alan Questrom
**Ex VP:* Tony Bartlett
**Ex VP:* Janet Dhillon
**Ex VP:* Brynn Evanson
**Ex VP:* Scott Laverty
**VP:* Vanessa Castagna

D-U-N-S 17-500-2914
J C PENNEY LIFE INSURANCE CO
JC PENNEY
(*Suby of* AEGON DIRECT MARKETING SERVICES INC) ★
2700 W Plano Pkwy, Plano, TX 75075-8205
Tel (972) 881-6000 *Founded/Ownrshp* 1967
Sales NA *EMP* 1,520
Accts Kpmg Peat Marwick Llp
SIC 6311 6321 Life insurance; Health insurance carriers
Ch Bd: Ted L Spurlock
CFO: Donald L Heise
**CFO:* Martha McDonald
Ex VP: George E Suiter
Sr VP: Thomas D McGahey
Sr VP: Joseph A Sartoris
IT Man: Tricia Brown
Sys/Mgr: Gary W Robinson
Genl Couns: Keith Wright

D-U-N-S 87-693-6295
■ J C PENNEY MEXICO INC
(*Suby of* JC PENNEY) ★
6501 Legacy Dr, Plano, TX 75024-3698
Tel (972) 431-1000 *Founded/Ownrshp* 1990
Sales 68.1MM^E *EMP* 3,500
SIC 5311 Department stores, non-discount
Pr: Mike Ullman
**Ch:* Allen Questron

J C PENNEY OPTICAL
See US VISION INC

J C PENNEY OPTICAL
See USV OPTICAL INC

D-U-N-S 06-253-3138 IMP/EXP
■ J C PENNEY PURCHASING CORP
JC PENNEY
(*Suby of* JC PENNEY) ★
6501 Legacy Dr, Plano, TX 75024-3698
Tel (972) 431-1000 *Founded/Ownrshp* 1959
Sales 359.1MM^E *EMP* 560
SIC 5137 5136 5023 Women's & children's clothing; Men's & boys' clothing; Home furnishings
Ch Bd: Mike Ullman
**CEO:* Marvin R Ellison
**CFO:* Michael P Dastugue
**Ex VP:* Michael Amend
**Ex VP:* Ken Mangone
**Sr VP:* Katheryn Burchett
**Sr VP:* Benita Casey
**Sr VP:* Siiri Dougherty
**Sr VP:* Lorraine Hitch
**VP:* Adil Raza
**VP:* L C Tucker

J C SALES
See SHIMS BARGAIN INC

D-U-N-S 01-464-2552
J CALNAN & ASSOCIATES INC
3 Batterymarch Park # 500, Quincy, MA 02169-7574
Tel (617) 801-0200 *Founded/Ownrshp* 1996
Sales 143.6MM *EMP* 65^E
Accts Lmhs Pc Norwell Massachus
SIC 8741 1542 Management services; Custom builders, non-residential
CEO: Jay Calnan
**Pr:* James Cahill
COO: Crowther Michael
**VP:* Michael Crowther
Exec: Rick Borden
Exec: David Ferreira
Snr PM: Bill McKenna

D-U-N-S 02-650-6485
J CINCO INC
JOHNSON OIL
1113 E Sarah Dewitt Dr, Gonzales, TX 78629-2518
Tel (830) 672-9574 *Founded/Ownrshp* 1958
Sales 335.6MM^E *EMP* 480
SIC 5172 5541 Petroleum products; Filling stations, gasoline
Pr: Fletcher Johnson
**Sec:* Jane Johnson
VP: Jeff Loomis

D-U-N-S 11-600-4417 IMP/EXP
J CREW INC
J. CREW WOMEN'S ACCESSORIES
(*Subý of* JCREW) ★
770 Broadway Fl 14, New York, NY 10003-9522
Tel (212) 209-8010 *Founded/Ownrshp* 2015
Sales 261.7MM^E *EMP* 800
SIC 5961 5621 5611 Women's apparel, mail order; Clothing, mail order (except women's); Women's clothing stores; Men's & boys' clothing stores
CEO: Millard S Drexler
Ch Bd: Nicholas Lamberti
COO: James Scully
COO: Jennifer Smith
CFO: Stuart Haseldon
Ex VP: Lynda Markoe
VP: Bobby Ashby
VP: Katrina R Clark
VP: Joseph Gaudio
VP: Angie Michaels
VP: Charlie Miller
VP: Katie Mitchell
VP: Michael Salmon
VP: Valerie Van Ogtrop

D-U-N-S 79-953-6271 IMP/EXP
J CREW OPERATING CORP
J.CREW
(*Suby of* JCREW GROUP INC) ★
770 Brdwy Fl 11 & 12, New York, NY 10003
Tel (212) 209-2500 *Founded/Ownrshp* 1997
Sales 333.6MM^E *EMP* 2,500
SIC 5961 5621 5611 5661 5632 6794 Mail order house; Women's apparel, mail order; Women's clothing stores; Men's & boys' clothing stores; Women's shoes; Men's shoes; Apparel accessories; Franchises, selling or licensing
CEO: Millard Drexler
**VP:* Tracy Gardner
**VP:* Nicholas Lamberti
**VP:* James Scully

J. CREW WOMEN'S ACCESSORIES
See J CREW INC

D-U-N-S 01-383-3868
J D ECKMAN INC (PA)
4781 Lower Valley Rd, Atglen, PA 19310-1767
Tel (610) 593-5300 *Founded/Ownrshp* 1946, 1977
Sales 141.6MM^E *EMP* 400
SIC 1611 Concrete construction: roads, highways, sidewalks, etc.
Pr: Mark S Eckman
**CFO:* Dennis Brubaker
Ex VP: Kenneth Kauffman
VP: Greg Burkhart
VP: David Maugle
**Prin:* Michael S Eckman
**Prin:* Virginia L Eckman
IT Man: Chris Bunting
Sfty Dirs: Richard Wittlinger
Opers Mgr: Bob Esposito

D-U-N-S 13-210-3169 IMP/EXP
J D FIELDS & CO INC
55 Waugh Dr Ste 1250, Houston, TX 77007-5840
Tel (281) 558-7199 *Founded/Ownrshp* 1985
Sales 193.1MM^E *EMP* 37
SIC 5051 7359 3443 Steel; Equipment rental & leasing; Pipe, standpipe & culverts
CEO: Jerry D Fields
**Pr:* Jay D Fields
**CFO:* Steve Friedrich
**Ex VP:* J Patrick Burk
Sls Mgr: Todd Fagen

D-U-N-S 00-946-2359
J D HEISKELL HOLDINGS LLC (CA)
J.D. HEISKELL AND COMPANY
1939 Hillman St, Tulare, CA 93274-1601
Tel (559) 685-6100 *Founded/Ownrshp* 2000
Sales 707.0MM^E *EMP* 322
SIC 5191 5999 Farm supplies; Feed & farm supply
Ch Bd: Scott T Hillman
**COO:* Ryan Pellett
**CFO:* Timothy J Regan
VP: Todd Gearheart
VP: Robert Hodgen
VP: Clark Jeary
VP: Randy W Spiegel
VP: Lori Wilke
VP Bus: Charles Tsatsos
Genl Mgr: Kevin Pray
Genl Mgr: Tom Sigler

J D R F
See JDRF INTERNATIONAL

D-U-N-S 13-161-2652 IMP/EXP
J D RUSH CORP
2 Northpoint Dr Ste 150, Houston, TX 77060-3200
Tel (281) 558-8004 *Founded/Ownrshp* 2003
Sales 100.0MM *EMP* 15
SIC 3498 5051 Fabricated pipe & fittings; Pipe & tubing, steel

Sr VP: Rick Whitfield
VP: George Clark
VP: Bobby Ford
VP Sls: Steve Pierson

D-U-N-S 02-151-5200 EXP
J D STREETT & CO INC
CITGO
144 Weldon Pkwy, Maryland Heights, MO 63043-3100
Tel (314) 432-6600 *Founded/Ownrshp* 1980
Sales 203.4MM *EMP* 240
Accts Bkd Llp St Louis Missouri
SIC 5171 5541 7389 5172 Petroleum bulk stations; Filling stations, gasoline; Packaging & labeling services; Engine fuels & oils
Pr: Newell A Baker Jr
* *Ch Bd:* Newell A Baker
* *CFO:* James A Schuering
Genl Mgr: Lee Rochnagel
Off Mgr: Dawn Harris
CIO: Lee Rucknagel
Opers Mgr: Rick Dumi

D-U-N-S 09-999-2430 IMP
J DAVID GLADSTONE INSTITUTES
1650 Owens St, San Francisco, CA 94158-2261
Tel (415) 734-2000 *Founded/Ownrshp* 1971
Sales 86.3MM *EMP* 370
SIC 8733

D-U-N-S 03-499-4624
J E MEURET GRAIN CO INC
101 N Franklin St, Brunswick, NE 68720
Tel (402) 842-2515 *Founded/Ownrshp* 1923
Sales 245.1MM *EMP* 33^E^
Accts Bmg Certified Public Accountan
SIC 5153 Grains
Pr: John J Meuret
* *Sec:* James Meuret
* *VP:* Pat Meuret
* *VP:* Patrick Meuret

J E ROBERT
See ROBERT CO INC J E

D-U-N-S 00-896-0122
J F AHERN CO (WI)
855 Morris St, Fond Du Lac, WI 54935-5611
Tel (920) 921-9020 *Founded/Ownrshp* 1880
Sales 233.9MM *EMP* 855
SIC 1711

D-U-N-S 79-241-9889
J F K JOHNSON REHABILITATION INSTITUTE
REHABILITATION MEDICINE
65 James St, Edison, NJ 08820-3947
Tel (732) 321-7070 *Founded/Ownrshp* 1963
Sales 49.8MM^E^ *EMP* 5,000
SIC 8093 Rehabilitation center, outpatient treatment
Pr: John McGee

D-U-N-S 00-257-0414
J F KIELY CONSTRUCTION CO INC
700 Mcclellan St, Long Branch, NJ 07740-5899
Tel (732) 222-4400 *Founded/Ownrshp* 1952
Sales 95.0MM^E^ *EMP* 225
SIC 1623 7353 Gas main construction; Heavy construction equipment rental
Pr: John F Kiely Jr
* *Pr:* John M Kiely
CFO: David Odor
VP: Scott Handel
* *VP:* Daniel Huber
* *VP:* Raymond Sexton
VP: Mark Taylor
Dir Bus: James Pagano

D-U-N-S 00-533-3658 IMP
J F SHEA CO INC (NV)
655 Brea Canyon Rd, Walnut, CA 91789-3078
Tel (909) 594-9500 *Founded/Ownrshp* 1881, 1981
Sales 2.1MMM^E^ *EMP* 2,600
SIC 3273 Ready-mixed concrete
CEO: Peter O Shea Jr
* *Pr:* John Francis Shea
* *CFO:* James Shontere
* *Treas:* Robert R O'Dell
* *VP:* Andy Roundtree
Dir Risk M: Jackie Huynh
Off Mgr: Lisa Jacobson
CIO: David Miller
Netwrk Eng: Kevin Hayes
Sfty Dirs: Victoria Petrosian
Board of Directors: Louise Clark

D-U-N-S 11-435-8625
J F TAYLOR INC
21610 S Essex Dr, Lexington Park, MD 20653-4239
Tel (301) 862-4744 *Founded/Ownrshp* 1983
Sales 83.1MM *EMP* 250
Accts Rsm Us Llp Mclean Virginia
SIC 8711 Consulting engineer; Electrical or electronic engineering
Pr: John F Taylor Sr
* *Sec:* Helen M Taylor
Ofcr: Robert Albertsen
* *VP:* David M Lowe
* *VP:* David W Sydnor
* *VP:* Jeffrey J Taylor
* *VP:* John F Taylor Jr
* *VP:* Mark J Taylor
Prgrm Mgr: Jan Griffith
Prgrm Mgr: David Hesse
Prgrm Mgr: Tammy Sparks

D-U-N-S 01-950-5429
J F WHITE CONTRACTING CO
(*Suby of* DRAGADOS CONSTRUCTION USA, INC.)
10 Burr St, Framingham, MA 01701-4692
Tel (508) 879-4700 *Founded/Ownrshp* 1924, 2016
Sales 205.8MM^E^ *EMP* 400
SIC 1622 Bridge, tunnel & elevated highway; Bridge construction; Highway construction, elevated; Tunnel construction
Pr: Peter T White
* *Ex VP:* Albert Peres Baucells
Ex VP: Kevin Egan
VP: Robert E Hoffman
VP: Bob Murphy

* *VP:* Stephen F White
Off Mgr: Karen Dionne
Off Mgr: Adrienne Medeiros
Off Mgr: Julie Perry
CIO: Karen Wuerfl

D-U-N-S 01-126-8927 IMP
J FLETCHER CREAMER & SON INC
(*Suby of* API GROUP INC) ★
101 E Broadway, Hackensack, NJ 07601-6846
Tel (201) 488-9800 *Founded/Ownrshp* 2016
Sales 91.3MM^E^ *EMP* 1,000
SIC 1623 1611 1771 1622 1629

D-U-N-S 02-780-2297
J FRANK SCHMIDT & SON CO
9500 Se 327th Ave, Boring, OR 97009-9710
Tel (503) 663-4128 *Founded/Ownrshp* 1946
Sales 93.2MM^E^ *EMP* 350
SIC 0783 2875 Planting services, ornamental tree; Fertilizers, mixing only
Pr: J Frank Schmidt I
* *Ex VP:* Jan Schmidt-Barkley
IT Man: Raymond Kerr

D-U-N-S 00-823-7505 IMP/EXP
J G BOSWELL CO (CA)
101 W Walnut St, Pasadena, CA 91103-3636
Tel (626) 356-7492 *Founded/Ownrshp* 1921
Sales 624.6MM^E^ *EMP* 2,000
SIC 0131 6552 Cotton; Subdividers & developers
CEO: James W Boswell
* *COO:* Sherm Railsback
* *CFO:* Steve Burish
* *Treas:* Cedrick Yoshomato
Board of Directors: James Maddox, Blake Quinn

D-U-N-S 07-921-9206
▲ **J G WENTWORTH CO**
201 King Of Prussia Rd # 501, Radnor, PA 19087-5148
Tel (484) 434-2300 *Founded/Ownrshp* 2013
Sales 296.3MM *EMP* 700^E^
Tkr Sym JGWE *Exch* OTO
SIC 7389 6798 Financial services; Mortgage investment trusts
CEO: Stewart A Stockdale
* *Ch Bd:* Alexander R Castaldi
CFO: Roger Gasper
CFO: Scott Stevens
Ex VP: Gregory A Schneider
Board of Directors: Robert C Griffin, Kevin Hammond, William J Morgan, Robert N Pomroy, Francisco J Rodriguez, Gerard Gerard Van Spaendon

D-U-N-S 84-968-4394
J H BERRA HOLDING CO INC
BERRA CONSTRUCTION
5091 Baumgartner Rd, Saint Louis, MO 63129-2821
Tel (314) 487-5617 *Founded/Ownrshp* 1994
Sales 88.3MM^E^ *EMP* 800^E^
SIC 6552 Subdividers & developers
Pr: John Berra Jr
* *Treas:* Robert Berra
VP: Joe Nicpon

D-U-N-S 00-610-6520
J H FINDORFF & SON INC (WI)
300 S Bedford St, Madison, WI 53703-3622
Tel (608) 257-5321 *Founded/Ownrshp* 1890, 1998
Sales 372.0MM^E^ *EMP* 500
SIC 1542 1541 8741 1522 Nonresidential construction; Commercial & office building, new construction; Industrial buildings, new construction; Construction management; Residential construction
Ch: Rich Lynch
* *Pr:* Richard M Lynch
* *CFO:* Daniel L Petersen
* *Ch:* F Curtis Hastings
VP: Mike Dillis
* *VP:* Tim J Stadelman
IT Man: Scott Noles
IT Man: Chuck Wood
Mktg Mgr: Nancy Mayek

D-U-N-S 00-500-6895 IMP/EXP
J H FLETCHER & CO
402 High St, Huntington, WV 25705-1747
Tel (304) 525-7811 *Founded/Ownrshp* 1983
Sales 214.0MM^E^ *EMP* 232
SIC 5082 3532 3743 3546 3541 Mining machinery & equipment, except petroleum; Mining machinery; Railroad equipment; Power-driven handtools; Machine tools, metal cutting type
CEO: Doug Hardman
* *Pr:* Robert O Duncan
* *Pr:* Raymond F Parks
* *CFO:* Jack Nistendirk
Bd of Dir: James Fletcher
* *VP:* Philip E Cline
Rgnl Mgr: Tim Martin
QA Dir: Paul Thomas
Dir IT: Gregory E Hinshaw
Plnt Mgr: Harold Newman
Ql Cn Mgr: Marc Endicott

D-U-N-S 96-867-8128
J H KELLY INVESTMENTS INC
821 3rd Ave, Longview, WA 98632-2105
Tel (360) 423-5510 *Founded/Ownrshp* 1923
Sales 190.0MM *EMP* 5
SIC 1711 Plumbing, heating, air-conditioning contractors
Pr: Dan Evans

D-U-N-S 00-890-4328
J H LARSON ELECTRICAL CO
10200 51st Ave N Ste B, Plymouth, MN 55442-4506
Tel (763) 545-1717 *Founded/Ownrshp* 1931
Sales 131.0MM^E^ *EMP* 186
SIC 5063 5074 5075 Electrical apparatus & equipment; Plumbing & hydronic heating supplies; Warm air heating equipment & supplies
Pr: Greg Pahl
* *Ch Bd:* C E Pahl
* *Ch Bd:* Charles E Pahl
* *Treas:* Lucas Pahl
Brnch Mgr: Richard Ewert
Brnch Mgr: Charlie Hendrickson
Brnch Mgr: Jan Jessen

Brnch Mgr: Gregg Miller
CIO: William Tapper
IT Man: Margie Westphal
Opers Mgr: Lynda Piel

D-U-N-S 00-446-1323
J H ROUTH PACKING CO (OH)
4413 W Bogart Rd, Sandusky, OH 44870-9648
Tel (419) 626-2251 *Founded/Ownrshp* 1947, 1919
Sales 160.0MM *EMP* 300
SIC 2011

J H T
See JOHNSON HEALTH TECH NORTH AMERICA INC

J H WHITNEY & CO
See WHITNEY & CO LLC

D-U-N-S 07-934-5726
J H WHITNEY CAPITAL PARTNERS LLC
130 Main St, New Canaan, CT 06840-5509
Tel (203) 716-6100 *Founded/Ownrshp* 2004
Sales 478.7MM^E^ *EMP* 4,505^E^
SIC 6799 Investors

J HILL OIL
See JAMIESON-HILL A GENERAL PARTNERSHIP

J I S
See JOB INDUSTRIAL SERVICES INC

D-U-N-S 78-958-3700
J IVERSON RIDDLE DEVELOPMENT CENTER
300 Enola Rd, Morganton, NC 28655-4625
Tel (828) 433-2800 *Founded/Ownrshp* 2006
Sales 42.7MM^E^ *EMP* 1,000
SIC 8211 Public elementary school

D-U-N-S 00-700-8113
J J B HILLIARD W L LYONS LLC
HILLIARD LYONS
(*Suby of* HL FINANCIAL SERVICES LLC) ★
500 W Jefferson St # 700, Louisville, KY 40202-2815
Tel (502) 588-8400 *Founded/Ownrshp* 2008
Sales 360.1MM^E^ *EMP* 1,150^E^
SIC 6211 Dealers, security; Brokers, security; Stock brokers & dealers; Bond dealers & brokers
Prin: James Allen
* *CFO:* Charles Grimley
Bd of Dir: Lora Norris
Ex VP: Randy Bugh
Ex VP: James Walters
Sr VP: Jack Brusewitz
Sr VP: Joe Bryant
Sr VP: Joe Cutsinger
Sr VP: Brendan Hosty
* *Sr VP:* Donald Merrifield
Sr VP: Kevin Mlincek
* *Sr VP:* George Moorin
Sr VP: Bill Munday
Sr VP: Shane Raymond
Sr VP: John Sousan
* *Sr VP:* Kenneth Wagner
VP: John Beery
VP: Ruth Blum
VP: Leslie Boor
VP: John R Bugh
VP: Laura Clark

D-U-N-S 05-026-4316
J J KELLER & ASSOCIATES INC
3003 Breezewood Ln, Neenah, WI 54956-9611
Tel (920) 722-2848 *Founded/Ownrshp* 1953
Sales 225.7MM *EMP* 1,300
SIC 2741 8742

J J TAYLOR CO
See JJ TAYLOR COMPANIES INC

D-U-N-S 01-485-0390 IMP
J J WHITE INC
5500 Bingham St, Philadelphia, PA 19120-2198
Tel (215) 722-1000 *Founded/Ownrshp* 1920
Sales 251.7MM^E^ *EMP* 1,500^E^
SIC 1711 1542 7699 Mechanical contractor; Commercial & office building contractors; Tank repair
Pr: James J White IV
CFO: Ed Purdy
* *CFO:* Edward W Purdy III

J. JILL
See JILL ACQUISITION LLC

D-U-N-S 17-813-8947 IMP/EXP
J JILL GROUP INC
4 Batterymarch Park, Quincy, MA 02169-7468
Tel (617) 376-4300 *Founded/Ownrshp* 2015
Sales 745.8M^E^ *EMP* 3,041
SIC 5961 5621 5661 5632

D-U-N-S 10-793-4937
J K MOVING & STORAGE INC
JK MOVING SERVICES LOUDOUN CO
44112 Mercure Cir Ste 1, Sterling, VA 20166-2017
Tel (703) 260-4282 *Founded/Ownrshp* 1982
Sales 90.6MM *EMP* 364
Accts Rsm Us Llp Mclean Virginia
SIC 4226 Special warehousing & storage
Pr: Charles S Kuhn
Pr: Paul Maginnis
CFO: Dave Harris
VP: Rocco Balsamo
VP: Andrea Bunch
VP: Vincent Burruano
VP: Ted Isaacson
VP: David Kordonowy
VP: David Macpherson
Admn Mgr: Tina Buckley
Genl Mgr: Tom Grass

D-U-N-S 03-916-2771 IMP
J KINGS FOOD SERVICE PROFESSIONALS INC
700 Furrows Rd, Holtsville, NY 11742-2001
Tel (631) 289-8401 *Founded/Ownrshp* 1974
Sales 377.4MM^E^ *EMP* 350
Accts Biscotti Toback & Company Cp

SIC 5149 5143 5144 5142 5148 Groceries & related products; Dairy products, except dried or canned; Poultry & poultry products; Packaged frozen goods; Fresh fruits & vegetables
* *Pr:* Greg Ferraro
CFO: Robert Deluca
Ex VP: Joel Panagakos
Exec: Christopher J Neary
Exec: Laura J Vonkampen
Store Mgr: Maria Calhoun
CTO: Ian Obrien
MIS Dir: Bob Daluka
IT Man: Gary Fernbach
IT Man: Jay Gavigan
IT Man: Diana Tempia

D-U-N-S 17-783-2698
J KNIPPER AND CO INC
1 Healthcare Way, Lakewood, NJ 08701-5400
Tel (732) 905-7878 *Founded/Ownrshp* 1986
Sales 113.9MM^E^ *EMP* 600
SIC 8742 Marketing consulting services
CEO: Jim Knipper
* *Pr:* Michael Laferrera
* *CFO:* Frank McNicholas
Sr VP: Jack Bryndza
* *Sr VP:* Linda E Hatt
* *Sr VP:* Eric Johnson
VP: Brad Clayton
VP: David Conklin
VP: Steve Grandsen
VP: Steve Gransden
VP: Steven Grasden
VP: Mike Griglik
VP: Gerri Treacy

J L COLEBROOK DIVISION
See G-III LEATHER FASHIONS INC

D-U-N-S 02-389-9719
J L CULPEPPER & CO INC
RICHMOND RESTAURANT SERVICE
201 Haley Rd, Ashland, VA 23005-2451
Tel (804) 752-6576 *Founded/Ownrshp* 1939
Sales 103.1MM^E^ *EMP* 98
SIC 5141 Groceries, general line
Pr: S Lynn Townsend
* *Ex VP:* Rhett Townsend
* *VP:* Patricia C Gibbs
* *VP:* Barbara Townsend

D-U-N-S 18-055-3984
J L DAVIS CO
211 N Colorado St, Midland, TX 79701-4696
Tel (432) 682-6311 *Founded/Ownrshp* 1987
Sales 350.0MM *EMP* 104
SIC 5172 4923 1311 Petroleum products; Gas transmission & distribution; Crude petroleum production; Natural gas production
Owner: James Lee Davis
MIS Dir: Shirley Weiler

J L G
See JLG INDUSTRIES INC

J. LEWIS COOPER CO.
See GREAT LAKES WINE & SPIRITS LLC

J M D
See J M DAVIDSON INC

D-U-N-S 06-237-1331
J M DAVIDSON INC
J M D
2564 County Road 1960, Aransas Pass, TX 78336-8960
Tel (361) 883-0983 *Founded/Ownrshp* 1982
Sales 106.4MM^E^ *EMP* 250^E^
SIC 1541 1731 3441 Industrial buildings, new construction; General electrical contractor; Fabricated structural metal
Pr: John M Davidson
* *VP:* Joe R Wallace
Genl Mgr: Nzilani Barry
* *Genl Mgr:* Justin Davidson

J M I
See JAMES MARINE INC

D-U-N-S 00-586-8245 IMP
J M SMITH CORP
INTEGRAL SOLUTIONS GROUP
101 W Saint John St # 305, Spartanburg, SC 29306-5150
Tel (864) 542-9419 *Founded/Ownrshp* 1944
Sales 2.4MMM *EMP* 1,050
SIC 5122 7374 Drugs, proprietaries & sundries; Data processing service
Ch Bd: William R Cobb
* *Pr:* Ken Couch
* *CFO:* James C Wilson Jr
Sr VP: Brian Purscell
VP: Linda Campbell
VP: Rick Simerly
Dir Risk M: Roy Meidinger
Natl Sales: Jim Hancock
Mktg Dir: Heidi Jameson

J M SMUCKER
See INTERNATIONAL MULTIFOODS CORP

D-U-N-S 00-446-1406 IMP/EXP
▲ **J M SMUCKER CO** (OH)
1 Strawberry Ln, Orrville, OH 44667-1298
Tel (330) 682-3000 *Founded/Ownrshp* 1897
Sales 7.8MMM *EMP* 6,910
Accts Ernst & Young Llp Akron Ohio
Tkr Sym SJM *Exch* NYS
SIC 2099 2033 2023 2087 2035 Syrups; Frosting, ready-to-use; Sandwiches, assembled & packaged: for wholesale market; Peanut butter; Jams, jellies & preserves: packaged in cans, jars, etc.; Jellies, edible, including imitation: in cans, jars, etc.; Vegetable juices: packaged in cans, jars, etc.; Fruit juices: packaged in cans, jars, etc.; Canned milk, whole; Beverage bases, concentrates, syrups, powders & mixes; Pickles, sauces & salad dressings
CEO: Richard K Smucker
* *Pr:* Mark T Smucker
CFO: Mark R Belgya
CFO: Jim Nielsen

Sr VP: Jeannette L Knudsen
Sr VP: Jill R Penrose
Plnt Mgr: Bill Erickson
VP Mktg: Tamara J Fynan
Sls Dir: Jessica Fording
Mktg Mgr: Catherine Belden
Mktg Mgr: Alison Hartnoll
Board of Directors: Kathryn W Dindo, Paul J Dolan, Jay L Henderson, Nancy Lopez Knight, Elizabeth Valk Long, Gary A Oatey, Sandra Pianalto, Alex Shumate, Timothy P Smucker

J MT
See JOHNSON MIRMIRAN & THOMPSON INC

D-U-N-S 11-752-4629
J P CULLEN & SONS INC
330 E Delavan Dr, Janesville, WI 53546-2711
Tel (608) 754-6601 *Founded/Ownrshp* 1981
Sales 407.2MM *EMP* 600
Accts Baker Tilly Virchow Krause Ll
SIC 1541 1542 Industrial buildings, new construction; Commercial & office building, new construction
Ch Bd: Mark A Cullen
**Pr:* David J Cullen
**CFO:* Stephen P Wisnefsky
VP: Kevin Hickman
**VP:* Larry D Rocole
**VP:* Daniel A Swanson
Off Mgr: Liz Hasenstein
IT Man: Daniel Maginot
Info Man: James Bacus
Sfty Mgr: Tom Gruman
Opers Mgr: Joe Martino

J P I LEASING
See JPI INVESTMENT CO LP

D-U-N-S 79-056-1273
■ J P MORGAN ASSET MANAGEMENT INC
(*Suby of* JPMORGAN CHASE & CO) ★
270 Park Ave Fl 12, New York, NY 10017-7924
Tel (212) 270-6000 *Founded/Ownrshp* 1995
Sales 101.1MM^E^ *EMP* 136
SIC 6211 6282 Investment firm, general brokerage; Investment advice
CIO: Gary Madich
**Chf Mktg O:* Benji Baer
Chf Inves: Michael Cembalest
VP: Megan Goett
Mng Dir: Daniel Hines
Mng Dir: Catherine Keating

D-U-N-S 10-836-1002
J P MORGAN CHASE FOUNDATION
270 Park Ave Fl 6, New York, NY 10017-7924
Tel (212) 270-6000 *Founded/Ownrshp* 1969
Sales 149.8MM *EMP* 5
SIC 8699 Charitable organization
CEO: Bruce McNamer
Owner: Lewis Jones
Pr: Dalila Wilson-Scott
Ch: Jeffrey C Walker
Ofcr: Stan Stanford
VP: Emily Beizer
VP: Mark Nofziger
VP: Douglas Schwarz
Exec: Michael Alix

D-U-N-S 03-847-4342
■ J P MORGAN SERVICES INC
(*Suby of* JPMORGAN CHASE & CO) ★
500 Stanton Christiana Rd, Newark, DE 19713-2105
Tel (302) 634-1000 *Founded/Ownrshp* 1996
Sales 47.7MM^E^ *EMP* 1,000
SIC 7374 8741 Data processing service; Management services
Pr: Rich J Johnson

J PAUL GETTY MUSEUM
See J PAUL GETTY TRUST

D-U-N-S 08-985-8969 IMP
J PAUL GETTY TRUST
J PAUL GETTY MUSEUM
1200 Getty Center Dr # 500, Los Angeles, CA 90049-1657
Tel (310) 440-7300 *Founded/Ownrshp* 1953
Sales 503.5MM *EMP* 1,500
SIC 8412

J. POLEP DISTRIBUTION SERVICES
See CONSUMER PRODUCT DISTRIBUTORS INC

D-U-N-S 18-373-9374
J R C TRANSPORTATION INC
47 Maple Ave, Thomaston, CT 06787-1901
Tel (860) 283-0207 *Founded/Ownrshp* 1985
Sales 88.5MM^E^ *EMP* 150
SIC 4213 4212 Trucking, except local; Local trucking, without storage
Pr: Raymond M Cappella

J R METALS
See MISA METALS INC

D-U-N-S 94-772-7368
■ J RAY MCDERMOTT & CO INC
(*Suby of* MCDERMOTT INTERNATIONAL INC) ★
1340 Poydras St Ste 1200, New Orleans, LA 70112-1232
Tel (504) 587-5000 *Founded/Ownrshp* 1994
Sales 330.9MM^E^ *EMP* 7,100
Accts Pricewaterhousecoopers Llp
SIC 1629 1389 1623 Marine construction; Industrial plant construction; Power plant construction; Construction, repair & dismantling services; Oil field services; Roustabout service; Servicing oil & gas wells; Pipeline construction
CEO: Bruce W Wilkinson
Pr: Robert H Rawle
CFO: Bruce F Longaker Jr
Ex VP: E Allen Womack Jr
Snr PM: Marc Zeringer

D-U-N-S 60-657-3996
J RAYMOND & ASSOCIATES INC
465 W Warren Ave, Longwood, FL 32750-4002
Tel (407) 339-2988 *Founded/Ownrshp* 1988
Sales 109.5MM *EMP* 30
Accts Tschopp Whitcomb & Orr Pa
SIC 1542 Commercial & office building, new construction; Commercial & office buildings, renovation & repair
Pr: John R Sofarelli
**VP:* Russ Suddeth
Sfty Mgr: Richard Cooney

J S
See JEL SERT CO

J S G
See JOHNSON SERVICE GROUP INC

D-U-N-S 19-683-5029
J S LEASING CO INC
SLAY INDUSTRIES
1441 Hampton Ave, Saint Louis, MO 63139-3115
Tel (314) 647-7529 *Founded/Ownrshp* 1979
Sales 149.7MM^E^ *EMP* 400^E^
SIC 7359 Equipment rental & leasing
CEO: Eugene Slay
**Pr:* Glen Slay
**Ex VP:* Gary Slay
Exec: Jill Garlich

J S W
See JSW STEEL (USA) INC

D-U-N-S 08-608-3193
J SMITH LANIER & CO
300 W 10th St, West Point, GA 31833-1212
Tel (706) 645-2211 *Founded/Ownrshp* 1983
Sales NA *EMP* 572
Accts Warrant Averett Atlanta Ga
SIC 6411 Life insurance agents; Property & casualty insurance agent; Fire loss appraisal
Ch Bd: D Gaines Lanier
Pr: Gary Ivey
CFO: Frank Plan
Ex VP: Scott Crawford
VP: Chris Bolt
Off Mgr: Rob Murphy
MIS Dir: Mike Milan

D-U-N-S 01-086-1201
J STANTON DAVID & ASSOCIATES INC
WENDY'S
714 W Michigan Ave, Jackson, MI 49201-1909
Tel (517) 784-4094 *Founded/Ownrshp* 1974
Sales 77.7MM^E^ *EMP* 2,300
SIC 5812 Fast-food restaurant, chain
Ch Bd: David J Stanton
VP: Alan Lecrone
IT Man: Jim Bunker
Mktg Dir: Dave Wenglekowski

D-U-N-S 02-479-4711
JT DAVENPORT & SONS INC
1144 Broadway Rd, Sanford, NC 27332-9793
Tel (919) 774-9444 *Founded/Ownrshp* 2012
Sales 108.7MM^E^ *EMP* 350^E^
SIC 5199

JT PACKARD
See THOMAS & BETTS POWER SOLUTIONS LLC

D-U-N-S 00-946-6111 IMP
JT THORPE & SON INC
(*Suby of* TERRA MILLENNIUM CORP) ★
1060 Hensley St, Richmond, CA 94801-2117
Tel (510) 233-2500 *Founded/Ownrshp* 1985
Sales 177.0MM *EMP* 550
Accts Armanino Llp San Ramon Calif
SIC 1741 8711 Refractory or acid brick masonry; Engineering services
CEO: Mark C Stutzman
Pr: Bryan Young
CFO: Michael P Elam
VP: Richard Giaramita
VP: Kevin Howard

D-U-N-S 18-646-1406
JT VAUGHN ENTERPRISES INC
VAUGHN CONSTRUCTION
10355 Westpark Dr, Houston, TX 77042-5312
Tel (713) 243-8300 *Founded/Ownrshp* 1988
Sales 216.4MM^E^ *EMP* 300
SIC 1542 Commercial & office building, new construction; Hospital construction
Pr: J T Vaughn Jr
**Pr:* Tom Vaughn
**Treas:* Bob Weeks
**Treas:* Robert Weeks
**VP:* Stephen Skabla
**VP:* Bill Vaughn
Off Mgr: Lillie Lewis
CIO: Rahul Deshmukh
Sfty Dir: Eloy Silva
Ql Cn Mgr: Pedro Gutierrez
Mktg Mgr: Christine Sellew

D-U-N-S 00-860-0256 IMP/EXP
JT WALKER INDUSTRIES INC
861 N Hercules Ave, Clearwater, FL 33765-2025
Tel (727) 461-0501 *Founded/Ownrshp* 1997
Sales 697.0MM^E^ *EMP* 5,000
SIC 3442 3089 3585 5193 Screens, window, metal; Window frames & sash, plastic; Parts for heating, cooling & refrigerating equipment; Nursery stock
CEO: Peter Desoto
**Pr:* Jay K Poppleton
CFO: Janet Sasenmyer
**VP:* Janet L Fasenmyer
**VP:* Michael Luther
Genl Mgr: Mark Paul
VP Mfg: David Hawkins
Sfty Dirs: Darlene Moffatt
VP Sls: Grant Tyson

D-U-N-S 00-294-5777 EXP
JTECH SALES LLC (FL)
CITRUS OLEO
6531 Park Of Cmrc Blvd Ste 170, Boca Raton, FL 33487
Tel (561) 995-0070 *Founded/Ownrshp* 1997
Sales 90.0MM *EMP* 35
SIC 5169 Chemicals & allied products
VP Mktg: Jim Coletta
Sls Dir: Ricki Tannenbaum

D-U-N-S 15-186-7363
J V LABORATORIES INC
(*Suby of* ST LUKE'S MEMORIAL HOSPITAL INC)
1320 Wisconsin Ave # 101, Racine, WI 53403-1978
Tel (262) 687-2150 *Founded/Ownrshp* 1991
Sales 396.7MM *EMP* 85^E^
SIC 8071 Medical laboratories
Pr: Kenneth Buser
Pharmcst: Joseph Menden

J W
See JACKSON WALKER LLP

J W POWERLINE CONSTRUCTION
See JIM F WEBB INC

D-U-N-S 00-699-1160
J WALTER THOMPSON CO LLC (DE)
J WALTER THOMPSON INTL DIV
(*Suby of* W P P) ★
466 Lexington Ave Ste 6r, New York, NY 10017-3186
Tel (212) 210-7000 *Founded/Ownrshp* 1864
Sales 612.2MM^E^ *EMP* 9,000
SIC 7311 Advertising agencies
CEO: Bob Jeffrey
Pr: Claire Capeci
Pr: Lynn Power
CEO: David Eastman
CFO: Lewis J Trencher
Ofcr: Erin Johnson
Ex VP: Mark Alhermizi
Ex VP: Joe Lagattuta
Ex VP: Lewis Trencher
VP: Amarjeet Thakur
Exec: Saurabh Saksena
Dir: Matt Gerber
Creative D: David Carvajal
Creative D: Winnie Chang
Creative D: Eddy Greenwood
Creative D: Nick Liatos
Creative D: Alex Martinez
Creative D: Alex Noble
Creative D: Manesh Swamy
Creative D: John Tsaganellias
Comm Dir: Anaka Kobzev

J WALTER THOMPSON INTL DIV
See J WALTER THOMPSON CO LLC

D-U-N-S 10-111-6986
J WALTER THOMPSON USA LLC
JWT DIRECT DIV
(*Suby of* WPP PLC)
466 Lexington Ave Ste 6r, New York, NY 10017-3186
Tel (212) 210-7000 *Founded/Ownrshp* 1980
Sales 61.6MM^E^ *EMP* 1,390
SIC 7311 Advertising agencies
Ch Bd: James B Patterson Jr
Pt: Jefftey Steir
**CEO:* Ronald S Burns
**Prin:* Robert L Jeffrey
Ex Dir: Josy Paul
CIO: James Hudson
MIS Dir: Ed Brenin

D-U-N-S 11-482-6410
J&B MEDICAL SUPPLY CO INC
ABCO
50496 Pontiac Trl Ste 500, Wixom, MI 48393-2090
Tel (800) 737-0045 *Founded/Ownrshp* 1996
Sales 104.7MM^E^ *EMP* 172^E^
SIC 5047 Medical equipment & supplies
CEO: Mary E Shaya
**COO:* Charlene Shaya
**CFO:* Abu Sheikh Bakar
CFO: Abu Sheikh
Sls Mgr: Jerry Rhea

J&H FAMILY STORES
See EXIT 76 CORP

J&J FAMILY OF FARMS
See J & J PRODUCE INC

D-U-N-S 07-162-8598
J&J STAFFING RESOURCES INC (NJ)
1814 Marlton Pike E # 210, Cherry Hill, NJ 08003-2058
Tel (856) 751-5050 *Founded/Ownrshp* 1972
Sales 117.1MM^E^ *EMP* 9,053
SIC 7363 Temporary help service
Pr: John E Malady
Off Mgr: Deb Murphy
Off Admin: Judy Piccione
VP Mktg: Sean Malady

J&J/INVISION
See J & J INDUSTRIES INC

D-U-N-S 09-872-1509 IMP
J&P CYCLES LLC
(*Suby of* MOTORSPORT AFTERMARKET GROUP INC) ★
13225 Circle Dr, Anamosa, IA 52205-7321
Tel (319) 462-4817 *Founded/Ownrshp* 2010
Sales 133.9MM^E^ *EMP* 250
SIC 5571 5013 Motorcycle parts & accessories; Motor vehicle supplies & new parts
Genl Mgr: Zach Parham
**Pr:* John Parham
**Treas:* Michael Moore
**Prin:* Thomas S Collins
Mktg Mgr: Rhyde Thomas

D-U-N-S 06-248-6238 IMP/EXP
J-M MANUFACTURING CO INC
JM EAGLE
5200 W Century Blvd, Los Angeles, CA 90045-5928
Tel (800) 621-4404 *Founded/Ownrshp* 1982
Sales 1.0MMM^E^ *EMP* 1,800
SIC 2821 3491 3084 Polyvinyl chloride resins (PVC); Water works valves; Plastics pipe
CEO: Walter Wang
CFO: Dick Oxley
VP: Neal Gordon
VP: Dan O'Connor
Exec: Paulette Sandstedt
**Prin:* Shirley Wang
Adm Dir: Autumn Carlson
Area Mgr: Brian Lang
Area Mgr: Mark Montgomery
Off Mgr: Sally Jefferson
Dir IT: Hank Lin

D-U-N-S 78-748-3960 EXP
J-POWER USA DEVELOPMENT CO LTD
(*Suby of* ELECTRIC POWER DEVELOPMENT CO., LTD.)
1900 E Golf Rd Ste 1030, Schaumburg, IL 60173-5076
Tel (847) 908-2800 *Founded/Ownrshp* 2005
Sales 235.6MM^E^ *EMP* 578^E^
SIC 4911 Generation, electric power
Pr: Mark Condon
Sr VP: Hirofumi Hinokawa
VP: Paul Peterson
VP: Masaru Sakai

D-U-N-S 96-555-9672
J-W ENERGY CO
15505 Wright Brothers Dr, Addison, TX 75001-4274
Tel (972) 233-8191 *Founded/Ownrshp* 2006
Sales 725.1MM^E^ *EMP* 700
SIC 1311 7353 3533 1381 Crude petroleum production; Natural gas production; Oil field equipment, rental or leasing; Oil & gas field machinery; Drilling oil & gas wells
CEO: Howard G Westerman
Pr: Jeff Brown
Pr: Perry A Harris
**Pr:* David A Miller
**Treas:* Lindon H Leners
**Ex VP:* Richard T Clement
VP: Larry Carpenter
**VP:* Richard S Davis
Snr Sftwr: Uday Karuppiah

D-U-N-S 00-677-1356 IMP
J-W OPERATING CO (TX)
COHORT ENERGY COMPANY
(*Suby of* J-W ENERGY CO) ★
15505 Wright Brothers Dr, Addison, TX 75001-4274
Tel (972) 233-8191 *Founded/Ownrshp* 1960
Sales 676.9MM^E^ *EMP* 700
SIC 1382 Oil & gas exploration services
CEO: Howard G Westerman
**Pr:* Tony Meyer
COO: Paul D Westerman
**Ex VP:* C D McDaniels
VP: Jeff Brown
VP: Adam Griffin
VP: Jim Matthias
Off Mgr: Marsha McIntyre
Dir IT: Deron Helgren
IT Man: Jim McKie
Opers Mgr: Peter Kowalczik

D-U-N-S 94-622-7774
■ J2 CLOUD SERVICES INC
(*Suby of* J2 GLOBAL INC) ★
6922 Hollywood Blvd # 500, Los Angeles, CA 90028-6125
Tel (323) 860-9200 *Founded/Ownrshp* 2014
Sales 599.0MM^E^ *EMP* 1,830^E^
SIC 4822 Telegraph & other communications
CEO: Nehemia Zucker
**Pr:* R Scott Turicchi
**CFO:* Kathleen M Griggs
CFO: Allen K Jones
CFO: Scott R Tuicchi
Sr Cor Off: Susan Park
Sr Cor Off: Jeff Shell
Ex VP: Michael Benevento
Ex VP: Tonia Oconnor
Ex VP: Bedi Singh
VP: Jeff Adelman
**VP:* Jeffrey D Adelman
VP: Kevin Feldman
VP: Ken Ford
VP: Timothy Johnson
VP: Kevin Mitchell
VP: Linda Silva
Exec: Anthony Ghosn
Comm Dir: Marc Sobul
Dir Bus: Charlene Christman
Board of Directors: Douglas Y Bech, Robert J Cresci, W Brian Kretzmer, Richard S Ressler, Stephen Ross, Michael P Schulhof

D-U-N-S 07-954-2179
▲ J2 GLOBAL INC
6922 Hollywood Blvd # 500, Los Angeles, CA 90028-6125
Tel (323) 860-9200 *Founded/Ownrshp* 1995
Sales 720.8MM *EMP* 2,315^E^
Tkr Sym JCOM *Exch* NGS
SIC 4822 Telegraph & other communications
CEO: Nehemia Zucker
Pr: R Scott Turicchi
VP: Kevin Feldman
VP: Ken Ford
VP: Christopher Goodman
VP: Gary Kapner
VP: Tim McLean
VP: Jeremy D Rossen
VP: Bedi Singh
VP: Paul Yee
Snr Sftwr: Mike Cronin
Board of Directors: Douglas Y Bech, Robert J Cresci, W Brian Kretzmer, Jonathan F Miller, Stephen Ross

D-U-N-S 18-554-5100 IMP/EXP
■ JA APPAREL CORP
(*Suby of* JA HOLDING INC) ★
6380 Rogerdale Rd, Houston, TX 77072-1624
Tel (877) 986-9689 *Founded/Ownrshp* 2006
Sales 162.4MM^E^ *EMP* 500
SIC 5136 Men's & boys' clothing
Pr: Anthony Sapienza
**Ch Bd:* Bill Watts
Pr: Kenton Selvey
**CFO:* Erick Spiel
Founder: Joseph Abboud
VP: Trudy Larson
VP: Tanja Siburg
Creative D: Bernardo Rojo
VP Sls: Natalie Condon
Board of Directors: Alberto Morabito

D-U-N-S 07-909-6391
■ JA HOLDING INC
(*Suby of* MENS WEARHOUSE INC) ★
650 5th Ave Fl 20, New York, NY 10019-7687
Tel (212) 586-9140 *Founded/Ownrshp* 2013
Sales 162.4MM^E *EMP* 500
SIC 5136 Men's & boys' clothing
Pr: Doug Ewert

D-U-N-S 00-690-3512
JA RIGGS TRACTOR CO
RIGGS CA
9125 Interstate 30, Little Rock, AR 72209-3703
Tel (501) 570-3100 *Founded/Ownrshp* 1927
Sales 175.4MM^E *EMP* 450
SIC 5082 5511 General construction machinery & equipment; New & used car dealers
Pr: Robert L Cress
**Pr:* Rob Riggs
VP: Denny Upton
Info Man: Keith Riggs
VP Sls: Skip Hokett
Mktg Dir: John Bryant
Sls Mgr: Jason McDonald

D-U-N-S 07-854-9761
JAB BEECH INC
2200 Pennsylvania Ave Nw, Washington, DC 20037-1709
Tel (516) 537-1040 *Founded/Ownrshp* 2012
Sales 2.2MMM^E *EMP* 6,087^E
SIC 6799 Investors
CEO: Peter Harf

D-U-N-S 04-181-0979
▲ JABIL CIRCUIT INC
10560 Dr Martin Luther, Saint Petersburg, FL 33716-3718
Tel (727) 577-9749 *Founded/Ownrshp* 1966
Sales 18.3MMM *EMP* 138,000
Accts Ernst & Young Llp Tampa Flor
Tkr Sym JBL *Exch* NYS
SIC 3672 Printed circuit boards
CEO: Mark T Mondello
**Ch Bd:* Timothy L Main
Pr: William E Peters
COO: William D Muir Jr
CFO: Forbes I J Alexander
**V Ch Bd:* Thomas A Sansone
Board of Directors: Martha F Brooks, Frank A Newman, John C Plant, Steven A Raymund, David M Stout

D-U-N-S 05-392-7708 IMP
■ JABIL CIRCUIT LLC
(*Suby of* JABIL CIRCUIT INC) ★
10560 Dr Martin, Saint Petersburg, FL 33716
Tel (727) 577-9749 *Founded/Ownrshp* 1992
Sales 302.5MM^E *EMP* 789
SIC 3672 Circuit boards, television & radio printed
Ch Bd: Tim L Main
Pr: William E Peters
CEO: Mark Tmondello
COO: William D Muir Jr
Treas: Sergio A Cadavid
Prin: Forbes IJ Alexander
IT Man: Sudhir Sahu

D-U-N-S 87-826-8432 IMP/EXP
JAC HOLDING CORP
(*Suby of* WYNNCHURCH CAPITAL LTD) ★
3937 Campus Dr, Pontiac, MI 48341-3124
Tel (248) 874-1800 *Founded/Ownrshp* 1994
Sales 189.9MM^E *EMP* 1,505
SIC 3089 Injection molding of plastics
CEO: Jack Falcon
**COO:* Mike Wood
**CFO:* Mike Vanloon
**VP:* Noel Ranka

D-U-N-S 05-880-6126 IMP/EXP
JAC PRODUCTS INC
3937 Campus Dr, Pontiac, MI 48341-3124
Tel (248) 874-1800 *Founded/Ownrshp* 2016
Sales 259.9MM^E *EMP* 36^E
SIC 3089 3714

D-U-N-S 01-228-8767 IMP
JAC VANDENBERG INC
100 Corporate Dr Ste 155, Yonkers, NY 10701-6838
Tel (914) 964-5900 *Founded/Ownrshp* 1947
Sales 180.9MM *EMP* 30
SIC 5148 Fruits, fresh
Pr: David L Schiro
**Treas:* Edward Paap
**VP:* Fred Vandenberg
Dir IT: Joseph McEwing
Ql Cn Mgr: George Innocenzo
Trfc Mgr: Brian Murphy
Sls Mgr: Steve Stedman

D-U-N-S 00-494-5642 IMP
JACHS NY LLC
SHIRT BY SHIRT USA
359 Broadway Fl 3, New York, NY 10013-3932
Tel (212) 334-4380 *Founded/Ownrshp* 2007
Sales 107.0MM *EMP* 21^E
SIC 5136 Nightwear, men's & boys'
Pr: Hayati Banastey
**COO:* Baris Ozturk

D-U-N-S 79-642-5853
■ JACINTOPORT INTERNATIONAL LLC
GLOBAL DISTRIBUTION CENTER
(*Suby of* SEABOARD CORP) ★
16398 Jacintoport Blvd, Houston, TX 77015-6586
Tel (281) 457-2415 *Founded/Ownrshp* 2007
Sales 87.0MM^E *EMP* 450
SIC 4491 Marine cargo handling
Ex VP: David Labbe
IT Man: Pete Tinsley

JACK & JILL D.S.D.
See SIMCO LOGISTICS INC

D-U-N-S 01-832-8260
JACK A ALLEN INC
ALLEN OIL
2105 Old State Route 7, Steubenville, OH 43952-4332
Tel (740) 282-4531 *Founded/Ownrshp* 1977
Sales 85.1MM^E *EMP* 65
SIC 5172 5983 5541 5411 Gasoline; Fuel oil dealers; Filling stations, gasoline; Convenience stores, independent
Pr: Gary Armentrout

D-U-N-S 00-696-5537
JACK COOPER TRANSPORT CO INC
1100 Walnut St Ste 2400, Kansas City, MO 64106-2186
Tel (816) 983-4000 *Founded/Ownrshp* 1939
Sales 767.8MM^E *EMP* 3,000
SIC 4213 7389 Automobiles, transport & delivery; Drive-a-way automobile service
Ch: T Michael Riggs
**CEO:* Robert Griffin
**Ex VP:* Rudy Bijleveld
**Ex VP:* Theo Ciupitu
VP: David Davis
VP: Donald Gallant
VP: Curtis Goodwin
**VP:* Craig Irwin
VP: Mark Kreger
VP: Craig McGrath
VP: Brian Varano

D-U-N-S 00-404-0325 IMP
■ JACK DANIEL DISTILLERY LEM MOTLOW PROP INC
JACK DANIELS WHISKEY
(*Suby of* BROWN FORMAN BEVERAGES WORLDWI) ★
Rr 1, Lynchburg, TN 37352-9801
Tel (931) 759-4221 *Founded/Ownrshp* 1939
Sales 90.1MM^E *EMP* 365
SIC 2085 Bourbon whiskey
VP: Steve Goodner
**CFO:* Danny Lamb

JACK DANIELS CONSTRUCTION
See PHAZE CONCRETE INC

D-U-N-S 83-781-4867 IMP
JACK DANIELS MOTORS INC
16-01 Mcbride Ave, Fair Lawn, NJ 07410-2800
Tel (201) 796-8500 *Founded/Ownrshp* 1972
Sales 103.6MM^E *EMP* 275^E
SIC 5511 Automobiles, new & used
Genl Mgr: Frank Devita
**Pr:* Michael V Daniels
**COO:* Greg Zulli
**CFO:* Ronald Dubin
Genl Mgr: Donald Chittum
Sls Mgr: Curtis Aldershof
Sls Mgr: Jack Daniels
Sales Asso: Terry Axel

JACK DANIELS WHISKEY
See JACK DANIEL DISTILLERY LEM MOTLOW PROP INC

D-U-N-S 09-826-5341
▲ JACK HENRY & ASSOCIATES INC
663 W Highway 60, Monett, MO 65708-8215
Tel (417) 235-6652 *Founded/Ownrshp* 1976
Sales 1.3MMM *EMP* 5,822
Accts Pricewaterhousecoopers Llp Ka
Tkr Sym JKHY *Exch* NGS
SIC 7373 Computer integrated systems design; Computer systems analysis & design
Ch Bd: John F Prim
Pr: David B Foss
CFO: Kevin D Williams
**V Ch Bd:* Matthew C Flanigan
Bd of Dir: Michael Marston
Ex VP: Michael Collins
VP: Esteban Castorena
VP: Mark S Forbis
VP: David McDaniel
Genl Mgr: Brian Hunter
Genl Mgr: Ron L Moses
Board of Directors: Jacqueline R Fiegel, Laura G Kelly, Thomas H Wilson Jr, Thomas A Wimsett

JACK IN THE BOX
See A 3 H FOODS LP

JACK IN THE BOX
See J & D RESTAURANT GROUP LLC

D-U-N-S 04-211-7200 IMP
▲ JACK IN BOX INC
9330 Balboa Ave, San Diego, CA 92123-1524
Tel (858) 571-2121 *Founded/Ownrshp* 1951
Sales 1.6MMM *EMP* 20,700
Tkr Sym JACK *Exch* NGS
SIC 5812 6794 Fast-food restaurant, chain; Franchises, selling or licensing
Ch Bd: Leonard A Comma
Pr: Keith Guilbault
CFO: Jerry P Rebel
Treas: Paul D Melancon
Chf Mktg O: Keith M Guilbault
Ofcr: Vanessa C Fox
Ex VP: Mark H Blankenship
Ex VP: Phillip H Rudolph
Sr VP: Elana M Hobson
Sr VP: Linda A Lang
VP: Carol Diraimo
VP: Dee Frustaglio
VP: Kathy Lama
VP: Brian Luscomb
VP: Raymond Pepper
VP: Eric Tunquist
VP: Deborah Williamson
Board of Directors: David L Goebel, Sharon P John, Madeleine A Kleiner, Michael W Murphy, James M Myers, David M Tehle, John T Wyatt

JACK LINK BEEF JERKY
See LINK SNACKS INC

JACK LINK'S BEEF JERKY
See S I L INC

D-U-N-S 06-928-1350
■ JACK MORTON WORLDWIDE INC
INTERPUBLIC GROUP OF COMPANIES
(*Suby of* INTERPUBLIC GROUP OF COMPANIES INC) ★
142 Berkeley St Ste 6, Boston, MA 02116-5143
Tel (617) 585-7000 *Founded/Ownrshp* 1998
Sales 242.4MM^E *EMP* 575
SIC 8748 8742 Communications consulting; Business planning & organizing services; Marketing consulting services
Ch Bd: Josh McCall
**Pr:* Tara Back
**CFO:* William Davis
Ex VP: Elizabeth Krato
Ex VP: Charlotte Merrell
Sr VP: Kate Crotty
Sr VP: Cyndi Davis
Sr VP: Ethan Gunning
Sr VP: Tom Michael
Sr VP: Steve Mooney
Sr VP: Abigail Walker
VP: Natalie Ackerman
VP: Alex Apthorpe
VP: Gary Baker
VP: Vince Belizario
VP: Theresa Brown
VP: Sheila Denneen
VP: Carley Faircloth
VP: Ross Fleckenstein
VP: Traci Kleinman
VP: Debbie Melkonian

D-U-N-S 05-387-6504 IMP
JACK NADEL INC
JACK NADEL INTERNATIONAL
8701 Bellanca Ave, Los Angeles, CA 90045-4411
Tel (310) 815-2600 *Founded/Ownrshp* 1953
Sales 106.0MM *EMP* 245
SIC 8742 5199 Incentive or award program consultant; Gifts & novelties
CEO: Craig Nadel
CFO: Bob Kritzler
**CFO:* Robert Kritzler
**Ch:* Jack Nadel
**Sr VP:* Debbie Abergel
**Sr VP:* Craig Reese
VP: Mark Hacker
VP: Damon Miller
VP: Paul Navabpour
**VP:* Athans Zafiropoulos
Exec: Scott Brown
Exec: Cathy Davis
Exec: Laird Eickmeyer
Exec: Stephanie Peyrefitte
**Exec:* Steve Widdicombe
Board of Directors: David Falato, Jeff Jacobs

JACK NADEL INTERNATIONAL
See JACK NADEL INC

D-U-N-S 01-427-6430 IMP/EXP
JACK WILLIAMS TIRE CO INC
JACK WLLAMS TIRE AUTO SVC CTRS
700 Rocky Glen Rd, Avoca, PA 18641-9529
Tel (570) 457-5000 *Founded/Ownrshp* 1969
Sales 241.0MM^E *EMP* 500
SIC 5531 5014 Automotive tires; Automobile tires & tubes; Truck tires & tubes
Ch Bd: William C Williams
**Pr:* Scott Williams
**CFO:* Frank J Chalk
**Treas:* Caroline Orourke
**Sec:* Sandra Williams
**VP:* Jason Williams
**VP:* Tracey Williams

JACK WLLAMS TIRE AUTO SVC CTRS
See JACK WILLIAMS TIRE CO INC

D-U-N-S 09-379-1184
JACKIES INTERNATIONAL INC
LUIGI'S FAMILY RESTAURANT
1554 W Peace St, Canton, MS 39046-5325
Tel (601) 855-0146 *Founded/Ownrshp* 1977
Sales 55.9MM^E *EMP* 1,200
SIC 5812 7011 Pizzeria, chain; Pizza restaurants; Steak restaurant; Family restaurants; Hotels & motels
Pr: S L Sethi
CFO: Jerry Beckwith
Treas: Sethi Raksha
**Sec:* Raksha Sethi
**VP:* Monica Sethi Harrigill
**VP:* John Kirk
**VP:* Dana Moreau
**VP:* Sunny Sethi

JACK'S FAMILY RESTAURANTS
See BIG JACK ULTIMATE HOLDINGS LP

JACKSON BOARD OF EDUCATION
See JACKSON COUNTY SCHOOL DISTRICT

D-U-N-S 62-019-9836
JACKSON CLINIC PHARMACY INC
JACKSON CLINIC PROF ASSN INF
(*Suby of* JACKSON CLINIC PROFESSIONAL ASSOCIATION) ★
828 N Parkway, Jackson, TN 38305-3032
Tel (731) 422-0330 *Founded/Ownrshp* 1970
Sales 90.5MM^E *EMP* 800
SIC 5912 Drug stores
Dir Lab: Doris Knott
Ansthlgy: Laura A Ermenc
Ansthlgy: John W Miles
Doctor: Salomon N Asmar MD

JACKSON CLINIC PROF ASSN INF
See JACKSON CLINIC PHARMACY INC

D-U-N-S 03-466-4938
JACKSON CLINIC PROFESSIONAL ASSOCIATION
828 N Parkway, Jackson, TN 38305-3032
Tel (731) 422-0200 *Founded/Ownrshp* 1970
Sales 118.9MM^E *EMP* 800
SIC 5912 8011 8062 Drug stores; Clinic, operated by physicians; General medical & surgical hospitals
CEO: Carl E Rudd
**Exec:* Beverly Waylie

D-U-N-S 07-313-4868
JACKSON COUNTY
415 E 12th St, Kansas City, MO 64106-2706
Tel (816) 881-3333 *Founded/Ownrshp* 1826
Sales NA *EMP* 2,000
Accts Kpmg Llp Kansas City Mo
SIC 9111 Executive offices;
Pr: Kathy Hearron
Pr: Heather Martin
Pr: Alicia Warren
COO: Rick Perry
Ofcr: Kenneth Bobb
Ofcr: Carl Carmoney
Ofcr: Randy Nygaard
Ofcr: Nicole Tigner
Genl Mgr: Ted Hunt
Dir IT: Connie Frey
IT Man: Barbara Casamento

D-U-N-S 03-726-1518
JACKSON COUNTY BOARD OF EDUCATION
4700 Col Vickery Rd, Ocean Springs, MS 39565-6632
Tel (228) 826-1757 *Founded/Ownrshp* 1930
Sales 22.4MM^E *EMP* 1,200
SIC 8211 School board
Ch Bd: Kenneth Fountain

D-U-N-S 10-064-5902
JACKSON COUNTY PUBLIC SCHOOLS
JACKSON COUNTY SCHOOL BOARD
2903 Jefferson St, Marianna, FL 32446-3445
Tel (850) 482-1200 *Founded/Ownrshp* 1900
Sales 58.0MM^E *EMP* 1,099
SIC 8211 Public elementary & secondary schools
Teacher Pr: Mary Skipper
HC Dir: Shirl A Williams
Board of Directors: Charlotte Gardner

D-U-N-S 07-598-0201
JACKSON COUNTY SCHNECK MEMORIAL HOSPITAL
SCHNECK MEDICAL CENTER
411 W Tipton St, Seymour, IN 47274-2363
Tel (812) 522-2349 *Founded/Ownrshp* 1940
Sales 132.1MM *EMP* 700
SIC 8062 General medical & surgical hospitals
Pr: Gary A Meyer
COO: Kim Ellerman
**CFO:* Warren Forgey
Exec: Ann Green
Exec: Allison Spurgeon
Dir Rx: Justin Brown
Chf Nrs Of: Vicki Johnson
Cmptr Lab: Denise Fleenor
Dir IT: Craig Rice
IT Man: Mellencamp Charlene
IT Man: Charlene Mellencamp

JACKSON COUNTY SCHOOL BOARD
See JACKSON COUNTY PUBLIC SCHOOLS

D-U-N-S 11-833-1383
JACKSON COUNTY SCHOOL DISTRICT
4700 Colonel Vickrey Rd, Vancleave, MS 39565
Tel (228) 826-1757 *Founded/Ownrshp* 2002
Sales 68.5MM *EMP* 1,403
SIC 8211 Public elementary & secondary schools
MIS Dir: David Besanzon
Teacher Pr: Laura McCool
Psych: Shanon Hinkle
Board of Directors: David Sims, Karen Tolbert, Randal Turner, Glen Dickerson J Keith Lee

D-U-N-S 19-331-1362
JACKSON COUNTY SCHOOL DISTRICT
JACKSON BOARD OF EDUCATION
1660 Winder Hwy, Jefferson, GA 30549-5458
Tel (706) 367-5151 *Founded/Ownrshp* 1950
Sales 48.5MM^E *EMP* 1,352
SIC 8211 Public elementary & secondary schools
Teacher Pr: Selena Blankenship

D-U-N-S 07-979-2161
JACKSON COUNTY SCHOOLS
1 School St, Ripley, WV 25271-1538
Tel (304) 372-7300 *Founded/Ownrshp* 1933
Sales 9.2MM^E *EMP* 1,147^E
SIC 8211 Public elementary & secondary schools
Teacher Pr: Jay Carnell
Instr Medi: Debbie Casto
HC Dir: Lisa Martin

D-U-N-S 00-381-3003
JACKSON ELECTRIC MEMBERSHIP CORP (GA)
JACKSON EMC
850 Commerce Rd, Jefferson, GA 30549-3329
Tel (706) 367-5281 *Founded/Ownrshp* 1938
Sales 527.7MM *EMP* 445
Accts Mcnair Mclemore Middlebrooks &
SIC 4911 Distribution, electric power
CEO: Randall Pugh
**COO:* Roy Stowe
**CFO:* Greg Keith
Exec: Lori McCutcheon
Dir IT: Ken Brand
Dir IT: Jeff Keen
Board of Directors: Steve Blair

JACKSON EMC
See JACKSON ELECTRIC MEMBERSHIP CORP

D-U-N-S 03-838-9347
JACKSON ENERGY AUTHORITY
351 Dr Martin Luther, Jackson, TN 38301
Tel (731) 422-7500 *Founded/Ownrshp* 2001
Sales 245.0MM *EMP* 425
Accts Alexander Thompson Arnold Pllc
SIC 4925 4911 4941 4952 Gas production and/or distribution; Electric services; Water supply; Sewerage systems
Ch: Ken Marston
**Pr:* Danny Wheeler
**VP:* Michael Baughn
VP: David Cowfer
IT Man: David Ridenhour
Snr Mgr: Barry Cross

D-U-N-S 00-877-9159
JACKSON ENERGY COOPERATIVE CORP
115 Jackson Energy Ln, Mc Kee, KY 40447-8847
Tel (606) 364-1000 *Founded/Ownrshp* 1938
Sales 96.6MM *EMP* 130
SIC 4911 Distribution, electric power
Pr: Carol Wright
Ch Bd: Phillip Thompson
Sec: Keith Binder
V Ch Bd: Landis Cornett
Chf Mktg O: Rodney Chrisman
Dist Mgr: Larry Lakes
Genl Mgr: Don Schaefer
Genl Mgr: Ruth Venable
CIO: Rodger Witt
Dir IT: Lindsy Russell
IT Man: Patrick Head

D-U-N-S 60-511-4644 IMP
JACKSON FAMILY WINES INC
VINEYARDS OF MONTEREY
421 And 425 Aviation Blvd, Santa Rosa, CA 95403
Tel (707) 544-4000 *Founded/Ownrshp* 1987
Sales 342.1MM^E *EMP* 1,000
SIC 2084 0172 5813 Wines; Grapes; Wine bar
Prin: Barbara Banke
Ex VP: Rick Tigner
Sr VP: David K Bowman
**VP:* Charles Shea
Mktg Dir: Jeff Ngo
Board of Directors: Barbara Banke, Larry Kitchen, Harry Wetzel

D-U-N-S 00-703-1453 IMP/EXP
JACKSON FURNITURE INDUSTRIES INC (TN)
CATNAPPER
1910 King Edward Ave Se, Cleveland, TN 37311-3076
Tel (423) 476-8544 *Founded/Ownrshp* 1933, 1986
Sales 167.4MM^E *EMP* 700
SIC 2512 Chairs: upholstered on wood frames; Living room furniture: upholstered on wood frames
Pr: W Ronald Jackson
**VP:* Roger T Jackson
**VP:* Virginia Matheny
VP: W Kay Stewart
Dir IT: Nicholas Townsend
Ql Cn Mgr: Matt Smith
VP Sls: Chuck Catterton
VP Sls: Tom Little

D-U-N-S 08-768-1537
JACKSON HEALTHCARE LLC (GA)
2655 Northwinds Pkwy, Alpharetta, GA 30009-2280
Tel (770) 643-5500 *Founded/Ownrshp* 1989
Sales 696.9MM *EMP* 784
SIC 7361 Labor contractors (employment agency)
Ch Bd: Richard L Jackson
Pt: Scott L'Heureux
**Pr:* R Shane Jackson
CFO: Loren Johnson
**CFO:* Douglas B Kline
**Ex VP:* Michael Hiffa
VP: Alan Frutchey
VP: Leslie Harrell
VP: Diana D Holmes
VP: David McAnally
VP: Karyn Mullins
VP: Doug Walker
Exec: Lurline Craig-Burke

D-U-N-S 07-987-9831
JACKSON HEALTHCARE STAFFING HOLDINGS LLC (GA)
2655 Northwinds Pkwy, Alpharetta, GA 30009-2280
Tel (770) 643-5500 *Founded/Ownrshp* 2007
Sales 565.0MM *EMP* 627
SIC 8099 Childbirth preparation clinic
CEO: Richard L Jackson
CFO: Douglas B Klein
VP: R Shane Jackson

D-U-N-S 60-751-7430 IMP
■ **JACKSON HMA LLC**
MERIT HEALTH CENTRAL
(*Suby of* COMMUNITY HEALTH SYSTEMS INC) ★
1850 Chadwick Dr, Jackson, MS 39204-3404
Tel (601) 376-1000 *Founded/Ownrshp* 2014
Sales 101.8MM^E *EMP* 850
SIC 8011 Clinic, operated by physicians
Pr: Wanda Aultman
Pr: Carole Newell
Nurse Mgr: Kimberly Hulitt
Doctor: Richard Miles MD
Pharmcst: Amanda Labuda
Occ Thrpy: Lisa Davis
HC Dir: Yvonne Sanchez

JACKSON HOLE GOLF & TENNIS
See GRAND TETON LODGE CO

D-U-N-S 08-932-3851
JACKSON HOLE MOUNTAIN RESORT CORP
3395 Cody Ln, Teton Village, WY 83025
Tel (307) 733-2292 *Founded/Ownrshp* 1963
Sales 91.4MM^E *EMP* 1,400^E
SIC 7999 6552 Recreation center; Aerial tramway or ski lift, amusement or scenic; Concession operator; Subdividers & developers
Ch: John L Kemmerer III
**Pr:* Jerry Blann
COO: Ned Wonson
Ofcr: Scott Horn
VP: Jessica Milligan
Comm Man: Anna Cole
Off Mgr: Trisha Taggart
Dir IT: Tobias Guttormson

D-U-N-S 03-405-4098
JACKSON HOSPITAL & CLINIC INC
1725 Pine St, Montgomery, AL 36106-1117
Tel (334) 293-8000 *Founded/Ownrshp* 1949
Sales 201.8MM *EMP* 1,400
SIC 8062 General medical & surgical hospitals
CEO: Joe B Riley
Pr: Larry Sherbett
**CFO:* Paul Peiffer
Trst: George Handey
Trst: Glenn Yates
VP: Richard Caldwell
**VP:* Sharon Goodison
**VP:* Michael James
**VP:* Janet McQueen
VP: Peter Verrecchia
Ex Dir: AGA Afgan

D-U-N-S 12-622-2400
■ **JACKSON HOSPITAL CORP**
REGIONAL HOSPITAL OF JACKSON
(*Suby of* QUORUM HEALTH CORP) ★
367 Hospital Blvd, Jackson, TN 38305-2080
Tel (731) 661-2000 *Founded/Ownrshp* 2016
Sales 92.6MM *EMP* 643^E
SIC 8062 General medical & surgical hospitals
CEO: Thomas D Miller
COO: Martin D Smith
CFO: Michael J Culotta
Chf Mktg O: Shaheed Koury

D-U-N-S 04-214-0483
JACKSON LABORATORY
600 Main St, Bar Harbor, ME 04609-1500
Tel (207) 288-6000 *Founded/Ownrshp* 1929
Sales 274.5MM *EMP* 1,300
SIC 8733 Noncommercial research organizations
CEO: Edison T Liu
**COO:* Charles E Hewett
**CFO:* Linda Jensen
CFO: M S Linda
CFO: Janice Vonbrook
CFO: Lee Willur
**Ch:* Brian Wruble
**Treas:* Edward Sameck
Bd of Dir: Alan D Macewan
Sr VP: Yun Wang
**VP:* Robert Braun
VP: James Fahey
**VP:* Michael E Hyde
VP: Luke Krebs
VP: Carol Lamb
VP: Kristen Rozansky
VP: Abigail Smith
Exec: Cathleen Lutz
Dir Lab: Kenneth Paigen
Assoc Dir: Ann G Burns
Assoc Dir: Wenning Qin

JACKSON LEWIS
See LEWIS P C JACKSON

D-U-N-S 11-829-8673
JACKSON MEMORIAL HOSPITAL
UHEALTH
1611 Nw 12th Ave, Miami, FL 33136-1096
Tel (305) 585-1111 *Founded/Ownrshp* 1997
Sales 883.0MM *EMP* 11,000^E
SIC 8062 General medical & surgical hospitals
Ch: Michael Kosnitzky
V Ch: John H Copeland
V Ch: Angel Medina
COO: Jerald Kaiser
COO: David R Small
CFO: Frank J J Barrett
CFO: Brian Dean
CFO: Mark Knight
Treas: Marcos J Lapciuc
**Treas:* Andres Murai Jr
Trst: Jorge L Arrizurieta
Trst: Joaquin Del Cueto
Trst: Ernesto A De La F
Trst: Nilda Peragallo
Trst: Dorrin D Rolle
Trst: Martin G Zilber
Ofcr: Theresa Wilson
Ex VP: Michael Butler
Ex VP: Steven Klein
VP: Abbe Bendel
VP: Ric Cuming

D-U-N-S 07-871-4921
JACKSON NATIONAL LIFE DISTRIBUTORS LLC
JNLD
(*Suby of* JACKSON NATIONAL LIFE INSURANCE CO INC) ★
7601 E Technology Way, Denver, CO 80237-3003
Tel (303) 488-3518 *Founded/Ownrshp* 2003
Sales NA *EMP* 826^E
SIC 6311 Life insurance carriers
Pr: Greg P Cicotte
Chf Cred: Daniel Wright
**Ex VP:* Clifford James Jack
Sr VP: Kevin Grant
**Sr VP:* Alison Reed
**VP:* Doug Mantelli
VP: David Thaxter
VP: Jack Zadigian
VP: Aron Zierdt
Sales Asso: Kenneth Garon

D-U-N-S 00-886-7897
JACKSON NATIONAL LIFE INSURANCE CO INC
(*Suby of* PRUDENTIAL PUBLIC LIMITED COMPANY)
1 Corporate Way, Lansing, MI 48951-1001
Tel (517) 381-5500 *Founded/Ownrshp* 1986
Sales NA *EMP* 3,500
SIC 6311 6282 6211 6411

D-U-N-S 00-402-2689 EXP
JACKSON NORTH MEDICAL CENTER
160 Nw 170th St, North Miami Beach, FL 33169-5576
Tel (305) 651-1100 *Founded/Ownrshp* 2006
Sales 25.2MM^E *EMP* 11,000^E
SIC 8011 8062 Medical centers; General medical & surgical hospitals
Dir Lab: Masoud Ketabchi
Pr: Jose Nunez
Dir Lab: Sherline Manzo
Dir Lab: Tracy Urruela
Dir Lab: Isis Zambrana
Sfty Dirs: Patricia Batchelder
Opers Mgr: Rogelio Borroto
Ansthlgy: Sarita Sharma

D-U-N-S 79-647-1980
JACKSON NURSE PROFESSIONALS LLC
(*Suby of* JACKSON HEALTHCARE LLC) ★
3452 Lake Lynda Dr # 200, Orlando, FL 32817-1481
Tel (205) 968-7500 *Founded/Ownrshp* 2006
Sales 85.0MM *EMP* 420
SIC 7363 Help supply services
Prin: Brett Doll
Genl Mgr: Pat Olear

D-U-N-S 07-597-3289
JACKSON OIL & SOLVENTS INC
JOES JUNCTION
1970 Kentucky Ave, Indianapolis, IN 46221-1914
Tel (317) 481-2244 *Founded/Ownrshp* 1979
Sales 109.1MM^E *EMP* 95
SIC 5172 5541 5983 5531 Gasoline; Fuel oil; Filling stations, gasoline; Fuel oil dealers; Automobile & truck equipment & parts
Pr: Monica S Heath
VP: Nathan Keith
VP: Ron Willis

D-U-N-S 00-820-2137 IMP
JACKSON PAPER CO
NEWELL PAPER CO OF COLUMBUS
4400 Mangum Dr, Flowood, MS 39232-2113
Tel (800) 844-5449 *Founded/Ownrshp* 1921
Sales 118.6MM^E *EMP* 195
Accts Swain Buckalwe & Collins Pa
SIC 5111 5113 5087 Fine paper; Paper & products, wrapping or coarse; Service establishment equipment; Janitors' supplies
Ch: Tommy Galyean
**Pr:* Noel Machost
**Sec:* Brenda Bernhard

JACKSON PARK HOSP & MED CTR
See JACKSON PARK HOSPITAL FOUNDATION

D-U-N-S 06-848-3981
JACKSON PARK HOSPITAL FOUNDATION (IL)
JACKSON PARK HOSP & MED CTR
7531 S Stony Island Ave # 1, Chicago, IL 60649-3954
Tel (773) 947-7500 *Founded/Ownrshp* 1960, 1959
Sales 112.5MM *EMP* 700
SIC 8062 General medical & surgical hospitals
Pr: Merritt J Hasbrouck
Pr: Asif Daud
**CFO:* Nelson Vasquez
Chf Mktg O: Lakshmi Dodda
Sr VP: Vernell Williams
VP: Margo Brooks-Pugh
Dir Lab: Jose Ruiz
Dir Rad: Cardell Gentry
Genl Mgr: Randall Smith
CIO: Thomas Pankow
IT Man: Jim Boland

D-U-N-S 07-944-7611
JACKSON PUBLIC SCHOOL DISTRICT LEASE CORP INC
JACKSON PUBLIC SCHOOLS
662 S President St, Jackson, MS 39201-5601
Tel (601) 960-8921 *Founded/Ownrshp* 1949
Sales 165.9MM^E *EMP* 4,200
SIC 8211 Public elementary & secondary schools
COO: Derick Williams
CFO: Rick Autrey
**CFO:* Michael Thomas
Ex Dir: Vicki Davidson
Ex Dir: Margrit Wallace
Dir Sec: Gerald Jones
MIS Dir: Stephan George
Pr Dir: Sherwin Johnson

JACKSON PUBLIC SCHOOLS
See JACKSON PUBLIC SCHOOL DISTRICT LEASE CORP INC

D-U-N-S 07-635-1543
JACKSON PUBLIC SCHOOLS
522 Wildwood Ave, Jackson, MI 49201-1013
Tel (517) 841-2200 *Founded/Ownrshp* 1876
Sales 43.0MM^E *EMP* 1,035
Accts Plante & Moran Pllc Portage
SIC 8211 Public combined elementary & secondary school; Public adult education school
MIS Dir: Richard Compton
Psych: Eric Baldwin

D-U-N-S 80-865-4479
JACKSON RANCHERIA CASINO & HOTEL
JACKSON RNCHERIA CASINO RESORT
12222 New York Ranch Rd, Jackson, CA 95642-9407
Tel (209) 223-1677 *Founded/Ownrshp* 1991
Sales 50.1MM^E *EMP* 1,000
SIC 7999 5812 7011 5813 Bingo hall; Game parlor; Eating places; Hotels & motels; Drinking places
Ch Bd: Margaret Dalton
Genl Mgr: Michael Turngren
IT Man: Carol Olney

JACKSON RNCHERIA CASINO RESORT
See JACKSON RANCHERIA CASINO & HOTEL

D-U-N-S 04-450-7085
JACKSON STATE UNIVERSITY
JSU
1400 J R Lynch St Ste 206, Jackson, MS 39217-0001
Tel (601) 979-2121 *Founded/Ownrshp* 1877
Sales 164.8MM^E *EMP* 2,000
SIC 8221 College, except junior
Pr: Ronald Mason Jr
Ofcr: Joseph Bradley
Ofcr: Detra Ward
**Ex VP:* Willie G Brown
VP: David Howard
VP: Felix Okojie
Assoc Dir: Timothy Abram
Assoc Dir: Donna Antoine-Lavigne
Dir Soc: Brenda Manuel
Comm Dir: Willie Foster
Ex Dir: Debra Buchanan

D-U-N-S 18-456-1611 IMP
JACKSON SUPPLY CO
JSC
6655 Roxburgh Dr Ste 100, Houston, TX 77041-5210
Tel (713) 849-5865 *Founded/Ownrshp* 1990
Sales 94.9MM^E *EMP* 85
SIC 5075 Air conditioning & ventilation equipment & supplies
Pr: Darla D Chakkalakal
**Ch:* James J Durrett
**Sec:* Tina Syzdek

JACKSON TOWNSHIP BOARD EDUCATN
See JACKSON TOWNSHIP SCHOOL DISTRICT

D-U-N-S 10-005-2323
JACKSON TOWNSHIP SCHOOL DISTRICT
JACKSON TOWNSHIP BOARD EDUCATN
151 Don Connor Blvd, Jackson, NJ 08527-3407
Tel (732) 833-4600 *Founded/Ownrshp* 1924
Sales 69.2MM^E *EMP* 1,114
Accts Suplee Clooney & Company Wes
SIC 8211 Public elementary school; Public junior high school; Public senior high school
**CFO:* Michelle Richardson
IT Man: Lincoln Mahabir
Schl Brd P: Barbara Fiero

D-U-N-S 08-073-8628
JACKSON WALKER LLP (TX)
J W
2323 Ross Ave Ste 600, Dallas, TX 75201-2725
Tel (214) 953-6000 *Founded/Ownrshp* 2008
Sales 116.2MM^E *EMP* 650
SIC 8111 General practice law office
Pt: C Wade Cooper
Pt: Howard Baskin
Pt: Carl C Butzer
Pt: Alan N Greenspan
Pt: Phillip R Jones
Pt: David Laney
Pt: Larry Langley
**Pt:* David T Moran
Pt: J S Rose
Pr: Sharon Stokes
Pr: Diane D Watters
**CFO:* Richard A Herlan

D-U-N-S 06-165-4513
JACKSON-MADISON COUNTY GENERAL HOSPITAL DISTRICT
WEST TENNESSEE HEALTH CARE
620 Skyline Dr, Jackson, TN 38301-3923
Tel (731) 541-5000 *Founded/Ownrshp* 1950
Sales 554.3MM *EMP* 5,000
SIC 8062 General medical & surgical hospitals
Pr: Bobby Arnold
COO: James Ross
**CFO:* Jeffrey Blankenship
**Ch:* Phil Bryant
Dir Rx: Sherry Osborne
Ex Dir: Damon Mays
Ex Dir: Bart Teague
Mng Dir: Jerry Barker
Off Mgr: Marva Sain
IT Man: Currie Higgs
Software D: Vickie Campbell

D-U-N-S 78-945-8010
JACKSON-MADISON COUNTY SCHOOL SYSTEM
310 N Parkway, Jackson, TN 38305-2712
Tel (731) 664-2500 *Founded/Ownrshp* 2006
Sales 114.7MM^E *EMP* 2,000
SIC 8211 Public elementary & secondary schools
IT Man: Holly Kellar
Pr Dir: Ginger Carver
Teacher Pr: Tiffany Green
HC Dir: Annette Wilson

D-U-N-S 16-153-9903
JACKSONS FOOD STORES INC
3450 E Commercial Ct, Meridian, ID 83642-8915
Tel (208) 888-6061 *Founded/Ownrshp* 1975
Sales 389.1MM^E *EMP* 1,000
SIC 5541 5411 Filling stations, gasoline; Convenience stores
Pr: John D Jackson
**Treas:* Jason Manning
Rgnl Mgr: Brody Kesler-Mauch
Dist Mgr: Toni Smith

JACKSONVILLE SHERIFFS OFFICE
See CITY OF JACKSONVILLE

D-U-N-S 07-831-4903
JACKSONVILLE UNIVERSITY
JACKSONVILLE UNIVERSITY DORMIT
2800 University Blvd N, Jacksonville, FL 32211-3394
Tel (904) 256-8000 *Founded/Ownrshp* 1934
Sales 119.2MM *EMP* 450
Accts Crowe Horwath Llp Tampa Fl
SIC 8221 University
Pr: Kerry D Romesburg
Treas: Charles Wodehouse
Ofcr: Erin McFeely
Ofcr: Wenying Xu
**VP:* Timothy Payne
VP: Gil Pomar Jr
Assoc Dir: David Stout
IT Man: Andrew Lee
IT Man: Dax Peters
Pgrm Dir: Christine Sapienza

JACKSONVILLE UNIVERSITY DORMIT
See JACKSONVILLE UNIVERSITY

D-U-N-S 83-127-4233 IMP
JACKTHREADS INC
(*Suby of* THRILLIST.COM) ★
568 Broadway Rm 607, New York, NY 10012-3260
Tel (646) 786-1980 *Founded/Ownrshp* 2005
Sales 136.2MM^E *EMP* 99^E
SIC 5136 Men's & boys' clothing

D-U-N-S 06-459-2611 IMP
JACMAR COMPANIES
SHAKEY'S PIZZA
300 Baldwin Park Blvd, City of Industry, CA 91746-1405
Tel (800) 834-8806 *Founded/Ownrshp* 1960
Sales 699.3MM^E *EMP* 900
SIC 5141 5812 6552 Groceries, general line; Fast-food restaurant, chain; Land subdividers & developers, commercial
Pr: James A Dal Pozzo
Ch Bd: William Tilley
CFO: David Reid
VP: Sonia Barajas
VP: Robert Hill
VP: Victor Santillan
IT Man: Amy Gehrig

D-U-N-S 08-689-3815 IMP
JACMEL JEWELRY INC (NY)
1385 Broadway Fl 8, New York, NY 10018-2102
Tel (718) 349-4300 *Founded/Ownrshp* 1977
Sales 100.0MM *EMP* 200^E
SIC 3911 Medals, precious or semiprecious metal
Pr: Jack Rahmey
CFO: Robert Passaro
Treas: Evan Barkley
VP: Morris Dweck

D-U-N-S 96-216-4125
JACO ENVIRONMENTAL INC
APPLIANCE RECYCLING OUTLET
18323 Bothell Everett Hwy # 110, Bothell, WA 98012-5246
Tel (425) 398-6200 *Founded/Ownrshp* 1999
Sales 102.7MM^E *EMP* 420
SIC 8748

D-U-N-S 06-120-1625
JACO HILL CO
4960 Adobe Rd, Twentynine Palms, CA 92277-1612
Tel (760) 361-1407 *Founded/Ownrshp* 2001
Sales 217.3MM *EMP* 4^E
Accts Moss Adams Llp Los Angeles C
SIC 5171 Petroleum bulk stations & terminals
Prin: Dan Jaco

D-U-N-S 05-642-0318
JACO OIL CO
3101 State Rd, Bakersfield, CA 93308-4931
Tel (661) 393-7000 *Founded/Ownrshp* 1970
Sales 442.7MM *EMP* 350
Accts Moss-Adams Llp Los Angeles C
SIC 5541 Filling stations, gasoline
CEO: T J Jamieson
**CFO:* Brian Busacca
**Sec:* Lee Jamieson
**VP:* Charles Mc Can
Area Supr: Ron Jonas

JACOB K JAVITS CONVENTION CTR
See NEW YORK CONVENTION CENTER OPERATING CORP

D-U-N-S 00-791-4922 IMP/EXP
JACOB STERN & SONS INC (PA)
ACME-HARDESTY CO.
1464 E Valley Rd, Santa Barbara, CA 93108-1241
Tel (805) 565-4532 *Founded/Ownrshp* 1857
Sales 98.5MM^E *EMP* 100
SIC 5169 5191 5199 Chemicals & allied products; Animal feeds; Greases, animal or vegetable
Pr: Phillip L Bernstein
Pr: Jeff Kenton
CEO: Doug Shreves
CFO: Chip Hull
VP: Jeff Peeler
Brnch Mgr: Jim Mazich
Dir IT: Dale Polekoff
QC Dir: Chris Lopez

D-U-N-S 00-336-6135 EXP
■ **JACOBS APPLIED TECHNOLOGY INC**
(*Suby of* JACOBS ENGINEERING GROUP INC) ★
2040 Bushy Park Rd, Goose Creek, SC 29445
Tel (843) 824-1100 *Founded/Ownrshp* 1945, 1990
Sales 133.1MM^E *EMP* 500
SIC 3559 3443 8711 1629 Petroleum refinery equipment; Vessels, process or storage (from boiler shops): metal plate; Petroleum, mining & chemical engineers; Industrial plant construction
Pr: Dan Gaa
Treas: John W Prosser Jr
Board of Directors: W R Kerler, Noel G Watson

JACOBS, BILL BMW
See BILL JACOBS MOTORSPORT HOLDINGS INC

D-U-N-S 05-712-0941
■ **JACOBS CONSTRUCTORS INC**
(*Suby of* JACOBS ENGINEERING GROUP INC) ★
4949 Essen Ln, Baton Rouge, LA 70809-3433
Tel (225) 769-7700 *Founded/Ownrshp* 1977
Sales 91.8MM^E *EMP* 500
SIC 1629 Industrial plant construction
VP: R Terry Jones
**Treas:* J W Prosser Jr

D-U-N-S 06-382-5236
■ **JACOBS ENGINEERING CO**
(*Suby of* JACOBS ENGINEERING GROUP INC) ★
1111 S Arroyo Pkwy, Pasadena, CA 91105-3254
Tel (626) 449-2171 *Founded/Ownrshp* 1979
Sales 98.4MM^E *EMP* 4,000
SIC 8711 1629 Engineering services; Chemical plant & refinery construction
CEO: Noel G Watson
**Pr:* C L Martin

D-U-N-S 07-410-3508 IMP/EXP
▲ **JACOBS ENGINEERING GROUP INC**
1999 Bryan St Ste 1200, Dallas, TX 75201-6823
Tel (214) 583-8500 *Founded/Ownrshp* 1947
Sales 10.9MMM *EMP* 64,000
Tkr Sym JEC *Exch* NYS
SIC 8711 1629 1541 8748 Engineering services; Construction & civil engineering; Building construction consultant; Industrial plant construction; Chemical plant & refinery construction; Oil refinery construction; Waste disposal plant construction; Industrial buildings & warehouses; Pharmaceutical manufacturing plant construction; Industrial buildings, new construction; Systems analysis & engineering consulting services; Systems analysis or design
Pr: Steven J Demetriou
Pr: Terence D Hagen
Pr: Andrew F Kremer
Pr: Joseph G Mandel
CFO: Kevin C Berryman
Bd of Dir: Julie Ellis
Div VP: Patrick McFarlin
Sr VP: William Benton Allen Jr
Sr VP: Cora L Carmody
Sr VP: Lori S Sundberg
Sr VP: Michael R Tyler
VP: Harry Breeden
VP: Dan Campagna
VP: Jannette Funderburk
VP: Michelle Jones
VP: Randy Lycans
VP: Keith McConnell
VP: Tom Nielsen
VP: Robert Norfleet
VP: Randy Walker
VP Bus Dev: Philip Luna
Board of Directors: Noel G Watson, Joseph R Bronson, Juan Jose Suarez Coppel, John F Coyne, Robert C Davidson Jr, Ralph E Eberhart, Dawne S Hickton, Linda Fayne Levinson, Peter J Robertson, Christopher M T Thompson

D-U-N-S 96-649-2188
JACOBS ENGINEERING GROUP MEDICAL PLAN TRUST
300 Frank H Ogawa Plz # 10, Oakland, CA 94612-2037
Tel (510) 457-0027 *Founded/Ownrshp* 2011
Sales 144.8MM *EMP* 2
SIC 8711 Engineering services

D-U-N-S 83-175-8359
■ **JACOBS ENGINEERING INC**
(*Suby of* JACOBS ENGINEERING GROUP INC) ★
155 N Lake Ave, Pasadena, CA 91101-1849
Tel (626) 578-3500 *Founded/Ownrshp* 1971
Sales 164.8MM^E *EMP* 748^E
SIC 8711 Engineering services
CEO: Craig L Martin
Dir IT: Gregory Gassett
IT Man: Mark Wishart
Netwrk Mgr: John Pratt

D-U-N-S 10-346-6004
JACOBS ENTERTAINMENT INC
(*Suby of* JACOBS INVESTMENTS INC) ★
17301 W Colfax Ave # 250, Golden, CO 80401-4891
Tel (303) 215-5196 *Founded/Ownrshp* 2001
Sales 98.0MM^E *EMP* 1,800^E
SIC 7993 7948 Coin-operated amusement devices; Horse race track operation
Ch Bd: Jeffrey P Jacobs
**Ch Bd:* Jeffrey Jacobs
**Pr:* Stephen R Roark
**COO:* Michael T Shubic
**CFO:* Brent Kramer
**Ex VP:* Emanuel J Cotronakis
VP: Dave Grunenwald
VP: Stan Guidroz
VP: Michael Shubic
Mktg Dir: Meera Rosser

D-U-N-S 80-581-7798
■ **JACOBS FACILITIES INC**
(*Suby of* JACOBS ENGINEERING GROUP INC) ★
501 N Broadway, Saint Louis, MO 63102-2131
Tel (314) 335-4000 *Founded/Ownrshp* 1999
Sales 420.7MM *EMP* 2,047
Accts Ernst & Young Llp Los Angeles
SIC 8712 8711 8713 8741 1542 1541 Architectural services; Architectural engineering; Engineering services; Civil engineering; Surveying services; Management services; Nonresidential construction; Industrial buildings & warehouses
Pr: Craig Martin
**VP:* Warren M Dean
**VP:* H Thomas Mc Duffie
**VP:* James J Scott
Netwrk Mgr: Kevin V Dickens
Mktg Dir: Stephanie Crouch

D-U-N-S 05-934-5124
■ **JACOBS FIELD SERVICES NORTH AMERICA INC**
(*Suby of* JACOBS ENGINEERING GROUP INC) ★
5995 Rogerdale Rd, Houston, TX 77072-1601
Tel (832) 351-6000 *Founded/Ownrshp* 1978
Sales 361.9MM^E *EMP* 2,300
SIC 8711 Engineering services; Electrical or electronic engineering
Pr: James E Dixon
**Treas:* John W Prosser Jr
**VP:* Walter Lisiewski

D-U-N-S 09-277-8182
JACOBS INDUSTRIES INC
JACOBS INTERACTIVE
8096 Excelsior Blvd, Hopkins, MN 55343-3415
Tel (612) 339-9500 *Founded/Ownrshp* 1977
Sales 89.9MM^E *EMP* 440
SIC 2841 2087 2099 2844 5084 6794 Detergents, synthetic organic or inorganic alkaline; Scouring compounds; Extracts, flavoring; Spices, including grinding; Toilet preparations; Printing trades machinery, equipment & supplies; Franchises, selling or licensing
Pr: Irwin Jacobs
CFO: David A Mahler
Exec: Patricia Jensen

JACOBS INTERACTIVE
See JACOBS INDUSTRIES INC

D-U-N-S 82-541-5359
■ **JACOBS INTERNATIONAL LTD INC**
(*Suby of* JACOBS ENGINEERING GROUP INC) ★
155 N Lake Ave, Pasadena, CA 91101-1849
Tel (626) 578-3500 *Founded/Ownrshp* 2002
Sales 85.0MM *EMP* 300
SIC 8711 Engineering services
Pr: Craig Martin
**Treas:* John W Prosser Jr
Sr VP: Bruce Mills
**VP:* Jeff Sanders

D-U-N-S 16-565-4109
JACOBS INVESTMENTS INC
11770 Us Highway 1 # 600, North Palm Beach, FL 33408-3032
Tel (561) 776-6050 *Founded/Ownrshp* 1975
Sales 182.7MM^E *EMP* 1,800^E
SIC 6211 7011 Investment firm, general brokerage; Casino hotel
Ch Bd: Jeffrey P Jacobs
CFO: Tom Hamilton

D-U-N-S 16-816-3017 IMP
■ **JACOBS P&C US INC**
(*Suby of* JACOBS ENGINEERING GROUP INC) ★
3600 Briarpark Dr, Houston, TX 77042-5206
Tel (713) 988-2002 *Founded/Ownrshp* 2013
Sales 152.3MM^E *EMP* 1,700^E
SIC 1629 Power plant construction
CEO: Inge Hansen
**Pr:* Craig L Martin
CFO: Dieter Shcheer
Sr VP: Dane Osborn
**VP:* Andrew Kremer
**VP:* Keith Vecchini
IT Man: Louis Caplan
IT Man: Jean Chessher
S&M/VP: Donna Rougeaux

D-U-N-S 14-453-3655
JACOBS PRIVATE EQUITY LLC
350 Round Hill Rd, Greenwich, CT 06831-3343
Tel (203) 413-4000 *Founded/Ownrshp* 2003
Sales 288.0MM^E *EMP* 10,400^E
SIC 4731 6282 6726 Freight transportation arrangement; Investment advisory service; Investment offices

D-U-N-S 00-792-3014
■ **JACOBS TECHNOLOGY INC** (TN)
(*Suby of* JACOBS ENGINEERING GROUP INC) ★
600 William Northern Blvd, Tullahoma, TN 37388-4729
Tel (931) 455-6400 *Founded/Ownrshp* 1980, 1999
Sales 4.0MMM^E *EMP* 11,000
SIC 8711 Aviation &/or aeronautical engineering
Pr: Robert Norfleet
Treas: John Prosser Jr
Ofcr: Jeffrey Clark
VP: Ken Burk
VP: Patrick Campbell
Prgrm Mgr: Mark Henscheid
Snr Sftwr: Randy Bone
IT Man: Donald Kinser
IT Man: Glen Ward
IT Man: Will Watson
Sftwr Eng: Nadean King

D-U-N-S 00-132-8772 IMP/EXP
■ **JACOBS VEHICLE SYSTEMS INC**
JAKE BRAKE
(*Suby of* FORTIVE CORP) ★
22 E Dudley Town Rd, Bloomfield, CT 06002-1440
Tel (860) 243-5222 *Founded/Ownrshp* 2016
Sales 118.4MM^E *EMP* 420
SIC 3519 Engines, diesel & semi-diesel or dual-fuel
Pr: Sergio Sgarbi
CFO: Chris Mulhall
Treas: Frank T McFaden
Treas: Kevin Potts
VP: Joao John Cullen
VP: Sebastian Hatch
VP: Robert Perkins
Genl Couns: Ann Schmidt

D-U-N-S 00-385-0856
JACOBSEN CONSTRUCTION CO INC
3131 W 2210 S, Salt Lake City, UT 84119-1267
Tel (801) 973-0500 *Founded/Ownrshp* 1998
Sales 260.9MM^E *EMP* 485
SIC 1542 1541 Commercial & office building, new construction; Industrial buildings, new construction
Pr: Douglas C Welling
COO: Jim Cavey
Ex VP: Doug Welling
VP: Kirk Dickamore
VP: Gary Ellis
VP: Gale Mair
VP: Jon Moody
VP: Matt Rich
VP: Jack Wixom
VP: Terry Wright
Exec: Matt Radke
Creative D: Dustin Smith
Comm Dir: Kareen Openshaw

JACOBSON COMPANIES
See JHCI HOLDINGS INC

D-U-N-S 95-746-4670
JACOBSON TRANSPORTATION CO INC
(*Suby of* JHCI ACQUISITION INC) ★
1275 Nw 128th St, Clive, IA 50325-7403
Tel (515) 262-1236 *Founded/Ownrshp* 1986
Sales 135.3MM^E *EMP* 300^E
SIC 4213 4731 Trucking, except local; Freight transportation arrangement
Ch Bd: Brian Lutt
**Pr:* Scott Temple
**CFO:* Jack Ingle
Sec: Marty Howard
Board of Directors: Ted Dardani, John Rachwalski

D-U-N-S 04-561-7883
JACOBSON WAREHOUSE CO INC
XPO LOGISTICS
(*Suby of* JHCI ACQUISITION INC) ★
3811 Dixon St, Des Moines, IA 50313-3907
Tel (515) 265-6171 *Founded/Ownrshp* 1968
Sales 808.7MM^E *EMP* 1,500
SIC 4226 4221 4225 8741 6552 4783 Special warehousing & storage; Farm product warehousing & storage; General warehousing & storage; Management services; Subdividers & developers; Packing & crating
Co-Pr: Tony Tegnelia
Ofcr: Marty Howard
Ofcr: Jack Ingle
Ofcr: Gordon Smith
Off Mgr: Carla Rees
CIO: Brian Kautz
Opers Mgr: Teresa Loffredo
Board of Directors: Ted Dardani, John Rachwalski

D-U-N-S 02-339-8191
JACOBUS ENERGY INC
QUICK FLASH FUEL
11815 W Bradley Rd, Milwaukee, WI 53224-2532
Tel (414) 577-0217 *Founded/Ownrshp* 1919
Sales 138.4MM^E *EMP* 259
SIC 5983 5172 Fuel oil dealers; Petroleum products
Pr: Eugene Jacobus
**CEO:* Chuck Jacobus Jr
**Treas:* Bob Heicher
**Ex VP:* Fred J Regenfuss
Sls Mgr: Cameron Walker

D-U-N-S 83-652-0882
■ **JACOR BROADCASTING OF COLORADO INC**
CLEAR CHANNEL
(*Suby of* IHEARTCOMMUNICATIONS INC) ★
4695 S Monaco St, Denver, CO 80237-3525
Tel (303) 631-2933 *Founded/Ownrshp* 1987
Sales 8.0MMM *EMP* 285
SIC 7313 Radio advertising representative
VP: Lee Larsen
**VP:* Pat Connors
Exec: Lorilynn Barker
Dir IT: Jeff Archer
Sls Dir: Tim Hager

D-U-N-S 07-770-8618 IMP
JACQUES MORET INC
MORET GROUP, THE
1411 Broadway Fl 8, New York, NY 10018-3565
Tel (212) 354-2400 *Founded/Ownrshp* 2002
Sales 300.0MM *EMP* 250^E
SIC 2339 5137 Women's & misses' athletic clothing & sportswear; Sportswear, women's & children's
Ch Bd: Ralph Harary
**Pr:* Joey Harary
CFO: Mark A Lopiparo
**Treas:* Jack Beyda
**VP:* Allan Sassoon

D-U-N-S 15-412-9563 IMP
JACUZZI BRANDS LLC
JACUZZI GROUP WORLDWIDE
13925 City Center Dr # 200, Chino Hills, CA 91709-5437
Tel (909) 606-1416 *Founded/Ownrshp* 1995
Sales 1.4MMM^E *EMP* 4,907
SIC 3842 Whirlpool baths, hydrotherapy equipment
CEO: Robert Rowen
**Pr:* Alex P Marini
Pr: Peter Munk
Pr: Robert I Rowan
**CFO:* David Broadbent
**CFO:* Dave Hellman
**CFO:* Jeffrey B Park
**Sr VP:* Steven C Barre
**Sr VP:* Marie S Dreher
Sr VP: Dorothy E Sander
VP: Todd Adams
VP: Francisco V Pu Al
**VP:* Diana E Burton
VP: Edmund L Krainski
VP: Howard Lederman
VP: Lillian C Macia
VP: Patricia Whaley

JACUZZI GROUP WORLDWIDE
See JACUZZI BRANDS LLC

D-U-N-S 00-634-0798 EXP
JACUZZI INC
JACUZZI OUTDOOR PRODUCTS
(*Suby of* JACUZZI GROUP WORLDWIDE) ★
14525 Monte Vista Ave, Chino, CA 91710-5721
Tel (909) 606-7733 *Founded/Ownrshp* 1989
Sales 600.7MM^E *EMP* 4,018
SIC 3088 3589 Plastics plumbing fixtures; Hot tubs, plastic or fiberglass; Tubs (bath, shower & laundry), plastic; Shower stalls, fiberglass & plastic; Swimming pool filter & water conditioning systems
CEO: Thomas Koos
**Ch Bd:* Roy A Jacuzzi
**Pr:* Donald C Devine

JACUZZI OUTDOOR PRODUCTS
See JACUZZI INC

D-U-N-S 00-914-0005 IMP
JACUZZI WHIRLPOOL BATH INC
(*Suby of* JACUZZI OUTDOOR PRODUCTS) ★
14525 Monte Vista Ave, Chino, CA 91710-5721
Tel (909) 606-1416 *Founded/Ownrshp* 1987
Sales 106.4MM^E *EMP* 800
SIC 3088 Tubs (bath, shower & laundry), plastic; Hot tubs, plastic or fiberglass
CEO: Thomas D Koos
**Pr:* Philip Weeks
Dir IT: Jeff Castillo

D-U-N-S 08-610-2316 IMP
JAE ELECTRONICS INC (CA)
(*Suby of* JAPAN AVIATION ELECTRONICS INDUSTRY, LIMITED)
142 Technology Dr Ste 100, Irvine, CA 92618-2430
Tel (949) 753-2600 *Founded/Ownrshp* 1977
Sales 161.4MM *EMP* 180
Accts Kakimoto Nagashima
SIC 5065 5088 3679 3829 3678 Connectors, electronic; Aircraft & space vehicle supplies & parts; Electronic circuits; Measuring & controlling devices; Electronic connectors

CEO: Noboru Norose
**Pr:* Shinsuke Takahashi
Genl Mgr: Glen Griffin
IT Man: Ira Shankar
Plnt Mgr: Antonio Serra
Sls Dir: Shawn O'Callaghan
Mktg Mgr: Mark Saubert
Manager: George Coddington
Sls Mgr: Steve Black

JAFFE BOOK SOLUTIONS
See GL GROUP INC

JAG COMPANIES
See NORTHEAST REMSCO CONSTRUCTION INC

D-U-N-S 07-916-9169
JAG COMPANIES INC
1433 State Route 34 Ste 5, Wall Township, NJ 07727-1613
Tel (732) 557-6100 *Founded/Ownrshp* 2010
Sales 159.1MM^E *EMP* 452
SIC 1623 1622 1629 1611 Water, sewer & utility lines; Bridge construction; Land clearing contractor; General contractor, highway & street construction
Owner: Juan A Gutierrez
CFO: Marco Afonso
**Prin:* Marco Guttierrez

D-U-N-S 02-257-7499
JAG FOOTWEAR ACCESSORIES AND RETAIL CORP
ENZO ANGIOLINI
(*Suby of* CAMUTO GROUP) ★
411 W Putnam Ave Fl 3, Greenwich, CT 06830-6261
Tel (239) 301-3001 *Founded/Ownrshp* 2016
Sales 100.0MM *EMP* 25
SIC 5139 Footwear
CEO: Alex Delcielo
**CFO:* Jeff Howald
**VP:* Chris D'Elia

D-U-N-S 13-726-0399 IMP
JAG FOOTWEAR ACCESSORIES AND RETAIL CORP
180 Rittenhouse Cir, Bristol, PA 19007-1618
Tel (215) 785-4000 *Founded/Ownrshp* 1983
Sales NA *EMP* 6,370
SIC 5621

D-U-N-S 04-633-9081
JAGUAR CARS INC
(*Suby of* JAGUAR CARS LIMITED)
555 Macarthur Blvd, Mahwah, NJ 07430-2327
Tel (201) 818-8500 *Founded/Ownrshp* 1989
Sales 100.4MM^E *EMP* 222
SIC 5012 5013 Automobiles & other motor vehicles; Automotive supplies & parts; Automotive supplies
Ch Bd: Nicholas V Scheele
**Pr:* Michael H Dale
VP: Richard N Beattie
VP: John G Crawford
VP: George J Frame
VP: Dale Gambill
IT Man: Ben Weiner
Board of Directors: John Edwards

JAGUAR CREDIT
See PRIMUS AUTOMOTIVE FINANCIAL SERVICES INC

JAKE BRAKE
See JACOBS VEHICLE SYSTEMS INC

JAKES CRAWFISH & SEAFOOD
See PACIFIC SEA FOOD CO INC

JAKE'S DISTRIBUTING COMPANY
See JAKES INC

D-U-N-S 00-973-6653 IMP
JAKES INC
JAKE'S DISTRIBUTING COMPANY
13400 Hollister Dr, Houston, TX 77086-1218
Tel (713) 868-1301 *Founded/Ownrshp* 1946
Sales 151.2MM^E *EMP* 140^E
SIC 5144 5142 5141 Eggs; Packaged frozen goods; Food brokers
Pr: Leonard M Bench
**CFO:* Michael C Bench
**Sec:* Patsy Sakowitz
Sr VP: Sam Sakowitz
**VP:* Kevin P Ullrich
IT Man: Ben Nguyen
Opers Mgr: Tony Anthony
Sls Mgr: Shane Childers
Sls Mgr: Brian Gosline
Snr Mgr: Kenny Goldstein

D-U-N-S 92-877-9826
▲ JAKKS PACIFIC INC
2951 28th St Ste 51, Santa Monica, CA 90405-2961
Tel (424) 268-9444 *Founded/Ownrshp* 1995
Sales 745.7MM *EMP* 775^E
Accts Bdo Usa Llp Los Angeles Cal
Tkr Sym JAKK *Exch* NGS
SIC 3944 Games, toys & children's vehicles
Pr: Stephen G Berman
COO: John J McGrath
CFO: Joel M Bennett
Board of Directors: Michael J Gross, Rex H Poulsen, Alexander Shoghi, Michael S Sitrick, Murray L Skala

D-U-N-S 09-545-6406 IMP/EXP
JAM DISTRIBUTING CO (TX)
(*Suby of* BRENNTAG NORTHEAST INC) ★
7010 Mykawa Rd, Houston, TX 77033-1132
Tel (713) 844-7788 *Founded/Ownrshp* 1946
Sales 166.7MM^E *EMP* 175
SIC 5172 Petroleum products; Lubricating oils & greases
CEO: Jeffrey Kramer
**CFO:* Richard Vogt
Ex VP: Brian Drake
Dir IT: John Joseph
Opers Mgr: Dan Greenwood
**VP Sls:* John Filak
**VP Sls:* Craig Goodrich
Sls Mgr: Todd Joosten
Sls Mgr: Vernon Reinhardt

Sales Asso: Stewart Johnson
Sales Asso: Brad Kageler

D-U-N-S 00-182-6627 IMP
JAMAICA BEARINGS CO INC (DE)
1700 Jericho Tpke Ste 1, New Hyde Park, NY 11040-4744
Tel (516) 326-1350 *Founded/Ownrshp* 1932, 1935
Sales 93.7MM^E *EMP* 85
SIC 5085 5088 Bearings; Aircraft & space vehicle supplies & parts
Ch Bd: Peter Negri
VP: Scott Carpenter
Prgrm Mgr: Shelley Johnson
MIS Mgr: Mark Hoffman
QC Dir: Michael Matrazzo
Manager: Wayne Rodriguez
Sales Asso: Dave Hufsmith
Sales Asso: Christopher Kozlowski

JAMAICA HOSPITAL
See MEDISYS HEALTH NETWORK INC

D-U-N-S 07-274-0426
JAMAICA HOSPITAL
JAMAICA HOSPITAL MEDICAL CENTE
8900 Van Wyck Expy Fl 4n, Jamaica, NY 11418-2897
Tel (718) 206-6290 *Founded/Ownrshp* 1892
Sales 422.6MM *EMP* 3,251
SIC 8062 General medical & surgical hospitals
CEO: Neil Foster Phillips
Chf Mktg O: Michael Hinck
Ofcr: Joylene Porter
**VP:* Manzar Sassani
Dir Rad: Kiran Chawla
Dir Sec: Charles Neacy
Cmptr Lab: Gloria Bento
IT Man: Alex Umansky
Pathlgst: Sicong Ren
Obsttrcn: Roopam Bhalla
Doctor: Donna Losco
Board of Directors: Ann Corrigan

JAMAICA HOSPITAL MEDICAL CENTE
See JAMAICA HOSPITAL

D-U-N-S 07-956-8179
JAMAICA HOSPITAL MEDICAL CENTER
8900 Van Wyck Expy, Jamaica, NY 11418-2897
Tel (718) 206-6000 *Founded/Ownrshp* 2014
Sales 415.7MM *EMP* 4^E
SIC 8011 Medical centers
CEO: Bruce J Flanz
**Ex VP:* Mounir F Doss
**Ex VP:* William Lynch
**VP:* Sheila Garvey
**VP:* Manzar Sassani

D-U-N-S 04-003-8796
JAMAR CO
ADSCO
(*Suby of* API GROUP INC) ★
4701 Mike Colalillo Dr, Duluth, MN 55807-2762
Tel (218) 628-1027 *Founded/Ownrshp* 1985
Sales 164.5MM *EMP* 200
SIC 1711 1761 1742 5033 7699 3444

D-U-N-S 14-660-1385
▲ JAMBA INC
6475 Christie Ave Ste 150, Emeryville, CA 94608-2259
Tel (510) 596-0100 *Founded/Ownrshp* 1990
Sales 161.6MM *EMP* 1,313
Tkr Sym JMBA *Exch* NGM
SIC 5812 6794 Soft drink stand; Franchises, selling or licensing
CEO: David A Pace
**Ch Bd:* Richard L Federico
Ofcr: Karen L Luey
Sr VP: Steve Adkins
Sr VP: Arnaud Joliff
Sr VP: Julie S Washington
Board of Directors: Michael A Depatie, Lorna C Donatone, Andrew R Heyer, James C Pappas, Glenn W Welling

JAMBA JUICE
See JUICE CLUB INC

D-U-N-S 02-959-4249 IMP
JAMCO AMERICA INC
(*Suby of* JAMCO CORPORATION)
1018 80th St Sw, Everett, WA 98203-6278
Tel (425) 347-4735 *Founded/Ownrshp* 1981
Sales 91.6MM^E *EMP* 350
SIC 3728 Aircraft parts & equipment
Pr: Norikazu Natsume
**VP:* Don Grissitt
**VP:* Masamichi Kato
**VP:* Scott Miller
**VP:* David Nelson
Prgrm Mgr: David Barrat
Prgrm Mgr: Clement Chandrabalan
Prgrm Mgr: Taro Kumashiro
Prgrm Mgr: John Norton
Prgrm Mgr: Joanne Roberts
Prgrm Mgr: Heli Trivedi

JAME COLEMAN CADILLAC
See BETHESDA INVESTMENT HOLDING CO INC

D-U-N-S 05-422-9034
■ JAMES A CUMMINGS INC
CUMMINGS GENERAL CONTRACTORS
(*Suby of* TUTOR PERINI CORP) ★
1 E Broward Blvd Ste 1300, Fort Lauderdale, FL 33301-1865
Tel (954) 484-1532 *Founded/Ownrshp* 2003
Sales 122.4MM *EMP* 114
Accts Deloitte & Touche Llp Los Ang
SIC 1542 1541 Commercial & office building, new construction; Industrial buildings, new construction
Pr: William R Derrer
**VP:* Geoffrey Bunnell
**VP:* Raymond Feuilliez De La
**VP:* Michael F Lanciault
**VP:* Robert Maphis
**VP:* Scott Pat
IT Man: Jonathan Alexander

D-U-N-S 00-812-2764 IMP
JAMES AVERY CRAFTSMAN INC (TX)
145 Avery Rd, Kerrville, TX 78028-7603
Tel (830) 895-6800 *Founded/Ownrshp* 1954
Sales 483.1MM^E *EMP* 1,438
SIC 3911 Jewelry, precious metal; Necklaces, precious metal; Earrings, precious metal; Rings, finger: precious metal
Pr: Christopher M Avery
**CFO:* Geroge Lee
**Ch:* Homer J Avery
**Ex VP:* Paul Avery
CIO: Harsha Bellur
IT Man: Jeremiah Parsons

JAMES B BEAM IMPORT
See JIM BEAM BRANDS CO

D-U-N-S 07-452-9520
JAMES B OSWALD CO
OSWALD COMPANIES, THE
1100 Superior Ave E # 1500, Cleveland, OH 44114-2544
Tel (216) 367-8787 *Founded/Ownrshp* 1970
Sales NA *EMP* 260
SIC 6411

D-U-N-S 07-593-2012
JAMES BROWN CO (GA)
(*Suby of* NCP 2 LP) ★
6908 Chapman Rd, Lithonia, GA 30058-5246
Tel (770) 482-6521 *Founded/Ownrshp* 1970, 2008
Sales 90.1MM^E *EMP* 570
Accts Grant Thornton Llp Atlanta
SIC 4213 Trucking, except local
CEO: Brian Kinsey
**Pr:* James W Brown
**CFO:* Barbara Leasure
**Sec:* Patricia A Brown
VP: Richard Jenkins
Rgnl Mgr: Randy Harris
Trfc Dir: Michael Lepors
Opers Mgr: Kevin Slaughter

JAMES C HUDSON CONSTRUCTION CO
See HUDSON CONSTRUCTION CO

D-U-N-S 13-495-1495
JAMES C JUSTICE COMPANIES INC
302 S Jefferson St # 400, Roanoke, VA 24011-1710
Tel (540) 776-7890 *Founded/Ownrshp* 2003
Sales 117.4MM^E *EMP* 520^E
SIC 6719 Investment holding companies, except banks
Pr: James C Justice II

D-U-N-S 03-733-4179
■ JAMES CONSTRUCTION GROUP LLC
(*Suby of* PRIMORIS SERVICES CORP) ★
18484 E Petroleum Dr, Baton Rouge, LA 70809-6130
Tel (225) 293-0274 *Founded/Ownrshp* 2009
Sales 495.3MM^E *EMP* 1,800^E
SIC 1611 1622 Highway & street construction; Bridge, tunnel & elevated highway
Pr: Danny Hester
**CFO:* Don Bonaventure
CFO: Alfons Theeuwes
**Ex VP:* Mike Killgore

D-U-N-S 07-975-0028
JAMES FORD OF WILLIAMSON LLC
3923 Route 104, Williamson, NY 14589-9592
Tel (800) 246-2000 *Founded/Ownrshp* 2013
Sales 175.0MM *EMP* 20
SIC 5511 Automobiles, new & used

D-U-N-S 09-343-5725
JAMES G PARKER INSURANCE ASSOCIATES
BACOME INSURANCE AGENCY
1753 E Fir Ave, Fresno, CA 93720-3840
Tel (559) 222-7722 *Founded/Ownrshp* 1978
Sales NA *EMP* 160
SIC 6411 Insurance agents
Pr: James G Parker
**Treas:* Janice W Parker
**VP:* Leroy Berrett
VP: John Cleveland
**VP:* Jon Parker
**VP:* Gerald Thompson
**VP:* Danny Todd
Off Mgr: Maureen Beshears
IT Man: Brandon Feemster
Prd Mgr: Megan A Hoover
Prd Mgr: Carrie Stubblefield

D-U-N-S 18-318-6113 IMP/EXP
JAMES HARDIE BUILDING PRODUCTS INC
JAMESHARDIE
(*Suby of* VICTORVILLE INDUSTRIAL MNRL) ★
26300 La Alameda Ste 400, Mission Viejo, CA 92691-8372
Tel (949) 348-1800 *Founded/Ownrshp* 1986
Sales 469.3MM^E *EMP* 400
SIC 5031 Building materials, exterior; Building materials, interior
CEO: Louis Gries
**CFO:* Matthew Marsh
**Treas:* Ginger Lester
**Ex VP:* Mark Fisher
**Ex VP:* Ryan Sullivan
VP: Dave Kessner
**VP:* Sandra Lamartine
Exec: Jamie Gilmer
Area Mgr: Aaron George
Area Mgr: Brian Horstmann
Sys Mgr: Leonard Ludwig

D-U-N-S 17-438-5328 IMP/EXP
JAMES HARDIE TRANSITION CO INC
VICTORVILLE INDUSTRIAL MNRL
(*Suby of* JAMES HARDIE HOLDINGS LIMITED)
26300 La Alameda Ste 400, Mission Viejo, CA 92691-8372
Tel (949) 348-1800 *Founded/Ownrshp* 1986
Sales 499.9MM^E *EMP* 1,300

SIC 3275 3523 3494 5072 Wallboard, gypsum; Fertilizing, spraying, dusting & irrigation machinery; Valves & pipe fittings; Hardware
Pr: Donald N Manson

JAMES HINES ADMINISTRATIVE CTR
See BOARD OF COOPERATIVE EDUCATIONAL SERVICES

D-U-N-S 07-018-6762
JAMES IRVINE FOUNDATION
1 Bush St Fl 8, San Francisco, CA 94104-4414
Tel (415) 777-2244 *Founded/Ownrshp* 1937
Sales 155.6MM *EMP* 36
SIC 6732 Charitable trust management
Pr: James Canales
Bd of Dir: Jane W Carney

D-U-N-S 07-201-3279
JAMES M PLEASANTS CO INC
JPM
603 Diamond Hill Ct, Greensboro, NC 27406-4617
Tel (336) 275-3152 *Founded/Ownrshp* 1987
Sales 106.7MM^E *EMP* 98
SIC 5075 3585 3561 3494 Warm air heating & air conditioning; Refrigeration & heating equipment; Pumps & pumping equipment; Valves & pipe fittings
Pr: J Chris Edmonson
**Pr:* Jamie Edmondson
VP: Pete Conroy
VP: Phil Farlow
VP: Chuck Moore
**VP:* G David Pleasants
Genl Mgr: Teresa Turner
Ql Cn Mgr: Shelley Tobin
Mktg Mgr: Chad Edmondson
Sls Mgr: Robert Harris

D-U-N-S 87-932-5355
JAMES MADISON UNIVERSITY INC
800 S Main St, Harrisonburg, VA 22807-0002
Tel (540) 568-6211 *Founded/Ownrshp* 1908
Sales 500.0MM *EMP* 1,700
SIC 8221 Colleges universities & professional schools
Pr: Jonathan R Alger
**CFO:* John Knight
Treas: Barbara Monger
Top Exec: Sharon Gasser
**Sr VP:* Charles W King
**VP:* Douglas Brown
VP: Douglas T Brown
VP: Joanne Carr
VP: Kimberly A Donohoe
VP: Dary Erwin
VP: Kathy Floyd
VP: Weston W Hatfield
VP: Carol Hurney
VP: Towana Moore
VP: Chris Pipkins
VP: Leslie Purtlebaugh
VP: Maranda Scott

D-U-N-S 17-347-4602 IMP
JAMES MARINE INC
J M I
4500 Clarks River Rd, Paducah, KY 42003-0823
Tel (270) 898-7392 *Founded/Ownrshp* 1986
Sales 261.3MM^E *EMP* 1,007
SIC 3731 4492 5541 3732 Barges, building & repairing; Shifting of floating equipment within harbors; Marine towing services; Marine service station; Boat building & repairing
CEO: C Ronald James
**Pr:* Phil Crabtree
**CFO:* Brandon Buchanan
Ex VP: Barry Gipson
**Ex VP:* Jeff James
**Sr VP:* Eric Crabtree
VP: Phillip Crabtree
**Genl Mgr:* Brent Gaines
CTO: Brian Brinkley

D-U-N-S 00-693-1331 IMP
JAMES MCHUGH CONSTRUCTION CO
(*Suby of* MCHUGH ENTERPRISES INC) ★
1737 S Michigan Ave, Chicago, IL 60616-1211
Tel (312) 986-8000 *Founded/Ownrshp* 1896
Sales 441.7MM^E *EMP* 750
SIC 1542 1522 1622 Hospital construction; Commercial & office building, new construction; Commercial & office buildings, renovation & repair; Hotel/motel & multi-family home construction; Bridge construction; Tunnel construction; Highway construction, elevated
Ch Bd: James P McHugh
**Pr:* Bruce E Lake
**CFO:* Patrick Seery
VP: Dale Hendrix
VP: Hoefflin James
**VP:* James R Mc Hugh
**VP:* James R McHugh
VP: Richard Mole
VP: Robert Mortimer
Exec: Steve Wiley
Dir IT: Richard Shin

D-U-N-S 01-501-0908
JAMES MORIEL
IMPERIAL TURF PRODUCTS
25701 Taladro Cir Ste B, Mission Viejo, CA 92691-3122
Tel (949) 240-3340 *Founded/Ownrshp* 1997
Sales 108.2MM *EMP* 7
Accts Haskell & White Llp Irvine C
SIC 5083 Lawn & garden machinery & equipment
Owner: James Moriel

D-U-N-S 94-735-7539 IMP
JAMES PERSE ENTERPRISES INC
JAMES PERSE LOS ANGELES
7373 Flores St, Downey, CA 90242-4011
Tel (323) 588-2226 *Founded/Ownrshp* 1994
Sales 89.2MM^E *EMP* 70
SIC 5136 5137 Men's & boys' clothing; Women's & children's clothing
CEO: James Perse
**CFO:* Karen Swanson
VP: Brett Brooks
VP: Kimberley Smith
CIO: Tom Stevenson

IT Man: Andy Bach
Mktg Mgr: Bach Andy
Sales Asso: Chloe Fugate

JAMES PERSE LOS ANGELES
See JAMES PERSE ENTERPRISES INC

D-U-N-S 00-658-1987
JAMES PETERSON SONS INC
PETERSON CONCRETE
N2251 Gibson Dr, Medford, WI 54451-9702
Tel (715) 748-3010 *Founded/Ownrshp* 1948
Sales 90.1MM *EMP* 130
Accts Wipfli Llp Eau Claire Wiscon
SIC 1611 General contractor, highway & street construction
Pr: John M Peterson
**VP:* Jeffery Peterson

D-U-N-S 02-122-8671 IMP
JAMES R GLIDEWELL DENTAL CERAMICS INC (CA)
GLIDEWELL LABORATORIES
4141 Macarthur Blvd, Newport Beach, CA 92660-2015
Tel (949) 440-2600 *Founded/Ownrshp* 1969
Sales 195.7MM[E] *EMP* 1,900
SIC 8072 Dental laboratories
CEO: James R Glidewell
**COO:* Greg Minzenmayer
**CFO:* Rob Grice
**CFO:* Glenn Sasaki
CFO: Glenn Sasaski
Ofcr: Brandon Nelson
VP: Anna Ameduri
**VP:* Jim Shuck
Exec: Vince Munoz
Genl Mgr: Ron Fichter
Genl Mgr: Paula La Bar

D-U-N-S 00-678-0662
JAMES R VANNOY & SONS CONSTRUCTION CO INC (NC)
VANNOY CONSTRUCTION
1608 Us Highway 221 N, Jefferson, NC 28640-9808
Tel (336) 846-7191 *Founded/Ownrshp* 1952
Sales 340.0MM *EMP* 315
Accts Coffey Lovins & Company Pllc
SIC 1542 1541 1799 Commercial & office building, new construction; Institutional building construction; Industrial buildings, new construction; Building site preparation
CEO: W Eddie Vannoy
Pr: J Mark Vannoy
VP: Bill Blank
VP: John J Montgomery

D-U-N-S 78-409-3502
JAMES RIVER COAL CO
901 E Byrd St Ste 1600, Richmond, VA 23219-4529
Tel (804) 780-3000 *Founded/Ownrshp* 1988
Sales 1.1MMM *EMP* 2,124[E]
SIC 1221 Bituminous coal & lignite-surface mining
Ch Bd: Peter T Socha
Chf Cred: Michael E Weber
VP: Samuel M Hopkins II
VP: Coy Lane
Dir Risk M: William B Murphy
Board of Directors: Alan F Crown, Ronald J Florjancic, Leonard J Kujawa, Joseph H Vipperman

D-U-N-S 07-786-3314
JAMES RIVER COAL SERVICE CO
(*Suby of* JAMES RIVER COAL CO) ★
901 E Byrd St Ste 1600, Richmond, VA 23219-4529
Tel (606) 878-7411 *Founded/Ownrshp* 1971
Sales 134.8MM[E] *EMP* 1,018
SIC 1222 1221 Underground mining, semibituminous; Strip mining, bituminous; Coal preparation plant, bituminous or lignite; Unit train loading facility, bituminous or lignite
CEO: Peter Socha
**Pr:* Talmadge M Mosley
**Pr:* Dexter Brian Patton III
**Treas:* Samuel Hopkins

D-U-N-S 05-890-1646 EXP
JAMES RIVER EQUIPMENT INC
11047 Leadbetter Rd, Ashland, VA 23005-3408
Tel (804) 748-9324 *Founded/Ownrshp* 1978
Sales 203.5MM[E] *EMP* 550
SIC 5084 5082 Industrial machinery & equipment; General construction machinery & equipment
Pr: Mark D Romer
**VP:* Rodger Hargis
Brnch Mgr: Clifford Applewhite
Genl Mgr: Will Barbee
Mktg Dir: Jim Erbesti
Sls Mgr: Dave Cumming
Sls Mgr: Ted Doran
Sls Mgr: Ronnie Rathbone

D-U-N-S 04-473-5298 EXP
JAMES RIVER EQUIPMENT VIRGINIA LLC
JOHN DEERE AUTHORIZED DEALER
11047 Leadbetter Rd, Ashland, VA 23005-3408
Tel (804) 798-6001 *Founded/Ownrshp* 2000
Sales 99.1MM[E] *EMP* 330
SIC 5082 General construction machinery & equipment
Pr: Mark Romer
VP: Irvin Marshall
IT Man: John Bussert
Sls Mgr: Steve Newton

D-U-N-S 12-644-1687
JAMES RIVER GROUP INC
(*Suby of* FRANKLIN HOLDINGS (BERMUDA) LTD)
1414 Raleigh Rd Ste 405, Chapel Hill, NC 27517-8834
Tel (919) 883-4171 *Founded/Ownrshp* 2007
Sales NA *EMP* 197
SIC 6411 Property & casualty insurance agent
CEO: Michael T Oakes
CFO: Gregg T Davis
Mktg Dir: John Clark

D-U-N-S 05-464-1865
JAMES WOOD MOTORS INC (TX)
2111 S Highway 287, Decatur, TX 76234-2722
Tel (940) 627-2177 *Founded/Ownrshp* 1970, 1978
Sales 92.9MM[E] *EMP* 215[E]
SIC 5511 Automobiles, new & used
Pr: James Wood
**CFO:* Thomas J Keenan
Treas: Tom Keenon
**VP:* Shirley Wood
Exec: Trynna R Roberts
Genl Mgr: Jeff Horn
Sls Dir: Amanda Williams
Sls Mgr: Will Lewis
Sls Mgr: Zach Rhine
Sls Mgr: Randall Wood

JAMESHARDIE
See JAMES HARDIE BUILDING PRODUCTS INC

D-U-N-S 60-584-9520
JAMESON HEALTH SYSTEM INC
JAMESON HOSPITAL
1211 Wilmington Ave, New Castle, PA 16105-2516
Tel (724) 658-9001 *Founded/Ownrshp* 1986
Sales 720.6M *EMP* 1,300
SIC 8062 General medical & surgical hospitals
Pr: Thomas White
**Ch Bd:* Chris Mitsos
**Pr:* Douglas Danko
COO: Donald Melonio
**CFO:* James Aubel
**Sec:* Steven Warner
Bd of Dir: Robert Bruce
**VP:* Neil Chessin
Dir IT: Kathleen Sanders
QC Dir: Debra Perretta
Plnt Mgr: Ken Jones
Board of Directors: Robert N Chambers, James L Gardner II MD, Walter Higgins, Thomas O'shane, John Sant, R Kay Thompson

JAMESON HOSPITAL
See JAMESON HEALTH SYSTEM INC

JAMESON INN
See PARK MANAGEMENT GROUP LLC

D-U-N-S 36-169-8392
JAMESON INNS INC
ROBERT COMPANY MARYLAND, J. E
(*Suby of* ROBERT COMPANY OF MARYLAND, J. E. (USED IN VA. BY ROBERT COMPANY, J. E.))
41 Perimeter Ctr E # 4100, Atlanta, GA 30346-1910
Tel (770) 512-0462 *Founded/Ownrshp* 2006
Sales 22.7MM[E] *EMP* 2,100
SIC 7011 1522 Hotels & motels; Hotel/motel, new construction
Ch Bd: Thomas W Kitchin
Pr: Craig R Kitchin
Treas: Martin D Brew
VP: Steven A Curlee
VP: William Doug Walker

D-U-N-S 07-498-4758
JAMESON MEMORIAL HOSPITAL
JHS
1211 Wilmington Ave, New Castle, PA 16105-2595
Tel (724) 658-9001 *Founded/Ownrshp* 1986
Sales 302.8MM *EMP* 1,150
SIC 8062 General medical & surgical hospitals
CEO: Douglas Danko
Dir Vol: Cyndee Adamo
**Pr:* Boud Tinko
**CFO:* James Aubel
**Sec:* Steven Warner
**VP:* Neil Chessin
Pr Dir: Lisa Lombardo
Nrsg Dir: Barbara Bernardi
Pharmcst: Terri Natale
Pharmcst: Heather Salata

D-U-N-S 00-211-5657 EXP
JAMESTOWN CONTAINER CORP (NY)
14 Deming Dr, Falconer, NY 14733-1697
Tel (716) 665-4623 *Founded/Ownrshp* 1956
Sales 127.6MM[E] *EMP* 445
SIC 2653 3086 Corrugated & solid fiber boxes; Packaging & shipping materials, foamed plastic
Ch Bd: Bruce Janowsky
**Sec:* Dick Weimer
VP: Richards Emmerick
**VP:* Joseph R Palmeri
Exec: Gary Yager
Genl Mgr: Larry Hudson
Mktg Dir: Bill Madl
Sls Mgr: Bill Benedict

JAMIESON FENCE SUPPLY
See JAMIESON MANUFACTURING CO

D-U-N-S 00-734-5259 IMP
JAMIESON MANUFACTURING CO
JAMIESON FENCE SUPPLY
4221 Platinum Way, Dallas, TX 75237-1617
Tel (214) 339-8384 *Founded/Ownrshp* 1965
Sales 94.8MM[E] *EMP* 124
SIC 5039 2499 Wire fence, gates & accessories; Fencing, docks & other outdoor wood structural products
CEO: B J Wallace
**Pr:* Richard Calhoun
**Ex VP:* Len Hoersten
**VP:* Monte Grissom
**VP:* J Ketterer
Rgnl Mgr: Chad Kearney
Brnch Mgr: Allen Duke
Brnch Mgr: Thomas Reeves
Brnch Mgr: Joel Schumacher
VP Opers: Mike Weaver
Sales Asso: Jesus Arzate

D-U-N-S 18-951-4284
JAMIESON-HILL A GENERAL PARTNERSHIP
J HILL OIL
3101 State Rd, Bakersfield, CA 93308-4931
Tel (661) 393-7000 *Founded/Ownrshp* 1978
Sales 183.7MM *EMP* 50
Accts Moss Adams Llp Los Angeles C
SIC 5541 6798 Filling stations, gasoline; Real estate investment trusts
Pt: W J Hill
**Pt:* Roy Sanders

JANDY POOL PRODUCTS
See ZODIAC POOL SYSTEMS INC

D-U-N-S 06-497-9992
JANE PHILLIPS MEDICAL CENTER
3450 E Frank Phillips Blvd, Bartlesville, OK 74006-2406
Tel (918) 338-3730 *Founded/Ownrshp* 2014
Sales 110.1MM *EMP* 4[E]
SIC 8011 Medical centers

D-U-N-S 12-433-4967
JANE PHILLIPS MEMORIAL MEDICAL CENTER INC
(*Suby of* ST JOHN HEALTH SYSTEM INC) ★
3500 E Frank Phillips Blvd, Bartlesville, OK 74006-2411
Tel (918) 333-7200 *Founded/Ownrshp* 1952
Sales 114.7MM *EMP* 900
Accts Deloitte Tax Llp Cincinnati
SIC 8062 General medical & surgical hospitals
Pr: David Stire
COO: Scott Smith
**CFO:* Mike Moore
Ofcr: Jennifer Dildine
**VP:* Susan Herron
VP: Amanda Mitchell
VP: Sue Parnell
**VP:* Scott C Phillips
Dir Inf Cn: Valerie Vieux
Dir Lab: Dale Kenney
Dir Rx: Erin Claiborne
Dir Bus: Brian Lawrence

D-U-N-S 07-923-0585
JANE STREET GROUP LLC
250 Vesey St, New York, NY 10281-1052
Tel (646) 759-6000 *Founded/Ownrshp* 2013
Sales 181.3MM[E] *EMP* 450[E]
SIC 6211 Investment firm, general brokerage

D-U-N-S 07-426-5794
JANEPHILLIPS HEALTH CROP
(*Suby of* ST JOHN HEALTH SYSTEM INC) ★
1923 S Utica Ave, Tulsa, OK 74104-6520
Tel (918) 273-3102 *Founded/Ownrshp* 1950
Sales 112.4MM *EMP* 1,050
SIC 8062 General medical & surgical hospitals
CEO: David Stire

JANESVILLE GAZETTE
See BLISS COMMUNICATIONS INC

D-U-N-S 10-008-3070
JANESVILLE SCHOOL DISTRICT
527 S Franklin St, Janesville, WI 53548-4779
Tel (608) 743-5000 *Founded/Ownrshp* 1856
Sales 76.5MM[E] *EMP* 1,395
SIC 8211 Public combined elementary & secondary school
CFO: Keith Pennington
CIO: Bently Turner
MIS Dir: Brandon Keirns
Dir IT: Steve Scholmann
Pr Dir: Bret Berg
Schl Brd P: Greg Ardrey
Teacher Pr: Scott Garner
HC Dir: Christine Wesling

D-U-N-S 14-712-1024
JANI-KING INTERNATIONAL INC
16885 Dallas Pkwy, Addison, TX 75001-5202
Tel (972) 991-0900 *Founded/Ownrshp* 1969
Sales 160.5MM *EMP* 550[E]
SIC 7349 Building maintenance services
Ch: James A Cavanaugh Jr
**Pr:* Jerry Crawford
**CFO:* Steve Hawkins
**Ex VP:* Charles Oney
**VP:* Jill Bean

D-U-N-S 84-744-4445 IMP
JANICKI INDUSTRIES INC
719 Metcalf St, Sedro Woolley, WA 98284-1420
Tel (360) 856-5143 *Founded/Ownrshp* 1994
Sales 106.9MM[E] *EMP* 630[E]
SIC 3728

D-U-N-S 10-115-5968
JANITRONICS INC
29 Sawyer Rd Ste 11, Waltham, MA 02453-3400
Tel (781) 647-5570 *Founded/Ownrshp* 1977
Sales 34.1MM[E] *EMP* 1,187
SIC 7349 Cleaning service, industrial or commercial
Pr: Donald Brecher
Treas: Marilyn Brecher
**VP:* Michael A Halliday

D-U-N-S 00-941-3477
JANJER ENTERPRISES INC
12150 Tech Rd, Silver Spring, MD 20904-1914
Tel (301) 625-5920 *Founded/Ownrshp* 1981
Sales 46.8MM[E] *EMP* 1,400
SIC 5812 8721 8741 Fast-food restaurant, chain; Accounting, auditing & bookkeeping; Restaurant management
Pr: Jerome Friedlander
**VP:* Jan Strompf

D-U-N-S 05-330-3897
JANNEY MONTGOMERY SCOTT LLC
PARKER HUNTER
(*Suby of* PENN MUTUAL LIFE INSURANCE CO) ★
1717 Arch St Fl 16, Philadelphia, PA 19103-2772
Tel (215) 665-6000 *Founded/Ownrshp* 1982
Sales 838.9MM[E] *EMP* 1,200
Accts Pricewaterhousecoopers Llp Ph
SIC 6211 Investment firm, general brokerage; Brokers, security
Ch Bd: Rudolph Sander
**Ch Bd:* Norman T Wilde Jr
**Pr:* James Wolitarsky
COO: William Hartman
COO: Michael Musson
COO: Stacey Polito
**V Ch Bd:* Charles B Cook Jr
Ex VP: David E Grice
**Ex VP:* William Jones
Ex VP: John Kline
Ex VP: Lance McCoy
**Ex VP:* Anthony Miller
Ex VP: Kimberly Nickerson
Ex VP: Randall Renneisen
Ex VP: Doug Walters
Ex VP: Christina Wright
**Sr VP:* Randall A Carbone
**Sr VP:* Gregory B McShea
Sr VP: Kevin Reed
**Sr VP:* Robert J Thielmann
Sr VP: Greg Torretta

D-U-N-S 01-207-8622 IMP
■ **JANOVIC-PLAZA INC**
(*Suby of* BENJAMIN MOORE & CO) ★
3035 Thomson Ave, Long Island City, NY 11101-3072
Tel (718) 392-3999 *Founded/Ownrshp* 1957
Sales 376.5MM[E] *EMP* 270
SIC 5198 5231 5023 5719 Paints; Paint brushes, rollers, sprayers; Wallcoverings; Paint; Paint brushes, rollers, sprayers & other supplies; Wallpaper; Window furnishings; Window furnishings
Pr: Paul Renn
**Prin:* Don Brady
Genl Mgr: Brian Budin

D-U-N-S 07-478-3689 IMP
■ **JANSPORT INC**
(*Suby of* VF CORP) ★
N850 County Road Cb, Appleton, WI 54914-8277
Tel (920) 734-5708 *Founded/Ownrshp* 1967
Sales 113.3MM[E] *EMP* 550
SIC 3949 3161 2339 2329 2321 Camping equipment & supplies; Traveling bags; Women's & misses' athletic clothing & sportswear; Men's & boys' sportswear & athletic clothing; Men's & boys' furnishings
Pr: Michael Cisler
CFO: Harvey Erickson
VP: Karin Apitz
VP: Richard Hayes
VP: Bill Howard
VP: Jim Koehne
**VP:* Bill Kramer
VP: Dan Small
VP: Paul Whitener
IT Man: Margaret Fisher
MIS Mgr: Margaret Fietzer
Board of Directors: Mackey McDonald

D-U-N-S 09-909-1753 IMP
■ **JANSSEN BIOTECH INC**
(*Suby of* JOHNSON & JOHNSON) ★
800 Ridgeview Dr, Horsham, PA 19044-3607
Tel (610) 651-6000 *Founded/Ownrshp* 1999
Sales 908.3MM[E] *EMP* 3,000
SIC 2834 2835 Pharmaceutical preparations; Drugs affecting parasitic & infective diseases; Drugs acting on the cardiovascular system, except diagnostic; In vitro diagnostics
Pr: Robert B Bazemore
**Treas:* Jay Fischbein
**VP:* Bruce Peacock
Assoc Dir: Jim Schaedel
Ex Dir: Elliot Barnathan
Ex Dir: Hugh Davis
Prgrm Mgr: Steve Tufillaro
DP Dir: Brenda Koob
IT Man: Tom Hill
Mktg Dir: Michael Cassano
Mktg Dir: Karen Lade

D-U-N-S 06-313-7772 IMP
■ **JANSSEN PHARMACEUTICALS INC**
(*Suby of* JOHNSON & JOHNSON) ★
1125 Trnton Harbourton Rd, Titusville, NJ 08560-1499
Tel (609) 730-2000 *Founded/Ownrshp* 1983
Sales 603.9MM[E] *EMP* 1,800
SIC 2833 2834 Anesthetics, in bulk form; Antihistamine preparations; Astringents, medicinal
Pr: Jennifer Taubert
CFO: Richard Gatens
**Treas:* Steve Bariahtaris
VP: Jim Barr
VP: Ed Hill
VP: Randall L Morrison
VP: Jose Sotoca
**VP:* Michael Yang
Exec: Gwenn Brown
Dir Surg: Vic Sipido
Dir Surg: Jim Witt

D-U-N-S 11-923-7597
■ **JANSSEN RESEARCH & DEVELOPMENT LLC**
(*Suby of* JOHNSON & JOHNSON) ★
920 Us Highway 202, Raritan, NJ 08869-1420
Tel (908) 704-4000 *Founded/Ownrshp* 2000
Sales 486.4MM[E] *EMP* 2,513
SIC 2834 8731 Pharmaceutical preparations; Commercial physical research
Ch: P A Paterson MD
Ofcr: Keke Ren
Ofcr: Paul Stoffels
VP: Marene Allison
VP: Gina Bilotti
**VP:* Nicholas C Dracopoli
**VP:* Yusri A Elsayed
**VP:* Joseph Erhardt
VP: Seema Kumar
VP: Kenneth Leahy
VP: Samuel Maldonado
VP: Thomas Manion
VP: Kristen Seggern
Dir Surg: Albert Leung
Assoc Dir: Andrew Carmen
Assoc Dir: Wanda Davis
Assoc Dir: Patricia Driver

D-U-N-S 07-996-1124
■ **JANUS CAPITAL CORP**
(*Suby of* JANUS CAPITAL GROUP INC) ★
151 Detroit St, Denver, CO 80206-4928
Tel (303) 333-3863 *Founded/Ownrshp* 2000
Sales 489.3MM[E] *EMP* 1,113[E]
SIC 6282 Manager of mutual funds, contract or fee basis; Investment counselors

Pr: Gerry Black
Treas: Scott S Grace
**Ex VP:* Darrell Watters
Sr VP: Stephanie Pierce
VP: Gwen E Royl
CIO: Jeff Kautz
Opers Mgr: Corie Carlson
Mktg Dir: Kim Blankenburg

D-U-N-S 02-449-6726
▲ JANUS CAPITAL GROUP INC
151 Detroit St, Denver, CO 80206-4928
Tel (303) 333-3863 *Founded/Ownrshp* 1969
Sales 1.0MMM *EMP* 1,272E
Tkr Sym JNS *Exch* NYS
SIC 6282 8741 Investment advice; Investment advisory service; Manager of mutual funds, contract or fee basis; Business management
CEO: Richard M Weil
**Ch Bd:* Glenn S Schafer
Pr: Enrique Chang
Pr: Bruce L Koepfgen
CFO: Jennifer J McPeek
Board of Directors: Jeffrey J Diermeier, Eugene Flood Jr, J Richard Fredericks, Deborah R Gatzek, Lawrence E Kochard, Arnold A Pinkston, Billie I Williamson

D-U-N-S 07-867-0677
JANUS GLOBAL HOLDINGS LLC
2229 Old Highway 95, Lenoir City, TN 37771-6747
Tel (865) 988-6063 *Founded/Ownrshp* 2012
Sales 219.5MM *EMP* 6,473
SIC 8742 Management consulting services
CEO: Matthew R Kaye
**Pr:* Alan Weakley
**CFO:* Steven Hile
VP: Matt Hulsey
VP: David T Johnson
Prgrm Mgr: Mark Fletcher
Opers Mgr: Mike Pate
Ql Cn Mgr: Donald Welch

D-U-N-S 60-575-5651
JANUS GLOBAL OPERATIONS LLC
(*Suby of* JANUS GLOBAL HOLDINGS LLC) ★
2229 Old Highway 95, Lenoir City, TN 37771-6747
Tel (865) 988-6063 *Founded/Ownrshp* 2012
Sales 219.5MM *EMP* 6,473
SIC 4959 7381 7373 7379 8742 Toxic or hazardous waste cleanup; Environmental cleanup services; Security guard service; Computer systems analysis & design; Computer related consulting services; Materials mgmt. (purchasing, handling, inventory) consultant; Site location consultant
CEO: Matthew R Kaye
Pr: Alan Weakley
CFO: Steven Hile
CFO: Lisa Jacobson
Ofcr: Kevin Kuklok
Sr VP: Michael King
VP: John South
Admn Mgr: Staci Monroe
MIS Dir: Joseph McLoughlin

D-U-N-S 05-347-7571 IMP/EXP
JANUS INTERNATIONAL GROUP LLC
135 Janus Intl Blvd, Temple, GA 30179
Tel (770) 562-2850 *Founded/Ownrshp* 2001
Sales 137.1MME *EMP* 375
Accts Nichols Cauley & Associates
SIC 3442 Metal doors
Pr: David Curtis
**Pr:* Jeff Higashi
**CFO:* Scott M Sannes CPA
VP: Dennis Johnson
VP: John McLane
**VP:* Vic Nettie
CIO: Dan Horton
IT Man: Greg Smith
Netwrk Eng: Kenneth Jorgensen
Sfty Mgr: Sonny Jarrett
Opers Mgr: Alan Campbell

D-U-N-S 03-445-3097
■ JANUS INTERNATIONAL HOLDING LLC
(*Suby of* JANUS CAPITAL CORP) ★
151 Detroit St, Denver, CO 80206-4805
Tel (303) 333-3863 *Founded/Ownrshp* 2004
Sales 81.3MME *EMP* 1,000E
SIC 6719 Investment holding companies, except banks
Ex VP: Augustus Cheh
Advt Dir: Emily Parkhurst
Mktg Mgr: Megan McCahill

D-U-N-S 07-520-7043 IMP/EXP
JAPAN PULP & PAPER (USA) CORP
(*Suby of* JAPAN PULP AND PAPER COMPANY LIMITED)
5928 S Malt Ave, Commerce, CA 90040-3504
Tel (323) 889-7750 *Founded/Ownrshp* 1974
Sales 1.1MMME *EMP* 537
SIC 5113 5093 5099 Cardboard & products; Waste paper; Pulpwood
CEO: Akihiko Watanabe
**CFO:* Yoshio Takai
CFO: Kazuhiko Yokozawa
**Exec:* Mark Roth

D-U-N-S 00-625-8115 EXP
JAPS-OLSON CO
7500 Excelsior Blvd, St Louis Park, MN 55426-4519
Tel (952) 932-9393 *Founded/Ownrshp* 2006
Sales 174.8MME *EMP* 650E
SIC 2752 7331 2791 2759 Letters, circular or form: lithographed; Calendars, lithographed; Coupons, lithographed; Addressing service; Mailing service; Typesetting; Commercial printing
**Pr:* Michael R Murphy
COO: Stephen Rhodes
**CFO:* Gary Petrangelo
**Ch:* Robert E Murphy
**Prin:* Kevin Beddor
IT Man: David Kreider
Software D: Matthew Scott
Prd Mgr: Julie Halverson
Prd Mgr: Tony Waska

S&M/VP: Monica Murphy
S&M/VP: Debbie Roth

JARDEN APPLIED MATERIALS
See SHAKESPEARE CO LLC

JARDEN BRANDS CONSUMABLES
See HEARTHMARK LLC

D-U-N-S 80-187-5980 IMP/EXP
■ JARDEN CORP
NEWELL BRANDS
(*Suby of* NEWELL BRANDS INC) ★
1800 N Military Trl # 210, Boca Raton, FL 33431-6376
Tel (561) 447-2520 *Founded/Ownrshp* 2015
Sales 8.6MMM *EMP* 17,000
Accts Pricewaterhousecoopers Llp Ne
SIC 3089 3634 Plastic containers, except foam; Plastic kitchenware, tableware & houseware; Electric housewares & fans; Electric household cooking appliances; Electric household cooking utensils; Personal electrical appliances
CEO: Michael B Polk
Pr: William A Burke
Sr VP: Jim Bennett
Genl Mgr: Matthew Shifrin
Opers Mgr: Sebastian Schroeder

D-U-N-S 05-398-3862 IMP
■ JARDEN ZINC PRODUCTS LLC
(*Suby of* NEWELL BRANDS) ★
2500 Old Stage Rd, Greeneville, TN 37745-3036
Tel (423) 639-8111 *Founded/Ownrshp* 1997
Sales 101.2MME *EMP* 200
SIC 2796 3364 3356 1031 2789 Photoengraving plates, linecuts or halftones; Zinc & zinc-base alloy die-castings; Zinc & zinc alloy bars, plates, sheets, etc.; Lead & zinc ores; Beveling of cards
Pr: Tom Wennogle
**VP:* Christine Mathews
Dir IT: Wiley Helton
Secur Mgr: Eddie Anderson
Sales Asso: Stephanie Hurt

D-U-N-S 78-567-7451
JARDINE HAWAII MOTOR HOLDINGS LTD
(*Suby of* JARDINE U S MOTOR HOLDINGS LIMITED (DE))
818 Kapiolani Blvd, Honolulu, HI 96813-5210
Tel (808) 592-5600 *Founded/Ownrshp* 1991
Sales 142.3MM *EMP* 88
SIC 5511 New & used car dealers
Pr: Fletcher Jones

JARED THE GALLERIA OF JEWELRY
See STERLING JEWELERS INC

JARIT
See INTEGRA LIFESCIENCES CORP

D-U-N-S 11-487-4527
JARRETT LOGISTICS SYSTEMS INC
1347 N Main St, Orrville, OH 44667-9761
Tel (330) 682-0099 *Founded/Ownrshp* 2004
Sales 100.0MM *EMP* 150
SIC 8742 4731 Transportation consultant; Freight transportation arrangement
Pr: Michael Jarrett
**VP:* Matt Angell
Dir Bus: Michael Rootes
Dir Bus: Leroy Schalk
IT Man: Aaron Schar

D-U-N-S 83-989-6441
JARRITOS INC
TIPP DISTRIBUTOR
500 W Overland Ave # 300, El Paso, TX 79901-1086
Tel (915) 594-1618 *Founded/Ownrshp* 1997
Sales 132.6MME *EMP* 153
SIC 5149 Groceries & related products
Pr: Ramon Carrasco
**Treas:* Francisco Hill Avendano
IT Man: Jose Hernandez
Sls Dir: Kevin Rose
Mktg Mgr: Erwin Chang
Manager: Donald Craig

D-U-N-S 16-160-4046 IMP/EXP
JARROW FORMULAS INC
1824 S Robertson Blvd, Los Angeles, CA 90035-4317
Tel (310) 204-6936 *Founded/Ownrshp* 1975
Sales 89.9MME *EMP* 90
SIC 5122 Vitamins & minerals
CEO: Ben Khowong
**Pr:* Jarrow L Rogovin
**Treas:* Clayton Dubose
**VP:* Michael Jacobs
Creative D: ARA Soghomonian
Dir IT: Charles Fischer
Mktg Mgr: Rory Lipsky

D-U-N-S 11-417-0330
JAS AMERICA HOLDING INC
(*Suby of* JAS WORLDWIDE SARL)
5424 Glenridge Dr, Atlanta, GA 30342-1342
Tel (770) 688-1240 *Founded/Ownrshp* 1998
Sales 160.3MME *EMP* 412
SIC 4731 Customhouse brokers; Domestic freight forwarding
Pr: Marco Rebuffi
**CFO:* Tahira Fumo
Mng Dir: Marc Dalais
Brnch Mgr: Shirley Macias
Brnch Mgr: Dirk Manegold
Brnch Mgr: Andre Voedisch
**CIO:* Paul Foster
Opers Mgr: Michael Jackstaedt
Mktg Mgr: Neerish Chooramun

D-U-N-S 00-952-5098 IMP/EXP
JAS D EASTON INC
5215 W Wiley Post Way # 130, Salt Lake City, UT 84116-3282
Tel (801) 526-6211 *Founded/Ownrshp* 1922
Sales 440.4MME *EMP* 1,800
SIC 3949 5091 6552 Baseball equipment & supplies, general; Archery equipment, general; Snow skiing equipment & supplies, except skis; Hockey equipment & supplies, general; Sporting & recreation goods; Subdividers & developers
CEO: Jim Easton
**Pr:* Tony Palma
**Pr:* Eric Watts
**VP:* John Cramer

D-U-N-S 61-464-6172 IMP/EXP
JAS FORWARDING (USA) INC
JAS FORWARDING WORLDWIDE
(*Suby of* JAS AMERICA HOLDING INC) ★
6165 Barfield Rd, Atlanta, GA 30328-4317
Tel (770) 688-1206 *Founded/Ownrshp* 1998
Sales 138.4MME *EMP* 412
SIC 4731 Customhouse brokers; Domestic freight forwarding
Pr: Adrian Emmenegger
COO: Graeme Robinson
CFO: Kerstin Roche
Ofcr: Bruce Jackson
VP: Steve Jeffery
VP: Marco Rebuffi
Ex Dir: Brig Hassan
Mng Dir: Johnny Delgado
Mng Dir: Juergen Erdt
Mng Dir: Nicolas Frate
Mng Dir: Laurent Gohet

JAS FORWARDING WORLDWIDE
See JAS FORWARDING (USA) INC

JASCO CUTTING TOOLS
See GRAYWOOD COMPANIES INC

D-U-N-S 08-256-7025 IMP/EXP
JASCO PRODUCTS CO LLC
10 E Memorial Rd Bldg B, Oklahoma City, OK 73114-2205
Tel (405) 752-0710 *Founded/Ownrshp* 1977
Sales 87.0MME *EMP* 250
SIC 5065 5064

D-U-N-S 09-292-8071 IMP/EXP
JASON HOLDINGS INC
411 E Wisconsin Ave # 2120, Milwaukee, WI 53202-4461
Tel (414) 277-9300 *Founded/Ownrshp* 2000
Sales NA *EMP* 1,500
SIC 2297 3465 3469 3844 3443

D-U-N-S 15-084-8877 IMP/EXP
■ JASON INC
JASON INDUSTRIES
(*Suby of* JPHI HOLDINGS INC) ★
411 E Wisconsin Ave, Milwaukee, WI 53202-4461
Tel (414) 277-9300 *Founded/Ownrshp* 2014
Sales 700.0MME *EMP* 3,500
SIC 3465 2297 3625 3469 3844 3443 Moldings or trim, automobile: stamped metal; Nonwoven fabrics; Noise control equipment; Metal stampings; Irradiation equipment; Boilers: industrial, power, or marine
Pr: David Cataldi
**Pr:* Srivas Prasad
**Pr:* Florestan Von Boxberg
**CFO:* Steve Cripe
**CFO:* Sarah Sutton
**VP:* John J Hengel
VP: Matt Oberski
Genl Couns: William P Schultz
Snr Mgr: Jeffry Quinn

D-U-N-S 00-170-7330 IMP/EXP
JASON INDUSTRIAL INC (NJ)
340 Kaplan Dr, Fairfield, NJ 07004-2567
Tel (973) 227-4904 *Founded/Ownrshp* 1965
Sales 85.6MME *EMP* 200
SIC 5084 3052 Textile machinery & equipment; Rubber & plastics hose & beltings
CEO: Philip Cohenca
**Ch Bd:* Emilia Cohenca
Ex VP: Peter H Batchelar
VP: Edward Menashe
VP: Albert Nacawa
VP: Roy Pyle
Sls Mgr: Darrell Gartner
Sls Mgr: Mark Mirchevich

JASON INDUSTRIES
See JASON INC

D-U-N-S 07-888-9261
▲ JASON INDUSTRIES INC
833 E Michigan St Ste 900, Milwaukee, WI 53202-5624
Tel (414) 277-9300 *Founded/Ownrshp* 2014
Sales 708.3MM *EMP* 4,600E
Tkr Sym JASN *Exch* NAS
SIC 3465 2297 3625 3469 3844 3443 Automotive stampings; Body parts, automobile: stamped metal; Nonwoven fabrics; Noise control equipment; Metal stampings; Irradiation equipment; Boilers: industrial, power, or marine
Ch Bd: Jeffry N Quinn
Pr: Brian K Kobylinski
CFO: Sarah C Sutton
Treas: John J Hengel
Sr VP: Steven G Carollo
Sr VP: Srivas Prasad
VP: Thomas L Doerr Jr
Board of Directors: James P Heffernan, Edgar G Hotard, James E Hyman, Mitchell I Quain, John Rutledge, James M Sullivan

JASON'S DELI
See DELI MANAGEMENT INC

D-U-N-S 09-242-4886 IMP
JASONS FOODS
208 E Helen Rd, Palatine, IL 60067-6955
Tel (847) 358-9901 *Founded/Ownrshp* 1978
Sales 135.0MME *EMP* 12
SIC 5144 5147 5142

JASPER ENGINE & TRANSM EXCHANGE
See JASPER ENGINE & TRANSMISSION EXCHANGE INC

D-U-N-S 01-645-8473
JASPER ENGINE & TRANSMISSION EXCHANGE INC
JASPER ENGINE & TRANSM EXCHAGE
(*Suby of* INDIANA TOOL & DIE) ★
815 Wernsing Rd, Jasper, IN 47546-8141
Tel (812) 482-1041 *Founded/Ownrshp* 1959
Sales 262.5MME *EMP* 1,500
SIC 5013 Automotive engines & engine parts
Ch Bd: Gervase Schwenk
**Pr:* Doug Bawel
**Treas:* Raymond Schwenk
**VP:* Mike Schwenk

D-U-N-S 01-764-6357 IMP
JASPER ENGINE & TRANSMISSION EXCHANGE INC
(*Suby of* INDIANA TOOL & DIE) ★
815 Wernsing Rd, Jasper, IN 47546-8141
Tel (812) 482-1041 *Founded/Ownrshp* 1958
Sales 154.7MME *EMP* 1,500
SIC 5013 Automotive engines & engine parts
CEO: Doug Bawel
**Ch Bd:* Gervase Schwenk
**Pr:* Zach Bawel
**Treas:* Raymond Schwenk
**VP:* Mike Schwenk
Brnch Mgr: Doug Sandow
Off Mgr: Trenton Smith

D-U-N-S 01-645-8481
JASPER ENGINE & TRANSMISSION EXCHANGE INC (KY)
(*Suby of* INDIANA TOOL & DIE) ★
815 Wernsing Rd, Jasper, IN 47546-8141
Tel (812) 482-1041 *Founded/Ownrshp* 1963
Sales 270.0MM *EMP* 1,500E
SIC 5013 7537 Automotive engines & engine parts; Automotive transmission repair shops
Pr: Doug Bawel
**Ch Bd:* Gervase Schwenk
**Treas:* Raymond Schwenk
**VP:* Mike Schwenk

D-U-N-S 00-639-8168 IMP/EXP
JASPER ENGINE EXCHANGE INC
INDIANA TOOL & DIE
815 Wernsing Rd, Jasper, IN 47546-8141
Tel (812) 482-1041 *Founded/Ownrshp* 1952
Sales 824.4MME *EMP* 1,500
SIC 3714 7538 6512 Rebuilding engines & transmissions, factory basis; Fuel systems & parts, motor vehicle; Gears, motor vehicle; General automotive repair shops; Nonresidential building operators
Ch Bd: Gervase Schwenk
**Pr:* Zachery Bawel
**CEO:* Douglas Bawel
CFO: Linda Bueltel
**Treas:* Raymond Schwenk
VP: Craig Hessenauer
VP: John Moser
VP: John Schroeder
**VP:* Mike Schwenk
Exec: Donald Casper
Exec: Jason Nord

JASPER GROUP
See JASPER SEATING CO INC

D-U-N-S 07-938-1439
JASPER PARENT LLC
9 W 57th St Ste 3100, New York, NY 10019-2701
Tel (212) 796-8500 *Founded/Ownrshp* 2013
Sales 1.8MMME *EMP* 10,790E
SIC 6211 Investment firm, general brokerage

D-U-N-S 13-244-5201 IMP
JASPER PRODUCTS LLC
(*Suby of* STREMICKS HERITAGE FOODS LLC) ★
3877 E 27th St, Joplin, MO 64804-3306
Tel (417) 206-3333 *Founded/Ownrshp* 2007
Sales 465.9MME *EMP* 400
SIC 5149 Health foods
Admn Mgr: Judy Rhinehart
Cmptr Lab: Amy Swan
IT Man: Kenneth Haubein
Ql Cn Mgr: Gina Becker

D-U-N-S 00-636-7239 IMP
JASPER RUBBER PRODUCTS INC
1010 1st Ave W, Jasper, IN 47546-3201
Tel (812) 482-3242 *Founded/Ownrshp* 1949, 2003
Sales 172.9MME *EMP* 750
SIC 3061 Mechanical rubber goods
Ch Bd: Jeffrey Geisler
**Pr:* Douglas Mathias
Pr: Laura Mohr
**CFO:* Marcus Oxley
Ex VP: Scott Ferguson
Ex VP: Scott Gehlhausen
**Ex VP:* R Keith Wyatt
**VP:* Lee Mincey
Dept Mgr: Drew Schmitt
Genl Mgr: Rebecca Beckman
MIS Dir: Valarie Frank
Board of Directors: Dow McCune, G Scott Schwinghammer

D-U-N-S 00-636-7767 IMP/EXP
JASPER SEATING CO INC
JASPER GROUP
225 Clay St, Jasper, IN 47546-3306
Tel (812) 482-3204 *Founded/Ownrshp* 1929, 1959
Sales 220.5MME *EMP* 920
SIC 2521 2531 2522 Wood office furniture; Chairs, office: padded, upholstered or plain: wood; School furniture; Office furniture, except wood
Pr: Elliott Michael
**VP:* Ronald Beck
Sls Mgr: Tonya Hief

D-U-N-S 96-292-5298 IMP
JASPER WELLER LLC
WELLER TRUCK PARTS
(*Suby of* INDIANA TOOL & DIE) ★
1500 Gezon Pkwy Sw, Grand Rapids, MI 49509-9585
Tel (616) 724-2000 *Founded/Ownrshp* 2014
Sales 124.6MME *EMP* 850

SIC 7538 5013 Truck engine repair, except industrial; Truck parts & accessories
COO: Paul Weller
*Prin: John Weller
Dir IT: Mark Huizinga
IT Man: Tim Mayo
Manager: Mike Kaniecki

JAT CREATIVE PDTS DIV LAFRANCE
See LA FRANCE CORP

D-U-N-S 08-120-0719
JAT OIL INC
600 W Main St, Chattanooga, TN 37402-4701
Tel (423) 629-6611 Founded/Ownrshp 1976
Sales 98.8MM[E] EMP 45
SIC 5172 Fuel oil
CEO: Pat Conroy
*Pr: William P Conroy Jr
*Sec: Melinda Hightower
*Prin: Bert Kaiser
*Prin: Brian Workman

JATF
See IUPAT DISTRICT COUNCIL 78

D-U-N-S 78-794-7951 IMP
JAVA TRADING CO LLC
DISTANT LANDS COFFEE
801 Houser Way N, Renton, WA 98057-5506
Tel (425) 917-2920 Founded/Ownrshp 2006
Sales 151.6MM[E] EMP 250
SIC 5149 2095 Coffee, green or roasted; Roasted coffee
CFO: Jim Ehchweiler

JAVIC WHOLESALE DIVISION
See STEIN GARDEN CENTERS INC

D-U-N-S 07-752-6739 IMP
JAVINE VENTURES INC
VARITEC SOLUTIONS
2851 W Kathleen Rd, Phoenix, AZ 85053-4053
Tel (602) 944-3330 Founded/Ownrshp 1988
Sales 183.6MM[E] EMP 275[E]
Accts Cordova & Jones Pc
SIC 5075 1731 Warm air heating equipment & supplies; Air conditioning & ventilation equipment & supplies; Electronic controls installation
Pr: Jack Kucera
VP: Marty Applebaum
VP: Allan Barinque
VP: Alex Radovan
IT Man: Dan Carlock
IT Man: Jimeen Hamblen
IT Man: Jim Sullivan
Sfty Dirs: Ronda Gill
Opers Supe: Astrid Cardenas
Opers Mgr: Nate Haugh
Opers Mgr: Gary Neely

JAX BROKERAGE
See CYPRESS TRUCK LINES INC

JAX UTILITIES & WATERPROOFING
See HASKELL CO INC

JAY AT PLAY
See JAY FRANCO & SONS INC

JAY C STORES
See JOHN C GROUB CO INC

D-U-N-S 86-816-0698 EXP
JAY CASHMAN INC
(Suby of JCI HOLDINGS LLC) ★
549 South St Bldg 19, Quincy, MA 02169-7318
Tel (617) 890-0600 Founded/Ownrshp 1994
Sales 200.0MM[E] EMP 300
SIC 1629 Marine construction
Pr: Dale H Pyatt
CFO: Andrew B Goldberg
VP: Michael Empey
VP: Richard Fernandez
VP: Robert Goodman
QA Dir: Joseph Ludwin
QA Dir: Aaron Sulkey
IT Man: John Doiron
VP Mktg: Kathleen Nolan

D-U-N-S 00-135-6963 IMP
JAY FRANCO & SONS INC (NY)
JAY AT PLAY
295 5th Ave Ste 312, New York, NY 10016-7106
Tel (212) 679-3022 Founded/Ownrshp 1949
Sales 188.7MM[E] EMP 160
SIC 5023 2211 Towels; Towels & toweling, cotton
Ch Bd: Joseph N Franco
CFO: Howard Weinreich
Treas: Marc Franco
VP: Joseph A Franco
Natl Sales: Bally Faudar
Sls Dir: Michele Judge

JAY GROUP, THE
See JAY GROUP LTD

D-U-N-S 05-676-5233 IMP
JAY GROUP INC
ORIBE
700 Indian Springs Dr, Lancaster, PA 17601-7800
Tel (717) 285-6200 Founded/Ownrshp 1970
Sales 84.9MM[E] EMP 273
SIC 5961 7389 7331 7319 5199 Catalog & mail-order houses; Telemarketing services; Direct mail advertising services; Distribution of advertising material or sample services; Packaging materials
Pr: Dana Chryst
*Ch Bd: J Freeland Chryst
*Pr: H Douglas Bushong
*Pr: Dana A Chryst
COO: Doug Fisher
CFO: Joseph Grabias
*CFO: Craig Robinson
*Sec: Michael P Boyer
*Sec: John J Shields
Bd of Dir: Matt Fitzgerald
VP: Paul Carton
VP: Tolga Demiralay
VP: David Durham
VP: Christopher Marett
VP: Howard Sadler
*VP: David E Wood
Exec: Kim Fairfield

D-U-N-S 78-951-6564 IMP/EXP
JAY GROUP LTD
JAY GROUP, THE
1450 Atlantic Ave, Rocky Mount, NC 27801-2714
Tel (252) 442-2139 Founded/Ownrshp 1991
Sales 98.9MM[E] EMP 130
Accts Dixon Hughes Goodman Llp Ral
SIC 5139 Footwear
CEO: David Jay
*CFO: John Kelly
*VP: Mark Elliott
*VP: Stephen Parsons
Off Admin: Marquita Macon

D-U-N-S 00-415-7145 IMP
JAY INDUSTRIES INC
BROSHCO FABRICATED PRODUCTS
150 Longview Ave E, Mansfield, OH 44903-4206
Tel (419) 524-3778 Founded/Ownrshp 1946
Sales 230.4MM[E] EMP 930
SIC 2531 3089 Seats, automobile; Injection molding of plastics
Pr: Rick R Taylor
*CFO: Rodger Loesch
*Treas: Carol Taylor
*Ex VP: Dave Benick
*VP: Paul Shatlock
*VP: Josh Taylor
*Prin: R G Taylor
Prgrm Mgr: Dan Shell
Telecom Ex: Mark Amicone
Prd Mgr: Jeffrey Spurlock
Sales Exec: Rodney Earick

D-U-N-S 01-658-6075
JAY PETROLEUM INC
PAK-A-SAK
533 S 200 W, Portland, IN 47371-8309
Tel (260) 726-9374 Founded/Ownrshp 1959
Sales 123.5MM EMP 420
Accts Bkd Llp Fort Wayne In
SIC 5411 5172 Convenience stores, chain; Gasoline
Pr: Ronald Freeman
*Sec: Timothy Caster
*VP: Chris Braun
*VP: Kevin Huffman

D-U-N-S 19-148-3986 IMP
JAYA APPAREL GROUP LLC
5175 S Soto St, Vernon, CA 90058-3620
Tel (323) 584-3500 Founded/Ownrshp 2005
Sales 110.0MM EMP 130
SIC 2339 2337 Women's & misses' jackets & coats, except sportswear; Shorts (outerwear): women's, misses' & juniors'; Women's & misses' suits & skirts
CEO: Jane Siskin
*CFO: Don Lewis
VP: Ingrid Saurer
Natl Sales: Katelyn Berberian
*Mktg Mgr: Jalal Elbasri

JAYC FOOD STORES
See KROGER LIMITED PARTNERSHIP I

D-U-N-S 05-122-1125 EXP
■ **JAYCO INC**
BOTTOM LINE RV
(Suby of THOR INDUSTRIES INC) ★
903 S Main St, Middlebury, IN 46540-8529
Tel (574) 825-5861 Founded/Ownrshp 2016
Sales 911.5MM[E] EMP 1,770
SIC 5013 3716 3792 Trailer parts & accessories; Motor homes; Recreational van conversion (self-propelled), factory basis; House trailers, except as permanent dwellings; Campers, for mounting on trucks; Camping trailers & chassis
Pr: Derald Bontrager
VP: Tadd K Jenkins
VP: Joseph Morthorst
VP Opers: Phil Geise
Sfty Dirs: Paul Gardner
Manager: Brian Lapray

D-U-N-S 13-047-4971
JAYNES COMPANIES
2906 Broadway Blvd Ne, Albuquerque, NM 87107-1506
Tel (505) 345-8591 Founded/Ownrshp 2002
Sales 167.3MM[E] EMP 300[E]
SIC 1611 General contractor, highway & street construction
VP: Donald Power
IT Man: Berube Mark

D-U-N-S 00-711-2253
JAYNES CORP (NM)
JAYNES STRUCTURES
(Suby of JAYNES COMPANIES) ★
2906 Broadway Blvd Ne, Albuquerque, NM 87107-1599
Tel (505) 345-8591 Founded/Ownrshp 1965
Sales 167.3MM[E] EMP 250
SIC 1542 1541 Hospital construction; School building construction; Commercial & office building, new construction; Industrial buildings, new construction
CEO: Rick Marquardt
*Pr: Shad James
*CFO: Tracy Utterback
Sr VP: William A Florez
VP: Krishna Reddi
Exec: Del Ameko
Genl Mgr: Daniel Sanchez
IT Man: Matt Ammerman
Sfty Mgr: Bryan Mitchell
Sls Mgr: Scott Villane

JAYNES STRUCTURES
See JAYNES CORP

D-U-N-S 05-265-3784
JAZZ CASINO CO LL C
HARRAH'S CASINO
8 Canal St, New Orleans, LA 70130-1601
Tel (504) 525-6260 Founded/Ownrshp 2008
Sales 38.3MM[E] EMP 2,500
SIC 7011 Casino hotel
MIS Mgr: Desmond Robinson

D-U-N-S 13-592-6363 IMP
JAZZ PHARMACEUTICALS INC
(Suby of JAZZ PHARMACEUTICALS PUBLIC LIMITED COMPANY)
3180 Porter Dr, Palo Alto, CA 94304-1288
Tel (650) 496-3777 Founded/Ownrshp 2012
Sales 1.3MMM EMP 626[E]
SIC 2834 Pharmaceutical preparations; Drugs acting on the central nervous system & sense organs
Ch Bd: Bruce C Cozadd
*CFO: Kathryn E Falberg
Bd of Dir: James Momtazee
*Ex VP: Russell J Cox
*Ex VP: Suzanne Sawochka Hooper
Ex VP: Jeffrey Tobias
VP: David Brabazon
VP: Laurie Hurley
VP: Michael Kelly
VP: Charles Lapree
VP: Kathee Littrell
VP: Shawn Mindus
VP: Craig Parker
VP: Michael Romanowicz
VP: Trudy Vanhove
VP: Trudy F Vanhove
Assoc Dir: Romy Alhadef
Assoc Dir: Roberta Bongers
Assoc Dir: Wendy Burton
Assoc Dir: Jeff Christensen
Assoc Dir: Yelena Khaymovich

D-U-N-S 11-057-3743 IMP
JAZZ SEMICONDUCTOR INC
TOWERJAZZ
(Suby of JAZZ TECHNOLOGIES INC) ★
4321 Jamboree Rd, Newport Beach, CA 92660-3007
Tel (949) 435-8000 Founded/Ownrshp 2007
Sales 221.4MM[E] EMP 805
SIC 3674 Wafers (semiconductor devices)
Ch Bd: Amir Elstein
*Pr: Itzhak Edrei
COO: Chang-Ou Lee
*COO: Rafi Mor
*CFO: Oren Shirazi
VP: Ilan Rabinovich
VP: Marco Racanelli
Dir Bus: Kazuo Inoue
Dir IT: Meir Siso
IT Man: William Krieger
IT Man: Alex Liu
Board of Directors: Donald Beall, Dwight Decker, Patrick R McCarter, Jerry Neal, Todd Newnam, R Douglas Norby, Donald Schrock

JAZZ TECHNOLOGIES, INC.
See TOWER US HOLDINGS INC

D-U-N-S 08-408-6131
JAZZY ELECTRONICS CORP
PYRAMID SOUND
1600 63rd St, Brooklyn, NY 11204-2713
Tel (718) 236-8000 Founded/Ownrshp 1977
Sales 103.4MM[E] EMP 125[E]
SIC 6512 5064 3651 Nonresidential building operators; High fidelity equipment; Household audio & video equipment
Pr: Zigmond Brach
*Pr: Jerry Brach

D-U-N-S 00-633-8552
▲ **JB HUNT TRANSPORT SERVICES INC**
615 Jb Hunt Corp Dr, Lowell, AR 72745
Tel (479) 820-0000 Founded/Ownrshp 1961
Sales 6.1MMM EMP 20,158
Tkr Sym JBHT Exch NGS
SIC 4213 4731 Trucking, except local; Freight transportation arrangement
Pr: John N Roberts III
*Ch Bd: Kirk Thompson
Pr: John McKuin
COO: Craig Harper
CFO: David G Mee
CFO: Jerry Walton
Ofcr: Paul R Bergant
Ex VP: Stuart L Scott
VP: Tracy Black
VP: Greg Breeden
VP: Mark Calcagni
VP: Andrew Deblock
VP: Brian Dieringer
VP: Mike Dougherty
VP: Bill Fedorchak
VP: Darren Field
VP: Jeff Franco
VP: Grant Hanby
VP: Michael Hinkle
VP: Derek Kennemer
VP: John Kuhlow

D-U-N-S 14-212-4614
JB JAMES CONSTRUCTION LLC
1881 Wooddale Blvd, Baton Rouge, LA 70806-1510
Tel (225) 927-3131 Founded/Ownrshp 2001
Sales 94.0MM[E] EMP 230
SIC 1611 Highway & street construction
Off Mgr: Monica Cornette
*Sls&Mrk Ex: Gerald Denley

JBFCS
See JEWISH BOARD OF FAMILY AND CHILDRENS SERVICES INC

JBG COMPANIES
See JBG PROPERTIES INC

JBG COMPANIES, THE
See JBG COMPANIES L L C

D-U-N-S 07-913-1226
JBG COMPANIES L L C
JBG COMPANIES, THE
4445 Willard Ave, Chevy Chase, MD 20815-3690
Tel (240) 333-3600 Founded/Ownrshp 2003
Sales 122.0MM[E] EMP 238[E]
SIC 6799 Investors
VP: Tom Brennan
Assoc VP: Anthony Greenberg
Ex VP: Robin Mosle
Sr VP: Judy Carter
Sr VP: Roni Kelley
Sr VP: Margaret Klarman
Sr VP: Rafael Muaiz
Sr VP: Michele Smith
VP: Joe Babarsky
VP: Michael Becker
VP: Edward Chaglassian
VP: Frank Draper
VP: ADI Englander
VP: Andrew Horn
VP: Stephen House
VP: Donna McKinnon
VP: Jennifer Michaels
VP: Bryan Moll
VP: James Nozar
VP: Ashesh Parikh
VP: James Reed

D-U-N-S 07-679-5207
JBG PROPERTIES INC
JBG COMPANIES
4445 Willard Ave Ste 400, Chevy Chase, MD 20815-4641
Tel (240) 333-3600 Founded/Ownrshp 1962
Sales 145.3MM[E] EMP 500
SIC 6531 6552 Real estate agents & managers; Subdividers & developers
Sr VP: Brooks A Blake
Sr VP: Krista Di Iaconi
Sr VP: Edward J Kopp
Sr VP: Kai Reynolds
VP: Adam Peters
Genl Mgr: Genny Hardesty
Board of Directors: Brian Coulter, Rob Stewart

JBR GOURMET FOODS
See JBR INC

D-U-N-S 09-706-5510 IMP/EXP
JBR INC
JBR GOURMET FOODS
1731 Aviation Blvd, Lincoln, CA 95648-9317
Tel (916) 258-8000 Founded/Ownrshp 1979
Sales 123.9MM[E] EMP 230[E]
SIC 2095 2099 Roasted coffee; Coffee roasting (except by wholesale grocers); Tea blending
CEO: Jon B Rogers
*VP: Barbara Rogers

D-U-N-S 07-951-2460
JBRE HOLDINGS LLC
8150 N Central Expy, Dallas, TX 75206-1815
Tel (214) 276-5504 Founded/Ownrshp 2014
Sales 96.1MM[E] EMP 855[E]
SIC 7539 6719 Brake repair, automotive; Investment holding companies, except banks

D-U-N-S 84-742-2631
JBRE LLC
JUST BRAKES
(Suby of JBRE HOLDINGS LLC) ★
8150 N Central Expy M1008, Dallas, TX 75206-1815
Tel (214) 276-5504 Founded/Ownrshp 2013
Sales 96.1MM[E] EMP 850
SIC 7539 Brake repair, automotive
Ch Bd: Perry Cloud
*CFO: Wil Saqueton
*VP: Bennet R Cloud
*VP: Clothilde Cloud
*VP: Leigh A Cloud
*VP: Leigh Anne Haugh
*VP: Stewart Manning
Dir IT: Jeff Payne
VP Mktg: Sarah Hamp
Mktg Dir: Judy Wish

D-U-N-S 00-491-9917
JBS CARRIERS INC
(Suby of JBS USA LLC) ★
2401 2nd Ave, Greeley, CO 80631-7205
Tel (866) 298-4573 Founded/Ownrshp 1988
Sales 130.0MM EMP 700[E]
SIC 4213 Trucking, except local
Pr: Rodrigo Horgath
Sfty Dirs: Mark Respass

D-U-N-S 55-647-0651
JBS FIVE RIVERS CATTLE FEEDING LLC
(Suby of JBS USA HOLDINGS LLC) ★
1770 Promontory Cir, Greeley, CO 80634-9039
Tel (970) 506-8000 Founded/Ownrshp 2008
Sales 106.7MM[E] EMP 720
SIC 0211 Beef cattle feedlots
CEO: Mike Thoren
Dir IT: Mike Shafer

D-U-N-S 08-618-6285
JBS PACKERLAND INC
I-57 SERVICE CENTER
(Suby of PACKERLAND HOLDINGS INC) ★
1330 Lime Kiln Rd, Green Bay, WI 54311-6044
Tel (920) 468-4000 Founded/Ownrshp 1994
Sales 122.1MM[E] EMP 1,000
SIC 2011 4213 Boxed beef from meat slaughtered on site; Trucking, except local
Ch Bd: George N Gillett Jr
*Pr: Richard V Vesta
VP: David Jagodzinske
VP: Jerry Shelton
Off Mgr: Dave Trimmer
Sfty Mgr: Jeremy Klingbeil
Sfty Mgr: Eric Plate

D-U-N-S 06-435-0234
JBS SOUDERTON INC
MOPAC
(Suby of JBS S/A)
249 Allentown Rd, Souderton, PA 18964-2207
Tel (215) 723-5555 Founded/Ownrshp 2008
Sales 172.3MM[E] EMP 1,550
SIC 2011 2077 2013 Beef products from beef slaughtered on site; Cured meats from meat slaughtered on site; Luncheon meat from meat slaughtered on site; Meat by-products from meat slaughtered on site; Animal & marine fats & oils; Sausages & other prepared meats
Prin: Keith Fratrick
Prin: Nicholas C Renzi
Genl Mgr: Joshua Duckworth

JBS SWIFT & CO.
See PROTEIN PROVIDERS INC

D-U-N-S 01-661-9637 EXP
JBS UNITED INC
4310 W State Road 38, Sheridan, IN 46069-9639
Tel (317) 758-4495 *Founded/Ownrshp* 1956
Sales 142.4MM^E *EMP* 400
SIC 2048 5153 0213 Livestock feeds; Grains; Hog feedlot
CEO: John B Swisher
**Pr:* Donald E Orr Jr
COO: Doug Webel
**VP:* John L McGraw
**VP:* Douglas M Webel
**Prin:* John Corbett
Plnt Mgr: Chris Wallace
Sls Mgr: Charlie Hild
Nutrtnst: Xiaojing Li

D-U-N-S 04-812-4978 IMP/EXP
JBS USA FOOD CO HOLDINGS
JBS USA, LLC
(*Subsy of* JBS USA HOLDINGS LLC) ★
1770 Promontory Cir, Greeley, CO 80634-9039
Tel (970) 506-8000 *Founded/Ownrshp* 2002, 2015
Sales 8.0MMM^E *EMP* 24,800
SIC 2011 Meat packing plants; Boxed beef from meat slaughtered on site; Pork products from pork slaughtered on site; Lamb products from lamb slaughtered on site
CEO: Andre Nogueira
Pr: Jim Herlihy
Pr: William Van Solkema
CFO: Denilson Molina
**Ch:* Wesley Batista
**Treas:* Gustavo Biscardi
**Sr VP:* Martin Dooley
Sr VP: Brad Lorenger
Sr VP: Jack Shandley
VP: John Bormann
VP: Kiersten Folb
VP: Del Holzer
VP: Chris Jensen
VP: Dathel Nimmons
VP: Geoffrey Scott
VP: Matthew D Wineinger

D-U-N-S 12-693-0226 IMP/EXP
JBS USA HOLDINGS LLC
(*Subsy of* JBS S/A)
1770 Promontory Cir, Greeley, CO 80634-9039
Tel (970) 506-8000 *Founded/Ownrshp* 2002
Sales 12.8MMM^E *EMP* 65,570
SIC 2011 5147 Meat packing plants; Beef products from beef slaughtered on site; Pork products from pork slaughtered on site; Lamb products from lamb slaughtered on site; Meats & meat products; Meats, cured or smoked; Meats, fresh
Pr: Wesley Batista
**CFO:* Andre Nogueira
Top Exec: Steve Snyder
Sr VP: Dan Halstrom
**Sr VP:* Brad Lorenger
VP: Leonard Huskey
VP: Geoffrey Scott
Dir IT: Jim Sehi
Plnt Mgr: Keith Strunk
Mktg Mgr: Lisa Brown
Mktg Mgr: John Punis

JBS USA, LLC
See JBS USA FOOD CO HOLDINGS

JBT
See JOHN BEAN TECHNOLOGIES CORP

JBT FOODTECH
See JBT FOODTECH CITRUS SYSTEMS

D-U-N-S 82-836-3262 IMP/EXP
JBT FOODTECH CITRUS SYSTEMS
JBT FOOD TECH
400 Fairway Ave, Lakeland, FL 33801-2468
Tel (863) 683-5411 *Founded/Ownrshp* 2008
Sales 91.5MM^E *EMP* 84^E
SIC 5169 Food additives & preservatives
CEO: John T Gremp
**Pr:* Thomas W Giacomini

D-U-N-S 01-968-4968
JC CANNISTRARO LLC
80 Rosedale Rd, Watertown, MA 02472-2234
Tel (617) 926-0092 *Founded/Ownrshp* 1963
Sales 205.4MM *EMP* 400
Accts Darmody Merlino & Co Llp Bos
SIC 1711 Plumbing contractors; Heating & air conditioning contractors; Fire sprinkler system installation
Pr: John C Cannistraro Jr
**CEO:* David G Cannistraro
**CFO:* Joseph Ccannistraro
CFO: Joseph Cannistraro
Exec: David Cannistraro
Div Mgr: Christopher Hill
IT Man: Riccardo Armand
IT Man: Davidson Saintus
Info Man: Mike Cannistraro
Sfty Dirs: Matthew Gifford

J.C. EHRLICH
See RENTOKIL NORTH AMERICA INC

D-U-N-S 00-389-9655 IMP
JC EHRLICH CHEMICAL CO
1125 Berkshire Blvd # 150, Reading, PA 19610-1218
Tel (610) 372-9700 *Founded/Ownrshp* 1928
Sales 674.5MM^E *EMP* 1,800
SIC 5191 Chemicals, agricultural; Pesticides
Pr: John Myers
**CFO:* David Waring
**VP:* John Tercha
Mktg Dir: Mary Hart

D-U-N-S 79-307-0689
■ **JC HIGGINS CORP**
(*Subsy of* EMCOR GROUP INC) ★
70 Hawes Way, Stoughton, MA 02072-1163
Tel (781) 341-1500 *Founded/Ownrshp* 1990
Sales 91.4MM^E *EMP* 600
SIC 1711 Mechanical contractor; Ventilation & duct work contractor; Heating & air conditioning contractors; Plumbing contractors
Pr: Bob Gallagher
**Ch Bd:* Joseph C Higgins
CFO: Ronald Ledeoux
**Sec:* Ron Cherkasly
**VP:* Robert Gallagher
**VP:* R Kevin Matz
**VP:* John W Shaughnessy
**VP:* Kevin Walsh

JC IMPORTS
See HOM FURNITURE INC

JC PENNEY
See JC PENNEY CORP INC

JC PENNEY
See J C PENNEY PURCHASING CORP

JC PENNEY
See J C PENNEY LIFE INSURANCE CO

JC PENNEY
See J C PENNEY EUROPE INC

D-U-N-S 00-698-8893 IMP/EXP
■ **JC PENNEY CORP INC**
JC PENNEY
(*Subsy of* J C PENNEY CO INC) ★
6501 Legacy Dr, Plano, TX 75024-3698
Tel (972) 431-1000 *Founded/Ownrshp* 1902
Sales 3.0MMM^E *EMP* 15,500^E
SIC 5311 5961 Department stores, non-discount; Catalog & mail-order houses; Catalog sales
CEO: Mike Ullman
**Ch:* Thomas Engibous
**Ex VP:* Joanne Bober
Sr VP: Timothy M Nichols
**Sr VP:* Ed Robben
**VP:* Ken Hicks
**VP:* E H Sweney
Genl Mgr: Monte Winterhalter
IT Man: Joni Dunstan
IT Man: Sherry Staber
Sftwr Eng: Jennifer Hinson

D-U-N-S 94-869-5184
JC RESORTS LLC
533 Coast Blvd S, La Jolla, CA 92037-4641
Tel (858) 605-2700 *Founded/Ownrshp* 1971
Sales 135.3MM^E *EMP* 1,200
SIC 8741 7992 7991 Hotel or motel management; Public golf courses; Physical fitness facilities
Pr: Paul Reed
**CFO:* Frank Levett
**VP:* Blaise Bartell
Genl Mgr: Maureen Carew

D-U-N-S 05-235-0741 IMP/EXP
JCB INC
(*Subsy of* J.C. BAMFORD EXCAVATORS LIMITED)
2000 Bamford Blvd, Pooler, GA 31322-9504
Tel (912) 447-2000 *Founded/Ownrshp* 1945
Sales 197.1MM^E *EMP* 250
SIC 5082 5084 3531 3537 General construction machinery & equipment; Materials handling machinery; Backhoes; Industrial trucks & tractors
Ch: John Patterson
**Pr:* Graeme Macdonald
CFO: David Miller
VP: Ken Bianco
VP: Ray Bingley
VP: Liam Brown
VP: Arjin Mirdha
VP: Dan Schmidt
VP: Mike Werner
Mng Dir: John Gill
Mng Dir: Paul Grys
Board of Directors: John J Patterson

D-U-N-S 82-861-2676 IMP
JCB MANUFACTURING INC
2000 Bamford Blvd, Pooler, GA 31322-9504
Tel (912) 447-2000 *Founded/Ownrshp* 1998
Sales 85.3MM^E *EMP* 250
SIC 5084 Industrial machinery & equipment
Pr: Arjun Mirdha
**CFO:* Nick Weate
**Ch:* John Patterson

D-U-N-S 07-851-4041
JCG FOODS OF ALABAMA LLC
764 George Cagle Dr, Collinsville, AL 35961-4296
Tel (256) 524-2147 *Founded/Ownrshp* 2012
Sales 119.3MM^E *EMP* 854
SIC 2038 Frozen specialties
CEO: Joseph Grendys

D-U-N-S 80-204-2689
JCG INDUSTRIES INC
4404 W Berteau Ave, Chicago, IL 60641-1907
Tel (847) 384-5940 *Founded/Ownrshp* 1992
Sales 121.3MM^E *EMP* 201
SIC 5144 Poultry products
Pr: Joseph Grendys
**Sec:* Mark J Kaminsky
Off Mgr: Bonnie Diviesti

JCI
See NORMAN YORK INTERNATIONAL

D-U-N-S 07-962-3791
JCI HOLDINGS LLC
549 South St Bldg 19, Quincy, MA 02169-7318
Tel (617) 890-0600 *Founded/Ownrshp* 2014
Sales 200.0MM^E *EMP* 300^E
SIC 1629 Marine construction
Pr: Dale H Pyatt

D-U-N-S 00-221-6091 IMP/EXP
JCI JONES CHEMICALS INC (NY)
1765 Ringling Blvd, Sarasota, FL 34236-6873
Tel (941) 330-1537 *Founded/Ownrshp* 1930
Sales 131.6MM^E *EMP* 250
SIC 2819 2842 Chlorine; Swimming pool & spa chemicals; Caustic soda; Ammonia, household; Bleaches, household: dry or liquid
CEO: Jeffrey W Jones
**CFO:* Dawn Irving
**Ex VP:* Tim Gaffney
**Ex VP:* Ryan Jones
VP: Wayne Hernandez
VP: Susan Jones
VP: Summer Mello
Off Mgr: Pam Nowaske
Dir IT: Zachary Dean
Sales Asso: Pat Mulhall

D-U-N-S 82-702-2877 IMP/EXP
JCIM US LLC
45000 Helm St Ste 200, Plymouth, MI 48170-6040
Tel (734) 254-3100 *Founded/Ownrshp* 2015
Sales 1.8MMM^E *EMP* 6,700^E
SIC 3089

JCP
See ICREST INTERNATIONAL LLC

D-U-N-S 78-648-9554
■ **JCP MEDIA INC**
JCP MEDIA, L.P.
(*Subsy of* J C PENNEY CO INC) ★
6501 Legacy Dr, Plano, TX 75024-3612
Tel (972) 431-1000 *Founded/Ownrshp* 1999
Sales 98.4MM^E *EMP* 5,008^E
SIC 8743 Public relations services
Pr: M J Boylson
**VP:* Jim Francois

JCP MEDIA, L.P.
See JCP MEDIA INC

D-U-N-S 94-264-7660
■ **JCP PUBLICATIONS CORP**
(*Subsy of* JC PENNEY) ★
6501 Legacy Dr, Plano, TX 75024-3612
Tel (972) 431-1000 *Founded/Ownrshp* 1996
Sales 71.8MM^E *EMP* 4,500
SIC 5311 Department stores
CEO: Ellen Questrom

JCPS
See JEFFERSON CITY PUBLIC SCHOOLS

J.CREW
See J CREW OPERATING CORP

D-U-N-S 36-230-8892
JCREW GROUP INC
(*Subsy of* CHINOS INTERMEDIATE HOLDINGS B INC) ★
770 Broadway Fl 11, New York, NY 10003-9512
Tel (212) 209-2500 *Founded/Ownrshp* 2011
Sales 2.5MMM *EMP* 15,300^E
SIC 5961 5621 5611 5632 Catalog & mail-order houses; Women's apparel, mail order; Clothing, mail order (except women's); Mail order house; Women's clothing stores; Men's & boys' clothing stores; Women's accessory & specialty stores; Apparel accessories
Ch Bd: Millard Drexler
Pr: Jenna Lyons
Pr: Michael Nicholson
Ex VP: Lynda Markoe
VP: Jeremy Brooks
CIO: Michelle Garvey
Board of Directors: James Coulter, John Danhakl, Jonathan Sokoloff, Stephen Squeri, Carrie Wheeler

JC'S 5 STAR OUTLET
See SB CAPITAL ACQUISITIONS LLC

D-U-N-S 18-577-2287
JCT HOLDING CO LLC
19007 W Highway 33, Sapulpa, OK 74066-7545
Tel (918) 227-1600 *Founded/Ownrshp* 2004
Sales 250.0MM *EMP* 231
SIC 4213 Refrigerated products transport
Pr: John M Christner
**COO:* Daniel L Christner
**CFO:* Darryl A Christner
VP: Bob Snell

D-U-N-S 00-800-6561
JD ABRAMS LP (TX)
TRANS-MOUNTAIN EQUIPMENT
(*Subsy of* ABRAMS INTERNATIONAL INC) ★
5811 Trade Center Dr # 1, Austin, TX 78744-1311
Tel (512) 322-4000 *Founded/Ownrshp* 1966
Sales 155.1MM *EMP* 750
Accts Schmi Broaddus Nugent Gano Pc
SIC 1611 1622 1629 3272 General contractor, highway & street construction; Bridge construction; Dam construction; Prestressed concrete products
Ch: Jon F Abrams
**Pt:* James D Abrams Sr
**Pt:* J Kelly Gallagher
**Pt:* Bob Underwood
CFO: Kelly Gallagher
VP: C Worrell
**Prin:* Steven Zbranek
Area Mgr: William G Duguay

J.D. BYRIDER
See BYRIDER SALES OF INDIANA S LLC

D-U-N-S 62-047-4510
JD BYRIDER SYSTEMS LLC
12802 Hmlton Crssing Blvd, Carmel, IN 46032-5424
Tel (317) 249-3000 *Founded/Ownrshp* 1989
Sales 146.9MM^E *EMP* 625
SIC 6794 5734 7538 7515 5521 Franchises, selling or licensing; Computer & software stores; General automotive repair shops; Passenger car leasing; Used car dealers
CEO: Steven E Wedding
COO: Rob Palmer
CFO: Brian Littleton
CFO: Phillip Ratkovic
VP: Thomas L Welter
Off Mgr: Elvia Ysasaga
Snr Sftwr: Daniel Davis
IT Man: Paul Pavich

D-U-N-S 12-447-5732 EXP
JD EQUIPMENT INC
JOHN DEERE AUTHORIZED DEALER
3979 Parkway Ln, Hilliard, OH 43026-1250
Tel (614) 527-8800 *Founded/Ownrshp* 1983
Sales 202.5MM^E *EMP* 200
SIC 5999 5083 Farm equipment & supplies; Agricultural machinery & equipment
CEO: Jeff Mitchell
**Pr:* Don K Mitchell Jr
**Treas:* Carla Mitchell
**VP:* Maxine Mitchell
Exec: Dick Landes
Store Mgr: Dave Donohue
Store Mgr: Kevin Finton
Store Mgr: Cody Kirkpatrick
Store Mgr: Michael Murphy
Sls Mgr: Joe Goettemoeller

J.D. HEISKELL AND COMPANY
See J D HEISKELL HOLDINGS LLC

D-U-N-S 02-772-9299
JD MELLBERG FINANCIAL
3067 W Ina Rd Ste 105, Tucson, AZ 85741-2106
Tel (520) 731-9000 *Founded/Ownrshp* 2011
Sales NA *EMP* 150
SIC 6311 Life insurance
Pr: Josh Mellberg
CFO: Douglas Lamb
Sr VP: Brent Matthew
IT Man: Eric Thiessen
VP Opers: Rosa Garcia

D-U-N-S 00-506-4381 IMP
JD NORMAN INDUSTRIES INC (IL)
787 W Belden Ave, Addison, IL 60101-4942
Tel (630) 458-3700 *Founded/Ownrshp* 1986, 2004
Sales 116.9MM^E *EMP* 350
SIC 3469 3496 3495 Metal stampings; Miscellaneous fabricated wire products; Wire springs
Pr: Justin D Norman
**VP:* Chey Becker-Varto
**VP:* Elizabeth Kousiakis
Prgrm Mgr: Paul Macduff
Opers Mgr: Timothy M Knight
Plnt Mgr: Alberto Hernandez
Ql Cn Mgr: Dinela Visan
Oper/Mgr: Charles Gibson

D-U-N-S 07-619-6526
JD POWER AND ASSOCIATES
(*Subsy of* XIO (UK) LLP)
3200 Park Center Dr Fl 13, Costa Mesa, CA 92626-7163
Tel (714) 621-6200 *Founded/Ownrshp* 2016
Sales 162.1MM^E *EMP* 800
SIC 8732 Survey service: marketing, location, etc.
Pr: Finbarr O'Neill
**CFO:* Joseph Damour
Sr VP: Deirdre Borrego
Sr VP: Keith Webster
VP: Deidre Borrego
VP: Greg Hoeg
VP: John Humphrey
VP: Jeff Leiman
**VP:* Jonathan Miller
VP: Diane Nott-Kilfoil
VP: Lindsay Rush
VP: David Sargent
VP: Brian Walters

D-U-N-S 82-610-0455
JD RAMMING PAVING MANAGEMENT LLC
RAMMING PAVING COMPANY
(*Subsy of* SUMMIT MATERIALS LLC) ★
9020 N Cpitl Of Texas Hwy, Austin, TX 78759-7279
Tel (512) 251-3713 *Founded/Ownrshp* 2011
Sales 92.6MM^E *EMP* 270
SIC 1611 1771 General contractor, highway & street construction; Concrete work
Pr: John D Ramming
Pt: Chuck Fuller
Pt: Dean Lundquist
Pt: Grant Shelton

D-U-N-S 94-260-3325
JDA SOFTWARE GROUP INC
(*Subsy of* RP CROWN PARENT LLC) ★
15059 N Scottsdale Rd # 400, Scottsdale, AZ 85254-2666
Tel (480) 308-3000 *Founded/Ownrshp* 2012
Sales 1.2MMM^E *EMP* 6,199^E
SIC 7371 Computer software development & applications
CEO: Baljit Dail
**Pr:* Hamish N J Brewer
COO: Scott Hamilton
**CFO:* Peter S Hathaway
**CFO:* Marc Levine
**Chf Cred:* Todd Johnston
Chf Mktg O: Larry Ferrere
**Ofcr:* Brian Boylan
**Ofcr:* Razat Gaurav
**Ofcr:* Enrique Rodriguez
Ex VP: Brian P Boylan
**Ex VP:* Thomas Dziersk
**Ex VP:* David Gai
Ex VP: Cindy Howton
Ex VP: Kevin Iaquinto
**Ex VP:* David Kennedy
**Ex VP:* David R King
**Ex VP:* John L Kopcke
Ex VP: Serge Massicotte
Ex VP: Jason B Zintak
Sr VP: David Johnston

D-U-N-S 18-390-2048
JDA SOFTWARE INC
(*Subsy of* JDA SOFTWARE GROUP INC) ★
15059 N Scottsdale Rd # 400, Scottsdale, AZ 85254-2666
Tel (480) 308-3000 *Founded/Ownrshp* 1985
Sales 1.0MMM *EMP* 794
SIC 7371 7373 Custom computer programming services; Computer integrated systems design
CEO: Baljit S Dail
**Pr:* Daniel J Maynard
**Ex VP:* Brian Boylan
**Ex VP:* Razat Gaurav

*Ex VP: Kevin Iaquinto
*Sr VP: Salil Joshi
Sr VP: Duane Kotsen
Sr VP: David Tidmarsh
VP: Gina Harmatiuk
VP: Aamer Rehman
QA Dir: Aftab Ahmed

D-U-N-S 02-779-4577 IMP
JDB INC
380 S Pacific Hwy, Woodburn, OR 97071-5931
Tel (503) 874-3000 Founded/Ownrshp 1980
Sales 168.0MM^E EMP 800
Accts Perkins & Company Pc Portl
SIC 2015 2013 Poultry slaughtering & processing; Prepared beef products from purchased beef
CEO: Glen Golomski
*CFO: Kristan Hoke
*VP: Rob Bruce
*VP: Terry Buford
*Prin: Don Kelley
IT Man: Deborah Miles

J.D.C.
See AMERICAN JEWISH JOINT DISTRIBUTION COMMITTEE INC

D-U-N-S 04-895-4572
JDM STEEL SERVICE INC
330 E Joe Orr Rd Unit 3, Chicago Heights, IL 60411-1296
Tel (708) 757-2092 Founded/Ownrshp 2005
Sales 100.0MM EMP 50^E
SIC 5051 4225 Metals service centers & offices; General warehousing & storage
Pr: Richard A Merlo
*Pr: George Cimbala
Pr: Paul Inbody
CFO: Jim Baranthouse
*VP: Paul Cravens
*VP: Gene Puk
Ql Cn Mgr: Ken Ray
VP Sls: Tom Zager

D-U-N-S 07-772-6172 IMP
JDRF INTERNATIONAL
J D R F
26 Broadway, New York, NY 10004-1703
Tel (212) 785-9500 Founded/Ownrshp 1970
Sales 205.4MM EMP 600^E
Accts Kpmg Llp New York Ny
SIC 8399 8733 Fund raising organization, non-fee basis; Noncommercial research organizations
Pr: Derek Rapp
*Ch Bd: Mark Fischer-Colbrie
*CFO: Mark Greene
*Ch: Robert Wood Johnson IV
*Treas: David W Nelms
Ex VP: Mania Boyder
*Ex VP: Richard Insel
Ex VP: David E Wheadon
Sr VP: Pam Gatz
Sr VP: Steven Griffen
Sr VP: Benita Shobe
Assoc Dir: Esther Latres
Assoc Dir: Sherri Lozano

D-U-N-S 02-822-7593 IMP/EXP
JDRUSH CO INC
(Suby of VARNER FAMILY LIMITED PARTNERSHIP) ★
5900 E Lerdo Hwy, Shafter, CA 93263-4023
Tel (661) 392-1900 Founded/Ownrshp 1957
Sales 111.0MM EMP 105
SIC 5051 Pipe & tubing, steel
CEO: James Varner
Sec: Paul Sahey
VP: Teri Seely

JDSU
See ACTERNA LLC

D-U-N-S 14-623-7875
■ JDSU ACTERNA HOLDINGS LLC
(Suby of VIAVI SOLUTIONS INC) ★
1 Milestone Center Ct, Germantown, MD 20876-7106
Tel (240) 404-1550 Founded/Ownrshp 2005
Sales 198.7MM^E EMP 1,700
SIC 3825 Instruments to measure electricity

D-U-N-S 00-890-6844 IMP
JE DUNN CONSTRUCTION CO
(Suby of JE DUNN CONSTRUCTION GROUP INC) ★
1001 Locust St, Kansas City, MO 64106-1904
Tel (816) 474-8600 Founded/Ownrshp 1924
Sales 2.9MMM EMP 1,635
Accts Kpmg Llp Kansas City Missour
SIC 1542 Commercial & office building, new construction
Ch Bd: Stephen D Dunn
Pr: Gordon E Landsford III
CFO: Beth A Soukup
V Ch Bd: William H Dunn Sr
Ex VP: William H Dunn Jr
Ex VP: Greg Nook
Ex VP: Tom Whittaker
Sr VP: John Rowlett
VP: David Barber
VP: Mike Bartlett
VP: Randall J Bredar
VP: Randall Bredar
VP: Curt Campbell
VP: Jeffrey Campbell
VP: Michael Clippinger
VP: Mike Cloud
VP: Charles Daniel
VP: Bill Dunn Jr
VP: Robert P Dunn
VP: Bill Edwards
VP: Paul Fenzl

D-U-N-S 00-783-6448
JE DUNN CONSTRUCTION GROUP INC (MO)
1001 Locust St, Kansas City, MO 64106-1904
Tel (816) 474-8600 Founded/Ownrshp 1981
Sales 2.9MMM EMP 2,090
Accts Kpmg Llp Kansas City Missour
SIC 1542 Commercial & office building, new construction
CEO: Gordon Lansford III
*Ch Bd: Stephen D Dunn
*V Ch: William H Dunn Sr
*Pr: Terrence P Dunn
CFO: Gordon E Lansford
*CFO: Beth Soukup
Ofcr: Tom Whittaker
*Ex VP: William H Dunn Jr
Ex VP: Gregory E Nook
Sr VP: Richard Beyer
*VP: Robert P Dunn
VP: Tom Raney
VP: Chris Sorensen
VP: Melanie Tucker
Board of Directors: Kevin A Dunn, Robert P Dunn, Robert A Long

D-U-N-S 15-362-9670
JE RICHARDS INC
(Suby of PHALCON LTD) ★
10401 Tucker St, Beltsville, MD 20705-2202
Tel (301) 345-1300 Founded/Ownrshp 2006
Sales 122.0MM EMP 500
SIC 1731

JE SPORT DIV
See JORDACHE LIMITED

D-U-N-S 07-758-0223 IMP
JEA
21 W Church St Fl 1, Jacksonville, FL 32202-3158
Tel (904) 665-6000 Founded/Ownrshp 1968
Sales 2.2MMM^E EMP 2,356
SIC 4911 1623 Electric services; Water, sewer & utility lines
CEO: Paul McElroy
*Pr: James Chancellor
CFO: Mary Arditti
*CFO: Melissa Dykes
Chf Mktg O: Jane McNally
*Ex VP: James Dickenson
VP: Randy Boswell
*VP: Mike Brost
VP: Bill Cutts
VP: Debbie Hayes
*VP: Brian Roche
Board of Directors: John Coxwell, Robert M Harris, Ernest Isaac Jr, Max K Morris, Pamela Quarles, John Schickel, Robert L Stein

D-U-N-S 03-013-8390 IMP
JEAN NELL ENTERPRISES INC
OUTDOORSMAN, THE
1 Nell Jean Sq 19, Beckley, WV 25801-2200
Tel (304) 253-0200 Founded/Ownrshp 1975
Sales 100.6MM EMP 9^E
SIC 5941 5082 5091 Archery supplies; Mining machinery & equipment, except petroleum; Sporting & recreation goods
Pr: Harry M Hylton
*Sec: Jerry Acord
*VP: Tracy W Hylton II
*VP: Warren Hylton

D-U-N-S 06-901-3605
JEANES HOSPITAL
(Suby of TEMPLE UNIVERSITY HEALTH SYSTEM INC) ★
7600 Central Ave, Philadelphia, PA 19111-2499
Tel (215) 728-2000 Founded/Ownrshp 1996
Sales 136.8MM EMP 1,100
SIC 8062 General medical & surgical hospitals
CEO: Dr Marc Hurowitz
*CEO: Linda J Grass
CFO: Joe Scully
*Treas: Thomas S Albanesi Jr
Bd of Dir: F P Buckman
Bd of Dir: George C Corson
Bd of Dir: Joseph Evans
Bd of Dir: Joan Randolph
Bd of Dir: Eleanor Reinhardt
Bd of Dir: Thomas Unkefer
Bd of Dir: Roger Wood

D-U-N-S 13-136-0935 IMP
JEANJER LLC
JUST FOR MEN DIV
1400 Broadway Fl 15, New York, NY 10018-5300
Tel (212) 944-1330 Founded/Ownrshp 1985
Sales 105.7MM^E EMP 3,000
SIC 2331 2337 2339 2369 Blouses, women's & juniors': made from purchased material; Suits: women's, misses' & juniors'; Slacks: women's, misses' & juniors'; Girls' & children's outerwear
Pr: Joe Nakash
*Treas: Ralph Nakash
*VP: AVI Naakash
Sls Mgr: Charles Flores

JEFF ANDERSON REGIONAL MED CTR
See ANDERSON REGIONAL MEDICAL CENTER

JEFFCO PUBLIC SCHOOLS
See JEFFERSON COUNTY SCHOOL DISTRICT NO R-1

D-U-N-S 06-777-8449
■ JEFFERIES GROUP LLC
(Suby of LEUCADIA NATIONAL CORP) ★
520 Madison Ave, New York, NY 10022-4213
Tel (212) 284-2550 Founded/Ownrshp 2013
Sales 3.2MMM EMP 3,915^E
SIC 6211 Investment bankers; Security brokers & dealers
Ch Bd: Richard B Handler
Pr: Joe Baidoo
Pr: Harshul Banthia
Pr: Bruce M Bossert
Pr: Michael Embry
Pr: Dean Osofsky
CFO: Peregrine C Broadbent
Treas: Kenneth Nehlsen
Treas: John Stacconi
Ex VP: Jeffrey Beckmen
Ex VP: Lloyd Feller
Ex VP: David Schwartz
Ex VP: Carl Toriello
Sr VP: Marion Guilbert
Sr VP: John Riedel
VP: Jeff Agnew
VP: Daniel Aharoni
VP: Vicki Andreadis
VP: Joshua Araujo
VP: Kim Atkinson
VP: Kenneth Bann
Board of Directors: Barry J Alperin, W Patrick Campbell, Richard G Dooley, Brian P Friedman, Maryanne Gilmartin, Joseph S Steinberg

D-U-N-S 04-310-3340
■ JEFFERIES LLC
(Suby of JEFFERIES GROUP LLC) ★
520 Madison Ave Fl 10, New York, NY 10022-4213
Tel (212) 284-2300 Founded/Ownrshp 1962, 1973
Sales 925.0MM^E EMP 1,050
SIC 6211 Brokers, security; Dealers, security
Ch Bd: Richard B Handler
*Pr: Patrice Blanc
Pr: Adam De Chiara
Pr: William F Farmer
Pr: Bradford L Klein
Pr: Michael J Richter
*Pr: John Shaw Jr
*CEO: Michael Alexander
*CFO: Peregrine C Broadbent
*CFO: Joseph Schenk
Treas: Paul Dolid
*Treas: Ronald Johnson
Assoc VP: Tony Cario
*Ex VP: Jonathan Cunningham
*Ex VP: Lloyd H Feller
*Ex VP: Chris Kanoff
*Ex VP: Curtis W Schade
*Ex VP: Clifford A Siegel
*Ex VP: Maxine Syrjamaki
*Ex VP: Andrew Whittaker
Sr VP: Kenneth Bann

D-U-N-S 07-034-2183
JEFFERSON CITY PUBLIC SCHOOLS
JCPS
315 E Dunklin St, Jefferson City, MO 65101-3197
Tel (573) 659-3000 Founded/Ownrshp 1838
Sales 55.4MM^E EMP 1,100
SIC 8211 Public elementary & secondary schools; Vocational high school; Elementary school
CFO: Jason Hoffman
Pr Dir: Amy Berendzen

JEFFERSON COUNTY
See COUNTY OF JEFFERSON

D-U-N-S 07-764-9044
JEFFERSON COUNTY ALABAMA
716 Richard Arrington Jr, Birmingham, AL 35203-0114
Tel (205) 731-2880 Founded/Ownrshp 1819
Sales NA EMP 4,077
SIC 9111 Executive offices;
Pr: Bettye Finecollins
CFO: George Tablack
Treas: Barry K Stephenson
CIO: Roosevelt Butler
Opers Mgr: Joe White

JEFFERSON COUNTY BOARD EDUCATN
See JEFFERSON COUNTY SCHOOL DISTRICT

D-U-N-S 06-298-4430
JEFFERSON COUNTY BOARD OF EDUCATION
JEFFERSON COUNTY PUB SCHOOLS
3332 Newburg Rd, Louisville, KY 40218-2414
Tel (502) 485-3011 Founded/Ownrshp 1884
Sales 1.1MMM^E EMP 14,000^E
Accts Strothman & Company Psc Loui
SIC 8211 8741 Public elementary & secondary schools; Specialty education; Management services
CFO: Cornelia Hardin
Ofcr: Larry Priddy
Dir Teleco: Gerald Evans
Dir Sec: Stanford Mullen
Psych: Traci Taylor

D-U-N-S 07-210-6743
JEFFERSON COUNTY BOARD OF EDUCATION
2100 Richard Arrington Jr, Birmingham, AL 35209-1298
Tel (205) 379-2000 Founded/Ownrshp 1914
Sales 194.0MM^E EMP 5,000
Accts Ronald L Jones
SIC 8211 9111 Public elementary & secondary schools; County supervisors' & executives' offices
Pr: Jennifer Parsons
Treas: Catherine Brockman
VP: Joe Morris
*VP: Ronald Rhodes

JEFFERSON COUNTY PUB SCHOOLS
See JEFFERSON COUNTY BOARD OF EDUCATION

D-U-N-S 07-663-5325
JEFFERSON COUNTY PUBLIC HOSPITAL DISTRICT 2
JEFFERSON HEALTHCARE
834 Sheridan St, Port Townsend, WA 98368-2443
Tel (360) 379-8031 Founded/Ownrshp 1975
Sales 94.5MM^E EMP 500
Accts Dingus Zarecor & Associates P
SIC 8062 General medical & surgical hospitals
CEO: Mike Glenn
Dir Vol: Marsha Goldman
*COO: Paula Dowdle
*CFO: Hilary Whittington
Exec: Heather Bailey
Dir Lab: Alice Smith
Chf Nrs Of: Joyce Cardinal
Chf Nrs Of: Jackie Mossakowski
Ex Dir: Brandie Manuel
Ex Dir: Clarence Tupper
Prac Mgr: Colleen Rodrigues

D-U-N-S 07-846-4998
JEFFERSON COUNTY PUBLIC SCHOOL DISTRICT
3332 Newburg Rd, Louisville, KY 40218-2414
Tel (502) 485-3011 Founded/Ownrshp 2012
Sales 20.0MM^E EMP 13,049^E
SIC 8211 Elementary & secondary schools
Prin: Shari Morelli
Dir Sec: David Self
MIS Dir: Raghu Seshadr
Pr Dir: Allison Martin
Teacher Pr: Tiffany Armour
Instr Medi: Paul Lanata
HC Dir: Anne Perryman

D-U-N-S 10-067-0876
JEFFERSON COUNTY SCHOOL DISTRICT
JEFFERSON COUNTY BOARD EDUCATN
1221 Gay St, Dandridge, TN 37725-4723
Tel (865) 397-3138 Founded/Ownrshp 1991
Sales 42.2MM^E EMP 1,000
SIC 8211 Public elementary & secondary schools
Trst: Ginger Franklin
CIO: Norma Huff
Pr Dir: Dominique Salaciak
Teacher Pr: Carol Baker
HC Dir: Mandy Schneitman

D-U-N-S 01-062-0565
JEFFERSON COUNTY SCHOOL DISTRICT NO R-1
JEFFCO PUBLIC SCHOOLS
1829 Denver West Dr # 27, Golden, CO 80401-3120
Tel (303) 982-6500 Founded/Ownrshp 1950
Sales 801.2MM EMP 12,000
Accts Cliftonlarsonallen Llp Broomf
SIC 8211 Public elementary & secondary schools; High school, junior or senior; Public combined elementary & secondary school
COO: Bob Smith
Treas: Jill Fellman
Ex Dir: Rich Waterman
Dir Sec: John McDonald
Prgrm Mgr: Alvin Tafoya
MIS Dir: Michael Gordon
Dir IT: Brent Heaviland
IT Man: Dawn Miller
Netwrk Eng: Michael Kent
Pr Dir: Diana Wilson
Schl Brd P: Ken Witt

D-U-N-S 07-953-4552
JEFFERSON COUNTY SCHOOLS
2100 Richard Arrington Jr, Birmingham, AL 35209-1298
Tel (205) 379-2000 Founded/Ownrshp 1914
Sales 39.1MM^E EMP 4,604^E
SIC 8211 Public elementary & secondary schools
HC Dir: Ken Storie

D-U-N-S 96-213-4578
JEFFERSON COUNTY SCHOOLS PUBLIC EDUCATION FOUNDATION
2100 Rich Arrington Jr Bl, Birmingham, AL 35203-1102
Tel (205) 379-2216 Founded/Ownrshp 1992
Sales 361.2M EMP 4,200
Accts Borland Benefield Birmingham
SIC 8699 Animal humane society
Ex Dir: Sally Price

D-U-N-S 79-307-6795
JEFFERSON ENERGY I LP
3104 Edloe St Ste 205, Houston, TX 77027-6022
Tel (713) 552-0002 Founded/Ownrshp 1993
Sales 98.5MM^E EMP 4
SIC 1389 5051 Oil field services; Tubing, metal
Pr: Edward T Cotham Jr
*Treas: John Storms
VP: Robert L Parker

JEFFERSON HEALTHCARE
See JEFFERSON COUNTY PUBLIC HOSPITAL DISTRICT 2

D-U-N-S 06-872-5910
JEFFERSON HOSPITAL
(Suby of HIGHMARK BLUE CRSS-BLUE SHIELD) ★
565 Coal Valley Rd, Clairton, PA 15025-3703
Tel (412) 267-6024 Founded/Ownrshp 2013
Sales 215.5MM^E EMP 2,000
SIC 8062 8063 8069 General medical & surgical hospitals; Psychiatric hospitals; Alcoholism rehabilitation hospital; Drug addiction rehabilitation hospital
Pr: John J Dempster
*V Ch: Gary W Deschamps
*COO: Robert A Frank Sr
CFO: Joanne Hachey
*Treas: C R Modispacher
VP: Dorothy Bellhouse
VP: Marcie Caplan
VP: Judy M Hall
Dir Lab: Brian Graper
Chf Nrs Of: Joy Peters
Dir IT: Jim Witenske

D-U-N-S 07-563-9096
JEFFERSON HOSPITAL ASSOCIATION INC
JEFFERSON REGIONAL MEDICAL CTR
1600 W 40th Ave, Pine Bluff, AR 71603-6301
Tel (870) 541-7100 Founded/Ownrshp 1966
Sales 170.8MM EMP 1,700
SIC 8062 General medical & surgical hospitals
Pr: Simpson M Tanya
Chf Rad: Melvin Hedgewood
CFO: Nathan Van Genderen
Chf Mktg O: Reid Pierce
*Ex VP: Tomas Harbuck
Dir Lab: Michael R Smith
Adm Dir: Andy Jenkins
Dir IT: Patrick Neece

D-U-N-S 36-152-9373 IMP
JEFFERSON INDUSTRIES CORP
6670 State Route 29, West Jefferson, OH 43162-9677
Tel (614) 879-5300 Founded/Ownrshp 1988
Sales 320.0MM EMP 750^E
SIC 3711 Chassis, motor vehicle
Pr: Shiro Shimokagi
*VP: Kazuhiko Hara
*VP: Hassan Saadat
*Exec: Steve Yoder
*Prin: Curtis A Loveland

JEFFERSON INSURANCE CO
See AGA SERVICE CO

Section I Businesses Alphabetically

D-U-N-S 02-718-2294 IMP/EXP
JEFFERSON IRON AND METAL BROKERAGE INC
3940 Montclair Rd Ste 300, Mountain Brk, AL 35213-2420
Tel (205) 803-5200 *Founded/Ownrshp* 1984
Sales 125.0MM *EMP* 22
SIC 5051 Ferrous metals; Miscellaneous nonferrous products
Pr: George Dreher
Ch: Paul Dreher
VP: Jim Nuckels

JEFFERSON LAB
See THOMAS JEFFERSON NATIONAL ACCELERATOR FACILITY

JEFFERSON MEDICAL COLLEGE
See THOMAS JEFFERSON UNIVERSITY

D-U-N-S 00-503-3612
JEFFERSON MEMORIAL COMMUNITY FOUNDATION 145
1450 Parkway W, Festus, MO 63028-2385
Tel (636) 638-1400 *Founded/Ownrshp* 2013
Sales 157.1MM *EMP* 3
SIC 8641 Civic social & fraternal associations

D-U-N-S 05-136-9977
JEFFERSON PARISH PUBLIC SCHOOL SYSTEM
501 Manhattan Blvd, Harvey, LA 70058-4443
Tel (504) 349-7600 *Founded/Ownrshp* 2010
Sales 388.6MME *EMP* 5,832E
SIC 8211 Public elementary & secondary schools
Dir Sec: James Hufft
Sfty Dirs: Lisa Gautreau
Pr Dir: Elizabeth Branley
HC Dir: Angie Ruiz

D-U-N-S 07-508-4178
JEFFERSON PARISH SCHOOL BOARD INC
501 Manhattan Blvd, Harvey, LA 70058-4443
Tel (504) 349-7803 *Founded/Ownrshp* 1955
Sales 65.7MM *EMP* 7,200E
Accts Mike B Gillespie Cpa Jennin
SIC 8211 School board
Pr: Cedric Floyd
*COO: Lale Geer
*CFO: Robert Fulton
IT Man: Vu Vuong

D-U-N-S 07-861-2197
JEFFERSON PARISH SHERIFFS OFFICE
SHERIFF NEWELL NORMAND
1233 Westbank Expy, Harvey, LA 70058-4462
Tel (504) 363-5500 *Founded/Ownrshp* 2007
Sales NA *EMP* 1,450E
SIC 9221 9223 Sheriffs' offices;
CFO: Paul Rivera
*CEO: Newell Normand
Ofcr: Steven Abadie
Ofcr: Steve Higgerson

JEFFERSON REGIONAL MEDICAL CTR
See JEFFERSON HOSPITAL ASSOCIATION INC

JEFFERSON-PILOT
See ABE ENTERCOM HOLDINGS LLC

D-U-N-S 04-917-5927
JEFFREY L LONDON
70 W Madison St Ste 4200, Chicago, IL 60602-4230
Tel (312) 583-2339 *Founded/Ownrshp* 2010
Sales 400.0MM *EMP* 900
SIC 8111 General practice attorney, lawyer
Owner: Jeffrey L London

D-U-N-S 00-514-1346 IMP/EXP
JEL SERT CO
J S
Conde St Rr 59, West Chicago, IL 60185
Tel (630) 231-7590 *Founded/Ownrshp* 1929
Sales 175.2MME *EMP* 277E
SIC 2087 2024 2099 5499 5143 Concentrates, flavoring (except drink); Fruit pops, frozen; Desserts, ready-to-mix; Beverage stores; Ice cream & ices
CEO: Gary Ricco
*Ch Bd: Charles T Wegner IV
*Pr: Kenneth E Wegner
CFO: Lori Bottoms
VP: Bob Clements
IT Man: Mike Gomolski
Plnt Mgr: Simon Richards
Prd Mgr: Carols Fregoso
VP Mktg: Jeff Saad
Mktg Dir: Carol Cummings
Mktg Dir: Susie Frausto
Board of Directors: Susie Frausto, Joan Wegner, John Wegner

JELD WEN INTERNATIONAL SUPPLY
See JELD-WEN INC

D-U-N-S 00-904-0288 IMP/EXP
JELD-WEN INC
JELD WEN INTERNATIONAL SUPPLY
(*Suby of* ONEX INVESTMENT CORP) ★
440 S Church St Ste 400, Charlotte, NC 28202-2064
Tel (800) 535-3936 *Founded/Ownrshp* 1960, 2011
Sales 1.5MMME *EMP* 2,000E
SIC 3442 5031 2421 Shutters, door or window: metal; Doors, combination, screen-storm; Building & structural materials, wood
Ch Bd: Kirk Hachigian
*CEO: Mark A Beck
*CFO: L Brooks Mallard
*Treas: Brian Luke
*Ex VP: Timothy R Craven
*Ex VP: John A Dinger
*Ex VP: Bob Merrill
*CIO: Krish Mani

D-U-N-S 00-911-8290 IMP
JELLY BELLY CANDY CO (CA)
1 Jelly Belly Ln, Fairfield, CA 94533-6741
Tel (707) 428-2800 *Founded/Ownrshp* 1900
Sales 215.6MME *EMP* 650
SIC 2064 Candy & other confectionery products
CEO: Robert M Simpson Jr
*Ch Bd: Herman G Rowland Sr
Pr: Albert Larson
*Pr: Robert Simpson
*Sec: Lisa Brasher
*V Ch Bd: William Kelley
Genl Mgr: Michael Pencek
VP Opers: Jeffrey Brown
*Genl Couns: John Di Giusto

D-U-N-S 08-211-3366
JEM RESTAURANT MANAGEMENT CORP
312 W Cromwell Ave, Fresno, CA 93711-6113
Tel (559) 435-9648 *Founded/Ownrshp* 1973
Sales 46.3MME *EMP* 1,200
SIC 5812 Fast-food restaurant, chain
Ch: Joseph F Desmond
*Pr: Richard Braden
VP: Steve Liles
IT Man: Pat Geston

D-U-N-S 05-799-1820 IMP/EXP
JEN-COAT INC
PROLAMINA
(*Suby of* PROLAMINA CORP) ★
132 N Elm St, Westfield, MA 01085-1644
Tel (413) 875-9861 *Founded/Ownrshp* 2011
Sales 166.5MME *EMP* 350
SIC 3554 Die cutting & stamping machinery, paper converting
CEO: Greg Tucker
*CFO: Eric Bradford
VP: James Kauffman

D-U-N-S 60-796-2107
JENISYS ENGINEERED PRODUCTS INC
VICWEST STEEL
404 E Dallas Rd, Grapevine, TX 76051-4110
Tel (817) 481-3521 *Founded/Ownrshp* 2000
Sales 79.5MME *EMP* 1,116
SIC 3444 Roof deck, sheet metal
Pr: Robert Dryburgh

JENKINS HYUNDAI
See DJ PROPERTY INVESTMENTS INC

JENKS INDEPENDENT SCHL DST 5
See JENKS PUBLIC SCHOOLS

D-U-N-S 05-821-0030
JENKS PUBLIC SCHOOLS
JENKS INDEPENDENT SCHL DST 5
205 E B St, Jenks, OK 74037-3906
Tel (918) 299-4415 *Founded/Ownrshp* 1906
Sales 75.6MME *EMP* 1,400
SIC 8211 Public elementary & secondary schools
Pr: Ron Barber
*VP: Chuck Forbes
VP: Jon Phillips
IT Man: Cody Way
Teacher Pr: Dana Ezell
Psych: James Cooper
Psych: Edie Winters
Psych: Julia Wood

D-U-N-S 15-528-3518 IMP
JENNE INC
33665 Chester Rd, Avon, OH 44011-1307
Tel (440) 835-0040 *Founded/Ownrshp* 1986
Sales 371.0MME *EMP* 200
SIC 7371 7382 Software programming applications; Security systems services
CEO: Dave Johnson
Ch Bd: Rose M Jenne
Pr: Dean M Jenne
Pr: Ray Jenne Jr
CFO: Christopher Anderle
CFO: Anthony R Grilli
CFO: Tony Grilli
Sr VP: Rick Coan
VP: William Brennan
IT Man: Joseph Lyons
Natl Sales: Peter Sandrev

D-U-N-S 05-319-7331
JENNER & BLOCK LLP
353 N Clark St Ste 3200, Chicago, IL 60654-5474
Tel (312) 222-9350 *Founded/Ownrshp* 1914
Sales 168.0MME *EMP* 833
SIC 8111 General practice law office
Pt: Ana R Bugan
Sr Pt: Charles McCarthy
Pt: Reena R Bajowala
Pt: Christine L Childers
Pt: Tom Cooke
Pt: Larry P Ellsworth
Pt: Peter M Gaines
Pt: Chris Gair
Pt: Robert Graham
Pt: Mark Heilbrun
Pt: Reginald J Hill
Pt: Eric S Jackson
Pt: Kenneth K Lee
Pt: Bradford P Lyerla
Pt: Kevin P Mullen
Pt: Thomas C Newkirk
Pt: Matt Oppenheim
Pt: Peter B Pope
Pt: Harry Sandick
Pt: Jerold S Solovy
Pt: Terrance Truax

D-U-N-S 07-012-8012
JENNIE EDMUNDSON MEMORIAL HOSPITAL
(*Suby of* NEBRASKA METHODIST HEALTH SYSTEM INC) ★
933 E Pierce St, Council Bluffs, IA 51503-4626
Tel (712) 396-6000 *Founded/Ownrshp* 1887
Sales 99.7MM *EMP* 750E
SIC 8062 General medical & surgical hospitals
Pr: Steven Baumert
Treas: Allan G Lozier
*Sec: Kathy Tisher
Bd of Dir: Clark Collett
VP: Michael Romano
Dir Env Sv: Dave Paul
Dir Sec: Charlie Kelly
Sls&Mrk Ex: Ed Rider
Dir Health: Jane Flury

D-U-N-S 07-133-3157
JENNIE STUART MEDICAL CENTER INC
320 W 18th St, Hopkinsville, KY 42240-1965
Tel (270) 887-0100 *Founded/Ownrshp* 1913
Sales 111.7MM *EMP* 750
Accts Bkd Llp Bowling Green Ky
SIC 8062 General medical & surgical hospitals
CEO: Eric Lee
Chf Rad: Michael Clark
*CFO: Greg Moore
Treas: Donna Russell
VP: Nancy Raines
Dir Lab: Carla C Wallace
Comm Man: Lisa Behm
CIO: Ken Robertson
Dir IT: Debbie Dickerson
Secur Mgr: Mike Prater
Mktg Dir: Ruth Childers

D-U-N-S 00-616-0766 EXP
■ JENNIE-O TURKEY STORE INC
(*Suby of* HORMEL FOODS CORP) ★
2505 Willmar Ave Sw, Willmar, MN 56201-2711
Tel (320) 235-2622 *Founded/Ownrshp* 1949
Sales 1.2MMME *EMP* 7,000
SIC 2015 0253 Turkey processing & slaughtering; Turkey farm
Pr: Glenn Leitch
*CFO: John Court
Sr VP: Robert A Tegt
VP: Steve Atchison
VP: Gary Matthys
VP: Patricia Solheid
Exec: Lili Alamo
Dir IT: Robert Merrill
IT Man: Carol Boie
IT Man: James Stark
VP Opers: Robert Wood

D-U-N-S 07-852-6531
■ JENNIE-O TURKEY STORE INTERNATIONAL INC
(*Suby of* JENNIE-O TURKEY STORE INC) ★
2505 Willmar Ave Sw, Willmar, MN 56201-2711
Tel (320) 235-2622 *Founded/Ownrshp* 2012
Sales 92.6MME *EMP* 1,466E
SIC 2015 Poultry slaughtering & processing
Prin: Earl Olson

D-U-N-S 15-480-6327 IMP
JENNIFER CONVERTIBLES INC
335 Crossways Park Dr, Woodbury, NY 11797-2066
Tel (516) 496-1900 *Founded/Ownrshp* 1986
Sales 100.7MME *EMP* 417
SIC 5712 6794 5021 Furniture stores; Patent owners & lessors; Furniture
Ch Bd: Fred J Love
*Pr: Rami Abada
VP: Nick Carpenter
VP: Meryl Gair
VP: Glenn Hillman
VP: Kevin Mattler
VP: Philip Rameshwar
VP: Ronald Turin
MIS Dir: George Marr
VP Sls: Marty Ehrlich
Board of Directors: Mark L Berman, Edward G Bohn, Kevin J Coyle

D-U-N-S 00-347-2081
JENNINGS INC L F (VA)
407 N Washington St # 200, Falls Church, VA 22046-3430
Tel (703) 241-1200 *Founded/Ownrshp* 1951, 1952
Sales 151.0MME *EMP* 300E
SIC 1542 Commercial & office building, new construction
CEO: Roberta G Jennings
*Pr: Robert R Rucks
*COO: Stanley L Reed
*Sec: Larlyn Jennings
*VP: Jonathan S Jennings
*VP: Michael Killelea
VP: John F Martin
VP: Gregg Monday
VP: Ed Sandidge

JENNMAR
See CALANDRA FRANK INC

D-U-N-S 04-720-5174 IMP/EXP
JENNMAR CORP
(*Suby of* JENNMAR) ★
258 Kappa Dr, Pittsburgh, PA 15238-2818
Tel (412) 963-9071 *Founded/Ownrshp* 1968
Sales 179.3MME *EMP* 560
SIC 3532 Mining machinery
Pr: Frank Calandra Jr
*COO: Mark Brandon
COO: Robert Wise
CFO: Tim Maziarz
*Ex VP: Karl Anthony Calandra
Ex VP: Tony Calandra
*VP: Jack Calandra
*VP: Al Campoli
VP: Hanjie Chen
*VP: David Hurd
VP: Gene Zurawsky

D-U-N-S 13-051-2221
JENNY CRAIG INC
(*Suby of* NORTH CASTLE PARTNERS LLC) ★
5770 Fleet St, Carlsbad, CA 92008-4700
Tel (760) 696-4000 *Founded/Ownrshp* 2013
Sales 130.5MME *EMP* 3,510
SIC 7299 6794 5149 5499 Diet center, without medical staff; Franchises, selling or licensing; Diet foods; Dietetic foods
CEO: Monty Sharma
*Ch Bd: Patricia Larchet
CFO: Paul Britton
*CFO: Jim Kelly
*Chf Mktg O: Leesa Eichberger
VP: Allen Arvig
*VP: Alan V Dobies
*VP: Doug Fisher
*VP: Shoukry Tiab
VP Mktg: Barbara Barry
*VP Mktg: Scott Parker
Board of Directors: Richard Laube, Bruce McConnell

D-U-N-S 78-550-9126
JENNY CRAIG WEIGHT LOSS CENTERS INC
(*Suby of* JENNY CRAIG INC) ★
5770 Fleet St, Carlsbad, CA 92008-4700
Tel (760) 696-4000 *Founded/Ownrshp* 2002
Sales 54.9MME *EMP* 2,900
SIC 7299 7991 Diet center, without medical staff; Weight reducing clubs
Pr: Dana Fiser
*Ch Bd: Kent Kreh
*Pr: Patti Larchet
*CEO: Jenny Craig
*CFO: James Kelly

D-U-N-S 96-895-1348
JENOPTIK NORTH AMERICA INC
(*Suby of* JENOPTIK AG)
16490 Innovation Dr, Jupiter, FL 33478-6449
Tel (561) 881-7400 *Founded/Ownrshp* 2009
Sales 53.8MME *EMP* 1,000
SIC 3827 Optical instruments & lenses
Pr: Albert Miranda
*Treas: Susan Wilder

D-U-N-S 00-482-7481
JENSEN CONSTRUCTION CO (IA)
JENSEN CRANE SERVICES
(*Suby of* RASMUSSEN GROUP INC) ★
5550 Ne 22nd St, Des Moines, IA 50313-2530
Tel (515) 266-5173 *Founded/Ownrshp* 1949
Sales 91.6MME *EMP* 250
SIC 1622 1629 Bridge construction; Pile driving contractor
Pr: Kurt Rasmussen
*Treas: Jeffry Rasmussen
*VP: Jeff Rasmussen
*VP: Dan Timmons
Dir IT: Carol Broman

D-U-N-S 05-051-2730
JENSEN CORPORATE HOLDINGS INC
1983 Concourse Dr, San Jose, CA 95131-1708
Tel (408) 446-1118 *Founded/Ownrshp* 1969
Sales 128.2MME *EMP* 450
SIC 0782 Landscape contractors
CEO: John Vlay
CFO: Paul Johnson
*CFO: Quang Trinh
*Div Pres: Donald Defever
*VP: Glenn Berry
*VP: Kirk Brown
*VP: Rodney W Morimoto
*Prin: Scott Mc Gilvray
*Prin: Duane Wasson
Brnch Mgr: Clint Christman

JENSEN CRANE SERVICES
See JENSEN CONSTRUCTION CO

JENSEN DISTRIBUTION SERVICES
See JENSEN-BYRD CO LLC

D-U-N-S 06-501-8178 IMP
JENSEN ENTERPRISES INC
JENSEN PRECAST
825 Steneri Way, Sparks, NV 89431-6312
Tel (775) 352-2700 *Founded/Ownrshp* 1966
Sales 152.2MME *EMP* 450
SIC 3272 Concrete products, precast
Pr: Tony Shanks
*Treas: Donald L Jensen
Chf Mktg O: Eric Jensen
VP Mfg: Leonard Smith
Sls&Mrk Ex: Mark Voiselle
Sls Mgr: Justin Caufield
Sls Mgr: Greg Taylor
Sales Asso: Brian Phenix
Genl Couns: Ty Cobb

D-U-N-S 03-504-3744
JENSEN HUGHES INC (MD)
3610 Commerce Dr Ste 817, Baltimore, MD 21227-1640
Tel (410) 737-8677 *Founded/Ownrshp* 1980, 2015
Sales 151.3MME *EMP* 758
SIC 8748 8711 8734 Business consulting; Fire protection engineering; Product testing laboratory, safety or performance
CEO: Paul Orzeske
*Pr: Dave Boswell
*Pr: Mickey Reiss
COO: Paul Sincaglia
*CFO: Michael McRae
CFO: Paula Sidlowski
*Chf Mktg O: George Toth
Ex VP: Doug True
Sr VP: Elizabeth Kleinsorg
VP: Jim Antell
VP: Hamid Bahadori
VP: Jack Brady
VP: Joseph Cappuccio
VP: Joe Castellano
VP: Scott Chong
VP: Mike Crowley
VP: Michael Ferreira
VP: Jeff Harper
VP: Tim Larose
VP: Renato Molina
VP: Eric Rosenbaum

D-U-N-S 02-911-9310
JENSEN MEAT CO INC
2550 Britannia Blvd # 101, San Diego, CA 92154-7408
Tel (619) 754-6450 *Founded/Ownrshp* 1958
Sales 122.3MME *EMP* 95
SIC 5147 Meats & meat products
CEO: Abel Olivera
*Co-Ownr: Jeff Hamann
*CFO: Sam Acuna
Prd Mgr: Edmundo Garcia

JENSEN PRECAST
See JENSEN ENTERPRISES INC

JENSEN, RALPH L JR
See RJR CONSULTING GROUP INC

D-U-N-S 04-445-3264 IMP/EXP
JENSEN USA INC (NC)
99 Aberdeen Loop, Panama City, FL 32405-6483
Tel (850) 271-8464 *Founded/Ownrshp* 1979
Sales 108.1MM^E *EMP* 150
SIC 5087 Laundry equipment & supplies
CEO: Jesper Jensen
**Pr:* Simon Nield
COO: Larry Jensen
**CFO:* Markus Schalch
**CFO:* Erik Vanderhagen
**VP:* Phyllis Decker
**VP:* Norbert Gittard
**VP:* Helmut Harfmann
VP: Mike McBride
**VP:* James Thorpe
**VP:* Mark Wingrove
Exec: Cindy Tisdale

D-U-N-S 00-794-3582 IMP
JENSEN-BYRD CO LLC (WA)
JENSEN DISTRIBUTION SERVICES
(*Suby of* ACE HARDWARE CORP) ★
314 W Riverside Ave, Spokane, WA 99201-0272
Tel (509) 624-1321 *Founded/Ownrshp* 1949, 2015
Sales 244.2MM^E *EMP* 230
SIC 5072 Hardware
CEO: Michael S Jensen
Pr: Micah Jensen Dunlap
Ofcr: Chris Jensen
Ex VP: Micah C Jensen
Ex VP: P Chris Jensen
VP: John Wade
Prgrm Mgr: Kaylee Paxton
Off Mgr: Ann Wissink
Natl Sales: Frank Trulin
Manager: Tom Peterson
Sls Mgr: Jacob Emmons

D-U-N-S 04-798-0821
JENZABAR INC
101 Huntington Ave # 2200, Boston, MA 02199-8087
Tel (617) 492-9099 *Founded/Ownrshp* 1998
Sales 87.0MM^E *EMP* 275
SIC 7372 Educational computer software
Ch Bd: Robert Maginn Jr
**Pr:* Ling Chai
**CFO:* Mimi Jespersen
**VP:* Ben Bassett
**VP:* Christian Hartigan
VP: Hans Kobler
VP: Erik Nilsson
**VP:* Sashi Parthasarathi
Exec: John Beahm
Snr Sftwr: AVI Neer
Snr Sftwr: Walter Plourde

D-U-N-S 04-941-0087 IMP
JEOL USA INC
(*Suby of* JEOL LTD.)
11 Dearborn Rd, Peabody, MA 01960-3862
Tel (978) 535-5900 *Founded/Ownrshp* 1962
Sales 92.5MM^E *EMP* 320
Accts Greene Rubin Miller & Pacino
SIC 5049 Scientific instruments
Pr: Peter Genovese
VP: Masuru Iwatani
VP: Robert Pohorenec
Rgnl Mgr: Craig Koht
Genl Mgr: Patrick McKinley
Sys/Mgr: Andy Dukehart
Natl Sales: Chris Rood
Manager: Robert Mierzwa

JEPPESEN A BOEING COMPANY
See JEPPESEN SANDERSON INC

D-U-N-S 00-706-1062 IMP
■ **JEPPESEN SANDERSON INC**
JEPPESEN A BOEING COMPANY
(*Suby of* BOEING CO) ★
55 Inverness Dr E, Englewood, CO 80112-5412
Tel (303) 799-9090 *Founded/Ownrshp* 1934, 2000
Sales 680.4MM^E *EMP* 3,200
SIC 2741 2731 8748 Miscellaneous publishing; Textbooks: publishing only, not printed on site; Systems analysis or design
CEO: Mark Van Tine
**Ch Bd:* Horst A Bergmann
COO: Margarita Kots
**COO:* Brad Thomann
**CFO:* Jepson Fuller
CFO: Bob Kurtz
VP: Paul Eckert
VP: Gary Minard
VP: Bernd B Montigny
VP: Sean Schwinn
VP: Alexander Shissel
VP: Carol Van Steensburg
VP: Mitchell Villanueva
VP: David Walker
VP: Mary Wild
Dir Bus: Russ Hoffman
Dir Bus: Juha Makikalli

D-U-N-S 15-211-1196
JER INVESTORS TRUST INC
1650 Tysons Blvd Ste 1600, Mc Lean, VA 22102-4846
Tel (703) 714-8000 *Founded/Ownrshp* 2004
Sales 108.1MM *EMP* 1^E
SIC 6798 Real estate investment trusts
CEO: Joseph E Robert Jr
**Pr:* Mark S Weiss
VP: John Murray

D-U-N-S 78-665-8380
JER PARTNERS LLC
ROBERT CO INC J E MCLEAN VA
(*Suby of* J E ROBERT) ★
1250 Conn Ave Nw Ste 700, Washington, DC 20036-2657
Tel (703) 714-8000 *Founded/Ownrshp* 2006
Sales 100.1MM^E *EMP* 2,566
SIC 6798 Real estate investment trusts
VP: Matthew Cady
VP: Aleksandar Obradovic
VP: Kelly Sheehy
Board of Directors: John Haymes, Kevin Nishimura

JEREMIAH
See CRAFTMADE INTERNATIONAL INC

D-U-N-S 60-503-9366
■ **JERNBERG INDUSTRIES LLC**
(*Suby of* HHI FORGING LLC) ★
328 W 40th Pl, Chicago, IL 60609-2815
Tel (773) 268-3004 *Founded/Ownrshp* 2006
Sales 105.7MM^E *EMP* 500^E
SIC 3462 3463 Iron & steel forgings; Nonferrous forgings
CEO: George Thanopoulos
Treas: Robert Koscicki
Genl Mgr: Michael Keslar

D-U-N-S 02-440-2836
JERNIGAN OIL CO INC
DUCK THRU FOOD STORES
415 Main St E, Ahoskie, NC 27910-3421
Tel (252) 332-2131 *Founded/Ownrshp* 1979
Sales 199.7MM *EMP* 350
Accts May & Place Pa Louisburg No
SIC 5411 5171 Convenience stores, independent; Petroleum bulk stations
Pr: James M Harrell
**Sec:* Jerry Harrell
Mktg Dir: Jerry Castelloe

D-U-N-S 80-453-9641
JEROME GROUP INC
RADIATION ONCOLOGY ASSOC PA
6 E Chestnut St, Augusta, ME 04330-5758
Tel (207) 626-1496 *Founded/Ownrshp* 1982
Sales 10.9MM^E *EMP* 1,000
SIC 8011 8062 Oncologist; General medical & surgical hospitals
Pr: Scott Bullock

JEROME KING
See BOARD OF SCHOOL COMMISSIONERS OF MOBILE COUNTY

D-U-N-S 02-913-8948 IMP
JEROMES FURNITURE WAREHOUSE
16960 Mesamint St, San Diego, CA 92127-2407
Tel (866) 633-4094 *Founded/Ownrshp* 1954
Sales 116.1MM^E *EMP* 420
SIC 5712 Furniture stores
Pr: Brian Woods
COO: Phil Kenney
**CFO:* Paul Sanford
VP: Pam Fettu
VP: Jim Navarra
VP Sls: Dave Brunson
Mktg Mgr: Glenn Weber

D-U-N-S 17-379-4561
JERRY ERWIN ASSOCIATES INC
12115 Ne 99th St Ste 1800, Vancouver, WA 98682-2334
Tel (800) 254-9442 *Founded/Ownrshp* 1986
Sales 112.5MM^E *EMP* 650
SIC 6552 6531 Subdividers & developers; Real estate managers
Pr: Jerry Erwin
**COO:* Cody Erwin
**VP:* John McNeil

JERRY LEIGH ENTERTAINMENT AP
See JERRY LEIGH OF CALIFORNIA INC

D-U-N-S 08-718-7944 IMP/EXP
JERRY LEIGH OF CALIFORNIA INC (CA)
JERRY LEIGH ENTERTAINMENT AP
7860 Nelson Rd, Van Nuys, CA 91402-6044
Tel (818) 909-6200 *Founded/Ownrshp* 1977
Sales 385.8MM^E *EMP* 550^E
SIC 5137 Women's & children's clothing
CEO: Andrew Leigh
**CFO:* Jeff Silver
Ex VP: Jonathan Hirsh
VP: Samira Jammal
VP Sls: Lisa Esserman
Art Dir: James Asuncion

D-U-N-S 02-763-5747 IMP
JERRYS BUILDING MATERIALS INC
JERRYS HOME IMPROVEMENT CENTER
2600 Highway 99 N, Eugene, OR 97402-9706
Tel (541) 689-1911 *Founded/Ownrshp* 1961
Sales 124.5MM^E *EMP* 450^E
SIC 5211

D-U-N-S 04-480-0324
JERRYS ENTERPRISES INC
JERRY'S FOODS
5125 Vernon Ave S, Edina, MN 55436-2104
Tel (952) 922-8335 *Founded/Ownrshp* 1958
Sales 504.0MM^E *EMP* 3,500
SIC 5411 5812 5251 Supermarkets, hypermarket; Restaurant, family: independent; Carry-out only (except pizza) restaurant; Hardware
CEO: Robert N Shadduck
**VP:* Kent Dixon
**VP:* David Gerdes
**VP:* Mike Jutz
**VP:* Tom Thueson

D-U-N-S 05-760-2401
JERRYS FAMOUS DELI INC
SOLLEY'S
12711 Ventura Blvd # 400, Studio City, CA 91604-2456
Tel (818) 766-8311 *Founded/Ownrshp* 1984
Sales 61.1MM^E *EMP* 1,800
SIC 5812 Restaurant, family: independent
Ch Bd: Isaac Starkman
Ch Bd: Guy Starkman
Pr: Jason Starkman
CFO: Christina Sterling
Rgnl Mgr: Billy Friedman

JERRY'S FOODS
See JERRYS ENTERPRISES INC

JERRYS HOME IMPROVEMENT CENTER
See JERRYS BUILDING MATERIALS INC

D-U-N-S 00-697-3358 IMP
■ **JERSEY CENTRAL POWER & LIGHT CO** (NJ)
(*Suby of* FIRSTENERGY CORP) ★
76 S Main St, Akron, OH 44308-1812
Tel (800) 736-3402 *Founded/Ownrshp* 1925
Sales 854.5MM^E *EMP* 1,413^E
Accts Pricewaterhousecoopers Llp C
SIC 4911 Electric services; Distribution, electric power; Generation, electric power; Transmission, electric power
Pr: Donald M Lynch
**CFO:* Marlene A Barwood
CFO: Mark T Clark
Treas: T G Howson
Treas: James F Pearson
Ex VP: Leila L Vespoli
Sr VP: Charles E Jones
Sr VP: David C Luff
VP: C Brooks
VP: William D Byrd
VP: Mark A Jones
VP: Charles D Lasky
VP: C A Mascari
VP: M P O'Flynn
VP: Harvey L Wagner
VP: R S Zechman
Board of Directors: Charles E Jones, Mark A Julian, Jesse T Williams Sr

D-U-N-S 07-754-2942
JERSEY CITY BOARD OF EDUCATION (INC)
JERSEY CITY PUBLIC SCHOOLS
346 Claremont Ave, Jersey City, NJ 07305-1634
Tel (201) 915-6202 *Founded/Ownrshp* 1895
Sales 198.1MM^E *EMP* 2,494^E
SIC 8211 School board
VP: John Reichart

D-U-N-S 06-750-5990
JERSEY CITY INCINERATOR AUTHORITY
501 State Rt 440, Jersey City, NJ 07305-4823
Tel (201) 432-4645 *Founded/Ownrshp* 1951
Sales 88.2MM^E *EMP* 174^E
SIC 4953 0782 4212 Recycling, waste materials; Lawn & garden services; Local trucking, without storage
CEO: Oren K Dabney
**CEO:* Oren K Dadney Sr
CFO: Shirley Marcano
**Ch:* Phillip T Flood
Ofcr: Raj Vasan
Comm Dir: Francis Lamparelli

D-U-N-S 07-930-8110
JERSEY CITY MEDICAL CENTER INC
LIBERTYHEALTH
(*Suby of* LIBERTYHEALTH) ★
355 Grand St, Jersey City, NJ 07302-4321
Tel (201) 915-2000 *Founded/Ownrshp* 1990
Sales 375.6MM *EMP* 1,942
SIC 8062 General medical & surgical hospitals
CEO: Joe Scott
Chf Path: Patricia Tsang
**Ch Bd:* James R Reilly
COO: Michael Prilutsky
CFO: Donald Parseghin
CFO: Domenic Segalla
Trst: Robert Lahita
Trst: Juan Perez
Ofcr: Rita Smith
VP: Richard Bonforte
Exec: Doug Cooper
Dir Lab: Rabhia Abdelhady
Dir Lab: Ting Shen
Dir Rad: Anthony Tramontana MD

JERSEY CITY PUBLIC SCHOOLS
See JERSEY CITY BOARD OF EDUCATION (INC)

D-U-N-S 07-979-9140
JERSEY CITY PUBLIC SCHOOLS
346 Claremont Ave, Jersey City, NJ 07305-1634
Tel (201) 915-6202 *Founded/Ownrshp* 2015
Sales 106.5MM^E *EMP* 3,603^E
SIC 8211 Public elementary & secondary schools
Pr: Vidya Gangadin
**VP:* John Reichart
Dir Sec: Arthur Youmans
MIS Dir: Debasis Gupta

D-U-N-S 00-780-2911
JERSEY COUNTY GRAIN CO
428 E Exchange St, Jerseyville, IL 62052-1715
Tel (618) 498-2183 *Founded/Ownrshp* 1931
Sales 88.0MM *EMP* 20
SIC 5153 5191 Grain elevators; Feed; Seeds: field, garden & flower
CEO: Mike Welburne
**Pr:* William Kuebrich
**Pr:* Tom Moore
**Sec:* Wayn Fuhler
**VP:* Rich Devergar
Div Mgr: Tom Deurinder
Genl Mgr: Michael Welbourne

JERSEY PAPER PLUS
See JPC ENTERPRISES INC

D-U-N-S 00-304-3338 IMP
JERSEY SHORE STEEL CO (PA)
70 Maryland Ave, Jersey Shore, PA 17740-7113
Tel (570) 753-3000 *Founded/Ownrshp* 1938, 1943
Sales 97.6MM^E *EMP* 400
SIC 3312 Rails, steel or iron
CEO: John C Schultz
**Treas:* Mark Scheffey
**Ex VP:* Peter D Schultz
Ql Cn Mgr: Mike Berry

D-U-N-S 00-537-8815 IMP
JERVIS B WEBB CO (MI)
(*Suby of* DAIFUKU CO., LTD.)
34375 W 12 Mile Rd, Farmington Hills, MI 48331-5624
Tel (248) 553-1000 *Founded/Ownrshp* 1919, 2007
Sales 228.7MM^E *EMP* 900
SIC 3535 3536 3462 3537 3613 Conveyors & conveying equipment; Overhead conveyor systems; Cranes & monorail systems; Cranes, industrial plant; Monorail systems; Iron & steel forgings; Chains, forged steel; Stacking machines, automatic; Tractors, used in plants, docks, terminals, etc.: industrial; Control panels, electric
Pr: Robertus Schmit
CEO: Dina Salehi
CFO: Tetsuya Hibi
VP: George Flintosh
VP: Christopher Murphy
VP: Parker Thomas III
VP Bus Dev: Christopher Lutz
Ex Dir: Dan Klepack
Admn Mgr: Bruce L Redman
CIO: John Jaynes
Dir IT: Don Lecroy

D-U-N-S 00-480-2112
JESCO INC
(*Suby of* YATES COMPANIES INC) ★
2020 Mccullough Blvd, Tupelo, MS 38801-7108
Tel (662) 842-3240 *Founded/Ownrshp* 2000
Sales 153.2MM *EMP* 600
Accts Rea Shaw Giffin & Stuart Ll
SIC 1541 Industrial buildings, new construction; Factory construction; Warehouse construction
Pr: Jerry Maxcy
**Ch Bd:* William Yates Jr
**Sec:* Tim Miles
**Sr VP:* Daniel Steele
VP: Trey Hard
VP: Sid McMillan

D-U-N-S 07-787-5532
JESSAMINE COUNTY BOARD OF EDUCATION (INC)
871 Wilmore Rd, Nicholasville, KY 40356-9462
Tel (859) 885-4179 *Founded/Ownrshp* 2003
Sales 79.2MM *EMP* 1,440
Accts Summers Mccrary & Sparks Psc
SIC 8211 School board
Ch Bd: Eugene Peel

D-U-N-S 05-037-1277 IMP
JESSICA MCCLINTOCK INC (CA)
2307 Broadway St, San Francisco, CA 94115-1291
Tel (415) 553-8200 *Founded/Ownrshp* 1970
Sales 85.4MM^E *EMP* 600
SIC 2361 2335 2844 Dresses: girls', children's & infants'; Women's, juniors' & misses' dresses; Perfumes, natural or synthetic
Pr: Jessica Mc Clintock
CFO: Dilip K Parekh
CTO: Lambert Dangilan

D-U-N-S 19-460-3478 IMP/EXP
JET CORR INC
CORRUGATING DIVISION
(*Suby of* PRATT INDUSTRIES (USA) INC) ★
1800 Sarasot Bus Pkwy Ne B, Conyers, GA 30013-5775
Tel (770) 929-1300 *Founded/Ownrshp* 1985
Sales 695.2MM^E *EMP* 3,500
SIC 2653 Boxes, corrugated: made from purchased materials
Pr: Gary B Byrd
**Ch Bd:* Richard Pratt
**CEO:* Brian McPheely
**COO:* Phillip Bulger
**CFO:* Aamir Anwar
**Ch:* Pratt Anthony
**VP:* Douglas Balyeat
**VP:* David J Kyles
**VP:* David Wiser

D-U-N-S 06-646-0874
JET FOOD STORES OF GEORGIA INC
1106 S Harris St, Sandersville, GA 31082-6904
Tel (478) 552-2588 *Founded/Ownrshp* 1988
Sales 88.0MM^E *EMP* 600
SIC 5411 Convenience stores, chain
Ch Bd: Phillip R Seay
**Pr:* Charles E Turner
**CFO:* Chuck Hancock

D-U-N-S 79-500-9414 IMP/EXP
JET INDUSTRIES INC
OZZ PROPERTIES
1935 Silverton Rd Ne, Salem, OR 97301-0181
Tel (503) 363-2334 *Founded/Ownrshp* 1977
Sales 141.4MM^E *EMP* 300
SIC 1711 1731 Heating & air conditioning contractors; Fire sprinkler system installation; Electrical work; Fire detection & burglar alarm systems specialization
Pr: Hunter Zeeb
**Pr:* Oliver Raab
**Pr:* Jeff Zeeb
VP: Oliver Rob
Genl Mgr: Tom Marshall
Genl Mgr: Ray Raab
IT Man: Chip Roker

D-U-N-S 08-374-8343
JET PEP INC
9481 Highway 278 W, Holly Pond, AL 35083
Tel (256) 796-2237 *Founded/Ownrshp* 1973
Sales 361.9MM *EMP* 75
SIC 5541 Filling stations, gasoline
Pr: Robert G Norris
**CFO:* Steve Gaines
**VP:* Darlene H Norris
Genl Mgr: Chuck Moore

D-U-N-S 03-994-0655
JET SPECIALTY INC
211 Market Ave, Boerne, TX 78006-3050
Tel (830) 331-9457 *Founded/Ownrshp* 1991
Sales 267.1MM *EMP* 171
Accts Weaver And Tidwell Llp San
SIC 5084 5085 Instruments & control equipment; Valves & fittings
Pr: Tom W Darter
**CFO:* Ted Williams
**VP:* Chad Darter
Store Mgr: Mike Derrick

Store Mgr: Matt Marney
IT Man: Chris Bruce
Sales Asso: Aaron Baker
Sales Asso: Britt Poynor
Sales Asso: Joseph Urias

D-U-N-S 07-958-6880
■ JET.COM INC
(*Suby of* WALMART) ★
221 River St Fl 8, Hoboken, NJ 07030-5891
Tel (844) 538-2255 *Founded/Ownrshp* 2016
Sales 320.7MM^E *EMP* 1,200^E
SIC 4813
CEO: Marc Lore
Pr: Stephanie Brensilver
Sr VP: John Turek
Prin: Nate Faust
Prin: Mike Hanrahan
Snr Mgr: Nora Ali

D-U-N-S 08-900-2799
▲ JETBLUE AIRWAYS CORP
2701 Queens Plz N, Long Island City, NY 11101-4020
Tel (718) 286-7900 *Founded/Ownrshp* 2000
Sales 6.4MMM *EMP* 16,862
Tkr Sym JBLU *Exch* NGS
SIC 4512 Air transportation, scheduled; Air passenger carrier, scheduled
Prin: Robin Hayes
**Ch Bd:* Joel Peterson
CFO: Mark D Powers
Treas: Jim Leddy
**V Ch Bd:* Frank Sica
Ex VP: James Hnat
Ex VP: Marty St George
VP: Alexander Chatkewitz
VP: Warren Christie
VP: Glenn Cusano
VP: Michael S Elliott
VP: Jim Hnat
VP: Robert C Land
VP: Marc Rabinowitz
VP: Bart Roberts
VP: John Ross
VP: Christopher Sangiovanni
VP: Brad Sheehan
VP: Martin St George
Exec: Rick Sawicki
Board of Directors: Jens Bischof, Peter Boneparth, David Checketts, Virginia Gambale, Stephan Gemkow, Ellen Jewett, Stanley McChrystal, Thomas Winkelmann

D-U-N-S 07-929-0856
JETMORE WIND LLC
15445 Innovation Dr, San Diego, CA 92128-3432
Tel (888) 903-6926 *Founded/Ownrshp* 2013
Sales 193.7MM^E *EMP* 826
SIC 4911 Electric services
Pr: Tristan Grimbert
VP: Ryan Pfaff

D-U-N-S 12-220-0355
JETOBRA INC
HOFFMAN ENTERPRISES
700 Connecticut Blvd, East Hartford, CT 06108-3222
Tel (877) 274-8207 *Founded/Ownrshp* 1979
Sales 108.1MM^E *EMP* 310^E
SIC 5511 New & used car dealers
Ch: Jeffrey S Hoffman
**Sec:* Phyllis B Keyes
**VP:* Matthew Hoffman

JETRO CASH & CARRY
See JETRO CASH AND CARRY ENTERPRISES LLC

JETRO CASH & CARRY
See JETRO HOLDINGS LLC

D-U-N-S 04-007-5780 IMP/EXP
JETRO CASH AND CARRY ENTERPRISES LLC
JETRO CASH & CARRY
(*Suby of* JRD HOLDINGS INC) ★
1524 132nd St, College Point, NY 11356-2440
Tel (718) 939-6400 *Founded/Ownrshp* 1976
Sales 1.8MMM^E *EMP* 1,000
SIC 5142 5046 5181 5147 5411 Packaged frozen goods; Restaurant equipment & supplies; Beer & other fermented malt liquors; Meats, fresh; Grocery stores
CEO: Stanley Fleishman
Sr Cor Off: Roger Chavez
Exec: Dan Stabile
Brnch Mgr: Enrique Gallard

D-U-N-S 96-561-1648 EXP
JETRO HOLDINGS LLC
JETRO CASH & CARRY
1506 132nd St, College Point, NY 11356-2440
Tel (718) 762-8700 *Founded/Ownrshp* 1990
Sales 4.3MMM^E *EMP* 5,000
SIC 5149 5141 5812 Organic & diet foods; Diet foods; Health foods; Groceries, general line; Caterers
**Mng Pt:* Glenn Fleischman
CFO: Brian Emmert

D-U-N-S 96-490-2394
JETT INDUSTRIES INC
(*Suby of* KIEWIT INFRASTRUCTURE CO) ★
121 Willow Ln, Colliersville, NY 13747
Tel (607) 433-2100 *Founded/Ownrshp* 2008
Sales 158.5MM^E *EMP* 4,270^E
SIC 1611 1623 Highway & street construction; Water & sewer line construction
Pr: Matthew P Centofante
**Treas:* Stephen S Thomas
**VP:* Daniel L Dubois
**VP:* Michael J Piechoski
**VP:* Scott A Schmidt
**VP:* Daniel A Shults

D-U-N-S 07-839-6625
JEUNESSE GLOBAL HOLDINGS LLC
(*Suby of* JEUNESSE, LLC)
650 Douglas Ave Ste 1020, Altamonte Springs, FL 32714-2554
Tel (407) 215-7414 *Founded/Ownrshp* 2010
Sales 84.6MM^E *EMP* 402^E

SIC 5999 Toilet preparations

D-U-N-S 07-144-9078
JEVIC TRANSPORTATION INC
(*Suby of* SUN CAPITAL PARTNERS INC) ★
1540 E Dundee Rd Ste 240, Palatine, IL 60074-8320
Tel (856) 764-1909 *Founded/Ownrshp* 2006
Sales 51.9MM^E *EMP* 1,100
SIC 4213 Contract haulers
Pr: David Gorman
Sr VP: Raymond Conlin
Sr VP: Joe Librizzi
VP: Dennis Ungrady

D-U-N-S 07-376-3450
JEVS HUMAN SERVICES
JEWISH EMPLYMENT VCTIONAL SVCS
1845 Walnut St Ste 700, Philadelphia, PA 19103-4713
Tel (215) 875-7387 *Founded/Ownrshp* 1941
Sales 54.1MM *EMP* 1,000
Accts Cliftonlarsonallen Llp Plymou
SIC 8322 8331 Substance abuse counseling; Vocational rehabilitation agency
Pr: Jay Spector
CFO: Bruce Fishberg
VP: Francis Kardos
Prgrm Mgr: Marjorie Carasquero
Genl Mgr: Rachel Aucott
IT Man: Debbie Bello
Mktg Dir: Krista Biesecker

D-U-N-S 00-506-8630
JEWEL OSCO INC
(*Suby of* ACME) ★
150 E Pierce Rd Ste 200, Itasca, IL 60143-1224
Tel (630) 551-2672 *Founded/Ownrshp* 1899
Sales 2.4MMM^E *EMP* 30,000
SIC 5411 2834 Supermarkets, chain; Proprietary drug products
Pr: Shane Sampson
**Pr:* Mike Withers
Treas: John F Boyd
**Treas:* Thomas P Heneghan
Sr VP: Gerald D Bay
Sr VP: Sherry M Smith
VP: Stephen C Bowater
VP: Gregory E Gullickson
VP: Robert L Hughes
VP: Linda K Massman
VP: Ronald T Mendes
VP: John C Owen
VP: Jeffrey Peszek
VP: Thomas S Rousonelos
VP: Thomas J Walter
VP: Roy C Whitmore
Exec: Nancy Franciose
Board of Directors: Jonathan L Scott, Alan D Stewart

JEWEL-OSCO
See NEW ALBERTSONS INC

D-U-N-S 00-643-6133
JEWELERS MUTUAL INSURANCE CO (WI)
24 Jewelers Park Dr, Neenah, WI 54956-3703
Tel (800) 558-6411 *Founded/Ownrshp* 1913
Sales NA *EMP* 160
SIC 6331 Fire, marine & casualty insurance: mutual
CEO: Darwin Copeman
Pr: Patrick Drummond
CFO: Paul Fuhrman
Treas: Kelly Kinas
Chf Mktg O: Trina Woldt
Sr VP: Tim Riedl
VP: Jared Ashland
VP: Chris Hartrich
Mktg Mgr: Sam Tassoul

JEWELERY MARKETING COMPANY
See DIAMLINK INC

JEWELRY AND HANDBANG WAREHOUSE
See TREES N TRENDS INC

D-U-N-S 79-252-8304 IMP
JEWELRY CHANNEL INC
LIQUIDATION CHANNEL
(*Suby of* VAIBHAV GLOBAL LIMITED)
100 Mchl Agl Way Ste 400d, Austin, TX 78728
Tel (512) 852-7000 *Founded/Ownrshp* 2007
Sales 198.3MM^E *EMP* 520
SIC 3679 Electronic circuits
CEO: Sunil Agrawal
**Pr:* Gerald Tempton
Ofcr: Shannon Becton
**Prin:* Sharon Kincaid
**Prin:* Reeta Sharma
Dir IT: Prasanta Gordon
Prd Dir: Michael Lacy
Board of Directors: Suresh Punjabi

JEWISH AGENCY FOR ISRAEL, THE
See JEWISH AGENCY FOR ISRAEL INC

D-U-N-S 06-120-3865
JEWISH AGENCY FOR ISRAEL INC
JEWISH AGENCY FOR ISRAEL, THE
111 8th Ave Fl 11, New York, NY 10011-5211
Tel (212) 284-6900 *Founded/Ownrshp* 1927
Sales 193.1MM *EMP* 6
Accts Loeb & Troper Llp New York N
SIC 8399 Fund raising organization, non-fee basis
Ch Bd: Jane Sherman
CFO: Didi Latina
**V Ch Bd:* Alan Shulman

D-U-N-S 07-103-7543
JEWISH BOARD OF FAMILY AND CHILDRENS SERVICES INC
JBFCS
135 W 50th St Fl 6, New York, NY 10020-1201
Tel (212) 582-9100 *Founded/Ownrshp* 1893
Sales 153.0MM^E *EMP* 2,000
Accts Loeb & Troper Llp New York N
SIC 8361 8322 Home for the emotionally disturbed; Individual & family services
CEO: David Rivel
**Ch Bd:* John Herman
**Pr:* Anthony E Mann
CFO: Helene Stone
**Ch:* Roger A Goldman
**Ch:* Joseph Kaplan
**Ch:* Jean L Troubh
Bd of Dir: Karim Lopez
Ex VP: Leonardo Rodriguez
**VP:* Lynn Korda Korll
Assoc Dir: Reginald Fuller
Dir Soc: Hope Larson

D-U-N-S 07-684-9124
JEWISH CHILD CARE ASSOCIATION OF NEW YORK
858 E 29th St, Brooklyn, NY 11210-2927
Tel (917) 808-4800 *Founded/Ownrshp* 1822
Sales 98.4MM *EMP* 950
SIC 8361 8399 Group foster home; Social service information exchange
CEO: Ronald E Richter
**Pr:* Barbara Salmanson
**CFO:* Steven Wolinsky
**Ch:* Peter Hauspurg
Sr VP: Foster Home
VP: David Goldstein
VP: Elizabeth Schnur
Brnch Mgr: Peter Gioiella
CIO: Sharon Cort
CTO: Mark Edelman
Dir IT: Antonio Garay

D-U-N-S 02-127-0905
JEWISH COMMUNAL FUND
575 Madison Ave Ste 703, New York, NY 10022-8591
Tel (212) 752-8277 *Founded/Ownrshp* 1972
Sales 390.1MM *EMP* 14
Accts Eisneramper Llp New York Ny
SIC 6732 Charitable trust management
Pr: Harold R Handler
**Sr VP:* Jose Virella
**VP:* Susan F Dickman
VP: Ellen Israelson
Assoc Dir: Igor Musayev
VP Admn: Jane Fraleigh

D-U-N-S 03-098-9701
JEWISH COMMUNITY FEDERATION OF SAN FRANCISCO PENINSULA MARIN & SONOMA COUNTIES
121 Steuart St Fl 7, San Francisco, CA 94105-1280
Tel (415) 777-0411 *Founded/Ownrshp* 1921
Sales 147.2MM *EMP* 110
Accts Rothstein Kass San Francisco
SIC 8399 Fund raising organization, non-fee basis
CEO: Jennifer Gorvitz
**CFO:* Bill Powers
VP: Carol Weitz
Assoc Dir: Bab Freiberg
IT Man: Kevin Ho
Mktg Dir: Angela Ingel

JEWISH COMMUNITY FOUNDATION
See COMMUNITY FUND OF UNITED JEWISH

D-U-N-S 87-463-0916
JEWISH COMMUNITY FOUNDATION
6505 Wilshire Blvd # 1200, Los Angeles, CA 90048-4906
Tel (323) 761-8700 *Founded/Ownrshp* 1955
Sales 134.0MM *EMP* 26
Accts Ernst & Young Us Llp San Dieg
SIC 8699 Charitable organization
Pr: Marvin Schotland
COO: Simone Savlov
**CFO:* Steve Shean
Trst: Bertrand I Gnsberg
Trst: Ronald L Eibow
Trst: Annette Shapiro
VP: Max Factor III
VP: Elliot Kristal
VP: Marsha Sussman
Genl Couns: Susan Mattisinko

JEWISH EMPLYMENT VCTIONAL SVCS
See JEVS HUMAN SERVICES

D-U-N-S 09-328-4578
JEWISH FEDERATION OF CLEVELAND
25701 Science Park Dr, Cleveland, OH 44122-7302
Tel (216) 593-2900 *Founded/Ownrshp* 1903
Sales 93.2MM *EMP* 130
Accts Lb Bdo Usa Llp Solon Oh
SIC 8399 Fund raising organization, non-fee basis
Pr: Steve Hoffman
**Ex VP:* Joel Fox
Sr VP: Barry Reis
**Prin:* E Joseph
Dir Sec: Jim Hartnett
Genl Mgr: Jennifer Schwarz
Counsel: Paul Feinberg

D-U-N-S 07-688-1671
JEWISH FEDERATION OF METROPOLITAN CHICAGO
30 S Wells St, Chicago, IL 60606-5054
Tel (312) 357-4790 *Founded/Ownrshp* 1900
Sales 137.1MM *EMP* 78
Accts Mcgladrey Llp Chicago Illino
SIC 8399 Community development groups
Pr: Steven B Nasatir
CFO: Michael Tarnoff
Assoc VP: Merle Cohen
Assoc VP: Donna Kahan
VP: Deborah Covington
Pgrm Dir: Jennifer Lande

D-U-N-S 06-499-2076
JEWISH FEDERATIONS OF NORTH AMERICA INC
25 Broadway Fl 17, New York, NY 10004-1015
Tel (212) 284-6500 *Founded/Ownrshp* 1935
Sales 184.7MM *EMP* 150
Accts Loeb & Troper Llp New York N
SIC 8399 Fund raising organization, non-fee basis
Pr: Howard M Rieger
**Ch Bd:* Joseph Kanser
**Ch Bd:* Michael Siegal
**Ch:* Robert Goldberg
VP: William Daroff
Prgrm Mgr: Alexandra Coffey
Snr Mgr: Ellen Frischberg
Board of Directors: Jerry Silverman

JEWISH HOME AND HOSP FOR AGED
See JEWISH HOME LIFECARE HARRY AND JEANETTE WEINBERG CAMPUS BRONX

D-U-N-S 15-558-3883
JEWISH HOME AND HOSPITAL
KITTAY HOUSE
100 W Kingsbridge Rd # 100, Bronx, NY 10468-3961
Tel (718) 579-0420 *Founded/Ownrshp* 1863
Sales 54.4MM^E *EMP* 1,000
SIC 6513 6531 Apartment building operators; Real estate managers
Pr: Sheldon Goldberg
**Ex Dir:* Arlene Richman

D-U-N-S 07-772-9606
JEWISH HOME LIFECARE HARRY AND JEANETTE WEINBERG CAMPUS BRONX
JEWISH HOME AND HOSP FOR AGED
120 W 106th St, New York, NY 10025-3923
Tel (212) 870-5000 *Founded/Ownrshp* 1866
Sales 54.1MM^E *EMP* 1,300^E
SIC 8051 Skilled nursing care facilities
Pr: Audrey Weiner
Pr: Donald Worton
CFO: Eileen Rivera
**CFO:* Thomas Ruggiero
Ofcr: Thomas Gilmartin
Sr VP: Frederic Bloch
Sr VP: Robert Davis
Sr VP: Bridget Gallagher
Sr VP: Audrey Wathen
VP: Kristine Cerchiara
VP: Svetlana Debellis
VP: Lois R Faust
VP: Gerald Garofalo
VP: Richard Nuefeld
**VP:* Kenneth J Sherman
Dir Lab: Silvia Myers

D-U-N-S 07-685-2649
JEWISH HOME LIFECARE MANHATTAN
GREENWALL PAVILION
120 W 106th St, New York, NY 10025-3923
Tel (212) 870-5000 *Founded/Ownrshp* 1872
Sales 95.9MM *EMP* 2,150
Accts Loeb & Troper Llp New York N
SIC 8361 7521 Home for the aged; Parking garage
Pr: Audrey Weiner
**CFO:* Thomas Gilmartin
**Sr VP:* Frederic L Bloch
**Sr VP:* Audrey Wathen
**VP:* Lois R Faust
**VP:* Thomas Ruggiero
Off Mgr: Elizabeth Cardamona
Dir IT: Robert Lanfranchi
IT Man: Danesh Singh
Nrsg Dir: Marie Rosenthal
HC Dir: Toyin Savage

JEWISH HOSP ST MRYS HEALTHCARE
See FOUR COURTS INC

D-U-N-S 13-040-1078
JEWISH HOSPITAL & ST MARYS HEALTHCARE INC
(*Suby of* KENTUCKYONE HEALTH SOURCE) ★
200 Abraham Flexner Way # 1, Louisville, KY 40202-1886
Tel (502) 587-4011 *Founded/Ownrshp* 2012
Sales 61.5MM^E *EMP* 8,100
SIC 8062 8082 General medical & surgical hospitals; Home health care services
Pr: David Laird
**Pr:* Joseph Gilene
**Treas:* Melvin Alexander
Trst: Susan Gatz
Trst: Louis Waterman
**Sr VP:* Kathleen M Haddix
VP: Joanne Berryman
VP: Sherri Craig
Nurse Mgr: Valerie Kennedy
Nurse Mgr: Missy Wethington
Dir QC: Ann Spencer

D-U-N-S 87-945-4783
JEWISH HOSPITAL CINCINNATI INC
PHYSICAL MEDICINE
3200 Burnet Ave, Cincinnati, OH 45229-3028
Tel (513) 569-2367 *Founded/Ownrshp* 1984
Sales 239.3MM *EMP* 4
Accts Deloitte Tax Llp Cincinnati
SIC 8031

D-U-N-S 78-222-2991
JEWISH HOSPITAL HEALTHCARE SERVICES INC
200 Abraham Flexner Way # 1, Louisville, KY 40202-2877
Tel (502) 587-4011 *Founded/Ownrshp* 2005
Sales 159.8MM^E *EMP* 8,125
Accts Ernst & Young Us Llp Chicago
SIC 8062 8082 General medical & surgical hospitals; Home health care services
Pr: Robert L Shircliff
**Ch Bd:* Louis Waterman
Sr VP: Ronald Greenberg
VP: Alice O Bridges
VP: Rick Buono
VP: Michael Collins
VP: Stephan French
VP: Ken Johnson
VP: Jeff Polson
Dir Case M: Bev Beckman
Dir Sec: Steve Collins

D-U-N-S 06-894-7431 IMP
JEWISH HOSPITAL LLC
4777 E Galbraith Rd, Cincinnati, OH 45236-2814
Tel (513) 686-3000 *Founded/Ownrshp* 1941
Sales 185.5MM^E *EMP* 1,700
SIC 8062 General medical & surgical hospitals
Ex VP: Aurora M Lambert
VP: Julie Clark
VP: Pam Vansant
VP: Donald Wayne
Exec: Janet Patterson
VP Admn: Janice Falstrom
Adm Dir: Roger Vorherr

Off Mgr: Mandy Genson
CTO: Maria Russo
Cmptr Lab: Betty Miller
Sfty Mgr: Sam Cordary

D-U-N-S 11-289-0132 IMP
JEWISH HOSPITAL OF CINCINNATI INC
(Suby of MERCY HEALTH PARTNERS) ★
4777 E Galbraith Rd, Cincinnati, OH 45236-2814
Tel (513) 686-3000 Founded/Ownrshp 2009
Sales 220.1MM EMP 2,500
SIC 8062 General medical & surgical hospitals
Pr: Steve Holman
CFO: William Jirgan
*VP: Donald L D
*VP: Kathy Smith
*Prin: Warren Falberg

D-U-N-S 07-443-0661
JEWISH UNITED FUND OF METROPOLITAN CHICAGO
30 S Wells St, Chicago, IL 60606-5056
Tel (312) 357-4805 Founded/Ownrshp 1949
Sales 105.3MM EMP 160
Accts Rsm Mcgladrey Inc Chicago Il
SIC 8399 Fund raising organization, non-fee basis
Pr: Steven B Nasatir
Bd of Dir: Stacy Saltzman
*VP: James Pinkston
Ex Dir: Scott Aaron
Off Mgr: Carly Greenspan
Pgrm Dir: Sarah Friedman
Pgrm Dir: Ruth Schachter

D-U-N-S 05-504-4028
JF ACQUISITION LLC
JONES & FRANK
1330 Saint Marys St # 210, Raleigh, NC 27605-1375
Tel (757) 857-5700 Founded/Ownrshp 2012
Sales 171.1MM^E EMP 207
SIC 5084 1799 7299 Pumps & pumping equipment; Service station equipment installation, maintenance & repair; Station operation services
Pr: Sterling Baker
*CFO: Jay Trepanier
*Ex VP: Scott Jones
*VP: Jeff Badgley
*VP: Tom Pera
*VP: Joe Wrightson
Opers Mgr: Roger Ewing
Sls Dir: Ed Perkins

D-U-N-S 00-451-2901
JF ALLEN CO INC (WV)
U.S 33 W Red Rock Rd, Buckhannon, WV 26201
Tel (304) 472-8890 Founded/Ownrshp 1946
Sales 116.0MM^E EMP 350
SIC 3271 1611 3273 3281 2951 Blocks, concrete or cinder: standard; General contractor, highway & street construction; Ready-mixed concrete; Cut stone & stone products; Asphalt paving mixtures & blocks
Pr: John C Allen
CFO: Darren Glover
Sr VP: Michael Griffith
VP: Delbert Leatherman
Ql Cn Mgr: Ed Phares

D-U-N-S 04-773-2136
JF ELECTRIC INC
100 Lake Front Pkwy, Edwardsville, IL 62025-2900
Tel (618) 797-5353 Founded/Ownrshp 1925
Sales 162.6MM EMP 550
SIC 1731 General electrical contractor
Pr: Greg Fowler
*Treas: Charles Fowler
VP: Larry Noble
VP: Jeff Sherman
Board of Directors: James Fowler

D-U-N-S 16-454-9151
JF LEHMAN & CO INC
110 E 59th St Fl 27, New York, NY 10022-1326
Tel (212) 634-0100 Founded/Ownrshp 1990
Sales 162.8MM^E EMP 570
SIC 6722 Management investment, open-end
*VP: David F Thomas
Mng Dir: Michael Cuff

D-U-N-S 09-119-6246 IMP
JF MONTALVO CASH AND CARRY INC
Amelia Ind Park 46, Guaynabo, PR 00968-8043
Tel (787) 781-2962 Founded/Ownrshp 1979
Sales 172.0MM^E EMP 562
SIC 5141 Groceries, general line
Pr: Juan F Montalvo

D-U-N-S 00-969-1940 IMP
JF SHEA CONSTRUCTION INC (CA)
SHEA HOMES FOR ACTIVE ADULTS
(Suby of J F SHEA CO INC) ★
655 Brea Canyon Rd, Walnut, CA 91789-3078
Tel (909) 595-4397 Founded/Ownrshp 1958
Sales 990.7MM^E EMP 2,200
SIC 1521 1622 6512

D-U-N-S 00-796-8175 IMP/EXP
JFC INTERNATIONAL INC (CA)
(Suby of KIKKOMAN CORPORATION)
7101 E Slauson Ave, Commerce, CA 90040-3622
Tel (323) 721-6100 Founded/Ownrshp 1958, 1969
Sales 323.7MM^E EMP 677
SIC 5149 Specialty food items
CEO: Yoshiyuki Ishigaki
*Pr: Hiroyuki Enomoto
VP: Masanori Takenaka
Genl Mgr: Derek Kaneko
IT Man: Sonia Benson
S&M/VP: Paul Iiyama

D-U-N-S 05-108-0653
JFC LLC
GNP COMPANY
(Suby of MASCHHOFFS LLC) ★
4150 2nd St S Ste 200, Saint Cloud, MN 56301-3994
Tel (320) 251-3570 Founded/Ownrshp 2013
Sales 222.9MM^E EMP 1,700
SIC 2015 0251 Chicken, processed; Broiling chickens, raising of

CEO: Michael Helgeson
Ex VP: Steve Jurek
*Ex VP: Tim Wensman
*Exec: Stephen R Jurek
Telecom Mg: Joy Schween
Sfty Mgr: Barbara Pyka
Sfty Mgr: Kari Waters
Mktg Mgr: Karla Hankes
Snr Mgr: Crystal Ganz
Snr Mgr: Wendy Gilk
Snr Mgr: Lucas Peterson

D-U-N-S 02-690-2705
JFK HEALTH SYSTEM INC
JFK MEDICAL CENTER
80 James St, Edison, NJ 08820-3938
Tel (732) 321-7000 Founded/Ownrshp 1982
Sales 768.2MM^E EMP 6,735
Accts Baker Tilly
SIC 8062 General medical & surgical hospitals
Pr: Raymond Fredericks
CFO: Richard Smith
*Ch: Dr Michael Kleiman
VP: Shir Higgins-Bouers
Dir Inf Cn: Judith Luschek
Comm Man: Daniel Sullivan
Chf Nrs Of: Jim Lindquist
Nurse Mgr: Michelle Siegel
Dir IT: Eileen Donnelly
Plnt Mgr: Mark Di Geronimno
Mktg Dir: Tom Casey

JFK MEDICAL CENTER
See JFK HEALTH SYSTEM INC

JFK MEDICAL CENTER
See COMMUNITY HOSPITAL GROUP INC

JFK MEDICAL CENTER
See MUHLENBERG REGIONAL MEDICAL CENTER INC

D-U-N-S 05-537-7966
JG BRANDS INC
10530 Nw 26th St Ste F201, Doral, FL 33172-5930
Tel (786) 597-1554 Founded/Ownrshp 2011
Sales 120.0MM EMP 3
SIC 5999 Mobile telephones & equipment
Pr: Jorbel J Griebeler

JGB
See GUILDNET INC

D-U-N-S 08-517-2005 IMP/EXP
JGB ENTERPRISES INC
115 Metropolitan Dr, Liverpool, NY 13088-5389
Tel (315) 451-2770 Founded/Ownrshp 1977
Sales 116.8MM EMP 240
SIC 3052 5085 3429

D-U-N-S 07-909-7248
JGC FOOD CO LLC (WA)
(Suby of JOSHUA GREEN CORPORATION)
1425 4th Ave Ste 420, Seattle, WA 98101-2218
Tel (206) 622-0420 Founded/Ownrshp 2012
Sales 92.5MM^E EMP 207^E
SIC 2099 2092 Food preparations; Fresh or frozen fish or seafood chowders, soups & stews
CEO: Joshua Green III
CFO: Claudia Pieropan

D-U-N-S 03-381-3395
JH HARVEY CO LLC
HARVEY'S SUPERMARKETS
(Suby of BI-LO HOLDING LLC) ★
107 S Davis St, Nashville, GA 31639-2113
Tel (704) 633-8250 Founded/Ownrshp 1950, 2014
Sales 313.7MM^E EMP 3,500
SIC 5411 Supermarkets, chain

JH INSTRUMENTS
See FCX PERFORMANCE INC

D-U-N-S 00-283-6070
JH KELLY LLC
(Suby of KELLY ELECTRIC GROUP) ★
821 3rd Ave, Longview, WA 98632-2105
Tel (360) 423-5510 Founded/Ownrshp 1971
Sales 201.4MM^E EMP 1,000
SIC 1711 Plumbing, heating, air-conditioning contractors; Mechanical contractor
CFO: Paul Furth
*VP: Robert Harris
*VP: Terry Major
DP Exec: Kevin Farley
Dir IT: Justin Cook
Dir IT: Craig Harrison
IT Man: Kevin Fleet
IT Man: Kellie Peterson
IT Man: Eric Smith
Sfty Dirs: Nicole McOmie
Mtls Mgr: Dale King

D-U-N-S 00-118-9638
JH LYNCH & SONS INC
50 Lynch Pl, Cumberland, RI 02864-5334
Tel (401) 333-4300 Founded/Ownrshp 2000
Sales 140.3MM^E EMP 300
SIC 1611 2951 Surfacing & paving; Asphalt & asphaltic paving mixtures (not from refineries)
Pr: Stephen P Lynch Jr
*VP: Frank Aceto
VP: Francis Foley
*VP: David C Lynch Sr
*VP: Harry E Myers III

D-U-N-S 07-848-7604
JH WHITNEY VI LP
130 Main St, New Canaan, CT 06840-5509
Tel (203) 716-6100 Founded/Ownrshp 2005
Sales 332.0MM^E EMP 10,900
SIC 6726 5812 Management investment funds, closed-end; Seafood restaurants
VP: Daniel T Harknett
*VP: Ann Kim

D-U-N-S 83-223-4988
JHCI ACQUISITION INC
(Suby of JACOBSON COMPANIES) ★
3811 Dixon St, Des Moines, IA 50313-3907
Tel (515) 265-6171 Founded/Ownrshp 2007
Sales 947.0MM^E EMP 3,500^E
SIC 4225 General warehousing
CEO: Brian Lutt
CFO: Jack Ingle
Treas: John Rachwalski
Sec: John Monsky

D-U-N-S 93-379-9731
JHCI HOLDINGS INC
JACOBSON COMPANIES
(Suby of XPO LOGISTICS EUROPE)
1275 Nw 128th St, Clive, IA 50325-7403
Tel (515) 265-6171 Founded/Ownrshp 2014
Sales 947.0MM^E EMP 3,500^E
SIC 4226 4221 4225 Special warehousing & storage; Farm product warehousing & storage; General warehousing & storage
Pr: Tony Tegnelia
Pr: Gordon Smith
Ofcr: Marty Howard
Ofcr: Jack Ingle
VP: Kraig Enyeart
VP: Tom Taylor
Brnch Mgr: Justin Andrews
Genl Mgr: Tom Fulhorst
Genl Mgr: Denny Ullo
Off Mgr: Carmen Parker
CIO: Brian Kautz

D-U-N-S 61-802-2149
JHPIEGO CORP
1615 Thames St Ste 310, Baltimore, MD 21231-3492
Tel (410) 537-1800 Founded/Ownrshp 1974
Sales 295.6MM EMP 1,800
SIC 8299 Educational services
Pr: Leslie Mancuso
*Ch Bd: Joseph Cooper
*COO: Edwin J Judd
*CFO: Ronald Geary
CFO: Ronald Gerair
*V Ch Bd: Theodore Poehler
Bd of Dir: C C Raffaeli
Ofcr: Antoinette Allsbrooks
Ofcr: Lee Ann
Ofcr: Rachel Favero
Ofcr: Rebecca Fielding
Ofcr: Leah Hart
Ofcr: Jaime Haver
Ofcr: George Hoyah
Ofcr: Kelly Kirby
Ofcr: Joy Mascardo
Ofcr: Angela Mercado
Ofcr: Stephanie Reinhardt
Ofcr: Deirdre Russo
Ofcr: Rachel Waxman
*Sr VP: Alain Damiba

JHS
See JAMESON MEMORIAL HOSPITAL

D-U-N-S 13-331-1030
JHT HOLDINGS INC
10801 Corporate Dr, Pleasant Prairie, WI 53158-1603
Tel (800) 558-3271 Founded/Ownrshp 1999
Sales 212.3MM^E EMP 1,180^E
SIC 4213 Trucking, except local
CEO: John Jarrington
CEO: John Harrington

D-U-N-S 05-964-7924
JID TRANSPORTATION LLC
158 61st St Apt 2, West New York, NJ 07093-2925
Tel (201) 362-0841 Founded/Ownrshp 2014
Sales 85.0MM EMP 1
SIC 3713 4212 7363 Truck cabs for motor vehicles; Truck rental with drivers; Truck driver services
Prin: Jaile Luis Diaz

JIFFY LUBE
See LUCOR INC

D-U-N-S 02-172-5379
JIFFY LUBE INTERNATIONAL INC
(Suby of SOPUS PRODUCTS) ★
700 Milam St, Houston, TX 77002-2806
Tel (713) 546-1400 Founded/Ownrshp 1986
Sales 270.8MM^E EMP 6,539^E
SIC 7549 Lubrication service, automotive
Pr: Marc C Graham
*Treas: David P Alderson II
*VP: Linda F Condit
*VP: Thomas M Mc Connell
*VP: Bradley F Stuebing
Off Mgr: Cheryl Wilson

D-U-N-S 00-501-6863
JIH TRUCKING LLC (MO)
1041 Camelot Gardens Dr, Saint Louis, MO 63125-3539
Tel (314) 487-7159 Founded/Ownrshp 2007
Sales 100.0MM EMP 6
SIC 4212 4213 Local trucking, without storage; Heavy hauling
Pr: Juso Hodzic

D-U-N-S 83-121-9295 IMP
JILL ACQUISITION LLC
J. JILL
(Suby of TOWERBROOK CAPITAL PARTNERS LP) ★
4 Batterymarch Park, Quincy, MA 02169-7468
Tel (617) 376-4300 Founded/Ownrshp 2015
Sales 573.5MM^E EMP 3,200
SIC 5961 5621 Catalog sales; Ready-to-wear apparel, women's
VP: Annette Buelow
Store Mgr: Nancy Hong

D-U-N-S 00-512-1447 IMP/EXP
JIM BEAM BRANDS CO
JAMES B BEAM IMPORT
(Suby of BEAM SUNTORY INC) ★
510 Lake Cook Rd Ste 200, Deerfield, IL 60015-4964
Tel (847) 948-8903 Founded/Ownrshp 1923, 1997
Sales 245.7MM^E EMP 985
SIC 2085 Distilled & blended liquors; Bourbon whiskey; Gin (alcoholic beverage); Vodka (alcoholic beverage)
CEO: Matthew J Shattock
*Pr: Richard B Reese
*Chf Mktg O: Rory Finlay
*Ex VP: Craig M Smith
*Ex VP: Joseph J Winkler
Sr VP: Beth Bronner
Sr VP: Mike Donohoe
Sr VP: Ed Moser
*Sr VP: Bob Probst
VP: Thomas J Flocco
VP: Mindy Mackenzie
VP: Florence Pramberger
VP: Marcio Ribeiro

JIM BURKE FORD
See FORD HABERFELDE

D-U-N-S 02-678-8356
JIM BURNS AUTOMOTIVE GROUP INC
PIONEER-LINCOLN-MERCURY
8230 Urbana Ave, Lubbock, TX 79424-4997
Tel (806) 747-3211 Founded/Ownrshp 1981
Sales 200.0MM EMP 250
SIC 5511 Automobiles, new & used; Pickups, new & used
Pr: James J Burns
*Sec: Richard Adams
*VP: James D Burns

D-U-N-S 01-775-8996
JIM CLICK INC (CA)
JIM CLICK NISSAN
780 W Competition Rd, Tucson, AZ 85705-6000
Tel (520) 884-4100 Founded/Ownrshp 1955
Sales 218.7MM^E EMP 750
SIC 5511 Automobiles, new & used
Pr: Christopher B Cotter
*CFO: Susan Artaz
*CFO: Bradley R Wise
*Ch: James H Click Jr
*VP: Robert Tuttle
Off Mgr: Eddy Yashar
Sls Mgr: Tim Manzano

JIM CLICK NISSAN
See JIM CLICK INC

JIM ELLIS DIRECT
See ELLIS ATLANTA JIM INC

D-U-N-S 07-314-5971
JIM F WEBB INC
J W POWERLINE CONSTRUCTION
2401 E Interstate 20, Midland, TX 79701-2059
Tel (432) 684-4388 Founded/Ownrshp 1974
Sales 277.1MM^E EMP 100
SIC 4911 Electric services
Pr: Benton Posey
*VP: Dustin Burris
VP: Justin Burris

D-U-N-S 06-865-6628
JIM HAWK TRUCK TRAILER INC
(Suby of HAWK JIM GROUP INC) ★
3119 S 9th St, Council Bluffs, IA 51501-7664
Tel (712) 366-2241 Founded/Ownrshp 1993
Sales 90.5MM^E EMP 275
SIC 5012 Trailers for trucks, new & used
Pr: James V Hawk
*Pr: David P Hawk
*CFO: Gene Dolan
CFO: Eugene Dollen
*Treas: James V Hawk III
Genl Mgr: Jack Croy
Genl Mgr: Jason Gerhardt
Genl Mgr: John Minard
Dir IT: Rick Nordman

D-U-N-S 17-519-0339
JIM KOONS MANAGEMENT CO
2000 Chain Bridge Rd, Vienna, VA 22182-2531
Tel (703) 448-7000 Founded/Ownrshp 1986
Sales 308.9MM^E EMP 165
SIC 8741

D-U-N-S 03-494-4215
JIM L SHETAKIS DISTRIBUTING CO
SHETAKIS WHOLESALERS
3840 Civic Center Dr A, North Las Vegas, NV 89030-7534
Tel (702) 940-3663 Founded/Ownrshp 1959
Sales 116.8MM^E EMP 60
SIC 5141 5046 Groceries, general line; Restaurant equipment & supplies
Pr: Charlie Jackson
*Treas: Andrew Dannin
VP: John Quinones

D-U-N-S 14-170-1354 EXP
JIMBOS JUMBOS INC
(Suby of HAMPTON FARMS) ★
185 Peanut Dr, Edenton, NC 27932-9604
Tel (252) 482-2193 Founded/Ownrshp 1946
Sales 150.6MM^E EMP 205
SIC 5159 Peanuts (bulk), unroasted
Pr: Dallas Barnes
*VP: William E McKeown
VP: Mike Partin
Genl Mgr: Hal Burns
Prd Mgr: Roy Thompson
Trfc Mgr: Eddie McNair
Sls Mgr: Marvin Smith

D-U-N-S 01-208-1543 IMP/EXP
JIMLAR CORP
CALVIN KLEIN FOOTWEAR
(Suby of MAX LEATHER) ★
350 5th Ave Lbby 8, New York, NY 10118-0223
Tel (212) 475-0787 Founded/Ownrshp 1962
Sales 97.0MM^E EMP 249^E
SIC 5139 Footwear
CEO: Jim Tarica
*Pr: Larry Tarica
*CEO: Ronald Ventricelli
*COO: Frank Vignola
*Ex VP: John Castella
*Ex VP: Vincent Destefano

VP: Joan Auerbach
VP: Dave Moore
**Prin:* Tom Tarica
IT Man: Jay D'Eloia
Web Prj Mg: Andrew Tarica

D-U-N-S 04-115-5425 IMP
JIMS SUPPLY CO INC
3530 Buck Owens Blvd, Bakersfield, CA 93308-4920
Tel (661) 324-6514 *Founded/Ownrshp* 1955
Sales 88.9MM^E *EMP* 85
SIC 5051 Steel
CEO: Doreen M Boylan
**CFO:* Bryan Boylan
**Sec:* Jennifer Drake
**VP:* Greg Boylan
**VP:* Jennice Boylan
**VP:* Dan Drake
Exec: Tim Moreno
Opers Mgr: Jeff Miller
Sales Asso: Kevin Been
Sales Asso: Hillary Boylan
Sales Asso: Robert Gorman

D-U-N-S 12-013-2977 IMP
JINNY BEAUTY SUPPLY CO INC
3587 Oakcliff Rd, Atlanta, GA 30340-3014
Tel (770) 734-9222 *Founded/Ownrshp* 1995
Sales 200.0MM *EMP* 300
SIC 5087 Beauty salon & barber shop equipment & supplies
Pr: Eddie Jhin

D-U-N-S 03-355-6924
JIPC MANAGEMENT INC
JOHN'S INCREDIBLE PIZZA CO
22342 Avenida Empresa # 220, Rcho STA Marg, CA 92688-2161
Tel (949) 916-2000 *Founded/Ownrshp* 1998
Sales 82.3MM^E *EMP* 1,000
SIC 8741 Restaurant management
Pr: John M Parlet

D-U-N-S 00-802-3181
▲ JIVE SOFTWARE INC
325 Lytton Ave Ste 200, Palo Alto, CA 94301-1489
Tel (650) 319-1920 *Founded/Ownrshp* 2001
Sales 195.7MM *EMP* 721^E
Accts Kpmg Llp Portland Oregon
Tkr Sym JIVE *Exch* NGS
SIC 7372 Prepackaged software; Application computer software
Pr: Elisa A Steele
Ch Bd: Anthony Zingale
Pr: Jeff Lautenbach
CFO: Bryan J Leblanc
Chf Mktg O: David Puglia
Ex VP: Ofer Ben-David
VP: Rob Brewster
VP: Leandra Fishman
VP: Eric Johnson
VP: Dilshad Simons
Comm Dir: Jason Khoury
Board of Directors: Margaret A Breya, Stephen R Darcy, Philip Koen, William A Lanfri, Thomas Reilly, Chuck J Robel, Theodore E Schlein, Gabrielle Toledano

D-U-N-S 00-695-0042 IMP
JJ HAINES & CO LLC (MD)
6950 Aviation Blvd, Glen Burnie, MD 21061-2531
Tel (410) 760-4040 *Founded/Ownrshp* 1874
Sales 278.0MM^E *EMP* 400
SIC 5023 Floor coverings; Carpets; Resilient floor coverings: tile or sheet; Wood flooring
Pr: Bruce Zwicker
**CFO:* John Coakley
**VP:* Terry Russell
Genl Mgr: Jim Claypool
Sls Mgr: Jay Friend

D-U-N-S 06-391-4121 IMP/EXP
JJTAYLOR COMPANIES INC
J J TAYLOR CO
655 N Highway A1a, Jupiter, FL 33477-4579
Tel (813) 247-4000 *Founded/Ownrshp* 1958
Sales 212.6MM^E *EMP* 600
SIC 5181 Ale; Beer & other fermented malt liquors
CEO: John J Taylor Jr
**Pr:* John J Taylor III
VP: Daniel Daul
CIO: Bruce Whitely
Mktg Mgr: Melissa Berger

D-U-N-S 06-762-3181 IMP
JJI LIGHTING GROUP INC
ALKCO LIGHTING COMPANY
(*Suby of* KONINKLIJKE PHILIPS N.V.)
11500 Melrose Ave, Franklin Park, IL 60131-1334
Tel (847) 451-3258 *Founded/Ownrshp* 2011
Sales 88.2MM^E *EMP* 650
SIC 3646 3648 3645 Commercial indusl & institutional electric lighting fixtures; Outdoor lighting equipment; Arc lighting fixtures; Floor lamps; Fluorescent lighting fixtures, residential; Table lamps; Wall lamps
Pr: James F Hayworth
**CFO:* Charles J Florio
CFO: John Walsh
**VP Admn:* Peter K Mitchell
Genl Mgr: Bob Haidinger

D-U-N-S 62-461-5345
JJJTB INC
3200 Flightline Dr, Lakeland, FL 33811-2848
Tel (863) 607-5600 *Founded/Ownrshp* 2004
Sales 260.6MM *EMP* 54^E
Accts Harman & Peaslee Pa Plant
SIC 4731 Truck transportation brokers
Pr: John J Jerue
**Treas:* E Luis Campano

JJS
See JOSEPH JINGOLI & SON INC

D-U-N-S 61-779-5229
JK & T WINGS INC
13405 W Star Dr Ste 2, Shelby Township, MI 48315-2706
Tel (586) 781-0591 *Founded/Ownrshp* 1996
Sales 98.3MM^E *EMP* 1,200
SIC 8741 Administrative management
Pr: Kent Ward

D-U-N-S 07-872-8635 IMP
JK IMAGING LTD
17239 S Main St, Gardena, CA 90248-3129
Tel (310) 755-6848 *Founded/Ownrshp* 2012
Sales 100.0MM *EMP* 100
SIC 5043 Cameras & photographic equipment
CEO: Joe Atick
**CFO:* Shu-Ping Wu

JK MOVING SERVICES LOUDOUN CO
See J K MOVING & STORAGE INC

D-U-N-S 16-318-6059 IMP
JL AUDIO INC
10369 N Commerce Pkwy, Miramar, FL 33025-3962
Tel (954) 443-1100 *Founded/Ownrshp* 1977
Sales 83.9MM^E *EMP* 265
SIC 5065 2519 Sound equipment, electronic; Fiberglass furniture, household: padded or plain
CEO: Lucio Proni
**Pr:* Andy Oxenhorn
**VP:* Clare Gates
**VP:* George Jenkins
VP: Jeff Scoon
Creative D: Andrew Sheehy
Dir IT: Ozzy Reyes
Opers Mgr: Darrell Chapman
Prd Mgr: Harry Lord
**VP Mktg:* Manville Smith
**VP Sls:* Carl Kennedy

J.L. FRENCH AUTO CASTINGS INC
See NEMAK AUTOMOTIVE CASTINGS INC

D-U-N-S 61-963-2701 IMP
JL FRENCH AUTOMOTIVE LLC
(*Suby of* JL FRENCH LLC) ★
3101 S Taylor Dr, Sheboygan, WI 53081-9401
Tel (920) 458-7724 *Founded/Ownrshp* 2004
Sales 128.1MM^E *EMP* 416^E
SIC 3465

D-U-N-S 04-726-0591 IMP/EXP
JL FRENCH LLC
3101 S Taylor Dr, Sheboygan, WI 53081-9401
Tel (920) 458-7724 *Founded/Ownrshp* 2007
Sales 622.7MM^E *EMP* 3,000
SIC 3363

JLA HOME
See E & E CO LTD

D-U-N-S 04-388-7728 IMP/EXP
■ JLG INDUSTRIES INC
J L G
(*Suby of* OSHKOSH CORP) ★
1 J L G Dr, Mc Connellsburg, PA 17233-9533
Tel (717) 485-5161 *Founded/Ownrshp* 2006
Sales 1.2MMM^E *EMP* 4,993
SIC 3531 Construction machinery; Aerial work platforms: hydraulic/elec. truck/carrier mounted; Cranes
Pr: Frank Nerenhausen
**Sr VP:* Timothy Morris
**VP:* Frank Cholewicki
VP: Shawn Kenny
VP: Wayne Lawson
VP: Tracey McKenzie
**VP:* Andrew Tacelosky
Prgrm Mgr: Tonya Metzler
Dir IT: Bill Belleville
Dir IT: Michael Bierly
IT Man: Chris Gambacurta

D-U-N-S 01-775-9761
JLJ HOME FURNISHINGS LLC
SLEEP STYLES
4776 Charlotte Hwy, Lancaster, SC 29720-7769
Tel (704) 239-8630 *Founded/Ownrshp* 2015
Sales 90.0MM^E *EMP* 12^E
SIC 5712 Furniture stores

D-U-N-S 96-166-4195
JLL PARTNERS FUND IV LP
450 Lexington Ave Fl 31, New York, NY 10017-3925
Tel (212) 286-8600 *Founded/Ownrshp* 2000
Sales 42.3MM^E *EMP* 1,040
SIC 6722 Money market mutual funds

D-U-N-S 62-707-1103
JLL PARTNERS INC
ACE CASH EXPRESS
450 Lexington Ave Fl 31, New York, NY 10017-3925
Tel (212) 286-8600 *Founded/Ownrshp* 1987
Sales 2.2MMM^E *EMP* 13,491
SIC 6799 6099 Investors; Check cashing agencies
Pr: Paul Levy
**COO:* Michael Schwartz
Ex VP: Wayne Schuchts
**VP:* Daniel Agroskin
**VP:* Kevin T Hammond
VP: Kevin Hammond
Mng Dir: Dalia Cohen

JM & A GROUP
See JM FAMILY ENTERPRISES INC

D-U-N-S 00-578-2519
JM BULLION INC (PA)
12655 N Cntl Expy Ste 800, Dallas, TX 75243
Tel (800) 276-6508 *Founded/Ownrshp* 2011
Sales 660.0MM *EMP* 41^E
SIC 5094 Bullion, precious metals
CEO: Michael Whitmeyer
**CFO:* Robert Byerley

JM EAGLE
See J-M MANUFACTURING CO INC

JM EAGLE
See PW EAGLE INC

JM FAMILY ENTERPRISES
See SOUTHEAST TOYOTA DISTRIBUTORS LLC

D-U-N-S 08-242-3435 EXP
JM FAMILY ENTERPRISES INC
JM & A GROUP
100 Jim Moran Blvd, Deerfield Beach, FL 33442-1702
Tel (954) 429-2000 *Founded/Ownrshp* 1969
Sales 1.4MMM^E *EMP* 3,800
SIC 5511 5012 5013 5531 New & used car dealers; Automobiles & other motor vehicles; Motor vehicle supplies & new parts; Automobile & truck equipment & parts
CEO: Colin Brown
Pr: Rosie Burkman
Pr: Diana Najm
**COO:* Ron Coombs
**CFO:* Brent D Burns
Treas: Donna McWilliams
Ofcr: Ken Yerves
Ex VP: Carmen S Johnson
Sr VP: Dan Chait
VP: Josh Bass
VP: Debbie Battisto
VP: Shawn Berg
VP: Alan Browdy
VP: Fred Brown
VP: Todd Clarke
VP: Andy Eccher
VP: Kim Fields
VP: Charles Gordon
VP: Hank Grooms
VP: Jan Moran
VP: Rajeev Ravindran
Board of Directors: Arline M Mc Nally, John J Mc Nally, James M Moran Jr, Janice M Moran, Patricia G Moran

D-U-N-S 00-255-4459 IMP/EXP
JM HUBER CORP (NJ)
499 Thornall St Ste 8, Edison, NJ 08837-2267
Tel (732) 603-3630 *Founded/Ownrshp* 1883
Sales 859.5MM^E *EMP* 4,000
Accts Kpmg Llp Short Hills Nj
SIC 0811 1311 1455 2493 2819 Timber tracts; Crude petroleum production; Kaolin mining; Strandboard, oriented; Industrial inorganic chemicals
Ch Bd: Mike Marberry
Pr: William B Goodspeed
Pr: Albert Landers
Pr: Andrew Trott
CFO: Jeffrey Jerome
CFO: Michael L Marberry
CFO: Jeff Prosinski
Treas: Lane Silverman
Sr VP: Donald Whaley
VP: Robert L Cornelius
VP: Robert Cornelius
VP: Robert Currie
VP: Joseph Dunning
VP: Bart Edwards
VP: Phyllis A Erikson
VP: William Fricker
VP: B Keidan
VP: Dan Krawczyk
VP: Daniel Krawczyk
VP: Carol Lynn Messer
VP: Marilyn Pearlman

D-U-N-S 12-181-3166
JM THOMAS FOREST PRODUCTS CO
2525 N Hwy 89 91, Ogden, UT 84404-2656
Tel (801) 782-8090 *Founded/Ownrshp* 1980
Sales 89.6MM^E *EMP* 90
Accts Pinnock Robbins Posey & Rich
SIC 5031 Building materials, exterior; Building materials, interior
Ch Bd: James Matthew Thomas
**Pr:* Bill Anderson
**CFO:* Carl Daines
Dir IT: Brandon Stevenson

D-U-N-S 02-532-3247 IMP
JMAC INC
200 W Nationwide Blvd # 1, Columbus, OH 43215-2561
Tel (614) 436-2418 *Founded/Ownrshp* 1980
Sales 96.0MM^E *EMP* 600^E
SIC 3325 5198 7999 5511 8741 Steel foundries; Paints; Ice skating rink operation; Automobiles, new & used; Financial management for business
Ch Bd: John P McConnell
**Pr:* Michael A Priest
**Prin:* George N Corey

JMC STEEL GROUP
See WHEATLAND TUBE LLC

D-U-N-S 13-046-0657
JMEG LP
EA ELECTRIC
13995 Diplomat Dr Ste 400, Farmers Branch, TX 75234-8804
Tel (972) 590-5555 *Founded/Ownrshp* 2002
Sales 164.8MM^E *EMP* 900
SIC 1731 Electrical work
Pt: Russell Ferraro
Pt: Gary Fraser
Pt: Jerry Mills
Pt: Bill Mitchell
Pt: Ray Naizer
Pt: John Wall
VP: Billy Tennison
Snr PM: Bill Lerow
Snr PM: Gene Speight

D-U-N-S 00-677-3709 IMP
JMF CO
2735 62nd Street Ct, Bettendorf, IA 52722-5599
Tel (563) 332-9200 *Founded/Ownrshp* 1948
Sales 100.0MM *EMP* 100
SIC 5074 Plumbing & hydronic heating supplies
CEO: Max Hansen
**Pr:* Bryan Micheelsem
**CFO:* Dallon Christensen
VP Sls: Bill Tinker
VP Sls: Bob Wilson

D-U-N-S 82-884-8437
■ JMH TRADEMARK INC
(*Suby of* A&F TRADEMARK INC) ★
6301 Fitch Path, New Albany, OH 43054-9269
Tel (614) 283-6500 *Founded/Ownrshp* 2002
Sales 474.8MM^E *EMP* 350
SIC 5611 Men's & boys' clothing stores
CEO: Michael S Jeffries

D-U-N-S 08-030-6586
JMJ CONSULTING GROUP INC
RELIABLE HEALTH CARE SOLUTIONS
1197 Perregrine Cir E, Saint Johns, FL 32259-2966
Tel (904) 538-0944 *Founded/Ownrshp* 2015
Sales 90.3MM *EMP* 3
SIC 5141 Groceries, general line
Pr: Phillip M Clayton

D-U-N-S 03-690-0761
JMJ FINANCIAL GROUP
26800 Aliso Viejo Pkwy # 200, Aliso Viejo, CA 92656-2625
Tel (949) 340-6336 *Founded/Ownrshp* 2010
Sales NA *EMP* 75
SIC 6162 Mortgage bankers
Pr: Virgil Kyle
**COO:* Thomas Kish
**CFO:* Ryan Robertson

D-U-N-S 04-121-9452
JMK AUTO SALES INC
JMK BMW
391-399 Rt 22 E, Springfield, NJ 07081
Tel (973) 379-7744 *Founded/Ownrshp* 1965
Sales 123.0MM *EMP* 145
SIC 7538 5511 General automotive repair shops; Automobiles, new & used
**Pr:* Roger J Kosempel
**Pr:* Cathie Maier
**Sec:* Cathryn Maier-Tajkowski
IT Man: Susan Arrogante
Sls Mgr: Mike Blomgren
Sls Mgr: Angelo Zito

JMK BMW
See JMK AUTO SALES INC

D-U-N-S 03-922-1398
JMM SERVICES INC
TEMPSTAR STAFFING
1431 N George St, York, PA 17404-2014
Tel (717) 848-1100 *Founded/Ownrshp* 2005
Sales 18.0MM *EMP* 1,050
SIC 7361 Employment agencies
Pr: Michael Rauch
**CFO:* Richard Spaw

D-U-N-S 10-638-1598
■ JMP GROUP INC
(*Suby of* JMP GROUP LLC) ★
600 Montgomery St # 1100, San Francisco, CA 94111-2702
Tel (415) 835-8900 *Founded/Ownrshp* 2015
Sales 206.3MM *EMP* 235^E
SIC 6211 Investment bankers
Ch Bd: Joseph A Jolson
Pr: Mark L Lehmann
Pr: Kevin Lynch
**Pr:* Carter D Mack
CFO: Raymond S Jackson
**V Ch Bd:* Craig R Johnson

D-U-N-S 08-010-1787
▲ JMP GROUP LLC
600 Montgomery St # 1100, San Francisco, CA 94111-2702
Tel (415) 835-8900 *Founded/Ownrshp* 2014
Sales 206.3MM^E *EMP* 235^E
Tkr Sym JMP *Exch* NYS
SIC 6211 Investment bankers
Ch Bd: Joseph A Jolson
**Pr:* Carter D Mack
CFO: Raymond S Jackson
CFO: Craig Kitchin
**V Ch Bd:* Craig R Johnson
VP: Andrew Welsh
Mng Dir: Donald Ellis
Mng Dir: Don More
Mng Dir: David Shapiro
Mng Dir: Gavin Slader
Mng Dir: Jorge Solares

JMS BUILDING SOLUTIONS, LLC
See PARAMOUNT BUILDING SOLUTIONS LLC

D-U-N-S 14-653-8306
JNET COMMUNICATIONS LLC
25 Independence Blvd # 103, Warren, NJ 07059-2706
Tel (203) 951-6400 *Founded/Ownrshp* 2003
Sales 90.0MM *EMP* 2,260
SIC 4899 1731 Data communication services; Cable television installation
CEO: David Jefferson
COO: Michael A Dennis
**CFO:* Eugene Caldwell

JNLD
See JACKSON NATIONAL LIFE DISTRIBUTORS LLC

D-U-N-S 00-653-8516 IMP
JO GALLOUP CO
SMITH INSTRUMENT
(*Suby of* GREAT LAKES AUTOMATION SUPPLY) ★
130 Helmer Rd N, Battle Creek, MI 49037-4900
Tel (269) 965-2303 *Founded/Ownrshp* 2012
Sales 157.8MM^E *EMP* 233
SIC 5051 5085 5162 Pipe & tubing, steel; Valves & fittings; Industrial fittings; Plastics materials & basic shapes
Pr: Martin U Ranly
**Sec:* James L Treadwell
Genl Mgr: Sheila Bailey
Genl Mgr: Richard Waters
CIO: Carl Bolles
Sales Exec: Tim Hayes
Sales Exec: Dave Komosinski
Sls&Mrk Ex: Scott Hodges
Sls Mgr: Jim Barnes

Sls Mgr: Dan Foster
Sls Mgr: Doug Riggs

JO-ANN FABRICS & CRAFTS
See JO-ANN STORES LLC

JO-ANN FABRICS & CRAFTS
See JO-ANN STORES HOLDINGS INC

D-U-N-S 07-946-3509
JO-ANN STORES HOLDINGS INC
JO-ANN FABRICS & CRAFTS
5555 Darrow Rd, Hudson, OH 44236-4054
Tel (888) 739-4120 *Founded/Ownrshp* 2012
Sales 3.3MMM^E *EMP* 19,626^E
SIC 5945 5949 5947 Arts & crafts supplies; Fabric stores piece goods; Notions, including trim; Patterns: sewing, knitting & needlework; Sewing supplies; Gifts & novelties
Pr: Roger Hawkins
Pr: Sue Walker
Sr VP: Karen Frey
Sr VP: David Goldston
VP: Christopher Ditullio
VP: Doug Robinson
VP: Scott Roubic
VP: Dennis Spence
VP: Joe Thibault
VP: Ed Weinstein
Exec: Robin Kaminski

D-U-N-S 00-294-4684 IMP
JO-ANN STORES LLC
JO-ANN FABRICS & CRAFTS
(*Suby of* JO-ANN FABRICS & CRAFTS) ★
5555 Darrow Rd, Hudson, OH 44236-4054
Tel (330) 656-2600 *Founded/Ownrshp* 2011
Sales 3.3MMM^E *EMP* 23,000
SIC 5945 5949 5947 Arts & crafts supplies; Fabric stores piece goods; Notions, including trim; Patterns: sewing, knitting & needlework; Sewing supplies; Gifts & novelties
Ch: Darrell Webb
**Pr:* Jill Soltau
CFO: Brian Carney
**CFO:* Jim Kerr
CFO: Wade Miquelon
**Ofcr:* Sharyn Hejcl
Ex VP: Lee Barnard
Ex VP: Chris Ditullio
Ex VP: Dotty Grexa
Ex VP: Gerturde Horn
Ex VP: Fred Johnson
Ex VP: Mary Lehman
Ex VP: Mary Marlinski
Ex VP: Bruce Schwallie
Ex VP: Rosalind Thompson
Ex VP: Debra Walker
Ex VP: Alma Zimmerman
Sr VP: Robert R Gerber
Sr VP: David Goldston
**Sr VP:* Riddianne Kline
Sr VP: Susan Van Benten

D-U-N-S 08-414-2785
JO-KELL INC (VA)
1716 Lambert Ct, Chesapeake, VA 23320-8913
Tel (757) 523-2900 *Founded/Ownrshp* 1977
Sales 84.3MM^E *EMP* 64
SIC 5063 8711 Electrical apparatus & equipment; Consulting engineer
CEO: Susan Kelly
**Pr:* Martin Kelly
**COO:* Adrian Marchi
CFO: John D Williamson
Sr VP: Jim Baur
Sls Mgr: John Kelly

D-U-N-S 15-070-7656
JOAH INC
(*Suby of* ACME) ★
250 E Parkcenter Blvd, Boise, ID 83706-3940
Tel (208) 395-6200 *Founded/Ownrshp* 1987
Sales 1.5MMM^E *EMP* 18,000
SIC 5411 Grocery stores
CEO: Lawrence R Johnston

D-U-N-S 79-101-6991
JOB 1 USA
(*Suby of* JOB1USA) ★
701 Jefferson Ave Ste 202, Toledo, OH 43604-6957
Tel (419) 255-5005 *Founded/Ownrshp* 1951
Sales 30.5MM^E *EMP* 1,012^E
SIC 7381 7363 7361 Security guard service; Protective services, guard; Temporary help service; Medical help service; Employment agencies; Executive placement
Pr: Bruce F Rumpf
**VP:* Sue Daniels
**VP:* Eloise Huston
**VP:* Don Reynolds
Area Mgr: Ken Curry
Area Mgr: Ray Kasparian
VP Opers: Carol Hayward
VP Sls: Stacie Moss
Sls Mgr: Jessica Weatherholtz

D-U-N-S 60-091-1981
JOB INDUSTRIAL SERVICES INC
J I S
1805 S Redwood Rd # 150, Salt Lake City, UT 84104-5151
Tel (801) 433-0901 *Founded/Ownrshp* 2005
Sales 99.7MM *EMP* 35
Accts Tanner Llc Salt Lake City Ut
SIC 8711 Construction & civil engineering
Pr: Jason Job
**Pr:* Eric Schomaker
COO: Steve Wendel
**CFO:* Jack Job
Dir IT: Ben Rand
Snr PM: Ryan Ranzenberger

JOB1USA
See RUMPF CORP

D-U-N-S 19-890-2624
JOBE MATERIALS LP
1150 Southview Dr Ste A, El Paso, TX 79928-5240
Tel (915) 298-9900 *Founded/Ownrshp* 2005
Sales 84.1MM^E *EMP* 430^E
SIC 3272 Concrete products
Genl Pt: Stanley Jobe
Pt: Irene Eperson
Dir Risk M: Hector Paquian
Genl Mgr: Victor Salcido
Trfc Dir: Henry Tellez
Ql Cn Mgr: Rey Loya

JOBS PLUS
See PLUS GROUP INC

D-U-N-S 06-210-6563
JOBSOHIO
41 S High St, Columbus, OH 43215-6170
Tel (614) 224-6446 *Founded/Ownrshp* 2011
Sales 121.7MM *EMP* 3
SIC 7361 Labor contractors (employment agency)
CFO: Kevin Giangola
Chf Mktg O: Scott Hanley
Chf Inves: John Minor
Ex Dir: Kristi Clouse
Mng Dir: Tracy Allen
Mng Dir: Ted Griffith
Mng Dir: Mark Patton
Mng Dir: Glenn Richardson
Mng Dir: Dana Saucier
Mktg Dir: Marlon Cheatham
Sls Dir: Lee Crume

D-U-N-S 00-168-3911 IMP
JOBSON MEDICAL INFORMATION LLC
440 9th Ave Fl 14, New York, NY 10001-1629
Tel (212) 274-7000 *Founded/Ownrshp* 2005
Sales 108.0MM^E *EMP* 403
SIC 2721 2741 Magazines: publishing & printing; Miscellaneous publishing
**CEO:* Michael Tansey
**CFO:* John Orr
Exec: Robert Amato
Mktg Dir: Nancy Ness
Assoc Ed: Patrisha Zabrycki

D-U-N-S 78-328-4656
JOCKEY INTERNATIONAL DOMESTIC INC
JOCKEY STORE
(*Suby of* JOCKEY USA) ★
2300 60th St, Kenosha, WI 53140-3889
Tel (262) 658-8111 *Founded/Ownrshp* 1986
Sales 91.3MM^E *EMP* 700
SIC 5651 5611 Family clothing stores; Men's & boys' clothing stores
Ch Bd: Donna Wolf Steigerwaldt
**Pr:* Edward C Emma
VP: Mark S Jaeger
CIO: Frank Schneider III
Telecom Mg: Tom Ruffalo
Telecom Mg: Bob Schultz
VP Opers: Marion Smith
Plnt Mgr: Danny Hayes
Mktg Mgr: Sara Fuhs

D-U-N-S 79-436-4828
JOCKEY INTERNATIONAL GLOBAL INC
JOCKEY STORE
(*Suby of* JOCKEY STORE) ★
2300 60th St, Kenosha, WI 53140-3889
Tel (262) 658-8111 *Founded/Ownrshp* 1986
Sales 89.8MM^E *EMP* 630
SIC 2211 5611 Underwear fabrics, cotton; Men's & boys' clothing stores
Pr: Edward Emma
**Pr:* Frank Sneider
**Treas:* Ron Kwasny

D-U-N-S 04-193-6840 IMP/EXP
JOCKEY INTERNATIONAL INC (WI)
JOCKEY USA
2300 60th St, Kenosha, WI 53140-3889
Tel (262) 658-8111 *Founded/Ownrshp* 1876, 1930
Sales 1.3MMM^E *EMP* 5,000
SIC 2254 2341 2322 Knit underwear mills; Underwear, knit; Women's & children's underwear; Men's & boys' underwear & nightwear
Ch Bd: Debra Steigerwaldt Waller
**Pr:* Peter J Hannes
**Pr:* Michael S Lapidus
**Pr:* Robert L Nolan
**Pr:* Byron Norsleet
**Pr:* Steven M Tolensky
CFO: Frank Schneider
Sr Cor Off: Conrad Lung
**Sr VP:* F Brad Beal
**VP:* Anne T Arbas
**VP:* Mark S Jaeger
**VP:* Ronald E Kwasny
VP: Jamie Lockard

JOCKEY STORE
See JOCKEY INTERNATIONAL DOMESTIC INC

JOCKEY STORE
See JOCKEY INTERNATIONAL GLOBAL INC

JOCKEY USA
See JOCKEY INTERNATIONAL INC

JOE G MALOOF & CO
See MALOOF DISTRIBUTING LLC

JOE KELLEY CONSTRUCTION
See KELLEY CONSTRUCTION INC

D-U-N-S 04-772-3192
JOE MACHENS FORD INC
JOE MACHENS FORD LINCOLN
1911 W Worley St, Columbia, MO 65203-1093
Tel (573) 445-4411 *Founded/Ownrshp* 1969
Sales 171.7MM^E *EMP* 800
SIC 5511 Automobiles, new & used; Pickups, new & used; Vans, new & used
Pr: Gary R Drewing
**VP:* David Machens
Dir Bus: Brian Neuner
Ex Dir: Mary Jo Henry
Off Mgr: Shirley Cornelison
Sls Mgr: Scott Cross
Sls Mgr: Ralph Dumas
Sls Mgr: Danny Hammack
Sls Mgr: John Milletics
Sls Mgr: Steve Rennells
Sls Mgr: Kerry Thomas

JOE MACHENS FORD LINCOLN
See JOE MACHENS FORD INC

D-U-N-S 05-720-8118 IMP/EXP
JOE PIPER INC
123 Industrial Dr, Birmingham, AL 35211-4445
Tel (205) 290-2211 *Founded/Ownrshp* 1954
Sales 107.7MM^E *EMP* 80
SIC 5113 Paperboard & products
Pr: Ann Piper Carpenter
CFO: Phillips Crabtree
**Treas:* Richard W Patterson
**VP:* Bill Miller
CIO: Terri Yearty
**VP Opers:* Mims Cooper
Sfty Mgr: Scott Moncrief
VP Sls: Joe Hobby

D-U-N-S 80-807-9284
JOE TORNANTE-MDP HOLDING LLC
233 S Beverly Dr, Beverly Hills, CA 90212-3886
Tel (310) 228-6800 *Founded/Ownrshp* 2007
Sales 354.0MM^E *EMP* 487^E
SIC 5145 5092 5112 2064 Confectionery; Candy; Chewing gum; Toys & games; Playing cards; Social stationery & greeting cards; Albums, scrapbooks & binders; Candy & other confectionery products; Lollipops & other hard candy

D-U-N-S 00-690-0898
JOE WHEELER ELECTRIC MEMBERSHIP CORP
25354 Al Highway 24, Trinity, AL 35673-5365
Tel (256) 552-2300 *Founded/Ownrshp* 1937
Sales 153.4MM *EMP* 108
Accts Jackson Thornton & Co Pc Mont
SIC 4911 Distribution, electric power
Pr: Neal Norwood
**Sec:* Rick Knouff

D-U-N-S 78-513-9630
JOE WHEELER EMC
25700 Al Highway 24, Trinity, AL 35673-5395
Tel (256) 552-2300 *Founded/Ownrshp* 2006
Sales NA *EMP* 40^E
SIC 6111 Rural Electrification Administration
CFO: Patrick Holmes
**Genl Mgr:* George Kitchens

JOEMC
See JONES-ONSLOW ELECTRIC MEMBERSHIP CORP

D-U-N-S 13-763-4309
JOERIS GENERAL CONTRACTORS LTD
823 Arion Pkwy, San Antonio, TX 78216-2922
Tel (210) 286-8696 *Founded/Ownrshp* 1983
Sales 351.0MM *EMP* 200
Accts Padgett Stratermann & Co San
SIC 1542 Commercial & office building, new construction
Genl Pt: Gary Joeris
**Pt:* Michelle Seward
**Pt:* Stephen Walter
CFO: Michelle Davis
Genl Mgr: Elva Rose
Off Mgr: Vicky Banks
VP Opers: John Casstevens
Sfty Mgr: Mark Bakeman
Snr PM: Bill Huber
Snr PM: Blake Larue

D-U-N-S 79-093-7150 IMP
JOERNS HEALTHCARE LLC
(*Suby of* QUAD-C JH HOLDINGS INC) ★
2430 Whit Park Dr Ste 100, Charlotte, NC 28273
Tel (704) 499-6000 *Founded/Ownrshp* 2006
Sales 293.0MM *EMP* 500
SIC 5047 Hospital furniture
CEO: Mark Ludwig
CFO: Travis Chester
**CFO:* Jim Shiller
VP: Partha Biswas
QA Dir: Mike Chellson
IT Man: Jeremy Laha
IT Man: Andrew Woolner

D-U-N-S 12-608-5120
JOERNS LLC
(*Suby of* QUAD-C JH HOLDINGS INC) ★
19748 Dearborn St, Chatsworth, CA 91311-6509
Tel (800) 966-6662 *Founded/Ownrshp* 1998
Sales 100.6MM^E *EMP* 300
SIC 5047 Hospital equipment & furniture
**CFO:* Mark Urbania

JOERNS RECOVERCARE
See RECOVERCARE LLC

JOES JEANS
See GBG WEST LLC

JOES JUNCTION
See JACKSON OIL & SOLVENTS INC

JOE'S SPORTS, OUTDOOR & MORE
See G I JOES INC

JOH ATLANTIC PARTNERS
See JOHNSON OHARE CO INC

D-U-N-S 00-235-0577 IMP/EXP
JOHANNA FOODS INC
20 Johanna Farms Rd, Flemington, NJ 08822
Tel (908) 788-2200 *Founded/Ownrshp* 1944
Sales 178.1MM^E *EMP* 540^E
SIC 2033 2026 Fruit juices: packaged in cans, jars, etc.; Fruit juices: fresh; Yogurt
Pr: Robert A Facchina
**CFO:* Richard Cook
VP: Steve Kovack
VP: Roque Lopez
VP: Donna Serio
VP: Steven Steigerwalt
VP Bus Dev: Chris Hirst
IT Man: Keith Kunkel
Info Man: Chris Rears
VP Mktg: Jim Rowe
Sls Mgr: Barbara Tumler

D-U-N-S 02-272-0288
JOHANNESONS INC
MARKET PLACE FOODS
2301 Johanneson Dr Nw, Bemidji, MN 56601-4101
Tel (218) 751-9644 *Founded/Ownrshp* 1975
Sales 88.3MM^E *EMP* 650
SIC 5411 Supermarkets, independent
CEO: Keith Johanneson
CFO: Carmen Nornenberg
**Sec:* Richard Johanneson

D-U-N-S 00-447-2403
JOHN A BECKER CO (OH)
BECKER ELECTRIC SUPPLY
1341 E 4th St, Dayton, OH 45402-2235
Tel (937) 226-1341 *Founded/Ownrshp* 1920
Sales 295.9MM^E *EMP* 231
SIC 5063 Electrical construction materials; Electrical supplies; Lighting fixtures; Motor controls, starters & relays: electric
CEO: Thomas J Becker
**Pr:* David Adkinson
**VP:* James Becker
**VP:* Mark Covey
**VP:* James Dichito

D-U-N-S 05-882-1778 IMP
JOHN A BIEWER LUMBER CO (MI)
812 S Riverside Ave, Saint Clair, MI 48079-5393
Tel (810) 329-4789 *Founded/Ownrshp* 1961, 2000
Sales 101.5MM^E *EMP* 300
SIC 2491 Structural lumber & timber, treated wood; Pilings, treated wood
Pr: Richard Biewer
CFO: Gary Olmstead
**Sec:* Brian B Biewer
**VP:* Timothy Biewer

JOHN A. CARUSI MIDDLE SCHOOL
See CHERRY HILL PUBLIC SCHOOL DISTRICT

JOHN ASCUAGA'S NUGGET
See SPARKS NUGGET INC

D-U-N-S 02-529-3481 IMP
▲ JOHN B SANFILIPPO & SON INC
FISCHER NUT COMPANY
1703 N Randall Rd, Elgin, IL 60123-7820
Tel (847) 289-1800 *Founded/Ownrshp* 1979
Sales 952.0MM *EMP* 1,300
Tkr Sym JBSS *Exch* NGM
SIC 2068 2064 2099 2096 2066 Nuts: dried, dehydrated, salted or roasted; Candy & other confectionery products; Peanut butter; Dessert mixes & fillings; Potato chips & similar snacks; Chocolate & cocoa products
Ch Bd: Jeffrey T Sanfilippo
**Pr:* Jasper B Sanfilippo Jr
**Pr:* Michael J Valentine
Sr VP: Frank S Pellegrino
VP: Robert J Sarlls
Dir Bus: Lisa Sanfilippo
CIO: James A Valentine
Prd Mgr: Rick Balfour
Sls Dir: Polly Rowland
Mktg Mgr: Karri Demarois
Board of Directors: Timothy R Donovan, Jim Edgar, James J Sanfilippo, Ellen C Taaffe, Mathias A Valentine, Daniel M Wright

D-U-N-S 82-705-5869
▲ JOHN BEAN TECHNOLOGIES CORP
JBT
70 W Madison St Ste 4400, Chicago, IL 60602-4546
Tel (312) 861-5900 *Founded/Ownrshp* 1994
Sales 1.1MMM *EMP* 4,200
Tkr Sym JBT *Exch* NYS
SIC 3556 3585 3537 Food products machinery; Refrigeration & heating equipment; Containers (metal), air cargo
Ch Bd: Thomas W Giacomini
CFO: Brian A Deck
Ex VP: James L Marvin
Ex VP: Mark K Montague
VP: Dave Burdakin
VP: Megan J Rattigan
Dir IT: Miki Hohnsen
Mktg Mgr: Per Friberg
Manager: Paul Butler
Sls Mgr: Jeff Dahl
Board of Directors: C Maury Devine, Edward L Doheny II, Alan D Feldman, James E Goodwin, Polly B Kawalek, James M Ringler

D-U-N-S 00-982-7346
JOHN C GRIMBERG CO INC
3200 Tower Oaks Blvd Fl 3, Rockville, MD 20852-4216
Tel (301) 881-5120 *Founded/Ownrshp* 1954
Sales 157.7MM^E *EMP* 215
SIC 1542 Commercial & office building, new construction; Commercial & office buildings, renovation & repair
Pr: Peter J Grimberg
**CEO:* John M Grimberg
**VP:* James L Graham
VP: John Greenwell
**VP:* Stephen J Grimberg
**VP:* John F Treseler
IT Man: Kevin Fox
Ql Cn Mgr: Matthew Messier
Ql Cn Mgr: Tom Niederberger

D-U-N-S 00-693-9672
JOHN C GROUB CO INC
JAY C STORES
900 A Ave E, Seymour, IN 47274-3239
Tel (812) 522-1998 *Founded/Ownrshp* 1863
Sales 71.8MM^E *EMP* 2,000
SIC 5411 Grocery stores, chain
Pr: James T McCoy
**Treas:* Thomas Bollinger
Ex Dir: Karen Bottomley
Opers Mgr: Don Belcher
Mktg Mgr: Mark Baker
Mktg Mgr: Tom Bolinger

D-U-N-S 04-301-8480
JOHN C LINCOLN HEALTH NETWORK
JOHN C LINCOLN HOSP - DEER VLY
250 E Dunlap Ave, Phoenix, AZ 85020-2825
Tel (602) 870-6060 *Founded/Ownrshp* 2015
Sales 584.5MM *EMP* 3,500
SIC 8062 8051

JOHN C LINCOLN HOSP - DEER VLY
See JOHN C LINCOLN HEALTH NETWORK

D-U-N-S 07-112-4788
JOHN CARROLL UNIVERSITY (OH)
1 John Carroll Blvd, University Heights, OH 44118-4581
Tel (216) 397-1886 *Founded/Ownrshp* 1886
Sales 96.0MM *EMP* 2,343[E]
Accts Bkd Llp Fort Wayne Indiana
SIC 8221 University
Pr: Robert L Niehoff
Treas: Richard F Mausser
VP: Carol Dietz
VP: Lanasia Douglas
VP: Taylor Hartman
VP: Richard Mausser
VP: Nate Napolitano
VP: Richard P Salmi
Exec: Duane Dukes
CIO: Michael Bestul
IT Man: William Barker

D-U-N-S 17-411-8190
JOHN CHRISTNER TRUCKING LLC
19007 W Highway 33, Sapulpa, OK 74066-7545
Tel (918) 248-3300 *Founded/Ownrshp* 1986
Sales 117.8MM[E] *EMP* 789
SIC 4213 Trucking, except local
Pr: John M Christner
**Treas:* Darryl Christner
**VP:* Daniel Christner
VP: Jim Redwine
**VP:* Bob Snell
Dir Risk M: Shannon Crowley
MIS Dir: Quek Song
Trfc Dir: Pete Galli
VP Sls: Greg Gorman
Mktg Dir: Jim Gomez

D-U-N-S 00-509-4347 IMP/EXP
JOHN CRANE INC
(*Suby of* SMITHS GROUP PLC)
227 W Monroe St Ste 1800, Chicago, IL 60606-5053
Tel (312) 605-7800 *Founded/Ownrshp* 1917, 1986
Sales 1.6MMM[E] *EMP* 6,180
SIC 3053 Gaskets & sealing devices; Packing materials
Pr: Duncan Gillis
Pr: Rhonda Winston
**CFO:* Eric Evans
**Treas:* Terrance P McNamara
Sr Cor Off: Paul Roberts
VP: Ruben Alvarez
VP: Ruben Bonales
VP: Colin Clark
VP: Marcio Costa
**VP:* John F Donatiello
**VP:* Andrew J Forrest
VP: Guy Hagen
**VP:* David Hill
VP: Luca Mazzei
VP: Robin Piotrowski
VP: Angelo Rizzo
**VP:* David Tallentire
VP: Joseph Trytek

D-U-N-S 14-831-2481
JOHN D AND CATHERINE T MACARTHUR FOUNDATION
140 S Dearborn St, Chicago, IL 60603-5202
Tel (312) 332-0101 *Founded/Ownrshp* 1970
Sales 575.3MM *EMP* 150[E]
SIC 7011 Hotels & motels
Pr: Julia Stasch
Chf Inves: Su Manske
Ofcr: Marlies Carruth
Ofcr: Allison Clark
Ofcr: Maurice Classen
Ofcr: Sean Harder
Ofcr: Alaina Harkness
Ofcr: Christina Lovely
Ofcr: Kristen Molyneaux
Ofcr: Lauren Pabst
Ofcr: Erin Sines
Ofcr: Jeff Ubois
VP: Cecilia A Conrad
VP: Joshua J Mintz
VP: Gary Samore
VP: Debra Schwartz
VP: Andrew Solomon
Assoc Dir: Daniel Dirnberger

D-U-N-S 01-010-0899 IMP
JOHN D ARCHBOLD MEMORIAL HOSPITAL
ARCHBOLD MEDICAL CENTER
915 Gordon Ave, Thomasville, GA 31792-6699
Tel (229) 228-2000 *Founded/Ownrshp* 1925
Sales 251.3MM *EMP* 2,700
SIC 8062 General medical & surgical hospitals
Pr: Perry Mustian
**Ch Bd:* Daniel Autry
Pr: Jim Bue
**CFO:* Skip Hightower
Trst: Edward Hall
Trst: James Hester
Trst: James Smith
**Sr VP:* John A Fischer
VP: Debbie Beeson
VP: John Carter
VP: Amy Griffin
VP: J Perry Mustian
VP: Grady Ramsey
Exec: Michael Crowley
Dir Inf Cn: Annette Warren
Dir Risk M: Kellie Odom
Board of Directors: Pryor Cornell, Cindy Parrish, Joy Salter, Zack Wheeler

JOHN DEERE
See ALLIED DIESEL INC

JOHN DEERE
See WEST SIDE TRACTOR SALES CO

JOHN DEERE
See WM NOBBE AND CO INC

JOHN DEERE
See RAY LEE EQUIPMENT CO LTD

JOHN DEERE
See 4 RIVERS EQUIPMENT LLC

JOHN DEERE
See ZAHM & MATSON INC

JOHN DEERE
See DEERE CREDIT INC

JOHN DEERE AUTHORIZED DEALER
See WESTERN BRANCH DIESEL INC

JOHN DEERE AUTHORIZED DEALER
See STRIBLING EQUIPMENT LLC

JOHN DEERE AUTHORIZED DEALER
See VALLEY POWER SYSTEMS INC

JOHN DEERE AUTHORIZED DEALER
See WASHINGTON TRACTOR INC

JOHN DEERE AUTHORIZED DEALER
See RIESTERER & SCHNELL INC

JOHN DEERE AUTHORIZED DEALER
See CENTRAL CAROLINA FARM & MOWER INC

JOHN DEERE AUTHORIZED DEALER
See MCLEAN IMPLEMENT INC

JOHN DEERE AUTHORIZED DEALER
See ERB EQUIPMENT CO INC

JOHN DEERE AUTHORIZED DEALER
See CARRICO IMPLEMENT CO INC

JOHN DEERE AUTHORIZED DEALER
See HONNEN EQUIPMENT CO

JOHN DEERE AUTHORIZED DEALER
See JAMES RIVER EQUIPMENT VIRGINIA LLC

JOHN DEERE AUTHORIZED DEALER
See MISSISSIPPI AG CO

JOHN DEERE AUTHORIZED DEALER
See AMERICAN IMPLEMENT INC

JOHN DEERE AUTHORIZED DEALER
See MURPHY TRACTOR & EQUIPMENT CO INC

JOHN DEERE AUTHORIZED DEALER
See ARENDS HOGAN WALKER LLC

JOHN DEERE AUTHORIZED DEALER
See GREENWAY EQUIPMENT INC

JOHN DEERE AUTHORIZED DEALER
See XYLEM DEWATERING SOLUTIONS INC

JOHN DEERE AUTHORIZED DEALER
See RDO CONSTRUCTION EQUIPMENT CO

JOHN DEERE AUTHORIZED DEALER
See PAPE MACHINERY INC

JOHN DEERE AUTHORIZED DEALER
See JD EQUIPMENT INC

JOHN DEERE AUTHORIZED DEALER
See SLOAN IMPLEMENT CO INC

D-U-N-S 00-693-4764
■ JOHN DEERE CAPITAL CORP
JOHN DEERE FINANCIAL
(*Suby of* JOHN DEERE FINANCIAL SERVICES INC) ★
10587 Double R Blvd # 100, Reno, NV 89521-8966
Tel (775) 786-5527 *Founded/Ownrshp* 1958
Sales NA *EMP* 1,713[E]
SIC 6153 Short-term business credit
Ch Bd: Samuel R Allen
**Pr:* Michael J Mack Jr
**CFO:* Rajesh Kalathur
Board of Directors: James M Field, David C Gilmore, Max A Guinn, Patrick E Mack, John C May, Lawrence W Sidwell

JOHN DEERE CNSTR RET SLS
See JOHN DEERE SHARED SERVICES INC

D-U-N-S 00-543-3693 EXP
■ JOHN DEERE CONSTRUCTION & FORESTRY CO (DE)
JOHN DEERE CONSTRUCTION EQP
(*Suby of* DEERE & CO) ★
1 John Deere Pl, Moline, IL 61265-8010
Tel (309) 765-8000 *Founded/Ownrshp* 1906, 1969
Sales 548.2MM[E] *EMP* 760
SIC 5084 5082 Industrial machinery & equipment; General construction machinery & equipment
Pr: Pierre Leroy
CFO: James A Davlin
**Treas:* Michael Mack
VP: Metro Hornbuckle
**VP:* J H Peterson
**VP:* James D White
Dir IT: Richard Kramer
Sls Mgr: Steve Allison

JOHN DEERE CONSTRUCTION EQP
See JOHN DEERE CONSTRUCTION & FORESTRY CO

JOHN DEERE FINANCIAL
See JOHN DEERE CAPITAL CORP

D-U-N-S 55-541-7799
■ JOHN DEERE FINANCIAL SERVICES INC
(*Suby of* DEERE & CO) ★
6400 Nw 86th St, Johnston, IA 50131-2945
Tel (515) 267-3000 *Founded/Ownrshp* 1988
Sales NA *EMP* 1,727
SIC 6141 Personal credit institutions
Ch Bd: Robert Lane
**Pr:* Jon D Volkert
**Treas:* James S Robertson
**VP:* Michael T Feeley
**VP:* Keith R Hanson
**VP:* James R Heseman
**VP:* James A Israel
**VP:* Eugene L Schotanus
**VP:* Steven E Warren
**Prin:* Michael P Orr
IT Man: Beth Ullmark
Board of Directors: Joseph W England, Bernard L Hardiek, Dennis E Hoffmann, Ferdinand F Korndorf, Robert W Lane, Pierre E Leroy

JOHN DEERE HEALTH
See UNITEDHEALTHCARE SERVICES CO OF RIVER VALLEY INC

D-U-N-S 19-427-1771
JOHN DEERE INSURANCE GROUP INC
(*Suby of* SENTRY INSURANCE A MUTUAL CO) ★
3400 80th St, Moline, IL 61265-5884
Tel (309) 765-8000 *Founded/Ownrshp* 1999
Sales NA *EMP* 1,453
SIC 6331 6321 6311 Fire, marine & casualty insurance & carriers; Automobile insurance; Accident & health insurance carriers; Life insurance carriers
Pr: Wayne Ashenberg
**Sr VP:* Robert Nixon
Sr VP: Dave Rodger
VP: Robert E Reko
VP: Robert D Schauenberg
VP: Martin Wilkinson
Dir IT: Rebecca Gordon

D-U-N-S 14-212-4762
■ JOHN DEERE SHARED SERVICES INC
JOHN DEERE CNSTR RET SLS
(*Suby of* JOHN DEERE CONSTRUCTION EQP) ★
1515 5th Ave Ste 200, Moline, IL 61265-1367
Tel (309) 765-0260 *Founded/Ownrshp* 1985
Sales 391.3MM *EMP* 372[E]
SIC 5082 Graders, motor
VP: Max Guinn

JOHN DEERE WATER
See RIVULIS IRRIGATION INC

D-U-N-S 00-695-8193
JOHN E GREEN CO (MI)
220 Victor St, Detroit, MI 48203-3116
Tel (313) 868-2400 *Founded/Ownrshp* 1909
Sales 210.2MM[E] *EMP* 600
Accts Plante & Moran Pllc
SIC 1711 Mechanical contractor; Fire sprinkler system installation
Ch Bd: Peter J Green
**Pr:* Michael J Green
**COO:* Rob Martin
CFO: Dave Hubbard
**CFO:* John Stelter
**Sec:* John R Green
Bd of Dir: Rick Westcott
**Ex VP:* Michael T Brunett
**Ex VP:* Charles Osborne
**VP:* Ed Fici
VP: Gary Fisk
VP: Todd Pugh
Board of Directors: Marian R Green, Michael J Green

D-U-N-S 03-093-9169
JOHN E RETZNER OIL CO INC
630 S Adams St, Versailles, IN 47042-9003
Tel (812) 609-4178 *Founded/Ownrshp* 2004
Sales 168.4MM *EMP* 5
Accts Brian P Hawkins Kaneohe Haw
SIC 5983 Fuel oil dealers
Pr: Adam Hanson

D-U-N-S 07-263-3985 IMP/EXP
JOHN F KENNEDY CENTER FOR PERFORMING ARTS
KENNEDY CENTER, THE
2700 F St Nw, Washington, DC 20566-0002
Tel (202) 416-8000 *Founded/Ownrshp* 1958
Sales 211.5MM *EMP* 1,144
Accts Bdo Usa Llp Bethesda Md
SIC 7922 7929 Performing arts center production; Entertainers & entertainment groups
Ex Dir: Michael Kaiser
**CFO:* Lynne Pratt
**Treas:* Roland Betts
Treas: Lynn Pratt
Trst: Donald J Hall Jr
VP: Eileen Andrews
VP: John Dow
VP: Kathy Kruse
Mng Dir: Vernon E Jordan Jr
CIO: Alan C Levine
Mktg Mgr: Monica Holt

D-U-N-S 03-170-8360
■ JOHN F KENNEDY SPACE CENTER
NASA
(*Suby of* NASA) ★
6225 Vectorspace Blvd, Titusville, FL 32780-8040
Tel (321) 867-5000 *Founded/Ownrshp* 1964
Sales NA *EMP* 16,799
SIC 9661 Space flight operations, government; Space research & development, government;
CFO: Nap Carroll
Sfty Mgr: Thomas Dwyer

D-U-N-S 04-388-3081
JOHN F MARTIN & SONS INC
55 Lower Hillside Rd, Stevens, PA 17578-9787
Tel (717) 336-2804 *Founded/Ownrshp* 1945
Sales 94.5MM *EMP* 160
SIC 2013 0212

D-U-N-S 00-883-4681
JOHN F OTTO INC (CA)
OTTO CONSTRUCTION
1717 2nd St, Sacramento, CA 95811-6214
Tel (916) 441-6870 *Founded/Ownrshp* 1958
Sales 142.7MM *EMP* 120
Accts Campbell Taylor & Company Ros
SIC 1542 1541 Commercial & office building, new construction; Industrial buildings, new construction
Pr: Carl Barrett
**Sec:* Carol Otto
**VP:* Rick McVey
**VP:* Allison Otto
**VP:* Elease Terry
Board of Directors: Allison Otto John W Otto C

D-U-N-S 03-103-2329 EXP
JOHN FABICK TRACTOR CO
CATERPILLAR AUTHORIZED DEALER
1 Fabick Dr, Fenton, MO 63026-2928
Tel (636) 343-5900 *Founded/Ownrshp* 1917
Sales 284.6MM[E] *EMP* 600
SIC 5082 7699 General construction machinery & equipment; Road construction & maintenance machinery; Construction equipment repair
Pr: Harry Fabick
**Treas:* James Jansen
**Ex VP:* Doug Fabick
Sls Mgr: Benny Walker

D-U-N-S 01-949-9520
JOHN GORE ORGANIZATION INC
BROADWAY ACROSS AMERICA
1619 Broadway Fl 9, New York, NY 10019-7412
Tel (917) 421-5400 *Founded/Ownrshp* 2004
Sales 473.0M *EMP* 1,843[E]
SIC 7922 Entertainment promotion
Ch Bd: John Gore
Pt: Glenn Hill
**CFO:* Paul Dietz
CFO: Liam Lynch
**Ch:* Peter Schneider
Treas: Stephen Conroy
Ex VP: Rich Jaffe
Ex VP: Seth Popper
VP: Jill Keyishian
Mktg Dir: Leslie Butler
Mktg Dir: Brittany Smith

D-U-N-S 00-820-2673 IMP
JOHN H CARTER CO INC (LA)
17630 Perkins Rd Ste West, Baton Rouge, LA 70810-3849
Tel (225) 751-3788 *Founded/Ownrshp* 1957
Sales 359.9MM[E] *EMP* 376
SIC 5084 Processing & packaging equipment
Pr: Michel E Sansovich III
**Sec:* Robert G Wagnon
**VP:* Danny W Childress
**VP:* Calvin Curtis Douglas
**VP:* Todd E Gilbertson
**VP:* Bruce D Lowrey
**VP:* Michael J Nicaud
Exec: Scott Stein
Netwrk Eng: Cory Curson
Opers Mgr: Randy Lambert
Sls Mgr: Jason Fontenot

D-U-N-S 00-327-4552 IMP/EXP
JOHN H HARLAND CO
2939 Miller Rd, Decatur, GA 30035-4086
Tel (770) 593-5050 *Founded/Ownrshp* 2007
Sales NA *EMP* 5,360
SIC 2782 2752 2761 7371 7379

JOHN HANCOCK
See HANCOCK NATURAL RESOURCE GROUP INC

D-U-N-S 95-692-8568
JOHN HANCOCK CORPORATE TAX CREDIT FUND I LP
200 Clarendon St, Boston, MA 02116-5021
Tel (617) 572-6000 *Founded/Ownrshp* 1995
Sales 98.4MM[E] *EMP* 8,000
SIC 7389 Personal service agents, brokers & bureaus
CEO: Dominic D'Aldssandro
V Ch: Michele Van Leer
Sr VP: Deborah H McAneny
Sr VP: Jean Peters
VP: Sam Davis
Mng Dir: John C Anderson
Mng Dir: John Garrison
Mng Dir: Philip Messina

D-U-N-S 09-039-5844
JOHN HANCOCK FINANCIAL SERVICES INC
(*Suby of* MANULIFE FINANCIAL CORPORATION)
200 Clarendon St, Boston, MA 02116-5021
Tel (617) 572-6000 *Founded/Ownrshp* 1999, 2004
Sales NA *EMP* 7,965
SIC 6311 6351 6411 8371 6321

D-U-N-S 00-695-2410 IMP
JOHN HANCOCK LIFE INSURANCE CO (USA)
(*Suby of* JOHN HANCOCK FINANCIAL SERVICES INC) ★
865 S Figueroa St # 3320, Los Angeles, CA 90017-2543
Tel (213) 689-0813 *Founded/Ownrshp* 1862, 2000
Sales 915.9MM[E] *EMP* 7,962
SIC 7389 6351 6371 6321 Financial services; Mortgage guarantee insurance; Pensions; Accident insurance carriers; Health insurance carriers
CEO: Emeritus D'Alessandro
**Pr:* David F D'Alessandro
Pr: Ross Fryer
CFO: Steve Finch
**Treas:* Gregory P Winn
Ofcr: Robert F Walters
Ex VP: James Bowhers
Ex VP: Kathleen M Graveline
Ex VP: Harold K Mosher
**Ex VP:* Robert R Reitano
Sr VP: John M Deciccio
Sr VP: John T Farady
Sr VP: Joel V Kamer
Sr VP: Peter M Mawn
VP: Scott Estey
VP: James Logan
VP: Randy Zipse

D-U-N-S 78-959-6327
JOHN HANCOCK MANULIFE
(*Suby of* MANULIFE FINANCIAL CORPORATION)
197 Clarendon St Fl 4, Boston, MA 02116-5010
Tel (617) 663-3000 *Founded/Ownrshp* 1991
Sales NA *EMP* 150
SIC 6411 Insurance agents & brokers

*COO: John G Vrysen
CFO: Howard Cronson
*CFO: Charles A Rizzo
Ofcr: Thomas Horack
Ex VP: Scott Hartz
Sr VP: Karen A McCafferty
VP: Jerard Beauchamp
*VP: Thomas Kinzler
VP: Diane Landers
VP: Kristine McManus
VP: Andrea Mercier
VP: Camille Mucci
VP: Peter Schofield
VP: Lisa Welch
Exec: Betty Gregware
Assoc Dir: Lawrence Riddell

D-U-N-S 78-959-6228
JOHN HANCOCK SIGNATURE SERVICES INC
101 Huntington Ave Fl 3, Boston, MA 02199-7607
Tel (617) 375-4708 Founded/Ownrshp 1990
Sales 87.2MM[E] EMP 1,000
Accts Ernst & Young Llp
SIC 6289 6282 Security transfer agents; Investment advice
VP: Daniel Ouellette
*Treas: Christopher M Meyer
Ofcr: Robin Costa
VP: Timothy Malloy
*VP: Charles McKenney
*VP: John Morin
Comm Man: Marc Davis
Dir IT: Ann Welch
IT Man: Rick Russell

JOHN HENRY HOLDINGS, INC.
See MPS HOLDCO INC

D-U-N-S 00-691-9823 IMP
JOHN I HAAS INC
HAAS HOP PRODUCTS
5185 Mcarthur Blvd Nw # 300, Washington, DC 20016-3341
Tel (202) 777-4800 Founded/Ownrshp 1916
Sales 110.5MM[E] EMP 360
SIC 0139 5159 Hop farm; Hops
CEO: Henry Von Eichel
Mng Pt: Regine Barth
*Pr: Alexander Barth
*CFO: Thomas Davis

D-U-N-S 12-154-3714
JOHN J KIRLIN INC
JOHN J MECHANICAL SERVICES DIV
515 Dover Rd Ste 2100, Rockville, MD 20850-1290
Tel (301) 424-3410 Founded/Ownrshp 1960
Sales 345.6MM[E] EMP 1,200
SIC 1711 Plumbing contractors; Warm air heating & air conditioning contractor
Pr: Wayne Day
*CFO: William Goodrum
*Ex VP: Michael Mack
IT Man: Tracy Stallone

D-U-N-S 60-302-4857 IMP
JOHN J KIRLIN INC
515 Dover Rd Ste 2200, Rockville, MD 20850-1290
Tel (301) 424-3410 Founded/Ownrshp 1989
Sales 113.2MM EMP 1,000
SIC 1711 Mechanical contractor
Pr: Robert Bacon

JOHN J MECHANICAL SERVICES DIV
See JOHN J KIRLIN INC

D-U-N-S 07-926-5468
JOHN L SCOTT INC
JOHN L SCOTT REAL ESTATE
1700 Nw Gilman Blvd # 300, Issaquah, WA 98027-5349
Tel (425) 392-1211 Founded/Ownrshp 1931
Sales 4.0MMM EMP 155
SIC 6531 6794 Real estate brokers & agents; Franchises, selling or licensing
Ch: J Lennox Scott
*COO: Phil McBride
VP: Laura Hurme

JOHN L SCOTT REAL ESTATE
See JOHN L SCOTT INC

D-U-N-S 02-117-8702
JOHN L SULLIVAN INVESTMENTS INC (CA)
ROSEVILLE TOYOTA
6200 Northfront Rd, Livermore, CA 94551-9507
Tel (916) 969-5911 Founded/Ownrshp 1980, 1992
Sales 113.5MM[E] EMP 330
SIC 5511 7538 Automobiles, new & used; Pickups, new & used; General automotive repair shops
Pr: John L Sullivan
*Sec: Steve Ruckels
*VP: David Rodgers
Sls Mgr: Branden Rudh

D-U-N-S 07-741-7533
JOHN L WORTHAM & SON LP
WORTHAM INSURANCE & RISK MGT
2727 Allen Pkwy, Houston, TX 77019-2115
Tel (713) 526-3366 Founded/Ownrshp 1915
Sales NA EMP 469
SIC 6411 Insurance agents, brokers & service
Pt: Fred C Burns
Genl Pt: Daniel Traber
V Ch: Richard Blades
V Ch: Charles Flournoy
VP: George Adkins
VP: Tony Pham
Assoc Dir: Stephen Bishop
Assoc Dir: Barbara Childers
Assoc Dir: Aaron Fowler
Assoc Dir: Enrique Gomez
Assoc Dir: Christine Pace
Assoc Dir: Stuart Petty

D-U-N-S 96-308-6017
JOHN M BELK EDUCATIONL ENDOWMENT
4201 Congress St Ste 470, Charlotte, NC 28209-4682
Tel (704) 357-1000 Founded/Ownrshp 2010
Sales 244.1MM EMP 2
SIC 8699 Charitable organization
Prin: Morris Katherine Belk

D-U-N-S 09-672-1352
JOHN M QUALY
QUALY INSURANCE AGENCY
701 Market St Ste 1070, Saint Louis, MO 63101-1851
Tel (314) 231-3931 Founded/Ownrshp 1992
Sales NA EMP 150
SIC 6411 6311 Insurance agents; Life insurance
Mng Pt: John Qualy
Ofcr: Matthew Banderman
Ofcr: Justin Hennessey

JOHN MICHAEL MOORETRAUMA CTR
See VIRGINIA WEST UNIVERSITY HOSPITALS INC

D-U-N-S 07-653-8594
JOHN MUIR HEALTH
1601 Ygnacio Valley Rd, Walnut Creek, CA 94598-3122
Tel (925) 947-4449 Founded/Ownrshp 1958
Sales 1.2MMM EMP 2,200
Accts Deloitte Tax Llp San Francisc
SIC 8062 General medical & surgical hospitals
CEO: Calvin Knight
V Ch: David L Goldsmith
V Ch: Tom Rundall
*Pr: Michael S Thomas
*Pr: Jane A Willemsen
COO: Lee Huskins
COO: Elizabeth Stallings
CFO: Chris Pass
Treas: Guy Henshaw
Treas: Malcolm J McAuley
Ex VP: Kenneth L Meehan
Sr VP: Donna Brackley
Sr VP: Jon Russell
VP: Lisa Foust
VP: Linda Jaffe
VP: Mitchell Zack
Exec: Nancy Cotton
Exec: Wende Weckbacher

JOHN MUIR MEDICAL CENTER
See JOHN MUIR PHYSICIAN NETWORK

D-U-N-S 11-133-8653
JOHN MUIR PHYSICIAN NETWORK
JOHN MUIR MEDICAL CENTER
1450 Treat Blvd, Walnut Creek, CA 94597-2168
Tel (925) 296-9700 Founded/Ownrshp 1997
Sales 243.9MM[E] EMP 3,612
SIC 8062 8069 8093 7363 General medical & surgical hospitals; Substance abuse hospitals; Substance abuse clinics (outpatient); Medical help service
VP: Lynn Baskett
VP: Mitchell Zack
Surgeon: Jatinder S Dhillon
Board of Directors: Patrick E Kavanaugh, Burton H Baker, Ronald K Mullin, Phillip Batchelor, Thomas Rundall, David A Birdsall, Stuart B Shikora, William F Cronk, Stephen L Davenport, Marilyn M Gardner, Janet E Gaston, William K Hoddick, Steven M Kaplan

D-U-N-S 01-001-2243
JOHN P PICONE INC
31 Garden Ln, Lawrence, NY 11559-1126
Tel (516) 239-1600 Founded/Ownrshp 1980
Sales 178.4MM[E] EMP 400
SIC 1611 1622 1623 1629 Highway & street construction; Bridge construction; Sewer line construction; Waste water & sewage treatment plant construction
Ch Bd: John P Picone
*Pr: Robert Taikina
*CEO: Gerald E Rossettie
*VP: Kenneth Durkin
*VP: Robert Wessels
Dir Bus: Jim Longworth
Genl Mgr: Michael Germano
Off Mgr: Sara Picone

D-U-N-S 03-818-5518 IMP/EXP
JOHN PAUL MITCHELL SYSTEMS
20705 Centre Pointe Pkwy, Santa Clarita, CA 91350-2967
Tel (661) 298-0400 Founded/Ownrshp 1980
Sales 158.4MM[E] EMP 174
SIC 5122 Hair preparations
CEO: John Paul Dejoria
COO: Luke Jacobellis
CFO: Rick Battalini
VP: Julia Provost
VP: Debbie White
Off Mgr: Carin Herman

JOHN PETER SMITH HOSPITAL
See TARRANT COUNTY HOSPITAL DISTRICT

JOHN Q HAMMONS HOTELS
See TUCSON HOTELS LP

D-U-N-S 03-178-3806
JOHN Q HAMMONS HOTELS MANAGEMENT LLC
300 S John Q Hammons Pkwy # 900, Springfield, MO 65806-2596
Tel (471) 864-7333 Founded/Ownrshp 2005
Sales 270.6MM[E] EMP 5,000
SIC 7011 Hotels & motels
CEO: Jacqueline Dowdy
*Sr VP: Greggory Groves
*Sr VP: Joe Morrissey
*Sr VP: Christopher Smith
*VP: Phill Burgess
Exec: Lacie Oels
Exec: Robin Shamel
Prin: Kathy Rutledge
Genl Mgr: Mark C Cherry
Genl Mgr: Brendan England
Genl Mgr: Lynnie Green

JOHN Q HAMMONS HOTELS RESORTS
See JOHN Q HAMMONS RVOCTR 12281989

D-U-N-S 07-831-6201
JOHN Q HAMMONS RVOCTR 12281989
JOHN Q HAMMONS HOTELS RESORTS
300 S John Q Hammons Pkwy # 9, Springfield, MO 65806-2518
Tel (417) 864-4300 Founded/Ownrshp 1951
Sales 453.2MM[E] EMP 9,000
SIC 7011 6733 Hotels & motels; Trusts
Trst: Jacqueline A Dowdy
*Co-Ownr: Kathy Rutledge
*Owner: Jacquie Dowdy

D-U-N-S 08-812-2895
JOHN R GRAHAM HEADACHE CENTER INC
FAULKNER HOSPITAL
1153 Centre St, Boston, MA 02130-3446
Tel (617) 983-7243 Founded/Ownrshp 2001
Sales 207.9MM EMP 1
SIC 8011 8062 Offices & clinics of medical doctors; General medical & surgical hospitals
CEO: David Trull
*Pr: Dr Dhirendra Bana
Dir Env Sv: Jeanne Barton

D-U-N-S 11-379-6630
JOHN S AND JAMES L KNIGHT FOUNDATION INC
200 S Biscayne Blvd # 3300, Miami, FL 33131-2349
Tel (305) 358-1061 Founded/Ownrshp 1950
Sales 182.6MM EMP 50
SIC 8399 Fund raising organization, non-fee basis
Pr: Alberto Ibarguen
*Ch: Robert W Briggs
*VP: Paula Ellis
*VP: Belinda Lawrence
VP: Michael Maness
*VP: Juan Martinez
*VP: Larry Meyer
*VP: Eric Newton
VP: Mayur Patel
VP: Andrew Sherry
Exec: Susan Gomez
Comm Man: Robertson Adams

D-U-N-S 00-838-2863 IMP
JOHN S FREY ENTERPRISES (CA)
1900 E 64th St, Los Angeles, CA 90001-2104
Tel (323) 583-4061 Founded/Ownrshp 1945
Sales 167.0MM[E] EMP 250
Accts Mcgladrey & Pullen Llp Pasad
SIC 3441 3444 6719 Building components, structural steel; Canopies, sheet metal; Investment holding companies, except banks
Ch Bd: John S Frey Jr
*Treas: Grace Lee

D-U-N-S 09-150-0090
JOHN SNOW INC (MA)
44 Farnsworth St Fl 7, Boston, MA 02210-1223
Tel (617) 482-9485 Founded/Ownrshp 1975, 1978
Sales 426.0MM EMP 297
SIC 8742 Hospital & health services consultant
Pr: Joel Lamstein
*COO: Alexander K Baker
Ofcr: Heather Casciato
Ofcr: Michel Othepa
Ofcr: Lora Shimp
Sr VP: Kristin Johnson
*VP: Patricia Fairchild
VP: Nancy Harris
*VP: Theo Lippeveld
VP: Richard Owens
Ex Dir: Penelope Riseborough

D-U-N-S 07-969-0284
JOHN SOULES ACQUISITIONS LLC (GA)
PRO VIEW FOODS
(Suby of JOHN SOULES FOODS INC) ★
311 Green St Nw Ste 500, Gainesville, GA 30501-3367
Tel (770) 532-3058 Founded/Ownrshp 2014
Sales 88.6MM[E] EMP 750
SIC 2015 Poultry, processed: cooked
CEO: John E Soules Sr
*Co-CEO: John Soules Jr
*Co-CEO: Mark Soules
Opers Mgr: Jerry Garrett

D-U-N-S 04-329-5765 IMP
JOHN SOULES FOODS INC
10150 Fm 14, Tyler, TX 75706-7145
Tel (903) 592-9800 Founded/Ownrshp 1985
Sales 313.9MM[E] EMP 1,225[E]
SIC 2013 2015 5147 Sausages & other prepared meats; Poultry slaughtering & processing; Meats & meat products
Ch Bd: John E Soules Sr
*CEO: John E Soules II
*CEO: Mark D Soules
*Ex VP: Thomas L Ellis

D-U-N-S 09-127-4936
JOHN STEWART CO
1388 Sutter St Ste 1100, San Francisco, CA 94109-5454
Tel (213) 833-1860 Founded/Ownrshp 2001
Sales 107.7MM[E] EMP 1,300
Accts Perotti And Carrade Larkspur
SIC 6531 6552 6726 Real estate managers; Subdividers & developers; Investors syndicates
Ch: John K Stewart
*CEO: Jack D Gardner
COO: Noah Schwartz
*CFO: Michael Smith-Heimer
*Sr VP: Dan Levine
Sr VP: Loren Sanborn
*Sr VP: Mari Tustin
VP: Steve McElroy
VP: Margaret Miller
Exec: Doug Schultz
Rgnl Mgr: Marsha Estrada

JOHN T MATHER MEMORIAL HOSP
See JOHN T MATHER MEMORIAL HOSPITAL OF PORT JEFFERSON NEW YORK INC

D-U-N-S 06-473-8859
JOHN T MATHER MEMORIAL HOSPITAL OF PORT JEFFERSON NEW YORK INC
JOHN T MATHER MEMORIAL HOSP
75 N Country Rd, Port Jefferson, NY 11777-2119
Tel (631) 476-2738 Founded/Ownrshp 1928
Sales 279.3MM EMP 1,700
SIC 8062 General medical & surgical hospitals
Pr: Kenneth D Roberts
Dir Vol: Dorothy Perricone
Pr: Theresa Grimes
COO: Joseph Cirrone
Chf Mktg O: Maryanne Gordon
VP: Mark Borek
*VP: Barbara Farruggia
VP: Steven Heiman
*VP: Joseph Josnowsky
*VP: Frank T Lettera
*VP: Diane Marotta
*VP: Kevin Murray
*VP: Wayne Shattes
VP: Loretta Wagner
Dir Rx: Olga Larios

D-U-N-S 92-720-3646
JOHN TEMPLETON FOUNDATION
300 Conshohocken State Rd # 500, Conshohocken, PA 19428-3815
Tel (610) 941-2828 Founded/Ownrshp 1987
Sales 281.6MM EMP 27
Accts Grant Thornton Llp Philadelph
SIC 8699 Charitable organization
Pr: Heather Templeton Dill
COO: Jack Shields
*Ex VP: Douglas W Scott
VP: Paul Wason
VP: Earl Whipple
Exec: Felicia Smith
Mng Dir: Jim Pitofsky
Dir IT: Mathew Bernold

D-U-N-S 06-441-0637 IMP
JOHN VARVATOS ENTERPRISES INC
26 W 17th St Fl 12, New York, NY 10011-5710
Tel (212) 812-8000 Founded/Ownrshp 2012
Sales 244.7MM[E] EMP 250[E]
SIC 5136 Apparel belts, men's & boys'
Ch Bd: John Varvatos
Exec: Vanessa Vega
Off Mgr: Nicole Russo
Sls&Mrk Ex: Faircloth Donna

D-U-N-S 80-838-6239
JOHN W DANFORTH CO
(Suby of JWD GROUP INC) ★
4770 Bickert Dr, Clarence, NY 14031-2206
Tel (716) 832-1940 Founded/Ownrshp 1992
Sales 105.0MM EMP 9[E]
SIC 1711 Plumbing, heating, air-conditioning contractors
Ch Bd: Kevin G Reilly
*Pr: Emmett L Reilly
*Sr VP: Patrick J Reilly
*VP: Nickolas Optis

D-U-N-S 03-420-0147
JOHN W STONE OIL DISTRIBUTOR LLC
87 1st St, Gretna, LA 70053-4746
Tel (504) 366-3401 Founded/Ownrshp 1946
Sales 456.3MM[E] EMP 300
SIC 5172 Diesel fuel; Fuel oil; Gasoline; Lubricating oils & greases
Exec: Anthony Odak

D-U-N-S 00-151-9248 IMP/EXP
▲ JOHN WILEY & SONS INC
111 River St Ste 2000, Hoboken, NJ 07030-5790
Tel (201) 748-6000 Founded/Ownrshp 1807
Sales 1.7MMM EMP 4,900
Tkr Sym JWA Exch NYS
SIC 2731 2721 Textbooks: publishing only, not printed on site; Books: publishing only; Statistical reports (periodicals): publishing only; Trade journals: publishing only, not printed on site
Pr: Mark J Allin
*Ch Bd: Matthew S Kissner
COO: John A Kritzmacher
Ex VP: Gary Rinck
Ex VP: John W Semel
Ex VP: Clay Stobaugh
Ex VP: Judy Verses
VP: Andy Cummings
VP: Eileen Dolan
VP: Mike Fenton
VP: Peter Gregory
VP: Joseph Marchetti
VP: Amanda L Miller
VP: M O'Leary
VP: Jay Ocallaghan
VP: Katharine Robson
VP: Edward Wates
VP: Hayley Wood
Exec: Don Fowley
Assoc Dir: Joseph Carpin
Assoc Dir: Paula Pita
Board of Directors: Mari J Baker, George Bell, Laurie A Leshin, Raymond W McDaniel Jr, Eduardo Menasce, William J Pesce, William B Plummer, Jesse C Wiley, Peter Booth Wiley

JOHN WILEY AND SONS
See WILEY PUBLISHING INC

D-U-N-S 78-501-6481
JOHN WOOD GROUP US HOLDINGS INC
WG
(Suby of JOHN WOOD GROUP P.L.C.)
17325 Park Row Ste 500, Houston, TX 77084-4932
Tel (281) 828-3500 Founded/Ownrshp 2006
Sales 250.4MM[E] EMP 420
SIC 4581 Aircraft servicing & repairing
VP: Michael Leonard
IT Man: Alberto Vasquez
Genl Couns: Robbie Brown

D-U-N-S 06-203-6483 IMP/EXP
JOHN ZINK CO LLC
JOHN ZINK HAMWORTHY COMBUSTION
(*Suby of* KOCH CHEMICAL TECHNOLOGY GROUP LLC) ★
11920 E Apache St, Tulsa, OK 74116-1300
Tel (918) 234-1800 *Founded/Ownrshp* 1999
Sales 293.8MM^E *EMP* 967
SIC 3823 Combustion control instruments
Pr: Casey Chambers
VP: Scott Fox
VP: Alan Gerber
Dir Rx: Rick Iwamoto
Dir Rx: Jay Karan
Mng Dir: Manuel Martinez
Off Mgr: Fred Moore
Tech Mgr: Jorge Kuhlenkamp
VP Opers: John Zink
Sfty Dirs: Paula J Huddleston
Plnt Mgr: Gary Goodnight

JOHN ZINK HAMWORTHY COMBUSTION
See JOHN ZINK CO LLC

D-U-N-S 06-966-5925
JOHNS HOPKINS ALL CHILDRENS HOSPITAL INC
ALL CHILDREN HEALTH SYSTEM
(*Suby of* JOHNS HOPKINS HEALTH SYS CORP) ★
501 6th Ave S, Saint Petersburg, FL 33701-4634
Tel (727) 898-7451 *Founded/Ownrshp* 2011
Sales 408.1MM *EMP* 2,325
SIC 8069 8062 Children's hospital; General medical & surgical hospitals
CEO: Jonathan Ellen
Chf Rad: Evan Harris
Dir Vol: Jeanne Stevens
**Ch Bd:* Mark Stroud
COO: Christopher Indelicato
CFO: Stenberg Arnold
**CFO:* Douglas Myers
**Treas:* J Kenneth Coppedge
Ofcr: Joe Marquart
Comm Dir: Andy Walker
Dir Rx: Kevin Olson
Dir Bus: Claude Amestoy

D-U-N-S 11-823-9458 IMP
JOHNS HOPKINS BAYVIEW MEDICAL CENTER INC
BMC BAYVIEW MEDICAL CENTER
(*Suby of* JOHNS HOPKINS HEALTH SYS CORP) ★
4940 Eastern Ave, Baltimore, MD 21224-2735
Tel (410) 550-0100 *Founded/Ownrshp* 1986
Sales 507.3MM *EMP* 3,300
SIC 8062 8051 General medical & surgical hospitals; Hospital, medical school affiliated with residency; Hospital, medical school affiliation; Skilled nursing care facilities; Extended care facility
Pr: Steven J Kravet
V Ch: James T Dresher
**Treas:* L Kenneth Grabill II
**Ofcr:* David Strapelli
**VP:* Craig Brodian
VP: Kenneth L Grabill
**VP:* Cheryl Koch
VP: Charles Reuland
**VP:* Joan H Williams
Div Mgr: Tiffani Panek
Mktg Dir: Sandy R Reusing

D-U-N-S 15-534-8113 EXP
JOHNS HOPKINS HEALTH SYS CORP
600 N Wolfe St, Baltimore, MD 21287-0005
Tel (410) 955-5000 *Founded/Ownrshp* 1986
Sales 3.7MMM^E *EMP* 13,000
SIC 8062 General medical & surgical hospitals
Pr: Ronald R Peterson
**Ch Bd:* C Micheal Amstrong
**CFO:* Ronald J Werthman
Sr VP: Deborah Baker
Sr VP: Bertrand M Emerson II
VP: Dalal Haldeman
**VP:* Beryl Rosenstein
VP: Steven Thompson
Doctor: Josef Coresh

JOHNS HOPKINS HOSPITAL, THE
See JOHNS HOPKINS MEDICINE INTERNATIONAL LLC

D-U-N-S 02-541-2417 IMP
JOHNS HOPKINS HOSPITAL
(*Suby of* JOHNS HOPKINS HEALTH SYS CORP) ★
1800 Orleans St, Baltimore, MD 21287-0010
Tel (410) 550-0730 *Founded/Ownrshp* 1867
Sales 1.8MMM *EMP* 12,000^E
SIC 8062 General medical & surgical hospitals
Pr: Ronald Peterson
V Ch: Michael Clark
**CFO:* Ronald Werthman
VP: Beryl Rosenstein
Adm Dir: Mary Beaudry
Off Mgr: Gail Jackson
Opers Mgr: Lisa Katulis
Surgeon: Emmanouil Pappou
Opthamlgy: Esen K Akpek
Opthamlgy: Cameron F Parsa
Opthamlgy: Donald J Zack

D-U-N-S 00-310-4478 EXP
JOHNS HOPKINS MEDICINE INTERNATIONAL LLC (MD)
JOHNS HOPKINS HOSPITAL, THE
600 N Wolfe St, Baltimore, MD 21287-0005
Tel (410) 955-1725 *Founded/Ownrshp* 1890
Sales 768.5MM^E *EMP* 7,000
SIC 8062 8221 Hospital, medical school affiliated with nursing & residency; Colleges universities & professional schools
CEO: Harris Benny
**COO:* Judy Reitz
Sr Cor Off: Donna Carey
Sr Cor Off: Dana Webster
Ofcr: Laura C Mezan
Sr VP: Jonathan Lewin
VP: Joanne Pollak
Dir Lab: Gerard Lutty
Assoc Dir: Barry Zirkin
Mktg Dir: Susan B Case
Mktg Mgr: Shannon Doolin

JOHNS HOPKINS REAL ESTATE
See DOME CORP

JOHNS HOPKINS REAL ESTATE
See BROADWAY SERVICES INC

D-U-N-S 00-191-0777
JOHNS HOPKINS UNIVERSITY (MD)
3400 N Charles St, Baltimore, MD 21218-2680
Tel (410) 516-8000 *Founded/Ownrshp* 1867
Sales 3.9MMM^E *EMP* 37,600
SIC 8221 University
Pr: Ronald J Daniels
Ch Bd: Anita Stone
Sr VP: Daniel G Ennis
Sr VP: Robert Lieberman
VP: Kathryn J Crecelius
VP: Stephen S Dunham
VP: Fred Newman
VP: Cheryl Resch
Assoc Dir: Louis Biggie
Assoc Dir: Charlene Knoerlein
Comm Dir: Mary Maushard

D-U-N-S 04-054-9461
JOHNS HOPKINS UNIVERSITY APPLIED PHYSICS LABORATORY LLC
APL
(*Suby of* JOHNS HOPKINS UNIVERSITY) ★
11100 Johns Hopkins Rd, Laurel, MD 20723-6005
Tel (240) 228-5000 *Founded/Ownrshp* 2009
Sales 1.0MMM *EMP* 37,600
SIC 8731 Commercial research laboratory
VP: Mike Buckley
VP: Michael Thompson
Ex Dir: Richard Roca
Prgrm Mgr: John Noble
IT Man: Teresa Colella
IT Man: Mary Lasky
Info Man: Jon Willig
Sftwr Eng: Timothy Gion
Sftwr Eng: Ronald Glaser
Sftwr Eng: Julio Guzman
Sftwr Eng: Onna Roberts

JOHN'S INCREDIBLE PIZZA CO
See JIPC MANAGEMENT INC

D-U-N-S 96-797-8594 IMP/EXP
JOHNS LONE STAR DISTRIBUTION GP LLC
11401 Granite St, Charlotte, NC 28273-6400
Tel (214) 340-0718 *Founded/Ownrshp* 1997
Sales 94.8MM^E *EMP* 100^E
SIC 5122 5149 Vitamins & minerals; Health foods
**CFO:* Chuck Letchman
**VP:* Frank Fenimore
**Genl Mgr:* Kelly Crawford
Plnt Mgr: Bill Paolella

D-U-N-S 04-542-6558 IMP/EXP
■ JOHNS MANVILLE CORP
JOHNS MANVILLE INTERNATIONAL
(*Suby of* BERKSHIRE HATHAWAY INC) ★
717 17th St Ste 800, Denver, CO 80202-3332
Tel (303) 978-2000 *Founded/Ownrshp* 1981
Sales 2.6MMM^E *EMP* 8,000
SIC 2952 1761 1742 Roofing materials; Roofing contractor; Insulation, buildings
Pr: Mary Rhinehart
COO: Thomas E Cook
Treas: W S Bullock
Sr VP: William J Ehner
Sr VP: Kenneth L Jensen
Sr VP: Michael P Kane
**Sr VP:* Michael Lawrence
**Sr VP:* Cynthia Meyer
**Sr VP:* Fred Stefan
**Sr VP:* Robert Wambolt
VP: Michael Benedict
VP: Lawrence J Blanford
VP: David Fisher
VP: Enno Henze
VP: Brien D Hodge
VP: Cindy Meyer
VP: Darrell Neumeyer
VP: Cynthia Ryan
**VP:* John Shellenberger
VP: Joseph Smith
VP: Kim Smolka

JOHNS MANVILLE INTERNATIONAL
See JOHNS MANVILLE CORP

JOHNSON & GALYON CONTRACTORS
See JOHNSON & GALYON INC

D-U-N-S 00-982-3808
JOHNSON & GALYON INC (TN)
JOHNSON & GALYON CONTRACTORS
1130 Atlantic Ave, Knoxville, TN 37917-3798
Tel (865) 688-1111 *Founded/Ownrshp* 1955, 1984
Sales 100.8MM *EMP* 100
SIC 1542 1541

D-U-N-S 00-130-7081 IMP/EXP
▲ JOHNSON & JOHNSON (NJ)
1 Johnson And Johnson Plz, New Brunswick, NJ 08933-0002
Tel (732) 524-0400 *Founded/Ownrshp* 1886
Sales 70.0MMM *EMP* 127,142
Accts Pricewaterhousecoopers Llp Fl
Tkr Sym JNJ *Exch* NYS
SIC 2676 2844 3841 3842 2834 Feminine hygiene paper products; Napkins, sanitary: made from purchased paper; Panty liners: made from purchased paper; Infant & baby paper products; Toilet preparations; Oral preparations; Toilet preparations; Powder: baby, face, talcum or toilet; Surgical & medical instruments; Surgical instruments & apparatus; Diagnostic apparatus, medical; Ophthalmic instruments & apparatus; Surgical appliances & supplies; Ligatures, medical; Sutures, absorbable & non-absorbable; Dressings, surgical; Pharmaceutical preparations; Drugs acting on the central nervous system & sense organs; Dermatologicals; Drugs affecting parasitic & infective diseases
Ch Bd: Alex Gorsky
CFO: Dominic J Caruso
Ch: Sandra E Peterson
Treas: Luis Toca
Ex VP: Peter M Fasolo
Ex VP: Ann Rewey
Ex VP: Michael H Ullmann
VP: Patricia Andradegordon
VP: David Atkins
VP: Jose L Azevedo
VP: Steve Berry
VP: Andy Brackett
VP: James Buschmeier
VP: Alan Cariski
VP: Erin Carney
VP: Angie Caswell
VP: Helaine Catalano
VP: Marianne Debacker
VP: David Decker
VP: Aldo Denti
VP: Ravi Desiraju
Board of Directors: Ronald A Williams, Mary C Beckerle, Mary Sue Coleman, D Scott Davis, Ian E L Davis, Mark B McClellan, Anne M Mulcahy, William D Perez, Charles Prince, A Eugene Washingtonm

D-U-N-S 00-234-7102 EXP
■ JOHNSON & JOHNSON CONSUMER INC
(*Suby of* JOHNSON & JOHNSON) ★
199 Grandview Rd, Skillman, NJ 08558-1303
Tel (908) 874-1000 *Founded/Ownrshp* 1879, 1959
Sales 498.3MM^E *EMP* 1,019
SIC 2834 Pharmaceutical preparations
Pr: C Watts
Pr: Rebecca Tillet
Treas: Robert W McMahon
VP: Mike Gowen
VP: Jerry B Hansen
VP: Ed Hemwall
VP: J Mahony
VP: Vicki Walker
Exec: Diana Mauro
Div/Sub He: Colin Watts
Board of Directors: Gerald Ostrov

D-U-N-S 12-215-2379 EXP
■ JOHNSON & JOHNSON INTERNATIONAL
(*Suby of* JOHNSON & JOHNSON) ★
475 Calle C Ste 200, Guaynabo, PR 00969-4293
Tel (787) 272-1905 *Founded/Ownrshp* 2004
Sales 160.6MM^E *EMP* 300
SIC 5122 Drugs, proprietaries & sundries
VP: Francis Boero

D-U-N-S 00-801-3583
■ JOHNSON & JOHNSON MEDICAL INC (NJ)
(*Suby of* ETHICON INC) ★
Us Rt 22, Somerville, NJ 08876
Tel (908) 218-0707 *Founded/Ownrshp* 1949
Sales 127.7MM^E *EMP* 3,128
SIC 3842 Surgical appliances & supplies
Pr: William Clarke

D-U-N-S 96-563-0150
JOHNSON & JOHNSON PATIENT ASSISTANCE FOUNDATION INC
1 Johnson And Johnson Plz, New Brunswick, NJ 08933-0001
Tel (732) 524-1394 *Founded/Ownrshp* 2010
Sales 787.8MM *EMP* 14^E
SIC 8699 Charitable organization
Prin: Nancy Moyer

D-U-N-S 00-406-0273 EXP
■ JOHNSON & JOHNSON VISION CARE INC (FL)
VISTAKON
(*Suby of* JOHNSON & JOHNSON) ★
7500 Centurion Pkwy, Jacksonville, FL 32256-0517
Tel (904) 443-1000 *Founded/Ownrshp* 1962
Sales 828.7MM^E *EMP* 3,500
SIC 3851 Contact lenses; Eyes, glass & plastic
Pr: Laura Angelini
**Ch Bd:* Ashley McEvoy
COO: Tim Newton
**CFO:* Nchacha E Etta
VP: Melissa Alfaro
**VP:* Madonna M Malin
Div/Sub He: D Keefer
Brnch Mgr: Bernard Walsh
Dir IT: Jim Sarka
IT Man: Marcos Matos
IT Man: Matthew Ryno

D-U-N-S 00-230-0051 IMP
JOHNSON & TOWERS INC (PA)
2021 Briggs Rd, Mount Laurel, NJ 08054-4618
Tel (856) 234-6990 *Founded/Ownrshp* 1926
Sales 88.0MM^E *EMP* 210
SIC 5084 5013 7699 7538 5085 Engines & parts, diesel; Automotive supplies & parts; Marine engine repair; General automotive repair shops; Diesel engine repair: automotive; Industrial supplies
CEO: Walter F Johnson
**CFO:* Thomas Hogan
**Sec:* Thomas M Dutterer
Sr VP: Robert Shomo
**VP:* David P Johnson

D-U-N-S 05-518-1036
JOHNSON & WALES UNIVERSITY INC
8 Abbott Park Pl, Providence, RI 02903-3775
Tel (401) 598-1000 *Founded/Ownrshp* 1947
Sales 529.2MM *EMP* 1,400
Accts Mcgladrey Llp Charlestown Ma
SIC 7011 Hotels & motels
Pr: Larry Rice
**Pr:* John A Yena
CFO: Joseph J Greene
**Treas:* Christopher Del Sesto
Treas: Christopher D Sesto
Trst: Dana Gaebe
Trst: Edward P Grace
Trst: Robert Taylor
Ofcr: Paul Brayman
Ofcr: William Day
Ofcr: Sandra Lawrence
Ofcr: Bryan Mullin
Top Exec: Paul J Colbert
**Ex VP:* John Bowen
Sr VP: Merlin A Deconti
Sr VP: Manuel Pimentel
VP: Taylor Anthony
VP: Marie Bernardo-Sousa
VP: Johannes Busch
VP: Kenneth Disaia
**VP:* Thomas Dwyer

JOHNSON APARTMENTS
See PATH FINDER SCHOOLS INC

JOHNSON BANK
See JOHNSON FINANCIAL GROUP INC

D-U-N-S 00-896-0288
JOHNSON BANK NA
(*Suby of* JOHNSON BANK) ★
1 S Main St Ste 100, Janesville, WI 53545-3977
Tel (262) 639-6010 *Founded/Ownrshp* 1855, 1990
Sales NA *EMP* 75
SIC 6021 National commercial banks
Pr: Scott K Kelly
**Chf Cred:* Dan Defnet
**VP:* Carolyn Beretta
**VP:* Larry Squire

D-U-N-S 86-744-6551 IMP
JOHNSON BROS BAKERY SUPPLY INC
10731 N Ih 35, San Antonio, TX 78233-6639
Tel (210) 590-2575 *Founded/Ownrshp* 1994
Sales 97.8MM^E *EMP* 74
SIC 5149 5046 Groceries & related products; Bakery equipment & supplies
Pr: Kevin G Johnson
**CFO:* Lorrena Paz
Genl Mgr: Randy Andres

D-U-N-S 02-284-7354
JOHNSON BROS CORP
(*Suby of* SOUTHLAND HOLDINGS LLC) ★
608 Henrietta Creek Rd, Roanoke, TX 76262-6339
Tel (813) 685-5101 *Founded/Ownrshp* 1959
Sales 111.8MM^E *EMP* 225
SIC 1623 1629 1622
CEO: Walter D Johnson
**Treas:* Benita Rueckert
**Ex VP:* John A Hogan Jr
**Ex VP:* Paul E Johnson
Sr VP: Joseph Michaels
**VP:* Roberto Elbo
**VP:* Zvonko Juric
**VP:* Jimmy W Kirkman
**VP:* David D Kofstad
**VP:* Joseph Michels
**VP:* Michael Swanson
**Exec:* Charlie L Humphries

D-U-N-S 00-886-7921 IMP/EXP
JOHNSON BROTHERS LIQUOR CO
1999 Shepard Rd, Saint Paul, MN 55116-3210
Tel (651) 649-5800 *Founded/Ownrshp* 1954
Sales 643.7MM^E *EMP* 2,000
SIC 5182 5149

JOHNSON BROTHERS LIQUOR CO FLA
See JOHNSON BROTHERS OF FLORIDA INC

D-U-N-S 80-985-0043 IMP
JOHNSON BROTHERS OF FLORIDA INC
JOHNSON BROTHERS LIQUOR CO FLA
(*Suby of* JOHNSON BROTHERS LIQUOR CO) ★
4520 S Church Ave, Tampa, FL 33611-2201
Tel (813) 832-4477 *Founded/Ownrshp* 1993
Sales 91.1MM^E *EMP* 223
SIC 5182 5149 Wine; Liquor; Juices
Pr: Frank Galante
**Ch:* Lynn Johnson
**VP:* Michael Johnson

JOHNSON CITY MEDICAL CENTER
See MOUNTAIN STATES HEALTH ALLIANCE

JOHNSON CONTRLS AUTHORIZED DLR
See MEIER SUPPLY CO INC

JOHNSON CONTRLS AUTHORIZED DLR
See CRESCENT PARTS & EQUIPMENT CO INC

JOHNSON CONTRLS AUTHORIZED DLR
See STANDARD SUPPLY AND DISTRIBUTING CO INC

JOHNSON CONTRLS AUTHORIZED DLR
See JOHNSON SUPPLY AND EQUIPMENT CORP

JOHNSON CONTRLS AUTHORIZED DLR
See BEHLER-YOUNG CO

JOHNSON CONTRLS AUTHORIZED DLR
See FAMOUS INDUSTRIES INC

JOHNSON CONTRLS AUTHORIZED DLR
See HABEGGER CORP

JOHNSON CONTRLS AUTHORIZED DLR
See BELL PUMP SERVICE CO

JOHNSON CONTRLS AUTHORIZED DLR
See HATFIELD AND CO INC

JOHNSON CONTRLS AUTHORIZED DLR
See MINGLEDORFFS INC

JOHNSON CONTRLS AUTHORIZED DLR
See GEMAIRE DISTRIBUTORS LLC

JOHNSON CONTRLS AUTHORIZED DLR
See WITTICHEN SUPPLY CO

JOHNSON CONTRLS AUTHORIZED DLR
See REFRICENTER OF MIAMI INC

JOHNSON CONTRLS AUTHORIZED DLR
See TROPIC SUPPLY INC

JOHNSON CONTRLS AUTHORIZED DLR
See KELE INC

JOHNSON CONTRLS AUTHORIZED DLR
See INDUSTRIAL CONTROLS DISTRIBUTORS LLC

JOHNSON CONTROLS
See GUSTAVE A LARSON CO

JOHNSON CONTROLS
See DWYER INSTRUMENTS INC

JOHNSON CONTROLS
See G W BERKHEIMER CO INC

D-U-N-S 84-065-2580 IMP/EXP
JOHNSON CONTROLS BATTERY GROUP INC
(Suby of JOHNSON CONTROLS INC) ★
5757 N Green Bay Ave, Milwaukee, WI 53209-4408
Tel (414) 524-1200 Founded/Ownrshp 1990
Sales 3.9MM^E EMP 4,000
SIC 3691 Storage batteries
CEO: Alex A Molinaroli
*Pr: Stephen A Roell
VP: Suzanne M Vincent
Sfty Mgr: Debra Nyenbrink

JOHNSON CONTROLS BATTLE
See HOOVER UNIVERSAL INC

D-U-N-S 18-204-5752
JOHNSON CONTROLS HOLDING CO INC
(Suby of JOHNSON CONTROLS INC) ★
5757 N Green Bay Ave, Milwaukee, WI 53209-4408
Tel (414) 524-1200 Founded/Ownrshp 1992
Sales 770.2MM^E EMP 10,500
SIC 6719 Personal holding companies, except banks
Dir IT: Richard Dean
IT Man: AGA Lasota

D-U-N-S 00-609-2860
JOHNSON CONTROLS INC (WI)
(Suby of JOHNSON CONTROLS INTERNATIONAL PUBLIC LIMITED COMPANY)
5757 N Green Bay Ave, Milwaukee, WI 53209-4408
Tel (414) 524-1200 Founded/Ownrshp 1885
Sales 36.8MMM EMP 139,000
SIC 2531 3714 3691 3822 8744 Seats, automobile; Motor vehicle body components & frame; Instrument board assemblies, motor vehicle; Lead acid batteries (storage batteries); Building services monitoring controls, automatic; Facilities support services
CEO: Alex A Molinaroli
Pr: George R Oliver
CFO: Brian Stief
Ex VP: Susan F Davis
VP: Brian J Cadwallader
VP: Suzanne M Vincent
Exec: Karen Brayton
Prgrm Mgr: Abdul Semia
Brnch Mgr: Dan Starsoneck
Genl Mgr: Michael A Wojtas
CIO: Therron Kokales

D-U-N-S 00-694-3039
JOHNSON COOPERATIVE GRAIN CO INC
304 E Highland Ave, Johnson, KS 67855
Tel (620) 492-6210 Founded/Ownrshp 1930
Sales 83.9MM EMP 68
SIC 5153 5191 5172 Grain elevators; Farm supplies; Feed; Fertilizer & fertilizer materials; Seeds: field, garden & flower; Petroleum products
CEO: David Corn
*Pr: Martie Floyd
*CFO: Rodney Friesen

D-U-N-S 07-307-3546
JOHNSON COUNTY COMMUNITY COLLEGE
12345 College Blvd, Overland Park, KS 66210-1283
Tel (913) 469-8500 Founded/Ownrshp 1968
Sales 53.4MM EMP 2,004
Accts Rubinbrown Llp Overland Park
SIC 8222 8221 Community college; Colleges universities & professional schools
Pr: Terry Calaway
Ofcr: Christopher Sager
VP: Denise Moore
Exec: Dian Jauregui-Smith
Ex Dir: Janelle Vogler
Store Mgr: Kenneth Behrmann
CIO: Wayne Brown
CTO: Nancy Harrington
CTO: Michael Whitmore
DP Dir: Cathleen Peterson
Cmptr Lab: Herbert Pfeifer

D-U-N-S 09-507-0251 IMP
JOHNSON ELECTRIC AUTOMOTIVE INC
(Suby of JOHNSON ELECTRIC HOLDINGS LIMITED)
47660 Halyard Dr, Plymouth, MI 48170-2453
Tel (734) 392-1022 Founded/Ownrshp 1976
Sales 125.9MM^E EMP 550^E
SIC 5013 8731 8742 Automotive supplies; Commercial physical research; Management consulting services
Pr: Patrick Wang
Sr VP: Yue Li
*VP: Winnie Wang
Admn Mgr: Eduardo Catta-Preta

D-U-N-S 08-438-0807
JOHNSON ELECTRIC NORTH AMERICA INC (CT)
(Suby of JOHNSON ELECTRIC HOLDINGS LIMITED)
47660 Halyard Dr, Plymouth, MI 48170-2453
Tel (734) 392-5300 Founded/Ownrshp 1976
Sales 550.0MM^E EMP 40,000
SIC 5063 3625 3674 8711 Motors, electric; Solenoid switches (industrial controls); Microcircuits, integrated (semiconductor); Engineering services
Ch: Patrick Shui-Chung Wang
VP: Thomas Roschke
Genl Mgr: Ivan Dominguez
Genl Mgr: Sharon Tecklenburg
Ql Cn Mgr: Darwin Thankaswamy
Sales Exec: Doug Eberle
Sls Mgr: Chad Reed

D-U-N-S 61-922-2060
JOHNSON FINANCIAL GROUP INC
JOHNSON BANK
555 Main St Ste 400, Racine, WI 53403-4615
Tel (262) 619-2700 Founded/Ownrshp 1988
Sales NA EMP 1,233
Accts Cliftonlarsonallen Llp Racine
SIC 6022 6021 6712 6733 6311 State commercial banks; National commercial banks; Bank holding companies; Trusts, except educational, religious, charity: management; Life insurance
Ch: Helen Johnson-Liepold
Pr: Jennifer Aceto
Pr: Kristin Braska
Pr: Louis Burg
Pr: Dave Burke
Pr: Gretchen Choynacki
Pr: Chris Estell
Pr: Korey Frey
Pr: Sharon George
Pr: Scott Gregory
Pr: Kyle J Hager
Pr: Mary R Helgerson
Pr: Sue Hullin
Pr: Vince Janecky
Pr: Susan Kutz
Pr: Robert Leibham
Pr: Larry Lukasavage
Pr: Dawn Merritt
Pr: Kristine Opatz
Pr: Bob Reinders
Pr: Rich Ricciardi
Board of Directors: Jane M Hutterly, S Curtis Johnson, John Jeffrey Louis III, Winifred J Marquart, Neal R Nottleson, Richard D Pauls, Alan J Ruud, John M Schroeder, Carol Scornicka

D-U-N-S 01-282-6991
JOHNSON FOOD SERVICES LLC
Forney Smter St Bldg 3290, Columbia, SC 29207
Tel (803) 782-1461 Founded/Ownrshp 2000
Sales 12.7MM^E EMP 1,200
SIC 5812 Eating places
Owner: Donald Johnson

D-U-N-S 82-848-0165
JOHNSON HEALTH TECH NORTH AMERICA INC
J H T
(Suby of JOHNSON HEALTH TECH CO., LTD.)
1600 Landmark Dr, Cottage Grove, WI 53527-8967
Tel (608) 839-1240 Founded/Ownrshp 1975
Sales 213.0MM^E EMP 350
SIC 5091 5941 Fitness equipment & supplies; Exercise equipment
Pr: Nathan Pyles
*COO: Robert Zande
*Ex VP: Stewart Kent Stevens
*VP: Mark Zabel
IT Man: Eric Chow

JOHNSON HEATER
See ARIZON COMPANIES INC

D-U-N-S 00-506-8382 IMP/EXP
■ **JOHNSON KADANT INC** (MI)
(Suby of KADANT INC) ★
805 Wood St, Three Rivers, MI 49093-1053
Tel (269) 278-1715 Founded/Ownrshp 1930, 2005
Sales 201.9MM^E EMP 1,600
Accts Ernst & Young Llp Boston Ma
SIC 3494 8711 1389 3052 1099 Steam fittings & specialties; Construction & civil engineering; Construction, repair & dismantling services; Rubber hose; Aluminum & beryllium ores mining
Pr: Greg Wedel

JOHNSON LEXUS OF RALEIGH
See HOL-DAV INC

D-U-N-S 00-691-0855 IMP/EXP
JOHNSON MACHINERY CO (CA)
CATERPILLAR AUTHORIZED DEALER
800 E La Cadena Dr, Riverside, CA 92507-8715
Tel (951) 686-4560 Founded/Ownrshp 1940
Sales 197.7MM^E EMP 385
SIC 5082 General construction machinery & equipment
Pr: William Johnson Jr
COO: Jerry Welch
*Ex VP: Kevin Kelly
*Ex VP: Matt Merickel
VP: Albert Sanchez
CTO: Bryn Glover
IT Man: Aiza Duarte
Netwrk Mgr: Rob Millerd
Opers Mgr: Duane Valantine
Mktg Dir: Darin Perry
Sls Mgr: Eric Johnson

D-U-N-S 05-627-8633
JOHNSON MIRMIRAN & THOMPSON INC
J M T
72 Loveton Cir, Sparks, MD 21152-9202
Tel (410) 329-3100 Founded/Ownrshp 1971
Sales 186.8MM EMP 1,350
Accts Cliftonlarsonallen Llp Balti
SIC 8711 Civil engineering
Ch Bd: Fred F Mirmiran
*Pr: Jack Moeller
Pr: Jonathan Ryan
CFO: Michael Kolar
*CFO: Rick Smulovitz
*Sr VP: Daniel Cheng
Sr VP: Douglas Rose
Sr VP: Brian Stickles
VP: Ben Asavakarin
VP: James Blake
VP: Mike Hild
VP: Jerry Jurick
VP: Sanjay Kumar
VP: April Showers
VP: Matthew Wolniak
Dir Bus: Jeanne Ruthloff

D-U-N-S 09-628-7990
JOHNSON OHARE CO INC
JOH ATLANTIC PARTNERS
1 Progress Rd, Billerica, MA 01821-5731
Tel (978) 663-9000 Founded/Ownrshp 1956
Sales 181.5MM^E EMP 580
SIC 5141 Food brokers
Ch: Harry O'Hare Sr
*Pr: John Saidnawey
*Sr VP: Carl Annese
*Sr VP: Will Martinez
VP: Phillip Allin
VP: Ron McLean
VP: Bobbie Ohare

JOHNSON OIL
See J CINCO INC

D-U-N-S 01-706-2621
JOHNSON OIL CO OF GAYLORD
JOHNSONS OIL & PROPANE COMPANY
507 S Otsego Ave, Gaylord, MI 49735-1718
Tel (989) 732-6014 Founded/Ownrshp 1954
Sales 97.7MM^E EMP 120
SIC 5171 5541 5983 Petroleum bulk stations; Filling stations, gasoline; Fuel oil dealers
Pr: Kevin Johnson
*Pr: Dale E Johnson
*VP: Steven Johnson

D-U-N-S 14-474-2129 IMP/EXP
▲ **JOHNSON OUTDOORS INC**
555 Main St, Racine, WI 53403-1000
Tel (262) 631-6600 Founded/Ownrshp 1970
Sales 433.7MM EMP 1,200
Tkr Sym JOUT Exch NGM
SIC 3949 3732 3812 Sporting & athletic goods; Skin diving equipment, scuba type; Camping equipment & supplies; Canoes, building & repairing; Kayaks, building & repairing; Sailboats, building & repairing; Navigational systems & instruments; Compasses & accessories
Ch Bd: Helen P Johnson-Leipold
CFO: David W Johnson
*V Ch Bd: Thomas F Pyle Jr
VP: Cynthia Georgeson
VP: Kelly T Grindle
VP: Bill Kelly
VP: William S Kelly
VP: John C Moon
VP: Joseph B Stella
VP: Alisa Swire
Assoc Dir: Jim Ness
Board of Directors: Kathy Button Bell, John M Fahey Jr, Edward F Lang, Terry E London, W Lee McCollum, Richard Sheahan

JOHNSON PROPERTIES
See JOHNSON STORAGE & MOVING CO HOLDINGS LLC

D-U-N-S 17-788-5548
JOHNSON SERVICE GROUP INC
J S G
1 E Oakhill Dr Ste 200, Westmont, IL 60559-5540
Tel (630) 655-3500 Founded/Ownrshp 1984
Sales 112.3MM^E EMP 5,600
SIC 7363 8711 Temporary help service; Engineering services
Pr: Louis Bertone
Sr VP: Michael Adelman
Sr VP: James Filarski
*VP: Dale Slater
VP: April Weston
Brnch Mgr: Lethea Davis
Brnch Mgr: Ben Shirley
IT Man: Stu Shipinski
Manager: Jamie Tran

JOHNSON STATE COLLEGE
See VERMONT STATE COLLEGES

D-U-N-S 03-052-8020
JOHNSON STORAGE & MOVING CO HOLDINGS LLC
JOHNSON PROPERTIES
7009 S Jordan Rd, Centennial, CO 80112-4219
Tel (303) 785-4300 Founded/Ownrshp 1995
Sales 164.0MM^E EMP 800
SIC 4213 4214 Household goods transport; Household goods moving & storage, local

D-U-N-S 00-842-4459
JOHNSON SUPPLY AND EQUIPMENT CORP (TX)
JOHNSON CONTRLS AUTHORIZED DLR
10151 Stella Link Rd, Houston, TX 77025-5398
Tel (713) 830-2300 Founded/Ownrshp 1977
Sales 100.0MM EMP 210
Accts Bkd
SIC 5075 Warm air heating equipment & supplies; Air conditioning & ventilation equipment & supplies
CEO: Carl I Johnson
*Pr: Richard W Cook
*CFO: Donald K Wile
*VP: James B Cook
*VP: Douglas Domgard
VP: Sonia Mendiola
VP: Darrell J Simoneaux
Brnch Mgr: John Klier
Store Mgr: Cody Steel

JOHNSONITE
See TARKETT USA INC

JOHNSONS OIL & PROPANE COMPANY
See JOHNSON OIL CO OF GAYLORD

D-U-N-S 04-261-9932 IMP/EXP
JOHNSONVILLE SAUSAGE LLC
N6928 Johnsonville Way, Sheboygan Falls, WI 53085
Tel (920) 453-6900 Founded/Ownrshp 1945
Sales 437.7MM^E EMP 1,400
SIC 2013 Sausages from purchased meat
CEO: Nick Meriggioli
*Ch Bd: Ralph Stayer
VP: Jena Goosen
VP: Lisa Lieffring
*VP: Laura Stayer
VP: Ralph C Stayer
Creative D: Tony Rammer
Dir Bus: Gene Rech
Rgnl Mgr: Brad Martin
CTO: Cory Bouck
Sfty Mgr: Phil Vaness
Board of Directors: Ralph Stayer

JOHNSTON CMMNCTIONS VOICE DATA
See G P JOHNSTON INC

JOHNSTON CNTY BD COMMISSIONERS
See COUNTY OF JOHNSTON

D-U-N-S 10-005-8676
JOHNSTON COUNTY SCHOOLS
2320 Us Highway 70 Bus E, Smithfield, NC 27577-7790
Tel (919) 934-6031 Founded/Ownrshp 1955
Sales 150.4MM^E EMP 3,500
SIC 8211 Public elementary & secondary schools
Pr Dir: Tracey Peedin-Jones
Teacher Pr: Brian Vetrano
HC Dir: Oliver Johnson

D-U-N-S 08-058-9716
JOHNSTON ENTERPRISES INC
WB JOHNSTON GRAIN COMPANY
411 W Chestnut Ave, Enid, OK 73701-2057
Tel (580) 233-5800 Founded/Ownrshp 1971
Sales 334.2MM^E EMP 30
SIC 5153 5191 Grains; Fertilizer & fertilizer materials; Seeds: field, garden & flower
Ch Bd: Lew Meibergen
*Pr: Butch Meibergen
COO: Dennis Craig
*CFO: Gary Tucker
*VP: Roger Henneke
VP: Joey Meibergen
Dir IT: Abraham Guerrero

JOHNSTON HEALTH
See JOHNSTON MEMORIAL HOSPITAL CORP

D-U-N-S 07-201-0713
JOHNSTON MEMORIAL HOSPITAL CORP
JOHNSTON HEALTH
509 N Brightleaf Blvd, Smithfield, NC 27577-4407
Tel (919) 934-8171 Founded/Ownrshp 2006
Sales 152.6MM EMP 1,200
SIC 8062 General medical & surgical hospitals
CEO: Chuck Elliott
Chf Rad: Kerry Chandler
Dir Vol: Farrah Nguyen
V Ch: David Mills
*COO: Ruth Marler
*COO: Jackie Ring
*CFO: Eddie Klein
VP: Teresa Chappell
*VP: April Culver
VP: Joyce Lassiter
*VP: Donald Pocock MD
Dir Lab: Daniel Rogers

D-U-N-S 07-902-0087
JOHNSTON MEMORIAL HOSPITAL INC
16000 Johnston Memorial D, Abingdon, VA 24211-7664
Tel (276) 258-1000 Founded/Ownrshp 1919
Sales 160.8MM^E EMP 2,500
Accts Pershing Yoakley & Associates
SIC 8062 8011 General medical & surgical hospitals; Offices & clinics of medical doctors
CEO: Sean Mc Murray
Chf OB: Brett A Manthey
*Treas: Fleming Ann
*Treas: Donald Jeanes
Ofcr: Haynes Melton
*Prin: Joanne Gilmer
*Prin: Jackie Phipps
*Prin: Michael Spiegler
Dir Health: Kim Ratliss

D-U-N-S 01-362-9928
JOHNSTON PAPER CO INC
2 Eagle Dr, Auburn, NY 13021-8696
Tel (315) 253-8435 Founded/Ownrshp 1976
Sales 161.8MM^E EMP 97
Accts Dermody Burke & Brown Cpas
SIC 5113 5084 Industrial & personal service paper; Towels, paper; Cups, disposable plastic & paper; Napkins, paper; Packaging machinery & equipment
Pr: Michael D May
*Treas: Thomas E Lewis
*VP: David Kristin May
MIS Dir: David Colbert

D-U-N-S 05-720-4187
JOHNSTON-WILLIS HOSPITAL NURSES ALUMNAE ASSOCIATION
1401 Johnston Willis Dr, North Chesterfield, VA 23235-4730
Tel (804) 560-5800 Founded/Ownrshp 1931
Sales 169.1MM^E EMP 3,000
SIC 8062 Hospital, AMA approved residency
CEO: Peter Marmerstein
CFO: Lynn Strader
Off Mgr: Ruth Michaud

JOHNSTONE SUP AUTHORIZED DLR
See WARE GROUP LLC

JOHNSTONE SUP S JACKSONVILLE
See WARE GROUP INC

D-U-N-S 06-343-8675 IMP/EXP
JOHNSTONE SUPPLY INC
11632 Ne Ainsworth Cir, Portland, OR 97220-9016
Tel (503) 256-3663 Founded/Ownrshp 1981
Sales 1.0MMM EMP 299
SIC 5075 5085 5063 5064

D-U-N-S 55-657-0968 IMP/EXP
■ **JOHNSTOWN AMERICA CORP**
FREIGHT CAR DIVISION
(Suby of FREIGHTCAR AMERICA INC) ★
17 Johns St, Johnstown, PA 15901-1531
Tel (814) 533-5000 Founded/Ownrshp 1991
Sales 107.4MM^E EMP 282^E
SIC 3743 Freight cars & equipment
Pr: Jim Hart
Treas: Joseph E McNeely
VP: Glen Karan
VP: Gary Somesn
Ql Cn Mgr: David St John

JOHNSTOWN TRIBUNE DEMOCRAT
See NEWSPAPER HOLDING INC

JOIE
See DUTCH LLC

D-U-N-S 04-853-1060
JOIE DE VIVRE HOSPITALITY LLC
530 Bush St Ste 501, San Francisco, CA 94108-3633
Tel (415) 835-0300 Founded/Ownrshp 1987
Sales 231.8MM EMP 2,000
SIC 8741 Hotel or motel management
CEO: Niki Leondakis
*CEO: Stephen T Conley Jr
Ex VP: Rick Colangelo
Ex VP: Greg Smith
Ex VP: Jorge Trevino
VP: Brett Blass
VP: Peter Gamez
VP: Karlene Holloman
VP: Dan Korn
VP: Gregory Weiss
Exec: Oliver Ridgeway
Exec: Sergio Rodriguez
Exec: Glafira Sorto

JOINT BOARD OF FAMILY PRACTICE
See GEORGIA HEALTH SCIENCES FOUNDATION INC

JOINT COMMISSION, THE
See JOINT COMMISSION ON ACCREDITATION OF HEALTHCARE ORGANIZATIONS

D-U-N-S 06-847-5391
JOINT COMMISSION ON ACCREDITATION OF HEALTHCARE ORGANIZATIONS
JOINT COMMISSION, THE
1 Renaissance Blvd, Oakbrook Terrace, IL 60181-4813
Tel (630) 792-5000 Founded/Ownrshp 1951
Sales 92.6MM^E EMP 936
Accts Kpmg Llp Chicago Il
SIC 8621 Medical field-related associations
Pr: Mark Chassin MD
*Pr: Dennis S O Leary MD
*Ex VP: Anne Marie Benedicto
VP: Anne Rooney
VP: Robert Wise
Assoc Dir: Steve Misenko
Assoc Dir: Ann Watt
Assoc Dir: Scott Williams
Ex Dir: M Hampel
Prgrm Mgr: Susan Murray
Prgrm Mgr: Andrea Zaba-Peabody

JOINT PENSION TRUST OF CHICAGO
See ELECTRICAL INSURANCE TRUSTEES

JOINT SCHOOL DIST 128
See MACKAY JOINT SCHOOL DIST 182

D-U-N-S 03-423-9678
JOINT SCHOOL DISTRICT
1303 E Central Dr, Meridian, ID 83642-7991
Tel (208) 350-5093 Founded/Ownrshp 2001
Sales 244.7MM EMP 99
SIC 8211 Public elementary & secondary schools

D-U-N-S 02-960-4402
JOINT SCHOOL DISTRICT 2
WEST ADA SCHOOL DISTRICT
1303 E Central Dr, Meridian, ID 83642-7991
Tel (208) 855-4500 Founded/Ownrshp 1950
Sales 257.6MM EMP 4,000
Accts Eide Bailly Llp Boise Idaho
SIC 8211 Public elementary & secondary schools
Admn Mgr: Jason Leforgee
Admn Mgr: Marilyn Renolds
Teacher Pr: Dave Roberts
Instr Medi: Dennis Hahs

JOINT TEST TACTICS & TRAINING
See JT3 LLC

JOINT VENTURE BETWEEN
See PHILADELPHIA ENERGY SOLUTIONS LLC

JOINT VENTURE BETWEEN THE CARL
See PHILADELPHIA ENERGY SOLUTIONS REFINING AND MARKETING LLC

D-U-N-S 05-384-6812
JOJOS CALIFORNIA (CA)
COCO'S
120 Chula Vis, San Antonio, TX 78232-2234
Tel (877) 225-4160 Founded/Ownrshp 1948, 1996
Sales 168.0MM^E EMP 9,000
SIC 5812 Fast-food restaurant, chain
Pr: David Devoy

JOLIET JUNIOR COLLEGE BKSTR
See JOLIET JUNIOR COLLEGE DISTRICT 525

D-U-N-S 06-995-9013
JOLIET JUNIOR COLLEGE DISTRICT 525
JOLIET JUNIOR COLLEGE BKSTR
1215 Houbolt Rd, Joliet, IL 60431-8800
Tel (815) 280-6767 Founded/Ownrshp 1901
Sales 24.6MM^E EMP 1,296
SIC 8222 Junior college
Pr: Debra S Daniels
VP: Judy Mitchell
*Prin: Kat Boehle
*Prin: Eric Monahan
*Prin: Frank Zeller

D-U-N-S 07-975-1194
JOLIET PUBLIC SCHOOLS DISTRICT 86
420 N Raynor Ave, Joliet, IL 60435-6065
Tel (815) 740-3196 Founded/Ownrshp 1857
Sales 132.0MM EMP 1,000
SIC 8211 Public elementary school
MIS Dir: John Armstrong
Pr Dir: Sandy Zalewski
Schl Brd P: Jeffery Pritz
Schl Brd P: Gwendolyn R Ulmer
Schl Brd P: Deborah Zeich
Psych: Debbie Cobb
Psych: Lauren Massey

D-U-N-S 05-704-4927 IMP
JOMAR INVESTMENTS INC
NEW LIFE TRANSPORT PARTS CTR
400 Gordon Indus Ct Sw, Byron Center, MI 49315-8354
Tel (616) 878-3633 Founded/Ownrshp 1972
Sales 177.0MM^E EMP 300
SIC 5013 Trailer parts & accessories
Pr: Robert L Hinton
Chf Mktg O: Scott Hammon
*VP: Michael J Hinton
*VP: Larry Yeager
Info Man: Tom Chandler
VP Opers: Robert Lindley
Opers Mgr: Raymond Peterson
*VP Sls: David P Broyles
Manager: Patrick Bailey
Manager: Adam Clugston
Manager: Don Dattilo

D-U-N-S 96-757-2041
JOMARSHE INVESTMENT GROUP INC
KELLER WILLIAMS REALTORS
1617 Nc Highway 66 S # 201, Kernersville, NC 27284-3828
Tel (336) 992-0200 Founded/Ownrshp 1999
Sales 89.0MM EMP 7
SIC 6531 Real estate agent, residential
Pr: Sam Rogers
*Pr: Samuel Wrogers
*Treas: Richard Woolridge
*Ex VP: Carol K Whicker
*VP: Shirley Ramsey

D-U-N-S 09-177-3820 IMP
JON-DON INC
400 Medinah Rd, Roselle, IL 60172-2329
Tel (630) 872-5401 Founded/Ownrshp 1978
Sales 120.1MM^E EMP 100
SIC 5087 Carpet & rug cleaning equipment & supplies, commercial; Janitors' supplies
Pr: John T Paolella
Brnch Mgr: Tim Wessels
Genl Mgr: Dwight Dahl
IT Man: Bill Piet
Natl Sales: Derek Zimmermann
Mktg Dir: Jacki Fry
Mktg Mgr: Michael Tolkson
Manager: Devin Bates
Manager: Rick Jensen
Manager: Ryan Meier
Sls Mgr: Sherry Essany

D-U-N-S 04-358-1626 IMP
JONAH BROOKLYN INC (CA)
YOGA SAK
9673 Topanga Canyon Pl, Chatsworth, CA 91311-4118
Tel (877) 964-2725 Founded/Ownrshp 2011
Sales 500.0MM EMP 5
SIC 2673 Wardrobe bags (closet accessories): from purchased materials
Pr: Daniel Meyers

D-U-N-S 07-938-0282
JONAH ENERGY LLC
(Suby of TEXAS PACIFIC GROUP) ★
707 17th St Ste 2700, Denver, CO 80202-3429
Tel (720) 577-1000 Founded/Ownrshp 2014
Sales 135.0MM^E EMP 147^E
SIC 1382 Oil & gas exploration services
CEO: Thomas M Hart III
*Pr: L Craig Manaugh
*VP: C Mark Brannum
*VP: David W Honeyfield
*VP: Rory Obyrne

D-U-N-S 16-048-5194 IMP
JONATHAN ADLER ENTERPRISES LLC
333 Hudson St Fl 7, New York, NY 10013-1031
Tel (212) 645-2802 Founded/Ownrshp 2004
Sales 90.1MM^E EMP 150
SIC 5023 Decorative home furnishings & supplies
VP: Denise Benn
VP: Susan Eydenberg
Genl Mgr: Q Bui
Store Mgr: Coy Barton
Store Mgr: Daniel Cotter
Store Mgr: Luis Cox
Store Mgr: Michael Deherrera
Store Mgr: Kristopher Docter
Store Mgr: Robert Dorsey
Store Mgr: Thomas Fisher
Store Mgr: Jacob Jasso

D-U-N-S 12-203-4978 IMP
JONATHAN LOUIS INTERNATIONAL LTD
544 W 130th St, Gardena, CA 90248-1502
Tel (323) 770-3330 Founded/Ownrshp 1985
Sales 220.3MM^E EMP 610
SIC 2512 Upholstered household furniture
CEO: Juan Valle
Pt: Javier Sanchez
Dir IT: Ushan Dalwis
IT Man: Jose Sandoval
VP Sls: Mary Bowling

D-U-N-S 09-396-8394
JONES & CARTER INC
COTTON SURVEYING COMPANY
6330 West Loop S Ste 150, Bellaire, TX 77401-2928
Tel (713) 777-5337 Founded/Ownrshp 1976
Sales 83.9MM^E EMP 511
SIC 8711 Civil engineering
CEO: Robert Aylward
Ex VP: Carlos Cotton
*Sr VP: Clayton Black
*Sr VP: Dwayne Hamilton
*Sr VP: Kristin Kautz
*Sr VP: Bryan Kennedy
*Sr VP: R Scott Knapp
*Sr VP: Kevin Krahn
*Sr VP: Robert Maxwell
Off Admin: Ralynn Reome
IT Man: Dean Errington

JONES & FRANK
See JF ACQUISITION LLC

D-U-N-S 00-484-0864
JONES BROS INC
JONES BROTHERS CONSTRUCTION CO
(Suby of JONES INVESTMENT HOLDING INC) ★
5760 Old Lebanon Dirt Rd, Mount Juliet, TN 37122-3393
Tel (615) 754-4710 Founded/Ownrshp 1964
Sales 106.4MM^E EMP 200
SIC 1622 1771 1794 1629 1611 Bridge construction; Driveway, parking lot & blacktop contractors; Excavation & grading, building construction; Land leveling; General contractor, highway & street construction
Ch Bd: Robert A Jones
*Pr: M Dale Mc Cullough
VP: Eugene M Hubbard
*VP: M Eugene Hubbard
*VP: Robert S Mc Culloch
*VP: Mann R P Pendleton

JONES BROTHERS CONSTRUCTION CO
See JONES BROS INC

D-U-N-S 12-094-0721
JONES CO
215 Pendleton St Ste A, Waycross, GA 31501-2330
Tel (912) 285-4011 Founded/Ownrshp 1982
Sales 547.3MM^E EMP 1,800
Accts Moore Colson And Company Pc
SIC 5541 5411 5172 Gasoline service stations; Grocery stores; Petroleum products
CEO: James C Jones III
*CFO: James A Walker Jr

D-U-N-S 07-193-2693
JONES COUNTY SCHOOL DISTRICT
JONES COUNTY SCHOOLS
5204 Highway 11 N, Ellisville, MS 39437-5072
Tel (601) 649-5201 Founded/Ownrshp 1900
Sales 47.2MM^E EMP 1,100
SIC 8211 9411 Public elementary & secondary schools; High school, junior or senior; Administration of educational programs
*CFO: Scott Lewis
Schl Brd P: Lester Boyles
Psych: Barbara Odom

JONES COUNTY SCHOOLS
See JONES COUNTY SCHOOL DISTRICT

D-U-N-S 07-674-4234
JONES DAY LIMITED PARTNERSHIP
901 Lakeside Ave E Ste 2, Cleveland, OH 44114-1190
Tel (216) 586-3939 Founded/Ownrshp 1893
Sales 1.0MMM^E EMP 4,600
SIC 8111 General practice law office
Pt: Jones Day
Pt: Brett P Barragate
*Pt: Dennis Barsky
*Pt: Patrick Belville
*Pt: Erin L Burke
Pt: Charles M Carberry
Pt: Tyrone R Childress
Pt: Peter D Clarke
*Pt: James A Cox
Pt: Thomas F Cullen Jr
Pt: Antonio F Dias
Pt: Lawrence C Dinardo
Pt: James R Dutro
Pt: Giles P Elliott
Pt: Noel J Francisco
Pt: Robert W Gaffey
Pt: Arman Galledari
Pt: Adam Greaves
Pt: Daniel C Hagen
Pt: Charles W Hardin Jr
*Pt: Harry I Johnson III

D-U-N-S 19-617-2639
■ JONES ENERGY HOLDINGS LLC
JONES ENERGY LIMITED
(Suby of JONES ENERGY INC) ★
807 Las Cimas Pkwy # 350, Austin, TX 78746-6193
Tel (512) 328-2953 Founded/Ownrshp 1988
Sales 131.6MM^E EMP 65^E
SIC 1311 1382 Crude petroleum production; Natural gas production; Oil & gas exploration services
Genl Pt: Jonny Jones
*CFO: Craig M Fleming
Ex VP: Robert J Brooks
*Sr VP: Jody Crook
Sr VP: Kristel Franklin
*Sr VP: Hal Hawthorne
Sr VP: Stephen Roberts
VP: Todd Wehner
IT Man: Ryan O'Dea

D-U-N-S 07-909-0501
▲ JONES ENERGY INC
807 Las Cimas Pkwy # 350, Austin, TX 78746-6193
Tel (512) 328-2953 Founded/Ownrshp 1988
Sales 197.4MM EMP 116
Tkr Sym JONE Exch NYS
SIC 1311 Crude petroleum & natural gas; Crude petroleum & natural gas production; Natural gas production
Ch Bd: Jonny Jones
*Pr: Mike S McConnell
COO: Eric Niccum
CFO: Robert J Brooks
Ex VP: Jeff Tanner
Board of Directors: Alan D Bell, Howard I Hoffen, Gregory D Myers, Robb L Voyles, Halbert S Washburn

JONES ENERGY LIMITED
See JONES ENERGY HOLDINGS LLC

D-U-N-S 18-592-3232
JONES FINANCIAL COMPANIES LLLP
12555 Manchester Rd, Saint Louis, MO 63131-3710
Tel (314) 515-2000 Founded/Ownrshp 1987
Sales 6.6MMM EMP 41,000
SIC 6211 6411 6163 Stock brokers & dealers; Investment firm, general brokerage; Advisory services, insurance; Loan brokers
Mng Pt: James D Weddle
Genl Pt: Norman L Eaker
Genl Pt: Tim Kirley
Genl Pt: James A Tricarico
CFO: Kevin D Bastien
Prin: Tom Migneron
Prin: John Rahal

D-U-N-S 04-006-2168 IMP/EXP
JONES GROUP INC
1411 Broadway Fl 15, New York, NY 10018-3410
Tel (212) 642-3860 Founded/Ownrshp 2014
Sales NA EMP 10,790
SIC 5632 5137 5139 5661 5641

D-U-N-S 07-950-3552
JONES HOLDINGS LLC
1411 Brdwy, New York, NY 10018
Tel (215) 785-4000 Founded/Ownrshp 2013
Sales 296.1MM^E EMP 400^E
SIC 5137 Women's & children's clothing
VP: Karen Curione
*CFO: Joseph T Donnalley

D-U-N-S 00-424-2561
JONES INDUSTRIAL HOLDINGS INC (TX)
806 Seaco Ct, Deer Park, TX 77536-3176
Tel (281) 479-6000 Founded/Ownrshp 1998
Sales 141.0MM^E EMP 450
SIC 3564 Air purification equipment
CEO: Bradley T Jones
*Pr: Stewart H Jones
*COO: Reagan Busbee

D-U-N-S 07-340-9864 EXP
JONES INTERNATIONAL LTD
JONES.COM
300 E Mineral Ave Ste 5, Littleton, CO 80122-2655
Tel (303) 792-3111 Founded/Ownrshp 1969
Sales 120.1MM^E EMP 330
SIC 4832 4841 7371 7372 Radio broadcasting stations, music format; Cable television services; Custom computer programming services; Prepackaged software
Ch Bd: Glenn R Jones
*Prin: Vincent Dibiase
*Prin: John Jennings

D-U-N-S 05-397-6747
JONES INVESTMENT HOLDING INC
5760 Old Lebanon Dirt Rd, Mount Juliet, TN 37122-3393
Tel (615) 754-4710 Founded/Ownrshp 1999
Sales 106.4MM^E EMP 200
SIC 1622 1771 1794 1611 Bridge, tunnel & elevated highway; Concrete work; Excavation work; Highway & street construction
Pr: Dan McCullch
Treas: Michael Randolph
VP: Robert S McCulloch
VP: William R Slinkard

D-U-N-S 15-453-7807 IMP
■ JONES LANG LASALLE AMERICAS INC
HOTELS & HOSPITALITY GROUP
(Suby of JONES LANG LASALLE INC) ★
200 E Randolph St # 4300, Chicago, IL 60601-6436
Tel (312) 782-5800 Founded/Ownrshp 1988
Sales 455.0M^E EMP 15,000
SIC 6282 1542 Investment advisory service; Commercial & office building contractors
CEO: Greg O'Brian
*Ch Bd: Sheila A Penrose
*Pr: Colin Dyer
*Pr: Peter Roberts
*Ex VP: Louis Breeding
*Ex VP: David Calverley
*Ex VP: Lauralee E Martin
*VP: Vendetta Blowe
VP: Peter Bulgarelli
VP: Beth Hayden
VP: Stephen Pollard

D-U-N-S 02-878-1060
▲ JONES LANG LASALLE INC
200 E Randolph St # 4300, Chicago, IL 60601-6537
Tel (312) 782-5800 Founded/Ownrshp 1997
Sales 5.9MMM EMP 61,500^E
Tkr Sym JLL Exch NYS
SIC 6512 6531 Commercial & industrial building operation; Real estate agents & managers
Pr: Christian Ulbrich
*Ch Bd: Sheila A Penrose
CFO: Christie B Kelly
Treas: Bryan J Duncan
Chf Mktg O: Charles J Doyle
Ofcr: James S Jasionowski
Ofcr: Patricia Maxson
Ex VP: Allan Frazier
Ex VP: David A Johnson
Ex VP: Mark J Ohringer
VP: Walter Lovell
Board of Directors: Hugo Bague, Dame Deanne Julius, Ming Lu, Bridget Macaskill, Martin H Nesbitt, Ann Marie Petach, Samuel A Di Piazza Jr

JONES NEW YORK
See AUTHENTIC BRANDS GROUP LLC

D-U-N-S 00-637-3633 IMP
JONES PLASTIC AND ENGINEERING CO LLC (KY)
2410 Plantside Dr, Louisville, KY 40299-2528
Tel (502) 491-3785 Founded/Ownrshp 1961
Sales 378.1MM^E EMP 1,310
SIC 3089 Injection molded finished plastic products
Genl Mgr: Chuck Flaherty
Ql Cn Mgr: Bruce Jones

D-U-N-S 80-763-9273 IMP
JONES STEPHENS CORP
PLUMBEST
(Suby of WORLD AND MAIN LLC) ★
3249 Moody Pkwy, Moody, AL 35004-2622
Tel (205) 640-7200 Founded/Ownrshp 2014
Sales 87.1MM^E EMP 220^E
SIC 5074 Plumbing & hydronic heating supplies; Plumbing fittings & supplies
CEO: Bryan Yazel
CFO: Ben Small
VP: Christopher Rowlin
VP: Garry L Taylor
Opers Mgr: Brian Owens
Manager: Darren Hayes

D-U-N-S 01-039-7404
JONES WALKER LLP
201 Saint Charles Ave # 5200, New Orleans, LA 70170-5000
Tel (504) 582-8000 Founded/Ownrshp 1982
Sales 180.0MM EMP 800
SIC 8111 General practice law office
Mng Pt: William H Hines

Pt: Jesse R Adams
Pt: Arnold I Havens
Pt: Matthew T Brown
Pt: Andre Burvant
Pt: Susan Chambers
Pt: Scott D Chenevert
Pt: Glen G Goodier
Pt: Curtis R Hearn
Pt: William Joyce
Pt: Robin McGuire
Pt: Marshall J Page III
Pt: John Reynolds
Pt: Coleman D Ridley
Pt: M Richard Schroeder
Pt: R Patrick Vance
Pr: Judy Way
CFO: Andrew Bruns
Chf Mktg O: Carol Todd Thomas
Trst Ofcr: Erin Allemand
Board of Directors: Miriam Wogan Henry, Robert S Lazarus, Joshua A Norris, Gary J Russo

D-U-N-S 09-307-0670
JONES WHOLESALE LUMBER CO INC
10761 Alameda St, Lynwood, CA 90262-1751
Tel (323) 567-1301 *Founded/Ownrshp* 1977
Sales 110.1MM *EMP* 45
SIC 5031 Lumber: rough, dressed & finished
CEO: Roderick M Jones
**Pr:* John M Cencak
**Sec:* Robert H Jones
**VP:* Rick Jones
Exec: Stephanie Jones
Sales Exec: John Pasqualetto
Sls Mgr: Craig Evans
Board of Directors: John M Cencak, Rick H Jones, Robert H Jones, Roderick M Jones

D-U-N-S 00-779-4191
JONES-ONSLOW ELECTRIC MEMBERSHIP CORP
JOEMC
259 Western Blvd, Jacksonville, NC 28546-5736
Tel (910) 353-1940 *Founded/Ownrshp* 1939
Sales 128.1MM *EMP* 151
Accts Adams Jenkins And Cheatham R
SIC 4911 Distribution, electric power
CEO: J Ronald McElheney
**CEO:* Jeff Clark
**Treas:* Thomas Waller
VP: Steve Goodson
**VP:* Michelle Hefner
VP: Carrie Peters
**Prin:* Horace Phillips

JONES.COM
See JONES INTERNATIONAL LTD

JON'S MARKETPLACE
See BERBERIAN ENTERPRISES INC

D-U-N-S 83-068-0422 IMP
JOON LLC
AJIN USA
(*Suby of* AJIN INDUSTRIAL CO., LTD.)
1500 County Road 177, Cusseta, AL 36852-2764
Tel (334) 756-8601 *Founded/Ownrshp* 2008
Sales 191.3MM^E *EMP* 500
Accts Choi Kim & Park Llp Montgome
SIC 3465 4214 Automotive stampings; Local trucking with storage
CEO: Jung Ho Sea
**COO:* Taechul Kim
Genl Mgr: Hyun Yun
Ql Cn Mgr: Young Park

D-U-N-S 06-795-6102
JOPLIN SCHOOL
310 W 8th St, Joplin, MO 64801-4302
Tel (417) 625-5200 *Founded/Ownrshp* 1874
Sales 88.9MM *EMP* 1,260
Accts Mense Churchwell & Mense Pc
SIC 8211 Public elementary school; Public junior high school; Public senior high school; Public vocational/technical school
Dir Vol: Dale Peterson
**CFO:* Paul Barr
Bd of Dir: Rhonda Randall
Bd of Dir: Pat Waldo
Dir IT: Susan Smith
IT Man: Ross Lauck
Pr Dir: Kelli Price
Psych: Barbara Brown
Psych: Morgan Ramsey

D-U-N-S 08-896-7005 IMP/EXP
JORDACHE ENTERPRISES INC
1400 Broadway Rm 1404b, New York, NY 10018-5336
Tel (212) 643-8400 *Founded/Ownrshp* 1978
Sales 1.3MMM^E *EMP* 8,000
SIC 2339 2325 2369 2331 2321 2361 Slacks: women's, misses' & juniors'; Men's & boys' trousers & slacks; Slacks: girls' & children's; Jackets: girls', children's & infants'; Shirts, women's & juniors': made from purchased materials; Men's & boys' furnishings; Shirts: girls', children's & infants'
CEO: Joe Nakash
**Sec:* Ralph Nakash
Ex VP: Eddie Benaderet
Ex VP: Bob Ross
Ex VP: Emzon Shung
VP: Charles Flores
**VP:* AVI Nakash
VP: Peter Sachs
Creative D: Saeryon Park
Mng Dir: Jonathan Bennett
Off Mgr: Bruce Byriel

D-U-N-S 11-060-0678 IMP
JORDACHE LIMITED
JE SPORT DIV
(*Suby of* JORDACHE ENTERPRISES INC) ★
1400 Broadway Rm 1404b, New York, NY 10018-5336
Tel (212) 944-1330 *Founded/Ownrshp* 1991
Sales 89.9MM^E *EMP* 200
SIC 5137 5136 6153 Women's & children's clothing; Men's & boys' clothing; Factoring services
Pr: Joseph Nakash
COO: Joseph Mansour
CFO: Joe Taylor
**Sec:* Ralph Nakash
Chf Mktg O: Shaul Nakash
Sr VP: Charles Flores
VP: Shaul Cohen
**VP:* AVI Nakash
VP: Ricky Ramnani
Netwrk Mgr: Hugh Bardsley
Sftwr Eng: Imran Elahi

D-U-N-S 80-852-3229
JORDAN CARRIERS INC
170 Highway 61 S, Natchez, MS 39120-5279
Tel (601) 446-8899 *Founded/Ownrshp* 1992
Sales 90.5MM^E *EMP* 490
SIC 4213 Contract haulers
Pr: Kenneth Jordan
**CFO:* Doug Jordan

D-U-N-S 19-686-4607
JORDAN CF CONSTRUCTION LLC
(*Suby of* JORDAN CF INVESTMENTS LLP) ★
7700 Cf Jordan Dr Ste 200, El Paso, TX 79912-8807
Tel (915) 877-3333 *Founded/Ownrshp* 1993
Sales 299.9MM *EMP* 500
Accts Schmid Broaddus Nugent Gano Pc
SIC 1542 1541 1522 Nonresidential construction; Industrial buildings & warehouses; Residential construction
Ch Bd: C F Jordan III
**Pr:* Darren G Woody
**CFO:* Cynthia Rogers
Off Mgr: Kelly Riley

D-U-N-S 83-612-7183
JORDAN CF INVESTMENTS LLP
7700 Cf Jordan Dr, El Paso, TX 79912-8808
Tel (915) 877-3333 *Founded/Ownrshp* 1993
Sales 301.9MM^E *EMP* 500
Accts Schmid Broaddus Nugent Gano Pc
SIC 1542 1541 1522 1611 Nonresidential construction; Industrial buildings & warehouses; Residential construction; Highway & street paving contractor; Grading
Ch: CF Paco Jordan
Pt: C F Jordan III

D-U-N-S 05-038-1243
JORDAN CO L P
399 Park Ave Fl 30, New York, NY 10022-4871
Tel (212) 572-0800 *Founded/Ownrshp* 1982
Sales 420.8MM^E *EMP* 290
SIC 6726

D-U-N-S 00-895-2855 EXP
JORDAN FORD LTD
13010 N Interstate 35, Live Oak, TX 78233-2644
Tel (210) 653-3673 *Founded/Ownrshp* 1946
Sales 83.7MM^E *EMP* 220
SIC 5511 Automobiles, new & used
Genl Mgr: Tom Murray
**Pt:* Charles Jordan
**Pt:* William A Jordan Jr
CFO: Mike Trompeter
Genl Mgr: Marc Cross

D-U-N-S 07-909-9262
JORDAN FOSTER CONSTRUCTION LLC (TX)
7700 Cf Jordan Dr Ste 200, El Paso, TX 79912-8807
Tel (915) 877-3333 *Founded/Ownrshp* 2013
Sales 176.2MM *EMP* 1,000
Accts Bkd Llp San Antonio Texas
SIC 1542 Commercial & office building, new construction
CFO: Cynthia Rogers
VP: John Goodrich
Dir IT: John Buraczyk
Sfty Dirs: Crystal Stewart
Mtls Mgr: Jerry Smith
Sfty Mgr: Damian Alvarez
Snr PM: Clint Henson

D-U-N-S 94-639-4111
JORDAN HEALTH CARE INC
JORDAN HEALTH SERVICES
(*Suby of* SKILLED CARE) ★
412 Texas Highway 37 S, Mount Vernon, TX 75457-6570
Tel (903) 537-3600 *Founded/Ownrshp* 1996
Sales 201.9MM^E *EMP* 13,000^E
SIC 8082 Home health care services
CEO: Dean Anthony Holland
**CFO:* Lance Cornell
**Sr VP:* Chad Wooten
**VP:* Gregg Cannady
VP: Renee Cheesman
**VP:* Tim Conroy
VP: George Hutto
**VP:* Kathy Poland
Off Admin: Antonio Alvarado
Dir IT: Patrick Egan
IT Man: Jeff Bonham

JORDAN HEALTH SERVICES
See JORDAN HEALTH CARE INC

D-U-N-S 17-576-0164
JORDAN HEALTH SYSTEMS INC
JORDAN HOSPITAL
275 Sandwich St, Plymouth, MA 02360-2183
Tel (508) 830-2388 *Founded/Ownrshp* 1901
Sales 212.8MM *EMP* 1,600
Accts Kpmg Llp Boston Massachusett
SIC 8741 8062 Hospital management; General medical & surgical hospitals
CEO: Peter J Holden
CFO: Jack Patricio
**Ch:* Wilfred Sheehan
**Treas:* Joseph Iannoni
Chf Mktg O: Bernard Durante
**Sr VP:* James Fanale
**VP:* Donna Doherty
**VP:* Andrea Holleran
VP: Cindy Outhouse
Exec: Bill McCarthy
Dir Rad: Ronald Goldberg

D-U-N-S 96-769-5904
JORDAN HEALTHCARE HOLDINGS INC
SKILLED CARE
412 Texas Highway 37 S, Mount Vernon, TX 75457-6570
Tel (903) 537-2445 *Founded/Ownrshp* 2010
Sales 1.5MMM^E *EMP* 13,000^E
SIC 6719 8082 Investment holding companies, except banks; Home health care services
CEO: Dean Holland

JORDAN HOSPITAL
See JORDAN HEALTH SYSTEMS INC

D-U-N-S 07-952-3668
JORDAN HOSPITAL CLUB INC
275 Sandwich St, Plymouth, MA 02360-2196
Tel (508) 830-2391 *Founded/Ownrshp* 1901
Sales 197.0MM *EMP* 1,600
SIC 8062 General medical & surgical hospitals
Pr: Peter Holden
**CFO:* Elliot Schwartz
CIO: Cheryl Crowley
Nrsg Dir: Christine Klucznik

D-U-N-S 18-915-8736 IMP/EXP
JORDAN INDUSTRIES INC
1751 Lake Cook Rd Ste 550, Deerfield, IL 60015-5658
Tel (847) 945-5591 *Founded/Ownrshp* 1988
Sales 592.6MM^E *EMP* 3,973
SIC 3621 3625 3714 3089 2759 5999 Motors, electric; Electric motor & generator auxiliary parts; Motor starters & controllers, electric; Motor vehicle engines & parts; Rebuilding engines & transmissions, factory basis; Gears, motor vehicle; Thermoformed finished plastic products; Labels & seals: printing; Art, picture frames & decorations; Picture frames, ready made
Ch Bd: John W Jordan II
Pr: Thomas H Quinn
CFO: Dan Drury
CFO: Michael Elia
CFO: Lisa M Ondrula
Treas: Gordon L Nelson
Sr VP: Joseph C Linen
Sr VP: Gordon Nelson
VP: Edward F Lilly
VP: Pam Ross
Dir Rx: Pal Hayer

D-U-N-S 06-086-9450 IMP/EXP
JORDAN MANUFACTURING CO INC
1200 S 6th St, Monticello, IN 47960-8200
Tel (574) 583-6008 *Founded/Ownrshp* 1986
Sales 128.2MM^E *EMP* 500^E
SIC 2392 5021 Cushions & pillows; Outdoor & lawn furniture
Pr: David N Jordan
VP: David Wolfe
Exec: Ashley Medley
CIO: Paul Suhr
Dir IT: Tara Bailey
Sfty Mgr: Keith Lehocky
Sales Exec: Cindy Caudle
VP Mktg: BJ Mursener
Sales Asso: Sean Wright

D-U-N-S 07-298-3406
JORDAN SCHOOL DISTRICT
7387 S Campus View Dr, West Jordan, UT 84084-5500
Tel (801) 280-3689 *Founded/Ownrshp* 1913
Sales 415.3MM *EMP* 5,900
Accts Squire & Company Pc Orem Ut
SIC 8211 Public elementary & secondary schools; Elementary school; Specialty education
Ofcr: Kurt Prusse
**VP:* Leah Voorhies
**Prin:* Richard S Osborn
**Prin:* Susan Pulsipher
Dir Sec: Jeff Beesley
Genl Mgr: Heather Ellingson
Off Admin: Wendy Johnson
IT Man: Denice Brown
Teacher Pr: June Lemaster
Psych: Jim Stewart
Nutrtnst: Karen Cloward

D-U-N-S 62-408-3684
JORDAN SPECIALTY PLASTICS INC
(*Suby of* JORDAN INDUSTRIES INC) ★
1751 Lake Cook Rd Ste 550, Deerfield, IL 60015-5624
Tel (847) 945-5591 *Founded/Ownrshp* 2006
Sales 152.4MM^E *EMP* 686^E
SIC 3089 3081 Plastic containers, except foam; Unsupported plastics film & sheet
Prin: Lisa Ondrula

D-U-N-S 96-376-3719
JORDAN VALLEY MEDICAL CENTER LP
(*Suby of* IASIS HEALTHCARE CORP) ★
3580 W 9000 S, West Jordan, UT 84088-8812
Tel (801) 561-8888 *Founded/Ownrshp* 1996
Sales 61.4MM *EMP* 1,300
SIC 8062 General medical & surgical hospitals
CEO: Steven M Anderson
CFO: Jerry Panter
Dir Inf Cn: Mary Jordan
Dir Inf Cn: Robyn Rollins-Root
Chf Nrs Of: Jolisa Catmull
Off Mgr: Laurie Madsen
Doctor: Patrick Vandenhazel

JORDANO'S FOOD SERVICE
See JORDANOS INC

D-U-N-S 02-937-9088 IMP
JORDANOS INC
JORDANO'S FOOD SERVICE
550 S Patterson Ave, Santa Barbara, CA 93111-2498
Tel (805) 964-0611 *Founded/Ownrshp* 1915
Sales 441.7MM^E *EMP* 500
SIC 5181 5182 5149 5141 5142 5148 Beer & other fermented malt liquors; Wine; Soft drinks; Groceries, general line; Packaged frozen goods; Fresh fruits & vegetables
CEO: Peter Jordano
CFO: Michael F Sieckowski
Ex VP: Jeffrey S Jordano
Opers Mgr: Dennis Merchant

D-U-N-S 01-967-8168 IMP
■ **JORDANS FURNITURE INC**
(*Suby of* BERKSHIRE HATHAWAY INC) ★
450 Revolutionary Dr, East Taunton, MA 02718-1369
Tel (508) 828-4000 *Founded/Ownrshp* 1999
Sales 270.5MM^E *EMP* 1,200
SIC 5712 Furniture stores
CEO: Barry Tatelman
**COO:* Peter Bolton
**CFO:* David Stavros
**Sec:* Steve Wholley
**VP:* Joshua Tatelman
Exec: Ethan Peterson
Dir Risk M: Denise Deslauriers
Dir IT: Peter Clark
Software D: Andrew Hanson
Sls Mgr: Ned Burke
Sls Mgr: Ken Ross

JORGENSEN STEEL AND ALUMINUM
See EARLE M JORGENSEN CO

D-U-N-S 06-490-0079 IMP
■ **JOS A BANK CLOTHIERS INC**
(*Suby of* MENS WEARHOUSE INC) ★
500 Hanover Pike, Hampstead, MD 21074-2002
Tel (410) 239-2700 *Founded/Ownrshp* 2014
Sales 774.0MM^E *EMP* 6,342
SIC 5611 5961 Men's & boys' clothing stores; Clothing accessories: men's & boys'; Clothing, mail order (except women's)
Pr: R Neal Black
**CEO:* Douglas S Ewert
**CEO:* Robert Wildrick
**CFO:* Jon W Kimmins
**CFO:* David E Ullman
Treas: Richard E Pitts
Chf Mktg O: James Singh
**Chf Mktg O:* James W Thorne
**Ex VP:* Robert B Hensley
**Ex VP:* Gary M Merry
VP: Carol Moore
VP: Nick Rizzi
VP: Brent Thompson
**VP:* Brian T Vaclavik

D-U-N-S 07-911-6847
JOSE MASSUH REVOCABLE TRUST
825 Brickell Bay Dr, Miami, FL 33131-2936
Tel (305) 358-1900 *Founded/Ownrshp* 1982
Sales 85.0MM *EMP* 48
SIC 5162 Plastics resins
Pr: Jose M Massuh

D-U-N-S 09-006-7786 IMP/EXP
JOSE SANTIAGO INC
5 Calle Marginal # 5, Bayamon, PR 00959-5530
Tel (787) 288-8835 *Founded/Ownrshp* 1902
Sales 190.9MM^E *EMP* 300
SIC 5142 5149 Meat, frozen: packaged; Canned goods: fruit, vegetables, seafood, meats, etc.
Pr: Jose Santiago
**Treas:* Eduardo Santiago
**VP:* Eduardo S Gonzalez
**VP:* Julio Julia

D-U-N-S 00-693-5571 IMP/EXP
JOSEPH BEHR & SONS INC
BEHR IRON & METAL
1100 Seminary St, Rockford, IL 61104-4644
Tel (815) 987-2755 *Founded/Ownrshp* 1906
Sales 254.9MM^E *EMP* 412
Accts Mc Gladrey & Pullen Cpas Roc
SIC 5093 Ferrous metal scrap & waste
CEO: Richard Behr
**CFO:* Leland R Foecking
MIS Dir: Dave Steneck
IT Man: David Lai
Mktg Dir: Jodi Behr

JOSEPH CORY COMPANIES
See CORY JOSEPH HOLDING LLC

JOSEPH GILENE, PRESIDENT
See LOUISVILLE HOSPITAL

D-U-N-S 02-938-5994
JOSEPH J ALBANESE INC
851 Martin Ave, Santa Clara, CA 95050-2903
Tel (408) 727-5700 *Founded/Ownrshp* 1974
Sales 158.5MM^E *EMP* 700
SIC 1771 Concrete work
Prin: Joseph J Albanese
Ofcr: Nick Dalis
VP: Leslie M Cusimano
Exec: Kevin Albanese
Exec: Stephanie Nguyen
Off Mgr: Melissa Delgado
CTO: John Formoso
VP Opers: Fil Calderon
VP Sls: Jeff Jacobs
VP Sls: Phil Roby
Sls Mgr: Ronald Vega

D-U-N-S 01-178-9237
JOSEPH JINGOLI & SON INC
JJS
100 Lenox Dr Ste 100, Lawrenceville, NJ 08648-2332
Tel (609) 896-3111 *Founded/Ownrshp* 1922
Sales 186.4MM^E *EMP* 350
SIC 1541 Industrial buildings & warehouses
CEO: Joseph R Jingoli Jr
**Pr:* Robert E Reager
**CFO:* Michael D Jingoli
VP: Frank Kark
Exec: Phillip Sheperd
Assoc Dir: Michael Burdalski
IT Man: Nick Tzanavaris
Genl Couns: Glenn Clouser
Snr PM: Richard Basso
Snr PM: David Christiansen
Snr PM: Neil Pelullo

D-U-N-S 62-618-6089
JOSEPH STOKES INSTITUTE OF RESEARCH
(*Suby of* CHILDRENS HOSP OF PA FNDTN) ★
3615 Civic Center Blvd, Philadelphia, PA 19104-4318
Tel (215) 590-3800 *Founded/Ownrshp* 2006
Sales 5.9MM^E *EMP* 1,819^E

SIC 8062 8733 General medical & surgical hospitals; Medical research
CEO: Steven Altschuler
Pr: George Marshalek
**Prin:* Peter C Adamson
Orthpdst: John M Flynn

D-U-N-S 00-693-2446 IMP/EXP
■ JOSEPH T RYERSON & SON INC
(*Suby of* RYERSON HOLDING CORP) ★
227 W Monroe St Fl 27, Chicago, IL 60606-5081
Tel (312) 292-5000 *Founded/Ownrshp* 1999
Sales 2.1MMM^E *EMP* 3,200
SIC 5051 5162 Metals service centers & offices; Steel; Aluminum bars, rods, ingots, sheets, pipes, plates, etc.; Miscellaneous nonferrous products; Plastics materials & basic shapes
Pr: Edward Lehner
CFO: Jay M Grapz
**CFO:* Erich Schnaufer
**Treas:* Robert Delaney
Treas: Terrance R Oges
Ex VP: Gary Niederpruem
**Sr VP:* Roger Lindsay
VP: Leslie M Norgren
**VP:* Mark Silver
Genl Mgr: Brain Kluge
Genl Mgr: Keith G Medick

D-U-N-S 00-776-9783
JOSH BIRT LLC
JOSHBIRT
2 Fordham Ave, Pittsburgh, PA 15229-1546
Tel (412) 719-7182 *Founded/Ownrshp* 2009
Sales 170.0MM *EMP* 4
SIC 7812 Motion picture & video production
Owner: Josh Birt

D-U-N-S 01-529-3232
JOSH MCDOWELL MINISTRY
(*Suby of* NEW LIFE PUBLICATIONS) ★
2001 W Plano Pkwy # 2400, Plano, TX 75075-8637
Tel (972) 907-1000 *Founded/Ownrshp* 2010
Sales 7.8MM^E *EMP* 1,667^E
SIC 8661 Religious organizations
Prin: Josh McDowell

JOSHBIRT
See JOSH BIRT LLC

D-U-N-S 18-827-6596 IMP/EXP
JOSHEN PAPER & PACKAGING CO
5800 Grant Ave, Cleveland, OH 44105-5608
Tel (216) 441-5600 *Founded/Ownrshp* 1988
Sales 386.6MM^E *EMP* 325
SIC 5113 5169 Bags, paper & disposable plastic; Cups, disposable plastic & paper; Boxes & containers; Sanitation preparations
CEO: Michelle Reiner
**Pr:* Bob Reiner
**CFO:* Joe Monroe
**VP:* John Caldwell
**VP:* Don Morgenroth
**Prin:* Elliot M Kaufman

JOSLIN CLINIC
See JOSLIN DIABETES CENTER INC

D-U-N-S 07-172-3084
JOSLIN DIABETES CENTER INC
JOSLIN CLINIC
1 Joslin Pl, Boston, MA 02215-5394
Tel (617) 732-2400 *Founded/Ownrshp* 1953
Sales 100.9MM *EMP* 600
Accts Cbiz Tofias Boston Ma
SIC 8011 Medical centers
CEO: John L Brooks III
**Pr:* C R Kahn MD
**CFO:* Rick Markello
Ofcr: Steve Flander
Ofcr: Christi Gabbay
**Ex VP:* Rajni Aneja
Sr VP: Martin Abrahamson
Sr VP: Paul O'Brien
VP: Catherine Carver
VP: Nandan Padukone
Dir Lab: Dan Jamieson
Dir Lab: Jennifer Lock
Assoc Dir: John Zrebiec

D-U-N-S 00-954-5658
■ JOSLYN SUNBANK CO LLC
(*Suby of* ESTERLINE TECHNOLOGIES CORP) ★
1740 Commerce Way, Paso Robles, CA 93446-3620
Tel (805) 238-2840 *Founded/Ownrshp* 2013
Sales 139.9MM^E *EMP* 500
SIC 3678 3643 5065 Electronic connectors; Connectors & terminals for electrical devices; Connectors, electronic
Prin: Angel Cruz
COO: Kim Lachance
Dir IT: Tim Bergquist
Software D: Lisa Blackburn
Mtls Mgr: Dana B Blakeslee
QI Cn Mgr: Gordon Krueger

D-U-N-S 14-788-2294 IMP/EXP
JOST CHEMICAL CO
8150 Lackland Rd, Saint Louis, MO 63114-4524
Tel (314) 428-4300 *Founded/Ownrshp* 1985
Sales 97.6MM^E *EMP* 200
SIC 2834 2819 Pharmaceutical preparations; Industrial inorganic chemicals
Pr: Jerry L Jost
Mng Dir: Nick Akers
Area Mgr: David Bohnenstiehl
QA Dir: Joel Kruse
IT Man: Howard Ashley
Manager: Sebastien Deloffre
Manager: Jackie Hsiao
Manager: Jerry Lynch

D-U-N-S 01-774-6207 IMP/EXP
JOST INTERNATIONAL CORP
(*Suby of* JOST-WERKE INTERNATIONAL BETEILIGUNGSVERWALTUNG GMBH)
1770 Hayes St, Grand Haven, MI 49417-9428
Tel (616) 846-7700 *Founded/Ownrshp* 2013
Sales 125.0MM *EMP* 424
SIC 3715 Truck trailers
Pr: Lee Brace
**Pr:* Greg Laarman
**VP:* Rich Carroll
VP: Mimi Dew
**VP:* Brian Moynihan
**VP:* Jens Polte
Dir IT: Linda Vaneizenga
IT Man: Linda Van Eizenga
VP Sls: Richard Carroll

D-U-N-S 04-834-1556 IMP/EXP
■ JOSTENS INC
(*Suby of* VISANT CORP) ★
3601 Minnesota Dr Ste 400, Minneapolis, MN 55435-6008
Tel (952) 830-3300 *Founded/Ownrshp* 2004
Sales 1.1MMM^E *EMP* 4,758^E
SIC 3911 2759 2741 Rings, finger: precious metal; Commercial printing; Invitation & stationery printing & engraving; Announcements: engraved; Yearbooks: publishing & printing
VP: Rick Cochran
Bd of Dir: Tagar C Olson
Sr VP: Marjorie Brown
Sr VP: John Larsen
VP: John Bibeault
**VP:* Keith Kugler
**VP:* Patrick Lambert
**VP:* Eric Loring
VP: Craig Rosenberger
Exec: Julie Holman
Dir Soc: Britta Bolm

D-U-N-S 03-349-0640 IMP
■ JOTALY INC
(*Suby of* RICHLINE GROUP INC) ★
1385 Broadway Fl 12, New York, NY 10018-6118
Tel (212) 886-6000 *Founded/Ownrshp* 1981
Sales 101.2MM^E *EMP* 750
SIC 3911 Jewelry, precious metal
Ch Bd: Ofer Azrielant
**VP:* John C Esposito
Dir IT: Fred Poluhovich
MIS Mgr: Marvin Pincus
VP Sls: Scott Lyle
VP Sls: John Peters
Snr Mgr: Michael Milgrom

JOURNAGAN CNSTR & AGGREGATES
See LEO JOURNAGAN CONSTRUCTION CO INC

JOURNAL
See SMALL NEWSPAPER GROUP

D-U-N-S 06-351-1216 IMP
JOURNAL BROADCAST GROUP INC
WSYM-TV
(*Suby of* DESK BC MERGER LLC) ★
720 E Capitol Dr, Milwaukee, WI 53212-1308
Tel (414) 799-9494 *Founded/Ownrshp* 1973
Sales 224.9MM^E *EMP* 1,000
SIC 4833 Television broadcasting stations
Pt: Bob Uecker
Ex VP: Debbie Turner
Ex VP: Steve Wexler
VP: Bill Berra
VP: David Bruce
VP: Dianne Downey
VP: Dominic Fails
VP: Bill Lutzen
VP: Brian McHale
VP: Bob Rosenthal
VP: Andrew Stewart
VP: Jim Thomas
Dir Soc: Molly Fay
Creative D: Doak Breen
Creative D: Walker Foard

D-U-N-S 00-607-7101 IMP/EXP
JOURNAL COMMUNICATIONS INC
333 W State St, Milwaukee, WI 53203-1305
Tel (414) 224-2000 *Founded/Ownrshp* 1882
Sales 428.4MM *EMP* 2,700^E
SIC 4832 4833 2711 2759 4813

D-U-N-S 07-614-3643
JOURNAL COMMUNITY PUBLISHING GROUP INC
(*Suby of* DESK BC MERGER LLC) ★
600 Industrial Dr, Waupaca, WI 54981-8814
Tel (715) 258-8450 *Founded/Ownrshp* 1971
Sales 104.5MM^E *EMP* 1,156
SIC 2741 2711 Shopping news: publishing & printing; Commercial printing & newspaper publishing combined
CEO: Elizabeth Brenner
Pr: David Honan
Exec: Susan Griffin
Genl Mgr: Linda Byars
Off Mgr: Sandy Ebner
Plnt Mgr: Terry Lodewegen

D-U-N-S 07-954-1886
■ JOURNAL MEDIA GROUP INC (WI)
(*Suby of* GANNETT CO INC) ★
333 W State St, Milwaukee, WI 53203-1305
Tel (414) 224-2000 *Founded/Ownrshp* 2015, 2016
Sales 441.0MM *EMP* 3,000^E
Accts Deloitte & Touche Llp Milwau
SIC 2711 Newspapers
Pr: Timothy E Stautberg
CFO: Jason R Graham
VP: Marty V Ozolins

JOURNAL OF BUSINESS
See COWLES PUBLISHING CO

JOURNAL OF CHEMICAL & ENGINEER
See AMERICAN CHEMICAL SOCIETY

D-U-N-S 15-411-8400
JOURNAL REGISTER CO
5 Hanover Sq Fl 25, New York, NY 10004-4008
Tel (212) 257-7212 *Founded/Ownrshp* 2013
Sales 828.3MM^E *EMP* 4,500
SIC 2711 Newspapers, publishing & printing
CEO: John Paton
Ch Bd: James W Hall
Pr: Paul Provost
CFO: Jeff Bairstow
Ex VP: Guy Gilmore
Ex VP: Michael Kuritzkes
Sr VP: William J Higginson
Sr VP: Allen J Mailman
Sr VP: Edward J Yocum Jr
VP: Jerry Bammel
VP: Jared Bean
VP: Eric Lamont Mayberry
VP: Brian McNamara

D-U-N-S 06-351-1224
JOURNAL SENTINEL INC
MILWAUKEE JOURNAL/SENTINEL
(*Suby of* DESK BC MERGER LLC) ★
333 W State St, Milwaukee, WI 53203-1305
Tel (414) 224-2000 *Founded/Ownrshp* 2015
Sales 387.4MM^E *EMP* 1,820
SIC 2711 Commercial printing & newspaper publishing combined
Pr: Tim Stautberg
**COO:* Elizabeth Brenner
**CFO:* Ken McNamee
**Sr VP:* Jason Graham
VP: Daryl Hively
VP: Martin Kaiser
VP: William M Kaiser
VP: Dani Longoria
**VP:* Marty Ozolins
Exec: Andre Fernandez
IT Man: Donna Riehle
Board of Directors: Paul Bonaiuto, Gerry Hinkley, W Martin Kaiser, Douglas Kiel, Thomas Massopust, David Meissner, George Stanley

D-U-N-S 07-199-3568
JOURNEY CHURCH COLORADO
8237 S Holly St Ste C, Centennial, CO 80122-4027
Tel (303) 921-5595 *Founded/Ownrshp* 2004
Sales 90.0MM *EMP* 9
SIC 8661 Churches, temples & shrines

D-U-N-S 11-777-5606
JOURNEYMAN CONSTRUCTION INC
7701 N Lamar Blvd Ste 100, Austin, TX 78752-1012
Tel (512) 247-7000 *Founded/Ownrshp* 2000
Sales 134.8MM *EMP* 55^E
Accts Kemp & Stich Pc San Antonio
SIC 1542 Commercial & office building contractors
Pr: Sam Kumar
Dir Risk M: David Gregorcyk

JOURNEYS KIDZ
See GENESCO INC

D-U-N-S 15-355-0793 IMP/EXP
▲ JOY GLOBAL INC
100 E Wisconsin Ave # 2780, Milwaukee, WI 53202-4127
Tel (414) 319-8500 *Founded/Ownrshp* 1884
Sales 2.3MMM *EMP* 15,400
Tkr Sym JOY *Exch* NYS
SIC 3532 Mining machinery; Drills & drilling equipment, mining (except oil & gas); Feeders, ore & aggregate
Pr: Edward L Doheny II
**Ch Bd:* John Nils Hanson
Pr: Michael W Sutherlin
COO: Randal W Baker
COO: Chuck Bruskin
CFO: James M Sullivan
Treas: Barbara Bolens
Chf Mktg O: Doug Blom
Ex VP: James A Chokey
Ex VP: John Fons
Ex VP: Sean D Major
Ex VP: Johannes S Maritz
VP: Matthew S Kulasa
VP: Greg Ladzinski
VP: Neil Massey
VP: Jeff Schmaling
VP: Mark Shaver
VP: Andre Williams
Exec: Val Lahti

D-U-N-S 00-731-7480 IMP
■ JOY GLOBAL LONGVIEW OPERATIONS LLC
(*Suby of* JOY GLOBAL INC) ★
2400 S Macarthur Dr, Longview, TX 75602
Tel (903) 237-7000 *Founded/Ownrshp* 2011
Sales 384.9MM^E *EMP* 2,500
SIC 3532 3533 3312 3531 Trucks (dollies), mining; Loading machines, underground: mobile; Well logging equipment; Drill rigs; Plate, steel; Plate, sheet & strip, except coated products; Construction machinery
Pr: Edward L Dokeny II
**Treas:* Kenneth J Stark
**Sr VP:* Brad C Rogers
**Sr VP:* N Pharr Smith
VP: Blazek Dave
**VP:* James M Sullivan
Sfty Mgr: Billie Porter

D-U-N-S 00-608-2275 IMP/EXP
■ JOY GLOBAL SURFACE MINING INC
(*Suby of* JOY GLOBAL INC) ★
4400 W National Ave, Milwaukee, WI 53214-3639
Tel (414) 671-4400 *Founded/Ownrshp* 1972
Sales 415.7MM^E *EMP* 2,700
SIC 3462 Construction or mining equipment forgings, ferrous
Pr: Mark Readinger
CFO: Donald C Roof
**Treas:* Ken Stark
VP: Pat Bartling
**VP:* John Diclemente
**VP:* Wayne Feasby
**VP:* Eugene Fuhrmann
**VP:* Mark Verdova
IT Man: Robin Pearsick
IT Man: Mark Schmidt

D-U-N-S 17-292-0225 IMP/EXP
■ JOY GLOBAL UNDERGROUND MINING LLC
MINING JOY MACHINERY
(*Suby of* JOY GLOBAL INC) ★
40 Pennwood Pl Ste 100, Warrendale, PA 15086-6526
Tel (724) 779-4500 *Founded/Ownrshp* 1994
Sales 800.7MM^E *EMP* 5,200
SIC 3535 3532 Conveyors & conveying equipment; Drills, bits & similar equipment
Pr: Wayne Hunnell
**Pr:* Michael Sutherlin
VP: Julie Beck
VP: Karina Livshin
**VP:* Michael S Olsen
Mfg Mgr: Chris Delaney
Mfg Mgr: Justin Massey
Plnt Mgr: Eddy Franken
Sls Mgr: Mike Harris
Sls Mgr: Billy Kirkpatrick
Sls Mgr: Wayne Thomas

D-U-N-S 00-891-6736 IMP/EXP
JOYCE LESLIE INC (NY)
186 Paterson Ave Ste 102, East Rutherford, NJ 07073-1837
Tel (201) 804-7800 *Founded/Ownrshp* 1947
Sales 357.8MM^E *EMP* 900
Accts Citrin Cooperman & Company Ll
SIC 3087 Custom compound purchased resins
CEO: Celia Clancy
**CFO:* Peter Left
**Treas:* Hermine Gewirtz
Board of Directors: Joyce Segal, Nancy Shapiro

D-U-N-S 16-136-1613 IMP
JOYCE MEYER MINISTRIES INC
LIFE IN THE WORD
700 Grace Pkwy, Fenton, MO 63026-5390
Tel (636) 349-0303 *Founded/Ownrshp* 1985
Sales 111.0MM *EMP* 537
Accts Stanfield & O Dell Pc Tulsa
SIC 8661 Non-church religious organizations
Pr: Joyce Meyer
CFO: Delanie Truty
Bd of Dir: Paul O Steen
**VP:* David Meyer
CIO: Robert Sanabria
Software D: Chad Singleton

D-U-N-S 96-882-1400
▲ JP ENERGY PARTNERS LP
600 Las Colinas Blvd E # 2000, Irving, TX 75039-5607
Tel (972) 444-0300 *Founded/Ownrshp* 2011
Sales 1.6MMM *EMP* 100^E
Tkr Sym JPEP *Exch* NYS
SIC 1321 Propane (natural) production
CEO: J Patrick Barley
COO: Jeremiah J Ashcroft III
**CFO:* Patrick Welch

D-U-N-S 15-096-9363
JP HOLDING CO INC
4020 W 73rd St, Anderson, IN 46011-9609
Tel (765) 778-6960 *Founded/Ownrshp* 2002
Sales 335.5MM^E *EMP* 800
SIC 4213 Trucking, except local
Pr: John Paugh

JP MORGAN
See JP MORGAN INVESTMENT MANAGEMENT INC

D-U-N-S 79-489-8841
■ JP MORGAN CLEARING CORP
(*Suby of* JP MORGAN SECURITIES LLC) ★
1 Metrotech Ctr N Lbby 4, Brooklyn, NY 11201-3878
Tel (212) 272-1000 *Founded/Ownrshp* 1991
Sales 148.3MM^E *EMP* 2,000
SIC 6289 6211 Exchange clearinghouses, security; Traders, security; Brokers, security
CEO: Michael Minikes
**Ch Bd:* James E Cayne
**COO:* Samuel L Molinaro
**Treas:* John Stacconi
**Ex VP:* Ronald M Hersch
VP: Robert Steinberg
**VP:* Colleen Sullivan
VP: Paul Tarantino
Genl Mgr: Mark Gianchetti
CTO: Paul Brock
IT Man: Alen Kahen

D-U-N-S 96-631-8255
■ JP MORGAN H&Q PRINCIPALS LP
(*Suby of* JPMORGAN CHASE & CO) ★
560 Mission St Fl 2, San Francisco, CA 94105-2915
Tel (415) 315-5000 *Founded/Ownrshp* 1999
Sales 113.4MM^E *EMP* 827
SIC 6211 6799 6282 7389 Security brokers & dealers; Underwriters, security; Investment bankers; Venture capital companies; Investment advisory service; Telephone services
Pt: William R Timken
Pt: Patrick J Allen
Pt: Steven M Machtinger
Pt: David M McAuliffe
Prin: Rupen Dolasia
Prin: Gene Eidenberg
Prin: Chris Hollenbeck

D-U-N-S 14-975-9912 IMP
■ JP MORGAN INVESTMENT MANAGEMENT INC
JP MORGAN
(*Suby of* JPMORGAN CHASE & CO) ★
270 Park Ave Fl 12, New York, NY 10017-7924
Tel (212) 483-2323 *Founded/Ownrshp* 1984
Sales 1.0MMM^E *EMP* 2,000
SIC 6722 Management investment, open-end
CEO: Eve Guernsey
VP: Kevin Abato
VP: Anna Andreeva
VP: Phil Anglim
VP: Rik Belenger
VP: Richard Berg
VP: Nicola Boone
VP: Gaylon Boyd

VP: Brent Chandaria
VP: Craig Demetres
VP: Lori A Deuberry
VP: Jeffrey Dreyfus
VP: Lisa Geffeney
VP: Yaritza N Jordan
VP: Patricia H Matthews
VP: Mary Messer
VP: Michael Pearce
VP: John Pietrunti
VP: Jaime Sadanandan
VP: Ashli B Smith
VP: Tara Torres

D-U-N-S 14-464-7393
■ JP MORGAN SECURITIES LLC
(*Suby of* JPMORGAN CHASE & CO) ★
383 Madison Ave Fl 9, New York, NY 10179-0001
Tel (212) 272-2000 *Founded/Ownrshp* 2010
Sales 1.6MMM^E *EMP* 6,000
SIC 6211 6282 6289 Security brokers & dealers; Underwriters, security; Traders, security; Brokers, security; Investment advisory service; Investment research; Exchange clearinghouses, security
CEO: James Edward Staley
**Pr:* Carlos Hernandez
Pr: Neal Rudowitz
COO: Jeffrey Bernstein
CFO: James Collins
**Treas:* Lisa Fitzgerald
VP: Brian Browne
Mng Dir: John Costango
Mng Dir: Anthony Jaffe
Mng Dir: Thomas Novack

D-U-N-S 03-348-3744
JP OIL CO LLC
JP OIL HOLDINGS
1604 W Pinhook Rd Ste 300, Lafayette, LA 70508-3729
Tel (337) 234-1170 *Founded/Ownrshp* 1975
Sales 1.2MMM^E *EMP* 100
SIC 1311

JP OIL HOLDINGS
See JP OIL CO LLC

D-U-N-S 80-659-6615
JP TURNER & CO LLC
(*Suby of* ARETEC GROUP INC) ★
1 Buckhead Plz 3060, Atlanta, GA 30305
Tel (404) 479-8300 *Founded/Ownrshp* 2014
Sales 112.6MM^E *EMP* 550
SIC 6211 Investment bankers
Pt: Tim McAfee
**Pt:* Bill Mello
**COO:* Dean Vernoia
**Ofcr:* Ed Woll
Ex VP: Mike Bresner
Sr VP: Richard Boatright
Sr VP: Philip Fatta
Sr VP: George Howard
Sr VP: Reed Lengel
Sr VP: Robert Omohundro
VP: Bill Laseter
VP: Jack Leniart
VP: Robert Malone
VP: Herman Mannings
VP: Jim Weaver
Exec: Tony Mowrer

D-U-N-S 06-428-2988
JPB FOUNDATION
9 W 57th St Ste 3800, New York, NY 10019-2701
Tel (212) 364-6266 *Founded/Ownrshp* 2011
Sales 962.3MM *EMP* 3
SIC 8641 Civic social & fraternal associations
Prin: April C Freilich
VP: Dana Bourland

D-U-N-S 05-350-6002
JPC ENTERPRISES INC
JERSEY PAPER PLUS
47 Brunswick Ave, Edison, NJ 08817-2576
Tel (732) 750-1900 *Founded/Ownrshp* 1993
Sales 97.2MM^E *EMP* 95
SIC 5113 Industrial & personal service paper; Bags, paper & disposable plastic; Boxes, paperboard & disposable plastic; Towels, paper
CEO: Steven Tabak
**Ch:* Joseph Tabak
VP: Steve Halper
Sales Asso: David Lerman

D-U-N-S 07-947-8422
■ JPHI HOLDINGS INC
(*Suby of* JASON INDUSTRIES INC) ★
411 E Wisconsin Ave, Milwaukee, WI 53202-4461
Tel (414) 277-9445 *Founded/Ownrshp* 2014
Sales 700.0MM^E *EMP* 3,500^E
SIC 3465 2297 3625 3469 3844 3443 Moldings or trim, automobile: stamped metal; Nonwoven fabrics; Noise control equipment; Metal stampings; Irradiation equipment; Boilers: industrial, power, or marine

D-U-N-S 02-233-6130
JPI APARTMENT CONSTRUCTION LP
600 Las Colinas Blvd E # 1800, Irving, TX 75039-5648
Tel (972) 556-1700 *Founded/Ownrshp* 1997
Sales 168.8MM^E *EMP* 1,170
SIC 1522 Apartment building construction
Pt: J Frank Miller III
CIO: Tom Bumpass

D-U-N-S 95-839-5410
JPI INVESTMENT CO LP
J P I LEASING
600 Las Colinas Blvd E # 1800, Irving, TX 75039-5648
Tel (972) 556-1700 *Founded/Ownrshp* 1991
Sales 181.8MM^E *EMP* 1,200
SIC 6552 Subdividers & developers
Prin: Bobby Page
CEO: J Frank Miller III

D-U-N-S 01-947-3763
JPI LIFESTYLE APARTMENT COMMUNITIES LP
600 Las Colinas Blvd E, Irving, TX 75039-5648
Tel (972) 556-1700 *Founded/Ownrshp* 1997
Sales 33.1MM^E *EMP* 1,200
SIC 6513 6552 Apartment building operators; Land subdividers & developers, residential
Mng Pt: J Frank Miller III
Genl Pt: Jpi I LP
Pt: GE Capital
VP: Amy Luce

D-U-N-S 13-186-8841
JPI MANAGEMENT LLC
JPI MANAGEMENT SERVICES
600 Las Colinas Blvd E, Irving, TX 75039-5648
Tel (972) 556-1700 *Founded/Ownrshp* 2009
Sales 30.6MM^E *EMP* 1,150
SIC 8741 Management services

JPI MANAGEMENT SERVICES
See JPI MANAGEMENT LLC

JPM
See JAMES M PLEASANTS CO INC

D-U-N-S 78-734-9021
■ JPMORGAN CAPITAL CORP
(*Suby of* BANC ONE FINANCIAL LLC) ★
55 W Monroe St, Chicago, IL 60603-5001
Tel (614) 248-5800 *Founded/Ownrshp* 1996
Sales 54.2MM^E *EMP* 2,368^E
SIC 8748 6726 Business consulting; Investment offices
Prin: Kristie McNab

D-U-N-S 04-767-5947
▲ JPMORGAN CHASE & CO
270 Park Ave Fl 38, New York, NY 10017-2014
Tel (212) 270-6000 *Founded/Ownrshp* 1968
Sales NA *EMP* 234,598^E
Tkr Sym JPM *Exch* NYS
SIC 6021 6211 6162 6141 National commercial banks; Security brokers & dealers; Mortgage bankers & correspondents; Automobile loans, including insurance; Financing: automobiles, furniture, etc., not a deposit bank
Ch Bd: James Dimon
Pr: Sophia Aceret
Pr: Joseph Andre
Pr: Ameen Budhwani
Pr: Antonio Cordero
Pr: Paul Davenport
Pr: Rome Del Rosario
Pr: Ernie Demetriades
Pr: Geri Dewitt
Pr: James Frost
Pr: Bridget Garcia
Pr: Jarrod Holt
Pr: Naveen Krishnamurthy
Pr: Pamela Lee
Pr: Sara Manfro
Pr: Tony Martin
Pr: Matt Messersmith
Pr: Ajay Nagrani
Pr: Myrisia Polohan
Pr: David Poon
Pr: Girish Purswani
Board of Directors: Lee R Raymond, Linda B Bammann, William C Weldon, James A Bell, Crandall C Bowles, Stephen B Burke, Todd A Combs, James S Crown, Timothy P Flynn, Laban P Jackson Jr, Michael A Neal

D-U-N-S 00-698-1831 IMP/EXP
■ JPMORGAN CHASE BANK NATIONAL ASSOCIATION
(*Suby of* JPMORGAN CHASE & CO) ★
1111 Polaris Pkwy, Columbus, OH 43240-2050
Tel (614) 436-3055 *Founded/Ownrshp* 1824
Sales NA *EMP* 170,538
Accts Federal Deposit Insurance Corp
SIC 6022 6099 6799 6211 6162 7389 State commercial banks; Travelers' checks issuance; Safe deposit companies; Real estate investors, except property operators; Investment bankers; Mortgage bankers; Credit card service
Ch Bd: James Dimon
**Pr:* Sean Friedman
Ofcr: Mercy Borjas
Assoc VP: Ed Eppick
Assoc VP: Megan Franzen
Assoc VP: Joe Gutman
Sr VP: Dave Cohen
Sr VP: Christopher Henry
Sr VP: Bradly Isbell
Sr VP: Larry Reccoppa
VP: Kristy Blue
VP: Vicki Cole
VP: Jim Defillippo
VP: Jennifer Elliott
VP: Anthony Galley
VP: Matthew W Gilligan
VP: Elizabeth Hogan
VP: Yardise Jones
VP: Ariel Lopez
VP: Shaney Lynde
VP: Sarah Merkey

D-U-N-S 96-459-6857
JPMORGAN CHASE VEBA TRUST FOR RETIREE
1 Chase Manhattan Plz, New York, NY 10005-1401
Tel (212) 552-2992 *Founded/Ownrshp* 2010
Sales 87.4MM *EMP* 28^E
SIC 6733 Trusts, except educational, religious, charity: management

D-U-N-S 79-871-8367
■ JPMORGAN INVESTMENT ADVISORS INC
(*Suby of* JPMORGAN CHASE & CO) ★
1111 Polaris Pkwy, Columbus, OH 43240-2031
Tel (614) 248-5800 *Founded/Ownrshp* 2005
Sales 104.5MM^E *EMP* 650
SIC 6282 Investment advisory service
Pr: David J Kundert

D-U-N-S 18-974-0608 IMP/EXP
■ JPS COMPOSITE MATERIALS CORP
JPS GLASS
(*Suby of* JPS INDUSTRIES INC) ★
2200 S Murray Ave, Anderson, SC 29624-3139
Tel (864) 836-8011 *Founded/Ownrshp* 1988
Sales 114.9MM^E *EMP* 325^E
SIC 3231 Products of purchased glass
Pr: M Gary Wallace
**VP:* Donald R Burnette
**VP:* Dieter R Wachter
IT Man: Brian Green
Tech Mgr: Mark Anderson
Sfty Mgr: Donnie Richey
Plnt Mgr: Donald Gunter
Plnt Mgr: Wes Young

JPS GLASS
See JPS COMPOSITE MATERIALS CORP

D-U-N-S 18-724-2797 IMP/EXP
■ JPS INDUSTRIES INC
(*Suby of* HANDY & HARMAN GROUP LTD) ★
2200 S Murray Ave, Anderson, SC 29624-3139
Tel (864) 239-3900 *Founded/Ownrshp* 2015
Sales 123.2MM^E *EMP* 900
SIC 2221 3081 Fiberglass fabrics; Unsupported plastics film & sheet
Pr: Mikel H Williams
**CFO:* Charles R Tutterow
VP: William Jackson
Tech Mgr: Mark Anderson
Plnt Mgr: Gary M Wallace

D-U-N-S 10-289-8335
JR ABBOTT CONSTRUCTION INC
3408 1st Ave S Ste 101, Seattle, WA 98134-1805
Tel (206) 467-8500 *Founded/Ownrshp* 1983
Sales 86.3MM^E *EMP* 144
Accts Berntson Porter And Co Pllc
SIC 1542 Commercial & office building, new construction; Commercial & office buildings, renovation & repair
Pr: John P McGowan
**CFO:* Mark C Seaman
**VP:* Doug J Klein
**VP:* Wendy P Newman
**VP:* Robert M Robertson
Exec: Denise Hubbard
CTO: Pete Ophoven
IT Man: Joel Hagemeyer
IT Man: Christine Mayes
Sfty Mgr: Ron Nelson
Snr PM: Tim Strand

D-U-N-S 02-103-9607 IMP
JR AUTOMATION TECHNOLOGIES LLC
EPOCH ROBOTICS
(*Suby of* JR TECHNOLOGY GROUP LLC) ★
13365 Tyler St, Holland, MI 49424-9421
Tel (616) 399-2168 *Founded/Ownrshp* 2004, 2015
Sales 200.0MM *EMP* 850^E
SIC 3549 Assembly machines, including robotic
Co-CEO: Bryan Jones
**CFO:* Barry Kohn
**Co-CEO:* Scot Lindemann

D-U-N-S 15-270-8244
JR DAVIS CONSTRUCTION CO INC
210 S Hoagland Blvd, Kissimmee, FL 34741-4534
Tel (407) 870-0066 *Founded/Ownrshp* 1985
Sales 109.4MM^E *EMP* 400
SIC 1629 1521 Land preparation construction; Land clearing contractor; Single-family housing construction
Pr: James B J Davis
**Treas:* Kimberly Buccellato
**Sec:* Tama Davis
Genl Mgr: Glenn Kelley

D-U-N-S 00-683-7165
JR FILANC CONSTRUCTION CO INC (CA)
740 N Andreasen Dr, Escondido, CA 92029-1414
Tel (760) 941-7130 *Founded/Ownrshp* 1952
Sales 137.2MM^E *EMP* 200
SIC 1623 1629 Pumping station construction; Waste water & sewage treatment plant construction
CEO: Mark E Filanc
**Pr:* Harry S Cosmos
**CFO:* Kevin Elliotts
**VP:* Vincent L Diaz

D-U-N-S 04-931-1673
JR MC DADE CO INC
J.R. MCDADE
1102 N 21st Ave, Phoenix, AZ 85009-3723
Tel (602) 258-7134 *Founded/Ownrshp* 1959
Sales 90.5MM^E *EMP* 170
SIC 5023 1752 Carpets; Carpet laying
Pr: Jack McDade

J.R. MCDADE
See JR MC DADE CO INC

D-U-N-S 00-907-3503 IMP/EXP
JR SIMPLOT CO
SIMPLOT WESTERN STOCKMEN'S
999 W Main St Ste 1300, Boise, ID 83702-9009
Tel (208) 336-2110 *Founded/Ownrshp* 1923
Sales 4.2MMM^E *EMP* 9,970
SIC 0211 2879 2037 2874 2873 Beef cattle feedlots; Agricultural chemicals; Potato products, quick frozen & cold pack; Vegetables, quick frozen & cold pack, excl. potato products; Fruits, quick frozen & cold pack (frozen); Phosphatic fertilizers; Ammonium phosphate; Nitrogenous fertilizers
Ch: Scott Simplot
**Pr:* William Whitacre
**CFO:* Annette Elg
CFO: Dennis Mogensen
**Treas:* Amber Post
Sr Cor Off: Maureen Duffy
Bd of Dir: David McDermott
Ex VP: Janss Franden
Sr VP: Alan Kahn
**Sr VP:* Garrett Lofto
**Sr VP:* Mark McKellar
**Sr VP:* Terry T Uhling
VP: James Crawford
VP: Roger Park
VP: Nick Spardy
VP: Stephen Vernon
Board of Directors: Stephen A Beebe, A Dale Dunn, Richard M Hormaechea, Robert J Lane, Joseph Marshall, Debbie McDonald, Gay C Simplot, J E Simplot, Scott R Simplot

D-U-N-S 07-978-3699
JR TECHNOLOGY GROUP LLC
13365 Tyler St, Holland, MI 49424-9421
Tel (616) 399-2168 *Founded/Ownrshp* 2015
Sales 225.0MM^E *EMP* 1,371^E
SIC 3549 Assembly machines, including robotic
Co-CEO: Bryan Jones
**CFO:* Barry Kohn
**Co-CEO:* Scot Lindemann

D-U-N-S 04-007-5723 IMP/EXP
JRD HOLDINGS INC
(*Suby of* JETRO CASH & CARRY) ★
1524 132nd St, College Point, NY 11356-2440
Tel (718) 762-8700 *Founded/Ownrshp* 1990
Sales 1.9MMM^E *EMP* 1,500
SIC 5141 5142 5147 5181 5194 Groceries, general line; Packaged frozen goods; Meats, fresh; Beer & other fermented malt liquors; Tobacco & tobacco products
Pr: Stanley Fleishman
**CFO:* Brian Emmert
**VP:* Richard Kirshner
CIO: Richard Grossman
Netwrk Mgr: Ravi Sahni
Opers Mgr: Russell Depaolis

JRJR NETWORKS
See JRJR33 INC

D-U-N-S 00-892-3196
▲ JRJR33 INC
JRJR NETWORKS
2950 N Harwood St Fl 22, Dallas, TX 75201-1034
Tel (469) 913-4115 *Founded/Ownrshp* 2007
Sales 113.9MM *EMP* 582
Tkr Sym JRJR *Exch* ASE
SIC 5499 5023 5122 2721 5251 Gourmet food stores; Spices & herbs; Decorative home furnishings & supplies; Cosmetics; Magazines: publishing & printing; Tools, hand
Ch Bd: John P Rochon
CFO: John P Walker
**V Ch Bd:* John Rochon Jr
Board of Directors: John W Bickel, Michael Bishop, Roy G C Damary, Bernard Ivaldi, William H Randall, Julie Rasmussen

D-U-N-S 85-944-3025
JRM CONSTRUCTION MANAGEMENT LLC
242 W 36th St Rm 901, New York, NY 10018-8957
Tel (212) 545-0500 *Founded/Ownrshp* 2007
Sales 155.0MM^E *EMP* 200
SIC 1542 Commercial & office building, new construction

D-U-N-S 05-427-7298
JRN INC (TN)
KFC
209 W 7th St, Columbia, TN 38401-3233
Tel (931) 381-3000 *Founded/Ownrshp* 1971
Sales 133.6MM^E *EMP* 4,000
SIC 5812

D-U-N-S 79-110-0944
JRS HOLDING INC
20445 W Capitol Dr, Brookfield, WI 53045-2745
Tel (262) 781-2626 *Founded/Ownrshp* 1985
Sales 106.3MM^E *EMP* 250
SIC 5511 Automobiles, new & used
Pr: John R Safro
**Pr:* Martin Thomas
**VP:* James Tessmer

D-U-N-S 15-380-2277 IMP/EXP
JS INTERNATIONAL SHIPPING CORP
JSI SHIPPING
1535 Rollins Rd Ste B, Burlingame, CA 94010-2305
Tel (650) 697-3963 *Founded/Ownrshp* 1986
Sales 214.2MM^E *EMP* 1,500
SIC 4731 Freight forwarding; Customhouse brokers
CEO: James G Cullen
VP: Scott French
VP: Bobby Solis
VP: Will Waller
Rgnl Mgr: Mike Singh
Brnch Mgr: Yvonne Angelo
Brnch Mgr: Jeff Beck
Brnch Mgr: Ramesh Raman
Genl Mgr: Richard Bryant
Genl Mgr: James Lin
IT Man: Izhar Burica

D-U-N-S 60-924-4793
JS VENTURES INC
APPLEBEE'S
2400 N Woodlawn Blvd # 230, Wichita, KS 67220-3989
Tel (316) 683-7799 *Founded/Ownrshp* 1989
Sales 57.3MM^E *EMP* 2,000
SIC 5812 Restaurant, family: chain
Pr: James Stevens

D-U-N-S 03-028-5265
JS WEST & COMPANIES
501 9th St, Modesto, CA 95354-3420
Tel (209) 577-3221 *Founded/Ownrshp* 1946
Sales 109.5MM^E *EMP* 300^E
SIC 5172 5211 5251 0723 5499 Gases, liquefied petroleum (propane); Lumber & other building materials; Lumber products; Hardware; Feed milling custom services; Eggs & poultry
CEO: Eric Benson

JSC
See JACKSON SUPPLY CO

D-U-N-S 14-572-9117
JSI RESEARCH AND TRAINING INSTITUTE INC
44 Farnsworth St Fl 7, Boston, MA 02210-1206
Tel (617) 482-9485 *Founded/Ownrshp* 1979
Sales 270.6MM *EMP* 135E
Accts Norman R Fougere Jr Cpa Dux
SIC 8742 Management consulting services
Pr: Joel H Lamstein
**COO:* Alexander K Baker
VP: Pat Fairchild
**VP:* Theo Lippeveld
Genl Mgr: Robert Schlink
IT Man: Lori Kiel
Tech Mgr: Wayne Zafft

JSI SHIPPING
See JS INTERNATIONAL SHIPPING CORP

D-U-N-S 05-366-8729 IMP/EXP
JSJ CORP
700 Robbins Rd, Grand Haven, MI 49417-2603
Tel (616) 842-6350 *Founded/Ownrshp* 1919
Sales 564.0MME *EMP* 2,568
SIC 3465 3469 3366 3089 3086 2522 Automotive stampings; Metal stampings; Stamping metal for the trade; Castings (except die): brass; Castings (except die): bronze; Injection molded finished plastic products; Plastics foam products; Chairs, office: padded or plain, except wood; Desks, office: except wood
Prin: Nelson Jacobson
**Pr:* Nelson Jacobson
**COO:* Barry Lemay
**COO:* Thomas J Rizzi
**CFO:* Martin Jennings
**CFO:* Michael D Metzger
**Ex VP:* Erick P Johnson
VP: Nelson C Jacobson
**VP:* Timothy Liang
**VP:* Jim Nutt
**VP:* Edward L Ozark

D-U-N-S 10-107-0709 IMP/EXP
JSJ FURNITURE CORP
IZZY
(*Suby of* JSJ CORP) ★
17237 Van Wagoner Rd, Spring Lake, MI 49456-9702
Tel (616) 847-6534 *Founded/Ownrshp* 2000
Sales 153.0MME *EMP* 710E
SIC 2521 Wood office furniture
CEO: Chuck Saylor
**Pr:* Nancy Dallinger
**Pr:* Rick Glasser
**Pr:* Gregg Masenthin
**COO:* Joan Hill
COO: Todd Robart
**CFO:* Eric Jorgensen
**VP:* Dan Vukcevich
Opers Mgr: Michael Sheridan
S&M/VP: Scott Reus

D-U-N-S 02-945-8197 IMP
JST CORP
(*Suby of* J.S.T. MFG. CO.,LTD.)
1957 S Lakeside Dr, Waukegan, IL 60085-8331
Tel (847) 473-1957 *Founded/Ownrshp* 1981
Sales 86.6MME *EMP* 500
SIC 5065 Connectors, electronic
Ch Bd: Atsuhiro Takahashi

D-U-N-S 19-287-4592
JST ENTERPRISES
5120 Summerhill Rd, Texarkana, TX 75503-1824
Tel (903) 794-3743 *Founded/Ownrshp* 1990
Sales 25.0MM *EMP* 1,000E
SIC 8741 Mexican restaurant
Pr: Joe Thomson
Treas: Gwen Dean

JSU
See JACKSON STATE UNIVERSITY

D-U-N-S 17-597-3163 IMP/EXP
JSW STEEL (USA) INC
J S W
(*Suby of* JSW STEEL LIMITED)
5200 E Mckinney Rd # 110, Baytown, TX 77523-8291
Tel (281) 383-2525 *Founded/Ownrshp* 2007
Sales 365.6MM *EMP* 696
Accts Braj Aggarwal Cpa Pc Hicksv
SIC 3317 3312 Steel pipe & tubes; Blast furnaces & steel mills; Tubes, steel & iron
Pr: Michael Fitch
**Sec:* Krishnamurty Karra
VP: Jason Jamieson
**VP:* Daniel E Meinzen
VP Sls: Charles Bartholomew
Manager: Joseph Dagro
Sales Asso: Terry Matney

D-U-N-S 79-693-5856
■ **JT CO INC**
(*Suby of* TOOTSIE ROLL INDUSTRIES INC) ★
7401 S Cicero Ave, Chicago, IL 60629-5818
Tel (773) 838-3400 *Founded/Ownrshp* 2013
Sales 16.4MME *EMP* 1,000
SIC 7389 Personal service agents, brokers & bureaus
Pr: Ellen R Gordon

D-U-N-S 87-289-4886
JT MAGEN & CO INC
44 W 28th St Fl 11, New York, NY 10001-4212
Tel (212) 790-4200 *Founded/Ownrshp* 1992
Sales 171.5MME *EMP* 150
SIC 1542 Nonresidential construction
CEO: Maurice Regan
**CFO:* Steven M Mount
Snr PM: Nick Parisi

D-U-N-S 07-838-1037
JT PACKARD LLC
275 Investment Ct, Verona, WI 53593-8787
Tel (800) 972-9778 *Founded/Ownrshp* 2002
Sales 322.8MME *EMP* 230
SIC 4911 Distribution, electric power

D-U-N-S 10-180-3963 IMP/EXP
JT SHANNON LUMBER CO INC
SHAMROCK PLANK FLOORING
2200 Cole Rd, Horn Lake, MS 38637-2300
Tel (662) 393-3765 *Founded/Ownrshp* 1982
Sales 127.4MME *EMP* 270
SIC 5031 3559 2421 Lumber: rough, dressed & finished; Kilns, lumber; Planing mills
CEO: Jack T Shannon Jr
COO: Jim Garrard
Mktg Mgr: Ryan Jones

D-U-N-S 15-809-1848
JT3 LLC
JOINT TEST TACTICS & TRAINING
821 Grier Dr, Las Vegas, NV 89119-3717
Tel (702) 492-2100 *Founded/Ownrshp* 2000
Sales 356.0MME *EMP* 2,000
SIC 8711 Engineering services
CFO: Daniel Wild
Sr VP: Jarrett Jordan
VP: Ralph Decker
VP: Matt Densmore
VP: Reynaldo Garza
VP: Paul Krause
Snr Sftwr: Dan Laforce

D-U-N-S 07-282-3693
JTB AMERICAS LTD
(*Suby of* JTB CORP.)
19700 Mariner Ave, Torrance, CA 90503-1648
Tel (310) 303-3750 *Founded/Ownrshp* 1991
Sales 140.2MME *EMP* 1,356
SIC 4724 Travel agencies
Pr: Tsuneo Irita

D-U-N-S 62-664-1815
JTD HEALTH SYSTEMS INC
SPEECH CENTER
200 Saint Clair Ave, Saint Marys, OH 45885-2400
Tel (419) 394-3335 *Founded/Ownrshp* 1953
Sales 90.0MM *EMP* 600
Accts Ernst & Young Llp Dayton Oh
SIC 8741 Hospital management
**Treas:* Jeff Vossler

D-U-N-S 61-531-0216 IMP/EXP
JTEKT AUTOMOTIVE TENNESSEE-MORRISTOWN INC
(*Suby of* JTEKT NORTH AMERICA INC) ★
5932 Commerce Blvd, Morristown, TN 37814-1051
Tel (423) 585-2544 *Founded/Ownrshp* 1989
Sales 99.9MME *EMP* 545E
SIC 3714 Power steering equipment, motor vehicle
Ch Bd: Ike Funahashi
**Pr:* Max Biery
CIO: Sandra Graves

D-U-N-S 80-827-6328 IMP/EXP
JTEKT AUTOMOTIVE TEXAS LP
(*Suby of* JTEKT NORTH AMERICA INC) ★
4400 Sterilite Dr, Ennis, TX 75119-7816
Tel (972) 878-1800 *Founded/Ownrshp* 2004
Sales 86.9MME *EMP* 405E
SIC 3714 Motor vehicle steering systems & parts
Pr: Murray Durham

D-U-N-S 07-372-3868 IMP/EXP
JTEKT NORTH AMERICA CORP
KOYO BEARINGS
(*Suby of* JTEKT CORPORATION)
29570 Clemens Rd, Westlake, OH 44145-1007
Tel (440) 835-1000 *Founded/Ownrshp* 1973
Sales 782.1MME *EMP* 1,907
SIC 5085 3562 Industrial supplies; Ball & roller bearings
CEO: Hirouki Kaijima
**COO:* Mike Davidson
COO: Sam Holt
**COO:* Ken Hopkins
**Sr VP:* Gary Bourque
**Sr VP:* James Gregory
**Sr VP:* Christelle Orzan
Assoc Dir: Emmanuel Pedersen
Prd Mgr: Michael Nienstedt
Sls Dir: Frank Bush
Sls Mgr: Dale Neumann

D-U-N-S 07-272-0399
JTEKT NORTH AMERICA INC
(*Suby of* JTEKT CORPORATION)
47771 Halyard Dr, Plymouth, MI 48170-2479
Tel (734) 454-1500 *Founded/Ownrshp* 1988
Sales 284.4MME *EMP* 1,000
SIC 5013 Motor vehicle supplies & new parts
Pr: Yoshio Tsuji
**VP:* Charles Brandt
Genl Mgr: Ben Simpson
Ql Cn Mgr: Andrea Jamieson

D-U-N-S 82-777-4225
■ **JTL GROUP INC**
KNIFE RIVER-BILLINGS
(*Suby of* KNIFE RIVER COAL MINING) ★
4014 Hesper Rd, Billings, MT 59106-3352
Tel (406) 655-2010 *Founded/Ownrshp* 1999
Sales 304.0MME *EMP* 2,200
SIC 1611 Highway & street construction
Pr: David K Zinke
**Treas:* Nancy K Christenson
**VP:* Terry Haven

JTM FOOD GROUP
See JTM PROVISIONS CO INC

D-U-N-S 01-762-5856
JTM PROVISIONS CO INC (OH)
JTM FOOD GROUP
200 Sales Ave, Harrison, OH 45030-1485
Tel (513) 367-4900 *Founded/Ownrshp* 1963
Sales 154.8MM *EMP* 350
SIC 2013 2051 Frozen meats from purchased meat; Buns, bread type: fresh or frozen
Pr: Anthony A Maas
VP: Scott Bonta
VP: Jamie Cronen
VP: Jeff Jung
**VP:* Jerome Maas
**VP:* John Maas Jr
**VP:* Joseph Maas
Manager: Steve Osuna
Plnt Mgr: Steve Chaney
Mktg Mgr: Jeff Dickman
Mktg Mgr: Ryan Kutzleb

D-U-N-S 05-436-4476 IMP
JTS ENTERPRISES OF TAMPA LIMITED (FL)
MCDONALD'S
4908 W Nassau St, Tampa, FL 33607-3827
Tel (813) 287-2231 *Founded/Ownrshp* 1958, 2005
Sales 134.7MME *EMP* 3,500
SIC 5812 Fast-food restaurant, chain
Genl Pt: Blake Casper
Pt: Allison Casper Adams
VP: Brian Wischnack
VP Opers: Rudy Garcia
VP Mktg: Bob Conigliaro
Sales Asso: Claudia Jacobo

JT'S LUMBER COMPANY
See RIVERHEAD BUILDING SUPPLY CORP

JUAREZ SALONS & SPAS
See GJS HOLDING LLC

D-U-N-S 06-926-3643 IMP
JUBILANT HOLLISTERSTIER LLC
HOLLISTER-STIER LABORATORIES
(*Suby of* JUBILANT LIFE SCIENCES LIMITED)
3525 N Regal St, Spokane, WA 99207-5788
Tel (509) 482-4945 *Founded/Ownrshp* 1999
Sales 151.8MME *EMP* 265
SIC 2834 Pharmaceutical preparations
CFO: Richard Freeman
**CEO:* Marcelo Morales
Sr VP: Bradley Larson
**VP:* Curtis L Gingles
**VP:* Jeffrey K Milligan
**VP:* Rabindra Sahoo
Genl Mgr: Sarah Hoyt
CIO: Jeff Milligan
QA Dir: Linda Rendon
Dir IT: Monica Thakrar
IT Man: Hunter Dennis

D-U-N-S 84-499-6637
JUBILEE CENTER
SAINT VINCENT'S
10330 N Meridian St, Indianapolis, IN 46290-1024
Tel (317) 415-5300 *Founded/Ownrshp* 1985
Sales 210.5MM *EMP* 15
SIC 8748 Educational consultant
Ex Dir: Izera McAfee-Day

D-U-N-S 02-772-3097
JUBITZ CORP
JUBITZ TRAVEL CENTER
33 Ne Middlefield Rd, Portland, OR 97211-1277
Tel (503) 283-1111 *Founded/Ownrshp* 1952
Sales 199.0MM *EMP* 230E
Accts Fordham Goodfellow Llp Hills
SIC 5541 4789 5014 7011 Filling stations, gasoline; Truck stops; Cargo loading & unloading services; Automobile tires & tubes; Hotels
Pr: Frederick D Jubitz
**CFO:* Rich Jansen
**VP:* Mark G Gram
**VP:* Victor D Stibolt
Dir IT: Grant Newcombe

JUBITZ TRAVEL CENTER
See JUBITZ CORP

D-U-N-S 07-551-3853
JUDGE GROUP INC
151 S Warner Rd Ste 100, Wayne, PA 19087-2125
Tel (610) 667-7700 *Founded/Ownrshp* 1970
Sales 323.3MM *EMP* 2,450
Accts Kreischer Miller Horsham Pa
SIC 7373 7361 7379 Computer integrated systems design; Executive placement; Computer related consulting services
CEO: Martin Judge Jr
Pr: Brian T Anderson
**Pr:* Bryan Anderson
Pr: Mick Angelichio
Pr: Edward Carmody
Pr: Stephen Green
**Pr:* Gary R Morris
Pr: Khang Nguyen
Pr: Richard W Schnell
Pr: Sanjay Shah
Pr: Raj Singh
COO: Jack Shields
**COO:* Katharine A Wiercinski
**CFO:* Robert G Alessandrini
CFO: Frank Barrett
Bd of Dir: Randolph Angermann
Bd of Dir: James Hahn
Assoc VP: Keith Elliott
Ex VP: Dennis F Judge Jr
Ex VP: Jared Rakes
Sr VP: Janet Harbour

JUDGE'S OFFICE
See COUNTY OF CAMERON

JUDICARY CURTS OF THE STATE LA
See JUDICIARY COURTS OF STATE OF LOUISIANA

JUDICIAL BRANCH OF STATE ARIZ
See JUDICIARY COURTS OF STATE OF ARIZONA

D-U-N-S 36-070-7004
JUDICIAL BRANCH STATE OF CONNECTICUT
(*Suby of* STATE OF CONNECTICUT) ★
231 Capitol Ave, Hartford, CT 06106-1548
Tel (860) 706-5146 *Founded/Ownrshp* 1818
Sales NA *EMP* 2,381
SIC 9211 State courts;
Admn Mgr: Patricia Gargiulo

D-U-N-S 36-070-9414
JUDICIAL COUNCIL OF CALIFORNIA
(*Suby of* STATE OF CALIFORNIA) ★
455 Golden Gate Ave # 1521, San Francisco, CA 94102-3667
Tel (415) 865-4200 *Founded/Ownrshp* 1850
Sales NA *EMP* 19,000
SIC 9211 State courts
Prin: Victoria Henley

D-U-N-S 36-070-8275
JUDICIAL COURTS OF STATE OF ILLINOIS
(*Suby of* STATE OF ILLINOIS) ★
Clerk Supreme Court Bldg, Springfield, IL 62704
Tel (217) 782-2035 *Founded/Ownrshp* 1818
Sales NA *EMP* 2,012
SIC 9111 9211 Governors' offices; Courts

D-U-N-S 36-070-5610
JUDICIARY COURTS OF COMMONWEALTH OF KENTUCKY
(*Suby of* COMMONWEALTH OF KENTUCKY) ★
700 Capital Ave Rm 231, Frankfort, KY 40601-3410
Tel (502) 564-6753 *Founded/Ownrshp* 1975
Sales NA *EMP* 2,700
SIC 9211 State courts;

D-U-N-S 36-070-6345
JUDICIARY COURTS OF COMMONWEALTH OF VIRGINIA
EXECUTIVE SECRETARY
(*Suby of* COMMONWEALTH OF VIRGINIA) ★
100 N 9th St, Richmond, VA 23219-2335
Tel (804) 786-6455 *Founded/Ownrshp* 1788
Sales NA *EMP* 2,485
SIC 9211 State courts;
**Prin:* Rebecca Schmidt

D-U-N-S 36-070-5321
JUDICIARY COURTS OF STATE OF ARIZONA
JUDICIAL BRANCH OF STATE ARIZ
(*Suby of* GOVERNORS OFFICE) ★
1501 W Washington St, Phoenix, AZ 85007-3225
Tel (602) 452-3300 *Founded/Ownrshp* 1863
Sales NA *EMP* 1,500
SIC 9211 State courts;
Ofcr: Don Barks

D-U-N-S 36-070-9893
JUDICIARY COURTS OF STATE OF ARKANSAS
SUPREME COURT CLERK OFFICE
(*Suby of* STATE OF ARKANSAS) ★
625 Marshall St Ste 1100, Little Rock, AR 72201-1021
Tel (501) 682-6849 *Founded/Ownrshp* 1836
Sales NA *EMP* 1,200
SIC 9211 State courts;
Admn Mgr: Debbie Blevins
Admn Mgr: Sheila Brewer
Admn Mgr: Danielle Brown
Admn Mgr: Alicia Christopher
Admn Mgr: Ashley Lackey
Admn Mgr: Brent Rowe
Admn Mgr: Margaret Wilson
Admn Mgr: Gary Wright
Dir IT: Tim Holthoff

D-U-N-S 36-070-9505
JUDICIARY COURTS OF STATE OF COLORADO
COLORADO JUDICIAL DEPARTMENT
(*Suby of* STATE OF COLORADO) ★
1300 N Broadway Ste 1200, Denver, CO 80203-2104
Tel (303) 837-3741 *Founded/Ownrshp* 1876
Sales NA *EMP* 3,500
SIC 9211 State courts;
CEO: Nancy E Rice
Ofcr: Sheila Graves
Ofcr: Fran Jamison
Ofcr: Stephanie Mauth
Ofcr: Byron Mitchell

D-U-N-S 36-070-5149
JUDICIARY COURTS OF STATE OF HAWAII
(*Suby of* STATE OF HAWAII) ★
417 S King St, Honolulu, HI 96813-2943
Tel (808) 539-4700 *Founded/Ownrshp* 1895
Sales NA *EMP* 1,200
SIC 9211 State courts;
Brnch Mgr: Thomas R Kelle

D-U-N-S 36-070-4456
JUDICIARY COURTS OF STATE OF INDIANA
(*Suby of* STATE OF INDIANA) ★
200 W Washington St # 217, Indianapolis, IN 46204-2728
Tel (317) 232-1930 *Founded/Ownrshp* 1816
Sales NA *EMP* 3,201
SIC 9211 State courts;
**CEO:* Brent Dickson

D-U-N-S 36-070-6329
JUDICIARY COURTS OF STATE OF IOWA
IOWA STATE JUDICIAL BRANCH
(*Suby of* STATE OF IOWA) ★
1111 E Court Ave, Des Moines, IA 50319-5003
Tel (515) 281-5241 *Founded/Ownrshp* 1846
Sales NA *EMP* 1,856
SIC 9211 State courts;
Prin: Lewis Lavorato Chf Jus
Ofcr: John Hawkins

D-U-N-S 36-070-5487
JUDICIARY COURTS OF STATE OF KANSAS
(*Suby of* STATE OF KANSAS) ★
301 Sw 10th Ave, Topeka, KS 66612-1500
Tel (785) 296-4873 *Founded/Ownrshp* 1891
Sales NA *EMP* 2,350
SIC 9211

D-U-N-S 36-070-6618
JUDICIARY COURTS OF STATE OF LOUISIANA
JUDICARY CURTS OF THE STATE LA
(*Suby of* STATE OF LOUISIANA) ★
400 Royal St Ste 4200, New Orleans, LA 70130-8102
Tel (504) 310-2300 *Founded/Ownrshp* 1812
Sales NA *EMP* 1,000
SIC 9211 State courts;

Ch: Pascal F Calogero Jr
**Brnch Mgr:* John T Olivier
Genl Mgr: Dejon Stewart

D-U-N-S 36-070-9356
JUDICIARY COURTS OF STATE OF MICHIGAN
(*Suby of* STATE OF MICHIGAN) ★
925 W Ottawa St, Lansing, MI 48915-1741
Tel (517) 373-0120 *Founded/Ownrshp* 1805
Sales NA *EMP* 1,150E
SIC 9211 State courts;
Prin: Robert P Young Jr
Ofcr: Michael Benedict
MIS Dir: Marcus Dobek
Dir IT: Mark Wing

D-U-N-S 36-070-6907
JUDICIARY COURTS OF STATE OF MINNESOTA
(*Suby of* STATE OF MINNESOTA) ★
25 Rev Dr Mlk Jr Blvd, Saint Paul, MN 55155-1500
Tel (651) 297-7650 *Founded/Ownrshp* 1857
Sales NA *EMP* 3,700
SIC 9211 State courts;

D-U-N-S 36-070-9547
JUDICIARY COURTS OF STATE OF MISSOURI
MISSOURI OFFC OF STATE CRT ADM
(*Suby of* STATE OF MISSOURI) ★
207 High St, Jefferson City, MO 65101
Tel (573) 751-4144 *Founded/Ownrshp* 1821
Sales NA *EMP* 1,400
SIC 9211 State courts;

D-U-N-S 36-070-6626
JUDICIARY COURTS OF STATE OF NEVADA
(*Suby of* STATE OF NEVADA) ★
201 S Carson St Ste 201, Carson City, NV 89701-4780
Tel (775) 684-1700 *Founded/Ownrshp* 1861
Sales NA *EMP* 1,051
SIC 9211 State courts;
Bd of Dir: Evie Lancaster
Ofcr: Debra Norvell

D-U-N-S 36-070-8283
JUDICIARY COURTS OF STATE OF NEW JERSEY
MANAGEMENT SERVICES DIVISION
(*Suby of* STATE OF NEW JERSEY) ★
25 Market St, Trenton, NJ 08611-2148
Tel (609) 984-0627 *Founded/Ownrshp* 1787
Sales NA *EMP* 1,699
SIC 9211 State courts;
Genl Mgr: Robert O'Neill

D-U-N-S 36-070-4332
JUDICIARY COURTS OF STATE OF NORTH CAROLINA
ADMINSTRATIVE OFFICE OF COURTS
(*Suby of* STATE OF NORTH CAROLINA) ★
2 E Morgan St, Raleigh, NC 27601-1568
Tel (919) 733-3723 *Founded/Ownrshp* 1789
Sales NA *EMP* 6,711E
SIC 9211 State courts;

D-U-N-S 36-070-5735
JUDICIARY COURTS OF STATE OF OREGON
(*Suby of* STATE OF OREGON) ★
1163 State St, Salem, OR 97301-2562
Tel (503) 986-5555 *Founded/Ownrshp* 1859
Sales NA *EMP* 1,715
SIC 9211 State courts
Prin: Wallace P Carson
VP: Mary M James
Genl Mgr: Susan Love
Genl Mgr: Susan Taylor

D-U-N-S 36-070-5040
JUDICIARY COURTS OF STATE OF TEXAS
SUPREME COURT OF TEXAS
(*Suby of* STATE OF TEXAS) ★
205 W 14th St Ste 600, Austin, TX 78701-1614
Tel (512) 463-1312 *Founded/Ownrshp* 1845
Sales NA *EMP* 1,049
SIC 9211 State courts;

D-U-N-S 36-070-6857
JUDICIARY COURTS OF STATE OF WASHINGTON
(*Suby of* GOVERNORS OFFICE) ★
Temple Of Justice, Olympia, WA 98504-0001
Tel (360) 357-2077 *Founded/Ownrshp* 1889
Sales NA *EMP* 1,586
SIC 9211 State courts;

D-U-N-S 36-070-9091
JUDICIARY COURTS OF STATE OF WEST VIRGINIA
WV SUPREME COURT OF APPEALS
(*Suby of* GOVERNORS OFFICE) ★
State Capital Bldg E100, Charleston, WV 25305
Tel (304) 558-0145 *Founded/Ownrshp* 1863
Sales NA *EMP* 1,172
SIC 9211 State courts;
Board of Directors: Steve Canterbury, Melissa Crawford, Angela Saunders

D-U-N-S 06-725-7329
JUDLAU CONTRACTING INC
(*Suby of* OHL USA INC) ★
2615 Ulmer St, Flushing, NY 11354-1144
Tel (718) 554-2320 *Founded/Ownrshp* 1981
Sales 465.2MM *EMP* 140
SIC 1611 1623 Highway & street paving contractor; Sewer line construction; Water main construction
CEO: Tom Iovino
Exec: John Ventimiglia
Ex Dir: Gustavo Monne
Sfty Mgr: Richard Longenecker
Opers Mgr: Vincent Sefershayan
Opers Mgr: Jorge Silva

Ql Cn Mgr: Mohammed Hasan
Ql Cn Mgr: Paresh Patel

D-U-N-S 02-649-2686 IMP
JUDSON ENTERPRISES INC
K-DESIGNERS
2440 Gold River Rd # 100, Rancho Cordova, CA 95670-6390
Tel (916) 631-9300 *Founded/Ownrshp* 1986
Sales 113.2MME *EMP* 650
SIC 2431 5031 Windows, wood; Windows
Pr: Larry D Judson
**CFO:* Tony Tobia
**VP:* Michael Burgess
**VP:* Brian Vidlock
Off Admin: Lane Black
Opers Mgr: Bryan Stanley
VP Sls: Mike Ferguson
Mktg Dir: Mike Kane
Mktg Dir: Morgan Mitchell
Mktg Dir: Matt Wenninger
Corp Couns: Tony Smith

D-U-N-S 01-054-2637
JUDSON INDEPENDENT SCHOOL DISTRICT
8012 Shin Oak Dr, Live Oak, TX 78233-2413
Tel (210) 945-5100 *Founded/Ownrshp* 1959, 2007
Sales 170.5MME *EMP* 3,500
Accts Abip Pc San Antonio Texas
SIC 8211 Public elementary & secondary schools; High school, junior or senior; Public special education school
CFO: Karen Robb
Ex Dir: Yvette Reyna

JUDSON PARK RETIREMENT
See AMERICAN BAPTIST HOMES OF WASHINGTON INC

D-U-N-S 80-101-1578
■ **JUICE CLUB INC**
JAMBA JUICE
(*Suby of* JAMBA INC) ★
6475 Christie Ave Ste 150, Emeryville, CA 94608-2259
Tel (510) 596-0100 *Founded/Ownrshp* 1991
Sales 492.5MME *EMP* 4,000
SIC 5812 6794 Soft drink stand; Franchises, selling or licensing
CEO: James D White
**CFO:* Donald D Breen
Treas: Erik Mattias
**Chf Mktg O:* Susan Shields
**Sr VP:* Paul Coletta
**Sr VP:* Karen Kelley
VP: Greg Schwartz
VP: Malia Spaulding
Genl Mgr: Norah Haufe
Genl Mgr: Eric Sheehan
Genl Mgr: Amy Sutherland

JUICE DIVISION
See AMERICAN FRUITS AND FLAVORS LLC

D-U-N-S 06-166-1641
JUICE PLUS CO LLC
140 Crescent Dr, Collierville, TN 38017-3374
Tel (901) 850-3000 *Founded/Ownrshp* 1969
Sales 105.3MME *EMP* 220
SIC 5149 Health foods
CEO: A Jay Martin
COO: Paulo Teixeira
CFO: Parker Harness
CFO: Stan Turk
Chf Mktg O: Douglas Arscott
VP: Ron Watkins
CIO: Dennis Wilson

D-U-N-S 07-860-1903
JUILLIARD SCHOOL
60 Lincoln Center Plz, New York, NY 10023-6588
Tel (212) 799-5000 *Founded/Ownrshp* 1905
Sales 131.1MM *EMP* 550
Accts Grant Thornton Llp New York
SIC 8299 7911 5942 8221 Music school; Dramatic school; Professional dancing school; Book stores; Colleges universities & professional schools
Pr: Joseph W Polisi
VP: Elizabeth Hurley
**VP:* Karen Wagner

D-U-N-S 05-463-6182
JULIE VILLA COLLEGE
1525 Greenspring Vly Rd, Stevenson, MD 21153-0641
Tel (410) 486-7000 *Founded/Ownrshp* 2010
Sales 124.9MM *EMP* 24E
SIC 8221 Colleges universities & professional schools
Prin: Kevin J Manning

D-U-N-S 08-043-3695
JUMIO CORP
(*Suby of* JUMIO HOLDINGS INC) ★
268 Lambert Ave, Palo Alto, CA 94306-2216
Tel (650) 424-8545 *Founded/Ownrshp* 2016
Sales 15.0MM *EMP* 1,085
SIC 7371 Custom computer programming services; Computer software development
CEO: Stephen Stuut
**CFO:* Colby Moosman
**Dir Risk M:* Robert Prigge
Genl Couns: James Cook

D-U-N-S 08-043-3700
JUMIO HOLDINGS INC
2711 Centerville Rd # 400, Wilmington, DE 19808-1660
Tel (650) 424-8545 *Founded/Ownrshp* 2016
Sales 27.9MME *EMP* 1,088
SIC 6719 7371 Investment holding companies, except banks; Custom computer programming services; Computer software development
Pr: Eric Byunn
**VP:* Benjamin Cukier

D-U-N-S 07-307-2266
JUNIOR COLLEGE DISTRICT OF METROPOLITAN KANSAS CITY MISSOURI
METROPOLITAN COMMUNITY COLLEGE
3200 Broadway Blvd, Kansas City, MO 64111-2408
Tel (816) 604-1000 *Founded/Ownrshp* 1964
Sales 48.7MM *EMP* 1,450
Accts Bkd Llp Kansas City Mo
SIC 8222 Community college
Ofcr: Adam Welsh
Assoc Dir: Mary Truex
Comm Man: Christina Medina
Mktg Dir: Roger Banbury
Nrsg Dir: Marjorie Thomason
Snr Mgr: Gary Hacker

D-U-N-S 07-199-5963
JUNIOR COLLEGE DISTRICT OF ST LOUIS
ST LOUIS COMMUNITY COLLEGE
300 S Broadway, Saint Louis, MO 63102-2800
Tel (314) 206-2150 *Founded/Ownrshp* 1962
Sales 113.3MME *EMP* 3,900
SIC 8222 Community college
CFO: Carla Chance
Ofcr: Daphne Walker-Thoth
VP: Ashok Agrawal
VP: Carolyn Jackson
VP: Jason McClelland
VP: Patrick Vaughn
VP: Thomas Walker
Ex Dir: Jeff Allen
Off Mgr: Teresa Huether
CIO: John Klimczak
CTO: Kate Baker

D-U-N-S 15-447-9166
■ **JUNIOR FOOD STORES OF WEST FLORIDA INC**
TOM THUMB
(*Suby of* GERBES SPRMKT / KING SOOPERS) ★
619 8th Ave, Crestview, FL 32536-2101
Tel (850) 587-5023 *Founded/Ownrshp* 1961
Sales 296.1MME *EMP* 1,250
SIC 5541 5411 Filling stations, gasoline; Convenience stores, chain
Pr: Mark W Salisbury
**Treas:* Scott M Henderson
**VP:* David Daigle
**VP:* William Mullen

D-U-N-S 60-423-2343
JUNIPER NETWORKS (US) INC
1133 Innovation Way, Sunnyvale, CA 94089-1228
Tel (408) 745-2000 *Founded/Ownrshp* 2015
Sales 185.0MME *EMP* 9,000
SIC 3577 Computer peripheral equipment
CEO: Mitchell Lee Gaynor
**Ch Bd:* Scott Kriens
CFO: Robyn Denholm
CFO: Kenneth Niven

D-U-N-S 94-679-2355 IMP
▲ **JUNIPER NETWORKS INC**
1133 Innovation Way, Sunnyvale, CA 94089-1228
Tel (408) 745-2000 *Founded/Ownrshp* 1996
Sales 4.8MMM *EMP* 9,058
Accts Ernst & Young Llp San Jose
Tkr Sym JNPR *Exch* NYS
SIC 3577 7372 Computer peripheral equipment; Prepackaged software
CEO: Rami Rahim
Ch Bd: Scott Kriens
CFO: Ken Miller
V Ch Bd: Pradeep Sindhu
Chf Cred: Vince Molinaro
Ex VP: Jonathan Davidson
Ex VP: David Yen
Ex VP: David W Yen
Sr VP: Marty Gavin
Sr VP: Daniel Hua
Sr VP: Brian Martin
Sr VP: Brian M Martin
VP: Joe Carson
VP: Parviz Gardner
VP: Lisa Guess
VP: Jason Hsieh
VP: John G Morrison
VP: Paul Obsitnik
VP: Hayley Tabor
Board of Directors: Robert M Calderoni, Gary Daichendt, Kevin Denuccio, Jim Dolce, Mercedes Johnson, Rahul Merchant, William R Stensrud

JUNO LIGHTING GROUP
See JUNO LIGHTING LLC

D-U-N-S 06-036-1276 IMP/EXP
JUNO LIGHTING LLC
JUNO LIGHTING GROUP
1300 S Wolf Rd, Des Plaines, IL 60018-1300
Tel (847) 827-9880 *Founded/Ownrshp* 1983
Sales 228.8MME *EMP* 1,000
SIC 3646 3645

D-U-N-S 87-804-5558
■ **JUPITER HOLDINGS INC**
(*Suby of* NORTHLAND INSURANCE) ★
1285 Northland Dr, Saint Paul, MN 55120-1374
Tel (952) 681-3005 *Founded/Ownrshp* 1993
Sales NA *EMP* 249E
SIC 6331 Fire, marine & casualty insurance & carriers
Ch Bd: Gene G Gopon

D-U-N-S 79-748-0332
JUPITER I LLC
OFFICESCAPES
9900 E 51st Ave, Denver, CO 80238-2430
Tel (303) 574-1115 *Founded/Ownrshp* 1998
Sales 112.8MME *EMP* 160
SIC 5021 Furniture
CFO: Joel Bolgrien
Opers Mgr: Al Mitze
Sales Exec: Sharie Grant
Sales Exec: Robert Sobota
Sls&Mrk Ex: Mary Bloomer
Sls Dir: Pauline Bargell

**Sls Dir:* Dana Good
Sls Mgr: Danna Squires

D-U-N-S 13-150-6958
JUPITER MEDICAL CENTER INC
1210 S Old Dixie Hwy, Jupiter, FL 33458-7205
Tel (561) 747-2234 *Founded/Ownrshp* 1979
Sales 192.8MM *EMP* 1,500
SIC 8062 8051 General medical & surgical hospitals; Skilled nursing care facilities
Ch Bd: Barrie Godown
**Pr:* Seldon Taub MD
COO: Elinor Rose
**COO:* Terri Wentz
**Treas:* Robert E Grogan MD
VP: Peter Gloggner
VP: Judy Magalhaes
**VP:* Thomas Murray MD
**VP:* Cathy Thomson MD
VP: Paula Zalucki
Dir Risk M: Terri Freeman
Dir Lab: Cathy Rogers
Dir Soc: Pamela M Slaski
Dir Rx: Alan Davis

D-U-N-S 07-814-3286
JURUPA UNIFIED SCHOOL DISTRICT
4850 Pedley Rd, Jurupa Valley, CA 92509-3966
Tel (951) 360-4100 *Founded/Ownrshp* 1963
Sales 99.4MME *EMP* 2,000
Accts Nigro & Nigro Pc Merrietta
SIC 8211 Public elementary school; Public junior high school; Public senior high school
**Pr:* Sheryl Schmidt
MIS Dir: Joshua Lewis
Psych: Esther Marquez

D-U-N-S 00-239-7982 IMP/EXP
JUST BORN INC (PA)
JUST BORN QUALITY CONFECTIONS
1300 Stefko Blvd, Bethlehem, PA 18017-6672
Tel (610) 867-7568 *Founded/Ownrshp* 1923
Sales 168.0MME *EMP* 550
SIC 2064 Candy & other confectionery products
Pr: Kevin McElvain
**Pr:* David Yale
**CEO:* Ross J Born
CFO: Ronald J Izewski
**Treas:* Jack M Shaffer
VP: Ron Arnold
VP: George Cinquegrana
VP: Ronald Izewski
VP: Norman G Jungmann
VP: David Stephens
VP: Rob Sweatman

JUST BORN QUALITY CONFECTIONS
See JUST BORN INC

JUST BRAKES
See JBRE LLC

D-U-N-S 07-945-0483
JUST ENERGY (US) CORP
(*Suby of* JUST ENERGY GROUP INC)
5251 Westheimr Rd # 1000, Houston, TX 77056-5414
Tel (713) 850-6784 *Founded/Ownrshp* 2001
Sales 85.7MME *EMP* 495
SIC 3621 4924 Power generators; Natural gas distribution
Pr: Deborah Merril
**Pr:* James Lewis
**CFO:* Beth Summers
**Ex VP:* Jonah Davids

JUST FOR MEN DIV
See JEANJER LLC

D-U-N-S 15-918-9278 IMP/EXP
JUST LIKE SUGAR INC
2020 Pama Ln, Las Vegas, NV 89119-4678
Tel (702) 483-6777 *Founded/Ownrshp* 2003
Sales 184.5MME *EMP* 1,300
SIC 2869 Sweeteners, synthetic
CEO: Mike Silver
**Pr:* Randall W Robirds
**Sec:* Gary L Silver

D-U-N-S 01-208-5403
JUST ONE MORE RESTAURANT CORP
1730 Rhode Island Ave Nw # 900, Washington, DC 20036-3101
Tel (202) 775-7256 *Founded/Ownrshp* 1945
Sales 21.1MME *EMP* 1,000
SIC 5812 5813 Steak restaurant; Bar (drinking places)
VP: Louise Bozzi
**Pr:* James Longo
**Treas:* Bruce Bozzi
Dir IT: Kelly McCardle

D-U-N-S 92-735-0215
JUSTICE AND PUBLIC SAFETY CABINET OF KENTUCKY
(*Suby of* EXECUTIVE OFFICE OF COMMONWEALTH OF KENTUCKY) ★
125 Holmes St Fl 2, Frankfort, KY 40601-2108
Tel (502) 564-7554 *Founded/Ownrshp* 1792
Sales NA *EMP* 4,400
SIC 9229
IT Man: Penny Quatman

JUSTICE BRANDS
See TWEEN BRANDS INC

D-U-N-S 00-410-4061
JUSTICE FAMILY GROUP LLC
101 Main St W, Wht Sphr Spgs, WV 24986-5063
Tel (304) 252-1074 *Founded/Ownrshp* 2009
Sales 96.9MME *EMP* 1,000E
SIC 8741 Management services

JUSTICE HOLDCO
See BURGER KING HOLDCO LLC

D-U-N-S 78-771-5051 IMP
■ JUSTIN BRANDS INC
JUSTIN ORIGINAL WORK BOOT
(*Suby of* ACME BRICK) ★
610 W Daggett Ave, Fort Worth, TX 76104-1103
Tel (817) 332-4385 *Founded/Ownrshp* 1991
Sales 97.0MM^E *EMP* 1,035
SIC 3144 3143 3149 Boots, canvas or leather: women's; Boots, dress or casual: men's; Work shoes, men's; Children's footwear, except athletic
Ch Bd: Randy Watson
**Pr:* Jaime Morgan
**CFO:* Herbert Beckwith Jr
**Sr VP:* Larry Nelson
**VP:* Lisa Lankes
VP: Scott C Milden
**VP:* Chuck Smallbach
VP: Chris Smith
VP: Rush Weston
IT Man: Malory Shank
Netwrk Mgr: Steven White

D-U-N-S 00-801-8772 IMP
■ JUSTIN INDUSTRIES INC (TX)
ACME BRICK
(*Suby of* BERKSHIRE HATHAWAY INC) ★
3024 Acme Brick Plz, Fort Worth, TX 76109-4104
Tel (817) 332-4101 *Founded/Ownrshp* 1891, 1916
Sales 512.0MM^E *EMP* 4,111
SIC 3251 3271 5211 5032 Brick clay: common face, glazed, vitrified or hollow; Concrete block & brick; Blocks, concrete or cinder: standard; Brick; Tile, ceramic; Brick, except refractory
Pr: Dennis D Knautz
**Pr:* Edward L Stout Jr
**CEO:* Warren Buffett
**Sec:* Judy B Hunter
VP: JT Dickenson
**VP:* J Randy Watson
VP Mktg: Bill Seidel

JUSTIN ORIGINAL WORK BOOT
See JUSTIN BRANDS INC

JUVENILE DETENTION CENTER
See COUNTY OF WEBB

D-U-N-S 80-748-7533
JUVENILE JUSTICE DIVISION CALIFORNIA
(*Suby of* CALIFORNIA DEPARTMENT OF CORRECTIONS & REHABILITATION) ★
1515 S St Ste 502s, Sacramento, CA 95811-7243
Tel (916) 323-2848 *Founded/Ownrshp* 1980
Sales NA *EMP* 42,000
SIC 9223 Prison, government;

D-U-N-S 01-663-8384 IMP
JV INDUSTRIAL COMPANIES LTD (TX)
JV PIPING
(*Suby of* ZACHRY HOLDINGS INC) ★
4040 Red Bluff Rd, Pasadena, TX 77503-3606
Tel (713) 568-2600 *Founded/Ownrshp* 1998, 2012
Sales 334.4MM^E *EMP* 2,500
SIC 7692 3441 8711 Welding repair; Building components, structural steel; Construction & civil engineering
Pt: Joe Vardell
Pt: John Durham
VP: David Herzog

JV PIPING
See JV INDUSTRIAL COMPANIES LTD

D-U-N-S 00-598-7268 IMP
JVCKENWOOD USA CORP (CA)
(*Suby of* JVC KENWOOD CORPORATION)
2201 E Dominguez St, Long Beach, CA 90810-1009
Tel (310) 639-9000 *Founded/Ownrshp* 1961, 1975
Sales 107.9MM^E *EMP* 170
Accts Deloitte & Touche Llp
SIC 5064 High fidelity equipment
Pr: Kuhiro Aigami
**CEO:* Joseph Glassett
**CFO:* Dilip Patki
Treas: Michael McConnell
**Ex VP:* Craig Geiger
**Ex VP:* Mark Jasin
VP: Dave Hoag
**VP:* Harvey D Mitnick
VP: Chris Montanez
VP: Tom Wineland
Genl Mgr: Steve Inoue
Board of Directors: Mark Jasin, Keith Lehmann

JVIS - USA
See JVIS INTERNATIONAL LLC

JVIS CRYSTAL AVENUE
See JVIS MANUFACTURING LLC

D-U-N-S 79-645-4655 IMP
JVIS INTERNATIONAL LLC
JVIS - USA
(*Suby of* JVIS USA LLC) ★
52048 Shelby Pkwy, Shelby Township, MI 48315-1787
Tel (586) 739-9542 *Founded/Ownrshp* 2015
Sales 291.6MM^E *EMP* 800^E
SIC 3089 Automotive parts, plastic
CEO: Jason Murar

D-U-N-S 96-468-0990 IMP
JVIS MANUFACTURING LLC
JVIS CRYSTAL AVENUE
(*Suby of* JVIS - USA) ★
1285 N Crystal Ave, Benton Harbor, MI 49022-9215
Tel (269) 927-8200 *Founded/Ownrshp* 2010
Sales 255.5MM^E *EMP* 300^E
SIC 5015 Automotive supplies, used
Pr: Jason Murar
**VP:* Mike Alexander
**VP:* Jack Fuery
**VP:* Arthur Hariskos
**VP:* Darius Preisler

D-U-N-S 04-494-0093
JVIS USA LLC
52048 Shelby Pkwy, Shelby Township, MI 48315-1787
Tel (586) 884-5700 *Founded/Ownrshp* 2006
Sales 324.0MM *EMP* 1,000
SIC 3089 Automotive parts, plastic
Ofcr: Lisa Tava

D-U-N-S 18-917-0715 IMP/EXP
■ JW ALUMINUM HOLDING CORP
(*Suby of* BLACKSTONE GROUP) ★
435 Old Mount Holly Rd, Goose Creek, SC 29445-2805
Tel (843) 572-1100 *Founded/Ownrshp* 2015
Sales 401.9MM^E *EMP* 809
SIC 3353 3497 Coils, sheet aluminum; Foil, aluminum; Metal foil & leaf
CEO: Lee McCarter
**COO:* Stan Brant
VP: Kevin Monroe
Dir IT: Tim Monahan
Plnt Mgr: Dale Ruben
Sales Asso: Stefani Weatherford
Snr Mgr: Chester Roush

D-U-N-S 92-698-3834
JW CHILDS ASSOCIATES LP
500 Totten Pond Rd Ste 6, Waltham, MA 02451-1924
Tel (617) 753-1100 *Founded/Ownrshp* 1995
Sales 371.9MM^E *EMP* 8,447
SIC 5812 Mexican restaurant
Pt: Arthur Byrne
Pt: John Childs
Pt: Philip Damiano
Pt: Alan Dowds
Pt: Dr Mitchell Eisenberg
Pt: David Fiorentino
CFO: Todd Fitzpatrick
VP: Kyle Casella
VP: Jeffrey Miller
VP: Hemanshu Patel
Dir IT: Jodie Urquhart

D-U-N-S 00-368-7044
JW HOME IMPROVEMENT LLC
849 Quince Orch, Gaithersburg, MD 20878
Tel (703) 899-3129 *Founded/Ownrshp* 2008
Sales 16.1MM^E *EMP* 2,020
SIC 7299 Home improvement & renovation contractor agency
Genl Mgr: Ed Quinones

D-U-N-S 04-716-9503 IMP
■ JW WILLIAMS INC
(*Suby of* FLINT ENERGY SERVICES INC) ★
2180 W Renauna Ave, Casper, WY 82601-9688
Tel (307) 237-8345 *Founded/Ownrshp* 1963
Sales 89.4MM^E *EMP* 147
SIC 3533 3443 3547 1761 3291 Gas field machinery & equipment; Oil field machinery & equipment; Vessels, process or storage (from boiler shops): metal plate; Heat exchangers, plate type; Structural mills (rolling mill equipment); Sheet metalwork; Abrasive metal & steel products
Pr: Alan Phrasher
CFO: Paul Boechler
Treas: Lynn Warden
Sls Mgr: Pat Keefe

D-U-N-S 16-114-7608 IMP
JWD GROUP INC
300 Colvin Woods Pkwy, Tonawanda, NY 14150-6976
Tel (716) 832-1940 *Founded/Ownrshp* 1985
Sales 172.6MM *EMP* 450
SIC 1711 1629 1623 Mechanical contractor; Warm air heating & air conditioning contractor; Fire sprinkler system installation; Waste water & sewage treatment plant construction; Pipeline construction
Ch Bd: Kevin Reilly
**Ex VP:* Nickolas Optis
**Ex VP:* Patrick Reilly
**VP:* Patrick Mc Parlane
**VP:* John Samar
**VP:* Gerald Wilson

JWT DIRECT DIV
See J WALTER THOMPSON USA LLC

D-U-N-S 19-357-7418
JX ENTERPRISES INC
1320 Walnut Ridge Dr, Hartland, WI 53029-8311
Tel (800) 810-3410 *Founded/Ownrshp* 2000
Sales 214.1MM^E *EMP* 580
SIC 5012 5511 7538 6159 7513 Trucks, commercial; Trucks, tractors & trailers: new & used; General truck repair; Truck finance leasing; Truck leasing, without drivers
Pr: Eric K Jorgensen
**Pr:* Randy Buenig
**CFO:* Mark Muskevitsch
Bd of Dir: Kevin Whitehill
VP: John Bidochka
**VP:* Kurt Jorgensen
Exec: Carolyn Eschenburg
Genl Mgr: Larry Raspor
Off Mgr: Pam Vopravil
Sales Exec: Tim Cahoon
Sales Exec: Corrie Confer

D-U-N-S 04-360-0840 IMP
JX NIPPON OIL & ENERGY USA INC
ENEOS
(*Suby of* JX NIPPON OIL & ENERGY CORPORATION)
20 N Martingale Rd # 300, Schaumburg, IL 60173-2412
Tel (847) 413-2188 *Founded/Ownrshp* 1960
Sales 126.0MM *EMP* 70
SIC 5172 Petroleum products
Pr: Motoshi Sunami
**Treas:* Shinichi Nakaya
**Treas:* Thomas Takahashi

K

K & B INDUSTRIES
See K&B MACHINE WORKS LLC

D-U-N-S 13-328-1303
K & C LLC
HEAVENER NURSING CENTER
204 W 1st St, Heavener, OK 74937-2062
Tel (918) 653-2484 *Founded/Ownrshp* 1997
Sales 142.8MM *EMP* 30
SIC 8059 Nursing home, except skilled & intermediate care facility

D-U-N-S 61-157-1485
K & G PETROLEUM LLC
10459 Park Meadows Dr # 101, Lone Tree, CO 80124-5305
Tel (303) 792-9467 *Founded/Ownrshp* 2002
Sales 93.6MM^E *EMP* 300^E
SIC 5541 Gasoline service stations
CFO: Bob Claar

K & I LUMBER CO
See KENTUCKY-INDIANA LUMBER CO INC

K & K CONSTRUCTION
See KENYON CONSTRUCTION INC

D-U-N-S 18-700-7372 IMP
K & K VETERINARY SUPPLY INC
K&K VETERINARY SUPPLY
675 Laura Ln, Tontitown, AR 72770
Tel (479) 361-1516 *Founded/Ownrshp* 1987
Sales 90.0MM *EMP* 117
SIC 5199 5047 5072 Pet supplies; Veterinarians' equipment & supplies; Power tools & accessories
Pr: John K Lipsmeyer
**VP:* Melissa S Lipsmeyer

K & L BEVERAGE CO
See K AND L DISTRIBUTORS INC

D-U-N-S 05-162-9467 IMP
K & M TIRE INC
965 Spencerville Rd, Delphos, OH 45833-2351
Tel (419) 695-1061 *Founded/Ownrshp* 1977
Sales 354.9MM *EMP* 500
SIC 5014 7538 5531 Tires & tubes; General automotive repair shops; Automotive tires
Pr: Ken Langhals
VP: Cheryl Gossard
VP: Paul Zurcher

D-U-N-S 04-659-2424 IMP/EXP
K & N ENGINEERING INC
1455 Citrus St, Riverside, CA 92507-1603
Tel (951) 826-4000 *Founded/Ownrshp* 1964
Sales 135.4MM^E *EMP* 580
SIC 3751 3599 3714 Handle bars, motorcycle & bicycle; Air intake filters, internal combustion engine, except auto; Filters: oil, fuel & air, motor vehicle
Ch: Jerry E Mall
**CEO:* Thomas McGann
**CEO:* Steven J Rogers
Software D: Allen Reyes
Prd Mgr: Vanessa Coombs
Prd Mgr: Jere Wall
Natl Sales: Jenna Jefferies
Sls&Mrk Ex: Bob Donovan
Snr Mgr: Dave Martis

D-U-N-S 87-713-5632
K & N MANAGEMENT INC
RUDY'S COUNTRY STR & BAR-B-QUE
11570 Research Blvd, Austin, TX 78759-4036
Tel (512) 418-0444 *Founded/Ownrshp* 1993
Sales 84.2MM^E *EMP* 450
SIC 5411 5812 Convenience stores, independent; Barbecue restaurant
Pr: Thomas K Schiller
Mng Pt: Dan Peabody
**VP:* Brian K Nolan

D-U-N-S 01-907-0283
■ K & R HOLDINGS INC
PARADIGM SOLUTIONS
(*Suby of* BEACON ROOFING SUPPLY INC) ★
400 Warren Ave, Portland, ME 04103-1109
Tel (207) 797-7950 *Founded/Ownrshp* 2014
Sales 95.4MM^E *EMP* 135
SIC 5033 3089 Siding, except wood; Insulation, thermal; Roofing, asphalt & sheet metal; Doors, folding: plastic or plastic coated fabric; Windows, plastic
Pr: Scott Koocher
**Sec:* Richard Robinov
**Prin:* Jerry Robinov
Brnch Mgr: Tom Leighton
IT Man: Denis Dube
Opers Mgr: Todd Cray
Mktg Dir: Tony Eldridge
Mktg Dir: Brian Mills
Sls Mgr: Scott Frazier
Sales Asso: Aaron B Frigon

D-U-N-S 55-623-2382
K & S GROUP INC
18601 Lyndn B Jhnsn 420, Mesquite, TX 75150-6439
Tel (214) 234-8871 *Founded/Ownrshp* 2005
Sales NA *EMP* 5
SIC 6411 Insurance agents, brokers & service
Pr: Richard Daiker
Div Mgr: Peggy Hogan
Div Mgr: Steve Rickenbacher
S&M/VP: Sophie Kheang

D-U-N-S 05-700-7502
K & S PROPERTY INC
CUMMINS BRIDGEWAY
21810 Clessie Ct, New Hudson, MI 48165-8573
Tel (248) 573-1600 *Founded/Ownrshp* 1971
Sales 110.0MM *EMP* 630
SIC 5084 3519 Engines & parts, diesel; Internal combustion engines
Pr: Gregory Boll
CFO: Ken Clark
Chf Mktg O: Matt Caldwell

D-U-N-S 01-737-7136
K & W CAFETERIAS INC
1391 Plaza West Dr, Winston Salem, NC 27103-1440
Tel (336) 760-0526 *Founded/Ownrshp* 1981
Sales 94.1MM^E *EMP* 2,940
SIC 5812 Cafeteria
CEO: Donald C Allred
**Pr:* Dax Allred
**Pr:* Jimmy Sizemore
**Treas:* R Leo Sasaki
**Ex VP:* Todd Smith

D-U-N-S 04-160-2160 IMP
K - O - I WAREHOUSE INC
K O I AUTO PARTS
(*Suby of* K O I) ★
2701 Spring Grove Ave, Cincinnati, OH 45225-2221
Tel (513) 357-2400 *Founded/Ownrshp* 1966
Sales 86.1MM^E *EMP* 147
SIC 5013 Automotive supplies & parts
Pr: David Wesselman
**CFO:* Tom Frank
**Sec:* Mary Riesenbeck
Rgnl Mgr: Marty Spegal

D-U-N-S 02-744-3043 IMP/EXP
K AND L DISTRIBUTORS INC (WA)
K & L BEVERAGE CO
3215 Lind Ave Sw, Renton, WA 98057-3320
Tel (206) 454-8800 *Founded/Ownrshp* 1942
Sales 118.4MM^E *EMP* 400
SIC 5182

K B I
See KYKLOS BEARING INTERNATIONAL LLC

K B R
See KBR HOLDINGS LLC

K B R
See KELLOGG BROWN & ROOT SERVICES INC

K C FOOD
See KWIK CHEK FOOD STORES INC

K C I
See KCI USA INC

K C I
See KCI HOLDINGS INC

K C P
See KIRTLAND CAPITAL PARTNERS LP

K D C
See KONIAG DEVELOPMENT CO LLC

K G E
See KANSAS GAS AND ELECTRIC CO

K H A M
See KAISER HOSPITAL ASSET MANAGEMENT INC

K HOVNANIAN
See HOVNANIAN ENTERPRISES INC

K HOVNANIAN
See K HOVNANIAN COMPANIES OF CALIFORNIA INC

D-U-N-S 86-781-0525
K HOVNANIAN COMPANIES OF CALIFORNIA INC
K HOVNANIAN
400 Exchange Ste 200, Irvine, CA 92602-1340
Tel (949) 222-7700 *Founded/Ownrshp* 1994
Sales 103.4MM^E *EMP* 150
SIC 1521 Single-family housing construction
Pr: Nicholas Pappas

D-U-N-S 16-161-7170
■ K HOVNANIAN COMPANIES OF NEW YORK INC
(*Suby of* K HOVNANIAN DEVELOPMENTS OF NEW YORK INC) ★
10 Rte 35, Red Bank, NJ 07701-5902
Tel (732) 747-7800 *Founded/Ownrshp* 1985
Sales 187.4MM^E *EMP* 2,900^E
SIC 6531 Real estate agents & managers
Pr: ARA Hovnanian
**Ch Bd:* Kevork Hovnanian
**Treas:* Kevin Hake
**Sr VP:* Peter Reinhart
**VP:* Paul Buchanan
**VP:* Larry Sorsby
CTO: John E Uln

D-U-N-S 61-714-5073
■ K HOVNANIAN DEVELOPMENTS OF NEW JERSEY INC
(*Suby of* K HOVNANIAN) ★
10 State Route 35, Red Bank, NJ 07701-5902
Tel (732) 747-7800 *Founded/Ownrshp* 1985
Sales 183.1MM^E *EMP* 500
SIC 1531 Operative builders
Prin: A Hovnanian
Ex Dir: Robert Jackson

D-U-N-S 79-180-1947
■ K HOVNANIAN DEVELOPMENTS OF NEW YORK INC
(*Suby of* K HOVNANIAN) ★
10 State Route 35, Red Bank, NJ 07701-5902
Tel (732) 747-7800 *Founded/Ownrshp* 1985
Sales 279.7MM^E *EMP* 1,565
SIC 1531 Operative builders
Ch Bd: ARA K Hovanian
**Pr:* James Corbett
Sls Dir: Julie Distel
Sls Mgr: Kim Weaver

D-U-N-S 12-929-5965
■ K HOVNANIAN HOLDINGS NJ LLC
(*Suby of* K HOVNANIAN DEVELOPMENTS OF NEW JERSEY INC) ★
110 W Front St, Red Bank, NJ 07701-1139
Tel (732) 747-7800 *Founded/Ownrshp* 2002
Sales 133.8MM *EMP* 3
SIC 6552 Subdividers & developers
Pr: ARA Hovnanian
CFO: Larry Sorsby

K HOVNANIAN HOMES
See K HOVNANIAN HOMES AT FAIRWOOD LLC

D-U-N-S 02-268-6208
■ K HOVNANIAN HOMES AT FAIRWOOD LLC
K HOVNANIAN HOMES
(*Suby of* K HOVNANIAN) ★
1802 Brightseat Rd # 500, Landover, MD 20785-4232
Tel (301) 772-8900 *Founded/Ownrshp* 2002

Sales 175.4MM[E] *EMP* 500
SIC 1531 1522 1521 Speculative builder, single-family houses; Townhouse developers; Condominium developers; Residential construction; Single-family housing construction
CFO: Christopher Spendley
CTO: Mary Phelan
Dir IT: Brian Patterson
VP Opers: Steve Snyder

D-U-N-S 79-611-9857
K I INVESTMENTS INC
(*Suby of* INTERAMERICANA TRADING CORP)
Ave 65 De Infntria St1179, San Juan, PR 00924
Tel (787) 622-0600 *Founded/Ownrshp* 1991
Sales 214.0MM *EMP* 230
SIC 6519 5012 5511 Sub-lessors of real estate; Automobiles; Automobiles, new & used
Pr: Kyffin D Simpson
CFO: Roberto Cabello
**VP:* Garry D Clarke
Genl Mgr: John Bowen

K I K
See KIK-SOCAL INC

D-U-N-S 02-730-5700
K INVESTMENTS LIMITED PARTNERSHIP
PERKINS FAMILY RESTAURANT
1500 Sycamore Rd Ste 10, Montoursville, PA 17754-9303
Tel (570) 327-0111 *Founded/Ownrshp* 1996
Sales 42.6MM[E] *EMP* 3,400
SIC 7011 5521 5712 Hotels & motels; Used car dealers; Furniture stores
Pt: Dan Klingerman

D-U-N-S 62-161-0344
K LINE AMERICA INC
(*Suby of* KAWASAKI KISEN KAISHA, LTD.)
8730 Stony Point Pkwy # 400, Richmond, VA 23235-1970
Tel (804) 560-3600 *Founded/Ownrshp* 1998
Sales 149.1MM[E] *EMP* 489
SIC 4412 4491 Deep sea foreign transportation of freight; Marine loading & unloading services
CEO: Shio Suzuki
**Sr VP:* David N Mills
**Sr VP:* Ishida Nubuo
VP: Maria Bodnar
**VP:* A Chai
VP: Ty Cheng
VP: David Daly
VP: Jim Harris
VP: David Xiao
Genl Mgr: Patricia Colombo
Genl Mgr: Nick Elliott

K M C P I
See ALLIANCE PHYSICIANS INC

D-U-N-S 02-914-0712
K MOTORS INC
TOYOTA OF EL CAJON
965 Arnele Ave, El Cajon, CA 92020-3001
Tel (619) 270-3000 *Founded/Ownrshp* 1990
Sales 142.4MM[E] *EMP* 186
SIC 5521 5013 5511 Used car dealers; Automotive supplies & parts; Automobiles, new & used
Pr: Robert Kaminsky
**Sec:* Kim Kaminsky
**VP:* Gary Kaminsky
Dir Bus: Khang Nguyen
Sls Mgr: Tan Nguyen
Sls Mgr: Paul Sphabmixay

D-U-N-S 05-322-4379
K NEAL PATRICK & ASSOCIATES INC
8210 Lakewood Ranch Blvd, Lakewood Ranch, FL 34202-5157
Tel (941) 328-1111 *Founded/Ownrshp* 1972
Sales 135.0MM[E] *EMP* 100
SIC 6531 Real estate managers
Pr: Patrick Neal
**VP:* James R Schier
**VP:* Mark Sochar

K O I
See KOI ENTERPRISES INC

K O I AUTO PARTS
See K - O - I WAREHOUSE INC

D-U-N-S 79-837-1233
K R DRENTH TRUCKING INC
KRD TRUCKING
20340 Stoney Island Ave, Chicago Heights, IL 60411-8657
Tel (708) 757-3333 *Founded/Ownrshp* 1987
Sales 86.6MM[E] *EMP* 325[E]
SIC 4212 Garbage collection & transport, no disposal
Pr: Thomas J Manzke
**Sec:* Kenneth S Drenth

K S I
See KS INDUSTRIES LP

K S L
See BONNEVILLE INTERNATIONAL CORP

K S S
See KEY SAFETY RESTRAINT SYSTEMS INC

K S S
See KEY SAFETY SYSTEMS INC

K SWISS
See K-SWISS INC

KT P
See KLEENTEST PRODUCTS CORP

KTT V-FOX 11
See FOX TELEVISION STATIONS LLC

K U B
See KNOXVILLE UTILITIES BOARD

D-U-N-S 07-261-0025 IMP
K&B MACHINE WORKS LLC
K & B INDUSTRIES
208 Rebeccas Pond Rd, Schriever, LA 70395-3307
Tel (985) 868-6730 *Founded/Ownrshp* 1974
Sales 133.4MM *EMP* 500
Accts K&B Machine Works Llc Hou
SIC 3599 Machine shop, jobbing & repair
Pr: Kenneth Wood Jr
**Sec:* Cathleen Wood
VP: Craig Cenac
Dir Risk M: Scott Hebert
QA Dir: Jeremy Griffin
Sales Exec: Steve Williams
Mktg Mgr: Chantal Haynes
Sls Mgr: Bennie Bourg

D-U-N-S 05-471-7319 IMP
K&D FUTURE INC (PA)
MEALEY'S FURNITURE WARMINSTER
(*Suby of* PARALLEL INVESTMENT PARTNERS LLC) ★
908 W Street Rd, Warminster, PA 18974-3124
Tel (215) 674-3555 *Founded/Ownrshp* 1970, 2006
Sales 115.4MM[E] *EMP* 165
SIC 5021 Beds & bedding; Mattresses
Pr: Dan Mealey
**Pr:* Kevin Mealey
Genl Mgr: Ryan Wm
Sales Exec: Joe Pietrowski

D-U-N-S 55-688-3627 IMP
■ **K&G MENS CO INC**
K&G MEN'S SUPERSTORE
(*Suby of* MENS WEARHOUSE INC) ★
6380 Rogerdale Rd, Houston, TX 77072-1624
Tel (281) 776-7000 *Founded/Ownrshp* 1999
Sales 166.1MM[E] *EMP* 1,500
SIC 5611 5621 Men's & boys' clothing stores; Women's clothing stores
CEO: Douglas S Ewert
**CFO:* Jon W Kimmins
**Ex VP:* Carole L Souvenir
**Sr VP:* Kelly M Dilts
**Sr VP:* William Evans Jr
VP: Scott R Saban
**Prin:* Laura Ann Smith

K&G MEN'S SUPERSTORE
See K&G MENS CO INC

K&K VETERINARY SUPPLY
See K & K VETERINARY SUPPLY INC

D-U-N-S 01-044-1459
K&L GATES LLP
210 6th Ave Ste 1100, Pittsburgh, PA 15222-2602
Tel (412) 355-6500 *Founded/Ownrshp* 1946
Sales 508.7MM[E] *EMP* 1,917
SIC 8111

K&W TRANSPORTATION
See CARLILE TRANSPORTATION SYSTEMS INC

D-U-N-S 96-887-1348
K+S MONTANA HOLDINGS LLC
(*Suby of* K+S FINANCE BELGIUM BVBA)
123 N Wacker Dr, Chicago, IL 60606-1743
Tel (312) 807-2000 *Founded/Ownrshp* 2009
Sales 835.6MM[E] *EMP* 2,911[E]
SIC 2899 Salt

D-U-N-S 83-243-6005
K+S SALT LLC
(*Suby of* K+S MONTANA HOLDINGS LLC) ★
123 N Wacker Dr Fl 6, Chicago, IL 60606-1743
Tel (844) 789-3991 *Founded/Ownrshp* 2009
Sales 1.1MMM[E] *EMP* 2,901
SIC 2899 5149 5169 Salt; Salt, edible; Salts, industrial
Ch: Norbert Steiner

D-U-N-S 15-588-1394
K-3 RESOURCES LP
K3 BMI
850 County Road 149, Alvin, TX 77511-1316
Tel (281) 585-2817 *Founded/Ownrshp* 2005
Sales 117.7MM[E] *EMP* 100[E]
SIC 1389 Oil field services
Genl Pt: Karlis Ercums III
Ofcr: Scott Haney

D-U-N-S 01-472-6256 EXP
K-C INTERNATIONAL LLC
EKMAN RECYCLING
(*Suby of* INTERCONTINENTAL CELLULOSE SLS) ★
1800 Rte 34 Ste 401, Wall Township, NJ 07719-9167
Tel (732) 202-9500 *Founded/Ownrshp* 1976
Sales 167.6MM[E] *EMP* 58[E]
SIC 5093 Waste paper & cloth materials
CEO: Frank Crowley
**Ch Bd:* Matts Ekman
**Ex VP:* Phil Epstein

K-DESIGNERS
See JUDSON ENTERPRISES INC

D-U-N-S 08-982-0161
K-FIVE CONSTRUCTION CORP (IL)
13769 Main St, Lemont, IL 60439-9371
Tel (630) 257-5600 *Founded/Ownrshp* 1977
Sales 90.0MM[E] *EMP* 80
SIC 1611 Highway & street construction
Pr: George Krug
**CFO:* Mark Asniegowski
**Treas:* Josephine M Krug
**VP:* Dennis Devitto
**VP:* Jennifer Krug
**VP:* Robert G Krug
VP: Steve Murphy
**VP:* Rick Sniegowski
Mktg Dir: Scott Pirkins

K-LOVE RADIO NETWORK
See EDUCATIONAL MEDIA FOUNDATION

D-U-N-S 03-113-3044
K-MAC ENTERPRISES INC
KFC
1820 S Zero St, Fort Smith, AR 72901-8400
Tel (479) 646-2053 *Founded/Ownrshp* 1964
Sales 128.7MM[E] *EMP* 3,000
SIC 5812 Fast-food restaurant, chain
Pr: Virgil S Fiori
**Ex VP:* Jon A Dyer
**Ex VP:* Sam Fiori
VP: Brent McGruder

K-STATE
See KANSAS STATE UNIVERSITY

D-U-N-S 01-979-9812
K-STATE-MRI BIODEFENSE COALITION LLC
(*Suby of* MIDWEST RESEARCH INSTITUTE) ★
425 Volker Blvd, Kansas City, MO 64110-2241
Tel (816) 753-7600 *Founded/Ownrshp* 2009
Sales 36.4MM[E] *EMP* 1,053[E]
SIC 6794 Patent owners & lessors
Pr: Thomas M Sack
**Ch Bd:* Tom Bowser
**CFO:* R Thomas Fleener
**VP:* Linda D Evans
**VP:* Roger Harris

D-U-N-S 04-443-6335 IMP
K-SWISS INC
K SWISS
(*Suby of* E-LAND WORLD LTD.)
31248 Oak Crest Dr, Westlake Village, CA 91361-4692
Tel (818) 706-5100 *Founded/Ownrshp* 2013
Sales 491.5MM[E] *EMP* 609[E]
SIC 3021 3911 Rubber & plastics footwear; Jewelry apparel
Pr: Larry Remington
Pr: Mark Miller
**COO:* Edward Flora
**CFO:* George Powlick
**Chf Mktg O:* Barney Waters
VP: Eric Sarin
Genl Mgr: Masaki Saito
CIO: Cheryl Kuchinka
CIO: Galen Uptgrant
Dir IT: Robert Sobel
VP Sls: Peter Worley

D-U-N-S 06-644-8726
K-SWISS SALES CORP
(*Suby of* K SWISS) ★
31248 Oak Crest Dr # 150, Westlake Village, CA 91361-4692
Tel (818) 706-5100 *Founded/Ownrshp* 1999
Sales 484.0MM *EMP* 242
SIC 3021 Rubber & plastics footwear
Pr: Cheryl Kuchinka

D-U-N-S 04-327-9504 IMP/EXP
■ **K-TRON INTERNATIONAL INC**
PENNSYLVANIA CRUSHER
(*Suby of* HILLENBRAND INC) ★
590 Woodbury Glassboro Rd, Sewell, NJ 08080-4558
Tel (856) 589-0500 *Founded/Ownrshp* 2010
Sales 102.9MM[E] *EMP* 727[E]
SIC 3532 3535 Feeders, ore & aggregate; Conveyors & conveying equipment
Ch Bd: Edward B Cloues II
**CFO:* Robert E Wisniewski
**Sr VP:* Kevin C Bowen
**Sr VP:* Lukas Guenthardt
**Sr VP:* Donald W Melchiorre
VP: Ronald Remick
VP: Mike Sullivan
Admn Mgr: Mary Vaccara
Genl Mgr: Kevin Buchler
Genl Mgr: John Collins
Mktg Mgr: Shari Lake

D-U-N-S 78-107-1642 EXP
■ **K-TRON INVESTMENT CO**
(*Suby of* PENNSYLVANIA CRUSHER) ★
300 Delaware Ave Ste 900, Wilmington, DE 19801-1671
Tel (856) 589-0500 *Founded/Ownrshp* 1990
Sales 101.6MM[E] *EMP* 190
SIC 3823 Industrial process control instruments
Pr: Kenneth Camp
CFO: Jacky McMorris
**Treas:* Dorit Bannett
Board of Directors: Andrew Byod, Amanda D Foster

D-U-N-S 14-823-0691
K-VA-T FOOD STORES INC
FOOD CITY
1 Food City Cir E, Abingdon, VA 24210-1100
Tel (800) 826-8451 *Founded/Ownrshp* 1955
Sales 1.8MMM[E] *EMP* 10,500
SIC 5411 5141 6512 Grocery stores, chain; Groceries, general line; Commercial & industrial building operation
Pr: Steven C Smith
**Pr:* Robert L Neeley
COO: Jesse A Lewis
**CFO:* Michael T Lockard
Ofcr: Trina Robertson
**Sr VP:* Thomas Hembree
VP: Saul Hernandez
VP: Robert Lounsberry
**VP:* Bob Sutherland
**VP:* Steve Trout
VP: Linda Zester
Exec: Pat Osborne

D-U-N-S 19-007-8621
▲ **K12 INC**
2300 Corporate Park Dr, Herndon, VA 20171-4838
Tel (703) 483-7000 *Founded/Ownrshp* 1999
Sales 872.7MM *EMP* 4,800
Tkr Sym LRN *Exch* NYS
SIC 8211 8299 Elementary & secondary schools; Educational services
CEO: Stuart J Udell
**Ch Bd:* Nathaniel A Davis
CFO: James J Rhyu
Ex VP: Allison B Cleveland
Ex VP: Howard D Polsky
Ex VP: Joseph P Zarella
Admn Mgr: Teresa Scaife
Board of Directors: Jon Q Reynolds Jr Andrew, Craig R Barrett, Guillermo Bron, Fredda J Cassell, Kevin P Chavous, Adam L Cohn, John M Engler, Steven B Fink

D-U-N-S 13-164-5215
K2 INDUSTRIAL SERVICES INC
4527 Columbia Ave 2, Hammond, IN 46327-1666
Tel (708) 928-4765 *Founded/Ownrshp* 2003
Sales 170.5MM[E] *EMP* 1,500
SIC 2842 1799 Specialty cleaning preparations; Coating, caulking & weather, water & fireproofing
CEO: Ted L Mansfield
**COO:* Rick Napier
**CFO:* Rich Bartell
**Prin:* Frank Davenport
**Prin:* David Johnson
Div Mgr: Anthony Simioli
Opers Mgr: Jose Padilla
Sls Mgr: Liz Beison

D-U-N-S 07-844-9326
K2 INSURANCE SERVICES LLC
514 Via De La Valle Ste 3, Solana Beach, CA 92075-2750
Tel (858) 866-8966 *Founded/Ownrshp* 2011
Sales NA *EMP* 97
SIC 6411 Insurance agents, brokers & service
CEO: Pat Kilkenny
**Pr:* Bob Kimmel
**COO:* Matt Lubien
**CFO:* Nathan Hunter

D-U-N-S 07-876-0536
K2 INTELLIGENCE LLC
845 3rd Ave Fl 15, New York, NY 10022-6818
Tel (212) 694-7000 *Founded/Ownrshp* 2010
Sales NA *EMP* 120[E]
SIC 6411 Inspection & investigation services, insurance
Pr: Jeremy M Kroll
**CEO:* James W Crystal
CFO: Phillip Sherman
Mng Dir: Brian Cairl
Mng Dir: Anne Cheney
Board of Directors: Thomas Glocer

D-U-N-S 03-587-5504 EXP
K2D INC
COLORADO PREMIUM FOOD
2035 2nd Ave, Greeley, CO 80631-7201
Tel (970) 313-4400 *Founded/Ownrshp* 1998
Sales 251.9MM[E] *EMP* 300[E]
SIC 5147 Meats & meat products
Pr: Kevin Lafleur
**CFO:* Michael Rodgers
VP: Ginny Hogan
VP: Rob Streight
QA Dir: Dolores Casillas
Ql Cn Mgr: Paul Lange
Sls Mgr: Joe Lafleur

D-U-N-S 07-933-2204
K2M GROUP HOLDINGS INC
600 Hope Pkwy Se, Leesburg, VA 20175-4428
Tel (703) 777-3155 *Founded/Ownrshp* 2010
Sales 216.0MM *EMP* 541
Tkr Sym KTWO *Exch* NGS
SIC 3842 Surgical appliances & supplies
Pr: Eric D Major
**Ch Bd:* Daniel A Pelak
CFO: Gregory S Cole
**Chf Mktg O:* John P Kostuik
Board of Directors: Brett P Brodnax, Carlos A Ferrer, Paul B Queally, Raymond A Ranelli, Sean M Traynor, Michael A Turpin

K3 BMI
See K-3 RESOURCES LP

D-U-N-S 04-790-7084 IMP
KABA ILCO CORP
(*Suby of* DORMAKABA HOLDING AG)
400 Jeffreys Rd, Rocky Mount, NC 27804-6624
Tel (252) 446-3321 *Founded/Ownrshp* 2005
Sales 173.0MM[E] *EMP* 1,250
Accts Pricewater House Coopers Llp
SIC 3429 Keys, locks & related hardware; Keys & key blanks; Locks or lock sets
Pr: Frank Belflower
Pr: Barb Cummings
CFO: Jack Miller
VP: Amerique Du Nord
Genl Mgr: Charles Murray
CIO: Ed White
Opers Mgr: Noel Baltzell
Ql Cn Mgr: Glenn Davis

D-U-N-S 00-417-5862
KABAM INC (DE)
795 Folsom St Fl 6, San Francisco, CA 94107-4226
Tel (415) 391-0817 *Founded/Ownrshp* 2006
Sales 127.6MM[E] *EMP* 800[E]
SIC 7371 Computer software development & applications; Computer software development
Pr: Kevin Chou
Pr: Nick Earl
**COO:* Chris Carvalho
**CFO:* Steve Klei
Ofcr: Scott Thomas
**Ex VP:* Kent Wakeford
Sr VP: Paxton R Cooper
Sr VP: Mike Delaet
Sr VP: Doug Inamine
VP: Jordan Edelstein
VP: Yoko Nakao
Creative D: Lori Hyrup
Board of Directors: Joe Kraus

D-U-N-S 02-563-3120
KABBAGE INC
730 Peachtree St Ne # 350, Atlanta, GA 30308-1226
Tel (855) 278-7084 *Founded/Ownrshp* 2010
Sales NA *EMP* 90
SIC 6153 Working capital financing
Ch Bd: Marc Gorlin
CEO: Robert Frohwein

COO: Kathryn T Petralia
CFO: Jeff Hodges
CFO: Simon Yoo
Chf Mktg O: Victoria Treyger
Ofcr: Rama RAO
CIO: Kevin Phillips
CTO: Amala Duggirala
Counsel: Azba Habib

D-U-N-S 79-316-6799
KABLE MEDIA SERVICES INC
(*Suby of* DFI HOLDINGS LLC) ★
14 Wall St Ste 4c, New York, NY 10005-2143
Tel (212) 705-4600 *Founded/Ownrshp* 2015
Sales 117.2MM^E *EMP* 29^E
SIC 5192 7389 Books, periodicals & newspapers; Building scale models
CEO: Michael P Duloc
Sr VP: Richard Noser
VP: Doug Knodle
Ex Dir: Daniel Byrne
Opers Mgr: Carl Arnold

D-U-N-S 61-734-9139
▲ KADANT INC
1 Technology Park Dr # 210, Westford, MA 01886-3139
Tel (978) 776-2000 *Founded/Ownrshp* 1991
Sales 390.1MM *EMP* 1,800^E
Tkr Sym KAI *Exch* NYS
SIC 3554 3321 2621 Paper industries machinery; Ductile iron castings; Pressed & molded pulp & fiber products
Pr: Jonathan W Painter
**Ch Bd:* William A Rainville
COO: Eric T Langevin
CFO: Michael J McKenney
Treas: Daniel Walsh
Ex VP: Jeffrey L Powell
VP: Sandra L Lambert
VP: Deborah S Selwood
Sls Mgr: Brian Rees
Board of Directors: John M Albertine, Thomas C Leonard, William P Tully

D-U-N-S 07-666-0513
KADLEC REGIONAL MEDICAL CENTER
888 Swift Blvd, Richland, WA 99352-3514
Tel (509) 946-4611 *Founded/Ownrshp* 1984
Sales 504.5MM *EMP* 2,668
SIC 8062 General medical & surgical hospitals
CEO: Lane Savitch
Mng Pt: Thomas Rado
**Pr:* Rand Wortman
COO: Jason Paslean
**CFO:* Julie Meek
Bd of Dir: Edward Temple
**VP:* Larry Christensen
**VP:* Jeffrey Clark
**VP:* Dale Hoekema
VP: Nathan Sheeran
**VP:* Bill Wingo
Exec: Anne Laucella
Exec: Asif Malik
Exec: Daniel Niendorff
Exec: James Severance
Dir Lab: Gene Werst
Dir Rx: Dave Pearson

D-U-N-S 04-677-8718
KADRMAS LEE & JACKSON INC
(*Suby of* KLJ SOLUTIONS CO) ★
1463 I94 Business Loop E, Dickinson, ND 58601-6434
Tel (701) 355-8400 *Founded/Ownrshp* 2001
Sales 112.8MM^E *EMP* 780
Accts Dickinson Nd
SIC 8711 8713 Engineering services; Civil engineering; Structural engineering; Electrical or electronic engineering; Surveying services
CEO: Niles Hushka
**Treas:* Dean Anagnost
**VP:* Barry Schuchard
Exec: Angela Miller
IT Man: Jon Artz
Sftwr Eng: Daphne Baseflug
Sfty Mgr: Troy Clark
Snr PM: Tracy Haag
Snr Mgr: Ron Williams

KAEC
See KENTUCKY ASSOCIATION OF ELECTRIC CO-OPERATIVES INC

D-U-N-S 09-960-4217 IMP/EXP
KAESER COMPRESSORS INC
(*Suby of* SIGMA-TEC GMBH)
511 Sigma Dr, Fredericksburg, VA 22408-7330
Tel (540) 898-5500 *Founded/Ownrshp* 2008
Sales 150.4MM^E *EMP* 489
Accts Rodl Langford De Kock Llp Atl
SIC 5084 Compressors, except air conditioning
Pr: Frank R Mueller
**VP:* Laurie L Pouliot
VP: Roy A Stuhlman
Comm Dir: Kaeser Compressors
Rgnl Mgr: Jignesh Shah
Area Mgr: Gabriel Atodiresei
Brnch Mgr: Kevin Gates
Brnch Mgr: Renny Kroge
Dist Mgr: Joe D'Orazio
Dist Mgr: Mark Olson
Genl Mgr: Jonathan Teo

KAFP
See KAISER ALUMINUM FABRICATED PRODUCTS LLC

D-U-N-S 87-813-9513
KAHALA BRANDS LTD
BLIMPIE
(*Suby of* GROUPE D'ALIMENTATION MTY INC)
9311 E Via De Ventura, Scottsdale, AZ 85258-3423
Tel (480) 362-4800 *Founded/Ownrshp* 2016
Sales 84.5MM^E *EMP* 1,203
SIC 5812 6794 Fast-food restaurant, chain; Franchises, selling or licensing
CEO: Michael Serruya
COO: Jeff Smit
VP: Renee Mitchell

D-U-N-S 02-687-5302
KAHLIG ENTERPRISES INC
BLUEBONNET MOTORS
351 S Interstate 35, New Braunfels, TX 78130-4894
Tel (830) 606-8011 *Founded/Ownrshp* 1984
Sales 89.2MM^E *EMP* 230
SIC 5511 Automobiles, new & used; Trucks, tractors & trailers: new & used
Pr: Clarence J Kahlig II
Pt: Wes Studdard
**VP:* Gary Kahlig
Exec: Jeff Nolan
Genl Mgr: William F Vaughn Jr
Sls Mgr: Ed Donaho
Sls Mgr: Alan Gullet
Sls Mgr: Bob Hasbrook
Sales Asso: Neil Bligh
Sales Asso: Alan Brucks

D-U-N-S 61-511-7744
KAHLIG MOTOR CO
NORTH PARK LEXUS
611 Lockhill Selma Rd, San Antonio, TX 78216-5041
Tel (210) 308-8900 *Founded/Ownrshp* 1994
Sales 167.2MM *EMP* 140
Accts Morrison Brown Argiz & Farra
SIC 5511 7515 Automobiles, new & used; Passenger car leasing
Pr: Clarence J Kahlig
**VP:* William F Vaughn Jr
**VP:* Lee Willis
Sls Mgr: Tom Murgers
Sales Asso: Leslie Hernandez
Sales Asso: Erik Joseph
Sales Asso: Jose Karam
Sales Asso: Darin Van Dusen

KAI
See KURARAY AMERICA INC

D-U-N-S 08-442-4043 IMP/EXP
KAI USA LTD
KERSHAW KNIVES
(*Suby of* SANSUI SHOJI K.K.)
18600 Sw Teton Ave, Tualatin, OR 97062-8841
Tel (503) 682-1966 *Founded/Ownrshp* 1974
Sales 102.4MM *EMP* 150^E
Accts Maginnis & Carey Llp Portlan
SIC 3421 Carving sets
Ch Bd: Koji Endo
**Ex VP:* Hiroshi Igarashi
Exec: Les Shields
Mktg Dir: Jeff Goddard
Mktg Dir: Tom Welk

KAIC
See KAISER ALUMINUM INVESTMENTS CO

D-U-N-S 08-027-6062
KAINOS GP LLC
2100 Mckinney Ave # 1600, Dallas, TX 75201-2171
Tel (214) 740-7300 *Founded/Ownrshp* 2013
Sales 143.0MM^E *EMP* 45
SIC 5812 Contract food services

D-U-N-S 00-921-3570
KAISER AEROSPACE & ELECTRONICS CORP
2701 Orchard Pkwy Ste 100, San Jose, CA 95134-2008
Tel (949) 250-1015 *Founded/Ownrshp* 2000
Sales NA *EMP* 3,580
SIC 3728

D-U-N-S 17-776-2192 EXP
▲ KAISER ALUMINUM CORP
27422 Portola Pkwy # 200, Foothill Ranch, CA 92610-2836
Tel (949) 614-1740 *Founded/Ownrshp* 1946
Sales 1.3MMM *EMP* 2,790
Accts Deloitte & Touche Llp Costa M
Tkr Sym KALU *Exch* NGS
SIC 3334 3353 3354 3355 Primary aluminum; Aluminum sheet, plate & foil; Aluminum rod & bar; Bars, extruded, aluminum; Rods, extruded, aluminum; Wire, aluminum: made in rolling mills; Cable, aluminum: made in rolling mills
Ch Bd: Jack A Hockema
V Ch: Carolyn Bartholomew
Pr: Keith A Harvey
COO: Jim Klinger
COO: Malcolm Wright
CFO: Daniel J Rinkenberger
Treas: Melinda C Ellsworth
Ex VP: Joseph Bellino
Ex VP: Peter S Bunin
Ex VP: John M Donnan
VP: David Conrow
VP: W S Lamb
VP: Del Miller
VP: Neal E West
Exec: Tim Freije
Exec: Mike Underwood
Board of Directors: Carolyn Bartholomew, David Foster, L Patrick Hassey, Teresa A Hopp, Alfred E Osborne Jr, Jack Quinn, Thomas M Van Leeuwen, Brett E Wilcox

D-U-N-S 78-704-3715 IMP
■ KAISER ALUMINUM FABRICATED PRODUCTS LLC
KAFP
(*Suby of* KAISER ALUMINUM CORP) ★
27422 Portola Pkwy # 200, Foothill Ranch, CA 92610-2831
Tel (949) 614-1740 *Founded/Ownrshp* 2006
Sales 917.9MM^E *EMP* 2,400
SIC 3353 3334 3354 3355 Aluminum sheet, plate & foil; Primary aluminum; Aluminum rod & bar; Wire, aluminum: made in rolling mills
Pr: Jack A Hockema
**CFO:* Joseph P Bellino
**VP:* John M Donnan

D-U-N-S 62-404-0619
■ KAISER ALUMINUM INVESTMENTS CO
KAIC
(*Suby of* KAISER ALUMINUM CORP) ★
27422 Portola Pkwy # 350, Foothill Ranch, CA 92610-2837
Tel (949) 614-1740 *Founded/Ownrshp* 2006
Sales 177.7MM^E *EMP* 2,400
SIC 3353 3334 3354 3355 Aluminum sheet, plate & foil; Primary aluminum; Aluminum rod & bar; Wire, aluminum: made in rolling mills
Pr: Jack A Hockema
**CFO:* Joseph P Bellino
**Treas:* Daniel J Rinkenberger
**VP:* John M Donnan

KAISER CNTRACT CLG SPCLSTS INC
See KAISER CONTRACT CLEANING SPECIALISTS LLC

D-U-N-S 96-743-0745
KAISER CONTRACT CLEANING SPECIALISTS LLC
KAISER CNTRACT CLG SPCLSTS INC
(*Suby of* PACKERS HOLDINGS LLC) ★
3691 Prism Ln, Kieler, WI 53812
Tel (608) 568-3413 *Founded/Ownrshp* 2010
Sales 36.9MM^E *EMP* 3,000^E
SIC 7349 Building maintenance services
CEO: Jeff Kaiser
VP: Anne Kaiser
Prin: Kevin Mc Donnell

D-U-N-S 96-783-5690
KAISER FDN HEALTH PLAN OF COLORADO
1 Kaiser Plz Ste 15l, Oakland, CA 94612-3610
Tel (510) 271-6611 *Founded/Ownrshp* 2011
Sales 3.2MMM *EMP* 15^E
Accts Pricewaterhousecoopers Llp Ph
SIC 8099 Childbirth preparation clinic

D-U-N-S 07-169-5183
KAISER FOUNDATION HEALTH PLAN INC (CA)
1 Kaiser Plz, Oakland, CA 94612-3610
Tel (510) 271-5800 *Founded/Ownrshp* 1955
Sales NA *EMP* 189,319
Accts Kpmg Llp San Francisco Ca
SIC 6324 Hospital & medical service plans; Health maintenance organization (HMO), insurance only; Dental insurance; Group hospitalization plans
Ch Bd: Bernard J Tyson
Chf Rad: John Rego
Pr: Gregory A Adams
Pr: Alan Johnson
**CFO:* Kathy Lancaster
**Chf Mktg O:* Patrick Courneya
Ofcr: Carla Barbaro
Ofcr: Daniel Garcia
Ex VP: Patrick T Courneya
Ex VP: Richard D Daniels
Ex VP: Arthur M Southam MD
**Sr VP:* Raymond J Baxter PHD
Sr VP: Bechara Choucair
**Sr VP:* Robert M Crane
**Sr VP:* J Clifford Dodd
**Sr VP:* Philip Fasano
**Sr VP:* Louise Liang MD
Sr VP: Louise L Liang MD
**Sr VP:* Laurence G O Neil
**Sr VP:* Paul B Records
Sr VP: Bernard Tyson
Board of Directors: Regina Benjamin, Judith A Johansen, Jenny J Ming, Edward Pei, Meg Porfido, Richard Shannon, Sandra P Thompkins, A Eugene Washington

D-U-N-S 04-070-7275
KAISER FOUNDATION HEALTH PLAN OF COLORADO
(*Suby of* KAISER FOUNDATION HEALTH PLAN INC) ★
10350 E Dakota Ave, Denver, CO 80247-1314
Tel (866) 239-1677 *Founded/Ownrshp* 1969
Sales NA *EMP* 7,000
SIC 6324 Hospital & medical service plans
Pr: Donna Lynne
**Pr:* Roland Lyon
Adm Dir: Shelly Dodd
IT Man: Gwyn Saylor

D-U-N-S 15-522-2102
KAISER FOUNDATION HEALTH PLAN OF GEORGIA INC
(*Suby of* KAISER FOUNDATION HEALTH PLAN INC) ★
3495 Piedmont Rd Ne # 9, Atlanta, GA 30305-1717
Tel (404) 364-7000 *Founded/Ownrshp* 1984
Sales NA *EMP* 1,111
SIC 6324 Hospital & medical service plans
CEO: George C Halvorson
**Pr:* Julie Miller-Phipps
**CFO:* Kathy Lancaster
VP: Jonna Kirkwood
VP: James F Linnane
Dir Lab: Tom Addington
Genl Mgr: Wendy Hennum
Telecom Mg: Teresa McBee
IT Man: Keith Bell
IT Man: Brian Faison
IT Man: Katrina McCarty

D-U-N-S 07-266-1143
KAISER FOUNDATION HEALTH PLAN OF MID-ATLANTIC STATES INC
(*Suby of* KAISER FOUNDATION HEALTH PLAN INC) ★
2101 E Jefferson St, Rockville, MD 20852-4908
Tel (301) 816-2424 *Founded/Ownrshp* 1995
Sales NA *EMP* 950
SIC 6324 Hospital & medical service plans
CEO: Bernard J Tyson
**Pr:* Kim Horn
**CEO:* George C Halvorson
**CEO:* Robert M Pearl
**Treas:* Thomas R Meier
Ofcr: Ken Hunter
**Sr VP:* Mitch Goodstein
**Sr VP:* Kathy Lancaster
**VP:* Gregory A Adams
VP: Sherri Locke
Exec: Jacqueline M Ennis
Dir Rx: Lyndsy Pinchevsky

D-U-N-S 04-491-0461
KAISER FOUNDATION HEALTH PLAN OF NORTHWEST (OR)
(*Suby of* KAISER FOUNDATION HEALTH PLAN INC) ★
500 Ne Multnomah St # 100, Portland, OR 97232-2023
Tel (503) 813-2440 *Founded/Ownrshp* 1942
Sales NA *EMP* 1,495
SIC 6324 Hospital & medical service plans
Pr: Bernard J Tyson
**CEO:* Andrew McCulloch
Sr VP: Robert Crane
IT Man: Merry Maese

D-U-N-S 05-305-2619 IMP
KAISER FOUNDATION HOSPITALS INC
KAISER PERMANENTE
(*Suby of* KAISER FOUNDATION HEALTH PLAN INC) ★
1 Kaiser Plz, Oakland, CA 94612-3610
Tel (510) 271-6611 *Founded/Ownrshp* 1948
Sales NA *EMP* 175,668
SIC 8062 8011 General medical & surgical hospitals; Medical centers
Pr: Bernard J Tyson
**Pr:* Janet Liang
**CFO:* Kathy Lancaster
Ofcr: James Malone
**Ex VP:* Patrick Courneya
Ex VP: Gail Lam
**Sr VP:* Daniel P Garcia
VP: Thomas Curtin
**VP:* Richard Daniels
VP: Susan Fleischman
VP: Jill Rivers
VP: Yvonne Webb
VP: Bill Wehrle
Exec: Donna Young
Comm Man: Anne Little
Board of Directors: A Eugene Washington

D-U-N-S 18-638-2701
▲ KAISER GROUP HOLDINGS INC
9300 Lee Hwy, Fairfax, VA 22031-6050
Tel (703) 934-3000 *Founded/Ownrshp* 2000
Sales 578.9MM^E *EMP* 915
Tkr Sym KGHI *Exch* OTO
SIC 4953 Non-hazardous waste disposal sites
Pr: Douglas W McMinn
**Ch Bd:* Frank E Williams Jr
CFO: Allen Stewart

D-U-N-S 11-099-2307
KAISER HOSPITAL ASSET MANAGEMENT INC
KHAM
(*Suby of* KAISER PERMANENTE) ★
1 Kaiser Plz 19l, Oakland, CA 94612-3610
Tel (510) 271-5910 *Founded/Ownrshp* 2003
Sales 178.6MM *EMP* 25
Accts Pricewaterhousecoopers Llp Ph
SIC 5047 Hospital equipment & supplies
Pr: Thoams R Meir
**Pr:* Thomas R Meier

D-U-N-S 15-278-9280
KAISER MIDWEST INC
808 Highway 34 W, Marble Hill, MO 63764-4302
Tel (573) 238-2675 *Founded/Ownrshp* 1990
Sales 136.4MM *EMP* 86^E
Accts Van De Ven Llc Cape Girardeau
SIC 5083 5084 Lawn machinery & equipment; Chainsaws
Pr: Stanley Crader
**Ch Bd:* Don Crader
**Sec:* Val Crader
**VP:* Becky Hurst
Sls Mgr: Kyle Kramer

KAISER PERMANENTE
See KAISER FOUNDATION HOSPITALS INC

KAISER PERMANENTE
See SOUTHERN CALIFORNIA PERMANENTE MEDICAL GROUP

KAISER PERMANENTE
See P C NORTHWEST PERMANENTE

D-U-N-S 83-279-6432
KAISER PERMANENTE INTERNATIONAL
1 Kaiser Plz, Oakland, CA 94612-3610
Tel (510) 271-5910 *Founded/Ownrshp* 2009
Sales 418.5MM^E *EMP* 10,337^E
SIC 8062 General medical & surgical hospitals
CEO: Bernard J Tyson
**CEO:* Raymond J Baxter
**CFO:* Kathy Lancaster
CFO: Michael Rowe
Sr VP: Donald Orndoff
VP: Lisa Koltun
VP: Elisa Mendel
VP: Jason Phillips
Exec: Elisa Lopez
Comm Man: Jennifer Delaura
IT Man: Joe Walden

KAISER-FRANCIS OIL COMPANY
See GBK CORP

D-U-N-S 07-241-7900 IMP
KAISER-FRANCIS OIL CO
PILGRIM DRILLING CO
(*Suby of* KAISER-FRANCIS OIL CO) ★
6733 S Yale Ave, Tulsa, OK 74136-3330
Tel (918) 494-0000 *Founded/Ownrshp* 1976
Sales 8.1MM *EMP* 2,087
Accts Hogantaylor Llp Tulsa Ok
SIC 1382 1311 Oil & gas exploration services; Crude petroleum & natural gas
Pr: George B Kaiser
**CFO:* Don Millican
Ex VP: Robert Waldo

*Ex VP: Jim Willis
Exec: Dee Cooper
Genl Mgr: Brian Jobe
CIO: Kirk Walker
CTO: Burris Smith
Mktg Mgr: Dale Gann

D-U-N-S 88-436-6527
KAISER-HILL CO LLC
11025 Dover St Unit 1000, Broomfield, CO 80021-5573
Tel (303) 966-7000 Founded/Ownrshp 1994
Sales 86.3MM^E EMP 1,500
Accts Kpmg Llp
SIC 4953 Radioactive waste materials, disposal
CEO: Alan M Parker
*COO: Nancy Tuor
*CFO: Leonard A Martinez
Prin: E Chandler Jr
Prin: Robert K Merkins

KAIWAH ISLAND CLUB
See KIAWAH RESORT ASSOCIATES

D-U-N-S 17-190-3342
KAIZEN RESTAURANTS INC
16500 Nw Bethany Ct # 150, Beaverton, OR 97006-6013
Tel (214) 221-7599 Founded/Ownrshp 2003
Sales 28.2MM^E EMP 1,000
SIC 5812 Fast-food restaurant, chain
Pr: Syed J Ahmad

D-U-N-S 02-472-6700 IMP
KAJIMA INTERNATIONAL INC
(Suby of KAJIMA USA INC) ★
3475 Piedmont Rd Ne # 1600, Atlanta, GA 30305-2954
Tel (404) 564-3900 Founded/Ownrshp 1998
Sales 737.9MM^E EMP 1,003
Accts Deloitte & Touche Llp
SIC 1541 3446 1542 Industrial buildings & warehouses; Architectural metalwork; Nonresidential construction
CEO: Shinya Urano
*Treas: Katsushi Norihama

D-U-N-S 07-228-6933
KAJIMA REAL ESTATE DEVELOPMENT INC
(Suby of KAJIMA USA INC) ★
3475 Pdmn Rd Ne Ste 1600, Atlanta, GA 30305-2993
Tel (404) 564-3900 Founded/Ownrshp 1964
Sales 287.2MM EMP 480
Accts Deloitte & Touche Llp New Yor
SIC 6552 Land subdividers & developers, commercial
Pr: Keisuke Koshijima
*CFO: Hiroshi Unno
*VP: Yoichi Tsuchiyama

D-U-N-S 18-942-6257 IMP
KAJIMA USA INC
(Suby of KAJIMA CORPORATION)
3475 Piedmont Rd Ne, Atlanta, GA 30305-2954
Tel (404) 564-3900 Founded/Ownrshp 1986
Sales 1.1MMM EMP 9,000
Accts Deloitte & Touche Llp Atlanta
SIC 1542 1541 6531 1522 6552 1622 Commercial & office building, new construction; Commercial & office buildings, renovation & repair; Factory construction; Industrial buildings, new construction; Renovation, remodeling & repairs: industrial buildings; Real estate agents & managers; Hotel/motel, new construction; Hotel/motel & multi-family home renovation & remodeling; Subdividers & developers; Bridge construction
CEO: Noriaki Ohashi
*CFO: Mitsuyoshi Tamura
Treas: Yoshitaka Mizunaka
Ex Dir: Hiroto Ichiki
IT Man: Ray Punzalan
VP Mktg: Noriyuki Sato
Mktg Mgr: Naoko Onishi

D-U-N-S 12-337-8049 IMP
KALAHARI DEVELOPMENT LLC
KALAHARI RESORTS
1305 Kalahari Dr, Wisconsin Dells, WI 53965
Tel (608) 254-5466 Founded/Ownrshp 1998
Sales 107.2MM^E EMP 1,800
SIC 7011 5812 5813 Hotels; Eating places; Drinking places
*CFO: Mary Spath
*Ex VP: William Otto
*VP: Shari Nelson

KALAHARI RESORT
See LMN DEVELOPMENT LLC

KALAHARI RESORTS
See KALAHARI DEVELOPMENT LLC

KALAMAZOO BOARD OF EDUCATION
See KALAMAZOO PUBLIC SCHOOL DISTRICT

D-U-N-S 06-222-3532
KALAMAZOO COLLEGE
1200 Academy St, Kalamazoo, MI 49006-3295
Tel (269) 337-7000 Founded/Ownrshp 1833
Sales 90.4MM EMP 297
SIC 8221

D-U-N-S 07-259-0433
KALAMAZOO PUBLIC SCHOOL DISTRICT
KALAMAZOO BOARD OF EDUCATION
1220 Howard St, Kalamazoo, MI 49008-1871
Tel (269) 337-0113 Founded/Ownrshp 1924
Sales 169.7MM EMP 2,000
Accts Plante & Moran Pllc Portage
SIC 8211 Public elementary & secondary schools; Public elementary school; Public junior high school; Public senior high school
Netwrk Mgr: Carol Patrick
Pr Dir: Lynn Chio
Pr Dir: Alex Lee
Pr Dir: G A Lee
HC Dir: Jill Reynolds

D-U-N-S 06-018-3498
KALAMAZOO VALLEY COMMUNITY COLLEGE
KVCC
6767 W O Ave, Kalamazoo, MI 49009-9606
Tel (269) 488-4400 Founded/Ownrshp 1980
Sales 44.5MM^E EMP 1,000
Accts Plante & Moran Pllc Portage
SIC 8222 Community college
Pr: Marilyn J Schlack
Assoc VP: Dean McCurdy
VP: Louise Anderson
VP: Dennis Bertch
VP: Jack Taylor
CTO: Robert Christensen
Netwrk Mgr: Ryan Cummings
Netwrk Mgr: David Lynch
Web Dev: Kerri S Totten

D-U-N-S 00-300-4389 IMP
KALAS MFG INC
167 Greenfield Rd, Lancaster, PA 17601-5814
Tel (717) 335-2360 Founded/Ownrshp 1958
Sales 88.1MM^E EMP 300
SIC 3357 3694 Nonferrous wiredrawing & insulating; Engine electrical equipment
COO: Jack Witwer
*CFO: Dennis M Melnyk
VP: Tim Gaalswyk
VP: Rick Kile
*VP: Jon J Wiig
Exec: Deb Brown
Exec: Rachel Heisey
CIO: Lauren Winslow
Dir IT: Richard Hause
Dir IT: Richard Kendall
IT Man: Wagaman Fred

D-U-N-S 84-078-4032
KALDI MANAGEMENT INC
4824 Winterset Dr Ste 100, Las Vegas, NV 89130-3612
Tel (702) 340-7283 Founded/Ownrshp 1979
Sales NA EMP 22
SIC 6099 Check cashing agencies
Pr: Steven R Kaldi

D-U-N-S 01-085-7238
KALEIDA HEALTH
726 Exchange St, Buffalo, NY 14210-1484
Tel (716) 859-8000 Founded/Ownrshp 1996
Sales 1.1MMM EMP 9,000
SIC 8062 General medical & surgical hospitals
Pr: James R Kaskie
*Ex VP: Toni L Booker
*Ex VP: Margaret Paroski
*Sr VP: Donald Boyd
VP: Daniel Farberman
VP: Lynne Ferraro
VP: Michael P Hughes
Dir Lab: Georgirene Vladutiu
Genl Mgr: Bauwin Lissa
Nurse Mgr: Barbara Kuppel
Mtls Dir: Diane Artieri

D-U-N-S 00-900-1132
KALIL BOTTLING CO (AZ)
931 S Highland Ave, Tucson, AZ 85719-6796
Tel (520) 624-1788 Founded/Ownrshp 1946
Sales 245.3MM^E EMP 800
SIC 2086 7359 Soft drinks: packaged in cans, bottles, etc.; Vending machine rental
Pr: George Kalil
*Sec: William Ourand
*VP: John P Kalil
Mfg Dir: Patrick Duncan

D-U-N-S 10-657-8826
KALISPELL REGIONAL HEALTHCARE SYSTEM
310 Sunnyview Ln, Kalispell, MT 59901-3129
Tel (406) 752-8991 Founded/Ownrshp 1982
Sales 2.9MM EMP 1,300
Accts Jordahl & Sliter Pllc Kalispe
SIC 8051 8011 4522 7352 Skilled nursing care facilities; Health maintenance organization; Physicians' office, including specialists; Ambulance services, air; Medical equipment rental
Pr: Velinda Stevens
*Ch Bd: Doug Nelson
Treas: William Freeman
*Treas: Charles T Pearce
Ofcr: Dave Sibert
VP: Tate Kreitenger
VP: Tate Kreitinger
QA Dir: Sandra Swanson
Netwrk Eng: Aaron Turner

D-U-N-S 01-036-7506
KALISPELL REGIONAL MEDICAL CENTER INC
KALISPELL REGIONAL MEDICAL CTR
310 Sunnyview Ln, Kalispell, MT 59901-3199
Tel (406) 752-5111 Founded/Ownrshp 1982
Sales 273.5MM EMP 1,800^E
SIC 8062

KALISPELL REGIONAL MEDICAL CTR
See KALISPELL REGIONAL MEDICAL CENTER INC

D-U-N-S 00-462-5435
KALITTA AIR LLC
818 Willow Run Airport, Ypsilanti, MI 48198-0899
Tel (734) 484-0088 Founded/Ownrshp 1999
Sales 216.5MM^E EMP 1,100^E
Accts Wright Griffen Davis Ann Arbo
SIC 4513 Air courier services
*CFO: Greg Strzynski
CIO: Chad Rider
CTO: Zoltan Kocis
Web Dev: Diane Schroeder
Opers Mgr: Tina Dewitt
Ql Cn Mgr: Rich Stone

D-U-N-S 12-168-0458
KALKREUTH ROOFING & SHEET METAL INC
53 14th St Ste 100, Wheeling, WV 26003-3433
Tel (304) 232-8540 Founded/Ownrshp 1984
Sales 106.1MM^E EMP 330
SIC 1761 3446 3444 3441 Roofing contractor; Sheet metalwork; Architectural metalwork; Sheet metalwork; Fabricated structural metal
Pr: John Kalkreuth
COO: Andrew Vanlandingham
Div VP: Dave Hesse
Div VP: Pat Hurley
*Ex VP: Jim Hurley
VP: Bill Lewis
*VP: Chad McLeish
Exec: Chad Smith
Div Mgr: Jeff Piazza
Genl Mgr: John Trifonoff
Sfty Dirs: Jeremy Dvorcek

D-U-N-S 03-307-3862 IMP/EXP
KALMAR SOLUTIONS LLC
CARGOTEC SERVICES USA
(Suby of CARGOTEC HOLDING INC) ★
415 E Dundee St, Ottawa, KS 66067-1543
Tel (785) 242-2200 Founded/Ownrshp 2011
Sales 152.0MM^E EMP 375
SIC 3537 3714 3713 3643 Industrial trucks & tractors; Fifth wheel, motor vehicle; Truck & bus bodies; Current-carrying wiring devices
Pr: Ton Case
Pr: Jorma Tirkkonen
CFO: Mike Manning
Treas: Bob Wills
IT Man: Jenie Montgomery
IT Man: Thomas Soderstrom

D-U-N-S 07-976-9729
KALTEX AMERICA INC (NY)
(Suby of KALTEX NORTH AMERICA INC) ★
350 5th Ave Ste 7100, New York, NY 10118-0110
Tel (212) 971-0575 Founded/Ownrshp 1987, 2002
Sales 161.0MM EMP 18
SIC 2339 2325 Jeans: women's, misses' & juniors'; Jeans: men's, youths' & boys'
Ch Bd: Rafael M Kalach
CEO: Hebe Schecter
CFO: Jennifer Mason

D-U-N-S 14-114-7525 IMP
KALTEX NORTH AMERICA INC
(Suby of KALTEX TEXTILES, S.A. DE C.V.)
350 5th Ave Ste 7100, New York, NY 10118-0110
Tel (212) 894-3200 Founded/Ownrshp 2002
Sales 199.0MM^E EMP 120
SIC 2392 Comforters & quilts: made from purchased materials
Ch Bd: Rafael Kalach

D-U-N-S 00-108-6198 IMP/EXP
KALWALL CORP (NH)
1111 Candia Rd, Manchester, NH 03109-5211
Tel (603) 627-3861 Founded/Ownrshp 1955
Sales 92.4MM^E EMP 450
SIC 3089 3083 Panels, building: plastic; Thermoplastic laminates: rods, tubes, plates & sheet
Pr: Richard Keller
COO: John Krzyston
CFO: Kathy Garfield
Treas: Richard Severance
*Sec: Katherine Garfield
*VP: Bruce M Keller
Rgnl Mgr: Tom Hon
DP Exec: Dan Cronin
IT Man: Elanchard Mathew
Netwrk Mgr: Doug Deland
Info Man: Paul Fisher

D-U-N-S 05-254-3188 IMP
■ **KAMAN AEROSPACE CORP**
(Suby of KAMAN AEROSPACE GROUP INC) ★
30 Old Windsor Rd, Bloomfield, CT 06002-1414
Tel (860) 242-4461 Founded/Ownrshp 1969
Sales 283.7MM^E EMP 1,326
SIC 3721 3728 Aircraft; Aircraft parts & equipment
Ch Bd: Neal J Keating
Pr: Gregory Steiner
Treas: Russ Jones
*Treas: Robert D Starr
Div Pres: Alphonse J Lariviere Jr
Div Pres: James C Larwood Jr
Div Pres: Gerald C Ricketts
Ofcr: Mark Stevens
VP: Jairaj Chetnani
VP: Clarence Close
VP: Janna L Drake
VP: Richard C Forsberg
VP: Philip A Goodrich
VP: Michael Lafleur
VP: Jeffrey Leeper
VP: James B Melvin
VP: Robert Renz
VP: Christopher Simmons
VP: Darlene R Smith
VP: John K Stockman
VP: Patrick Wheeler
Board of Directors: Neal J Keating

D-U-N-S 78-279-7583 IMP/EXP
■ **KAMAN AEROSPACE GROUP INC**
(Suby of KAMAN CORP) ★
1332 Blue Hills Ave, Bloomfield, CT 06002-5302
Tel (860) 243-7100 Founded/Ownrshp 1945
Sales 501.3MM^E EMP 1,678
SIC 3721 3724 3728 3769 Aircraft; Aircraft engines & engine parts; Aircraft parts & equipment; Guided missile & space vehicle parts & auxiliary equipment
Pr: Gregory L Steiner
Treas: William Denninger Jr
*Treas: Robert D Starr
Div Pres: James C Larwood Jr
Sr VP: Patrick Owens
Sr VP: Patrick Renehan
VP: Richard C Forsberg
VP: Philip A Goodrich
VP: Nancy A L'Esperance
VP: Michael Lafleur
VP: Christopher Simmons
VP: Gary V Tenison
VP: Gary Tenison
VP: Pat Wheeler
VP: Patrick J Wheeler

D-U-N-S 00-115-5225 IMP/EXP
▲ **KAMAN CORP**
1332 Blue Hills Ave, Bloomfield, CT 06002-5302
Tel (860) 243-7100 Founded/Ownrshp 1945
Sales 1.7MMM EMP 5,258
Accts Pricewaterhousecoopers Llp Ha
Tkr Sym KAMN Exch NYS
SIC 5085 3721 3728 Industrial supplies; Bearings; Power transmission equipment & apparatus; Pistons & valves; Helicopters; Aircraft parts & equipment; Roto-blades for helicopters; Flaps, aircraft wing; Wing assemblies & parts, aircraft
Ch Bd: Neal J Keating
Pr: Thomas McNerney
Pr: Gregory L Steiner
CFO: Robert D Starr
Ofcr: Gregory T Troy
Sr VP: Ronald M Galla
Sr VP: Phillip A Goodrich
Sr VP: Shawn G Lisle
VP: Pat Sullivan
Exec: Terry Fogarty
Brnch Mgr: Eddie Roberts
Board of Directors: Brian E Barents, E Reeves Callaway III, Karen M Garrison, A William Higgins, Scott E Kuechle, George E Minnich, Jennifer M Pollino, Thomas W Rabaut, Richard J Swift

D-U-N-S 07-731-6412 IMP
■ **KAMAN INDUSTRIAL TECHNOLOGIES CORP**
(Suby of KAMAN CORP) ★
1 Vision Way, Bloomfield, CT 06002-5321
Tel (860) 687-5000 Founded/Ownrshp 1974
Sales 955.4MM^E EMP 2,141
SIC 3491 5085 Industrial valves; Industrial supplies
CEO: Neal J Keating
*Pr: Steven J Smidler
*Treas: Robert D Starr
*Sr VP: Ronald M Galla
*Sr VP: Gary J Haseley
*Sr VP: Roger S Jorgensen
*Sr VP: Thomas A Weihsmann
*VP: Kyle Ahlinger
*VP: Jeffrey M Brown
*VP: Thomas M Caputo
*VP: Anthony L Clark
VP: Robert F Go
*VP: Philip A Goodrich
*VP: Tom R Holtry
*VP: Michael J Kelly
*VP: David H Mayer
*VP: Michael J Pastore
*VP: Carmen Rivera
*VP: Donald O Roland
*VP: Abraham D Samaro
VP: Steve Smidler
Board of Directors: Neal J Keating

D-U-N-S 06-220-4573
■ **KAMATICS CORP**
(Suby of KAMAN AEROSPACE GROUP INC) ★
1330 Blue Hills Ave, Bloomfield, CT 06002-5303
Tel (860) 243-9704 Founded/Ownrshp 1971
Sales 95.8MM^E EMP 425
SIC 3451 3562 3724 3728 Screw machine products; Ball & roller bearings; Aircraft engines & engine parts; Aircraft parts & equipment
CEO: Neal J Keating
Pr: Robert G Paterson
*Treas: Robert D Starr
Ex VP: Steven J Smidler
Ex VP: Gregory L Steiner
Sr VP: Ronald M Galla
Sr VP: Philip A Goodrich
VP: Mathew Mormino
VP: Jeff Post
VP: Patrick C Sullivan
VP: John Tedone
Board of Directors: Neal J Keating, Gregory L Steiner

D-U-N-S 00-535-4899 IMP/EXP
KAMAX LP
(Suby of KAMAX HOLDING GMBH & CO. KG)
500 W Long Lake Rd, Troy, MI 48098-4540
Tel (248) 879-0200 Founded/Ownrshp 1995, 1935
Sales 135.4MM^E EMP 400
SIC 3452 Bolts, nuts, rivets & washers; Bolts, metal; Rivets, metal
VP: David Winn
COO: Wolfgang Ruoff
VP: Theresa Neutze
Ql Cn Mgr: Christopher Pierik
Snr Mgr: Jeff Kollhoff
Snr Mgr: Wayne Powell

D-U-N-S 15-138-9954
KAMCO BUILDING SUPPLY CORP OF PENNSYLVANIA
(Suby of KAMCO SUPPLY CORP) ★
1100 Township Line Rd, Chester, PA 19013-1446
Tel (610) 364-1356 Founded/Ownrshp 1986
Sales 85.9MM^E EMP 57
SIC 5031 Building materials, exterior; Building materials, interior
Pr: Charles Dougherty
*Treas: Carl Ingram
*VP: John W Sheehy
VP: Scott Weiss
Genl Mgr: Glenn Reilly
Genl Mgr: John Rymiszewski

D-U-N-S 01-257-0651 IMP
KAMCO SUPPLY CORP
80 21st St, Brooklyn, NY 11232-1138
Tel (718) 840-1700 Founded/Ownrshp 1969
Sales 174.6MM^E EMP 150
SIC 5031 5033 Lumber: rough, dressed & finished; Plywood; Building materials, interior; Building materials, exterior; Roofing & siding materials
Pr: Allan B Swerdlick
*CFO: Raymond Barter
Sr VP: Faisal M Sarkhou
VP: Steve Cangialosi
Brnch Mgr: Cesar Chavez
Dir IT: Seth Mayers
Trfc Mgr: Al Rodrugez
Mktg Dir: Evan Meyers

Sls Mgr: Thomas Nigro
Sales Asso: Adam Blackwell

D-U-N-S 05-518-2042 IMP
KAMCO SUPPLY CORP OF BOSTON
181 New Boston St, Woburn, MA 01801-6203
Tel (508) 587-1500 *Founded/Ownrshp* 1981
Sales 163.7MM^E *EMP* 200
SIC 5032 5031 5039 5023 5033 Brick, stone & related material; Building materials, exterior; Building materials, interior; Doors, garage; Ceiling systems & products; Floor coverings; Insulation materials
Pr: James F Scaia
VP: David Kovacs
Sls Mgr: Mike Williams

KAMEHAMEHA SCHOOLS
See TRUSTEES OF ESTATE OF BERNICE PAUAHI BISHOP

D-U-N-S 13-601-5781 IMP
KAMILCHE CO
1301 5th Ave Ste 2700, Seattle, WA 98101-2675
Tel (206) 224-5800 *Founded/Ownrshp* 1961
Sales 422.6MM^E *EMP* 2,870
SIC 2621 2611 2421 2435 2431 Paper mills; Pulp mills; Lumber: rough, sawed or planed; Plywood, hardwood or hardwood faced; Doors, wood
Pr: Colin Moseley
**Treas:* Colley Nancy L
**VP:* Reed Jr Wm G

D-U-N-S 82-463-9822 IMP/EXP
KAMIN LLC
KAMIN PERFORMANCE MINERALS
822 Huber Rd, Macon, GA 31217-9208
Tel (478) 750-5410 *Founded/Ownrshp* 2008
Sales 142.2MM^E *EMP* 350^E
SIC 3295 Earths, ground or otherwise treated
CEO: Rankin Hobbs
**Pr:* Harlan Archer
Pr: Doug Carter
VP: Warren McPhillips
VP: Roddy Wells
IT Man: Lou Gatti

KAMIN PERFORMANCE MINERALS
See KAMIN LLC

KAMINO INTERNATIONAL TRANSPORT
See TIGERS (USA) GLOBAL LOGISTICS INC

D-U-N-S 00-781-9709
KAMO ELECTRIC COOPERATIVE INC
KAMO POWER
500 S Kamo Dr, Vinita, OK 74301-4613
Tel (918) 256-5551 *Founded/Ownrshp* 1941
Sales 334.9MM^E *EMP* 154
Accts Bkd Llp Oklahoma City Oklah
SIC 4911 Transmission, electric power
CEO: J Chris Cariker
COO: Theodore Hilmes
CFO: Ann Hartne
**CFO:* Ann Hartness
Exec: Terry Brown
**Prin:* Howard E Freeman
**Prin:* W S Warner
**Prin:* J G Williams
**CIO:* Walter Kenyon
Sls Dir: Bryan Thompson

KAMO POWER
See KAMO ELECTRIC COOPERATIVE INC

D-U-N-S 04-691-5948
KAMPGROUNDS OF AMERICA INC
550 N 31st St Ste 400, Billings, MT 59101-1123
Tel (406) 248-8135 *Founded/Ownrshp* 1960
Sales 176.9MM^E *EMP* 830
SIC 6794 7033 Franchises, selling or licensing; Campgrounds
CEO: Jim Rogers
Pr: Erik Gothberg
**Pr:* Patrick C Hittmeier
**CFO:* John J Burke
VP: Mike Bresnahan
VP: Jeff Sutherland
**VP:* Michael E Zimmerman
Comm Man: Susan Austin
Rgnl Mgr: Greg Taylor
IT Man: Patty Hunter
Mktg Mgr: Chris Fairlee

D-U-N-S 03-862-6149
KAMPS INC
KAMPS WOOD RESOURCES
2900 Peach Ridge Ave Nw, Grand Rapids, MI 49534-1333
Tel (616) 453-9676 *Founded/Ownrshp* 1973
Sales 168.0MM^E *EMP* 650
SIC 2448 2499 Pallets, wood; Mulch, wood & bark
Pr: Bernard Kamps
COO: Bill Viveen
**CFO:* Ken Haines
Mng Dir: Jaap Schalken
VP Mktg: Tom Bodbyl

D-U-N-S 96-156-0091
KAMPS PROPANE INC
1262 Dupont Ct, Manteca, CA 95336-6003
Tel (209) 858-6000 *Founded/Ownrshp* 1996
Sales 100.0MM^E *EMP* 400
SIC 5171 Petroleum terminals
Pr: John Kamps
**CFO:* Jan Peterson
**VP:* Terry Ayres
Dir IT: Isaac Partain
Sfty Mgr: Mike Konanz

KAMPS WOOD RESOURCES
See KAMPS INC

D-U-N-S 80-824-6461 IMP
KAMTEK INC
(*Suby of* COSMA ENGINEERING) ★
1595 Sterilite Dr, Birmingham, AL 35215-4189
Tel (205) 327-7000 *Founded/Ownrshp* 2008
Sales 205.9MM^E *EMP* 600
SIC 3714 Motor vehicle parts & accessories
Genl Mgr: Bill Jones

D-U-N-S 07-413-9007
KAN-DI-KI LLC
DIAGNOSTIC LABS & RDLGY
2820 N Ontario St, Burbank, CA 91504-2015
Tel (818) 549-1880 *Founded/Ownrshp* 2008
Sales 74.5MM^E *EMP* 1,500
SIC 8071 Testing laboratories; X-ray laboratory, including dental
VP: Brian Tees
Area Mgr: Nedd Sherbanee
Sls Mgr: Jose Toribio

KANA
See KAY TECHNOLOGY HOLDINGS INC

D-U-N-S 19-519-1650
■ **KANA SOFTWARE INC**
VERINT
(*Suby of* VERINT SYSTEMS INC) ★
2550 Walsh Ave Ste 120, Santa Clara, CA 95051-1345
Tel (650) 614-8300 *Founded/Ownrshp* 2014
Sales 109.3MM^E *EMP* 790
SIC 7372 Prepackaged software
CEO: Mark Duffell
Pr: William A Bose
Pr: Brett White
CFO: Brian Allen
**CFO:* Jeff Wylie
Bd of Dir: Robert Frick
Bd of Dir: Tom Galvin
**Chf Mktg O:* James Norwood
Ofcr: Jay A Jones
Ex VP: Mark A Angel
Ex VP: David Milam
**Sr VP:* Jim Bureau
**Sr VP:* Amy Mosher
Sr VP: Chad A Wolf
VP: Joseph Ansanelli
VP: Peter Morton
VP: Michael Wolfe

D-U-N-S 00-418-0683 IMP/EXP
KANAN ENTERPRISES INC
KING NUT COMPANIES
31900 Solon Rd, Solon, OH 44139-3536
Tel (440) 248-8484 *Founded/Ownrshp* 1927
Sales 96.1MM^E *EMP* 300^E
SIC 2068 2034 Nuts: dried, dehydrated, salted or roasted; Fruits, dried or dehydrated, except freeze-dried
Pr: Martin Kanan
**Ch:* Michael Kanan
**VP:* Matthew Kanan
Sales Exec: Lynn Gordon

D-U-N-S 06-894-5844 EXP
KANAWAY SEAFOODS INC
ALASKA GENERAL SEAFOODS
(*Suby of* JIM PATTISON INDUSTRIES LTD)
6425 Ne 175th St, Kenmore, WA 98028-4808
Tel (425) 485-7755 *Founded/Ownrshp* 1986
Sales 94.8MM^E *EMP* 352^E
SIC 2091 Canned & cured fish & seafoods
Pr: Gordon Lindquist
Off Mgr: Jessica Hgester

D-U-N-S 05-160-8412
KANAWHA COUNTY BOARD OF EDUCATION
200 Elizabeth St, Charleston, WV 25311-2197
Tel (304) 348-7770 *Founded/Ownrshp* 1863
Sales 167.4MM^E *EMP* 3,770
SIC 8211 School board
Pr: Robin Rector
VP: Ron Canestraro
Exec: Carol Hamric
Genl Mgr: Kim Thompson
Psych: Vicki Broce
Psych: AMi Campbell
Psych: Sonya Christian
Psych: Ann Flynt
Psych: Lynn Gattlieb
Psych: Janice Moss
Psych: Don Todd

D-U-N-S 12-375-3493
KANAWHA COUNTY SCHOOLS
KANAWHA COUNTY SCHOOLS ACADEMY
200 Elizabeth St, Charleston, WV 25311-2197
Tel (304) 348-7770 *Founded/Ownrshp* 1863
Sales 75.7MM^E *EMP* 3,594^E
SIC 8211 Public senior high school; Public junior high school
Dir Sec: Charlie Warner
MIS Dir: Jerry Legg
Pr Dir: Ron Pauley
Schl Brd P: Robin Rector
Teacher Pr: Carol Hamrick
Psych: Jennifer Jackfert
Psych: Janice Standish
HC Dir: Brenda Isaac

KANAWHA COUNTY SCHOOLS ACADEMY
See KANAWHA COUNTY SCHOOLS

D-U-N-S 07-710-3054
KANDERS & CO INC
2 Sound View Dr Ste 3, Greenwich, CT 06830-6471
Tel (203) 552-9600 *Founded/Ownrshp* 1999
Sales NA *EMP* 1,805
SIC 6159 Small business investment companies
Pr: Warren B Kanders

D-U-N-S 00-781-3140 IMP
KANE CO
6500 Kane Way, Elkridge, MD 21075-6000
Tel (410) 799-3200 *Founded/Ownrshp* 1945
Sales 58.2MM *EMP* 1,500
SIC 4212 Local trucking, without storage; Furniture moving, local: without storage
Ch Bd: John M Kane
**COO:* Ronald H Meliker
**CFO:* David J Korotkin
VP: Jim Durfee
VP: Steve Gilbert
VP: Brad Jones
Admn Mgr: Lolita Williams
Brnch Mgr: Mark Warner
Genl Mgr: John Tenuta

Off Mgr: Tina Chism
Dir IT: Rich Santers

D-U-N-S 03-271-3497 IMP/EXP
KANE FURNITURE CORP
KANE'S FURNITURE
5700 70th Ave N, Pinellas Park, FL 33781-4238
Tel (727) 545-9555 *Founded/Ownrshp* 1948
Sales 203.9MM^E *EMP* 900
SIC 5712

D-U-N-S 11-257-0551
KANE IS ABLE INC
3 Stauffer Industrial Par, Taylor, PA 18517-9628
Tel (570) 344-9801 *Founded/Ownrshp* 1995
Sales 127.0MM^E *EMP* 500
SIC 4213 4222 4225 4214 Trucking, except local; Warehousing, cold storage or refrigerated; Storage, frozen or refrigerated goods; General warehousing; Local trucking with storage
**Ch Bd:* Lee Stucky
**CFO:* Eugene J Kane Jr
Sr VP: Anne E Cooper
Sr VP: John W Hurst
Sr VP: Satu Mehta
Off Mgr: Freddie Floyd
Mktg Dir: Alex Stark

D-U-N-S 06-809-3483 IMP/EXP
KANEKA AMERICAS HOLDING INC
(*Suby of* KANEKA CORPORATION)
6250 Underwood Rd, Pasadena, TX 77507-1061
Tel (281) 474-7084 *Founded/Ownrshp* 1982
Sales 89.1MM^E *EMP* 300
SIC 2023

D-U-N-S 07-844-7033 IMP/EXP
KANEKA NORTH AMERICA LLC
(*Suby of* KANEKA AMERICAS HOLDING INC) ★
6161 Underwood Rd, Pasadena, TX 77507-1096
Tel (281) 474-7084 *Founded/Ownrshp* 2012
Sales 89.1MM^E *EMP* 300^E
SIC 2821 3081 2023 Plastics materials & resins; Unsupported plastics film & sheet; Dry, condensed, evaporated dairy products
Pr: Kazuhiko Fujii
**Ex VP:* Steven Skarke
**VP:* Bruce Duerringer
**VP:* Alvin Proctor
**VP:* William Renaud

D-U-N-S 00-193-1344 IMP/EXP
KANEMATSU USA INC (NY)
(*Suby of* KANEMATSU CORPORATION)
500 5th Ave Fl 29, New York, NY 10110-2999
Tel (212) 704-9400 *Founded/Ownrshp* 1951
Sales 433.0MM^E *EMP* 100
SIC 5084 5051 5065 5153 Industrial machinery & equipment; Steel; Ferrous metals; Nonferrous metal sheets, bars, rods, etc.; Electronic parts & equipment; Electronic parts; Grains
Pr: Katsumi Morita
Treas: Yoshio Tajima
Treas: Taro Unno
Div/Sub He: Sigehiro Yamanaka
Div Mgr: Kenji Ogiso
Genl Mgr: K Koshiyama
Off Mgr: Bob Schwartz
Info Man: Tera Seiji

D-U-N-S 05-457-8716
KANEQUIP INC
KUBOTA AUTHORIZED DEALER
(*Suby of* KUBOTA AUTHORIZED DEALER) ★
1152 Pony Express Hwy, Marysville, KS 66508-8647
Tel (785) 562-2377 *Founded/Ownrshp* 1999
Sales 117.0MM^E *EMP* 167
SIC 5046 5083 Commercial equipment; Farm & garden machinery
**CEO:* James Meinhardt

D-U-N-S 07-635-6562
KANEQUIP INC
KUBOTA AUTHORIZED DEALER
18035 E Us Highway 24, Wamego, KS 66547-9790
Tel (785) 456-2041 *Founded/Ownrshp* 1966
Sales 117.0MM^E *EMP* 167
SIC 5999 5083 Farm machinery; Farm & garden machinery
Pr: James Meinhardt
**VP:* Jim Burke
Off Mgr: April Goff
Store Mgr: Mike Brown
IT Man: Jason Baity
Sales Asso: Karisa Bryan

KANE'S FURNITURE
See KANE FURNITURE CORP

KANGAROO EXPRESS
See PANTRY INC

D-U-N-S 08-410-2870
KANSAS ATHLETICS INC
(*Suby of* UNIVERSITY OF KANSAS) ★
1651 Naismith Dr, Lawrence, KS 66045-4069
Tel (785) 864-7050 *Founded/Ownrshp* 1925
Sales 103.7MM *EMP* 434
Accts Bkd Kansas City Mo
SIC 8699 Athletic organizations

D-U-N-S 00-716-9584 IMP
KANSAS CITY BOARD OF PUBLIC UTILITIES
BPU
540 Minnesota Ave, Kansas City, KS 66101-2930
Tel (913) 573-9000 *Founded/Ownrshp* 1909
Sales 232.6MM *EMP* 1,772
SIC 4931 4941 Electric & other services combined; Water supply
Pr: David Alvey
CFO: Lori Austin
Bd of Dir: Mary Gonzales
Bd of Dir: Thomas Groneman
Ofcr: Kristina Daggett
**Prin:* Don L Gray
Adm Dir: Laurie Brough
CIO: Spurlynn Byers

Cmptr Lab: Frank Liu
Sfty Dirs: Teresa Grimes

D-U-N-S 00-696-5834
KANSAS CITY LIFE INSURANCE CO
3520 Broadway Blvd, Kansas City, MO 64111-2565
Tel (816) 753-7000 *Founded/Ownrshp* 1895
Sales NA *EMP* 446^E
Accts Kpmg Llp Kansas City Missour
SIC 6311 6411 Life insurance; Life insurance carriers; Life insurance agents
Ch Bd: R Philip Bixby
Pr: Kris Jones
Pr: Mike Kershner
**CFO:* Tracy W Knapp
**V Ch Bd:* Walter E Bixby
Ofcr: Kelly Ullom
Sr VP: Charles R Duffy
Sr VP: Donald E Krebs
Sr VP: A Craig Mason Jr
Sr VP: Mark A Milton
Sr VP: Stephen E Ropp
VP: Bill Browning
VP: Kathryn Church
VP: Timothy Knott
VP: David A Laird
VP: Francis P Lemery
VP: Tom Morgan
VP: Richard Ropp
VP: J Todd Salash
Board of Directors: Kevin G Barth, William R Blessing, Michael Braude, John C Cozad, Richard L Finn, Cecil R Miller, Mark A Milton, William A Schalekamp

D-U-N-S 00-696-5842 IMP
■ **KANSAS CITY POWER & LIGHT CO**
GREAT PLAINS ENERGY
(*Suby of* GREAT PLAINS ENERGY INC) ★
1200 Main St Ste 114, Kansas City, MO 64105-2100
Tel (816) 556-2200 *Founded/Ownrshp* 2001
Sales 1.7MMM *EMP* 2,935^E
Accts Deloitte & Touche Llp Kansas
SIC 4911 Generation, electric power; Transmission, electric power; Distribution, electric power
Ch Bd: Terry Bassham
COO: Scott H Heidtbrink
CFO: James C Shay
Treas: Michael W Cline
Chf Cred: Ellen E Fairchild
Ex VP: Marcus Jackson
Sr VP: Heather A Humphrey
VP: Steven P Busser
VP: Chuck Caisley
Dir IT: Mitch Krysa
Telecom Mg: Marc McFall
Board of Directors: David L Bodde, Randall C Ferguson Jr, Gary D Forsee, Scott D Grimes, Thomas D Hyde, James A Mitchell, Ann D Murtlow, John J Sherman, Linda H Talbott

D-U-N-S 04-366-7385
KANSAS CITY PUBLIC SCHOOLS (MO)
2901 Troost Ave, Kansas City, MO 64109-1538
Tel (816) 418-7000 *Founded/Ownrshp* 1867
Sales 238.8MM^E *EMP* 4,700
Accts Mcgladrey Llp Kansas City Mi
SIC 8211 Public elementary & secondary schools
**CFO:* Rebecca Lee Gwin
**CFO:* Allan Tunis
**Ex Dir:* Thomas Brenneman
HC Dir: Tonia Gilbert

D-U-N-S 00-194-2218
▲ **KANSAS CITY SOUTHERN**
427 W 12th St, Kansas City, MO 64105-1403
Tel (816) 983-1303 *Founded/Ownrshp* 1962
Sales 2.4MMM *EMP* 6,670^E
Accts Kpmg Llp Kansas City Missour
Tkr Sym KSU *Exch* NYS
SIC 4011 Railroads, line-haul operating
CEO: David L Starling
**Ch Bd:* Robert J Druten
Pr: Rito Arredondo
Pr: Jose Guillermo Zozaya Delano
Pr: Mick Fenley
Pr: Gil Niesen
Pr: Patrick J Ottensmeyer
COO: Jeffrey M Songer
CFO: Michael W Upchurch
Bd of Dir: Angie Hoover
Chf Mktg O: Brian D Hancock
Ex VP: Daniel Avramovich
Ex VP: Warren K Erdman
Sr VP: Brian H Bowers
Sr VP: Lora Cheatum
Sr VP: John S Jacobsen
Sr VP: Michael J Naatz
Sr VP: Mary K Stadler
Sr VP: Richard M Zuza
Board of Directors: Lu M Cordova, Henry R Davis, Antonio O Garza Jr, David F Garza, David F Garza, Thomas A McDonnell, Rodney E Slater

D-U-N-S 00-696-5859
■ **KANSAS CITY SOUTHERN RAILWAY CO**
(*Suby of* KANSAS CITY SOUTHERN) ★
427 W 12th St, Kansas City, MO 64105-1403
Tel (816) 983-1303 *Founded/Ownrshp* 1900
Sales 223.7MM^E *EMP* 880^E
SIC 4011 4213 Railroads, line-haul operating; Trucking, except local
Ch Bd: Landon H Rowland
**COO:* David R Ebbrecht
**Sr VP:* Mike Naatz
**Sr VP:* Jeff Songer
Sr VP: Robert B Terry
VP: Wayne Godlewski
VP: D Morris Godwin
VP: Mark A Redd
VP: Michael Smith
VP: T Scot Stottlemyre
VP: Steve Truitt

KANSAS CITY STAR, THE
See CYPRESS MEDIA LLC

D-U-N-S 17-593-7804
KANSAS DEPARTMENT FOR CHILDREN AND FAMILIES
(*Suby of* EXECUTIVE OFFICE OF STATE OF KANSAS) ★
915 Sw Harrison St, Topeka, KS 66612-1505
Tel (785) 368-6358 *Founded/Ownrshp* 1861
Sales NA *EMP* 6,256
SIC 9441 9431 Administration of social & manpower programs; ; Administration of public health programs;

D-U-N-S 00-252-2832
KANSAS DEPARTMENT OF CORRECTIONS
(*Suby of* EXECUTIVE OFFICE OF STATE OF KANSAS) ★
714 Sw Jackson St Fl 3, Topeka, KS 66603-3721
Tel (785) 296-3317 *Founded/Ownrshp* 1861
Sales NA *EMP* 3,100
SIC 9223 Prison, government;
Pr: Dennis Williams
Treas: Camie Borsdorf
VP: Karen Rohling

D-U-N-S 17-607-8103
KANSAS DEPARTMENT OF TRANSPORTATION
EXECUTIVE OFFCE OF THE STATE
(*Suby of* EXECUTIVE OFFICE OF STATE OF KANSAS) ★
700 Sw Harrison St # 500, Topeka, KS 66603-3964
Tel (785) 296-3501 *Founded/Ownrshp* 1868
Sales NA *EMP* 3,000ᴱ
Accts Cliftonlarsonallen Llp Broom
SIC 9621
Dir: Chris Herrick
Prgrm Mgr: Sondra Clark
IT Man: Roger Moore
Pr Mgr: Kirk Hutchinson
Sls Mgr: Julie Prather
Board of Directors: Mike Crow, Marcia Ferrill, Lon Ingram, Dale Jost, Julie Lorenz, Ben Nelson, Dan Scherschligt, Bob Stacks, Ed Young

D-U-N-S 09-582-9693
KANSAS ELECTRIC POWER COOPERATIVE INC
KEPCO
600 Sw Corporate Vw, Topeka, KS 66615-1233
Tel (785) 273-7010 *Founded/Ownrshp* 1975
Sales 174.1MM *EMP* 24
Accts Bkd Llp Tulsa Ok
SIC 4911 Distribution, electric power
CEO: Thuck Terrill
Trst: KS Altamont
Trst: KS Mankato
Trst: KS Meade
Trst: KS Pratt
Trst: KS Wellington

D-U-N-S 00-694-4151
■ **KANSAS GAS AND ELECTRIC CO**
K G E
(*Suby of* WESTAR ENERGY INC) ★
120 E 1st St N, Wichita, KS 67202-2001
Tel (316) 721-1899 *Founded/Ownrshp* 1909
Sales 368.7MMᴱ *EMP* 1,900
SIC 4911 Generation, electric power; Transmission, electric power; Distribution, electric power
Pr: William B Moore
VP: Caroline Williams

D-U-N-S 04-114-6432 IMP
KANSAS STATE UNIVERSITY
K-STATE
110 Anderson Hall, Manhattan, KS 66506-0100
Tel (785) 532-6210 *Founded/Ownrshp* 1863
Sales 552.7MM *EMP* 5,168
SIC 8221 University
Pr: Richard B Myers
**Sr VP:* April Mason
VP: Amy Auch
VP: Tatiana Nzinkeu
VP: Elizabeth A Unger
Exec: Christopher Havenstein
Dir Risk M: Theo Brooks
Assoc Dir: Terri Lee
Comm Dir: Heather Wagoner
Adm Dir: Janette Jensen
Netwrk Eng: Caterina Scoglio

D-U-N-S 07-628-2235
KANSAS STATE UNIVERSITY FOUNDATION INC
KSU FOUNDATION
1800 Kimball Ave Ste 200, Manhattan, KS 66502-3373
Tel (785) 532-6266 *Founded/Ownrshp* 1944
Sales 133.8MM *EMP* 100
Accts Bkd Llp Kansas City Mo
SIC 7389 Fund raising organizations
CEO: Gary Hellebust
**CEO:* Fred Scholick
**CFO:* Greg Lohrentz
IT Man: Josh Gfeller
IT Man: Chuck Gould

D-U-N-S 06-794-2904
KANSAS TURNPIKE AUTHORITY
9401 E Kellogg Dr, Wichita, KS 67207-1804
Tel (316) 682-4537 *Founded/Ownrshp* 1953
Sales 106.7MM *EMP* 500
Accts Allen Gibbs & Houlik Lc W
SIC 4785 Toll road operation
Pr: Michael L Johnston
**COO:* Alan Bakaitis
**Sec:* Les Donovan
Ofcr: Matt Lawson
Sfty Dirs: Merlin Eck

D-U-N-S 07-625-7427
KANSAS UNIVERSITY ENDOWMENT ASSOCIATION
KU ENDOWMENT
1891 Constant Ave, Lawrence, KS 66047-3743
Tel (785) 832-7400 *Founded/Ownrshp* 1891
Sales 142.2MM *EMP* 170
SIC 6732

D-U-N-S 92-922-8021
KANSAS UNIVERSITY PHYSICIANS INC
UNIVERSITY OF KANSAS
3901 Rainbow Blvd, Kansas City, KS 66160-8500
Tel (913) 362-2128 *Founded/Ownrshp* 1995
Sales 346.3MM *EMP* 480
Accts Bkd Llp Kansas City Mo
SIC 8011 Clinic, operated by physicians
CEO: Jim Albertson
Dir IT: Sean Roberts
Tech Mgr: Jim Gergen
Surgeon: Joseph Noland
Doctor: Kirk Benson
Doctor: Ronald Torline
Board of Directors: Keith Baskin

D-U-N-S 17-329-9827
KANTAR MEDIA INTELLIGENCES INC
TNS MEDIA INTELLIGENCE
(*Suby of* TNS GROUP HOLDINGS LIMITED)
11 Madison Ave Fl 12, New York, NY 10010-3643
Tel (800) 497-8450 *Founded/Ownrshp* 2005
Sales 95.0MMᴱ *EMP* 677
SIC 7313 Newspaper advertising representative; Magazine advertising representative; Radio advertising representative
CEO: Terry Kent
**Pr:* George Carens
Pr: Ron Mulliken
COO: Dave Kostolansky
COO: Darren Smith
**CFO:* Amy Silverstein
Ex VP: Bridget Armstrong
Ex VP: Paul Fiolek
Sr VP: Carl Dickens
**Sr VP:* Diane Laura
Sr VP: Libby Macdonald
Sr VP: Cheryl G Max
**Sr VP:* Joel Pacheco
Sr VP: Anita Watkins
VP: Scott Bernberg
VP: Pete Davis
VP: Beth Desautels
VP: Ziad Elmously
VP: Dave Emery
VP: Erin Fish
VP: Todd Isaacson

D-U-N-S 62-361-1188
KANTAR OPERATIONS
(*Suby of* W P P) ★
3333 Warrenville Rd # 400, Lisle, IL 60532-1462
Tel (630) 505-0066 *Founded/Ownrshp* 2006
Sales 64.3MMᴱ *EMP* 2,000
SIC 8732 Market analysis or research
Pr: Beth Teehan
**CFO:* Lee Larocque
VP: Mark Laforest
IT Man: Cook Jim

D-U-N-S 03-127-9367
KANZA COOPERATIVE ASSOCIATION
102 N Main St, Iuka, KS 67066-9401
Tel (620) 546-2231 *Founded/Ownrshp* 1915
Sales 300.0MM *EMP* 150
SIC 5153 5191 5541 4221 Grains; Farm supplies; Fertilizer & fertilizer materials; Chemicals, agricultural; Filling stations, gasoline; Grain elevator, storage only
CEO: Bruce Krehbiel
COO: Jeff Bolen
**CFO:* Brad Riley
IT Man: Anthony Holmes
Sls Mgr: Mickaela Bonnewell

D-U-N-S 15-518-4435 IMP/EXP
KANZAKI SPECIALTY PAPERS INC
(*Suby of* OJI IMAGING MEDIA CO.,LTD.)
20 Cummings St, Ware, MA 01082-1716
Tel (413) 967-6204 *Founded/Ownrshp* 1993
Sales 86.0MMᴱ *EMP* 233
SIC 2672 Coated & laminated paper
Pr: Stephen P Hefner
**VP:* David Gonsalves
**VP:* Stephen Hefner
**VP:* Joshua Polak
**VP:* Peter Sawosi
Sls Dir: Frank Neffinger
Sls Mgr: Frank Messemger

D-U-N-S 12-511-8872 IMP/EXP
KAO SPECIALTIES AMERICAS LLC
(*Suby of* KAO CORPORATION)
243 Woodbine St, High Point, NC 27260-8339
Tel (336) 878-4230 *Founded/Ownrshp* 1999
Sales 244.5MMᴱ *EMP* 152
SIC 5169 Chemicals & allied products
Ofcr: Gerald Sykes
Dir Lab: Steve Williams
Cmptr Lab: Gwen Glover
Opers Mgr: Keisha Barrett
VP Sls: Kenji Omori
Mktg Mgr: Warren Kotacska
Sls Mgr: Harriet Gayle
Sls Mgr: Mark Hellriegel
Sls Mgr: Chitose Page

D-U-N-S 00-425-1617 IMP/EXP
KAO USA INC
(*Suby of* KAO CORPORATION)
2535 Spring Grove Ave, Cincinnati, OH 45214-1729
Tel (513) 421-1400 *Founded/Ownrshp* 1988
Sales 553.5MMᴱ *EMP* 1,100
SIC 2844 2841 Cosmetic preparations; Face creams or lotions; Soap: granulated, liquid, cake, flaked or chip
Pr: Bill Gentner
**Pr:* John Nosek
VP: Steve Cagle
VP: Mark Cushman
VP: Satoshi Onitsuka
VP: Glen Spurrier
VP: John Sullivan
VP: Jayson Zoller
Assoc Dir: Brian Haavig
Assoc Dir: Neil Larrance
CIO: Bob Garriot

D-U-N-S 04-454-1019 IMP
KAOLIN MUSHROOM FARMS INC
649 W South St, Kennett Square, PA 19348-3417
Tel (610) 444-4800 *Founded/Ownrshp* 1985
Sales 138.4MMᴱ *EMP* 491
SIC 0182 Mushroom spawn, production of
Pr: Michael Pia
**VP:* John Pia
Sfty Mgr: Richard Rush

D-U-N-S 07-766-1890
■ **KAPALUA LAND CO LTD**
PLANTATION ESTATES
(*Suby of* MAUI LAND & PINEAPPLE COMPANY, INC.)
1000 Kapalua Dr, Lahaina, HI 96761-9028
Tel (808) 669-5622 *Founded/Ownrshp* 1975
Sales 619.2MMᴱ *EMP* 462
SIC 6552 6512 Land subdividers & developers, commercial; Commercial & industrial building operation
CEO: David C Cole
Ch Bd: Richard Cameron
Treas: Darryl Chai
Ex VP: Paul J Meyer
VP: Robert M McNatt
VP: Thomas J Selby

KAPCO GLOBAL
See KIRKHILL AIRCRAFT PARTS CO

D-U-N-S 96-954-1155
KAPIOLANI MEDICAL CENTER AT PALI MOMI
55 Merchant St, Honolulu, HI 96813-4306
Tel (808) 486-6000 *Founded/Ownrshp* 2011
Sales 122.6MMᴱ *EMP* 2
Accts Ernst & Young Us Llp Honolulu
SIC 8322 Emergency shelters
Prin: Arnobit
Ofcr: Teresa Pytel

D-U-N-S 06-628-1080
KAPIOLANI MEDICAL CENTER FOR WOMEN AND CHILDREN
HAWAII PACIFIC HEALTH
(*Suby of* HAWAII PACIFIC HEALTH) ★
1319 Punahou St, Honolulu, HI 96826-1001
Tel (808) 535-7401 *Founded/Ownrshp* 1890
Sales 371.4MM *EMP* 1,378
SIC 8069 Maternity hospital; Children's hospital
CEO: Martha Smith
VP: Dew-Anne Langcaon
Surgeon: Devin Puapong
Obsttrcn: Tod Aeby
Obsttrcn: Leticia Diniega
Obsttrcn: Angela M Pratt
Doctor: Kent Kumashiro
Doctor: Cherilyn Yee

D-U-N-S 87-805-7330
KAPL INC
KNOLLS ATOMIC POWER LABORATORY
2401 River Rd, Schenectady, NY 12309-1103
Tel (877) 527-5522 *Founded/Ownrshp* 1993
Sales 315.9MMᴱ *EMP* 2,600
SIC 8731 Energy research
Ch Bd: Michael F Quinn
**Treas:* Janet L McGregor
Exec: Len Yanazzo
Mng Dir: Emmanuel Seiz
Brnch Mgr: John Freeh

KAPLAN & CRAWFORD DODGE WORLD
See DAR CARS DODGE INC

D-U-N-S 78-738-9337
KAPLAN AT OLD BRIDGE INC
KAPLAN COMPANIES
433 River Rd, Highland Park, NJ 08904-1918
Tel (732) 846-5900 *Founded/Ownrshp* 1983
Sales 200.0MM *EMP* 180
SIC 6552 Land subdividers & developers, residential
CEO: Michael Kaplan
**Pr:* Jason Kaplan
CFO: Stevenz Sprauss
**VP:* Morris Kaplan
Sales Exec: Rose Kramer
Mktg Dir: Christina Santowasso

KAPLAN COLLEGE
See KAPLAN HIGHER EDUCATION LLC

KAPLAN COMPANIES
See KAPLAN AT OLD BRIDGE INC

KAPLAN EDUCATIONAL CENTERS
See KAPLAN INC

D-U-N-S 05-246-7201
■ **KAPLAN HIGHER EDUCATION LLC**
(*Suby of* KAPLAN EDUCATIONAL CENTERS) ★
900 North Point Pkwy # 250, Alpharetta, GA 30005-8901
Tel (770) 360-6100 *Founded/Ownrshp* 1988
Sales 241.1MMᴱ *EMP* 5,141
SIC 8221 8244 Colleges universities & professional schools; Business & secretarial schools
Pr: Jefffrey Conlon
COO: Andrew Rosen
CFO: Lionel Lenz
Sr VP: Elaine Neely
Sr VP: Matthew Seelye
VP: Kevin L Corser

D-U-N-S 08-179-7110
■ **KAPLAN HIGHER EDUCATION LLC**
KAPLAN COLLEGE
(*Suby of* KAPLAN HIGHER EDUCATION LLC) ★
9055 Balboa Ave, San Diego, CA 92123-1509
Tel (858) 279-4500 *Founded/Ownrshp* 1989
Sales 35.8MMᴱ *EMP* 2,000
SIC 8249 Medical training services
Pr: Mike Seifert
Prin: Vickie Davis

D-U-N-S 06-607-6837
■ **KAPLAN INC**
KAPLAN EDUCATIONAL CENTERS
(*Suby of* GRAHAM HOLDINGS CO) ★
6301 Kaplan Univ Ave, Fort Lauderdale, FL 33309-1905
Tel (212) 492-5800 *Founded/Ownrshp* 1984
Sales 297.1MMᴱ *EMP* 6,388
SIC 8299 7361 7372 2731 Educational services; Tutoring school; Reading school, including speed reading; Employment agencies; Prepackaged software; Book publishing
Ch: Andrew S Rosen
Mng Pt: David Kaplan
Pr: Howard Benson
**Pr:* Eric Cantor
Pr: Maria Closs
Pr: Hal Jones
**Pr:* Thomas C Leppert
Pr: Donna Skibbe
**CEO:* Jonathan N Grayer
COO: Prodeep Ghosh
CFO: Scott August
**CFO:* Robert L Lane
CFO: David Munns
**CFO:* Matthew Seelye
Chf Mktg O: Eric Plath
Ofcr: M J Miller
Ofcr: Sharon Miller
**Ex VP:* Veronica Dillon
**Ex VP:* Vince Pisano
**Ex VP:* Darrell Splithoff
Sr VP: Wade Dyke

D-U-N-S 07-852-8400
■ **KAPLAN K12 LEARNING SERVICES LLC**
(*Suby of* KAPLAN EDUCATIONAL CENTERS) ★
395 Hudson St Fl 4, New York, NY 10014-3669
Tel (888) 527-5268 *Founded/Ownrshp* 2012
Sales 14.0MMᴱ *EMP* 7,383
SIC 8299 Educational services
CEO: John Polstein
**Treas:* Matthew Seelye
**VP:* Janice Block
VP: Jeffery Elie
**VP:* Mark Freidberg

D-U-N-S 04-797-5966
KAPPA KAPPA GAMMA FOUNDATION
KAPPA KAPPA GAMMA FRATERNITY
530 E Town St, Columbus, OH 43215-4820
Tel (614) 228-6515 *Founded/Ownrshp* 1870
Sales 6.1MM *EMP* 1,000
Accts Crowe Horwath Llp Columbus O
SIC 8641 Fraternal associations
Dir IT: Jane Steiner
Mktg Dir: Ashley Moyer

KAPPA KAPPA GAMMA FRATERNITY
See KAPPA KAPPA GAMMA FOUNDATION

D-U-N-S 15-286-1642
KAPPA MEDIA GROUP INC
40 Skippack Pike, Fort Washington, PA 19034-1100
Tel (215) 643-5800 *Founded/Ownrshp* 2000
Sales 153.4MMᴱ *EMP* 465
SIC 2721 2741 5111 Magazines: publishing only, not printed on site; Miscellaneous publishing; Printing paper
Pr: Nick Karabots
Treas: William Mainwaring
VP: William J Bonner

KAPSTONE
See LONGVIEW FIBRE PAPER AND PACKAGING INC

D-U-N-S 82-865-1799 IMP/EXP
■ **KAPSTONE CHARLESTON KRAFT LLC**
(*Suby of* KAPSTONE PAPER AND PACKAGING CORP) ★
5600 Virginia Ave, North Charleston, SC 29406-3612
Tel (843) 745-3000 *Founded/Ownrshp* 2008
Sales 196.8MMᴱ *EMP* 1,088ᴱ
SIC 2621 Bag paper

D-U-N-S 17-443-2070
■ **KAPSTONE CONTAINER CORP**
(*Suby of* KAPSTONE PAPER AND PACKAGING CORP) ★
1601 Blairs Ferry Rd Ne, Cedar Rapids, IA 52402-5805
Tel (319) 393-3610 *Founded/Ownrshp* 2011
Sales 202.6MMᴱ *EMP* 135ᴱ
SIC 2653 Sheets, corrugated: made from purchased materials
CEO: Roger Stone
**Pr:* Matthew Kaplan
**Pr:* Timothy P Keneally
**Pr:* Randy J Nebel
Pr: Ingrid Santiago
**VP:* Andrea K Tarboxm
IT Man: Stephen Weeks

D-U-N-S 79-092-8936 EXP
■ **KAPSTONE KRAFT PAPER CORP**
(*Suby of* KAPSTONE PAPER AND PACKAGING CORP) ★
1101 Skokie Blvd Ste 300, Northbrook, IL 60062-4124
Tel (252) 533-6000 *Founded/Ownrshp* 2006
Sales 281.5MMᴱ *EMP* 453
SIC 2621 Packaging paper
Pr: Timothy Keneally
Bd of Dir: Earl Shapiro
VP: Tim Keneally

D-U-N-S 60-714-1442 EXP
▲ **KAPSTONE PAPER AND PACKAGING CORP**
1101 Skokie Blvd Ste 300, Northbrook, IL 60062-4124
Tel (847) 239-8800 *Founded/Ownrshp* 2005
Sales 2.7MMM *EMP* 6,440
Tkr Sym KS *Exch* NYS
SIC 2621 Paper mills
Ch Bd: Roger W Stone
**Pr:* Matthew Kaplan
Pr: Timothy P Keneally
Pr: Randy J Nebel
**CFO:* Andrea K Tarbox

*VP: Kathryn D Ingraham
VP: Antionette Meyers
*VP: Mark A Niehus
Ql Cn Mgr: Jim Yarborough
Board of Directors: David P Storch, Robert J Bahash, John M Chapman, Paula H J Cholmondeley, Jonathan R Furer, David G Gabriel, Brian R Gamache, Ronald J Gidwitz, Matthew H Paull, Maurice S Reznik

D-U-N-S 07-963-2828
■ KAPSTONE RECEIVABLES LLC
(Suby of KAPSTONE PAPER AND PACKAGING CORP) ★
1101 Skokie Blvd Ste 300, Northbrook, IL 60062-4124
Tel (270) 393-2559 Founded/Ownrshp 2014
Sales 6.0MM^E EMP 1,356^E
SIC 7322 Collection agency, except real estate

D-U-N-S 80-056-7534
▲ KAR AUCTION SERVICES INC
13085 Hmlton Crssing Blvd, Carmel, IN 46032-1412
Tel (800) 923-3725 Founded/Ownrshp 2007
Sales 2.6MMM EMP 14,400^E
Tkr Sym KAR Exch NYS
SIC 5012 6153 5521 Automobiles & other motor vehicles; Automotive brokers; Financing of dealers by motor vehicle manufacturers organ.; Used car dealers
Ch Bd: James P Hallett
COO: Donald S Gottwald
CFO: Eric M Loughmiller
Chf Cred: Thomas J Caruso
Ex VP: Warren W Byrd
Ex VP: Lisa Pierce
Ex VP: Rebecca C Polak
Ex VP: Lisa A Price
Ex VP: Benjamin Skuy
Ex VP: David Vignes
VP: Michael Eliason
Board of Directors: Todd F Bourell, Donna R Ecton, Mark E Hill, J Mark Howell, Lynn Jolliffe, Michael R Kestner, John P Larson, Stephen E Smith

D-U-N-S 80-055-0019
KAR HOLDINGS II LLC
13085 Hamil Cross Blvd St Ste 500, Carmel, IN 46032
Tel (317) 815-1100 Founded/Ownrshp 2006
Sales 3.3MMM^E EMP 13,253
SIC 5012 6153 Automobiles & other motor vehicles; Automotive brokers; Commercial vehicles; Short-term business credit; Financing of dealers by motor vehicle manufacturers organ.
Treas: James E Money
Netwrk Eng: Garrett Baggs

D-U-N-S 04-242-8037
KAR NUT PRODUCTS CO
KAR'S NUTS
1200 E 14 Mile Rd Ste A, Madison Heights, MI 48071-1421
Tel (248) 588-1903 Founded/Ownrshp 1967
Sales 140.3MM^E EMP 140
SIC 5145 2068 Confectionery; Nuts: dried, dehydrated, salted or roasted
Pr: Ernest L Nicolay III
*VP: William P Elam
Exec: Nick Nicolay
IT Man: Thomas H Long
Prd Mgr: Bill Leva
Mktg Dir: John Koskovich
Sls Mgr: Scott McKinnon

D-U-N-S 12-947-9924
■ KAR PRODUCTS
(Suby of BARNES GROUP INC) ★
1301 E 9th St Ste 700, Cleveland, OH 44114-1800
Tel (216) 416-7200 Founded/Ownrshp 2005
Sales 100.5MM^E EMP 1,200
SIC 5013 5084 5072 Automotive supplies & parts; Automobile glass; Hydraulic systems equipment & supplies; Pneumatic tools & equipment; Screws; Nuts (hardware); Bolts; Washers (hardware)
Prin: Ronald Koskela

KARCHER NORTH AMERICA
See C-TECH INDUSTRIES INC

D-U-N-S 07-703-0773 IMP/EXP
KARCHER NORTH AMERICA INC
(Suby of ALFRED KARCHER GMBH & CO. KG)
4555 Airport Way Fl 4, Denver, CO 80239-5801
Tel (303) 762-1800 Founded/Ownrshp 2006
Sales 348.1MM^E EMP 1,018
SIC 3635 5084 Household vacuum cleaners; Cleaning equipment, high pressure, sand or steam
CEO: Hannes Subert
*CFO: Peter Lynch
Treas: Roland Deibler
VP: Chris Doerr
Sales Exec: Debbie Castro
Sls Dir: Steve Bowie
Mktg Mgr: David Hults
Sls Mgr: Patrick Battaglia
Snr Mgr: Tunseth Amber

KAREL MANUFACTURING
See LORENZ INC

KARI OUT COMPANY
See PERK-UP INC

D-U-N-S 02-557-8170
KARL KNAUZ MOTORS INC
775 Rockland Rd, Lake Bluff, IL 60044-2208
Tel (847) 615-3670 Founded/Ownrshp 1961
Sales 86.6MM^E EMP 280
SIC 5511 Automobiles, new & used
Pr: William R Madden
*Owner: H William Knauz
*Sec: Ingeborg Knauz
Genl Mgr: James Astuno
Telecom Ex: Jeff Lefevbre
IT Man: Ann Morocco

KARL MALONE TOYOTA
See M & M AUTOMOTIVE INC

D-U-N-S 07-529-3423 IMP
KARL STORZ ENDOSCOPY-AMERICA INC
(Suby of KARL STORZ GMBH & CO. KG)
2151 E Grand Ave, El Segundo, CA 90245-5017
Tel (424) 218-8100 Founded/Ownrshp 1971
Sales 300.3MM^E EMP 900^E
SIC 3841 5047 Surgical & medical instruments; Medical equipment & supplies
CEO: Charles Wilhelm
*CFO: Dean Ditto
VP: Barbara Durant
*VP: Mark Green
VP: Jean L Hopper
VP: Cristina Lee
Ex Dir: Mark Heinemeyer
Genl Mgr: Cory Alcala
CIO: Matt Butcher
Tech Mgr: James Singer
Opers Supe: Cynthia Adams

D-U-N-S 78-091-3190
KARL STORZ ENDOVISION INC
(Suby of KARL STORZ GMBH & CO. KG)
91 Carpenter Hill Rd, Charlton, MA 01507-5274
Tel (508) 248-9011 Founded/Ownrshp 1989
Sales 130.2MM^E EMP 400
SIC 3841 Surgical & medical instruments
Pr: Gary Macker
*Owner: Sybill Storz
Genl Mgr: Bruce Watkins
Off Mgr: Kelli Banas
CTO: Thomas Richard
QA Dir: Jason Johnson
QA Dir: Jodi Peck
Mfg Dir: Thomas Caron
QC Dir: Tina Seifert
Opers Mgr: Bill Kirk
Prd Mgr: Rich Santora

D-U-N-S 83-253-7976 IMP
KARL STORZ IMAGING INC
(Suby of KARL STORZ GMBH & CO. KG)
175 Cremona Dr, Goleta, CA 93117-5502
Tel (805) 845-3617 Founded/Ownrshp 1984
Sales 118.0MM^E EMP 350
SIC 3841 Optometers
CEO: Gary A Macker
VP: Jim Fish
Mng Dir: Jerry Xu
Prgrm Mgr: Bradford Lim
Genl Mgr: Daniel McMahon
CTO: Karl Storz
Dir IT: David Chatenever
Dir IT: Craig Pannett
Sls Dir: Anna Fritz
Mktg Mgr: Rich Crandall
Sls Mgr: Mike Bateman

D-U-N-S 08-473-8566 EXP
KARLIN FOODS CORP (IL)
1845 Oak St Ste 19, Northfield, IL 60093-3022
Tel (847) 441-8330 Founded/Ownrshp 1977
Sales 128.8MM EMP 17
Accts Hdb Llc Chicago Il
SIC 2034 Dehydrated fruits, vegetables, soups
Pr: Mitchell Karlin
*Treas: Donna Hastings
Manager: Keith Creel
Sls Mgr: Michael Frick

D-U-N-S 07-952-3495
KARMA AUTOMOTIVE LLC
(Suby of WANXIANG AMERICA CORP) ★
3080 Airway Ave, Costa Mesa, CA 92626-6034
Tel (714) 723-3247 Founded/Ownrshp 2014
Sales 158.3MM^E EMP 300^E
SIC 3711 Motor vehicles & car bodies
*Pr: Tom Corcoran
*VP: Ronald Samaco

D-U-N-S 80-457-8487
KARNAVATI HOLDINGS INC
(Suby of NIRMA LIMITED)
9401 Indian Creek Pkwy # 1000, Overland Park, KS 66210-2007
Tel (913) 344-9500 Founded/Ownrshp 2008
Sales 554.2MM^E EMP 649
SIC 1479 Salt & sulfur mining

KARNS FOOD
See KARNS PRIME AND FANCY FOOD LTD

D-U-N-S 06-977-5781
KARNS PRIME AND FANCY FOOD LTD (PA)
KARNS FOOD
675 Silver Spring Rd, Mechanicsburg, PA 17050-2846
Tel (717) 766-6477 Founded/Ownrshp 1959
Sales 112.4MM^E EMP 800
SIC 5411

D-U-N-S 07-922-7654
KARPELES FREIGHT SERVICES INC
(Suby of DB US HOLDING CORP) ★
150 Albany Ave, Freeport, NY 11520-4702
Tel (516) 377-3000 Founded/Ownrshp 2013
Sales 205.0M^E EMP 2,039^E
SIC 4731 Freight transportation arrangement
CEO: Malcolm Heath
*CFO: Donna Hanson Prantl

KAR'S NUTS
See KAR NUT PRODUCTS CO

D-U-N-S 04-201-8184 IMP
KARSTEN MANUFACTURING CORP (AZ)
PING
2201 W Desert Cove Ave, Phoenix, AZ 85029-4912
Tel (602) 870-5000 Founded/Ownrshp 1959
Sales 319.3MM^E EMP 1,400
SIC 3949 3398 3363 3325 8711 7997 Golf equipment; Metal heat treating; Aluminum die-castings; Steel foundries; Civil engineering; Country club, membership
CEO: John A Solheim
CFO: George Drewry
Treas: Dawn M Grove
*Treas: Michael T Trueblood
*Ex VP: K Louis Solheim
*Ex VP: Louise Solheim
*VP: Rawleigh Grove
*VP: Stacey S Pauwels
CTO: Stacey Solheim
Plnt Mgr: Pat Patrick
Snr Mgr: Jolana Dyson

KAS-KEL
See KASSON & KELLER INC

KASAI NORTH AMERICA, INC.
See M-TEK INC

D-U-N-S 93-357-4316
KASASA LTD
BANCVUE
4516 Seton Center Pkwy, Austin, TX 78759-5370
Tel (512) 418-9590 Founded/Ownrshp 2004
Sales 106.6MM^E EMP 318^E
SIC 7371 7373 7379 Computer software systems analysis & design, custom; Computer integrated systems design; Computer related consulting services
Prin: Don Shafer
*Pr: Martin D Sunde
*CEO: Gabriel Krajicek
*CFO: Jeremy Foster
Chf Mktg O: Keith Brannan
Ex VP: Stan Goudeau
Sr VP: Bob Brandt
Sr VP: Lori Peterson
Sr VP: Tom Snyder
VP: Nathan Baumeister
VP: Sean Downing
VP: Grant Gerthoffer
VP: Paul Hamby
VP: Michael Lee
VP: Kelly L Payne
VP: Craig Raughton
Exec: Dawn Lewis
Exec: Lorie McDonald
Exec: Jason Seale

KASMIR FABRICS
See FRANK KASMIR ASSOCIATES INC

D-U-N-S 00-121-0749 IMP/EXP
KASON INDUSTRIES INC
KASON MID-WEST
57 Amlajack Blvd, Newnan, GA 30265-1093
Tel (770) 251-1422 Founded/Ownrshp 1928
Sales 83.8MM^E EMP 360
SIC 3589

KASON MID-WEST
See KASON INDUSTRIES INC

D-U-N-S 00-809-2983
KASPAR WIRE WORKS INC
959 State Highway 95 N, Shiner, TX 77984-5883
Tel (361) 594-3327 Founded/Ownrshp 1898
Sales 109.0MM^E EMP 650
SIC 3496 Miscellaneous fabricated wire products
Pr: Dan A Kaspar
*Treas: Douglas D Kaspar
*VP: David C Kaspar

D-U-N-S 96-928-1120
KASPER ASL LTD
180 Rittenhouse Cir, Bristol, PA 19007-1618
Tel (215) 785-4000 Founded/Ownrshp 2003
Sales NA EMP 2,240
SIC 2337

D-U-N-S 94-216-9343 IMP/EXP
KASPER GROUP LLC
1412 Broadway Fl 5, New York, NY 10018-3330
Tel (212) 354-4311 Founded/Ownrshp 1995
Sales 350.0MM EMP 250
SIC 2335 Women's, juniors' & misses' dresses
Pr: Gregg Marks
*CFO: Daniel Fishman
Board of Directors: Arthur Levine, Lester Schreiber, Meredith Warz

D-U-N-S 00-207-7196 IMP
KASSON & KELLER INC (NY)
KAS-KEL
60 School St, Fonda, NY 12068-4809
Tel (518) 853-3421 Founded/Ownrshp 1946
Sales 173.8MM^E EMP 900
SIC 3442 3089 1521 3231 Window & door frames; Windows, plastic; Single-family housing construction; Products of purchased glass
Ch Bd: William Keller III
*Ex VP: James P Keller
VP: Drue Wallach
CIO: Greg Spencer
Sls Mgr: Mark Empie
Sls Mgr: Matthew Sullivan

D-U-N-S 62-079-9382
KAST CONSTRUCTION CO LLC
701 Nrthpint Pkwy Ste 400, West Palm Beach, FL 33407
Tel (561) 689-2910 Founded/Ownrshp 2005
Sales 203.5MM EMP 125
Accts Ef Alvarez & Company Pa
SIC 1531 Operative builders
Pr: Michael Neal
VP: Dave Demay
VP: Page McKee
Dir Bus: Ashlee Figg

D-U-N-S 01-739-6172 IMP
KATANA RACING INC
KATANA RACING WHL & TIRE DISTR
14407 Alondra Blvd, La Mirada, CA 90638-5504
Tel (562) 977-8565 Founded/Ownrshp 1998
Sales 123.4MM^E EMP 105^E
Accts Agoplan & Baboghli Torrance
SIC 5013 5014 Wheels, motor vehicle; Automobile tires & tubes; Truck tires & tubes
CEO: ARA Tchaghlassian
Genl Mgr: Joe Garcia

KATANA RACING WHL & TIRE DISTR
See KATANA RACING INC

D-U-N-S 16-280-4855
KATCH
2381 Rosecrans Ave # 400, El Segundo, CA 90245-4917
Tel (310) 219-6200 Founded/Ownrshp 2002
Sales 140.0MM EMP 70
SIC 7311 Advertising agencies
CEO: Patrick Quigley
VP: Betsy Niksefat
Dir Bus: Jeff Sweetser
*Dir IT: Robert Chrone
Board of Directors: Jamie Montgomery, Rory O'-driscoll

D-U-N-S 04-005-9230 IMP/EXP
▲ KATE SPADE & CO
2 Park Ave Fl 8, New York, NY 10016-5613
Tel (212) 354-4900 Founded/Ownrshp 1976
Sales 1.2MMM EMP 3,600
Tkr Sym KATE Exch NYS
SIC 2331 5651 5136 5137 5961 Women's & misses' blouses & shirts; Family clothing stores; Unisex clothing stores; Men's & boys' clothing; Women's & children's clothing; Catalog & mail-order houses
CEO: Craig A Leavitt
*Ch Bd: Nancy J Karch
Pr: George M Carrara
CFO: Thomas Linko
*Chf Cred: Deborah J Lloyd
Sr VP: Timothy F Michno
Sr VP: Linda Yanussi
VP: Robert Karpf
VP: Patricia Peters
VP: Carmen Vieira
Exec: William Higley
Board of Directors: Lawrence S Benjamin, Raul J Fernandez, Carsten Fischer, Kenneth B Gilman, Kenneth P Kopelman, Douglas Mack, Jan Singer, Doreen A Toben

D-U-N-S 00-592-6030 EXP
■ KATE SPADE LLC
(Suby of KATE SPADE & CO) ★
2 Park Ave Fl 8, New York, NY 10016-5613
Tel (201) 295-6000 Founded/Ownrshp 1990
Sales 399.5MM^E EMP 190
SIC 5137 5632 Handbags; Handbags
CEO: Craig A Leavitt
*Pr: George M Carrara
*Sr VP: Mary Beech
*Sr VP: Christopher Di Nardo
*Sr VP: Bill Higley
VP: Donna Chiffriller
VP: John Cullina
VP: Phillip Rosenzweig
Ex Dir: Al Mateo
Netwrk Eng: Charles Shepard

D-U-N-S 06-401-2008
KATHERINE SHAW BETHEA HOSPITAL
KSB HOSPITAL
403 E 1st St, Dixon, IL 61021-3187
Tel (815) 288-5531 Founded/Ownrshp 1893
Sales 135.3MM EMP 1,000
SIC 8062

D-U-N-S 82-550-0791
KATMAI GOVERNMENT SERVICES LLC
(Suby of OUZINKIE NATIVE CORP) ★
11001 Omalley Centre Dr # 204, Anchorage, AK 99515-3096
Tel (907) 333-7000 Founded/Ownrshp 2007
Sales 85.0MM^E EMP 812^E
SIC 3812 Search & navigation equipment
CEO: R David Stephens
*Pr: Shane Harvey
*CFO: Thomas Clements
*Ex VP: Cynthia Vanden Berg
Dir IT: Jeff Hall

D-U-N-S 04-182-7986 IMP/EXP
■ KATO ENGINEERING INC
EMERSON INDUSTRIAL AUTOMATION
(Suby of EMERSON ELECTRIC CO) ★
2075 Howard Dr W, North Mankato, MN 56003-9921
Tel (507) 345-2716 Founded/Ownrshp 1998
Sales 113.0MM^E EMP 350
SIC 3621 3643 3625 Motors & generators; Current-carrying wiring devices; Relays & industrial controls
CEO: David N Farr
Brnch Mgr: Doug Rohlk
Genl Mgr: Nate Wenner
Dir IT: Will Bauman
VP Opers: Kevin Newman
Sls Mgr: Dave Miller

D-U-N-S 83-872-2361
KATO KAGAKU CO LTD
HYATT REGENCY CHICAGO
151 E Wacker Dr, Chicago, IL 60601-3764
Tel (312) 565-1234 Founded/Ownrshp 1989
Sales 130.6MM^E EMP 1,300
SIC 6512 7011 Hotels & motels
Pr: Eiichi Kato
Sr VP: Peter Norman
*VP: Shoji Kato
Assoc Dir: Lori Ramos
Ex Dir: Erica Korpi
Genl Mgr: Randy Thompson

D-U-N-S 02-003-4351
KATTEN MUCHIN ROSENMAN LLP
525 W Monroe St Ste 1900, Chicago, IL 60661-3718
Tel (312) 902-5200 Founded/Ownrshp 1974
Sales 263.3MM^E EMP 1,731
SIC 8111

D-U-N-S 09-391-6377 IMP/EXP
KATUN CORP
BLMGTN
(Suby of MONOMOY CAPITAL PARTNERS LP) ★
10951 Bush Lake Rd # 100, Minneapolis, MN 55438-2391
Tel (952) 941-9505 Founded/Ownrshp 2008
Sales 390.6MM^E EMP 1,060
SIC 5112 Photocopying supplies
Pr: Carlyle Singer
Pr: Jan Bolin

*Pr: Todd Mavis
Treas: Tom Wallace
Sr VP: Russell S John
Rgnl Mgr: Bridget McGlenn
Sales Exec: Prima Juniar
Sls&Mrk Ex: Mauricio Gonzalez
Mktg Mgr: Cornelis Alderlieste
Mktg Mgr: Matthew Oconnor
Mktg Mgr: Dan Stewart

D-U-N-S 02-081-4232
KATY INDEPENDENT SCHOOL DISTRICT
6301 S Stadium Ln, Katy, TX 77494-1057
Tel (281) 396-6000 Founded/Ownrshp 1919
Sales 443.4MM[E] EMP 6,631
SIC 8211 Elementary & secondary schools; High school, junior or senior
Pr: Bryan Michalsky
*Pr: Rebecca Fox
*CFO: William L Moore
*Treas: Charles Griffin
Bd of Dir: Neal Howard
Bd of Dir: Tom Law
*VP: Joe M Adams
*VP: Henry Dibrell
Ex Dir: Brian Malechuk
Ex Dir: Ron Pleasant
Dir Sec: Peggy Caruso

D-U-N-S 14-557-9491
KATY INDEPENDENT SCHOOL DISTRICT DARE ADVISORY BOARD INC
20380 Franz Rd, Katy, TX 77449-5600
Tel (281) 396-2500 Founded/Ownrshp 1999
Sales 47.0MM[E] EMP 7,000[E]
Accts Null-Lairson Pc Cpas Houst
SIC 8211 Public elementary & secondary schools

D-U-N-S 04-463-8369
▲ KATY INDUSTRIES INC
11840 Westline Industrial, Saint Louis, MO 63146-3329
Tel (314) 656-4321 Founded/Ownrshp 1967
Sales 113.9MM EMP 301[E]
Tkr Sym KATY Exch OTO
SIC 3589 2673 Commercial cleaning equipment; Food storage & trash bags (plastic)
Pr: Robert L Guerra
*Ch Bd: Richard A Mark
CFO: Curt A Kroll
VP: Brian G Nichols
Board of Directors: Christopher W Anderson, Daniel B Carroll, Pamela Carrol Crigler, Samuel P Frieder

KATZ COMMUNICATIONS
See KATZ MEDIA GROUP INC

D-U-N-S 88-354-1302
■ KATZ MEDIA GROUP INC
KATZ COMMUNICATIONS
(Suby of IHEARTCOMMUNICATIONS INC) ★
125 W 55th St Fl 11, New York, NY 10019-5385
Tel (212) 315-0956 Founded/Ownrshp 1993
Sales 25.7MM[E] EMP 1,300
SIC 7313 Radio, television, publisher representatives
CEO: Stuart O Olds
CEO: Mark Rosenthal
*CFO: Robert Damon
Bd of Dir: Pamela Peterson
Ex VP: Stacey Lynn Schulman
Ex VP: Jay Zeitchik
VP: Donna Bell
*VP: James E Beloyianis
VP: Michelle Blevins
VP: Mike Bramel
*VP: Joe Brewer
VP: Bill Carroll
VP: Megan Carson
VP: Steve Diamond
VP: Russell Fielder
VP: Emily Ginsburg
VP: Noel Goldman
VP: Mark Goldstein
VP: Trevor Heaton
VP: Kim Jack
VP: Dimitri Kotsis

D-U-N-S 80-887-4408
■ KATZ MILLENNIUM SALES & MARKETING INC
(Suby of KATZ COMMUNICATIONS) ★
125 W 55th St Frnt 3, New York, NY 10019-5936
Tel (212) 424-6000 Founded/Ownrshp 1990
Sales 17.6MM[E] EMP 1,300
SIC 7313 Radio, television, publisher representatives
Pr: James E Beloyianis
CEO: Stuart O Olds

D-U-N-S 17-510-1401 IMP
KATZKIN LEATHER INC
6868 W Acco St, Montebello, CA 90640-5441
Tel (323) 725-1243 Founded/Ownrshp 1998
Sales 102.1MM[E] EMP 265
SIC 5199 2531 Leather & cut stock; Seats, automobile
Pr: Brook Mayberry
Pr: Jim Roberson
Rgnl Mgr: Bill North
Mktg Dir: Miles Hubbard

KAUAI COFFEE CO
See MASSIMO ZANETTI BEVERAGE USA INC

D-U-N-S 12-272-1587
KAUAI ISLAND UTILITY COOPERATIVE
4463 Pahee St Ste 1, Lihue, HI 96766-2000
Tel (808) 246-4300 Founded/Ownrshp 2002
Sales 179.3MM EMP 159
Accts Moss Adams Llp Portland Oreg
SIC 4911 Generation, electric power
Pr: Dennis Esaki
*Ch Bd: Allan Smith
*CEO: David J Bissell
*CFO: Karissa Jonas
*Treas: Peter Yukimura
*V Ch Bd: Jan Tenbruggencate
Exec: Pia Gregorio
Comm Man: Jim Kelly
*Prin: Carol Bain
*Prin: Karen Baldwin
*Prin: Patrick Gegen

D-U-N-S 19-331-5272
KAUAI SCHOOL DISTRICT
(Suby of OFFICE OF SUPERINTENDENT) ★
3060 Eiwa St Ste 305, Lihue, HI 96766-1876
Tel (808) 274-3502 Founded/Ownrshp 2002
Sales 29.9MM[E] EMP 1,887[E]
SIC 8211 9411 Public elementary & secondary schools; Administration of educational programs

D-U-N-S 18-611-6802 IMP
KAUFFMAN TIRE INC
2832 Anvil Block Rd, Ellenwood, GA 30294-2301
Tel (404) 762-4944 Founded/Ownrshp 1978
Sales 327.8MM[E] EMP 600
SIC 5014 5531 Automobile tires & tubes; Automotive tires
Pr: John Kauffman
*CFO: Susan Reeves
CFO: Reeves Susan
*Ex VP: Tom Money
VP: Richard Alderman
VP: Allen Battista
Sales Asso: Brian Massey
Sales Asso: Chester Mejia

D-U-N-S 10-140-5397 IMP
■ KAUTEX INC
(Suby of TEXTRON INC) ★
750 Stephenson Hwy, Troy, MI 48083-1103
Tel (248) 616-5100 Founded/Ownrshp 1996
Sales 2.8MMM[E] EMP 16,000
SIC 3714 Motor vehicle parts & accessories; Instrument board assemblies, motor vehicle; Bumpers & bumperettes, motor vehicle
Pr: Vicente Perez-Lucerga
COO: Hanno Neizer
Treas: Mary F Lovejoy
Ex VP: Edward Certisimo
Ex VP: Klaus Konig
Sr VP: James Heffner
VP: Rob Abfall
VP: Mark Ankenbauer
*VP: John H Bracken
VP: Mira Eigler
VP: Klaus Esser
VP: Arnold M Friedman
VP: Greg Fuller
VP: James M Heethuis
VP: Paul Luft
VP: Andrew Quibell
VP: Norman B Richter
VP: Ann T Willamson

D-U-N-S 00-826-7262 EXP
KAVLICO CORP
(Suby of C S T) ★
1461 Lawrence Dr, Thousand Oaks, CA 91320-1311
Tel (805) 523-2000 Founded/Ownrshp 1958
Sales 316.2MM[E] EMP 1,400
SIC 3679 3829 3823 Transducers, electrical; Measuring & controlling devices; Industrial instrmnts msrmnt display/control process variable
Pr: Martha Sullivan
VP: Alison Roelke
VP: Carmine Villani
Genl Mgr: Todd Jensen
Manager: John Andrews
Manager: Arron Bickerton
Manager: Lynn Koch
Manager: Christopher Mussat
Manager: Scott Purvis
Manager: Patrick Thomas

D-U-N-S 03-759-1419 IMP
■ KAVO DENTAL TECHNOLOGIES LLC
PELTON & CRANE
(Suby of DANAHER CORP) ★
11729 Fruehauf Dr, Charlotte, NC 28273-6507
Tel (888) 275-5286 Founded/Ownrshp 1980
Sales 120.7MM[E] EMP 465
SIC 5047 Dental equipment & supplies
Bd of Dir: Scott Fraser
VP: Robert Winter
Dir IT: Mike Sherman
IT Man: Jamie Allen
IT Man: Ben Chapman
IT Man: Michael Santy
Tech Mgr: Dianne V Kistler
Prd Mgr: Christine Meaney
VP Sls: Bob Joyce
Sls Dir: Brian Sommerhauser
Manager: Steve Dumas

D-U-N-S 62-096-0732
KAWAILOA DEVELOPMENT LLP
POIPU BAY RESORT
1571 Poipu Rd Ste 3063, Koloa, HI 96756-9402
Tel (808) 742-1234 Founded/Ownrshp 1987
Sales 44.7MM[E] EMP 1,000
SIC 7011 7992 Hotels & motels; Public golf courses
Pt: Jun Fukada
Exec: Alison Higa

D-U-N-S 04-660-3379 IMP/EXP
KAWASAKI MOTORS CORP USA
(Suby of KAWASAKI HEAVY INDUSTRIES, LTD.)
26972 Burbank, Foothill Ranch, CA 92610-2506
Tel (949) 837-4683 Founded/Ownrshp 1967
Sales 242.9MM[E] EMP 530
SIC 5012 5013 5084 5091 Motorcycles; Motorcycle parts; Engines, gasoline; Boats, canoes, watercrafts & equipment
Pr: Masatoshi Tsurutani
*Ofcr: Richard N Beattie
*Exec: Terunori Kitajima
Ex Dir: Tom Leimkuhler
Dist Mgr: Jim Bullard
Dist Mgr: Joe Butt
Dist Mgr: Chip Dongara
Dist Mgr: Hersh Gooden
Dist Mgr: John Kochanek
Dist Mgr: Scott Lincourt
Dist Mgr: Chris Morton

D-U-N-S 17-556-6215 IMP
KAWASAKI MOTORS MANUFACTURING CORP USA
(Suby of KAWASAKI HEAVY INDUSTRIES, LTD.)
6600 Nw 27th St, Lincoln, NE 68524-8904
Tel (402) 476-6600 Founded/Ownrshp 1981
Sales 328.0MM[E] EMP 2,000
SIC 3751 5571 Motorcycles & related parts; Motorcycle dealers; Motorcycle parts & accessories
Pr: Matt Kurushima
*Genl Mgr: Naoshi Kato

D-U-N-S 07-463-4593
KAWEAH DELTA HEALTH CARE DISTRICT GUILD
KAWEAH DELTA MEDICAL CENTER
400 W Mineral King Ave, Visalia, CA 93291-6237
Tel (559) 624-2000 Founded/Ownrshp 1961
Sales 475.4MM EMP 3,200
SIC 8062 Hospital, AMA approved residency
CEO: Donna Archer
*CEO: Lindsay K Mann
*CFO: Gary Herbst
Treas: May Stevens
Sr VP: Thomas Rayner
VP: Janet Danielson
Dir Inf Cn: Katherine Wittman
Dir Lab: David Peterson
Ex Dir: Lucile Gibbs
Ex Dir: Scott Lunsford
Nurse Mgr: Kari Bentson

KAWEAH DELTA MEDICAL CENTER
See KAWEAH DELTA HEALTH CARE DISTRICT GUILD

D-U-N-S 00-175-8333 IMP/EXP
■ KAWNEER CO INC (GA)
(Suby of ARCONIC INC) ★
555 Guthridge Ct Tech, Norcross, GA 30092
Tel (770) 449-5555 Founded/Ownrshp 1906, 1998
Sales 491.4MM[E] EMP 2,900
SIC 3442 3446 Metal doors; Architectural metalwork
Pr: Glen Morrison
*CFO: Peter Hong
*VP: Bob Leylend
*VP: Leslie McDole
Exec: Jane Ashley

D-U-N-S 00-323-7021 IMP/EXP
■ KAY CHEMICAL CO (NC)
(Suby of ECOLAB INC) ★
8300 Capital Dr, Greensboro, NC 27409-9790
Tel (336) 668-7290 Founded/Ownrshp 1963
Sales 139.6MM[E] EMP 620
SIC 2842 Specialty cleaning preparations
Pr: Ching-Meng Chew
*CFO: George G Harris
Bd of Dir: Douglas Baker
Bd of Dir: Barbara Beck
Bd of Dir: Leslie Biller
Bd of Dir: Jerry Grundhofer
Bd of Dir: Joel Johnson
Bd of Dir: Jerry Levin
Bd of Dir: Robert Lumpkins
Bd of Dir: Richard D Schutter
Bd of Dir: John Zillmer
*Sr VP: Bob Sherwood
VP: Doug Douthitt
*VP: Michael A Hickey
*VP: Robert Inchaustegui
*VP: Judy M McNamara

D-U-N-S 83-305-7073
■ KAY TECHNOLOGY HOLDINGS INC
KANA
(Suby of VERINT ACQUISITION LLC) ★
2500 Sand Hill Rd Ste 300, Menlo Park, CA 94025-7063
Tel (650) 289-2481 Founded/Ownrshp 2014
Sales 138.6MM EMP 12[E]
SIC 7372 Prepackaged software
Pr: Jason Klein
Prin: Thomas Barnds
Snr Sftwr: Gomathy Anusuyaraj
Software D: Shanmu Balasubramanian

KAYCO
See KENOVER MARKETING CORP

D-U-N-S 10-163-3782 IMP/EXP
KAYDON CORP
(Suby of ATLAS MANAGEMENT INC) ★
2723 S State St Ste 300, Ann Arbor, MI 48104-6188
Tel (734) 747-7025 Founded/Ownrshp 2013
Sales 634.2MM[E] EMP 2,187[E]
SIC 3562 3569 3592 3053 3621 3679 Ball & roller bearings; Ball bearings & parts; Roller bearings & parts; Filters, general line: industrial; Pistons & piston rings; Gaskets & sealing devices; Sliprings, for motors or generators; Electronic circuits
Pr: Timothy J Heasley
COO: Pierre Demandolx
*Sr VP: Peter C Dechants
*VP: Debra K Crane
VP: Tracy Crosson
VP: John Genova
*VP: Laura Kowalchik
VP: Kevin Lechene
CIO: Greg Billingsley
Sls Dir: Donald Baran
Sls Dir: Scott Herrala

D-U-N-S 07-329-5230
KAYE SCHOLER LLP
250 W 55th St Fl 4, New York, NY 10019-7639
Tel (212) 836-8000 Founded/Ownrshp 2007
Sales 219.5MM[E] EMP 1,200
SIC 8111 General practice law office
Mng Pt: Barry Willner
Pt: James Blank
Pt: Gary Gartner
Pt: Peter L Haviland
Pt: Jeffrey Scheine
Pt: Gary R Silverman
Pt: Rhonda R Trotter
Pt: William E Wallace Jr
Mng Pt: Michael B Solow
Ch Bd: Stanley Pierre-Louis
Ch Bd: David J Stoll
Ofcr: Cliff Hook

D-U-N-S 00-104-6432 IMP
KAYEM FOODS INC (MA)
75 Arlington St, Chelsea, MA 02150-2365
Tel (781) 933-3115 Founded/Ownrshp 1909
Sales 129.3MM[E] EMP 490
SIC 2011 2013 Meat packing plants; Smoked meats from purchased meat; Sausages from purchased meat
Pr: Ralph O Smith
COO: Paul Egan
*Treas: Stephan Monkiewicz
*VP: Peter Monkiewicz
VP: Chris Reisner
QA Dir: Carli Maisano
IT Man: Mark Whitney
Plnt Mgr: Steve Tapley
Prd Mgr: Ernesto Barrezueta
Sales Exec: Joellen West
Mktg Mgr: Katie Monkiewicz
Board of Directors: Michael Mulrain, Lawrence Siff

D-U-N-S 00-792-0796 IMP
■ KAYO OIL CO
CONOCO
(Suby of PHILLIPS PETROLEUM CO) ★
600 N Dairy Ashford Rd, Houston, TX 77079-1100
Tel (281) 293-1000 Founded/Ownrshp 1940, 1959
Sales 367.9MM[E] EMP 3,450
SIC 5541 5411 Gasoline service stations; Convenience stores, independent
Pr: Archie Dunham
*Treas: M W Espinosa
*VP: J S Hill

KAYSER AUTOMOTIVE GROUP
See FORD KAYSER INC

D-U-N-S 00-148-2033 IMP/EXP
KAYSER-ROTH CORP
NO NONSENSE
(Suby of GOLDEN LADY COMPANY SPA)
102 Corporate Center Blvd, Greensboro, NC 27408-3172
Tel (336) 852-2030 Founded/Ownrshp 1999
Sales 422.9MM[E] EMP 2,200
SIC 2252 2251 5961 8741 3842 Men's, boys' & girls' hosiery; Socks; Women's hosiery, except socks; Women's apparel, mail order; Management services; Surgical appliances & supplies
Pr: Kevin Toomey
VP: Gianni Orsini
Exec: Joey Schmissrauter
Genl Mgr: Kathy Mann
Genl Mgr: Julia Townsend
MIS Dir: Kevin Aliff
QA Dir: Donna Lerner
Tech Mgr: Stacy Chadwell
Trfc Mgr: Nancy Davenport
Sales Exec: Robin Rayfield
Mktg Dir: Karen Morrow

D-U-N-S 00-606-9496 IMP
■ KAYTEE PRODUCTS INC (WI)
(Suby of CENTRAL GARDEN & PET CO) ★
521 Clay St, Chilton, WI 53014-1477
Tel (920) 849-2321 Founded/Ownrshp 1866, 1997
Sales 100.1MM[E] EMP 500
SIC 2048 Bird food, prepared; Feed supplements; Feeds, specialty: mice, guinea pig, etc.
CEO: William E Brown
VP: Jim Glassford
Dir Lab: Cindy Pederson
Dir IT: Mark Doff
Dir IT: Sherry Satler
Software D: Richard Best
VP Mfg: Steve Parker
VP Opers: John Williams
Mfg Dir: John Rollmann
Sfty Mgr: Rita Bollini
Sfty Mgr: Fernando Yebra

D-U-N-S 00-148-3890 IMP/EXP
KAZ INC (NY)
(Suby of HELEN OF TROY LIMITED)
400 Donald Lynch Blvd # 300, Marlborough, MA 01752-4733
Tel (508) 490-7000 Founded/Ownrshp 1936, 2011
Sales 132.6MM[E] EMP 2,500
SIC 8082 2834 5047 Home health care services; Pharmaceutical preparations; Medical & hospital equipment
Treas: Amanda Wilson
*Chf Mktg O: Christophe Coudray
VP: Marcus Allemann
VP: Rajesh Kasbekar
Creative D: Jennifer Petersen
Prgrm Mgr: Jeff Cross
Prgrm Mgr: Matthew Lagarto
Prgrm Mgr: Janet Talbot
Prd Mgr: Garrett Dewitt
VP Mktg: John Wojcik
Mktg Dir: Brian Carboni

D-U-N-S 05-363-7893
KAZI FOODS CORP OF HAWAII
KFC
560 N Nimitz Hwy Ste 214, Honolulu, HI 96817-5380
Tel (808) 550-4100 Founded/Ownrshp 1998
Sales 32.7MM[E] EMP 1,175
SIC 5812 Fast-food restaurant, chain
Pr: Zubair Kazi
*CFO: Shambhu Acharya
*VP: Brian Burr
Genl Mgr: Steve Johnson

KB CREATIVE NETWORK
See KIRSHENBAUM BOND SENECAL & PARTNERS LLC

D-U-N-S 08-661-9223
KB FRAMERS LLC
5795 Rogers St, Las Vegas, NV 89118-3017
Tel (702) 873-9451 Founded/Ownrshp 1998
Sales 16.2MM[E] EMP 1,000
SIC 1751 1521 Framing contractor; Single-family housing construction

D-U-N-S 17-772-3061
▲ KB HOME
10990 Wilshire Blvd Fl 5, Los Angeles, CA 90024-3902
Tel (310) 231-4000 *Founded/Ownrshp* 1957
Sales 3.0MMM *EMP* 1,590
Accts Ernst & Young Llp Los Angeles
Tkr Sym KBH *Exch* NYS
SIC 1531 6351 6162 Operative builders; Speculative builder, single-family houses; Condominium developers; Speculative builder, multi-family dwellings; Surety insurance; Mortgage guarantee insurance; Credit & other financial responsibility insurance; Mortgage bankers & correspondents
Pr: Jeffrey T Mezger
Pr: Randy Carpenter
Pr: Brian Kunec
Pr: Glen Longarini
Pr: Matt Mandino
Pr: Amy McReynolds
CFO: Jeff J Kaminski
Ex VP: Nick Franklin
Ex VP: Albert Z Praw
Ex VP: Brian J Woram
Sr VP: William R Hollinger
Sr VP: Thomas F Norton
Sr VP: Jill Peters
Sr VP: Albert Praw
Sr VP: Tom Silk
VP: Dale Ahrendt
VP: A Anthony
VP: Kevin Beall
VP: Daniel Bridleman
VP: James Caldwell
VP: Michael Carver
Board of Directors: Stephen F Bollenbach, Timothy W Finchem, Stuart Gabriel, Thomas W Gilligan, Kenneth M Jastrow II, Robert L Johnson, Melissa Lora, Robert L Patton Jr Michael

D-U-N-S 80-915-7068 IMP
KBC GROUP INC
3400 109th St, Des Moines, IA 50322-8104
Tel (515) 270-2417 *Founded/Ownrshp* 1993
Sales 112.9MM^E^ *EMP* 100
SIC 1542 5083 Agricultural building contractors; Agricultural machinery & equipment
Pr: Peter Bratney
CFO: Obrasio Brawn

D-U-N-S 04-918-4633
KBE BUILDING CORP
76 Batterson Park Rd # 1, Farmington, CT 06032-2571
Tel (860) 284-7424 *Founded/Ownrshp* 1966
Sales 92.0MM^E^ *EMP* 155
SIC 1542 1541 Shopping center construction; Commercial & office building, new construction; Renovation, remodeling & repairs: industrial buildings
Pr: Michael Kolakowski
**CFO:* Tim O'Brien
**Sr VP:* Eric Brown
**Sr VP:* Simon Etzel
**VP:* Robert G Dunn
**VP:* Dan Hannon
VP: Anthony Maselli
**VP:* Gary Sherman
Exec: Tim Obrien
Dir Risk M: Lori Bonini
Admn Mgr: Patricia Moody

D-U-N-S 13-723-6456
KBF AMSTERDAM PARTNERS
SAGAMORE APARTMENTS
189 W 89th St, New York, NY 10024-1959
Tel (212) 712-2661 *Founded/Ownrshp* 2006
Sales 30.4MM^E^ *EMP* 1,828
SIC 6531 Real estate agents & managers
Prin: Larry Lipton
Prin: Michael Herrington

KBP FOODS
See FOSR LLC

D-U-N-S 03-231-1284 IMP
■ KBR CONSTRUCTION CO LLC
(*Suby of* B E & K INC) ★
3000 Riverchase Galleria, Hoover, AL 35244-2315
Tel (205) 972-6538 *Founded/Ownrshp* 1980
Sales 874.7MM^E^ *EMP* 6,000^E^
SIC 1541 1796 1711 1629 1799 1521 Industrial buildings, new construction; Paper/pulp mill construction; Machinery installation; Mechanical contractor; Industrial plant construction; Athletic & recreation facilities construction; Single-family housing construction

D-U-N-S 62-155-9876
■ KBR HOLDINGS LLC
K B R
(*Suby of* KBR INC) ★
601 Jefferson St Ste 7911, Houston, TX 77002-4003
Tel (713) 753-4176 *Founded/Ownrshp* 2006
Sales 4.6MMM^E^ *EMP* 20,010
Accts Kpmg Llp
SIC 1629 8711 8741 Industrial plant construction; Dams, waterways, docks & other marine construction; Engineering services; Construction management
Pr: William P Utt
**CFO:* Cedric Burgher
**Treas:* Charles E Schneider
**VP:* Zac Nagle

D-U-N-S 78-407-2626 IMP/EXP
▲ KBR INC
601 Jefferson St Ste 3400, Houston, TX 77002-7901
Tel (713) 753-3011 *Founded/Ownrshp* 2006
Sales 5.1MMM *EMP* 22,000
Tkr Sym KBR *Exch* NYS
SIC 1629 8711 8741 Land preparation construction; Industrial plant construction; Dams, waterways, docks & other marine construction; Engineering services; Petroleum, mining & chemical engineers; Construction & civil engineering; Management services; Business management; Construction management
Ch Bd: Loren K Carroll
Pr: Stuart J B Bradie
Pr: John T Derbyshire
Pr: J Jay Ibrahim
Pr: Roy B Oelking Jr
Pr: Andrew R D Pringle
CFO: Brian K Ferraioli
Ex VP: Eileen G Akerson
Ex VP: Jan Egil Braendeland
Ex VP: K Graham Hill
Ex VP: Ian J Mackey
VP: Lynn Nazareth
VP: Nelson E Rowe Sr
VP: Martin Siddle

KBR-KELLOGG BROWN
See KELLOGG BROWN & ROOT LLC

D-U-N-S 04-101-4242
■ KBRWYLE TECHNOLOGY SOLUTIONS LLC
(*Suby of* KBR INC) ★
7000 Columbia Gateway Dr # 100, Columbia, MD 21046-3151
Tel (410) 964-7000 *Founded/Ownrshp* 2016
Sales 810.7MM^E^ *EMP* 3,500
SIC 4899 8711 Satellite earth stations; Engineering services
Pr: Roger Wiederkeh

KBS
See KOCH BUSINESS SOLUTIONS LP

D-U-N-S 01-006-3048
KBS INC (VA)
8050 Kimway Dr, Richmond, VA 23228-2831
Tel (804) 262-0100 *Founded/Ownrshp* 1975
Sales 180.7MM *EMP* 130
Accts Lewis & Company Pc Chesape
SIC 1542 Commercial & office building, new construction
Pr: Bill Paulette
**CFO:* James Lipscombe
**Ex VP:* Dennis Lynch
**VP:* John Gillenwater
**VP:* Steve Satterfield
**VP:* Sam Stocks
Sales Exec: Matthew S Gass

D-U-N-S 96-342-6734
KBS REAL ESTATE INVESTMENT TRUST II INC
KBS SOR WESTMOOR CENTER
800 Nwport Ctr Dr Ste 700, Newport Beach, CA 92660
Tel (949) 417-6500 *Founded/Ownrshp* 2008
Sales 165.3MM *EMP* 2^E^
SIC 6799 Investors
CEO: Charles Schreiber Jr
CFO: David E Snyder

D-U-N-S 96-210-4944
KBS REAL ESTATE INVESTMENT TRUST III INC
620 Newport Center Dr # 1300, Newport Beach, CA 92660-8013
Tel (949) 417-6500 *Founded/Ownrshp* 2010
Sales 315.7MM *EMP* 2
SIC 6798 Real estate investment trusts
CEO: Charles J Schreiber Jr

KBS SOR WESTMOOR CENTER
See KBS REAL ESTATE INVESTMENT TRUST II INC

D-U-N-S 83-069-8333
KBS STRATEGIC OPPORTUNITY REIT INC
620 Newport Center Dr, Newport Beach, CA 92660-6420
Tel (949) 417-6500 *Founded/Ownrshp* 2008
Sales 112.1MM *EMP* 2
Accts Ernst & Young Llp Irvine Ca
SIC 6798 Real estate investment trusts
CEO: Keith D Hall
**Pr:* Peter B McMillan
**CFO:* David E Snyder

D-U-N-S 79-034-5107
■ KBW LLC
(*Suby of* STIFEL FINANCIAL CORP) ★
787 7th Ave Fl 4, New York, NY 10019-6018
Tel (212) 887-7777 *Founded/Ownrshp* 2013
Sales 133.5MM^E^ *EMP* 537^E^
SIC 6211 Security brokers & dealers; Investment bankers; Security brokers & dealers
VP: Dan Frascone
VP: Sharad Daswani
VP: Brian Estaphan

D-U-N-S 08-036-3755
KBWB OPERATIONS-RICE LLC
1120 Alps Rd, Wayne, NJ 07470-3704
Tel (973) 339-8899 *Founded/Ownrshp* 2014
Sales 45.6MM^E^ *EMP* 2,500^E^
SIC 8051 8361 Skilled nursing care facilities; Geriatric residential care

D-U-N-S 06-442-1410
■ KC DISTANCE LEARNING INC
(*Suby of* K12 INC) ★
830 Ne Holladay St # 100, Portland, OR 97232-5106
Tel (503) 731-5427 *Founded/Ownrshp* 2010
Sales 21.5MM^E^ *EMP* 2,744^E^
SIC 8299 Educational services
Pr: Caprice Young
VP: Gregg Levin
**VP:* Kathi Littmann
Dir Surg: Rebecca Tomasini
Dir Bus: Anton Leof
VP Mktg: Janet Johnson

KCG
See KNIGHT CAPITAL AMERICAS LP

D-U-N-S 07-881-4681
▲ KCG HOLDINGS INC
545 Washington Blvd, Jersey City, NJ 07310-1607
Tel (201) 222-9400 *Founded/Ownrshp* 2012
Sales 1.3MMM *EMP* 1,093^E^
Tkr Sym KCG *Exch* NYS
SIC 6211 6282 Security brokers & dealers; Investment advice
CEO: Daniel Coleman
COO: Nick Ogurtsov
CFO: Steffen Parratt
VP: Thomas Duffy
VP: Timothy Liang
VP: Yumi OH
VP: Parin Shah
VP: Catherine Xu
Mng Dir: Douglas Borden
Mng Dir: Christopher Renkowski
CTO: Jonathan Ross
Board of Directors: Charles S Haldeman Jr, Rene Kern, James T Milde, John C Morris, Daniel F Schmitt, Stephen Schuler, Laurie M Shahon, Daniel Tierney

D-U-N-S 03-981-5410 IMP
KCG INC
REW MATERIALS
15720 W 108th St Ste 100, Lenexa, KS 66219-1338
Tel (913) 438-4142 *Founded/Ownrshp* 1993
Sales 361.4MM^E^ *EMP* 250
SIC 5032 2992 Drywall materials; Lubricating oils & greases
Pr: Rick J Rew
**Pr:* James W Bedsworth Sr
COO: Kim Gray
**CFO:* James W Bedsworth Jr
**VP:* Jeff Butts
CTO: Kenneth Greenwell
IT Man: Todd Thielbar
Opers Mgr: Allen Bristow
Sales Asso: Mike Muse

KCI
See KINETIC CONCEPTS INC

D-U-N-S 03-105-6690
KCI CONSTRUCTION CO
10315 Lake Bluff Dr, Saint Louis, MO 63123-7245
Tel (314) 894-8888 *Founded/Ownrshp* 2005
Sales 129.5MM^E^ *EMP* 215
SIC 1542 1611 1629 Specialized public building contractors; Highway & street construction; Industrial plant construction
Pr: Doug Jones
**VP:* Tom Huster
**VP:* Ron Webel Huth
**VP:* Brent Krueger

D-U-N-S 84-703-1770 IMP/EXP
KCI HOLDING USA INC
(*Suby of* KONECRANES FINANCE OY)
4401 Gateway Blvd, Springfield, OH 45502-9339
Tel (937) 525-5533 *Founded/Ownrshp* 1993
Sales 183.5MM^E^ *EMP* 2,500
SIC 3536 Cranes, industrial plant
Sr VP: Bernie D'Ambrosi
CFO: Guy Shoumaker
**Treas:* Amy Corbisier
**Treas:* Steve Mayes
**VP:* Guy Shumaker
Board of Directors: Teo Ottola, Tom Sothard

D-U-N-S 60-510-8141
KCI HOLDINGS INC
K C I
936 Ridgebrook Rd, Sparks Glencoe, MD 21152-9390
Tel (410) 316-7800 *Founded/Ownrshp* 1988
Sales 160.6MM *EMP* 1,001
Accts Grant Thornton Llp Baltimore
SIC 8711 1799 Consulting engineer; Petroleum storage tank installation, underground
CEO: Terry F Neimeyer
**CFO:* Christine Koski
**Ex VP:* William Franswick
VP: Joseph Blaney
Off Mgr: Michael Ebner
Off Mgr: Robert Macoy
Software D: Brendan Carroll
Software D: James Somerville
Sfty Mgr: Jim Shumaker
Opers Mgr: Laurie Arensdorf
Opers Mgr: Michelle Burgess

D-U-N-S 08-499-3344
KCI TECHNOLOGIES INC
(*Suby of* K C I) ★
936 Ridgebrook Rd, Sparks, MD 21152-9390
Tel (410) 316-7800 *Founded/Ownrshp* 1955, 1988
Sales 123.5MM *EMP* 1,000
Accts Grant Thornton Llp Baltimore
SIC 8711 Consulting engineer
CEO: Terry F Neimeyer
**Pr:* Harvey Floyd
**CFO:* Donald A McConnell
**Ex VP:* Nathan J Beil
Sr VP: Scott Lang
**Sr VP:* Charles A Phillips Jr
**VP:* Edward D Berger
VP: Stephen Drumm
**VP:* Christopher Griffith
VP: Stephen Redding
**VP:* Kenneth H Trout
Assoc Dir: Heidi Hammel

D-U-N-S 10-272-6734
KCI USA INC
K C I
(*Suby of* ACELITY LP INC) ★
12930 W Interstate 10, San Antonio, TX 78249-2248
Tel (800) 275-4524 *Founded/Ownrshp* 1991
Sales 344.7MM^E^ *EMP* 1,071
SIC 7352 3842 5047 Medical equipment rental; Surgical appliances & supplies; Medical & hospital equipment
Pr: Joseph F Woody
**Ex VP:* Robert P Hureau
**VP:* Peter Arnold
**VP:* David Ball
**VP:* John T Bibb
**VP:* Jim Cunniff
**VP:* Butch Hulse
**VP:* Rohit Kashyap
**VP:* David Lillback
**VP:* Mike Matthews
**VP:* Ron Silverman

KCLS
See KING COUNTY LIBRARY SYSTEM

KCMC HOME HEALTH & HOSPICE
See KERSHAW HEALTH MEDICAL CENTER

D-U-N-S 07-863-2165
KCP HOLDCO INC
603 W 50th St, New York, NY 10019-7029
Tel (212) 265-1500 *Founded/Ownrshp* 2012
Sales 98.8MM^E^ *EMP* 1,600
SIC 3143 3171 5661 5632 5611
CEO: Paul Blum

D-U-N-S 00-696-6055 IMP/EXP
■ KCP&L GREATER MISSOURI OPERATIONS CO
(*Suby of* GREAT PLAINS ENERGY INC) ★
1200 Main St Fl 30, Kansas City, MO 64105-2122
Tel (816) 556-2200 *Founded/Ownrshp* 1986
Sales 242.9M^E^ *EMP* 2,213
SIC 4911 Generation, electric power; Transmission, electric power; Distribution, electric power
CEO: Terry D Bassham
**Treas:* Michael W Cline
**Sr VP:* Paul Perkins
**VP:* Jim Alberts
**VP:* Kevin E Bryant
**VP:* Lora C Cheatman
**VP:* Carl Churchman
**VP:* F Dana Crawford
**VP:* Stephen T Easley
**VP:* Ellen Fairchild
**VP:* Chris B Giles
**VP:* Scott Heidtbrink
**VP:* William P Herdegen
**VP:* Maria Jenks
**VP:* Todd Kobayashi
**VP:* Marvin L Rollison
**VP:* Richard A Spring
**VP:* Chuck Tickles
**VP:* Lori A Wright
Board of Directors: Dr David L Bodde, Michael J Chesser, William H Downey, Mark A Ernst, Randall C Ferguson Jr, Luis A Jimenez, James A Mitchell, William C Nelson, Dr Linda H Talbott

D-U-N-S 80-034-3878
■ KCPC HOLDINGS INC
(*Suby of* SP PLUS CORP) ★
2401 21st Ave S Ste 200, Nashville, TN 37212-5309
Tel (615) 297-4255 *Founded/Ownrshp* 2012
Sales 112.7MM^E^ *EMP* 18,940^E^
SIC 7521 Automobile parking
CEO: Monroe Carell Jr
**VP:* Seth H Hollander

D-U-N-S 05-333-6145
KCR INTERNATIONAL TRUCKS INC
(*Suby of* SUMMIT HOLDINGS) ★
7700 Ne 38th St, Kansas City, MO 64161-9410
Tel (816) 455-1833 *Founded/Ownrshp* 1999
Sales 83.0MM^E^ *EMP* 199
SIC 5511 5531 7538 7513 Trucks, tractors & trailers: new & used; Truck equipment & parts; Truck engine repair, except industrial; Truck leasing, without drivers
CEO: Richard Sweebe
COO: Rocky Zinser
CFO: Scott Gill

D-U-N-S 07-932-5091
KCS HOLDINGS LLC (MO)
8001 Nw 106th St, Kansas City, MO 64153-2379
Tel (515) 266-4100 *Founded/Ownrshp* 2013
Sales 200.0MM *EMP* 1
SIC 6719

D-U-N-S 80-181-6091 EXP
KCS INTERNATIONAL INC
CRUISER YACHTS
804 Pecor St, Oconto, WI 54153-1761
Tel (920) 834-2211 *Founded/Ownrshp* 1993
Sales 213.6MM^E^ *EMP* 1,000
SIC 3732 Boats, fiberglass: building & repairing
Pr: Mark Pedersen
**Ch:* Kenneth C Stock
MIS Dir: Sue Hoffman

KCTCS
See KENTUCKY COMMUNITY AND TECHNICAL COLLEGE SYSTEM

KD
See KRIZ-DAVIS CO

KDC CONSTRUCTION
See CIRKS CONSTRUCTION INC

D-U-N-S 78-783-6758 IMP
KDDI AMERICA INC
KDDI MOBILE
(*Suby of* KDDI CORPORATION)
825 3rd Ave Fl 3, New York, NY 10022-9526
Tel (212) 295-1200 *Founded/Ownrshp* 2003
Sales 95.3MM^E^ *EMP* 164
SIC 4813 7375 7374 8743 Long distance telephone communications; On-line data base information retrieval; Data processing & preparation; Sales promotion
Pr: Satoru Manabe
Pr: Yoichi Iwaki
**CFO:* Masato Takei
Chf Mktg O: Akihiko Yamaguchi
Ex VP: Masahiro Yamamoto
VP: Hiromu Naratani
**VP:* Takami Teshigawara
VP: Hiroshi Uchida
Ex Dir: Shin Shinohara
Genl Mgr: Takashi Shigeno
Dir IT: Ray Okayama

KDDI MOBILE
See KDDI AMERICA INC

D-U-N-S 04-089-2317 IMP
■ KDI TRANSITION CO INC
KERR HEALTH CARE CENTERS
(*Suby of* WALGREENS) ★
3220 Spring Forest Rd, Raleigh, NC 27616-2822
Tel (412) 828-1884 *Founded/Ownrshp* 2013
Sales 385.8MM^E^ *EMP* 2,400
SIC 5912 Drug stores
CEO: Anthony N Civello

KDIC FM RADIO
See TRUSTEES OF GRINNELL COLLEGE

D-U-N-S 02-014-9550 IMP
KDM HOLDING INC
(*Suby of* LHOIST SA)
3700 Hulen St, Fort Worth, TX 76107-6816
Tel (817) 732-8164 *Founded/Ownrshp* 1997
Sales 472.2MM[E] *EMP* 1,200
SIC 3274 Lime; Quicklime
CEO: Ludwig De Mot

KDM SCREEN PRINTING
See KDM SIGNS INC

D-U-N-S 05-510-4525
KDM SIGNS INC
KDM SCREEN PRINTING
10450 Medallion Dr, Cincinnati, OH 45241-3199
Tel (513) 769-1932 *Founded/Ownrshp* 1984
Sales 101.9MM[E] *EMP* 337
SIC 2759 3993 Commercial printing; Screen printing; Signs & advertising specialties
Pr: Robert J Kissel
CFO: William Holbrook
**Sec:* Kathy McQueen
CTO: Lisa Carr
Dir IT: Brian Combs
IT Man: Brad Williamson
Plnt Mgr: Bonnie Kissel
Prd Mgr: Katie Murphy
Sales Exec: Dominick Cuocci
Sales Exec: Steve Jenner
Sales Exec: Charlie H Leavitt

D-U-N-S 15-594-3111
KEAN UNIVERSITY REALTY FOUNDATION INC
RAPE SURVIVAL CENTER
1000 Morris Ave Ste 1, Union, NJ 07083-7133
Tel (908) 527-2000 *Founded/Ownrshp* 1855
Sales 146.3MM[E] *EMP* 1,900
SIC 8221 College, except junior
Pr: Dawood Farahi
Dir IT: Joe Marinello

D-U-N-S 07-951-2488
KEANE GROUP HOLDINGS LLC
11200 Westheimer Rd # 900, Houston, TX 77042-3229
Tel (713) 960-0381 *Founded/Ownrshp* 2011
Sales 418.6MM[E] *EMP* 650[E]
SIC 1381 7353 4212 Drilling oil & gas wells; Oil well drilling equipment, rental or leasing; Petroleum haulage, local

KEANY PRODUCE COMPANY
See P J K FOOD SERVICE CORP

D-U-N-S 19-515-6500
KEARFOTT CORP
(*Suby of* ASTRONAUTICS CORP OF AMERICA) ★
1150 Mcbride Ave Ste 1, Woodland Park, NJ 07424-2564
Tel (973) 785-6000 *Founded/Ownrshp* 1988
Sales 163.2MM[E] *EMP* 1,050
Accts Bdo Seidman Llp Milwaukee W
SIC 3812 Search & navigation equipment
Pr: Ronald E Zelazo
COO: Jane Owen
CFO: Stephen G Givant
Genl Mgr: Sandra Cookson
Genl Mgr: Middleton John
Genl Mgr: Natasha McLucas
IT Man: Scott Mekechnie
IT Man: William Mitchener
Mfg Mgr: Dave Cardy

D-U-N-S 04-319-0198 IMP/EXP
KEARNEY-NATIONAL INC
COTO TECHNOLOGY
(*Suby of* DYSON-KISSNER-MORAN CORP) ★
565 5th Ave Fl 4, New York, NY 10017-2424
Tel (212) 661-4600 *Founded/Ownrshp* 1988
Sales 238.0MM[E] *EMP* 1,780
SIC 3679 3694 3714 3625 Electronic switches; Engine electrical equipment; Fuel systems & parts, motor vehicle; Relays & industrial controls
Ch Bd: Robert R Dyson
**VP:* Marc Feldman

D-U-N-S 07-544-5866
■ **KEARNY BANK**
(*Suby of* KEARNY BANK) ★
120 Passaic Ave, Fairfield, NJ 07004-3523
Tel (973) 244-4500 *Founded/Ownrshp* 1943
Sales NA *EMP* 135
SIC 6022 State commercial banks
CEO: Craig L Montanaro
**CFO:* Albert Gossweiler
**Treas:* Frank Milley
Ofcr: Donna Portuesi
**Sr VP:* Sharon Jones
VP: Frank Coronato
VP: Dennita Peterkin
VP: Nancy Slingland
Exec: Kimberly Manfrado
Board of Directors: Kathleen Fisher, John Hopkins, Bernard Leung M D, Richard Masch, James Mason, Robert Miller

D-U-N-S 09-222-6356
■ **KEARNY BANK**
(*Suby of* KEARNY FINANCIAL CORP) ★
120 Passaic Ave, Fairfield, NJ 07004-3523
Tel (973) 244-4500 *Founded/Ownrshp* 1884, 2001
Sales NA *EMP* 255
SIC 6035 Federal savings banks
Ch Bd: John Mazur
**CFO:* William Ledgerwood
**Treas:* Albert E Gossweiler
**Treas:* Frank Milley
Ex VP: Eric Heyer
Ex VP: Patrick Joyce
Ex VP: Bill Ledgerwood
Sr VP: Jeff Apostolou
VP: Peter Cappello
**VP:* Coronato Frank
VP: Valentin Kazanovich
VP: Timothy Swanson
VP: Tracy Tripucka
Board of Directors: Raymond E Chandonnet, Christopher D Petermann

KEARNY FEDERAL SAVINGS BANK
See KEARNY MHC

D-U-N-S 16-982-0748
▲ **KEARNY FINANCIAL CORP**
120 Passaic Ave, Fairfield, NJ 07004-3523
Tel (973) 244-4500 *Founded/Ownrshp* 2001
Sales NA *EMP* 491[E]
Tkr Sym KRNY *Exch* NGS
SIC 6035 Savings institutions, federally chartered
Pr: Craig L Montanaro
**Ch Bd:* John J Mazur Jr
COO: William C Ledgerwood
CFO: Eric B Heyer
Ex VP: Sharon Jones
Ex VP: Erika K Parisi
VP: Peter A Cappello

D-U-N-S 16-960-1841
KEARNY MHC
KEARNY FEDERAL SAVINGS BANK
120 Passaic Ave, Fairfield, NJ 07004-3523
Tel (973) 244-4500 *Founded/Ownrshp* 2001
Sales NA *EMP* 556
SIC 6035 Savings institutions, federally chartered
**Ch Bd:* John J Mazur
COO: Erika Sacher
Treas: William Ledgerwood
Sr VP: Patrick Joyce
VP: Allan Cronheim
VP: Grace Cruz-Beyer
VP: Cheryl Lyons
VP: Donna Porcaro
VP: Marry Webb
Dir IT: Tim Swanson
Site Mgr: Anna Wright

D-U-N-S 80-972-0860
KEARNY PUBLIC SCHOOLS
100 Davis Ave, Kearny, NJ 07032-3328
Tel (201) 955-5000 *Founded/Ownrshp* 2008
Sales 24.8MM[E] *EMP* 1,087[E]
SIC 8211 Public elementary & secondary schools
Bd of Dir: Barbara Cifelli
Bd of Dir: Mercedes Davidson
Bd of Dir: James Hill
**VP:* Paul Castelli
Dir IT: Neil Brohm
Psych: Frank Armenio
Psych: Alexandra Garcia

KEATING BUILDING COMPANY
See DANIEL J KEATING CONSTRUCTION CO

D-U-N-S 07-933-9971 IMP
KECK HOSPITAL OF USC
1500 San Pablo St, Los Angeles, CA 90033-5313
Tel (800) 872-2273 *Founded/Ownrshp* 2013
Sales 761.1MM *EMP* 77[E]
SIC 8011 Health maintenance organization
CFO: Kamyar Afshar
Dir Lab: Jay S Ana
HC Dir: Mike Fong

D-U-N-S 01-330-9888
KEDRION BIOPHARMA INC
KEDRION MELVILLE
(*Suby of* KEDRION SPA)
400 Kelby St Ste 11, Fort Lee, NJ 07024-2938
Tel (201) 242-8900 *Founded/Ownrshp* 2011
Sales 242.6MM *EMP* 19
SIC 8099 Plasmapherous center
CEO: Paolo Marcucci
**COO:* Chris Lamb
**CFO:* John Menapace

KEDRION MELVILLE
See KEDRION BIOPHARMA INC

D-U-N-S 09-918-5076
■ **KEDS LLC**
(*Suby of* STRIDE RITE CORP) ★
500 Totten Pond Rd Ste 1, Waltham, MA 02451-1924
Tel (617) 824-6000 *Founded/Ownrshp* 1979
Sales 110.9MM[E] *EMP* 500
SIC 5139 5661 Footwear, athletic; Shoes; Shoe stores
Pr: Pamela Salkovitz
CFO: Frank Karuso
Treas: Gordon W Johnson
VP: Stephanie H Brocoum
VP: John J Nannicelli
Genl Mgr: Peter Charles
Genl Mgr: Julie Forsyth
VP Mktg: Sue Dooley

D-U-N-S 00-132-6065 IMP/EXP
■ **KEEBLER CO**
(*Suby of* KELLOGG CO) ★
1 Kellogg Sq, Battle Creek, MI 49017-3534
Tel (269) 961-2000 *Founded/Ownrshp* 2001
Sales 1.4MMM[E] *EMP* 12,000
SIC 2052 2051 Cookies; Crackers, dry; Cones, ice cream; Pretzels; Bread, cake & related products
Pr: David McKay

D-U-N-S 01-209-1427
■ **KEEFE BRUYETTE & WOODS INC**
(*Suby of* KBW LLC) ★
787 7th Ave Fl 4, New York, NY 10019-6080
Tel (212) 887-7777 *Founded/Ownrshp* 1962
Sales 131.7MM[E] *EMP* 450
Accts Ernst & Young Llp New York N
SIC 6211 Brokers, security; Dealers, security; Investment bankers
Pr: Andrew M Senchak
CEO: Thomas Michaud
CFO: Jeff Fox
CFO: Robert Giambrone
Ex VP: Will Allen
Ex VP: Dennis O'Rourke
Ex VP: James B Penny
Ex VP: Peter J Wirth
Sr VP: Nikolei Bjorkedal
Sr VP: Bernard Caffrey
Sr VP: Charles Crowley
Sr VP: Thomas M Ekert
Sr VP: Tim Guba
Sr VP: Philip Haggard
Sr VP: Rick Jeffrey
Sr VP: Mary Johnstone
Sr VP: Edward Kreppein
Sr VP: Bryce Nucera
Sr VP: Roger Puccio-Johnson
Sr VP: Patrick Ryan
Sr VP: Arthur Sarzen

D-U-N-S 55-666-2851 IMP
KEEFE GROUP LLC
KEEFE SUPPLY COMPANY
(*Suby of* NAG LLC) ★
10880 Linpage Pl, Saint Louis, MO 63132-1008
Tel (314) 963-8700 *Founded/Ownrshp* 2003
Sales 98.4MM[E] *EMP* 1,140[E]
SIC 7389 Packaging & labeling services
CEO: James Theiss
Pr: Tim Nichols
**CEO:* John Spesia
VP: Dana Dierdorf
VP: Ken Dubinsky
VP: Paul Eifert
VP: Margarita Groark
**VP:* Paul Scherer
Dir Bus: Ann Hogan
Plnt Mgr: Tony Demartino
Mktg Mgr: Holly Karleskint

KEEFE SUPPLY COMPANY
See KEEFE GROUP LLC

KEELEY COMPANIES, THE
See L KEELEY CONSTRUCTION CO

KEEN FOOTWEAR
See KEEN INC

D-U-N-S 14-159-0559 IMP/EXP
KEEN INC
KEEN FOOTWEAR
515 Nw 13th Ave, Portland, OR 97209-3000
Tel (503) 402-1520 *Founded/Ownrshp* 2006
Sales 142.7MM[E] *EMP* 125[E]
SIC 5139 5661 Footwear; Footwear, athletic
CEO: Rory Fuerst
**CFO:* John Barron
Sr VP: Francisco Garbayo
VP: Tyler Lamotte
Mktg Mgr: Perry Laukens
Snr Mgr: Aaron Baker
Board of Directors: Robin Smith

D-U-N-S 84-755-1541
KEEN LIVE INC
2789 W Main St Ste 4, Wappingers Falls, NY 12590-1524
Tel (845) 790-0813 *Founded/Ownrshp* 2006
Sales 950.0MM *EMP* 4
SIC 7336 Creative services to advertisers, except writers
, *Pr:* Walter Soyka

D-U-N-S 00-986-9801
KEEN TRANSPORT INC
(*Suby of* PLATINUM EQUITY LLC) ★
1951 Harrisburg Pike, Carlisle, PA 17015-7304
Tel (717) 243-6685 *Founded/Ownrshp* 2012
Sales 156.7MM[E] *EMP* 550
SIC 4213 Heavy machinery transport
CEO: Christopher R Easter
**Treas:* Kenneth Sheibley
**Ex VP:* Elizabeth Keen
**VP:* Dan Higgins
VP: Jesse Keen
**VP:* Alan Shilvock
Off Admin: Melissa Nelson
VP Opers: Paul Ross

D-U-N-S 18-874-4916
KEENA STAFF INC
KEENA STAFFING SERVICES
2 Progress Blvd, Queensbury, NY 12804-3202
Tel (518) 793-9825 *Founded/Ownrshp* 1985
Sales 73.6MM[E] *EMP* 1,800
SIC 7361 7363 Employment agencies; Temporary help service
Owner: Connie Gerarde
VP Opers: Michael Niles

KEENA STAFFING SERVICES
See KEENA STAFF INC

D-U-N-S 06-668-8441
KEENAN & ASSOCIATES
2355 Crenshaw Blvd # 200, Torrance, CA 90501-3395
Tel (310) 212-3344 *Founded/Ownrshp* 1972
Sales NA *EMP* 675
SIC 6411 Insurance brokers
Ch Bd: John Keenan
**CEO:* Sean Smith
**COO:* Davis Seres
Ex VP: Dave Dewenter
**Sr VP:* Henry Loubet
VP: Toni Hendel
VP: Robert Herrmann
VP: Tim Keenan
**VP:* Keith Pippard
IT Man: Betti Pasquale

D-U-N-S 13-195-7722 EXP
KEENAN HOPKINS SCHMIDT AND STOWELL CONTRACTORS INC
KHS&S CONTRACTORS
5422 Bay Center Dr # 200, Tampa, FL 33609-3437
Tel (813) 627-2219 *Founded/Ownrshp* 1984
Sales 93.8MM *EMP* 350
Accts B2d Semago Tampa Florida
SIC 1542 1742 Commercial & office building, new construction; Plastering, drywall & insulation
**Pr:* Michael R Cannon
COO: Philip Cherne
**CFO:* Lynda Licht
CFO: Dennis Norman
**Sr VP:* Michael Carrigan
**Sr VP:* Daniel F Casey Jr
**Sr VP:* Thomas J Gibbons
**Sr VP:* Neal W Harris Jr
**Sr VP:* Tony L Hemgesberg
**Sr VP:* Robert C Luker
**Sr VP:* Robert J McCarthy
**Sr VP:* Erik S Santiago
**VP:* Robert Evans
VP: Tony Hemgesberg
**VP:* Ted Malone
**VP:* Thomas Pickford
**VP:* Matthew Pollard
**VP:* Richard Pollicino
**VP:* Jess Robinson
**VP:* Angela Sechrest
VP: Derek Stevens

D-U-N-S 00-929-0032 IMP
KEENAN HOPKINS SUDER & STOWELL CONTRACTORS INC
KHS & S CONTRACTORS
5109 E La Palma Ave Ste A, Anaheim, CA 92807-2066
Tel (714) 695-3670 *Founded/Ownrshp* 1996
Sales 291.1MM[E] *EMP* 2,000
Accts Moore Stephens Wurth Frazer An
SIC 1742 1751 1743 1741 1721 Plastering, plain or ornamental; Carpentry work; Terrazzo, tile, marble, mosaic work; Masonry & other stonework; Painting & paper hanging
Pr: David Suder
**COO:* Philip Cherne
**CFO:* Dennis Norman
Sr VP: Mark Gill
**Sr VP:* John Platon
VP: Jeff Miller
VP: Kelly Sell
CIO: Chuck Mook
IT Man: Thad Orrell

D-U-N-S 07-133-6465 IMP
KEENELAND ASSOCIATION INC
4201 Versailles Rd, Lexington, KY 40510-9662
Tel (859) 288-4236 *Founded/Ownrshp* 1936
Sales 117.7MM[E] *EMP* 100
SIC 5154 7948 0751 Auctioning livestock; Thoroughbred horse racing; Livestock services, except veterinary
CEO: Bill Thomason
**Ch Bd:* James E Bassett III
**Treas:* Stanley H Jones
**VP:* Vince Gabbert

D-U-N-S 00-115-5159 IMP
KEENEY MANUFACTURING CO
PLUMB PAK MEDICAL
1170 Main St, Newington, CT 06111-3098
Tel (603) 239-6371 *Founded/Ownrshp* 1923
Sales 126.6MM *EMP* 500
SIC 3432 5074 Plumbers' brass goods: drain cocks, faucets, spigots, etc.; Plumbing fittings & supplies
CEO: Robert S Holden
Ch: Jean Hanna Holden
Treas: Kenneth L Collett
Ex VP: James H Holden
VP: Edwin F Atkins
VP: Ken Colete
VP: Stephen A Cooke
VP: Rachel Garate
VP: Chris Jeffers
VP: Wayne Moore
Exec: Patrick Flynn
Exec: Dawn Lawson
Board of Directors: Virginia Holden Atkins, Jessica Holden

D-U-N-S 07-918-1985 IMP/EXP
KEHE DISTRIBUTORS HOLDINGS LLC
1245 E Diehl Rd Ste 200, Naperville, IL 60563-4816
Tel (630) 343-0000 *Founded/Ownrshp* 2010
Sales 221.8MM[E] *EMP* 4,500
SIC 5149 Groceries & related products; Specialty food items; Pickles, preserves, jellies & jams; Spices & seasonings
Pr: Brandon Barnholt
CFO: Chris Meyers

D-U-N-S 00-543-7033 IMP/EXP
KEHE DISTRIBUTORS LLC
KEHE SOLUTIONS
1245 E Diehl Rd Ste 200, Naperville, IL 60563-4816
Tel (630) 343-0000 *Founded/Ownrshp* 1952
Sales 3.8MMM[E] *EMP* 3,400
SIC 5149 Groceries & related products; Specialty food items; Pickles, preserves, jellies & jams; Spices & seasonings
Pr: Brandon Barnholt
COO: Gene Carter
CFO: Christopher Meyers
CFO: Timothy J Wiggins
Chf Cred: Mike Leone
Sr VP: Annette Roder
VP: Ted Beilman
VP: Bill Gianaras
VP: David Klein
VP: Gary Messmore
VP: Jon Mollman
VP: Joe Shannon
VP: Ronald Turner
VP: Gordon Walker
VP: Mike Weger
VP: Scott Widtfeldt

KEHE SOLUTIONS
See KEHE DISTRIBUTORS LLC

D-U-N-S 01-611-0509 IMP
KEIHIN CAROLINA SYSTEM TECHNOLOGY LLC
(*Suby of* KEIHIN NORTH AMERICA INC) ★
4047 Mcnair Rd, Tarboro, NC 27886-9055
Tel (252) 641-6750 *Founded/Ownrshp* 1997
Sales 190.6MM[E] *EMP* 468
SIC 3694 3625 3714 Automotive electrical equipment; Actuators, industrial; Motor vehicle parts & accessories
Pr: Shigeo Umesaki
Pr: Nobuaki Suzuki
Pr: Mamoru Tanaka
Pr: Masahiro Wakaki
Pr: Gregory S Young
Sls Mgr: Mike Jones

D-U-N-S 16-688-6429 IMP
KEIHIN IPT MFG LLC
(*Suby of* KEIHIN NORTH AMERICA INC) ★
400 W New Rd, Greenfield, IN 46140-3001
Tel (317) 462-3015 *Founded/Ownrshp* 2001
Sales 228.8MME *EMP* 2,000
SIC 3714 Fuel systems & parts, motor vehicle
Pr: Koki Onuma
**Treas:* Mamoru Tanaka
**VP:* Gregory S Young

D-U-N-S 19-243-8042 IMP
KEIHIN NORTH AMERICA INC
(*Suby of* KEIHIN CORPORATION)
2701 Enterprise Dr # 100, Anderson, IN 46013-6101
Tel (765) 298-6030 *Founded/Ownrshp* 1988
Sales 1.0MMM *EMP* 4,591
Accts Ernst & Young Llp Columbus O
SIC 3714 Fuel systems & parts, motor vehicle; Manifolds, motor vehicle; Motor vehicle engines & parts
Pr: Koki Onuma
**Treas:* Toru Sugihara
VP: Greg Trusty
**VP:* Greg York
**VP:* Gregory S Young
**Prin:* Sosuke Sese
**Prin:* Masami Watanabe

D-U-N-S 96-931-7143 IMP/EXP
KEIHIN THERMAL TECHNOLOGY OF AMERICA INC
10500 Oday Harrison Rd, Mount Sterling, OH 43143-9474
Tel (740) 869-3000 *Founded/Ownrshp* 2011
Sales 110.0MME *EMP* 475
SIC 5013 3714 Automotive engines & engine parts; Motor vehicle engines & parts
Pr: Tatsuhiko Arai
**VP:* Scott Amortimer
Genl Mgr: Scott Mortimer
Sfty Mgr: Robert Feltz

KEISER UNIVERSITY
See EVERGLADES COLLEGE INC

D-U-N-S 07-928-1153
KEITH DAVIS
DAVIS TRUCKING SERVICES
3574 Boxtown Rd, Memphis, TN 38109-3300
Tel (901) 496-6477 *Founded/Ownrshp* 2010
Sales 386.4MM *EMP* 5
SIC 4213 Contract haulers
Owner: Keith Davis
Co-Ownr: Rochelle Davis

D-U-N-S 00-419-0419 IMP
■ **KEITHLEY INSTRUMENTS INC**
(*Suby of* TEKTRONIX INC) ★
28775 Aurora Rd, Solon, OH 44139-1891
Tel (440) 248-0400 *Founded/Ownrshp* 2010
Sales 83.2MME *EMP* 490E
SIC 3825 3823 7371 Instruments to measure electricity; Test equipment for electronic & electric measurement; Multimeters; Semiconductor test equipment; Computer interface equipment for industrial process control; Computer software development
Pr: Joseph P Keithley
**COO:* Linda C Rae
**CFO:* Mark J Plush
**VP:* Philip R Etsler
VP: Alan S Gaffney
**VP:* Mark A Hoersten
VP: Mark Hoersten
**VP:* Larry L Pendergrass
Exec: Michelle Ferguson
Exec: Ron Rich
Prgrm Mgr: Tom Ohlsen

D-U-N-S 05-663-1328 IMP
KEITHLY-WILLIAMS SEEDS INC
420 Palm Ave, Holtville, CA 92250-1156
Tel (760) 356-5533 *Founded/Ownrshp* 1981
Sales 100.0MME *EMP* 75
Accts Swain & Kennerson
SIC 5191 0721 0181 Seeds: field, garden & flower; Crop seeding services; Seeds, vegetable: growing of
CEO: Kelly G Kiehtly
**CFO:* Walt Williams
**VP:* Mary Bornt
**VP:* Pat Cooley
Off Mgr: Lupita Madrid
Dir IT: Gerald Juettner
IT Man: Greg Estrada
Netwrk Eng: Wendy Vega
Sls Mgr: Jose Gudino

KEL-SAN PRODUCTS
See KELSAN INC

D-U-N-S 00-386-6022
KEL-TECH INC (TX)
(*Suby of* CLARIANT CORP) ★
3408 E State Highway 158, Midland, TX 79706-4240
Tel (432) 684-4700 *Founded/Ownrshp* 1983, 2016
Sales 95.0MM *EMP* 300E
SIC 1389 8731 Oil field services; Chemical laboratory, except testing
Pr: Kenneth Golder
**Treas:* Jennifer Morningstar
Tech Mgr: John Mosley
Plnt Mgr: Dennis Wallace
Mktg Dir: Clifton Struck

D-U-N-S 00-678-3765
KELCHNER INC (OH)
(*Suby of* WOOD GROUP PSN LIMITED)
50 Advanced Dr, Springboro, OH 45066-1805
Tel (937) 704-9890 *Founded/Ownrshp* 1948, 2015
Sales 93.0MM *EMP* 375E
SIC 1794 1389 Excavation work; Mud service, oil field drilling; Bailing wells
CEO: Todd Kelchner
**Pr:* Troy Norvell
VP: Jeff Kelchner
VP: Kevin Weckel

D-U-N-S 06-858-3749 IMP
KELCO INDUSTRIES INC
1425 Lake Ave, Woodstock, IL 60098-7419
Tel (815) 334-3600 *Founded/Ownrshp* 1962
Sales 90.8MME *EMP* 842
SIC 3599 3069 3494 3585 3544 3625 Flexible metal hose, tubing & bellows; Molded rubber products; Valves & pipe fittings; Expansion joints pipe; Heating equipment, complete; Air conditioning units, complete: domestic or industrial; Industrial molds; Relays, for electronic use; Switches, electronic applications
Ch Bd: Michael J Kelly
**Pr:* Kevin G Kelly
**VP:* Marietta Kelly

D-U-N-S 06-614-5236 IMP
KELE INC
JOHNSON CONTRLS AUTHORIZED DLR
3300 Brother Blvd, Memphis, TN 38133-8950
Tel (901) 382-6084 *Founded/Ownrshp* 2004
Sales 106.6MME *EMP* 230
SIC 5075 3822 3829 Air conditioning & ventilation equipment & supplies; Auto controls regulating residntl & coml environmt & applncs; Measuring & controlling devices
CEO: Tim Vargo
**CFO:* Keith Mayer
CFO: Keith Mayor
CFO: Mike Phillips
VP: Dean Mueller
Exec: Johnny Enoch
Genl Mgr: Janet Flickinger
IT Man: Tom Ovidio
IT Man: Donna Pineau
VP Sls: Tom Benson
VP Sls: Anthony Gardner

D-U-N-S 05-035-5460 IMP
KELLEHER CORP
KELLEHER LUMBER COMPANY
1543 5th Ave, San Rafael, CA 94901-1806
Tel (415) 454-8861 *Founded/Ownrshp* 1972
Sales 109.6MME *EMP* 200
SIC 5031 Lumber: rough, dressed & finished; Millwork; Molding, all materials
CEO: Donald J Kelleher
**Sec:* Donna Kelleher
**VP:* Jeffrey Barnes
IT Man: Shawn Maloney
Sales Exec: Dave Westlake

KELLEHER LUMBER COMPANY
See KELLEHER CORP

D-U-N-S 61-675-8074 IMP/EXP
KELLER FOUNDATIONS LLC
(*Suby of* KELLER GROUP PLC)
7550 Teague Rd Ste 300, Hanover, MD 21076-1807
Tel (410) 551-8200 *Founded/Ownrshp* 1991
Sales 889.4MME *EMP* 3,000
SIC 1799 8711 Building site preparation; Engineering services
Pr: Robert M Rubright
CFO: Dan Jor
**CFO:* Dan Jordan
VP: George Burke
VP: Robin Johnson
**VP:* Richard N Yale
Dir Risk M: Kim Smith
Off Mgr: Rose Brown
Dir IT: Brian Seymour

KELLER GRADUATE SCHOOL MGT
See DEVRY UNIVERSITY INC

D-U-N-S 00-614-2566
KELLER INC
KELLER PLNNRS/RCHTCTS/BUILDERS
N216 State Highway 55, Kaukauna, WI 54130-8401
Tel (920) 766-5795 *Founded/Ownrshp* 1960
Sales 112.1MME *EMP* 185
Accts Schenck Sc - Appleton Wi
SIC 1542 1541 7336 Commercial & office building contractors; Industrial buildings & warehouses; Commercial art & graphic design
Pr: Wayne Stellmacher
**VP:* Gerald Cohen
**VP:* Steven Klessig
**VP:* Douglas Stecker
VP Opers: Jerry Cohen
Opers Mgr: Tom Fricke

D-U-N-S 03-903-3337
KELLER INDEPENDENT SCHOOL DISTRICT
KELLER ISD
350 Keller Pkwy, Keller, TX 76248-2249
Tel (817) 744-1000 *Founded/Ownrshp* 1911
Sales 310.7MM *EMP* 3,400
Accts Weaver And Tidwell Llp Fort
SIC 8211 Public elementary & secondary schools; Public elementary school; Public junior high school; Public senior high school
Pr: Steve Dunmore
Psych: Dana Benton

KELLER ISD
See KELLER INDEPENDENT SCHOOL DISTRICT

KELLER PLNNRS/RCHTCTS/BUILDERS
See KELLER INC

D-U-N-S 00-948-2837 IMP
KELLER SUPPLY CO (WA)
LEISURE SUPPLY
3209 17th Ave W, Seattle, WA 98119-1792
Tel (206) 285-3300 *Founded/Ownrshp* 1952
Sales 339.0MME *EMP* 410
SIC 5074 Plumbing & hydronic heating supplies
CEO: Neil Keller
**Pr:* Michael P Murphy
**CFO:* George W Debell
**VP:* Stuart Sulman
Brnch Mgr: Matt Marshall
Brnch Mgr: David Warner
Dist Mgr: Dan Page
IT Man: Nancy Beveridge
IT Man: Bruce Dahl
IT Man: Mike Fey
IT Man: Scott Hilsen

KELLER WILLIAMS REALTORS
See KELLER WILLIAMS REALTY INC

KELLER WILLIAMS REALTORS
See JOMARSHE INVESTMENT GROUP INC

D-U-N-S 19-858-6807
KELLER WILLIAMS REALTY INC
KELLER WILLIAMS REALTORS
1221 S Mo Pac Expy # 400, Austin, TX 78746-7650
Tel (512) 327-3070 *Founded/Ownrshp* 1983
Sales 127.2MME *EMP* 170
SIC 6531 Real estate agent, residential
CEO: Mark Willis
**Pr:* Mary Tennant
**COO:* Jim Talbot
**CFO:* Ann Yett
**Ch:* MO Anderson
**Ch:* Gary Keller
Ofcr: Byron Ellington
VP: Kristan Cole
VP: Carol Drake
VP: Sharon Gibbons
VP: David Osborn
VP: Jay Papasan
VP: Ron Patulski
VP: Christian Ross
VP: Bill Soteroff
VP: Cary Sylvester

D-U-N-S 18-141-7143
KELLERMEYER BERGENSONS SERVICES LLC
1575 Henthorne Dr, Maumee, OH 43537-1372
Tel (419) 867-4300 *Founded/Ownrshp* 2001
Sales 535.0MME *EMP* 12,000
SIC 7349 Building & office cleaning services
CEO: Mark Minasian
**COO:* Paul Jones
**CFO:* Brett Himes
VP: Mike Mese
Area Mgr: Francisco Emperador
VP Sls: Gene Paja

D-U-N-S 87-920-3776 IMP
KELLEX CORP
33390 Liberty Pkwy, North Ridgeville, OH 44039-2600
Tel (440) 327-4428 *Founded/Ownrshp* 2007
Sales 85.5MME *EMP* 149
SIC 5021 Office & public building furniture
Pr: Chris Rice
CEO: Bryan Beam
CFO: Quez Little
VP: Vicki Elliott
VP: Lew English
VP: Doug Fawcett
VP: Nancy Wilson

D-U-N-S 00-696-9893 EXP
KELLEY BEAN CO INC (NE)
2407 Circle Dr, Scottsbluff, NE 69361-1791
Tel (308) 635-6438 *Founded/Ownrshp* 1927, 1947
Sales 112.6MME *EMP* 225
SIC 5153 2034 Beans, dry: bulk; Grain elevators; Dehydrated fruits, vegetables, soups
Pr: Kevin L Kelley
**CFO:* Lee Glenn
Genl Mgr: Judd Keller
Off Mgr: Kim Fertufon
Opers Mgr: Juan Carrizales
Plnt Mgr: Brian Kaman

D-U-N-S 13-928-1513
KELLEY BLUE BOOK CO INC
(*Suby of* COX AUTOMOTIVE) ★
195 Technology Dr, Irvine, CA 92618-2402
Tel (949) 770-7704 *Founded/Ownrshp* 2010
Sales 92.6MME *EMP* 500
SIC 2721 Trade journals: publishing only, not printed on site
CEO: Jared Rowe
**CFO:* John Morrison
Comm Man: Andrea Suh
Snr Sftwr: Stephen Pettinato
Snr Ntwrk: John Chang
CIO: Dave Templeton
CTO: Jeff McCombs
Web Dev: Kym Huang
Mktg Mgr: Dean Orman
Snr PM: Melody Chu

D-U-N-S 00-820-5213
KELLEY BROTHERS CONTRACTORS INC (MS)
401 County Farm Rd, Waynesboro, MS 39367-8772
Tel (601) 735-2541 *Founded/Ownrshp* 1955
Sales 97.6MME *EMP* 115
SIC 1389 1382 1381 Oil field services; Oil & gas exploration services; Drilling oil & gas wells
Pr: Jerry Kelley
**Treas:* Bessie Kelley
**VP:* Thomas O Kelley Jr

D-U-N-S 09-419-7613
KELLEY CONSTRUCTION INC (KY)
JOE KELLEY CONSTRUCTION
12550 Lake Station Pl, Louisville, KY 40299-6394
Tel (502) 239-2848 *Founded/Ownrshp* 2000, 1978
Sales 90.9MME *EMP* 120E
SIC 1542 Commercial & office building, new construction
Pr: Joseph T Kelley Jr
**VP:* Mark Kelley

D-U-N-S 07-861-0094
KELLEY DRYE & WARREN LLP
101 Park Ave Fl 30, New York, NY 10178-3099
Tel (212) 808-7800 *Founded/Ownrshp* 1835, 1836
Sales 155.4MME *EMP* 1,100
SIC 8111 General practice law office
Mng Pt: James J Kirk
Pt: John Callagy
Pt: Merrill B Stone
Mng Pt: Kathleen Cannon
Mng Pt: Richard S Chargar
Mng Pt: David E Fink
Mng Pt: Michael S Insel
Mng Pt: Henry T Kelly
Mng Pt: Lauri A Mazzuchetti
Mng Pt: Robert I Steiner
Mng Pt: Lewis Rose
Mng Pt: Andrew M White
Dir Soc: John Bergin

D-U-N-S 00-693-5654
KELLEY WILLIAMSON CO (IL)
KW LUBES
1132 Harrison Ave, Rockford, IL 61104-7290
Tel (815) 397-9410 *Founded/Ownrshp* 1924
Sales 176.9MME *EMP* 480
SIC 5541 5411 5171 Filling stations, gasoline; Convenience stores, independent; Petroleum bulk stations
Pr: John Griffin
CFO: Kim Schmidt
VP: Mark Long
Dist Mgr: Suzanne Dorsey-Sterling

D-U-N-S 12-424-1402
KELLEY-CLARKE LLC
(*Suby of* ACOSTA SALES & MARKETING) ★
6600 Corporate Ctr Pkwy, Jacksonville, FL 32216-0973
Tel (904) 281-9800 *Founded/Ownrshp* 1982
Sales 111.9MME *EMP* 2,200
SIC 5141 Food brokers
Ch Bd: Gary Chartrand

KELLEYAMERIT FLEET SERVICES
See KELLEYAMERIT HOLDINGS INC

D-U-N-S 83-317-2468
KELLEYAMERIT HOLDINGS INC
KELLEYAMERIT FLEET SERVICES
1331 N Calif Blvd Ste 150, Walnut Creek, CA 94596-4535
Tel (877) 512-6374 *Founded/Ownrshp* 2010
Sales 98.4MME *EMP* 1,500
SIC 8741 Management services
CEO: Gary Herbold
**Pr:* Robert Brauer
**COO:* Amein Punjani
**CFO:* Dan Williams
VP: Lorraine Brady
Dir IT: Marlene Welsh
Board of Directors: Gary Herbold, Dan Williams

D-U-N-S 01-081-0893 IMP/EXP
■ **KELLOGG BROWN & ROOT LLC**
KBR-KELLOGG BROWN
(*Suby of* K B R) ★
601 Jefferson St Ste 100, Houston, TX 77002-7911
Tel (713) 753-2000 *Founded/Ownrshp* 2005
Sales 2.8MMME *EMP* 20,010
SIC 8711 1629 Engineering services; Industrial plant construction
CEO: Stuart Bradie
CFO: Sue Carter
CFO: Brian Ferraioli
Ex VP: Andrew D Farley
Ex VP: Farhan Mujib
Comm Dir: Susan Wasley
CTO: Van Sickels

D-U-N-S 92-966-6709 IMP
■ **KELLOGG BROWN & ROOT SERVICES INC**
K B R
(*Suby of* K B R) ★
200 12th St S Ste 300, Arlington, VA 22202-5401
Tel (703) 526-7500 *Founded/Ownrshp* 1996
Sales 421.2MME *EMP* 20,010
SIC 8741 Construction management
Pr: John Derbyshire
**Pr:* William P Utt
VP: David Swindle

KELLOGG CMNTY COLLEGE BK STR
See KELLOGG COMMUNITY COLLEGE FOUNDATION

D-U-N-S 00-535-6209 IMP/EXP
▲ **KELLOGG CO**
1 Kellogg Sq, Battle Creek, MI 49017-3534
Tel (269) 961-2000 *Founded/Ownrshp* 1906
Sales 13.5MMM *EMP* 33,577
Accts Pricewaterhousecoopers Llp De
Tkr Sym K *Exch* NYS
SIC 2043 2041 2052 2051 2038 Cereal breakfast foods; Corn flakes: prepared as cereal breakfast food; Rice: prepared as cereal breakfast food; Wheat flakes: prepared as cereal breakfast food; Flour & other grain mill products; Cookies; Crackers, dry; Pastries, e.g. danish: except frozen; Waffles, frozen
Ch Bd: John A Bryant
CFO: Ronald L Dissinger
CFO: Gunther Plosch
Sr VP: Margaret R Bath
Sr VP: Jim Call
Sr VP: Alistair D Hirst
Sr VP: Samantha J Long
Sr VP: Paul T Norman
Sr VP: Doug Vandevelde
VP: Mike Mickunas
VP: Donald O Mondano
VP: Sharron Moss-Higham
VP: Marsha Wolf
Exec: Melissa Kenney
Assoc Dir: Megan Carcano
Assoc Dir: Lores Tome
Board of Directors: Cynthia Hardin Milligan, Stephanie A Burns, Rogelio M Rebolledo, John T Dillon, Carolyn Tastad, Richard W Dreiling, Noel Wallace, Gordon Gund, Zachary Gund, James M Jenness, Donald R Knauss, Ann McLaughlin Korologos, Mary A Laschinger

D-U-N-S 07-929-3312
KELLOGG COMMUNITY COLLEGE FOUNDATION (MI)
KELLOGG CMNTY COLLEGE BK STR
450 North Ave, Battle Creek, MI 49017-3306
Tel (269) 965-4142 *Founded/Ownrshp* 1957, 1998
Sales 20.9MM *EMP* 1,000
Accts Plante & Moran Pllc Portage
SIC 8222 Community college

Ch: Jonathan D Byrd
**Pr:* Dennis Bona
**Treas:* Matthew A Davis
**VP:* Jill Booth
VP: Catherine Waugh
Exec: Bob Reynolds
Dir Rx: Michael Gagnon
VP Admn: Robert Rimkus
CIO: Robert Reynolds
MIS Dir: Kelli Cowell
Nrsg Dir: Cynthia Sublett
Board of Directors: Adam R Dingwall, Chad W Smith

D-U-N-S 07-971-1967
■ KELLOGG NORTH AMERICA CO
(*Suby of* KEEBLER CO) ★
1 Kellogg Sq, Battle Creek, MI 49017-3534
Tel (269) 961-2000 *Founded/Ownrshp* 1997
Sales 228.8MM[E] *EMP* 5,037[E]
SIC 2052 Cookies
Pr: David McKay

D-U-N-S 06-951-8371 EXP
■ KELLOGG SALES CO
KELLOGG'S
(*Suby of* KELLOGG CO) ★
1 Kellogg Sq, Battle Creek, MI 49017-3534
Tel (269) 961-2000 *Founded/Ownrshp* 1923
Sales 670.2MM[E] *EMP* 1,000
SIC 5149 Breakfast cereals
Pr: Carlos Gutierrez
**Pr:* Jim Jenneff
CFO: Raymond Held
VP: Alistair Hirst

D-U-N-S 79-802-7512 EXP
■ KELLOGG USA INC
(*Suby of* KELLOGG CO) ★
1 Kellogg Sq, Battle Creek, MI 49017-3534
Tel (269) 961-2000 *Founded/Ownrshp* 1906
Sales 1.1MMM[E] *EMP* 5,882
SIC 2043 Cereal breakfast foods
Pr: John Bryant
Bd of Dir: Dorothy A Johnson
Ex VP: Jonathan Wilson
VP: Alistair Hirst
**Prin:* David Pfanzelter

KELLOGG'S
See KELLOGG SALES CO

D-U-N-S 11-412-5490 IMP
KELLSTROM AEROSPACE LLC
14400 Nw 77th Ct Ste 306, Miami Lakes, FL 33016-1592
Tel (847) 233-5800 *Founded/Ownrshp* 2002
Sales 149.1MM[E] *EMP* 83
SIC 5088 Aircraft engines & engine parts
VP: Dixie Newton
S&M/VP: Elmer Davis
Sls Dir: Petra Titze
Sales Asso: Robert Scotland

D-U-N-S 11-412-5698
KELLSTROM COMMERCIAL AEROSPACE INC
KELLSTROM MATERIALS
450 Medinah Rd, Roselle, IL 60172-2329
Tel (630) 351-8813 *Founded/Ownrshp* 2015
Sales 88.9MM[E] *EMP* 322
SIC 5088 Transportation equipment & supplies
CEO: Roscoe Musselwhite
**CEO:* Jeff Lund
**CFO:* Oscar Torres
IT Man: Frank Slawinski
Sls Dir: Pauline Esty

KELLSTROM MATERIALS
See KELLSTROM COMMERCIAL AEROSPACE INC

D-U-N-S 00-512-0431 IMP/EXP
KELLWOOD CO LLC
(*Suby of* SUN CAPITAL PARTNERS INC) ★
600 Kellwood Pkwy Ste 200, Chesterfield, MO 63017-5809
Tel (314) 576-3100 *Founded/Ownrshp* 1961, 2008
Sales 723.9MM[E] *EMP* 1,132
SIC 5136 5137 Men's & boys' clothing; Women's & children's clothing
CEO: Lynn Shanahan
Pr: Marc Babins
Pr: Janice Sullivan
Treas: Roger D Joseph
Sr Cor Off: Phil Iosca
Ex VP: Mary P Hinson
Ex VP: Thomas H Pollihan
VP: Stephen R Beluk Jr
VP: J David Larocca
VP: Jeff Rand
VP: Donald E Riley
Exec: Joe Rutz

D-U-N-S 08-260-5106
KELLY & ASSOCIATES INSURANCE GROUP INC (MD)
1 Kelly Way, Sparks Glencoe, MD 21152-9484
Tel (410) 527-3400 *Founded/Ownrshp* 1976
Sales NA *EMP* 350
SIC 6411 Insurance brokers
Pr: Francis X Kelly III
**Ch Bd:* Francis X Kelly Jr
**CFO:* Craig Horner
Bd of Dir: Rebecca Pellegrini
Ex VP: Bryan Kelly
**Ex VP:* Joan Kelly
VP: Kitty Bollinger
VP: Jason J Danner
VP: Kathleen Gier
**VP:* Bryan Keely
**VP:* David Kelly
VP: Brandon Luckett
VP: Michele Sargent
VP: Sherry Shilling
Exec: Tara Gaskins

D-U-N-S 80-095-6323
KELLY CAPITAL GROUP INC
12730 High Bluff Dr # 250, San Diego, CA 92130-3023
Tel (619) 687-5000 *Founded/Ownrshp* 1994
Sales 95.2MM[E] *EMP* 845[E]
SIC 6733 Personal investment trust management
CEO: Michael Kelly
**Pr:* Kenneth R Satterlee
CFO: Greg Bowen
VP: Sean Murphy

KELLY ELECTRIC
See TOWNSEND CORP

KELLY ELECTRIC GROUP
See KELLY JH HOLDING LLC

D-U-N-S 01-728-3156
KELLY JH HOLDING LLC
KELLY ELECTRIC GROUP
821 3rd Ave, Longview, WA 98632-2105
Tel (360) 423-5510 *Founded/Ownrshp* 1998
Sales 201.4MM[E] *EMP* 1,000
Accts Pricewaterhousecoopers Llp Po
SIC 1711 1542 1731 Plumbing, heating, air-conditioning contractors; Nonresidential construction; Electrical work
CFO: Paul Furth

D-U-N-S 02-098-1965
KELLY MANAGEMENT CORP
KELLY PONTIAC
2415 S Babcock St Ste C, Melbourne, FL 32901-5369
Tel (321) 768-2424 *Founded/Ownrshp* 1973
Sales 211.2MM[E] *EMP* 425
SIC 5511 Automobiles, new & used
Ch Bd: Edward J Kelly Jr
**Pr:* Robert P Kelly
Board of Directors: Gregory W Kelly, Robert T Kelly

D-U-N-S 04-288-4580
KELLY MITCHELL GROUP INC (MO)
8229 Maryland Ave, Saint Louis, MO 63105-3643
Tel (314) 727-1700 *Founded/Ownrshp* 1998
Sales 140.5MM[E] *EMP* 1,200
SIC 7371 7373 Custom computer programming services; Computer integrated systems design
CEO: Cassandra Sanford
**Pr:* Mark Locigno
**CFO:* Rebecca Boyer
Mng Dir: Shannon Hernandez

D-U-N-S 00-796-5619 IMP
KELLY PAPER CO (CA)
(*Suby of* LINDENMEYR CENTRAL) ★
288 Brea Canyon Rd, Walnut, CA 91789-3087
Tel (909) 859-8200 *Founded/Ownrshp* 1936, 2012
Sales 283.2MM[E] *EMP* 315
SIC 5111 5943 Printing paper; Office forms & supplies
Pr: Janice Gottesman
COO: Rod Schaar
Dist Mgr: Robert Soto
Store Mgr: Jeffrey Jurisprudencia
Store Mgr: Waylon Obrien
Store Mgr: Joseph Patterson
DP Exec: Arthur Guerrero

D-U-N-S 12-834-5381 IMP/EXP
KELLY PIPE CO LLC
LINE PIPE INTERNATIONAL
(*Suby of* SHOJI JFE TRADE AMERICA INC) ★
11680 Bloomfield Ave, Santa Fe Springs, CA 90670-4608
Tel (562) 868-0456 *Founded/Ownrshp* 2014
Sales 218.6MM[E] *EMP* 285
SIC 5051 Pipe & tubing, steel
Ch: Eddy Ogawa
**CEO:* Leonard Gross
**CEO:* Steve Livingston
**CFO:* Leo Mann
**CFO:* Hideki Matsumoto
**VP:* Mark Brozek
**VP:* Cullen King
VP: Kevin Roberts
**VP:* John N Wolfson
Brnch Mgr: Doug Badger
Brnch Mgr: Barry Henning

KELLY PONTIAC
See KELLY MANAGEMENT CORP

D-U-N-S 00-695-8318
▲ KELLY SERVICES INC
999 W Big Beaver Rd, Troy, MI 48084-4716
Tel (248) 362-4444 *Founded/Ownrshp* 1946
Sales 5.5MMM *EMP* 8,100
Tkr Sym KELYA *Exch* NGS
SIC 7363 Temporary help service
Pr: Carl T Camden
**Ch Bd:* Terence E Adderley
COO: George S Corona
CFO: Olivier G Thirot
Ex VP: John Healy
Sr VP: Teresa S Carroll
Sr VP: Peter W Quigley
Sr VP: Antonina M Ramsey
Sr VP: Natalia A Shuman
VP: Carol Curtis
VP: John Drew
VP: Cathy Hunt
VP: Laura S Lockhart
VP: Juanita Moore-Riles
VP: Mike Orsini
VP: Martin Schlenker
VP: Rich Struble
VP: Brittna Valenzuela
VP: Adam Watkins
VP: David Weeks
Exec: Amy Campbell
Board of Directors: Carol M Adderley, Robert S Cubbin, Jane E Dutton, Terrence B Larkin, Conrad L Mallett Jr, Leslie A Murphy, Donald R Parfet, B Joseph White

D-U-N-S 00-692-2553 IMP/EXP
KELLY TRACTOR CO
8255 Nw 58th St, Doral, FL 33166-3493
Tel (305) 592-5360 *Founded/Ownrshp* 1933
Sales 181.9MM[E] *EMP* 415
SIC 5082 5083 7359 7353 5084 7699 Construction & mining machinery; Farm & garden machinery; Equipment rental & leasing; Heavy construction equipment rental; Industrial machinery & equipment; Industrial machinery & equipment repair; Agricultural equipment repair services
Pr: Patrick L Kelly
**Treas:* Bridget G Duncan
**Sr VP:* David K Julian
**Sr VP:* Nicholas D Kelly
VP: Dan Christofferson
**VP:* K David Julian
Genl Mgr: Juan Alvarez
Genl Mgr: John Socol
Software D: Ernesto Leon
Advt Mgr: Nelda Figueiredo
Manager: Mark Becker
Board of Directors: Eileen Kelly, Marjorie Kelly, Evelyn J Shelley

D-U-N-S 00-912-5303 IMP/EXP
KELLY-MOORE PAINT CO INC
KELLY-MOORE PAINTS
987 Commercial St, San Carlos, CA 94070-4018
Tel (650) 592-8337 *Founded/Ownrshp* 1946
Sales 719.7MM[E] *EMP* 1,500
SIC 2851 Paints: oil or alkyd vehicle or water thinned; Lacquers, varnishes, enamels & other coatings; Removers & cleaners
Ch Bd: Steve DeVoe
**CFO:* Roy George
VP: James Alberts
VP: Michael Black
VP: Daniel Englert
VP: Karl Jaranillo
VP: Rusty Martindale
**VP:* James Maul
VP: Todd Wirdzek
**VP:* Mark A Zielinski
Genl Mgr: Clarence Jones
Board of Directors: L Dale Crandall, Steve Devoe, Christine McCall, Bill Moore Jr

KELLY-MOORE PAINTS
See KELLY-MOORE PAINT CO INC

D-U-N-S 10-834-9937
KELSAN INC
KEL-SAN PRODUCTS
5109 N National Dr, Knoxville, TN 37914-6512
Tel (865) 525-7132 *Founded/Ownrshp* 1983
Sales 107.7MM[E] *EMP* 125
SIC 5087 5169 7699 Cleaning & maintenance equipment & supplies; Janitors' supplies; Specialty cleaning & sanitation preparations; Industrial equipment services
Ch Bd: Tillman J Keller III
**Pr:* J Ken Bodie
**CEO:* Vincent Keller
CFO: Stanley Johnson
**CFO:* Kyle Kirchhofer
Dir IT: Todd Allen
Opers Mgr: Alvin Huffine
Sls Mgr: Tim Hyman
Sls Mgr: Andy Smith

D-U-N-S 01-710-4563
KELSER CORP
111 Roberts St Ste D, East Hartford, CT 06108-3666
Tel (860) 610-2200 *Founded/Ownrshp* 1981
Sales 89.4MM *EMP* 53
SIC 5045 Computers; Computer peripheral equipment; Computer software
Pr: Barry Kelly
VP Opers: Tom Sharp

D-U-N-S 14-473-5433 IMP/EXP
KELSEY-HAYES CO
(*Suby of* LUCASVARITY AUTOMOTIVE HOLDING CO) ★
12001 Tech Center Dr, Livonia, MI 48150-2122
Tel (734) 812-6979 *Founded/Ownrshp* 2010
Sales 125.2MM[E] *EMP* 308
SIC 3714 Motor vehicle parts & accessories; Motor vehicle engines & parts; Motor vehicle body components & frame; Motor vehicle electrical equipment
Pr: Edward Carpenter

KELSEY-SEYBOLD CLINIC
See KELSEY-SEYBOLD MEDICAL GROUP PLLC

D-U-N-S 62-468-0559
KELSEY-SEYBOLD MEDICAL GROUP PLLC
KELSEY-SEYBOLD CLINIC
11511 Shadow Creek Pkwy, Pearland, TX 77584-7298
Tel (713) 442-0000 *Founded/Ownrshp* 1992
Sales 230.4MM[E] *EMP* 2,800
SIC 8011 5912 Offices & clinics of medical doctors; Physicians' office, including specialists; Drug stores
Ch Bd: Spencer Berthelsen
**CFO:* John Sperry
**Sec:* Tejash Patel
**V Ch Bd:* Azam Kundi
Ofcr: Mike Fitzgerald
VP: Kenneth Janis
VP: Michael Newmark
VP: Philip Price
VP: Nicholas Ro
Exec: David Miller
Dir Rad: Carla Antley
Dir Bus: Peter Wertheim
Board of Directors: Herbert Ashe MD, James Boland MD, P K Champion MD, Michael Condit MD Chb, John Hughes MD, Donald Owens MD Sec-Treas, Marilyn Rice MD, Julie Toll MD

D-U-N-S 16-855-3332 IMP
KELTA INC
141 Rodeo Dr, Edgewood, NY 11717-8378
Tel (631) 789-5000 *Founded/Ownrshp* 2003
Sales 112.7MM[E] *EMP* 1,000[E]
SIC 3089 3643 3661 Plastic hardware & building products; Current-carrying wiring devices; Telephone & telegraph apparatus
Pr: Parag Mehta

D-U-N-S 07-890-4901 IMP
KEM KREST LLC
3221 Magnum Dr, Elkhart, IN 46516-9021
Tel (574) 389-2650 *Founded/Ownrshp* 2008
Sales 115.4MM[E] *EMP* 150
SIC 5169 5013 5085 4783 4225 Chemicals & allied products; Motor vehicle supplies & new parts; Industrial supplies; Packing & crating; General warehousing & storage
CEO: Amish Shah
**CFO:* David Weaver
Opers Supe: Jonathan Paige
Mktg Mgr: Mindy Brooks

D-U-N-S 78-842-1808 IMP
▲ KEMET CORP
2835 Kemet Way, Simpsonville, SC 29681-6298
Tel (864) 963-6300 *Founded/Ownrshp* 1919
Sales 734.8MM *EMP* 8,800[E]
Accts Ernst & Young Llp Greenville
Tkr Sym KEM *Exch* NYS
SIC 3675 Electronic capacitors
CEO: Per-Olof Loof
**Ch Bd:* Frank G Brandenberg
CFO: William M Lowe Jr
Treas: Richard J Vatinelle
Ofcr: Susan B Barkal
Ofcr: Stefano Vetralla
Ex VP: Assal David
Ex VP: Charles C Meeks Jr
Sr VP: R James Assaf
Sr VP: Phillip M Lessner
Sr VP: Claudio Lollini
Sr VP: Andreas Meier
Sr VP: Robert S Willoughby
VP: Michael L Raynor
Board of Directors: Wilfried Backes, Joseph V Borruso, Jacob T Kozubei, E Erwin Maddrey II, Robert G Paul

KEMI
See KENTUCKY EMPLOYERS MUTUAL INSURANCE AUTHORITY

KEMIN FOODS
See KEMIN INDUSTRIES INC

D-U-N-S 00-527-4287 IMP/EXP
KEMIN INDUSTRIES INC (IA)
KEMIN FOODS
2100 Maury St, Des Moines, IA 50317-1100
Tel (515) 559-5100 *Founded/Ownrshp* 1961
Sales 315.7MM[E] *EMP* 919
SIC 2834

D-U-N-S 03-387-0585 IMP
KEMIRA CHEMICALS INC
KEMIRA SPECIALITY CHEMICALS
(*Suby of* KEMIRA OYJ)
1000 Parkwood Cir Se # 500, Atlanta, GA 30339-2131
Tel (863) 533-5990 *Founded/Ownrshp* 2002
Sales 220.8MM[E] *EMP* 350
SIC 2869 2819 Industrial organic chemicals; Industrial inorganic chemicals
CEO: Carolina Den Brok-Perez
**Pr:* Hannu Melarti
**CFO:* Belinda Rosario
**Ex VP:* Harri Kerminen
Ex VP: Antti Salminen
VP: Pedro Materan
Mng Dir: David Goult
Off Mgr: Carmen Willson
Tech Mgr: Christoffer Odman
Site Mgr: Duncan Carr
Site Mgr: Kemira Kemi

KEMIRA SPECIALITY CHEMICALS
See KEMIRA CHEMICALS INC

D-U-N-S 62-794-5702 IMP/EXP
KEMIRA WATER SOLUTIONS INC
(*Suby of* KEMIRA OYJ)
1000 Parkwood Cir Se # 500, Atlanta, GA 30339-2131
Tel (770) 436-1542 *Founded/Ownrshp* 1988
Sales 269.2MM[E] *EMP* 750
SIC 2899 Water treating compounds
**CFO:* Belinda Rosario
**Treas:* Daniel Britt

KEMP
See SPX FLOW TECHNOLOGY USA INC

KEMPER A UNITRIN BUSINESS
See KEMPER INDEPENDENCE INSURANCE CO

D-U-N-S 61-193-5909
▲ KEMPER CORP
1 E Wacker Dr, Chicago, IL 60601-1474
Tel (312) 661-4600 *Founded/Ownrshp* 1990
Sales NA *EMP* 5,600[E]
Tkr Sym KMPR *Exch* NYS
SIC 6331 6321 6311 6141 Fire, marine & casualty insurance; Property damage insurance; Fire, marine & casualty insurance: stock; Accident & health insurance; Life insurance; Life insurance carriers; Automobile loans, including insurance
Pr: Joseph P Lacher Jr
**Ch Bd:* Robert J Joyce
CFO: Frank J Sodaro
Chf Inves: John M Boschelli
Ofcr: Shekar G Jannah
Ex VP: Naimish P Patel
Sr VP: Charles T Brooks
Sr VP: Christine Theros Mullins
VP: Tracy Berwick
VP: C Thomas Evans Jr
VP: Elizabeth Lupetini
VP: Denise Lynch
VP: Steve McGinley
VP: Richard Roeske
Board of Directors: George N Cochran, Kathleen M Cronin, Douglas G Geoga, Thomas M Goldstein, Lacy M Johnson, Christopher B Sarofim, David P Storch

D-U-N-S 11-486-8818
■ KEMPER INDEPENDENCE INSURANCE CO
KEMPER A UNITRIN BUSINESS
(*Suby of* KEMPER CORP) ★
12926 Gran Bay Pkwy W, Jacksonville, FL 32258-4469
Tel (904) 245-5600 *Founded/Ownrshp* 1998
Sales NA *EMP* 900
SIC 6411 Insurance agents, brokers & service; Patrol services, insurance
Pr: Denise I Lynch
**Treas:* Edwin P Schultz
Ex VP: Thomas McDaniel
**Sr VP:* Steven S Andrews
Exec: Peter Walker
Genl Mgr: Bob Sallustio
MIS Dir: Beverly Roman
Dir IT: Patricia Connor
Dir IT: Dorothy Langley
IT Man: Cindy Berger
IT Man: Charles Blumberg

KEMPER INSURANCE
See BB&T INSURANCE SERVICES INC

KEMPER INSURANCE
See RYAN ROBERTSON AND ASSOCIATES INC

KEMPER INSURANCE
See UNITED AGENCIES INC

KEMPER INSURANCE
See INTERWEST INSURANCE SERVICES INC

KEMPER INSURANCE
See WILLIAM RAVEIS REAL ESTATE INC

KEMPER LESNIK ORGANIZATION
See KEMPER SPORTS INC

D-U-N-S 09-253-3959
KEMPER SPORTS INC
KEMPER LESNIK ORGANIZATION
500 Skokie Blvd Ste 444, Northbrook, IL 60062-2844
Tel (847) 850-1818 *Founded/Ownrshp* 1989
Sales 213.2MME *EMP* 4,250
SIC 8743 7941 7992 Public relations services; Promotion service; Sports clubs, managers & promoters; Basketball club; Public golf courses
CEO: Steven K Skinner
**Pr:* Josh W Lesnik
**CFO:* Brian Milligan
**Treas:* Robert L Wallace
**Ex VP:* Gary S Binder
**Ex VP:* Ben Blake
**Sr VP:* Amy Littleton
**VP:* Steve Argo
**VP:* Tom Valdiserri

D-U-N-S 85-855-8166
KEMPER SPORTS MANAGEMENT INC
(*Suby of* KEMPER LESNIK ORGANIZATION) ★
500 Skokie Blvd Ste 444, Northbrook, IL 60062-2844
Tel (847) 850-1818 *Founded/Ownrshp* 1978
Sales 93.9MME *EMP* 2,000
SIC 7999 Golf professionals
Ch: Steven H Lesnik
**Owner:* Jim Stegall
**Pr:* Josh W Lesnik
**CEO:* Stephen K Skinner
**CFO:* Brian Milligan
**Ex VP:* Gary S Binder
**Ex VP:* Ben Blake
Ex VP: James R Seeley
Sr VP: Barrett Eiselman
**Sr VP:* Andrew Fleming
Sr VP: Douglas Hellman
Sr VP: Eric Jonke
Sr VP: Tom Valdiserri
VP: John C Clark
VP: Andy Crosson
VP: Daniel F Cunningham
VP: Barnaby Dinges
VP: David Goltz
VP: Keith Hanley
VP: Hank Hickox
VP: Steve Kelley

D-U-N-S 00-625-9501 IMP
KEMPS LLC
(*Suby of* DAIRY FARMERS OF AMERICA INC) ★
1270 Energy Ln, Saint Paul, MN 55108-5225
Tel (651) 379-6500 *Founded/Ownrshp* 1914
Sales 171.1MME *EMP* 1,060
SIC 2026 2024

KEN GARFF AUTOMOTIVE GROUP
See GARFF ENTERPRISES INC

D-U-N-S 01-845-0718 IMP
KEN MILLER SUPPLY INC (OH)
1537 Blachleyville Rd, Wooster, OH 44691-9752
Tel (330) 264-9146 *Founded/Ownrshp* 1959
Sales 117.5MME *EMP* 70
SIC 5084 Oil field tool joints
CEO: Kirk Miller
**CEO:* Lindy Chandler
Sls Mgr: Troy Poling
Board of Directors: Jack Miller

D-U-N-S 08-382-0639
KEN SMALL CONSTRUCTION INC (CA)
6205 District Blvd, Bakersfield, CA 93313-2141
Tel (661) 617-1700 *Founded/Ownrshp* 1968, 1960
Sales 146.0MME *EMP* 2,000
SIC 1623

KEN-CREST SERVICES
See KENCREST SERVICES

D-U-N-S 06-605-3455 IMP
KEN-MAC METALS INC
(*Suby of* THYSSENKRUPP RAW MATERIALS USA) ★
17901 Englewood Dr, Cleveland, OH 44130-3454
Tel (440) 891-1480 *Founded/Ownrshp* 1994
Sales 332.7MME *EMP* 230
SIC 5051 Nonferrous metal sheets, bars, rods, etc.; Aluminum bars, rods, ingots, sheets, pipes, plates, etc.
Pr: Larry Parsons
Sr VP: Tim Yost
VP: Scott H Seabeck

D-U-N-S 60-634-9025
KENAI DRILLING LIMITED
6430 Cat Canyon Rd, Santa Maria, CA 93454-9712
Tel (805) 937-7871 *Founded/Ownrshp* 1978
Sales 307.9MME *EMP* 271
SIC 1381 Drilling oil & gas wells
Pr: Tim Crist
**COO:* David Arias
**CFO:* David Uhler
**VP:* Rex Northern
Opers Mgr: Gene Kramer

D-U-N-S 10-064-2099
KENAI PENINSULA BOROUGH SCHOOL DISTRICT
148 N Binkley St, Soldotna, AK 99669-7520
Tel (907) 714-8888 *Founded/Ownrshp* 1964
Sales 168.0MM *EMP* 1,104
Accts Bdo Usa Llp Anchorage Alask
SIC 8211 Public elementary & secondary schools
Treas: Marty Anderson
Dir Risk M: Julie Cisco
IT Man: Shelley Stockdale
Info Man: Bob Jones

D-U-N-S 02-053-4637
KENAN ADVANTAGE GROUP INC
4366 Mount Pleasant St Nw, North Canton, OH 44720-5446
Tel (877) 999-2524 *Founded/Ownrshp* 2010
Sales 1.4MMME *EMP* 4,923
SIC 4213 4212 Trucking, except local; Liquid petroleum transport, non-local; Local trucking, without storage; Petroleum haulage, local
CEO: Dennis Nash
**Ch Bd:* Lee Shaffer
**Pr:* Bruce Blaise
**COO:* Douglas Allen
CFO: Jim Appleton
**CFO:* Carl H Young
CFO: Carl Young
Treas: Jerry Hoover
Ex VP: Bill Downey
**Ex VP:* Rex Molder
**Ex VP:* Kevin Spencer
Ex VP: Dennis Waller
VP: Mike Calnon
VP: Richard Cole
VP: Charlie Delacey
VP: Justin Jeffers
VP: R Molder
VP: William Prevost
VP: John Rakoczy
VP: Bruce Stockton
VP: Steve Welty

D-U-N-S 00-346-1233
KENAN TRANSPORT LLC
(*Suby of* KENAN ADVANTAGE GROUP INC) ★
100 Europa Dr Ste 170, Chapel Hill, NC 27517-2310
Tel (919) 967-8221 *Founded/Ownrshp* 2001
Sales 117.6MME *EMP* 1,674
SIC 4212 4213 Local trucking, without storage; Trucking, except local; Liquid petroleum transport, non-local
Pr: Lee P Shaffer
**Treas:* William L Boone
Treas: Carl H Young
**VP:* John Krovic
**VP:* Dennis Waller
**VP Mktg:* Gary Knutson

D-U-N-S 07-153-1586
KENCO GROUP INC
KENCO LOGISTIC SERVICES
2001 Riverside Dr Ste 3100, Chattanooga, TN 37406
Tel (423) 622-1113 *Founded/Ownrshp* 1968
Sales 1.6MMME *EMP* 4,000
SIC 4225 6512 General warehousing; Nonresidential building operators
CEO: Jane Kennedy Greene
Ch Bd: James D Kennedy Jr
Pr: Sheila Crane
CEO: Gerald Perritt
COO: David Caines
CFO: Dwight Crawley
VP: Jimmy Glascock
Genl Mgr: Kevin Charles
Genl Mgr: Chuck Cobb
Genl Mgr: Kal Dawson
Genl Mgr: Grant Denton

KENCO LOGISTIC SERVICES
See KENCO GROUP INC

D-U-N-S 08-239-6024
KENCO LOGISTIC SERVICES INC
520 W 31st St, Chattanooga, TN 37410-1115
Tel (423) 756-5552 *Founded/Ownrshp* 1950
Sales 87.4MME *EMP* 2,500
SIC 4225 4783 Warehousing, self-storage; Crating goods for shipping
Ch Bd: James D Kennedy III
**Pr:* Gary Mayfield

D-U-N-S 78-446-4489
KENCREST SERVICES
KEN-CREST SERVICES
960 Harvest Dr Ste 100a, Blue Bell, PA 19422-1900
Tel (610) 825-9360 *Founded/Ownrshp* 1984
Sales 107.1MM *EMP* 1,200
Accts Bbd Llp Philadelphia Pa
SIC 8361 8322 8351 Residential care for the handicapped; Individual & family services; Child day care services
Pr: Herta Clements
**CFO:* Tonia McNeal
**Ex Dir:* Jim McFalls
**Ex Dir:* W James McFalls
**Ex Dir:* Bill Nolan
Off Mgr: Sheila Fehrenbach
Netwrk Mgr: Margaret Rothenberger
Mktg Mgr: Mik Gregoire
Nrsg Dir: Rosemarie Kehoe
Pgrm Dir: Gary Clofine
Snr Mgr: Stephanie Brown

D-U-N-S 06-831-9388
KENDALL AUTOMOTIVE GROUP INC (OR)
1400 Executive Pkwy # 400, Eugene, OR 97401-6712
Tel (541) 335-4000 *Founded/Ownrshp* 1963
Sales 195.9MME *EMP* 675
SIC 5511

D-U-N-S 06-584-9168
KENDALL ELECTRIC INC
GREAT LAKES AUTOMATION SUPPLY
5101 S Sprinkle Rd, Portage, MI 49002-2049
Tel (800) 632-5422 *Founded/Ownrshp* 1973
Sales 352.5MME *EMP* 950
SIC 5063 7629 5084

D-U-N-S 62-683-9211
■ KENDALL HEALTHCARE GROUP LTD
KENDALL REGIONAL MEDICAL CTR
(*Suby of* HOSPITAL COPORATION OF AMERICA) ★
11750 Sw 40th St, Miami, FL 33175-3530
Tel (305) 227-5500 *Founded/Ownrshp* 1991
Sales 80.6MME *EMP* 1,700
SIC 8062 General medical & surgical hospitals
CEO: Scott A Cihak
CFO: Michael Houston
CFO: Mauricio E Sirvent
Pathlgst: Miguel M Gonzalez

D-U-N-S 04-886-5851 IMP/EXP
KENDALL IMPORTS LLC
KENDALL TOYOTA
10943 S Dixie Hwy, Miami, FL 33156-3752
Tel (305) 666-1784 *Founded/Ownrshp* 1998
Sales 195.5MME *EMP* 425
SIC 5511 5521 Automobiles, new & used; Used car dealers
IT Man: Luis Garcia
Sls Mgr: Ruben Diaz

D-U-N-S 00-603-3271
KENDALL REGIONAL MEDICAL CENTER INC
11750 Sw 40th St, Miami, FL 33175-3530
Tel (305) 223-3000 *Founded/Ownrshp* 2007
Sales 371.3MM *EMP* 3
SIC 8011 Medical centers
Prin: Karen Hennington
COO: Martha Garcia
CFO: Ricardo Pavon
VP: Manuel Mantecon
Dir Sec: Hugo Gonzalez
Dir IT: Denise Lopez
Mktg Dir: Agatha Samuel
Doctor: Jose Torrent
Nrsg Dir: Carmen Hamilton
Occ Thrpy: Karen Henington
Diag Rad: Orlando C Enrizo

KENDALL REGIONAL MEDICAL CTR
See KENDALL HEALTHCARE GROUP LTD

KENDALL TOYOTA
See KENDALL IMPORTS LLC

D-U-N-S 96-630-9135
KENDALL WEST BAPTIST HOSPITAL INC
(*Suby of* BAPTIST HEALTH SOUTH FLORIDA INC) ★
9555 Sw 162nd Ave, Miami, FL 33196-6408
Tel (786) 467-2000 *Founded/Ownrshp* 2003
Sales 201.2MM *EMP* 138
Accts Deloitte & Touche Llp
SIC 8062 General medical & surgical hospitals
CEO: Javier Hernandez Lichtl

KENDLE GOVERNMENT SERVICES
See KENDLE INTERNATIONAL LLC

D-U-N-S 01-696-8919
■ KENDLE INTERNATIONAL LLC (OH)
KENDLE GOVERNMENT SERVICES
(*Suby of* INC RESEARCH LLC) ★
3201 Beechleaf Ct, Durham, NC 27703
Tel (919) 876-9300 *Founded/Ownrshp* 1989, 2011
Sales 115.5MME *EMP* 3,105E
SIC 8731 Medical research, commercial
CEO: James T Ogle
Treas: Anthony L Forcellini
Chf Mktg O: Thomas E Stilgenbauer
VP: Sarah Beeby
VP: James P Burns Jr
VP: Sylva H Collins
VP: Karen L Crone
VP: Philip J W Davies
VP: Gregg Dearhammer
VP: Michael J Gallagher
VP: Pierre Geoffroy
VP: Ross J Horsburgh
VP: Dennis Hurley
VP: J Michael Sprafka
VP: Patricia A Steigerwald
VP: Satish Tripathi

D-U-N-S 09-687-3666
KENECO INC
123 N 8th St, Kenilworth, NJ 07033-1108
Tel (908) 241-3700 *Founded/Ownrshp* 2000
Sales 350.0MM *EMP* 3
SIC 3535 Conveyors & conveying equipment
Pr: William Van Loan III
**VP:* Thomas Hoefenkrieg

D-U-N-S 08-623-0542
KENERGY CORP (KY)
6402 Old Corydon Rd, Henderson, KY 42420-9392
Tel (270) 926-4141 *Founded/Ownrshp* 1999
Sales 375.6MM *EMP* 155
SIC 4911 Distribution, electric power
Pr: Stanford Noveick
**Ch:* Robert White
Bd of Dir: William H Reid
**VP:* William Reid
**VP:* Steve Thompson
Comm Man: Renee Jones
Dist Mgr: Tim Miller

D-U-N-S 60-264-3827
KENEXA CORP
IBM
(*Suby of* SALARY.COM LLC) ★
650 E Swedesford Rd # 200, Wayne, PA 19087-1628
Tel (877) 971-9171 *Founded/Ownrshp* 1987
Sales 187.8MME *EMP* 2,744
SIC 7361 7371 Placement agencies; Computer software systems analysis & design, custom
Ch Bd: Nooruddin S Karsan
Genl Pt: John Rutherford
Pr: Addison Grimes
Pr: Kevin Horigan
Pr: Troy A Kanter
CFO: Donald F Volk
VP: Zach Canaday
VP: Andrew Jackson
VP: Archie L Jones Jr
Mng Dir: Tim Collins
CTO: James P Restivo

KENLAKE FOODS
See INTER AMERICAN PRODUCTS INC

D-U-N-S 08-596-4591
KENMOR ELECTRIC CO LP (TX)
(*Suby of* HEICO COMPANIES L L C) ★
8330 Hansen Rd, Houston, TX 77075-1004
Tel (713) 869-0171 *Founded/Ownrshp* 1976, 1997
Sales 98.1MME *EMP* 400
SIC 1731 General electrical contractor
Pr: John C Quebe
**Ex VP:* Joe Martin
VP: Kip Farrington
**VP:* Jeff Hinton
**VP:* Steve Parris
Snr PM: Stu Jardine

D-U-N-S 01-748-1797 IMP
KENMORE CONSTRUCTION CO INC
700 Home Ave, Akron, OH 44310-4190
Tel (330) 762-8936 *Founded/Ownrshp* 1956
Sales 103.3MME *EMP* 200E
SIC 1611 5032 General contractor, highway & street construction; Sand, construction
Pr: William A Scala
VP: Matt Moravec
VP: Thomas Postak
**VP:* Paul Scala
VP: Jerry Stanoch
Snr PM: Dustin Thonen

D-U-N-S 03-022-8522
KENMORE MERCY HOSPITAL (NY)
(*Suby of* CATHOLIC HEALTH SYSTEM INC) ★
2950 Elmwood Ave Fl 6, Kenmore, NY 14217-1390
Tel (716) 447-6100 *Founded/Ownrshp* 1951, 1997
Sales 168.5MM *EMP* 1,000
SIC 8062 8059 8011 General medical & surgical hospitals; Nursing home, except skilled & intermediate care facility; Medical centers
Pr: Mary Hoffman
Pr: Patricia Marcus
QA Dir: Kathy Coughlin
Pr Mgr: Dawn Cwierley

D-U-N-S 07-979-9142
KENMORE-TONAWANDA UNION FREE SCHOOL DISTRICT
1500 Colvin Blvd, Buffalo, NY 14223-1118
Tel (716) 874-8400 *Founded/Ownrshp* 2015
Sales 11.2MME *EMP* 1,593E
SIC 8211 Public elementary & secondary schools
Trst: Chris Pashler
Ofcr: Melanie Kamens
VP: Andrew Gianni
Genl Mgr: Diane Voght
Genl Mgr: Margaret Weglarski
Pr Dir: Patrick Moses
HC Dir: Debra Cerey

D-U-N-S 01-841-2283
■ KENNAMETAL HOLDINGS EUROPE INC
(*Suby of* KENNAMETAL INC) ★
1600 Technology Way, Latrobe, PA 15650-4647
Tel (724) 539-5000 *Founded/Ownrshp* 2000
Sales 110.6MME *EMP* 900E
SIC 6719 Investment holding companies, except banks
Pr: John R Tucker
**Treas:* Brian E Kelly

D-U-N-S 00-439-7659 IMP
▲ KENNAMETAL INC (PA)
600 Grant St Ste 5100, Pittsburgh, PA 15219-2706
Tel (412) 248-8200 *Founded/Ownrshp* 1938, 1943
Sales 2.1MMM *EMP* 11,200
Tkr Sym KMT *Exch* NYS
SIC 3545 3532 3531 3313 3399 Machine tool accessories; Cutting tools for machine tools; Bits for use on lathes, planers, shapers, etc.; Tool holders; Mining machinery; Bits, except oil & gas field tools, rock; Auger mining equipment; Construction machinery attachments; Blades for graders, scrapers, dozers & snow plows; Snow plow attachments; Screeds & screeding machines; Electrometallurgical products; Tungsten carbide powder; Metal powders, pastes & flakes
Pr: Ronald M De Feo
Ch Bd: Lawrence W Stranghoener
CFO: Jan Kees Van Gaalen
VP: Judith L Bacchus
VP: Robert J Clemens
VP: Michelle Keating
Board of Directors: Cindy L Davis, Philip A Dur, William J Harvey, William M Lambert, Timothy R McLevish, Steven H Wunning

D-U-N-S 15-595-9463 EXP
KENNECOTT CORP
(*Suby of* RIO TINTO AMERICA INC) ★
8315 W 3595 S, Magna, UT 84044-3406
Tel (801) 913-8335 *Founded/Ownrshp* 1979
Sales 12.7MMME *EMP* 3,065
SIC 1041 1021 1061 1221 Gold ores; Copper ore mining & preparation; Molybdenum ores mining; Surface mining, bituminous
Ch Bd: Oscar L Groeneveld

Pr: Jonathon Leslie
CFO: Roger Johnson
Ofcr: James Elegante
Sr VP: Bruce Farmer
Sr VP: William Orchow
Sr VP: Richard Pierce
Dir IT: Richard Landinghan
Sls Mgr: Jim Cowley

D-U-N-S 61-996-8779 EXP
KENNECOTT UTAH COPPER LLC
RIO TINTO REGIONAL CENTER
(*Suby of* KENNECOTT CORP) ★
4700 W Daybreak Pkwy, South Jordan, UT 84009-5120
Tel (801) 204-2000 *Founded/Ownrshp* 1982
Sales 12.6MMM[E] *EMP* 2,400
SIC 1021 1041 1044 1061

D-U-N-S 12-303-2732
KENNEDY AUTOMOTIVE GROUP INC
620 Bustleton Pike, Feasterville Trevose, PA 19053-6054
Tel (215) 357-6600 *Founded/Ownrshp* 1955
Sales 179.0MM[E] *EMP* 341
SIC 5511 Automobiles, new & used
Prin: J Michael Kennedy
**Treas:* Kurt Kennedy
Sales Asso: Tom Hockemeier
Sales Asso: Matt Robinson

KENNEDY CENTER, THE
See JOHN F KENNEDY CENTER FOR PERFORMING ARTS

KENNEDY COMPANIES, THE
See KENNEDY CULVERT & SUPPLY CO

D-U-N-S 06-569-5751
KENNEDY CULVERT & SUPPLY CO
KENNEDY COMPANIES, THE
125 6th Ave Ste 100, Mount Laurel, NJ 08054-1801
Tel (856) 813-5000 *Founded/Ownrshp* 1973
Sales 110.4MM[E] *EMP* 130
SIC 5085 Industrial supplies
Pr: Robert A Kennedy Sr
**Pr:* Robert A Kennedy Jr
Sales Asso: Michael Gaughan
Sales Asso: Michael Mascola
Sales Asso: Bob Thomas

D-U-N-S 11-433-6910
KENNEDY HEALTH CARE FOUNDATION INC
18 E Laurel Rd, Stratford, NJ 08084-1327
Tel (856) 661-5100 *Founded/Ownrshp* 1983
Sales 135.0MM[E] *EMP* 2,800[E]
SIC 6733 4119 8051 6531 7361 8721 Trusts; Ambulance service; Extended care facility; Real estate managers; Nurses' registry; Accounting services, except auditing
Ch Bd: Joseph Maressa
Pr: A R Pirolli
VP: Joseph M Lario

KENNEDY HEALTH SYSTEM
See KENNEDY UNIVERSITY HOSPITAL INC

D-U-N-S 07-696-1481
KENNEDY HEALTH SYSTEM INC
1099 White Horse Rd, Voorhees, NJ 08043-4405
Tel (856) 566-5200 *Founded/Ownrshp* 1982
Sales 479.7MM[E] *EMP* 4,000
SIC 8062 Hospital, medical school affiliated with residency
CEO: Martin A Bieber
**Pr:* Richard E Murray
**CEO:* Joseph W Devine
**COO:* Joseph Hummel
**CFO:* Gary Perrinoni
**Sr VP:* Joseph Lario
VP: Kevin J Caracciolo
VP: Michael P Dennis
VP: Daniel L Herriman
VP: Suzette Martella
Sales Exec: Mary Darrow

KENNEDY HOUSE SYSTEM
See KENNEDY MEMORIAL HOSPITAL UNIVERSITY MEDICAL CENTER INC

D-U-N-S 06-487-2518
KENNEDY KRIEGER CHILDRENS HOSPITAL INC (MD)
707 N Broadway, Baltimore, MD 21205-1832
Tel (443) 923-9400 *Founded/Ownrshp* 1937
Sales 146.9MM *EMP* 1,200
Accts Sc&H Tax & Advisory Services L
SIC 8069 Children's hospital
Pr: Dr Gary Goldstein
**COO:* James M Anders Jr
**CFO:* Michael Neuman
Psych: Chrissy Cox

D-U-N-S 15-534-2371
KENNEDY KRIEGER INSTITUTE INC
707 N Broadway, Baltimore, MD 21205-1888
Tel (443) 923-9200 *Founded/Ownrshp* 1986
Sales 237.0MM *EMP* 2,500
Accts Pricewaterhousecoopers Llp B
SIC 8069 Children's hospital
Pr: Gary W Goldstein
**COO:* James M Anders Jr
**CFO:* Michael Neuman
VP: Jim Anders
VP: Robert Findling
VP: Larry Triplett
Dir Soc: Michele Huffman
Nurse Mgr: Yvonne Paraway
Sfty Dirs: John Gattus
Psych: Thomas Ley
Board of Directors: Dorothy Hamill, William J Toomey II

D-U-N-S 11-337-9890
KENNEDY MEMORIAL HOSPITAL UNIVERSITY MEDICAL CENTER INC
KENNEDY HOUSE SYSTEM
(*Suby of* KENNEDY HEALTH SYSTEM INC) ★
1099 White Horse Rd Fl 3, Voorhees, NJ 08043-4405
Tel (856) 566-2000 *Founded/Ownrshp* 2002
Sales 455.1MM *EMP* 2
SIC 8062 General medical & surgical hospitals

D-U-N-S 07-838-4413
KENNEDY UNIVERSITY HOSPITAL INC
KENNEDY HEALTH SYSTEM
435 Hurffvl Cross Keys Rd, Turnersville, NJ 08012-2453
Tel (856) 582-2500 *Founded/Ownrshp* 1965
Sales 147.4MM[E] *EMP* 4,000
SIC 8221 Colleges universities & professional schools
CEO: Joe Devine
**Ch:* John P Silvestri
**Treas:* Michele A Fletcher
**Prin:* Marty Bieber

D-U-N-S 04-493-3943
KENNEDY WIEDEN INC
224 Nw 13th Ave, Portland, OR 97209-2920
Tel (503) 937-7000 *Founded/Ownrshp* 1983
Sales 129.0MM[E] *EMP* 928
SIC 7311 Advertising agencies
Pr: Dave W Luhr
**Pr:* Dan G Wieden
VP: Antony Goldstein
VP: Dave Luhr
VP: Keith McLellan
Assoc Dir: Patrick Mauro
Creative D: Aaron Allen
Creative D: Hal Curtis
Creative D: Susan Hoffman
Creative D: Stuart Jennings
Mng Dir: Trish Adams

D-U-N-S 82-535-0007
▲ KENNEDY-WILSON HOLDINGS INC
151 El Camino Dr, Beverly Hills, CA 90212-2704
Tel (310) 887-6400 *Founded/Ownrshp* 1977
Sales 603.7MM *EMP* 495[E]
Tkr Sym KW *Exch* NYS
SIC 6531 6799 Real estate agent, commercial; Real estate agent, residential; Investors
Ch Bd: William J McMorrow
CFO: Justin Enbody
Ex VP: Fred Cordova
**Ex VP:* Kent Mouton
Ex VP: Matt Windisch
Sr VP: In Ku Lee
Mng Dir: Jennifer Hall

D-U-N-S 04-652-4260
KENNEDY/JENKS CONSULTANTS INC
303 2nd St Ste 300s, San Francisco, CA 94107-3632
Tel (415) 243-2150 *Founded/Ownrshp* 1919
Sales 138.7MM[E] *EMP* 450
Accts Hood & Strong Llp San Francis
SIC 8711 Consulting engineer
Ch: Gary Carlton
**Pr:* Keith A London
**CFO:* Patrick J Courtney
**Ch:* Lynn Takaichi
Ofcr: Don Weiden
VP: Michael Greenspan
VP: Patrick Huston
VP: Sachi Itagaki
VP: Craig W Lichty
VP: John Rayner
VP: Dennis Sanchez
VP: Kim Tanner

D-U-N-S 15-739-5641
KENNER & CO INC
437 Madison Ave Ste 3601, New York, NY 10022-7019
Tel (212) 319-2300 *Founded/Ownrshp* 1986
Sales 399.2MM[E] *EMP* 2,800
SIC 6211 Investment firm, general brokerage
Pr: Jeffrey Kenner
**Mng Dir:* Thomas Wolf

D-U-N-S 10-291-9388 IMP
KENNERLEY-SPRATLING INC
2116 Farallon Dr, San Leandro, CA 94577-6604
Tel (510) 351-8230 *Founded/Ownrshp* 1982
Sales 129.5MM[E] *EMP* 400
SIC 3089 3082 Injection molding of plastics; Unsupported plastics profile shapes
CEO: Richard Spratling
**CFO:* Bill Roure
VP: Ed Lopez
**Prin:* Paul Hoefler
**VP Sls:* Jeffrey Cranor

D-U-N-S 62-775-8923
KENNESAW STATE UNIVERSITY
BOARD OF RGNTS OF THE UNVRSTY
(*Suby of* GEORGIA BOARD OF REGENTS) ★
1000 Chastain Rd Nw, Kennesaw, GA 30144-5591
Tel (770) 423-6000 *Founded/Ownrshp* 1966
Sales 265.8MM[E] *EMP* 3,000
Accts Russell W Hinton-State Audito
SIC 8221 Colleges universities & professional schools
Pr: Daniel S Papp
COO: Debbie Chimeno
COO: Richard Corhen
**COO:* Randy Hinds
CFO: Paula Campbell
Bd of Dir: Richard W Whiteside
Ofcr: Lynn Kirkland
Assoc Dir: Michael Dutcher
Assoc Dir: McCree Lake
Assoc Dir: Carolyn E Lliottfarino
Assoc Dir: Kristi S McMillan
Assoc Dir: Ruth A Middleton
Assoc Dir: Karen S Ohlsson
Assoc Dir: Vincenzo A Patone
Assoc Dir: Christine L Storey
Assoc Dir: Caryn Young

D-U-N-S 03-721-7064
KENNESTONE HOSPITAL AT WINDY HILL INC
WELL STAR
(*Suby of* WELLSTAR HEALTH SYSTEM INC) ★
677 Church St Ne, Marietta, GA 30060-1101
Tel (770) 793-5000 *Founded/Ownrshp* 1972
Sales 821.3MM *EMP* 2,950
SIC 8062 General medical & surgical hospitals
CEO: Thomas E Hill
**CFO:* Dick Stovall
Ofcr: Andre Hayden
VP: Adam Thompson
Exec: Cecelia Byers
Dir Rx: Bill Gonzalez
Ex Dir: Don Burton
Ex Dir: Edward J Peterson
Prac Mgr: Jen Gaines
Doctor: Eugene McNatt
Doctor: Don Shaffer
Board of Directors: James Coffey, Richard Hammonds

D-U-N-S 96-960-9390
KENNESTONE HOSPITAL INC
805 Sandy Plains Rd, Marietta, GA 30066-6340
Tel (770) 792-5023 *Founded/Ownrshp* 2011
Sales 948.4MM *EMP* 15[E]
Accts Pricewaterhousecoopers Llp Ph
SIC 8062 General medical & surgical hospitals
CEO: Reynold J Jennings

D-U-N-S 07-644-8257 IMP
KENNETH COLE PRODUCTIONS INC
603 W 50th St, New York, NY 10019-7051
Tel (212) 265-1500 *Founded/Ownrshp* 2012
Sales 804.5MM[E] *EMP* 1,600[E]
SIC 3143 3144 3171 5661 5632 5611 Men's footwear, except athletic; Women's footwear, except athletic; Handbags, women's; Purses, women's; Shoe stores; Women's boots; Men's shoes; Women's accessory & specialty stores; Apparel accessories; Costume jewelry; Handbags; Men's & boys' clothing stores
Ch: Kenneth Cole
V Ch: Paul Blum
**Pr:* Mia Dellosso-Caputo
Pr: Chris Nakatani
Pr: Joshua Schulman
**CEO:* Marc Schneider
**CFO:* David P Edelman
Ex VP: Michael Devirgilio
Sr VP: Henrik Madsen
Sr VP: Lori Wagner
VP: Derek Benson
VP: Regina Gorinshteyn
VP: Richard Hardy
VP: Gayle Kasuba
VP: Alicia Molitor
VP: Dan Riley
VP: Joe Scarpellino
VP: Brian Weaver
VP: Chris Yoham

D-U-N-S 10-336-4068
KENNETH CORP
GARDEN GROVE HOSPITAL
12601 Garden Grove Blvd, Garden Grove, CA 92843-1908
Tel (714) 537-5160 *Founded/Ownrshp* 1951
Sales 84.5MM *EMP* 615
SIC 8062 General medical & surgical hospitals
CEO: Edward Mirzabegian
**Ch Bd:* Hassan Alkhouli
CFO: Mary B Formy
VP: Carla Glaze
Dir Risk M: Bader Elghussein
Dir Risk M: Jacinto Panes
Dir Lab: Susan David
Dir Rx: Leslie Wolder
CIO: Debbie Horgan
Dir QC: Ahmad Imran
Ansthlgy: Christopher Lui

KENNETH NORRIS CANCER HOSPITAL
See TENET HEALTH SYSTEMS NORRIS INC

D-U-N-S 03-472-0631 IMP
■ KENNETH O LESTER CO INC
PFG CUSTOMIZED DISTRIBUTION
(*Suby of* P F G) ★
245 N Castle Heights Ave, Lebanon, TN 37087-2741
Tel (615) 444-9901 *Founded/Ownrshp* 1988
Sales 2.0MMM[E] *EMP* 1,700
SIC 5141 5142 5148 Groceries, general line; Packaged frozen goods; Fruits, fresh
Pr: Craig Hoskins
VP: Kevin Lester
**VP:* Robert Provalenko
**VP:* Jeff Ray
Genl Mgr: Chris Flynn
IT Man: Gil Helms
Info Man: Bill Huston
Software D: Alan Combs
Sftwr Eng: Damon Dodson
VP Sls: John Hogan

D-U-N-S 06-133-6231
KENNETH RAININ FOUNDATION
155 Grand Ave Ste 1000, Oakland, CA 94612-3779
Tel (510) 625-5200 *Founded/Ownrshp* 1997
Sales 135.3MM *EMP* 17[E]
SIC 8999 Scientific consulting
Pr: Jennifer A Rainin
Ofcr: Paula Ambrose
Ofcr: Kimberly Krivacic

KENNEWICK GENERAL HOSPITAL
See KENNEWICK PUBLIC HOSPITAL DISTRICT

D-U-N-S 07-183-9781
KENNEWICK PUBLIC HOSPITAL DISTRICT
KENNEWICK GENERAL HOSPITAL
900 S Auburn St, Kennewick, WA 99336-5621
Tel (509) 586-6111 *Founded/Ownrshp* 1952
Sales 177.9MM *EMP* 540
SIC 8062 General medical & surgical hospitals
CEO: Louis Koussa
**Owner:* Darren Szendre
**CFO:* Jerry Paule
**VP:* Vik Johnson

D-U-N-S 07-096-8151
KENNEWICK SCHOOL DISTRICT 17
1000 W 4th Ave, Kennewick, WA 99336-5533
Tel (509) 222-5000 *Founded/Ownrshp* 1884
Sales 99.7MM[E] *EMP* 2,600
SIC 8211 9411

D-U-N-S 00-145-7845 IMP/EXP
KENNEY MANUFACTURING CO (RI)
1000 Jefferson Blvd, Warwick, RI 02886-2200
Tel (401) 739-2200 *Founded/Ownrshp* 1914
Sales 123.1MM[E] *EMP* 600
SIC 2591 3261 2511 3699 3499 2541 Drapery hardware & blinds & shades; Mini blinds; Window shades; Bathroom accessories/fittings, vitreous china or earthenware; Storage chests, household: wood; Security devices; Magnetic shields, metal; Display fixtures, wood
Pr: Leslie M Kenney
**Ch Bd:* G D Kenney
CFO: Bruce Bialy
CFO: Joseph Desouse
Bd of Dir: Harry Schult
CTO: Tom Choy
IT Man: Rick Ferreira
Natl Sales: Paul Grimes
Sls&Mrk Ex: Sally Voas
Sls Dir: Steve Brayer

D-U-N-S 02-518-5455
KENNICOTT BROS CO
AMC FLORAL INTERNATIONAL
1638 W Hubbard St, Chicago, IL 60622-6681
Tel (312) 492-8200 *Founded/Ownrshp* 1881, 2000
Sales 109.1MM[E] *EMP* 229
SIC 5193 Flowers, fresh; Artificial flowers; Florists' supplies; Planters & flower pots
CEO: Red Kennicott
**Pr:* Gary Doran
**Pr:* Gustavo Gilchrist
**CEO:* Harrison Kennicott
**CFO:* Randy Smestad

D-U-N-S 02-583-7287 EXP
■ KENNY CONSTRUCTION A GRANITE CO
(*Suby of* KENNY INDUSTRIES INC) ★
2215 Sanders Rd Ste 400, Northbrook, IL 60062-6114
Tel (847) 919-8200 *Founded/Ownrshp* 1985
Sales 157.6MM[E] *EMP* 500[E]
SIC 1622 1611 1629 1623 1541 Bridge construction; Tunnel construction; General contractor, highway & street construction; Subway construction; Power plant construction; Water, sewer & utility lines; Industrial buildings & warehouses
Pr: John E Kenny Jr
**CFO:* Gene Huebner
CFO: Robert Strong
**Treas:* Joan Rose
**Ex VP:* Patrick B Kenny
Board of Directors: Michael Africk, Michael Futch

D-U-N-S 17-787-6745
■ KENNY INDUSTRIES INC
(*Suby of* GRANITE CONSTRUCTION INC) ★
2215 Sanders Rd Ste 400, Northbrook, IL 60062-6114
Tel (847) 919-8200 *Founded/Ownrshp* 1985
Sales 334.8MM[E] *EMP* 1,000[E]
SIC 1611 1622 1629 1623 1541 6552 Highway & street construction; Highway construction, elevated; Bridge construction; Tunnel construction; Subway construction; Sewer line construction; Industrial buildings & warehouses; Subdividers & developers
Pr: John E Kenny Jr
**Treas:* Joan E Rose
**Ex VP:* Patrick Kenny
VP: Theodore Budd
VP: Dan Zarletti
Dir Risk M: John Tuisl
MIS Dir: David Jean
Mktg Dir: Larry Dunlap

D-U-N-S 78-786-0501
KENNY PIPE & SUPPLY INC
811 Cowan St, Nashville, TN 37207-5623
Tel (615) 242-5909 *Founded/Ownrshp* 1992
Sales 115.5MM[E] *EMP* 190
SIC 5074 Plumbing fittings & supplies
Pr: William H Kenny Jr
CFO: Gerald Drennan
**Treas:* Thomas J Guzik Jr
VP: David Gordon
**VP:* Howard Hodges
**VP:* Randy McKnight
Brnch Mgr: Hudson Cole
Brnch Mgr: Chris Finley
Brnch Mgr: Britt Norris
Off Mgr: Kathy Duer
Mktg Mgr: Jake Hester

D-U-N-S 02-328-4516
KENOSHA BEEF INTERNATIONAL LTD
BIRCHWOOD TRANSPORT
3111 152nd Ave, Kenosha, WI 53144-7630
Tel (800) 541-1684 *Founded/Ownrshp* 1936
Sales 184.3MM[E] *EMP* 755
SIC 2011 Meat packing plants
CEO: Charles Vignieri
**Pr:* Dennis Vignieri
**CFO:* Jerome D King
Off Mgr: Sherri Peaslee
Ql Cn Mgr: Tom Sereno
S&M/VP: Dave Vankampen

KENOSHA MEDICAL CENTER
See UNITED HOSPITAL SYSTEM INC

D-U-N-S 09-634-4197
KENOSHA UNIFIED SCHOOL DISTRICT 1
3600 52nd St, Kenosha, WI 53144-2664
Tel (262) 359-6300 *Founded/Ownrshp* 1967
Sales 160.9MM[E] *EMP* 2,093
SIC 8211 Public elementary school; Secondary school
Pr: Rebecca Stevens
COO: Mark Aslakson
CFO: Tarik Hamdan

*CFO: Tina Schmitz
*Treas: Carl Bryan
*VP: Jo Ann Taube
Exec: Brian Bieri
Exec: Athena Burmeister
Exec: Joel Dutton
Exec: Adam Rogahn
*Ex Dir: Ms Sheronda Glass

D-U-N-S 94-817-7175 IMP/EXP
KENOVER MARKETING CORP
KAYCO
72 Hook Rd, Bayonne, NJ 07002-5007
Tel (718) 369-4600 Founded/Ownrshp 1996
Sales 86.2MM EMP 180[E]
Accts Saul N Friedman & Co Brookl
SIC 5141 Groceries, general line
Pr: Ilan Ron
*VP: Moshe Doppelt
*VP: Effe Landsberg

D-U-N-S 00-106-3114 IMP/EXP
KENS FOODS INC (MA)
1 Dangelo Dr, Marlborough, MA 01752-3066
Tel (508) 229-1100 Founded/Ownrshp 1958
Sales 278.0MM[E] EMP 920
Accts Mayer Hoffman Mccann Pc Cam
SIC 2033 Barbecue sauce: packaged in cans, jars, etc.
Pr: Frank A Crowley III
COO: Bob Merchant
*CFO: James Sutherby
*VP: Brian L Crowley
VP: Mark Holbrook
VP: John Pritchard
*VP: Joseph Shay
VP: Al Slingluff
VP: Bob Wynne
CTO: Michael George
QA Dir: Maria Kefalas

D-U-N-S 00-526-9923 IMP/EXP
KENT CORP (IA)
2905 N Highway 61, Muscatine, IA 52761-5809
Tel (563) 264-4211 Founded/Ownrshp 1943
Sales 613.2MM[E] EMP 1,800
SIC 2869 2085 2046 2048 Alcohols, industrial: denatured (non-beverage); Grain alcohol for beverage purposes; Corn starch; Corn oil, refined; Livestock feeds; Poultry feeds
COO: G A Kent
*CFO: D A Jones
Board of Directors: Jeff Underwood

D-U-N-S 83-261-2415
KENT COUNTY CMH AUTHORITY
NETWORK 180
790 Fuller Ave Ne, Grand Rapids, MI 49503-1918
Tel (616) 336-3765 Founded/Ownrshp 2008
Sales 136.2MM EMP 120
Accts Bdo Usa Llp Grand Rapids Mi
SIC 8069 Drug addiction rehabilitation hospital
Ex Dir: Scott Gilman
Ex Dir: Bonnie Huntley

D-U-N-S 06-985-5195
KENT COUNTY MEMORIAL HOSPITAL
HOSPITALITY SHOP
455 Toll Gate Rd, Warwick, RI 02886-2770
Tel (401) 737-7000 Founded/Ownrshp 1946
Sales 318.3MM EMP 1,850
SIC 8062 General medical & surgical hospitals
Pr: Michael Dacey
Chf OB: Maural Colavitta
Chf Rad: Julie Armada
Treas: Polly E Leonard Do
Trst: James R Hagety
Trst: Daniel B Reardon
Ofcr: Caren Santos
VP: Dan Callahan
VP: Alicia Condon
VP: Joseph Dipietro
Dir Risk M: Ruth Denehy
Dir Lab: Lois Beauparlant
Dir Rad: Stevens L Bruce
Dir Rad: Rogovitz M David
Dir Rad: Williams C Mihael
Dir Rad: Silva Rafael

D-U-N-S 02-088-5463
KENT COUNTY OF (INC)
NETWORK 180
300 Monroe Ave Nw Unit 1, Grand Rapids, MI 49503-2206
Tel (616) 632-7580 Founded/Ownrshp 1836
Sales NA EMP 2,000
Accts Rehmann Robson Llc Grand Rapi
SIC 9111 Executive offices;

D-U-N-S 07-706-5928
KENT GENERAL HOSPITAL
MILFORD MEMORIAL HOSPITAL
(Suby of BAYHEALTH MEDICAL CENTER INC) ★
640 S State St, Dover, DE 19901-3599
Tel (302) 674-4700 Founded/Ownrshp 1921
Sales 537.3MM EMP 2,600[E]
SIC 8062 General medical & surgical hospitals
Exec: Kia L Evans
Doctor: Richard Dushuttle
HC Dir: Courtney Breasure

D-U-N-S 07-258-4329
KENT INTERMEDIATE SCHOOL DISTRICT
KENT ISD
2930 Knapp St Ne, Grand Rapids, MI 49525-7006
Tel (616) 364-1333 Founded/Ownrshp 1903
Sales 243.5MM EMP 1,000
Accts Maner Costerisan Pc Lansing
SIC 8211 Public elementary & secondary schools
*Pr: Andrea Haidle
CFO: James McLian
*Treas: Steve Zinger
*VP: Claudia Bajema
Prin: Gail Persons
Doctor: Frank Schwartz

KENT ISD
See KENT INTERMEDIATE SCHOOL DISTRICT

D-U-N-S 08-355-7173
KENT MOORE CABINETS LTD (TX)
501 Industrial Blvd, Bryan, TX 77803-2012
Tel (979) 775-2906 Founded/Ownrshp 1971
Sales 101.3MM[E] EMP 400
SIC 2434 Wood kitchen cabinets; Vanities, bathroom: wood
Pr: R Kent Moore
*CFO: Eric Carter
VP: Casey Moore
VP: Dale Tolmsoff
VP: John Trclek

D-U-N-S 00-694-1926 EXP
KENT NUTRITION GROUP INC (IA)
EVERGREEN MILLS DIVISION
(Suby of KENT CORP) ★
1600 Oregon St, Muscatine, IA 52761-1404
Tel (866) 647-1212 Founded/Ownrshp 1927, 1946
Sales 149.9MM[E] EMP 400
SIC 2048 Livestock feeds; Poultry feeds
Pr: D T Tubandt
*Pr: Rich Dwyer
*Treas: M R Dunsmore
*Treas: Larry Schaapveld
*Treas: D B Tinio
Rgnl VP: D R Beck
VP: R J Dennis
VP: J M Dougherty
VP: Gary L Mercer
*VP: Kevin Zeimet
MIS Dir: Doug McDermid

D-U-N-S 01-317-8363
KENT SCHOOL DISTRICT
12033 Se 256th St, Kent, WA 98030-6643
Tel (253) 373-7000 Founded/Ownrshp 1942
Sales 292.3MM EMP 3,505
Accts Troy Kelley Olympia Washingt
SIC 8211 Public elementary & secondary schools; Public senior high school; Public junior high school; Public elementary school
MIS Dir: Danni Phiffer
Pr Dir: Chris Loftis
Teacher Pr: Moriah Martin

D-U-N-S 10-197-2362 IMP
KENT SECURITY SERVICES INC
14600 Biscayne Blvd, North Miami, FL 33181-1212
Tel (305) 919-9400 Founded/Ownrshp 1982
Sales 47.3MM[E] EMP 1,000[E]
SIC 7381 7299 Protective services, guard; Security guard service; Valet parking
CEO: Gil Neuman
*Ch Bd: Shlomi Alexander
*Pr: Shelly Tygielski
*CFO: Orly Alexander
VP: Ovadiya Aharonoff
Exec: Newman Gil
*Prin: Alon Alexander
Off Mgr: Rosemary Curillo

D-U-N-S 06-154-0704 IMP
KENT SPORTING GOODS CO INC
433 Park Ave, New London, OH 44851-1314
Tel (419) 929-7021 Founded/Ownrshp 1961
Sales 135.8MM[E] EMP 575
SIC 3949 Water sports equipment
CEO: Robert Archer
*Pr: J Robert Tipton
CFO: John Archer
*CFO: John A Clark
*VP: Marlene Sipp
VP: Wayne Walters
*VP: Brian C Zaletel
Exec: Russell Gaskill
Info Man: John Clark
Plnt Mgr: Hank Wiggins
VP Mktg: Lisa Rankine
Board of Directors: Dennis Campbell

D-U-N-S 04-107-1101
KENT STATE UNIVERSITY
1500 Horning Rd, Kent, OH 44242-0001
Tel (330) 672-3000 Founded/Ownrshp 1910
Sales 474.6MM EMP 5,466
Accts Dave Yost Columbus Ohio
SIC 8221 University
Pr: Lester A Lefton
Trst: Sandra W Harbrecht
Trst: Gina C Spencer
Ofcr: Anthony Davis
Ofcr: John Ditrick
Ofcr: Alice Ickes
Ofcr: Richard O'Neill
Ofcr: Wayne Parker
Ofcr: Nancy Shefchuk
Ofcr: Trisha Synder
Ofcr: Miguel Witt
Assoc VP: Cynthia Crimmins
Sr VP: Robert G Frank
VP: Iris E Harvey
VP: Gregory Jarvie
VP: Thomas R Neumann
Exec: Zouheir N Kahwaji
Assoc Dir: Scott McKinney
Assoc Dir: Roberto Uribe

D-U-N-S 08-002-0877
KENTON COUNTY SCHOOL DISTRICT
1055 Eaton Dr, Ft Wright, KY 41017-9655
Tel (859) 344-8888 Founded/Ownrshp 1884
Sales 1.9MM[E] EMP 1,750
SIC 8211 Public elementary & secondary schools; Public senior high school; Public junior high school; Public elementary school

D-U-N-S 06-091-5824
KENTON COUNTY SCHOOL DISTRICT EDUCATIONAL FOUNDATION INC
1055 Eaton Dr, Ft Wright, KY 41017-9655
Tel (859) 344-8888 Founded/Ownrshp 1938
Sales 121.1MM[E] EMP 1,750
Accts Bertke & Spaks Inc Crestvie
SIC 8399 Fund raising organization, non-fee basis
Pr: Karen Collins
Dir Sec: Teal Nally
Genl Mgr: Steve Jablonowski
MIS Dir: Chris Setters

Pr Dir: Kim Banta
Pr Dir: Jessica Dykes
Teacher Pr: Mike Tolliver
Instr Medi: Chris Kendall
HC Dir: Paula Rust
Board of Directors: Robert Lape

D-U-N-S 00-639-8416 IMP
KENTUCKY ASSOCIATION OF ELECTRIC COOPERATIVES INC
KAEC
4515 Bishop Ln, Louisville, KY 40218-4507
Tel (502) 451-2430 Founded/Ownrshp 1943
Sales 88.2MM EMP 186
SIC 3612 2721 7629 5063 Power transformers, electric; Periodicals: publishing only; Electrical equipment repair, high voltage; Power transmission equipment, electric
CFO: Tim Hargrove
CIO: Mike McHargue
Sls&Mrk Ex: Gary Burnett

D-U-N-S 05-011-2098
KENTUCKY COMMUNITY AND TECHNICAL COLLEGE SYSTEM
KCTCS
300 N Main St, Versailles, KY 40383-1245
Tel (859) 256-3100 Founded/Ownrshp 1999
Sales 536.0M EMP 9,000
Accts Dean Dorton Allen Ford Pllc L
SIC 8222 Community college
Pr: Jay Box
Ofcr: Kathie Stamper
*VP: Kenneth Walker
Off Admin: Laura Bates
Off Admin: Darlene West
Dir IT: Null G Gabbar
Netwrk Mgr: Robert Tucker
HC Dir: Shelbie Hugle
Genl Couns: Beverly Haverstock

D-U-N-S 92-735-0090
KENTUCKY DEPARTMENT OF PARKS
(Suby of TOURISM ARTS AND HERITAGE CABINET) ★
Capital Plaza Tower 10th, Frankfort, KY 40601
Tel (502) 564-2172 Founded/Ownrshp 1924
Sales NA EMP 1,300
SIC 9512 Land, mineral & wildlife conservation;

D-U-N-S 92-748-5847
KENTUCKY DEPT OF TECHNICAL EDUCATION
(Suby of KENTUCKY EDUCATION AND WORK FORCE DEVELOPMENT CABINET) ★
500 Mero St Ste 2, Frankfort, KY 40601-1957
Tel (502) 564-4286 Founded/Ownrshp 1792
Sales NA EMP 1,100
SIC 9411 9441 State education department; ; Income maintenance programs;
*Ex Dir: John Marks
Pgrm Dir: Kara Burkett

D-U-N-S 92-741-0555
KENTUCKY EDUCATION AND WORK FORCE DEVELOPMENT CABINET
(Suby of EXECUTIVE OFFICE OF COMMONWEALTH OF KENTUCKY) ★
500 Mero St Ste 3, Frankfort, KY 40601-1957
Tel (502) 564-6606 Founded/Ownrshp 1990
Sales NA EMP 1,179[E]
SIC 9441 9111 Income maintenance programs; ; Executive offices;
*Pr: Gerry Don Crump
*VP: James Spencer

D-U-N-S 92-753-4313
KENTUCKY EDUCATION AND WORKFORCE DEVELOPMENT CABINET
500 Mero St Ste 3, Frankfort, KY 40601-1957
Tel (502) 564-0372 Founded/Ownrshp 1994
Sales NA EMP 2,500
SIC 9411 Administration of educational programs;
Ofcr: Charles L Harman

D-U-N-S 92-605-2622
KENTUCKY EMPLOYERS MUTUAL INSURANCE AUTHORITY
KEMI
250 W Main St Ste 900, Lexington, KY 40507-1724
Tel (859) 425-7800 Founded/Ownrshp 1994
Sales NA EMP 210
SIC 6331 Workers' compensation insurance
Pr: Roger Fries
COO: Mary Colvin
*Ex VP: Jon Stewart
*VP: Michelle Landers
Dir IT: Nancy Maglothin
Dir IT: Kathy Phelps
IT Man: Teresa Willett
Software D: Adam Dickison
Software D: Jesse Smith
Sftwr Eng: Ryan Peters
Mktg Dir: Brian Worthen

D-U-N-S 80-169-9422
KENTUCKY FARM BUREAU INSURANCE AGENCY INC
(Suby of FB INSURANCE CO) ★
9201 Bunsen Pkwy, Louisville, KY 40220-3792
Tel (502) 495-5000 Founded/Ownrshp 1962
Sales NA EMP 138
SIC 6411 Insurance agents, brokers & service
CEO: Bradley R Smith
Treas: Paula Kessler

D-U-N-S 00-694-5380
KENTUCKY FARM BUREAU MUTUAL INSURANCE CO
FB INSURANCE COMPANY
9201 Bunsen Pkwy, Louisville, KY 40220-3792
Tel (502) 495-5000 Founded/Ownrshp 1943
Sales NA EMP 680
SIC 6411 Property & casualty insurance agent
CEO: Bradley R Smith
*Pr: Mark Haney
COO: Bradley B Smith

*Treas: Nathan C Anguiano
VP: Paul Diersing
VP: Kelly Hall
Exec: Bruce Brown
Exec: Treasa Jenkins
Exec: Ryan Wood
Genl Mgr: David Ellington
CTO: Steven McCormick

D-U-N-S 14-779-3632
■ **KENTUCKY FRIED CHICKEN CORP**
KENTUCKY FRIED CHICKEN CORP DE
(Suby of KFC ENTERPRISES INC) ★
1441 Gardiner Ln, Louisville, KY 40213-1914
Tel (502) 874-8300 Founded/Ownrshp 1997
Sales 488.4MM[E] EMP 25,000
SIC 5812 6794 Fast-food restaurant, chain; Franchises, selling or licensing
Pr: David C Novak

KENTUCKY FRIED CHICKEN CORP DE
See KENTUCKY FRIED CHICKEN CORP

D-U-N-S 79-868-0989 IMP/EXP
■ **KENTUCKY FRIED CHICKEN OF LOUISVILLE INC**
KFC
(Suby of YUM BRANDS INC) ★
1441 Gardiner Ln, Louisville, KY 40213-1914
Tel (502) 874-8300 Founded/Ownrshp 1997
Sales 28.5MM[E] EMP 1,000
SIC 5812 Fast-food restaurant, chain
Pr: Gregg Dedrick

D-U-N-S 02-412-3473
KENTUCKY LAKE OIL CO INC (KY)
POCKETS CONVENIENCE STORE
620 S 4th St, Murray, KY 42071-2680
Tel (270) 753-1323 Founded/Ownrshp 1932, 1973
Sales 111.8MM EMP 170
Accts Alexander Thompson Arnold Pllc
SIC 5541 5571 5171 5411 Filling stations, gasoline; Motorcycles; Petroleum terminals; Convenience stores, independent
CEO: Chuck Baker

D-U-N-S 09-538-5068
KENTUCKY MEDICAL SERVICES FOUNDATION INC
2333 Alumni Park Plz # 200, Lexington, KY 40517-4012
Tel (859) 257-7910 Founded/Ownrshp 1978
Sales 306.6MM EMP 150
Accts Dean Dorton Allen Ford Pllc L
SIC 8721 Billing & bookkeeping service
Pr: Marc Randall
*VP: Raleigh Jones
*Ex Dir: Darrell Griffith
CIO: Bill Merritt
MIS Dir: Sherri Mayberry
IT Man: John Tripure
Mktg Dir: Dawn Wilson

D-U-N-S 92-741-1611
KENTUCKY OFFICE OF ATTORNEY GENERAL
(Suby of EXECUTIVE OFFICE OF COMMONWEALTH OF KENTUCKY) ★
Capitol Building Rm 100, Frankfort, KY 40601
Tel (502) 696-5615 Founded/Ownrshp 1792
Sales NA EMP 2,365[E]
SIC 9199 General government administration;

D-U-N-S 00-500-3934
KENTUCKY OIL AND REFINING CO (KY)
156 Ky Oil Vlg, Betsy Layne, KY 41605
Tel (606) 478-2303 Founded/Ownrshp 1956
Sales 143.0MM[E] EMP 150
SIC 5171 5541 Petroleum bulk stations & terminals; Filling stations, gasoline
Pr: Dale Tomlinson
*Sec: Jessie Tomlinson
VP: Thomas S Stanley III
*VP: Chris Tomlinson

KENTUCKY RX COALITION
See UNIVERSITY OF KENTUCKY

D-U-N-S 00-694-4938 IMP
■ **KENTUCKY UTILITIES CO INC** (KY)
(Suby of LG&E AND KU ENERGY LLC) ★
1 Quality St, Lexington, KY 40507-1462
Tel (502) 627-2000 Founded/Ownrshp 1912
Sales 1.7MMM EMP 945[E]
SIC 4911 Electric services; Distribution, electric power; Generation, electric power; Transmission, electric power
Ch Bd: Victor A Staffieri
CFO: Kent W Blake
VP: Gary E Blake
VP: Roger Smith
VP: Paul W Thompson
VP: John Voyles
CTO: Dave Collett
Board of Directors: S Bradford Rives, Vincent Sorgi, William H Spence, Paul A Thompson

D-U-N-S 00-791-5929
■ **KENTUCKY WEST VIRGINIA GAS CO**
(Suby of EQT CORP) ★
748 N Lake Dr, Prestonsburg, KY 41653-1283
Tel (606) 886-2311 Founded/Ownrshp 1927
Sales 99.2MM[E] EMP 240
SIC 1311 1389 4922 Natural gas production; Servicing oil & gas wells; Natural gas transmission

D-U-N-S 02-406-7175 IMP
KENTUCKY-INDIANA LUMBER CO INC
K & I LUMBER CO
(Suby of US LBM HOLDINGS LLC) ★
4010 Collins Ln, Louisville, KY 40245-1644
Tel (502) 637-1401 Founded/Ownrshp 1959, 2014
Sales 149.4MM[E] EMP 220
SIC 5031 2439 2431 Lumber, plywood & millwork; Plywood; Millwork; Pallets, wood; Trusses, wooden roof; Millwork
Pr: Bob Deferraro

D-U-N-S 94-301-0475
KENTUCKYONE HEALTH INC
KENTUCKYONE HEALTH SOURCE
(*Suby of* CHI) ★
200 Abraham Flexner Way, Louisville, KY 40202-2877
Tel (502) 587-4011 *Founded/Ownrshp* 1982
Sales 107.1MM *EMP* 9,777[E]
Accts Catholic Health Initiatives E
SIC 8099 Medical services organization
Ch: Robert M Hewett
**Pr:* Ruth W Brinkley
**Pr:* David Laird
**Treas:* Melvin Alexander
Sr VP: Angie Ely
**VP:* Ronald J Farr
VP: Neva Francis
VP: David Joos
Surgeon: Stephen Self

D-U-N-S 04-325-0436
KENTUCKYONE HEALTH MEDICAL GRO
100 E Liberty St Ste 100, Louisville, KY 40202-1441
Tel (502) 315-1458 *Founded/Ownrshp* 2015
Sales 188.7MM *EMP* 2[E]
SIC 8099 Health & allied services

KENTUCKYONE HEALTH SOURCE
See KENTUCKYONE HEALTH INC

KENTUCKYONE HEALTH SOURCE
See SAINT JOSEPH HEALTH SYSTEM INC

D-U-N-S 07-970-7055
KENTWOOD DTC LLC
5690 Dtc Blvd Ste 600w, Greenwood Village, CO 80111-3224
Tel (303) 773-3399 *Founded/Ownrshp* 1981, 2007
Sales 1.9MMM *EMP* 68
SIC 6531 7389 Real estate brokers & agents; Relocation service
CEO: Peter Niederman

D-U-N-S 07-927-8230
KENTWOOD PUBLIC SCHOOLS
5820 Eastern Ave Se, Grand Rapids, MI 49508-6200
Tel (616) 455-4400 *Founded/Ownrshp* 1959
Sales 31.5M *EMP* 1,161
Accts Bdo Usa Llp Kalamazoo Michi
SIC 8211 Public combined elementary & secondary school
IT Man: Karen Slaby
Opers Mgr: Ellen Rankin
Manager: Carey Williamson
Psych: Jennifer Galloway

D-U-N-S 00-695-8326 IMP
KENWAL STEEL CORP (MI)
KENWEL STEEL BURNS HARBOR
8223 W Warren Ave, Dearborn, MI 48126-1615
Tel (313) 739-1000 *Founded/Ownrshp* 1947
Sales 109.3MM[E] *EMP* 230
SIC 5051 Steel
Ch Bd: Kenneth Eisenberg
**COO:* David Bazzy
**CFO:* Frank Jernevcic
**VP:* Larry Bogner
**VP:* Jon Davidson

KENWEL STEEL BURNS HARBOR
See KENWAL STEEL CORP

KENWORTH NORTHWEST
See MARSHALLS HOLDING CO

D-U-N-S 00-895-4687 IMP
KENWORTH SALES CO (UT)
TRANSPORT FINANCE
2125 S Constitution Blvd, West Valley City, UT 84119-1219
Tel (801) 487-4161 *Founded/Ownrshp* 1945
Sales 267.5MM[E] *EMP* 700
Accts Poston Denney & Killpack Pllc
SIC 5012 5013 7538 3519 Trucks, commercial; Truck parts & accessories; General truck repair; Diesel engine repair: automotive; Engines, diesel & semi-diesel or dual-fuel
Pr: R Kyle Treadway
**CFO:* Lance Jorgensen
Exec: Jim Dreher
Brnch Mgr: Rick Worthen
Genl Mgr: Tom Berg
Genl Mgr: John Holmstrom
Genl Mgr: Tucker Morgan
Off Mgr: Cathie Hobson
Off Admin: Bonita Latimer
Telecom Ex: Dave Rasmussen
Sls Mgr: Chuck Knorr

D-U-N-S 93-160-4235
KENYON COMPANIES
2602 N 35th Ave, Phoenix, AZ 85009-1311
Tel (602) 233-1191 *Founded/Ownrshp* 1992
Sales 69.2MM[E] *EMP* 1,400
SIC 1742 2819 Stucco work, interior; Industrial inorganic chemicals
Ch Bd: John W Kenyon III
**CFO:* Daniel Bang

D-U-N-S 11-512-0123
KENYON CONSTRUCTION INC
K & K CONSTRUCTION
4001 W Indian School Rd, Phoenix, AZ 85019-3314
Tel (602) 484-0080 *Founded/Ownrshp* 1978
Sales 162.0MM[E] *EMP* 1,500
SIC 1742 Stucco work, interior
Ch Bd: John W Kenyon III
**CFO:* Daniel Bang
**VP:* Bonnie Mason

D-U-N-S 07-593-1662
KENYON PLASTERING INC
(*Suby of* K & K CONSTRUCTION) ★
4001 W Indian School Rd, Phoenix, AZ 85019-3314
Tel (602) 233-1191 *Founded/Ownrshp* 1995
Sales 87.6MM[E] *EMP* 800
SIC 1742 Stucco work, interior
Pr: John W Kenyon III
**Treas:* Daniel Bang
**Prin:* Brian Chien

KEOKUK STEEL CASTINGS CO
See MATRIX METALS LLC

D-U-N-S 00-630-4766
KEOLIS AMERICA INC
(*Suby of* GROUPE KEOLIS SAS)
3003 Washington Blvd, Arlington, VA 22201-2194
Tel (301) 251-5612 *Founded/Ownrshp* 2008
Sales 278.8MM[E] *EMP* 1,875[E]
SIC 4111 Passenger rail transportation
CEO: Steve Townsend

D-U-N-S 78-901-4847
KEOLIS TRANSIT AMERICA INC
(*Suby of* KEOLIS AMERICA INC) ★
6053 W Century Blvd # 900, Los Angeles, CA 90045-6400
Tel (310) 981-9500 *Founded/Ownrshp* 2006
Sales 158.9MM[E] *EMP* 1,205
Accts Windes & Mcclaughry Cpas Lon
SIC 4119 7699 Local passenger transportation; Customizing services
Pr: Michael Griffus
**CFO:* Joseph Cardoso
**CFO:* Francis Homan
Ex VP: Kevin Adams
**Ex VP:* Dwight D Brashear
Sr VP: Michael Ake
Sr VP: Stephen Helriegel
Sr VP: Sandi Hill
Sr VP: Drew Jones
**Sr VP:* Mark Levitt
**Sr VP:* Cindi Ritter
**Sr VP:* Larry Slagle
**Sr VP:* Brian Sullivan
**Sr VP:* Scott Williams
VP: Ryan Adams
VP: Christina Bird

KEP AMERICAS
See CELANESE AMERICAS LLC

KEPCO
See KANSAS ELECTRIC POWER COOPERATIVE INC

D-U-N-S 18-476-8547 IMP
KEPPEL AMFELS LLC
(*Suby of* KEPPEL OFFSHORE & MARINE LTD)
20000 State Highway 48, Brownsville, TX 78521-8910
Tel (956) 831-8220 *Founded/Ownrshp* 2016
Sales 235.0MM *EMP* 1,532
Accts Burton Mccumber & Cortez Llp
SIC 1629 3731 1389 3449 3546 3443 Oil refinery construction; Shipbuilding & repairing; Oil & gas wells: building, repairing & dismantling; Miscellaneous metalwork; Power-driven handtools; Fabricated plate work (boiler shop)
CEO: Ho Yuen
**COO:* G S Tan
**CFO:* Tim Lin
CFO: Wong Ngiam
**VP:* Gilberto Elisonto
**VP:* Thomas Mc Coy
**VP:* Eric Phua
Ex Dir: Aziz Merchant
CIO: Juan Saldana

KEPRO
See KEYSTONE PEER REVIEW ORGANIZATION INC

D-U-N-S 78-617-5786
■ **KERASOTES SHOWPLACE THEATRES LLC**
(*Suby of* AMC ENTERTAINMENT INC) ★
224 N Des Plns Ste 200, Chicago, IL 60661
Tel (312) 756-3360 *Founded/Ownrshp* 2010
Sales 71.1MM[E] *EMP* 2,200
SIC 7832 Motion picture theaters, except drive-in
CEO: Anthony Kerasotes
**Pr:* Dean Kerasotes
**CFO:* James Debruzzi
Software D: Bill Scott

D-U-N-S 07-837-3084
KERING AMERICAS INC
(*Suby of* KERING)
3 E 57th St, New York, NY 10022-2557
Tel (212) 238-3010 *Founded/Ownrshp* 1990
Sales 501.6M[E] *EMP* 1,075
SIC 8742 Business consultant
Pr: Laurent Claquin
**CFO:* Andrew McNaulty
Treas: Daniel Byrnes

D-U-N-S 06-909-7256
KERLEY BIOKIMICA INC
33707 Prairieview Ln, Oconomowoc, WI 53066
Tel (262) 567-8840 *Founded/Ownrshp* 1997
Sales 24.0MM[E] *EMP* 1,082
SIC 7389 Artists' agents & brokers
Pr: Abbas A Fadel
**VP:* Micheal Green

D-U-N-S 02-016-7425
KERN COMMUNITY COLLEGE DISTRICT (CA)
CERRO COSO COMM COLLEGE
2100 Chester Ave, Bakersfield, CA 93301-4014
Tel (661) 336-5100 *Founded/Ownrshp* 1961
Sales 37.2MM *EMP* 1,269
Accts Matson And Isom Redding Cali
SIC 8222 Community college
CEO: Sandra Serrano
VP: Andrea Thorson
Netwrk Mgr: Mike Arnold
Web Dev: Richard Robinson
Netwrk Eng: Jeremy Horton
Netwrk Eng: Juan Lucero
Sfty Dirs: Sheila Shearer
Teacher Pr: John Means

D-U-N-S 11-880-5860
KERN COUNTY SUPERINTENDENT OF SCHOOLS EDUCATIONAL SERVICES FOUNDATION
1300 17th St, Bakersfield, CA 93301-4504
Tel (661) 636-4000 *Founded/Ownrshp* 1900
Sales 465.8M[E] *EMP* 1,400
Accts Brown Armstrong Accountancy Co
SIC 8211 Public elementary & secondary schools
**CEO:* Chris Hall
Prin: Janice Barricklow
Prin: Denis Desmond
Ex Dir: Gregory Rhoten
IT Man: Alan Wells
Netwrk Eng: Deana Claflin
Netwrk Eng: Jerry Heap
Schl Brd P: Ronald G Froelick

D-U-N-S 01-071-6280
KERN HIGH SCHOOL DST
5801 Sundale Ave, Bakersfield, CA 93309-7908
Tel (661) 827-3100 *Founded/Ownrshp* 1893
Sales 409.5MM *EMP* 2,000
Accts Mayer Hoffman Mccann Pc Bak
SIC 8211 Public elementary & secondary schools
Prin: Jim Caswell
Prin: Robert Schneider
Dir Sec: Mike Collier
Genl Mgr: David Chalupa
CTO: Don Wilmot
Pr Dir: Jason George
Instr Medi: Debra Thorson
HC Dir: Amy Greene

D-U-N-S 08-838-7469
KERN REGIONAL CENTER (CA)
3200 N Sillect Ave, Bakersfield, CA 93308-6333
Tel (661) 327-8531 *Founded/Ownrshp* 1971
Sales 153.2MM *EMP* 178
Accts Barbich Hooper King Dill Hoffm
SIC 8322 Association for the handicapped
Ex Dir: Michal Clark
**CEO:* Duane Law
**CFO:* Jerry Bowman

D-U-N-S 62-161-7372
■ **KERN RIVER GAS SUPPLY CORP**
KERN RIVER GAS TRANSMISSION
(*Suby of* BERKSHIRE HATHAWAY ENERGY CO) ★
2755 E Cottonwood Pkwy # 300, Salt Lake City, UT 84121-6949
Tel (801) 937-6000 *Founded/Ownrshp* 1985
Sales 118.5MM[E] *EMP* 160
SIC 4922 Pipelines, natural gas
Pr: Gary W Hoogeveen
**VP:* Robert S Checketts
VP: Laura Demman
**VP:* Micheal Dunn
**VP:* John T Dushinske
VP: Patricia M French
**VP:* Mary Kay Miller
**VP:* J Gregory Porter
**VP:* Bret W Reich
**VP:* Richard Stapler
Plnt Mgr: Shane Allgood

KERN RIVER GAS TRANSMISSION
See KERN RIVER GAS SUPPLY CORP

D-U-N-S 19-935-4556 IMP/EXP
■ **KERR CORP**
(*Suby of* ANALYTIC ENDODONTICS) ★
1717 W Collins Ave, Orange, CA 92867-5422
Tel (714) 516-7400 *Founded/Ownrshp* 1987
Sales 285.7MM[E] *EMP* 1,431
SIC 3843 Dental materials; Dental laboratory equipment; Impression material, dental; Dental hand instruments
CEO: Damien McDonald
Pr: Philip Read
**Pr:* Steve Semmelmayer
**Treas:* Steve Dunkerken
VP: Lars Gehlbach
**VP:* Leo Pranitis
VP: Dr Edward Shellard
VP: Mark Yorba
Rgnl Mgr: Brian Kolb
Dist Mgr: Kerry Fowler
IT Man: Trish Tazelaar

D-U-N-S 04-166-8047 IMP/EXP
■ **KERR GROUP LLC**
(*Suby of* BERRY PLASTICS CORP) ★
1846 Charter Ln Ste 209, Lancaster, PA 17601-6773
Tel (812) 424-2904 *Founded/Ownrshp* 2008
Sales 99.7MM[E] *EMP* 780
SIC 3089 Closures, plastic; Jars, plastic; Tubs, plastic (containers); Plastic containers, except foam
Pr: Richard D Hofmann
Pr: Steven Rafter
**COO:* Peter A Siebert
**CFO:* Robert C Rathsam
**Ex VP:* Lawrence C Caldwell
VP: Bruce T Cleevely
VP: Kathy Cruse
VP: James T Farley
VP: James A Foy
VP: Mark R Fricke
**VP:* Timothy E Guhl
VP: Robert J Kiely
VP: Megan Petry
VP: John W Rogers
VP: Thomas G Ryan
VP: Thomas E Sweeney

KERR HEALTH CARE CENTERS
See KDI TRANSITION CO INC

KERR NORTON STRACHAN AGENCY
See NORTON LILLY INTERNATIONAL INC

D-U-N-S 00-902-8598 IMP/EXP
KERR PACIFIC CORP
PENDLETON FLOUR MILLS
1211 Sw 6th Ave, Portland, OR 97204-1001
Tel (503) 221-1301 *Founded/Ownrshp* 1986
Sales 275.0MM[E] *EMP* 297
SIC 5141 2041 Food brokers; Flour & other grain mill products
Pr: Christopher W Labbe
**CFO:* Dean Wakuzawa
**VP:* Timothy Kerr

KERR YOUTH & FAMILY SERVICES
See ALBERTINA KERR CENTERS

D-U-N-S 11-072-1003 IMP/EXP
■ **KERR-MCGEE CORP**
(*Suby of* ANADARKO PETROLEUM CORP) ★
1201 Lake Robbins Dr, Spring, TX 77380-1181
Tel (832) 636-1000 *Founded/Ownrshp* 2006
Sales 248.1MM[E] *EMP* 3,200
SIC 2816 2819 1311 1221 1222 Titanium dioxide, anatase or rutile (pigments); Boron compounds, not from mines; Crude petroleum production; Natural gas production; Bituminous coal & lignite-surface mining; Bituminous coal-underground mining
Pr: Karl F Kurz
Sr VP: David A Hger
VP: Tom Adams
VP: Richard C Buterbaugh
VP: Darrell E Hollek
VP: Mary Mikkelson
Exec: Charles A Meloy
Exec: Frank Patterson

D-U-N-S 10-192-3303 IMP/EXP
KERRY HOLDING CO
KERRY INGREDIENTS & FLAVOURS
(*Suby of* KERRY GROUP PUBLIC LIMITED COMPANY)
3330 Millington Rd, Beloit, WI 53511-9542
Tel (608) 363-1200 *Founded/Ownrshp* 1998
Sales 1.0MMM[E] *EMP* 2,313
SIC 2099 2079 2023 2022 2087 Food preparations; Seasonings: dry mixes; Edible fats & oils; Dry, condensed, evaporated dairy products; Natural cheese; Beverage bases, concentrates, syrups, powders & mixes
CEO: Gerry Behan
Pr: Daryl Adel
VP: Kevin Andreson
VP: Dennis Fechhelm
VP: Melissa Kuehl
IT Man: Bruce Tubbs
VP Opers: Michael Leahy
Mfg Dir: Eimear McGettrick

D-U-N-S 10-751-7591 IMP/EXP
KERRY INC
KERRY INGREDIENTS & FLAVOURS
(*Suby of* KERRY INGREDIENTS & FLAVOURS) ★
3330 Millington Rd, Beloit, WI 53511-9542
Tel (608) 363-1200 *Founded/Ownrshp* 1983
Sales 920.7MM[E] *EMP* 1,800
SIC 2099 Food preparations
Pr: Michael O'Neill
**CFO:* Elerina Conneely
**Sr VP:* Mike Gransee
VP: Jacques Boudreau
VP: Gordon Pincaerd
Genl Mgr: Kumar Govindasamy
IT Man: Matt Beschta
VP Opers: Ryan O'Toole
Mktg Mgr: Eric Borchardt
Mktg Mgr: Michael Spoon
Genl Couns: Lanny Schimmel

KERRY INGREDIENTS & FLAVOURS
See KERRY HOLDING CO

KERRY INGREDIENTS & FLAVOURS
See KERRY INC

D-U-N-S 09-763-7144
KERSHAW COUNTY SCHOOL DISTRICT
2029 W Dekalb St, Camden, SC 29020-2093
Tel (803) 432-8416 *Founded/Ownrshp* 1970
Sales 70.0MM *EMP* 1,400
SIC 8211 Public combined elementary & secondary school
**CFO:* Donnie Wilson
**Ch:* Mr Ron Blackmon
Ex Dir: Alisa Goodman
Ex Dir: John Thompson
Pr Dir: Maryanne A Byrd
Teacher Pr: Claire Champion
Psych: Jacqueline Deas
HC Dir: Tarry McGovern

D-U-N-S 03-009-8404
KERSHAW HEALTH MEDICAL CENTER
KCMC HOME HEALTH & HOSPICE
1315 Roberts St, Camden, SC 29020-3737
Tel (803) 432-4311 *Founded/Ownrshp* 1958
Sales 100.0MM *EMP* 575
SIC 8062 8051 8082 General medical & surgical hospitals; Skilled nursing care facilities; Home health care services
CEO: Email Terry Gunn
**Ch Bd:* Jay Green
**Pr:* Donnie J Weeks
**COO:* Susan Outen
CFO: Richard Humphrey
**CFO:* Rick Humphrey
**Ex VP:* Mike Bunch
**VP:* Angie Johnson
**VP:* Gloria Keeffe
**VP:* Angela Nettles
Dir Rx: Doug Murray

KERSHAW KNIVES
See KAI USA LTD

D-U-N-S 00-409-0387
KERZNER INTERNATIONAL NORTH AMERICA INC
INTERNATIONAL SUPPLIERS
1000 S Pine Island Rd, Plantation, FL 33324-3906
Tel (954) 809-2000 *Founded/Ownrshp* 1996
Sales 129.3MM[E] *EMP* 3,220
SIC 7011

KESSLER COLLECTION
See KESSLER ENTERPRISE INC

D-U-N-S 15-098-5661
KESSLER ENTERPRISE INC
KESSLER COLLECTION
4901 Vineland Rd Ste 650, Orlando, FL 32811-7195
Tel (407) 996-9999 *Founded/Ownrshp* 1984
Sales 212.7MM[E] *EMP* 1,200
SIC 8741 7011 Administrative management; Hotels
Ch: Richard C Kessler
**VP:* Dantzler Day B

Section I
Businesses Alphabetically

VP: Tara Bonner
Exec: Eric Barnett
Exec: Geir Kilen
Ex Dir: Walter Deppe
Genl Mgr: Nick Saltmarsh
IT Man: Jack Buck
Mktg Dir: Amanda Kliegl
Mktg Mgr: Kelly Lasserman
Manager: Rachel Atkinson

D-U-N-S 80-655-5376
KESSLER FAMILY LLC
FRIENDLY'S
410 White Spruce Blvd, Rochester, NY 14623-1608
Tel (585) 424-5277 *Founded/Ownrshp* 1999
Sales 43.0MM[E] *EMP* 1,500
SIC 5812 Restaurant, family: chain

D-U-N-S 07-932-9579
■ KESSLER INSTITUTE FOR REHABILITATION INC
SELECT PHYSICAL THEREPAHY AND
(*Suby of* SELECT PHYSICAL THEREPAHY) ★
1199 Pleasant Valley Way, West Orange, NJ 07052-1424
Tel (973) 731-3600 *Founded/Ownrshp* 1948
Sales 215.1MM *EMP* 1,706
SIC 8069 8093 Specialty hospitals, except psychiatric; Rehabilitation center, outpatient treatment
**Chf Mktg O:* Bruce M Gans
VP: Lonnie L Busby
VP: Michael Glickert
VP: Barry Kirschbaum
VP: Ron Logue
VP: Judd Patricia
VP: Gail Solomon
Exec: Steve Koltenuk
Exec: Patty Stern
Assoc Dir: Maria Esconi
Dir Rx: Neil Schulman

D-U-N-S 78-962-2677
■ KESSLER REHABILITATION CORP
(*Suby of* SELECT PHYSICAL THEREPAHY) ★
1199 Pleasant Valley Way, West Orange, NJ 07052-1424
Tel (973) 731-3600 *Founded/Ownrshp* 2003
Sales 226.2MM *EMP* 1,363
SIC 8062 General medical & surgical hospitals
Pr: Kenneth W Aitchison
Sr VP: Bonnie A Evans
VP: William Rosa
Dir Pat Ca: Karen Liszner
Dir Inf Cn: Rita Guellnitz
Dir Rx: Neil Schuman
VP Admn: Sue Kida
QA Dir: Joan Alverzo
Dir IT: Donna Nadeau
Sfty Dirs: Cliff Lassiter
Plnt Mgr: Bill Oconnor

D-U-N-S 14-722-2785 IMP/EXP
■ KESTER INC
(*Suby of* ILLINOIS TOOL WORKS INC) ★
800 W Thorndale Ave, Itasca, IL 60143-1341
Tel (630) 616-4000 *Founded/Ownrshp* 2004
Sales 86.5MM[E] *EMP* 500
SIC 3356 Solder: wire, bar, acid core, & rosin core
Pr: Steven L Martindale
**Pr:* Roger Savage
IT Man: Jim Mullin
Mktg Mgr: Mike Gonzalez

D-U-N-S 08-029-5901
KESTRA FINANCIAL INC
(*Suby of* STONE POINT CAPITAL LLC) ★
1250 Capital Of Tex, West Lake Hills, TX 78746-6446
Tel (512) 697-6890 *Founded/Ownrshp* 2016
Sales 407.2MM[E] *EMP* 300[E]
SIC 7389 Financial services
Pr: James Poer
COO: John Vanderheyden
CFO: Shaugn Stephen Stanley
Genl Mgr: Bredt Norwood

D-U-N-S 08-030-9106
KESTRA INVESTMENT SERVICES LLC
(*Suby of* KESTRA FINANCIAL INC) ★
1250 Capital Of Texas Hwy, West Lake Hills, TX 78746-6446
Tel (512) 697-6940 *Founded/Ownrshp* 2016
Sales 406.8MM *EMP* 250
SIC 6211 Security brokers & dealers
CFO: Kelly Yin

KETCHIKAN NORTHERN SALES
See NORTHERN SALES CO INC

D-U-N-S 01-057-4247
■ KETCHUM INC
(*Suby of* OMNICOM GROUP INC) ★
1285 Avenue Of The Americ, New York, NY 10019-6029
Tel (646) 935-3900 *Founded/Ownrshp* 1996
Sales 186.4MM[E] *EMP* 1,345[E]
SIC 8743 Public relations services; Public relations & publicity
CEO: Raymond L Kotcher
Sr Pt: Lorraine Thelian
Pt: Thomas Barritt
Pr: Tyler Durham
Pr: Debra Forman
Pr: Barri Rafferty
Ofcr: Michael O'Brien
Ofcr: Paul M Rand
Ofcr: Stephen Waddington
Ex VP: Matthew Afflixio
Ex VP: Lori Beecher
Ex VP: Joseph Kelliher
Ex VP: Marcus Peterzell
Sr VP: Jon Chin
Sr VP: Cheryl Damian
Sr VP: Kim Essex
Sr VP: Genevieve Hilton
Sr VP: Sandy Hu
Sr VP: Jill Bratina Kermes
Sr VP: Dean McBeth
VP: Aimee Alvarez

D-U-N-S 12-327-7923
KETTERING ADVENTIST HEALTHCARE
KETTERING HEALTH NETWORK
3535 Southern Blvd, Dayton, OH 45429-1221
Tel (937) 298-4331 *Founded/Ownrshp* 1982
Sales 605.4MM[E] *EMP* 6,800[E]
SIC 8741 Hospital management
Pr: Roy Chew
**Pr:* Frank Perez
Treas: Edward Mann
Ofcr: Bill White
VP: Jon Larrabee
VP: Andy Lehman
VP: Christina Turner
**VP:* Russ Wethell
VP: Gregory Wise
VP: Larry Zumstein
Dir Rx: Steve Motil

D-U-N-S 07-127-2843
KETTERING CITY SCHOOL DISTRICT
3750 Far Hills Ave, Dayton, OH 45429-2506
Tel (937) 499-1400 *Founded/Ownrshp* 1841
Sales 96.5MM *EMP* 782
Accts Mary Taylor Cpa Dayton Oh
SIC 8211 Public elementary school; Public junior high school; Public senior high school
**Treas:* Steven G Clark
Assoc Dir: Tony Foust
Snr Mgr: Michele Massa

KETTERING HEALTH NETWORK
See KETTERING ADVENTIST HEALTHCARE

D-U-N-S 07-128-8450
KETTERING MEDICAL CENTER (OH)
CHARLES F KETTERING MEM HOSP
(*Suby of* KETTERING HEALTH NETWORK) ★
3535 Southern Blvd, Kettering, OH 45429-1298
Tel (937) 298-4331 *Founded/Ownrshp* 1959
Sales 570.9MM[E] *EMP* 3,100[E]
Accts Clark Schaefer Hackett & Co D
SIC 8062 Hospital, professional nursing school; Hospital, medical school affiliated with nursing & residency
CEO: Jarrod McNaughton
Chf Rad: J Bidell
**Pr:* Roy Chew
**Pr:* Terri Day
**CEO:* Fred Manchur
CFO: Russ Wetherell
Ex VP: Todd Anderson
Ex VP: Terry Burns
Sr VP: Rebecca Lewis
Sr VP: Wally Sackett
VP: Tom Gross

D-U-N-S 18-350-0131 IMP
KETTLE CUISINE LLC
330 Lynnway Ste 405, Lynn, MA 01901-1713
Tel (617) 409-1100 *Founded/Ownrshp* 1986
Sales 105.0MM *EMP* 250[E]
SIC 2032 2035 Soups, except seafood: packaged in cans, jars, etc.; Soups & broths: canned, jarred, etc.; Seasonings & sauces, except tomato & dry
CEO: Liam McClennon
**CFO:* Trent Shute
**Sr VP:* Lorie Donnelly
**Sr VP:* Nick Murphy
**VP:* Tim Adler
VP: Julie Bonney
VP: Dennis Flynn
VP: Ken Murray
Exec: Joseph Ascoli
Exec: Volker Frick
QA Dir: Karen Bishop-Carbone

D-U-N-S 09-699-5642 EXP
■ KETTLE FOODS INC
(*Suby of* DIAMOND FOODS LLC) ★
3125 Kettle Ct Se, Salem, OR 97301-5572
Tel (503) 364-0399 *Founded/Ownrshp* 2010
Sales 163.7MM[E] *EMP* 550
SIC 2096 Potato chips & similar snacks
CEO: Paul Davis
**Pr:* Cameron Healy
**CFO:* Marc Cramer

D-U-N-S 03-770-4855 IMP/EXP
KEURIG GREEN MOUNTAIN INC
(*Suby of* ACORN HOLDINGS B.V.)
33 Coffee Ln, Waterbury, VT 05676-8900
Tel (802) 244-5621 *Founded/Ownrshp* 2015
Sales 4.5MMM *EMP* 6,000
SIC 5046 Coffee brewing equipment & supplies
Pr: Brian P Kelley
**CFO:* Peter G Leemputt
**Chf Mktg O:* Mark Baynes
**Ofcr:* Michael Cunningham
VP: Deb Crowther
VP: Tom Ferguson
VP: Denis Graus
**VP:* Kevin Hartley
VP: Jim Martin
VP: Chris McMahon
VP: Tara Murphy
VP: Stacy Nelms
VP: Stephen Sabol
VP: James Travis
VP: Luis Viso
Dir Bus: Bill McCauley

D-U-N-S 00-503-6330 IMP/EXP
▲ KEWAUNEE SCIENTIFIC CORP
2700 W Front St, Statesville, NC 28677-2894
Tel (704) 873-7202 *Founded/Ownrshp* 1906
Sales 128.6MM *EMP* 645
Tkr Sym KEQU *Exch* NGM
SIC 3821 2599 Laboratory furniture; Worktables, laboratory; Laboratory apparatus, except heating & measuring; Laboratory equipment: fume hoods, distillation racks, etc.; Factory furniture & fixtures; Work benches, factory
Pr: David M Rausch
**Ch Bd:* William A Shumaker
CFO: Thomas D Hull III
VP: David Rausch
VP: Michael G Rok
Telecom Ex: Peggy Lambert

Tech Mgr: Harry Klaver
VP Sls: Dana L Dahlgren
Manager: Lee Dyer
Board of Directors: John C Campbell Jr, Keith M Gehl, Margaret B Pyle, David S Rhind, John D Russell, Donald F Shaw

KEY AMERICA
See KEYSTONE GROUP HOLDINGS INC

D-U-N-S 04-354-8049
KEY BENEFIT ADMINISTRATORS INC
E-ZBENEFITS
8330 Allison Pointe Trl, Indianapolis, IN 46250-1682
Tel (317) 284-7100 *Founded/Ownrshp* 1979, 1992
Sales NA *EMP* 275
SIC 6371 Pension, health & welfare funds
Pr: Mike Goodman
**CFO:* Bradley Ray
VP: Tiffany Alsabrook
VP: Patrick Bridgeman
VP: Kris Cardell
VP: Anita Dust
**VP:* Wally T Gray
VP: Dale Kaliser
VP: Jamie Light
VP: Bruce Miller
Snr Sftwr: Mona Houston

KEY COMMERCIAL MORTGAGE
See KEY EQUIPMENT FINANCE INC

D-U-N-S 10-407-5551
KEY CONSTRUCTION INC
741 W 2nd St N, Wichita, KS 67203-6004
Tel (316) 263-9515 *Founded/Ownrshp* 1978
Sales 195.4MM *EMP* 210
SIC 1542 1541 Commercial & office building, new construction; Industrial buildings, new construction
CEO: Kenneth A Wells
Pr: Troy Heckart
**Pr:* David E Wells
**Ex VP:* Richard McCafferty
Exec: John Hoffman
Exec: John Walker Jr
Dir Bus: John Hoover
Genl Mgr: Josh Kippenbrger
VP Opers: David Messmore
VP Sls: Greg Fogle
Mktg Dir: Lisa Byrne

D-U-N-S 00-798-9262
KEY COOPERATIVE
SCE
13585 620th Ave, Roland, IA 50236-8061
Tel (515) 388-4341 *Founded/Ownrshp* 1936
Sales 371.5MM *EMP* 180
SIC 5153 5541 2048 5191 Grains; Filling stations, gasoline; Livestock feeds; Fertilizers & agricultural chemicals
Pr: Bob Finch
**Treas:* Dave Vander Pol
Chf Mktg O: Cindy Vandonselaar
**VP:* Rick Fopma
Comm Dir: Sara Clausen
Genl Mgr: Rich Adams
Genl Mgr: Jim Magnuson
Sfty Dirs: Mark Gaunt

D-U-N-S 93-191-7546 IMP
KEY ENERGY DRILLING INC
(*Suby of* KEY ENERGY SERVICES INC) ★
1301 Mckinney St Ste 1800, Houston, TX 77010-3057
Tel (432) 620-0300 *Founded/Ownrshp* 1995
Sales 138.0MM[E] *EMP* 283
SIC 1381 Drilling oil & gas wells
Pr: Newton W Wilson III
V Ch: James Byerlotzer
COO: Dick Alario
**VP:* J Marshall Dodson
VP: J Dodson
**VP:* Kimberly R Frye
Dist Mgr: Roger Henderson
Div Mgr: REO Brownlee

D-U-N-S 03-768-0964 EXP
KEY ENERGY SERVICES INC
1301 Mckinney St Ste 1800, Houston, TX 77010-3057
Tel (713) 651-4300 *Founded/Ownrshp* 1978
Sales 792.3MM *EMP* 4,300
Accts Grant Thornton Llp Houston T
SIC 1389 1381 1311 Servicing oil & gas wells; Drilling oil & gas wells; Crude petroleum production; Natural gas production
Pr: Robert W Drummond
CFO: J Marshall Dodson
Sr VP: Scott P Miller
Sr VP: Jeffrey S Skelly
VP: Dennis Brown
VP: Mark A Cox
VP: Marshall Dodson
VP: Jeff Skelly
Mfg Dir: Don Gregory
Opers Mgr: Keith Stahn
Board of Directors: Lynn R Coleman, Kevin P Collins, William D Fertig, W Phillip Marcum, Ralph S Michael III, William F Owens, Robert K Reeves, Mark H Rosenberg, Arlene M Yocum

D-U-N-S 03-106-2883
■ KEY EQUIPMENT FINANCE INC
KEY COMMERCIAL MORTGAGE
(*Suby of* KEYBANK NATIONAL ASSOCIATION) ★
1000 S Mccaslin Blvd, Superior, CO 80027-9437
Tel (800) 539-2968 *Founded/Ownrshp* 1996
Sales 162.8MM[E] *EMP* 400
SIC 7359 Equipment rental & leasing
Pr: Linda A Grandstaff
Pr: Gale Burket
Ofcr: Cynthia George
Sr VP: Mark Hoffman
VP: Kaileen Almond
VP: Shawn Arnone
VP: Henry Bissell
VP: Mark Brandt
VP: Mark Casel
VP: Colleen Daly
VP: Scott Daugherty
VP: Douglas L Dupy
VP: Amy Gestal

VP: James Gulka
VP: Margaret Gutierrez
VP: Robert Hawley
VP: Tim Keel
VP: Toni Larson
VP: Richard Lawson
VP: Dan S Little
VP: Thomas Lulich

KEY FOOD
See DANS SUPREME SUPER MARKETS INC

D-U-N-S 01-257-3358
KEY FOOD STORES CO-OPERATIVE INC
1200 South Ave, Staten Island, NY 10314-3413
Tel (718) 370-4200 *Founded/Ownrshp* 1937
Sales 893.2MM *EMP* 84[E]
Accts Anchin Block & Anchin Llp Ne
SIC 5141 Groceries, general line
CEO: Dean Janeway
**Ch Bd:* Lawrence Mandel
Pr: Richard Grobman
Treas: Anthony Bileddo
VP: Salvatore Bonavita
VP: George Knobloch
Mktg Mgr: Paul Gelardi

D-U-N-S 02-412-0867
KEY IMPACT SALES & SYSTEMS INC
1701 Crossroads Dr, Odenton, MD 21113-1110
Tel (410) 381-1239 *Founded/Ownrshp* 1981
Sales 102.7MM[E] *EMP* 500
SIC 8742 Marketing consulting services; New products & services consultants
CEO: Daniel Cassidy
**Pr:* Randy Wieland
COO: Carl Benkovich
**COO:* Eric Frost
**CFO:* Kathleen Mooy
**Ex VP:* Rob Monroe
**Sr VP:* Butch Cassidy
Sr VP: Joe Hargadon
VP: Cass Ahern
**VP:* Eric Garvin
VP: Lane Gordon
**VP:* Tony Odorissio
**VP:* Gary Vonck
VP: Peter Voss
Exec: Anthony Mowry

KEY OIL CO
See KEYSTOPS LLC

D-U-N-S 09-942-3043 IMP
KEY PLASTICS LLC
19575 Victor Pkwy Ste 400, Livonia, MI 48152-7026
Tel (248) 449-6100 *Founded/Ownrshp* 2009
Sales 1.0MMM[E] *EMP* 3,600
SIC 3089 7389 Automotive parts, plastic; Design services
Ch Bd: Eugene Davis
**CEO:* Terry Gohl
**CFO:* Jonathan Ball
CFO: Rex Carlile
Treas: Rachel Burns
VP: Adrian Stull
S&M/VP: Gene Stull

D-U-N-S 09-032-6765 IMP/EXP
KEY SAFETY RESTRAINT SYSTEMS INC
K S S
(*Suby of* K S S) ★
7000 19 Mile Rd, Sterling Heights, MI 48314-3210
Tel (586) 726-3800 *Founded/Ownrshp* 1997
Sales 234.4MM[E] *EMP* 1,264
SIC 3714 3674 3679 Motor vehicle steering systems & parts; Bumpers & bumperettes, motor vehicle; Instrument board assemblies, motor vehicle; Radiation sensors; Resonant reed devices, electronic

D-U-N-S 18-065-6753 IMP
KEY SAFETY SYSTEMS INC
K S S
7000 19 Mile Rd, Sterling Heights, MI 48314-3210
Tel (586) 726-3800 *Founded/Ownrshp* 2016
Sales 2.3MMM[E] *EMP* 6,000
SIC 2399 3714 Seat belts, automobile & aircraft; Motor vehicle steering systems & parts
Pr: Jason Luo
Pr: Jennifer Duke
Pr: Jeff Taylor
Treas: Tom Wolf
**Treas:* Natalia Zaryckyj
Ofcr: Kellie Whelan
Ofcr: Erin Witte
Sr VP: Andrew Auten
**Sr VP:* Larry Casey
**Sr VP:* Tom Dono
**Sr VP:* Ron Feldeisen
**Sr VP:* Joe Perkins
VP: Angela Baker
VP: Cecilia Bury
VP: Anne Cutaiar
VP: Robert Daley
VP: Lara Deleone
VP: Rachel Galusha
VP: Cathy Green
VP: Terri Kolo
VP: Anthony Lanza

D-U-N-S 07-782-9695 IMP/EXP
▲ KEY TECHNOLOGY INC
150 Avery St, Walla Walla, WA 99362-4703
Tel (509) 529-2161 *Founded/Ownrshp* 1948
Sales 120.0MM *EMP* 546[E]
Accts Grant Thornton Llp Seattle W
Tkr Sym KTEC *Exch* NGM
SIC 3556 2834 Food products machinery; Pharmaceutical preparations
Pr: John J Ehren
CFO: Jeffrey T Siegal
Sr VP: Stephen M Pellegrino
Sr VP: Louis C Vintro
VP: Michael Nichols
VP: Louis Vintro
Area Mgr: Trae Buchert
IT Man: Ken McGarvey
IT Man: Joe Starr
Sftwr Eng: David Alford
Netwrk Eng: Ray Trees

Board of Directors: Robert M Averick, Richard Lawrence, John E Pelo, Michael L Shannon, Charles H Stonecipher, Donald A Washburn, Paul J Wolf, Frank L A Zwerts

D-U-N-S 04-844-0424 IMP
▲ KEYTRONIC CORP
KEYTRONICEMS
4424 N Sullivan Rd, Spokane Valley, WA 99216-1593
Tel (509) 928-8000 *Founded/Ownrshp* 1969
Sales 484.9MM *EMP* 4,866
Tkr Sym KTCC *Exch* NGM
SIC 3577 Computer peripheral equipment
Pr: Craig D Gates
Ch Bd: Patrick Sweeney
CFO: Brett R Larsen
Ofcr: Dave Manky
Ex VP: Douglas G Burkhardt
Ex VP: Philip S Hochberg
VP: Lawrence J Bostwick
VP: Ed Carter
VP: Frank Crispigna III
VP: Duane D Mackleit
Genl Mgr: Tony Meger
Board of Directors: James R Bean, Ronald F Klawitter

D-U-N-S 18-787-1702
■ KEYBANC CAPITAL MARKETS INC
MCDONALD FINANACIAL GROUP
(*Suby of* KEYCORP) ★
800 Superior Ave E # 1400, Cleveland, OH 44114-2613
Tel (800) 553-2240 *Founded/Ownrshp* 1999
Sales NA *EMP* 2,200
SIC 6021 6211 National commercial banks; Security brokers & dealers
Pr: Randy Paine
**CEO:* Douglas Preiser
**CFO:* Robert D Moran Jr
Chf Cred: William Hayden
Assoc VP: Joseph Angeloro
Sr VP: John Conner
Sr VP: Mitch Miller
VP: Jason Black
VP: Blair Kaplan
VP: Ken Patsey
VP: Jon Wakim

D-U-N-S 83-001-1057
■ KEYBANK EB MANAGED GUARANTEED INVESTMENT CONTRACT FUND
MAGIC FUND
(*Suby of* KEYBANK NATIONAL ASSOCIATION) ★
127 Public Sq, Cleveland, OH 44114-1217
Tel (216) 689-3000 *Founded/Ownrshp* 2009
Sales 326.9MM^E *EMP* 1,600^E
SIC 6722 Money market mutual funds
Prin: Joseph Dedek
Sr VP: Kathleen Foley
Sr VP: Stephen Holler
Sr VP: Daniel Mismas
Sr VP: Poppie Parish
VP: Larry Bauer
VP: Thompson Guy
VP: Suzi Redlin
Brnch Mgr: Sue Bentz
Brnch Mgr: Dana Leon
Brnch Mgr: Joe Voytik

D-U-N-S 06-603-5056
■ KEYBANK NATIONAL ASSOCIATION
(*Suby of* KEYCORP) ★
127 Public Sq Ste 5600, Cleveland, OH 44114-1226
Tel (800) 539-2968 *Founded/Ownrshp* 1958
Sales NA *EMP* 13,483
SIC 6021 6022 6159 National commercial banks; State commercial banks; Automobile finance leasing
CEO: R B Heisler
**Pr:* Patrick Auletta
Pr: Mark R Danahy
Ofcr: Thomas C Stevens
Ex VP: Alfred Carpetto
**Ex VP:* Tom Tulodzieski
Sr VP: Michael Bellardine
Sr VP: Dave Brown
Sr VP: Robin Cottingham
Sr VP: Deborah Kennedy
Sr VP: Dori Nelson-Hollis
Sr VP: Elizabeth Patacek
Sr VP: Eric Peiffer
Sr VP: Babette Schubert
VP: William Bresch
VP: Jill Dalton
VP: Jeffrey Eades
VP: Albert B Holding
VP: Dan Koszczewski
VP: Aneta Kuzma
VP: Sheila Meister

D-U-N-S 00-294-5293
▲ KEYCORP (OH)
127 Public Sq, Cleveland, OH 44114-1306
Tel (216) 689-3000 *Founded/Ownrshp* 1958
Sales NA *EMP* 13,483
Tkr Sym KEY *Exch* NYS
SIC 6021 6141 6211 National commercial banks; Personal credit institutions; Automobile & consumer finance companies; Consumer finance companies; Financing: automobiles, furniture, etc., not a deposit bank; Investment bankers; Brokers, security
Ch Bd: Beth E Mooney
CFO: Donald R Kimble
Ofcr: Craig A Buffie
Dir Risk M: William L Hartmann
CIO: Amy G Brady

D-U-N-S 14-718-0418 IMP
KEYENCE CORP OF AMERICA
(*Suby of* KEYENCE CORPORATION)
669 River Dr Ste 403, Elmwood Park, NJ 07407-1361
Tel (201) 930-0100 *Founded/Ownrshp* 1985
Sales 167.4MM^E *EMP* 300
SIC 3825 5084 3674 Instruments to measure electricity; Measuring & testing equipment, electrical; Semiconductors & related devices
Prin: Katsuhiro Yoshii
COO: Rick Scrofani
CFO: Katz Iizuka
Area Mgr: Tony Ocampo
Genl Mgr: Tiffany Stallworth
Off Mgr: Michael Montgomery
IT Man: Adam Preuss
Tech Mgr: Andrew Kominek
Tech Mgr: Wesley McBride
Tech Mgr: Hideki Nishikawa
Info Man: Katsu Yoshii

KEYKERT
See KIEKERT USA INC

D-U-N-S 00-395-9251 IMP
KEYMARK CORP (NY)
1188 Cayadutta St, Fonda, NY 12068
Tel (518) 853-3421 *Founded/Ownrshp* 1964, 1988
Sales 228.8MM^E *EMP* 600
SIC 3354 3479 3471 Aluminum extruded products; Painting of metal products; Anodizing (plating) of metals or formed products
Ch Bd: William L Keller III
Pr: Gus Brotsis
**COO:* Tony Maiolo
**CFO:* Brad Harring
**Ex VP:* James P Keller
Genl Mgr: Kelly Fernet
VP Opers: Bob Channell
Plnt Mgr: Shawn Gavin
Plnt Mgr: Leo Slecton
Ql Cn Mgr: Robert Dubois
Ql Cn Mgr: Jeff Thompson

D-U-N-S 84-858-9669
KEYNOTE LLC
KEYNOTE SYSTEMS
777 Mariners Island Blvd, San Mateo, CA 94404-5083
Tel (650) 376-3033 *Founded/Ownrshp* 2013
Sales 144.5MM^E *EMP* 495^E
SIC 7374 7373

KEYNOTE SYSTEMS
See KEYNOTE LLC

KEYS ENERGY SERVICE
See UTILITY BOARD OF CITY OF KEY WEST

KEYSER ENERGY
See HOP ENERGY LLC

D-U-N-S 07-929-7662
▲ KEYSIGHT TECHNOLOGIES INC
1400 Fountaingrove Pkwy, Santa Rosa, CA 95403-1738
Tel (707) 577-5030 *Founded/Ownrshp* 1939
Sales 2.9MMM *EMP* 10,250^E
Tkr Sym KEYS *Exch* NYS
SIC 3825 Instruments to measure electricity; Microwave test equipment; Oscillators, audio & radio frequency (instrument types)
Pr: Ronald S Nersesian
**Ch Bd:* Paul N Clark
CFO: Neil Dougherty
Sr VP: Jay Alexander
Sr VP: Stephen Williams
Genl Mgr: Kari Fauber
Tech Mgr: Otto Lee
Sftwr Eng: Sue Leake
Board of Directors: James G Cullen, Charles J Dockendorff, Jean M Halloran, Richard Hamada, Robert A Rango, Mark Templeton

D-U-N-S 83-032-6448
KEYSPAN CORP
(*Suby of* NATIONAL GRID USA) ★
1 Metrotech Ctr Fl 1, Brooklyn, NY 11201-3949
Tel (718) 403-1000 *Founded/Ownrshp* 1998
Sales 8.6MMM^E *EMP* 9,595
SIC 4924 Natural gas distribution
CEO: Robert B Catell
CFO: Fred Yam
VP: Walter Burke
VP: Cathy Gamble
VP: Marilyn Lennon
VP: Elaine Weinstein
IT Man: Valerie Debono
Counsel: Brian Mulcahy

KEYSPAN ENERGY
See NATIONAL GRID CORPORATE SERVICES LLC

D-U-N-S 05-310-6352
KEYSPAN GAS EAST CORP (NY)
NATIONAL GRID
(*Suby of* KEYSPAN CORP) ★
175 Old Country Rd, Hicksville, NY 11801
Tel (718) 403-1000 *Founded/Ownrshp* 1998
Sales 239.0MM^E *EMP* 1,500
SIC 4924 Natural gas distribution
Pr: William J Akley
**CFO:* David B Doxsee
Ex VP: Joseph Giordano
**VP:* Robert Teetz
**VP:* Martin Wheatcroft
Genl Mgr: Arthur Olsen
Opers Mgr: Aaron Choo
Counsel: Cynthia Clark
Board of Directors: Nickolas Stavropoulus

D-U-N-S 00-916-4914 IMP
KEYSTON BROS (INC) (CA)
(*Suby of* KUDZU FABRICS INC) ★
1000 Holcomb Wds Pkwy # 111, Roswell, GA 30076-2588
Tel (770) 587-2555 *Founded/Ownrshp* 1868, 2001
Sales 108.0MM^E *EMP* 210
SIC 5199 5131 5191 Automobile fabrics; Upholstery fabrics, woven; Saddlery
CEO: Dan Duncan Jr
**COO:* Ron Crumbley
**CFO:* Dennis Alieksaites
**Ex VP:* Jeff Gower
**Sr VP:* Heather H Breedlove
**Sr VP:* Joel Brook
Sr VP: Keyston Bros
**Sr VP:* Ann Duncan
**Sr VP:* Paul Radke
**Sr VP:* Ron Steik
**VP:* Greg Chaffee
Exec: Brooke Duncan

D-U-N-S 05-254-8492
■ KEYSTONE AMERICA INC
SERIVCE CORP INTERNATIONAL
(*Suby of* SCI) ★
2685 Henderson Dr, Jacksonville, NC 28546-5239
Tel (910) 347-2595 *Founded/Ownrshp* 1955
Sales 93.5MM^E *EMP* 10
SIC 7261 Funeral home
Genl Mgr: Johnny Thompson
Genl Mgr: Tina Wagoner
**Off Mgr:* Christina Wagoner

D-U-N-S 80-075-3498 IMP/EXP
■ KEYSTONE AUTOMOTIVE HOLDINGS INC
(*Suby of* LKQ CORP) ★
44 Tunkhannock Ave, Exeter, PA 18643-1221
Tel (570) 655-4514 *Founded/Ownrshp* 2014
Sales 532.6MM^E *EMP* 1,896
SIC 5013 5531 Automotive supplies & parts; Automotive supplies; Tools & equipment, automotive; Automotive parts
Pr: Edward H Orzetti
**Pr:* Edward H Orzetti
**CFO:* Richard S Paradise
VP: Bill Rogers
VP: Ralph Ruzzi

D-U-N-S 05-923-0151 IMP/EXP
■ KEYSTONE AUTOMOTIVE INDUSTRIES INC
(*Suby of* LKQ CORP) ★
655 Grassmere Park, Nashville, TN 37211-3659
Tel (615) 781-5200 *Founded/Ownrshp* 2007
Sales 1.0MMM^E *EMP* 5,000
SIC 5013 5531 3714 Automotive supplies & parts; Automotive parts; Motor vehicle parts & accessories
CEO: Robert L Wagman
Treas: Frank Erlain
Ex VP: Al Ronco
VP: Barnett L Gershen
VP: Dwain K Lanier
VP: John M Palumbo
VP: Kim D Wood
Comm Man: Elier Rodriguez
**Prin:* John S Quinn
Genl Mgr: Sean Bickers
Genl Mgr: Ralph Hairsine

D-U-N-S 04-671-1743 IMP
■ KEYSTONE AUTOMOTIVE INDUSTRIES MN INC
NORTH STAR BUMPER
(*Suby of* KEYSTONE AUTOMOTIVE INDUSTRIES INC) ★
3615 Marshall St Ne, Minneapolis, MN 55418-1005
Tel (612) 789-1919 *Founded/Ownrshp* 1997
Sales 132.7MM^E *EMP* 800
SIC 5013 3312 3465 Automotive supplies & parts; Wheels; Body parts, automobile: stamped metal
Pr: Joseph Hlosten
**VP:* Rob Wagman
Genl Mgr: Joe Hernandez
Mktg Dir: Barry Harris

D-U-N-S 16-094-2363 IMP
■ KEYSTONE AUTOMOTIVE INDUSTRIES TN INC
(*Suby of* KEYSTONE AUTOMOTIVE INDUSTRIES INC) ★
655 Grassmere Park, Nashville, TN 37211-3659
Tel (615) 781-5200 *Founded/Ownrshp* 2007
Sales 179.2MM^E *EMP* 500
SIC 5013 Automotive supplies & parts
Pr: Joseph M Holsten
CTO: Mike Marlo
VP Sls: Joe Turner

D-U-N-S 01-167-8799 IMP/EXP
■ KEYSTONE AUTOMOTIVE OPERATIONS INC
(*Suby of* LKQ CORP) ★
44 Tunkhannock Ave, Exeter, PA 18643-1221
Tel (570) 655-4514 *Founded/Ownrshp* 2014
Sales 846.8MM^E *EMP* 1,724
SIC 5531 5013 Automotive parts; Automotive supplies & parts
Pr: Edward Orzetti
CFO: Bryant P Bynum
CFO: Richard Paradise
VP: Kevin Canavan
VP: Rudy Esteves
VP: Murthy Sathya
Dir IT: Robert Lewis
Opers Mgr: Rob Ford
Opers Mgr: Greg Phillips
Sls Mgr: Pat Saunders

D-U-N-S 05-671-9883 IMP
■ KEYSTONE AUTOMOTIVE WAREHOUSE
(*Suby of* KEYSTONE AUTOMOTIVE HOLDINGS INC) ★
44 Tunkhannock Ave, Exeter, PA 18643-1221
Tel (570) 655-4514 *Founded/Ownrshp* 1972
Sales 173.9MM^E *EMP* 750
SIC 5013 Automotive supplies & parts; Automotive supplies; Tools & equipment, automotive
Prin: Joseph Amato
**Prin:* James Chebalo
**Prin:* Leonard Ross

KEYSTONE CLEARWATER SOLUTIONS
See WATER SOLUTIONS HOLDINGS LLC

KEYSTONE CONCRETE PLACEMENT
See STEWART BUILDERS INC

D-U-N-S 00-512-9309 IMP
■ KEYSTONE CONSOLIDATED INDUSTRIES INC
(*Suby of* CONTRAN CORP) ★
5430 Lyndon B Johnson Fwy # 1740, Dallas, TX 75240-2601
Tel (800) 441-0308 *Founded/Ownrshp* 1889
Sales 244.1MM^E *EMP* 1,121
SIC 3312 3315 Bar, rod & wire products; Rods, iron & steel: made in steel mills; Wire products, steel or iron; Wire & fabricated wire products; Fencing made in wiredrawing plants; Barbed & twisted wire; Welded steel wire fabric
CEO: Chris Armstrong
Ch Bd: Glenn R Simmons
Pr: C Vic Stirnaman
CFO: Richard Burkhart
CFO: Bert E Downing Jr
VP: Mark S Brachbill
VP: Kelly D Luttmer
Exec: Fredrick Olness
CTO: Saundra Hess

D-U-N-S 14-702-3449
■ KEYSTONE EDUCATION AND YOUTH SERVICES LLC
(*Suby of* UNIVERSAL HEALTH SERVICES INC) ★
3401 West End Ave Ste 400, Nashville, TN 37203-6847
Tel (615) 250-0000 *Founded/Ownrshp* 2000
Sales 15.4MM^E *EMP* 2,200^E
SIC 8299 8322 Educational services; Child related social services
VP: Buddy Turner

D-U-N-S 10-719-0969
KEYSTONE FAMILY HEALTH PLAN
KEYSTONE FIRST
200 Stevens Dr, Philadelphia, PA 19113-1520
Tel (215) 937-8000 *Founded/Ownrshp* 1996
Sales NA *EMP* 1,500
SIC 6324 Hospital & medical service plans
Pr: Russell R Gianforcaro
Treas: Steven H Bohner
Sr VP: Carol Muldoon
VP: Scott Bass
QA Dir: Thomas McCloskey
QA Dir: John Perkins
Tech Mgr: Ed Malinowski

KEYSTONE FIRST
See KEYSTONE FAMILY HEALTH PLAN

KEYSTONE FOODS
See EQUITY GROUP EUFAULA DIVISION LLC

D-U-N-S 10-460-2169 EXP
KEYSTONE FOODS EQUITY GROUP
(*Suby of* M & M RESTAURANT SUPPLY) ★
7220 Us Highway 19, Camilla, GA 31730-7432
Tel (229) 336-9747 *Founded/Ownrshp* 1994
Sales 3.8MM^E *EMP* 2,570^E
SIC 2099 Food preparations

D-U-N-S 06-988-8717
KEYSTONE FOODS LLC
M & M RESTAURANT SUPPLY
(*Suby of* MARFRIG GLOBAL FOODS S/A.)
905 Airport Rd Ste 400, West Chester, PA 19380-5984
Tel (610) 667-6700 *Founded/Ownrshp* 2010
Sales 2.7MMM *EMP* 11,000
SIC 2013 2015 5087

D-U-N-S 01-589-6806
KEYSTONE GROUP HOLDINGS INC
KEY AMERICA
4901 Vineland Rd Ste 350, Orlando, FL 32811-7192
Tel (813) 225-4650 *Founded/Ownrshp* 1996
Sales 41.7MM^E *EMP* 1,375
SIC 7389 7261 Brokers' services; Funeral home
CEO: Steven Tidwell
**Pr:* Steve Tidwell
**COO:* Jim Price
**CFO:* Steve Shaffer
**VP:* Gary Baker
**VP:* Richard Wood
Sales Exec: Mark Burley

D-U-N-S 16-166-6771
KEYSTONE HEALTH PLAN EAST INC
(*Suby of* BLUE CROSS) ★
1901 Market St Ste 1000, Philadelphia, PA 19103-1475
Tel (215) 241-2001 *Founded/Ownrshp* 1991
Sales NA *EMP* 696
Accts Deloitte & Touche Llp Philade
SIC 6324 8011 Health maintenance organization (HMO), insurance only; Health maintenance organization
CEO: Joseph Frick
**Pr:* G Fred Dibona Jr
**COO:* John A Daddis
**CFO:* Thomas F Pappalardo
Sr VP: Stephen Udvarhelyi I

D-U-N-S 12-967-3443
KEYSTONE HOLDINGS LLC
10 Nw 42nd Ave Ste 700, Miami, FL 33126-5473
Tel (305) 567-1577 *Founded/Ownrshp* 2002
Sales 938.1MM^E *EMP* 6,102
SIC 8711 3053 3081 3082 3545 Construction & civil engineering; Gaskets, packing & sealing devices; Unsupported plastics film & sheet; Unsupported plastics profile shapes; Machine tool accessories
CFO: Steve Rasa

D-U-N-S 01-205-9553
KEYSTONE HUMAN SERVICES
124 Pine St, Harrisburg, PA 17101-1208
Tel (717) 232-7509 *Founded/Ownrshp* 1999
Sales 11.5MM *EMP* 3,500
Accts Keystone Human Services Harri
SIC 8322 Individual & family services
Pr: Dennis W Felty
COO: Norman Whitman
CFO: Charles Sweeder
**Sr VP:* Charles J Hooker III
VP: Lora Ball
VP: Christina Diehl
VP: Fatima Dumbuya
VP: John Ferdinand
VP: Eileen Scott
Ex Dir: Carol A Amy
Ex Dir: Robert Bausinger

KEYSTONE INDUSTRIES
See MYCONE DENTAL SUPPLY CO INC

KEYSTONE MERCY HEALTH PLAN
See MERCY HEALTH PLAN INC

D-U-N-S 15-542-1159
KEYSTONE PEER REVIEW ORGANIZATION INC
KEPRO
777 E Park Dr, Harrisburg, PA 17111-2754
Tel (717) 564-8288 *Founded/Ownrshp* 2014
Sales 34.4MM^E *EMP* 1,000
SIC 8099

D-U-N-S 00-210-3174 IMP
KEYSTONE POWDERED METAL CO (PA)
251 State St, Saint Marys, PA 15857-1658
Tel (814) 781-1591 *Founded/Ownrshp* 1927
Sales 129.6MM^E *EMP* 770
SIC 3499 Friction material, made from powdered metal
Pr: Richard T Maxstadt
**Treas:* Douglas I Thomas
**VP:* John Cerroni
VP: Paul Orr
**VP:* Michael Werner
Genl Mgr: Pete Imbrogno
Plnt Mgr: Randy Dacanal
Plnt Mgr: Curt Lindell
Ql Cn Mgr: Julia Marusiak

D-U-N-S 92-781-1950
■ KEYSTONE RV CO
(*Suby of* THOR INDUSTRIES INC) ★
2642 Hackberry Dr, Goshen, IN 46526-6811
Tel (574) 534-9430 *Founded/Ownrshp* 2001
Sales 475.5MM^E *EMP* 1,851
SIC 3792 Travel trailers & campers; Travel trailer chassis; Campers, for mounting on trucks
Pr: H Coleman Davis III
**COO:* David Chupp
**CFO:* Tonya Lucchese
**Treas:* Lon Franklin
Ex VP: Tonja Lucchese
Ex VP: Mike Rheinheimer
VP: David Thomas
Exec: Bill Wilson
Comm Man: Jim Mac
CTO: Kevin Silcox
Netwrk Mgr: Brian Mann

D-U-N-S 05-608-2233
KEYSTONE SERVICE SYSTEMS INC
(*Suby of* KEYSTONE HUMAN SERVICES) ★
124 Pine St, Harrisburg, PA 17101-1208
Tel (717) 232-7509 *Founded/Ownrshp* 1972
Sales 121.6MM *EMP* 3,000
Accts Keystone Human Services Harri
SIC 8361 Home for the mentally handicapped
CEO: Robert J Baker
**Pr:* Dennis W Felty
**CFO:* Charles J Hooker III
**Treas:* Roger W Burns

D-U-N-S 00-893-7922
KEYSTONE SHIPPING CO
(*Suby of* CHAS KURZ & CO INC)
1 Bala Plz Ste 600, Bala Cynwyd, PA 19004-1496
Tel (610) 617-6800 *Founded/Ownrshp* 1941
Sales 89.8MM^E *EMP* 1,000
SIC 4731 4412 4424 Agents, shipping; Deep sea foreign transportation of freight; Coastwide transportation, freight
Pr: Robert K Kurz
**Treas:* J A Wassel
VP: Louis Cavaliere
**VP:* Mitchell K Koslow
**VP:* Donald R Kurz
IT Man: Mary Specht
VP Opers: Bruce Fernie
Board of Directors: J F Fricko

D-U-N-S 05-758-9384
KEYSTOPS LLC
KEY OIL CO
376 Reasonover Ave, Franklin, KY 42134-4003
Tel (270) 586-8283 *Founded/Ownrshp* 1999
Sales 584.6MM *EMP* 200
Accts Bkd Llp Bowling Green Kentuc
SIC 5541 5171 Truck stops; Petroleum bulk stations

KEYTRONICEMS
See KEYTRONIC CORP

D-U-N-S 07-879-1834
■ KEYW CORP
(*Suby of* KEYW HOLDING CORP) ★
250 Clark St, North Andover, MA 01845-1018
Tel (978) 682-7767 *Founded/Ownrshp* 2012
Sales 292.4MM^E *EMP* 1,100^E
SIC 7371 8713 7389 Computer software systems analysis & design, custom; Photogrammetric engineering; Photogrammatic mapping

D-U-N-S 82-711-0136
■ KEYW CORP
(*Suby of* KEYW HOLDING CORP) ★
7740 Milestone Pkwy # 400, Hanover, MD 21076-1754
Tel (443) 733-1600 *Founded/Ownrshp* 2008
Sales 311.8MM^E *EMP* 1,100
Accts Grant Thornton Llp Baltimore
SIC 8711 8748 Engineering services; Testing services
Pr: William J Weber
CEO: John G Hannon
COO: Mark Willard
CFO: John Krobath
CFO: Caroline S Pisano
VP: Brian W Hobbs
VP: John D Johns
VP: Gerard Roccanova
VP: Jack Russell
Prgrm Mgr: Peter Buckingham
Prgrm Mgr: Milton Duran
Board of Directors: Pierre Chao

D-U-N-S 96-166-5820
▲ KEYW HOLDING CORP
7740 Milestone Pkwy # 400, Hanover, MD 21076-1754
Tel (443) 733-1600 *Founded/Ownrshp* 2008
Sales 311.8MM *EMP* 1,173^E
Tkr Sym KEYW *Exch* NGS
SIC 7373 7372 8731 7375 Computer integrated systems design; Prepackaged software; Computer (hardware) development; Information retrieval services
Pr: William J Weber
**Ch Bd:* Caroline S Pisano
COO: Mark A Willard
CFO: Michael J Alber
Ofcr: Kimberly J Dechello
Ex VP: Michele Cook
Ex VP: Chris Fedde
Board of Directors: Deborah A Bonanni, William I Campbell, Shephard Hill, Chris Inglis, Kenneth A Minihan, Arthur L Money, Mark Sopp

D-U-N-S 10-795-8845
KEZI INC
KEZI TV 9
2975 Chad Dr, Eugene, OR 97408-7427
Tel (541) 485-5611 *Founded/Ownrshp* 1983
Sales 84.2MM^E *EMP* 250
SIC 4833 6512 4813 Television broadcasting stations; Commercial & industrial building operation;
Ch Bd: Carolyn S Chambers
**Pr:* Scott Chambers
IT Man: Jim Plummer
Sls Mgr: Mike Boring

KEZI TV 9
See KEZI INC

KFC
See LUIHN FOOD SYSTEMS INC

KFC
See K-MAC ENTERPRISES INC

KFC
See KAZI FOODS CORP OF HAWAII

KFC
See JRN INC

KFC
See HOMETOWN ENTERPRISES INC

KFC
See WEST QUALITY FOOD SERVICE INC

KFC
See MORGANS RESTAURANT OF PENNSYLVANIA INC

KFC
See POLLYS INC

KFC
See NORTHWEST RESTAURANTS INC

KFC
See KENTUCKY FRIED CHICKEN OF LOUISVILLE INC

KFC
See SUMMERWOOD CORP

KFC
See SHAMROCK CO

D-U-N-S 04-143-4838
■ KFC CORP (DE)
(*Suby of* KENTUCKY FRIED CHICKEN CORP DE) ★
1900 Colonel Sanders Ln, Louisville, KY 40213-1970
Tel (502) 874-8300 *Founded/Ownrshp* 1997
Sales 488.4MM^E *EMP* 24,000
SIC 5812 6794 Fast-food restaurant, chain; Franchises, selling or licensing
CEO: David Novak
**Pr:* Chuck Rawley
COO: Tony Mastropaolo
CFO: Kathy Corsi
**Chf Cred:* Terry Davenport
Ofcr: Joanne Towery
VP: Matt Kelly
VP: Jerry Merritt
VP: Jeff Rager
Genl Mgr: Melinda Rafuse
Tech Mgr: Martine Macdonald

D-U-N-S 14-779-3517
■ KFC ENTERPRISES INC
(*Suby of* YUM BRANDS INC) ★
1441 Gardiner Ln, Louisville, KY 40213-1957
Tel (502) 895-3227 *Founded/Ownrshp* 1984
Sales 488.4MM^E *EMP* 25,438^E
SIC 5812 Fast-food restaurant, chain
Prin: Greg Dedick
**CFO:* Kathleen Corsi
**VP:* R Scott Toop

D-U-N-S 05-682-2653
■ KFC NATIONAL MANAGEMENT CO
(*Suby of* KFC CORP (DE)) ★
1441 Gardiner Ln, Louisville, KY 40213-1957
Tel (502) 874-8300 *Founded/Ownrshp* 1969
Sales 452.3MM^E *EMP* 20,000
SIC 5812 Fast-food restaurant, chain
Ch: Anne P Byerlein
**Pr:* Cheryl A Bachelder
**Pr:* Chuck Rawley
COO: Mark Cosby
**Treas:* Kathleen Corsi
**Treas:* Debbie Medley
Sr VP: Rob Saxton
VP: Amy Sherwood
VP: Michael Tierney
**VP:* R Scott Toop
VP: Nikki Weis
Dir Surg: Niel Bronzo

D-U-N-S 00-467-0829
■ KFORCE GOVERNMENT HOLDINGS INC
(*Suby of* KFORCE INC) ★
1001 E Palm Ave, Tampa, FL 33605-3551
Tel (813) 552-5000 *Founded/Ownrshp* 2000
Sales 77.8MM^E *EMP* 1,095
SIC 6719 Investment holding companies, except banks
CEO: Patrick Moneymaker
**Ofcr:* William Turner

D-U-N-S 06-570-3209
■ KFORCE GOVERNMENT SOLUTIONS INC
(*Suby of* KFORCE GOVERNMENT HOLDINGS INC) ★
2677 Prosperity Ave # 100, Fairfax, VA 22031-4928
Tel (703) 245-7350 *Founded/Ownrshp* 2006
Sales 99.8MM^E *EMP* 948
SIC 7379 Computer related consulting services
CEO: Patrick D Moneymaker
V Ch: Richard M Cocchiaro
CFO: Marc M Herman
Treas: Judy M Genshino
Ofcr: Mike Ettore
Ofcr: Randy Marmon
Ofcr: Richard Orpin
**Sr VP:* Karen L Bell
Sr VP: Michael R Blackman
Sr VP: Andrew Thomas
VP: Anton T Hartman
VP: David Kelly
VP: Kathleen Massie
VP: Virg Palumbo
VP Bus Dev: Graham Palmer

D-U-N-S 05-828-7814
▲ KFORCE INC
1001 E Palm Ave, Tampa, FL 33605-3551
Tel (813) 552-5000 *Founded/Ownrshp* 1994
Sales 1.3MMM *EMP* 2,800
Tkr Sym KFRC *Exch* NGS
SIC 7363 7361 Help supply services; Employment agencies
Ch Bd: David L Dunkel
Pr: Joseph J Liberatore
COO: Kye L Mitchell
COO: Jeffrey Neal
CFO: David M Kelly
**V Ch Bd:* Howard W Sutter
Chf Cred: Robert W Edmund
Chf Mktg O: Jeffrey T Neal
Ofcr: Peter M Alonso
Ofcr: Michael R Blackman
Sr VP: Jeffrey B Hackman
VP: Robin Bair
VP: Jennifer Cirrito
VP: Rob Edmund
VP: Brandon Lion
VP: Raymond Morganti
Board of Directors: John N Allred, Richard M Cocchiaro, Ann E Dunwoody, Mark F Furlong, Elaine D Rosen, N John Simmons, Ralph E Struzziero, A Gordon Tunstall

D-U-N-S 07-937-8967
KFORCE SERVICES CORP
1001 E Palm Ave, Tampa, FL 33605-3551
Tel (813) 552-3734 *Founded/Ownrshp* 2014
Sales 24.0MM^E *EMP* 1,000
SIC 7361 Employment agencies
CEO: David Dunkel

D-U-N-S 17-669-0378
KGBO HOLDINGS INC
4289 Ivy Pointe Blvd, Cincinnati, OH 45245-0002
Tel (513) 831-2600 *Founded/Ownrshp* 2006
Sales 2.2MMM *EMP* 2,150^E
Accts Barnes Dennig & Co Ltd Ci
SIC 4731 Truck transportation brokers
Pr: Kenneth Oaks
Sr Cor Off: Ryan Legg
Ex VP: Kerry Byrne
VP: Nathan Knipper
VP: Matt McConnell
CIO: Matthew Long
Software D: Sheldon Diltz
Software D: Trent Dues
Software D: Clifford Still
Software D: Justin Watren
Opers Mgr: Lucas Jenkins

D-U-N-S 16-927-5489
■ KGEN HOT SPRING LLC
(*Suby of* ENTERGY ARKANSAS INC) ★
696 Black Branch Rd, Malvern, AR 72104-6897
Tel (501) 609-4600 *Founded/Ownrshp* 2012
Sales 1.6MMM^E *EMP* 10^E
SIC 4911 Electric services

KGP LOGISTICS
See KGP TELECOMMUNICATIONS INC

D-U-N-S 11-336-4301
KGP PRODUCTS INC
PREMIER
(*Suby of* KGP LOGISTICS) ★
600 New Century Pkwy, New Century, KS 66031-1101
Tel (800) 755-1950 *Founded/Ownrshp* 2006
Sales 112.9MM^E *EMP* 236^E
SIC 3661 Telephones & telephone apparatus; Facsimile equipment
CEO: Kathleen G Putrah
Exec: Randy Aldridge
Dir Bus: Richard Snyder
Prgrm Mgr: Bradly Griggs
VP Opers: Richard Summers
Sales Asso: Kgp Stevanov

D-U-N-S 14-850-4814
KGP TELECOMMUNICATIONS INC
KGP LOGISTICS
3305 Highway 60 W, Faribault, MN 55021-4869
Tel (507) 334-2268 *Founded/Ownrshp* 1975
Sales 1.0MMM^E *EMP* 1,248
SIC 5065 Telephone equipment
CEO: Kathleen G Putrah
**Pr:* Trevor Putrah
**CFO:* Stuart Romenesko
CFO: Don Shaffer
VP: Steven Locke
IT: Cheryl Riggle
Sls Mgr: Charlie Fuller
Counsel: Kari Carter
Snr Mgr: David Lembke
Board of Directors: Kathleen G Putrah, Trevor Putrah

KHOU-TV CHANNEL 11
See KHOU-TV INC

D-U-N-S 10-267-2284
■ KHOU-TV INC
KHOU-TV CHANNEL 11
(*Suby of* BELO FOUNDATION) ★
1945 Allen Pkwy, Houston, TX 77019-2596
Tel (713) 284-1011 *Founded/Ownrshp* 1984
Sales 87.2MM^E *EMP* 440
SIC 4833 Television broadcasting stations
Pr: Susan Mc Eldoon
**Treas:* Carey P Hendrickson
**Treas:* Guy H Kerr
IT Man: Linda Deprado

KHS & S CONTRACTORS
See KEENAN HOPKINS SUDER & STOWELL CONTRACTORS INC

KHS DIVISION
See KHS USA INC

D-U-N-S 09-739-4241 IMP/EXP
KHS USA INC
KHS DIVISION
(*Suby of* KHS GMBH)
880 Bahcall Ct, Waukesha, WI 53186-1801
Tel (262) 797-7200 *Founded/Ownrshp* 1868
Sales 117.1MM^E *EMP* 400
SIC 3556 Beverage machinery; Pasteurizing equipment, dairy machinery
**Pr:* Michael Brancato
Pr: Jeffrey Camargo
COO: Johann Grabenweger
COO: Marc Hartmann
**CFO:* Jim Elliott
Admn Mgr: Wendy Brucker
Genl Mgr: Ravindra R Kanetkar
Genl Mgr: Jay Steinbrecher
CIO: Paul Turinske
Dir IT: Terry Kerns
IT Man: Paul Fisher

KHS&S CONTRACTORS
See KEENAN HOPKINS SCHMIDT AND STOWELL CONTRACTORS INC

KHUDAIRI GROUP
See AZKU INC

KI
See KRUEGER INTERNATIONAL INC

D-U-N-S 80-267-0687 IMP
KIA MOTORS AMERICA INC
(*Suby of* KIA MOTORS CORPORATION)
111 Peters Canyon Rd, Irvine, CA 92606-1790
Tel (949) 468-4800 *Founded/Ownrshp* 1992
Sales 1.2MMM^E *EMP* 3,000
SIC 5511 5013 8741 Automobiles, new & used; Automotive supplies & parts; Management services
CEO: Byung M Ahn
COO: Peter Nochar
**COO:* Michael Sprague
**Ex VP:* Tom Loveless
**Ex VP:* John Yoon
VP: John Crowe
VP: Allen Farquer
Ex Dir: Julie Kurcz
Dir IT: Richard Lin
Mktg Mgr: John Carney
Mktg Mgr: Travis Long

D-U-N-S 87-725-6862 IMP/EXP
KIA MOTORS MANUFACTURING GEORGIA INC
KMMG
(*Suby of* KIA MOTORS AMERICA INC) ★
7777 Kia Pkwy, West Point, GA 31833-4897
Tel (706) 902-7777 *Founded/Ownrshp* 2006
Sales 942.9MM^E *EMP* 3,000^E
SIC 5511 Automobiles, new & used
CEO: Hyun Jong Shin
CFO: Kang In
**CFO:* Jae Cheon Jeong
**CFO:* In Ho Kang
IT Man: Regina Farmer
Opers Mgr: Narae Cho
Ql Cn Mgr: Chris Tarver
Genl Couns: Deborah Walker
Snr Mgr: Ted Arnold
Snr Mgr: Arch Griggs
Snr Mgr: Dw Kim

KIAWAH ISLAND GOLFTNNIS RSORT
See KIAWAH ISLAND INN CO

D-U-N-S 82-462-9836
KIAWAH ISLAND INN CO
KIAWAH ISLAND GOLFTNNIS RSORT
1 Sanctuary Beach Dr, Johns Island, SC 29455-5434
Tel (843) 768-6000 *Founded/Ownrshp* 1993
Sales 105.0MM^E *EMP* 1,200
SIC 7011 Resort hotel
Pr: Roger Warren
Mng Pt: Pat McKinney
**COO:* Brian Gerard
VP: Jonathan Barth
Exec: Lawrence Brubaker
Exec: Terri Hall
Exec: Patt Tamasy
**Prin:* Tom Bewley
**Prin:* Dan Dipmars
**Prin:* Mike Vegis
**Genl Mgr:* Bill Lacey

D-U-N-S 18-956-8694 IMP
KIAWAH RESORT ASSOCIATES
KAIWAH ISLAND CLUB
245 Gardners Cir, Johns Island, SC 29455-5471
Tel (843) 768-3400 *Founded/Ownrshp* 1988
Sales 115.4MM^E *EMP* 250
SIC 6552 Subdividers & developers
Pt: Charles P Darby III
CTO: Amanda Mole
Pr Dir: Mike Touhill
Mktg Mgr: Scott Kublin
Mktg Mgr: Rachel Moore

KICHLER LIGHTING
See L D KICHLER CO

D-U-N-S 62-105-6100
KICKAPOO TRADITIONAL TRIBE OF TEXAS
2212 Rosita Valley Rd, Eagle Pass, TX 78852-2503
Tel (830) 773-2105 *Founded/Ownrshp* 1989
Sales 100.0MM *EMP* 1,300
SIC 8322 Individual & family services
**CFO:* Robert F Kuhnemund
Ofcr: Juan Ventura

D-U-N-S 01-158-6153 IMP/EXP
KID BRANDS INC
1 Meadowlands Plz Ste 803, East Rutherford, NJ 07073-2152
Tel (201) 405-2400 *Founded/Ownrshp* 1963
Sales 188.1MM *EMP* 201[E]
SIC 2399 3944

KIDDE FIRE FIGHTING
See KIDDE FIRE PROTECTION INC

D-U-N-S 62-757-8016 IMP/EXP
■ **KIDDE FIRE PROTECTION INC**
KIDDE FIRE FIGHTING
(*Suby of* UNITED TECHNOLOGIES CORP) ★
350 E Union St, West Chester, PA 19382-3450
Tel (610) 363-1400 *Founded/Ownrshp* 2009
Sales 282.7MM[E] *EMP* 2,450[E]
SIC 3669 3999 3823 Fire detection systems, electric; Fire extinguishers, portable; Temperature instruments: industrial process type
Pr: John Hargreaves
Treas: Bill Langan
Sr VP: Holly O Paz
VP: Dean Byrne
VP: John Dowling
Exec: Bill Keegan

KIDDE FIRE SYSTEM
See KIDDE-FENWAL INC

KIDDE SAFETY
See WALTER KIDDE PORTABLE EQUIPMENT INC

D-U-N-S 60-695-5318 EXP
■ **KIDDE TECHNOLOGIES INC**
FENWAL SAFETY SYSTEMS
(*Suby of* KIDDE FIRE FIGHTING) ★
4200 Airport Dr Nw, Wilson, NC 27896-8630
Tel (252) 237-7004 *Founded/Ownrshp* 1989
Sales 92.0MM[E] *EMP* 730
SIC 3728 Aircraft parts & equipment
Pr: Terry Hayden
**Pr:* Brent Ehmke
**CFO:* W Thomas Ramsey
VP: John J Shea
Genl Mgr: Dennis Bissonnette
Genl Mgr: Vincent Rowe
Sfty Dirs: Brent Ehmeke
Sfty Mgr: Jeff Henchel
Sls Dir: Martin Sturla
Board of Directors: Ronald V Daggon, J Michael Harper, Alton D Slay, James W Stansberry, John E Sullivan, Lewis B Sykes, Douglas J Vaday

D-U-N-S 19-974-4715 IMP/EXP
■ **KIDDE-FENWAL INC**
KIDDE FIRE SYSTEM
(*Suby of* UNITED TECHNOLOGIES CORP) ★
400 Main St, Ashland, MA 01721-2150
Tel (508) 881-2000 *Founded/Ownrshp* 2010
Sales 209.5MM[E] *EMP* 650
SIC 3669 3823 3825 3822 3643 3625 Fire detection systems, electric; Temperature instruments: industrial process type; Instruments to measure electricity; Auto controls regulating residntl & coml environmt & applncs; Current-carrying wiring devices; Relays & industrial controls
Pr: Michael C Burcham
**Treas:* Martin Fernandez
VP: Dennis Jackson
VP: David Olchowski
**Prin:* John Vernon
Prgrm Mgr: Kishor Trivedi
Genl Mgr: Jerry Connolly
Snr Sftwr: Walter Greene
CIO: Bob Coleman
MIS Dir: Jim Livingstone
QA Dir: Larry Rodkey

D-U-N-S 07-925-3801
KIDDER MATHEWS LLC (WA)
601 Union St Ste 4720, Seattle, WA 98101-1356
Tel (206) 296-9600 *Founded/Ownrshp* 2009
Sales 97.0MM *EMP* 450
SIC 6531 Real estate agent, commercial
CEO: Jeffrey S Lyon
**Pr:* Bill Frame
**COO:* Gordon K Buchan
Assoc VP: James Gaglione
Assoc VP: Jeffrey Hutchins
Assoc VP: Erik Swanson
Assoc VP: Cody Winchester
**Ex VP:* Brian Hatcher
**Ex VP:* D Keith Kaiser
**Ex VP:* Reed W Payne
**Ex VP:* Peter K Shorett
Sr VP: Karen Benoit
Sr VP: Martin Church
Sr VP: Christopher J Corr
Sr VP: Gregg Domanico
Sr VP: Arielle Dorman
Sr VP: Mark Fraser
Sr VP: Ronald King
Sr VP: Steven Klein
Sr VP: James Lees
Sr VP: Joe Lynch

D-U-N-S 82-726-8249
KIDS IN NEED FOUNDATION
3055 Kettering Blvd # 119, Moraine, OH 45439-1900
Tel (937) 296-1230 *Founded/Ownrshp* 2008
Sales 121.9MM *EMP* 19[E]
Accts Lb Brady Ware & Schoenfeld Inc
SIC 8641 Civic social & fraternal associations
Ex Dir: David Smith
Mktg Dir: David Ledsinger

D-U-N-S 86-081-8152
KIDSPEACE NATIONAL CENTERS OF NEW YORK INC
5300 Kidspeace Dr, Orefield, PA 18069-2098
Tel (800) 992-9543 *Founded/Ownrshp* 1991
Sales 47.4MM *EMP* 3,601
SIC 8322 Child guidance agency
Pr: C T O'Donnell
CFO: James Horan
**VP:* Richard A Boyer
VP: Michael Slack
Ex Dir: Scott Merritt
Genl Mgr: Denise Card
Genl Mgr: Nora Culley
Genl Mgr: Conniejo Dicruttalo
Genl Mgr: Kelly Hukmani
CTO: Jay Robinson
IT Man: Paula Knouse

D-U-N-S 07-365-1143
KIDSPEACE NATIONAL CENTERS OF NORTH AMERICA INC
4085 Independence Dr, Schnecksville, PA 18078-2574
Tel (610) 799-8353 *Founded/Ownrshp* 1886
Sales 16.4MM *EMP* 2,070
SIC 8322

D-U-N-S 61-416-1115 IMP
KIEKERT USA INC
KEYKERT
(*Suby of* KIEKERT AG)
46941 Liberty Dr, Wixom, MI 48393-3603
Tel (248) 960-4100 *Founded/Ownrshp* 1987
Sales 87.8MM[E] *EMP* 500
SIC 3714 Motor vehicle body components & frame
CEO: Karl Krause
**Ex VP:* Matthias Berg
**Ex VP:* Guido Hanel
Ex VP: Diana Korner
**Ex VP:* Andrea Kusemann
Ex VP: Ulrich Nass
**Ex VP:* Jrgen Peulen
Prgrm Mgr: Brian Couture
IT Man: Mendez Armando
IT Man: Dave Ennis
Plnt Mgr: Chuck Bartley

KIENLEN CONSTRUCTORS
See ALBERICI CORP

D-U-N-S 15-397-3581
KIER CONSTRUCTION CORP
3710 Quincy Ave, Ogden, UT 84403-1934
Tel (801) 627-1414 *Founded/Ownrshp* 1986
Sales 88.9MM *EMP* 57
Accts Wsrp Llc Ogden Utah
SIC 1522 1542 1541 Multi-family dwelling construction; Nonresidential construction; Industrial buildings, new construction
Pr: Stephen J Kier
**Treas:* Brent Openshaw
**VP:* Scott J Kier

D-U-N-S 18-965-7138
KIEWIT BUILDING GROUP INC
(*Suby of* KIEWIT CORP) ★
302 S 36th St Ste 500, Omaha, NE 68131-3894
Tel (402) 977-4500 *Founded/Ownrshp* 2005
Sales 844.1MM[E] *EMP* 1,047[E]
Accts Kpmg Llp Omaha Ne
SIC 1521 General remodeling, single-family houses
Pr: Joseph R Lempka
**Treas:* Stephen S Thomas
**Sr VP:* Michael J Colpack
**Sr VP:* Ronald C Duce
**Sr VP:* J D Vetter
**Sr VP:* Kevin P Welker
**Sr VP:* Lance K Wilhelm
**VP:* Becky S Golden
**VP:* Raymond D Hallquist
**VP:* Michael J Piechoski
VP: Mitchell Pirnie
**VP:* Herb J Reuss
**VP:* Tobin A Schropp
**VP:* William L Schwarten
**VP:* Don E Sloane
**VP:* Terry L White
**VP:* Randall D Zuke
Exec: Andy Stine
Board of Directors: Scott L Cassels

D-U-N-S 15-454-9877 IMP
KIEWIT CORP
(*Suby of* PETER KIEWIT SONS INC) ★
3555 Farnam St Ste 1000, Omaha, NE 68131-3302
Tel (402) 342-2052 *Founded/Ownrshp* 1991
Sales 19.3MMM[E] *EMP* 10,441
Accts Kpmg Llp Omaha Ne
SIC 1542 1541 1611 1622 1629 Commercial & office building contractors; Industrial buildings & warehouses; Highway & street paving contractor; Bridge construction; Tunnel construction; Highway construction, elevated; Marine construction
CEO: Bruce E Grewcock
Treas: Anne Begley
Treas: Stephen S Thomas
Treas: Michael Whetstine
Ex VP: Scott L Cassels
Ex VP: Richard W Colf
Ex VP: Doug Legursky
Ex VP: Douglas E Patterson
Sr VP: Steven Hansen
Sr VP: Lance Wilhelm
VP: Robert Alder
VP: Chris Bantner
VP: Stephen Carter
VP: Larry Cochran
VP: Mike Colpack
VP: Frank Ratajski
VP: James Rowings
Exec: Mary Brown
Exec: Catherine French
Dir Risk M: Phil Dehn

D-U-N-S 96-336-7920
KIEWIT INDUSTRIAL GROUP INC
(*Suby of* KIEWIT CORP) ★
3555 Farnam St, Omaha, NE 68131-3311
Tel (402) 342-2052 *Founded/Ownrshp* 2005
Sales 3.4MMM *EMP* 20
Accts Kpmg Llp Omaha Ne
SIC 1629 Power plant construction
Pr: Douglas E Patterson
Ex VP: Richard A Lanoha

D-U-N-S 05-882-2412 IMP
KIEWIT INFRASTRUCTURE CO (DE)
(*Suby of* KIEWIT CORP) ★
Kiewit Plz, Omaha, NE 68131
Tel (402) 342-2052 *Founded/Ownrshp* 1981
Sales 4.3MMM[E] *EMP* 9,000
SIC 1541 1542 1629 1622 1522 Industrial buildings & warehouses; Warehouse construction; Nonresidential construction; Commercial & office building contractors; Institutional building construction: Stadium construction; Subway construction; Tunnel construction; Residential construction
Pr: Bruce Grewcock
**CFO:* Michael J Piechoski
**Treas:* Stephen S Thomas
**Ex VP:* H E Adams
**Ex VP:* David J Miles
**VP:* Stephen P Allen
**VP:* Parke D Ball
**VP:* Michael K Breyer
**VP:* Craig A Briggs
**Prin:* Scott L Cassels

D-U-N-S 96-336-8050
KIEWIT INFRASTRUCTURE GROUP INC
(*Suby of* KIEWIT CORP) ★
3555 Farnam St, Omaha, NE 68131-3311
Tel (402) 342-2052 *Founded/Ownrshp* 2014
Sales 6.0MMM[E] *EMP* 50[E]
SIC 1611 1622 Highway & street construction; Bridge, tunnel & elevated highway
Pr: Scott L Cassels
Ex VP: R Michael Phelps

D-U-N-S 05-507-6616
KIEWIT INFRASTRUCTURE SOUTH CO
(*Suby of* KIEWIT CORP) ★
Kiewit Plz No 1044, Omaha, NE 68131
Tel (402) 342-2052 *Founded/Ownrshp* 1969
Sales 603.0MM *EMP* 333
Accts Kpmg Llp Omaha Nebraska
SIC 1622 1611 Bridge, tunnel & elevated highway; Highway & street construction
Pr: David J Miles
**CFO:* Connie Lanoha
**Treas:* Stephen S Thomas
**VP:* Howard L Barton Jr
**VP:* Stephen Paul Carter Jr
**VP:* Timothy J Cleary
**VP:* Ricardo Cummings
**VP:* William D Glaser
**VP:* Mark D Langford
**VP:* Jeffrey P Petersen
**VP:* Michael J Piechoski
**VP:* John D Proskovec
**VP:* Joseph Richard
**VP:* Randall P Sanman
**VP:* Keith N Sasich
**VP:* Tobin A Schropp
**VP:* S Van Groves

D-U-N-S 07-423-2216 IMP
KIEWIT INFRASTRUCTURE WEST CO
(*Suby of* KIEWIT CORP) ★
4004 S 60th St, Omaha, NE 68117-1220
Tel (402) 342-2052 *Founded/Ownrshp* 1982
Sales 1.4MMM[E] *EMP* 2,625
Accts Kpmg Llpomaha Nebraska
SIC 1611 1629 1541 1622 1623 Highway & street construction; Highway & street paving contractor; Grading; Land preparation construction; Dam construction; Industrial plant construction; Marine construction; Industrial buildings & warehouses; Bridge, tunnel & elevated highway; Water, sewer & utility lines
Pr: Scott L Cassels
**CFO:* Trent M Demulling
Treas: Stephen S Thomas
**Ex VP:* H E Adams
**Ex VP:* David J Miles
**Ex VP:* Alfredo E Sori
**Sr VP:* Jeffrey P Petersen
**Sr VP:* Eric M Scott
**Sr VP:* A T Skoro
**Sr VP:* Matt L Swinton
**Sr VP:* Eugene D Van Wagner III
**Sr VP:* J D Vetter
**Sr VP:* Jamie D Wisenbaker
**VP:* Jeffrey C Arviso
**VP:* Kent A Boden
**VP:* Steven J Caniglia
**VP:* Jeffrey Ellis
**VP:* Paul H Giuntini
**VP:* Erik A Nelson
**VP:* Andrew J Peplow
**VP:* Terrence L Robinson

D-U-N-S 79-329-0354
KIEWIT MINING GROUP INC
Q BUILDING
(*Suby of* KIEWIT INFRASTRUCTURE CO) ★
Kiewit Plz, Omaha, NE 68131
Tel (402) 342-2052 *Founded/Ownrshp* 1991
Sales 147.1MM[E] *EMP* 150
SIC 1241 Coal mining services
Pr: Christopher J Murphy
**Treas:* Michael J Whetstine
**VP:* Michael J Piechoski
**VP:* Anthony A Ritter

D-U-N-S 01-553-9344 IMP/EXP
KIEWIT OFFSHORE SERVICES LTD
(*Suby of* PETER KIEWIT SONS INC) ★
2440 Kiewit Rd, Ingleside, TX 78362-5101
Tel (361) 775-4300 *Founded/Ownrshp* 2001
Sales 210.9MM[E] *EMP* 500
SIC 1623 Oil & gas line & compressor station construction
CEO: Bruce Grewcock
**Pr:* Myron Rodrigue
**Pr:* Fuat Sezer
**VP:* Jeffrey J Gordon
**VP:* Michael J Piechoski
**VP:* Tobin A Schropp
Sfty Dirs: Rand Magee

D-U-N-S 84-067-0470
KIEWIT OFFSHORE SERVICES LTD
(*Suby of* PETER KIEWIT SONS INC) ★
Kiewit Plz, Omaha, NE 68131
Tel (402) 342-2052 *Founded/Ownrshp* 2001
Sales 201.5MM[E] *EMP* 2,368
SIC 3441 Fabricated structural metal
Pr: Fuat Sezer
**Treas:* Stephen S Thomas
**VP:* Michael J Piechoski
**VP:* Tobin A Schropp

D-U-N-S 61-320-1029 IMP
KIEWIT TEXAS CONSTRUCTION LP
GILBERT TEXAS CONSTRUCTION
(*Suby of* KIEWIT FRONTIER INC)
13119 Old Denton Rd, Fort Worth, TX 76177-2403
Tel (817) 337-7000 *Founded/Ownrshp* 1989
Sales 121.6MM[E] *EMP* 559
Accts Kpmg Llp
SIC 1611 Airport runway construction
CEO: Bruce Grewcock
Pt: Kiewit Frontier
Prin: William D Glaser
Prin: Wh Murphy
Prin: Michael F Norton
Prin: Jeffrey P Petersen
Prin: Michael J Piechoski
Prin: John D Proskovec
Prin: Timothy S Riley
Prin: Keith N Sasich
Prin: Tobin A Schropp

D-U-N-S 10-229-1812
KIEWIT WESTERN CO
(*Suby of* KIEWIT CORP) ★
3888 E Broadway Rd, Phoenix, AZ 85040-2924
Tel (602) 437-7878 *Founded/Ownrshp* 1981
Sales 143.6MM *EMP* 1,672
Accts Kpmg Llp Omaha Ne
SIC 1622 1629 1794 1611 1623 Bridge, tunnel & elevated highway; Land preparation construction; Excavation & grading, building construction; General contractor, highway & street construction; Water main construction; Pipeline construction
CEO: Bruce Grewcock
**Pr:* H John Jansen
**Ex VP:* H E Adams
**Ex VP:* Scott L Cassels
**Ex VP:* Ken E Riley
**Ex VP:* Randall P Sanman
**Sr VP:* Craig A Briggs
**Sr VP:* Stan M Driver
**Sr VP:* Gregory A Hill
**Sr VP:* Richard H Raine
**VP:* Michaek K Breyer
**VP:* Kenneth W Hanna
**VP:* Troy L Heckmaster
**VP:* Thomas R Howell
**VP:* Gray D Kite
**VP:* Dwight Metcalf
**VP:* Michael J Piechoski
**VP:* Tobin A Schropp
**VP:* Wayne D Thomas

KIK CUSTOM PRODUCTS
See MARIETTA HOLDING CORP INC

D-U-N-S 84-864-7657 IMP
KIK CUSTOM PRODUCTS INC
KIK DANVILLE
(*Suby of* KIK CUSTOM PRODUCTS INC)
1 W Hegeler Ln, Danville, IL 61832-8341
Tel (217) 442-1400 *Founded/Ownrshp* 1989
Sales 716.3MM *EMP* 2,500
SIC 2841 2842 2843 2844 Soap & other detergents; Specialty cleaning, polishes & sanitation goods; Surface active agents; Toilet preparations
Pr: William Smith
**Prin:* Bill Smith

KIK DANVILLE
See KIK CUSTOM PRODUCTS INC

D-U-N-S 11-785-4153
KIK INTERNATIONAL HOUSTON INC
(*Suby of* KIK HOLDCO COMPANY INC)
2921 Corder St, Houston, TX 77054-3401
Tel (713) 747-8710 *Founded/Ownrshp* 1993
Sales 390.2MM[E] *EMP* 3,000
SIC 5999 Cleaning equipment & supplies
CEO: David Cynamon
VP Sls: Christopher Benning

D-U-N-S 05-148-2784
KIK-SOCAL INC
K I K
(*Suby of* KIK INTERNATIONAL HOUSTON INC) ★
9028 Dice Rd, Santa Fe Springs, CA 90670-2520
Tel (562) 946-6427 *Founded/Ownrshp* 1999
Sales NA *EMP* 3,000
SIC 2842 Bleaches, household: dry or liquid; Fabric softeners; Ammonia, household; Cleaning or polishing preparations
CEO: Jeffrey M Nodland
**Pr:* Stratis Katsiris
**Pr:* William Smith
**CFO:* Ben W Kaak
Genl Mgr: Greg Wiese

D-U-N-S 02-920-6547 IMP
KIKKOMAN SALES USA INC
(*Suby of* KIKKOMAN CORPORATION)
50 California St Ste 3600, San Francisco, CA 94111-4760
Tel (415) 956-7750 *Founded/Ownrshp* 1957
Sales 86.2MM[E] *EMP* 60
SIC 5149 2035 Specialty food items; Pickles, sauces & salad dressings
CEO: Yuzaburo Mogi
**Treas:* Nakamura Mitsunodu
Treas: Mitsunobu Nakamura
Mktg Dir: Deborah Carpenter
Manager: Helen Robert
Mktg Mgr: Jane Foreman
Sls Mgr: Jorge Ortiz

Sls Mgr: Be Reese
Sls Mgr: Seiichiro Shimoda
Sls Mgr: Yasuhiro Yamazaki

D-U-N-S 86-807-3888
KILGORE COMPANIES LLC
KILGORE PAVING & MAINTANCE
(*Suby of* SUMMIT MATERIALS LLC) ★
7057 W 2100 S, Salt Lake City, UT 84128-8430
Tel (801) 250-0132 *Founded/Ownrshp* 2010
Sales 130.0MM^E *EMP* 379
SIC 1721 Pavement marking contractor
Genl Mgr: Jason Kilgore
IT Man: Brian Hall
Sfty Dirs: Rich Kauss

D-U-N-S 01-824-3985 IMP/EXP
KILGORE FLARES CO LLC
(*Suby of* CHG GROUP INC) ★
155 Kilgore Rd, Toone, TN 38381-7850
Tel (731) 228-5200 *Founded/Ownrshp* 2001
Sales 94.3MM^E *EMP* 1^E
SIC 2899 3728 Chemical preparations; Countermeasure dispensers, aircraft
Pr: James Williams
COO: Nick Vlahakis
CFO: Eric Rangen
Treas: Karen Moore
Prgrm Mgr: Chris Byrd
Prgrm Mgr: Mike Wehmeyer
Admn Mgr: Barbra Yarborough
CIO: John Dixon
CTO: Mark Driber
QA Dir: Craig Walgren
Dir IT: Alan Phillips

KILGORE PAVING & MAINTANCE
See KILGORE COMPANIES LLC

D-U-N-S 08-330-7348
KILLEEN INDEPENDENT SCHOOL DISTRICT
200 N W S Young Dr, Killeen, TX 76543-4025
Tel (254) 336-0000 *Founded/Ownrshp* 1882
Sales 418.2MM *EMP* 6,200^E
Accts Lott Vernon & Company Pc K
SIC 8211 Public elementary & secondary schools
**Pr:* Carlos Cole Jr
**CFO:* Megan Bradley
**VP:* Joshua Ayers
Ex Dir: Bonnie Tomczyk
Brnch Mgr: Don Webster
Telecom Mg: Russ Jarret
Netwrk Mgr: John Hocking
Pr Dir: Shannon Rideout
Sls Mgr: Amberly Mills
Schl Brd P: Terry Delano
Psych: Jane Verran

D-U-N-S 00-242-1121
KILLINGTON/PICO SKI RESORT PARTNERS LLC
(*Suby of* POWDR CORP) ★
4763 Killington Rd, Killington, VT 05751-9746
Tel (802) 422-3333 *Founded/Ownrshp* 1986, 2008
Sales 21.0MM^E *EMP* 1,500^E
SIC 7011 Ski lodge
Pr: Mike Solimano
**Sr VP:* Herwig Demschar
VP: Jeff Temple

D-U-N-S 07-587-5500
KILPATRICK TOWNSEND & STOCKTON LLP
HYDREL
1100 Peachtree St Ne, Atlanta, GA 30309-4501
Tel (404) 815-6500 *Founded/Ownrshp* 1874
Sales 242.2MM^E *EMP* 1,225
SIC 8111 General practice attorney, lawyer
Mng Pt: Susan M Spaeth
Pt: William E Dorris
Pt: Thomas J Dougherty
Pt: Keith Harper
Pt: Gerald A Jeutter
Pt: Wyck A Knox
Pt: Nils Sk Ld
Pt: Diane Prucino
Pt: Hayden J Silver
Pt: David B Whelpley
Mng Pt: Susan Mspaeth
COO: Gary G Dacey
CFO: John B Murphy
Ofcr: Sarah H Bazen
Assoc Dir: John Page
Assoc Dir: Sue Wilder

D-U-N-S 05-239-0192
▲ KILROY REALTY CORP
12200 W Olympic Blvd # 200, Los Angeles, CA 90064-1044
Tel (310) 481-8400 *Founded/Ownrshp* 1997
Sales 581.2MM *EMP* 232^E
Tkr Sym KRC *Exch* NYS
SIC 6798 Real estate investment trusts
Ch Bd: John Kilroy
COO: Jeffrey Hawken
CFO: Tyler Rose
Bd of Dir: Anna Orlando
Ex VP: Tracy Murphy
Ex VP: Heidi Roth
Ex VP: David Simon
Ex VP: Justin Smart
Sr VP: John T Fucci
Sr VP: Rob Swartz
VP: James Gwilliam
Board of Directors: Edward Brennan, Jolie Hunt, Scott Ingraham, Gary Stevenson, Peter Stoneberg

D-U-N-S 10-557-0084
KILROY REALTY LP
12200 W Olympic Blvd # 200, Los Angeles, CA 90064-1044
Tel (310) 481-8400 *Founded/Ownrshp* 1996
Sales 581.2MM *EMP* 226^E
SIC 6798 Real estate investment trusts
Pr: John B Kilroy Jr
Genl Pt: Kilroy Realty Corporation
CFO: Tyler H Rose

KIMBALL CORPORATE, THE
See KIMBALL ELECTRONICS GROUP LLC

KIMBALL DISTRIBUTIONS
See KIMBALL ELECTRONICS INC

D-U-N-S 94-560-3392 IMP/EXP
■ KIMBALL ELECTRONICS GROUP LLC
KIMBALL CORPORATE, THE
(*Suby of* KIMBALL ELECTRONICS INC) ★
1205 Kimball Blvd, Jasper, IN 47546-0017
Tel (812) 634-4000 *Founded/Ownrshp* 2015
Sales 941.8MM^E *EMP* 3,510
SIC 3571 Electronic computers
Pr: Donald D Charron
**Pr:* James C Thyen
**CFO:* Michael K Sergesketter
**Ch:* Douglas A Habig
**Treas:* Adam Smith
VP: Steve Korn
**VP:* Gary W Schwartz
**VP:* Kevin R Smith
Exec: Marla Haas
Board of Directors: Greg Bannick, Dennis Gradler

D-U-N-S 00-909-3311 IMP
KIMBALL ELECTRONICS INC (UT)
KIMBALL DISTRIBUTIONS
2233 S 300 E, Salt Lake City, UT 84115-2803
Tel (801) 466-0569 *Founded/Ownrshp* 1921
Sales 88.1MM^E *EMP* 200
SIC 5065 5063 Electronic parts & equipment; Electrical apparatus & equipment
Pr: Richard A Kimball Jr
**Ch:* Richard Kimball Sr
**Treas:* Ray M Schenk

D-U-N-S 13-152-2401
▲ KIMBALL ELECTRONICS INC
1205 Kimball Blvd, Jasper, IN 47546-0017
Tel (812) 634-4000 *Founded/Ownrshp* 1961
Sales 842.0MM *EMP* 4,500^E
Accts Deloitte & Touche Llp Indiana
Tkr Sym KE *Exch* NGS
SIC 3672 Printed circuit boards
Ch Bd: Donald D Charron
CFO: Michael K Sergesketter
Chf Cred: John H Kahle
VP: Roger Chang
VP: Janusz F Kasprzyk
VP: Steven T Korn
VP: Sandy A Smith
VP: Christopher J Thyen
Ql Cn Mgr: Gregory Hessler
Board of Directors: Gregory J Lampert, Colleen C Repplier, Geoffrey L Stringer, Thomas J Tischhauser, Christine M Vujovich

D-U-N-S 13-920-4783
■ KIMBALL ELECTRONICS MANUFACTURING INC
(*Suby of* KIMBALL CORPORATE) ★
1600 Royal St, Jasper, IN 47549-1022
Tel (812) 482-1600 *Founded/Ownrshp* 2014
Sales 702.0MM^E *EMP* 825
SIC 3679 Electronic circuits
Ch Bd: Douglas Habig
**Pr:* Don Charron

D-U-N-S 08-875-3710 IMP
■ KIMBALL ELECTRONICS TAMPA INC
(*Suby of* KIMBALL CORPORATE) ★
1205 Kimball Blvd, Jasper, IN 47546-0017
Tel (812) 634-4000 *Founded/Ownrshp* 1993
Sales 228.8MM^E *EMP* 952
SIC 3679 3672 Electronic circuits; Printed circuit boards
Pr: Donald D Charron
**CFO:* Michael K Sergesketter
**Treas:* Gregory R Kincer
**Treas:* R G Kincer
**VP:* Michelle R Schroeder
Dir: Marilyn Cooper
Dir IT: Brad Schulz
Mtls Mgr: Sherri Roos
Opers Mgr: Jerry Anderson
Opers Mgr: Mahmod Zand
Prd Mgr: Shawn Woods

D-U-N-S 79-473-2313 IMP
■ KIMBALL FURNITURE GROUP LLC
(*Suby of* KIMBALL INTERNATIONAL INC) ★
1600 Royal St, Jasper, IN 47549-1022
Tel (812) 482-1600 *Founded/Ownrshp* 1988
Sales 1.0MMM^E *EMP* 4,947^E
SIC 2521 2522 Wood office furniture; Office furniture, except wood
Pr: Donald W Van Winkle
**Treas:* R Gregory Kincer
**VP:* Michelle R Schroeder
**VP:* James C Thyen
Board of Directors: Brian K Habig, Polly Kawalek, Christina M Vujovich, Jack R Wentworth, John Hagig Alan B Graf Jr

KIMBALL HILL HOMES
See KIMBALL HILL INC

D-U-N-S 02-492-3799
KIMBALL HILL INC
KIMBALL HILL HOMES
5999 New Wilke Rd Ste 306, Rolling Meadows, IL 60008-4503
Tel (847) 364-7300 *Founded/Ownrshp* 1969
Sales 153.7MM^E *EMP* 900
SIC 1521 1531 New construction, single-family houses; Operative builders; Condominium developers; Cooperative apartment developers; Speculative builder, multi-family dwellings
CEO: David K Hill
**Ch Bd:* Ken Love
Pr: Isaac Heimbinder
CFO: Gene Rowehl
Sr VP: Hal Barber
Sr VP: Robert J Bob Ryan
Board of Directors: Diane Hill

D-U-N-S 00-636-5803 IMP/EXP
▲ KIMBALL INTERNATIONAL INC
1600 Royal St, Jasper, IN 47549-1022
Tel (812) 482-1600 *Founded/Ownrshp* 1939
Sales 635.1MM *EMP* 2,894^E
Tkr Sym KBAL *Exch* NGS
SIC 2511 2512 2521 2522 2517 Wood household furniture; Upholstered household furniture; Wood office furniture; Office furniture, except wood; Stereo cabinets, wood; Television cabinets, wood
Ch Bd: Robert F Schneider
Pr: Donald W Van Winkle
CFO: Michelle R Schroeder
Ofcr: Lonnie P Nicholson
Ex VP: Gary W Schwartz
VP: Julia E Heitz Cassidy
VP: R Gregory Kincer
VP: Steven T Korn
VP: Stephanie Martin
VP: Lisa A Schmidt
VP: Michael S Wagner
Board of Directors: Patrick E Connolly, Susan B Frampton, Timothy J Jahnke, Kristine L Juster, Kimberly K Ryan, Geoffrey L Stringer, Thomas J Tischhauser, Christine M Vujovich

D-U-N-S 07-827-2713
KIMBALL MEDICAL CENTER INC
BARNABAS HEALTH
600 River Ave, Lakewood, NJ 08701-5281
Tel (732) 363-1900 *Founded/Ownrshp* 1911
Sales 108.9MM *EMP* 1,500^E
Accts Withumsmithbrown Pc Morristow
SIC 8062 General medical & surgical hospitals
Pr: Michael Mimoso
Pr: Susan Hernandez
**CFO:* Paul Rouvell
**VP:* Judy Colorado
VP: Elizabeth Deblock
VP: Kelly Fulton
**VP:* Caryl Russo
Dir Risk M: Cathy Johnson
Dir Case M: Anne White
Dir IT: Kim Good
Mtls Mgr: Jonohan Ango

KIMBALL MIDWEST
See MIDWEST MOTOR SUPPLY CO

D-U-N-S 79-731-2147 IMP
■ KIMBALL OFFICE INC
(*Suby of* KIMBALL FURNITURE GROUP LLC) ★
1600 Royal St, Jasper, IN 47549-1022
Tel (812) 482-1600 *Founded/Ownrshp* 2016
Sales 299.0MM^E *EMP* 2,500
Accts Deloitte & Touche Llp Indiana
SIC 2522 Office desks & tables: except wood
Pr: Michael Wagner
**Ch Bd:* Douglas A Habig
**Pr:* James C Thyen
**Treas:* R Gregory Kincer
**V Ch Bd:* Thomas L Habig
Ex VP: Randall L Catt
**VP:* C Allen Parker
**Exec:* John T Thyen
Dir Bus: Denise Meagles
Genl Mgr: Jim Duncan
CIO: Gary Schwartz

D-U-N-S 08-708-2491 IMP
KIMBER MFG INC
1 Lawton St, Yonkers, NY 10705-2617
Tel (914) 964-0771 *Founded/Ownrshp* 1996
Sales 92.3MM^E *EMP* 330
SIC 3599 Machine shop, jobbing & repair
Ch Bd: Leslie Edelmen
VP: Benny Kokia
VP: Doron Segal
Mng Dir: Abdool Jamal
CTO: Boaz Hayik
Dir IT: Gerry Keho
Mfg Dir: Robert Nemergut
Mfg Mgr: Kieran Kelly
VP Sls: Ryan Busse
Mktg Mgr: Celia Crane

D-U-N-S 00-403-9053 IMP/EXP
KIMBERLAND SWAN HOLDINGS INC
(*Suby of* PERRIGO CO) ★
1 Swan Dr, Smyrna, TN 37167-2099
Tel (615) 459-8900 *Founded/Ownrshp* 1898, 1992
Sales 275.0MM *EMP* 825
SIC 2844 Toilet preparations
Pr: All Goia
VP Sls: Greg Plummer

D-U-N-S 00-607-2136
▲ KIMBERLY-CLARK CORP
351 Phelps Dr, Irving, TX 75038-6540
Tel (972) 281-1200 *Founded/Ownrshp* 1872
Sales 18.5MMM *EMP* 43,000^E
Tkr Sym KMB *Exch* NYS
SIC 2621 2676 Paper mills; Facial tissue stock; Toilet tissue stock; Sanitary tissue paper; Sanitary paper products; Towels, napkins & tissue paper products; Feminine hygiene paper products; Infant & baby paper products
Ch Bd: Thomas J Falk
CFO: Maria Henry
Chf Mktg O: Scott Usitalo
Ofcr: Lizanne C Gottung
Sr VP: Sandra Macquillan
Sr VP: Thomas J Mielke
Exec: Salli Nickolai
Exec: Melody Villarreal
Assoc Dir: Christine Johanski
Dir Soc: Lauren Murphy
CIO: Suja Chandrasekaran
Board of Directors: Marc J Shapiro, John F Bergstrom, Michael D White, Abelardo E Bru, Robert W Decherd, Fabian T Garcia, Mae C Jemison, James M Jenness, Nancy J Karch, Christa S Quarles, Ian C Read

D-U-N-S 07-975-9020
KIMBERLY-CLARK PROFESSIONAL
1400 Holcomb Bridge Rd, Roswell, GA 30076-2190
Tel (800) 241-3146 *Founded/Ownrshp* 2015
Sales 119.9MM^E *EMP* 491^E
SIC 3589 Commercial cleaning equipment
VP: Chuck Goerg
VP: Aaron Powell
VP: Angie Scott
Exec: Antonio Bell
Exec: Diane Fitzgerald
Exec: Steven Hohol
Assoc Dir: Cheryl Sanzere
Creative D: Jonathan Franz
Comm Man: Heather Peace
CIO: Normand Gagnier
Software D: Wendy Cocke

KIMBLE CHASE
See CHASE SCIENTIFIC GLASS INC

D-U-N-S 00-250-1211 IMP/EXP
KIMBLE CHASE LIFE SCIENCE AND RESEARCH PRODUCTS LLC (NJ)
KONTES OF CALIFORNIA
1022 Spruce St, Vineland, NJ 08360-2841
Tel (865) 717-2600 *Founded/Ownrshp* 1934, 2007
Sales 159.5MM^E *EMP* 1,200
SIC 3231 Medical & laboratory glassware: made from purchased glass
CEO: Klaus Walber
CFO: Randy Baughman
VP: Ken Falkowi
VP: Bradley Hogg
VP Sls: Ken Falkowitz
Board of Directors: Axel Herberg, Gerhard Schulze

KIMBLE CLAY & LIMESTONE
See KIMBLE CO

D-U-N-S 04-106-7869
KIMBLE CO
KIMBLE CLAY & LIMESTONE
3596 State Route 39 Nw, Dover, OH 44622-7232
Tel (330) 343-1226 *Founded/Ownrshp* 1952
Sales 1.3MMM^E *EMP* 185
SIC 1221

D-U-N-S 83-467-4566
KIMBLE COMPANIES INC
ACE DISPOSAL
3596 State Route 39 Nw, Dover, OH 44622-7232
Tel (330) 343-5665 *Founded/Ownrshp* 1994
Sales 146.7MM^E *EMP* 191
SIC 4953 Refuse collection & disposal services
Pr: Keith Kimble
**Sec:* Rick Kimble
VP: Eric Kimble
**VP:* Greg Kimble
Genl Mgr: Scott Walter
Genl Mgr: Don Zaucha
Off Mgr: Stacey McAfee
IT Man: Mike Yates
Sls Mgr: Ed Lee
Sales Asso: Tom Morris
Genl Couns: Nathan Vaughan

KIMBRELL'S FURNITURE
See FURNITURE DISTRIBUTORS INC

D-U-N-S 07-943-2815
KIMCO FACILITY SERVICES LLC
KIMCO SERVICES
6055 Lakeside Commons Dr, Macon, GA 31210-5790
Tel (478) 752-7000 *Founded/Ownrshp* 2014
Sales 200.0MM *EMP* 3,000
SIC 7349 Janitorial service, contract basis
CFO: James Fritze
Sr VP: Edward Pim
Area Mgr: David Tolson

KIMCO GOVERNMENT SERVICES
See KIMCO STAFFING SERVICES INC

D-U-N-S 06-803-3117 IMP
▲ KIMCO REALTY CORP
3333 New Hyde Park Rd # 100, New Hyde Park, NY 11042-1205
Tel (516) 869-9000 *Founded/Ownrshp* 1966
Sales 993.9MM *EMP* 546
Tkr Sym KIM *Exch* NYS
SIC 6798 Real estate investment trusts
Pr: Conor C Flynn
Ch Bd: Milton Cooper
CFO: Glenn G Cohen
VP: Scott Onufrey
VP: Julio Ramon
Genl Couns: Michael Parry
Board of Directors: Philip E Coviello, Richard G Dooley, Frank Lourenso, Richard B Saltzman, Joe Grills

KIMCO SERVICES
See KIMCO FACILITY SERVICES LLC

D-U-N-S 16-126-7430
KIMCO STAFFING SERVICES INC
KIMCO GOVERNMENT SERVICES
17872 Cowan, Irvine, CA 92614-6010
Tel (949) 331-1199 *Founded/Ownrshp* 1986
Sales 177.3MM^E *EMP* 4,000
SIC 7361 Employment agencies
CEO: Kim I Megonigal
**Pr:* Lisa Pierson
**VP:* Steven Bradley
VP: Thomas Megonigal
Exec: Leticia Kelch
Brnch Mgr: Peggy Best
Off Mgr: Windy McNay
Dir IT: Barbara Heeger
Dir IT: Azeddine Ouhida
IT Man: Tony Bruno
IT Man: Feras Elfar

D-U-N-S 06-109-9131
KIMLEY-HORN AND ASSOCIATES INC
(*Suby of* APHC INC) ★
421 Fayetteville St # 600, Raleigh, NC 27601-1777
Tel (919) 677-2000 *Founded/Ownrshp* 1967
Sales 556.6MM^E *EMP* 2,500
SIC 8711 Engineering services
Pr: John C Atz
**Ch Bd:* Brooks Peed
**CFO:* Mark Wilson
**Treas:* David McEntee
Sr VP: John Benditz
Sr VP: Steve Daugherty
Sr VP: Mike Kiefer
Sr VP: Pierre Pretorius
Sr VP: Mark Tabor
Sr VP: Roy Wilshire

Sr VP: Jon Wilson
VP: Raj Christian
VP: Johnathan Dorman
VP: Dave Leistiko
VP: Kevin Roberson
Board of Directors: Brooks Peed

D-U-N-S 19-647-3557
KIMMINS CONTRACTING CORP
(*Suby of* KIMMINS CORP) ★
1501 E 2nd Ave, Tampa, FL 33605-5005
Tel (813) 248-3878 *Founded/Ownrshp* 1983
Sales 91.3MME *EMP* 320
SIC 1623 Water, sewer & utility lines
Pr: Joseph Williams
CFO: Ray Rowland
**Sec:* Norm Dominiak
**VP:* Candice Agosto
**VP:* Mike O Brien
**VP:* John Zemina
Off Mgr: Winnie Jackson
Sfty Mgr: Domenic Deamicis

D-U-N-S 17-568-4018 IMP
KIMMINS CORP
1501 E 2nd Ave, Tampa, FL 33605-5005
Tel (813) 248-3878 *Founded/Ownrshp* 1985
Sales 148.2MME *EMP* 327
SIC 1799 1795 1522 Decontamination services; Asbestos removal & encapsulation; Demolition, buildings & other structures; Apartment building construction; Multi-family dwelling construction
Pr: Francis M Williams
**Sec:* Joseph M Williams
**VP:* Karl Burgin

D-U-N-S 10-346-6231
KIMPTON HOTEL & RESTAURANT GROUP LLC
(*Suby of* INTERCONTINENTAL HOTELS GROUP PLC)
222 Kearny St Ste 200, San Francisco, CA 94108-4537
Tel (415) 397-5572 *Founded/Ownrshp* 2001
Sales 935.1MME *EMP* 7,500
SIC 8741 Hotel or motel management
CEO: Mike Depatie
Pr: Donald Ograd y
**COO:* Mike Defrino
**COO:* Niki Leondakis
**CFO:* Ben Rowe
**Ex VP:* Joe Long
Ex VP: Joseph Long
**Ex VP:* Judy Miles
Ex VP: Gregory J Wolkom
Sr VP: James Alderman
Sr VP: Christine Lawson
Sr VP: James Lin
Sr VP: Greg Smith
VP: Alan Baer
VP: Mark Campbell
VP: Scott Gingerich
VP: Pete Koerner
VP: Jin Lee
VP: Jack Levy
VP: Andrea Mue
VP: David O'Malley

D-U-N-S 05-132-4093 IMP
■ **KINCAID FURNITURE CO INC**
(*Suby of* LA-Z-BOY INC) ★
240 Pleasant Hill Rd, Hudson, NC 28638-2244
Tel (828) 728-3261 *Founded/Ownrshp* 1988
Sales 111.2MME *EMP* 550
SIC 2511 2512 Wood household furniture; Upholstered household furniture
Pr: Steven M Kincaid
Pr: Tim Annas
Sr VP: Ryan Allen
Sr VP: Bob Lemons
VP: Reggie Probst
Creative D: Seth Olsen
Brnch Mgr: Clarence Gilbert
Snr Sftwr: Reba Baldwin
Snr Sftwr: Jason Winkler
DP Dir: Jack Debonis
Dir IT: Don Gregory

D-U-N-S 04-247-8961
■ **KINCAID GENERATION LLC**
(*Suby of* DYNEGY INC) ★
4 Miles W Of Kincaid, Kincaid, IL 62540
Tel (217) 237-4311 *Founded/Ownrshp* 2016
Sales 122.2MME *EMP* 140
Accts Deloitte & Touche Llp Richmo
SIC 4911 Generation, electric power
Mng Dir: James Klenki
CFO: Douglas Black

KINCAID'S
See RESTAURANTS UNLIMITED INC

KINCO CONSTRUCTION
See KINCO CONSTRUCTORS LLC

D-U-N-S 07-567-1289
KINCO CONSTRUCTORS LLC
KINCO CONSTRUCTION
12600 Lawson Rd, Little Rock, AR 72210-2711
Tel (501) 225-7606 *Founded/Ownrshp* 2001
Sales 86.8MME *EMP* 185
SIC 1542 1541 Nonresidential construction; Industrial buildings & warehouses
CEO: Doug Wasson
**VP:* Marc Dillard
**VP:* William Fletcher
VP: Clay Gordon
**VP:* Keith Jacks
Genl Mgr: Brian Strickland

KIND FOODS
See KIND LLC

D-U-N-S 87-940-8680 IMP
KIND LLC
KIND FOODS
1372 Broadway Frnt 3, New York, NY 10018-6123
Tel (855) 884-5463 *Founded/Ownrshp* 1994
Sales 221.8MME *EMP* 500
SIC 5141 Groceries, general line
VP: Rodrigo Zuloaga
Comm Dir: Erin Pineda
Comm Man: Meghan Kelleher
CTO: Khaled Abohalima
VP Opers: Doris Rivera
Mktg Mgr: Tara Buchan
Mktg Mgr: Amy Mixa
Mktg Mgr: Kathryne Nahoum
Sls Mgr: Seth Brody

KINDER MORGAN
See EL PASO TENNESSEE PIPELINE CO LLC

D-U-N-S 07-507-9822 IMP/EXP
■ **KINDER MORGAN BULK TERMINALS LLC**
(*Suby of* KINDER MORGAN ENERGY PARTNERS LP) ★
1001 Louisiana St # 1000, Houston, TX 77002-5089
Tel (713) 369-9000 *Founded/Ownrshp* 1998
Sales 244.0MME *EMP* 767
SIC 4491 Marine terminals; Stevedoring
Pr: Steven J Kean
**CEO:* Richard D Kinder
**CFO:* Kimberly Allen Dang

D-U-N-S 03-512-3850 IMP/EXP
■ **KINDER MORGAN ENERGY PARTNERS LP**
(*Suby of* KMI) ★
1001 La St Ste 1000, Houston, TX 77002
Tel (713) 369-9000 *Founded/Ownrshp* 2014
Sales 12.5MMM *EMP* 11,075
SIC 4613 4925 4922 4226 4619 5171 Refined petroleum pipelines; Gasoline pipelines (common carriers); Gas production and/or distribution; Liquefied petroleum gas, distribution through mains; Natural gas transmission; Pipelines, natural gas; Storage, natural gas; Petroleum & chemical bulk stations & terminals for hire; Coal pipeline operation; Petroleum terminals
CEO: Richard D Kinder
Pr: Duane Kokinda
Pr: Tom Martin
CFO: Kimberly A Dang
VP: Bill Henderson

D-U-N-S 80-040-8192
▲ **KINDER MORGAN INC**
KMI
1001 La St Ste 1000, Houston, TX 77002
Tel (713) 369-9000 *Founded/Ownrshp* 2006
Sales 14.4MMM *EMP* 11,290
Tkr Sym KMI *Exch* NYS
SIC 4922 Natural gas transmission; Pipelines, natural gas; Storage, natural gas
Pr: Steven J Kean
Ch Bd: Richard D Kinder
Pr: Ian D Anderson
Pr: Jesse Arenivas
Pr: Thomas A Martin
Pr: Ronald G McClain
Pr: John W Schlosser
CFO: Kimberly Allen
CFO: Kimberly A Dang
VP: Meli Armstrong
VP: David Barrow
VP: Holly Breaux
VP: Gary Buchler
VP: Gabrielle Butler
VP: Paul Davis
VP: David R Deveau
VP: Robert D Dillard
VP: James Holland
VP: McGee Johnny
VP: Gary Lamphier
VP: Brian Mahler
Board of Directors: Joel V Staff, Ted A Gardner, Robert F Vagt, Anthony W Hall Jr, Perry M Waughtal, Gary L Hultquist, Ronald L Kuehn Jr, Deborah A Macdonald, Michael C Morgan, Arthur C Reichstetter, C Park Shaper, William A Smith

D-U-N-S 00-694-3500 IMP/EXP
■ **KINDER MORGAN KANSAS INC**
(*Suby of* KMI) ★
1001 La St Ste 1000, Houston, TX 77002
Tel (713) 369-9000 *Founded/Ownrshp* 2007
Sales 1.0MMME *EMP* 7,931
SIC 4922 4924 Natural gas transmission; Pipelines, natural gas; Natural gas distribution
CEO: Richard D Kinder
**Pr:* C Park Shaper
**COO:* Steven J Kean
CFO: Kimberly A Dang
VP: Joseph Listengart
Prin: Henry Cornell
Prin: Deborah A Macdonald
Prin: Michael Miller
Prin: Michael C Morgan
Prin: Kenneth A Pontarelli
Prin: Fayez Sarofim
Board of Directors: Henry Cornell, Deborah A Macdonald, Michael Miller, Michael C Morgan, Kenneth A Pontarelli, Joel V Staff, John Stokes, R Baran Tekkora, Glenn A Youngkin

D-U-N-S 13-988-7975
■ **KINDER MORGAN LIQUIDS TERMINALS LLC**
(*Suby of* KINDER MORGAN ENERGY PARTNERS LP) ★
500 Dallas St Ste 1000, Houston, TX 77002-4718
Tel (713) 369-8758 *Founded/Ownrshp* 1975
Sales 282.6MME *EMP* 1,000E
SIC 4226 Oil & gasoline storage caverns for hire
CEO: Richard D Kinder
Pr: John Schlosser
CFO: Kimberly Dang
Treas: David D Kinder
Ex VP: Steven J Kean
VP: Joseph Listengart
Prin: Jeff Armstrong

D-U-N-S 02-918-8021
■ **KINDER MORGAN MATERIALS SERVICES LLC**
(*Suby of* KINDER MORGAN ENERGY PARTNERS LP) ★
333 Rouser Rd Ste 4601, Moon Township, PA 15108-2773
Tel (412) 264-6068 *Founded/Ownrshp* 2002
Sales 180.0MME *EMP* 5,485
SIC 4011 Railroads, line-haul operating
VP: Arthur Rudolph
VP: Michael Chutz
**Genl Mgr:* Brian Seaman

D-U-N-S 14-359-8048
■ **KINDER MORGAN PRODUCTION CO LP**
(*Suby of* KINDER MORGAN ENERGY PARTNERS LP) ★
1001 La St Ste 1000, Houston, TX 77002
Tel (800) 525-3752 *Founded/Ownrshp* 2007
Sales 221.8MME *EMP* 435E
SIC 5172 Crude oil
CEO: Richard Kinder

KINDERCARE
See MULBERRY CHILDCARE CENTERS INC

D-U-N-S 11-617-4533
KINDERCARE EDUCATION LLC
C D C
650 Ne Holladay St # 1400, Portland, OR 97232-2096
Tel (503) 872-1300 *Founded/Ownrshp* 2016
Sales 1.1MMME *EMP* 32,000
SIC 8299 Music school
CEO: Tom Wyatt
**Ex VP:* WEI-LI Chong
VP: Deborah Bordonaro
Dist Mgr: Jennifer Thomas
Dist Mgr: Jennifer R Thompson

D-U-N-S 60-366-9052
KINDERCARE LEARNING CENTERS LLC
(*Suby of* C D C) ★
650 Ne Holladay St # 1400, Portland, OR 97232-2096
Tel (503) 872-1300 *Founded/Ownrshp* 2005
Sales 661.3MME *EMP* 24,000
SIC 8351 Group day care center
CEO: John T Wyatt
**CEO:* Thomas A Heymann
**CFO:* Dan R Jackson
**Sr VP:* Edward L Brewington
**Sr VP:* S Wray Hutchinson
**Sr VP:* Eva M Kripalani
**Sr VP:* Bruce Walters
Ex Dir: Jacquie Ciccia
Ex Dir: Casey Crost
Ex Dir: Michelle Grubb
Ex Dir: Melonie Hilstad
Board of Directors: Richard J Goldstein, Henry R Kravis, Michael W Michelson, Scott C Nuttall, George R Roberts

D-U-N-S 16-276-4414
KINDERHOOK INDUSTRIES LLC
521 5th Ave Fl 34, New York, NY 10175-3301
Tel (212) 201-6780 *Founded/Ownrshp* 2003
Sales 171.1MME *EMP* 540
SIC 6799 Investors
CFO: Lisa Schmidt
VP: Louis Aurelio
VP: Michael Zoch

KINDRED
See GREATER PEORIA SPECIALTY HOSPITAL LLC

D-U-N-S 02-250-3642
■ **KINDRED DEVELOPMENT 17 LLC**
KINDRED HOSPITAL MELBORNE
(*Suby of* KINDRED HEALTHCARE INC) ★
765 W Nasa Blvd, Melbourne, FL 32901-1815
Tel (321) 409-4044 *Founded/Ownrshp* 2008
Sales 18.2MME *EMP* 1,493E
SIC 8062 General medical & surgical hospitals

D-U-N-S 13-153-0511
▲ **KINDRED HEALTHCARE INC**
680 S 4th St, Louisville, KY 40202-2412
Tel (502) 596-7300 *Founded/Ownrshp* 1998
Sales 7.0MMM *EMP* 102,000
Tkr Sym KND *Exch* NYS
SIC 8062 8051 8322 8082 General medical & surgical hospitals; Skilled nursing care facilities; Rehabilitation services; Home health care services
Pr: Benjamin A Breier
**Ch Bd:* Phyllis R Yale
Pr: Jason Zachariah
COO: Kent H Wallace
CFO: Stephen D Farber
Sr VP: William M Altman
Sr VP: Barbara L Baylis
Sr VP: Vincent S Hambright
Sr VP: Joseph Landenwich
Sr VP: Sandra Long
Sr VP: David Mikula
Sr VP: Brian L Pugh
Sr VP: Hank Robinson
Sr VP: Robert Schmidt
VP: Michael Bean
VP: Vonda Black
VP: Kathleen Border
VP: Tony Dickamore
VP: Edward Goddard
VP: Mike Grannan
VP: Jeffrey M Jasnoff
Board of Directors: Joel Ackerman, Jonathan D Blum, Thomas P Cooper, Paul J Diaz, Heyward R Donigan, Richard Goodman, Christopher T Hjelm, Frederick J Kleisner, Lynn Simon

D-U-N-S 08-966-6478
■ **KINDRED HEALTHCARE OPERATING INC**
(*Suby of* KINDRED HEALTHCARE INC) ★
680 S 4th St, Louisville, KY 40202-2412
Tel (502) 596-7300 *Founded/Ownrshp* 1998
Sales 649.5MME *EMP* 7,800
SIC 8051 Extended care facility
CFO: Chris Porter
Treas: Steven L Monaghan
Sr VP: William M Altman
Sr VP: Barbara L Baylis
Sr VP: Michael W Beal
Sr VP: Michael Beal
Sr VP: Peter D Corless
Sr VP: Anthony Disser
Sr VP: Dennis J Hansen
Sr VP: David G Henderson
Sr VP: Donna G Kelsey
Sr VP: Joseph L Landenwich
Sr VP: Ruth A Lusk
Sr VP: Gregory C Miller
Sr VP: James J Novak
Sr VP: Russel D Ragland
Sr VP: M S Riedman
Sr VP: Donald H Robinson
Sr VP: Traci K Shelton
Sr VP: Richard H Starke
Sr VP: T S Turner

KINDRED HOSPITAL MELBORNE
See KINDRED DEVELOPMENT 17 LLC

KINDRED HOSPITAL-MID WEST DST
See KINDRED HOSPITALS LIMITED PARTNERSHIP

D-U-N-S 94-567-0289
■ **KINDRED HOSPITALS LIMITED PARTNERSHIP**
KINDRED HOSPITAL-MID WEST DST
(*Suby of* KINDRED HEALTHCARE INC) ★
1313 Saint Anthony Pl, Louisville, KY 40204-1740
Tel (502) 587-7001 *Founded/Ownrshp* 1994
Sales 84.1MME *EMP* 650
SIC 8069 Specialty hospitals, except psychiatric
CFO: Debra Michaelek
VP: Rich Chatman
Dir Lab: Lisa Brown
IT Man: Catherine Gooch
IT Man: Sue Revlett
IT Man: James Rogers
IT Man: Leslie Wright
Opers Mgr: Gina Warrene
Mktg Dir: Mark Mourer
Doctor: Emma Cornell
HC Dir: Wendy Barnes

D-U-N-S 07-840-6637
■ **KINDRED NURSING CENTERS EAST LLC**
(*Suby of* KINDRED HEALTHCARE OPERATING INC) ★
680 S 4th St, Louisville, KY 40202-2412
Tel (502) 596-7300 *Founded/Ownrshp* 1998
Sales 109.7MME *EMP* 5,500
SIC 8051 Skilled nursing care facilities
Dir Surg: Rose Michels

D-U-N-S 14-558-1141
■ **KINDRED NURSING CENTERS LIMITED PARTNERSHIP**
ROYAL OAKS HEALTH CARE & REHAB
(*Suby of* KINDRED HEALTHCARE OPERATING INC) ★
3500 Maple Ave, Terre Haute, IN 47804-1732
Tel (502) 596-7300 *Founded/Ownrshp* 1998
Sales 93.1MME *EMP* 6,174E
SIC 8051 Skilled nursing care facilities
Sr VP: Arthur L Rothgerber
Off Mgr: Heather Dickerson
Nrsg Dir: Vanessa Atkinson Rn
HC Dir: Bre Fox

D-U-N-S 09-270-5375
KINECTA FEDERAL CREDIT UNION
1440 Rosecrans Ave, Manhattan Beach, CA 90266-3702
Tel (310) 643-5400 *Founded/Ownrshp* 1994
Sales NA *EMP* 450
SIC 6061 Federal credit unions
CEO: Keith Sultemeier
**Pr:* Randall G Dotemoto
**Pr:* Douglas C Wicks
**CEO:* Steve Lumm
**COO:* Joseph E Whitaker
**CFO:* Gregory C Talbott
Ofcr: David Roth
Sr VP: Brian Ctti
Sr VP: Kevin Faulkner
VP: Bruce Bingham
VP: Curt Byers
**VP:* Steven J Glouberman
**VP:* Sharon Moseley
VP: Ali Sadri

D-U-N-S 84-131-2569
KINECTA FINANCIAL & INSURANCE SERVICES LLC
(*Suby of* KINECTA FEDERAL CREDIT UNION) ★
1440 Rosecrans Ave, Manhattan Beach, CA 90266-3702
Tel (310) 643-5400 *Founded/Ownrshp* 2009
Sales NA *EMP* 16E
SIC 6061 Federal credit unions

D-U-N-S 96-955-7008 IMP/EXP
KINETEK INC
25 Northwest Point Blvd # 900, Elk Grove Village, IL 60007-1044
Tel (224) 265-1290 *Founded/Ownrshp* 2012
Sales 246.1MME *EMP* 2,578E
SIC 3621 3566 3613

D-U-N-S 08-313-9394 IMP
KINETIC CONCEPTS INC
KCI
(*Suby of* CHIRON HOLDINGS INC) ★
12930 W Interstate 10, San Antonio, TX 78249-2248
Tel (800) 531-5346 *Founded/Ownrshp* 2011
Sales 1.5MMME *EMP* 5,500
SIC 3842 Surgical appliances & supplies
Pr: Joseph F Woody
**Ch Bd:* Ronald A Matricaria
**Pr:* Catherine M Burzik
**Pr:* Stephen D Seidel
Pr: Joseph Woody
**CFO:* William Brown
**CFO:* Robert Hureau
**CFO:* Martin J Landon
Ex VP: Cameron McKennit
Ex VP: Debbie Mitchell
Ex VP: Margie Morales

Ex VP: Mike Schaeffer
Sr VP: Peter Arnold
**Sr VP:* R James Cravens
Sr VP: Michael Delvacchio
Sr VP: Mike Mathews
**VP:* John T Bibb
**VP:* Mike Helbock
VP: Rohit Kashyap
**VP:* Theresa McCutcheon
Exec: Jerry Ferris

D-U-N-S 06-355-2194
KINETIC SYSTEMS INC
(*Suby of* KINETICS HOLDING GMBH)
48400 Fremont Blvd, Fremont, CA 94538-6505
Tel (510) 683-6000 *Founded/Ownrshp* 2012
Sales 179.6MM^E *EMP* 500
SIC 1711 Mechanical contractor
CEO: Peter Maris
**COO:* Norm Escover
**CFO:* Martin Kaus
Treas: Seth Cuni
Sr VP: Todd Graves
VP: Jose Bre A
VP: Joachim Biggen
VP: Abby Heskett
Genl Mgr: J Rgen Schr Der
Genl Mgr: Jnrgen Schr Der
Off Mgr: Shannon Johnson

D-U-N-S 06-888-9344 IMP
KINETICO INC
WATER ONE QUALITY WTR SYSTEMS
(*Suby of* AXEL JOHNSON INC) ★
10845 Kinsman Rd, Newbury, OH 44065-8702
Tel (440) 564-9111 *Founded/Ownrshp* 2006, 2005
Sales 106.5MM^E *EMP* 427
SIC 3589 5074

D-U-N-S 05-649-7493 IMP/EXP
KINEXO
800 Tiffany Blvd Ste 300, Rocky Mount, NC 27804-1807
Tel (252) 407-2000 *Founded/Ownrshp* 1991
Sales 350.0MM *EMP* 85
SIC 5141 Food brokers
Pr: Todd Williams
**VP:* Heather Glascock
**VP:* Bill Taylor

D-U-N-S 00-407-4431 IMP/EXP
KING & PRINCE SEAFOOD CORP
(*Suby of* NIPPON SUISAN (USA) INC) ★
1 King And Prince Blvd, Brunswick, GA 31520-8668
Tel (912) 261-7025 *Founded/Ownrshp* 2005
Sales 83.1MM^E *EMP* 500
SIC 2092

D-U-N-S 06-454-1881
KING & SPALDING LLP
1180 Peachtree St, Atlanta, GA 30309
Tel (404) 572-4600 *Founded/Ownrshp* 1885
Sales 341.1MM^E *EMP* 1,927
SIC 8111 General practice law office
Ch Bd: Robert Hays
Pt: Juan M Alcal
Pt: Raymond E Baltz
Pt: Eleanor Banister
Pt: Patricia T Barmeyer
Pt: W Randall Bassett
Pt: Crayton L Bell
Pt: Paul R Bessette
Pt: Michael J Biles
Pt: James F Bowe
Pt: Gregory N Etzel
Pt: John S Herbert
Pt: Abraham NM Shashy
Pt: Geoffrey R Unger
Mng Pt: Alan Prince
Mng Pt: Timothy T Scott
COO: Derek J Hardesty
Ofcr: Kevin A Cavanaugh
Exec: Chris Jackson
Assoc Dir: Barry Lloyd

D-U-N-S 09-791-9794 EXP
KING AMERICA FINISHING INC
1351 Scarboro Hwy, Sylvania, GA 30467-7607
Tel (912) 863-4511 *Founded/Ownrshp* 2001
Sales 95.1MM^E *EMP* 450
SIC 2211 2261 Broadwoven fabric mills, cotton; Dyeing cotton broadwoven fabrics
CEO: George Renaldi III
**Pr:* Mike Beasley

KING ARCHITECTURAL METALS
See KING SUPPLY CO LLC

D-U-N-S 00-799-7935
KING ARTHUR FLOUR CO INC
BAKER'S STORE, THE
135 Us Route 5 S, Norwich, VT 05055-9430
Tel (802) 649-3881 *Founded/Ownrshp* 1984
Sales 100.0MM *EMP* 350
SIC 5149 5961 5461 8299 Flour; Bakery products; Catalog & mail-order houses; Bakeries; Educational service, nondegree granting: continuing educ.
Pr: Steve Voigt
Sls Mgr: Leigh Woods

D-U-N-S 06-549-6387
KING ARTHUR FLOUR CO INC
(*Suby of* BAKERS STORE) ★
62 Fogg Farm Rd, White River Junction, VT 05001-9485
Tel (802) 649-3881 *Founded/Ownrshp* 1790
Sales 89.0MM^E *EMP* 270
SIC 5149 Flour
Ch Bd: Frank E Sands II
**Pr:* Steven P Voigt
**VP:* Brinna Sands
VP Sls: Beth Kluge

D-U-N-S 04-030-2395
KING CANNON INC
FUDDRUCKERS
60 River St, Beverly, MA 01915-4223
Tel (978) 921-7438 *Founded/Ownrshp* 1998
Sales 38.5MM^E *EMP* 2,075
SIC 5812 Restaurant, family: chain
Pr: Bryce L King

D-U-N-S 93-005-7807
KING COUNTY HOUSING AUTHORITY
TALL CEDARS MOBILE COURT
401 37th St Se, Auburn, WA 98002-8006
Tel (206) 205-8837 *Founded/Ownrshp* 1994
Sales 103.0MM *EMP* 14^E
SIC 6515 Mobile home site operators
Prin: Liz Hlavaty
Comm Dir: Rhonda Rosenberg
Ex Dir: Stephen Norman

D-U-N-S 80-837-4248
KING COUNTY LIBRARY SYSTEM
KCLS
960 Newport Way Nw, Issaquah, WA 98027-2702
Tel (425) 369-3200 *Founded/Ownrshp* 1942
Sales 110.0MM *EMP* 1,364
SIC 8231 Libraries
Bd of Dir: Kathryn Brown
Bd of Dir: Julia Shaw
VP: Mark Whitaker
Assoc Dir: Kay Johnson
Ex Dir: Charlene Richards

D-U-N-S 07-184-0789
KING COUNTY PUBLIC HOSPITAL DISTRICT 2
EVERGREEN HOSPITAL MEDICAL CEN
12040 Ne 128th St, Kirkland, WA 98034-3013
Tel (425) 899-2769 *Founded/Ownrshp* 1967
Sales 565.8MM *EMP* 2,400
SIC 8062 General medical & surgical hospitals
CEO: Bob Malte
**COO:* Neil Johnson
**VP:* Jack Handley
Dir Lab: Mary Munchak
CIO: Tom Martin
CIO: Jamie Tripp
Cmptr Lab: Christie Brown
Dir QC: Beverly Hodge
QC Dir: Kathy Schoenrock
Opers Mgr: Chuck Davis
Opers Mgr: Maria Sheild

D-U-N-S 01-288-7738
KING COUNTY PUBLIC HOSPITAL DISTRICT NO 2
EVERGREEN HEALTHCARE
12040 Ne 128th St, Kirkland, WA 98034-3013
Tel (425) 899-1000 *Founded/Ownrshp* 1971
Sales 301.2MM *EMP* 2,800
Accts Kpmg Llp Seattle Wa
SIC 8741 Restaurant management
CEO: Steve Brown
Sr VP: Chrissy Yamada
VP: Jack Handley
Chf Nrs Of: Nancee R Hofmeister
Ex Dir: Mark Magistrale
QA Dir: Kathy Schoenrock
Dir IT: Benjamin Trigg
Ql Cn Mgr: Albert Cabrera
Doctor: Aileen Mickey
Doctor: Terry Pheifer

KING EMPLOYER SERVICES
See OASIS OUTSOURCING INC

D-U-N-S 00-813-3084
KING FISHER MARINE SERVICE LP
159 Hwy 316, Port Lavaca, TX 77979
Tel (361) 552-6751 *Founded/Ownrshp* 1998
Sales 102.6MM *EMP* 350^E
SIC 1629

D-U-N-S 79-120-0947
KING HOLDING CORP
360 N Crescent Dr, Beverly Hills, CA 90210-4874
Tel (586) 254-3900 *Founded/Ownrshp* 2006
Sales NA *EMP* 7,970
SIC 3452 3465 3469 3089 5072

D-U-N-S 00-699-5443
KING KULLEN GROCERY CO INC (NY)
185 Central Ave, Bethpage, NY 11714-3929
Tel (516) 733-7100 *Founded/Ownrshp* 1930
Sales 707.7MM^E *EMP* 4,500
SIC 5411 Supermarkets, chain
Ch Bd: Ronald Conklin
**Ch Bd:* Brian C Cullen
**Ch Bd:* Bernard Kennedy
**Pr:* J Donald Kennedy
**Sr VP:* James Flynn
**VP:* Joseph Brown
**VP:* James Carey
**VP:* Thomas K Cullen
**VP:* Joseph E Eck
**VP:* Anthony Femminella
Exec: John Santoro

D-U-N-S 08-012-7225
KING MEAT SERVICE INC
4215 Exchange Ave, Vernon, CA 90058-2604
Tel (323) 835-8989 *Founded/Ownrshp* 2015
Sales 90.0MM^E *EMP* 38
SIC 5147 Meats & meat products
Prin: Shunong Yan
**CEO:* Bei Zhi Yan

KING NUT COMPANIES
See KANAN ENTERPRISES INC

D-U-N-S 80-958-7413 IMP
■ **KING PHARMACEUTICALS LLC**
PFIZER
(*Suby of* PFIZER INC) ★
501 5th St, Bristol, TN 37620-2304
Tel (423) 989-8000 *Founded/Ownrshp* 2011
Sales 379.6MM^E *EMP* 2,637
SIC 2834 Pharmaceutical preparations
Pr: Brian A Markison
Pr: Tim Leonard
CFO: John Shumate
**CFO:* Joseph Squicciarino
Ofcr: Eric G Carter
Ex VP: Richard Buecheler
Ex VP: Michael H Davis
Ex VP: Sarah Faust
Ex VP: Dennis O'Brien
Ex VP: Dennis Obrien
Ex VP: Henry Richards
VP: Ray Feagins
VP: John J Howarth
VP: John Howarth
VP: Gary Powers
VP: Dean Slack
**VP:* Bryan Supran
VP: Jeff Taylor
VP: Linda Wase
Exec: Ryan Kochenower
Dir Rx: Sajani Mehta

D-U-N-S 00-793-3492 EXP
KING RANCH INC
3 Riverway Ste 1600, Houston, TX 77056-1967
Tel (832) 681-5700 *Founded/Ownrshp* 1853
Sales 318.2MM^E *EMP* 776
SIC 0212 2711 5083 5948 Beef cattle except feedlots; Newspapers, publishing & printing; Agricultural machinery; Leather goods, except luggage & shoes
Pr: Robert Underbrink
**CFO:* Bill Gardiner
**CFO:* William J Gardiner
**Ch:* James H Clement Jr
Treas: Tracy Janik
**VP:* Michael Z Rhyne
Oper/Dir: Stephen J Kleberg

D-U-N-S 61-858-8206 IMP/EXP
KING SUPPLY CO LLC
KING ARCHITECTURAL METALS
9611 E R L Thornton Fwy, Dallas, TX 75228-5618
Tel (214) 388-9834 *Founded/Ownrshp* 1990
Sales 129.3MM^E *EMP* 320
SIC 5039 5051 Architectural metalwork; Metals service centers & offices
Pr: Stewart E King
VP: Kathy King
**VP:* Kathy Walker

KING SYSTEMS
See AMBU INC

D-U-N-S 96-101-2978
KING TELESERVICES LLC
48 Wall St Fl 23, New York, NY 10005-2922
Tel (718) 238-7924 *Founded/Ownrshp* 1996
Sales 43.7MM^E *EMP* 1,500
SIC 7389 Brokers' services

D-U-N-S 17-847-5638
KING VENTURE INC
BURGER KING
17800 N Laurel Park Dr, Livonia, MI 48152-3985
Tel (248) 357-6182 *Founded/Ownrshp* 1981
Sales 130.2MM^E *EMP* 3,200
SIC 5812 Fast-food restaurant, chain
Pr: Mark S Schostak
CFO: Ken Stanecki
**Ch:* Alexandre Behring
VP: Paula Goldman-Spinner
VP: Mark London
VP: J M McFee
VP: Lori Schechter
**VP:* David W Schostak
Software D: David Johns

D-U-N-S 11-511-4654 IMP
KINGMAN HOSPITAL INC
KINGMAN REGIONAL MEDICAL CENTE
3269 N Stockton Hill Rd, Kingman, AZ 86409-3619
Tel (928) 757-2101 *Founded/Ownrshp* 1980
Sales 277.5MM *EMP* 1,300
Accts Bkd Llp Colorado Springs Co
SIC 8062 General medical & surgical hospitals
CEO: Brian Turney
**Pr:* Pat Shook
COO: Eileen Pressler
Bd of Dir: Barbara Merritt
VP: Lisa Dreer
**VP:* Judy Stahl
Dir Inf Cn: Debbie Demarce
Dir Risk M: Karol Collison
Dir Lab: Michael Oursler
Dir Lab: Roger Rasmussen
Assoc Dir: Sandy Savage

KINGMAN REGIONAL MEDICAL CENTE
See KINGMAN HOSPITAL INC

D-U-N-S 14-473-2554 IMP/EXP
KINGPIN HOLDINGS LLC
10 S Wacker Dr Ste 3175, Chicago, IL 60606-7407
Tel (312) 876-1275 *Founded/Ownrshp* 2003
Sales 87.1MM^E *EMP* 8,841
SIC 7933 Duck pin center

D-U-N-S 61-929-9709
KINGPIN INTERMEDIATE CORP
(*Suby of* KINGPIN HOLDINGS LLC) ★
10 S Wacker Dr, Chicago, IL 60606-7453
Tel (312) 876-1275 *Founded/Ownrshp* 2004
Sales 344.0M *EMP* 8,841
SIC 7933 Duck pin center
Pr: Thomas J Formolo
CFO: Stephen D Satterwhite
VP: Richard A Lobo

D-U-N-S 96-615-4887
KINGS BAY SERVICES GROUP LLC
3755 S Cptl Of Tx Hwy # 35, Austin, TX 78704-8810
Tel (931) 241-1183 *Founded/Ownrshp* 2011
Sales 950.0M *EMP* 1,100
SIC 7349 Janitorial service, contract basis

D-U-N-S 19-353-7008
KINGS COUNTY OFFICE OF EDUCATION
1144 W Lacey Blvd, Hanford, CA 93230-5956
Tel (559) 589-7026 *Founded/Ownrshp* 1942
Sales NA *EMP* 1,468
Accts Borchardt Corona & Faeth Fre
SIC 9411 County supervisor of education, except school board
**Bd of Dir:* John Boogaard
**Bd of Dir:* William Gundaker
**Bd of Dir:* Joe Hammond
**Bd of Dir:* Larella Howe
**Bd of Dir:* Jim Kilner
IT Man: Jamie Dial
IT Man: Corryne Montgomery
IT Man: Kim Spicer
IT Man: Natalie Wilson
Sys Mgr: Karen Sherwood

KINGS DAUGHTERS HEALTH
See BETHANY CIRCLE OF KINGS DAUGHTERS OF MADISON INDIANA INC

D-U-N-S 07-930-2762
KINGS DAUGHTERS HEALTH SYSTEM INC
2201 Lexington Ave, Ashland, KY 41101-2843
Tel (606) 408-4000 *Founded/Ownrshp* 2010
Sales 465.2MM^E *EMP* 4,200^E
Accts Baker Tilly Virchow Krause Llp
SIC 8062 General medical & surgical hospitals
CEO: Fred Jackson
**Treas:* Jeff Treasure

KING'S DAUGHTERS HOSPITAL
See SCOTT & WHITE MEMORIAL HOSPITAL

KING'S DAUGHTERS' MEDICAL CENT
See PORTSMOUTH HOSPITAL CORP

D-U-N-S 11-038-5262
KINGS DAUGHTERS MEDICAL CENTER
2201 Lexington Ave, Ashland, KY 41101-2843
Tel (606) 408-4000 *Founded/Ownrshp* 2002
Sales 82.6MM *EMP* 1,437^E
SIC 8062 General medical & surgical hospitals
Pr: Fred Jackson
Pr: Ron Henson
Chf Mktg O: Elaine Corbitt
VP: Philip Fioret
VP: Larry Higgins
VP: Rob Walters
Exec: Lisa Reynolds
Dir Risk M: Cherene Fannin
Dir Lab: Donna Flocker
Dir Rad: Robert Penkava
Dir Rad: Alvin Schwarz

KING'S DAUGHTERS MEDICAL CTR
See ASHLAND HOSPITAL CORP

D-U-N-S 08-025-2723
■ **KINGS DOMINION LLC**
(*Suby of* CEDAR FAIR LP) ★
1 Cedar Point Dr, Sandusky, OH 44870-5259
Tel (419) 626-0830 *Founded/Ownrshp* 2016
Sales 3.2MM^E *EMP* 3,009^E
SIC 7996 Amusement parks

KINGS ELECTRONICS
See WINCHESTER ELECTRONICS CORP

KING'S FISH HOUSE
See UNIVERSITY RESTAURANT GROUP INC

D-U-N-S 01-813-7539
KINGS FORD INC
9555 Kings Auto Mall Rd, Cincinnati, OH 45249-8309
Tel (513) 683-0220 *Founded/Ownrshp* 1979
Sales 90.0MM *EMP* 75
SIC 5511

D-U-N-S 08-110-7745
KINGS HAWAIIAN HOLDING CO INC
19161 Harborgate Way, Torrance, CA 90501-1316
Tel (310) 755-7100 *Founded/Ownrshp* 1996
Sales 144.0MM^E *EMP* 278
SIC 2051 5812 Bread, all types (white, wheat, rye, etc): fresh or frozen; Restaurant, family: independent
Pr: Mark Taira
**Sec:* Leatrice Taira
VP: Luis Cupajita
VP: Rich Fitzgerald
**VP:* Curtis Taira

D-U-N-S 60-423-0263 IMP
KINGS SEAFOOD CO LLC
555 EAST
3185 Airway Ave Ste J, Costa Mesa, CA 92626-4601
Tel (310) 451-4595 *Founded/Ownrshp* 2005
Sales 81.0MM^E *EMP* 1,500^E
SIC 5812 Seafood restaurants
Pr: A Samuel King
**COO:* Rj Thomas
**CFO:* Roger Doan
Genl Mgr: Hollie Azevedo
Genl Mgr: Jeff Brower
Genl Mgr: Michelle Corley
Genl Mgr: Justin Dickens
Genl Mgr: Cindy Farrant
Genl Mgr: David Petty
Mktg Mgr: Matt Foley

D-U-N-S 00-787-5354 IMP
KINGS SUPER MARKETS INC
(*Suby of* KB HOLDING, INC.)
700 Lanidex Plz Ste 2, Parsippany, NJ 07054-2705
Tel (973) 463-6300 *Founded/Ownrshp* 1936, 2016
Sales 363.8MM^E *EMP* 2,500
SIC 5411 Supermarkets, chain
Ch Bd: Judith Spires
**Pr:* Richard Durante
**CFO:* Patrick Dentato
**Ex VP:* Fred Brohm
Exec: Jennifer Keane
Genl Mgr: Cheryl Goode
Sls Mgr: Tony Ruccio

D-U-N-S 06-829-8306
KINGSBROOK JEWISH MEDICAL CENTER INC (NY)
585 Schenectady Ave Ste 2, Brooklyn, NY 11203-1809
Tel (718) 604-5000 *Founded/Ownrshp* 1926
Sales 218.4MM *EMP* 2,100
SIC 8062 General medical & surgical hospitals
CEO: Linda Brady
COO: Harold McDonald
CFO: John Schmitt
S&M/VP: Clare Small

D-U-N-S 15-370-7620 IMP/EXP
KINGSBURG APPLE PACKERS INC
KINGSBURG ORCHARDS
10363 Davis Ave, Kingsburg, CA 93631-9539
Tel (559) 897-5132 *Founded/Ownrshp* 1984
Sales 137.3MM^E *EMP* 450
SIC 5148 Fruits, fresh
Pr: George H Jackson
**Treas:* Colleen Jackson

KINGSBURG CENTER
See SUNBRIDGE CARE ENTERPRISES WEST LLC

KINGSBURG ORCHARDS
See KINGSBURG APPLE PACKERS INC

D-U-N-S 00-321-8294 IMP
KINGSDOWN INC
126 W Holt St, Mebane, NC 27302-2622
Tel (919) 563-3531 *Founded/Ownrshp* 1904
Sales 103.9MM *EMP* 330
SIC 2515 Mattresses, innerspring or box spring; Box springs, assembled
Pr: Frank Hood
Pr: David Kresser
Pr: Lance McElreath
Ex VP: Damewood Kevin
**Sr VP:* Joe Schmoeller
VP: Scott Cecil
VP: Cindy McIntyre
Genl Mgr: Mike Shoe
CIO: Ken Creager
VP Mfg: John Farnham
VP Mfg: Abdul Majid

D-U-N-S 06-464-1798 IMP
■ **KINGSFORD PRODUCTS CO LLC**
(*Suby of* CLOROX CO) ★
1221 Broadway Ste 1300, Oakland, CA 94612-2072
Tel (510) 271-7000 *Founded/Ownrshp* 1973
Sales 144.0MM^E *EMP* 684
SIC 2861 2099 2035 2033 2879 Charcoal, except activated; Dressings, salad: dry mixes; Dressings, salad: raw & cooked (except dry mixes); Barbecue sauce: packaged in cans, jars, etc.; Insecticides, agricultural or household
Pr: Richard T Conti
**Pr:* A W Biebl
**CFO:* Karen Rose
**Treas:* L L Hoover
**VP:* B C Blewett

D-U-N-S 06-808-6529
KINGSLEY CONSTRUCTORS INC
25250 Borough Park Dr # 106, Spring, TX 77380-3565
Tel (281) 363-1979 *Founded/Ownrshp* 1976
Sales 88.3MM^E *EMP* 220^E
SIC 1623 1611 Underground utilities contractor; General contractor, highway & street construction
Pr: J D Kingsley Sr
**Sec:* Tawna H Kingsley
VP: Brad Kingssley

KINGSPAN - ASI
See KINGSPAN INSULATED PANELS INC

D-U-N-S 06-785-6211 IMP/EXP
KINGSPAN INSULATED PANELS INC
KINGSPAN - ASI
(*Suby of* KINGSPAN INSULATED PANELS LTD)
726 Summerhill Dr, Deland, FL 32724-2021
Tel (386) 626-6789 *Founded/Ownrshp* 1987
Sales 131.9MM^E *EMP* 440^E
SIC 3448 Prefabricated metal buildings
Pr: Russell Shiels
**VP:* Ilhan Eser
**VP:* Carlo Vezza

KINGSTON CITY SCHOOLS CNSLD
See CITY SCHOOL DISTRICT KINGSTON NY

D-U-N-S 61-175-6065
KINGSTON HEALTHCARE CO
KINGSTON RESIDENCE
1 Seagate Ste 1960, Toledo, OH 43604-1592
Tel (419) 247-2880 *Founded/Ownrshp* 1989
Sales 95.5MM *EMP* 565
Accts William Vaughan Company Maume
SIC 8059 8741 Nursing home, except skilled & intermediate care facility; Personal care home, with health care; Nursing & personal care facility management
Pr: M George Rumman
**Treas:* Larry A Nirschl
**VP:* Kent Libbe
Ex Dir: Joanna Hunter
Rgnl Mgr: Beth Connors
Rgnl Mgr: Becky Housman
QA Dir: Travis Grasley
Pr Dir: Colleen Doyle
Mktg Mgr: Amy Peters
Nrsg Dir: Rachel Mamere
HC Dir: Kristen Cooksey
Board of Directors: Bruce Dukeman, Bruce G Thompson, F D Wolfe

KINGSTON RESIDENCE
See KINGSTON HEALTHCARE CO

D-U-N-S 19-781-9683 IMP/EXP
KINGSTON TECHNOLOGY CO INC
(*Suby of* KINGSTON TECHNOLOGY CORP) ★
17600 Newhope St, Fountain Valley, CA 92708-4220
Tel (714) 435-2600 *Founded/Ownrshp* 1987
Sales 613.6MM^E *EMP* 4,000
SIC 3577

D-U-N-S 80-122-2238 IMP
KINGSTON TECHNOLOGY CORP
17600 Newhope St, Fountain Valley, CA 92708-4298
Tel (714) 445-3495 *Founded/Ownrshp* 1987
Sales 825.5MM^E *EMP* 4,150
SIC 3674 Semiconductors & related devices
CEO: John Tu
VP: Samson Gong
**Prin:* David Leong
**Prin:* David Sun
Dist Mgr: Daniel Reilly
QA Dir: Diep MAI

Dir IT: Sal Maciel
Software D: Karen O'Bryan
Art Dir: Marion Strupp

D-U-N-S 01-146-4133
KINGSWAY CHARITIES INC (VA)
1119 Commonwealth Ave, Bristol, VA 24201-2629
Tel (276) 466-3014 *Founded/Ownrshp* 1993
Sales 189.6MM *EMP* 9
Accts Brown Edwards & Company Ll
SIC 8699 Charitable organization
Ch Bd: John Gregory

D-U-N-S 03-758-1167
KINGWOOD MEDICAL CENTER
22999 Highway 59 N # 134, Kingwood, TX 77339-4449
Tel (281) 348-8000 *Founded/Ownrshp* 1996
Sales 256.3MM *EMP* 1,200
SIC 8011 Medical centers
CEO: Melinda Stephenson

KINNEY
See FOOT LOCKER RETAIL INC

KINNEY DRUGS
See KPH HEALTHCARE SERVICES INC

KINNEY PARKING
See KINNEY SYSTEM INC

D-U-N-S 07-523-1852
■ **KINNEY SYSTEM INC**
KINNEY PARKING
(*Suby of* CENTRAL PARKING CORP) ★
60 Madison Ave Fl 7, New York, NY 10010-1600
Tel (212) 889-2056 *Founded/Ownrshp* 1998
Sales 24.5MM^E *EMP* 1,800
SIC 7521 8742 Parking lots; Parking garage; Industry specialist consultants
Pr: James H Bond
**CFO:* Stephen A Tisdell
Ex VP: Daniel Stark
MIS Dir: Anna Guidone
**MIS Dir:* Lewis Katz
MIS Dir: Charles Monteleone
Opers Mgr: Sylvia Rios

D-U-N-S 13-088-9033 IMP
KINPLEX CORP
200 Heartland Blvd, Edgewood, NY 11717-8380
Tel (631) 242-4800 *Founded/Ownrshp* 1984
Sales 93.5MM^E *EMP* 353
SIC 3589 Commercial cooking & foodwarming equipment
Pr: Penny Hunter
**VP:* Daniel Schwartz

D-U-N-S 01-257-4513
■ **KINRAY INC**
(*Suby of* CARDINAL HEALTH INC) ★
15235 10th Ave, Whitestone, NY 11357-1233
Tel (718) 767-1234 *Founded/Ownrshp* 2010
Sales 221.8MM^E *EMP* 1,000
SIC 5122 Drugs & drug proprietaries; Druggists' sundries
Ch Bd: Michael C Kaufmann
**Pr:* Stewart Rahr
Ex VP: Tom Pelizza
Exec: Bruce Geller
Exec: Joann Santarelli
Exec: Jeffrey Smith
Software D: Eugene Senderovich
Manager: Joe Caccavale
Art Dir: Jason Callori

D-U-N-S 03-875-5232 IMP
■ **KINRO MANUFACTURING INC**
(*Suby of* STARQUEST PRODUCTS) ★
200 Mmaroneck Ave Ste 301, White Plains, NY 10601
Tel (817) 483-7791 *Founded/Ownrshp* 1997
Sales 130.0MM^E *EMP* 1,250
SIC 3442 Metal doors, sash & trim
Pr: Jason Lippert
**CFO:* Gary McPhail
**VP:* Scott Mereness

D-U-N-S 10-246-8360 IMP
■ **KINRO MANUFACTURING INC**
STARQUEST PRODUCTS
(*Suby of* DREW INDUSTRIES INC) ★
3501 County Road 6 E, Elkhart, IN 46514-7663
Tel (574) 535-1125 *Founded/Ownrshp* 1982
Sales 426.7MM^E *EMP* 2,000
SIC 3442 Screen doors, metal; Screens, window, metal; Storm doors or windows, metal
Pr: Jason Lippert
VP: Tom Beasley
**VP:* Dominic Gattuso
VP: Tom Gattuso
**Prin:* Scott Mereness
Off Mgr: Jenith Kele
MIS Dir: Howard Grainger
Sfty Mgr: Carl Lamb
Plnt Mgr: John Becker

D-U-N-S 80-754-5777 EXP
KINROSS GOLD USA INC
(*Suby of* KINROSS GOLD CORPORATION)
5075 S Syracuse St, Denver, CO 80237-2712
Tel (775) 829-1666 *Founded/Ownrshp* 1993
Sales 794.3MM^E *EMP* 1,573
Accts Deloitte & Touche Llp
SIC 1041 1044 Gold ores; Silver ores
Pr: James Fowler
**Treas:* Brian Penny
**Treas:* P Kristopher Sims
**VP:* Richard Dye
Off Mgr: Ron Law
Cmptr Lab: Cherie Mondragon
Sfty Mgr: Michael Moore
HC Dir: Bob Sweeden

D-U-N-S 19-882-2293
KINSALE HOLDINGS INC
VALIDANT
475 Sansome St Ste 700, San Francisco, CA 94111-3129
Tel (415) 400-2600 *Founded/Ownrshp* 2005
Sales 116.4MM^E *EMP* 250

SIC 5122 Pharmaceuticals
CEO: Brian Healy
**Pr:* Michael Beatrice
VP: Maya Kraft
VP: Helm Siegel
QA Dir: Richard Stonehouse

D-U-N-S 01-515-1186 IMP
KINSLEY CONSTRUCTION INC
KINSLEY MANUFACTURING
2700 Water St, York, PA 17403-9306
Tel (717) 741-3841 *Founded/Ownrshp* 1960
Sales 756.2MM^E *EMP* 1,284
SIC 1541 1542 1611 Industrial buildings, new construction; Warehouse construction; Commercial & office building, new construction; Shopping center construction; Highway & street paving contractor
Ch Bd: Robert A Kinsley
Pr: Jonathan R Kinsley
Treas: Jerry L Caslow
Ex VP: Daniel M Driver
VP: Dennis J Falvey
VP: Patrick A Kinsley
VP: Timothy J Kinsley
VP: Steven Schrum
Dir Bus: Ronnie Brouillard
Rgnl Mgr: Ken Stoutzenberger
CTO: Russ Witmer

KINSLEY MANUFACTURING
See KINSLEY CONSTRUCTION INC

D-U-N-S 17-704-1993 IMP
KINSTON NEUSE CORP
(*Suby of* CROWN LIFT TRUCKS) ★
2000 Dobbs Farm Rd, Kinston, NC 28504-8907
Tel (252) 522-3088 *Founded/Ownrshp* 1987
Sales 114.4MM^E *EMP* 250
SIC 3537 Pallet loaders & unloaders
Pr: James F Dicke III
**Ch Bd:* James Dicke II
**VP:* Bradley Smith
**VP:* Kent W Spille
Exec: Beverly Andrews
Plnt Mgr: Mike Sperati

D-U-N-S 06-193-1689 IMP/EXP
KINTETSU WORLD EXPRESS (USA) INC
(*Suby of* KINTETSU WORLD EXPRESS, INC.)
1 Jericho Plz Ste 100, Jericho, NY 11753-1635
Tel (516) 933-7100 *Founded/Ownrshp* 1969
Sales 220.0MM^E *EMP* 703
SIC 4731 Freight forwarding; Customhouse brokers
CEO: Takashi Chris Bamba
Treas: Nobukazu Tani
**VP:* Luke Nakano
**VP:* Hideto Tazura
**Prin:* Joji Tomiyama
Brnch Mgr: Giancarlo Console
Genl Mgr: Michael Goh
VP Opers: Gerard Berger
Opers Mgr: Tinh Ly
Opers Mgr: Noel Wong
Sls Mgr: Rod Noche

D-U-N-S 08-031-1384
KINZE MANUFACTURING INC
2172 M Ave, Williamsburg, IA 52361-8563
Tel (319) 668-1300 *Founded/Ownrshp* 1965
Sales 89.5MM^E *EMP* 500^E
SIC 3523

D-U-N-S 13-572-1921
KIPP DC
2600 Virginia Ave Nw # 900, Washington, DC 20037-1905
Tel (202) 223-4505 *Founded/Ownrshp* 2000
Sales 106.0MM *EMP* 750
Accts Rsm Us Llp Gaithersburg Md
SIC 8211
Ex Dir: Susan Schaeffler
**Pr:* Allison Fansler
**CFO:* Jane Hoffman

KIPP HOUSTON PUBLIC SCHOOLS
See KIPP INC

D-U-N-S 94-795-0879 IMP
KIPP INC
KIPP HOUSTON PUBLIC SCHOOLS
10711 Kipp Way Dr, Houston, TX 77099-2675
Tel (832) 328-1051 *Founded/Ownrshp* 1995
Sales 125.9MM *EMP* 100^E
Accts Blazek & Vetterling Houston
SIC 8211
Pr: Brian McCabe
**CFO:* John Murphy
Dir Soc: Deanna Sheaffer
Off Mgr: Glenda Castillo
Off Mgr: Adriana Stovall
IT Man: Colleen Dippel
Mktg Mgr: Lupita Talley

D-U-N-S 10-588-9752 IMP/EXP
KIRBY - SMITH MACHINERY INC
6715 W Reno Ave, Oklahoma City, OK 73127-6590
Tel (888) 861-0219 *Founded/Ownrshp* 1983
Sales 321.5MM *EMP* 385
Accts Eidebailly Oklahoma City Okl
SIC 7353 5082 7692 Heavy construction equipment rental; Road construction equipment; General construction machinery & equipment; Welding repair
Pr: Ed Kirby
**VP:* Ben Graham
Brnch Mgr: Bruce Taylor
Div Mgr: Kevin D Phillips
IT Man: JD Young
S&M/Mgr: Glen Townsend
Sales Asso: Todd Coffey

D-U-N-S 00-592-7744 EXP
■ **KIRBY BUILDING SYSTEMS LLC** (TN)
(*Suby of* NUCOR CORP) ★
124 Kirby Dr, Portland, TN 37148-2003
Tel (615) 325-4165 *Founded/Ownrshp* 1957, 2007
Sales 104.1MM^E *EMP* 293
SIC 3448 Prefabricated metal buildings
Genl Mgr: Mark Specht

**Plnt Mgr:* Mike Newton
**Sls Mgr:* Dan Cook

D-U-N-S 02-079-7296 IMP/EXP
▲ **KIRBY CORP**
55 Waugh Dr Ste 1000, Houston, TX 77007-5834
Tel (713) 435-1000 *Founded/Ownrshp* 1921
Sales 2.1MMM *EMP* 3,250^E
Tkr Sym KEX *Exch* NYS
SIC 4449 7699 Intracoastal (freight) transportation; River transportation, except on the St. Lawrence Seaway; Marine engine repair
Pr: David W Grzebinski
**Ch Bd:* Joseph H Pyne
Pr: William G Ivey
Pr: Dorman L Strahan
CFO: C Andrew Smith
Treas: Renato A Castro
Ex VP: Mel R Jodeit
Ex VP: Andrew Smith
Ex VP: Steven Valerius
Sr VP: Joseph H Reniers
VP: Gregory Culp
VP: Ronald A Dragg
VP: James F Farley
VP: Charles R Ferrer
VP: Stephen Holcomb
VP: David R Mosley
Dir Risk M: Alton Peralta
Board of Directors: Richard J Alario, Barry E Davis, C Sean Day, Monte J Miller, Richard R Stewart, William M Waterman

D-U-N-S 02-538-5568
KIRBY FOODS INC
IGA
8745 W Higgins Rd, Chicago, IL 60631-2704
Tel (217) 352-2600 *Founded/Ownrshp* 2001
Sales 127.6MM^E *EMP* 950
SIC 5411

D-U-N-S 00-793-1223 IMP
■ **KIRBY INLAND MARINE LP**
(*Suby of* KIRBY CORP) ★
55 Waugh Dr Ste 1000, Houston, TX 77007-5834
Tel (713) 435-1000 *Founded/Ownrshp* 1948, 1969
Sales 170.6MM^E *EMP* 1,950
SIC 4449 Intracoastal (freight) transportation
Mng Pt: William Ivey
Mng Pt: Joseph H Pyne
Mng Pt: Carl Whitlach
Ex VP: James C Guidry
Ex VP: William G Ivey
Ex VP: Mel R Jodeit
Ex VP: Norman Nolen
VP: Ronald C Dansby

D-U-N-S 62-142-3987
■ **KIRBY OFFSHORE MARINE LLC**
(*Suby of* KIRBY CORP) ★
55 Waugh Dr Ste 1000, Houston, TX 77007-5834
Tel (713) 435-1000 *Founded/Ownrshp* 2011
Sales 706.5MM^E *EMP* 992^E
SIC 5172 4212 4213 Petroleum products; Petroleum haulage, local; Liquid petroleum transport, non-local
Genl Pt: Timothy J Casey
Pt: Richard P Falcinelli
Pt: Terrence P Gill
Pt: Gregory J Haslinsky
Pt: Thomas M Sullivan
Dir IT: John Carl

D-U-N-S 00-175-3755 IMP
KIRBY RISK CORP
KIRBY RISK ELECTRICAL SUPPLY
1815 Sagamore Pkwy N, Lafayette, IN 47904-1765
Tel (765) 448-4567 *Founded/Ownrshp* 1926
Sales 401.3MM *EMP* 950
Accts Bkd Llp Indianapolis In
SIC 5063 7694 3599 3679 3629 Electrical supplies; Electric motor repair; Machine shop, jobbing & repair; Harness assemblies for electronic use: wire or cable; Capacitors, fixed or variable
Pr: James K Risk III
**CFO:* Jason J Bricker
CFO: Jason Bricker
VP: Doug Gutridge
Area Mgr: Jon Davis
CTO: Todd Jackson
Dir IT: Scott Davis
IT Man: Lesley Macdowall
Mtls Mgr: Diane Lantz
Plnt Mgr: John Mack
Plnt Mgr: Jim Smith
Board of Directors: Robert B Truitt

KIRBY RISK ELECTRICAL SUPPLY
See KIRBY RISK CORP

D-U-N-S 80-968-1369 IMP/EXP
KIRBY SALES CO INC
1920 W 114th St, Cleveland, OH 44102-2344
Tel (216) 228-2400 *Founded/Ownrshp* 1923
Sales 120.7MM^E *EMP* 500
SIC 3635 Household vacuum cleaners
Pr: Mike Nichols
**VP:* H K Bell
VP: William Bell
VP: Tina Yurek
**Prin:* Bud Miley
Dept Mgr: Tom Tibbits
MIS Dir: Anthony Morris
IT Man: Joseph Gardner
Opers Mgr: Michael Rowan
Mktg Mgr: Laura Winkelmann

KIRBY VACUUM CLEANER
See SCOTT FETZER CO

KIRCHHFF-CNSIGLI CNSTR MGT LLC
See CONSIGLI CONSTRUCTION NY LLC

KIRCHMAN BROTHERS
See STAFFORD-SMITH INC

D-U-N-S 06-311-1405
KIRKHILL AIRCRAFT PARTS CO
KAPCO GLOBAL
3120 Enterprise St, Brea, CA 92821-6236
Tel (714) 223-5400 *Founded/Ownrshp* 1972

Sales 221.5MM^E *EMP* 300
SIC 5088 3728 Aircraft & parts; Aircraft parts & equipment
Pr: Andrew Todhunter
Pr: John Valentine
VP: Ron Basbas
VP: Lynann Collins
VP: Pete Curti
VP: Hector Sardinas
VP: John Valantine
VP: Terry Vieira
Assoc Dir: Cesar Chaves
Dir Bus: Jim Kuwik
Mng Dir: Paul Ferri

D-U-N-S 00-825-5168 IMP
■ KIRKHILL-TA CO
(*Suby of* ESTERLINE TECHNOLOGIES CORP) ★
300 E Cypress St, Brea, CA 92821-4007
Tel (714) 529-4901 *Founded/Ownrshp* 1919
Sales 267.5MM^E *EMP* 1,100
SIC 3069 Reclaimed rubber & specialty rubber compounds
Pr: Richard B Lawrence
**CEO:* Michael R Johnson
**VP:* Rick Gentle
**VP:* Steve Lautenschlager
VP: Larry Pierce
**VP:* Jim Sweeney
Dir IT: Lester Fountain
Dir IT: Ali Sarhangpour
Ql Cn Mgr: Kenneth Kaler

D-U-N-S 06-861-3447
KIRKLAND & ELLIS LLP
300 N La Salle Dr # 2400, Chicago, IL 60654-5412
Tel (312) 862-2000 *Founded/Ownrshp* 1920, 1968
Sales 539.6MM^E *EMP* 2,400
SIC 8111 General practice attorney, lawyer; General practice law office
Pt: Robert B Ellis
Pt: Greg S Arovas
Pt: Eugene F Assaf
Pt: David A Breach
Pt: Richard M Cieri
Pt: Mark Filip
Pt: Michael P Foradas
Pt: David Fox
Pt: Richard C Godfrey
Pt: Jay P Lefkowitz
Pt: Linda K Myers
Pt: Stephen L Richie
Pt: James H M Sprayregen
Pt: Matthew E Steinmetz
Pt: Graham White
CFO: Christian Cooley
**CFO:* Nicholas J Willmott
**Ch:* Jeffrey C Hammes
Treas: Jeff Hohner
Exec: Gregg Kirchhoefer
Assoc Dir: Myroslawa Bojczuk

D-U-N-S 03-042-5250
▲ KIRKLANDS INC
5310 Maryland Way, Brentwood, TN 37027-5091
Tel (615) 872-4800 *Founded/Ownrshp* 1966
Sales 561.8MM *EMP* 6,821^E
Tkr Sym KIRK *Exch* NGS
SIC 5999 5947 Art, picture frames & decorations; Gift shop
Pr: W Michael Madden
**Ch Bd:* R Wilson Orr III
Treas: Ashley Deffenbaugh
Ofcr: Adam C Holland
Ex VP: Michelle R Graul
VP: Karla Q Calderon
VP: Anthony J Debruno
VP: James W Harris
VP: Philip H Rogers
Store Mgr: Jason Baril
Store Mgr: Vicki Beaver
Board of Directors: Robert E Alderson, Steven J Collins, Carl T Kirkland, Miles T Kirkland, Susan S Lanigan, Jeffrey C Owen

KIRKLIN CLINIC
See UNIVERSITY OF ALABAMA HEALTH SERVICES FOUNDATION PC

D-U-N-S 87-804-7943
KIRKWOOD COMMUNITY COLLEGE FOUNDATION
6301 Kirkwood Blvd Sw, Cedar Rapids, IA 52404-5260
Tel (319) 398-5411 *Founded/Ownrshp* 1966
Sales 3.6MM *EMP* 1,750
Accts Mcgladrey Llp Cedar Rapids I
SIC 8222 Community college
Pr: Steve Caves
**Treas:* George Grask
**Treas:* Lois Nanke
**VP:* John Bloomhall
VP: Jim Choate
VP: Kathy Hall
VP: Bill Lamb
**Ex Dir:* Rick Anderson
Ex Dir: Al Rowe
Ex Dir: Dawn Wood
Prgrm Mgr: Dale Monroe

D-U-N-S 08-678-6738
KIRKWOOD R-VII SCHOOL DISTRICT
11289 Manchester Rd, Saint Louis, MO 63122-1122
Tel (314) 213-6100 *Founded/Ownrshp* 1863
Sales 84.2MM *EMP* 683
Accts Schowalter & Jabouri Pc St
SIC 8211 Public elementary & secondary schools
Off Admin: Mary Hart
Schl Brd P: Matt Cottler

KIRLIN'S HALLMARK
See KIRLINS INC

D-U-N-S 02-577-0199 IMP
KIRLINS INC
KIRLIN'S HALLMARK
532 Maine St, Quincy, IL 62301-3932
Tel (217) 222-0813 *Founded/Ownrshp* 1948
Sales 54.7MM *EMP* 1,600
Accts Danielle M Fleer Quincy Ill
SIC 5947 Greeting cards
Ch Bd: Dale Kirlin Jr
**Pr:* Gary Kirlin
Site Mgr: Mary Durbin

D-U-N-S 96-804-2361
KIRSCHENMAN ENTERPRISES SALES LP
12826 Edison Hwy, Edison, CA 93220
Tel (661) 366-5736 *Founded/Ownrshp* 2009
Sales 100.0MM *EMP* 300
SIC 7389 Brokers, business: buying & selling business enterprises
Genl Pt: Wayde Kirschenman

D-U-N-S 18-181-5424
KIRSHENBAUM BOND SENECAL & PARTNERS LLC
KB CREATIVE NETWORK
160 Varick St Fl 4, New York, NY 10013-1273
Tel (646) 336-9400 *Founded/Ownrshp* 2013
Sales 84.6MM^E *EMP* 350
Accts Stephen M Smith & Company Llc
SIC 7311 Advertising agencies
CEO: Lori Senecal
Mng Pt: Stephen Fick
Pr: Robin D Hafitz
CFO: Chris Mozolewski
**Ch:* Richard Kirshenbaum
Chf Mktg O: Bill Grogan
VP: Lisa Zakarin
Assoc Dir: Michael King
Creative D: Mike Abell
Creative D: Michael Craven
Creative D: Isidoro Debellis
Creative D: Kevin Gentile
Creative D: Jonah Levine
Creative D: Kathi Stark
Creative D: Nic Wehmeyer

D-U-N-S 94-337-6277 IMP/EXP
KIRTLAND CAPITAL PARTNERS LP
K C P
3201 Entp Pkwy Ste 200, Beachwood, OH 44122
Tel (216) 593-0100 *Founded/Ownrshp* 1992
Sales 237.5MM^E *EMP* 998^E
SIC 5051 3312 3498 3494 3492 3317 Metals service centers & offices; Tubes, steel & iron; Fabricated pipe & fittings; Valves & pipe fittings; Fluid power valves & hose fittings; Steel pipe & tubes
Pt: Corrie Menary
VP: Corrine Menary

D-U-N-S 09-268-0222
KISATCHIE CORP
9258 Highway 84, Winnfield, LA 71483-7560
Tel (318) 628-4116 *Founded/Ownrshp* 1978
Sales 29.4MM^E *EMP* 1,100
SIC 8741 Nursing & personal care facility management
Pr: Teddy R Price

D-U-N-S 07-458-5795
KISHWAUKEE COMMUNITY HOSPITAL
GREEN LEAF GIFT SHOP
(*Suby of* KISHHEALTH SYSTEM)
1 Kish Hospital Dr, Dekalb, IL 60115-9602
Tel (815) 756-1521 *Founded/Ownrshp* 1970
Sales 165.1MM *EMP* 150^E
SIC 8062 General medical & surgical hospitals
COO: Bhagavatlal Morker
**CFO:* Loren Foelske
Ansthlgy: Mark A Nessim

D-U-N-S 86-738-3606
KISSICK CONSTRUCTION CO INC
8131 Indiana Ave, Kansas City, MO 64132-2507
Tel (816) 363-5530 *Founded/Ownrshp* 1994
Sales 98.3MM^E *EMP* 200
SIC 1541 1623 1771 1794 Industrial buildings, new construction; Water, sewer & utility lines; Concrete work; Excavation & grading, building construction
Pr: Jim Kissick
**VP:* Pete Browne
VP Opers: Dennis Richardson
Mtls Mgr: Rick White

D-U-N-S 18-739-8797
KISSIMMEE UTILITY AUTHORITY (INC)
1701 W Carroll St, Kissimmee, FL 34741-6804
Tel (407) 933-7777 *Founded/Ownrshp* 1985
Sales 299.7MM^E *EMP* 300
Accts Purvis Gray & Company Gainesv
SIC 4911 Electric services
Pr: James C Welsh
Pr: Cindy Herrera
CFO: Lisa Davis
Treas: Michelle Daboin
Bd of Dir: Kathleen Thacker
Ofcr: Scott Reaves
**VP:* Kenneth L Davis
**VP:* Chris Gent
**VP:* Jeffery S Gray
**VP:* Wilbur Hill
VP: Brian Horton
**VP:* Joseph Hostetlar
VP: Susan Postans

KISTLER-OBRIEN FIRE PROTECTION
See GEO W KISTLER INC

D-U-N-S 60-438-4164 IMP
KISWIRE PINE BLUFF INC
(*Suby of* KISWIRE LTD.)
5100 Industrial Dr S, Pine Bluff, AR 71602-3109
Tel (870) 247-2444 *Founded/Ownrshp* 2014
Sales 108.4MM^E *EMP* 300
SIC 3312 2296 Wire products, steel or iron; Steel tire cords & tire cord fabrics
CEO: Mike Morris
**Pr:* David Minnick
**Sec:* Beverly Barrett
Plnt Mgr: Nicholas Boyan
Plnt Mgr: Charley Chen

KIT PAK
See PACKAGING UNLIMITED LLC

D-U-N-S 07-883-0302
■ KIT ZELLER INC
(*Suby of* KAMAN INDUSTRIAL TECHNOLOGIES CORP) ★
1000 University Ave # 800, Rochester, NY 14607-1286
Tel (585) 254-8840 *Founded/Ownrshp* 2012
Sales 235.4MM^E *EMP* 200
SIC 5063 Electrical apparatus & equipment
Pr: Steve Snidler
**Sr VP:* Dary Haseley
VP Opers: Joe Bertalli
Sales Asso: Dwight Roth

D-U-N-S 18-112-7358
KITCHELL CONTRACTORS INC OF ARIZONA
(*Suby of* KITCHELL CORP) ★
1707 E Highland Ave # 200, Phoenix, AZ 85016-4640
Tel (602) 264-4411 *Founded/Ownrshp* 1950
Sales 102.7MM^E *EMP* 472
SIC 1541 1542 1521 Industrial buildings, new construction; Commercial & office building, new construction; Specialized public building contractors; Single-family housing construction

D-U-N-S 00-901-0984
KITCHELL CORP (AZ)
1707 E Highland Ave # 100, Phoenix, AZ 85016-4668
Tel (602) 264-4411 *Founded/Ownrshp* 1962
Sales 822.7MM^E *EMP* 946
Accts Mayer Hoffman Mccann Pc Ph
SIC 1542 1541 1521 8711 5078 6552 Commercial & office building, new construction; Specialized public building contractors; Industrial buildings, new construction; Single-family housing construction; Engineering services; Refrigeration equipment & supplies; Subdividers & developers
Pr: Jim Swanson
**Ch:* William C Schubert
**Treas:* William J Judge
**VP:* Jeffrey W Allen
**VP:* Russell A Fox
**VP:* Mark J Pendelton

KITCHEN AND BATH GALLERY
See SUPPLY NEW ENGLAND INC

D-U-N-S 08-153-7912 IMP
■ KITCHEN COLLECTION LLC
LE GOURMET CHEF
(*Suby of* NACCO INDUSTRIES INC) ★
71 E Water St, Chillicothe, OH 45601-2577
Tel (740) 773-9150 *Founded/Ownrshp* 2011
Sales 1.2MMM^E *EMP* 2,487
Accts Mcgladrey & Pullen
SIC 5719 Kitchenware
CEO: Greg Trepp
Treas: L J Kennedy
VP: Carla Ison
VP: Roger Metzger
VP: Randy Sklenar
VP: Robert Strenski
Rgnl Mgr: Daniel Russeau
Dir IT: Conrad Dana
IT Man: Mark Gawelek

KITCHEN FACTOR , THE
See EAST HAVEN BUILDERS SUPPLY - US LBM LLC

D-U-N-S 78-475-1067
■ KITCHENAID INC
(*Suby of* MAYTAG APPLIANCES) ★
101 E Maple St, Canton, OH 44720-2517
Tel (330) 499-9200 *Founded/Ownrshp* 1989
Sales 518.7MM^E *EMP* 16,700^E
SIC 5064 Electric household appliances
Ch Bd: Leonard A Hadley
VP: R J Elsaesser
VP: Gregory Puplin
VP Sls: Marty Armstrong

KITCHEN'S SEAFOOD
See TAMPA BAY FISHERIES INC

D-U-N-S 82-756-3631
KITE REALTY GROUP TRUST
30 S Meridian St Ste 1100, Indianapolis, IN 46204-3565
Tel (317) 577-5600 *Founded/Ownrshp* 2004
Sales 347.0MM *EMP* 141^E
Accts Ernst & Young Llp Indianapoli
SIC 6798 Real estate investment trusts
Ch Bd: John A Kite
Pr: Thomas K McGowan
CFO: Daniel R Sink
Trst: Gerald Moss
Ex VP: Scott E Murray
Rgnl Mgr: Brian Hector
Rgnl Mgr: Karly Kilroy
Rgnl Mgr: Daniel Martin
CTO: Alvin Kite
Snr PM: Doug Kirby
Snr PM: Matthew Van Dyke

KITTAY HOUSE
See JEWISH HOME AND HOSPITAL

D-U-N-S 01-642-2016 IMP
KITTLES HOME FURNISHINGS CENTER INC
ETHAN ALLEN GALLERY
8600 Allisonville Rd, Indianapolis, IN 46250-1583
Tel (317) 849-5300 *Founded/Ownrshp* 1969
Sales 161.4MM^E *EMP* 750
SIC 5712 5719 Furniture stores; Bedding & bedsprings; Lighting, lamps & accessories; Pictures & mirrors
Ch Bd: James L Kittle Jr
**Pr:* John F Durkott
**CEO:* Eric Easter
CFO: Lisa Hudak
Off Mgr: Eve Teeters
Dir IT: Thomas Wirt
Site Mgr: Mike Halteman
Site Mgr: Brian Helmerick
Site Mgr: Joy Perkins
Sales Exec: Sara E Graves
Sls&Mrk Ex: Ferd Burgman

D-U-N-S 09-253-1409 IMP/EXP
KITTRICH CORP
1585 W Mission Blvd, Pomona, CA 91766-1233
Tel (714) 736-1000 *Founded/Ownrshp* 1978
Sales 210.1MM^E *EMP* 500
SIC 2591 2392 2381 Blinds vertical; Household furnishings; Fabric dress & work gloves
CEO: Robert Friedland
VP: Jon Klevesahl
Mng Ofcr: Marissa Delasalas
MIS Dir: Walter Kampschuur
Natl Sales: Rico Burgos
Natl Sales: Scott Livingston
Mktg Dir: Gus Lejano
Sls Mgr: Jan Meere
Sls Mgr: Aaron Rose

D-U-N-S 13-754-3369 IMP/EXP
KITZ CORP OF AMERICA
(*Suby of* KITZ CORPORATION)
10750 Corporate Dr, Stafford, TX 77477-4008
Tel (281) 491-7333 *Founded/Ownrshp* 1984
Sales 85.0MM *EMP* 38
Accts Hein & Associates Llp Housto
SIC 5085 Valves & fittings
Pr: James Walther
**Ch:* Hirofumi Fujhara
VP: Darrell Lueckemeyer
Ex Dir: Hideki Ozawa
Div Mgr: Eric Olson

D-U-N-S 00-979-7333
KJELLSTROM AND LEE INC
1607 Ownby Ln, Richmond, VA 23220-1318
Tel (804) 288-0082 *Founded/Ownrshp* 1999
Sales 100.0MM *EMP* 200^E
SIC 1541 1542 Industrial buildings, new construction; Renovation, remodeling & repairs: industrial buildings; Commercial & office building, new construction; Commercial & office buildings, renovation & repair
Pr: Peter S Alcorn
**Ch Bd:* Donald B Garber
**Sr VP:* H Fulton Sensabaugh
**VP:* Roger D Young
**Prin:* N David Kjellstrom
**Prin:* Harry G Lee
Snr PM: David Turner

D-U-N-S 80-625-6132
▲ KKR & CO LP
9 W 57th St Ste 4200, New York, NY 10019-2707
Tel (212) 750-8300 *Founded/Ownrshp* 2007
Sales 1.0MMM *EMP* 1,196^E
Tkr Sym KKR *Exch* NYS
SIC 6282 6799 Investment advice; Manager of mutual funds, contract or fee basis; Venture capital companies
Ch Bd: Henry R Kravis
Genl Pt: KKR M LLC
Genl Pt: Paul Raether
Ch Bd: George R Roberts
VP: Aidan Bailey
VP: Joanne Casey
VP: Cecelia Gilroy
VP: Samir Shah
Mng Dir: Saleena R Goel
Mng Dir: Gary Jacobs
Mng Dir: David Liu

D-U-N-S 80-031-8599
■ KKR FINANCIAL HOLDINGS LLC
(*Suby of* KKR FUND HOLDINGS LP) ★
555 California St Fl 50, San Francisco, CA 94104-1701
Tel (415) 315-3620 *Founded/Ownrshp* 2014
Sales 375.2MM *EMP* 4^E
Accts Deloitte & Touche Llp San Fra
Tkr Sym KFH *Exch* NYS
SIC 6798 6282 Mortgage investment trusts; Manager of mutual funds, contract or fee basis
Pr: William J Janetschek
**COO:* Jeffrey B Van Horn
CFO: Thomas N Murphy

D-U-N-S 08-005-4916
■ KKR FUND HOLDINGS LP
(*Suby of* KKR & CO LP) ★
9 W 57th St Fl 41, New York, NY 10019-2701
Tel (212) 230-9742 *Founded/Ownrshp* 2014
Sales 375.2MM^E *EMP* 4^E
SIC 6798 Real estate investment trusts

D-U-N-S 82-632-9364
KKR MILLENNIUM GP LLC
9 W 57th St Ste 4150, New York, NY 10019-2701
Tel (212) 750-8300 *Founded/Ownrshp* 2001
Sales 178.9MM^E *EMP* 4,850
SIC 2515 Mattresses, innerspring or box spring
Pr: Lawrence J Rogers

D-U-N-S 08-042-5533
▲ KKR PRA INVESTORS LP
4130 Parklake Ave Ste 400, Raleigh, NC 27612-4462
Tel (919) 786-8200 *Founded/Ownrshp* 2013
Sales 1.6MMM^E *EMP* 12,000^E
SIC 6722 6726 Management investment, open-end; Management investment funds, closed-end
Pr: Colin Shannon
**CFO:* Linda Baddour

D-U-N-S 01-093-6193 IMP/EXP
▲ KLA-TENCOR CORP (CA)
1 Technology Dr, Milpitas, CA 95035-7916
Tel (408) 875-3000 *Founded/Ownrshp* 1975
Sales 2.9MMM *EMP* 5,580
Tkr Sym KLAC *Exch* NGS
SIC 3827 3825 7699 7629 Optical instruments & lenses; Optical test & inspection equipment; Semiconductor test equipment; Optical instrument repair; Electronic equipment repair
Pr: Richard P Wallace
**Ch Bd:* Edward W Barnholt
CFO: Bren D Higgins
Treas: Vishal Pathak
Ex VP: Ahmad A Khan
Ex VP: Michael D Kirk
Ex VP: Bin-Ming B Tsai
Sr VP: Virendra A Kirloskar

VP: Lance Glasser
Sys Mgr: Gary Taan
Sftwr Eng: Ying Huang
Board of Directors: Robert M Calderoni, John T Dickson, Kevin J Kennedy, Gary B Moore, Robert A Rango, David C Wang

D-U-N-S 80-813-1262
KLAMATH FALLS INTERCOMMUNITY HOSPITAL AUTHORITY
SKYLAKES MEDICAL CENTER
2865 Daggett Ave, Klamath Falls, OR 97601-1106
Tel (541) 883-6150 *Founded/Ownrshp* 1967
Sales NA *EMP* 9
SIC 6162 Bond & mortgage companies
Pr: Paul Stewart
**VP:* Joe Chamberland
**VP:* Leslie Flick
**VP:* Sarah Whities
**VP:* Don York
Ansthlgy: Charles T Gonsowski
Ansthlgy: Vincent D Herr
Ansthlgy: Stefan J Jodko
Ansthlgy: Todd J Kirschenmann
Ansthlgy: John R Pattee
Ansthlgy: Eric B Swetland

D-U-N-S 09-615-5098 IMP
KLAUSSNER CORP (NC)
KLAUSSNER HOME FURNISHINGS
405 Lewallen Rd, Asheboro, NC 27205-6111
Tel (888) 732-5948 *Founded/Ownrshp* 1979
Sales 521.6MM^E *EMP* 2,100
SIC 2512 Upholstered household furniture
Ch Bd: Hans Klaussner
CFO: David O Bryant
Sec: Scott Kauffman
Ex VP: J B Davis
VP: Darren York
VP Mfg: Rick Kite

D-U-N-S 00-347-1463 IMP/EXP
KLAUSSNER FURNITURE INDUSTRIES INC (NC)
KLAUSSNER HOME FURNISHINGS
(*Suby of* KLAUSSNER HOME FURNISHINGS) ★
405 Lewallen Rd, Asheboro, NC 27205-6111
Tel (336) 625-6174 *Founded/Ownrshp* 1964, 2013
Sales 316.7MM^E *EMP* 1,200^E
SIC 2512 Upholstered household furniture
CEO: Bill Wittenberg
**Pr:* Claud William Wittenber
**CFO:* David O Bryant
**Treas:* Scott Kauffman
VP: Len Burke
VP: Jason Neal
CIO: Mike Cook
Plnt Mgr: Glen Kahn

KLAUSSNER HOME FURNISHINGS
See KLAUSSNER FURNITURE INDUSTRIES INC

KLAUSSNER HOME FURNISHINGS
See KLAUSSNER CORP

D-U-N-S 15-691-3998
KLB CONSTRUCTION INC
3405 121st St Sw, Lynnwood, WA 98087-1549
Tel (425) 355-7335 *Founded/Ownrshp* 1984
Sales 88.3MM^E *EMP* 250
SIC 1623 1611 Underground utilities contractor; General contractor, highway & street construction
Pr: Kelly Bosa
**CFO:* Corey Christenson

KLEAN-STRIP
See WM BARR & CO INC

D-U-N-S 16-816-5814 IMP/EXP
KLEEN TEST PRODUCTS CORP
K T P
(*Suby of* MERIDIAN SPECIALTY YARN GROUP) ★
1611 S Sunset Rd, Port Washington, WI 53074-9673
Tel (262) 284-6600 *Founded/Ownrshp* 1943
Sales 134.1MM^E *EMP* 500^E
SIC 2842 2675 Cleaning or polishing preparations; Paper die-cutting
Pr: Bill Ahlborn
Admn Mgr: Nicole Kenehan
IT Man: Foga Zellermayer
Prd Mgr: Patrick Bichler
Ql Cn Mgr: Bob Beffa
Natl Sales: Robert Boyer

D-U-N-S 05-104-3313 EXP
KLEEN-TEX INDUSTRIES INC
101 N Greenwood St Ste C, Lagrange, GA 30240-2632
Tel (706) 882-0111 *Founded/Ownrshp* 1967
Sales 83.5MM^E *EMP* 550
SIC 3069 2273 2392 Sheeting, rubber or rubberized fabric; Mats & matting; Mops, floor & dust
CEO: Bruce Howard
**Sr VP:* Duncan Allen
Sls Mgr: Lee Fox

D-U-N-S 01-275-3299
KLEET LUMBER CO INC
777 Park Ave, Huntington, NY 11743-3993
Tel (631) 427-7060 *Founded/Ownrshp* 1946
Sales 91.4MM^E *EMP* 89
SIC 5031 Lumber, plywood & millwork
Pr: Howard Kleet
Pr: Gene Wolff
**Treas:* Warren Kleet
Chf Mktg O: Jon Bieslien
**VP:* Linda Nussbaum
Exec: Jane Ricci
Store Mgr: Ray Nurnberger
IT Man: William Shultz
Sales Asso: Louis Kleet
Sales Asso: Glenn Landberg
Sales Asso: Tom Legere

D-U-N-S 07-392-2270
KLEIN INDEPENDENT SCHOOL DISTRICT
KLEIN ISD
7200 Spring Cypress Rd, Spring, TX 77379-3215
Tel (832) 249-4000 *Founded/Ownrshp* 1988
Sales 511.4MM *EMP* 5,691
Accts Hereford Lynch Sellars & Kir
SIC 8211 Public elementary school; Public junior high school; Public senior high school
Pr: Steven E Smith
CFO: Tonya Little
Bd of Dir: Jamal Hazzan
Ofcr: Susan Green
VP: Ronnie K Anderson
VP: Lorraine R Pratt
Assoc Dir: Donald Chiu
Comm Man: Denise McLean
Dir Sec: David Kimberly
Brnch Mgr: Bob Grove
Dir IT: Judy Schwietzer

KLEIN ISD
See KLEIN INDEPENDENT SCHOOL DISTRICT

D-U-N-S 00-514-9141 IMP/EXP
KLEIN TOOLS INC
450 Bond St, Lincolnshire, IL 60069-4225
Tel (847) 821-5500 *Founded/Ownrshp* 1958
Sales 341.9MM^E *EMP* 1,000
SIC 3423 3199 Hand & edge tools; Belting for machinery: solid, twisted, flat, etc.: leather; Safety belts, leather
Pr: Thomas R Klein
Pr: Thomas R Klein Jr
CFO: Verne Tuite
Ex VP: John J McDevitt
VP: James Finneman
Dist Mgr: Richard Adinolfi
Dist Mgr: David Inman
Dist Mgr: Dan Pierce
Dist Mgr: Raymond Tormey
Dist Mgr: Vince Waldvogel
Genl Mgr: Ryan Wojtkiewicz

D-U-N-S 60-621-7524
KLEINFELDER ASSOCIATES
(*Suby of* KLEINFELDER GROUP INC) ★
550 W C St Ste 1200, San Diego, CA 92101-3532
Tel (619) 831-4600 *Founded/Ownrshp* 1985
Sales 51.0MM^E *EMP* 1,500
SIC 8748 Environmental consultant
Pr: George J Pierson
**COO:* Bart Patton
**CFO:* John Pilkington
**Sr VP:* Larry Peterson
**VP:* Russ Carey
**CTO:* Russ Erbes
Board of Directors: Craig Vaughn, Rich Young

D-U-N-S 14-470-8682
KLEINFELDER GROUP INC
550 W C St Ste 1200, San Diego, CA 92101-3532
Tel (619) 831-4600 *Founded/Ownrshp* 1985
Sales 258.9MM *EMP* 1,800^E
Accts Grant Thornton Llp San Diego
SIC 8711 Consulting engineer
Pr: George J Pierson
Pr: Sharon Province
CFO: Carl D Lowman
Chf Mktg O: Bart Schubert
VP: Robert Benamati
VP: Timothy Bradley
VP: Suad Cisic
VP: Joe Cormier
VP: Raymond Ferrara
VP: Gary Higashi
VP: Diana Salazar
Dir Lab: Uly Panuncialman

D-U-N-S 04-600-7506
KLEINFELDER INC
(*Suby of* KLEINFELDER GROUP INC) ★
550 W C St Ste 1200, San Diego, CA 92101-3532
Tel (619) 831-4600 *Founded/Ownrshp* 1985
Sales 175.4MM *EMP* 1,800
SIC 8711 8712 Consulting engineer; Architectural engineering
Ch Bd: Kevin Pottmeyer
CFO: Jon Holmgren
**CFO:* Carl Lowman
**VP:* Michael P Kesler
**Prin:* John Moossazaeeh
Genl Mgr: John Moossazadeh
Sales Exec: Lisa Vomero-Inouye

D-U-N-S 00-609-3975 IMP
KLEMENT SAUSAGE CO INC (WI)
(*Suby of* BLUE RIBBON) ★
1036 W Juneau Ave 400, Milwaukee, WI 53233-1447
Tel (414) 744-2330 *Founded/Ownrshp* 1927, 2014
Sales 122.3MM^E *EMP* 355
SIC 2013 Sausages from purchased meat
CEO: Ray Booth
**Pr:* George Lampros
**CFO:* Tom Klement
**Sec:* James W Gustafson
Ex VP: Jack Belke
VP: Steve Feye
VP: Dan Sotski
Rgnl Mgr: Don Treichel
Area Mgr: Don Gordon
Sfty Mgr: Dennis Rousseau
Natl Sales: Pete Aschenbrenner

D-U-N-S 96-884-1494 IMP
KLG USA LLC
20 W King St, Port Jervis, NY 12771-3061
Tel (845) 856-5311 *Founded/Ownrshp* 1996
Sales 183.3MM^E *EMP* 1,000
SIC 2844 7389 2834 Toilet preparations; Packaging & labeling services; Pharmaceutical preparations
Ch Bd: Joseph Healey
**Pr:* Rob Edmonds
COO: James Skelton
Ofcr: Carol Starr
VP: Jack Fallon
VP: Robert Jaegly

D-U-N-S 96-731-5297
KLINGBEIL CAPITAL MANAGEMENT LLC
500 W Wilson Bridge Rd, Worthington, OH 43085-2238
Tel (614) 396-4919 *Founded/Ownrshp* 2000
Sales 137.0MM^E *EMP* 300
SIC 6799 8741 Real estate investors, except property operators; Management services
CEO: James D Klingbeil Jr
VP: Kasey Stevens

D-U-N-S 00-694-2148
KLINGER COMPANIES INC
2015 7th St, Sioux City, IA 51101-2003
Tel (712) 277-3900 *Founded/Ownrshp* 1919
Sales 216.0MM^E *EMP* 600
Accts Henjes Conner & Williams Pc
SIC 1542 1541 Commercial & office building contractors; Industrial buildings, new construction
CEO: John W Gleeson
**CFO:* Jodi A Miller
**Treas:* Robert J Desmidt
Pharmcst: Elliot Paige

D-U-N-S 10-652-2225
KLJ SOLUTIONS CO
4585 Coleman St, Bismarck, ND 58503-0431
Tel (701) 355-8400 *Founded/Ownrshp* 2001
Sales 112.8MM^E *EMP* 780
SIC 8711 8713 Engineering services; Civil engineering; Structural engineering; Electrical or electronic engineering; Surveying services
CEO: Niles Hushka
**Pr:* Gene Jackson
**CFO:* Dean Anagnost
**Sr VP:* Mark Anderson
**Sr VP:* Lanny Harris
**Prin:* Barry Schuchard

D-U-N-S 00-977-9083
KLLM INC
KLLM TRANSPORT SERVICES
(*Suby of* KLLM TRANSPORT SERVICES LLC) ★
135 Riverview Dr, Richland, MS 39218-4401
Tel (601) 932-8616 *Founded/Ownrshp* 1975
Sales 284.5MM^E *EMP* 1,500
SIC 4213 Refrigerated products transport; Trailer or container on flat car (TOFC/COFC)
Pr: James M Richards Jr
COO: Richards James
CFO: Terry Thornton
Ofcr: Mark Lewis
Sr VP: Jim Richards
**VP:* Kirk Blankenship
**VP:* Greg Carpenter
VP: C Clark
VP: Andy Morris
**VP:* Wilson Risinger
VP: Vince Schott
**VP:* Milton Tallant Jr
Exec: Catherine Dennis

KLLM TRANSPORT SERVICES
See KLLM INC

D-U-N-S 04-532-1841
KLLM TRANSPORT SERVICES LLC
135 Riverview Dr, Jackson, MS 39218-4401
Tel (601) 939-2545 *Founded/Ownrshp* 2000
Sales 371.8MM^E *EMP* 1,650
SIC 4213 Trucking, except local; Refrigerated products transport; Trailer or container on flat car (TOFC/COFC)
CEO: James M Richards Jr
Ch Bd: William Liles III
CEO: Jim Richards
CFO: Kevin Adams
CFO: John P Hammonds
VP: Greg Carpenter
VP: David Carter
VP: Milton Tallant Jr

D-U-N-S 95-985-5081 IMP/EXP
KLN ENTERPRISES INC
400 Lakeside Dr, Perham, MN 56573-2202
Tel (218) 346-7000 *Founded/Ownrshp* 1995
Sales 305.4MM^E *EMP* 1,235
SIC 2047 2064 Dog & cat food; Candy & other confectionery products
CEO: Kenneth Nelson
**COO:* Kurt Nelson
**CFO:* Wayne Caughey
CTO: Robert Kinlund
Sls Mgr: Brian Smith

D-U-N-S 06-984-2789 IMP/EXP
KLOCKNER NAMASCO HOLDING CORP
(*Suby of* KLOECKNER & CO USA BETEILIGUNGS GMBH)
500 Colonial Center Pkwy # 500, Roswell, GA 30076-8853
Tel (678) 259-8800 *Founded/Ownrshp* 2011
Sales 2.1MMM^E *EMP* 2,400
SIC 5051 Steel; Aluminum bars, rods, ingots, sheets, pipes, plates, etc.
CEO: Bill Partalis
CFO: Kirk Johnson

D-U-N-S 06-033-6104 IMP/EXP
KLOCKNER PENTAPLAST OF AMERICA INC
(*Suby of* KP INTERNATIONAL HOLDING GMBH)
3585 Kloeckner Rd, Gordonsville, VA 22942-6148
Tel (540) 832-1400 *Founded/Ownrshp* 1982
Sales 482.4MM^E *EMP* 3,247
SIC 3081 4213 Plastic film & sheet; Trucking, except local
Pr: Michael P Ryan
Ch Bd: Wayne Hewett
Treas: Aida Garay
Treas: Eric Sigler
VP: Bob Kramer
VP: Tracy Scott
VP: David Veasey
Genl Mgr: Klaus Huessner
CTO: Steve Henley
MIS Dir: Shawn Wilson
Netwrk Mgr: Lisa Walton

D-U-N-S 10-172-9374 IMP/EXP
KLOCKNER PENTAPLAST PARTICIPATION LLC
3585 Kloeckner Rd, Gordonsville, VA 22942-6148
Tel (540) 832-3600 *Founded/Ownrshp* 2001
Sales NA *EMP* 1,284^E
SIC 3081 4213

D-U-N-S 60-527-1803
KLOCKNER USA HOLDING INC
(*Suby of* KLOCKNER & CO SE)
500 Colonial Center Pkwy # 500, Roswell, GA 30076-8853
Tel (678) 259-8800 *Founded/Ownrshp* 2004
Sales 175.3MM^E *EMP* 1,329
SIC 6799 5051 Investors; Steel
Prin: Bill Partalis

D-U-N-S 79-997-3094 IMP/EXP
KLOECKNER METALS CORP
(*Suby of* KLOCKNER NAMASCO HOLDING CORP) ★
500 Colonial Center Pkwy # 500, Roswell, GA 30076-8853
Tel (678) 259-8800 *Founded/Ownrshp* 1997
Sales 2.1MMM^E *EMP* 2,400
SIC 5051 Ferrous metals; Nonferrous metal sheets, bars, rods, etc.; Metal wires, ties, cables & screening
**CFO:* Kirk Johnson
Ofcr: Jeffrey Friedman
VP: Jason Albro
VP: Clarence Cavignac
VP: Bob Cromley
VP: Warren Daubenspeck
VP: Andrea Moseley
Dept Mgr: Terry Weaver
Brnch Mgr: James Boedeker
Genl Mgr: Bill Loveland
Genl Mgr: Travis Nishi

D-U-N-S 00-424-8837
KLOSTERMAN BAKING CO (OH)
4760 Paddock Rd, Cincinnati, OH 45229-1047
Tel (513) 242-5667 *Founded/Ownrshp* 1900
Sales 218.4MM^E *EMP* 630
SIC 2051 Bread, cake & related products; Bread, all types (white, wheat, rye, etc): fresh or frozen; Cakes, bakery: except frozen; Yeast goods, sweet: except frozen
Pr: Kenneth Klosterman
**COO:* Dennis Wiltshire
**VP:* Ed Piasecki
VP: Jason Shingleton
Plnt Mgr: Lawrence Moore
Mktg Dir: Amy Ott

D-U-N-S 00-819-8186 IMP/EXP
KLUMB LUMBER CO (MS)
KLUMB SOUTHERN DIVISION
1080 River Oaks Dr Sa200, Flowood, MS 39232-9779
Tel (601) 932-6070 *Founded/Ownrshp* 1945
Sales 160.2MM *EMP* 140
SIC 5031 Lumber: rough, dressed & finished
Pr: Vicki Klumb O'Neill
**Pr:* Steve Funchess
**Pr:* Vicki O'Neill
**CEO:* C E Klumb Jr
**CFO:* Randall Hudson

KLUMB SOUTHERN DIVISION
See KLUMB LUMBER CO

D-U-N-S 96-335-3227
■ **KLUNE HOLDINGS INC**
(*Suby of* PCC) ★
7323 Coldwater Canyon Ave, North Hollywood, CA 91605-4206
Tel (818) 503-8100 *Founded/Ownrshp* 2010
Sales 131.6MM *EMP* 760
SIC 3728 Aircraft parts & equipment
CEO: Allen Ronk
CFO: Clom Plunkett
CFO: Ken Ward
Comm Man: Vicky Dalton
Ex Dir: Lisa Lujan
Genl Mgr: Al Eddert
Genl Mgr: Micheal Meehan
QA Dir: Eric Vorlage
IT Man: Eugene Humphreys
IT Man: Lee Shurie
Ql Cn Mgr: Gill Nierhoff

D-U-N-S 03-038-7286 IMP
■ **KLUNE INDUSTRIES INC**
(*Suby of* KLUNE HOLDINGS INC) ★
7323 Coldwater Canyon Ave, North Hollywood, CA 91605-4206
Tel (818) 503-8100 *Founded/Ownrshp* 2012
Sales 131.1MM^E *EMP* 757
SIC 3728 Aircraft parts & equipment
CEO: Joseph I Snowden
**CFO:* Kenneth Ward
Prgrm Mgr: Greg Brooks
Prgrm Mgr: Ian Davis
Genl Mgr: Kurt Spielman
IT Man: Kurt Olson
QC Dir: Mark Claire
Opers Mgr: Don Ewin
Ql Cn Mgr: Matthew Walkawicz
Sls&Mrk Ex: Bill Durante
Board of Directors: Jake Blumenthal, Gordon Clune, Richard Crowell, Tom Epley, Richard Roeder, Allen Ronk

KLX AEROSPACE SOLUTIONS
See M & M AEROSPACE HARDWARE INC

D-U-N-S 07-957-9685
▲ **KLX INC**
1300 Corporate Center Way # 200, Wellington, FL 33414-8594
Tel (561) 383-5100 *Founded/Ownrshp* 1974
Sales 1.5MMM *EMP* 3,500^E
Tkr Sym KLXI *Exch* NGS
SIC 3728 2911 1381 Aircraft parts & equipment; Fractionation products of crude petroleum, hydrocarbons; Service well drilling
Ch Bd: Amin J Khoury
Pr: Thomas P McCaffrey
CFO: Michael F Senft
VP: John Cuomo
VP: Roger Franks
VP: Gary Roberts
VP: Gary J Roberts
Board of Directors: John T Collins, Peter V Del Presto, Richard G Hamermesh, Benjamin A Hardesty, Stephen M Ward Jr, Theodore L Weise, John T Whates

D-U-N-S 18-641-3477
KM2 SOLUTIONS LLC
112 Christine Dr, Downingtown, PA 19335-1518
Tel (610) 213-1408 *Founded/Ownrshp* 2004
Sales 41.3MM^E *EMP* 1,000
SIC 8742 Financial consultant

D-U-N-S 00-896-5873 IMP/EXP
■ KMART CORP
(*Suby of* KMART HOLDING CORP) ★
3333 Beverly Rd, Hoffman Estates, IL 60179-0001
Tel (847) 286-2500 *Founded/Ownrshp* 1916
Sales 7.5MMM^E *EMP* 45,000
SIC 5311 5912 5399 Department stores; Drug stores; Army-Navy goods
Pr: Edward Lampert
**Pr:* Ronald D Doirie
Treas: Ryan Deutsch
**Treas:* Scott E Huckins
Div VP: Todd Troldahl
VP: Tom Aiello
VP: Ken Lejkowski
VP: John Pigott
VP: Lisa Schultz
VP Bus Dev: Andy Coleman
Dist Mgr: Kory Weber

D-U-N-S 13-197-8533 IMP
■ KMART HOLDING CORP
(*Suby of* SEARS HOLDINGS CORP) ★
3333 Beverly Rd, Hoffman Estates, IL 60179-0001
Tel (847) 286-2500 *Founded/Ownrshp* 2003
Sales 7.5MMM^E *EMP* 45,000^E
Accts Bdo Seidman Llp Troy Mi
SIC 5311 Department stores, discount
Chf Mktg O: Alasdair James
CFO: Robert Schriesheim
Treas: James F Gooch
Chf Mktg O: Paul Guyardo
Chf Mktg O: Mike Valle
Ofcr: Peter Whitsett
Ofcr: Thomas E Zielecki
Ex VP: Ronald Boire
Sr VP: Karen A Austin
Sr VP: James E Defebaugh
Sr VP: Dane Drobny
Sr VP: Donald J Germano
Sr VP: John D Goodman
Sr VP: William Harkel
Sr VP: James P Mixon
Sr VP: Irv Neger
Sr VP: William Phelan
Sr VP: Leslie Schultz
VP: Robert Riecker
VP: Judith Rusch
Board of Directors: W Bruce Johnson, Aylwin B Lewis, Allen R Ravas

KMC MUSIC
See ROKR DISTRIBUTION US INC

KME FIRE APPARATUS
See KOVATCH MOBILE EQUIPMENT CORP

D-U-N-S 00-974-1745 IMP/EXP
▲ KMG CHEMICALS INC (TX)
300 Throckmorton St, Fort Worth, TX 76102-2921
Tel (817) 761-6100 *Founded/Ownrshp* 1992
Sales 297.9MM *EMP* 657
Tkr Sym KMG *Exch* NYS
SIC 2899 Chemical preparations
Pr: Christopher T Fraser
CFO: Marcelino Rodriguez
VP: Roger C Jackson
VP: Ernest C Kremling
Board of Directors: Gerald G Ermentrout, James F Gentilcore, George W Gilman, Robert Harrer, John C Hunter III, Fred C Leonard, Karen A Twitchell

D-U-N-S 80-126-0154 IMP/EXP
■ KMG ELECTRONIC CHEMICALS INC
(*Suby of* KMG CHEMICALS INC) ★
300 Throckmorton St, Fort Worth, TX 76102-2921
Tel (817) 761-6100 *Founded/Ownrshp* 2007
Sales 92.5MM^E *EMP* 272
SIC 1629 Chemical plant & refinery construction
CEO: Christopher T Fraser
**CFO:* John V Sobchak
**Treas:* Pam Birkholz
**VP:* Ernest C Kremling II

D-U-N-S 78-964-1875 IMP
■ KMG-BERNUTH INC
(*Suby of* KMG CHEMICALS INC) ★
300 Throckmorton St, Fort Worth, TX 76102-2921
Tel (817) 761-6100 *Founded/Ownrshp* 1996
Sales 91.7MM^E *EMP* 118
SIC 5169 2869 Chemicals, industrial & heavy; Industrial organic chemicals
Ch Bd: David L Hatcher
**Pr:* Neal Butler
**Treas:* John V Sobchak
**VP:* Michael A Hoffman
**VP:* Roger Jackson
**VP:* Ernest C Kremling III

KMI
See KINDER MORGAN INC

D-U-N-S 78-812-4980
KMM TELECOMMUNICATIONS INC
9 Law Dr Ste 13, Fairfield, NJ 07004-3233
Tel (844) 566-8488 *Founded/Ownrshp* 1991
Sales 723.1MM^E *EMP* 175
Accts Dorfman Abrams Music Llc Sad
SIC 7629 4225 Telecommunication equipment repair (except telephones); General warehousing
CEO: Katherine McConvey
**Pr:* Nick Shanker
**CFO:* Kofi Dadu
CFO: Bill Teja
VP: Dennis Smith
VP: Robert Suastegui
VP: Chawn M Tate
Opers Mgr: Reggie Humphrey

KMMG
See KIA MOTORS MANUFACTURING GEORGIA INC

D-U-N-S 03-060-7774 IMP
KMS INC
811 E Waterman St Ste 1, Wichita, KS 67202-4716
Tel (316) 264-8833 *Founded/Ownrshp* 1976
Sales 83.2MM *EMP* 25
SIC 5199 5141 General merchandise, non-durable; Groceries, general line
Pr: Michael S Jabara
CFO: Steven Jess
**VP:* Garrell Dombaugh
**VP:* Larry McKee

D-U-N-S 19-217-5040 EXP
■ KMT REFRIGERATION INC
KOLPAK
(*Suby of* MANITOWOC FOODSERVICE COMPANIES LLC) ★
2915 Tennessee Ave N, Parsons, TN 38363-5046
Tel (731) 847-6361 *Founded/Ownrshp* 1997
Sales 85.2MM^E *EMP* 1,100
SIC 3585 3448 1711 Refrigeration equipment, complete; Prefabricated metal components; Refrigeration contractor
Genl Mgr: Gerry Senion
**Treas:* Glen Tellock

D-U-N-S 00-602-4699 IMP/EXP
KNAPE & VOGT MANUFACTURING CO (MI)
(*Suby of* WIND POINT PARTNERS VI LP) ★
2700 Oak Industrial Dr Ne, Grand Rapids, MI 49505-6081
Tel (616) 459-3311 *Founded/Ownrshp* 1898, 2006
Sales 189.8MM^E *EMP* 640
SIC 2542 2541 3429 Partitions & fixtures, except wood; Shelving, office & store: except wood; Fixtures: display, office or store: except wood; Wood partitions & fixtures; Shelving, office & store, wood; Display fixtures, wood; Furniture builders' & other household hardware
CEO: Peter Martin
**Ch Bd:* Bill Denton
COO: Dan Suttorp
**VP:* Gordon Kirsch
**VP:* John J Master
VP: Rick McQuigg
**VP:* Daniel D Pickett
VP: Michael Van Rooy
Sls&Mrk Ex: Jim Dahlke
Manager: Kelly Makin

D-U-N-S 62-366-5853 IMP
KNAPP LOGISTICS AUTOMATION INC
2124 Barrett Park Dr Nw # 100, Kennesaw, GA 30144-3602
Tel (678) 388-2880 *Founded/Ownrshp* 1997
Sales 100.0MM *EMP* 100
SIC 3559 Foundry machinery & equipment
CEO: Josef Mentzer
**Sec:* Shan Powell
Ofcr: Michael Hanh
Ofcr: Frank Kraus
VP: Michael Hahn
Dir Bus: Kevin Reader
Genl Mgr: Bernhard Rottenbuecher
**CTO:* Roland Kohloka
Sys Mgr: Thomas Reisinger
Manager: Heimo Robosch
Sls Mgr: Gerhard Weigand

D-U-N-S 05-511-5059 IMP
KNAPP MEDICAL CENTER
1401 E 8th St, Weslaco, TX 78596-6640
Tel (956) 968-8567 *Founded/Ownrshp* 2005
Sales 99.8MM *EMP* 1,000
Accts Bkd Llp Houston Tx
SIC 8011 Offices & clinics of medical doctors
CEO: Bill Adams
Chf Path: Alberto P Gonzalez
Chf Rad: Michael Decandia
**Pr:* James Summersett
CFO: Dinah Gonzales
CFO: Curtis Haley
Dir OR: Tamara Leonard
Dir Risk M: Ruben Garza
Dir Lab: Roberto Velasquez
Dir Rx: Claudia Sander
Off Mgr: Rick Hidalgo

D-U-N-S 13-487-5983 IMP
KNAUF INSULATION INC
(*Suby of* GEBR. KNAUF VERWALTUNGSGESELLSCHAFT KG)
1 Knauf Dr, Shelbyville, IN 46176-8626
Tel (317) 398-4434 *Founded/Ownrshp* 1979
Sales 484.8MM^E *EMP* 1,126
SIC 3229 Glass fiber products
CEO: Tony Robson
**Pr:* Mark Andrews
**CFO:* Robert Claxton
Top Exec: Barry Lynham
**VP:* Jeffery Brisley
**VP:* Jon Pereira
VP: Joe Rogers
Area Mgr: Kieran Stephenson
Brnch Mgr: Aaron Wine
Dir IT: Geoff Hickman
IT Man: George Henry

D-U-N-S 14-434-5147 IMP
KNAUF INSULATION LLC
979 Batesville Rd Ste B, Greer, SC 29651-6819
Tel (517) 629-9464 *Founded/Ownrshp* 2014
Sales 125.3MM^E *EMP* 500
SIC 3296 Fiberglass insulation
CEO: Mark Andrews
VP: Jeffrey Knight
IT Man: Greg Sanford

D-U-N-S 15-454-8564
KNECHT LLC
320 West Blvd, Rapid City, SD 57701-2671
Tel (605) 342-4840 *Founded/Ownrshp* 2016
Sales 115.0MM *EMP* 349^E
SIC 5211 5251 Lumber & other building materials; Builders' hardware
Pr: Craig Bradshaw
**CFO:* Pat Beans
Genl Mgr: Wallace Bork

D-U-N-S 82-893-4989
KNIA HOLDINGS INC
110 Hopkins St, Buffalo, NY 14220-2131
Tel (914) 241-7430 *Founded/Ownrshp* 2006
Sales NA *EMP* 1,070
SIC 6719 Investment holding companies, except banks
Pr: James Kohlberg

KNIFE RIVER COAL MINING
See KNIFE RIVER CORP

D-U-N-S 00-696-2096 IMP
■ KNIFE RIVER CORP
KNIFE RIVER COAL MINING
(*Suby of* MDU RESOURCES GROUP INC) ★
1150 W Century Ave, Bismarck, ND 58503-0942
Tel (701) 530-1400 *Founded/Ownrshp* 1922, 1988
Sales 1.1MMM^E *EMP* 2,370
SIC 1442 3273 1221 Construction sand & gravel; Ready-mixed concrete; Bituminous coal & lignite-surface mining
Pr: Dave Barney
**Ch Bd:* Martin White
**CEO:* Bill Schneider
**Treas:* Larry E Hansen
Ofcr: Steve Baeth
**VP:* Larry Duppong
VP: Mary Johnson
VP: Steve Mote
Genl Mgr: Alrick Hale
Off Admin: Wendi Frarey
IT Man: Joe Barthelemy

D-U-N-S 04-725-8306
■ KNIFE RIVER CORP - NORTH CENTRAL
(*Suby of* KNIFE RIVER COAL MINING) ★
4787 Shadowwood Dr Ne, Sauk Rapids, MN 56379-9431
Tel (320) 251-9472 *Founded/Ownrshp* 2007
Sales 142.5MM^E *EMP* 750
SIC 1611 1442 3273 2951 Highway & street paving contractor; Gravel mining; Ready-mixed concrete; Asphalt paving mixtures & blocks
CEO: David C Barney
**VP:* Michael Bauerly
Sls Mgr: Alan Johnson

D-U-N-S 00-904-1427 IMP
■ KNIFE RIVER CORP - NORTHWEST (OR)
(*Suby of* KNIFE RIVER COAL MINING) ★
32260 Old Highway 34, Tangent, OR 97389-9770
Tel (541) 928-6491 *Founded/Ownrshp* 1962
Sales 167.7MM^E *EMP* 575
SIC 1611 3273 General contractor, highway & street construction; Ready-mixed concrete
Pr: Brian R Gray
**Ch Bd:* Martin A White
**Pr:* David Ball
**CEO:* Terry D Hildestad
Ex VP: Dave Bull
**VP:* Stephen Frey
Trfc Dir: Amanda Pinner
Opers Supe: Fred Sondermayer

KNIFE RIVER-BILLINGS
See JTL GROUP INC

D-U-N-S 83-587-4892
■ KNIGHT CAPITAL AMERICAS LP
KCG
(*Suby of* KNIGHT CAPITAL GROUP INC) ★
545 Washington Blvd Ste 1, Jersey City, NJ 07310-1607
Tel (800) 544-7508 *Founded/Ownrshp* 1998
Sales 101.4MM^E *EMP* 481
SIC 6211 Security brokers & dealers
Mng Pt: Thomas M Joyce
Pt: James P Smyth Sr
Pt: Gregory C Voetsch
COO: Philip Gough
Software D: Zia Chowdhury
Software D: Vincent Harvey
Software D: Alexander Kondratskiy
Software D: Vlad Lazarenko
Software D: Ujwal Ovaleker
Software D: Chung Tsao
Software D: Hua Yu

D-U-N-S 01-820-3229
■ KNIGHT CAPITAL GROUP INC
(*Suby of* KCG HOLDINGS INC) ★
545 Washington Blvd Ste 1, Jersey City, NJ 07310-1607
Tel (201) 222-9400 *Founded/Ownrshp* 1995, 2013
Sales 590.0MM^E *EMP* 1,524^E
SIC 6211 6282 Security brokers & dealers; Investment advice
CEO: Daniel B Coleman
Pr: Scott Crammond
Pr: Rohit Khandekar
Pr: Loren Messina
Pr: Anna Rossi
Pr: Bhavin Shah
Pr: Parin Shah
Pr: Jianzhang Xu
**COO:* Steven Bisgay
CFO: Steffen Parratt
Bd of Dir: Rory O'Kane
Ofcr: Nick Ogurtsov
Assoc VP: Beth Mills
**Ex VP:* Leonard J Amoruso
**Sr VP:* Glenn T Callen
VP: Glen Alvarado
VP: Amanda Anderson
VP: Brad Bagdis
VP: Michael Bell
VP: Ricky Bhatt
VP: Michael Bita
Board of Directors: William L Bolster, Martin Brand, James W Lewis, James T Milde, Matthew Nimetz, Christopher C Quick, Daniel F Schmitt, Laurie M Shahon, Fred Tomczyk

D-U-N-S 96-304-6946
KNIGHT FOUNDATION
1 Sw Bowerman Dr, Beaverton, OR 97005-0979
Tel (503) 671-3500 *Founded/Ownrshp* 2010
Sales 165.8MM *EMP* 2
Accts Pricewaterhousecoopers Llp Sa
SIC 8699 Charitable organization
Prin: Lisa McKillips

D-U-N-S 02-258-1537
KNIGHT HAWK COAL LLC
500 Cutler Trico Rd, Percy, IL 62272-2716
Tel (618) 426-3662 *Founded/Ownrshp* 1998
Sales 494.9MM^E *EMP* 380
SIC 1241 1222 Coal mining services; Bituminous coal-underground mining
Dir Risk M: Jenna Parsons
Genl Mgr: Keith Dailey
Off Mgr: Neil Bradley
IT Man: Jason Thies
Plnt Mgr: Dale Winter

D-U-N-S 62-759-2843
KNIGHT PROTECTIVE SERVICE INC
6411 Ivy Ln Ste 320, Greenbelt, MD 20770-1405
Tel (301) 808-4669 *Founded/Ownrshp* 1988
Sales 20.4MM^E *EMP* 1,500
Accts Mccalin & Associates Philadel
SIC 7381 Security guard service
Pr: Macon Sims Jr
VP: Denisha Logan

D-U-N-S 61-595-6992
▲ KNIGHT TRANSPORTATION INC
20002 N 19th Ave, Phoenix, AZ 85027-4250
Tel (602) 269-2000 *Founded/Ownrshp* 1989
Sales 1.1MMM *EMP* 6,196
Tkr Sym KNX *Exch* NYS
SIC 4213 4212 Trucking, except local; Local trucking, without storage
Pr: David A Jackson
**Ch Bd:* Kevin P Knight
COO: Kevin Quast
CFO: Adam W Miller
**V Ch Bd:* Gary J Knight
Ex VP: James E Updike Jr
Exec: Matt Rosen
Opers Mgr: Michael Evertsen
Board of Directors: Michael Garnreiter, Richard C Kraemer, Richard J Lehmann, G D Madden, Kathryn L Munro, Roberta Roberts Shank, Robert E Synowicki Jr

D-U-N-S 18-764-3754 IMP/EXP
KNIGHT-CHEMSTAR INC
9204 Emmott Rd, Houston, TX 77040-3328
Tel (713) 466-8751 *Founded/Ownrshp* 2002
Sales 363.3MM *EMP* 10
SIC 5169 5172 Chemicals & allied products; Industrial chemicals; Petroleum products; Naptha
Pr: Steve Knight

D-U-N-S 15-369-6930 IMP/EXP
■ KNIGHTS APPAREL INC
ALTA GRACIA
(*Suby of* HANESBRANDS INC) ★
5475 N Blackstock Rd, Spartanburg, SC 29303-4702
Tel (864) 587-9690 *Founded/Ownrshp* 2015
Sales 217.8MM^E *EMP* 325^E
SIC 5091 5699 Sporting & recreation goods; Sports apparel
CEO: Joseph Bozich
**Pr:* Donnie Hodge
**CFO:* Jay R Cope

KNIGHTS INN
See WYNDHAM HOTEL GROUP LLC

D-U-N-S 04-120-5329 IMP
KNIGHTS OF COLUMBUS
1 Columbus Plz Ste 1700, New Haven, CT 06510-3326
Tel (203) 752-4000 *Founded/Ownrshp* 1882
Sales NA *EMP* 2,300
SIC 6411 8641 Insurance agents & brokers; Fraternal associations
VP: Robert Tracz
Pr: Niki Kratzert
COO: Ed Mullen
CFO: Terry Lescoe
**Treas:* Logan Ludwig
Treas: Michael J O'Connor
Ex VP: Thomas Smith
VP: Lynn Hussey
VP: Patrick Korten
VP: Gilles Marchand
VP: Anthony Minopoli
VP: Barry Nickerson

D-U-N-S 04-777-7131
KNOBBE MARTENS OLSON & BEAR LLP
2040 Main St Fl 14, Irvine, CA 92614-8214
Tel (949) 760-0404 *Founded/Ownrshp* 1962
Sales 95.3MM^E *EMP* 600
SIC 8111 General practice law office
Mng Pt: Steven J Nataupsky
**Pt:* William B Bunker
**Pt:* Drew S Hamilton
**Pt:* Ned Israelsen
**Pt:* Steven Nataupsky
**Pt:* William H Nieman
**Pt:* Darrell L Olson
**Pt:* Arthur S Rose
**Pt:* Joseph R RE
**Pt:* Edward A Schlatter
**Pt:* John B Sganga
**Pt:* Gerard Von Hoffman III
Mng Pt: Adeel Akhtar
**Mng Pt:* James B Bear
Mng Pt: Ned A Israelsen
VP: Daniel Henry
VP: Charles Schill
VP: Edward Treska
Dir Bus: Krista Hosseinzadeh

D-U-N-S 78-131-6096 EXP
▲ KNOLL INC
1235 Water St, East Greenville, PA 18041-2202
Tel (215) 679-7991 *Founded/Ownrshp* 1938
Sales 1.1MMM *EMP* 3,386
Tkr Sym KNL *Exch* NYS

SIC 2521 2522 2299 Wood office furniture; Panel systems & partitions (free-standing), office: wood; Chairs, office: padded, upholstered or plain: wood; Office furniture, except wood; Panel systems & partitions, office: except wood; Chairs, office: padded or plain, except wood; Upholstery filling, textile
CEO: Andrew B Cogan
*Ch Bd: Burton B Staniar
COO: Joseph T Coppola
CFO: Craig B Spray
Ex VP: Benjamin A Pardo
Sr VP: Michael A Pollner
VP: Bernadette Baker
VP: Michael Benigno
VP: Carl Hohmann
VP: Marie Kessler
VP: Charlie Lieb
VP: Patrick Oleary
Board of Directors: Kathleen G Bradley, Stephen F Fisher, Jeffrey A Harris, Sidney Lapidus, John G Maypole, Sarah E Nash, Stephanie Stahl

KNOLLS ATOMIC POWER LABORATORY
See KAPL INC

D-U-N-S 08-055-8406
KNOLLWOOD MANOR GENESIS ELDERCARE
KNOLLWOOD MANOR NURSING HOME
1221 Waugh Chapel Rd, Gambrills, MD 21054-1608
Tel (410) 987-1644 Founded/Ownrshp 1960, 1994
Sales 505.2MM EMP 84
SIC 8051 8052 Skilled nursing care facilities; Intermediate care facilities
Exec: Todd Jones
Off Mgr: Audrea Matthews

KNOLLWOOD MANOR NURSING HOME
See KNOLLWOOD MANOR GENESIS ELDERCARE

D-U-N-S 93-264-6748
KNOLOGY BROADBAND INC
1241 Og Skinner Dr, West Point, GA 31833-1789
Tel (706) 645-8553 Founded/Ownrshp 1998
Sales NA EMP 1,157E
SIC 4841

D-U-N-S 09-801-3613
KNOLOGY INC
(Suby of WOW) ★
1241 Og Skinner Dr, West Point, GA 31833-1789
Tel (334) 644-2611 Founded/Ownrshp 2012
Sales 487.4MME EMP 1,861E
SIC 4813 4841 ; Cable television services
CEO: Rodger L Johnson
COO: Jack Hearst
CFO: Felix L Boccucci Jr
VP: Anthony J Palermo Jr
VP: Wendy Wills
Genl Mgr: Deb Hines
Genl Mgr: Kevin Nolan
Plng Mgr: Lynn Hall
Netwrk Eng: David Reale

D-U-N-S 80-135-6317 IMP
KNORR BRAKE HOLDING CORP
(Suby of KNORR-BREMSE AG)
748 Starbuck Ave, Watertown, NY 13601-1620
Tel (315) 786-5356 Founded/Ownrshp 1990
Sales 1.2MMME EMP 5,304
SIC 3743 5013 Railroad equipment; Motor vehicle supplies & new parts
Pr: Heinz Hermann Thiele
Snr Mgr: Jerry Autry

D-U-N-S 55-607-2163 IMP
KNORR BRAKE TRUCK SYSTEMS CO
NEW YORK AIR BRAKE
(Suby of KNORR BRAKE HOLDING CORP) ★
748 Starbuck Ave, Watertown, NY 13601-1620
Tel (315) 786-5200 Founded/Ownrshp 1990
Sales 1.1MMME EMP 3,194
Accts Kpmg Llp
SIC 3743 Brakes, air & vacuum: railway
Pr: Heinz Hermann Thiele
*Pr: Mike Hawthorne
CFO: Cheri Lamarche
*CFO: J Paul Morgan
Treas: Kathleen Gosnell
*V Ch Bd: Peter Riedlinger
VP: Scott Burkhart
VP: Kishor Pendse
VP: Karen Tichenor
Exec: Paul Morgan
Prgrm Mgr: Mark Pettit

KNOTT'S BERRY FARM
See BERRY KNOTTS FARM LLC

D-U-N-S 00-300-2680 IMP/EXP
KNOUSE FOODS COOPERATIVE INC
800 Pach Glen Idaville Rd, Peach Glen, PA 17375-0001
Tel (717) 677-8181 Founded/Ownrshp 1949
Sales 414.3MME EMP 1,200
SIC 2033 Fruits: packaged in cans, jars, etc.; Fruit juices: packaged in cans, jars, etc.; Fruit pie mixes & fillings: packaged in cans, jars, etc.; Apple sauce: packaged in cans, jars, etc.
Pr: Kenneth E Guise Jr
*Treas: Craig M Hinkle
*VP: Thomas M Denisco
*VP: Richard W Esser
*VP: Emery C Etter Jr
*VP: Eugene Kelly
VP: Eugene F Kelly
*VP: Linda Kelly
MIS Mgr: Harold Heller
Opers Mgr: Arlene Jennings
Plnt Mgr: Binkley Mike

D-U-N-S 09-279-8354
KNOWLANS SUPER MARKETS INC
FESTIVAL FOODS
111 County Road F E, Vadnais Heights, MN 55127-6933
Tel (651) 483-9242 Founded/Ownrshp 1955
Sales 92.2MME EMP 600
SIC 5411 Supermarkets, independent
CEO: Marie Aarthun
Store Dir: Rick Ubel
Genl Mgr: Kevin Donovan
Genl Mgr: Frank Kirchner

D-U-N-S 07-925-8305
▲ KNOWLES CORP
1151 Maplewood Dr, Itasca, IL 60143-2058
Tel (630) 250-5100 Founded/Ownrshp 2013
Sales 1.0MMM EMP 12,000E
Tkr Sym KN Exch NYS
SIC 3651 3675 Household audio & video equipment; Audio electronic systems; Microphones; Speaker systems; Electronic capacitors
Pr: Jeffrey S Niew
*Ch Bd: Jean-Pierre M Ergas
Pr: Paul M Dickinson
Pr: Christian U Scherp
Pr: Gordon A Walker
Pr: David W Wightman
COO: Daniel J Giesecke
CFO: John S Anderson
Sr VP: Alexis Bernard
Sr VP: Raymond D Cabrera
Sr VP: Thomas G Jackson
VP: Bryan E Mittelman
Board of Directors: Keith L Barnes, Hermann Eul, Ronald Jankov, Richard K Lochridge, Donald Macleod

D-U-N-S 00-511-5902
■ KNOWLES ELECTRONICS HOLDINGS INC
(Suby of KNOWLES CORP) ★
1151 Maplewood Dr, Itasca, IL 60143-2058
Tel (630) 250-5100 Founded/Ownrshp 1954, 2014
Sales 228.8MME EMP 2,420
SIC 3679 3625 3651 8731 6159 Transducers, electrical; Headphones, radio; Solenoid switches (industrial controls); Sound reproducing equipment; Engineering laboratory, except testing; Commercial research laboratory; Loan institutions, general & industrial
Ch Bd: Jean-Pierre M Ergas
*Pr: Michael A Adell
*Pr: Jeffrey S Niew
*CFO: John S Anderson
*Sr VP: Raymond D Cabrera
*Sr VP: Paul M Dickinson
*VP: Pat Cavanagh
*VP: James H Moyle
*VP: Stephen D Petersen
*Prin: John J Zei

D-U-N-S 02-529-6208 IMP
■ KNOWLES ELECTRONICS LLC
(Suby of KNOWLES CORP) ★
1151 Maplewood Dr, Itasca, IL 60143-2071
Tel (630) 250-5100 Founded/Ownrshp 1999
Sales NA EMP 2,418
SIC 3679 3842 Transducers, electrical; Hearing aids
Pr: Jeffrey Niew
Pr: Pete Loeppert
*Sr VP: John Anderson
VP: Mike Adell
VP: Ray Cabrera
VP: Jignesh Sampat
Plng Mgr: Nancy Jing
QA Dir: Peter Maus
Dir IT: Vikas Jain
Dir IT: Mike Kochis
IT Man: Chris Hees

D-U-N-S 07-934-4242
■ KNOWLES INTERMEDIATE HOLDING INC
(Suby of KNOWLES CORP) ★
1151 Maplewood Dr, Itasca, IL 60143-2058
Tel (630) 250-5100 Founded/Ownrshp 2014
Sales 126.1ME EMP 5,003E
SIC 6799 Investors

D-U-N-S 82-777-4720
KNOX & ASSOCIATES LLC
CHRISTIAN J KNOX & ASSOCIATES
615 Candlewood Ct, Lodi, CA 95242-4646
Tel (209) 365-1567 Founded/Ownrshp 1978
Sales 51.7MME EMP 3,000
SIC 8741 5812 Restaurant management; Eating places
Pt: Chris Knox
*Pt: David Knox
*Pt: Michael Pettit

D-U-N-S 05-884-1073
KNOX COMMUNITY HOSPITAL
1330 Coshocton Ave, Mount Vernon, OH 43050-1495
Tel (740) 393-9000 Founded/Ownrshp 1977
Sales 140.3MM EMP 628
SIC 8062 General medical & surgical hospitals
CEO: Bruce White
CEO: Sheila Cochran
*CFO: Michael Ambrosiani
VP: Judy Schwartz
Chf Nrs Of: Sandra Beidelschies
Mktg Dir: Jeffrey Scott
Orthpdst: Michael Sullivan
Surgeon: Paul Taiganides
Pharmcst: Melissa Palausky
Pgrm Dir: Rachail Risko

D-U-N-S 07-132-0501
KNOX COUNTY HOSPITAL
GOOD SAMARITAN HOSPITAL
305 S 5th St, Vincennes, IN 47591-1117
Tel (812) 882-5220 Founded/Ownrshp 1908, 2001
Sales 291.1MM EMP 1,900
Accts Bkd Llp Indianapolis In
SIC 8062 General medical & surgical hospitals
Pr: Robert D McLin
Chf Path: Cathy Freeman
COO: Daryl Waldrige
COO: Darryl Waldrup
VP: Charles Hedde
VP: Emily Heineke
VP: Scott Kaminski
VP: Margaret Pfeiffer
VP: Adam Thacker
Dir Risk M: Michael Smith
Dir Rx: Jim Eskew

D-U-N-S 00-338-0888
■ KNOXVILLE NEWS-SENTINEL CO
(Suby of JOURNAL MEDIA GROUP INC) ★
2332 News Sentinel Dr, Knoxville, TN 37921-5766
Tel (865) 523-3131 Founded/Ownrshp 2015
Sales 85.2MME EMP 580
SIC 2711 Newspapers, publishing & printing
Pr: Bruce Hartmann
*Sr VP: Mark G Contreras
*VP: Rusty Coats
*VP: Jack McElroy
Advt Dir: Frank B Hughes

D-U-N-S 00-338-7560
KNOXVILLE UTILITIES BOARD
K U B
(Suby of CITY OF KNOXVILLE) ★
445 S Gay St, Knoxville, TN 37902-1125
Tel (865) 594-7324 Founded/Ownrshp 1939, 1986
Sales 733.3MM EMP 500
Accts Rodefer Moss & Co Pllc Knox
SIC 4911 4924 4941 4952 Electric services; Natural gas distribution; Water supply; Sewerage systems
CEO: Mintha Roach
*Ex VP: Bill Elmore
*Sr VP: Eddie Black
*Sr VP: Susan Edwards
Sr VP: Roby Trotter
VP: Debbie M Boles
*VP: Mike Bolin
VP: Derwin Haygood
*VP: Mark Walker
Genl Mgr: Rosalind Wood
CIO: Derwin Haegood

KNUTSON CONSTRUCTION SERVICES
See KNUTSON HOLDINGS INC

D-U-N-S 13-073-2332
KNUTSON CONSTRUCTION SERVICES INC
(Suby of KNUTSON CONSTRUCTION SERVICES) ★
7515 Wayzata Blvd, Minneapolis, MN 55426-1621
Tel (763) 546-1400 Founded/Ownrshp 1985
Sales 101.8MME EMP 400
SIC 1542 1541

D-U-N-S 14-466-2632
KNUTSON HOLDINGS INC
KNUTSON CONSTRUCTION SERVICES
7515 Wayzata Blvd, Minneapolis, MN 55426-1621
Tel (763) 546-1400 Founded/Ownrshp 1985
Sales 132.8MME EMP 400E
SIC 1542 1541 Commercial & office building, new construction; Industrial buildings, new construction
Pr: Steven O Curry
*CFO: Michael D Wolf
*VP: Dave Foley

D-U-N-S 60-315-5482 IMP/EXP
KOBE STEEL USA HOLDINGS INC
(Suby of KOBE STEEL, LTD.)
535 Madison Ave Fl 5, New York, NY 10022-4214
Tel (212) 751-9400 Founded/Ownrshp 1905
Sales 248.9MME EMP 1,512
SIC 3542 3089 Extruding machines (machine tools), metal; Injection molding of plastics
Pr: Hiroya Kawasaki
Dir IT: Carrie Dugan
IT Man: Onuma Hideki
IT Man: Kazuhiro Ono

D-U-N-S 60-972-8423 IMP/EXP
KOBELCO COMPRESSORS AMERICA INC
(Suby of KOBE STEEL, LTD.)
1450 W Rincon St, Corona, CA 92880-9205
Tel (951) 739-3030 Founded/Ownrshp 1990
Sales 173.9MME EMP 280
SIC 1623 3563 Oil & gas line & compressor station construction; Air & gas compressors; Air & gas compressors including vacuum pumps
CEO: Takaaki Hayata
*CTO: Mohamad A Gauhar

D-U-N-S 07-972-5044
KOCH AG & ENERGY SOLUTIONS LLC
4111 E 37th St N, Wichita, KS 67220-3203
Tel (316) 828-8310 Founded/Ownrshp 2008
Sales 215.2MME EMP 650E
SIC 5191 Fertilizers & agricultural chemicals
Pr: Chase Koch

D-U-N-S 05-447-0351
KOCH AIR LLC (IN)
(Suby of KOCH HVAC DISTRIBUTION INC) ★
1900 W Lloyd Expy, Evansville, IN 47712-7506
Tel (812) 962-5200 Founded/Ownrshp 1999, 1936
Sales 150.0MM EMP 182
Accts Harding Shymanski & Company
SIC 5075 Air conditioning & ventilation equipment & supplies
Pr: James H Muehlbauer
*VP: Glen Muehlbauer
Sls Mgr: Allan Jones

D-U-N-S 06-461-8676
KOCH BUSINESS SOLUTIONS LP
KBS
(Suby of KOCH INDUSTRIES INC) ★
4111 E 37th St N, Wichita, KS 67220-3203
Tel (316) 828-5500 Founded/Ownrshp 2007
Sales 91.2MME EMP 240E
SIC 8748 Business consulting
Pt: David Robertson
Mng Pt: Becci Biagini
Dir IT: Frank Walker
IT Man: Matthew Carnahan

D-U-N-S 10-332-6216 IMP/EXP
KOCH CHEMICAL TECHNOLOGY GROUP LLC
(Suby of KOCH RESOURCES LLC) ★
4111 E 37th St N, Wichita, KS 67220-3203
Tel (316) 828-8515 Founded/Ownrshp 2001
Sales 314.2MME EMP 1,103E
SIC 3443 Metal parts
CEO: Charles Koch
*Pr: David Robertson
*Ex VP: David Koch
VP: Bradley E Haddock
Counsel: Krisyn Wood

KOCH COMPANIES
See STAN KOCH & SONS TRUCKING INC

D-U-N-S 00-637-0357 IMP
KOCH ENTERPRISES INC
14 S 11th Ave, Evansville, IN 47712-5020
Tel (812) 465-9800 Founded/Ownrshp 1873
Sales 1.0MMME EMP 2,482
Accts Harding Shymanski & Company
SIC 3363 5075 3559 5084 2891 3069 Aluminum die-castings; Air conditioning equipment, except room units; Metal finishing equipment for plating, etc.; Industrial machinery & equipment; Sealants; Adhesives; Molded rubber products
Ch: Robert Koch
*Pr: Kevin R Koch
COO: James H Muelbauer
*CFO: Susan E Parsons
IT Man: Kevin Peveler
Mktg Dir: Jennifer Slade

D-U-N-S 60-208-4618 IMP
KOCH FERTILIZER LLC
(Suby of KOCH AG & ENERGY SOLUTIONS LLC) ★
4111 E 37th St N, Wichita, KS 67220-3203
Tel (316) 828-5010 Founded/Ownrshp 2001
Sales 179.4MME EMP 314
SIC 2873 5169 2813 Nitrogenous fertilizers; Chemicals & allied products; Industrial gases
Treas: Richard Dinkel

D-U-N-S 00-338-5127 EXP
KOCH FOODS INC
1300 W Higgins Rd, Flowood, MS 39232
Tel (601) 732-8911 Founded/Ownrshp 1948
Sales 1.8MMME EMP 3,984
SIC 5144 Poultry: live, dressed or frozen (unpackaged); Poultry products; Eggs
CEO: Joseph Grendys
CFO: Mark Kaminsky
VP: John Marler
QI Cn Mgr: Anita Scott

D-U-N-S 00-819-5638 EXP
KOCH FOODS OF MISSISSIPPI LLC (MS)
(Suby of KOCH FOODS INC) ★
4688 Highway 80, Morton, MS 39117-3472
Tel (601) 732-8911 Founded/Ownrshp 1981, 1999
Sales 613.9MME EMP 3,534
SIC 2015 Chicken, processed: fresh; Chicken, processed: frozen; Chicken, slaughtered & dressed
Exec: Neil Valentine

D-U-N-S 03-106-5394
KOCH HVAC DISTRIBUTION INC
(Suby of KOCH ENTERPRISES INC) ★
1900 W Lloyd Expy, Evansville, IN 47712-5138
Tel (812) 962-5200 Founded/Ownrshp 1997
Sales 150.1MME EMP 191
Accts Harding Shymanski And Company
SIC 5075 Warm air heating & air conditioning; Compressors, air conditioning; Condensing units, air conditioning
Ch Bd: Robert L Koch II
*Pr: James H Muehlbauer
*CFO: Cindy Spaetti
Treas: Cindy Mitchell
*Sec: Susan E Parsons

D-U-N-S 00-694-4334 IMP/EXP
KOCH INDUSTRIES INC
4111 E 37th St N, Wichita, KS 67220-3298
Tel (316) 828-5500 Founded/Ownrshp 1961
Sales 26.6MMME EMP 70,000
SIC 5172 2911 5169 Petroleum products; Petroleum refining; Chemicals & allied products
CEO: Charles G Koch
COO: J F Gostkowski
COO: Bill Hohns
COO: Allen Wright
CFO: Steven Feilmeier
CFO: Sam Soliman
Ex VP: Richard Fink
Ex VP: Brad Sanders
VP: Brian Boulter
VP: James Faith
VP: Lori Little
VP: Rick Moncrief
VP: Tim Nicol
VP: Steve Pankey
VP: Paul R Wheeler
VP: Jeff Wilson
Dir Risk M: Jeff Parke

D-U-N-S 02-518-9853 EXP
KOCH MEAT CO INC (IL)
KOCH POULTRY
(Suby of KOCH FOODS INC) ★
1300 Higgins Rd Ste 100, Park Ridge, IL 60068-5766
Tel (847) 384-8018 Founded/Ownrshp 1959
Sales 265.5MME EMP 405
SIC 5142 5144 Poultry, frozen: packaged; Poultry: live, dressed or frozen (unpackaged); Poultry products
Pr: Joseph Grundy
*Sec: Mark Kaminsky
Plnt Mgr: David Lebla

D-U-N-S 04-169-7244 IMP/EXP
KOCH MEMBRANE SYSTEMS INC
(Suby of KOCH-GLITSCH LP) ★
850 Main St, Wilmington, MA 01887-3388
Tel (978) 694-7000 Founded/Ownrshp 1999
Sales 121.2MME EMP 480
SIC 3569 3564 Separators for steam, gas, vapor or air (machinery); Air purification equipment
Ch Bd: David H Koch
*Pr: Manny Singh
*COO: Mark Farrell
*Treas: Jeanne R Hernandez
VP: Joseph Gullotta
Div/Sub He: William Ekyamp
Rgnl Mgr: Martin Howard
IT Man: Thomas McCarthy
Opers Mgr: Timothy May

VP Sls: Jeffrey Conley
Sls Dir: Coley Ali
Board of Directors: John M Van Gelder

KOCH POULTRY
See KOCH MEAT CO INC

D-U-N-S 14-298-1278
KOCH RESOURCES LLC
(*Suby of* KOCH INDUSTRIES INC) ★
4111 E 37th St N, Wichita, KS 67220-3203
Tel (316) 828-5500 *Founded/Ownrshp* 2003
Sales 2.2MMM^E *EMP* 10,000^E
SIC 6221 2911 Commodity traders, contracts; Petroleum refining
CEO: Charles G Koch
Pr: David L Robertson
Ex VP: David H Koch
Genl Mgr: Wade Marquardt
Genl Mgr: Anthony Sementelli

KOCH SUPPLY & TRADING
See KS&T INTERNATIONAL HOLDINGS LP

D-U-N-S 03-115-9093 IMP/EXP
KOCH SUPPLY & TRADING LP
KOCH SUPPLY AND TRADING
(*Suby of* KOCH INDUSTRIES INC) ★
4111 E 37th St N, Wichita, KS 67220-3203
Tel (316) 828-5500 *Founded/Ownrshp* 2001
Sales 237.6MM^E *EMP* 350
SIC 2911 Petroleum refining
CEO: Charles G Koch
Pt: Bradford T Sanders
Pr: Steve Mawer
CFO: Bradley C Hall
Ex VP: Mark Dobbins
Ex VP: Bill Kovach
IT Man: Donnie Aschenbrenner
IT Man: Tim Shanfelt

KOCH SUPPLY AND TRADING
See KOCH SUPPLY & TRADING LP

D-U-N-S 00-732-4916 IMP/EXP
KOCH-GLITSCH LP
(*Suby of* KOCH INDUSTRIES INC) ★
4111 E 37th St N, Wichita, KS 67220-3203
Tel (316) 828-5110 *Founded/Ownrshp* 1913, 1997
Sales 259.8MM^E *EMP* 900
SIC 3443 Vessels, process or storage (from boiler shops): metal plate
Pt: Robert Difulgentiz
Pt: Vince Dailey
Pt: Matt Sherwood
Bd of Dir: John Gelder
Opers Mgr: Robert Brown
Plnt Mgr: Jim Snodgrass
VP Sls: Christoph Ender
Sls Mgr: Kate Caddick
Sls Mgr: Fred Cash

KOCKUMS CANCAR CHIP-N-SAW
See USNR LLC

D-U-N-S 07-595-2713
KOCOLENE MARKETING LLC
2060 1st Ave, Seymour, IN 47274-3321
Tel (812) 522-2224 *Founded/Ownrshp* 1973
Sales 188.9MM^E *EMP* 580^E
SIC 5541 5411 Gasoline service stations; Convenience stores, independent

D-U-N-S 07-909-0540 IMP/EXP
KODAK ALARIS INC
(*Suby of* KODAK ALARIS HOLDINGS LIMITED)
2400 Mount Read Blvd # 1175, Rochester, NY 14615-2744
Tel (585) 290-2891 *Founded/Ownrshp* 2013
Sales 300.7MM^E *EMP* 700^E
SIC 3861 Photographic equipment & supplies
CEO: Jeff Goodman
Pr: Rick Costanzo
**Pr:* Rick Costanzom
**Pr:* Dennis Olbrich
**Pr:* Nicki Zongrone
**CFO:* Mark Alflatt

D-U-N-S 14-456-8631
KODIAK FRESH PRODUCE LLC
KODIAK PRODUCE
1033 E Maricopa Fwy, Phoenix, AZ 85034-5505
Tel (602) 253-2236 *Founded/Ownrshp* 2005
Sales 207.3MM^E *EMP* 225
SIC 5148

KODIAK OIL & GAS CORP.
See WHITING CANADIAN HOLDING CO ULC

KODIAK PRODUCE
See KODIAK FRESH PRODUCE LLC

D-U-N-S 01-754-9353
KOENIG EQUIPMENT INC
15213 State Route 274, Botkins, OH 45306-9586
Tel (937) 693-5000 *Founded/Ownrshp* 1974
Sales 200.0MM *EMP* 210
SIC 5999 0782 Farm equipment & supplies; Lawn & garden services
CEO: Raymond Koenig
**Pr:* Aaron Koenig
**Treas:* Gene Derringer
Chf Mktg O: Marguerite Kleinedler
**VP:* Jack Koenig

D-U-N-S 14-791-8601 EXP
KOFAX INC
(*Suby of* KOFAX LIMITED) ★
15211 Laguna Canyon Rd, Irvine, CA 92618-3146
Tel (949) 783-1000 *Founded/Ownrshp* 1985
Sales 270.0MM^E *EMP* 505
SIC 3577 7371 Input/output equipment, computer; Computer software development
CEO: Reynolds C Bish
CFO: Stefan Gaiser
CFO: Paul Smith
**Ex VP:* Howard Dratler
**Ex VP:* Jim Nicol
Ex VP: Wm B Weller
Sr VP: Karl Doyle
Sr VP: Steven Porter
**Sr VP:* Lynne Scheid
Sr VP: Owen Taraniuk
VP: Colleen Edwards
VP: Wayne Ford
VP: Rupert Grafendorfer
VP: Brad Hamilton
VP: Phillip Jones
VP: Dermot McCauley
VP: David Tankersley
VP: Tom Ullman

D-U-N-S 07-925-6419
KOFAX LIMITED
(*Suby of* LEXMARK INTERNATIONAL INC) ★
15211 Laguna Canyon Rd, Irvine, CA 92618-3146
Tel (949) 783-1000 *Founded/Ownrshp* 2015
Sales 276.5MM^E *EMP* 1,400^E
SIC 7372 Prepackaged software; Business oriented computer software
CEO: Reynolds C Bish
**CFO:* James Arnold Jr
Chf Mktg O: Grant Johnson
Ex VP: Bradford Weller
CTO: Anthony Macciola
Dir IT: Johnathan Corrington
Dir IT: Joe Fiedler
VP Sls: Craig Roy

KOHL WHOLESALE
See N KOHL GROCER CO

KOHLBERG & COMPANY
See KOHLBERG & CO LLC

D-U-N-S 01-255-0153
KOHLBERG & CO LLC
KOHLBERG & COMPANY
111 Radio Circle Dr, Mount Kisco, NY 10549-2609
Tel (914) 241-7430 *Founded/Ownrshp* 1987
Sales 8.9MMM^E *EMP* 37,730
SIC 6726 6211 Investment offices; Security brokers & dealers
Treas: Walter W Farley
VP: Tom Gaffney
VP: Ted Jeon
VP: David A Lorch
VP: Benjamin Mao
VP: Joseph Regent
VP: Jean Roberts
VP: Mary-Ann Sievert
VP: Zachary Viders
Prin: Marion H Antonini
Prin: George T Brophy

D-U-N-S 06-022-3393 IMP/EXP
■ **KOHLBERG KRAVIS ROBERTS & CO LP**
(*Suby of* KKR & CO LP) ★
9 W 57th St Ste 4200, New York, NY 10019-2707
Tel (212) 750-8300 *Founded/Ownrshp* 1976
Sales 884.9MM^E *EMP* 1,014^E
SIC 6726

D-U-N-S 96-277-1775
KOHLBERG SPORTS GROUP INC
(*Suby of* KOHLBERG & CO) ★
111 Radio Circle Dr, Mount Kisco, NY 10549-2609
Tel (914) 241-7430 *Founded/Ownrshp* 2010
Sales 878.3M^E *EMP* 5,025^E
SIC 3949 Hockey equipment & supplies, general

D-U-N-S 08-001-7466
KOHLBERG TE INVESTORS VII-B LP
(*Suby of* KOHLBERG & CO) ★
111 Radio Circle Dr, Mount Kisco, NY 10549-2609
Tel (914) 241-7430 *Founded/Ownrshp* 2015
Sales 114.1M^E *EMP* 2,542^E
SIC 6799 Investors

D-U-N-S 00-607-3225 IMP/EXP
KOHLER CO
444 Highland Dr, Kohler, WI 53044-1500
Tel (920) 457-4441 *Founded/Ownrshp* 1873
Sales 8.0MMM^E *EMP* 30,000^E
Accts Pricewaterhousecooper Llp
SIC 3431 3432 3261 2511 2521 3519 Plumbing fixtures: enameled iron cast iron or pressed metal; Bathroom fixtures, including sinks; Plumbing fixture fittings & trim; Bathroom accessories/fittings, vitreous china or earthenware; Plumbing fixtures, vitreous china; Wood household furniture; Wood office furniture; Gasoline engines
Pr: K David Kohler
Pr: Scott Anderson
Pr: Jeff Mueller
Pr: Jim Westdorp
Treas: John Suralik
Sr VP: Delbert P Haas
**Sr VP:* Laura E Kohler
Sr VP: James M Robinson
VP: Amy Adams
VP: Barbara Bergin
VP: Natalie A Black
VP: Elizabeth Brady
VP: Daniel Brohn
VP: Steven Cassady
VP: Ryan Cloud
VP: Bill Coisineau
VP: Gerard Gallenberger
VP: Underwood Gregg
VP: Delbert Haas
VP: Joe Hnilicka
VP: Otto Kopietzki
Board of Directors: Natalie A Black, John M Kohler Jr Director, Jeff M Fettig, William C Foote, Glen H Hiner, Jeffrey A Joerres, Rachael D Kohler, Michael H Thaman

D-U-N-S 08-906-6484 IMP/EXP
KOHLER INTERIORS FURNITURE CO
MCGUIRE FURNITURE
(*Suby of* KOHLER CO) ★
1105 22nd St Se, Hickory, NC 28602-9670
Tel (828) 624-7000 *Founded/Ownrshp* 1986
Sales 208.8MM^E *EMP* 716^E
SIC 2511 5021 Wood household furniture; Household furniture
Pr: Rachel D Kohler
CFO: Martin D Agard

Sr VP: Rick Vaughn
Genl Mgr: Mitch Stotts

D-U-N-S 78-740-8996
▲ **KOHLS CORP**
N56w17000 Ridgewood Dr, Menomonee Falls, WI 53051-7096
Tel (262) 703-7000 *Founded/Ownrshp* 1962
Sales 19.2MMM *EMP* 140,000
Accts Ernst & Young Llp Milwaukee
Tkr Sym KSS *Exch* NYS
SIC 5311 5961 Department stores; Department stores, non-discount; Catalog & mail-order houses
Ch Bd: Kevin Mansell
COO: Sona Chawla
CFO: Wesley S McDonald
Ofcr: Richard D Schepp
Sr Ex VP: Tom Kingsbury
Sr Ex VP: John Worthington
Ex VP: Nancy Feldman
Ex VP: Debby Fisher
Ex VP: Telvin Jeffries
Ex VP: Amy Kocourek
Ex VP: Sarah Masterson
Ex VP: Teresa Sabish
VP: Annette Adams
VP: Linn Allison
VP: Joseph Bagby
VP: Sunil S Bhardwaj
VP: Randy Blackburn
VP: Nancy Blok-Anderson
VP: Carrie Brown-Schmidt
VP: Scott Conant
VP: Brent Cook
Board of Directors: Peter Boneparth, Steven A Burd, Dale E Jones, Jonas Prising, John E Schlifske, Frank V Sica, Stephanie A Streeter, Nina G Vaca, Stephen E Watson

D-U-N-S 15-420-2360 IMP
■ **KOHLS DEPARTMENT STORES INC**
(*Suby of* KOHLS CORP) ★
N56w17000 Ridgewood Dr, Menomonee Falls, WI 53051-7096
Tel (262) 703-7000 *Founded/Ownrshp* 1992
Sales 16.9MMM^E *EMP* 126,000
SIC 5311 Department stores, non-discount
CEO: Kevin Mansell
**COO:* Sona Chawla
CFO: Wesley S McDonald
**Chf Cred:* Michelle Gass
**Ex VP:* Kenneth Bonning
Ex VP: Donald A Brennan
Ex VP: David J Campisi
Ex VP: Chris Capuano
Ex VP: Joanne Crevoiserat
Ex VP: Peggy Eskenasi
Ex VP: Telvin Jeffries
Ex VP: John Lesko
Ex VP: Richard Leto
Sr VP: Shakeel Farooque
Sr VP: Bernard Powers
VP: Jack H Boyle
VP: John M Worthington
Exec: Krisi Adams
Exec: Michael Clevinger
Exec: Edward Collins
Exec: William Cushing
Board of Directors: James D Ericson, Frank V Sica, Herbert Simon, Peter M Sommerhauser, R Elton White

D-U-N-S 00-167-5623 IMP
KOI ENTERPRISES INC
K O I
(*Suby of* FISHER AUTO PARTS INC) ★
2701 Spring Grove Ave, Cincinnati, OH 45225-2221
Tel (513) 357-2400 *Founded/Ownrshp* 2014
Sales 612.2MM^E *EMP* 1,000
SIC 5013 5531 Automotive supplies & parts; Automotive & home supply stores
Pr: David Wesselman
**Treas:* Greg Steppe
IT Man: Chuck Smith

D-U-N-S 01-017-7031
■ **KOKO OHA INVESTMENTS INC** (HI)
(*Suby of* PAR PACIFIC HOLDINGS INC) ★
1100 Alakea St Fl 8, Honolulu, HI 96813-2833
Tel (808) 535-5999 *Founded/Ownrshp* 2007, 2015
Sales 110.4MM^E *EMP* 900^E
SIC 5172 6719 Petroleum products; Service station supplies, petroleum; Personal holding companies, except banks
Pr: Jim R Yates
CFO: Kaiyo Sayle Hirashima
VP: David C Hulihee
VP: Bill D Mills
VP: Keith M Yoshida

D-U-N-S 10-064-8146
KOKOMO SCHOOL CORP
LAFAYETTE PARK ELEMENTARY MIDD
1500 S Washington St, Kokomo, IN 46902-2011
Tel (765) 455-8000 *Founded/Ownrshp* 1993
Sales 79.1MM^E *EMP* 1,100
SIC 8211 Public elementary & secondary schools
**Treas:* Joyce Aaron
**Treas:* Geralynn Smalling
Bd of Dir: Ted Schuck
Dir Soc: Cynthia Evans
Dir Bus: Michelle Kronk
MIS Dir: Richard Arroyo
Cmptr Lab: Judy Wininger
Tech Mgr: Adam Heady
Opers Mgr: Dwight Cline
Pr Dir: Dave Barnes
Board of Directors: James Little

D-U-N-S 10-769-8706 IMP
KOKOSING CONSTRUCTION CO INC
(*Suby of* KOKOSING INC) ★
886 Mckinley Ave, Columbus, OH 43222-1187
Tel (614) 228-1029 *Founded/Ownrshp* 1981
Sales 583.6MM^E *EMP* 1,061
Accts Crowe Horwath Llp South Bend
SIC 1611 1622 1629 1542 1541 1623 General contractor, highway & street construction; Highway & street paving contractor; Bridge construction; Waste water & sewage treatment plant construction; Commercial & office building, new construction; Industrial buildings, new construction; Renovation, remodeling & repairs: industrial buildings; Sewer line construction; Water main construction
CEO: W Barth Burgett
**CFO:* Timothy Freed
**CFO:* James H Geiser
CFO: James Graves
**Ex VP:* Marsha Rinehart
**Sr VP:* Daniel J Compston
**Sr VP:* Daniel Walker
VP: Valerie Matusik
VP: John Neighbors
Area Mgr: Bart Moody
Genl Mgr: Joe A Celuch

D-U-N-S 07-778-7984 IMP
KOKOSING CONSTRUCTION INC
1516 Timken Rd, Wooster, OH 44691-9401
Tel (330) 263-4168 *Founded/Ownrshp* 2002
Sales 92.8MM^E *EMP* 2,500
SIC 1611 Highway & street paving contractor
Pr: Brian Burgett

D-U-N-S 07-981-3347
KOKOSING INC
6235 Wstrville Rd Ste 200, Westerville, OH 43081
Tel (614) 212-5700 *Founded/Ownrshp* 2015
Sales 718.7MM^E *EMP* 1,900
Accts Crowe Horwath Llp South Bend
SIC 1611 General contractor, highway & street construction; Highway & street paving contractor
**Pr:* Dan Compston

D-U-N-S 88-425-8369
KOKUSAI SEMICONDUCTOR EQUIPMENT CORP
(*Suby of* HITACHI KOKUSAI ELECTRIC INC.)
2460 N 1st St Ste 290, San Jose, CA 95131-1024
Tel (408) 456-2750 *Founded/Ownrshp* 1992
Sales 109.3MM *EMP* 96
SIC 5065 7629 Semiconductor devices; Communication equipment; Electronic equipment repair
CEO: Fumiyuki Kanai
**CFO:* Kenichi Sato
VP Sls: Len Elias

D-U-N-S 00-612-7294 IMP/EXP
KOLBE & KOLBE MILLWORK CO INC (WI)
KOLBE WINDOWS & DOORS
1323 S 11th Ave, Wausau, WI 54401-5980
Tel (715) 842-5666 *Founded/Ownrshp* 1973
Sales 254.9MM^E *EMP* 1,150
SIC 5031 2431 Millwork; Window frames, wood; Doors, wood
CEO: Mike Salsieder
Pr: Judith Gorski
Pr: George Waldvogle
VP: Donald Huehnerfuss
VP: George Waldvogel
Rgnl Mgr: Steve Charuka
Rgnl Mgr: Jerry Jorgenson
Rgnl Mgr: Ted Olear
Genl Mgr: Scott Orlikowski
Dir IT: Dusten Tornow
VP Mfg: Jeffrey De Lonay

KOLBE WINDOWS & DOORS
See KOLBE & KOLBE MILLWORK CO INC

D-U-N-S 96-947-5763 IMP/EXP
■ **KOLBERG-PIONEER INC**
(*Suby of* ASTEC INDUSTRIES INC) ★
700 W 21st St, Yankton, SD 57078-1506
Tel (605) 665-9311 *Founded/Ownrshp* 1997
Sales 112.0MM^E *EMP* 420
SIC 3532 3531 3535 Mining machinery; Construction machinery; Conveyors & conveying equipment
Pr: Jeff May
VP: Bill Carpenter
Advt Mgr: Curt Peterka

D-U-N-S 78-217-1946
KOLL MANAGEMENT SERVICES INC
4343 Von Karman Ave # 150, Newport Beach, CA 92660-2099
Tel (949) 833-3030 *Founded/Ownrshp* 1997
Sales 29.1MM^E *EMP* 2,400
SIC 6531 8741 Real estate managers; Management services
Ch Bd: Donald M Koll

D-U-N-S 00-111-7290 IMP/EXP
■ **KOLLMORGEN CORP** (NY)
DANAHER MOTION
(*Suby of* FORTIVE CORP) ★
203a W Rock Rd, Radford, VA 24141-4026
Tel (540) 639-2495 *Founded/Ownrshp* 1951, 2016
Sales 495.4MM^E *EMP* 2,025
SIC 3621 3825 3827 3861 Motors & generators; Servomotors, electric; Generators & sets, electric; Motors, electric; Test equipment for electronic & electrical circuits; Periscopes; Densitometers
Pr: Michael Wall
Pr: John Boyland
VP: Ray Butler
VP: Hil Johnson
VP: Andrew McCauley
Snr Sftwr: Thomas Bannish
Sftwr Eng: Carol Wasolowski
Mtls Mgr: Shawn Jones
Ql Cn Mgr: Frank Sadlowski

D-U-N-S 93-213-5148
KOLLSMAN INC
(*Suby of* ELBIT SYSTEMS OF AMERICA LLC) ★
220 Daniel Webster Hwy, Merrimack, NH 03054-4837
Tel (603) 889-2500 *Founded/Ownrshp* 1995
Sales 92.8MM^E *EMP* 550
SIC 3812 3629 Search & navigation equipment; Electrochemical generators (fuel cells)
Pr: Ranaan Horowitz
**COO:* Yuval Ramon
VP: Joann Lifehood

Genl Mgr: Holly Donahue
IT Man: Keith Czulno
IT Man: David Merry
IT Man: Lynwood Shaw
IT Man: Mike Villanueva
Sys Mgr: Ed Rosenbloom
VP Opers: Real Madore
Opers Mgr: Erin Krajewski

KOLLSMAN INSTRUMENT DIVISION
See SEQUA CORP

D-U-N-S 00-772-7829 IMP/EXP
KOLMAR AMERICAS INC
(Suby of KOLMAR GROUP AG)
10 Middle St Ph, Bridgeport, CT 06604-4229
Tel (203) 873-2078 Founded/Ownrshp 1998
Sales 196.2MM[E] EMP 24
SIC 5172 Petroleum products
Pr: Rafael Aviner
CFO: Kevin Luddy
*VP: Paul Francis Teta

KOLMAR INC. / PORT JERVIS
See KOLMAR LABORATORIES INC

D-U-N-S 00-153-5103 IMP/EXP
KOLMAR LABORATORIES INC (DE)
KOLMAR INC. / PORT JERVIS
(Suby of CORPORATION DEVELOPPEMENT KNOWLTON INC)
20 W King St, Port Jervis, NY 12771-3061
Tel (845) 856-5311 Founded/Ownrshp 1937, 2015
Sales 133.2MM[E] EMP 700[E]
SIC 2844

KOLPAK
See KMT REFRIGERATION INC

KOMAR COMPANY, THE
See CHARLES KOMAR & SONS INC

D-U-N-S 13-410-6595 IMP
KOMAR INTIMATES LLC
(Suby of KOMAR CO) ★
90 Hudson St, Jersey City, NJ 07302-3900
Tel (212) 725-1500 Founded/Ownrshp 2011
Sales 88.0MM EMP 880
SIC 5621 Women's clothing stores; Women's sportswear
CEO: Charles Komar
CFO: Mary Taibbi

D-U-N-S 61-875-0772 IMP/EXP
KOMATSU AMERICA CORP
(Suby of KOMATSU LTD.)
1701 Golf Rd Ste 1-100, Rolling Meadows, IL 60008-4234
Tel (847) 437-5800 Founded/Ownrshp 1970
Sales 1.6MMM[E] EMP 4,000
SIC 5082 3532 3531 Mining machinery & equipment, except petroleum; Mining machinery; Construction machinery
Ch Bd: Rod Schrader
Pr: Max Masayuki Moriyama
COO: Hisashi Shinozuka
Ex VP: Ken Furuse
Ex VP: Gary Kasbeer
Ex VP: Noboru Sato
Sr VP: Nob Sato
VP: Dan Funcannon
VP: Ed Powers
VP: Hiroshi Yasuda
Prin: Dave Grzelak

D-U-N-S 14-490-7193 IMP/EXP
KOMATSU AMERICA INDUSTRIES LLC
(Suby of KOMATSU AMERICA CORP) ★
1701 Golf Rd Ste 1-100, Rolling Meadows, IL 60008-4234
Tel (847) 437-5800 Founded/Ownrshp 1998
Sales 150.0MM EMP 47
SIC 5084 Metal refining machinery & equipment

D-U-N-S 09-000-2577 IMP/EXP
KOMODIDAD DISTRIBUTORS INC
GATSBY
156 Km 58 8, Caguas, PR 00727
Tel (787) 746-3188 Founded/Ownrshp 1965
Sales 192.8MM[E] EMP 475
Accts De Angel & Compania San Juan
SIC 5137 5136 5094 Women's & children's clothing; Women's & children's lingerie & undergarments; Women's & children's accessories; Men's & boys' clothing; Jewelry
Pr: Jorge Galliano
*VP: Carlos Galliano
Genl Mgr: Gisela Cartagena

D-U-N-S 93-186-1272
▲ KONA GRILL INC
7150 E Camelback Rd # 220, Scottsdale, AZ 85251-1233
Tel (480) 922-8100 Founded/Ownrshp 1998
Sales 143.0MM EMP 2,743
Accts Ernst & Young Llp Phoenix Ar
Tkr Sym KONA Exch NGM
SIC 5812 6794 Grills (eating places); Franchises, selling or licensing
Pr: Berke Bakay
*Ch Bd: James R Jundt
COO: Zach Bredemann
CFO: Christi Hing
VP: Angie Cesario
VP: Rachel Luther
VP: Marci Rude
Exec: Dusty Crane
Exec: Ahmed Ibrahim
Exec: Alfredo Romero
Exec: Benjamin Theis
Exec: Willard Thompson
Board of Directors: Richard J Hauser, Marcus E Jundt, Leonard M Newman, Steven W Schussler, Anthony L Winczewski

D-U-N-S 01-562-1964 IMP/EXP
KONAMI GAMING INC
(Suby of KONAMI HOLDINGS CORPORATION)
585 Konami Cir, Las Vegas, NV 89119-3754
Tel (702) 616-1400 Founded/Ownrshp 2011
Sales 397.4MM EMP 405
SIC 5092 3999 Bingo games & supplies; Slot machines
Pr: Satoshi Sakamoto
*Pr: Jay Canaday
*COO: Steve Sutherland
*Sr VP: Thomas A Jingoli
QA Dir: Erdulfo Devicente
Netwrk Eng: Brian Alu
Ql Cn Mgr: David Duperault

D-U-N-S 11-320-4846 IMP
KONE ELEVATOR
(Suby of KONE HOLLAND B.V.)
1 Kone Ct, Moline, IL 61265-1380
Tel (309) 764-6771 Founded/Ownrshp 1981
Sales 76.2MM[E] EMP 4,200
SIC 7699 3534 Elevators: inspection, service & repair; Elevators & equipment
Sls Mgr: Ty Jewell
Sales Asso: Matt Delks

D-U-N-S 00-526-2308 IMP/EXP
KONE INC
(Suby of KONE OYJ)
1 Kone Ct, Moline, IL 61265-1380
Tel (309) 764-6771 Founded/Ownrshp 1956, 1965
Sales 895.3MM[E] EMP 4,295
SIC 7699 3534 1796 Elevators: inspection, service & repair; Escalators, passenger & freight; Walkways, moving; Dumbwaiters; Elevator installation & conversion
CEO: Larry Wash
*CFO: Eriikka Sderstrm
Ofcr: Frank Manuella
*Sr VP: Dennis Gerard
*Sr VP: David McFadden
*Sr VP: Charles Moore
*Sr VP: Kenneth E Schmid Jr
*Sr VP: Kurt Stepaniak
VP: Minna Aula
VP: Jeffrey Blum
VP: Stephen Cox
VP: Wayne Elias
VP: Timo Pakarinen
VP: Alexander Vitt

D-U-N-S 80-474-9505 IMP/EXP
KONECRANES INC
(Suby of KONECRANES ABP)
4401 Gateway Blvd, Springfield, OH 45502-9339
Tel (937) 525-5533 Founded/Ownrshp 2014
Sales 565.1MM[E] EMP 2,100
SIC 3536 Cranes, industrial plant
Pr: Pekka Lundmark
Pr: Pete Robbins
CFO: Teuvo R Ki
*Treas: Steve Mayes
*VP: Bernard D'Ambrosi Jr
*VP: Keith Kings
VP: Jaakko Koppinen
*VP: Steve Kosir
*VP: Sirpa Poitsalo
*VP: Kim Sullivan
*VP: Mark Ubl
VP: Debbie Yost
Board of Directors: Teo Ottola, Tom Sothard

KONGSBERG AUTO POWER PRDCT SYS
See KONGSBERG POWER PRODUCTS SYSTEMS I INC

KONGSBERG AUTOMOTIVE
See KONGSBERG HOLDING III INC

D-U-N-S 60-663-3337 IMP
KONGSBERG AUTOMOTIVE INC
(Suby of KONGSBERG AUTOMOTIVE ASA)
27275 Haggerty Rd Ste 610, Novi, MI 48377-3635
Tel (248) 468-1300 Founded/Ownrshp 2008
Sales 263.2MM[E] EMP 900
SIC 3714 Motor vehicle parts & accessories; Heaters, motor vehicle
CEO: Hans Peter Havdal
*Ex VP: Joachim Magnusson
*Ex VP: Jarle Nymoen
*Ex VP: Anders Nystrm
*Ex VP: Trond Stabekk
Genl Mgr: Scott Trayer
Board of Directors: Hans Peter Havdal

D-U-N-S 82-774-1971
KONGSBERG HOLDING III INC
KONGSBERG AUTOMOTIVE
(Suby of KONGSBERG AUTOMOTIVE ASA)
27275 Haggerty Rd Ste 610, Novi, MI 48377-3635
Tel (248) 468-1300 Founded/Ownrshp 2008
Sales 271.8MM[E] EMP 2,500
SIC 3714 Motor vehicle parts & accessories
Pr: Raymond Boyma

D-U-N-S 08-202-1296 IMP
KONGSBERG POWER PRODUCTS SYSTEMS I INC
KONGSBERG AUTO POWER PRDCT SYS
(Suby of KONGSBERG AUTOMOTIVE) ★
300 S Cochran St, Willis, TX 77378-9034
Tel (936) 856-2971 Founded/Ownrshp 2008
Sales 203.5MM[E] EMP 2,300
SIC 3714 Motor vehicle parts & accessories; Antisway devices, motor vehicle
Ex VP: Scott Paquette
*VP: Jonathan Reeve

D-U-N-S 12-521-2154
KONIAG DEVELOPMENT CO LLC
K D C
(Suby of KONIAG INC) ★
3800 Centerpoint Dr # 502, Anchorage, AK 99503-5961
Tel (907) 561-2668 Founded/Ownrshp 2002
Sales 246.0MM EMP 820
Accts Kpmg Llp Anchorage Ak
SIC 8741 6719 Management services; Investment holding companies, except banks
Pr: Thomas Panamaroff
*Ch Bd: Elizabeth Perry

D-U-N-S 07-820-3361
KONIAG INC
3800 Cntrpoint Dr Ste 502, Kodiak, AK 99615
Tel (907) 486-2530 Founded/Ownrshp 1972
Sales 251.5MM EMP 834
Accts Kpmg Llp Anchorage Ak
SIC 6552 6519 6719 Subdividers & developers; Landholding office; Investment holding companies, except banks
*Ch Bd: Ronald Unger
*Pr: Thomas Panamaroff
*CEO: Christopher Morgan
*CEO: Elizabeth Perry
CFO: Will Anderson
*Ch: Ron Unger
*Ex VP: Jessica Graham
VP: Debbie Lukin

D-U-N-S 00-170-7322 IMP/EXP
KONICA MINOLTA BUSINESS SOLUTIONS USA INC
MINOLTA BUSINESS SYSTEMS
(Suby of KONICA MINOLTA HOLDINGS USA INC) ★
100 Williams Dr, Ramsey, NJ 07446-2907
Tel (201) 825-4000 Founded/Ownrshp 1959
Sales 437.8MM[E] EMP 590
SIC 5044 5045 Office equipment; Copying equipment; Computers, peripherals & software; Printers, computer
CEO: Toshimitsu Taiko
Pr: Daniel Davidson
Pr: Ernest Iovine
CFO: Mark Crossley
CFO: John Thielke
Ex VP: Kazuhiro Goto
Sr VP: Mark Bradord
Sr VP: Barbara Stainbrook
VP: Milo Bump
VP: Brian Cupka
VP: Todd G Foote
VP: David Hartman
VP: Todd Jones
VP: Michael Kinnick
VP: Todd Lalor
VP: Nelson T Lin
VP: Peder Malchow
VP: Richard Mamola
VP: Barry Nickerson
VP: Martin Noci
VP: Keith Okamoto
Board of Directors: Jun Haraguchi, William Troxil

D-U-N-S 06-929-3090 IMP/EXP
KONICA MINOLTA HEALTHCARE AMERICAS INC
(Suby of KONICA MINOLTA HOLDINGS USA INC) ★
411 Newark Pompton Tpke, Wayne, NJ 07470-6657
Tel (973) 633-1500 Founded/Ownrshp 1989
Sales 120.0MM EMP 85
SIC 5047 3861 3845 Medical & hospital equipment; Photographic equipment & supplies; Electromedical equipment
Pr: Mr David Widmann
*CFO: Jerry Liebowitz
Treas: Ken Nozaki
Ex VP: Kirk Ichijo
Sr VP: Brian T Noyes
Dist Mgr: George Mitchell
CIO: Nelson T Lin
IT Man: Michael Hunstein
Sys Mgr: Karunasagar Narla
VP Sls: Richard Miller
Mktg Mgr: Steven Eisner

D-U-N-S 13-825-6677 IMP
KONICA MINOLTA HOLDINGS USA INC
(Suby of KONICA MINOLTA, INC.)
100 Williams Dr, Ramsey, NJ 07446-2907
Tel (201) 825-4000 Founded/Ownrshp 2004
Sales 713.8MM[E] EMP 605[E]
SIC 5043 5065 5044 5047 Photographic equipment & supplies; Photographic cameras, projectors, equipment & supplies; Photographic processing equipment; Facsimile equipment; Tapes, audio & video recording; Office equipment; Duplicating machines; Microfilm equipment; Photocopy machines; X-ray film & supplies; X-ray machines & tubes
Pr: Hideki Okamura
VP: Richard Miller
Mktg Mgr: Steven Eisner
Sls Mgr: Randall Peck

D-U-N-S 61-004-5643 IMP
KONICA MINOLTA SUPPLIES MANUFACTURING USA INC
(Suby of KONICA MINOLTA HOLDINGS USA INC) ★
51 Hatfield Ln, Goshen, NY 10924-6712
Tel (845) 294-8400 Founded/Ownrshp 1987
Sales 100.0MM EMP 75
Accts Kpmg Llp Short Hills Nj
SIC 3861 Toners, prepared photographic (not made in chemical plants)
Pr: Miyako Asai
MIS Dir: Gary Gould

D-U-N-S 96-177-6069
KONING RESTAURANTS INTERNATIONAL LC
PIZZA HUT
15600 Nw 15th Ave, Miami, FL 33169-5604
Tel (305) 430-1200 Founded/Ownrshp 1999
Sales 47.5MM[E] EMP 2,000
SIC 5812 Pizzeria, chain
CEO: Alfredo Salas
CFO: Omar Sezer
Genl Couns: Elliot Tunis

KONTES OF CALIFORNIA
See KIMBLE CHASE LIFE SCIENCE AND RESEARCH PRODUCTS LLC

D-U-N-S 10-588-9732
KONVISSER CUSTOM SOFTWARE
5109 Deer Run Cir, Orchard Lake, MI 48323-1510
Tel (248) 682-0717 Founded/Ownrshp 2002
Sales 214.1MM EMP 2
Accts Steakley & Gilbert Pc Okla
SIC 7371 Custom computer programming services
Owner: Mark Konvisser

D-U-N-S 82-866-3349
KONY INC
7380 W Sand Lake Rd # 390, Orlando, FL 32819-5290
Tel (407) 730-5669 Founded/Ownrshp 2008
Sales 240.2MM[E] EMP 1,000
SIC 7372 Application computer software
Pr: Thomas Hogan
Pr: Jim Lambert
*Treas: Lesli Whisenant
*Ex VP: Hollie Castro
Sr VP: John Stewart
VP: Jonathan Best
VP: Oscar Clarke
VP: Carlos Falconi
VP: Theresa Heinz
*VP: John Joyce
VP: Jean Kondo
VP: Les Russell
VP: Andrew Timblin
*VP: Robert Turner
VP: Steve Ware
Assoc Dir: Prabhakar Cherukuri

KOO KOO ROO
See BROSNA INC

KOOL PAK
See NESS HOLDING CO

KOOL SMILES
See BENEVIS LLC

D-U-N-S 80-951-5377
KOONTZ CONSTRUCTION INC
755 E Mulberry Ave # 100, San Antonio, TX 78212-3129
Tel (210) 826-2600 Founded/Ownrshp 2015
Sales 145.0MM EMP 82
SIC 1542 1522 Nonresidential construction; Commercial & office building contractors; Hotel/motel & multi-family home construction
Pr: Bart C Koontz
*Pr: Henry Serry
*CFO: Troves B Gilbert
*Ex VP: Chris Corso
*VP: Robert Grier
Genl Couns: Erwin Caban

KOONTZ-WAGNER
See KW SERVICES LLC

D-U-N-S 01-641-6893
KOORSEN FIRE & SECURITY INC
2719 N Arlington Ave, Indianapolis, IN 46218-3300
Tel (317) 542-1800 Founded/Ownrshp 1968
Sales 230.2MM[E] EMP 625
SIC 5099 7389 5199 5063 1731

D-U-N-S 02-106-2989 IMP
KOOS MANUFACTURING INC
BIG STAR
2741 Seminole Ave, South Gate, CA 90280-5550
Tel (323) 249-1000 Founded/Ownrshp 1985
Sales 98.4MM[E] EMP 800
SIC 7389 Sewing contractor
Pr: U Yul Ku
*VP: Kee H Fong
*VP: John Hur

KOOTENAI HEALTH
See KOOTENAI HOSPITAL DISTRICT

D-U-N-S 07-183-6936
KOOTENAI HOSPITAL DISTRICT
KOOTENAI HEALTH
2003 Kootenai Health Way, Coeur D Alene, ID 83814-6051
Tel (208) 625-4000 Founded/Ownrshp 1956
Sales 398.8MM EMP 2,776
SIC 8062 8063 8093 8734 General medical & surgical hospitals; Psychiatric hospitals; Rehabilitation center, outpatient treatment; Radiation dosimetry laboratory
Chf Rad: Albert Martinez
*CFO: Kim Webb
Chf Mktg O: Walter Fairfax
VP: Joe Bujak
*VP: Jeremy S Evans
Dir Risk M: Lorraine Olshesky
Chf Nrs Of: Joan Simon
Genl Mgr: Jennifer Bean
CIO: Steve Garske
Sls&Mrk Ex: Mike Regan
VP Mktg: Cathy Kendrick

D-U-N-S 96-785-6167
KOP KLINE PLAZA LLC
BRIXMOR PROPERTY GROUP
450 Lexington Ave Fl 13, New York, NY 10017-3956
Tel (212) 661-9890 Founded/Ownrshp 2004
Sales 500.0MM EMP 800
SIC 6512 Nonresidential building operators
*Ex VP: Steven Siegel

D-U-N-S 61-343-4856
▲ KOPPERS HOLDINGS INC
436 7th Ave, Pittsburgh, PA 15219-1826
Tel (412) 227-2001 Founded/Ownrshp 1988
Sales 1.6MMM EMP 2,142
Tkr Sym KOP Exch NYS
SIC 2865 2491 2895 3312 2899 Cyclic crudes, coal tar; Poles, posts & pilings: treated wood; Carbon black; Coke produced in chemical recovery coke ovens; Coke oven products (chemical recovery); Chemical preparations
Pr: Leroy M Ball Jr
*Ch Bd: David M Hillenbrand
CFO: Michael J Zugay
Treas: Louann E Tronsberg-Deihle
Sr VP: Steven R Lacy
Board of Directors: Cynthia A Baldwin, Sharon Feng,

Albert J Neupaver, Louis L Testoni, Stephen R Tritch, T Michael Young

D-U-N-S 19-699-1582 IMP/EXP

■ KOPPERS INC
(*Suby of* KOPPERS HOLDINGS INC) ★
436 7th Ave, Pittsburgh, PA 15219-1826
Tel (412) 227-2001 *Founded/Ownrshp* 1988
Sales 644.5MM[E] *EMP* 1,589
SIC 2865 2491 3312 2899 Cyclic crudes, coal tar; Poles, posts & pilings: treated wood; Coke produced in chemical recovery coke ovens; Coke oven products (chemical recovery); Oils & essential oils
Pr: Leroy M Ball Jr
Pr: Robert Dashevsky
CFO: Leroy Ball
Treas: Louann Deihle
Sr VP: Paul A Goydan
Sr VP: Steven R Lacy
Sr VP: Thomas D Loadman
VP: Ernest S Bryon
VP: Ernest Byron
VP: Randall Collins
VP: James T Dietz
VP: Jim Dietz
VP: Donald E Evans
VP: Leslie Hyde
VP: Tom Loadman
VP: Mark R McCormack
VP: Markus Spiess
VP: Robert Wombles
Exec: Heidi Branthoover
Exec: Kelly Hester
Board of Directors: Cynthia A Baldwin, David M Hillenbrand Phd, James C Stalder, T Michael Young

D-U-N-S 00-211-2944 EXP

■ KOPPERS PERFORMANCE CHEMICALS INC (GA)
(*Suby of* KOPPERS INC) ★
1016 Everee Inn Rd, Griffin, GA 30224-4733
Tel (770) 228-8434 *Founded/Ownrshp* 1934
Sales 114.7MM[E] *EMP* 200
SIC 2491 Preserving (creosoting) of wood
Pr: Paul A Goydan
Treas: Tracie McCormick
**Chf Mktg O:* Gary Converse
Dir IT: Ken Brooks

KORBEL CHAMPAGNE CELLERS
See F KORBEL & BROS

KORDIAL NTRNTS PROF SPPLEMENTS
See PROGRESSIVE LABORATORIES INC

D-U-N-S 00-809-1071 IMP/EXP

KORDSA INC
(*Suby of* KORDSA GLOBAL ENDUSTRIYEL IPLIK VE KORD BEZI SANAYI VE TICARET ANONIM SIRKETI)
4501 N Access Rd, Chattanooga, TN 37415-3816
Tel (423) 643-8300 *Founded/Ownrshp* 2005
Sales 391.6MM[E] *EMP* 1,200
SIC 5169 Chemicals & allied products
VP: Mesut Ada
**Treas:* Darrell Smutz
**Treas:* Charlise Way
CIO: Richard Massey

D-U-N-S 15-135-6615 IMP

KORG USA INC
(*Suby of* KORG INC.)
316 S Service Rd, Melville, NY 11747-3228
Tel (631) 390-6500 *Founded/Ownrshp* 1985
Sales 84.5MM[E] *EMP* 112
SIC 5099 Musical instruments; Musical instruments parts & accessories
Ch Bd: Joseph Castronovo
**Sr VP:* Mitch Colby
VP: Andy Rossi
Genl Mgr: Sakae Yoshinaga
Software D: Brittany Sajeski
Netwrk Eng: Joseph Roy
Natl Sales: Aj Reitz
VP Sls: Joseph Bredau
Mktg Mgr: Scott Fiesel
Mktg Mgr: Jennifer Lewis
Mktg Mgr: Barry Seiden

KORN FERRY
See KORN/FERRY INTERNATIONAL

D-U-N-S 07-649-4129

■ KORN FERRY HAY GROUP INC
(*Suby of* KORN FERRY) ★
33 S 6th St Ste 4900, Minneapolis, MN 55402-3716
Tel (612) 339-0927 *Founded/Ownrshp* 2013
Sales 91.3MM[E] *EMP* 575
SIC 8742

D-U-N-S 05-223-9530

▲ KORN/FERRY INTERNATIONAL
KORN FERRY
1900 Avenue Stars, Los Angeles, CA 90067
Tel (310) 552-1834 *Founded/Ownrshp* 1969
Sales 1.3MMM *EMP* 6,947
Tkr Sym KFY *Exch* NYS
SIC 8742 7361 Management consulting services; Executive placement
Pr: Gary D Burnison
**Ch Bd:* George T Shaheen
V Ch: Melanie Kusin
CEO: Stephen Kaye
CEO: Byrne Mulrooney
CFO: Robert P Rozek
VP: Sanitourian Armen
VP: Mike Carlin
VP: Roy Dar
VP: Marat Fookson
VP: David Grant
VP: Erika Joseph
VP: Karin Lucas
VP: Mark Neal
VP: Don Spetner
Exec: Melissa M Spezzano
Board of Directors: Doyle N Beneby, William R Floyd, Christina A Gold, Jerry P Leamon, Debra J Perry, Harry L You

D-U-N-S 07-934-1415

KOROSEAL INTERIOR PRODUCTS LLC
3875 Embassy Pkwy Ste 110, Fairlawn, OH 44333-8334
Tel (330) 668-7600 *Founded/Ownrshp* 2014
Sales 100.0MM[E] *EMP* 639[E]
SIC 3081 3089 3069 Floor or wall covering, unsupported plastic; Battery cases, plastic or plastic combination; Wallcoverings, rubber
CEO: Rich Runkel
COO: John Farrell
CFO: Richard Garcia
Ex VP: Eric Wroldsen
VP: Barb Leyba
Genl Mgr: Bill Calhoun
Genl Mgr: Thomas Roche
Dir IT: Nichole Sprutte
Plnt Mgr: Fred Yeagle
Manager: Sharlene Murtagh
Manager: Jim Price

D-U-N-S 60-590-3293

■ KORRY ELECTRONICS CO
(*Suby of* ESTERLINE TECHNOLOGIES CORP) ★
11910 Beverly Park Rd, Everett, WA 98204-3529
Tel (425) 297-9700 *Founded/Ownrshp* 1989
Sales 108.8MM[E] *EMP* 675
SIC 3613 Switchgear & switchboard apparatus; Panel & distribution boards & other related apparatus; Control panels, electric
Pr: Richard Brad Lawrence
**CFO:* Robert D George
**VP:* Frank E Houston
Prgrm Mgr: Don Glass
Prgrm Mgr: Sidney Lull
Genl Mgr: Fern Hansen
Snr Sftwr: Rik Lambey
Snr Sftwr: Chris Lykken
IT Man: Robert Eikenberry
Info Man: Betsy Jordan
Prd Mgr: Connie Trias

KORTE COMPANY, THE
See KORTE CONSTRUCTION CO

D-U-N-S 08-163-9411

KORTE CONSTRUCTION CO
KORTE COMPANY, THE
5700 Oakland Ave Ste 275, Saint Louis, MO 63110-1375
Tel (314) 231-3700 *Founded/Ownrshp* 1958
Sales 119.9MM *EMP* 170
Accts Rubinbrown Llp Saint Louis
SIC 1541 1542 Industrial buildings & warehouses; Commercial & office building, new construction
Pr: Todd Korte
Pr: Greg Korte
COO: Jason Mantle
CFO: William D Bououris
Ch: Ralph Korte
Sec: Susan Bowman
Ex VP: Thomas V Korte
Sr VP: Dennis Araujo
Sr VP: Dennis Calvert
Sr VP: Thomas Lyerla
VP: Chris Gilliam

D-U-N-S 36-192-2446 IMP

■ KOS PHARMACEUTICALS INC
(*Suby of* ABBVIE INC) ★
1 Cedarbrook Dr, Cranbury, NJ 08512-3618
Tel (609) 495-0500 *Founded/Ownrshp* 2006
Sales 52.2MM[E] *EMP* 1,361[E]
SIC 2834 Pharmaceutical preparations
CEO: Adrian Adams

D-U-N-S 07-407-9948

KOSAIR CHILDRENS HOSPITAL
(*Suby of* NORTON HOSPITALS INC) ★
231 E Chestnut St Ste 100, Louisville, KY 40202-3800
Tel (502) 629-6000 *Founded/Ownrshp* 1886
Sales 171.0MM[E] *EMP* 1,500
SIC 8062 General medical & surgical hospitals
Pr: Thomas D Kmetz
CFO: Jeffrey Lilly
**VP:* Jeff Lilly
Dir Rx: Edward Leist
IT Man: David Ross
Opthamlgy: Paul Rychwalski

D-U-N-S 11-857-4672

KOSHAN INC
PAYLESS FOODS
23501 Avalon Blvd, Carson, CA 90745-5522
Tel (310) 830-8241 *Founded/Ownrshp* 1984
Sales 87.6MM[E] *EMP* 550
SIC 5411 Grocery stores, independent
CEO: Bijan H Rodd
**Treas:* Frank Hendizadeh
**VP:* Sami Khoshbin

D-U-N-S 00-694-1298

KOSS CONSTRUCTION CO (IA)
5830 Sw Drury Ln, Topeka, KS 66604-2262
Tel (785) 228-2928 *Founded/Ownrshp* 1912
Sales 127.8MM[E] *EMP* 350
SIC 1611

KOST TIRE & MUFFLER
See KOST TIRE DISTRIBUTORS INC

D-U-N-S 01-412-5108 IMP

KOST TIRE DISTRIBUTORS INC
KOST TIRE & MUFFLER
200 Holleder Pkwy, Binghamton, NY 13904
Tel (607) 723-9471 *Founded/Ownrshp* 1982
Sales 138.8MM[E] *EMP* 308
SIC 5014 5531 7538 Tires & tubes; Automotive tires; General automotive repair shops
Ch Bd: Michael G Kost
**VP:* David Kost
VP: Erwin Kost Jr
**VP:* Sam Kost
Opers Mgr: Dan Getter

D-U-N-S 11-081-1192

KOUNTRY WOOD PRODUCTS LLC
352 Shawnee St, Nappanee, IN 46550-9061
Tel (574) 773-5673 *Founded/Ownrshp* 1998
Sales 85.9MM[E] *EMP* 425
SIC 2434 5211 5031 Wood kitchen cabinets; Cabinets, kitchen; Kitchen cabinets
CEO: Ola Yoder
Pr: Perry Miller
CFO: Greg Shank
VP: Virgil Yoder
Sfty Dirs: Dan Mains
Prd Mgr: Howard Miller

D-U-N-S 02-459-3790

KOURY CORP
2275 Vanstory St Ste 200, Greensboro, NC 27403-3623
Tel (336) 299-9200 *Founded/Ownrshp* 1955
Sales 43.8MM[E] *EMP* 1,000
SIC 6512 6513 Commercial & industrial building operation; Shopping center, property operation only; Apartment building operators
Ch: Koury
**Pr:* Steve Showfety
VP: Ron Mack

KOVACH BUILDING ENCLOSURES
See KOVACH INC

D-U-N-S 07-447-2275 IMP/EXP

KOVACH INC
KOVACH BUILDING ENCLOSURES
3195 W Armstrong Pl, Chandler, AZ 85286-6602
Tel (480) 926-9292 *Founded/Ownrshp* 1969
Sales 96.1MM[E] *EMP* 200
SIC 1761 Roofing contractor; Siding contractor
Pr: Stephen E Kovach IV
**Pr:* Scott Bourdo

D-U-N-S 15-214-4010 IMP/EXP

KOVATCH MOBILE EQUIPMENT CORP
KME FIRE APPARATUS
(*Suby of* ASV) ★
1 Industrial Complex, Nesquehoning, PA 18240-1499
Tel (570) 669-9461 *Founded/Ownrshp* 2016
Sales 168.3MM[E] *EMP* 765
Accts Fegley & Associates Pc Plymou
SIC 3711 Chassis, motor vehicle; Fire department vehicles (motor vehicles), assembly of; Automobile assembly, including specialty automobiles
Pr: John I Kovatch
VP: Ken Creese
VP: Jeff Kahler
Rgnl Mgr: Tim Besser
Off Mgr: Janena Young
Sls Mgr: Stan Ptaszkowski
Sales Asso: Doug Burrell
Sales Asso: Bill Powell
Sales Asso: Pat Sullivan
Sales Asso: Kevin Todd

D-U-N-S 10-227-7308 IMP

KOWALSKI COMPANIES INC
KOWALSKIS WOODBURY MKT WINE SP
8505 Valley Creek Rd, Woodbury, MN 55125-2342
Tel (651) 578-8800 *Founded/Ownrshp* 1984
Sales 205.3MM[E] *EMP* 1,200
SIC 5411 Supermarkets
Pr: James S Kowalski
**COO:* Kristin Kowalski
**CFO:* Tom Beauchamp
**VP:* Mary Anne Kowalski
Store Mgr: Doug Borsch
Store Mgr: Dan Niggeler
CTO: Steve Beaird
MIS Dir: Bob Kowalski
VP Opers: Dale Riley
Mktg Dir: Laurie Bell

KOWALSKIS WOODBURY MKT WINE SP
See KOWALSKI COMPANIES INC

D-U-N-S 94-339-2522

KOYITLOTSINA LIMITED
1603 College Rd Ste 2, Fairbanks, AK 99709-4175
Tel (907) 452-8119 *Founded/Ownrshp* 1980
Sales 89.6MM[E] *EMP* 650
Accts Rjg Pc Fairbanks Alaska
SIC 6798 8744 7349 Real estate investment trusts; Facilities support services; Building maintenance services
Pr: Christopher Simon
CFO: Lynn Laycock
CFO: R Lynn Laycock CPA
**Treas:* Julia Simon
**VP:* Fred Bifelt
Adm Dir: Julie Gasparro

KOYO BEARINGS
See JTEKT NORTH AMERICA CORP

D-U-N-S 83-256-3774 IMP

KOYO BEARINGS NORTH AMERICA LLC
(*Suby of* KOYO BEARINGS) ★
4895 Dressler Rd Nw Ste B, Canton, OH 44718-2571
Tel (330) 994-0890 *Founded/Ownrshp* 2009
Sales 340.6MM[E] *EMP* 1,444
SIC 3562 Ball & roller bearings
Pr: Ken Hopkins
Genl Mgr: Bryan Spinney

D-U-N-S 05-097-3130 IMP

KP LLC (OR)
13951 Washington Ave, San Leandro, CA 94578-3220
Tel (510) 346-0729 *Founded/Ownrshp* 1929, 1967
Sales 113.9MM[E] *EMP* 300
SIC 2752 7334 7331 7374 7389 8742 Commercial printing, lithographic; Photocopying & duplicating services; Direct mail advertising services; Computer graphics service; Subscription fulfillment services: magazine, newspaper, etc.; Marketing consulting services
CEO: Joe Atturio
Ofcr: Paul Braverman
Exec: Dorothy Yell
Prgrm Mgr: Rachel Lee
CIO: Thomas Middleton
Opers Mgr: Aaron King
VP Mktg: Brett Olszewski

D-U-N-S 13-610-3970

KPC HEALTHCARE INC
1301 N Tustin Ave, Santa Ana, CA 92705-8619
Tel (714) 953-3652 *Founded/Ownrshp* 2004
Sales 449.3MM[E] *EMP* 3,012
SIC 8062 6719 General medical & surgical hospitals; Investment holding companies, except banks
Pr: Suzanne Richards
**Ch Bd:* Kali Chaudhuri
**CFO:* John Collins
CFO: Kathy Hammack
Bd of Dir: William Thomas
VP: Randy Overturf
Dir Lab: Nancy W Davis
Chf Nrs Of: Patricia Rives
CIO: SRI Yarramsetti
Pharmcst: Thinh Tran
HC Dir: Zoha Zabihi
Board of Directors: Robert Jameson, Michael Metzler, Fernando Niebla, William E Thomas

KPFF CONSULTING ENGINEERS
See KPFF INC

D-U-N-S 04-247-7729

KPFF INC
KPFF CONSULTING ENGINEERS
1601 5th Ave Ste 1600, Seattle, WA 98101-3665
Tel (206) 622-5822 *Founded/Ownrshp* 1960
Sales 169.7MM[E] *EMP* 900
SIC 8711 Consulting engineer; Civil engineering; Structural engineering
Pr: John Gavan
Mng Pt: Brian Raji
**CFO:* Steve Dill
**VP:* Molly Wilcox
Admn Mgr: Dan Allwardt
Div Mgr: Jenny Lockheimers
Off Mgr: Kim Anderson
Off Mgr: Marylou Hoffman
Off Mgr: Kacy Rufener
Off Admin: Leo Castillo
Dir IT: Paul Weir

D-U-N-S 00-586-9581 IMP

KPH HEALTHCARE SERVICES INC (NY)
KINNEY DRUGS
29 E Main St, Gouverneur, NY 13642-1401
Tel (315) 287-3600 *Founded/Ownrshp* 1903, 2008
Sales 915.4MM *EMP* 3,400
SIC 5912 Drug stores
Ch Bd: Craig Painter
**Pr:* Bridget-Ann Hart
COO: Bridget Hart
**Ex VP:* Stephen McCoy
VP: Scott Bouchard
**VP:* Michael Burgess
VP: Owen Halloran
**VP:* David C McClure
Exec: Mary Austin
Rgnl Mgr: Dale Myatt
Genl Mgr: Elaine Easley
Board of Directors: John Dyer, Warren Wolfson

D-U-N-S 08-033-9043

KPI CAPITAL HOLDINGS INC
437 Madison Ave Fl 36, New York, NY 10022-7001
Tel (479) 443-1455 *Founded/Ownrshp* 2015
Sales 76.1MM[E] *EMP* 2,800[E]
SIC 6719 3363 3312 Investment holding companies, except banks; Aluminum die-castings; Tool & die steel
Pr: Jeffrey Kenner

D-U-N-S 08-033-9024

KPI HOLDINGS INC
(*Suby of* KPI CAPITAL HOLDINGS INC) ★
437 Madison Ave Fl 36, New York, NY 10022-7001
Tel (479) 443-1455 *Founded/Ownrshp* 2008
Sales 50.8MM[E] *EMP* 2,800[E]
SIC 6719 3363 3312 Investment holding companies, except banks; Aluminum die-castings; Tool & die steel
Pr: Jeffrey Kenner
CFO: W Craig Potter

D-U-N-S 05-017-1381

KPI INTERMEDIATE HOLDINGS INC
(*Suby of* KPI HOLDINGS INC) ★
481 S Shiloh Dr, Fayetteville, AR 72704-7552
Tel (479) 443-1455 *Founded/Ownrshp* 2008
Sales 719.4MM[E] *EMP* 2,800[E]
SIC 3363 3312 Aluminum die-castings; Tool & die steel
Pr: Jeffrey Kenner
**CFO:* W Craig Potter
**VP:* Jeff Blaschke
**VP:* Jay Scott Bull

D-U-N-S 82-779-6579

KPLT HOLDINGS INC
(*Suby of* KOHLBERG & CO) ★
111 Radio Circle Dr, Mount Kisco, NY 10549-2609
Tel (914) 241-7430 *Founded/Ownrshp* 2008
Sales NA *EMP* 29,060
SIC 6719 Investment holding companies, except banks
Prin: Gordon Woodward
**Sec:* Seth Hollander

D-U-N-S 00-166-7906

KPMG LLP
(*Suby of* KPMG TAKS END EDVAIZORI, TOO)
345 Park Ave Lowr Ll4, New York, NY 10154-0016
Tel (212) 758-9700 *Founded/Ownrshp* 1994
Sales 4.6MMM[E] *EMP* 24,097
SIC 8721 Certified public accountant
CEO: John Veihmeyer
Pt: Brian M Ambrose
Pt: J Richard Andrews Jr
Pt: Patrick L Arsers
Pt: Charles J Bachand
Pt: Jeffrey S Berman
Pt: Kyle A Bibb
Pt: Charles Bruce
Pt: Patricia Carey
Pt: Dominick P Cavuoto
Pt: Charles I Johnson III
Pt: Stephen N Chase

Pt: Joann Chavez
Pt: R Matthew Clark
Pt: Robert D Cleveland
Pt: Charles E Cochran
Pt: Brian Cooper
Pt: Jim Craycroft
Pt: Steven L Cross
Pt: Brian L Cumberland
Pt: Anthony Dalessio

D-U-N-S 07-115-9078 IMP/EXP
KPS CAPITAL PARTNERS LP
485 Lexington Ave Fl 31, New York, NY 10017-2641
Tel (212) 338-5100 *Founded/Ownrshp* 1998
Sales 2.2MMM^E *EMP* 7,789
SIC 3541 6722 3545 5084 Machine tools, metal cutting type; Management investment, open-end; Machine tool accessories; Industrial machinery & equipment
Mng Pt: Michael G Psaros
Pt: Jay Bernstein
Pt: Raquel Palmer
Pt: David Shapiro

D-U-N-S 08-010-0463
KPS GLOBAL LLC
4201 N Beach St, Fort Worth, TX 76137-3212
Tel (817) 281-5121 *Founded/Ownrshp* 2015
Sales 120.5MM^E *EMP* 800^E
SIC 3089 3585 Panels, building: plastic; Refrigeration & heating equipment
CEO: Jack Bowling
**CFO:* Dan Zeddy
VP: Glenn Kaufman
**VP:* Eojin Lee

D-U-N-S 07-934-6140
■ **KPS LLC** (OH)
(*Suby of* KROGER CO) ★
1014 Vine St, Cincinnati, OH 45202-1141
Tel (513) 762-4000 *Founded/Ownrshp* 2013
Sales 179.7MM^E *EMP* 1^E
SIC 5141 Groceries, general line
CEO: W Rodney McMullen

D-U-N-S 06-209-2895 IMP/EXP
KRACO ENTERPRISES LLC
505 E Euclid Ave, Compton, CA 90222-2890
Tel (310) 639-0666 *Founded/Ownrshp* 2008
Sales 101.2MM^E *EMP* 164
SIC 5531 3069 5013 Automotive & home supply stores; Hard rubber & molded rubber products; Motor vehicle supplies & new parts
Pr: Lawrence McIsaac
CFO: Blake Barnett
CFO: Dennis Jolicoeur
Sr VP: John Fiumefreddo
Sr VP: Steve Lazzara
VP: Roger McCallen
Dir Sec: Marvin Todd
Prgrm Mgr: Gary Steinberg
Natl Sales: Oscar Martinez

KRAFT FOODS
See KRAFT PIZZA CO INC

KRAFT FOODS
See MONDELEZ PUERTO RICO LLC

D-U-N-S 03-901-0590 IMP/EXP
KRAFT FOODS GROUP INC
3 Lakes Dr, Northfield, IL 60093-2754
Tel (847) 646-2000 *Founded/Ownrshp* 2015
Sales 16.5MMM^E *EMP* 22,100
SIC 2022 3411 2095 2043 2035 2087

D-U-N-S 80-571-1723
KRAFT GROUP LLC
1 Patriot Pl, Foxboro, MA 02035-1374
Tel (508) 384-4230 *Founded/Ownrshp* 1995
Sales 981.7MM^E *EMP* 5,000^E
SIC 2653 Boxes, corrugated: made from purchased materials
Pr: Jonathan A Kraft
**CFO:* Michael Quattromani
**Ch:* Robert Kraft
Exec: Al Labelle
Genl Mgr: Brian Earley
Counsel: Marie Coukos

D-U-N-S 07-932-0220
▲ **KRAFT HEINZ CO**
1 Ppg Pl, Pittsburgh, PA 15222-5415
Tel (412) 456-5700 *Founded/Ownrshp* 2013
Sales 18.3MMM *EMP* 42,000^E
Tkr Sym KHC *Exch* NGS
SIC 2033 2038 2032 2098 Tomato sauce: packaged in cans, jars, etc.; Frozen specialties; Baby foods, including meats: packaged in cans, jars, etc.; Bean sprouts: packaged in cans, jars, etc.; Soups, except seafood: packaged in cans, jars, etc.; Macaroni & spaghetti
CEO: Bernardo Hees
Ch Bd: Alexandre Behring
CFO: Paulo Basilio
V Ch Bd: John T Cahill
Ex VP: Tom Corley
Ex VP: Eduardo Pelleissone
Sr VP: James Savina
VP: Michael Crouse
VP: Julie Groetsch
VP: Michael Mullen
Plnt Mgr: Kevin Griffin
Board of Directors: Gregory E Abel, Warren E Buffett, Tracy Britt Cool, Jeanne P Jackson, Jorge Paulo Lemann, Mackey J McDonald, John C Pope, Marcel Herrmann Telles

D-U-N-S 04-200-9001 EXP
KRAFT PIZZA CO INC (WI)
KRAFT FOODS
(*Suby of* WONKA BAMBOOZLE) ★
1 Kraft Ct, Glenview, IL 60025
Tel (847) 646-2000 *Founded/Ownrshp* 1962, 2010
Sales 237.2MM^E *EMP* 1,500
SIC 2038 Pizza, frozen; Snacks, including onion rings, cheese sticks, etc.
Pr: David S Johnson
Pr: Peter Boyle
Pr: Barbara M Ford
Ex VP: Rajesh Garg
**VP:* Gregory P Banks
**VP:* Brian T Jansen
**VP:* Randal S Tworek
IT Man: Mark Downs
QI Cn Mgr: Debra Reyes
Manager: Michele Malo

D-U-N-S 01-922-4120 IMP/EXP
KRAFT POWER CORP
199 Wildwood Ave, Woburn, MA 01801-2024
Tel (781) 938-9100 *Founded/Ownrshp* 1965
Sales 148.7MM^E *EMP* 160
SIC 5084 7699 Industrial machinery & equipment; Industrial machine parts; Industrial machinery & equipment repair
Pr: Owen M Duffy
Exec: Patty Rappa
Genl Mgr: Angela Chamtigny
Sls Mgr: Dave Barstow
Sls Mgr: Derwin Fancher

D-U-N-S 07-326-6330
KRAMER LEVIN NAFTALIS & FRANKEL LLP
1177 Ave Of The Americas, New York, NY 10036-2714
Tel (212) 715-9236 *Founded/Ownrshp* 1968
Sales 107.7MM^E *EMP* 700^E
SIC 8111 General practice law office
Pt: Paul S Pearlman
Mng Pt: Alexander Marquardt
VP: Elliott Baldeon
VP: Wadie Sanbar
Genl Couns: Gary Naftalis
Genl Couns: Stephen Zide
Counsel: Fabienne Arrighi
Counsel: Jeffrey Braun
Counsel: Michael Korotkin
Counsel: Philippe Mauduit
Counsel: Eve Preminger

D-U-N-S 03-038-8672 IMP/EXP
KRAMER-WILSON CO INC
CENTURY NATIONAL
6345 Balboa Blvd Ste 190, Encino, CA 91316-1515
Tel (818) 760-0880 *Founded/Ownrshp* 1969
Sales NA *EMP* 670
SIC 6331 Fire, marine & casualty insurance & carriers
CEO: Weldon Wilson
**Pr:* Kevin Wilson
**CFO:* Daniel Sherrin

KRAMM HALTHCARE REHABILITATION
See KRAMM HEALTHCARE CENTER INC

D-U-N-S 04-093-8664
KRAMM HEALTHCARE CENTER INC
KRAMM HALTHCARE REHABILITATION
(*Suby of* KRAMM NRSING HM REHABILITATION) ★
743 Mahoning St, Milton, PA 17847-2232
Tel (570) 742-2681 *Founded/Ownrshp* 1982
Sales 832.9MM^E *EMP* 330
SIC 8051 Skilled nursing care facilities
Pr: Jeffrey Kramm
**Prin:* Steven Kramm DMD
**Prin:* Randall L Kramm

KRAMM NRSING HM REHABILITATION
See KRAMM NURSING HOME INC

D-U-N-S 08-087-7665
KRAMM NURSING HOME INC (PA)
KRAMM NRSING HM REHABILITATION
(*Suby of* MID-ATLANTIC HEALTH CARE LLC) ★
245 E 8th St, Watsontown, PA 17777-1033
Tel (570) 538-2561 *Founded/Ownrshp* 1968
Sales 832.9MM^E *EMP* 330
SIC 8051 Skilled nursing care facilities
Pr: Randall D Kramm
**Treas:* Jeffrey S Kramm
**VP:* Janet S Kramm
VP: Steven R Kramm

D-U-N-S 61-857-0162 IMP
KRAMS ENTERPRISES INC
ARDEN-BENHAR MILLS
30400 Telg Rd Ste 200, Bingham Farms, MI 48025
Tel (248) 415-8500 *Founded/Ownrshp* 1986
Sales 194.2MM^E *EMP* 887
SIC 2392 Household furnishings; Cushions & pillows; Dishcloths, nonwoven textile: made from purchased materials; Towels, fabric & nonwoven: made from purchased materials
Pr: Bob Sachs
**Pr:* Robert S Sachs
**Sec:* Kenneth Sachs
**Ex VP:* John F Connell
**Ex VP:* Ronald P Zemenak
Sr VP: Charles Thompson
**VP:* Stephen M Ezer
**VP:* Martha M Sachs
**VP:* William N Sachs
Plnt Mgr: Al Smith

D-U-N-S 00-698-6483 IMP
KRASDALE FOODS INC (DE)
65 W Red Oak Ln Ste 2, White Plains, NY 10604-3614
Tel (914) 694-6400 *Founded/Ownrshp* 1907
Sales 1.1MMM^E *EMP* 530
SIC 5141 Groceries, general line
CEO: Charles Krasne
VP: Michael Chayet
VP: Leonard Pesce
VP: Catherine Taibi
Dir Bus: John Coppola
CIO: Simon Barker
Dir IT: Sara Marcy
Dir IT: Michael McShane
Opers Mgr: Dan Sheehan
S&M/VP: Rich Desimone

D-U-N-S 83-264-7247
▲ **KRATON CORP**
15710 John F Kennedy Blvd # 300, Houston, TX 77032-2347
Tel (281) 504-4700 *Founded/Ownrshp* 2000
Sales 1.0MMM *EMP* 2,029^E
Tkr Sym KRA *Exch* NYS
SIC 2821 Plastics materials & resins
Pr: Kevin M Fogarty
**Ch Bd:* Dan F Smith
CFO: Stephen E Tremblay
Ofcr: Melinda S Conley
Ofcr: Holger R Jung
Ofcr: Suzanne Pesgens
Sr VP: Lothar F P Freund
VP: Damian T Burke
VP: James L Simmons
VP Mfg: J Fernando C Haddad
Board of Directors: Anna C Catalano, Steven J Demetriou, Dominique Fournier, John J Gallagher III, Barry J Goldstein, Francis S Kalman, Karen A Twitchell

D-U-N-S 82-790-0320 IMP
■ **KRATON POLYMERS LLC**
(*Suby of* KRATON CORP) ★
15710 John F Kennedy Blvd # 300, Houston, TX 77032-2347
Tel (281) 504-4700 *Founded/Ownrshp* 2000
Sales 302.8MM^E *EMP* 917^E
SIC 2822 Ethylene-propylene rubbers, EPDM polymers
Pr: Kevin M Fogarty
Pr: Robert Newman
**COO:* David A Bradley
**CFO:* Stephen E Tremblay
VP: Thomas Abrey
VP: Richard Brennan
VP: Damian Burke
VP: William H Davis
VP: William Davis
**VP:* Stephen W Duffy
VP: Lothar P Freund
VP Bus Dev: Eli Ben
Exec: Bing Yang
Board of Directors: Nathan H Wright, Richard C Brown, Kelvin L Davis, Steven J Demetriou, Barry J Goldstein, Michael G Macdougall, Kevin G O'brien, Dan F Smith, Karen A Twitchell, Timothy J Walsh

D-U-N-S 01-833-0279 IMP/EXP
■ **KRATON POLYMERS US LLC**
(*Suby of* KRATON POLYMERS LLC) ★
15710 John F Kennedy Blvd # 300, Houston, TX 77032-2347
Tel (281) 504-4700 *Founded/Ownrshp* 1999
Sales 197.4MM^E *EMP* 520
SIC 2822 Synthetic rubber
CEO: Kevin M Fogarty
Treas: Stan Rice
**Ex VP:* Stephen E Tremblay
**Sr VP:* Lothar P Freund
**Sr VP:* Holger R Jung
**VP:* Melinda S Conley
**VP:* G Scott Lee
VP: Eli B Shoshan

D-U-N-S 78-625-0902
■ **KRATOS DEFENSE & ROCKET SUPPORT SERVICES INC**
(*Suby of* KRATOS DEFENSE & SECURITY SOLUTIONS INC) ★
4820 Estgate Mall Ste 200, San Diego, CA 92121
Tel (858) 812-7300 *Founded/Ownrshp* 2004
Sales 265.4MM^E *EMP* 1,607
SIC 8711 Engineering services
Pr: Eric M Demarco
CFO: Gary Accord
**Treas:* Laura L Siegal
VP: Michael W Fink
Board of Directors: William A Hoglund

D-U-N-S 88-445-7813
▲ **KRATOS DEFENSE & SECURITY SOLUTIONS INC**
4820 Estgate Mall Ste 200, San Diego, CA 92121
Tel (858) 812-7300 *Founded/Ownrshp* 1995
Sales 657.1MM *EMP* 3,600
Accts Deloitte & Touche Llp San Die
Tkr Sym KTOS *Exch* NGS
SIC 3761 8711 8744 7382 Guided missiles & space vehicles; Engineering services; Facilities support services; Security systems services
Pr: Eric M Demarco
**Ch Bd:* William Hoglund
Pr: Gerald Beaman
Pr: Phillip Carrai
Pr: David Carter
Pr: Benjamin Goodwin
Pr: Thomas Mills
CFO: Deanna Lund
CFO: Deanna H Lund
Bd of Dir: Amy Zegart
Ex VP: Richard Selvaggio
VP: George Baker
VP: Taylor Boswell
VP: Richard Duckworth
VP: Charles Farmer
VP: Mike Fink
VP: Scott McKee
VP: Marie Mendoza
VP: Mark Schmitt
VP: Marc Shapiro
VP: Michael Smith
Board of Directors: Scott Anderson, Scot Jarvis, Jane Judd, Samuel Liberatore, Amy Zegart

D-U-N-S 61-532-1911
KRAUSE HOLDINGS INC
6400 Westown Pkwy, West Des Moines, IA 50266-7709
Tel (515) 226-0128 *Founded/Ownrshp* 1990
Sales 509.0MM^E *EMP* 3,500
SIC 5411 Convenience stores, chain
Pr: Kyle J Krause
COO: Dennis Folden
**Treas:* Craig A Bergstrom
**Treas:* Brian J Thompson

D-U-N-S 06-259-6115 IMP/EXP
KRAUSS-MAFFEI CORP
(*Suby of* KRAUSSMAFFEI GROUP GMBH)
7095 Industrial Rd, Florence, KY 41042-2930
Tel (859) 283-0200 *Founded/Ownrshp* 1966
Sales 95.4MM^E *EMP* 147
SIC 5084 3559 Chemical process equipment; Plastic products machinery; Plastics working machinery; Chemical machinery & equipment
CEO: Paul Caprio
**CFO:* Sandy Winter
VP: Reiner Bunnenberg
VP: Martin Mack
VP: John Mead
**VP:* Sandra K Winter
CIO: Jeff Spurlock
Dir IT: George Tucker
Sfty Mgr: Rick Hawk
Opers Mgr: Mark Giesey
Prd Mgr: Sam Milanese

D-U-N-S 80-002-8297 IMP
KRAVET FABRICS INC
225 Central Ave S, Bethpage, NY 11714-4990
Tel (516) 293-2000 *Founded/Ownrshp* 2002
Sales 92.5MM^E *EMP* 500^E
SIC 2392 Mattress pads
CEO: Cary Kravet
Telecom Mg: Mike Degroso
Opers Mgr: Elliot Halem
Genl Couns: Lisa Kravet

D-U-N-S 00-196-5987 IMP
KRAVET INC
LEE JOFA
225 Cent Ave S, Bethpage, NY 11714
Tel (516) 293-2000 *Founded/Ownrshp* 1917
Sales 494.9MM^E *EMP* 500
SIC 5131 5198 2392 Upholstery fabrics, woven; Drapery material, woven; Trimmings, apparel; Wallcoverings; Household furnishings
Ch Bd: Cary Kravet
Pr: Robert Duban
CFO: Frank Nardolillo
**CFO:* Mike Wilbur
Ex VP: Steve Prada
Dir IT: Eugene Cordi

KRD TRUCKING
See K R DRENTH TRUCKING INC

D-U-N-S 09-236-4702 IMP
KREHER STEEL CO LLC
1550 N 25th Ave, Melrose Park, IL 60160-1801
Tel (708) 345-8180 *Founded/Ownrshp* 1996
Sales 140.0MM^E *EMP* 200
SIC 5051 Bars, metal
VP: Kim Tremmel
Genl Mgr: Fred Rust
Mktg Dir: Tim Lambert
Sls Mgr: Dave Trump

KREIDER DAIRY FARMS
See KREIDER FARMS

D-U-N-S 02-435-4755 EXP
KREIDER FARMS
KREIDER DAIRY FARMS
1461 Lancaster Rd, Manheim, PA 17545-9768
Tel (717) 665-4415 *Founded/Ownrshp* 1935
Sales 97.0MM^E *EMP* 450
SIC 0291 General farms, primarily animals
Pr: Ronald Kreider
**Ch:* Noah W Kreider Jr
**VP:* Dave Andrews
Exec: Terri Turner
VP Opers: Tom Beachler

D-U-N-S 00-642-2406 IMP
■ **KREMERS URBAN PHARMACEUTICALS INC**
(*Suby of* LANNETT CO INC) ★
1101 C Ave W, Seymour, IN 47274-3342
Tel (812) 523-5347 *Founded/Ownrshp* 1930
Sales 124.6MM^E *EMP* 350^E
SIC 2834 Tablets, pharmaceutical; Syrups, pharmaceutical
CEO: Arthur P Bedrosian
**Pr:* George Stevenson
**CEO:* Arthur P Bedrosian
**CFO:* Mary Ellen Campion
**CFO:* Martin P Galvan
**Treas:* Jon Thiel
**Chf Cred:* Frank Stiefel
**VP:* John M ABT
**VP:* Xiu Xiu Cheng
VP: Michael Dornhecker
**VP:* Kevin Smith
VP: Susan Witham
Board of Directors: Arthur P Bedrosian

D-U-N-S 08-393-7086
KRESGE FOUNDATION (MI)
3215 W Big Beaver Rd, Troy, MI 48084-2818
Tel (248) 643-9630 *Founded/Ownrshp* 1924
Sales 203.7MM *EMP* 27
SIC 6732 Charitable trust management
Pr: John Marshall
Pr: Sharon Zimmerman
COO: Donna Snider
Ofcr: Bryan Hogle
Ofcr: Helen D Johnson
Ofcr: Chris Kabel
Ofcr: Fred Karnas
Ofcr: Neesha Modi
Ofcr: Regina Smith
VP: Robert Manilla
VP: ARI Simon

D-U-N-S 09-030-4056
KRESS STORES OF PUERTO RICO INC
CLICK
598 Calle A, San Juan, PR 00920-2102
Tel (787) 783-5374 *Founded/Ownrshp* 1972
Sales 95.4MM^E *EMP* 2,000
Accts Goas Psc San Juan Puerto Ric
SIC 7389 8741 Purchasing service; Personnel management
Pr: Mark J Berezdivin
**CFO:* Moises Berezdivin
**VP:* Jeff Berezdivin
**VP:* Vivian Lazoff
Corp Couns: David Solomainy

D-U-N-S 16-757-8017
KRESTMARK INDUSTRIES LP
3950 Bastille Rd Ste 100, Dallas, TX 75212-5903
Tel (214) 237-5055 *Founded/Ownrshp* 2016
Sales 105.6MM[E] *EMP* 400
SIC 3442 3089 Storm doors or windows, metal; Windows, plastic
Pr: William E Robinson
**Pt:* Joe Fojtasek
VP: Steve Rosenthal
Dept Mgr: Mike Prindle
Sales Exec: Felix Hicks
Sls&Mrk Ex: Lou Simi

D-U-N-S 85-971-4151
KRG CAPITAL PARTNERS LLC
1800 Larimer St Ste 2200, Denver, CO 80202-1417
Tel (303) 390-5001 *Founded/Ownrshp* 1996
Sales 349.2MM[E] *EMP* 1,667
SIC 6726 8742 6411 Investment offices; Management consulting services; Insurance agents, brokers & service
Mng Pt: Bruce Rogers
Pr: Daniel E Greenleaf
COO: Colton King
Ofcr: Kevin Rohnstock
VP: Piotr Biezychudek
VP: E S Cho
VP: Christopher Pusey
VP: Bennett Thompson

D-U-N-S 00-643-9814
KRIETE TRUCK CENTER MILWAUKEE INC
MILWAUKEE TRUCK SALES
4444 W Blue Mound Rd, Milwaukee, WI 53208-3670
Tel (414) 258-8484 *Founded/Ownrshp* 1951
Sales 118.8MM[E] *EMP* 230
SIC 5511 New & used car dealers; Trucks, tractors & trailers: new & used
Ch: Roger H Kriete
**Pr:* David Kriete
**VP:* George Pavin
Sls Mgr: Diana Sirovina

KRIS TV CHANNEL SIX
See GULF COAST BROADCASTING CO

D-U-N-S 01-265-0750 IMP/EXP
KRISPY KREME DOUGHNUT CORP
(*Suby of* KRISPY KREME DOUGHNUTS INC) ★
259 S Stratford Rd, Winston Salem, NC 27103-1817
Tel (336) 724-2484 *Founded/Ownrshp* 2000
Sales 16.2MM[E] *EMP* 3,360
SIC 5461 2051 Doughnuts; Pies; Pastries; Doughnuts, except frozen; Pies, bakery: except frozen; Buns, sweet: except frozen
CEO: Tony Thompson
Ch Bd: James H Morgan
Pr: Darryl R Marsch
Pr: Kenneth A May
Pr: John Tate
Treas: Douglas R Muir
Chf Mktg O: Duane Chambers
Ex VP: J Paul Breitbach
Ex VP: John N Mc Aleer
Sr VP: Randy S Casstevens
Sr VP: L Stephen Hendrix
Sr VP: Robert E L Hodges
Sr VP: Fred W Mitchell
VP: R Michael Cecil
VP: Dwayne Chambers
VP: Timothy Honeycutt
VP: Stanley N Lowry
VP: Philip R S Waugh Jr
Board of Directors: Frank E Guthrie, Joseph A McAleer, Robert L McCoy, Steven D Smith

D-U-N-S 11-638-7510 IMP/EXP
KRISPY KREME DOUGHNUTS INC
(*Suby of* COTTON PARENT INC) ★
370 Knollwood St Ste 500, Winston Salem, NC 27103-1865
Tel (336) 726-8876 *Founded/Ownrshp* 2016
Sales 518.7MM *EMP* 5,200
SIC 5461 5149 2051 Doughnuts; Bakery products; Doughnuts, except frozen
Pr: Tony Thompson
Pr: Dan L Beem
CFO: G Price Cooper
Sr VP: Cynthia A Bay
Sr VP: Tom Kuharcik
VP: Cathleen D Allred
VP: Nathan Mucha
VP: Corena Norris-Mccluney
VP: Amy Stroud
Dir IT: Darrell Walker
Site Mgr: Mike Dillon

KRIST FOOD MARTS
See KRIST OIL CO

D-U-N-S 01-677-4762
KRIST OIL CO
KRIST FOOD MARTS
303 Selden Rd, Iron River, MI 49935-1899
Tel (906) 265-6144 *Founded/Ownrshp* 1954
Sales 192.8MM[E] *EMP* 535
SIC 5541 5411

D-U-N-S 00-891-0150
KRIZ-DAVIS CO
KD
2400 W 3rd St, Grand Island, NE 68803-5324
Tel (308) 382-2230 *Founded/Ownrshp* 1953
Sales 148.5MM[E] *EMP* 217
SIC 5063 Electrical apparatus & equipment
Pr: Timothy P Berry
**VP:* David Brown
**VP:* Ralph J Knobbe
Brnch Mgr: Steve Chambers
Div Mgr: Glen Barritt
Div Mgr: Dan Bond
Div Mgr: Sam Herzog
Div Mgr: Ted Myers
Div Mgr: Josh Phillips
Div Mgr: Shelly Willis
Opers Mgr: Steve Barnes

KROENKE SPORTS & ENTERTAINMENT
See KROENKE SPORTS HOLDINGS LLC

D-U-N-S 04-178-5028
KROENKE SPORTS HOLDINGS LLC
KROENKE SPORTS & ENTERTAINMENT
1000 Chopper Cir, Denver, CO 80204-5805
Tel (303) 405-1100 *Founded/Ownrshp* 1999
Sales 137.4MM[E] *EMP* 835[E]
SIC 7941 Sports field or stadium operator, promoting sports events
Prin: Stan Kroenke
Ex VP: Paul Andrews
VP: Mike Kurowski
VP: Shawn Stokes
VP: Mark Wagner
Ex Dir: Dick Brockmeier
Ex Dir: Kelley Kocher
Ex Dir: Jeremy Short
Dir IT: Rick Schoenhuls
VP Mktg: Tom Philind
Pr Mgr: Lesley Linscott

KROGER
See FRED MEYER STORES INC

KROGER
See BAKERS SUPERMARKETS INC

D-U-N-S 00-699-9528
▲ KROGER CO
1014 Vine St Ste 1000, Cincinnati, OH 45202-1100
Tel (513) 762-4000 *Founded/Ownrshp* 1883
Sales 109.8MMM *EMP* 431,140
Tkr Sym KR *Exch* NYS
SIC 5411 5912 5541 5944 Supermarkets, chain; Supermarkets, 66,000-99,000 square feet; Convenience stores, chain; Drug stores; Gasoline service stations; Jewelry stores
Ch Bd: W Rodney McMullen
Pr: Colleen Juergensen
Pr: Pam Matthews
CFO: J Michael Schlotman
Treas: Todd A Foley
Bd of Dir: Carol McLemore
Ofcr: Kevin M Dougherty
Ex VP: Christopher T Hjelm
Ex VP: Frederick J Morganthall II
Ex VP: Don Rosanova
Sr VP: Sukanya R Madlinger
Sr VP: Alessandro Tosolini
Sr VP: Mark C Tuffin
VP: Mary Adcock
VP: Jessica C Adelman
VP: Stuart W Aitken
VP: Peter Barth
VP: James R Callahan
VP: Robert W Clark
VP: Michael J Donnelly
VP: William A Douglas
Board of Directors: Bobby S Shackouls, Nora A Aufreiter, Robert D Beyer, Anne Gates, Susan J Kropf, Jorge P Montoya, Clyde R Moore, Susan M Phillips, James A Runde, Ronald L Sargent

D-U-N-S 12-713-0537 IMP
■ KROGER CO
(*Suby of* KROGER CO) ★
2000 Nutter Farms Ln, Delaware, OH 43015-9195
Tel (740) 657-2124 *Founded/Ownrshp* 2003
Sales 71.8MM[E] *EMP* 1,000
SIC 5411 Supermarkets, chain
Pr: Bruce Macaulay

D-U-N-S 36-143-0114 IMP
■ KROGER LIMITED PARTNERSHIP I
JAYC FOOD STORES
(*Suby of* KROGER CO) ★
1014 Vine St Ste 1000, Cincinnati, OH 45202-1119
Tel (513) 762-4000 *Founded/Ownrshp* 1997
Sales 257.6MM[E] *EMP* 1,456
SIC 5411 Grocery stores
Pt: Carver Johnson

D-U-N-S 07-939-6092
■ KROGER SPECIALTY PHARMACY HOLDINGS I INC
(*Suby of* KROGER CO) ★
6435 Hazeltine National, Orlando, FL 32822-5158
Tel (626) 932-1600 *Founded/Ownrshp* 2012, 2016
Sales 850.0MM *EMP* 140
SIC 6719 Investment holding companies, except banks
CEO: Dominic Meffe
CFO: Vincent Cook
Ofcr: Tom Dervin
Ofcr: Joan Schuckenbrock

D-U-N-S 00-344-8060
■ KROGER TEXAS LP
AMERICA'S BEVERAGE COMPANY
(*Suby of* KROGER CO) ★
19245 David Memorial Dr, Shenandoah, TX 77385-8778
Tel (713) 507-4800 *Founded/Ownrshp* 1999
Sales 1.2MMM[E] *EMP* 2,500
SIC 5141 5411 Groceries, general line; Supermarkets, chain
Pt: Bill Breetz

D-U-N-S 10-148-7239
KROLL LLC
(*Suby of* CORPORATE RISK HOLDINGS LLC) ★
600 3rd Ave Fl 4, New York, NY 10016-1919
Tel (212) 593-1000 *Founded/Ownrshp* 2010
Sales 559.0MM[E] *EMP* 3,098
SIC 7381 8742 8748 7389 Detective services; Private investigator; Industry specialist consultants; Business consulting; Tenant screening service
Recvr: Chris Hughes
Pr: Mark R Williams
CFO: Glenn R King Jr
CFO: Ken Roche
Ex VP: David R Fontaine
Ex VP: Howard Smith
Sr VP: Lee Kirschbaum
Sr VP: Tom Parker
VP: Melissa Outlaw
VP: Patricia Pizzo
VP: Scott Williams

D-U-N-S 14-758-7240 IMP
KROLL ONTRACK LLC
(*Suby of* KROLL LLC) ★
9023 Columbine Rd, Eden Prairie, MN 55347-4182
Tel (952) 937-5161 *Founded/Ownrshp* 2002
Sales 414.5MM[E] *EMP* 1,500
SIC 7374 7372 Data processing & preparation; Application computer software
CEO: Mark R Williams
Pr: Ravi Sathyanna
COO: Lee B Lewis
COO: Gregory A Olson
Bd of Dir: Ben Allen
Sr VP: Craig Carpenter
Sr VP: Greg Olson
Sr VP: Cathleen Peterson
VP: Shawn Abbas
VP: John M Bujan
VP: Todd R Johnson
VP: Lee Lewis
VP: Neil Sathyanna
VP: Josh Zylbershlag

D-U-N-S 04-594-8429 IMP/EXP
KRONES INC
(*Suby of* KRONES AG)
9600 S 58th St, Franklin, WI 53132-9107
Tel (414) 409-4000 *Founded/Ownrshp* 1966
Sales 99.8MM[E] *EMP* 570
Accts Kpmg Llp
SIC 3565 Bottling machinery: filling, capping, labeling
CEO: Holger Beckmann
COO: Michael M Wiebe
Ex VP: Timothy A Raymond
VP: Andrea Meza
VP: Roland Pokorny
VP: Claudius Wolf
Dir Risk M: Doris Mayer
Mng Dir: Feuring Heiko
Div Mgr: Dave Niemuth
Genl Mgr: Sebastian Delgado
QA Dir: Anne Goetv

D-U-N-S 92-929-0682 IMP
KRONHEIM CO INC
(*Suby of* NATIONAL DISTRIBUTING CO INC) ★
8201 Stayton Dr, Jessup, MD 20794-9633
Tel (410) 724-3300 *Founded/Ownrshp* 1997
Sales 160.0MM *EMP* 300
SIC 5182 5181 Wine & distilled beverages; Beer & other fermented malt liquors
Ch Bd: Jay Davis
**Pr:* Pat Vogel

D-U-N-S 02-611-5521 IMP
■ KRONOS (US) INC
(*Suby of* KRONOS LOUISIANA INC) ★
14950 Heathrow Ste 230, Houston, TX 77032
Tel (281) 423-3300 *Founded/Ownrshp* 1986
Sales 221.8MM[E] *EMP* 7,300
SIC 5169 Acids
CEO: Bobby D O Brien
**COO:* James Buch
**COO:* Klemens T Schlater
**CFO:* Gregory M Swalwell
**Ch:* Steven L Watson
**VP:* Brian W Christian

D-U-N-S 80-576-8897
KRONOS ACQUISITION CORP
(*Suby of* KRONOS PARENT CORP) ★
297 Billerica Rd, Chelmsford, MA 01824-4119
Tel (978) 250-9800 *Founded/Ownrshp* 2007
Sales 1.5MMM[E] *EMP* 4,128
SIC 7372 7373 6726 Prepackaged software; Computer integrated systems design; Investment offices
Ch: Mark S AIN
**CEO:* Aron J AIN
**CFO:* Mark Julien

D-U-N-S 08-255-0211
KRONOS FOODS CORP
1 Kronos, Glendale Heights, IL 60139-1965
Tel (773) 847-2250 *Founded/Ownrshp* 2016
Sales 104.9MM[E] *EMP* 350[E]
SIC 2013 2051 5141 5963 Prepared beef products from purchased beef; Breads, rolls & buns; Food brokers; Food services, direct sales
CEO: Howard C Eirinberg
Pr: Patrick Costello
Pr: Marilyn Kelly
Sr VP: Pat Costello
Sr VP: Bob Michaels
VP: George Liggett
VP: Jesse Pratt
VP: Bobby Verros
VP Opers: Mara Deura

D-U-N-S 09-427-3653 IMP/EXP
KRONOS INC (MA)
(*Suby of* KRONOS ACQUISITION CORP) ★
297 Billerica Rd, Chelmsford, MA 01824-4119
Tel (978) 250-9800 *Founded/Ownrshp* 1977, 2007
Sales 1.6MMM[E] *EMP* 4,128
SIC 7372 7373 Prepackaged software; Computer integrated systems design
Ch Bd: Mark S AIN
Pr: Joel Hauff
CEO: Aron J AIN
CFO: Mark Julien
Ex VP: Vince Devlin
Sr VP: Peter C George
Sr VP: Lenley Hensarling
Sr VP: James J Kizielewicz
Sr VP: James Kizielewicz
Sr VP: John O'Brien
Sr VP: Christopher R Todd
VP: David Almeda
VP: Michael Biery
VP: Peter Broderick
VP: Renee Cacchillo
VP: Doug Clute
VP: Robert Collins
VP: Charlie Dewitt
VP: Dave Gilbertson
VP: Nobu Hara
VP: Jim Haugen

D-U-N-S 96-535-0411
■ KRONOS INTERNATIONAL INC
(*Suby of* KRONOS WORLDWIDE INC) ★
5430 L B Johnson Fwy 1700, Dallas, TX 75240
Tel (972) 233-1700 *Founded/Ownrshp* 2004
Sales 748.0MM[E] *EMP* 91[E]
Accts Pricewaterhousecoopers Llp Da
SIC 2816 Inorganic pigments
Pr: Steven L Watson

D-U-N-S 08-019-3151
■ KRONOS LOUISIANA INC
(*Suby of* KRONOS WORLDWIDE INC) ★
3300 Bayou Dinde Rd, Westlake, LA 70669-8102
Tel (337) 882-1774 *Founded/Ownrshp* 1989
Sales 221.8MM[E] *EMP* 7,303[E]
SIC 2816 Titanium dioxide, anatase or rutile (pigments)
Pr: Bobby D O'Brien
**VP:* Kelly D Luttmer
**VP:* Gregory M Swalwell

D-U-N-S 07-929-6464
KRONOS PARENT CORP
297 Billerica Rd, Chelmsford, MA 01824-4119
Tel (978) 250-9800 *Founded/Ownrshp* 2007
Sales 1.6MMM[E] *EMP* 4,128
SIC 7372 7373 Prepackaged software; Computer integrated systems design
Pr: Aron J AIN
**Treas:* Mark V Julien
**VP:* Alyce Moore

D-U-N-S 60-712-1258
▲ KRONOS WORLDWIDE INC
5430 Lbj Fwy Ste 1700, Dallas, TX 75240-2620
Tel (972) 233-1700 *Founded/Ownrshp* 1989
Sales 1.3MMM *EMP* 2,280[E]
Tkr Sym KRO *Exch* NYS
SIC 2816 Titanium dioxide, anatase or rutile (pigments)
Pr: Bobby D O'Brien
Pr: Benjamin R Corona
COO: James Buch
CFO: Gregory M Swalwell
Treas: John A St Wrba
Ex VP: Brian W Christian
Ex VP: Robert D Graham
VP: Clarence B Brown III
VP: Steven S Eaton
VP: Tim C Hafer
VP: Janet G Keckeisen
VP: Patricia A Kropp
VP: A Andrew R Louis
VP: Kelly Luttmer
VP: H Joseph Maas
VP: Andrew B Nace
VP: Courtney J Riley
VP: John A Sunny
Board of Directors: Keith R Coogan, Loretta J Feehan, John E Harper, Cecil H Moore Jr, Thomas P Stafford, R Gerald Turner, C Kern Wildenthal

D-U-N-S 08-011-6781
KRONOSPAN INC
1 Kronsopan Way, Eastaboga, AL 36260-5316
Tel (256) 741-8755 *Founded/Ownrshp* 1989
Sales 104.5MM[E] *EMP* 227[E]
SIC 2431 2295 Panel work, wood; Laminating of fabrics
Pr: Klaus Kohler
**CFO:* Timothy Pack

KRS
See KWAJALEIN RANGE SERVICES LLC

D-U-N-S 03-267-2651 IMP/EXP
KRUEGER INTERNATIONAL INC
KI
1330 Bellevue St, Green Bay, WI 54302-2197
Tel (920) 468-8100 *Founded/Ownrshp* 1986
Sales 617.2MM *EMP* 2,300
Accts Baker Tilly Virchow Krause Llp
SIC 2531 School furniture
CEO: Richard J Resch
**Pr:* Brian Krenke
**CFO:* Kelly Andersen
**VP:* Dean Lindsley
VP: Gary Van
Prgrm Mgr: Brian Kontny
Dist Mgr: John Shearer
Dir IT: Tim Lasecki
Netwrk Eng: Eric Fleming
Netwrk Eng: Craig Nowak
Opers Mgr: Terry Brown

D-U-N-S 07-061-9820 IMP
KRUGER LTD
1513 Absco Dr, Longs, SC 29568-8815
Tel (843) 399-2165 *Founded/Ownrshp* 2004
Sales 102.0MM *EMP* 6
SIC 5199 Gifts & novelties
Pr: Joe Kruger
**Owner:* Richard Kruger
**Sec:* Joanne Kruger

D-U-N-S 00-986-8142
KRUSE INVESTMENT CO INC
31120 W St, Goshen, CA 93227
Tel (559) 302-1000 *Founded/Ownrshp* 1936
Sales 571.8MM[E] *EMP* 312
SIC 6799

D-U-N-S 00-792-0804
KRYSTAL CO (GA)
KRYSTAL RESTAURANT
(*Suby of* ARGONNE CAPITAL GROUP LLC) ★
1455 Lincoln Pkwy E # 600, Dunwoody, GA 30346-2200
Tel (423) 757-1550 *Founded/Ownrshp* 1932, 2012
Sales 332.6MM[E] *EMP* 7,056
SIC 5812 6794 American restaurant; Franchises, selling or licensing
CEO: James F Exum Jr
**CFO:* James W Bear
**CFO:* Carl Jakaitis
**Chf Mktg O:* Jason Abelkop
**Ofcr:* Tom Murrill

*Sr VP: Michael C Bass
VP: Gordon L Davenport Jr
VP: Misty Didal
VP: Scott Gallagher
VP: Glen R Griffiths
VP: Chris Kermode

KRYSTAL RESTAURANT
See KRYSTAL CO

KS
See KULITE SEMICONDUCTOR PRODUCTS INC

D-U-N-S 17-221-9458
KS ENERGY SERVICES LLC
19705 W Lincoln Ave, New Berlin, WI 53146-1720
Tel (262) 574-5100 Founded/Ownrshp 2004
Sales 146.8MM^E EMP 300
SIC 1623 Gas main construction
Pr: Dennis Klumb Jr
*Treas: Shawn Klumb
*VP: Michael Klumb Sr
*VP: Tom Schaitel Sr
Area Mgr: Troy Anderson

D-U-N-S 15-471-0680
KS INDUSTRIES LP
K S I
6205 District Blvd, Bakersfield, CA 93313-2141
Tel (661) 617-1700 Founded/Ownrshp 2002
Sales 303.5MM^E EMP 2,500
SIC 1623 Water, sewer & utility lines
CEO: Kevin Small
VP: Doug Erickson
CIO: Jerry Janzen
VP Opers: Allan Faughn
Snr PM: David Aguirre
Snr PM: Steve Napier

D-U-N-S 96-923-1104
KS INTERNATIONAL LLC
3601 Eisenhower Ave # 600, Alexandria, VA 22304-6426
Tel (703) 676-3253 Founded/Ownrshp 2011
Sales 173.4MM EMP 1^E
Accts Mcgladrey Mclean Va
SIC 1522 Renovation, hotel/motel

D-U-N-S 61-843-3064 IMP
KS KOLBENSCHMIDT US INC
(Suby of KSPG HOLDING USA INC) ★
1731 Industrial Pkwy N, Marinette, WI 54143-3704
Tel (715) 732-0181 Founded/Ownrshp 1992
Sales 175.0MM^E EMP 870
SIC 3592 Pistons & piston rings
Pr: Donald L Cameron
VP: Don Cameron
VP: Mark Lennart
*VP: Robert W Steffens
VP: Robert Steffers
*VP: Robert G Turcott
Dir IT: Yeujun Huang
Sfty Mgr: Debbie Vandercook
Opers Mgr: Jim Weidman
Plnt Mgr: Mark M Greenlund
Ql Cn Mgr: Ron Stromgren

D-U-N-S 06-185-4456
KS MANAGEMENT SERVICES LLC (TX)
(Suby of KELSEY-SEYBOLD CLINIC) ★
2727 W Holcombe Blvd, Houston, TX 77025-1669
Tel (713) 442-0000 Founded/Ownrshp 1949
Sales NA EMP 2,400
SIC 8741 Management services
CFO: John Sperry
VP: Mike Fitzgerald
VP Mktg: Phil Price
Doctor: Nancy Byrd

D-U-N-S 80-840-8319
KS&T INTERNATIONAL HOLDINGS LP
KOCH SUPPLY & TRADING
(Suby of KOCH RESOURCES LLC) ★
4111 E 37th St N, Wichita, KS 67220-3203
Tel (316) 828-5500 Founded/Ownrshp 2002
Sales 107.5MM^E EMP 279^E
SIC 2911 Petroleum refining

D-U-N-S 80-186-9843 IMP/EXP
KSB AMERICA CORP
(Suby of PAB PUMPEN- UND ARMATUREN- BETEILIGUNGSGESELLSCHAFT MIT BESCHRANKTER HAFTUNG)
4415 Sarellen Rd, Richmond, VA 23231-4428
Tel (804) 222-1818 Founded/Ownrshp 1969
Sales 221.7MM^E EMP 508
Accts Ernst & Young Llp
SIC 3561 3494 3625 5084 Industrial pumps & parts; Pipe fittings; Actuators, industrial; Pumps & pumping equipment
*Sec: Karen M Wood
Prin: William A Leech

KSB HOSPITAL
See KATHERINE SHAW BETHEA HOSPITAL

D-U-N-S 07-949-0154
KSF ACQUISITION CORP
SLIMFAST
(Suby of KSF INTERMEDIATE CORP) ★
11780 Us Highway 1 400n, Palm Beach Gardens, FL 33408-3007
Tel (561) 231-6548 Founded/Ownrshp 2014
Sales 143.0MM EMP 41^E
SIC 5122 Vitamins & minerals
*CEO: Chris Tisi
*CFO: Doug Reader
*Ex VP: Paul Gagliano

D-U-N-S 08-027-5448
KSF HOLDINGS LLP
(Suby of KAINOS GP LLC) ★
2100 Mckinney Ave # 1600, Dallas, TX 75201-1803
Tel (214) 740-7300 Founded/Ownrshp 2014
Sales 143.0MM^E EMP 44^E
SIC 5149 Health foods
Mng Pt: Andrew Rosen
Pt: Nirav Shah
Pt: Bob Sperry

D-U-N-S 08-027-5432
KSF INTERMEDIATE CORP
(Suby of KSF HOLDINGS LLP) ★
11780 Us Highway 1 400n, Palm Beach Gardens, FL 33408-3007
Tel (866) 726-2272 Founded/Ownrshp 2014
Sales 143.0MM^E EMP 42^E
SIC 6733 Trusts
CEO: Andrew Rosen
VP: Nirav Shah
VP: Bob Sperry

D-U-N-S 11-286-1315 IMP
KSI TRADING CORP
CRS AUTOMOTIVE COOLING PDTS
100a Wade Ave, South Plainfield, NJ 07080-1311
Tel (908) 754-7154 Founded/Ownrshp 1987
Sales 90.0MM^E EMP 103
SIC 5013 Automotive supplies & parts
Pr: Wayne Jan
Sales Exec: Chuck Lee

D-U-N-S 78-932-7947
KSL ARIZONA HOLDINGS III INC
ARIZONA BILTMORE RESORT & SPA
2400 E Missouri Ave, Phoenix, AZ 85016-3106
Tel (602) 955-6600 Founded/Ownrshp 2000
Sales 13.0MM^E EMP 1,150
SIC 7011 5812 7991 5813 Resort hotel; Eating places; Spas; Drinking places
Pr: Scott M Dalecio

D-U-N-S 78-883-1233
KSL CAPITAL PARTNERS LLC
100 Saint Paul St Ste 800, Denver, CO 80206-5144
Tel (720) 284-6400 Founded/Ownrshp 2005
Sales 262.8MM^E EMP 1,035
SIC 6799 Investors
CFO: Eric Resnick
VP Sls: Michael E Rickson
Sls Mgr: Nicole German
Sls Mgr: Jana Thompson

D-U-N-S 05-805-1160
KSL MEDIA INC
15910 Ventura Blvd # 900, Encino, CA 91436-2809
Tel (212) 468-3395 Founded/Ownrshp 2003
Sales 365.9MM^E EMP 130
SIC 7319 Media buying service
Ch Bd: Kalman Liebowitz
*Pr: Hank Cohen
*CFO: Russell Meisels
Sr VP: Tyler Liebowitz
VP: Christina Selbaris
Mng Dir: Fran McCreary

D-U-N-S 00-527-9109
KSL RECREATION MANAGEMENT OPERATIONS LLC (DE)
50905 Avenida Bermudas, La Quinta, CA 92253-8910
Tel (760) 564-8000 Founded/Ownrshp 2003
Sales NA EMP 8,000
SIC 7992 7011

D-U-N-S 78-476-2150
KSM CORP
(Suby of KSM COMPONENT CO., LTD.)
1959 Concourse Dr, San Jose, CA 95131-1708
Tel (408) 514-2400 Founded/Ownrshp 2003
Sales 100.0MM EMP 500
SIC 3674 Semiconductors & related devices
CEO: Jooswan Kim
*Pr: Harvinder P Singh

D-U-N-S 62-198-1059 IMP
KSPG HOLDING USA INC
(Suby of RHEINMETALL AG)
1731 Industrial Pkwy N, Marinette, WI 54143-3704
Tel (715) 732-0181 Founded/Ownrshp 2005
Sales 375.7MM^E EMP 1,800
SIC 3592 3714 6719 Pistons & piston rings; Bearings, motor vehicle; Investment holding companies, except banks
Pr: Dr Peter Merten
Ex VP: Richard A Posz
VP: Robert G Turcott
Board of Directors: Dr Joerg-Martin Friedrich

D-U-N-S 96-890-7621 IMP
KSPG NORTH AMERICA INC
1731 Industrial Pkwy N, Marinette, WI 54143-3704
Tel (715) 732-0181 Founded/Ownrshp 2011
Sales 53.0MM^E EMP 1,000^E
SIC 3592 Pistons & piston rings
CEO: Don Cameron
*CFO: Rick Posz

KSU FOUNDATION
See KANSAS STATE UNIVERSITY FOUNDATION INC

KTA SUPER STORES
See PUNA PLANTATION HAWAII LIMITED

D-U-N-S 86-765-1155
KTB SERVICES LLC
EXPERT AIR
1108 Cedar Bayou Rd, Baytown, TX 77520-2926
Tel (281) 428-7344 Founded/Ownrshp 2009
Sales 204.0MM EMP 12
SIC 1711 Plumbing, heating, air-conditioning contractors

D-U-N-S 10-911-1372
KTG (USA) LP
(Suby of KRUGER PRODUCTS L.P.)
400 Mahannah Ave, Memphis, TN 38107-1021
Tel (901) 260-3900 Founded/Ownrshp 2013
Sales 134.5MM^E EMP 265
SIC 2621 Towels, tissues & napkins: paper & stock
Pt: Phil Shearing
Snr Mgr: Randy Adams

D-U-N-S 12-198-2664 IMP
KTH PARTS INDUSTRIES INC
1111 State Route 235 N, Saint Paris, OH 43072-9680
Tel (937) 663-5941 Founded/Ownrshp 1984
Sales 219.4MM^E EMP 826
SIC 3714 Motor vehicle parts & accessories
Pr: Toshio Inoue
*Ex VP: Sanichi Kanai
Exec: Doug Surber
*Prin: Fumio Takeuchi
Admn Mgr: Andrew Donahoe
Ql Cn Mgr: Joey Bechtel

KU ENDOWMENT
See KANSAS UNIVERSITY ENDOWMENT ASSOCIATION

D-U-N-S 11-323-0569 IMP
KUAKINI HEALTH SYSTEM
347 N Kuakini St, Honolulu, HI 96817-2382
Tel (808) 536-2236 Founded/Ownrshp 1900
Sales 1.1MM EMP 1,400
Accts Delo Itte Tax Llp Honolulu H
SIC 8062 General medical & surgical hospitals
Pr: Gary K Kajiwara
*COO: Gregg Oishi
*CFO: Quin Ogawa
CFO: Quinn Ogawa
*VP: June Drumeller
*VP: Nobuyuki Miki
QA Dir: Vicki Philbin

D-U-N-S 07-770-1613
KUAKINI MEDICAL CENTER
(Suby of KUAKINI HEALTH SYSTEM) ★
347 N Kuakini St, Honolulu, HI 96817-2381
Tel (808) 547-9231 Founded/Ownrshp 1995
Sales 133.5MM EMP 1,216
Accts Deloitte Tax Llp Honolulu Hi
SIC 8062 General medical & surgical hospitals
Pr: Gary Kajiwara
*Treas: Chuck Gee
Ofcr: Tamlyn Miyagawa
*Sr VP: Gregg Oishi
*VP: Dawn Ching
*VP: June Drumeller
Dir Rx: Wendy Zarella
Brnch Mgr: Scott Lopes
Brnch Mgr: Ida Thiede
Info Man: Terri Hara
Opers Mgr: Rob Muranaka

KUBOTA
See HOOBER INC

KUBOTA AUTHORIZED DEALER
See COLUMBUS EQUIPMENT CO

KUBOTA AUTHORIZED DEALER
See GARTON TRACTOR INC

KUBOTA AUTHORIZED DEALER
See KANEQUIP INC

KUBOTA AUTHORIZED DEALER
See KANEQUIP INC

D-U-N-S 36-066-5376 IMP/EXP
KUBOTA MANUFACTURING OF AMERICA CORP
(Suby of KUBOTA USA INC) ★
2715 Ramsey Rd, Gainesville, GA 30501-7526
Tel (770) 532-0038 Founded/Ownrshp 1988
Sales 203.5MM^E EMP 850
SIC 3524 3537 Lawn & garden tractors & equipment; Industrial trucks & tractors
CEO: Hironobu Kubota
*CFO: Takehiro Ueda
*CFO: Hirokazu Yoshida
*Treas: Walter Ouchi
*Ex VP: Kaz Monodane
*VP: Yasu Hiyama
Exec: John Harris
CIO: Phil Sutton
IT Man: Kevin Rainey

D-U-N-S 06-207-4828 IMP/EXP
KUBOTA TRACTOR CORP
(Suby of KUBOTA USA INC) ★
3401 Del Amo Blvd, Torrance, CA 90503-1636
Tel (310) 370-3370 Founded/Ownrshp 1972
Sales 422.6MM^E EMP 470
SIC 5083 3531 3799 Tractors, agricultural; Farm equipment parts & supplies; Construction machinery; Recreational vehicles
Pr: Yuichi Kitao
Pr: Masto Yoshikawa
Treas: Kosuke Ota
VP: Shingo Banada
Prin: Susan Holmes
Admn Mgr: Sharon McConnell
Dist Mgr: Bob Gertner
Dist Mgr: Mike Jacobson
CTO: Jack Cross
IT Man: Hiro Kuge
VP Opers: Alex Woods

D-U-N-S 18-339-9005 IMP
KUBOTA USA INC
(Suby of KUBOTA CORPORATION)
3401 Del Amo Blvd, Torrance, CA 90503-1636
Tel (310) 370-3370 Founded/Ownrshp 1986
Sales 942.4MM^E EMP 1,500
SIC 5083 3577 5051 3531 3571 Tractors, agricultural; Disk & diskette equipment, except drives; Castings, rough: iron or steel; Loaders, shovel: self-propelled; Electronic computers
Pr: Yoshiharu Nishiguchi
*Sec: Hiro Okino
Ofcr: Toby Anderson
Top Exec: Sid Winecoop

D-U-N-S 13-301-5722 IMP
KUDZU FABRICS INC
2154 River Cliff Dr, Roswell, GA 30076-3904
Tel (770) 641-0379 Founded/Ownrshp 1999
Sales 108.0MM^E EMP 212
SIC 5199 5131 5191 Automobile fabrics; Upholstery fabrics, woven; Saddlery
Pr: Dan M Duncan Jr
CEO: Dee Dunkins
VP: Ann Duncan

D-U-N-S 00-985-3664 IMP/EXP
KUEHNE + NAGEL INC
BLUE ANCHOR LINE
(Suby of KUEHNE + NAGEL INVESTMENT INC) ★
10 Exchange Pl Fl 19, Jersey City, NJ 07302-4935
Tel (201) 413-5500 Founded/Ownrshp 1992
Sales 1.6MMM^E EMP 3,300
SIC 4731 Freight forwarding
Pr: Bob Mohok
V Ch: Bernd Wrede
Pr: Bill Spiker
CFO: Markus Blanka-Graff
*CFO: Michael Schimpf
*CFO: Gerard Van Kesteren
Sr VP: Dave Mabon
*Sr VP: Greg Martin
VP: Bill Aldridge
VP: Steven Atcheson
*VP: Juerg Bandle
VP: Steve Bridgland
VP: Rick Delpaz
VP: Phil Denning
VP: Graeme Egan
VP: John Franklin
VP: Jeff Grogan
VP: Jon Hettrick
VP: Nadine Jones
VP: Steve Kuchta
VP: Claudine Lewis

D-U-N-S 80-736-8360
KUEHNE + NAGEL INVESTMENT INC
(Suby of KUHNE + NAGEL INTERNATIONAL AG)
10 Exchange Pl Fl 19, Jersey City, NJ 07302-4935
Tel (201) 413-5500 Founded/Ownrshp 1992
Sales 1.8MMM^E EMP 5,306^E
SIC 4731 Foreign freight forwarding
CEO: Reinhard Lange
*Pr: John Hextall
*CFO: Gerard Van Kesteren
*Ex VP: Peter Messerli
*VP: Klaus-Michael Kuehne
Opers Mgr: Paul Norris

D-U-N-S 01-123-9167 IMP/EXP
KUEHNE CHEMICAL CO INC
86 N Hackensack Ave, Kearny, NJ 07032-4673
Tel (973) 589-0700 Founded/Ownrshp 1966
Sales 118.3MM^E EMP 200
SIC 2819 4226 2812 Sodium & potassium compounds, exc. bleaches, alkalies, alum.; Special warehousing & storage; Alkalies & chlorine
Pr: Donald Nicolai
*CFO: Bill Paulin
Genl Mgr: Kelly Ward
Sfty Mgr: Tony Dias
Sfty Mgr: Tony Diaz

D-U-N-S 00-608-3240 IMP/EXP
KUHN NORTH AMERICA INC
(Suby of KUHN SA)
1501 W 7th Ave, Brodhead, WI 53520-1637
Tel (608) 897-4508 Founded/Ownrshp 2002
Sales 204.2MM^E EMP 630
SIC 3523 3531 Feed grinders, crushers & mixers; Spreaders, fertilizer; Construction machinery
CEO: Thierry Krier
CFO: Scott Rupprecht
Mng Dir: Roland Rieger
Store Mgr: Tad Allen
Dir IT: Laurent Maurer
Opers Mgr: Fabien Moreau
Sls Dir: Craig Pados
Mktg Mgr: Frank O Brien
Sls Mgr: Grant Hansel

KUHNLE BROS TRUCKING
See KUHNLE BROTHERS INC

D-U-N-S 00-294-6523
KUHNLE BROTHERS INC (OH)
KUHNLE BROS TRUCKING
14905 Cross Creek Pkwy, Newbury, OH 44065-9788
Tel (440) 564-7168 Founded/Ownrshp 1963
Sales 270.0MM EMP 150
Accts Demarchi & Associates Clevela
SIC 4213 4212 Trucking, except local; Local trucking, without storage
CEO: Kim Taylor Kuhnle
*Treas: Robert Russell

D-U-N-S 01-125-7615
KUIKEN BROTHERS CO INC
6-02 Fair Lawn Ave, Fair Lawn, NJ 07410-1219
Tel (201) 796-2082 Founded/Ownrshp 1912
Sales 150.0MM EMP 270
Accts Massood & Company Pa Totowa
SIC 5211 5031 3272 Lumber & other building materials; Building materials, exterior; Building materials, interior; Concrete stuctural support & building material
Pr: Douglas Kuiken
*VP: Nicholas M Fuiken
*VP: Henry Kuiken
Sfty Dirs: Louis Cicchella
Sales Asso: Darlene Bryant
Sales Asso: Michael Conte
Sales Asso: Mitch Falk

KUKA AEROSPACE
See KUKA SYSTEMS NORTH AMERICA LLC

D-U-N-S 05-332-9082 IMP
KUKA SYSTEMS NORTH AMERICA LLC
KUKA AEROSPACE
(Suby of KUKA SYSTEMS GMBH)
6600 Center Dr, Sterling Heights, MI 48312-2666
Tel (586) 795-2000 Founded/Ownrshp 1935, 2007
Sales 572.0MM EMP 940
SIC 3549 Assembly machines, including robotic
Pr: Lawrence A Drake
*CFO: Paul Ambros
CFO: Ryan Carrithers
VP: Mike Larose
VP: Gary Tino
Snr Ntwrk: Nick Consiglio
Dir IT: Michael Fera
Software D: Dustin Zagumny
Mfg Mgr: Bill Cardella

Plnt Mgr: Scott Higuchi
Snr Mgr: Jason Aldinger

KULICKE & SOFFA
See KULICKE AND SOFFA INDUSTRIES INC

D-U-N-S 00-235-1203
▲ KULICKE AND SOFFA INDUSTRIES INC (PA)
KULICKE & SOFFA
1005 Virginia Dr, Fort Washington, PA 19034-3101
Tel (215) 784-6000 *Founded/Ownrshp* 1951
Sales 627.1MM *EMP* 2,373ᴱ
Tkr Sym KLIC *Exch* NGS
SIC 3674 Semiconductors & related devices; Integrated circuits, semiconductor networks, etc.
CFO: Jonathan H Chou
**Ch Bd:* Garrett E Pierce
CFO: Claudia Stadler
Sr VP: Irene Lee
Sr VP: Yih-Neng Lee
Sr VP: Lester Wong
VP: Robert Hanson
VP: Deepak Sood
VP: Nelson Wong
Snr Sftwr: Todd Leitzel
Snr Sftwr: Sameer Raheja
Board of Directors: Brian R Bachman, Peter T Kong, Chin Hu Lim, Gregory F Milzcik

D-U-N-S 00-180-3089
KULITE SEMICONDUCTOR PRODUCTS INC (NJ)
KS
1 Willow Tree Rd, Leonia, NJ 07605-2239
Tel (201) 461-0900 *Founded/Ownrshp* 1959
Sales 123.0MM *EMP* 828
SIC 3728 3829

D-U-N-S 61-532-2414 IMP
KUM & GO LC
(*Suby of* KRAUSE HOLDINGS INC) ★
6400 Westown Pkwy, West Des Moines, IA 50266-7709
Tel (515) 226-0128 *Founded/Ownrshp* 1997
Sales 509.0MMᴱ *EMP* 3,000
SIC 5411 Convenience stores, chain
Ch: William A Krause
CEO: Kyle J Krause
COO: Mark Hastings
CFO: Craig Bergstrom
CFO: Brian Thompson
Ex VP: Dennis Folden
VP: James Brandt
Ex Dir: Pat Fellers
Netwrk Eng: Bill Kaminski

D-U-N-S 78-950-8959
KUMON NORTH AMERICA INC
(*Suby of* KUMON INSTITUTE OF EDUCATION CO.,LTD.)
300 Frank W Burr Blvd # 6, Teaneck, NJ 07666-6703
Tel (201) 928-0444 *Founded/Ownrshp* 1989
Sales 149.3MM *EMP* 781
Accts Citrin Cooperman & Company Ll
SIC 8299 Educational services
Pr: Minoru Tanabe
CFO: John Miller
CFO: Joseph Nativo
VP: James F Coakley Jr
**VP:* Kazutaka Kubo
**VP:* Robert Lichtenstein
VP: Matt Lupsha
**VP:* Toshi Yoseda
Brnch Mgr: Caroline Rostkowski
Software D: Joe Larkin
Mktg Mgr: Tammy Monroe

KUNA FOOD SERVICE
See KUNA MEAT CO INC

D-U-N-S 08-738-8893
KUNA GOOD NEIGHBORS INC (ID)
12689 S Five Mile Rd, Kuna, ID 83634-2661
Tel (208) 362-1907 *Founded/Ownrshp* 1990
Sales 197.0MM *EMP* 15
SIC 8611 Community affairs & services
Pr: Patricia Hamm
Sec: Janie Arnold

D-U-N-S 03-105-8423 IMP
KUNA MEAT CO INC
KUNA FOOD SERVICE
704 Kuna Industrial Ct, Dupo, IL 62239-1823
Tel (618) 286-4000 *Founded/Ownrshp* 1994
Sales 137.9MMᴱ *EMP* 105
SIC 5144 5142 5147 5169 5149 5148 Poultry & poultry products; Packaged frozen goods; Meats & meat products; Specialty cleaning & sanitation preparations; Sanitation preparations; Groceries & related products; Fresh fruits & vegetables
Pr: Daniel F Bippen
CFO: Paul Vlaich

KUNI AUTOMOTIVE
See KUNI ENTERPRISES LLC

D-U-N-S 78-785-0705
KUNI ENTERPRISES LLC
KUNI AUTOMOTIVE
(*Suby of* HOLMAN AUTOMOTIVE GROUP INC) ★
8035 Lenexa Dr, Overland Park, KS 66214-3609
Tel (360) 553-7350 *Founded/Ownrshp* 2016
Sales 360.0MMᴱ *EMP* 1,000
SIC 5511 New & used car dealers
Genl Mgr: Joe Allis
Genl Mgr: Brad Castonguay

D-U-N-S 00-300-2433
KUNZLER & CO INC
652 Manor St, Lancaster, PA 17603-5108
Tel (717) 299-6301 *Founded/Ownrshp* 1961
Sales 123.4MMᴱ *EMP* 500
SIC 2011 2013 Meat packing plants; Smoked meats from purchased meat
Pr: Christian C Kunzler III
CFO: John Younk
**VP:* John S Kunzler
MIS Dir: Steve Henry

Mktg Mgr: Tim Vance
Sls Mgr: Betty Ann Loht

D-U-N-S 02-081-1123 IMP
KURABE AMERICA CORP
37735 Interchange Dr, Farmington Hills, MI 48335-1030
Tel (248) 939-5803 *Founded/Ownrshp* 2006
Sales 15.5MMᴱ *EMP* 1,100
SIC 7699 7549 Professional instrument repair services; High performance auto repair & service
CEO: Yasuto Kanazawa
**Pr:* Takenobu Kanazawa

D-U-N-S 96-493-4756
KURANI PIZZA INC
PIZZA HUT
2825 Breckinridge Blvd # 150, Duluth, GA 30096-7600
Tel (770) 923-2313 *Founded/Ownrshp* 1994
Sales 57.3MMᴱ *EMP* 2,559
SIC 5812 Pizzeria, chain
Pr: Sultan Kurani
Off Mgr: Aneela Huwaja

D-U-N-S 94-809-5245 IMP/EXP
KURARAY AMERICA INC
KAI
(*Suby of* KURARAY HOLDINGS USA INC) ★
2625 Bay Area Blvd # 600, Houston, TX 77058-1523
Tel (281) 474-1592 *Founded/Ownrshp* 2000
Sales 246.0MMᴱ *EMP* 220
SIC 2821 3081 3843 Vinyl resins; Polyvinyl film & sheet; Glue, dental
Pr: George Avdey
Sr VP: Bob Chvala
VP: David Schreckengost
VP: Toshio Suzuki
Tech Mgr: Ray Jouett
Opers Mgr: Eric Bass
Opers Mgr: Michael Iwanski
Plnt Mgr: Glen Pubentz
Sales Exec: Derek Harvey
Sales Exec: Kenneth Perry
Natl Sales: Rick Evans

D-U-N-S 17-470-8540 EXP
KURARAY HOLDINGS USA INC
(*Suby of* KURARAY CO., LTD.)
2625 Bay Area Blvd, Houston, TX 77058-1523
Tel (713) 495-7311 *Founded/Ownrshp* 1996
Sales 246.0MMᴱ *EMP* 235
SIC 5047 5049 2821 Dental equipment & supplies; Optical goods; Vinyl resins
Pr: Yuichi Kawarasaki

D-U-N-S 07-440-3312 IMP/EXP
KURIYAMA OF AMERICA INC (IL)
(*Suby of* KURIYAMA HOLDINGS CORPORATION)
360 E State Pkwy, Schaumburg, IL 60173-5335
Tel (847) 755-0360 *Founded/Ownrshp* 1968
Sales 94.4MMᴱ *EMP* 150
SIC 5085 3052 Hose, belting & packing; Rubber & plastics hose & beltings
Pr: Lester A Kraska
**Treas:* Fred Bobzien
**VP:* Motohiro Majikima
VP: Motohiro Majikina
Exec: Tsutomu Hitomi
Genl Mgr: Brian Dutton
Genl Mgr: Hassan Salim
IT Man: Dura Hose
Board of Directors: Brian Dutton, Thomas Hanyok, Terry Jackson, Gary Kammes, Gary Kammes

D-U-N-S 05-968-0165 IMP
KURT MANUFACTURING CO INC
5280 Main St Ne, Minneapolis, MN 55421-1594
Tel (763) 572-1500 *Founded/Ownrshp* 1946
Sales 120.4MMᴱ *EMP* 410
SIC 3499 3545 3363 3728 3842 3365 Machine bases, metal; Vises, machine (machine tool accessories); Aluminum die-castings; Gears, aircraft power transmission; Wheelchairs; Aluminum foundries
Ch: William G Kuban
**Pr:* Steven Carlsen
**CEO:* Paul Lillyblad
COO: Jerry Meistad
**VP:* Kelli Watson
Exec: Brad Carlstrom
Dept Mgr: Darren Kitz
Genl Mgr: Jeff Lenz
CIO: Michael Scipioni
Dir IT: Tom Moore
IT Man: Dan Cooke

D-U-N-S 00-325-6450
KURT SALMON US LLC (GA)
HEALTH CARE MGT COUNSELORS
(*Suby of* ACCENTURE PUBLIC LIMITED COMPANY)
1355 Peachtree St Ne # 900, Atlanta, GA 30309-3257
Tel (404) 892-0321 *Founded/Ownrshp* 1935
Sales 123.5MMᴱ *EMP* 1,003
SIC 8742

KURT WEISS FLORIST
See KURT WEISS GREENHOUSES INC

D-U-N-S 01-352-2008 IMP
KURT WEISS GREENHOUSES INC
KURT WEISS FLORIST
95 Main St, Center Moriches, NY 11934-1703
Tel (631) 878-2500 *Founded/Ownrshp* 1960
Sales 432.8MMᴱ *EMP* 1,000
SIC 0181 5193 Plants, potted: growing of; Plants, potted
Pr: Russell Weiss
**VP:* Kirk Weiss
VP: Wayne Weiss

D-U-N-S 13-048-0437
KUSHNER COMPANIES INC
WESTMINSTER MANAGEMENT
666 5th Ave Fl 15, New York, NY 10103-0001
Tel (212) 527-7000 *Founded/Ownrshp* 1984
Sales 175.6MMᴱ *EMP* 650
SIC 1521 6513 6531 6512 1522 1531 New construction, single-family houses; Townhouse construction; Apartment building operators; Condominium manager; Cooperative apartment manager; Real estate brokers & agents; Multiple listing service, real estate; Nonresidential building operators; Apartment building construction; Co-op construction; Condominium construction; Condominium developers; Cooperative apartment developers
Pr: Charles Kushner
CFO: Lawrence Lipton
VP: Gladys Vanterpool
**Genl Mgr:* Richard Stadtmauer
Genl Couns: Sampson Schmitt

D-U-N-S 96-955-7532 IMP
KUSS FILTRATION INC
2150 Industrial Dr, Findlay, OH 45840-5402
Tel (419) 423-9040 *Founded/Ownrshp* 2011
Sales 192.6MMᴱ *EMP* 600
SIC 3569 Filters, general line: industrial
CEO: Hasnain R Merchant
**Ch Bd:* Nick Galambos
**CFO:* John Byrnes
CFO: Tom Hogan
**VP:* Gary L Rickle
VP: Gary Rickle
**Prin:* Scott Salsburey
**Prin:* George Starring
IT Man: Bonnie Stansberry
Mtls Mgr: Tim Meyers

D-U-N-S 96-332-2540
KUSSY INC
QUALITY FLOORING JACKSON HOLE
1260 Huff Ln Ste B, Jackson, WY 83001-8504
Tel (307) 739-9465 *Founded/Ownrshp* 1995
Sales 116.2MM *EMP* 2
SIC 1752 5713 Carpet laying; Floor covering stores
Pr: Richard Kussy
**Sec:* Kimmi Kussy
Off Mgr: Kimberly Townsend

KUSTOM FOOD
See UWAJIMAYA INC

KUSTOM PAK
See TUR-PAK FOODS INC

D-U-N-S 07-800-6301
KUTAK ROCK LLP
1650 Farnam St Fl 2, Omaha, NE 68102-2103
Tel (402) 346-6000 *Founded/Ownrshp* 1965
Sales 147.7MMᴱ *EMP* 750
SIC 8111 General practice law office; General practice attorney, lawyer
Mng Pt: David L Amsden
Mng Pt: James D Arundel
Mng Pt: Katherine A Carey
Mng Pt: Michael L Curry
Mng Pt: Seth D Kirshenberg
Mng Pt: Jay Selanders
V Ch: Robert D Irvin
CFO: Vicki L Young
VP: Erin Thompson
Exec: Fred Clingman
Genl Mgr: Robert D Binderup

KUTZTOWN BOLOGNA
See GODSHALLS QUALITY MEATS INC

KUVERA INTERNATIONAL
See VINMAR INTERNATIONAL HOLDINGS LTD

D-U-N-S 79-338-6194
KVAERNER NORTH AMERICAN CONSTRUCTION INC
701 Technology Dr, Canonsburg, PA 15317-9529
Tel (724) 416-6900 *Founded/Ownrshp* 2011
Sales 476.2MMᴱ *EMP* 1,500
SIC 1542 8741

KVCC
See KALAMAZOO VALLEY COMMUNITY COLLEGE

KVEO TV
See COMMUNICATIONS CORP OF AMERICA

D-U-N-S 09-320-7215 IMP/EXP
▲ KVH INDUSTRIES INC
50 Enterprise Ctr, Middletown, RI 02842-5279
Tel (401) 847-3327 *Founded/Ownrshp* 1978
Sales 184.6MM *EMP* 567
Tkr Sym KVHI *Exch* NGS
SIC 3663 3812 Mobile communication equipment; Navigational systems & instruments
Ch Bd: Martin A Kits Van Heyningen
COO: Brent C Bruun
CFO: John McCarthy
Ex VP: Daniel R Conway
Sr VP: Robert J Balog
VP: Brian Arthur
VP: Patricio Baez
VP: Brent Brunn
VP: Christopher Burnett
VP: Felise B Feingold
**VP:* Robert W B Kits Van Heyningen
VP: Robert K Van Heyningen
Board of Directors: Mark S Ain, Stanley K Honey, Bruce J Ryan, Charles R Trimble

KW COMPANIES
See KW INTERNATIONAL INC

D-U-N-S 96-244-3677
KW INTERNATIONAL INC
KW COMPANIES
18655 Bishop Ave, Carson, CA 90746-4028
Tel (310) 747-1380 *Founded/Ownrshp* 1996
Sales 236.8MMᴱ *EMP* 600
SIC 4731 4226 8744 Freight transportation arrangement; Freight forwarding; Special warehousing & storage; Facilities support services
CEO: Kil Won Jin
**CFO:* Dj Kim
VP: Karen Cho
VP Admn: Dan Schrader
Ex Dir: Julie Gerberding
Genl Mgr: Aron Park

D-U-N-S 86-837-4406
KW INTERNATIONAL LLC
10880 Alcott Dr, Houston, TX 77043-2040
Tel (713) 468-9581 *Founded/Ownrshp* 2004
Sales 115.7MMᴱ *EMP* 170
SIC 3533 Oil & gas field machinery
CEO: Don Ray
Pr: John Thompson
**COO:* Joe Craft
**CFO:* Tom S Simms
Exec: Kari Cromeens
Dir Bus: Tom Owoc
Mfg Dir: Jeff Wagner
Sls Dir: Zac Henderson

KW LUBES
See KELLEY WILLIAMSON CO

D-U-N-S 15-003-2774
KW PROPERTY MANAGEMENT LLC
KW PROPERTY MGT & CONSULTING
8200 Nw 33rd St Ste 300, Doral, FL 33122-1942
Tel (305) 476-9188 *Founded/Ownrshp* 2004
Sales 88.9MMᴱ *EMP* 630ᴱ
SIC 6531 Real estate managers
Ex Dir: Katalina Cruz
Genl Mgr: Mirian Padin
Off Mgr: Ernesto Moreno

KW PROPERTY MGT & CONSULTING
See KW PROPERTY MANAGEMENT LLC

D-U-N-S 00-546-2460
KW SERVICES LLC
KOONTZ-WAGNER
3801 Voorde Dr Ste B, South Bend, IN 46628-1643
Tel (574) 232-2051 *Founded/Ownrshp* 1921, 2013
Sales 87.7MMᴱ *EMP* 140
SIC 6719 1799 5063 Investment holding companies, except banks; Service station equipment installation, maintenance & repair; Switchgear
Prin: Heather Webb
Pr: Paul M Witek
VP: William G Harlan Jr
VP: Stephen J Vivian

D-U-N-S 11-435-3365
KWAJALEIN RANGE SERVICES LLC
KRS
(*Suby of* BECHTEL NATIONAL INC) ★
4975 Bradford Dr Nw # 600, Huntsville, AL 35805-1929
Tel (256) 890-8536 *Founded/Ownrshp* 2002
Sales 162.0MMᴱ *EMP* 1,500
SIC 8744 Facilities support services
Sls Mgr: Gerard Sims

KWIK CHEK FOOD STORES
See KWIK CHEK REAL ESTATE TRUST INC

D-U-N-S 15-469-3741
KWIK CHEK FOOD STORES INC
K C FOOD
2207 N Center St, Bonham, TX 75418-2112
Tel (903) 583-7484 *Founded/Ownrshp* 1975
Sales 160.2MMᴱ *EMP* 425
Accts Fox Byrd & Company Pc Dal
SIC 5541 5411 Filling stations, gasoline; Convenience stores, independent
Pr: Doyce Taylor
**CFO:* Becky Moore
**VP:* Bobby Mc Craw
Sales Exec: Sherry Capehart

D-U-N-S 10-528-6640
KWIK CHEK REAL ESTATE TRUST INC
KWIK CHEK FOOD STORES
2207 N Center St, Bonham, TX 75418-2112
Tel (903) 583-7481 *Founded/Ownrshp* 1998
Sales 86.1MM *EMP* 50
SIC 6798 Real estate investment trusts
Pr: Doyce Taylor
**VP:* Bobby McCraw
Prd Mgr: Lance Davis

D-U-N-S 03-127-2206
■ KWIK SHOP INC
(*Suby of* KROGER CO) ★
734 E 4th Ave, Hutchinson, KS 67501-2274
Tel (620) 669-8504 *Founded/Ownrshp* 2001
Sales 207.1MMᴱ *EMP* 1,507
SIC 5411 Convenience stores, chain
Pr: Micheal Hoffman
**CFO:* Mike Gerwert
Treas: Scott Henderson
**VP:* Pat Edwards
**VP:* Kenny Nuss
Dist Mgr: Neal Sewyer
Dir IT: Dennis Farrell
VP Opers: Brian Fisher
Mktg Mgr: Dennis Abshier

D-U-N-S 05-903-9339
KWIK TRIP INC
1626 Oak St, La Crosse, WI 54603-2308
Tel (608) 781-8988 *Founded/Ownrshp* 1971
Sales 2.6MMMᴱ *EMP* 10,500
Accts Mcgladrey & Pullen Llp Minne
SIC 5921 5993 5541 5983 5461 Liquor stores; Tobacco stores & stands; Filling stations, gasoline; Fuel oil dealers; Bakeries
Pr: Don Zietlow
**Treas:* Scott Teigen
**VP:* Steve Loehr
**VP:* Greg Olson
**VP:* Thomas Reinhart
**VP:* Robert Thorud
**VP:* Steve Zietlow
Dir Risk M: Stephanie Thompson
Genl Mgr: Gretchen Knudson-Stuhr
Genl Mgr: Jill Thompson
CTO: Nick Adams

KWIKEE
See SOUTHERN GRAPHIC SYSTEMS LLC

D-U-N-S 60-286-0520 IMP
KWIKSET CORP
SPECTRUM BRANDS HDWR HM IMPRV
19701 Da Vinci, Foothill Ranch, CA 92610-2622
Tel (949) 672-4000 *Founded/Ownrshp* 2012
Sales 1.1MMM^E *EMP* 3,200
SIC 3429

D-U-N-S 05-208-1908
KWS INC
STAAB MANAGEMENT CO
3048 W Stolley Park Rd, Grand Island, NE 68801-7227
Tel (308) 382-1053 *Founded/Ownrshp* 1981
Sales 43.7MM^E *EMP* 1,400
SIC 5812 Pizzeria, chain
Pr: Kenneth Staab
**Treas:* Dean Olson

D-U-N-S 00-794-0117 IMP/EXP
KYANITE MINING CORP (VA)
BUFFALO WOOD PRODUCTS DIV
30 Willis Mountain Ln, Dillwyn, VA 23936
Tel (434) 983-2085 *Founded/Ownrshp* 1928, 1945
Sales 179.4MM^E *EMP* 300
SIC 1459 Kyanite mining
Pr: Dixon Jr Gene Bishop
**Treas:* Ron Hudgins
**VP:* Dixon Guy Bishop
DP Exec: Dilip Jain
IT Man: Lakshmi Bertram
VP Opers: Barry Jones
S&M/VP: Hank Jamerson

D-U-N-S 18-368-8837 IMP
KYB AMERICAS CORP
(*Suby of* KYB CORPORATION)
2625 N Morton St, Franklin, IN 46131-8820
Tel (317) 736-7774 *Founded/Ownrshp* 2001
Sales 155.0MM^E *EMP* 1,000
SIC 3714 8711 Shock absorbers, motor vehicle; Engineering services
Pr: Hiroaki Hirayama
**Pr:* A Tanaka
CFO: Richard A Smith
Genl Mgr: Wade Cunningham
Genl Mgr: Sal Milioto
Manager: Ryan Dickerman
Sls Mgr: Corey Davis

D-U-N-S 80-960-8750 IMP
KYKLOS BEARING INTERNATIONAL LLC
K B I
2509 Hayes Ave, Sandusky, OH 44870-5359
Tel (419) 627-7000 *Founded/Ownrshp* 2008
Sales 149.0MM^E *EMP* 900
SIC 3714 Bearings, motor vehicle
Pr: George Thanopoulos
Exec: Chris Kettereer
Opers Supe: Christopher Marquart
Manager: Terence Kehres

D-U-N-S 06-869-2732
KYNETIC LLC
225 Washington St, Conshohocken, PA 19428-4122
Tel (484) 534-8100 *Founded/Ownrshp* 2011
Sales 352.7MM^E *EMP* 920
SIC 8741 5961 Business management; Catalog & mail-order houses
CEO: Michael G Rubin
**CFO:* Michael R Conn
**VP:* Saj Cherian
**VP:* Brian L Miles
Exec: Todd Sandler
Genl Couns: Jonathan S Schoenfeld

D-U-N-S 03-319-4572
KYO-YA HOTELS & RESORTS LP
(*Suby of* KOKUSAI KOGYO KANRI CO., LTD.)
2255 Kalakaua Ave Fl 2, Honolulu, HI 96815-2515
Tel (808) 931-8600 *Founded/Ownrshp* 1961
Sales 247.6MM^E *EMP* 3,638
SIC 7011 5812 5813 Hotels & motels; Eating places; Bar (drinking places)
Pr: Takamasa Osano
Pr: Greg Dichkens
COO: Ernest Nishizaki
Sr VP: Nobutada Nagai
Exec: Kevin Gleason
Exec: Nona Tamanaha
Mng Dir: William Hurley
IT Man: Ken Sato
Sys/Mgr: Allan Sato
Pr Dir: Dara Young
Board of Directors: Kenichi Uchida

D-U-N-S 17-451-9678
KYOCERA AMERICA INC
8611 Balboa Ave, San Diego, CA 92123-1580
Tel (858) 576-2600 *Founded/Ownrshp* 1978
Sales 90.5MM^E *EMP* 50
SIC 3674

D-U-N-S 06-446-5503 IMP/EXP
■ KYOCERA DOCUMENT SOLUTIONS AMERICA INC
(*Suby of* KYOCERA DOCUMENT SOLUTIONS INC.)
225 Sand Rd, Fairfield, NJ 07004-1575
Tel (973) 808-8444 *Founded/Ownrshp* 1973
Sales 193.3MM^E *EMP* 700
SIC 5044 5084 5065 Photocopy machines; Printing trades machinery, equipment & supplies; Facsimile equipment
CEO: Norihiko INA
**CFO:* Nicholas Maimone
CFO: Nicholas Naimone
Ex VP: Yoshihiro Suzuki
VP: Ed Bialecki
VP: Mark Ohara
Area Mgr: Greg Bezdek
Area Mgr: James Robinson
Genl Mgr: Dennis Lees
Dir IT: Ashwin Bhansali
Dir IT: Mano Misra
Board of Directors: Tetsuo Kuba, Takashi Kuki, Nicholas Maimone, John Rigby, Calvin Rosen

D-U-N-S 07-849-5083 IMP
■ KYOCERA INDUSTRIAL CERAMICS CORP
KYOCERA USA
(*Suby of* KYOCERA INTERNATIONAL INC) ★
100 Industrial Park Rd, Hendersonville, NC 28792-9011
Tel (828) 693-0241 *Founded/Ownrshp* 1990
Sales 101.0MM^E *EMP* 310
SIC 5065 5013 5085 Electronic parts & equipment; Connectors, electronic; Semiconductor devices; Heaters, motor vehicle; Industrial tools
Pr: David M Williams

D-U-N-S 04-789-6097 IMP/EXP
■ KYOCERA INTERNATIONAL INC
(*Suby of* KYOCERA CORPORATION)
8611 Balboa Ave, San Diego, CA 92123-1580
Tel (858) 576-2600 *Founded/Ownrshp* 1969
Sales 203.6MM^E *EMP* 150^E
SIC 5043 Cameras & photographic equipment
Pr: Robert Whisler
CFO: Mark Umemura
Sr Cor Off: Kevin King
**VP:* William Edwards
**VP:* George Woodworth
Assoc Dir: Bill Cassidy
Genl Mgr: Dean Fledderjohn
QA Dir: Robert Bruening
Prd Mgr: Brad Demilio
Ql Cn Mgr: Agustin Guevara
Mktg Mgr: Katie Shaw

KYOCERA USA
See KYOCERA INDUSTRIAL CERAMICS CORP

D-U-N-S 15-753-6822 IMP
KYOWA AMERICA CORP
(*Suby of* KYOWA ELECTRIC AND CHEMICAL CO.,LTD.)
1039 Fred White Blvd, Portland, TN 37148-8369
Tel (615) 323-2194 *Founded/Ownrshp* 1973
Sales 171.4MM^E *EMP* 447
SIC 5162 Plastics basic shapes
Pr: Sumito Furuya
VP: K Nakazawa
**VP:* Fumio Tomita

KYRENE DE LOS CERRITOS SCHOOL
See KYRENE SCHOOL DISTRICT

D-U-N-S 07-983-6257
KYRENE ELEMENTARY DISTRICT
8700 S Kyrene Rd, Tempe, AZ 85284-2108
Tel (480) 541-1000 *Founded/Ownrshp* 2015
Sales 6.3MM^E *EMP* 1,480^E
SIC 8211

D-U-N-S 02-165-7069
KYRENE SCHOOL DISTRICT
KYRENE DE LOS CERRITOS SCHOOL
8700 S Kyrene Rd, Tempe, AZ 85284-2197
Tel (480) 541-1000 *Founded/Ownrshp* 1888
Sales 153.0MM^E *EMP* 2,000
SIC 8211 Public elementary school
**VP:* Bernadette Coggins
VP: Michelle Hirsch
Pr Dir: Kelly Alexander
Pr Dir: Nancy Dudenhoffer
Teacher Pr: Mary Jane Rincon
HC Dir: Vickie Burke

D-U-N-S 00-602-1141 EXP
■ KYSOR INDUSTRIAL CORP
KYSOR WARREN
(*Suby of* MANITOWOC CO INC) ★
2227 Welbilt Blvd, Trinity, FL 34655-5130
Tel (727) 376-8600 *Founded/Ownrshp* 1925, 2009
Sales 228.6MM^E *EMP* 1,342
SIC 3585 3714 Refrigeration & heating equipment; Refrigeration equipment, complete; Counters & counter display cases, refrigerated; Air conditioning condensers & condensing units; Motor vehicle engines & parts; Heaters, motor vehicle; Radiators & radiator shells & cores, motor vehicle; Air conditioner parts, motor vehicle
Pr: Richard Osborne
**Treas:* Donald Holmes

KYSOR PANEL SYSTEMS
See WELBILT WALK-INS LP

KYSOR WARREN
See KYSOR INDUSTRIAL CORP

D-U-N-S 02-322-4250 IMP
KYUNGSHIN AMERICA CORP
(*Suby of* KYUNGSHIN CORPORATION)
1201 Og Skinner Dr, West Point, GA 31833-1789
Tel (706) 645-1595 *Founded/Ownrshp* 2008
Sales 354.6MM^E *EMP* 114^E
SIC 3714 Motor vehicle parts & accessories; Automotive wiring harness sets
CEO: Seung Kwan Lee
**CFO:* Chang Jun Lee

D-U-N-S 15-077-1652 EXP
KYUNGSHIN-LEAR SALES AND ENGINEERING LLC
(*Suby of* KYUNGSHIN AMERICA CORP) ★
100 Smothers Rd, Montgomery, AL 36117-5505
Tel (334) 413-0575 *Founded/Ownrshp* 2003
Sales 354.6MM *EMP* 105
Accts Mancera Sc Ciudad Juarez Ch
SIC 3714 Automotive wiring harness sets
CEO: Richard Ocallaghan
**Pr:* Seung Kwan Lee
**Genl Mgr:* Charles Kim

L

L & A JUICE
See LANGER JUICE CO INC

D-U-N-S 08-313-9311 IMP
L & F DISTRIBUTORS LLC
3900 N Mccoll Rd, McAllen, TX 78501-9160
Tel (956) 687-7751 *Founded/Ownrshp* 2007
Sales 188.6MM^E *EMP* 250
SIC 5181 Beer & other fermented malt liquors
Exec: Robert Rubio
IT Man: John Beagle
IT Man: John Duran
IT Man: Gabriel Gomez
Mktg Mgr: Brian Desmond
Sls Mgr: Dion Ruiz
Sls Mgr: Biff Wright

D-U-N-S 17-365-9574
L & G MORTGAGEBANC INC
8151 E Evans Rd Ste 10, Scottsdale, AZ 85260-3648
Tel (408) 905-5140 *Founded/Ownrshp* 1985
Sales NA *EMP* 1,000^E
SIC 6162 Mortgage bankers
Ch Bd: Alan D Levin
**CEO:* Mitchell Ginsberg
**VP:* Laura Cohen

D-U-N-S 03-568-8795
L & H CO INC
MEADE ELECTRIC CO
2215 York Rd Ste 304, Oak Brook, IL 60523-4004
Tel (630) 571-7200 *Founded/Ownrshp* 1980
Sales 350.2MM^E *EMP* 2,000
SIC 1731 1611 1623 3621 Electrical work; Lighting contractor; General contractor, highway & street construction; Oil & gas pipeline construction; Motors, electric
Pr: John S Lizzadro

D-U-N-S 00-953-3068 IMP
L & L NURSERY SUPPLY INC (CA)
UNIGRO
2552 Shenandoah Way, San Bernardino, CA 92407-1845
Tel (909) 591-0461 *Founded/Ownrshp* 1953
Sales 204.9MM^E *EMP* 275
SIC 5191 2875 2449 5193 Insecticides; Fertilizer & fertilizer materials; Soil, potting & planting; Potting soil, mixed; Wood containers; Flowers & florists' supplies
Ch Bd: Lloyd Swindell
Pr: Harvey Luth
**Pr:* Tom Medhurst
VP: Mike Fuson
Genl Mgr: Damian Mendoza
IT Man: Larry Tabert
Natl Sales: Craig Patrick

D-U-N-S 00-537-1414 IMP/EXP
L & L PRODUCTS INC
(*Suby of* L& L PRODUCTS) ★
160 Mclean, Bruce Twp, MI 48065-4919
Tel (586) 336-1600 *Founded/Ownrshp* 1958
Sales 181.6MM^E *EMP* 775
SIC 3053 Gaskets & sealing devices; Gaskets, all materials
CEO: John Ligon
**Pr:* Tom Klieno
**Ch:* Larry R Schmidt
**Treas:* Robert M Ligon
Prgrm Mgr: Tom Kleino

D-U-N-S 01-257-8514 IMP
L & R DISTRIBUTORS INC
9301 Avenue D, Brooklyn, NY 11236-1899
Tel (718) 272-2100 *Founded/Ownrshp* 1956
Sales 1.4MMM^E *EMP* 950
SIC 5122 5131 Druggists' sundries; Notions
CEO: Marc J Bodner
**Pr:* E Reilly Murray
**CFO:* Edward Musantry
**Ex VP:* Annette Lucas
**Sr VP:* Arthur C Walker
**VP:* Ray Delio
MIS Mgr: George Heudelo

L & S AVIATION LUBRICANTS
See EXXONMOBIL OIL CORP

D-U-N-S 05-308-8829
L & S ELECTRIC INC
5101 Mesker St, Schofield, WI 54476-3056
Tel (715) 359-3155 *Founded/Ownrshp* 1970
Sales 85.4MM *EMP* 350
Accts Gassner Co Sc Wausau Wi
SIC 7694 5063 8711 3613 Electric motor repair; Motors, electric; Motor controls, starters & relays: electric; Electrical or electronic engineering; Control panels, electric
Pr: Jeremy A Lewitzke
**CFO:* David Krause
Ofcr: Jeff Wendorf
**Ex VP:* Paul Gullickson
VP: Louis Barto
VP: Elaine Lane
VP: John Sturm
Exec: Marsha Wadzinski
Genl Mgr: Jody Frieders
Genl Mgr: Jamie Studinski
CTO: Dave Felton

D-U-N-S 17-808-0446 IMP
L & W INC
ADVANCE ENGINEERING
17757 Woodland Dr, New Boston, MI 48164-9265
Tel (734) 397-6300 *Founded/Ownrshp* 1985
Sales 559.1MM^E *EMP* 1,500
SIC 3469 3465 3441 3429 Stamping metal for the trade; Automotive stampings; Fabricated structural metal; Manufactured hardware (general)
Ch Bd: Wayne D Jones
**Pr:* Scott L Jones
COO: Joyce Miller
**COO:* Steven Schafer
CFO: John Meng
CFO: Kurt Vaaler
**Treas:* Bob Koss
VP: Kim Casper
**VP:* Mark Lorenger
Info Man: Barry Cloke
VP Opers: Jim Swainston

D-U-N-S 05-662-5908 IMP/EXP
L & W SUPPLY CORP
DOBY BUILDING SUPPLY
(*Suby of* ABC SUPPLY CO) ★
550 W Adams St, Chicago, IL 60661-3665
Tel (312) 606-4000 *Founded/Ownrshp* 2016
Sales 1.4MMM^E *EMP* 3,250
SIC 5032 Plastering materials
Pr: Jennifer F Scanlon
VP: John W Cain
VP: Kevin Corrigan
VP: Jake Gress
VP: Tim Mahaffey
Rgnl Mgr: Matt Myers
Rgnl Mgr: Don Wolf
Brnch Mgr: Jack Martin
Brnch Mgr: Debra Newbern
Brnch Mgr: Carl Roy
Brnch Mgr: Chad Thompson

L A CARE HEALTH PLAN
See LOCAL INITIATIVE HEALTH AUTHORITY FOR LOS ANGELES COUNTY

L A GIRL
See BEAUTY 21 COSMETICS INC

D-U-N-S 00-377-9931 IMP/EXP
L A HEARNE CO (CA)
512 Metz Rd, King City, CA 93930-2503
Tel (831) 385-5441 *Founded/Ownrshp* 1938, 1960
Sales 88.2MM^E *EMP* 105
SIC 5191 0723 5699 4214 2048 5261 Fertilizers & agricultural chemicals; Bean cleaning services; Grain drying services; Seed cleaning; Western apparel; Local trucking with storage; Livestock feeds; Lawn & garden supplies
Pr: Francis Giudici
**Ch Bd:* Dennis Hearne
**VP:* Frank Hearne

L A PHILHARMONIC
See LOS ANGELES PHILHARMONIC ASSOCIATION

D-U-N-S 02-280-6475 IMP
L AND M SUPPLY INC
TRUE VALUE
1200 E Us Highway 169, Grand Rapids, MN 55744-3235
Tel (218) 326-9451 *Founded/Ownrshp* 1963
Sales 111.6MM^E *EMP* 450
SIC 5251 5331 5013 Hardware; Variety stores; Motor vehicle supplies & new parts
CEO: Terry Matteson
**Sec:* Donald Ley
Store Mgr: Greg Yanish
Software D: Shawn Matteson

D-U-N-S 79-337-4034
L B & B ASSOCIATES INC
9891 Broken Land Pkwy # 400, Columbia, MD 21046-1165
Tel (301) 621-3944 *Founded/Ownrshp* 1992
Sales 250.3MM^E *EMP* 1,308^E
SIC 8744 7338 4225 8742 8748 4581 Facilities support services; Secretarial & court reporting; General warehousing & storage; Transportation consultant; Safety training service; Fixed base operator
Pr: F Edward Brandon
**COO:* David Van Scoyoc
**CFO:* Rachel Rakes
Ofcr: Shannon Klisiewicz
**Sr VP:* Jeff Mendenhall
**Sr VP:* Reginald Spence
**VP:* Alexander Torrance
**Exec:* Frederick Franz
Exec: Rick Franz

D-U-N-S 00-439-2619 IMP/EXP
▲ L B FOSTER CO (TX)
LBFOSTER
415 Holiday Dr Ste 1, Pittsburgh, PA 15220-2793
Tel (412) 928-3417 *Founded/Ownrshp* 1902
Sales 624.5MM *EMP* 1,406
Tkr Sym FSTR *Exch* NGS
SIC 3312 3272 3317 Railroad crossings, steel or iron; Structural shapes & pilings, steel; Ties, railroad: concrete; Concrete products, precast; Steel pipe & tubes
Pr: Robert P Bauer
**Ch Bd:* Lee B Foster II
CFO: David J Russo
Sr VP: John F Kasel
Sr VP: Alexandre Kosmala
VP: Merry L Brumbaugh
VP: Samuel K Fisher
VP: Patrick J Guinee
VP: Gregory W Lippard
VP: Konstantinos Papazoglou
Opers Mgr: Jerry Logston
Board of Directors: Dirk Junge, G Thomas McKane, Diane B Owen, Robert S Purgason, William H Rackoff, Suzanne B Rowland, Bradley S Vizi

D-U-N-S 00-512-1546
L B INDUSTRIES INC
LALLY PIPE & TUBE DIVISION
8770 Railroad Dr, Taylor Mill, KY 41015-9096
Tel (859) 431-8300 *Founded/Ownrshp* 1934
Sales 110.0MM *EMP* 100
SIC 5051

L BRANDS
See MAST INDUSTRIES INC

D-U-N-S 02-247-2468 IMP/EXP
▲ L BRANDS INC
LBRANDS
3 Limited Pkwy, Columbus, OH 43230-1467
Tel (614) 415-7000 *Founded/Ownrshp* 1963
Sales 12.1MMM *EMP* 87,900
Accts Ernst & Young Llp Grandview
Tkr Sym LB *Exch* NYS
SIC 5632 5961 5621 5999 Lingerie (outerwear); Lingerie & corsets (underwear); Women's apparel, mail order; Women's clothing stores; Toiletries, cosmetics & perfumes
Ch Bd: Leslie H Wexner
Pr: Nicholas P M Coe

Pr: Sharen J Turney
COO: Charles C McGuigan
CFO: Stuart B Burgdoerfer
Board of Directors: Raymond Zimmerman, E Gordon Gee, Dennis S Hersch, Donna A James, David T Kollat, Jeffrey H Miro, Michael G Morris, Stephen D Steinour, Allan R Tessler, Abigail S Wexner

D-U-N-S 79-691-9447 IMP
■ L BRANDS STORE DESIGN & CONSTRUCTION INC
LIMITED
(*Suby of* LBRANDS) ★
3 Ltd Pkwy, Columbus, OH 43230
Tel (614) 415-7000 *Founded/Ownrshp* 1990
Sales 148.4MM^E *EMP* 230
SIC 1542 Commercial & office building, new construction
Pr: Gene Torcha
Pr: James McFate
**Treas:* Timothy Faber
Assoc VP: George Arenschield
Assoc VP: Michael Bruch
Assoc VP: Jacqueline Hoskins
Assoc VP: Bryan Yuris
Ex VP: Peter M Horvath
Ex VP: Martyn Redgrave
Ex VP: Scott Taylor
Ex VP: Margaret M Wright
Sr VP: Wendy Arlin
Sr VP: Sheena Foley
Sr VP: Todd Helvie
Sr VP: Lauren Richardson
Sr VP: Edward Wolf
VP: Marvin Clayton
**VP:* Rick Felice
VP: Kent Kleeberger
VP: Andy Lane
VP: Kim Menz

L C C C
See LORAIN COUNTY COMMUNITY COLLEGE DISTRICT

L C E
See LIFE CYCLE ENGINEERING INC

D-U-N-S 13-138-1402
L C VIRGINIA
4600 Fairfax Dr Ste 1004, Arlington, VA 22203-1553
Tel (703) 524-5454 *Founded/Ownrshp* 2016
Sales 86.0MM^E *EMP* 400
SIC 1541 1542 1522 Industrial buildings & warehouses; Nonresidential construction; Residential construction
Pr: David Ridenour
Pr: Alfred McNeal
Sr VP: Francois Antypas
VP: Frank Autypos
VP: Boglios Malkhossion
Board of Directors: Thomas M Haythe, Dimitri D Papadopaulos, Elias Sotoripoulos

L CATTERTON
See CATTERTON PARTNERS CORP

D-U-N-S 00-446-0317 IMP
L D KICHLER CO (OH)
KICHLER LIGHTING
7711 E Pleasant Valley Rd, Cleveland, OH 44131-5532
Tel (216) 573-1000 *Founded/Ownrshp* 1938
Sales 133.9MM^E *EMP* 645
SIC 3645 3648 3641 Residential lighting fixtures; Lighting equipment; Electric lamps
CEO: Tony Davidson
**Ch Bd:* Harold S Minoff
**Ch:* Barry Minoff
**VP:* Roy Minoff
**VP:* David Pamer

D-U-N-S 06-367-7579 EXP
L E BELL CONSTRUCTION CO INC
1226 County Road 11, Heflin, AL 36264-3533
Tel (256) 253-2434 *Founded/Ownrshp* 1972
Sales 129.8MM^E *EMP* 300
SIC 1623 Oil & gas pipeline construction
Pr: Larry Bell
Sec: Jimmie Taylor
Ofcr: Tama Estes
VP: Michael Bell
VP: Dan Norton
VP: Jackson Norton
Exec: Elizabeth Bell
Dir IT: Dennis Daniel
Sfty Dirs: Sierra Coleman

D-U-N-S 00-613-4183 IMP
L E JONES CO
1200 34th Ave, Menominee, MI 49858-1695
Tel (906) 863-1043 *Founded/Ownrshp* 1946
Sales 83.5MM^E *EMP* 390
SIC 3592 3545 Valves, engine; Machine tool accessories
CEO: David Doll
**Ch Bd:* Peter Vennema
**VP:* Douglas Dooley
VP Sls: Lawrence Bowsher

D-U-N-S 00-693-1661
■ L E MYERS CO
(*Suby of* MYR GROUP INC) ★
1701 Golf Rd Ste 3-1012, Rolling Meadows, IL 60008-4276
Tel (847) 290-1891 *Founded/Ownrshp* 1982
Sales 120.7MM^E *EMP* 280
SIC 1623 Electric power line construction
Ch Bd: William A Koertner
**Pr:* Richard S Swartz Jr
**Treas:* Marco A Martinez
**Sr VP:* William Green
**VP:* John A Fluss Sr
Opers Mgr: Warren Beert

L E S
See LOUISIANA ENERGY SERVICES LLC

D-U-N-S 79-008-1814
L E SIMMONS & ASSOCIATES INC
SCF PARTNERS
600 Travis St Ste 6600, Houston, TX 77002-2921
Tel (713) 227-7888 *Founded/Ownrshp* 1989
Sales 479.4MM^E *EMP* 5,006
SIC 6799 Venture capital companies
Pr: L E Simmons
Pt: Ray A Ballantyne
**Pt:* Anthony F Deluca
Pr: David Clark
**VP:* Nicholas B Drake
**VP:* Theresa W Eaton
VP: Logan Walters

D-U-N-S 00-678-1769
L F DRISCOLL CO LLC
(*Suby of* STRUCTURE TONE INC) ★
401 E City Ave Ste 500, Bala Cynwyd, PA 19004-1124
Tel (610) 668-0950 *Founded/Ownrshp* 1929, 2009
Sales 900.0MM^E *EMP* 296
Accts Deloitte & Touche Llp Parsipp
SIC 8741 Construction management
Pr: Frank M Stulb
CFO: Rich Pirollo
Ex VP: Robert J Miller
Ex VP: Robert Miller
VP: John Defazio
VP: Michael F Delaney
VP: Ken J Innella
VP: Kenneth J Innella
VP: Thomas McDonald
Exec: Peggy Cowan
Exec: Ed Hanzel
Exec: George Schaefer
Dir Bus: Trish Harrington

D-U-N-S 01-065-0414
L G BARCUS AND SONS INC
1430 State Ave, Kansas City, KS 66102-4469
Tel (913) 621-1100 *Founded/Ownrshp* 1941
Sales 100.9MM^E *EMP* 125
SIC 1629 1622 Pile driving contractor; Bridge construction
Pr: Richard W Hoener
**Ch Bd:* Douglas G Barcus
**CFO:* Stephen Kimsey
**V Ch Bd:* Lawrence G Barcus
**VP:* David Grossman
VP: Joshua Shorley
**VP:* Dale E Stockfleth
Rgnl Mgr: Todd Kalwei
Off Mgr: Jan Provost

D-U-N-S 00-792-0390
L G EVERIST INC (IA)
300 S Phillips Ave # 200, Sioux Falls, SD 57104-6322
Tel (712) 552-1347 *Founded/Ownrshp* 1876
Sales 449.4MM^E *EMP* 260
SIC 1442 1429 Common sand mining; Gravel mining; Quartzite, crushed & broken-quarrying; Riprap quarrying
CEO: Rick Everist
CFO: John Henkhaus
**CFO:* Steve Mousel
**VP:* Rob Everist
VP: Todd Schuver
**VP:* Jay Van Den Top
VP: Jay Den Den Top
VP: Jay Den Top
VP: Jay Den Den Top
VP: Jay Den Top
Area Mgr: Richard C Schneider

L G H
See LOWELL GENERAL HOSPITAL

D-U-N-S 05-325-1679 IMP/EXP
■ L G SOURCING INC
(*Suby of* LOWES COMPANIES INC) ★
1605 Curtis Bridge Rd, North Wilkesboro, NC 28659
Tel (866) 578-0563 *Founded/Ownrshp* 1997
Sales 92.8MM^E *EMP* 40
SIC 5023 5031 2499 Home furnishings; Decorative home furnishings & supplies; Building materials, exterior; Building materials, interior; Picture & mirror frames, wood
Pr: Mike Menser
**Treas:* Benjamin S Adams Jr
**VP:* David R Green

D-U-N-S 80-560-3698
L GARY HART ASSOCIATED
13381 440th Ave Sw, East Grand Forks, MN 56721-9004
Tel (520) 297-3237 *Founded/Ownrshp* 2006
Sales 805.6MM *EMP* 1
SIC 8733 Medical research
Owner: Lawrence Gary Hart

L HAMRICK'S
See HAMRICKS INC

D-U-N-S 17-266-0524
L I C H CORP
339 Hicks St, Brooklyn, NY 11201-5509
Tel (718) 780-1000 *Founded/Ownrshp* 1984
Sales 46.1MM^E *EMP* 3,200
SIC 8062 8092 5912

D-U-N-S 08-163-1459
L KEELEY CONSTRUCTION CO
KEELEY COMPANIES, THE
500 S Ewing Ave Ste G, Saint Louis, MO 63103-2944
Tel (314) 421-5933 *Founded/Ownrshp* 1976
Sales 144.3MM *EMP* 50
SIC 1541 1611 1623 Industrial buildings, new construction; Highway & street paving contractor; Sewer line construction
Prin: Rusty Keeley
**Pr:* LP Rusty Keeley Jr

D-U-N-S 01-957-2577 IMP
L KNIFE & SON INC
GREAT BREWERS
35 Elder Ave, Kingston, MA 02364-1503
Tel (781) 585-2364 *Founded/Ownrshp* 1963
Sales 118.1MM^E *EMP* 200
SIC 5181 5182 Beer & other fermented malt liquors; Wine
Pr: Timothy G Sheehan
**Treas:* Douglas S Macdonald
VP: Jeffrey Annis
VP: Tom Schreibel
**Prin:* Gerald Sheehan
Genl Mgr: JC Panio
Off Mgr: Kerri Lydon
VP Opers: Brian McGuire
Opers Mgr: Jim Burke
Opers Mgr: Ryan Wells
Sales Exec: Marvin Beasley

D-U-N-S 00-109-4382 IMP/EXP
L L BEAN INC (ME)
15 Casco St, Freeport, ME 04033-0002
Tel (207) 552-2000 *Founded/Ownrshp* 1934
Sales 1.1MMM^E *EMP* 5,000
SIC 5961 5621 5611 5941 5661 5948

D-U-N-S 04-503-3453
L LYON WILLIAM & ASSOCIATES INC
LYON REAL ESTATE
3640 American River Dr, Sacramento, CA 95864-5953
Tel (916) 978-4200 *Founded/Ownrshp* 1946
Sales 73.1MM^E *EMP* 1,062
SIC 8741 Management services
CEO: Larry Knapp
**Pr:* Jean LI
Pr: Jim Waters
**CEO:* Patrick M Shea
CFO: Michael Levedahl
Exec: Bruce Dolder
Exec: Richard Paiko
Off Mgr: David Falcone
Off Admin: Jessica Boatman
Off Admin: Andy Siau
Mktg Dir: Cathy Harrington

D-U-N-S 00-790-2380
■ L M BERRY AND CO
(*Suby of* BELLSOUTH ENTERPRISES INC)
3170 Kettering Blvd, Moraine, OH 45439-1924
Tel (937) 296-2121 *Founded/Ownrshp* 1910
Sales 59.4MM^E *EMP* 2,600
SIC 7311 2741 Advertising agencies; Miscellaneous publishing
Pr: Daniel J Graham
Exec: Scott Pomeroy
IT Man: James Oreilly
Sls&Mrk Ex: Carol Betts

L M H
See LAWRENCE MEMORIAL HOSPITAL

L M I
See LOGISTICS MANAGEMENT INSTITUTE

D-U-N-S 00-601-3346 IMP/EXP
L PERRIGO CO (MI)
(*Suby of* PERRIGO CO) ★
515 Eastern Ave, Allegan, MI 49010-9070
Tel (269) 673-8451 *Founded/Ownrshp* 1887, 1981
Sales 1.8MMM^E *EMP* 9,200
SIC 2834 Pharmaceutical preparations
CEO: Joseph Papa
**Ch Bd:* David Gibbons
Ex VP: Celeste Smith
**Prin:* Arthur J Shannon
Ql Cn Mgr: Andrea Kirk
Ql Cn Mgr: David Troff
S&M/VP: Don Smith

L R G
See LIFTED RESEARCH GROUP INC

D-U-N-S 80-841-1263
L S F 5 ACCREDITED INVESTMENTS LLC
(*Suby of* LONE STAR FUND V (US) LP) ★
717 N Harwood St Ste 2200, Dallas, TX 75201-6515
Tel (214) 754-8300 *Founded/Ownrshp* 2007
Sales 242.7MM^E *EMP* 2,705^E
SIC 6798 Real estate investment trusts
Prin: Benjamin D Velvin III

D-U-N-S 00-112-5681 IMP
▲ L S STARRETT CO (MA)
121 Crescent St, Athol, MA 01331-1915
Tel (978) 249-3551 *Founded/Ownrshp* 1880
Sales 209.6MM *EMP* 1,804
Tkr Sym SCX *Exch* NYS
SIC 3545 3423 3999 3425 3823 Precision measuring tools; Micrometers; Verniers (machinists' precision tools); Calipers & dividers; Rules or rulers, metal; Carpenters' hand tools, except saws: levels, chisels, etc.; Tape measures; Saw blades for hand or power saws; Saws, hand: metalworking or woodworking; Industrial instrmnts msrmnt display/control process variable
Pr: Douglas A Starrett
CFO: Francis J O'Brien
VP: Anthony M Aspin
VP: James B Taylor
Genl Mgr: David J Whitham
Ql Cn Mgr: Dexter Carlson
Ql Cn Mgr: Brian Morris
Natl Sales: Rick Marble
Board of Directors: Salvador De Camargo Jr, Richard B Kennedy, Ralph G Lawrence, David A Lemoine, Terry A Piper, Stephen F Walsh

L U A
See LUMBERMENS UNDERWRITING ALLIANCE

D-U-N-S 00-223-3872 IMP
L& JG STICKLEY INC (NY)
1 Stickley Dr, Manlius, NY 13104-2485
Tel (315) 682-5500 *Founded/Ownrshp* 1895, 1974
Sales 272.4MM^E *EMP* 1,200
SIC 2511 2519 Wood household furniture; Household furniture, except wood or metal: upholstered
Ch Bd: Aminy I Audi
**Pr:* Edward Audi
**CFO:* John Brogan
Prd Mgr: Jim Christman

L& L PRODUCTS
See ZEPHYROS INC

D-U-N-S 78-647-4325
L&L ENERGY INC
130 Andover Park E # 200, Tukwila, WA 98188-2909
Tel (206) 264-8065 *Founded/Ownrshp* 2006
Sales 198.9MM *EMP* 1,364
Tkr Sym LLEN *Exch* OTC
SIC 1241 1221 5052 Coal mining services; Bituminous coal & lignite-surface mining; Coal
CFO: Ian G Robinson
**VP:* Clayton Fong
Genl Mgr: Paul Lee

D-U-N-S 13-415-8141
L&S SERVICES LLC
501 W Broad St, Smithville, TN 37166-1111
Tel (615) 597-6278 *Founded/Ownrshp* 2003
Sales 17.4MM^E *EMP* 1,000
SIC 5812 Contract food services
CFO: Bill Stencer

L-3 COMMUNICATION & THALES
See AVIATION COMMUNICATION & SURVEILLANCE SYSTEMS LLC

D-U-N-S 00-725-0079
■ L-3 COMMUNICATIONS AVIONICS SYSTEMS INC
BF GOODRICH AVIONICS SYS
(*Suby of* L-3 COMMUNICATIONS CORP) ★
5353 52nd St Se, Grand Rapids, MI 49512-9702
Tel (616) 977-6837 *Founded/Ownrshp* 2003
Sales 83.1MM^E *EMP* 479
SIC 3812 Aircraft flight instruments; Gyroscopes; Automatic pilots, aircraft; Radar systems & equipment
CEO: Michael T Strianese
**Pr:* Jay Lafoy
VP: Doug Pell
Dir IT: Henry Vlieg

D-U-N-S 05-910-6484
■ L-3 COMMUNICATIONS CINCINNATI ELECTRONICS CORP
(*Suby of* L-3 COMMUNICATIONS CORP) ★
7500 Innovation Way, Mason, OH 45040-9695
Tel (513) 573-6100 *Founded/Ownrshp* 2004
Sales 147.3MM^E *EMP* 735
SIC 3812 3769 3823 Detection apparatus: electronic/magnetic field, light/heat; Missile guidance systems & equipment; Guided missile & space vehicle parts & auxiliary equipment; Infrared instruments, industrial process type
Ch: Patrick J Sweeney
**CEO:* Russ Walker
**CFO:* David Monaco
**VP:* Doug Becker
**VP:* Mark Dapore
**VP:* Ed English
**VP:* Vance King
**VP:* Gregg Ridgley
VP Admn: Dale E Lhmann
Prgrm Mgr: Jeff Raines
Off Admin: Kathy Buck
Board of Directors: Doug Foster, Kevin Haurin, George Macomber, Alison McKinnon

D-U-N-S 00-889-8884
■ L-3 COMMUNICATIONS CORP (GA)
(*Suby of* L-3 COMMUNICATIONS HOLDINGS INC) ★
600 3rd Ave, New York, NY 10016-1901
Tel (212) 697-1111 *Founded/Ownrshp* 1997
Sales 3.5MMM *EMP* 38,000^E
SIC 3812 3663 3669 3679 3769 Search & navigation equipment; Aircraft control systems, electronic; Telemetering equipment, electronic; Receiver-transmitter units (transceiver); Amplifiers, RF power & IF; Signaling apparatus, electric; Intercommunication systems, electric; Microwave components; Guided missile & space vehicle parts & auxiliary equipment
Ch Bd: Michael T Strianese
Pr: Christopher E Kubasik
CFO: Ralph G D'Ambrosio
Sr VP: Steven M Post
VP: Dan Azmon
Dir IT: Niki Montoya
Sftwr Eng: Eric Colegate
S&M/VP: Vince Longhi
Board of Directors: Alan H Washkowitz, Claude R Canizares, Thomas A Corcoran, Ann E Dunwoody, Lewis Kramer, Robert B Millard, Lloyd W Newton, Vincent Pagano Jr, H Hugh Shelton, Arthur L Simon

D-U-N-S 08-015-8524
L-3 COMMUNICATIONS CORP
COMMUNICATIONS SYSTEM WEST
322 N 2200 W, Salt Lake City, UT 84116-2922
Tel (801) 594-2000
Sales NA *EMP* 3,800
SIC 3812

D-U-N-S 19-237-2860 IMP
■ L-3 COMMUNICATIONS CORP
(*Suby of* L-3 COMMUNICATIONS HOLDINGS INC) ★
9 Akira Way, Londonderry, NH 03053-2037
Tel (603) 626-4800 *Founded/Ownrshp* 2010
Sales 228.8MM^E *EMP* 1,100
SIC 3827 Optical instruments & lenses
Pr: Todd Stirtzinger
Prgrm Mgr: Dante D'Amato
Genl Mgr: James Collins
Genl Mgr: Melissa Sawyer
Snr Sftwr: Mark Dobrosielski
CIO: Geoff Ziminsky
IT Man: Suzanne Allen

D-U-N-S 55-661-8267 IMP
■ L-3 COMMUNICATIONS ELECTRON TECHNOLOGIES INC
(*Suby of* L-3 COMMUNICATIONS HOLDINGS INC) ★
3100 Lomita Blvd, Torrance, CA 90505-5104
Tel (310) 517-6000 *Founded/Ownrshp* 2000
Sales 159.9MM^E *EMP* 658
SIC 3671 3764 Traveling wave tubes; Guided missile & space vehicle propulsion unit parts
CEO: Michael Strianese
VP: Frank Lucca
Genl Mgr: Alan Piring
Genl Mgr: Robert Vasquez

IT Man: Mike Luna
IT Man: April Parker

D-U-N-S 00-889-8843 IMP/EXP
▲ L-3 COMMUNICATIONS HOLDINGS INC
600 3rd Ave, New York, NY 10016-1901
Tel (212) 697-1111 *Founded/Ownrshp* 1997
Sales 10.4MMM *EMP* 38,000
Tkr Sym LLL *Exch* NYS
SIC 3663 3669 3679 3812 3769 Telemetering equipment, electronic; Receiver-transmitter units (transceiver); Signaling apparatus, electric; Intercommunication systems, electric; Microwave components; Search & navigation equipment; Guided missile & space vehicle parts & auxiliary equipment
Ch Bd: Michael T Strianese
Pr: Steve Kantor
Pr: Christopher E Kubasik
Pr: John S Mega
Pr: Mark Von Schwarz
CFO: Ralph G D'Ambrosio
Ex VP: Curtis Brunson
Sr VP: Richard A Cody
Sr VP: Ann D Davidson
Sr VP: Charles R Davis
VP: Dan Azmon
VP: Ronald Cook
VP: Ronald Mandler
Dir Bus: Chris Scalia
Board of Directors: Claude R Canizares, Thomas A Corcoran, Ann E Dunwoody, Lewis Kramer, Robert B Millard, Lloyd W Newton, Vincent Pagano Jr, H Hugh Shelton, Arthur L Simon

D-U-N-S 11-364-1703
■ L-3 COMMUNICATIONS INTEGRATED SYSTEMS LP
(*Suby of* L-3 COMMUNICATIONS HOLDINGS INC) ★
1309 Ridge Rd Ste 401, Rockwall, TX 75087-4226
Tel (903) 455-3450 *Founded/Ownrshp* 2002
Sales 1.2MMM^E *EMP* 23,000^E
SIC 4581 Aircraft maintenance & repair services
Pr: John McNellis
Pt: Robert Drews
Pr: Sylvain Bdard
Pr: Jim Gibson
Pr: Alison J Hartley
Ex VP: Nick V Farah
Ex VP: Mark Von Schwarz
Sr VP: Tim Keenan
VP: Nick Farah
VP: Ed Gloviak
VP: Randy Hall
VP: Russell Martin
VP: S Gordon Walsh
Exec: Joe Burns
Dir Bus: Joseph Siniscalchi

D-U-N-S 09-144-1089 IMP
■ L-3 COMMUNICATIONS VERTEX AEROSPACE LLC
(*Suby of* L-3 COMMUNICATIONS CORP) ★
555 Industrial Dr S, Madison, MS 39110-9072
Tel (601) 856-2274 *Founded/Ownrshp* 1977, 2004
Sales 425.8MM^E *EMP* 4,000^E
Accts Pricewaterhousecoopers Llp
SIC 4581 5088 Aircraft maintenance & repair services; Aircraft & parts
CEO: Michael T Strianese
**CFO:* Ralph G D'Ambrosio
**Ex VP:* Curtis Brunson
**Sr VP:* Richard A Cody
**Sr VP:* Steven M Post
**VP:* Dave Merriam
**VP:* R Steve Sinqfield
VP: Steve Sinquefield
Prgrm Mgr: Tom Rachfalski
Prgrm Mgr: William Staber
Dir IT: Lisa Scott

D-U-N-S 04-160-3077
■ L-3 FUZING AND ORDNANCE SYSTEMS INC
(*Suby of* L-3 COMMUNICATIONS HOLDINGS INC) ★
3975 Mcmann Rd, Cincinnati, OH 45245-2307
Tel (513) 943-2000 *Founded/Ownrshp* 1998
Sales 228.8MM^E *EMP* 575
SIC 3483 Arming & fusing devices for missiles
CEO: Michael T Strianese
Pr: Eric Ellis
CFO: Ralph G D'Ambrosio
Ex VP: Curtis Brunson
Sr VP: Richard A Cody
Sr VP: Steven M Post
VP: Richard Hunter
Prgrm Mgr: Leo Brun
Prgrm Mgr: Jim Ferrando
Prgrm Mgr: James Webb
Genl Mgr: Heidi Sims
Board of Directors: Mark Clark, Roy B York

L-3 INTERSTATE ELECTRONICS
See INTERSTATE ELECTRONICS CORP

L-3 SPD ELECTRICAL SYSTEMS
See SPD ELECTRICAL SYSTEMS INC

L-COM GLOBAL CONNECTIVITY
See L-COM INC

D-U-N-S 04-019-9572 IMP/EXP
L-COM INC (MA)
L-COM GLOBAL CONNECTIVITY
(*Suby of* INFINITE RF HOLDINGS INC) ★
50 High St Fl 3, North Andover, MA 01845-2620
Tel (800) 343-1455 *Founded/Ownrshp* 1982, 2016
Sales 137.0MM^E *EMP* 413
SIC 3678 3577 3357 Electronic connectors; Computer peripheral equipment; Nonferrous wiredrawing & insulating
Pr: Edward J Caselden
**CFO:* George Walter
Ex VP: Bill Miller
Sr VP: Chris Long
VP: William Byrd
Genl Mgr: Mark Desousa
Mfg Dir: Tom Barczak

D-U-N-S 05-198-2569
L-O CORONADO HOTEL INC
1500 Orange Ave, Coronado, CA 92118-2918
Tel (619) 435-6611 *Founded/Ownrshp* 1886, 2015
Sales 8.1MM^E *EMP* 1,350
SIC 7011 5812 5813 5941 Hotels; Eating places; Cocktail lounge; Tennis goods & equipment
Pr: Tod Shallon
IT Man: Vic Duvela
Mktg Mgr: Stephanie Jourdan

L-T-D COMMODITIES
See LTD COMMODITIES LLC

D-U-N-S 05-165-8516
L/B WATER SERVICE INC
LB WATER
540 S High St, Selinsgrove, PA 17870-1302
Tel (570) 374-2355 *Founded/Ownrshp* 2002
Sales 106.8MM^E *EMP* 196
SIC 5074 Plumbing fittings & supplies; Pipes & fittings, plastic; Plumbing & heating valves
CEO: Shawn Pulford
**COO:* Robert Dagle
**CFO:* Michael Schaeffer
Chf Mktg O: Don Bush
Off Mgr: Tanya Worley
**MIS Mgr:* Brian Shirk
Sales Asso: Loyal Butts
Sales Asso: Ginny Capello
Sales Asso: Joshua Dickert
Sales Asso: Jim Haworth
Sales Asso: Clint Inch
Board of Directors: James App, William R Everly, Matt Markunas, Mark Pulaski, Walter Vannuys

D-U-N-S 02-073-6880
LA ASOCIACION NACIONAL PRO PERSONAS MAYORES (CA)
NAT'L ASSN FOR HISPANIC ELDERL
234 E Colo Blvd Ste 300, Pasadena, CA 91101
Tel (626) 564-1988 *Founded/Ownrshp* 1975
Sales 13.1MM *EMP* 1,330^E
SIC 8322 Social service center
Pr: Carmela G Lacayo
**Ch Bd:* Maria Ramirez
**Treas:* Carole Kracer

LA BODEGA MEAT AND PRODUCE
See LA BODEGA MEAT INC

D-U-N-S 78-414-9663 IMP
LA BODEGA MEAT INC
LA BODEGA MEAT AND PRODUCE
14330 Gillis Rd, Farmers Branch, TX 75244-3717
Tel (972) 926-6129 *Founded/Ownrshp* 2004
Sales 211.9MM *EMP* 99
SIC 5147 Meat brokers
Pr: Mario Nafal
COO: Jose Torres
**VP:* Khaled Nafal
VP Opers: Terry Wiseman

LA BONITA
See DIANAS MEXICAN FOOD PRODUCTS INC

D-U-N-S 01-651-1011 IMP/EXP
LA BREA BAKERY CAFE INC
(*Suby of* LA BREA BAKERY HOLDINGS INC) ★
14490 Catalina St, San Leandro, CA 94577-5516
Tel (818) 742-4242 *Founded/Ownrshp* 1998
Sales 103.0MM^E *EMP* 1,200
SIC 2051 2052 2053 Bread, cake & related products; Cookies & crackers; Frozen bakery products, except bread
CEO: John Yamin
**COO:* Ronan Minahan
Mktg Mgr: Magen Linden

D-U-N-S 10-624-3681
LA BREA BAKERY HOLDINGS INC
(*Suby of* ARYZTA AG)
14490 Catalina St, San Leandro, CA 94577-5516
Tel (818) 742-4242 *Founded/Ownrshp* 2001
Sales 162.3MM^E *EMP* 1,200
SIC 2051 Bread, all types (white, wheat, rye, etc): fresh or frozen
CEO: John Yamin
Sr VP: Paul Cannon
VP: Conor Costello
Genl Mgr: Tom Bent
Mktg Mgr: Sigalle Feit

D-U-N-S 82-569-4193
LA CADENA INVESTMENTS INC
3750 University Ave # 610, Riverside, CA 92501-3366
Tel (909) 733-5000 *Founded/Ownrshp* 1983
Sales 71.8MM^E *EMP* 35,000
SIC 5411

D-U-N-S 07-015-9157
LA CLINICA DE LA RAZA INC
1450 Fruitvale Ave Fl 3, Oakland, CA 94601-2313
Tel (510) 535-4000 *Founded/Ownrshp* 1971
Sales 79.1MM^E *EMP* 2,000
Accts Moss Adams Llp San Francisco
SIC 8099 Medical services organization
CEO: Jane Garcia
**CFO:* Patricia Aguilera
Dir: Amy Debower
CTO: Tina Buop
Dir IT: Fernando Cortez

D-U-N-S 05-220-4949
LA COSTENA USA INC
(*Suby of* LA COSTEIA VIZCAYA SOCIEDAD LIMITADA)
8755 S Rita Rd, Tucson, AZ 85747-9106
Tel (520) 663-4720 *Founded/Ownrshp* 2006
Sales 251.4MM^E *EMP* 835
SIC 2032 Beans & bean sprouts, canned, jarred, etc.
CEO: Albert Basauri
**Pr:* Vincent Rodea

LA COUNTY MUSEUM OF ART
See MUSEUM ASSOCIATES

LA CURACAO
See ADIR INTERNATIONAL LLC

D-U-N-S 15-284-5061 IMP/EXP
■ LA DARLING CO LLC
THORCO INDUSTRIES
(*Suby of* MARMON RETAIL SERVICES INC) ★
1401 Highway 49b, Paragould, AR 72450-3139
Tel (870) 239-9564 *Founded/Ownrshp* 1960
Sales 407.6MM^E *EMP* 1,500
SIC 2541 2542 Store fixtures, wood; Fixtures, store: except wood; Racks, merchandise display or storage: except wood; Shelving, office & store: except wood
Pr: Randy Guthrie
CFO: Bobby Wallis
**Prin:* Kenneth Recor
Snr Mgr: Jim Murray
Snr Mgr: Tim Williams

LA FEDE ITALIAN FOODS
See ACE ENDICO CORP

LA FITNESS
See FITNESS INTERNATIONAL LLC

D-U-N-S 02-324-8727
LA FORCE INC
1060 W Mason St, Green Bay, WI 54303-1863
Tel (920) 497-7100 *Founded/Ownrshp* 1954
Sales 169.0MM^E *EMP* 412
SIC 5072 5031 3442 Builders' hardware; Doors; Window & door frames
CEO: Kenneth Metzler
**Pr:* Brian Mannering
**Treas:* Jill M Pruski
**VP:* Michael Latour
**VP:* Jeff McGlachlin
Genl Mgr: Pat Connelly
CIO: Jeff Mc Glachlin
IT Man: Tery Mallon
Trfc Dir: Andy Roznowski
Plnt Mgr: Dave Allison
Plnt Mgr: Dave Watson
Board of Directors: Harold Breliant, Tony Cinquini, Tom Gaible, James La Force, Patricia La Force, Bruce Massey

D-U-N-S 00-227-5436 IMP/EXP
LA FRANCE CORP
JAT CREATIVE PDTS DIV LAFRANCE
1 Lafrance Way, Concordville, PA 19331
Tel (610) 361-4300 *Founded/Ownrshp* 1946
Sales 131.3MM *EMP* 1,827
Accts Cliftonlarsonallen Llp Plymo
SIC 3089 3364 3993 5013 7389 Injection molded finished plastic products; Zinc & zinc-base alloy die-castings; Name plates: except engraved, etched, etc.: metal; Automotive supplies & parts; Design services
Ch: John J Teti
**Pr:* George Barrar
**CFO:* Thomas Sheehan
**Ex VP:* Alan Grodnitzky
**VP:* Brian McHenry
**VP:* Peter Peroni
VP: Lou Venancio
Genl Mgr: Fran Vespa
Dir IT: Brandon Hilkert
Ql Cn Mgr: Kai Zhang
Mktg Mgr: Amanda Kalbrosky

D-U-N-S 12-271-7866
■ LA GRANGE ACQUISITION LP
ENERGY TRANSFER COMPANY
(*Suby of* ENERGY TRANSFER PARTNERS LP) ★
8111 Westchester Dr, Dallas, TX 75225-6140
Tel (214) 981-0700 *Founded/Ownrshp* 2002
Sales 448.2MM^E *EMP* 500^E
SIC 4922 Natural gas transmission
Pt: Kelcy L Warren
**Pt:* Ray Davis
**Pt:* Mackie McCrea
**Pr:* Marshall S McCrea
**Pr:* Matthew S Ramsey
**CFO:* Thomas E Long
VP: Ken English
Off Admin: Rachel McPheeters
Plnt Mgr: Larry Gray
Snr PM: John Bilhartz

D-U-N-S 04-423-9606
LA GRANGE MEMORIAL HOSPITAL INC
ADVENTIST MIDWEST HEALTH
5101 Willow Springs Rd, La Grange, IL 60525-2600
Tel (708) 352-1200 *Founded/Ownrshp* 1946, 1999
Sales 110.7MM^E *EMP* 1,754
SIC 8062 General medical & surgical hospitals
CEO: Rick Wright
CFO: Paul Ziegele
VP: Theodore Suchy
Dir Rx: Dave Tsang
CIO: Rich Razwadowski
Pharmcst: Lue Baker
Pharmcst: Anne Bran
Pharmcst: Mike Datro
Pharmcst: Glen Grames
Pharmcst: Swee Quah
Pharmcst: Ray Silhan
Board of Directors: Keren Gonzalez

D-U-N-S 07-812-6554
LA GRANGE TROUP COUNTY HOSPITAL AUTHORITY
FLORENCE HAND NURSING HOME
1514 Vernon Rd, Lagrange, GA 30240-4131
Tel (706) 882-1411 *Founded/Ownrshp* 1936
Sales 73.5MM^E *EMP* 1,315
SIC 8062 8051 General medical & surgical hospitals; Skilled nursing care facilities
Pr: Gerald Fulke
**CFO:* Paul Perrotti
CFO: Esther Rainey
CFO: Monty Wallace
Ofcr: Marjorie Scott
CIO: Bob Honeycutt
Mktg Dir: Jan Nichols
Obsttrcn: Madhavi Naik
Ansthlgy: Jung Ahn
Doctor: Sylvester Ejeh
Doctor: Bruce James

D-U-N-S 02-410-2451
LA JOYA INDEPENDENT SCHOOL DISTRICT
200 W Expressway 83, La Joya, TX 78560-4002
Tel (956) 580-2000 *Founded/Ownrshp* 1926
Sales 172.0MM^E *EMP* 2,800
Accts Reyna & Garza Pllc Cpa S Tx
SIC 8211 Public elementary & secondary schools
**Pr:* Juan Jos Jj Pea Jr
MIS Dir: Frank Rivera
Instr Medi: Perriann Huntley

LA MESA DISPOSAL
See EDCO DISPOSAL CORP INC

D-U-N-S 05-927-6444
LA MESA R V CENTER INC
7430 Copley Park Pl, San Diego, CA 92111-1122
Tel (858) 874-8001 *Founded/Ownrshp* 1972
Sales 209.8MM^E *EMP* 450
SIC 5561 7538 Motor homes; Travel trailers: automobile, new & used; Recreational vehicle parts & accessories; Recreational vehicle repairs
CEO: James R Kimbrell
**Pr:* James Walters
VP: Laree Howell
Sales Exec: Terry Bridgewater
Sales Exec: Duane Rivera
Mktg Mgr: Stephen Love
Sls Mgr: Thomas Chelone
Sls Mgr: Jan Mosegaard
Sls Mgr: Miguel Sanchez

D-U-N-S 07-872-8987
LA MESA-SPRING VALLEY SCHOOL DISTRICT
4750 Date Ave, La Mesa, CA 91942-9214
Tel (619) 668-5700 *Founded/Ownrshp* 1915
Sales 88.3MM^E *EMP* 1,500
Accts Christywhite Accountancy Corpo
SIC 8211 Public elementary & secondary schools
Bd of Dir: Craig Wood
Ex VP: Courtney Lanier
VP: Kathy Haase
Off Mgr: Marla Locklar
Off Admin: Ariana Najera
Schl Brd P: Bob Duff
Psych: Melissa Mackie
HC Dir: Jody Bonduranstron

LA PETITE ACADEMY
See LPA INVESTMENT LLC

D-U-N-S 02-722-9863
LA PETITE ACADEMY INC
(*Suby of* LA PETITE HOLDINGS CORP) ★
21333 Haggerty Rd Ste 300, Novi, MI 48375-5537
Tel (877) 861-5078 *Founded/Ownrshp* 1994
Sales 143.2MM^E *EMP* 9,791^E
Accts Deloitte & Touche Llp Chicago
SIC 8351 Child day care services; Preschool center; Montessori child development center
Ch Bd: Stephen P Murray
**CEO:* Barbara J Beck
**COO:* Leigh-Ellen Louie
**CFO:* Mark R Bierley
VP: Joan K Singleton
VP: Bill Van Huis
IT Exec: Walt Tracy
CIO: Hugh W Tracy

D-U-N-S 07-833-1475
LA PETITE HOLDINGS CORP
(*Suby of* LEARNING CARE GROUP (US) INC) ★
21333 Haggerty Rd Ste 300, Novi, MI 48375-5537
Tel (248) 697-9000 *Founded/Ownrshp* 1993
Sales 143.2MM^E *EMP* 9,728^E
SIC 8351 Child day care services; Preschool center; Montessori child development center

D-U-N-S 00-387-3627
LA PLATA ELECTRIC ASSOCIATION INC
45 Stewart St, Durango, CO 81303-7915
Tel (970) 247-5786 *Founded/Ownrshp* 1939
Sales 109.2MM *EMP* 113
Accts Bkd Llp Denver Co
SIC 4911 Distribution, electric power
CEO: Steve Gregg
CFO: John Bloom
Bd of Dir: Nancy Andrews
**Prin:* Emery Maez
Dir IT: Harry Peterson
IT Man: Gail Aalund

D-U-N-S 07-960-3827
LA PLAYA BEACH ASSOCIATES LLC
1000 E Hllandale Bch Blvd, Hallandale Beach, FL 33009-4433
Tel (954) 668-2505 *Founded/Ownrshp* 2014
Sales 100.0MM *EMP* 20
SIC 6552 Land subdividers & developers, residential

LA PORTE HOSPITAL & HLTH SVCS
See IUHLP LIQUIDATION INC

D-U-N-S 08-022-1199
■ LA PORTE HOSPITAL CO LLC
(*Suby of* COMMUNITY HEALTH SYSTEMS INC) ★
1007 Lincolnway, La Porte, IN 46350-3290
Tel (219) 326-1234 *Founded/Ownrshp* 2016
Sales 38.4MM^E *EMP* 1,700^E
SIC 8062 General medical & surgical hospitals
Pr: Thor Thordarson
Treas: Barbara Werner
VP: Jeffrey Anderson
VP: Connie Ford
MIS Dir: Jennifer Hawkins
HC Dir: Rhonda Willis

D-U-N-S 08-086-5645
LA PORTE INDEPENDENT SCHOOL DISTRICT
1002 San Jacinto St, La Porte, TX 77571-5481
Tel (281) 604-7000 *Founded/Ownrshp* 2005
Sales 104.7MM *EMP* 1,200
Accts Weaver And Tidwell Llp Houst
SIC 8211 Public elementary & secondary schools
Dir Sec: David Knowles

Pr Dir: Terri Cook
Teacher Pr: Isela Montes

D-U-N-S 07-929-3385
▲ LA QUINTA HOLDINGS INC
909 Hidden Rdg Ste 600, Irving, TX 75038-3822
Tel (214) 492-6600 *Founded/Ownrshp* 1968
Sales 1.0MMM *EMP* 7,426
Tkr Sym LQ *Exch* NYS
SIC 7011 Hotels & motels; Hotel, franchised
Pr: Keith A Cline
**Ch Bd:* Mitesh B Shah
COO: John W Cantele
COO: John Cantele
CFO: James H Forson
Chf Mktg O: Julie M Cary
Ex VP: Mark M Chloupek
Ex VP: Rajiv K Trivedi
Board of Directors: James R Abrahamson, Glenn Alba, Scott O Bergren, Alan J Bowers, Henry G Cisneros, Giovanni Cutaia, Brian Kim, Gary M Sumers

LA QUINTA INN
See LQ MANAGEMENT LLC

D-U-N-S 03-718-5329 IMP/EXP
■ LA QUINTA LLC
(*Suby of* LA QUINTA HOLDINGS INC) ★
909 Hidden Rdg Ste 600, Irving, TX 75038-3822
Tel (214) 492-6600 *Founded/Ownrshp* 2006
Sales 364.2MM^E *EMP* 9,400
SIC 7011 6794 8741 Hotels & motels; Franchises, selling or licensing; Hotel or motel management
Pr: Wayne B Goldberg
Pr: Feliz Jarvis
Pr: Gerald Rodriguez
**CFO:* Robert Harshbarber
CFO: Robert M Harshberger
CFO: David L REA
Sr Cor Off: Clive Bode
**Ex VP:* Julie Cary
Ex VP: Murry Cathlina
**Ex VP:* Mark M Chloupek
Ex VP: Mark Chloupek
**Ex VP:* Keith A Cline
**Ex VP:* Angelo J Lombardi
**Ex VP:* Rajiv K Trivedi
Sr VP: David Bradtke
Sr VP: Donna Cooper
Sr VP: Alise Deeb
**Sr VP:* James Forson
Sr VP: John A Novak
VP: Christina Cernuch
VP: Oliver Evancho

LA RAZA
See IMPREMEDIA LLC

LA SALLE UNIVERSITY
See LASALLE UNIVERSITY

D-U-N-S 62-759-9988
LA SIERRA UNIVERSITY
4500 Riverwalk Pkwy, Riverside, CA 92505-3332
Tel (951) 785-2000 *Founded/Ownrshp* 1968
Sales 87.6MM *EMP* 282
Accts Ahern Adcock Devlin Llp River
SIC 8221 University
CEO: Randal R Wisbey
VP: Frankie Findlay
**VP:* David Geriguis
VP: David Lofthouse
VP: Marjorie Robinson
Dir Sec: Doug Nophsker
Cmptr Lab: Richard Rakijian
Sfty Mgr: Christine Bartholomew
Mktg Dir: Douglas Clark
Mktg Dir: Julie Narducd
Pr Dir: Darren Goltiao

D-U-N-S 13-969-3261
LA SPECIALTY PRODUCE CO
SAN FRANSISCO SPECIALITY PROD
13527 Orden Dr, Santa Fe Springs, CA 90670-6338
Tel (562) 741-2200 *Founded/Ownrshp* 1985
Sales 377.0MM^E *EMP* 475
SIC 5148 Fresh fruits & vegetables
Pr: Michael Glick
**VP:* Kathleen Glick
Exec: Joycee Del Toro
Opers Mgr: Scott Mathews

LA TESTING
See EMSL ANALYTICAL INC

D-U-N-S 08-721-2270
LA TORTILLA FACTORY INC (CA)
3300 Westwind Blvd, Santa Rosa, CA 95403-8273
Tel (707) 586-4000 *Founded/Ownrshp* 1977
Sales 151.9MM^E *EMP* 310
SIC 5149 2051 Specialty food items; Bakery products; Bread, cake & related products
CEO: Samuel Carlos Tamayo
**Pr:* Carlos G Tamayo
VP: Katie Evans
**VP:* Jonna Greene
VP: Paula Stockert
**Prin:* Sam Tamayo
Dist Mgr: Jake Hammack
IT Man: Clarke Katz
Sfty Mgr: Maria Villegas
Opers Mgr: Mark Malliot
Plnt Mgr: Carlos Mojica

D-U-N-S 04-211-4341
LA VALENCIANA AVOCADOS CORP (TX)
RAMON VALENCIA ESPINOZA
214 N 16th St Ste 127, McAllen, TX 78501-7984
Tel (956) 994-0561 *Founded/Ownrshp* 2011
Sales 85.0MM *EMP* 175
SIC 5148 0179 Fruits; Avocado orchard
Pr: Sergio F Zurita-Valencia
Off Mgr: Dulce Soliz

LA VOX THE HOUSTON NEWSPAPER
See LA VOZ PUBLISHING CORP

D-U-N-S 10-701-5406
LA VOZ PUBLISHING CORP
LA VOX THE HOUSTON NEWSPAPER
4747 Southwest Fwy, Houston, TX 77027-6901
Tel (713) 664-4404 *Founded/Ownrshp* 1980
Sales 26.1MM^E *EMP* 1,000
SIC 2711 Newspapers: publishing only, not printed on site
VP: Erquiaga Angel

LA-Z-BOY
See LZB MANUFACTURING INC

D-U-N-S 00-504-2841 IMP/EXP
▲ LA-Z-BOY INC (MI)
1 La Z Boy Dr, Monroe, MI 48162
Tel (734) 242-1444 *Founded/Ownrshp* 1927
Sales 1.5MMM *EMP* 8,270
Tkr Sym LZB *Exch* NYS
SIC 2512 2511 5712 Chairs: upholstered on wood frames; Couches, sofas & davenports: upholstered on wood frames; Recliners: upholstered on wood frames; Rockers: upholstered on wood frames; Wood household furniture; Furniture stores
Ch Bd: Kurt L Darrow
CFO: Louis M Riccio Jr
Treas: Greg Brinks
Ofcr: J Douglas Collier
Sr VP: Mark S Bacon Sr
Sr VP: Darrell D Edwards
Sr VP: Darrell Edwards
Sr VP: Steven Kincaid
VP: Allred Britt
VP: Aaron Brown
VP: James Chickini
VP: David Jones
VP: Gary Lake
VP: Michael Martinelli
VP: Lynn McFerrin
VP: Brian Mossor
VP: Peg Mueller
VP: Ginger Murner
VP: Kim Roussey
VP: Julie Sullivan
VP: Drew Sweeney
Board of Directors: Richard M Gabrys, David K Hehl, Edwin J Holman, Janet E Kerr, Michael T Lawton, H George Levy, W Alan McCollough

D-U-N-S 62-788-7990
LAB HOLDINGS INC
8500 Normandale Lake Blvd # 1750, Minneapolis, MN 55437-3864
Tel (612) 607-1700 *Founded/Ownrshp* 1999
Sales 353.0MM^E *EMP* 1,400^E
SIC 8734 8731 Hazardous waste testing; Soil analysis; Water testing laboratory; Commercial physical research
CEO: Rodney Burwell

LAB SAFETY SUPPLY
See GHC SPECIALTY BRANDS LLC

LABATT FOOD SERVICE
See LABATT INSTITUTIONAL SUPPLY CO INC

D-U-N-S 83-094-3812
LABATT FOOD SERVICE LLC
(*Suby of* LABATT FOOD SERVICE) ★
4500 Industry Park Dr, San Antonio, TX 78218-5427
Tel (210) 661-4216 *Founded/Ownrshp* 2007
Sales 103.0MM^E *EMP* 235^E
SIC 8742 Restaurant & food services consultants
Pr: Blair Labatt
COO: Al Silva
VP: Jason Beinart
VP: Tony Canti
VP: Rodney Carrillo
VP: Chas Demott
**VP:* Alfredo Silvia
Brnch Mgr: Pat Wilson
Dist Mgr: Tony McCormick
Genl Mgr: Frank Anglin
Genl Mgr: Dean Atkinson

D-U-N-S 04-627-5301
LABATT INSTITUTIONAL SUPPLY CO INC (TX)
LABATT FOOD SERVICE
4500 Industry Park Dr, San Antonio, TX 78218-5427
Tel (210) 661-4216 *Founded/Ownrshp* 1968
Sales 542.6MM^E *EMP* 1,200
SIC 5141

LABCORP OF AMERICA
See LABORATORY CORP OF AMERICA

D-U-N-S 05-531-9482
LABINAL LLC
LABINAL POWER SYSYEMS
(*Suby of* SAFRAN USA INC) ★
3790 Russell Newman Blvd # 100, Denton, TX 76208-2936
Tel (940) 272-5700 *Founded/Ownrshp* 1993
Sales 408.8MM^E *EMP* 900
SIC 3728 Aircraft parts & equipment
Pr: Jorge Ortega
**Treas:* David Anderson
IT Man: Carl Johnson

LABINAL POWER SYSYEMS
See LABINAL LLC

D-U-N-S 86-930-5961 IMP
LABINAL SALISBURY LLC
(*Suby of* SAFRAN USA INC) ★
600 Glen Ave, Salisbury, MD 21804-5250
Tel (410) 548-7800 *Founded/Ownrshp* 2010
Sales 137.2MM^E *EMP* 800^E
SIC 3728 Aircraft parts & equipment
Pr: Greg Moffitt
Ex VP: Bill Caputo
**VP:* Marc Renick
Genl Mgr: James Smith

D-U-N-S 18-922-2334 IMP
■ LABONE INC
QUEST DIAGNOSTICS
(*Suby of* QUEST DIAGNOSTICS INC) ★
10101 Renner Blvd, Lenexa, KS 66219-9752
Tel (913) 888-1770 *Founded/Ownrshp* 2005
Sales 62.7MM^E *EMP* 1,500
SIC 8071 6411 Testing laboratories; Blood analysis laboratory; Urinalysis laboratory; Insurance information & consulting services
VP: Joseph Benage
Pr: Barry Bauer
Pr: Gene Matarazzo
Ofcr: Aaron Atkinson
Ex VP: Patrick L James
Sr VP: Darren Dombrosky
**VP:* Troy Hartman
VP: Monica Learned
Dir Lab: Connie Ballard
Mng Dir: L P James
Rgnl Mgr: Teri Leibson

LABOR, COMMISSIONER OF
See GEORGIA DEPARTMENT OF LABOR

LABOR FINDERS
See DMD INC

D-U-N-S 96-489-7917
LABOR HEALTH & WELTR FNDNE CA
220 Campus Ln, Fairfield, CA 94534-1497
Tel (707) 864-2800 *Founded/Ownrshp* 2010
Sales 157.2MM *EMP* 2
Accts Hemming Morse Cpa S And Consul
SIC 8099

D-U-N-S 80-367-7769
LABOR MANAGEMENT HEALTHCARE FU
3786 Broadway St, Buffalo, NY 14227-1123
Tel (716) 601-7980 *Founded/Ownrshp* 2007
Sales 199.1MM *EMP* 7^E
Accts Toski & Co Cpas Pc Buffalo N
SIC 8011 Clinic, operated by physicians
Prin: Vicki Martino

D-U-N-S 12-355-1108
■ LABOR READY MIDWEST INC
(*Suby of* TRUEBLUE INC) ★
1015 A St Unit A, Tacoma, WA 98402-5122
Tel (253) 383-9101 *Founded/Ownrshp* 1998
Sales 38.5MM^E *EMP* 2,600
SIC 7363 Temporary help service
Pr: Joe Sambataro

D-U-N-S 12-357-3011
■ LABOR READY NORTHWEST INC
(*Suby of* TRUEBLUE INC) ★
P.O. Box 2910 (98401-2910)
Tel (253) 383-9101 *Founded/Ownrshp* 1998
Sales 86.8MM^E *EMP* 5,310
SIC 7363 Temporary help service
Pr: Richard King

D-U-N-S 12-353-6794
■ LABOR READY SOUTHEAST III LP
(*Suby of* TRUEBLUE INC) ★
1015 A St Unit A, Tacoma, WA 98402-5122
Tel (253) 383-9101 *Founded/Ownrshp* 1998
Sales 75.2MM^E *EMP* 2,000
SIC 7363 Temporary help service
Prin: Robert Breen

D-U-N-S 12-355-8145
■ LABOR READY SOUTHEAST INC
(*Suby of* TRUEBLUE INC) ★
1016 S 28th St, Tacoma, WA 98409-8020
Tel (253) 383-9101 *Founded/Ownrshp* 2000
Sales 107.3MM^E *EMP* 1,830
SIC 7363 Temporary help service
CEO: Joe Sambataro

D-U-N-S 08-028-9921
LABOR READY SOUTHWEST INC
1015 A St Unit A, Tacoma, WA 98402-5122
Tel (800) 610-8920 *Founded/Ownrshp* 1998
Sales 22.9MM^E *EMP* 6,000
SIC 7361 Employment agencies

D-U-N-S 01-282-2243 IMP
■ LABORATORY CORP OF AMERICA
LABCORP OF AMERICA
(*Suby of* LABORATORY CORP OF AMERICA HOLDINGS) ★
358 S Main St Ste 458, Burlington, NC 27215-5837
Tel (336) 229-1127 *Founded/Ownrshp* 1997
Sales 1.1MMM^E *EMP* 10,953
SIC 8071

D-U-N-S 86-142-2434
▲ LABORATORY CORP OF AMERICA HOLDINGS
358 S Main St, Burlington, NC 27215-5837
Tel (336) 229-1127 *Founded/Ownrshp* 1971
Sales 8.6MMM *EMP* 50,000
Tkr Sym LH *Exch* NYS
SIC 8071 Medical laboratories; Testing laboratories; Pathological laboratory
Ch Bd: David P King
Pr: William E Klitgaard
Pr: Jonathan Zung
CEO: Deborah Keller
CFO: Glenn A Eisenberg
Ofcr: Lisa J Uthgenannt
Sr VP: Lance V Berberian
Sr VP: Edward T Dodson
VP: Mark Schroeder

D-U-N-S 08-648-5455
LABORATORY SCIENCES OF ARIZONA LLC
(*Suby of* BANNER RESEARCH INSTITUTE) ★
1255 W Washington St, Tempe, AZ 85281-1210
Tel (602) 685-5000 *Founded/Ownrshp* 1996
Sales 88.9MM^E *EMP* 1,760^E
SIC 8071 8011 8331 Medical laboratories; Clinic, operated by physicians; Job training & vocational rehabilitation services; Job counseling
CEO: David A Dexter

**CFO:* Jennifer Andrew
VP: Suzanne Moss
Ex Dir: Anne T Daley
Rgnl Mgr: Nikki Surento
**CIO:* Robert Dowd

D-U-N-S 06-156-2641 IMP/EXP
LABORATORY SUPPLY CO
LABSCO
(*Suby of* FRAZIER HEALTHCARE II LP) ★
1951 Bishop Ln Ste 300, Louisville, KY 40218-1950
Tel (800) 888-5227 *Founded/Ownrshp* 2011
Sales 117.5MM^E *EMP* 200
SIC 5047 Medical & hospital equipment; Medical laboratory equipment
CEO: Hendrik Struik
Pr: Dan Eckert
CFO: George Willett
Sec: Charles E Davis Jr
Ex VP: Joel Weihe
VP: Charles E Davis Sr
VP: John Hardesky
Exec: Jennifer Howard
Opers Mgr: James Ardoin
Opers Mgr: Scott Rohrman
Snr Mgr: Phil Dieckhoff
Board of Directors: Rod Wolford

LABORERS CMBNED FNDS WSTN PNNS
See LABORERS COMBINED FUNDS OF WESTERN PENNSYLVANIA

D-U-N-S 08-756-1346
LABORERS COMBINED FUNDS OF WESTERN PENNSYLVANIA
LABORERS CMBNED FNDS WSTN PNNS
12 8th St, Pittsburgh, PA 15222-3617
Tel (412) 263-0900 *Founded/Ownrshp* 1978
Sales NA *EMP* 49
Accts Deloitte & Touche Llp Pittsbu
SIC 6371 Pension funds
Pr: Paul A Quarantillo
CFO: Paul A Qurntillo
**Sec:* John Busse
IT Man: Robert Buzzanco

D-U-N-S 80-202-5192
LABORERS HEALTH & WELFARE TRUST FUND FOR SOUTHERN
4399 Santa Anita Ave # 200, El Monte, CA 91731-1648
Tel (626) 279-3000 *Founded/Ownrshp* 2007
Sales 163.1MM *EMP* 3
Accts Miller Kaplan Arase Llp North
SIC 8631 Labor unions & similar labor organizations

D-U-N-S 07-760-8913
LABORERS INTERNATIONAL UNION OF NORTH AMERICA (DC)
LIUNA
905 16th St Nw, Washington, DC 20006-1703
Tel (202) 737-8320 *Founded/Ownrshp* 1903
Sales 98.7MM *EMP* 231
SIC 8631 Labor union
Pr: Terence M O'Sullivan
**Sec:* Armand E Sabitoni
Genl Couns: Michael Barrett
Genl Couns: Stephanie McCarthy

D-U-N-S 07-442-1058
LABORERS PENSION & WELFARE FUNDS
HEALTH AND WELFARE DEPT OF THE
11465 W Cermak Rd, Westchester, IL 60154-5768
Tel (708) 562-0200 *Founded/Ownrshp* 1950
Sales NA *EMP* 82^E
Accts Bansley And Kiener Llp Chicag
SIC 6371 Pension funds; Union welfare, benefit & health funds; Welfare pensions
MIS Dir: Rini Collo

D-U-N-S 96-454-4576
LABORERS-EMPLOYERS BENEFIT PLAN COLLECTION TRUST
905 16th St Nw, Washington, DC 20006-1703
Tel (202) 393-7344 *Founded/Ownrshp* 2010
Sales NA *EMP* 2^E
Accts Calibre Cpa Group Pllc Washin
SIC 6411 Pension & retirement plan consultants
Prin: Tracey Barrick

LABORS LOCAL NO 472
See HEAVY & GENERAL CONSTRUCTION LABORERS UNION LOCAL NO 472

LABOUR DEPARTMENT
See HARBOR HOSPITAL CENTER INC

LABSCO
See LABORATORY SUPPLY CO

D-U-N-S 79-691-3192
LABWARE HOLDINGS INC
3 Mill Rd Ste 102, Wilmington, DE 19806-2154
Tel (302) 658-8444 *Founded/Ownrshp* 1988
Sales 110.0MM *EMP* 450
SIC 7371 7372 6719 Computer software development & applications; Business oriented computer software; Personal holding companies, except banks
Pr: Vance Kershner
**VP:* David Nixon

D-U-N-S 07-478-1584
LAC DU FLAMBEAU BAND OF LAKE SUPERIOR CHIPPEWA INDIANS (INC)
LAC DU FLAMBEAU TRIBAL COUNCIL
418 Little Pines Rd, Lac Du Flambeau, WI 54538-9124
Tel (715) 588-3303 *Founded/Ownrshp* 1936
Sales 163.0MM^E *EMP* 2,122
SIC 8011 7999 5411 5541 8031 Medical centers; Bingo hall; Grocery stores, independent; Filling stations, gasoline; Offices & clinics of osteopathic physicians
Pr: Thomas Maulson
**Treas:* Rose Mitchell
**Treas:* Mary Peterson
**VP:* Michael Ellen

LAC DU FLAMBEAU TRIBAL COUNCIL
See LAC DU FLAMBEAU BAND OF LAKE SUPERIOR CHIPPEWA INDIANS (INC)

LACERA
See LOS ANGELES COUNTY EMPLOYEES RETIREMENT ASSOCIATION

D-U-N-S 95-821-2029 IMP
LACEY MANUFACTURING CO LLC
(*Suby of* PEP) ★
1146 Barnum Ave, Bridgeport, CT 06610-2794
Tel (203) 336-7427 *Founded/Ownrshp* 2008
Sales 94.0MM^E *EMP* 310
SIC 3841 3089 Surgical instruments & apparatus; Injection molding of plastics
Pr: Ken Lisk
CFO: Robin Bergman

D-U-N-S 07-915-9141
LACKAWANNA COUNTY GOVERNMENT (PA)
200 Adams Ave, Scranton, PA 18503-1607
Tel (570) 963-6800 *Founded/Ownrshp* 1878
Sales NA *EMP* 1,400
SIC 9611 9199 Consumer protection office, government; Economic development agency, government; Civil rights commission, government

D-U-N-S 09-933-1811 IMP
LACKAWANNA PRODUCTS CORP
8545 Main St Ste 1, Williamsville, NY 14221-7457
Tel (716) 633-1940 *Founded/Ownrshp* 1982
Sales 109.0MM^E *EMP* 70
SIC 5191 5153 Animal feeds; Grains
Ch Bd: Tunney Murchie
**Pr:* David A Olshan

D-U-N-S 06-594-0512
LACKMANN FOOD SERVICE INC
LACKMANN FOOD SVCE
303 Crossways Park Dr, Woodbury, NY 11797-2099
Tel (516) 364-2300 *Founded/Ownrshp* 1963
Sales 32.1MM^E *EMP* 1,200
SIC 5812 Sandwiches & submarines shop
CEO: Matthew Lackmann
**Pr:* Peter Alessio
**CEO:* Andrew Lackmann
Exec: Cathie Reis
Dist Mgr: Michael Franzese

LACKMANN FOOD SVCE
See LACKMANN FOOD SERVICE INC

D-U-N-S 61-681-1659
LACKS ENTERPRISES INC
5460 Cascade Rd Se, Grand Rapids, MI 49546-6406
Tel (616) 949-6570 *Founded/Ownrshp* 1985
Sales 841.7MM^E *EMP* 2,800
SIC 3089 Molding primary plastic
Pr: Richard Lacks Jr
**Treas:* Chester Anisko
**Ex VP:* Kurt Lacks
VP: Dave McNulty
**Prin:* John Lacks
**Prin:* Chris Walker
Dir Sec: Aj Ponstein
Prgrm Mgr: Nick Velting
Genl Mgr: Bob Bieri
Genl Mgr: Jeff Lacross
CTO: Green Jim

D-U-N-S 02-648-6253 IMP
LACKS EXTERIOR SYSTEMS LLC
LACKS TRIM SYSTEMS
(*Suby of* LACKS ENTERPRISES INC) ★
5460 Cascade Rd Se, Grand Rapids, MI 49546-6406
Tel (616) 949-6570 *Founded/Ownrshp* 1966
Sales 443.1MM^E *EMP* 1,700
SIC 3089 Plastic hardware & building products
CFO: Chet Anisko
CFO: Mike Clover
**VP:* Kurt Lacks

D-U-N-S 00-601-4666 IMP
LACKS INDUSTRIES INC
REM DIE CASTING
(*Suby of* LACKS ENTERPRISES INC) ★
5460 Cascade Rd Se, Grand Rapids, MI 49546-6499
Tel (616) 949-6570 *Founded/Ownrshp* 1964
Sales 151.6MM^E *EMP* 1,900
SIC 3089

LACKS TRIM SYSTEMS
See LACKS EXTERIOR SYSTEMS LLC

D-U-N-S 02-682-0175 IMP/EXP
LACKS VALLEY STORES LTD
1300 San Patricia Dr, Pharr, TX 78577-2158
Tel (956) 702-3361 *Founded/Ownrshp* 1935
Sales 181.1MM^E *EMP* 800
SIC 5712 5722

D-U-N-S 00-696-7798
■ **LACLEDE GAS CO** (MO)
(*Suby of* SPIRE INC) ★
700 Market St, Saint Louis, MO 63101-1829
Tel (314) 342-0878 *Founded/Ownrshp* 1857
Sales 1.0MMM *EMP* 2,169
SIC 4924 Natural gas distribution
Pr: Steven L Lindsey
**Ch Bd:* Suzanne Sitherwood
**CFO:* Steven P Rasche
VP: D P Abernathy
VP: Muawiya A Huneidi
VP: Peter J Palumbo Jr
Board of Directors: Mark C Darrell, C Craig Dowdy

L.A.CO.
See SANITATION DISTRICT OF LOS ANGELES COUNTY DISTRICT 2

LACOE
See LOS ANGELES COUNTY OFFICE OF EDUCATION

D-U-N-S 18-612-1208
LACOSTA INC
PREMIER FACILITY SERVICES ILL
440 W Bonner Rd, Wauconda, IL 60084-1102
Tel (847) 526-9556 *Founded/Ownrshp* 1988
Sales 114.8MM^E *EMP* 2,800^E
SIC 7349 Building & office cleaning services
Pr: Karla Mota
VP: Mark Cones
VP: Bill McKenna
Rgnl Mgr: Ann Donnelley
Opers Mgr: Charles Haithcock

D-U-N-S 11-622-7315 IMP
LACROSSE FOOTWEAR INC
(*Suby of* ABC-MART,INC.)
17634 Ne Airport Way, Portland, OR 97230-4999
Tel (503) 262-0110 *Founded/Ownrshp* 1983
Sales 113.1MM^E *EMP* 713^E
SIC 3021 Rubber & plastics footwear
CEO: Joseph P Schneider
Pr: Yasushi Akaogi
Pr: Robert Sasaki
CFO: David P Carlson
VP: Joseph Fahey
VP: Wayne Lorek
VP: Nina Palludan
VP: Robert G Rinehart
VP Admn: Greg S Inman
CTO: Debbie Hess
Mktg Dir: Laurie Dunn-Thomas
Board of Directors: Stephen F Loughlin, Charles W Smith, John D Whitcombe, William H Williams

D-U-N-S 13-168-7790 IMP/EXP
LACTALIS AMERICAN GROUP INC
SORRENTO LACTALIS
(*Suby of* PARMALAT SPA)
2376 S Park Ave, Buffalo, NY 14220-2670
Tel (716) 823-6262 *Founded/Ownrshp* 1980
Sales 501.7MM^E *EMP* 1,500
SIC 2022 Cheese, natural & processed
CEO: Frederick Bouisset
VP: Pierre Lorieau
VP: Paul Peterson
VP: Elena Umanskaya
Exec: Peggy Weittenhiller
Dir IT: William Packard
Plnt Mgr: Donald Lahrs
Ql Cn Mgr: Amelie Depuydt
Natl Sales: Mark Baskin
Natl Sales: Jeffrey Pugliese
Natl Sales: Ed Sullivan

D-U-N-S 02-906-8202 IMP/EXP
LACTALIS DELI INC
(*Suby of* SORRENTO LACTALIS) ★
77 Water St Fl Mezz, New York, NY 10005-4421
Tel (212) 758-6666 *Founded/Ownrshp* 1980
Sales 185.4MM^E *EMP* 765
SIC 5143 2022 Cheese; Cheese, natural & processed
CEO: Frederick Bouisset
**Pr:* Philippe Surget
CFO: Michael Picirillo
VP: Alain Gerard
Dir Soc: Cecile Hollman
**Prin:* Erick Boutry
QA Dir: Loren Green
IT Man: Michael Vendura
VP Sls: Yann Connan
Sls Dir: Julien Lapraz
Mktg Mgr: Marjolaine Besnard

D-U-N-S 60-584-4505
LACY DISTRIBUTION INC
(*Suby of* LDI LTD LLC) ★
54 Monument Cir Ste 800, Indianapolis, IN 46204-2949
Tel (317) 237-5400 *Founded/Ownrshp* 1989
Sales 253.8MM^E *EMP* 1,550
SIC 5015 Automotive parts & supplies, used
Ch: Andre Lacy
MIS Dir: Kathy Randell
IT Man: Brian Reed
IT Man: Vangie Sison

D-U-N-S 07-908-9494
▲ **LADDER CAPITAL CORP**
345 Park Ave Fl 8, New York, NY 10154-0017
Tel (212) 715-3170 *Founded/Ownrshp* 2008
Sales 442.7MM *EMP* 73^E
Tkr Sym LADR *Exch* NYS
SIC 6798 6162 Real estate investment trusts; Mortgage bankers & correspondents
CEO: Brian Harris
Pr: Michael Mazzei
COO: Pamela McCormack
CFO: Marc Fox
CIO: Greta Guggenheim
Genl Couns: Kelly Porcella

D-U-N-S 06-516-0819
LADEKI RESTAURANT GROUP
ROPPONGI
7596 Eads Ave Ste 200, La Jolla, CA 92037-4899
Tel (858) 454-2222 *Founded/Ownrshp* 1998
Sales 43.7MM^E *EMP* 2,000
SIC 8741 Restaurant management
Pr: Sami Ladeki
**CFO:* Anthony Kulick
Genl Mgr: Richard Stephan
VP Opers: Dan Smith

D-U-N-S 00-222-7036
▲ **LADENBURG THALMANN FINANCIAL SERVICES INC** (FL)
4400 Biscayne Blvd Fl 12, Miami, FL 33137-3212
Tel (305) 572-4100 *Founded/Ownrshp* 1876
Sales 1.1MMM *EMP* 1,522^E
Accts Eisner Amper Llp New York Ne
Tkr Sym LTS *Exch* ASE
SIC 6211 6282 Investment bankers; Investment firm, general brokerage; Investment advisory service
Pr: Richard J Lampen
**Ch Bd:* Phillip Frost
COO: Adam Malamed
CFO: Brett Kaufman
**V Ch Bd:* Howard M Lorber
**Ex VP:* Mark Zeitchick
Sr VP: Joseph Giovanniello Jr
Sr VP: Oksana Poznak
VP: John D Cornetta
VP: Michael Mundo
Dir IT: Coe Mark

D-U-N-S 06-647-7480
LADIES PROFESSIONAL GOLF ASSOCIATION
LPGA
100 International Golf Dr, Daytona Beach, FL 32124-1082
Tel (386) 274-6200 *Founded/Ownrshp* 1950
Sales 121.3MM *EMP* 85
Accts Grant Thornton Llp Orlando F
SIC 8699 Professional golf association
Ex Dir: Tim Erensen
CIO: Jack Sumner

LADWP
See LOS ANGELES DEPARTMENT OF WATER AND POWER

D-U-N-S 02-520-7622
LADY LITTLE FOODS INC (IL)
PRIMERRO FROZEN FOODS
2323 Pratt Blvd, Elk Grove Village, IL 60007-5918
Tel (847) 806-1440 *Founded/Ownrshp* 1960, 1984
Sales 141.7MM^E *EMP* 420
SIC 2038 2099 Pizza, frozen; Food preparations
**CEO:* Rick Anderson
**CFO:* James Sharwarko
VP: Mark Pickett
Dir Bus: David Foran
Dir IT: Eric Parker
Dir IT: Ellie Stevanovic
VP Opers: Steven Kunkle
Opers Mgr: Jim Dinklenburg
Opers Mgr: Lee Hodson
Sls Mgr: Terry Clark

D-U-N-S 04-279-1152 IMP/EXP
LAERDAL MEDICAL CORP
167 Myers Corners Rd, Wappingers Falls, NY 12590-3869
Tel (845) 297-7770 *Founded/Ownrshp* 1967
Sales 83.0MM^E *EMP* 310
SIC 5047 3845 3841 Medical & hospital equipment; Oxygen therapy equipment; Defibrillator; Surgical & medical instruments
Pr: Clyde Patrickson
Ch Bd: David Johnson
Bd of Dir: Cindy Baxter
Exec: Dan Baumgardner
Exec: Kim Keller
Creative D: Ramon Sosa
Rgnl Mgr: George Besant
QA Dir: Ronald Weyhrauch
Dir IT: David Diprete
Opers Mgr: Wendy Faulkner
VP Sls: Joseph Pahlow
Board of Directors: Hans H Dahll, Tore Laerdal

D-U-N-S 11-531-8230 IMP
LAFARGE BUILDING MATERIALS INC
(*Suby of* LAFARGE NORTH AMERICA INC) ★
8700 W Bryn Mawr Ave 300n, Chicago, IL 60631-3512
Tel (678) 746-2000 *Founded/Ownrshp* 2009
Sales 615.8MM^E *EMP* 2,600
SIC 3241 3274 3273 3271 Masonry cement; Natural cement; Portland cement; Lime; Ready-mixed concrete; Blocks, concrete or cinder: standard
CEO: Jean M Lechene
**CEO:* Peter L Keeley
**CFO:* Robert Fiolek

D-U-N-S 13-148-6177
LAFARGE MID-ATLANTIC LLC
300 E Joppa Rd Ste 200, Baltimore, MD 21286-3015
Tel (410) 847-9445 *Founded/Ownrshp* 1986
Sales 100.6MM^E *EMP* 500
SIC 3273 1422 Ready-mixed concrete; Crushed & broken limestone
Opers Supe: James Wallace

D-U-N-S 06-756-8246 IMP
LAFARGE NORTH AMERICA INC
(*Suby of* LAFARGE)
8700 W Bryn Mawr Ave Ll, Chicago, IL 60631-3535
Tel (703) 480-3600 *Founded/Ownrshp* 1977
Sales 4.0MMM^E *EMP* 16,600
SIC 3241 3273 3272 3271 1442 2951 Cement, hydraulic; Portland cement; Ready-mixed concrete; Concrete products; Precast terrazo or concrete products; Prestressed concrete products; Cylinder pipe, prestressed or pretensioned concrete; Blocks, concrete or cinder: standard; Construction sand & gravel; Construction sand mining; Gravel mining; Asphalt paving mixtures & blocks; Paving mixtures; Asphalt & asphaltic paving mixtures (not from refineries)
Pr: John Stull
**CEO:* Bernard L Kasriel
**CEO:* Isaac Preston
CFO: John Cheong
**CFO:* Robert Fiolek
Ex VP: Ulrich Glaunach
Ex VP: Jean-Marc Lech Ne
VP: Ed Claggett
VP: Carlos Espina
VP: Sandip Ghose
**VP:* Peter Keeley
VP: Stephen Smith
VP: David Tucker
Dir Soc: Mariann Amog
Board of Directors: Michel Rose, Marshall A Cohen, Lawrence M Tanenbaum, Philippe P Dauman, Gerald H Taylor, Bruno Lafont, Claudine B Malone, Blythe J McGarvie, James M Micali, Robert W Murdoch, Bertin F Nadeau, John D Redfern

D-U-N-S 16-087-5381
LAFARGE WEST INC
WESTERN PAVING CONSTRUCTION
(*Suby of* LAFARGE NORTH AMERICA INC) ★
10170 Church Ranch Way # 200, Westminster, CO 80021-6060
Tel (303) 657-4355 *Founded/Ownrshp* 2003
Sales 207.7MM^E *EMP* 1,400
SIC 5032 1611 3273

D-U-N-S 93-308-8643 IMP
LAFAYETTE 148 INC
148 Lafayette St Fl 2, New York, NY 10013-3115
Tel (646) 708-7010 *Founded/Ownrshp* 1996
Sales 159.6MM *EMP* 250^E
Accts Friedman Llp New York Ny
SIC 5137 Women's & children's accessories
Pr: Deirdre Quinn
VP: Amy Goodwin
DP Exec: Albert Chu
Dir IT: Kinsen Siu
Sls Dir: Candace Amesbury
Mktg Mgr: Clarissa Zhu

D-U-N-S 07-505-4536
LAFAYETTE CITY PARISH CONSOLIDATED GOVERNMENT
705 W University Ave, Lafayette, LA 70506-3543
Tel (337) 291-8353 *Founded/Ownrshp* 1840
Sales NA *EMP* 2,022
Accts Kolder Champagne Slaven & Co
SIC 9111 Executive offices;
Pr: Walter S Comeaux Jr
Ofcr: Scott McIver
Ofcr: Kelly Theriot
Exec: Paul Mouton
**Adm/Dir:* Rebecca Lalumia
Snr Mgr: Robert Benoit
Snr Mgr: Kurt Bourg

D-U-N-S 04-136-4522
LAFAYETTE COLLEGE
730 High St, Easton, PA 18042-1761
Tel (610) 330-5000 *Founded/Ownrshp* 1826
Sales 265.7MM *EMP* 675^E
Accts Cliftonlarsonallen Llp Plymou
SIC 8221 Colleges universities & professional schools
Pr: Alison Byerly
Assoc VP: Craig Becker
Ex VP: Olivia Andersen
VP: Jackie Cirincione
VP: Katherine Cook
VP: Kristin Garbarini
VP: Alexander Gordon
**VP:* James Krivoski
VP: Robert J Massa
VP: Brian McAtee
VP: Bethany Rack
VP: Elise Reynolds
VP: Kanako Shibano
VP: Karolina Vera
VP: Eugene Warnick
Assoc Dir: Dave Block
Assoc Dir: Maureen Walz
Assoc Dir: David Woglom

D-U-N-S 80-968-1476
LAFAYETTE CONSOLIDATED GOVERNMENT
705 W University Ave, Lafayette, LA 70506-3543
Tel (337) 291-8200 *Founded/Ownrshp* 2008
Sales NA *EMP* 2,500
Accts Kolder Champagne Slaven & Co
SIC 9111 Executive offices
Pr: Joel Robideaux
CFO: Lorrie Toups
Comm Man: Mark Pope
Genl Mgr: Sheila Courville

LAFAYETTE EXTENDED CARE
See PRIME HEALTHCARE LLC

D-U-N-S 96-633-3457
LAFAYETTE GENERAL HEALTH SYSTEM INC
LGH
1214 Coolidge Blvd, Lafayette, LA 70503-2621
Tel (337) 289-8125 *Founded/Ownrshp* 2002
Sales 585.1MM *EMP* 2,600^E
Accts Laporte Apac Metairie La
SIC 8062 General medical & surgical hospitals
Ch Bd: Clay M Allen
**Pr:* David Callecod

LAFAYETTE GENERAL HOSP GIFT SP
See LAFAYETTE GENERAL MEDICAL CENTER INC

D-U-N-S 04-342-7426
LAFAYETTE GENERAL MEDICAL CENTER INC (LA)
LAFAYETTE GENERAL HOSP GIFT SP
1214 Coolidge Blvd, Lafayette, LA 70503-2621
Tel (337) 289-7991 *Founded/Ownrshp* 1905
Sales 428.9MM *EMP* 1,626
SIC 8062 General medical & surgical hospitals
Ex Dir: Caroline Huval
Pr: Wendy Alexander
Sr VP: Susan Johnson
Ex Dir: John Burdin
Pharmcst: Michael Moresi

D-U-N-S 19-598-7248
LAFAYETTE GENERAL SURGICAL HOSPITAL LLC
1000 W Pinhook Rd Ste 100, Lafayette, LA 70503-2460
Tel (337) 289-8095 *Founded/Ownrshp* 2003
Sales 17.2MM *EMP* 1,200
SIC 8062 General medical & surgical hospitals
Genl Mgr: Cian Robinson

LAFAYETTE INTERIOR FASHIONS
See LAFAYETTE VENETIAN BLIND INC

D-U-N-S 02-087-8674
LAFAYETTE PARISH SCHOOL BOARD
113 Chaplin Dr, Lafayette, LA 70508-2101
Tel (337) 521-7000 *Founded/Ownrshp* 1870
Sales 345.4MM *EMP* 3,400
Accts Kolder Champagne Slaven & Co
SIC 8211 School board
Pr: Tommy Angelle
**Pr:* Hunter Beasley

D-U-N-S 04-962-3921
LAFAYETTE PARISH SCHOOL SYSTEM
113 Chaplin Dr, Lafayette, LA 70508-2101
Tel (337) 521-7000 *Founded/Ownrshp* 1870
Sales 31.3MM[E] *EMP* 3,400
SIC 8211 Public elementary & secondary schools
Off Admin: Phyllis Collette
Off Admin: Paula Jameyson
Schl Brd P: Tommy Angelle
Teacher Pr: Bruce C Leininger
Instr Medi: Patrick Hanisee

LAFAYETTE PARK ELEMENTARY MIDD
See KOKOMO SCHOOL CORP

D-U-N-S 07-206-0163
LAFAYETTE SCHOOL CORP
2300 Cason St, Lafayette, IN 47904-2692
Tel (765) 771-6000 *Founded/Ownrshp* 1963
Sales 75.1MM[E] *EMP* 1,200
Accts State Board Of Accounts India
SIC 8211 Public elementary & secondary schools; Public elementary school; Public junior high school; Public senior high school
CFO: Carol Kilver
**CFO:* Eric Rody
**Treas:* Robert Forman
**VP:* Rebecca Sprague
Off Mgr: Diane Troxel
Software D: Larry Guentert
Netwrk Eng: Doug Simon

LAFAYETTE STEEL AND ALUM SLS
See OSCAR WINSKI CO INC

LAFAYETTE STEEL PROCESSING
See OLYMPIC STEEL LAFAYETTE INC

D-U-N-S 00-508-0908 IMP/EXP
LAFAYETTE VENETIAN BLIND INC
LAFAYETTE INTERIOR FASHIONS
3000 Klondike Rd, West Lafayette, IN 47906-5210
Tel (765) 464-2500 *Founded/Ownrshp* 1950
Sales 173.7MM[E] *EMP* 1,000
SIC 2591 2391 Drapery hardware & blinds & shades; Venetian blinds; Mini blinds; Blinds vertical; Draperies, plastic & textile: from purchased materials
Pr: Joseph N Morgan
Mng Pt: Rebecca Dexter
CFO: Tom Moore
**Sec:* Dennis Morgan
CIO: Doug Corley
Dir IT: Joseph Lamay
IT Man: Rick Haan
Mktg Mgr: Tom Robinson

D-U-N-S 09-354-6901
LAFOURCHE PARISH SCHOOL BOARD INC
LAFOURCHE PUBLIC SCHOOLS
805 E 7th St, Thibodaux, LA 70301-3606
Tel (985) 446-5631 *Founded/Ownrshp* 1906
Sales 88.5MM[E] *EMP* 2,218
Accts Stagni & Company Llc Thiboda
SIC 8211 Public elementary & secondary schools
Bd of Dir: Gregg Stall
Genl Mgr: Lafon Ortis
IT Man: Ben Gautreaux
Psych: Elizabeth Hodnett

D-U-N-S 07-980-2903
LAFOURCHE PARISH SCHOOL DISTRICT
805 E 7th St, Thibodaux, LA 70301-3606
Tel (985) 446-5631 *Founded/Ownrshp* 2015
Sales 58.1MM[E] *EMP* 2,006[E]
SIC 8211 Public elementary & secondary schools
Pr Dir: Floyd Benoit
Schl Brd P: Julie Breaux
Teacher Pr: Louis Voiron
HC Dir: Charles Michel

LAFOURCHE PUBLIC SCHOOLS
See LAFOURCHE PARISH SCHOOL BOARD INC

D-U-N-S 78-246-9498
LAGARDERE NORTH AMERICA INC
(*Suby of* LAGARDERE MEDIA)
60 E 42nd St Ste 1940, New York, NY 10165-6201
Tel (212) 477-7373 *Founded/Ownrshp* 2004
Sales 551.5MM[E] *EMP* 7,024[E]
SIC 2721 Magazines: publishing only, not printed on site
Sr VP: David Leckey
**VP:* Richard Rabinowitz

D-U-N-S 00-816-1523 IMP/EXP
■ **LAGASSE INC**
LAGASSE SWEET
(*Suby of* MICROUNITED DIVISION) ★
1 Parkway North Blvd # 100, Deerfield, IL 60015-2554
Tel (847) 627-7000 *Founded/Ownrshp* 1996
Sales 856.4MM[E] *EMP* 500
SIC 5087 5141 Janitors' supplies; Food brokers
Pr: Paul Barrett
**VP:* Eric A Blanchard
**VP:* Robert J Kelderhouse
Genl Mgr: Bob Machlinski
Opers Mgr: Vic Moretti
Mktg Mgr: Sara McCarthy
Manager: Tim Aland
Manager: David Friend
Manager: Cory Jones
Manager: Jorge Lara
Manager: Chuck Mannato

LAGASSE SWEET
See LAGASSE INC

D-U-N-S 04-607-2344
LAGRASSO BROS INC
5001 Bellevue St, Detroit, MI 48211-3278
Tel (313) 579-1455 *Founded/Ownrshp* 1944
Sales 96.5MM[E] *EMP* 108
SIC 5148 Fruits, fresh; Vegetables, fresh
Pr: Thomas La Grasso Jr
Pr: Steve Schultz
**VP:* Frank La Grasso
**VP:* Joseph H La Grasso
**VP:* Michael La Grasso
Exec: Barbara Lehto
IT Man: Alex Lagrasso

D-U-N-S 14-448-2429
LAGUNA DEVELOPMENT CORP
14500 Central Ave Sw I40, Albuquerque, NM 87121-1450
Tel (505) 352-7877 *Founded/Ownrshp* 1998
Sales 113.6MM[E] *EMP* 1,400
SIC 7011 5411 Casino hotel; Grocery stores, independent
Ch: Debra Haaland
**CEO:* Jerry Smith
**COO:* Kevin Greer
**CFO:* Howard Funchess
Board of Directors: Debra Haaland

D-U-N-S 86-788-6848
LAGUNA WOODS VILLAGE
24351 El Toro Rd, Laguna Beach, CA 92653
Tel (949) 597-4267 *Founded/Ownrshp* 1964
Sales 29.4MM[E] *EMP* 1,000
SIC 6531 Real estate agents & managers

D-U-N-S 04-170-6300
LAHEY CLINIC FOUNDATION INC
(*Suby of* LAHEY HEALTH SYSTEM INC) ★
41 Mall Rd, Burlington, MA 01805-0002
Tel (781) 273-5100 *Founded/Ownrshp* 2012
Sales 1.6MMM[E] *EMP* 5,000[E]
Accts Pricewaterhousecoopers Llp Bo
SIC 8059 Rest home, with health care
Pr: David M Barrett MD
Treas: Timothy P O'Connor
IT Man: Jim Drewett
Ansthlgy: Carl J Borromeo
Ansthlgy: Michael D Kaufman
Opthamlgy: Geetha K Athappilly
Opthamlgy: Patrick L Bessette
Diag Rad: Nancy D Baker

D-U-N-S 18-345-2549
LAHEY CLINIC HOSPITAL INC
(*Suby of* LAHEY CLINIC FOUNDATION INC) ★
41 Mall Rd, Burlington, MA 01805-0002
Tel (781) 273-5100 *Founded/Ownrshp* 2012
Sales 816.6MM *EMP* 5,000
SIC 8062 General medical & surgical hospitals
CEO: Howard R Grant JD
**CEO:* David Barrett MD
COO: Richard Bias
**Ch:* Bernard Gordon
Treas: Timothy P Connor
Ofcr: Kathleen Jose
Sr VP: Derek C Bellin
**VP:* Donna Cameron
IT Man: Elizabeth Gardner
Netwrk Mgr: John Proctor
Pgrm Dir: Vincent Sites

D-U-N-S 88-385-0364
LAHEY CLINIC INC
LAHEY CLINIC MEDICAL CENTER
(*Suby of* LAHEY CLINIC FOUNDATION INC) ★
41 Mall Rd, Burlington, MA 01805-0002
Tel (781) 744-5100 *Founded/Ownrshp* 1923
Sales 816.6MM *EMP* 5,000
SIC 8062 General medical & surgical hospitals
CEO: Joanne Conroy
V Ch: James W Henderson
**Pr:* Howard R Grant JD
COO: Jeffrey P Doran
COO: Robert J Schneider
**CFO:* Timothy P Oconnor
Trst: Eric M Bailey
Trst: Craig R Benson
Trst: Bernard Cammarata
Trst: Charles M Leighton
Trst: Robert L Reynolds
Ofcr: David J Schoetz Jr
Ex VP: Richard W Nesto
VP: Allen S Danis
VP: Elizabeth Garvin
Assoc Dir: Roe Sherman
Dir Rad: Richard J Guarino

LAHEY CLINIC MEDICAL CENTER
See LAHEY CLINIC INC

D-U-N-S 07-860-1824
LAHEY HEALTH SYSTEM INC
41 Mall Rd, Burlington, MA 01805-0001
Tel (781) 744-5100 *Founded/Ownrshp* 2011
Sales 5.4MM *EMP* 5,079[E]
Accts Feeley & Driscoll Pc Boston
SIC 8059 Rest home, with health care
Pr: Howard R Grant
**Treas:* Timothy P O'Connor
VP: Eric Berger
Doctor: Ghazwan Acash
Doctor: Yevgeniy Arshanskiy

D-U-N-S 62-794-2048
LAHR CONSTRUCTION CORP
LECESSE CONSTRUCTION COMPANY
75 Thruway Park Dr Ste 1, West Henrietta, NY 14586-9793
Tel (585) 334-4490 *Founded/Ownrshp* 1990
Sales 120.0MM *EMP* 95
SIC 1521 1541 Single-family housing construction; Industrial buildings & warehouses
Pr: Andrew Hislop
**COO:* Tayloe M Call
CFO: Evelyn Hartwell
**Ch:* Gary Henehan
**Treas:* David Luxenberg
Treas: Bill Tehan
**VP:* William O Hanlon
VP: Bill Ohanlon
**VP:* Christopher Phillips
Genl Mgr: Chuck Little
IT Man: Elaine Nikish

LAICO INDUSTRIES
See LIFETIME ASSISTANCE INC

D-U-N-S 13-387-1439
LAIDLAW INTERNATIONAL INC
FIRSTGROUP AMERICA
(*Suby of* FIRSTGROUP PLC)
55 Shuman Blvd Ste 400, Naperville, IL 60563-8248
Tel (214) 849-8100 *Founded/Ownrshp* 2007
Sales 1.0MMM[E] *EMP* 17,200
SIC 4151 4131 School buses; Intercity bus line
Pr: Kevin E Benson
CFO: Jeffrey W Sanders
Treas: Jeffrey A McDougle
Ex VP: Beth B Corvino
VP: Bill Shuman
VP: Beverly A Wyckoff
Exec: Diane Orndorff
Exec: Dean Suhre

D-U-N-S 10-647-8105
LAIDLAW TRANSIT SERVICES INC
(*Suby of* FIRST GROUP OF AMERICA) ★
600 Vine St Ste 1400, Cincinnati, OH 45202-2426
Tel (513) 241-2200 *Founded/Ownrshp* 2007
Sales 124.4MM[E] *EMP* 6,000
SIC 4131 Intercity & rural bus transportation
Pr: Mike Rushin
CFO: Larry Sisel
**VP:* Jeff C Baker

D-U-N-S 00-696-3805
LAIRD NORTON CO LLC (MN)
801 2nd Ave Ste 1700, Seattle, WA 98104-1520
Tel (206) 464-5245 *Founded/Ownrshp* 1855
Sales 568.6MM[E] *EMP* 7,500
SIC 5211 Home centers
Pr: Jeffery Vincent
**Ch Bd:* Elizabeth Williams
**CFO:* Kim Hillyard
**CFO:* Nick Pavelich

D-U-N-S 00-253-1317 IMP/EXP
LAIRD PLASTICS INC
5800 Campus Circle Dr E, Irving, TX 75063-2701
Tel (469) 299-7000 *Founded/Ownrshp* 1944, 2004
Sales 446.4MM[E] *EMP* 500[E]
SIC 5162 3089 Plastics materials; Plastics sheets & rods; Plastics film; Windows, plastic
Pr: Mark W Kramer
**CFO:* Wilfredo W Figueras
CFO: Dolores Willis
**Ch:* Douglas T McNair
**Ex VP:* Peter Edelstein
VP: Gerald Burnett
VP: Larry A Stafford
Exec: Chris Muth
Brnch Mgr: Gary King
Sales Asso: Dale Bartley
Sales Asso: Mark Baskerville

D-U-N-S 00-216-1685 IMP/EXP
LAIRD TECHNOLOGIES INC
(*Suby of* LAIRD PLC)
3481 Rider Trl S, Earth City, MO 63045-1110
Tel (636) 898-6000 *Founded/Ownrshp* 1938, 1991
Sales 420.9MM[E] *EMP* 1,440
SIC 3469 3663 Stamping metal for the trade; Cellular radio telephone
CEO: David Lockwood
**Pr:* Tom Cochran
CFO: Jonathan Silver
Ofcr: Marty Rapp
VP: Craig Fix
VP: Scott Lordo
Dir Rx: Steven Ye
Mng Dir: Dirk Rasmussen
Prgrm Mgr: Yang Cao
Prgrm Mgr: Shane Demarais
Prgrm Mgr: Thomas Fouchard
Board of Directors: W Brewster Kopp, Paul Kozloff, John Thomas O'donnell, Thomas Witmer

D-U-N-S 00-819-3799 IMP/EXP
LAITRAM LLC
220 Laitram Ln, Harahan, LA 70123-5308
Tel (504) 733-6000 *Founded/Ownrshp* 1949
Sales 367.5MM[E] *EMP* 1,400
SIC 3535 3556 7359 3446 6719 Conveyors & conveying equipment; Food products machinery; Equipment rental & leasing; Stairs, staircases, stair treads: prefabricated metal; Investment holding companies, except banks
CIO: Donald Lalonde
Board of Directors: Andrew B Lapeyre, Charles Lapeyre, James M Lapeyre Jr, Philip F Lapeyre, Robert S Lapeyre, Monique Lapeyre McCleskey

D-U-N-S 80-029-9047
LAKE AREA CORN PROCESSORS CO-OPERATIVE
46269 Sd Highway 34, Wentworth, SD 57075-6934
Tel (605) 483-2676 *Founded/Ownrshp* 1999
Sales 96.4MM *EMP* 40
Accts Mcgladrey & Pullen Llp Des M
SIC 2869 Ethanolamines
Pr: Greg Vanzaten
**Treas:* Roger Orton
**VP:* Doyle Paul

D-U-N-S 80-554-3845
LAKE ATK CITY AMMUNITION
101 N M 7 Hwy, Independence, MO 64056
Tel (816) 796-7101 *Founded/Ownrshp* 2000
Sales 228.8MM[E] *EMP* 2,800
SIC 3761 Rockets, space & military, complete
CEO: Mark W Deyoung
**Pr:* Karen Davis
**VP:* Mark Hissong

D-U-N-S 85-842-1030
LAKE CAPITAL MANAGEMENT LLC
676 N Michigan Ave # 3900, Chicago, IL 60611-2896
Tel (312) 640-7050 *Founded/Ownrshp* 1995
Sales 633.2MM[E] *EMP* 11,735
SIC 6799

LAKE CAPOTE PARK
See SOUTHERN UTE INDIAN TRIBE

LAKE CATHERINE FOOTWEAR CO
See MUNRO & CO INC

D-U-N-S 07-701-4660
LAKE CENTRAL SCHOOL CORP
8260 Wicker Ave, Saint John, IN 46373-9711
Tel (219) 365-8507 *Founded/Ownrshp* 1967
Sales 68.8MM[E] *EMP* 1,300
SIC 8211 Public combined elementary & secondary school; Public special education school
Treas: Lorri Miskus
**Prin:* Al Gandolfi
Dir Sec: Brett Sidenbender
Dir IT: Rick Moreno

LAKE CHARLES MEMORIAL HOSPITAL
See SOUTHWEST LOUISIANA HOSPITAL ASSOCIATION

D-U-N-S 12-511-8294
LAKE CHARLES MEMORIAL HOSPITAL
1701 Oak Park Blvd, Lake Charles, LA 70601-8911
Tel (337) 494-2121 *Founded/Ownrshp* 2002
Sales 132.5MM *EMP* 4[E]
SIC 8011 General & family practice, physician/surgeon
Prin: James Maze

D-U-N-S 08-792-0831
■ **LAKE CITY BANK**
(*Suby of* LAKELAND FINANCIAL CORP) ★
202 E Center St, Warsaw, IN 46580-2853
Tel (574) 267-6144 *Founded/Ownrshp* 1999
Sales NA *EMP* 400
SIC 6022 6163 State commercial banks; Loan brokers
Pr: David M Findlay
**Ch Bd:* Michael L Kubacki
CFO: Lisa M O'Neill
Chf Cred: Michael E Gavin
Chf Inves: Andrew R Haddock
Ofcr: Lisa Fitzgerald
Ofcr: Laura Hartley
Ofcr: Dave Hume
Ofcr: Eric Neuenschwander
Ofcr: Kristi Parker
Ofcr: Leslie E Rohrer
Ofcr: Michelle Wedeven
Ex VP: Kevin L Deardorff
Sr VP: Joe Kessie
Sr VP: Meyer Kretchman
Sr VP: Bill Redman
Sr VP: Jonathan P Steiner
Sr VP: James Westerfield
VP: Patricia Culp
VP: Drew D Dunlavy
VP: Lisa Fulton
Board of Directors: Blake W Augsburger, Daniel F Evans Jr, Brian J Smith, Brad Toothaker, Ron Truex

LAKE COUNTY ADMINISTRATION CEN
See COUNTY OF LAKE

LAKE COUNTY BOCC
See COUNTY OF LAKE

D-U-N-S 07-674-8870
LAKE COUNTY COMMUNITY COLLEGE DISTRICT
LAKELAND COMMUNITY COLLEGE
7700 Clocktower Dr, Willoughby, OH 44094-5198
Tel (440) 525-7000 *Founded/Ownrshp* 1967
Sales 17.3MM *EMP* 1,100[E]
Accts Ciuni & Panichi Inc Clevela
SIC 8222 Community college
Pr: Morris W Beverage Jr
**CFO:* Michael E Mayher
**VP:* Mary Ann Plakeley
**VP:* Dawn Plante
**Prin:* Margaret Sbartow
Off Admin: Bernice Connolly
CTO: Travis Okel
Psych: Sarah Amoroso
Psych: Ricky Amster
Psych: Alan Kirsh
Psych: Bonnie Shinhearl

D-U-N-S 07-686-5260
LAKE COUNTY OF INDIANA
LAKE COUNTY PARKS
2293 N Main St, Crown Point, IN 46307-1854
Tel (219) 755-3465 *Founded/Ownrshp* 1937
Sales NA *EMP* 2,552
SIC 9111
**Treas:* Peggy Holinga
Ex Dir: Milan Grozdanich
Genl Mgr: Anna Nunez
IT Man: Lori Burke

LAKE COUNTY PARKS
See LAKE COUNTY OF INDIANA

D-U-N-S 05-191-9041
LAKE COUNTY PRESS INC
98 Noll St, Waukegan, IL 60085-3031
Tel (847) 336-4333 *Founded/Ownrshp* 1970
Sales 87.0MM[E] *EMP* 223[E]
SIC 2791 7334 Typesetting; Blueprinting service
Pr: Ralph L Johnson
Pr: Dan Smith
Pr: Ned Steck
**Sr VP:* Peter Douglas
**Sr VP:* Robert Hilliard
Sr VP: Russ Schoenherr
**VP:* Russell Schoenherr
Exec: Maryann Pope
Dir IT: Abraham Garcia
Opers Mgr: Mark Hammel
Plnt Mgr: Dan Murphy

D-U-N-S 07-921-4185
LAKE COUNTY SCHOOLS
201 W Burleigh Blvd, Tavares, FL 32778-2407
Tel (352) 253-6500 *Founded/Ownrshp* 1950
Sales 123.6MM[E] *EMP* 3,777
Accts Auditor General State Of Flori
SIC 8211 Public elementary & secondary schools; Public elementary school; Public junior high school; Public senior high school
**Ch:* Larry Metz
Exec: Carolyn Samuel
Dir Risk M: Lauren Deridder
Ex Dir: Carman Cullen
Dir IT: John Taylor
Info Man: Harris Jacobs

D-U-N-S 78-748-1746 IMP
LAKE COURT MEDICAL SUPPLIES INC
27733 Groesbeck Hwy, Roseville, MI 48066-2758
Tel (800) 860-3130 *Founded/Ownrshp* 1991
Sales 88.9MM[E] *EMP* 65[E]
SIC 5047 Medical equipment & supplies
Pr: Charles Elliott
**CFO:* Sandy Wagner
VP Sls: Phil Benvenuti
Sls Mgr: Dan Neill

D-U-N-S 01-535-0379
■ LAKE CUMBERLAND REGIONAL HOSPITAL LLC
(*Suby of* LIFEPOINT HEALTH INC) ★
305 Langdon St, Somerset, KY 42503-2750
Tel (606) 679-7441 *Founded/Ownrshp* 1998
Sales 227.1MM *EMP* 3
SIC 8031 Offices & clinics of osteopathic physicians
CEO: Timothy Bess
CFO: Steve Sloan
Dir Risk M: Diann Vanhook
**Prin:* Nagma Zafar
Nurse Mgr: Amy Reynolds
Cmptr Lab: Regina Strong
Mktg Mgr: Cecil Helton
Ansthlgy: Lalitkumar V Patel
Doctor: Andrea Woodroof

D-U-N-S 01-350-3255
LAKE ELSINORE UNIFIED SCHOOL DISTRICT
ACOUNTS PAYABLE DEPT
545 Chaney St, Lake Elsinore, CA 92530-2712
Tel (951) 253-7000 *Founded/Ownrshp* 1884
Sales 93.4MM[E] *EMP* 1,919
SIC 8211 Public elementary school
Dir Sec: Julie Scranton
IT Man: Carol Cole
Teacher Pr: Samuel Wensel

D-U-N-S 79-731-5348
LAKE ERIE COLLEGE OF OSTEOPATHIC MEDICINE INC
LECOM
1858 W Grandview Blvd, Erie, PA 16509-1025
Tel (814) 866-3986 *Founded/Ownrshp* 1993
Sales 124.6MM *EMP* 180
Accts Carbis Walker Llp Pittsburgh
SIC 8221 Colleges universities & professional schools
Pr: John M Ferretti
**CFO:* Richard Olinger
Ofcr: Edward Yeung
**VP:* Hershey Bell
**VP:* Silvia M Ferretti
**VP:* Irving Freeman
Dir Sec: Jack Hines
IT Man: Keith Hein
VP Mktg: Robert George

D-U-N-S 55-627-8224
■ LAKE FOREST BANK AND TRUST CO
(*Suby of* WINTRUST FINANCIAL CORP) ★
727 N Bank Ln Fl 1, Lake Forest, IL 60045-1898
Tel (847) 234-2882 *Founded/Ownrshp* 1991
Sales NA *EMP* 211
SIC 6022 State commercial banks
Pr: David E Lee
Ch Bd: Edward Wehmer
CFO: David A Dykstra
Ch: John J Meierhoff
Bd of Dir: Jack Frigo
Ofcr: Zack Adamovic
Ofcr: Lisa Meggs
Ofcr: Katie Wiswald
Ex VP: Lynn Cleave
Ex VP: Kurt Prinz
Sr VP: David Bruskin
Sr VP: James Draths
Sr VP: Lori Higgins
Sr VP: Thomas Littau
Sr VP: Steve Madden
Sr VP: Stephen Milota
VP: Christopher Baker
VP: Paul Blake
VP: Kelly B Breasbois
VP: Brad Bremen
VP: Tom Groth

D-U-N-S 07-458-3899
LAKE FOREST COLLEGE
555 N Sheridan Rd, Lake Forest, IL 60045-2399
Tel (847) 234-3100 *Founded/Ownrshp* 1857
Sales 104.4MM *EMP* 385[E]
SIC 8221 College, except junior
V Ch: Peter G Schiff
**Pr:* Stephen D Schutt
**Treas:* Leslie T Chapman
Trst: Daniel Gescheidle
Trst: Robert Lansing
VP: Leslie Chapman
VP: Lisa Hinkley
**VP:* Philip R Hood
**VP:* Bill Motzer
**VP:* Fred Vansickle
Schl Brd P: David Harris

D-U-N-S 61-672-1148
LAKE FOREST HOSPITAL FOUNDATION
660 N Westmoreland Rd, Lake Forest, IL 60045-1659
Tel (847) 234-5600 *Founded/Ownrshp* 1982
Sales 63.9MM[E] *EMP* 1,500
SIC 8062 General medical & surgical hospitals
CEO: Thomas McAsee
Chf Rad: Ahmed Faraq
Bd of Dir: Robert Shaw
VP: Mathew Koschmann
Dir Risk M: Richard Paulus
Dir Rx: Satya RAO
Ex Dir: Jane Paley
Brnch Mgr: Vida Ludington
Genl Mgr: Rich Menely
Dir IT: Sue Atkinson
Mktg Dir: Colleen Scrivner

LAKE GRANBURY MEDICAL CENTER
See GRANBURY HOSPITAL CORP

D-U-N-S 00-654-5164
LAKE HARLEYSVILLE STATES INSURANCE CO
(*Suby of* HARLEYSVILLE GROUP INC) ★
600 E Front St Ste 200, Traverse City, MI 49686-2892
Tel (231) 946-6390 *Founded/Ownrshp* 1915
Sales NA *EMP* 50
Accts Kpmg Llp
SIC 6331 Fire, marine & casualty insurance; Property damage insurance
Pr: Daniel E Barr
Treas: Mark Cummins
VP: Richard A Fasa

D-U-N-S 03-882-5283
LAKE HEALTH TRIPOINT MEDICAL CENTER
7590 Auburn Rd, Painesville, OH 44077-9176
Tel (440) 375-8100 *Founded/Ownrshp* 2011
Sales 324.4MM *EMP* 34[E]
SIC 8062 General medical & surgical hospitals
Prin: Donna M Kuta
Sr VP: Richard Cicero
Dir Rx: Beth Krause

D-U-N-S 55-689-5949
LAKE HOSPITAL SYSTEMS
7956 Tyler Blvd, Mentor, OH 44060-4806
Tel (440) 255-6400 *Founded/Ownrshp* 2005
Sales 309.6MM *EMP* 1
Accts Plante & Moran Pllc Columbus
SIC 8062 General medical & surgical hospitals
Prin: Paul V Miotto MD

D-U-N-S 07-559-8359
LAKE LAND COLLEGE
5001 Lake Land Blvd, Mattoon, IL 61938-9366
Tel (217) 234-5253 *Founded/Ownrshp* 1967
Sales 18.4MM *EMP* 1,012
Accts Doehring Winders & Co Llp
SIC 8222 8221 Junior college; Community college; Colleges universities & professional schools
Pr: Scott Lensink
**VP:* Ray Rieck

D-U-N-S 07-257-7042
LAKE MICHIGAN CREDIT UNION
C U FINANCIAL GROUP
4027 Lake Dr Se Ste 100, Grand Rapids, MI 49546-8812
Tel (616) 242-9790 *Founded/Ownrshp* 1933
Sales NA *EMP* 130
SIC 6062 State credit unions, not federally chartered
Ch Bd: Dr Marinus Swets
Pr: Sandy Jelinski
V Ch Bd: Rodger Northuis
Ofcr: Melinda Ball
Ofcr: Chuck Bauss
Ofcr: Mark Breon
Ofcr: Jason Pewinski
Ofcr: Bill Wilson
Sr VP: Jim Koessel
VP: Audrey Andrews
VP: Keane Blaszczynski
VP: Sheri Crump
VP: Peter Dann
VP: Carla Grice
VP: Sara Hendrickson
VP: Dan McLean
VP: Jason Ryba
VP: Bill Schirmer

LAKE MOULTRIE NURSING HOME
See SAINT STEPHEN NURSING FACILITY INC

D-U-N-S 61-195-5613
LAKE NORMAN REGIONAL MEDICAL CENTRE
171 Fairview Rd, Mooresville, NC 28117-9500
Tel (704) 660-4000 *Founded/Ownrshp* 2003
Sales 136.1MM *EMP* 21[E]
SIC 8062 General medical & surgical hospitals
CEO: Greg Lowe

LAKE NRMAN CHRYSLER JEEP DODGE
See TT OF LAKE NORMAN LLC

D-U-N-S 02-084-2068
LAKE ORION COMMUNITY SCHOOLS
315 N Lapeer St, Lake Orion, MI 48362-3165
Tel (248) 693-5400 *Founded/Ownrshp* 1890
Sales 91.5MM *EMP* 1,000
Accts Plante & Moran Pllc Auburn Hi
SIC 8211 Public elementary & secondary schools; School board
Psych: Jared Wood

D-U-N-S 07-077-2268
■ LAKE POINTE MEDICAL CENTER LTD
(*Suby of* TENET HEALTHCARE CORP) ★
6800 Scenic Dr, Rowlett, TX 75088-4552
Tel (972) 412-2273 *Founded/Ownrshp* 1987
Sales 148.5MM *EMP* 700[E]
SIC 8011 Medical centers
CEO: Brett Lee
Dir Inf Cn: Maria Sparks
Chf Nrs Of: Debbie Moeller
Dir IT: Charles Sitzes
IT Man: Susan Miklis

D-U-N-S 02-433-7461
LAKE PRESTON COOPERATIVE ASSOCIATION
LAKE PRESTON FARM SUPPLY
106 2nd St Nw, Lake Preston, SD 57249
Tel (605) 847-4414 *Founded/Ownrshp* 1939
Sales 125.9MM *EMP* 30
Accts Gardiner Thomsen Pc Sioux
SIC 5153 5191 5172 Grains; Fertilizer & fertilizer materials; Feed; Chemicals, agricultural; Petroleum products

LAKE PRESTON FARM SUPPLY
See LAKE PRESTON COOPERATIVE ASSOCIATION

D-U-N-S 07-176-4062
LAKE REGION HEALTHCARE CORP
LAKE REGION REHAB SERVICE
712 S Cascade St, Fergus Falls, MN 56537-2913
Tel (218) 736-8000 *Founded/Ownrshp* 2005
Sales 131.3MM *EMP* 868[E]
Accts Eidebailly Llp Fargo North
SIC 8062 General medical & surgical hospitals
CEO: Larry Schulz
**Ch Bd:* Stephen Rufer
**Pr:* Paul Wilson
**CFO:* Brett Longtin
**CFO:* Edward Strand
**Treas:* Dennis Emmen
Sr VP: Jeff Shackor
Dir OR: Holly Leonard
Dir Rx: Mark Dewey
Dir Rx: Brett A Leitch
IT Man: Michael Blank

D-U-N-S 04-229-6665
■ LAKE REGION MANUFACTURING INC
LAKE REGION MEDICAL
(*Suby of* LAKE REGION MEDICAL INC) ★
100 Fordham Rd, Wilmington, MA 01887-2168
Tel (952) 361-2515 *Founded/Ownrshp* 2014
Sales 431.4MM[E] *EMP* 1,630
SIC 3841 3845 Surgical instruments & apparatus; Electromedical equipment
Ch Bd: Donald J Spence
**CEO:* Joe Fleischhacker
VP: Sharon Barber
Ql Cn Mgr: David Devett
Sales Asso: Steve Rudin

LAKE REGION MEDICAL
See LAKE REGION MANUFACTURING INC

LAKE REGION MEDICAL
See ACCELLENT LLC

D-U-N-S 79-955-4931 IMP
■ LAKE REGION MEDICAL INC
(*Suby of* INTEGER HOLDINGS CORP) ★
100 Fordham Rd, Wilmington, MA 01887-2168
Tel (978) 570-6900 *Founded/Ownrshp* 2015
Sales 827.0MM[E] *EMP* 3,190
SIC 3841 Surgical & medical instruments
Pr: Donald J Spence
**CFO:* Richard E Johnson
VP: Jeremy M Farina
VP: Jeremy Friedman
VP: William Gaffney
**VP:* Ron Honig
Site Mgr: Carol Simon
Prd Mgr: Christopher Metcalf
Corp Couns: Kimberly Jarman

LAKE REGION REHAB SERVICE
See LAKE REGION HEALTHCARE CORP

D-U-N-S 08-500-8217
LAKE REGIONAL HEALTH SYSTEM
LAKE REGIONAL HOSPITAL
54 Hospital Dr, Osage Beach, MO 65065-3050
Tel (573) 348-8000 *Founded/Ownrshp* 1973
Sales 175.9MM *EMP* 1,300
Accts Bkd Llp Springfield Missouri
SIC 8062 General medical & surgical hospitals
CEO: Michael E Henze
**Pr:* Dennis Michaelree
**VP:* Cory Ten Bensel
Sys/Dir: Cynthia Otradovec

LAKE REGIONAL HOSPITAL
See LAKE REGIONAL HEALTH SYSTEM

LAKE SHORE CAMPUS
See LOYOLA UNIVERSITY OF CHICAGO INC

LAKE SHORE ORTHOPEDICS
See ILLINOIS BONE & JOINT INSTITUTE

D-U-N-S 06-048-7915
LAKE SPIRIT TRIBE
816 3rd Ave N, Fort Totten, ND 58335-9998
Tel (701) 766-1270 *Founded/Ownrshp* 1870
Sales NA *EMP* 1,000
SIC 9131 0191 2394 2298 7999 Indian reservation; General farms, primarily crop; Canvas & related products; Sails: made from purchased materials; Camouflage nets, not made in weaving mills; Gambling establishment
Ch Bd: Myra Pierson
V Ch: Joel Redfox
**Sec:* Bryan Pierson
Ex Dir: Linda Thompson

D-U-N-S 09-827-9276 IMP
LAKE STATES LUMBER INC
CEDAR CREEK LUMBER
(*Suby of* CEDAR CREEK LLC) ★
312 S Chester St, Sparta, WI 54656-1813
Tel (608) 269-6714 *Founded/Ownrshp* 2016
Sales 170.0MM *EMP* 200
SIC 5031

D-U-N-S 10-008-0670
LAKE STEVENS SCHOOL DISTRICT
EDUCATIONAL SERVICE CENTER
12309 22nd St Ne, Lake Stevens, WA 98258-9500
Tel (425) 335-1500 *Founded/Ownrshp* 1928
Sales 80.3MM *EMP* 1,000
Accts Briann Sontag Cgfm
SIC 8211 Public elementary & secondary schools; Public junior high school; Public senior high school
Pr Dir: Jayme Taylor
Teacher Pr: Ken Collins
HC Dir: Randy Celori

D-U-N-S 02-083-5294
LAKE WALLED CONSOLIDATED SCHOOL DISTRICT
850 Ladd Rd Bldg D, Walled Lake, MI 48390-3019
Tel (248) 956-2000 *Founded/Ownrshp* 1922
Sales 186.5MM *EMP* 1,482
Accts Plant & Moran Pllc Auburn Hil
SIC 8211 Public elementary school; Public junior high school; Public senior high school; Public vocational/technical school
Genl Mgr: Teri Les
Netwrk Mgr: Mark Williams
Psych: Scott Nolan

D-U-N-S 08-683-5287
LAKE WASHINGTON SCHOOL DISTRICT
16250 Ne 74th St, Redmond, WA 98052-7817
Tel (425) 936-1200 *Founded/Ownrshp* 1944
Sales 207.8MM[E] *EMP* 3,100
SIC 8211 Public elementary school; Public junior high school; Public senior high school; Public special education school
Bd of Dir: Ravi Shahani
Off Mgr: Brenda Nunn
Off Mgr: Brigitte Tennis
Off Mgr: Ann Yasui
MIS Dir: Tim Kreiger
Pr Dir: Kathyrn Reith
Teacher Pr: Pat Fowler-Fung
HC Dir: Molly Houghton

LAKE ZURICH SCHOOL DISTRICT 95
See COMMUNITY UNIT SCHOOL DISTRICT 95

LAKEHEAD CONSTRUCTORS, INC..
See LAKEHEAD CONSTRUCTORS INC

D-U-N-S 00-880-7679
LAKEHEAD CONSTRUCTORS INC
LAKEHEAD CONSTRUCTORS, INC..
(*Suby of* LAKEHEAD HOLDING CORP) ★
2916 Hill Ave, Superior, WI 54880-5560
Tel (715) 392-5181 *Founded/Ownrshp* 1955
Sales 103.5MM[E] *EMP* 250[E]
SIC 1541 1542 Industrial buildings, new construction; Renovation, remodeling & repairs: industrial buildings; Commercial & office building contractors
CEO: Brian C Maki
**Pr:* Dennis M Hallberg
**Sec:* Mark Hubbard
**VP:* Don Odermann
Genl Mgr: Bruce Beste

D-U-N-S 16-196-2261
LAKEHEAD HOLDING CORP
2916 Hill Ave, Superior, WI 54880-5504
Tel (715) 392-5181 *Founded/Ownrshp* 1987
Sales 103.5MM[E] *EMP* 250
Accts Mcgladrey & Pullen
SIC 1541 1542 Industrial buildings, new construction; Renovation, remodeling & repairs: industrial buildings; Commercial & office building contractors
Pr: Dennis M Hallberg

LAKELAND AUTO MALL
See MUTZ MOTORS LTD PARTNERSHIP

D-U-N-S 80-876-7933
▲ LAKELAND BANCORP INC
250 Oak Ridge Rd, Oak Ridge, NJ 07438-8906
Tel (973) 697-2000 *Founded/Ownrshp* 1989
Sales NA *EMP* 551[E]
Tkr Sym LBAI *Exch* NGS
SIC 6022 State commercial banks
Pr: Thomas J Shara
**Ch Bd:* Mary Ann Deacon
COO: Robert A Vandenbergh
CFO: Joseph F Hurley
Chf Cred: James R Noonan
Ofcr: Ronald E Schwarz
Ofcr: David S Yanagisawa
Ex VP: Jeffrey J Buonforte
Ex VP: Timothy J Matteson
Sr VP: Mary Kaye Nardone
VP: Thomas F Splaine Jr
Board of Directors: Stephen R Tilton Sr, Bruce D Bohuny, Edward B Deutsch, Brian Flynn, Mark J Fredericks, Lawrence R Inserra Jr, Thomas J Marino, Robert E McCracken, Robert B Nicholson III, Joseph P O'dowd

D-U-N-S 18-726-9873
■ LAKELAND BANK
(*Suby of* LAKELAND BANCORP INC) ★
2717 Route 23, Newfoundland, NJ 07435-1441
Tel (973) 697-2040 *Founded/Ownrshp* 1988
Sales NA *EMP* 541
SIC 6022 State commercial banks
CEO: Thomas J Shara
**Ch Bd:* Mary Ann Deacon
V Ch: Bruce G Bohuny
Pr: Bill Schachtel
**Pr:* Robert A Vandenbergh
**CFO:* Joseph Hurley
Treas: Hannah Shea-Nomer
**Chf Cred:* James R Noonan
Ofcr: Laurie Corcoran
Ofcr: R David Korngruen
Ofcr: Lisa Nienaber
Ofcr: Frank Walka
Sr Ex VP: Stewart McClure
Ex VP: Michele M Gilchrist
**Ex VP:* Timothy J Matteson
Ex VP: Ronald Schwarz
Sr VP: Thomas Keady
Sr VP: Gail Martin
Sr VP: Maureen Martin
Sr VP: Mark McCoy
**Sr VP:* Rita Myers

D-U-N-S 96-468-1469
LAKELAND CARE DISTRICT
N6654 Rolling Meadows Dr, Fond Du Lac, WI 54937-9471
Tel (920) 906-5100 *Founded/Ownrshp* 2010
Sales NA *EMP* 175[E]
SIC 6321 Accident & health insurance
Ex Dir: Katie Mnuk
CFO: Dan Bizub
Ql Cn Mgr: Katie Calmes

D-U-N-S 07-056-4992
LAKELAND CENTRAL SCHOOL DISTRICT OF SHRUB OAK INC
1086 E Main St, Shrub Oak, NY 10588-1507
Tel (914) 245-1700 *Founded/Ownrshp* 1951
Sales 161.6MM *EMP* 1,200

SIC 8211 Public combined elementary & secondary school
Prin: Dr George Stone
Treas: Maryanne Oconnor
Off Admin: Nancy Gentile
Psych: Laurainne Mosca
Psych: Shari Sakovits

D-U-N-S 07-614-7321
LAKELAND COLLEGE
W3718 South Dr, Plymouth, WI 53073-4878
Tel (920) 565-2111 *Founded/Ownrshp* 1862
Sales 33.5MM *EMP* 1,123
Accts Schenck Cpas Green Bay Wisco
SIC 8221 College, except junior
Ch: Robert T Melzer
**Pr:* Daniel Eck
**Pr:* Stephen Gould
**CFO:* Joseph Botana II
Assoc VP: Beth Borgen
Sr VP: Dan Eck
VP: Meg Albrinck
VP: Nete Dehme
VP: Anthony Fessler
VP: Andre Glass
VP: Tim Stromiska
VP: Zach Voelz

LAKELAND COMMUNITY COLLEGE
See LAKE COUNTY COMMUNITY COLLEGE DISTRICT

D-U-N-S 10-235-6003
▲ LAKELAND FINANCIAL CORP
202 E Center St, Warsaw, IN 46580-2842
Tel (574) 267-6144 *Founded/Ownrshp* 1983
Sales NA *EMP* 518[E]
Tkr Sym LKFN *Exch* NGS
SIC 6022 State commercial banks
Pr: David M Findlay
**Ch Bd:* Michael L Kubacki
CFO: Lisa M O'Neill
Ex VP: Kevin L Deardorff
Ex VP: Eric H Ottinger

LAKELAND HEALTH
See LAKELAND REGIONAL HEALTH SYSTEM

LAKELAND HEALTH MEDICAL CENTER
See LAKELAND HOSPITALS AT NILES AND ST JOSEPH INC

D-U-N-S 06-678-0400
LAKELAND HOSPITALS AT NILES AND ST JOSEPH INC
LAKELAND HEALTH MEDICAL CENTER
1234 Napier Ave, Saint Joseph, MI 49085-2112
Tel (800) 968-0115 *Founded/Ownrshp* 1977
Sales 327.1MM *EMP* 4,000
Accts Plante & Moran Pllc
SIC 8062 General medical & surgical hospitals
Pr: Loren B Hamel
**Pr:* David Burghart
**CEO:* Ray Cruse
**CEO:* Melinda Graham-Gruber
**CFO:* Timothy Calhoun
VP: Laurie Fleming
VP: David O'Conner
VP: Mary Ann Peter
Dir Rx: Mark Paulson
Ex Dir: Dave Koch
Prgrm Mgr: Beth Benjiman

D-U-N-S 05-588-3458 EXP
▲ LAKELAND INDUSTRIES INC
3555 Vtrans Mem Hwy Ste C, Ronkonkoma, NY 11779-7636
Tel (631) 981-9700 *Founded/Ownrshp* 1982
Sales 99.6MM *EMP* 1,211[E]
Tkr Sym LAKE *Exch* NGM
SIC 3842 2389 Personal safety equipment; Clothing, fire resistant & protective; Gloves, safety; Disposable garments & accessories
Pr: Christopher J Ryan
CFO: Teri W Hunt
Sr VP: Charles D Roberson
Board of Directors: James M Jenkins, A John Kreft, Thomas McAteer

D-U-N-S 00-901-9619
LAKELAND MEDICAL HEALTH CENTER
1234 Napier Ave, Saint Joseph, MI 49085-2112
Tel (269) 982-4935 *Founded/Ownrshp* 2010
Sales 344.1MM *EMP* 3
SIC 8099 Health & allied services

LAKELAND PHARMACY
See MIKE STUART ENTERPRISES INC

D-U-N-S 79-849-7756
LAKELAND REGIONAL HEALTH SYSTEM
LAKELAND HEALTH
1234 Napier Ave, Saint Joseph, MI 49085-2112
Tel (269) 983-8300 *Founded/Ownrshp* 1985
Sales 650.0MM *EMP* 2,430
Accts Plante & Moran Pllc St Jose
SIC 8741 Hospital management; Nursing & personal care facility management; Business management
COO: Daniel Bacchiocchi
**VP:* Ray Cruse
VP: Laurie Fleming
**VP:* Lowell Hamel
Dir Rx: Mark Paulson
Ex Dir: Dave Koch
Ex Dir: Jann Totzke
Prgrm Mgr: Beth Benjiman
CIO: Dorita Metzger
CTO: Jim Paulin
Dir IT: Peggy Juhl

D-U-N-S 96-344-5049
LAKELAND REGIONAL HEALTH SYSTEMS INC
1324 Lakeland Hills Blvd, Lakeland, FL 33805-4543
Tel (863) 687-1100 *Founded/Ownrshp* 1986
Sales 730.7MM *EMP* 3,124
Accts Kpmg Llp Tampa Fl
SIC 8062 General medical & surgical hospitals
Pr: Jack T Stephens
Assoc VP: Ana Kalman
**VP:* Paul A Powers
Exec: Karen Stebbins
Netwrk Eng: Brett Powell
Pharmcst: Natalie Pope

D-U-N-S 06-025-3150
LAKELAND REGIONAL MEDICAL CENTER INC
LRMC
1324 Lakeland Hills Blvd, Lakeland, FL 33805-4500
Tel (863) 687-1100 *Founded/Ownrshp* 1986
Sales 674.4MM *EMP* 3,100
Accts Kpmg Llp Tampa Fl
SIC 8062 General medical & surgical hospitals
CEO: Elaine C Thompson
**Pr:* Tim Regan
Treas: Dick Schaw
Sr VP: Janine Wiggins
VP: Wendell Blake
VP: Carl Gil
VP: Pat Gilen
VP: Vesta Hudson
VP: Debra Lineberger
VP: Debra Marion
VP: Mary A Pater
VP: Jeff Payne
Exec: Michelle Benjamin
Dir Risk M: Jennifer Szanyi
Dir Rad: John Badshaw
Dir Rad: Thelma Chisholm
Dir Rad: Thelma L Chishom
Dir Rad: Larry M Dietrich
Dir Rad: Carol J Ebersole

LAKENORMAN REGIONAL MED CTR
See MOORESVILLE HOSPITAL MANAGEMENT ASSOCIATES LLC

D-U-N-S 12-284-3381
■ LAKESHORE ENERGY SERVICES LLC
CENTERPOINT ENERGY
(*Suby of* CENTERPOINT ENERGY SERVICES RETAIL LLC) ★
1415 La St Ste 4200, Houston, TX 77002
Tel (888) 200-3788 *Founded/Ownrshp* 2008
Sales 173.8MM[E] *EMP* 35
Accts Grant Thornton Llp Tulsa Ok
SIC 4924 Natural gas distribution
VP: Hilarion Lopez

D-U-N-S 02-879-7546 IMP/EXP
LAKESHORE EQUIPMENT CO INC
LAKESHORE LEARNING MATERIALS
2695 E Dominguez St, Carson, CA 90895-1000
Tel (310) 537-8600 *Founded/Ownrshp* 1992
Sales 420.7MM[E] *EMP* 1,800
SIC 5999 5961 Education aids, devices & supplies; Educational supplies & equipment, mail order; Toys & games (including dolls & models), mail order
Pr: Michael A Kaplan
CFO: Mike Baltzer
**CFO:* Renee Bille
CFO: Karen Townsend
CFO: Renee Villea
**Treas:* Joshua Kaplan
Sr VP: Tony Gioia
VP: Jeniffer Centazzo
**VP:* Charles P Kaplan
VP: Pamela Moreno
VP: Bob Musso
VP: Mario Savastano

D-U-N-S 02-949-4105
LAKESHORE HEALTH PARTNERS
3235 N Wellness Dr 120b, Holland, MI 49424-8035
Tel (616) 399-9522 *Founded/Ownrshp* 2010
Sales 69.0MM[E] *EMP* 1,198[E]
SIC 8062 General medical & surgical hospitals
Prin: Dale Sowders
Off Mgr: Nicole Eardley

LAKESHORE LEARNING MATERIALS
See LAKESHORE EQUIPMENT CO INC

D-U-N-S 00-360-9633
LAKESHORE MANAGEMENT GROUP INC (IL)
70 E Lake St Ste 1600, Chicago, IL 60601-7446
Tel (773) 981-1452 *Founded/Ownrshp* 1997
Sales 18.1MM[E] *EMP* 1,500
SIC 7991 Health club
CEO: Robert Johnson
**Pr:* Jordon Kaiser
**Treas:* Walter Kaiser
**Ex VP:* Michael Sons
**VP:* Michael Dow

D-U-N-S 07-877-8361
LAKESHORE RECYCLING SYSTEMS LLC
LAKESHORE WASTE SERVICES
6132 Oakton St, Morton Grove, IL 60053-2718
Tel (773) 685-8811 *Founded/Ownrshp* 2012
Sales 136.6MM[E] *EMP* 419
SIC 4953 Refuse systems
CEO: Alan T Handley
Mng Pt: Joshua Connell
Exec: Jessica Amaya
IT Man: Kamran Jamal
VP Opers: John J Larsen

LAKESHORE WASTE SERVICES
See LAKESHORE RECYCLING SYSTEMS LLC

LAKESIDE FAMILY PHYSICIANS
See NOVANT HEALTH INC

LAKESIDE FAMILY PHYSICIANS
See PRESBYTERIAN MEDICAL CARE CORP

D-U-N-S 00-607-2037 IMP/EXP
LAKESIDE FOODS INC (WI)
808 Hamilton St, Manitowoc, WI 54220-5326
Tel (920) 684-3356 *Founded/Ownrshp* 1921
Sales 396.3MM[E] *EMP* 970
SIC 2033 2037 2032 2038 Canned fruits & specialties; Vegetables & vegetable products in cans, jars, etc.; Fruits & fruit products in cans, jars, etc.; Jams, jellies & preserves: packaged in cans, jars, etc.; Frozen fruits & vegetables; Canned specialties; Frozen specialties
Pr: Glen Telleck
Pr: Denise Kitzerow
Pr: Joel Yanda
QI Cn Mgr: Brian Herbrand
Mktg Mgr: Todd Eucke
Board of Directors: Elizabeth Kocourek, Henry F White Jr

D-U-N-S 05-835-2022 IMP
LAKESIDE INDUSTRIES INC
6505 226th Pl Se Ste 200, Issaquah, WA 98027-8905
Tel (425) 313-2600 *Founded/Ownrshp* 1952
Sales 403.0MM[E] *EMP* 750
SIC 1611 2951 5032 Highway & street paving contractor; Asphalt & asphaltic paving mixtures (not from refineries); Gravel
Ch: Rhoady R Lee Jr
**Pr:* Michael J Lee
**CEO:* Timothy Lee Jr
**CFO:* Hank Waggoner
Bd of Dir: Mike Smith
Exec: Sharon Lee
CTO: Bruce Fyfe
IT Man: Eric Carlson
IT Man: Doug Stillgebauer
Mtls Mgr: Greg Nachatilo
Sfty Mgr: Mike O'Neil

D-U-N-S 11-753-2507
LAKESIDE INTERNATIONAL LLC
LAKESIDE INTERNATIONAL TRUCKS
11000 W Silver Spring Dr, Milwaukee, WI 53225-3134
Tel (414) 353-4800 *Founded/Ownrshp* 1995
Sales 141.8MM[E] *EMP* 285
SIC 5511 5531 7538 7532 6159 7513 Trucks, tractors & trailers: new & used; Truck equipment & parts; General truck repair; Body shop, trucks; Truck finance leasing; Truck rental, without drivers
CEO: William K Reilley
**Pr:* Bill Reilley Jr
**CFO:* Jim Daugherty
Genl Mgr: Jeff Hitt
Genl Mgr: Peter Klein
Genl Mgr: Jim Kraschinsky
Sales Asso: David Considine

LAKESIDE INTERNATIONAL TRUCKS
See LAKESIDE INTERNATIONAL LLC

D-U-N-S 09-892-9524
LAKEVIEW CENTER INC
1221 W Lakeview Ave, Pensacola, FL 32501-1836
Tel (850) 432-1222 *Founded/Ownrshp* 1961
Sales 231.9MM *EMP* 1,900[E]
Accts Ernst & Young Llp
SIC 8069 8093 7389 7371 7373 Specialty hospitals, except psychiatric; Substance abuse hospitals; Alcoholism rehabilitation hospital; Drug addiction rehabilitation hospital; Substance abuse clinics (outpatient); Detoxification center, outpatient; Personal service agents, brokers & bureaus; Custom computer programming services; Computer integrated systems design
Pr: Gary L Bembry
COO: Tra Williams
CFO: Allison Hill
CFO: Xan Smith
Ex VP: John Bilbrey
VP: Rich Gilmartin
VP: Dennis Goodspeed
VP: Shawn Salamida
Exec: Sandy Whitaker
Ex Dir: Alicia Hall

D-U-N-S 19-146-6739
LAKEVIEW FARMS LLC
1600 Gressel Dr, Delphos, OH 45833-9153
Tel (419) 695-9925 *Founded/Ownrshp* 2015
Sales 108.6MM[E] *EMP* 230
SIC 2026 2099 2022 Cream, sour; Dips, sour cream based; Dips, except cheese & sour cream based; Gelatin dessert preparations; Cheese, natural & processed
Pr: Ernest E Graves
**Treas:* Martin Garlock
**VP:* John Kopilchack
Dir IT: Doug Metzger
QI Cn Mgr: Lynda Stewart

D-U-N-S 07-839-0061
LAKEVIEW HOSPITAL
630 Medical Dr, Bountiful, UT 84010-4908
Tel (801) 292-6231 *Founded/Ownrshp* 2012
Sales 85.1MM *EMP* 144[E]
SIC 8062 General medical & surgical hospitals
Ex Dir: Bobby Braun
Doctor: Scott H West MD
Pharmcst: Greg Mendiola
Occ Thrpy: Robert Braun
Diag Rad: Richard J Pope
Snr Mgr: Bernadette Waldrop

D-U-N-S 07-763-7569
LAKEVIEW MEDICAL CENTER INC OF RICE LAKE
1700 W Stout St, Rice Lake, WI 54868-5000
Tel (715) 234-1515 *Founded/Ownrshp* 1920
Sales 86.9MM *EMP* 360[E]
SIC 8062 General medical & surgical hospitals
Pr: Edward H Wolf
Dir Vol: Tammy Koger
CFO: Jackie Klein
Treas: Delores Bantz
**VP:* Scott Moebius
Dir OR: Kelly Flach
Dir Rx: Ken Engel
Dir Pat Ac: Ann Gleichert
IT Man: Eric Pelle
Doctor: Daniel Lochmann

D-U-N-S 96-973-6201
LAKEVIEW REGIONAL MEDICAL CENTER
95 Judge Tanner Blvd, Covington, LA 70433-7507
Tel (985) 867-3800 *Founded/Ownrshp* 2005
Sales 102.8MM *EMP* 12
SIC 8069 Cancer hospital
Ch: Bruce Ennis
Chf Rad: Steve Pflug
CFO: Tim Breslin
Off Mgr: Melissa Bourque
Telecom Mg: Marilyn Summerville
Occ Thrpy: John Gerhold
Snr Mgr: Randy Provensal

D-U-N-S 01-039-2751
LAKEVILLE AREA PUBLIC SCHOOLS
LAKEVILLE PUBLIC SCHOOL
8670 210th St W, Lakeville, MN 55044-7000
Tel (952) 232-2000 *Founded/Ownrshp* 2000
Sales 131.5MM *EMP* 1,270
Accts Malloy Montague Karnowski R
SIC 8211 Public elementary & secondary schools
Pr Dir: Amy Olson
**Schl Brd P:* Roz Peterson
**Schl Brd P:* Michelle Volk
Teacher Pr: Tony Massaros
Board of Directors: Stan Frederickson, Gayle Smaley-Rader, Lonnie Smith, Linda Swanson, Greg Utchetc

LAKEVILLE PUBLIC SCHOOL
See LAKEVILLE AREA PUBLIC SCHOOLS

D-U-N-S 08-094-8540
LAKEWOOD BOARD OF EDUCATION (INC) (NJ)
LAKEWOOD PUBLIC SCHOOLS
200 Ramsey Ave, Lakewood, NJ 08701-2085
Tel (732) 730-1606 *Founded/Ownrshp* 1910, 1970
Sales 174.4MM *EMP* 1,000[E]
SIC 8211 School board
Pr: Isaac Zlatkin
**VP:* Tracey Tift
Dir Sec: John Stillwell
Schl Brd P: Aida Gonzalez

D-U-N-S 08-448-8139
LAKEWOOD HEALTH SYSTEM
49725 County 83, Staples, MN 56479-5280
Tel (218) 894-1515 *Founded/Ownrshp* 1973
Sales 98.3MM *EMP* 800[E]
SIC 8062 8051 General medical & surgical hospitals; Extended care facility
Pr: Tim Rice
Dir Vol: Marnie Pogreba
**CFO:* Jim Dregney
Bd of Dir: Julie Benson
Dir IT: Jim Thurner
Pharmcst: Alissa Kuepers
Pharmcst: Michelle Lundquist
HC Dir: Mary Fitcher
HC Dir: Shauna Olson
HC Dir: Shauna Stokes

D-U-N-S 07-778-2241
LAKEWOOD HOSPITAL ASSOCIATION
CLEVELAND CLINIC HEALTH SYSTEM
(*Suby of* CLEVELAND CLINIC HEALTH SYSTEM) ★
14519 Detroit Ave, Lakewood, OH 44107-4383
Tel (216) 529-7160 *Founded/Ownrshp* 1907
Sales 94.0MM *EMP* 750
SIC 8062 General medical & surgical hospitals
CEO: Fred Degrandis
VP: W C Geiger III
Cmptr Lab: Barb Garrard
Doctor: Krisin Broadben

D-U-N-S 94-094-6226
LAKEWOOD MIDSTREAM LLC
(*Suby of* ENERGY SPECTRUM PARTNERS VI LP) ★
6655 S Lewis Ave Ste 200, Tulsa, OK 74136-1031
Tel (918) 392-9356 *Founded/Ownrshp* 2013
Sales 98.1MM *EMP* 122
SIC 4932 Gas & other services combined
Genl Mgr: Scott Rachels

LAKEWOOD PUBLIC SCHOOLS
See LAKEWOOD BOARD OF EDUCATION (INC)

LAKIN TIRE OF CALIF
See LAKIN TIRE WEST INC

D-U-N-S 06-861-7570 EXP
LAKIN TIRE WEST INC
LAKIN TIRE OF CALIF
15305 Spring Ave, Santa Fe Springs, CA 90670-5645
Tel (562) 802-2752 *Founded/Ownrshp* 1918
Sales 101.9MM[E] *EMP* 180[E]
SIC 5014 5531 Tires, used; Automotive & home supply stores
CEO: Robert Lakin
**VP:* David Lakin
VP: Randolph Roth
VP: Randy Roth
IT Man: Phuc Dinh
MIS Mgr: David Hui

D-U-N-S 03-095-4713
LAKOTA LOCAL SCHOOL DISTRICT
5572 Princeton Rd, Liberty Twp, OH 45011-9726
Tel (513) 874-5505 *Founded/Ownrshp* 1970
Sales 90.4MM[E] *EMP* 1,800[E]
SIC 8211 Public elementary school; Public junior high school; Public senior high school
Treas: Beth Dodson
**Treas:* Jenni Logan
Prin: Clayton Ash
Prin: Matthew Glover
Prin: Linda Lee
Prin: Cathleen Newkirk
Prin: David Pike
Prin: Ed Rudder
Prin: Ron Spurlock
Prin: David Tobergte
Prin: Robert Winterberger
Board of Directors: Ben Dibble, Ray Murray, Lynda Oconnor, Todd Parnell, Julie Shaffer

D-U-N-S 80-921-3817
LALA BRANDED PRODUCTS LLC
GILSA DAIRY PRODUCTS
(*Suby of* CHANVIM ENGINEERING (INDIA) PRIVATE LIMITED)
8750 N Central Expy # 400, Dallas, TX 75231-6417
Tel (214) 459-1100 *Founded/Ownrshp* 2016
Sales 122.2MM[E] *EMP* 300[E]
SIC 5143 Dairy products, except dried or canned

CEO: Scot Rank
VP: Diego Rosenfledt

D-U-N-S 16-188-4416
LALLY PIPE & TUBE CO
(*Suby of* LALLY PIPE & TUBE DIVISION) ★
8770 Railroad Dr, Taylor Mill, KY 41015-9096
Tel (606) 371-5600 *Founded/Ownrshp* 1984
Sales 120.0MM *EMP* 100
SIC 5014 Tires & tubes
Pr: Timothy Lally
**Ch Bd:* John B Lally
**VP:* Brendan Lally

LALLY PIPE & TUBE DIVISION
See L B INDUSTRIES INC

D-U-N-S 03-813-7956 IMP
▲ LAM RESEARCH CORP
4650 Cushing Pkwy, Fremont, CA 94538-6401
Tel (510) 572-0200 *Founded/Ownrshp* 1980
Sales 5.8MMM *EMP* 7,300
Tkr Sym LRCX *Exch* NGS
SIC 3674 Semiconductors & related devices; Wafers (semiconductor devices)
Pr: Martin B Anstice
**Ch Bd:* Stephen G Newberry
COO: Timothy M Archer
CFO: Douglas R Bettinger
Treas: Cfa Go
Ex VP: Richard A Gottscho
Sr VP: Gary Bultman
VP: John Daugherty
VP: Robert Dunsford
VP: Zach Hatcher
VP: David J Hemker
VP: Dinesh Kalakkad
VP: Stephen Keeney
VP: Thorsten Lill
VP: Mike Morita
VP: Rangesh Raghavan
Board of Directors: Eric K Brandt, Michael R Cannon, Christine A Heckart, Catherine P Lego, Youssef A El-Mansy, Rick Tsai

D-U-N-S 78-812-1481
▲ LAMAR ADVERTISING CO
5321 Corporate Blvd, Baton Rouge, LA 70808-2506
Tel (225) 926-1000 *Founded/Ownrshp* 1902
Sales 1.3MMM *EMP* 3,200
Tkr Sym LAMR *Exch* NGS
SIC 7312 6798 Outdoor advertising services; Billboard advertising; Poster advertising, outdoor; Real estate investment trusts
Ch Bd: Kevin P Reilly Jr
Pr: Jon Funk
Pr: Kellye Williams
CEO: Sean E Reilly
CFO: Keith A Istre
VP: Shauna Forsythe
VP: Neal Gatherum
VP: Bill Ripp
Off Mgr: Janice Olafson
Opers Mgr: Brian Duncan
Board of Directors: John Maxwell Hamilton, John E Koerner III, Stephen P Mumblow, Thomas V Reifenheiser, Anna Reilly, Wendell Reilly

D-U-N-S 09-964-4353
LAMAR CO SCHOOL SYSTEM
LAMAR COUNTY SCHOOL DISTRICT
424 Martin Luther King Dr, Purvis, MS 39475-5028
Tel (601) 794-1030 *Founded/Ownrshp* 1900
Sales 50.7MM^E *EMP* 1,200
SIC 8211 Public elementary & secondary schools
Prin: Tess R Smith
Dir Sec: Steve Rosser
HC Dir: Josette Sirmon

D-U-N-S 82-763-3632
LAMAR COMMUNITY CARE CENTER LLC
WINDHAM HOUSE OF HATTIESBURG
(*Suby of* COMMCARE CORP) ★
37 Hillcrest Dr Ofc, Hattiesburg, MS 39402-8622
Tel (601) 264-0058 *Founded/Ownrshp* 2008
Sales 5.5MM *EMP* 1,035^E
SIC 8051 Skilled nursing care facilities

LAMAR COMPANIES
See LAMAR TEXAS LIMITED PARTNERSHIP

D-U-N-S 08-356-9764
LAMAR CONSOLIDATED INDEPENDENT SCHOOL DISTRICT (INC)
CSID
3911 Avenue I, Rosenberg, TX 77471-3901
Tel (832) 223-0000 *Founded/Ownrshp* 1947
Sales 261.6MM^E *EMP* 4,200
Accts Null-Lairson Pc Houston Tx
SIC 8211 Public combined elementary & secondary school; Public senior high school
**Pr:* Julie Thompson
**VP:* Rhonda Zacharias
**Prin:* Sam Hopkins
Pr Dir: Mike Rockwood
Teacher Pr: Kathleen Bowen
HC Dir: Judy Smith

D-U-N-S 00-485-3651
LAMAR CONSTRUCTION CO
4404 Central Pkwy, Hudsonville, MI 49426-7831
Tel (616) 662-2933 *Founded/Ownrshp* 1999
Sales 211.7MM *EMP* 125^E
SIC 1542 1541

LAMAR COUNTY SCHOOL DISTRICT
See LAMAR CO SCHOOL SYSTEM

D-U-N-S 06-953-6118
■ LAMAR MEDIA CORP
(*Suby of* LAMAR ADVERTISING CO) ★
5321 Corporate Blvd, Baton Rouge, LA 70808-2506
Tel (225) 926-1000 *Founded/Ownrshp* 1902
Sales 1.3MMM *EMP* 3,200
SIC 7312 Outdoor advertising services; Billboard advertising; Poster advertising, outdoor
CEO: Sean E Reilly
**Ch Bd:* Kevin P Reilly Jr
Pr: Kellye Moody
CFO: Keith A Istre
Mktg Dir: Cheryl Zimmermann
Board of Directors: John Maxwell Hamilton, John E Koerner III, Stephen P Mumblow, Thomas Reifenheiser, Anna Reilly, Wendell S Reilly

D-U-N-S 14-720-6515
LAMAR TEXAS LIMITED PARTNERSHIP
LAMAR COMPANIES
5321 Corporate Blvd, Baton Rouge, LA 70808-2506
Tel (800) 235-2627 *Founded/Ownrshp* 1995
Sales 71.6MM^E *EMP* 3,000
SIC 7312 Outdoor advertising services

D-U-N-S 96-731-5706
LAMAR UNIVERSITY
LAMAR UNIVERSITY-BEAUMONT
(*Suby of* TEXAS STATE UNIVERSITY SYSTEM) ★
4400 S M L King Jr Pkwy, Beaumont, TX 77705-5748
Tel (409) 880-8932 *Founded/Ownrshp* 1923
Sales 89.4MM^E *EMP* 836
SIC 8221 University
Prin: Carroll David
VP: Kevin Smith
Dir Lab: Robert Corbett
Dir IT: Fatai Oyejobi

LAMAR UNIVERSITY-BEAUMONT
See LAMAR UNIVERSITY

LAMB WESTON
See WESTON LAMB HOLDINGS INC

D-U-N-S 08-959-4506 EXP
LAMBERT VET SUPPLY LLC
714 5th St, Fairbury, NE 68352-2626
Tel (402) 729-3044 *Founded/Ownrshp* 1994
Sales 151.3MM^E *EMP* 92
SIC 5047 Veterinarians' equipment & supplies
CFO: John Gabel CPA
Genl Mgr: Shannon Snider
IT Man: Nels Sorensen
Mktg Dir: Michael Koehn
Mktg Mgr: Mandy Fortik

D-U-N-S 79-667-6117
LAMBERTI SYNTHESIS USA INC
(*Suby of* LAMBERTI SPA)
4001 N Hawthorne St, Chattanooga, TN 37406-1314
Tel (423) 697-0526 *Founded/Ownrshp* 2006
Sales 10.1MM^E *EMP* 3,000
SIC 8741 Management services
Pr: Anthony Philip
Tech Mgr: Luigi Merli

D-U-N-S 06-545-1080
LAMERS BUS LINES INC (WI)
2407 S Point Rd, Green Bay, WI 54313-5498
Tel (920) 496-3600 *Founded/Ownrshp* 1944
Sales 146.7MM^E *EMP* 1,300
SIC 4151 4142 4119 4725 4141 School buses; Bus charter service, except local; Local passenger transportation; Limousine rental, with driver; Tour operators; Local bus charter service
Prin: Allen Lamers

D-U-N-S 14-759-0731 IMP/EXP
LAMEX FOODS INC
(*Suby of* LAMEX FOODS EUROPE LIMITED)
8500 Normandale Ste 1150, Bloomington, MN 55437
Tel (952) 844-0585 *Founded/Ownrshp* 1986
Sales 501.2MM *EMP* 47
SIC 5144 5147 Poultry: live, dressed or frozen (unpackaged); Meats & meat products
CEO: Phillip O Wallace
**Pr:* Steven Anderson
**VP:* Mark Barrett
VP: Dave Huber
**VP:* Robert Lucas
**Prin:* Mark Ryder
Off Admin: Luz Hernandez
Opers Mgr: Megan Abbott

D-U-N-S 11-434-1506 IMP
LAMI PRODUCTS INC
860 Welsh Rd, Huntingdon Valley, PA 19006-6000
Tel (215) 947-5333 *Founded/Ownrshp* 1976
Sales 207.8MM^E *EMP* 450
SIC 5199

D-U-N-S 02-187-7436
LAMINATE CO (VA)
AMERICAN STAIR AND CABINETRY
6612 James Madison Hwy, Haymarket, VA 20169-2713
Tel (703) 753-0699 *Founded/Ownrshp* 1980, 1991
Sales 107.1MM^E *EMP* 253
SIC 5031 2431 Kitchen cabinets; Staircases, stairs & railings
CEO: John Lombardozzi
**VP:* John Hall
**VP:* Mary Jeanne Helton

D-U-N-S 00-808-2976 IMP
■ LAMONS GASKET CO
(*Suby of* TRIMAS CORP) ★
7300 Airport Blvd, Houston, TX 77061-3932
Tel (713) 547-9527 *Founded/Ownrshp* 1945, 2002
Sales 200.9MM^E *EMP* 495
SIC 3053 5085 Gaskets, all materials; Hose, belting & packing
Pr: Kurt Allen
Tech Mgr: Kris Kolb
Mtls Mgr: Jeff Warren
Mktg Dir: Dave Metzer
Sls Mgr: Ron Kovilaritch

LAMONT COMMUNITY HEALTH CENTER
See CLINICA SIERRA VISTA

LAMONTS GIFTS & SUNDRY
See FOOD PANTRY LTD

D-U-N-S 00-696-3342
LAMPERT YARDS INC (MN)
LAMPERTS
1850 Como Ave, Saint Paul, MN 55108-2715
Tel (651) 695-3600 *Founded/Ownrshp* 1887
Sales 142.2MM^E *EMP* 500
SIC 5211 1521 2439 2426

LAMPERTS
See LAMPERT YARDS INC

D-U-N-S 00-643-8162 IMP/EXP
LAMPLIGHT FARMS INC (WI)
(*Suby of* ZEBCO) ★
W140n4900 Lilly Rd, Menomonee Falls, WI 53051-7035
Tel (262) 781-9590 *Founded/Ownrshp* 1964, 1965
Sales 132.8MM^E *EMP* 301
SIC 3648 3999 3229 2911 Lighting equipment; Candles; Pressed & blown glass; Oils, illuminating
Pr: Joel R Borgardt
**VP:* Thomas Risch

D-U-N-S 08-111-0124 IMP/EXP
LAMPS PLUS INC
20250 Plummer St, Chatsworth, CA 91311-5300
Tel (818) 886-5267 *Founded/Ownrshp* 1976
Sales 273.0MM^E *EMP* 1,200
SIC 5719 Lighting, lamps & accessories
CEO: Dennis K Swanson
**COO:* Jerry Bass
**CFO:* Clark Linstone
VP: Chuck Ackerman
VP: Elie Boutros
Dist Mgr: Iskender Berberoglu
Store Mgr: Eric Fairchild
Store Mgr: Azher Khan
Store Mgr: Edwin Uhey
Dir IT: Gary Shapiro
IT Man: John Dunn

D-U-N-S 05-602-7980
LAMPTON-LOVE INC
(*Suby of* ERGON INC) ★
2829 Lakeland Dr Ste 1505, Jackson, MS 39232-8880
Tel (601) 933-3400 *Founded/Ownrshp* 1967
Sales 129.7MM^E *EMP* 328
SIC 5171 Petroleum bulk stations & terminals
Ch Bd: Leslie B Lampton Sr
**Pr:* Robert Love
VP: Don Davis
**VP:* Ken Hodges
VP: Robert H Lampton
VP: Easterling Rusty
**VP:* Kathryn Stone
IT Man: Mike Donaldson

D-U-N-S 01-778-6245 IMP
■ LAMRITE WEST INC
DARICE
(*Suby of* MICHAELS COMPANIES INC) ★
14225 Pearl Rd, Strongsville, OH 44136-8711
Tel (440) 238-7318 *Founded/Ownrshp* 1964
Sales 175.3MM^E *EMP* 600
SIC 5999 5199 5092 Artists' supplies & materials; Artificial flowers; Art goods & supplies; Toys & hobby goods & supplies
Pr: Michael Catanzarite
**CFO:* Joe Rudolph
**VP:* David Catanzarite

D-U-N-S 62-661-9949
LAN CARGO SA
(*Suby of* LATAM AIRLINES GROUP S.A.)
6500 Nw 22nd St, Miami, FL 33122-2234
Tel (786) 265-6000 *Founded/Ownrshp* 1990
Sales 87.3MM^E *EMP* 800^E
SIC 4789 Cargo loading & unloading services
CEO: Christian Ureta
**COO:* Federico Germani
COO: Eduardo Vial
**CFO:* Andres Bianchi

D-U-N-S 06-629-0602 IMP
LANAI RESORTS LLC
LODGE AT KOELE
(*Suby of* CASTLE & COOKE, INC.)
1311 Fraser Ave, Lanai City, HI 96763
Tel (808) 565-3000 *Founded/Ownrshp* 2012
Sales 533.3MM^E *EMP* 800
SIC 6552 6512 Land subdividers & developers, commercial; Commercial & industrial building operation
**COO:* Kurt Matsumoto
**Sr VP:* Arlan Chun
**Sr VP:* Lesley Kaneshiro
**VP:* Kimberly Miyazawa Frank
VP: John Uchiyama

LANCASTER
See MERIT DISTRIBUTION GROUP LLC

D-U-N-S 05-429-5456
LANCASTER CENTRAL SCHOOLS DISTRICT
177 Central Ave, Lancaster, NY 14086-1897
Tel (716) 686-3200 *Founded/Ownrshp* 1950
Sales 96.6MM *EMP* 900
Accts Drescher & Malecki Llp Buffal
SIC 8211 9411 Public elementary school; Public junior high school; Public senior high school; Kindergarten; Administration of educational programs
**CIO:* Edward Myszka
Pr Dir: Patricia Burgio
Teacher Pr: Cheryl Reukauf

LANCASTER CNTY SCHL DISTRCT 1
See LINCOLN PUBLIC SCHOOLS INC

D-U-N-S 00-192-8035 IMP/EXP
▲ LANCASTER COLONY CORP (OH)
37 W Broad St Ste 500, Columbus, OH 43215-4177
Tel (614) 224-7141 *Founded/Ownrshp* 1961
Sales 1.1MMM *EMP* 2,600
Tkr Sym LANC *Exch* NGS
SIC 2035 2038 Dressings, salad: raw & cooked (except dry mixes); Seasonings & sauces, except tomato & dry; Frozen specialties
Ch Bd: John B Gerlach Jr
Pr: David A Ciesinski
CFO: Douglas A Fell

D-U-N-S 08-471-3015
LANCASTER COUNTY SCHOOL DISTRICT
300 S Catawba St, Lancaster, SC 29720-2458
Tel (803) 286-6972 *Founded/Ownrshp* 1935
Sales 116.3MM *EMP* 1,600
Accts Mcgregor & Company Llp Columb
SIC 8211 Public elementary & secondary schools
**CFO:* Tony Walker
Ex Dir: Lydia Quinn
Dir IT: Scott Johnson
Pr Dir: David Knight
Schl Brd P: Robert Parker
HC Dir: Kathy Durbin

D-U-N-S 08-162-3241 IMP
LANCASTER FOODS LLC (DE)
(*Suby of* GUEST SERVICES INC) ★
7700 Conowingo Ave, Jessup, MD 20794-9473
Tel (410) 799-0010 *Founded/Ownrshp* 1983, 1992
Sales 221.8MM^E *EMP* 280
SIC 5148 Fresh fruits & vegetables
Pr: John Gates
**VP:* Jerold Chadwick
**VP:* Kevin Jones
Dir IT: George Gutierrez
Sls Mgr: Christina Sikorski

D-U-N-S 60-644-6227
LANCASTER GENERAL HEALTH
555 N Duke St, Lancaster, PA 17602-2250
Tel (717) 290-5511 *Founded/Ownrshp* 1983
Sales 27.5MM *EMP* 5,000
SIC 8062 General medical & surgical hospitals
Pr: Thomas Beeman
**Ch Bd:* Robert Bolinger
CFO: F Joseph Byroick
Ex VP: Jan L Bergen
Sr VP: F J Byorick
Sr VP: Joseph Byorick
Sr VP: Robert Macina
Sr VP: Regina Mingle
VP: Kay A Brady
VP: Geoffrey Eddowes
Dir Rx: Rich Paoletti
Board of Directors: Mark A Brazitis, Robert P Macina

D-U-N-S 06-978-4924
LANCASTER GENERAL HOSPITAL
LGH
555 N Duke St, Lancaster, PA 17602-2207
Tel (717) 544-5511 *Founded/Ownrshp* 1893
Sales 920.2MM *EMP* 7,000
SIC 8062 Hospital, professional nursing school with AMA residency
CEO: Jan L Bergen
Chf Rad: Leigh S Shuman
CFO: Dennis R Roemer
Ex VP: Robert P Macina
Ex VP: Joel Perlish
Sr VP: Jan Bergen
Sr VP: Gary Davidson
Sr VP: Lee M Duke II
Sr VP: Geoffrey W Eddowes
VP: Joseph Byorick
VP: Carolyn Carlson
VP: Norma Ferndinand
VP: Christopher Maley
VP: Regina Mingle
VP: Rich Paoletti
VP: Joseph Puskar
VP: Doug Rinehart
VP: Susan Wynne

D-U-N-S 09-999-9492
LANCASTER SCHOOL DISTRICT
44711 Cedar Ave, Lancaster, CA 93534-3216
Tel (661) 948-4661 *Founded/Ownrshp* 1890
Sales 118.4MM^E *EMP* 2,500
Accts Christy White Accountancy Corp
SIC 8211 Public elementary & secondary schools
Genl Mgr: Michele Bowers
CFO: Leona Smith
Genl Mgr: Jeanette Tigert
Mktg Dir: Patricia Burgio
HC Dir: Jullie Eutsler

D-U-N-S 09-187-3984
LANCASTER-LEBANON INTERMEDIATE UNIT 13 (INC)
1020 New Holland Ave, Lancaster, PA 17601-5606
Tel (717) 606-1600 *Founded/Ownrshp* 1971
Sales 83.7M^E *EMP* 1,800
Accts Trout Ebersole & Groff Llp La
SIC 8299 Educational services
Ex Dir: Cynthia Burkhart
**CFO:* Gina Brillhart
Instr Medi: Pam Mc Artney
Instr Medi: Pam McCartney

D-U-N-S 05-455-0140
LANCE INVESTIGATION SERVICE INC
1438 Boston Rd, Bronx, NY 10460-4963
Tel (718) 893-1400 *Founded/Ownrshp* 1965
Sales 18.8MM^E *EMP* 1,800
Accts Zeligson Granito & Epstein L
SIC 7381 1731 Protective services, guard; Detective services; Fire detection & burglar alarm systems specialization
Pr: Ralph V Johnson
**VP:* Lance W Johnson
Genl Mgr: Mark Creighton

LANCE PRIVATE BRANDS
See VISTA BAKERY INC

D-U-N-S 04-701-3412 IMP/EXP
LANCER CORP
INDUSTRIAS LANCERMEX SA DE CV
(*Suby of* HOSHIZAKI AMERICA INC) ★
6655 Lancer Blvd, San Antonio, TX 78219-4735
Tel (210) 661-6964 *Founded/Ownrshp* 1969
Sales 168.4MM^E *EMP* 515
SIC 3585 Ice making machinery; Soda fountain & beverage dispensing equipment & parts; Beer dispensing equipment; Carbonators, soda water
Pr: Luis Alvarez
VP: Jose A Canales
VP: David Ewing
VP: Richard Laughlin
VP: Chuck Thomas

D-U-N-S 80-735-4410
LANCER INSURANCE CO
1 Fairchild Ct Ste 200, Plainview, NY 11803-1720
Tel (541) 472-0950 Founded/Ownrshp 1985
Sales NA EMP 430
SIC 6331 Fire, marine & casualty insurance
Pr: David P Delaney Jr
Pr: Kim Aquilino
*CFO: Alistair T Lind
CFO: Alistair Lind
Ex VP: Timothy Delaney
Ex VP: Thomas L Theiler
VP: Paul Berne
VP: Robert Burns
VP: Michael Byrne
*VP: Bob Crescenzo
VP: Leslie Drake
VP: Pamela Marin
VP: Kieran McGowan
VP: Matthew Mushorn
VP: Randy O'Neill
VP: Timothy O'Sullivan
VP: John Petrilli
*VP: Gail Riley
VP: Ed Temkin
Exec: Erin Ford
Exec: Gail Reilly

D-U-N-S 04-252-4272 EXP
LANCO INTERNATIONAL INC
LANTECH LOGISTICS
3111 167th St, Hazel Crest, IL 60429-1025
Tel (708) 596-5200 Founded/Ownrshp 1954
Sales 190.9MM[E] EMP 650
SIC 3531 8711 5084 3536 7353 3537 Construction machinery; Designing: ship, boat, machine & product; Cranes, industrial; Cranes, overhead traveling; Heavy construction equipment rental; Industrial trucks & tractors
Pr: John J Lanigan Jr
*CFO: Stephen J Bayers
*Ex VP: Mike T Lanigan
*Ex VP: William P Lanigan
*VP: Jack Wepfer
Genl Mgr: C Rog
VP Sls: Ray Tippit
Board of Directors: Daniel P Lanigan

LAND & PERSONNEL MANAGEMENT
See HALL MANAGEMENT CORP

D-U-N-S 07-845-6993 EXP
■ LAND N SEA DISTRIBUTING INC (FL)
LAND N SEA FORT MYERS
(Suby of BRUNSWICK CORP) ★
3131 N Andrews Avenue Ext, Pompano Beach, FL 33064-2118
Tel (954) 792-9971 Founded/Ownrshp 1975
Sales 244.3MM[E] EMP 350
SIC 5088 5091 5046 5531 Marine supplies; Sporting & recreation goods; Commercial equipment; Automotive parts
Pr: Thomas Schuessler
Pr: Carl Parisi
*VP: David R Swick
*VP: Judith P Zelisko
MIS Dir: Betty Alvarez

LAND N SEA FORT MYERS
See LAND N SEA DISTRIBUTING INC

LAND OLAKES ANIMAL MILK PDTS
See PURINA ANIMAL NUTRITION LLC

D-U-N-S 00-625-3835 IMP/EXP
LAND OLAKES INC (TN)
4001 Lexington Ave N, Arden Hills, MN 55126-2998
Tel (651) 375-2222 Founded/Ownrshp 1921
Sales 14.9MMM EMP 9,144
SIC 2879

D-U-N-S 96-826-2048
LAND OSUN MANAGEMENT CORP
FASTTRACK FOODS
3715 Nw 97th Blvd Ste A, Gainesville, FL 32606-7373
Tel (352) 333-3011 Founded/Ownrshp 1988
Sales 118.5MM[E] EMP 300
SIC 5541 5411 Filling stations, gasoline; Convenience stores
Pr: Alan Fogg
*VP: Stephen Fogg
*VP: Richard Rentz

LAND PRIDE
See GREAT PLAINS MANUFACTURING INC

LAND ROVER
See FRED LAVERY CO

LAND ROVER METRO WEST
See FOREIGN MOTORS WEST INC

D-U-N-S 83-837-0682
LAND SOUTHERN CO LLC
WESTHAVEN REALTY
1550 W Mcewen Dr Ste 200, Franklin, TN 37067-1771
Tel (615) 778-3150 Founded/Ownrshp 1995
Sales 146.3MM[E] EMP 250[E]
SIC 6552 Subdividers & developers
CEO: Tim Downey
Pr: Brian Sewell
CFO: Ken Howell
VP: Michael McNally
VP: Kathy Shelling
VP: Cliff Smith
VP: Tim Snook
VP: Creighton Wright
Mng Dir: Tom Fous
Genl Mgr: Shelley Homer
VP Mktg: Jena Armistead

D-U-N-S 07-576-3540
LAND TITLE GUARANTEE CO INC
3033 E 1st Ave Ste 600, Denver, CO 80206-5625
Tel (303) 321-1880 Founded/Ownrshp 1994
Sales NA EMP 600
SIC 6411 Insurance agents, brokers & service;
Ch Bd: Bill Vollbracht
*Pr: John E Fryer Sr
*CFO: Dan Every
Ofcr: Debi Bright
Ofcr: Sarah Dorman
Ofcr: Dave Fischer
Ofcr: Sandra Johnson
Ofcr: Ben Lowe
Ofcr: David Quarles
Ofcr: Scott Seymour
Ofcr: Kim Shultz
Ofcr: Robin Trent
Ex VP: John Freyer
*Sr VP: Brian Hamilton
VP: Diane Evans
*VP: John E Fryer Jr
VP: Randy Gibbons
VP: Peter Griffiths
VP: Mike Heber

D-U-N-S 11-751-6757
LAND VIEW INC
20504 4th St, Rupert, ID 83350-9428
Tel (208) 531-4100 Founded/Ownrshp 1984
Sales 86.1MM[E] EMP 150
SIC 2879 2873 2874 5999 5261 5169 Agricultural chemicals; Nitrogenous fertilizers; Phosphatic fertilizers; Feed & farm supply; Fertilizer; Chemicals & allied products; Alkalines & chlorine
Pr: Roy Young
CFO: Lance Whitney
*VP: Gregg M Harman
*VP: V Paul Hobson
Exec: Lance Wihitney
Opers Mgr: Jake Harman

D-U-N-S 61-925-8734
LAND-AIR EXPRESS OF NEW ENGLAND LTD
59 Avenue C, Williston, VT 05495-8109
Tel (800) 639-3095 Founded/Ownrshp 1990
Sales 89.3MM[E] EMP 650
SIC 4214

D-U-N-S 87-805-3321 EXP
■ LAND-O-SUN DAIRIES LLC
PET DAIRY
(Suby of DEAN FOODS CO) ★
2900 Bristol Hwy, Johnson City, TN 37601-1502
Tel (423) 283-5700 Founded/Ownrshp 1998
Sales 242.8MM[E] EMP 1,900
SIC 2026 2024 5143 Fluid milk; Ice cream & frozen desserts; Dairy products, except dried or canned
Pr: Rick Fehr
*CFO: Loren White
Treas: A M Allem
Treas: A Allem
MIS Dir: Rod Barnett

D-U-N-S 12-283-9462
LANDAIR TRANSPORT INC
1 Landair Way, Greeneville, TN 37743-2577
Tel (423) 783-1300 Founded/Ownrshp 2002
Sales 94.7MM[E] EMP 951[E]
SIC 4213 4225 Trucking, except local; General warehousing & storage
CEO: John A Tweed
*CFO: Chris E Horner
*Ch: Scott M Niswonger
*Sr VP: Matt T Anderson
*Sr VP: Gary Funk
*Sr VP: Kris Kohls
Sr VP: Earnie Seibert
*VP: Jim Massengill
*VP: Richard Roberts
Genl Mgr: Mike Chesser
Dir IT: Chris Dolese

D-U-N-S 83-224-2692
LANDAU APARTMENTS LIMITED PARTNERSHIP
1321 S Broad St, Clinton, SC 29325-9430
Tel (864) 833-3215 Founded/Ownrshp 2009
Sales 40.3MM[E] EMP 3,900
SIC 6513 Apartment building operators
Prin: Margaret Stannard
Sr VP: Leeann Morein

D-U-N-S 04-217-0829 IMP/EXP
LANDAU UNIFORMS INC
8410 W Sandidge Rd, Olive Branch, MS 38654-3412
Tel (662) 895-7200 Founded/Ownrshp 1959
Sales 98.8MM[E] EMP 500[E]
SIC 2326 2337 2339 Work uniforms; Medical & hospital uniforms, men's; Uniforms, except athletic: women's, misses' & juniors'; Women's & misses' outerwear
CEO: Bruce Landau
*Pr: Nathaniel Landau
*Sec: Nancy E Russell
Ofcr: Jenny Cook
*VP: Gregg A Landau
Rgnl Mgr: Jason Bowen
Dept Mgr: Janice Credille
MIS Dir: Ron Richins
Web Dev: Arsenio Macapaz
Software D: Andy Blankenship
Mfg Dir: Sergio Gonzalez
Board of Directors: Dale Scott

D-U-N-S 18-980-7159
▲ LANDAUER INC
2 Science Rd, Glenwood, IL 60425-1586
Tel (708) 755-7000 Founded/Ownrshp 1987
Sales 151.3MM EMP 600[E]
Accts Bdo Usa Llp Chicago Il
Tkr Sym LDR Exch NYS
SIC 8734 5047 3829 Radiation laboratories; Radiation dosimetry laboratory; Instruments, surgical & medical; X-ray film & supplies; Measuring & controlling devices
Pr: Michael P Kaminski
*Ch Bd: Michael T Leatherman
Pr: Peter Cempellin
CFO: Dan Fujii
Sr VP: Michael R Kennedy
Sr VP: G Douglas King
VP: Dick Berning
VP: Doug King
Exec: Douglas R Gipson
CTO: Sue Morrow
Dir IT: Barry Barovick
Board of Directors: Jeffrey A Bailey, Robert J Cronin, William G Dempsey, Teri G Fontenot, David D Meador, Stephen C Mitchell, Thomas M White

D-U-N-S 01-299-5176
■ LANDCARE USA INC
(Suby of SERVICEMASTER CO LLC) ★
2603 Augusta Dr Ste 1300, Houston, TX 77057-5428
Tel (713) 692-6371 Founded/Ownrshp 1998, 1999
Sales 33.2MM[E] EMP 2,000
SIC 0783 0782 Planting, pruning & trimming services; Tree trimming services for public utility lines; Removal services, bush & tree; Highway lawn & garden maintenance services; Landscape contractors
Ch Bd: William F Murdy
*Sr VP: William L Fiedler
*Sr VP: Kenneth V Garcia
*VP: Harold D Cranston
*VP: Peter C Forbes

D-U-N-S 12-154-8270
LANDCARE USA LLC
5295 Westview Dr Ste 100, Frederick, MD 21703-8306
Tel (301) 874-3300 Founded/Ownrshp 2011
Sales 200.0MM[E] EMP 3,000
SIC 0782 Landscape contractors; Lawn services
CEO: Joseph Michael Bogan
CFO: Dan Krems
VP: John A Mann
VP: Kevin Sherwood
Exec: Richard Klein
VP Opers: Darrell Ennes
Opers Mgr: Tim Drake
Genl Couns: Jim Ballard

D-U-N-S 09-546-2867
LANDDESIGN INC
223 N Graham St, Charlotte, NC 28202-1431
Tel (704) 333-0325 Founded/Ownrshp 1978
Sales 166.0MM[E] EMP 85
SIC 0781

D-U-N-S 17-707-0794
▲ LANDEC CORP
3603 Haven Ave, Menlo Park, CA 94025-1010
Tel (650) 306-1650 Founded/Ownrshp 1986
Sales 541.1MM EMP 552[E]
Accts Ernst & Young Llp San Franci
Tkr Sym LNDC Exch NGS
SIC 2033 5148 5999 Fruits: packaged in cans, jars, etc.; Vegetables: packaged in cans, jars, etc.; Fresh fruits & vegetables; Medical apparatus & supplies
Pr: Molly A Hemmeter
*Ch Bd: Steven Goldby
COO: Ronald L Midyett
CFO: Gregory S Skinner
VP: Steven P Bitler
VP: Larry D Hiebert
Board of Directors: Albert D Bolles, Frederick Frank, Tonia Pankopf, Catherine A Sohn, Gary T Steele, Robert Tobin

LANDERS MCLARTY CHEVROLET
See R M L HUNTSVILLE CHEVROLET LLC

D-U-N-S 11-973-2696
LANDESK SOFTWARE INC
SHAVLIK
698 W 10000 S Ste 500, South Jordan, UT 84095-4054
Tel (801) 208-1500 Founded/Ownrshp 2002
Sales 237.6MM[E] EMP 810[E]
SIC 7371 Computer software development & applications
Pr: Stephen M Daly
Pt: John White
*CFO: Mark McBride
*Chf Mktg O: Steve Morton
Ex VP: Josh Baxter
Ex VP: Tom Davis
VP: Michael W Hall
*VP: Matthew Smith
Dir Sec: Linda Gilliam
Rgnl Mgr: Ashley Chesley
Rgnl Mgr: Giuseppe Ferrari

LANDIS GYR
See LANDIS+GYR HOLDCO2 LLC

D-U-N-S 16-456-7484
LANDIS+GYR HOLDCO2 LLC
LANDIS GYR
(Suby of LANDIS & GYR HOLDINGS PTY LTD)
30000 Mill Creek Ave, Alpharetta, GA 30022-1584
Tel (678) 258-1500 Founded/Ownrshp 2004
Sales 104.5MM[E] EMP 375
Accts Deloitte & Touche Llp
SIC 7389 Meter readers, remote
CEO: Andreas Umbach
*COO: Jerry Figurilli
*COO: Richard Mora
*CFO: Jonathan Elmer
*CFO: John Lutz
*Ex VP: Roger Amhof
*Ex VP: Ellie Doyle
*Ex VP: Dieter Hecht
Ex VP: Chris Hickman
*Ex VP: Oliver Iltisberger
*Ex VP: Prasanna Venkatesan
*VP: Randolph Houchins

D-U-N-S 00-510-5408
LANDIS+GYR INC (GA)
LANDISGYR
(Suby of LANDIS+GYR AG)
30000 Mill Creek Ave, Alpharetta, GA 30022-1584
Tel (678) 258-1500 Founded/Ownrshp 2002
Sales 650.7MM[E] EMP 5,139
SIC 3825 Meters: electric, pocket, portable, panelboard, etc.; Measuring instruments & meters, electric; Demand meters, electric
CEO: Richard Mora
*CEO: Andreas Umbach
*CFO: Jonathan Elmer
VP: Tim Hilton
VP: Eric Seiter
*VP: Donald Shipley
VP: Prasanna Venkatesan
Prgrm Mgr: Charlie Estes
Area Mgr: Calvin Bargsley
Area Mgr: Randy Riley
Snr Sftwr: Cheng Zhu

LANDISGYR
See LANDIS+GYR INC

D-U-N-S 02-019-6890
LANDLOVERS LLC
LOANS 4 HOMES
1833 Executive Dr Ste 105, Oconomowoc, WI 53066-4841
Tel (262) 560-9786 Founded/Ownrshp 2001
Sales NA EMP 20
SIC 6163 Mortgage brokers arranging for loans, using money of others

D-U-N-S 01-411-5248
LANDMARK APARTMENT TRUST INC
4901 Dickens Rd Ste 101, Richmond, VA 23230-1952
Tel (804) 237-1335 Founded/Ownrshp 2005
Sales 262.2MM EMP 768[E]
SIC 6798 6513

LANDMARK AVIATION
See PIEDMONT HAWTHORNE AVIATION LLC

D-U-N-S 87-933-0330
LANDMARK BANK NATIONAL ASSOCIATION
(Suby of THE LANDRUM COMPANY INC)
801 E Broadway, Columbia, MO 65201-4855
Tel (573) 449-3911 Founded/Ownrshp 2009
Sales NA EMP 355
SIC 6021 National commercial banks
Pr: Jeffrey Maclellan
Treas: Kris Bloom
Chf Inves: Nicholas Thurwanger
Ofcr: Tennille Dorsey
Ofcr: Theresa Gehlken
Ofcr: Beth Moore
Ofcr: Joe Ritter
Ofcr: Kim Staton
Sr VP: Ron Bennett
Sr VP: Brenda Emerson
Sr VP: Susan Gowin
Sr VP: Sam Henry
Sr VP: Josh Herron
Sr VP: Cheryl Jarvis
Sr VP: Larry R Niedergerke
VP: Craig Bowser
VP: Cathy Eubank
VP: Laura Glass
VP: Jo Mooney
VP: David Mordy
VP: Aaron Quarles

D-U-N-S 06-833-8367 IMP
LANDMARK COMMUNITY NEWSPAPERS LLC
(Suby of LANDMARK MEDIA ENTERPRISES LLC) ★
601 Taylorsville Rd, Shelbyville, KY 40065-9125
Tel (502) 633-4334 Founded/Ownrshp 1973
Sales 221.6MM[E] EMP 1,280
SIC 2711 2759 Commercial printing & newspaper publishing combined; Commercial printing
Pr: Michael Abernathy
*VP: Dan Sykes
Dir IT: James Bryant
Dir IT: Danny Correll
Opers Mgr: Jay Bondurant

D-U-N-S 06-833-8359
LANDMARK COMMUNITY NEWSPAPERS OF KENTUCKY LLC (NM)
(Suby of LANDMARK COMMUNITY NEWSPAPERS LLC) ★
601 Taylorsville Rd, Shelbyville, KY 40065-9125
Tel (502) 633-4334 Founded/Ownrshp 1968, 2015
Sales 47.8MM[E] EMP 1,100
SIC 2711 2752 Commercial printing & newspaper publishing combined; Commercial printing, lithographic
Pr: Michael Abernathy
Board of Directors: John O Wynne

D-U-N-S 11-916-8722
LANDMARK CONSTRUCTION CO INC
3255 Industry Dr, North Charleston, SC 29418-8453
Tel (843) 552-6186 Founded/Ownrshp 1967
Sales 95.4MM[E] EMP 150
SIC 1542 1541 1623 1771 1794 Commercial & office building, new construction; Industrial buildings, new construction; Water, sewer & utility lines; Concrete work; Excavation work; Excavation & grading, building construction
Ch Bd: Ann B Mixson
*Pr: Cynthia Mixson
Treas: Cynthia M Eagerton
*VP: Fredrick B Mixson
Sls&Mrk Ex: Kristian Murphy

D-U-N-S 04-078-9380
LANDMARK CREDIT UNION
5445 S Westridge Dr, New Berlin, WI 53151-7948
Tel (262) 796-4500 Founded/Ownrshp 1933
Sales NA EMP 435
SIC 6062 State credit unions, not federally chartered
CEO: Jay Magulski
*Ch Bd: Michael Maxwell
*Pr: Ron Kase
Sr VP: Eric Kase
Sr VP: David Powers
VP: Donald Cohen
VP: Betty Feierstein
VP: Kyle Mather
VP: Sharon Mather
VP: Charles Schuyler
Brnch Mgr: Kristy Gray

D-U-N-S 80-258-1467
LANDMARK EVENT STAFFING SERVICES INC
4131 Harbor Walk Dr, Fort Collins, CO 80525-4855
Tel (714) 293-4248 Founded/Ownrshp 2006
Sales 14.1MM EMP 5,053
SIC 7381 7389 Security guard service;
Pr: Peter Kranske
*CEO: Michael Harrison

Dir Soc: Mike Serie
Brnch Mgr: Glen Freeman
Opers Mgr: Erik Rodrigues

D-U-N-S 82-935-7727
LANDMARK FBO LLC
SIGNATURE FLIGHT SUPPORT
(*Suby of* EXECUTIVE BEECHCRAFT) ★
1500 Citywest Blvd # 600, Houston, TX 77042-2280
Tel (713) 895-9243 *Founded/Ownrshp* 2016
Sales 513.7MM^E *EMP* 1,492^E
SIC 4581 Airports, flying fields & services
CEO: Daniel T Bucaro
Treas: Marlene Henry
VP: Skip Madsen
Genl Mgr: Richard Collins
Genl Mgr: Jeff Miller
Genl Mgr: Chris Paul
Genl Mgr: Brett Shade
Dir IT: David Armato
VP Opers: Tad Hamilton
Opers Mgr: Vernon McIntyre
Opers Mgr: Gonzalo Montoya

D-U-N-S 06-801-0586
LANDMARK FOOD CORP
LANDMARK FOODS
865 Waverly Ave, Holtsville, NY 11742-1109
Tel (631) 654-4500 *Founded/Ownrshp* 1973
Sales 87.3MM^E *EMP* 90
Accts Laurence Rothblatt & Company
SIC 5142 5141 5148 5147 Packaged frozen goods; Groceries, general line; Fruits, fresh; Meats & meat products
Ch Bd: Gordon Kerner
* *Sec:* Victor Cardinali Jr

LANDMARK FOODS
See LANDMARK FOOD CORP

D-U-N-S 06-722-1796
■ **LANDMARK GRAPHICS CORP**
(*Suby of* HALLIBURTON DELAWARE INC) ★
2107 Citywest Blvd Bldg 2, Houston, TX 77042-2827
Tel (713) 839-2000 *Founded/Ownrshp* 1996
Sales 125.1MM^E *EMP* 1,946
SIC 7371 7373 Software programming applications; Computer-aided design (CAD) systems service
VP: Jonathan Lewis
* *Pr:* Peter Bernard
* *Ex VP:* Al Escher
Ex VP: Beverly Stafford
* *VP:* Jeff Donnellan
* *VP:* Christian Garcia
* *VP:* Glenn Goodwin
VP: Paul Koeller
VP: Maggie Montaigne
* *VP:* William Trebinski
Exec: Brian Moloney
Board of Directors: David Lesar

D-U-N-S 10-582-7166
LANDMARK INDUSTRIES HOLDINGS LTD
TIMEWISE FOOD STORES
11111 S Wilcrest Dr, Houston, TX 77099-4310
Tel (713) 789-0310 *Founded/Ownrshp* 1983
Sales 121.9MM^E *EMP* 900
SIC 5411 5541 Convenience stores, independent; Filling stations, gasoline
Pt: Marshall Dujka
* *Pt:* J Kent Brotherton
* *Pt:* Robert E Duff
* *Pt:* Stephen C Dujka
Dist Mgr: Walter Graham
Dist Mgr: Tammika Pete
Dir IT: Lynn Venckus
IT Man: Nathan Wells
Mktg Dir: April Rocha
Mktg Mgr: Randy Krause
Sls Mgr: Stephen McQuarrie

D-U-N-S 82-853-8988
LANDMARK MEDIA ENTERPRISES LLC
150 Granby St, Norfolk, VA 23510-1604
Tel (757) 351-7000 *Founded/Ownrshp* 2008
Sales 800.0MM *EMP* 4,600
SIC 2711 5045 2721 6531 Newspapers, publishing & printing; Computer software; Periodicals; Real estate listing services
Ch Bd: Frank Batten Jr
* *Pr:* Jack J Ross
* *CFO:* Teresa F Blevins
* *Treas:* Colleen R Pittman
* *Ex VP:* Guy R Friddell III

LANDMARK MEDICAL CENTER
See PRIME HEALTHCARE SERVICES-LANDMARK LLC

D-U-N-S 07-572-6141
LANDMARK MEDICAL CENTER
115 Cass Ave, Woonsocket, RI 02895-4731
Tel (401) 769-4100 *Founded/Ownrshp* 1988
Sales 117.5MM *EMP* 1,200
SIC 8062

D-U-N-S 00-886-6840
LANDMARK SERVICES COOPERATIVE
1401 Landmark Dr, Cottage Grove, WI 53527-8984
Tel (608) 819-3115 *Founded/Ownrshp* 1933
Sales 418.1MM *EMP* 400
SIC 4221 5171 5191 1711 Grain elevator, storage only; Petroleum bulk stations; Feed; Seeds: field, garden & flower; Fertilizer & fertilizer materials; Plumbing, heating, air-conditioning contractors
CEO: Bob Carlson
* *Pr:* John Blaska
* *COO:* Mike Elder
* *Ex VP:* Doug Cropp
* *VP:* Junior Manthe
Mktg Mgr: Heather Benson

D-U-N-S 01-761-7171 IMP
LANDMARK STRUCTURES I LP
1665 Harmon Rd, Fort Worth, TX 76177-6522
Tel (817) 439-8888 *Founded/Ownrshp* 2000
Sales 88.2MM^E *EMP* 254
Accts Broder Pineider And Ford Llp
SIC 1791 7699 Storage tanks, metal: erection; Tank repair & cleaning services
Genl Pt: Doug Lamon
Pt: Chris Lamon
Pt: Eric Lamon
Pt: Jim Pitts
CIO: Tim Jobin
Tech Mgr: Michael Faubel
Sfty Dirs: Laurel Almeter

LANDMARK THEATRES
See SILVER CINEMAS ACQUISITION CO

D-U-N-S 03-133-1051 IMP/EXP
LANDOLL CORP
1900 North St, Marysville, KS 66508-1271
Tel (785) 562-5381 *Founded/Ownrshp* 1963
Sales 95.9MM^E *EMP* 460
SIC 3728 3715 3523 3537 Aircraft parts & equipment; Deicing equipment, aircraft; Truck trailers; Plows, agricultural: disc, moldboard, chisel, listers, etc.; Trailers & wagons, farm; Forklift trucks
Pr: Don Landoll
COO: Jeff Keating
* *Treas:* Dan Caffrey
Assoc VP: Melisa Treff
VP: John Schmidt
IT Man: Craig McCurdy
IT Man: Lynn Ranaball
IT Man: Lynn Ronnebaum
VP Mktg: Wayne Carroll
Mktg Dir: Shawn Rose
Mktg Mgr: Mike Irish

D-U-N-S 15-449-7846
LANDOR INTERNATIONAL INC
2120 Staples Mill Rd # 300, Richmond, VA 23230-2917
Tel (804) 346-8200 *Founded/Ownrshp* 1985
Sales 96.4MM^E *EMP* 345
SIC 6552 8741 4724 Subdividers & developers; Management services; Travel agencies
CEO: John L Holt III
* *Pr:* Ronald T Holt
COO: Virginia H Eyler
CFO: Bert Holt
VP: John Ruch
Software D: James Moncrieff

LANDROVER NORTHPOINT
See HENNESSY CADILLAC INC

D-U-N-S 82-546-7629
LANDRYS GAMING INC
(*Suby of* LANDRYS SEAFOOD HOUSE) ★
1510 West Loop S, Houston, TX 77027-9505
Tel (713) 850-1010 *Founded/Ownrshp* 1980
Sales 174.6MM^E *EMP* 3,500^E
SIC 7011 Casino hotel
Pr: Tilman J Fertitta
* *Treas:* Rick Liem

D-U-N-S 10-266-4935 IMP
LANDRYS INC
LANDRY'S SEAFOOD HOUSE
(*Suby of* FERTITTA GROUP INC) ★
1510 West Loop S, Houston, TX 77027-9505
Tel (713) 850-1010 *Founded/Ownrshp* 2010
Sales 2.0MMM^E *EMP* 30,000
SIC 5812 Eating places; Seafood restaurants
CEO: Tilman J Fertitta
Pr: Jeffrey L Cantwe
Pr: Wayne Stancil
* *CFO:* Richard H Liem
* *CFO:* Rick Lim
* *Ofcr:* K Kelly Roberts
* *Ex VP:* Steven L Scheinthal
* *Sr VP:* Jeffrey L Cantwell
Sr VP: Lori Kittle
VP: Nicki Keenan
VP: Joseph Leighy
VP: William Story
VP: Peter Wagle

LANDRY'S SEAFOOD HOUSE
See LANDRYS INC

D-U-N-S 02-519-7609
▲ **LANDS END INC**
1 Lands End Ln, Dodgeville, WI 53595-0001
Tel (608) 935-9341 *Founded/Ownrshp* 1963
Sales 1.4MMM *EMP* 6,000
Tkr Sym LE *Exch* NAS
SIC 5961 5611 5621

LANDSBERG ORORA
See ORORA PACKAGING SOLUTIONS

D-U-N-S 11-273-5840 IMP
LANDSCAPE DEVELOPMENT INC
28447 Witherspoon Pkwy, Valencia, CA 91355-4174
Tel (661) 295-1970 *Founded/Ownrshp* 1983
Sales 85.0MM^E *EMP* 500
SIC 0782 5039 Lawn & garden services; Landscape contractors; Soil erosion control fabrics
CEO: Gary Horton
* *CFO:* Jenny Lunde
* *CFO:* Tim Myers
* *VP:* Casper Correll
Off Mgr: Patrick Reinoso
IT Man: Bruce Pedersen
Sales Exec: Caroline De Biase
Snr PM: Glenn Austin

D-U-N-S 04-923-8363 IMP/EXP
LANDSCAPE FORMS INC
7800 E Michigan Ave, Kalamazoo, MI 49048-9506
Tel (269) 381-0396 *Founded/Ownrshp* 1969
Sales 98.8MM^E *EMP* 299
SIC 2531 2522 2511 2449 3648

D-U-N-S 13-989-7941
LANDSCAPE INNOVATIONS LLC
11101 Fairview 189, Eagle, ID 83616
Tel (208) 841-7666 *Founded/Ownrshp* 2002
Sales 90.0MM *EMP* 14
SIC 0781 Landscape counseling & planning

D-U-N-S 06-478-9787 IMP
LANDSCAPE STRUCTURES INC
601 7th St S, Delano, MN 55328-8605
Tel (763) 972-3391 *Founded/Ownrshp* 1971
Sales 1.0MMM *EMP* 230^E
SIC 3949 2531 Playground equipment; Picnic tables or benches, park
CEO: Steven King
* *Pr:* Pat Faust
CFO: Fred Caslavka
Bd of Dir: Charlie Thomas
Genl Mgr: Elaine Harkess
CIO: Sally Prinsen
IT Man: Matt Frank
IT Man: Harold Harris
IT Man: Amy J Madson
Sls Mgr: Mike Fingeroth
Sls Mgr: Steve Hare

D-U-N-S 08-021-9421
LANDSCAPES UNLIMITED LLC
1201 Aries Dr, Lincoln, NE 68512-9338
Tel (402) 423-6653 *Founded/Ownrshp* 1976
Sales 212.6MM^E *EMP* 500
SIC 1629 Golf course construction
COO: Alesia Schepers
CFO: Mike Surls
Treas: Myrna J Kubly
VP: Eric Heskje
VP: Matt Stotler
Exec: Myrna Kubly
Rgnl Mgr: Ty Arndt
Genl Mgr: Renae Feilmeier
Genl Mgr: Tim Halpine
Genl Mgr: Mark Ruhga
Dir IT: Brad Jurgensen

LANDSHIRE SANDWICHES
See TROVERCO INC

D-U-N-S 78-778-4487 EXP
■ **LANDSTAR GLOBAL LOGISTICS INC**
(*Suby of* LANDSTAR SYSTEM HOLDINGS INC) ★
13410 Sutton Park Dr S, Jacksonville, FL 32224-5270
Tel (904) 390-4751 *Founded/Ownrshp* 2005
Sales 122.1MM^E *EMP* 1,200
SIC 4731 Foreign freight forwarding
Pr: Patrick J O'Malley
* *CFO:* Kevin Stout
* *VP:* John J Collins
* *VP:* Michael K Kneller
* *VP:* Patrick J Murphy

D-U-N-S 00-877-8847 IMP
■ **LANDSTAR LIGON INC**
(*Suby of* LANDSTAR SYSTEM HOLDINGS INC) ★
13410 Sutton Park Dr S, Jacksonville, FL 32224-5270
Tel (904) 398-9400 *Founded/Ownrshp* 1982
Sales 126.5MM^E *EMP* 900
SIC 4213 Trucking, except local; Building materials transport; Contract haulers
CEO: Jim Gattoni
* *Pr:* Henry H Gerkens
Ex VP: Rachel Gupton
VP: Al Jordan
* *VP:* Larry Thomas
Exec: Patrick J Malley

D-U-N-S 19-466-0387
■ **LANDSTAR SYSTEM HOLDINGS INC**
(*Suby of* LANDSTAR SYSTEM INC) ★
13410 Sutton Park Dr S, Jacksonville, FL 32224-5270
Tel (904) 398-9400 *Founded/Ownrshp* 1988
Sales 616.4MM^E *EMP* 1,200
SIC 4213 Trucking, except local; Contract haulers; Building materials transport
Pr: Henry H Gerkens
* *Pr:* James B Gattoni
Ex VP: Robert Brasher
VP: Frank Albanese
* *VP:* Joe Beacom
QA Dir: Renee Nelson
QA Dir: Patricia Wong
Dir IT: John Bradley
Dir IT: Paula Deppe
IT Man: Michael Cashner
Opers Mgr: Jim Rigdon

D-U-N-S 62-386-4857
▲ **LANDSTAR SYSTEM INC**
13410 Sutton Park Dr S, Jacksonville, FL 32224-5270
Tel (904) 398-9400 *Founded/Ownrshp* 1968
Sales 3.3MMM *EMP* 1,223^E
Tkr Sym LSTR *Exch* NGS
SIC 4789 Cargo loading & unloading services
Pr: James B Gattoni
* *Ch Bd:* Diana M Murphy
COO: Joseph J Beacom
CFO: L Kevin Stout
Chf Mktg O: Patrick J O'Malley
VP: Mike Ebensteiner
VP: Michael K Kneller
VP: Kevin Stout
VP: Larry S Thomas
Netwrk Mgr: Bruce Wallace
Natl Sales: Mike Dean
Board of Directors: David G Bannister, Michael A Henning, Anthony J Orlando, Larry J Thoele

D-U-N-S 08-022-0906
LANDUS COOPERATIVE
2321 N Loop Dr Ste 220, Ames, IA 50010-8218
Tel (515) 817-2100 *Founded/Ownrshp* 1906
Sales 287.6MM^E *EMP* 703^E
SIC 5153 Grain elevators
CEO: Milan Kucerak

D-U-N-S 04-193-5875 IMP
LANE AUTOMOTIVE INC
MOTOR STATE DISTRIBUTING
8300 Lane Dr, Watervliet, MI 49098-9583
Tel (269) 463-4113 *Founded/Ownrshp* 1965
Sales 159.5MM^E *EMP* 200
SIC 5013 5531 Automotive supplies & parts; Speed shops, including race car supplies
Pr: George Lane
Pr: Dean Akins
Pr: Bill Hartman
Pr: Bryan Postelli
* *Treas:* David Lane
* *VP:* Doug Lane
Dir IT: Jerry Drake
Dir IT: Brad Picardat
Dir IT: Brian Robbins
Dir IT: Eddie Smith
IT Man: Dan Kirby

D-U-N-S 00-891-7668 IMP
■ **LANE BRYANT INC**
(*Suby of* CATHERINES) ★
3344 Morse Xing, Columbus, OH 43219-3092
Tel (614) 476-9281 *Founded/Ownrshp* 2001
Sales 1.1MMM^E *EMP* 9,000
SIC 5621 Ready-to-wear apparel, women's
CEO: Linda Heasley
* *Pr:* Lorna E Nagler
Sr VP: Elizabeth Crystal
VP: Luann Bett
VP: Shannon Gatti
VP: Nick Haffer
VP: Patti Mockler
VP: Rona Orbovich
VP: Theresa Sullivan
Creative D: Mike Teal
Dir Bus: Margie Hegg

D-U-N-S 13-120-3309
LANE CLEARWATER LIMITED PARTNERSHIP
LANE INDUSTRIES
1200 Shermer Rd, Northbrook, IL 60062-4500
Tel (847) 498-6650 *Founded/Ownrshp* 1985
Sales 100.0MM *EMP* 50
SIC 7011 Hotels

LANE COMPANY
See LANE SERVICES LLC

D-U-N-S 04-898-0288
LANE COMMUNITY COLLEGE
4000 E 30th Ave, Eugene, OR 97405-0640
Tel (541) 463-3000 *Founded/Ownrshp* 1964
Sales 52.6MM^E *EMP* 1,888
Accts Kenneth Kuhns & Co Salem Or
SIC 8222 Community college
Pr: Mary Spilde
Bd of Dir: Jay Lamb
Ofcr: Joan Aschim
VP: James Bailey
VP: Jackie Bryson
VP: Anna K Malliris
VP: Wendy Shaeffer
VP: Roxanne Watson
Exec: Dennis Carr
CIO: Bill Hughes
CIO: Bill Shoots

D-U-N-S 00-691-7504
LANE CONSTRUCTION CORP
(*Suby of* LANE INDUSTRIES INC) ★
90 Fieldstone Ct, Cheshire, CT 06410-1212
Tel (203) 235-3351 *Founded/Ownrshp* 1902
Sales 1.1MMM *EMP* 3,500
Accts Pricewaterhousecoopers Llp Ha
SIC 1622 1611 1629 3272 5032 Highway construction, elevated; Bridge construction; Airport runway construction; Subway construction; Dam construction; Power plant construction; Building materials, except block or brick: concrete; Paving materials
Pr: Robert E Alger
Pr: Thomas R Larson
* *CFO:* James M Ferrell
* *Treas:* Vincent J Caiola
* *Ex VP:* David F Benton
* *Ex VP:* Micheal M Cote
* *Ex VP:* Jay S Cruickshank
* *Ex VP:* Donald P Dobbs
* *Ex VP:* Kirk D Junco
VP: Farid Hamad
VP: Michael L Johnson
VP Bus Dev: Dennis Galligan
Dir Bus: George Hassfurter

LANE FURNITURE
See LFI WIND DOWN INC

LANE INDUSTRIES
See LANE CLEARWATER LIMITED PARTNERSHIP

D-U-N-S 10-125-8739
LANE INDUSTRIES INC
(*Suby of* SALINI IMPREGILO SPA)
90 Fieldstone Ct, Cheshire, CT 06410-1212
Tel (203) 235-3351 *Founded/Ownrshp* 2015
Sales 1.2MMM *EMP* 4,500
Accts Pricewaterhousecoopers Llp Ha
SIC 1629 1611 5032 3272 1622 Subway construction; Dam construction; Power plant construction; Airport runway construction; Paving materials; Building materials, except block or brick: concrete; Highway construction, elevated; Bridge construction
Pr: Robert Alger
Treas: Vincent Caiola
Ex VP: Mike Cote
Ex VP: Donald Dobbs
Ex VP: James Ferrell
Ex VP: Kirk Junco
VP: David Benton
VP: Jay Cruickshank

D-U-N-S 06-958-6006
LANE POWELL PC (OR)
1420 5th Ave Ste 4200, Seattle, WA 98101-2375
Tel (206) 223-7000 *Founded/Ownrshp* 1880
Sales 91.4MM *EMP* 420
Accts Moss Adams Llp Seattle Washi
SIC 8111 Legal services
Pr: Charles W Riley Jr
COO: Randy L Leitzke
* *VP:* Thomas W Sondag
Dir Bus: Sanjiv N Kripalani
Counsel: Michaela A Lbon
Counsel: Leigh D Stephenson-Kuhn

D-U-N-S 61-526-9045
LANE SERVICES LLC
LANE COMPANY
303 Perimeter Ctr N # 200, Atlanta, GA 30346-3402
Tel (678) 681-7200 *Founded/Ownrshp* 2005

Sales 39.8MM^E *EMP* 1,000
SIC 6512 Property operation, retail establishment
Genl Couns: Eric Hade

D-U-N-S 07-453-0320
LANE STEEL CO INC (PA)
4 River Rd Ste 2, Mc Kees Rocks, PA 15136-2810
Tel (412) 331-1400 *Founded/Ownrshp* 1982
Sales 89.3MM *EMP* 55
Accts Listwak Finke & Associates P
SIC 5051 Plates, metal
Ch: Al Gedeon
**Pr:* Paul D Gedeon
**VP:* Kathleen Gedeon
**VP:* Michael J Gedeon
**VP:* Richard H Zabrowski

LANG EXPLORATORY DRLG DL MAHER
See LONGYEAR CO

D-U-N-S 19-141-1016
LANGAN ENGINEERING AND ENVIRONMENTAL SERVICES INC
(*Suby of* LANGAN ENGINEERING ENVIRONMENTAL SURVEYING AND LANDSCAPE ARCHITECTURE DPC) ★
300 Kimball Dr, Parsippany, NJ 07054-2181
Tel (201) 794-6900 *Founded/Ownrshp* 2013
Sales 208.0MM^E *EMP* 550
SIC 8711 Consulting engineer
Ch Bd: Andrew J Ciancia
**Pr:* David T Gockel
**CFO:* William Kraekel
Ex VP: Richard Rodgers
Sr VP: Guy Archambault
Sr VP: Archabal Roger
Sr VP: Jeffrey Smith
Admn Mgr: George Kelley
Genl Mgr: Leonard Savino
CIO: Sameh Ishak
Netwrk Eng: Jon Desalvatore

D-U-N-S 07-870-3163
LANGAN ENGINEERING ENVIRONMENTAL SURVEYING AND LANDSCAPE ARCHITECTURE DPC (NY)
300 Kimball Dr Ste 4, Parsippany, NJ 07054-2184
Tel (973) 560-4900 *Founded/Ownrshp* 2012, 1970
Sales 208.0MM^E *EMP* 730^E
SIC 8711 8748 1389 0781 Engineering services; Environmental consultant; Testing, measuring, surveying & analysis services; Landscape architects
Ch Bd: Andrew J Ciancia
**Pr:* David T Gockel
**CFO:* William Kraekel
**Ex VP:* Richard D Rodgers
**Ex VP:* Philip G Smith
Prin: Nicholas De Rose
Prin: Rudolph P Frizzi
Prin: Ronald A Fuerst
Prin: George P Kelley
Prin: George E Leventis
Prin: John D Plante

D-U-N-S 00-330-0506 EXP
LANGDALE CO
1202 Madison Hwy, Valdosta, GA 31601-6033
Tel (229) 242-7450 *Founded/Ownrshp* 1894
Sales 108.5MM^E *EMP* 425^E
SIC 2421 2491 7011 7699 5031 5171 Sawmills & planing mills, general; Planing mills; Preserving (creosoting) of wood; Motels; Knife, saw & tool sharpening & repair; Lumber: rough, dressed & finished; Petroleum bulk stations & terminals
Pr: John W Langdale III
Ch Bd: Harley Langdale Jr
CFO: Gregory J Miller
Treas: Delores M Parrish
VP: Larry Fudge
VP: James Harley Langdale
VP: Chris Reid
VP: Donald K Warren
Genl Mgr: Ronnie Lightsey
Sls Mgr: Rick Sanders

D-U-N-S 08-718-3737 IMP/EXP
LANGER JUICE CO INC (CA)
L & A JUICE
16195 Stephens St, City of Industry, CA 91745-1718
Tel (626) 336-3100 *Founded/Ownrshp* 1957
Sales 155.3MM^E *EMP* 250
SIC 2037 Fruit juices
Pr: Nathan Langer
**Treas:* Bruce Langer
**VP:* David Langer
S&M/VP: Jenny San

D-U-N-S 62-243-7205
LANGFORD SERVICES INC
6480 State Road 60 E, Lake Wales, FL 33898-9721
Tel (863) 528-2242 *Founded/Ownrshp* 2006
Sales 200.0MM *EMP* 22
SIC 8999 Actuarial consultant
Pr: Robert Dean Langford
**VP:* Janet Langford

D-U-N-S 03-017-6028
LANGLADE HOSPITAL - HOTEL DIEU OF ST JOSEPH OF ANTIGO WISCONSIN (WI)
112 E 5th Ave, Antigo, WI 54409-2710
Tel (715) 623-2331 *Founded/Ownrshp* 1933
Sales 98.9MM *EMP* 800
Accts Wipfli Llp Wausau Wi
SIC 8062 General medical & surgical hospitals
CEO: David R Schneider
CFO: Pat Tincher
VP: Sarah Olafson
Sls&Mrk Ex: Betsy Kommers
Mktg Dir: Betsy Kommerf
Pathlgst: Tracy Cousins

D-U-N-S 17-000-9687
LANGUAGE LINE HOLDINGS INC
1 Lower Ragsdale Dr # 2, Monterey, CA 93940-5747
Tel (831) 648-5800 *Founded/Ownrshp* 2004
Sales 76.1MM^E *EMP* 1,000^E
SIC 7389 Translation services
CEO: Dennis Dracup
**CFO:* Matthew Gibbs

D-U-N-S 84-268-2999
LANIER PARKING HOLDINGS INC
LANIER PARKING SOLUTIONS
233 Peachtree St Ne # 2600, Atlanta, GA 30303-1510
Tel (404) 881-6076 *Founded/Ownrshp* 1989
Sales 84.3MM *EMP* 2,000
Accts Habif Arogeti And Wynne Llp A
SIC 7521 Automobile parking
CEO: Jerry Skillett
**Pr:* Bijan Eghtedari
**COO:* Richard C Graham
CFO: Brian Dubay
**CFO:* David A Klarman
**CFO:* Karen Quinn
**Ex VP:* Micheal Brown
**Ex VP:* Scott Diggs
Ex VP: Glenn Kirtz
Ex VP: Glenn Kurtz
VP: Bret Almassy
VP: James Commers
VP: Andrea Gappell

LANIER PARKING SOLUTIONS
See LANIER PARKING HOLDINGS INC

D-U-N-S 15-063-4004 IMP
LANIER WORLDWIDE INC
(*Suby of* RICOH USA INC) ★
4667 N Royal Atlanta Dr, Tucker, GA 30084-3802
Tel (770) 493-2100 *Founded/Ownrshp* 2011
Sales 1.2MMM^E *EMP* 7,350
Accts Kpmg Llp
SIC 5044 5999 7359 7629 Office equipment; Telephone & communication equipment; Business machine & electronic equipment rental services; Business machine repair, electric
Pr: Nori Goto
VP: Tony Eugene Amason
**VP:* Randy Humphrey
VP: Masayoshi Ikeda
VP: Steven McBrayer
**VP:* Mark Miller
VP: Bradford L Nelson
**VP:* Paul Nix
**VP:* Barry Ward
Dist Mgr: Shaun Prendergast
Info Man: Jan Prior
Board of Directors: Y Mizutani, K Yoshida

LANKFORD - SYSCO FOOD SERVICES
See SYSCO EASTERN MARYLAND LLC

LANL FOUNDATION
See LOS ALAMOS NATIONAL LABORATORY FOUNDATION

D-U-N-S 00-227-7481
▲ LANNETT CO INC
9000 State Rd, Philadelphia, PA 19136-1615
Tel (215) 333-9000 *Founded/Ownrshp* 1942
Sales 542.4MM *EMP* 502^E
Tkr Sym LCI *Exch* NYS
SIC 2834 Pharmaceutical preparations
CEO: Arthur P Bedrosian
**Ch Bd:* Jeffrey Farber
CFO: Martin P Galvan
Chf Cred: Kristie Stephens
VP: John M ABT
VP: Mahendra Dedhiya
VP: Robert Ehlinger
VP: John Kozlowski
Dir Lab: Helen Libman
VP Sls: Kevin R Smith
Board of Directors: David Drabik, James M Maher, Albert Paonessa III, Paul Taveira

D-U-N-S 09-369-2408 IMP/EXP
■ LANOGA CORP
UNITED BUILDING CENTERS
(*Suby of* PROBUILD HOLDINGS LLC) ★
17946 Ne 65th St, Redmond, WA 98052-4963
Tel (425) 883-4125 *Founded/Ownrshp* 2006
Sales 432.8MM^E *EMP* 5,600
SIC 5211 5031

D-U-N-S 04-127-4325
LANPHERE ENTERPRISES INC
BEAVERTON HONDA
12505 Sw Brdwy St, Beaverton, OR 97005
Tel (503) 643-5577 *Founded/Ownrshp* 1964
Sales 307.8MM^E *EMP* 675
SIC 5571 5511 5261 Motorcycle dealers; Automobiles, new & used; Lawn & garden equipment
Ch Bd: Robert D Lanphere Sr
**Pr:* Robert D Lanphere Jr
**CFO:* Robb Walther
**Sec:* Sharon Lenz
Bd of Dir: Sabra Burge
Dir Bus: Bill Stallard
**Prin:* Pat Blanchat
**Prin:* Ryan Malone
Genl Mgr: Dave Jachter
IT Man: Greg Miller
Sfty Dirs: Debbie Lanphere

D-U-N-S 02-083-5245
LANSE CREUSE PUBLIC SCHOOLS
24076 Frdrick Pankow Blvd, Clinton Township, MI 48036
Tel (586) 783-6300 *Founded/Ownrshp* 1954
Sales 52.1MM^E *EMP* 1,200
Accts Plante & Moran Pllc Clinton
SIC 8211 Public elementary & secondary schools; High school, junior or senior; Vocational high school
Pr Dir: Kelly Allen
Schl Brd P: Linda McLatcher

D-U-N-S 00-313-6587 IMP
LANSING BUILDING PRODUCTS INC (VA)
8501 Sanford Dr, Richmond, VA 23228-2812
Tel (804) 266-8893 *Founded/Ownrshp* 1957
Sales 374.9MM^E *EMP* 750
SIC 5033 5031 5032 Roofing & siding materials; Windows; Brick, stone & related material
Pr: Hunter Lansing
Pr: Steve Mosby
CFO: Mason Chapman
Ex VP: John Witt
Sr VP: Kevin Kuchem
VP: Kevin Kruchem
VP: Ted Lansing
VP: Lynn Whyte
VP: Jeff Wietholter
Rgnl Mgr: John Martin
Brnch Mgr: Jason Abbott
Board of Directors: W B Douglass III

D-U-N-S 07-633-6882
LANSING COMMUNITY COLLEGE
610 N Capitol Ave, Lansing, MI 48933-1212
Tel (517) 483-1957 *Founded/Ownrshp* 1957
Sales 41.5MM *EMP* 2,500
Accts Rehmann Robson Llc Jackson
SIC 8222 Community college
CEO: Brent Knight
**CFO:* Catherine Fisher
Assoc VP: Elva Revilla
Ex VP: Gary Vankempen
Sr VP: Lisa W Sharpe
Ex Dir: Deborah Cole
Dir IT: Jonathan Deforest
Dir IT: Karl Dietrich
Dir IT: Gary Heisler
Dir IT: Randy Jobksi
Dir IT: Jonathan Kavanagh

D-U-N-S 61-094-3115 IMP
LANSING L MPT L C
MAGNA POWERTRAIN LANSING
(*Suby of* MAGNA POWERTRAIN TROY) ★
3140 Spanish Oak Dr Ste A, Lansing, MI 48911-4291
Tel (517) 316-1013 *Founded/Ownrshp* 2005
Sales 205.9MM^E *EMP* 140
SIC 3714 Motor vehicle engines & parts
Mtls Mgr: Heather Bickford

D-U-N-S 06-132-0255
LANSING MALL LIMITED PARTNERSHIP
(*Suby of* ROUSE PROPERTIES LLC) ★
5330 W Saginaw Hwy, Lansing, MI 48917-6207
Tel (517) 321-0145 *Founded/Ownrshp* 2012
Sales 175.2MM^E *EMP* 1,450
SIC 6512 7311 Shopping center, property operation only; Advertising agencies
CEO: Ric Clark
**Ch Bd:* Matthew Bucksbaum
**Pr:* Robert A Michaels
**CFO:* Bernard Freibaum
VP: Linda White
**Prin:* John Bucksbaum

LANSING MANOR APARTMENTS
See SENIOR RELATED WORLD LLC

D-U-N-S 00-896-4884 IMP
■ LANSING MPS INC (MI)
(*Suby of* JOHN HENRY HOLDINGS INC) ★
5800 W Grand River Ave, Lansing, MI 48906-9111
Tel (517) 323-9000 *Founded/Ownrshp* 1946, 2004
Sales 237.2MM^E *EMP* 1,800
SIC 2759 2731 2761 3089 2671 Commercial printing; Screen printing; Letterpress printing; Tags: printing; Books: publishing & printing; Continuous forms, office & business; Identification cards, plastic; Packaging paper & plastics film, coated & laminated
CEO: Marc Shore
**Pr:* Dennis Kaltman
**Treas:* Greg Bomers
MIS Dir: Jane Schaffer
Dir IT: Frank Golupski
VP Mktg: Erin Willigan
Mktg Dir: Brenda Vaughn

D-U-N-S 07-637-3687
LANSING SCHOOL DISTRICT
519 W Kalamazoo St, Lansing, MI 48933-2080
Tel (517) 755-1000 *Founded/Ownrshp* 1847
Sales 81.3MM^E *EMP* 2,000
Accts Maner Costerisan & Ellis Pc
SIC 8211 Public elementary & secondary schools
VP: Steve Maiville
Opers Supe: Jeff Vanderlaan

D-U-N-S 01-719-5611 IMP/EXP
LANSING TRADE GROUP LLC
10975 Benson Dr Ste 400, Overland Park, KS 66210-2137
Tel (913) 748-3000 *Founded/Ownrshp* 2006
Sales 3.1MMM^E *EMP* 400
SIC 5153 6221 Grains; Commodity contracts brokers, dealers
CEO: William E Krueger
**COO:* Mark Odonnell
CFO: Mark O'Donnell
Ex VP: Tom Carew
Ex VP: Tom Irmen
**Ex VP:* Scott Mills
VP: Weston Heide
VP: Mike Lemke
VP: Dwight Pflipsen
VP: Eric Watts
Dir Bus: Scott Wernimont

LANTECH LOGISTICS
See LANCO INTERNATIONAL INC

D-U-N-S 05-759-4749 IMP/EXP
LANTECH.COM LLC
11000 Bluegrass Pkwy, Louisville, KY 40299-2399
Tel (502) 267-4200 *Founded/Ownrshp* 1971
Sales 103.3MM *EMP* 390
Accts Crowe Horwath Llp Louisville
SIC 3565 Packaging machinery
Sr VP: Allison Myers
VP: Chris Kist
Exec: Cathy Taylor
QA Dir: Rusty Cuyler
Opers Mgr: Annette Noel
Sales Exec: Jim Lancaster
Natl Sales: Neil Bennett
Natl Sales: Mike Castelli
Mktg Dir: Paul Stewart
Mktg Mgr: Robert Habermehl
Mktg Mgr: Alden Swartz

D-U-N-S 07-854-0805
▲ LANTHEUS HOLDINGS INC
331 Treble Cove Rd, North Billerica, MA 01862-2849
Tel (978) 671-8001 *Founded/Ownrshp* 1956
Sales 293.4MM *EMP* 474^E
Accts Deloitte & Touche Llp Boston
Tkr Sym LNTH *Exch* NGM
SIC 2835 2834 In vitro & in vivo diagnostic substances; Pharmaceutical preparations
Pr: Mary Anne Heino
CFO: John Bakewell
CFO: Jack Crowley
Chf Mktg O: Cesare Orlandi
VP: Michael Duffy

D-U-N-S 17-678-6812 IMP
LANTHEUS MEDICAL IMAGING INC
(*Suby of* LANTHEUS MI INTERMEDIATE INC) ★
331 Treble Cove Rd, North Billerica, MA 01862-2849
Tel (978) 671-8001 *Founded/Ownrshp* 2008
Sales 123.6MM^E *EMP* 519^E
SIC 3841 2834 Diagnostic apparatus, medical; Pharmaceutical preparations
Pr: Jeffrey Bailey
Pr: Peter Card
COO: Mary Anne Heino
CFO: John K Bakewell
Chf Mktg O: Cesare Orlandi
VP: Michael Duffy
VP: Bob Gaffey
VP: Cyrille Villeneuve
Assoc Dir: Sunil Anklekar
Assoc Dir: Tracy Foucault
Assoc Dir: Meara Murphy
Assoc Dir: John Singelais
Assoc Dir: Robyn Strassel
Assoc Dir: MB Whittington
Board of Directors: David Burgstahler, Samuel Leno, Brian Markison, Patrick O'niell

D-U-N-S 07-959-5362
LANTHEUS MI INTERMEDIATE INC
331 Treble Cove Rd, North Billerica, MA 01862-2849
Tel (978) 671-8001 *Founded/Ownrshp* 2007
Sales 301.6MM *EMP* 519^E
SIC 3841 2834 Diagnostic apparatus, medical; Pharmaceutical preparations
Pr: Jeffrey Bailey
CFO: John K Bakewell

D-U-N-S 10-910-2376
LANTIS ENTERPRISES INC
4755 E Colorado Blvd, Spearfish, SD 57783-9405
Tel (605) 642-7736 *Founded/Ownrshp* 1990
Sales 89.6MM^E *EMP* 2,500
SIC 8051 8052 Skilled nursing care facilities; Intermediate care facilities
CEO: Travis Lantis
**Pr:* Will Lantis
**Sec:* Mary Ellen Lantis
**Ex Dir:* Lynne Follmer
CTO: Greg Rinard

D-U-N-S 03-654-1787 IMP
LANTMANNEN UNIBAKE USA INC
(*Suby of* LANTMANNEN UNIBAKE HOLDING A/S)
5007 Lincoln Ave Ste 300, Lisle, IL 60532-4187
Tel (630) 963-4781 *Founded/Ownrshp* 1993
Sales 192.0MM^E *EMP* 360
SIC 5142 Bakery products, frozen
Comm Man: Mira Perander
Genl Mgr: Giulio Anceschi
Genl Mgr: Greg Harnwell
Natl Sales: Monia Parker
Mktg Mgr: Susan Koss

D-U-N-S 14-585-8770 IMP/EXP
LANXESS CORP
(*Suby of* LANXESS DEUTSCHLAND GMBH)
111 Parkwest Dr, Pittsburgh, PA 15275-1112
Tel (800) 526-9377 *Founded/Ownrshp* 2004
Sales 846.5MM^E *EMP* 1,620
SIC 2869 2821 2822 2816 2819 Industrial organic chemicals; Amines, acids, salts, esters; Aldehydes & ketones; Plastics materials & resins; Plasticizer/additive based plastic materials; Synthetic rubber; Butadiene rubbers; Inorganic pigments; Industrial inorganic chemicals
Pr: Flemming B Bjoernslev
CFO: Ray Newhouse
Ofcr: Judith Trautman
Top Exec: Ralph Gierga
Top Exec: James Kok
VP: Christof Krogmann
VP: Wolfgang Oehlert
Exec: Asmita Bhalla
Exec: Erin Bunda
Exec: Martin Bury
Exec: Shilpi Nemlekar
Comm Man: Philippe Van Wassenhove

D-U-N-S 60-855-6809 IMP/EXP
LANXESS SYBRON CHEMICALS INC
(*Suby of* LANXESS CORP) ★
200 Birmingham Rd, Birmingham, NJ 08011
Tel (609) 893-1100 *Founded/Ownrshp* 2000
Sales 131.0MM^E *EMP* 913
SIC 2843 2899 3589 Surface active agents; Textile processing assistants; Water treating compounds; Water filters & softeners, household type
Pr: Markus Linke

D-U-N-S 08-895-1939
LANYON SOLUTIONS INC
RESERVEAMERICA
717 N Harwood St Ste 2200, Dallas, TX 75201-6515
Tel (817) 226-5656 *Founded/Ownrshp* 2013
Sales 100.0MM *EMP* 850
SIC 5734 Software, business & non-game
CEO: David Bonnette
**CFO:* John Mills
Ofcr: Matt Ehrlichman
Ex VP: Kevin Biggs
Sr VP: Kourosh Vossoughi
VP: Kristin Carroll
VP: Andy George
Exec: Elisa Cheng
Snr Sftwr: Bridget Oflaherty

QA Dir: Todd Jansky
Web Dev: Alan Tree

LAPEER REGION MEDICAL CENTER
See MCLAREN LAPEER REGION

D-U-N-S 82-868-9617
LAPEER REGIONAL MEDICAL CENTER
(*Suby of* MCLAREN HEALTH CARE CORP) ★
1375 N Main St, Lapeer, MI 48446-1350
Tel (810) 667-5500 *Founded/Ownrshp* 2013
Sales 121.7MM *EMP* 800
SIC 8062 General medical & surgical hospitals
Pr: Philip Incarnati
**COO:* Michael Taylor
CFO: Mary Beth
**CFO:* Dave Mazurkiewicz
**Ex VP:* Michael McKenna
**Sr VP:* Gregory Lane
**Prin:* Barton Buxton

D-U-N-S 00-693-0986 IMP
LAPHAM-HICKEY STEEL CORP (IL)
5500 W 73rd St, Chicago, IL 60638-6587
Tel (708) 496-6111 *Founded/Ownrshp* 1926, 1956
Sales 252.3MM^E *EMP* 450
SIC 5051 3398 3355 3317 3316 Bars, metal; Strip, metal; Tubing, metal; Metal heat treating; Aluminum rolling & drawing; Steel pipe & tubes; Cold finishing of steel shapes
Pr: William M Hickey Jr
**CFO:* Bob Piland
Ex VP: Steve Ford
VP: Jeff Hobson
VP: Rick Oconnell
**Prin:* Bill Hickey
Brnch Mgr: Mike Dedic
CIO: Marylou Olsen
Dir IT: Christine Colon
IT Man: Robert Carlisle
IT Man: Mandy O'Brien

D-U-N-S 96-412-7398
LAPORTE HOSPITAL INC
Tunnel 7 Lincoln Way, La Porte, IN 46350
Tel (219) 326-2305 *Founded/Ownrshp* 2010
Sales 155.8MM *EMP* 39^E
SIC 8062 General medical & surgical hospitals
Prin: Sarah Evans Barker

D-U-N-S 94-801-2596 IMP
LAPP HOLDING NA INC
(*Suby of* LAPP BETEILIGUNGS-KG)
29 Hanover Rd, Florham Park, NJ 07932-1408
Tel (973) 660-9700 *Founded/Ownrshp* 1988
Sales 150.1MM^E *EMP* 199^E
SIC 3355 Aluminum wire & cable
Pr: Marc Mackin
Ex VP: Tom McPherson

D-U-N-S 08-298-3172 IMP
LAPP USA LLC
(*Suby of* LAPP HOLDING NA INC) ★
29 Hanover Rd, Florham Park, NJ 07932-1408
Tel (973) 660-9700 *Founded/Ownrshp* 1976
Sales 126.2MM^E *EMP* 132
SIC 5063 3678 Control & signal wire & cable, including coaxial; Electronic connectors
Pr: Andreas Lapp
**COO:* Marc K Mackin
Ex VP: Thomas Barmann
**Ex VP:* Rob Conway
Ex VP: Geoff Grace
Ex VP: David Solano
**VP:* George Dann
VP: Marybeth Marx
VP: Randy Sadler
CTO: Jay Cordero
CTO: Keith Myrick

LAR LU
See WINCRAFT INC

D-U-N-S 07-576-2971
LARAMIE COUNTY SCHOOL DISTRICT 1
2810 House Ave, Cheyenne, WY 82001-2860
Tel (307) 771-2100 *Founded/Ownrshp* 1890
Sales 245.9MM *EMP* 1,600
Accts Mcgee Hearne & Paiz Llp Che
SIC 8211 Private elementary & secondary schools
CEO: Mark Stock
Bd of Dir: Alfred Atkins
Bd of Dir: Anne Beckle

D-U-N-S 05-757-0640
LAREDO INDEPENDENT SCHOOL DISTRICT EDUCATIONAL FOUNDATION
LAREDO ISD
1702 Houston St, Laredo, TX 78040-4906
Tel (956) 795-3200 *Founded/Ownrshp* 1946
Sales 194.7MM^E *EMP* 3,701
Accts Weaver And Tidwell Llp Housto
SIC 8211 Public elementary & secondary schools
**CFO:* Flor Ayala
**CFO:* Alvaro Perez
Ex Dir: David Garza
Off Mgr: Avelina Rodriguez
Dir IT: Elizabeth Garcia

LAREDO ISD
See LAREDO INDEPENDENT SCHOOL DISTRICT EDUCATIONAL FOUNDATION

D-U-N-S 05-511-6214 IMP
■ LAREDO MEDICAL CENTER
(*Suby of* COMMUNITY HEALTH SYSTEMS INC) ★
1700 E Saunders St, Laredo, TX 78041-5474
Tel (956) 796-5000 *Founded/Ownrshp* 2003
Sales 309.5MM *EMP* 1,600
SIC 8062 General medical & surgical hospitals
CEO: Aaron Hazard
**Pr:* Abraham Martinez
**COO:* John Ulbricht
**CFO:* Ed Romero
Dir Risk M: Veronica Gonzalez
Dir Lab: Edna Solis
Dir Rad: David Claudio
Dir Rx: Elizabeth Kaczmarek
Mtls Dir: Gloria Pineda
Ansthlgy: Luis R Ramos

D-U-N-S 07-833-0012
▲ LAREDO PETROLEUM INC
15 W 6th St Ste 1800, Tulsa, OK 74119-5412
Tel (918) 513-4570 *Founded/Ownrshp* 2006
Sales 606.6MM *EMP* 340^E
Tkr Sym LPI *Exch* NYS
SIC 1311 Crude petroleum & natural gas production
Ch Bd: Randy A Foutch
CFO: Richard C Buterbaugh
Sr VP: Kenneth E Dornblaser
Sr VP: Daniel C Schooley
VP: Michael T Beyer
Exec: Patrick J Curth
Mktg Mgr: Ben Klein
Board of Directors: Peter R Kagan, James R Levy, B Z Parker, Pamela S Pierce, Francis Rooney, Myles W Scoggins, Edmund P Segner III, Donald D Wolf

D-U-N-S 80-583-1901
■ LAREDO REGIONAL MEDICAL CENTER L P
DOCTORS HOSPITAL OF LAREDO
(*Suby of* UNIVERSAL HEALTH SERVICES INC) ★
1700 E Saunders St, Laredo, TX 78041-5474
Tel (956) 796-5000 *Founded/Ownrshp* 1999
Sales 149.0MM *EMP* 300
SIC 8062 8071 General medical & surgical hospitals; Medical laboratories
Pt: Rene Lopez
Genl Pt: Alan B Miller
Pt: Marc Miller
Dir Teleco: Maribel Mata

LAREDO WATERWORKS SYSTEM
See CITY OF LAREDO

D-U-N-S 61-361-9782
LARGO CONCRETE INC
2741 Walnut Ave Ste 110, Tustin, CA 92780-7040
Tel (714) 731-3600 *Founded/Ownrshp* 1989
Sales 93.6MM^E *EMP* 500
SIC 1771

LARGO MED CTR
See LARGO MEDICAL CENTER INC

D-U-N-S 60-991-6762 IMP
■ LARGO MEDICAL CENTER INC
LARGO MED CTR
(*Suby of* HOSPITAL COPORATION OF AMERICA) ★
201 14th St Sw, Largo, FL 33770-3199
Tel (727) 588-5200 *Founded/Ownrshp* 1984
Sales 224.4MM^E *EMP* 755^E
SIC 8062 General medical & surgical hospitals
CEO: Anthony Degina
**Pr:* Richard H Satcher
**CFO:* Robert Billings
**Treas:* Vicky A Chiszar
IT Man: Joe Parise
Mktg Mgr: Holly Borota
Ansthlgy: Jonathan W Dunn
Ansthlgy: Karen Lalonde
Ansthlgy: Lucas Nourse
Doctor: Paul Steele
Diag Rad: Cuong Nguyen

D-U-N-S 05-515-1166 IMP
■ LARIAT SERVICES INC
CHAPPARAL DRILLING FLUIDS
(*Suby of* SANDRIDGE ENERGY INC) ★
123 Robert S Kerr Ave, Oklahoma City, OK 73102-6406
Tel (405) 753-5500 *Founded/Ownrshp* 2010
Sales 307.6MM^E *EMP* 888^E
SIC 1382 Oil & gas exploration services
Opers Mgr: Eldon Burns
Opers Mgr: Neil Kincade

D-U-N-S 07-608-9622
LARKIN COMMUNITY HOSPITAL INC
7031 Sw 62nd Ave, South Miami, FL 33143-4701
Tel (305) 757-5707 *Founded/Ownrshp* 1997
Sales 101.5MM *EMP* 1,225^E
SIC 8062 General medical & surgical hospitals
Pr: Jack Michel
CFO: Estephany Giraldo

D-U-N-S 80-810-7242
LARON PHARMA INC
500 Office Center Dr # 400, Fort Washington, PA 19034-3219
Tel (267) 575-1470 *Founded/Ownrshp* 2006
Sales 300.0MM *EMP* 15
SIC 2834 5122 Pharmaceutical preparations; Pharmaceuticals
CEO: Afoluso Adesanya
**Pr:* Adenekan H Adesanya

D-U-N-S 01-765-2074
LAROSAS INC
2334 Boudinot Ave, Cincinnati, OH 45238-3492
Tel (513) 347-5660 *Founded/Ownrshp* 1954
Sales 76.0MM^E *EMP* 1,500
SIC 5812 6794 5141 5921 Pizzeria, chain; Franchises, selling or licensing; Groceries, general line; Wine
**CFO:* Michael J Selker
**Ch:* Donald S Larosa
**Treas:* Joanne Larosa
Treas: Joanne L Rosa
**Sec:* Mark Larosa
Exec: Pete Buscani
Mktg Mgr: Beth Reupert
Sls Mgr: Gary Galloway

D-U-N-S 18-160-0016 IMP
LARROC INC
6420 Boeing Dr, El Paso, TX 79925-1007
Tel (915) 772-3733 *Founded/Ownrshp* 1987
Sales 148.1MM *EMP* 25
Accts Lauterbach Borschow & Company
SIC 5141 5149 Groceries, general line; Groceries & related products
Owner: Enrique Munoz
**Prin:* Olga Munoz

D-U-N-S 08-015-9438
LARRY H MILLER GROUP OF COMPANIES
LHM GROUP
9350 S 150 E Ste 1000, Sandy, UT 84070-2721
Tel (801) 563-4100 *Founded/Ownrshp* 1979, 2013
Sales 841.4MM^E *EMP* 2,000
SIC 8741 Business management
CEO: Clark Whitworth
Ex VP: Jay Francis
Ex VP: Steve Starks
Mktg Mgr: Doug Petersen
Mktg Mgr: Jon Sullivan
Sls Mgr: Dave Whitmer

D-U-N-S 82-946-0117
LARRY H MILLER THEATRES INC
MEGAPLEX
(*Suby of* LHM GROUP) ★
35 E 9270 S, Sandy, UT 84070-2660
Tel (801) 304-4500 *Founded/Ownrshp* 1998
Sales 29.9MM^E *EMP* 1,100
SIC 7832 Motion picture theaters, except drive-in
CFO: Steve Tarbet

D-U-N-S 16-069-1288
LARSEN & TOUBRO INFOTECH LIMITED
(*Suby of* LARSEN AND TOUBRO LIMITED)
2035 State Route 27 # 3000, Edison, NJ 08817-3351
Tel (732) 248-6111 *Founded/Ownrshp* 1997
Sales 478.6MM *EMP* 20,000
Accts Ramesh Sarva Cpa Pc For
SIC 7379 Computer related consulting services
CEO: Sanjay Jalona
**CFO:* Ashok Sonthalia
**Ex VP:* Sunil Pande
VP: Harsh Naidu
Ex Dir: Shankar Raman

D-U-N-S 02-330-8141
LARSEN COOPERATIVE CO
8290 County Hwy T, Larsen, WI 54947-9701
Tel (920) 982-1111 *Founded/Ownrshp* 1919
Sales 179.5MM *EMP* 150
SIC 5191 5172 5541

D-U-N-S 05-175-3546
LARSON GROUP
TLG
3026 N Mulroy Rd, Strafford, MO 65757-7213
Tel (417) 865-5355 *Founded/Ownrshp* 2000
Sales 359.7MM *EMP* 64^E
Accts Roberts Mckenzie Mangan & Cu
SIC 3713 Truck & bus bodies
Prin: Glenn Larson
VP: Don Porthan
VP: Mike Thurston
Off Mgr: Kathy Griffith
Off Mgr: Carrie Walsh
Sls Dir: Roger Sherwood

D-U-N-S 80-795-0613 IMP
LARSON MANUFACTURING CO INC
(*Suby of* LARSON MANUFACTURING CO OF SOUTH DAKOTA INC) ★
2333 Eastbrook Dr, Brookings, SD 57006-2899
Tel (605) 692-6115 *Founded/Ownrshp* 1954
Sales 99.2MM^E *EMP* 240
SIC 5031 Doors & windows; Windows
Pr: Dale Larson
Pr: Bill Retterath
**Sec:* Craig H Johnson
VP: Dan Beinhorn
Ex Dir: Maree Larson
Genl Mgr: Daren Meints
MIS Dir: Ted Weinrich
Sfty Dirs: Scott Hegdahl
Sfty Mgr: Joel Osbeck
Plnt Mgr: Steven Wagner
VP Sls: Todd Stratmoen

D-U-N-S 00-622-6237
LARSON MANUFACTURING CO OF SOUTH DAKOTA INC
2333 Eastbrook Dr, Brookings, SD 57006-2899
Tel (605) 692-6115 *Founded/Ownrshp* 1964
Sales 173.7MM^E *EMP* 1,000
SIC 3442 Metal doors, sash & trim; Metal doors; Screen & storm doors & windows
Pr: Dale Larson
Treas: Maree Larson

D-U-N-S 00-617-2589 IMP/EXP
■ LARSON-JUHL US LLC (GA)
(*Suby of* ALBECCA INC) ★
3900 Steve Reynolds Blvd, Norcross, GA 30093-3090
Tel (770) 279-5200 *Founded/Ownrshp* 1893, 2002
Sales 111.0MM *EMP* 1,172
SIC 2499 3499 2431 Picture frame molding, finished; Picture frames, metal; Millwork
CEO: Drew P Van Pelt
Pr: Mark Marschke
VP: Lynn Duncan
VP: Brad Laporte
Genl Mgr: Damien Howard
Genl Mgr: Mark Nichols
Genl Mgr: Paul Noble
QA Dir: Bertha Ray
Dir IT: Mike Trammel
Opers Supe: Kevin Roman
Opers Mgr: Nick Budzilovich

D-U-N-S 11-416-5694
■ LAS CRUCES MEDICAL CENTER LLC
MOUNTAINVIEW REGIONAL MED CTR
(*Suby of* COMMUNITY HEALTH SYSTEMS INC) ★
4311 E Lohman Ave, Las Cruces, NM 88011-8255
Tel (575) 556-7600 *Founded/Ownrshp* 2007
Sales 98.6MM^E *EMP* 700
SIC 8062 General medical & surgical hospitals
CFO: Gene Alexander
Prin: Denten Park
Adm Dir: Jennifer Jimenez
Surgeon: Edward Sweetser

LAS CRUCES PUBLIC RELATIONS OF
See LAS CRUCES PUBLIC SCHOOLS

D-U-N-S 09-413-8740
LAS CRUCES PUBLIC SCHOOLS
LAS CRUCES PUBLIC RELATIONS OF
505 S Main St Ste 249, Las Cruces, NM 88001-1243
Tel (575) 527-5893 *Founded/Ownrshp* 1938
Sales 172.3MM^E *EMP* 3,100
Accts Moss Adams Llp Albuquerque N
SIC 8211 Public elementary & secondary schools; Public elementary school; Public junior high school; Public senior high school
Prin: Irene Gomez
Genl Mgr: Dorothy Irion
MIS Dir: Terry Stuart
Pr Dir: Jo Galvan-Nash
Teacher Pr: Elizabeth Marrufo
Teacher Pr: Tracy O'Hara
HC Dir: Sandy Peugh

D-U-N-S 07-901-0708
LAS VEGAS CONVENTION & VISITORS AUTHORITY
LAS VEGAS CONVENTION CENTER
3150 Paradise Rd, Las Vegas, NV 89109-9096
Tel (702) 892-0711 *Founded/Ownrshp* 1955
Sales 329.0MM *EMP* 1,100
Accts Piercy Bowler Taylor & Kern L
SIC 7389 Advertising, promotional & trade show services
Pr: Rossi Ralenkotter
Treas: Jennifer Diblasi
Bd of Dir: Steve Stallworth
**Sr VP:* Terry Jicinsky
Sr VP: Cathy Tull
VP: Caroline Coyle
VP: Lisa Culpepper
VP: Jeremy Handel
VP: Miles Rodela
VP: Rafael Villanueva
Ex Dir: Meg McVdaniel

LAS VEGAS CONVENTION CENTER
See LAS VEGAS CONVENTION & VISITORS AUTHORITY

D-U-N-S 00-959-6032
LAS VEGAS PAVING CORP
4420 S Decatur Blvd, Las Vegas, NV 89103-5803
Tel (702) 251-5800 *Founded/Ownrshp* 1958
Sales 270.7MM^E *EMP* 700
SIC 1611 1629 8711

D-U-N-S 86-753-7917
LAS VEGAS RESORT HOLDINGS LLC
SLS LAS VEGAS
2535 Las Vegas Blvd S, Las Vegas, NV 89109-1137
Tel (702) 761-7702 *Founded/Ownrshp* 2007
Sales 153.0MM^E *EMP* 2,500
SIC 7011 Casino hotel
CFO: Michael Morgan

LAS VEGAS REVIEW-JOURNAL
See STEPHENS MEDIA LLC

D-U-N-S 16-720-2667
▲ LAS VEGAS SANDS CORP
3355 Las Vegas Blvd S, Las Vegas, NV 89109-8941
Tel (702) 414-1000 *Founded/Ownrshp* 2004
Sales 11.6MMM *EMP* 46,500
Tkr Sym LVS *Exch* NYS
SIC 7011 Casino hotel; Resort hotel
Ch Bd: Sheldon G Adelson
**Pr:* Robert G Goldstein
CFO: Patrick Dumont
Ex VP: Ira H Raphaelson
VP: Justin Beltram
VP: Gideon Berkowitz
VP: Travis Phillips
VP: David Pitney
VP: Norbert Riezler
VP: Stana Subaric
Comm Dir: Dawn Britt
Comm Man: Paul Dungo

D-U-N-S 17-891-8330
■ LAS VEGAS SANDS LLC
VENETIAN, THE
(*Suby of* LAS VEGAS SANDS CORP) ★
3355 Las Vegas Blvd S, Las Vegas, NV 89109-8941
Tel (702) 414-1000 *Founded/Ownrshp* 1988
Sales 375.1MM^E *EMP* 10,000
SIC 7011 Casino hotel
Ch Bd: Sheldon Adelson
Pr: Frederick Kraus
**Pr:* William Weidner
**COO:* Michael Alan Leven
COO: Bill Weidner
**Ex VP:* Bradley H Stone
**Sr VP:* Robert Goldstein
Sr VP: Scott Henry
Sr VP: Robert Rozek
VP: Chad Forster
VP: David Pitney
VP: Jeff Zabriskie
Comm Man: Paul Dungo

D-U-N-S 04-167-0829 IMP
LAS VEGAS VALLEY WATER DISTRICT
1001 S Valley View Blvd, Las Vegas, NV 89107-4447
Tel (702) 870-2011 *Founded/Ownrshp* 1947
Sales 336.4MM *EMP* 1,200
Accts Piercy Bowler Taylor & Kern L
SIC 4941 Water supply
Genl Mgr: Patricia Mulroy
CFO: David Wright
**Treas:* Cary M Casey
Ofcr: Mary Macdonald
Ofcr: Terri Robertson
Ex VP: Cynthia Bodnar
**Exec:* Karen Hayes
Exec: Lori Mitchell
Exec: Richard Wimmer
**Prin:* John Entsminger
Genl Mgr: Kimberly Villani
Board of Directors: Yvonne Atkinson Gates, Myrna Williams

D-U-N-S 03-493-8928
LAS-CAL CORP
TACO BELL
3225 S Rainbow Blvd # 102, Las Vegas, NV 89146-6216
Tel (702) 880-5818 *Founded/Ownrshp* 1967
Sales 59.1MM[E] *EMP* 1,500
SIC 5812 Fast-food restaurant, chain
Pr: Bill Allmon
**VP:* David Bonanni
**VP:* Dewey Doolen
Admn Mgr: Wendye Lee

LASALLE BRISTOL
See BRISTOL LASALLE CORP

D-U-N-S 80-700-2204
LASALLE HOTEL OPERATING PARTNERSHIP LP
(*Suby of* LASALLE HOTEL PROPERTIES) ★
7550 Wisconsin Ave Fl 10, Bethesda, MD 20814-3559
Tel (301) 941-1500 *Founded/Ownrshp* 2007
Sales 977.0MM[E] *EMP* 35
SIC 8741 Hotel or motel management
CEO: Michael D Barnello
Ch Bd: Stuart L Scott

D-U-N-S 07-322-7121
LASALLE HOTEL PROPERTIES
7550 Wisconsin Ave # 100, Bethesda, MD 20814-6599
Tel (301) 941-1500 *Founded/Ownrshp* 1998
Sales 1.2MMM *EMP* 35
SIC 6798 Real estate investment trusts
Pr: Michael D Barnello
COO: Alfred L Young
CFO: Kenneth G Fuller
CFO: Rhonda K Raphael
CFO: Bruce A Riggins
Ofcr: Kenneth Shoop
Board of Directors: Denise M Coll, Jeffrey T Foland, Darryl Hartley-Leonard, William S McCalmont, Stuart L Scott, Donald A Washburn

D-U-N-S 83-153-3521
LASALLE INCOME & GROWTH FUND IV
I & G BELLEVUE
200 E Randolph St Fl 44, Chicago, IL 60601-6520
Tel (312) 228-2087 *Founded/Ownrshp* 2005
Sales 101.6MM *EMP* 12
Accts Deloitte & Touche Llp Chicago
SIC 6531 Real estate agents & managers

D-U-N-S 10-664-5414
■ **LASALLE INVESTMENT MANAGEMENT INC**
(*Suby of* JONES LANG LASALLE INC) ★
333 W Wacker Dr Ste 2000, Chicago, IL 60606-1288
Tel (312) 782-5800 *Founded/Ownrshp* 1957
Sales 88.8MM[E] *EMP* 150[E]
SIC 6531 Real estate agents & managers
CEO: Jeff Jacobson
**CEO:* Jason Kern
COO: Gerardo Ruiz
Treas: Brian Hake
Chf Inves: Wade Judge
Ofcr: Jeremy Snoad
Sr VP: Stephen Adams
Sr VP: Adam Caskey
Sr VP: Chris Harris
Sr VP: Edmund Lee
Sr VP: Erick Paulson
Sr VP: Clyde Rawlings
Sr VP: Kim Woodrow
VP: Chris Akins
VP: Peter Bulgarelli
VP: Hank Feibusch
VP: Nick Firth
VP: Janet Healy
VP: Lucas Kimmel
VP: Richard Kleinman
VP: Marci McCready

D-U-N-S 07-161-7880
LASALLE UNIVERSITY
LA SALLE UNIVERSITY
1900 W Olney Ave, Philadelphia, PA 19141-1199
Tel (215) 951-1000 *Founded/Ownrshp* 1863
Sales 123.4MM *EMP* 900
Accts Kpmg Llp Philadelphia Pa
SIC 8221 University
Pr: Colleen M Hanycz
Pr: Jon C Aroulis
**Treas:* David C Fleming
VP: Swee-Lim Chia
VP: James Moore
VP: Rose L Pauline
Exec: Chris Kane
Exec: Royer Smith
Assoc Dir: Mark A Badstubner
Ex Dir: Stephen McGonigle
Ex Dir: Steve Melick

D-U-N-S 11-136-7202 IMP/EXP
LASCO FITTINGS INC
(*Suby of* AALBERTS INDUSTRIES N.V.)
414 Morgan St, Brownsville, TN 38012-9324
Tel (800) 776-2756 *Founded/Ownrshp* 2007
Sales 231.4MM[E] *EMP* 490
SIC 3494 Valves & pipe fittings
Pr: John C McDonald
Treas: Daniel J Disser
**VP:* Randy Stewart
Plnt Mgr: Jack Shamburger
Ql Cn Mgr: Tom Allen
Manager: David Beyer
Manager: Don Caver
Manager: Bryan Jackman

LASER DIVISION
See SPECTRA-PHYSICS INC

D-U-N-S 82-713-5021 IMP
LASERMASTERS LLC
LMI SOLUTIONS
4857 W Van Buren St, Phoenix, AZ 85043-3814
Tel (602) 278-5234 *Founded/Ownrshp* 1997
Sales 95.1MM[E] *EMP* 750[E]
SIC 3861 Toners, prepared photographic (not made in chemical plants)
Plnt Mgr: Juan Camargo
Mktg Dir: Christian Pepper

D-U-N-S 18-772-5569
LASERSHIP INC
1912 Woodford Rd Ste Ll, Vienna, VA 22182-3740
Tel (703) 761-9030 *Founded/Ownrshp* 1986
Sales 135.9MM[E] *EMP* 475
SIC 7389 Courier or messenger service
CEO: Ali Dilmaghani
**Pr:* Fred Aryan
**COO:* Helen Campbell
**CFO:* Kathleen Hughes
**CFO:* Guy Jackson
**Ex VP:* Mehran Aliakbar
**Ex VP:* Blake W Averill
VP: Averill Blake
VP: Joseph Jarvis
Exec: Rene Tingleff
Dir Risk M: Mimi Connelly

LASHIP
See NORTH AMERICAN FABRICATORS LLC

LASIK
See TLC VISION (USA) CORP

D-U-N-S 02-337-6853
LASKO GROUP INC
820 Lincoln Ave, West Chester, PA 19380-4469
Tel (610) 692-7400 *Founded/Ownrshp* 1997
Sales 226.1MM[E] *EMP* 1,400
SIC 4789 3634 Railroad car repair; Ceiling fans
Pr: Oscar Lasko
Pr: Vasanthi Iyer
**Ex VP:* Edward Mc Assey
Web Dev: Eric Miller
Software D: Kelly Nie
Ql Cn Mgr: Louis Delarosa
Genl Couns: Bradford Brush

D-U-N-S 00-232-9779 IMP/EXP
LASKO PRODUCTS INC (PA)
GALAXY FANS & HEATERS
(*Suby of* LASKO GROUP INC) ★
820 Lincoln Ave, West Chester, PA 19380-4469
Tel (610) 692-7400 *Founded/Ownrshp* 1906
Sales 209.9MM[E] *EMP* 1,000
SIC 4789 3585 3564 Railroad car repair; Refrigeration & heating equipment; Blowers & fans
Pr: William Lasko
**CFO:* Yen Tsai
Treas: Pat Farrell
**Treas:* Patricia Farrell
**VP:* Edward McAssey
**VP:* James Perella
Software D: Jonathan Hartline
Manager: Julian Quiroz
Ql Cn Mgr: George Gilley
Mktg Dir: Inger D Heller
Manager: Andy Yarbrough

D-U-N-S 05-250-4122
LASON INC
(*Suby of* HOV SERVICES INC) ★
11850 Hempstead Rd # 270, Houston, TX 77092-6013
Tel (713) 957-0800 *Founded/Ownrshp* 2010
Sales 62.2M[E] *EMP* 1,058[E]
SIC 7376 Computer facilities management
CEO: Hector Suarez

D-U-N-S 00-235-7549 IMP/EXP
LASSONDE PAPPAS AND CO INC
(*Suby of* PAPPAS LASSONDE HOLDINGS INC) ★
1 Collins Dr Ste 200, Carneys Point, NJ 08069-3640
Tel (856) 455-1000 *Founded/Ownrshp* 2011
Sales 450.0MM *EMP* 600
SIC 2033 Fruit juices: packaged in cans, jars, etc.; Fruits: packaged in cans, jars, etc.
CEO: Mark A McNeil
CFO: Marc Friedant
**Ch:* Jean Gattuso
Chf Mktg O: Mary Rachide
VP: Craig Ablin
VP: Robert Crawford
VP: Rick Jochums
VP: Mike Luciano
VP: Pat Nicolino
Exec: Lilya Hernadez
Dir IT: Mark Gillmore

D-U-N-S 00-798-4933
LASSUS BROS OIL INC
LASSUS HANDY DANDY
1800 Magnavox Way, Fort Wayne, IN 46804-1540
Tel (260) 436-1415 *Founded/Ownrshp* 1925, 1972
Sales 221.0MM *EMP* 375
Accts Krouse Kern & Co Inc Fort
SIC 5541 5411 Filling stations, gasoline; Convenience stores, independent
Pr: Todd Lassus
COO: Mike Bates
**CFO:* David Fledderjohann
Exec: Greg Smith

LASSUS HANDY DANDY
See LASSUS BROS OIL INC

D-U-N-S 10-149-5778 IMP/EXP
LASTAR INC
(*Suby of* LEGRAND FRANCE)
3555 Kettering Blvd, Moraine, OH 45439-2014
Tel (937) 224-0639 *Founded/Ownrshp* 2014
Sales 166.8MM[E] *EMP* 420
SIC 3678 Electronic connectors
CEO: John Selldorf
Opers Mgr: Jason Arnold
Sls Dir: Michelle Brad
Mktg Mgr: Kalee Maloy
Mktg Mgr: Denise Scarpelli

LASTEC
See WOOD-MIZER HOLDINGS INC

D-U-N-S 79-094-4545
LATAM AIRLINES GROUP SA INC
(*Suby of* LATAM AIRLINES GROUP S.A.)
6500 Nw 22nd St, Miami, FL 33122-2234
Tel (786) 265-6050 *Founded/Ownrshp* 2007
Sales 91.1MM[E] *EMP* 800
SIC 4512 Air transportation, scheduled
VP: Pablo Chiozza
**Treas:* Eduardo Opazo
Bd of Dir: Juan Sierra
Sr VP: Enrique Hirmas
Exec: Andres Fernandez
Genl Mgr: Maximiliano Naranjo
CTO: Salvador Jofre
Mktg Mgr: Ursula Velarde
Sls Mgr: Karl Hecht

D-U-N-S 03-012-8614
LATAMSCIENCE LLC
2151 S Le Jeune Rd # 307, Miami, FL 33134-4200
Tel (305) 871-0701 *Founded/Ownrshp* 2007
Sales 92.7MM *EMP* 41
SIC 8731 8999 Medical research, commercial; Scientific consulting
CEO: Edmundo G Stahl
**COO:* Annette O Austin
**CFO:* Gustavo Zingg

D-U-N-S 00-692-5721
LATEX CONSTRUCTION CO INC (GA)
1353 Farmer Rd Nw, Conyers, GA 30012-3488
Tel (770) 760-0820 *Founded/Ownrshp* 1946
Sales 157.3MM[E] *EMP* 400[E]
Accts Birdsong & Associates Llc Su
SIC 1623 Oil & gas pipeline construction; Water main construction
Pr: John D Stotz
**Sec:* Tim B Elder
**VP:* David Williams
Genl Mgr: Holly Andrews

D-U-N-S 07-622-1159
LATHAM & WATKINS LLP
355 S Grand Ave Ste 1000, Los Angeles, CA 90071-3419
Tel (213) 485-1234 *Founded/Ownrshp* 1934, 1972
Sales 931.1MM[E] *EMP* 4,100
SIC 8111 Legal services
Mng Pt: Robert Dell
Pt: Christopher J Allen
Pt: James P Beaubien
Pt: Joseph A Bevash
Pt: Jos Luis Blanco
Pt: Jose Luis Blanco
Pt: James E Brandt
Pt: Rowland Cheng
Pt: John Clair
Pt: Nicholas A Cline
Pt: Fabio Coppola
Pt: Michael E Dillard
Pt: Olivier Du Mottay
Pt: Alice S Fisher
Pt: Mark A Flagel
Pt: Thomas Fox
Pt: Peter M Gilhuly
Pt: David A Gordon
Pt: Ursula Hyman
Pt: Holger Iversen
Pt: Jorg Kirchner

D-U-N-S 00-395-7099 IMP/EXP
LATHAM INTERNATIONAL INC
787 Watervliet Shaker Rd, Latham, NY 12110-2211
Tel (518) 783-7776 *Founded/Ownrshp* 2004
Sales 218.9MM[E] *EMP* 300
SIC 3086 3081 Plastics foam products; Vinyl film & sheet
Pr: Mark Laven
CFO: Chuck Ryan
QA Dir: Ryan Legere
VP Opers: Gary Whitcher
Sfty Mgr: Lynn Hyatt
Plnt Mgr: Tom Correll
Sls Mgr: Marc Thomas

D-U-N-S 79-887-0457 IMP
LATHAM MANUFACTURING CORP
FORT WAYNE POOLS
787 Watervliet Shaker Rd, Latham, NY 12110-2211
Tel (518) 783-7776 *Founded/Ownrshp* 2004
Sales 142.7MM[E] *EMP* 300
SIC 3086 3081 3083 3949

D-U-N-S 96-338-0139 EXP
LATHAM POOL PRODUCTS INC
787 Watervliet Shaker Rd, Latham, NY 12110-2211
Tel (518) 951-1000 *Founded/Ownrshp* 2010
Sales 119.9MM[E] *EMP* 300[E]
SIC 3949 Swimming pools, except plastic
Pr: Mark Laven
VP: Ron Crowley
VP: John McGough
Dir IT: Gary Jones
VP Sls: Richard Piontkowski
Mktg Dir: Michelle Zollinger
Sls Dir: Bill Wiley
Manager: Andrew Gawinski
Manager: Aaron Young
Sls Mgr: Kieth Dodge

D-U-N-S 07-303-3888
LATHROP & GAGE LLP
2345 Grand Blvd Ste 2200, Kansas City, MO 64108-2618
Tel (816) 292-2000 *Founded/Ownrshp* 1970
Sales 117.7MM[E] *EMP* 645
SIC 8111 General practice law office
Mng Pt: Mark Bluhm
Pt: Joel B Voran
VP: Brett C Bogan
Counsel: Amanda Cochran
Counsel: Stacy Harper
Counsel: Anthony Janiuk
Counsel: Lauren Katunich
Counsel: George G Matava
Counsel: Leslie E Miller
Counsel: Jenny Mosh
Counsel: Maurice Osullivan

LATHROP PAINT
See HIRSHFIELDS INC

D-U-N-S 00-116-8343 IMP/EXP
LATICRETE INTERNATIONAL INC (CT)
1 Laticrete Park N 91, Bethany, CT 06524-3444
Tel (203) 393-0010 *Founded/Ownrshp* 1962
Sales 134.8MM[E] *EMP* 350
SIC 2899 2891

D-U-N-S 07-495-6582
LATROBE AREA HOSPITAL INC
(*Suby of* EXCELA HEALTH HOLDING CO INC) ★
1 Mellon Way, Latrobe, PA 15650-1197
Tel (724) 537-1000 *Founded/Ownrshp* 1908
Sales 82.3MM[E] *EMP* 1,060[E]
SIC 8062 General medical & surgical hospitals
Pr: Peggy Hayden

D-U-N-S 00-439-3468 IMP/EXP
■ **LATROBE SPECIALTY METALS CO LLC**
(*Suby of* CARPENTER TECHNOLOGY CORP) ★
2626 Ligonier St, Latrobe, PA 15650-3246
Tel (724) 537-7711 *Founded/Ownrshp* 2012
Sales 271.5MM[E] *EMP* 860
SIC 3312 3369 Tool & die steel; Castings, except die-castings, precision
CEO: Toni Thene
**VP:* Dale Mikus
VP: Dave Murray
Area Mgr: Craig Ridilla
Area Mgr: Eric Thomson
Genl Mgr: Conni Stahl
Genl Mgr: Mark Weberding
IT Man: Leon Nusselt
IT Man: Randall Strayer

D-U-N-S 01-921-7355 IMP/EXP
■ **LATROBE SPECIALTY METALS DISTRIBUTION INC**
(*Suby of* CARPENTER TECHNOLOGY CORP) ★
1551 Vienna Pkwy, Vienna, OH 44473-8703
Tel (330) 609-5137 *Founded/Ownrshp* 2012
Sales 95.0MM[E] *EMP* 82
SIC 5051 3312 Steel; Stainless steel
Ch Bd: Gregory A Pratt
**VP:* Timothy R Armstrong
**VP:* Thomas F Cramsey
**VP:* James D Dee
**VP:* Matthew S Enoch
**VP:* David Murray
**VP:* Joe Wakeling
Mktg Mgr: Tim Wise

LATSHAW DRILLING
See MUSTANG HEAVY HAUL LLC

D-U-N-S 11-530-3096
LATSHAW DRILLING & EXPLORATION CO
LATSHAW DRLG CO
4500 S 129th East Ave # 150, Tulsa, OK 74134-5801
Tel (918) 355-4380 *Founded/Ownrshp* 1981
Sales 444.3MM[E] *EMP* 1,100[E]
SIC 1381 Drilling water intake wells
Pr: Trent B Latshaw
Dir Risk M: Cindy Lozano
Dir Bus: Steve McCoy
Dir IT: Brusse James
Sfty Mgr: Jason Fox
Opers Mgr: Joey Stockton

LATSHAW DRLG CO
See LATSHAW DRILLING & EXPLORATION CO

D-U-N-S 08-892-2091
LATTER & BLUM INC
430 Notre Dame St, New Orleans, LA 70130-3610
Tel (504) 525-1311 *Founded/Ownrshp* 1986
Sales 53.8MM[E] *EMP* 1,000
SIC 6531 Real estate brokers & agents; Appraiser, real estate
Ch Bd: Robert W Merrick
**Pr:* Arthur Sterbcow
**CFO:* Robert C Penick
**Ex VP:* Patrick Egan
Off Mgr: Heather Sweatman
Dir IT: Gillian Sims

D-U-N-S 10-301-7299 IMP
▲ **LATTICE SEMICONDUCTOR CORP**
111 Sw 5th Ave Ste 700, Portland, OR 97204-3641
Tel (503) 268-8000 *Founded/Ownrshp* 1983
Sales 405.9MM *EMP* 1,146[E]
Tkr Sym LSCC *Exch* NGS
SIC 3674 Integrated circuits, semiconductor networks, etc.
Pr: Darin G Billerbeck
**Ch Bd:* John Bourgoin
COO: Glen Hawk
VP: Stefan Beck
VP: Byron Brown
VP: Byron W Milstead
VP: Rick White
Dir IT: Dan Martin
Dir IT: Mike Orr
Sftwr Eng: Andrew Lin
VP Sls: Andy Chin
Board of Directors: Robin A Abrams, Robert R Herb, Mark E Jensen, D Jeffrey Richardson, Frederick D Weber

D-U-N-S 02-632-9623 IMP
LATTIMORE MATERIALS CO LP
LATTIMORE READY MIX
(*Suby of* AGGREGATE INDUSTRIES MGT) ★
15900 Dooley Rd, Addison, TX 75001-4243
Tel (972) 221-4646 *Founded/Ownrshp* 1990
Sales 225.6MM[E] *EMP* 1,100
SIC 3273 1422 1442 Ready-mixed concrete; Limestones, ground; Sand mining
Pt: Scott Chrimes

LATTIMORE READY MIX
See LATTIMORE MATERIALS CO LP

D-U-N-S 15-799-1774 EXP
LAU INDUSTRIES INC
SUPREME FAN/INDUSTRIAL AIR
(*Suby of* JOHNSON CONTROLS INC) ★
4509 Springfield St, Dayton, OH 45431-1042
Tel (937) 476-6500 *Founded/Ownrshp* 1990
Sales 192.1MM[E] *EMP* 1,865[E]
SIC 3564 Ventilating fans: industrial or commercial
Pr: Damian Macaluso
**VP:* Dan Disser
**VP:* Christopher Wampler

L'AUBERGE DU LAC CASINO RESORT
See PNK (LAKE CHARLES) LLC

D-U-N-S 02-125-1236
LAUDERDALE COUNTY BOARD OF EDUCATION
LAUDERDALE COUNTY SCHOOL SYS
355 County Road 61, Florence, AL 35634-2559
Tel (256) 760-1300 *Founded/Ownrshp* 1889
Sales 77.3MM *EMP* 1,000
SIC 8211 School board
Ch Bd: Jerry Fulmer

D-U-N-S 07-895-5176
LAUDERDALE COUNTY SCHOOL DISTRICT
410 Constitution Ave Fl 3, Meridian, MS 39301-5161
Tel (601) 482-9746 *Founded/Ownrshp* 1833
Sales 38.0MM *EMP* 1,120
SIC 8211 Public elementary & secondary schools
HC Dir: Diane Freeman

LAUDERDALE COUNTY SCHOOL SYS
See LAUDERDALE COUNTY BOARD OF EDUCATION

D-U-N-S 07-979-9000
LAUDERDALE COUNTY SCHOOL SYSTEM
355 County Road 61, Florence, AL 35634-2559
Tel (256) 760-1300 *Founded/Ownrshp* 2015
Sales 43.2MM[E] *EMP* 1,000[E]
SIC 8211 Public elementary & secondary schools
Ch: Jerry Fulmer
Dir Sec: John Mansell
MIS Dir: Jason Truiet
Schl Brd P: Chad Holden
HC Dir: Brenda Foster
HC Dir: Kelly Stanhope

D-U-N-S 06-774-9382
LAUGHLIN RECREATIONAL ENTERPRISES INC
1650 S Casino Dr, Laughlin, NV 89029-1512
Tel (702) 298-2535 *Founded/Ownrshp* 1973
Sales 43.2MM[E] *EMP* 2,000
SIC 6512 Nonresidential building operators
Pr: Donald J Laughlin

D-U-N-S 05-014-8220 IMP/EXP
LAUGHLIN-CARTRELL INC
12850 Ne Hendricks Rd, Carlton, OR 97111
Tel (503) 852-7151 *Founded/Ownrshp* 1982
Sales 96.2MM[E] *EMP* 13
Accts Boldt Carlisle & Smith Salem
SIC 5191 Feed; Fertilizer & fertilizer materials
Pr: Tillman J Stone
**Ch Bd:* Robert S Laughlin
**VP:* Lawrence Kubes

LAUNCH EQUIPMENT SUPPORT SHOP
See UNITED SPACE ALLIANCE LLC

D-U-N-S 96-709-7515
LAURA AND JOHN ARNOLD FOUNDATION
2800 Post Oak Blvd # 225, Houston, TX 77056-6100
Tel (713) 554-1349 *Founded/Ownrshp* 2008
Sales 418.7MM *EMP* 2
SIC 8699 Charitable organization
Ch: Laura E Arnold
**Pr:* Denis Calacrese
**Ch:* John Arnold
**Treas:* Elizabeth Banks
VP: Josh B McGee

D-U-N-S 12-183-6816 IMP
LAURAND ASSOCIATES INC
11 Grace Ave Ste 405, Great Neck, NY 11021-2417
Tel (516) 829-8821 *Founded/Ownrshp* 2000
Sales 110.0MM *EMP* 8
SIC 5051 Aluminum bars, rods, ingots, sheets, pipes, plates, etc.
Pr: Laurence A Goldfarb
Opers Mgr: Patricia Romero

D-U-N-S 16-190-7613
LAUREATE EDUCATION INC
650 S Exeter St Fl 7, Baltimore, MD 21202-4574
Tel (410) 843-6100 *Founded/Ownrshp* 2007
Sales 765.0MM[E] *EMP* 23,210
SIC 8299 Educational services
Ch Bd: Douglas L Becker
Pr: Raph Appadoo
Pr: Neal Cohen
Pr: Paula R Singer
CFO: Eilif Serck-Hanssen
Bd of Dir: Wolf H Engst
Ex VP: Daniel M Nickel
Sr VP: Robert W Zentz
VP: Alan Ferayorni
VP: Ken Neimo
VP: Cristina O'Naghten
VP: Hernando Ramirez
VP: Chris Symanoskie
Board of Directors: George Munoz, Judith Rodin, Robert B Zoellick

D-U-N-S 07-131-9966
LAUREL COUNTY BOARD OF EDUCATION
LAUREL COUNTY PUBLIC SCHOOLS
718 N Main St, London, KY 40741-1222
Tel (606) 862-4608 *Founded/Ownrshp* 1925
Sales 90.0MM *EMP* 1,300
SIC 8211 Public senior high school; Public junior high school; Public elementary school

LAUREL COUNTY PUBLIC SCHOOLS
See LAUREL COUNTY BOARD OF EDUCATION

D-U-N-S 00-799-1979
LAUREL GROCERY CO LLC (KY)
129 Barbourville Rd, London, KY 40744-9301
Tel (606) 878-6601 *Founded/Ownrshp* 1920, 1944
Sales 459.1MM[E] *EMP* 411
SIC 5141 5147 5122 5143 Groceries, general line; Meats, fresh; Drugs, proprietaries & sundries; Dairy products, except dried or canned
**V Ch:* Winston Griffin
CFO: Doug George
VP: Dan Osborne
Exec: Barry Williams

D-U-N-S 78-599-2520
LAUREL HEALTH CARE CO
(*Suby of* LAUREL HEALTH CARE CO OF NORTH WORTHTINGTON) ★
8181 Worthington Rd Uppr, Westerville, OH 43082-8071
Tel (614) 794-8800 *Founded/Ownrshp* 1992
Sales 52.4MM[E] *EMP* 1,041[E]
SIC 8741 Nursing & personal care facility management
Pr: Bradford Payne
CFO: Lynette Mocksherman
**VP:* Jack Alcott
**VP:* Carol Bailey
**VP:* Timothy Patton
Dir IT: Kelly Foster
Doctor: Lynette Mochsherman
Doctor: Colleen Robinson

D-U-N-S 83-607-5028
LAUREL HEALTH CARE CO OF NORTH WORTHTINGTON
8181 Worthington Rd, Westerville, OH 43082-8067
Tel (614) 794-8800 *Founded/Ownrshp* 1995
Sales 158.5MM[E] *EMP* 2,018
SIC 8059 8741 Nursing home, except skilled & intermediate care facility; Nursing & personal care facility management
Pr: Brad Payne

D-U-N-S 10-805-0394
LAUREL HEALTH SYSTEM INC
22 Walnut St, Wellsboro, PA 16901-1526
Tel (570) 724-1010 *Founded/Ownrshp* 1989
Sales 670.3M *EMP* 1,100
SIC 8082 8741 8011 Home health care services; Management services; Offices & clinics of medical doctors
CEO: Steven P Johnson
CFO: Ron Gilbert
**Treas:* Craig Litchfield
**Ex VP:* Jan E Fisher
**VP:* Ronald M Gilbert Jr
CIO: Joseph F Bubacz Jr
Opers Mgr: Ben Weiskopff
Pharmcst: Craig Konzen
Pgrm Dir: Susan Sticklin

D-U-N-S 07-806-3831
LAUREL HILL INC
(*Suby of* HMR ADVANTAGE HEALTH SYSTEMS INC) ★
716 E Cedar Rock St, Pickens, SC 29671-2324
Tel (864) 878-4739 *Founded/Ownrshp* 1969
Sales 569.4MM *EMP* 225
SIC 8052 8051 Intermediate care facilities; Skilled nursing care facilities
Prin: Mary Reed
**Sec:* John P O'Brien Jr
Sr VP: David Salmon
**VP:* Larry Lollis
Exec: Heather Harbinson

D-U-N-S 08-620-9269
LAUREL HOLDINGS INC
111 Roosevelt Blvd, Johnstown, PA 15906-2736
Tel (814) 533-5777 *Founded/Ownrshp* 1974
Sales 92.4MM[E] *EMP* 311
SIC 4941 5063 3599 4724 7349 Water supply; Batteries, dry cell; Machine shop, jobbing & repair; Travel agencies; Janitorial service, contract basis
Pr: Kim Kunkle
Treas: Mike Brosig

D-U-N-S 07-116-9841
LAUREL SAND & GRAVEL INC
SW BARRICK & SONS
14504 Greenview Dr # 210, Laurel, MD 20708-3225
Tel (410) 792-7234 *Founded/Ownrshp* 1982
Sales 133.8MM[E] *EMP* 215
SIC 1422 1442 Crushed & broken limestone; Construction sand & gravel
Pr: Ronald Matovick
VP: Ed Barhauser
**VP:* Edward Barnhouser

LAURELWOOD CLC
See CLC OF LAUREL LLC

D-U-N-S 19-853-7367
LAUREN CORP
901 S 1st St, Abilene, TX 79602-1502
Tel (325) 670-9660 *Founded/Ownrshp* 1988
Sales 613.2MM *EMP* 1,700
SIC 1629 Chemical plant & refinery construction; Power plant construction; Oil refinery construction
Pr: C Cleve Whitener
CFO: Thomas Modisett

D-U-N-S 12-092-8700
LAUREN ENGINEERS & CONSTRUCTORS INC
(*Suby of* LAUREN CORP) ★
901 S 1st St, Abilene, TX 79602-1502
Tel (325) 670-9660 *Founded/Ownrshp* 1994
Sales 582.5MM *EMP* 1,100
SIC 1541 Industrial buildings & warehouses
CEO: C Cleve Whitener
**Pr:* Randal Lipps
CFO: Dale Crawford
**CFO:* Thomas Modisett
Treas: Christopher R Keays
Ex VP: Bob Fasciana
**Ex VP:* Ron Johnson
**Ex VP:* Clint Rosenbaum
VP: Robert W Roy
VP: Gary Young
Off Admin: Cheryl Cline

D-U-N-S 19-449-7405
LAUREN HOLDING INC
781 North St, Greenwich, CT 06831-3105
Tel (239) 514-7329 *Founded/Ownrshp* 2005
Sales 180.0MM[E] *EMP* 100
SIC 6211 Investment bankers
Pr: Lauren Corrigan

D-U-N-S 00-398-3269 IMP
LAUREN INTERNATIONAL LTD (OH)
LAUREN MANUFACTURING
2228 Reiser Ave Se, New Philadelphia, OH 44663-3334
Tel (330) 339-3373 *Founded/Ownrshp* 1965
Sales 174.7MM[E] *EMP* 450
Accts Four Fifteen Group Canton Oh
SIC 3069 Molded rubber products
Pr: Kevin E Gray
**CFO:* David Gingrich
Exec: Sheryl Montan
Genl Mgr: Eric Alander
Genl Mgr: Jim Nixon
Telecom Ex: Cindy Felgenhauer
Tech Mgr: Chris Porter
Sftwr Eng: Jonathan Gentsch
Mktg Dir: Joe Hasbrouck
Mktg Dir: Cynthia Miller
Sls Dir: Paul Kessler
Board of Directors: Philip Eykamp, Dale Foland, Kevin Gray, William High, Thad Rosenberry

LAUREN MANUFACTURING
See LAUREN INTERNATIONAL LTD

D-U-N-S 00-379-3205
LAURENS ELECTRIC COOPERATIVE INC (SC)
2254 Highway 14, Laurens, SC 29360-5164
Tel (864) 682-3141 *Founded/Ownrshp* 1939
Sales 113.9MM *EMP* 160
Accts Mclemor Middlebrooks Macon
SIC 4911 Distribution, electric power
Pr: J David Wasson Jr
Board of Directors: Helen Abrams, Louis Harrison, Ralph Hendrix, V Pres

D-U-N-S 02-531-2724 IMP/EXP
LAURIDSEN GROUP INC
2425 Se Oak Tree Ct, Ankeny, IA 50021-7102
Tel (515) 289-7600 *Founded/Ownrshp* 1994
Sales 171.6MM[E] *EMP* 750
SIC 2099 Food preparations
Pr: John F Wheeler
**VP:* Mel Berg
**VP:* Jerry Frankl
VP: Christine Lauridsen
**VP:* Louis Russell
Sls Dir: Bill Petersen
Manager: Jamie Pope
Nutrtnst: Joy Campbell

LAUSD
See LOS ANGELES UNIFIED SCHOOL DISTRICT

LAVALETTE FOODFAIR
See FORTHS FOODS INC

D-U-N-S 19-487-6132 IMP
LAVAZZA PREMIUM COFFEES CORP
(*Suby of* LUIGI LAVAZZA SPA)
120 Wall St Fl 27, New York, NY 10005-4011
Tel (212) 725-8800 *Founded/Ownrshp* 2001
Sales 110.8MM *EMP* 75
Accts Funaro & Co Pc New York Ny
SIC 5149 Coffee, green or roasted
CEO: Rich Andrews
CFO: Ricky Chetarpaul
VP: Giuseppe Lavazza
Rgnl Mgr: Patrizia E Tucker
Sls&Mrk Ex: Debbie Grabarz
Mktg Dir: Tonia Mancino
Mktg Mgr: Danielle Goldman

D-U-N-S 82-987-6528
LAVIDA COMMUNITIES INC
500 Stevens Ave Ste 100, Solana Beach, CA 92075-2055
Tel (858) 792-9300 *Founded/Ownrshp* 2009
Sales 12.8MM[E] *EMP* 1,228
SIC 6513 6512 6531 6553 Apartment building operators; Nonresidential building operators; Real estate agents & managers; Cemetery subdividers & developers
Prin: J Wickliffe Peterson

LAVIE CARE CENTER
See SEA CREST HEALTH CARE MANAGEMENT LLC

D-U-N-S 17-352-2707 EXP
LAVOI CORP
EPI BREADS
1749 Tullie Cir Ne, Atlanta, GA 30329-2305
Tel (404) 325-1016 *Founded/Ownrshp* 1985
Sales 93.3MM[E] *EMP* 280
SIC 2045 2053 2051 5149 Prepared flour mixes & doughs; Frozen bakery products, except bread; Bread, cake & related products; Breads, rolls & buns; Bakery products
CEO: Bob Gansel
**CFO:* Jim Kelley
**Ch:* Nicholas Mulliez

D-U-N-S 00-781-3587
LAW CO INC
345 N Rverview St Ste 300, Wichita, KS 67203
Tel (316) 268-0200 *Founded/Ownrshp* 1959
Sales 118.9MM[E] *EMP* 250
Accts Gj & Company Llc Wichita Ka
SIC 1542 1522 Nonresidential construction; Multi-family dwelling construction
Ch: Richard Kerschen
**Pr:* Dennis Kerschen
**Treas:* Josh Gordon
**Ex VP:* Marc Porter
VP: Hassan Jabara
**VP:* Doug Kimple
**VP:* Bill Reynolds
CTO: Andrew Bustraan

D-U-N-S 17-729-2034
LAW ENFORCEMENT HEALTH BENEFITS INC
LEHB
2233 Spring Garden St, Philadelphia, PA 19130-3511
Tel (215) 763-8290 *Founded/Ownrshp* 1987
Sales 125.1MM *EMP* 19
Accts Fischer Dorwart Pc Audubon N
SIC 8621 Health association

LAW MED PERSONNEL
See AUTOMATION PERSONNEL SERVICES INC

LAW OFFCES DAN NEWLIN PARTNERS
See DANIEL J NEWLIN PA

D-U-N-S 82-797-0265
LAW OFFICES OF ETHERIDGE & OUGRAH LLP
340 N Sam Houston Pkwy E, Houston, TX 77060-3305
Tel (832) 563-3620 *Founded/Ownrshp* 2008
Sales 100.0MM *EMP* 4
SIC 8111 Legal services
Genl Pt: Krishna Ougrah
Pt: Chad Etheridge

D-U-N-S 07-401-7252
LAWLEY SERVICE INC
GMAC INSURANCE
361 Delaware Ave, Buffalo, NY 14202-1622
Tel (716) 849-8618 *Founded/Ownrshp* 1939
Sales NA *EMP* 200
SIC 6411 Insurance agents, brokers & service
Ch Bd: William J Lawley Sr
**Pr:* Christopher Ross
CFO: Mark Higgins
Sr VP: Todd Tevens
**VP:* Todd F Best
**VP:* Mike Lawley
Mktg Mgr: Fred Holender
Sls Mgr: John Beecher
Sls Mgr: Peter Braun
Sls Mgr: Kirk Lawley
Sls Mgr: Joe O'Connor

D-U-N-S 19-408-4547
■ **LAWNWOOD MEDICAL CENTER INC**
LAWNWOOD MEDICAL REGIONAL CTR
(*Suby of* HOSPITAL COPORATION OF AMERICA) ★
1700 S 23rd St, Fort Pierce, FL 34950-4899
Tel (772) 461-4000 *Founded/Ownrshp* 1994
Sales 300.0MM *EMP* 1,200
SIC 8062 8063 8069 General medical & surgical hospitals; Psychiatric hospitals; Specialty hospitals, except psychiatric
CEO: Rodney Smith
**CFO:* Robert Dunwoody Jr
Nurse Mgr: Debbie Boyer
Dir IT: Ramiro Duran
Surgeon: Chris Cromwell
Surgeon: Victor R Dasilva
Surgeon: Brad McCollom
Surgeon: Christian Schuetz
Surgeon: William Stanton
Ansthlgy: Ali M Ahed-Elain
Ansthlgy: Celestine O Kwune

LAWNWOOD MEDICAL REGIONAL CTR
See LAWNWOOD MEDICAL CENTER INC

D-U-N-S 06-925-3946 IMP
LAWRENCE & MEMORIAL HOSPITAL INC
(*Suby of* LAWRENCE MEMORIAL) ★
365 Montauk Ave, New London, CT 06320-4769
Tel (860) 442-0711 *Founded/Ownrshp* 1912, 2005
Sales 339.2MM *EMP* 2,200
SIC 8011 8062 Offices & clinics of medical doctors; General medical & surgical hospitals
Pr: Bruce D Cummings
**Ch Bd:* Ulysses Hammond
COO: Cynthia Kane
**Treas:* Fred Conti
VP: Maureen Anderson
VP: Lugene Inzana
Exec: Sal Argento
Dir OR: Karen Buck
**Prin:* Timothy Bates
Off Mgr: Lisa Longo
Nurse Mgr: Debra Merola
Board of Directors: Timothy Bates

D-U-N-S 62-341-6211
LAWRENCE + MEMORIAL CORP
LAWRENCE MEMORIAL
365 Montauk Ave, New London, CT 06320-4700
Tel (860) 442-0711 *Founded/Ownrshp* 1984
Sales 3.4MM *EMP* 2,253
Accts Lb Pricewaterhousecoopers Llp
SIC 8741 Hospital management
Pr: Bruce D Cummings
**Ch:* Ulysses B Hammond
**VP:* Crista Durand
**VP:* Dan Rissi
**VP:* William Stanley
**VP:* Lauren Williams
Dir Lab: Judy Portelance

LAWRENCE BERKELEY NATIONAL LAB
See UNITED STATES DEPARTMENT OF ENERGY BERKELEY OFFICE

D-U-N-S 07-060-6854 IMP
LAWRENCE BERKELEY NATIONAL LAB
1 Cyclotron Rd, Berkeley, CA 94720-8099
Tel (510) 486-6792 *Founded/Ownrshp* 1989
Sales 206.1MM[E] *EMP* 6,000
SIC 8071 Medical laboratories; Biological laboratory; Testing laboratories
COO: Glenn D Kubiak
CFO: Kim Williams
VP: Jim Garbe
Dir Lab: Jeff Anderson
Prgrm Mgr: Brian Heimberg
Prgrm Mgr: Max WEI
Admn Mgr: Carmen Ross
CIO: Rosio Alvarez
CIO: Craig Leres
IT Man: Steve Bakaley
Netwrk Eng: Miriam Brafman

LAWRENCE BROTHERS
See MAL ENTERPRISES INC

D-U-N-S 00-510-6174 EXP
LAWRENCE FOODS INC
2200 Lunt Ave, Elk Grove Village, IL 60007-5685
Tel (847) 437-2400 *Founded/Ownrshp* 1930

Sales 101.4MM^E *EMP* 250
SIC 2033 2099 Canned fruits & specialties; Food preparations
CEO: Lester Lawrence
Ex VP: Keith Appling
VP: Jeffrey Jenniges
Genl Mgr: Andy Balafas
IT Man: Kim Pantano
Ql Cn Mgr: Sravani Chancharem
Sls Mgr: Pat Dineen
**Genl Couns:* Marc R Lawrence
Snr Mgr: Shawn Andre

D-U-N-S 07-951-7611
LAWRENCE GENERAL HOSPITAL
(*Suby of* LGH CHARITABLE TRUST INC) ★
1 General St, Lawrence, MA 01841-2997
Tel (978) 683-4000 *Founded/Ownrshp* 1875
Sales 203.7MM *EMP* 1,405
SIC 8062 General medical & surgical hospitals
**Pr:* Joseph S Mc Manus
COO: Denise Palumbo
CFO: Deborah Wilson
**Ex VP:* Gerard Foley
VP: Daniel Concaugh
VP: Theresa Dunn
VP: Elizabeth Hale
VP: Robin Hynds
**VP:* Robert Tremblay
Exec: Susan Daley
Dir Lab: Richard Battles
Dir Lab: Terry Scuderi

D-U-N-S 07-915-8881
LAWRENCE HOLDING INC
(*Suby of* HUAXIANG CO., LTD.)
803 S Black River St, Sparta, WI 54656-2221
Tel (608) 269-6911 *Founded/Ownrshp* 2011
Sales 120.0MM^E *EMP* 1,200^E
SIC 3469 3089 3544 Stamping metal for the trade; Automotive parts, plastic; Special dies, tools, jigs & fixtures
VP: Bruce Dinger

D-U-N-S 07-270-1832
LAWRENCE HOSPITAL CENTER
LAWRENCE MEDICAL ASSOCIATE
55 Palmer Ave, Bronxville, NY 10708-3491
Tel (914) 787-1000 *Founded/Ownrshp* 1988
Sales 212.8MM *EMP* 15,000
SIC 8062 General medical & surgical hospitals
Pr: Edward M Dinan
**CFO:* Murray Askinazi
Chf Mktg O: Mark Fox
**Ex VP:* James Y Lee
**VP:* Timothy J Hughes
**VP:* James Keogh
VP: Rachel Negron
Dir Inf Cn: Mary A Hauff
Dir Case M: Eileen Mullaney
Dir Lab: Jackie Reiner
Dir Rx: Lisa Oronzio
Board of Directors: George Austin, Paul Brenner, Arthur Nagle

LAWRENCE LIVERMORE NAT LAB
See UNITED STATES DEPARTMENT OF ENERGY LIVERMORE OFFICE

LAWRENCE MEDICAL ASSOCIATE
See LAWRENCE HOSPITAL CENTER

LAWRENCE MEMORIAL
See LAWRENCE + MEMORIAL CORP

D-U-N-S 96-112-3254
LAWRENCE MEMORIAL HOSPITAL
L M H
325 Maine St, Lawrence, KS 66044-1360
Tel (785) 505-5000 *Founded/Ownrshp* 1996
Sales 198.7MM *EMP* 1,200^E
SIC 8062 General medical & surgical hospitals
Pr: Gene Meyer
Chf Rad: James Mandigo
**CFO:* Simon Scholtz
**VP:* Sheryle D Amico
**VP:* Carolyn Bowmer
**VP:* Janice Early
**VP:* Dana Hale
**VP:* Karen Shumate
**VP:* Deborah Thompson
**VP:* Kathy Clausing Willis
Dir Rx: Michael Bennett

D-U-N-S 07-305-3282
LAWRENCE MEMORIAL HOSPITAL ENDOWMENT ASSOCIATION
LMH
(*Suby of* L M H) ★
330 Arkansas St Ste 201, Lawrence, KS 66044-1335
Tel (785) 505-3318 *Founded/Ownrshp* 1921
Sales 3.4MM *EMP* 1,200
Accts Ss&C Solutions Inc Lawrence
SIC 8051 8062 Skilled nursing care facilities; General medical & surgical hospitals
CEO: Gene Meyer
**Pr:* Eugene W Meyer
**Pr:* Deborah Thomson
**CFO:* Simon Scholtz
**VP:* Sheryle D Amico
**VP:* Carolyn Bowmer
**VP:* Janice Early
**VP:* Kathy Clausing Willis
CIO: Jane A Maskus
Board of Directors: Kelli Hilmes, Patrick Parker, Terri Barnes, Kevin Howser, Teresa Sikes, Connie Bores, Nancy Knagg, Patty Winslow, Connie Broers, Corey Koester, Stacy Cope, Allyson Leland, Cheryl D'amico, Angela Lowe, Tom Damewood, Denise Martinek, Linda Gall, Patrick Mc Cool, Dana Hale, Debbie Miers, Joan Harvey, Lida Osbern

LAWRENCE MIDDLE SCHOOL
See LAWRENCE UNION FREE SCHOOL DISTRICT

LAWRENCE PHOTO-GRAPHIC
See HEARTLAND IMAGING COMPANIES INC

LAWRENCE PUBLIC SCHOOLS
See LAWRENCE SCHOOL DISTRICT

D-U-N-S 03-069-3642
LAWRENCE PUBLIC SCHOOLS
110 Mcdonald Dr, Lawrence, KS 66044-1055
Tel (785) 832-5000 *Founded/Ownrshp* 1966
Sales 107.1MM^E *EMP* 1,700
SIC 8211 Public combined elementary & secondary school
Pr: Leonard Ortiz
**Treas:* Katharine S Johnson
**VP:* Sue Morgan
Teacher Pr: Samrie Devin

D-U-N-S 80-433-7111
LAWRENCE SCHOOL DISTRICT
LAWRENCE PUBLIC SCHOOLS
233 Haverhill St, Lawrence, MA 01840-1405
Tel (978) 975-5905 *Founded/Ownrshp* 1848
Sales 156.0MM *EMP* 2,300^E
SIC 8211 Public elementary & secondary schools
Ch Bd: William Lantigua
Ch Bd: Samuel Reyes
Dir Sec: Jesus Hernandez
MIS Dir: Long Nguyen
Pr Dir: Lynne Garcia
Instr Medi: Greg Limperis
Psych: Janette Diaz
HC Dir: Mary Lou Bergeron

LAWRENCE TRANSPORTATION
See LTX INC

D-U-N-S 00-278-0666 IMP
LAWRENCE TRANSPORTATION SYSTEMS INC (VA)
UNITED VAN LINES
872 Lee Hwy, Roanoke, VA 24019-8516
Tel (540) 966-4000 *Founded/Ownrshp* 1932
Sales 118.0MM^E *EMP* 500
Accts J Moore & Company Pc Roan
SIC 4225 4213 4212 General warehousing; Household goods transport; Local trucking, without storage
CEO: Weldon S Lawrence
**Pr:* Ronald E Spangler
**Treas:* Lawrence Harris
VP: Peer Segelke
Brnch Mgr: Billy Wills
Sfty Dirs: Joyce Ray
Natl Sales: Regina Durnal
VP Sls: Barry Barnes

D-U-N-S 04-046-6716
LAWRENCE UNION FREE SCHOOL DISTRICT
LAWRENCE MIDDLE SCHOOL
195 Broadway, Lawrence, NY 11559-1737
Tel (516) 295-7000 *Founded/Ownrshp* 1890
Sales 93.4MM *EMP* 755
Accts Cullen & Danowski Llp Port J
SIC 8211 Public junior high school
Genl Mgr: Kathleen Halbach
IT Man: Lee Comeau
Psych: Dianne McCarthy

D-U-N-S 10-872-8254 IMP
LAWRENCE WHOLESALE LLC
DERIVAMAR
4353 Exchange Ave, Vernon, CA 90058-2619
Tel (323) 235-7525 *Founded/Ownrshp* 2000
Sales 759.0MM *EMP* 30
SIC 5147 Meat brokers
CEO: Mark Liszt
**COO:* Max Liszt
**CFO:* Robert Francis

D-U-N-S 82-999-3976
LAWRENCEVILLE SCHOOL
TRUSTEES OF LAWRENCEVILLE SCHO
2500 Main St, Lawrenceville, NJ 08648-1699
Tel (609) 896-0400 *Founded/Ownrshp* 1700
Sales 90.8MM *EMP* 490^E
Accts Withum Smith Brown Pc Princet
SIC 8211 Private elementary & secondary schools
CEO: Elizabeth A Duffy
Trst: Fahad Al-Rashid
Trst: Frederick McCord
Trst: Raymond Viault
Trst: Loyal Wilson
Ofcr: Miyuki Kaneko
Assoc Dir: Leslie Duffy
Genl Mgr: Robert Freeman
Dir IT: Niki Emanuel
Dir IT: Alyssa Totoro
Info Man: Tracey Allen

D-U-N-S 00-543-8890 IMP/EXP
▲ LAWSON PRODUCTS INC
8770 W Bryn Mawr Ave # 639, Chicago, IL 60631-3526
Tel (773) 304-5050 *Founded/Ownrshp* 1952
Sales 275.8MM *EMP* 1,500
Tkr Sym LAWS *Exch* NGS
SIC 5072 5085 5084 5013 Hardware; Nuts (hardware); Rivets; Screws; Fasteners & fastening equipment; Industrial fittings; Hose, belting & packing; Welding machinery & equipment; Automotive supplies & parts; Automotive servicing equipment
Pr: Michael G Decata
Ch Bd: Ronald B Port
Pr: John J Murray
CFO: Ronald J Knutson
Ex VP: Steve R Broome
Ex VP: Neil E Jenkins
Sr VP: Lawrence Krema
Sr VP: Shane T McCarthy
VP: Elizabeth Abrahamson
VP: Matthew Brown
VP: Kevin Hoople
VP: Ron Knutson
Board of Directors: Andrew B Albert, I Steven Edelson, James S Errant, Lee S Hillman, Thomas S Postek, Wilma J Smelcer

D-U-N-S 96-805-9019 IMP
LAWTER INC
(*Suby of* LAWTER CAPITAL B.V.)
200 N La Salle St # 2600, Chicago, IL 60601-1060
Tel (312) 662-5700 *Founded/Ownrshp* 2011
Sales 156.6MM^E *EMP* 582
SIC 2899 2851 Chemical preparations; Paints & allied products
Pr: Ichiro Taninaka
**Ch:* Yoshihiro Hasegawa
Treas: Hideo Takahira
**Chf Cred:* Rich Tuttle
**VP:* Peter Biesheuvel

D-U-N-S 08-247-1038
LAWTON PUBLIC SCHOOL DISTRICT I-008
753 Nw Fort Sill Blvd, Lawton, OK 73507-5421
Tel (580) 357-6900 *Founded/Ownrshp* 1901, 1902
Sales 162.0MM^E *EMP* 2,200
SIC 8211 Public elementary & secondary schools; Public elementary school; Public junior high school; Public senior high school
CFO: Dianne Branstette
Dir Sec: David Hornbeck
Pr Dir: Lynn Cordes
HC Dir: Chris Sharkey

D-U-N-S 07-622-0433
■ LAWYERS TITLE CO
(*Suby of* FIDELITY NATIONAL FINANCIAL INC) ★
7530 N Glenoaks Blvd, Burbank, CA 91504-1052
Tel (818) 767-0425 *Founded/Ownrshp* 1984
Sales NA *EMP* 786
SIC 6361 6531 Real estate title insurance; Escrow agent, real estate
CEO: Edward Zerwekh
**Sr VP:* Edward Beierle
**VP:* Steve Bauer
**VP:* William Star

D-U-N-S 00-794-1180
■ LAWYERS TITLE INSURANCE CORP
(*Suby of* FIDELITY NATIONAL FINANCIAL INC) ★
601 Riverside Ave, Jacksonville, FL 32204-2946
Tel (888) 866-3684 *Founded/Ownrshp* 1988, 2008
Sales NA *EMP* 11,000
SIC 6361 7372 5734 Guarantee of titles; Real estate title insurance; Prepackaged software; Computer peripheral equipment; Computer software & accessories
CEO: Theodore L Chandler Jr
Pr: Kenneth Astheimer
Pr: Melissa A Hill
Pr: Jeffrey C Selby
Pr: Albert V Will
Ex VP: Ross W Dorneman
Ex VP: G William Evans
Ex VP: Margaret M Foster
Ex VP: Michelle H Gluck
Ex VP: Richard P Gonzalez
Ex VP: John A Magness
Ex VP: Glyn Nelson
Ex VP: John M Obzud
Ex VP: Lynn M Riedel
Ex VP: James E Sindoni
Ex VP: William C Thornton
Ex VP: Jeffrey D Vaughan
Ex VP: Marcy A Welburn
VP: Marty Austin
VP: Jordan Kanter
VP: Toni Reichow

D-U-N-S 12-647-1676
LAY MANAGEMENT CORP OF GEORIGA
790 Dixon Rd Apt J7, Jonesboro, GA 30238-3165
Tel (678) 558-5631 *Founded/Ownrshp* 2002
Sales 35.6MM^E *EMP* 2,000
SIC 8741 Management services
Pr: David Lay
**VP:* Laquallis McGee

D-U-N-S 00-696-5917 IMP
▲ LAYNE CHRISTENSEN CO
1800 Hughes Landing Blvd, The Woodlands, TX 77380-1682
Tel (281) 475-2600 *Founded/Ownrshp* 1800
Sales 683.0MM *EMP* 2,680
Accts Deloitte & Touche Llp Houston
Tkr Sym LAYN *Exch* NGS
SIC 1781 1623 5084 1481 8748 Water well drilling; Water well servicing; Water, sewer & utility lines; Materials handling machinery; Pumps & pumping equipment; Water pumps (industrial); Nonmetallic minerals development & test boring; Mine exploration, nonmetallic minerals; Test boring for nonmetallic minerals; Environmental consultant
Pr: Michael J Caliel
**Ch Bd:* David A B Brown
Pr: Leslie F Archer
Pr: Larry D Purlee
Pr: Ronald Thalacker
CFO: J Michael Anderson
Ofcr: Steven F Crooke
Sr VP: Kevin P Maher
Board of Directors: J Samuel Butler, Robert R Gilmore, Alan P Krusi, John T Nesser III, Nelson Obus

D-U-N-S 04-905-9702 IMP
■ LAYNE HEAVY CIVIL INC
(*Suby of* LAYNE CHRISTENSEN CO) ★
4520 N State Road 37, Orleans, IN 47452-9035
Tel (812) 865-3232 *Founded/Ownrshp* 2005
Sales 463.3MM^E *EMP* 650
SIC 1623 1781 1629 Water main construction; Sewer line construction; Pumping station construction; Water well drilling; Waste disposal plant construction
Pr: Mark Accetturo
Treas: Steven Crooke
**Treas:* James R Easter
Ex VP: Jerry Fanska
Ex VP: Patrick Schmidt
VP: Kevin Collenbaugh
VP: Mark Harris
**VP:* Larry Purlee
VP: William K Reynolds
**VP:* Jim Stutler
**VP:* Andrew M Zalla
Board of Directors: Patrick Schmidt- Dir

D-U-N-S 13-073-4267 IMP
■ LAYNE INLINER LLC
(*Suby of* LAYNE HEAVY CIVIL INC) ★
4520 N State Rd State 37, Orleans, IN 47452
Tel (812) 865-3232 *Founded/Ownrshp* 2002
Sales 118.7MM^E *EMP* 295
SIC 1623 Water, sewer & utility lines
CEO: Jeff Reynolds
**Ch Bd:* David AB Brown

D-U-N-S 00-780-9676
LAYTON COMPANIES INC
ROCKY MOUNTAIN PIES
9090 S Sandy Pkwy, Sandy, UT 84070-6409
Tel (801) 568-9090 *Founded/Ownrshp* 1948
Sales 105.3MM^E *EMP* 650^E
SIC 1542 1541 Commercial & office building, new construction; Industrial buildings, new construction
Pr: David S Layton
**CFO:* Dallis Christensen
**Sec:* Gerald Monson
**Ex VP:* Jason Hill
Ex VP: John Thornton
**Ex VP:* Bryan Webb
VP: Craig Bergstrom
VP: Chris Jensen
VP: Bill Munck
Dir IT: John Zinger
Sfty Mgr: Trevor Austin

D-U-N-S 82-698-7083
LAZ KARP ASSOCIATES INC
15 Lewis St Fl 5, Hartford, CT 06103-2503
Tel (860) 522-7641 *Founded/Ownrshp* 2003
Sales 20.9MM^E *EMP* 7,000
SIC 7521 1799 Automobile parking; Parking lot maintenance
Pr: Jeffery Karp
**CEO:* Alan Lazowski
**VP:* Michael Kuziak

D-U-N-S 96-746-7569
LAZ KARP ASSOCIATES LLC
15 Lewis St Fl 5, Hartford, CT 06103-2503
Tel (860) 522-7641 *Founded/Ownrshp* 2007
Sales 718.9MM^E *EMP* 7,000
SIC 1799 Parking lot maintenance
CEO: Alan B Lazowski
**Pr:* Jeffrey N Karp
**COO:* Michael J Kuziak
**CFO:* Nathan Owen
**Treas:* Raymond H Skoglund
Ofcr: Heather Mortimer

D-U-N-S 00-736-9516
LAZ PARKING LTD
(*Suby of* LAZ KARP ASSOCIATES LLC) ★
9333 Genesee Ave Ste 220, San Diego, CA 92121-2113
Tel (858) 587-8888 *Founded/Ownrshp* 1981
Sales 32.5MM^E *EMP* 6,000
SIC 7521 Parking lots
CEO: Alan Lazowski
**Treas:* Raymond Skoglund
**VP:* Bert Kaplowitz

D-U-N-S 10-851-2856 IMP
LAZ PARKING LTD LLC
(*Suby of* LAZ KARP ASSOCIATES LLC) ★
15 Lewis St Fl 5, Hartford, CT 06103-2500
Tel (860) 713-2030 *Founded/Ownrshp* 1981
Sales 248.1MM^E *EMP* 2,003
SIC 7521 Parking garage
CEO: Alan Lazowski
Pr: Terrance Gilmore
Pr: Steven Gresh
**Pr:* Jeffrey N Karp
Pr: Todd Lawson
Pr: Joe Leightner
Rgnl VP: Steven Greshis
Ex VP: Kynn Knight
**VP:* Mike Kusiak
VP: Philip Oropesa
Dir Bus: Jason Marovick

D-U-N-S 62-086-2677
LAZ-MD HOLDINGS LLC
(*Suby of* LAZARD LTD)
30 Rockefeller Plz, New York, NY 10112-0015
Tel (212) 632-6000 *Founded/Ownrshp* 2004
Sales 379.1MM^E *EMP* 2,511
SIC 6211 6221 Flotation companies; Investment certificate sales; Commodity contracts brokers, dealers
CEO: Charles Ward III
Mng Dir: William B Buchanan

D-U-N-S 78-412-9830
LAZARD ASSET MANAGEMENT LLC
(*Suby of* LAZARD FRERES & CO LLC) ★
30 Rockefeller Plz Fl 57, New York, NY 10112-0015
Tel (212) 632-1890 *Founded/Ownrshp* 2002
Sales NA *EMP* 63^E
SIC 6351 Assessment associations, surety & fidelity insurance
Sr VP: Bruce Bickerton
Sr VP: Rohit Chopra
**Sr VP:* James F Harmon
Sr VP: Peter Kashanek
Sr VP: Christopher Komosa
**Sr VP:* Richard Kowal
Sr VP: Erik McKee
Sr VP: Alex Montoya
Sr VP: SRI Nadesan
Sr VP: Richard K Owal
Sr VP: Edward Rosenfeld
VP: Kerryn Andrews
VP: Ramana Bondugula
VP: Elena S Cfa
VP: Giuseppe R Cfa
**VP:* Stephen S Clair
VP: Joann Disantis
VP: Neal Doying
VP: Dylan Heck
VP: John Labadia
VP: Kevin Ledger

D-U-N-S 00-698-6723
LAZARD FRERES & CO LLC
(*Suby of* LAZARD LTD)
30 Rockefeller Plz, New York, NY 10112-0015
Tel (212) 632-6000 *Founded/Ownrshp* 1992
Sales 502.9MM^E *EMP* 1,300
SIC 6211 Dealers, security; Investment bankers
Ch Bd: Kenneth M Jacobs
**COO:* Alexander F Stern
Sr VP: John Ceglia
VP: Michael Basil
VP: Patrick Fouhy
VP: Chris Leelum
VP: Adrian Merkt
Dir Risk M: Zoe Chen
Mng Dir: Charles Burgdorf
Mng Dir: Joseph Cassanelli
Mng Dir: James Donald

D-U-N-S 02-611-5597
LAZARD GROUP LLC
(*Suby of* LAZARD LTD)
30 Rockefeller Plz, New York, NY 10112-0015
Tel (212) 632-6000 *Founded/Ownrshp* 1848
Sales 2.4MMM *EMP* 2,523^E
SIC 6282 6211 Investment advisory service; Investment bankers; Securities flotation companies
Ch Bd: Kenneth M Jacobs
V Ch: Gary Parr
Pr: Beth Butler
COO: Alexander F Stern
CFO: Matthieu Bucaille
**Chf Inves:* Ashish Bhutani
Sr VP: Greg Bernhardt
Sr VP: Kenneth Colton
Sr VP: Guy Fiumarelli
Sr VP: Tom Franzese
Sr VP: Elena Geraci
Sr VP: Anthony Lombardi
Sr VP: Jean-Daniel Malan
Sr VP: Claire Nordin
Sr VP: Andrew Rogers
Sr VP: Nicholas Sordoni
VP: Michael Adelman
VP: Paul Aristy
VP: William Genao
VP: Jeff Heite
VP: Joe Mallilo
Board of Directors: Andrew M Alper, Steven J Heyer, Sylvia Jay, Philip A Laskawy, Laurent Mignon, Richard D Parsons, Hal S Scott, Michael J Turner

D-U-N-S 78-672-0776
▲ LAZARUS ENERGY HOLDINGS LLC
LAZARUS ENERGY SERVICES
801 Travis St Ste 2100, Houston, TX 77002-5705
Tel (713) 850-0500 *Founded/Ownrshp* 2006
Sales 222.2MM^E *EMP* 70
SIC 2911 Petroleum refining
Genl Mgr: Jonathan Carroll
Brnch Mgr: Tommy Byrd
Brnch Mgr: Fred Marshall
Genl Mgr: Jason Heuring

LAZARUS ENERGY SERVICES
See BLUE DOLPHIN ENERGY CO

LAZARUS ENERGY SERVICES
See LAZARUS ENERGY HOLDINGS LLC

D-U-N-S 01-514-9599
LAZER SPOT INC
6525 Shiloh Rd Ste 900, Alpharetta, GA 30005-1615
Tel (770) 886-6851 *Founded/Ownrshp* 2015
Sales 308.4MM^E *EMP* 1,300
SIC 0762 4212 Farm management services; Farm to market haulage, local
CEO: Wesley Newsome
**COO:* Adam Newsome
**CFO:* Clay Herron
**Ex VP:* Jerry Edwards
**Ex VP:* Phil Newsome
VP: Steven Hogan
VP: Brent Parker
Rgnl Mgr: John Chambers
Rgnl Mgr: Corey Johnson
VP Opers: David Mumbauer

LAZYDAYS RV CAMPGROUND
See LDRV HOLDINGS CORP

D-U-N-S 10-118-9434 IMP
LB STEEL LLC
TOPEKA METAL SPECIALTIES
15700 Lathrop Ave, Harvey, IL 60426-5118
Tel (708) 331-2600 *Founded/Ownrshp* 2001
Sales 151.2MM^E *EMP* 350
SIC 3599

LB WATER
See L/B WATER SERVICE INC

LBFOSTER
See L B FOSTER CO

D-U-N-S 79-119-8976
LBI MEDIA HOLDINGS INC
(*Suby of* LIBERMAN BROADCASTING INC) ★
1845 W Empire Ave, Burbank, CA 91504-3402
Tel (818) 563-5722 *Founded/Ownrshp* 2007
Sales 117.5MM *EMP* 697^E
SIC 4832 4833 Radio broadcasting stations; Television broadcasting stations
Pr: Lenard Liberman
**COO:* Winter Horton
CFO: Blima Tuller
Sr VP: Andy Weir
Sls Mgr: Ozzie Mendoza

D-U-N-S 05-406-0405 EXP
LBM ADVANTAGE INC
ENAP
555 Hudson Valley Ave # 200, New Windsor, NY 12553-4748
Tel (845) 564-4900 *Founded/Ownrshp* 1967
Sales 314.7MM^E *EMP* 117
SIC 5031 Lumber: rough, dressed & finished; Building materials, exterior; Building materials, interior
CEO: Stephen J Sallah
**Ex VP:* Paul Dean
**VP:* Tom Molloy
VP: Brad Waller
Exec: Bob Carson
**Exec:* Duncan Facey
Exec: Thomas Molloy
Exec: Scott Reiser
Natl Sales: David Merryman
Mktg Mgr: Donna Cramsie
Manager: Neal Bavousett

D-U-N-S 08-015-9368
LBM BORROWER LLC
1000 Corporate Grove Dr, Buffalo Grove, IL 60089-4550
Tel (877) 787-5267 *Founded/Ownrshp* 2015
Sales 1.9MMM^E *EMP* 1,207^E
SIC 5031 Building materials, exterior

LBRANDS
See L BRANDS INC

LBUSD
See LONG BEACH UNIFIED SCHOOL DISTRICT

LCAS
See LORAIN COUNTY AUTOMOTIVE SYSTEMS INC

D-U-N-S 15-324-8695
LCC INTERNATIONAL INC
(*Suby of* TECH MAHINDRA LIMITED)
2201 Coop Way Ste 600, Herndon, VA 20171
Tel (703) 873-2065 *Founded/Ownrshp* 1996
Sales 186.0MM^E *EMP* 5,500^E
SIC 4813 4812 Telephone communication, except radio; Data telephone communications; Radio telephone communication
Pr: Kenneth Young
**Sr Pt:* Keith Paglusch
CFO: Simone D Carri
**CFO:* Rebecca Stahl
Treas: Louis Salamone Jr
**Sr VP:* Brian J Dunn
Sr VP: Doreen Trant
**VP:* Nancy O Feeney
Mng Dir: Ozgur Gulle
Genl Mgr: Arnaldo Palamidessi
Genl Mgr: Jarek Woroszy

LCEC
See LEE COUNTY ELECTRIC COOPERATIVE INC

D-U-N-S 05-492-7000
LCI HOLDCO LLC
(*Suby of* HOSPITAL ACQUISITION LLC) ★
5340 Legacy Dr Ste 150, Plano, TX 75024-3131
Tel (469) 241-2100 *Founded/Ownrshp* 2012
Sales 450.6MM^E *EMP* 7,800^E
SIC 8069 8051 Specialty hospitals, except psychiatric; Skilled nursing care facilities
CEO: Phillip B Douglas
**COO:* Stuart Archer
**Ex VP:* Grant B Asay
**Sr VP:* Greg Floyd

LCI HOLDING COMPANY, INC.
See ICL HOLDING CO INC

D-U-N-S 60-656-0233 IMP/EXP
■ LCI HOLDINGS INC
(*Suby of* KATE SPADE & CO) ★
5901 W Side Ave, North Bergen, NJ 07047-6451
Tel (201) 295-6300 *Founded/Ownrshp* 1988
Sales 399.6MM^E *EMP* 6,800
SIC 5651 5136 5137 5094 5122 5944 Family clothing stores; Men's & boys' clothing; Women's & children's clothing; Jewelry; Perfumes; Jewelry stores
CEO: Paul R Charron
**CFO:* Mike Scarpa
**Treas:* Robert Vill
VP: Steven Duva
**VP:* Elaine H Goodell
Exec: Patty Polise
**CIO:* John Sullivan
MIS Dir: John Ference
Counsel: Christopher Dinardo

D-U-N-S 07-835-8372
■ LCI INTERMEDIATE HOLDCO INC
(*Suby of* LCI HOLDING CO INC) ★
5340 Legacy Dr Bldg 4150, Plano, TX 75024-3178
Tel (469) 241-2100 *Founded/Ownrshp* 2005
Sales 33.9MM^E *EMP* 11,100
SIC 8069 8051 Specialty hospitals, except psychiatric; Skilled nursing care facilities
CEO: Phillip B Douglas

LCPS
See LOUDOUN COUNTY PUBLIC SCHOOL DISTRICT

D-U-N-S 00-810-6866 IMP/EXP
LCR-M LIMITED PARTNERSHIP
PLUMBING WAREHOUSE, THE
(*Suby of* WEINSTEIN SUPPLY) ★
6232 Siegen Ln, Baton Rouge, LA 70809-4157
Tel (225) 292-9910 *Founded/Ownrshp* 1995
Sales 223.4MM^E *EMP* 650
SIC 5074 Pipes & fittings, plastic; Plumbing & heating valves; Plumbers' brass goods & fittings
Genl Pt: Richard Klau
**Pt:* C Tom Bromley
**Pt:* Mark D Hanley
**Pt:* Karen V Landry
**Pt:* John D Lyle
**Pt:* A Lavoy Moore
**Pt:* Karl W Triche
Treas: C Pappo
Exec: Cherie Bourgeois
Genl Mgr: Roderick Johnson

LCRA
See LOWER COLORADO RIVER AUTHORITY

LCUB
See LENOIR CITY UTILITIES BOARD

LCW WIRELESS
See LEAP WIRELESS INTERNATIONAL INC

D-U-N-S 96-545-6275
LD COMMODITIES CITRUS HOLDINGS LLC
(*Suby of* LOUIS DREYFUS CO NORFOLK) ★
40 Danbury Rd, Wilton, CT 06897-4441
Tel (203) 761-2000 *Founded/Ownrshp* 2016
Sales 85.6MM^E *EMP* 124^E
SIC 6221 Commodity contracts brokers, dealers
Pr: Peter Hahn
Pr: Robert Eckert
COO: H Thomas Hayden
Treas: Serge Stepanov
VP: Erik Anderson
VP: Mark Gerardi
VP: Jeffery Zanchelli

D-U-N-S 00-906-2597 EXP
LD MCFARLAND CO LIMITED
MCFARLAND CASCADE
1640 E Marc St, Tacoma, WA 98421
Tel (253) 572-5670 *Founded/Ownrshp* 1916
Sales 125.8MM^E *EMP* 500
SIC 2499 2491 2411 Poles, wood; Poles & pole crossarms, treated wood; Logging
CEO: B Corry Mc Farland
Pr: Wayne Wilkinson
VP: L W Docter
VP: Greg D Mc Farland
Manager: Terry Berg

D-U-N-S 18-850-5213 IMP
LD PRODUCTS INC
4INKJETS.COM
3700 Cover St, Long Beach, CA 90808-1782
Tel (562) 986-6940 *Founded/Ownrshp* 2005
Sales 149.8MM^E *EMP* 150
Accts Woo San Ramon Ca
SIC 5045 2621 Printers, computer; Stationery, envelope & tablet papers
CEO: Aaron Leon
**Sr VP:* Patrick Devane
QA Dir: David Calkins
QA Dir: Eric Chun
IT Man: Michael Fernandez
Software D: Lewis Lee
Software D: Huy Nguyen
Netwrk Eng: James Easter
Snr Mgr: Chad Abercrombie
Snr Mgr: Brenna Welch

LDC HOLDING INC.
See LOUIS DREYFUS CO HOLDING INC

LDF FOOD GROUP
See LDF SALES & DISTRIBUTING INC

D-U-N-S 09-144-3333
LDF FOOD GROUP INC
WENDY'S
10610 E 26th Cir N, Wichita, KS 67226-4536
Tel (316) 630-0677 *Founded/Ownrshp* 1977
Sales 5.0MM *EMP* 1,400
SIC 5812 Fast-food restaurant, chain
Ch Bd: Larry D Fleming
**Pr:* Don Haynes
**Treas:* Dennis Kirkhart
Sr VP: Jim Cook
**VP:* Rick Albrecht

D-U-N-S 10-407-5874
LDF SALES & DISTRIBUTING INC
LDF FOOD GROUP
10610 E 26th Cir N, Wichita, KS 67226-4536
Tel (316) 636-5575 *Founded/Ownrshp* 1950
Sales 419.4MM^E *EMP* 1,500^E
SIC 5181 Beer & other fermented malt liquors
Ch Bd: Larry D Fleming
**Sr VP:* Dennis Kirkhart
**VP:* Rick Albreck
**VP:* David Alferd
Area Mgr: Garry Davis
Area Mgr: Chris Oleson
IT Man: Chris Herman
VP Opers: Brad Knott

D-U-N-S 05-116-6782
LDI LOGISTICS INC
(*Suby of* LACY DISTRIBUTION INC) ★
54 Monument Cir Ste 800, Indianapolis, IN 46204-2949
Tel (317) 237-5400 *Founded/Ownrshp* 2010
Sales 253.8MM^E *EMP* 1,000
SIC 4731 Agents, shipping; Brokers, shipping
CEO: Ja Lacy
**Treas:* Jon Black
**VP:* Bill Himebrook
**VP:* Ryan Polk

D-U-N-S 78-871-3063
LDI LTD LLC
54 Monument Cir Ste 800, Indianapolis, IN 46204-2949
Tel (317) 237-5400 *Founded/Ownrshp* 1987
Sales 18.9MM^E *EMP* 7,415
SIC 6719 Investment holding companies, except banks
Ch Bd: Andre B Lacy
**CEO:* Ja Lacy
VP: Margot Eccles
**VP:* Bill Himebrook
VP: Ryan Polk
VP: Joyce Schooley

D-U-N-S 05-876-3913
LDI MECHANICAL INC
1587 E Bentley Dr, Corona, CA 92879-1738
Tel (951) 340-9685 *Founded/Ownrshp* 1985
Sales 103.7MM^E *EMP* 400^E
SIC 1711 Heating & air conditioning contractors
Pr: Lloyd Smith
CFO: Robert Sylvester
Chf Mktg O: Bridgett Robinson
Ofcr: Derek Schaper
**Sr VP:* Mike Smith
Sr VP: Sandy Smith
**VP:* Steve Buren
**VP:* Jeff Minarik

D-U-N-S 78-581-5312
■ LDR HOLDING CORP
(*Suby of* ZIMMER BIOMET HOLDINGS INC) ★
13785 Res Blvd Ste 200, Austin, TX 78750
Tel (512) 344-3333 *Founded/Ownrshp* 2016
Sales 164.4MM *EMP* 290
SIC 3841 Surgical & medical instruments
Pr: Christophe Lavigne
CFO: Robert McNamara
Ex VP: Scott Way
VP: Herve Dinville
VP Sls: Andre Potgieter
Manager: Tim Elrod
Board of Directors: Joseph Aragona, William W Burke, Matthew Crawford, Kevin M Lalande, Alan Milinazzo, Thomas A Raffin, Pierre Remy, Stefan Widensohler

D-U-N-S 08-136-7104
LDRV HOLDINGS CORP
LAZYDAYS RV CAMPGROUND
6130 Lazy Days Blvd, Seffner, FL 33584-2968
Tel (813) 246-4333 *Founded/Ownrshp* 2004
Sales 293.8MM^E *EMP* 500^E
SIC 5561 Travel trailers: automobile, new & used; Motor homes; Recreational vehicle parts & accessories
Pr: John Horton
CFO: Randall Lay
Sls Mgr: James Paredes
Sales Asso: Todd Wallace

D-U-N-S 80-041-5940
LDS HOSPITAL
8th Ave C St, Salt Lake City, UT 84143-0001
Tel (801) 408-1100 *Founded/Ownrshp* 1983
Sales 256.4MM *EMP* 48^E
SIC 8062 General medical & surgical hospitals
Pr: Bill Nelson
COO: Becky Kapp
VP: Sandra Smith
Exec: Heather Ashby
Exec: Mary Virden
Dir Rad: Edgar J Booth
Dir Rad: Margaret F Ensign
Dir Rad: Frank V Gabor
Dir Rad: Colleen P Harker
Dir Rad: John M Jacobs
Dir Rad: Denise Rodgers

LE BONHEUR CHILDREN'S HOSPITAL
See METHODIST HEALTHCARE MEMPHIS HOSPITALS

D-U-N-S 08-470-7694 IMP/EXP
LE CREUSET OF AMERICA INC
(*Suby of* LE CREUSET)
114 Bob Gifford Blvd, Early Branch, SC 29916-4138
Tel (803) 943-4308 *Founded/Ownrshp* 1977
Sales 139.5MM^E *EMP* 400
SIC 5023 Kitchen tools & utensils
CEO: Faye Gooding
**Sec:* Andrew J Belger Jr
VP: Donald Hilberand
Rgnl Mgr: Denise Vargo
VP Mktg: Stephen Jones

D-U-N-S 07-879-2909
LE DUFF AMERICA INC
12201 Merit Dr Ste 900, Dallas, TX 75251-3139
Tel (214) 540-1867 *Founded/Ownrshp* 2011
Sales 283.1MM^E *EMP* 7,690^E
SIC 5812 American restaurant
CEO: Claude Bergeron
**COO:* Miguel Fernandez
**CFO:* Mike Clock

LE GOURMET CHEF
See KITCHEN COLLECTION LLC

D-U-N-S 60-339-8488
LE JEUNE STEEL CO
(*Suby of* API GROUP INC) ★
118 W 60th St, Minneapolis, MN 55419-2319
Tel (612) 861-3321 *Founded/Ownrshp* 1989
Sales 180.3MM *EMP* 105
Accts Kpmg Llp Minneapolis Mn
SIC 3441 Fabricated structural metal; Building components, structural steel; Fabricated structural metal for bridges
Pr: Jim Torborg
CFO: Bryan L Kuha
**Treas:* Gregory Keup
**Sr VP:* Mike Histon
MIS Dir: Clay Kimber

D-U-N-S 05-372-3094
LE MOYNE COLLEGE
1419 Salt Springs Rd, Syracuse, NY 13214-1301
Tel (315) 445-4100 *Founded/Ownrshp* 1946
Sales 123.2MM *EMP* 500
Accts Kpmg Llp Albany Ny
SIC 8221 College, except junior
Pr: Linda Lamura
Treas: Thomas Oneil
**Treas:* Roger W Stackpoole
VP: Bill Brower
VP: Allison Herholtz
VP: Deborah Melzer
MIS Dir: Michael Donlin

LE PAIN QUOTIDIEN
See PQ NEW YORK INC

D-U-N-S 01-302-3549
LE PETIT PAIN HOLDINGS LLC
676 N Michigan Ave, Chicago, IL 60611-2883
Tel (312) 981-3770 *Founded/Ownrshp* 2013
Sales 170.6MM^E *EMP* 1,473^E
SIC 2051 Bakery: wholesale or wholesale/retail combined

LE SUEUR CHEESE DIVISION
See DAVISCO FOODS INTERNATIONAL INC

D-U-N-S 00-624-9627 IMP
LE SUEUR INC (MN)
ALUMINUM DIV
1409 Vine St, Le Sueur, MN 56058-1125
Tel (507) 665-6204 Founded/Ownrshp 1946
Sales 110.9MM[E] EMP 630
SIC 3363 3089 3544 3369 Aluminum die-castings; Injection molding of plastics; Special dies, tools, jigs & fixtures; Nonferrous foundries
CEO: Mark C Mueller
Pr: Henry J Prevot
CFO: Larry Busch
Treas: Janet Mueller
Genl Mgr: Mike Horton
Genl Mgr: Michael Jindra
CTO: Dave Gagnon
Info Man: Karl Lamm
Sfty Mgr: Eric Retzlaff
Mfg Mgr: John Acker
Plnt Mgr: Nick Schroer

D-U-N-S 60-201-7709 IMP
■ **LEACH GARNER - A BERKSHIRE HATHAWAY CO**
(Suby of STERN METALS, INC.)
49 Pearl St, Attleboro, MA 02703-3940
Tel (508) 222-7400 Founded/Ownrshp 2012
Sales 178.6MM[E] EMP 500
SIC 5094 Jewelry & precious stones
Pr: Joe White
VP: Dennis Breneiser
*VP: Fred Poluhovich
VP Mktg: Peter Clark
VP Mktg: Dick Smith
Mktg Dir: Ed Rigano

D-U-N-S 08-258-8559
■ **LEACH INTERNATIONAL CORP**
ESTERLINE POWER SYSTEMS
(Suby of ESTERLINE TECHNOLOGIES CORP) ★
6900 Orangethorpe Ave, Buena Park, CA 90620-1390
Tel (714) 736-7537 Founded/Ownrshp 1919, 2004
Sales 256.6MM[E] EMP 1,000
SIC 3679 Electronic circuits
CEO: Richard Brad Lawrence
*Pr: Mark Thek
VP: Diana Bourcier
*VP: Alain Durand
Dir Bus: Franck Kolczak
Ex Dir: Grace Quintero
MIS Dir: Phil Sealana
Sftwr Eng: David Lawton
VP Sls: Tim Ostrosky
S&M/VP: Frank Breslin

LEADER DRUG STORE
See LITTLE CO OF MARY HOSPITAL

LEADING COMMUNICATION CONTRS
See PRINCE TELECOM LLC

D-U-N-S 18-865-3042
LEAF COMMERCIAL CAPITAL INC
2005 Market St Fl 14, Philadelphia, PA 19103-7009
Tel (800) 819-5556 Founded/Ownrshp 1995
Sales NA EMP 230
SIC 6159 7359 Equipment & vehicle finance leasing companies; Equipment rental & leasing
Ch Bd: Crit S Dement
*Pr: Miles Herman
*CFO: Robert Moskovitz
Treas: Matthew Goldenberg
*Ex VP: David English
Sr VP: Nicholas Capparelli
VP: Paul Tyczkowski
Genl Mgr: John Beard
CTO: Earle Compton
IT Man: Mike McKie
Sls Dir: Bob Herman

D-U-N-S 78-449-6283 EXP
LEAF RIVER CELLULOSE LLC
(Suby of GP CELLULOSE LLC) ★
157 Buck Creek Rd, New Augusta, MS 39462-6070
Tel (601) 964-8411 Founded/Ownrshp 2004
Sales 128.9MM[E] EMP 300
SIC 2676 Diapers, paper (disposable): made from purchased paper
IT Man: Brad Hoefler

D-U-N-S 01-053-6910
LEANDER INDEPENDENT SCHOOL DISTRICT
204 W South St, Leander, TX 78641-1719
Tel (512) 570-0000 Founded/Ownrshp 1948
Sales 124.2MM[E] EMP 2,700
SIC 8211 Public elementary school; Public junior high school; Public senior high school
Assoc Dir: Michael Howard
Comm Dir: Dick Ellis
Ex Dir: Nancy Scott
Dir Sec: Russell Summers
Pr Dir: Lisa Napper

D-U-N-S 03-807-4188
■ **LEAP WIRELESS INTERNATIONAL INC**
LCW WIRELESS
(Suby of AT&T INC) ★
7337 Trade St, San Diego, CA 92121-2423
Tel (858) 882-6000 Founded/Ownrshp 1998
Sales 1.3MMM[E] EMP 2,984[E]
SIC 4812 Radio telephone communication
CEO: S Douglas Hutcheson
*Pr: Jerry V Elliott
COO: Cherrie Nanninga
*CFO: R Perley McBride
*Ofcr: William D Ingram
Ofcr: Perley McBride
Sr VP: Erik Gerson
Sr VP: Colin E Holland
Sr VP: Anne Liu
Sr VP: Aaron P Maddox
Sr VP: Catherine Shackleford
Sr VP: Leonard C Stephens
VP: John H Casey III
*VP: Amy Wakeham
Board of Directors: Nick W Jones

D-U-N-S 87-928-8470 IMP/EXP
LEAPFROG ENTERPRISES INC
6401 Hollis St Ste 100, Emeryville, CA 94608-1463
Tel (510) 420-5000 Founded/Ownrshp 2015
Sales 339.1MM EMP 579
SIC 3944 Games, toys & children's vehicles
CEO: Nick Delany
*Pr: William To
Ex VP: Nancy G Macintyre
Ex VP: Nancy Macintyre
Ex VP: Nancy G Mcintyre
Sr VP: William K Campbell
Sr VP: Craig R Hendrickson
Sr VP: Hilda S West
VP: Robert L Lattuga
VP: Karen L Luey
VP: Sarah Mason
VP: Sarah Shin
VP: Chris Spalding
VP: Scott A Steinberg
VP: Jill Waller
Exec: Diane Andreoli

D-U-N-S 15-780-3792
LEAR CAPITAL INC
1990 S Bundy Dr Ste 600, Los Angeles, CA 90025-5256
Tel (310) 571-0190 Founded/Ownrshp 2013
Sales 360.0MM[E] EMP 72
SIC 6211 Mineral, oil & gas leasing & royalty dealers
Pr: Kevin Demerit
CFO: Scott Robinson
Mktg Dir: Cher Cusumano

D-U-N-S 17-559-2476
▲ **LEAR CORP**
21557 Telegraph Rd, Southfield, MI 48033-4248
Tel (248) 447-1500 Founded/Ownrshp 1917
Sales 18.2MMM EMP 136,200
Accts Ernst & Young Llp Detroit Mi
Tkr Sym LEA Exch NYS
SIC 3714 2531 2396 3643 Motor vehicle electrical equipment; Instrument board assemblies, motor vehicle; Automotive wiring harness sets; Motor vehicle body components & frame; Seats, automobile; Automotive & apparel trimmings; Current-carrying wiring devices
Pr: Matthew J Simoncini
V Ch: James Vandenberghe
Pr: Jay K Kunkel
Pr: Frank C Orsini
Pr: Raymond E Scott
CFO: Jeffrey H Vanneste
Treas: Jeff Mayer
Ex VP: Terrence B Larkin
Ex VP: Terry Larkin
Sr VP: Thomas A Didonato
Sr VP: Melvin L Stephens
VP: Dean M Ackerman
VP: Jason Cardew
VP: Oscar Dominguez
VP: Steve Gardon
VP: Dan Golles
VP: Jeneanne Hanley
VP: Mario Krug
VP: James L Murawski
VP: Nicholas Pearson
VP: Lisa Samartino
Board of Directors: Richard H Bott, Thomas P Capo, Jonathan F Foster, Mary Lou Jepsen, Kathleen A Ligocki, Conrad L Mallett Jr, Donald L Runkle, Gregory C Smith, Henry D G Wallace

D-U-N-S 96-055-9383 IMP/EXP
■ **LEAR OPERATIONS CORP**
(Suby of LEAR CORP) ★
21557 Telegraph Rd, Southfield, MI 48033-4248
Tel (248) 447-1500 Founded/Ownrshp 1995
Sales 372.2MM[E] EMP 4,011
SIC 3089 Plastic processing
Pr: Robert Rossiter
*Treas: Sherri Burgess

D-U-N-S 06-243-7058
LEARFIELD COMMUNICATIONS INC
505 Hobbs Rd, Jefferson City, MO 65109-5788
Tel (573) 893-7200 Founded/Ownrshp 2013
Sales 192.0MM[E] EMP 465
SIC 4832 4841 Radio broadcasting stations; Cable & other pay television services
Pr: Clyde G Lear
Ex VP: Doug A Bax
VP: John Raleigh
VP: David A Rawlings
*VP: Andy Rollings
VP: James A Worsham
Genl Mgr: Ryan Grant
Genl Mgr: Thomas Morris

D-U-N-S 00-723-4313 IMP
LEARJET INC
BOMBARDIER AVIATION SERVICES
(Suby of BOMBARDIER INC)
1 Learjet Way, Wichita, KS 67209-2924
Tel (316) 946-2000 Founded/Ownrshp 1990
Sales 1.0MMM[E] EMP 4,482
SIC 3721 3812 Aircraft; Search & navigation equipment
VP: Jim Ziegler
CFO: Sylvie Desjardins
Treas: Cody Chandler
VP: Paul Comeau
VP: Chris Crawshaw
VP: Ed Thomas
Prgrm Mgr: Brian Botts
Dir IT: Jocelyn Gauthier
IT Man: Matt Ediger
IT Man: Kassi McCabe
Sls Mgr: Nic Aliaga

D-U-N-S 10-125-9596
LEARN
44 Hatchetts Hill Rd, Old Lyme, CT 06371-1512
Tel (860) 434-4800 Founded/Ownrshp 1966
Sales 37.6MM EMP 1,000[E]
Accts Cohn Reznick Llp New London
SIC 8299 Educational services
Ex Dir: Dr Eileen Howley
*CEO: Mary Royce
*CFO: Jean Paul Leblanc
*Ex Dir: Virginia Seccombe
Off Mgr: Gail Foley

D-U-N-S 96-824-6061
LEARNING CARE GROUP (US) INC
21333 Haggerty Rd Ste 300, Novi, MI 48375-5537
Tel (248) 697-9000 Founded/Ownrshp 2014
Sales 627.6MM[E] EMP 17,000[E]
SIC 8351 Child day care services
CEO: Barbara J Beck
*COO: Leigh-Ellen Louie
*CFO: Robert T Vanhees

D-U-N-S 80-727-4923
LEARNING CARE GROUP INC
(Suby of LA PETITE ACADEMY) ★
130 S Jefferson St # 300, Chicago, IL 60661-3687
Tel (312) 469-5656 Founded/Ownrshp 1993
Sales 420.8MM EMP 6
Accts Deloitte & Touche Llp Chicago
SIC 8351 Child day care services
Pr: Gary A Graves
*Ch Bd: Stephen P Murray
CFO: Neil P Dyment
Treas: Daniel J Knight
Ofcr: William H Van Huis
VP: Lawrence Appell
VP: William C Buckland
VP: Gregory S Davis
VP: Stephan Laudicino
VP: Lisa J Miskimins
VP: Leah L Oliva
VP: Stephanie L Pasche
VP: Hugh W Tracy

D-U-N-S 93-395-1618
LEARNING CARE GROUP INC
(Suby of LEARNING CARE GROUP (US) INC) ★
21333 Haggerty Rd Ste 300, Novi, MI 48375-5537
Tel (248) 697-9000 Founded/Ownrshp 2008
Sales 438.9MM[E] EMP 17,000
SIC 8351 8299 Child day care services; Educational services
Ch Bd: Benjamin Jacobson
Pr: Mark R Bierley
Pr: Teri Davies
CEO: Barbara J Beck
COO: Kathryn L Myers
CFO: Frank M Jerneycic
CFO: Robert Vanhees
Chf Cred: Daniel Follis Jr
Chf Mktg O: John Lichtenberg
VP: William Burgess
VP: Linda Cassidy
VP: Ahmad Malik
VP: Anne Manousos
VP: Kathryn Peel
VP: Tim Truly
Exec: Judy Duncan
Exec: Scott W Smith
Comm Dir: Lydia Cisaruk

D-U-N-S 09-946-4729
▲ **LEARNING TREE INTERNATIONAL INC**
13650 Dulles Tech Dr # 400, Herndon, VA 20171-4649
Tel (703) 709-9119 Founded/Ownrshp 1974
Sales 94.8MM EMP 727
Tkr Sym LTRE Exch OTO
SIC 8243 Data processing schools
CEO: Richard A Spires
*Ch Bd: David C Collins
Pr: Max Shevitz
CFO: David W Asai
VP: Dan Rush
VP: Knut Skare
Exec: Lyle Davis
Dir Rx: Timothy Vatne
Dir Sec: Gregory L Adams
CIO: Magnus Nylund
Opers Mgr: Ian Huckle
Board of Directors: Howard A Bain III, Mary C Collins, Henri Hodara, W Mathew Juechter, John R Phillips

D-U-N-S 04-182-8294 EXP
LEASE PLAN USA INC
LEASEPLAN
(Suby of LEASEPLAN CORPORATION N.V.)
1165 Sanctuary Pkwy, Alpharetta, GA 30009-4797
Tel (770) 933-9090 Founded/Ownrshp 1983
Sales 1.8MMM EMP 550
SIC 7515 8741 Passenger car leasing; Management services
Pr: Michael A Pitcher
COO: Mark Flanders
CFO: George Astrauckas
*CFO: David G Dahm
Sr VP: Brian Barber
*Sr VP: John Jaje
*Sr VP: Paul Kennedy
*Sr VP: Tim Martin
Sr VP: Bryan Steele
*Sr VP: Jon Toups
VP: Robert O Hughes
VP: Dan Shive
VP: Michael Wren
Board of Directors: Hans Peter Lutzenkirchen, Abe Tomas

LEASEPLAN
See LEASE PLAN USA INC

D-U-N-S 14-497-8772 IMP/EXP
LEATHERMAN TOOL GROUP INC
12106 Ne Ainsworth Cir, Portland, OR 97220-9001
Tel (503) 253-7826 Founded/Ownrshp 1983
Sales 89.0MM[E] EMP 450[E]
SIC 3421

D-U-N-S 02-765-1090
LEATHERS ENTERPRISES INC
LEATHERS OIL COMPANY
255 Depot St, Fairview, OR 97024
Tel (503) 661-1244 Founded/Ownrshp 1959
Sales 94.8MM EMP 75
SIC 5541 6519 Filling stations, gasoline; Real property lessors
Pr: Lila Leathers-Fitz
*VP: Kathryn Leathers
*Prin: Brent Leathers

LEATHERS OIL COMPANY
See LEATHERS ENTERPRISES INC

D-U-N-S 00-759-7313
LEAVITT GROUP ENTERPRISES INC
216 S 200 W, Cedar City, UT 84720-3207
Tel (435) 586-1555 Founded/Ownrshp 1962
Sales NA EMP 1,272
Accts Bdo Usa Llp Las Vegas Nv
SIC 6153 8741 6411 Working capital financing; Management services; Insurance agents, brokers & service
CEO: Eric Leavitt
*Treas: Craig O Marchant
Bd of Dir: Mike Chidester
*Sr VP: Bruce Crankshaw
*Sr VP: Nathan Esplin
*Sr VP: Rod Leavitt
*Sr VP: Kelly Russell
VP: Julie Beezley
VP: Robert Carrington
*VP: Michael Chidester
VP: Gregory Gates
VP: Mary Grandy
VP: Cathy Huntsman
VP: Bracken Longhurst
VP: Greg Massey
VP: Terri Peckinpaugh
VP: Derek Snow
VP: Chris Utterback
VP: Guy Wallrath

D-U-N-S 10-329-2082
LEBANESE AMERICAN UNIVERSITY
211 E 46th St Fl 3, New York, NY 10017-2912
Tel (212) 203-4333 Founded/Ownrshp 1950
Sales 203.6MM EMP 13
Accts Lb Plante & Moran Pllc Auburn
SIC 8221 University
Pr: Dr Joseph G Jabbra

LEBANON COMMUNITY HOSPITAL
See MID-VALLEY HEALTHCARE INC

D-U-N-S 01-057-7724
LEBANON COUNTY
400 S 8th St Ste 1, Lebanon, PA 17042-6794
Tel (717) 274-2801 Founded/Ownrshp 1813
Sales NA EMP 1,190
SIC 9111 Executive offices;
Treas: Sally Neuin
IT Man: Stephanie Axarlis
IT Man: Brian Deiderick
IT Man: James Holtry

LEBANON FORD
See FORD LEBANON INC

D-U-N-S 09-566-8091
■ **LEBANON HMA LLC**
UNIVERSITY MEDICAL CENTER HOSP
(Suby of HMA) ★
1411 W Baddour Pkwy, Lebanon, TN 37087-2513
Tel (615) 444-8262 Founded/Ownrshp 2003
Sales 99.5MM EMP 700
SIC 8062 General medical & surgical hospitals
CEO: Vins Cherry
*CEO: Matt Caldwell
*COO: Greg Carda
Doctor: Haroon Kahn
Doctor: Robert Patti
Pharmcst: Tom Keifer
HC Dir: Andria Oliver

D-U-N-S 00-300-5477 IMP/EXP
LEBANON SEABOARD CORP (PA)
1600 E Cumberland St, Lebanon, PA 17042-8323
Tel (717) 273-1685 Founded/Ownrshp 1947
Sales 147.6MM EMP 300
SIC 5191 2875 2048

LEBANON SUPPLY COMPANY
See INDEPENDENT STAVE CO LLC

D-U-N-S 00-130-4534 IMP
LEBHAR-FRIEDMAN INC (NY)
CHAIN STORES AGE
150 W 30th St Fl 19, New York, NY 10001-4119
Tel (212) 756-5000 Founded/Ownrshp 1925
Sales 111.5MM[E] EMP 460
SIC 2721 2711 Magazines: publishing only, not printed on site; Newspapers: publishing only, not printed on site
Pr: J Roger Friedman
*Pr: Daniel J Mills
Ex Dir: Katherine Boccaccio
Sls Dir: Michael Morrissey
Assoc Ed: Drew Buono

LECESSE CONSTRUCTION COMPANY
See LAHR CONSTRUCTION CORP

D-U-N-S 03-651-9767
LECHASE CONSTRUCTION SERVICES LLC
205 Indigo Creek Dr, Rochester, NY 14626-5100
Tel (585) 254-3510 Founded/Ownrshp 1997
Sales 538.6MM[E] EMP 780
SIC 1541 1542 Industrial buildings, new construction; Renovation, remodeling & repairs: industrial buildings; Nonresidential construction; Institutional building construction; Commercial & office building, new construction; Commercial & office buildings, renovation & repair
CEO: William H Goodrich
*Pr: William H Goodrich
*Pr: William L Mack
Pr: Thomas W Porter
COO: Bill B Goodrich
*Ch: Wayne Le Chase
VP: Richard Allen
VP: H Brewer
VP: William Herbert
VP: Raymond R Lechase
VP: Michael J Mallon
VP: Jim Matteson
VP: James Mulcahy
VP: Gary Roth
VP: Brian J Russo
*Exec: Raymond F Lechase II
Dir Risk M: Michelle Keller

D-U-N-S 18-344-1732
LECLAIRRYAN A PROFESSNL CORP
951 E Byrd St Fl 8, Richmond, VA 23219-4055
Tel (804) 783-2003 Founded/Ownrshp 1989
Sales 124.4MM^E EMP 715
SIC 8111 General practice law office
CEO: David C Freinberg
Mng Pt: Gilles Cariou
Mng Pt: Xavier Normand
*Ch Bd: Gary D Leclair
*Pr: Micheal L Hern
*COO: Dennis M Ryan
*CFO: Joseph D Cheely
*VP: Douglas L Sbertoli
CIO: Howard Phillips

D-U-N-S 00-506-8861
LECO CORP
TEM-PRESS DIVISION
3000 Lakeview Ave, Saint Joseph, MI 49085-2319
Tel (269) 983-5531 Founded/Ownrshp 1936
Sales 298.8MM^E EMP 725
Accts Bdo Usa Llp Kalamazoo Mi
SIC 4493 3821 3826 3825 3823 3264 Boat yards, storage & incidental repair; Marine basins; Laboratory apparatus, except heating & measuring; Chemical laboratory apparatus; Analytical instruments; Instruments to measure electricity; Industrial instrmnts msrmnt display/control process variable; Porcelain electrical supplies
Pr: Carl S Warren
*Pr: B John Hawkins
*Pr: Larry S O'Brien
*Pr: Elizabeth S Warren
*Ex VP: Christopher J Warren
*VP: Joel D Debruyne
Genl Mgr: Melissa Rogers
IT Man: Kevin McNitt
Web Dev: Tyler Newton
Ql Cn Mgr: Bradley Wilson
Sls Dir: Nick Hall

LECOM
See LAKE ERIE COLLEGE OF OSTEOPATHIC MEDICINE INC

LEDBETTER PACKING
See EMPIRE PACKING CO LP

D-U-N-S 78-670-6296
LEDCOR CMI INC
6405 Mira Mesa Blvd # 100, San Diego, CA 92121-4120
Tel (602) 595-3017 Founded/Ownrshp 2003
Sales 158.5MM^E EMP 5,000
SIC 1541 1611 1629 1623 1522 8999 Industrial buildings & warehouses; Highway & street construction; Mine loading & discharging station construction; Industrial plant construction; Pipeline construction; Condominium construction; Communication services
CEO: David W Lede

D-U-N-S 07-633-0500
LEDCOR CONSTRUCTION INC
LEDCOR GROUP
(Suby of LEDCOR HOLDINGS INC)
6405 Mira Mesa Blvd # 100, San Diego, CA 92121-4120
Tel (858) 527-6400 Founded/Ownrshp 2001
Sales 92.1MM^E EMP 150
SIC 1542 Commercial & office building, new construction
CEO: Christopher Bourassa
*CFO: James Logan
VP: Lee Coonfer
VP: Ron Hughes
Exec: Dave Jeffrey

LEDCOR GROUP
See LEDCOR CONSTRUCTION INC

D-U-N-S 17-434-5934
LEDGEWOOD HEALTH CARE CORP
LEDGEWOOD NURSING CARE CENTER
87 Herrick St, Beverly, MA 01915-2773
Tel (978) 524-6100 Founded/Ownrshp 1984
Sales 1.4MMM EMP 140
SIC 8051 Skilled nursing care facilities
*Pr: James Dunn
*Treas: Greg Sorrell
*VP: Richard Blinn

LEDGEWOOD NURSING CARE CENTER
See LEDGEWOOD HEALTH CARE CORP

D-U-N-S 08-028-7250
LEDVANCE LLC
(Suby of OSRAM SYLVANIA INC) ★
200 Ballardvale St, Wilmington, MA 01887-1074
Tel (978) 570-3000 Founded/Ownrshp 2015
Sales 1.2MMM^E EMP 1,281^E
SIC 5063 Lighting fixtures
CEO: Jes Munk Hansen

D-U-N-S 00-713-1501
■ **LEE APPAREL CO INC** (PA)
(Suby of VF CORP) ★
1 Lee Dr, Shawnee Mission, KS 66202-3620
Tel (913) 789-0330 Founded/Ownrshp 1889
Sales 583.8MM^E EMP 10,300
SIC 2325 2339 Jeans: men's, youths' & boys'; Jeans: women's, misses' & juniors'
Pr: Terry Lay
Pr: Claudia Broddus
CFO: Mike Mitchell
Board of Directors: William C Hardy, G G Johnson, Mackey J McDonald, Frank C Pickard III, L R Pugh

D-U-N-S 13-161-2335 IMP
LEE BROS FOODSERVICES INC
LEE INDUSTRIAL CATERING
660 E Gish Rd, San Jose, CA 95112-2707
Tel (408) 275-0700 Founded/Ownrshp 1985
Sales 94.7MM^E EMP 150
SIC 5141 5142 Groceries, general line; Packaged frozen goods
CEO: Chieu Van Le

*VP: Huong Le
*VP: Jimmy Lee
MIS Dir: David Hui

D-U-N-S 00-116-2395 IMP
LEE CO (CT)
2 Pettipaug Rd, Westbrook, CT 06498-1500
Tel (860) 399-6281 Founded/Ownrshp 1949, 1948
Sales 221.5MM^E EMP 915
SIC 3823 3841 3812 3728 3714 Fluidic devices, circuits & systems for process control; Surgical & medical instruments; Search & navigation equipment; Aircraft parts & equipment; Motor vehicle parts & accessories
Pr: William W Lee
*CFO: Alex M Corl
*Ch: Leighton Lee III
*Ex VP: Robert M Lee
VP: William Buckridge
VP: Reid Hanford
VP: Bob Hawtin
Exec: Michael Curtis
Dist Mgr: Ryan Dieterle
Dist Mgr: Leland Parker
Dist Mgr: Jeff Svadlenak

D-U-N-S 06-908-8680
LEE CO (TN)
TENNESEE LEE COMPANY
331 Mallory Station Rd, Franklin, TN 37067-8257
Tel (615) 567-1000 Founded/Ownrshp 1965
Sales 165.1MM EMP 820
SIC 1711 Plumbing contractors; Warm air heating & air conditioning contractor; Refrigeration contractor
CEO: William B Lee
*Pr: Richard C Perko
Pr: Gerry Vance
*CFO: Roy B Osborne
*Ex VP: Gerald R Vance
*Sr VP: Stuart L Price
VP: Amanda Lee
*VP: Steve Scott
Off Mgr: Anne McPhaill
Dir IT: Tom Goddard
Dir IT: Chris Young

D-U-N-S 79-151-5455
LEE CONTRACTING INC
LEE INDUSTRIAL CONTRACTING
631 Cesar E Chavez Ave, Pontiac, MI 48342-1074
Tel (888) 833-8776 Founded/Ownrshp 1995
Sales 115.6MM^E EMP 150
SIC 1731 1542 1541 Electrical work; Commercial & office building, new construction; Industrial buildings, new construction
Pr: Edward E Lee

D-U-N-S 00-384-0337
LEE COUNTY ELECTRIC COOPERATIVE INC
LCEC
4980 Bayline Dr, Fort Myers, FL 33917-3998
Tel (800) 599-2356 Founded/Ownrshp 1940
Sales 405.9MM EMP 400
SIC 4911 Electric services
CEO: Dennie Hamilton
*CFO: Donald Schleicher
IT Man: Susan Crisafulli
IT Man: Stanley Hyde
IT Man: Frederic Kunzi
Software D: Cindy Neumann
Netwrk Eng: Brian Klepper
Mktg Dir: Barbara Panellino
Mktg Mgr: Melissa Miller

D-U-N-S 06-743-9703
LEE COUNTY OF (INC)
106 Hillcrest Dr, Sanford, NC 27330-4021
Tel (919) 718-4600 Founded/Ownrshp 1907
Sales NA EMP 1,105
Accts Thompson Price Scott Adams
SIC 9111 County supervisors' & executives' offices
Ofcr: Bettina Seymoure
Ofcr: Omayra Zagada
IT Man: Core Eckel
IT Man: Kyle Edwards

D-U-N-S 06-591-2354
LEE COUNTY PUBLIC SCHOOLS
(Suby of COUNTY OF LEE) ★
2855 Colonial Blvd, Fort Myers, FL 33966-1012
Tel (239) 337-8523 Founded/Ownrshp 1934
Sales 845.4MM EMP 1,000
Accts Auditor General State Of Flori
SIC 8211 Public elementary & secondary schools; Elementary school; High school, junior or senior
Bd of Dir: Cathleen Morgan
Ex Dir: William Tubb

D-U-N-S 07-989-3932
LEE COUNTY SCHOOL DISTRICT
2410 Society Hill Rd, Opelika, AL 36804-4830
Tel (334) 705-6000 Founded/Ownrshp 2015
Sales 34.0MM^E EMP 1,200^E
SIC 8211 Public elementary & secondary schools
Ofcr: Margie Smith
Teacher Pr: Michelle Washington

D-U-N-S 10-005-8734
LEE COUNTY SCHOOLS
106 Gordon St, Sanford, NC 27330-3960
Tel (919) 774-6226 Founded/Ownrshp 1977
Sales 59.3MM^E EMP 1,000
SIC 8211 Public elementary & secondary schools; School board
Bd of Dir: Sylvia Womble

D-U-N-S 01-441-9532
LEE COUNTY SHERIFF DEPARTMENT
14750 6 Mile Cypress Pkwy, Fort Myers, FL 33912-4406
Tel (239) 477-1000 Founded/Ownrshp 1887
Sales NA EMP 1,800
SIC 9221 Police protection

LEE DESIGN STUDIO
See LEE SUPPLY CORP

D-U-N-S 17-705-7627
LEE ELECTRICAL CONSTRUCTION INC
12828 Us Highway 15 501, Aberdeen, NC 28315-4902
Tel (910) 944-9728 Founded/Ownrshp 1985
Sales 144.6MM^E EMP 500
SIC 1731 Lighting contractor; Electric power systems contractors
Pr: Jerry Lee
*VP: Donald Lee
IT Man: Kim Jordn
Sfty Dirs: Todd Williams

D-U-N-S 00-526-4064
▲ **LEE ENTERPRISES INC**
201 N Harrison St Ste 600, Davenport, IA 52801-1924
Tel (563) 383-2100 Founded/Ownrshp 1890
Sales 614.3MM EMP 4,500
Tkr Sym LEE Exch NYS
SIC 2711 Newspapers
Pr: Kevin D Mowbray
Pr: John M Humenik
CFO: Jayne Behal
CFO: Ronald A Mayo
*Ch: Mary E Junck
VP: Nathan E Bekke
VP: Paul M Farrell
VP: Robert P Fleck
VP: Robert Fleck
VP: James A Green
VP: Bill Masterson
VP: Michael E Phelps
*VP: Gregory P Schermer
Board of Directors: Richard R Cole, Nancy S Donovan, Leonard J Elmore, Brent Magid, William E Mayer, Herbert W Moloney III, Andrew E Newman, Mark B Vittert

LEE FINANCIAL SERVICES
See FRESNO TRUCK CENTER

LEE HEALTH
See LEE MEMORIAL HEALTH SYSTEM

D-U-N-S 08-040-7810
LEE HECHT HARRISON LLC
(Suby of ADECCO GROUP AG)
50 Tice Blvd Ste 115, Woodcliff Lake, NJ 07677-8429
Tel (201) 930-9333 Founded/Ownrshp 1974
Sales 203.6MM^E EMP 1,180
SIC 8742 8741 Management consulting services; Management services
Pr: Peter Alcide
*CFO: Karine Storm
Treas: Joann McCullough
*Ofcr: Massimiliano Savarese
*Ex VP: Barbara Barra
*Ex VP: Kevin Gagan
*Ex VP: James Greenway
*Ex VP: Waseem Razzaq
Sr VP: Reuben Cohen
Sr VP: Ed Epstein
Sr VP: John Farrell
Sr VP: Hayley French
VP: Adam Alexander
VP: Rosanne M Altrows
VP: Murielle Antille
VP: James Appleby
VP: Pam Brahos
VP: Karen Burke
VP: Kim Cherry
VP: Patti Nuttycombe Cochran
VP: Isabel Corbeil

LEE INDUSTRIAL CATERING
See LEE BROS FOODSERVICES INC

LEE INDUSTRIAL CONTRACTING
See LEE CONTRACTING INC

D-U-N-S 04-846-1024 IMP/EXP
LEE INDUSTRIES INC
210 4th St Sw, Conover, NC 28613-2628
Tel (828) 464-8318 Founded/Ownrshp 1969
Sales 89.7MM^E EMP 400
SIC 2512 Couches, sofas & davenports: upholstered on wood frames; Chairs: upholstered on wood frames
Pr: Bill G Coley
Exec: Angi Houston
Dir IT: Marvin Cutshall
Plnt Mgr: Dick Coffey
Plnt Mgr: Darryl Leonhardt

D-U-N-S 95-834-2917
■ **LEE JEANS CO INC**
(Suby of VF CORP) ★
9001 W 67th St, Merriam, KS 66202-3699
Tel (913) 384-4000 Founded/Ownrshp 2000
Sales 7.7MM^E EMP 2,350^E
SIC 2325 2339 2369 Jeans: men's, youths' & boys'; Jeans: women's, misses' & juniors'; Jeans: girls', children's & infants'
Pr: Mike Lettera
VP: Kent Pech

LEE JOFA
See KRAVET INC

D-U-N-S 08-898-6179
LEE KENNEDY CO INC
122 Quincy Shore Dr Ste 1, Quincy, MA 02171-2906
Tel (617) 825-6930 Founded/Ownrshp 1978
Sales 276.2MM EMP 75
Accts Feeley & Driscoll Pc Bosto
SIC 1542 Commercial & office buildings, renovation & repair; Commercial & office building, new construction
Ch Bd: Lee M Kennedy
*CFO: Michael Heath
*Sr VP: Chris Pennie
*VP: Eugene Kennedy

D-U-N-S 04-092-3021
LEE LEWIS CONSTRUCTION INC
7810 Orlando Ave, Lubbock, TX 79423-1942
Tel (806) 797-8400 Founded/Ownrshp 1975
Sales 141.9MM^E EMP 200
SIC 1542 1541 Commercial & office building, new construction; Industrial buildings & warehouses

Treas: Kelly Messersmith
VP: James Candle

D-U-N-S 83-100-1685
LEE MEMORIAL HEALTH SYSTEM
LEE HEALTH
2776 Cleveland Ave, Fort Myers, FL 33901-5864
Tel (239) 343-2000 Founded/Ownrshp 2009
Sales 760.6MM^E EMP 13,000^E
SIC 8011 Offices & clinics of medical doctors
CEO: James R Nathan
*COO: Lawrence Antonucci
*CFO: Mike German
Ofcr: Larry Antonucci
Ofcr: Lisa Sgarlata
Ofcr: Charles Swain
VP: Deborah Metcalf
Assoc Dir: William A Bookless
Dir Rx: Steve Kelsey
Adm Dir: Claude W Houle
*Ex Dir: Robert Johns

D-U-N-S 01-052-0674
LEE MEMORIAL HEALTH SYSTEM FOUNDATION INC (FL)
BRIGHT IDEAS GIFT SHOP
2776 Cleveland Ave, Fort Myers, FL 33901-5864
Tel (239) 343-2000 Founded/Ownrshp 1916
Sales 807.9MM^E EMP 7,870
SIC 8741 8062 8082 8051 Hospital management; General medical & surgical hospitals; Home health care services; Skilled nursing care facilities
Pr: James R Nathan
Dir Vol: Jill Palmer
CFO: Michael German
Treas: Marilyn Stout
Bd of Dir: Jessica Carter
Bd of Dir: George Kenneke
Bd of Dir: Guy Rhoades
Bd of Dir: Hatton Rogers
Bd of Dir: Alexander Roulston
Bd of Dir: Julie K Smith
*Ofcr: C B Rebsamen
Ofcr: Charles Swain
VP: Jennifer Higgins
Dir Lab: Susan Lawless
Comm Dir: Brandy Church
Dir Rx: Koth Cassavaugh

D-U-N-S 08-536-9044
LEE MEMORIAL HOSPITAL INC
(Suby of LEE HEALTH) ★
2776 Cleveland Ave, Fort Myers, FL 33901-5855
Tel (239) 343-2000 Founded/Ownrshp 1916
Sales 760.5MM EMP 1,159
SIC 8062 General medical & surgical hospitals
Pr: Jim Nathan
V Ch: Nancy McGovern
CFO: Dennis Pettigrew
Chf Mktg O: Scott Nygaard
Exec: Elvia Fernandez
Exec: Frank Rosa
Exec: Jason Yost
Dir OR: Kandy Dewitt
Dir Risk M: Mary Lorah
CIO: Sherri Widen
Opers Mgr: Andrea Adams

D-U-N-S 03-735-6572
LEE MEMORIAL WOMENS HEALTH PRO
(Suby of LEE HEALTH) ★
4761 S Cleveland Ave, Fort Myers, FL 33907-1375
Tel (239) 343-9734 Founded/Ownrshp 2010
Sales 172.1MM^E EMP 2,210^E
SIC 8099 Health & allied services
Prin: Julie Adams

D-U-N-S 00-516-0635
■ **LEE PUBLICATIONS INC** (DE)
TIMES-NEWS, THE
(Suby of LEE ENTERPRISES INC) ★
201 N Harrison St Ste 600, Davenport, IA 52801-1918
Tel (563) 383-2100 Founded/Ownrshp 1972, 2002
Sales 258.4MM^E EMP 2,500
SIC 2711 Newspapers: publishing only, not printed on site
VP: Brian E Kardell
VP: Gregory Schermer
VP: Carl Schmidt

LEE RANCH COAL
See PEABODY NATURAL RESOURCES CO

D-U-N-S 01-145-3792
LEE REGIONAL HEALTH SYSTEM INC
132 Walnut St Ste 3, Johnstown, PA 15901-1621
Tel (814) 533-0751 Founded/Ownrshp 1981
Sales 23.3MM^E EMP 1,487
SIC 8399 Fund raising organization, non-fee basis
Ch Bd: John W Augustine
CFO: Kelly Blake
VP: Robert E Barrett

D-U-N-S 00-293-6920 IMP/EXP
LEE STEEL CORP (MI)
45525 Grand River Ave, Novi, MI 48374-1308
Tel (855) 533-7833 Founded/Ownrshp 1947
Sales 100.0MM EMP 65
SIC 5051

D-U-N-S 07-867-5566
LEE SUMMER HOLDINGS LLC
600 Travis St Ste 5800, Houston, TX 77002-3008
Tel (713) 993-4610 Founded/Ownrshp 2006, 2012
Sales 152.7MM^E EMP 999^E
SIC 6799 Venture capital companies

D-U-N-S 01-395-1447 IMP
LEE SUPPLY CO INC
305 1st St, Charleroi, PA 15022-1427
Tel (724) 483-3543 Founded/Ownrshp 1954
Sales 120.2MM EMP 127
Accts Rd Hoag & Associates Pc
SIC 5082 5084 Mining machinery & equipment, except petroleum; Industrial machinery & equipment
CEO: Michael H Lee
*Pr: Kevin M Lee
CFO: K Deutsch
*CFO: David Lee

Treas: Eileen Nucci
**VP:* Shawn Lee
Sales Asso: Jeff Dumm
Sales Asso: John Kite
Sales Asso: George Milkent

D-U-N-S 00-604-5678
LEE SUPPLY CORP
LEE DESIGN STUDIO
6610 Guion Rd, Indianapolis, IN 46268-2534
Tel (317) 290-2500 *Founded/Ownrshp* 1973, 1980
Sales 133.8MM^{E} *EMP* 190
SIC 5074 5075 5064 5085 5031 Plumbing & hydronic heating supplies; Air conditioning & ventilation equipment & supplies; Electric household appliances; Industrial supplies; Lumber, plywood & millwork
Pr: Robert T Lee
**Treas:* Charles Lee
Brnch Mgr: Jeff Bymaster
Brnch Mgr: Kevin Kreutzberger
IT Man: David Barnes

D-U-N-S 16-703-0290
LEE THOMAS H EQUITY FUND V LIMITED PARTNERSHIP
100 Federal St Ste 3500, Boston, MA 02110-1802
Tel (617) 737-3261 *Founded/Ownrshp* 2007
Sales 224.5MM^{E} *EMP* 8,040
SIC 3585 3444 3634 2431 3699 Refrigeration & heating equipment; Sheet metalwork; Electric housewares & fans; Millwork; Electrical equipment & supplies
Genl Pt: Thomas H Lee

D-U-N-S 07-153-5728
LEE UNIVERSITY
1120 N Ocoee St Ste 102, Cleveland, TN 37311-4475
Tel (423) 614-8000 *Founded/Ownrshp* 1946
Sales 99.1MM^{E} *EMP* 635
Accts Elliott Davis Decosimo Llc Pll
SIC 8221 8661 College, except junior; Religious organizations
Pr: Paul Conn
Store Mgr: Skip Gienapp
CTO: Amanda Gilkeson
Dir IT: William Lamb
IT Man: Crystal Dake

LEEANN CHIN RESTAURANT
See CHIN LEEANN INC

LEEDO CABINETRY
See LEEDO MANUFACTURING CO LP

D-U-N-S 05-030-6729 IMP
LEEDO MANUFACTURING CO LP (TX)
LEEDO CABINETRY
10707 Corp Dr Ste 250, Stafford, TX 77477
Tel (866) 465-3336 *Founded/Ownrshp* 2001
Sales 104.6MM^{E} *EMP* 500^{E}
SIC 2434 Wood kitchen cabinets; Vanities, bathroom: wood
Pr: David Mullis
CFO: Michelle Baker
CFO: Howard Maymon
Ch: George Hagle
Ofcr: Cindy Ward
VP: David Burke
Genl Mgr: John Dodrill
Mfg Dir: Julia Gross
Sfty Mgr: Don Kaingely
Sfty Mgr: Don Kingery
Opers Mgr: Darren Schmidt

D-U-N-S 15-374-6201 IMP/EXP
LEEDSWORLD INC
(*Suby of* POLYCONCEPT NORTH AMERICA INC) ★
400 Hunt Valley Rd, New Kensington, PA 15068-7059
Tel (724) 334-9000 *Founded/Ownrshp* 1983
Sales 401.9MM^{E} *EMP* 800^{E}
SIC 5199 5111 5112 3172 3161 2394 Advertising specialties; Writing paper; Writing instruments & supplies; Personal leather goods; Luggage; Canvas & related products
CEO: Michael Bernstein
**Pr:* David Nicholson
CFO: Martin Vuono
Opers Mgr: Mike Strobel
VP Sls: Samuel Dibiase
Mktg Mgr: Martin Dornisch
Mktg Mgr: Patty Solar

D-U-N-S 05-458-1848 IMP
LEEMAH CORP
155 S Hill Dr, Brisbane, CA 94005-1203
Tel (415) 394-1288 *Founded/Ownrshp* 1971
Sales 101.9MM^{E} *EMP* 300
SIC 3671 3672 3669 3663 3577 Electron tubes; Printed circuit boards; Intercommunication systems, electric; Radio & TV communications equipment; Computer peripheral equipment
CEO: Efrem Mah
**Pr:* Bing Hong Mah
**CFO:* Warren Gee

LEER
See TRUCK ACCESSORIES GROUP LLC

D-U-N-S 08-069-3591
LEES SUMMIT R-7 SCHOOL DISTRICT
301 Ne Tudor Rd, Lees Summit, MO 64086-5702
Tel (816) 986-1000 *Founded/Ownrshp* 1889
Sales 136.4MM^{E} *EMP* 2,503
SIC 8211 Public elementary school; Public junior high school; Public senior high school
Ex Dir: Eric P Flack
Genl Mgr: Willeta Chance
Sfty Mgr: Willard Parks

D-U-N-S 02-510-4311
LEESAR INC
LEESAR REGIONAL SERVICE CENTER
2727 Winkler Ave, Fort Myers, FL 33901-9358
Tel (239) 939-8800 *Founded/Ownrshp* 1998
Sales 218.8MM *EMP* 280
Accts Bobbitt Pittenger & Company Pa
SIC 5047 Medical equipment & supplies
Pr: Robert Simpson
**CEO:* Bob Simpson
**CFO:* Gayle Reynolds
**VP:* Paul McWhinnie
Ex Dir: Dan Fitzgerald
IT Man: Vickie Dragich

LEESAR REGIONAL SERVICE CENTER
See LEESAR INC

D-U-N-S 79-661-9922
■ **LEESBURG KNITTING MILLS INC**
(*Suby of* FRUIT OF LOOM) ★
400 Industrial Blvd, Leesburg, AL 35983-3745
Tel (256) 526-8522 *Founded/Ownrshp* 1998
Sales 58.1MM^{E} *EMP* 1,470
SIC 2281 0724 Yarn spinning mills; Cotton ginning
Pr: Jim Browning

D-U-N-S 01-082-1858
LEESBURG REGIONAL MEDICAL CENTER INC
600 E Dixie Ave, Leesburg, FL 34748-5999
Tel (352) 323-5762 *Founded/Ownrshp* 1986
Sales 222.2MM *EMP* 1,900
Accts Kpmg Llp Greensboro Nc
SIC 8062 General medical & surgical hospitals
**CEO:* Don Henderson
**Sr VP:* Diane Harden
**VP:* Phyllis Baum
VP: Alex Chang
Nurse Mgr: Michelle Currie
CIO: Dave Steele
Netwrk Mgr: Fraysur Dale
Sls&Mrk Ex: Marc Westerman
Pathlgst: David Rizzuto

LEESBURG REGIONAL MEDICAL CTR
See CENTRAL FLORIDA HEALTH ALLIANCE INC

D-U-N-S 06-687-2706 IMP/EXP
■ **LEESON ELECTRIC CORP**
(*Suby of* REGAL BELOIT CORP) ★
1051 Cheyenne Ave, Grafton, WI 53024-9541
Tel (262) 377-8810 *Founded/Ownrshp* 2000
Sales 72.4MM^{E} *EMP* 1,000
SIC 3621 Motors, electric
VP: Mike Catania
VP: Keith Tipper
DP Exec: Ben He
Manager: Mark Baake
Sales Asso: Lori Volkert

D-U-N-S 16-080-8502 IMP
LEEVAC SHIPYARDS JENNINGS LLC
(*Suby of* CARI CO) ★
111 Bunge St, Jennings, LA 70546
Tel (337) 824-2210 *Founded/Ownrshp* 1998
Sales 104.9MM^{E} *EMP* 260
SIC 3731 Shipbuilding & repairing
CEO: Christian G Vaccari
Pr: Dan Gaiennie
**VP:* Richard Ortego
**VP:* Troy W Skelton

D-U-N-S 03-219-5245
LEEVERS FOODS PARTNERSHIP LLP
501 4th St Se, Devils Lake, ND 58301-3703
Tel (701) 662-8646 *Founded/Ownrshp* 1997
Sales 92.5MM^{E} *EMP* 950
SIC 5411 Grocery stores
Pr: Robert Leevers
**VP:* Al Hanson

D-U-N-S 83-309-0264
LEEWARD MEMBER LLC
6688 N Central Expy # 500, Dallas, TX 75206-3914
Tel (214) 515-1100 *Founded/Ownrshp* 2009
Sales 87.1MM^{E} *EMP* 110
SIC 4911 Generation, electric power
CEO: Craig Carson
**CEO:* David Smith
**VP:* Andrew Flanagan
**VP:* Greg Flowers
**VP:* Christopher Loehr
Board of Directors: Randy Barnes, Matthew McGowan

D-U-N-S 14-838-0348
LEEWARD OAHU SCHOOL DISTRICT
(*Suby of* OFFICE OF SUPERINTENDENT) ★
601 Kamokila Blvd Ste 418, Kapolei, HI 96707-2036
Tel (808) 564-6066 *Founded/Ownrshp* 1950
Sales 80.6MM^{E} *EMP* 2,000
SIC 8211 9411 Public elementary & secondary schools;

D-U-N-S 04-915-5591
LEFRAK ORGANIZATION INC
40 W 57th St Fl 23, New York, NY 10019-4011
Tel (212) 707-6600 *Founded/Ownrshp* 1905
Sales 89.7MM *EMP* 245
SIC 6513 6512

D-U-N-S 05-279-5525
LEGACY BUSINESS SOLUTIONS LLC
1144 Shine Ave, Myrtle Beach, SC 29577-1503
Tel (843) 945-4358 *Founded/Ownrshp* 2013
Sales 7.4MM^{E} *EMP* 1,300
SIC 7011 Hotels & motels; Resort hotel
Ex Dir: Nabil Ghanan

D-U-N-S 18-794-4491
LEGACY COMMUNITY HEALTH SERVICES INC
1415 California St, Houston, TX 77006-2602
Tel (713) 830-3000 *Founded/Ownrshp* 1982
Sales 93.9MM *EMP* 132
Accts Bkd Llp Springfield Mo
SIC 8093 8011 Specialty outpatient clinics; Offices & clinics of medical doctors
Ch Bd: Ray Purser
**COO:* Jeff Perry
**CFO:* Ben Glisan
**CFO:* Judi McNall
**Ex Dir:* Katy Caldwell
IT Man: Theron Bretz
VP Opers: Michelle Barrera

LEGACY COMPANIES, THE
See GREENFIELD WORLD TRADE INC

D-U-N-S 07-962-7919
■ **LEGACY EDUCATION ALLIANCE INC**
(*Suby of* TIGRENT INC) ★
1612 Cape Coral Pkwy E, Cape Coral, FL 33904-9618
Tel (239) 542-0643 *Founded/Ownrshp* 2014
Sales 87.1MM *EMP* 208
Tkr Sym LEAI *Exch* OTC
SIC 8299 Educational service, nondegree granting: continuing educ.
CEO: Anthony C Humpage
**Ch Bd:* James K Bass
COO: Iain Edwards
CFO: Christian Baeza
Ofcr: James E May
VP: Brenda Kalscheuer
Board of Directors: Peter W Harper, Cary Sucoff

D-U-N-S 05-097-3098
LEGACY EMANUEL HOSPITAL & HEALTH CENTER
2801 N Gantenbein Ave, Portland, OR 97227-1623
Tel (503) 413-2200 *Founded/Ownrshp* 1912
Sales 705.0MM *EMP* 3,619
SIC 8062 General medical & surgical hospitals; Hospital, AMA approved residency
Pr: George J Brown MD
Ex Dir: Lisa Harris
CIO: Matthew Calais
Doctor: Duncan Neilson

D-U-N-S 02-247-0635
LEGACY EQUIPMENT INC
(*Suby of* GA WEST & CO INC) ★
12526 Celeste Rd, Chunchula, AL 36521-3578
Tel (251) 679-1965 *Founded/Ownrshp* 2008
Sales 105.8MM *EMP* 10
SIC 5046 Commercial equipment
Pr: Gary A West

D-U-N-S 01-802-3770
LEGACY FARMERS COOPERATIVE
6566 County Road 236, Findlay, OH 45840-9769
Tel (419) 423-2611 *Founded/Ownrshp* 1989
Sales 278.4MM *EMP* 122
Accts Balestra Harr & Scherer Cpas
SIC 5153 5191 5984 2875 2048 2041 Grains; Farm supplies; Seeds: field, garden & flower; Fertilizer & fertilizer materials; Liquefied petroleum gas dealers; Fertilizers, mixing only; Prepared feeds; Flour & other grain mill products
Pr: Mark Sunderman
**Ch Bd:* Andrew Jones
**Treas:* Gary Herringshaw
**V Ch Bd:* Marvin Maas
VP: William Tong
Brnch Mgr: Tom Bowman
Brnch Mgr: Tim Meyer
Brnch Mgr: Steve Welty
IT Man: Sam Clark
VP Mktg: Brice Berry
VP Mktg: Gale Berry

D-U-N-S 07-782-4337 IMP
LEGACY FARMS LLC
6625 Caballero Blvd, Buena Park, CA 90620-1131
Tel (714) 736-1800 *Founded/Ownrshp* 1991
Sales 96.4MM^{E} *EMP* 120
SIC 5148 Fresh fruits & vegetables
**Prin:* Rick Baxter
**Prin:* Vince Mendoza
**Prin:* Ron Shimizu
**Prin:* Wally Sinner
Genl Mgr: Kevin Shimizu
Genl Mgr: Phil Trotter
Sales Asso: Steve Bradley

D-U-N-S 04-980-6789
LEGACY GOOD SAMARITAN HOSPITAL AND MEDICAL CENTER
LEGACY GOOD SAMARITAN MED CTR
1015 Nw 22nd Ave, Portland, OR 97210-3025
Tel (503) 413-7711 *Founded/Ownrshp* 1989
Sales 318.7MM *EMP* 1,900
SIC 8069

LEGACY GOOD SAMARITAN MED CTR
See LEGACY GOOD SAMARITAN HOSPITAL AND MEDICAL CENTER

D-U-N-S 03-079-8441
LEGACY HEALTH
1919 Nw Lovejoy St, Portland, OR 97209-1503
Tel (503) 415-5600 *Founded/Ownrshp* 1970
Sales 1.6MMM *EMP* 8,000
SIC 8011 Medical centers
CEO: George J Brown MD
V Ch: Wilma G Kaplan
COO: Mike Newcomb
CFO: Dave Eager
CFO: Linda Hoff
**Treas:* Kelly A Higgins
Ofcr: Allyson Anderson
Ofcr: Jonathan Avery
**Ofcr:* Carol Bradley Rn
Ofcr: Carla D Harris
Ofcr: Bryce Helgerson
Ofcr: Bronwyn Houston
Ofcr: Lori Morgan
Ofcr: Gretchen Nichols
**Sr VP:* Maureen Bradley
**Sr VP:* Rob Dewitt
**Sr VP:* Trent Green
Sr VP: John Kenagy
Sr VP: Lewis Low
VP: Maureen A Bradley
VP: Molly Burchell

LEGACY HEALTH SERVICES
See DMD MANAGEMENT INC

D-U-N-S 55-741-4815 IMP
LEGACY HOUSING LTD
4801 Mark Iv Pkwy, Fort Worth, TX 76106-2217
Tel (817) 624-7565 *Founded/Ownrshp* 2005
Sales 109.0MM *EMP* 500^{E}
SIC 2451 Mobile homes, personal or private use
Genl Pt: Kenny Shipley
Pt: Conley Bigham
Pt: Curtis Hodgson
COO: Mick Barker
CFO: Jeff Burt
Exec: Dionesia Flores
Genl Mgr: Ray McKay
Opers Mgr: Andy Nauert
Sales Exec: Christi Lancaster
Sls Mgr: Ed Spaeth
Genl Couns: Drew Chapman

D-U-N-S 15-401-9673
LEGACY MERIDIAN PARK HOSPITAL
19300 Sw 65th Ave, Tualatin, OR 97062-7706
Tel (503) 692-1212 *Founded/Ownrshp* 1984
Sales 188.0MM *EMP* 458
SIC 8062 8011 General medical & surgical hospitals; Primary care medical clinic
CEO: George J Brown
**COO:* Mike Newcomb
**CFO:* Linda Hoff
**Sr VP:* Carol Bradley
**Sr VP:* David Eager

D-U-N-S 14-769-4160
LEGACY MOUNT HOOD MEDICAL CENTER
24800 Se Stark St, Gresham, OR 97030-3378
Tel (503) 674-1122 *Founded/Ownrshp* 1984
Sales 136.4MM *EMP* 306
SIC 8062 5912 Hospital, affiliated with AMA residency; Drug stores
Pr: George J Brown
Off Mgr: Kelly Buker
Doctor: Michael Frommlet

D-U-N-S 12-280-2262
LEGACY PARTNERS RESIDENTIAL INC
(*Suby of* STEELWAVE INC) ★
4000 E 3rd Ave Ste 600, Foster City, CA 94404-4828
Tel (650) 571-2250 *Founded/Ownrshp* 1995
Sales 62.8MM^{E} *EMP* 1,000
SIC 8741 Management services
Ch Bd: C Preston Butcher
CFO: Tim McCarthy
**CFO:* Gary J Rossi
Sr VP: Bob Phipps
Mng Dir: Spencer R Stuart Jr

D-U-N-S 78-280-1414
▲ **LEGACY RESERVES LP**
303 W Wall St Ste 1800, Midland, TX 79701-5106
Tel (432) 689-5200 *Founded/Ownrshp* 2005
Sales 338.7MM *EMP* 379^{E}
Tkr Sym LGCY *Exch* NGS
SIC 1311 Crude petroleum & natural gas; Crude petroleum & natural gas production
Pr: Paul T Horne
Genl Pt: Legacy Reserves GP
**Ch Bd:* Cary D Brown
CFO: James Daniel Westcott
Ex VP: Kyle Hammond
VP Bus Dev: Shad Frazier
VP Opers: Paul Horne
Board of Directors: Dale A Brown, William R Granberry, G Larry Lawrence, Kyle A McGraw, William D Sullivan, Kyle D Vann

LEGACY SUPPLY CHAIN SERVICES
See TRI-STARR MANAGEMENT SERVICES INC

D-U-N-S 06-080-1929
LEGACY VISITING NURSE ASSOCIATION
LEGENCY VISITING NURSE ASSOC
(*Suby of* LEGACY HEALTH) ★
815 Ne Davis St, Portland, OR 97232-2964
Tel (503) 220-1000 *Founded/Ownrshp* 1902
Sales 12.8MM *EMP* 5,094
Accts Kpmg Llp Portland Or
SIC 8399 5999 8082 Health systems agency; Hospital equipment & supplies; Home health care services
Pr: Steve Johnson
VP: Dave Loboy
VP: Russ McGillivray
VP: Darwin Murray
VP: Brian Smith
VP: Jeff Vinson
Div Mgr: Stephen Fischer
Div Mgr: Doug Fisher
Div Mgr: Tom Mulligan
Genl Mgr: Chuck Whitaker
IT Man: Brandi Payton

D-U-N-S 00-339-6025 IMP/EXP
■ **LEGACY VULCAN LLC**
(*Suby of* VULCAN MATERIALS CO) ★
1200 Urban Center Dr, Vestavia, AL 35242-2545
Tel (205) 298-3000 *Founded/Ownrshp* 2007
Sales 3.3MMM^{E} *EMP* 6,598
SIC 1422 1423 1442 2951 3273 Crushed & broken limestone; Crushed & broken granite; Construction sand mining; Gravel mining; Paving mixtures; Ready-mixed concrete
CFO: Daniel F Sansone
Pr: John L Holland
**Pr:* John R McPherson
Sr VP: Guy M Badgett
**Sr VP:* William F Denson III
Sr VP: James W Smack
**Sr VP:* Robert A Wason IV
**VP:* Ejaz A Khan
VP: Michael R Mills
VP: James W O'Brien
Brnch Mgr: Rob McMahan

D-U-N-S 08-001-1459
■ **LEGACY VULCAN LLC**
(*Suby of* VULCAN MATERIALS CO) ★
1200 Urban Center Dr, Shoal Creek, AL 35242-2545
Tel (205) 298-3000 *Founded/Ownrshp* 2015
Sales 21.7MM *EMP* 4,623^{E}
SIC 1422 1423 1442 2951 3273

D-U-N-S 03-942-7831
■ **LEGACYSTAR SERVICES LLC**
(*Suby of* NUSTAR ENERGY LP) ★
2435 N Central Expy # 700, Richardson, TX 75080-2753
Tel (972) 699-4062 *Founded/Ownrshp* 2005

Sales 18.5MM^E *EMP* 1,078
SIC 4613 5172 Refined petroleum pipelines; Gasoline; Diesel fuel
VP: Howard C Wadsworth

D-U-N-S 05-083-7962 IMP
■ LEGACYTEXAS BANK
(*Suby of* LEGACYTEXAS FINANCIAL GROUP INC) ★
5851 Legacy Cir Ste 1200, Plano, TX 75024-5968
Tel (972) 578-5000 *Founded/Ownrshp* 2014
Sales NA *EMP* 285
SIC 6022 State commercial banks
CEO: Donald R St Clair
**Pr:* Phil Dyer
Pr: Gayland Lawshe
Pr: Kathy Miller
**CFO:* Rewaz Chowdhury
**Ofcr:* Jeff G Chase
Ofcr: Nikki Hood
Ofcr: Susan M Keene
Sr Ex VP: Alan Williams
Ex VP: Mays Davenport
Ex VP: Pam Smithey
Ex VP: Dan Strother
Ex VP: Steve Young
Sr VP: Kari Anderson
Sr VP: Pamela Austin
Sr VP: Pam Best
Sr VP: Michael Murray
Sr VP: Brad Schneider
Sr VP: Dawn Velekei
Sr VP: Becky Walters
Sr VP: Angela Webb

D-U-N-S 15-406-8956
▲ LEGACYTEXAS FINANCIAL GROUP INC
5851 Legacy Cir, Plano, TX 75024-5966
Tel (972) 578-5000 *Founded/Ownrshp* 2010
Sales NA *EMP* 856^E
Tkr Sym LTXB *Exch* NGS
SIC 6022 State commercial banks
Pr: Kevin J Hanigan
**Ch Bd:* Anthony J Levecchio
COO: Scott A Almy
CFO: J Mays Davenport
VP: Jamie Richardson
Dir IT: Larry Montoux

D-U-N-S 02-379-8291
LEGAL & GENERAL AMERICA INC
(*Suby of* LEGAL AND GENERAL ASSURANCE SOCIETY LIMITED)
3275 Bennett Creek Ave, Frederick, MD 21704-7608
Tel (800) 638-8428 *Founded/Ownrshp* 1981
Sales NA *EMP* 309^E
SIC 6411 6311 Insurance agents, brokers & service; Life insurance
Ex VP: James Galli
**Sr VP:* Thomas Sima
VP: Grant Andrew
VP: Gwin Banks
**VP:* Ramanathan Esau
VP: Keron Parker
VP: Lolita Stowers
VP: Troy Thompson
Dir Risk M: Amy B Butler
Dir Soc: Anita Macmaster
QA Dir: Brian Pavlick

D-U-N-S 17-267-7929
LEGAL ACQUISITIONS SUPPORT SERVICES LLC
1170 Peachtree St Ne # 1200, Atlanta, GA 30309-7649
Tel (404) 546-7290 *Founded/Ownrshp* 2004
Sales 134.6MM *EMP* 76
SIC 6531 Real estate agent, commercial

D-U-N-S 07-329-7541
LEGAL AID SOCIETY
199 Water St Frnt 3, New York, NY 10038-3526
Tel (212) 577-3346 *Founded/Ownrshp* 1876
Sales 241.1MM *EMP* 1,600
Accts Rsm Us Llp New York Ny
SIC 8111 Legal aid service
Ch Bd: Richard J Davis
**Pr:* Blaine Sogg
Ofcr: Patricia Bath
VP: Adriene Holder
Genl Couns: Janet Sabel
Board of Directors: Gregory A Markel

D-U-N-S 10-790-5085
LEGAL SEA FOODS LLC
1 Seafood Way, Boston, MA 02210-2702
Tel (617) 530-9000 *Founded/Ownrshp* 1950
Sales 127.7MM^E *EMP* 3,000
SIC 5812 5146 5961 Seafood restaurants; Fish & seafoods; Catalog & mail-order houses
Ch Bd: George Berkowitz
**Pr:* Roger Berkowitz
Pr: Jeffrey Lipson
**CFO:* Mark Synnott
**Treas:* Mary Cronin
VP: Richard Heller
VP: William P Holler
VP: Brian Schwanke
Ex Dir: Janet Sutherby
MIS Dir: Diane Mortesen
Sfty Mgr: Marney Whittaker

D-U-N-S 02-029-4500
■ LEGAL SERVICES CORP (DC)
(*Suby of* EXECUTIVE OFFICE OF UNITED STATES GOVERNMENT) ★
3333 K St Nw Ste 1, Washington, DC 20007-3522
Tel (202) 295-1500 *Founded/Ownrshp* 1974
Sales 377.8MM^E *EMP* 130
Accts Withum Smith & Brown Pc Phila
SIC 6732 9199 Trusts: educational, religious, etc.; General government administration;
Pr: James Sandman
**Treas:* David Richardson
**VP:* Ronald Flagg
**VP:* Lynn A Jennings
**CIO:* Peter Campbell
Counsel: Rebecca Weir

D-U-N-S 08-248-5350
LEGALSHIELD (TN)
(*Suby of* MIDOCEAN PARTNERS) ★
1 Prepaid Way, Ada, OK 74820-5813
Tel (323) 325-3198 *Founded/Ownrshp* 1976, 2011
Sales 130.2MM^E *EMP* 719^E
SIC 8111 General practice attorney, lawyer
Ch Bd: Ralph Mason III
Pr: Glenn Petersen
**Pr:* Alan Fearnley
Pr: James Rosseau
**Pr:* Harland C Stonecipher
**CEO:* Jeff Bell
**COO:* Randy Harp
COO: Kathy Pinson
**CFO:* Steve Williamson
**Chf Mktg O:* Mark Brown
**Ofcr:* David Coffey
Ex VP: Darnell Self
Sr VP: Bob Levy
VP: Steve Baker
VP: John Long
VP: Vicky Mapp
VP: Linda Masoli
**VP:* Keri Norris
**VP:* Kathleen S Pinson
VP: Charles Rosenberry
VP: Keith Sherman

LEGENCY VISITING NURSE ASSOC
See LEGACY VISITING NURSE ASSOCIATION

D-U-N-S 04-945-5606
LEGEND ENERGY SERVICES LLC
5801 Broadway Ext Ste 210, Oklahoma City, OK 73118-7491
Tel (405) 600-1264 *Founded/Ownrshp* 2010
Sales 90.0MM *EMP* 210
SIC 1389 Cementing oil & gas well casings
CEO: Trey Ingram
**COO:* Matt Goodson
**CFO:* Josh Pruett
Opers Mgr: Reid Thompson

D-U-N-S 00-126-7967
LEGEND HEALTH SYSTEMS INC
LEGEND PHARMACY
1111 Broadhollow Rd # 319, Farmingdale, NY 11735-4820
Tel (631) 630-4713 *Founded/Ownrshp* 1999
Sales 200.0MM *EMP* 60
SIC 5912 Drug stores
Pr: John Marmero

LEGEND HEALTHCARE
See WIND RIVER GROUP PT LLC

LEGEND PHARMACY
See LEGEND HEALTH SYSTEMS INC

D-U-N-S 82-907-4587 IMP
LEGENDS HOSPITALITY LLC
(*Suby of* LEGENDS HOSPITALITY MANAGEMENT LIMITED LIABILITY CO) ★
400 Bradacrest Dr Ste 200, Bloomfield, NJ 07003
Tel (973) 707-2800 *Founded/Ownrshp* 2008
Sales 91.9MM^E *EMP* 645^E
SIC 7929 Entertainers
CEO: Michael Rawlings
**Pr:* Martin Greenspun
**Pr:* Daniel Smith
**COO:* Michael Ondrejko
**CFO:* David Hammer

D-U-N-S 01-895-2728
LEGENDS HOSPITALITY MANAGEMENT LIMITED LIABILITY CO
(*Suby of* LEGENDS HOSPITALITY HOLDING COMPANY, LLC)
61 Broadway Ste 2400, New York, NY 10006-2835
Tel (646) 977-8521 *Founded/Ownrshp* 2007
Sales 91.9MM^E *EMP* 672^E
SIC 8741 8744 8742 Business management; Facilities support services; Hospital & health services consultant; Food & beverage consultant; Merchandising consultant
CEO: Mike Rawlings
**Pr:* Marty Greenspun
**COO:* Dan Smith
**CFO:* Jim Sheppard
**Sr VP:* Amy Phillips
**Sr VP:* Mike Phillips
VP: Todd Fleming
VP: Jon Muscalo
VP Sls: Al Guido

D-U-N-S 10-145-8883
▲ LEGG MASON INC
100 International Dr, Baltimore, MD 21202-4673
Tel (410) 539-0000 *Founded/Ownrshp* 1899
Sales 2.6MMM *EMP* 3,066^E
Tkr Sym LM *Exch* NYS
SIC 6282 6211 6162 Manager of mutual funds, contract or fee basis; Investment advisory service; Security brokers & dealers; Brokers, security; Dealers, security; Traders, security; Mortgage bankers
Ch Bd: Joseph A Sullivan
Pr: Frank Meisel
Pr: Mark Nigro
CFO: Gregg Gorman
CFO: Peter H Nachtwey
Ofcr: Ursula Schliessler
Ex VP: Thomas K Hoops
Ex VP: Terence Johnson
Ex VP: Thomas C Merchant
VP: David Chow
VP: Karen Corso
VP: James Crowley
VP: Tom Galloway
VP: Mary C Gay
VP: John Hogan
VP: Michael Komori
VP: Vinny Laverty
VP: Paul McKenna
VP: Richard Merson
VP: Maria Oberhofer
VP: Sandra Palmer
Board of Directors: Kurt L Schmoke, Robert E Angelica, Carol Anthony Davidson, Barry W Huff, Dennis M Kass, Cheryl Gordon Krongard, John V Murphy, John H Myers, W Allen Reed, Margaret Milner Richardson

D-U-N-S 00-714-0064 IMP/EXP
▲ LEGGETT & PLATT INC
1 Leggett Rd, Carthage, MO 64836-9649
Tel (417) 358-8131 *Founded/Ownrshp* 1883
Sales 3.9MMM *EMP* 20,000
Tkr Sym LEG *Exch* NYS
SIC 2515 2514 3495 2392 2542 3363 Box springs, assembled; Mattresses, innerspring or box spring; Chair & couch springs, assembled; Bedsprings, assembled; Frames for box springs or bedsprings: metal; Beds, including folding & cabinet, household: metal; Wire springs; Mattress pads; Fixtures: display, office or store: except wood; Aluminum die-castings
Pr: Karl G Glassman
**Ch Bd:* R Ted Enloe III
**CFO:* Matthew C Flanigan
Sr VP: Jack D Crusa
Sr VP: David M Desonier
Sr VP: J Mitchell Dolloff
Sr VP: Scott S Douglas
Sr VP: Russell J Iorio
VP: William Avise
VP: Perry E Davis
VP: Scott Douglas
VP: David Dupon
VP: Jason Jewett
VP: Joe Kupillas
VP: Todd Nechtem
VP: Dennis S Park
VP: Tracey Pressior
VP: Tammy M Trent
Dir Bus: Bren Flanigan
Board of Directors: Robert E Brunner, Robert G Culp III, Manuel A Fernandez, Joseph W McClanathan, Judy C Odom, Phoebe A Wood

D-U-N-S 79-620-6993
LEGISLATIVE OFFICE OF COMMONWEALTH OF PENNSYLVANIA
(*Suby of* COMMONWEALTH OF PENNSYLVANIA) ★
Main Capitol Bldg Rm 225, Harrisburg, PA 17120-0001
Tel (717) 787-5962 *Founded/Ownrshp* 1901
Sales NA *EMP* 2,583
SIC 9121 Legislative bodies, state & local;

D-U-N-S 80-955-8802
LEGISLATIVE OFFICE OF FLORIDA
(*Suby of* STATE OF FLORIDA) ★
400 S Monroe St, Tallahassee, FL 32399-6536
Tel (850) 488-4505 *Founded/Ownrshp* 1845
Sales NA *EMP* 2,515
SIC 9121 Legislative bodies, state & local;

D-U-N-S 80-388-9302
LEGISLATIVE OFFICE OF MICHIGAN
(*Suby of* STATE OF MICHIGAN) ★
George Romney Building, Lansing, MI 48933
Tel (517) 373-3400 *Founded/Ownrshp* 1837
Sales NA *EMP* 1,308
SIC 9121 Legislative bodies, state & local;

D-U-N-S 80-748-1031
LEGISLATIVE OFFICE OF STATE OF CONNECTICUT
GENERAL ASSEMBLY
(*Suby of* STATE OF CONNECTICUT) ★
300 Capitol Ave, Hartford, CT 06106-1553
Tel (860) 240-0100 *Founded/Ownrshp* 1788
Sales NA *EMP* 40,970
SIC 9121 Legislative bodies;
V Ch: Bob Duff
Dir IT: Paquette Thomas
Mktg Dir: Carmen M Calderon
Mktg Dir: Heidi J Lawrence
Mktg Dir: Diane Mazar-Roberts

D-U-N-S 80-534-7168
LEGISLATIVE OFFICE OF STATE OF MINNESOTA
(*Suby of* STATE OF MINNESOTA) ★
100 Rev Dr M L King Jr Bl, Saint Paul, MN 55155-0001
Tel (651) 296-2146 *Founded/Ownrshp* 1858
Sales NA *EMP* 1,038
SIC 9121 Legislative bodies, state & local;
MIS Dir: Laurie Lashbrook

D-U-N-S 87-807-2719
LEGISLATIVE OFFICE OF STATE OF MISSOURI
(*Suby of* STATE OF MISSOURI) ★
201 W Capitol Ave, Jefferson City, MO 65101-1556
Tel (573) 751-3829 *Founded/Ownrshp* 1820
Sales NA *EMP* 1,262
SIC 9121 Legislative bodies, state & local;
Prin: Matt Bount
**Prin:* Jay Nixon

D-U-N-S 80-719-6688
LEGISLATIVE OFFICE STATE OF NY
NEW YORK STATE ASSEMBLY
(*Suby of* STATE OF NEW YORK) ★
State Capital Bldg, Albany, NY 12248-0001
Tel (518) 455-4100 *Founded/Ownrshp* 1788
Sales NA *EMP* 3,519
SIC 9121 Legislative bodies, state & local;
Prin: Sheldon Silver
Comm Dir: Carla Downie
Comm Dir: Michele McCarthy
Pr Dir: Maylene Thurton
Counsel: Abby Brinkerhoff
Counsel: Jermaine Brookshire
Counsel: Nadia Gareeb

D-U-N-S 80-673-2327
LEGISLATIVE OFFICE TEXAS
(*Suby of* STATE OF TEXAS) ★
1200 N Congress Ave Ste 2, Austin, TX 78701
Tel (512) 463-0001 *Founded/Ownrshp* 1845
Sales NA *EMP* 4,258
SIC 9121 Legislative bodies, state & local;

LEGO BRAND RETAIL
See LEGO SYSTEMS INC

D-U-N-S 06-483-5549 IMP/EXP
LEGO SYSTEMS INC
LEGO BRAND RETAIL
(*Suby of* LEGO A/S)
555 Taylor Rd, Enfield, CT 06082-2372
Tel (860) 749-2291 *Founded/Ownrshp* 1973
Sales 679.7MM^E *EMP* 1,450
SIC 3944 5092 Erector sets, toy; Structural toy sets; Blocks, toy; Toys & hobby goods & supplies
Pr: Soren Torp Laursen
CFO: John Goodwin
Chf Mktg O: Julia Goldin
VP: John Coughlin
MIS Dir: Kevin Flynn
Dir IT: Scott Silvia
Mktg Dir: Leslie Jenkins
Mktg Mgr: Shawn Curtis
Mktg Mgr: Annemarie De Munnik
Mktg Mgr: Isabel Graham
Mktg Mgr: Ashley Merritt
Board of Directors: V H Andersen, Niels Christian Jensen

D-U-N-S 13-210-0673
LEGRAND HOLDING INC
(*Suby of* LEGRAND FRANCE)
60 Woodlawn St, West Hartford, CT 06110-2326
Tel (860) 233-6251 *Founded/Ownrshp* 1984
Sales 1.2MMM^E *EMP* 2,736
SIC 3643 6719 Current-carrying wiring devices; Investment holding companies, except banks
CEO: John P Selldorff
**Pr:* Giles Schnep
**Treas:* Robert Julian
**VP:* Antoine Burel
VP: Ken Freeman
VP: Susan Rochford
Genl Mgr: Tom Macerollo
DP Dir: Doug Fikse
DP Dir: Mark Panico
Dir IT: Glenn Olson
Sftwr Eng: Shelley Lockwood

D-U-N-S 01-981-2339
LEGRAND NORTH AMERICA LLC
(*Suby of* LEGRAND HOLDING INC) ★
60 Woodlawn St, West Hartford, CT 06110-2326
Tel (860) 233-6251 *Founded/Ownrshp* 2005
Sales 134.4MM^E *EMP* 983^E
SIC 8711 Electrical or electronic engineering
Pr: John Selldorff
Treas: James Laperriere
VP: Robert Julian
VP: Tom Plantamura
VP Sls: Dan Settles

LEHB
See LAW ENFORCEMENT HEALTH BENEFITS INC

D-U-N-S 06-856-5803
LEHIGH BLUE PRINT CO INC
BUTLER DIGITAL SERVICES
2000 Butler St, Easton, PA 18042-4682
Tel (610) 253-3303 *Founded/Ownrshp* 1971
Sales 190.0MM *EMP* 3
SIC 7334 Photocopying & duplicating services; Blueprinting service
Pr: Lynn Fitzgerald
VP: Jeffery L Fitzgerald

D-U-N-S 00-131-6355 IMP
LEHIGH CEMENT CO LLC
(*Suby of* HANSON LEHIGH INC) ★
300 E John Carpenter Fwy, Irving, TX 75062-2727
Tel (877) 534-4442 *Founded/Ownrshp* 2008, 2011
Sales 870.6MM^E *EMP* 2,249
SIC 3241 3273 5032 Portland cement; Ready-mixed concrete; Aggregate
Ch Bd: Helmut S Erhard
**Pr:* Robert Breyer
COO: Paul Jurgens
CFO: Mike Lewis
**CFO:* Larry A Prudhomme
Ch: Donald Fallon
VP: Larry Baloun
**VP:* Jeffry H Brozyna
VP: Helmut Leube
VP: Thor Lindberg
VP: Gerhard Muehlbeyer
VP: Pierre Rogmar
VP: Gerhard Seitz
VP: F R Snyder
VP: Erich Sulzer
VP: Peter B Tait
Exec: R M Memmer

D-U-N-S 09-641-3575 IMP/EXP
■ LEHIGH CONSUMER PRODUCTS LLC
LEHIGH GROUP, THE
(*Suby of* NEWELL BRANDS) ★
3901 Liberty St, Aurora, IL 60504-8122
Tel (630) 851-7330 *Founded/Ownrshp* 2003
Sales 151.8MM^E *EMP* 300
SIC 3965 2298 3462 3452 8742 Fasteners, buttons, needles & pins; Ropes & fiber cables; Iron & steel forgings; Bolts, nuts, rivets & washers; Financial consultant
Pr: Thomas Russo

LEHIGH GROUP, THE
See LEHIGH CONSUMER PRODUCTS LLC

D-U-N-S 08-866-5393 IMP/EXP
■ LEHIGH OUTFITTERS LLC
(*Suby of* ROCKY BRANDS INC) ★
39 E Canal St, Nelsonville, OH 45764-1247
Tel (740) 753-1951 *Founded/Ownrshp* 2005
Sales 104.7MM^E *EMP* 1,600
SIC 5661 5139 Men's shoes; Women's shoes; Shoes
Pr: Joseph J Sebes
VP: Darius Dabek
Genl Mgr: Nicole Zawerton
Sls Mgr: Grant Kimes
Sls Mgr: Matthew Rainville

LEHIGH PHOENIX
See PHOENIX COLOR CORP

D-U-N-S 15-247-7717 IMP
LEHIGH SOUTHWEST CEMENT CO
(*Suby of* HANSON LEHIGH INC) ★
2300 Clayton Rd Ste 300, Concord, CA 94520-2175
Tel (972) 653-5500 *Founded/Ownrshp* 2011
Sales 112.0MM[E] *EMP* 334
SIC 3241 2891 5032 5211 Portland cement; Masonry cement; Pozzolana cement; Cement, except linoleum & tile; Cement; Cement
CEO: Dan Harrington
VP: Zale Asbell
VP: Mike Lewis
VP: Mike Roth
Mng Dir: Alex Schwartz
VP Sls: Bill Boughton

D-U-N-S 06-857-0936
LEHIGH UNIVERSITY
27 Memorial Dr W Unit 8, Bethlehem, PA 18015-3005
Tel (610) 758-3000 *Founded/Ownrshp* 1865
Sales 307.1MM[E] *EMP* 4,000
Accts Kpmg Llp Philadelphia Pa
SIC 8221 University
Pr: Alice P Gast
Trst: Nancy M Beran
Trst: Robert L Brown
Trst: James J Duane
Trst: Oldrich Foucek
Trst: John E McGlad
Ofcr: Mark Ferencin
Ofcr: Ricky Rupp
Ex VP: John D Simon
VP: Toni Isreal
VP: Max Muheim
Assoc Dir: David Sudol

LEHIGH VALLEY HEALTH NETWORK
See NORTHEASTERN PENNSYLVANIA HEALTH CORP

D-U-N-S 10-620-7889
LEHIGH VALLEY HEALTH NETWORK INC
1247 S Cedar Crest Blvd, Allentown, PA 18103-6298
Tel (610) 402-8000 *Founded/Ownrshp* 1982
Sales 1.6MMM *EMP* 12,000
Accts Kpmg Llp Philadelphia Pennsy
SIC 8062 General medical & surgical hospitals
Pr: Elliot J Sussman
**Ch Bd:* J B Reily
V Ch: Richard Mackenzie
**CEO:* Ronald Swinfard
COO: Terry Capuano
CFO: Edward O'Dea
Ch: Michael Pasquale
Trst: John T Dickson
Trst: Edward M Mullin
Sr VP: Anne Panik
VP: Dorothy Jacquez
VP: Brian Leader
VP: Stephanie Marshall
**VP:* Stuart Paxton
VP: Mary Tirrell
VP: Lise Twiford
VP: Keith Weinhold
Dir Rx: Annmarie Higgins
Dir Rx: Mary B Karoly

D-U-N-S 15-074-5404
LEHIGH VALLEY HEALTH SERVICES INC
(*Suby of* LEHIGH VALLEY HEALTH NETWORK INC) ★
2166 S 12th St, Allentown, PA 18103-8701
Tel (610) 791-3682 *Founded/Ownrshp* 1983
Sales 114.0MM[E] *EMP* 625
SIC 4813 8741 8721 Telephone communication, except radio; Management services; Accounting, auditing & bookkeeping

D-U-N-S 06-857-2015
LEHIGH VALLEY HOSPITAL INC
LEHIGH VLY HOSP - CEDAR CREST
(*Suby of* LEHIGH VALLEY HEALTH NETWORK INC) ★
1200 S Cedar Crest Blvd, Allentown, PA 18103-6202
Tel (610) 402-8000 *Founded/Ownrshp* 1971
Sales 1.5MMM[E] *EMP* 12,000
SIC 8062 General medical & surgical hospitals
CEO: Ronald Swinfard
**Ch Bd:* William Hecht
**Ch Bd:* J B Reilly
**COO:* Stuart Paxton
**CFO:* Vaughn C Gower
CFO: Vaughn Gower
**CFO:* Edward O'Dea
Sr VP: Harry Lukens
Sr VP: Anne Panik
Dir Rad: Gary Marshall
Prac Mgr: Shannon Bickert

D-U-N-S 83-769-3522
LEHIGH VALLEY PHYSICIANS GROUP
(*Suby of* LEHIGH VALLEY HEALTH NETWORK INC) ★
1605 N Cedar Crest Blvd # 110, Allentown, PA 18104-2351
Tel (610) 439-7500 *Founded/Ownrshp* 1993
Sales 198.1MM[E] *EMP* 1,500[E]
SIC 8011 General & family practice, physician/surgeon
Ex Dir: Joseph Lyons
Prac Mgr: Debra Hontz
Prgrm Mgr: Richard Bowers
Pathlgst: Elizabeth Dellers
Doctor: Wayne Stephens

D-U-N-S 80-483-2152
LEHIGH VALLEY RESTAURANT GROUP INC
RED ROBIN
6802a Hamilton Blvd, Allentown, PA 18106-9644
Tel (610) 481-0436 *Founded/Ownrshp* 1993
Sales 75.6MM[E] *EMP* 2,000
SIC 5812 Restaurant, family: chain
CEO: James W Ryan
**CFO:* Chris Defrain
**Sec:* Lucinda Lobach
Ofcr: David Novick
**VP:* Joseph Fusco Jr
Genl Mgr: Joe McCarthy
Genl Mgr: Tischelle Wolfe
IT Man: Ed Kruczek
VP Opers: Mike Axiotis
Snr Mgr: Patricia Sobaru

LEHIGH VLY HOSP - CEDAR CREST
See LEHIGH VALLEY HOSPITAL INC

D-U-N-S 92-903-8545 EXP
LEHMAN DEALERSHIP ENTERPRISES INC
21400 Nw 2nd Ave, Miami, FL 33169-2126
Tel (305) 653-7111 *Founded/Ownrshp* 1984
Sales 84.9MM[E] *EMP* 243[E]
SIC 5511 Automobiles, new & used
Pr: William Lehman Jr

D-U-N-S 00-703-6676
LEHMAN-ROBERTS CO
1111 Wilson St, Memphis, TN 38106-2329
Tel (901) 774-4000 *Founded/Ownrshp* 1939
Sales 165.2MM[E] *EMP* 400
SIC 1611 2951 Highway & street paving contractor; Asphalt & asphaltic paving mixtures (not from refineries)
Pr: Patrick Nelson
Treas: Gilbert Wilson
**VP:* Johnny Driver
**VP:* John Paul Finerson
**VP:* David Greene
**VP:* Jobe Madison
Ql Cn Mgr: Dale Brewer

LEI AG SEATTLE
See LOWE ENTERPRISES INC

D-U-N-S 08-293-0884 IMP/EXP
LEICA BIOSYSTEMS RICHMOND INC (IL)
5205 Rte 12, Richmond, IL 60071
Tel (815) 678-2000 *Founded/Ownrshp* 1977
Sales 234.7MM[E] *EMP* 775
SIC 3842

D-U-N-S 19-442-7571 IMP
LEICA CAMERA INC
(*Suby of* LEICA CAMERA AG)
1 Pearl Ct Unit A, Allendale, NJ 07401-1658
Tel (201) 995-0051 *Founded/Ownrshp* 1990
Sales 85.7MM *EMP* 63
Accts Wilkin & Guttenplan Pc East
SIC 5043 Cameras & photographic equipment; Photographic cameras, projectors, equipment & supplies
Pr: Roger W Horn
**VP:* Raymond L Tomaselli

D-U-N-S 15-351-0730 IMP
■ **LEICA MICROSYSTEMS INC**
(*Suby of* DANAHER CORP) ★
1700 Leider Ln, Buffalo Grove, IL 60089-6622
Tel (847) 405-0123 *Founded/Ownrshp* 1986
Sales 113.0MM[E] *EMP* 400
SIC 3827 3841 3821 Optical instruments & lenses; Optical instruments & apparatus; Diagnostic apparatus, medical; Laboratory apparatus & furniture
Pr: Matthias Weber
Treas: Charles Schwertner
**Sec:* Albin Szklany
**VP:* Karen Bergendorf
VP: Chip Clark
VP: Christopher McMahon
Genl Mgr: Cynthia Manley
Netwrk Mgr: Vincent Amoranto
Sftwr Eng: Craig Sacco
Ql Cn Mgr: Lynne Dobson
Sales Exec: Doug Giszczynski
Board of Directors: Daniel L Comas, Robert L Comas, Terrence Grant, Robert S Lutz, Vincent Vaccerelli

D-U-N-S 04-430-6348
■ **LEIDOS ASPEN SYSTEMS CORP**
LOCKHEED MARTIN ASPEN
(*Suby of* LEIDOS HOLDINGS INC) ★
700 N Frederick Ave, Gaithersburg, MD 20879-3328
Tel (301) 240-7000 *Founded/Ownrshp* 2016
Sales 81.9MM[E] *EMP* 1,651
SIC 7374 7379 7389 Data processing service; Computer related consulting services; Financial services
Pr: Albert Lampert
**Treas:* Linda J Dybiec
**Ex VP:* Eugene Brannock

D-U-N-S 15-999-0456
■ **LEIDOS BIOMEDICAL RESEARCH INC**
(*Suby of* LEIDOS INC) ★
1050 Boyles St, Frederick, MD 21702-9242
Tel (301) 846-5031 *Founded/Ownrshp* 2000
Sales 1.0MMM[E] *EMP* 19,000[E]
SIC 8733 Noncommercial research organizations
Pr: David Heimbrook
**Treas:* David Bufter
**Ex VP:* Douglas Scott
VP: Darlene Rosmarino
Genl Mgr: Robert Mason
IT Man: Laura Knott
Netwrk Mgr: William Boyer
Web Dev: Jason Holbert

D-U-N-S 05-165-0752
■ **LEIDOS ENGINEERING LLC**
(*Suby of* LEIDOS INC) ★
11951 Freedom Dr, Reston, VA 20190-5640
Tel (571) 526-6000 *Founded/Ownrshp* 2007
Sales 328.1MM[E] *EMP* 849
SIC 8711 1541 Engineering services; Industrial buildings & warehouses
CEO: Roger Krone
Mng Pt: Tom Roach
V Ch: Connie Mullins
Pr: Ken Morris
Treas: Stephen Bingham
VP: Wally Hunt
VP: Napoliello Jeff
VP: Charles Weaver
Creative D: David Benham
Dir Bus: Randal Paquette
Mng Dir: Michael Wright

D-U-N-S 05-860-5858
■ **LEIDOS GOVERNMENT SERVICES INC**
LOCKHEED MARTIN GOV SVC, INC.
(*Suby of* LEIDOS HOLDINGS INC) ★
700 N Frederick Ave, Gaithersburg, MD 20879-3328
Tel (856) 486-5156 *Founded/Ownrshp* 2016
Sales 97.8MM[E] *EMP* 4,873
SIC 7379 7373 7374 7372 Computer related consulting services; Computer integrated systems design; Computer systems analysis & design; Data processing services; Data entry service; Application computer software
Pr: Harvey Braswell

D-U-N-S 61-164-1312
▲ **LEIDOS HOLDINGS INC**
11951 Freedom Dr Ste 500, Reston, VA 20190-5650
Tel (571) 526-6000 *Founded/Ownrshp* 1969
Sales 5.0MMM *EMP* 18,000
Tkr Sym LDOS *Exch* NYS
SIC 8731 7371 7373 8742 3674 Commercial physical research; Energy research; Environmental research; Medical research, commercial; Computer software development; Systems engineering, computer related; Training & development consultant; Integrated circuits, semiconductor networks, etc.
Ch Bd: Roger A Krone
Pr: Deborah H Alderson
Pr: Richard Deason
Pr: Michael Giblin
Pr: Richard Mitchell
Pr: Larry J Peck
Pr: George T Singley III
CFO: James C Reagan
Ofcr: Sarah Allen
Ex VP: Sarah K Allen
Ex VP: Michael Leiter
Ex VP: Vincent A Maffeo
Ex VP: William A Roper Jr
Sr VP: Ranjit S Chadha
Sr VP: Lucy Reilly Fitch
Sr VP: John R Hartley
Sr VP: David Lacquement
Sr VP: Paul E Levi
Sr VP: Steven Russell
VP: James Bahel
VP: Mike Eddings

D-U-N-S 05-478-1240 EXP
■ **LEIDOS INC**
(*Suby of* LEIDOS HOLDINGS INC) ★
11951 Freedom Dr Ste 500, Reston, VA 20190-5650
Tel (571) 526-6000 *Founded/Ownrshp* 1969
Sales 5.0MMM *EMP* 19,000
Accts Deloitte & Touche Llp Mclean
SIC 8731 7373 Commercial physical research; Energy research; Environmental research; Medical research, commercial; Systems engineering, computer related
Ch Bd: Roger A Krone
Pr: Paul Desantis
Pr: Dale Napier
Ofcr: Sarah Allen
Ex VP: Tom Aikens
Ex VP: James E Cuff
Ex VP: Deborah Lee James
Ex VP: Michael E Leiter
Ex VP: Vincent A Maffeo
Sr VP: Julius Caesar
Sr VP: Paul E Levi
Sr VP: Terry M Ryan
Sr VP: Kenneth P Sharp
Sr VP: Travis Slocumb
Sr VP: Jennifer E Smith
Sr VP: Paul W Sullivan
Sr VP: John Sweeney
VP: Marjorie Bailey
VP: Michele Brown
VP: Jessica Campbell
VP: Tod Comin
Board of Directors: David G Fubini, John J Hamre, Miriam E John, John J Jumper, Harry M J Kraemer Jr, Gary S May, Lawrence C Nussdorf, Robert S Shapard, Noel B Williams

D-U-N-S 04-803-5351
■ **LEIDOS INTEGRATED TECHNOLOGY LLC**
(*Suby of* LEIDOS HOLDINGS INC) ★
700 N Frederick Ave, Gaithersburg, MD 20879-3328
Tel (301) 240-7000 *Founded/Ownrshp* 2016
Sales 117.6MM[E] *EMP* 5,000
SIC 8741 Management services

D-U-N-S 61-737-9607
■ **LEIDOS TECHNICAL SERVICES INC**
(*Suby of* LEIDOS HOLDINGS INC) ★
700 N Frederick Ave, Gaithersburg, MD 20879-3328
Tel (301) 240-7000 *Founded/Ownrshp* 2016
Sales 98.2MM[E] *EMP* 1,000
SIC 8731 Electronic research
Pr: Linda Renfro
Treas: Janet L Mc Gregor
Treas: Robert W Powell Jr
Ex VP: Michael F Camardo
VP: Philip J Duke
VP Bus: Kenneth F Morton

D-U-N-S 05-264-3350 EXP
LEIF JOHNSON FORD INC
TRUCK CITY FORD
501 E Koenig Ln, Austin, TX 78751-1426
Tel (512) 454-3711 *Founded/Ownrshp* 1947
Sales 174.3MM[E] *EMP* 410
SIC 5521 5511 Used car dealers; Automobiles, new & used
CEO: Robert Johnson
Pt: Curt Johnson
CFO: Bill Sullivan
VP: Brook A Broesche
Genl Mgr: Fred Trudeau
Netwrk Eng: Mark Codington
Sales Exec: Chris Tohill
Mktg Mgr: Chris Stclair
Sls Mgr: Jeff Buhl
Sls Mgr: Ben Celis
Sls Mgr: Chip Clester

D-U-N-S 03-551-8237
LEILA A MANKARIOUS
MASSACHUSETS EYE EAR INFERMERY
(*Suby of* MASSACHUSETTS EYE AND EAR INFIRMARY & PHYSICIAN STAFF INC) ★
243 Charles St, Boston, MA 02114-3002
Tel (617) 573-3413 *Founded/Ownrshp* 2001
Sales 228.0MM *EMP* 4
Accts Lb Pricewaterhousecoopers Llp
SIC 8011 Offices & clinics of medical doctors
Owner: Leila A Mankarious PHD
Treas: Joseph B Nadol Jr

D-U-N-S 03-947-9332 IMP/EXP
■ **LEINER HEALTH PRODUCTS INC**
(*Suby of* ARCO PHARMACEUTICAL) ★
901 E 233rd St, Carson, CA 90745-6204
Tel (631) 200-2000 *Founded/Ownrshp* 1952
Sales 157.2MM[E] *EMP* 1,500
SIC 2834 5122 Vitamin, nutrient & hematinic preparations for human use; Vitamins & minerals
CEO: Jeffrey A Nagel
Pr: Robert J La Ferriere
Pr: Crystal Wright
**CFO:* Michael Collins
**V Ch Bd:* Harvey Kamil
Sr VP: Patrick Dunn
VP Mktg: Brenda Cheng

D-U-N-S 02-131-7003
LEISURE CARE LLC
999 3rd Ave Ste 4500, Seattle, WA 98104-4075
Tel (800) 327-3490 *Founded/Ownrshp* 2003
Sales 138.2MM[E] *EMP* 1,900
SIC 8361 Residential care
**CFO:* Judy Marczewski

D-U-N-S 62-161-1466 EXP
LEISURE PROPERTIES LLC
CROWNLINE BOATS
11884 Country Club Rd, West Frankfort, IL 62896-5064
Tel (618) 937-6426 *Founded/Ownrshp* 1990
Sales 177.2MM[E] *EMP* 550
SIC 3732 Boats, fiberglass: building & repairing
**Pr:* Scott Lahrman
CFO: Guy Coons

D-U-N-S 04-429-8685
LEISURE SPORTS INC
CLUBSPORT OF PLEASANTON
4670 Willow Rd Ste 100, Pleasanton, CA 94588-8587
Tel (925) 600-1966 *Founded/Ownrshp* 1991
Sales 213.0MM[E] *EMP* 1,300
SIC 6719 Investment holding companies, except banks; Personal holding companies, except banks
Pr: Steve Gilmour
**CFO:* Patrick O'Brien

LEISURE SUPPLY
See KELLER SUPPLY CO

D-U-N-S 07-302-6106 IMP/EXP
LEISURE TIME PRODUCTS LLC
BACKYARD DISCOVERY
3001 N Rouse St, Pittsburg, KS 66762-2404
Tel (620) 232-2400 *Founded/Ownrshp* 2015
Sales 202.9MM[E] *EMP* 1,020
SIC 3089 3949 2452

D-U-N-S 03-120-8390
LEISZLER OIL CO INC
SHORT STOP
8228 Southport Dr, Manhattan, KS 66502-8116
Tel (785) 632-5648 *Founded/Ownrshp* 1971
Sales 139.4MM[E] *EMP* 175
Accts Sink Gordon & Associates Llp
SIC 5171 5411 5541 Petroleum bulk stations; Grocery stores; Gasoline service stations
Pr: Charles Arthur III
**VP:* Alison R Leiszler
Area Supr: Brian Rankin

LEITH AUTO CENTER SERVICE
See LEITH INC

D-U-N-S 04-736-8238
LEITH INC
LEITH AUTO CENTER SERVICE
5607 Capital Blvd, Raleigh, NC 27616-2933
Tel (919) 876-5432 *Founded/Ownrshp* 1968
Sales 288.3MM[E] *EMP* 800
SIC 5511 7515 7513 5012 Automobiles, new & used; Pickups, new & used; Passenger car leasing; Truck rental & leasing, no drivers; Automobiles & other motor vehicles
Pr: Michael J Leith
**COO:* Linda Leith
Off Mgr: Kathy Braswell
CIO: David Prince
Mktg Mgr: Don Sigmon
Sls Mgr: Russ Clark
Sls Mgr: Josh Greene
Sls Mgr: Wayne Hunter
Sls Mgr: Warren Taylor

D-U-N-S 00-921-4214 IMP
LELAND STANFORD JUNIOR UNIVERSITY
STANFORD LINEAR ACCELERATOR CTR
2575 Sand Hill Rd, Menlo Park, CA 94025-7015
Tel (650) 723-2300 *Founded/Ownrshp* 1891
Sales 3.5MMM[E] *EMP* 15,000
Accts Pricewaterhousecoopers Llp Sa
SIC 8221 8069 8062 University; Children's hospital; General medical & surgical hospitals
Pr: John Hennessy
**CFO:* Randall S Livingston
VP: Bill Clebsch
**VP:* Debra Zumwalt
Software D: Jim Chiang
Doctor: Eugene Carragee
Snr Mgr: Martin Nordby
Snr Mgr: Ram Rayaroth
Snr Mgr: Ken Rubino
Snr Mgr: Peter Schuh

D-U-N-S 02-327-2776 IMP
LEMANS CORP (WI)
3501 Kennedy Rd, Janesville, WI 53545-8884
Tel (608) 758-1111 *Founded/Ownrshp* 1967
Sales 801.7MM[E] *EMP* 1,000
SIC 5013 Motor vehicle supplies & new parts; Motorcycle parts
Ch Bd: Fred Fox
CFO: Mark Scharenbroch
VP: Mike Collins
Genl Mgr: Lynne Severson
Mktg Dir: Tucker Rocky

D-U-N-S 78-978-3685
LEMBI GROUP INC
2101 Market St, San Francisco, CA 94114-1321
Tel (415) 861-1111 Founded/Ownrshp 1990
Sales 14.3MM^E EMP 1,510^E
SIC 6531 Real estate managers
Pr: Frank Lembi
*VP: Walter Lembi

D-U-N-S 12-417-3860
LEMEK LLC
PANERA BREAD
8184 Lark Brown Rd # 101, Elkridge, MD 21075-3403
Tel (443) 552-0700 Founded/Ownrshp 1998
Sales 85.0MM^E EMP 2,200
SIC 5812 Fast-food restaurant, chain
IT Man: Kevin Gandel

D-U-N-S 06-656-6969
LEMO USA INC
(Suby of INTERLEMO USA INC) ★
635 Park Ct, Rohnert Park, CA 94928-7940
Tel (707) 206-3700 Founded/Ownrshp 1986
Sales 94.4MM^E EMP 100
SIC 5065 3678 Connectors, electronic; Electronic connectors
CEO: Dinshaw Pohwala
Genl Mgr: Win Baerthel
CTO: Michael Grieco
Opers Mgr: Mike Perry
Mktg Mgr: Julie Carlson

D-U-N-S 01-640-2765
LEMOINE CO L L C
214 Jefferson St Ste 200, Lafayette, LA 70501-7050
Tel (337) 896-7720 Founded/Ownrshp 2015
Sales 149.8MM^E EMP 200
SIC 1542 Nonresidential construction
CEO: Leonard K Lemoine
COO: Van Champagne
*CFO: Donald Broussard Jr
VP: Robert Rice
Dir Bus: Rachel Fousch
Div Mgr: William Lemoine
Off Mgr: Shelly Schexnayder
Off Admin: Kristen Cory
Sfty Dirs: James Wallace
Sfty Mgr: Aaron Vincent
Opers Mgr: Tim Burdette

LEN STOLER FORD
See LEN STOLER INC

D-U-N-S 04-415-1389 EXP
LEN STOLER INC
LEN STOLER FORD
11275 Reisterstown Rd, Owings Mills, MD 21117-1997
Tel (410) 581-7000 Founded/Ownrshp 1985
Sales 154.2MM^E EMP 410
SIC 5511 Automobiles, new & used
Pr: Barry Stoler
*CFO: David Leibowitz
CFO: Dave Liebowitz
*VP: James Berg
*Prin: Len Stoler
Genl Mgr: Dave McBrearty
Sls Mgr: Richard Browne
Sls Mgr: Phillip Pate
Sls Mgr: Damian Shepard
Sales Asso: Chelsea Jefferson
Sales Asso: Joe Michalski
Board of Directors: Roslyn Stoler

D-U-N-S 03-258-5549
LENAPE REGIONAL HIGH SCHOOL DISTRICT
93 Willow Grove Rd, Shamong, NJ 08088-8961
Tel (609) 268-2588 Founded/Ownrshp 1954
Sales 163.4MM EMP 1,200
Accts Holman Frenia Allison Pc M
SIC 8211 High school, junior or senior
MIS Dir: Mike Haas
Teacher Pr: Paige Macgregor
Instr Medi: John Donaldson

D-U-N-S 18-798-4265 IMP
LENAWEE STAMPING CORP
VAN ROB TECUMSEH
(Suby of VAN-ROB INC)
1200 E Chicago Blvd, Tecumseh, MI 49286-8605
Tel (517) 423-2400 Founded/Ownrshp 2006
Sales 103.1MM^E EMP 330
SIC 3465 Body parts, automobile: stamped metal
Pr: Allan Power
Mfg Mgr: Greg Darling

LEND LASE US CNSTR HLDINGS INC
See LENDLEASE (US) CONSTRUCTION HOLDINGS INC

LEND LEASE
See LENDLEASE (US) CONSTRUCTION LMB INC

D-U-N-S 00-759-5861
LEND LEASE (US) INC
(Suby of LENDLEASE CONSTRUCTION HOLDINGS (EUROPE) LIMITED)
250 Civic Center Dr, New York, NY 10166
Tel (212) 592-6700 Founded/Ownrshp 1992
Sales 349.0MM^E EMP 3,097
SIC 6799 6552 Investors; Subdividers & developers
Pr: Peter A Marchetto

D-U-N-S 02-750-0848
LEND LEASE AMERICAS INC
200 Park Ave Fl 9, New York, NY 10166-0999
Tel (212) 592-6700 Founded/Ownrshp 1997
Sales 146.3MM^E EMP 450
SIC 1542 1541 Nonresidential construction; Industrial buildings & warehouses

D-U-N-S 12-780-7704 IMP
LENDERLIVE NETWORK INC
710 S Ash St Ste 200, Denver, CO 80246-1989
Tel (303) 226-8000 Founded/Ownrshp 1999
Sales 136.2MM^E EMP 376^E
SIC 4813 6163 ; Loan brokers
CEO: Rick Seehausen
COO: Dick Solheim
CFO: Adam Nichols
Chf Mktg O: Kim Starley
Sr VP: Donna Clayton
Sr VP: Steve Crawford
Sr VP: Len Franco
Sr VP: Bob Fulton
Sr VP: Richard R Holsclaw
Sr VP: Kevin Kelley
Sr VP: Jan Kidder
Sr VP: Karen Morehart
Sr VP: Reid Nelson
Sr VP: Eric Prosperi
Sr VP: Richard Sauerwein
Sr VP: Mitch Tanenbaum
VP: Pete Butler
VP: Bob Crittenden
VP: Eric Seabrook

D-U-N-S 88-353-4281
LENDING SOLUTIONS INC
2200 Point Blvd Ste 110, Elgin, IL 60123-7868
Tel (847) 844-2200 Founded/Ownrshp 1994
Sales NA EMP 400
SIC 6153 7389 Short-term business credit; Financial services
Ch: Mark E Johnson
*Pr: Lee Kolquist
Pr: Robert Macari
Pr: Jim Milano
*CEO: David Kushner
*Ex VP: Dave Brooke
VP: Karin Brown
VP: Jeff Frantz
*VP: Mike Karst
VP: Ed Swanson
*VP: Thomas R Zak

D-U-N-S 80-122-0836
▲ LENDINGCLUB CORP
71 Stevenson St Ste 300, San Francisco, CA 94105-2985
Tel (415) 632-5600 Founded/Ownrshp 2006
Sales NA EMP 1,382^E
Tkr Sym LC Exch NYS
SIC 6153 Working capital financing
Pr: Scott Sanborn
Pr: Kolya Klimenko
COO: Sameer Gulati
CFO: Carrie Dolan
Chf Cred: Sandeep Bhandari
Chf Cred: Patrick Dunne
Chf Mktg O: Scott Sanbourne
Sr VP: Bruce Marcellus
Sr VP: Zhi Zhou
VP: Joanne Chang
VP: Andrew Deringer
VP: Roger Dickerson
VP: Beth Haiken
VP: Mitchel Harad
VP: Avia Kay
VP: Kal Majmundar
VP: Margaret Murn
VP: David O'Brien
VP: Jordan Olivier
VP: Stephanie Reiter
VP: Richard Southwick
Board of Directors: Daniel Ciporin, Jeffrey Crowe, John J Mack, Mary Meeker, John C Morris, Lawrence Summers, Simon Williams

D-U-N-S 82-818-4429
▲ LENDINGTREE INC
11115 Rushmore Dr, Charlotte, NC 28277-3442
Tel (704) 541-5351 Founded/Ownrshp 2008
Sales NA EMP 312^E
Tkr Sym TREE Exch NGM
SIC 6163 6531 Loan brokers; Real estate brokers & agents
Ch Bd: Douglas R Lebda
Pr: Neil Salvage
COO: Nikul Patel
CFO: Gabriel Dalporto
VP Bus Dev: Bruce Cook
CTO: Paul Onnen
Snr Mgr: Sharon Northcutt
Board of Directors: Neal Dermer, Robin Henderson, Peter Horan, Steven Ozonian, Craig Troyer

D-U-N-S 62-235-2490 IMP
LENDLEASE (US) CONSTRUCTION HOLDINGS INC
LEND LASE US CNSTR HLDINGS INC
(Suby of LENDLEASE CONSTRUCTION HOLDINGS (EUROPE) LIMITED)
200 Park Ave Fl 9, New York, NY 10166-0999
Tel (212) 592-6700 Founded/Ownrshp 1999
Sales 563.6MM^E EMP 730
SIC 1542 1541 8742 Commercial & office building, new construction; Industrial buildings, new construction; Construction project management consultant
Ch: Jeffrey L Arfsten
*CEO: Robert McNamara
COO: Ron Clarkson
*COO: Dan Labbad
*CFO: Tony Lombardo
*Treas: Brad Robinson
Sr Cor Off: Suzn Head
Top Exec: Ray Dardenne
Ex VP: Jeff Arfsten
Ex VP: Jeff Riemer
Ex VP: Linda Sjogren
Ex VP: Thomas Tether
Sr VP: Bruce Berardi
Sr VP: Rick Wehmeier
VP: Kelly Benedict
VP: Kevin Bowen
VP: Richard Caster
VP: Majid Fanik
VP: Brian Fleming
VP: Marie Halloran
VP: Jason Hier

D-U-N-S 00-892-4029
LENDLEASE (US) CONSTRUCTION INC (FL)
(Suby of LEND LASE US CNSTR HLDINGS INC) ★
200 Park Ave Fl 9, New York, NY 10166-0999
Tel (212) 592-6700 Founded/Ownrshp 1987
Sales 563.6MM^E EMP 661
SIC 1541 1542 1522 8741 8742 Industrial buildings, new construction; Hospital construction; Commercial & office building, new construction; Shopping center construction; Religious building construction; Hotel/motel, new construction; Construction management; Construction project management consultant
Pr: Jeff Arfsten
COO: Dan Labbad
CFO: Alex Cockerton
*Treas: Brad Robinson
Ex VP: Michael M Feigin
Ex VP: Linda Sjogren
Sr VP: Steven Sommer
VP: William Connor
VP: Dennis Sawyer
VP: Gerry Stern
*Prin: George Keppler
Board of Directors: Dale Connor

D-U-N-S 09-698-1824 IMP
LENDLEASE (US) CONSTRUCTION LMB INC (NY)
LEND LEASE
(Suby of M/L BOVIS HOLDINGS LTD) ★
200 Park Ave Fl 9, New York, NY 10166-0999
Tel (212) 592-6700 Founded/Ownrshp 1979, 1999
Sales 173.4MM^E EMP 465^E
SIC 1522 1541 1542 8741 8742 Residential construction; Industrial buildings, new construction; Nonresidential construction; Management services; Management consulting services
Pr: Ralph Esposito
*Treas: Brad Robinson
Ofcr: Daloris Grohman
VP: John Anania
Mng Dir: Daniel Labbad
IT Man: Dennis Griffeth

D-U-N-S 08-722-2936
LENDLEASE (US) PUBLIC PARTNERSHIPS LLC
(Suby of LENDLEASE CORPORATION LIMITED)
1201 Demonbreun St # 800, Nashville, TN 37203-3140
Tel (615) 963-2600 Founded/Ownrshp 1999
Sales 115.3MM^E EMP 399
SIC 1522 Residential construction
Ex VP: Bruce Anderson
*CFO: Simon Benson
*Treas: Brad Robinson
Mng Dir: Peter Brecht
Mng Dir: Murray Coleman
Mng Dir: Eduardo Sposito
Genl Mgr: Ann Arnold
QC Dir: Tim Kelley
Sfty Mgr: James Steinke

D-U-N-S 95-848-3414
LENDMARK FINANCIAL SERVICES LLC
2118 Usher St Nw, Covington, GA 30014-2434
Tel (678) 625-6500 Founded/Ownrshp 2013
Sales NA EMP 500
SIC 6162 Loan correspondents
CEO: Robert W Aiken
Pr: Christie Hall
Pr: Paulette Jones
Pr: Vincent Kelley
*CFO: Wayne Taylor
Chf Cred: Al Appelman
Chf Mktg O: Ethan Andelman
Ofcr: Nicole Adams
VP: Rick Clayton
VP: Richard Davis
VP: Sharlene Goolsby
VP: Robert Greenhaw
VP: Becky Hewison
VP: Gary Levar
VP: Chris McKinley
VP: Brian Waichunas

D-U-N-S 00-450-0575 IMP/EXP
LENMORE INC (PA)
WIMCO METALS
401 Penn Ave, Pittsburgh, PA 15221-2135
Tel (412) 243-8000 Founded/Ownrshp 1915
Sales 91.4MM EMP 30
Accts Lally & Co Llc Pittsburgh
SIC 5093 Nonferrous metals scrap
Prin: Glen S Gross
*Pr: Morris E Gross

LENNAR BUILDERS
See LENNAR HOMES OF CALIFORNIA INC

D-U-N-S 05-537-8061 EXP
▲ LENNAR CORP
700 Nw 107th Ave Ste 400, Miami, FL 33172-3154
Tel (305) 559-4000 Founded/Ownrshp 1954
Sales 9.4MMM EMP 7,749^E
Accts Deloitte & Touch Llp Miami F
Tkr Sym LEN Exch NYS
SIC 1531 6552 6163 Operative builders; Condominium developers; Townhouse developers; Subdividers & developers; Loan brokers
CEO: Stuart A Miller
Pr: Richard Beckwitt
COO: Jonathan M Jaffe
CFO: Bruce E Gross
Treas: Diane J Bessette
Bd of Dir: Janice Stucker
Ex VP: Al Lee
Ex VP: Tom Lytle
Ex VP: Linda L Reed
Ex VP: Robert Santos
VP: Marshall H Ames
VP: Mark Bacon
VP: Dustin Barker
VP: Jim Bowersox
VP: Jeff Clemens
VP: Tom Garlock
VP: Ryan Gatchalian
VP: Scott Handt
VP: Daris Horn
VP: Steve Leach
VP: Steve Lutton
Board of Directors: Irving Bolotin, Steven L Gerard, Theron I Gilliam Jr, Sherrill W Hudson, Sidney Lapidus, Teri P McClure, Armando Olivera, Jeffrey Sonnenfeld

D-U-N-S 60-734-2284
■ LENNAR FINANCIAL SERVICES LLC
(Suby of US HOME) ★
700 Nw 107th Ave Ste 400, Miami, FL 33172-3139
Tel (305) 559-4000 Founded/Ownrshp 2002
Sales NA EMP 2,000^E
SIC 6162 6153 6361 6411 7382 Mortgage bankers; Short-term business credit; Title insurance; Insurance agents, brokers & service; Security systems services
Pr: David McCain
*CFO: Nancy Kaminsky
*Ch: Allan Pekor
*Treas: Janice Munoz
*Ex VP: Linda Reed
VP: Diane J Bessette
VP: John Jessup
IT Man: Brian Seveland

D-U-N-S 03-249-7497 EXP
■ LENNAR HOMES INC
(Suby of LENNAR CORP) ★
730 Nw 107th Ave Ste 300, Miami, FL 33172-3104
Tel (305) 559-4000 Founded/Ownrshp 1969
Sales 502.0MM^E EMP 600
SIC 1531 Operative builders
Pr: Stuart A Miller
*Pr: Rick Beckwitt
Pr: Ric Rojas
*COO: Jonathan M Jaffe
COO: Samantha Thompson
*VP: Diane J Bessette
*VP: Bruce Gross
*VP: Janice Munoz
VP: Michael Petrolino
IT Man: Belis Izquierdo
IT Man: Chris Oakes

D-U-N-S 12-947-5534 IMP
■ LENNAR HOMES LLC
(Suby of LENNAR CORP) ★
700 Nw 107th Ave Ste 400, Miami, FL 33172-3139
Tel (305) 559-4000 Founded/Ownrshp 1954
Sales 214.4MM^E EMP 325^E
SIC 1531 Operative builders
Treas: Jacqui Desouza
IT Man: Joe Timme
Sales Asso: Kathy Eller

D-U-N-S 94-951-9342
■ LENNAR HOMES OF CALIFORNIA INC
LENNAR BUILDERS
(Suby of LENNAR HOMES INC) ★
25 Enterprise Ste 400, Aliso Viejo, CA 92656-2712
Tel (949) 349-8000 Founded/Ownrshp 1996
Sales 135.5MM^E EMP 311
SIC 1521 6552 New construction, single-family houses; Subdividers & developers
CEO: Stuart Miller
VP Opers: Bob Tummolo

LENNOX
See INNOVATIVE HEARTH PRODUCTS LLC

D-U-N-S 00-528-8840 IMP/EXP
■ LENNOX INDUSTRIES INC
(Suby of LENNOX INTERNATIONAL INC) ★
2100 Lake Park Blvd, Richardson, TX 75080-2254
Tel (972) 497-5000 Founded/Ownrshp 1904
Sales 1.9MMM^E EMP 5,500
SIC 5075

D-U-N-S 13-956-4538
▲ LENNOX INTERNATIONAL INC
2140 Lake Park Blvd, Richardson, TX 75080-2252
Tel (972) 497-5350 Founded/Ownrshp 1895
Sales 3.4MMM EMP 10,000
Tkr Sym LII Exch NYS
SIC 3585 3621 Refrigeration & heating equipment; Furnaces, warm air: electric; Air conditioning units, complete: domestic or industrial; Refrigeration equipment, complete; Coils, for electric motors or generators
Ch Bd: Todd M Bluedorn
COO: Mark Rakowski
CFO: Mark Piccirillo
CFO: Joseph W Reitmeier
Treas: Nelson Hoffman
Ofcr: Daniel M Sessa
Ex VP: Prakash Bedapudi
Ex VP: Harry J Bizios
Ex VP: Terry L Johnston
Ex VP: David W Moon
Ex VP: Douglas L Young
VP: Chuck Donnelly
VP: Keith Nash
VP: Roy A Rumbough Jr
VP: Elliot Zimmer
Board of Directors: Todd J Teske, Janet K Cooper, John E Major, Max H Mitchell, John W Norris III, Karen H Quintos, Kim K Rucker, Paul W Schmidt, Terry D Stinson, Gregory T Swienton

D-U-N-S 00-969-0264
LENOIR CITY UTILITIES BOARD
LCUB
200 Depot St, Lenoir City, TN 37771-2917
Tel (865) 376-4421 Founded/Ownrshp 1938
Sales 102.0MM^E EMP 134
SIC 4911 Distribution, electric power
Genl Mgr: Freddie Nelson
VP: Jinni Redmond
Genl Mgr: Shannon Littleton

D-U-N-S 07-557-9847
LENOIR COUNTY BOARD OF EDUCATION INC
2017 W Vernon Ave, Kinston, NC 28504-3329
Tel (252) 527-1109 Founded/Ownrshp 1920
Sales 57.3MM^E EMP 1,134^E
SIC 8211 School board
Ch Bd: Jon Sargeant

D-U-N-S 07-979-8926
LENOIR COUNTY PUBLIC SCHOOLS
2017 W Vernon Ave, Kinston, NC 28504-3329
Tel (252) 527-1109 Founded/Ownrshp 2015
Sales 50.0MM^E EMP 1,212^E
SIC 8211 Public elementary & secondary schools

MIS Dir: Sheila Heath
Pr Dir: Patrick Holmes
Teacher Pr: Robin Roberson
Psych: Toni Braswell

D-U-N-S 07-201-0093
LENOIR MEMORIAL HOSPITAL INC
DOWN EAST MEDICAL SUPPLY
100 Airport Rd, Kinston, NC 28501-1634
Tel (252) 522-7000 *Founded/Ownrshp* 1950
Sales 101.6MM *EMP* 811
SIC 8062 General medical & surgical hospitals
Pr: Gary Black
Chf Path: Michael Haddad
**CFO:* Sarah Mayo
**Treas:* Mary Cauley
Dir Risk M: Donna Floyd
Dir Rad: Mark A Adkins
Dir Rx: Dale Hardy
CIO: Karl Vanderstouw
Mtls Dir: Dennis Boykin
Ansthlgy: Preecha Bhotiwihok
Doctor: Elaine Penuel

D-U-N-S 02-912-2207 IMP
LENORE JOHN & CO
1250 Delevan Dr, San Diego, CA 92102-2437
Tel (619) 232-6136 *Founded/Ownrshp* 1966
Sales 143.9MM[E] *EMP* 270
SIC 5149 5182 5181 Soft drinks; Mineral or spring water bottling; Wine; Liquor; Beer & other fermented malt liquors
CEO: John G Lenore
**Pr:* Jamie Lenore

D-U-N-S 15-334-5173 IMP
LENOVO (UNITED STATES) INC
LENOVO INTERNATIONAL
(*Suby of* LENOVO GROUP LIMITED)
1009 Think Pl, Morrisville, NC 27560-9002
Tel (919) 294-2500 *Founded/Ownrshp* 2005
Sales 863.3MM[E] *EMP* 1,968
SIC 3571 Electronic computers
CEO: Yang Yuanqing
Ch Bd: Liu Chuanzhi
Pr: Liu Jun
Pr: Gianfranco Lanci
CFO: Wong W Ming
CFO: Zhou Qingtong
Chf Mktg O: Deepak Advani
Ofcr: David Roman
Sr VP: Kenneth Dipietro
Sr VP: Van Duijl
Sr VP: Rory Reed
Sr VP: Gerry P Smith
Sr VP: Milko Van Duijl
VP: Greg Ausley
VP: WEI Guan
VP: David Hill
VP: Charlie Mulgrove
Exec: John Mayr
Exec: Virginia McAfee
Exec: Michael Mullen
Comm Man: Stephanie Shi

D-U-N-S 07-909-8933
LENOVO HOLDING CO INC
1009 Think Pl, Morrisville, NC 27560-9002
Tel (919) 294-0600 *Founded/Ownrshp* 2007
Sales 128.4MM[E] *EMP* 315[E]
SIC 3571 Personal computers (microcomputers)
Sales Asso: Katie O'Connor

LENOVO INTERNATIONAL
See LENOVO (UNITED STATES) INC

D-U-N-S 07-876-5314 IMP
LENOVO US FULFILLMENT CENTER LLC
(*Suby of* LENOVO HOLDING CO INC) ★
6540 Franz Warner Pkwy, Whitsett, NC 27377-9215
Tel (919) 294-0477 *Founded/Ownrshp* 2007
Sales 128.4MM[E] *EMP* 266[E]
SIC 3571 Electronic computers
Chf Mktg O: Joel Mondshane
VP: Timothy Carroll
VP: Wilfredo Sotolongo
Ex Dir: Bill Perez
Prgrm Mgr: Robert Graziano
Snr Mgr: Kristen Iadanza

LENOX HILL HOSPITAL
See LHH CORP

D-U-N-S 01-560-7462
LENOX HILL HOSPITAL
210 E 64th St Fl 4, New York, NY 10065-7471
Tel (212) 472-8872 *Founded/Ownrshp* 2010
Sales 885.4MM *EMP* 45[E]
SIC 8062 General medical & surgical hospitals
Owner: Dr Afsaneh Latifi
Psych: Jennifer L Oratio
Surgeon: W N Scott

D-U-N-S 83-002-6741 IMP/EXP
LENOX HOLDINGS INC
DANSK
1414 Radcliffe St Fl 1, Bristol, PA 19007-5418
Tel (267) 525-7800 *Founded/Ownrshp* 2009
Sales 242.3MM *EMP* 1,098
SIC 3229 3161 5719 5948 Tableware, glass or glass ceramic; Luggage; Briefcases; Traveling bags; China; Glassware; Luggage & leather goods stores
Pr: Lester Gribetz
CEO: Peter B Cameron
COO: Jerome Ciszewskiis
CFO: Steve Oaconnell
Ch: Barry Bramley
Treas: Stephen O'Connell
Sr VP: James Wilson
VP: Diane Bezak
VP: Robert Bishop
VP: Timothy Carder
VP: Sherri Crisenbery
VP: David Desiderio
VP: David Enright
VP: Buzz Leer
VP: Mike Lubka
VP: Jim Peikon
VP: Gregory Petro
VP: Dan Schutzman

D-U-N-S 82-968-2355 IMP
LENS VISION-EASE CORP
VISION-EASE LENS
7000 Sunwood Dr Nw, Ramsey, MN 55303-5160
Tel (763) 576-3930 *Founded/Ownrshp* 2006
Sales 169.7MM[E] *EMP* 1,200
SIC 3851 Eyeglasses, lenses & frames
CEO: John Weber
**CFO:* Richard G Faber
**Ch:* Doug Hepper
**Treas:* Bradley D Carlson

D-U-N-S 00-234-5502 IMP
LENTZ MILLING CO (PA)
2045 N 11th St, Reading, PA 19604-1201
Tel (610) 921-0666 *Founded/Ownrshp* 1941
Sales 111.4MM[E] *EMP* 150
SIC 5149 5142 Baking supplies; Flour; Yeast; Sugar, refined; Bakery products, frozen
Pr: Edward T Lentz
Ofcr: Scott Gullo
**VP:* James H Lentz

LEO A DALY
See LEO A DALY CO

D-U-N-S 00-728-4011
LEO A DALY CO
LEO A DALY
8600 Indian Hills Dr, Omaha, NE 68114-4039
Tel (808) 521-8889 *Founded/Ownrshp* 1915
Sales 162.2MM *EMP* 750
Accts Bkd Llp Omaha Ne
SIC 8712 Architectural engineering
Ch Bd: Leo A Daly III
Pr: Dennis W Petersen
VP: John Andrews
VP: Craig Carr
VP: Brian Rice
VP: Avery M Sarden
VP: Kurt Ubbelohde
Dir Bus: Cheri N Pavlik
Dir IT: Edward Ockerman II
IT Man: Brian Compton
IT Man: Brooke Grammier

D-U-N-S 83-038-0015
LEO A DALY/BURNS & MCCONNELL JOINT VENTURE
8600 Indian Hills Dr, Omaha, NE 68114-4039
Tel (402) 391-8111 *Founded/Ownrshp* 2009
Sales 29.0MM[E] *EMP* 3,000
SIC 8712 8711 Architectural services; Architectural engineering; Architectural engineering; Engineering services; Consulting engineer
Prin: Randy Pope

D-U-N-S 00-692-8956
LEO BURNETT CO INC
A R C
(*Suby of* PUBLICIS GROUPE S A)
35 W Wacker Dr Fl 21, Chicago, IL 60601-1755
Tel (312) 220-5959 *Founded/Ownrshp* 1999, 2002
Sales 271.4MM[E] *EMP* 2,000[E]
SIC 7311 3993 Advertising agencies; Signs & advertising specialties
CEO: Thomas L Bernardin
**Pr:* Bob Raidt
**Pr:* Richard Stoddart
CEO: Leo Burnett Milan
**CFO:* Patrick Dumouchel
CFO: Robert Maloney
Treas: Peter Tallboys
Ofcr: Miguel A Furones
Ofcr: Klista Hill
Ex VP: Nina Abnee
Ex VP: Christopher Andrews
Ex VP: Mark Blears
Ex VP: Steve Bonnell
Ex VP: Jennifer Cacioppo
**Ex VP:* Jim Carlton
**Ex VP:* Amy Cheronis
Ex VP: Denny Grant
Ex VP: Karen Green
**Ex VP:* Michelle Kristula Green
Ex VP: Alison McConnell
Ex VP: Kent Middleton

D-U-N-S 00-744-1777
LEO JOURNAGAN CONSTRUCTION CO INC
JOURNAGAN CNSTR & AGGREGATES
3003 E Chestnut Expy, Springfield, MO 65802-2580
Tel (417) 869-7222 *Founded/Ownrshp* 1948
Sales 94.8MM[E] *EMP* 147
SIC 1422 1611 1623 Crushed & broken limestone; Highway & street construction; Sewer line construction
Ch: Leo Journagan
**Pr:* Allen Journagan
**Treas:* John View
**VP:* Dale Popejoy
Brnch Mgr: Stan Workman

D-U-N-S 80-136-9369 IMP
LEOCH BATTERY CORP
19751 Descartes Unit A, Foothill Ranch, CA 92610-2620
Tel (949) 588-5853 *Founded/Ownrshp* 2003
Sales 30.9MM[E] *EMP* 11,000[E]
SIC 3621 Storage battery chargers, motor & engine generator type
Pr: Hui Peng
Sls Dir: John Stanphill
Sls Mgr: Kelly Liu

LEON AUTOMOTIVE INTERIORS
See LEON INTERIORS INC

D-U-N-S 08-193-6650
LEON COUNTY SCHOOL BOARD
2757 W Pensacola St, Tallahassee, FL 32304-2907
Tel (850) 487-7100 *Founded/Ownrshp* 1924
Sales 216.2MM[E] *EMP* 5,030[E]
Accts David W Martin Cpa Tallahas
SIC 8211 School board
Ch: Deedee Rasmussen
Bd of Dir: Alva S Striplin
Comm Man: Chris Petley
Ex Dir: Belinda Kelly
Ex Dir: Forrest Van Camp
IT Man: Tom Vogelgesang

D-U-N-S 00-492-9688
LEON COUNTY SCHOOL DISTRICT
2757 W Pensacola St, Tallahassee, FL 32304-2907
Tel (850) 487-7100 *Founded/Ownrshp* 1981
Sales 134.9MM[E] *EMP* 4,000[E]
SIC 8211 Public elementary & secondary schools; Public elementary school; Public junior high school; Public senior high school
Chf Mktg O: Marvin Henderson
Exec: VI Dennis
Dir Lab: Andreka Rittman
Prgrm Mgr: Ashley Scott
CIO: Bill Nimmons
MIS Dir: Chris Petley
Sfty Dirs: Carl Green
Psych: Megan Davis

D-U-N-S 07-844-0875
LEON FLAGLER HOLDINGS LLC
LEON MEDICAL CENTER
(*Suby of* LEON MEDICAL CENTERS INC) ★
7950 Nw 5th Ct, Miami, FL 33150-2833
Tel (305) 631-3900 *Founded/Ownrshp* 2008
Sales 30.3MM[E] *EMP* 1,891[E]
SIC 8011 Offices & clinics of medical doctors

D-U-N-S 11-872-3170 IMP
LEON INTERIORS INC
LEON AUTOMOTIVE INTERIORS
(*Suby of* MOTUS INTEGRATED TECHNOLOGIES) ★
88 E 48th St, Holland, MI 49423-9307
Tel (616) 531-7970 *Founded/Ownrshp* 2015
Sales 265.9MM[E] *EMP* 600
SIC 3089 3714 3086 Molding primary plastic; Motor vehicle parts & accessories; Plastics foam products
CEO: Shannon White
Opers Mgr: Christopher Mayeaux

D-U-N-S 07-850-3015
LEON MANAGEMENT INTERNATIONAL INC (FL)
11501 Sw 40th St Fl 2, Miami, FL 33165-3313
Tel (305) 642-5366 *Founded/Ownrshp* 2012
Sales 155.7MM[E] *EMP* 1,904[E]
SIC 8741 Business management
Pr: Benjamin Leon III
Ch: Benjamin J Leon
Treas: Silvia Leon
VP: Silvia J Maury

LEON MEDICAL CENTER
See LEON FLAGLER HOLDINGS LLC

D-U-N-S 94-723-7210 EXP
LEON MEDICAL CENTERS INC
(*Suby of* LEON MANAGEMENT INTERNATIONAL INC) ★
11501 Sw 40th St, Miami, FL 33165-3313
Tel (305) 559-2881 *Founded/Ownrshp* 1986
Sales 155.7MM[E] *EMP* 1,900
SIC 8011 Offices & clinics of medical doctors; Medical centers
Pr: Benjamin Leon Jr
**Pr:* Benjamin I Leon
**Treas:* Silvia Leon
VP: Marcus Gomez Sr
VP: Carlos Nuez Sr

LEONA GROUP ARIZONA
See SMITH ACADEMY FOR EXCELLENCE INC

LEONA GROUP ARIZONA
See LEONA GROUP L L C

D-U-N-S 01-545-2535
LEONA GROUP L L C
2125 University Park Dr # 250, Okemos, MI 48864-5903
Tel (517) 333-9030 *Founded/Ownrshp* 1996
Sales 85.8MM[E] *EMP* 1,200[E]
SIC 8742 Management consulting services
CEO: William Coats
CFO: Patrick Lawrence

D-U-N-S 87-623-7012
LEONA GROUP L L C
LEONA GROUP ARIZONA
7878 N 16th St Ste 150, Phoenix, AZ 85020-4470
Tel (602) 953-2933 *Founded/Ownrshp* 1996
Sales 91.6MM[E] *EMP* 1,600
SIC 8211 Private junior high school
CEO: Dr Bill Coats
**COO:* Michele Kaye
CFO: Patrick Lawrence
Ex VP: Derrick Shelton
Off Mgr: Kathy Thommasson
Off Admin: Vanessa Roman

D-U-N-S 96-795-6033
LEONA M AND HARRY B HELMSLEY CHARITABLE TRUST
230 Park Ave, New York, NY 10169-0005
Tel (212) 679-3600 *Founded/Ownrshp* 2011
Sales 175.4MM *EMP* 16[E]
SIC 6733 Trusts
CEO: John R Ettinger
CFO: Leigh Bonney
Chf Inves: Rosalind Hewsenian
Ofcr: Rachel Norman
Ofcr: Benjamin Williams
Comm Dir: Kevin Cavanaugh
Genl Couns: Sarah E Paul
Pgrm Dir: Shelley Stingley

D-U-N-S 83-542-0001
LEONARD FAMILY CORP
647 Steves Ave, San Antonio, TX 78210-3819
Tel (210) 532-3241 *Founded/Ownrshp* 1994
Sales 158.8MM[E] *EMP* 605
SIC 5147 Meats, fresh
Pr: Kenneth E Leonard
CFO: Russell Saldik

D-U-N-S 61-680-5719
LEONARD GREEN & PARTNERS LP
11111 Santa Monica Blvd # 2000, Los Angeles, CA 90025-3354
Tel (310) 954-0444 *Founded/Ownrshp* 1989
Sales 3.1MMM[E] *EMP* 14,266
SIC 6211 Investment bankers
Pt: Jonathan D Sokoloff
**Pt:* John M Baumer
**Pt:* John G Danhakl
**Pt:* James Halper
**Pt:* Peter J Nolan
**Pt:* Jonathan A Sciffer
**COO:* Lily W Chang
COO: Lily Chang
CFO: Franklin Cody
**CFO:* Cody L Franklin
VP: Jeffrey Suer
VP: Alyse Wagner
Exec: Cody Franklin

D-U-N-S 00-285-7555
LEONARD S FIORE INC (PA)
5506 6th Ave Rear, Altoona, PA 16602-1295
Tel (814) 946-3686 *Founded/Ownrshp* 1954
Sales 123.0MM[E] *EMP* 250
Accts Harry K Sickler Associates T
SIC 1542 Commercial & office building, new construction
Pr: Richard F Fiore Sr
**Ch:* Leonard S Fiore Jr
**Ex VP:* Michael A Fiore
**VP:* Richard F Fiore Jr
**VP:* Joseph Irwin

LEONARDO LO CASCIO SELECTIONS
See WINEBOW INC

D-U-N-S 09-477-4630
LEONARDTOWN SCHOOL DISTRICT
P.O. Box 641 (20650-0641)
Tel (301) 475-4250 *Founded/Ownrshp* 2001
Sales 13.1MM[E] *EMP* 1,400
SIC 8211 Public elementary & secondary schools
Prin: Joan Kozlovsky

LEONA'S NEIGHBORHOOD PLACE
See LEONAS PIZZERIA INC

D-U-N-S 01-346-6727
LEONAS PIZZERIA INC (IL)
LEONA'S NEIGHBORHOOD PLACE
3931 S Leavitt St, Chicago, IL 60609-2203
Tel (773) 843-0050 *Founded/Ownrshp* 1987
Sales 35.1MM[E] *EMP* 1,100
SIC 5812 5813 Pizzeria, independent; Italian restaurant; Caterers; Drinking places
Pr: Leon Toia
**CFO:* Doug Quinn
**VP:* Salvatore P Toia
CTO: Tina Niera

D-U-N-S 87-686-1881 IMP/EXP
LEONI WIRING SYSTEMS INC
(*Suby of* LEONISCHE HOLDING INC) ★
3100 N Campbell Ave # 101, Tucson, AZ 85719-2315
Tel (520) 741-0895 *Founded/Ownrshp* 2005
Sales 756.8MM[E] *EMP* 2,100
SIC 3643 8741 5063 Current-carrying wiring devices; Management services; Wire & cable
CEO: Martin Gloesslein
**Pr:* Juergen Linhard
**CFO:* Larry Finkenthal
CFO: Jesus Lozoya
**CFO:* Jay Meridew

D-U-N-S 83-186-8109
LEONISCHE HOLDING INC
(*Suby of* LEONI BORDNETZ-SYSTEME GMBH)
2861 N Flowing Wells Rd, Tucson, AZ 85705-9397
Tel (520) 741-0895 *Founded/Ownrshp* 2010
Sales 806.5MM[E] *EMP* 178[E]
SIC 3679 Harness assemblies for electronic use: wire or cable
Prin: Martin Gloesslein

D-U-N-S 09-678-6447
LEOPARDO COMPANIES INC (IL)
LEOPARDO CONSTRUCTION
5200 Prairie Stone Pkwy, Hoffman Estates, IL 60192-3709
Tel (847) 783-3000 *Founded/Ownrshp* 1979
Sales 115.9MM[E] *EMP* 300[E]
SIC 1542 8741 Commercial & office building, new construction; Commercial & office buildings, renovation & repair; Construction management
CEO: James A Leopardo
**Pr:* Rick Mattioda
**CFO:* John Ward
**Sr VP:* Mike Behm
**Sr VP:* Pierre Cowart
**Sr VP:* Rick Dupraw
**Sr VP:* Mike Leopardo
VP: Todd Andrlik
VP: Scott Higgins
VP: Anthony Iannessa
VP: John Leopardo
**VP:* Sal T Leopardo
Exec: John Cotsiopoulos
Exec: Damian Eallonardo
Exec: Christopher Novak

LEOPARDO CONSTRUCTION
See LEOPARDO COMPANIES INC

D-U-N-S 00-110-5741
■ **LEPAGE BAKERIES INC**
COUNTRY KITCHEN
(*Suby of* FLOWERS FOODS INC) ★
11 Adamian Dr, Auburn, ME 04210-8304
Tel (207) 783-9161 *Founded/Ownrshp* 2012
Sales 181.9MM[E] *EMP* 525
SIC 2051 5461 Bread, cake & related products; Bread, all types (white, wheat, rye, etc): fresh or frozen; Doughnuts, except frozen; Rolls, bread type: fresh or frozen; Bakeries
Pr: Andy Barowsky

D-U-N-S 00-707-6664 IMP/EXP
LEPRINO FOODS CO
1830 W 38th Ave, Denver, CO 80211-2200
Tel (303) 480-2600 *Founded/Ownrshp* 1955, 1965
Sales 1.9MMM^E *EMP* 3,700
SIC 2022 Cheese, natural & processed
CEO: James G Leprino
Pr: Larry J Jensen
Treas: Dan Alonzi
Sr VP: Mike Cureton
Sr VP: Michael L Reidy
VP: Richard Barz
VP: Adriel Fuentes
VP: Tom Hegarty
VP: David J Kielsmeier
VP: Joel Krein
VP: Edith A Quartey
VP: Rob Schwartz
VP: Dan Vecchiarelli
VP: Daniel A Vecchiarelli
Exec: Julia Lambert
Dir Risk M: Steven Levine
Assoc Dir: Melissa Bischoff
Assoc Dir: Bridget Lyons
Board of Directors: Michael Leprino

D-U-N-S 83-223-0804
LERETA LLC
1123 Park View Dr, Covina, CA 91724-3748
Tel (626) 543-1765 *Founded/Ownrshp* 2009
Sales 336.2MM^E *EMP* 450
SIC 6211 6541 6361 Tax certificate dealers; Title search companies; Real estate title insurance
CEO: John Walsh
Pr: Brett Bennett
Pr: Glenn McCarthy
Pr: Daniel Telles
**COO:* James V Micali
CFO: Tyler Page
CFO: Sharon Yokoyama
**Ex VP:* Chris Masten
Sr VP: Lily Akimoff
**Sr VP:* Richard Yonis
VP: Mike Blaha
VP: Kevin Brown
VP: Jonnine Eras
VP: Dominique Froesch
VP: Sharon Goody
VP: Bronson Quon
VP: John Short
VP: Ted Smith
VP: Adrienne Williams
VP: Dave Wilson

D-U-N-S 14-925-4182 IMP
■ **LERNER NEW YORK HOLDING INC**
(*Suby of* NEW YORK & CO INC) ★
450 W 33rd St Fl 3, New York, NY 10001-2632
Tel (212) 736-1222 *Founded/Ownrshp* 2002
Sales 67.8MM^E *EMP* 2,100
SIC 5621 Women's clothing stores
Pr: Richard Crystal
Sr VP: Hope Grey
Dist Mgr: Tony Lynch
IT Man: Greg England
IT Man: Anthony Rizzo
Snr Mgr: Joann Fassett

D-U-N-S 00-698-6814 IMP
■ **LERNER NEW YORK INC** (DE)
(*Suby of* NEW YORK & CO INC) ★
330 W 34th St Fl 7, New York, NY 10001-2406
Tel (212) 884-2000 *Founded/Ownrshp* 1985, 2002
Sales 206.5MM^E *EMP* 2,100
SIC 5621 Women's clothing stores
Ch Bd: Gregory Scott
**Ch Bd:* Richard Crystal
**CFO:* Sheamus Toal
Ex VP: Jackie Corso
**Ex VP:* John E Dewolf III
**Ex VP:* Leslie Goldmann
Ex VP: Hope Grey
**Ex VP:* Sandra Brooslin Viviano
VP: Jinn Chung
VP: Susan Reiss
Dist Mgr: Michelle Ghelfi

LEROY SOMER NA DIV EMERSON ELC
See LEROY-SOMER INC

D-U-N-S 79-052-5752 EXP
■ **LEROY-SOMER INC**
LEROY SOMER NA DIV EMERSON ELC
(*Suby of* EMERSON ELECTRIC CO) ★
669 Natchez Trace Dr, Lexington, TN 38351-4125
Tel (731) 967-3000 *Founded/Ownrshp* 1999
Sales 170.6MM^E *EMP* 800^E
SIC 3621 Motors & generators; Power generators
**Pr:* Dan Ray
Opers Mgr: Joey Morris
Sls Dir: Charles Ketron

LES
See LINCOLN ELECTRIC SYSTEM

D-U-N-S 03-537-6441
LES OLSON CO
3244 S 300 W, Salt Lake City, UT 84115-3411
Tel (435) 586-2345 *Founded/Ownrshp* 1956
Sales 144.7MM^E *EMP* 170
SIC 5044 Office equipment
Ch Bd: L Ray Olson
Pr: Larry G Olson
Treas: James Robert Olson Jr
Treas: Lisa Olson Thaller
VP: Richard Moore
VP: Larry Troy Olson
VP: Matt Olson
VP: Thomas P Olson
IT Man: Eric Swink
Opers Mgr: Clayton Olson
Sls Mgr: Gary Facer

LES SCHWAB TIRE CENTERS
See LES SCHWAB WAREHOUSE CENTER INC

D-U-N-S 02-776-6617
LES SCHWAB TIRE CENTERS OF IDAHO INC
(*Suby of* LES SCHWAB TIRE CENTERS) ★
646 Nw Madras Hwy, Prineville, OR 97754-1444
Tel (541) 447-4136 *Founded/Ownrshp* 1959
Sales 210.4MM^E *EMP* 990
SIC 5531 Automotive tires; Automotive accessories
Pr: John M Britton
**Ch Bd:* Margaret S Denton
Pr: G Phillip Wick
CFO: John Cuniff
Treas: Gerald V Darnell
Treas: James A Goad
Chf Mktg O: Dale Thompson
Ex VP: Richard W Priday
VP: Ken Edwards
Exec: Tom Freedman
Mktg Dir: John Maloney

D-U-N-S 07-072-3986
LES SCHWAB TIRE CENTERS OF PORTLAND INC
(*Suby of* LES SCHWAB TIRE CENTERS) ★
20900 Cooley Rd, Bend, OR 97701-3406
Tel (541) 447-4136 *Founded/Ownrshp* 1973
Sales 307.9MM^E *EMP* 1,552
SIC 5531 Automotive tires; Automotive accessories
Ch Bd: Margaret Schwab Denton
Pr: John Britton
Pr: G Phillip Wick
CFO: Thomas Freedman
Treas: Gerald V Darnell
Ex VP: Richard W Priday

D-U-N-S 04-978-9522 IMP
LES SCHWAB TIRE CENTERS OF WASHINGTON INC
(*Suby of* LES SCHWAB TIRE CENTERS) ★
20900 Cooley Rd, Bend, OR 97701-3406
Tel (541) 447-4136 *Founded/Ownrshp* 1976
Sales 360.0MM^E *EMP* 400^E
SIC 5531 Automotive tires; Automotive accessories
Ch: Richard Borgman
**Pr:* John Britton
CFO: Jack Cuniff
CFO: Gery Darnell
**CFO:* James Goad Jr
Ex VP: Richard W Priday
**Ex VP:* Dan Roberts
**VP:* Corey J Parks
**Prin:* CAM Durrell
Ex Dir: Dwayne Glemser
Brnch Mgr: Mike Crakes

D-U-N-S 04-126-9697 IMP
LES SCHWAB WAREHOUSE CENTER INC
LES SCHWAB TIRE CENTERS
20900 Cooley Rd, Bend, OR 97701-3406
Tel (541) 447-4136 *Founded/Ownrshp* 1958
Sales 2.3MMM^E *EMP* 5,680
SIC 5014 7534 5531 Automobile tires & tubes; Tire recapping; Automotive & home supply stores
CEO: Richard Borgman
**Pr:* John Britton
**CFO:* Tom Freedman
**Treas:* Gerald V Darnell
Chf Mktg O: Dale Thompson
**VP:* Dick Borgman
VP: Jerry Darnielle
**VP:* Larry Henderson
**VP:* Phil Powell
**VP:* Dan Roberts
**VP:* Doug Smith
Board of Directors: Denny Denton, Alan L Schwab, Diana Tomseth, Matthew S Tomseth

D-U-N-S 61-856-0601 IMP/EXP
LESAFFRE INTERNATIONAL CORP
(*Suby of* LESAFFRE ET COMPAGNIE)
7475 W Main St, Milwaukee, WI 53214-1552
Tel (414) 615-3300 *Founded/Ownrshp* 1977
Sales 223.8MM^E *EMP* 596
SIC 2099 Yeast
Ch Bd: Denise Lesaffre
**Pr:* John Riesch
**CFO:* Geoffrey O'Connor
**Treas:* Cary Levinson
**VP:* Chris Kaltenbach
**VP:* Chris Katenbach

D-U-N-S 17-683-9009 IMP/EXP
LESAFFRE YEAST CORP
RED STAR YEAST COMPANY
(*Suby of* LESAFFRE INTERNATIONAL CORP) ★
7475 W Main St, Milwaukee, WI 53214-1552
Tel (414) 615-3300 *Founded/Ownrshp* 1994
Sales 217.4MM^E *EMP* 448
SIC 5149 Groceries & related products
Ch Bd: Lucien Lesaffre
**Pr:* John Riesch
COO: George Parry
**CFO:* Geoff O'Connor
Treas: Geoffrey O Connor
Area Mgr: Stan Denton
CIO: Bryan Jocques
Dir IT: Ken Massey
Manager: John Phillips
Manager: Detlef Werner
Sls Mgr: Bruce Patterson

D-U-N-S 11-872-9917
LESAINT LOGISTICS LLC
868 W Crossroads Pkwy, Romeoville, IL 60446-4332
Tel (630) 243-5950 *Founded/Ownrshp* 2006
Sales 103.3MM^E *EMP* 232
SIC 4731 4225 8742 Freight transportation arrangement; General warehousing & storage; Materials mgmt. (purchasing, handling, inventory) consultant
Pr: Jeff Pennington
CFO: Lon Purdy
Ex VP: Dino Moler
VP: Bill Lansaw
Sales Exec: Jamie Blake

D-U-N-S 00-445-3825 EXP
■ **LESCO INC** (OH)
(*Suby of* DEERE & CO) ★
1385 E 36th St, Cleveland, OH 44114-4114
Tel (216) 706-9250 *Founded/Ownrshp* 1962, 2007
Sales 215.1MM^E *EMP* 1,122
SIC 5191 5083 5261 Grass seed; Lawn machinery & equipment; Mowers, power; Nurseries; Lawn & garden equipment; Lawn & garden supplies
Pr: Jeffrey L Rutherford
Ch Bd: J Martin Erbaugh
COO: Bruce K Thorn
CFO: Michael A Weisbarth
Sr VP: Steven Cochran
VP: Mark Hradil
VP: Amy McGahan
VP: Kathleen M Minahan
VP: Lisa Zone
Exec: Cristy Cote
Prin: Vincent C Fornes

D-U-N-S 06-157-6252 IMP/EXP
LESEA BROADCASTING CORP
WHME TV 46
61300 Ironwood Rd, South Bend, IN 46614-9019
Tel (574) 291-8200 *Founded/Ownrshp* 1972
Sales 99.8MM^E *EMP* 240
SIC 4833 4832 Television broadcasting stations; Gospel; Religious
Pr: Peter Sumrall
**Treas:* David E Sumrall
Ofcr: David Ellsworth
Ex VP: Michael Young
**VP:* Andrew Sumrall
Genl Mgr: Keith Passon
Genl Mgr: Lisa Slayton
Off Mgr: Idell Stelly
Opers Mgr: Swinehart Mike
Sls Mgr: Lori Kauffman
Sls Mgr: Anna Riblet

D-U-N-S 00-176-8910
LESLEY UNIVERSITY
29 Everett St, Cambridge, MA 02138-2702
Tel (617) 868-9600 *Founded/Ownrshp* 1942
Sales 100.6MM *EMP* 800
Accts Mayer Hoffman Mccann Pc Bosto
SIC 8221 College, except junior
Pr: Joseph B Moore
**COO:* Charles Gilroy
COO: Edmund Toomey
**Treas:* Robert Sage
VP: Lori Ayotte
CIO: Karen Boudreaushea
MIS Dir: Scott Boulet
Info Man: Kevin Murphy
Pgrm Dir: Sylvia Cowan
Pgrm Dir: Linda Grisham
Pgrm Dir: Prudence King

D-U-N-S 04-573-9182
■ **LESLIE COUNTY TELEPHONE CO**
(*Suby of* TDS TELECOMMUNICATIONS CORP) ★
22076 Main St, Hyden, KY 41749-8568
Tel (606) 672-2303 *Founded/Ownrshp* 1988
Sales 237.0MM^E *EMP* 2,700
SIC 4813 Local telephone communications
CEO: David A Wittwer

D-U-N-S 13-041-0467
LESLIE RESOURCES INC
1021 Tori Dr, Hazard, KY 41701-6670
Tel (606) 439-0946 *Founded/Ownrshp* 2007
Sales 184.9MM^E *EMP* 3,991
SIC 1221 Surface mining, bituminous
Ch Bd: Larry Addington

D-U-N-S 79-386-5697 IMP
LESLIES HOLDINGS INC
3925 E Broadway Rd # 100, Phoenix, AZ 85040-2966
Tel (602) 366-3999 *Founded/Ownrshp* 2007
Sales 2.8MMM^E *EMP* 3,200
SIC 5999 Swimming pool chemicals, equipment & supplies
CEO: Larry Hayward
**Pr:* Michael L Hatch
**CFO:* Steven L Ortega
Sr VP: Janet I McDonald
Exec: Gail Griffin
CIO: Janet Macdonald
Software D: Steve Silva

D-U-N-S 05-010-6095 IMP/EXP
LESLIES POOLMART INC
LESLIE'S POOLS
(*Suby of* LESLIES HOLDINGS INC) ★
2005 E Indian School Rd, Phoenix, AZ 85016-6113
Tel (602) 366-3999 *Founded/Ownrshp* 2007
Sales 2.8MMM^E *EMP* 3,200^E
SIC 5091 Swimming pools, equipment & supplies
Ch Bd: Lawrence H Hayward
Pr: Michael L Hatch
CFO: Steven L Ortega
Sr VP: Brian P Agnew
Sr VP: Brian Agnew
Sr VP: Stephen Blakeslee
Sr VP: Kory Klecker
VP: Kean Corrigan
VP: Roy Steves
VP: Len Tamboer
Dir IT: Ed Joneiack
Board of Directors: Edward C Agnew, John M Baumer, John G Danhakl, Michael J Fourticq

LESLIE'S POOLS
See LESLIES POOLMART INC

D-U-N-S 08-364-5130
LESTER BUILDING SYSTEMS LLC
1111 2nd Ave S, Lester Prairie, MN 55354-1003
Tel (320) 395-5212 *Founded/Ownrshp* 2004
Sales 96.4MM^E *EMP* 300
SIC 2452 Prefabricated buildings, wood
Area Mgr: Andy Howell
Area Mgr: Craig Nieland
Area Mgr: Thomas Reilly
Genl Mgr: Mark Billstrom
Genl Mgr: Craig Loger
IT Man: Bruce Minor
Plnt Mgr: Marty Schermann
Mktg Mgr: Jeannette Raufeisen
Sls Mgr: Butch Boehler
Sls Mgr: Brad Hovden
Snr Mgr: Glenn Maesse

D-U-N-S 03-644-5448
LESTER E COX MEDICAL CENTER
COX HEALTH
305 S National Ave # 500, Springfield, MO 65802-3420
Tel (417) 269-6000 *Founded/Ownrshp* 1906
Sales 206.1MM^E *EMP* 6,000
SIC 8011 Medical centers
Pr: Robert Bezanson
**CEO:* Steve Edwards
**CFO:* Jake McWay
VP: Jim Anderson
**VP:* John Duff
Dir Rad: Martin M Anbari
Brnch Mgr: John R Carlile
Plnt Mgr: Rod Schaffer
Doctor: Bryan Finke
Doctor: Marie McGettigan

D-U-N-S 07-303-7343
LESTER E COX MEDICAL CENTERS
COXHEALTH
1423 N Jefferson Ave, Springfield, MO 65802-1917
Tel (417) 269-3000 *Founded/Ownrshp* 1906
Sales 918.9MM *EMP* 9,100
SIC 8062 8069 General medical & surgical hospitals; Drug addiction rehabilitation hospital
CEO: Steven D Edwards
Chf Rad: Bryan Hall
Dir Vol: Barbara Frogue
**CFO:* Jacob McWay
CFO: David Strong
Ofcr: Tracy Mitchell
Ofcr: Ron Pronger
VP: Betty Breshears
VP: John Duff
VP: Laurie Duff
VP: Robert L Ferguson
VP: John Fry
VP: Karen Kramer
VP: Bruce Robison
VP: Dan Sontheimer
Dir Risk M: Steve Brown
Dir Risk M: Charity Elmer
Comm Dir: Yvette Williams

D-U-N-S 15-034-7268 IMP
LETCO GROUP LLC
LIVING EARTH
1901 Cal Crossing Rd, Dallas, TX 75220-7005
Tel (972) 506-8575 *Founded/Ownrshp* 2007
Sales 83.9MM^E *EMP* 230
SIC 2875 Compost; Potting soil, mixed
Pr: Mark Rose
Brnch Mgr: Paul Tomaso
Genl Mgr: Jeff Robnett

D-U-N-S 04-926-6976 IMP/EXP
LETICA CORP
52585 Dequindre Rd, Rochester Hills, MI 48307-2321
Tel (248) 652-0557 *Founded/Ownrshp* 1968
Sales 773.4MM^E *EMP* 1,800
SIC 2656 3089 Sanitary food containers; Plastic containers, except foam
Ch Bd: Ilija Letica
**Treas:* Gudrun Letica
Ex VP: Mara Letica
VP: Charles Dorger
**VP:* Albert J Gustafson
VP: Anton Letica
VP: Don Stonehouse
VP: Brian Vautaw
Off Mgr: June Phillips
CIO: Bob Stone
Netwrk Mgr: Tony Diponio

D-U-N-S 80-000-0705
LETS GO INC
(*Suby of* HARVARD STUDENT AGENCIES INC) ★
67 Mount Auburn St, Cambridge, MA 02138-4961
Tel (617) 495-9659 *Founded/Ownrshp* 1960
Sales 1.7MM^E *EMP* 1,000
SIC 2741 Miscellaneous publishing
Genl Mgr: Anne Chisholm
Snr Sftwr: David Powers
Dir IT: Doug Hoffman
IT Man: Mark Ting
Mktg Mgr: Caitlin Loveitt

D-U-N-S 02-661-8207
LETSOS CO
8435 Westglen Dr, Houston, TX 77063-6311
Tel (713) 783-3200 *Founded/Ownrshp* 1953
Sales 152.7MM^E *EMP* 325
SIC 1711 7623 Mechanical contractor; Plumbing contractors; Warm air heating & air conditioning contractor; Air conditioning repair
Pr: James N Letsos III
**CFO:* Mark Letsos
**Ex VP:* John G Letsos
CIO: Jason Feng
Snr PM: Alan Mikulenka

D-U-N-S 10-114-7676 IMP
LETTIRE CONSTRUCTION CORP
334 E 110th St 336, New York, NY 10029-3105
Tel (212) 996-6640 *Founded/Ownrshp* 1984
Sales 150.0MM^E *EMP* 90
SIC 1531 Operative builders
Pr: Nicholas Lettire
**VP:* Gerard Lettire
Snr PM: Chris Cardona
Snr PM: Dan Hlavac

D-U-N-S 07-686-4396
LETTUCE ENTERTAIN YOU ENTERPRISES INC
5419 N Sheridan Rd, Chicago, IL 60640-1964
Tel (773) 878-7340 *Founded/Ownrshp* 1971
Sales 127.0MM^E *EMP* 3,500
SIC 5812 8741 Eating places; Restaurant management
CEO: Kevin Brown

Pt: Perry H Fuselier
**Pr:* Manford Joast
**Pr:* Robert Wattel
**Ch:* Richard Melman
Ex VP: Susan Chernoff
Ex VP: Susie Southgate-Fox
VP: Michael Haley
VP: Jean Joho
VP: Page Louisell
VP: Gabino Sotelino
**VP:* Jay Stieber
Exec: Juan Diaz
Exec: Daniel Espinoza
Exec: Anthony Martin
Exec: Thierry Tritsch
Exec: Luis Trujillo
Dir Risk M: Craig Hudson
Dir Soc: Allison Gallese
Dir Soc: Kimberly Sasai

D-U-N-S 03-594-3984
LETTUCE ENTERTAIN YOU TOO INC
5419 N Sheridan Rd # 116, Chicago, IL 60640-1900
Tel (773) 878-7340 *Founded/Ownrshp* 1971
Sales 134.1MM^E *EMP* 5,000
SIC 5812 5813 Restaurant, family: independent; Cocktail lounge
Pr: Richard Melman
**V Ch Bd:* Charles Haskell
Ex VP: Jay Stieber
**VP:* Robert Wattell
Genl Mgr: Ian Oser
Off Mgr: Peter Wong
IT Man: Thomas Muno

D-U-N-S 04-525-6922 IMP
▲ **LEUCADIA NATIONAL CORP** (NY)
520 Madison Ave Bsmt A, New York, NY 10022-4357
Tel (212) 460-1900 *Founded/Ownrshp* 1968
Sales 11.6MMM *EMP* 13,300^E
Tkr Sym LUK *Exch* NYS
SIC 6798 6211 1382 2011 2426 Real estate investment trusts; Investment certificate sales; Investment bankers; Oil & gas exploration services; Boxed beef from meat slaughtered on site; Dimension, hardwood
CEO: Richard B Handler
**Ch Bd:* Joseph S Steinberg
**Pr:* Brian P Friedman
CFO: Teresa S Gendron
Treas: Rocco J Nittoli
Ex VP: Michael J Sharp
VP: John M Dalton
VP: Steven Kaplan
Mng Dir: Jimmy Hallac
Dir IT: Amy Dowse
Board of Directors: Linda L Adamany, Robert D Beyer, Francisco L Borges, W Patrick Campbell, Robert E Joyal, Jeffrey C Keil, Michael T O'kane, Stuart H Reese

D-U-N-S 07-520-9510
LEUKEMIA & LYMPHOMA SOCIETY INC
LLS
3 International Dr # 200, Rye Brook, NY 10573-7501
Tel (914) 949-5213 *Founded/Ownrshp* 1949
Sales 281.6MM *EMP* 825
SIC 8699 8399 8322 8011 8733 8621

D-U-N-S 04-577-6796 IMP
LEUPOLD & STEVENS INC
14400 Nw Greenbrier Pkwy, Beaverton, OR 97006-5791
Tel (503) 526-1400 *Founded/Ownrshp* 1944
Sales 107.5MM^E *EMP* 500^E
SIC 3827 Telescopic sights; Lens mounts; Binoculars
Pr: Calvin S Johnston
**Ch Bd:* Jim Clark
Pr: Fritz Kaufman
**Pr:* Howard Werth
CFO: Howard D Werth
VP: Scott Cain
VP: Kimberly King
VP: Kevin Trepa
VP: Wayne Waycloud
Genl Mgr: Mark Kowalski
Genl Mgr: Wilson Timothy
Board of Directors: Don R Kania, Dennis Spindler

D-U-N-S 07-833-0696
LEVEL 10 CONSTRUCTION LP
1050 Entp Way Ste 250, Sunnyvale, CA 94089
Tel (408) 747-5000 *Founded/Ownrshp* 2011
Sales 200.0MM *EMP* 220
Accts Lautze
SIC 1542 Commercial & office buildings, renovation & repair
Pr: Dennis Giles
CFO: Jim Evans

D-U-N-S 00-697-0263
▲ **LEVEL 3 COMMUNICATIONS INC**
1025 Eldorado Blvd, Broomfield, CO 80021-8254
Tel (720) 888-1000 *Founded/Ownrshp* 1884
Sales 8.2MMM *EMP* 12,500^E
Tkr Sym LVLT *Exch* NYS
SIC 4813 7373 7374 Telephone communication, except radio; Computer integrated systems design; Data processing & preparation
Pr: Jeff K Storey
**Ch Bd:* James O Ellis Jr
Pr: Hector R Alonso
Pr: Dave Mueller
CFO: Sunit S Patel
Ex VP: Angela Porter
Sr VP: Andrew Edison
Sr VP: Eric J Mortensen
VP: Jennifer Baker
VP: Treva Belt
VP: Mike Benjamin
VP: Jenny Bennett
VP: Joe Brooks
VP: Craig Burns
VP: Vickie Byrne
VP: Bruce Carver
VP: Jeff Collins
VP: Jerry Cox
VP: Gabriel Del
VP: Brianw Donnelly
VP: Stephen Dunton
Board of Directors: Kevin P Chilton, Steven T Clontz, Irene M Esteves, T Michael Glenn, Spencer B Hays, Peter Seah Lim Huat, Michael J Mahoney, Kevin W Mooney, Peter Van Oppen

D-U-N-S 07-309-0917
■ **LEVEL 3 COMMUNICATIONS LLC**
(*Suby of* LEVEL 3 FINANCING INC) ★
1025 Eldorado Blvd, Broomfield, CO 80021-8254
Tel (720) 888-2750 *Founded/Ownrshp* 1998, 1997
Sales 1.5MMM^E *EMP* 5,300
Accts Kpmg Llp Denver Co
SIC 4813 7373 Telephone communication, except radio; Computer integrated systems design
Pr: Jeff Storey
CFO: Sunit A Patel
**Ex VP:* Sunit Patel
**Ex VP:* Thomas C Stortz
**Sr VP:* Robin Grey
VP: Edward Macatee
**Prin:* Charles C Miller III

D-U-N-S 78-350-2458
■ **LEVEL 3 FINANCING INC**
(*Suby of* LEVEL 3 COMMUNICATIONS INC) ★
1025 Eldorado Blvd, Broomfield, CO 80021-8254
Tel (720) 888-1000 *Founded/Ownrshp* 1990
Sales 1.6MMM^E *EMP* 5,300^E
SIC 4813 Telephone communication, except radio
CEO: James Crowe
**Pr:* Kevin O'Hara
**CFO:* Sunit Patel
**Ex VP:* Thomas Stortz
**Sr VP:* Eric Mortensen

D-U-N-S 86-950-2971
■ **LEVEL 3 TELECOM HOLDINGS LLC**
(*Suby of* TW TELECOM LLC) ★
10475 Park Meadows Dr, Littleton, CO 80124-5433
Tel (303) 566-1000 *Founded/Ownrshp* 1998
Sales 700.8MM^E *EMP* 2,800^E
SIC 4813 Telephone communication, except radio
VP: Joseph Bivona
VP: Travis Ewert
VP: Marilyn Finfrock
VP: Zac Jacobson
VP: Jill Stuart
VP: Atilla Tinic
VP: Marc Willency
VP: Henry Yu
Snr Mgr: Teri Antonio
Snr Mgr: Bob Carlson
Snr Mgr: Suren Rodrigues

D-U-N-S 01-950-6133
■ **LEVEL 3 TELECOM LLC**
TW TELECOM, LLC
(*Suby of* LEVEL 3 COMMUNICATIONS INC) ★
10475 Park Meadows Dr, Littleton, CO 80124-5433
Tel (303) 566-1000 *Founded/Ownrshp* 2014
Sales 1.8MMM^E *EMP* 3,397
SIC 4813 Telephone communication, except radio; Local & long distance telephone communications;
CEO: Larissa L Herda
**Pr:* John T Blount
**CEO:* Jeff Storey
**CFO:* Mark A Peters
Sr VP: Tina A Davis
Sr VP: Robert W Gaskins
Sr VP: Julie A Rich
Sr VP: Jill R Stuart
VP: Don Stryszko

D-U-N-S 03-840-9868
LEVI RAY & SHOUP INC
LRS
2401 W Monroe St, Springfield, IL 62704-1439
Tel (217) 793-3800 *Founded/Ownrshp* 1979
Sales 205.6MM *EMP* 603
Accts Rsm Us Llp Springfield Illin
SIC 7371 5045 7379 Custom computer programming services; Computer software development; Computers, peripherals & software; Computer related consulting services
Pr: Richard H Levi
Sr VP: Gregory Collins
**Sr VP:* John Howerter
**VP:* Pam Benad
**VP:* Max Dillahunty
**VP:* Brian Huggins
VP: Kevin Huxley
MIS Dir: Scott Richardson
Dir IT: Steve Madonia
IT Man: Christine Ford
IT Man: Matthew Rivera

D-U-N-S 00-910-9273 IMP/EXP
LEVI STRAUSS & CO
1155 Battery St, San Francisco, CA 94111-1264
Tel (415) 501-6000 *Founded/Ownrshp* 1853
Sales 4.4MMM *EMP* 12,500
SIC 2325 2339 2321 2331 2337 2329 Jeans: men's, youths' & boys'; Slacks, dress: men's, youths' & boys'; Jeans: women's, misses' & juniors'; Slacks: women's, misses' & juniors'; Athletic clothing: women's, misses' & juniors'; Men's & boys' furnishings; Shirts, women's & juniors': made from purchased materials; T-shirts & tops, women's: made from purchased materials; Skirts, separate: women's, misses' & juniors'; Jackets (suede, leatherette, etc.), sport: men's & boys'; Athletic (warmup, sweat & jogging) suits: men's & boys'
Pr: Charles V Bergh
**Ch Bd:* Stephen C Neal
Pr: Carrie Ask
Pr: Roy Bagattini
Pr: Lisa Collier
Pr: James Curleigh
Pr: Seth M Ellison
Pr: Marc Rosen
CFO: Harmit Singh
Chf Cred: Kelly McGinnis
Ofcr: Elizabeth Wood
Ex VP: David Love
Sr VP: Douglas Conklyn
Sr VP: Seth R Jaffe
VP: Manuela Bellini
VP: Heidi Manes
VP: Wade Webster
Board of Directors: Troy Alstead, Jill Beraud, Robert A Eckert, Spencer C Fleischer, Mimi L Haas, Peter E Haas Jr, Christopher McCormick, Jenny Ming, Patricia Salas Pineda

LEVINE CHILDREN'S HOSPITAL
See CAROLINAS MEDICAL CENTER AT HOME LLC

D-U-N-S 18-858-0922
LEVINE LEICHTMAN CAPITAL PARTNERS INC
LLCP
335 N Maple Dr Ste 130, Beverly Hills, CA 90210-5162
Tel (310) 275-5335 *Founded/Ownrshp* 1994
Sales 280.3MM^E *EMP* 966
SIC 6799 Investors
CEO: Lauren B Leichtman
Pr: Arthur E Levine
CFO: Steve Hogan
Assoc Dir: Matthew Rich
Mng Dir: Paul W Drury
Mng Dir: Matthew G Frankel
Mng Dir: Monica J Holec
Mng Dir: Ronnie Kaplan
Mng Dir: Brad Parish
Mng Dir: John P Romney
Mng Dir: Andrew M Schwartz

LEVIN'S FURNITURE
See SAM LEVIN INC

D-U-N-S 00-123-3089 IMP/EXP
LEVITON MANUFACTURING CO INC
201 N Service Rd, Melville, NY 11747-3138
Tel (631) 812-6000 *Founded/Ownrshp* 1990
Sales 1.5MMM^E *EMP* 6,095
SIC 3643 3613 3357 3674 3694 3678 Current-carrying wiring devices; Caps & plugs, electric: attachment; Connectors, electric cord; Sockets, electric; Fuses, electric; Nonferrous wiredrawing & insulating; Building wire & cable, nonferrous; Diodes, solid state (germanium, silicon, etc.); Transistors; Engine electrical equipment; Electronic connectors
Pr: Donald J Hendler
**Pr:* Daryoush Larizadeh
**CFO:* Mark Baydarian
**V Ch Bd:* Stephen Sokolow
VP: Steve Campolo
VP: John Lamontagne
Exec: Gina De Burgo
Rgnl Mgr: Joseph Helm
Rgnl Mgr: Shady Youssef
Genl Mgr: Cesar Monroy
Off Mgr: Jean Cervantes
Board of Directors: Shirley Leviton

D-U-N-S 04-432-4515 IMP
LEVITZ FURNITURE CORP
(*Suby of* LEVITZ HOME FURNISHINGS, INC.)
300 Crossways Park Dr, Woodbury, NY 11797-2035
Tel (516) 682-0481 *Founded/Ownrshp* 1936
Sales 206.2MM^E *EMP* 2,700
SIC 5712 Furniture stores; Bedding & bedsprings
Ch Bd: Larry Zigerelli
**CFO:* Kathy Guinnessey
**Sr VP:* Jane Gilmartin
**Prin:* Tom Baumlin
Board of Directors: Tom Baumlin

D-U-N-S 00-137-9288 IMP
LEVY GROUP INC (NY)
LIZ CLAIBORNE COATS
1333 Broadway Fl 9, New York, NY 10018-1064
Tel (212) 398-0707 *Founded/Ownrshp* 1995
Sales 101.8MM^E *EMP* 250
SIC 2337 2385 Women's & misses' suits & coats; Jackets & vests, except fur & leather: women's; Raincoats, except vulcanized rubber: purchased materials
Ch Bd: Jack Arthur Levy
**Ch:* Donald Levy
**VP:* Lawrence Levy
**VP:* Richard Levy
Ql Cn Mgr: Rich Albom

D-U-N-S 61-716-8034
LEVY R & H LIMITED PARTNERSHIP
980 N Michigan Ave # 400, Chicago, IL 60611-4501
Tel (312) 664-8200 *Founded/Ownrshp* 1989
Sales 244.5MM^E *EMP* 7,000
SIC 5812 Contract food services
Pt: Lawrence F Levy
Pt: Andrew Lansing
Pt: Robert Seiffert
VP: Alison Weber
Exec: Leo Dominguez
Sls Mgr: Brooke Beck

D-U-N-S 00-941-8286
LEWIS & CLARK COLLEGE (OR)
0615 Sw Palatine Hill Rd, Portland, OR 97219-7879
Tel (503) 768-7000 *Founded/Ownrshp* 1867
Sales 119.7MM *EMP* 800
Accts Moss Adams Llp Portland Oreg
SIC 8221 College, except junior; Professional schools
Pr: Thomas J Hochstettler
Sr Pt: Portland John Jr
**Pr:* Barry Glassner
Trst: James Gardner
Trst: Frederick Jubitz
Trst: Randy Massengale
Trst: Owen Panner
Trst: Edward Perkins
Trst: Ronald Ragen
Trst: Robert Ridgley
Trst: Joan Smith
Trst: Charles Spalding
Trst: Ann Swindells
Trst: John Wright
Ex VP: Peter Chang
**VP:* Jane Monnig Atkinson
VP: Richard J Bettega
**VP:* David Ellis
VP: Gregory A Volk
Dir Lab: David Dean
Dir Lab: Lisa Holmes

D-U-N-S 03-392-1719
LEWIS AND RAULERSON INC
1759 State St, Waycross, GA 31501-6714
Tel (912) 283-5951 *Founded/Ownrshp* 1939
Sales 110.3MM^E *EMP* 50
SIC 5171 Petroleum bulk stations
Pr: Bill F Raulerson
**Ex VP:* David Turner
**Sr VP:* Clay Parker
**VP:* Carl Lewis
Off Mgr: Phylis Dixon
MIS Dir: William Woodard
Dir IT: Andrew Brauda

D-U-N-S 00-625-0427 IMP
LEWIS BOLT & NUT CO (MN)
30105 6th Ave, La Junta, CO 81050-9502
Tel (719) 384-5400 *Founded/Ownrshp* 1992
Sales 83.4MM^E *EMP* 150
SIC 3452 Bolts, nuts, rivets & washers
Pr: Mark Paper
**VP:* Dave Barry
**VP:* Cheryl Masias
**VP:* Cheryl McIntosh
VP: Jeremy Soden
**VP Mfg:* Carl Zimmerman
Plnt Mgr: Brett McIntosh
Sls Mgr: Robert Fiorio

D-U-N-S 09-642-7059
LEWIS BRISBOIS BISGAARD & SMITH LLP
633 W 5th St Ste 4000, Los Angeles, CA 90071-2074
Tel (213) 250-1800 *Founded/Ownrshp* 1979
Sales 227.1MM^E *EMP* 2,200
SIC 8111 General practice law office
Mng Pt: Robert F Lewis
Pt: Christopher P Bisgaard
Pt: Roy M Brisbois
Mgr Info S: Michael Yu
Counsel: John Skalak

D-U-N-S 00-629-7113 IMP
LEWIS BROTHERS BAKERIES INC (MO)
500 N Fulton Ave, Evansville, IN 47710-1571
Tel (812) 425-4642 *Founded/Ownrshp* 1925
Sales 700.5MM^E *EMP* 2,500
SIC 2051 5149 Bread, all types (white, wheat, rye, etc): fresh or frozen; Buns, bread type: fresh or frozen; Rolls, sweet: except frozen; Doughnuts, except frozen; Groceries & related products
Pr: R Jack Lewis Jr
Pr: John West
COO: Tom Woods Jr
**Treas:* Jeffery J Sankovitch
VP: Rodger Lesh
VP: Carol Stratman
Genl Mgr: Carl Finfrock
Genl Mgr: Harry Lincoln
Off Mgr: Laura Abernathy
Plnt Mgr: Nathan Ponder
Mktg Dir: Tracy Wingo

D-U-N-S 00-894-2088 IMP
LEWIS DRUGS INC
LEWIS FAMILY DRUGS
2701 S Minn Ave Ste 1, Sioux Falls, SD 57105-4787
Tel (605) 367-2800 *Founded/Ownrshp* 1942
Sales 175.8MM^E *EMP* 675
SIC 5912 Drug stores
Pr: Mark Griffin
Pr: Bill Ladwig
COO: Neilsen David
**COO:* David Nielson
**CFO:* Scott Cross
Ofcr: Herb Rosin
VP: Dave Nielsen
Dir Rx: Jim Rasmussen
CTO: Naomi Graves
IT Man: Kevin Riley

LEWIS ENERGY GROUP
See LEWIS RESOURCE MANAGEMENT LLC

D-U-N-S 85-911-8379
LEWIS ENERGY GROUP LP
10101 Reunion Pl Ste 1000, San Antonio, TX 78216-4157
Tel (210) 384-3200 *Founded/Ownrshp* 1998
Sales 889.5MM^E *EMP* 1,000
SIC 1311

LEWIS FAMILY DRUGS
See LEWIS DRUGS INC

D-U-N-S 85-962-5287
LEWIS FOOD TOWN INC
3131 Pawnee St, Houston, TX 77054-3302
Tel (713) 746-3600 *Founded/Ownrshp* 1994
Sales 238.3MM^E *EMP* 1,700
SIC 5411 Supermarkets, chain
Pr: Ross Lewis
**Sec:* Billy G Drews

D-U-N-S 60-420-6664
LEWIS LEASE CRUTCHER WA LLC
HOLYOKE FINE HOMES
(*Suby of* W LEASE LEWIS CO) ★
2200 Western Ave, Seattle, WA 98121-1921
Tel (206) 264-1985 *Founded/Ownrshp* 1989
Sales 136.6MM^E *EMP* 275
SIC 1542 1521 Commercial & office building, new construction; Single-family housing construction
CEO: Bart Ricketts
CFO: J Philo Hall
CFO: John Hall
CFO: Philo Hall
Ch: Bill Lewis
Div/Sub He: Jeff Cleator
Admn Mgr: Jan Vancourt
Brnch Mgr: Tim Carpenter
Off Mgr: Gary Smith
Opers Mgr: Matt Pearson
Mktg Dir: Carey Smith

D-U-N-S 00-792-0630
LEWIS MERIWETHER ELECTRIC COOPERATIVE (TN)
1625 Highway 100, Centerville, TN 37033-1023
Tel (931) 729-3558 *Founded/Ownrshp* 1939

Sales 96.5MM EMP 82
Accts Winnett Associates Pllc Shel
SIC 4911 Distribution, electric power
Pr: Keith Carnahan
*Ch Bd: Dr Zachary Hutchens
*CFO: Randy James
*V Ch Bd: Andrew Porch
Dist Mgr: Jason Graves
Board of Directors: Jessie Wallace, Ronny Averett, Bill Webb, Reed Dreaden, Johnnie Ruth Elrod, Raymond Fussell, Tommy Graham, Larry Mayberry, Jeff Perry DDS, Wayne Qualls, Cass Rye

D-U-N-S 07-280-9924
LEWIS P C JACKSON
JACKSON LEWIS
1133 Weschester Ave, White Plains, NY 10604
Tel (914) 872-8060 Founded/Ownrshp 1958
Sales 323.1MM^E EMP 1,160
SIC 8111 General practice law office
Prin: Ana C Shields
Pt: Brooks R Amiot
Pt: Richard J Hafets
Pt: Emmett F McGee
Pt: Larry R Seegull
Mng Pt: David Block
Mng Pt: Danny Jarrett
Mng Pt: Richard McAtee
Mng Pt: Joseph Saccomano
Mng Pt: Richard Schey
Mng Pt: Mickey Silberman
CFO: Diana Ferreira
Ch: Vincent Cino
Sr VP: Elissa Ali
Sr VP: Leighton Dawkins
VP: Thomas Alexander
VP: Brenda Hernandez
VP: Rhonda James

D-U-N-S 13-120-4059
LEWIS PAPER INTERNATIONAL INC
LEWIS PAPER PLACE
1400 S Wolf Rd Ste 100, Wheeling, IL 60090-6524
Tel (847) 520-3386 Founded/Ownrshp 1980
Sales 84.4MM^E EMP 158
SIC 5111 Printing paper
CEO: Miriam W Lewis
*Pr: Robert J Zessis
*Sr VP: Yvonne M Jewson
Dir IT: Shari F Necheles
Manager: Bob Grasse

LEWIS PAPER PLACE
See LEWIS PAPER INTERNATIONAL INC

D-U-N-S 07-842-7294
LEWIS RESOURCE MANAGEMENT LLC
LEWIS ENERGY GROUP
(Suby of LEWIS ENERGY GROUP LP) ★
10101 Reunion Pl Ste 1000, San Antonio, TX 78216-4157
Tel (210) 384-3200 Founded/Ownrshp 1983
Sales 559.4MM EMP 250
Accts Bkd Llp San Antonio Texas
SIC 4924 Natural gas distribution
Pr: Rodney R Lewis
*VP: Rick Price

D-U-N-S 06-792-1775
LEWIS TREE SERVICE INC
300 Lucius Gordon Dr, West Henrietta, NY 14586-9686
Tel (585) 436-3208 Founded/Ownrshp 2000
Sales 423.4MM^E EMP 2,950
SIC 0783 Tree trimming services for public utility lines
Ch Bd: A C Fred Engelfried
*Pr: Richard C Alt
Pr: Steven Gould
*Pr: Thomas R Rogers
*CFO: Joseph L Redman
*CFO: James W Stenger
*Sr VP: R Douglas Roof
*VP: Daniel Oberlies
VP: Stephen Polozie
VP: Doug Roof
Area Mgr: Joshua Pinto

D-U-N-S 06-996-4104
LEWIS UNIVERSITY
1 University Pkwy, Romeoville, IL 60446-1832
Tel (815) 838-0500 Founded/Ownrshp 1932
Sales 166.7MM EMP 500
Accts Selden Fox Ltd Oak Brook Il
SIC 8221 University
Pr: Brother James Gaffney
CFO: Rhonda Y Pilgrim
Treas: Gregory Maruszak
*Ex VP: Wayne J Draudt
*Sr VP: Robert C Derose
*Sr VP: Joseph T Falese
*Sr VP: Raymond Kennelly
VP: Robert De Rose
VP: Barbara Reidy
Comm Man: Samuel Enyia
Snr Ntwrk: Kimberly Jupiter-King
Board of Directors: A Board of Directors

D-U-N-S 02-611-2081
■ **LEWIS-GALE HOSPITAL INC**
LEWIS-GALE MEDICAL CENTER
(Suby of HOSPITAL COPORATION OF AMERICA) ★
1900 Electric Rd, Salem, VA 24153-7494
Tel (540) 776-4000 Founded/Ownrshp 1998
Sales 285.2MM EMP 1,400^E
SIC 8062 General medical & surgical hospitals
CEO: Victor Giovanetti
*Pr: James Thweatt Jr
*COO: Charlotte Tyson
CFO: Angela Bainter
CFO: William Bainter
*CFO: Angela Reynolds
Dir Rx: Joe Ciezkowski
Off Mgr: Rick Harmon
MIS Dir: Beth Cole
HC Dir: Anita Wilhelm

LEWIS-GALE MEDICAL CENTER
See LEWIS-GALE HOSPITAL INC

LEWIS-GOETZ & CO - CORP HDQTR
See LEWIS-GOETZ AND CO INC

D-U-N-S 00-253-0335 IMP/EXP
LEWIS-GOETZ AND CO INC (PA)
LEWIS-GOETZ & CO - CORP HDQTR
(Suby of ERIKS N.V.)
650 Washington Rd Ste 500, Pittsburgh, PA 15228-2714
Tel (800) 937-9070 Founded/Ownrshp 1935, 1991
Sales 637.1MM^E EMP 1,039
SIC 5085 Rubber goods, mechanical
Pr: Donald E Evans
COO: David A Chrnock
Treas: Rick Rozman
VP: Dave Adkins
*VP: Eelco De Graaf
VP: Stacey Fedorka
VP: Rich Holderman
VP: John Jurgensen
Brnch Mgr: Casey Olson
Dist Mgr: Matt Bunker
Genl Mgr: Ryan Dolbeck

LEWISBINS
See ORBIS CORP

D-U-N-S 01-058-3649
LEWISTOWN HOSPITAL
400 Highland Ave, Lewistown, PA 17044-1198
Tel (717) 248-5411 Founded/Ownrshp 1905
Sales 97.3MM EMP 900^E
SIC 8062 8221

D-U-N-S 07-137-2338
LEWISVILLE INDEPENDENT SCHOOL DISTRICT
1800 Timber Creek Rd, Flower Mound, TX 75028-1146
Tel (469) 713-5200 Founded/Ownrshp 1877
Sales 597.0MM EMP 4,500
SIC 8211

D-U-N-S 08-022-3859
LEWISVILLE INDEPENDENT SCHOOL DISTRICT
LISD
1565 W Main St Ste 101, Lewisville, TX 75067-2616
Tel (469) 713-5200 Founded/Ownrshp 2016
Sales 5.2MM^E EMP 7,000
SIC 8211 Public combined elementary & secondary school
Psych: Dave Thompson

LEX TV
See LEXINGTON INSURANCE CO

D-U-N-S 00-166-4465 IMP
LEXA INTERNATIONAL CORP (DE)
1 Landmark Sq Ste 407, Stamford, CT 06901-2601
Tel (203) 326-5200 Founded/Ownrshp 1920
Sales 452.7MM^E EMP 1,204
Accts Citrin Cooperman & Company Ll
SIC 5171 3822 Petroleum bulk stations & terminals; Auto controls regulating residntl & coml environmt & applncs
Ch Bd: Antonia Axson Johnson
V Ch: Goeran P Ennerfelt
V Ch Bd: P Goeran Ennerfelt
VP: John Pascale
VP: Charles W Seitz

D-U-N-S 11-873-0472
LEXAMAR CORP
(Suby of DECOMA ADMARK) ★
100 Lexamar Dr, Boyne City, MI 49712-9799
Tel (231) 582-3163 Founded/Ownrshp 1987
Sales 141.1MM^E EMP 325
SIC 3089 Injection molded finished plastic products
Pr: Al Powers
Dir Lab: Ken Bradley
Prgrm Mgr: Mike Severn
IT Man: Tom Schlueter
Sls Mgr: Tom Stewart

D-U-N-S 15-423-7234 IMP
LEXICON INC
SCHUECK STEEL
8900 Fourche Dam Pike, Little Rock, AR 72206-3806
Tel (501) 490-4200 Founded/Ownrshp 1996
Sales 301.7MM EMP 1,500
Accts Frost Pllc Little Rock Arka
SIC 1629 3441 Industrial plant construction; Fabricated structural metal
CEO: Eugene Riley Jr
*Pr: Patrick T Schueck
*Treas: Jeff D Weatherly
*VP: John Bailey
VP: Phillip Connor
*VP: Mark A Davis
*VP: Gary Loyd
*VP: Brian Rutherford
Dir IT: Jason Richmond
Opers Mgr: Chris Reynolds
Board of Directors: Thomas Schueck

D-U-N-S 83-817-9638
▲ **LEXICON PHARMACEUTICALS INC**
8800 Technology Forest Pl, The Woodlands, TX 77381-1160
Tel (281) 863-3000 Founded/Ownrshp 1995
Sales 130.0MM EMP 120^E
Tkr Sym LXRX Exch NGS
SIC 2834 Pharmaceutical preparations
Pr: Lonnel Coats
*Ch Bd: Raymond Debbane
Chf Mktg O: Pablo Lapuerta
Top Exec: Alex Santini
Ex VP: Alan J Main
Ex VP: Jeffrey L Wade
VP: Brian Crum
VP: Christophe Person
Ex Dir: Kenneth Kassler-Taub
Ex Dir: Chris Warner
Opers Mgr: Dawn Bright
Board of Directors: Philippe J Amouyal, Samuel L Barker, Robert J Lefkowitz, Alan S Nies, Frank P Palantoni, Christopher J Sobecki, Judith L Swain

D-U-N-S 78-667-5111
LEXINGTON CORPORATE ENTERPRISES INC
17725 Volbrecht Rd, Lansing, IL 60438-4542
Tel (708) 418-0700 Founded/Ownrshp 2005
Sales 116.5MM^E EMP 200
SIC 5075 1711 Warm air heating & air conditioning; Warm air heating & air conditioning contractor
Pr: Raymond Mungo
*Ex VP: David Yanow
*VP: Timothy M Scott

D-U-N-S 14-484-6250
LEXINGTON COUNTY HEALTH SERVICES DISTRICT INC
2720 Sunset Blvd, West Columbia, SC 29169-4810
Tel (803) 791-2000 Founded/Ownrshp 1988
Sales 893.9MM^E EMP 6,000^E
Accts Kpmg Llp Atlanta Ga
SIC 8062 8011 8299 8051 General medical & surgical hospitals; Clinic, operated by physicians; Educational service, nondegree granting: continuing educ.; Skilled nursing care facilities
Pr: Michael Biediger
*COO: Tod Augsburger
*VP: Melinda P Kruzner
Dir IT: Donna Lyles

LEXINGTON COUNTY HLTH SVCS DST
See LEXINGTON MEDICAL CENTER

D-U-N-S 10-007-1471
LEXINGTON COUNTY SCHOOL DISTRICT NO 1
100 Tarrar Springs Rd, Lexington, SC 29072-3835
Tel (803) 821-1000 Founded/Ownrshp 1952
Sales 370.2M EMP 3,500
Accts Burkett Burkett & Burkett Cpa
SIC 8211 Public elementary & secondary schools
*CFO: John Butler
Treas: Byron Sistare
Ofcr: Jonaire McClary
Exec: Daniel Powell
Dir IT: Harriet Zwart
Schl Brd P: Debra Knight
Psych: Cameron Anderson
Psych: Amy Long

LEXINGTON COUNTY SCHOOL DST 2
See BOOKLAND CAYCE SCHOOL DISTRICT NO 2

D-U-N-S 18-770-3574 IMP/EXP
LEXINGTON FURNITURE INDUSTRIES INC
LEXINGTON HOME BRANDS
1300 National Hwy, Thomasville, NC 27360-2318
Tel (336) 474-5300 Founded/Ownrshp 2002
Sales 633.2MM^E EMP 3,000
SIC 2512 Upholstered household furniture
Pr: Phil Haney
CFO: Craig Spooner
VP: Robert Stamper
VP Sls: Doug Hartzog
VP Sls: Art Negrin

LEXINGTON HEALTH NETWORK
See ROYAL MANAGEMENT CORP

D-U-N-S 11-246-0964
LEXINGTON HOLDINGS INC
WEB:WWW.ALTOONAHOSPITAL.ORG
620 Howard Ave, Altoona, PA 16601-4804
Tel (814) 946-2204 Founded/Ownrshp 2008
Sales 2.2MM EMP 1,575
SIC 8741 Hotel or motel management
CEO: James W Barner
*Treas: David J Duncan

LEXINGTON HOME BRANDS
See LEXINGTON FURNITURE INDUSTRIES INC

LEXINGTON INDUSTRIES
See FULTON COUNTY A R C

D-U-N-S 00-695-2519
■ **LEXINGTON INSURANCE CO**
LEX TV
(Suby of NATIONAL UNION FIRE INSURANCE CO OF PITTSBURGH PA) ★
99 High St Fl 23, Boston, MA 02110-2320
Tel (617) 330-1100 Founded/Ownrshp 1965
Sales NA EMP 312
SIC 6331 Fire, marine & casualty insurance
Pr: Jeremy Johnson
Pr: Thomas McLaughlin
*Treas: Robert Jacobson
Treas: Dean Owens
Sr VP: Sharyl Bales
Sr VP: Frank Douglas
Sr VP: George R Statts
VP: Nick Anselmo
VP: Thomas Grandmaison
VP: Ken Morrison
VP: Fred Owen
VP: Keith Peacock
VP: William Whitehead

D-U-N-S 06-933-3797
LEXINGTON MEDICAL CENTER (SC)
LEXINGTON COUNTY HLTH SVCS DST
(Suby of LEXINGTON COUNTY HEALTH SERVICES DISTRICT INC) ★
2720 Sunset Blvd, West Columbia, SC 29169-4810
Tel (803) 791-2000 Founded/Ownrshp 1971, 1988
Sales 863.9MM EMP 5,616^E
Accts Kpmg Llp Atlanta Ga
SIC 8062 General medical & surgical hospitals
Pr: Tod Augsburger
Chf Rad: Layne Clemenz
Pr: Deborah Hunt
*CFO: Melinda Kruzner
Sr VP: Roger Sipe
VP: Cindy Rohman
VP: DK Walker
Exec: Marguerite O'Brien
Comm Dir: Mark Shelley
Store Mgr: Chris Beasley
Nurse Mgr: Kim Diamond

D-U-N-S 08-248-1433
LEXINGTON NURSING HOME INC
632 Se 3rd St, Lexington, OK 73051-9902
Tel (405) 527-6531 Founded/Ownrshp 1977
Sales 158.3MM EMP 61
SIC 8052 Intermediate care facilities
Pr: Gerald Lawson

D-U-N-S 80-834-0954
LEXINGTON REALTY TRUST
1 Penn Plz Ste 4015, New York, NY 10119-4015
Tel (212) 692-7200 Founded/Ownrshp 1993
Sales 430.8MM EMP 48^E
SIC 6798 Real estate investment trusts
Pr: T Wilson Eglin
*Ch Bd: E Robert Roskind
CFO: Patrick Carroll
*V Ch Bd: Richard J Rouse
Ex VP: Nabil Andrawis
Ex VP: Joseph S Bonventre
Ex VP: Joseph Bonventre
Ex VP: Beth Boulerice
Ex VP: Lara Johnson
Sr VP: Heather Gentry
VP: James Dudley
VP: Paul Wood
Exec: Irfan Butt
Board of Directors: Richard S Frary, James Grosfeld, Claire A Koeneman, Kevin W Lynch, Harold First

D-U-N-S 60-821-3187 IMP
LEXINGTON RUBBER GROUP INC
QSR
(Suby of QUALITY SYNTHETIC RUBBER) ★
1700 Highland Rd, Twinsburg, OH 44087-2221
Tel (330) 425-8472 Founded/Ownrshp 1988
Sales 91.5MM^E EMP 410
SIC 3069 Hard rubber & molded rubber products
CEO: Randy Ross
*CFO: Dennis Welhouse
Plnt Mgr: Mike Berry

D-U-N-S 07-979-8951
LEXINGTON SCHOOL DISTRICT 01
100 Tarrar Springs Rd, Lexington, SC 29072-3835
Tel (803) 321-1002 Founded/Ownrshp 2015
Sales 88.4MM^E EMP 2,870^E
SIC 8211 Public elementary & secondary schools

D-U-N-S 80-756-2181
LEXINGTON SCHOOL DISTRICT 5
MAINTENANCE DEPARTMENT
1020 Dutchfork Rd, Ballentine, SC 29002
Tel (803) 732-8011 Founded/Ownrshp 2000
Sales 193.7MM EMP 13
Accts Derrick Stubbs & Stith Llp
SIC 8211 Public elementary & secondary schools

D-U-N-S 02-042-8777
LEXINGTON-FAYETTE URBAN COUNTY GOVERNMENT
LFUCG
200 E Main St, Lexington, KY 40507-1310
Tel (859) 258-3100 Founded/Ownrshp 1775
Sales NA EMP 2,772
Accts Dean Dorton Allen Ford Pllc
SIC 9121 9111 ; ; Executive offices
Prin: Jim Gray
Ofcr: Sally Hamilton
Ofcr: Daryll Trumbo
Comm Dir: Susan Straub
Ex Dir: Kay Sargent
CIO: Aldona Valicenti
MIS Dir: Michael Nugent
Dir IT: Chad Cottle
IT Man: Philip Shaw
Opers Mgr: Kevin Bennett

D-U-N-S 16-200-7871 IMP
LEXISNEXIS GROUP
(Suby of REED BUSINESS INFORMATION) ★
9443 Springboro Pike, Miamisburg, OH 45342-5490
Tel (937) 865-6800 Founded/Ownrshp 2008
Sales 630.2MM^E EMP 3,507^E
SIC 7375 2741 Data base information retrieval; Miscellaneous publishing
CEO: Kurt Sanford
Pr: Michael Lamb
CEO: Doug Kaplan
CFO: Rebecca Schmitt
Bd of Dir: Floyd Clarke
Ofcr: Mike Higgins
Ex VP: Ian McDougall
Ex VP: Vijay Raghavan
Ex VP: Jeff Reihl
Ex VP: Doreen Tyburski
Ex VP: Alex Watson
Sr VP: Lisa Agona
Sr VP: Christopher Ainsley
Sr VP: Carol Dibattiste
Sr VP: Kate Holden
Sr VP: Mark Norman
Sr VP: Joanna Stone
Sr VP: Donald Welsko
VP: Lisa Baumgarten
VP: John Birch
VP: Jim Christiansen

LEXISNEXIS MATTHEW BENDER
See MATTHEW BENDER & CO INC

D-U-N-S 15-293-0061
LEXISNEXIS RISK ASSETS INC
CHOICEPOINT
(Suby of REED ELSEVIER US HOLDINGS INC) ★
1105 N Market St Ste 501, Wilmington, DE 19801-1253
Tel (770) 752-6000 Founded/Ownrshp 1997
Sales NA EMP 5,000
SIC 8411 7375 8721 7323 Information bureaus, insurance; Information retrieval services; Accounting, auditing & bookkeeping; Credit reporting services
Ch Bd: Derek V Smith
*Pr: Douglas C Curling
*CFO: Kenneth Fogarty
*CFO: David E Trine
*Ex VP: David T Lee
Ex VP: Dan H Rocco
*Ex VP: Steven W Surbaugh
VP: Alton Adams

VP: Donald Welsko
Snr Sftwr: Ahsan Ul-Haque
Tech Mgr: Mark Sulimirski

D-U-N-S 06-011-7244
LEXISNEXIS RISK SOLUTIONS INC
(*Suby of* CHOICEPOINT) ★
1000 Alderman Dr, Alpharetta, GA 30005-4101
Tel (678) 694-6000 *Founded/Ownrshp* 1975
Sales 564.9MM^E *EMP* 5,000
SIC 8748 Business consulting
CEO: Bill Madison
Ch Bd: Derek V Smith
Pr: Douglas C Curling
Ex VP: David T Lee
Ex VP: Vijay Raghavan
Ex VP: Donald Welsko
Sr VP: Lisa Agona
Sr VP: Scott Sessler
VP: Jennifer Lemming
Prin: Haywood Talcove
Dir Sec: Angelo Bryant

D-U-N-S 61-208-4517 IMP/EXP
LEXJET LLC
1605 Main St Ste 400, Sarasota, FL 34236-5853
Tel (941) 330-1210 *Founded/Ownrshp* 1994
Sales 93.1MM^E *EMP* 100
SIC 5045 5112 5111 2672 5043 Computers, peripherals & software; Computer paper; Printing & writing paper; Thermoplastic coated paper: made from purchased materials; Cameras & photographic equipment
Pr: Ronald T Simkins
CFO: Gina Mascio
Sr VP: Pete Petersen
**VP:* Author Lambert

D-U-N-S 83-442-9078 IMP
LEXMARK CARPET MILLS INC
285 Kraft Dr, Dalton, GA 30721-1502
Tel (706) 277-3000 *Founded/Ownrshp* 1993
Sales 114.4MM^E *EMP* 245^E
SIC 2273 Carpets & rugs
CEO: Paul Cleary
Pr: Justin Cash
CFO: James Butler
VP: Scott Austin
Mktg Dir: Tammy Horn

D-U-N-S 18-064-1441
LEXMARK ENTERPRISE SOFTWARE LLC
(*Suby of* LEXMARK INTERNATIONAL INC) ★
8900 Renner Blvd, Lenexa, KS 66219-3049
Tel (913) 422-7525 *Founded/Ownrshp* 2004
Sales 321.3MM^E *EMP* 1,140
SIC 7371 7372 Computer software development; Prepackaged software
CEO: Scott Coons
**COO:* Darren Knipp
**Ex VP:* David Lintz
**VP:* Cary Decamp
VP: Nita Patel
Genl Mgr: David Wadler
Manager: Jeff Rapp
Sales Asso: Beth Deeds
Sales Asso: Shawn Vialle
Snr Mgr: Jackie Tucker

D-U-N-S 62-333-1717 IMP
LEXMARK INTERNATIONAL INC
740 W New Circle Rd, Lexington, KY 40511-1876
Tel (859) 232-2000 *Founded/Ownrshp* 2016
Sales 3.5MMM *EMP* 13,000
SIC 3577 Printers, computer
Pr: David Reeder
Pr: Paul A Rooke
Treas: Alice Bowen
Ex VP: Martin S Canning
VP: Gary Bourland
VP: Carlos Bretos
VP: Brad Clay
VP: Patrick Cox
VP: Efrain Escobedo
VP: Kyle Farmer
VP: Barry Fortson
VP: Olavo Guerra
VP: Tony Moffett
VP: Keith Moody
VP: Patrick Oliver
VP: Robert J Patton
VP: Chris Saunders
VP: Mark Sisk
VP: Rick Thompson
VP: Allen Waugerman
VP: Brett Wheeler

D-U-N-S 07-372-2878
LEXMED INC
LMC EXTENDED CARE
(*Suby of* LEXINGTON COUNTY HEALTH SERVICES DISTRICT INC) ★
815 Old Cherokee Rd, Lexington, SC 29072-9041
Tel (803) 359-5181 *Founded/Ownrshp* 1989
Sales 30.0MM *EMP* 2,653
Accts Kpmg Llp Atlanta Ga
SIC 8051 Skilled nursing care facilities
Pr: Mike Biediger
Phys Thrpy: Janet Haltiwanger
Board of Directors: Mary Ball, Ken Shelton

LEXTRON ANIMAL HEALTH
See ANIMAL HEALTH INTERNATIONAL INC

LEXUS OF GREENWICH
See GRIFFIN MANAGEMENT CO INC

LEXUS OF KNOXVILLE
See T & W OF KNOXVILLE INC

LEXUS OF SACRAMENTO
See RPM LUXURY AUTO SALES INC

LEXUS SANTA MONICA
See VOLKSWAGEN SANTA MONICA INC

D-U-N-S 01-400-7462
LEZZER HOLDINGS INC
LEZZER LUMBER
311 Schofield St, Curwensville, PA 16833-1433
Tel (814) 236-0220 *Founded/Ownrshp* 1954
Sales 93.5MM^E *EMP* 142
SIC 5211 Bathroom fixtures, equipment & supplies; Millwork & lumber; Insulation material, building
CEO: Michael F Lezzer
**Pr:* David M Lezzer
**Treas:* Margaret Lezzer
**Treas:* Julie A Seighman
**Ex VP:* Kenneth C Lezzer
**VP:* Elizabeth Lezzer

LEZZER LUMBER
See LEZZER HOLDINGS INC

D-U-N-S 10-158-5990
LEZZER LUMBER INC
(*Suby of* LEZZER LUMBER) ★
311 Schofield St, Curwensville, PA 16833-1433
Tel (814) 236-0220 *Founded/Ownrshp* 1983
Sales 84.0MM^E *EMP* 373^E
SIC 5211 Lumber & other building materials
Pr: Maurice Lezzer
**Pr:* Dave Lezzer
**COO:* John Lloyd
**CFO:* Jay Lee
**Treas:* Julie Seighman
Manager: Josh Ritchie
Sales Asso: Nate Sopic

D-U-N-S 96-474-1784 IMP
LF MENS GROUP LLC
(*Suby of* MAX LEATHER) ★
1359 Broadway Fl 21, New York, NY 10018-7824
Tel (646) 839-7000 *Founded/Ownrshp* 2011
Sales 106.6MM^E *EMP* 200^E
SIC 5136 Men's & boys' clothing

D-U-N-S 07-880-1541 IMP
LF SOURCING SPORTSWEAR LLC
(*Suby of* LI & FUNG (HONG KONG) LIMITED)
1359 Broadway Fl 18, New York, NY 10018-7839
Tel (646) 943-8505 *Founded/Ownrshp* 2012
Sales 200.0MM *EMP* 30
SIC 5611 Clothing, sportswear, men's & boys'
Pr: Jason Kra
Sr VP: Kathleen Ferraro
VP: Michelle Chen

D-U-N-S 06-188-2820
LFC ENTERPRISES INC
SIX L'S PACKING
315 New Market Rd E, Immokalee, FL 34142-3509
Tel (239) 657-3117 *Founded/Ownrshp* 2001
Sales 91.0MM^E *EMP* 369^E
SIC 5431 Fruit stands or markets
Pr: Kent Shoemaker
**VP:* Darren Micelle
**VP:* Gerry Odell

D-U-N-S 05-869-9836 EXP
LFI WIND DOWN INC
LANE FURNITURE
(*Suby of* THOMASVILLE FURNITURE) ★
5380 Highway 145 S, Tupelo, MS 38801-0811
Tel (662) 566-7211 *Founded/Ownrshp* 1998
Sales 709.5MM^E *EMP* 3,600
SIC 2512 Recliners: upholstered on wood frames; Couches, sofas & davenports: upholstered on wood frames
Pr: Greg Roy
**CFO:* Vance Johnston
**Treas:* Steven G Rolls
**Sr VP:* Meridith Graham
**VP:* Jon D Botsford
VP: Gean Pierce
Sfty Dirs: Doug Maxwell

LFUCG
See LEXINGTON-FAYETTE URBAN COUNTY GOVERNMENT

D-U-N-S 19-465-5882 IMP/EXP
LG CHEM AMERICA INC
(*Suby of* LG CHEM, LTD.)
910 Sylvan Ave, Englewood Cliffs, NJ 07632-3306
Tel (201) 816-2000 *Founded/Ownrshp* 2009
Sales 486.0MM^E *EMP* 35
SIC 5099 5169 5199 Containers: glass, metal or plastic; Detergents & soaps, except specialty cleaning; General merchandise, non-durable
Pr: Richard Do
**Prin:* Jay Kim

D-U-N-S 02-904-9590 IMP
LG ELECTRONICS ALABAMA INC
(*Suby of* LG GROUP AIC) ★
201 James Record Rd Sw, Huntsville, AL 35824-1513
Tel (256) 772-0623 *Founded/Ownrshp* 2004
Sales 108.7MM^E *EMP* 600
SIC 3651 3695 5064 5085 5065 4225 Television receiving sets; Video recording tape, blank; Microwave ovens, non-commercial; Industrial supplies; Tapes, audio & video recording; General warehousing & storage
Pr: SOO M Kim
**Pr:* Bon-Joon Koo
**CFO:* Michael Woo
Ex VP: Dermot J Boden
Ex VP: Reginald J Bull
VP: Rick B Calacci
VP: John H Riddle
VP: Scott Williams
VP: Richard Wingate
**Prin:* Havis Kwon
Snr Mgr: Taryn Brucia

D-U-N-S 94-171-6508 IMP
LG ELECTRONICS MOBILECOMM USA INC
LG INFOCOMM U.S.A.
(*Suby of* LG GROUP AIC) ★
10225 Willow Creek Rd, San Diego, CA 92131-1639
Tel (858) 635-5300 *Founded/Ownrshp* 1996
Sales 129.4MM^E *EMP* 150
SIC 5065 3663 Mobile telephone equipment; Radio & TV communications equipment
CEO: Wayne Park
**Pr:* Kyung Joo Hwang
**Treas:* Jae Dong Han
Ofcr: Sarah Knight
VP: Naveen Jain
VP: Eric Ley
VP: M Ehtisham Rabbani
IT Man: Ross Joseph
Sfty Dirs: Jenni Chun
Natl Sales: Stephanie Kohler
Manager: Peter Lane

D-U-N-S 07-009-4818 IMP/EXP
LG ELECTRONICS USA INC
LG GROUP AIC
(*Suby of* LG ELECTRONICS INC.)
1000 Sylvan Ave, Englewood Cliffs, NJ 07632-3318
Tel (201) 816-2000 *Founded/Ownrshp* 1975
Sales 9.7MMM *EMP* 2,500
Accts Kpmg Llp
SIC 5064 3651 Electrical appliances, television & radio; Electrical appliances, major; Electrical entertainment equipment; Air conditioning appliances; Household audio & video equipment
Pr: William Cho
**CFO:* Soohan Bae
CFO: Byeong Choi
CFO: Eunji Jung
Sr VP: Rick Calacci
Sr VP: James Fishler
Sr VP: Kevin McNamara
Sr VP: John Riddle
Sr VP: Jay Vandenbree
VP: Jeff Dowell
VP: Kevin Holian
VP: Ehtisham Rabbani

LG GROUP AIC
See LG ELECTRONICS USA INC

D-U-N-S 14-912-0367 IMP/EXP
LG HAUSYS AMERICA INC
(*Suby of* LG HAUSYS, LTD.)
900 Circle 75 Pkwy Se # 15, Atlanta, GA 30339-3035
Tel (678) 486-8210 *Founded/Ownrshp* 1988
Sales 116.0MM^E *EMP* 250^E
SIC 2541 Counter & sink tops
CFO: Yuku Kang
Ex VP: David Thoresen
VP: Simon OH
**Prin:* Bongsoo Kim
**Prin:* Anthony Rivera
**Prin:* Cathy Scutier
Natl Sales: Michelle Wheeler
Sls Dir: Don Luther
Mktg Mgr: Lee Heemun
Sls Mgr: Jodie Simpson
Sales Asso: Daniel Shin

LG INFOCOMM U.S.A.
See LG ELECTRONICS MOBILECOMM USA INC

LG SEED
See AGRELIANT GENETICS LLC

D-U-N-S 62-110-1484 IMP
■ **LG&E AND KU ENERGY LLC**
(*Suby of* PPL CORP) ★
220 W Main St Ste 1400, Louisville, KY 40202-5301
Tel (502) 627-2000 *Founded/Ownrshp* 2010
Sales 3.1MMM *EMP* 3,482
Accts Ernst & Young Llp Louisville
SIC 4911 4931 4932 4924 Generation, electric power; Transmission, electric power; Distribution, electric power; Electric & other services combined; Gas & other services combined; Natural gas distribution
Ch Bd: Victor A Staffieri
CFO: Kent W Blake
Sr VP: Paula Pottinger
VP: Laura Douglas
VP: George Siemens
Prgrm Mgr: Michelle Lynch
Dept Mgr: Lesley Pienaar
CIO: Charles Ransdell
IT Man: Anthony Hall
IT Man: Matthew Littlefield
IT Man: Robert Rose
Board of Directors: S Bradford Rives, Vincent Sorgi, William H Spence, Paul W Thompson

D-U-N-S 00-610-3696
■ **LG&E AND KU SERVICES CO** (KY)
(*Suby of* LG&E AND KU ENERGY LLC) ★
220 W Main St Ste 1400, Louisville, KY 40202-5301
Tel (502) 627-2000 *Founded/Ownrshp* 2000
Sales 904.7MM^E *EMP* 1,000^E
SIC 4911 Electric services
CEO: Victor Staffieri
**CFO:* Kent Blake
**Treas:* Dan Arbough
Dir Bus: Douglas Schetzel
Prgrm Mgr: Shirley Campbell
Dir IT: Kathy Butler

D-U-N-S 17-477-6273
LGD MANAGEMENT LP
608 Sandau Rd, San Antonio, TX 78216-4131
Tel (210) 564-0100 *Founded/Ownrshp* 2005
Sales 11.5MM^E *EMP* 2,300
SIC 8741 Management services
Prin: Dave Sheffield

D-U-N-S 18-865-1327
LGE ELECTRICAL SALES INC
INDEPENDENT PWR SYSTEMS & LGE
(*Suby of* INDEPENDENT ELECTRIC SUPPLY INC) ★
650 University Ave # 218, Sacramento, CA 95825-6726
Tel (916) 563-2737 *Founded/Ownrshp* 1994
Sales 97.1MM^E *EMP* 325
SIC 5063 Electrical apparatus & equipment
Pr: Gerald W Gierke
**Sec:* Raymond G Landgraf
**VP:* David E Evans
Sales Asso: Mike McQuiddy

LGH
See LANCASTER GENERAL HOSPITAL

LGH
See LAFAYETTE GENERAL HEALTH SYSTEM INC

D-U-N-S 14-412-5945
LGH CHARITABLE TRUST INC
1 General St, Lawrence, MA 01841-2961
Tel (978) 683-4000 *Founded/Ownrshp* 1985
Sales 203.7MM^E *EMP* 1,405
SIC 8082 Home health care services
Pr: Dianne J Anderson
**Pr:* Joseph S McManus
**COO:* Gerard Foley
**CFO:* Robert B Tremblay
CFO: Robert B Tremlay
**VP:* Denise Palumbo
Doctor: Peter Cole

LGI
See LUIS GARRATON INC

D-U-N-S 07-912-8694
▲ **LGI HOMES INC**
1450 Lake Robbins Dr # 430, The Woodlands, TX 77380-3294
Tel (281) 362-8998 *Founded/Ownrshp* 2003
Sales 630.2MM *EMP* 489
Tkr Sym LGIH *Exch* NGS
SIC 1531 Operative builders; Speculative builder, single-family houses
Ch Bd: Eric T Lipar
Pr: Michael Snider
CFO: Charles Merdian
Chf Mktg O: Rachel Eaton
Ofcr: Margaret Britton
Ex VP: Jack Lipar
Board of Directors: Ryan Edone, Duncan Gage, Bryan Sansbury, Steven Smith, Robert Vaharadian

D-U-N-S 00-976-0948
LGI INTERNATIONAL INC
(*Suby of* LIBERTY GLOBAL INC) ★
12300 Liberty Blvd, Englewood, CO 80112-7009
Tel (720) 875-5800 *Founded/Ownrshp* 2013
Sales 289.8MM^E *EMP* 1,510
SIC 4841 Cable television services
Ch Bd: John C Malone
**Treas:* Graham Hollis
**V Ch Bd:* Robert Bennett
**Sr VP:* Miranda Curtis
**Sr VP:* Bernard Dvorak
**Sr VP:* David Koff
**Sr VP:* David Leonard

D-U-N-S 03-127-8844
LGL RECYCLING LLC (FL)
2401 Pga Blvd, Palm Beach Gardens, FL 33410-3590
Tel (561) 582-6688 *Founded/Ownrshp* 2000
Sales 110.3MM^E *EMP* 185
Accts Divine Blalock Martin Sellari
SIC 4953 Recycling, waste materials
CEO: Charles Gusmano

LGS
See LITTLE GENERAL STORE INC

D-U-N-S 78-943-4953
LGS INNOVATIONS LLC
13665 Dulles Technology D, Herndon, VA 20171-4639
Tel (866) 547-4243 *Founded/Ownrshp* 2006
Sales 247.5MM^E *EMP* 650
SIC 4813 Telephone communication, except radio
CEO: Kevin L Kelly
**Pr:* Edward M Eldridge Jr
**CFO:* Debra Pfaff
**Treas:* Michael Slane
**Sr VP:* Daniel Bigbie
**VP:* Robert Farr
**VP:* John Fitzgerald
**CIO:* Richard Martin
**Genl Couns:* Michael D Garson

D-U-N-S 62-098-6042 IMP/EXP
LGS SPECIALTY SALES LTD
1 Radisson Plz Fl 10, New Rochelle, NY 10801-5767
Tel (718) 542-2200 *Founded/Ownrshp* 1990
Sales 156.2MM *EMP* 15
Accts Rogoff & Company Pc New York
SIC 5141 5148 Food brokers; Fresh fruits & vegetables
Pr: Luke Sears

LH
See LIQUIDHUB INC

D-U-N-S 01-038-6472
▲ **LHC GROUP INC**
901 Hugh Wallis Rd S, Lafayette, LA 70508-2511
Tel (337) 233-1307 *Founded/Ownrshp* 1994
Sales 816.3MM *EMP* 10,922
Tkr Sym LHCG *Exch* NGS
SIC 8082 8322 Home health care services; Rehabilitation services
Ch Bd: Keith G Myers
Pr: Donald D Stelly
CFO: Joshua L Proffitt
Ofcr: Melynda Boothe
VP: Chris Gill
VP: Marcus D Macip
Off Mgr: Marty Bacon
Nrsg Dir: Sherry Cameron
Board of Directors: Dan S Wilford, Monica F Azare, John B Breaux, John L Indest, George A Lewis, Ronald T Nixon, Christopher S Shackelton, Wilbert J Tauzin, Kenneth E Thorpe, Brent Turner

D-U-N-S 07-104-5397 IMP
LHH CORP
LENOX HILL HOSPITAL
(*Suby of* NSLIJ) ★
100 E 77th St, New York, NY 10075-1850
Tel (212) 434-2000 *Founded/Ownrshp* 2010
Sales 790.5MM *EMP* 2,955
SIC 8062 General medical & surgical hospitals
Ex Dir: Franck Danza
VP: John Connolly
Assoc Dir: Maxine Cenac
Dir Rad: Kristin Byrne
Dir Rx: Paul Nowierski
Adm Dir: Ann Oswald
Prgrm Mgr: Janice Coleman
Nurse Mgr: Novella Mikhaylov
MIS Dir: Robert Dulak

IT Man: Nicole Dichiara
IT Man: Dimitry Frivel

LHI
See LOGISTICS HEALTH INC

LHM GROUP
See LARRY H MILLER GROUP OF COMPANIES

D-U-N-S 15-154-9649 IMP
LHOIST NORTH AMERICA INC
(*Suby of* LIME HOLDING INC) ★
3700 Hulen St, Fort Worth, TX 76107-6816
Tel (817) 732-8164 *Founded/Ownrshp* 1985
Sales 483.1MM^E *EMP* 450
SIC 3274

D-U-N-S 03-483-0794 IMP
LHOIST NORTH AMERICA OF TENNESSEE INC
EAST REGIONAL OFFICE
(*Suby of* LHOIST NORTH AMERICA INC) ★
750 Old Hickory Blvd 200-2, Brentwood, TN 37027-4592
Tel (615) 259-4222 *Founded/Ownrshp* 2006
Sales 201.9MM^E *EMP* 250
SIC 1422 Crushed & broken limestone
CEO: Ludwig De Mot
VP: Jim West

D-U-N-S 80-541-0953
LHP HOSPITAL GROUP INC
2400 Dallas Pkwy Ste 450, Plano, TX 75093-4373
Tel (972) 943-1700 *Founded/Ownrshp* 2008
Sales 228.8MM^E *EMP* 1,210^E
SIC 8062 General medical & surgical hospitals
CEO: John F Holland
CFO: John Abreu
CFO: John W Ehrie
CFO: David Nosacka
Div Pres: Paul A Kappelman
Ex VP: Rebecca Hurley
Ex VP: Jim Shannon
Sr VP: Larry Schunder
Sr VP: Timothy Wons
VP: Patricia Ball
VP: Ed Davidson
VP: Edward T Davidson Jr
VP: Edward Davidson
VP: Don Fentem
VP: Lonnie Garrison
VP: Andrew Montgomery
VP: Shane Olivier
VP: Brian Padgett
VP: Maureen Potter
Board of Directors: Frederick A Hessler

LI-COR BIO SCIENCES
See LI-COR INC

D-U-N-S 06-223-7961
LI-COR INC
LI-COR BIO SCIENCES
4647 Superior St, Lincoln, NE 68504-1357
Tel (402) 467-3576 *Founded/Ownrshp* 1971
Sales 100.0MM^E *EMP* 335^E
SIC 3826 Analytical instruments
Pr: William W Biggs
Treas: Craig A Jessen
Sr VP: Lyle Middendorf
VP: Greg Biggs
VP: Dan Hile
VP: Dr Mike Olive
VP: Kerry Petersen
Software D: Thad Meyer
Mfg Dir: Mark Kurtenbach

D-U-N-S 83-985-7344
LIAISON TECHNOLOGIES INC
3157 Royal Dr Ste 200, Alpharetta, GA 30022-2484
Tel (770) 642-5000 *Founded/Ownrshp* 2000
Sales 137.1MM^E *EMP* 328
SIC 7373 Systems integration services
CEO: Robert A Renner
Pr: Sanjiv Bhalodai
CFO: Larry Mieldezis
Ofcr: Rob Consoli
Ofcr: Manish Gupta
Ofcr: Hmong Vang
Ex VP: Bruce Chen
Ex VP: Jaymie Forrest
Sr VP: Peter Rodenhauser
VP: Barry Nelson
Off Mgr: Deb Waid
Board of Directors: Jon Duke, Clark Golestani

D-U-N-S 15-284-5202 IMP/EXP
■ **LIBBEY GLASS INC**
(*Suby of* LIBBEY INC) ★
300 Madison Ave Fl 4, Toledo, OH 43604-2634
Tel (419) 325-2100 *Founded/Ownrshp* 1993
Sales 523.8MM^E *EMP* 2,172
SIC 3229 3231 Tableware, glass or glass ceramic; Products of purchased glass
Ex VP: Richard Reynolds
**Treas:* Ken Boerger
VP: L Frederick Ashton
**VP:* Daniel P Ibele
**VP:* Susan A Kovach
VP: Timothy T Paige
VP: John A Zarb
MIS Dir: Dave Johnson
Board of Directors: Carlos V Duno, William A Foley, Peter C McC Howell, Deborah G Miller, Carol B Moerdyk, John C Orr, Terence P Stewart

D-U-N-S 80-598-3335 EXP
▲ **LIBBEY INC**
300 Madison Ave, Toledo, OH 43604-1561
Tel (419) 325-2100 *Founded/Ownrshp* 1888
Sales 825.2MM *EMP* 6,543
Tkr Sym LBY *Exch* ASE
SIC 3229 3262 Glass furnishings & accessories; Tableware, glass or glass ceramic; Bowls, glass; Ashtrays, glass; Tableware, vitreous china
Ch Bd: William A Foley
CFO: Sherry L Buck
Treas: Gary Doner
Ofcr: Annunciata Cerioli
VP: Kenneth A Boerger
VP: Antoine Jordans
VP: Jeff Joyce
VP: Susan A Kovach
VP: Timothy Paige
VP: Karen Startzman
VP: Salvador Minarro Villalobos
Board of Directors: Carlos V Duno, Ginger M Jones, Theo Killion, Eileen A Mallesch, Deborah G Miller, Carol B Moerdyk, John C Orr

D-U-N-S 08-742-6268
LIBERAL SCHOOL DISTRICT
401 N Kansas Ave, Liberal, KS 67901-3329
Tel (620) 604-1010 *Founded/Ownrshp* 1964
Sales 221.4MM *EMP* 700
Accts Byron Bird & Associates Chtd
SIC 8211 Public elementary & secondary schools; High school, junior or senior; Vocational high school
IT Man: Kayla James
Pr Dir: Jason McAfee
Psych: Mary Hall
HC Dir: Michelle Hay

D-U-N-S 05-645-1214
LIBERMAN BROADCASTING INC
1845 W Empire Ave, Burbank, CA 91504-3402
Tel (818) 729-5300 *Founded/Ownrshp* 1988
Sales 265.0MM^E *EMP* 830
SIC 4832 Radio broadcasting stations
CEO: Lenard D Liberman
**Pr:* Jose Liberman
**CFO:* Frederic T Boyer
**VP:* Winter Horton
**VP:* Eduardo Leon
**VP:* Blima Tuller
Exec: Bill Garcia
Dir IT: Fernando Rodriguez
Natl Sales: Benny Herzog
Natl Sales: Albert Hoot
Natl Sales: Mark Whitt

D-U-N-S 07-832-6764 IMP
LIBERTAS COPPER LLC
HUSSEY COPPER
100 Washington St, Leetsdale, PA 15056-1000
Tel (724) 251-4200 *Founded/Ownrshp* 1848, 2011
Sales 266.7MM^E *EMP* 575
SIC 3366 3351 Copper foundries; Copper rolling & drawing
CEO: John Harrington
**CFO:* Brian Benjamin

D-U-N-S 02-704-0443 EXP
LIBERTO SPECIALTY CO INC
RICOS PRODUCTS
830 S Presa St, San Antonio, TX 78210-1375
Tel (210) 222-1415 *Founded/Ownrshp* 1909
Sales 87.0MM^E *EMP* 140
SIC 5046 5145 Commercial cooking & food service equipment; Confectionery
CEO: Frank G Liberto
**Pr:* Tony Liberto
CFO: Jeremy Poledge
**CFO:* Jeremy Powledge
Creative D: Michelle Scott

D-U-N-S 13-157-5961
LIBERTY 53 SCHOOL DISTRICT
LIBERTY PUBLIC SCHOOL
8 Victory Ln Ste 100, Liberty, MO 64068-2371
Tel (816) 736-5300 *Founded/Ownrshp* 1885
Sales 157.5MM *EMP* 2,200
Accts Westbrook & Co Pc Richmon
SIC 8211 Public combined elementary & secondary school
**CFO:* Carol Embree
Dir Sec: Gary Majors
MIS Dir: Trey Katzer
Pr Dir: Eleen Stewart
HC Dir: Kathy Ellermeier

D-U-N-S 00-691-7579
LIBERTY BANK
315 Main St, Middletown, CT 06457-3338
Tel (860) 344-7200 *Founded/Ownrshp* 1825
Sales NA *EMP* 512
SIC 6036 6163 6022 Savings institutions, not federally chartered; Loan brokers; State commercial banks
Pr: Chandler J Howard
COO: Robin Fujio
CFO: Thomas J Pastorello
Ofcr: Gerard M Kusinski
Ex VP: Deborah C Bochain
Ex VP: Ronald J Catrone
Ex VP: Robert Parry
Sr VP: Barry J Abramowitz
Sr VP: Stephen Barlow
Sr VP: Patricia D Jatkevicius
Sr VP: Don Peruta
VP: Thomas A Ballachino
VP: Thomas Ballachino
VP: Glenn Davis
VP: Damaris Garcia
VP: Brian Hedge
VP: Maryann Lentz
VP: Leslie McKillip
VP: Sue Murphy
VP: Anthony Rosado
VP: John Taylor
Board of Directors: Michael Helfgott, David E A Carson, Grace Sawyer Jones, David G Carter, Lawrence McHugh, William T Christopher, Timothy Ryan, Jean M D'aquila, Richard W Tomc, David Director, Mark R Gingras, Winona S Goings, Gary Gomola, Steve J Gorss

D-U-N-S 03-633-3482
LIBERTY BANK
318 E Main St, Siloam Springs, AR 72761-3232
Tel (479) 524-8101 *Founded/Ownrshp* 1960
Sales NA *EMP* 60
SIC 6022 State commercial banks
Pr: Art Morris
Board of Directors: D E Allen Jr, Roderick Allen, Robert Brown, Hank Harrison, Charles Jones, Mark Simmons, Dr Duane Thomas

D-U-N-S 01-463-9389 IMP/EXP
■ **LIBERTY BELL EQUIPMENT CORP**
MEDCO
(*Suby of* MICROUNITED DIVISION) ★
3201 S 76th St, Philadelphia, PA 19153-3215
Tel (215) 492-6700 *Founded/Ownrshp* 2014
Sales 220.3MM^E *EMP* 165^E
SIC 5013 Automobile service station equipment; Tools & equipment, automotive; Body repair or paint shop supplies, automotive
Pr: Andrew A Keim
**Sec:* Don Bernhardt
Area Mgr: Aj Eppler
Dir IT: Eric Stern
Natl Sales: Michael Ferris
Sls Mgr: Joseph Regan
Sales Asso: David Becerra
Sales Asso: Rick Victory
Snr Mgr: Christine Carratello

D-U-N-S 07-955-9539
LIBERTY BROADBAND CORP
12300 Liberty Blvd, Englewood, CO 80112-7009
Tel (720) 875-5700 *Founded/Ownrshp* 2014
Sales 91.1MM *EMP* 23,900
Tkr Sym LBRDK *Exch* NGS
SIC 4841 4899 Cable & other pay television services; Closed circuit television services; Data communication services
Pr: Gregory B Maffei
**Ch Bd:* John C Malone
CFO: Mark D Carleton
Board of Directors: Richard R Green, J David Wargo, John E Welsh III

D-U-N-S 61-437-3822 IMP
LIBERTY CABLEVISION OF PUERTO RICO LLC
(*Suby of* LIBERTY GLOBAL INC) ★
Urb Indl Tres Monjitas 1, San Juan, PR 00918
Tel (787) 766-0909 *Founded/Ownrshp* 2012
Sales 121.3MM^E *EMP* 350^E
SIC 4841 Cable television services
CEO: Ron Dorchester
**CFO:* Jorge Hernandez

D-U-N-S 79-339-8728 IMP
LIBERTY CABLEVISION OF PUERTO RICO LLC
Urb Industrial Tres Monj, San Juan, PR 00919
Tel (787) 657-3050 *Founded/Ownrshp* 2005
Sales NA *EMP* 1,500
SIC 4841

D-U-N-S 00-647-8234 IMP
LIBERTY CARTON CO (MN)
(*Suby of* LIBERTY DIVERSIFIED INTERNATIONAL INC) ★
870 Louisiana Ave S, Golden Valley, MN 55426-1672
Tel (763) 540-9600 *Founded/Ownrshp* 1932
Sales 196.0MM^E *EMP* 1,000
SIC 2653 Boxes, corrugated: made from purchased materials; Display items, corrugated: made from purchased materials
Ch Bd: Michael Fiterman
**COO:* Daniel Zdon
**CFO:* Byron Wieberdink
**Ex VP:* David Lenzen
**VP:* Ronda Bayer
**VP:* Michael Snowball

D-U-N-S 04-493-5542
LIBERTY CORP
(*Suby of* RAYCOM MEDIA INC) ★
135 S Main St Ste 1000, Greenville, SC 29601-2781
Tel (864) 609-8111 *Founded/Ownrshp* 2005
Sales 71.2MM^E *EMP* 1,400
SIC 4833 Television broadcasting stations
Ch Bd: W Hayne Hipp
**Pr:* James M Keelor
**CFO:* Howard L Schrott
Bd of Dir: John H Mullin
Bd of Dir: Eugene E Stone
VP: David Black
**VP:* Martha G Williams
Off Admin: Kay Oken
Netwrk Mgr: Kevin Flynn

D-U-N-S 10-064-6173
LIBERTY COUNTY BOARD OF EDUCATION
200 Bradwell St, Hinesville, GA 31313-2706
Tel (912) 876-2162 *Founded/Ownrshp* 1900
Sales 101.7MM *EMP* 1,800
Accts Greg S Griffin State Auditor
SIC 8211 School board
Ch Bd: Lily Baker
Ex Dir: Mindy Yanzetich
Netwrk Eng: Annette Roberts

D-U-N-S 07-979-9718
LIBERTY COUNTY SCHOOL SYSTEM
200 Bradwell St, Hinesville, GA 31313-2706
Tel (912) 876-2161 *Founded/Ownrshp* 2015
Sales 14.7MM^E *EMP* 1,633^E
SIC 8211 Public elementary & secondary schools
Pr Dir: Patricia Crane
Teacher Pr: Michele Dasher
HC Dir: Mary Alexander

D-U-N-S 78-086-4406
LIBERTY DENTAL PLAN OF CALIFORNIA INC
340 Commerce Ste 100, Irvine, CA 92602-1358
Tel (949) 223-0007 *Founded/Ownrshp* 2001
Sales NA *EMP* 300
SIC 6324 Dental insurance
**CFO:* Maja Kapic
Ex VP: John Carvelli
Sls Dir: Kia Hussain

D-U-N-S 06-145-6489 IMP/EXP
LIBERTY DIVERSIFIED INTERNATIONAL INC
5600 Highway 169 N, New Hope, MN 55428-3096
Tel (763) 536-6600 *Founded/Ownrshp* 1972
Sales 652.6MM^E *EMP* 1,820
SIC 2653 2631 5112 2542 3089 5961 Boxes, corrugated: made from purchased materials; Paperboard mills; Stationery & office supplies; Fixtures, office: except wood; Fixtures, store: except wood; Partitions for floor attachment, prefabricated: except wood; Shelving, office & store: except wood; Plastic containers, except foam; Plastic kitchenware, tableware & houseware; Plastic processing; Injection molding of plastics; Mail order house
Ch Bd: Michael Fiterman
**Pr:* Mark S Schumacher
**CFO:* Byron Wieberdink
CFO: Byron Wiedredink
**Ex VP:* David Lenzen
**VP:* Ronda Bayer
**VP:* Sally Bredehoft
**VP:* Michael Snowball
Genl Mgr: Todd Gardner
CIO: Alla Johnson

D-U-N-S 07-851-5476
LIBERTY ENERGY UTILITIES (NEW HAMPSHIRE) CORP
LIBERTY UTILITIES
(*Suby of* LIBERTY UTILITIES CO) ★
15 Buttrick Rd, Londonderry, NH 03053-3305
Tel (905) 287-2061 *Founded/Ownrshp* 2011
Sales 340.6MM^E *EMP* 655^E
SIC 1311 Crude petroleum & natural gas
Pr: Victor Del Vecchio
VP: Chris Thompson
Genl Mgr: Lester Melton
Opers Mgr: Deon Scott
Snr Mgr: Joel Ames

D-U-N-S 80-145-3577
■ **LIBERTY ENTERTAINMENT INC**
(*Suby of* DIRECTV GROUP HOLDINGS LLC) ★
2230 E Imperial Hwy, El Segundo, CA 90245-3504
Tel (310) 964-5000 *Founded/Ownrshp* 2009
Sales 98.7MM^E *EMP* 1,071^E
SIC 4841 Cable & other pay television services

D-U-N-S 05-407-6583 IMP
LIBERTY FRUIT CO INC
1247 Argentine Blvd, Kansas City, KS 66105-1508
Tel (913) 238-4606 *Founded/Ownrshp* 1965
Sales 113.6MM^E *EMP* 351
Accts Mayer Hoffman Mccann Pc Le
SIC 5148 Fruits, fresh; Vegetables, fresh
CEO: Arnold Caviar
**Pr:* Allen Caviar
**Ex VP:* Reade Sievert
VP: Michael Logan
Exec: David Smith
CIO: Cory Caviar
**VP Opers:* Mike Logan
Ql Cn Mgr: Ana Deshpande

D-U-N-S 78-463-3906
LIBERTY GLOBAL INC
(*Suby of* LIBERTY GLOBAL PLC)
1550 Wewatta St Ste 1000, Denver, CO 80202-6300
Tel (303) 220-6600 *Founded/Ownrshp* 1999
Sales 4.9MMM^E *EMP* 22,000^E
SIC 4841 4813 Cable & other pay television services;
Pr: Michael T Fries
COO: John Riley
CFO: Charles H R Bracken
Ex VP: Bernard G Dvorak
Ex VP: Bryan H Hall
Ex VP: Bryan Hall
Sr VP: Amy M Blair
Sr VP: Graham King
Sr VP: Elizabeth Markowski
Sr VP: Albert Rosenthaler
Sr VP: Jim Ryan
Sr VP: Andrea Salvato
Sr VP: Rick Westerman
VP: Richard Abbott
VP: Pamela Coe
VP: Phil Colby
VP: Terry Davis
VP: John Gowen
VP: Wade Haufschild
VP: Jim Jewell
VP: Bob Leighton

D-U-N-S 94-930-4430
LIBERTY HAMPSHIRE CO LLC
(*Suby of* GUGGENHEIM PARTNERS LLC) ★
227 W Monroe St, Chicago, IL 60606-5055
Tel (312) 827-0100 *Founded/Ownrshp* 2011
Sales NA *EMP* 535^E
SIC 6141 Personal credit institutions
Pt: Thomas Irvin
CIO: Sean P Connelly
Dir IT: Louis Celiberti

D-U-N-S 00-134-3870 IMP/EXP
■ **LIBERTY HARDWARE MFG CORP**
(*Suby of* MASCO CORP) ★
140 Business Park Dr, Winston Salem, NC 27107-6539
Tel (336) 769-4077 *Founded/Ownrshp* 1942, 1997
Sales 379.9MM^E *EMP* 393
SIC 5072 Hardware
Pr: Rick Roetken
**CFO:* Mark Stull
VP: Robert Buck
**VP:* Ronnie Murray
Comm Dir: Chris Lemnios
Web Dev: Steven Tisdale
Natl Sales: Brooke Taylor
VP Mktg: Gail Jacobson
VP Mktg: Dianne Pisarek
Mktg Dir: Dax Allen
Sls Mgr: Daniel Shore
Board of Directors: Rick Roetken

D-U-N-S 14-244-9771
■ **LIBERTY HEALTHCARE GROUP INC**
LIBERTY MEDICAL SUPPLY
(*Suby of* POLYMEDICA CORPORATION)
8881 Liberty Ln, Port Saint Lucie, FL 34952-3477
Tel (772) 398-7257 *Founded/Ownrshp* 1997
Sales 71.8MM^E *EMP* 2,037
SIC 5961 Pharmaceuticals, mail order
Pr: Joan Dp Kennedy
Pr: Harvey Frank A

Pr: Frank A Harvey
Pr: Bob Mark
COO: Peter McKenzie
COO: Arlene Rodriguez
CFO: Johnathan Star
Treas: Peter Gaylord
VP: Marc Lamrouex
VP: Henrik Sandell
Exec: Devin Anderson

D-U-N-S 78-733-6817
LIBERTY HEALTHCARE SYSTEM INC
LIBERTYHEALTH
(*Suby of* SAINT BARNABAS HEALTH CARE SYS) ★
355 Grand St, Jersey City, NJ 07302-4321
Tel (318) 251-9458 *Founded/Ownrshp* 2014
Sales 379.2MM[E] *EMP* 2,600
SIC 8062 General medical & surgical hospitals
CEO: Stephen Kirby
**Pr:* Joseph F Scott
VP: Kirat Kharode
Ex Dir: Bill Cook
Prgrm Mgr: Jenna Whiteside
CIO: Arne Larsen
VP Opers: Sue Smith
Sfty Dirs: Marcel Sanchez

D-U-N-S 82-812-5463
LIBERTY HOMECARE GROUP LLC
2334 S 41st St, Wilmington, NC 28403-5502
Tel (910) 815-3122 *Founded/Ownrshp* 2002
Sales 30.4MM[E] *EMP* 3,500
SIC 8082 Home health care services
CFO: Joe Calcutt

D-U-N-S 15-518-3924
LIBERTY INSURANCE CORP
(*Suby of* LIBERTY MUTUAL HOLDING CORP) ★
175 Berkeley St, Boston, MA 02116-5066
Tel (617) 357-9500 *Founded/Ownrshp* 1983
Sales NA *EMP* 15
SIC 6331 Fire, marine & casualty insurance; Property damage insurance
Pr: Edmund Francis Kelly
**Treas:* Julianna Coyle

D-U-N-S 79-065-7378
▲ LIBERTY INTERACTIVE CORP
12300 Liberty Blvd, Englewood, CO 80112-7009
Tel (720) 875-5300 *Founded/Ownrshp* 1991
Sales 9.9MMM *EMP* 22,080
Tkr Sym QVCA *Exch* NGS
SIC 4841 5961 Cable & other pay television services; Television, home shopping
Pr: Gregory B Maffei
**Ch Bd:* John C Malone
CFO: Mark D Carleton
CFO: Christopher W Shean
Ofcr: Albert E Rosenthaler
Board of Directors: Richard N Barton, Michael A George, M Ian G Gilchrist, Evan D Malone, David E Rapley, M Lavoy Robison, Larry E Romrell, Mark V Vadon, Andrea L Wong

D-U-N-S 87-481-9428 IMP/EXP
■ LIBERTY INTERACTIVE LLC
(*Suby of* LIBERTY INTERACTIVE CORP) ★
12300 Liberty Blvd, Englewood, CO 80112-7009
Tel (720) 875-5400 *Founded/Ownrshp* 1994
Sales 8.7MMM[E] *EMP* 22,000
SIC 5961 4841 7819 4813 Television, home shopping; Cable & other pay television services; Services allied to motion pictures; Telephone communication, except radio
Pr: Gregory B Maffei
**CFO:* Christopher W Shean

D-U-N-S 84-742-7960
LIBERTY INTERNATIONAL HOLDINGS INC
(*Suby of* LIBERTY MUTUAL HOLDING CO INC) ★
175 Berkeley St, Boston, MA 02116-5066
Tel (617) 357-9500 *Founded/Ownrshp* 1994
Sales NA *EMP* 3,684
SIC 6331 Fire, marine & casualty insurance
Pr: David Long
**Ch Bd:* Thomas Ramey
**CFO:* Paul Condrin
IT Man: Jennifer Fernald
Board of Directors: Gary L Countryman, Robert Gruhl, Edmond Kelly, Chris Mansfield, Stewart Steffey

D-U-N-S 01-336-6260
LIBERTY INTERNATIONAL UNDERWRITERS USA
LIBERTY INTL UNDERWRITERS USA
(*Suby of* LIBERTY MUTUAL INSURANCE CO) ★
55 Water St Fl 23, New York, NY 10041-0024
Tel (212) 208-4100 *Founded/Ownrshp* 1811, 1999
Sales NA *EMP* 450
SIC 6331 Fire, marine & casualty insurance
Pr: David Cohen
Pr: Tommy Laurendine
CFO: Nick Creatura
**Ofcr:* Michael Finnegan
Ofcr: Colleen Lyons
**Ofcr:* Jessica Rogin
Sr VP: William Bell
Sr VP: Diana Cossetti
Sr VP: Richard J Kirnbauer
Sr VP: Jane McCarthy
Sr VP: Rick Niehaus
Sr VP: Mike Nukk
VP: Phyllis Barone
VP: Keith Brennan
VP: Robert Capicchioni
VP: Richard Falcinelli
VP: Tony Glenn
VP: Hugh Gormley
VP: Richard Kirnbauer
VP: Robert Maier
VP: Paul V Meer

LIBERTY INTL UNDERWRITERS USA
See LIBERTY INTERNATIONAL UNDERWRITERS USA

D-U-N-S 07-865-9157
▲ LIBERTY MEDIA CORP
12300 Liberty Blvd, Englewood, CO 80112-7009
Tel (720) 875-5400 *Founded/Ownrshp* 2011
Sales 4.8MMM *EMP* 3,503
Tkr Sym LMCA *Exch* NGS
SIC 4841 Cable & other pay television services
Pr: Gregory B Maffei
**Ch Bd:* John C Malone
CFO: Mark D Carleton
CFO: Christopher W Shean
VP: Randy Lazzell
CTO: Albert E Rosenthaler
Snr Mgr: Roger Mortensen
Board of Directors: Robert R Bennett, Brian M Deevy, M Ian G Gilchrist, Evan D Malone, David E Rapley, Larry E Romrell, Andrea L Wong

LIBERTY MEDICAL SUPPLY
See LIBERTY HEALTHCARE GROUP INC

LIBERTY MUTUAL
See EMPLOYERS INSURANCE OF WAUSAU A MUTUAL CO

LIBERTY MUTUAL
See HELMSMAN MANAGEMENT SERVICES LLC

LIBERTY MUTUAL AGENCY MARKETS
See LIBERTY-USA CORP

D-U-N-S 00-695-2527
LIBERTY MUTUAL FIRE INSURANCE CO INC
(*Suby of* LIBERTY MUTUAL GROUP INC) ★
175 Berkeley St, Boston, MA 02116-5066
Tel (617) 357-9500 *Founded/Ownrshp* 1908
Sales NA *EMP* 1,503
SIC 6331 Fire, marine & casualty insurance
Ch Bd: Gary L Countryman
**Pr:* Edmund F Kelly
**CFO:* J Paul Chondrin
CFO: James Condrin
Sr VP: Christopher C Mansfield

D-U-N-S 10-834-9981
LIBERTY MUTUAL GROUP INC
(*Suby of* LMHC MASSACHUSETTS HOLDINGS INC) ★
175 Berkeley St, Boston, MA 02116-5066
Tel (617) 357-9500 *Founded/Ownrshp* 2001
Sales NA *EMP* 50,000
SIC 6331 6321 6351 7389 Fire, marine & casualty insurance; Workers' compensation insurance; Automobile insurance; Burglary & theft insurance; Accident insurance carriers; Health insurance carriers; Reinsurance carriers, accident & health; Liability insurance; Fidelity or surety bonding; Fidelity responsibility insurance; Financial services
Ch Bd: Edmund F Kelly
**Pr:* David H Long
Pr: Timothy Zepnick
COO: Kirk Maddern
**Treas:* Laurance H S Yahia
Dir Risk M: John McCabe
Genl Mgr: Martin Bourlot
IT Man: Denise Riopel
Opers Mgr: Todd Reimer
Sls Dir: John Lemire
Sls Mgr: Carrie Ragle

D-U-N-S 06-721-5793 IMP/EXP
LIBERTY MUTUAL HOLDING CO INC
175 Berkeley St, Boston, MA 02116-5066
Tel (617) 357-9500 *Founded/Ownrshp* 2001
Sales NA *EMP* 50,000
Accts Ernst & Young Llp Boston Ma
SIC 6331 6351 7389 Fire, marine & casualty insurance; Workers' compensation insurance; Automobile insurance; Burglary & theft insurance; Surety insurance; Liability insurance; Financial services
Pr: David H Long
**Ch Bd:* Edmund F Kelly
COO: James M Hinchley
**CFO:* Dennis J Langwell
CFO: Thomas Obrien
**Treas:* Laurance H S Yahia
Assoc VP: Lijia Guo
Ex VP: Mark A Butler
**Ex VP:* J Paul Condrin III
Ex VP: William Gourley
Ex VP: John Oconnell
Ex VP: Laurie Peterson
Ex VP: Daniel Rioux
Ex VP: Paul A Rodliff
Sr VP: Edward J Gramer
**Sr VP:* Christopher C Mansfield
Sr VP: James M McGlennon
Sr VP: Thomas Moylan
Sr VP: Robert T Muleski
Sr VP: Ram Ramkalawan
Sr VP: Helen E Sayles
Board of Directors: Thomas J May, Michael J Babcock, Stephen F Page, Gary C Butler, Ellen A Rudnick, Charles I Clough Jr, Martin P Slark, Gary L Countryman, William C Van Faasen, Nicholas M Donofrio, Annette M Verschuren, Francis A Doyle III, John P Hamill, Marian L Heard, John P Manning

D-U-N-S 78-770-4162
LIBERTY MUTUAL HOLDING CORP
(*Suby of* LIBERTY MUTUAL INSURANCE CO) ★
175 Berkeley St, Boston, MA 02116-5066
Tel (617) 357-9500 *Founded/Ownrshp* 1999
Sales NA *EMP* 250
SIC 6331 Fire, marine & casualty insurance
Pr: Edmund Kelly

D-U-N-S 00-695-2535 IMP/EXP
LIBERTY MUTUAL INSURANCE CO
(*Suby of* LIBERTY MUTUAL GROUP INC) ★
175 Berkeley St, Boston, MA 02116-5066
Tel (617) 357-9500 *Founded/Ownrshp* 1912
Sales NA *EMP* 50,000
SIC 6331 6321 6351 7389 Fire, marine & casualty insurance; Workers' compensation insurance; Automobile insurance; Burglary & theft insurance; Accident insurance carriers; Health insurance carriers; Reinsurance carriers, accident & health; Liability insurance; Fidelity or surety bonding; Fidelity responsibility insurance; Personal service agents, brokers & bureaus
Pr: David H Long
Pr: Brian Roth
V Ch: Martin Slark
Pr: Constance Bayne
Pr: Francisco Campos
**Pr:* J Paul Condrin III
**Pr:* Christopher L Peirce
Pr: Derek R Sproule
CEO: Fernando Cmbara Lodigiani
CFO: James P Condrin
**CFO:* Dennis J Langwell
CFO: Debra Pooley
Treas: Juliana M Coyle
**Treas:* Laurance Hs Yahia
Bd of Dir: Matthew Coyle
Bd of Dir: Francis Doyle
Bd of Dir: Marian Heard
Bd of Dir: John Manning
Bd of Dir: Annette Verschuren
**Ex VP:* Neeti Bhalla
**Ex VP:* J Eric Brosius

D-U-N-S 96-352-5675
LIBERTY N & R CTR OF MECKLENBURG
3700 Shamrock Dr, Charlotte, NC 28215-3218
Tel (704) 940-8367 *Founded/Ownrshp* 2010
Sales 1.2MMM *EMP* 10[E]
SIC 8051 Skilled nursing care facilities
Prin: Ronald McNeill

D-U-N-S 00-690-0385
■ LIBERTY NATIONAL LIFE INSURANCE CO
(*Suby of* TORCHMARK CORP) ★
100 Cncourse Pkwy Ste 350, Hoover, AL 35244
Tel (205) 325-2722 *Founded/Ownrshp* 1900
Sales NA *EMP* 1,090
SIC 6321 6311 Accident insurance carriers; Life insurance carriers
Pr: Roger Smith
Sr Cor Off: Kenneth Hunt
Sr Cor Off: James Sedgwick
**Chf Mktg O:* Andrew W King
**Ex VP:* Steve Dichiaro
Ex VP: Vurl Duce
**Sr VP:* C Fletcher
Sr VP: Wester A Gray
**Sr VP:* Jack A Kelley Jr
VP: G Burns
VP: Chou H Ceng
**VP:* Chou Hung Cheng
**VP:* John Chou
**VP:* Robert Dobbs
**VP:* West Graves
VP: Michael Hadder
Div/Sub He: Scot Ferguson

D-U-N-S 07-787-2679
LIBERTY NORTHWEST INSURANCE CORP
(*Suby of* LIBERTY MUTUAL INSURANCE CO) ★
650 Ne Holladay St, Portland, OR 97232-2045
Tel (503) 239-5800 *Founded/Ownrshp* 1983
Sales NA *EMP* 950
SIC 6331 Workers' compensation insurance
Pr: Julie Burnett
Ex VP: Matthew Nickerson
**VP:* Mary Augustyn
VP: Mark Backstrom
VP: Tom Becker
VP: James Scott
Software D: Lance Poehler

D-U-N-S 96-950-7206 IMP
LIBERTY OILFIELD SERVICES LLC
950 17th St Ste 2000, Denver, CO 80202-2801
Tel (303) 515-2800 *Founded/Ownrshp* 2011
Sales 500.0MM *EMP* 150
SIC 1382 Oil & gas exploration services
CEO: Scott Tiedgen
Pr: Ron Gusek
**CFO:* Michael Stock

D-U-N-S 15-287-0932 IMP
LIBERTY PACKING CO LLC
MORNING STAR COMPANY THE
724 Main St, Woodland, CA 95695-3491
Tel (209) 826-7100 *Founded/Ownrshp* 2001
Sales 131.8MM[E] *EMP* 120[E]
SIC 5148 Vegetables
Ex Dir: Kim Higgs

D-U-N-S 02-061-9175
LIBERTY PROPERTY LIMITED PARTNERSHIP
(*Suby of* LIBERTY PROPERTY TRUST) ★
500 Chesterfield Pkwy, Malvern, PA 19355-8707
Tel (610) 648-1700 *Founded/Ownrshp* 1994
Sales 808.7MM *EMP* 433
Accts Ernst & Young Llp Philadelphi
SIC 6512 Nonresidential building operators
Ch Bd: William P Hankowsky
Genl Pt: Liberty Property Trust
CFO: George J Alburger Jr
VP: Albert J Kraft III
VP: Anthony Nichols Jr

D-U-N-S 06-571-9254
LIBERTY PROPERTY TRUST
500 Chesterfield Pkwy, Malvern, PA 19355-8707
Tel (610) 648-1700 *Founded/Ownrshp* 1972
Sales 808.7MM *EMP* 384[E]
SIC 6798 Real estate investment trusts
Ch Bd: William P Hankowsky
CFO: Christopher J Papa
Ex VP: Michael T Hagan
Sr VP: James J Mazzarelli
Sr VP: Mary Beth Morrissey
VP: Shelby Christensen
VP: John Gattuso
VP: Chris Herrick
VP: Albert Kraft III
VP: James Maneri
VP: Mary B Morrissey
VP: Jeff Patti
VP: Sue Petruno
VP: Andy Petry
VP: Erin Plourde
VP: Don Schoenheider
VP: Gary Taylor
VP: Chris Warth
VP: Stephen Whitley
Board of Directors: Frederick F Bucholz, Thomas C Deloach Jr, Katherine Elizabeth Dietze, Antonio F Fernandez, Daniel P Garton, M Leanne Lachman, David L Lingerfelt, Frederic J Tomczyk

LIBERTY PUBLIC SCHOOL
See LIBERTY 53 SCHOOL DISTRICT

D-U-N-S 00-213-3445 IMP/EXP
LIBERTY PUMPS INC (NY)
7000 Appletree Ave, Bergen, NY 14416-9446
Tel (800) 543-2550 *Founded/Ownrshp* 1965, 1975
Sales 86.1MM *EMP* 130
Accts Freedmaxick Cpas Pc Buffalo
SIC 3561 Pumps, domestic: water or sump
**CFO:* Dennis Burke
**VP:* Allan Davis
VP: Rebecca Evangelista
VP: Gary Volk
Exec: Randy Waldron
Sfty Dirs: Judith Pfoltzer
Ql Cn Mgr: Mike Schuff
Natl Sales: Chuck Schwabe
Manager: Steve Ritsema
Sls Mgr: John Deluca

D-U-N-S 07-948-6581
■ LIBERTY QVC HOLDING LLC
(*Suby of* LIBERTY INTERACTIVE CORP) ★
12300 Liberty Blvd, Englewood, CO 80112-7009
Tel (484) 701-3777 *Founded/Ownrshp* 2003, 1998
Sales 8.7MMM[E] *EMP* 17,600[E]
SIC 4841 5961 Cable & other pay television services; Television, home shopping
Pr: Gregory B Maffei

D-U-N-S 19-638-1842 IMP
■ LIBERTY SAFE AND SECURITY PRODUCTS INC
(*Suby of* COMPASS DIVERSIFIED HOLDINGS) ★
1199 W Utah Ave, Payson, UT 84651-9749
Tel (801) 925-1000 *Founded/Ownrshp* 1988
Sales 94.6MM[E] *EMP* 350[E]
SIC 3499 Safes & vaults, metal
Pr: Kim Waddoups
**COO:* Steve Allred
**CFO:* Greg Clements
**Ch:* David Heidecorn
Mktg Mgr: Brandon Payne
Sls Mgr: Dan David
Board of Directors: Todd Atkinson

D-U-N-S 07-961-4050
LIBERTY SPAIN INSURANCE GROUP LLC
(*Suby of* LIBERTY MUTUAL HOLDING CO INC) ★
175 Berkeley St, Boston, MA 02116-5066
Tel (617) 357-9500 *Founded/Ownrshp* 2004
Sales NA *EMP* 1,200[E]
SIC 6311 Life insurance

D-U-N-S 07-847-6518
▲ LIBERTY TAX INC
1716 Corp Landing Pkwy, Virginia Beach, VA 23454-5681
Tel (757) 493-8855 *Founded/Ownrshp* 1996
Sales 173.4MM *EMP* 1,332
Tkr Sym TAX *Exch* NGM
SIC 7291 Tax return preparation services
Ch Bd: John T Hewitt
CFO: Kathleen E Donovan
VP: Richard G Artese
VP: Michael S Piper
VP: Vanessa M Szajnoga
Board of Directors: Gordon D'angelo, John R Garel, Thomas Herskovits, Robert M Howard, Steven Ibbotson, Ross N Longfield, Ellen M McDowell, George T Robson

D-U-N-S 96-490-6007
LIBERTY TIRE RECYCLING LLC
1251 Waterfront Pl # 400, Pittsburgh, PA 15222-4261
Tel (412) 562-1700 *Founded/Ownrshp* 2005
Sales 311.4MM[E] *EMP* 1,100[E]
SIC 5093 4953 8744 Scrap & waste materials; Recycling, waste materials;
CEO: Jeffrey D Kendall
**COO:* Thomas Womble
**CFO:* Dale Van Steenberg
**Sr VP:* Ronald B Carlson
Sr VP: Kurt Meyer
VP: Gregory Cummings
VP: Dan Drakulich
VP: Kyle Eastman
VP: Peter Ellis
**VP:* Andrew C Russell
Dir Risk M: Richard Gustashaw

LIBERTY TRAVEL
See FLIGHT CENTRE TRAVEL GROUP (USA) INC

D-U-N-S 07-946-8907
▲ LIBERTY TRIPADVISOR HOLDINGS INC
12300 Liberty Blvd, Englewood, CO 80112-7009
Tel (720) 875-5200 *Founded/Ownrshp* 2013
Sales 1.5MMM *EMP* 3,258[E]
Tkr Sym LTRPB *Exch* NGS
SIC 7374 Data processing & preparation
Ch Bd: Gregory B Maffei
CFO: Brian J Wendling
**Ofcr:* Albert E Rosenthaler

D-U-N-S 06-600-1074
LIBERTY UNIVERSITY INC
1971 University Blvd, Lynchburg, VA 24515-0002
Tel (434) 582-2000 *Founded/Ownrshp* 1972
Sales 988.8MM *EMP* 7,200
Accts Dixon Hughes Goodman Llp Glen
SIC 8221 University
Pr: Jerry Lamon Falwell Jr

*CFO: Don Moon
Assoc VP: Larry Shackleton
*Sr VP: Mark Hine
*VP: Ronald E Hawkins
VP: Barry Moore
VP: Johnnie Moore Jr
Assoc Dir: Sarah Dean
Assoc Dir: Rena Lindevaldsen
Ex Dir: Jay Himes
Off Admin: Andrew Bailey

D-U-N-S 07-942-1883
■ LIBERTY USA HOLDINGS LLC
(Suby of LIBERTY INTERACTIVE CORP) ★
12300 Liberty Blvd, Englewood, CO 80112-7009
Tel (720) 875-5300 Founded/Ownrshp 2007
Sales 7.2MMM^E EMP 18,210
SIC 4841 Cable & other pay television services

D-U-N-S 01-437-2809 IMP
LIBERTY USA INC
VENDOR FRIENDS
920 Irwin Run Rd, West Mifflin, PA 15122-1092
Tel (412) 461-2700 Founded/Ownrshp 1997
Sales 109.5MM^E EMP 100
SIC 5194 5145 5122 5141

LIBERTY UTILITIES
See LIBERTY ENERGY UTILITIES (NEW HAMPSHIRE) CORP

D-U-N-S 83-040-8873
LIBERTY UTILITIES (ENERGYNORTH NATURAL GAS) CORP
ENERGYNORTH NATURAL GAS, INC.
(Suby of LIBERTY UTILITIES) ★
15 Buttrick Rd, Londonderry, NH 03053-3305
Tel (603) 328-2700 Founded/Ownrshp 2012
Sales 165.1MM^E EMP 300
SIC 4924 Natural gas distribution
Pr: Victor Del Vecchio
Genl Mgr: Matthew Minghella
IT Man: Peter Buddell
Opers Mgr: Harold Woods
Counsel: Todd Wiley

D-U-N-S 04-440-0604
LIBERTY UTILITIES (PARK WATER) CORP
(Suby of LIBERTY UTILITIES (CANADA) CORP)
9750 Washburn Rd, Downey, CA 90241-5625
Tel (562) 923-0711 Founded/Ownrshp 2016
Sales 90.9MM^E EMP 146
SIC 4941 Water supply
Pr: Greg Sorensen
*CFO: Chris Alario
Sr VP: Jeanne Marie Bruno
VP: Mary Young
Snr Ntwrk: Timothy Liang
IT Man: Shaival Hora
IT Man: Rick Mayers

D-U-N-S 07-831-3643
LIBERTY UTILITIES CO
(Suby of ALGONQUIN POWER & UTILITIES CORP)
12725 W Indian School Rd, Avondale, AZ 85392-9520
Tel (905) 465-4500 Founded/Ownrshp 2010
Sales 414.6MM^E EMP 658^E
SIC 4939 Combination utilities
Pr: David Pasieka
Opers Supe: Ryan Blattel
Opers Supe: Carol Byars

D-U-N-S 01-327-2620
LIBERTY-EYLAU INDEPENDENT SCHOOL DISTRICT
2901 Leopard Dr, Texarkana, TX 75501-7817
Tel (903) 832-1535 Founded/Ownrshp 1974
Sales 26.7MM EMP 1,153
Accts Thomas & Thomas Llp Texarkana
SIC 8211 Public elementary & secondary schools; School board
Schl Brd P: Christina Walker
Teacher Pr: Laronda Graf
Teacher Pr: Amy Nix
Psych: Terri Brooks

D-U-N-S 02-126-7588
LIBERTY-USA CORP
LIBERTY MUTUAL AGENCY MARKETS
(Suby of LIBERTY MUTUAL INSURANCE CO) ★
62 Maple Ave, Keene, NH 03431-1625
Tel (603) 352-3221 Founded/Ownrshp 1999
Sales NA EMP 400
SIC 6411 Property & casualty insurance agent
Pr: Gary Gregg

LIBERTYHEALTH
See JERSEY CITY MEDICAL CENTER INC

LIBERTYHEALTH
See LIBERTY HEALTHCARE SYSTEM INC

D-U-N-S 03-949-2238
LIBERTYTOWN USA 2 INC
13131 Dairy Ashford Rd # 230, Sugar Land, TX 77478-4396
Tel (832) 295-5024 Founded/Ownrshp 2007
Sales 136.7MM^E EMP 675
SIC 6719 Investment holding companies, except banks
CEO: Philip Morrison
*Sec: Gregory Rossmiller

D-U-N-S 78-879-0434
■ LIBRARY OF CONGRESS
(Suby of CONGRESS UNITED STATES) ★
101 Independence Ave Se, Washington, DC 20540-0002
Tel (202) 707-5000 Founded/Ownrshp 1800
Sales 143.0MM^E EMP 4,213
SIC 8231 9121 Libraries; Legislative bodies;
Bd of Dir: Jane Gilchrist
Ofcr: Molly Johnson
Top Exec: Roberta Goldblatt
Top Exec: Judy Lu
Top Exec: Sarah Ozturk
Top Exec: Sharon Tsai
Top Exec: Helena Zinkham
Exec: Jay Miller
Exec: Littlejohn Tom
Exec: Michael Zech
Assoc Dir: Bessie Alkisswani
Comm Dir: David Early

LICKING COUNTY COMMISSIONERS
See COUNTY OF LICKING

D-U-N-S 78-675-9134
LICKING MEMORIAL HEALTH SYSTEMS
1320 W Main St, Newark, OH 43055-1822
Tel (740) 348-4000 Founded/Ownrshp 1984
Sales 209.7MM EMP 1,700
Accts Mountjoy Chilton Medley Llp C
SIC 8741 6411 Hospital management; Insurance agents, brokers & service
CFO: Rob Montagnese
*Pr: Robert Montagnese
*VP: Sallie Arnett
Off Mgr: Kathy Watters
Doctor: Brad Bernacki

LICKING MEMORIAL HLTH SYSTEMS
See LICKING MEMORIAL HOSPITAL

D-U-N-S 04-642-4750
LICKING MEMORIAL HOSPITAL (OH)
LICKING MEMORIAL HLTH SYSTEMS
(Suby of LICKING MEMORIAL HEALTH SYSTEMS) ★
1320 W Main St, Newark, OH 43055-3699
Tel (740) 348-4137 Founded/Ownrshp 1898, 1986
Sales 201.3MM EMP 1,143^E
SIC 8062 General medical & surgical hospitals
Pr: Robert A Montagnese
*VP: Sallie Arnett
*VP: Craig Cairns
VP: Ann Hubbuch
*VP: Veronica Link
VP: Rhonda Maddern
*VP: Christine McGee
VP: Ann Peterson
*VP: Cynthia L Webster
VP: Debboe Yooung
VP: Debbie Young
Dir Rx: Jeff Smith

D-U-N-S 01-051-4541
LICKING RIVER RESOURCES INC
(Suby of US COAL CORP) ★
6301 Old Richmond Rd, Lexington, KY 40515-9730
Tel (859) 223-8820 Founded/Ownrshp 2001
Sales 97.2MM^E EMP 180
SIC 1241 Coal mining services
Pr: John A Collins
*VP: Chris Lacy
*VP: Kenneth Whitt

LICR FUND
See LUDWIG INSTITUTE FOR CANCER RESEARCH

D-U-N-S 61-856-7630
LICT CORP
401 Theodore Fremd Ave, Rye, NY 10580-1422
Tel (914) 921-8821 Founded/Ownrshp 1989
Sales 638.5MM^E EMP 2,885
Accts Kpmg Llp New York Ny
SIC 4813 4841 4833 Telephone communication, except radio; Cable & other pay television services; Television broadcasting stations
Ch Bd: Mario J Gabelli
*CEO: Robert E Dolan
*COO: James Dabramo
*Sr VP: Evelyn Jerden
VP: Stephen J Moore
*VP Admn: Thomas J Hearity

LIDESTRI FOOD AND DRINK
See LIDESTRI FOODS INC

D-U-N-S 09-440-5503 IMP
LIDESTRI FOODS INC
LIDESTRI FOOD AND DRINK
815 Whitney Rd W, Fairport, NY 14450-1030
Tel (585) 377-7700 Founded/Ownrshp 1998
Sales 246.1MM^E EMP 750
SIC 3221 2033 Bottles for packing, bottling & canning: glass; Canned fruits & specialties; Spaghetti & other pasta sauce: packaged in cans, jars, etc.
CEO: John Lidestri
*CFO: John Veterer
VP: Tony Bash
*VP: Edward Salzano
*VP: Donna Yanicky
Creative D: Mary Demarco
*Prin: Joe Ferrigno
*Prin: Robert Schiefer
Mng Dir: Jeff Lalonde
Off Admin: Dawn Trippy
CIO: John Matrachisia

D-U-N-S 95-604-1339 IMP
■ LIDS CORP
(Suby of JOURNEYS KIDZ) ★
7555 Woodland Dr, Indianapolis, IN 46278-2705
Tel (888) 564-4287 Founded/Ownrshp 2004
Sales 417.4MM^E EMP 2,730
SIC 5699 Sports apparel
Pr: Jack Ladsey
Mng Pt: Casey Walts
*Pr: Kenneth J Kocher
*COO: Joseph Glenn Campbell
*CFO: Richard E Cramer
CFO: Richard E Cramr
CFO: Kevin Thimjon
Treas: Brooke Nichols
Ex VP: Charlie Brodt
Sr VP: Scott Molander
VP: Robert J Dennis
Comm Man: Tracy Brink

D-U-N-S 15-276-0567
LIEBEL-FLARSHEIM CO LLC
(Suby of GUERBET)
1034 S Brentwood Blvd, Saint Louis, MO 63117-1223
Tel (314) 654-8625 Founded/Ownrshp 1986
Sales 200.0MM EMP 1,100
SIC 1541 Pharmaceutical manufacturing plant construction
Pr: Jean-Frantois Blanc
*VP: Bruno Bonnemain

D-U-N-S 00-430-9647 IMP/EXP
LIEBERT CORP
VERTIV
(Suby of CORTES NP ACQUISITION CORP) ★
1050 Dearborn Dr, Columbus, OH 43085-4709
Tel (614) 888-0246 Founded/Ownrshp 2016
Sales 1.1MMM^E EMP 2,999
SIC 3585 3613 7629 Air conditioning equipment, complete; Regulators, power; Electronic equipment repair
Pr: Steve Hassell
Pr: Robert P Bauer
Pr: Robert Yopko
Treas: Thomas Vennemeyer
Ex VP: Scott Barbour
Ex VP: Gary Godek
Ex VP: W Odell
Sr VP: James Good
VP: Phil Arlinghaus
VP: Tom Bennett
VP: Jim Benson
VP: John Carey
VP: Bob Daniel
VP: Jim Good
VP: Joe Jones
VP: John Judge
VP: Fred Lancia
VP: Gorie Lapointe
VP: Steve Madara
VP: George Mulligan
VP: Peter Panfil

D-U-N-S 14-108-1930
LIEBERT NORTH AMERICA INC
(Suby of VERTIV) ★
1050 Dearborn Dr, Columbus, OH 43085-4709
Tel (614) 888-0246 Founded/Ownrshp 1999
Sales 185.5MM^E EMP 1,800
SIC 3699 3585 Electrical equipment & supplies; Refrigeration & heating equipment
Pr: Robert P Bauer
VP: James Good

D-U-N-S 05-404-2296 IMP
LIEBHERR MINING & CONSTRUCTION EQUIPMENT INC
LIEBHERR MINING EQUIPMENT
(Suby of LIEBHERR-INTERNATIONAL S.A.)
4100 Chestnut Ave, Newport News, VA 23607-2420
Tel (757) 245-5251 Founded/Ownrshp 1970
Sales 399.3MM^E EMP 950
SIC 5082 5084 3532 Construction & mining machinery; Excavating machinery & equipment; Cranes, construction; Road construction & maintenance machinery; Machine tools & accessories; Mining machinery
*Pr: Ronald E Jacobson
*Ex VP: Cooke Cheri
Ex VP: Cheri Cooke
Ex VP: Georg Diesch
*Ex VP: Hogue Lena
VP: Cort Reiser
Sftwr Eng: Douglas Rilee
VP Opers: Jochen Faber
Trfc Mgr: Angela Fizzano
Sls Mgr: Derek Alband

LIEBHERR MINING EQUIPMENT
See LIEBHERR MINING & CONSTRUCTION EQUIPMENT INC

D-U-N-S 00-597-2443 IMP
■ LIEBOVICH BROS INC (IL)
(Suby of RELIANCE STEEL & ALUMINUM CO) ★
2116 Preston St, Rockford, IL 61102-1975
Tel (815) 987-3200 Founded/Ownrshp 1940
Sales 300.1MM^E EMP 559
SIC 5051 Ferrous metals
Pr: Michael J Tulley

D-U-N-S 02-530-8318
■ LIEBOVICH STEEL & ALUMINUM CO
(Suby of LIEBOVICH BROS INC) ★
2116 Preston St, Rockford, IL 61102-1975
Tel (815) 987-3200 Founded/Ownrshp 1989
Sales 300.0MM EMP 559^E
SIC 5051 Metals service centers & offices
Pr: Michael Shanley
Pr: Greg Liebovich
Pr: Michael P Shanley

D-U-N-S 78-366-0074
LIFE AND SPECIALTY VENTURES LLC
LSV
17500 Chenal Pkwy Ste 500, Little Rock, AR 72223-9059
Tel (501) 378-2910 Founded/Ownrshp 2005
Sales 206.9MM^E EMP 1,200^E
SIC 6719 Personal holding companies, except banks
CEO: Jason Mann
*CFO: Mark Langston
Ex VP: Edward Murphy
IT Man: Brandy Stults

D-U-N-S 03-067-1002
LIFE CARE CENTERS OF AMERICA INC
3570 Keith St Nw, Cleveland, TN 37312-4309
Tel (423) 472-9585 Founded/Ownrshp 1975
Sales 10.3MM EMP 29,000
SIC 8051 8052 Skilled nursing care facilities; Intermediate care facilities
Ch Bd: Forrest L Preston
Pr: Bryan A Cook
*Pr: Beecher Hunter
Ex VP: Mohney Ralph
Sr VP: Norma Cooper
Sr VP: Terry Henry
Sr VP: Carol Hulgan
Sr VP: Carson Mike
Sr VP: Don Provonsha
VP: Bobby Holder
*VP: Lisa Lay
VP: Rick Mountz
VP: Dick Odenthal
VP: Tyler Owens
VP: Sue Payne
VP: Mary Pfeifer
VP: Pamela Rau
VP: James Sanner
VP: Rick Starke
VP: David Starrett
VP: Richard Swanker

D-U-N-S 18-795-5141
LIFE CARE HOME HEALTH SERVICES CORP
4723 W Atl Ave Ste 21, Delray Beach, FL 33445
Tel (561) 272-5866 Founded/Ownrshp 1988
Sales 30.2MM^E EMP 1,500
SIC 8082 7361 Home health care services; Nurses' registry
VP: Mary Harrison
*VP: Debbie Dacus
Exec: Kevin Meyer

LIFE CHURCH
See LIFE COVENANT CHURCH INC

D-U-N-S 08-699-8382
LIFE COVENANT CHURCH INC
LIFE CHURCH
4600 E 2nd St, Edmond, OK 73034-7550
Tel (405) 680-5433 Founded/Ownrshp 1997
Sales 89.6MM EMP 1,800
Accts Cole & Reed Pc Oklahoma Cit
SIC 8661 Non-denominational church
Pr: Craig Groeschel
*CFO: Cathi Linch
*VP: Bobby Gruenewald
*VP: Jerry Hurley
Comm Dir: Apr Ross
Snr Mgr: Mark Allen
Snr Mgr: Ian Brown
Snr Mgr: Al Garza

D-U-N-S 08-863-0264
LIFE CYCLE ENGINEERING INC
L C E
4360 Corporate Rd Ste 100, North Charleston, SC 29405-7439
Tel (843) 744-7110 Founded/Ownrshp 1976
Sales 91.1MM EMP 600
SIC 7371 7373 7376 7379 8711 Custom computer programming services; Computer integrated systems design; Computer facilities management; Computer related maintenance services; Engineering services
CEO: Robert Fei
Ch Bd: James Fei
CFO: Robert Bendetti
Sr VP: Bill Guin
Sr VP: Manuel Lovgren
Sr VP: Mark Ruby
Sr VP: Greg Walls
VP: Martin Baker
VP: Edward S Godfrey
VP: Jerry Vevon
Admn Mgr: Randy Heisler
Board of Directors: James R Fei, Robert F Fei

LIFE EXT QLTY SPPLMNTS VTAMINS
See LIFE EXTENSION FOUNDATION INC

D-U-N-S 13-839-2407
LIFE EXTENSION FOUNDATION INC
LIFE EXT QLTY SPPLMNTS VTAMINS
3600 W Coml Blvd Ste 100, Fort Lauderdale, FL 33309
Tel (954) 766-8433 Founded/Ownrshp 1977
Sales 180.0MM^E EMP 350
SIC 8733 Medical research
CEO: Paul Gilner
VP: Luke Huber
CIO: Bill Faloon
CTO: Ben Best
Manager: Jeff Thomas
Sls Mgr: Jeff Knowles
Snr Mgr: Suzanne Lang

D-U-N-S 02-416-0767 IMP/EXP
■ LIFE FITNESS INC (IL)
(Suby of BRUNSWICK CORP) ★
9525 Bryn Mawr Ave Fl 6, Rosemont, IL 60018-5249
Tel (847) 288-3300 Founded/Ownrshp 1999
Sales 175.0MM^E EMP 617^E
SIC 3949 Exercise equipment
Pr: Chris E Clawson
Ex VP: Jay Megna
Sr VP: Tom Zentefis
VP: Greg Highsmith
Exec: Tim Wild
Dir Soc: Kristin Risner
Creative D: Jim Layer
Prgrm Mgr: Maggie Anderson
Prgrm Mgr: Greg Topel
Genl Mgr: Chris Connor
CIO: Jesse Sturtlader

LIFE IN THE WORD
See JOYCE MEYER MINISTRIES INC

D-U-N-S 00-791-3957
■ LIFE INSURANCE CO OF NORTH AMERICA (PA)
(Suby of CIGNA) ★
1601 Chestnut St, Philadelphia, PA 19192-0003
Tel (215) 761-1000 Founded/Ownrshp 1956, 2001
Sales NA EMP 1,500
SIC 6321 6311 Accident insurance carriers; Health insurance carriers; Life insurance carriers
Sr VP: Joseph M Fitzgerald
*CFO: Jean Walker
*Treas: Paul Bergsteinsson
*Sr VP: Richard A Brownmiller
*Sr VP: Gregory Deming
*Sr VP: Kevin Gravatt
*Sr VP: Kathleen McEndy
*Sr VP: Eric M Reisenwitz
*Sr VP: Julian Romeu
*Sr VP: Jerold H Rosenblum
VP: Steven G Mellas

D-U-N-S 79-782-8092
LIFE RE CORP
(Suby of SWISS REINSURANCE AMERICA) ★
175 King St, Armonk, NY 10504-1606
Tel (914) 828-8500 Founded/Ownrshp 1988
Sales NA EMP 946
SIC 6311 6321 Life reinsurance; Reinsurance carriers, accident & health
Ch Bd: Rodney A Hawes Jr
*COO: Jacques E Dubois

*Ex VP: W Weldon Wilson
*VP: Patricia Harrigan

D-U-N-S 10-991-3587
LIFE SCIENCES RESEARCH INC
(Suby of LION HOLDINGS INC) ★
Mettlers Rd, East Millstone, NJ 08875
Tel (732) 649-9961 Founded/Ownrshp 2001
Sales 69.3MM[E] EMP 1,648[E]
SIC 8731 Commercial physical research; Biological research; Commercial physical research; Commercial research laboratory
CEO: Andrew Baker
*Pr: Brian Cass
CFO: Richard Michaelson
CFO: Richard A Michelson
Dir Bus: David Halverson
Dir Bus: Melanie Hann
Dir IT: Don Wagner
VP Opers: Julian Griffiths

D-U-N-S 92-615-0277
▲ LIFE STORAGE INC
6467 Main St, Williamsville, NY 14221-5856
Tel (716) 633-1850 Founded/Ownrshp 1985
Sales 366.6MM EMP 1,429
Tkr Sym LSI Exch NYS
SIC 6798 Real estate investment trusts
CEO: David L Rogers
*Ch Bd: Robert J Attea
*Pr: Kenneth F Myszka
COO: Edward F Killeen
CFO: Andrew J Gregoire
CIO: Paul T Powell
Board of Directors: Mark G Barberio, Arthur L Havener Jr, Charles E Lannon, Stephen R Rusmisel

D-U-N-S 18-215-8873 IMP/EXP
■ LIFE TECHNOLOGIES CORP
(Suby of THERMO FISHER SCIENTIFIC INC) ★
5781 Van Allen Way, Carlsbad, CA 92008-7321
Tel (760) 603-7200 Founded/Ownrshp 1997
Sales 3.0MMM[E] EMP 10,000
SIC 2836 2835 Biological products, except diagnostic; In vitro & in vivo diagnostic substances
CEO: Seth Hoogasian
Pr: Mark P Stevenson
CEO: Seth H Hoogasian
Ofcr: John A Cottingham
VP: Mark Gardner
VP: Steve Glover
VP: Kelli Richard
VP: Cheri Walker
Prgrm Mgr: Daniel Alessi
CTO: Willard Woods
Dir IT: Ravi Gupta
Board of Directors: Seth H Hoogasian

D-U-N-S 78-430-7084 IMP
LIFE TIME FITNESS INC
(Suby of LTF HOLDINGS INC) ★
2902 Corporate Pl, Chanhassen, MN 55317-4773
Tel (952) 229-7543 Founded/Ownrshp 2015
Sales 967.6MM[E] EMP 22,500
SIC 7997 Membership sports & recreation clubs
Pr: Bahram Akradi
COO: Jeffrey G Zwiefel
CFO: Eric J Buss
Ex VP: Jess R Elmquist
Ex VP: Tami A Kozikowski
Sr VP: John M Hugo
VP: Ryan Berk
VP: Marie Damato
Dir Soc: Krystel Reierson
Creative D: Lydia Anderson
Creative D: Carrie Stafford

D-U-N-S 13-148-0618
LIFEBRIDGE HEALTH INC
2401 W Belvedere Ave, Baltimore, MD 21215-5216
Tel (410) 601-5653 Founded/Ownrshp 1985
Sales 120.1MM EMP 6,000[E]
Accts Sc&H Tax & Advisory Services L
SIC 8062 General medical & surgical hospitals
CEO: Neil M Meltzer
*Ch Bd: Howard Weiss
COO: Jeff Watson
*CFO: David Krajewski
*Sr VP: Aric Spitulnik
Dir Rx: John D Bona
IT Man: Steven Sandler
Opers Mgr: Lisa Mules
Ansthlgy: Mark Coleman
Ansthlgy: Sukhjit Sandhu
Ansthlgy: William Su

LIFECARE ASSURANCE COMPANY
See 21ST CENTURY LIFE AND HEALTH CO INC

D-U-N-S 60-470-7935
LIFECARE ASSURANCE CO INC
(Suby of LIFECARE ASSURANCE CO) ★
21600 Oxnard St Fl 16, Woodland Hills, CA 91367-4976
Tel (818) 887-4436 Founded/Ownrshp 1980
Sales NA EMP 246
SIC 6321 6411 6311 Accident & health insurance; Insurance agents, brokers & service; Life insurance
Pr: James Glickman
*COO: Alan S Hughes
*CFO: Daniel J Disipio
*VP: Peter Diffley
*VP: Gwen D Franklin
*VP: Jay R Peters
*VP: Jim Rogers
*VP: Kirk R Shearburn
*VP Admn: Dick Sato
Dir IT: Ivan Banev

LIFECARE FAMILY OF HOSPITALS
See LIFECARE HOLDINGS INC

D-U-N-S 10-123-0931 IMP
LIFECARE HOLDINGS INC
LIFECARE FAMILY OF HOSPITALS
(Suby of LCI HOLDCO LLC) ★
5340 Legacy Dr Ste 150, Plano, TX 75024-3131
Tel (469) 241-2100 Founded/Ownrshp 1993
Sales 450.6MM[E] EMP 4,500[E]
SIC 8069 8051 Specialty hospitals, except psychiatric; Skilled nursing care facilities
Ch Bd: Phillip B Douglas
*COO: Stuart Archer
*COO: Frank J Battafarano
*CFO: Stuart A Walker
Ofcr: Pat A Denney
*Ex VP: Grant B Asay
Ex VP: Grant Asay
*Sr VP: Catherine A Conner
Sr VP: Greg Floyd
Sr VP: Leroy F Thompson Jr
*VP: Maegan Bowman
VP: Diane H Partridge
Board of Directors: Karen H Bechtel, William Hamburg, William P Johnston, William H McMullan Jr, Stephen H Wise

LIFECARE HOSPITALS WISCONSIN
See NEW LIFECARE HOSPITALS OF MILWAUKEE LLC

D-U-N-S 15-722-4205 IMP
LIFECELL CORP
(Suby of CHIRON HOLDINGS INC) ★
1 Millennium Way, Branchburg, NJ 08876-3876
Tel (908) 947-1100 Founded/Ownrshp 2011
Sales 428.0MM EMP 600[E]
SIC 2836 Biological products, except diagnostic
CEO: Joe Woody
CFO: Steve Sovieski
Sr VP: Lisa N Collera
Sr VP: Bruce Lamb
VP: John Harper
VP: Adrian Roji
Prgrm Mgr: Lara Minakas
Rgnl Mgr: Kevin Greene
Rgnl Mgr: Ken Knab
IT Man: Tina Carter
IT Man: Jennifer G Schaefer
Board of Directors: Timothy E Guertin

LIFELINE
See RIVERSIDE REGIONAL MEDIAL CENTER

D-U-N-S 08-003-0042 IMP
LIFELINE SYSTEMS CO
PHILIPS LIFELINE
(Suby of PHILIPS CONSUMER LIFESTYLE) ★
111 Lawrence St, Framingham, MA 01702-8171
Tel (508) 988-1000 Founded/Ownrshp 2014
Sales 212.2MM[E] EMP 897
SIC 3669 Emergency alarms
Pr: Kimberly O'Laughlin
Pr: Gerard Van Spaendonck
Ch: L D Shapiro
Treas: James Mark Mattern II
Sr VP: Edward M Bolesky
Sr VP: Richard M Reich
Sr VP: Donald G Strange
VP: Paul Cavanaugh
VP: John D Giannetto
VP: Nick Padula
VP: Mark T Rutherford
VP: Leonard E Wechsler
Dir Surg: Leverda Wallace

D-U-N-S 15-080-2932
LIFELINK FOUNDATION INC
LIFELINK TISSUE BANK
9661 Delaney Creek Blvd, Tampa, FL 33619-5121
Tel (813) 253-2640 Founded/Ownrshp 1982
Sales 100.7MM EMP 500
Accts Cbiz Mhm Llc Clearwater Fl
SIC 8099 Medical services organization
Ch Bd: Dana L Shires Jr
*Pr: Dennis F Heinrichs
*CFO: Bryan Mc Donald
VP: Mich M Eggsware
VP: Barbara Leeka
VP: Bobbie Pierson
Dir Risk M: Lynn Smith
Dir Lab: Maria Jackson
Brnch Mgr: John Stockman
Genl Mgr: Tina Ray
Dir IT: Ken Morley

D-U-N-S 05-364-5099
LIFELINK HOUSING CORP
1900 Spring Rd Ste 300, Oak Brook, IL 60523-1480
Tel (630) 368-0817 Founded/Ownrshp 1987
Sales 22.4M EMP 1,000
SIC 6513 Retirement hotel operation
CEO: Rev Carl A Zimmerman

LIFELINK TISSUE BANK
See LIFELINK FOUNDATION INC

D-U-N-S 36-070-9336
▲ LIFELOCK INC
60 E Rio Salado Pkwy # 400, Tempe, AZ 85281-9129
Tel (480) 682-5100 Founded/Ownrshp 2005
Sales 587.4MM EMP 938[E]
Tkr Sym LOCK Exch NYS
SIC 7382 Protective devices, security
Pr: Hilary A Schneider
*V Ch: Todd Davis
CFO: Douglas C Jeffries
CFO: Chris G Power
Ofcr: Douglas Jeffries
Ex VP: Scott Carter
Ex VP: Ignacio Martinez
Ex VP: Sharon Segev
Sr VP: Finn Faldi
Sr VP: Dev Patel
VP: Kimberly Allman
VP: Peter Levinson
VP: Martin Morzynski
VP: Marco Wirasinghe
VP: Aaron Zitzer
Board of Directors: Gary S Briggs, David Cowan, Roy A Guthrie, Albert A Pimentel, Thomas J Ridge, Jaynie Miller Studenmund

D-U-N-S 60-264-3934
■ LIFEMARK HOSPITALS OF FLORIDA INC
PALMETTO GENERAL HOSPITAL
(Suby of TENET HEALTHCARE CORP) ★
2001 W 68th St, Hialeah, FL 33016-1801
Tel (305) 823-5000 Founded/Ownrshp 1985
Sales 262.8MM EMP 1,400
SIC 8062 General medical & surgical hospitals
CEO: Ana Mederos
Chf Rad: Jose Becerra
*COO: Gina C Diaz
*CFO: Oscar Vicente
Dir Bus: Vilma H Medio
Dir IT: Pedro Nevarez
Mktg Mgr: Vilma Cestino
Pathlgst: Frederick Lancet
Ansthlgy: Thottankara Bhaskaran
Doctor: Edward L Gheiler
Doctor: Nuria M Lawson

D-U-N-S 12-182-8156
LIFENET HEALTH
1864 Concert Dr, Virginia Beach, VA 23453-1903
Tel (757) 464-4761 Founded/Ownrshp 1982
Sales 210.0MM EMP 500
Accts Kpmg Llp Mc Lean Va
SIC 8099 Organ bank
CEO: Rony Thomas
CFO: Don Berkstreer
CFO: Gordon Berkstresser
CFO: Gordon Berkstressor
Ofcr: James Clagett
VP: Michael Borgeson
VP: Richard Flores
VP: Terry Joe
VP: Perry Lange
VP: Steve Linz
VP: Christina Pierce
VP: Michael Plew
VP: Michael Poole
VP: Donald Pritchard
VP: Tom Sander
VP: Patrick Thompson

D-U-N-S 19-805-4350
▲ LIFEPOINT HEALTH INC
330 Seven Springs Way, Brentwood, TN 37027-5098
Tel (615) 920-7000 Founded/Ownrshp 1997
Sales 5.2MMM[E] EMP 41,427
Accts Ernst & Young Llp Nashville
Tkr Sym LPNT Exch NGS
SIC 8062 8742 General medical & surgical hospitals; Hospital, medical school affiliated with nursing & residency; Hospital & health services consultant
Ch Bd: William F Carpenter III
Pr: Donald J Bivacca
Pr: David M Dill
Pr: R Scott Raplee
Pr: Jeffrey G Seraphine
CFO: Michael S Coggin
CFO: Leif M Murphy
CFO: Bradley Owens
Treas: Phillip Gilbertson
Ofcr: Russell L Holman
VP: Pam Belcher
VP: Jamie Davis
VP: Fabio Fallico
VP: Richard Flores
VP: Christy Green
VP: William Hoffman
VP: Sean Kerkhove
VP: Christopher Monte
VP: Ed O'Dell
VP: Brad Owens
VP: Peter Radetich
Board of Directors: Gregory T Bier, Kermit Crawford, Richard H Evans, Dewitt Ezell Jr, Michael P Haley, Marguerite W Kondracke, John E Maupin Jr, Reed V Tuckson, Owen G Shell Jr

D-U-N-S 94-436-0908
■ LIFEPOINT OF LAKE CUMBERLAND LLC
DUKE LIFEPOINT HEALTHCARE
(Suby of HISTORIC LIFEPOINT HOSPITALS INC) ★
305 Langdon St, Somerset, KY 42503-2750
Tel (606) 679-7441 Founded/Ownrshp 2002
Sales 104.0MM[E] EMP 1,100
SIC 8062 8082 General medical & surgical hospitals; Home health care services
CFO: Steve Frenatz
Dir Lab: Dorothy Skidmore
Dir Pat Ac: Kevin Albert
QC Dir: Diann Vanhook
Pharmcst: Ron Wright
HC Dir: Patty Ruckel

LIFEPOINT/NORTON HEALTHCARE
See RHN CLARK MEMORIAL HOSPITAL LLC

D-U-N-S 15-340-9313 IMP
■ LIFESCAN INC
(Suby of JOHNSON & JOHNSON) ★
965 Chesterbrook Blvd, Chesterbrook, PA 19087-5614
Tel (800) 227-8862 Founded/Ownrshp 1986
Sales 318.0MM[E] EMP 1,500
SIC 2835 3841 Blood derivative diagnostic agents; Medical instruments & equipment, blood & bone work
CEO: Valerie Asbury
*CFO: James Buschmeier
VP: Glenn Johnson
*VP: Lee Ty
Dir Bus: Anthony Delizza
Dir Bus: Mark Zenz
Dir Bus: Mark T Zenz
Prgrm Mgr: Rita Ducharme
Prgrm Mgr: Robert Guillou
CIO: Madeline Fackler
DP Dir: Damyanti Patel

D-U-N-S 08-713-2502
LIFESPACE COMMUNITIES INC
100 E Grand Ave Ste 200, Des Moines, IA 50309-1835
Tel (515) 288-5805 Founded/Ownrshp 1976
Sales 221.5MM EMP 1,875
Accts Clifton Larson Allen Llp Minn
SIC 8059 Rest home, with health care
CEO: Scott M Harrison
CFO: Larry Smith
Treas: Larry M Smith
Comm Dir: Lisa Ryan
Ex Dir: Tim Smith

D-U-N-S 87-816-3674
LIFESPAN CORP
167 Point St Ste 2b, Providence, RI 02903-4771
Tel (401) 444-3500 Founded/Ownrshp 1986
Sales 156.6MM[E] EMP 8,000
Accts Lb Kpmg Llp Providence Ri
SIC 8011 Clinic, operated by physicians; Internal medicine, physician/surgeon; Physical medicine, physician/surgeon
CEO: Timothy J Babineau MD
Bd of Dir: Carol Lewis
Ex VP: Cathy Duquette
Ex VP: Boyd King
Ex VP: Eva Owens
Sr VP: Richard J Goldberg
Sr VP: Frederick J Macri
Sr VP: Karen Rosene Montella
Sr VP: Peter Snyder
Dir Risk M: Valerie Till
Dir Soc: Kim Borek
Dir Rad: Rick Gold

D-U-N-S 04-007-4742
LIFESPIRE INC (NY)
A.C.R.M.D
1 Whitehall St Fl 9, New York, NY 10004-2141
Tel (212) 741-0100 Founded/Ownrshp 1951
Sales 102.8MM EMP 1,600
Accts Mbaf Cpas Llc Valhalla Ny
SIC 8322 Individual & family services
CEO: Mark Van Voorst
Pr: Peter Valvo
*CFO: Keith Lee
Ex VP: Kamelia Kameli
VP: Laura Hill
VP: Leslie Verghese

D-U-N-S 82-481-5708
LIFESTAR RESPONSE CORP
(Suby of FALCK USA INC) ★
3710 Commerce Dr Ste 1006, Halethorpe, MD 21227-1653
Tel (631) 289-1100 Founded/Ownrshp 2011
Sales 67.2MM[E] EMP 1,604[E]
SIC 4119 Ambulance service
CEO: Jon Colin
*Pr: Daniel Platt
*CFO: James T Buonincontri
VP: Doug Tisdale
Opers Mgr: Jack Metz
Opers Mgr: Dennis Poole
Mktg Dir: Daniel Brown

D-U-N-S 09-166-2924
LIFETIME ASSISTANCE INC
LAICO INDUSTRIES
425 Paul Rd, Rochester, NY 14624-4721
Tel (585) 247-2255 Founded/Ownrshp 1978
Sales 63.7MM EMP 1,300
Accts Lb Bonadio & Co Llp Pittsford
SIC 8322 6512 Association for the handicapped; Nonresidential building operators
CEO: James Branciforte
CFO: Kevin Judge
Mng Dir: Pearl Nettles
Genl Mgr: Ronnie Urquhart
Pgrm Dir: Dennis Brown

D-U-N-S 11-521-3613 IMP/EXP
▲ LIFETIME BRANDS INC
1000 Stewart Ave, Garden City, NY 11530-4814
Tel (516) 683-6000 Founded/Ownrshp 1945
Sales 587.6MM EMP 1,454[E]
Tkr Sym LCUT Exch NGS
SIC 3421 5023 5719 Cutlery; Home furnishings; Kitchen tools & utensils; Stainless steel flatware; Kitchenware; Cutlery; Glassware
Ch Bd: Jeffrey Siegel
Pr: Daniel Siegel
*COO: Ronald Shiftan
CFO: Laurence Winoker
Board of Directors: Michael J Jeary, John Koegel, Cherrie Nanninga, Craig Phillips, Dennis E Reaves, Michael J Regan, Sara Genster Robling, William U Westerfield

LIFETIME CARE
See GENESEE REGION HOME CARE ASSOCIATION INC

LIFETIME COMPOSITES
See WOODBRIDGE CORP

D-U-N-S 10-330-5082
LIFETIME ENTERTAINMENT SERVICES LLC
LIFETIME TELEVISION
(Suby of AETN INTERNATIONAL) ★
235 E 45th St, New York, NY 10017-3305
Tel (212) 424-7000 Founded/Ownrshp 2009
Sales 191.5MM[E] EMP 720
SIC 4841 Cable television services
Ex VP: Rick Haskins
VP: Richard Basso
VP: Cathy Christiano
VP: Rachel Gruhin
IT Man: Joe Zine
Software D: Milton Baumwolspiner
Opers Mgr: Warren Lenard
VP Mktg: Kimberly Dobson
VP Mktg: Lee Heffernan
Mktg Mgr: Julie Harnik
Mktg Mgr: Frances Seda

LIFETIME HEALTH
See GENESEE VALLEY GROUP HEALTH ASSOCIATION

LIFETIME HEALTH COMPANIES, THE
See LIFETIME HEALTHCARE INC

D-U-N-S 18-000-4629
LIFETIME HEALTHCARE INC
LIFETIME HEALTH COMPANIES, THE
165 Court St, Rochester, NY 14647-0001
Tel (585) 454-1700 Founded/Ownrshp 1997
Sales NA EMP 7,000[E]
SIC 6324 6321 Group hospitalization plans; Accident & health insurance
CEO: David H Klein

*Ch Bd: Mary A Bellardini
VP: Jonathan Kaplan

D-U-N-S 14-541-1034 IMP/EXP
LIFETIME LLC
LIFETIME PRODUCTS
Freeport Ctr Bldg D-11, Clearfield, UT 84016
Tel (801) 776-1532 Founded/Ownrshp 2003
Sales 124.6MM^E EMP 1,200^E
SIC 3089 Plastic processing
Genl Mgr: Heidi Moulton

LIFETIME PRODUCTS
See LIFETIME LLC

D-U-N-S 14-845-5041 IMP/EXP
LIFETIME PRODUCTS INC
Freeport Ctr Bldg D-11, Clearfield, UT 84016
Tel (801) 776-1532 Founded/Ownrshp 1986
Sales 683.5MM^E EMP 1,800
SIC 2519 3949 2531 2511 Garden furniture, except wood, metal, stone or concrete; Basketball equipment & supplies, general; Public building & related furniture; Wood household furniture
Pr: Richard Hendrickson
Pr: Jo Healy
*Sec: Mark E Whiting
Sr VP: Clinton Morris
Sr VP: Vince Rhoton
*VP: Brent Allen
VP: Brett Horstmann
CIO: John Bowden
Mfg Mgr: Jeremy Rhead
Opers Mgr: Amanda Steed
Board of Directors: Kathy Mower

LIFETIME TELEVISION
See LIFETIME ENTERTAINMENT SERVICES LLC

D-U-N-S 05-437-5308
LIFETOUCH CHURCH DIRECTORIES AND PORTRAITS INC (MN)
(Suby of LIFETOUCH INC) ★
11000 Viking Dr Ste 400, Eden Prairie, MN 55344-7242
Tel (952) 826-4000 Founded/Ownrshp 1962, 1995
Sales 36.2MM^E EMP 1,424
SIC 7221 2741 Photographic studios, portrait; Directories: publishing & printing
CEO: Paul Harmel
*CFO: Randy Pladson

D-U-N-S 00-696-2351
LIFETOUCH INC (MN)
11000 Viking Dr, Eden Prairie, MN 55344-7242
Tel (952) 826-4000 Founded/Ownrshp 1936, 1977
Sales 902.7MM^E EMP 26,175
SIC 7221 7812 2741 Photographer, still or video; School photographer; Video tape production; Yearbooks: publishing & printing
Ch Bd: Paul Harmel
*Pr: Jake Barker
Pr: Tim Flanagan
*CFO: Randolph J Pladson
VP: Michael Anderson
VP: Tom Booth
VP: Glenn Elo
VP: Kelly Georger
VP: Kelvin Miller
VP: Michael Mullen
VP: Mark Schoenrock
VP: Rj Singh
VP: Cindy Vetsch
VP: Thomas Wargolet

D-U-N-S 13-073-3546
LIFETOUCH NATIONAL SCHOOL STUDIOS INC
(Suby of LIFETOUCH INC) ★
11000 Viking Dr Ste 300, Eden Prairie, MN 55344-7242
Tel (952) 826-4000 Founded/Ownrshp 1946
Sales 236.8MM^E EMP 5,000
SIC 7221 School photographer
CEO: Paul Harmel
Treas: Randolph J Pladson
VP: Jim Haeg
VP: Dale Knudsen
VP: Ted L Koenecke
VP: Mark Schoenrock
VP: George M Ward
Opers Mgr: Wes Westlund
Mktg Dir: Jennifer Stein
Sls Mgr: Tara Arensdorf
Sales Asso: Brandon Boulware

D-U-N-S 05-516-3604
LIFETOUCH PORTRAIT STUDIOS INC
(Suby of LIFETOUCH INC) ★
11000 Viking Dr, Eden Prairie, MN 55344-7235
Tel (952) 826-4335 Founded/Ownrshp 1983
Sales 77.7MM^E EMP 2,200
SIC 7221 Photographer, still or video
Ch Bd: Richard P Erickson
CEO: Paul Harmel
Treas: James V O'Halloran Jr
VP: Gail Thurmer
Prin: John Anderson
Prin: James Campbell
Prin: Ted Koenecke
Prin: Randolph Pladson
Brnch Mgr: Andrea Parmer
Mktg Mgr: Amie Mayo
Board of Directors: Donald Goldfus, Richard A Hassel, Robert Larson, John L Reid, Phillip Samper

D-U-N-S 96-300-2795
■ **LIFETRUST AMERICA INC**
(Suby of FIVE STAR QUALITY CARE INC) ★
113 Seaboard Ln Ste 150a, Franklin, TN 37067-8296
Tel (615) 342-0601 Founded/Ownrshp 2004
Sales 25.2MM^E EMP 1,000
SIC 8361 8051 8052 8059 Residential care; Skilled nursing care facilities; Intermediate care facilities; Nursing home, except skilled & intermediate care facility; Rest home, with health care
CEO: Pat Mulloy
CFO: Jim Bauchiero

D-U-N-S 55-705-3266
▲ **LIFEVANTAGE CORP**
9785 S Monroe St Ste 300, Sandy, UT 84070-4282
Tel (801) 432-9000 Founded/Ownrshp 1988
Sales 190.3MM EMP 166^E
Tkr Sym LFVN Exch NAS
SIC 2834 Pharmaceutical preparations
Pr: Darren Jensen
*Ch Bd: Garry Mauro
COO: Robert Urban
CFO: Mark Jaggi
*V Ch Bd: Dave Manovich
Sr VP: Ryan Thompson
Dir Sec: Justin Rose
Board of Directors: Michael A Beindorff, David S Manovich, George E Metzger, Richard Okumoto, David Toole

D-U-N-S 80-126-6201
LIFEWATCH CORP
(Suby of LIFEWATCH AG)
10255 W Higgins Rd # 100, Rosemont, IL 60018-5608
Tel (847) 720-2100 Founded/Ownrshp 2006
Sales 159.9MM^E EMP 601
Accts Pricewaterhousecoopers Llp
SIC 8099 5047 3845 Physical examination & testing services; Patient monitoring equipment; Electro-medical equipment; Electrocardiographs
Prin: Brent Cohen
*CFO: Kobi Ben Efraim
CFO: Francis J Leonard
Ex VP: Jake Mendelsohn
VP: Dan Pawlik
VP: Michael Turchi
*CIO: Jake Mehndelson
Sls Dir: Leigh Kelly
Mktg Mgr: Blair Dagenhart
Sls Mgr: Julie Hamilton

D-U-N-S 79-793-6734
LIFEWATCH SERVICES INC
(Suby of LIFEWATCH CORP) ★
10255 W Higgins Rd # 100, Rosemont, IL 60018-5608
Tel (847) 720-2100 Founded/Ownrshp 2000
Sales 149.0MM^E EMP 600
SIC 5047 8099 3845 8071 Patient monitoring equipment; Electro-medical equipment; Physical examination service, insurance; Health screening service; Physical examination & testing services; Electrocardiographs; Testing laboratories
CEO: Stephan Rietiker
*Pr: Roger K Richardson
*CFO: Kobi Ben Efraim
*CFO: Mike Turchi
*Prin: Yacov Geva

D-U-N-S 00-404-0010 IMP
LIFEWAY CHRISTIAN RESOURCES OF SOUTHERN BAPTIST CONVENTION (TN)
B & H PUBLISHERS
1 Lifeway Plz, Nashville, TN 37234-1001
Tel (615) 251-2000 Founded/Ownrshp 1891
Sales 487.4MM EMP 2,477
Accts Ernst & Young Llp Nashville
SIC 5942 5963 2731 5999 5735 5947 Books, religious; Direct selling establishments; Book publishing; Religious goods; Compact discs; Records; Gift shop
CEO: Thom S Rainer
Assoc VP: Bruce Grubbs
*Ex VP: Brad Waggoner
VP: Jim Baird
VP: Bill Crayton
VP: Craig Featherstone
*VP: Eric Geiger
VP: Tim Hill
*VP: Cossy Pachares
*VP: Jerry Rhyne
VP: Amanda Sloan
*VP: Ed Stetzer
VP: Tim Vineyard
*VP: Selma Wilson
Dir Rx: Bill Craig

D-U-N-S 15-303-2214 IMP
▲ **LIFEWAY FOODS INC**
6431 Oakton St, Morton Grove, IL 60053-2727
Tel (847) 967-1010 Founded/Ownrshp 1986
Sales 118.5MM EMP 370^E
Tkr Sym LWAY Exch NGM
SIC 2023 2026 Dry, condensed, evaporated dairy products; Fluid milk; Kefir; Yogurt; Fermented & cultured milk products
Pr: Julie Smolyansky
*Ch Bd: Ludmila Smolyansky
COO: Edward P Smolyansky
CFO: John P Waldron
Board of Directors: Renzo Bernardi, Paul Lee, Mariano Lozano, Jason Scher

D-U-N-S 96-191-1224
LIFEWISE HEALTH PLAN OF OREGON
(Suby of PREMERA BLUE CROSS) ★
2020 Sw 4th Ave Ste 1000, Portland, OR 97201-4965
Tel (503) 295-6707 Founded/Ownrshp 2008
Sales NA EMP 2^E
SIC 6321 Accident & health insurance
Pr: Majd El-Azma
VP: Sharon Sitton
IT Man: Scott Rossow
Sales Exec: Kay McGinnis
Manager: Cathy Harber
Sls Mgr: Majd Elazma

D-U-N-S 00-308-4209 IMP
■ **LIFOAM INDUSTRIES LLC** (MD)
(Suby of NEWELL BRANDS) ★
9999 E 121st, Belcamp, MD 21017
Tel (866) 770-3626 Founded/Ownrshp 1954, 2000
Sales 253.0MM^E EMP 500
SIC 3086 Plastics foam products
CEO: John Cantlin
*CFO: Cris Keller
IT Man: Dale Bargar
Sls Mgr: Brian Stiefel

D-U-N-S 06-387-5967
LIFT INC
3745 Hempland Rd, Mountville, PA 17554-1545
Tel (717) 295-1800 Founded/Ownrshp 2003
Sales 109.1MM^E EMP 220
SIC 5084 7353 Lift trucks & parts; Cranes & aerial lift equipment, rental or leasing
Pr: Donald G Herman
*VP: Kirk W Sears
Exec: Larry Spyker
Sales Exec: Dave Corey
Sales Asso: Stephen Sanger

D-U-N-S 02-547-6185 IMP/EXP
LIFT SOURCE INC
ATLAS TOYOTA MATERIAL HANDLING
1815 Landmeier Rd, Elk Grove Village, IL 60007-2420
Tel (847) 678-3450 Founded/Ownrshp 2010
Sales 118.0MM^E EMP 330
SIC 5999 5084

D-U-N-S 06-912-8655 IMP/EXP
LIFTED RESEARCH GROUP INC
L R G
7 Holland, Irvine, CA 92618-2506
Tel (949) 581-1144 Founded/Ownrshp 1999
Sales 102.4MM^E EMP 100^E
SIC 5136 Men's & boys' clothing
Pr: Robert D Wright
VP: Mike Schillmoeller
VP: Zach Wright
Mktg Mgr: Kevin Delaney
Mktg Mgr: Mike Posner
Sls Mgr: Paul Hauke
Sls Mgr: Nick Terrio

LIFTMASTER
See CHAMBERLAIN GROUP INC

D-U-N-S 14-878-9923 IMP
LIFTONE LLC
(Suby of CATERPILLAR AUTHORIZED DEALER) ★
440 E Westinghouse Blvd, Charlotte, NC 28273-5769
Tel (704) 588-1300 Founded/Ownrshp 2012
Sales 187.3MM^E EMP 560^E
SIC 5084 Materials handling machinery
Pr: Bill Ryan
CFO: Peter Nelson
Sls Mgr: Mike Wagner

D-U-N-S 00-128-8463 IMP
■ **LIGGETT GROUP LLC**
(Suby of VGR HOLDING LLC) ★
100 Maple Ln, Mebane, NC 27302-8160
Tel (919) 304-7700 Founded/Ownrshp 2006
Sales 111.8MM^E EMP 449
SIC 2111 Cigarettes
CEO: Ronald J Bernstein
Pr: Greg Sulin
*Ex VP: James A Taylor
*VP: Lynda Amey
*VP: Steven H Erikson
*VP: Jerry R Loftin
*VP: John R Long
VP Opers: Tim Jackson
VP Opers: Bill Turner
Opers Mgr: Richard Spaugh
Counsel: Marc Bell

D-U-N-S 78-443-4784
LIGHT TOWER FIBER LLC
LIGHTOWER FIBER NETWORKS
80 Central St Ste 240, Boxborough, MA 01719-1245
Tel (978) 264-6000 Founded/Ownrshp 2007
Sales 145.4MM^E EMP 223
SIC 4899

LIGHTHOUSE COUNTY COMMONS APTS
See RICHLIEU ASSOCIATES

D-U-N-S 11-342-1309
LIGHTHOUSE ELECTRIC CO INC
1957 Route 519, Canonsburg, PA 15317-5128
Tel (724) 873-3500 Founded/Ownrshp 1984
Sales 134.3MM^E EMP 400
SIC 1731 General electrical contractor
CEO: Anthony Mikec
*Pr: Todd A Mikec
*Sec: P Douglas Brock
VP: Joshua Eckenrode
*VP: Mark A Mikec

D-U-N-S 05-931-4921
LIGHTHOUSE GUILD INTERNATIONAL INC
15 W 65th St, New York, NY 10023-6601
Tel (212) 769-6200 Founded/Ownrshp 2013
Sales 849.4MM EMP 24^E
SIC 8322 8042 Individual & family services; Social services for the handicapped; Offices & clinics of optometrists
Ch Bd: James M Dubin
*CEO: Alan R Morse
CFO: Elliott J Hagler
*CFO: Christina Wong
*Treas: Sarah Smith
Sr VP: Kellyanne Caivano
Ex Dir: Susan Laventure
Genl Mgr: Lester Marks

D-U-N-S 00-837-6060
LIGHTHOUSE HOSPICE
(Suby of HARDEN HEALTHCARE SERVICES LLC) ★
100 College St, Round Rock, TX 78664-4415
Tel (866) 678-0505 Founded/Ownrshp 2011
Sales 3.7MM^E EMP 2,358^E
SIC 8052 Personal care facility

D-U-N-S 06-471-7816
LIGHTHOUSE HOSPICE
(Suby of HARDEN HEALTHCARE SERVICES LLC) ★
305 Coke Ave Ste 140, Hillsboro, TX 76645-2685
Tel (254) 710-9800 Founded/Ownrshp 2011
Sales 2.0MM^E EMP 2,021^E
SIC 8082 8069 Home health care services; Specialty hospitals, except psychiatric
Prin: Celeste McCraw

D-U-N-S 12-753-2539
LIGHTHOUSE INSURANCE GROUP INC
AUSTIN-POWELL-LANKES AGENCY
877 E 16th St, Holland, MI 49423-9130
Tel (616) 392-6900 Founded/Ownrshp 1960
Sales NA EMP 145
SIC 6411 6331 6321 6311 Insurance agents, brokers & service; Fire, marine & casualty insurance; Accident & health insurance; Life insurance
Pr: Pam Allard
*Pr: Thomas Helmstter
*Sec: James C Schippers
Ofcr: Tracy Bremmer
Dir Risk M: Gene Reed
*Prin: Kathleen Andersen
Brnch Mgr: Vern Borgman
Brnch Mgr: Kerri Woolverton
IT Man: Bruce Bos
Mktg Mgr: Jeff Beyer
Mktg Mgr: Anna Constant

D-U-N-S 17-445-4678 IMP/EXP
LIGHTING HOLDINGS INTERNATIONAL LLC
4 Manhattanville Rd, Purchase, NY 10577-2139
Tel (845) 306-1850 Founded/Ownrshp 1985
Sales 69.3MM^E EMP 1,400
SIC 3641 5719 5063 4225 3643 3229 Electric lamps & parts for generalized applications; Lamps & lamp shades; Lighting fixtures; General warehousing; Current-carrying wiring devices; Lamp sockets & receptacles (electric wiring devices); Pressed & blown glass
CEO: Dionne Gadsden
*CEO: Steve Imgham
*CFO: William Drexles
Ex VP: Jan Germis
Ex VP: Tom Mullally
Ex VP: Marcos Paganini
VP: Gregory Barry

D-U-N-S 80-961-6142
LIGHTNING FLUID SERVICES INC
1310 Southwood St, Alice, TX 78332-3923
Tel (361) 396-0801 Founded/Ownrshp 2007
Sales 371.5MM^E EMP 12
SIC 1389 7389 Oil field services;
Pr: William Starns

D-U-N-S 78-909-7623
LIGHTNING HOCKEY LP
TAMPA BAY LIGHTNING, THE
(Suby of TAMPA BAY SPORTS ENTERTAINMENT LLC) ★
401 Channelside Dr, Tampa, FL 33602-5400
Tel (813) 301-6500 Founded/Ownrshp 2008
Sales 52.2MM^E EMP 1,200
SIC 7941 Ice hockey club
Pr: Steve Griggs
CEO: Tod Leiweke
Ch: Jeff Vinik
Ex VP: Jarrod Dillon
Ex VP: Jamie Spencer
Ex VP: Bill Wickett
Genl Mgr: Darryl Benge

LIGHTOWER FIBER NETWORKS
See LIGHT TOWER FIBER LLC

D-U-N-S 09-142-7708 IMP
LIGHTS OF AMERICA INC (CA)
611 Reyes Dr, Walnut, CA 91789-3098
Tel (909) 594-7883 Founded/Ownrshp 1977
Sales 296.0MM^E EMP 1,200
SIC 3645 3646 7629 3641 Fluorescent lighting fixtures, residential; Fluorescent lighting fixtures, commercial; Electrical repair shops; Electric lamps
CEO: Usman Vakil
*Ex VP: Farooq Vakil
Genl Mgr: Anjum Rokerya
Mktg Mgr: Brian Halliwell

D-U-N-S 00-365-2906
LIGHTSOURCE CREATIVE SERVICES INC
121 La Porte Ave, Fort Collins, CO 80524-4379
Tel (970) 224-2806 Founded/Ownrshp 1996
Sales 150.0MM EMP 10
SIC 7336 Commercial art & graphic design
Pr: Matt Faye
*VP: Lisa Malmquist

D-U-N-S 14-940-0819
LIGHTSTONE GROUP LLC
460 Park Ave Rm 1300, New York, NY 10022-1861
Tel (212) 616-9969 Founded/Ownrshp 2002
Sales 781.3MM^E EMP 10,780
SIC 6531 Real estate agents & managers
CEO: David Lichtenstein
Pr: Christian Gabrielsen
*Pr: Mitchell C Hochberg
*CFO: Donna Brandin
*Ex VP: Arvind K Bajaj
*Ex VP: Pamela Z Meadows
Sr VP: Mark Green
Sr VP: Lauren Levin
Sr VP: Jonathan Rabinow
VP: Akiva Elazary
VP: Joshua Kornberg
VP: Josh Rubinger
Dir Risk M: Peggy Brockmann
Creative D: Audra Tuskes

LIGHTWORKS OF STEAMBOAT
See ASPEN ELECTRIC AND SUPPLY INC

D-U-N-S 05-123-8835
LIGHTYEAR CAPITAL LLC
9 W 57th St, New York, NY 10019-2701
Tel (212) 328-0555 Founded/Ownrshp 2001
Sales 174.6MM^E EMP 966
SIC 6726 Investment offices
CFO: Ellan Hayon
Bd of Dir: Mark Vassallo
Ex VP: Julie Miller
Ex VP: Michael Mooney
VP: Jay Comerford
VP: David Cynn
VP: Kevin Doldan
*Prin: David W Glenn
Mng Dir: Chris Casciato

Mng Dir: Michael Doppelt
Mng Dir: Lori Forlano

D-U-N-S 08-573-2852
LIGON INDUSTRIES LLC
1927 1st Ave N Ste 500, Birmingham, AL 35203-4000
Tel (205) 322-3302 *Founded/Ownrshp* 1998
Sales 619.1MME *EMP* 2,155
SIC 3365 3593 3325 3471 3714 3446 Aluminum foundries; Fluid power cylinders & actuators; Alloy steel castings, except investment; Chromium plating of metals or formed products; Cylinder heads, motor vehicle; Architectural metalwork

LIL' DUTCH MAID COOKIES
See ABIMAR FOODS INC

D-U-N-S 06-529-1361
LIL THRIFT FOOD MARTS INC
1007 Arsenal Ave, Fayetteville, NC 28305-5329
Tel (910) 433-4490 *Founded/Ownrshp* 1971
Sales 93.7MME *EMP* 300
Accts Cherry Bekaert & Holland Llp
SIC 5541 5411 Filling stations, gasoline; Convenience stores, chain
CEO: Chris Neal
**Pr:* Vance B Neal

LILA DOYLE NURSING CARE FCILTY
See OCONEE MEDICAL CENTER

D-U-N-S 87-825-1966
LILJA CORP
229 Rickenbacker Cir, Livermore, CA 94551-7616
Tel (925) 454-9544 *Founded/Ownrshp* 1992
Sales 84.7MME *EMP* 240
SIC 1541 Industrial buildings & warehouses
CEO: Walter Bowe
**Pr:* William Field
**COO:* Mike Simmons
**CFO:* Matt Costenbader
**VP:* Michael Simmons

D-U-N-S 00-701-8377 IMP
LILLY CO
3613 Knight Arnold Rd, Memphis, TN 38118-2729
Tel (901) 363-6000 *Founded/Ownrshp* 1919
Sales 131.2MME *EMP* 183
Accts Reynolds Bone & Griesbeck Plc
SIC 5084 7699 7359 5046 Lift trucks & parts; Materials handling machinery; Industrial truck repair; Equipment rental & leasing; Shelving, commercial & industrial
Pr: Thomas J Clark III
**COO:* Eric Wisher

LILLY DEL CARIBE
See ELI LILLY INDUSTRIES INC

LILLY PULITZER
See SUGARTOWN WORLDWIDE LLC

LILLY SOFTWARE ASSOCIATES
See INFOR (US) INC

D-U-N-S 96-304-9908
LILY CARES FOUNDATION INC
Lilly Corporate Center, Indianapolis, IN 46285-0001
Tel (317) 277-9109 *Founded/Ownrshp* 2010
Sales 503.3MM *EMP* 2
SIC 8699 Charitable organization

D-U-N-S 01-922-7354
LILY TRANSPORTATION CORP
145 Rosemary St Ste D3, Needham, MA 02494-3251
Tel (781) 247-1300 *Founded/Ownrshp* 1958
Sales 111.5MME *EMP* 500
SIC 4213 4212 Trucking, except local; Local trucking, without storage
CEO: John Simourian II
**Ch Bd:* John A Simourian
**CFO:* Stephen Dmohowski
CFO: Derica Rice
CFO: Vern Sherman
**Ex VP:* James E Walker
Sr VP: Jim Lavery
**VP:* Jonathan L Baldi
VP: Eric Bromage
VP: Peter Crowley
**VP:* Jack Poor
VP: David Powell

LIMA MEMORIAL HEALTH SYSTEM
See LIMA MEMORIAL HOSPITAL

D-U-N-S 01-292-1818
LIMA MEMORIAL HOSPITAL
LIMA MEMORIAL HEALTH SYSTEM
(*Suby of* LIMA MEMORIAL JOINT OPERATING CO) ★
1001 Bellefontaine Ave, Lima, OH 45804-2899
Tel (419) 228-3335 *Founded/Ownrshp* 1984
Sales 172.3MM *EMP* 1,500E
SIC 8062 General medical & surgical hospitals
Pr: Michael Swick
**VP:* Bob Armstrong
Comm Dir: Janis Daley
Ansthlgy: Kyung W Park

D-U-N-S 07-980-7440
LIMA MEMORIAL JOINT OPERATING CO
1001 Belelfontaine Ave, Lima, OH 45804
Tel (419) 228-5165 *Founded/Ownrshp* 1998
Sales 176.1MM *EMP* 1,500
SIC 8062 General medical & surgical hospitals
Pr: Michael Swick
**CFO:* Eric Pohjala

D-U-N-S 19-962-3414 IMP
LIMA REFINING CO
(*Suby of* HUSKY ENERGY INC)
1150 S Metcalf St, Lima, OH 45804-1145
Tel (419) 226-2300 *Founded/Ownrshp* 2007
Sales 173.5MME *EMP* 400E
SIC 2911 Petroleum refining
CEO: William Kalsse
**Pr:* Gregory King
Sr VP: Todd Neu
Opers Mgr: Patrick Conrath

D-U-N-S 00-791-5960
■ **LIMBACH CO LLC**
(*Suby of* LIMBACH FACILITY SVC) ★
31 35th St, Pittsburgh, PA 15201-1917
Tel (412) 359-2173 *Founded/Ownrshp* 1901
Sales 261.8MME *EMP* 850
SIC 1711 Plumbing, heating, air-conditioning contractors
CEO: Charles A Bacon III
**Pr:* Craig Sasser
**CFO:* Dennis Sacco
Sr VP: David R Leathes
Exec: Veronica Onorato
Plng Mgr: Rich Miller
Plng Mgr: Steve Norris'
CTO: Robert Wilder
Opers Mgr: Chris Richardson
Snr PM: Brad Brown
Snr PM: Greg Fox

D-U-N-S 10-157-9738
■ **LIMBACH FACILITY SERVICES LLC**
LIMBACH FACILITY SVC
(*Suby of* LIMBACH HOLDINGS LLC) ★
31 35th St, Pittsburgh, PA 15201-1917
Tel (412) 359-2100 *Founded/Ownrshp* 2002
Sales 291.8MME *EMP* 1,011
SIC 1711 8741 Plumbing, heating, air-conditioning contractors; Administrative management
CEO: Charles A Bacon
COO: Kristopher Thorne
**CFO:* John Jordan Jr
VP: Mike Balistreri
VP: Kevin Labrecque
VP: David Leathers
Brnch Mgr: Robert Morgan
IT Man: Rick Davidson
Sls Mgr: Tony White

LIMBACH FACILITY SVC
See LIMBACH FACILITY SERVICES LLC

D-U-N-S 88-447-1509
▲ **LIMBACH HOLDINGS LLC**
31 35th St, Pittsburgh, PA 15201-1917
Tel (412) 359-2173 *Founded/Ownrshp* 1994
Sales 292.0MME *EMP* 1,066
SIC 1711 Plumbing, heating, air-conditioning contractors
Ch: Charles A Bacon
**CFO:* John T Jordan Jr

D-U-N-S 03-147-4096
LIME ENERGY CO
4 Gateway Ctr Fl 4, Newark, NJ 07102-4073
Tel (201) 416-2575 *Founded/Ownrshp* 1997
Sales 112.6MM *EMP* 270
SIC 1711 8711 Mechanical contractor; Energy conservation engineering
Pr: C Adam Procell
**Ch Bd:* Andreas Hildebrand
CFO: Bruce D Torkelson

D-U-N-S 60-246-6088 IMP
LIME HOLDING INC
(*Suby of* KDM HOLDING INC) ★
3700 Hulen St, Fort Worth, TX 76107-6816
Tel (817) 732-8164 *Founded/Ownrshp* 1981
Sales 472.2MME *EMP* 500
SIC 3274 Lime; Quicklime; Hydrated lime; Dolomitic lime, dead-burned dolomite
CEO: Ludwig De Mot

D-U-N-S 08-013-8237
LIMECOM INC (FL)
6303 Blue Lagoon Dr, Miami, FL 33126-6002
Tel (786) 408-6743 *Founded/Ownrshp* 2015
Sales 108.2MM *EMP* 10
Accts Lopez Levi Lowenstein Pa C
SIC 4899 Data communication services
Pr: Orlando Taddeo
**CFO:* Daniel Contreras

D-U-N-S 02-955-1756
▲ **LIMELIGHT NETWORKS INC**
222 S Mill Ave Ste 800, Tempe, AZ 85281-2899
Tel (602) 850-5000 *Founded/Ownrshp* 2001
Sales 170.9MM *EMP* 509E
Accts Ernst & Young Llp Phoenix Ar
Tkr Sym LLNW *Exch* NGS
SIC 7372 7375 Application computer software; Business oriented computer software; Information retrieval services; On-line data base information retrieval
Pr: Robert A Lento
CFO: Sajid Malhotra
Ofcr: George E Vonderhaar
Sr VP: Michael D Disanto
VP: Kurt Silverman
Snr Ntwrk: Wayne Bouchard
Sftwr Eng: Nick Sherman
VP Opers: Dan Carney
VP Sls: Andy Clark
Mktg Mgr: Natascha Wilhelm
Sls Mgr: Michael Glynn
Board of Directors: Walter D Amaral, Gray Hall, Jeffrey T Fisherm Joseph H, Mark Midle, David C Peterschmidt

D-U-N-S 07-210-6628
LIMESTONE COUNTY BOARD OF EDUCATION
300 S Jefferson St, Athens, AL 35611-2549
Tel (256) 232-5353 *Founded/Ownrshp* 1900
Sales 107.7MME *EMP* 1,200
SIC 8211 School board
Pr: Brett McGill
Board of Directors: Dr William Berry, John Blankenship, Joel Glaze, Mike Poff, Fred Robertson Jr, Shelly Towe

D-U-N-S 07-979-8750
LIMESTONE COUNTY SCHOOL DISTRICT
300 S Jefferson St, Athens, AL 35611-2549
Tel (256) 232-5353 *Founded/Ownrshp* 2015
Sales 15.0MME *EMP* 1,096E
SIC 8211 Public elementary & secondary schools
Bd of Dir: Charles Shoulders
Teacher Pr: Tommy Hunter

D-U-N-S 08-015-2819
LIMETREE BAY TERMINALS LLC
(*Suby of* ARCLIGHT CAPITAL PARTNERS LLC) ★
1 Estate Hope, Christiansted, VI 00820
Tel (340) 692-3000 *Founded/Ownrshp* 2015
Sales 200.0MM *EMP* 525
SIC 4225 General warehousing & storage
CEO: Darius Sweet
**VP:* Keith Neil
**VP:* Sloan Schawyer

LIMEVILLE QUARRY
See MARTIN LIMESTONE INC

D-U-N-S 05-313-8812 IMP/EXP
LIMEX SICAR LTD CO
SICAR FARMS
701 Trinity St, Mission, TX 78572-1624
Tel (956) 581-6080 *Founded/Ownrshp* 2010
Sales 99.1MM *EMP* 150
SIC 5148 Fresh fruits & vegetables
CEO: Luis Jorge Gudino Ochoa
**CFO:* Alberto Albarran Moreno
Opers Mgr: Rosbel Ruiz
**VP Sls:* Dan Edmeier

LIMITED, THE
See LIMITED STORES LLC

LIMITED
See L BRANDS STORE DESIGN & CONSTRUCTION INC

D-U-N-S 04-231-5093 IMP/EXP
LIMITED STORES LLC
LIMITED, THE
(*Suby of* SUN CAPITAL PARTNERS INC) ★
7775 Walton Pkwy Ste 400, New Albany, OH 43054-8203
Tel (614) 289-2200 *Founded/Ownrshp* 2007
Sales 2.1MMME *EMP* 18,000
SIC 5621 5941 5632 Ready-to-wear apparel, women's; Sporting goods & bicycle shops; Apparel accessories
CFO: Stuart Burgdoerfer
Treas: Timothy Faber
VP: Jenn M Jong
VP: Martyn Redgrave
Plng Mgr: Chris Bichsel
Store Mgr: Christina Newton

D-U-N-S 00-691-4105 IMP/EXP
▲ **LIMONEIRA CO**
1141 Cummings Rd Ofc, Santa Paula, CA 93060-9783
Tel (805) 525-5541 *Founded/Ownrshp* 1893
Sales 100.3MM *EMP* 333E
Accts Ernst & Young Llp Los Angeles
Tkr Sym LMNR *Exch* NGM
SIC 0723 0174 0179 6531 6799 Fruit (fresh) packing services; Citrus fruits; Lemon grove; Orange grove; Avocado orchard; Real estate agents & managers; Real estate leasing & rentals; Commodity investors
Pr: Harold S Edwards
**Ch Bd:* Gordon E Kimball
COO: Gus Gunderson
CFO: Joseph D Rumley
CFO: Joseph Rumley
**V Ch Bd:* John W Blanchard
**V Ch Bd:* Robert M Sawyer
Ofcr: Jocelyn Hernandez
Sr VP: Alex M Teague
Genl Mgr: Lee Nesbitt
Sls Mgr: Maria Vargas
Board of Directors: John W H Merriman, Ronald Michaelis, Donald R Rudkin, Scott S Slater

D-U-N-S 08-526-1308 IMP/EXP
LIMSON TRADING INC
1300 Gezon Pkwy Sw, Grand Rapids, MI 49509-9300
Tel (616) 530-3110 *Founded/Ownrshp* 1998
Sales 126.9MM *EMP* 13
SIC 5141 Food brokers
Pr: David Lee Gray
VP: Barbara Kuiper
Genl Mgr: Jagtar Nijjar
Ql Cn Mgr: Katie Kolarik

D-U-N-S 11-852-5831
LIN R ROGERS ELECTRICAL CONTRACTORS INC
2050 Marconi Dr Ste 100, Alpharetta, GA 30005-2077
Tel (770) 772-3400 *Founded/Ownrshp* 1983
Sales 131.4MM *EMP* 1,100
Accts Moore Stephens Tiller Llc Dul
SIC 1731 General electrical contractor
Ch: Lin R Rogers
**VP:* Jamal Chehimi
**VP:* Benedict Cramer
**VP:* Jason Hayes
**VP:* Lindsey Rogers Schoultz
**VP:* Ken Sisson
**Prin:* Linda Chaney
VP Sls: Ron Gilcrease

D-U-N-S 79-143-1067
■ **LIN TELEVISION CORP**
(*Suby of* MEDIA GENERAL INC) ★
701 Brazos St Ste 800, Austin, TX 78701-2556
Tel (512) 774-6110 *Founded/Ownrshp* 2014
Sales 674.9MME *EMP* 5,300E
SIC 4833 Television broadcasting stations
Pr: Vincent L Sadusky
CFO: Richard J Schmaeling

D-U-N-S 10-320-3431
LIN TV CORP
1 W Exchange St Ste 305, Providence, RI 02903-1095
Tel (401) 454-2880 *Founded/Ownrshp* 1966
Sales 553.4MM *EMP* 2,558E
SIC 4833 7311

D-U-N-S 00-289-5597
LINBECK GROUP LLC
(*Suby of* AQUINAS CORP) ★
3900 Essex Ln Ste 1200, Houston, TX 77027-5486
Tel (713) 621-2350 *Founded/Ownrshp* 1964
Sales 295.1MME *EMP* 500
SIC 1542 Commercial & office building, new construction; Shopping center construction; Hospital construction
Ch Bd: Chuck Greco
CEO: David Stueckler
CFO: Bill Riegler
Ex VP: Bill Scott
VP: John Sylvester
Snr PM: Tom Hale
Board of Directors: Allen Nagel, Edwin H Wingate

LINC GROUP
See ABM FACILITY SOLUTIONS GROUP LLC

D-U-N-S 80-057-4019
LINC LOGISTICS CO
12755 E 9 Mile Rd, Warren, MI 48089-2621
Tel (586) 467-1500 *Founded/Ownrshp* 2012
Sales 98.0MME *EMP* 1,500
SIC 8742

D-U-N-S 62-220-4774
LINCARE HOLDINGS INC
(*Suby of* LINDE AG)
19387 Us Highway 19 N, Clearwater, FL 33764-3102
Tel (727) 530-7700 *Founded/Ownrshp* 2012
Sales 891.9MME *EMP* 13,216E
SIC 8082 8093 Home health care services; Specialty outpatient clinics
CEO: John P Byrnes
**Pr:* Shawn S Schabel
**CFO:* Paul G Gabos
Dist Mgr: Nan Pearson

D-U-N-S 08-642-1534
LINCARE INC
(*Suby of* LINCARE HOLDINGS INC) ★
19387 Us Highway 19 N, Clearwater, FL 33764-3102
Tel (727) 530-7700 *Founded/Ownrshp* 1972, 1990
Sales 651.3MME *EMP* 10,841
SIC 8082 5999 Home health care services; Hospital equipment & supplies
CEO: Kristen Hoefer
Pr: Vanessa Hager
**COO:* Greg McCarthy
CFO: Jim Emmanuel
CFO: Morris Kunofsky
**CFO:* Crispin Teufel
Ofcr: Jenna Pedersen
Ofcr: Jenna Petersen
Dist Mgr: Kyle Baxter
CIO: Gary Wolfifer
Dir IT: Don Crisp

D-U-N-S 36-257-6431
LINCHRIS HOTEL CORP
269 Hanover St Ste 2, Hanover, MA 02339-2245
Tel (781) 826-8824 *Founded/Ownrshp* 1985
Sales 90.7MME *EMP* 1,219
SIC 7011 Hotels & motels
CEO: Christopher Gistis
**Pr:* Michael Sullivan
**CFO:* Glenn Gistis
**Sr VP:* Robb M Moskowitz
Sr VP: Robb Moskowitz
**VP:* Dennis Jakubowski
**VP:* Liz Jobin

D-U-N-S 00-806-0170
LINCOLN BUILDERS INC
1809 Nrthpinte Ln Ste 201, Ruston, LA 71270
Tel (318) 255-3822 *Founded/Ownrshp* 1982
Sales 104.4MM *EMP* 85
Accts The Robinette Firm Apac Monr
SIC 1542 Commercial & office building, new construction; Commercial & office buildings, renovation & repair
CEO: Danny Graham
**Sec:* Lynn Hutchinson
Dir Bus: Ayres Bradford

LINCOLN COMPOSITES
See LINCOLN HEXAGON INC

LINCOLN COUNTY PUBLIC SCHOOLS
See LINCOLN COUNTY SCHOOL DISTRICT

D-U-N-S 19-301-6540
LINCOLN COUNTY SCHOOL DISTRICT
LINCOLN COUNTY PUBLIC SCHOOLS
353 N Generals Blvd, Lincolnton, NC 28092-3558
Tel (704) 732-2261 *Founded/Ownrshp* 1994
Sales 73.3MME *EMP* 1,600
SIC 8211 Public elementary & secondary schools
Genl Mgr: Pamela McBryde
IT Man: Kathy Houser
IT Man: Peggy Lafferty
Pr Dir: Sandra Andrews
Schl Brd P: Candi Burgin
Schl Brd P: Carl Robinson

D-U-N-S 07-979-9694
LINCOLN COUNTY SCHOOLS
10 Marland Ave, Hamlin, WV 25523-1058
Tel (304) 824-3033 *Founded/Ownrshp* 2015
Sales 7.1MME *EMP* 2,000E
SIC 8211 Public elementary & secondary schools
HC Dir: Teresa Ryan

D-U-N-S 18-995-3891
▲ **LINCOLN EDUCATIONAL SERVICES CORP**
200 Executive Dr Ste 340, West Orange, NJ 07052-3303
Tel (973) 736-9340 *Founded/Ownrshp* 1946
Sales 193.2MM *EMP* 2,398
Tkr Sym LINC *Exch* NGS
SIC 8222 Technical institute
CEO: Scott M Shaw
**Ch Bd:* J Barry Morrow
CFO: Brian K Meyers

D-U-N-S 07-178-3596 IMP/EXP
■ **LINCOLN ELECTRIC CO**
(*Suby of* LINCOLN ELECTRIC HOLDINGS INC) ★
22801 Saint Clair Ave, Euclid, OH 44117-1199
Tel (216) 481-8100 *Founded/Ownrshp* 1895
Sales 1.4MMME *EMP* 3,500

SIC 3548 Arc welding generators, alternating current & direct current; Electrodes, electric welding
Ch: Christopher L Mapes
Pr: Steven B Hedlund
Treas: Marsha Anderson
**Ex VP:* Frederick G Stueber
**Sr VP:* Geoffrey P Allman
**Sr VP:* Anthony Battle
VP: Michael S Mintun
VP: Steven R Summer
VP: Steven R Sumner
**Prin:* John Lincoln
Brnch Mgr: H Elliott

D-U-N-S 00-419-9048 IMP/EXP
▲ LINCOLN ELECTRIC HOLDINGS INC (OH)
22801 Saint Clair Ave, Cleveland, OH 44117-2524
Tel (216) 481-8100 *Founded/Ownrshp* 1895
Sales 2.5MMM *EMP* 10,000ᴱ
Accts Ernst & Young Llp Cleveland
Tkr Sym LECO *Exch* NGS
SIC 3548 Welding apparatus; Welding & cutting apparatus & accessories; Arc welding generators, alternating current & direct current
Pr: Christopher L Mapes
V Ch: Jeff Graham
Pr: George D Blankenship
Pr: Thomas A Flohn
Pr: Mathias Hallmann
Pr: Steven B Hedlund
Pr: Adel A Mir
Pr: David J Nangle
Pr: Fred Steuber
CFO: Vincent K Petrella
Treas: Mike Quinn
Ofcr: Gabriel Bruno
Ex VP: Michele R Kuhrt
Ex VP: Frederick G Stueber
Sr VP: Geoffrey P Allman
Sr VP: Michael J Whitehead
VP: Tim Keller

D-U-N-S 78-598-5248 IMP
■ LINCOLN ELECTRIC INTERNATIONAL HOLDING CO
(*Suby of* LINCOLN ELECTRIC HOLDINGS INC) ★
22801 Saint Clair Ave, Euclid, OH 44117-2524
Tel (216) 481-8100 *Founded/Ownrshp* 2000
Sales 352.3MMᴱ *EMP* 9,000ᴱ
SIC 3548 Welding apparatus
Ch: John Stropki
Dist Mgr: William Dotson
Genl Mgr: Dave Snider
Off Mgr: John Hach
IT Man: Keith Beaubien
IT Man: Stephanie Homa
Sales Exec: Mary A Beck
Natl Sales: David Mazak
Snr Mgr: George Slogik

D-U-N-S 82-959-7348
LINCOLN ELECTRIC SYSTEM
LES
1040 O St, Lincoln, NE 68508-3609
Tel (402) 475-4211 *Founded/Ownrshp* 1966
Sales 394.0MMᴱ *EMP* 453ᴱ
SIC 4911 Electric services
CEO: Kevin Wailes
COO: Doug Bantam
CFO: Keith Brown
VP: Keith U Brown
VP: Jason Fortik
VP: Douglas Friendt
VP: Dan Pudenz
VP: Russ Reno
VP: Shelley Sahling-Zart
Prgrm Mgr: Janet Chung
Prgrm Mgr: David Skipton

LINCOLN FINANCIAL
See LINCOLN NATIONAL INVESTMENT COMPANIES INC

D-U-N-S 18-753-9218
■ LINCOLN FINANCIAL ADVISORS CORP
(*Suby of* LINCOLN NATIONAL LIFE INSURANCE CO) ★
1300 S Clinton St, Fort Wayne, IN 46802-3506
Tel (800) 237-3813 *Founded/Ownrshp* 1968
Sales NA *EMP* 354
SIC 6311 6282 8748 8742 Life insurance carriers; Investment advisory service; Business consulting; Management consulting services
Pr: Robert W Dineen
**CEO:* Dennis R Glass
**COO:* Lucy Gafe
**Treas:* Jeffrey Coutts
VP: Duane Bernt
VP: Thomas Kaeher
VP: Susan Stalteri
**VP:* Ronald W Turpin
VP: Kenneth Wagner
**Prin:* Bob Dineen

D-U-N-S 02-749-8042
■ LINCOLN FINANCIAL SECURITIES CORP
(*Suby of* LNC) ★
1 Granite Pl, Concord, NH 03301-3258
Tel (603) 226-5000 *Founded/Ownrshp* 2007
Sales 110.0MM *EMP* 480
SIC 6722 Mutual fund sales, on own account
Pr: Christopher Flint
CFO: Keith Ryan
**Treas:* Jack Westen
Ex VP: Andrew A McElwee Jr
Ex VP: Harold L Morrison Jr
VP: Lisa S Clifford
VP: Dave Furman
VP: Margaret A Salamy
Opers Mgr: Tonya Amick

LINCOLN FINANCIAL SPORTS, INC.
See RAYCOM SPORTS NETWORK INC

D-U-N-S 08-673-1593
LINCOLN GENERAL INSURANCE CO
(*Suby of* KINGSWAY FINANCIAL SERVICES INC)
3501 Concord Rd Ste 120, York, PA 17402-8606
Tel (717) 757-0000 *Founded/Ownrshp* 1977
Sales NA *EMP* 465
SIC 6331 Fire, marine & casualty insurance
Pr: Gary J Orndorff
**Pr:* Scott D Wollney
VP: Timothy Kirk
IT Man: Kelly Dale
IT Man: Steven Schulze

D-U-N-S 06-219-6485
LINCOLN HARRIS LLC
4725 Piedmont Row Dr, Charlotte, NC 28210-4270
Tel (704) 331-0917 *Founded/Ownrshp* 1998
Sales 139.0MMᴱ *EMP* 658
SIC 6531 6552 Real estate agents & managers; Subdividers & developers
CEO: John W Harris III
Ex VP: Ronald K Steen
Sr VP: David Connor
Sr VP: Jubal Early
Sr VP: Carter Houchins
Sr VP: Ridr Knowlton
Sr VP: Dave Oddo
VP: Tracy Dodson
VP: Richard Faulkenberry
VP: Sara Hogan
VP: Brett Kennedy
VP: Matt Larson
VP: Betsy McIntyre
VP: Doug Millett
VP: Jackie Selle
VP: Patrick Stark
VP: Kaler Walker
VP: Marshall Williamson

D-U-N-S 04-130-2506
LINCOLN HERITAGE LIFE INSURANCE CO
(*Suby of* LONDEN INSURANCE GROUP INC) ★
4343 E Camelback Rd # 400, Phoenix, AZ 85018-2705
Tel (800) 750-6404 *Founded/Ownrshp* 1975
Sales NA *EMP* 100
SIC 6311 6411 Life insurance carriers; Insurance agents, brokers & service
CEO: Jack W Londen
**Pr:* Thomas Londen
**CFO:* Larry Schuneman
**Treas:* Dean Lathrop
**Sr VP:* Mary Johnson
**VP:* James Jerome
VP: Alex Londen
**VP:* Keith Perkins
**VP:* Doug Turner
Brnch Mgr: Ryan Farnsworth
VP Mktg: Norman Beazer

D-U-N-S 05-267-3359
LINCOLN HERITAGE LIFE INSURANCE CO
(*Suby of* LONDEN INSURANCE GROUP INC) ★
920 S Spring St, Springfield, IL 62704-2725
Tel (602) 957-1650 *Founded/Ownrshp* 2010
Sales NA *EMP* 1ᴱ
SIC 6311 Life insurance
Pr: Larry Schuneman
VP: Melanie Bearden

D-U-N-S 18-528-3772 IMP/EXP
LINCOLN HEXAGON INC
LINCOLN COMPOSITES
(*Suby of* HEXAGON COMPOSITES ASA)
5150 Nw 40th St, Lincoln, NE 68524
Tel (402) 470-5000 *Founded/Ownrshp* 2005
Sales 127.3MMᴱ *EMP* 300
SIC 3714 Gas tanks, motor vehicle
Pr: John D Schimenti

D-U-N-S 96-215-0335 IMP
LINCOLN HOLDINGS LLC
MONUMENTAL SPORTS & ENTRMT
627 N Glebe Rd Ste 850, Arlington, VA 22203-2129
Tel (202) 266-2200 *Founded/Ownrshp* 1999
Sales 63.0MMᴱ *EMP* 1,668ᴱ
SIC 7941 Sports clubs, managers & promoters
CFO: Peter Biche

D-U-N-S 00-446-8161 IMP/EXP
LINCOLN INDUSTRIAL CORP
(*Suby of* SKF MOTION TECHNOLOGIES) ★
5148 N Hanley Rd, Saint Louis, MO 63134-2419
Tel (314) 679-4200 *Founded/Ownrshp* 1912, 2010
Sales 128.2MMᴱ *EMP* 415
SIC 3569 3559 3561 3714 Lubricating equipment; Lubricating systems, centralized; Lubrication equipment, industrial; Lubrication machinery, automatic; Automotive related machinery; Automotive maintenance equipment; Pumps & pumping equipment; Industrial pumps & parts; Motor vehicle parts & accessories
Pr: Robert Law
Dist Mgr: Mark Pendergrass
Dist Mgr: Jerry Robinson
IT Man: Mike Gargac
IT Man: Bhavdip Shah
Ql Cn Mgr: Matthew Maidlow
Sales Exec: Steve Kornet
Sls Mgr: Aric Durr

D-U-N-S 15-454-8507 IMP
LINCOLN INDUSTRIES INC
600 W E St, Lincoln, NE 68522-1399
Tel (402) 475-3671 *Founded/Ownrshp* 1952
Sales 106.8MMᴱ *EMP* 550ᴱ
SIC 3471 3441 Electroplating & plating; Fabricated structural metal
CEO: Marc Le Baron
Pr: Thomas Hance
CFO: Andy Hunzeker
VP: Lori Saale
VP: Scott Weishaar
VP Bus: Matt Nyberg
VP Opers: Doug Custer
Ql Cn Mgr: Brandon Noerrlinger
Snr Mgr: Lucius Rippeteau
Snr Mgr: Dustin Young

D-U-N-S 07-283-5903
LINCOLN INTERMEDIATE UNIT 12
65 Billerbeck St, New Oxford, PA 17350-9375
Tel (717) 624-4616 *Founded/Ownrshp* 1971
Sales 36.6MMᴱ *EMP* 1,700
SIC 8299 Educational services
Ex Dir: Dr Leeann Zeroth

D-U-N-S 15-984-2020
LINCOLN INTERNATIONAL LLC
500 W Madison St Ste 3900, Chicago, IL 60661-4595
Tel (312) 580-8339 *Founded/Ownrshp* 1996
Sales 108.9MMᴱ *EMP* 190
Accts Mcgladrey Llp Chicago Illin
SIC 6211 Investment bankers
CEO: Robert B Barr
COO: Ivan Marina
VP: Greg Alkhas
VP: Mohit Bajpai
VP: Shruti Chaturvedi
VP: Anthony Crisman
VP: Jeff Foydl
VP: Brian Garfield
VP: Cynthya Goulet
VP: Christopher Gresh
VP: Neal Hawkins
VP: Robert M Horak
VP: Megha Jain
VP: Mark Jones-Pritchard
VP: Harry Kalmanowicz
VP: Bharathi Kannan
VP: Phillip Knotts
VP: Ningti Li
VP: Natalie Marjancik
VP: Saurin Mehta
VP: Vicki Mortimer

D-U-N-S 06-573-2406
LINCOLN INVESTMENT PLANNING LLC
601 Office Center Dr # 200, Fort Washington, PA 19034-3232
Tel (215) 887-8111 *Founded/Ownrshp* 1969
Sales 93.5MMᴱ *EMP* 220
SIC 6211 6282 Mutual funds, selling by independent salesperson; Brokers, security; Investment advice
Ch Bd: Edward S Forst Sr
**Pr:* Edward S Forst Jr
CFO: N Marr
**Treas:* Harry Forst
Chf Mktg O: Neil D Wernick
Ofcr: Matthew Attanucci
Ofcr: Raymond P Donnelly
Ofcr: Michael La Monda
Ofcr: Beth Peckman
Ofcr: Barry Rawls
Ofcr: Ronald Sherratt
Ofcr: Stanley Startzell
Ofcr: Jody Tolomeo
Ofcr: William Wilson
Sr VP: Steve Flax
Sr VP: Stephen Quickel
**VP:* Thomas Forst
VP: Dierdre Koerick

D-U-N-S 16-201-1647 IMP/EXP
LINCOLN MANUFACTURING INC
31209 Fm 2978 Rd, Magnolia, TX 77354-2388
Tel (281) 252-9494 *Founded/Ownrshp* 1997
Sales 162.0MMᴱ *EMP* 400
Accts David B Saba Cpa
SIC 3533 5082 Oil & gas field machinery; Oil field equipment
Pr: Eric Ward
**Treas:* David S Carnahan
VP: John Burns
Genl Mgr: Jacob Sponseller
Dir IT: James Dampier
IT Man: Rex Hebert
Mfg Mgr: Eric Bilbo
Ql Cn Mgr: Eric Norton
Sales Exec: Tammy Walker
Sls Mgr: Jose Negrete
Sales Asso: Alex Ward

D-U-N-S 00-468-2203
LINCOLN MEDICAL AND MENTAL HEALTH CENTER
NEW YORK CITY HEALTH AND HOSPI
(*Suby of* NEW YORK CITY HLTH & HOSPITALS) ★
234 E 149th St, Bronx, NY 10451-5504
Tel (718) 579-5000 *Founded/Ownrshp* 2011
Sales 530.5MM *EMP* 72ᴱ
SIC 8062 General medical & surgical hospitals
Ex Dir: Milton Nunez
Dir Rx: Michael Thomas
Ansthlgy: Jean R Maurice
Doctor: Jean Cadet
HC Dir: Lebby Delgado

D-U-N-S 04-946-7251
LINCOLN MEMORIAL UNIVERSITY
6965 Cumberland Gap Pkwy, Harrogate, TN 37752-8231
Tel (423) 869-3611 *Founded/Ownrshp* 1897
Sales 96.2MM *EMP* 400ᴱ
Accts Rodefer Moss & Co Pllc Knoxvi
SIC 8221 University
Pr: B James Dawson
**VP:* Cynthia Whitt
CIO: Richard Lewallen
Opers Supe: Kelly Nunn
Psych: Amy Spurlock
HC Dir: Janette Martin
HC Dir: Lisa Travis
HC Dir: Emily Weyant

LINCOLN MERCURY
See SUTTON FORD INC

LINCOLN NATIONAL CHINA INC
See CHINA FW INC

D-U-N-S 04-640-0180
▲ LINCOLN NATIONAL CORP
LNC
150 N Rad Chester Rd A305 Ste A, Radnor, PA 19087
Tel (484) 583-1400 *Founded/Ownrshp* 1968
Sales NA *EMP* 9,312ᴱ
Tkr Sym LNC *Exch* NYS
SIC 6311 6321 6371 6722 6411 6282 Life insurance; Health insurance carriers; Reinsurance carriers, accident & health; Pensions; Pension funds; Welfare pensions; Management investment, open-end; Insurance agents, brokers & service; Insurance agents & brokers; Property & casualty insurance agent; Investment advisory service
Pr: Dennis R Glass
**Ch Bd:* William H Cunningham
Pr: Belinda Fairbanks
Pr: Wilford H Fuller
Pr: Jeff Hamilton
Pr: Audrey Im
Pr: Mark E Konen
Pr: Jennifer Petruccelli
Pr: Howard Polk
Pr: Darla Roche
Pr: Andy Scanlon
Pr: Dan Schaecher
Pr: Lance Schulz
Pr: Carl Semmler
Pr: Jennifer Sheriff
Pr: Marcie Weber
Pr: Kristen Winsko
COO: Teresa Sayre
CFO: Randal J Freitag
Chf Inves: Ellen Cooper
Ofcr: Lisa M Buckingham
Board of Directors: Deirdre P Connelly, George W Henderson III, Eric G Johnson, Gary C Kelly, M Leanne Lachman, Michael F Mee, William Porter Payne, Patrick S Pittard, Isaiah Tidwell

D-U-N-S 96-629-5565
LINCOLN NATIONAL CORP VOLUNTARY EMPLOYEE BENEFICIARY ASSN
150 N Radnor Chester Rd, Radnor, PA 19087-5252
Tel (484) 583-1669 *Founded/Ownrshp* 2011
Sales 117.4MM *EMP* 2
SIC 8699 Membership organizations

D-U-N-S 92-621-8652
■ LINCOLN NATIONAL INVESTMENT COMPANIES INC
LINCOLN FINANCIAL
(*Suby of* LNC) ★
200 E Berry St, Fort Wayne, IN 46802-2731
Tel (260) 455-2000 *Founded/Ownrshp* 1995
Sales 208.7MMᴱ *EMP* 4,000
SIC 6282 6722 Investment advice; Management investment, open-end
Pr: Jon Boscia

D-U-N-S 00-693-7163
■ LINCOLN NATIONAL LIFE INSURANCE CO
(*Suby of* LNC) ★
1300 S Clinton St, Fort Wayne, IN 46802-3506
Tel (260) 455-2000 *Founded/Ownrshp* 1998
Sales NA *EMP* 3,470
SIC 6411 Insurance agents, brokers & service
Pr: Dennis Glass
Pr: Paul E Gibson
Pr: John H Gotta
Pr: Eric Patterson
**CFO:* Frederick Crawford
Treas: Rise Taylow
**Ex VP:* Charles Cornelio
Sr VP: John Addison
Sr VP: Michael Burns
Sr VP: Sandra Callahan
Sr VP: Donald Dibble
Sr VP: Robert Dineen
Sr VP: Charles Elam II
Sr VP: Randal Freitag
Sr VP: Mark Konen
Sr VP: Marvin Maynard
Sr VP: Douglas Miller
Sr VP: William Seawell II
Sr VP: Kenneth Solon
Sr VP: Richard Stange
VP: Richard Corwin
Board of Directors: Keith Ryan

D-U-N-S 00-699-6763
■ LINCOLN NATIONAL LIFE INSURANCE CO
(*Suby of* LNC) ★
100 N Greene St, Greensboro, NC 27401-2547
Tel (336) 691-3000 *Founded/Ownrshp* 2007
Sales NA *EMP* 8,000
SIC 6411 6321 6324 Insurance agents, brokers & service; Accident insurance carriers; Health insurance carriers; Hospital & medical service plans
Pr: Dennis R Glass
**CFO:* Randal J Freitag
**Ex VP:* Adam G Ciongoli
Board of Directors: George William Henderson I

D-U-N-S 80-130-5913
■ LINCOLN NATIONAL RISK MANAGEMENT INC
(*Suby of* LNC) ★
1670 Magnavox Way, Fort Wayne, IN 46804-1536
Tel (260) 455-2000 *Founded/Ownrshp* 1998
Sales NA *EMP* 3,650
SIC 6411 Insurance agents, brokers & service
Pr: Jon Boscia
**VP:* Lowry Scensrud
VP: Russell Sviever

D-U-N-S 80-793-8928 IMP/EXP
LINCOLN PAPER AND TISSUE LLC
50 Katadin Ave, Lincoln, ME 04457-1307
Tel (207) 794-0600 *Founded/Ownrshp* 2004
Sales 198.7MMᴱ *EMP* 400
SIC 2621

D-U-N-S 10-065-0431
LINCOLN PARISH WILDLIFE FEDERATION
410 S Farmerville St, Ruston, LA 71270-4655
Tel (318) 255-1430 *Founded/Ownrshp* 1880
Sales 81.0MM *EMP* 1,104
Accts Allen Green & Williamson Llp
SIC 8211 School board
CFO: Yoland Dade
Psych: Marilyn Rushing

LINCOLN PLASTICS
See PCE INC

LINCOLN PROPERTY CO
See LPC COMMERCIAL SERVICES INC

D-U-N-S 00-295-3008 IMP/EXP
LINCOLN PROPERTY CO
LPC
2000 Mckinney Ave # 1000, Dallas, TX 75201-1954
Tel (214) 740-3300 *Founded/Ownrshp* 1979
Sales 369.2MM^E *EMP* 3,985
SIC 6531 Real estate managers
Pr: A Mack Pogue
Pr: Tim Byrne
CFO: William A Macneil
CFO: Dennis Streit
Treas: Nancy Davis
Ex VP: Brian Byrne
Ex VP: JeffT Courtwright
Ex VP: Kevin Keane
Ex VP: Ellis L Shamburger
Sr VP: Tony Bartlett
Sr VP: Tony R Bartlett
Sr VP: Greg Cahill
Sr VP: Scott Caldwell
Sr VP: Adriano Calvanese
Sr VP: David Connor
Sr VP: Mike Crockett
Sr VP: Charlie Giammalva
Sr VP: Billy J Grant
Sr VP: Rex Lowe
Sr VP: Michael Maloney
Sr VP: John R Miller

D-U-N-S 13-936-3295 IMP/EXP
LINCOLN PROVISION INC
CHICAGO GOURMET STEAKS
824 W 38th Pl, Chicago, IL 60609-1415
Tel (773) 254-2400 *Founded/Ownrshp* 1985
Sales 86.2MM^E *EMP* 125^E
SIC 5142 5147 Packaged frozen goods; Meats & meat products
Pr: James J Stevens
**Pr:* Jim J Stevens Jr
CFO: Niteen Joshi
**VP:* Mark Stevens
Genl Mgr: Jon Schaffner
Ql Cn Mgr: Dulce Figueroa

D-U-N-S 07-289-8737
LINCOLN PUBLIC SCHOOLS INC
LANCASTER CNTY SCHL DISTRCT 1
5905 O St, Lincoln, NE 68510-2235
Tel (402) 436-1000 *Founded/Ownrshp* 1854
Sales 417.5MM *EMP* 6,950
Accts Hsmc-Orizon Kansas City Omah
SIC 8211 Public senior high school; Public junior high school; Public elementary school
Treas: Kirk Adams
VP: Lance Francisco
VP: Lorinda Rice
CIO: Wade Gibson
DP Exec: Lisa Bogus
Instr Medi: Mary Reiman
HC Dir: Matt Avey

D-U-N-S 03-513-8510
■ LINCOLN SYSCO INC
(*Suby of* SYSCO CORP) ★
900 King Bird Rd, Lincoln, NE 68521-3009
Tel (402) 423-1031 *Founded/Ownrshp* 1959
Sales 299.3MM^E *EMP* 460
SIC 5148 5142 5143 5141 5087 5113 Fresh fruits & vegetables; Soup, frozen; Dairy products, except dried or canned; Cheese; Groceries, general line; Restaurant supplies; Industrial & personal service paper; Cups, disposable plastic & paper; Napkins, paper; Towels, paper
Pr: Bill Delaney
**Pr:* Kim B Brown
CFO: Fred Schmidt
**Sr VP:* Brian Beach
VP Bus Dev: Gregory Munger
MIS Dir: Michael Chase
Dir IT: Ken Waltke
Sfty Mgr: Suraya Kamelian
Opers Mgr: Shari Hupka
Sls Mgr: Timothy Peterzen
Sls Mgr: David Slagle

D-U-N-S 07-754-9285
■ LINCOLN TECHNICAL INSTITUTE INC
(*Suby of* LINCOLN EDUCATIONAL SERVICES CORP) ★
200 Executive Dr Ste 340, West Orange, NJ 07052-3397
Tel (718) 246-4001 *Founded/Ownrshp* 1999
Sales 67.5MM^E *EMP* 1,200
Accts Deloitte & Touche Llp Parsipp
SIC 8222 Technical institute
Ch Bd: Shaun Mc Alamt
CFO: Cesar Riveiro
**Treas:* Nicholas Raspa
VP: Alexandra Luster
VP: Brian Meyers
Genl Mgr: Marcy Gadeck
VP Opers: Stephen Buchenot
VP Opers: Deborah Ramentol

D-U-N-S 15-399-6012 IMP
LINCOLNSHIRE MANAGEMENT INC
780 3rd Ave Rm 4000, New York, NY 10017-2173
Tel (212) 319-3633 *Founded/Ownrshp* 1987
Sales 144.6MM^E *EMP* 400
SIC 6211 7389 3599 Investment bankers; Automobile recovery service; Catapults
Pr: Thomas J Maloney
VP: Drew Shea
Comm Man: Bill Buttrick
Prin: W A Shea
Mng Dir: James Binch
Mng Dir: C K Clay
Mng Dir: Phil Jakeway
Mng Dir: Philip Kim
Mng Dir: Pieter Kodde
Mng Dir: James McLaughlin
Mng Dir: James McNair

D-U-N-S 15-287-1591
LINCOLNWAY ENERGY LLC
59511 Lincoln Hwy, Nevada, IA 50201-7992
Tel (515) 232-1010 *Founded/Ownrshp* 2006
Sales 101.1MM *EMP* 41
Accts Rsm Us Llp Des Moines Iowa
SIC 2869 2861 Ethyl alcohol, ethanol; Ethanolamines; Ethyl acetate, natural
Pr: Eric Hakmiller
**Ch Bd:* JeffTaylor
CFO: Rick Ogle
**Treas:* Terrill Wycoff
**V Ch Bd:* Brian Conrad
Off Mgr: Kay Gammon
Board of Directors: William Couser, Timothy Fevold, Gregory Geoffroy, James Hill, Kurt Olson, Rick Vaughan

D-U-N-S 96-730-4309
▲ LINDBLAD EXPEDITIONS HOLDINGS INC
509 7th St Nw, Washington, DC 20004-1600
Tel (202) 654-7060 *Founded/Ownrshp* 2010
Sales 209.9MM *EMP* 72^E
Tkr Sym LIND *Exch* NAS
SIC 6799 Investors
Ch Bd: Mark D Ein
**CFO:* L Dyson Dryden

D-U-N-S 06-542-3485 IMP/EXP
LINDE ENGINEERING NORTH AMERICA INC
LINDE ENGINEERING US
(*Suby of* LINDE HOLDINGS LLC) ★
6100 S Yale Ave Ste 1200, Tulsa, OK 74136-1905
Tel (918) 477-1200 *Founded/Ownrshp* 1982
Sales 139.3MM^E *EMP* 260
SIC 3567 8711 Incinerators, metal: domestic or commercial; Industrial engineers
Pr: Joerg Linsenmaier
Pr: Samir J Serhan
CFO: Laurie Brown
Treas: Gabriela Redondo
VP: Emerson Rhodes
Sfty Mgr: Verna Harrison
Snr PM: James A Deisinger

LINDE ENGINEERING US
See LINDE ENGINEERING NORTH AMERICA INC

D-U-N-S 80-556-8339 IMP/EXP
LINDE GAS NORTH AMERICA LLC
(*Suby of* LINDE GROUP) ★
200 Somerset Corp Blvd # 7000, Bridgewater, NJ 08807-2882
Tel (908) 464-8100 *Founded/Ownrshp* 2006
Sales 936.7MM^E *EMP* 3,700
SIC 2813 Oxygen, compressed or liquefied; Nitrogen; Argon; Hydrogen
Ch: Mark D Weller
**Pr:* Patrick F Murphy
**CEO:* Dr Wolfgang Reitzle
VP: Philippe D Brunet

D-U-N-S 00-417-4819 IMP/EXP
LINDE GAS USA LLC
(*Suby of* LINDE AG)
200 Somset Cor B Ste 7000, Bridgewater, NJ 08807
Tel (908) 464-8100 *Founded/Ownrshp* 2007
Sales 121.9MM^E *EMP* 600^E
SIC 2813 5084 Oxygen, compressed or liquefied; Nitrogen; Acetylene; Hydrogen; Welding machinery & equipment
Pr: Patrick Murphy
**Treas:* Jonathan Hoy
**Ex VP:* Mark Weller
**Sr VP:* John Brull
VP: Gene Allen
VP: David Johnston
Netwrk Mgr: Marryann Sicola
Plnt Mgr: Terry Phipps

LINDE GROUP
See LINDE NORTH AMERICA INC

D-U-N-S 13-160-2331
LINDE HOLDINGS LLC
(*Suby of* LINDE GROUP) ★
6100 S Yale Ave Ste 1200, Tulsa, OK 74136-1905
Tel (918) 477-1200 *Founded/Ownrshp* 2005
Sales 139.3MM^E *EMP* 389
SIC 8711 Engineering services
IT Man: Ben Beckham
Opers Mgr: Shirley Bunch

D-U-N-S 00-136-8141 IMP/EXP
LINDE LLC
(*Suby of* LINDE GROUP) ★
200 Somerset Corporate Bl, Bridgewater, NJ 08807-2882
Tel (908) 464-8100 *Founded/Ownrshp* 2006
Sales 1.2MMM^E *EMP* 3,700
SIC 2813 3569 3561 3823 Oxygen, compressed or liquefied; Nitrogen; Argon; Hydrogen; Gas separators (machinery); Pumps & pumping equipment; Industrial flow & liquid measuring instruments
COO: Joe Dagostino
Treas: Lisa Gaschler
Ofcr: Solms Wittig
Top Exec: Valerie Egan
Top Exec: Susan Ross
VP: Cliff Caldwell
Mng Dir: Sanjiv Lamba
Brnch Mgr: Pablo Pacheco
Genl Mgr: Gene Allen
Genl Mgr: Christian Lafleur
Dir IT: Bruce Turnbull

D-U-N-S 10-624-8008 IMP/EXP
LINDE NORTH AMERICA INC
LINDE GROUP
(*Suby of* LINDE AG)
200 Somerset Corporate Bl, Bridgewater, NJ 08807-2882
Tel (908) 464-8100 *Founded/Ownrshp* 1983
Sales 2.2MMM^E *EMP* 3,700^E
SIC 2813 3569 3559 3561 3511 3823 Industrial gases; Oxygen, compressed or liquefied; Nitrogen; Argon; Gas producers, generators & other gas related equipment; Cryogenic machinery, industrial; Pumps & pumping equipment; Turbines & turbine generator sets; Flow instruments, industrial process type
Pr: Pat Murphy
Pr: Frederic Jagush
Ex VP: Kenneth Linde
Genl Mgr: Zhishan Ben
CIO: Konstantin Fiedler
Dir IT: Bruce Turnbull
Plnt Mgr: Al Espy
Plnt Mgr: Kristie Hawkins
Plnt Mgr: Daniel Kahan
Plnt Mgr: Robert Mathers
Plnt Mgr: Keith Neanover

D-U-N-S 05-594-0043 IMP
LINDE PROCESS PLANTS INC
6100 S Yale Ave Ste 1200, Tulsa, OK 74136-1905
Tel (918) 477-1200 *Founded/Ownrshp* 2002
Sales 86.1MM^E *EMP* 389
SIC 3444 8711 1629

D-U-N-S 09-282-9055
LINDEN LLC
111 S Wacker Dr Ste 3350, Chicago, IL 60606-4306
Tel (312) 506-5657 *Founded/Ownrshp* 1998
Sales 111.2MM^E *EMP* 151^E
SIC 6726 Management investment funds, closed-end
CFO: Douglass W Vandegrift

D-U-N-S 01-402-0283
LINDEN UNIFIED SCHOOL DISTRICT
18527 E Highway 26, Linden, CA 95236-9584
Tel (209) 887-3894 *Founded/Ownrshp* 1965
Sales 45.0MM^E *EMP* 1,006
SIC 8211 Public elementary & secondary schools; School board
MIS Dir: Shelly Campigli
Schl Brd P: Marvin Vaccarezza

D-U-N-S 15-731-2620
LINDENGROVE INC
LINDENGROVE NURSING HOMES
13700 W National Ave # 9, New Berlin, WI 53151-9503
Tel (262) 797-4600 *Founded/Ownrshp* 1986
Sales 51.0MM *EMP* 1,000
Accts Wipfli Llp Milwaukee Wi
SIC 8051 5912 Convalescent home with continuous nursing care; Drug stores
CEO: Linda Joel
**CFO:* Mark Sperka
**Prin:* Robert Schaefer
Ex Dir: Dave Rindfleisch

D-U-N-S 96-351-7201
LINDENGROVE MUKWONAGO
837 County Road Nn E, Mukwonago, WI 53149-1013
Tel (262) 363-6830 *Founded/Ownrshp* 2010
Sales 505.1MM *EMP* 23^E
SIC 8051

LINDENGROVE NURSING HOMES
See LINDENGROVE INC

LINDENHURST PUBLIC SCHOOL
See LINDENHURST UNION FREE SCHOOL DISTRICT

D-U-N-S 06-594-8036
LINDENHURST UNION FREE SCHOOL DISTRICT
LINDENHURST PUBLIC SCHOOL
350 Daniel St, Lindenhurst, NY 11757-3547
Tel (631) 226-6441 *Founded/Ownrshp* 1930
Sales 45.5MM^E *EMP* 1,000
SIC 8211 Public elementary & secondary schools
VP: Edward J Murphy Jr
Dir IT: Kelly Waters
IT Man: Edward Salina
Pr Dir: Alison De Maria
Board of Directors: Cathy Donato Sectry Bussin

LINDENMEYR CENTRAL
See CENTRAL NATIONAL GOTTESMAN INC

D-U-N-S 07-696-4410
LINDENWOOD UNIVERSITY
209 S Kingshighway St, Saint Charles, MO 63301-1695
Tel (636) 949-2000 *Founded/Ownrshp* 2006
Sales 185.0MM *EMP* 1,200
Accts Kpmg Llp Columbus Oh
SIC 8221 University
Pr: James D Evans
Dir Recs: Adam Ulrich
**CFO:* David Kandel
Treas: John Hammond
VP: John Oldani
VP: Jann R Weitzel
Comm Dir: Scott Queen
Ex Dir: Brian Rivolta
CTO: Jann Weitdel
Dir IT: Scott Spinner
Mktg Dir: Mark Abney

D-U-N-S 00-411-2884 IMP/EXP
LINDER INDUSTRIAL MACHINERY CO (FL)
(*Suby of* SUMITOMO CORPORATION)
1601 S Frontage Rd # 100, Plant City, FL 33563-2004
Tel (813) 754-2727 *Founded/Ownrshp* 1953, 1996
Sales 158.1MM^E *EMP* 470
SIC 5082 7353 Construction & mining machinery; Heavy construction equipment rental
Pr: John L Coughlin
CFO: Hank Bolding
**CFO:* Peggy H Smith
Ex VP: Robert Olejniczak
VP: Chet Miller
VP: Eric Teague
Exec: Alan Nucci
Off Mgr: Ann Moore
Netwrk Mgr: Don Knox
Mktg Dir: Melissa Hancock
Mktg Mgr: Dan Sherman

D-U-N-S 01-625-5852 IMP/EXP
LINDER INDUSTRIAL MACHINERY CO
SUMIQUIP
(*Suby of* SUMITOMO CORPORATION)
1601 S Frontage Rd # 100, Plant City, FL 33563-2004
Tel (813) 754-2727 *Founded/Ownrshp* 1953
Sales 321.6MM^E *EMP* 1,004^E
SIC 5082 General construction machinery & equipment
Ch: Jeff Cox
**Pr:* Hitoshi Kai
**CFO:* Peggy Smith
**VP:* Max Kobyashi
**VP:* Masanori Osada

LINDSAY CADILLAC OF ALEXANDRIA
See LINDSAY MOTOR CAR CO

D-U-N-S 06-864-5696 EXP
▲ LINDSAY CORP
2222 N 111th St, Omaha, NE 68164-3817
Tel (402) 829-6800 *Founded/Ownrshp* 1955
Sales 516.4MM *EMP* 1,366^E
Accts Kpmg Llp Omaha Ne
Tkr Sym LNN *Exch* NYS
SIC 3523 3599 3443 Irrigation equipment, self-propelled; Machine & other job shop work; Pipe, standpipe & culverts
Pr: Richard W Parod
**Ch Bd:* Michael C Nahl
Pr: C Mike Harris
Pr: Randy A Wood
CFO: Brian L Ketcham
Treas: Mark A Roth
Ex VP: David B Downing
VP: Eric R Arneson
Board of Directors: Robert E Brunner, Michael N Christodolou, W Thomas Jagodinski, David B Rayburn, Michael D Walter, William F Welsh II

LINDSAY GOLDBERG
See GOLDBERG LINDSAY & CO LLC

D-U-N-S 08-006-3929
LINDSAY GOLDBERG LLC
630 5th Ave Fl 30, New York, NY 10111-0204
Tel (212) 651-1100 *Founded/Ownrshp* 2005
Sales 449.0MM^E *EMP* 210^E
SIC 6799 Investors
VP: Rachael A Wagner

D-U-N-S 02-620-0256 IMP
■ LINDSAY MANUFACTURING LLC
(*Suby of* LINDSAY CORP) ★
2222 N 111th St, Omaha, NE 68164-3817
Tel (402) 829-6800 *Founded/Ownrshp* 2006
Sales 94.6MM^E *EMP* 500
SIC 3523 3599 3499 3443 Irrigation equipment, self-propelled; Machine & other job shop work; Barricades, metal; Pipe, standpipe & culverts
Pr: Richard W Parod
CFO: Jim Raabe
Treas: David B Downing
VP: Eric R Arneson
VP: Eric Arneson
VP: Scott Marion
VP: James Raabe
VP: Mark A Roth
VP: Jim Shearer
VP: Reuben P Srinivasan
Rgnl Mgr: Richard B Hall

D-U-N-S 02-362-9355 IMP
LINDSAY MOTOR CAR CO
LINDSAY CADILLAC OF ALEXANDRIA
1525 Kenwood Ave, Alexandria, VA 22302-2319
Tel (703) 998-6600 *Founded/Ownrshp* 1953
Sales 164.2MM^E *EMP* 150
SIC 5511 Automobiles, new & used
CEO: Danny Niblett
**VP:* Charles T Lindsay Jr
**Prin:* Chris Lindsay
Sales Asso: Frank Passarelli

D-U-N-S 13-239-1327 IMP
LINDT & SPRUNGLI (USA) INC
(*Suby of* CHOCOLADEFABRIKEN LINDT & SPRUNGLI AG)
1 Fine Chocolate Pl, Stratham, NH 03885-2592
Tel (603) 778-8100 *Founded/Ownrshp* 1925
Sales 285.4MM^E *EMP* 650
SIC 2066 5149 5441 Chocolate; Chocolate; Candy
CEO: Daniel Studer
CFO: Ray Tice
Top Exec: Rocio Perez
Mng Dir: Jaques Amey
Off Mgr: Mica Magee
CTO: Leesa Daw
Dir IT: Richard Hauck
IT Man: John Walter
VP Opers: Robert E Michalski
Manager: Chris Ball
Natl Sales: Mauro Curti

LINE PIPE INTERNATIONAL
See KELLY PIPE CO LLC

D-U-N-S 07-854-5588
LINEAGE LOGISTICS HOLDINGS LLC
17911 Von Karman Ave # 400, Irvine, CA 92614-6209
Tel (800) 678-7271 *Founded/Ownrshp* 2011
Sales 1.5MMM^E *EMP* 3,000^E
SIC 4222 Warehousing, cold storage or refrigerated
Pr: Greg Lehmkuhl
**Pr:* Timothy Dayton
**Pr:* Paul Hendricksen
**Pr:* Mike McClendon
**CEO:* Bill Hendricksen
CFO: Jeremy Breaux
**CFO:* Todd Nelson
Ofcr: Allen Merrill
**Ex VP:* Tim Smith
Sr VP: Greg Bryan
**Sr VP:* Scott Chapman
VP: Len Anderson
**VP:* Calvin Austin
**VP:* Marcus Lester
**VP:* Patrick Stimpert

D-U-N-S 07-909-2447
LINEAGE LOGISTICS LLC
(*Suby of* LINEAGE LOGISTICS HOLDINGS LLC) ★
17911 Von Karman Ave # 400, Irvine, CA 92614-6209
Tel (800) 678-7271 *Founded/Ownrshp* 2013
Sales 129.0MM^E *EMP* 175^E
SIC 4222 Cheese warehouse; Warehousing, cold storage or refrigerated

CEO: Bill Hendricksen
CFO: Jeremy Breaux
CFO: Richard French
Ex VP: Tim Smith
Sr VP: Greg Bryan
Sr VP: John Dittrick
VP: Ken Hudson
Genl Mgr: Paul Alberty
Genl Mgr: Willie Ashford
Genl Mgr: Pat Ballweber
Genl Mgr: Randy Benish

D-U-N-S 96-243-7096
■ LINEAGE POWER HOLDINGS INC
GE CRITICAL POWER
(Suby of GENERAL ELECTRIC CO) ★
601 Shiloh Rd, Plano, TX 75074-7210
Tel (974) 244-9288 Founded/Ownrshp 2007
Sales 171.9MM[E] EMP 2,300[E]
SIC 6719 Investment holding companies, except banks
CEO: Craig Witsoe
*CFO: Skip Sorenson
IT Man: Jeffry Ruff
VP Mktg: Trent Waterhouse

D-U-N-S 96-508-1180
LINEAR CONTROLS INC
107 1/2 Commission Blvd, Lafayette, LA 70508-3514
Tel (337) 839-9702 Founded/Ownrshp 2004
Sales 150.5MM[E] EMP 200
SIC 5063 Electrical apparatus & equipment
CEO: Andre Clemons
CFO: Dawn Quibodeaux
Sfty Dirs: Randall Thomassie

D-U-N-S 03-253-3788 IMP
▲ LINEAR TECHNOLOGY CORP
1630 Mccarthy Blvd, Milpitas, CA 95035-7487
Tel (408) 432-1900 Founded/Ownrshp 1981
Sales 1.4MMM EMP 4,868
Tkr Sym LLTC Exch NGS
SIC 3674 Integrated circuits, semiconductor networks, etc.
CEO: Lothar Maier
*Ch Bd: Robert H Swanson Jr
COO: Alexander R McCann
COO: Henry Zhang
CFO: Paul Coghlan
CFO: Donald P Zerio
VP: Paul Chantalat
VP: Richard Nickson
VP: Donald Paulus
VP: Steve Pietkiewicz
VP: David A Quarles
VP: Robert Reay
VP: Erik M Soule
Board of Directors: Arthur C Agnos, John J Gordon, David S Lee, Richard M Moley, Thomas S Volpe

D-U-N-S 03-093-3881
LINEBARGER GOGGAN BLAIR & SAMPSON LLP
2700 Via Fortuna Ste 400, Austin, TX 78746-7997
Tel (512) 447-6675 Founded/Ownrshp 2009
Sales 139.4MM[E] EMP 1,500
SIC 8111

LINENS OF THE WEEK
See ALSCO INC

D-U-N-S 19-947-0878
■ LINETEC
(Suby of APOGEE ENTERPRISES INC) ★
7500 Stewart Ave, Wausau, WI 54401-9064
Tel (715) 843-4100 Founded/Ownrshp 1983
Sales 91.4MM[E] EMP 430
SIC 3442 Metal doors, sash & trim
Co-Ownr: Rick Marshall
Co-Ownr: Andy Joswiak
VP: Terri Dayan
VP: Rob Houchens
Sfty Mgr: Brian Stratton
Opers Mgr: Paul Bratz
Plnt Mgr: Ray Kroll
Ql Cn Mgr: Cara Bahlow
Sls Mgr: Wendy Taylor
Sales Asso: Tami Wirth

LINFINITY MICROELECTRONICS
See MICROSEMI CORP - ANALOG MIXED SIGNAL GROUP

D-U-N-S 15-694-6196
■ LINGER LONGER DEVELOPMENT CO
REYNOLDS PLANTATION
(Suby of METLIFE INC) ★
100 Linger Longer Rd, Greensboro, GA 30642-7427
Tel (888) 298-3119 Founded/Ownrshp 2012
Sales 297.2MM[E] EMP 600
SIC 6552 7997 Land subdividers & developers, residential; Golf club, membership; Tennis club, membership; Swimming club, membership
CEO: Dan Dupree
Pt: Bill Dewitt
*CEO: Dan Dupree
*CEO: Rob Mitchel
*CFO: Rex Rohm
VP: Glenn Winslette
Sales Exec: Ron Kalpak
Board of Directors: Dan Dupree

LINGUASYS
See ASPECT SOFTWARE INC

D-U-N-S 83-565-6224
LINK AMERICA LLC
3002 Century Dr, Rowlett, TX 75088-7542
Tel (972) 463-0050 Founded/Ownrshp 1994
Sales 179.0MM[E] EMP 26
SIC 8748

LINK ENGINEERING COMPANY
See LINK GROUP INC

D-U-N-S 96-758-0957 IMP
LINK GROUP INC
LINK ENGINEERING COMPANY
43855 Plymouth Oaks Blvd, Plymouth, MI 48170-2539
Tel (734) 453-0800 Founded/Ownrshp 2010
Sales 95.2MM[E] EMP 377
SIC 5013 Truck parts & accessories
CEO: Roy Link
*CFO: Derek Stoneburg

D-U-N-S 18-898-4827 IMP
LINK SNACKS INC
JACK LINK BEEF JERKY
1 Snack Food Ln, Minong, WI 54859-4405
Tel (715) 466-2234 Founded/Ownrshp 1987
Sales 123.0MM[E] EMP 320
SIC 2013

D-U-N-S 15-451-4814 IMP/EXP
LINK-BELT CONSTRUCTION EQUIPMENT CO LP LLLP
LINK-BELT CRANES
(Suby of SUMITOMO HEAVY INDUSTRIES, LTD.)
2651 Palumbo Dr, Lexington, KY 40509-1233
Tel (859) 263-5200 Founded/Ownrshp 1986
Sales 245.8MM[E] EMP 796
SIC 3531 Cranes
Pr: Chuck Martz
VP: John Claflin
VP: Russ Hopper
VP: Don Moore
VP: Melvin Porter
VP: Dan Quinn
VP: Bill Stramer
Genl Mgr: Kelly Ghani
MIS Dir: Mike Neal
IT Man: Tim Nance
IT Man: Sonny Smyth

LINK-BELT CRANES
See LINK-BELT CONSTRUCTION EQUIPMENT CO LP LLLP

D-U-N-S 12-913-3893
▲ LINKEDIN CORP
2029 Stierlin Ct Ste 200, Mountain View, CA 94043-4655
Tel (650) 687-3600 Founded/Ownrshp 2003
Sales 2.9MMM EMP 9,372[E]
Accts Deloitte & Touche Llp San Jos
Tkr Sym LNKD Exch NYS
SIC 7375 On-line data base information retrieval
CEO: Jeffrey Weiner
*Ch Bd: Reid Hoffman
CFO: Steven Sordello
Sr VP: Michael J Callahan
Sr VP: Michael Gamson
Sr VP: Mike Gamson
Sr VP: J Kevin Scott
Sr VP: Kevin Scott
Sr VP: Shannon Stubo
VP: Justin Bingham
VP: Michael Callahan
VP: Ted Harvey
VP: Isaac Josephson
VP: Fred Kofman
VP: Adam Nash
VP: Jeff Ownby
VP: Emily Parsons
VP: Gary Schneider
VP: Scott Shute
VP: Sue Taylor
VP: Pat Wadors

LINKS2CARE
See LOVING CARE AGENCY INC

LINKSHARE CORPORATION
See RAKUTEN MARKETING LLC

D-U-N-S 19-510-8220 IMP
LINKSYS LLC
(Suby of BELKIN COMPONENTS) ★
131 Theory, Irvine, CA 92617-3045
Tel (949) 270-8500 Founded/Ownrshp 2013
Sales 613.9MM[E] EMP 630
SIC 5065 Electronic parts & equipment; Communication equipment
Ex VP: J Pocock
Rgnl Mgr: David Boyd
Rgnl Mgr: Michael Peters
Genl Mgr: Andrew Tay
Sls Mgr: Jeff Cortez
Snr Mgr: Chingwei Chang

D-U-N-S 84-315-4258
LINKUS ENTERPRISES LLC
18631 Lloyd Ln, Anderson, CA 96007-8459
Tel (530) 229-9197 Founded/Ownrshp 2000
Sales 148.3MM[E] EMP 650[E]
SIC 1623 5731 4813 Telephone & communication line construction; Antennas, satellite dish;
CEO: Horacio Guzman
*COO: John Daily
*VP: Dant Morris

D-U-N-S 07-988-6378
■ LINN ACQUISITION CO LLC
(Suby of LINN ENERGY LLC) ★
600 Travis St Ste 4900, Houston, TX 77002-3017
Tel (281) 840-4000 Founded/Ownrshp 2013
Sales 641.6MM[E] EMP 123
SIC 1311 Crude petroleum production

D-U-N-S 00-787-2237
LINN CO-OPERATIVE OIL CO
325 35th St, Marion, IA 52302-3815
Tel (319) 377-4881 Founded/Ownrshp 1930
Sales 150.0MM EMP 72
SIC 5153 5171 5191

D-U-N-S 13-212-1125
▲ LINN ENERGY LLC
600 Travis St Ste 5100, Houston, TX 77002-3092
Tel (281) 840-4000 Founded/Ownrshp 2005
Sales 2.8MMM EMP 1,760[E]
Tkr Sym LINEQ Exch OTO
SIC 1311 Crude petroleum & natural gas
Ch Bd: Mark E Ellis
COO: Arden L Walker Jr
CFO: David B Rottino
Sr VP: Thomas E Emmons
Sr VP: Jamin B McNeil
Sr VP: Candice J Wells
VP: Abdon Rangel
VP: Charlene Ripley
VP: Tanya Smith
CIO: Tony Williams
IT Man: Tom Marshioni
Board of Directors: David D Dunlap, Stephen J Hadden, Michael C Linn, Joseph P McCoy, Jeffrey C Swoveland

LINN HOUSE
See AIDS HEALTHCARE FOUNDATION

D-U-N-S 80-781-9573
■ LINN OPERATING INC
(Suby of LINN ENERGY LLC) ★
600 Travis St Ste 5100, Houston, TX 77002-3092
Tel (713) 227-1868 Founded/Ownrshp 2007
Sales 287.4MM[E] EMP 400[E]
SIC 1382 Oil & gas exploration services
Pr: Michael Linn
*COO: Mark Ellis
*CFO: Kolja Rockov
*Sr VP: Lisa Anderson
*Sr VP: Roland Keddie
*Sr VP: Charlene Ripley
*Sr VP: Arden Walker
Netwrk Eng: Jose Colion
Counsel: Sasha Vaikhman

D-U-N-S 07-864-9152
▲ LINNCO LLC
600 Travis St Ste 5100, Houston, TX 77002-3092
Tel (281) 840-4000 Founded/Ownrshp 2012
Sales 181.8MM[E] EMP 1,800[E]
Accts Kpmg Llp Houston Texas
Tkr Sym LNCOQ Exch OTO
SIC 1311 Crude petroleum & natural gas; Natural gas production
Ch Bd: Mark E Ellis
COO: Arden L Walker Jr
CFO: Kolja Rockov
CFO: David B Rottino
Sr VP: Thomas E Emmons
Sr VP: Jamin B McNeil
Sr VP: Jamin McNeil
VP: Candice J Wells

D-U-N-S 00-541-5893
LINNEA BASEY CANCER RESOURCE CENTER
ST ANTHONY HOSPITAL
11600 W 2nd Pl, Lakewood, CO 80228-1527
Tel (773) 484-1000 Founded/Ownrshp 1995
Sales 388.3MM EMP 1
SIC 8069 Cancer hospital
Chf Nrs Of: Kate Bechtold

D-U-N-S 14-038-9763
LINQUEST CORP
5140 W Goldleaf Cir # 400, Los Angeles, CA 90056-1299
Tel (323) 924-1600 Founded/Ownrshp 2003
Sales 91.1MM[E] EMP 475
SIC 8711 Aviation &/or aeronautical engineering
Ch Bd: Leon Biederman
*COO: Ronald B Gorda
*CFO: Matthew C Lyons
*VP: Joe Dodd
*VP: Scott Stowe
*VP: Pat Talty
*VP: Rich Williams
*VP: Greg Young
Board of Directors: John Alexovich, Leon Biederman, Joe Dodd, Ronald Gorda, Matthew Lyons, Scott Stowe, Pat Talty

D-U-N-S 62-393-1557
LINROC COMMUNITY SERVICES CORP
Linden Blvd At Brookdale, Brooklyn, NY 11212
Tel (718) 240-5656 Founded/Ownrshp 1985
Sales 52.8MM[E] EMP 2,000
SIC 8741 Nursing & personal care facility management; Hospital management
Pr: Frank Maddalena
*CFO: Jeff Davis

D-U-N-S 78-407-6809
LINSALATA CORP
(Suby of TRANSTAR HOLDING CO) ★
5900 Landerbrook Dr # 280, Cleveland, OH 44124-4029
Tel (440) 684-1400 Founded/Ownrshp 2005
Sales 724.7MM[E] EMP 2,300[E]
SIC 5013 Automotive supplies & parts
Pr: Monte Ahuja
*Pr: Eric V Bacon
*Pr: Daniel L Desantis
*Pr: Stephen B Perry
*Pr: Gregory L Taber
*CFO: Jeffrey R Marshall
*VP: Mark A Kirk

D-U-N-S 86-812-7168 IMP
LINTECH INTERNATIONAL LLC
7705 Ne Industrial Blvd, Macon, GA 31216-7745
Tel (877) 546-8324 Founded/Ownrshp 2007
Sales 93.0MM[E] EMP 72
SIC 5169 Chemicals, industrial & heavy
CEO: Julie Hinson-Vanbrunt
Mng Pt: Thomas Hinson
VP: Randy N Waldman
Exec: Roger Shaw
Opers Mgr: Randy Griffin
Sls Mgr: Rick Diener

D-U-N-S 00-443-1185 IMP
■ LINVATEC CORP (FL)
CONMED LINVATEC
(Suby of CONMED CORP) ★
11311 Concept Blvd, Largo, FL 33773-4908
Tel (727) 392-6464 Founded/Ownrshp 1963, 1997
Sales 214.6MM[E] EMP 900
SIC 3842 3841 2821 Surgical appliances & supplies; Surgical instruments & apparatus; Elastomers, nonvulcanizable (plastics)
CEO: Curt Hartman
*Pr: Joseph Darling
*CFO: Luke A Pomilio
*Treas: Terence M Berge
*VP: Heather Cohen
*VP: Daniel S Jonas
Prgrm Mgr: William Mazurek
Genl Mgr: Gingerlee Haas
QA Dir: Sam Mancuso
VP Mfg: Mark Snyder
Opers Mgr: Darren Gussey

LINZER PRODUCTS
See AHI INVESTMENT INC

D-U-N-S 00-136-7739 IMP
LINZER PRODUCTS CORP (NY)
(Suby of LINZER PRODUCTS) ★
248 Wyandanch Ave, West Babylon, NY 11704-1506
Tel (631) 253-3333 Founded/Ownrshp 1892, 1988
Sales 100.0MM EMP 450
SIC 5198 3991 Paint brushes, rollers, sprayers; Paint & varnish brushes
Pr: Brent Swenson
*Treas: Mark Saji
VP: Ted Robinson
Natl Sales: Joe Dichiria
Sls Mgr: John Reimer

D-U-N-S 00-424-4083 IMP/EXP
LION APPAREL INC (OH)
(Suby of LION GROUP INC) ★
7200 Poe Ave Ste 400, Dayton, OH 45414-2798
Tel (937) 898-1949 Founded/Ownrshp 1930
Sales 237.1MM[E] EMP 760
SIC 2311 Firemen's uniforms: made from purchased materials; Military uniforms, men's & youths': purchased materials; Policemen's uniforms: made from purchased materials
CEO: Steve Schwartz
*Pr: Stephen A Schwartz
Treas: Richard Musick
VP: John Granby
VP: Mark Smith
*Prin: Mark Berliant
*Prin: Mark Jahnke
*Prin: Stephen Schwartz
Prgrm Mgr: Brian Stephens
Dir IT: Linda King
Dir IT: Larry Tieman

D-U-N-S 80-205-5579 EXP
LION COPOLYMER HOLDINGS LLC
36191 Highway 30, Geismar, LA 70734-3526
Tel (225) 673-8871 Founded/Ownrshp 2007
Sales 246.8MM[E] EMP 474
SIC 2891 Adhesives & sealants

D-U-N-S 07-963-6182
LION ELASTOMER HOLDINGS LLC
(Suby of LION COPOLYMER HOLDINGS LLC) ★
36191 Highway 30, Geismar, LA 70734-3526
Tel (225) 673-8871 Founded/Ownrshp 2014
Sales 162.2MM[E] EMP 251
SIC 2822 Synthetic rubber
Pr: Jesse Zeringue
CFO: Neil Jurkovic
VP: Jeff Jordan

D-U-N-S 13-571-7622 IMP/EXP
LION ELASTOMERS LLC
(Suby of LION ELASTOMER HOLDINGS LLC) ★
1615 Main St, Port Neches, TX 77651-3039
Tel (409) 722-8321 Founded/Ownrshp 2003
Sales 162.2MM[E] EMP 250
SIC 2822 Synthetic rubber
Pr: Jesse Zeringue
*CFO: Neil Jurkovic
*VP: Jeff Jordan

D-U-N-S 80-779-0600
LION GABLES REALTY LIMITED PARTNERSHIP
3399 Peachtree Rd Ne, Atlanta, GA 30326-1120
Tel (404) 923-5500 Founded/Ownrshp 1993
Sales 88.8MM[E] EMP 1,251[E]
SIC 6531 Real estate managers
CEO: David D Finch

D-U-N-S 07-986-8052
LION GROUP INC
7200 Poe Ave Ste 400, Dayton, OH 45414-2798
Tel (937) 898-1949 Founded/Ownrshp 2014
Sales 87.8MM[E] EMP 760
SIC 6719 Investment holding companies, except banks
*Treas: James Disanto
*Treas: Richard Musick
Exec: Lauras Dvareckas
Off Mgr: Alisa Young
Dir IT: Larry Tieman
Software D: David Feverston
Ql Cn Mgr: Diane Best
Manager: Jon Nelson

D-U-N-S 83-289-2215
LION HOLDINGS INC
Mettlers Rd, East Millstone, NJ 08875
Tel (732) 649-9961 Founded/Ownrshp 2009
Sales 69.3MM[E] EMP 1,648[E]
SIC 8731 Commercial physical research; Biological research; Commercial physical research; Commercial research laboratory
CEO: Andrew H Baker
*CFO: Richard Michaelson

D-U-N-S 13-122-5211
■ LION OIL CO
(Suby of DELEK US HOLDINGS INC) ★
7102 Commerce Way, Brentwood, TN 37027-2896
Tel (615) 771-6701 Founded/Ownrshp 1985
Sales 284.8MM[E] EMP 600
SIC 2911 4612 5172 Gasoline blending plants; Diesel fuels; Jet fuels; Asphalt or asphaltic materials, made in refineries; Crude petroleum pipelines; Petroleum products
Pr: Lee Lampton
*Sec: Kathy Stone
*VP: George Ishee
*VP: Ronnie Jackson
*VP: William W Lampton
VP: John Wallace
VP Mfg: Don Davis
Sls Mgr: Steve Thweatt

D-U-N-S 00-467-1400
▲ LIONBRIDGE TECHNOLOGIES INC
1050 Winter St Ste 2300, Waltham, MA 02451-1407
Tel (781) 434-6000 *Founded/Ownrshp* 1996
Sales 559.9MM *EMP* 6,000^E
Accts Pricewaterhousecoopers Llp Bo
Tkr Sym LIOX *Exch* NGM
SIC 7389 7374 7371 Translation services; Data processing & preparation; Computer software development & applications
Ch Bd: Rory J Cowan
COO: Satish Maripuri
CFO: Marc Litz
Sr VP: Marc Osofsky
Sr VP: Paula Barbary Shannon
Sr VP: Richard Tobin
VP: Peggy Shukur
Dir IT: Oyvand Kalvestad
Prd Mgr: Niamh Counihan
Secur Mgr: Rakhi Wadhwani
Sls&Mrk Ex: Beth Flaherty
Board of Directors: Edward A Blechschmidt, Michael G Dallas, Guy L De Chazal, Susan Kantor, Susan Kantor, Paul Kavanagh, Jack Noonan, James Quella, Claude Sheer

LIONMARK CNSTR COMPANIES
See LIONMARK CONSTRUCTION COMPANIES LLC

D-U-N-S 00-383-3290
LIONMARK CONSTRUCTION COMPANIES LLC (MO)
LIONMARK CNSTR COMPANIES
1620 Woodson Rd, Saint Louis, MO 63114-6129
Tel (314) 991-2180 *Founded/Ownrshp* 1932
Sales 230.7MM^E *EMP* 334
SIC 1611 2951 1622 General contractor, highway & street construction; Resurfacing contractor; Asphalt & asphaltic paving mixtures (not from refineries); Bridge construction
Pr: Edward Gomes Jr
**CFO:* Thomas Feldmann
**VP:* Gene Allen
**VP:* Roy Burns
VP: Henry Schmitt
MIS Dir: Todd Ledbetter

D-U-N-S 06-125-0531
LIONS GATE ENTERTAINMENT INC
(*Suby of* LIONS GATE ENTERTAINMENT CORP)
2700 Colorado Ave Ste 200, Santa Monica, CA 90404-5502
Tel (310) 449-9200 *Founded/Ownrshp* 2006
Sales 1.7MMM^E *EMP* 536
SIC 7812 Motion picture production & distribution
Ch Bd: Jon Feltheimer
V Ch: Michael Burns
Pr: Steven Beeks
Pr: Joseph Drake
Pr: Erik Feig
Pr: Sarah Greenberg
Pr: Tim Palen
CFO: James Keegan
CFO: Jim Keegan
Ex VP: Julie Fontaine
Ex VP: David C Friedman
Ex VP: B Gladstone
Ex VP: Gary Goodman
Ex VP: Ken Katsumoto
Ex VP: Lara Kazandjian
Ex VP: Patricia Laucella
Ex VP: Audrey Lee
Ex VP: Wayne Levin
Ex VP: David Luner
Ex VP: Courtney Mun
Ex VP: Ross Pollack
Board of Directors: Gordon Crawford

D-U-N-S 00-640-2820 IMP/EXP
LIPARI FOODS OPERATING CO LLC
26661 Bunert Rd, Warren, MI 48089-3650
Tel (586) 447-3500 *Founded/Ownrshp* 2011
Sales 611.0MM^E *EMP* 700^E
SIC 5146 5145 5149

D-U-N-S 00-886-8127 IMP
LIPMAN BROTHERS LLC (TN)
411 Great Circle Rd, Nashville, TN 37228-1403
Tel (615) 244-2230 *Founded/Ownrshp* 1939, 1966
Sales 311.4MM^E *EMP* 170
SIC 5182 Wine & distilled beverages
**Sec:* Stefan Banks
**Sec:* Ken Howell
**VP:* Greg Naiser
**VP:* Richard Thibus
Off Mgr: Janet Pruitt
Dir IT: John Pamplin
Info Man: Kevin Hippler
Opers Mgr: Ken Vanderpool
Natl Sales: Scott Gstell
VP Mktg: Paul Grand
Sls Dir: Charlie Jackson

LIPMAN PRODUCE
See LIPMAN-TEXAS LLC

LIPMAN PRODUCE
See CUSTOM-PAK INC

D-U-N-S 07-831-8182
LIPMAN-TEXAS LLC (FL)
LIPMAN PRODUCE
315 New Market Rd E, Immokalee, FL 34142-3509
Tel (239) 657-4421 *Founded/Ownrshp* 1930
Sales 172.0MM^E *EMP* 251^E
SIC 5148 Fruits, fresh
Pr: Kent Shoemaker
**VP:* Darren Micelle

D-U-N-S 04-322-2470 IMP
■ LIPPERT COMPONENTS INC
HOME-STYLE INDUSTRIES
(*Suby of* DREW INDUSTRIES INC) ★
3501 County Road 6 E, Elkhart, IN 46514-7663
Tel (800) 551-9149 *Founded/Ownrshp* 1997
Sales 1.0MMM^E *EMP* 5,109
SIC 3711 3469 3444 3714 Chassis, motor vehicle; Stamping metal for the trade; Metal roofing & roof drainage equipment; Motor vehicle parts & accessories
CEO: Jason Lippert
Ch Bd: L Douglas Lippert
Pr: Shane Duncan
Pr: Scott Mereness
CFO: Todd Blyly
CFO: Joshua Lippert
CFO: Grant Williams
VP: Chuck Bell
VP: Jim Chamberlain
VP: Conny Holcombe
VP: April Klein
VP: Robert Kuhns
VP: Phil Myers
VP: John Ries
VP: Josh Roan

LIPPINCOTT WILLIAMS & WILKIN
See WOLTERS KLUWER HEALTH INC

D-U-N-S 07-538-1186
LIPSCOMB UNIVERSITY (TN)
DAVID LIPSCOMB CAMPUS SCHOOL
1 University Park Dr, Nashville, TN 37204-3956
Tel (615) 966-1000 *Founded/Ownrshp* 1891
Sales 167.1MM *EMP* 550^E
Accts Lbmc Pc Brentwood Tn
SIC 8221 8211 Colleges universities & professional schools; Private combined elementary & secondary school
Pr: L Randolph Lowry III
**CFO:* Danny Taylor
VP: Melba Buchanan
VP: Larry Cochran
VP: Nancy Durham
VP: Mark McFerran
VP: Scott Sager
VP: Deby Samuels
Assoc Dir: Karin Hensley
Dir Soc: Naomi Lutz
Comm Man: Beth Morrow

D-U-N-S 83-258-9563
LIPSEY LOGISTICS WORLDWIDE LLC
5600 Brainerd Rd Ste E2, Chattanooga, TN 37411-5336
Tel (678) 336-1180 *Founded/Ownrshp* 2005
Sales 640.0MM^E *EMP* 128
SIC 4731 5499 Domestic freight forwarding; Water: distilled mineral or spring
CEO: Joseph Lipsey III
Sr VP: Neal Chibba
VP: Marc Stewart

D-U-N-S 08-248-6341 IMP
LIPSEYS LLC
7277 Exchequer Dr, Baton Rouge, LA 70809-4910
Tel (225) 755-1333 *Founded/Ownrshp* 1977, 1953
Sales 373.4MM *EMP* 60
SIC 5091

D-U-N-S 06-649-3292 IMP
LIPTIS PHARMACEUTICALS USA INC
110 Red Schoolhouse Rd, Spring Valley, NY 10977-7032
Tel (845) 627-0260 *Founded/Ownrshp* 1995
Sales 125.2MM^E *EMP* 1,022
SIC 2834 Pharmaceutical preparations
CEO: Sherin Awad
**Pr:* Dick Klaus
**VP:* Jenny Avalos

D-U-N-S 00-194-2499 IMP/EXP
LIQUI-BOX CORP (OH)
480 Schrock Rd Ste G, Columbus, OH 43229-1092
Tel (804) 325-1400 *Founded/Ownrshp* 1963
Sales 568.9MM^E *EMP* 1,100
SIC 2673 3585 3089 3081 5149 Plastic bags: made from purchased materials; Soda fountain & beverage dispensing equipment & parts; Plastic containers, except foam; Blow molded finished plastic products; Injection molded finished plastic products; Plastic film & sheet; Mineral or spring water bottling
Pr: Ken Swanson
**CFO:* Lou Marmo
Sr VP: Greg Gard
Sr VP: Anthony Rizzo
VP: Dave Klopp

D-U-N-S 06-915-7287 IMP
LIQUID INVESTMENTS INC (CA)
3840 Via De La Valle # 300, Del Mar, CA 92014-4268
Tel (858) 509-8510 *Founded/Ownrshp* 1981
Sales 167.5MM^E *EMP* 629
Accts Robert R Redwitz & Co Irvin
SIC 5181 5145 5182 Beer & other fermented malt liquors; Fountain supplies; Wine
CEO: Ron L Fowler
**Ex VP:* Mark Herculson

D-U-N-S 00-380-3897
LIQUID TRANSPORT CORP
(*Suby of* DANA TRANSPORT SYSTEM INC) ★
8470 Allison Pointe Blvd # 400, Indianapolis, IN 46250-4365
Tel (317) 841-4200 *Founded/Ownrshp* 1949, 2006
Sales 96.5MM^E *EMP* 300
SIC 4213 Contract haulers
Prin: Ronald B Dana
CFO: Arthur G Bortolini
Dir IT: Chuck Applequist
Trfc Dir: Jim Wharton
S&M/VP: Donald L Grossett

LIQUIDATION CHANNEL
See JEWELRY CHANNEL INC

D-U-N-S 02-813-1535
LIQUIDHUB INC
LH
(*Suby of* LIQUIDHUB INDIA PRIVATE LIMITED)
500 E Swedesford Rd # 300, Wayne, PA 19087-1614
Tel (610) 688-6531 *Founded/Ownrshp* 2001
Sales 141.6MM^E *EMP* 562^E
SIC 8748 Business consulting
Pr: Jonathan A Brassington
**Pt:* Robert T Kelley
**COO:* Stephen Racioppo
**CFO:* Dave Murray
IT Man: Gitesh Suchak
Sftwr Eng: Mahfuz Omer

D-U-N-S 93-335-1611
▲ LIQUIDITY SERVICES INC
1920 L St Nw Fl 6, Washington, DC 20036-5004
Tel (202) 467-6868 *Founded/Ownrshp* 2000
Sales 316.4MM *EMP* 1,179
Accts Ernst & Young Llp Mclean Vir
Tkr Sym LQDT *Exch* NGS
SIC 7389 Auction, appraisal & exchange services
Ch Bd: William P Angrick III
CFO: Jorge A Celaya
Ex VP: Holger Schwarz
VP: Dan Beck
VP: James E Williams
Dir Bus: Alysa Regen
Prgrm Mgr: Jeremy Logan
CIO: Leoncio S Casusol
CTO: Ben Brown
CTO: Benjamin D Faett
Info Man: Dawne Wright
Board of Directors: Philip A Clough, George H Ellis, Patrick W Gross, Beatriz Infante, Edward J Kolodzieski, Jaime Mateus-Tique

D-U-N-S 00-302-9741
LIQUOR CONTROL BOARD PENNSYLVANIA (PA)
PLCB
(*Suby of* GOVERNORS OFFICE) ★
Nw Office Bldg 910, Harrisburg, PA 17124-0001
Tel (717) 787-7963 *Founded/Ownrshp* 1933
Sales NA *EMP* 4,011
SIC 9651 Alcoholic beverage control board, government;
Ch: Patrick J Stapleton III
VP: Steve Reider

LIQUORS DIVISION
See V SUAREZ & CO INC

D-U-N-S 00-716-7914 IMP
LIRO ENGINEERS INC
3 Aerial Way, Syosset, NY 11791-5501
Tel (516) 938-5476 *Founded/Ownrshp* 1984
Sales 126.4MM *EMP* 475
Accts Marc L Montaruli Cpa Pc Is
SIC 1522 Hotel/motel & multi-family home construction
CEO: Rocco Trotta
**Ch Bd:* Luis Tormenta
**Sr VP:* Michael Burton
**Sr VP:* Lawrence S Roberts
**VP:* Michael Bailey
**VP:* Peter Gerbasi
**VP:* Michael Rennard
Mktg Dir: Andrew Weinberg

LISD
See LEWISVILLE INDEPENDENT SCHOOL DISTRICT

D-U-N-S 10-343-1300
LISI INC
1600 W Hillsdale Blvd # 100, San Mateo, CA 94402-3770
Tel (650) 348-4131 *Founded/Ownrshp* 1976
Sales NA *EMP* 140
SIC 6411 Insurance agents
Ch Bd: Philip Lebherz
**CEO:* Becky Patel
**VP:* Tamara Henderson
**Ex Dir:* Ken Doyle
**Ex Dir:* Hadley Weiler
Mktg Mgr: Shannon Carboni
Mktg Mgr: Frank Estrada
Mktg Mgr: Jeff Hoss
Mktg Mgr: Michele Isaly
Manager: Sandra Bealu
Manager: Christina Diamantis

D-U-N-S 00-506-3854 IMP
LIST INDUSTRIES INC
401 Jim Moran Blvd, Deerfield Beach, FL 33442-1781
Tel (954) 429-9155 *Founded/Ownrshp* 1936
Sales 144.4MM^E *EMP* 504
SIC 2541 5021 2542 Lockers, except refrigerated: wood; Lockers; Lockers (not refrigerated): except wood
Pr: Herbert A List Jr
COO: Keith Ronshausen
Ofcr: Thomas D Champa
VP: Greg Louden
Exec: Diego Bentacur
Rgnl Mgr: Boyd Bryson
Rgnl Mgr: Bob Geurtze
Rgnl Mgr: Jeff Lovelace
Genl Mgr: Robert Espineira
Genl Mgr: Dan Fay
VP Mfg: Dave Cole

D-U-N-S 00-290-1676
LITCHFIELD ELEMENTARY SCHOOL DISTRICT 79 (AZ)
272 E Sagebrush St, Litchfield Park, AZ 85340-4934
Tel (623) 535-6000 *Founded/Ownrshp* 1924
Sales 47.9MM^E *EMP* 1,000
Accts Cronstrom Osuch & Company Sc
SIC 8211 Public elementary & secondary schools
Dir IT: Paul Clark

D-U-N-S 04-664-1825
LITCO PETROLEUM INC
EXPRESS SHOPS
323 Highway 72 W, Corinth, MS 38834-5408
Tel (662) 287-1471 *Founded/Ownrshp* 1988
Sales 194.9MM^E *EMP* 600
Accts Nail Mckinney Professional Ass
SIC 5541 5172 5411 Filling stations, gasoline; Gasoline; Convenience stores
Pr: Taft Little

D-U-N-S 05-117-1130 IMP
LITEHOUSE INC
LITEHOUSE SPECIALTY FOODS
100 Litehouse Dr, Sandpoint, ID 83864-0528
Tel (208) 920-2000 *Founded/Ownrshp* 1977
Sales 214.5MM *EMP* 450
SIC 2035 2033 Dressings, salad: raw & cooked (except dry mixes); Jams, including imitation: packaged in cans, jars, etc.
CEO: Jim Frank
**CEO:* Edward Hawkins Jr
**CFO:* Kelly Prior
Treas: Betty Menser
**VP:* Paul Kusche
**VP:* Dan Munson
**VP:* Daren Parsons
Dir Lab: Valerie Allan
Plnt Mgr: Susan Serne

LITEHOUSE SPECIALTY FOODS
See LITEHOUSE INC

D-U-N-S 02-952-5789 IMP/EXP
LITEX INDUSTRIES LIMITED
3401 Trinity Blvd, Grand Prairie, TX 75050-4239
Tel (972) 871-4350 *Founded/Ownrshp* 1980
Sales 151.6MM^E *EMP* 344
SIC 5064 5063 Fans, household: electric; Lighting fixtures
CEO: John Mares
VP: Harold Wolfson Hwolf
VP: Peter WEI
IT Man: Kevin Sullivan
Natl Sales: Greg Pronti
Sls Mgr: Tom Gray

D-U-N-S 05-221-3907
▲ LITHIA MOTORS INC
150 N Bartlett St, Medford, OR 97501-6032
Tel (541) 776-6401 *Founded/Ownrshp* 1946
Sales 7.8MMM *EMP* 9,574^E
Tkr Sym LAD *Exch* NYS
SIC 5511 5531 5013 7539 Automobiles, new & used; Automotive parts; Automotive supplies & parts; Automotive repair shops
Ch Bd: Sidney B Deboer
Pr: Bryan B Deboer
CFO: Christopher Holzshu
Sr VP: Jeffrey B Deboer
Sr VP: Scott A Hillier
Sr VP: George C Liang
VP: Mark Smith
Genl Mgr: Stephen Bates
Genl Mgr: Larry Hook
Genl Mgr: Lonnie Lewis
Genl Mgr: Mark McCarthy

D-U-N-S 09-671-9125
LITHKO CONTRACTING LLC
5353 Hmlton Middletown Rd, Liberty Twp, OH 45011-2407
Tel (513) 863-5100 *Founded/Ownrshp* 1994
Sales 162.0MM^E *EMP* 450
SIC 1771 Concrete work; Foundation & footing contractor; Flooring contractor; Concrete repair
Pr: Robert Strobel
**VP:* Perry Hausfeld
Sfty Dirs: Andy Zimmerman

D-U-N-S 00-833-0946 IMP
LITHOGRAPHIX INC
12250 Crenshaw Blvd, Hawthorne, CA 90250-3332
Tel (323) 770-1000 *Founded/Ownrshp* 1979
Sales 163.7MM^E *EMP* 325
SIC 2752 2759 Commercial printing, lithographic; Commercial printing
Pr: Herbert Zebrack
**CFO:* Victor Wolfe
**Sec:* Jeffrey Zebrack
VP: Ariel Minguez
VP: Layne Morey
VP: George Wolden
VP: Jeff Zebrack
Sales Exec: Charlotte Lee

LITHONIA LIGHTING
See ACUITY BRANDS LIGHTING INC

D-U-N-S 00-521-2246
▲ LITTELFUSE INC
8755 W Higgins Rd Ste 500, Chicago, IL 60631-2701
Tel (773) 628-1000 *Founded/Ownrshp* 1927
Sales 867.8MM *EMP* 8,800
Accts Grant Thornton Llp Chicago I
Tkr Sym LFUS *Exch* NGS
SIC 3613 3679 Fuses & fuse equipment; Electronic circuits
Ch Bd: Gordon Hunter
COO: David W Heinzmann
CFO: Meenal A Sethna
Sr VP: Matthew J Cole
Sr VP: Ian Highley
Sr VP: Deepak Nayar
Sr VP: Dieter Roeder
Sr VP: Michael P Rutz
VP: Dal Ferbert
Board of Directors: Cary T Fu, Anthony Grillo, John E Major, William P Noglows, Ronald L Schubel

D-U-N-S 04-808-2747 IMP
LITTLE CAESAR ENTERPRISES INC
LITTLE CAESAR'S
(*Suby of* LITTLE CAESARS) ★
2211 Woodward Ave, Detroit, MI 48201-3400
Tel (313) 983-6000 *Founded/Ownrshp* 1959
Sales 346.1MM^E *EMP* 6,000
SIC 5812 6794 5141 5046 8741 Pizzeria, chain; Franchises, selling or licensing; Groceries, general line; Cooking equipment, commercial; Restaurant equipment & supplies; Management services
Ch Bd: Michael Ilitch
Pr: William Crystler
Pr: David Scrivano
CEO: Christopher Ilitch
CFO: Scott Fischer
Treas: Matthew Greenough
VP: John Beasley
VP: Greg Martino
VP: Rick Muse

VP: Darrell Snygg
Mktg Dir: Brad Jandrew

LITTLE CAESAR'S
See LITTLE CAESAR ENTERPRISES INC

LITTLE CAESAR'S
See ILITCH HOLDINGS INC

LITTLE COMPANY MARY HOSPITAL
See LITTLE CO OF MARY HOSPITAL AND HEALTH CARE CENTERS

LITTLE COMPANY MARY SVC AREA
See PROVIDENCE LITTLE CO OF MARY MEDICAL CENTER-TORRANCE

D-U-N-S 04-094-0348 IMP
LITTLE CO OF MARY HOSPITAL
LEADER DRUG STORE
(*Suby of* PROVIDENCE HEALTH SYSTEM-SOUTHERN CALIFORNIA) ★
4101 Torrance Blvd, Torrance, CA 90503-4664
Tel (310) 540-7676 *Founded/Ownrshp* 1957
Sales 8.5MM *EMP* 1,200
Accts Clark Nuber Ps Bellevue Wa
SIC 8062 8051 General medical & surgical hospitals; Skilled nursing care facilities
CEO: Joseph Zanetta
COO: Francesca Wachs
**CFO:* Elizabeth Zuanich
VP: Mary Reyes
IT Man: John Kanehailua
Netwrk Mgr: Ryan Lew
Sls Mgr: Marvin Murphy

D-U-N-S 04-702-2827
LITTLE CO OF MARY HOSPITAL AND HEALTH CARE CENTERS
2800 GIFT SHOP, THE
2800 W 95th St, Evergreen Park, IL 60805-2701
Tel (708) 422-6200 *Founded/Ownrshp* 1893
Sales 128.5MM^E *EMP* 2,000
SIC 8062 Hospital, AMA approved residency
Pr: Dennis Riley
Chf OB: Robert M Bonaminio
**COO:* Mary Freyer
CFO: Carl Carrier
**CFO:* Raymond Snowden
Treas: Dennis Kelly
**Treas:* Thomas Sahey
VP: Mary Quick
VP: Kevin Rehder
Exec: Carol Martinez
QA Dir: Cindy Deuser

D-U-N-S 96-959-1861
LITTLE CO OF MARY HOSPITAL AND HEALTH CARE CENTERS
LITTLE COMPANY MARY HOSPITAL
2800 W 95th St, Evergreen Park, IL 60805-2795
Tel (708) 422-6200 *Founded/Ownrshp* 1893
Sales 173.2MM *EMP* 2,200
SIC 8062 General medical & surgical hospitals
CEO: Dennis Reilly
**COO:* Mary Freyer
Ofcr: Marcus Schausele
Exec: Susan Arnold
Comm Man: Cheryl Conroy
Ex Dir: Marilyn Daley
Dir IT: Gary Nalley
IT Man: Cheryl Teale
Opers Mgr: Jill Fuggett
Surgeon: Nancy J Taft
Obsttrcn: Monica M Christmas

LITTLE CO OF MARYS HOSPITAL
See PHYSICIAN MATCH

D-U-N-S 08-225-3063
LITTLE GENERAL STORE INC
LGS
4036 Robert C. Byrd Dr, Beckley, WV 25801
Tel (304) 253-9592 *Founded/Ownrshp* 1975
Sales 111.8MM^E *EMP* 650
SIC 5411 Convenience stores
CEO: Greg Darby
**CEO:* Corey Beasley
**Prin:* Gloria Tolbert
Site Mgr: Della Blankenship
Mktg Dir: Don Bolen

D-U-N-S 00-718-9699
■ **LITTLE GIANT PUMP CO LLC** (OK)
(*Suby of* FRANKLIN ELECTRIC CO INC) ★
301 N Macarthur Blvd, Oklahoma City, OK 73127-6616
Tel (405) 947-2511 *Founded/Ownrshp* 1940, 2006
Sales 88.2MM^E *EMP* 500
SIC 3561 Pumps, domestic: water or sump; Cylinders, pump
Pr: Norman Heidebrecht
Treas: James Nicholson
VP: Ted Foti
CIO: Rich Fehrmann
Dir IT: Thomas Strotman

D-U-N-S 00-613-2294 IMP/EXP
LITTLE RAPIDS CORP (WI)
GRAHAM PROFESSIONAL PRODUCTS
2273 Larsen Rd, Green Bay, WI 54303-4809
Tel (920) 490-5400 *Founded/Ownrshp* 1925
Sales 85.2MM^E *EMP* 460
SIC 2621

LITTLE ROCK PUBLIC SCHOOLS
See LITTLE ROCK SCHOOL DISTRICT

D-U-N-S 04-064-4007
LITTLE ROCK SCHOOL DISTRICT
LITTLE ROCK PUBLIC SCHOOLS
810 W Markham St, Little Rock, AR 72201-1306
Tel (501) 447-1000 *Founded/Ownrshp* 1875
Sales 332.6MM *EMP* 4,000
Accts Hudson Cisne & Co Llp Littl
SIC 8211 Public elementary & secondary schools
VP: Keith Richardson
Exec: Donna Muldrew
Dir Sec: Ronald Self
Prgrm Mgr: Sheketa McKisick
Pr Dir: Pamela L Smith
Schl Brd P: Greg Adams
Teacher Pr: Ronda Benton
Psych: Kay Coleman
HC Dir: Margo Bushmiaer

LITTLE SIOUX CORN PROCESSORS
See LSCP LLLP

D-U-N-S 02-255-0177
LITTLE SIOUX CORN PROCESSORS LLC
LSCP
4808 F Ave, Marcus, IA 51035-7070
Tel (712) 376-2800 *Founded/Ownrshp* 2000
Sales 350.0MM *EMP* 46^E
Accts Christianson & Associates Pll
SIC 2869 Ethyl alcohol, ethanol
Ch Bd: Ron Wetherell
**CFO:* Gary Grotjohn
**V Ch Bd:* Myron Pingel
**Genl Mgr:* Steve Roe

LITTLE STORE , THE
See BEST OIL CO

D-U-N-S 04-270-4692 IMP/EXP
LITTLE TIKES CO
(*Suby of* MGA ENTERTAINMENT INC) ★
2180 Barlow Rd, Hudson, OH 44236-4199
Tel (330) 650-3000 *Founded/Ownrshp* 1967
Sales 242.9MM^E *EMP* 2,100
SIC 3944 2519

LITTLE YANKEE
See ASSOCIATED GROCERS OF MAINE INC

D-U-N-S 95-682-1326 IMP/EXP
LITTLEJOHN & CO LLC
8 Sound Shore Dr Ste 303, Greenwich, CT 06830-7254
Tel (203) 552-3500 *Founded/Ownrshp* 1996
Sales 2.1MMM^E *EMP* 6,860
SIC 6799 Investors
Pr: Michael I Klein
**Pr:* Brian Ramsay
**Ch:* Angus C Littlejohn Jr
VP: Andrew Goodrich
**VP:* Drew Greenwood
**VP:* Steven B Kalter
**VP:* Gentry Klein
**VP:* Brian W Michaud
Ex Dir: Ivan Nedds
Mng Dir: Richard Maybaum
Mng Dir: Steven Raich

D-U-N-S 07-875-8919
LITTLER MENDELSON PC
333 Bush St Fl 34, San Francisco, CA 94104-2874
Tel (415) 433-1940 *Founded/Ownrshp* 1956
Sales 397.1MM^E *EMP* 1,500
SIC 8111 General practice law office
CEO: Thomas J Bender
**Ch Bd:* Robert Millman
**Pr:* Marko Mrkonich
**Treas:* Steven R Mc Cown
VP: Scott Hultsman
CIO: Jennifer Dunn
Info Man: Yahya Alhafid
Info Man: Mark Nau
Web Dev: Kirk Won
Counsel: Gina M Chang
Counsel: Craig Dickinson
Board of Directors: Wesley J Fastiff, Wendy Wallner

D-U-N-S 06-990-5735
LITTLETON HOSPITAL ASSOCIATION
LITTLETON REGIONAL HOSPITAL
600 Saint Johnsbury Rd, Littleton, NH 03561-3442
Tel (603) 444-9000 *Founded/Ownrshp* 1906
Sales 83.1MM *EMP* 320
SIC 8062 General medical & surgical hospitals
CEO: Warren K West
COO: Peter Wright
CFO: Bob Fotter
Ofcr: Linda Gilmore
Dir Lab: Kim Miller
Dir Rad: Rob Mach
Dir Pat Ac: Ron Ness
Snr Ntwrk: Eric Perkins
Dir IT: Cindy Richards
Pr Dir: Gail Clark
Doctor: Stephen Goldberg

LITTLETON REGIONAL HOSPITAL
See LITTLETON HOSPITAL ASSOCIATION

D-U-N-S 19-160-5237
LITTON LOAN SERVICING LP
4828 Loop Central Dr # 104, Houston, TX 77081-2193
Tel (713) 960-9676 *Founded/Ownrshp* 2011
Sales NA *EMP* 1,190
SIC 6162

LIUNA
See LABORERS INTERNATIONAL UNION OF NORTH AMERICA

D-U-N-S 61-415-2143
▲ **LIVE NATION ENTERTAINMENT INC**
9348 Civic Center Dr Lbby, Beverly Hills, CA 90210-3642
Tel (310) 867-7000 *Founded/Ownrshp* 2005
Sales 7.2MMM *EMP* 7,700
Accts Ernst & Young Llp Los Angeles
Tkr Sym LYV *Exch* NYS
SIC 7922 7389 7941 Entertainment promotion; Theatrical production services; Theatrical companies; Promoters of shows & exhibitions; Sports clubs, managers & promoters
Pr: Michael Rapino
Ch Bd: Arthur Fogel
**Ch Bd:* Greg Maffei
Pr: Ron Bension
Pr: Mark Campana
Pr: John Reid
Pr: Alan Ridgeway
Pr: Bob Roux
COO: Joe Berchtold
CFO: Kathy Willard
Ex VP: John Carnahan
Ex VP: Lisa Licht
VP: Zack Allison
VP: Maili Bergman
VP: John D D'Esposito
VP: George Duran
VP: Dave Fortin
VP: Brett Gallagher
VP: Mike Garcia
VP: Jon Greenwood
VP: Craig Hoover
Board of Directors: Mark Shapiro, Mark Carleton, Jonathan Dolgen, Ari Emanuel, Ted Enloe, Jeff Hinson, Jimmy Iovine, Peggy Johnson, Jim Kahan, Randall Mays

D-U-N-S 18-122-8891
LIVE NATION MUSIC GROUP TEXAS INC
2000 West Loop S Ste 1300, Houston, TX 77027-3512
Tel (713) 693-8152 *Founded/Ownrshp* 2005
Sales 6.4MMM *EMP* 250
Accts Ernst & Young Llp Los Angeles
SIC 7922 6512 Theatrical producers & services; Theater building, ownership & operation
CEO: Michael Rapino
**VP:* David Cheadle
VP: Michael McGaw
**VP:* Michael Sanchez

D-U-N-S 00-819-0576
■ **LIVE NATION WORLDWIDE INC**
(*Suby of* LIVE NATION ENTERTAINMENT INC) ★
220 W 42nd St, New York, NY 10036-7200
Tel (917) 421-5100 *Founded/Ownrshp* 2007
Sales 216.1MM^E *EMP* 3,000
SIC 7922 Theatrical producers & services
Pr: Brian Becker
**CFO:* Ed Stacey
**Ex VP:* Steve Smith
**VP:* Leeann Gliha
**Genl Couns:* Dale Head

D-U-N-S 07-992-0050
LIVE OAK BANCSHARES INC (NC)
1741 Tiburon Dr, Wilmington, NC 28403-6244
Tel (910) 790-5867 *Founded/Ownrshp* 2008
Sales NA *EMP* 366
Tkr Sym LOB *Exch* NGS
SIC 6022 State commercial banks
Ch Bd: James S Mahan III
**Pr:* Neil L Underwood
COO: Gregory B Thompson
CFO: S Brett Caines
**V Ch Bd:* William L Williams III
Chf Cred: Steven J Smits
CIO: Thomas A Hill
Genl Couns: Gregory W Seward
Board of Directors: William H Cameron, Diane B Glossman, Glen F Hoffsis, Donald W Jackson, Howard K Landis III, Jerald L Pullins

D-U-N-S 82-963-5999
LIVE OAK BANKING CO
1741 Tiburon Dr, Wilmington, NC 28403-6244
Tel (910) 790-5867 *Founded/Ownrshp* 2008
Sales NA *EMP* 30
SIC 6153 Working capital financing
**Ch Bd:* James S Mahan III
**Pr:* Neil L Underwood
CFO: Lawrence Brobst
CFO: Lawrence S Brobt
**CFO:* Brett Caines
Treas: Betty Norris
Chf Cred: Caroline Esmond
Ofcr: Allyson Burkett
Ofcr: Jamie Crisafulli
Ofcr: Anne Pierce
Ofcr: Anna Taylor

D-U-N-S 78-013-4276
■ **LIVE OAK PERRY AND SOUTH GEORGIA RAILWAY CO**
(*Suby of* NORFOLK SOUTHERN RAILWAY CO) ★
3 Commercial Pl, Norfolk, VA 23510-2108
Tel (757) 629-2600 *Founded/Ownrshp* 1991
Sales 21.1MM^E *EMP* 1,281^E
SIC 4011 Railroads, line-haul operating
Pr: Paul R Rudder

D-U-N-S 94-615-9233
▲ **LIVEPERSON INC**
475 10th Ave Fl 5, New York, NY 10018-9722
Tel (212) 609-4200 *Founded/Ownrshp* 1995
Sales 239.0MM *EMP* 1,006^E
Tkr Sym LPSN *Exch* NAS
SIC 7371 4813 Computer software development & applications;
Ch Bd: Robert P Locascio
CFO: Daniel R Murphy
Top Exec: Robert Janecek
Ex VP: Dustin Dean
Ex VP: Monica L Greenberg
Sr VP: Daryl Carlough
Sr VP: Key Compton
Sr VP: Michael Montour
Sr VP: Jeremy Sokolic
Mng Dir: James Troiano
Prgrm Mgr: Michael Pagnotta
Board of Directors: Peter Block, Kevin C Lavan, David Vaskevitch, William G Wesemann

D-U-N-S 07-959-4591
LIVER AND PANCREAS CENTER UNIVERSITY OF MARYLAND ST JOSEPH MEDICAL CENTER
HODES LIVER & PANCREAS CENTER
(*Suby of* UNIVERSITY MD ST JSEPH MED CTR) ★
7505 Osler Dr Ste 303, Towson, MD 21204-7738
Tel (410) 427-2024 *Founded/Ownrshp* 2014
Sales 199.6M^E *EMP* 1,006^E
SIC 8062 Hospital, medical school affiliation
Prin: Deborah Hartley

D-U-N-S 07-015-9694
LIVERMORE VALLEY JOINT UNIFIED SCHOOL DISTRICT
685 E Jack London Blvd, Livermore, CA 94551-1855
Tel (925) 606-3200 *Founded/Ownrshp* 1966
Sales 79.8MM^E *EMP* 1,600
Accts Nigro & Nigro Pc Marrieta Ca
SIC 8211 Public elementary & secondary schools
**CEO:* Anders W Lundberg
Bd of Dir: Julie Elfin

D-U-N-S 05-098-2958
LIVERPOOL CENTRAL SCHOOL DISTRICT
195 Blackberry Rd, Liverpool, NY 13090-3047
Tel (315) 622-7148 *Founded/Ownrshp* 1950
Sales 156.8MM *EMP* 1,300
Accts Ciaschi Dietershagen Little
SIC 8211 Public elementary school; Public junior high school; Public senior high school
Ex Dir: Lorraine Burrows
**Ex Dir:* Katharine Phillips
Dir Sec: Michael McCarthy
Genl Mgr: Dan Burns
MIS Dir: Bonnie Mangicaro
Dir IT: Tillotson Lind
Netwrk Mgr: Ronald Richardson

D-U-N-S 08-648-0865
LIVHOME INC
5670 Wilshire Blvd # 500, Los Angeles, CA 90036-5682
Tel (800) 807-5854 *Founded/Ownrshp* 1999
Sales 64.0MM^E *EMP* 1,329
SIC 8322 Geriatric social service
Ch Bd: Mike Nicholson
**Ofcr:* Cody D Legler
VP: Maureen Kehan
Ex Dir: Bruce Gratland
Ex Dir: David Posner

LIVING EARTH
See LETCO GROUP LLC

LIVING ESSENTIALS
See INNOVATION VENTURES LLC

LIVING HOPE PHYSIOTHERAPY
See PHYSIOTHERAPY ASSOCIATES INC

D-U-N-S 02-250-0606
LIVING SOCIAL INC
1445 New York Ave Nw # 200, Washington, DC 20005-2157
Tel (877) 521-4191 *Founded/Ownrshp* 2007
Sales 684.3MM^E *EMP* 4,900^E
SIC 5961
Pr: Gautam Thakar
**Treas:* Dan Frederico
Sr VP: Jake Maas
Sr VP: Nick Macey
Sr VP: Mitch Spolan
VP: Keith Dufresne
Exec: Alexandria Whaley
**Prin:* Timothy O'Shaughnessy
Snr Sftwr: Cloves Carneiro
Snr Sftwr: Chris Gibson
Snr Sftwr: Darrell Rivera
Board of Directors: Paul Guyardo

D-U-N-S 12-966-7825 IMP
LIVING SPACES FURNITURE LLC
14501 Artesia Blvd, La Mirada, CA 90638-5805
Tel (714) 523-2000 *Founded/Ownrshp* 2003
Sales 85.6MM^E *EMP* 200^E
SIC 5712 5021 Furniture stores; Furniture
VP: Rene Interiano
VP: George Kavorkian
VP: Luke Parker
Genl Mgr: Jennifer Aguayo
IT Man: Marsha Chapman
Software D: Kylan Swank
Opers Mgr: Jay Martinez
Mktg Mgr: Elizabeth Alvarez

D-U-N-S 00-513-3874
LIVINGSTON INTERNATIONAL INC
(*Suby of* LIVINGSTON INTERNATIONAL INC)
670 Young St, Tonawanda, NY 14150-4103
Tel (716) 692-3100 *Founded/Ownrshp* 1945, 1983
Sales 260.8MM^E *EMP* 900
SIC 4731 Customhouse brokers
CEO: Steven C Preston
**Pr:* Roy Coburn
**Pr:* Peter Luit
**CFO:* Chris McMullen
**Sr VP:* Victor Dsouza
**VP:* Wendy Archambault
**VP:* Cora Di Pietro
**VP:* Stephane Ethier
Exec: Jeff Rohl

D-U-N-S 02-416-0452
LIVINGSTON INTERNATIONAL INC
(*Suby of* LIVINGSTON INTERNATIONAL INC)
141 W Jackson Blvd 1510a, Chicago, IL 60604-2992
Tel (630) 766-0202 *Founded/Ownrshp* 1986
Sales 132.9MM^E *EMP* 636^E
SIC 7389 Brokers' services
CEO: Steve Preston
**Pr:* Roy Coburn
Pr: Matt Goodman
**Pr:* Christopher Logan
**CFO:* Chris McMullen
**CFO:* Sharon Sritong
**Ofcr:* Craig E Conway
**Sr VP:* Victor Dsouza
**VP:* Wendy Archambault
**VP:* Stephane Ethier
**VP:* Bob Perkins
**VP:* David Schulingkamp
**VP:* Catherine Townsend

D-U-N-S 17-776-9924
LIVINGSTON MACHINERY CO
5201 S Highway 81, Chickasha, OK 73018-9613
Tel (405) 224-5056 *Founded/Ownrshp* 1987
Sales 101.4MM *EMP* 129
SIC 5083 5999 7699 5261 Agricultural machinery; Farm equipment parts & supplies; Farm machinery; Agricultural equipment repair services; Lawnmowers & tractors
Pr: Shawn Skaggs
IT Man: Jeremy Owens
Sls Dir: Michael Boyd

D-U-N-S 09-490-9413
LIVINGSTON PARISH SCHOOL DISTRICT
13909 Florida Blvd, Livingston, LA 70754-6340
Tel (225) 686-7044 Founded/Ownrshp 2005
Sales 106.8MM^E EMP 2,404
SIC 8211 Public elementary & secondary schools
*Pr: Keith Martin
Exec: Lloyd Degeneres
Exec: Dennis Delee
Exec: Stacey Milton
Exec: Stacey Wise
Dir Sec: Wendy Gill
Admn Mgr: Patricia Davis
IT Man: Lonnie Luce
HC Dir: Jennifer Wilkinson

D-U-N-S 07-423-6662
LIVONIA PUBLIC SCHOOL DISTRICT
LIVONIA PUBLIC SCHOOLS
15125 Farmington Rd, Livonia, MI 48154-5413
Tel (734) 744-2500 Founded/Ownrshp 1918
Sales 195.1MM EMP 2,100
Accts Plante & Moran Pllc Auburn H
SIC 8211 Public elementary & secondary schools; Public senior high school; Public junior high school; Public elementary school
Bd of Dir: Lynda L Scheel
Trst: Eileen McDonnell
IT Man: Steven R Mezzadri
Netwrk Mgr: Jim Seay
Pr Dir: Mary Benoit
Pr Dir: Donna McDowell
Schl Brd P: Mark Johnson
Teacher Pr: Dana Whinnery
HC Dir: Jennifer Taiariol
Pgrm Dir: Jay Young

LIVONIA PUBLIC SCHOOLS
See LIVONIA PUBLIC SCHOOL DISTRICT

LIZ CLAIBORNE COATS
See LEVY GROUP INC

D-U-N-S 96-803-3576
LJ/HAH HOLDINGS CORP
2750 High Meadow Cir, Auburn Hills, MI 48326-2796
Tel (248) 340-4100 Founded/Ownrshp 2016
Sales 146.8MM^E EMP 3,168
SIC 2891 3714 Adhesives & sealants; Motor vehicle parts & accessories
CEO: Larry Williams

LJUNGSTRM
See ARVOS HOLDING LLC

D-U-N-S 79-785-9832
LKN COMMUNICATIONS INC
GE PLANNING
134 Medical Park Rd # 105, Mooresville, NC 28117-8526
Tel (704) 260-3323 Founded/Ownrshp 1992
Sales 7.2MM^E EMP 1,110
SIC 4813 Local & long distance telephone communications;
CEO: Charles Barker
*Ch Bd: Robert Stevanovski
*Pr: Gregory Provenzano
*CFO: Brian Krass
*CFO: Jim Mulzahy
VP: Hayri Barutcu
*VP: Michael Cupisz
*VP: Dave Stevanovski

D-U-N-S 02-811-7104
▲ LKQ CORP
500 W Madison St Ste 2800, Chicago, IL 60661-2506
Tel (312) 621-1950 Founded/Ownrshp 1998
Sales 7.1MMM EMP 31,100^E
Tkr Sym LKQ Exch NGS
SIC 5093 5015 Automotive wrecking for scrap; Motor vehicle parts, used; Automotive parts & supplies, used
Pr: Robert L Wagman
*Ch Bd: Joseph M Holsten
*CFO: Dominick Zarcone
*Sr VP: Robert A Alberico
Sr VP: Ashley T Brooks
*Sr VP: Victor M Casini
Sr VP: Walter P Hanley
Sr VP: Justin L Jude
*VP: Michael S Clark
Exec: Bradley Willen
Dist Mgr: Daryl Masters
Board of Directors: A Clinton Allen, Robert M Hanser, Blythe J McGarvie, Paul M Meister, John F O'brien, William M Webster IV

D-U-N-S 78-498-0240 IMP
LL BEAN INTERNATIONAL
(Suby of L L BEAN INC) ★
15 Casco St, Freeport, ME 04033-0002
Tel (207) 865-4761 Founded/Ownrshp 2000
Sales 1.8MM^E EMP 1,000^E
SIC 5961 Catalog & mail-order houses
Ch Bd: Shawn Gorman
*VP: Kierston Vansoest
*Prin: Christopher J McCormick

LLC, CARL ZEISS NTS
See CARL ZEISS MICROSCOPY LLC

LLC, FORCE AMERICA DISTRG
See FORCE AMERICA INC

LLCP
See LEVINE LEICHTMAN CAPITAL PARTNERS INC

D-U-N-S 07-838-3402 IMP/EXP
LLFLEX LLC
1225 W Burnett Ave, Louisville, KY 40210-1879
Tel (502) 635-6331 Founded/Ownrshp 2011
Sales 100.0MM EMP 141
SIC 2672

D-U-N-S 14-193-3494 IMP
LLOG EXPLORATION CO LLC
1001 Ochsner Blvd Ste 200, Covington, LA 70433-8152
Tel (504) 833-7700 Founded/Ownrshp 2002
Sales 875.8MM^E EMP 75^E
Accts Ernst & Young Llp New Orleans
SIC 1311 1382 Crude petroleum & natural gas; Oil & gas exploration services
CEO: Scott Gutterman
Sr VP: Tim Lindsey
VP: Mike Altobelli
VP: Jay Cole
VP: Bruce Cooley
IT Man: Terry Hovis

D-U-N-S 05-391-4094
LLOG EXPLORATION OFFSHORE LLC (LA)
1001 Ochsner Blvd Ste 200, Covington, LA 70433-8152
Tel (985) 801-4300 Founded/Ownrshp 1996
Sales 162.7MM^E EMP 100
SIC 1382 Oil & gas exploration services
*Ch Bd: Gerald A Boelte
*Ex VP: Kevin P Guilbeau

LLOYD CREATIVE TEMPORARIES
See LLOYD STAFFING INC

D-U-N-S 10-585-2016
LLOYD STAFFING INC
LLOYD CREATIVE TEMPORARIES
445 Broadhollow Rd # 119, Melville, NY 11747-3631
Tel (631) 777-7600 Founded/Ownrshp 1971
Sales 56.1MM^E EMP 1,500
SIC 7363 Temporary help service
CEO: Merrill Banks
*Pr: Keith Banks
*CFO: Vincent J Albanese
CFO: Russell Owens
CFO: Kim Unruh
*VP: Jason Banks
*VP: Donna Caputo
*VP: Carolyn Doyle
*VP: Marc Lester
*VP: Nancy Schuman
CIO: Joseph R Brennskag

D-U-N-S 14-737-1335
LLOYDS ILLINOIS INC
(Suby of LLOYD'S MARKET ASSOCIATION)
181 W Madison St Ste 3870, Chicago, IL 60602-4541
Tel (312) 407-6200 Founded/Ownrshp 2004
Sales NA EMP 15
SIC 6411 Insurance information & consulting services
Pr: Maryanne Swaim
*CFO: John W O'Hara
VP: Keith Wenckowski

D-U-N-S 06-815-6215
LLP ROBINS KAPLAN
ROBINS KAPLAN MILLER & CIRESI
800 Lasalle Ave Ste 2800, Minneapolis, MN 55402-2039
Tel (612) 349-8500 Founded/Ownrshp 1938
Sales 109.5MM^E EMP 600
SIC 8111 Legal services
Ch: Martin R Lueck
Genl Pt: Dick Nigon
Pt: Robert Auchter
Pt: V R Denham Jr
Pt: Keith Styles
Mng Pt: Cole Fauver
Mng Pt: Kenneth Freeling
Mng Pt: Steven A Schumeister
Opers Mgr: Adam Pugh
Counsel: Richard Gill
Counsel: Sue Halverson

LLS
See LEUKEMIA & LYMPHOMA SOCIETY INC

LLU
See LOMA LINDA UNIVERSITY

LLUMC
See LOMA LINDA UNIVERSITY MEDICAL CENTER

D-U-N-S 05-288-5311 IMP/EXP
LM WIND POWER BLADES (ND) INC
LM WIND POWER LITTLE ROCK
(Suby of LM WIND POWER HOLDING A/S)
1580 S 48th St, Grand Forks, ND 58201-3808
Tel (701) 780-9910 Founded/Ownrshp 1998
Sales 299.4MM^E EMP 880^E
SIC 3511 3621 Turbines & turbine generator sets & parts; Motors & generators
CEO: Roland M Sunden
*CFO: Dominique Yates
*Treas: Sean R O Leary
*VP: Randy L Fox
VP: Kenneth Kaser
VP: Christopher Springham
Exec: Gerald Muizelaar
*CTO: Frank V Nielsen

LM WIND POWER LITTLE ROCK
See LM WIND POWER BLADES (ND) INC

LMAERO
See LOCKHEED MARTIN AERONAUTICAL CO

LMC
See LUMBERMENS MERCHANDISING CORP

LMC EXTENDED CARE
See LEXMED INC

LMGI
See LOCKHEED MARTIN GLOBAL INC

LMH
See LAWRENCE MEMORIAL HOSPITAL ENDOWMENT ASSOCIATION

D-U-N-S 10-854-4672
LMHC MASSACHUSETTS HOLDINGS INC
(Suby of LIBERTY MUTUAL HOLDING CO INC) ★
175 Berkeley St, Boston, MA 02116-5066
Tel (617) 357-9500 Founded/Ownrshp 2001
Sales NA EMP 50,000
SIC 6331 6321 6351 7389 Fire, marine & casualty insurance; Workers' compensation insurance; Automobile insurance; Burglary & theft insurance; Accident insurance carriers; Health insurance carriers; Reinsurance carriers, accident & health; Liability insurance; Fidelity or surety bonding; Fidelity responsibility insurance; Financial services
Ch Bd: Edmund F Kelly
VP: Galen Potts

D-U-N-S 04-129-7664
▲ LMI AEROSPACE INC
411 Fountain Lakes Blvd, Saint Charles, MO 63301-4352
Tel (636) 946-6525 Founded/Ownrshp 1948
Sales 375.1MM EMP 1,945
Tkr Sym LMIA Exch NGS
SIC 3728 Aircraft parts & equipment
Pr: Daniel G Korte
Pr: Jay Inman
CFO: Clifford C Stebe Jr
Chf Cred: Renee Skonier
Ofcr: Jennifer L Alfaro
VP: David Fillmore
VP: Jason Lawson
Comm Dir: Amy Horton
Dir Bus: Kenneth Scherwinski
Prgrm Mgr: Mark Reardon
Genl Mgr: Jim Bauer
Board of Directors: Gerald E Daniels, John S Eulich, Sanford S Neuman, Judith W Nothup, John N Roeder, Ronald S Sakes, Steven K Shaffer, Gregory L Summe

LMI SOLUTIONS
See LASERMASTERS LLC

D-U-N-S 18-188-7816
LMN DEVELOPMENT LLC
KALAHARI RESORT
7000 Kalahari Dr, Sandusky, OH 44870-8628
Tel (419) 433-7200 Founded/Ownrshp 2003
Sales 67.3MM^E EMP 1,000^E
SIC 7011 7996 5091 Resort hotel; Amusement parks; Water slides (recreation park)
Pr: Todd Nelson
CFO: Mary Bonte-Stath
Genl Mgr: Brian Shanle

D-U-N-S 78-370-2590
LMS INTELLIBOUND INC
6525 The Corners Pkwy, Norcross, GA 30092-3344
Tel (770) 724-0564 Founded/Ownrshp 1998
Sales 85.5MM^E EMP 1,600
SIC 4225 General warehousing & storage
CEO: Steve Taylor
*Pr: William Harper
Genl Mgr: William Davis Jr
Opers Mgr: Mike Henleben

LNC
See LINCOLN NATIONAL CORP

D-U-N-S 14-078-7743 IMP
LNG FREEPORT DEVELOPMENT L P
333 Clay St Ste 5050, Houston, TX 77002-4101
Tel (713) 980-2888 Founded/Ownrshp 2002
Sales 104.6MM^E EMP 99
Accts Ernst & Young Llp Houston Tx
SIC 4922 Pipelines, natural gas
CEO: Michael S Smith
Pr: Charles Reimer
Pr: Jody Sumrall
CFO: Hugh Urbantke
CFO: Hugh Urbantkes
VP: Bryan Frey
VP: Bobby Gaspard
VP: Todd McLaughlin
VP: Anne Rappold
VP: Jerry Smith
VP: John Tobola

D-U-N-S 00-302-1078
LNP MEDIA GROUP INC
BUSINESS INTELLHGENCER JOURNAL
8 W King St, Lancaster, PA 17603-3824
Tel (717) 291-8811 Founded/Ownrshp 1928
Sales 124.1MM^E EMP 550^E
SIC 2711 2752

D-U-N-S 02-682-5807
LNR PROPERTY LLC
(Suby of STARWOOD PROPERTY TRUST INC) ★
1601 Washington Ave # 800, Miami Beach, FL 33139-3164
Tel (305) 695-5500 Founded/Ownrshp 2010
Sales 128.7MM^E EMP 480
SIC 6513 Apartment building operators
VP: Shahram M Siddiqui
*Pr: Jeffrey P Krasnoff
COO: Cory Olson
*COO: Ronald E Schrager
Chf Mktg O: Yesenia Marcos
VP: Brett Birkeland
VP: Natan Bresler
*VP: Robert Cherry
VP: Tom Creasy
*VP: Zena M Dickstein
VP: Seth Fisher
VP: Hector Gomez
VP: Kevin Hanson
VP: Robert J Kates
VP: Juan Mira
VP: Joakim Mortensen
VP: Ken Oneill
VP: Rina Paniry
VP: Rich Pietrykowski
VP: Arne Shulkin
VP: Leah Solomon

LO LO CHICKEN AND WAFFLES
See CUTCHALL MANAGEMENT CO INC

D-U-N-S 94-811-6207 IMP
LOAD TRAIL LLC
220 Farm Road 2216, Sumner, TX 75486-4648
Tel (903) 783-3900 Founded/Ownrshp 1996
Sales 109.7MM EMP 410^E
Accts Bkd Llp Dallas Texas
SIC 3799 Trailers & trailer equipment
IT Man: Shane Richard

D-U-N-S 17-165-2485 EXP
LOADCRAFT INDUSTRIES LTD
3811 N Bridge St, Brady, TX 76825
Tel (325) 597-2911 Founded/Ownrshp 2004
Sales 104.6MM^E EMP 365^E
SIC 3533 Oil & gas field machinery
Mng Pt: Terry McIver
*Pt: Donald Barley
*Pt: Cary Brown
*Pt: Dale Brown
*Pt: Ray Jones
*Pt: Grady McIver
CFO: Luis Collazo
VP: Steven Richards
VP Sls: Gary Weatherman

LOAF 'N JUG
See MINI MART INC

D-U-N-S 83-022-5707
LOANDEPOT.COM LLC
26642 Towne Centre Dr, Foothill Ranch, CA 92610-2808
Tel (949) 474-1322 Founded/Ownrshp 2010
Sales NA EMP 5,000
SIC 6162 Mortgage bankers
CEO: Anthony Hsieh
Pr: David Norris
CFO: Jon Frojen
Ofcr: Diana Harvey
Ex VP: Peter Macdonald
Ex VP: Chad Smith
Ex VP: Bryan Sullivan
Sr VP: Michael H Wilson
CTO: Dominick Marchetti

LOANS 4 HOMES
See LANDLOVERS LLC

D-U-N-S 05-291-7143
LOBAR INC (PA)
1 Old Mill Rd, Dillsburg, PA 17019-1620
Tel (717) 432-9728 Founded/Ownrshp 1967
Sales 107.9MM^E EMP 175^E
SIC 1541 1542 8741 1629 1731 7371

LOBO DISTRIBUTING
See PHOENIX BEVERAGES INC

D-U-N-S 06-557-4683 IMP/EXP
LOC PERFORMANCE PRODUCTS INC
13505 N Haggerty Rd, Plymouth, MI 48170-4251
Tel (734) 453-2300 Founded/Ownrshp 1971
Sales 88.0MM^E EMP 225
SIC 3541 Machine tools, metal cutting type
CEO: Victor Vojcek
*Pr: Lou Burr
*COO: Jason Atkinson
*CFO: Thomas Horne
Prgrm Mgr: Paul Menosky
Genl Mgr: Jeff Hanson
IT Man: J B Pergeau
IT Man: Jessica Segarra
QC Dir: Tim Horner
Sls Mgr: David Sepesi

D-U-N-S 02-626-4713
LOCAL & WESTERN OF TEXAS INC
5445 La Sierra Dr Ste 100, Dallas, TX 75231-3463
Tel (214) 750-6633 Founded/Ownrshp 1986
Sales 147.2MM EMP 12
SIC 5142

D-U-N-S 04-754-6858
LOCAL 25 SEIU WELFARE FUND
SEIU LOCAL 25 WELFARE FUND
111 E Wacker Dr Ste 1700, Chicago, IL 60601-4504
Tel (312) 240-1600 Founded/Ownrshp 1968
Sales NA EMP 19
Accts Bansley And Kiener Llp Chicag
SIC 6371 Pension, health & welfare funds

D-U-N-S 96-780-7319
LOCAL 94 94A 94B HEALTH & BENEFIT TRUST FUND IUOE AFL-CIO
331 W 44th St 337, New York, NY 10036-5402
Tel (212) 541-9880 Founded/Ownrshp 2011
Sales 106.5MM EMP 13^E
Accts Schultheis & Panettieri Llp H
SIC 8631 Labor unions & similar labor organizations
Pr: Kuba Brown

D-U-N-S 07-966-2289
LOCAL CORP
LOCAL.COM
7555 Irvine Center Dr, Irvine, CA 92618-2930
Tel (949) 784-0800 Founded/Ownrshp 1999
Sales 83.1MM EMP 93^E
SIC 7311 Advertising agencies
Ch Bd: Frederick G Thiel
CFO: Kenneth S Cragun
Ofcr: Scott Reinke
Sr VP: Erick Herring
Sr VP: George Kellerman
VP: Peter Chang
VP: Eileen Licitra
VP: Mark Wallin
CTO: Michael Plonski
VP Mktg: Jennifer Black
Sls Dir: Laura Gaffney
Board of Directors: Norman K Farra Jr, Philip K Fricke, David M Hughes, John M Payne, John E Rehfeld

LOCAL GOVERNMENT
See COUNTY OF COCHISE

D-U-N-S 93-184-9285
LOCAL INITIATIVE HEALTH AUTHORITY FOR LOS ANGELES COUNTY
L A CARE HEALTH PLAN
1055 W 7th St Fl 11, Los Angeles, CA 90017-2751
Tel (213) 694-1250 Founded/Ownrshp 1995
Sales NA EMP 900
Accts Deloitte & Touche Llp Los Ang
SIC 6324 Hospital & medical service plans
CEO: Howard A Kahn
*COO: John Wallace

*CFO: Tim Reilly
Bd of Dir: Andrea Van Hook
*Chf Mktg O: Gertrude Carter
Exec: Elaine Batchlor
Comm Dir: Andrea Hook
Dir IT: Keith Tan
Info Man: Ibnu Kurniawan
Mktg Dir: Cherie Fields
Mktg Mgr: Linh Tran

D-U-N-S 00-202-6797
■ LOCAL MEDIA GROUP INC (NY)
(Suby of NEW MEDIA INVESTMENT GROUP INC) ★
40 Mulberry St, Middletown, NY 10940-6302
Tel (845) 341-1100 Founded/Ownrshp 1936, 2013
Sales 414.4MM^E EMP 2,900
SIC 2711 7313 Newspapers: publishing only, not printed on site; Newspaper advertising representative
Pr: John Wilcox
*COO: William T Kennedy
*CFO: Jonathan Kahan
*CFO: William A Zurilla
*Ch: Patrick Purcell
Treas: David Stewart
*Sr VP: Kurt Lozier
*VP: Patricia Gatto
Dir IT: David Foglia
Dir IT: David Laders
IT Man: Gregory Bryant

D-U-N-S 79-508-5401
■ LOCAL TV LLC
(Suby of TRIBUNE MEDIA CO) ★
300 Dave Cowans Dr, Newport, KY 41071-4570
Tel (859) 448-2700 Founded/Ownrshp 2013
Sales 179.2MM^E EMP 800
SIC 4833 Television broadcasting stations
*CFO: Ted Kuhlman

LOCAL WINE TOURS
See TERLATO WINE GROUP LTD

LOCAL.COM
See LOCAL CORP

LOCCITANE EN PROVENCE
See LOCCITANE INC

D-U-N-S 07-944-7092
LOCCITANE INC
120 Herrod Blvd, Dayton, NJ 08810-1528
Tel (212) 696-9098 Founded/Ownrshp 2014
Sales 63.4MM^E EMP 1,400
SIC 5999 Toiletries, cosmetics & perfumes
Sr VP: Benoit Mennegand

D-U-N-S 87-826-8200 EXP
LOCCITANE INC
LOCCITANE EN PROVENCE
(Suby of L'OCCITANE INTERNATIONAL SA)
1430 Broadway Fl 2, New York, NY 10018-9227
Tel (212) 333-4880 Founded/Ownrshp 1995
Sales 266.2MM^E EMP 600
SIC 5122 5999 5961 Drugs, proprietaries & sundries; Perfumes; Toiletries, cosmetics & perfumes; Cosmetics & perfumes, mail order
Pr: Reinold Geiger
*CFO: Francois Cambours
Treas: Wilfrid Poisnel
VP: Stephanie Guinard
Pr Mgr: Nicole Parker
Snr Mgr: Juan Buenano

LOCHBRIDGE
See CW PROFESSIONAL SERVICES LLC

D-U-N-S 84-792-5666 IMP/EXP
■ LOCHINVAR LLC
(Suby of A O SMITH CORP) ★
300 Maddox Simpson Pkwy, Lebanon, TN 37090-5366
Tel (615) 889-8900 Founded/Ownrshp 2011
Sales 98.6MM^E EMP 375
SIC 3639 3443 5074 Hot water heaters, household; Boilers: industrial, power, or marine; Plumbing & hydronic heating supplies
Pr: William L Vallett Jr
*Pr: Bill Vallett Jr
*Ex VP: Jeff Vallett
VP: Michelle Hibdon
QA Dir: La'mar Franklin
IT Man: Patti McFarland
Sfty Mgr: Ron Briley
Opers Mgr: Ava Brewington
Plnt Mgr: Michael Boatright
Plnt Mgr: Bill Rodgers
Ql Cn Mgr: Lee Poplin

D-U-N-S 07-843-2044
LOCKE LORD LLP
2200 Ross Ave Ste 2800, Dallas, TX 75201-2750
Tel (214) 740-8000 Founded/Ownrshp 1916
Sales 382.4MM^E EMP 1,150
SIC 8111 General practice law office
Ch: Jerry K Clements
Pt: Kay W McCurdy
Mng Pt: Bill Kelty
Mng Pt: Robert D Miller
CFO: Greg D Aunan
CFO: Mary Ann Jay
Ch: Don M Glendenning
Treas: Leldon Walenta
VP: Shonn Brown
Exec: Philip Cooper
Ex Dir: Miles Holsworth

D-U-N-S 00-720-5206 IMP
LOCKE SUPPLY CO
LOCKE WHOLESALE HTG & COOLG
1300 Se 82nd St, Oklahoma City, OK 73149-4400
Tel (405) 635-3230 Founded/Ownrshp 1955
Sales 396.0MM^E EMP 900
SIC 5063 5074 5075 1711

LOCKE WHOLESALE HTG & COOLG
See LOCKE SUPPLY CO

D-U-N-S 05-541-7968
LOCKHART GEOPHYSICAL CO
1600 Broadway Ste 1660, Denver, CO 80202-4915
Tel (303) 592-5220 Founded/Ownrshp 1981
Sales 191.3MM^E EMP 150^E
SIC 1382

D-U-N-S 94-858-6433 IMP/EXP
■ LOCKHEED MARTIN AERONAUTICAL CO
LMAERO
(Suby of LOCKHEED MARTIN CORP) ★
86 S Cobb Dr Se, Marietta, GA 30063-0001
Tel (770) 494-4411 Founded/Ownrshp 1951
Sales 228.8MM^E EMP 7,600
SIC 3721 3812 7699 3769 Aircraft; Search & navigation equipment; Aircraft & heavy equipment repair services; Guided missile & space vehicle parts & auxiliary equipment
Pr: Ralph Heath
*VP: Larry J McQuien
Genl Mgr: Lee Ryant
Snr Ntwrk: Mike Gibson
Corp Couns: Tressa Q Deandrade

D-U-N-S 11-917-3318 IMP
■ LOCKHEED MARTIN AIRCRAFT CENTER
(Suby of LOCKHEED MARTIN CORP) ★
244 Terminal Rd, Greenville, SC 29605-5508
Tel (864) 422-6262 Founded/Ownrshp 1984
Sales 464.4MM^E EMP 8,200
SIC 3721 4581 Aircraft; Motorized aircraft; Airport hangar rental; Aircraft cleaning & janitorial service
CEO: Raymond A Burick
*Pr: Steven Kreger

LOCKHEED MARTIN ASPEN
See LEIDOS ASPEN SYSTEMS CORP

D-U-N-S 83-495-1691
▲ LOCKHEED MARTIN CORP
6801 Rockledge Dr, Bethesda, MD 20817-1877
Tel (301) 897-6000 Founded/Ownrshp 1995
Sales 46.1MMM EMP 126,000
Accts Ernst & Young Llp Mclean Vi
Tkr Sym LMT Exch NYS
SIC 3761 3721 3663 3764 3812 3728 Space vehicles, complete; Guided missiles, complete; Ballistic missiles, complete; Guided missiles & space vehicles, research & development; Aircraft; Research & development on aircraft by the manufacturer; Satellites, communications; Propulsion units for guided missiles & space vehicles; Guided missile & space vehicle engines, research & devel.; Warfare countermeasure equipment; Missile guidance systems & equipment; Sonar systems & equipment; Radar systems & equipment; Aircraft parts & equipment; Research & dev by manuf., aircraft parts & auxiliary equip
Ch Bd: Marillyn A Hewson
CFO: Bruce L Tanner
Treas: Kenneth R Possenriede
Ofcr: Gene Holloway
Ex VP: Richard F Ambrose
Ex VP: Dale P Bennett
Ex VP: Orlando P Carvalho
Ex VP: Richard H Edwards
Ex VP: Craig Gabbard
Ex VP: William Graham
Ex VP: Paul Hommert
Sr VP: Maryanne R Lavan
VP: Brian P Colan
VP: Joe Garland
VP: Michael Gutierrez
VP: Cory A Miller
VP: Glenn Miller
VP: Steve O'Bryan
VP: David Trulio
VP: Jim L Valentine
VP: Jeffrey Wilcox
Board of Directors: Joseph W Ralston, Daniel F Akerson, Anne Stevens, Nolan D Archibald, Rosalind G Brewer, David B Burritt, Bruce A Carlson, James O Ellis Jr, Thomas J Falk, Ilene S Gordon, James M Loy

D-U-N-S 12-054-9840
■ LOCKHEED MARTIN ENERGY RESEARCH CORP
(Suby of LOCKHEED MARTIN CORP) ★
1 Bethel Valley Rd, Oak Ridge, TN 37830-8050
Tel (865) 574-1000 Founded/Ownrshp 1996
Sales 98.4MM^E EMP 4,000
SIC 8733 Noncommercial research organizations
Pr: Alvin W Trivelpiece
IT Man: David Rose

D-U-N-S 07-841-6354
■ LOCKHEED MARTIN GLOBAL INC
LMGI
(Suby of LOCKHEED MARTIN CORP) ★
497 Electronics Pkwy # 5, Liverpool, NY 13088-5394
Tel (315) 456-2982 Founded/Ownrshp 2012
Sales 352.3MM^E EMP 3,000^E
SIC 3812 Search & navigation equipment
Pr: Dale M Johnson
VP: Christopher Gregoire
VP: Kenneth Possenriede

D-U-N-S 17-019-7748
■ LOCKHEED MARTIN GLOBAL TELECOMMUNICATIONS INC
(Suby of BT LATAM HOLDINGS ONE, INC.)
1600 Tysons Blvd Ste 550, Mc Lean, VA 22102-4892
Tel (703) 556-9500 Founded/Ownrshp 2002
Sales 183.2MM^E EMP 927
SIC 4813 1731 Local & long distance telephone communications; ; Fiber optic cable installation
Pr: Kenneth Possenriede
*Pr: George Kappaz
*CFO: Ian Gerrard
*Ch: Brian Thompson
*Ex VP: Philip Walker
*VP: David C Preiss
*VP: Rena H Whitney
Ex Dir: Arlan Stehney

D-U-N-S 12-050-5032
■ LOCKHEED MARTIN GLOBAL TELECOMMUNICATIONS LLC
(Suby of LOCKHEED MARTIN CORP) ★
6560 Rock Spring Dr, Bethesda, MD 20817-1145
Tel (301) 571-7135 Founded/Ownrshp 1963
Sales 267.5MM^E EMP 1,000^E
SIC 4813 Telephone communication, except radio
CEO: Marillyn A Hewson
Treas: Wesley D Minami
VP: Steven F Bell
VP: Jerome W Breslow
VP: Peter Clyne
VP: Susan Miller
VP: Susan L Sallet
VP: Christophe Wallers
VP: Warren Y Zeger
Exec: Bruce L Crockett
Snr Sftwr: Kevin Carroll

LOCKHEED MARTIN GOV SVC, INC.
See LEIDOS GOVERNMENT SERVICES INC

D-U-N-S 83-619-6972
■ LOCKHEED MARTIN INTEGRATED SYSTEMS INC
(Suby of LOCKHEED MARTIN SERVICES INC) ★
6801 Rockledge Dr, Bethesda, MD 20817-1803
Tel (856) 486-5000 Founded/Ownrshp 1996
Sales 1.1MMM^E EMP 5,668
SIC 3812 Search & navigation equipment
CEO: Marillyn A Hewson
*Pr: Richard J Masi
*Ex VP: Richard F Ambrose
*Ex VP: Dale P Bennett
*VP: Sondra L Barbour
*VP: Bruce L Tanner

D-U-N-S 02-311-0377
■ LOCKHEED MARTIN LOGISTIC SERVICES INC
LOCKHEED MARTIN LOGISTIC SVCS
(Suby of LOCKHEED MARTIN CORP) ★
244 Terminal Rd, Greenville, SC 29605-5508
Tel (864) 236-3552 Founded/Ownrshp 1997
Sales 69.4MM^E EMP 3,000
SIC 4581 Aircraft servicing & repairing
Pr: Edward J Bergin
CFO: Connie Mearkle
*VP: Thomas Barthel

LOCKHEED MARTIN LOGISTIC SVCS
See LOCKHEED MARTIN LOGISTIC SERVICES INC

D-U-N-S 94-860-4350
■ LOCKHEED MARTIN LOGISTICS MANAGEMENT INC
(Suby of LOCKHEED MARTIN CORP) ★
244 Terminal Rd, Greenville, SC 29605-5508
Tel (864) 277-7230 Founded/Ownrshp 1980
Sales 95.9MM^E EMP 3,200
SIC 8742 Management consulting services
Pr: David Pozak

D-U-N-S 80-525-8373
■ LOCKHEED MARTIN SERVICES INC
(Suby of LOCKHEED MARTIN CORP) ★
700 N Frederick Ave, Gaithersburg, MD 20879-3328
Tel (301) 240-7669 Founded/Ownrshp 1993
Sales 1.1MMM^E EMP 20,000
SIC 8711 8741 8742 Engineering services; Management services; Management consulting services
CEO: Marillyn A Hewson
*Treas: Mike Mittrione
*Ex VP: Bruce L Tanner

D-U-N-S 03-204-6666 IMP
■ LOCKHEED MARTIN SIPPICAN INC
(Suby of LOCKHEED MARTIN CORP) ★
7 Barnabas Rd, Marion, MA 02738-1421
Tel (508) 748-3399 Founded/Ownrshp 2004
Sales 102.9MM^E EMP 450
SIC 3812 3826 3499 3672 3829 3845 Warfare counter-measure equipment; Environmental testing equipment; Target drones, for use by ships: metal; Printed circuit boards; Physical property testing equipment; Electromedical equipment
Pr: Latisha Rourke
*Pr: William E Walsh Jr
*CFO: James J Hickey
*VP: Douglas J Dapprich
*VP: Lawrence C Hall
*VP: Thomas L Jarbeau
*VP: James Langenheim
*VP: Bernard Mitchell
*VP: Donna M O'Connor
*VP: Kenneth R Possenriede
Exec: Donna Hogan
Board of Directors: Richard I Arthur, Thomas Corcoran, Alan Holt, George E Melton, William E Walsh Jr, Claudius Watts

D-U-N-S 13-930-7151 IMP
■ LOCKHEED MARTIN SPACE OPERATIONS LLC
(Suby of LOCKHEED MARTIN CORP) ★
700 N Frederick Ave, Gaithersburg, MD 20879-3328
Tel (301) 240-7000 Founded/Ownrshp 1994
Sales 265.5MM^E EMP 19,000^E
SIC 4789 Space flight operations, except government
Pr: Jay Honeycutt
*Sr VP: Ken Reightler
*VP: J R Kline

D-U-N-S 18-294-9776 IMP/EXP
■ LOCKHEED MARTIN TRAINING SOLUTIONS
(Suby of LOCKHEED MARTIN CORP) ★
100 Global Innovation Cir, Orlando, FL 32825-5003
Tel (407) 306-4000 Founded/Ownrshp 1995
Sales 175.4MM^E EMP 506^E
SIC 3728 Military aircraft equipment & armament
Pr: Nick Ali
Pr: Doug Greenlaw
*CEO: Marillyn A Hewson
*CFO: Bruce L Tanner

Treas: John C McCarthy
VP: Glenn Brown
*VP: Harold Browning
VP: William Carithers
VP: James Craig
VP: Thomas Dorsey
Prgrm Mgr: Michael Bond

LOCKTON COMPANIES
See LOCKTON INC

D-U-N-S 15-345-5555
LOCKTON COMPANIES LLC - PACIFIC SERIES
LOCKTON INSURANCE BROKERS
(Suby of LOCKTON COMPANIES) ★
725 S Figueroa St Fl 35, Los Angeles, CA 90017-5435
Tel (213) 689-0500 Founded/Ownrshp 2006
Sales NA EMP 350
SIC 6411 Insurance brokers
COO: Leonard Fodemski
Pt: Philip Hurrle
Mng Pt: Debbie Day
*Pr: Timothy J Noonan
COO: Gary Petrosino
*CFO: Leonard G Fodemski
Assoc VP: Shelly Noble-Seavall
Ex VP: Mark Carlin
Ex VP: Mark Cwizkel
Sr VP: Eileen M Bacon
Sr VP: Rex Cook
Sr VP: Blake Graeber
Sr VP: Keith Ohrstrom
Sr VP: Au Sandy
Sr VP: Jim Silicani
Sr VP: Keli Tomack
Sr VP: Viesha Treadwell
VP: Scott C Bastian
VP: Karen Daugherty
VP: Bryan Davis
VP: Edward Gallagher

D-U-N-S 16-137-3857
LOCKTON INC
LOCKTON COMPANIES
444 W 47th St Ste 900, Kansas City, MO 64112-1906
Tel (816) 960-9000 Founded/Ownrshp 1966
Sales NA EMP 1,361
SIC 6411 Property & casualty insurance agent; Insurance agents; Life insurance agents
Ch: David M Lockton
Pr: Joe Agnello
Pr: Bob Irvin
Pr: Chris Keith
Pr: Thomas J Schaffler
CEO: Tony Gusmao
*CEO: John Lumelleau
*COO: Mark Henderson
COO: Ross Reda
COO: Jason Richardson
*COO: Glenn Spencer
*CFO: Henry Bond
*V Ch Bd: Ron Lockton
Ex VP: Michael Andler
Ex VP: Jim Caldwell
Ex VP: Kevin Cummings
Sr VP: David Bachrach
Sr VP: Chris Bartnik
Sr VP: Ray Beegle
Sr VP: Mickey Brown
Sr VP: William Butler

LOCKTON INSURANCE BROKERS
See LOCKTON COMPANIES LLC - PACIFIC SERIES

D-U-N-S 09-194-5261 IMP
LOCKWOOD INTERNATIONAL INC
TY VALVE
10203 Wallisville Rd, Houston, TX 77013-4115
Tel (866) 898-2583 Founded/Ownrshp 1977
Sales 282.4MM^E EMP 200
SIC 5085 Valves & fittings
Pr: Mike Lockwood
CFO: Mark Lindsey
*VP: Tom Lockwood
VP: Pat Murphy
Brnch Mgr: Cameron Dawe
Dist Mgr: Dennis Hough
Off Mgr: Lisa Weeks
Dir IT: Chris Beard
Snr PM: Cliff Houk

LOCUST RIDGE QUARRY
See HAINES & KIBBLEHOUSE INC

D-U-N-S 14-219-5648 IMP
LODERS CROKLAAN USA LLC
(Suby of LODERS CROKLAAN B.V.)
24708 W Durkee Rd, Channahon, IL 60410-5249
Tel (815) 730-5200 Founded/Ownrshp 2002
Sales 90.5MM EMP 180
SIC 2079 Edible oil products, except corn oil
Prin: Julian Veitch
CFO: Mike Molenkamp
*Prin: Yeow Seng Lee
*Prin: William Troy
IT Man: Clay Bonham
IT Man: Jian Ming
Opers Mgr: Craig Nelson

LODGE AT KOELE
See LANAI RESORTS LLC

D-U-N-S 04-313-5698
LODGIAN INC
(Suby of LSREF LODGING INVESTMENTS LLC) ★
2002 Summit Blvd Ste 300, Brookhaven, GA 30319-6403
Tel (404) 364-9400 Founded/Ownrshp 1998, 2010
Sales 132.8MM^E EMP 3,046
SIC 7011 5813 Hotels & motels; Drinking places
Pr: Daniel E Ellis
COO: Michael W Amaral
*CFO: James A Maclennan
*Sr VP: Bryan Esposito
*Sr VP: Thomas Rosati
*VP: Donna B Cohen
*VP: James R McGrath
Brnch Mgr: Charito Monis
Brnch Mgr: Michael Patel

Genl Mgr: Jack Bhakta
Genl Mgr: Mark Brown
Board of Directors: W Blair Allen, John W Allison, Stewart J Brown, Paul J Garity, Stephen P Grathwohl, Michael J Grondahl, Alex R Lieblong, Mark S Oei

D-U-N-S 15-409-2068
LODGING ENTERPRISES LLC
AMERICAN HT INCOME PRPTS REIT
(*Suby of* AMERICAN HOTEL INCOME PROPERTIES REIT INC.)
8080 E Central Ave # 180, Wichita, KS 67206-2371
Tel (316) 630-6300 *Founded/Ownrshp* 2013
Sales 108.9MM^E *EMP* 1,010
SIC 7011 8741 6552 Hotels & motels; Management services; Subdividers & developers
Pr: William Burgess
**Treas:* David Mitchell
Dir IT: Dan Carpententer

D-U-N-S 96-842-0468
LODGING RLJTRUST L P
(*Suby of* RLJ LODGING TRUST) ★
3 Bethesda Metro Ctr # 1000, Bethesda, MD 20814-5330
Tel (301) 280-7777 *Founded/Ownrshp* 2011
Sales 1.1MMM *EMP* 9^E
Accts Pricewaterhousecoopers Llp Mc
SIC 7011 Vacation lodges
Pr: Thomas Baltimore
CFO: Leslie D Hale
VP: Susan Sloan
VP Admn: Anita Wells

D-U-N-S 07-467-3807
LODI MEMORIAL HOSPITAL ASSOCIATION INC
975 S Fairmont Ave, Lodi, CA 95240-5118
Tel (209) 334-3411 *Founded/Ownrshp* 1945
Sales 120.3MM *EMP* 1,050
Accts Ernst & Young Llp Roseville
SIC 8062 General medical & surgical hospitals
CEO: Joseph P Harrington
Chf OB: Jane M Maloney
Dir Recs: Ellen M Donald
Pr: Jana Van Os
COO: Jim Russell
**CFO:* Terrence Deak
Sr Cor Off: Becky Cook
Ofcr: Mark Sey
**VP:* Debbe Moreno
Exec: Mark Wallace
Dir Inf Cn: Donna Salvi
Dir Inf Cn: Gerg Woolf
Dir Lab: Karla Theis
Dir Rad: Erik Yasumoto
Dir Rx: Sandy Atwater

D-U-N-S 08-244-8093
LODI UNIFIED SCHOOL DISTRICT
1305 E Vine St, Lodi, CA 95240-3179
Tel (209) 331-7000 *Founded/Ownrshp* 1967
Sales 297.0MM *EMP* 3,516
Accts Gilbert Associates Inc Sacr
SIC 8211 Public elementary & secondary schools
**Pr:* Mr Ron Heberle
**VP:* Mr Joe Nava
Prgrm Mgr: Josephine Fierro
Trfc Dir: Virginia Connolly
Trfc Dir: Margie Duran
Trfc Dir: Sandy Torris
Opers Supe: Susan Martin
Teacher Pr: Amber Jaeger
Instr Medi: Gabriela Vazquez
HC Dir: Jon Price

D-U-N-S 00-196-4451 IMP
LOEB ELECTRIC CO (OH)
UNISTRUT-COLUMBUS
1800 E 5th Ave Ste A, Columbus, OH 43219-2592
Tel (614) 294-6351 *Founded/Ownrshp* 1911
Sales 185.1MM^E *EMP* 155
SIC 5063 Electrical apparatus & equipment; Lighting fixtures; Circuit breakers; Wire & cable
Pr: Charles A Loeb
**CFO:* Jeff Blunt
**Prin:* M J Walsh
Brnch Mgr: Bill Gannon
Genl Mgr: Debbie Coffmon
Sales Asso: Emily Kershaw
Sales Asso: Tina Weis
Sales Asso: Dale Wilson

D-U-N-S 02-520-8315
LOEBER MOTORS INC
4255 W Touhy Ave, Lincolnwood, IL 60712-1933
Tel (847) 675-1000 *Founded/Ownrshp* 1936
Sales 315.0MM *EMP* 110
SIC 5511 Automobiles, new & used
Mktg Dir: Pam Hartley
Sales Asso: Hubert Banasiuk
Sales Asso: James Jajou
Sales Asso: Vitas Markevicius
Sales Asso: John Mathis
Sales Asso: Paul Michalczyk
Sales Asso: Mark Sarros

D-U-N-S 60-180-7183 IMP
LOEHMANNS HOLDINGS INC
(*Suby of* ISTITHMAR WORLD)
2500 Halsey St Frnt 1, Bronx, NY 10461-3692
Tel (718) 409-2000 *Founded/Ownrshp* 2006
Sales 185.0MM^E *EMP* 1,784
SIC 5621 5661 3171 Ready-to-wear apparel, women's; Women's shoes; Women's handbags & purses
CEO: Steven Newman
**Pr:* Robert N Friedman
**COO:* Robert Glass
**Co-Ch Bd:* William J Fox
**Co-Ch Bd:* Joseph Nusim
CTO: Ramona Horibata

D-U-N-S 00-787-4563 IMP
LOEHMANNS INC (DE)
(*Suby of* LOEHMANNS HOLDINGS INC) ★
2500 Halsey St, Bronx, NY 10461-3637
Tel (718) 409-2000 *Founded/Ownrshp* 1921, 2000
Sales 180.3MM^E *EMP* 1,700
SIC 5621 Ready-to-wear apparel, women's
Pr: Robert N Friedman
**Ch Bd:* Steven Newman
**COO:* Robert Glass
Ex VP: Lesley Heller
VP: Christine Guerriero
VP: Patti Lally-Cahan
Store Mgr: Courtney Abrams
Store Mgr: Andrew Collins

LOEWS
See DIAMOND OFFSHORE DRILLING INC

D-U-N-S 00-698-6905 IMP/EXP
▲ LOEWS CORP
667 Madison Ave Fl 7, New York, NY 10065-8087
Tel (212) 521-2000 *Founded/Ownrshp* 1954
Sales NA *EMP* 16,700
Tkr Sym L *Exch* NYS
SIC 6331 6311 1381 4922 7011 Property damage insurance; Fire, marine & casualty insurance: stock; Life insurance carriers; Drilling oil & gas wells; Pipelines, natural gas; Hotels
Pr: James S Tisch
**Ch Bd:* Andrew H Tisch
Pr: Jerry Meade
COO: Jack Adler
CFO: David B Edelson
Sr VP: Gary W Garson
Sr VP: Kenneth I Siegel
Sr VP: Richard W Scott
VP: Gail Gordon
VP: Jonathan D Kantor
Natl Sales: Julio Marrero
Board of Directors: Ken Miller, Lawrence S Bacow, Anthony Welters, Ann E Berman, Joseph L Bower, Charles D Davidson, Charles M Diker, Jacob A Frenkel, Paul J Fribourg, Walter L Harris, Philip A Laskawy

LOEWS HOTELS & RESORTS
See LOEWS HOTELS HOLDING CORP

D-U-N-S 12-157-0840
■ LOEWS HOTELS HOLDING CORP
LOEWS HOTELS & RESORTS
(*Suby of* LOEWS CORP) ★
667 Madison Ave, New York, NY 10065-8029
Tel (212) 521-2000 *Founded/Ownrshp* 1983
Sales 253.8MM^E *EMP* 2,723
SIC 7011 Hotels
CEO: S Kirk Kinsell
COO: Jack W Bernsmeier
**CFO:* Vincent Dunleavy
**Ch:* Jonathan M Tisch
Ex VP: Ken Siegel
Sr VP: Elizabeth Harlow
Sr VP: Thomas Staab
VP: Elif Bali
**VP:* Gary Garson
VP: Stephanie Hinckley
VP: Jonathan Nathanson
VP: Michael Palmeri
VP: Richard Scott
VP: Jeffrey Stewart
Exec: Ron Cope

LOEWS HTELS AT UNVRSAL ORLANDO
See UCF HOTEL VENTURE

LOFFREDO FRESH PRODUCE CO
See LOFFREDO GARDENS INC

D-U-N-S 04-704-9580
LOFFREDO GARDENS INC
LOFFREDO FRESH PRODUCE CO
4001 Sw 63rd St, Des Moines, IA 50321-1607
Tel (816) 421-7480 *Founded/Ownrshp* 1970
Sales 113.2MM^E *EMP* 330
SIC 5148 Vegetables, fresh; Fruits, fresh
Pr: Gene Loffredo
**COO:* Steve Winders
**CFO:* Mark Zimmerman
**Treas:* Larry E Loffredo
**VP:* John J Loffredo
Off Mgr: Lisa Beener
IT Man: Ryan Meier
IT Man: Ryan Meir
Opers Mgr: John Davis
Plnt Mgr: Dean Riis
Ql Cn Mgr: Marcy Billings

LOFT
See ANN INC

D-U-N-S 88-487-8034 IMP
■ LOFTHOUSE BAKERY PRODUCTS INC
RALCORP FROZEN BAKERY PRODUCTS
(*Suby of* TREEHOUSE PRIVATE BRANDS INC) ★
215 N 700 W Ste A10, Ogden, UT 84404-1342
Tel (801) 776-3500 *Founded/Ownrshp* 2007
Sales 230.1MM^E *EMP* 550^E
SIC 5149 Bakery products
Pr: K J Hunt
**Pr:* David P Skarie
**VP:* S K Harris
Genl Mgr: Mark Stoner

D-U-N-S 03-591-6907
LOFTIN EQUIPMENT CO
2111 E Highland Ave # 255, Phoenix, AZ 85016-4795
Tel (800) 437-4376 *Founded/Ownrshp* 1976
Sales 136.5MM^E *EMP* 100^E
SIC 5063 5084 5999 Generators; Engines & parts, diesel; Electronic parts & equipment
Pr: Mark Loftin
**Pr:* John Haney
**VP:* Charles Loftin
Sls Dir: Tom Kelly

D-U-N-S 06-933-6832
LOFTON CORP (LA)
LOFTON STAFFING SERVICES
9414 Interline Ave, Baton Rouge, LA 70809-1911
Tel (225) 924-0200 *Founded/Ownrshp* 1979
Sales 128.6MM^E *EMP* 5,800
SIC 7361

D-U-N-S 82-886-2990
LOFTON SECURITY SERVICE INC
9405 Interline Ave, Baton Rouge, LA 70809-1912
Tel (225) 906-2200 *Founded/Ownrshp* 2003
Sales 13.5MM *EMP* 1,300
SIC 7381 Guard services
Pr: T Bret Lofton
**Treas:* G Bart Lofton
IT Man: John Babin
Opers Mgr: Greg Theriot

LOFTON STAFFING SERVICES
See LOFTON CORP

D-U-N-S 13-040-0799 IMP/EXP
LOGAN ALUMINUM INC
200 Gate Two Rd 2rd, Russellville, KY 42276
Tel (270) 755-6000 *Founded/Ownrshp* 1985
Sales 228.8MM^E *EMP* 960
SIC 3355 Aluminum rolling & drawing
Pr: Randy Schumaker
**COO:* Dan Minwell
**CFO:* Gary Grohovsky

D-U-N-S 61-157-9160
LOGAN CONTRACTORS SUPPLY INC
4101 106th St, Urbandale, IA 50322-7949
Tel (515) 253-9048 *Founded/Ownrshp* 1990
Sales 97.9MM^E *EMP* 90
SIC 5082 General construction machinery & equipment; Road construction equipment
Pr: Bruce Logan
**CEO:* Jerry L Logan
**VP:* Jeff Logan
Brnch Mgr: Scott Dyvad
Brnch Mgr: Shane Seymour
Sales Exec: Jon Krueger
Sales Exec: Dave Potter
VP Sls: Nick Sinn
Mktg Dir: Jim Stills
Sls Mgr: Scott Mouw
Sales Asso: George Goad

D-U-N-S 07-979-8977
LOGAN COUNTY SCHOOLS
506 Holly Ave, Logan, WV 25601-3306
Tel (304) 792-2060 *Founded/Ownrshp* 2015
Sales 6.1MM^E *EMP* 1,295^E
SIC 8211 Public elementary & secondary schools
Dir Sec: David Thompson

D-U-N-S 11-045-6469
■ LOGAN GENERAL HOSPITAL LLC
LOGAN REGIONAL MEDICAL CENTER
(*Suby of* HISTORIC LIFEPOINT HOSPITALS INC) ★
20 Hospital Dr, Logan, WV 25601-3452
Tel (304) 831-1101 *Founded/Ownrshp* 2002
Sales 94.8MM *EMP* 100
SIC 8011 Medical centers
CEO: John Walker
Chf Path: Alex Racadag
Chf OB: Suthipan Chevy
COO: Tim Harclerode
VP: Meridith Moody
Exec: Suzanne Jackson
Dir OR: Lisa Fordyce
Dir Inf Cn: Dawn Vandal
Dir Risk M: Michael Meadows
**Prin:* Med Records
Plnt Mgr: Harold McMillen

D-U-N-S 12-826-4111 IMP/EXP
LOGAN OIL TOOLS INC
11006 Lucerne St, Houston, TX 77016-1920
Tel (281) 219-6613 *Founded/Ownrshp* 1999
Sales 129.9MM^E *EMP* 330
SIC 5082 Oil field equipment
CEO: Gerald Hage
Pr: Daniel Craig
**CEO:* David Barr
**CFO:* Larry Kelster
Ex VP: Paul Deutch
VP: Eloy Palacios
Rgnl Mgr: Ted Crisp
Rgnl Mgr: John Pope
Dist Mgr: Guy Lee
Dist Mgr: C Wall
Dist Mgr: Kevin Williams

LOGAN REGIONAL MEDICAL CENTER
See LOGAN GENERAL HOSPITAL LLC

D-U-N-S 08-307-9566 IMP
LOGAN SQUARE ALUMINUM SUPPLY INC
REMODELERS SUPPLY CENTER
2500 N Pulaski Rd, Chicago, IL 60639-2107
Tel (773) 235-2500 *Founded/Ownrshp* 1979
Sales 91.9MM^E *EMP* 400
SIC 5211 3089 Lumber & other building materials; Windows, plastic
Pr: Louis Silver
Brnch Mgr: Dave Lambert

D-U-N-S 79-179-5412 IMP
LOGANS ROADHOUSE INC
(*Suby of* LRI HOLDINGS INC) ★
3011 Armory Dr Ste 300, Nashville, TN 37204-3721
Tel (615) 885-9056 *Founded/Ownrshp* 2010
Sales 408.8MM^E *EMP* 7,000^E
SIC 5812 Steak restaurant
Pr: Samuel N Borgese
**Ch Bd:* Mike Andres
**Pr:* Sam Borgese
**CFO:* James J Hagan
Sr VP: Maria Rivera
VP: Stephen Anderson
**VP:* Amy Bertauski
VP: Karen Davis
CTO: Scott Workman
Info Man: Scott Devor

LOGIC ELECTRONIC MFG SVCS
See LOGIC PD INC

D-U-N-S 07-257-7059 IMP
LOGIC PD INC
LOGIC ELECTRONIC MFG SVCS
6201 Bury Dr, Eden Prairie, MN 55346-1720
Tel (952) 646-1191 *Founded/Ownrshp* 1981
Sales 165.8MM^E *EMP* 490
SIC 3672 8711 Printed circuit boards; Engineering services
Pr: Bruce Dewitt
**COO:* Lisa Walker
**CFO:* Sandy Bell
**Chf Cred:* Jason Volovich
**VP:* Lorri Anderson
**VP:* Mona Phaff
VP: Jackie Torfin
**VP:* Eric Wilkowske
Prgrm Mgr: Eric Olson
Sftwr Eng: Mark Herscher

D-U-N-S 80-764-3150
LOGICALIS INC
(*Suby of* LOGICALIS US HOLDINGS INC) ★
1 Penn Plz Ste 5130, New York, NY 10119-5160
Tel (212) 596-7160 *Founded/Ownrshp* 2000
Sales 386.3MM *EMP* 700
Accts Deloitte & Touche Llp Detroit
SIC 5045 Computers, peripherals & software
CEO: Vince Deluca
COO: Mark Rogers
**COO:* Michael Souders
**Ex VP:* Eric Tilds
**Sr VP:* Mike Martin
Sr VP: Jim Reichwein
**Sr VP:* Dan Sytsma
Mng Dir: Stuart Hendry
Mng Dir: Andreas Riepen
Prac Mgr: Jack Waite
Prgrm Mgr: Stephen Thompson

D-U-N-S 96-856-7060
LOGICALIS US HOLDINGS INC
(*Suby of* LOGICALIS GROUP LIMITED)
1 Penn Plz, New York, NY 10119-0002
Tel (212) 596-7160 *Founded/Ownrshp* 2000
Sales 465.2MM *EMP* 702
Accts Deloitte & Touche Llp Detroit
SIC 5045 Computers, peripherals & software
CEO: Vince Deluca
**COO:* Michael Souders
**CFO:* Rich Pirrotta
**Ex VP:* Eric Tilds
**Sr VP:* Dan Sytsma
VP: Jim Cook

D-U-N-S 93-252-1776
■ LOGISTICARE SOLUTIONS LLC
(*Suby of* PROVIDENCE SERVICE CORP) ★
1275 Peachtree St Ne Fl 6, Atlanta, GA 30309-3580
Tel (404) 888-5800 *Founded/Ownrshp* 1999
Sales 1.0MMM *EMP* 2,000
Accts Kpmg Llp Atlanta Georgia
SIC 4731 Transportation agents & brokers
CEO: Herman Schwarz
COO: Robin Hamilton
**COO:* Jim McGean
CFO: Thomas E Oram
Sr VP: Chuck Dezearn
VP: Sandy Reifel
VP: Caroline Smyth
CIO: Rob Cornell
**CIO:* Ed Ringer
IT Man: Vance Hendley
Sfty Mgr: Gordon McInnis

D-U-N-S 13-146-8071
■ LOGISTICS HEALTH INC
LHI
(*Suby of* OPTUM INC) ★
328 Front St S, La Crosse, WI 54601-4023
Tel (866) 284-8788 *Founded/Ownrshp* 1999
Sales 86.6MM^E *EMP* 900^E
SIC 8011 Health maintenance organization
CEO: Donald J Weber
Pr: Jon Lewis
**COO:* Brian D Hafner
**Chf Mktg O:* David Tornberg MD
VP: Tom Hamilton
**VP:* Armagan Islamoglu
**VP:* Tom Walch
Exec: John Makepeace
Exec: Denise Thompson
Rgnl Mgr: Tricia Parker
Web Dev: Koshia Campbell

D-U-N-S 07-966-8583
LOGISTICS HOLLINGSWORTH GROUP LLC
14225 W Warren Ave, Dearborn, MI 48126-1456
Tel (313) 768-1400 *Founded/Ownrshp* 1999
Sales 196.6MM *EMP* 700^E
SIC 7389 Packaging & labeling services
CEO: Stephen Barr
**Pr:* R James Lapointe
**COO:* Michael T McNamara
**VP:* Martha Chalifoux

D-U-N-S 87-721-4569
■ LOGISTICS INSIGHT CORP
OAKLAND LOGISTICS SERVICE
(*Suby of* UNIVERSAL LOGISTICS HOLDINGS INC) ★
12755 E 9 Mile Rd, Warren, MI 48089-2621
Tel (586) 467-1500 *Founded/Ownrshp* 2015
Sales 128.4MM^E *EMP* 1,000
SIC 8742 Transportation consultant
CEO: H E Wolfe
**CFO:* David Crittenden
**Sr VP:* M Akkanen
Sr VP: Don Berquist
Dir Bus: John Avenia
Dir Bus: Jeff Paluk
Rgnl Mgr: Samuel Gentile
Genl Mgr: Chuck Downing
Genl Mgr: Mark Gillette
Genl Mgr: Jim Kelly
Genl Mgr: Seth Kohman

D-U-N-S 05-338-5738 IMP
LOGISTICS MANAGEMENT INSTITUTE
L M I
7940 Jones Branch Dr, Mc Lean, VA 22102-3381
Tel (703) 917-9800 *Founded/Ownrshp* 1961
Sales 242.9MM *EMP* 841
SIC 8742

LOGISTICS PLANNING SERVICES
See HALL ENTERPRISES INC

D-U-N-S 12-569-4591 IMP/EXP
LOGISTICS PLUS INC
1406 Peach St Ste 3, Erie, PA 16501-1879
Tel (814) 461-7600 *Founded/Ownrshp* 1996
Sales 89.2MM^E *EMP* 160
SIC 4731 Truck transportation brokers
Pr: Jim Berlin
**CFO:* Frank Humes
Treas: Lena Jia
Ofcr: Rini Angelina
**Sr VP:* Gretchen Seth
**VP:* Fred Rizzuto
Exec: George Horetsky
Dir Bus: Mohammed Omar
Brnch Mgr: Jenny Melgert

D-U-N-S 02-423-7877 IMP
LOGITECH INC (CA)
(*Suby of* LOGITECH INTERNATIONAL S.A.)
7700 Gateway Blvd, Newark, CA 94560-1046
Tel (510) 795-8500 *Founded/Ownrshp* 1982
Sales 2.0MMM^E *EMP* 5,000
Accts Kpmg Llp Santa Clara Califor
SIC 3577 Computer peripheral equipment; Input/output equipment, computer
Pr: Bracken P Darrell
**Ch Bd:* Guerrino De Luca
Sr VP: Joseph Sullivan
VP: Michele Hermann
VP: Nikki Montgomery
IT Man: Scott Cameron
IT Man: Vlad Kuusk
IT Man: Jason Linse
IT Man: Andi Siripoke
Netwrk Mgr: Antonio Berrio
Netwrk Mgr: Sanjay Dhar

D-U-N-S 12-941-1836
LOGIX COMMUNICATIONS LP
(*Suby of* ASTRA CAPITAL MANAGEMENT LLC) ★
2950 North Loop W Ste 140, Houston, TX 77092-8806
Tel (713) 862-2000 *Founded/Ownrshp* 2016
Sales 92.7MM *EMP* 330
Accts Hein & Associates Llp Housto
SIC 4813 Local & long distance telephone communications
CEO: Matt Murphy
**COO:* Will Sears
**CFO:* Patrick Lentz
VP: Ken Bonvillian
VP: Anthony Brown
VP: Terry Burnside
VP: Glenn Taylor
VP: Michael Watson
**CTO:* Shane Schillag
VP Opers: John Skidmore
S&M/VP: Josh Schlensker

D-U-N-S 07-527-6931
LOGIX FEDERAL CREDIT UNION
2340 N Hollywood Way, Burbank, CA 91505-1124
Tel (888) 718-5328 *Founded/Ownrshp* 1937
Sales NA *EMP* 350
SIC 6061 Federal credit unions
Pr: David Styler
**COO:* Dave Styler
**CFO:* Ana Fonseca
Ofcr: Sean Brown
Ofcr: Jesse Burk
Ofcr: Kara Buss
Ofcr: Anthony Carusa
Ofcr: Jeff Chen
Ofcr: Nuvia Espana
Ofcr: Irma Heffner
Ofcr: Staci Hermann
Ofcr: Gabriel Mann
Ofcr: Kathleen Mason
Ofcr: Donna Matthews
Ofcr: Shawn McKendry
Ofcr: Summer O'Neil
Ofcr: Tina Orellana
Ofcr: Lisa Perez
Ofcr: Alonso Rivas
Ofcr: Carol Salgado
Ofcr: Staci Somerville

D-U-N-S 17-589-5205
▲ LOGMEIN INC
320 Summer St Ste 100, Boston, MA 02210-1701
Tel (781) 638-9050 *Founded/Ownrshp* 2003
Sales 271.6MM *EMP* 1,006^E
Tkr Sym LOGM *Exch* NGS
SIC 7372 7379 Prepackaged software; Computer related consulting services
Pr: William R Wagner
**Ch Bd:* Michael K Simon
CFO: Edward K Herdiech
Chf Mktg O: W Sean Ford
Sr VP: Lawrence M D'Angelo
Sr VP: Michael J Donahue
VP: Kevin Bardos
VP: Tibor Biczo
VP: Larry D'Angelo
VP: Matt Duffy
VP: W Ford
VP: Adam Michelson
Board of Directors: Steven J Benson, Steven G Chambers, Michael J Christenson, Edwin J Gillis, Gregory W Hughes, Marilyn Matz

D-U-N-S 19-519-8788
LOGO HOLDINGS I CORP
626 W Main St, Louisville, KY 40202-2972
Tel (502) 637-5443 *Founded/Ownrshp* 2012
Sales 303.8MM^E *EMP* 2,410^E
SIC 3577 Graphic displays, except graphic terminals
Pr: Hank Baughman

D-U-N-S 04-219-7289
LOGO HOLDINGS II CORP
(*Suby of* LOGO HOLDINGS I CORP) ★
626 W Main St, Louisville, KY 40202-2972
Tel (502) 637-5443 *Founded/Ownrshp* 2012
Sales 125.2MM^E *EMP* 2,405^E
SIC 6719 7336 Investment holding companies, except banks; Graphic arts & related design
Pr: Hank Baughman

D-U-N-S 82-997-8766 IMP
LOGOMARK INC
1201 Bell Ave, Tustin, CA 92780-6420
Tel (714) 675-6100 *Founded/Ownrshp* 1992
Sales 164.7MM^E *EMP* 250
SIC 5199 Advertising specialties
Pr: Trevor Gnesin
Sr VP: Brian P Padian
Prd Dir: Errol Bouchet
VP Sls: Brian Padian
Manager: Erica Ehlers
Manager: Jaclyn Gerard

D-U-N-S 07-831-6141 IMP
LOGOPLASTE USA INC
(*Suby of* LOGOPLASTE PORTUGAL, LDA)
14420 N Van Dyke Rd, Plainfield, IL 60544-5867
Tel (815) 230-6961 *Founded/Ownrshp* 2006
Sales 100.0MM *EMP* 200
SIC 3085 Plastics bottles
CEO: Filipe De Botton

D-U-N-S 17-938-9650
LOGRHYTHM INC
4780 Pearl East Cir, Boulder, CO 80301-2472
Tel (303) 245-9074 *Founded/Ownrshp* 2005
Sales 134.0MM^E *EMP* 250^E
SIC 7372 Business oriented computer software
CEO: Andy Grolnick
CFO: Mark Vellequette
Ch: Chris Petersen
Sr VP: Bill Smith
VP: David Anthony
VP: Ross Brewer
VP: James Carder
VP: Mike Reagan
VP: Nancy Reynolds
Prgrm Mgr: Beth Petersen
Off Mgr: Christine Sznip
Board of Directors: Karen Blasing, Todd Headley, Robert Lentz, Dick Williams

D-U-N-S 03-106-2771 IMP
LOHR DISTRIBUTING CO INC
LOHR FINE WINES SPIRITS
1100 S 9th St, Saint Louis, MO 63104-3597
Tel (314) 436-8299 *Founded/Ownrshp* 1964
Sales 97.6MM^E *EMP* 120
SIC 5181 Beer & other fermented malt liquors
Pr: Ronald K Lohr
**VP:* Kurt Leinauer
**VP:* Steven E Lohr
CTO: Bob Weber
Sales Exec: Marty Sheahan
Sls Mgr: Gerry Armstrong
Sls Mgr: Robert Gassoff

LOHR FINE WINES SPIRITS
See LOHR DISTRIBUTING CO INC

D-U-N-S 15-774-1414
LOJAC ENTERPRISES INC
1401 Toshiba Dr, Lebanon, TN 37087-2588
Tel (615) 449-1401 *Founded/Ownrshp* 1986
Sales 97.0MM^E *EMP* 250
SIC 1611 1794 5032 Highway & street paving contractor; Excavation & grading, building construction; Asphalt mixture
Ch Bd: B F Jack Lowery
**Pr:* Donald G Chambers
CFO: Kellie Mires
Div Mgr: Russ Williams
Dir IT: Nic Morris
Board of Directors: W C Bill Marks

D-U-N-S 04-893-0218 IMP
■ LOJACK CORP
(*Suby of* CALAMP CORP) ★
40 Pequot Way, Canton, MA 02021-2306
Tel (781) 302-4200 *Founded/Ownrshp* 2016
Sales 156.7MM^E *EMP* 490^E
SIC 3699 Security devices; Security control equipment & systems
Pr: Randy L Ortiz
**CFO:* Kenneth L Dumas
Treas: Joe Barros
Bd of Dir: Marcia Hooper
**Sr VP:* Emad Isaac
Sr VP: Jose Oxholm
VP: Joe Castelli
VP: Manlio Huacuja
VP: Kevin Mullins
VP: Susan Munro
VP: Jose Oxholm-Uribe
VP: Bob Shumaker
VP: Scott Tripp

D-U-N-S 62-497-6924 EXP
LOKEY AUTOMOTIVE GROUP INC
LOKEY NISSAN
27850 Us Highway 19 N, Clearwater, FL 33761-4902
Tel (888) 275-8388 *Founded/Ownrshp* 1990
Sales 88.7MM^E *EMP* 300
SIC 5511 7532 Automobiles, new & used; Collision shops, automotive
Pr: Paul B Lokey
**COO:* Tb Staton
**CFO:* Angel Aaron
Sales Asso: Mark Brown
Sales Asso: Matt Melillo

LOKEY MERCEDES
See LOKEY MOTOR GROUP INC

D-U-N-S 18-372-6595 EXP
LOKEY MOTOR GROUP INC
LOKEY MERCEDES
19820 Us Highway 19 N, Clearwater, FL 33764-5016
Tel (727) 530-1661 *Founded/Ownrshp* 1957
Sales 90.9MM^E *EMP* 260
SIC 5511 Automobiles, new & used
Pr: Philip E Lokey
**VP:* Sharon Boraski

LOKEY NISSAN
See LOKEY AUTOMOTIVE GROUP INC

D-U-N-S 00-965-6273
LOMA LINDA UNIVERSITY
LLU
11060 Anderson St, Loma Linda, CA 92350-1736
Tel (909) 558-4540 *Founded/Ownrshp* 1909
Sales 848.7MM^E *EMP* 7,000
SIC 8221 University
Pr: Richard H Hart
**Ex VP:* Ruthita J Fike
**Ex VP:* H Roger Hadley
**Ex VP:* Kevin J Lang
**Sr VP:* Rachelle B Bussell
**Sr VP:* Verlon Strauss
Exec: Kevin Boggs
Ex Dir: Nellie Killion
Ex Dir: Janelle Pyke

D-U-N-S 09-224-6990
LOMA LINDA UNIVERSITY HEALTH CARE
(*Suby of* LLU) ★
11370 Anderson St # 3900, Loma Linda, CA 92350-1715
Tel (909) 558-2806 *Founded/Ownrshp* 1967
Sales 846.2MM^E *EMP* 4,814^E
SIC 8062 8011 8051 5999 Hospital, medical school affiliated with residency; Medical centers; Extended care facility; Convalescent equipment & supplies
Pr: Richard Hart
**CEO:* Rosita Fike
Assoc Dir: Maxine Ullery
Ex Dir: Padmini Davamony
Ex Dir: Rhodes Rigsby
Off Mgr: Lyn Edgemon
Off Mgr: Terry Merrick
Pathlgst: Mia Perez
Obsttrcn: Kathleen M Lau
Doctor: Evelyn Choo
Pharmcst: Norman M Haada

D-U-N-S 83-754-7017
LOMA LINDA UNIVERSITY HEALTH CARE
11175 Campus St, Loma Linda, CA 92350-1700
Tel (909) 558-4729 *Founded/Ownrshp* 1901
Sales 166.4MM *EMP* 1,100
SIC 8011 Offices & clinics of medical doctors
Pr: Roger Hadley MD
**V Ch:* David B Hinshaw Jr
VP: James Pappas

D-U-N-S 08-034-6300
LOMA LINDA UNIVERSITY HEALTHCARE
(*Suby of* LLU) ★
350 Commercial Rd Ste 101, San Bernardino, CA 92408-3764
Tel (909) 558-7132 *Founded/Ownrshp* 1909
Sales 2.4MM^E *EMP* 2,000
SIC 8221 Colleges universities & professional schools
Pr: Richard H Hart

D-U-N-S 07-688-6571
LOMA LINDA UNIVERSITY MEDICAL CENTER
LLUMC
(*Suby of* LOMA LINDA UNIVERSITY HEALTH CARE) ★
11234 Anderson St, Loma Linda, CA 92354-2871
Tel (909) 558-4000 *Founded/Ownrshp* 1980
Sales 846.2MM *EMP* 4,676
SIC 8062 8011 8051 5999 Hospital, medical school affiliated with residency; Medical centers; Extended care facility; Medical apparatus & supplies
CEO: Richard H Hart
Dir Recs: Brenda Taylor
**Pr:* James Jesse
**Treas:* Noni Patchett
**VP:* Richard Catalano
Adm Dir: Paul B Simms
Ex Dir: David Colwell
Ex Dir: Cindy Schmidt
CIO: Robert Blades
Dir IT: Bobby CHI
IT Man: Don Cole

D-U-N-S 02-212-4796
LOMAR DISTRIBUTING INC
(*Suby of* HY-VEE INC) ★
2500 Dixon St, Des Moines, IA 50316-1871
Tel (515) 244-3105 *Founded/Ownrshp* 1990
Sales 137.3MM^E *EMP* 100
SIC 5143 5149 Cheese; Specialty food items
Pr: Brandon Lampkin
Treas: Michael Skokan
VP: William E Sales Jr

D-U-N-S 80-168-4119
LOMBARD INTERNATIONAL AGENCY INC
1 Liberty Pl Ste 1650, Philadelphia, PA 19103-7312
Tel (484) 530-4800 *Founded/Ownrshp* 1994
Sales NA *EMP* 129^E
SIC 6411 Insurance agents, brokers & service
CEO: Michael Gordon
**COO:* Kent C Keim
**CFO:* James Hom
**Ex VP:* Joseph A Fillip Jr
**Ex VP:* Ken Kilbane
**Sr VP:* Paul J Sulek

D-U-N-S 15-292-2456
LOMBARDY HOLDINGS INC
3166 Hrseless Carriage Rd, Norco, CA 92860-3612
Tel (951) 808-4550 *Founded/Ownrshp* 1996
Sales 85.0MM *EMP* 400
SIC 1623 5211 Telephone & communication line construction; Cable television line construction; Electrical construction materials
CEO: Marc Laulhere

D-U-N-S 07-020-6800
LOMPOC UNIFIED SCHOOL DISTRICT
1301 N A St, Lompoc, CA 93436-3516
Tel (805) 742-3300 *Founded/Ownrshp* 1960
Sales 59.1MM^E *EMP* 1,300
SIC 8211 Public elementary & secondary schools; Public elementary school; Public senior high school; Public adult education school
Pr Dir: Brian Jarancko
Teacher Pr: Mary Ludziglan

D-U-N-S 00-901-7823
LONDEN INSURANCE GROUP INC
4343 E Camelback Rd # 400, Phoenix, AZ 85018-2705
Tel (602) 957-1650 *Founded/Ownrshp* 1963
Sales NA *EMP* 150
SIC 6311 6321 8741 Life insurance carriers; Accident insurance carriers; Administrative management
Ch Bd: Jack W Londen
Pr: Thomas Londen
CFO: Larry Schuneman
Sr VP: Dean Lathrop
VP: Monica Sole
Software D: Ben Ludkiewicz
VP Mktg: Doug Turner
Mktg Mgr: Fran McGovern
Pgrm Dir: Paula Rodriguez

D-U-N-S 00-811-0322 IMP
LONE STAR BAKERY INC
6905 Us Highway 87 E, China Grove, TX 78263-6029
Tel (210) 648-6400 *Founded/Ownrshp* 1889
Sales 130.2MM^E *EMP* 400
SIC 2053 2051 Frozen bakery products, except bread; Bread, cake & related products
Pr: Mac S Morris Jr
**VP:* Tracy Fletcher
**VP:* Deborah Morris
QA Dir: Brandee Mata
Sfty Mgr: Andris Ozolins
Opers Mgr: Glen Finch
Manager: Christina Zavala

D-U-N-S 04-032-5706
LONE STAR COLLEGE SYSTEM
LSC SYSTEM OFFICE
5000 Research Forest Dr, The Woodlands, TX 77381-4356
Tel (832) 813-6500 *Founded/Ownrshp* 1972
Sales 190.9MM^E *EMP* 5,137
SIC 8222 Junior college
Off Admin: Danny Osburn
CTO: Richard Fitzmaurice
MIS Dir: Allen Rice
Dir IT: Oscar Ramos
IT Man: Carolyn Poe
S&M/Dir: Fritz Guthrie
HC Dir: Marilyn Dement
Pgrm Dir: Taffy Daussin

D-U-N-S 08-040-2692
LONE STAR DAIRY PRODUCTS LLC
401 Highway 60, Canyon, TX 79015-1927
Tel (806) 567-5623 *Founded/Ownrshp* 2015
Sales 100.0MM *EMP* 60
SIC 2023 Baby formulas; Cream substitutes; Condensed milk; Powdered cream
Prin: Cody Gruwell

LONE STAR FORD
See SONIC AUTOMOTIVE OF TEXAS LP

D-U-N-S 06-028-6759
LONE STAR FUND IV (US) LP
2711 N Haskell Ave, Dallas, TX 75204-2911
Tel (214) 754-8300 *Founded/Ownrshp* 2001
Sales 3.4MMM^E *EMP* 47,026^E
SIC 6726 Investment offices
Pr: Andre Collin
Prin: Len Allen
Prin: John Grayken
Mktg Dir: Brad Haga

D-U-N-S 80-913-0482
LONE STAR FUND V (US) LP
(*Suby of* LONE STAR PARTNERS V, L. P.)
2711 N Haskell Ave # 1700, Dallas, TX 75204-2922
Tel (214) 754-8300 *Founded/Ownrshp* 2004
Sales 13.0MMM^E *EMP* 2,350
SIC 6799 5812 Real estate investors, except property operators; Steak & barbecue restaurants; Steak restaurant
Ch Bd: John Grayken
VP: Jeffrey Kert

D-U-N-S 83-158-4672
LONE STAR FUNDS
2711 N Haskell Ave # 1700, Dallas, TX 75204-2911
Tel (214) 754-8300 *Founded/Ownrshp* 1995
Sales 672.6MM^E *EMP* 1,200^E
SIC 6211 Investment firm, general brokerage
Pr: Andre Collin
VP: Kevin Barner
VP: Kevin Carlson
VP: Leigh REA
Mng Dir: Grant Wilbeck
Off Admin: Kim Roberts
Genl Couns: Michael Thomson

D-U-N-S 62-211-7521
LONE STAR HOLDINGS LLC
LONE STAR OVERNIGHT
6500 River Place Blvd # 2, Austin, TX 78730-1155
Tel (512) 873-8067 *Founded/Ownrshp* 2002
Sales 126.1MM^E *EMP* 600
SIC 4215 4513 4212 Package delivery, vehicular; Parcel delivery, vehicular; Package delivery, private air; Delivery service, vehicular
CEO: Rick Jones
Genl Pt: Gary Gunter
Pt: Keith Jaeger
Pt: George Stephens
Pr: Richard Jones
Dir IT: Bill Bartley

D-U-N-S 00-126-5321 IMP
LONE STAR INDUSTRIES INC
BUZZI UNICEM
(*Suby of* BUZZI UNICEM USA) ★
10401 N Meridian St # 400, Indianapolis, IN 46290-1154
Tel (317) 706-3314 *Founded/Ownrshp* 1919, 1999
Sales 223.6MM^E *EMP* 751
SIC 3241 3273 Portland cement; Ready-mixed concrete
Pr: Massimo Toso
**CFO:* Nancy Krial
**VP:* Patrick Lydon

D-U-N-S 10-720-3346
LONE STAR MILK PRODUCERS INC
2716 Commerce St, Wichita Falls, TX 76301-8051
Tel (817) 781-1194 Founded/Ownrshp 2000
Sales 180.2MM^E EMP 135^E
SIC 5143 Milk
Pr: James G Baird
*COO: Sonia Fabian
*Sec: Felice M Baird
*VP: W C Barton
Off Mgr: Felice Baired

LONE STAR NATIONAL BANCSHARES
See LONE STAR NATIONAL BANK SHARES NEVEDA

LONE STAR NATIONAL BANCSHARES-
See LONE STAR NATIONAL BANK

D-U-N-S 00-924-7144
LONE STAR NATIONAL BANCSHARES—TEXAS INC (TX)
LONE STAR NATIONAL BANK
4500 N 10th St Ste 305, McAllen, TX 78504-2969
Tel (956) 781-4321 Founded/Ownrshp 1995
Sales NA EMP 643
Accts Smith Fankhauser Voigt & Watso
SIC 6712 6021 Bank holding companies; National commercial banks
Ch: Alonzo Cantu
*Pr: S David Deanda
*CFO: George R Carruthers
Ex VP: Ed Borges
VP: Abrana Gonzalez
Brnch Mgr: Desi Walker

LONE STAR NATIONAL BANK
See LONE STAR NATIONAL BANCSHARES—TEXAS INC

D-U-N-S 10-275-6954
LONE STAR NATIONAL BANK
LONE STAR NATIONAL BANCSHARES-
(Suby of LONE STAR NATIONAL BANCSHARES) ★
520 E Nolana Ave Ste 110, McAllen, TX 78504-2681
Tel (956) 781-4321 Founded/Ownrshp 1998
Sales NA EMP 143
SIC 6021 National commercial banks
Ch Bd: Alonzo Cantu
*Ch Bd: Oscar R Gonzalez
*Pr: S David De Anda
*CEO: A Javier Rodriguez
*CFO: David Penoli
Ofcr: Marvelia Butler
Ofcr: Sochi Guerra
Ofcr: Javier Pena
Ex VP: Valerie Cardenas
*Ex VP: George R Carruthers
Ex VP: Marco Garcia
*Ex VP: Sam De La Garza
*Ex VP: Angie Vera-Oliva
Sr VP: Tom Bynum
Sr VP: Leonel Garcia
Sr VP: Kenneth Grams
VP: Veronica Cantu
VP: Roberto Contreras
VP: Jennifer Gil
VP: Jaime Gorina
VP: Eva Markum

D-U-N-S 12-675-7983
LONE STAR NATIONAL BANK SHARES NEVEDA
LONE STAR NATIONAL BANCSHARES
(Suby of LONE STAR NATIONAL BANK) ★
100 W Ferguson St, Pharr, TX 78577-9517
Tel (956) 781-4321 Founded/Ownrshp 1998
Sales NA EMP 143
SIC 6021 National commercial banks
CEO: A Jabier Rodriguez
V Ch: Oscar Gonzalez
CFO: George Carruthers

D-U-N-S 96-823-1550
■ LONE STAR NGL LLC
(Suby of ENERGY TRANSFER PARTNERS LP) ★
800 E Sonterra Blvd # 400, San Antonio, TX 78258-3940
Tel (210) 403-7300 Founded/Ownrshp 2011
Sales 229.1MM^E EMP 200
SIC 1321 Natural gas liquids
CEO: Kelcy L Warren
*Pr: Marshall S McCrea III
*CFO: Martin Salinas
*Sr VP: Thomas P Mason

D-U-N-S 80-952-1516
■ LONE STAR NGL PIPELINE LP
(Suby of LONE STAR NGL LLC) ★
1300 Main St 10, Houston, TX 77002-6803
Tel (210) 403-7300 Founded/Ownrshp 2011
Sales 90.3MM^E EMP 200^E
SIC 4924 1321 Natural gas distribution; Natural gas liquids
Pt: Kelcy L Warren
Pt: Marshall S McCrea III
Pt: Martin Salinas Jr
Dir Surg: Josie Castrejana

LONE STAR OVERNIGHT
See LONE STAR HOLDINGS LLC

LONE STAR PERIODICALS
See NEWS GROUP INC

D-U-N-S 83-320-9047
LONE STAR REAL ESTATE FUND (US) LP
2711 N Haskell Ave, Dallas, TX 75204-2911
Tel (214) 754-8300 Founded/Ownrshp 2007
Sales 455.5MM^E EMP 3,050^E
SIC 6733 Private estate, personal investment & vacation fund trusts
Pt: Louis Paletta

D-U-N-S 78-618-1792
LONE STAR STEAKHOUSE & SALOON OF KANSAS INC
5055 W Park Blvd Ste 500, Plano, TX 75093-2587
Tel (972) 295-8600 Founded/Ownrshp 2006
Sales 462.1MM^E EMP 19,750
SIC 5812

D-U-N-S 03-427-5227
LONE STAR STEAKHOUSE & SALOON OF OHIO INC (OH)
224 E Douglas Ave Ste 700, Wichita, KS 67202-3424
Tel (972) 295-8600 Founded/Ownrshp 2001
Sales 32.2MM^E EMP 1,375
SIC 5812 Steak restaurant
Prin: Louie Elliot
VP Opers: Mark Mednansky

D-U-N-S 03-411-6785
LONE STAR STEAKS INC (NC)
5055 W Park Blvd Ste 500, Plano, TX 75093-2587
Tel (972) 295-8600 Founded/Ownrshp 1989
Sales 46.2MM^E EMP 1,300
SIC 5812

D-U-N-S 00-750-5464 IMP/EXP
■ LONE STAR TECHNOLOGIES INC
(Suby of UNITED STATES STEEL CORP) ★
15660 Dallas Pkwy Ste 500, Dallas, TX 75248-3354
Tel (972) 770-6401 Founded/Ownrshp 1942
Sales 263.7MM^E EMP 2,699
SIC 3317 3312 Steel pipe & tubes; Welded pipe & tubes; Well casing, wrought: welded, lock joint or heavy riveted; Seamless pipes & tubes; Sheet or strip, steel, hot-rolled
CEO: Rhys J Best
*Pr: Joseph Alvarado
*CFO: Charles J Keszler
VP: Nikhil Amin
*VP: Robert F Spears

D-U-N-S 18-746-3781
LONE STAR TRANSPORTATION LLC
(Suby of DASEKE LONE STAR INC) ★
1100 Northway Dr, Fort Worth, TX 76131-1425
Tel (817) 306-1000 Founded/Ownrshp 2014
Sales 122.5MM^E EMP 456
SIC 4213 Heavy machinery transport
Pr: J Kevin Jordan
*VP: Douglas Miller
*VP: R Scott Wheeler
Opers Mgr: James Hester

LONESTAR
See DOUGLASS DISTRIBUTING RETAIL CO INC

LONESTAR ELECTRIC SUPPLY
See 1155 DISTRIBUTOR PARTNERS LLC

D-U-N-S 02-026-9952
LONESTAR FREIGHTLINER GROUP LLC (TX)
WICHITA FALLS FREIGHTLINER
2051 Hughes Rd, Grapevine, TX 76051-7317
Tel (817) 428-9736 Founded/Ownrshp 2001
Sales 420.7MM EMP 580
Accts Lane Gorman Trubitt Pllc Dal
SIC 5511 7538 Trucks, tractors & trailers: new & used; General truck repair
COO: Dan Steven
*Pt: Clay Corley
*Pt: Jay Simmons
*Pr: Vic Corley
*CFO: James Bennie
Genl Mgr: Kent Noble

D-U-N-S 12-230-9131
LONG & FOSTER COMPANIES INC
14501 George Carter Way # 1, Chantilly, VA 20151-1788
Tel (888) 462-9111 Founded/Ownrshp 1968
Sales 56.8MMM EMP 2,500
SIC 6531 6794 Real estate brokers & agents; Franchises, selling or licensing
CEO: P Wesley Foster Jr
*Treas: Betty F Foster
VP: Mahood Fonville
Dir Risk M: Glen Phillips
Brnch Mgr: Dottie Faust
IT Man: Sam Jackson
Mktg Dir: Monika Russell
Mktg Dir: Eileen Saccheri
Sales Asso: Marla Baines
Sales Asso: Bob T Clark
Sales Asso: Marta Granados

LONG BEACH CITY COLLEGE
See LONG BEACH COMMUNITY COLLEGE DISTRICT

D-U-N-S 14-508-7321
LONG BEACH COMMUNITY COLLEGE DISTRICT
LONG BEACH CITY COLLEGE
4901 E Carson St, Long Beach, CA 90808-1706
Tel (562) 938-5020 Founded/Ownrshp 1928
Sales 389.0MM EMP 2,812^E
SIC 8222 Community college
Pr: Eloy Ortiz Oakley
*Pr: Mark Bowen
*Pr: Roberto Uranga
CFO: Eloy Oakley
*VP: Dr Thomas J Clark
*VP: Jeffrey A Kellogg
*VP: Douglas W Otto
Exec: Dean Hopkins
Assoc Dir: Timothy Mittan
Ex Dir: CHI-Chung Keung
Genl Mgr: Dana Heathcott

D-U-N-S 13-346-2556
LONG BEACH MEMORIAL MEDICAL CENTER
MILLER CHILDREN'S HOSPITAL
(Suby of MEMORIAL CARE MEDICAL CENTERS) ★
2801 Atlantic Ave Fl 2, Long Beach, CA 90806-1701
Tel (562) 933-2000 Founded/Ownrshp 1907
Sales 624.0MM EMP 6,000
SIC 8062 General medical & surgical hospitals
CEO: John Bishop
*Pr: Barry Arbuckle PHD
*COO: Tamra Kaplan
*COO: Suize Reinsvold
COO: Susie Reinsvold
Treas: Michael Trainotti
*Sr VP: Judy Fix
*Sr VP: Scott Joslyn
VP: Roshawn Blunt
VP: Pamela Chevreaux
VP: Myra Gregorian
VP: Donna Hartman
VP: Linda Hoff
VP: Gerald Olson
*VP: Thomas Poole
VP: Kevin Torres
VP: Annette Walker
Dir Risk M: Rachel Nealeigh

LONG BEACH PAIN CENTER
See HEALTHSMART PACIFIC INC

D-U-N-S 07-294-8854
LONG BEACH UNIFIED SCHOOL DISTRICT
LBUSD
1515 Hughes Way, Long Beach, CA 90810-1865
Tel (562) 997-8000 Founded/Ownrshp 1945
Sales 921.9MM^E EMP 15,000
Accts Vicenti Lloyd Stutzman Llp
SIC 8211 Public elementary & secondary schools; Public junior high school; Public senior high school
COO: Darlene Martin
CFO: Lawrence Bozanich
VP: John McGinnis
Exec: Leticia Rodriguez
Adm Dir: Paul Bailey
Ex Dir: Jim Mahoney
Ex Dir: Judy Seal
Dir Sec: Thomas Hickman
DP Exec: Tanya Robertson
IT Man: William Craychee
IT Man: Ryan Noble

D-U-N-S 02-452-2963 IMP
LONG BEVERAGE INC (NC)
10500 World Trade Blvd, Raleigh, NC 27617-4246
Tel (919) 481-2738 Founded/Ownrshp 1950, 1976
Sales 116.8MM^E EMP 195
SIC 5181 5149 Beer & other fermented malt liquors; Groceries & related products
Pr: Rodney M Long
*VP: David N Long
Exec: William Tyre

LONG BUILDING ENVIRONMENTS
See LONG BUILDING TECHNOLOGIES INC

D-U-N-S 06-274-4495
LONG BUILDING TECHNOLOGIES INC
LONG BUILDING ENVIRONMENTS
5001 S Zuni St, Littleton, CO 80120-1071
Tel (303) 975-2100 Founded/Ownrshp 1965
Sales 163.5MM^E EMP 279
SIC 5075 1711 Air conditioning & ventilation equipment & supplies; Heating & air conditioning contractors
CEO: Jeff Long
*Pr: Mark A Balent
*VP: Jeffrey C Long
Assoc Dir: Scott Papay
Brnch Mgr: Joe Moran
Genl Mgr: Matthew Ramey
Off Mgr: Cheri Lingk
Opers Mgr: Peter Samuelson
Mktg Mgr: Fred Sullivan

D-U-N-S 00-283-1667
LONG FENCE CO INC (DC)
8545 Edgeworth Dr, Capitol Heights, MD 20743-3790
Tel (301) 350-2400 Founded/Ownrshp 1938
Sales 95.2MM EMP 440
SIC 1799

LONG ISLAND BLOOD SERVICES
See NEW YORK BLOOD CENTER INC

D-U-N-S 05-935-2799
LONG ISLAND COLLEGE HOSPITAL INC
(Suby of SUNY DOWNSTATE MEDICAL CENTER) ★
450 Clarkson Ave, Brooklyn, NY 11203-2012
Tel (718) 780-1000 Founded/Ownrshp 2010
Sales 83.1MM^E EMP 2,500
SIC 8062 9431 General medical & surgical hospitals;
Pr: Rita Battles
*CFO: Thomas Pfeiffer
Off Mgr: Denise Lisita
Off Mgr: Debbie Salliey
Opers Mgr: Leon ABO
Obsttrcn: Sanford Lederman
Doctor: Maxine Orris
Diag Rad: Mercedes Washington

LONG ISLAND COMMUNITY FOUNDATI
See NEW YORK COMMUNITY TRUST AND COMMUNITY FUNDS INC

D-U-N-S 07-917-1134
LONG ISLAND ELECTRIC UTILITY SERVCO LLC
333 Earle Ovington Blvd, Uniondale, NY 11553-3610
Tel (516) 719-9810 Founded/Ownrshp 2012
Sales 4.3MMM^E EMP 2,500
SIC 4911 Electric services
Pr: Dave Daly

D-U-N-S 06-474-4014
LONG ISLAND HOME (NY)
BROADLAWN MNNER NURSG CARE CTR
(Suby of NSLIJ) ★
400 Sunrise Hwy, Amityville, NY 11701-2508
Tel (631) 264-4000 Founded/Ownrshp 2012, 1882
Sales 101.6MM EMP 1,112
SIC 8063 8051 8099 8011 Hospital for the mentally ill; Convalescent home with continuous nursing care; Blood related health services; Internal medicine practitioners
CEO: Robert E Detor
*CFO: Patricia A Porter
Admn Mgr: Annamaria Digrigoli
MIS Dir: Douglas Simpson
Dir QC: Ken Corbin

D-U-N-S 06-472-7027 IMP/EXP
LONG ISLAND JEWISH MEDICAL CENTER
(Suby of NSLIJ) ★
27005 76th Ave, New Hyde Park, NY 11040-1496
Tel (516) 465-2600 Founded/Ownrshp 1949
Sales 1.5MMM EMP 1,214
SIC 8062 8063 8069 General medical & surgical hospitals; Psychiatric hospitals; Children's hospital
CEO: Michael J Dowling
Dir Recs: Patricia Hennelly
COO: Charles M Trunz
CFO: Robert S Shapiro
Ofcr: John Sandhusen
Sr VP: Joseph Cabral
Sr VP: Donna Drummond
Exec: Andrea Vambutas
Dir OR: Veronica Petersen
Dir Soc: Nancy Geller
Off Mgr: Paul Pugliese

D-U-N-S 13-355-1270
LONG ISLAND POWER AUTHORITY
PSEGLI AS AGENT FOR LIPA
333 Earle Ovington Blvd # 403, Uniondale, NY 11553-3606
Tel (516) 222-7700 Founded/Ownrshp 1986
Sales 115.8MM^E EMP 100^E
Accts Kpmg Llp Melville Ny
SIC 4911 Generation, electric power; Transmission, electric power
CEO: Michael D Hervey
CFO: Thomas Falcone
*CFO: Herbert L Hogue
*VP: Michael Deering
*VP: Kenneth Kane
Dir Risk M: Corey Horowitz
Counsel: Joseph Wiener

D-U-N-S 00-699-2929
LONG ISLAND RAIL ROAD CO (NY)
MTA LONG ISLAND RAIL ROAD
(Suby of M T A) ★
9027 Sutphin Blvd, Jamaica, NY 11435-3647
Tel (718) 558-4704 Founded/Ownrshp 1834, 1966
Sales 667.5MM^E EMP 7,000
SIC 4111 Commuter rail passenger operation
Pr: Helena Williams
CFO: Nicholas Di Mola
CFO: Nicholas Mola
Ex VP: Albert Cosenza
VP: Thomas Prendergast

D-U-N-S 06-593-3103
LONG ISLAND UNIVERSITY
700 Northern Blvd, Greenvale, NY 11548-1327
Tel (516) 299-2535 Founded/Ownrshp 1926
Sales 388.9MM EMP 3,300
Accts Kpmg Llp Melville Ny
SIC 8221 University
Pr: Dr Kimberly R Cline
Pr: Kitty Rockett
*Pr: David Steinberg PHD
*CFO: Robert Altholz
VP: Lucille Ambrosio
VP: Melodee Gandia
VP: Jeffrey Kane
VP: Paola Kleinman
VP: Lori Knapp
Exec: Nancy Sissons
Assoc Dir: Jamie Apicella
Assoc Dir: Eric Jean
Assoc Dir: Beth Koval
Dir Rx: Joseph Bova
Board of Directors: Susanne Flower, James Newell, Patricia Stephens, David Sterling

D-U-N-S 00-651-5118
LONG JOHN SILVERS RESTAURANT INC
(Suby of YORKSHIRE GLOBAL RESTAURANTS INC) ★
1441 Gardiner Ln, Louisville, KY 40213-1914
Tel (502) 874-3000 Founded/Ownrshp 1946
Sales 64.6MM^E EMP 1,000
SIC 5812 6794 Fast-food restaurant, chain; Franchises, selling or licensing
Pr: David Deno
*CFO: Mark Plummer
Treas: Cheri Leistner
*Sr VP: Forrest Ragsdale

D-U-N-S 00-420-5732
LONG POINT DEVELOPMENT LLC
TERRANEA RESORT
100 Terranea Way, Rancho Palos Verdes, CA 90275-1013
Tel (310) 265-2800 Founded/Ownrshp 2004
Sales 59.7MM^E EMP 1,000
SIC 7011 Resort hotel

LONG PRAIRIE PACKING
See ROSENS DIVERSIFIED INC

D-U-N-S 04-671-2444
LONG PRAIRIE PACKING CO INC
(Suby of LONG PRAIRIE PACKING) ★
100 Bridgepoint Curv # 249, South Saint Paul, MN 55075-5503
Tel (651) 552-8230 Founded/Ownrshp 1975
Sales 106.9MM^E EMP 1,462
SIC 2011 Meat packing plants; Beef products from beef slaughtered on site
CEO: Thomas J Rosen
*Pr: Greg Benedict
*Treas: Robert Hovde

D-U-N-S 96-860-0841
LONG TERM CARE GROUP INC
LTCG
(Suby of STONE POINT CAPITAL LLC) ★
11000 Prairie Lakes Dr, Eden Prairie, MN 55344-3885
Tel (952) 516-6800 Founded/Ownrshp 2014
Sales NA EMP 1,000
SIC 6411 Insurance agents & brokers
CEO: Peter Goldstein
Pr: Peter Levine
*COO: Rob Frederick
*CFO: Dean Miller
*Chf Mktg O: Stephen K Holland
Chf Mktg O: Mark Regan

Ex VP: Patrick Yount
Sr VP: Colleen Huberman
**Sr VP:* Keith Jasper
Sr VP: Terri Judge
Sr VP: Paul Kay
Sr VP: Kelly Lundgren
**Sr VP:* Eileen Tell
VP: Chad Bellin
VP: Jim Bruha
VP: Doug Foote
**VP:* Adam Hoffman
VP: David McGuire
VP: Bradley Schumacher

LONG-LEWIS FORD
See LONG-LEWIS INC

D-U-N-S 00-690-0088 IMP
LONG-LEWIS INC (AL)
LONG-LEWIS FORD
2551 Highway 150, Hoover, AL 35244-3533
Tel (205) 989-3673 *Founded/Ownrshp* 1906, 1986
Sales 164.9MM^E *EMP* 350
SIC 5511 5072

D-U-N-S 00-346-0144
LONGLEY SUPPLY CO
2018 Oleander Dr, Wilmington, NC 28403-2336
Tel (910) 762-7793 *Founded/Ownrshp* 1946
Sales 83.1MM^E *EMP* 100
SIC 5074 5063 5075 Plumbing fittings & supplies; Electrical supplies; Warm air heating & air conditioning
Pr: Emily Longley
Treas: Henry Longley Jr
IT Man: Joey Clark
Sls Mgr: Mark Matz
Sales Asso: Brent Bunn
Sales Asso: Sam McKenzie
Sales Asso: David Pigott

D-U-N-S 05-683-3833 IMP
LONGMONT UNITED HOSPITAL
1950 Mountain View Ave, Longmont, CO 80501-9865
Tel (303) 651-5111 *Founded/Ownrshp* 1955
Sales 170.1MM *EMP* 1,100
SIC 8062 General medical & surgical hospitals
CEO: Mitchell Carson
Pr: Darleen Savage
**CFO:* Neil W Bertrand
CFO: Mona McCarthy
Treas: Patti Rosquist
Ofcr: Carol Smith
VP: Becky Herman
Exec: Warren Laughlin
Dir Rx: John Ives
Off Mgr: Jackie Nagell
Dir QC: Kelley Degarate

D-U-N-S 78-326-3551 IMP
■ **LONGS DRUG STORES CALIFORNIA INC**
(*Suby of* LONGS DRUG STORES CORP) ★
1 Cvs Dr, Woonsocket, RI 02895-6146
Tel (925) 937-1170 *Founded/Ownrshp* 1938
Sales 1.4MMM^E *EMP* 18,999
SIC 5912 Drug stores; Proprietary (non-prescription medicine) stores
Pr: Harold Somerset

D-U-N-S 00-691-0004
■ **LONGS DRUG STORES CORP**
(*Suby of* CVS HEALTH CORP) ★
1 Cvs Dr, Woonsocket, RI 02895-6146
Tel (401) 770-1830 *Founded/Ownrshp* 1938, 2008
Sales 1.5MMM^E *EMP* 21,900
SIC 5912 5961 Drug stores; Proprietary (non-prescription medicine) stores; Pharmaceuticals, mail order
Ch Bd: Warren F Bryant
**COO:* Todd J Vasos
**CFO:* Steven F McCann
**Treas:* Roger L Chelemedos
**Sr VP:* William J Rainey
VP: Charles Armstrong
VP: Lee Klein
VP: Brian T McAndrews
VP: Brad McTeer
VP: Bruce Mentch
VP: Alan Pope
VP: Larry Prato

D-U-N-S 93-394-8820 IMP
LONGSTREET CLINIC P C
NORTHEAST GA INPATIENT SVCS
725 Jesse Jewell Pkwy Se, Gainesville, GA 30501-3834
Tel (770) 718-1122 *Founded/Ownrshp* 1994
Sales 110.0MM *EMP* 634
SIC 8011 Clinic, operated by physicians
CEO: Amelia Mimi Collins
**COO:* T Loren Funk
**CFO:* J Allen Butts
Opers Mgr: Kimberlee Joyce
Obsttrcn: Michael P Connor
Obsttrcn: Karen D Dillard
Obsttrcn: Karen D Illar
Obsttrcn: Ross Jacobson
Nutrtnst: Sheenagh King
Doctor: Janet G Boone
Doctor: Philip R Male

D-U-N-S 00-901-0471 IMP
LONGUST DISTRIBUTING INC (AZ)
2432 W Birchwood Ave, Mesa, AZ 85202-1064
Tel (480) 820-6244 *Founded/Ownrshp* 1975, 2005
Sales 113.0MM^E *EMP* 165
SIC 5023 Floor coverings; Resilient floor coverings: tile or sheet; Carpets; Wood flooring
Pr: Steve Wallace
**CFO:* William Bobertz
**Sr VP:* John Laird
**Sr VP:* Drew Mittelstaedt
Mktg Mgr: Debbie Hendy
Manager: Joe Felix

D-U-N-S 60-680-5984
LONGVIEW BRIDGE AND ROAD LTD
792 Skinner Ln, Longview, TX 75605-7352
Tel (903) 663-0264 *Founded/Ownrshp* 1989
Sales 131.3MM^E *EMP* 400^E
SIC 1611 1622 1794 General contractor, highway & street construction; Bridge construction; Excavation work
Pt: Larry Johnson
Genl Pt: Lb R LLC
Pt: Alan Woods

D-U-N-S 00-904-1443 IMP/EXP
■ **LONGVIEW FIBRE PAPER AND PACKAGING INC**
KAPSTONE
(*Suby of* KAPSTONE PAPER AND PACKAGING CORP) ★
300 Fibre Way, Longview, WA 98632-1199
Tel (360) 425-1550 *Founded/Ownrshp* 2013
Sales 413.2MM^E *EMP* 999
SIC 2621 Paper mills
CEO: Roger W Stone
**Pr:* Matthew Kaplan
**CFO:* Andrea K Tarbox
**VP:* Lou Loosbrock
VP: Ivan Olsen
VP: Richard Parker
VP: Todd Price
VP: Janet Wade
Exec: Bruce Warrick
**Prin:* Randy Nebel
CTO: Rosemary Purcell

D-U-N-S 80-775-6598
LONGVIEW HOLDING CORP
(*Suby of* ROCKWOOD SERVICE CORP) ★
43 Arch St, Greenwich, CT 06830-6512
Tel (203) 869-6734 *Founded/Ownrshp* 2005
Sales 318.8MM^E *EMP* 2,600
SIC 6719 1389 Personal holding companies, except banks; Testing, measuring, surveying & analysis services
Pr: Peter O Scannell
**CFO:* John P Lockwood
**VP:* Harald B Findlay

LONGVIEW I S D
See LONGVIEW INDEPENDENT SCHOOL DISTRICT

D-U-N-S 01-047-6513
LONGVIEW INDEPENDENT SCHOOL DISTRICT
LONGVIEW I S D
1301 E Young St, Longview, TX 75602-2251
Tel (903) 753-0206 *Founded/Ownrshp* 1909
Sales 96.1MM *EMP* 1,302
Accts Karen A Jacks & Associates P
SIC 8211 Public elementary & secondary schools
Bd of Dir: John Preston
Prin: Bonnie Bogue
Prin: Sarah Bridges
Prin: Carl Briley
Prin: Jacqueline Burnett
Prin: Linda Dorsey
Prin: Vernessa Gentry
Prin: Linda Lister
Prin: Lola Moore
Prin: Mary L Reed
Prin: Nancy Welch

D-U-N-S 18-791-5277
■ **LONGVIEW MEDICAL CENTER LP**
LONGVIEW REGIONAL MEDICAL CTR
(*Suby of* COMMUNITY HEALTH SYSTEMS INC) ★
2901 4th St, Longview, TX 75605-5128
Tel (903) 758-1818 *Founded/Ownrshp* 2007
Sales 318.1MM *EMP* 676
SIC 8062 8099 General medical & surgical hospitals; Medical services organization
Genl Pt: Jim Kendrick
Pt: Jill Bayless
Pt: Todd Johnson
COO: Roy Finch
Dir Rx: Gary Duty
Prin: Vicki Briggs
VP Sls: Stacey Newman
Doctor: Richard English
Nrsg Dir: Stephanie Foster
HC Dir: Wendy Hill

LONGVIEW REGIONAL MEDICAL CTR
See LONGVIEW MEDICAL CENTER LP

D-U-N-S 61-280-2256
LONGWOOD COMMUNITY LIVING CENTER
200 Long St, Booneville, MS 38829-4306
Tel (662) 728-6234 *Founded/Ownrshp* 1992
Sales 402.1MM *EMP* 72
SIC 8051 Skilled nursing care facilities
Pr: Douglas Wright Jr
Board of Directors: Dewitt Crawford

D-U-N-S 06-197-7427 EXP
LONGWOOD LINCOLN-MERCURY INC
DE LAND TOYOTA
3505 N Us Highway 17 92, Longwood, FL 32750-3771
Tel (407) 322-4884 *Founded/Ownrshp* 1979
Sales 87.0MM^E *EMP* 307^E
SIC 5511 Automobiles, new & used
Pr: Stephen R Parks
**Sec:* Greg Corless
Dir IT: Andy Harris

D-U-N-S 08-008-0831
LONGWOOD MANAGEMENT CORP
LONGWOOD MANOR SANITARIUM
4032 Wilshire Blvd Fl 6, Los Angeles, CA 90010-3425
Tel (213) 389-6900 *Founded/Ownrshp* 1964
Sales 169.4MM^E *EMP* 2,000
SIC 8742 6513 General management consultant; Retirement hotel operation
CEO: David Friedmand
**Pr:* Jacob Friedman
CFO: Zaid Pervaiz
**Treas:* Lea Friedman
**VP:* Irving Friedman

LONGWOOD MANOR SANITARIUM
See LONGWOOD MANAGEMENT CORP

D-U-N-S 83-612-1053 IMP/EXP
LONGYEAR CO
LANG EXPLORATORY DRLG DL MAHER
(*Suby of* BOART LONGYEAR CO) ★
10808 S River Front Pkwy, South Jordan, UT 84095-5759
Tel (801) 972-6430 *Founded/Ownrshp* 1974
Sales 507.4MM^E *EMP* 700
SIC 1481 Test boring for nonmetallic minerals
CEO: Richard Obrien
**Pr:* Paul Brunner
COO: Kipp Craig
**CFO:* Joe Ragan
**CFO:* Ron Sellwood
**Sr VP:* Brad Baker
**Sr VP:* Kent Hoots
VP: Denis Depres
Sls&Mrk Ex: Bill Johnson

D-U-N-S 83-156-6187
LONGYEAR HOLDINGS INC
(*Suby of* BOART LONGYEAR LIMITED)
2340 W 1700 S, Salt Lake City, UT 84104-4229
Tel (801) 972-6430 *Founded/Ownrshp* 2005
Sales 4.3MMM^E *EMP* 9,500
SIC 1481 3532 3559 Test boring for nonmetallic minerals; Drills & drilling equipment, mining (except oil & gas); Concrete products machinery
Ch Bd: Michael Moore
**Ch Bd:* David McLemore
**Pr:* Paul Brunner
**Pr:* Blake Cavit
**Sr VP:* Fab Rasetti
Dir IT: Jason Pehrson
Dir IT: Kevin Vaughan
Tech Mgr: Jessi Pettey
Manager: Sharon Condrat

D-U-N-S 07-887-4294
LONZA AMERICA INC (DE)
(*Suby of* LONZA GROUP AG)
90 Boroline Rd Ste 1, Allendale, NJ 07401-1629
Tel (201) 316-9200 *Founded/Ownrshp* 1980
Sales 499.7MM^E *EMP* 2,201
SIC 8731 Biotechnical research, commercial
CEO: Stephan Borgas
**Ch Bd:* Werner J Bauer
**Ch Bd:* Rolf Soiron
CFO: Raymond French
Chf Mktg O: Michael Frizberg
VP: James Coletta
Comm Man: Teri McCarthy
Mktg Dir: Christian Rose

D-U-N-S 09-314-9750 EXP
LONZA BIOLOGICS INC
(*Suby of* LONZA AMERICA INC) ★
101 International Dr, Portsmouth, NH 03801-2815
Tel (603) 610-4500 *Founded/Ownrshp* 1993
Sales 228.8MM^E *EMP* 476
SIC 2834 Pharmaceutical preparations
Pr: Stephan Kutzer
CFO: Rob Schauder
CFO: Roland Waibel
**Treas:* Alexander Hoy
Assoc Dir: Neil Bergeron
Telecom Ex: Randall Spayd
CIO: Thomas Salvetti
QA Dir: Kristina Siegenthaler
IT Man: Jeff Lundin
Sftwr Eng: Anna Myers
VP Opers: Gerhard Klement

D-U-N-S 00-164-3170 IMP/EXP
LONZA INC (NY)
(*Suby of* LONZA AMERICA INC) ★
90 Boroline Rd Ste 1, Allendale, NJ 07401-1629
Tel (201) 316-9200 *Founded/Ownrshp* 1958
Sales 245.2MM^E *EMP* 549
SIC 2899 2869 2819 Chemical preparations; Industrial organic chemicals; Industrial inorganic chemicals
CEO: Jeanne Thomas
**CFO:* Andrew Hoy
Top Exec: David Smith
VP: Konstantina Katcheves
VP: Dorothea Klein
VP: Mark Miller
VP: Roman Quinter
VP: Tony Sandonato
**VP:* Scott Waldman
VP: Dominik Werner
Exec: Van Basel
Exec: Basel Comer
Exec: Basel Merkt
Exec: Chu Slough
Exec: Basel Studer
Dir Risk M: Patrick Boylan
Board of Directors: Roland Waibel

D-U-N-S 60-909-5955 IMP
LONZA WALKERSVILLE INC
(*Suby of* LONZA GROUP AG)
8830 Biggs Ford Rd, Walkersville, MD 21793-8415
Tel (301) 898-7025 *Founded/Ownrshp* 2007
Sales 129.5MM^E *EMP* 480
SIC 2836 Biological products, except diagnostic
Pr: Shawn Cavanagh
CFO: Andy Long
Ofcr: Edward Flynn
Dir Bus: Richard Giles
CTO: Daniel Marshak
QA Dir: Juanquina Thomas
IT Man: Cathy Boyd
IT Man: Tracey Hamilton
Prd Mgr: Jennifer Dilks
Natl Sales: Ethan Brookes
Mktg Mgr: Colleen Florex

LOOKOUT RIDGE
See AGSTAR FINANCIAL SERVICES ACA

D-U-N-S 05-637-0109
LOOMIS ARMORED US LLC
(*Suby of* LOOMIS AB)
2500 Citywest Blvd # 2300, Houston, TX 77042-9000
Tel (713) 435-6700 *Founded/Ownrshp* 2006
Sales 687.0MM *EMP* 8,000
SIC 7381 4789 Armored car services; Cargo loading & unloading services
Pr: Lars Blecko
Pr: Kendall Walker
**COO:* Chuck Obrien
**CFO:* Marcus Hagegard
**CFO:* Patrick Otero
VP: Mark Clark
**VP:* Shirley R Jefferies
**VP:* Sarah Kattapong
Genl Mgr: Jasmine Taillon

D-U-N-S 10-167-6310
LOOMIS CO
850 N Park Rd, Wyomissing, PA 19610-1307
Tel (610) 374-4040 *Founded/Ownrshp* 1950
Sales NA *EMP* 375
SIC 6411 8742 Insurance agents, brokers & service; Policyholders' consulting service; Management consulting services
Pr: James R Loomis
**Treas:* Kathy Schlegel
Ex VP: Sandy Cuccaro
Sr VP: Debbie Hayes
VP: Joe Reedy
VP Opers: Tom Forsberg
Opers Mgr: Eric Sandoe

D-U-N-S 02-692-6816
LOOMIS INTERNATIONAL INC
100 N Richey St, Pasadena, TX 77506-1055
Tel (713) 477-7148 *Founded/Ownrshp* 1996
Sales 93.5MM^E *EMP* 100
SIC 1389 Testing, measuring, surveying & analysis services; Gas field services; Pipe testing, oil field service
Pr: Larry C Johnson
**CFO:* Ryan McMinn
Sfty Mgr: Kathy Nouis
Sls&Mrk Ex: Kent Padgett

D-U-N-S 00-695-2568
LOOMIS SAYLES & CO LP (MA)
(*Suby of* NATIXIS GLOBAL ASSET MANAGEMENT LP) ★
1 Financial Ctr Fl 34, Boston, MA 02111-2660
Tel (617) 482-2451 *Founded/Ownrshp* 1926, 1968
Sales 275.0MM^E *EMP* 525
SIC 6282 Investment counselors
CEO: Robert J Blanding
V Ch: Daniel Fuss
Pr: Keith Beaudin
Pr: Kevin Charleston
Treas: Paul Scherber
Chf Inves: Jae Park
Ofcr: Jean Loewenberg
Ofcr: Don Ryan
Ex VP: John Gallagher
VP: Rita Aisner
VP: David Beach
VP: John Bell
VP: Neil Burke
VP: Frank Caparrotta
VP: Dana Chamberlain
VP: Thomas Finucane
VP: Rob Forker
VP: Dozier Gardner
VP: Daniel Garuti
VP: Grover Heintz
VP: Christopher Hermance
Board of Directors: Paul Sherba, David Waldman

D-U-N-S 09-418-1633 IMP/EXP
LOOP LLC
LOUISIANA OFFSHORE OIL PORT
137 Northpark Blvd, Covington, LA 70433-5071
Tel (985) 632-6970 *Founded/Ownrshp* 1972
Sales 143.7MM^E *EMP* 128
SIC 1389 Oil field services
Pr: Robert Thompson
VP: Jill Shane

D-U-N-S 02-766-4478 IMP/EXP
LOPAREX LLC
EASY MASK
(*Suby of* LOPAREX HOLDING B.V.)
1255 Crescent Green # 400, Cary, NC 27518-8132
Tel (919) 678-7700 *Founded/Ownrshp* 2005
Sales 273.0MM^E *EMP* 732
SIC 2672 Coated paper, except photographic, carbon or abrasive
CEO: Michael Apperson
**COO:* Jack Taylor
CFO: John Mays
Tech Mgr: Chip Sheeran
Tech Mgr: Bruce Unruh
Software D: Yelong Cui
Software D: Tammy Martin
Snr Mgr: Melissa King

D-U-N-S 09-476-8702
LOPEZ FOODS INC
6016 Nw 120th Ct, Oklahoma City, OK 73162-1729
Tel (405) 603-7500 *Founded/Ownrshp* 1968
Sales 400.0MM *EMP* 1,564
SIC 2013 2011 Prepared beef products from purchased beef; Sausages from purchased meat; Bacon, side & sliced: from purchased meat; Meat packing plants
CEO: Ed Sanchez
**Ch Bd:* John C Lopez
**COO:* James D English
Exec: Michelle Wagner
Opers Mgr: Eric Underwood
Mktg Mgr: Alfred Fernandez
Sls Mgr: Brenda Gomez

D-U-N-S 80-528-5871
LOPEZ HEALTH SYSTEMS INC
2209 N Highway 83, Crystal City, TX 78839-1756
Tel (830) 374-3525 *Founded/Ownrshp* 1990
Sales 21.1MM^E *EMP* 1,300
SIC 8082 Home health care services
Pr: Amparo Lopez
CFO: Raul Flores
**VP:* Victor Lopez
IT Man: Caesar Lopez

LOPEZ HOUSTON METALS
See LOPEZ SCRAP METAL INC

D-U-N-S 07-508-7528 IMP/EXP
LOPEZ SCRAP METAL INC
LOPEZ HOUSTON METALS
351 N Nevarez Rd, El Paso, TX 79927-4120
Tel (915) 859-0770 *Founded/Ownrshp* 1970
Sales 103.3MM *EMP* 52
Accts Pena Briones Mcdaniel & Co E
SIC 5093 3341 Ferrous metal scrap & waste; Nonferrous metals scrap; Secondary nonferrous metals
Pr: Isidro Lopez
**Treas:* Hector E Lopez

D-U-N-S 06-148-8144 IMP
LOR INC
ROLLINS RANCHES
2170 Piedmont Rd Ne, Atlanta, GA 30324-4135
Tel (404) 486-5600 *Founded/Ownrshp* 1978
Sales 149.4MM^E^ *EMP* 1,426
SIC 6799 5084 3443 Investors; Pumps & pumping equipment; Fabricated plate work (boiler shop)
CEO: R Randall Rollins
Pr: Gary W Rollins
CEO: Randall Rollins

LORAIN BOARD OF EDUCATION
See LORAIN CITY SCHOOL DISTRICT

D-U-N-S 07-675-5412
LORAIN CITY SCHOOL DISTRICT
LORAIN BOARD OF EDUCATION
2350 Pole Ave, Lorain, OH 44052-4301
Tel (440) 233-2232 *Founded/Ownrshp* 1900
Sales 65.0MM^E^ *EMP* 1,500
SIC 8211 Public elementary & secondary schools
**Treas:* Dale Weber
IT Man: Diana Miglets
Teacher Pr: Carol Gottschling

D-U-N-S 19-146-5491 IMP
LORAIN COUNTY AUTOMOTIVE SYSTEMS INC
LCAS
(*Suby of* CHEMICAL) ★
7470 Industrial Pkwy Dr, Lorain, OH 44053-2070
Tel (440) 960-7470 *Founded/Ownrshp* 1996
Sales 215.7MM^E^ *EMP* 1,718
SIC 3714 Motor vehicle engines & parts
CEO: Arvind Pradhan
**CFO:* Tom Rockwell

D-U-N-S 07-778-0674
LORAIN COUNTY COMMUNITY COLLEGE DISTRICT
L C C C
1005 Abbe Rd N, Elyria, OH 44035-1613
Tel (440) 365-5222 *Founded/Ownrshp* 1961
Sales 129.8MM^E^ *EMP* 1,400^E^
Accts Balestra Harr & Scherer Cpas
SIC 8222 Community college
Pr: Roy A Church
V Ch: Andy Gurd
**VP:* Quentin Potter
IT Man: Laurie Carlberg
Sls Mgr: Julie Cantrell
Sls Mgr: Susan Sturm
Pgrm Dir: Craig Peneff

LORAIN COUNTY TREASURER
See COUNTY OF LORAIN

D-U-N-S 94-681-6212
▲ LORAL SPACE & COMMUNICATIONS INC
565 5th Ave, New York, NY 10017-2413
Tel (212) 697-1105 *Founded/Ownrshp* 2005
Sales 869.9MM^E^ *EMP* 441
Accts Deloitte & Touche Llp New Yor
Tkr Sym LORL *Exch* NGS
SIC 3663 4899 Satellites, communications; Satellite earth stations; Data communication services
Pr: AVI Katz
COO: Gregory Clark
CFO: John Capogrossi
VP: Barry Sitler
CTO: David N Wendling
Opers Mgr: Bill Lueckfeld

D-U-N-S 13-384-6969
■ LORAL SPACECOM CORP
(*Suby of* LORAL SPACE & COMMUNICATIONS INC) ★
565 5th Ave Fl 19, New York, NY 10017-2431
Tel (212) 697-1105 *Founded/Ownrshp* 1997
Sales 869.4MM *EMP* 2,000
Accts Deloitte & Touche Llp New Yor
SIC 3663 Satellites, communications
CEO: Michael Targoff
**Treas:* Richard Mastoloni

D-U-N-S 01-034-5452 IMP/EXP
LORAM MAINTENANCE OF WAY INC
3900 Arrowhead Dr, Hamel, MN 55340-9529
Tel (763) 478-6014 *Founded/Ownrshp* 1954
Sales 326.9MM^E^ *EMP* 1,100
SIC 3743 Railway maintenance cars
Pr: Philip J Homan
**VP:* Joe Carlin
**VP:* Don Cherrey
**VP:* Tom Dejoseph
**VP:* Jim Perkins
Exec: Peter Hauer
VP Opers: Darwin Isdahl
Ql Cn Mgr: Tab Ashwill
Manager: Gary Kohnert
Manager: Rolf Swanson
Manager: Bill Walls

D-U-N-S 62-340-2687 IMP
LORD & TAYLOR LLC
(*Suby of* HUDSON'S BAY COMPANY)
424 5th Ave, New York, NY 10018-2771
Tel (212) 391-3344 *Founded/Ownrshp* 2006
Sales 1.4MMM^E^ *EMP* 9,000
SIC 5621 5611 5632 5999 Women's clothing stores; Men's & boys' clothing stores; Women's accessory & specialty stores; Cosmetics
CEO: Russ Hardin
**CFO:* Michael Culhane
CFO: Don Perinchies
Treas: Danielle Calabrese
**Treas:* Lucas Evans
**Chf Mktg O:* Amy Avitabile
Sr VP: Roger W Adams
Sr VP: Robert Cole
VP: Amy Avitable
VP: Christina Callas
VP: Eileen Dileo
VP: Jack Fitzmaurice
VP: Laura Gallant
VP: Beth Hastie
**VP:* John Manos
VP: Maria Maurmann
VP: Marti Moore
VP: Irene Newman
VP: Tara Oliver
VP: Laurie Pappaceno
VP: Christopher Peters

D-U-N-S 01-212-2123
LORD ABBETT & CO LLC
90 Hudson St Fl 10, Jersey City, NJ 07302-3900
Tel (201) 827-2000 *Founded/Ownrshp* 1950
Sales 269.9MM^E^ *EMP* 509
SIC 6282 Investment advisory service
Pt: Daria L Foster
**Pt:* Stacy P Allen
**Pt:* Zane Brown
**Pt:* Paul Hilstad
**Pt:* W T Hudson
**Pt:* Robert G Morris
**Pt:* Robert Noelke
Mng Pt: Robert S Dow
COO: Joan A Binstock
Chf Inves: Robert Gerber
Ex VP: Frederick Ruvkun
VP: Kenneth Cutler
VP: Peter Smith
VP: John Walsh
Comm Man: Jason Farago

D-U-N-S 00-503-1281 IMP/EXP
LORD CORP (PA)
111 Lord Dr, Cary, NC 27511-7923
Tel (877) 275-5673 *Founded/Ownrshp* 1940
Sales 848.2MM *EMP* 3,256
SIC 2891 3724 3728 2851

D-U-N-S 00-213-6794 IMP/EXP
LOREAL USA INC
L'OREAL USA PRODUCTS
(*Suby of* L'OREAL)
10 Hudson Yards Fl 30, New York, NY 10001-2159
Tel (212) 818-1500 *Founded/Ownrshp* 1953, 1994
Sales 11.3MMM^E^ *EMP* 18,860
SIC 5122 2844

L'OREAL USA PRODUCTS
See LOREAL USA INC

D-U-N-S 02-592-4770
LOREN BUICK & PONTIAC INC (IL)
PONTIAC IN GLENVIEW
1610 Waukegan Rd, Glenview, IL 60025-2108
Tel (847) 729-8900 *Founded/Ownrshp* 1947
Sales 114.9MM *EMP* 80
SIC 5511 5521 Automobiles, new & used; Used car dealers
CEO: Irving Segeal
**Pr:* Paula Segal

D-U-N-S 00-445-6729 IMP
LOREN COOK CO (OH)
2015 E Dale St, Springfield, MO 65803-4637
Tel (417) 869-6474 *Founded/Ownrshp* 1941
Sales 157.8MM^E^ *EMP* 700
SIC 3564 Exhaust fans: industrial or commercial; Ventilating fans: industrial or commercial; Blowing fans: industrial or commercial
Ch Bd: Gerald A Cook
Pr: Steve Burney
Treas: Gerald A Cook Jr
VP: Mannie Brahman
VP: Victor Colwell
VP: Loren Cook II

D-U-N-S 96-800-2824 IMP
LORENZ INC
KAREL MANUFACTURING
280 Campillo St Ste G, Calexico, CA 92231-3200
Tel (760) 356-1019 *Founded/Ownrshp* 1993
Sales 94.7MM^E^ *EMP* 400
SIC 3699 Electrical equipment & supplies
Pr: Zaven Arakelian
Dir IT: Sergio Chao-Bushoven
IT Man: Isabel Garcia

D-U-N-S 16-060-4802
LORETTO HEALTH AND REHABILITATION CENTER
700 E Brighton Ave, Syracuse, NY 13205-2201
Tel (315) 469-1991 *Founded/Ownrshp* 2003
Sales 57.6MM *EMP* 2,000
SIC 8322 Rehabilitation services
Ch Bd: J Andrew Breuer
**Sec:* John A Cirando
VP: Penny Abulencia
IT Man: Angela Newcomb

D-U-N-S 07-230-9966
LORIG CONSTRUCTION CO
250 E Touhy Ave, Des Plaines, IL 60018-2658
Tel (847) 298-0360 *Founded/Ownrshp* 1986
Sales 89.5MM^E^ *EMP* 300
SIC 1622 Bridge construction; Viaduct construction; Highway construction, elevated
Ch: Max Lorig
**Pr:* David H Lorig
Snr PM: Woody Griffin

D-U-N-S 61-737-9169 EXP
LORILLARD TOBACCO CO LLC
714 Green Valley Rd, Greensboro, NC 27408-7018
Tel (336) 335-6600 *Founded/Ownrshp* 1989
Sales NA *EMP* 2,700
SIC 2111

D-U-N-S 03-971-3409
LORIS GIFTS INC
LORI'S HOSPITAL GIFT SHOPS
2125 Chenault Dr Ste 100, Carrollton, TX 75006-4936
Tel (972) 759-5000 *Founded/Ownrshp* 1997
Sales 181.4MM^E^ *EMP* 1,400
SIC 5947 8099 5999

LORI'S HOSPITAL GIFT SHOPS
See LORIS GIFTS INC

D-U-N-S 03-059-9302
■ LOS ALAMITOS MEDICAL CENTER INC
(*Suby of* TENET HEALTHCARE CORP) ★
3751 Katella Ave, Los Alamitos, CA 90720-3113
Tel (714) 826-6400 *Founded/Ownrshp* 1970
Sales 25.4M *EMP* 1,105
Accts Stan Diliberto Cpa Cfp Inc Se
SIC 8062 General medical & surgical hospitals
CEO: Kent Clayton
**Pr:* Alice Livingood
**Pr:* Margaret Watkins
Mtls Mgr: Wendy Roberts
Doctor: Juan Rodriguez

LOS ALAMOS NATIONAL LABORATORY
See LOS ALAMOS NATIONAL SECURITY LLC

D-U-N-S 09-383-8014 IMP
LOS ALAMOS NATIONAL LABORATORY FOUNDATION
LANL FOUNDATION
1112 Plaza Del Norte, Espanola, NM 87532-3216
Tel (505) 753-8890 *Founded/Ownrshp* 1997
Sales 2.8MM *EMP* 10,751
Accts Weiner & Co
SIC 8699 Charitable organization
CEO: Jenny Parks
**CFO:* Mihaela Popa Simil
**Treas:* Wayne Kennedy
Bd of Dir: Jeffrey Howlel
**VP:* Rich Marquez
**VP:* Libbie Martinez
Snr Mgr: Keith Lindsay

D-U-N-S 17-525-2894
LOS ALAMOS NATIONAL SECURITY LLC
LOS ALAMOS NATIONAL LABORATORY
105 Central Park Sq, Los Alamos, NM 87544-4019
Tel (877) 723-4101 *Founded/Ownrshp* 2006
Sales 605.2MM^E^ *EMP* 11,000^E^
SIC 8748 Business consulting
Ofcr: Patrice Stevens
Assoc Dir: Alan Bishop
Prgrm Mgr: Darryl Gardner
Prgrm Mgr: Robert Margevicius
Prgrm Mgr: Barbara Wolf
Admn Mgr: Mike Barr
IT Man: Brian Martinez
Netwrk Eng: Alex Montano
Snr Mgr: James Bossert
Snr Mgr: John Sarrao

D-U-N-S 60-406-1895
LOS ALTOS FOOD PRODUCTS INC
450 Baldwin Park Blvd, City of Industry, CA 91746-1407
Tel (626) 330-6555 *Founded/Ownrshp* 1988
Sales 139.9MM^E^ *EMP* 105
Accts Sotomayor & Associates Llp P
SIC 5143 Cheese
Pr: Raul Andrade
CFO: Corin Andrade
VP: Alin Andrade
**VP:* Gloria Andrade
Opers Mgr: John Clements

LOS ANGELES ANGELS OF ANAHEIM
See ANGELS BASEBALL LP

D-U-N-S 04-093-0096
LOS ANGELES CITY COLLEGE
(*Suby of* LOS ANGELES COMMUNITY COLLEGE DISTRICT) ★
855 N Vermont Ave, Los Angeles, CA 90029-3588
Tel (323) 953-4000 *Founded/Ownrshp* 2005
Sales 135.2MM^E^ *EMP* 1^E^
SIC 8222 Junior college
VP: Art Taylor
Dir IT: Beau Blaser
Dir IT: Bo Ser
Opers Mgr: Ronda Guess
Doctor: John Al-Amin

D-U-N-S 07-226-6174 IMP
LOS ANGELES COMMUNITY COLLEGE DISTRICT
770 Wilshire Blvd, Los Angeles, CA 90017-3719
Tel (213) 891-2000 *Founded/Ownrshp* 1929
Sales 452.8MM^E^ *EMP* 8,500
Accts Kpmg Llp Irvine Ca
SIC 8222 Community college
**Pr:* Scott Svonkin
Ofcr: Shawn Gordon
Ofcr: Lynn Gross
Ex VP: Adriana Barrera
VP: Tina Park
VP: Nancy Pearlman
CIO: Larry Choi
Dir IT: Rob Alworth
IT Man: Mee L Kyon
Opers Supe: Nat Yangsamran
Pr Dir: Steve Springer

D-U-N-S 11-312-1024
LOS ANGELES COUNTY DEVELOPMENTAL SERVICES FOUNDATION
FRANK D LANTERMAN REGIONAL CEN
3303 Wilshire Blvd # 700, Los Angeles, CA 90010-1704
Tel (213) 383-1300 *Founded/Ownrshp* 1979
Sales 147.3MM^E^ *EMP* 180
SIC 8099 8322 8093 Medical services organization; Individual & family services; Mental health clinic, outpatient
Ex Dir: Dianne Anand
COO: Maureen Wilson
Bd of Dir: Frank Lanterman
VP: Marjorie Heller
Brnch Mgr: John Walker
Opers Mgr: Martha Aguirre

D-U-N-S 08-302-0297
LOS ANGELES COUNTY EMPLOYEES RETIREMENT ASSOCIATION
LACERA
300 N Lake Ave Ste 720, Pasadena, CA 91101-5674
Tel (626) 564-6000 *Founded/Ownrshp* 1938
Sales NA *EMP* 340
Accts Brown Armstrong Bakersfield
SIC 6371 Pension funds
CEO: Gregg Rademather
V Ch: John Barger
Bd of Dir: Bonnie Nolley
VP: Ana Chang
VP: Margaret Shuler
Exec: Renee Henry
Prin: Lisa Mazzocco
Div Mgr: Ricki Contreras
Snr Ntwrk: Irwin Devries
CTO: Robert Whitten
IT Man: Ray Sare

D-U-N-S 04-405-5523
LOS ANGELES COUNTY METROPOLITAN TRANSPORTATION AUTHORITY
1 Gateway Plz Fl 25, Los Angeles, CA 90012-3745
Tel (323) 466-3876 *Founded/Ownrshp* 1964
Sales 699.1MM^E^ *EMP* 9,800
SIC 4111 Bus line operations; Subway operation
CEO: Arthur Leahy
**CEO:* Rick Thorpe
**COO:* Carolyn Flowers
COO: James T Gallagher
COO: Lonnie Mitchell
**CFO:* Nalini Ahuja
Ofcr: Ann Kerman
Ofcr: Frank Shapiro
Ofcr: Bronwen Trice
Ex VP: Cynthia Gibson
Exec: Brian Mahaffey
Board of Directors: Yvonne B Burke, Doug Failing, John Fasana, David Fleming, Richard Katz, Bonnie Lowenthal, Pam O'conner, Bernard Parks, Zev Yaroslavsky

D-U-N-S 60-288-0189
LOS ANGELES COUNTY OFFICE OF EDUCATION
LACOE
9300 Imperial Hwy, Downey, CA 90242-2813
Tel (562) 922-6111 *Founded/Ownrshp* 1852
Sales 747.3MM *EMP* 4,000
Accts Vavrinek Trine Day & Co Ll
SIC 8211 Specialty education
CEO: Rudell S Freer
**Pr:* Rebecca J Turrentine
Bd of Dir: Douglas Boyd
Bd of Dir: Alex Johnson
Bd of Dir: Maria Yepes
**VP:* Katie Braude
Exec: Margo Minecki
Ex Dir: Verne Newman
Ex Dir: Patricia Smith
Prgrm Mgr: Aleece Kelly
Prgrm Mgr: Anna Whalen

LOS ANGELES COUNTY TAX COLLECT
See COUNTY OF LOS ANGELES

D-U-N-S 10-387-2516
LOS ANGELES DEPARTMENT OF WATER AND POWER
LADWP
111 N Hope St, Los Angeles, CA 90012-2607
Tel (213) 367-4211 *Founded/Ownrshp* 1902
Sales 4.2MMM^E^ *EMP* 9,000^E^
Accts Kpmg Llp Los Angeles Ca
SIC 4941 4911 Water supply; Electric services
Pr: Mel Levine
CFO: Phil Leiber
**CFO:* Philip Leiver
Ofcr: David H Wiggs Jr
Sr Inv Off: Jeremy Wolfson
VP: Kevin Brown
VP: Desmond Johnson
VP: Brendon Owens
VP: Dan Raftevold
VP: Ann Santilli
VP: Demarlo Sims

D-U-N-S 16-514-3348
LOS ANGELES FIREMAN RELIEF ASSOCIATION INC
WIDOWS, ORPHANS AND DISABLED F
2900 W Temple St, Los Angeles, CA 90026-4516
Tel (800) 244-3439 *Founded/Ownrshp* 1906
Sales 86.4MM *EMP* 41
Accts Harrington Group Cpas Llp S
SIC 8322 Emergency social services
Pr: Barry G Hedberg
**VP:* John Kitchens

D-U-N-S 05-922-2430
LOS ANGELES PHILHARMONIC ASSOCIATION
L A PHILHARMONIC
151 S Grand Ave, Los Angeles, CA 90012-3034
Tel (213) 972-7300 *Founded/Ownrshp* 1934
Sales 145.5MM *EMP* 2,000
Accts Lb Singerlewak Llp Los Angele
SIC 7929 Entertainers & entertainment groups
CEO: Deborah Borda
**Ch:* David C Bohnett
Bd of Dir: Doris Christy
Bd of Dir: Rafael G Mendez
Ofcr: Sheri Broedlow
IT Man: Ronna Compton
Genl Couns: Mona Patel
Snr Mgr: Malorie Barbee
Snr Mgr: Jeff Wallace

D-U-N-S 12-215-0431
LOS ANGELES POLICE RELIEF ASSOCIATION INC
600 N Grand Ave, Los Angeles, CA 90012-2212
Tel (213) 674-3701 *Founded/Ownrshp* 1939

Sales 206.1MM *EMP* 21[E]
Accts Romberger Wilson & Beeson Inc
SIC 8641 Fraternal associations

D-U-N-S 00-838-2400 IMP
■ LOS ANGELES TIMES COMMUNICATIONS LLC
(*Suby of* TRONC INC) ★
202 W 1st St Ste 500, Los Angeles, CA 90012-4401
Tel (213) 237-3700 *Founded/Ownrshp* 2014
Sales 990.9MM[E] *EMP* 4,285[E]
SIC 2711 Newspapers, publishing & printing
CEO: Austin Beutner
Ofcr: Don Reis
Ex VP: Kathy Thomson
VP: Penn Jones
VP: Jack Kemp
VP: Crane Kenney
VP: Johanna Maska
CTO: Scott Sullivan
VP Sls: Ken Depaola

D-U-N-S 07-528-4901 IMP
LOS ANGELES UNIFIED SCHOOL DISTRICT
LAUSD
333 S Beaudry Ave Ste 209, Los Angeles, CA 90017-5141
Tel (213) 241-1000 *Founded/Ownrshp* 1853
Sales 4.4MMM[E] *EMP* 65,231
SIC 8211 Public elementary & secondary schools
Bd of Dir: Marquerite Lamotte
Bd of Dir: Maria Ventura
VP: Flores Aguilar
Comm Dir: Isidro Armenta
Dir Sec: Steven Zipperman
Admn Mgr: Susan Babit
Admn Mgr: Ellen Chambers
Genl Mgr: Sabrina Thomas
Off Admin: Gwen Northern
MIS Dir: Marjorie Josaphat
Dir IT: Paul Ishimaru

D-U-N-S 06-944-8736
LOS FRESNOS CONSOLIDATED INDEPENDENT SCHOOL DISTRICT
600 N Mesquite St, Los Fresnos, TX 78566-3634
Tel (956) 233-4407 *Founded/Ownrshp* 1920
Sales 111.5MM *EMP* 1,600
Accts Pattillo Brown & Hill Llp
SIC 8211 Public elementary & secondary schools
**CFO:* David Young
Bd of Dir: Kristy Atkinson
Bd of Dir: Juan Mendoza
Bd of Dir: Monica Ramos
Bd of Dir: Ruben Trevino
VP: Rey Farias
Exec: Marlen Marquez
Dir Sec: Joe Vasquez
CTO: Carlos Santillana
IT Man: John Danielson
IT Man: Jesse Gonzalez

D-U-N-S 07-155-3739 IMP
LOS RIOS COMMUNITY COLLEGE DISTRICT (CA)
1919 Spanos Ct, Sacramento, CA 95825-3981
Tel (916) 568-3041 *Founded/Ownrshp* 1964
Sales 92.2MM *EMP* 7,000
Accts Gilbert Associates Inc Sacr
SIC 8222 Community college
VP: Sheryl Gessford
Store Mgr: Maria Hyde
IT Man: Kevin Flash
Psych: Leila Stone
Snr Mgr: Cheryl Sears

D-U-N-S 80-621-4680 IMP/EXP
■ LOS ROBLES HOSPITAL & MEDICAL CENTER
COLUMBIA HCA
(*Suby of* HOSPITAL COPORATION OF AMERICA) ★
215 W Janss Rd, Thousand Oaks, CA 91360-1899
Tel (805) 497-2727 *Founded/Ownrshp* 1978
Sales 465.9MM *EMP* 35[E]
SIC 8062 General medical & surgical hospitals
CEO: Greg Angle
Chf Path: Wayne Schultheis
Chf Rad: Barry Klein
Dir Rad: David Clark
Dir Rx: Les Rukasin
Dir Sec: Patrick Smith
MIS Dir: Alex Bryar
Dir IT: Alex Brier
Dir IT: Alex Bryer
Mktg Dir: Kris Carraway
Pathlgst: Robin Rawson

LOSS AND RISK ADVISORS
See BARNEY & BARNEY INC

D-U-N-S 01-171-5836 IMP
LOSURDO FOODS INC
BEL-CAPRI
20 Owens Rd, Hackensack, NJ 07601-3297
Tel (201) 343-6680 *Founded/Ownrshp* 1959
Sales 100.9MM[E] *EMP* 150
SIC 5141 2022 2033 2045 Groceries, general line; Natural cheese; Tomato sauce: packaged in cans, jars, etc.; Pizza doughs, prepared: from purchased flour
Pr: Marc Jx Losurdo
**Pr:* Bjorn Hermann
**Treas:* Maria Losurdo
**Ex VP:* Marc Losurdo

D-U-N-S 15-416-8306
LOTT INDUSTRIES INC
3350 Hill Ave, Toledo, OH 43607-2937
Tel (419) 534-4980 *Founded/Ownrshp* 1955
Sales 9.0MM *EMP* 1,001
SIC 8331 8741 Sheltered workshop; Management services
CEO: Jeff Holland

D-U-N-S 03-435-7772
LOTT OIL CO INC
1855 South Dr, Natchitoches, LA 71457-2658
Tel (318) 356-5858 *Founded/Ownrshp* 1963
Sales 107.2MM[E] *EMP* 194
SIC 5171 Petroleum bulk stations
Pr: Luther W Lott Jr
**Sec:* Daniel J Broderick
**VP:* John W Dewitt
Dir Risk M: Jerry Arnold
Prd Dir: Mark Massia
Sls Mgr: David Dollar

D-U-N-S 10-544-2016
LOTTE HOTEL NEW YORK PALACE LLC
NEW YORK PALACE HOTEL, THE
(*Suby of* HOTEL LOTTE CO., LTD.)
455 Madison Ave, New York, NY 10022-6845
Tel (212) 888-7000 *Founded/Ownrshp* 2015
Sales 64.6MM[E] *EMP* 1,000
SIC 7011 Hotels
CEO: Song Yong-Dok
Dir Sec: Jim Byrne
**Genl Mgr:* Becky Hubbard
Sls Mgr: Elizabeth Malinowski

D-U-N-S 00-477-0459
LOTUS COMMUNICATIONS CORP (CA)
3301 Barham Blvd Ste 200, Los Angeles, CA 90068-1358
Tel (323) 512-2225 *Founded/Ownrshp* 1959
Sales 111.7MM[E] *EMP* 391
SIC 4832 Radio broadcasting stations
Pr: Howard Kalmenson
**Treas:* William H Shriftman
**Sr VP:* Jim Kalmenson
**Sr VP:* Jerry Roy
**VP:* Jasmin Dorismond
Genl Mgr: Kevin O'Rorke

D-U-N-S 92-763-7355
LOTUS INTERNATIONAL CO
6880 Commerce Blvd, Canton, MI 48187-4457
Tel (734) 245-0140 *Founded/Ownrshp* 1995
Sales 281.9MM *EMP* 520
SIC 8711 3651 1221 Consulting engineer; Television receiving sets; Bituminous coal & lignite-surface mining
Pr: Madan M Sharma
**CFO:* Sam Venkat
Sales Exec: Prasad Koppolu

LOU ANA FOODS
See VENTURA FOODS LLC

LOU BACDRODT CHEVY MAZDA
See B C S S LTD

D-U-N-S 62-394-3586
LOU FUSZ AUTOMOTIVE NETWORK INC
925 N Lindbergh Blvd, Saint Louis, MO 63141-5934
Tel (314) 997-3400 *Founded/Ownrshp* 1988
Sales 395.3MM[E] *EMP* 900
SIC 5511 5531 5521 Automobiles, new & used; Automotive parts; Automobiles, used cars only
Pr: Randy Fusz
**Pr:* Louis Fusz Jr
Treas: Martha Fusz
**Sec:* Peter Ramey
Bd of Dir: Pete Fusz
Genl Mgr: Jim Shelton
Telecom Ex: Linda McDonald
IT Man: John Bissell
Mktg Dir: Ted Stranz
Sls Mgr: Tom Capstick
Sls Mgr: Jim Davies

D-U-N-S 03-103-6858
LOU FUSZ MOTOR CO
LOU FUSZ PONTIAC
(*Suby of* LOU FUSZ AUTOMOTIVE NETWORK INC) ★
10329 Old Olive Street Rd, Saint Louis, MO 63141-5921
Tel (314) 994-1500 *Founded/Ownrshp* 1990
Sales 300.0MM *EMP* 400
SIC 5511 7514 Automobiles, new & used; Rent-a-car service
Ch Bd: Louis J Fusz Sr
**Pr:* Louis Fusz Jr
**Treas:* Martha Fusz
Sls Mgr: Ron Franklin Jr

LOU FUSZ PONTIAC
See LOU FUSZ MOTOR CO

D-U-N-S 19-464-0272 IMP/EXP
LOUD TECHNOLOGIES INC
(*Suby of* SUN MACKIE LLC) ★
16220 Wood Red Rd Ne, Woodinville, WA 98072-9061
Tel (425) 892-6500 *Founded/Ownrshp* 1988
Sales 126.2MM[E] *EMP* 533
SIC 3651 Household audio & video equipment; Audio electronic systems; Loudspeakers, electrodynamic or magnetic; Music distribution apparatus
Pr: Rodney E Olson
**Pr:* Mark Graham
**COO:* James Stewart
COO: Jim Stewart
**CFO:* Case Kuehn
Treas: William A Garrard
Ex VP: Kenton Forsythe
Ex VP: Robert A McDonald
Ex VP: Paul Rice
Sr VP: Ken Berger
Sr VP: Kenneth P Berger
Sr VP: Shawn C Powers
VP: John Boudreau
VP: Scott T King
**VP:* Mark E Kuchenrither
**VP:* Jason H Neimark
VP: Larry Pendergrass
**VP:* Clarence E Terry
Dir Rx: Christopher Mael
Board of Directors: Kevin J Calhoun, Jon W Gacek, C Daryl Hollis, George R Rea, R Lynn Skillen, Thomas V Taylor

D-U-N-S 03-032-0832
LOUDOUN COUNTY
1 Harrison St Se Fl 1, Leesburg, VA 20175-3102
Tel (703) 777-0100 *Founded/Ownrshp* 1757
Sales NA *EMP* 6,999
Accts Cherry Bekaert Llp Tysons Cor
SIC 9199 ; General government administration
**Treas:* H Roger Zurn Jr
Ofcr: Matthew Bisgaier
Ofcr: Caitlyn Dinger
Ofcr: Lance Kelley
Ofcr: Heather Rosenberg
Ofcr: Steven Schochet
Prgrm Mgr: Van Armstrong
Admn Mgr: Laura Dove
Admn Mgr: Becky Edmondson
Div Mgr: Michael Burke
Genl Mgr: Janet Romanchyk

D-U-N-S 18-872-7911
LOUDOUN COUNTY PUBLIC SCHOOL DISTRICT
LCPS
21000 Education Ct, Broadlands, VA 20148-5526
Tel (571) 252-1000 *Founded/Ownrshp* 1757
Sales 1.0MMM *EMP* 9,822
SIC 8211 Public elementary & secondary schools
Adm Dir: Michael J Lunsford
Dir Sec: Suzanne G Devlin
IT Man: Andrew Leith
Pr Dir: Wayde B Byard

D-U-N-S 18-051-0281
LOUDOUN HEALTHCARE INC
INOVA LOUDOUN HOSPITAL
(*Suby of* INOVA HEALTH SYSTEM) ★
44045 Riverside Pkwy, Leesburg, VA 20176-5101
Tel (703) 777-3300 *Founded/Ownrshp* 2005
Sales 32.7MM[E] *EMP* 1,300
SIC 8062 8059 General medical & surgical hospitals; Nursing home, except skilled & intermediate care facility
Pr: J Knox Singleton
**CEO:* Rodney Huebbers
**CFO:* Glenn Zirbfer
Off Mgr: Karen Evans

D-U-N-S 06-936-5807
LOUDOUN HOSPITAL CENTER (VA)
INOVA FAIRFAX HOSPITAL
(*Suby of* INOVA FAIRFAX HOSPITAL) ★
44045 Riverside Pkwy, Leesburg, VA 20176-5101
Tel (703) 858-6000 *Founded/Ownrshp* 1912, 1930
Sales 302.5MM *EMP* 1,000[E]
SIC 8062 General medical & surgical hospitals
Pr: Randall Kelley
Chf Rad: Allen Joseph
**Pr:* J Knox Singleton
COO: Susan Carroll
**CFO:* Glenn Zirbser
Dir Rad: Deborah N Blair
**Prin:* Rhonda Kohnen
Nurse Mgr: Cindy Andrejasich
Mtls Mgr: Lance Greene
Pathlgst: Nahla Acoury
Occ Thrpy: Cathy Christopher

D-U-N-S 80-445-7039
LOUDOUN MEDICAL GROUP PC
224d Cornwall St Nw, Leesburg, VA 20176-2700
Tel (703) 737-6010 *Founded/Ownrshp* 2000
Sales 83.9MM[E] *EMP* 1,000
SIC 8011 Medical centers
Ch Bd: Kevin P O Connor MD
**CEO:* Marybeth Tamasy
**Treas:* John Andrew
Exec: Karen Feely
Exec: Marybeth Tamsay
**Prin:* Michael Kavanagh MD
Doctor: John Cook

LOUIS A WEISS MEMORIAL HOSPITAL
See VHS ACQUISITION SUBSIDIARY NUMBER 3 INC

D-U-N-S 14-332-3439
LOUIS BERGER AND ASSOCIATES INC
412 Mount Kemble Ave, Morristown, NJ 07960-6666
Tel (973) 407-1000 *Founded/Ownrshp* 2005
Sales 58.8MM[E] *EMP* 3,000
SIC 8711 Consulting engineer
Pr: Nicolas Masucci
**VP:* Gul Khan

D-U-N-S 04-388-1093
LOUIS BERGER GROUP INC
(*Suby of* BERGER GROUP HOLDINGS INC) ★
412 Mount Kemble Ave, Morristown, NJ 07960-6666
Tel (973) 407-1000 *Founded/Ownrshp* 1963
Sales 224.6MM[E] *EMP* 534
SIC 8748 8712 8711 Economic consultant; Architectural services; Consulting engineer
Pr: Thomas Lewis
**Ch Bd:* Fredric S Berger
Pr: Anatoly Hochstein
**Pr:* Meg Lassarat
**COO:* James G Bach
**CFO:* Simon Hemming
**CFO:* Luke McKinnon
Treas: Horacio Alvarez
Ex VP: Rick Falconio
**Ex VP:* Larry D Walker
Sr VP: Bob Schmidt
VP: Jack Gundrum
VP: Aida Jimenez
VP: Gregory Matthews
**VP:* Thomas Nicastro
VP: Jeffrey Willis

D-U-N-S 96-209-9425
LOUIS BERGER SERVICES INC
(*Suby of* BERGER GROUP HOLDINGS INC) ★
80 International Dr # 130, Greenville, SC 29615-6953
Tel (864) 385-7500 *Founded/Ownrshp* 2012
Sales 95.5MM[E] *EMP* 1,000[E]
SIC 6719 Investment holding companies, except banks
CEO: Steve Townes
Pr: Andrew V Bailey II
CFO: Jeffrey Hartman
VP: Paul Chamberlain
VP: Nancy Grigsby
DP Exec: Klaffky Richard
VP Opers: Keith Moncrief
VP Opers: Suzanne Mueller

D-U-N-S 96-511-0190 IMP/EXP
LOUIS DREYFUS CITRUS INC
(*Suby of* LD COMMODITIES CITRUS HOLDINGS LLC) ★
355 9th St, Winter Garden, FL 34787-3651
Tel (407) 656-1000 *Founded/Ownrshp* 1996
Sales 85.6MM[E] *EMP* 425
SIC 2037 2033 Fruit juice concentrates, frozen; Canned fruits & specialties
Pr: Perry Aulie
COO: Ciro Echesortu
VP: Bill Ballenden
**VP:* Robert Eckert
VP: Gabriela S Ldcommodities
Mng Dir: Miguel Catella
Sls Dir: Jeff Graham

D-U-N-S 80-040-0983 EXP
LOUIS DREYFUS CO COTTON LLC
ALLENBERG COTTON CO.
(*Suby of* LOUIS DREYFUS CO NORFOLK) ★
7255 Goodlett Farms Pkwy, Cordova, TN 38016-4909
Tel (901) 383-5000 *Founded/Ownrshp* 2016
Sales 107.3MM[E] *EMP* 100[E]
SIC 5159 5131 Cotton merchants & products; Textiles, woven
CEO: Joe Nicosia
COO: Thomas F Malone Jr
Ch: Jerry D Harris
Ofcr: Luciano Cocito
Ex VP: Frank M Weathersby

D-U-N-S 80-009-2590
LOUIS DREYFUS CO HOLDING INC
LDC HOLDING INC.
(*Suby of* LOUIS DRYFUS CMMODITIES NA LLC) ★
40 Danbury Rd Ste 3, Wilton, CT 06897-4441
Tel (203) 761-2000 *Founded/Ownrshp* 2006
Sales 306.6MM[E] *EMP* 2,000
SIC 6719 Investment holding companies, except banks
CEO: Thomas Malone
**CFO:* Robert Eckert

D-U-N-S 96-543-4793
LOUIS DREYFUS CO LLC
LOUIS DREYFUS COMPANY NORFOLK
(*Suby of* LDC HOLDING INC) ★
40 Danbury Rd, Wilton, CT 06897-4441
Tel (402) 844-2680 *Founded/Ownrshp* 2010
Sales 830.1MM[E] *EMP* 1,300
Accts Ernst & Young Llp Stamford C
SIC 6221 Commodity contracts brokers, dealers
CEO: Thomas Malone
**CFO:* Robert Eckert

D-U-N-S 07-959-4501
LOUIS DREYFUS CO NA LLC
LOUIS DRYFUS CMMODITIES NA LLC
(*Suby of* LOUIS DREYFUS HOLDING B.V.)
40 Danbury Rd, Wilton, CT 06897-4441
Tel (203) 761-2000 *Founded/Ownrshp* 2014
Sales 310.0MM[E] *EMP* 3,331[E]
SIC 5153 Grain & field beans
CEO: Thomas Malone
**CFO:* Robert Eckert

LOUIS DREYFUS COMPANY NORFOLK
See LOUIS DREYFUS CO LLC

D-U-N-S 60-899-0552
LOUIS DREYFUS HOLDING CO INC
(*Suby of* IMPALA SAS)
10 Westport Rd Ste 200, Wilton, CT 06897-4548
Tel (203) 761-2000 *Founded/Ownrshp* 1976
Sales 140.7MM[E] *EMP* 1,749
SIC 6221 5153 6512 6531 1311 Commodity traders, contracts; Grains; Commercial & industrial building operation; Real estate managers; Natural gas production
Pr: Hal Wolkin
Treas: Richard D Gray

D-U-N-S 01-015-5372
LOUIS DREYFUS US LLC
SANGAMON TRANSPORTATION
(*Suby of* LDC HOLDING INC) ★
40 Danbury Rd, Wilton, CT 06897-4441
Tel (203) 761-2000 *Founded/Ownrshp* 1940, 2006
Sales 11.7MMM[E] *EMP* 2,000
SIC 6221 Commodity contracts brokers, dealers
Ch: Serge Schoen
**CFO:* Robert G Eckert
**CFO:* Claude Ehlinger
**Treas:* Sean Colvin
**Treas:* Serge A Stepanov
Ofcr: Reina Barcan
**Sr VP:* Hal Wolkin
**VP:* Mr Don Carlson
**VP:* Mark Gerardi
VP: Sean Martin
Brnch Mgr: Steven Ederle

LOUIS DRYFUS CMMODITIES NA LLC
See LOUIS DREYFUS CO NA LLC

LOUIS GLICK AND COMPANY
See LOUIS GLICK DIAMOND CORP

D-U-N-S 04-157-5283
LOUIS GLICK DIAMOND CORP
LOUIS GLICK AND COMPANY
810 7th Ave Fl 28, New York, NY 10019-9000
Tel (212) 259-0300 *Founded/Ownrshp* 1945
Sales 90.6MM[E] *EMP* 55
SIC 5094 3911 Diamonds (gems); Precious stones & metals; Jewelry, precious metal
Pr: Louis Glick
CFO: Aaron Cohen
Mng Dir: Pinchus Menche

D-U-N-S 00-890-1928 EXP
LOUIS PADNOS IRON AND METAL CO (MI)
185 W 8th St, Holland, MI 49423-3107
Tel (616) 396-6521 *Founded/Ownrshp* 1905
Sales 362.9MM *EMP* 450
SIC 5093 4491 3599

D-U-N-S 01-702-8713
LOUIS T OLLESHEIMER & SON INC
605 E 12 Mile Rd, Madison Heights, MI 48071-2568
Tel (248) 544-3900 Founded/Ownrshp 1999
Sales 174.6MM^E EMP 74
SIC 5033 5082 Roofing & siding materials; Construction & mining machinery
Treas: Barbara Ollesheimer
*Pr: James R Ollesheimer

D-U-N-S 07-813-4616 IMP/EXP
LOUIS WURTH AND CO
(Suby of WURTH GROUP OF NORTH AMERICA INC) ★
895 Columbia St, Brea, CA 92821-2917
Tel (714) 529-1771 Founded/Ownrshp 1975
Sales 111.7MM^E EMP 305
SIC 5072 5198 Furniture hardware; Stain
Pr: Vito Mancini
*Pr: Tom Mauss
*CFO: Ed McGraw
VP: Bob Shine
Opers Mgr: Andy Gette
Opers Mgr: Paul Wilson
VP Sls: Don Scardami
Sls Mgr: Bill Donnelly
Sales Asso: Greg Walker

D-U-N-S 07-793-4461
LOUISE OBICI MEMORIAL HOSPITAL INC
OBICI HEALTH SYSTEMS
2800 Godwin Blvd, Suffolk, VA 23434-8038
Tel (757) 934-4000 Founded/Ownrshp 1950
Sales 182.9MM EMP 1,272
Accts Boyce Spady & Moore Plc Suffo
SIC 8062 General medical & surgical hospitals
Pr: William C Giermak
Pr: David Bernd
CFO: William A Carpenter
Off Mgr: Terry Christovich

D-U-N-S 05-324-2009 IMP
LOUISE PARIS LTD (NY)
HIGHWAY
1407 Broadway Rm 1405, New York, NY 10018-2843
Tel (212) 354-5411 Founded/Ownrshp 1977
Sales 157.5MM EMP 63
SIC 5137 Women's & children's clothing
Ch Bd: Salomon Barnathan
*VP: Albert Barnathan

LOUISEVILLE
See LOUISVILLE LADDER INC

D-U-N-S 78-704-7901
LOUISIANA BOARD OF REGENTS
1201 N 3rd St Ste 6-200, Baton Rouge, LA 70802-5243
Tel (225) 342-4253 Founded/Ownrshp 1974
Sales NA EMP 6,983
SIC 9411 Administration of educational programs;
Ofcr: Kimberly Small

D-U-N-S 96-576-7838
LOUISIANA CHILDRENS MEDICAL CENTER INC
CHILDREN'S HOSPITAL
200 Henry Clay Ave, New Orleans, LA 70118-5720
Tel (504) 896-9581 Founded/Ownrshp 1997
Sales 21.3MM EMP 6,100^E
Accts Laporte Apac Metairie La
SIC 8069 Children's hospital
Pr: Mary Perrin
Mktg Dir: Nicole Marinello
Mngd Care: Cindy Nuesslein

D-U-N-S 00-818-7494
■ **LOUISIANA COCA-COLA BOTTLING CO LIMITED**
(Suby of COCA-COLA REFRESHMENTS USA INC) ★
5601 Citrus Blvd, New Orleans, LA 70123-5508
Tel (504) 818-7000 Founded/Ownrshp 1986
Sales 108.6MM^E EMP 1,700
SIC 2086 5962 Soft drinks: packaged in cans, bottles, etc.; Merchandising machine operators
VP: Lowry Kline
Treas: Joyce Lavinder
VP: Bernard Bommier
VP: Paul Gordon
VP: Pamela Kimmet
Genl Mgr: Rick Kehr

D-U-N-S 13-177-8354
LOUISIANA CRANE & CONSTRUCTION LLC
1045 Highway 190, Eunice, LA 70535-2947
Tel (337) 550-6217 Founded/Ownrshp 2001
Sales 243.0MM EMP 130
SIC 7389 7353 1623 Crane & aerial lift service; Cranes & aerial lift equipment, rental or leasing; Oil & gas line & compressor station construction
CEO: Logan Fournerat
*CFO: Douglas Marbantel
Sales Asso: Robert Deshotel

D-U-N-S 80-992-7429
LOUISIANA DEPARTMENT OF CHILDREN AND FAMILY SERVICES
(Suby of EXECUTIVE OFFICE OF STATE OF LOUISIANA) ★
627 N 4th St, Baton Rouge, LA 70802-5343
Tel (225) 342-4220 Founded/Ownrshp 1989
Sales NA EMP 4,700
SIC 9441 Administration of social & manpower programs;
Genl Couns: Steve Mayer

D-U-N-S 80-992-7056
LOUISIANA DEPARTMENT OF ENVIRONMENTAL QUALITY
OFFICE OF THE SECRETARY
(Suby of EXECUTIVE OFFICE OF STATE OF LOUISIANA) ★
602 N 5th St, Baton Rouge, LA 70802-5312
Tel (225) 219-3953 Founded/Ownrshp 1984
Sales NA EMP 1,000
SIC 9511 Air, water & solid waste management;
Pr: Peggy Hatch

D-U-N-S 80-992-7064
LOUISIANA DEPARTMENT OF HEALTH AND HOSPITALS
(Suby of EXECUTIVE OFFICE OF STATE OF LOUISIANA) ★
628 N 4th St, Baton Rouge, LA 70802-5342
Tel (225) 342-9500 Founded/Ownrshp 1975
Sales NA EMP 4,000
SIC 9431 Administration of public health programs;
*CFO: Pam Diaz
Chf Nrs Of: Mary Fontenelle
*Prin: Courtney N Phillips
*Prin: Jerry Phillips
Off Admin: Tammy Brumfield
Telecom Mg: Chris Parish
IT Man: Anita Milling

D-U-N-S 94-199-3305
LOUISIANA DEPARTMENT OF MILITARY AFFAIRS
(Suby of EXECUTIVE OFFICE OF STATE OF LOUISIANA) ★
6400 Saint Claude Ave, New Orleans, LA 70117-1456
Tel (504) 278-8071 Founded/Ownrshp 1812
Sales NA EMP 2,600
SIC 9711 9451 National Guard; ; Administration of veterans' affairs;
*Pr: Bennett C Landreneau

D-U-N-S 93-892-0949
LOUISIANA DEPARTMENT OF PUBLIC EDUCATION
(Suby of EXECUTIVE OFFICE OF STATE OF LOUISIANA) ★
1201 N 3rd St, Baton Rouge, LA 70802-5243
Tel (225) 342-3836 Founded/Ownrshp 1974
Sales NA EMP 1,000
SIC 9411 Administration of educational programs;
Exec: Gwendolyn Scott
DP Exec: Rizwan Ahmed
IT Man: Janet Broussard

D-U-N-S 09-366-9286
LOUISIANA DEPARTMENT OF PUBLIC SAFETY & CORRECTIONS
(Suby of EXECUTIVE OFFICE OF STATE OF LOUISIANA) ★
7919 Independence Blvd, Baton Rouge, LA 70806-6409
Tel (225) 925-6006 Founded/Ownrshp 2000
Sales NA EMP 3,000
SIC 9221 State police;
IT Man: Rexford McDonald

D-U-N-S 80-992-7403
LOUISIANA DEPARTMENT OF PUBLIC SAFETY AND CORRECTIONS
(Suby of EXECUTIVE OFFICE OF STATE OF LOUISIANA) ★
504 Mayflower St, Baton Rouge, LA 70802-6419
Tel (225) 342-6740 Founded/Ownrshp 1983
Sales NA EMP 8,123^E
SIC 9229 9223 Public order & safety statistics centers; ; Correctional institutions;
Genl Mgr: Kim Eiland
Dir IT: Terence Clair

D-U-N-S 80-992-7759
LOUISIANA DEPARTMENT OF TRANSPORTATION AND DEVELOPMENT
(Suby of EXECUTIVE OFFICE OF STATE OF LOUISIANA) ★
1201 Capitol Access Rd, Baton Rouge, LA 70802-4438
Tel (225) 379-1232 Founded/Ownrshp 1977
Sales NA EMP 5,500
SIC 9111 Executive offices

D-U-N-S 09-365-6432
LOUISIANA DIVISION OF ADMINISTRATION
(Suby of EXECUTIVE OFFICE OF STATE OF LOUISIANA) ★
1201 N 3rd St Ste 7-20, Baton Rouge, LA 70802-5243
Tel (225) 342-7000 Founded/Ownrshp 1960
Sales NA EMP 1,500
SIC 9199
CEO: Mark Drennon

D-U-N-S 12-732-6911
LOUISIANA DOCK CO LLC
(Suby of ACL TRANSPORTATION SERVICES LLC) ★
1701 Utica Pike, Jeffersonville, IN 47130-4747
Tel (812) 288-0100 Founded/Ownrshp 2007
Sales 741.0MM EMP 18^E
SIC 7389 Personal service agents, brokers & bureaus
Off Mgr: Kristin Rubino

D-U-N-S 13-663-1004 IMP/EXP
LOUISIANA ENERGY SERVICES LLC
L E S
(Suby of URENCO LIMITED)
275 Andrews Hwy, Eunice, NM 88231
Tel (575) 394-4646 Founded/Ownrshp 2004
Sales 277.9MM^E EMP 301^E
SIC 1094 Uranium-radium-vanadium ores
CEO: Gregory O D Smith
*CFO: Paul Mason
*Sec: Perry Robinson

D-U-N-S 15-075-9678
LOUISIANA EXTENDED CARE CENTERS INC
SENIOR VILLAGE NURSING HOME
763 Avery Blvd N, Ridgeland, MS 39157-5218
Tel (601) 956-8884 Founded/Ownrshp 1983
Sales 520.0MM EMP 487
SIC 8051 8052 Skilled nursing care facilities; Intermediate care facilities
Pr: Glynn Beebe
*CEO: David Stallard
*VP: Lansing Kolb
*VP: Joe Sadler

D-U-N-S 06-021-2974
LOUISIANA FARM BUREAU CASUALTY INSURANCE CO (LA)
FARM BUREAU INSURANCE
(Suby of FARM BUREAU INSURANCE) ★
9516 Airline Hwy, Baton Rouge, LA 70815-5501
Tel (225) 922-6200 Founded/Ownrshp 1981
Sales NA EMP 240
SIC 6411 Insurance agents, brokers & service
CEO: Gerald Garnett
*Pr: Ronald Roy Anderson
*Treas: Dennis Griffin
*VP: Jack Anderson
VP: Gail Chisum
*VP: Steven Walter Ingram
*VP: H Wynne Jacobs
*VP: Mickey Nugent
*VP: John Stenmark
*VP: Thomas Young
*VP: Linda Zaunbrecher
Board of Directors: David Hillman, Carl Loop Jr, Donald Patman, David Waide, David Winkles Jr

D-U-N-S 06-263-1809 IMP
■ **LOUISIANA GENERATING LLC**
(Suby of NRG ENERGY INC) ★
211 Carnegie Ctr, Princeton, NJ 08540-6299
Tel (609) 524-4500 Founded/Ownrshp 2000
Sales 286.4MM^E EMP 463
SIC 4911 Generation, electric power; Transmission, electric power
Pr: Jeff Baudier

D-U-N-S 06-951-7761
LOUISIANA HEALTH SERVICE AND INDEMNITY CO
BLUE CROSS
5525 Reitz Ave, Baton Rouge, LA 70809-3802
Tel (225) 295-3307 Founded/Ownrshp 1934
Sales NA EMP 1,500
Accts Neal D King Cpa-King Lejeune
SIC 6321 6324 6411 Health insurance carriers; Group hospitalization plans; Insurance agents, brokers & service
Pr: Mike Reitz
*CFO: Adam Short
Sr VP: Tej Shah
VP: Jacqueline Addison
VP: Robert Drelick
VP: Milam Ford
VP: Charles Landreneau
VP: Rodney Rone
VP: Mary Saporito
VP: Dean Simon
VP: Tony Wittman

D-U-N-S 87-801-5858
LOUISIANA I GAMING LP
BOOMTOWN BELLE CASINO
4132 Peters Rd, Harvey, LA 70058-1805
Tel (504) 366-7711 Founded/Ownrshp 1994
Sales 21.7MM^E EMP 1,200
SIC 7999 Gambling establishment
Prin: Michael Kosnett
Advt Dir: Erica Blanchard
Mktg Mgr: Phyllis Wiseman

D-U-N-S 00-694-7204 IMP/EXP
LOUISIANA MACHINERY CO LLC
CATERPILLAR
3799 W Airline Hwy, Reserve, LA 70084-5717
Tel (985) 536-1121 Founded/Ownrshp 1960
Sales 259.7MM^E EMP 400
SIC 5082 7699 7353

LOUISIANA OFFSHORE OIL PORT
See LOOP LLC

D-U-N-S 80-915-4958 IMP
LOUISIANA PIGMENT CO LP
3300 Bayou Dinde Rd, Westlake, LA 70669-8102
Tel (337) 882-7000 Founded/Ownrshp 1993
Sales 220.8MM^E EMP 500
SIC 2816 Titanium dioxide, anatase or rutile (pigments)
Pt: Greg Godfrey
CFO: Cisneros Richard
Dir Lab: Dwayne Courville
Genl Mgr: Doug Weaver
CTO: John Hammond
Sfty Dirs: John Dubose
Plnt Mgr: Tim J Hall

D-U-N-S 07-320-0334 EXP
LOUISIANA RICE MILL LLC
4 S Avenue D, Crowley, LA 70526-5657
Tel (337) 783-9777 Founded/Ownrshp 2003
Sales 252.5MM^E EMP 100
SIC 2044 Rice milling
Sfty Mgr: Janice Cart

D-U-N-S 80-855-8662
LOUISIANA RIVERBOAT GAMING PARTNERSHIP
DIAMOND JACKS CASINO & RESORT
711 Diamondjacks Blvd, Bossier City, LA 71111-5046
Tel (318) 678-7633 Founded/Ownrshp 1993
Sales 37.3MM^E EMP 1,200
SIC 7999 Gambling establishment
Pt: G Dan Marshall
Pt: Joe Collings
Pr: Raymond Cook
Secur Mgr: Greg Jackson
Secur Mgr: Sean McCloud

D-U-N-S 07-505-0765 IMP/EXP
LOUISIANA STATE UNIVERSITY
LOUISIANA STATE UNIVERSITY A&M
(Suby of LOUISIANA STATE UNIVERSITY) ★
202 Himes Hall, Baton Rouge, LA 70803-0001
Tel (225) 578-2760 Founded/Ownrshp 1860
Sales 1.3MMM^E EMP 26,000
SIC 8221

D-U-N-S 94-005-0792
LOUISIANA STATE UNIVERSITY
3810 W Lkshore Dr Ste 111, Baton Rouge, LA 70808
Tel (225) 578-2760 Founded/Ownrshp 1970
Sales 1.7MMM EMP 26,000
SIC 8221

LOUISIANA STATE UNIVERSITY A&M
See LOUISIANA STATE UNIVERSITY

D-U-N-S 06-974-6725
LOUISIANA TECH UNIVERSITY
1100 Hull Ave, Ruston, LA 71270-5551
Tel (318) 257-3267 Founded/Ownrshp 1894
Sales 130.8MM^E EMP 1,230
SIC 8221 University
Pr: Daniel D Reneau
*VP: Dr Kenneth W REA
*VP: Joseph R Thomas Jr

D-U-N-S 09-859-6901
LOUISIANA WHOLESALE DRUG CO INC
GOOD NEIGHBOR PHARMACY
2085 I 49 S Service Rd, Sunset, LA 70584
Tel (337) 662-1040 Founded/Ownrshp 1979
Sales 350.0MM EMP 75
Accts John S Dowling & Company Ope
SIC 5122 5912 Drugs & drug proprietaries; Druggists' sundries; Drug stores
*Pr: Gayle R White
CFO: Ricky Ducote
*VP: Carl Savoie

D-U-N-S 78-995-0326
LOUISIANA WORKERS COMPENSATION CORP
LWCC
2237 S Acadian Thruway, Baton Rouge, LA 70808-2371
Tel (225) 924-7788 Founded/Ownrshp 1991
Sales NA EMP 250^E
SIC 6331 Workers' compensation insurance
CEO: Kristin W Wall
Pr: Jill Breard
Pr: Patricia Canning
*Pr: Stephen W Cavanaugh
*Pr: Christian Wall
*Ch: Donald T Boysie Bollinger
Bd of Dir: Hampton Johnson
Assoc VP: Sandra Mayfield
Sr VP: William B Bangs
*Sr VP: Paul Buffone
*Sr VP: Mike De Laat
*Sr VP: John Hawie
*Sr VP: Jeffrey H Skagg
*Sr VP: Michael Stiltner
VP: Mike Delaat
VP: Jeffrey Skaggs
*VP: Michel J Stiltner

D-U-N-S 06-150-0534 IMP/EXP
▲ **LOUISIANA-PACIFIC CORP**
414 Union St Ste 2000, Nashville, TN 37219-1711
Tel (615) 986-5600 Founded/Ownrshp 1972
Sales 1.8MMM EMP 4,800
Tkr Sym LPX Exch NYS
SIC 2493 2436 2435 2421 2431 Strandboard, oriented; Particleboard products; Fiberboard, other vegetable pulp; Hardboard, tempered; Panels, softwood plywood; Panels, hardwood plywood; Veneer stock, hardwood; Lumber: rough, sawed or planed; Moldings & baseboards, ornamental & trim
CEO: Curtis M Stevens
*Ch Bd: E Gary Cook
COO: Brad Southern
CFO: Sallie B Bailey
Ex VP: Brian E Luoma
Ex VP: W Bradley Southern
Sr VP: Neil Sherman
Sr VP: Michael Sims
Exec: Jennifer Thomas
Tech Mgr: Robert Miller
Opers Mgr: Traci Hale
Board of Directors: Tracy A Embree, Daniel K Frierson, Kurt M Landgraf, Colin D Watson, John W Weaver

D-U-N-S 09-538-1984 IMP
LOUISVILLE & JEFFERSON COUNTY METROPOLITAN SEWER DISTRICT
700 W Liberty St, Louisville, KY 40203-1911
Tel (502) 540-6000 Founded/Ownrshp 1946
Sales 450.1MM^E EMP 600
Accts Crowe Horwath Llp Louisville
SIC 4952 Sewerage systems
Ex Dir: James Parrott
CFO: Chad Collier

D-U-N-S 00-637-1926 IMP/EXP
LOUISVILLE BEDDING CO INC
10400 Bunsen Way, Louisville, KY 40299-2500
Tel (502) 491-3370 Founded/Ownrshp 1889
Sales 184.7MM^E EMP 750
SIC 2392 3949 Mattress pads; Sporting & athletic goods
Pr: Stephen Elias
Ch Bd: Steve Elias
COO: Mary Jo Kissel
Genl Mgr: Kevin O'Connell
VP Mktg: Kim Robertson
VP Sls: Denise Matlack
Board of Directors: Prentice E Brown, Thomas Buetow, Robert Hill, John Minihan, Michael Seago, Gary Sterling, Alice Walter

D-U-N-S 00-694-5505 IMP
■ **LOUISVILLE GAS AND ELECTRIC CO** (KY)
(Suby of LG&E AND KU ENERGY LLC) ★
220 W Main St Ste 1400, Louisville, KY 40202-5301
Tel (502) 627-2000 Founded/Ownrshp 1913, 2010
Sales 1.4MMM EMP 1,029^E
SIC 4931 4911 4924 Electric & other services combined; Generation, electric power; Transmission, electric power; Distribution, electric power; Natural gas distribution
Ch Bd: Victor A Staffieri
*COO: Paul W Thompson
CFO: Kent W Blake
VP: Douglas Laura
Prgrm Mgr: Bill Cooper
CIO: Eric Slavinsky
QA Dir: Abby Hedges

IT Man: Eric Peek
Web Dev: Barry Rowe
Netwrk Eng: Jason Hamm
Sfty Mgr: Robert Mercke
Board of Directors: S Bradford Rives, Vincent Sorgi, William H Spence

D-U-N-S 12-099-0457
LOUISVILLE HOSPITAL
JOSEPH GILENE, PRESIDENT
217 E Chestnut St, Louisville, KY 40202-1821
Tel (502) 587-1100 *Founded/Ownrshp* 2002
Sales 856.0M^E *EMP* 3,500
SIC 8062 General medical & surgical hospitals
Pr: Joseph Gilene

D-U-N-S 03-761-8217 IMP/EXP
LOUISVILLE LADDER INC
LOUISEVILLE
7765 National Tpke # 190, Louisville, KY 40214-4803
Tel (502) 636-2811 *Founded/Ownrshp* 2005
Sales 182.0MM^E *EMP* 850
SIC 2499 Ladders, wood
Pr: Ricardo Clausse
**VP:* Florinda E Altamirano
IT Man: Stephen Dean
Sls Dir: Robert Zimmerman
Manager: Tim Veasman
Sls Mgr: Luis Pastrana

LOUISVILLE METRO
See LOUISVILLE-JEFFERSON COUNTY METRO GOVERNMENT

D-U-N-S 02-407-1110 IMP
LOUISVILLE TILE DISTRIBUTORS INC (KY)
CAMEO MARBLE
4520 Bishop Ln, Louisville, KY 40218-4508
Tel (502) 452-2037 *Founded/Ownrshp* 1955
Sales 161.1MM^E *EMP* 280
SIC 5032 5211 1743 Marble building stone; Ceramic wall & floor tile; Tile, ceramic; Terrazzo, tile, marble, mosaic work
Ch Bd: Aubrey J Wilcox
**Pr:* Robert Deangelis
**Pr:* Jerry G Short
CFO: Howard Passamanack
**Ex VP:* Carolyn Wilcox
**VP:* Robert Knabel
Opers Mgr: Tony Visco
Sls Mgr: Marty Vaughn
Sls Mgr: Al Williams

D-U-N-S 04-117-2545
LOUISVILLE WATER CO
550 S 3rd St, Louisville, KY 40202-1839
Tel (502) 569-3600 *Founded/Ownrshp* 1854
Sales 363.2MM^E *EMP* 447
Accts Crowe Howart Llp Louisville
SIC 4941 Water supply
Pr: James H Brammell
Pr: Dawn Czajka
Pr: David Vogel
COO: Helena Dahman
CFO: Robert Miller
Treas: Amber Halloran
Chf Mktg O: Barbara Crow
VP: Barbara Dickens
VP: Karla Teasley
Exec: Jim Smith
IT Man: John Baum

D-U-N-S 07-313-5584
LOUISVILLE-JEFFERSON COUNTY METRO GOVERNMENT
LOUISVILLE METRO
527 W Jefferson St, Louisville, KY 40202-2814
Tel (502) 574-2003 *Founded/Ownrshp* 1779
Sales NA *EMP* 6,500
Accts Crowe Horwath Llp Louisville
SIC 9111 Executive offices;
CFO: Jane Driskell
**CFO:* Daniel Frockt
Brnch Mgr: Dolores Delahanty
Brnch Mgr: Ted Pullen
Plnt Mgr: Jerry Abramson

LOUP CITY HEALTH
See ROSE LANE HOME

LOUP POWER DISTRICT
See LOUP RIVER PUBLIC POWER DISTRICT

D-U-N-S 06-863-9764
LOUP RIVER PUBLIC POWER DISTRICT
LOUP POWER DISTRICT
2404 15th St, Columbus, NE 68601-5021
Tel (402) 564-3171 *Founded/Ownrshp* 1933
Sales 96.8MM^E *EMP* 132
Accts Dana F Cole & Company Llp G
SIC 4911 ; Generation, electric power; Distribution, electric power; Transmission, electric power
Pr: Neal Suess
V Ch: Jim Donoghue
V Ch: Donald Pearson
**CFO:* Kim Grubaugh
Bd of Dir: Larry Zach
**VP:* David Bell
**VP:* Kendall Christensen
**VP:* Ron Ziola
IT Man: Les Hardesty
Sfty Mgr: Rick Prater

LOURDES HEALTH NETWORK
See OUR LADY OF LOURDES HOSPITAL AT PASCO

LOURDES HEALTH SYSTEM
See LOURDES MEDICAL CENTER OF BURLINGTON COUNTY

LOURDES HOSPITAL
See OUR LADY OF LOURDES MEMORIAL HOSPITAL INC

LOURDES HOSPITAL
See MERCY HEALTH PARTNERS - LOURDES INC

D-U-N-S 87-766-8814
LOURDES HOSPITAL
169 Riverside Dr, Binghamton, NY 13905-4198
Tel (607) 798-5111 *Founded/Ownrshp* 1987
Sales 14.6MM^E *EMP* 1,800
SIC 8062 General medical & surgical hospitals
Pr: John Oneil
**CFO:* Brian Regan
**VP:* Kathlyn Appler

D-U-N-S 79-987-9569 EXP
LOURDES MEDICAL CENTER OF BURLINGTON COUNTY
LOURDES HEALTH SYSTEM
(*Suby of* NEW JERSEY HEART INSTITUTE) ★
218 Sunset Rd, Willingboro, NJ 08046-1110
Tel (609) 835-2900 *Founded/Ownrshp* 1998
Sales 122.9MM *EMP* 528^E
SIC 8062 General medical & surgical hospitals
CEO: Alexander Hatala
Exec: John Scullan
Nurse Mgr: Doreen McCay

D-U-N-S 79-649-0857
LOURDES MEDICAL CENTER OF BURLINGTON COUNTY A NEW JERSEY NONPROFIT CORP
(*Suby of* CATHOLIC HEALTH EAST) ★
218 Sunset Rd, Willingboro, NJ 08046-1110
Tel (609) 835-2900 *Founded/Ownrshp* 2007
Sales 59.4MM *EMP* 3,495^E
Accts Deloitte Tax Llp Philadelphia
SIC 8062 General medical & surgical hospitals
Prin: Randall Maguire

LOVE BOX COMPANY, LLC
See PRATT (LOVE BOX) LLC

D-U-N-S 79-196-8378 IMP
LOVE CULTURE INC
2423 E 23rd St, Los Angeles, CA 90058-1201
Tel (614) 625-4781 *Founded/Ownrshp* 2007
Sales 150.2MM^E *EMP* 1,000^E
SIC 5621

D-U-N-S 06-195-2268
LOVED ONES IN HOME CARE LLC
144 7th Ave, South Charleston, WV 25303-1452
Tel (304) 744-4081 *Founded/Ownrshp* 1999
Sales 15.0MM *EMP* 1,200
SIC 8082 Visiting nurse service
CEO: Donna Skeen
**COO:* Jenna Skeen
Genl Mgr: Ronald Locke

D-U-N-S 04-591-1138
LOVELACE BIOMEDICAL & ENVIRONMENTAL RESEARCH INSTITUTE
INHALATION TOXICOLOGY RES INST
(*Suby of* LOVELACE RESPIRATORY RESEARCH INSTITUTE)
2425 Ridgecrest Dr Se, Albuquerque, NM 87108-5127
Tel (505) 348-9400 *Founded/Ownrshp* 1975
Sales 114.7MM *EMP* 465
Accts Moss Adams Llp Albuquerque N
SIC 8733 Medical research
**Pr:* Ross Leclaire
**Treas:* Richard McGivney
Board of Directors: Robert Rubin

D-U-N-S 60-279-1881
LOVELACE HEALTH SYSTEM INC
(*Suby of* AHS NEW MEXICO HOLDINGS, INC.)
4101 Indian School Rd Ne # 110, Albuquerque, NM 87110-3991
Tel (800) 808-7363 *Founded/Ownrshp* 2003
Sales 310.9MM^E *EMP* 3,183^E
SIC 8062 General medical & surgical hospitals
Pr: Ron Stern
**CFO:* Stephen Forney
Ofcr: Tobey Merlin
**VP:* Clint Adams
VP: Carole Henry
Dir Case M: Vicki Broshious
Off Mgr: Brenda Yantorn
Netwrk Eng: Rene Ruiz
VP Sls: Nanci George
Mktg Dir: Serena Lyons
Doctor: James Poliner

D-U-N-S 03-304-0353
LOVES TRAVEL STOPS & COUNTRY STORES INC
10601 N Pennsylvania Ave, Oklahoma City, OK 73120-4108
Tel (405) 302-6500 *Founded/Ownrshp* 1964
Sales 4.7MMM^E *EMP* 10,600
SIC 5541 5411 5947 Truck stops; Convenience stores, independent; Gift, novelty & souvenir shop
Ch Bd: Tom E Love
Pr: Frank Love
CFO: Doug Stussi
Ex VP: Kevin Asbury
Ex VP: Tom Edwards
Ex VP: Shane Wharton
VP: Reg Kennerty
VP: Terry Ross
VP: Jim Xenos
Genl Mgr: Shane Anderson
Genl Mgr: Chad Hinds

LOVE'S TRVL STOPS CNTRY STORES
See MUSKET CORP

D-U-N-S 95-887-5205
LOVING CARE AGENCY INC
LINKS2CARE
(*Suby of* EPIC HEALTH SERVICES INC) ★
611 Rte 46 W Ste 200, Hasbrouck Heights, NJ 07604
Tel (201) 403-9300 *Founded/Ownrshp* 2015
Sales 265.3MM^E *EMP* 6,500
SIC 8011 8082 Pediatrician; Home health care services
Pr: Glen R Cavallo
**CFO:* Patrick Patton
Sr VP: Karen Dargo-Mullahey
**Sr VP:* George Herchenroether
Brnch Mgr: Charlene Scharf
CTO: Stacey Evanuik

LOVING HANDS HM HLTH CARE SVCS
See LOVING HANDS LTD

D-U-N-S 12-228-2460
LOVING HANDS LTD
LOVING HANDS HM HLTH CARE SVCS
676 Winters Ave Ste 1, Paramus, NJ 07652-3913
Tel (201) 265-3523 *Founded/Ownrshp* 1984
Sales 27.6MM^E *EMP* 1,200
SIC 7363 8082 Medical help service; Home health care services
CFO: Paul Provost
**VP:* Nick Provost

D-U-N-S 02-011-6729
LOVITT & TOUCHE INC
7202 E Rosewood St # 200, Tucson, AZ 85710-1368
Tel (520) 722-3000 *Founded/Ownrshp* 1969
Sales NA *EMP* 200
SIC 6411 Insurance agents & brokers
Pr: Steven D Touche
**CFO:* Denise Birger
**VP:* Joseph C Dhuey
**VP:* Mary Katherine Krugman
VP: Matthew Nelson
VP: Jody Sarchett
**VP:* John L Shearman
**VP:* David Mark Wilder
IT Man: Ian Crawford

D-U-N-S 13-190-4286 IMP/EXP
LOW & BONAR INC
BONAR, INC
(*Suby of* COLBOND HOLDING B.V.)
1301 Sand Hill Rd, Enka, NC 28728
Tel (828) 665-5000 *Founded/Ownrshp* 2000
Sales 121.2MM^E *EMP* 226
SIC 5199 3296 2899 2297 2221

LOW COST POWER
See VERDE ENERGY USA INC

D-U-N-S 10-389-0356
LOWE ENTERPRISES INC
LEI AG SEATTLE
11777 San Vicente Blvd # 900, Los Angeles, CA 90049-6615
Tel (310) 820-6661 *Founded/Ownrshp* 2011
Sales 739.9MM^E *EMP* 5,000
SIC 6531 6552 Real estate managers; Subdividers & developers
Pr: Robert J Lowe
V Ch: Brian T Prinn
Pr: Joseph Heredia
Pr: Rachel Pederson
Pr: James Sabatier
Pr: Rick Swagerty
CFO: William Raphae
Ex VP: Jeffrey Allen
Ex VP: Jeffrey L Allen
Ex VP: Janice Diehl
Ex VP: Peter O'Keeffe
Ex VP: Matthew H Walker
Sr VP: Lynda S Cook
Sr VP: James H Daugherty
Sr VP: John M Demarco
Sr VP: Gordon A Howe
Sr VP: John Lee
Sr VP: Peter R O'Keeffe
Sr VP: Mark S Rivers
Sr VP: Robert M Weekley
VP: Jeffery Allen

D-U-N-S 07-952-1928
LOWELL CITY OF (INC)
375 Merrimack St Rm 27, Lowell, MA 01852-5939
Tel (978) 970-4200 *Founded/Ownrshp* 1826
Sales NA *EMP* 3,000
SIC 9311
**CFO:* Thomas Moses
CIO: Mir N Fernandez

LOWELL ENGINEERING
See MAGNA MIRRORS NORTH AMERICA LLC

D-U-N-S 01-944-1377
LOWELL GENERAL HOSPITAL
L G H
295 Varnum Ave, Lowell, MA 01854-2193
Tel (978) 937-6000 *Founded/Ownrshp* 1891
Sales 419.3MM *EMP* 3,000^E
SIC 8062 Hospital, professional nursing school
Pr: Normand E Deschene
Chf Rad: Scott Abel
Chf Rad: Jonas Berman
**Ch Bd:* Clementine Alexis
**COO:* Joseph White
CFO: Maureen Belley
**CFO:* Susan Green
**CFO:* Richard Jeffcote
Treas: Thomas Rubricki
**Ex VP:* Joseph Jody White III
Sr VP: Michelle Davis
**VP:* Amy Hoey
**VP:* Wayne E Pasanen
Dir Risk M: Tatiana Schultz
Dir Lab: Leslie Davis
Dir Soc: Kathy Sullivan
Dir Rad: Michelle O'Brien
Dir Rx: Paul Lavoie

D-U-N-S 04-075-0317
LOWENSTEIN SANDLER LLP
65 Livingston Ave Ste 2, Roseland, NJ 07068-1725
Tel (973) 597-2500 *Founded/Ownrshp* 1978
Sales 146.4MM^E *EMP* 568
SIC 8111 General practice law office
CEO: Gary M Wingens
Pt: Michele J Alexander
Pt: David M Banker
Pt: Daniel J Barkin
Pt: Nicole Denise Bearce
V Ch: Herschel S Weinstein
CFO: William B Farrell
Treas: Robert G Minion
Sec: Bruce D Shoulson
Ofcr: Donatella Verrico
Exec: Alice De Lancey

D-U-N-S 07-145-4888
LOWER BUCKS HOSPITAL
(*Suby of* PRIME HEALTHCARE SERVICES INC) ★
501 Bath Rd, Bristol, PA 19007-3190
Tel (215) 785-9200 *Founded/Ownrshp* 2012
Sales 77.1MM *EMP* 1,400
SIC 8062 General medical & surgical hospitals
CEO: Peter Adamo
**CEO:* Linda J Grass
**COO:* Matt Shelak
**CFO:* Courtney Coffman
**Prin:* Pete Caldwell

D-U-N-S 04-322-6885
LOWER COLORADO RIVER AUTHORITY
LCRA
3700 Lake Austin Blvd, Austin, TX 78703-3504
Tel (512) 473-3200 *Founded/Ownrshp* 1934
Sales 1.0MMM *EMP* 1,800
Accts Baker Tilly Virchow Krause Llp
SIC 4911 4941 1629 Distribution, electric power; Water supply; Waste water & sewage treatment plant construction
Ch: Timothy Timmerman
V Ch: Hughes G Abell
CFO: Brady Edwards
CFO: John Miesmer
**CFO:* Richard Williams
Bd of Dir: John H Mathews
**Ex VP:* John Hofmann
**Ex VP:* Bill Lauderback
VP: Bobby R Phillips
Area Supr: Bobby Fohn
Dist Mgr: Melinda Armbuster

D-U-N-S 78-647-4049
■ **LOWER KEYS MEDICAL CENTER**
(*Suby of* HMA) ★
5900 College Rd, Key West, FL 33040-4342
Tel (305) 294-5531 *Founded/Ownrshp* 1989
Sales 117.6MM *EMP* 487
SIC 8062 General medical & surgical hospitals
CEO: Nicki Will
Dir Lab: Peggy Spencer
Dir IT: Donna Snapp
Doctor: Daniel Gill
Nrsg Dir: Kim Bassett Rn
HC Dir: Leslie Dish
HC Dir: Stanley Padfield

D-U-N-S 00-699-7142 IMP/EXP
▲ **LOWES COMPANIES INC** (NC)
1000 Lowes Blvd, Mooresville, NC 28117-8520
Tel (704) 758-1000 *Founded/Ownrshp* 1946
Sales 59.0MMM *EMP* 270,000
Accts Deloitte & Touche Llp Charlot
Tkr Sym LOW *Exch* NYS
SIC 5211 5031 5722 5064 Lumber & other building materials; Building materials, exterior; Building materials, interior; Household appliance stores; Electrical appliances, television & radio
Ch Bd: Robert A Niblock
COO: Rick D Damron
CFO: Robert F Hull Jr
Treas: Judy Davis
Treas: Tiffany L Mason
Chf Cred: Ross W McCanless
Bd of Dir: Shannon Efird
Ofcr: Marshall A Croom
Ofcr: Michael A Jones
Ofcr: Brent G Kirby
Ofcr: Michael P McDermott
Ofcr: Jennifer L Weber
Ex VP: Joseph Abry
Ex VP: Michael K Brown
Ex VP: Douglas Evans
Ex VP: Bob Gfeller
Ex VP: J Michael Mabry Jr
Ex VP: Joseph M Mabry
Sr VP: Maureen Ausura
Sr VP: Cedric T Coco
Sr VP: Ronnie E Damron

LOWE'S FOOD STORES, INC.
See LOWES FOODS LLC

D-U-N-S 04-451-5187
LOWES FOODS LLC
LOWE'S FOOD STORES, INC.
(*Suby of* ALEX LEE INC) ★
1381 Old Mill Cir Ste 200, Winston Salem, NC 27103-1497
Tel (336) 659-2429 *Founded/Ownrshp* 1984
Sales 1.2MMM *EMP* 8,000
Accts Stocks Smith Campbell & Dend
SIC 5411 Supermarkets, chain
Ch Bd: Boyd Lee George
**Pr:* Timothy Lowe
Prac Mgr: Donna Cline
Board of Directors:

D-U-N-S 01-881-0275 IMP/EXP
■ **LOWES HOME CENTERS LLC**
(*Suby of* LOWES COMPANIES INC) ★
1605 Curtis Bridge Rd, Wilkesboro, NC 28697-2263
Tel (336) 658-4000 *Founded/Ownrshp* 1958
Sales 28.0MMM^E *EMP* 209,850
SIC 5211 5031 5722 5064 Lumber & other building materials; Building materials, exterior; Building materials, interior; Household appliance stores; Electrical appliances, television & radio
CEO: Robert Niblock
**Pr:* Larry D Stone
**CFO:* Robert F Hull Jr
**Treas:* James A Cook III
**Ex VP:* Gregory M Bridgeford
**Ex VP:* Micheal K Brown
**Ex VP:* Joseph M Mabry Jr
**Sr VP:* Maureen K Ausura
**Sr VP:* Matthew V Hollifield
IT Man: Steven Wright
Opers Mgr: Larry Cayton

LOWE'S MARKET
See PAY AND SAVE INC

LOWGRADE LUMBER
See SILVARIS CORP

D-U-N-S 15-338-2205
LOWNDES COUNTY BOARD OF EDUCATION INC
1592 Norman Dr, Valdosta, GA 31601-3581
Tel (229) 245-2250 *Founded/Ownrshp* 1871
Sales 98.1MM *EMP* 131E
Accts Greg S Griffin Atlanta Geor
SIC 8211 School board
Ch Bd: Brian Browning
CFO: Susan S Swader

D-U-N-S 07-979-9733
LOWNDES COUNTY SCHOOLS
1592 Norman Dr, Valdosta, GA 31601-3581
Tel (229) 245-2250 *Founded/Ownrshp* 2015
Sales 108.5MM *EMP* 1,002E
SIC 8211 Public elementary & secondary schools

LOWRANCE SMRAD B G GFREE BRNDS
See NAVICO INC

D-U-N-S 08-674-5452 IMP/EXP
LOWRY HOLDING CO INC
LOWRY SOLUTIONS
9420 Maltby Rd, Brighton, MI 48116-8801
Tel (810) 229-7200 *Founded/Ownrshp* 1979
Sales 135.1MME *EMP* 135E
SIC 5045 2672 8742 7373 5044 5734 Computers, peripherals & software; Coated & laminated paper; Management consulting services; Systems integration services; Office equipment; Computer & software stores
CEO: Michael Lowry
**CFO:* Mark Muehlenbeck
**Ex VP:* Steven R Lowry
VP: Jeff Polly
Mktg Dir: Michelle Borum
Sls Dir: Geoff Pollak
Mktg Mgr: Pam Turner

LOWRY SOLUTIONS
See LOWRY HOLDING CO INC

D-U-N-S 00-333-9157 IMP
LOXCREEN CO INC
(*Suby of* M-D BUILDING PRODUCTS INC) ★
1630 Old Dunbar Rd, West Columbia, SC 29172-1936
Tel (803) 822-1600 *Founded/Ownrshp* 1947, 2012
Sales 112.9MME *EMP* 600
SIC 3354 3442 3089 Aluminum extruded products; Screen doors, metal; Storm doors or windows, metal; Screens, window, metal; Extruded finished plastic products
CEO: John Parrish
**COO:* Joe T Comitale
**VP:* Howard McClure
**VP:* Ronald B Rhymer
**VP:* Fred Vermeer
**VP:* Rick Wheeler
Opers Mgr: Ronald Clayton

D-U-N-S 07-194-4649
■ LOYAL AMERICAN LIFE INSURANCE CO
(*Suby of* CIGNA HEALTH AND LIFE INSURANCE CO) ★
250 E 5th St Fl 8, Cincinnati, OH 45202-4119
Tel (800) 633-6752 *Founded/Ownrshp* 2012
Sales NA *EMP* 235
SIC 6311 Life insurance
Pr: Charles Schaper
**Ch Bd:* Robert A Adams
**COO:* Jane Rollinson
**CFO:* W Randolph Samples
**Ex VP:* Mark Muething
**Sr VP:* Edward C Dahmer Jr
**Sr VP:* Linda McGhee

D-U-N-S 83-101-7848
LOYAL SOURCE GOVERNMENT SERVICES LLC
12612 Challenger Pkwy # 365, Orlando, FL 32826-2759
Tel (407) 306-8441 *Founded/Ownrshp* 2011
Sales 56.0MM *EMP* 1,000
SIC 8062 General medical & surgical hospitals
Prgrm Mgr: Jeff Henderson

D-U-N-S 07-294-6239
LOYOLA MARYMOUNT UNIVERSITY INC
1 Lmu Dr Ste 100, Los Angeles, CA 90045-2677
Tel (310) 338-2700 *Founded/Ownrshp* 1911
Sales 349.8MM *EMP* 1,449
Accts Pricewaterhousecoopers Llp L
SIC 8211 Elementary & secondary schools
Pr: Timothy Law Snyder
Pr: Rick Garcia
**Treas:* Caroline Wilhelm
Assoc VP: Michael Wong
Ex VP: David Zuercher
VP: Robert Caro
VP: Thomas Fleming
**VP:* Victor J Gold
VP: Gregory Hadzinski
VP: Evelynne Scarboro
VP: Lynne Scarboro
VP: Dennis Slon
Assoc Dir: Joseph C McNicholas
Assoc Dir: Maureen Pacino
Dir: Mark Peacor
Dir: Lynn Witherspoon

D-U-N-S 07-492-7740
LOYOLA UNIVERSITY MARYLAND INC
5000 York Rd Ste 200, Baltimore, MD 21212-4437
Tel (410) 617-2000 *Founded/Ownrshp* 1852
Sales 285.5MM *EMP* 2,066
SIC 8221 College, except junior
Pr: Bryan Linnane
**Treas:* John A Palmucci
Ofcr: Julie Ryder
Assoc VP: Anne Young
Ex VP: Eric Campos
Ex VP: Christopher Kutner
Ex VP: Jordan Sowinski
VP: Marc Camille
**VP:* Susan Donovan
VP: Connor Kennedy
VP: Meghan Lynch
VP: Chris Monin
VP: Micaela Murphy
VP: Brendan O'Neill
VP: Taylor Reddan
VP: Peter Scacco
**VP:* David Sears
VP: Evan Wagenfeld
VP: Amy Wolfson
Exec: Helen Aberle
Assoc Dir: Randy Wallace

D-U-N-S 96-391-0265
LOYOLA UNIVERSITY MEDICAL CENTER
2160 S 1st Ave, Maywood, IL 60153-3328
Tel (708) 216-9000 *Founded/Ownrshp* 2010
Sales 1.2MMM *EMP* 19
SIC 8011 Physicians' office, including specialists
Prin: Patrick Stiff MD
VP: Leonard Vertuno
Off Mgr: Marie Chemik
Off Mgr: Rich Novotny
Pathlgst: Valdas Gasilionis
Pathlgst: Meiha Guo
Doctor: Myles N Sheeha MD
Pharmcst: Renee Petzel

D-U-N-S 00-820-3309 IMP
LOYOLA UNIVERSITY NEW ORLEANS INC
6363 Saint Charles Ave, New Orleans, LA 70118-6195
Tel (504) 865-2011 *Founded/Ownrshp* 1912
Sales 120.1MM *EMP* 1,000
Accts Carr Riggs & Ingram Llc New
SIC 8221 University
Pr: Rev Kevin W Wildes S J
CFO: Rhonda Cartwright
CFO: Linda Richard
Trst: James Bradley
VP: John Calamia
VP: Jin Huang
VP: Ana Morales
Ex Dir: Bret Jacobs
CTO: Vicki McNeil

D-U-N-S 07-436-8911 IMP/EXP
LOYOLA UNIVERSITY OF CHICAGO INC
LAKE SHORE CAMPUS
1032 W Sheridan Rd, Chicago, IL 60660-1537
Tel (773) 274-3000 *Founded/Ownrshp* 1870
Sales 540.0MM *EMP* 10,500
Accts Deloitte & Touche Llp Chicag
SIC 8221 University
Pr: Jo Ann Rooney
Trst: John F Cuneo
Trst: Frank W Hogan
Trst: Robert L Parkinson
Trst: Joseph A Power
VP: Susan Malisch
VP: Terry Moritz
VP: Kelly Shannon
VP: Frank Tortorella
Off Admin: Gina Lopez
Netwrk Mgr: David Wieczorek

D-U-N-S 00-725-9484 IMP/EXP
LOZIER CORP (NE)
6336 John J Pershing Dr, Omaha, NE 68110-1122
Tel (402) 457-8000 *Founded/Ownrshp* 1937
Sales 481.7MME *EMP* 2,490
Accts Rsm Us Llp Omaha Nebraska
SIC 2541 2542 Store fixtures, wood; Partitions & fixtures, except wood
Pr: Sheri L Andrews
**CFO:* Steve Franz
**Ch:* Allan Lozier
**Treas:* Jan Muller
Ex VP: Troy Wilhelm
VP: Bob Braun
VP: Jay Daily
**VP:* Dave Gnuse
VP: William Naidenovich
VP: Neil Sherman
VP: Carlson Tammy

D-U-N-S 12-194-6362 EXP
LOZIER STORE FIXTURES LLC
(*Suby of* LOZIER CORP) ★
6336 John J Pershing Dr, Omaha, NE 68110-1100
Tel (402) 457-8000 *Founded/Ownrshp* 2013
Sales 84.6MME *EMP* 300
SIC 5046 Store machines; Shelving, commercial & industrial
Pr: Sheri Andrews
Treas: Jan Muller

LP ACQUISITION
See PULITZER INC

D-U-N-S 96-701-2852
LP COLUMBIA LLC
SIGNATURE HEALTHCARE COLUMBIA
(*Suby of* SIGNATURE HEALTHCARE LLC) ★
1410 Trotwood Ave, Columbia, TN 38401-4901
Tel (931) 388-6443 *Founded/Ownrshp* 2011
Sales 950.0M *EMP* 11,375
SIC 8051 Skilled nursing care facilities
Prin: Deirdre M McManus

D-U-N-S 07-936-0241
LP HARRODSBURG LLC
HARRODSBURG HEALTH & REHAB CTR
(*Suby of* SIGNATURE HEALTHCARE LLC) ★
853 Lexington Rd, Harrodsburg, KY 40330-1260
Tel (859) 734-7791 *Founded/Ownrshp* 2014
Sales 90.4MME *EMP* 13,957
SIC 8051 Skilled nursing care facilities
Prin: John Harrison
Prin: Rafael Ramos
Prin: E Joseph Steier

D-U-N-S 13-233-2466
LPA INVESTMENT LLC
LA PETITE ACADEMY
21333 Haggerty Rd Ste 300, Novi, MI 48375-5537
Tel (866) 244-5384 *Founded/Ownrshp* 1998
Sales 420.0MM *EMP* 12,800E
SIC 8351 Child day care services
Pr: Graves Gary
**Pr:* Gary Graves
Off Mgr: Dan Knight

LPC
See LINCOLN PROPERTY CO

D-U-N-S 62-337-6605
LPC COMMERCIAL SERVICES INC
LINCOLN PROPERTY CO
2000 Mckinney Ave # 1000, Dallas, TX 75201-1954
Tel (202) 513-6710 *Founded/Ownrshp* 1990
Sales 204.6MME *EMP* 565
SIC 6552 Land subdividers & developers, commercial; Land subdividers & developers, residential
Ch: William C Duvall
**Ch:* Mack Pogue
**Treas:* Nancy A Davis
**Ofcr:* William Hickey
**VP:* John Paul Price
Dir IT: Anthony Hernandez
IT Man: Todd Hawkins
IT Man: Jay Kenney

D-U-N-S 10-561-9212
LPC CRUDE OIL INC
408 W Wall St Ste B, Midland, TX 79701-4460
Tel (432) 682-8555 *Founded/Ownrshp* 2002
Sales 90.2MME *EMP* 100
SIC 5172 Crude oil
Pr: Steve Mills
VP: Daniel Carter

D-U-N-S 12-062-2055
LPG ENTERPRISES INC
MCDONALD'S
12854 Eastridge Dr Ne, Albuquerque, NM 87112-4715
Tel (505) 299-4155 *Founded/Ownrshp* 1980
Sales 30.5MME *EMP* 1,000
Accts Horne Cpas & Business Advisors
SIC 5812 Fast-food restaurant, chain
Pr: Larry Garcia
**VP:* Pearlene Garcia

LPGA
See LADIES PROFESSIONAL GOLF ASSOCIATION

D-U-N-S 78-882-3016
▲ LPL FINANCIAL HOLDINGS INC
LPLFH
75 State St Ste 2401, Boston, MA 02109-1823
Tel (617) 423-3644 *Founded/Ownrshp* 1989
Sales 4.2MMM *EMP* 3,410
Tkr Sym LPLA *Exch* NGS
SIC 6211 6282 6091 Security brokers & dealers; Investment advisory service; Investment counselors; Nondeposit trust facilities
Ch Bd: Mark S Casady
Pr: Dan H Arnold
CFO: Matthew J Audette
Div Pres: J Andrew Kalbaugh
Div Pres: William P Morrissey Jr
Ofcr: Michelle Oroschakoff
Mng Dir: David P Bergers
Mng Dir: Tracy Calder
Mng Dir: Victor P Fetter
Mng Dir: Thomas Gooley
Mng Dir: Stace Hilbrant

D-U-N-S 03-496-3751
■ LPL FINANCIAL LLC
LPL FINANCIAL SERVICES
(*Suby of* LPL HOLDINGS INC) ★
4707 Executive Dr, San Diego, CA 92121-3091
Tel (800) 877-7210 *Founded/Ownrshp* 1989
Sales 671.4MME *EMP* 986
SIC 6211 Brokers, security
Ch Bd: Todd A Robinson
Mng Pt: Rodney Medina
**Ch Bd:* Mark Casady
Pr: Scott Fewin
**COO:* Esther Stearns
CFO: William Maher
**CFO:* Becky S Shulman
**V Ch Bd:* David H Butterfield
Ex VP: David Akellian
**Ex VP:* Gina Cannella
Ex VP: David Reich
Sr VP: Patrick Cox
Sr VP: Neil Devoe
**Sr VP:* Jeffrey Kleintop
Sr VP: Michael Watson
VP: Andrew Blake
VP: Anthony Henry
VP: Kristine Koczajowski
VP: Andrew Poe

LPL FINANCIAL SERVICES
See LPL FINANCIAL LLC

D-U-N-S 60-315-8502
■ LPL HOLDINGS INC
(*Suby of* LPLFH) ★
4707 Executive Dr, San Diego, CA 92121-3091
Tel (858) 450-9606 *Founded/Ownrshp* 2005
Sales 693.2MME *EMP* 1,200E
SIC 6211 Brokers, security; Dealers, security
CEO: Mark Casady
Pr: Rebecca Power
Ex VP: Robert Comfort
Sr VP: Christopher Defrank
Sr VP: Stephen Lank
Sr VP: Thomas Seeburger
VP: Jen Bergman
VP: John Gurski
VP: Allison Harris
VP: Carolyn McCarthy
VP: Bill McFarlane
VP: John Milder
VP: Terri Payne
VP: Marc Ravenscroft
VP: Scott Witeby
Dir Bus: Jeremy Hudson

LPLFH
See LPL FINANCIAL HOLDINGS INC

D-U-N-S 11-899-7266
LPS INTEGRATION INC
5300 Virginia Way Ste 100, Brentwood, TN 37027-2309
Tel (866) 706-7904 *Founded/Ownrshp* 2002
Sales 87.2MM *EMP* 72
Accts Horne Llp Ridgeland Mississi
SIC 5045 7379 Computers, peripherals & software; Computer related consulting services
CEO: Todd Sanford
**Pr:* Chris McMillen
**CEO:* David Linzy
**COO:* Frank Pulliza
**CFO:* Theresa Chester
VP: Gregg Ambulos
VP: Bill McClanahan
Snr Ntwrk: Matt Lang
Sales Asso: Andrew Gray

D-U-N-S 83-174-3179
■ LPS REAL ESTATE GROUP INC
(*Suby of* BLACK KNIGHT INFOSERV LLC) ★
2050 Main St Ste 400, Irvine, CA 92614-8270
Tel (949) 681-4700 *Founded/Ownrshp* 2006
Sales 33.2MME *EMP* 1,401E
SIC 7374 Data processing & preparation
Pr: Jay Gaskill

D-U-N-S 06-118-9981
■ LQ MANAGEMENT LLC (GA)
LA QUINTA INN
(*Suby of* LA QUINTA HOLDINGS INC) ★
909 Hidden Rdg Ste 600, Irving, TX 75038-3822
Tel (214) 492-6600 *Founded/Ownrshp* 2005
Sales 634.0MME *EMP* 7,426
SIC 7011 Hotels & motels
Pr: Wayne B Goldberg
**Pr:* Keith A Cline
**COO:* John W Cantele
COO: Angelo Lambardi
COO: William McCalmont
**CFO:* James H Forson
Bd of Dir: Francis Cash
**Chf Mktg O:* Julie M Cary
**Ex VP:* Mark M Chloupek
Ex VP: Mark La Bissoniere
**Ex VP:* Rajiv K Trivedi
Sr VP: Stephen T Parker
VP: Henry Cope
VP: Vicki Cutwright
VP: Ivonne Laboy
VP: James Marshall
VP: Hoang Nguyen
VP: David Sims
VP: Gary Zodrow

D-U-N-S 08-031-5957
LRC EAGLES LANDING GP LLC (TN)
555 Perkins Ext, Memphis, TN 38117-4410
Tel (901) 435-7716 *Founded/Ownrshp* 2015, 2016
Sales 122.0MM *EMP* 5
SIC 6798 6531 Real estate investment trusts; Real estate leasing & rentals
CEO: Pierce Ledbetter
**COO:* Terri Benskin
**CFO:* Jeff Ezekiel

D-U-N-S 07-396-8455
LRGHEALTHCARE
HEALTHLINK
80 Highland St, Laconia, NH 03246-3298
Tel (603) 524-3211 *Founded/Ownrshp* 1898
Sales 174.2MM *EMP* 1,600
SIC 8062 General medical & surgical hospitals
CEO: Thomas A Clairmont
Ex VP: Henry D Lipman
**Sr VP:* Henry Lipman
**Sr VP:* Ellen Wolff
Comm Dir: Ron Blackey
Ex Dir: Mary Wilson
Dir Pat Ac: Joyce Bluhm
Off Mgr: Brenda Ford
IT Man: Scott Vachon
Netwrk Eng: Bruce Veilleux
Doctor: Carolyn Drake

D-U-N-S 79-042-5610
LRI HOLDINGS INC
(*Suby of* ROADHOUSE PARENT INC) ★
3011 Armory Dr Ste 300, Nashville, TN 37204-3721
Tel (615) 885-9056 *Founded/Ownrshp* 2010
Sales 614.3MM *EMP* 14,885E
SIC 5812 6794 Steak restaurant; Franchises, selling or licensing
Pr: Samuel N Borgese
CFO: Edmund J Schwartz
Chf Mktg O: Len A Van Popering
Sr VP: Mariahilda Rivera
CIO: John C Laporte

LRMC
See LAKELAND REGIONAL MEDICAL CENTER INC

D-U-N-S 96-855-5362
■ LRR ENERGY LP
(*Suby of* VANGUARD NATURAL RESOURCES LLC) ★
1111 Bagby St Ste 4600, Houston, TX 77002-2559
Tel (713) 292-9510 *Founded/Ownrshp* 2015
Sales 187.9MM *EMP* 153
SIC 1311 Crude petroleum & natural gas
CEO: Scott W Smith
CFO: Richard A Robert
VP: Christopher Butta
VP: Britt Pence

D-U-N-S 01-702-5115
LRR FOOD INC
850 76th St Sw, Grand Rapids, MI 49518
Tel (810) 629-1383 *Founded/Ownrshp* 1960
Sales 144.1MME *EMP* 2,000
SIC 5411 5921 Supermarkets, independent; Beer (packaged); Wine
Ch Bd: Russell V Gilder Jr
**Pr:* Lisa Van Gilder

LRS
See LEVI RAY & SHOUP INC

D-U-N-S 84-015-9318 EXP
LS ENERGIA INC
1200 S Pine Island Rd # 420, Plantation, FL 33324-4413
Tel (954) 628-3059 *Founded/Ownrshp* 1995
Sales 300.0MM *EMP* 100
SIC 1731 Energy management controls
Pr: Jose Tamayo

LS TRAVEL RETAIL NORTH AMERICA
See HDS RETAIL NORTH AMERICA LP

D-U-N-S 07-975-0271
LS1 LLC
RITE WAY SERVICE, LLC
(Suby of DIVERSIFIED MAINTENANCE SYSTEMS LLC) ★
331 1st Ave N, Birmingham, AL 35204-4904
Tel (205) 251-9249 Founded/Ownrshp 2014
Sales 78.0MM EMP 2,800^E
SIC 7349 Janitorial service, contract basis
CEO: David Ramon
Ex Dir: Steven Lea
Off Mgr: Dana McClinton

D-U-N-S 08-374-2403
LS1 LLC (AL)
RITE WAY SERVICE
331 1st Ave N, Birmingham, AL 35204-4904
Tel (205) 251-9249 Founded/Ownrshp 2014
Sales NA EMP 2,200
SIC 7349

D-U-N-S 12-258-8510 IMP/EXP
■ **LSB CHEMICAL LLC**
(Suby of LSB INDUSTRIES INC) ★
16 S Pennsylvania Ave, Oklahoma City, OK 73107-7024
Tel (405) 235-4546 Founded/Ownrshp 1983
Sales 130.3MM^E EMP 364
SIC 2819 2873 2892 Sulfuric acid, oleum; Nitric acid; Ammonium nitrate, ammonium sulfate; Explosives
Pr: Paul Rydlund
*VP: Larry D Fitzwater
*VP: Brian Lewis
*VP: Dallas C Robinson

D-U-N-S 03-365-3770
■ **LSB CORP**
(Suby of PEOPLES UNITED FINANCIAL INC) ★
30 Massachusetts Ave # 8, North Andover, MA 01845-3458
Tel (978) 725-7500 Founded/Ownrshp 2010
Sales NA EMP 1,946^E
SIC 6022 State commercial banks
CEO: Gerald T Mulligan
*CFO: Diane L Walker

D-U-N-S 04-686-0979
▲ **LSB INDUSTRIES INC**
16 S Pennsylvania Ave, Oklahoma City, OK 73107-7024
Tel (405) 235-4546 Founded/Ownrshp 1968
Sales 711.7MM EMP 1,928
Tkr Sym LXU Exch NYS
SIC 3822 3585 3567 2873 Hydronic controls; Heat pumps, electric; Heating units & devices, industrial: electric; Ammonium nitrate, ammonium sulfate; Anhydrous ammonia; Fertilizers: natural (organic), except compost; Urea
Pr: Daniel D Greenwell
Ch Bd: Jack E Golsen
COO: Richard Aldridge
CFO: Mark T Behrman
Ex VP: John Diesch
Ex VP: David R Goss
Ex VP: Brian Lewis
Ex VP: Richard S Sanders Jr
Sr VP: Michael J Foster
Sr VP: Phil Gough
VP: James Murray
VP: Robert Porter
VP: Dallas Robinson
VP: Michael Sullivan
Board of Directors: Jonathan S Bobb, Mark T Genender, Barry H Golsen, William G Murdy, Joseph E Reece, Richar W Roedel, Lynn F White

D-U-N-S 08-042-9308
LSC COMMUNICATIONS US LLC
35 W Wacker Dr, Chicago, IL 60601-1723
Tel (844) 572-5720 Founded/Ownrshp 2016
Sales 262.5MM^E EMP 1,276^E
SIC 1623 Telephone & communication line construction

LSC SYSTEM OFFICE
See LONE STAR COLLEGE SYSTEM

LSCP
See LITTLE SIOUX CORN PROCESSORS LLC

D-U-N-S 11-415-0548 IMP/EXP
LSCP LLLP
LITTLE SIOUX CORN PROCESSORS
(Suby of LSCP) ★
4808 F Ave, Marcus, IA 51035-7070
Tel (712) 376-2800 Founded/Ownrshp 2001
Sales 232.4MM EMP 46
Accts Christianson & Associates Pll
SIC 4925 5191 Gas production and/or distribution; Manufactured gas, production & distribution; Animal feeds
CFO: Gary Grotjohn
Genl Mgr: Steve Roe

LSF INTERACTIVE
See GEARY LSF GROUP INC

D-U-N-S 02-692-5465
LSF5 BI-LO HOLDINGS LLC
WINN-DIXIE
(Suby of LONE STAR FUND V (US) LP) ★
5050 Edgewood Ct, Jacksonville, FL 32254-3601
Tel (904) 783-5000 Founded/Ownrshp 2005
Sales 12.8MMM^E EMP 177,959^E
SIC 5411 Convenience stores, chain
Pr: R Randall Onstead Jr

D-U-N-S 07-960-8470
LSF5 CACTUS LLC
5055 W Park Blvd Ste 500, Plano, TX 75093-2587
Tel (281) 830-0055 Founded/Ownrshp 2014
Sales 270.1MM^E EMP 2,970^E
SIC 6799 Investors

D-U-N-S 07-856-8804
LSF5 WAGON HOLDINGS LLC
2711 N Haskell Ave # 1700, Dallas, TX 75204-2911
Tel (214) 515-6824 Founded/Ownrshp 2007
Sales 52.0MM^E EMP 6,890
SIC 5812 5813 Eating places; Drinking places
CEO: John P Grayken

LSG SKY CHEFS
See SKY CHEFS INC

D-U-N-S 15-467-9252 IMP
LSG SKY CHEFS USA INC
(Suby of LSG LUFTHANSA SERVICE HOLDING AG)
6191 N State Highway 161 # 100, Irving, TX 75038-2290
Tel (972) 793-9000 Founded/Ownrshp 2001
Sales 592.8MM^E EMP 7,321
Accts Price Waterhousecoopers Llp D
SIC 5812 5962 Caterers; Contract food services; Coffee shop; Merchandising machine operators
CFO: Jens Theuerkorn
*CFO: Patrick Tolbertp
Treas: Jamie Rafftesaeth
*Sr VP: Pat Berkelbaugh
Web Dev: Ben Galaviz
Netwrk Eng: Joel Nola

D-U-N-S 01-244-4253 IMP
LSI CORP
(Suby of AVAGO TECHNOLOGIES US INC) ★
1320 Ridder Park Dr, San Jose, CA 95131-2313
Tel (408) 433-8000 Founded/Ownrshp 2014
Sales 361.3M EMP 5,272
Accts Perrone & Associates Morgan H
SIC 3674 Microcircuits, integrated (semiconductor)
Pr: Abhijit Y Talwalkar
*COO: D Jeffrey Richardson
*CFO: Bryon Look
Ex VP: Jeff Hoogenboom
*Ex VP: Jean F Rankin
Ex VP: Frank A Tornghi
*Sr VP: Gautam Srivastava
VP: Phil Bullinger
*CTO: Gregory L Huff

D-U-N-S 08-093-4375
▲ **LSI INDUSTRIES INC**
10000 Alliance Rd, Blue Ash, OH 45242-4706
Tel (513) 793-3200 Founded/Ownrshp 1976
Sales 322.2MM EMP 1,292^E
Accts Grant Thornton Llp Cincinnat
Tkr Sym LYTS Exch NGS
SIC 3648 3993 3663 Lighting equipment; Floodlights; Public lighting fixtures; Area & sports luminaries; Electric signs; Light communications equipment
Pr: Dennis W Wells
*Ch Bd: Gary P Kreider
CFO: Ronald S Stowell
Ex VP: Andrew J Foerster
Sr VP: Sylvia Astrop
Info Man: Steve Minor
Plnt Mgr: Michael Wright
Sales Exec: Brian Sherlock
Sls Dir: Don Mann
Manager: Marc Sheff
Sls Mgr: Jeff Hutchinson
Board of Directors: Robert P Beech, John K Morgan, Wilfred T O'gara, Mark A Serrianne, James P Sferra, Robert A Steele

D-U-N-S 12-227-3303 IMP
■ **LSI LIGHTRON INC**
(Suby of LSI INDUSTRIES INC) ★
500 Hudson Valley Ave, New Windsor, NY 12553-4744
Tel (845) 562-5500 Founded/Ownrshp 2000
Sales 189.3MM^E EMP 1,000
SIC 3646 5063 Commercial indusl & institutional electric lighting fixtures; Electrical apparatus & equipment
CEO: Gene Littman
Pr: Barry White

D-U-N-S 05-543-1836 IMP
LSIS USA INC
2000 Millbrook Dr, Lincolnshire, IL 60069-3630
Tel (847) 941-8240 Founded/Ownrshp 2012
Sales 221.8MM^E EMP 23,000
SIC 5063 Power wire & cable
Pr: Min Dokko

D-U-N-S 94-987-5884
LSQ FUNDING GROUP LC
(Suby of LSQ GROUP LLC) ★
2600 Lucien Way Ste 100, Maitland, FL 32751-7064
Tel (407) 206-0022 Founded/Ownrshp 1996
Sales NA EMP 55
SIC 6153 Factoring services
Ch Bd: Max Eliscu
Pr: Joe Kiefer
COO: Roger Allen
CFO: Terry Ragsdale
Ofcr: Stan Carpenter
Ex VP: Tyler Grady
Ex VP: Pat McMonagle
Ex VP: Tanya Plotnikoff
VP: Tanya Boczek
VP: Heather Lyons
VP: Bob Reagen
Exec: Matt Durfee
Creative D: Damien Wolf

D-U-N-S 07-984-3614
LSQ GROUP LLC
2600 Lucien Way Ste 100, Maitland, FL 32751-7064
Tel (407) 206-0022 Founded/Ownrshp 2015
Sales NA EMP 55^E
SIC 6153 Factoring services

D-U-N-S 96-250-6437
LSREF LODGING INVESTMENTS LLC
(Suby of LONE STAR REAL ESTATE FUND (US) LP) ★
2711 N Haskell Ave, Dallas, TX 75204-2911
Tel (214) 754-8300 Founded/Ownrshp 2010
Sales 175.0MM^E EMP 3,046^E
SIC 6798 Real estate investment trusts
Pt: Louis Paletta

D-U-N-S 80-867-8262
LSRI HOLDINGS INC
(Suby of LANDRYS SEAFOOD HOUSE) ★
1510 West Loop S, Houston, TX 77027-9505
Tel (713) 850-1010 Founded/Ownrshp 1993
Sales 1.3MMM^E EMP 16,000
SIC 5812 Seafood restaurants; Steak & barbecue restaurants
Ch Bd: Tilman J Fertitta
*CFO: Rick Lim
*Ex VP: Richard E Ervin
Ex VP: Richard E Rvin
*Ex VP: Steve Scheinthal

LSV
See LIFE AND SPECIALTY VENTURES LLC

D-U-N-S 79-528-4793
▲ **LTC PROPERTIES INC**
2829 Townsgate Rd Ste 350, Westlake Village, CA 91361-3019
Tel (805) 981-8655 Founded/Ownrshp 1992
Sales 136.2MM EMP 22^E
Tkr Sym LTC Exch NYS
SIC 6798 Real estate investment trusts
Ch Bd: Wendy L Simpson
CFO: Pamela J Shelley-Kessler
Treas: Caroline L Chikhale
Ex VP: Clint B Malin
Sr VP: Brent P Chappell
Sr VP: Douglas Korey
VP: Caroline Wong

LTCG
See LONG TERM CARE GROUP INC

D-U-N-S 02-519-5116 IMP/EXP
LTD COMMODITIES LLC
L-T-D COMMODITIES
2800 Lakeside Dr, Bannockburn, IL 60015-1280
Tel (847) 295-6058 Founded/Ownrshp 2001
Sales 372.8MM^E EMP 1,500^E
SIC 5961 5947 Catalog & mail-order houses; Gift, novelty & souvenir shop
Pr: Sheldon Leibowitz
*CEO: Michael Hara
COO: Dion Bell
Genl Mgr: Rick Disclafani
IT Man: Tim Christoff
Sftwr Eng: Patricia Hindes

LTD HOSPITALITY GROUP
See LTD MANAGEMENT CO LLC

D-U-N-S 80-007-1920
LTD MANAGEMENT CO LLC
LTD HOSPITALITY GROUP
1564 Crossways Blvd, Chesapeake, VA 23320-2841
Tel (757) 420-0900 Founded/Ownrshp 1991
Sales 84.2MM^E EMP 800^E
SIC 8741 8721 Hotel or motel management; Accounting, auditing & bookkeeping
Pr: Dilip Desai
Mng Pt: Tejal Desai
Mng Pt: Kush Thakkar
*Pr: Bharat Shah
Sr VP: Prakash J Rajamani
*Sr VP: Kimberly Schlick
Dir IT: Tony Parrow
Sls Dir: Dawn Anderson
Sls Dir: Amy Gilliam
Sls Mgr: Stephanie Eckes
Sls Mgr: Lisa Hahn

LTD PARTS
See BBB INDUSTRIES LLC

D-U-N-S 07-988-1824
LTF HOLDINGS INC
2902 Corporate Pl, Chanhassen, MN 55317-4560
Tel (952) 380-0303 Founded/Ownrshp 2015
Sales 773.5MM EMP 22,500^E
SIC 6719 Investment holding companies, except banks
Ch Bd: Bahram Akradi

D-U-N-S 02-594-0156
LTG LONESTAR TRUCK GROUP EAST LLC
SHREVEPORT TRUCK CENTER
2051 Hughes Rd, Grapevine, TX 76051-7317
Tel (817) 428-9736 Founded/Ownrshp 2007
Sales 127.6MM EMP 215^E
SIC 5531

D-U-N-S 61-574-5168 IMP
LTI HOLDINGS INC
BOYD
(Suby of SNOW PHIPPS GROUP LLC) ★
600 S Mcclure Rd, Modesto, CA 95357-0520
Tel (209) 236-1111 Founded/Ownrshp 2013
Sales 704.0MM^E EMP 2,664
SIC 3069 2822 Hard rubber & molded rubber products; Rubber automotive products; Synthetic rubber
Pr: Mitch Aiello
*CFO: Kurt Wetzel

D-U-N-S 08-013-5595
LTS BUYER LLC
80 Central St, Boxborough, MA 01719-1245
Tel (978) 264-6001 Founded/Ownrshp 2012
Sales 553.5MM EMP 900
Accts Deloitte & Touche Llp Boxboro
SIC 4899 Communication signal enhancement network system
Pr: Robert Shanahan
COO: Jason Campbell
CFO: Eric Sandman
Treas: Gerard Ahearn
VP: David Mayer
Dir Risk M: Doug Dalissandro
CTO: Philip Olivero

D-U-N-S 07-964-6567
LTS GROUP HOLDINGS LLC
80 Central St Ste 240, Boxborough, MA 01719-1245
Tel (978) 264-6001 Founded/Ownrshp 2014
Sales 196.1MM^E EMP 880^E
SIC 3661 Fiber optics communications equipment
CEO: Robert Shanahan
*CFO: Eric Sandman

D-U-N-S 78-766-0513 IMP/EXP
LTS LOHMANN THERAPY SYSTEMS CORP
(Suby of LTS LOHMANN THERAPIE-SYSTEME AG)
21 Henderson Dr, West Caldwell, NJ 07006-6607
Tel (973) 575-5170 Founded/Ownrshp 2009
Sales 228.8MM^E EMP 1,000
SIC 2834 Pharmaceutical preparations
CEO: Wolfgang Hartwig
*CFO: H Werner Lscher
*CFO: Gregory Webink
*Chf Mktg O: Tim Schlange
Ofcr: Peter Schwarz
*VP: Kenneth Rogers
*VP: Dave Sacks
*VP: Salvatore Sascatta
*VP: Wolfgang Schafer
QA Dir: Christopher Bogart
Ql Cn Mgr: Patricia Townsend

D-U-N-S 18-730-4951
LTX INC
LAWRENCE TRANSPORTATION
1515 Industrial Dr Nw, Rochester, MN 55901-0792
Tel (507) 282-6715 Founded/Ownrshp 1987
Sales 95.9MM^E EMP 456
SIC 4213 Refrigerated products transport
Ch Bd: Steve Lawrence
*Pr: George C Wilson
*CFO: Jayson Crell

D-U-N-S 08-548-4384
LUBAR & CO INC
700 N Water St Ste 1200, Milwaukee, WI 53202-4259
Tel (414) 291-9000 Founded/Ownrshp 1977
Sales 245.3MM^E EMP 511^E
SIC 6722 Management investment, open-end
Pr: David Lubar
*Pt: Vince Shiely
*CFO: David Bauer
*Ch: Sheldon Lubar
Bd of Dir: John Becker
*Prin: David Kuehl

D-U-N-S 07-166-0492
LUBBOCK COUNTY HOSPITAL DISTRICT
UNIVERSITY MEDICAL CENTER
602 Indiana Ave, Lubbock, TX 79415-3364
Tel (806) 775-8200 Founded/Ownrshp 1978
Sales 444.2MM EMP 2,000
SIC 8062 Hospital, medical school affiliation
Pr: David Allison
Sr VP: Jeff Dane
Sr VP: Kimberly Judd
VP: Adrienne Cozart
Dir Case M: Joyce Timmons
Dir Lab: Harry Ng
Off Mgr: Cecelia Garcia
CIO: Bill Eubanks
Dir IT: Shane Terrell
IT Man: Renee Staggs
Obsttrcn: Sharon Shoulders

D-U-N-S 02-033-3878
LUBBOCK INDEPENDENT SCHOOL DISTRICT
1628 19th St, Lubbock, TX 79401-4832
Tel (806) 766-1000 Founded/Ownrshp 1907
Sales 307.6MM EMP 3,300
Accts Bolinger Segars Gilbert & Mo
SIC 8211 Public adult education school; Public elementary school; Public junior high school; Public senior high school
COO: Jennifer Walden
Exec: Bill Tarro
Comm Dir: Nancy Sharp
Ex Dir: Kami Finger
Dir Sec: Jody Scifers
Off Admin: Amber Constancio
Dir IT: Bill Landis
IT Man: Carolyn Jordan
Sales Asso: Anush Gharibyan

D-U-N-S 82-676-3737
LUBE HOLDINGS INC
(Suby of LUBE AGGREGATOR INC)
101 Chestnut Ave, Sharon, PA 16146-1751
Tel (724) 981-3123 Founded/Ownrshp 2004
Sales 90.4MM^E EMP 512^E
SIC 6719 Investment holding companies, except banks
CEO: Greg Lippert

LUBE-TECH
See LUBRICATION TECHNOLOGIES INC

D-U-N-S 10-315-0074 IMP/EXP
LUBERSKI INC
HIDDEN VILLA RANCH
310 N Harbor Blvd Ste 205, Fullerton, CA 92832-1954
Tel (714) 680-3447 Founded/Ownrshp 1991
Sales 260.0MM^E EMP 261
SIC 5144 5143 Eggs; Milk; Cheese
CEO: Timothy Luberski
CFO: Don Lawson
*Ex VP: Robert J Kelly
*Ex VP: Greg Schneider
*Ex VP: Michael Sencer
*VP: Tim Clausen
VP Mktg: Nick Jioras
Mktg Mgr: Brandy Gamoning
Mktg Mgr: Jasen Urena
Sls Mgr: April Canepa
Sls Mgr: Tim Cohen

D-U-N-S 86-720-5866 IMP/EXP
LUBERSKI INC
HIDDEN VILLA RANCH
(Suby of HIDDEN VILLA RANCH) ★
310 N Harbor Blvd Ste 205, Fullerton, CA 92832-1954
Tel (714) 680-3447 Founded/Ownrshp 1987
Sales 260.0MM EMP 261^E
SIC 5144 Eggs
Pr: Tim E Luberski
*CFO: Don Lawson
*Ex VP: Robert J Kelly

Section I Businesses Alphabetically

*Ex VP: Greg Schneider
*Ex VP: Michael Sencer

LUBRICANT ADDITIVES
See LUBRIZOL CORP

D-U-N-S 06-652-5163 IMP
LUBRICATION TECHNOLOGIES INC
LUBE-TECH
900 Mendelssohn Ave N, Minneapolis, MN 55427-4387
Tel (763) 545-0707 Founded/Ownrshp 1993
Sales 181.1MM^E EMP 165
SIC 5172 5169 Lubricating oils & greases; Chemicals & allied products
CEO: Christian Bame
COO: Eric Jackson
Genl Mgr: Dave Stascavage
Dir IT: Todd Matvick
Prd Mgr: Scott Hanson
VP Sls: Adam Sylvester

D-U-N-S 01-237-6732 IMP/EXP
■ LUBRIZOL ADVANCED MATERIALS INC
(Suby of LUBRICANT ADDITIVES) ★
9911 Brecksville Rd, Brecksville, OH 44141-3201
Tel (216) 447-5000 Founded/Ownrshp 2004
Sales 1.1MMM^E EMP 2,780
SIC 2899 2891 3088 2834 3629 Chemical preparations; Adhesives & sealants; Plastics plumbing fixtures; Pharmaceutical preparations; Electronic generation equipment
CEO: James L Hambrick
*Pr: Rick Tolin
*CFO: Brian A Valentine
*VP: John J King
Opers Mgr: Debbie McKee
Mktg Mgr: Carol Durgan

D-U-N-S 00-417-2565 IMP/EXP
■ LUBRIZOL CORP
LUBRICANT ADDITIVES
(Suby of BERKSHIRE HATHAWAY INC) ★
29400 Lakeland Blvd, Wickliffe, OH 44092-2298
Tel (440) 943-4200 Founded/Ownrshp 2011
Sales 6.1MMM^E EMP 14,043
SIC 2899 2869 Oil treating compounds; Industrial organic chemicals
Pr: James L Hambrick
*COO: Stephen F Kirk
*CFO: Charles P Cooley
*CFO: Suzanne F Day
*CFO: Brian A Valentine
VP: Donald W Bogus
VP: Yannick Couedic
VP: Stephen A Di Biase
VP: Ka-Pl Hoh
VP: Phil Hruska
*VP: John J King
VP: Tim Mandilakis
VP: Don Martens
*VP: Larry D Norwood
VP: Brian Pitts
*VP: Eric R Schnur
VP: Eric Schnur
VP: Gregory D Taylor
VP: Mike Vaughn
VP: James Zhang
Exec: Edward Godlewsky

D-U-N-S 02-701-4984
▲ LUBYS INC
13111 Nw Fwy Ste 600, Houston, TX 77040-6392
Tel (713) 329-6800 Founded/Ownrshp 1947
Sales 402.6MM EMP 8,352
Tkr Sym LUB Exch NYS
SIC 5812 Restaurant, family: chain
Pr: Christopher J Pappas
*Ch Bd: Gasper Mir III
*COO: Peter Tropoli
CFO: K Scott Gray
*V Ch Bd: Judith B Craven
VP: Steven Barrow
Area Mgr: Edward Davis
Genl Mgr: Dennis Donahoe
Genl Mgr: Kenneth R Lance
Prd Mgr: Aaron Cerda
Board of Directors: Gerald W Bodzy, Arthur Rojas Emerson, Jill Griffin, J S B Jenkins, Frank Markantonis, Joe C McKinney, Harris J Pappas

D-U-N-S 60-390-8950
■ LUBYS RESTAURANTS LIMITED PARTNERSHIP
(Suby of LUBYS INC) ★
13111 Nw Fwy Ste 600, Houston, TX 77040-6392
Tel (713) 329-6800 Founded/Ownrshp 1996
Sales 238.9MM^E EMP 7,320
SIC 5812 Cafeteria
Ch: Gasper Mir III
*Pr: Chris Pappas
*Pr: Christopher J Pappas
Pr: Dan J Rathmell
*COO: Peter Tropoli
Treas: Roland Gonzalez
*Sr VP: Benjamin T Coutee
*Sr VP: K Scott Gray
VP: Ronald Bass
Dir IT: Steven G Barrow
IT Man: Michele Whitley

D-U-N-S 00-608-6425 IMP
■ LUCAS-MILHAUPT INC
(Suby of HANDY & HARMAN) ★
5656 S Pennsylvania Ave, Cudahy, WI 53110-2453
Tel (414) 769-6000 Founded/Ownrshp 1942
Sales 125.1MM^E EMP 328^E
SIC 3356 Nonferrous rolling & drawing
Pr: John Whitenack
VP: Pam King
CTO: John Gapinski
CTO: Brian Hughes
CTO: Joseph Shapiro
Sls Mgr: Tom Semonic

D-U-N-S 62-035-8387
LUCASVARITY AUTOMOTIVE HOLDING CO
(Suby of TRW AUTOMOTIVE INC) ★
12001 Tech Center Dr, Livonia, MI 48150-2122
Tel (734) 855-2600 Founded/Ownrshp 2003
Sales 125.2MM^E EMP 1,840^E
SIC 3714 Motor vehicle parts & accessories

D-U-N-S 13-438-8524
LUCENT JEWELERS INC
1200 Ave Of Americas, New York, NY 10036
Tel (212) 869-2820 Founded/Ownrshp 1999
Sales 167.7MM^E EMP 1,100
SIC 5094 Diamonds (gems)
Pr: Harry Savalia
*VP: Nilesh Savalia

LUCENT POLYMERS ACQUISITION
See LUCENT POLYMERS INC

D-U-N-S 96-943-0958 EXP
■ LUCENT POLYMERS INC
LUCENT POLYMERS ACQUISITION
(Suby of CITADEL PLASTICS HOLDINGS INC) ★
1700 Lynch Rd, Evansville, IN 47711-2848
Tel (812) 421-2216 Founded/Ownrshp 2013
Sales 103.7MM^E EMP 100
SIC 5162 Resins; Plastics resins
Pr: Kevin Kuhnash
*Treas: Tracy Ripple
Sfty Mgr: Brian Edge

D-U-N-S 01-826-3301 IMP
LUCENT TECHNOLOGIES INTERNATIONAL INC
(Suby of ALCATEL-LUCENT USA INC) ★
600 Mountain Ave 700, New Providence, NJ 07974-2008
Tel (908) 582-8500 Founded/Ownrshp 1996
Sales 152.3MM EMP 400
SIC 5065 Communication equipment
Pr: Janet O'Rourke
CFO: Scott Ashby
Assoc VP: Brian Witt
VP: Jeff Jaffe
VP: Thomas Miller
CTO: Peter Busschbach
CTO: Ruell Levesque
VP Sls: Alain Penel

D-U-N-S 08-434-8143
LUCIA MAR UNIFIED SCHOOL DISTRICT
LUCIA MAR USD
602 Orchard Ave, Arroyo Grande, CA 93420-4000
Tel (805) 474-3000 Founded/Ownrshp 1966
Sales 54.9MM^E EMP 1,000
Accts Vavrinek Trine Day & Co Ll
SIC 8211 Public elementary & secondary schools
Trst: Vern Dahl
Trst: Colleen Martin
Trst: Vicki Meagher
Trst: Don Stewart
Prin: Bob Mistele
Pr Dir: Amy Jacobs
Schl Brd P: Mark Millis

LUCIA MAR USD
See LUCIA MAR UNIFIED SCHOOL DISTRICT

D-U-N-S 06-912-5441 IMP
LUCILE SALTER PACKARD CHILDRENS HOSPITAL AT STANFORD
725 Welch Rd, Palo Alto, CA 94304-1601
Tel (650) 497-8000 Founded/Ownrshp 1919
Sales 1.1MMM EMP 1,100^E
Accts Pricewaterhousecoopers Llp Bo
SIC 8069 8082 5912 Children's hospital; Home health care services; Drug stores & proprietary stores
Pr: Christopher Dawes
*CFO: Timothy W Carmack
VP: Gary May
Chf Nrs Of: Paul Shuttleworth
Off Mgr: Laurie Jones
IT Man: Mila Walker
Pharmcst: Diane Stanton
Board of Directors: Susan Bostrom, John Levin

LUCK STONE CENTRAL SERVICES
See LUCK STONE CORP

D-U-N-S 00-287-5227 IMP/EXP
LUCK STONE CORP (VA)
LUCK STONE CENTRAL SERVICES
515 Stone Mill Dr, Manakin Sabot, VA 23103-3261
Tel (804) 784-3383 Founded/Ownrshp 1923
Sales 770.3MM^E EMP 750
SIC 1423 2899 3281 5211 8741 Crushed & broken granite; Chemical preparations; Cut stone & stone products; Masonry materials & supplies; Management services
Ch Bd: Charles S Luck IV
*Pr: John A Legore
*CFO: Roy B Goodman
Ex VP: Wayne Feigenbutz
*VP: William R Chenault
VP: John Legore
VP: Jim H Ness
VP: Luck Stone
*VP: James H Van Ness
Plnt Mgr: Jamey Epps
Snr Mgr: Audrey Storm

D-U-N-S 00-541-8462
LUCKEY FARMERS INC (OH)
1200 W Main St, Woodville, OH 43469-9701
Tel (419) 849-2711 Founded/Ownrshp 1918
Sales 129.2MM^E EMP 115
SIC 5153 Grain elevators
CEO: Daniel Walski
IT Man: Andrew Gladden

D-U-N-S 61-472-9275 IMP/EXP
LUCKY BRAND DUNGAREES LLC
540 S Santa Fe Ave, Los Angeles, CA 90013-2233
Tel (213) 443-5700 Founded/Ownrshp 2013
Sales 479.8MM^E EMP 477
SIC 2325 2339 Dungarees: men's, youths' & boys'; Jeans: men's, youths' & boys'; Jeans: women's, misses' & juniors'
CEO: Carlos Alberini
Pr: Timothy Mack
CFO: Nigel Kershaw
Sr VP: Courtney Lynch
VP: Alyson Barker
VP: Allison Engel
VP: Robert Fagan
Store Mgr: Christopher Baldwin
Store Mgr: Ashleigh Bargiol
Store Mgr: Madison Bechthold
Store Mgr: Heather Carder

LUCKY LIL'S
See TOWN PUMP INC

D-U-N-S 78-625-8488
LUCKY STRIKE ENTERTAINMENT INC
15260 Ventura Blvd # 1110, Sherman Oaks, CA 91403-5346
Tel (818) 933-3752 Founded/Ownrshp 2004
Sales 241.6MM^E EMP 1,712
SIC 3949 5812 5813 Bowling alleys & accessories; American restaurant; Bar (drinking places)
Pr: Steven Foster
Genl Mgr: Tiffany Newsome
Genl Mgr: Justin Rosenberg
Genl Mgr: Eric Wills
VP Sls: Derek Duronslet
Mktg Dir: Desiree Clode
Mktg Dir: Mark Loewinger
Mktg Dir: Bryan Mundy
Mktg Dir: Brandon Thomsen
Sls Dir: Colleen O'Grady
Sls Mgr: Justina Goyette

D-U-N-S 13-722-0195
LUCKY STRIKE ENTERTAINMENT LLC
LUCKY STRIKE LANES
(Suby of LUCKY STRIKE ENTERTAINMENT INC) ★
15260 Ventura Blvd # 1110, Sherman Oaks, CA 91403-5346
Tel (323) 467-7776 Founded/Ownrshp 2002
Sales 70.0MM^E EMP 1,662
SIC 7933 Ten pin center
Sls Dir: Lyndell Massengale

LUCKY STRIKE LANES
See LUCKY STRIKE ENTERTAINMENT LLC

D-U-N-S 80-748-1999
LUCOR INC
JIFFY LUBE
790 Pershing Rd, Raleigh, NC 27608-2712
Tel (919) 828-9511 Founded/Ownrshp 1998
Sales 75.0MM^E EMP 2,011
SIC 7549 Lubrication service, automotive
Ch Bd: Stephen P Conway
*Pr: Jerry B Conway
*CFO: Kendall A Carr
VP: David Barnett
VP: Michael Davis
VP: Brady R Thompson
Mktg Mgr: Barbara Wallen

D-U-N-S 07-590-9465
■ LUCY LEE HOSPITAL INC
NORTH CAMPUS
(Suby of HMA) ★
2620 N Westwood Blvd, Poplar Bluff, MO 63901-3396
Tel (573) 785-7721 Founded/Ownrshp 2003
Sales 42.2MM^E EMP 1,300
SIC 8062 General medical & surgical hospitals
CEO: Bruce Eady
COO: Cliff Yeager
COO: Mike Youngmann
CFO: John Erickson
CFO: Paul Peiffer
*Ex VP: John Bollmer

D-U-N-S 07-482-8344
LUCY W HAYES TRAINING SCHOOL FOR DECONESSES & MISSIONARIES INC
SIBLEY MEMORIAL HOSPITAL
(Suby of JOHNS HOPKINS HEALTH SYS CORP) ★
5255 Loughboro Rd Nw, Washington, DC 20016-2633
Tel (202) 537-4257 Founded/Ownrshp 2012
Sales 252.6MM EMP 1,500
SIC 8062 General medical & surgical hospitals
Pr: Richard O Davis
VP: Tera Eaton
VP: Gem Henry
VP: Mary Lethbridge
QA Dir: Sonja McLean
Web Prj Mg: Kristen Dusen
Opthamlgy: Sarah Merrill
Doctor: Kim Cox
Doctor: Michelle Divito
Doctor: Kathleen Haywood
Doctor: Michael Lee

D-U-N-S 00-802-5447
LUDLUM MEASUREMENTS INC
501 Oak St, Sweetwater, TX 79556-3209
Tel (325) 235-5494 Founded/Ownrshp 1962
Sales 88.5MM^E EMP 500
SIC 3829 3826 3824 3823 Nuclear radiation & testing apparatus; Analytical instruments; Fluid meters & counting devices; Industrial instrmnts msrmnt display/control process variable
Pr: Donald G Ludlum
CFO: Ed Emerson
*CFO: Jeanie McPherson
*VP: Larry M Ludlum
VP: Jamie Witt
Genl Mgr: Larry Place
Genl Mgr: John Spaulding
DP Exec: Patrick Brand
IT Man: Tony Tillman
Prd Mgr: Keith Brock
VP Sls: Mick Truitt

D-U-N-S 00-469-3565
LUDWIG INSTITUTE FOR CANCER RESEARCH
LICR FUND
666 3rd Ave Fl 28, New York, NY 10017-4030
Tel (212) 450-1500 Founded/Ownrshp 1973
Sales 95.6MM EMP 703
Accts Kpmg Ag
SIC 8733 Medical research
Ch: John L Notter
*Pr: Edward A McDermott Jr
Ofcr: Jonathan Skipper
VP: Xing Chen
Ex Dir: Andrew Simpson
Snr Mgr: Gary Odonnell

LUFKIN DAILY NEWS
See COX TEXAS PUBLICATIONS INC

D-U-N-S 00-809-0375 IMP/EXP
■ LUFKIN INDUSTRIES LLC
(Suby of GENERAL ELECTRIC CO) ★
601 S Raguet St, Lufkin, TX 75904-3951
Tel (936) 634-2211 Founded/Ownrshp 2013
Sales 11.5MM^E EMP 4,700^E
SIC 3561 3321 3462 Pumps & pumping equipment; Pumps, oil well & field; Gray iron castings; Ductile iron castings; Iron & steel forgings; Pump, compressor & turbine forgings
Pr: John F Glick
*Chf Cred: Alejandro Cestero
*Ofcr: Christopher L Boone
Ex VP: Serena Fanucchi
VP: Mark E Crews
*VP: Brian J Gifford
VP: C D Hay
VP: Larry Hoes
*VP: Scott Semlinger
Genl Mgr: Ramses Habib
Off Admin: Leighanne McDonald

D-U-N-S 00-784-9169
LUHR BROS INC (IL)
250 W Sand Bank Rd, Columbia, IL 62236-1044
Tel (618) 281-4106 Founded/Ownrshp 1939
Sales 134.7MM EMP 400
SIC 1629 Dams, waterways, docks & other marine construction
Ch Bd: Twyla Luhr
*Pr: Michael Luhr
COO: Steve Glenn
Treas: Sheryl Metzger
Ofcr: Lloyd Miller
*VP: William R Gardner
*VP: Jay Luhr
*VP: William G Shaw
Genl Mgr: Ronnie Inman
CTO: John Bergman
Dir IT: Tammy Duffy

D-U-N-S 05-273-4878
LUIGINOS INC
MID CONTINENT WAREHOUSE CO
(Suby of YU SING) ★
1325 Port Terminal Rd, Duluth, MN 55802-2642
Tel (218) 722-1427 Founded/Ownrshp 1968, 1991
Sales 25.5MM^E EMP 1,300
SIC 4222 4225 Warehousing, cold storage or refrigerated; General warehousing
Pr: Jeno Paulucci

LUIGI'S FAMILY RESTAURANT
See JACKIES INTERNATIONAL INC

D-U-N-S 02-461-5924 IMP
LUIHN FOOD SYSTEMS INC (NC)
KFC
2950 Gateway Centre Blvd, Morrisville, NC 27560-9615
Tel (919) 850-0558 Founded/Ownrshp 1966
Sales 45.7MM^E EMP 1,200
SIC 5812 Fast-food restaurant, chain
Pr: S Allan Luihn
COO: Cindy McFalls
Treas: Donna Luihn
*VP: Allan J Luihn
Genl Mgr: Tammy Flower
Genl Mgr: Sandra Haines
Genl Mgr: Susan Miller
Sales Exec: Arturo Hernandez
Mktg Dir: Theresa Eberwein

D-U-N-S 09-002-0777 IMP
LUIS GARRATON INC
LGI
Luchetti Ind Park Rd 28 C, Bayamon, PR 00961
Tel (787) 788-6100 Founded/Ownrshp 1948
Sales 85.9MM EMP 250
Accts Falcon Sanchez & Associates P
SIC 5122 5141 Pharmaceuticals; Cosmetics, perfumes & hair products; Groceries, general line
Pr: Raul Rodriguez Font
*Treas: Maria Victoria Leon Freire
*VP: Rafael Rodriguez

D-U-N-S 00-203-3710 IMP
LUITPOLD PHARMACEUTICALS INC (NY)
(Suby of DAIICHI SANKYO COMPANY, LIMITED)
5 Ramsey Rd, Shirley, NY 11967-4701
Tel (631) 924-4000 Founded/Ownrshp 1946, 1970
Sales 221.3MM^E EMP 800
SIC 2834 Pharmaceutical preparations
Ch: Mary Jane Helenek
VP: Gopal Anyarambhatla
VP: Gretchen Fritz
Genl Mgr: William Berger
QA Dir: John Maiero
QA Dir: Michael Setiadi
Dir IT: Gennine Kelly
IT Man: Darrin Turner
Netwrk Mgr: Greg Miller
Netwrk Eng: Ken Kinkead
Sfty Mgr: Liz Tilton

LUJACK'S NORTHPARK AUTO PLAZA
See QUAD CITY AUTOMOTIVE GROUP LLC

D-U-N-S 08-665-5198 IMP
LUK CLUTCH SYSTEMS LLC
(Suby of LUK USA LLC) ★
3401 Old Airport Rd, Wooster, OH 44691-9544
Tel (330) 264-4383 Founded/Ownrshp 2004
Sales 117.9MM^E EMP 1,000^E
SIC 3714 3568 3566 Motor vehicle parts & accessories; Clutches, motor vehicle; Power transmission equipment; Speed changers, drives & gears
VP: David Marlar

MIS Mgr: Hans Peter Seiter
Ql Cn Mgr: Mason Russell
Board of Directors: Siegfried Kronmueller

D-U-N-S 15-212-2359 IMP/EXP
LUK TRANSMISSION SYSTEMS LLC
(*Suby of* LUK USA LLC) ★
3401 Old Airport Rd, Wooster, OH 44691-9544
Tel (330) 264-4383 *Founded/Ownrshp* 2004
Sales 228.8MM[E] *EMP* 640
SIC 3714 3566 Motor vehicle parts & accessories; Speed changers, drives & gears

D-U-N-S 17-094-9692 IMP
LUK USA LLC
(*Suby of* SCHAEFFLER GROUP USA INC) ★
3401 Old Airport Rd, Wooster, OH 44691-9544
Tel (330) 264-4383 *Founded/Ownrshp* 2009
Sales 346.8MM[E] *EMP* 1,000[E]
SIC 3714 Motor vehicle parts & accessories
CEO: Klaus Rosenfeld
**Pr:* Marc McGrath
VP: Marc McGrath
**VP:* Ashi Uppal
Exec: Steven Bushman
CIO: Tom Miller
Plnt Mgr: Al McAfoos

D-U-N-S 12-665-2010 IMP
■ **LUKE PAPER CO**
NEWPAGE
(*Suby of* VERSO CORP) ★
300 Pratt St, Luke, MD 21540-1015
Tel (301) 359-3311 *Founded/Ownrshp* 2015
Sales 195.3MM[E] *EMP* 1,000[E]
SIC 2621 Paper mills
Pr: George F Martin
Sr VP: Stacy Mazza

LUKE THEIS CONTRACTORS
See LUKE THEIS ENTERPRISES INC

D-U-N-S 10-863-3561
LUKE THEIS ENTERPRISES INC
LUKE THEIS CONTRACTORS
14120 State Route 568, Findlay, OH 45840-9428
Tel (419) 422-2040 *Founded/Ownrshp* 1969
Sales 122.0MM *EMP* 57
SIC 1542 1541 1521 Nonresidential construction; Industrial buildings & warehouses; New construction, single-family houses
Pr: Luke Theis

D-U-N-S 01-229-6021
LUKOIL AMERICAS CORP
(*Suby of* LUKOIL, PAO)
505 5th Ave Fl 9, New York, NY 10017-4921
Tel (212) 421-4141 *Founded/Ownrshp* 1997
Sales 105.9MM[E] *EMP* 624
SIC 1311 Crude petroleum & natural gas
Ch Bd: Vadim Guzman
**CEO:* Robert Ferluga

LULULEMON ATHLETICA USA
See LULULEMON USA INC

D-U-N-S 01-206-0918
LULULEMON USA INC
LULULEMON ATHLETICA USA
(*Suby of* LULULEMON ATHLETICA CANADA INC)
2201 140th Ave E, Sumner, WA 98390-9711
Tel (604) 732-6124 *Founded/Ownrshp* 2002
Sales 4.0MM *EMP* 5,000[E]
SIC 5137 5331 Women's & children's sportswear & swimsuits; Variety stores
Pr: Laurent Potdevin

D-U-N-S 09-497-2973
LUMASENSE TECHNOLOGIES INC
3301 Leonard Ct, Santa Clara, CA 95054-2054
Tel (408) 727-1600 *Founded/Ownrshp* 2003
Sales 130.2MM[E] *EMP* 421
SIC 3823 3845 3829 3825 Industrial instrmnts msrmnt display/control process variable; Temperature instruments: industrial process type; Industrial process control instruments; Electromedical equipment; Measuring & controlling devices; Instruments to measure electricity
CEO: Steve Abely
**Pr:* Vivek Joshi
Pr: Steve Uhlir
**VP:* Subra Sankar
VP: Brett Sargent
**VP:* Ronald Sutton
VP: Victor Wong
**VP:* Diane Wotus
Area Mgr: Bob Mintz
Off Mgr: Mary Jenkins
IT Man: Wlodek Czeczot

D-U-N-S 06-109-5071
LUMBEE RIVER ELECTRIC MEMBERSHIP CORP
605 E 4th Ave, Red Springs, NC 28377-1668
Tel (910) 843-7932 *Founded/Ownrshp* 1940
Sales 126.6MM *EMP* 121
Accts Dixon Hughes Goodman Llp Danv
SIC 4911 Distribution, electric power
**CEO:* Perry Cummings
**VP:* Carmen Dietrich
**VP:* Angela Revels-Bullard
**VP:* Robert Stricklend
Exec: Craig Davis
**Genl Mgr:* Ronnie Hunt
Genl Mgr: Misha Melvin

D-U-N-S 00-599-1641 IMP
LUMBER CITY CORP (CA)
NEIMAN-REED LUMBER CO
20525 Nordhoff St Ste 210, Chatsworth, CA 91311-6135
Tel (818) 407-3888 *Founded/Ownrshp* 1948, 1986
Sales 131.8MM[E] *EMP* 550
SIC 5211 5031 Lumber & other building materials; Lumber, plywood & millwork
CEO: Jesse A Ruf
CFO: John Lyons

D-U-N-S 96-197-6698
▲ **LUMBER LIQUIDATORS HOLDINGS INC**
3000 John Deere Rd, Toano, VA 23168-9332
Tel (757) 259-4280 *Founded/Ownrshp* 1994
Sales 978.7MM *EMP* 1,842
Tkr Sym LL *Exch* NYS
SIC 5211 Lumber & other building materials
CEO: Dennis R Knowles
CFO: Martin Agard
CFO: Gregory A Whirley Jr
CIO: Christopher Tomsen
Board of Directors: W Stephen Cannon, Douglas T Moore, John M Presley, Peter B Robinson, Martin F Roper, Thomas D Sullivan, Nancy M Taylor, Jimmie L Wade

D-U-N-S 94-901-2280 IMP/EXP
■ **LUMBER LIQUIDATORS INC**
HUSKY HARDWOOD FLOORS
(*Suby of* LUMBER LIQUIDATORS HOLDINGS INC) ★
3000 John Deere Rd, Toano, VA 23168-9332
Tel (757) 259-4280 *Founded/Ownrshp* 1994
Sales 449.9MM[E] *EMP* 788
SIC 5031 5211 Hardboard; Lumber products
CEO: Robert Lynch
COO: Dennis R Knowles
CFO: Everett T Daniel
CFO: Daniel E Terrell
Ofcr: Sandra C Whitehouse
Sr VP: E Jean Matherne
VP: James J Costa
VP: Ken Strohschein
Board of Directors: Macon F Brock Jr, Douglas T Moore, John M Presley, Martin F Roper, Thomas D Sullivan, Richard D Tadler

LUMBER PDTS HOLDINGS & MGT CO
See LUMBER PRODUCTS AN OREGON CORP

D-U-N-S 00-790-8759 IMP/EXP
LUMBER PRODUCTS AN OREGON CORP
LUMBER PDTS HOLDINGS & MGT CO
5200 Meadows Rd Ste 150, Lake Oswego, OR 97035-0066
Tel (503) 692-3322 *Founded/Ownrshp* 1938
Sales 95.6MM[E] *EMP* 540
SIC 5031 Lumber: rough, dressed & finished; Plywood; Doors
Pr: Peter J Hall
**Pr:* Edward C Hostmann
**COO:* Craig Hall
**CFO:* Bart Walker
Admn Mgr: Carla Singler
Opers Mgr: A Swindlehurst
Sales Exec: John McMains

D-U-N-S 06-181-2087 IMP
LUMBERMEN ASSOCIATES INC
2101 Hunter Rd, Bristol, PA 19007
Tel (215) 785-4600 *Founded/Ownrshp* 1961
Sales 107.0MM *EMP* 65
Accts Kreischer Miller Horsham Pen
SIC 5031 Lumber: rough, dressed & finished
Pr: Thomas J Deegan
**CFO:* Brian R Cassel
**Treas:* Timothy M Deegan
**Ex VP:* Thomas C Coleman

D-U-N-S 00-656-7465
LUMBERMENS INC (MI)
ROSEWOOD WORKS
4433 Stafford Ave Sw, Grand Rapids, MI 49548-4124
Tel (616) 261-3200 *Founded/Ownrshp* 1955, 1986
Sales 237.0MM[E] *EMP* 270
SIC 5033 5031 5198 Roofing, asphalt & sheet metal; Shingles, except wood; Insulation, thermal; Doors & windows; Windows; Paneling, wood; Molding, all materials; Stain
Pr: Roger Vanderheide
**Ex VP:* Douglas Rathbun
VP: Henry Bouma
VP: Randy Martin
VP: Dave Mulder
**VP:* Steve Petersen
VP: Steve Peterson
Manager: Tim Karcher
Sls Mgr: Alan Albert
Sales Asso: Jeff Brown
Sales Asso: Larry Greer

D-U-N-S 00-893-9803 EXP
LUMBERMENS MERCHANDISING CORP
LMC
137 W Wayne Ave, Wayne, PA 19087-4018
Tel (610) 293-3678 *Founded/Ownrshp* 1935
Sales 221.8MM[E] *EMP* 200
SIC 5031 5072 Lumber: rough, dressed & finished; Millwork; Plywood; Wallboard; Builders' hardware
Pr: John Somerville Jr
**Pr:* Annamarie Genther
**Treas:* Anthony J Decarlo
Top Exec: Christopher Hart
**Sr VP:* John L Broomell
**Sr VP:* David J Gonze
**VP:* Kathleen M Butcosk
VP: Kathleen Butcosk
**VP:* Vern Dando
**VP:* John Keeley
**VP:* Andrew J Toombs
Board of Directors: Douglas R Kuiken, Douglas E Ashy Sr, Kenneth L Lawson Jr, W A Bissette, Kenneth J Lehman, Jeffrey B Brown, Michael F Lezzer, David M Campbell, David Majeski, C Christopher Cluss, Joel C Robinson Jr, Farrell L Goble, Steven C Steinman, George W Hodges, Alfred J Torrisi, Thomas J Hughes, Charles L Kirchner

D-U-N-S 07-628-0528
LUMBERMENS UNDERWRITING ALLIANCE
L U A
1905 Nw Corporate Blvd, Boca Raton, FL 33431-7315
Tel (561) 994-1900 *Founded/Ownrshp* 1973
Sales NA *EMP* 226
SIC 6331 6411 6311 Fire, marine & casualty insurance & carriers; Insurance agents, brokers & service; Life insurance
Ch Bd: Christine Lynn
**Pr:* Bill Broich
Pr: Gary Lambert
**CEO:* Jan Carlsson
**CFO:* Jeff Poirier
**VP:* Mindy Appel
**VP:* Mary Moore
**VP:* Wil Nance
VP: Michael North
VP: Craig Smith
Rgnl Mgr: Chris Jacobson

D-U-N-S 14-242-3826
LUMENATE TECHNOLOGIES LP
16633 Dallas Pkwy Ste 450, Addison, TX 75001-6811
Tel (972) 248-8999 *Founded/Ownrshp* 2003
Sales 96.0MM[E] *EMP* 240
SIC 7379 Computer related consulting services
Pt: Reagan Dixon
Pt: Chad Hodges
Pt: Collin Miles
Pt: Jeff Stoll
Pr: Ethan Simmons
VP: Denisa Bravenec
VP: Gary Derheim
VP: Chris Harrington
Dir Sec: Mark Seay
Sls Dir: Steve Lonon
Snr PM: Wayne Grant

D-U-N-S 88-362-4843 IMP
LUMENIS INC
(*Suby of* LUMENIS LTD.)
2033 Gateway Pl Ste 200, San Jose, CA 95110-3714
Tel (408) 764-3000 *Founded/Ownrshp* 1992
Sales 228.9MM[E] *EMP* 600
SIC 5047 Therapy equipment
CEO: Tzipi Ozer Armon
**Ch Bd:* Harel Beit-On
**Pr:* Abner Ray
COO: Zivi Nedivisioni
**CFO:* Shlomi Cohen
CFO: Laurie Hanover
**CFO:* Kevin Morano
**Ex VP:* Mono Grencel
VP: Kevin McGann
**VP:* Hadas Padan
**VP:* Roy Ramati

D-U-N-S 07-981-7523
▲ **LUMENTUM HOLDINGS INC**
400 N Mccarthy Blvd, Milpitas, CA 95035-5112
Tel (408) 546-5483 *Founded/Ownrshp* 1979
Sales 903.0MM *EMP* 1,850[E]
Accts Pricewaterhousecoopers Llp Sa
Tkr Sym LITE *Exch* NGS
SIC 3669 3674 3826 Emergency alarms; Semiconductors & related devices; Optical isolators; Analytical instruments; Laser scientific & engineering instruments
Pr: Alan Lowe
**Ch Bd:* Martin A Kaplan
**Pr:* Alan S Lowe
COO: Vince Retor
CFO: Aaron Tachibana
Ex VP: Jason Reinhardt
Plng Mgr: Michael Tang
Board of Directors: Harold L Covert, Penelope A Herscher, Brian J Lillie, Samuel F Thomas

D-U-N-S 12-499-8217 IMP/EXP
LUMILEDS LLC
PHILIPS LUMILEDS LIGHTING CO
370 W Trimble Rd, San Jose, CA 95131-1008
Tel (408) 964-2900 *Founded/Ownrshp* 1999
Sales 208.3MM[E] *EMP* 470[E]
SIC 3825 Electrical energy measuring equipment
CEO: Pierre Yves Lesaicherre
**COO:* Ajay Marathe
Ex VP: Steve Barlow
**Sr VP:* Klemens Brunner
**Sr VP:* Mircea-Irimia Buzgar-Nazare
Sr VP: Emmanuel Dieppedalle
Sr VP: Pascal Popis
**VP:* Alex Kirk
VP: Paul Van Der Plas

D-U-N-S 10-950-6043 IMP
LUMINANT GENERATION CO LLC
ENERGY FUTURE HOLDINGS
(*Suby of* TXU ENERGY) ★
1601 Bryan St, Dallas, TX 75201-3401
Tel (214) 812-4600 *Founded/Ownrshp* 2001
Sales 1.1MMM[E] *EMP* 2,000[E]
SIC 4911 3621 Electric services; Power generators
Pr: Mac McFarland
**CFO:* Robert Frenzel
**Sr VP:* Richard R Federwisch
**Sr VP:* Joseph C Ho
**Sr VP:* Stpehen G Horn

D-U-N-S 04-463-2834
LUMINANT MINING CO LLC
TXU
(*Suby of* TXU ENERGY INDUSTRIES CO) ★
1601 Bryan St, Dallas, TX 75201-3401
Tel (214) 812-4600 *Founded/Ownrshp* 2002
Sales 815.2MM[E] *EMP* 653
SIC 1221 Bituminous coal & lignite-surface mining
Pr: David A Campbell
CFO: Paul Keglevic
V Ch Bd: Mike Greene
Ex VP: M A McFarland
Sr VP: Richard R Federwisch
Sr VP: Robert C Frenzel
Prin: Paul M Keglevic

D-U-N-S 07-829-6029 IMP
LUMINATOR TECHNOLOGY GROUP LLC
900 Klein Rd, Plano, TX 75074-3712
Tel (972) 424-6511 *Founded/Ownrshp* 2014
Sales 88.9MM[E] *EMP* 400
SIC 3613 3643 3646 3647 Switchgear & switchboard apparatus; Current-carrying wiring devices; Commercial indusl & institutional electric lighting fixtures; Aircraft lighting fixtures
Pr: AVI Zisman
**VP:* Steven Boyd
**VP:* Dan Kelleher
**VP:* Nick Moolenijzer
Exec: Gregg Evans
VP Sls: Riko Yap
Sls Mgr: Thomas Jacobsson

D-U-N-S 14-156-2020
LUMINENT MORTGAGE CAPITAL INC
1 Commerce Sq, Philadelphia, PA 19103-1415
Tel (215) 564-5900 *Founded/Ownrshp* 2003
Sales 520.8MM *EMP* 26[E]
SIC 6798 Real estate investment trusts
Pr: Zachary H Pashel
**Ch Bd:* Craig A Cohen
CFO: Karen Chang
Sr VP: Dimitri Papatheoharis

D-U-N-S 96-547-6641
▲ **LUMINEX CORP**
12212 Technology Blvd, Austin, TX 78727-6100
Tel (512) 219-8020 *Founded/Ownrshp* 1995
Sales 237.7MM *EMP* 797[E]
Tkr Sym LMNX *Exch* NGS
SIC 3841 8731 Diagnostic apparatus, medical; Commercial physical research; Biological research
Pr: Nachum Shamir
**Ch Bd:* G Walter Loewenbaum
CFO: Harriss T Currie
Sr VP: Nancy M Fairchild
Sr VP: Randall Myers
Sr VP: Richard W Rew II
VP: Chuck Collins
Assoc Dir: John Geddes
Snr Sftwr: Donald Conner
Sftwr Eng: Shane Torgerson
VP Mfg: Steven Back
Board of Directors: Robert J Cresci, Stephen L Eck, Thomas W Erickson, Jay B Johnston, Kim D Kever, Kevin M McNamara, Edward A Ogunro

LUMINEX HD&F COMPANY
See LUMINEX HOME DECOR & FRAGRANCE HOLDING CORP

D-U-N-S 08-026-6528
LUMINEX HOME DECOR & FRAGRANCE HOLDING CORP
LUMINEX HD&F COMPANY
10521 Millington Ct, Blue Ash, OH 45242-4022
Tel (513) 563-1113 *Founded/Ownrshp* 2016
Sales 260.9MM[E] *EMP* 1,200[E]
SIC 5023 2844 Decorative home furnishings & supplies; Toilet preparations
CEO: Calvin Johnston

D-U-N-S 00-698-7028
LUMMUS OVERSEAS CORP
CB & I LUMMUS GLOBAL INC
(*Suby of* CHICAGO BRIDGE & IRON CO) ★
1515 Broad St, Bloomfield, NJ 07003-3002
Tel (973) 893-1515 *Founded/Ownrshp* 1907, 2007
Sales 210.0MM[E] *EMP* 4,000
SIC 8711 1629 8741 Engineering services; Industrial plant construction; Construction management
Pr: Martin W Gross
**Ex VP:* K Farid
**VP:* M Duplantier
**VP:* M J Ford Jr

D-U-N-S 07-834-4519
▲ **LUMOS NETWORKS CORP**
1 Lumos Plz, Waynesboro, VA 22980-4549
Tel (540) 946-2000 *Founded/Ownrshp* 2011
Sales 204.2MM *EMP* 593[E]
Tkr Sym LMOS *Exch* NGS
SIC 4813 Telephone communication, except radio;
Pr: Timothy G Biltz
**Ch Bd:* Robert E Guth
CFO: Johan G Broekhuysen
Ex VP: Joseph E McCourt Jr
Sr VP: Diego Anderson
Sr VP: William G Davis Jr
Sr VP: Thomas E Ferry
Sr VP: Mary McDermott
Sr VP: Jeffrey Miller
Genl Mgr: Pam McGown
Board of Directors: Peter D Aquino, Lawrence J Askowitz, Shawn F O'donnell, William M Pruellage, Michael K Robinson, Michael T Sicoli, Jerry E Vaughn

D-U-N-S 05-056-3808
LUNAN CORP
414 N Orleans St Ste 402, Chicago, IL 60654-8002
Tel (312) 645-9898 *Founded/Ownrshp* 1967
Sales 48.4MM[E] *EMP* 1,000[E]
Accts Crowe Chizek Oak Brook Il
SIC 5812 Fast-food restaurant, chain
Pr: Gregory Schulson
**Ch Bd:* Michael Schulson
**CFO:* Steve Ganek
**VP:* Brendan Casey
VP Opers: Jeff Winograd
Mktg Dir: Janet Broline

D-U-N-S 04-294-5715
LUND BROWN ENTERPRISES LLC
7490 Clubhouse Rd Ste 200, Boulder, CO 80301-3720
Tel (303) 530-2900 *Founded/Ownrshp* 2010
Sales 229.9MM[E] *EMP* 6,000
SIC 6794 Franchises, selling or licensing
Owner: Dewey R Brown

D-U-N-S 96-156-6502
LUND FOOD HOLDINGS INC
LUNDS & BYERLYS
4100 W 50th St Ste 100, Minneapolis, MN 55424-1272
Tel (952) 927-3663 *Founded/Ownrshp* 1997
Sales 540.8MM[E] *EMP* 4,500
SIC 5411 Supermarkets, chain
CEO: Russell T Lund III
Pr: Russell Lund
Genl Mgr: Dave Detloff
Genl Mgr: Tom Gordon
Genl Mgr: Patty Horton
Genl Mgr: Dave Jones
Genl Mgr: Gary Larges
Genl Mgr: Mike Macrae
Genl Mgr: Todd Moffitt
Genl Mgr: Diane Stehura
Genl Mgr: Heather Wicklander

D-U-N-S 14-851-0928 IMP
LUND INC
DEFLECTA SHIELD
(*Suby of* TRADESMAN TRUCK ACCESSORIES) ★
4325 Hamilton Mill Rd # 400, Buford, GA 30518-8848
Tel (678) 804-3767 *Founded/Ownrshp* 2007
Sales 168.5MM[E] *EMP* 500
SIC 3714 Motor vehicle parts & accessories; Bumpers & bumperettes, motor vehicle; Sun roofs, motor vehicle; Wind deflectors, motor vehicle
CEO: George Scherff
**Pr:* Mitch Fogle
**COO:* Bob Chapman
COO: Robert Chapman
**CFO:* Glenn A Hollis
**CFO:* Bill White
**VP:* Tammy Gracek
VP: Harry Samp
**VP:* Matt Stanesic
**VP:* Joe Thompson
Exec: Billy Bibb

D-U-N-S 96-880-5536
LUND INTERNATIONAL HOLDING CO
TRADESMAN TRUCK ACCESSORIES
4325 Hamilton Mill Rd, Buford, GA 30518-8835
Tel (678) 804-3767 *Founded/Ownrshp* 2007
Sales 259.8MM[E] *EMP* 500[E]
SIC 3714 3713 Motor vehicle parts & accessories; Bumpers & bumperettes, motor vehicle; Sun roofs, motor vehicle; Wind deflectors, motor vehicle; Truck beds
Pr: Mitch Fogle
**Pr:* Gre Bernardo
**COO:* Tammy Gracek
**CFO:* Mark Stanko
**Sr VP:* Joe Thompson

D-U-N-S 00-583-2613
■ **LUNDA CONSTRUCTION CO** (WI)
(*Suby of* TUTOR PERINI CORP) ★
620 Gebhardt Rd, Black River Falls, WI 54615-9152
Tel (715) 284-2322 *Founded/Ownrshp* 1938, 2011
Sales 389.0MM *EMP* 1,785
Accts Deloitte & Touche Llp Los Ang
SIC 1622 8711 Bridge construction; Engineering services
Pr: Larry Lunda
**CFO:* Carl Holmquist
VP: Dennis Behnke
**VP:* Tom Braun
VP: John Ostrowski
**VP:* Richard Slifka
IT Man: Michael Haun
Sfty Dirs: William Olson
Mtls Mgr: Wayne Baumgartner

D-U-N-S 01-834-3595
LUNDBECK LLC (IL)
(*Suby of* H. LUNDBECK A/S)
6 Parkway N Ste 400, Deerfield, IL 60015-2522
Tel (847) 282-1000 *Founded/Ownrshp* 2000, 2009
Sales 172.5MM[E] *EMP* 674[E]
SIC 2834 5122 Pharmaceutical preparations; Pharmaceuticals
CEO: Sean Nolan
**CFO:* Curtis Rhine
Ofcr: Erik Eglite
VP: Erik Allikmets
VP: Dan Brennan
VP: Charles R Krikorian
VP: Randall Owen
Assoc Dir: Ron Mihalcean
Dir Bus: Bradon Kashfian
Mng Dir: Franz Blatnek
Area Mgr: Michael Romano

LUNDS & BYERLYS
See LUND FOOD HOLDINGS INC

LUNDS & BYERLYS HIGHLAND PARK
See LUNDS INC

D-U-N-S 02-291-6134
LUNDS INC
LUNDS & BYERLYS HIGHLAND PARK
4100 W 50th St Ste 100, Minneapolis, MN 55424-1272
Tel (952) 927-3663 *Founded/Ownrshp* 1961
Sales 185.1MM[E] *EMP* 1,709
SIC 5411 Supermarkets, chain
CEO: Russell T Lund III
**Treas:* Von Martin
**VP:* Jim Geisler
Store Mgr: Steve Bishop

D-U-N-S 08-915-3071 IMP
LUPIN PHARMACEUTICALS INC
(*Suby of* LUPIN LIMITED)
111 S Calvert St Fl 21, Baltimore, MD 21202-6174
Tel (410) 576-2000 *Founded/Ownrshp* 2003
Sales 270.5MM[E] *EMP* 407[E]
SIC 5122 Drugs & drug proprietaries
CEO: Vinita Gupta
**Pr:* Paul McGarty
**CFO:* William Gileza
Top Exec: Alok Sharma
VP: Pramod Dahibhate
VP: Nitin Vadia
Exec: Amit Malani
Mng Dir: Kamal Sharma
Genl Mgr: Pradeep Bhagwat
Genl Mgr: Amrut Naik
Off Mgr: Leslie Leader

D-U-N-S 17-011-6409
LUPTON VENTURES INC
1405 14th St, Fort Lupton, CO 80621-2718
Tel (303) 659-9767 *Founded/Ownrshp* 2004
Sales 93.2MM[E] *EMP* 170
SIC 3353 Aluminum sheet, plate & foil
CEO: Jeff Frim

LURCAT
See DAMICO & PARTNERS INC

D-U-N-S 02-406-3877 IMP
LUSAMERICA FOODS INC
16480 Railroad Ave, Morgan Hill, CA 95037-5210
Tel (408) 294-6622 *Founded/Ownrshp* 1976
Sales 128.8MM[E] *EMP* 150[E]
SIC 5146 5142 Fish, fresh; Fish, frozen, unpackaged; Packaged frozen goods
CEO: Fernando Luis Frederico
**VP:* Anna Frederico
Exec: Nicole Silva
MIS Dir: Paula Silva
Manager: Jason Beaulieu
VP Sls: Eric Critchlow
Sls Mgr: Randy Fairbanks

D-U-N-S 00-958-5464
LUSARDI CONSTRUCTION CO
1570 Linda Vista Dr, San Marcos, CA 92078-3880
Tel (760) 744-3133 *Founded/Ownrshp* 1947
Sales 138.3MM[E] *EMP* 250
SIC 1542 1541

D-U-N-S 80-041-0602
LUTHER BURBANK CORP
520 3rd St Fl 4, Santa Rosa, CA 95401-6414
Tel (707) 523-9898 *Founded/Ownrshp* 2007
Sales 134.9MM[E] *EMP* 168[E]
SIC 8211 Elementary & secondary schools
CEO: George Mancini

LUTHER BURBANK SAVINGS CORP
See BURBANK LUTHER SAVINGS

D-U-N-S 78-794-8876
LUTHER HOLDING CO
3701 Alabama Ave S, Minneapolis, MN 55416-5156
Tel (763) 593-5755 *Founded/Ownrshp* 1989
Sales 240.9MM[E] *EMP* 700
SIC 5511 7515 7513 6512 6552 5611 Automobiles, new & used; Pickups, new & used; Vans, new & used; Passenger car leasing; Truck leasing, without drivers; Commercial & industrial building operation; Subdividers & developers; Men's & boys' clothing stores
Pr: David Luther
**Pr:* R Daniel Luther
**Treas:* C David Luther
VP: Mike Gallagher
IT Man: Dan Johnson

D-U-N-S 84-180-1186
LUTHER HOSPITAL
HEALTHWORKS
733 W Clairemont Ave, Eau Claire, WI 54701-6101
Tel (715) 838-3060 *Founded/Ownrshp* 1986
Sales 230.8MM *EMP* 5
SIC 8011 Occupational & industrial specialist, physician/surgeon

D-U-N-S 09-704-7872
LUTHER KING CAPITAL MANAGEMENT CORP
301 Commerce St Ste 1600, Fort Worth, TX 76102-4190
Tel (817) 429-6256 *Founded/Ownrshp* 1979
Sales 331.3MM[E] *EMP* 1,314
SIC 6282 Investment counselors
Pr: John Luther King Jr
**Treas:* Lisa Rettew
**VP:* David Dowler
**VP:* Paul Greenwell
**VP:* Scot Hollmann
**VP:* Mark Johnson
**VP:* Bryan King
**VP:* Trisha Kroutil
**VP:* Jim Krrigan
**VP:* Allan Marshall
VP: David May
**VP:* Joan Maynard
VP: Greg McCoy
**VP:* Vince Melashenko
VP: Scott Neuendorf
**VP:* Jim Orser
**VP:* Steve Purvis
**VP:* Jacob Smith
**VP:* Bill Uhlemeyer
**VP:* Gary Walsh
**VP:* Michael Yeager

D-U-N-S 07-134-0608
LUTHER MIDELFORT MAYO HEALTH SYSTEM
733 W Clairemont Ave, Eau Claire, WI 54701-6101
Tel (715) 838-5353 *Founded/Ownrshp* 1992
Sales NA *EMP* 1,076
SIC 6324 8011 Health maintenance organization (HMO), insurance only; Clinic, operated by physicians
CEO: Randall Linton
Off Mgr: Betty Savall

D-U-N-S 06-855-0441
LUTHERAN CHURCH - MISSOURI SYNOD
1333 S Kirkwood Rd, Saint Louis, MO 63122-7226
Tel (314) 965-9000 *Founded/Ownrshp* 1847
Sales 145.2MM *EMP* 325[E]
Accts Brown Smith Wallace Llc S
SIC 8661 Lutheran Church
Pr: Matthew Harrison
Pr: Peter Meier
**COO:* Ron Schultz
**CFO:* Jerald Wulf
VP: Dorothy Kaestner
**VP:* Herbert Miller
Off Mgr: Diane Grimm

D-U-N-S 60-331-2331
LUTHERAN GENERAL MEDICAL GROUP S C
1775 Dempster St Ste 10, Park Ridge, IL 60068-1143
Tel (847) 795-2800 *Founded/Ownrshp* 1906
Sales 55.0MM[E] *EMP* 1,000
SIC 8093

D-U-N-S 62-067-9688
■ **LUTHERAN HEALTH NETWORK OF INDIANA LLC**
(*Suby of* QUORUM HEALTH RESOURCES LLC) ★
2123 Lincolnway Ct, Fort Wayne, IN 46819-2140
Tel (260) 479-3550 *Founded/Ownrshp* 2001
Sales 123.3MM[E] *EMP* 1,060
SIC 6719 Investment holding companies, except banks
Pr: Brian Bauer
COO: Bernard A Niezer
VP: Krista Quinones

D-U-N-S 00-417-8799
LUTHERAN HEART HOSPITAL
BANNER HEART HOSPITAL
6750 E Baywood Ave, Mesa, AZ 85206-1749
Tel (480) 854-5000 *Founded/Ownrshp* 1998
Sales 132.0MM *EMP* 4
SIC 8062 General medical & surgical hospitals
CEO: Laura Robertson
Exec: Matthew James

D-U-N-S 80-964-5182
LUTHERAN HOME ALBEMARLE PROPERTY INC
24724 S Business 52, Albemarle, NC 28001-8179
Tel (704) 982-8191 *Founded/Ownrshp* 2004
Sales 219.1M *EMP* 1,000
Accts Langdon & Company Llp Garneer
SIC 6531 Real estate managers
CEO: Ted W Goins Jr
**Treas:* Annette S Conrad

LUTHERAN HOME FOR THE AGED
See LUTHERAN LIFE COMMUNITIES

LUTHERAN HOSPITAL
See LUTHERAN MEDICAL CENTER (INC)

LUTHERAN HOSPITAL - LA CROSSE
See GUNDERSEN LUTHERAN MEDICAL CENTER INC

LUTHERAN HOSPITAL OF INDIANA
See IOM HEALTH SYSTEM LP

D-U-N-S 02-429-8938
■ **LUTHERAN HOSPITAL OF INDIANA LP**
(*Suby of* COMMUNITY HEALTH SYSTEMS INC) ★
7950 W Jefferson Blvd, Fort Wayne, IN 46804-4160
Tel (260) 479-3434 *Founded/Ownrshp* 2009
Sales 38.5MM[E] *EMP* 5,000
SIC 8062 General medical & surgical hospitals
CEO: Byan Bauer

D-U-N-S 16-449-4291
LUTHERAN LIFE COMMUNITIES
LUTHERAN HOME FOR THE AGED
800 W Oakton St, Arlington Heights, IL 60004-4602
Tel (847) 368-7400 *Founded/Ownrshp* 1984
Sales 6.8MM *EMP* 1,200
SIC 8052 Intermediate care facilities
CEO: Roger Paulsberg
CEO: Tim Leone
Opers Mgr: Lonnie Lehman
HC Dir: Marlette Borland
HC Dir: Deanna Orsi

D-U-N-S 18-952-6163
LUTHERAN MEDICAL CENTER
8300 W 38th Ave, Wheat Ridge, CO 80033-6005
Tel (303) 425-4500 *Founded/Ownrshp* 1959
Sales 68.1M[E] *EMP* 2,100
SIC 8011 7389 8082 8331 Offices & clinics of medical doctors; Fund raising organizations; Home health care services; Manpower training
CEO: Grant Wicklund
CFO: James Doyle

D-U-N-S 07-690-3129
LUTHERAN MEDICAL CENTER (INC)
LUTHERAN HOSPITAL
(*Suby of* CLEVELAND CLINIC HEALTH SYSTEM) ★
1730 W 25th St, Cleveland, OH 44113-3108
Tel (216) 696-4300 *Founded/Ownrshp* 1895
Sales 91.9MM *EMP* 800
SIC 8062 8011 8069 General medical & surgical hospitals; Offices & clinics of medical doctors; Specialty hospitals, except psychiatric
CEO: David Pesre MD
Dir Recs: Pat Koch
**CFO:* Christopher Winters
Dir OR: Amyu Boone
Dir Case M: Cathleen Lawley
Off Mgr: Virginia R Tipton
Doctor: Leslie J Gilbert MD
Doctor: Leslie Gilbert
Doctor: Michelle Rader
Diag Rad: J Bradley Burns
Diag Rad: Howard S Cahn

D-U-N-S 16-027-8776
LUTHERAN SENIOR SERVICES
1150 Hanley Industrial Ct, Saint Louis, MO 63144-1910
Tel (314) 968-9313 *Founded/Ownrshp* 1985
Sales 187.0MM *EMP* 2,254
Accts Cliftonlarsonallen Llp St L
SIC 8361 Geriatric residential care
Pr: John Kotovsky
Pr: Michael Raso
**COO:* Linda M Detring
**CFO:* Paul Ogier
CFO: Gary Winchell
CFO: Gary M Winschel
CFO: Gary Winshel
Ofcr: Ellen Harmon
VP: Gary Anderson
VP: Lea A Coates
VP: Linda Detring
VP: Sue Duncan
VP: Mary P Lazare
Exec: Michelle Wetter
Creative D: Kathi Bell

D-U-N-S 13-967-6936
LUTHERAN SERVICES FLORIDA INC
3627a W Waters Ave, Tampa, FL 33614-2783
Tel (813) 868-4438 *Founded/Ownrshp* 1982
Sales 150.8MM *EMP* 565
Accts Cbiz Mhm Llc Clearwater Fl
SIC 8322 Social service center
Pr: Samuel M Sipes
**Pr:* Christopher J Card
Ofcr: Angie Henderson
VP: Angela W Combs
**VP:* Michael Seeraj
**VP:* George Wallace
**VP:* David Yarborough
Ex Dir: Fred Tausig

D-U-N-S 07-106-3077
LUTHERAN SERVICES FOR AGING INC
1416 S Martin Luther, Salisbury, NC 28144
Tel (704) 637-2870 *Founded/Ownrshp* 1960
Sales 86.8MM *EMP* 2,800
Accts Dixon Hughes Goodman Llp Rale
SIC 8051 8052 8059 Convalescent home with continuous nursing care; Intermediate care facilities; Rest home, with health care
Pr: Ted W Grins Jr
**CFO:* Kirby Nickerson
VP: Ted Hakala

D-U-N-S 07-972-8721
LUTHERAN SOCIAL SERVICE OF MINNESOTA (MN)
2485 Como Ave, Saint Paul, MN 55108-1469
Tel (651) 642-5990 *Founded/Ownrshp* 1865
Sales 89.3MM *EMP* 2,300
Accts Cliftonlarsonallen Llp Minnea
SIC 8322 Individual & family services
CEO: Jodi Harpstead
**Pr:* Mark A Peterson
**CFO:* Ken Borle
**CFO:* Patrick Thueson
VP: Daniel Holmgren
**VP:* Joyce Norals
Prgrm Mgr: Jen Fairbourne
Prgrm Mgr: Tara Giese
Prgrm Mgr: Duncan Gregory
Prgrm Mgr: Cari Logan
Prgrm Mgr: Eva Margolis

D-U-N-S 07-685-5626
LUTHERAN SOCIAL SERVICES OF ILLINOIS
1001 E Touhy Ave Ste 50, Des Plaines, IL 60018-5817
Tel (847) 635-4600 *Founded/Ownrshp* 1965
Sales 97.7MM *EMP* 2,014
Accts Baker Tilly Virchow Krause Llp
SIC 8322 6514 6513 Social service center; Senior citizens' center or association; Social services for the handicapped; Dwelling operators, except apartments; Apartment building operators
CEO: Mark A Stutrud
Dir Vol: Diane Bergquist
V Ch: Paul Olson
**Pr:* Rev Frederick Aigner
**CFO:* Gerald E Noonan
Treas: Frank Chiarella
**VP:* Susan E Gregory
**VP:* Gean M Johnson
VP: Larry Lutey
VP: David Novak
Assoc Dir: Mike Davis
Assoc Dir: Tracy Sadlon

D-U-N-S 06-984-0817
LUTHERAN SOCIAL SERVICES OF MICHIGAN
8131 E Jefferson Ave, Detroit, MI 48214-2691
Tel (313) 823-7700 *Founded/Ownrshp* 1934
Sales 103.0MM *EMP* 1,250
Accts Bdo Usa Llp Grand Rapids Mi
SIC 8051 8322 Skilled nursing care facilities; Individual & family services
Pr: Mark Stutrud
**CFO:* Gerald Benjamin
Ofcr: David Goodrich
VP: Dave Barcus
**VP:* Jerald W Benjamin
**VP:* Sean De Four
**VP:* Robert Louis
**VP:* Vickie Thompson
Prgrm Mgr: Trish Harris
CIO: Frank Sellgren
IT Man: Louis Prues

D-U-N-S 06-046-0730
LUTHERAN SOCIAL SERVICES OF WISCONSIN AND UPPER MICHIGAN INC
647 W Virginia St Ste 200, Milwaukee, WI 53204-1535
Tel (262) 896-3446 *Founded/Ownrshp* 1882
Sales 55.5MM *EMP* 2,300
Accts Lb Baker Tilly Virchow Krause
SIC 8322 8082 Social service center; Home health care services
Pr: David N Larson
CFO: Patrick Thueson
VP: Christy Brown
Ex Dir: Heather Yaeger
Prgrm Mgr: Gregory Duncan
Prgrm Mgr: Diane Shuck
Genl Mgr: Amanda Holland
Dir IT: Daniel Mertz

D-U-N-S 10-234-8315
LUTHERAN UNIVERSITY ASSOCIATION INC
VALPARAISO UNIVERSITY
1700 Chapel Dr, Valparaiso, IN 46383-4520
Tel (219) 464-5000 *Founded/Ownrshp* 1925
Sales 116.9MM[E] *EMP* 1,000
SIC 8221 University
Pr: Mark A Heckler
Treas: Sarah Robertson
Trst: Susan Hooker
Assoc VP: Kerry Hutchinson
**VP:* Charley E Gillispie
VP: Lisa Hollander
VP: Stephanie York
Exec: Trevor Richardson
Assoc Dir: Rasha Abed
Assoc Dir: John Kuka
Assoc Dir: Kristi Rensberger

D-U-N-S 00-239-0912 EXP
LUTRON ELECTRONICS CO INC (PA)
7200 Suter Rd, Coopersburg, PA 18036-1249
Tel (610) 282-3800 *Founded/Ownrshp* 1964
Sales 569.5MM[E] *EMP* 1,500[E]
SIC 3625 Control equipment, electric
Ch Bd: Susan Hakkarainen
**Pr:* Michael W Pessina
CFO: Frank Parrillo
VP: Stephanie Deutsch
VP: Gail Jancsics

VP: Paul Lobo
VP: Oscar Mendez
**VP:* Walter S Peake
Exec: Eric Lind
Exec: Mark Rose
CTO: Chuck Mills

D-U-N-S 14-713-0058 IMP/EXP
LUVATA GRENADA LLC
(*Suby of* NORDIC CAPITAL SVENSKA AB)
3984 Highway 51 S, Grenada, MS 38901-9318
Tel (662) 226-3421 *Founded/Ownrshp* 2005
Sales 832.8MM^E *EMP* 4,000
SIC 3621 3585 Coils, for electric motors or generators; Refrigeration equipment, complete
Ch: John Peter Leesi
**Ch Bd:* Hannu Wahlroos
**Pr:* Dennis Appel
Pr: Juha Korhonen
**CFO:* Ron Beal
**CFO:* Jyrki Vesaluoma
**Treas:* Scott Neece
VP: Mike Schwartz
Genl Mgr: Dave Anderson
Genl Mgr: Brenda Gleaton
Opers Mgr: Kathy Brazil

LUX BOND CO
See INFOR INC

LUXFER GAS CYLINDER
See LUXFER INC

D-U-N-S 06-448-3704 IMP/EXP
LUXFER INC
LUXFER GAS CYLINDER
(*Suby of* BA HOLDINGS) ★
3016 Kansas Ave Bldg 1, Riverside, CA 92507-3445
Tel (336) 578-4515 *Founded/Ownrshp* 1996
Sales 118.2MM^E *EMP* 370
SIC 3728 3354 Aircraft parts & equipment; Shapes, extruded aluminum
Pr: John Rhodes
Pr: Anthony Barnes
Ex VP: Michael J Reynolds
Sr VP: Hendy Holrowd
Sr VP: William Schuler
VP: Micheal Edwards
Exec: Andy Beaden
Mng Dir: David Rix
IT Man: Richard Lintin

LUXOR HOTEL & CASINO
See RAMPARTS INC

LUXOTICA SERVICE CENTER
See LUXOTTICA RETAIL NORTH AMERICA INC

LUXOTTICA GROUP
See LUXOTTICA US HOLDINGS CORP

D-U-N-S 79-101-3642 IMP
LUXOTTICA RETAIL NORTH AMERICA INC
LUXOTICA SERVICE CENTER
(*Suby of* LUXOTTICA GROUP) ★
4000 Luxottica Pl, Mason, OH 45040-8114
Tel (513) 765-6000 *Founded/Ownrshp* 1998
Sales 3.3MMM^E *EMP* 14,000
SIC 5995 Contact lenses, prescription
Prin: Thomas L Buehler
**COO:* Kerry Bradley
COO: Miah Sullivan
**CFO:* Jack Dennis
Treas: Joseph Gaglioti
Assoc VP: Peter Grimes
Assoc VP: Jeanine McHugh
Ex VP: Tom Coleman
**Ex VP:* Valeric Giacobbi
**VP:* Vito Giannola
VP: Erwin Hinteregger
VP: Frank Kudlac

D-U-N-S 07-486-7966
LUXOTTICA US HOLDINGS CORP
LUXOTTICA GROUP
(*Suby of* LUXOTTICA GROUP SPA)
12 Harbor Park Dr, Port Washington, NY 11050-4649
Tel (516) 484-3800 *Founded/Ownrshp* 1999
Sales 3.9MMM^E *EMP* 35,000
SIC 5048 5099 5995 5999 Frames, ophthalmic; Lenses, ophthalmic; Sunglasses; Eyeglasses, prescription; Sunglasses
CEO: Andrea Guerra
**Ch Bd:* Vito Giannola
Treas: Vito Giannnola
**Treas:* Vito Gianolla
**VP:* Michael Boxer
VP: Susan Eyvazzadeh
**VP:* Dan Socci
**Prin:* Claudio De Vecchio
Dir IT: Claudio Delvechio
Dir IT: Wayne Lange
VP Sls: Jack Dampier

D-U-N-S 01-856-1159
LUXURY BRAND HOLDINGS INC
ROSS-SIMONS
(*Suby of* FREEMAN SPOGLI & CO LLC) ★
9 Ross Simons Dr, Cranston, RI 02920-4581
Tel (401) 463-3100 *Founded/Ownrshp* 2002
Sales 120.0MM *EMP* 300
Accts Deloitte & Touche Llp Hartfor
SIC 5944 Jewelry stores
Pr: Darrell Ross
COO: Robert J Simone
CFO: David Pawlak
CFO: Robert Pulciani
VP: Larry Davis
VP: Terry Matthews
Genl Mgr: Chris Temple

D-U-N-S 08-033-2206
LUXURY HOME FURNISHINGS LLC
STAR FURNITURE
130 S Merkle Rd, Columbus, OH 43209-1938
Tel (661) 610-0299 *Founded/Ownrshp* 2016
Sales 2.5MMM *EMP* 15
SIC 5712 Furniture stores

D-U-N-S 18-291-5900
■ **LUXURY LINENS OF NASHVILLE INC**
BURLINGTON COAT FACTORY
(*Suby of* BURLINGTON COAT FACTORY WAREHOUSE CORP) ★
1830 N Route 130, Burlington, NJ 08016-3017
Tel (609) 387-7800 *Founded/Ownrshp* 1987
Sales 39.2MM^E *EMP* 1,000
SIC 5719 Linens
Pr: Jack Moore
**VP:* Richard Rynda

D-U-N-S 06-051-3058
LUZERNE COUNTY
200 N River St, Wilkes Barre, PA 18711-1004
Tel (570) 825-1500 *Founded/Ownrshp* 1900
Sales NA *EMP* 2,087
Accts Zelenkofske Axelrod Llc Harri
SIC 9111 Executive offices;
V Ch: Edward Brominski
**Ch:* Gregory Skrepnak
Genl Mgr: David Pedri
IT Man: Mauro Dimauro

LUZIANNE
See REILY FOODS CO

D-U-N-S 96-856-6377
LV GAMING VENTURES LLC
M RESORT SPA CASINO, THE
12300 Las Vegas Blvd S, Henderson, NV 89044-9506
Tel (702) 797-1000 *Founded/Ownrshp* 2011
Sales 34.8MM^E *EMP* 1,600
SIC 7011 7991

D-U-N-S 03-244-6122
LV HIERS INC
253 Florida Ave, Macclenny, FL 32063-2419
Tel (904) 259-2314 *Founded/Ownrshp* 2004
Sales 118.6MM *EMP* 12
SIC 5171

D-U-N-S 80-637-5411
LVB ACQUISITION HOLDING LLC
56 E Bell Dr, Warsaw, IN 46582-6989
Tel (574) 267-6639 *Founded/Ownrshp* 2006
Sales NA *EMP* 9,279
SIC 3842 3841 3845

D-U-N-S 80-638-1773
■ **LVB ACQUISITION INC**
(*Suby of* ZIMMER BIOMET HOLDINGS INC) ★
56 E Bell Dr, Warsaw, IN 46582-6989
Tel (574) 267-6639 *Founded/Ownrshp* 2015
Sales 3.2MMM^E *EMP* 9,279
SIC 3842 3841 3845 Implants, surgical; Supports: abdominal, ankle, arch, kneecap, etc.; Surgical appliances & supplies; Medical instruments & equipment, blood & bone work; Surgical instruments & apparatus; Suction therapy apparatus; Electromedical apparatus; Ultrasonic medical equipment, except cleaning
Co-Pr: Stephen Ko
Co-Pr: Michael Dal Ballo
Co-Pr: Andrew Rhee
Co-Pr: Jeffrey Rhodes

D-U-N-S 00-655-1229
LVDE CORP (TX)
INDIAN CREEK HYDRO
5100 San Felipe St 244e, Houston, TX 77056-3600
Tel (713) 840-1489 *Founded/Ownrshp* 2010, 2014
Sales 100.0MM *EMP* 20
SIC 4911 Distribution, electric power
Ch Bd: Robert Klein
**CEO:* Daneil Dygert

D-U-N-S 07-864-1443
■ **LVGV LLC**
M RESORT SPA CASINO
(*Suby of* PENN NATIONAL GAMING INC) ★
12300 Las Vegas Blvd S, Henderson, NV 89044-9506
Tel (702) 797-1000 *Founded/Ownrshp* 2013
Sales 160.0MM *EMP* 1,600
SIC 7011 7991 Casino hotel; Resort hotel; Spas
Pr: Bob Sheldon
Exec: Sheung Choi
Exec: Kc Chua
Netwrk Mgr: Gary Greene
Mktg Dir: Becky Romijn

LVH-LAS VEGAS HOTEL & CASINO
See COLONY RESORTS LVH ACQUISITIONS LLC

D-U-N-S 80-620-5548
LVI HOLDING CORP
(*Suby of* NORTHSTAR GROUP SERVICES INC) ★
80 Broad St Fl 3, New York, NY 10004-2209
Tel (212) 951-3660 *Founded/Ownrshp* 2008
Sales 47.1MM^E *EMP* 2,000
SIC 1799 Asbestos removal & encapsulation
CEO: Scott E State
CFO: Paul S Cutrone
Treas: Joseph Annarumma
VP: Robert S Hogan
Board of Directors: Robert R Buck, Richard F Ferrucci, Daniel J Hennessey, Brian Simmons

D-U-N-S 18-772-3577
LVI PARENT CORP
(*Suby of* NORTHSTAR GROUP HOLDINGS LLC) ★
370 7th Ave Ste 1803, New York, NY 10001-3969
Tel (212) 951-3660 *Founded/Ownrshp* 2002
Sales 371.8MM *EMP* 3,500^E
Accts Grant Thornton Llp New York
SIC 1795 Demolition, buildings & other structures
Pr: Scott E State
CFO: Paul S Cutrone

D-U-N-S 14-471-6771 IMP
LVMH MOET HENNESSY LOUIS VUITTON INC
(*Suby of* SOFIDIV)
19 E 57th St, New York, NY 10022-2506
Tel (212) 931-2700 *Founded/Ownrshp* 1980
Sales 1.4MMM^E *EMP* 5,000
SIC 5948 5199 Luggage, except footlockers & trunks; Anatomical specimens & research material
CEO: Mark Weber
COO: Gary Hahn
VP: Robert Mihin
Dir IT: Bob Swierczek

LVMH MOET HNNSSY LOUIS VUITTON
See STARBOARD CRUISE SERVICES INC

LWCC
See LOUISIANA WORKERS COMPENSATION CORP

D-U-N-S 04-181-3077 IMP
LWIN FAMILY CO
HISSHO SUSHI
11949 Steele Creek Rd, Charlotte, NC 28273-3773
Tel (704) 926-2200 *Founded/Ownrshp* 1989
Sales 110.5MM^E *EMP* 100
SIC 5146 Fish & seafoods
Pr: Philip Maung
Opers Mgr: Lily Wang
Opers Mgr: Yuan Wang
Mktg Dir: Vanessa Curry
Snr Mgr: Chee Chang

LXR RESORTS
See WIND HOTELS HOLDINGS INC

D-U-N-S 00-113-9963 IMP
▲ **LYDALL INC** (CT)
1 Colonial Rd, Manchester, CT 06042-2307
Tel (860) 646-1233 *Founded/Ownrshp* 1969
Sales 524.5MM *EMP* 2,100
Tkr Sym LDL *Exch* NYS
SIC 2297 3053 2899 2631 3714 3564 Nonwoven fabrics; Gaskets, all materials; Insulating compounds; Automobile board; Filters: oil, fuel & air, motor vehicle; Oil strainers, motor vehicle; Filters, air: furnaces, air conditioning equipment, etc.
Pr: Dale G Barnhart
Pr: Paul A Marold
COO: Franck Valton
CFO: Scott M Deakin
Treas: James V Laughlan
Chf Mktg O: Pat Blanc
Ofcr: Chad A McDaniel
VP: Jim Posa
VP: Erika H Turner
VP Bus Dev: David Glenn
Off Admin: Sherry Savastio
Board of Directors: Kathleen Burdett, W Leslie Duffy, Matthew T Farrell, Marc T Giles, William D Gurley, Suzanne Hammett, S Carl Soderstrom Jr

D-U-N-S 08-543-8430 IMP
■ **LYDALL THERMAL/ACOUSTICAL INC**
METALS
(*Suby of* LYDALL INC) ★
1243 Buck Shoals Rd, Hamptonville, NC 27020-7624
Tel (336) 468-8522 *Founded/Ownrshp* 1977
Sales 115.3MM^E *EMP* 618
SIC 3441 Fabricated structural metal
Pr: Dale G Barnhart
**Sr VP:* Joe Abbruzzi

D-U-N-S 87-490-8010 IMP
LYDEN OIL CO
30692 Tracy Rd, Walbridge, OH 43465-9775
Tel (419) 666-1948 *Founded/Ownrshp* 1919
Sales 140.7MM *EMP* 167
Accts Rehmann Robson Llc Toledo Oh
SIC 5172 Lubricating oils & greases
Pr: Breen Lyden
**VP:* Paul Lyden
Off Mgr: Dave Stratton

D-U-N-S 00-942-4680
LYDIG CONSTRUCTION INC
11001 E Montgomery Dr, Spokane Valley, WA 99206-4714
Tel (509) 534-0451 *Founded/Ownrshp* 1996
Sales 195.4MM^E *EMP* 130
Accts Moss Adams Llp Spokane Washi
SIC 1542 1541 Commercial & office building, new construction; Industrial buildings, new construction
CEO: Larry Swartz
**CFO:* Mark Bray
Ofcr: Taylor Brown
**VP:* William Gottschalk
**VP:* Kenneth Schwartz
CTO: Jon Edwards
Dir IT: Orlando Solano
Sfty Dirs: Paul Moorman
Mktg Mgr: Heather Brown
Snr PM: Andrew Johnson
Snr PM: Randy Smith

D-U-N-S 00-409-3472
LYKES BROS INC (FL)
400 N Tampa St Ste 1900, Tampa, FL 33602-4776
Tel (813) 223-3911 *Founded/Ownrshp* 1875
Sales 88.1MM^E *EMP* 250
SIC 0174 6331 Citrus fruits; Agricultural insurance
Ch Bd: Howell L Ferguson
**Pr:* Carl J Bauman
**Pr:* Charles P Lykes Jr
**CEO:* Michael L Carrere
COO: Angela J Whitaker
**CFO:* Fred Bennett
CFO: Frederick J Bennett
**Ex VP:* Hiram P Hampton
**VP:* Joe Collins
VP: Mark E Jackson
VP: Pete Priolo
VP: Richard P Russo
VP: William P Taulbee II
**VP:* Elizabeth A Waters
VP: Thomas A Webster

D-U-N-S 01-823-0573
LYKINS COMPANIES INC
LYKINS ENERGY SOLUTIONS
5163 Wlfpn Plsnt Hl Rd, Milford, OH 45150-9632
Tel (513) 831-8820 *Founded/Ownrshp* 1948
Sales 164.8MM^E *EMP* 235
SIC 5172 4213 5411 Gasoline; Diesel fuel; Fuel oil; Trucking, except local; Convenience stores, chain
CEO: Jeff Lykins
**CFO:* Robert J Manning
VP: Greg Belisle
VP: Mary Eisnaugle
Div Mgr: Diana Brown
Div Mgr: Mike Schmid
Div Mgr: Joyce Spizzirri
Genl Mgr: James Siefert
MIS Dir: Linda Bock
Trfc Dir: Terry Murray
S&M/VP: Robert Manning

LYKINS ENERGY SOLUTIONS
See LYKINS COMPANIES INC

D-U-N-S 09-062-9395
LYKINS OIL CO
(*Suby of* LYKINS ENERGY SOLUTIONS) ★
5163 Wlfpn Plsnt Hl Rd, Milford, OH 45150-9632
Tel (513) 831-8820 *Founded/Ownrshp* 1948
Sales 143.2MM^E *EMP* 125
SIC 5172 5983 Gasoline; Diesel fuel; Fuel oil; Lubricating oils & greases; Fuel oil dealers
Pr: D Jeff Lykins
**CFO:* Robert J Manning
Chf Mktg O: Mary U Gray
**VP:* Ronald Lykins
IT Man: Sandy Howard

D-U-N-S 02-802-1061 IMP
LYMAN GROUP INC
201 East St, Woodland, CA 95776-3523
Tel (530) 662-5442 *Founded/Ownrshp* 1963
Sales 84.0MM^E *EMP* 63
SIC 5191 Chemicals, agricultural; Fertilizer & fertilizer materials
Ch: Leslie F Lyman
**Pr:* Johnny Council
**CFO:* Scott Mansell
**VP:* Walt Johnson

LYMAN LUMBER COMPANY
See BEP/LYMAN LLC

D-U-N-S 00-891-0622
LYMAN-RICHEY CORP
(*Suby of* ASH GROVE CEMENT CO) ★
4315 Cuming St, Omaha, NE 68131-1014
Tel (402) 556-3600 *Founded/Ownrshp* 1884, 1935
Sales 157.2MM^E *EMP* 400
SIC 3273 1442 3271 5211 5032 Ready-mixed concrete; Construction sand & gravel; Construction sand mining; Gravel mining; Concrete block & brick; Lumber & other building materials; Brick, stone & related material
Pr: Patrick J Gorup
**Pr:* Kevin D Schmidt
**Treas:* Mark F Osborn
Treas: Mark Osborn
Ex VP: Kevin Schmidt
Exec: Gordon Wellensiek
Brnch Mgr: John Stueve
Genl Mgr: Doug Harrison
Genl Mgr: Jarod Hendricks
Dir IT: Allen Miller
VP Mktg: Mark Deetz

D-U-N-S 07-475-5265
LYNCHBURG COLLEGE
1501 Lakeside Dr, Lynchburg, VA 24501-3113
Tel (434) 544-8100 *Founded/Ownrshp* 1917
Sales 67.4MM *EMP* 1,077^E
Accts Brown Edwards & Company Llp
SIC 8221 College, except junior
Pr: Kenneth R Garren
VP: Steve L Bright
VP: Rita Detwiler
Off Mgr: Deborah Brown
Off Mgr: Olivia Downey
Web Dev: Tracy Chase
HC Dir: Mandi Dolan

D-U-N-S 94-195-8394 IMP
LYNCO DISTRIBUTION INC
LYNCO PRODUCTS
1410 11th St W, Milan, IL 61264-2264
Tel (309) 787-2300 *Founded/Ownrshp* 2002
Sales 148.3MM^E *EMP* 150
SIC 5199 Variety store merchandise
Pr: Edward Lampo
Pr: Jerry Follette
CFO: John Mitchell
**VP:* Anthony J Alexander
CIO: Bill Hintz
VP Opers: Christopher Cartelli
Mktg Mgr: Lizabeth Wilson

LYNCO PRODUCTS
See LYNCO DISTRIBUTION INC

D-U-N-S 09-639-4697
LYND CO
8000 W Interstate 10 # 1200, San Antonio, TX 78230-3872
Tel (210) 798-8114 *Founded/Ownrshp* 1979
Sales 87.4MM^E *EMP* 787
SIC 6513 6512 Apartment hotel operation; Commercial & industrial building operation
CEO: Michael Lynd
**Pt:* Samuel J Kasparek
Pr: Lisa Bednarz
**CFO:* Sean Kiehne
**Ex VP:* Jeffrey Weissman
**VP:* Randy Brown
**VP:* Lucille Hebert
**VP:* Michael J Lynd Jr
**VP:* Patricia A Lynd
**VP:* Paul Valdez
**Prin:* Monique Allen

D-U-N-S 00-696-1734
LYNDALE TERMINAL CO (MN)
HOLIDAY STATION STORES
4567 American Blvd W, Minneapolis, MN 55437-1123
Tel (952) 830-8700 *Founded/Ownrshp* 1932, 1969
Sales 301.2MM^E *EMP* 4,500
SIC 5311 5411 5541 Department stores; Supermarkets, chain; Convenience stores; Gasoline service stations
Pr: Ronald Erickson
**VP:* Gerald Erickson

D-U-N-S 05-932-0788 IMP
LYNDEN AIR FREIGHT INC
LYNDEN INTERNATIONAL
(*Suby of* LYNDEN INC) ★
18000 Intl Blvd Ste 700, Seatac, WA 98188-4202
Tel (206) 777-5300 *Founded/Ownrshp* 1970
Sales 133.0MM *EMP* 2,500ᴱ
SIC 4731

D-U-N-S 06-277-4674 IMP/EXP
LYNDEN INC (WA)
18000 Intl Blvd Ste 800, Seatac, WA 98188-4263
Tel (206) 241-8778 *Founded/Ownrshp* 1947
Sales 1.0MMMᴱ *EMP* 2,500
SIC 4213 4731 4424 Trucking, except local; Domestic freight forwarding; Coastwide transportation, freight
Pr: Jonathan Burdick
Ch Bd: Jim Jansen
COO: Alex McKallor
COO: Alexander McKallor
CFO: Brad McKeown
VP: Everett H Billingslea
VP: John Kaloper
VP: Ji Kim
VP: Stephanie Littleton
VP: Don Reid
VP: Ann Suver

LYNDEN INTERNATIONAL
See LYNDEN AIR FREIGHT INC

D-U-N-S 88-490-1588
LYNDON STATE COLLEGE
LYNDON STATE COLLEGE AMER
(*Suby of* JOHNSON STATE COLLEGE) ★
1001 College Rd, Lyndonville, VT 05851
Tel (802) 626-6200 *Founded/Ownrshp* 1961
Sales 113.6MM *EMP* 220
Accts Berry Dunn Mcneil & Parker
SIC 8221 College, except junior
Pr: Carol Moore
Ex Dir: Sylvia Plumb
Store Mgr: Raymond Dubois
Store Mgr: Anita Little
Dir IT: Michael Dente
Snr Mgr: Stephen Nichipor

LYNDON STATE COLLEGE AMER
See LYNDON STATE COLLEGE

LYNN COMMUNITY HEALTH CENTER
See LYNN COMMUNITY HEALTH INC

D-U-N-S 03-083-4915
LYNN COMMUNITY HEALTH INC
LYNN COMMUNITY HEALTH CENTER
269 Union St, Lynn, MA 01901-1314
Tel (781) 581-3900 *Founded/Ownrshp* 1972
Sales 86.1MM *EMP* 375ᴱ
Accts Feeley & Driscoll Pc Bosto
SIC 8093 Specialty outpatient clinics
Ex Dir: Lori Abrams Berry
IT Man: AMR Mostafa

D-U-N-S 14-718-3818 IMP
LYNN PRODUCTS INC
PUREFORMANCE CABLES
2645 W 237th St, Torrance, CA 90505-5269
Tel (310) 530-5966 *Founded/Ownrshp* 1982
Sales 146.3MMᴱ *EMP* 1,000
SIC 3577 3357 Computer peripheral equipment; Fiber optic cable (insulated)
Pr: Hsinyu Lin
**Treas:* Chun MEI Shei
**VP:* Eric Tseng
IT Man: Hugh Jass
Sls Mgr: Dan Miller

D-U-N-S 80-363-7297
LYNN PUBLIC SCHOOLS
100 Bennett St, Lynn, MA 01905-3004
Tel (781) 593-1680 *Founded/Ownrshp* 1647
Sales 11.5MMᴱ *EMP* 2,000
SIC 8211 Public elementary & secondary schools
Dir Sec: Oran Wright
Area Mgr: Ben Johnson
MIS Dir: Daniel McManus
Teacher Pr: Barbara Rafuse
HC Dir: Kathleen McNulty
HC Dir: Dennis Thompson

LYNN REGIONAL CANCER CENTER OF
See BOCA RATON REGIONAL HOSPITAL INC

LYNN REGIONAL CANCER INSTITUTE
See BACO RATON COMMUNITY HOSPITAL INC

D-U-N-S 07-131-0197
LYNN UNIVERSITY INC (FL)
3601 N Military Trl, Boca Raton, FL 33431-5598
Tel (561) 237-7000 *Founded/Ownrshp* 1963, 1971
Sales 87.3MM *EMP* 500
Accts Crowe Horwath Llp Boca Raton
SIC 8221 College, except junior
Pr: Donald E Ross
**Treas:* John Mortimer
**Chf Mktg O:* Sherrie Weldon
**Ex VP:* Jack Sites
**VP:* Anthony Casale
**VP:* Kathleen Cheek-Milby
**VP:* Jan Glitz
**VP:* Gregory Malfitano
VP: Phillip Riordan
Dir Sec: Mike McMurry
Netwrk Mgr: Kevin Kerr

D-U-N-S 09-745-2676
■ **LYNNFIELD DRUG INC**
FREEDOM DRUG
(*Suby of* CURASCRIPT SPECIALTY DIST) ★
12 Kent Way Ste 120, Byfield, MA 01922-1221
Tel (978) 499-1400 *Founded/Ownrshp* 2001
Sales 165.0MM *EMP* 100
SIC 5912 5961 Drug stores; Pharmaceuticals, mail order
Pr: Kim Rondeau
VP: Keith Ebling
VP: Chris Houston
Pharmcst: Frank Seamster

D-U-N-S 07-527-8630
LYNWOOD UNIFIED SCHOOL DISTRICT
11321 Bullis Rd, Lynwood, CA 90262-3600
Tel (310) 639-5627 *Founded/Ownrshp* 1950
Sales 93.0MMᴱ *EMP* 1,700
Accts Nigro Nigro & White Pc Mur
SIC 8211 Public elementary & secondary schools
VP: Oscar Espinoza
Psych: Eugenia Sung
HC Dir: Kavin Dobson

LYNX
See CENTRAL FLORIDA REGIONAL TRANSPORTATION AUTHORITY

LYNX POWER SYSTEMS
See SIGNAL POINT SYSTEMS INC

D-U-N-S 09-300-8118 IMP
LYON CONKLIN & CO INC
(*Suby of* FERGUSON ENTERPRISES INC) ★
4501 Hollins Ferry Rd # 140, Baltimore, MD 21227-4623
Tel (410) 540-4880 *Founded/Ownrshp* 2001
Sales 83.8MMᴱ *EMP* 250
SIC 5075 5051 Warm air heating & air conditioning; Air conditioning & ventilation equipment & supplies; Warm air heating equipment & supplies; Sheets, metal
CEO: Frank Roach
**Pr:* David Brown
VP Mktg: George Tilghman

D-U-N-S 80-050-3919
LYON COUNTY SCHOOL DISTRICT
25 Joe Parr Way, Yerington, NV 89447-2315
Tel (775) 463-3006 *Founded/Ownrshp* 2007
Sales 64.6MM *EMP* 1,125
Accts Schettler Macy & Silva Llc Re
SIC 8211 Public elementary & secondary schools
Ofcr: Alvin McNeil
Dir Sec: Shani Dues
Brnch Mgr: David Fulstone
MIS Dir: Alan Medeiros
IT Man: Julie Gibbs
HC Dir: Marva Clevan

D-U-N-S 07-882-8502 IMP
LYON LLC
(*Suby of* ECHELON CAPITAL LLC) ★
420 N Main St, Montgomery, IL 60538-1367
Tel (630) 892-8941 *Founded/Ownrshp* 2013
Sales 110.6MMᴱ *EMP* 278ᴱ
SIC 2542 Shelving, office & store: except wood
CEO: Louise E Berg
**CFO:* Robert Miller
**Ex VP:* William Guo
**Ex VP:* Matthew Zakaras
Dist Mgr: Bill Countryman
Dist Mgr: Jeremy Dennis
Dist Mgr: Bryan Lenz
Dist Mgr: Jeff Majnarich
Dist Mgr: Jeff Shuler
Dist Mgr: Mike Wilgus
IT Man: Margi Washington

LYON REAL ESTATE
See L LYON WILLIAM & ASSOCIATES INC

LYON SHEET METAL WORKS DIV
See CORRIGAN BROTHERS INC

D-U-N-S 00-511-9474 IMP/EXP
LYON WORKSPACE PRODUCTS LLC
420 N Main St, Montgomery, IL 60538-1367
Tel (630) 892-8941 *Founded/Ownrshp* 2015
Sales 96.0MMᴱ *EMP* 500
SIC 2542 Shelving, office & store: except wood; Lockers (not refrigerated): except wood; Cabinets: show, display or storage: except wood
COO: Douglas M Harrison
Dist Mgr: Robert Brossell
Plnt Mgr: Mike Pine

D-U-N-S 19-412-3154 IMP/EXP
LYONDELL CHEMICAL CO
(*Suby of* LYONDELLBASELL INDUSTRIES INC) ★
1221 Mckinney St Ste 300, Houston, TX 77010-2036
Tel (713) 309-7200 *Founded/Ownrshp* 2007
Sales 3.0MMMᴱ *EMP* 7,340
SIC 2869 2911 Industrial organic chemicals; Olefins; Ethylene; Propylene, butylene; Gasoline blending plants; Oils, fuel; Jet fuels; Oils, lubricating
Pr: Morris Gelb
Pr: Dave Prilutski
CFO: Alan S Bigman
CFO: Robert Blakley
CFO: Karyn Ovelmen
Ofcr: Craig B Glidden
Ofcr: Jeff Kaplan
Ex VP: Charlie Graham
Sr VP: Kevin W Brown
Sr VP: C Bart De Jong
Sr VP: Edward J Dineen
Sr VP: Cees Los
Sr VP: Patrick D Quarles
Sr VP: Timothy D Roberts
Sr VP: Karen Swindler
Sr VP: Jackie Wolf
VP: Russell T Crockett Jr
VP: Paul Davies
VP: Kevin Denicola
VP: Earl Ehlers
VP: J R Fontenot

D-U-N-S 18-184-3095
LYONDELL CHEMICAL WORLDWIDE INC
1221 Mckinney St Ste 1600, Houston, TX 77010-2006
Tel (713) 652-7200 *Founded/Ownrshp* 2009
Sales NA *EMP* 6,892ᴱ
SIC 2869

D-U-N-S 80-155-0802 IMP
LYONDELLBASELL INDUSTRIES INC
(*Suby of* LYONDELLBASELL INDUSTRIES HOLDINGS B.V.)
1221 Mckinney St Ste 700, Houston, TX 77010-2045
Tel (713) 309-7200 *Founded/Ownrshp* 2007
Sales 3.1MMMᴱ *EMP* 7,340
SIC 2821 Polymethyl methacrylate resins (plexiglass)
CEO: Jim Gallogly
CFO: Robert Blakley
CFO: Bill Wright
**Ex VP:* Craig Glidden
**Ex VP:* Karyn Ovelmen
**Ex VP:* Bob Patele
**Ex VP:* Tim Roberts
Sr VP: Steve F Kennedy
VP: George Easterling
**VP:* Morris Gelb
VP: Wendy McCready
VP: Douglas Pike
VP: Sam Smolik
VP: Paul Turner
VP: Mark Wilson
Dir Risk M: Gerald Obrien

D-U-N-S 62-375-4876
LYONS GROUP LTD
334 Boylston St Ste 501, Boston, MA 02116-3492
Tel (617) 262-2605 *Founded/Ownrshp* 1980
Sales 86.3MM *EMP* 1,000ᴱ
SIC 8741 Restaurant management
Pr: Patrick T Lyons
**Treas:* Edward J Sparks

D-U-N-S 04-166-1042 IMP/EXP
LYONS MAGNUS INC
3158 E Hamilton Ave, Fresno, CA 93702-4163
Tel (559) 268-5966 *Founded/Ownrshp* 1967
Sales 226.7MMᴱ *EMP* 600
SIC 2033 2026 2087 Jams, including imitation: packaged in cans, jars, etc.; Jellies, edible, including imitation: in cans, jars, etc.; Preserves, including imitation: in cans, jars, etc.; Fruit pie mixes & fillings: packaged in cans, jars, etc.; Yogurt; Syrups, flavoring (except drink); Extracts, flavoring
Pr: Robert E Smittcamp
**Sec:* Muriel Smittcamp
VP Mktg: Jim Davis

D-U-N-S 00-821-4074
LYONS SPECIALTY CO LLC
A A VENDING SERVICE DIV
2800 La Highway 1 N, Port Allen, LA 70767-3417
Tel (225) 356-1319 *Founded/Ownrshp* 1923
Sales 131.2MM *EMP* 80
SIC 5194 5145 5149 Tobacco & tobacco products; Confectionery; Groceries & related products
COO: Raetzsch Hugh
VP: Davis Aquin
Genl Mgr: Charles Schimmel

D-U-N-S 84-448-4704
LYRIC HEALTH CARE LLC
7150 Columbia Gateway Dr J, Columbia, MD 21046-2972
Tel (443) 539-2369 *Founded/Ownrshp* 1998
Sales NA *EMP* 4,300
SIC 8059

D-U-N-S 06-858-4846 IMP
LYRIC OPERA OF CHICAGO
20 N Wacker Dr Ste 860, Chicago, IL 60606-2899
Tel (312) 332-2244 *Founded/Ownrshp* 1954
Sales 85.4MM *EMP* 100
SIC 7922 Opera company
Exec: Madeleine Walsh
IT Man: Rene Calvo
Prd Mgr: April Busch
Mktg Dir: Tracy Galligher
Mktg Dir: Lisa Middleton
Mktg Mgr: Emily Lange

D-U-N-S 02-649-9454
LYTX INC
9785 Towne Centre Dr, San Diego, CA 92121-1968
Tel (858) 430-4000 *Founded/Ownrshp* 1998
Sales 99.1MMᴱ *EMP* 400
SIC 3812 Search & navigation equipment; Search & detection systems & instruments
CEO: Brandon Nixon
**COO:* David Riordan
**CFO:* Paul J Pucino
**CFO:* Kelli Richard
**Chf Mktg O:* Kara Kerker
Ex VP: Doron Lurie
**Ex VP:* Drew Martin
**Sr VP:* Shelley Bennett
**Sr VP:* Julie Cunningham
**Sr VP:* Eliot Feldstein
**VP:* Tom Fisher
VP: Paul Jones
VP: Patrick Shipley
VP: Greg Vacchiano
Exec: David Brandos
Board of Directors: Thomas Darcy, Marco Thompson

D-U-N-S 80-859-0413 IMP/EXP
■ **LZB MANUFACTURING INC**
LA-Z-BOY
(*Suby of* LA-Z-BOY INC) ★
1 Lazboy Dr, Monroe, MI 48162-5138
Tel (734) 242-1444 *Founded/Ownrshp* 2004
Sales 159.3MMᴱ *EMP* 801
SIC 2512 Upholstered household furniture
Pr: Mark S Bacon Sr
**CFO:* Louis M Riccio
**Treas:* Greg A Brinks
**VP:* R Rand Tucker

M

D-U-N-S 04-107-2349
M & B ASPHALT CO INC
1525 W Seneca Cnty Rd 42, Tiffin, OH 44883
Tel (419) 992-4235 *Founded/Ownrshp* 1958
Sales 85.7MMᴱ *EMP* 38
SIC 1429 2951 1611 2952 1771

D-U-N-S 02-071-1438 IMP
M & D INDUSTRIES CORP (OK)
SONIC DRIVE-IN
2701 W I 44 Service Rd # 102, Oklahoma City, OK 73112-3775
Tel (405) 942-2936 *Founded/Ownrshp* 1975
Sales 75.0MM *EMP* 1,800
SIC 5812 Drive-in restaurant
Pr: Dan Winters
**VP:* Marvin D Jirous

D-U-N-S 03-908-7705
M & F FIRST CORP
134 W Washington St, Kosciusko, MS 39090-3633
Tel (662) 289-5121 *Founded/Ownrshp* 1890
Sales NA *EMP* 456ᴱ
SIC 6022

D-U-N-S 88-398-3413
M & F WORLDWIDE CORP
(*Suby of* MACANDREWS & FORBES HOLDINGS INC) ★
35 E 62nd St, New York, NY 10065-8014
Tel (212) 572-8600 *Founded/Ownrshp* 2011
Sales 2.6MMMᴱ *EMP* 9,000
SIC 5149 8741 2782 Flavourings & fragrances; Business management; Checkbooks
Pr: Barry F Schwartz
**Pr:* Christine M Taylor
**Treas:* Alison M Horowitz
VP: Steven Fasman
VP: Alison Horowitz
Board of Directors: Stephen G Taub, Philip E Beekman, Carl B Webb, William C Bevins, Martha L Byorum, Charles T Dawson, Theo W Folz, John M Keane, Paul M Meister, Ronald O Perelman, Bruce Slovin

M & I TRUST
See MARSHALL & ILSLEY TRUST CO NATIONAL ASSOCIATION

D-U-N-S 10-158-9620
M & J MANAGEMENT CORP
MCDONALD'S
147 Delta Dr, Pittsburgh, PA 15238-2805
Tel (412) 963-6550 *Founded/Ownrshp* 1968
Sales 41.4MMᴱ *EMP* 1,000
Accts Horovitz Rudoy & Roteman Llc
SIC 5812 Fast-food restaurant, chain
Pr: Michael J Delligatti
**Treas:* Daniel Hubert
**VP:* Daniel T Deligatti

M & K QUALITY TRUCK SALES
See M & K TRUCK AND TRAILER INC

D-U-N-S 79-042-0632 EXP
M & K TRUCK AND TRAILER INC
M & K QUALITY TRUCK SALES
8800 Byron Commerce Dr Sw, Byron Center, MI 49315-8491
Tel (616) 583-2100 *Founded/Ownrshp* 1989
Sales 107.0MMᴱ *EMP* 166ᴱ
SIC 5511 4212 Trucks, tractors & trailers: new & used; Local trucking, without storage
Pr: Ron Meyering
Genl Mgr: Bob Devink
Off Mgr: Rainelle Jansma

D-U-N-S 06-917-2294 EXP
■ **M & M AEROSPACE HARDWARE INC** (FL)
KLX AEROSPACE SOLUTIONS
(*Suby of* KLX INC) ★
10000 Nw 15th Ter, Doral, FL 33172-2754
Tel (305) 925-2600 *Founded/Ownrshp* 1974, 2014
Sales 221.8MMᴱ *EMP* 300
SIC 5088 Aircraft equipment & supplies
CEO: Robert J Khoury
**Pr:* Werner Lieberherr
COO: Terry Bond
**Sr VP:* Thomas P McCaffrey
**VP:* Sean Cromie
VP: Michael Senft
Exec: Yanida Bacallao
**Prin:* Bob Marchetti
Prgrm Mgr: Julia Mahadni
Genl Mgr: Holger Assman
Genl Mgr: Tracy Eutsey

D-U-N-S 02-975-9904
M & M AUTOMOTIVE INC
KARL MALONE TOYOTA
11453 S Lone Peak Pkwy, Draper, UT 84020-8872
Tel (801) 553-5800 *Founded/Ownrshp* 1997
Sales 125.0MM *EMP* 175
SIC 5511 Automobiles, new & used
Pr: Karl A Malone
**VP:* Andrew Madsen
**VP:* Gregory S Miller

M & M RESTAURANT SUPPLY
See KEYSTONE FOODS LLC

D-U-N-S 00-687-0612
M & M SERVICE CO INC
130 N Chiles St, Carlinville, IL 62626-1684
Tel (217) 854-4516 *Founded/Ownrshp* 1931, 1999
Sales 251.5MM *EMP* 165
Accts Cliftonlarsonallen Llp Norma
SIC 5153 5191 5171 Grain elevators; Feed; Fertilizer & fertilizer materials; Petroleum bulk stations
Pr: Gary Meyers
VP: Emmet Bennett
**VP:* Mark Prose
Genl Mgr: Brad Klaus

D-U-N-S 02-644-1498
M & M TRANSPORT SERVICES INC (MA)
643 Manley St, West Bridgewater, MA 02379-1002
Tel (508) 521-6201 *Founded/Ownrshp* 1990
Sales 84.5MMᴱ *EMP* 400
SIC 4213 4212 Trucking, except local; Local trucking, without storage
Pr: Mark Warsofsky
Trfc Dir: Steve Rossi
Sfty Mgr: Charles Cooper

D-U-N-S 09-123-6802
M & O AGENCIES INC (AZ)
MAHONEY GROUP, THE
(*Suby of* SOUTHWESTERN FINANCIAL CORPORATION)
1835 S Extension Rd, Mesa, AZ 85210-5942
Tel (480) 730-4920 *Founded/Ownrshp* 1960, 2001
Sales NA *EMP* 195
SIC 6411 Insurance agents, brokers & service

Ch: Glendon D Nelson
**Pr:* Steven Goble
VP: Glen Luglan
Brnch Mgr: Richard Perry
Snr Mgr: Yanira Roman

D-U-N-S 07-833-8806
M & R HIGH POINT HOLDINGS INC
402 High Point Dr Ste 101, Cocoa, FL 32926-6602
Tel (321) 631-0245 *Founded/Ownrshp* 2011
Sales 580.3MM *EMP* 2
Accts James Moore & Co Pl Gaine
SIC 6719 Holding companies
Prin: Mahesh R Shah

D-U-N-S 15-175-1161 IMP
M & R PRINTING EQUIPMENT INC
M & R SALES AND SERVICE
(*Suby of* M&R PRINTING) ★
440 Medinah Rd, Roselle, IL 60172-2329
Tel (800) 736-6431 *Founded/Ownrshp* 1993
Sales 134.3MM^E *EMP* 400
SIC 3555 3552 5084 Printing trades machinery; Printing machinery, textile; Printing trades machinery, equipment & supplies
CEO: Richard Hoffman
**Pr:* Ronnie Riggs
CFO: Howard Bloom
**VP:* Richard Nesladek
VP: Dave Zimmer
CIO: Clarence Rupert
IT Man: Perry Boyce
Netwrk Eng: Patryk Wasilewski
Plnt Mgr: Larry Iaccino

M & R SALES AND SERVICE
See M & R PRINTING EQUIPMENT INC

D-U-N-S 15-100-8331
M & R UNITED INC
DAIRY QUEEN
402 High Point Dr Ste 101, Cocoa, FL 32926-6602
Tel (321) 631-0245 *Founded/Ownrshp* 1985
Sales 94.4MM *EMP* 30
Accts James Moore & Co Pl Gaine
SIC 5812 5411 Ice cream stands or dairy bars; Convenience stores, independent
Pr: Mahesh R Shah
**VP:* Rashmi Shah

M 3
See M3 INSURANCE SOLUTIONS INC

M A C
See MAC VALVES INC

M A C
See MIKUNI AMERICAN CORP

D-U-N-S 00-890-4385 IMP
M A MORTENSON CO
MORTENSON CONSTRUCTION
(*Suby of* M A MORTENSON COMPANIES INC) ★
700 Meadow Ln N, Minneapolis, MN 55422-4837
Tel (763) 522-2100 *Founded/Ownrshp* 1954
Sales 1.6MMM^E *EMP* 1,730
Accts Pricewaterhousecoopers Llp Mi
SIC 1542 1629 Institutional building construction; Commercial & office building, new construction; Industrial plant construction; Power plant construction; Waste water & sewage treatment plant construction
CEO: Thomas F Gunkel
**Pr:* Daniel L Johnson
**COO:* Thomas W Wacker
CFO: Eric Brekke
**CFO:* Sandra G Sponem
Treas: Jennifer Facciani
Sr VP: Paul V Campbell
Sr VP: Bob Hansen
Sr VP: Robert J Nartonis
Sr VP: John Ohman
**Sr VP:* Paul I Cossette
Sr VP: Tom Wacker
Sr VP: John Wood
VP: Rick Clevette
VP: Mark Ruffino
VP: Allen Troshinsky
Exec: Erik Youngquist
Dir Risk M: Krista Twesme
Dir Bus: Nathan Lingard

D-U-N-S 13-073-1797 IMP
M A MORTENSON COMPANIES INC
700 Meadow Ln N, Minneapolis, MN 55422-4837
Tel (763) 522-2100 *Founded/Ownrshp* 1983
Sales 1.6MMM^E *EMP* 2,000
Accts Pricewaterhousecoopers Llp Mi
SIC 1542 1629 Institutional building construction; Commercial & office building, new construction; Industrial plant construction; Power plant construction; Waste water & sewage treatment plant construction
CEO: M A Mortenson Jr
**Pr:* Tom Gunkel
**CFO:* Peter A Conzemius
CFO: Sandy Sponem
VP: Bill Patt
Snr PM: Rob Weise

M A O
See MID-AMERICA OVERSEAS INC

D-U-N-S 04-739-2741
M ARTHUR GENSLER JR & ASSOCIATES INC (CA)
2 Harrison St Fl 4, San Francisco, CA 94105-6127
Tel (415) 433-3700 *Founded/Ownrshp* 1965
Sales 1.0MMM *EMP* 5,000
Accts Burr Pilger Mayer Inc San Fra
SIC 8712 Architectural services
Co-CEO: Andy Cohen
**Ch Bd:* Robin Klehr Avia
**CFO:* Linda Harvard
**Co-CEO:* Diane Hoskins
Ofcr: Robert Clough
Ofcr: Dee Rendleman
Ofcr: Tina Riedell
Prin: John Adams
Prin: Lisa Amster
Prin: Sarah Bader
Prin: Kenneth P Baker

M B
See MARQUEZ BROTHERS INTERNATIONAL INC

M B C I
See NCI GROUP INC

D-U-N-S 10-200-4306
M B FAYETTE SPECIALISTS INC
FAYETTE IMPORT
1588 Highway 85 N, Fayetteville, GA 30214-4054
Tel (770) 461-3784 *Founded/Ownrshp* 2001
Sales 113.2MM *EMP* 15
SIC 7538 General automotive repair shops
Pr: Ronnie Taylor
**VP:* Douglas Horgen

M B I
See MBI ENERGY LOGISTICS LLC

D-U-N-S 00-791-9442
M B KAHN CONSTRUCTION CO INC (TN)
101 Flintlake Rd, Columbia, SC 29223-7851
Tel (803) 736-2950 *Founded/Ownrshp* 1927
Sales 322.6MM *EMP* 429
Accts Elliott Davis Decosimo Columb
SIC 1542 8742 Nonresidential construction; Construction project management consultant
Pr: William H Neely
COO: Dave Petty
VP: Hayley Bowers
VP: Jack Brown
Off Mgr: Marsha Raines
VP Opers: L Davis Petty
Site Mgr: Andy Finley
Site Mgr: Jimmy Jatt
Site Mgr: Randy Stoner
Mktg Mgr: Peggy Riddick
Board of Directors: Alan B Kahn, Charles B Kahn, Ronald L McCall

M B S
See MANITOWOC BEVERAGE SYSTEMS INC

D-U-N-S 00-512-1181 IMP
M BLOCK & SONS INC
BLOCK HOUSE
5020 W 73rd St, Bedford Park, IL 60638-6612
Tel (708) 728-8400 *Founded/Ownrshp* 1947
Sales 206.8MM^E *EMP* 400
SIC 5064 5023 Electrical appliances, television & radio; Home furnishings
Pr: Bruce Levy
**CFO:* Edward C Roels
**VP:* David Dewes
**VP:* Jody Fellows
**VP:* Mark McManus

D-U-N-S 06-283-2845
M BRADY & ASSOCIATES
9753 Independence Ave, Chatsworth, CA 91311-4318
Tel (818) 700-8813 *Founded/Ownrshp* 1979
Sales 130.0MM *EMP* 15
SIC 5082 General construction machinery & equipment
Pr: Michael E Brady

M C
See MORGAN ADVANCED CERAMICS INC

M C A
See MAIL CONTRACTORS OF AMERICA INC

M C A
See MERCHANDISING CORP OF AMERICA INC

M C ASSEMBLY
See M C TEST SERVICE INC

M C C
See MERCURY CASUALTY CO

D-U-N-S 06-788-6625
M C HOLDINGS INC
MCMM
5709 Education Dr Apt 205, Cheyenne, WY 82009-6308
Tel (307) 514-1510 *Founded/Ownrshp* 1987
Sales 82.1MMM *EMP* 15,600
SIC 6719 7389 Personal holding companies, except banks;
Pr: Erich Lynch

M C L CAFETERIAS
See MCL INC

M C M
See MUNILLA CONSTRUCTION MANAGEMENT LLC

D-U-N-S 14-705-1874 IMP
M C TEST SERVICE INC
M C ASSEMBLY
(*Suby of* MC ASSEMBLY HOLDINGS INC) ★
425 North Dr, Melbourne, FL 32934-9209
Tel (321) 956-3052 *Founded/Ownrshp* 2007
Sales 267.4MM^E *EMP* 1,600^E
SIC 3672 8734 Printed circuit boards; Testing laboratories
Pr: George W Moore
Pr: Jay Sing
**COO:* Luis Ramirez
**CFO:* Mark McReynolds
CFO: Mark McReyonlds
**VP:* Vicki Cooke
VP: Tim Jameson
**VP:* Jake Kulp
Prgrm Mgr: Dianne Karelovich
Sls Mgr: Gary Baltimore

D-U-N-S 07-849-5998
M CASPERSON ENTERPRISE LLC (UT)
MICHAEL CASPERSON
220 S 100 E, St George, UT 84770-3425
Tel (800) 275-8802 *Founded/Ownrshp* 2011
Sales 43.5MM^E *EMP* 1,099
SIC 5063 1731 Burglar alarm systems; Fire detection & burglar alarm systems specialization

M D I
See MERCHANTS DISTRIBUTORS LLC

M D L
See MERYL DIAMOND LTD

M D P
See MADISON DEARBORN PARTNERS LLC

D-U-N-S 11-153-2524
M D WISE INC
1200 Madison Ave Ste 400, Indianapolis, IN 46225-1616
Tel (317) 822-7300 *Founded/Ownrshp* 1994
Sales 457.5MM *EMP* 48
Accts Crowe Horwath Llp Dallas Tx
SIC 8621 Health association
Pr: Charlotte Macbeth
Sls Mgr: Caroline Doebbeling

M E A
See MATANUSKA ELECTRIC ASSOCIATION INC

M E A N
See MUNICIPAL ENERGY AGENCY OF NEBRASKA (INC)

M E F A
See MASSACHUSETTS EDUCATIONAL FINANCING AUTHORITY

M E G
See MILLER ENVIRONMENTAL GROUP INC

M E I
See CRANE PAYMENT INNOVATIONS INC

D-U-N-S 92-978-3587
■ M E S HOLDING CORP
EMCOR CONSTRUCTION SERVICES
(*Suby of* EMCOR GROUP INC) ★
301 Merritt 7, Norwalk, CT 06851-1070
Tel (203) 849-7800 *Founded/Ownrshp* 1994
Sales 367.3MM^E *EMP* 700^E
SIC 1711 1731 Plumbing, heating, air-conditioning contractors; Electrical work
Pr: Tony Guzzi
**VP:* Leicle Chesser

M F I
See MITSUI FOODS INC

M F S
See MASSACHUSETTS FINANCIAL SERVICES CO

D-U-N-S 79-346-6632 IMP
M G H HEALTH SERVICES CORP
GENERAL HOSPITAL
55 Fruit St, Boston, MA 02114-2696
Tel (617) 724-0567 *Founded/Ownrshp* 1986
Sales 18.4MM^E *EMP* 1,400^E
SIC 8082 8059 8071 8062 Home health care services; Personal care home, with health care; Medical laboratories; General medical & surgical hospitals
Pr: James Mongan
**VP:* Jay Pieper

D-U-N-S 79-142-4385
■ M G I C MORTGAGE INSURANCE CORP
(*Suby of* MGIC INVESTMENT) ★
250 E Kilbourn Ave, Milwaukee, WI 53202-3102
Tel (414) 347-6480 *Founded/Ownrshp* 1987
Sales NA *EMP* 900
SIC 6351 Mortgage guarantee insurance
Pr: Kurt Culver
**CFO:* J Michael Lauer
**Sr VP:* Joseph J Ziino
VP: Merri L Elkins
**VP:* Mike Mead
**VP:* Patrick Sinks

M G M
See MGM HOLDINGS INC

D-U-N-S 06-386-9846 IMP/EXP
M H EBY INC
MH EBY TRAILERS
1194 Main St, Blue Ball, PA 17506
Tel (800) 292-4752 *Founded/Ownrshp* 1938
Sales 100.0MM *EMP* 375
SIC 3713 5012 Truck bodies (motor vehicles); Trailers for trucks, new & used
Pr: Mennoh EBY Jr
**Pr:* N Travis EBY
**VP:* Nicholas A EBY

M H EQUIPMENT COMPANY
See MH LOGISTICS CORP

M H M
See METHODIST HEALTHCARE MINISTRIES OF SOUTH TEXAS INC

M H TECHNOLOGIES
See WALKER ENGINEERING INC

D-U-N-S 00-543-4766 IMP/EXP
M HOLLAND CO
400 Skokie Blvd Ste 600, Northbrook, IL 60062-7906
Tel (847) 272-7370 *Founded/Ownrshp* 1948
Sales 533.2MM^E *EMP* 150
SIC 5162 Plastics resins
Pr: Edward J Holland
**CFO:* Patrick McKune
**VP:* Marc Fern
VP: Dwight Morgan
DP Dir: Joaan Guy
Dir IT: Douglas Goldstein
VP Opers: Peter Nutley
QI Cn Mgr: Robert Burton
Manager: Kevin Barnes
Sls Mgr: Keith Carlson
Sls Mgr: Tim Costigan

M I
See MEASUREMENT INC

M I C
See MITSUBISHI INTERNATIONAL CORP

M I C
See MOTORS INSURANCE CORP

M I G
See MANUFACTURERS INDUSTRIAL GROUP LLC

M I P
See MITSUBISHI INTERNATIONAL POLYMER-TRADE CORP

M IT INTERNATIONAL
See DISTRIBUTION INTERNATIONAL SOUTHWEST INC

D-U-N-S 00-446-2032 IMP/EXP
M K MORSE CO
1101 11th St Se, Canton, OH 44707-3400
Tel (330) 453-8187 *Founded/Ownrshp* 1963, 2001
Sales 91.8MM^E *EMP* 450^E
SIC 3425 Saw blades for hand or power saws
CEO: Nancy Sonner
**Owner:* Sally Dale
**Pr:* James Batchelder
**CFO:* Thomas Herrick Jr
**Treas:* George Briercheck
Exec: Janet Morse
Off Mgr: Teidre Lazarides
Opers Mgr: Tom Capone
VP Sls: Paul Schoellman
Manager: Benjamin Harrison
Sls Mgr: Tod Benson
Board of Directors: Sally Dale

M L B
See MLB ADVANCED MEDIA LP

M L B
See MAJOR LEAGUE BASEBALL ENTERPRISES INC

M L B
See MAJOR LEAGUE BASEBALL PROPERTIES INC

D-U-N-S 80-741-6842
M L E HOLDINGS INC
1301 W 400 N, Orem, UT 84057-4442
Tel (801) 224-0589 *Founded/Ownrshp* 2007
Sales 135.3MM^E *EMP* 789^E
SIC 2531 2522 2521 Public building & related furniture; Office desks & tables: except wood; Panel systems & partitions, office: except wood; Chairs, office: padded or plain, except wood; Tables, office: except wood; Wood office furniture; Wood office chairs, benches & stools; Chairs, office: padded, upholstered or plain: wood; Panel systems & partitions (free-standing), office: wood
Ch: Gregory Wilson

M M I
See MONEY MANAGEMENT INTERNATIONAL INC

M M I
See MARKETING MANAGEMENT INC

M MODAL
See MMODAL INC

D-U-N-S 04-643-4676
M O DION & SONS INC (CA)
1543 W 16th St, Long Beach, CA 90813-1210
Tel (714) 540-5535 *Founded/Ownrshp* 1930, 1986
Sales 143.5MM *EMP* 115
Accts Windes Inc Long Beach Cali
SIC 5172 Gasoline; Diesel fuel; Lubricating oils & greases
CEO: Pat Cullen
**Pr:* Matt Cullen
**CEO:* Patrick B Cullen
**CFO:* Bill Frank
Genl Mgr: Brian Busby

M P G
See MEDIA PLANNING GROUP USA LLC

D-U-N-S 82-908-0188
M P I INTERNATIONAL INC
2129 Austin Ave, Rochester Hills, MI 48309-3668
Tel (608) 764-5416 *Founded/Ownrshp* 1969
Sales 280.1MM^E *EMP* 975^E
SIC 3462 3714 3469 Automotive forgings, ferrous: crankshaft, engine, axle, etc.; Motor vehicle transmissions, drive assemblies & parts; Metal stampings
CEO: Mike Bryant
**CFO:* Michael Niemiec
**VP:* Robert Kuth

M P S
See MILWAUKEE PUBLIC SCHOOLS (INC)

M P S
See MACMILLAN HOLDINGS LLC

M R L
See MONTANA RAIL LINK INC

M RESORT SPA CASINO
See LVGV LLC

M RESORT SPA CASINO, THE
See LV GAMING VENTURES LLC

M S
See NATIONAL MULTIPLE SCLEROSIS SOCIETY

M S C INDUSTRIAL SUPPLY
See SID TOOL CO INC

D-U-N-S 05-018-2841
M S D WAYNE TOWNSHIP
1220 S High School Rd, Indianapolis, IN 46241-3127
Tel (317) 243-8251 *Founded/Ownrshp* 2010
Sales NA *EMP* 1,320^E
SIC 9111 City & town managers' offices
Dir Sec: Doug Scheffel
MIS Dir: Pete Just
Dir IT: Mark Lutey
IT Man: Kayanne Klinker
IT Man: Heather Newman
Pr Dir: Mary Lang
Schl Brd P: Shirley Deckard
Schl Brd P: Stan Ellis
Schl Brd P: Mike Nance
Teacher Pr: Dave Marcotte
Teacher Pr: Shenia Suggs

D-U-N-S 07-098-7227 IMP/EXP
M S INTERNATIONAL INC
MSI
2095 N Batavia St, Orange, CA 92865-3101
Tel (714) 685-7500 *Founded/Ownrshp* 1983
Sales 552.1MM^E *EMP* 1,000
SIC 5032 Brick, stone & related material
CEO: Manahar R Shah
**Pr:* Rajesh Shah
**Sec:* Chandrika M Shah
Ofcr: Marlene Ramirez
VP: Sanjay Sanghvi
VP: Ryan Wiener
Dir Bus: Haij Sult
Ex Dir: Steve Rowe
Brnch Mgr: Sunil Etha
Opers Mgr: Manish NJ
Sls Dir: Dharmesh Balsara

M S W
See MAHOMED SALES & WAREHOUSING LLC

D-U-N-S 00-102-0718 IMP
M S WALKER INC (MA)
20 3rd Ave, Somerville, MA 02143-4404
Tel (617) 776-6700 *Founded/Ownrshp* 1931, 1949
Sales 142.1MM^E *EMP* 200
SIC 5182 Liquor
Pr: Harvey Allen
Treas: Richard A Sandler
VP: Steve Blanchard
VP: Doug Shaw
Dir Soc: Christine Bono
Genl Mgr: Jeff Allen
Info Man: William Livingstone
Opers Mgr: Jeffrey Walsh
Natl Sales: Steven Riley
Mktg Dir: Ken Anderson
Mktg Mgr: Justin Shaw

D-U-N-S 01-422-6351 IMP/EXP
M SIMON ZOOK CO
ZOOK MOLASSES CO
4960 Horseshoe Pike, Honey Brook, PA 19344-1361
Tel (800) 327-4406 *Founded/Ownrshp* 1934
Sales 141.4MM^E *EMP* 170
SIC 5149 2048 4013 Molasses, industrial; Prepared feeds; Railroad terminals
Pr: Sally L Martin
**COO:* Larry E Martin
**CFO:* Dean Johnson
Trfc Dir: Brian Suter
QC Dir: Oscar Brunner
Sls&Mrk Ex: Ron Glessner

D-U-N-S 01-285-1705
M SPIEGEL & SONS OIL CORP (NY)
S O S FUELS DIV
10 E Village Rd, Tuxedo Park, NY 10987-4512
Tel (845) 351-4700 *Founded/Ownrshp* 1964
Sales 136.7MM *EMP* 38
Accts Weiser Mazars Llp Woodbury N
SIC 5172 5983 Gasoline; Fuel oil; Diesel fuel; Fuel oil dealers
CEO: Richard Spiegel
**Treas:* Robert Spiegel

M T A
See METROPOLITAN TRANSPORTATION AUTHORITY

M T C
See MUTUAL TRADING CO INC

M T C
See MANAGEMENT & TRAINING CORP

M T C
See METROPOLITAN TRANSPORTATION COMMISSION

M T E
See MONROE TRUCK EQUIPMENT INC

M T F
See MUSCULOSKELETAL TRANSPLANT FOUNDATION INC

D-U-N-S 15-693-1347 IMP/EXP
M T G LLC
GMT
Carre 175km 27 2 Hc 34 Bo, Caguas, PR 00725
Tel (787) 783-1988 *Founded/Ownrshp* 1989
Sales 96.3MM *EMP* 225
Accts Marques-Guillermety Cpa Ps
SIC 5147 Meats & meat products
Pr: Sam Ramos Cordova
**VP:* Sammy Ramos Montes

M T M
See MEDICAL TRANSPORTATION MANAGEMENT INC

M T S
See MARTIN TRANSPORTATION SYSTEMS INC

M U D
See METROPOLITAN UTILITIES DISTRICT

D-U-N-S 03-804-9532
M V M INC
44620 Guilford Dr Ste 150, Ashburn, VA 20147-6063
Tel (571) 223-4500 *Founded/Ownrshp* 1979
Sales 2.9MM *EMP* 4,100
Accts Lo Brarenwalsh & Associates I
SIC 7381 8741 Detective & armored car services; Management services
Pr: Dario O Marquez
**COO:* David Westrate
**CFO:* Joseph D Stanton
**Ex VP:* Kevin P Marquez
**Sr VP:* Louie T McKinney
**VP:* Maria Campos
Admn Mgr: Margie Cebrian
IT Man: Imad Samha

M W E
See MCDERMOTT WILL & EMERY LLP INC

M X R
See MERRY X-RAY CHEMICAL CORP

D-U-N-S 17-564-6611 IMP
M&A TECHNOLOGY INC
EDUBUYERS
2045 Chenault Dr, Carrollton, TX 75006-5021
Tel (972) 490-5803 *Founded/Ownrshp* 1985
Sales 176.4MM^E *EMP* 90
SIC 5045 7373 Computers, peripherals & software; Systems integration services
Pr: Magdy S Elwany
**Sr VP:* Donna Shepard
Sr VP: Donna Zweback
**VP:* Tom Garrett
Dir Bus: Alok Sarna
Prgrm Mgr: Christie Hite
CTO: Val Overbey
Mktg Mgr: Herb Emerson
Manager: Amy Thomas
Sls Mgr: Donna Shepherd
Snr Mgr: Pamela Moore

D-U-N-S 78-802-1681
M&C HOTEL INTERESTS INC
RICHFIELD TECHNICAL SERVICES
(*Suby of* MILLENNIUM HOTELS & RESORTS) ★
6560 Greenwood Plaza Blvd # 300, Greenwood Village, CO 80111-4980
Tel (303) 779-2000 *Founded/Ownrshp* 1991
Sales 77.5MM^E *EMP* 2,300
SIC 8741 8712 6321 6331 7389 Hotel or motel management; Architectural services; Accident & health insurance carriers; Workers' compensation insurance; Purchasing service
Pr: Paul T Underhill
**Sr VP:* Lyle L Boll

D-U-N-S 84-165-5538 IMP
M&C HOTEL INTERESTS INC
MILLENNIUM HOTELS & RESORTS
(*Suby of* MILLENNIUM & COPTHORNE HOTELS PLC)
7600 E Orchard Rd 230s, Greenwood Village, CO 80111-2553
Tel (303) 779-2000 *Founded/Ownrshp* 2000
Sales 356.6MM^E *EMP* 5,000
SIC 7011 Hotels
CEO: John Arnett
**Pr:* Robert Morse
VP: Janlyn Mahlman

D-U-N-S 02-281-2697 IMP
M&G DURAVENT INC
(*Suby of* M & G GROUP EUROPE B.V.)
877 Cotting Ct, Vacaville, CA 95688-9354
Tel (707) 446-1786 *Founded/Ownrshp* 2010
Sales 119.6MM^E *EMP* 400
SIC 3444 Metal ventilating equipment
Pr: Brooks Sherman
**VP:* Victor Lambert

D-U-N-S 00-802-5355 IMP/EXP
■ **M&M MANUFACTURING INC**
M&M MANUFACTURING, LLC
(*Suby of* MITEK INDUSTRIES INC) ★
4001 Mark Iv Pkwy, Fort Worth, TX 76106-4129
Tel (817) 336-2311 *Founded/Ownrshp* 1958, 2015
Sales 156.9MM^E *EMP* 480
SIC 3444 Ducts, sheet metal
Pr: Rob Felton
COO: Robert Felton
**VP:* Melvin Nobles
**VP:* Steve Priester
**VP:* Michael D Stepp
**VP:* Jim Strong

M&M MANUFACTURING, LLC
See M&M MANUFACTURING INC

D-U-N-S 08-047-3849
M&Q HOLDINGS LLC
3 Earl Ave, Schuylkill Haven, PA 17972-8961
Tel (570) 385-4991 *Founded/Ownrshp* 2015
Sales 86.5MM^E *EMP* 400^E
SIC 3089 6719 Plastic processing; Investment holding companies, except banks
Pr: Michael Schmal

D-U-N-S 87-855-0516 IMP
M&R HOLDINGS INC
M&R PRINTING
440 Medinah Rd, Roselle, IL 60172-2329
Tel (630) 858-6101 *Founded/Ownrshp* 1993
Sales 134.3MM^E *EMP* 400
SIC 3552 Printing machinery, textile
Pr: Richard Hoffman
**VP:* Howard Bloom
**VP:* Richard Nesladek

M&R PRINTING
See M&R HOLDINGS INC

M&T
See MANUFACTURERS AND TRADERS TRUST CO

D-U-N-S 07-279-6022 IMP/EXP
▲ **M&T BANK CORP**
1 M&T Plz Fl 5, Buffalo, NY 14203
Tel (716) 635-4000 *Founded/Ownrshp* 1969
Sales NA *EMP* 17,476
Tkr Sym MTB *Exch* NYS
SIC 6022 State commercial banks
Ch Bd: Robert G Wilmers
**V Ch:* Robert T Brady
**Pr:* Mark J Czarnecki
Pr: Whitney Lee
CFO: Ren F Jones
CFO: Darren J King
Treas: D Scott N Warman
Ofcr: Robert J Bojdak
Ofcr: Richard S Gold
Trst Ofcr: Doris P Meister
Ex VP: Janet M Coletti
Ex VP: William J Farrell II
Ex VP: Brian E Hickey
Ex VP: Gino A Martocci
Ex VP: Kevin J Pearson
Ex VP: Michael J Todaro
Ex VP: Michele D Trolli
VP: Kimberly Barker
VP: Beth Beshaw
VP: Scott Boli
VP: Jolene Falkner

D-U-N-S 93-974-4819
■ **M&T BANK NATIONAL ASSOCIATION**
(*Suby of* M&T BANK CORP) ★
48 Main St, Oakfield, NY 14125-1044
Tel (800) 528-6532 *Founded/Ownrshp* 1995
Sales 227.3MM *EMP* 45^E
SIC 8611 Regulatory associations
Ch: Robert G Wilmers
**Pr:* Robert E Sadler Jr
Ex VP: Harry R Stainrook
Sr VP: James A Gately
Sr VP: Richard A Lammert
Sr VP: Alfred F Luhr III
Sr VP: William H Mabee

D-U-N-S 78-848-8336
■ **M&T MORTGAGE CORP**
(*Suby of* M&T) ★
1 Fountain Plz, Buffalo, NY 14203-1420
Tel (716) 842-5445 *Founded/Ownrshp* 1991
Sales NA *EMP* 1,050
SIC 6162 Mortgage bankers; Mortgage brokers, using own money
Sr VP: Michael Drury
Pr: Rosaria Carnevale
Ofcr: Stephen Harrington
Ofcr: Len Soldano
Ofcr: Jennifer Yates
Ex VP: Brian Hickey
**Sr VP:* Michael Todaro
Sr VP: Jeffrey A Wellington
VP: Scott Eakin
VP: Teresa Eller
VP: Michael Freer
VP: Rich Gold
VP: Donna Gorney
VP: Laura Greenfield
VP: Joseph Hassett
VP: Gary Hutchings
VP: Mary Isakov
VP: Sharon Obrien
VP: George Oliver
VP: Ralph Partlow
VP: Craig Schwartz
Board of Directors: Emerson L Brumback, Michael P Pinto, Robert E Sadler Jr

D-U-N-S 12-982-1018
M+W AMERICAS INC
(*Suby of* M+W FACILITY ENGINEERING GMBH)
1001 Klein Rd Ste 400, Plano, TX 75074-3751
Tel (972) 535-7300 *Founded/Ownrshp* 1990
Sales 266.1MM^E *EMP* 920
SIC 3433 8712 8711 8741 Solar heaters & collectors; Architectural services; Architectural engineering; Engineering services; Construction & civil engineering; Construction management
VP: Jose Rivas
**COO:* Gary C Baughman
CFO: Hannes Rosenthaler
Dir IT: Martin Boekeloo
Dir IT: Don Yeaman
Mktg Mgr: Al Hannah
Sls Mgr: Martin Schutz
Snr PM: Dan Olsen
Board of Directors: Ron Oakley, Robert Wills

D-U-N-S 62-114-7255 IMP
M+W US INC
(*Suby of* M+W GROUP GMBH)
201 Fuller Rd Ste 400, Albany, NY 12203-3621
Tel (518) 266-3400 *Founded/Ownrshp* 2005
Sales 265.9MM^E *EMP* 400
SIC 1542 8711 Nonresidential construction; Engineering services
CEO: Ron Oakley
**COO:* Gary Baughman
**CFO:* Bob Wills
**Ex VP:* James Ellington
**VP:* Dan Mariani
**VP:* Greg Meyers
**VP:* Jose M Rivas
**VP:* Ken Toliver
Board of Directors: Ron Oakley Bob Wills Gary

D-U-N-S 00-718-8063 IMP/EXP
M-D BUILDING PRODUCTS INC
4041 N Santa Fe Ave, Oklahoma City, OK 73118-8512
Tel (405) 528-4411 *Founded/Ownrshp* 2000
Sales 253.6MM^E *EMP* 600
SIC 3442 Weather strip, metal; Moldings & trim, except automobile: metal
CEO: Loren A Plotkin
**CFO:* Kathryn McKinney
**Ch:* Richard Gaugler
**Ex VP:* Larry Sanford
**Ex VP:* Steve Wright
Sr VP: Lynn Ely
IT Man: Travis Cleek
Plnt Mgr: Tom Stark
Board of Directors: Brent Gooden, Rick Moore

M-DCPS SCHOOL BOARD
See SCHOOL BOARD OF MIAMI-DADE COUNTY

D-U-N-S 16-080-1585 IMP/EXP
M-I LLC
M-I SWACO A SCHLUMBERGER CO
(*Suby of* SCHLUMBERGER) ★
5950 N Course Dr, Houston, TX 77072-1626
Tel (281) 561-1300 *Founded/Ownrshp* 1994
Sales 3.6MMM^E *EMP* 3,500
SIC 1389 2865 2869 8711 8741 Oil field services; Mud service, oil field drilling; Cyclic crudes & intermediates; Industrial organic chemicals; Engineering services; Management services
CEO: Paal Kibsgaard
**Pr:* Joe Bacho
**Ex VP:* Simon Ayat
**Ex VP:* Ashok Belani
**Ex VP:* J-F Poupeau
Sr VP: Bryan Dudman
VP: Richard Chandler
**VP:* Stephanie Cox
**VP:* Alan McLean
Genl Mgr: Rusty Adams
Genl Mgr: Kevin Gautreaux

M-I SWACO A SCHLUMBERGER CO
See M-I LLC

D-U-N-S 02-849-2770 IMP/EXP
M-L HOLDINGS CO
4601 Washington Blvd, Baltimore, MD 21227-4460
Tel (410) 242-6500 *Founded/Ownrshp* 1997
Sales 134.7MM^E *EMP* 165
SIC 5082 6719 Crushing, pulverizing & screening machinery; Investment holding companies, except banks
Prin: Tom Logan
**Prin:* John Logan
**Prin:* Robert Matz

D-U-N-S 88-437-4521
M-PLAN INC
(*Suby of* THE HEALTH CARE GROUP LLC)
8802 N Meridian St # 100, Indianapolis, IN 46260-5318
Tel (317) 963-9700 *Founded/Ownrshp* 1989
Sales NA *EMP* 255
SIC 6324 6411 Health maintenance organization (HMO), insurance only; Insurance agents, brokers & service
Pr: Alex Slabosky
**CFO:* Connie Brown
Ex Dir: Ceresa Beason
Board of Directors: Chuck Mihalik, Kathleen Shook, Alex Slabosky

D-U-N-S 06-193-7319 IMP/EXP
M-SKO IAS HOLDINGS INC
MAG IAS HOLDINGS, INC.
(*Suby of* MAG IAS GMBH)
1395 Brickell Ave Ste 800, Miami, FL 33131-3302
Tel (786) 871-2904 *Founded/Ownrshp* 2012
Sales 790.0MM^E *EMP* 4,919
SIC 5084 Machine tools & accessories
Pr: Moshe Meidar
Ex VP: Gregory Vereschagin
**VP:* Liad Meidar
**VP:* Hillit R Meidar-Alfi

D-U-N-S 17-433-2072 IMP/EXP
M-TEK INC
KASAI NORTH AMERICA, INC.
(*Suby of* KASAI KOGYO CO., LTD.)
1020 Volunteer Pkwy, Manchester, TN 37355-6461
Tel (931) 728-4122 *Founded/Ownrshp* 1986
Sales 546.9MM^E *EMP* 2,422
SIC 3089 3714 3429 Injection molded finished plastic products; Motor vehicle parts & accessories; Manufactured hardware (general)
CEO: Masaki Sugisawa
**Pr:* Koji Hori
**Pr:* N Onedara
Treas: Tatsuo Kase
Treas: Bob Miller
**Treas:* Shinichi Yasukawa
**Sr VP:* Koichi Yoshida
VP: Kazuhiro Kobayashi
VP: Bobby Locke
Prgrm Mgr: Lyndon Davidson
Genl Mgr: Jim Leyhew

M/A-COM
See MACOM TECHNOLOGY SOLUTIONS INC

D-U-N-S 07-164-9743
▲ **M/I HOMES INC** (OH)
3 Easton Oval Ste 500, Columbus, OH 43219-6011
Tel (614) 418-8000 *Founded/Ownrshp* 1973
Sales 1.4MMM *EMP* 1,008
Tkr Sym MHO *Exch* NYS
SIC 1531 6162 Speculative builder, single-family houses; Townhouse developers; Mortgage bankers & correspondents
Ch Bd: Robert H Schottenstein
Pr: Thomas W Jacobs
Pr: Ronald H Martin
Pr: Fred J Sikorski
**CFO:* Phillip G Creek
Sr VP: Paul S Rosen
VP: David Balcerzak
VP: Kevin D Stewart
Opers Mgr: Nancy Wilson
S&M/VP: Desiree Davis
Mktg Mgr: Kimberly Jackson
Board of Directors: Friedrich K M Bohm, William H Carter, Michael P Glimcher, Nancy J Kramer, Norman L Traeger, Sharen Jester Turney

D-U-N-S 14-786-0761
M/L BOVIS HOLDINGS LTD
(*Suby of* LENDLEASE CORPORATION LIMITED)
200 Park Ave Fl 9, New York, NY 10166-0999
Tel (212) 592-6700 *Founded/Ownrshp* 1988
Sales 173.4MM^E *EMP* 600
SIC 1522 1541 1542 8741 8742 Residential construction; Industrial buildings & warehouses; Nonresidential construction; Management services; Management consulting services
Pr: Dale Connor

D-U-N-S 07-860-7184
M10 INC
817 W Main St, Brownsville, WI 53006-1439
Tel (920) 583-3132 *Founded/Ownrshp* 2010
Sales 493.4MM^E *EMP* 5,000^E
Accts Grant Thornton Llp Appleton
SIC 6719 Investment holding companies, except banks
CEO: Ruth Michels

D-U-N-S 15-156-7427 IMP
M3 ENGINEERING & TECHNOLOGY CORP
2051 W Sunset Rd Ste 101, Tucson, AZ 85704-1722
Tel (520) 293-1488 *Founded/Ownrshp* 1986
Sales 128.3MM *EMP* 470
Accts Beachfleischman Pc Tucson Ar
SIC 8741 8712 8711 Construction management; Architectural services; Consulting engineer
Pr: Daniel H Neff
**Sr VP:* Douglas Austin

*Sr VP: Thomas L Drielick
*Sr VP: Dennis Mulligan
*VP: Lee Becker
*VP: Patrick W Dugan
*VP: Peter A Erath
*VP: Conrad E Huss
*VP: David E Sitterud

D-U-N-S 09-854-8159
M3 INSURANCE SOLUTIONS INC (WI)
M 3
828 John Nolen Dr, Madison, WI 53713-1424
Tel (608) 273-0655 Founded/Ownrshp 1968, 1970
Sales NA EMP 200
SIC 6411 Insurance agents
Pr: Michael E Victorson
Pt: Christine Kenyon
Pr: Ed Rapee III
Ex VP: Thomas Golden
Ex VP: Richard F Kekula
Ex VP: Michael J Moore
Ex VP: Michael Moore
Ex VP: Rich Twietmeyer
VP: James Lutcf
VP: Hernan Tocuyo
VP: Jim Yeager
Dir Risk M: Chris Halverson
Dir Soc: Traci Mandell
Dir Bus: Claire Flitcroft

D-U-N-S 05-856-5857
M3 MIDSTREAM LLC
600 Travis St Ste 5600, Houston, TX 77002-2909
Tel (713) 783-3000 Founded/Ownrshp 2010
Sales 126.1MM^E EMP 180
SIC 1311 Natural gas production
CEO: Frank Tsuru
Pr: Mark Kraus
Pr: Chris Pearce
*COO: Brant Baird
*Ch: Bill Pritchard
*VP: George Francisco
Dir Bus: Keith Hickey

D-U-N-S 96-380-3536
MA ACQUISITION CO LLC
501 Galveston St, Wichita Falls, TX 76301-5906
Tel (940) 397-2100 Founded/Ownrshp 2010
Sales 83.1MM^E EMP 251
SIC 6733 Personal investment trust management
CEO: Ron Duncan

D-U-N-S 94-240-8766
MA FEDERAL INC
IGOV.COM
12030 Sunrise Valley Dr # 300, Reston, VA 20191-3447
Tel (703) 356-1160 Founded/Ownrshp 1996
Sales 130.5MM^E EMP 100^E
Accts Cherry Bekaert & Holland Ll
SIC 5045 Accounting machines using machine readable programs
CEO: Patrick A Neven
*Pr: Michael Tyrrell
*CFO: Steven Hamric
*Sr VP: Walter Hupalo
*VP: Chuck Reiche
VP: Tom Walsh
VP Bus Dev: Sean Thompson
Dir Bus: Peter Davis

D-U-N-S 08-001-8421
MA INDUSTRIAL JV LLC
5683 Hines Dr, Ann Arbor, MI 48108-7901
Tel (734) 585-9500 Founded/Ownrshp 2015
Sales 724.4MM^E EMP 5,800^E
SIC 3585 3679 6719 Parts for heating, cooling & refrigerating equipment; Hermetic seals for electronic equipment; Investment holding companies, except banks
CEO: Gregory L Christopher

D-U-N-S 15-509-3172 IMP/EXP
MA LABORATORIES INC
MA LABS
2075 N Capitol Ave, San Jose, CA 95132-1009
Tel (408) 941-0808 Founded/Ownrshp 1988
Sales 241.3MM^E EMP 600
SIC 5045

MA LABS
See MA LABORATORIES INC

D-U-N-S 00-817-2157 IMP/EXP
MA PATOUT & SON LIMITED LLC
3512 J Patout Burns Rd, Jeanerette, LA 70544-7122
Tel (337) 276-4592 Founded/Ownrshp 1911
Sales 267.3MM EMP 413
Accts Broussard Poche Llp Lafayette
SIC 2061 Raw cane sugar; Blackstrap molasses made from sugar cane; Cane syrup made from sugar cane
Ch Bd: Frank W Patout
*CEO: Craig Caillier
*CFO: Randall K Romero
*Treas: J Jared Patout
Genl Mgr: Jerome Fitch
Genl Mgr: Robert B Patout
Board of Directors: William Patout III

MAA
See MID-AMERICA APARTMENT COMMUNITIES INC

D-U-N-S 16-850-0127
MAALT LP
MAALT TRANSPORT
4413 Carey St, Fort Worth, TX 76119-4219
Tel (817) 205-0460 Founded/Ownrshp 2004
Sales 106.8MM^E EMP 400
SIC 4225 4731 General warehousing & storage; Truck transportation brokers
Pt: Martin Robertson
Pt: Gary Humphreys
VP: Steve McCarley

MAALT TRANSPORT
See MAALT LP

D-U-N-S 84-800-4248 IMP/EXP
MAAX US CORP
(Suby of MAAX BATH INC)
7767 Elm Creek Blvd N # 310, Maple Grove, MN 55369-7041
Tel (877) 438-6229 Founded/Ownrshp 2009
Sales 163.5MM^E EMP 1,200
SIC 3088 Plastics plumbing fixtures
CEO: Mark Gold
VP: David Lipkin
*Prin: Paul Golden

D-U-N-S 03-746-2488
MABANK INDEPENDENT SCHOOL DISTRICT
310 E Market St, Mabank, TX 75147-2311
Tel (903) 880-1300 Founded/Ownrshp 1900
Sales 35.8MM EMP 1,107
Accts Smith Lambright & Associates
SIC 8211 Public elementary & secondary schools
Instr Medi: James Pate
HC Dir: Pam Odom

MABSC
See MEGGITT AIRCRAFT BRAKING SYSTEMS CORP

MAC
See METROPOLITAN AIRPORTS COMMISSION

D-U-N-S 02-488-8972
MAC ACQUISITION OF KANSAS LLC (KS)
6750 Lyndon B Johnson Fwy, Dallas, TX 75240-6512
Tel (972) 674-4300 Founded/Ownrshp 2013
Sales 205.1MM^E EMP 10,000
SIC 5812

D-U-N-S 00-620-7005
MAC ARTHUR CO (MN)
WEEKES FOREST PRODUCTS
2400 Wycliff St, Saint Paul, MN 55114-1268
Tel (651) 646-2773 Founded/Ownrshp 1913, 2004
Sales 700.0M EMP 1,000
SIC 5033 3448

D-U-N-S 03-785-7976
MAC CONSTRUCTION & EXCAVATING INC
1908 Unruh Ct, New Albany, IN 47150-6948
Tel (812) 284-4250 Founded/Ownrshp 1980
Sales 102.4MM^E EMP 200
SIC 1623 1622 1794 Water main construction; Sewer line construction; Highway construction, elevated; Bridge construction; Excavation & grading, building construction
CEO: Chad Unruh
*Pr: Travis Unruh
*Pr: Victor O Unruh
*CEO: Jean M Unruh
CFO: Christopher Bane
VP Admn: Bryan Wickens
Sfty Mgr: Neal Biggs
VP Sls: Michael Lyttle
Sls Dir: Rusty Crosier

D-U-N-S 08-356-0490
MAC HAIK ENTERPRISES
11757 Katy Fwy Ste 1500, Houston, TX 77079-1794
Tel (281) 496-7788 Founded/Ownrshp 1974
Sales 192.4MM^E EMP 720
SIC 5511 Automobiles, new & used; Pickups, new & used; Vans, new & used
Owner: Mac Haik
CFO: Bill Blackwell
Sr VP: Ron Marshall
Sr VP: Brandon Poynter
VP: Amy Jankowski
VP: Christina Logan
VP: Rachel Schipul
Dir Risk M: Nathan Walker
Sls Dir: Chris Ferguson

D-U-N-S 00-508-6376 IMP
MAC LEAN-FOGG CO
MACLEAN FASTENERS
1000 Allanson Rd, Mundelein, IL 60060-3804
Tel (847) 566-0010 Founded/Ownrshp 1925
Sales 1.3MMM^E EMP 4,500
SIC 3678 3452 3089 3061 3492 3451 Electronic connectors; Nuts, metal; Bolts, metal; Screws, metal; Plastic processing; Automotive rubber goods (mechanical); Fluid power valves & hose fittings; Screw machine products
*Pr: Duncan A L Maclean
*CFO: George H Cook
VP: Tom Macdonald
VP: Rob Whitney
Prgrm Mgr: Christian Muehlich
*Off Admin: Brian Duffy
IT Man: Ash Shah
Mfg Mgr: Bob Allcox
Plnt Mgr: Drew Ammons
Ql Cn Mgr: Pratik Shah
Snr Mgr: Jeff Degner
Board of Directors: Andrew Silvernail, Paul F Anderson, Dean Gestal, Stanford J Goldblatt, Stephen M Gordon, Juergen Harnisch, Thomas R Hodgson, Barry L Maclean, David B Maclean, Duncan Maclean

MAC LIQUID TANK TRAILER
See MAC LTT INC

D-U-N-S 96-978-7907
MAC LTT INC
MAC LIQUID TANK TRAILER
(Suby of MAC TRAILER MANUFACTURING INC) ★
1400 Fairchild Ave, Kent, OH 44240-1818
Tel (330) 474-3795 Founded/Ownrshp 2011
Sales 125.2MM^E EMP 150^E
SIC 3569 Assembly machines, non-metalworking
Pr: Jim Maiorana
Genl Mgr: Carol McNutt
Plnt Mgr: Ken Grosswiller

D-U-N-S 80-382-5939 IMP
MAC MANUFACTURING INC
14599 Commerce St Ne, Alliance, OH 44601-1003
Tel (330) 823-9900 Founded/Ownrshp 1995
Sales 367.1MM^E EMP 1,300
SIC 3715 5012 Truck trailers; Trailers for trucks, new & used; Truck bodies
*Sec: Jenny Conny
*VP: Dan Tubbs

D-U-N-S 04-253-1533
■ **MAC NEAL MEMORIAL HOSPITAL ASSOCIATION**
(Suby of VANGUARD HEALTH SYSTEMS INC) ★
3249 Oak Park Ave, Berwyn, IL 60402-3429
Tel (708) 783-9100 Founded/Ownrshp 1931
Sales 265.5MM EMP 1,053
SIC 8062 General medical & surgical hospitals
CEO: Scott Steiner
*CFO: ME Cleary
*CFO: Sharon Oxendale
QC Dir: Jan Machanis
Pgrm Dir: Jenny Wasielewski

D-U-N-S 60-820-8773 IMP/EXP
MAC NEIL AUTOMOTIVE PRODUCTS LIMITED
WEATHERTECH
1 Macneil Ct, Bolingbrook, IL 60440-4903
Tel (630) 769-1500 Founded/Ownrshp 1989
Sales 110.9MM^E EMP 130^E
SIC 5531 5013 Automotive accessories; Automotive supplies
CEO: David Mac Neil
Pr: David Iverson
*Pr: Allan Thom
*CFO: Les Veatch
VP: Michael Bishop
VP: Al Thom
Exec: Jeff Plude
CTO: Thomas Virzi
Plnt Mgr: Jeremy Simkowski
Sales Asso: Konrad Fitzgerald
Art Dir: Sam Ezzo

D-U-N-S 00-407-9141 IMP/EXP
MAC PAPERS INC
3300 Phillips Hwy, Jacksonville, FL 32207-4312
Tel (904) 396-5312 Founded/Ownrshp 1964
Sales 1.0MMM^E EMP 870
SIC 5112 5111 Envelopes; Fine paper
Ch Bd: Frank S McGehee
Pr: David S McGehee
CEO: Sutton McGehee
CFO: John W Brent
Sec: Jonathan Y Rogers
Sr VP: Jerry Shane
VP: Darnell M Babbit
VP: Steve Bethea
VP: Dave Boynton
VP: Stephen L Collins
*VP: Thomas R McGehee Jr
Board of Directors: Ann Mc Gehee, Delia Mc Gehee, Delia Mc Gehee II, Ann M Riley

D-U-N-S 80-003-2112
MAC PARENT LLC
(Suby of ROMANOS MACARONI GRILL) ★
3100 S Gessner Rd Ste 125, Houston, TX 77063-3744
Tel (832) 649-2260 Founded/Ownrshp 2015
Sales 323.7MM^E EMP 7,500^E
SIC 5812 6794 Grills (eating places); Franchises, selling or licensing
Pr: John Gilbert
Exec: Jamie French
Exec: Todd Olson
Genl Mgr: Stephanie Chappell
Genl Mgr: Stacy Clift
Genl Mgr: Bryan Davis
Genl Mgr: Joel Diaz
Genl Mgr: Adam Goldstone
Genl Mgr: Danny Hadfield
Genl Mgr: Rich Kalafut
Genl Mgr: Elizabeth Lee

D-U-N-S 79-821-8780 IMP/EXP
MAC TRAILER MANUFACTURING INC
14599 Commerce St Ne, Alliance, OH 44601-1003
Tel (330) 823-9900 Founded/Ownrshp 1992
Sales 149.4MM^E EMP 400^E
SIC 3715 5012 5013 5015 7539 Truck trailers; Trailers for trucks, new & used; Truck bodies; Motor vehicle supplies & new parts; Motor vehicle parts, used; Trailer repair
Pr: Mike Conny
COO: John Raymond
*CFO: Bill Ogden
*Treas: Jenny Conny
*VP: Ben Childers
VP: Tay Griffith
*VP: David Sandor
CIO: Dennis Postiy
IT Man: Dennis Posty

D-U-N-S 00-535-4295 IMP
MAC VALVES INC
M A C
30569 Beck Rd, Wixom, MI 48393-2842
Tel (248) 624-7700 Founded/Ownrshp 1948
Sales 161.4MM^E EMP 890
SIC 3492 3494 3491 Control valves, fluid power: hydraulic & pneumatic; Valves & pipe fittings; Industrial valves
Pr: Robert Neff
*Treas: Martha C Welch
*VP: Douglas Mc Cuiston
VP: Matthew Neff
Dept Mgr: Doug Hipps
Plnt Mgr: John Haar
VP Sls: Douglas McCuiston

D-U-N-S 01-340-5901
MACALESTER COLLEGE
200 Amherst St, Saint Paul, MN 55105-1912
Tel (651) 698-8650 Founded/Ownrshp 1874
Sales 97.7MM EMP 1^E
SIC 8299 Educational services
Pr: Brian C Rosenberg
*Prin: Carleton Macy

D-U-N-S 07-762-6778
MACALESTER COLLEGE
1600 Grand Ave, Saint Paul, MN 55105-1899
Tel (651) 696-6000 Founded/Ownrshp 1874
Sales 110.9MM EMP 750
Accts Cliftonlarsonallen Llp Minnea
SIC 8221 College, except junior
Pr: Brian Rosenberg
*CFO: David Wheaton
Treas: Kenneth Tivey
VP: D Brown
Assoc Dir: Angi Faiks
Assoc Dir: Paul Odegaard
Assoc Dir: Robin Ruthenbeck
Prgrm Mgr: Christian Nelson
Telecom Mg: Kelly Borke
IT Man: Jacob Dorer
Web Dev: Zach Bajaber

MACALLISTER ENGINE POWER
See MACALLISTER MACHINERY CO INC

D-U-N-S 00-693-8419 IMP/EXP
MACALLISTER MACHINERY CO INC
MACALLISTER ENGINE POWER
7515 E 30th St, Indianapolis, IN 46219-1192
Tel (317) 545-2151 Founded/Ownrshp 1941
Sales 1.3MMM EMP 1,850
SIC 5082 7699 5013 Tractors, construction; General construction machinery & equipment; Construction equipment repair; Automotive supplies & parts
Ch Bd: Pershing E Macallister
*Pr: Christopher E Macallister
*CFO: David Baldwin
Genl Mgr: Mike Doyle
Genl Mgr: Lisa Harless
Genl Mgr: Dan Zachary
CTO: Chris Scott
Dir IT: Garry Buechlar
Dir IT: Gary Buechler
IT Man: Bobby Saint
Software D: Jan Guzman

D-U-N-S 00-695-8573 IMP/EXP
MACALLISTER MACHINERY CO INC
MICHIGAN CAT
24800 Novi Rd, Novi, MI 48375-2414
Tel (248) 349-4800 Founded/Ownrshp 1943, 2011
Sales 497.6MM EMP 648
SIC 5082 General construction machinery & equipment
Pr: Chris Macallister
*COO: Bill Hodges
*CFO: Dave Baldwin
VP: Arnold Strouse
Netwrk Mgr: Jeremy Parkinson

D-U-N-S 87-830-4849 IMP/EXP
MACANDREWS & FORBES HOLDINGS INC
35 E 62nd St, New York, NY 10065-8014
Tel (212) 572-8600 Founded/Ownrshp 1993
Sales 5.7MMM^E EMP 60,637
SIC 7819 Film processing, editing & titling: motion picture
CEO: Ronald O Perelman
*Pr: Paul M Meister
Sr Ex VP: William C Bevins
Ex VP: Steven Fasman
Ex VP: Eric Rose
*Sr VP: David L Kennedy
Sr VP: Evan Knisely
VP: Michael Borofsky
VP: Geoffrey Chow
VP: Floyd Clarke
*VP: Steven M Cohen
VP: Michelle Galdos
VP: Ron Goffinet
VP: Timothy Murphy
VP: Debbie Perelman

D-U-N-S 11-291-9956 IMP/EXP
MACANDREWS & FORBES INC
(Suby of MACANDREWS & FORBES HOLDINGS INC) ★
38 E 63rd St, New York, NY 10065-8027
Tel (212) 688-9000 Founded/Ownrshp 1991
Sales 2.1MMM^E EMP 25,000^E
SIC 2844 2087 2121 7819 2721 2731

D-U-N-S 96-626-8513
MACAULAY BROWN INC
MACB
2933 Bunker Hill Ln # 220, Santa Clara, CA 95054-1124
Tel (937) 426-3421 Founded/Ownrshp 2011
Sales 2.5MM^E EMP 1,500
SIC 8711 Engineering services
Ex Dir: Vicki Summers

D-U-N-S 07-925-3831
MACAULAY-BROWN INC
1951 Polaris Rd, Finksburg, MD 21048-2070
Tel (937) 426-3421 Founded/Ownrshp 2014
Sales 27.1MM^E EMP 1,900
SIC 8711 Electrical or electronic engineering
VP: Victoria Summers

D-U-N-S 09-650-0483
MACAULAY-BROWN INC (OH)
MACB
4021 Executive Dr, Beavercreek, OH 45430-1062
Tel (937) 426-3421 Founded/Ownrshp 1979, 2002
Sales 434.5MM^E EMP 2,000
SIC 8711 8733 Engineering services; Research institute
Pr: Sidney E Fuchs
CEO: Sid Fuchs
*CFO: Michael C Zeiser
*Ofcr: Mike Ritter
Sr VP: Mike Beauchamp
Sr VP: Mark Chadason
Sr VP: Fred Norman
Sr VP: William Pratt
Sr VP: Donald Raines
Sr VP: Jim Soos
*VP: Dave Bramlage
VP: Sigrid Calandra
VP: John Graziano
*VP: Mia Kerivan-Omalley
VP: Troy Kohler
VP: Bernie Murtaugh
VP: Phil Nielsen
VP: Alan Puterbaugh
VP: Patrick Simpson

VP: Leigh Thompson
VP: Greg Yadzinski
Board of Directors: Bruce Lesser, Kevin Soder

D-U-N-S 94-970-8598
MACAYO RESTAURANTS LLC
1480 E Bethany Home Rd # 130, Phoenix, AZ 85014-2022
Tel (602) 264-1831 *Founded/Ownrshp* 1946
Sales 51.1MM^E *EMP* 1,000
SIC 5813 5812 5149 Bar (drinking places); Mexican restaurant; Groceries & related products
Genl Mgr: Juan Gonzales
IT Man: Rebecca Bustillos
IT Man: Naji Ibrahem

MACB
See MACAULAY-BROWN INC

MACB
See MACAULAY BROWN INC

MACDERMID GRAPHICS SOLUTION
See MACDERMID PRINTING SOLUTIONS LLC

D-U-N-S 00-116-4599 IMP/EXP
■ MACDERMID INC (CT)
MACDERMID PRFMCE SOLUTIONS
(*Suby of* PLATFORM SPECIALTY PRODUCTS CORP) ★
245 Freight St, Waterbury, CT 06702-1818
Tel (203) 575-5700 *Founded/Ownrshp* 1922, 2007
Sales 613.6MM^E *EMP* 1,500^E
SIC 2899 2842 2874 2992 2752 3577 Chemical preparations; Plating compounds; Rust resisting compounds; Stencil correction compounds; Cleaning or polishing preparations; Phosphates; Lubricating oils; Offset & photolithographic printing; Printers & plotters
Ch Bd: Daniel H Leever
**CFO:* Frank J Monteiro
**Treas:* Michael V Kennedy
Ex VP: Peter Kukanskis
Ex VP: John Malfettone
**VP:* John L Cordani
Sfty Mgr: Sherrie Gillis

MACDERMID PRFMCE SOLUTIONS
See MACDERMID INC

D-U-N-S 87-802-8430 IMP/EXP
■ MACDERMID PRINTING SOLUTIONS LLC
MACDERMID GRAPHICS SOLUTION
(*Suby of* MACDERMID PRFMCE SOLUTIONS) ★
5210 Phillip Lee Dr Sw, Atlanta, GA 30336-2217
Tel (404) 472-0072 *Founded/Ownrshp* 1994
Sales 249.9MM^E *EMP* 1,131
SIC 3555 Printing plates
Ch Bd: David Beckerman
CFO: Gerry Miller
**Ex VP:* Gerard Loeb
Dir Rx: Patrick Mullaney
Brnch Mgr: John P Brice O

D-U-N-S 14-162-9753
MACDONALD MOTT GROUP INC
111 Wood Ave S Ste 5, Iselin, NJ 08830-2700
Tel (973) 379-3400 *Founded/Ownrshp* 2001
Sales 507.4MM *EMP* 2,500
Accts Bdo Usa Llp Woodbridge Nj
SIC 8711 Engineering services
Pr: Nicholas Denichilo
**Treas:* Jeff Hilla
VP: Patrick Natale
IT Man: Peter Ling
Snr PM: Kevin Bollinger
Snr PM: Anthony Gagliostro
Snr PM: John Green
Snr PM: Steven Morey
Snr PM: Lisa Taylor

D-U-N-S 13-163-7956
MACDONALD-MILLER FACILITY SOLUTIONS INC
7717 Detroit Ave Sw, Seattle, WA 98106-1903
Tel (206) 763-9400 *Founded/Ownrshp* 2002
Sales 95.8MM^E *EMP* 300
SIC 1711 1731 Heating & air conditioning contractors; Electronic controls installation
Pr: Gus Simonds
**CFO:* Stephanie Gebhardt
**Treas:* Steve Nicholes
**Sec:* Tyler Kopet
Sr VP: Reagan Perry
VP: Bret Lovely
**VP:* Steven Lovely
**Prin:* Frederic J Sigmond
**Prin:* Derrick Simonds
IT Man: Lilay Gebreigziabher
Sfty Dirs: Lee Pyfrom

D-U-N-S 02-016-5585
▲ MACERICH CO (MD)
401 Wilshire Blvd Ste 700, Santa Monica, CA 90401-1452
Tel (310) 394-6000 *Founded/Ownrshp* 1965
Sales 1.2MMM *EMP* 997
Tkr Sym MAC *Exch* NYS
SIC 6798 Real estate investment trusts
Ch Bd: Arthur M Coppola
**Pr:* Edward C Coppola
COO: Robert D Perlmutter
CFO: Thomas E O'Hern
Ofcr: Eric V Salo
Ex VP: Randy L Brant
VP: Erik Johnson
VP: Bob Jones
VP: Bob Kirk
VP: Mark Klein
VP: Olivia Leigh
VP: Lynn Lovell
VP: John Perry
VP: Mechelle Peters
VP: David Piper
VP: Fred Yeries
VP Bus Dev: Coleen McNelis
Board of Directors: John H Alschuler, Steven R Hash, Frederick S Hubbell, Diana M Laing, Mason G Ross, Steven L Soboroff, Andrea M Stephen, John M Sullivan

D-U-N-S 19-428-5904
MACH 1 GLOBAL SERVICES INC
MACH1
1530 W Broadway Rd, Tempe, AZ 85282-1131
Tel (480) 921-3900 *Founded/Ownrshp* 1988
Sales 127.9MM^E *EMP* 210
SIC 4731 4212 Freight forwarding; Local trucking, without storage
CEO: Jamie Fletcher
**COO:* Rob Lively
COO: Robert Lively
VP: Rick Batia
VP: Justin Panasewicz
VP: David Scappe
Admn Mgr: Chris Beaudoin
Dist Mgr: Edward Garcia
Dist Mgr: Tom Pittman
Dist Mgr: Kari Thomsen
Dist Mgr: Peggy Weaver
Board of Directors: Kathleen Entzminger, Michael Entzminger, Jamie Fletcher

D-U-N-S 07-928-7530 IMP
MACH SPEED HOLDINGS LLC
APOLLO BRANDS
(*Suby of* TRANSITION CAPITAL PARTNERS LP) ★
7200 Bishop Rd Ste 280, Plano, TX 75024-3639
Tel (214) 978-3800 *Founded/Ownrshp* 2011
Sales 125.0MM^E *EMP* 75
SIC 5091 5065 3679

MACH1
See MACH 1 GLOBAL SERVICES INC

MACHACKEMACH APARTMENTS
See PJ HOUSING PRESERVATION LP

D-U-N-S 06-530-0535
MACHINE & WELDING SUPPLY CO
ARC3 GASES SOUTH
(*Suby of* ARC3 GASES INC) ★
1660 Us Highway 301 S, Dunn, NC 28334-6791
Tel (910) 892-4016 *Founded/Ownrshp* 2013
Sales 103.6MM^E *EMP* 260
SIC 5084 5169 Welding machinery & equipment; Industrial gases
Pr: Emmett C Aldredge Jr
**VP:* Emmett C Aldredge III
**VP:* Jeff Johnson
Exec: Scott Coats
Brnch Mgr: Jan McLamb
Store Mgr: Keith Benfield
IT Man: Christopher Aldredge
IT Man: Terry Tew
Manager: Jim Weedman

MACHINE CLOTHING COMPANY
See BILLION TOWER INTL LLC

MACHINE TOOL DIVISION
See GROB SYSTEMS INC

MACHINE TOOLS SUPPLY
See MT SUPPLY INC

MACHLINK-MUSCATINE POWER & WTR
See MUSCATINE POWER & WATER (INC)

MACI
See MICHIGAN AUTOMOTIVE COMPRESSOR INC

MACK AND PARKER
See HUB INTERNATIONAL OF ILLINOIS LIMITED

D-U-N-S 08-772-7186 EXP
MACK CLEVELAND SALES INC
PERFORMANCE TRUCK
1263 Us Highway 59 N, Cleveland, TX 77327-2877
Tel (281) 593-8888 *Founded/Ownrshp* 1977
Sales 128.9MM^E *EMP* 270
SIC 5012 Trucks, commercial; Truck tractors; Trailers for trucks, new & used
Pr: RC Sweeten
**VP:* Skipper Martin
Brnch Mgr: Ronnie Newton
Sls Mgr: Chase Robinson
Sales Asso: Joshua Cunningham

D-U-N-S 80-489-3105
MACK ENERGY CORP
PIPE & SUPPLY
11344 Lovington Hwy, Artesia, NM 88210-9634
Tel (575) 748-1288 *Founded/Ownrshp* 1990
Sales 528.2MM^E *EMP* 500
SIC 1311 2911 Crude petroleum & natural gas; Oils, fuel; Oils, lubricating
Pr: Mack C Chase
**CFO:* Brad Bartek
**VP:* Robert Chase
Off Admin: Crissa Carter
Dir IT: Rodney Carter

D-U-N-S 05-022-7250 IMP
MACK GROUP INC
608 Warm Brook Rd, Arlington, VT 05250-8570
Tel (802) 375-2511 *Founded/Ownrshp* 1997
Sales 490.6MM^E *EMP* 1,400
Accts Gallagher Flynn & Company Ll
SIC 3089 3577 6719 Plastic processing; Injection molding of plastics; Injection molded finished plastic products; Computer peripheral equipment; Investment holding companies, except banks
Pr: Donald S Kandall III
**CFO:* Florence Belnap
**Sec:* Randy Boduch
Comm Dir: Julie Horst
Board of Directors: Raymond E Burns, William H Cooley, Jane Gardner, Nancy Kendall, William S Kendell

D-U-N-S 00-421-4466
MACK INDUSTRIES INC (OH)
MACK TRANSPORT
1321 Industrial Pkwy N # 500, Brunswick, OH 44212-6358
Tel (330) 460-7005 *Founded/Ownrshp* 1932, 1958
Sales 160.1MM^E *EMP* 500
SIC 3272 1771 Burial vaults, concrete or precast terrazzo; Septic tanks, concrete; Manhole covers or frames, concrete; Concrete work

Sec: Betsy Mack Nespeca
**Pr:* Betsy Mack-Nespeca

D-U-N-S 00-206-8096 IMP/EXP
MACK MOLDING CO INC
(*Suby of* MACK GROUP INC) ★
608 Warm Brook Rd, Arlington, VT 05250-8570
Tel (802) 375-2511 *Founded/Ownrshp* 1997
Sales 299.0MM^E *EMP* 1,000
SIC 3089 3577 Plastic processing; Computer peripheral equipment
Pr: Donald S Kendall III
Pr: Jeff Somple
**Pr:* Jeffrey Somple
**VP:* Randy Boduch
Dept Mgr: Martin Drobek
Genl Mgr: Don Boucher
Plnt Mgr: Marc Colety
Ql Cn Mgr: William Hackett
Ql Cn Mgr: Sharon Herrick
Ql Cn Mgr: Nate James
Mktg Dir: Julie Horst

D-U-N-S 80-789-5362 IMP
MACK TECHNOLOGIES INC
(*Suby of* MACK GROUP INC) ★
27 Carlisle Rd, Westford, MA 01886-3644
Tel (978) 392-5500 *Founded/Ownrshp* 1997
Sales 185.3MM^E *EMP* 700
SIC 3577 3571 Computer peripheral equipment; Electronic computers
Pr: John Kovach
**Sec:* Florence M Belnap
VP: Steve Barbera
Dir Bus: Jody Smith
Snr Sftwr: Mark Kendall
IT Man: Vic Montiverdi
Manager: Les Clark
Sls&Mrk Ex: Peter McDonald
Board of Directors: Jeffrey T Somple

MACK TRANSPORT
See MACK INDUSTRIES INC

D-U-N-S 04-232-1117 IMP/EXP
MACK TRUCKS INC
(*Suby of* AB VOLVO)
7825 National Service Rd, Greensboro, NC 27409-9667
Tel (336) 291-9001 *Founded/Ownrshp* 2001
Sales 1.6MMM^E *EMP* 4,500
SIC 3711 3714 5012 6141 6153 7538 Motor trucks, except off-highway, assembly of; Truck tractors for highway use, assembly of; Motor vehicle parts & accessories; Truck tractors; Financing: automobiles, furniture, etc., not a deposit bank; Installment sales finance, other than banks; Financing of dealers by motor vehicle manufacturers organ.; General truck repair; Truck engine repair, except industrial
Pr: Stephen Roy
Pr: Michael Maddox
**Treas:* Stephen Polzer
Treas: Dave Smith
**Treas:* David Smith
Treas: Richard Welch
Sr Cor Off: Catherine Ragobert
Ex VP: Guy Clabeau
Ex VP: Dennis R Slagle
Ex VP: Sam Torrence
Ex VP: Mike Werth
Sr VP: Kevin Flaherty
**Sr VP:* Stan Janis
Sr VP: Bruno Linsolas
**Sr VP:* Frank Meehan
Sr VP: Harold W Wiegel
VP: Chad Cross
VP: Jason Hardy
**VP:* Bruce Hollenback
VP: Martin Kleker
VP: Patrick Meehan

D-U-N-S 07-514-3230 IMP/EXP
▲ MACK-CALI REALTY CORP
343 Thornall St, Edison, NJ 08837-2206
Tel (732) 590-1000 *Founded/Ownrshp* 1994
Sales 594.8MM *EMP* 530^E
Tkr Sym CLI *Exch* NYS
SIC 6798 Real estate investment trusts
CEO: Mitchell E Rudin
**Ch Bd:* William L Mack
Pr: Michael J Demarco
Pr: Robert Andrew Marshall
CFO: Anthony Krug
Ch: Marshall B Tycher
Ex VP: Christopher Delorenzo
VP: Bill Donaleski
VP: Nicholas Mitarotonda Jr
CIO: Ricardo Cardoso
Board of Directors: Alan S Bernikow, Kenneth M Duberstein, Nathan Gantcher, Jonathan Litt, David S Mack, Alan G Philibosian, Irvin D Reid, Rebecca Robertson, Vincent Tese

D-U-N-S 78-424-2518
MACK-CALI REALTY L P
4 Becker Farm Rd Ste 104, Roseland, NJ 07068-1734
Tel (973) 577-2472 *Founded/Ownrshp* 1998
Sales 594.8MM *EMP* 2
Accts Pricewaterhousecoopers Llp Ne
SIC 6798 Real estate investment trusts
CEO: Mitchell Hersh
Pr: Mitchell E Hersh

D-U-N-S 80-315-5365
MACKAY JOINT SCHOOL DIST 182
JOINT SCHOOL DIST 128
411 Rose Ave, Mackay, ID 83251-7702
Tel (208) 588-2896 *Founded/Ownrshp* 1996
Sales 121.2MM *EMP* 36
Accts Balukoff Lindstrom & Co Pa
SIC 8211 Public elementary & secondary schools
Prin: Brandon Farris

D-U-N-S 00-625-6317 EXP
MACKAY MITCHELL ENVELOPE CO LLC (MN)
2100 Elm St Se, Minneapolis, MN 55414-2533
Tel (612) 331-9311 *Founded/Ownrshp* 1959, 2000
Sales 117.0MM^E *EMP* 350
SIC 2677 Envelopes
CFO: Tim Chesiak
CFO: Timothy Cheslak
VP: Reid Anderson
VP: Michael Becker
VP: Brian Bomberger
VP: Joseph Claeys
VP: Bill Levoir
VP: Wayne Logeais
IT Man: Joan Samuelson
Plnt Mgr: Jeff Peterson

MACKENZIE FORD
See MACKENZIE MOTOR CO

D-U-N-S 02-765-5562
MACKENZIE MOTOR CO
MACKENZIE FORD
4151 Se Tualatin Vly Hwy, Hillsboro, OR 97123-7951
Tel (503) 693-1133 *Founded/Ownrshp* 1987
Sales 85.4MM^E *EMP* 250
SIC 5511 5521 Automobiles, new & used; Used car dealers
Off Mgr: Lisa Bishops
Dir IT: Dave Leslie
Sls Mgr: Shaun Weber

D-U-N-S 10-867-7444
MACKIN BOOK CO
MACKIN LIBRARY MEDIA
3505 County Road 42 W, Burnsville, MN 55306-3803
Tel (952) 895-9540 *Founded/Ownrshp* 1985
Sales 190.9MM^E *EMP* 350^E
SIC 5192 Books
CEO: Randal Heise
**VP:* Kay M Heise
Comm Dir: Troy Mikell
Dir IT: Pavel Yurevich
Sftwr Eng: Meyers Gordon
Natl Sales: Ryan C Thomas
Sales Asso: Mark Caldwell
Sales Asso: Robin Cole
Sales Asso: Susan Dalton
Sales Asso: Bob Dearen
Sales Asso: Erin Segreto

MACKIN LIBRARY MEDIA
See MACKIN BOOK CO

MACLEAN - DIXIE
See MACLEAN POWER LLC

MACLEAN FASTENERS
See MAC LEAN-FOGG CO

D-U-N-S 80-818-8903 IMP
MACLEAN POWER LLC
MACLEAN - DIXIE
(*Suby of* MACLEAN FASTENERS) ★
481 Munn Rd E Ste 300, Fort Mill, SC 29715-8462
Tel (847) 455-0014 *Founded/Ownrshp* 1998
Sales 140.5MM^E *EMP* 350^E
SIC 3493 Helical springs, hot wound: railroad equipment etc.
Pr: Duncan Maclean
IT Man: Mike Estes

MACLEAN POWER SYSTEMS
See MACLEAN POWER TN LLC

D-U-N-S 07-866-9547 IMP
MACLEAN POWER TN LLC
MACLEAN POWER SYSTEMS
(*Suby of* MACLEAN FASTENERS) ★
1465 Industrial Park Dr, Trenton, TN 38382-3937
Tel (847) 566-0010 *Founded/Ownrshp* 2012
Sales 200.2MM^E *EMP* 1,000
SIC 3679 Electronic loads & power supplies
Genl Mgr: Dhruva Mandal

MACMILLAN
See HOLTZBRINCK PUBLISHERS LLC

D-U-N-S 95-973-7925 IMP/EXP
MACMILLAN HOLDINGS LLC
M P S
(*Suby of* HOLTZBRINCK PUBLISHERS HOLDINGS LIMITED)
175 5th Ave, New York, NY 10010-7703
Tel (646) 307-5151 *Founded/Ownrshp* 1998
Sales 478.9MM^E *EMP* 1,668
SIC 2721 2731

D-U-N-S 03-233-7594 IMP/EXP
MACMILLAN OIL CO OF FLORIDA INC
2955 E 11th Ave, Hialeah, FL 33013-3599
Tel (305) 691-7814 *Founded/Ownrshp* 1995
Sales 106.9MM^E *EMP* 45
SIC 5172 Petroleum products
Pr: Amancio Alonso
VP: Frank Saldana
Genl Mgr: Danny Alonso
Genl Mgr: William Putnam

D-U-N-S 11-850-3549 IMP
MACMILLAN PUBLISHERS INC
(*Suby of* MACMILLAN LIMITED)
175 5th Ave Ste 400, New York, NY 10010-7726
Tel (646) 307-5151 *Founded/Ownrshp* 1982
Sales 138.5MM^E *EMP* 1,200
Accts Ernst & Young Llp
SIC 2731 5192 Books: publishing only; Books
CEO: John Sargent
CFO: Libby Marenco
**Treas:* Mike Ross
Sr VP: Jamie Demas
VP: Jaime Ariza
VP: Jeffrey Capshew
VP: Erin Coffey
VP: Ken Holland
VP: Sharon Laday
VP: Tom Stouras
**VP:* Philip Swartz
Assoc Dir: Kathryn Little
Board of Directors: Nicholas G Beam Shaw

D-U-N-S 00-193-7150 IMP/EXP
MACMILLAN PUBLISHING GROUP LLC
PALAGRAVE MACMILLAN
(*Suby of* M P S) ★
175 5th Ave, New York, NY 10010-7703
Tel (212) 674-5151 *Founded/Ownrshp* 1952
Sales 134.3MM^E *EMP* 455
SIC 2731 5192 Books: publishing only; Books
Pr: Sally Richardson
Ex VP: Jeff Dodes
VP: Adriana Coada
Exec: Laurie Chittenden
Mktg Mgr: Erin Cox
Mktg Mgr: Kym Giacoppe
Mktg Mgr: Courtney Reed
Mktg Mgr: Eileen Rothschild
Mktg Mgr: Gianna Terrranova
Art Dir: David Rotstein
Art Dir: Michael Storrings

MACNEAL HOSPITAL
See VHS OF ILLINOIS INC

MACOM
See MINDSPEED TECHNOLOGIES INC

D-U-N-S 96-338-9726
▲ MACOM TECHNOLOGY SOLUTIONS HOLDINGS INC
100 Chelmsford St, Lowell, MA 01851-2694
Tel (978) 656-2500 *Founded/Ownrshp* 2009
Sales 420.6MM *EMP* 1,100^E
Tkr Sym MTSI *Exch* NGS
SIC 3674 Semiconductors & related devices
Ch Bd: John Ocampo
Pr: John Croteau
CFO: Robert McMullan
Sr VP: Walter Baker
Sr VP: Alex Behfar
Sr VP: Robert Dennehy
Sr VP: Donghyun Thomas Hwang
Sr VP: John Kennedy
Sr VP: Michael Murphy
Sr VP: Preetinder Virk

D-U-N-S 82-776-9154
■ MACOM TECHNOLOGY SOLUTIONS INC
M/A-COM
(*Suby of* MACOM TECHNOLOGY SOLUTIONS HOLDINGS INC) ★
100 Chelmsford St, Lowell, MA 01851-2694
Tel (978) 656-2500 *Founded/Ownrshp* 1999
Sales 331.5MM^E *EMP* 915
SIC 3663 3679 Radio & TV communications equipment; Microwave components
Pr: John Croteau
CFO: Robert Mc Mullan
CFO: Bob McMullan
Sr VP: Robert Dennehy
Sr VP: Thomas Hwang
Sr VP: Michael Murphy
Sr VP: Preetinder Virk
Prin: James Rame
Genl Mgr: Karen Hanlon
Genl Mgr: Ron Karfelt
Opers Mgr: Paul Bovaird

D-U-N-S 06-189-0612
MACOMB COMMUNITY COLLEGE
14500 E 12 Mile Rd, Warren, MI 48088-3896
Tel (586) 445-7306 *Founded/Ownrshp* 1999
Sales 126.0MM *EMP* 2,000^E
SIC 8221 College, except junior
Pr: James Jacobs
Ofcr: Sophia Carroll
Ofcr: Keith Gurney
**VP:* Elizabeth Argiri
VP: Robert Penkala
DP Exec: Robert Kansa
IT Man: Richard McMillan
Pr Mgr: Jeanne Nicol

MACOMB DAILY
See 21ST CENTURY NEWSPAPERS INC

D-U-N-S 08-394-2607 IMP
MACOMB GROUP INC (MI)
MACOMB PIPE & SUPPLY
6600 15 Mile Rd, Sterling Heights, MI 48312-4512
Tel (586) 274-4100 *Founded/Ownrshp* 1977, 1991
Sales 166.9MM *EMP* 398
Accts Gordon Advisors Pc Troy Mi
SIC 5085 Industrial supplies; Valves & fittings
CEO: William McGivern Jr
**Ex VP:* Keith Schatko
**VP:* Dick Dixon
**VP:* Steve Dixon
**VP:* James Tucker
Brnch Mgr: Zackariah Cook
Brnch Mgr: Gary Phillips
Natl Sales: Chuck Raymond
Sales Asso: Craig Davidson
Sales Asso: Chris Wernet

D-U-N-S 07-841-7169
MACOMB INTERMEDIATE SCHOOL DISTRICT
MISD
44001 Garfield Rd, Clinton Township, MI 48038-1100
Tel (586) 228-3479 *Founded/Ownrshp* 1951
Sales 399.9MM^E *EMP* 14,000
SIC 8211 Public elementary & secondary schools; Public special education school; School for the retarded; School for physically handicapped
CEO: Paul Bodiya
Bd of Dir: Gus Demas
Bd of Dir: Elaine Martin
Bd of Dir: Michael Scott
Bd of Dir: Mark Titus
Exec: Sherry Kenward
Ex Dir: Regina Delegato
IT Man: Kathy Francis

D-U-N-S 95-901-4556
MACOMB OAKLAND REGIONAL CENTER INC
16200 19 Mile Rd, Clinton Township, MI 48038-1103
Tel (586) 263-8700 *Founded/Ownrshp* 1972
Sales 198.2MM *EMP* 300
SIC 8093 Mental health clinic, outpatient
CEO: Gerald Provencal
**CFO:* Richard Stone
VP: Carrie Gerdeman
VP: John Torrone
Exec: Peter Lynch
CIO: Dan Manzardo
IT Man: Debbie Conway
IT Man: Mark Morehouse

MACOMB PIPE & SUPPLY
See MACOMB GROUP INC

D-U-N-S 02-745-6656
MACON WATER AUTHORITY
790 2nd St, Macon, GA 31201-6800
Tel (478) 464-5600 *Founded/Ownrshp* 1966
Sales 121.6MM^E *EMP* 200
Accts Mauldin And Jenkins Llc Maco
SIC 4941 4952 Water supply; Sewerage systems
Ch Bd: Frank C Amerson Jr
Ex Dir: Tony Rojas

MACPHERSON'S
See ART SUPPLY ENTERPRISES INC

D-U-N-S 88-443-9795
MACQUARIE CAPITAL (USA) INC
(*Suby of* MACQUARIE GROUP LIMITED)
125 W 55th St Frnt 3, New York, NY 10019-5936
Tel (212) 231-1000 *Founded/Ownrshp* 2007
Sales 231.9MM^E *EMP* 600^E
SIC 6211 Security brokers & dealers
Ch Bd: Robert Redmond
V Ch: Rob Redmond
**Pr:* Michael McLauchlan
Assoc Dir: John Fullam
Dir IT: Alan Broom

D-U-N-S 79-884-6036 IMP/EXP
MACQUARIE ENERGY LLC
(*Suby of* MACQUARIE GROUP LIMITED)
500 Dallas St 31, Houston, TX 77002-4800
Tel (713) 275-6100 *Founded/Ownrshp* 2005
Sales 359.3MM^E *EMP* 265
SIC 6221 Commodity traders, contracts
CEO: Nicholas O'Kane
**Pr:* Tim Bourn
**Treas:* Trent Byerley
**VP:* Matthew D'Agostino
**VP:* David Louw
Assoc Dir: Nathan Salisbury

D-U-N-S 92-984-9404 IMP
MACQUARIE HOLDINGS (USA) INC
125 W 55th St Fl 8, New York, NY 10019-5369
Tel (212) 231-1000 *Founded/Ownrshp* 1994
Sales 781.2MM^E *EMP* 1,500^E
SIC 6211 Security brokers & dealers
CEO: Oliver Yates
**Ch Bd:* Nicholas James Butcher
**Pr:* Alyssa Bonebrake
COO: Sarosh Irani

D-U-N-S 17-748-7654 IMP
▲ MACQUARIE INFRASTRUCTURE CORP
125 W 55th St, New York, NY 10019-5369
Tel (212) 231-1000 *Founded/Ownrshp* 2004
Sales 1.6MMM *EMP* 3,300^E
Tkr Sym MIC *Exch* NYS
SIC 5172 4581 4785 7521 4932 Petroleum products; Aircraft maintenance & repair services; Airports & flying fields; Toll road operation; Automobile parking; Outdoor parking services; Indoor parking services; Gas & other services combined
CEO: James Hooke
**Ch Bd:* Martin Stanley
CFO: Liam Stewart
VP: Hugh Miller
Dir Sec: Elise Hubert
Mng Dir: John Kim
Admn Mgr: Adrienne Cavallaro
Board of Directors: Norman H Brown Jr, George W Carmany III, Henry E Lentz, William H Webb

D-U-N-S 07-965-4048
MACQUARIE INFRASTRUCTURE PARTNERS II INTERNATIONAL LP
125 W 55th St, New York, NY 10019-5369
Tel (212) 231-1310 *Founded/Ownrshp* 2008
Sales 761.8MM^E *EMP* 1,069^E
SIC 6282 Investment advisory service
CEO: Christopher J Leslie

D-U-N-S 83-596-4461 IMP
■ MACRO RETAILING LLC
SUPER SHOE STORES
(*Suby of* B H SHOE HOLDINGS INC) ★
10365 Mount Savage Rd Nw, Cumberland, MD 21502-4925
Tel (301) 722-6563 *Founded/Ownrshp* 1994
Sales 86.0MM *EMP* 500
SIC 5661 Shoe stores
Pr: James Issler
**VP:* Marc Hamburg

D-U-N-S 01-062-6351
▲ MACROGENICS INC
9704 Medical Center Dr, Rockville, MD 20850-3343
Tel (301) 251-5172 *Founded/Ownrshp* 2000
Sales 100.8MM *EMP* 269
Tkr Sym MGNX *Exch* NGS
SIC 2834 Pharmaceutical preparations
Pr: Scott Koenig
**Ch Bd:* Paulo Costa
CFO: James Karrels
Treas: Lynn Cilinski
Sr VP: Eric Risser
Sr VP: Atul Saran
Sr VP: Thomas Spitznagel
Sr VP: Jon Wigginton
VP: Joan A Brandt
VP: Stanford Stewart
Dir Sec: Ezio Bonvini
Board of Directors: Matthew Fust, Kenneth Galbraith, Edward Hurwitz, David Stump

D-U-N-S 00-128-3845
MACROMEDIA INC (NJ)
150 River St, Hackensack, NJ 07601-7110
Tel (201) 646-4000 *Founded/Ownrshp* 1895, 1921
Sales 353.1MM^E *EMP* 1,521^E
SIC 2711 2721 Newspapers, publishing & printing; Periodicals
Ch Bd: Malcolm A Borg
**Treas:* Charles W Gibney
**VP:* Stephen A Borg
Board of Directors: Sandra A Borg, David L Cohen Esq

MAC'S CONVENIENCE STORES
See SHERMAN V ALLEN INC

D-U-N-S 11-318-1585
MACS CONVENIENCE STORES LLC
CIRCLE K
(*Suby of* ALIMENTATION COUCHE-TARD INC)
4080 W Jnathan Moore Pike, Columbus, IN 47201-8667
Tel (812) 379-9227 *Founded/Ownrshp* 2012
Sales 552.4MM^E *EMP* 3,773
SIC 5411 Convenience stores, chain

MACTAC
See MORGAN ADHESIVES CO LLC

MACY'S
See MACYS.COM INC

D-U-N-S 03-718-3790
■ MACYS CORPORATE SERVICES INC
BLOOMINGDALE'S
(*Suby of* MACYS INC) ★
7 W 7th St Ste 1100, Cincinnati, OH 45202-2419
Tel (513) 579-7000 *Founded/Ownrshp* 2004
Sales 123.4MM^E *EMP* 620^E
SIC 5311 Department stores, non-discount
CEO: Terry J Lundgren
**Pr:* Jeffrey Gennette
**CFO:* Karen M Hoguet
Chf Mktg O: Peter Sachse

D-U-N-S 83-231-1906
■ MACYS CREDIT AND CUSTOMER SERVICES INC
(*Suby of* MACYS RETAIL HOLDINGS INC) ★
9111 Duke Blvd, Mason, OH 45040-8999
Tel (513) 398-5221 *Founded/Ownrshp* 1994
Sales 108.7MM^E *EMP* 3,000
SIC 7389 7322 6141 Credit card service; Adjustment & collection services; Personal credit institutions
Pr: Michael Gatio
Ex VP: Dave Faulk
VP: Felicia Williams
VP Mktg: Jon Rosenbaum

D-U-N-S 60-249-4650 IMP
■ MACYS FLORIDA STORES LLC
(*Suby of* MACYS RETAIL HOLDINGS INC) ★
7 W 7th St Fl 17, Cincinnati, OH 45202-2468
Tel (513) 579-7000 *Founded/Ownrshp* 2008
Sales 504.2MM^E *EMP* 8,273
SIC 5311 Department stores, non-discount

D-U-N-S 00-698-7135 IMP/EXP
▲ MACYS INC
7 W 7th St, Cincinnati, OH 45202-2424
Tel (513) 579-7000 *Founded/Ownrshp* 1830
Sales 27.0MMM *EMP* 157,900
Accts Kpmg Llp Cincinnati Ohio
Tkr Sym M *Exch* NYS
SIC 5311 Department stores
Ch Bd: Terry J Lundgren
Pr: Jeffrey Gennette
CFO: Karen M Hoguet
Ofcr: William S Allen
Ofcr: Robert B Harrison
Ofcr: Jeffrey A Kantor
Ofcr: Molly Langenstein
Ofcr: Peter Sachse
Ex VP: Joel A Belsky
Ex VP: Dennis J Broderick
Ex VP: Thomas Cody
Ex VP: Mike Dervos
Ex VP: Muriel Gonzalez
Ex VP: Douglas W Sesler
VP: David Aldahl
VP: Todd Anyan
VP: Chuck ABT
VP: Susan Babb
VP: Christopher Babbitt
VP: Maureen Balent
VP: Linda Balicki
Board of Directors: Paul C Varga, Francis S Blake, Craig E Weatherup, Stephen F Bollenbach, Marna C Whittington, John A Bryant, Deirdre P Connelly, Leslie D Hale, William H Lenehan, Sara Levinson, Joyce M Roche, Annie Young-Scrivner

D-U-N-S 83-108-3055
■ MACYS MERCHANDISING CORP
(*Suby of* MACYS RETAIL HOLDINGS INC) ★
151 W 34th St, New York, NY 10001-2101
Tel (212) 695-4400 *Founded/Ownrshp* 2009
Sales 86.7MM^E *EMP* 1,003
SIC 5311 Department stores, non-discount
Ch Bd: Jeffrey A Kantor
**Pr:* Terry J Lundgren
**VP:* Susan Robinson

MACYS MERCHANDISING GROUP
See MACYS MERCHANDISING GROUP INC

D-U-N-S 36-127-7069 IMP
■ MACYS MERCHANDISING GROUP INC
MACYS MERCHANDISING GROUP
(*Suby of* MACYS INC) ★
11 Penn Plz Fl 10, New York, NY 10001-2027
Tel (646) 429-6000 *Founded/Ownrshp* 1985
Sales 122.5MM^E *EMP* 1,155^E
SIC 5699 5399 Western apparel; Army-Navy goods
Pr: Leonard Marcus
Pr: Brett Foster
**CFO:* Harry Frenkel
Sr VP: Nancy Johnson
VP: Kevin Cernich
VP: Andrew Dachisen
VP: Denise Filchner
VP: Margaret Grioli
Comm Dir: Anthony Fusco
Sys Mgr: Pavel Tsiporkin
Mktg Mgr: Sara Koppel

D-U-N-S 87-796-0807 IMP/EXP
■ MACYS RETAIL HOLDINGS INC
(*Suby of* MACYS INC) ★
7 W 7th St Ste 1100, Cincinnati, OH 45202-2419
Tel (513) 579-7000 *Founded/Ownrshp* 1994
Sales 9.6MMM^E *EMP* 111,000
SIC 5311 Department stores, non-discount
CEO: Terry Lundgren
**Pr:* Jeffrey Gennette
**CFO:* Karen Hoguet
Dir Risk M: Ronald E Godfry

D-U-N-S 93-787-2620 IMP/EXP
■ MACYS SYSTEMS AND TECHNOLOGY INC
(*Suby of* MACYS RETAIL HOLDINGS INC) ★
5985 State Bridge Rd, Duluth, GA 30097-8208
Tel (678) 474-2000 *Founded/Ownrshp* 1994
Sales 233.2MM^E *EMP* 740
SIC 7374 Data processing & preparation
Ch Bd: Thomas L Cole
**Pr:* Larry Lewark
**CFO:* Faye Glance
**Treas:* Karen Hoguet
Sr VP: Mike Manougian
VP: Mitch Borger
**VP:* Dennis Broderick
VP: Gian Cacioppo
VP: Andrew Koller
**VP:* Gary Nay
VP: Dave Seeley
VP: Dave Seely
**VP:* Robert Seppelt
**VP:* John R Sims
VP: Joe Tirocke

D-U-N-S 78-652-3790 IMP/EXP
■ MACYS WEST STORES INC
(*Suby of* MACYS INC) ★
7 W 7th St Fl 17, Cincinnati, OH 45202-2468
Tel (513) 579-7000 *Founded/Ownrshp* 1999
Sales 2.0MMM^E *EMP* 34,000
SIC 5311

D-U-N-S 01-178-0678
■ MACYS.COM INC
MACY'S
(*Suby of* MACYS RETAIL HOLDINGS INC) ★
7 W 7th St, Cincinnati, OH 45202-2424
Tel (513) 579-7000 *Founded/Ownrshp* 1997
Sales 6.8MMM^E *EMP* 111,000^E
SIC 5961 5311 Mail order house; Department stores
Ch Bd: Peter R Sachse
VP: Stacy Goldberg
VP: Darren Stoll
VP: Patricia Stromberg
**Prin:* Kent Anderson
S&M/VP: Gary Ostrager

D-U-N-S 06-167-9650
MAD ANTHONYS INC
ANTHONYS SEAFOOD
10502 Ne 37th Cir Bldg 8, Kirkland, WA 98033-7920
Tel (425) 455-0732 *Founded/Ownrshp* 1972
Sales 77.9MM^E *EMP* 1,500
SIC 5812 5813 Seafood restaurants; Chicken restaurant; Cocktail lounge
Pr: Herbert M Gould III
VP: Jeff Arnot
**VP:* Herbert Milton Gould IV
VP: Herbert Gould
Genl Mgr: Andrew Miller
Genl Mgr: Mary Nance
Genl Mgr: Vicki Westberg
Mktg Mgr: Lisa M Jones

D-U-N-S 18-760-8005 IMP
MAD ENGINE INC
6740 Cobra Way Ste 100, San Diego, CA 92121-4102
Tel (858) 558-5270 *Founded/Ownrshp* 1987
Sales 97.8MM^E *EMP* 180
Accts Smith Mandel & Associates Llp
SIC 2261 Screen printing of cotton broadwoven fabrics
CEO: Danish Gajiani
**Pr:* Alby Amato
Pr: George Dodge
CFO: Jack Fiedler
Ex VP: Faizan Bakaki
**Ex VP:* Faizan Bakali
Sr VP: Angelina Yagudayev
**VP:* Carolyn Foreman
**VP:* Clarinda Orng
Mktg Dir: Jessica Barrameda

MAD WINGS
See SIMMONS PREPARED FOODS INC

MADAME TUSSAUDS NEW YORK
See MERLIN ENTERTAINMENTS GROUP US LLC

D-U-N-S 06-849-7080 IMP/EXP
MADDEN COMMUNICATIONS INC
901 Mittel Dr, Wood Dale, IL 60191-1118
Tel (630) 787-2200 *Founded/Ownrshp* 1960
Sales 173.8MM *EMP* 340
Accts Deloitte & Touche Llp Chicago
SIC 2752 Commercial printing, offset
Ch Bd: James P Donahugh
Pr: Sean Madden
COO: John McMahon
CFO: Thomas Nickele
Sr VP: Larry Gundrum
VP: Kevin Heniff
Exec: Amy Sebastian
MIS Dir: Ken Myers
Software D: Steve Swithers

D-U-N-S 00-285-5955
MADDEN CONTRACTING CO LLC (LA)
11288 Hwy 371, Minden, LA 71055
Tel (318) 377-0927 *Founded/Ownrshp* 1955

Sales 95.0MM *EMP* 175
Accts Broussard & Company Cpas Llc
SIC 1611 2951 General contractor, highway & street construction; Asphalt & asphaltic paving mixtures (not from refineries)
**Pr:* James D Madden
**Treas:* Lyda Madden
**VP:* S Douglas Madden
Genl Mgr: Ray Delia
Off Mgr: Bob Moorehead

MADDOX OIL COMPANY
See WORKMAN OIL CO

MADE2MANAGE SYSTEMS
See APTEAN HOLDINGS INC

D-U-N-S 07-018-0245
MADERA COMMUNITY HOSPITAL
MCH
1250 E Almond Ave, Madera, CA 93637-5696
Tel (559) 675-5555 *Founded/Ownrshp* 1975
Sales 92.1MM *EMP* 800[E]
SIC 8062 General medical & surgical hospitals
CEO: Evan J Rayner
Pr: Mary Aguirre
CFO: Donna Tooley
Genl Mgr: Betty Ortega
Sls Dir: Robert Poythress
Doctor: Khalid Rauf
HC Dir: Zafar Sheikh

D-U-N-S 79-402-6807
MADERA UNIFIED SCHOOL DISTRICT
1902 Howard Rd, Madera, CA 93637-5167
Tel (559) 675-4500 *Founded/Ownrshp* 2011
Sales 123.1MM[E] *EMP* 2,000
Accts Vavrinek Trine Day & Co Fres
SIC 8211 Public elementary & secondary schools
Ofcr: Isabel Barreras
Dir Sec: Brett Moglia
MIS Dir: Joseph Halford
Dir IT: Tomas Galvan
Dir IT: Paul Parkey
Teacher Pr: Ken Alberson

MADISN-NIDA BD COOP EDCTL SVCS
See MADISON-ONEIDA COUNTY BOCES (INC)

D-U-N-S 07-384-9200
MADISON AREA TECHNICAL COLLEGE DISTRICT
MATC
(*Suby of* WISCONSIN TECHNICAL COLLEGE SYSTEM BOARD) ★
1701 Wright St, Madison, WI 53704-2599
Tel (608) 246-6100 *Founded/Ownrshp* 1938
Sales 119.9MM[E] *EMP* 3,500
Accts Clifton Larson Allen Llp Milw
SIC 8222 Technical institute
Pr: Jack E Daniels III
VP: Brian Woestman
VP Admn: Jerry Collingwood
CIO: David Wallace
Pgrm Dir: Lynea Lavoy
Pgrm Dir: Garilyn Truttschel
Snr Mgr: Rona McNeil
Snr Mgr: Jim Russell

D-U-N-S 08-547-8605
MADISON CAPITAL FUNDING LLC
(*Suby of* NEW YORK LIFE INSURANCE CO) ★
30 S Wacker Dr Ste 3700, Chicago, IL 60606-7462
Tel (312) 596-6900 *Founded/Ownrshp* 2001
Sales NA *EMP* 55
SIC 6163 Loan brokers
**Ofcr:* Andrew Bucolo
Sr VP: Joshua Niedner
Sr VP: Marc Pressler
VP: Dave Kulakofsky
VP: Tricia Marks
VP: Christopher Martin
VP: Pete Notter
VP: Timothy Schifer
Exec: Devon Russell
Off Mgr: Rebecca Sekosky
Mktg Mgr: Maryellen Hurtado

D-U-N-S 92-985-0949 IMP
MADISON CAPITAL PARTNERS CORP
500 W Madison St Ste 3890, Chicago, IL 60661-4593
Tel (312) 277-0323 *Founded/Ownrshp* 1994
Sales 194.6MM[E] *EMP* 2,150
SIC 3542 8741 Machine tools, metal forming type; Management services
Pr: Larry W Gies
CFO: Brent Campbell
**CFO:* John E Udelhofen
**VP:* Aaron J Vangetson
Mng Dir: Christopher Domke
IT Man: Aaron Vangetson

D-U-N-S 10-000-0629
MADISON COUNTY BOARD OF EDUCATION
1275 Jordan Rd, Huntsville, AL 35811-9378
Tel (256) 852-2557 *Founded/Ownrshp* 1908
Sales 76.7MM[E] *EMP* 1,800
Accts Ronald L Jones
SIC 8211 School board

D-U-N-S 86-857-3692
MADISON COUNTY COMMISSIONS
SHARON JOHNSTON PARK RESV
783 Coleman Rd, New Market, AL 35761-9103
Tel (256) 379-2132 *Founded/Ownrshp* 1978
Sales 87.1MM *EMP* 5
SIC 7999 Recreation center

D-U-N-S 00-722-0387
MADISON COUNTY SCHOOL DISTRICT
476 Highland Colony Pkwy, Ridgeland, MS 39157-8727
Tel (601) 879-3000 *Founded/Ownrshp* 1957
Sales 74.0MM[E] *EMP* 1,343
Accts Kimberly Alford Cpa
SIC 8211 Public elementary & secondary schools
VP: Karen Baker
VP: Shannon James
DP Dir: Liz Risher
Pr Dir: Ellen Aregood
Teacher Pr: Stephanie Hobson
Teacher Pr: Shay Williamson
Psych: Judy Statham
Psych: Kay Weems

D-U-N-S 07-407-0632
MADISON COUNTY SCHOOL DISTRICT
550 S Keeneland Dr, Richmond, KY 40475-3232
Tel (859) 624-4500 *Founded/Ownrshp* 1932
Sales 68.2MM[E] *EMP* 1,500
SIC 8211 Public senior high school; Public junior high school; Public elementary school

D-U-N-S 07-979-8996
MADISON COUNTY SCHOOLS
1275 Jordan Rd, Huntsville, AL 35811-9378
Tel (256) 852-2557 *Founded/Ownrshp* 2015
Sales 97.6MM[E] *EMP* 1,800[E]
SIC 8211 Public elementary & secondary schools
Dir Sec: Kerry Wilkerson
IT Man: Duane Thompson
Plnt Mgr: Brent Simons
Plnt Mgr: Steve Walker
Pr Dir: John Sutherland
Teacher Pr: Ken Kubik
Instr Medi: Vickey Sullivan
Psych: Beverly Young
HC Dir: Donna Stiles

D-U-N-S 60-359-2978
MADISON DEARBORN PARTNERS IV LP
70 W Madison St Ste 3800, Chicago, IL 60602-4342
Tel (312) 895-1000 *Founded/Ownrshp* 2000
Sales 951.3MM[E] *EMP* 14,000
SIC 5031 8744 Building materials, exterior; Facilities support services
Mng Dir: Benjamin D Chereskin
VP: Michael Kreger
Mng Dir: Timothy M Hurd
CIO: Stephen Heinmiller

D-U-N-S 17-063-4286
MADISON DEARBORN PARTNERS LLC
M D P
70 W Madison St Ste 4600, Chicago, IL 60602-4215
Tel (312) 895-1000 *Founded/Ownrshp* 1998
Sales 2.2MMM[E] *EMP* 8,800
SIC 6726 6722 Investment offices; Management investment, open-end
Co-CEO: Paul J Finnegan
Pt: Harry Kraemer
Treas: Francisco Isla
**Co-CEO:* Samuel Mencoff
VP: Karla J Bullard
VP: Sam Mencoff
VP: Vivek Pattipati
IT Man: Sal Arcos
Sls Dir: Amy Craver

D-U-N-S 00-695-8433
MADISON ELECTRIC CO
MADISON ELECTRONICS
31855 Van Dyke Ave, Warren, MI 48093-1047
Tel (586) 825-0200 *Founded/Ownrshp* 1914
Sales 98.3MM[E] *EMP* 200
Accts Baker Tilly Virchow Krause Llp
SIC 5063 3679 Electrical construction materials; Electrical supplies; Lighting fixtures; Harness assemblies for electronic use: wire or cable
Pr: Brett Schneider
**CFO:* Benjamin Rosenthal
**Treas:* Jordan Glass
**VP:* Scott Leemaster
**VP:* Richard Sonenklar
VP: John Waitz
**VP:* Jon Waitz
Opers Mgr: Chuck Braidwood

MADISON ELECTRONICS
See MADISON ELECTRIC CO

D-U-N-S 00-794-6346
■ **MADISON GAS AND ELECTRIC CO** (WI)
MGE ENERGY
(*Suby of* MGE ENERGY INC) ★
133 S Blair St, Madison, WI 53788-0002
Tel (608) 252-7000 *Founded/Ownrshp* 1896
Sales 564.0MM *EMP* 695[E]
SIC 4931 Electric & other services combined
Ch Bd: Gary J Wolter
CFO: Jeffrey C Newman
Bd of Dir: Jean M Biddick
Sr VP: Lynn K Hobbi
VP: James G Bidlingmaier
VP: Kristine A Euclide
VP: Mark T Maranger
VP: Peter J Waldron
Board of Directors: Mark D Bugher, F Curtis Hastings, Regina M Millner, John R Nevin, James L Possin, Thomas R Stolper

D-U-N-S 07-997-3581
MADISON INDUSTRIES HOLDINGS LLC
500 W Madison St Ste 3890, Chicago, IL 60661-4593
Tel (312) 277-0156 *Founded/Ownrshp* 2013
Sales 191.6MM[E] *EMP* 740[E]
SIC 6719 5051 3443 3316 Investment holding companies, except banks; Steel; Fabricated plate work (boiler shop); Cold finishing of steel shapes
Pr: Larry W Gies
**Treas:* John E Udelhofen
Sr VP: Aaron J Vangetson

D-U-N-S 04-436-6847 IMP/EXP
MADISON INDUSTRIES INC
295 5th Ave Ste 512, New York, NY 10016-7103
Tel (212) 679-5110 *Founded/Ownrshp* 1967
Sales 117.4MM[E] *EMP* 550
SIC 2392 5023 Household furnishings; Comforters & quilts: made from purchased materials; Pillowcases: made from purchased materials; Mattress protectors, except rubber; Home furnishings
Ch Bd: Michael Schwartz

D-U-N-S 00-327-3208
MADISON INDUSTRIES INC OF GEORGIA
(*Suby of* JOHN S FREY ENTERPRISES) ★
1035 Iris Dr Sw, Conyers, GA 30094
Tel (770) 483-4401 *Founded/Ownrshp* 1947
Sales 121.5MM[E] *EMP* 250
SIC 1541 3444 Industrial buildings, new construction; Sheet metalwork
CEO: John S Frey Jr
**Treas:* Grace Lee
**VP:* H Michael Davis

D-U-N-S 02-046-6561
MADISON METROPOLITAN SCHOOL DISTRICT
MMSD
545 W Dayton St, Madison, WI 53703-1995
Tel (608) 663-1879 *Founded/Ownrshp* 1963
Sales 173.7MM[E] *EMP* 4,006
SIC 8211 Public elementary & secondary schools; Secondary school
Pr: James Howard
**Treas:* Beth Moss
**VP:* Marj Passman
Ex Dir: Marggie Banker
Ex Dir: Cynthia Green
Dir IT: Mark Anderson
HC Dir: Sally Zirbel-Donisch

MADISON MINE SUPPLY CO
See WATERLOO COAL CO INC

D-U-N-S 13-579-5172 IMP/EXP
MADISON ONE HOLDINGS LLC
BOUMATIC
2001 S Stoughton Rd, Madison, WI 53716-2849
Tel (608) 222-3484 *Founded/Ownrshp* 2002
Sales 87.4MM[E] *EMP* 350
SIC 3523 Dairy equipment (farm); Milking machines
CFO: Allen Vail
Dir IT: Bob Schaefer

MADISON PAPER INDUSTRIES
See MADISON UPM

MADISON PERFORMANCE GROUP
See 488 PERFORMANCE GROUP INC

D-U-N-S 19-665-1954 IMP
MADISON PRECISION PRODUCTS INC
(*Suby of* METTS CORPORATION)
94 E 400 N, Madison, IN 47250-9599
Tel (812) 273-4702 *Founded/Ownrshp* 2009
Sales 175.7MM[E] *EMP* 500
SIC 3363 3365 Aluminum die-castings; Aluminum foundries
Pr: Michihiko Kato
Treas: Lisa Franklin
**Ex VP:* Ken Degler
**VP:* Randy Boyd
**VP:* David A Sutherland
**Prin:* Kazuyoshi Matsushita
IT Man: John Higgins
Sfty Mgr: Vicky Georgiev
Plnt Mgr: Kevin Turner
Sls Mgr: Masahiko Koto
Snr Mgr: Chub McNeeley

D-U-N-S 17-867-8863
MADISON SECURITY GROUP INC
31 Kirk St, Lowell, MA 01852-1028
Tel (978) 459-5911 *Founded/Ownrshp* 2004
Sales 34.0MM *EMP* 1,500
SIC 6289 Security custodians
Pr: Joan Fiore
Pr: James Doyle
**VP:* Tim Grover
Brnch Mgr: Al Medeiros

MADISON SQUARE GARDEN COMPANY
See MSG SPORTS & ENTERTAINMENT LLC

D-U-N-S 07-994-0571
MADISON SQUARE GARDEN CO
2 Penn Plz Fl 15, New York, NY 10121-1703
Tel (212) 465-6000 *Founded/Ownrshp* 1879
Sales 1.1MMM *EMP* 8,900
Accts Kpmg Llp
Tkr Sym MSG *Exch* NYS
SIC 7941 Sports clubs, managers & promoters; Sports field or stadium operator, promoting sports events; Sports promotion; Stadium event operator services
Pr: David O'Connor
**Ch Bd:* James L Dolan
CFO: Donna Coleman
Ex VP: Lawrence J Burian
Sr VP: Robert J Lynn
Sr VP: Joseph F Yospe
Board of Directors: Vincent Tese, Charles F Dolan, Kristin A Dolan, Thomas C Dolan, Wilt Hildenbrand, Richard D Parsons, Nelson Peltz, Alan D Schwartz, Scott M Sperling, Brian G Sweeney

D-U-N-S 04-683-3278
MADISON TITLE AGENCY LLC
1125 Ocean Ave Ste 1, Lakewood, NJ 08701-4577
Tel (732) 905-9400 *Founded/Ownrshp* 1998
Sales NA *EMP* 150[E]
SIC 6411
Pr: Joseph Rosenbaum
Ofcr: Dina Schwarzman
Ofcr: Yehudis Zarum
Mng Dir: Sol Kinraich
Genl Couns: Debra Smith
Counsel: Eliezer Shaffren

D-U-N-S 00-312-3629 IMP
MADISON UPM
MADISON PAPER INDUSTRIES
1 Main St, Madison, ME 04950-1220
Tel (207) 696-3307 *Founded/Ownrshp* 2007
Sales 180.0MM[E] *EMP* 225
SIC 2621

D-U-N-S 00-607-1716 IMP
MADISON-KIPP CORP
201 Waubesa St, Madison, WI 53704-5728
Tel (608) 244-3511 *Founded/Ownrshp* 2015
Sales 131.3MM[E] *EMP* 500[E]
SIC 3363 Aluminum die-castings
Pr: Tony Koblinski
**CFO:* Mark Daniel
Sfty Dirs: Alina Walcek
Mfg Mgr: Mike Dykstra
Opers Mgr: Mari Fuller
Opers Mgr: Dave Grebe
Prd Mgr: Brian Strohmenger
Ql Cn Mgr: Jay Laughlin
Sls Dir: David Gustafson
Snr Mgr: Tom Wiedenbeck

D-U-N-S 01-078-1573
MADISON-ONEIDA COUNTY BOCES (INC)
MADISN-NIDA BD COOP EDCTL SVCS
4937 Spring Rd, Verona, NY 13478-3526
Tel (315) 361-5500 *Founded/Ownrshp* 1968
Sales 88.8MM[E] *EMP* 750
Accts D Arcangelo & Co Llp Rome Ny
SIC 8211 Public elementary & secondary schools
**Treas:* Sandra J Foley
IT Man: Rebecca Lewis
IT Man: Joan Sotherden
Opers Mgr: David Phelps
Instr Medi: Diana Wendell

D-U-N-S 00-824-6316 IMP
■ **MADISON/GRAHAM COLOR GRAPHICS INC**
COLORGRAPHICS
(*Suby of* CENVEO CORP) ★
150 N Myers St, Los Angeles, CA 90033-2109
Tel (323) 261-7171 *Founded/Ownrshp* 1953
Sales 120.9MM[E] *EMP* 380
SIC 2752 7336 2796 Commercial printing, lithographic; Graphic arts & related design; Platemaking services
CEO: Cappy Childs
**Pr:* Chris Madison
CFO: Ralph Strong
**VP:* Arthur Bell
VP: Ken Stout
Trfc Mgr: Tony Hernandez
Sls Mgr: Kirk Bennett

D-U-N-S 00-731-8926 EXP
MADIX INC
500 Airport Rd, Terrell, TX 75160-5200
Tel (214) 515-5400 *Founded/Ownrshp* 1962
Sales 293.2MM[E] *EMP* 1,100
Accts Jamison Money Farmer & Co Pc
SIC 2542 2541 Partitions & fixtures, except wood; Fixtures, store: except wood; Shelving, office & store: except wood; Wood partitions & fixtures; Display fixtures, wood
Ch Bd: Alan H Sharaway
**Pr:* Thomas A Satterfield
**V Ch Bd:* Walter S Dowdle
CIO: Al Cantrel
Dir IT: Al Cantrell
IT Man: Jeff Carney
S&M/VP: Shawn Kahler

D-U-N-S 06-989-5837
MADLYN AND LEONARD ABRAMSON CENTER FOR JEWISH LIFE
POLISHER RESEARCH INSTITUTE
1425 Horsham Rd, North Wales, PA 19454-1320
Tel (215) 371-3000 *Founded/Ownrshp* 1891
Sales 61.7MM *EMP* 1,000
SIC 8051 8069 6513 Extended care facility; Geriatric hospital; Retirement hotel operation
CEO: Carol A Irvine
V Ch: Leonard Cantor
**V Ch:* Seth Lehr
V Ch: Saul Reibstein
**Pr:* Frank Podietz
**COO:* Valerie G Palmieri
**CFO:* Mark T Wasserman
VP: Robin Brandies
**VP:* Andy Bronstein
VP: Sean Gregson
**VP:* Michael B Steinberg
VP: Staci Warsaw
Exec: Karen Baldwin

D-U-N-S 04-091-2479
MADONNA REHABILITATION HOSPITAL
PROACTIVE
5401 South St, Lincoln, NE 68506-2150
Tel (402) 413-3000 *Founded/Ownrshp* 1966
Sales 110.9MM *EMP* 1,400
SIC 8051 Skilled nursing care facilities
Pr: Paul Dongilli Jr
Dir Recs: Charlene Dunbar
Ofcr: Jodi Blowers
VP: John Glenn
Dir Rad: Elizabeth Edwards
Dir Rx: Ingrid Songster
Dir Rx: Marsha Wagner
Dir IT: Bob Heydon
Sfty Dirs: Davie Shutzer-Hill
Opers Supe: Dawn Yanks
Pr Dir: Lori Paulsen
Board of Directors: Lynn Roper, Thomas Smith

MADRAG 10 SPOT
See 618 MAIN CLOTHING CORP

D-U-N-S 00-166-5322
MAERSK INC (NY)
MAERSK LINE
(*Suby of* A.P. MOLLER - MAERSK A/S)
180 Park Ave Ste 105, Florham Park, NJ 07932-1054
Tel (973) 514-5000 *Founded/Ownrshp* 1943, 2005
Sales 1.1MMM[E] *EMP* 3,000
SIC 4731 4491 4412 Agents, shipping; Stevedoring; Deep sea foreign transportation of freight
CEO: Sren Skou
**Ch Bd:* Russell J Brunner
**COO:* Morten Engelstoft
**CFO:* Morten K Nicolaisen
**Treas:* Pat Arnesen
**Chf Cred:* Philip V Connors
Bd of Dir: William S Stavropoulos
**Sr VP:* Doug Ceva
**Sr VP:* Kurt Mc Elroy
VP: Kevin Denman

VP: Neil W Magargal
VP: James P Philbin
Exec: Eric Herman

MAERSK LINE
See MAERSK INC

D-U-N-S 04-099-0913 IMP
MAERSK LINE LIMITED
(Suby of MAERSK LINE) ★
1 Commercial Pl Fl 20, Norfolk, VA 23510-2126
Tel (757) 857-4800 Founded/Ownrshp 1983
Sales 156.6MM[E] EMP 900[E]
SIC 4499 Steamship leasing
Pr: J Russell Bruner
Pr: Greg Moore
*CFO: Steven Hadder
*Chf Cred: William Kenwall
*Sr VP: Michael Hopkins
VP: Richard F Boyle
VP: Richard Boyle
*VP: Rick Boyle
VP: Ed Hanley
VP: Edward F Hanley
VP: R Gregory Moore
*Exec: Stephen Carmel
Dir Risk M: Lina Fennig
Board of Directors: John P Clancey,charles T, Harold W Gehman, Joe L Roby

D-U-N-S 79-101-2644
MAFCO CONSOLIDATED GROUP INC
(Suby of MACANDREWS & FORBES HOLDINGS INC) ★
35 E 62nd St, New York, NY 10065-8014
Tel (212) 572-8600 Founded/Ownrshp 1995
Sales 266.8MM[E] EMP 4,500
SIC 2121 2131 2869 Cigars; Smoking tobacco; Flavors or flavoring materials, synthetic
Ch Bd: Ronald O Perelman

D-U-N-S 00-132-5836
MAFCOTE INC
MIAMI WABASH PAPER
108 Main St Ste 3, Norwalk, CT 06851-4640
Tel (203) 847-8500 Founded/Ownrshp 1975
Sales 113.8MM[E] EMP 350
SIC 2631 2657 2679 2671

D-U-N-S 60-248-6391 IMP/EXP
MAG AEROSPACE INDUSTRIES INC
MONOGRAM SYSTEMS
(Suby of ZODIAC AEROSPACE)
1500 Glenn Curtiss St, Carson, CA 90746-4012
Tel (310) 631-3800 Founded/Ownrshp 1989
Sales 176.8MM[E] EMP 350
SIC 3431 3728 Plumbing fixtures: enameled iron cast iron or pressed metal; Portable chemical toilets, metal; Aircraft parts & equipment
Pr: Sebastien Weber
*CFO: Mark Scott
Sr VP: Olivier Zarrouati
*VP: Tim Birbeck
*VP: Mike Nieves
VP: Steve Schuetze
*VP Sls: David Conrad
Sls Mgr: Caryn Larks

MAG IAS HOLDINGS, INC.
See M-SKO IAS HOLDINGS INC

D-U-N-S 05-285-3454 IMP
MAG INSTRUMENT INC
2001 S Hellman Ave, Ontario, CA 91761-8019
Tel (909) 947-1006 Founded/Ownrshp 1955
Sales 181.0MM[E] EMP 910[E]
SIC 3648 Flashlights
CEO: Anthony Maglica
*Ofcr: Brent Flaharty
*Ofcr: Malissa Peace
VP: John Maglica
*VP: James Zecchini
MIS Dir: Cody Becker
*VP Sls: Thomas K Richardson
Sls Dir: Adrian Dare
Sls Dir: John Teskoski
Board of Directors: Jennifer Cimaglia, Anthony S Maglica, Dorothy Maglica, John Maglica

D-U-N-S 06-695-2748
MAG MUTUAL INSURANCE AGENCY LLC
3525 Piedmont Rd Ne 8-600, Atlanta, GA 30305-1556
Tel (404) 842-5600 Founded/Ownrshp 1988
Sales NA EMP 300
SIC 6351 6411 Liability insurance; Insurance agents, brokers & service
Chf Mktg O: Mary G Gregg

MAGAGNINI
See INTELLISWIFT SOFTWARE INC

D-U-N-S 07-525-8202
MAGAZINE PUBLISHERS OF AMERICA
PUBLISHERS INFORMATION BUREAU
810 7th Ave Fl 24, New York, NY 10019-5873
Tel (212) 872-3700 Founded/Ownrshp 1919
Sales 91.9MM[E] EMP 47
SIC 8611 Trade associations
Pr: Nina B Link
*Ex VP: Ellen Oppenheim
Sr VP: Rita Cohen

D-U-N-S 03-386-6880
MAGBEE BROS LUMBER AND SUPPLY CO INC (GA)
MAGBEE CONTRACTORS SUPPLY
1065 Bankhead Hwy, Winder, GA 30680-8415
Tel (678) 425-2600 Founded/Ownrshp 1954
Sales 103.8MM[E] EMP 211
SIC 2431 5211 3531 2439 Millwork; Lumber & other building materials; Construction machinery; Structural wood members
CEO: Robert G Magbee

MAGBEE CONTRACTORS SUPPLY
See MAGBEE BROS LUMBER AND SUPPLY CO INC

D-U-N-S 07-215-9460 IMP/EXP
MAGEE-WOMENS HOSPITAL OF UPMC
(Suby of UPMC HEALTH BENEFITS) ★
300 Halket St, Pittsburgh, PA 15213-3108
Tel (412) 641-1000 Founded/Ownrshp 1912
Sales 823.0MM EMP 2,300
SIC 8062 Hospital, affiliated with AMA residency
Pr: Leslie C Davis
*Ch Bd: William Pietragallo
COO: William Cook
COO: Ketul Patel
CFO: Ilene Simmons
*Treas: Peter Eisenbrandt
Chf Mktg O: Richard L Sweet
Dir Lab: Monica Daood
Dir Lab: Edward Smith
Adm Dir: Nicole Travis
Mng Dir: Marguerite Bonaventura

D-U-N-S 09-824-4796 IMP
MAGELLAN AIRCRAFT SERVICES LLLP
(Suby of MAGELLAN AVIATION GROUP LLLP) ★
2345 Township Rd Ste B, Charlotte, NC 28273-0119
Tel (704) 504-9204 Founded/Ownrshp 1998
Sales 128.6MM EMP 100
Accts Bdo Usa Llp Charlotte North
SIC 5088 Aircraft equipment & supplies
Pr: William Polyi
*Pt: Robert G Fessler
*CFO: Lawrence E Grogan
VP: Ken Auen

D-U-N-S 16-810-2445
MAGELLAN AVIATION GROUP LLLP
2345 Township Rd Ste B, Charlotte, NC 28273-0119
Tel (704) 504-9204 Founded/Ownrshp 2008
Sales 133.1MM EMP 100
Accts Bdo Usa Llp Charlotte Nc
SIC 5088 Aircraft engines & engine parts
Pt: David G Fessler
Pt: Niall Duggan
Pt: Robert G Fessler
Pt: Jerry Gerry
Pt: Larry Grogan
Pt: John McDonnell
Pt: Willam Polyi
Pt: Declan Treacy
Pt: Peter Zutty
VP: Jon Lobello

D-U-N-S 07-309-2199
■ **MAGELLAN BEHAVIORAL HEALTH SERVICE LLC**
(Suby of MAGELLAN HEALTH INC) ★
55 Nod Rd, Avon, CT 06001-3819
Tel (860) 507-1900 Founded/Ownrshp 1997
Sales 98.1MM[E] EMP 5,100
SIC 8322 Referral service for personal & social problems
Pr: Renee Lerer MD
Chf Mktg O: Shareh Ghani
Sr VP: Joann Albright
Sr VP: Kariena Greiten
Sr VP: Chris Hause
Sr VP: Anne McCabe
Sr VP: Linton Newlin
Sr VP: Cynthia Pigg
Sr VP: Bob Sawicki
Sr VP: Renie Shapiro
Sr VP: Glenn Stanton
VP: Craig Churn
VP: Shelly Scott
VP: Riwan Sheaprio
VP: Cadia Thone
Dir Lab: Heather Chadwick

D-U-N-S 04-969-3732
▲ **MAGELLAN HEALTH INC**
4800 N Scottsdale Rd, Scottsdale, AZ 85251-7630
Tel (602) 572-6050 Founded/Ownrshp 1969
Sales 3.5MMM EMP 8,700
Tkr Sym MGLN Exch NGS
SIC 8063 8011 5122 Psychiatric hospitals; Radiologist; Pharmaceuticals
Ch Bd: Barry M Smith
CEO: Sam K Srivastava
CFO: Jonathan N Rubin
Ofcr: Caskie Lewis-Clapper
Ex VP: Robert Lagalia
Sr VP: David W Carter
Sr VP: John Littel
Sr VP: Melissa Rose
CTO: Srinivas Koushik
Board of Directors: John O Agwunobi, Michael S Diament, Perry G Fine, Kay Coles James, G Scott Mackenzie, William J McBride, Michael P Ressner, Mary F Sammons

D-U-N-S 12-670-5347
■ **MAGELLAN HEALTHCARE INC**
(Suby of MAGELLAN HEALTH INC) ★
14100 Magellan Plz, Maryland Heights, MO 63043-4644
Tel (410) 953-1000 Founded/Ownrshp 1999
Sales NA EMP 1,900
SIC 6324 Health maintenance organization (HMO), insurance only
CEO: Henry Harbin
*Pr: Dan Messina
*Ex VP: Michael F Murphy

D-U-N-S 06-601-5611
■ **MAGELLAN MEDICAID ADMINISTRATION INC**
COMPUTER COMPANY, THE
(Suby of MAGELLAN HEALTH INC) ★
11013 W Broad St Ste 500, Glen Allen, VA 23060-6017
Tel (804) 548-0100 Founded/Ownrshp 1968
Sales 91.7MM[E] EMP 1,100
SIC 7374 8093 6411 8741 Computer processing services; Specialty outpatient clinics; Substance abuse clinics (outpatient); Mental health clinic, outpatient; Insurance claim processing, except medical; Medical insurance claim processing, contract or fee basis; Administrative management
Pr: Timothy Nolan
Treas: Irene Shapiro
*VP: James Council
VP: Richard A Holloway
VP: Mark Huntley
VP: Linton C Newlin
VP: Jonathan Rubin
VP: Joseph E Whitters
VP: Edward L Wristen
Snr PM: Kenneth Cheek

D-U-N-S 13-912-2738
■ **MAGELLAN MIDSTREAM HOLDINGS GP LLC**
(Suby of MAGELLAN MIDSTREAM PARTNERS LP) ★
1 One Williams Ctr Bsmt 2, Tulsa, OK 74172-0172
Tel (918) 574-7000 Founded/Ownrshp 2003
Sales 69.5MM[E] EMP 1,127
SIC 4613 Refined petroleum pipelines
Pt: Don R Wellendorf
Pt: John D Chandler
Pt: Lonny E Townsend

D-U-N-S 16-015-8069 IMP
▲ **MAGELLAN MIDSTREAM PARTNERS LP**
1 Williams Ctr Bsmt 2, Tulsa, OK 74172-0172
Tel (918) 574-7000 Founded/Ownrshp 2000
Sales 2.1MMM EMP 1,640
Tkr Sym MMP Exch NYS
SIC 5171 4613 Petroleum bulk stations & terminals; Refined petroleum pipelines; Gasoline pipelines (common carriers)
Ch Bd: Michael N Mears
Genl Pt: Magellan GP
CFO: Aaron L Milford
Sr VP: Lisa J Korner
VP: Robb Barnes
VP: Jerry Jefferson
Netwrk Eng: Ken Umezawa
Board of Directors: Lori A Gobillot, Edward J Guay

D-U-N-S 07-940-5006
■ **MAGELLAN PARTNERS RX INC**
(Suby of MAGELLAN HEALTH INC) ★
55 Nod Rd, Avon, CT 06001-3819
Tel (860) 507-1900 Founded/Ownrshp 2013
Sales 29.8MM[E] EMP 5,030[E]
SIC 8063 Psychiatric hospitals
CEO: Barry M Smith

D-U-N-S 00-718-7305 IMP
■ **MAGELLAN PIPELINE CO LP**
(Suby of MAGELLAN MIDSTREAM PARTNERS LP) ★
1 Williams Ctr, Tulsa, OK 74172-0140
Tel (918) 574-7000 Founded/Ownrshp 2003
Sales 157.2MM[E] EMP 435
SIC 4613 Gasoline pipelines (common carriers)
Pt: Don Wellendorf
Pt: Jeff Holman

D-U-N-S 11-205-9741
■ **MAGELLAN TERMINALS HOLDINGS LP**
(Suby of MAGELLAN MIDSTREAM PARTNERS LP) ★
1 One Williams Ctr Bsmt 2, Tulsa, OK 74172-0172
Tel (918) 574-7000 Founded/Ownrshp 2001
Sales 199.2MM[E] EMP 174
SIC 5171 Petroleum terminals
Pt: Don R Wellendorf
VP: Lisa Korner

MAGENTO COMMERCE
See X.COMMERCE INC

D-U-N-S 04-018-1120
■ **MAGGIANOS INC**
MAGGIANO'S LITTLE ITALY
(Suby of BRINKER INTERNATIONAL INC) ★
6820 Lyndon B Johnson Fwy, Dallas, TX 75240-6511
Tel (972) 980-9917 Founded/Ownrshp 1994
Sales 75.3MM[E] EMP 1,555
SIC 5812 Italian restaurant
Pr: Roger Thomson
*CFO: Chuck Sonsteby
*Sr VP: David Doyle
Genl Mgr: Todd Houchin

MAGGIANO'S LITTLE ITALY
See MAGGIANOS INC

MAGIC AIRE
See UNITED ELECTRIC CO LP

MAGIC FUND
See KEYBANK EB MANAGED GUARANTEED INVESTMENT CONTRACT FUND

MAGIC HAT BREWING COMPANY
See INDEPENDENT BREWERS UNITED CORP

D-U-N-S 07-852-8568
MAGIC JOHNSON ENTERPRISES INC
9100 Wilshire Blvd 700e, Beverly Hills, CA 90212-3423
Tel (310) 247-2033 Founded/Ownrshp 1991
Sales 505.2MM[E] EMP 10,100[E]
SIC 8743 7389 Promotion service; Music recording producer
CEO: Earvin Johnson Jr
COO: Kawanna Brown
VP Opers: Sheila Ewing
Sls&Mrk Ex: Christine Simmons
Genl Couns: Brad Young

MAGIC KITCH'N
See PITCO FRIALATOR INC

D-U-N-S 07-881-9314
MAGIC LEAP INC
1855 Griffin Rd Ste B454, Dania Beach, FL 33004-2247
Tel (954) 889-7010 Founded/Ownrshp 2011
Sales 162.6MM[E] EMP 200[E]
SIC 7371 Computer software development
*CFO: Russell Burke
*Chf Mktg O: Brenda Freeman
Chf Mktg O: Brian Wallace
*Ofcr: Rio Caraeff
Sr VP: Yannick Pellet
VP: Graeme Devine

MAGIC MART
See AMMARS INC

D-U-N-S 02-088-7949
MAGIC STEEL CORP
4242 Clay Ave Sw Ste 2, Grand Rapids, MI 49548-3034
Tel (616) 532-4071 Founded/Ownrshp 1974
Sales 170.0MM[E] EMP 103
SIC 5051

D-U-N-S 11-069-2956
MAGIC STEEL SALES LLC
(Suby of MAGIC STEEL CORP) ★
4242 Clay Ave Sw Ste 2, Grand Rapids, MI 49548-3034
Tel (616) 532-4071 Founded/Ownrshp 1974
Sales 170.0MM EMP 62
SIC 5051

D-U-N-S 00-895-1501
MAGIC VALLEY ELECTRIC COOPERATIVE INC
1 3/4 Mi W Hwy 83, Mercedes, TX 78570
Tel (866) 225-5683 Founded/Ownrshp 1937
Sales 163.5MM[E] EMP 217[E]
Accts Bolinger Segars Gilbert And Mo
SIC 4911 Electric services
Pr: Martin E Garcia
*Treas: M G Dyers
*Sec: Barbara S Miller
*VP: Reynaldo L Lopez
*Genl Mgr: John W Herrera

D-U-N-S 04-727-2542
MAGIC VALLEY FRESH FROZEN LLC
MAGIC VALLEY FROZEN
3701 W Military Hwy, McAllen, TX 78503-4403
Tel (956) 994-8947 Founded/Ownrshp 2014
Sales 198.8MM[E] EMP 275
SIC 5142 Frozen vegetables & fruit products

MAGIC VALLEY FROZEN
See MAGIC VALLEY FRESH FROZEN LLC

D-U-N-S 07-916-7630
MAGIC WORKFORCE SOLUTIONS LLC
(Suby of MAGIC JOHNSON ENTERPRISES INC) ★
9100 Wilsh Blvd Ste 700e, Beverly Hills, CA 90212
Tel (310) 246-6153 Founded/Ownrshp 2007
Sales 2.1MM[E] EMP 4,532[E]
SIC 8743 Promotion service
CEO: Earvin Johnson
*Pr: Eric Holoman
*COO: Kawanna Brown

D-U-N-S 07-964-2334
MAGIC WORKFORCE SOLUTIONS LLC
(Suby of MAGIC JOHNSON ENTERPRISES INC) ★
840 Ernest W Barrett Pkwy, Kennesaw, GA 30144-6816
Tel (770) 420-4759 Founded/Ownrshp 2014
Sales 264.2M[E] EMP 3,399[E]
SIC 7361 Employment agencies

D-U-N-S 00-518-1789 IMP/EXP
MAGID GLOVE & SAFETY MANUFACTURING CO LLC (IL)
1300 Naperville Dr, Romeoville, IL 60446-1043
Tel (773) 384-2070 Founded/Ownrshp 1946
Sales 117.0MM[E] EMP 862
SIC 3151 2381 5699 3842 2326 Gloves, leather: work; Gloves, work: woven or knit, made from purchased materials; Work clothing; Surgical appliances & supplies; Men's & boys' work clothing
Opers Mgr: Harvey Cohen
Pr: Marc Grubert
Pr: Susan Salcines
Treas: Sheldon Cohen
Sr VP: Lee Cohen
VP: Richard Allaire
VP: Peter Baltes
VP: Matt Montanez
Dist Mgr: Ken Barrick
Dist Mgr: Damon Cassell
Dist Mgr: Kevin Feeley

MAGNA
See NORPLAS INDUSTRIES INC

MAGNA
See COSMA AMERICA HOLDINGS INC

D-U-N-S 11-551-3702 IMP
MAGNA CARTOP SYSTEMS OF AMERICA INC
(Suby of MAGNA INTERNATIONAL INC)
2725 Commerce Pkwy, Auburn Hills, MI 48326-1789
Tel (248) 836-4500 Founded/Ownrshp 1999
Sales 122.5MM[E] EMP 673[E]
SIC 2394 Convertible tops, canvas or boat: from purchased materials
Genl Mgr: Shawn Bentley
Sls Dir: Jim Horaney
Sls Dir: Dave Noel

D-U-N-S 00-698-9255
MAGNA CARTA COMPANIES INC (DE)
1 Park Ave Fl 15, New York, NY 10016-5802
Tel (212) 591-9500 Founded/Ownrshp 1925
Sales NA EMP 706
SIC 6331 Fire, marine & casualty insurance
Ch Bd: A L Furgatch
*Pr: John T Hill II
*Sr VP: David A Lawless
VP: Mark Battistelli
*VP: Larry Gaddy
*VP: Louis Masucci
*VP: Theodore Smyk
*VP: Grace H Yang
DP Exec: David Peterson
Corp Couns: Viviana Monasterio

MAGNA COSMA BDY CHASSIS GROUP
See EAGLE BEND MFG INC

MAGNA DRIVE AUTO AMER DIV
See DRIVE AUTOMOTIVE INDUSTRIES OF AMERICA INC

D-U-N-S 95-883-4210 IMP
MAGNA ELECTRONICS INC
(*Suby of* MAGNA MIRRORS OF AMERICA INC) ★
10410 N Holly Rd, Holly, MI 48442-9332
Tel (810) 606-0444 *Founded/Ownrshp* 1996
Sales 174.5MM^E *EMP* 350
SIC 3672 3679 Printed circuit boards; Electronic circuits
Pr: Carlos Mazzorine
Dir Bus: Michael Manchester
Sys Mgr: Axel Nix
Sftwr Eng: Gordon Fincannon
Sftwr Eng: Jeff Kanoza
Sftwr Eng: Brian Tedesco
Mtls Mgr: Dennis Hamilton
Sfty Mgr: Bob Carmack
Plnt Mgr: Tom Beattie
Plnt Mgr: Bill Uitos
Ql Cn Mgr: Shannon Gibson

D-U-N-S 18-205-5137 IMP/EXP
MAGNA EXTERIORS OF AMERICA INC
DECOMA ADMARK
(*Suby of* MAGNA INTERNATIONAL INC)
750 Tower Dr, Troy, MI 48098-2863
Tel (248) 631-1100 *Founded/Ownrshp* 1987
Sales 1.0MMM^E *EMP* 2,400
SIC 3714 3544 8711 Motor vehicle body components & frame; Forms (molds), for foundry & plastics working machinery; Engineering services
CEO: Donald J Walker
**Pr:* Guenther Apfalter
**COO:* Tom J Skudutis
**CFO:* Vincent J Galifi
**Ex VP:* Marc Neeb
**VP:* William Frederiksen
**VP:* S Randall Smallbone
Prgrm Mgr: Terri Mezel
Prgrm Mgr: Dean Parks
Genl Mgr: Grahame Burrow
Genl Mgr: John Schultz

D-U-N-S 83-040-1456
MAGNA INTERNATIONAL OF AMERICA INC
(*Suby of* MAGNA INTERNATIONAL INC)
750 Tower Dr 7000, Troy, MI 48098-2863
Tel (248) 729-2400 *Founded/Ownrshp* 1987
Sales 2.1MMM^E *EMP* 8,678^E
SIC 3714 Motor vehicle parts & accessories
Pr: Donald Walker
**Pr:* Marc Neeb
COO: Tom Skudutis
**Ex VP:* Vincent J Galifi
**Ex VP:* Swamy Kotagiri
**Ex VP:* Jeffrey O Palmer
VP: Scott Paradise
Genl Mgr: David O'Connell
QA Dir: Jim Vanderweel

D-U-N-S 00-603-1561 IMP/EXP
MAGNA MIRRORS NORTH AMERICA LLC
LOWELL ENGINEERING
(*Suby of* MAGNA INTERNATIONAL INC)
6151 Bancroft Ave Se, Alto, MI 49302-9313
Tel (616) 868-6122 *Founded/Ownrshp* 1954, 1990
Sales 242.5MM^E *EMP* 1,100
SIC 3231 3442 Mirrors, truck & automobile: made from purchased glass; Metal doors, sash & trim
Pr: Carlos Mazzorin

D-U-N-S 00-601-1936 EXP
MAGNA MIRRORS OF AMERICA INC (MI)
(*Suby of* MAGNA INTERNATIONAL OF AMERICA INC) ★
5085 Kraft Ave Se, Grand Rapids, MI 49512-9707
Tel (616) 942-0163 *Founded/Ownrshp* 1905, 2008
Sales 2.0MMM^E *EMP* 8,000
SIC 3231 3647 3827 Mirrors, truck & automobile: made from purchased glass; Windshields, glass: made from purchased glass; Dome lights, automotive; Automotive lighting fixtures; Optical instruments & lenses
CEO: James L Brodie
Sr VP: Niall R Lynam
Prgrm Mgr: Don Duclos
Prgrm Mgr: Anna Marmann
Prgrm Mgr: Brian McGuire
Genl Mgr: Marcia Kort
Mtls Mgr: Aaron Pallas
Opers Mgr: Nathan Denman
Prd Mgr: David Fox
Prd Mgr: Mark Steinmetz
Ql Cn Mgr: Kevin Pluff

D-U-N-S 61-727-2898 IMP
MAGNA MODULAR SYSTEMS INC
MAGNA TEAM SYSTEMS
(*Suby of* DECOMA ADMARK) ★
1800 Nathan Dr, Toledo, OH 43611-1091
Tel (419) 324-3387 *Founded/Ownrshp* 2008
Sales 202.5MM^E *EMP* 350
Accts Ernst & Young Llp Toronto Ca
SIC 3714 Motor vehicle body components & frame
CEO: Grahhame Burrow
**Genl Mgr:* Keith McMahon

MAGNA POWERTRAIN LANSING
See LANSING L MPT L C

D-U-N-S 84-915-9988 IMP
MAGNA POWERTRAIN OF AMERICA INC
(*Suby of* MAGNA INTERNATIONAL INC)
1870 Technology Dr, Troy, MI 48083-4232
Tel (248) 597-7811 *Founded/Ownrshp* 1992
Sales 92.6MM^E *EMP* 151
SIC 5013 Automotive supplies
CEO: Donald J Walker
Mng Pt: George Silveira
Bd of Dir: Eric Richardson
Assoc VP: ABI Arigbabu
Ex VP: CHI Liu
Sr VP: Daniela Lia
Sr VP: Jack Tran
Prgrm Mgr: Monica Khokhar
Prgrm Mgr: Edwin Paredes
Genl Mgr: Stephen Brand
IT Man: Keith Gerds

MAGNA POWERTRAIN TROY
See MAGNA POWERTRAIN USA INC

D-U-N-S 16-563-2527 IMP
MAGNA POWERTRAIN USA INC
MAGNA POWERTRAIN TROY
(*Suby of* MAGNA POWERTRAIN INC)
1870 Technology Dr, Troy, MI 48083-4232
Tel (248) 680-4900 *Founded/Ownrshp* 2004
Sales 535.9MM^E *EMP* 2,983
SIC 3714 Motor vehicle engines & parts
Pr: Jake Hirsch
Opers Mgr: Teri Freeburn

D-U-N-S 78-301-6538 IMP
MAGNA SEATING OF AMERICA INC
INTIER AUTOMOTIVE SEATING
(*Suby of* MAGNA INTERNATIONAL INC)
39600 Lewis Dr Ste 216, Novi, MI 48377-2953
Tel (248) 553-8094 *Founded/Ownrshp* 1985
Sales 558.1MM^E *EMP* 2,377
SIC 3714 Motor vehicle parts & accessories
Pr: Joseph Pittel
**Pr:* Mike Bisson
Pr: John Oilar
Ex VP: Michael McCarthy
**VP:* Glen Copeland
Prgrm Mgr: John Radford
Mktg Mgr: Nuncha Maranon

MAGNA TEAM SYSTEMS
See MAGNA MODULAR SYSTEMS INC

D-U-N-S 03-245-4357 IMP/EXP
MAGNABLEND INC
326 N Grand Ave, Waxahachie, TX 75165-2220
Tel (972) 938-2028 *Founded/Ownrshp* 2012
Sales 182.0MM^E *EMP* 420
SIC 2899

D-U-N-S 15-580-8285 EXP
■ **MAGNATRAX CORP**
(*Suby of* NUCOR CORP) ★
1220 Old Alpharetta Rd # 310, Alpharetta, GA 30005-3972
Tel (678) 455-3360 *Founded/Ownrshp* 2007
Sales 118.7MM^E *EMP* 1,800
SIC 3448 3442 3479 4213 3444 Prefabricated metal buildings; Prefabricated metal components; Metal doors; Coating of metals & formed products; Trucking, except local; Metal roofing & roof drainage equipment
CEO: Harry R Lowe
**CFO:* James D Frias
**Ex VP:* Allen Capsuto

D-U-N-S 55-684-6835 IMP/EXP
MAGNELL ASSOCIATE INC
ABS COMPUTER TECHNOLOGIES
(*Suby of* NEWEGG.COM) ★
17560 Rowland St, City of Industry, CA 91748-1114
Tel (562) 695-8823 *Founded/Ownrshp* 1990
Sales 2.1MMM^E *EMP* 900
Accts Pricewaterhousecoopers Llp L
SIC 5045 Computers & accessories, personal & home entertainment
CEO: James Wu
**VP:* Craig Hayes
VP: Howard Tong
Dir Sec: Albert Whale
IT Man: Charlie Chan
IT Man: Albert Chong
**VP Sls:* Hip Lee
Genl Couns: Lee Cheng
Board of Directors: Robert Cheng

D-U-N-S 16-657-2615 IMP
■ **MAGNEQUENCH INC**
(*Suby of* MOLYCORP MINERALS CANADA ULC)
237 S Pendleton Ave Ste C, Pendleton, IN 46064-1187
Tel (765) 778-7809 *Founded/Ownrshp* 1999
Sales 148.1MM^E *EMP* 1,300
SIC 3499 Magnets, permanent: metallic
Pr: Constantine Karayanno
**Ch Bd:* Hong Zhang
**Pr:* Archibald Cox Jr
**COO:* Gary Riley
**CFO:* K C Ashok
**Sr VP:* Shannon Song
Off Mgr: Missy Wilson

D-U-N-S 00-791-7966 IMP/EXP
MAGNESITA REFRACTORIES CO (PA)
(*Suby of* MAGNESITA REFRATARIOS S A)
425 S Salem Church Rd, York, PA 17408-5955
Tel (717) 792-3611 *Founded/Ownrshp* 1941, 2008
Sales 121.2MM^E *EMP* 500
SIC 3297 3274 1422 Dolomite or dolomite-magnesite brick & shapes; Lime; Dolomite, crushed & broken-quarrying
Pr: Otto Levy
**Sec:* Kelly L Myers
**VP:* Paul A Dydek
VP: Gustavo Franco
**Prin:* Ronaldo Iabrudi Dos Santos Per
Rgnl Mgr: Mark Zikesch
Off Mgr: Lorie Baker
Snr Ntwrk: Lloyd West
Dir IT: Don Griffin
IT Man: Mark Messner
**VP Mfg:* Ricky D Gladfelter
Board of Directors: Flavio Rezende Barbosa, David A Gregory, Ronaldo Iabrudi Dos Santos

D-U-N-S 02-495-6344
MAGNESS OIL CO
CIRCLE K
167 Tucker Cemetery Rd, Gassville, AR 72635-8701
Tel (870) 425-4353 *Founded/Ownrshp* 1960
Sales 92.3MM^E *EMP* 120
SIC 5171 5541 5411 Petroleum bulk stations; Filling stations, gasoline; Convenience stores, independent
Pr: Benny W Magness
CFO: Richard Simmons
**VP:* Jeffrey W Magness

D-U-N-S 96-996-7731 IMP
MAGNETATION LLC
102 Ne 3rd St Ste 120, Grand Rapids, MN 55744-2868
Tel (218) 398-0079 *Founded/Ownrshp* 2010
Sales 100.0MM *EMP* 475
SIC 1011 Iron ore mining
Ch Bd: Larry Lehtinen
**Pr:* Matt Lehtinen
**CFO:* Joe Broking
**VP:* David Chappie
IT Man: Justin Haar
Opers Mgr: Dustin Robinson

D-U-N-S 11-753-1954 IMP
■ **MAGNETEK INC**
MAGNETEK MATERIAL HANDLING
(*Suby of* COLUMBUS MCKINNON CORP) ★
N49w13650 Campbell Dr, Menomonee Falls, WI 53051-7051
Tel (262) 783-3500 *Founded/Ownrshp* 2015
Sales 110.9MM^E *EMP* 328
SIC 3625 Relays & industrial controls; Control equipment, electric; Electric controls & control accessories, industrial
Pr: Peter M McCormick
**CFO:* Marty J Schwenner
**VP:* Scott S Cramer
VP: Richard Heppe
**VP:* Hungsun S Hui
**VP:* Michael J Stauber

MAGNETEK MATERIAL HANDLING
See MAGNETEK INC

D-U-N-S 03-829-1837 IMP
MAGNETI MARELLI POWERTRAIN USA LLC
(*Suby of* MAGNETI MARELLI SPA)
2101 Nash St, Sanford, NC 27330-6338
Tel (919) 776-4111 *Founded/Ownrshp* 1975
Sales 126.9MM^E *EMP* 500^E
SIC 3714 3592 Fuel systems & parts, motor vehicle; Carburetors, pistons, rings, valves
CFO: Marco Manzi
VP: Earl Losey
Prgrm Mgr: Dario Gaffoglio
Prgrm Mgr: Michael Harral
Prgrm Mgr: Scott Shultz
Snr Sftwr: Kuntal Mukherjee
Plnt Mgr: Joe Machado
Prd Mgr: Ronnie L Wilson
Ql Cn Mgr: Bob Lombard

MAGNETIC TECHNOLOGY
See ARNOLD MAGNETIC TECHNOLOGIES CORP

D-U-N-S 02-353-6386
MAGNETIC TICKET & LABEL CORP
MT&L CARD PRODUCTS
(*Suby of* HOSPITAL FORMS & SYSTEMS) ★
8719 Diplomacy Row, Dallas, TX 75247-5401
Tel (214) 634-8600 *Founded/Ownrshp* 1982
Sales 104.4MM^E *EMP* 400
SIC 2679 Labels, paper: made from purchased material
Pr: Peter A Pyhrr
**Sr VP:* Stan Welker
VP: Dave Fehrman
**VP:* Barbara Fulenwiter
VP: Michael Hale
VP: Reiner Vanooteghem
VP: Stanley Walker
MIS Mgr: Helmut Lilischkies
VP Sls: Adam Wittekind

D-U-N-S 08-982-4684 EXP
MAGNETROL INTERNATIONAL INC
705 Enterprise St, Aurora, IL 60504-8149
Tel (630) 723-6600 *Founded/Ownrshp* 1979, 1978
Sales 93.4MM^E *EMP* 364
SIC 3823 3699 3643 3625 3541 Level & bulk measuring instruments, industrial process; Flow instruments, industrial process type; Electrical equipment & supplies; Current-carrying wiring devices; Relays & industrial controls; Machine tools, metal cutting type
Pr: Jeffrey K Swallow
Pr: John Benway
**COO:* John E Heiser
**CFO:* Marlin K Underwood
Assoc Dir: Julie Bjorkman
Ex Dir: Bill Hendrick
QA Dir: Rich Forst
IT Man: Darren Meyer
IT Man: Paul Rymek
Sfty Mgr: Brad Stroud
Mfg Mgr: Steve Meier

D-U-N-S 15-126-6269 IMP
MAGNI GROUP INC
390 Park St Ste 300, Birmingham, MI 48009-3400
Tel (248) 647-4500 *Founded/Ownrshp* 1986
Sales 86.7MM^E *EMP* 170
SIC 2899 3479 Rust resisting compounds; Coating, rust preventive
Ch: David E Berry
**Pr:* Tim Berry
VP: Jack Benson
VP: Robert Keagy
VP: Kamlesh Passi
VP: Doug Paul
VP: Kirk Weaver
Dir IT: Laurel Emerick
IT Man: Thomas Devilbiss
Opers Mgr: Richard Misplay
VP Mktg: Thomas McIntosh

D-U-N-S 18-920-6287 IMP
■ **MAGNIFIQUE PARFUMES AND COSMETICS INC**
PERFUMANIA
(*Suby of* PERFUMANIA INC) ★
5900 N Andrews Ave # 500, Fort Lauderdale, FL 33309-2370
Tel (954) 335-9100 *Founded/Ownrshp* 1987
Sales 152.8MM^E *EMP* 1,500
SIC 5999 Perfumes & colognes
Pr: Michael W Katz
VP: Bill Reger
VP: A M Young

D-U-N-S 08-029-7033
MAGNITUDE PARENT HOLDINGS LLC
200 N Point Ctr E Ste 200, Alpharetta, GA 30022-8274
Tel (678) 323-2500 *Founded/Ownrshp* 2015
Sales NA *EMP* 3,350
SIC 6719 Investment holding companies, except banks

D-U-N-S 00-696-4654
MAGNOLIA ELECTRIC POWER ASSOCIATION
3012 Highway 98 E, McComb, MS 39648-9463
Tel (601) 876-5671 *Founded/Ownrshp* 1938
Sales 90.3MM *EMP* 73
Accts Wilson & Biggs Pllc Ridgeland
SIC 4911 Distribution, electric power
Pr: Hollis Alford
**COO:* Tony Nettles
VP: Dennis Wilson
**Genl Mgr:* Darrell Smith
Dir IT: Lawrence Weems
Opers Mgr: Aaron Achord
Board of Directors: Noel Andrews, John P Ard, John Mc Cabe, Bruce McCaffrey, Jerry Sisco, Jewell H Smith

D-U-N-S 96-373-8034
MAGNOLIA HEALTH SYSTEMS INC
9480 Prority W Dr, Indianapolis, IN 46240
Tel (317) 818-1240 *Founded/Ownrshp* 1997
Sales 67.3MM^E *EMP* 2,000
SIC 8099 Medical services organization
Pr: Stuart Reed
**VP:* Michael Reed

D-U-N-S 80-669-6766
MAGNOLIA INDEPENDENT SCHOOL DISTRICT
31141 Nichols Sawmill Rd, Magnolia, TX 77355-6032
Tel (281) 356-3571 *Founded/Ownrshp* 2007
Sales 68.7MM^E *EMP* 1,500^E
SIC 8211 Public elementary & secondary schools; Public elementary school; Public junior high school; Public senior high school
**CFO:* Erich Morris
Adm Dir: John Roch
Dir Sec: Garrett Matej
Dir IT: Melissa Beale
Pr Dir: Marsha Little
Psych: Kim Ayres
Psych: Lisa Kennedy
Psych: Bonnie McCoy

D-U-N-S 02-102-4872
MAGNOLIA MANAGEMENT CORP
763 Avery Blvd N, Ridgeland, MS 39157-5218
Tel (601) 956-8884 *Founded/Ownrshp* 1979
Sales 21.3MM^E *EMP* 1,300
SIC 8051

D-U-N-S 07-859-2417
MAGNOLIA REGIONAL HEALTH CENTER FOUNDATION INC
SECURITY & EMERGENCY MANAGMENT
611 Alcorn Dr, Corinth, MS 38834-9321
Tel (662) 293-1000 *Founded/Ownrshp* 1965
Sales 149.6MM^E *EMP* 928
SIC 8062 General medical & surgical hospitals
CEO: Ronny Humes
**COO:* Angela Nowlin
**CFO:* Brian Craven
VP: Gene Combest
VP: Amy McBride
VP: David Parker
VP: Pam Wallis
Dir Inf Cn: Amy Gray
Dir Rx: Todd Cox
CIO: Brian Davis
CIO: Bill Jones MD

D-U-N-S 62-162-5883
MAGNUM HUNTER RESOURCES CORP
909 Lake Carolyn Pkwy # 600, Irving, TX 75039-3926
Tel (832) 369-6986 *Founded/Ownrshp* 2005
Sales 154.1MM *EMP* 440^E
Accts Bdo Usa Llp Dallas Texas
SIC 1311 Crude petroleum & natural gas; Crude petroleum & natural gas production
Pr: John K Reinhart
Ch Bd: Gary C Evans
COO: Keith Yankowsky
CFO: Joseph C Daches
CFO: Michael R Koy
Ex VP: Glenn Dawson
Ex VP: R Glenn Dawson
Ex VP: H C Ferguson III
Ex VP: Ronald Ormand
Sr VP: Richard S Farrell
Sr VP: Paul M Johnston
Sr VP: Donald Kirkendall
Sr VP: Kirk J Trosclair
VP: Chris Benton
VP: Debbie Funderburg
VP: Charlie Gibson
VP: Chris Hewitt
VP: David Lipp
VP: Matthew H Rucker
VP: Nicole Thurmond
VP: Richard Vickery
Board of Directors: J Raleigh Bailes Sr, Victor G Carrillo, Roderick Duckworth, Stephen H Hurley, Joel L McClaugherty, Jeff Swanson

D-U-N-S 11-360-8228
MAGNUM INSURANCE AGENCY CO INC
4259 N Western Ave, Chicago, IL 60618-2815
Tel (773) 539-2102 *Founded/Ownrshp* 1981
Sales NA *EMP* 200
SIC 6411 Insurance agents, brokers & service
Ch Bd: Craig Lamm
**Pr:* Ericka Ariza
**Pr:* Ericka Ceballos
VP: Christopher Roman

D-U-N-S 79-344-6006 IMP
■ MAGNUM MANAGEMENT CORP
(Suby of CEDAR FAIR LP) ★
1 Cedar Point Dr, Sandusky, OH 44870-5259
Tel (419) 627-2334 Founded/Ownrshp 1983
Sales 91.1MM^E EMP 800
SIC 4785 6552 7996 Toll bridge operation; Subdividers & developers; Amusement parks
CEO: Richard L Kinzel
VP: Clark Culbertson
VP: Craig J Freeman
VP: Jim Rein
VP: Alan L Schwartz
Off Mgr: Lois A Lawrence
Dir IT: Renae Weaver

D-U-N-S 93-848-3815
MAGNUM STAFFING SERVICES INC
2900 Smith St Ste 250, Houston, TX 77006-3445
Tel (713) 658-0068 Founded/Ownrshp 1996
Sales 45.2MM^E EMP 1,250
SIC 7363 Manpower pools; Labor resource services
Pr: Caroline Brown
*CFO: Darrel Brown
Dir IT: Steve Bowen

D-U-N-S 06-583-5050 IMP/EXP
MAGOTTEAUX INC
(Suby of MAGOTTEAUX INTERNATIONAL SA)
725 Cool Springs Blvd # 200, Franklin, TN 37067-2704
Tel (615) 385-3055 Founded/Ownrshp 1970
Sales 99.2MM^E EMP 450
SIC 3369 Castings, except die-castings, precision
CEO: Bernard Goblet
*Pr: Walter Mersch
Exec: M Devalckeneer
Exec: V Warbrouck
Tech Mgr: Joseph Cesarini
Plnt Mgr: Tim Carr
Ql Cn Mgr: Bart Johnson
Sls Mgr: Freddy Debock

D-U-N-S 00-506-6126
MAGPIE INTERNET COMMUNICATIONS CORP (CA)
PLANETMAGPIE
2762 Bayview Dr, Fremont, CA 94538-6518
Tel (510) 344-1200 Founded/Ownrshp 1998
Sales 200.0MM EMP 15
SIC 4813 7379 7374 ; ; ; ; Computer graphics service
Pr: Robert Douglas
*VP: Doreyne Douglas

D-U-N-S 06-437-8433
MAGUIRE INSURANCE AGENCY INC
VALLEY FORGE INSURANCE BRKG
(Suby of PHILADELPHIA CONSOLIDATED HOLDING CORP) ★
1 Bala Plz Ste LI34, Bala Cynwyd, PA 19004-1400
Tel (610) 617-7900 Founded/Ownrshp 2002
Sales NA EMP 1,374
SIC 6411 Insurance agents
Pr: James J Maguire Jr
*COO: Chris J Maguire
*CFO: Craig P Keller
*Chf Mktg O: Sean S Sweeney

MAHAR MEDICAL
See MAHAR TOOL SUPPLY CO INC

D-U-N-S 01-736-5420
MAHAR TOOL SUPPLY CO INC
MAHAR MEDICAL
112 Williams St, Saginaw, MI 48602-1441
Tel (989) 799-5530 Founded/Ownrshp 1978
Sales 96.5MM^E EMP 114
SIC 5085

D-U-N-S 00-167-0488 IMP
■ MAHARAM FABRIC CORP (NY)
(Suby of HERMAN MILLER INC) ★
74 Horseblock Rd, Yaphank, NY 11980-9757
Tel (631) 582-3434 Founded/Ownrshp 1932
Sales 196.4MM^E EMP 290
SIC 5131 7389 Textiles, woven; Styling of fashions, apparel, furniture, textiles, etc.
Ch Bd: Donald Maharam
Ex VP: Bruce Madden
VP: Manny Feldson
VP: Annette Schaih
*Prin: Michael Maharam
Genl Mgr: Jackie Kleinman
Dir IT: Sal Deaugustino

D-U-N-S 92-685-0926 IMP/EXP
MAHINDRA USA INC
(Suby of MAHINDRA AND MAHINDRA LIMITED)
9020 Jackrabbit Rd # 600, Houston, TX 77095-3397
Tel (281) 449-7771 Founded/Ownrshp 1995
Sales 285.8MM EMP 130
Accts Kahanek Franke & Associates
SIC 5083 Tractors, agricultural
Ch: Anand Mahindra
*Pr: Anita Arjundas
*CFO: Hetal Shah
*VP: Cleo Frankline
*Prin: Mani Iyer
IT Man: Rajesh Mishra
IT Man: Rajesh Tiwaskar
Opers Mgr: Jerry Murillo
VP Mktg: Cleo Franklin
Snr Mgr: Gena Medeiros

D-U-N-S 79-646-6303 IMP
MAHLE AFTERMARKET INC
(Suby of MAHLE INDUSTRIES INC) ★
23030 Mahle Dr, Farmington, MI 48335-2606
Tel (248) 347-9700 Founded/Ownrshp 2007
Sales 113.5MM^E EMP 200^E
SIC 5013 Automotive engines & engine parts
Ch Bd: Arnd Franz
*Ch: Prof Dr LNG Heinz K Junker
Genl Mgr: Dan Moody
VP Sls: Ken Carter
Mktg Mgr: Melissa Kirk

D-U-N-S 10-675-7271 IMP
MAHLE BEHR CHARLESTON INC
(Suby of MAHLE BEHR USA INC) ★
4500 Leeds Ave Ste 101, Charleston, SC 29405-8515
Tel (843) 745-1233 Founded/Ownrshp 1994
Sales 121.8MM^E EMP 1,000
SIC 3714 Radiators & radiator shells & cores, motor vehicle; Air conditioner parts, motor vehicle; Motor vehicle engines & parts
Pr: Hans Lange
Exec: Antoinette Barnes
Exec: Paula Horn

D-U-N-S 36-286-6233 IMP/EXP
MAHLE BEHR DAYTON LLC
(Suby of MAHLE BEHR GMBH & CO. KG)
1600 Webster St, Dayton, OH 45404-1144
Tel (937) 369-2900 Founded/Ownrshp 2002
Sales 272.4MM EMP 1,120
SIC 3714 Motor vehicle parts & accessories
Ch Bd: Ing Heinz K Junker
*Pr: Wolf Hennig Scheider
*CEO: Willm Uhlenbecker
*CFO: Christopher Arkwright
*CFO: Milan Belans
*VP: Bruce Moorehouse

D-U-N-S 07-991-3550
MAHLE BEHR MANUFACTURING MANAGEMENT INC
2700 Daley Dr, Troy, MI 48083-1949
Tel (248) 735-3623 Founded/Ownrshp 2015
Sales 2.0MMM EMP 14,000
SIC 5013 3714 Automotive supplies & parts; Air conditioner parts, motor vehicle
VP: Wilm Uhlenbecker

D-U-N-S 62-281-5975 IMP
MAHLE BEHR USA INC
(Suby of MAHLE GMBH)
2700 Daley Dr, Troy, MI 48083-1949
Tel (248) 743-3700 Founded/Ownrshp 2013
Sales 1.0MMM^E EMP 3,182
SIC 3714 Radiators & radiator shells & cores, motor vehicle; Air conditioner parts, motor vehicle; Motor vehicle engines & parts
Pr: Wilm Uhlenbecker
*VP: Dean Arneson
VP Opers: Uwe Gerber

D-U-N-S 09-637-2883 IMP/EXP
MAHLE ENGINE COMPONENTS USA INC
(Suby of MAHLE GMBH)
1 Mahle Dr, Morristown, TN 37815
Tel (423) 581-6603 Founded/Ownrshp 1976
Sales 239.2MM^E EMP 1,000
SIC 3592 3443

D-U-N-S 18-201-4555 IMP
MAHLE FILTER SYSTEMS NORTH AMERICA INC
(Suby of MAHLE GMBH)
906 Butler Dr, Murfreesboro, TN 37127-6137
Tel (615) 895-5572 Founded/Ownrshp 2001
Sales 167.9MM^E EMP 500
SIC 3714 Motor vehicle engines & parts; Cleaners, air, motor vehicle; Filters: oil, fuel & air, motor vehicle
Ch: Wolf-Henning Scheider
VP: Joe Strong
Exec: John McGough
CIO: Christina Siharaj
Dir IT: Herb Strandberg
IT Man: Greg Ireland
VP Opers: Frank Lengsfeld
Opers Mgr: Eddie Nelson
Ql Cn Mgr: Beverly Chesebro
Ql Cn Mgr: Rick Corum
Ql Cn Mgr: Yuri Garcia

D-U-N-S 61-055-4433 IMP
MAHLE INDUSTRIES INC
(Suby of MAHLE GMBH)
23030 Mahle Dr, Farmington Hills, MI 48335-2606
Tel (248) 305-8200 Founded/Ownrshp 2015
Sales 158.4MM^E EMP 215
SIC 3714 Motor vehicle parts & accessories
Ch: Prof Dr Heinz Junker
Pr: Roland Zitt
Treas: Ralf R Roske
VP: Jerry W Dillard
IT Man: Uwe Thumlert

D-U-N-S 01-320-8702
MAHOMED SALES & WAREHOUSING LLC (IN)
M S W
8258 Zionsville Rd, Indianapolis, IN 46268-1627
Tel (317) 472-5800 Founded/Ownrshp 1997
Sales 100.0MM^E EMP 80
SIC 4225 3714 General warehousing & storage; Motor vehicle parts & accessories
CEO: Yousuf Mohamed
Pr: James Brown
VP: Keith Kanipe

MAHONEY GROUP, THE
See M & O AGENCIES INC

D-U-N-S 02-064-3706
MAHONING COUNTY
BOARD MHNING CNTY CMMISSIONERS
21 W Boardman St Ste 200, Youngstown, OH 44503-1416
Tel (330) 740-2130 Founded/Ownrshp 1845
Sales NA EMP 1,500
SIC 9121 County commissioner;
Dir IT: Jake Williams

MAHONING VLY HMTOLOGY ONCOLOGY
See TRUMBULL MEMORIAL HOSPITAL FOUNDATION

D-U-N-S 00-120-5640 IMP
MAHR FEDERAL INC
(Suby of CARL MAHR HOLDING GMBH)
1144 Eddy St, Providence, RI 02905-4511
Tel (401) 784-3100 Founded/Ownrshp 1999
Sales 86.6MM^E EMP 300
SIC 5084 Instruments & control equipment
Pr: Tony Picone
Mng Pt: Ulrich Kaspar
*CFO: John Robinson
*VP: Kurt Braun
VP: Eddy Hochwart
Mng Dir: Anna Nagar
Dist Mgr: Sam Banerjea
Dist Mgr: John Buck
Dist Mgr: Pete Erins
Dist Mgr: Catherine Norton
Dist Mgr: Thomas Remington

D-U-N-S 07-849-4263
MAIDENFORM
485 Us Highway 1 S, Iselin, NJ 08830-3009
Tel (732) 621-2216 Founded/Ownrshp 2012
Sales 43.3MM^E EMP 1,200
SIC 2341 Women's & children's underwear

D-U-N-S 36-421-6445 IMP
■ MAIDENFORM BRANDS INC
(Suby of HANESBRANDS INC) ★
485 Us Highway 1 S, Iselin, NJ 08830-3009
Tel (888) 573-0299 Founded/Ownrshp 2013
Sales 133.5MM^E EMP 1,230^E
SIC 2341 2342 5621 Women's & children's underwear; Women's & children's undergarments; Bras, girdles & allied garments; Brassieres; Foundation garments, women's; Girdles & panty girdles; Women's specialty clothing stores; Ready-to-wear apparel, women's
CEO: Maurice S Reznik
Pr: Malcolm Robinson
COO: Christopher W Vieth
Ofcr: Anthony D'Onofrio
Ex VP: Patrick J Burns
Ex VP: Nanci Prado
Ex VP: Gayle Weibley Wolman
Sr VP: Steven Castellano
Sr VP: Patricia J Royak
VP: Gayle Webley
Netwrk Mgr: John Hascup

D-U-N-S 00-146-7893 IMP
MAIDENFORM INC
TRUE FORM
485f Us Highway 1 S # 120, Iselin, NJ 08830-3055
Tel (732) 621-2500 Founded/Ownrshp 1999
Sales NA EMP 1,120
SIC 2341 2342

D-U-N-S 07-927-5610
■ MAIDENFORM LLC
(Suby of HANESBRANDS INC) ★
1000 E Hanes Mill Rd, Winston Salem, NC 27105-1384
Tel (336) 519-8080 Founded/Ownrshp 2013
Sales 314.7MM^E EMP 1,120^E
SIC 5137 Lingerie
Prin: Joia Johnson

MAIDSTONE COFFEE
See TIM HORTONS USA INC

MAIL BOXES ETC
See UPS STORE INC

D-U-N-S 15-424-6623
MAIL CONTRACTORS OF AMERICA INC
M C A
3800 N Rodney Parham Rd # 301, Little Rock, AR 72212-2489
Tel (501) 280-0500 Founded/Ownrshp 1956
Sales 125.0MM^E EMP 1,200
SIC 4212 Mail carriers, contract
Pr: Don Salmon
CFO: Bryan Wilson
VP: Sheila McDonald
Exec: John Beasley
IT Man: Robert Peacock

MAILTRUST
See RACKSPACE US INC

D-U-N-S 05-738-1535
MAIMONIDES MEDICAL CENTER
4802 10th Ave, Brooklyn, NY 11219-2916
Tel (718) 581-0598 Founded/Ownrshp 1906
Sales 890.0MM EMP 6,382
SIC 8062 General medical & surgical hospitals
Ch Bd: Martin D Payson
Dir Recs: Sylvia Semenskaya
Dir Vol: Alla Zats
*Ch Bd: Martin D Payson
*Pr: Pamela Brier
Pr: William Howe
Pr: Lori White
COO: Dominick Stanzione
*COO: Dominque Stanzione
*CFO: Robert Naldi
Chf Mktg O: Ivonne Colonna
Ex VP: David I Cohen
VP: Marcel Biberfeld
VP: Bob Cruz
VP: Frank Degratto
VP: Thomas Doherty
VP: Walter J Fahey
VP: Maxine Fielding
VP: Douglas Jablon
VP: Brigid Klein
VP: Joyce Leahy

D-U-N-S 00-958-4996 IMP
MAIN ELECTRIC SUPPLY CO
3600 W Segerstrom Ave, Santa Ana, CA 92704-6408
Tel (949) 833-3052 Founded/Ownrshp 1946
Sales 350.8MM^E EMP 300
SIC 5063 Electrical apparatus & equipment
Pr: Scott R Germann
*COO: Paul Vowels
*CFO: Karen Morris
Dept Mgr: Christine Baeza
Brnch Mgr: Carlos Balencia
Brnch Mgr: Maurice Orozco
Brnch Mgr: Rob Siler
Brnch Mgr: Carlos Valencia
Genl Mgr: Curtis Slocum
Dir IT: Mark Arnold
Dir IT: Rod Knight

D-U-N-S 06-122-0377
MAIN EVENT ENTERTAINMENT LP
6652 Pinecrest Dr Ste 100, Plano, TX 75024-2940
Tel (972) 406-2600 Founded/Ownrshp 1998
Sales 64.5MM^E EMP 1,000
SIC 7929 5813 5812 Entertainers; Drinking places; Eating places
CEO: Charlie Keegan
CFO: Chandra McCormack
CFO: Dough Novak
VP: Walter Lovell
Creative D: Dana Jones
Genl Mgr: Jennifer Donovan
Tech Mgr: James Morningstar
Tech Mgr: Dave Sawer
Opers Mgr: Jason Calotis
Opers Mgr: Tj Leonard
VP Mktg: Sherri Landry

MAIN EXECUTIVE OFFICE
See PARISH OF JEFFERSON

D-U-N-S 17-344-7855
MAIN LINE HEALTH INC
MAIN LINE HLTH HOSP OPERATIONS
(Suby of MAIN LINE HEALTH SYSTEM) ★
3803 West Chester Pike # 250, Newtown Square, PA 19073-2336
Tel (484) 565-1644 Founded/Ownrshp 1985
Sales 1.6MMM EMP 5,840^E
SIC 8741 Administrative management
Pr: John J Lynch III
*CFO: Mike Buongiorno
Sr VP: Donald C Arthur
*Sr VP: Brian T Corbett
Sr VP: Brian Corbett
Sr VP: Lydia Hammer
Sr VP: Kenneth Kirbey
*Sr VP: Kenneth E Kirby
*Sr VP: Joann M Magnatta
Sr VP: Eileen McAnally
Sr VP: Sarah A Peterson
*Sr VP: Barbara Wadsworth
*Sr VP: Paul Yakulis
VP: Joel A Port
Exec: Walter Kanhofer
Dir Rx: Richard Centafont

D-U-N-S 96-401-4278
MAIN LINE HEALTH SYSTEM
240 N Radnor Chester Rd, Radnor, PA 19087-5170
Tel (610) 225-6200 Founded/Ownrshp 1995
Sales 1.6MMM EMP 17,485
Accts Pricewaterhousecoopers Llp P
SIC 5999 8059 8361 8062 Hearing aids; Personal care home, with health care; Rehabilitation center, residential: health care incidental; Hospital, AMA approved residency
Pr: Jack Lynch
Chf Mktg O: Stanton Smullens
*Sr VP: Thomas Mendicino
CIO: James Hauck
CIO: Deborah Krau

D-U-N-S 10-963-1929
MAIN LINE HEALTHCARE
2 Industrial Blvd Ste 400, Paoli, PA 19301-1645
Tel (610) 648-1644 Founded/Ownrshp 1985
Sales 231.7MM EMP 760
SIC 8099 8011 Medical services organization; Physicians' office, including specialists
CEO: Michael Buongiorno
*Pr: Eric Mankin MD

MAIN LINE HLTH HOSP OPERATIONS
See MAIN LINE HEALTH INC

D-U-N-S 07-548-4121
MAIN LINE HOSPITALS INC
BRYN MAWR HOSPITAL
(Suby of MAIN LINE HEALTH SYSTEM) ★
130 S Bryn Mawr Ave, Bryn Mawr, PA 19010-3121
Tel (610) 526-3000 Founded/Ownrshp 1892
Sales 1.2MMM EMP 10,800
SIC 8062 General medical & surgical hospitals
CEO: Leland I White
Dir Vol: Joanne Marciante
*Pr: Andrea Gilbert
*CEO: Jack Lynch
*CFO: Michael J Buongiorno
*Sr VP: Brian T Corbett
VP: Michael Bouongiono
VP: Joel Port
VP: Harm Scherpbier
VP: Karen Thomas
VP: Chris Torres
Dir Risk M: Denise Murphy
Dir Lab: Glen Bull
Dir Rad: Emma Simpson

D-U-N-S 96-939-9398
MAIN LINE SERVICES
950 E Haverford Rd # 110, Bryn Mawr, PA 19010-3851
Tel (484) 337-8480 Founded/Ownrshp 2011
Sales 122.8MM EMP 4^E
Accts Pricewaterhousecoopers Llp Ph
SIC 8011 Medical centers

D-U-N-S 07-963-5712
MAIN STEEL LLC
2200 Pratt Blvd, Elk Grove Village, IL 60007-5917
Tel (847) 916-1220 Founded/Ownrshp 2014
Sales 153.6MM^E EMP 234
SIC 3312 Stainless steel
CEO: Tom Modrowski
*CFO: Paul Patek
VP Sls: James Henry

MAIN STREET AMERICA GROUP, THE
See NGM INSURANCE CO

MAIN STREET AMERICA GROUP, THE
See MAIN STREET AMERICA GROUP INC

D-U-N-S 80-040-5289
MAIN STREET AMERICA GROUP INC
MAIN STREET AMERICA GROUP, THE
4601 Touchton Rd E # 3300, Jacksonville, FL 32246-4485
Tel (904) 642-3000 Founded/Ownrshp 2005

Sales NA *EMP* 983^E
SIC 6411 Insurance agents, brokers & service
Pr: Thomas M Van Berkel
Pr: Chris Cox
Pr: Tiffany Daly
Pr: Joe Meholic
Pr: Dave Randle
COO: Steve Peeters
CFO: Amy Frederick
Treas: Ed Kuhl
Assoc VP: Deb Jansen
Assoc VP: Lisa Murman
Assoc VP: Ron Profaizer
Sr VP: Jeff Kusch
VP: Brian Beggs
VP: Mark Berger
VP: Dean Dorman
VP: Doug Eden
VP: Bruce Fox
VP: Tom Frazier
VP: Dan Gaynor
VP: Dave Medvidofsky
VP: David S Medvidofsky
Board of Directors: Chris Doerr

D-U-N-S 84-006-2905
▲ MAIN STREET CAPITAL CORP
1300 Post Oak Blvd, Houston, TX 77056-3043
Tel (713) 350-6000 *Founded/Ownrshp* 2007
Sales 143.2MM *EMP* 38
Accts Grant Thornton Llp Dallas Te
Tkr Sym MAIN *Exch* NYS
SIC 6211 Investment firm, general brokerage
Ch Bd: Vincent D Foster
Pr: Dwayne L Hyzak
CFO: Brent D Smith
Chf Cred: Curtis L Hartman
Ex VP: Rodger A Stout
VP: Shannon D Martin
VP: Katherine S Silva
Mng Dir: Travis L Haley
Mng Dir: Nicholas T Meserve
CIO: David L Magdol
Mktg Dir: Jessica Hart
Board of Directors: Michael Appling Jr, Joseph E Canon, Arthur L French, J Kevin Griffin, John E Jackson, Brian E Lane, Stephen B Solcher

D-U-N-S 79-324-8241
MAIN STREET NATURAL GAS INC
104 Townpark Dr Nw, Kennesaw, GA 30144-5508
Tel (770) 590-1000 *Founded/Ownrshp* 2006
Sales 135.0MM *EMP* 50
SIC 4922 Natural gas transmission
CEO: Arthur C Corbin
**CFO:* Susan G Reeves

D-U-N-S 13-105-6707
MAIN STREET OPERATING CO INC
(*Suby of* HARDAWAY GROUP INC) ★
615 Main St, Nashville, TN 37206-3603
Tel (615) 254-5461 *Founded/Ownrshp* 1986
Sales 93.5MM^E *EMP* 238
SIC 1542 1541 1521 6531 Commercial & office building, new construction; Industrial buildings & warehouses; New construction, single-family houses; Real estate managers
Ch Bd: Stan H Hardaway
**Sec:* Kerry P Sloan
VP: Linda Guinn CPA

D-U-N-S 10-544-6327
MAINE BEHAVIORAL HEALTHCARE
SPRING HARBOR HOSPITAL
(*Suby of* MAINEHEALTH) ★
123 Andover Rd, Westbrook, ME 04092-3848
Tel (207) 761-2200 *Founded/Ownrshp* 1999
Sales 67.7MM *EMP* 1,100
Accts Mainehealth Portland Me
SIC 8062 General medical & surgical hospitals
Pr: Dennis King
CEO: Patrica Davis
COO: Mary Jane Krebs
CFO: Mike Abbatiello
Ex VP: Greg A Bowers
Dir Rx: Gary Roy
Nurse Mgr: Nancy Masteller
CIO: Robert Rague
CTO: Marjorie Wiggins
HC Dir: Mary Jean Mork

D-U-N-S 18-636-1127
MAINE COMMUNITY COLLEGE SYSTEM
MCCS
323 State St, Augusta, ME 04330-7131
Tel (207) 629-4000 *Founded/Ownrshp* 1986
Sales 58.6MM^E *EMP* 1,200
Accts Baker Newman & Noyes Portland
SIC 8222 Junior colleges & technical institutes
Pr: John Fitzsimmons
**CFO:* David Daigler
Ex Dir: Carolanne Dube
IT Man: Mary Lapointe

D-U-N-S 80-904-5594
MAINE DEPARTMENT OF HEALTH AND HUMAN SERVICES
(*Suby of* EXECUTIVE OFFICE OF STATE OF MAINE) ★
221 State St, Augusta, ME 04330-6846
Tel (207) 287-1716 *Founded/Ownrshp* 1975
Sales NA *EMP* 2,800
SIC 9441 9431 Administration of social & manpower programs; ; Administration of public health programs;
**CEO:* William Boeschenstein

D-U-N-S 80-904-5966
MAINE DEPARTMENT OF TRANSPORTATION
(*Suby of* EXECUTIVE OFFICE OF STATE OF MAINE) ★
16 State House Sta, Augusta, ME 04333-0016
Tel (207) 624-3000 *Founded/Ownrshp* 1972
Sales NA *EMP* 2,500
SIC 9621 Regulation, administration of transportation;

D-U-N-S 01-901-5304 IMP
MAINE DRILLING AND BLASTING INC
544 Brunswick Ave, Gardiner, ME 04345-6026
Tel (207) 582-4300 *Founded/Ownrshp* 1966
Sales 137.4MM^E *EMP* 300
SIC 1629 Blasting contractor, except building demolition
Pr: William D Purington
**Treas:* Timothy R Maynard
**VP:* Ted Purington Jr
VP: Daniel Werner
Div Mgr: Travis Martzall
MIS Dir: Troy Beaulieu
Dir IT: Dale A Thomas
IT Man: Ken Smith
Web Prj Mg: Bill Purrington
Sfty Mgr: Bruce Lawler
Opers Mgr: Mike Bell

D-U-N-S 79-806-2881
MAINE EMPLOYERS MUTUAL INSURANCE CO
MEMIC
261 Commercial St, Portland, ME 04101-4622
Tel (207) 791-3300 *Founded/Ownrshp* 1993
Sales NA *EMP* 250
Accts Johnson Lambert Llp Atlanta
SIC 6331 Workers' compensation insurance
Pr: John T Leonard
**Sr VP:* Michael Bourque
Sr VP: Donald V Hale
**Sr VP:* Catherine Lamson
Sr VP: John Marr
**Sr VP:* Robert S Mc Mann
VP: Dan Cote
Exec: Rebecca Leclair
Dir IT: Steve Hughes
Info Man: David Fournier
Sales Asso: Stephen Badger

D-U-N-S 11-207-6513
MAINE GENERAL MEDICAL CENTER INC
149 North St, Waterville, ME 04901-4974
Tel (207) 872-4190 *Founded/Ownrshp* 1991
Sales 166.7MM^E *EMP* 3,000
SIC 8011 Medical centers
Pr: Scott Bullock

D-U-N-S 07-173-2663
MAINE MEDICAL CENTER (ME)
22 Bramhall St, Portland, ME 04102-3175
Tel (207) 662-0111 *Founded/Ownrshp* 1870
Sales 1.0MMM *EMP* 5,000
SIC 8062 8071 6513 Hospital, AMA approved residency; Medical laboratories; Apartment building operators
Pr: Richard Petersen
V Ch: Christopher W Emmons
COO: Jeffrey D Sanders
Sr VP: Mark A Harris
VP: Peter W Bates
VP: Barry Blumenfeld
VP: Wayne Clark
VP: George L Higgins
VP: Ann Keillor
VP: Chausse Paul
VP: Maureen Van Benthuysen
Dir Lab: Marcia Waterman
Assoc Dir: Daniel Spratt
Dir Soc: Cindy Tack
Dir Rx: Brian Marden
Dir Env Sv: Charlie Papa

D-U-N-S 08-318-1347
MAINE MUNICIPAL ASSOCIATION
60 Community Dr, Augusta, ME 04330-9486
Tel (207) 621-2645 *Founded/Ownrshp* 1936
Sales 114.8MM^E *EMP* 112
SIC 8611 Business associations
CEO: Christopher Lockwood
**CFO:* Martin Hanish
CFO: Gordon Tibbetts
Treas: Pamela Griffith
Trst: Jolan Ippolito
Ex VP: Miles Theeman
Sr VP: Kenneth Payne
Dir Bus: Tamara Butts

MAINE MUTUAL GROUP
See MMG INSURANCE CO

D-U-N-S 06-705-3512 IMP
MAINE OXY-ACETYLENE SUPPLY CO
ATLANTIC SAFETY AND SUPPLY
22 Albiston Way, Auburn, ME 04210-4869
Tel (207) 784-5788 *Founded/Ownrshp* 1929
Sales 92.8MM^E *EMP* 200
SIC 5169 5084 Industrial gases; Welding machinery & equipment
Pr: Dan Guerin
**Prin:* John Conrad
**Prin:* Carolyn Flanigan

D-U-N-S 08-687-7115
MAINE STATE HOUSING AUTHORITY (ME)
353 Water St, Augusta, ME 04330-6113
Tel (207) 626-4600 *Founded/Ownrshp* 1969
Sales NA *EMP* 123
Accts Baker Newman & Noyes Llc Por
SIC 6162 Mortgage bankers
Ex Dir: John Gallagher
Pt: Lisa Lavigne
**Treas:* Thomas Cary
Bd of Dir: Sheryl Gregory
Bd of Dir: Elizabeth Horning
Bd of Dir: David G Lemoine
Off Mgr: Eric Winne
Off Admin: Jody Rollins

MAINE SUNDAY TELEGRAM
See MTM OLDCO INC

D-U-N-S 01-058-8499
MAINE TOWNSHIP HIGH SCHOOL DISTRICT 207
1177 S Dee Rd, Park Ridge, IL 60068-4379
Tel (847) 696-3600 *Founded/Ownrshp* 1902
Sales 155.9MM *EMP* 975
Accts Mcgladrey Llp Chicago Illino
SIC 8211 High school, junior or senior
**Pr:* Margaret McGrath
**VP:* Donna Pellar
Pr Dir: Dave Berry
Teacher Pr: Debra Michalik
Psych: Katelyn Pantke
Psych: Cynthia Perez
Psych: Nicole Rinaldi

D-U-N-S 04-511-2679
MAINE TURNPIKE AUTHORITY
2360 Congress St Ste 1, Portland, ME 04102-1999
Tel (207) 842-4030 *Founded/Ownrshp* 1977
Sales 127.0MM *EMP* 340
Accts Macpage Llc South Portland M
SIC 4785 Toll road operation
Pr: Paul E Violette

D-U-N-S 10-119-1526
MAINE VETERANS HOMES
460 Civic Center Dr, Augusta, ME 04330-7902
Tel (207) 622-0075 *Founded/Ownrshp* 1977
Sales 92.2MM *EMP* 1,000
SIC 8052 Intermediate care facilities
CEO: Kelley Kash
**CFO:* Robert St Pierre

D-U-N-S 15-971-9582
MAINEGENERAL HEALTH
35 Medical Center Pkwy, Augusta, ME 04330-8160
Tel (207) 626-1000 *Founded/Ownrshp* 1997
Sales 423.2MM *EMP* 3,800
Accts Baker Newman Noyes Portland
SIC 8062 General medical & surgical hospitals
Pr: Charles Hays
**COO:* Paul Stein
**CFO:* Michael Koziol
CFO: Kenneth Payne
Sr VP: Kash Basavappa
VP: Crowley Barbara
VP: Wendy Manter
Dir Risk M: Elliot Sarantakos
Nurse Mgr: Tania Dawson
IT Man: Dan Burgess
IT Man: Marcia Feaby

D-U-N-S 07-746-1754
MAINEGENERAL MEDICAL CENTER
(*Suby of* MAINEGENERAL HEALTH) ★
35 Medical Center Pkwy, Augusta, ME 04330-8160
Tel (207) 626-1289 *Founded/Ownrshp* 1997
Sales 378.7MM *EMP* 2,200
Accts Baker Newman & Noyes Portlan
SIC 8062 General medical & surgical hospitals
CEO: Chuck Hays
Chf Rad: Jonathan J Hallenbeck
Ofcr: Jane Belanye
**Ofcr:* Charles Hays
Ofcr: Georgia Kosciusko
Sr VP: Gail Evans
Exec: Stephen Walsh
Dir Risk M: Elliott Sarantakos
Dir: Michelle Ayotte
Comm Dir: Paul Tobey
Dir Rx: Andrea Gimpel-Blanchar
Comm Man: Barbara Martin

D-U-N-S 85-858-2372
MAINEHEALTH
110 Free St, Portland, ME 04101-3576
Tel (207) 661-7001 *Founded/Ownrshp* 1987
Sales 59.4MM *EMP* 2,100
Accts Mainehealth Rectortown Va
SIC 8741 Hospital management; Nursing & personal care facility management
Pr: William Caron
**Treas:* Frank G McGinty
Trst: Richard L Roy
Chf Inves: John Heye
Ex VP: Frank McGinty
Ex VP: Albert Swallow
VP: Paul Chausse
**VP:* Mark Harris
Adm Dir: Marsha Waterman
Genl Mgr: Bobbi Shirley
Off Mgr: Joanne Sarlo
Board of Directors: Hanson D Louis

D-U-N-S 00-225-1197
MAINES PAPER & FOOD SERVICE INC (NY)
101 Broome Corporate Pkwy, Conklin, NY 13748-1507
Tel (607) 779-1200 *Founded/Ownrshp* 1919, 1960
Sales 1.9MMM^E *EMP* 1,000
SIC 5142 5113 5141 5087 5147 5146 Packaged frozen goods; Industrial & personal service paper; Groceries, general line; Janitors' supplies; Meats, fresh; Seafoods
Co-Ch Bd: David Maines
**Pr:* Christopher Mellon
**Co-Ch Bd:* William Maines
VP: Stephanie Lacoe
VP: Jeff Sault
VP: Steve Stoner
Dir Bus: Bradley Hurlburt
Dir Bus: Brooks Teeter
Rgnl Mgr: Dan Rosenthal
Admn Mgr: Christina Phillips
Trfc Dir: Anna Shafer

D-U-N-S 06-461-8572 IMP/EXP
MAINFREIGHT INC
(*Suby of* MAINFREIGHT LIMITED)
1400 Glenn Curtiss St, Carson, CA 90746-4030
Tel (310) 900-1974 *Founded/Ownrshp* 2007
Sales 310.8MM^E *EMP* 310
SIC 4731 Domestic freight forwarding; Foreign freight forwarding
Pr: John Hepworth
**CEO:* Christopher Coppersmith
**VP:* John Eshuis
Sls Mgr: Michelle Merino

D-U-N-S 62-691-6779
MAINLINE INFORMATION SYSTEMS INC
1700 Summit Lake Dr, Tallahassee, FL 32317-7942
Tel (850) 219-5000 *Founded/Ownrshp* 1989
Sales 479.8MM *EMP* 568
Accts Kpmg Llp Jacksonville Fl
SIC 7373 7379 7371 Value-added resellers, computer systems; Computer related consulting services; Computer software systems analysis & design, custom
Pr: Richard Kearney
Treas: Joseph P Elebash
Ex VP: John R McCarthy
Sr VP: Sherrie E Kishbaugh
VP: Sandy Carter
VP: Mary Debartolo
VP: Ray Lee
VP: Greg Schneider
Admn Mgr: Charles E Vianey
Snr Sftwr: Kenneth Dean
Snr Sftwr: Raymond Horton

D-U-N-S 10-724-1895
MAINSCAPE INC
13418 Britton Park Rd, Fishers, IN 46038-3583
Tel (317) 577-3155 *Founded/Ownrshp* 1985
Sales 99.9MM^E *EMP* 500
SIC 0781 Landscape counseling & planning
Pr: Mark W Forsythe
Pr: Lee White
**Treas:* Bruce H Torrance
**VP:* Zygmunt Mazanowski III
IT Man: Jill Dougherty
VP Opers: Nate Hyde
Opers Mgr: Samuel Reimold

D-U-N-S 05-499-9933
■ MAINSOURCE BANK
(*Suby of* MAINSOURCE FINANCIAL GROUP INC) ★
201 N Broadway St, Greensburg, IN 47240-1701
Tel (812) 663-4711 *Founded/Ownrshp* 1991
Sales NA *EMP* 388
SIC 6035 Savings institutions, federally chartered
Pr: Daryl R Tressler
Pr: Daniel Cobb
Dir IT: Philip Dickey

D-U-N-S 15-060-3892
▲ MAINSOURCE FINANCIAL GROUP INC
2105 N State Road 3 Byp, Greensburg, IN 47240-9539
Tel (812) 663-0157 *Founded/Ownrshp* 1982
Sales NA *EMP* 841^E
Tkr Sym MSFG *Exch* NGS
SIC 6022 State commercial banks; State trust companies accepting deposits, commercial
Ch Bd: Archie M Brown Jr
CFO: James M Anderson
Chf Cred: Chris Bower
Board of Directors: Charles J Thayer, Kathleen L Bardwell, William G Barron, Vincent A Berta, D J Hines, Erin P Hoeflinger, Thomas M O'brien, Lawrence R Rueff, John G Seale, John T Smith

MAINTECH ACQUISITION
See TRIANGLE SERVICES INC

MAINTENANCE DEPARTMENT
See LEXINGTON SCHOOL DISTRICT 5

D-U-N-S 09-067-7436
MAINTENANCE STAFF INC
122 W 8th St, Long Beach, CA 90813-4371
Tel (562) 493-3982 *Founded/Ownrshp* 1994
Sales 18.0MM^E *EMP* 2,600
SIC 7349 Janitorial service, contract basis
Pr: Vivian M Frahm

D-U-N-S 78-444-0484 IMP
MAINTENANCE SUPPLY HEADQUARTERS LP
12315 Parc Crest Dr # 100, Stafford, TX 77477-2408
Tel (281) 530-6300 *Founded/Ownrshp* 2006
Sales 118.7MM^E *EMP* 65^E
SIC 5072 Hardware
Mng Pt: Richard Penick
Pt: Terri Moll
Pt: David Ryle
Dir IT: George Juarez
Natl Sales: Todd Mancini
Natl Sales: Wes Williams
Sls Mgr: Paul Brown
Sales Asso: Tonya Presby

D-U-N-S 03-395-6184
MAINVUE HOMES LLC
(*Suby of* CCX) ★
1110 112th Ave Ne Ste 202, Bellevue, WA 98004-4571
Tel (425) 646-4022 *Founded/Ownrshp* 2011
Sales 150.0MM *EMP* 90
SIC 7389 1521 Interior design services; Single-family housing construction
IT Man: Randy Hutton

D-U-N-S 03-365-0576
MAIPF
17456 N Laurel Park Dr # 130, Livonia, MI 48152-3981
Tel (734) 464-1100 *Founded/Ownrshp* 2010
Sales NA *EMP* 4^E
SIC 6331 Automobile insurance
Prin: Terri Miller

D-U-N-S 80-011-9992
■ MAJESCO
(*Suby of* MASTEK LIMITED)
412 Mount Kemble Ave 110c, Morristown, NJ 07960-6675
Tel (973) 461-5200 *Founded/Ownrshp* 1992
Sales 113.3MM *EMP* 2,134
Tkr Sym MJCO *Exch* ASE
SIC 7372 7371 Prepackaged software; Computer software development
Pr: Ketan Mehta
**Ch Bd:* Arun K Maheshwari
COO: Edward Ossie
CFO: Farid Kazani
Ex VP: William Freitag
Ex VP: Chad Hersh
Ex VP: Prateek Kumar
Ex VP: Tilakraj Panjabi
Ex VP: Manish D Shah

D-U-N-S 83-036-1551
MAJESTIC HOLDCO LLC
1 Buffington Harbor Dr, Gary, IN 46406-3000
Tel (702) 388-2400 *Founded/Ownrshp* 1996

Sales 85.4MME EMP 2,750E
SIC 7011 Casino hotel
CEO: Peter M Liguori

D-U-N-S 01-047-0388
MAJESTIC MISSISSIPPI LLC
BARDEN MISSISSIPPI GAMING, LLC
(Suby of MAJESTIC STAR CASINO LLC) ★
711 Lucky Ln, Robinsonville, MS 38664-9141
Tel (662) 363-5825 Founded/Ownrshp 2001
Sales 44.7MME EMP 1,175
SIC 7011 Casino hotel
CEO: Don H Barden
Pr: Patrick Lowery
COO: Kirk Saylor
*CFO: Jon S Bennett
VP: Adolph Lepre
CIO: Michael Flowers
IT Man: Marilyn Young
Advt Dir: Sheila Stafford
Mktg Dir: Amy Belk
Mktg Dir: Sheila Stansford

MAJESTIC STAR CASINO
See BARDEN COMPANIES INC

D-U-N-S 83-798-0077
MAJESTIC STAR CASINO LLC
(Suby of MAJESTIC HOLDCO LLC) ★
5524 S Fort Apache Rd # 120, Las Vegas, NV 89148-7669
Tel (702) 386-0226 Founded/Ownrshp 2001
Sales 85.4MME EMP 2,700E
SIC 7011 Casino hotel
Ch Bd: Cezar Froelich
Mng Pt: John Risner
CEO: Peter Liguori
CFO: Jon Bennett
Exec: Jack Binion
Genl Mgr: David S Schugar
Board of Directors: Patrick R Cruzen, Michelle R Sherman Nicki, John A Obrien

MAJESTIC STEEL SERVICE
See MAJESTIC STEEL USA INC

D-U-N-S 09-497-2056 IMP/EXP
MAJESTIC STEEL USA INC
MAJESTIC STEEL SERVICE
31099 Chagrin Blvd # 150, Cleveland, OH 44124-5930
Tel (440) 786-2666 Founded/Ownrshp 1979
Sales 255.8MME EMP 278
SIC 5051 Sheets, metal; Structural shapes, iron or steel
CEO: Dennis Leebow
*Pr: Todd Leebow
COO: Aaron Housiaux
*CFO: Susan Suvak
Chf Mktg O: Steve Chiles
*Ex VP: Jonathan Leebow
Sales Asso: Ed Sweeney

MAJESTIC THEATER
See GETTYSBURG COLLEGE

D-U-N-S 94-724-5288 EXP
MAJOR AUTOMOTIVE COMPANIES INC
4340 Northern Blvd, Long Island City, NY 11101-1020
Tel (718) 625-6753 Founded/Ownrshp 1995
Sales 96.5MME EMP 513
SIC 5511 Automobiles, new & used
Ch Bd: Bruce Bendell

D-U-N-S 18-612-4954 IMP
MAJOR BRANDS INC
6701 Southwest Ave, Saint Louis, MO 63143-2623
Tel (314) 645-1843 Founded/Ownrshp 1988
Sales 195.6MME EMP 632
SIC 5182 5181 Wine & distilled beverages; Beer & ale
CEO: Susan B McCollum
*Pr: Robert N Epsten
COO: Randy Simpson
*CFO: Jim Havel
*Treas: Thomas Schawang
VP: Rau Danny
VP: Mark Quinn
*VP: David Vittor
Exec: Cyndi Nelson
Exec: Michelle Reichardt
Mktg Dir: Fred Nachbar

D-U-N-S 00-790-8312
MAJOR EAGLE INC
MC DONALD WHOLESALE COMPANY
2350 W Broadway, Eugene, OR 97402-2704
Tel (541) 345-8421 Founded/Ownrshp 1927
Sales 207.2MME EMP 330
Accts Isler Cpa Eugene Or
SIC 5181 5141 5194 5142 Beer & other fermented malt liquors; Groceries, general line; Smoking tobacco; Packaged frozen goods
Ch: Weir W Mc Donald
*Pr: Charles R Huey
*CFO: Gary Thomsen
*VP: Steve Hayes
*VP: Jack Willis
*Prin: Lote Mason
Sales Asso: Tom Ocumpaugh
Sales Asso: Shawn Wojack

D-U-N-S 07-597-1689
MAJOR HOSPITAL
150 W Washington St, Shelbyville, IN 46176-1236
Tel (317) 392-3211 Founded/Ownrshp 1930
Sales 115.2MM EMP 950
SIC 8062 8011 General medical & surgical hospitals; Offices & clinics of medical doctors
Pr: Jack Horner
*CFO: Ralph Mercuri
CFO: Robin Nichols
Bd of Dir: Nancy E Dayhoff
Exec: Lloyd Lewis
Dir Lab: Mark Andrews
Dir Lab: Kimberly Six
Doctor: Carrie Lipp
Doctor: E Miller
Doctor: Danielle D Turnak
Board of Directors: Richard Bishopp, Nancy Dayhoff, Richard Hidy, Dorine Wolsiefer

D-U-N-S 07-685-1476
MAJOR LEAGUE BASEBALL ENTERPRISES INC
M L B
245 Park Ave, New York, NY 10167-0002
Tel (212) 931-7500 Founded/Ownrshp 1915
Sales 289.9MME EMP 300
Accts Ernst & Young Us Llp Indianap
SIC 4833 8699 Television broadcasting stations; Athletic organizations
*Pr: Bob Bowman
*COO: Tony Petitti
CFO: Jonathan D Mariner
*CFO: Bob Starkey
*Chf Cred: Pat Courtney
Ex VP: Rob Manfred
Ex VP: Frank Robinson
VP: Aixa Garcia
VP: Mark Haden
VP: John Quinones
VP: Jim Small
VP: Christopher Tully
Dir Soc: Ashley Scherer

D-U-N-S 07-885-8115
MAJOR LEAGUE BASEBALL PROPERTIES INC
M L B
(Suby of M L B) ★
245 Park Ave Fl 34, New York, NY 10167-0002
Tel (212) 931-7800 Founded/Ownrshp 1966
Sales 97.9MME EMP 150
SIC 6794 4833 8748 Copyright buying & licensing; Television broadcasting stations; Publishing consultant
Pr: Timothy J Brosnan
*Ch Bd: Robert Bowman
Ex VP: Jonathan Mariner
*VP: Thomas C Brasuell
VP: Howard Smith
*VP: Kathleen Torres
Software D: Gene Zilberstein
Genl Couns: Ethan Orlinsky

MAJOR PHARMACEUTICALS
See HARVARD DRUG GROUP L L C

D-U-N-S 01-239-7170 IMP
MAJOR WORLD CHEVROLET LLC
4340 Northern Blvd, Long Island City, NY 11101-1020
Tel (718) 937-3700 Founded/Ownrshp 2014
Sales 91.7MME EMP 250E
SIC 5511 7515 7538 5521 New & used car dealers; Passenger car leasing; General automotive repair shops; Used car dealers
Counsel: Eric Kelpz

MAKALLON LA JOLLA PROPERTIES
See MAKAR PROPERTIES LLC

D-U-N-S 12-229-4028
MAKAR ANAHEIM LLC
ANAHEIM HILTON & TOWERS
777 W Convention Way, Anaheim, CA 92802-3425
Tel (714) 740-4431 Founded/Ownrshp 2007
Sales 25.9MME EMP 1,200
SIC 7011 Hotels
CFO: Bruce Hayden
Genl Mgr: Shaun Robinson
Dir IT: Tracy Hansen
Sls Mgr: Laurie Calaunan

D-U-N-S 03-838-9305
MAKAR PROPERTIES LLC
MAKALLON LA JOLLA PROPERTIES
4100 Macarthur Blvd # 150, Newport Beach, CA 92660-2063
Tel (949) 255-1100 Founded/Ownrshp 2001
Sales 357.1MME EMP 1,200E
SIC 6552 1542 Land subdividers & developers, commercial; Commercial & office building, new construction
CEO: Paul P Makarechian
*Pr: Peter Ciaccia
*COO: Douglas Kiel
Ex VP: Sandy Weissbard
Mktg Dir: Laura Foster
Counsel: Ira Lebovic

D-U-N-S 05-514-2751
MAKE CORP (IL)
1 S 450 Smmit Ave Ste 165, Oakbrook Terrace, IL 60181
Tel (630) 376-0646 Founded/Ownrshp 1981
Sales 22.7MME EMP 192E
Accts Kutchins Robbins & Diamond Lt
SIC 7379 Computer related consulting services
Pr: Karen Wilson
*CFO: Steve Wilson
VP: Charlie Macconnachie

MAKE-A-WISH, AMERICA
See MAKE-A-WISH FOUNDATION OF AMERICA

D-U-N-S 62-475-9932
MAKE-A-WISH FOUNDATION OF AMERICA
MAKE-A-WISH, AMERICA
4742 N 24th St Ste 400, Phoenix, AZ 85016-4862
Tel (602) 279-9474 Founded/Ownrshp 1983
Sales 89.1MM EMP 118
Accts Cliftonlarsonallen Llp Phoeni
SIC 8322 Children's aid society
Pr: David Williams
Dir Vol: Stephanie Smith
Pr: Rose Farr
COO: Dennis Covelli
COO: Pam Keough
*COO: Kurt Kroemer
CFO: Della Cherchia
CFO: Ed Kendall
*CFO: Paul Melhorne
CFO: John Stetner
Bd of Dir: Steven Hill
Ofcr: Kimberly Deardorff
Ofcr: Czerina Garcia
Ofcr: Gabrielle Peterson
VP: Paul Allvin
VP: Amy Alvarez
VP: Tracey T Burnett

VP: Pamela Clark
VP: Steven Henderson
VP: Sylvia Hopkins
VP: Paul Kirchgraber

D-U-N-S 01-596-7125 IMP
MAKERBOT INDUSTRIES LLC
(Suby of MOJO) ★
1 Metrotech Ctr Fl 21, Brooklyn, NY 11201-3949
Tel (347) 334-6800 Founded/Ownrshp 2009
Sales 90.2MME EMP 300
SIC 3621 3625 5084 Motors & generators; Actuators, industrial; Industrial machinery & equipment
CEO: Jenny Lawton
VP: Carla Echevarria
Ex Dir: Joanne Swanson
Snr Sftwr: Quynh Dinh
QA Dir: Ray Cheng
IT Man: Jason Friske
Web Dev: Tony Buser
Web Dev: Umar Khokhar
Opers Mgr: Matthew Jones
Plnt Mgr: Diana Pincus
Ql Cn Mgr: Alyssa Coligado

D-U-N-S 02-855-0564 IMP
■ **MAKERS OF KAL INC**
HEALTHWAY
(Suby of NUTRACEUTICAL INTERNATIONAL CORP) ★
1500 Kearns Blvd, Park City, UT 84060-7226
Tel (435) 655-6000 Founded/Ownrshp 1995
Sales 115.2MME EMP 450
SIC 5122 Vitamins & minerals
Pr: Bruce Hough
*CEO: Frank W Gay II
*CFO: Cory McQueen

D-U-N-S 78-588-6284 IMP/EXP
MAKHTESHIM AGAN OF NORTH AMERICA INC
ADAMA US
(Suby of ADAMA AGRICULTURE B.V.)
3120 Highwoods Blvd # 100, Raleigh, NC 27604-0012
Tel (919) 256-9300 Founded/Ownrshp 1991
Sales 200.0MM EMP 210
SIC 2879 Agricultural chemicals
Pr: Rob Williams
*CFO: Craig Lupton-Smith
VP: Carlos Danilowicz
Snr Mgr: Hollie Altice
Snr Mgr: Dennis Fuller
Snr Mgr: Kevin Hutcheson
Snr Mgr: Ellen Mueller
Snr Mgr: Austin Tinsley

D-U-N-S 00-423-4183 IMP/EXP
MAKINO INC (OH)
(Suby of MAKINO MILLING MACHINE CO., LTD.)
7680 Innovation Way, Mason, OH 45040-9695
Tel (513) 573-7200 Founded/Ownrshp 1887
Sales 191.4MME EMP 646
SIC 3541 Machine tools, metal cutting type
Pr: Donald Lane
Pr: Thomas Clark
Pr: Robert Henry
VP: Ronald Brown
*VP: Bob Henry
VP: Tom Slager
IT Man: Chris Voniheim
Mktg Dir: Craig Voss
Mktg Mgr: Mark Rentschler
Snr Mgr: Laura Klinger
Snr Mgr: David Walton

D-U-N-S 18-810-0010 IMP/EXP
MAKITA CORP OF AMERICA
(Suby of MAKITA USA INC) ★
2650 Buford Hwy, Buford, GA 30518-6045
Tel (770) 932-2901 Founded/Ownrshp 1984
Sales 112.1MME EMP 400
SIC 3546 Power-driven handtools
Pr: Minio Owzeki
*VP: Tim Donovan
Plnt Mgr: Larry Peck
Manager: Darnell D Nunez
Manager: Brett Rose

D-U-N-S 07-271-5428 IMP/EXP
MAKITA USA INC
(Suby of MAKITA CORPORATION)
14930 Northam St, La Mirada, CA 90638-5753
Tel (714) 522-8088 Founded/Ownrshp 1970
Sales 310.3MME EMP 560
SIC 5072 Power handtools
CEO: Hiroshi Tsujimura
Sr VP: Richszrd Chapman
*VP: Rich Chapman
*VP: Ron Schachter
VP: Jonathan Speaks
VP: Mack Tokui
Dist Mgr: Robert Shelton
Sls&Mrk Ex: Porter Lilly
Advt Mgr: Bill Austin
Manager: Alfred Alvarez
Manager: Mike Gilbert

D-U-N-S 17-523-9677
■ **MAKO SURGICAL CORP**
(Suby of STRYKER CORP) ★
2555 Davie Rd, Davie, FL 33317-7424
Tel (866) 647-6256 Founded/Ownrshp 2013
Sales 110.8MME EMP 436
SIC 3842 Orthopedic appliances; Trusses, orthopedic & surgical
Pr: Maurice R Ferre
*CFO: Fritz L Laporte
*Sr VP: Menashe R Frank
Sr VP: Christopher R Marrus
Sr VP: Christopher Marrus
Sr VP: Steven J Nunes
VP: Louis Arata
VP: Ivan Delevic
VP: Ivan Develic
VP: Larry Gibbons
VP: Duncan Moffat

D-U-N-S 06-421-6823
MAL ENTERPRISES INC
LAWRENCE BROTHERS
300 Hailey St, Sweetwater, TX 79556-4774
Tel (325) 236-6351 Founded/Ownrshp 1972
Sales 124.7MME EMP 750
SIC 5411 Grocery stores, independent
Pr: Jay Lawrence
*Treas: Larry N Hoover
*Sec: Mildred A Lawrence
*VP: Kyle Lawrence
*VP: Tere L Lawrence
Genl Mgr: Penny Hernandez

MALARKEY ROOFING PRODUCTS
See HERBERT MALARKEY ROOFING CO

D-U-N-S 61-891-3701
MALCO ENTERPRISES OF NEVADA INC
BUDGET RENT-A-CAR
7120 Haven St, Las Vegas, NV 89119-4102
Tel (702) 736-1212 Founded/Ownrshp 1989
Sales 97.3MME EMP 300
SIC 5521 7514 7513 Automobiles, used cars only; Passenger car rental; Truck rental, without drivers
*CFO: Steve Badilla
*VP: Larry Mallo
IT Man: Tim Stewart

D-U-N-S 04-503-1267 IMP
MALCOLM DRILLING CO INC
92 Natoma St Ste 400, San Francisco, CA 94105-2685
Tel (415) 901-4400 Founded/Ownrshp 1968
Sales 819.9MME EMP 5,650E
SIC 1799 Building site preparation; Boring for building construction
CEO: John M Malcolm
*Pr: Terry Tucker
Treas: Derek Yamashita
Sr VP: Chase Chappelle
*VP: Heinrich Majewski
*VP: John Roe
VP: Bruce Wilhelm
Dist Mgr: Roberto Lopez
Off Mgr: Barbara Keen
Off Admin: Ciara McGinn
Info Man: Seechai Kwan

D-U-N-S 07-927-3485
▲ **MALIBU BOATS INC**
5075 Kimberly Way, Loudon, TN 37774-6469
Tel (865) 458-5478 Founded/Ownrshp 1982
Sales 252.9MM EMP 540
Tkr Sym MBUU Exch NGM
SIC 3732 Boat building & repairing
CEO: Jack D Springer
*Ch Bd: Michael K Hooks
COO: Ritchie L Anderson
CFO: Wayne R Wilson
VP: Dan L Gasper
Board of Directors: James R Buch, Ivar S Chhina, Michael J Connolly, Phillip S Estes, Mark W Lanigan, Peter E Murphy, John E Stokely

D-U-N-S 05-136-7969 IMP
■ **MALIBU BOATS LLC**
(Suby of MALIBU BOATS INC) ★
5075 Kimberly Way, Loudon, TN 37774-6469
Tel (865) 458-5478 Founded/Ownrshp 1982
Sales 125.4MME EMP 509
SIC 3732 Boats, fiberglass: building & repairing
COO: Ritchie L Anderson
CFO: Wayne R Wilson
Exec: Holly Fiegle
S&M/VP: Eric Bondy
Mktg Dir: Hugh Michael
Sls Dir: Scott Davenport

D-U-N-S 78-248-4273
▲ **MALIBU ENTERTAINMENT WORLDWIDE INC**
717 N Harwood St Ste 1650, Dallas, TX 75201-6501
Tel (214) 210-8701 Founded/Ownrshp 1985
Sales 67.0MME EMP 1,100
Tkr Sym MBEW Exch OTO
SIC 1629 7999 Athletic & recreation facilities construction; Recreation center
Pr: Richard Beckert
*Ch Bd: Richard N Beckert
*CFO: Scott Wheeler
Sec: Eric Terry
*Sec: Robert Whitman
VP: Kenneth R Grissom
Mfg Dir: Rebecca Henderson
Board of Directors: Daniel A Decker, Julia E Demerau, L Scott Demerau, James T Hands, William M Kearns Jr, Steven D Scheetz, Bert W Wasserman

D-U-N-S 16-367-9744
■ **MALL AT MONTGOMERYVILLE LP**
(Suby of SIMON PROPERTY GROUP LP) ★
115 W Washington St, Indianapolis, IN 46204-3420
Tel (215) 362-1600 Founded/Ownrshp 2014
Sales 16.3MME EMP 5,001
SIC 6512 Shopping center, property operation only
Ch Bd: David Simon
Pr: Richard S Sokolov

MALLARD FOOD SHOP
See MALLARD OIL CO

D-U-N-S 04-591-8182
MALLARD OIL CO
MALLARD FOOD SHOP
1502 Dr Martin Luther, Kinston, NC 28501
Tel (252) 527-0364 Founded/Ownrshp 1968
Sales 103.5MME EMP 250
SIC 5171 5983 5984 Petroleum bulk stations; Fuel oil dealers; Liquefied petroleum gas, delivered to customers' premises
Ch Bd: Felix Harvey
*Pr: Frank Famularo
Genl Mgr: Mickey Connor

D-U-N-S 04-702-1092 IMP/EXP
MALLINCKRODT LLC
MALLINCKRODT PHARMACEUTICALS
(*Suby of* MALLINCKRODT PUBLIC LIMITED COMPANY)
675 Jmes S Mcdonnell Blvd, Hazelwood, MO 63042-2379
Tel (314) 654-2000 *Founded/Ownrshp* 2011
Sales 1.8MMM^E *EMP* 5,500
SIC 3841 3829 2834 2833 Surgical & medical instruments; Catheters; Anesthesia apparatus; Medical diagnostic systems, nuclear; Pharmaceutical preparations; Analgesics; Codeine & derivatives; Opium derivatives
Pr: Mark Trudeau
CFO: Matthew Harbaugh
Sr VP: Thomas Berry
Sr VP: Peter Edwards
VP: Ralph Heasley
CIO: Shrikant Ramachandran
IT Man: George Norton
Sfty Dirs: Ken Coffey
Pharmcst: Steve Kosierowski
Snr Mgr: Neal McDaniel

MALLINCKRODT PHARMACEUTICALS
See MALLINCKRODT LLC

D-U-N-S 05-287-7409 IMP/EXP
MALLORY ALEXANDER INTERNATIONAL LOGISTICS LLC (TN)
MALLORY TRANSPORTATION SYSTEM
4294 Swinnea Rd, Memphis, TN 38118-6620
Tel (901) 367-9400 *Founded/Ownrshp* 1925
Sales 219.4MM^E *EMP* 510
SIC 4731 4225 4789 Customs clearance of freight; General warehousing; Pipeline terminal facilities, independently operated
Pr: W Neely Mallory III
**COO:* Tina Newman
VP: Lamar Black
VP Sls: Donna Lemm

D-U-N-S 07-640-9390 IMP
MALLORY CO
RAIN OR SHINE
1040 Industrial Way, Longview, WA 98632-1039
Tel (360) 636-5750 *Founded/Ownrshp* 1975
Sales 250.7MM^E *EMP* 205
SIC 5099 Safety equipment & supplies
CEO: Timothy Loy
COO: Shawn Murray
Opers Mgr: Tisha Proudfit
Opers Mgr: Lorene Simmons
Sls Mgr: Steve Johnson

D-U-N-S 96-584-5022
MALLORY SAFETY AND SUPPLY LLC
(*Suby of* RAIN OR SHINE) ★
1040 Industrial Way, Longview, WA 98632-1039
Tel (360) 636-5750 *Founded/Ownrshp* 1999
Sales 239.1MM^E *EMP* 203^E
SIC 5099 8331 Safety equipment & supplies; Job training & vocational rehabilitation services
Pr: Tim Loy
**COO:* Shawn Murray
Sls Mgr: Carrie Sawvel
Sls Mgr: Scott Watkins

MALLORY TRANSPORTATION SYSTEM
See MALLORY ALEXANDER INTERNATIONAL LOGISTICS LLC

MALLOY ELECTRIC BEARING & SUP
See D M G INC

D-U-N-S 78-812-0145 IMP/EXP
MALNOVE HOLDING CO INC
13434 F St, Omaha, NE 68137-1181
Tel (402) 330-1100 *Founded/Ownrshp* 1991
Sales 231.3MM^E *EMP* 622
SIC 2657 Folding paperboard boxes
Ch: Paul Malnove
**CFO:* James K Belcher

D-U-N-S 01-435-6125 EXP
MALNOVE INC OF FLORIDA (NE)
(*Suby of* MALNOVE HOLDING CO INC) ★
10500 Canada Dr, Jacksonville, FL 32218-4968
Tel (904) 696-1600 *Founded/Ownrshp* 1956, 1948
Sales 119.9MM^E *EMP* 622
SIC 2657 Folding paperboard boxes
CEO: Paul Malnove
VP: Peter Hofmann

D-U-N-S 00-891-4178 IMP
MALOOF DISTRIBUTING LLC
JOE G MALOOF & CO
701 Comanche Rd Ne, Albuquerque, NM 87107-4105
Tel (505) 345-1218 *Founded/Ownrshp* 1946
Sales 199.4MM^E *EMP* 2,300
SIC 5181 5149 Beer & other fermented malt liquors; Tea; Water, distilled
CFO: Keith Hartnett

D-U-N-S 00-201-1179 EXP
MALT PRODUCTS CORP (NJ)
88 Market St, Saddle Brook, NJ 07663-4830
Tel (201) 845-4420 *Founded/Ownrshp* 1939, 1962
Sales 182.0MM^E *EMP* 650
SIC 2083 2087 Malt; Malt byproducts; Flavoring extracts & syrups
VP: Joe Hickenbottom
**Pr:* Amy Targen
**Pr:* Ronald G Targen
**Treas:* Nathan Mandelbaum

D-U-N-S 19-674-9159
MAMA ROSAS LLC
(*Suby of* HGGC LLC) ★
1910 Fair Rd, Sidney, OH 45365-8906
Tel (937) 498-4511 *Founded/Ownrshp* 2011
Sales 293.4MM^E *EMP* 300^E
SIC 5141 5142 Groceries, general line; Food brokers; Packaged frozen goods; Bakery products, frozen
CEO: Scott McNair

D-U-N-S 05-021-3495
MAMARONECK UNION FREE SCHOOL DISTRICT
1000 W Boston Post Rd, Mamaroneck, NY 10543-3399
Tel (914) 220-3000 *Founded/Ownrshp* 1850
Sales 115.8MM^E *EMP* 821
SIC 8211 Public senior high school; Public junior high school; Public elementary school

D-U-N-S 00-698-7200 IMP
MAMIYE BROTHERS INC (NJ)
MAMIYE SALES
1385 Brdwy Fl 18, New York, NY 10018
Tel (212) 279-4150 *Founded/Ownrshp* 1946, 2001
Sales 270.0MM^E *EMP* 260
SIC 5137 Sportswear, women's & children's; Sweaters, women's & children's
Pr: Hyman Mamiye
Treas: Abraham Mamiye
VP: Abe Mamiye
VP: Stephen Mamiye
Div Mgr: Nathan Mamiye
Dir IT: Emil Lavagno
Dir IT: Mark Snyder
Sls Dir: Caitlin Ciancimino

MAMIYE SALES
See MAMIYE BROTHERS INC

D-U-N-S 07-956-9701
▲ MAMMOTH ENERGY PARTNERS LP
4727 Gaillardia Pkwy # 200, Oklahoma City, OK 73142-1923
Tel (405) 265-4600 *Founded/Ownrshp* 2014
Sales 359.9MM *EMP* 914^E
SIC 1389 1381 Construction, repair & dismantling services; Oil field services; Drilling oil & gas wells
CEO: Arty Straehla
Genl Pt: Mammoth E LLC
CFO: Mark Layton

D-U-N-S 02-864-8061 IMP
MAMMOTH MOUNTAIN SKI AREA LLC
(*Suby of* STARWOOD CAPITAL GROUP LLC) ★
10001 Minaret Rd, Mammoth Lakes, CA 93546
Tel (760) 934-2571 *Founded/Ownrshp* 2005
Sales 137.9MM *EMP* 350
Accts Pricewaterhousecoopers Llp S
SIC 7011 5812 Ski lodge; Resort hotel; Eating places
Pt: David Cummings
CFO: Mark Clausen
**Ofcr:* Erik Forsell
VP: Bruce Burton
Exec: Caroline Casey
Genl Mgr: Bridget Sisson
Genl Mgr: Luis Villanueva
Dir IT: Greg Dallas
IT Man: Stacey Crockett
IT Man: Phil Romero
Sys Mgr: Paul Deangelis

MAMMOTONE
See DEVICOR MEDICAL PRODUCTS INC

D-U-N-S 19-321-1021
MANA DEVELOPMENT LLC
MANNA BREAD DEVELOPMENT
2339 11th St, Encinitas, CA 92024-6604
Tel (760) 944-1070 *Founded/Ownrshp* 2008
Sales 368.8MM^E *EMP* 3,000
SIC 5149 Bakery products
Pt: Patrick Rogers

D-U-N-S 07-887-0292 IMP
MANA PRODUCTS INC
YOUR NAME PROFESSIONAL BRAND
3202 Queens Blvd Fl 6, Long Island City, NY 11101-2341
Tel (718) 361-2550 *Founded/Ownrshp* 1975
Sales 289.0MM^E *EMP* 800^E
SIC 2844 5122 Cosmetic preparations; Cosmetics
Ch: Nikos Mouyiaris
**CFO:* Lawrence Weinstock
Ex VP: N Masturzo
**Ex VP:* Barbara Novick
VP: George Alexandrou
**VP:* Edward Ewankov
VP: George Lambridis
VP: Bruce Meyer
**VP:* Dennis Roberts
**VP:* Bob Salem
VP: Debi Theis
Creative D: Aloise Levesque
Dir Bus: Eleni Spencer

D-U-N-S 01-879-4438
MANAFORT BROTHERS INC (CT)
414 New Britain Ave, Plainville, CT 06062-2065
Tel (860) 229-4853 *Founded/Ownrshp* 1922
Sales 138.7MM^E *EMP* 500
SIC 1794 1771 1622 1795 4953 Excavation work; Foundation & footing contractor; Bridge, tunnel & elevated highway; Wrecking & demolition work; Recycling, waste materials
Pr: James Manafort Jr
**CFO:* Robert King
**Sec:* Lauren Manafort
Bd of Dir: Ann Catelli
VP: Amanda J Fagan
**VP:* David Manafort
VP: Frank Manafort
**VP:* Jon Manafort
**VP:* Michael Tarsi
Info Man: Mike Daversa
Sfty Mgr: John Overhiser

D-U-N-S 60-121-7979
■ MANAGED HEALTH NETWORK
(*Suby of* HEALTH NET INC) ★
2370 Kerner Blvd, San Rafael, CA 94901-5546
Tel (415) 460-8168 *Founded/Ownrshp* 1990
Sales NA *EMP* 1,300
SIC 6324 8099 8093 8011 Hospital & medical service plans; Health maintenance organization (HMO), insurance only; Medical services organization; Specialty outpatient clinics; Offices & clinics of medical doctors
CEO: Jeffrey Bairstow
Pr: Jerry Coil
Pr: Steven Sell
COO: Linda Brisbane
COO: Jonathan Wormhoudt
CFO: John Volkober
VP: Al Gross
VP: Dena Maddox
Ex Dir: Brian Oleary
Board of Directors: John Crockerin

D-U-N-S 03-920-3740
MANAGEMENT & TRAINING CORP
M T C
500 N Market Place Dr # 100, Centerville, UT 84014-1711
Tel (801) 693-2600 *Founded/Ownrshp* 1980
Sales 753.7MM *EMP* 9,500
Accts Kpmg Llp Salt Lake City Ut
SIC 8744 8331 7349 8741 8249 Jails, privately operated; Job training services; Building maintenance services; Business management; Vocational schools; Civil service training school
Pr: Scott Marquardt JD
**Pr:* Roberts T Jones
CFO: Randy King
**CFO:* Lyle J Parry
Ex VP: Neil Adler
**Sr VP:* Sergio Molina
**Sr VP:* John Pedersen
**Sr VP:* Odie Washington
VP: Dawn Call
VP: JC Conner
VP: Lynette Greenwell
VP: Lonnie Hall
VP: Mike Murphy
VP: Greg Niblett

D-U-N-S 09-407-1511
MANAGEMENT ANALYSIS & UTILIZATION INC
MAU WORKFORCE SOLUTIONS
501 Greene St Ste 100, Augusta, GA 30901-4400
Tel (706) 722-6806 *Founded/Ownrshp* 1973
Sales 174.4MM^E *EMP* 175
Accts Cherrybekaert Llp Augusta Ge
SIC 7361 Employment agencies
Ch Bd: William G Hatcher Sr
**Pr:* Randall Hatcher
Site Mgr: Brent Moore
Mktg Mgr: Brett Yardley

MANAGEMENT CO
See DRURY HOTELS CO LLC

MANAGEMENT COMPANY
See FORD RESTAURANT GROUP INC

D-U-N-S 08-018-9973
MANAGEMENT CONSULTING INC
MANCON
2503 Se 17th Ave, Cape Coral, FL 33910
Tel (239) 458-3611 *Founded/Ownrshp* 2016
Sales 12.0MM^E *EMP* 1,000
SIC 5531 5087 Automotive parts; Janitors' supplies
Pr: Richard Clarke

D-U-N-S 11-337-7659
MANAGEMENT CONSULTING INC
MANCON
1961 Diamond Springs Rd, Virginia Beach, VA 23455-2319
Tel (757) 460-0879 *Founded/Ownrshp* 1983
Sales 402.7MM^E *EMP* 900
SIC 8742 Management consulting services
Pr: Richard Clarke
**Co-Ownr:* Robert Clarke
VP: David Bibby
**VP:* David Meadows
Prgrm Mgr: Rex Allen
Sls Mgr: Bart Consford

D-U-N-S 06-874-6346
MANAGEMENT SCIENCE ASSOCIATES INC (PA)
6565 Penn Ave, Pittsburgh, PA 15206-4490
Tel (412) 362-2000 *Founded/Ownrshp* 1963
Sales 113.7MM^E *EMP* 750
SIC 8742 7371

D-U-N-S 07-171-3085
MANAGEMENT SCIENCES FOR HEALTH INC
200 Rivers Edge Dr, Medford, MA 02155-5479
Tel (617) 250-9500 *Founded/Ownrshp* 1971
Sales 303.3MM *EMP* 400
Accts Tonneson & Company Inc Wakefi
SIC 8742 Hospital & health services consultant
Pr: Jonathan Quick
**COO:* Paul Auxila
**CFO:* Vickie Barrow Klein
VP: John Gatto
VP: Mary Jamar
IT Man: Patrick Louis

D-U-N-S 06-258-6704
MANAGEMENT SENIOR LLC MORNINGSTAR
MORNING STAR
7555 E Hampden Ave # 501, Denver, CO 80231-4830
Tel (303) 750-5522 *Founded/Ownrshp* 2005
Sales 8.6MM^E *EMP* 1,200
SIC 6513 Apartment building operators
CEO: Ken Jaeger
**COO:* Kimberly Erickson
**CFO:* Matt Turner

MANAGEMENT SERVICES DIVISION
See JUDICIARY COURTS OF STATE OF NEW JERSEY

D-U-N-S 96-884-1978
■ MANAGEMENT SHIP LLC GENCO
(*Suby of* GENCO SHIPPING & TRADING LTD) ★
299 Park Ave Fl 12, New York, NY 10171-0002
Tel (646) 443-8550 *Founded/Ownrshp* 2005
Sales 58.0M^E *EMP* 1,227^E
SIC 8748 Business consulting
CFO: John C Wobensmith

D-U-N-S 80-136-9617
MANAGEMENT SSS INC
MSSS
Roosevlt Av 145a Fl 3, San Juan, PR 00918
Tel (787) 758-7700 *Founded/Ownrshp* 2004
Sales 69.3MM^E *EMP* 2,000
SIC 8742

D-U-N-S 04-840-7589
MANAGEMENT SYSTEMS INTERNATIONAL INC (DC)
MSI
(*Suby of* COFFEY INTERNATIONAL LIMITED)
200 12th St S, Arlington, VA 22202-5400
Tel (703) 979-7100 *Founded/Ownrshp* 1981
Sales 138.7MM *EMP* 250
Accts Kpmg Llp Mclean Va
SIC 8742 General management consultant
Pr: Lawrence Cooley
COO: Laurie Flamholtz
**CFO:* Paul J Wise
**Exec:* Marina Fanning
IT Man: Ausaf Alavi

D-U-N-S 96-614-0704
MANAGEMENT TEMPORARY & CONTRACT EMPLOYMENT SERVICES INC
145 A Roosevelt Ave, San Juan, PR 00919
Tel (787) 758-7700 *Founded/Ownrshp* 2005
Sales 40.0MM *EMP* 1,000
Accts Robert John Santiago Cpa San
SIC 8742 Human resource consulting services
Pr: Alma I Acosta
Sls Mgr: Iillyak Negroni

MANAGEMENT TRUST, THE
See MANAGEMENT TRUST ASSOCIATION INC

D-U-N-S 82-550-2201
MANAGEMENT TRUST ASSOCIATION INC
MANAGEMENT TRUST, THE
15661 Red Hill Ave # 201, Tustin, CA 92780-7300
Tel (714) 285-2626 *Founded/Ownrshp* 2011
Sales 135.0MM^E *EMP* 550
SIC 6733 Trusts
CEO: William B Sasser

D-U-N-S 96-733-8075
MANAGEMENT-ILA MANAGED HEALTH CARE TRUST FUND
111 Broadway Fl 5, New York, NY 10006-1901
Tel (212) 766-5700 *Founded/Ownrshp* 2011
Sales 491.6MM *EMP* 3
Accts Desena & Company Cpas East Ha
SIC 8741 Management services

MANAGERS FUNDS
See AMG FUNDS LLC

D-U-N-S 08-095-0181
MANALAPAN-ENGLISHTOWN REGIONAL SCHOOL DISTRICT
54 Main St, Englishtown, NJ 07726-1529
Tel (732) 786-2500 *Founded/Ownrshp* 1878
Sales 84.6MM *EMP* 535
Accts Jump Perry And Company Llp
SIC 8211 Public elementary & secondary schools
Bd of Dir: Brian Graime
Adm Dir: Patricia Resnyk
MIS Dir: Maribeth Cruz
Teacher Pr: Joanne Monroe
HC Dir: Georgianna Petillo

D-U-N-S 02-583-7865
MANAN TOOL & MANUFACTURING INC
241 W Palatine Rd, Wheeling, IL 60090-5824
Tel (847) 637-3333 *Founded/Ownrshp* 2006
Sales 109.3MM^E *EMP* 1,112
SIC 3541 3841 Machine tools, metal cutting type; Needles, suture
Prin: Werner Mittermeier

MANATEE COUNTY GOVERNMENT
See COUNTY OF MANATEE

D-U-N-S 06-025-9314
■ MANATEE MEMORIAL HOSPITAL
(*Suby of* UNIVERSAL HEALTH SERVICES INC) ★
206 2nd St E, Bradenton, FL 34208-1000
Tel (941) 746-5111 *Founded/Ownrshp* 1992
Sales 249.8MM *EMP* 1,450
SIC 8062 General medical & surgical hospitals
CEO: Kevin DiLallo
CFO: Karen Sullivan
**CFO:* Mark Tierney
Exec: Garry Grant
Prac Mgr: Anne Sirois
Nurse Mgr: Priscilla Cooper
DP Exec: Troy Beaubien
Pathlgst: Hung-WEI Lee
Anesthlgy: Alan K Gilman
Anesthlgy: Ngoc T Nguyen
Opthamlgy: Eric L Berman
Board of Directors: Bert Beard, Troy Beaubies, Betty Chambliss, Beth Heinz, Andrew Knoch, Mike Lorraine, Alberto Montalvo, Barbara Raney, Ron Walter

MANATI MEDICAL CENTER
See DORADO HEALTH INC

D-U-N-S 07-189-4505
MANATT PHELPS & PHILLIPS LLP
11355 W Olympic Blvd Fl 2, Los Angeles, CA 90064-1656
Tel (310) 312-4000 *Founded/Ownrshp* 1965
Sales 188.3MM^E *EMP* 850
SIC 8111

D-U-N-S 00-782-0491 IMP
MANATTS INC
1775 Old 6 Rd, Brooklyn, IA 52211-7731
Tel (641) 522-9206 *Founded/Ownrshp* 1948
Sales 280.4MM^E *EMP* 475
SIC 1611 1442 2951 3273 Highway & street paving contractor; Airport runway construction; Sand mining; Gravel mining; Concrete, asphaltic (not from refineries); Ready-mixed concrete
**Treas:* J C Miller

VP: Anthony J Manatt
**VP:* Gerald J Manatt Jr
**VP:* Michael J Manatt
Div Mgr: Dennis Gallagher

D-U-N-S 08-770-8756
MANCAN INC
48 1st St Nw, Massillon, OH 44647-5450
Tel (330) 832-4595 *Founded/Ownrshp* 1976
Sales 124.8MM^E *EMP* 5,000
SIC 7361 Employment agencies
Pr: Jonathan P Mason
**Sec:* Bonnie Mason
VP: Amy King
**Prin:* F Stuart Wilkins
Brnch Mgr: Jerry Miller
Dir IT: Mike Morris

D-U-N-S 06-817-3608
MANCHA DEVELOPMENT CO LLC
BURGER KING
24422 Avenida De La Carlo, Laguna Hills, CA 92653-3603
Tel (951) 271-4100 *Founded/Ownrshp* 1979
Sales 87.3MM^E *EMP* 2,000
SIC 5812 Fast-food restaurant, chain
CEO: Vince F Eupierre
CFO: Brent Dunkin
**CFO:* Frank Velasco
Dir IT: Scott Nakamura

D-U-N-S 78-945-7756
MANCHESTER BOARD OF EDUCATION
MANCHESTER PUBLIC SCHOOLS
45 N School St, Manchester, CT 06042-2010
Tel (860) 647-3442 *Founded/Ownrshp* 2006
Sales 60.7MM^E *EMP* 1,400^E
SIC 8211 Public elementary & secondary schools
**Genl Mgr:* Patricia Brooks
Opers Mgr: Susan Grady
HC Dir: Mary J Quistorff

D-U-N-S 07-732-5645
MANCHESTER MEMORIAL HOSPITAL INC
ECHN
71 Haynes St, Manchester, CT 06040-4188
Tel (860) 646-1222 *Founded/Ownrshp* 1919
Sales 183.1MM *EMP* 1,056
SIC 8062 General medical & surgical hospitals
Owner: Marc Lory
Chf Path: Dennis G O'Neill
Sr VP: Dennis Mc Conville
VP: Mary Powers
Dir Rad: Dan Delgallo
Dir Bus: Kevin Murphy
Adm Dir: Rosanne Williams
CIO: Charles Covin
IT Man: Nicholas Jamieson
Pathlgst: Monica Srodon
Ansthlgy: John W McCarrick

D-U-N-S 05-348-9188 IMP
■ **MANCHESTER PARADIGM INC**
PARADIGM PRECISION
(*Suby of* GE AVIATION SYSTEMS LLC) ★
967 Parker St, Manchester, CT 06042-2208
Tel (860) 646-4048 *Founded/Ownrshp* 2004
Sales 137.2MM^E *EMP* 575
SIC 3728 Aircraft assemblies, subassemblies & parts
Pr: Michael Grunza
**Pr:* James Donahu
**VP:* William W Booth
**VP:* Steve Lindsey

MANCHESTER PUBLIC SCHOOLS
See MANCHESTER BOARD OF EDUCATION

D-U-N-S 80-948-8828
MANCHESTER SCHOOL DISTRICT
45 N School St, Manchester, CT 06042-2010
Tel (860) 647-3442 *Founded/Ownrshp* 2010
Sales 10.9MM^E *EMP* 1,100
SIC 8211 Elementary & secondary schools
Dir Sec: Max Cohen
Pr Dir: Suzanne Angeloni
Teacher Pr: Nilsa Taylor
HC Dir: Linda Hodgkins

D-U-N-S 14-846-5008 IMP/EXP
MANCHESTER TANK & EQUIPMENT CO INC
(*Suby of* MCWANE CAST IRON PIPE CO) ★
1000 Corporate Centre Dr # 300, Franklin, TN 37067-6206
Tel (615) 370-6104 *Founded/Ownrshp* 1945
Sales 244.1MM^E *EMP* 1,050
SIC 3443 Industrial vessels, tanks & containers; Fuel tanks (oil, gas, etc.): metal plate; Tanks, standard or custom fabricated: metal plate
CEO: Larry Whitehead
**Pr:* Robert Graumann
Pr: Steve H Harris
**VP:* Danny M Clymer
**VP:* Tom Freeland
VP: Brian Skinner
VP: Scott Viebranz
**VP:* D Harrison Whitehead
Genl Mgr: Erick Hart
IT Man: Mike Lurty
Opers Mgr: Jim Young

MANCON
See MANAGEMENT CONSULTING INC

MANCON
See MANAGEMENT CONSULTING INC

MANDALAY BAY RESORT AND CASINO
See MANDALAY RESORT GROUP

D-U-N-S 06-778-3738
■ **MANDALAY RESORT GROUP**
MANDALAY BAY RESORT AND CASINO
(*Suby of* MGM RESORTS INTERNATIONAL) ★
3950 Las Vegas Blvd S, Las Vegas, NV 89119-1005
Tel (702) 693-7120 *Founded/Ownrshp* 2005
Sales 541.0MM^E *EMP* 28,000
SIC 7011 7999 7996 Casino hotel; Gambling & lottery services; Gambling establishment; Gambling machines, operation; Theme park, amusement
CEO: Michael S Ensign
Pr: Clark Dumont
**Pr:* James J Murren
**Pr:* Glenn Schaeffer
COO: Felix Rapapport
CFO: James Murren
**Treas:* Daniel J D'Arrigo
Sr VP: Tony Alamo
Sr VP: Steve Greathouse
Sr VP: Gregg Solomon
VP: Danielle Babillino
VP: Chris Baldizan
VP: Mark Bennett
**VP:* Yvette Landau
**VP:* Les Martin
VP: Bill Monson
VP: Michael Starr
VP: George Togliatti
Exec: Christopher Deright
Exec: Elizabeth Dicandilo
Exec: Brian Elledge

MANDEE
See A & M (2015) LLC

D-U-N-S 92-942-6104 IMP
MANDO AMERICA CORP
(*Suby of* MANDO CORPORATION)
4201 N Park Dr, Opelika, AL 36801-9667
Tel (334) 364-3600 *Founded/Ownrshp* 1996
Sales 905.0MM *EMP* 1,000
SIC 3714 Air brakes, motor vehicle
Ch Bd: Chung In-Yung
Genl Mgr: Michael S Gaertner
Sls Mgr: Cuk Lee

MANE CALAFORNIA
See MANE INC

D-U-N-S 03-288-9151 IMP
MANE INC (OH)
MANE CALAFORNIA
(*Suby of* MANE USA INC) ★
2501 Henkle Dr, Lebanon, OH 45036-7794
Tel (513) 248-9876 *Founded/Ownrshp* 1998
Sales 93.8MM^E *EMP* 340
SIC 2087 2099 Flavoring extracts & syrups; Food preparations
Ch Bd: Jean Mane
**Pr:* Ken Hunter
Sec: Stacie Bennison
VP: Jill Fleury
VP: Martha Kimbrough
VP: Deborah Knighton
VP: Syed Shamil
Opers Mgr: Barney Bussey
Plnt Mgr: Jim Abel
VP Sls: Birgit Benayoun
VP Sls: Dallas Stokes

D-U-N-S 04-768-5581 IMP
MANE USA INC
(*Suby of* V MANE FILS)
60 Demarest Dr, Wayne, NJ 07470-6702
Tel (973) 633-5533 *Founded/Ownrshp* 1956
Sales 154.9MM^E *EMP* 526
SIC 2869 Perfumes, flavorings & food additives
Pr: Michel Mane
CFO: Taphiana Remick
VP: Bob Bagnato
VP Opers: Larry Deraney
Mktg Mgr: Jason Boland

D-U-N-S 61-176-2733
MANGANARO INDUSTRIES INC
52 Cummings Park, Woburn, MA 01801-2123
Tel (781) 937-8880 *Founded/Ownrshp* 1982
Sales 36.2MM^E *EMP* 1,000
SIC 1742 1741 1799 1743 Drywall; Acoustical & ceiling work; Masonry & other stonework; Fireproofing buildings; Tile installation, ceramic
**Treas:* David Manganaro

D-U-N-S 19-149-8943
MANGANARO MIDATLANTIC LLC
6405d Ammendale Rd, Beltsville, MD 20705-1203
Tel (301) 937-0580 *Founded/Ownrshp* 2003
Sales 101.2MM^E *EMP* 600
SIC 1741 1742 1799 Masonry & other stonework; Acoustical & ceiling work; Waterproofing
Pr: Tom Vagrin

D-U-N-S 00-253-4058 IMP
MANGAR INDUSTRIES INC (PA)
MANGAR MEDICAL PACKAGING
(*Suby of* OLIVER-TOLAS HEALTHCARE PACKG) ★
97 Britain Dr, New Britain, PA 18901-5193
Tel (215) 230-0300 *Founded/Ownrshp* 1986, 2016
Sales 128.6MM^E *EMP* 225
Accts Spear Coyne & Company Ltd Do
SIC 2671 Packaging paper & plastics film, coated & laminated
Pr: Jerry Bennish
CFO: Ann Buckley
VP: Don Hanson
Dir Bus: Mark Foster
Mng Dir: June Cowger
Off Mgr: Janet West
IT Man: Rob Gibbs
Mfg Mgr: Duc Nguyen

MANGAR MEDICAL PACKAGING
See MANGAR INDUSTRIES INC

D-U-N-S 82-871-3805
MANHATTAN AND BRONX SURFACE TRANSIT OPERATING AUTHORITY
PUBLIC TRANSPORTATION
(*Suby of* PUBLIC TRANSPORTATION) ★
2 Broadway, New York, NY 10004-2207
Tel (718) 694-1000 *Founded/Ownrshp* 2008
Sales 1.1MMM *EMP* 5,021^E
SIC 4111 Local & suburban transit
Prin: Walter Weinert

D-U-N-S 78-548-4387
▲ **MANHATTAN ASSOCIATES INC**
2300 Windy Ridge Pkwy Se 1000n, Atlanta, GA 30339-5675
Tel (770) 955-7070 *Founded/Ownrshp* 1990
Sales 556.3MM *EMP* 2,930
Accts Ernst & Young Llp Atlanta Ge
Tkr Sym MANH *Exch* NGS
SIC 7373 7372 5045 Computer integrated systems design; Systems software development services; Prepackaged software; Computers, peripherals & software; Computer peripheral equipment; Printers, computer; Computers
Pr: Eddie Capel
CFO: Linda C Pinne
CFO: Dennis B Story
Ofcr: Andrew Cooper
Ex VP: Jeffrey B Cashman
Sr VP: Terry Geraghty
Sr VP: Robert G Howell
Sr VP: Henri Seroux
Sr VP: Sanjeev Siotia
Sr VP: Usha Tirumala
VP: Jeff Baum
VP: Marvin Lee
VP: Bruce Richards
VP: Ken Shipp
VP: Joshua Whitmire
Board of Directors: Brian J Cassidy, Edmond I Eger III, John J Huntz Jr, Dan J Lautenbach, Thomas E Noonan

D-U-N-S 09-400-6814 IMP
MANHATTAN BEACHWEAR INC
10700 Valley View St, Cypress, CA 90630-4835
Tel (714) 892-7354 *Founded/Ownrshp* 2011
Sales 196.6MM^E *EMP* 400
SIC 2339 Bathing suits: women's, misses' & juniors'; Beachwear: women's, misses' & juniors'; Athletic clothing: women's, misses' & juniors'; Sportswear, women's
CEO: Allan Colvin
**Pr:* Brenda West
**CFO:* Michael Conway
CFO: William Singletary
VP: Anne Kelly
VP: Michelle Leblanc
Netwrk Mgr: Jennifer Moh
Mfg Dir: Jose Marquez
VP Merchng: Howie Greller
Pr Mgr: Carrie Seifert

D-U-N-S 09-297-2231 IMP
MANHATTAN BEER DISTRIBUTORS LLC
955 E 149th St, Bronx, NY 10455-5021
Tel (718) 292-9300 *Founded/Ownrshp* 1970
Sales 662.5MM^E *EMP* 1,400
SIC 5181 Beer & ale
COO: Bill Bessette
CFO: George Wertheimer
VP: Bill Deluca
VP: William Deluca
VP: Damian Rippon
Dir Bus: Ender Berrios
MIS Dir: Ziad El-Jamal
Dir IT: Vlad Eljamal
Info Man: Todd White
Sfty Dirs: Mike Gabriel
Sls Dir: Richard Hourihan

D-U-N-S 07-104-0810
MANHATTAN COLLEGE CORP
4513 Mnhttan College Pkwy, Bronx, NY 10471-4004
Tel (718) 862-8000 *Founded/Ownrshp* 1853
Sales 122.0MM^E *EMP* 496^E
SIC 8221 University
**Pr:* Brennan O'Donnell PHD
**CFO:* Matthew S McManness
VP: William Bisset
VP: Ann Burke
VP: Robert A Mahan
Assoc Dir: Mercy Alonso
Dir: Stephen White
Comm Man: Lydia Gray
Ex Dir: Harry Welsh
Off Mgr: Grace Cabrera
Off Mgr: Carol McTiernan
Board of Directors: John Lawler, Valentine A Lehr

D-U-N-S 04-546-1498
MANHATTAN CONSTRUCTION (FLORIDA) INC
MANHATTAN CONSTRUCTION COMPANY
(*Suby of* MANHATTAN CONSTRUCTION GROUP INC) ★
3705 Westview Dr Ste 1, Naples, FL 34104-4033
Tel (239) 643-6000 *Founded/Ownrshp* 1974
Sales 137.5MM^E *EMP* 500
SIC 1542 8712 1531 1521 8741 Commercial & office building, new construction; Architectural services; Operative builders; Single-family housing construction; Construction management
Pr: Robert Koenig
**Ch Bd:* Robert Carsello
**Pr:* Fred Pezeshkan
**Treas:* Jim Lawson
**Ex VP:* Thomas Williams
**Sr VP:* Thomas Abraham
**VP:* Bill Dean
VP: Tom Kramer

MANHATTAN CONSTRUCTION COMPANY
See MANHATTAN CONSTRUCTION (FLORIDA) INC

D-U-N-S 05-395-9755 IMP
MANHATTAN CONSTRUCTION CO
(*Suby of* ROONEY HOLDINGS INC) ★
5601 S 122nd East Ave, Tulsa, OK 74146-6912
Tel (918) 583-6900 *Founded/Ownrshp* 1896
Sales 680.1MM^E *EMP* 1,100
SIC 1542 Institutional building construction
Pr: John Reyhan
COO: George Kolczun
**CFO:* Kevin Moore
**Treas:* Jim Lawson
**Ex VP:* Robert Bowen
Ex VP: Frank Fralick
**Ex VP:* Bob Vecera
VP: Todd Fultz
VP: Tom Kramer
VP: George Kreis
**VP:* George Kreiss
VP: Michael Lauder
VP: Bob Postma
Exec: Joe Arnold
Exec: Jon Clark
Exec: Bob Jack
Dir Bus: BJ Brundage
Comm Man: Brent Dostal

D-U-N-S 83-163-0673
MANHATTAN CONSTRUCTION GROUP INC
(*Suby of* ROONEY HOLDINGS INC) ★
5601 S 122nd East Ave, Tulsa, OK 74146-6912
Tel (918) 878-3341 *Founded/Ownrshp* 2009
Sales 137.6MM^E *EMP* 524
SIC 1542 Nonresidential construction
Pr: Kevin Moore
Ex VP: Elmon Henry
Sfty Mgr: Julie Lovelace

D-U-N-S 15-135-0378
MANHATTAN PSYCHIATRIC CENTER
1 Wards Is Ofc 2, New York, NY 10035-6011
Tel (646) 672-6767 *Founded/Ownrshp* 1896
Sales 40.1MM^E *EMP* 1,400
SIC 8063 Psychiatric hospitals
Ex Dir: Eileen Consilvio
**Ex Dir:* Steve Rebinowitz
Ex Dir: Yvette Wilson
CIO: Jeff Fox

D-U-N-S 04-255-4782
MANHATTAN ROAD & BRIDGE CO
(*Suby of* ROONEY HOLDINGS INC) ★
5601 S 122nd East Ave, Tulsa, OK 74146-6912
Tel (918) 583-6900 *Founded/Ownrshp* 1956
Sales 127.9MM^E *EMP* 350^E
SIC 1622 Bridge construction
Pr: Mike Webb
**Ex VP:* Todd Saxton
VP: Mark Windle
**Prin:* Kendall Adams
**Prin:* Bobby J Lee
**Prin:* Jack J Lee
Sfty Dirs: Ashley Godsey
Sfty Dirs: Nick Taylor

D-U-N-S 16-169-7347 EXP
MANHEIM INVESTMENTS INC
(*Suby of* COX AUTOMOTIVE INC) ★
6205 Pachtree Dunwoody Rd, Atlanta, GA 30328-4524
Tel (866) 626-4346 *Founded/Ownrshp* 1991
Sales 1.3MMM^E *EMP* 20,000
SIC 5012 Automobile auction
CEO: Sanford H Schwartz
**Pr:* Dennis Berry
**Treas:* Robert E Gartin

MANHEIM PITTSBURGH
See MANHEIM REMARKETING INC

D-U-N-S 02-145-0549 EXP
MANHEIM REMARKETING INC
MANHEIM PITTSBURGH
(*Suby of* MANHEIM INVESTMENTS INC) ★
21095 Route 19, Cranberry Township, PA 16066-5907
Tel (724) 452-5555 *Founded/Ownrshp* 1968
Sales 221.8MM^E *EMP* 2,000
SIC 5012 Automobile auction
Pr: Dean H Eisner
**Treas:* Richard J Jacobson
**VP:* Maria L Friedman
MIS Mgr: Jerry Stich

D-U-N-S 14-709-3582
MANHEIM REMARKETING INC
(*Suby of* COX AUTOMOTIVE INC) ★
6325 Pchtree Dnwody Rd Ne, Atlanta, GA 30328-4545
Tel (678) 645-2067 *Founded/Ownrshp* 1985
Sales 191.0MM^E *EMP* 350^E
SIC 5012 Automobile auction
Pr: Dean H Eisner
Exec: Debbie Harris
Snr Mgr: Chuck Konfrst

D-U-N-S 08-192-3526
MANIILAQ ASSOCIATION
MANIILAQ HEALTH CENTER
733 2nd Ave Ferguson Bldg, Kotzebue, AK 99752
Tel (907) 442-3311 *Founded/Ownrshp* 1967
Sales 111.9MM *EMP* 620
Accts Lb Altman Rogers & Company Ko
SIC 8062 8741 General medical & surgical hospitals; Management services
Pr: Helen Bolen
CFO: Craig Moen
Bd of Dir: Brad Reich
**VP:* Barbara Janitscheck
Dir IT: Christina Hensley

MANIILAQ HEALTH CENTER
See MANIILAQ ASSOCIATION

D-U-N-S 09-656-2244
MANIKEN LLC
8621 Robert Fulton Dr # 100, Columbia, MD 21046-2620
Tel (410) 290-1400 *Founded/Ownrshp* 1971
Sales 125.0MM *EMP* 160
SIC 6512 Commercial & industrial building operation
Pt: Richard Alter
Pt: Louis Lapenna
CFO: Ed Kouneski
Sr VP: Owen J Rouse Jr

D-U-N-S 10-203-3925 IMP
MANIS LUMBER CO
WHEELER'S
15 Old Airport Rd Nw, Rome, GA 30165-2001
Tel (706) 232-2400 *Founded/Ownrshp* 1986
Sales 97.0MM^E *EMP* 560
SIC 5031 5211 Lumber, plywood & millwork; Lumber & other building materials
Pr: James T Manis
**CEO:* Mark W Manis
Sfty Dirs: Wayne White
Opers Mgr: Garrett Manis

D-U-N-S 78-540-9392 IMP
▲ **MANITEX INTERNATIONAL INC**
9725 Industrial Dr, Bridgeview, IL 60455-2304
Tel (708) 430-7500 *Founded/Ownrshp* 1993
Sales 386.7MM *EMP* 961^E

Tkr Sym MNTX *Exch* NAS
SIC 3537 3536 Industrial trucks & tractors; Forklift trucks; Lift trucks, industrial: fork, platform, straddle, etc.; Hoists, cranes & monorails
Ch Bd: David J Langevin
Pr: Lubomir T Litchev
Pr: Andrew M Rooke
CFO: David H Gransee
Ex VP: Steve Kiefer
VP: Scott Rolston
Board of Directors: Ronald M Clark, Robert S Gigliotti, Frederick B Knox, Marvin B Rosenberg, Stephen J Tober

D-U-N-S 14-441-2640
MANITO SUPER 1 FOODS INC
240 W Hayden Ave, Hayden Lake, ID 83835-8194
Tel (208) 772-5722 *Founded/Ownrshp* 1985
Sales 118.6MM^E *EMP* 800
SIC 5411 Supermarkets, independent
**Pr:* Ronald Mc Intire

D-U-N-S 00-607-0031 IMP/EXP
MANITOU AMERICAS INC (WI)
GEHL COMPANY
(*Suby of* MANITOU BF)
1 Gehl Way, West Bend, WI 53095-3463
Tel (262) 334-9461 *Founded/Ownrshp* 1859, 2008
Sales 275.1MM^E *EMP* 848
SIC 3531 3523 Backhoes, tractors, cranes, plows & similar equipment; Dozers, tractor mounted: material moving; Cranes; Excavators: cable, clamshell, crane, derrick, dragline, etc.; Farm machinery & equipment; Haying machines: mowers, rakes, stackers, etc.; Balers, farm: hay, straw, cotton, etc.; Harvesters, fruit, vegetable, tobacco, etc.
Pr: Daniel Miller
**Ch Bd:* William D Gehl
COO: Malcolm F Moore
CFO: Thomas Rettler
Treas: James J Monnat
VP: James C Green
VP: Daniel Mier
VP: Daniel L Miller
VP: Michael J Mulcahy
Prin: Lori Heidecker
Ex Dir: Anthony Safia
Board of Directors: John T Byrnes, Richard J Fotsch, John W Splude, Dr Hermann Viets

D-U-N-S 06-162-7712 IMP/EXP
■ **MANITOWOC BEVERAGE SYSTEMS INC**
M B S
(*Suby of* MANITOWOC CO INC) ★
2100 Future Dr, Sellersburg, IN 47172-1874
Tel (419) 861-0800 *Founded/Ownrshp* 1998
Sales 352.0MM^E *EMP* 3,000
SIC 3585 Soda fountain & beverage dispensing equipment & parts
Pr: Terry D Growcock
**CEO:* John Barber
**Treas:* Glenn E Tellock
VP: David Mosteller
**Prin:* Robert R Friedl
Opers Mgr: Mike Kascak
Ql Cn Mgr: Gary Herrmann

D-U-N-S 00-607-3183
▲ **MANITOWOC CO INC** (WI)
2400 S 44th St, Manitowoc, WI 54220-5846
Tel (920) 684-4410 *Founded/Ownrshp* 1902
Sales 3.4MMM *EMP* 11,000
Accts Pricewaterhousecoopers Llp M
Tkr Sym MTW *Exch* NYS
SIC 3536 3537 3531 3585 Hoists, cranes & monorails; Cranes, overhead traveling; Cranes, industrial plant; Trucks, tractors, loaders, carriers & similar equipment; Cranes; Excavators: cable, clamshell, crane, derrick, dragline, etc.; Ice making machinery; Refrigeration equipment, complete; Soda fountain & beverage dispensing equipment & parts; Ice boxes, industrial
Pr: Barry L Pennypacker
COO: Charles Hornbaker
CFO: David J Antoniuk
CFO: Carl J Laurino
Treas: Therese C Houlahan
Treas: Jose Maya
Sr VP: Thomas J Angst
Sr VP: Carl Laurino
Sr VP: Thomas G Musial
Sr VP: Andreas G Weishaar
VP: Keith Boerschinger
VP: Ashok Bonde
VP: Ted Bratthauar
VP: Eric Etchart
VP: Mark Haupt
VP: Josef Matosevic
VP: Bob Norlander
VP: Louis F Raymond
VP: Clifford Samuels
VP: Randy White
Board of Directors: Jose Maria Alapont, Robert G Bohn, Donald M Condon Jr, Anne M Cooney, Kenneth W Krueger, Jesse A Lynn, C David Myers, John C Pfeifer

MANITOWOC CRANE GROUP
See GROVE US LLC

D-U-N-S 96-511-8755 IMP/EXP
■ **MANITOWOC CRANES LLC**
(*Suby of* MANITOWOC CO INC) ★
2401 S 30th St, Manitowoc, WI 54220-5919
Tel (920) 684-6621 *Founded/Ownrshp* 1996
Sales 125.0MM^E *EMP* 362^E
SIC 3531 Construction machinery
VP: Lb Smith
VP Bus Dev: Paul A Boggs
DP Dir: Dave Patrikus
VP Opers: Daniel Kaltenbaugh
Sfty Mgr: Corey Zeddies
Ql Cn Mgr: David Dahleen

D-U-N-S 96-752-3382
■ **MANITOWOC FOODSERVICE COMPANIES LLC**
(*Suby of* MANITOWOC FOODSERVICE INC) ★
2227 Welbilt Blvd, Trinity, FL 34655-5130
Tel (727) 375-7010 *Founded/Ownrshp* 2015
Sales 470.1MM^E *EMP* 1,500
SIC 6719 Investment holding companies, except banks
CEO: Hubertus M Muehlhaeuser
COO: Josef Matosevic
CFO: John O Stewart
Manager: Kenny Smith

D-U-N-S 08-015-6097
▲ **MANITOWOC FOODSERVICE INC**
2227 Welbilt Blvd, Trinity, FL 34655-5130
Tel (727) 375-7010 *Founded/Ownrshp* 2015
Sales 494.3MM^E *EMP* 1,500^E
Tkr Sym MFS *Exch* NYS
SIC 3585 3589 Air conditioning equipment, complete; Food warming equipment, commercial
Pr: Hubertus Muehlhaeuser
COO: Josef Matosevic
CFO: John O Stewart
Sr VP: Richard N Caron
Sr VP: Phil Dei Dolori
Sr VP: Maurice D Jones
Sr VP: Chris Karssiens
Sr VP: Andreas G Weishaar
Sr VP: Bob Wonder
Sls Dir: Rick Zuehlke

D-U-N-S 05-529-8384 IMP
MANITOWOC TOOL AND MACHINING LLC
MTM
4211 Clipper Dr, Manitowoc, WI 54220-4115
Tel (920) 682-8825 *Founded/Ownrshp* 1965
Sales 95.0MM^E *EMP* 300^E
SIC 3441 Fabricated structural metal
Pr: Scott J Mertens
Pr: Steve Schiller
**CFO:* Jean Hansen
Ql Cn Mgr: Henry Butkovich

MANKATO AREA PUBLIC SCHOOL
See INDEPENDENT SCHOOL DISTRICT NO 77

D-U-N-S 00-949-1770 IMP/EXP
MANKE LUMBER CO INC
SUPERIOR WOOD TREATING
1717 Marine View Dr, Tacoma, WA 98422-4192
Tel (253) 572-6252 *Founded/Ownrshp* 1952
Sales 98.9MM^E *EMP* 450
SIC 2421 2491 2499 Lumber: rough, sawed or planed; Wood preserving; Poles & pole crossarms, treated wood; Posts, treated wood; Flooring, treated wood block; Mulch or sawdust products, wood
Pr: Charles Manke
Chf Mktg O: Randy Jordan
**VP:* James Manke

D-U-N-S 60-284-1488
MANKO WINDOW SYSTEMS INC
800 Hayes Dr, Manhattan, KS 66502-5087
Tel (785) 776-9643 *Founded/Ownrshp* 1989
Sales 95.1MM^E *EMP* 375
SIC 3442 1799 5039 Metal doors, sash & trim; Store fronts, prefabricated, metal; Glass tinting, architectural or automotive; Glass construction materials
Pr: Gary Jones
COO: Bill Ulrich
CFO: Bill Ulrich
**Sec:* Joe Jones
VP: Kevin Dix
**VP:* Steve Jones
Exec: Debbie Rowe
Site Mgr: Kevin Bauer
Sfty Mgr: Nick Markson
Plnt Mgr: Joe Modean
Sales Exec: Scott Leiker

D-U-N-S 16-025-7473 IMP
MANN + HUMMEL INC
(*Suby of* MANN + HUMMEL GMBH)
6400 S Sprinkle Rd, Portage, MI 49002-9706
Tel (269) 329-3900 *Founded/Ownrshp* 1996
Sales 1.9MMM^E *EMP* 1,000
SIC 3559 3585 Plastics working machinery; Dehumidifiers electric, except portable
Pr: Alfred Weber

D-U-N-S 11-282-7332 IMP
MANN + HUMMEL USA INC
(*Suby of* MANN + HUMMEL INC) ★
6400 S Sprinkle Rd, Portage, MI 49002-9706
Tel (269) 329-3900 *Founded/Ownrshp* 1983
Sales 899.0MM^E *EMP* 500
SIC 3089 3714 Injection molding of plastics; Motor vehicle parts & accessories
CEO: Alfred Weber
**Pr:* Frank B Jehle
Pr: Julie Thomas
**Pr:* Emese Weissenbacher

D-U-N-S 02-906-5273
MANN PACKING CO INC
1333 Schilling Pl, Salinas, CA 93901-4535
Tel (831) 422-7405 *Founded/Ownrshp* 1945
Sales 132.4MM^E *EMP* 500
SIC 0723 4783 0722 Vegetable packing services; Packing & crating; Crop harvesting
CEO: Lorri Koster
**Pr:* Michael Jarrod
**CFO:* William Beaton
**Ch:* Richard Ramsey
Board of Directors: Don Nucci, William Ramsey

D-U-N-S 17-150-7473 IMP
MANN+HUMMEL FILTRATION TECHNOLOGY GROUP INC
(*Suby of* MANN+HUMMEL FILTRATION TECHNOLOGY INTERMEDIATE HOLDINGS INC) ★
1 Wix Way, Gastonia, NC 28054-6142
Tel (704) 869-3300 *Founded/Ownrshp* 2004
Sales 884.7MM^E *EMP* 5,543^E
SIC 3714 5013 Motor vehicle brake systems & parts; Filters: oil, fuel & air, motor vehicle; Motor vehicle body components & frame; Automotive supplies & parts
Pr: Keith Wilson
**Pr:* Jorge Schertel
**CFO:* Steven Klueg
Sr VP: Greg Dillman
Sr VP: Dave Sturgess
Sr VP: Kay Teixeira
Dist Mgr: Tom Hildebrand
CIO: Karl Westrick
Mktg Mgr: Georgianne Dickey

D-U-N-S 17-221-4814 IMP/EXP
MANN+HUMMEL FILTRATION TECHNOLOGY HOLDINGS INC
1 Wix Way, Gastonia, NC 28054-6142
Tel (704) 869-3300 *Founded/Ownrshp* 2016
Sales 3.0MMM^E *EMP* 5,615^E
SIC 3714

D-U-N-S 17-221-4194
MANN+HUMMEL FILTRATION TECHNOLOGY INTERMEDIATE HOLDINGS INC
(*Suby of* MANN + HUMMEL USA INC) ★
1 Wix Way, Gastonia, NC 28054-6142
Tel (704) 869-3300 *Founded/Ownrshp* 2004
Sales 899.0MM *EMP* 5,632^E
Accts Deloitte & Touche Llp Charlot
SIC 3714 Filters: oil, fuel & air, motor vehicle; Connecting rods, motor vehicle engine; Motor vehicle brake systems & parts
Pr: Keith A Wilson
Ch Bd: James S McElya
CFO: Steven P Klueg
Sr VP: Dave McColley
Sr VP: David E Sturgess
Sr VP: Kay Teixeira
VP: Dave Sturgess
CIO: Karl J Westrick
Genl Couns: Maggie Drozd

D-U-N-S 15-763-8458 IMP/EXP
MANN+HUMMEL FILTRATION TECHNOLOGY US LLC
(*Suby of* MANN+HUMMEL FILTRATION TECHNOLOGY GROUP INC) ★
1 Wix Way, Gastonia, NC 28054-6142
Tel (704) 869-3300 *Founded/Ownrshp* 2004
Sales 331.2MM^E *EMP* 657
SIC 3714 Filters: oil, fuel & air, motor vehicle
Sr VP: Dave McColley
S&M/VP: Jeff Blocher
Pdt Mgr: Brad Drake
Pdt Mgr: Tim Tarte

D-U-N-S 78-101-4944 IMP
MANN+HUMMEL PUROLATOR FILTERS LLC
OE FILTERS
(*Suby of* MANN + HUMMEL INC) ★
3200 Natal St, Fayetteville, NC 28306-2845
Tel (910) 425-4181 *Founded/Ownrshp* 2006
Sales 1.0MMM *EMP* 1,000^E
SIC 3569 Filters
CEO: Alfred Weber
**CFO:* Frank B Jehle

MANNA BREAD DEVELOPMENT
See MANA DEVELOPMENT LLC

D-U-N-S 84-055-6351
▲ **MANNATECH INC**
600 S Royal Ln Ste 200, Coppell, TX 75019-3828
Tel (972) 471-7400 *Founded/Ownrshp* 1993
Sales 180.2MM *EMP* 287^E
Tkr Sym MTEX *Exch* NGS
SIC 2833 Medicinals & botanicals
Pr: Alfredo Bala
**Ch Bd:* J Stanley Fredrick
Pr: Yong Jae Park
Pr: Christopher J Simons
CFO: David A Johnson
Treas: Ronald D Norman
**V Ch Bd:* Robert A Toth
Sr VP: Joel Bikman
VP: Russell Wood
Opers Mgr: MEI Khoo
Art Dir: Scott Shelton
Board of Directors: Linda K Ferrell, Gerald E Gilbert, Larry A Jobe, Kevin Robbins, Eric W Schrier

D-U-N-S 07-368-6594
MANNING & NAPIER ADVISORS LLC
290 Woodcliff Dr Ste 300, Fairport, NY 14450-4298
Tel (800) 551-0224 *Founded/Ownrshp* 1970
Sales 176.2MM^E *EMP* 425
SIC 6282 8742 7375 Investment advisory service; Management consulting services; On-line data base information retrieval
CEO: Patrick Cunningham
**Pr:* B Reuben Auspitz
**Pr:* Jeff S Coons
CFO: Brian Foster
**CFO:* James Mikolaichik
**Treas:* William Manning
VP: Donna Dhont
VP: Chris Labounty
VP: Colin Schleifer
**Prin:* Fonda Herrick
CTO: Peer Boerner

D-U-N-S 96-913-8333
▲ **MANNING & NAPIER INC**
290 Woodcliff Dr Ste 300, Fairport, NY 14450-4298
Tel (585) 325-6880 *Founded/Ownrshp* 1970
Sales 327.8MM *EMP* 525^E
Tkr Sym MN *Exch* NYS
SIC 6282 8742 6722 Investment advice; Investment advisory service; Management consulting services; Management investment, open-end
CEO: William Manning
Pr: Jeffrey S Coons
CFO: James Mikolaichik
Ofcr: Richard B Yates
Trst Ofcr: Megan Henry
Ex VP: Charles H Stamey
VP: Jason Badesha
VP: Cary Clayborn
VP: Stephanie Cochran
VP: Antony Desorbo
VP: Ben Gorton
VP: Greg Hodges
VP: Chris Labounty
VP: Russell M Mergelas
VP: Scott Musick
VP: Winston Nelson
VP: Deanna Perry
VP: Scott Pilchard
VP: Michael Purcell
VP: Chris Roop
VP: Kyle C Ryan
Board of Directors: Richard Barrington, Richard Goldberg, Barbara Goodstein, Michael E Jones, Edward J Pettinella, Geoffrey Rosenberger

D-U-N-S 00-234-9256 IMP/EXP
MANNINGTON MILLS INC (NJ)
MANNINGTON RSILIENT FLOORS DIV
75 Mannington Mills Rd, Salem, NJ 08079-2009
Tel (856) 935-3000 *Founded/Ownrshp* 1915
Sales 775.5MM^E *EMP* 2,390
SIC 3996 3253 2273 2435 Hard surface floor coverings; Wall tile, ceramic; Floor tile, ceramic; Rugs, tufted; Carpets, hand & machine made; Veneer stock, hardwood; Hardwood plywood, prefinished; Panels, hardwood plywood; Plywood, hardwood or hardwood faced
Ch Bd: Keith S Campbell
**Pr:* Thomas S Davis
**COO:* Russel Grizzel
CFO: Debbie Freels
**Treas:* Francis J Norris
Sr VP: Edward Duncan
VP: Alonzo Burns
VP: Barbara Gallagher
VP: Mark Hollinger
VP: Dave Kitts
VP: Jay Kopelson

MANNINGTON RSILIENT FLOORS DIV
See MANNINGTON MILLS INC

MANOR CARE
See HCR MANORCARE MEDICAL SERVICES OF FLORIDA LLC

D-U-N-S 78-398-3414
■ **MANOR CARE INC**
(*Suby of* CARLYLE GROUP L P) ★
333 N Summit St Ste 103, Toledo, OH 43604-2617
Tel (419) 252-5500 *Founded/Ownrshp* 2007
Sales 1.0MMM^E *EMP* 1,500
SIC 8051 8082 8062 Extended care facility; Home health care services; General medical & surgical hospitals
Pr: Paul A Ormond
**COO:* Stephen L Guillard
**CFO:* Steven M Cavanaugh
CFO: Kedon Shaw
VP: Nancy A Edwards
VP: John K Graham
VP: Lynn M Hood
VP: John I Remenar
**VP:* Spencer C Moler
VP: Linda E Neumann
VP: David B Parker
**VP:* Richard A Parr II
Exec: Doug Pearson

D-U-N-S 04-954-6781
■ **MANOR CARE OF AMERICA INC**
(*Suby of* MANOR CARE INC) ★
333 N Summit St Ste 103, Toledo, OH 43604-2617
Tel (419) 252-5500 *Founded/Ownrshp* 1998
Sales 116.0MM^E *EMP* 700
SIC 8051 8062 8082 Extended care facility; General medical & surgical hospitals; Home health care services
Pr: Paul A Ormond
**COO:* M Keith Weikel
**CFO:* Geoffrey G Myers
VP: William Kinschner
**VP:* Muriy Mercier

D-U-N-S 05-022-3239
MANOR INDEPENDENT SCHOOL DISTRICT
10335 Us Highway 290 E, Manor, TX 78653-4686
Tel (512) 278-4000 *Founded/Ownrshp* 1900
Sales 101.9MM *EMP* 1,200
Accts Maxwell Locke & Ritter Llp Au
SIC 8211 Public elementary school; Public junior high school; Public senior high school
Pr Dir: Abby Chalmers
Teacher Pr: Martivel Sedillo
HC Dir: Linda Townsend

MANORCARE HLTH SRVCES- KENOSHA
See HEARTLAND-WASHINGTON MANOR OF KENOSHA WI LLC

MANORWOOD HOMES
See COMMODORE CORP

MANPOWER
See RIGHT MANAGEMENT INC

MANPOWER
See HAT LIMITED PARTNERSHIP

MANPOWER
See CPM LTD INC

D-U-N-S 07-615-2776
■ **MANPOWER INC OF NEW YORK**
(*Suby of* MANPOWERGROUP INC) ★
100 W Manpower Pl, Milwaukee, WI 53212-4030
Tel (414) 961-1000 *Founded/Ownrshp* 1953
Sales 116.0MM^E *EMP* 700
SIC 7363 Manpower pools
Pr: Jeff Joerres
**Pr:* Jonas Prising
Ofcr: Mark Toth
VP: Sherri Albinger
VP: William F Carollo
**VP:* Terry Hueneke
**VP:* James J Katte
**VP:* Walter Kozlowski
VP: Julie Krey

*VP: Douglas Krueger
VP: Byrne Luft
VP: Patricia Puccinelli
VP: Mike Stull

D-U-N-S 78-201-5911
▲ MANPOWERGROUP INC
100 W Manpower Pl, Milwaukee, WI 53212-4030
Tel (414) 961-1000 Founded/Ownrshp 1948
Sales 19.3MMM EMP 27,000
Tkr Sym MAN Exch NYS
SIC 7363 7361 Help supply services; Temporary help service; Office help supply service; Employment agencies; Executive placement
Ch Bd: Jonas Prising
Pr: Darryl Green
CFO: John T McGinnis
Sr VP: Richard D Buchband
Exec: Roxanne Hollingsworth
Exec: Michael J Van Handel
Brnch Mgr: Bryant Lucio
Brnch Mgr: Linda Ragsdale
Brnch Mgr: Antonice Thomas
Genl Mgr: Louise Whitelaw
Opers Supe: Ann Schnee
Board of Directors: Edward J Zore, Gina R Boswell, William Downe, John F Ferraro, Patricia Hemingway Hall, Julie M Howard, Roberto Mendoza, Paul Read, Elizabeth P Sartain, John R Walter

MANSFIELD BLANKING DIV
See SHILOH CORP

D-U-N-S 96-869-1241
MANSFIELD ENERGY CORP
1025 Airport Pkwy, Gainesville, GA 30501-6813
Tel (678) 450-2000 Founded/Ownrshp 2010
Sales 5.2MMM EMP 450E
Accts Smith & Howard Cpas Atlanta
SIC 5172 4212 1796 Petroleum products; Petroleum haulage, local; Pollution control equipment installation
CEO: Michael F Mansfield
*Pr: John Byrd
*Treas: Mike Davino

D-U-N-S 06-138-1935
MANSFIELD INDEPENDENT SCHOOL DISTRICT (TX)
605 E Broad St, Mansfield, TX 76063-1766
Tel (817) 299-6300 Founded/Ownrshp 1912
Sales 321.2MM EMP 4,228
Accts Whitley Penn Llp Houston Tex
SIC 8211 Public elementary school; Public junior high school; Public senior high school
Admn Mgr: Gary Manns
IT Man: Juanita Dorsette

D-U-N-S 03-372-3990
MANSFIELD OIL CO OF GAINESVILLE INC
(Suby of MANSFIELD ENERGY CORP) ★
1025 Airport Pkwy, Gainesville, GA 30501-6833
Tel (678) 450-2000 Founded/Ownrshp 1957
Sales 5.2MMM EMP 259E
SIC 5172

D-U-N-S 19-614-6781 IMP/EXP
MANSFIELD PLUMBING PRODUCTS LLC
(Suby of ORGANIZACION CORONA S A)
150 E 1st St, Perrysville, OH 44864-9421
Tel (419) 938-5211 Founded/Ownrshp 2004
Sales 156.1MME EMP 698
SIC 3261 3463 3088 3431 3432 5074 Vitreous plumbing fixtures; Plumbing fixture forgings, nonferrous; Plastics plumbing fixtures; Bathtubs: enameled iron, cast iron or pressed metal; Shower stalls, metal; Plumbing fixture fittings & trim; Plumbing fittings & supplies
Pr: Jim Morando
CFO: Phillip Taggart
Dir IT: Jake Bright
Dir IT: Jeff Lutz
Netwrk Mgr: Brian Fuhrmann
VP Mfg: Sergio Villegas
Prd Mgr: Dale Lepp
VP Mktg: Richard Oreagan
Manager: Bill Halsted

D-U-N-S 00-794-2824 IMP/EXP
MANSON CONSTRUCTION CO (WA)
(Suby of MANSON CONSTRUCTION HOLDING CO) ★
5209 E Marginal Way S, Seattle, WA 98134-2409
Tel (206) 762-0850 Founded/Ownrshp 1905
Sales 407.2MM EMP 750
SIC 1629

D-U-N-S 19-409-7960
MANSON CONSTRUCTION HOLDING CO
5209 E Marginal Way S, Seattle, WA 98134-2409
Tel (206) 762-0850 Founded/Ownrshp 2012
Sales 295.5MME EMP 751E
SIC 1629 Marine construction
Pr: Eric V Haug

D-U-N-S 06-012-4047
MANTECA UNIFIED SCHOOL DISTRICT
2271 W Louise Ave, Manteca, CA 95337-8381
Tel (209) 825-3200 Founded/Ownrshp 1966
Sales 87.8MME EMP 1,400
Accts Vavrinek Trine Day & Co Ll
SIC 8211 Public combined elementary & secondary school
*Prin: Frank Gonzales
Dir IT: Colby Clark
Pr Dir: Victoria Brunn
HC Dir: Bhatti Rupinder

MANTECH ADVANCED SYSTEMS INTL
See MANTECH SYSTEMS ENGINEERING CORP

D-U-N-S 83-891-8183
■ MANTECH GRAY HAWK SYSTEMS INC
(Suby of MANTECH INTERNATIONAL CORP) ★
7799 Leesburg Pike 700s, Falls Church, VA 22043-2408
Tel (703) 610-9232 Founded/Ownrshp 2005
Sales 60.9MME EMP 5,600
SIC 7373 7378 Systems integration services; Computer maintenance & repair
CEO: Harry Howton
*Pr: Marshall Godwin
*Sr VP: Michael Weixel
Board of Directors: Jeffrey S Brown, Geroge J Pederson, Kevin M Phillips

D-U-N-S 05-351-8312
▲ MANTECH INTERNATIONAL CORP
12015 Lee Jackson Hwy, Fairfax, VA 22033-3300
Tel (703) 218-6000 Founded/Ownrshp 1968
Sales 1.5MMM EMP 7,100E
Tkr Sym MANT Exch NGS
SIC 7373 8711 7379 Systems software development services; Systems engineering, computer related; Engineering services; Computer related consulting services
Ch Bd: George J Pedersen
Pr: Louis M Addeo
*CFO: Judith L Bjornaas
*CFO: Kevin M Phillips
Chf Mktg O: Carl Buising
Ex VP: Jeffrey S Brown
Ex VP: Bonnie J Cook
Ex VP: Stuart Davis
Ex VP: Carlos S Echalar
Ex VP: Daniel J Keefe
Ex VP: Sally Sullivan
Ex VP: Stan Surrette
Sr VP: Christopher Bishop
Sr VP: Michael Brogan
Sr VP: Matthew E Candy
Sr VP: Stephen J Comber
Sr VP: Stephen Comber
Sr VP: Damian Dipippa
Sr VP: Robert P Frisbie
Sr VP: Paul T Gentile
Sr VP: H Christopher Goodrich
Board of Directors: Richard L Armitage, Mary K Bush, Barry G Campbell, Walter R Fatzinger Jr, Richard J Kerr, Kenneth A Minihan, Stephen W Porter

D-U-N-S 17-424-5993
■ MANTECH SYSTEMS ENGINEERING CORP
MANTECH ADVANCED SYSTEMS INTL
(Suby of MANTECH INTERNATIONAL CORP) ★
12015 Lee Jackson Hwy, Fairfax, VA 22033-3300
Tel (703) 218-6000 Founded/Ownrshp 1985
Sales 122.6MME EMP 2,501
SIC 7373 8711 Systems engineering, computer related; Engineering services
CEO: George J Pedersen
*Pr: Kenneth J Farquhar
*Treas: John A Moore Jr
*Ex VP: Jeffrey S Brown
*Ex VP: M Stuart Davis
*Ex VP: Sally Sullivan
*Sr VP: Matthew P Galaski
*VP: Louis M Addeo
*VP: Kent A Bridges
*VP: Kevin M Phillips
QC Dir: Liz Burnett

D-U-N-S 80-100-8228
■ MANTECH TELECOMMUNICATIONS AND INFORMATION SYSTEMS CORP
(Suby of MANTECH INTERNATIONAL CORP) ★
12015 Lee Jackson Mem Hwy, Fairfax, VA 22033-3300
Tel (703) 218-6000 Founded/Ownrshp 1982
Sales 92.6MME EMP 1,113
SIC 7373 Computer systems analysis & design
Pr: Dan Keefe
*Prin: Ronald R Spoehl
Ex Dir: Hunter Trice
Snr Sftwr: Ben Newman
Software D: Nathaniel Hall

D-U-N-S 06-631-6522 IMP
MANUAL WOODWORKERS & WEAVERS INC
3737 Howard Gap Rd, Hendersonville, NC 28792-3174
Tel (828) 692-7333 Founded/Ownrshp 1974
Sales 101.9MME EMP 506E
SIC 2392 Household furnishings
Pr: Travis L Oates
*CFO: James Clarke
*Co-Pr: Molly Oates Sherrill
Genl Mgr: Randy Gilliland

D-U-N-S 00-697-6724
■ MANUFACTURERS AND TRADERS TRUST CO
M&T
(Suby of WILMINGTON TRUST CORP) ★
1 M And T Plz, Buffalo, NY 14203-2309
Tel (716) 842-4200 Founded/Ownrshp 1856, 2011
Sales NA EMP 14,243
SIC 6022 State commercial banks
CEO: Robert G Wilmers
*V Ch: Carl L Campbell
Pr: Jim Ahrens
*CFO: Michael P Pinto
*Ofcr: Richard S Gold
*Ex VP: Emerson L Brumback
*Ex VP: Atwood Collins III
*Ex VP: John F Cook
Sr VP: Nicholas Lambrow
VP: Evis Daum
VP: Tom Esposito
VP: Robert S Graber
VP: Patti Haan
VP: Courtney Herbert
VP: Sharon O'Brien
VP: Wenting Qin
VP: Leslie Wallace
VP: Scott Weber

D-U-N-S 96-826-0323 IMP/EXP
■ MANUFACTURERS CHEMICALS LLC
(Suby of SYNALLOY CORP) ★
4325 Old Tasso Rd Ne, Cleveland, TN 37312-5836
Tel (423) 476-6666 Founded/Ownrshp 1919
Sales 173.3MME EMP 406
SIC 2899 Chemical preparations
Pr: Larry Sloan
*Ex VP: J Greg Gibson
*Ex VP: Kevin Hrebenar
*VP: Ron Smesny

D-U-N-S 01-073-0120 IMP
MANUFACTURERS INDUSTRIAL GROUP LLC
M I G
659 Natchez Trace Dr, Lexington, TN 38351-4125
Tel (731) 968-3601 Founded/Ownrshp 1997
Sales 113.3MME EMP 407
SIC 3499 2531

D-U-N-S 86-938-0840
MANUFACTURERS SERVICES LIMITED
(Suby of CELESTICA INC)
300 Baker Ave Ste 106, Concord, MA 01742-2131
Tel (978) 287-5630 Founded/Ownrshp 2004
Sales 171.7MME EMP 2,280
SIC 3571 3577 3572 3661 3663 Electronic computers; Computer peripheral equipment; Computer storage devices; Telephone sets, all types except cellular radio; Cellular radio telephone
VP Opers: John Boucher
Treas: Sean T Lannan
Sr Cor Off: Robert Donahue
Sr Cor Off: Albert Motini
Chf Cred: Tom Pugh
Bd of Dir: Robert Bradshaw
Bd of Dir: George Chamillard
Bd of Dir: Thompson Dean
Bd of Dir: Jeffrey Fishman
Bd of Dir: John Fort
Bd of Dir: Dermott O'Flanagan
Bd of Dir: John J Walsh
Bd of Dir: William Weyand
Bd of Dir: Curtis Wozniak
Bd of Dir: Karl Wyss
Ofcr: Rodolfo Archbold
Ex VP: Bruce Leasure
Ex VP: Bert Notini
Ex VP: James N Poor
VP: Richard Buckingham
VP: Frank Coyle

D-U-N-S 00-318-5758
MAOLA MILK AND ICE CREAM CO LLC (NC)
(Suby of MARVA MAID DAIRY DIVISION) ★
305 Avenue C, New Bern, NC 28560-3113
Tel (252) 638-1131 Founded/Ownrshp 1935, 2003
Sales 87.3MME EMP 335E
SIC 2026 2024 Fluid milk; Ice cream, bulk
Chf Mktg O: Ricky Bennet
Genl Mgr: Danny Lovell
*Genl Mgr: Steve Nicoll
Genl Mgr: Tony Norbut
CIO: Lisa Dixon
IT Man: Amy Horrell
Sfty Mgr: Sue Shivar

D-U-N-S 06-858-8789
MAP INTERNATIONAL (INC)
MEDICAL ASSISTANCE PROGRAMS
4700 Glynco Pkwy, Brunswick, GA 31525-6901
Tel (912) 265-6010 Founded/Ownrshp 1954
Sales 547.0MM EMP 200
Accts Capincrouse Llp Atlanta Geo
SIC 8399 Health & welfare council
Pr: Steve Stirling
*CEO: Chok-Pin Foo
*CFO: Daniel C Reed
*Ch: Immanuel Phangaraj
Ofcr: Candace Rowell
Ofcr: Lauren Wright
VP: Edwin Corr
Assoc Dir: Jacqueline Cameron

MAP OF EASTON
See MOLDED ACOUSTICAL PRODUCTS OF EASTON INC

D-U-N-S 02-494-1077
MAPCO EXPRESS INC
(Suby of COPEC INC.)
7102 Commerce Way, Brentwood, TN 37027-2896
Tel (615) 771-6701 Founded/Ownrshp 2016
Sales 714.1MME EMP 1,800
SIC 5541 5411 Gasoline service stations; Convenience stores, chain
Pr: Uzi Yemin
COO: Lyn Gregory
CFO: Ed Morgan
VP: Keith Johnson
VP Mktg: Paul Pierce

D-U-N-S 14-834-5382 IMP/EXP
MAPEI CORP
(Suby of MAPEI SPA)
1144 E Newport Center Dr, Deerfield Beach, FL 33442-7725
Tel (954) 246-8888 Founded/Ownrshp 1988
Sales 320.6MME EMP 875
SIC 2891 Adhesives
Pr: Luigi Di Geso
Dir Bus: Laith Haboubi
Prin: Rainer Blair
IT Man: Don Olaski
IT Man: Walt Reister
Plnt Mgr: Claude Brouin
Manager: Mike Granatowski
Board of Directors: Dr Giorgio Squinzi

D-U-N-S 05-525-4867
MAPFRE INSURANCE CO
901 Franklin Ave, Garden City, NY 11530-2933
Tel (516) 564-8000 Founded/Ownrshp 2011
Sales NA EMP 2
SIC 6411 Insurance agents, brokers & service
Pr: Gerral Felson

D-U-N-S 16-757-9080
MAPFRE PRAICO CORP
(Suby of MAPFRE AMERICA SA)
297 Ave Chardon Urb Tres, San Juan, PR 00918
Tel (787) 250-6500 Founded/Ownrshp 2004
Sales NA EMP 600E
SIC 6411 Insurance agents & brokers
CEO: Raul Costilla
*Ch Bd: Antonio Huertas
VP: Antonio Esposito

D-U-N-S 10-583-1531
MAPFRE USA CORP
(Suby of MAPFRE, SA)
211 Main St, Webster, MA 01570-2249
Tel (508) 943-9000 Founded/Ownrshp 2008
Sales NA EMP 2,373
SIC 6331 Fire, marine & casualty insurance; Automobile insurance
Pr: Jaime Tamayo
*CFO: Randall V Becker
CFO: Jose Martinez
*Treas: Robert E McKenna
VP: Patrick J McDonald
VP: Michael Sher
MIS Dir: Julio Morales
IT Man: Ines J Torres
Info Man: Ray Perez
Snr Mgr: Steven Keller
Snr Mgr: Maria Molina

D-U-N-S 00-302-3272
MAPLE DONUTS INC (PA)
3455 E Market St, York, PA 17402-2696
Tel (717) 757-7826 Founded/Ownrshp 1946, 1975
Sales 86.6MME EMP 250
SIC 2051 5461 Doughnuts, except frozen; Bakeries
Pr: Charles F Burnside
*Treas: Susan M Burnside
*VP: Ralph E Wooten
Sls Dir: Damian Burnside

D-U-N-S 03-270-5838
MAPLE GROVE HOSPITAL CORP
9875 Hospital Dr, Maple Grove, MN 55369-4648
Tel (763) 581-1000 Founded/Ownrshp 2006
Sales 151.1MM EMP 34E
Accts Deloitte & Touche Llp Minneap
SIC 8062 General medical & surgical hospitals
Pr: Andrew S Cochrane
Dir Rx: Megan Matack
CIO: Pat Taffe
Pathlgst: Sue Schlafmann
Doctor: Leigh Rowan-Kelly
Pharmcst: Kirsten Bosch
Pharmcst: Kelly Hadsall
Cert Phar: Casey Timm
Snr Mgr: Sheryl Vugteveen

MAPLE LEAF FARMS
See MAPLE LEAF INC

D-U-N-S 01-652-2823 IMP/EXP
MAPLE LEAF FARMS INC
SERENADE FOODS
(Suby of MAPLE LEAF FARMS) ★
9166 N 200 E, Milford, IN 46542-9722
Tel (574) 453-4500 Founded/Ownrshp 1967
Sales 9.6MME EMP 1,100
SIC 0259 2015 Duck farm; Duck slaughtering & processing
Ch Bd: Terry L Tucker
*Pr: John Tucker
*CFO: John Kidiger
*CFO: Scott Reinholt
Mktg Dir: Cindy Cline
Mktg Dir: Cindy Turk
Manager: Dave Diehm

D-U-N-S 15-342-7885 IMP/EXP
MAPLE LEAF INC
MAPLE LEAF FARMS
101 E Church St, Leesburg, IN 46538-7701
Tel (574) 453-4455 Founded/Ownrshp 1958
Sales 9.6MME EMP 1,100
SIC 0259 2015 5159 Duck farm; Ducks, processed; Chicken, processed; Feathers
Pr: Terry L Tucker B S
*CFO: Scott Reinholt
*Co-Pr: Scott Tucker
*VP: Mike Turk
Dir Lab: Rhonda Murdoch
*Prin: John Tucker
CTO: Jeff Lohser
Mktg Mgr: Megan Reinholt
Sls Mgr: John Palumbo

D-U-N-S 08-024-8650
MAPLE MOUNTAIN ENTERPRISES INC (NV)
588 S 2000 W, Springville, UT 84663-3047
Tel (801) 418-2000 Founded/Ownrshp 1994
Sales 225.0MME EMP 200E
SIC 2023 Dietary supplements, dairy & non-dairy based
CEO: Robert Conlee

D-U-N-S 16-182-0212 IMP/EXP
MAPLE MOUNTAIN GROUP INC
NEWAYS
(Suby of MAPLE MOUNTAIN ENTERPRISES INC) ★
588 S 2000 W, Springville, UT 84663-3047
Tel (801) 418-2000 Founded/Ownrshp 2006
Sales 225.0MME EMP 200
SIC 5999 Toiletries, cosmetics & perfumes
CEO: Robert S Conlee
*Pr: Bruce Murdock
*COO: Josh Kirschbaum
*CFO: Nate Brown
CFO: Debbie Stiner
*Treas: Glen L Tuttle
Chf Mktg O: Robert Finigan
*VP: Brian D Baxter
Dir Soc: Callie Rose
Mng Dir: Tomomi Kosugi
Mng Dir: Paul Vanwynsberghe

D-U-N-S 00-301-6409 IMP
MAPLE PRESS CO (PA)
MAPLE-VAIL
480 Willow Springs Ln, York, PA 17406-6047
Tel (717) 764-5911 Founded/Ownrshp 1903
Sales 224.6MME EMP 350
SIC 2732 2791 2789 2752 Books: printing & binding; Photocomposition, for the printing trade; Bookbinding & related work; Commercial printing, lithographic
CEO: James S Wisotzkey
*Ch Bd: John U Wisotzkey
VP: Bill Long
Genl Mgr: Andrew Van Sprang

Plnt Mgr: Curt Dolinger
Sales Exec: Shirley Baker

D-U-N-S 03-181-3538
MAPLE RIVER GRAIN & AGRONOMY LLC
1630 1st Ave S, Casselton, ND 58012-3910
Tel (701) 347-4465 *Founded/Ownrshp* 1904
Sales 147.0MM *EMP* 14
Accts Burke Myers & Associates Ltd
SIC 5153 5191 Grain elevators; Farm supplies

MAPLE-VAIL
See MAPLE PRESS CO

MAPLEHURST BAKERIES
See WESTON FOODS US INC

D-U-N-S 04-113-3034 EXP
MAPLEHURST BAKERIES LLC
(*Suby of* MAPLEHURST BAKERIES) ★
50 Maplehurst Dr, Brownsburg, IN 46112-9085
Tel (317) 858-9000 *Founded/Ownrshp* 2009
Sales 311.7MM^E *EMP* 1,031
SIC 2051 Cakes, pies & pastries
VP: Kevin Whitlock
VP: Jonathan Feigen
VP: Donald Niemeyer
VP: Carl Singer

D-U-N-S 06-800-5743
MAPLEHURST FARMS INC
936 S Moore Rd, Rochelle, IL 61068-9789
Tel (815) 562-8723 *Founded/Ownrshp* 1997
Sales 178.2MM^E *EMP* 75
SIC 5153 2879 4212 Grain & field beans; Agricultural chemicals; Local trucking, without storage
CEO: Carol Hayenga
**Pr:* Lyn Carmichael
**CFO:* Barbara Koehnke
Opers Mgr: Steve Delhotal

D-U-N-S 05-579-7609 IMP
MAPLES INDUSTRIES INC
2210 Moody Ridge Rd, Scottsboro, AL 35768-4114
Tel (256) 259-1327 *Founded/Ownrshp* 1984
Sales 452.9MM^E *EMP* 1,850^E
SIC 2273 Rugs, tufted
Pr: John Maples
**Pr:* John W Maples Jr
CFO: William Martin
Exec: Charlotte McDowel
CIO: Jackie Ba
Dir IT: Jacki Bass

D-U-N-S 00-211-9386
MAPLEVALE FARMS INC (NY)
2063 Allen Street Ext, Falconer, NY 14733-1710
Tel (716) 355-4114 *Founded/Ownrshp* 1969, 1975
Sales 119.0MM^E *EMP* 110
SIC 5141 Food brokers
Ch Bd: Douglas Neckers
**VP:* Bruce Neckers
Dist Mgr: Stuart Foster
Sfty Mgr: Alan McIntyre
Opers Mgr: Gary Neckers
Sls Mgr: Joe Boland
Sls Mgr: Dave Panek
Sales Asso: Jerry Costantini

D-U-N-S 78-267-1804
MAPP CONSTRUCTION LLC
344 3rd St, Baton Rouge, LA 70801-1307
Tel (225) 757-0111 *Founded/Ownrshp* 2003
Sales 120.0MM^E *EMP* 150
Accts Hannis T Bourgeois Llp Bato
SIC 1542 Commercial & office building, new construction; Commercial & office buildings, renovation & repair
Pr: Michael Polito
**CFO:* John McKowen
VP: Dana Emberton
**VP:* Mark Lahaye
VP: Richard Setliff
Opers Mgr: Vernon Anderson

MAPS
See NEW CO-OPERATIVE INC

MAQUET
See DATASCOPE CORP

D-U-N-S 83-089-5319 IMP
MAQUET CARDIOVASCULAR US SALES LLC
MAQUET MEDICAL SYSTEMS USA
(*Suby of* MAQUET GMBH)
45 Barbour Pond Dr, Wayne, NJ 07470-2094
Tel (201) 995-8700 *Founded/Ownrshp* 2009
Sales 144.5MM^E *EMP* 483^E
SIC 5047 Medical equipment & supplies
Pr: Raoul Quintero
**CFO:* Maximo Nougues
**Sr VP:* Philip Freed

D-U-N-S 16-802-1850 IMP
MAQUET INC
MAQUET MEDICAL SYSTEM USA
(*Suby of* GETINGE AB)
45 Barbour Pond Dr, Wayne, NJ 07470-2094
Tel (973) 709-7000 *Founded/Ownrshp* 2003
Sales 290.2MM^E *EMP* 842^E
SIC 5047 Medical & hospital equipment; Medical equipment & supplies
CEO: Raoul Quintero
Rgnl Mgr: Goran Steiner
Rgnl Mgr: Guochao Yang
Dir IT: Tyrone Marnotes
Software D: Kjell Elster
Opers Mgr: George Skeens
VP Sls: Serge Exshaw
VP Sls: Christoph Lenze
Sls Dir: Jim Hartman
Mktg Mgr: Gregory Johnson
Sls Mgr: Leo Marin

MAQUET MEDICAL SYSTEM USA
See MAQUET INC

MAQUET MEDICAL SYSTEMS USA
See MAQUET CARDIOVASCULAR US SALES LLC

D-U-N-S 06-902-8728 IMP
■ **MAR COR PURIFICATION INC** (PA)
(*Suby of* CANTEL MEDICAL CORP) ★
4450 Township Line Rd, Skippack, PA 19474
Tel (800) 633-3080 *Founded/Ownrshp* 1970
Sales 163.8MM^E *EMP* 600
SIC 3569 3677 Filters; Filtration devices, electronic
Pr: Curt Weitnauer
**VP:* Andrew G Stitzinger
Mtls Mgr: Kate M Getty

D-U-N-S 03-106-5410 EXP
MAR-CONE APPLIANCE PARTS CO
MARCONE SUPPLY
1 Cityplace Dr Ste 400, Saint Louis, MO 63141-7065
Tel (877) 993-9196 *Founded/Ownrshp* 1932
Sales 291.2MM^E *EMP* 650
SIC 5064 Appliance parts, household
Ch Bd: Mitchell Markow
**Pr:* Jim Souers
Sr VP: Dave Cook
VP: John Carroll
Brnch Mgr: Gregory Brown
Brnch Mgr: Terry Fluri
Sales Exec: Christopher Harris
Mktg Mgr: Isaac Williams
Sls Mgr: Paul Dooley

D-U-N-S 60-123-1657 EXP
MAR-JAC POULTRY INC
PROCESSING DIVISION
(*Suby of* MARJAC HOLDINGS LLC) ★
1020 Aviation Blvd, Gainesville, GA 30501-6839
Tel (770) 531-5000 *Founded/Ownrshp* 1954
Sales 282.8MM^E *EMP* 1,200^E
Accts Frost Pllc Little Rock Arka
SIC 0254 Poultry hatcheries
CEO: Al B Jamal
**CEO:* J Pete Martin
**CFO:* Mulham Shbeib
**CFO:* Mirza M Yaqub
VP: Donald Bull
**VP:* Doug Carnes
VP: Charlie Howington
VP: Ron Weaver
Rgnl Mgr: Michael Melenick
Brnch Mgr: Taylor Sipsy
Manager: Clifford Ross

D-U-N-S 07-932-5490
MAR-JAC POULTRY MS LLC
261 Marshall Durbin Dr, Waynesboro, MS 39367-3033
Tel (601) 735-3132 *Founded/Ownrshp* 2014, 2013
Sales 114.3MM^E *EMP* 1,000
SIC 2048 Prepared feeds
Genl Mgr: Dwayne Rawson

MAR-KELL SEAL
See QUADION LLC

D-U-N-S 01-763-7968 IMP
MARAMONT CORP
5600 1st Ave, Brooklyn, NY 11220-2550
Tel (718) 439-8900 *Founded/Ownrshp* 1981
Sales 108.9MM^E *EMP* 450
SIC 2099 8322 Ready-to-eat meals, salads & sandwiches; Salads, fresh or refrigerated; Sandwiches, assembled & packaged: for wholesale market; Individual & family services
Pr: George Chivari
**CFO:* Linda Jannzzkowski
MIS Dir: Barry Mittelmann

D-U-N-S 06-887-0880
MARANA AEROSPACE SOLUTIONS INC
(*Suby of* RELATIVITY CAPITAL LLC) ★
24641 E Pinal Air Park Rd, Marana, AZ 85653-9504
Tel (520) 682-4181 *Founded/Ownrshp* 2011
Sales 144.4MM^E *EMP* 673
SIC 4581 Aircraft maintenance & repair services; Aircraft servicing & repairing
CEO: James F Martin
Pr: Mike Michaels
**Sec:* Gayla Bella
Sr VP: Greg Mitchell
**VP:* Colin Buxton
VP: Michael Melvin
**VP:* Lou Moore
**VP:* Carl Shultz
**Prin:* Greg Emerson
VP Opers: Jack Keating
Sfty Mgr: Karen Hoskinson

D-U-N-S 07-983-6348
MARANA UNIFIED SCHOOL DISTRICT
11279 W Grier Rd, Marana, AZ 85653-9609
Tel (520) 682-4749 *Founded/Ownrshp* 2015
Sales 47.8MM^E *EMP* 1,173^E
SIC 8211 Public elementary & secondary schools
CFO: Dan Contorno
Ex Dir: Russell Federico
CTO: Bob Thomas
IT Man: Jan Truitt
HC Dir: Irisan Manalo

D-U-N-S 10-000-1668
MARANA UNIFIED SCHOOL DISTRICT PARENT/CITIZEN ORGANIZATION
11279 W Grier Rd, Marana, AZ 85653-9609
Tel (520) 682-3243 *Founded/Ownrshp* 1941
Sales 68.4MM^E *EMP* 1,600
SIC 8211 Public elementary & secondary schools
**Pr:* Dan Post
Exec: Brian Lundenbach
Dir IT: Dan Hunt
IT Man: Judith Braeutigam
Psych: Kimberly Bernazanni
Psych: Leatanya Koppa
Psych: Pam Settles

D-U-N-S 11-207-4179
MARATHON ASSET MANAGEMENT LP
1 Bryant Park Fl 38, New York, NY 10036-6737
Tel (212) 500-3000 *Founded/Ownrshp* 1998
Sales 84.1MM^E *EMP* 190^E
SIC 6282 Manager of mutual funds, contract or fee basis
CEO: Bruce Richards
COO: Andrew Rabinowitz
Ofcr: Christine Chartouni
Sr VP: Matthew Breckenridge
Sr VP: Nishi Kapoor
Sr VP: Robert Manley
Sr VP: Jelena Petrovic
VP: Nitin Chexal
VP: Jason Eidelstein
VP: Richard Horn
VP: Anupam Ladha
VP: Natalie Louie
VP: Michael Lynch
VP: Jared Z Mintz
VP: Michael Passantino
VP: Arthur Rosenberg

D-U-N-S 02-333-5987
MARATHON CHEESE CORP
304 East St, Marathon, WI 54448-9643
Tel (715) 443-2211 *Founded/Ownrshp* 1954
Sales 303.3MM^E *EMP* 2,000
SIC 2022 5143

D-U-N-S 62-487-3139 IMP/EXP
■ **MARATHON EQUIPMENT CO (DELAWARE)**
(*Suby of* DOVER ENGINEERED SYSTEMS INC) ★
Highway 9 S, Vernon, AL 35592
Tel (205) 695-9105 *Founded/Ownrshp* 1990
Sales 106.8MM^E *EMP* 540
SIC 3589 Commercial cooking & foodwarming equipment
Pr: Pat Carroll
**CFO:* Darren Bird
VP: Mitch Covington
**VP:* Tom Vatter
VP: Dave Young
Dir IT: Christina Harris
Manager: Tom Bailey
Manager: Robby Dehart
Manager: Jim Loeffler
Manager: Ryan Ottman
Manager: Michael Ryan

D-U-N-S 02-026-1079
■ **MARATHON INTERNATIONAL OIL CO**
(*Suby of* MARATHON PIPE LINE) ★
5555 San Felipe St # 2796, Houston, TX 77056-2796
Tel (713) 629-6600 *Founded/Ownrshp* 1961
Sales 166.4MM^E *EMP* 2,000
SIC 1311 1382 6519 Crude petroleum production; Natural gas production; Oil & gas exploration services; Real property lessors
Pr: V G Beghini
**VP:* D C Gerard
**VP:* K M Henning

D-U-N-S 01-326-0497
MARATHON MEDIA GROUP LLC
737 N Michigan Ave # 2060, Chicago, IL 60611-5660
Tel (312) 640-9700 *Founded/Ownrshp* 1996
Sales 90.1MM^E *EMP* 546
SIC 4832 Radio broadcasting stations
Sr Cor Off: Jared Golden
Ex VP: Bruce Buzil
VP: Jeffrey Mulder

D-U-N-S 05-512-2568 IMP/EXP
■ **MARATHON OIL CO**
MARATHON PIPE LINE
(*Suby of* MARATHON OIL CORP) ★
5555 San Felipe St # 2796, Houston, TX 77056-2799
Tel (713) 629-6600 *Founded/Ownrshp* 1981
Sales 1.0MMM^E *EMP* 3,000
SIC 2911 5171 5541 1311 4612 4613 Petroleum refining; Gasoline blending plants; Intermediate distillates; Heavy distillates; Petroleum bulk stations; Petroleum terminals; Filling stations, gasoline; Crude petroleum production; Natural gas production; Crude petroleum pipelines; Refined petroleum pipelines
Pr: Clarence P Cazalot Jr
COO: Jim Christie
Sr VP: Philip E Behrman
Sr VP: G D Golder
Sr VP: Steven B Hinchman
Sr VP: Steve J Lowden
Sr VP: Mary E Peters
Prin: Jeffrey L Hayman
Dir IT: Anne Hunt
Opers Mgr: William Browne

D-U-N-S 00-202-8801
▲ **MARATHON OIL CORP** (DE)
5555 San Felipe St # 2796, Houston, TX 77056-2796
Tel (713) 629-6600 *Founded/Ownrshp* 1887
Sales 5.8MMM *EMP* 2,611
Accts Pricewaterhousecoopers Llp Ho
Tkr Sym MRO *Exch* NYS
SIC 1311 2911 5171 5541 Crude petroleum & natural gas; Crude petroleum production; Natural gas production; Petroleum refining; Petroleum bulk stations & terminals; Gasoline service stations
Pr: Lee M Tillman
**Ch Bd:* Dennis H Reilley
CFO: Pat Wagner
CFO: Patrick J Wagner
Ex VP: Sylvia J Kerrigan
Ex VP: T Mitch Little
Ex VP: David E Roberts Jr
Ex VP: John Sult
Sr VP: G David Golder
Sr VP: Steven J Lowden
Sr VP: Mary Ellen Peters
VP: Frank W Bassetti
VP: Trevor Chargois
VP: Mohamed Harp
VP: Billie Hysong
VP: Catherine L Krajicek
VP: Garry Peiffer
VP: Lance W Robertson
VP: Christopher Roeser
VP: Doug Rogers
VP: Robert Sovine
Board of Directors: Gregory H Boyce, Pierre Brondeau, Chadwick C Deaton, Philip Lader, Michael E J Phelps

D-U-N-S 96-299-3101 IMP
■ **MARATHON PETROLEUM CO LP**
(*Suby of* MARATHON PETROLEUM CORP) ★
539 S Main St, Findlay, OH 45840-3229
Tel (419) 422-2121 *Founded/Ownrshp* 1997
Sales 27.3MMM^E *EMP* 24,210
SIC 5172 2951 2865 Gasoline; Asphalt paving mixtures & blocks; Cyclic crudes & intermediates
CEO: Gary Heminger
Pt: Brad Allsop
Pt: Mary Ellen Peters
Pt: J Michael Wilder
Pr: Ronald G Becker
CFO: Donald Templin
Sr VP: Tom Kelley
VP: Pamela Beall
VP: Pamela Km Beall
VP: Anthony R Kenney
VP: C Michael Palmer
VP: Craig Pierson
VP: Donald Wehrly

D-U-N-S 96-839-3996
▲ **MARATHON PETROLEUM CORP**
539 S Main St, Findlay, OH 45840-3229
Tel (419) 422-2121 *Founded/Ownrshp* 2009
Sales 72.2MMM *EMP* 45,440^E
Tkr Sym MPC *Exch* NYS
SIC 2911 5172 Petroleum refining; Gasoline
Ch Bd: Gary R Heminger
CFO: Timothy T Griffith
Sr VP: Raymond L Brooks
Sr VP: Thomas M Kelley
Sr VP: C Michael Palmer
Sr VP: John S Swearingen
VP: Sarah Fowler
VP: John J Quaid
VP: Donald W Wehrly
VP: J Michael Wilder
Comm Man: Chris Fox
Board of Directors: Evan Bayh, Charles E Bunch, David A Daberko, Steven A Davis, Donna A James, James E Rohr, Frank M Semple, John W Snow, John P Surma

D-U-N-S 08-042-2184
■ **MARATHON PETROLEUM SUPPLY LLC**
(*Suby of* MARATHON PETROLEUM CORP) ★
539 S Main St, Findlay, OH 45840-3229
Tel (419) 422-2121 *Founded/Ownrshp* 1997
Sales 57.3MM^E *EMP* 2,000
SIC 2911 Petroleum refining

MARATHON PIPE LINE
See MARATHON OIL CO

D-U-N-S 00-790-2836 IMP
■ **MARATHON PIPE LINE LLC**
(*Suby of* MARATHON PETROLEUM CORP) ★
539 S Main St Ste 7614, Findlay, OH 45840-3229
Tel (419) 422-2121 *Founded/Ownrshp* 2011
Sales 124.6MM^E *EMP* 487
SIC 4612 4613 Crude petroleum pipelines; Refined petroleum pipelines
CEO: Gary R Heminger
VP: Pamela K Beall
VP: Clifford C Cook
VP: R K McCord
VP: Rodney P Nichols
VP: John Parziale
VP: Michael A Peak
VP: G L Peiffer
VP: Mary E Peters
VP: J D Sparkman
VP: Jerry C Welch
Exec: Steve Cummins

D-U-N-S 07-228-0027
MARBORG INDUSTRIES
728 E Yanonali St, Santa Barbara, CA 93103-3233
Tel (805) 963-1852 *Founded/Ownrshp* 1974
Sales 154.3MM^E *EMP* 254
Accts Bartlett Pringle & Wolf Llp
SIC 4953 7359 7699 4212 Rubbish collection & disposal; Portable toilet rental; Septic tank cleaning service; Local trucking, without storage
Pr: Mario Borgatello Jr
**VP:* David Borgatello
Dir Risk M: Alan Coulter
Off Mgr: Roberto Medina
IT Man: Dennis Taylor

MARC ECKO COLLECTION
See MEE APPAREL LLC

D-U-N-S 09-448-7477 IMP
MARC GLASSMAN INC
MARC'S XPECT DRUGS
5841 W 130th St, Cleveland, OH 44130-9308
Tel (216) 265-7700 *Founded/Ownrshp* 1978
Sales 1.4MMM^E *EMP* 7,000
SIC 5331 Variety stores
Ch Bd: Marc Glassman
**Pr:* Kevin Yaugher
**CFO:* Beth Weiner
VP: Bob Guddy
VP: Mark Hartkop
VP: Jim Hocking
VP: Melanie Petropoulos
**Prin:* Harold E Leidner
Off Mgr: Michelle McFadden
IT Man: Stephanie Seney
Opers Mgr: Jim Howe

MARC LIFE
See MUNICH AMERICAN REASSURANCE CO PAC INC

D-U-N-S 82-707-4753 IMP/EXP
MARCAL MANUFACTURING LLC
SOUNDVIEW PAPER COMPANY
(*Suby of* SOUNDVIEW PAPER MILLS LLC) ★
1 Market St, Elmwood Park, NJ 07407-1401
Tel (201) 703-6225 *Founded/Ownrshp* 2008
Sales 279.2MM^E *EMP* 800^E
SIC 2676 Sanitary paper products; Towels, paper: made from purchased paper; Napkins, paper: made from purchased paper; Toilet paper: made from purchased paper

COO: Karl Meyers
CFO: Mike Roth
VP: Ray Heuchling
VP: Greg Kane
Exec: Mj J Dickson
VP Opers: Ben Wenberg
VP Sls: Jim Rochford
Sls Dir: Mike Conciatori
Mktg Mgr: Ginny Fjermestad
Manager: Larry Broderick
Manager: Jim Forrester

D-U-N-S 07-846-3743
MARCAL PAPER MILLS LLC
(*Suby of* SOUNDVIEW PAPER MILLS LLC) ★
1 Market St, Elmwood Park, NJ 07407-1493
Tel (201) 791-0852 *Founded/Ownrshp* 2008
Sales 199.1MM[E] *EMP* 800
SIC 2676 Sanitary paper products
Sr VP: Robert Jackson
Sfty Mgr: Donna McGauley

D-U-N-S 80-123-6142 IMP/EXP
MARCEGAGLIA USA INC
(*Suby of* MARCEGAGLIA SPECIALTIES SPA)
1001 E Waterfront Dr, Munhall, PA 15120-1098
Tel (412) 462-2185 *Founded/Ownrshp* 1991
Sales 110.7MM[E] *EMP* 135
SIC 3317 3312 Welded pipe & tubes; Iron & steel: galvanized, pipes, plates, sheets, etc.; Stainless steel
Pr: Francesco Tabarrini
Pr: David Cornelius
CEO: Antonio Marcegaglia
CFO: Robert Minster

D-U-N-S 06-134-4883
MARCH OF DIMES FOUNDATION
1275 Mamaroneck Ave, White Plains, NY 10605-5298
Tel (914) 428-7100 *Founded/Ownrshp* 1938
Sales 195.8MM *EMP* 1,200
Accts Kpmg Llp New York Ny
SIC 8399 Fund raising organization, non-fee basis
Pr: Jennifer L Howse
V Ch: Janice Icenhower
**COO:* Jane Massey
COO: Jane E Massey
CFO: Richard E Mulligan
**Ch:* Ken May
**Treas:* Childs Al
Treas: Nancy T Lukitsch
Trst: Jos F Cordero
Trst: Billy B Hill
VP: Kimberly Haywood
VP: Frank P Lynch
**VP:* Richard Mulligan

D-U-N-S 12-814-9932
▲ MARCHEX INC
520 Pike St Ste 2000, Seattle, WA 98101-2319
Tel (206) 331-3300 *Founded/Ownrshp* 2003
Sales 143.0MM *EMP* 375[E]
Tkr Sym MCHX *Exch* NGS
SIC 7313 Electronic media advertising representatives
Ch Bd: Anne Mills
Sr Pt: Brian Brock
**Ch Bd:* Anne Devereux-Mills
CFO: Michael A Arends
**V Ch Bd:* Nicolas Hanauer
Sr VP: Brooks McMahon
VP: Todd Wilson
Dir Risk M: Gary Nafus
Dir Sec: Greg Nelson
Snr Sftwr: Jacob Lucas
IT Man: Doug Redway
Board of Directors: Dennis Cline, Ian Morris, M Wayne Wisehart

D-U-N-S 83-293-4660
■ MARCHI THERMAL SYSTEMS INC
(*Suby of* UCT) ★
3108 Diablo Ave, Hayward, CA 94545-2702
Tel (510) 300-1500 *Founded/Ownrshp* 2015
Sales 112.8MM[E] *EMP* 1,087[E]
SIC 3826 Thermal analysis instruments, laboratory type
CEO: James E Hawthorne

D-U-N-S 07-727-7648 IMP/EXP
MARCHON EYEWEAR INC
(*Suby of* C V S OPTICAL LAB DIV) ★
201 Old Country Rd Fl 3, Melville, NY 11747-2731
Tel (631) 756-8530 *Founded/Ownrshp* 2008
Sales 210.1MM[E] *EMP* 1,055
SIC 5048 Frames, ophthalmic; Optometric equipment & supplies
Ch Bd: Claudio Gottardi
**COO:* Marty Fox
**CFO:* Phil Hibbert
VP: Pierre Bessez
VP: Riccardo Cadorin
VP: Ken Clay
VP: Mark Ginsberg
VP: Ron Kitt
VP: Susan Kressman
VP: Len Lasalandra
VP: Joe Paek
VP: Achille Rachello
VP: ISO Sides
VP: Micha Siebenhandl
VP: Michelle Skinner
VP: Jeff Stern
VP: Nicola Zotta
Exec: Krista Kester

MARCO COMPANY, THE
See MARCO DISPLAY SPECIALISTS LP

D-U-N-S 11-876-9884 IMP/EXP
MARCO DISPLAY SPECIALISTS LP
MARCO COMPANY, THE
3209 Marquita Dr, Fort Worth, TX 76116-5120
Tel (817) 244-8300 *Founded/Ownrshp* 2001
Sales 114.6MM *EMP* 500
Accts Weaver And Tidwell Llp Fort
SIC 2521 2541 3993 3089 3081 Tables, office: wood; Store & office display cases & fixtures; Signs & advertising specialties; Washers, plastic; Unsupported plastics film & sheet
CFO: Jon W Stewart
Opers Mgr: Danny Towne

D-U-N-S 96-487-6010 IMP
MARCO DISPLAY SPECIALISTS LP
(*Suby of* MARCO CO) ★
3209 Marquita Dr, Fort Worth, TX 76116-5120
Tel (817) 244-8300 *Founded/Ownrshp* 1984
Sales 92.4MM[E] *EMP* 500
SIC 2541 3993 Store & office display cases & fixtures; Signs & advertising specialties
Prin: Darrell L Cooper
CFO: Jon Stewart

D-U-N-S 00-527-3735 IMP
MARCO GROUP INTERNATIONAL INC
3425 E Locust St, Davenport, IA 52803-3534
Tel (563) 324-2519 *Founded/Ownrshp* 1944
Sales 90.5MM[E] *EMP* 90[E]
SIC 5084 5032 Industrial machinery & equipment; Sand, construction
Pr: Michael W Marthens
CFO: Dennis F Dedecker
VP: Cheryl Lester
VP: Annette Rettig
VP: Stuart Swint
IT Man: Samantha Hayen
VP Opers: Matt Molumby
Opers Mgr: Chad Dragon
Opers Mgr: Ricky Richoux
VP Sls: James Claassen
VP Sls: Jeff Schopmeyer
Board of Directors: Michael W Marthens

D-U-N-S 06-285-9558
MARCO TECHNOLOGIES LLC
4510 Heatherwood Rd, Saint Cloud, MN 56301-9500
Tel (320) 259-3000 *Founded/Ownrshp* 2015
Sales 350.7MM[E] *EMP* 1,210
SIC 7371 4813 7313 7812

D-U-N-S 08-975-1499 IMP/EXP
MARCOLIN USA EYEWEAR CORP
VIVA INTERNATIONAL GROUP
(*Suby of* MARCOLIN SPA)
3140 Rte 22, Branchburg, NJ 08876-3548
Tel (800) 345-8482 *Founded/Ownrshp* 2013
Sales 214.4MM[E] *EMP* 550
SIC 5099 5048 Sunglasses; Ophthalmic goods; Frames, ophthalmic; Lenses, ophthalmic
CEO: Giovanni Zoppas
**CEO:* Sabrizio Gamberini
CFO: Frfank Dwyer
**CFO:* Paolo Piazza
**CFO:* Sal Rianna
**Ch:* Vittorio Levi
Sr VP: Jan Cory
VP: Alexandra Gil
VP: Harry Scheer
Sls Mgr: Jeff Pech
Sales Asso: Scott Harrison

D-U-N-S 03-028-9941 IMP/EXP
MARCOLIN USA INC
(*Suby of* MARCOLIN SPA)
3140 Us Highway 22, Branchburg, NJ 08876-3548
Tel (480) 951-7174 *Founded/Ownrshp* 2008
Sales 87.7MM[E] *EMP* 300
SIC 5048
Ch: Vittorio Levi
**Pr:* Maurizio Marcolin
**CEO:* Giovanni Zoppas
**CFO:* Joseph Ivenz
Sr VP: Ben Wolf
VP: Bob Dunn
VP: Greg Pollock
VP: Tom Seltze

D-U-N-S 19-439-1124
MARCON & BOYER INC
DUGGAN AND MARCON
645 Hamilton St Ste 300, Allentown, PA 18101-2191
Tel (610) 866-5959 *Founded/Ownrshp* 1981
Sales 121.3MM[E] *EMP* 670
SIC 3448 1742 1743 1799 Panels for prefabricated metal buildings; Drywall; Tile installation, ceramic; Fireproofing buildings
Pr: L Charles Marcon
**Sec:* Kenneth H Kline Jr
**Sr VP:* Frank B Boyer
VP: Michael Anthony
**VP:* Robert H Handschue

MARCONE SUPPLY
See MAR-CONE APPLIANCE PARTS CO

D-U-N-S 79-111-8276
MARCOR ENTERPRISES INC
(*Suby of* PREMIUM TRANSPORTATION STAFFING INC) ★
190 Highland Dr, Medina, OH 44256-3199
Tel (330) 722-7974 *Founded/Ownrshp* 1996
Sales 130.0MM *EMP* 20[E]
SIC 7363 Employee leasing service
CEO: William Schoenstein
**Pr:* Nancy Normile

MARCRAFT APPAREL GROUP
See MARCRAFT CLOTHES INC

D-U-N-S 06-430-3308 IMP
MARCRAFT CLOTHES INC
MARCRAFT APPAREL GROUP
301 Island Rd, Mahwah, NJ 07430-2127
Tel (201) 828-2085 *Founded/Ownrshp* 1972
Sales 89.7MM[E] *EMP* 80
SIC 5136 Suits, men's & boys'
Ch Bd: Sheldon Brody
**Pr:* Gary Brody
**COO:* Gary Daily
**CFO:* Brad Goldstein

MARC'S XPECT DRUGS
See MARC GLASSMAN INC

D-U-N-S 06-474-9864
MARCUM LLP
750 3rd Ave Fl 11, New York, NY 10017-2716
Tel (212) 485-5500 *Founded/Ownrshp* 1951
Sales 273.0MM[E] *EMP* 1,360
SIC 8721 Certified public accountant
Genl Pt: Jeffrey M Weiner
Sr Pt: David Appel
Pt: James T Ashe
Pt: David Bukzin
Pt: Bart H Friedman
Pt: Lawrence Schienthal
Pt: James Smart
CFO: Edward Scicchitano
Dir Bus: Victor Tricarico
QA Dir: Matt Mitzen
IT Man: Peter Ziello

D-U-N-S 11-329-1710
MARCUS & MILLICHAP CO
777 S California Ave, Palo Alto, CA 94304-1102
Tel (650) 494-1400 *Founded/Ownrshp* 1971
Sales 68.9MM[E] *EMP* 1,308
SIC 6531 Real estate brokers & agents
Ch: George M Marcus
**Pr:* Harvey E Green
CFO: Martin E Louie
**CFO:* Alex Yamolinski
Sr VP: William E Hughes Jr
VP: Brett Hatcher
VP: Rick Peltz
VP: Kent Williams
CIO: Ken Sayward
**Corp Couns:* Robert Kennis
Snr Mgr: Yitzie Sommer

D-U-N-S 02-297-6130
▲ MARCUS & MILLICHAP INC
23975 Park Sorrento # 400, Calabasas, CA 91302-4014
Tel (818) 212-2250 *Founded/Ownrshp* 1971
Sales 689.0MM *EMP* 611[E]
Tkr Sym MMI *Exch* NYS
SIC 6531 Buying agent, real estate
Pr: John J Kerin
**Ch Bd:* George M Marcus
**Ch Bd:* William A Millichap
CFO: Martin E Louie
Ex VP: Gene A Berman
Ex VP: Mark L Myers
Sr VP: Paul Davis
VP: Cliff David
VP: Jay Lybik
VP: Bill Rose
VP: Philip Saglimbeni
Exec: Hessam Nadji
Assoc Dir: Charles Hilding
Assoc Dir: David Sperling
Board of Directors: Norma J Lawrence, Nicholas F Macclanahan, George T Shaheen, Don C Watters

D-U-N-S 06-912-5151
MARCUS & MILLICHAP REAL ESTATE INVESTMENT SERVICES OF INDIANA INC
(*Suby of* MARCUS & MILLICHAP CO) ★
2626 Hanover St, Palo Alto, CA 94304-1132
Tel (650) 494-1400 *Founded/Ownrshp* 1971
Sales 23.0MM[E] *EMP* 1,300
SIC 6531 Real estate brokers & agents
Pr: Harvey E Green
**Ch Bd:* George M Marcus
**Co-Ch Bd:* William A Millichap
Sr VP: Michael Mele
VP: Kevin McCrann

D-U-N-S 05-874-2347
▲ MARCUS CORP
100 E Wisconsin Ave # 1, Milwaukee, WI 53202-4107
Tel (414) 905-1000 *Founded/Ownrshp* 1935
Sales 488.0MM *EMP* 7,000[E]
Tkr Sym MCS *Exch* NYS
SIC 7011 7833 Hotels & motels; Resort hotel; Drive-in motion picture theaters
Pr: Gregory S Marcus
Ch Bd: Stephen H Marcus
Pr: Joseph S Khairallah
COO: Ralph Marcus
CFO: Douglas A Neis
Treas: Doug Neis
Ex VP: Rolando B Rodriguez
VP: Chris Anderson
VP: Andrea Foster
VP: Mark Gramz
VP: Tom Kissinger
Exec: Thomas F Kissinger
Dir Soc: Kristi Johnson
Board of Directors: Allan H Selig, David M Baum, Brian J Stark, James D Ericson, Katherine M Gehl, Diane Marcus Gershowitz, Bronson J Haase, Timothy E Hoeksema, Daniel F McKeithan Jr, Philip L Milstein, Bruce J Olson

D-U-N-S 09-770-4894 IMP/EXP
MARCUS FOOD CO
240 N Rock Rd Ste 246, Wichita, KS 67206-2245
Tel (316) 686-7649 *Founded/Ownrshp* 1980
Sales 212.3MM *EMP* 23
SIC 5144 5142

MARCUS HOTELS AND RESORTS
See MARCUS HOTELS INC

D-U-N-S 80-789-9760
■ MARCUS HOTELS INC
MARCUS HOTELS AND RESORTS
(*Suby of* MARCUS CORP) ★
100 E Wisconsin Ave, Milwaukee, WI 53202-4107
Tel (414) 905-1200 *Founded/Ownrshp* 1990
Sales 250.0MM[E] *EMP* 3,500
SIC 7011 Hotels
Pr: Joseph Khairallah
**Sr VP:* Chris Anderson
Sr VP: Andrea Foster
Sr VP: Tom Mason
**Sr VP:* Thomas P Riley
VP: Bill Eichelberg
**VP:* Gary Gentile
VP: Kevin M Hickman
VP: Brett Huske
VP: Ted Lorenzi
**VP:* Steve Martin
VP: David Morley
VP: Duane Quintana
VP: Scott Richter
VP: Scott Schoenberger
VP: Pam Seidl
VP: Michael Swasey
VP: Susan Terry
VP: Chad Waetzig
VP: Jim Waldvogel

D-U-N-S 06-689-0880
■ MARCUS THEATRES CORP
(*Suby of* MARCUS CORP) ★
100 E Wisconsin Ave, Milwaukee, WI 53202-4107
Tel (414) 905-1500 *Founded/Ownrshp* 1935
Sales 70.2MM[E] *EMP* 1,050
SIC 7832 Motion picture theaters, except drive-in
Pr: Bruce J Olson
Treas: Doug Neis
Chf Mktg O: Ann Stadler
Ofcr: Kim Lueck
Ex VP: Mark Gramz
Sr VP: Samuel Gourley
Sr VP: Gregory Marcus
VP: Tom Kissinger
VP: Rick Neals
VP: Jeff Tomachek
Exec: Chris Colello

D-U-N-S 03-413-3173 IMP
MARDEL INC (OK)
VALUES BY DESIGN
7727 Sw 44th St, Oklahoma City, OK 73179-4815
Tel (405) 745-1300 *Founded/Ownrshp* 1981
Sales 87.7MM *EMP* 714
SIC 5999 5943 Religious goods; Office forms & supplies
CEO: Mart Green
**Ch Bd:* David Green
CIO: Joe Warfield
MIS Dir: Diana King
VP Opers: Jason Green
Mktg Mgr: Kelly Black

D-U-N-S 01-901-1311 IMP
MARDENS INC
MARDEN'S SURPLUS & SALVAGE
184 College Ave, Waterville, ME 04901-6220
Tel (207) 873-6111 *Founded/Ownrshp* 1963
Sales 122.3MM[E] *EMP* 850
SIC 5311 Department stores, discount
Pr: Harold A Marden
**Treas:* John E Marden
**VP:* David M Marden
Trfc Mgr: Tim Nason

MARDEN'S SURPLUS & SALVAGE
See MARDENS INC

D-U-N-S 18-606-1370 IMP
MAREK BROTHERS SYSTEMS INC
2115 Judiway St, Houston, TX 77018-5834
Tel (713) 681-9213 *Founded/Ownrshp* 1948
Sales 205.0MM[E] *EMP* 907
SIC 1742 Drywall
CEO: R Stan Marek Jr
**Pr:* Paul A Marek
**Pr:* R Stan Marek
**CFO:* Doyle Crow
CFO: Charles Grogan
Off Mgr: BJ Simmons

D-U-N-S 96-005-8824 IMP
MAREL INC
(*Suby of* MAREL HF.)
8145 Flint St, Lenexa, KS 66214-3301
Tel (913) 888-9110 *Founded/Ownrshp* 1995
Sales 100.0MM[E] *EMP* 120
SIC 5046 Commercial cooking & food service equipment
Pr: Einar Einarsson
**CFO:* Deborah Bernas
**VP:* Larry Campbell
**VP:* Troels Svendsen
**VP:* David Whitem
Area Mgr: Gabe Arriaga
Area Mgr: Kim Balle
Area Mgr: Larry Couch
Area Mgr: Donn Larue
Genl Mgr: Steini Gretarsson
Dir IT: Louie Bardic

D-U-N-S 00-327-7589 IMP
MAREL STORK POULTRY PROCESSING INC
(*Suby of* MAREL HF.)
1024 Airport Pkwy, Gainesville, GA 30501-6814
Tel (770) 532-7041 *Founded/Ownrshp* 1975
Sales 113.5MM[E] *EMP* 220
SIC 3556 3535 Poultry processing machinery; Meat processing machinery; Overhead conveyor systems
CEO: Anton De Weerd
**Pr:* Einar Einarsson
VP: Mark Finnimore
**VP:* Mike Sales
Software D: Raymond Strawn
Mfg Mgr: Michael Otterbach
Manager: Scott Moore
Manager: Brian Shamblin
Sales Asso: Brad Baranick
Snr Mgr: Phil Lamb
Snr Mgr: Rod Liming

MARGARET HOLMES
See MCCALL FARMS INC

MARGARET R PARDEE MEMORIAL HOS
See HENDERSON COUNTY HOSPITAL CORP

D-U-N-S 07-563-2476
MARGARITAS MANAGEMENT GROUP INC
TIO JANS MRGRITAS MEXICAN REST
200 Griffin Rd Ste 1, Portsmouth, NH 03801-7145
Tel (603) 430-8905 *Founded/Ownrshp* 1993
Sales 59.2MM[E] *EMP* 1,200
SIC 5812 Mexican restaurant
CEO: John Pellitier
CFO: Mario Mancini
**CFO:* Bonnie Monahan
**Sec:* E Stanton Bagley
VP: Kelly Parkinson
**VP:* David Pelletier
Dir Soc: Dan Lederer
Genl Mgr: Mark Lakeman

Genl Mgr: Ryan O'Leary
Genl Mgr: Greg Tatarian

D-U-N-S 80-835-8233
MARGARITAVILLE ENTERPRISES LLC
6900 Turkey Lake Rd # 200, Orlando, FL 32819-4707
Tel (407) 224-3213 *Founded/Ownrshp* 2006
Sales 184.2MM[E] *EMP* 1,000
SIC 5087 Restaurant supplies
CEO: John Cohlan
**CFO:* Eric Forward

D-U-N-S 11-504-3887 IMP
MARIAK INDUSTRIES INC
MARIAK WINDOW FASHION
575 W Manville St, Rancho Dominguez, CA 90220-5509
Tel (310) 661-4400 *Founded/Ownrshp* 1987
Sales 170.7MM[E] *EMP* 380
SIC 5023 2591 Vertical blinds; Blinds vertical
CEO: Leo Elinson
**VP:* Patrice Elinson

MARIAK WINDOW FASHION
See MARIAK INDUSTRIES INC

D-U-N-S 05-310-8619
MARIAM INC (MD)
DARCAR
12210 Cherry Hill Rd, Silver Spring, MD 20904-1968
Tel (888) 841-9679 *Founded/Ownrshp* 1982, 1981
Sales 479.9MM[E] *EMP* 1,000
SIC 5511 Automobiles, new & used
Pr: John R Darvish
Bd of Dir: Laverne Hawkins
**VP:* George D Noel
Exec: Abdoul Keita
Genl Mgr: Hess Darvish
Genl Mgr: Hesham Elhamayel
Genl Mgr: Lalin Gallart
Genl Mgr: James Onderdonk
Genl Mgr: Marvin Rawls
Genl Mgr: Ashanti Shackleford
Genl Mgr: Jason Waltrup

D-U-N-S 07-861-1742 IMP
MARIAN INC
2787 S Freeman Rd, Monticello, IN 47960-7742
Tel (574) 583-3464 *Founded/Ownrshp* 2011
Sales 186.8MM[E] *EMP* 3,000
SIC 3699 Electrical welding equipment; Electron beam metal cutting, forming or welding machines; Electron linear accelerators; Electronic training devices
Pr: Fred Ennis

D-U-N-S 07-724-1008
MARIAN MEDICAL CENTER
MARIAN REGIONAL MEDICAL CENTER
1400 E Church St, Santa Maria, CA 93454-5906
Tel (805) 739-3000 *Founded/Ownrshp* 1970
Sales 324.8MM *EMP* 1,000
SIC 8062

MARIAN REGIONAL MEDICAL CENTER
See MARIAN MEDICAL CENTER

D-U-N-S 00-796-3945 IMP/EXP
MARIANI PACKING CO INC (CA)
500 Crocker Dr, Vacaville, CA 95688-8706
Tel (707) 452-2800 *Founded/Ownrshp* 1982
Sales 131.9MM[E] *EMP* 350
SIC 0723 2034 5148 Fruit (farm-dried) packing services; Fruit drying services; Dried & dehydrated fruits; Fresh fruits & vegetables
CEO: Mark A Mariani
**V Ch:* George Sousa Jr
CFO: Forrest Chandler
**Sec:* Marian Ciabattari
**Ex VP:* Craig Mackley
**Ex VP:* Paul Mariani
VP: Scott Fulihara
**VP:* George Sousa Sr

D-U-N-S 04-557-0736 IMP/EXP
MARIANNA INDUSTRIES INC
11222 I St Ste A, Omaha, NE 68137-1238
Tel (402) 593-0211 *Founded/Ownrshp* 1968
Sales 316.8MM[E] *EMP* 300[E]
SIC 5122 2844 7231 Drugs, proprietaries & sundries; Hair preparations; Cosmetics; Toilet preparations; Shampoos, rinses, conditioners: hair; Hair preparations, including shampoos; Cosmetic preparations; Beauty shops
VP: William Cosentino
**CFO:* Robert Campney
**CFO:* Annette Eggert
Treas: Lori C Christensen
Exec: Folkers Mitch
**Prin:* Michael Cosentino

MARIANNE'S
See UBI LIQUIDATING CORP

D-U-N-S 03-953-2713
MARIBEL RESENDIZ
TAVO VASQUEZ DISTRIBUTING
711 Mispola Dr, Laredo, TX 78046
Tel (956) 236-2907 *Founded/Ownrshp* 2016
Sales 132.0MM *EMP* 2
SIC 5199 Charcoal
Owner: Maribel Resendiz

D-U-N-S 07-449-1515
MARICOPA COUNTY COMMUNITY COLLEGE DISTRICT
2411 W 14th St, Tempe, AZ 85281-6941
Tel (480) 731-8000 *Founded/Ownrshp* 1962
Sales 293.5MM[E] *EMP* 11,000
SIC 8222

D-U-N-S 18-650-7216
MARICOPA COUNTY SPECIAL HEALTH CARE DISTRICT
MARICOPA INTEGRATED HEALTH SYS
2601 E Roosevelt St, Phoenix, AZ 85008-4973
Tel (602) 344-5726 *Founded/Ownrshp* 2005
Sales 533.2MM[E] *EMP* 4,000[E]
SIC 8062 Hospital, AMA approved residency
CEO: Steve Purves
V Ch: David Drachman
COO: Bill Van Askie
Ofcr: Andrea Prado
Sr VP: Mike Robertson
Dir OR: Deana Manning
Dir Inf Cn: Rita Neibaur
Dir Risk M: Mary Mc Kelvey
Dir Risk M: Mary McKelvey
Dir Soc: Laura Smith
Dir Rx: Ken Prayzer

MARICOPA INTEGRATED HEALTH SYS
See MARICOPA COUNTY SPECIAL HEALTH CARE DISTRICT

D-U-N-S 15-129-0546
MARIE CALLENDER PIE SHOPS INC
MARIE CALLENDER'S PIE SHOPS
(*Suby of* PERKINS FAMILY RESTAURANT) ★
6075 Poplar Ave Ste 800, Memphis, TN 38119-4717
Tel (901) 766-6400 *Founded/Ownrshp* 2006
Sales 56.9MM[E] *EMP* 2,000
SIC 5812 Restaurant, family: chain
Pr: Phillip Ratner
VP: Nick Saba
VP: Jim Vickers

MARIE CALLENDER'S PIE SHOPS
See MARIE CALLENDER PIE SHOPS INC

MARIE CALLENDER'S PIE SHOPS
See CASTLE HARLAN PARTNERS III LP

D-U-N-S 85-856-7605
MARIETTA CITY SCHOOLS (INC)
250 Howard St Ne, Marietta, GA 30060-1953
Tel (770) 422-3500 *Founded/Ownrshp* 1892
Sales 73.5MM[E] *EMP* 1,400
Accts Bambo Sonaike Cpa Llc Mariett
SIC 8211 Elementary & secondary schools
Bd of Dir: Margaret Barfield
Bd of Dir: Jeanie Carter
**Prin:* Harold T Barnett
**Prin:* Dayton Hibbs
**Prin:* Dr Donna Ryan
MIS Dir: David Digiovanni
MIS Dir: John Pickering
Pr Dir: Sommer Vega

D-U-N-S 01-076-5394 IMP/EXP
MARIETTA CORP
(*Suby of* KIK CUSTOM PRODUCTS) ★
37 Huntington St, Cortland, NY 13045-3098
Tel (607) 753-6746 *Founded/Ownrshp* 2004
Sales 334.0MM[E] *EMP* 1,500
SIC 2844 2834 2541 Cosmetic preparations; Toilet preparations; Druggists' preparations (pharmaceuticals); Store & office display cases & fixtures
CEO: Donald W Sturdivant
COO: Eileen Anderson
**CFO:* Perry Morgan
**Treas:* James Matthews
**Sr VP:* Chris Calhoun
**Sr VP:* Beth Corl
**Sr VP:* Ray Ferretti
**Sr VP:* David Hempson
Sr VP: Brian Oneil
VP: Beth Boyd
VP: Lisa Bruce
VP: Rob Chichester

D-U-N-S 00-327-7217 IMP/EXP
MARIETTA DRAPERY & WINDOW COVERINGS CO INC
22 Trammell St Sw, Marietta, GA 30064-3371
Tel (770) 428-3335 *Founded/Ownrshp* 1975
Sales 83.2MM[E] *EMP* 170
SIC 5023 2391 2591 2392 Window furnishings; Venetian blinds; Vertical blinds; Window shades; Draperies, plastic & textile: from purchased materials; Mini blinds; Blinds vertical; Venetian blinds; Bedspreads & bed sets: made from purchased materials
CEO: Douglas C Bentley
**Pr:* Andrew F Bentley
**CFO:* Frederick A Bentley
Sls Mgr: Darrell Duffel

D-U-N-S 07-462-7592 IMP/EXP
MARIETTA ERAMET INC
(*Suby of* ERAMET HOLDING MANGANESE)
16705 State Route 7, Marietta, OH 45750-8519
Tel (740) 374-1000 *Founded/Ownrshp* 1999
Sales 112.4MM[E] *EMP* 205
SIC 3313 Ferroalloys
CFO: Michel Masci
CFO: Marc Blanquart
Dept Mgr: Dean Douglass
Telecom Ex: Julie King

D-U-N-S 60-871-4882
MARIETTA HOLDING CORP INC
KIK CUSTOM PRODUCTS
37 Huntington St, Cortland, NY 13045-3096
Tel (607) 753-6746 *Founded/Ownrshp* 2015
Sales 340.0MM[E] *EMP* 1,501
SIC 6719 2841 Investment holding companies, except banks; Soap: granulated, liquid, cake, flaked or chip
CEO: Donald W Sturdivant
**Pr:* Brian O'Neil
**CFO:* Perry Morgan
**Treas:* James Mattews
**Sr VP:* David P Hempson
**Sr VP:* Dan Keefe

D-U-N-S 06-871-7859
MARIETTA MEMORIAL HOSPITAL INC
401 Matthew St, Marietta, OH 45750-1699
Tel (740) 374-1400 *Founded/Ownrshp* 1984
Sales 378.0MM *EMP* 1,100
SIC 8062 8069 General medical & surgical hospitals; Alcoholism rehabilitation hospital
Ch Bd: Tom Tucker
**Pr:* J Stott Cantley
**CFO:* Eric Young
**Treas:* Glen Hale
**VP:* Orive E Fischer
Ex Dir: Wendy Brewer
Genl Mgr: Diana Chapman
Genl Mgr: Inge Chenoweth
Off Mgr: Wanda Lowers
IT Man: Brian Taylor
Pharmcst: Robert Kuhn

MARIETTA POWER
See BOARD OF LIGHTS AND WATER

D-U-N-S 07-868-1812
MARIKA LLC
5553-B Bandini Blvd, Bell, CA 90201
Tel (323) 888-7755 *Founded/Ownrshp* 2011
Sales 135.0MM[E] *EMP* 100
SIC 2339 Athletic clothing: women's, misses' & juniors'; Women's & misses' athletic clothing & sportswear

D-U-N-S 82-960-2338
MARIN CLEAN ENERGY
MCE CLEAN ENERGY
1125 Tamalpais Ave, San Rafael, CA 94901-3221
Tel (415) 464-6028 *Founded/Ownrshp* 2008
Sales 100.6MM *EMP* 32
Accts Vavrinek Trine Day & Company
SIC 3264 Porcelain electrical supplies
CEO: Dawn Weisz
Comm Dir: Jamie Tuckey

D-U-N-S 02-000-5732
MARIN COMMUNITY COLLEGE DISTRICT
COLLEGE OF MARIN
835 College Ave, Kentfield, CA 94904-2590
Tel (415) 457-8811 *Founded/Ownrshp* 1926
Sales 43.7MM[E] *EMP* 1,100
SIC 8222 8221 Community college; Colleges universities & professional schools
Pr: David Wayne Coon
**VP:* Albert Harrison
**VP:* Gregory Nelson
**VP:* Stephanie O'Brien
Mng Dir: Andrea Liguori

D-U-N-S 06-885-8851
MARIN GENERAL HOSPITAL (CA)
(*Suby of* MARIN HEALTHCARE DISTRICT) ★
250 Bon Air Rd, Kentfield, CA 94904-1784
Tel (415) 925-7000 *Founded/Ownrshp* 1947, 2010
Sales 342.3MM *EMP* 1,100
SIC 8062 8011 General medical & surgical hospitals; Offices & clinics of medical doctors
CEO: Lee Domanico
**CEO:* David Bradley
**CFO:* Theresa Daughton
Treas: Nadder Mirsepassi
VP: Goonasagrie Naidoo
VP: Denise Perry
Exec: Linda Lang
Dir Risk M: Jan Sams
Comm Dir: Jamie Maites
Surgeon: James Reid
Obsttrcn: Tim Jefferson
Board of Directors: Robert Macinnes

D-U-N-S 16-710-4830
MARIN HEALTHCARE DISTRICT
100b Drakes Landing Rd, Greenbrae, CA 94904-2438
Tel (415) 464-2090 *Founded/Ownrshp* 2000
Sales 342.3MM[E] *EMP* 1,101[E]
SIC 8062 General medical & surgical hospitals
Chf Mktg O: Joe Sklar
CIO: Somayaji Bulusu

D-U-N-S 83-287-7877
▲ MARIN SOFTWARE INC
123 Mission St Fl 27, San Francisco, CA 94105-1681
Tel (415) 399-2580 *Founded/Ownrshp* 2006
Sales 108.5MM *EMP* 511[E]
Tkr Sym MRIN *Exch* NYS
SIC 7374 Data processing & preparation
Ch Bd: Christopher Lien
CFO: Catriona M Fallon
Ex VP: Stephen E Kim
Off Mgr: Faith Harris
Web Dev: Chris Mielke
Software D: Brandon Chen
Sftwr Eng: Kapil Duraphe
Sftwr Eng: Cary Young
Mktg Dir: Jennifer Madison
Mktg Mgr: Brenda Ton
Mktg Mgr: Jena Yost
Board of Directors: Paul R Auvil III, James J Barrese, L Gordon Crovitz, Bruce W Dunlevie, Donald P Hutchison, Allan Leinwand

D-U-N-S 09-998-7158
MARINA ASSOCIATES LTD
HARRAHS ATLANTIC CY CASINO HT
777 Harrahs Blvd, Atlantic City, NJ 08401-1911
Tel (609) 441-5000 *Founded/Ownrshp* 1979
Sales 59.2MM[E] *EMP* 2,949
SIC 7011 5812 Casino hotel; Eating places
CEO: Timothy Wilmott
Exec: Jim Byrnes
CTO: Arlene Guzan

D-U-N-S 96-243-5975
MARINA CLUB CONDOMINIUM
655 Absecon Blvd Ste B, Atlantic City, NJ 08401-2573
Tel (609) 348-0040 *Founded/Ownrshp* 2010
Sales 15.1MM[E] *EMP* 1,828
SIC 6513 Apartment building operators
Prin: Larry Lipton

MARINA DEL REY HOSPITAL
See CFHS HOLDINGS INC

D-U-N-S 17-855-8909
MARINA DISTRICT DEVELOPMENT CO LLC
BORGATA HOTEL CASINO AND SPA
1 Borgata Way, Atlantic City, NJ 08401-1946
Tel (609) 317-1000 *Founded/Ownrshp* 1995
Sales 738.2MM[E] *EMP* 7,000[E]
Accts Deloitte & Touche Llp Las Ve
SIC 7011 Casino hotel; Resort hotel
Pr: Tom Ballance
CFO: Ellis Landau
Sr VP: Joe Lupo
VP: Bill Callihan
VP: Ted Herzchel
VP: Signe Huff
VP: Nicolas Kurban
VP: Jay B Rosenthal
VP: Drew Schlesinger
VP: Hugh Turner
Exec: Patty Conroy

D-U-N-S 82-758-1641
MARINA DISTRICT FINANCE CO INC
BORGATA HOTEL CASINO & SPA
(*Suby of* BORGATA HOTEL CASINO AND SPA) ★
1 Borgata Way, Atlantic City, NJ 08401-1946
Tel (609) 317-1000 *Founded/Ownrshp* 2000
Sales 738.2MM *EMP* 5,709
SIC 7011 Hotels & motels
Pr: Keith E Smith
COO: Robert L Boughner
CFO: Josh Hirsberg
Board of Directors: William S Boyd, Marianne Boyd Johnson

D-U-N-S 07-882-8839 IMP
■ MARINE ACQUISITION (US) INC
SEASTAR SOLUTIONS
(*Suby of* AMERICAN SECURITIES LLC) ★
640 N Lewis Rd, Limerick, PA 19468-1228
Tel (610) 495-7011 *Founded/Ownrshp* 2011, 2013
Sales 221.8MM[E] *EMP* 892[E]
SIC 3531 5551 Marine related equipment; Marine supplies & equipment
Exec: Kimberly Koennecker
Genl Mgr: Dave Wolfe
Pdt Mgr: Richard Lawrence

D-U-N-S 07-023-0389 IMP
■ MARINE ACQUISITION CORP
SEASTAR SOLUTIONS
(*Suby of* AMERICAN SECURITIES LLC) ★
1 Sierra Pl, Litchfield, IL 62056-3029
Tel (217) 324-9400 *Founded/Ownrshp* 2014
Sales 124.1MM[E] *EMP* 300[E]
SIC 5088 Marine propulsion machinery & equipment; Marine supplies
Pr: Yvan Cote
VP: Thomas Douglass
Sales Exec: Susie Strauss
Mktg Mgr: Laurie Louvier

MARINE CORPS COMMUNITY SVCS
See MORALE WELFARE RECREATION ACTIVITY

MARINE CORPS INTELLIGENCE
See UNITED STATES MARINE CORPS

D-U-N-S 10-251-2501 IMP/EXP
MARINE HARVEST USA LLC
(*Suby of* MARINE HARVEST ASA)
8550 Nw 17th St Ste 105, Doral, FL 33126-1036
Tel (305) 591-8550 *Founded/Ownrshp* 2011
Sales 400.0MM *EMP* 262
SIC 5146 Seafoods
Mng Dir: Gian F Nattero
Treas: Chris Leighton

D-U-N-S 82-981-9981
■ MARINE HOLDING US CORP
(*Suby of* ZODIAC POOL SOLUTIONS NORTH AMERICA INC) ★
6000 Condor Dr, Moorpark, CA 93021-2601
Tel (805) 529-2000 *Founded/Ownrshp* 2004
Sales 141.1MM[E] *EMP* 653
SIC 6799 Investors
Pr: Francois Miralle
**CFO:* Joel Silva
**Sec:* Mark Cortell

D-U-N-S 62-606-8456
MARINE PRESERVATION ASSOCIATION INC
MPA
20645 N Pima Rd Ste 100, Scottsdale, AZ 85255-5595
Tel (480) 991-5500 *Founded/Ownrshp* 1990
Sales 95.1MM *EMP* 3
SIC 8611 Trade associations
Pr: Robert Aldag
Treas: Stephen E Fortino

D-U-N-S 01-281-2702
▲ MARINE PRODUCTS CORP
2801 Buford Hwy Ne # 520, Brookhaven, GA 30329-2143
Tel (404) 321-7910 *Founded/Ownrshp* 2000
Sales 207.0MM *EMP* 767[E]
Tkr Sym MPX *Exch* NYS
SIC 3732 Boat building & repairing; Boats, fiberglass: building & repairing
Pr: Richard A Hubbell
**Ch Bd:* R Randall Rollins
CFO: Ben M Palmer
**VP:* Linda H Graham
Board of Directors: Bill J Dismuke, Larry L Prince, Gary W Rollins, Henry B Tippie, James B Williams

D-U-N-S 61-839-8580 EXP
MARINE SPILL RESPONSE CORP
MSRC
220 Spring St Ste 500, Herndon, VA 20170-6207
Tel (703) 326-5600 *Founded/Ownrshp* 1990
Sales 113.9MM *EMP* 450
Accts Bdo Usa Llp Mc Lean Va
SIC 4959 Oil spill cleanup
Pr: Steve Ben
**CFO:* Christine Murphy
IT Man: Keith Whitney
Opers Supe: Dusty Henry
Sfty Mgr: Chris Muzzy
Genl Couns: Regina Pace
Snr Mgr: Buzz Leonard
Snr Mgr: Steve Simon

D-U-N-S 00-292-9946
▲ MARINEMAX INC (FL)
2600 Mccormick Dr Ste 200, Clearwater, FL 33759-1029
Tel (727) 531-1700 *Founded/Ownrshp* 1998
Sales 942.0MM *EMP* 1,289
Tkr Sym HZO *Exch* NYS

SIC 5551 Boat dealers; Motor boat dealers; Canoe & kayak dealers; Sailboats & equipment
Ch Bd: William H McGill Jr
**CFO:* Michael H McLamb
Ex VP: Charles A Cashman
Ex VP: William Brett McGill
VP: Chuck Cashman
VP: Anthony E Cassella Jr
Genl Mgr: Bryan Douglas
Sls Mgr: Romy Decena
Board of Directors: George Borst, Hilliard M Eure III, Evelyn V Follit, Clint Moore, Charles R Oglesby, Joseph A Watters

MARINER FINANCE
See MILESTONE PARTNERS MANAGEMENT CO LP

D-U-N-S 06-725-7501
MARINER HEALTH CARE INC
MARINER HEALTHCARE MANAGEMENT
(*Suby of* NATIONAL SENIOR CARE INC) ★
1 Ravinia Dr Ste 1500, Atlanta, GA 30346-2115
Tel (678) 443-7000 *Founded/Ownrshp* 2004
Sales 4.1MMM[E] *EMP* 35,000
SIC 5912 8051 8093 8741 8062 3443 Drug stores; Extended care facility; Mental retardation hospital; Rehabilitation center, outpatient treatment; Nursing & personal care facility management; Hospital, affiliated with AMA residency; Chambers & caissons
CEO: Harry Grunstein
**CEO:* Tony E Oglesby
CFO: Kevin Seramur
CFO: Bernard Turk
**Treas:* Boyd P Gentry
Ex VP: Michael Boxer
CIO: Sara Goldberg
QA Dir: Angela Jackson
Plnt Mgr: Ariel Valladolid

MARINER HEALTHCARE MANAGEMENT
See MARINER HEALTH CARE INC

MARINO WARE DIVISION
See WARE INDUSTRIES INC

D-U-N-S 05-845-1840 IMP
MARIO CAMACHO FOODS LLC
(*Suby of* ANGEL CAMACHO ALIMENTACION SL)
2502 Walden Woods Dr, Plant City, FL 33566-7167
Tel (813) 305-4534 *Founded/Ownrshp* 1937, 2007
Sales 85.0MM *EMP* 25
SIC 5148 Vegetables, fresh
Pr: Shawn Kaddoura
IT Man: Ken Starling

D-U-N-S 10-439-6275
MARIO SINACOLA & SONS EXCAVATING INC
10950 Research Rd, Frisco, TX 75033-2042
Tel (214) 387-3900 *Founded/Ownrshp* 1981
Sales 156.9MM[E] *EMP* 400
SIC 1794 Excavation work
Pr: James M Sinacola
CFO: Neil Motley
**Sec:* David G Sinacola
VP: Daren Lesley
**VP:* Neal Mortley
Genl Mgr: Mark Lohse
Sfty Dirs: Ben Baldwin
Trfc Dir: Deybis Perez

D-U-N-S 60-910-3429
■ **MARIO TRICOCIS HAIR SALON & DAY SPA**
(*Suby of* RED DOOR SPA) ★
900 N Michigan Ave # 1850, Chicago, IL 60611-1542
Tel (800) 874-2624 *Founded/Ownrshp* 1989
Sales 7.3MM[E] *EMP* 1,600
SIC 7231 Hairdressers; Cosmetology & personal hygiene salons
Pr: Mario Tricoci

D-U-N-S 01-082-5271
■ **MARION COMMUNITY HOSPITAL INC**
COLUMBIA HCA
(*Suby of* HOSPITAL COPORATION OF AMERICA) ★
1431 Sw 1st Ave, Ocala, FL 34471-6500
Tel (352) 401-1000 *Founded/Ownrshp* 1994
Sales 301.5MM *EMP* 1,100[E]
SIC 8062 General medical & surgical hospitals
Prin: Samuel N Hazen
Chf Rad: John Cain
COO: Nathan Vooys
VP: Lori McGriff
Dir Lab: Jim Certa
Dir Rx: Jerry Cummings
QA Dir: Carol Marlin
IT Man: Holly McEachern
Mktg Dir: Marilyn Robinson
Doctor: Odest Cannon
Doctor: Margaret L Cohen

D-U-N-S 05-048-1118
MARION COMMUNITY SCHOOLS
750 W 26th St, Marion, IN 46953-2929
Tel (765) 662-2546 *Founded/Ownrshp* 1890
Sales 45.0MM[E] *EMP* 1,000
SIC 8211 Public elementary & secondary schools
Treas: Patricia Nauman
Comm Dir: Patricia Gibson
Prgrm Mgr: Michele Kelsay

MARION COUNTY AUDITOR OFFICE
See COUNTY OF MARION

D-U-N-S 07-322-8454
MARION COUNTY BOARD OF COUNTY COMMISSIONERS
601 Se 25th Ave, Ocala, FL 34471-2690
Tel (352) 438-2323 *Founded/Ownrshp* 1944
Sales NA *EMP* 1,500
Accts Purgis Gray And Company Llp
SIC 9111 Executive offices;
Ch Bd: Stan Ncctain
**Ch Bd:* Cherly Stone

D-U-N-S 08-966-8917
MARION COUNTY BOARD OF EDUCATION INC
200 Gaston Ave, Fairmont, WV 26554-2739
Tel (304) 367-2100 *Founded/Ownrshp* 1930
Sales 48.1MM[E] *EMP* 1,210
SIC 8211 School board
Pr: Richard Pellegrin
**Treas:* Kim Wade

MARION COUNTY PUBLIC SCHL SYS
See MARION COUNTY PUBLIC SCHOOLS

D-U-N-S 07-832-0868
MARION COUNTY PUBLIC SCHOOLS
MARION COUNTY PUBLIC SCHL SYS
512 Se 3rd St, Ocala, FL 34471-2212
Tel (352) 671-7700 *Founded/Ownrshp* 1844
Sales 322.1MM[E] *EMP* 5,000
SIC 8211 Public elementary & secondary schools
Prin: Mike Graff
Prin: Walt Miller
Ex Dir: Carmen Maines
Dir Sec: Brian Marcum
MIS Dir: Scott Hansen
MIS Dir: Vickye Vaughns
Pr Dir: Kevin Christian

D-U-N-S 08-002-1703
MARION COUNTY SCHOOL BOARD
512 Se 3rd St, Ocala, FL 34471-2200
Tel (352) 671-7700 *Founded/Ownrshp* 1844
Sales 369.9MM *EMP* 7[E]
SIC 8211 School board
Ch Bd: Angie Boynton

D-U-N-S 01-099-4809
MARION COUNTY SCHOOL TRANSPORTATION
(*Suby of* MARION COUNTY BOARD OF EDUCATION INC) ★
614 Virginia Ave, Fairmont, WV 26554-5130
Tel (304) 367-2161 *Founded/Ownrshp* 2001
Sales 8.0MM[E] *EMP* 1,148[E]
SIC 4151 School buses
Prin: Tj James

D-U-N-S 07-979-9725
MARION COUNTY SCHOOLS
200 Gaston Ave, Fairmont, WV 26554-2739
Tel (304) 367-2100 *Founded/Ownrshp* 2015
Sales 9.3MM[E] *EMP* 1,013[E]
SIC 8211 Public elementary & secondary schools
MIS Dir: Sally Morgan
Teacher Pr: Andy Neptune

D-U-N-S 06-906-5449
MARION GENERAL HOSPITAL INC (OH)
(*Suby of* OHIOHEALTH CORP) ★
1000 Mckinley Park Dr, Marion, OH 43302-6397
Tel (740) 383-8400 *Founded/Ownrshp* 1955, 1986
Sales 181.5MM *EMP* 1,300[E]
SIC 8062 Hospital, AMA approved residency
Pr: John Sanders
Ofcr: Michael Cruea
Dir OR: Evelyn Dean
Dir Risk M: Christina Richards
Dir Lab: Christian Rizo
Dir Rx: Justin Hamper
Adm Dir: Karen Jones
IT Man: Dave Carmichael
Plnt Mgr: Mitch Chambers
Mktg Dir: Gary Blair
Pathlgst: Niranjan Shah

D-U-N-S 07-596-3397
MARION GENERAL HOSPITAL INC
441 N Wabash Ave, Marion, IN 46952-2690
Tel (765) 660-6000 *Founded/Ownrshp* 1902
Sales 166.5MM *EMP* 1,212
Accts Blue & Co Llc Indianapolis
SIC 8062 General medical & surgical hospitals
Pr: Paul L Usher
Dir Vol: Sheila Stewart
Bd of Dir: Jeffrey Bragg
Ofcr: Elijah Bilbee
Dir Inf Cn: Barbara Eppley
Adm Dir: Doug Truitt
Doctor: Nabi Sharif
Doctor: Muni Theertham
Pharmcst: Elaine Greene
Pharmcst: Margaret Miller

D-U-N-S 04-013-9735
■ **MARION HOSPITAL CORP**
HEARTLAND REGIONAL MEDICAL CTR
(*Suby of* QUORUM HEALTH CORP) ★
3333 W Deyoung St, Marion, IL 62959-5884
Tel (618) 998-7800 *Founded/Ownrshp* 2016
Sales 103.8MM[E] *EMP* 817
SIC 8062 8011 General medical & surgical hospitals; Offices & clinics of medical doctors
Pr: Michael J Culotta
Dir Lab: Tara Ferguson
Chf Nrs Of: Melissa Adkins
CIO: Larry Koch
Surgeon: Rachel Trather
Phys Thrpy: Amy Dyer

D-U-N-S 10-554-2802
MARION INDUSTRIES INC
(*Suby of* EG INDUSTRIES) ★
999 Kellogg Pkwy, Marion, OH 43302-1791
Tel (740) 223-0075 *Founded/Ownrshp* 1999
Sales 228.8MM[E] *EMP* 753
SIC 3714 Motor vehicle wheels & parts
Ch Bd: James R Conway
**Pr:* Jerome Curtis
**CEO:* Rick Charville
Sr Cor Off: Louis Scutellaro
**VP:* Gerald Lehrke
Genl Mgr: Myron Crowell
Mtls Mgr: Jason Leuthold

D-U-N-S 07-865-9843
MARION VA MEDICAL CENTER
2401 W Main St, Marion, IL 62959-1188
Tel (618) 993-1122 *Founded/Ownrshp* 2012
Sales 4.3MM[E] *EMP* 1,464[E]
SIC 8062 General medical & surgical hospitals
Prin: Casey George
Pharmcst: Sandra Colson
Pharmcst: Amy Okeefe

D-U-N-S 12-915-5144
■ **MARION WEST COMMUNITY HOSPITAL**
OCALA REGIONAL MEDICAL CENTER
(*Suby of* HOSPITAL COPORATION OF AMERICA) ★
4600 Sw 46th Ct, Ocala, FL 34474-5783
Tel (352) 291-3000 *Founded/Ownrshp* 2002
Sales 82.7MM[E] *EMP* 1,200
SIC 8062 General medical & surgical hospitals
CEO: Garry Karsner
**CEO:* Rex Etheredge
Ofcr: Ginger Carroll
Snr Mgr: Scott Hankinson

D-U-N-S 07-964-1763
MARIPOSA INTERMEDIATE HOLDINGS LLC
(*Suby of* NEIMAN MARCUS GROUP INC) ★
1618 Main St, Dallas, TX 75201-4720
Tel (214) 743-7600 *Founded/Ownrshp* 2013
Sales 4.9MMM[E] *EMP* 16,500[E]
SIC 5311 Department stores

D-U-N-S 02-067-1178
MARIST COLLEGE
3399 North Rd, Poughkeepsie, NY 12601-1387
Tel (845) 575-3000 *Founded/Ownrshp* 1929
Sales 239.2MM *EMP* 1,300
Accts Grant Thornton Llp New York
SIC 8221 College, except junior
Pr: Dennis J Murray
Pr: Danny Szpiro
**CFO:* John Pecchia
Ex VP: Summer Bourlier
Ex VP: Jeffrey Brackett
Ex VP: Roy Merolli
VP: Mary Abu
VP: Allison Bolch
**VP:* Geoffrey L Brackett
VP: Austin Christensen
VP: Deborah Dicaprio
VP: Debbie Dzielecki
VP: Briana Holmes
VP: Andrew James
VP: Shawn Kaylor
VP: Croix Laconsay
VP: Jeanie Plecenik
VP: Joe Pugilese
VP: Deborah Raikes
VP: Deborah Raikes-Colbert
VP: Hollie Randall

D-U-N-S 00-696-7921
MARITZ HOLDINGS INC (MO)
1375 N Highway Dr, Fenton, MO 63099-0001
Tel (636) 827-4000 *Founded/Ownrshp* 1923
Sales 1.2MMM *EMP* 2,955
Accts Kpmg Llp St Louis Mo
SIC 4725 8748 8732 4899 Arrangement of travel tour packages, wholesale; Employee programs administration; Market analysis or research; Data communication services
CEO: W Stephen Maritz
**Pr:* John McArthur
Pr: Lisa Weaner
**CFO:* James W Kienker
CFO: Rick Ramos
Sr Ex VP: John F Risberg
Div VP: Kari McGraw
**Sr VP:* Richard T Ramos
**Sr VP:* John Risberg
VP: Ken Abendschein
VP: Dave Caldwell
VP: Carlos Dunlap
VP: Jill Eichwald
VP: Terry Erwin
VP: John Farley
VP: Matt Glazer
VP: Mindy McGrath
VP: Dick Oconnor
VP: Richard Packer
VP: Beth Schelske
VP: Tom Wilson

D-U-N-S 82-914-3192
MARITZ LLC
(*Suby of* MARITZ HOLDINGS INC) ★
1375 N Highway Dr, Fenton, MO 63099-0001
Tel (636) 827-4000 *Founded/Ownrshp* 2008
Sales 57.6MM[E] *EMP* 2,500
SIC 4725 8748 8732 4899 Arrangement of travel tour packages, wholesale; Employee programs administration; Market analysis or research; Data communication services

D-U-N-S 05-397-6585
MARITZ TRAVEL CO
(*Suby of* MARITZ HOLDINGS INC) ★
1395 N Highway Dr, Fenton, MO 63026-1929
Tel (636) 827-4000 *Founded/Ownrshp* 1955
Sales 218.9MM[E] *EMP* 1,363
SIC 4724 Travel agencies
CEO: Steve Maritz
**Pr:* Christine Duffy
COO: Dennis Hummel
**CFO:* Rich Ramos
**Exec:* John Risberg
IT Man: Saeid Banankhah
Ql Cn Mgr: Aruna Garlapaty
Psych: Ginger Narens
Snr PM: Julie Reinheimer
Board of Directors: Christie Hicks

D-U-N-S 07-963-7115
MARITZCX HOLDINGS LLC
(*Suby of* MARITZ HOLDINGS INC) ★
3451 N Triumph Blvd, Lehi, UT 84043-4991
Tel (385) 695-2800 *Founded/Ownrshp* 2014
Sales 276.5M[E] *EMP* 1,500
SIC 8742 6719 Management consulting services; Investment holding companies, except banks
Pr: Carine Clark
Pt: JD Jeppson
Pr: Chris Cottle
**COO:* Troy Monney
**CFO:* Todd Miceli
Chf Mktg O: Troy L Monney
Sr VP: Chad Latimer
VP: Justin Thompson
VP: Dennis Wood
Prgrm Mgr: Matthew McEwen
Prgrm Mgr: Lisa Oneill

D-U-N-S 06-852-5286
MARITZCX RESEARCH LLC (MO)
(*Suby of* MARITZ HOLDINGS INC) ★
1355 N Highway Dr, Fenton, MO 63026-1935
Tel (636) 827-4000 *Founded/Ownrshp* 1967, 1974
Sales 86.6MM[E] *EMP* 700
SIC 8732 Market analysis or research
Pr: Michael Brereton
**COO:* Gary Eversole
Treas: Richard T Ramos
Div VP: Karan Schmiderer
**Ex VP:* Jim Stone
VP: Jeanne Baker
VP: Randal D Brandt
VP: Dennis Hummel
VP: Michael Kyritsis
**VP:* Eric Levy
IT Man: Rick Lemp

D-U-N-S 15-693-9969 EXP
MARJAC HOLDINGS LLC
1020 Aviation Blvd, Gainesville, GA 30501-6839
Tel (770) 531-5000 *Founded/Ownrshp* 1954
Sales 300.1MM[E] *EMP* 1,200[E]
Accts Moore Stephens Frost Little R
SIC 2015 Chicken slaughtering & processing

MARJAM SUPPLY COMPANY
See MARJAM SUPPLY CO INC

D-U-N-S 09-577-3107 IMP
MARJAM SUPPLY CO INC
MARJAM SUPPLY COMPANY
885 Conklin St, Farmingdale, NY 11735-2400
Tel (631) 249-4900 *Founded/Ownrshp* 1979
Sales 400.1MM *EMP* 614
SIC 5211 5031 Lumber & other building materials; Building materials, interior
Pr: Mark Buller
**VP:* James Buller

D-U-N-S 04-682-0197
MARK DUNNING INDUSTRIES
MDI
100 Race Track Rd, Dothan, AL 36303-0911
Tel (334) 983-1506 *Founded/Ownrshp* 1980
Sales 129.9MM[E] *EMP* 250
SIC 4953 Garbage: collecting, destroying & processing
Pr: J Mark Dunning

D-U-N-S 18-756-3648
MARK FACEY & CO
225 N Main St Ste 500, Bristol, CT 06010-4997
Tel (800) 237-0938 *Founded/Ownrshp* 1986
Sales 52.3MM[E] *EMP* 2,000
SIC 7389

D-U-N-S 12-092-7475 IMP/EXP
MARK FOODS INC
20 W 22nd St Ste 901, New York, NY 10010-5878
Tel (212) 255-6048 *Founded/Ownrshp* 2002
Sales 200.0MM *EMP* 10
SIC 5146 Seafoods
Pr: Barry Markman
Genl Mgr: JB Henderson

D-U-N-S 09-577-4279
MARK GOLDEN MAINTENANCE LTD INC
420 Doughty Blvd Ste 4, Inwood, NY 11096-1356
Tel (516) 239-3400 *Founded/Ownrshp* 1979, 1986
Sales 19.1MM[E] *EMP* 1,150
SIC 7349 5087 Cleaning service, industrial or commercial; Janitors' supplies
Pr: Robert Golden
**VP:* Mark Ashkinazy

MARK ONE CONSTRUCTION CO
See MARK ONE ELECTRIC CO INC

D-U-N-S 00-716-8230
MARK ONE ELECTRIC CO INC (MO)
MARK ONE CONSTRUCTION CO
909 Troost Ave, Kansas City, MO 64106-3088
Tel (816) 842-7023 *Founded/Ownrshp* 1947, 1974
Sales 94.6MM[E] *EMP* 200
SIC 1731 General electrical contractor
Pr: Rosana Privitera Biondo
**VP:* Anthony L Privitera II
**VP:* Joseph A Privitera
**VP:* Josephine A Privitera
**VP:* Richard Sheldrake
Off Mgr: Stephen Sprouse

D-U-N-S 10-828-7939
MARK TRAVEL CORP
FUNJET VACATIONS
8907 N Port Washington Rd, Milwaukee, WI 53217-1634
Tel (414) 228-7472 *Founded/Ownrshp* 1974
Sales 125.2MM[E] *EMP* 1,000
SIC 4725 Arrangement of travel tour packages, wholesale
CEO: William E Lamacchia
COO: Kevin Froemming
**COO:* Thomas E Meier
**CFO:* William Lamacchia Jr
Ex VP: Bob Lacroix
Ex VP: Ray Snisky
**VP:* Randi Becker
**VP:* Ron Jacobs
VP: Lisa Kosiski
**VP:* Sharon Lamacchia
VP: Tammy Lee
VP: Bill L Macchia
VP: Sharon Macchia
VP: Howard McCalla
VP: Terry Morrison
VP: Scott Praven
VP: Tricia Valentine
Dir Bus: Tom Brussow

D-U-N-S 94-338-6987
■ **MARKEL AMERICAN INSURANCE CO**
(*Suby of* MARKEL CORP) ★
N14w23800 Stone Ridge Dr # 300, Waukesha, WI 53188-1144
Tel (262) 548-9880 *Founded/Ownrshp* 1986
Sales NA *EMP* 100E
SIC 6411 Insurance agents, brokers & service
Ch Bd: Anthony Markel
**Pr:* Timberlee T Grove
**Pr:* Audrey Hanken
**V Ch Bd:* Steven Markel
**VP:* John Dwyer

D-U-N-S 00-313-4582
▲ **MARKEL CORP** (VA)
4521 Highwoods Pkwy, Glen Allen, VA 23060-6148
Tel (804) 747-0136 *Founded/Ownrshp* 1930
Sales NA *EMP* 10,600E
Accts Kpmg Llp Richmond Virginia
Tkr Sym MKL *Exch* NYS
SIC 6331 6211 Fire, marine & casualty insurance & carriers; Property damage insurance; Underwriters, security
Co-CEO: Thomas S Gayner
**Ch Bd:* Alan I Kirshner
Pr: F Michael Crowley
Pr: Britton L Glisson
Pr: Brian Gray
CFO: Anne G Waleski
Co-CEO: Richard R Whitt III
Ex VP: Gerard Albanese Jr
Dir IT: Jason Delmore
Board of Directors: Jay M Weinberg, J Alfred Broaddus Jr, Richard R Whitt, K Bruce Connell, Debora J Wilson, Douglas C Eby, Thomas S Gayner, Stewart M Kasen, Lemuel E Lewis, Darrell D Martin, Michael O'reilly, Michael J Schewel

D-U-N-S 80-489-1802
■ **MARKEL INSURANCE CO**
(*Suby of* MARKEL CORP) ★
4600 Cox Rd Ste 100, Glen Allen, VA 23060-6753
Tel (800) 431-1270 *Founded/Ownrshp* 1986
Sales NA *EMP* 251
SIC 6411 Insurance agents, brokers & service
Pr: Britton L Glisson
VP: George D Faison Jr
VP: Emmett Morgan
VP: Mark Nichols
VP: Robin Russo
VP: Mary Allen Waller
VP: Thomas F Wisneski
Mktg Mgr: Linda Lee

D-U-N-S 62-162-5425
■ **MARKEL MIDWEST**
(*Suby of* MARKEL CORP) ★
10 Parkway N Ste 100, Deerfield, IL 60015-2526
Tel (847) 572-6000 *Founded/Ownrshp* 1978
Sales NA *EMP* 100
SIC 6351 Liability insurance
Ch: Steven A Markel
**Pr:* Anthony F Markel

D-U-N-S 10-173-2030
■ **MARKEL SERVICE INC**
(*Suby of* MARKEL CORP) ★
4600 Cox Rd Ste 100, Glen Allen, VA 23060-6753
Tel (804) 747-0136 *Founded/Ownrshp* 1980
Sales NA *EMP* 197E
SIC 6411 Insurance brokers
Pr: Anthony F Markel
**Ch Bd:* Alan I Kirshner
**V Ch Bd:* Steven A Markel
Sr VP: Karen Passey
**VP:* Bruce Kay

D-U-N-S 83-264-8096
■ **MARKEL VENTURES INC**
(*Suby of* MARKEL CORP) ★
4521 Highwoods Pkwy, Glen Allen, VA 23060-6148
Tel (804) 747-0136 *Founded/Ownrshp* 2005
Sales 336.3MME *EMP* 503E
SIC 8741 Business management
**Pr:* Thomas S Gayner
**Treas:* Anne G Waleski

D-U-N-S 00-108-5158 IMP
■ **MARKEM-IMAJE CORP**
(*Suby of* DOVER ENGINEERED SYSTEMS INC) ★
150 Congress St, Keene, NH 03431-4307
Tel (603) 352-1130 *Founded/Ownrshp* 1928
Sales 387.5MME *EMP* 2,800
SIC 2893

D-U-N-S 00-978-3127
MARKET & JOHNSON INC
2350 Galloway St, Eau Claire, WI 54703-3441
Tel (715) 834-1213 *Founded/Ownrshp* 1968
Sales 218.2MM *EMP* 250
Accts Wipfli Llp Eau Claire Wisco
SIC 1542 1541 Hospital construction; School building construction; Institutional building construction; Industrial buildings, new construction
CEO: Dan Market

D-U-N-S 79-741-2236 IMP/EXP
MARKET AMERICA INC
(*Suby of* MARKET AMERICA WORLDWIDE INC) ★
1302 Pleasant Ridge Rd, Greensboro, NC 27409-9415
Tel (336) 605-0040 *Founded/Ownrshp* 2002
Sales 305.3MME *EMP* 650E
SIC 5199 General merchandise, non-durable
Pr: Ridinger
COO: Marc Ashley
Ex VP: Joe Bolyard
Ex VP: Dennis Franks
Ex VP: Marty Weismann
Sr VP: Loren Ridinger
VP: Eddie Alberty
VP: Gene Wallace
Creative D: William Treadwell
Dir IT: Regan Spencer

D-U-N-S 11-487-3388
MARKET AMERICA WORLDWIDE INC
1302 Pleasant Ridge Rd, Greensboro, NC 27409-9415
Tel (336) 605-0040 *Founded/Ownrshp* 2002
Sales 412.0MME *EMP* 730
Accts Dixon Hughes Goodman Llp High
SIC 5199 General merchandise, non-durable
CEO: Ridinger
**Pr:* James H Ridinger
**COO:* Marc Ashley
**Ex VP:* Dennis Franks
**Ex VP:* Martin Weissman
**Sr VP:* Loren Ridinger
**VP:* Kevin Buckman

MARKET BASKET
See DEMOULAS SUPER MARKETS INC

MARKET BASKET
See RETAIL INVESTORS OF TEXAS LTD

D-U-N-S 07-201-1992
MARKET BASKET PRODUCE INC
(*Suby of* MARKET BASKET) ★
875 East St, Tewksbury, MA 01876-1495
Tel (978) 851-8000 *Founded/Ownrshp* 1973
Sales 11.4MME *EMP* 7,000
SIC 5411 Supermarkets, chain
Pr: A T Demoulas
**Treas:* Donald Mulligan
**Treas:* D H Sullivan

D-U-N-S 07-842-9180
MARKET BASKET STORES INC
(*Suby of* MARKET BASKET) ★
2420 Nederland Ave, Nederland, TX 77627-6048
Tel (409) 727-3104 *Founded/Ownrshp* 1975
Sales 216.9MME *EMP* 2,000
SIC 5411 Supermarkets
CEO: Bruce C Thompson
**Pr:* Skylar Thompson
CFO: Thomas Cormier
Sr VP: Keith Dauterive
**VP:* Alletta Thompson
CTO: Danny Wallace
Dir IT: Jed Watts

D-U-N-S 10-319-0351 EXP
MARKET DAY LLC
(*Suby of* GORDON FOOD SERVICE INC) ★
1300 Gezon Pkwy Sw, Wyoming, MI 49509-9300
Tel (630) 285-1470 *Founded/Ownrshp* 2013
Sales 327.4MME *EMP* 1,300
SIC 5141 Food brokers
Pr: Kristine Holtz
CFO: Mary Larson
Ex VP: William S Sivak
Software D: Bill Raymond

D-U-N-S 05-628-0576
MARKET INDUSTRIES LTD
(*Suby of* UTI (US) HOLDINGS INC) ★
110 N Marine Dr, Portland, OR 97217-8030
Tel (503) 283-2405 *Founded/Ownrshp* 2006
Sales 141.8MME *EMP* 180E
SIC 4731 4213 Brokers, shipping; Contract haulers
Pr: Gary Wilson
**Pr:* Garry Wilson
Mktg Mgr: Randy Giovanetti

MARKET LOGISTICS
See MARKET TRANSPORT LTD

D-U-N-S 09-625-1343
MARKET OF CHOICE INC (OR)
PRICE CHOPPER
2580 Willakenzie Rd, Eugene, OR 97401-4805
Tel (541) 345-3349 *Founded/Ownrshp* 1978
Sales 108.8MME *EMP* 700
SIC 5411 Supermarkets, independent
Pr: Richard L Wright Jr
**CFO:* Lawrence Brody
Exec: Marcus Whittaker
Genl Mgr: Heinz Beierling
Genl Mgr: Dorothy Jones

MARKET PLACE FOODS
See JOHANNESONS INC

D-U-N-S 60-544-6251
MARKET STRATEGIES INC
MARKET STRATEGIES INTL
17430 College Pkwy, Livonia, MI 48152-2363
Tel (734) 542-7600 *Founded/Ownrshp* 1989
Sales 127.3MME *EMP* 860
SIC 8742 8732 Marketing consulting services; Market analysis or research
Ch Bd: Andrew Morrison PHD
**Pr:* George Wilkerson
**CEO:* Rob Stone PHD
**COO:* Reginald Baker
**CFO:* Philip Giroux
Sr VP: Kenneth V Athaide
VP: Lindsey Dickman
**VP:* Leona Foster
VP: Alexander Gage
VP: Katherine Katy
VP: Erin Leedy
VP: David Paull
VP: Farrell Wilson

MARKET STRATEGIES INTL
See MARKET STRATEGIES INC

D-U-N-S 14-467-1067
MARKET TRACK LLC
233 S Wacker Dr, Chicago, IL 60606-7147
Tel (312) 529-5102 *Founded/Ownrshp* 2012
Sales 71.9MME *EMP* 1,102E
SIC 8742 Management consulting services
CEO: Dennis Moore
**Ch Bd:* Wayne Mincey
**CFO:* Tim Burditt
**Ofcr:* Paul Salay
VP: Lei Jin

D-U-N-S 07-643-7417
MARKET TRANSPORT LTD
MARKET LOGISTICS
(*Suby of* MARKET INDUSTRIES LTD) ★
110 N Marine Dr, Portland, OR 97217-8097
Tel (503) 283-3279 *Founded/Ownrshp* 2008
Sales 141.8MME *EMP* 375
SIC 4213 Contract haulers; Refrigerated products transport
Pr: Greg P Galbraith
VP: Mike Olsen
VP: Gary Wilson
CIO: Jay Hemmady
Opers Mgr: Guy Cook
Opers Mgr: Kathy Korb
Opers Mgr: Tae No

D-U-N-S 15-586-4528
▲ **MARKETAXESS HOLDINGS INC**
299 Park Ave Fl 10, New York, NY 10171-3804
Tel (212) 813-6000 *Founded/Ownrshp* 2000
Sales 303.1MM *EMP* 342E
Tkr Sym MKTX *Exch* NGS
SIC 6211 Security brokers & dealers; Bond dealers & brokers; Stock brokers & dealers; Stock option dealers
Ch Bd: Richard M McVey
CFO: Antonio L Delise
VP: Bill Barnett
CIO: Nicholas Themelis
IT Man: Daniel Jacobson
Web Dev: Reginald Hunt
Board of Directors: Steven L Begleiter, Stephen P Casper, Jane Chwick, William F Cruger, David G Gomach, Carlos M Hernandez, Ronald M Hersch, John Steinhardt, James J Sullivan

D-U-N-S 08-108-9372
MARKETFARE FOODS LLC
(*Suby of* GREENCORE US HOLDINGS) ★
222 Rosewood Dr Fl 2, Danvers, MA 01923-4502
Tel (978) 716-2530 *Founded/Ownrshp* 2012
Sales 99.1MME *EMP* 400
SIC 5142 Packaged frozen goods
CEO: Liam McClennon
VP: Bill Stanley

D-U-N-S 06-840-1285
MARKETING ALLIANCE GROUP INC
AMERICAN DISPLAY & FIXTURE
2830 N Dug Gap Rd Sw, Dalton, GA 30720-4946
Tel (706) 277-9707 *Founded/Ownrshp* 1998
Sales 176.9MME *EMP* 600E
SIC 2752 Commercial printing, lithographic
CEO: Bryan Hair
**Pr:* Brian Hair
**CFO:* Frank Grant
CTO: Donnie Bowers
Sales Exec: Phyllis Davis
Natl Sales: John Kile
Natl Sales: Paige Spurlock
Sls Mgr: Sandy McDowell
Sls Mgr: Mike Oric
Sls Mgr: Josh Young

MARKETING ARM, THE
See MARKETING ARM INC

D-U-N-S 96-168-2341
■ **MARKETING ARM INC**
MARKETING ARM, THE
(*Suby of* OMNICOM GROUP INC) ★
1999 Bryan St Fl 18, Dallas, TX 75201-3136
Tel (214) 259-3200 *Founded/Ownrshp* 1999
Sales 88.5MME *EMP* 255E
SIC 8742 Marketing consulting services
CEO: Ray Clark
Pr: Mark Talkington
**COO:* Brad Penman
**CFO:* Jennifer Henry
**Chf Mktg O:* Daniel G Belmont
**Ex VP:* Nowell Upham
Sr VP: Eric Holmen
Sr VP: Mike Paley
Sr VP: Jordis Rosenquest
VP: Tony Amador
VP: Alison Delzell
**VP:* Erin Dwyer
**VP:* Jeff Erickson
**VP:* Jason Katz
VP: Dan Keats
VP: Michelle Palmer
VP: Trina Roffino
VP: Lara Beth Seager
VP: Melvin Strobbe
VP: James Welsh
Assoc Dir: Steven Meyers
Board of Directors: Michael Rodriguez

D-U-N-S 07-318-4335 IMP/EXP
MARKETING MANAGEMENT INC
M M I
4717 Fletcher Ave, Fort Worth, TX 76107-6826
Tel (817) 731-4176 *Founded/Ownrshp* 1966
Sales 93.1MME *EMP* 215
SIC 5141 Food brokers
Pr: Wesley Williams
**Treas:* Kimberly R Pease
Sr Cor Off: Herbert Poledna
**VP:* Paul Nichols
VP: Gregory Pohlmann
Comm Dir: Joni Grulke
Off Mgr: Jackie Mason
Snr Ntwrk: Tyronne Foster
Sales Exec: Coleman Anderson
VP Sls: Ed Mieskoski
Art Dir: Tom Schuller

D-U-N-S 05-432-7866
MARKETING STORE WORLDWIDE L L C
(*Suby of* PERSECO CO DIV) ★
55 W Monroe St Fl 14, Chicago, IL 60603-5005
Tel (312) 614-4600 *Founded/Ownrshp* 1991
Sales 87.0MME *EMP* 1,000
SIC 7311 8742 Advertising agencies; Marketing consulting services
Pt: Mark Landolt
**COO:* Howard Katz
**VP:* Robert Bredy

VP: Michael Jenneman
Creative D: Shelford Chandler
CIO: Bill Pittges
Art Dir: Robert Lee
Snr PM: Holly Findling

D-U-N-S 82-830-0637
MARKETO INC
(*Suby of* MILESTONE HOLDCO, INC.)
901 Mariners Island Blvd, San Mateo, CA 94404-1592
Tel (650) 376-2300 *Founded/Ownrshp* 2016
Sales 209.8MM *EMP* 949E
SIC 7371 7372 Custom computer programming services; Computer software writing services; Prepackaged software
CEO: Phillip M Fernandez
COO: Jason L Holmes
CFO: Brian K Kinion
Chf Mktg O: Chandar Pattabhiram
Ex VP: Lynne Biggar
Ex VP: Steven M Winter
Sr VP: Robin Ritenour
Sr VP: Margo Smith
VP: Joan Burke
Creative D: Davis Lee
Snr Sftwr: Bharath R Nukala

MARKETPLACE
See WINN-DIXIE STORES INC

MARKETPLACE CHAPLAINS USA
See MARKETPLACE MINISTRIES INC

D-U-N-S 78-461-4752
MARKETPLACE MINISTRIES INC
MARKETPLACE CHAPLAINS USA
2001 W Plano Pkwy, Dallas, TX 75201
Tel (972) 941-4400 *Founded/Ownrshp* 1984
Sales 14.9MM *EMP* 1,200
Accts Capin Crouse Llp Dallas Tx
SIC 8661 Religious organizations
CEO: Gilford A Stricklin
**Pr:* Richard Dewtt
Ex VP: Ann Stricklin
**Sr VP:* C G Maclin
VP: George Cotter
**VP:* Chaley Quackenbush
VP: Joel Rayfield
**VP:* Dan Shotts
VP: Jim Tereschuk
Snr Mgr: Joseph Bennett
Snr Mgr: Clint Beymer

D-U-N-S 02-731-7551 IMP
MARKETS LLC
COST CUTTERS
4350 Cordata Pkwy, Bellingham, WA 98226-8019
Tel (360) 714-9797 *Founded/Ownrshp* 1909
Sales 161.4MME *EMP* 800
SIC 5411 Supermarkets, chain
**CFO:* Aaron Tam
VP: Andrew Baum
Dist Mgr: James Estes
Off Mgr: Lindsey Kelley
CIO: Rick N Treese
Netwrk Mgr: Michael Zamora
VP Opers: Clark Jordan
Mktg Dir: Dean Priestman
Pr Dir: Sue Cole
Mktg Mgr: Geri Reichenbach

D-U-N-S 17-189-9326
MARKETSOURCE INC
(*Suby of* ALLEGIS GROUP INC) ★
11700 Great Oaks Way, Alpharetta, GA 30022-2448
Tel (770) 674-5000 *Founded/Ownrshp* 1991
Sales 98.4MME *EMP* 8,500
SIC 8742 Marketing consulting services
Pr: Rick Haviland
**Ex VP:* Mike Christensen
VP: Steve Carlisle
**VP:* Bob Hunter
VP: Randy Luffman
Ex Dir: Deborah Keeney
CIO: Steve Bonvissuto
Sls Dir: John Bowers
Sales Asso: Jim Confer

D-U-N-S 17-196-0172
■ **MARKETSTAR CORP**
(*Suby of* OMNICOM GROUP INC) ★
2475 Washington Blvd, Ogden, UT 84401-2315
Tel (801) 393-1155 *Founded/Ownrshp* 1999
Sales 98.4MME *EMP* 2,500
SIC 8742 Marketing consulting services
CEO: David Treadway
**COO:* Aaron Tracy Hall
CFO: Harris Ej
**CFO:* Elroy J Harris
VP: Vaughn Aust
VP: Aaron T Exec
VP Bus Dev: Millie Davis
VP Admn: Paul Stout
Area Mgr: Mark Braddy
Area Mgr: Shawn Cosky
Dir IT: Russell Reid

MARKETTE STORES, THE
See WEST OIL INC

D-U-N-S 82-757-6930
MARKIT GROUP LIMITED
620 8th Ave Fl 35, New York, NY 10018-1693
Tel (212) 931-4900 *Founded/Ownrshp* 2001
Sales 1.0MM *EMP* 3,000
SIC 7374 Data processing service
CEO: Lance Uggla
Pr: Amit Joshi
Ex VP: Shane Akeroyd
Ex VP: Chip Carver
VP: Allan Barshtak
VP: Peter Boyes
VP: Holly Chen
VP: Priyanka Chetia
VP: Ann Criqui
VP: Boris Dainson
VP: Alex Gurman
VP: Jonathan Hadden
VP: Fred Henkel
VP: Jasmine Ho
VP: Carly Hodgkiss

VP: Jamie Hull
VP: Leah Jordan
VP: Meg Liebenstein
VP: Chris Melton
VP: Gavan Nolan
VP: Kaushal Parikh

D-U-N-S 06-390-9308
MARKIT INC
250 Mill St Ste 303, Rochester, NY 14614-1026
Tel (585) 777-4018 *Founded/Ownrshp* 1999
Sales 524.0MM *EMP* 70ᴱ
SIC 8742 Sales (including sales management) consultant
Pr: Dmitri Tereschenko
VP: Victoria Kogan
VP: Krishna Shetty
Mng Dir: Claire Lobo

D-U-N-S 10-172-1798
MARKIT NORTH AMERICA INC
(*Suby of* MARKIT GROUP LIMITED)
620 8th Ave Fl 35, New York, NY 10018-1693
Tel (212) 931-4900 *Founded/Ownrshp* 2004
Sales 182.0MMᴱ *EMP* 350ᴱ
SIC 6289 Financial reporting
Pr: Kevin Gould
**CEO:* Lance Uggla

D-U-N-S 08-603-5958
MARKLOGIC CORP
999 Skyway Rd Ste 200, San Carlos, CA 94070-2722
Tel (650) 655-2300 *Founded/Ownrshp* 2004
Sales 177.4MMᴱ *EMP* 525ᴱ
SIC 7371 Computer software development & applications
Pr: Gary Bloom
CFO: Peter Norman
CFO: Dave Ponzini
Chf Mktg O: Michaline Todd
Ofcr: Catherine Chan
Ex VP: Keith Carlson
Ex VP: John Shap
Sr VP: Gary Lang
VP: David Gorbet
VP: Andrew Grygiel
VP: David Martin
VP: John Pomeroy
VP: Kevin Shelly
VP: Mark Tice
VP: Ted Yarnell
Dir Bus: Jeff Faraday
Board of Directors: Tom Banahan, Gary Bloom, Mark Kvamme, Christopher Lindblad, Greg J Santora

D-U-N-S 00-692-5515
MARKS & MORGAN JEWELERS INC (GA)
(*Suby of* SIGNET HOLDINGS LTD)
375 Ghent Rd, Fairlawn, OH 44333-4601
Tel (330) 668-5000 *Founded/Ownrshp* 1924
Sales 57.3MMᴱ *EMP* 1,200
SIC 5944

D-U-N-S 07-105-0330
MARKS PANETH LLP
685 3rd Ave Fl 4, New York, NY 10017-8408
Tel (212) 503-8800 *Founded/Ownrshp* 1966
Sales 106.7MMᴱ *EMP* 560ᴱ
SIC 8721 Certified public accountant
Mng Pt: Mark Levenfus
Pt: Steven L Brass
Mng Pt: Harry Moehringer
CFO: Brian L Fox
CFO: Brian Fox
Chf Mktg O: Diane Paoletta
Admn Mgr: Myrta Maldonado
Mktg Mgr: Kelly Parkhurst
Snr Mgr: David Greenberg
Snr Mgr: Joshua Hartman
Snr Mgr: Moshe Landy

D-U-N-S 36-246-2322
MARKSMAN SECURITY CORP
1700 Nw 49th St Ste 110, Fort Lauderdale, FL 33309-3798
Tel (954) 771-9755 *Founded/Ownrshp* 2003
Sales 34.4MMᴱ *EMP* 1,500ᴱ
SIC 7382 7381 Security systems services; Security guard service
CEO: Ezekiel A Kaufman
**Pr:* Mark E Radi
Site Mgr: Everett Hunley

MARKSTEIN BEVERAGE COMPANY
See MARKSTEIN BEVERAGE CO OF SACRAMENTO

D-U-N-S 02-880-0589 IMP
MARKSTEIN BEVERAGE CO OF SACRAMENTO
MARKSTEIN BEVERAGE COMPANY
60 Main Ave, Sacramento, CA 95838-2034
Tel (916) 920-3911 *Founded/Ownrshp* 1974
Sales 120.6MMᴱ *EMP* 150
SIC 5181 5149 Beer & ale; Soft drinks; Mineral or spring water bottling
CEO: Hayden Markstein
**Ch Bd:* Richard Markstein
**Pr:* Steve Markstein
Ex VP: Markstein Hayden

D-U-N-S 03-449-6146
■ **MARKWEST ENERGY PARTNERS LP**
(*Suby of* MPLX LP) ★
1515 Arapahoe St, Denver, CO 80202-3150
Tel (303) 925-9200 *Founded/Ownrshp* 2002, 2015
Sales 2.1MMM *EMP* 1,404ᴱ
SIC 1321 4922 1389 Natural gas liquids; Fractionating natural gas liquids; Natural gasoline production; Pipelines, natural gas; Storage, natural gas; Gas compressing (natural gas) at the fields; Processing service, gas
Pr: Frank M Semple
CFO: Nancy K Buese
Treas: Stephen C Newman
Treas: Stephen Newman
VP: Tiffany Kenyon
VP: Scott Parker
VP: Ron Spingler
VP: Bryan Teets
Area Mgr: Ron Smith
Plnt Mgr: Greg Bezdec

MARKWEST HYDROCARBON, INC.
See MARKWEST HYDROCARBON LLC

D-U-N-S 18-835-4799 EXP
■ **MARKWEST HYDROCARBON LLC**
MARKWEST HYDROCARBON, INC.
(*Suby of* MARKWEST ENERGY PARTNERS LP) ★
1515 Arapahoe St, Denver, CO 80202-3150
Tel (303) 290-8700 *Founded/Ownrshp* 2008
Sales 396.8MMᴱ *EMP* 318ᴱ
SIC 1321 4924 Fractionating natural gas liquids; Propane (natural) production; Isobutane (natural) production; Butane (natural) production; Natural gas distribution
Pr: Frank M Semple
Pr: Dan Cory
COO: John C Mollenkopf
CFO: Nancy K Buese
CFO: Nancy K Masten-Buese
Treas: Andrew L Schroeder
Sr VP: C Corwin Bromley
Sr VP: Randy S Nickerson
VP: Richard A Ostberg
VP: Richard Ostberg
Board of Directors: Michael L Beatty, Donald C Heppermann, William A Kellstrom, Anne E Mounsey, Karen Rogers, William F Wallace, Donald D Wolf

D-U-N-S 11-331-3969 IMP
MARKWINS INTERNATIONAL CORP
22067 Ferrero, Walnut, CA 91789-5214
Tel (909) 595-8898 *Founded/Ownrshp* 1987
Sales 296.4MM *EMP* 302
Accts Mcgladrey Llp Los Angeles Ca
SIC 2844 Cosmetic preparations
Pr: Sung-Tsei Eric Chen
Pr: Jeff Rogers
**CFO:* Leslie H Hernandez
VP: Mark Law
VP: Evelyn Wang
Genl Mgr: Alberto Cuellar
CTO: Hon Ly
IT Man: Caroline Chiu
VP Sls: Dan Stoecklein
Mktg Dir: Wilson Fennelly
Mktg Dir: Patti Hair

D-U-N-S 04-974-9075
MARLABS INC
1 Corporate Pl S Fl 3, Piscataway, NJ 08854-6116
Tel (732) 694-1000 *Founded/Ownrshp* 1996
Sales 139.1MMᴱ *EMP* 900
SIC 7371 Computer software development & applications
Pr: Vadakekkara Siby A
Pt: Sandhya Durai
**Pr:* Balram Srinivasan
**CFO:* Krishnan Ramachandran
**VP:* Jay Nair
Exec: Seema Adhangale
**Prin:* Sanjay Vidyadharan
QA Dir: Mohankrishna Mannava
IT Man: Rajesh Arora
Sftwr Eng: Sandeep Kumar
Sls Mgr: Sharon L Vastano

D-U-N-S 07-825-2350
MARLBORO TOWNSHIP BOARD OF EDUCATION
1980 Township Dr, Marlboro, NJ 07746-2247
Tel (732) 972-2000 *Founded/Ownrshp* 1925
Sales 88.7MM *EMP* 9
Accts Walter J Brash Pine Brook N
SIC 8211 School board
Pr: Debbie Mattos
Bd of Dir: Victoria Dean
Bd of Dir: Dara Enny
Bd of Dir: Michael Lilonsky
Bd of Dir: Joanne Liu-Rudel
Bd of Dir: Craig Marshall
Bd of Dir: Robyn Wolfe
Bd of Dir: Ellen WEI Xu
**VP:* Stephen Shifrinson
Tech Mgr: Lee Quackenbush

D-U-N-S 13-310-7164
■ **MARLETTE HOMES**
(*Suby of* OAKWOOD HOMES) ★
400 W Elm Ave, Hermiston, OR 97838-1021
Tel (541) 567-5546 *Founded/Ownrshp* 2009
Sales 127.4MMᴱ *EMP* 624ᴱ
SIC 3999 Advertising curtains
Pr: Walter E Wells
Genl Mgr: David Debusk
Mtls Mgr: Kc Cannell
Sls&Mrk Ex: Darlene Newman
Sls Mgr: Jim Johanson

D-U-N-S 00-713-1816 IMP
■ **MARLEY CO LLC**
S P X
(*Suby of* SPX CORP) ★
13515 Balntyn Corp Pl, Charlotte, NC 28277-2706
Tel (704) 752-4400 *Founded/Ownrshp* 1922, 2001
Sales 485.0MMᴱ *EMP* 2,600
SIC 3443 3433 3586 3561 3634 Cooling towers, metal plate; Heat exchangers, plate type; Heating equipment, except electric; Measuring & dispensing pumps; Pumps & pumping equipment; Heating units, electric (radiant heat): baseboard or wall
CEO: Steve Zeller
**CFO:* Patrick J O'Leary
VP: Darren Dickson
**VP:* Robert B Foreman
**VP:* Christopher J Kearney
VP: Sue Simmonds
Info Man: Patrick Barry
Board of Directors: Robert E Drury, G A Eisenberg

D-U-N-S 07-913-8997
■ **MARLEY ENGINEERED PRODUCTS LLC**
(*Suby of* SPX CORP) ★
470 Beauty Spot Rd E, Bennettsville, SC 29512-2770
Tel (843) 479-4006 *Founded/Ownrshp* 2002
Sales 100.0MM *EMP* 360
SIC 3634 Fans, exhaust & ventilating, electric: household; Electric household fans, heaters & humidifiers
Pr: John Swann
Manager: Sean Pesce

D-U-N-S 82-549-1082
■ **MARLIN BUSINESS BANK**
(*Suby of* MARLIN BUSINESS SERVICES CORP) ★
2795 E Cottonwood Pkwy # 120, Salt Lake City, UT 84121-7092
Tel (888) 479-9111 *Founded/Ownrshp* 2005
Sales NA *EMP* 25ᴱ
SIC 6111 Federal & federally sponsored credit agencies
Pr: Raymond Dardano
**Ofcr:* George F Coburn

D-U-N-S 13-838-8793
▲ **MARLIN BUSINESS SERVICES CORP**
300 Fellowship Rd, Mount Laurel, NJ 08054-1201
Tel (888) 479-9111 *Founded/Ownrshp* 1997
Sales 89.7MM *EMP* 314ᴱ
Tkr Sym MRLN *Exch* NGS
SIC 7389 7359 6022 Financial services; Equipment rental & leasing; State commercial banks
CEO: Jeffrey A Hilzinger
**Ch Bd:* Lawrence J Deangelo
Pr: Bob Basile
Pr: Greg Dietrich
Pr: Kathy McGurk
COO: Edward J Siciliano
CFO: William Taylor Kamp Jr
Sr VP: Edward R Dietz
VP: Dan Castellini
VP: Ronald Queen
VP: Karen Shields
VP: David Sowell
Board of Directors: John J Calamari, Scott Heimes, Matthew J Sullivan, J Christopher Teets, James W Wert

D-U-N-S 19-096-3749
MARLIN ENERGY LLC
3861 Ambassador Caffery P, Lafayette, LA 70503-5270
Tel (337) 769-0032 *Founded/Ownrshp* 2003
Sales 88.0MMᴱ *EMP* 35ᴱ
SIC 1311 1382 Crude petroleum & natural gas production; Oil & gas exploration services

D-U-N-S 80-044-9055
MARLIN EQUITY PARTNERS LLC
338 Pier Ave, Hermosa Beach, CA 90254-3617
Tel (310) 364-0100 *Founded/Ownrshp* 2016
Sales 3.2MMMᴱ *EMP* 8,300
SIC 6282 Investment advisory service
CFO: Barbara Luzzatto
Ex VP: John McCurry
VP: Doug Bayerd
VP: Andrew Lawson
Exec: Marcia Fish
Exec: Robb Warwick
Genl Couns: AZ Virji

D-U-N-S 82-615-9175
MARLIN HOLDCO LP
3301 Benson Dr Ste 601, Raleigh, NC 27609-7331
Tel (919) 325-3000 *Founded/Ownrshp* 2007
Sales 688.6MMᴱ *EMP* 1,601
SIC 4953

D-U-N-S 83-289-3460 IMP
■ **MARMAXX OPERATING CORP**
T.J. MAXX
(*Suby of* TJ MAXX) ★
770 Cochituate Rd, Framingham, MA 01701-4666
Tel (508) 390-1000 *Founded/Ownrshp* 1989
Sales 3.2MMMᴱ *EMP* 20,000
SIC 5311 5651 Department stores, discount; Family clothing stores
Pr: Ernie Herrman
**VP:* Jeffrey Naylor
Plng Mgr: Katie Schopp
IT Man: Ann Dalton

D-U-N-S 96-227-3814
■ **MARMON DISTRIBUTION SERVICES INC**
(*Suby of* MARMON HOLDINGS INC) ★
225 E Cunningham St, Butler, PA 16001-6018
Tel (724) 283-3000 *Founded/Ownrshp* 2009
Sales 162.2MMᴱ *EMP* 960
SIC 5051 4213 Metals service centers & offices; Trucking, except local
Pr: Alan Wilkinson
**CFO:* Andrew N Seka
MIS Dir: Jay Powell
Opers Mgr: Greg Paugh
Corp Couns: Bambi Tucker

D-U-N-S 01-021-6679 IMP
■ **MARMON GROUP LLC** (CA)
PAN AMERICAN SCREW DIV
(*Suby of* UNION TANK CAR CO) ★
181 W Madison St Ste 2600, Chicago, IL 60602-4504
Tel (312) 372-9500 *Founded/Ownrshp* 1973
Sales 510.9MMᴱ *EMP* 358
SIC 3452 5072 Bolts, nuts, rivets & washers; Bolts, nuts & screws
CEO: Frank Ptak

D-U-N-S 79-587-1581
■ **MARMON GROUP LLC**
(*Suby of* MARMON HOLDINGS INC) ★
181 W Madison St Ste 2600, Chicago, IL 60602-4504
Tel (312) 372-9500 *Founded/Ownrshp* 2012
Sales 1.0MMMᴱ *EMP* 1,700
SIC 8748 Business consulting
CEO: Frank Ptak
**Treas:* Robert C Gluth
**VP:* James Angus
VP: Mark Carrier
VP: Leon Drake
**VP:* Kenneth P Fischl
VP: Don Hannon
**VP:* Randy Rizzo
**VP:* Robert Schaumann
VP: Loren Veltrop
**VP:* Robert W Webb
**VP:* Henry J West

D-U-N-S 05-227-8728 IMP/EXP
■ **MARMON HOLDINGS INC**
(*Suby of* BERKSHIRE HATHAWAY INC) ★
181 W Madison St Ste 2600, Chicago, IL 60602-4504
Tel (312) 372-9500 *Founded/Ownrshp* 2008
Sales 6.0MMMᴱ *EMP* 20,881
Accts Deloitte & Touche Llp Chicago
SIC 5051 3351 3743 4741 3423 3589 Metals service centers & offices; Copper pipe; Tubing, copper & copper alloy; Wire, copper & copper alloy; Railway motor cars; Rental of railroad cars; Caulking tools, hand; Can openers, not electric; Water treatment equipment, industrial; Water purification equipment, household type
Pr: Frank Ptak
**V Ch:* John Nichols
**CFO:* Robert K Lorch
**Ch:* Thomas J Pritzker
**Sr VP:* Robert W Webb
VP: Robert C Gluth

D-U-N-S 04-525-6138 IMP/EXP
■ **MARMON INDUSTRIAL LLC**
(*Suby of* MARMON HOLDINGS INC) ★
181 W Madison St Fl 26, Chicago, IL 60602-4510
Tel (312) 372-9500 *Founded/Ownrshp* 1995
Sales 810.4MMᴱ *EMP* 5,188
SIC 3743 4741 3589 6159 3965 3492 Railway motor cars; Rental of railroad cars; Water treatment equipment, industrial; Machinery & equipment finance leasing; Fasteners; Control valves, fluid power: hydraulic & pneumatic
Pr: John Nichols
CFO: Bob Lorch
Sr VP: Robert W Webb
VP: Lawrence Rist

D-U-N-S 07-919-5591
■ **MARMON RETAIL & END USER TECHNOLOGIES INC**
(*Suby of* MARMON HOLDINGS INC) ★
181 W Madison St Fl 26, Chicago, IL 60602-4510
Tel (312) 372-9500 *Founded/Ownrshp* 2013
Sales 400.0MMᴱ *EMP* 125ᴱ
SIC 2599 Restaurant furniture, wood or metal
Prin: Robert B Davidson

D-U-N-S 07-874-5765 IMP
■ **MARMON RETAIL PRODUCTS INC**
RETAIL HOME IMPROVEMENT PDTS
(*Suby of* MARMON RETAIL & END USER TECHNOLOGIES INC) ★
1002 Industrial Way, Crothersville, IN 47229-9415
Tel (812) 793-2929 *Founded/Ownrshp* 2012
Sales 400.0MMᴱ *EMP* 125
SIC 3357 3351 Nonferrous wiredrawing & insulating; Copper rolling & drawing
Genl Mgr: Jared Argyle
**Prin:* Paul Ridsdale
Genl Mgr: Robert Kennedy

D-U-N-S 60-621-1287
■ **MARMON RETAIL SERVICES INC**
(*Suby of* MARMON HOLDINGS INC) ★
181 W Madison St, Chicago, IL 60602-4510
Tel (312) 332-0317 *Founded/Ownrshp* 2002
Sales 400.0MMᴱ *EMP* 1,600ᴱ
SIC 2541 2542 Store fixtures, wood; Fixtures, store: except wood

D-U-N-S 04-817-5764 EXP
■ **MARMON UTILITY LLC**
(*Suby of* MARMON HOLDINGS INC) ★
53 Old Wilton Rd, Milford, NH 03055-3119
Tel (603) 673-2040 *Founded/Ownrshp* 1996
Sales 124.6MMᴱ *EMP* 200
SIC 3357 Communication wire

D-U-N-S 00-791-0052 IMP/EXP
■ **MARMON/KEYSTONE LLC**
(*Suby of* BERKSHIRE HATHAWAY INC) ★
225 E Cunningham St, Butler, PA 16001-6018
Tel (724) 283-3000 *Founded/Ownrshp* 1907
Sales 265.9MMᴱ *EMP* 950
SIC 5051 4213

D-U-N-S 07-340-6332 IMP
■ **MARMOT MOUNTAIN LLC**
(*Suby of* NEWELL BRANDS) ★
5789 State Farm Dr # 100, Rohnert Park, CA 94928-6308
Tel (707) 544-4590 *Founded/Ownrshp* 1974
Sales 101.2MMᴱ *EMP* 200
SIC 2329

D-U-N-S 05-591-0528
MARNELL GAMING LLC
COLORADO BELL AND CASINO
2100 S Casino Dr, Laughlin, NV 89029-1514
Tel (702) 298-4000 *Founded/Ownrshp* 2006
Sales 226.5MMᴱ *EMP* 2,800ᴱ
SIC 7999 Gambling establishment
VP: Raymond Gradisher

D-U-N-S 80-733-2973
MARNELL SHER GAMING LLC
12300 Las Vegas Blvd S, Henderson, NV 89044-9506
Tel (702) 797-1000 *Founded/Ownrshp* 2006
Sales 91.3MMᴱ *EMP* 1,350ᴱ
SIC 7011 Resort hotel
Pr: Anthony A Marnell III
**CFO:* James Barrett
CFO: Jason Early
**Ex VP:* Kari Dimler
**Ex VP:* Joseph Magliarditi
Sr VP: Bruce Howard
**VP:* Jay Francis
**VP:* Cherisse Nicastro
**VP:* Stan Tims
**VP:* Robert Willis
Dir Sec: Maria Santo

MARONDA HOMES
See MARONDA INC

D-U-N-S 05-930-1606
MARONDA INC
MARONDA HOMES
11 Timberglen Dr, Imperial, PA 15126-9267
Tel (724) 695-1200 *Founded/Ownrshp* 1972
Sales 149.1MM^E *EMP* 380
SIC 6552 1521 Subdividers & developers; New construction, single-family houses
Ch Bd: William J Wolf
**Pr:* Ron Wolf
**Sec:* Ronald W Wolf

D-U-N-S 08-322-0848 IMP/EXP
MAROON GROUP LLC
1390 Jaycox Rd, Avon, OH 44011-1372
Tel (440) 937-1000 *Founded/Ownrshp* 1977
Sales 93.8MM^E *EMP* 56
SIC 5169 Chemicals & allied products
CEO: Mark Reichard
**COO:* Mike McKenna
**CFO:* Brian Wilson
**Chf Cred:* Howard Hubert
**CTO:* Mark Maroon
Mktg Dir: Keith Stricker
Sls Mgr: Rodger Cram

D-U-N-S 05-896-8942
MAROUS BROTHERS CONSTRUCTION INC
1702 Joseph Lloyd Pkwy, Willoughby, OH 44094-8028
Tel (440) 951-3904 *Founded/Ownrshp* 1980
Sales 138.1MM^E *EMP* 300
SIC 1521 1751 Single-family housing construction; Carpentry work
Pr: Adelbert Marous
**Sec:* Kenneth Marous
**VP:* Scott Marous
Genl Mgr: Douglas Richardson
Genl Mgr: Jeff Roush
Off Mgr: Karen Fonovic
Sfty Mgr: Keith Taylor
Opers Mgr: Bruce Asp
Manager: Ken Weinberg
Snr PM: John Marinelli

MARQUARDT HEATING
See HOPSON OIL CO INC

D-U-N-S 07-085-0102 IMP
MARQUARDT SWITCHES INC (DE)
(*Suby of* MARQUARDT GMBH)
2711 Us Route 20, Cazenovia, NY 13035-9405
Tel (315) 655-8050 *Founded/Ownrshp* 1975
Sales 219.7MM *EMP* 555
Accts Fust Charles Chambers Llp Syr
SIC 3625 3613 Switches, electric power; Switchgear & switchboard apparatus
Pr: Jochen Becker
**Ch Bd:* Harold Marquardt
**CFO:* John Jelfo

D-U-N-S 07-477-8614 IMP
MARQUETTE GENERAL HOSPITAL INC
420 W Magnetic St, Marquette, MI 49855-2794
Tel (906) 228-9440 *Founded/Ownrshp* 1973
Sales 212.3MM *EMP* 3,100
SIC 8062 General medical & surgical hospitals
CEO: A Gary Muller
CFO: Shawn Beaudry
CFO: Don Grisham
**CFO:* Gary Worden
**VP:* Mark Aho
VP: Richard Jones
**VP:* Paulette J Lindberg
Exec: James Gallagher
Dir Inf Cn: Julie Maki
Brnch Mgr: Judy Bramshneider
Nurse Mgr: Nancy Firestone

MARQUETTE GROUP
See GENERAL YELLOW PAGES CONSULTANTS INC

D-U-N-S 00-643-9962
MARQUETTE UNIVERSITY (WI)
1250 W Wisconsin Ave, Milwaukee, WI 53233-2225
Tel (414) 288-7223 *Founded/Ownrshp* 1861, 1881
Sales 418.6MM *EMP* 3,000^E
Accts Kpmg Llp Milwaukee Wi
SIC 8221 University
Pr: Rev Scott Pilarz
Pr: Jeff Janz
**CFO:* John C Lamb
VP: Larren Barron
VP: David Buckholdt
VP: Melissa Frank
VP: Tom Ganey
VP: Meghan Hamilton
VP: Kendra Jorandby
VP: Bradley Kwaterski
VP: Christopher Miller
VP: Betsy Philipose
VP: Carmel Ruffolo
VP: Sally Sutko
VP: Lindsey Usher
VP: Erika Zoller
Assoc Dir: Sue McKeon
Assoc Dir: Todd McMahon
Dir Soc: Julie Kuligowski

D-U-N-S 82-525-1903 IMP/EXP
MARQUEZ BROTHERS ENTERPRISES INC
15480 Valley Blvd, City of Industry, CA 91746-3325
Tel (626) 330-3310 *Founded/Ownrshp* 1993
Sales 88.3MM^E *EMP* 200
SIC 5141 Groceries, general line
Pr: Gustavo Marquez
CFO: Dave Villanueva
**VP:* Jaime Marquez
**VP:* Juan Marquez
VP Opers: Francisco Lara

D-U-N-S 04-523-3020 IMP
MARQUEZ BROTHERS INTERNATIONAL INC
M B
5801 Rue Ferrari, San Jose, CA 95138-1857
Tel (408) 960-2700 *Founded/Ownrshp* 1981
Sales 208.6MM^E *EMP* 600
SIC 2022 Natural cheese
CEO: Gustavo Marquez
CFO: David Villaneuva
CFO: David Villanueva
**Ex VP:* Jaime Marquez
IT Man: Ames Gross
Opers Mgr: Keith Rodriguez
Mktg Dir: Lydia Rmarquez
Mktg Mgr: Robert Gallegos
Manager: Elizabeth Ambriz
Sls Mgr: Hannia Parrales

D-U-N-S 00-231-4230 EXP
MARQUIP LLC
(*Suby of* BW PAPERSYSTEMS) ★
1300 N Airport Rd, Phillips, WI 54555-1527
Tel (715) 339-2191 *Founded/Ownrshp* 2000, 2001
Sales 132.4MM^E *EMP* 543
Accts Ernst & Young Llp St Louis
SIC 3554 Box making machines, paper
Dir IT: Bill Martin

MARQUIP WARD UNITED
See WARD MACHINERY CO

MARQUIS CENTENNIAL
See MARQUIS COMPANIES I INC

D-U-N-S 79-345-1857
MARQUIS COMPANIES I INC
MARQUIS CENTENNIAL
725 Se 202nd Ave, Portland, OR 97233-6105
Tel (503) 665-3118 *Founded/Ownrshp* 1989
Sales 138.3MM^E *EMP* 1,015
SIC 8741 Nursing & personal care facility management
Pr: Phillip G Fogg Jr
**VP:* Gary A Wart
IT Man: Lani B Bennett
VP Mktg: Charles Bloom

D-U-N-S 07-148-0057
MARRANO CORP
2730 Transit Rd, Buffalo, NY 14224-2523
Tel (716) 675-1200 *Founded/Ownrshp* 1963
Sales 85.0MM *EMP* 50
SIC 1521 New construction, single-family houses; Townhouse construction
Pr: Patrick Marrano
Ex VP: Michael Kreamer
Exec: Lawrence Reger
VP Sls: John M Manns
Sales Asso: Linda Van Nortwick

MARRIOTT
See SUNRISE CONNECTICUT AVENUE ASSISTED LIVING LLC

MARRIOTT
See SAGE HOSPITALITY RESOURCES LLC

D-U-N-S 80-850-6526
■ **MARRIOTT CORP**
(*Suby of* MARRIOTT INTERNATIONAL INC) ★
4040 Central Florida Pkwy, Orlando, FL 32837-7662
Tel (407) 206-2300 *Founded/Ownrshp* 2007
Sales 33.9MM^E *EMP* 1,000
SIC 7011 Hotels & motels
CEO: Steve Contos

D-U-N-S 01-300-5702
▲ **MARRIOTT INTERNATIONAL INC**
10400 Fernwood Rd, Bethesda, MD 20817-1102
Tel (301) 380-3000 *Founded/Ownrshp* 1971
Sales 14.4MMM *EMP* 127,500
Tkr Sym MAR *Exch* NGS
SIC 7011 6794 6531 Hotels & motels; Franchises, selling or licensing; Time-sharing real estate sales, leasing & rentals
Pr: Arne M Sorenson
Ch Bd: John Willard Marriott Jr
Pr: David Grissen
Pr: Alex Kyriakidis
Pr: Craig S Smith
CFO: Kathleen K Oberg
Bd of Dir: Ron Couget
Ofcr: David A Rodriguez
Ex VP: Anthony G Capuano
Ex VP: Carolyn B Handlon
Ex VP: Kevin Kimball
Ex VP: Susan Levenson
Ex VP: Pamela Murray
Ex VP: Edward A Ryan
Sr VP: Shafiq Khan
VP: Jim Abramson
VP: Kathi Borkholder
VP: Cindy Braak
VP: Leigh Brummerhoff
VP: Kathy Cheung
VP: Lauren Chewning
Board of Directors: Mary K Bush, Deborah Marriott Harrison, Frederick A Henderson, Lawrence W Kellner, Debra L Lee, George Munoz, Steven S Reinemund, W Mitt Romney, Susan C Schwab

D-U-N-S 11-539-4611
■ **MARRIOTT OWNERSHIP RESORTS INC**
(*Suby of* MARRIOTT VACATIONS WORLDWIDE CORP) ★
6649 W Wood Blvd Ste 500, Orlando, FL 32821-6066
Tel (863) 688-7700 *Founded/Ownrshp* 2011
Sales 623.2MM^E *EMP* 6,500
SIC 7011 Hotels & motels
Pr: Stephen P Weisz
**CFO:* Victora Dolan
**CFO:* Tamara Glover
**Sec:* W David Mann
**Ofcr:* Michael E Yonker
Sr VP: Don Baarman
Sr VP: Lee Cunningham
Sr VP: Ronald Wilensky
VP: Chris Brink
**VP:* Sterling D Colton
VP: John Geller
VP: Terry Henderson
VP: Mary Keeble
VP: Reggie Plummer
VP: Lynne Roach
VP: Miguel Ruano
VP: Zach Sonberg
Exec: Bruce Rohman
Board of Directors: Richard E Marriott

D-U-N-S 15-262-6180
■ **MARRIOTT RESORTS HOSPITALITY CORP**
(*Suby of* MARRIOTT OWNERSHIP RESORTS INC) ★
6649 W Wood Blvd Ste 500, Orlando, FL 32821-6066
Tel (407) 206-6000 *Founded/Ownrshp* 1998
Sales 56.3MM^E *EMP* 2,000^E
SIC 7011 Hotels & motels
Pr: Stephen P Weisz
**CFO:* Karl Sweeney
**Treas:* Raymond G Murphy
Ex VP: Bob Miller
**VP:* William J Love

D-U-N-S 96-978-3906
▲ **MARRIOTT VACATIONS WORLDWIDE CORP**
6649 Westwood Blvd, Orlando, FL 32821-8029
Tel (407) 206-6000 *Founded/Ownrshp* 2011
Sales 1.8MMM *EMP* 10,000^E
Tkr Sym VAC *Exch* NYS
SIC 6531 7011 Real estate agents & managers; Resort hotel
Pr: Stephen P Weisz
**COO:* R Lee Cunningham
COO: Robert A Miller
**CFO:* John E Geller Jr
Ofcr: Dwight D Smith
**Ex VP:* Clifford M Delorey
**Ex VP:* James H Hunter IV
Ex VP: Lizabeth Kane-Hanan
Ex VP: Brian E Miller
Ex VP: Wanda Schlett
Ex VP: Michael E Yonker
VP: Troy Asche
VP: Bob Bukovic
VP: Darla Everitt
VP: David Holton
VP: Douglas Kelly
VP: Ed Kinney
VP: Alan Marshall
VP: Andy Stanko
Board of Directors: C E Andrews, Raymond L Gellein Jr, Thomas J Hutchinson III, William W McCarten, Dianna F Morgan

D-U-N-S 80-835-3952
■ **MARRIOTT WORLDWIDE CORP**
(*Suby of* MARRIOTT INTERNATIONAL INC) ★
10400 Fernwood Rd, Bethesda, MD 20817-1102
Tel (301) 634-5100 *Founded/Ownrshp* 1978
Sales 90.4MM^E *EMP* 3,270^E
SIC 7011 Hotels & motels

D-U-N-S 78-587-4363
■ **MARRIOTT WORLDWIDE SALES AND MARKETING INC**
(*Suby of* MARRIOTT WORLDWIDE CORP) ★
10400 Fernwood Rd, Bethesda, MD 20817-1102
Tel (301) 634-5100 *Founded/Ownrshp* 1998
Sales 90.3MM^E *EMP* 3,636
SIC 8741 Hotel or motel management
Pr: J W Marriott Jr
**VP:* Joseph Ryan
**VP:* William Shaw

D-U-N-S 06-392-1274 IMP
MARS 2000 INC
CLEAR CHOICE
40 Agnes St, Providence, RI 02909-3418
Tel (401) 421-5275 *Founded/Ownrshp* 1996
Sales 109.6MM^E *EMP* 850
SIC 3089 Molding primary plastic
Pr: Karl J Krikorian
**CFO:* Claudette Soucy
Genl Mgr: Bibianna Roggero
Opers Mgr: Wayne Roggero

D-U-N-S 03-681-4572 IMP/EXP
MARS CHOCOLATE NORTH AMERICA LLC
(*Suby of* MARS INC) ★
800 High St, Hackettstown, NJ 07840-1552
Tel (908) 852-1000 *Founded/Ownrshp* 1950
Sales 1.1MMM^E *EMP* 2,675
SIC 2064 2066 Candy & other confectionery products; Chocolate & cocoa products
Pr: Todd R Lachman
CFO: Paul Davies
VP: Mark Mattia
**VP:* Jim Murphy
**VP:* Mike Wittman

D-U-N-S 00-828-5991 IMP/EXP
MARS FOOD US LLC
(*Suby of* MARS INC) ★
2001 E Cashdan St Ste 201, Rancho Dominguez, CA 90220-6438
Tel (310) 933-0670 *Founded/Ownrshp* 1968
Sales 151.0MM^E *EMP* 616
SIC 2044 Rice milling
VP: Vreij Kolandjian
VP: Robert Kozlowicz
Exec: Lorraine Beranello

D-U-N-S 00-325-0685 IMP/EXP
MARS INC
6885 Elm St, Mc Lean, VA 22101-6031
Tel (703) 821-4900 *Founded/Ownrshp* 1952
Sales 5.3MMM^E *EMP* 80,000
SIC 2044 2024 2066 2064 5812 Enriched rice (vitamin & mineral fortified); Ice cream, packaged: molded, on sticks, etc.; Chocolate candy, solid; Candy & other confectionery products; Chocolate candy, except solid chocolate; Candy bars, including chocolate covered bars; Caterers
Pr: Grant Reid
**CFO:* Claus Aagaard
Treas: R E Barns
Ex VP: Jacqueline B Mars
Sr VP: Richard Continelli
VP: Henry Azcarraga
VP: Nici Bush
**VP:* John Donofrio
VP: Peter Littlewood
VP: Phil Moody
VP: Alberto Mora
VP: Richard Ware
Dir Bus: Mandy Heyes

D-U-N-S 00-713-4919 IMP/EXP
MARS PETCARE US INC
(*Suby of* MARS INC) ★
315 Cool Springs Blvd, Franklin, TN 37067-1632
Tel (615) 807-4626 *Founded/Ownrshp* 1995
Sales 1.0MMM^E *EMP* 2,671
SIC 2047 Dog & cat food; Cat food; Dog food
Pr: Douglas J Cahill
**Pr:* Grant F Reid
**CFO:* Philip K Woodlief
**VP:* Richard A Hannasch
**VP:* David Horton
**VP:* Joseph J Meyers
**Prin:* Luc Mongeau
Genl Mgr: Jeff Suttner
Mktg Mgr: Lisa Campbell

D-U-N-S 02-247-9752
MARS SUPER MARKETS INC
9627 Philadelphia Rd # 100, Baltimore, MD 21237-4155
Tel (410) 590-0500 *Founded/Ownrshp* 1952
Sales 245.4MM^E *EMP* 1,700
SIC 5411 Supermarkets, chain
Pr: E Philip Hanlon
**Ex VP:* Christopher D'Anna
**Ex VP:* Theodore D'Anna
**Sr VP:* Philip Hanlon
VP: Matt Drummond
**VP:* Thomas Veystrk

D-U-N-S 11-536-6387
MARSAU ENTERPRISES INC
1209 N 30th St, Enid, OK 73701-2700
Tel (580) 233-3910 *Founded/Ownrshp* 1980
Sales 100.0MM *EMP* 600
SIC 1389 Construction, repair & dismantling services
Pr: Marlin Esau
**VP:* Rob Niles
Sales Asso: Terry Alexander

D-U-N-S 05-709-4476
MARSDEN HOLDING LLC
2124 University Ave W, Saint Paul, MN 55114-1838
Tel (651) 641-1717 *Founded/Ownrshp* 1952
Sales 600.2MM^E *EMP* 8,000
SIC 1731 Safety & security specialization
Pr: Maureen Hill
Pr: Matt Johnson
Pr: Eric Zinkel
Treas: Daniel G McCarthy
VP: Ray Cole
VP: Cory Krug
VP Opers: Dave Nowacki
Opers Mgr: Robin Kemp
Sls&Mrk Ex: Tony Curtis
Sls Dir: Mark Nelson
Mktg Mgr: Kelly T Williamson
Board of Directors: Carla Smith

MARSH
See SEITLIN & CO

D-U-N-S 83-262-3008
■ **MARSH & MCLENNAN AGENCY LLC**
(*Suby of* MARSH LLC) ★
360 Hamilton Ave Ste 930, White Plains, NY 10601-1847
Tel (914) 397-1600 *Founded/Ownrshp* 2008
Sales NA *EMP* 3,093^E
SIC 6411 Insurance brokers
**Pr:* Benjamin F Allen
**COO:* William Corrigan
**Sr VP:* Ben Newman
**Sr VP:* Sharon Werner

D-U-N-S 04-156-4378 IMP/EXP
▲ **MARSH & MCLENNAN COMPANIES INC**
1166 Avenue Of The Americ, New York, NY 10036-2728
Tel (212) 345-5000 *Founded/Ownrshp* 1871
Sales NA *EMP* 60,000
Tkr Sym MMC *Exch* NYS
SIC 6411 6282 8742 Insurance brokers; Insurance agents; Insurance information & consulting services; Policyholders' consulting service; Investment advisory service; Investment research; Compensation & benefits planning consultant; General management consultant
Pr: Daniel S Glaser
**Ch Bd:* H Edward Hanway
Ch Bd: Peter Zaffino
V Ch: John T Sinnott
Pr: Michael Anderson
Pr: Alexander Moczarski
Pr: Julie Windsor
CEO: Ricardo Brockmann
CEO: Mark Feuer
CEO: Martin South
COO: Georg Braeuchle
COO: Emichael Caulfield
COO: Judy Chang
COO: Joseph J Fico
COO: Charles Fry
COO: David Lessing
COO: Bill Pieron
COO: Bill Pieroni
COO: Jane D Roche
CFO: Matthew B Artley
CFO: Jerome H Bailey
Board of Directors: R David Yost, Anthony K Anderson, Anthony K Anderson, Oscar Fanjul, Elaine La Roche, Steven A Mills, Bruce P Nolop, Marc D Oken, Morton O Schapiro, Lloyd M Yates

D-U-N-S 15-114-5844
■ **MARSH AFFINITY GROUP SERVICES**
(*Suby of* SEABURY & SMITH (DELAWARE) INC) ★
12421 Meredith Dr, West Des Moines, IA 50398-0002
Tel (515) 243-1900 *Founded/Ownrshp* 1984
Sales NA *EMP* 400
SIC 6411 Insurance brokers
Pr: Kirke Dorweiler
Treas: Alan Bieler
**Treas:* Jeffrey Schlingbum
VP: Terry Boettcher
**VP:* Thomas R Hopkins
VP: Tom Kristensen
MIS Dir: Larry Alberty

MARSH BELLOFRAM COR
See BELLOFRAM CORP

D-U-N-S 00-323-3111 IMP
MARSH FURNITURE CO
MARSH KITCHENS
1001 S Centennial St, High Point, NC 27260-8126
Tel (336) 884-7363 Founded/Ownrshp 1906
Sales 95.9MME EMP 550
SIC 2434 5712 2421

MARSH KITCHENS
See MARSH FURNITURE CO

D-U-N-S 07-940-4169
■ **MARSH LLC**
(Suby of MARSH & MCLENNAN COMPANIES INC) ★
1166 Avenue Of The Americ, New York, NY 10036-2750
Tel (212) 345-5000 Founded/Ownrshp 1999
Sales NA EMP 5,073E
SIC 6411 6282 8742 Insurance brokers; Insurance agents; Insurance information & consulting services; Policyholders' consulting service; Investment advisory service; Investment research; Compensation & benefits planning consultant; General management consultant
Pr: Peter Zaffino
Sr VP: John G Doran
Sr VP: Meredith Frick
Sr VP: Dana Gannon
Sr VP: James Holland
Sr VP: Jamie Kagan
Sr VP: Chris E Klouda
Sr VP: Charles Moran
Sr VP: Charity O'Sullivan
Sr VP: Paige Turner
Sr VP: Nicholas Warren
VP: Nigel Armitage
VP: Daniel Balmat
VP: Karlie Beal
VP: Mark Bernstein
VP: Jay Caruso
VP: Michael Kalady
VP: Sara Kinley
VP: Deborah Miller
VP: Elaine Nelli
VP: Haylen Stevens

D-U-N-S 11-122-4189
MARSH MCLENNAN
540 W Madison St Ste 1200, Chicago, IL 60661-3600
Tel (312) 627-6000 Founded/Ownrshp 2002
Sales NA EMP 600E
SIC 6411
CFO: Sean Shover
Ex VP: David Reed
Sr VP: Jim Anderson
Sr VP: Laurie Bahr
Sr VP: Denise N Banks
Sr VP: Lisa Bastick
Sr VP: Susan Denecke
Sr VP: Denise Fitzpatrick
Sr VP: Christopher Freund
Sr VP: Meredith Frick
Sr VP: Cindy Hernandez
Sr VP: Robert Hong
Sr VP: Kim Joyal
Sr VP: Peter Keane
Sr VP: Dan Kelley
Sr VP: Jim O'Hara
Sr VP: Linda Puccio
Sr VP: Dennis Quinilty
Sr VP: Stephen Stewart
Sr VP: Paul Therrien
Sr VP: Kathleen Warren

D-U-N-S 05-843-6098
■ **MARSH RISK & INSURANCE SERVICES INC**
MMC
(Suby of MARSH & MCLENNAN COMPANIES INC) ★
777 S Figueroa St # 2200, Los Angeles, CA 90017-5800
Tel (213) 624-5555 Founded/Ownrshp 1997
Sales NA EMP 687
SIC 6411 Insurance brokers
Mng Dir: Paul Gibbs
Sr VP: Melody Schwartz
Mng Dir: Steve Flynn

D-U-N-S 00-694-0282 IMP
MARSH SUPERMARKETS CO LLC
(Suby of MARSH SUPERMARKETS HOLDING LLC) ★
9800 Crosspoint Blvd, Indianapolis, IN 46256-3300
Tel (317) 594-2406 Founded/Ownrshp 1931
Sales 2.1MMME EMP 13,300
SIC 5411 Supermarkets, chain; Convenience stores, chain; Supermarkets, 55,000-65,000 square feet (superstore); Supermarkets, 66,000-99,000 square feet
Ch Bd: Frank Lazaran
*CFO: Robert J Riesbeck
VP: Harlen Brinson
VP: Terry Huser
VP: Ronald Sims
Mng Ofcr: Danny Omalla
Comm Man: Bryan Zerfas
IT Man: Alan Doty

D-U-N-S 62-370-0916
MARSH SUPERMARKETS HOLDING LLC
9800 Crosspoint Blvd, Indianapolis, IN 46256-3300
Tel (317) 594-2100 Founded/Ownrshp 2006
Sales 2.1MMME EMP 14,000
SIC 5411 Supermarkets, chain; Convenience stores, chain; Supermarkets, 55,000-65,000 square feet (superstore); Supermarkets, 66,000-99,000 square feet
Pr: Thomas R O Boyle Jr
COO: Dennis Crook
COO: Bill Holsworth
*CFO: Terry Huser
Sr Cor Off: Ronald Sims
Ex VP: Mark Varner
VP: Jodi D Marsh
Admn Mgr: Jay Cluck
Admn Mgr: John Nightengale
Store Mgr: Christopher Shepard

D-U-N-S 00-174-9258
■ **MARSH USA INC** (DE)
(Suby of MARSH & MCLENNAN COMPANIES INC) ★
1166 Ave Of The Americas, New York, NY 10036-2708
Tel (212) 345-6000 Founded/Ownrshp 1923, 1969
Sales NA EMP 38,000
SIC 6411 6331 6351 6282 Insurance brokers; Insurance agents; Fire, marine & casualty insurance: stock; Property damage insurance; Boiler insurance; Surety insurance bonding; Fidelity or surety bonding; Investment advisory service
Ch Bd: Joseph Mc Sweeny
V Ch: Heidi Miller
V Ch: Steven Schloss
Pr: Henry S Allen
Pr: Timothy J Mahoney Jr
Pr: Joseph M McSweeny
Pr: Alexander Moczarksi
Pr: Adalja Ruchir
Pr: Alexander W Vietor
CEO: Peter Zaffino
COO: Bill Pieroni
CFO: Douglas Davis
CFO: Patricia Hagemann
CFO: Courtney Leimkuhler
CFO: Christopher Murphy
Ofcr: Scott Gilbert
Sr VP: Ann M Avnet
Sr VP: Harold Dorbin
Sr VP: Machua Millett
Sr VP: Michael Murphy
Sr VP: Helen Vrabel

D-U-N-S 80-273-0275
MARSHALL & ILSLEY TRUST CO NATIONAL ASSOCIATION
M & I TRUST
(Suby of BMO FINANCIAL CORP) ★
111 E Kilbourn Ave # 200, Milwaukee, WI 53202-6633
Tel (414) 287-8700 Founded/Ownrshp 1973
Sales 107.1MME EMP 700
SIC 6733 Private estate, personal investment & vacation fund trusts
CEO: Kenneth Krei
*Pr: Morry L Birnbaum
*Pr: David W Schulz
Ofcr: Carrie Handler
Trst Ofcr: Thomas Tuttle
Sr VP: William Curtis
VP: Timothy Bonin
VP: William Crain
VP: Forrest Dupre
VP: Christopher Gloe
*VP: Anthony L Lesczwaski
VP: Todd Perala

D-U-N-S 16-184-4105
MARSHALL & STERLING ENTERPRISES INC
THEODORE TUNICK INSURANCE
110 Main St Ste 4, Poughkeepsie, NY 12601-3080
Tel (845) 454-0800 Founded/Ownrshp 1864
Sales NA EMP 350
SIC 6411 Insurance agents, brokers & service
Ch Bd: Timothy E Dean
*CFO: Tim Rychcik
*VP: Betty Fanelli
VP: Pat Malleolo
*VP: Frank S Maranto
VP: John Morgan
VP: Jeremy Schokman
VP: Mario Vtniello
Dir Risk M: Frank Murano
Rgnl Mgr: Chet Schneider
Brnch Mgr: Mark Robertson

D-U-N-S 00-833-3635
■ **MARSHALL & SWIFT/BOECKH LLC**
(Suby of CORELOGIC INC) ★
10001 W Innovation Dr # 102, Milwaukee, WI 53226-4851
Tel (262) 780-2800 Founded/Ownrshp 2014
Sales NA EMP 350
SIC 6411 Property & casualty insurance agent
Sr VP: Mark Burkhart
VP: Rick Carlberg
VP: Jerry Fox
VP: Dhaval Vasavada
Tech Mgr: Ed Martinez
Info Man: Patrick Kobylanski
VP Sls: David Berenson
VP Sls: Dick Brooks
VP Sls: Kerry Macca
Mktg Mgr: Kayla Merker
Sls Mgr: Robert Blythe

D-U-N-S 07-896-2719
MARSHALL COUNTY HEALTH CARE AUTHORITY
MARSHALL MEDICAL CENTER SOUTH
2505 Us Highway 431, Boaz, AL 35957-5908
Tel (256) 894-6600 Founded/Ownrshp 1956
Sales 143.5MM EMP 1,200
SIC 8062 Hospital, professional nursing school
CEO: Gary R Gore
*CFO: Kathy Nelson
Dir Soc: Libby McClendon

D-U-N-S 07-059-5921
MARSHALL DENNEHEY WARNER COLEMAN & GOGGIN PC
2000 Market St Fl 23, Philadelphia, PA 19103-7006
Tel (215) 575-2600 Founded/Ownrshp 1960
Sales 176.8MME EMP 1,047
SIC 8111 General practice law office
Ch Bd: Christopher E Dougherty
*Ch Bd: Peter S Miller
Pr: Janet Lewis
*CEO: Thomas A Brophy
*CEO: Robert Coleman
*Ch: Philip B Toran
*Sr VP: Thomas De Lorenzo
*Sr VP: Scott G Dunlop
*Sr VP: Niki Ingram
*Sr VP: Kathleen McGrath
*Sr VP: Mark Thompson
Board of Directors: Coleen Bannon, Mari Anne Boyne, Liz Brown, Patti Day, Karen Rudderow, Larry Schempp

MARSHALL DURBIN FARMS
See MARSHALL DURBIN FOOD CORP

D-U-N-S 00-796-0263
MARSHALL DURBIN FOOD CORP
MARSHALL DURBIN FARMS
(Suby of PROCESSING DIVISION) ★
2830 Commerce Blvd, Irondale, AL 35210-1216
Tel (205) 841-7315 Founded/Ownrshp 1967, 2014
Sales 194.7MME EMP 1,200
SIC 0252 0254 2048 0251 2015 5144 Chicken eggs; Chicken hatchery; Poultry feeds; Broiling chickens, raising of; Chicken slaughtering & processing; Poultry: live, dressed or frozen (unpackaged)
Pr: Melissa Durbin
*CFO: Mark Jeter
*Sec: Elise Durbin
*VP: Freddie Mitchell
*VP: David Bart Payne

MARSHALL HEALTH CARE &
See MARSHALL NURSING SERVICES INC

MARSHALL HOSPITAL
See MARSHALL MEDICAL CENTER

D-U-N-S 06-780-5069
MARSHALL MEDICAL CENTER
MARSHALL HOSPITAL
1100 Marshall Way, Placerville, CA 95667-6533
Tel (530) 622-1441 Founded/Ownrshp 1959
Sales 229.3MM EMP 1,500
SIC 8062 8071 8082 General medical & surgical hospitals; Medical laboratories; X-ray laboratory, including dental; Home health care services
CEO: James Whipple
Dir Vol: Jennifer Fiterre
*COO: Shannon Truesdell
*CFO: Laurie Eldridge
Genl Mgr: Marlene Markowich
Genl Mgr: Lynda Vernon
Dir IT: Kimberley Bunch
IT Man: Ronnie Cabusora
Pathlgst: Michael Berry
Doctor: Roger Gallant
Doctor: Reginald Rice

MARSHALL MEDICAL CENTER FAMILY
See UNIVERSITY PHYSICIANS & SURGEONS INC

MARSHALL MEDICAL CENTER SOUTH
See MARSHALL COUNTY HEALTH CARE AUTHORITY

D-U-N-S 07-931-9895
MARSHALL MEDICAL CENTER SOUTH
2505 Us Highway 431, Boaz, AL 35957-5908
Tel (256) 593-8310 Founded/Ownrshp 2014
Sales 143.5MM EMP 30E
SIC 8011 Physicians' office, including specialists
Owner: Larry W Greer

D-U-N-S 10-763-6953 IMP/EXP
■ **MARSHALL MIDDLEBY INC**
MIDDLEBY COOKING SYSTEMS GROUP
(Suby of MIDDLEBY CORP) ★
1400 Toastmaster Dr, Elgin, IL 60120-9274
Tel (847) 289-0204 Founded/Ownrshp 1983
Sales 275.0MME EMP 1,200
SIC 3556 3585 3631 Ovens, bakery; Mixers, feed, except agricultural; Refrigeration equipment, complete; Household cooking equipment
Ch Bd: William F Whitman Jr
*Pr: Selim A Bassoul
*CFO: David B Baker
*Treas: Martin Lindsay

D-U-N-S 09-773-9023
MARSHALL NURSING SERVICES INC
MARSHALL HEALTH CARE &
9 Beal St, Machias, ME 04654-1002
Tel (207) 255-3387 Founded/Ownrshp 1996
Sales 362.7MM EMP 110
Accts Downeast Accounting Bangor M
SIC 8051 Extended care facility
Dir Recs: Patricia Rocco
Dir Soc: Adrianne Lemos
Dir Env Sv: Patrick Dennison
Off Mgr: Helen P Dennison
Nrsg Dir: Shannon Todd
Board of Directors: Peter Marshall

D-U-N-S 07-918-7678
■ **MARSHALL PHYSICIAN SERVICES LLC**
MESA MEDICAL GROUP
(Suby of TEAMHEALTH) ★
1792 Alysheba Way Ste 150, Lexington, KY 40509-2285
Tel (877) 601-6372 Founded/Ownrshp 2013
Sales 28.5MME EMP 1,410E
SIC 8011 Freestanding emergency medical center
Pr: James Foster MD
Pr: John Mullins
Chf Mktg O: Christophe R Pund MD
Chf Mktg O: T J Richardson MD
HC Dir: Douglas Smith

MARSHALL REGIONAL MEDICAL CENT
See HARRISON COUNTY HOSPITAL ASSOCIATION

D-U-N-S 03-494-0130 IMP
MARSHALL RETAIL GROUP LLC
MARSHALL ROUSSO
3755 W Sunset Rd Ste A, Las Vegas, NV 89118-3931
Tel (702) 385-5233 Founded/Ownrshp 2014
Sales 163.9MME EMP 850
SIC 5661 5621 5641 5611 Men's shoes; Women's shoes; Women's clothing stores; Women's sportswear; Ready-to-wear apparel, women's; Children's & infants' wear stores; Men's & boys' clothing stores
CEO: Todd Marshall
*Pr: Michael Wilkins

MARSHALL ROUSSO
See MARSHALL RETAIL GROUP LLC

MARSHALL UNIV GRADUATE COLLEGE
See MARSHALL UNIVERSITY

D-U-N-S 06-813-0798
MARSHALL UNIVERSITY
MARSHALL UNIV GRADUATE COLLEGE
1 John Marshall Dr, Huntington, WV 25755-0003
Tel (304) 696-2385 Founded/Ownrshp 1837
Sales 174.8MM EMP 1,632
Accts Cliftonlarsonallen Llp Plymou
SIC 8221 University
Pr: Gary White
*Pr: Dan Angel PHD
*Sr VP: Herbert J Karlet
Sr VP: Anita Lockridge
*VP: Dr Betty Cleckley
VP: Calvin Kent
VP: George Lambros
VP: John Maher
VP: Ted Massey
*VP: Dr Charles McKown
VP: Ginny Painter
VP: Isabelle Rogner
Exec: Marcia Harrison
Comm Dir: Luke Lassiter

D-U-N-S 07-665-9127
MARSHALLS HOLDING CO
KENWORTH NORTHWEST
20220 International Blvd, Seatac, WA 98198-5703
Tel (206) 433-5911 Founded/Ownrshp 1997
Sales 89.9MM EMP 180
SIC 5012 5013 Trucks, commercial; Truck parts & accessories
Pr: Marshall Cymbaluk
*VP: Kathreen Cymbaluk

D-U-N-S 04-341-1693 IMP/EXP
■ **MARSHALLS OF MA INC** (MA)
(Suby of TJ MAXX) ★
770 Cochituate Rd, Framingham, MA 01701-4666
Tel (508) 390-1000 Founded/Ownrshp 1958
Sales 1.6MMME EMP 20,000
SIC 5651 5719 Family clothing stores; Beddings & linens
Pr: Richard Sherr
Treas: Mary B Reynolds
VP: David Averill
Dist Mgr: Chris Jones
Dist Mgr: Mark Landis
Store Mgr: Richard Rapolla
MIS Dir: Bob Hernandez
MIS Dir: Carol Hubert
IT Man: Ken Kozikowski
Mfg Mgr: Lyn Costello
Opers Mgr: Jerry Rosei

D-U-N-S 87-844-0411
■ **MARSHALS SERVICE UNITED STATES**
(Suby of UNITED STATES DEPARTMENT OF JUSTICE) ★
3601 Pennsy Dr, Landover, MD 20785-1612
Tel (202) 307-9001 Founded/Ownrshp 1789
Sales NA EMP 4,000
SIC 9221 Marshals' offices, police;

D-U-N-S 07-981-7262
MARSHFIELD CLINIC HEALTH SYSTEM INC
1000 N Oak Ave, Marshfield, WI 54449-5702
Tel (715) 387-5511 Founded/Ownrshp 2012
Sales 768.3MME EMP 363E
SIC 8011 Clinic, operated by physicians
CEO: Susan Turney
*COO: Daniel Ramsey
*CFO: John Cook
*Treas: Tim Peterson
Doctor: John Hayes
Doctor: Shereif Rezkalla
Doctor: Param Sharma

D-U-N-S 07-477-6030
MARSHFIELD CLINIC INC
(Suby of MARSHFIELD CLINIC HEALTH SYSTEM INC) ★
1000 N Oak Ave, Marshfield, WI 54449-5702
Tel (715) 387-5511 Founded/Ownrshp 1916
Sales 768.3MME EMP 363
Accts Kpmg Llp Columbus Oh
SIC 8011 Clinic, operated by physicians
Pr: Brian H Ewert MD
V Ch: Mark J Bradley
*CFO: Gary Jankowski
CFO: Brent Miler
*Treas: Mark A Lepage
Treas: Mark Lepage
Ofcr: Steve Youso
*VP: Douglas Reding MD
*VP: C Todd Stewart
Dir Lab: Pamela Carter
Dir Rx: Dick Gritt

D-U-N-S 00-406-7125 IMP/EXP
■ **MARSHFIELD DOORSYSTEMS INC** (DE)
(Suby of MASONITE INTERNATIONAL CORP) ★
1401 E 4th St, Marshfield, WI 54449-4555
Tel (715) 384-2141 Founded/Ownrshp 2000, 2011
Sales 90.1MME EMP 662
SIC 2431 3442 Doors, wood; Metal doors
CEO: Donald Bergman
*Pr: Jerry Mannigel
Sfty Mgr: Mark Meurette
Manager: Doug Bachand
Manager: Jim Dawson

D-U-N-S 10-402-4708 IMP/EXP
MARTCO LLC
ROYOMARTIN
(Suby of ROYOMARTIN) ★
2189 Memorial Dr, Alexandria, LA 71301-3610
Tel (318) 448-0405 Founded/Ownrshp 1981
Sales 246.2MME EMP 1,100
SIC 2493 2435 Strandboard, oriented; Plywood, hardwood or hardwood faced
VP: Joe Mackay
VP: Scott Poole
VP: Mickey Rachal
VP: Terry Secrest
CTO: Brian Harpe
Software D: John Laponsie
Sls Mgr: Wayne Miller
Genl Couns: Ray Brown

MARTEC INTERNATIONAL
See CARL F EWIG INC

D-U-N-S 00-486-6257
▲ MARTEN TRANSPORT LTD
129 Marten St, Mondovi, WI 54755-1700
Tel (715) 926-4216 *Founded/Ownrshp* 1946
Sales 664.9MM *EMP* 3,577ᴱ
Tkr Sym MRTN *Exch* NGS
SIC 4213 Refrigerated products transport; Contract haulers
Ch Bd: Randolph L Marten
Pr: Timothy M Kohl
COO: Bob Smith
COO: Robert G Smith
CFO: James J Hinnendael
Ex VP: Timothy P Nash
Sr VP: John H Turner
Dir IT: Randy Baier
Sys Admin: Kevin Ingvalson
Mktg Dir: Greg Cernjar
Sls Dir: Christopher A Douglass
Board of Directors: Jerry M Bauer, Ronald R Booth, Robert L Demorest, Larry B Hagness, G Larry Owens, Thomas J Winkel

D-U-N-S 03-009-8313 IMP/EXP
MARTEX FIBER SOUTHERN CORP
3200b Southport Rd, Spartanburg, SC 29302-5327
Tel (864) 583-6412 *Founded/Ownrshp* 1975
Sales 86.5MMᴱ *EMP* 185ᴱ
SIC 5093

D-U-N-S 80-181-6570
MARTHA JEFFERSON HEALTH SERVICES CORP
MARTHA JEFFERSON WNS HLTH CTR
500 Martha Jefferson Dr, Charlottesville, VA 22911-4668
Tel (434) 654-7000 *Founded/Ownrshp* 1903
Sales 24.5M *EMP* 1,600
SIC 8741 Hospital management
Ch: Peter Brooks
**Pr:* James E Haden
**Ch:* William Achenbach
**Treas:* J Michael Burrus

D-U-N-S 04-698-9141
MARTHA JEFFERSON HOSPITAL
(*Suby of* SENTARA CNCER NTWRK NORFOLK CI) ★
500 Martha Jefferson Dr, Charlottesville, VA 22911-4668
Tel (434) 982-7000 *Founded/Ownrshp* 2011
Sales 258.7MM *EMP* 2,768ᴱ
Accts Kpmg Llp Norfolk Virginia
SIC 8062 General medical & surgical hospitals
CEO: James E Haden
**CFO:* Joseph Burris
**Treas:* J Michael Burris
VP: Amy Black
VP: Ray Mishler
Nurse Mgr: Abby Denby
Pathlgst: Hunt M Lll
Doctor: Wayne Nye
Diag Rad: Christopher D Cook
HC Dir: Bonnie Diehr

D-U-N-S 93-399-8817
MARTHA JEFFERSON HOSTIPAL
(*Suby of* MARTHA JEFFERSON HOSPITAL) ★
459 Locust Ave, Charlottesville, VA 22902-4871
Tel (434) 982-7000 *Founded/Ownrshp* 1986
Sales 5.5MMᴱ *EMP* 2,660ᴱ
SIC 8082 Home health care services
Pr: James Haden

MARTHA JEFFERSON WNS HLTH CTR
See MARTHA JEFFERSON HEALTH SERVICES CORP

D-U-N-S 08-170-2024 IMP
■ MARTHA STEWART LIVING OMNIMEDIA INC
(*Suby of* SEQUENTIAL BRANDS GROUP INC) ★
601 W 26th St Rm 900, New York, NY 10001-1143
Tel (212) 827-8000 *Founded/Ownrshp* 2015
Sales 141.9MM *EMP* 274ᴱ
SIC 2721 2731 4813 7812 Magazines: publishing only, not printed on site; Book publishing; ; Motion picture production & distribution, television
CEO: Daniel W Dienst
Pr: Jacqueline Landaeta
CFO: Kenneth P West
CFO: Kenneth West
Chf Cred: Martha Stewart
Ex VP: Ann Casey Bukawyn
Ex VP: Shelley S Nandkeolyar
Ex VP: Eric Pike
Sr VP: Allison Jacques
Sr VP: Janet Stein
VP: Ruth Feldman
Dir Risk M: Joe Lagani

D-U-N-S 12-672-8356
MARTHAS VINEYARD MORTGAGE CO LLC
107 Beach Rd Ste 101, Vineyard Haven, MA 02568-5524
Tel (508) 696-1801 *Founded/Ownrshp* 2000
Sales NA *EMP* 2
SIC 6163 Mortgage brokers arranging for loans, using money of others

MARTIGNETTI COMPANIES
See MARTIGNETTI CORP

D-U-N-S 87-620-3373
MARTIGNETTI CORP
MARTIGNETTI COMPANIES
500 John Hancock Rd, Taunton, MA 02780-7379
Tel (781) 278-2000 *Founded/Ownrshp* 1991
Sales 215.8MMᴱ *EMP* 394
SIC 5182 5921 Wine; Liquor; Liquor stores; Wine; Hard liquor
Pr: Carl J Martignetti
**Treas:* Carmine A Martignetti

D-U-N-S 04-102-9208 IMP
MARTIGNETTI GROCERY CO INC
CAROLINA WINE COMPANY
500 John Hancock Rd, Taunton, MA 02780-7379
Tel (781) 278-2000 *Founded/Ownrshp* 1986
Sales 372.5MMᴱ *EMP* 700ᴱ
SIC 5182 Liquor
Pr: Carmine Martignetti
**Treas:* Carl Martignetti

D-U-N-S 02-499-7314
MARTIN & BAYLEY INC
HUCK'S
1311a W Main St, Carmi, IL 62821-1389
Tel (618) 382-2334 *Founded/Ownrshp* 2001
Sales 285.5MMᴱ *EMP* 1,500
Accts Harding Shymanski & Company
SIC 5411 Convenience stores
CEO: Todd Jenney
**Pr:* Mark Bayley
CFO: Michael Logan
**Ch:* Frank Bayley
**V Ch Bd:* Charles Martin
VP: Teresa Knasel
VP: John Long
VP: Ken Pearson
**VP:* Jim Whetstone
Brnch Mgr: Sheila Jolly
Div Mgr: Eddie Allen

D-U-N-S 04-389-2777
■ MARTIN AGENCY INC
INGENUITY MEDIA GROUP
(*Suby of* INTERPUBLIC GROUP OF COMPANIES INC) ★
1 Shockoe Plz, Richmond, VA 23219-4132
Tel (804) 649-1496 *Founded/Ownrshp* 1994
Sales 88.4MMᴱ *EMP* 600
SIC 7331 7311 8743 7313 Direct mail advertising services; Advertising agencies; Public relations services; Radio, television, publisher representatives
Ch Bd: John Adams Jr
Pt: Ren J Ferran
**CEO:* Matthew Williams
**COO:* Beth Rilee-Kelley
**CFO:* Rene J Ferran
CFO: Terry Thompson
**CFO:* Janet White
Sr VP: Kathy Snead
VP: Carmina Drummond
VP: Emily Eldridge
VP: Carey Ely
VP: Darren Foot
VP: Randy Freisner
VP: Deb Hagan
VP: Marge Hickman
VP: Deanna Maneker
VP: John McAdorey
VP: David Muhlenfeld
VP: Lorri Riddle
VP: Clifford Searles
VP: Tom Sparks

D-U-N-S 04-607-8366
MARTIN AND SNYDER PRODUCT SALES CO
8880 Hubbell St, Detroit, MI 48228-2396
Tel (313) 272-4900 *Founded/Ownrshp* 1966
Sales 152.6MM *EMP* 27
Accts Plante & Moran Pllc Ann Arbo
SIC 5194 5145 Tobacco & tobacco products; Candy; Chewing gum
Pr: Frank Daiza
Treas: Kathleen Spence
**VP:* George Daiza

MARTIN ASPHALT
See MARTIN PRODUCT SALES LLC

D-U-N-S 60-213-6632
MARTIN ATTEA
ATTEA APPLIANCE
1509 Clinton St, Buffalo, NY 14206-3008
Tel (716) 822-0378 *Founded/Ownrshp* 1988
Sales 206.5MM *EMP* 2ᴱ
Accts Morgan Beyer & Wayne Cpa P
SIC 5064 5722 Electrical appliances, major; Electric household appliances, major
Owner: Martin Attea

D-U-N-S 02-204-4762
MARTIN BROTHERS DISTRIBUTING CO INC
6623 Chancellor Dr, Cedar Falls, IA 50613-6966
Tel (319) 266-1775 *Founded/Ownrshp* 2001
Sales 546.7MMᴱ *EMP* 400
SIC 5141 5169 5046 5087 Groceries, general line; Chemicals & allied products; Restaurant equipment & supplies; Service establishment equipment
**Pr:* John Martin
CFO: Gerald Johnson
**Treas:* Martin Jeff
Netwrk Mgr: Lee Winterscheidt
Sales Exec: Michael Moss
Manager: Dean Schwartz
Sls Mgr: Brian Hathcock

D-U-N-S 03-372-4097
MARTIN CAR FINANCING INC
MARTIN, MILTON TOYOTA
3150 Mlton Mrtn Tyota Way, Gainesville, GA 30507-8200
Tel (770) 532-4355 *Founded/Ownrshp* 1961
Sales 89.5MM *EMP* 76
Accts Ross Lane & Company Llc Atla
SIC 5511 Automobiles, new & used
Pr: Milton M Martin
**Sec:* Carole Hope
Exec: Jimmy Hernandez
Sales Exec: Evan Martin

D-U-N-S 00-818-4608
MARTIN COMPANIES LLC ROM
2189 Memorial Dr, Alexandria, LA 71301-3610
Tel (318) 445-1973 *Founded/Ownrshp* 1923
Sales 249.0MMᴱ *EMP* 1,200
SIC 0811 Timber tracts; Timber tracts, softwood
CEO: Jonathan E Martin
**Pr:* Roy O Martin III
**Sr VP:* E Scott Poole

D-U-N-S 08-632-4068
MARTIN COUNTY BOARD OF EDUCATION
300 N Watts St, Williamston, NC 27892-2056
Tel (252) 792-1575 *Founded/Ownrshp* 1919
Sales 34.0MMᴱ *EMP* 1,027
SIC 8211 School board
Ch Bd: Addie Leggett

D-U-N-S 80-091-4319
MARTIN COUNTY SCHOOL DISTRICT
500 Se Ocean Blvd, Stuart, FL 34994-2572
Tel (772) 219-1200 *Founded/Ownrshp* 1945
Sales 149.0MMᴱ *EMP* 2,831
Accts David W Martin Cpa Tallahas
SIC 8211 Public elementary & secondary schools; Elementary school; Finishing school, secondary; High school, junior or senior
Dir Sec: Mark Coco
MIS Dir: Katharine Preston
Dir IT: Chris Hall
Opers Mgr: Mark Cocco
Pr Dir: Jamie Adcock
Teacher Pr: Richard Bilay

D-U-N-S 01-041-1015
MARTIN ENERGY SERVICES LLC
(*Suby of* MARTIN RESOURCE MANAGEMENT CORP) ★
3 Riverway Ste 400, Houston, TX 77056-1947
Tel (713) 350-6800 *Founded/Ownrshp* 1999
Sales 1.2MMM *EMP* 250
SIC 5171 4492 5172 5551 Petroleum terminals; Marine towing services; Diesel fuel; Gasoline; Service station supplies, petroleum; Marine supplies
CEO: Ruben S Martin
**CFO:* Robert D Bondurant
**Sr VP:* Damon King
VP: George Dodgen

D-U-N-S 02-568-2873 IMP/EXP
MARTIN ENGINEERING CO
1 Martin Pl, Neponset, IL 61345-9766
Tel (309) 852-2384 *Founded/Ownrshp* 1944
Sales 180.5MMᴱ *EMP* 850
SIC 3829 3532 Measuring & controlling devices; Mining machinery; Flotation machinery (mining machinery); Cleaning machinery, mineral
Pr: Scott E Hutter
**COO:* Robert Nogaj
**CFO:* Ronald Ron J Vick
**Ch:* Edwin Peterson
**VP:* Robert J Nogaj
Exec: Sue Nolasco
Mng Dir: Michael Hengl
Div Mgr: Adam Childs
Genl Mgr: Edward Peterson
IT Man: Mark Luciani
Opers Supe: Oleksiy Yakovlenko

D-U-N-S 00-394-3342
MARTIN ENGLE & ASSOCIATES INC (MO)
EM
5565 Glenridge Connector # 900, Atlanta, GA 30342-4797
Tel (678) 553-4400 *Founded/Ownrshp* 1997
Sales NA *EMP* 1,514
SIC 6411 Insurance adjusters
Pr: John Quinn
**CFO:* Michael Bavely
**CFO:* Janice Warford
**Treas:* Christopher McCoy
**Ofcr:* Bruce Boggs
**Ofcr:* Martha Boggs
**Ex VP:* Melissa Christ
Sr VP: John Ketch
Sr VP: Bentley Laytin
**VP:* Stephen Beene
**VP:* Jay Campbell
**VP:* W Todd Evans
**VP:* J Robert Gambell
**VP:* Don Ouzts
**VP:* Joseph Slane
Exec: Rick Haggis
Board of Directors: Kevin L Engle

MARTIN GENERAL STORES
See MARTIN OIL CO

MARTIN GUITAR COMPANY, THE
See C F MARTIN & CO INC

D-U-N-S 00-403-1076 IMP
MARTIN INC (AL)
MARTIN INDUSTRIAL SUPPLY
125 N Court St, Florence, AL 35630-4739
Tel (256) 383-3131 *Founded/Ownrshp* 1934
Sales 223.9MMᴱ *EMP* 220
SIC 5085 Industrial supplies
Ch Bd: Edith Martin Ruggles
**Pr:* Donald F Ruggles
**VP:* D Gordon Ruggles
Genl Mgr: Candy Linam
Sls Mgr: Chad Allred
Sls Mgr: Chris Maye

MARTIN INDUSTRIAL SUPPLY
See MARTIN INC

D-U-N-S 00-694-4003
MARTIN K EBY CONSTRUCTION CO INC (KS)
(*Suby of* EBY CORP) ★
2525 E 36th Cir N, Wichita, KS 67219-2303
Tel (316) 268-3500 *Founded/Ownrshp* 1937
Sales 93.2MM *EMP* 150ᴱ
SIC 1542 Commercial & office building contractors
Pr: Michael A Grier
**Ch Bd:* James R Grier III
CFO: Adam Dunn
**CFO:* R Adam Dunn
**Sec:* Linda Walton
Bd of Dir: Starla Criser
Bd of Dir: Gordon Kessler
**Ex VP:* Kurt T Grier
Board of Directors: James R Grier III, Kurt T Grier, Michael A Grier

D-U-N-S 00-790-9880 IMP
MARTIN LIMESTONE INC
LIMEVILLE QUARRY
(*Suby of* BUFFALO CRUSHED STONE) ★
3580 Division Hwy, East Earl, PA 17519-9217
Tel (717) 335-4500 *Founded/Ownrshp* 1933, 1946
Sales 202.4MMᴱ *EMP* 1,151
SIC 3273 3271 1611 1422 8741 5211 Ready-mixed concrete; Blocks, concrete or cinder: standard; Highway & street paving contractor; Crushed & broken limestone; Business management; Lumber & other building materials
Pr: Howard Winey
Treas: Dale Good
**VP:* Donald Detwiler
**VP:* Paul I Detwiler Jr
Off Mgr: Dale Kershner
Sfty Mgr: John Palm

D-U-N-S 00-922-6262
MARTIN MANAGEMENT GROUP INC
1048 Ashley St Ste 401, Bowling Green, KY 42103-2453
Tel (270) 783-8080 *Founded/Ownrshp* 1998
Sales 210.4MMᴱ *EMP* 600
SIC 5511 Automobiles, new & used
Pr: Lee Michaelson
Ex VP: Dave Alexander
Mktg Mgr: Cory Glass

D-U-N-S 80-975-0912 IMP/EXP
▲ MARTIN MARIETTA MATERIALS INC
2710 Wycliff Rd, Raleigh, NC 27607-3033
Tel (919) 781-4550 *Founded/Ownrshp* 1993
Sales 3.5MMM *EMP* 7,300
Tkr Sym MLM *Exch* NYS
SIC 1423 1422 1442 3295 3297 Crushed & broken granite; Crushed & broken limestone; Construction sand & gravel; Magnesite, crude: ground, calcined or dead-burned; Heat resistant mixtures
Ch Bd: C Howard Nye
CFO: Anne H Lloyd
Ex VP: Roselyn R Bar
Sr VP: Daniel L Grant
Sr VP: Dana F Guzzo
Sr VP: Donald A McCunniff
VP: Steve Bruce
VP: Dana Guzzo
VP: Dean Hardy
VP: John Mohr
VP: Shelby Olsen
Board of Directors: Sue W Cole, John J Koraleski, David G Maffucci, William E McDonald, Michael J Quillen, Dennis L Rediker, Stephen P Zelnak Jr

D-U-N-S 00-793-6560 IMP
■ MARTIN MARIETTA MATERIALS SOUTHWEST INC
(*Suby of* MARTIN MARIETTA MATERIALS INC) ★
5710 W Hausman Rd Ste 121, San Antonio, TX 78249-1646
Tel (210) 208-4400 *Founded/Ownrshp* 1934
Sales 661.9MMᴱ *EMP* 635
SIC 1422 3273 2951 3274 1442 Crushed & broken limestone; Ready-mixed concrete; Concrete, asphaltic (not from refineries); Hydrated lime; Quicklime; Construction sand & gravel
Pr: Howard C Nye
**CFO:* Anne H Lloyd
**Sr VP:* Roselyn R Bar
**Sr VP:* Daniel L Grant
**Sr VP:* Dana F Guzzo
**VP:* W D Bankston
**VP:* David L Wenzel
IT Man: Chris Clark
Board of Directors: G R Phillipson, William S Yearsley

D-U-N-S 15-465-7449
MARTIN MEMORIAL HEALTH SYSTEMS INC
200 Se Hospital Ave, Stuart, FL 34994-2346
Tel (772) 287-5200 *Founded/Ownrshp* 1983
Sales 542.4MM *EMP* 2,972
SIC 8741 8062 Hospital management; Nursing & personal care facility management; General medical & surgical hospitals
Pr: Mark E Robitaille
Chf Rad: Eileen McGlynn
CFO: Chuck Cleaver
Chf Mktg O: Howard Robbins MD
**Sr VP:* L Mark Cocorullo
**Sr VP:* Donna H Griffith
Sr VP: Donna Griffith
**Sr VP:* Robert L Lord Jr
**Sr VP:* Karen Ripper
**Sr VP:* Michael Skehan
**VP:* Amy Barry
**VP:* John Tagliareni
Dir Risk M: Sharon Beiser

D-U-N-S 07-846-7651
MARTIN MEMORIAL MEDICAL CENTER INC (FL)
MARTIN MEMORIAL MEDICAL CTR S
(*Suby of* MARTIN MEMORIAL HEALTH SYSTEMS INC) ★
200 Se Hospital Ave, Stuart, FL 34994-2346
Tel (772) 287-5200 *Founded/Ownrshp* 1938, 1967
Sales 434.4MM *EMP* 2,972ᴱ
SIC 8062 General medical & surgical hospitals
Pr: Mark Robitaille
**CFO:* Chuck Cleaver
**CFO:* L Mark Cocorullo
**Treas:* John Lowenberg
**Sr VP:* Donna H Griffith
Sr VP: Howard M Robbins
**VP:* Craig Chindemi
VP: Edmund Collins
Dir Risk M: Julie Pike
Dir Bus: Carol Plato-Nicosia
Adm Dir: Carol Plato

MARTIN MEMORIAL MEDICAL CTR S
See MARTIN MEMORIAL MEDICAL CENTER INC

D-U-N-S 09-967-6020
▲ MARTIN MIDSTREAM PARTNERS LP
4200 Stone Rd, Kilgore, TX 75662-6935
Tel (903) 983-6200 *Founded/Ownrshp* 1951
Sales 1.0MMM *EMP* 871E
Tkr Sym MMLP *Exch* NGS
SIC 5171 4226 1321 4424 2819 2875 Petroleum bulk stations & terminals; Petroleum bulk stations; Petroleum terminals; Petroleum & chemical bulk stations & terminals for hire; Natural gas liquids production; Coastwide transportation, freight; Sulfur, recovered or refined, incl. from sour natural gas; Fertilizers, mixing only
Pr: Ruben S Martin
Genl Pt: Martin Midstream GP LLC
CFO: Robert D Bondurant
Exec: Muggs Athey
VP Mktg: Kelly McCorkle

MARTIN, MILTON TOYOTA
See MARTIN CAR FINANCING INC

D-U-N-S 94-363-1598
MARTIN MONTGOMERY CONTRACTORS LLC
8245 Tournament Dr # 300, Memphis, TN 38125-8898
Tel (901) 374-9400 *Founded/Ownrshp* 1995
Sales 97.0MM *EMP* 125
SIC 1542 1541 8741 Commercial & office building, new construction; Commercial & office buildings, renovation & repair; Industrial buildings, new construction; Renovation, remodeling & repairs: industrial buildings; Construction management
CEO: H Montgomery Martin
VP: Scott Barnes
**VP:* George Bratton
**VP:* Jeff Emerson
**VP:* Richard T Meena
**VP:* Joel Thomas

D-U-N-S 01-385-9160
MARTIN OIL CO
MARTIN GENERAL STORES
528 N 1st St, Bellwood, PA 16617-1922
Tel (814) 742-8438 *Founded/Ownrshp* 1962
Sales 98.4MM *EMP* 202
SIC 5983 5171 5541 5411

D-U-N-S 82-994-3989 EXP
■ MARTIN OPERATING PARTNERSHIP LP
(*Suby of* MARTIN MIDSTREAM PARTNERS LP) ★
4200 Stone Rd, Kilgore, TX 75662-6935
Tel (903) 983-6200 *Founded/Ownrshp* 1956
Sales 412.9MME *EMP* 708
SIC 5172 Petroleum products
Pr: Ruben S Martin III
CFO: Bob Bondurang
Ex VP: Chris Booth
VP: Joe McCreery

MARTIN PREFERRED LOGISTICS
See PREFERRED FOODS MARTIN L P

D-U-N-S 13-956-3332 IMP/EXP
MARTIN PRODUCT SALES LLC
MARTIN ASPHALT
(*Suby of* MARTIN RESOURCE MANAGEMENT CORP) ★
4200 Stone Rd, Kilgore, TX 75662-6935
Tel (903) 983-6200 *Founded/Ownrshp* 1986
Sales 321.5MME *EMP* 206
SIC 5052 5032 5172 Sulfur; Asphalt mixture; Crude oil
Pr: Ruben S Martin III
**COO:* Randall L Tauscher
CFO: Bob Bondurant
**Ex VP:* Robert D Bondurant
**VP:* Chris Booth
Sls Mgr: Brian Federico

D-U-N-S 14-711-1751 IMP/EXP
MARTIN RESOURCE MANAGEMENT CORP
4200 Stone Rd, Kilgore, TX 75662-6935
Tel (903) 983-6200 *Founded/Ownrshp* 1963
Sales 2.4MMM *EMP* 2,300
Accts Kpmg Llp Dallas Texas
SIC 2911 4924 5984 5172 Gases & liquefied petroleum gases; Natural gas distribution; Liquefied petroleum gas, delivered to customers' premises; Fuel oil; Crude oil; Gases, liquefied petroleum (propane)
Pr: Ruben S Martin III
COO: Randall L Tauscher
**CFO:* Bob Bondurant
CFO: Robert D Bondurant
**Treas:* Wesley M Skelton
Sr VP: Mike Ginzel
Sr VP: Ed Grimm
Sr VP: Scot A Shoup
VP: Kyle Dickard
VP: Al Foley
VP: Mike Lawrence
VP: Johnnie Murry
VP: Michael Newton
VP: Tom Redd
VP: Doug Towns
**VP:* Douglas Towns
Dir Risk M: Mike Murley

D-U-N-S 00-802-9613 IMP
MARTIN SPROCKET & GEAR INC (TX)
3100 Sprocket Dr, Arlington, TX 76015-2898
Tel (817) 258-3000 *Founded/Ownrshp* 1951
Sales 367.1MME *EMP* 1,700
SIC 3566 3568 3535 3321 3462 3429

D-U-N-S 02-548-8891
MARTIN SULLIVAN INC
250 E Main St Ste 402, Galesburg, IL 61401-4723
Tel (309) 343-1423 *Founded/Ownrshp* 1926
Sales 111.8MME *EMP* 85
SIC 5083 5261 Agricultural machinery & equipment; Lawn & garden equipment
CEO: Mark Kleine
**Pr:* Jim Haynes
Manager: Bill Sullivan

D-U-N-S 08-044-2595
MARTIN SUSTAINABLE RESOURCES LLC
ROYOMARTIN
2189 Memorial Dr, Alexandria, LA 71301-3610
Tel (318) 448-0405 *Founded/Ownrshp* 2015, 2016
Sales 247.7MME *EMP* 1,181
SIC 2493 2435 Strandboard, oriented; Plywood, hardwood or hardwood faced

D-U-N-S 05-966-6834
MARTIN TRANSPORT INC
(*Suby of* MARTIN RESOURCE MANAGEMENT CORP) ★
4200 Stone Rd, Kilgore, TX 75662-6935
Tel (281) 860-4313 *Founded/Ownrshp* 1951
Sales 180.0MM *EMP* 1,000
SIC 4213 Trucking, except local
CEO: Ruben S Martin III
**CEO:* Ruben S Martin III
**Treas:* Wesley M Skelton
**Sr VP:* Johnny Murry

D-U-N-S 03-861-0200
MARTIN TRANSPORTATION SYSTEMS INC
M T S
7300 Clyde Park Ave Sw, Byron Center, MI 49315-8387
Tel (616) 455-8850 *Founded/Ownrshp* 1997
Sales 270.8MME *EMP* 1,000
SIC 4212 Local trucking, without storage
Pr: Richard M Dabney
**CFO:* Don Armbrester
**Treas:* Altimore Harrison Jr
Trfc Dir: Kristy Overdyk

D-U-N-S 05-786-1650 IMP/EXP
MARTIN-BROWER CO L L C
(*Suby of* REYES HOLDINGS LLC) ★
6250 N River Rd Ste 9000, Rosemont, IL 60018-4241
Tel (847) 227-6500 *Founded/Ownrshp* 1998
Sales 2.2MMME *EMP* 3,900
SIC 5142 5113 5149 5087 Packaged frozen goods; Industrial & personal service paper; Groceries & related products; Restaurant supplies
Pr: Gregory Nickele
**COO:* Robert McGonigle
**CFO:* Joseph Tomczak
CFO: Bill Williams
**Ch:* J Christopher Reyes
**Treas:* Kurt Roemer
**Ex VP:* David K Reyes
**Ex VP:* M Jude Reyes
**Sr VP:* Dan Doheny
**Sr VP:* Nicholas L Giampietro
VP: Pearson Claire
VP: Brent Clarke
Exec: Randy French

D-U-N-S 08-838-9408 IMP
MARTIN-HARRIS CONSTRUCTION LLC
(*Suby of* BIG-D CAPITAL CORP) ★
3030 S Highland Dr, Las Vegas, NV 89109-1047
Tel (702) 385-5257 *Founded/Ownrshp* 2014
Sales 154.8MME *EMP* 140E
SIC 1541 1542 Warehouse construction; Specialized public building contractors
Pr: Frank E Martin
Ofcr: Manuel Lopez
**Sr VP:* Guy Martin
VP: Ray Newmiller

MARTINDALE FEED MILL
See ALAN RITCHEY INC

D-U-N-S 12-437-6786 IMP
MARTINREA AUTOMOTIVE-STRUCTURES (USA) INC
TKA FABCO
(*Suby of* MARTINREA INDUSTRIES INC) ★
2800 Livernois Rd Ste 450, Troy, MI 48083-1253
Tel (248) 823-5700 *Founded/Ownrshp* 2006
Sales 209.4MME *EMP* 450
SIC 3714 Motor vehicle parts & accessories
Pr: Nick Orlando
Genl Mgr: Richard Haveman
Genl Mgr: Kurt Spencer
Plnt Mgr: Leo La Bla

D-U-N-S 80-179-1075 IMP
MARTINREA HOPKINSVILLE LLC
(*Suby of* MARTINREA INTERNATIONAL INC)
1500 Frank Yost Ln, Hopkinsville, KY 42240-6818
Tel (270) 475-2000 *Founded/Ownrshp* 1998
Sales 275.2MME *EMP* 340E
SIC 5013 Automotive engines & engine parts
Pr: Tim Parys
Prgrm Mgr: Leo Chau
Prgrm Mgr: Cliff Duncan
Prgrm Mgr: Al Trout
Genl Mgr: Kurt Spencer
Genl Mgr: Tom Troyan
Ql Cn Mgr: Dan Brown
Ql Cn Mgr: David Noster
Ql Cn Mgr: Lynn Sakal
Snr Mgr: David Klawes
Snr Mgr: Jerry Miller

D-U-N-S 10-307-8213 IMP
MARTINREA INDUSTRIES INC
(*Suby of* MARTINREA INTERNATIONAL INC)
10501 Mi State Road 52, Manchester, MI 48158-9432
Tel (734) 428-2400 *Founded/Ownrshp* 2002
Sales 392.7MME *EMP* 1,350
SIC 3714 3317 3089 3544 Motor vehicle parts & accessories; Steel pipe & tubes; Plastic containers, except foam; Special dies, tools, jigs & fixtures
CEO: Morris Rowlett
**Ch Bd:* Robert Wildeboer
**Pr:* Fred Jaekel
**CFO:* Robert Eckert
**CFO:* Nick Orlando
Genl Mgr: Tom Troyan
Ql Cn Mgr: Charles Muhammad

D-U-N-S 82-972-1799 IMP
MARTINREA JONESVILLE LLC
(*Suby of* MARTINREA INTERNATIONAL INC)
260 Gaige St, Jonesville, MI 49250-9431
Tel (517) 849-2195 *Founded/Ownrshp* 2009
Sales 155.6MME *EMP* 700E
SIC 3465 Body parts, automobile: stamped metal
CEO: Nick Orlando
Genl Mgr: Pete Bertolni

D-U-N-S 07-939-1325
MARTINREA RIVERSIDE LLC
(*Suby of* MARTINREA INTERNATIONAL INC)
5233 Nw 41st St, Riverside, MO 64150-7815
Tel (816) 587-0875 *Founded/Ownrshp* 2014
Sales 90.8MME *EMP* 300
SIC 3465 Automotive stampings
Ch: Robert Wildeboer

D-U-N-S 01-394-7551 IMP
MARTINS FAMOUS PASTRY SHOPPE INC
1000 Potato Roll Ln, Chambersburg, PA 17202-8897
Tel (717) 263-9580 *Founded/Ownrshp* 1957
Sales 165.8MME *EMP* 464
SIC 2051 Rolls, bread type: fresh or frozen; Buns, bread type: fresh or frozen
Pr: James A Martin
**Treas:* Donna F Martin
**VP:* Ronald G Gipe
**VP:* James Martin
VP: Tony Martin
Dir IT: Karl Hansen
Manager: Vernon McCauley
Sales Asso: Amy Reed

MARTIN'S FOOD CENTER VT
See MARTINS FOODS OF S BURLINGTON INC

MARTIN'S FOOD MARKET
See GIANT FOOD STORES LLC

D-U-N-S 05-276-5294
MARTINS FOODS OF S BURLINGTON INC (VT)
MARTIN'S FOOD CENTER VT
(*Suby of* HANNAFORD SUPERMARKET & PHRM) ★
145 Pleasant Hill Rd, Scarborough, ME 04074-9309
Tel (207) 883-2911 *Founded/Ownrshp* 1969
Sales 188.3MME *EMP* 3,087
SIC 5411 Supermarkets, chain
Pr: Hugh G Farrington
Ch Bd: James L Moody Jr
Treas: Gary Bowne
Prin: Ronald Hodge
Board of Directors: Judy S Thompson, Richard H Wadhams Jr, Judith A White

D-U-N-S 00-235-4637
MARTINS POINT HEALTH CARE INC (ME)
USFHP AT MARTIN'S POINT
331 Veranda St Ste 1, Portland, ME 04103-5544
Tel (207) 774-5801 *Founded/Ownrshp* 1971
Sales 571.8MM *EMP* 729
Accts Baker Newman & Noyes Portland
SIC 8093 Specialty outpatient clinics
Pr: Dr David Howes
**Ch Bd:* Michael Thomas
**COO:* Larry Henry
**CFO:* Dale Bradford
CFO: Dennis Reese
Treas: George Campbell
**Bd of Dir:* Katherine Greenleaf
VP: Jeffry Bland
VP: Ann Connelly
VP: Judy Cote
Off Mgr: Julie Trimmer

D-U-N-S 04-640-0701
MARTINS SUPER MARKETS INC
760 Cotter St, South Bend, IN 46613-1824
Tel (574) 234-5848 *Founded/Ownrshp* 1947
Sales 356.9MME *EMP* 3,100
SIC 5411 Supermarkets, independent
Pr: Robert E Bartels Jr
**Ch Bd:* Robert E Bartels
CIO: Scott Johnson
IT Man: Ed Delaurelle
VP Opers: Tom Killelea

MARTORI FARMS
See EAGLE PRODUCE LLC

D-U-N-S 00-167-0876 IMP/EXP
MARUBENI AMERICA CORP (NY)
(*Suby of* MARUBENI CORPORATION)
375 Lexington Ave, New York, NY 10017-5644
Tel (212) 450-0100 *Founded/Ownrshp* 1951
Sales 7.1MMME *EMP* 4,175
Accts Ernst & Young Llp New York N
SIC 5131 5084 5012 5169 5172 5094 Textiles, woven; Industrial machinery & equipment; Automobiles & other motor vehicles; Industrial chemicals; Petroleum products; Crude oil; Fuel oil; Gasoline; Precious metals
VP: Jerome E Barnett
COO: Yuichi Ishimaru
COO: Shigemi Naito
Treas: Hironori Hanada
Sr Cor Off: Tom Mustico
Bd of Dir: Yoshiya Toyoda
Ex VP: Toru Nishimi
Sr VP: Shinichiro Kawazoe
VP: Jerome Barnett
VP: Shinji Kawauchi
VP: Makoto Okada
VP: Eric Smith
VP: Daniel Welt
VP: Koji Yamanaka
Exec: Toru Nashimi

D-U-N-S 80-644-0467
MARUBENI AUTO & CONSTRUCTION MACHINERY (AMERICA) INC
(*Suby of* MARUBENI CORPORATION)
450 Lexington Ave, New York, NY 10017-3904
Tel (212) 450-0447 *Founded/Ownrshp* 2002
Sales 136.6MME *EMP* 325
SIC 5082 7353 7699 General construction machinery & equipment; Heavy construction equipment rental; Construction equipment repair
Pr: Takuji Harada

D-U-N-S 82-639-2479 EXP
MARUBENI POWER SERVICES INC
(*Suby of* MARUBENI CORPORATION)
375 Lexington Ave, New York, NY 10017-5644
Tel (212) 450-0640 *Founded/Ownrshp* 2005
Sales 94.3MM *EMP* 1,061E
Accts Ernst & Young Llp Atlanta Ga
SIC 1629 4911 8711 Power plant construction; Electric services; Engineering services
Prin: Takehiro Nakamura
CFO: Eisuke Kamide
**Ex VP:* Richard Straebel
Sr VP: Shinichiro Kawazoe
**Sr VP:* Xavier Tournier
VP: Abby Saigal
VP: Hiroshi Tachitachi
**VP:* Daniel Welt
**VP:* Hiroki Yamamoto
Counsel: Thomas Blinten

D-U-N-S 78-727-6633 IMP/EXP
MARUBENI SPECIALTY CHEMICALS INC
(*Suby of* MARUBENI AMERICA CORP) ★
10 Bank St Ste 740, White Plains, NY 10606-1952
Tel (914) 428-8900 *Founded/Ownrshp* 1991
Sales 186.2MM *EMP* 62
Accts Ernst & Young Llp New York N
SIC 5169 Chemicals, industrial & heavy
Pr: Jo Harada
**VP:* Tsuyoshi Honkawa
Genl Mgr: Toshinori Takeyama

D-U-N-S 04-307-1377 IMP
MARUBENI-ITOCHU STEEL AMERICA INC
MISA
(*Suby of* MARUBENI-ITOCHU STEEL INC.)
150 E 42nd St Fl 7, New York, NY 10017-5612
Tel (212) 660-6000 *Founded/Ownrshp* 2001
Sales 721.0MME *EMP* 1,358
Accts Deloitte & Touche Llp New Yor
SIC 5051 Metals service centers & offices
CEO: Takeshi Mitomi
**Ch Bd:* Katsuya Masai
**CFO:* Shuji Suzuki
VP: Shohei Tanaka
Genl Mgr: Hidefumi Ogita
Genl Mgr: Namiki Toshio-Cgomisa
VP Sls: Bradley Miller
Sls Mgr: David Lyster
Counsel: Akira Takahashi

D-U-N-S 06-460-7096 IMP/EXP
MARUCHAN INC
(*Suby of* TOYO SUISAN KAISHA, LTD.)
15800 Laguna Canyon Rd, Irvine, CA 92618-3103
Tel (949) 789-2300 *Founded/Ownrshp* 1972
Sales 261.3MME *EMP* 600
SIC 2098 Noodles (e.g. egg, plain & water), dry
CEO: Noritaka Sumimoto
Dir IT: Takashi Ueno
IT Man: Gary Leeper
Prd Mgr: Satoshi Asano
Sls&Mrk Ex: James R Santo
Manager: Gregg Sommer

D-U-N-S 16-727-8261
MARUHA CAPITAL INVESTMENT INC
(*Suby of* MARUHA NICHIRO CORPORATION)
2101 4th Ave Ste 1700, Seattle, WA 98121-2377
Tel (206) 382-0640 *Founded/Ownrshp* 2001
Sales 391.7MME *EMP* 204E
SIC 6799 2091 Investors; Seafood products: packaged in cans, jars, etc.
Pr: Hiroshi Okazaki
**Treas:* Tatsuya Yamamoto
**VP:* Katsuhiko Uota

MARVA MAID DAIRY DIVISION
See MARYLAND AND VIRGINIA MILK PRODUCERS COOPERATIVE ASSOCIATION INC

D-U-N-S 18-582-5569 IMP
■ MARVEL ENTERTAINMENT LLC
(*Suby of* WALT DISNEY CO) ★
135 W 50th St Fl 7, New York, NY 10020-1201
Tel (212) 576-4000 *Founded/Ownrshp* 2009
Sales 97.1MME *EMP* 300E
SIC 2721 6794 3944 7929 Comic books: publishing only, not printed on site; Magazines: publishing only, not printed on site; Patent buying, licensing, leasing; Electronic games & toys; Entertainment service
CEO: Isaac Perlmutter
Pr: Michael Helfant
Pr: Timothy E Rothwell
COO: Michael Halfant
COO: Ralph Lancellotti
CFO: Kenneth P West
Ex VP: David Maisel
Ex VP: John Turitzin
VP: Mitchell Bell
VP: David Grant
VP: Jeff Klein
VP: Cort Lane
VP: Karim Zreik
VP Bus Dev: Benjamin Hung

D-U-N-S 00-512-0050 IMP/EXP
MARVEL GROUP INC (DE)
3843 W 43rd St, Chicago, IL 60632-3409
Tel (773) 523-4804 *Founded/Ownrshp* 1946, 2003
Sales 94.1MME *EMP* 440
SIC 2522 Office furniture, except wood
Pr: John J Dellamore
VP: Chris Bone
VP: Joe Fortin
VP: Michael Glab
VP: Ken Wolfanger
IT Man: Grace Bukowski
Web Prj Mg: Mike Edwards
VP Mfg: Ed Lencioni

D-U-N-S 95-881-9906 IMP
MARVELL SEMICONDUCTOR INC
(*Suby of* MARVELL TECHNOLOGY GROUP LTD)
5488 Marvell Ln, Santa Clara, CA 95054-3606
Tel (408) 222-2500 *Founded/Ownrshp* 1995
Sales 587.8MM^E *EMP* 1,900
SIC 3674 Semiconductors & related devices
CEO: Sehat Sutardja
**COO:* Weili Dai
**CFO:* George Hervey
**CFO:* Michael Rashkin
Bd of Dir: John Kassakian
Assoc VP: Dansey Steve
VP: Alan Armstrong
VP: Allan Brown
VP: James Laufman
VP: Sukhi Nagesh
VP: Thomas Savage
Board of Directors: John Gabriel Kassakian

D-U-N-S 86-798-7323 IMP
MARVELL TECHNOLOGY GROUP LTD
(*Suby of* MARVELL TECHNOLOGY GROUP LTD)
5488 Marvell Ln, Santa Clara, CA 95054-3606
Tel (408) 222-2500 *Founded/Ownrshp* 1991
Sales 282.2MM^E *EMP* 1,410^E
SIC 6719 Personal holding companies, except banks
**Ch Bd:* Richard S Hill
**CFO:* George A De Urioste
Ex VP: Thomas Lagatta
VP: Alan Armstrong
VP: Matthew Gloss
VP: James Laufman
VP: Abuzar Saeed
VP: Moshe Steiner
VP: Pantas Sutardja
Prgrm Mgr: Gary Zimmerman
Dept Mgr: Michael Bogachek

D-U-N-S 00-956-6167 IMP
MARVIN ENGINEERING CO INC
MARVIN GROUP, THE
261 W Beach Ave, Inglewood, CA 90302-2904
Tel (310) 674-5030 *Founded/Ownrshp* 1963
Sales 225.6MM^E *EMP* 700
SIC 3728 Aircraft parts & equipment
CEO: Gerald M Friedman
**Pr:* Howard Gussman
COO: Jim Fish
COO: Oded Nechustan
**CFO:* Leon Tsimmerman
VP: Howard Guman
VP: Seth Silverstein
Prgrm Mgr: Bob Perryman
Prgrm Mgr: Robert Sammons
CIO: Barry Yarkoni
MIS Dir: Bill Allin
Board of Directors: David Gussman, Madeline Gussman

MARVIN GROUP, THE
See MARVIN ENGINEERING CO INC

D-U-N-S 00-616-4511 IMP
MARVIN LUMBER AND CEDAR CO (MN)
MARVIN WINDOWS & DOORS
Hwy 11 & W Lake St, Warroad, MN 56763
Tel (218) 386-1430 *Founded/Ownrshp* 1920
Sales 553.3MM^E *EMP* 3,573
SIC 2431

MARVIN WINDOWS & DOORS
See MARVIN LUMBER AND CEDAR CO

MARVIN WINDOWS AND DOORS
See MARVIN WINDOWS OF TENNESSEE INC

D-U-N-S 11-527-9168 IMP/EXP
MARVIN WINDOWS OF TENNESSEE INC
MARVIN WINDOWS AND DOORS
101 Marvin Dr, Ripley, TN 38063-7365
Tel (731) 635-5190 *Founded/Ownrshp* 1980
Sales 87.1MM^E *EMP* 700
SIC 2431 3231 Doors, wood; Doors, glass: made from purchased glass
CEO: John W Marvin
**Pr:* Susan Marvin

D-U-N-S 08-997-6385 IMP
MARVINS LLC
BUILDING MATERIALS & HOME CTRS
(*Suby of* CENTRAL NETWORK RETAIL GROUP LLC) ★
7480 Parkway Dr Ste 100, Leeds, AL 35094-4823
Tel (205) 702-7305 *Founded/Ownrshp* 2015
Sales 152.4MM^E *EMP* 550
SIC 5211 5074 5031 5072

D-U-N-S 83-764-7585
■ **MARY BLACK HEALTH SYSTEMS INC**
(*Suby of* QUORUM HEALTH RESOURCES LLC) ★
1700 Skylyn Dr, Spartanburg, SC 29307-1041
Tel (864) 573-3000 *Founded/Ownrshp* 1999
Sales 68.7MM^E *EMP* 1,100
SIC 8062 General medical & surgical hospitals
CEO: Sean Dardeau
**CFO:* Micheal Mart
Dir Rx: William Galarneau
**Ex Dir:* Glenn A Robinson
Nurse Mgr: Lisa Dill
Dir IT: Jeff Nash
Mktg Dir: Connie Legrand

D-U-N-S 13-166-8738
MARY BLACK MEMORIAL HOSPITAL INC
1700 Skylyn Dr, Spartanburg, SC 29307-1061
Tel (864) 573-3004 *Founded/Ownrshp* 1932
Sales 156.6MM *EMP* 99
SIC 8062 General medical & surgical hospitals
Pr: Treresa Landers
Dir Vol: Teresa Vickers
COO: David Cope
CFO: Richard Meyer
Ofcr: Nancy White
Dir OR: Chris Terrill
Dir Risk M: Beth Van Orsdale
Dir Rad: Beverly O' Sullivan
Dir Rx: Bill Galarneau
Dir Env Sv: Bill Blackwell
Off Mgr: Christina Banks
Board of Directors: Kelly Hill, Theresa Landers

D-U-N-S 07-929-2645
MARY FREE BED REHABILITATION HOSPITAL
235 Wealthy St Se, Grand Rapids, MI 49503-5247
Tel (616) 242-0300 *Founded/Ownrshp* 1913
Sales 63.4MM^E *EMP* 1,100
Accts Plante & Moran Pllc Grand Ra
SIC 8069 8093 Specialty hospitals, except psychiatric; Rehabilitation center, outpatient treatment
CEO: Kent Riddle
**Ch Bd:* David Muir
**Pr:* William Blessing
COO: Dave Holsworth
**Treas:* Chad Bush
VP: Jeff Garber
VP: Jen Lannon
VP: Curt Meyer
VP: Margaret Nault
VP: Tim Pietryga
VP: Tom Stranz

D-U-N-S 08-560-0307
MARY GREELEY MEDICAL CENTER
1111 Duff Ave, Ames, IA 50010-5745
Tel (515) 239-6730 *Founded/Ownrshp* 1969
Sales 177.0MM *EMP* 75
SIC 8082 Home health care services
Sls Mgr: Julie Hill
HC Dir: Connie Dudding

D-U-N-S 82-526-7912
MARY GREELEY MEDICAL CENTER FOUNDATION
(*Suby of* CITY OF AMES) ★
1111 Duff Ave, Ames, IA 50010-5745
Tel (515) 239-2011 *Founded/Ownrshp* 1969
Sales 1.9MM *EMP* 1,400
Accts Rsm Us Llp Des Moines Ia
SIC 8062 General medical & surgical hospitals
Pr: Brian Dieter
**CFO:* Michael Tretina
**VP:* Neal Loes
**VP:* Lynn Whisler
Dir Case M: Darla Handsaker
Off Mgr: Tricia Clausen
Pr Dir: Keith Sullivan
Board of Directors: Connie Dudding, Selden Spencer

MARY HITCHCOCK MEMORIAL HOSP
See MAXIFACIAL DENTAL SURGERY

D-U-N-S 06-991-0297
MARY HITCHCOCK MEMORIAL HOSPITAL
DARTMOUTH-HITCHCOCK
1 Medical Center Dr, Lebanon, NH 03756-1000
Tel (603) 650-5000 *Founded/Ownrshp* 1889
Sales 894.4MM *EMP* 8,000^E
SIC 8062

D-U-N-S 06-600-2734
MARY IMMACULATE HOSPITAL INC
BON SECOURS MARY
2 Bernardine Dr, Newport News, VA 23602-4499
Tel (757) 886-6440 *Founded/Ownrshp* 1956
Sales 186.2MM *EMP* 850^E
Accts Deloitte Tax Lp Atlanta Ga
SIC 8062 8099 Hospital, affiliated with AMA residency; Blood related health services
CEO: Richard Hanson
**CEO:* John Barrett
**Ex VP:* Cynthia Farrand
HC Dir: Cynthia Miller

D-U-N-S 02-067-2820
MARY IMOGENE BASSETT HOSPITAL
BASSETT MEDICAL CENTER
1 Atwell Rd, Cooperstown, NY 13326-1394
Tel (607) 547-3456 *Founded/Ownrshp* 1924
Sales 412.6MM *EMP* 3,200
Accts Lb Kpmg Llp Albany Ny
SIC 8011 8062 5999 General medical & surgical hospitals; Offices & clinics of medical doctors; Hearing aids
Pr: Vance M Brown
COO: Bertine McKenna
CFO: Sue Andrews
Chf Cred: Steven Heneghan
Top Exec: William J Richtsmeier
VP: Kenneth Deans
VP: Brian Tiffany
Dir Case M: Lorry Stubley
Genl Mgr: Carol Smola
Off Mgr: Suzanne Tompson
Off Mgr: Brian Wright
Board of Directors: Scott Barrett, Richard Beebe

D-U-N-S 13-955-7789 IMP/EXP
MARY KAY HOLDING CORP
16251 Dallas Pkwy, Addison, TX 75001-6820
Tel (972) 687-6300 *Founded/Ownrshp* 1985
Sales 741.5MM^E *EMP* 3,600
SIC 5963 3961 3172 4724 Cosmetic sales, house-to-house; Compacts, except precious metal; Cosmetic bags; Travel agencies
Ch Bd: Richard Rogers
Mng Pt: Jennifer Koneval
**Pr:* David B Holl
**CFO:* Terry Smith
**Sr VP:* Nathan Moore
VP: Olga Camacho-Ryan
VP: Sharon Drobeck
VP: Shelia Galliher
VP: Israel Gonzales
VP: Paul Jones
VP: Charlie Moss
VP: Alex Walder
VP: Patricia Wanderley
VP: Leonor Warren

D-U-N-S 04-999-4452 IMP/EXP
MARY KAY INC
(*Suby of* MARY KAY HOLDING CORP) ★
16251 Dallas Pkwy, Addison, TX 75001-6820
Tel (972) 687-6300 *Founded/Ownrshp* 1988
Sales 741.5MM^E *EMP* 3,500^E
SIC 5963 Cosmetic sales, house-to-house
Pr: David Holl
CFO: Deborah Gibbins
CFO: Sherry Polonsky
**CFO:* Terry Smith
Ex VP: Kregg Jodie
Ex VP: Russel Mack
Ex VP: Myra O'Barker
Ex VP: Darrell Overcash
**Sr VP:* Nathan Moore
Sr VP: Wilbur Smither
VP: Myra A Barker
VP: Laura Beitler
**VP:* Patrick Cargo
VP: Shelia Galliher
VP: Israel Gonzales
VP: Terry Jacks
VP: Adrie Lee
VP: Eva Liebermann
VP: Laura McKinney
VP: Mike Scott
VP: Shaya Seward

D-U-N-S 07-697-5077
MARY LANNING MEMORIAL HOSPITAL ASSOCIATION
715 N Saint Joseph Ave, Hastings, NE 68901-4451
Tel (402) 463-4521 *Founded/Ownrshp* 1914
Sales 149.4MM *EMP* 950^E
SIC 8062 General medical & surgical hospitals
COO: Mark Callahan
**Pr:* Eric Barber
**Pr:* Brad Meet
Bd of Dir: Robert Anderson
Sr VP: Joann Lomax
VP: Bruce Curright
VP: Shawn Riggs
VP: Charlene Sanders
Chf Nrs Of: Ronda Ehly
CIO: Aaron Young
Dir IT: Sherrie Hollister
Board of Directors: Patrick Kern

D-U-N-S 05-261-0235 IMP/EXP
MARY LEE PACKAGING CORP
GILSTER-MARY LEE
615 Saint Marys Rd, Perryville, MO 63775-1836
Tel (573) 547-1705 *Founded/Ownrshp* 1969
Sales 1.0MMM^E *EMP* 4,200
SIC 2043 2099 3089 2098 Corn flakes: prepared as cereal breakfast food; Syrups; Plastic containers, except foam; Macaroni & spaghetti
Pr: Donald E Welge
**Treas:* Michael W Welge
Dir IT: Rick Hayden

D-U-N-S 07-942-3851
MARY RUTAN HOSPITAL
(*Suby of* MARY RUTAN HEALTH ASSOCIATION OF LOGAN COUNTY)
205 E Palmer Rd, Bellefontaine, OH 43311-2298
Tel (937) 592-4015 *Founded/Ownrshp* 1983
Sales 96.0MM *EMP* 700
Accts Plante & Moran Pllc Columbus
SIC 8062 General medical & surgical hospitals
Ch Bd: Thomas Simon
CFO: Tammy Bowen
**VP:* Ron Carmen
Dir Lab: Robert J Bailey
Dir IT: Jerome Hoover
Opers Mgr: Glenn Durfor
HC Dir: Pattie S Hinkel

MARY WASHINGTON HEALTHCARE
See WASHINGTON HEALTHCARE PHYSICIANS MARY

D-U-N-S 12-574-8582
MARYHAVEN CENTER OF HOPE INC
(*Suby of* CATHOLIC HLTH SVCS LONG ISLAND) ★
51 Terryville Rd, Port Jeff STA, NY 11776-1359
Tel (631) 474-4120 *Founded/Ownrshp* 1934
Sales 58.2MM *EMP* 1,600
Accts Pricewaterhousecoopers Llp Ne
SIC 8322 7389 Social services for the handicapped; Fund raising organizations
CEO: Lewis Grossman
**CFO:* Susan Barrett
IT Man: Mark Lubranski

D-U-N-S 19-623-0841 IMP
MARYL GROUP INC
MARYL PACIFIC CONSTRUCTION
55 Merchant St Ste 2000, Honolulu, HI 96813-4329
Tel (808) 545-2920 *Founded/Ownrshp* 1986
Sales 116.3MM^E *EMP* 180
SIC 6552 1542 Subdividers & developers; Shopping center construction
Pr: Mark Richards
**CFO:* Tiffiany Trang
**Ex VP:* Mark Kong
**VP:* Cheryl Richards

MARYL PACIFIC CONSTRUCTION
See MARYL GROUP INC

D-U-N-S 00-323-9563
MARYLAND AND VIRGINIA MILK PRODUCERS COOPERATIVE ASSOCIATION INC (VA)
MARVA MAID DAIRY DIVISION
1985 Isaac Newton Sq W # 200, Reston, VA 20190-5031
Tel (703) 742-6800 *Founded/Ownrshp* 1920
Sales 1.3MMM *EMP* 550
Accts Herliem & Company Inc Reading
SIC 5143 2026 5084 Milk; Fluid milk; Food industry machinery
Pr: Dwayne Myers
**CFO:* Jorge Gonzalez
**Treas:* Jay Bryant
Treas: Robert Shore
**VP:* R Steven Graybeal
**VP:* Richard Mosemann
CTO: Kathy Rice
Dir IT: Kathleen Short
Opers Mgr: Craig Gentry
Sales Exec: Michael Curtis
Board of Directors: Lenard Kresge, Sam Tressler, Laird Bowman, C Richard Mosemann Jr, Jeff Wooten, Laird Bowman, David Pool, Edwin Fry, David Pool, Edwin Fry, Fred Rowe, R Steven Graybeal, Fred Rowe, Brian Haugh, W W Sanford III, Matthew Hoff, Kevin Satterwhite, Matthew Hoff, Timothy Stoner, Lenard Kresge, Ray Thrush

D-U-N-S 87-889-4849
MARYLAND DEPARTMENT OF HEALTH & MENTAL HYGIENE
(*Suby of* EXECUTIVE OFFICE OF STATE OF MARYLAND) ★
201 W Preston St Fl 5, Baltimore, MD 21201-2301
Tel (410) 767-6500 *Founded/Ownrshp* 1776
Sales NA *EMP* 7,500
SIC 9431 Administration of public health programs;
Pr: John Commers
Ofcr: Heather Peters
Assoc Dir: Debbie Badawi
Assoc Dir: Michael Howard
Ex Dir: Susan Tucker
Genl Mgr: Kenneth Keys
IT Man: James Hermann
IT Man: Harrison Smith
Pharmcst: Joseph Glass
Cert Phar: John Wagner
Snr Mgr: Tammi Speights

D-U-N-S 09-057-2780
MARYLAND DEPARTMENT OF HUMAN RESOURCES
(*Suby of* EXECUTIVE OFFICE OF STATE OF MARYLAND) ★
311 W Saratoga St, Baltimore, MD 21201-3500
Tel (410) 767-7109 *Founded/Ownrshp* 1999
Sales NA *EMP* 7,020
SIC 9441 Administration of social & human resources;
Ofcr: Dawn Dent
Ofcr: Becky Gray
Ofcr: Aaron Vonmoore
Dist Mgr: Daniel Allotey
Dist Mgr: Ann Mitchell
Off Mgr: Christine Seipp
Off Admin: Janice Jewson
Pgrm Dir: J D Carrington

D-U-N-S 87-993-1251
MARYLAND DEPARTMENT OF JUVENILE SERVICES
(*Suby of* EXECUTIVE OFFICE OF STATE OF MARYLAND) ★
120 W Fayette St, Baltimore, MD 21201-3741
Tel (410) 230-3333 *Founded/Ownrshp* 1984
Sales NA *EMP* 1,000
SIC 9223 Prison, government;
VP: Mathew Fonseca
CIO: Elizabeth Wright
Telecom Mg: Nancy Seidman
IT Man: Michael Dibattista

D-U-N-S 87-820-7505
MARYLAND DEPARTMENT OF NATURAL RESOURCES
(*Suby of* EXECUTIVE OFFICE OF STATE OF MARYLAND) ★
580 Taylor Ave Bldg E3, Annapolis, MD 21401-2363
Tel (410) 260-8100 *Founded/Ownrshp* 1989
Sales NA *EMP* 1,460
SIC 9512 Land, mineral & wildlife conservation;
Plnt Mgr: Donald Mackall

D-U-N-S 87-813-7462 IMP/EXP
MARYLAND DEPARTMENT OF TRANSPORTATION
MDOT
(*Suby of* EXECUTIVE OFFICE OF STATE OF MARYLAND) ★
7201 Corporate Center Dr, Hanover, MD 21076-1415
Tel (410) 865-1037 *Founded/Ownrshp* 1971
Sales 3.8MMM *EMP* 1,000^E
Accts Sb & Company Llc Hunt Valley
SIC 8748 9621 Business consulting;
Ofcr: Jackie Arnie
**Prin:* Robert Ehrlich
**Prin:* Donald A Halligan
VP Mktg: Lisa Dickerson
VP Mktg: Trent M Kittleman
VP Mktg: Trent Kittleman
VP Mktg: Jim Ports
Snr Mgr: Carin Michel

D-U-N-S 87-901-6178
MARYLAND DEPT OF PUBLIC SAFETY & CORRECTIONAL SERVICES
DPSCS
(*Suby of* EXECUTIVE OFFICE OF STATE OF MARYLAND) ★
300 E Joppa Rd Ste 1000, Towson, MD 21286-3068
Tel (410) 339-5000 *Founded/Ownrshp* 1956
Sales NA *EMP* 11,626
SIC 9223 Prison, government;
Ofcr: Danielle Leuking
VP: Donna Wiltshire
Genl Mgr: Tekia Jackson
Genl Mgr: Farid Keshavarz
Software D: Oyefeso Bola
Sls&Mrk Ex: Loreto Vogel
Snr Mgr: Kevin Combs

D-U-N-S 15-120-1896
MARYLAND ECONOMIC DEVELOPMENT CORP
MEDCO
300 E Lombard St Ste 1000, Baltimore, MD 21202-3228
Tel (410) 727-8049 *Founded/Ownrshp* 1984
Sales 139.8MM *EMP* 80
Accts Sc&H Tax & Advisory Services L
SIC 8742 Construction project management consultant
Pr: Martin G Knott Jr
**Ch Bd:* Leonard R Sachs
CFO: Henry A Berliner
**Ex Dir:* Robert Brennan

MARYLAND EXEC OFC OF THE STATE
See ENVIRONMENT MARYLAND DEPARTMENT OF

D-U-N-S 19-064-7404
MARYLAND FOODS INC
CHILI'S
1960 Gallows Rd Ste 200, Vienna, VA 22182-3827
Tel (703) 827-0320 *Founded/Ownrshp* 1988
Sales 35.8MM^E *EMP* 2,500
Accts Watkins Meegan Drury & Compa
SIC 5812 5813 Restaurant, family: chain; American restaurant; Bar (drinking places)
Pr: Linda Hardee
**Sec:* Louise Sawyer
**VP:* Edmund Spivack

MARYLAND GENERAL HEALTH SYSTEM
See MARYLAND GENERAL HOSPITAL INC

D-U-N-S 06-939-8303
MARYLAND GENERAL HOSPITAL INC
MARYLAND GENERAL HEALTH SYSTEM
(*Suby of* UMMC) ★
827 Linden Ave, Baltimore, MD 21201-4606
Tel (410) 225-8000 *Founded/Ownrshp* 1911
Sales 210.4MM *EMP* 1,100
SIC 8062 General medical & surgical hospitals
Pr: Brian Bailey
**Ch Bd:* Marily Carp
**VP:* Donald E Ray

D-U-N-S 00-466-8831
MARYLAND HOSPITALITY INC (VA)
MHI HOTELS
6411 Ivy Ln Ste 510, Greenbelt, MD 20770-1405
Tel (301) 474-3307 *Founded/Ownrshp* 1957
Sales 21.9MM^E *EMP* 1,500
SIC 7011 8741 8742 Hotels; Management services; Management consulting services
Pr: Kim Sims
CFO: William Zaiser
**VP:* Christopher Sims
**VP:* Steven Smith
IT Man: Jametta Wagner

D-U-N-S 06-938-8296
MARYLAND INSTITUTE
ART STORE CENTER
1300 W Mount Royal Ave, Baltimore, MD 21217-4134
Tel (410) 383-2063 *Founded/Ownrshp* 1957
Sales 121.7MM *EMP* 400^E
Accts Kpmg Llp Mc Lean Va
SIC 8221 Colleges universities & professional schools
Pr: Fred Lazarus IV
Pr: Douglas Frost
CFO: Douglas Mann
Assoc VP: Susan Miltenberger
Assoc VP: Diane Prengaman
VP: Theresa Bedoya
Assoc Dir: Tyree George
Assoc Dir: Lynn Marsha
Adm Dir: Diana Caldwell
Ex Dir: Kathy Cowan
Off Mgr: Carla Brown

MARYLAND JOCKEY CLUB
See PIMLICO RACING ASSOCIATION INC

D-U-N-S 00-695-0976 IMP
MARYLAND SOUTHERN ELECTRIC COOPERATIVE INC (MD)
SMECO
15035 Burnt Store Rd, Hughesville, MD 20637-2699
Tel (301) 274-3111 *Founded/Ownrshp* 1937
Sales 490.0MM *EMP* 375
Accts Adams Jenkins Cheatham Pc Mid
SIC 4911 Transmission, electric power; Distribution, electric power
Pr: A Joseph Slater
**COO:* Kenneth M Capps
**CFO:* Sonja M Cox
CFO: Thomas E Kandel
**Ch:* Joseph V Stone
**Treas:* Kenneth L Dyson
**Sec:* Fern Brown
**Sr VP:* Joseph Trentacosta
VP: Andrew Yeskie
IT Man: Jolene Burger
Tech Mgr: Kelli Baldwin
Board of Directors: Daniel W Dyer, Richard A Winkler

D-U-N-S 87-804-5038
MARYLAND STATE DEPARTMENT OF EDUCATION
(*Suby of* EXECUTIVE OFFICE OF STATE OF MARYLAND) ★
200 W Baltimore St, Baltimore, MD 21201-2549
Tel (410) 767-0462 *Founded/Ownrshp* 1991
Sales NA *EMP* 1,478
SIC 9411 Administration of educational programs;
Adm Dir: Vincent Tyler
Ex Dir: Ned F Sparks
Rgnl Mgr: Susan Copsey
Rgnl Mgr: Dolores Harmon
Rgnl Mgr: Loretta Wallace
Off Mgr: Jasmine Brown
Snr Mgr: Xavier Richards

MARYLAND STEEL SPARROWS POINT
See E2 ACQUISITION CORP

D-U-N-S 96-376-4019
MARYLAND TRASPORTATION AUTHORITY
2400 Ste 115, Baltimore, MD 21224
Tel (410) 537-5710 *Founded/Ownrshp* 2010
Sales 22.5MM^E *EMP* 1,000
SIC 4785 Toll operations
Prin: Allen Garman

D-U-N-S 04-549-4457 IMP/EXP
MARYLAND-NATIONAL CAPITAL PARK AND PLANNING COMMISSION
6611 Kenilworth Ave # 103, Riverdale, MD 20737-1332
Tel (301) 454-1540 *Founded/Ownrshp* 1927
Sales 133.1MM^E *EMP* 5,000
SIC 7999 Recreation services
Ex Dir: Patricia C Barney
**Sec:* Joseph C Zimmerman
IT Man: Dianna Napier

D-U-N-S 11-207-4948
MARYLANE HOSPITAL
BAY STATE MEDICAL CENTER
759 Chestnut St, Springfield, MA 01199-1001
Tel (413) 794-5436 *Founded/Ownrshp* 2002
Sales 979.4MM *EMP* 10^E
SIC 8082 Home health care services
Prin: Joanne Ohare

D-U-N-S 07-675-8887 IMP
MARYMOUNT HOSPITAL INC
(*Suby of* CLEVELAND CLINIC HEALTH SYSTEM) ★
9500 Euclid Ave, Cleveland, OH 44195-0001
Tel (216) 581-0500 *Founded/Ownrshp* 2000
Sales 149.5MM *EMP* 500
SIC 8062 8063 8051 8082 General medical & surgical hospitals; Psychiatric hospitals; Skilled nursing care facilities; Home health care services
CEO: David Kilarski
Off Mgr: Bi Welch

D-U-N-S 04-055-4214
MARYMOUNT UNIVERSITY
2807 N Glebe Rd, Arlington, VA 22207-4299
Tel (703) 284-1500 *Founded/Ownrshp* 1950
Sales 100.1MM *EMP* 625
Accts Brown Edwards & Company Llp B
SIC 8221 University
Pr: James E Bundschuh
**Pr:* Matthew D Shank
CFO: George Lasnier
VP: Sherri Hughes
**VP:* Ralph Kidder
VP: Emily Mahony
VP: Linda McMahon
Exec: Vanessa Lim
Dir Risk M: Margaret Axelrod
Assoc Dir: Jennifer Webb
DP Exec: Barbara Favola

MARYSVILLE AUTO PLANT
See HONDA OF AMERICA MFG INC

D-U-N-S 10-000-7186
MARYSVILLE JOINT UNIFIED SCHOOL DISTRICT
1919 B St, Marysville, CA 95901-3731
Tel (530) 741-6000 *Founded/Ownrshp* 1966
Sales 82.9MM^E *EMP* 1,553
SIC 8211 Public elementary & secondary schools
Ex Dir: Lennie Tate

D-U-N-S 80-949-1558
MARYVIEW HOSPITAL
MARYVIEW MEDICAL CENTER
3636 High St, Portsmouth, VA 23707-3270
Tel (757) 398-2200 *Founded/Ownrshp* 1984
Sales 96.2MM^E *EMP* 1,397
SIC 8062 General medical & surgical hospitals
Ch: Dick Hansen
**Ch:* Dominick Calgi
**Ch:* Bray J Robert
**Sec:* Michael Kerner
Off Mgr: Sharon M Teller

MARYVIEW MEDICAL CENTER
See MARYVIEW HOSPITAL

D-U-N-S 02-021-5245
MARYVILLE HEALTHCARE & REHABILITATION
MARYVLL HLTHCR & REHAB CTR
1012 Jamestown Way, Maryville, TN 37803-5865
Tel (865) 984-7400 *Founded/Ownrshp* 1997
Sales 994.1MM *EMP* 100
SIC 8322 Rehabilitation services
Pr: Joe Naples
CFO: Joe Michaels
Off Mgr: Lori Casey
Sls&Mrk Ex: Susan Robinson
Nrsg Dir: Amanda Smith

MARYVLL HLTHCR & REHAB CTR
See MARYVILLE HEALTHCARE & REHABILITATION

MARYWOOD RETREAT CENTER
See DIOCESE OF ST AUGUSTINE INC

D-U-N-S 08-816-5972
MASCARO CONSTRUCTION CO LP
1720 Metropolitan St, Pittsburgh, PA 15233-2260
Tel (412) 321-4901 *Founded/Ownrshp* 1997
Sales 212.0MM *EMP* 220
Accts Henry Rossi & Co Llp Monroe
SIC 1542 Commercial & office building, new construction; Commercial & office buildings, renovation & repair
Genl Pt: John C Mascaro Jr
Pt: Jeffrey Mascaro
Pt: John C Mascaro Sr
Pt: Michael Mascaro
Pt: Charles Solkovy
Dir Bus: Michael Ellis
Sfty Mgr: Patrick Marsilio
Sfty Mgr: Amanda Presto
Sfty Mgr: Amanda Smoker

D-U-N-S 19-600-5990
MASCHHOFFS LLC
7475 State Route 127, Carlyle, IL 62231-3103
Tel (618) 594-2125 *Founded/Ownrshp* 2005
Sales 552.1MM^E *EMP* 1,859
SIC 0213 Hogs
Pr: Mark Greenwood
**Ch Bd:* Kenneth Maschhoff
CFO: Jason Logsdon
VP: Aaron M Gaines
Assoc Dir: Kevin Van

D-U-N-S 04-831-8133 IMP/EXP
MASCO BATH CORP (TN)
MASCO BATH SOUTH
8445 Keystone Xing # 100, Indianapolis, IN 46240-2496
Tel (317) 254-5959 *Founded/Ownrshp* 1984
Sales NA *EMP* 1,450
SIC 3088 3842

MASCO BATH SOUTH
See MASCO BATH CORP

D-U-N-S 00-503-4749 IMP
■ **MASCO BUILDER CABINET GROUP**
(*Suby of* MASCO CORP) ★
5353 W Us Highway 223, Adrian, MI 49221-8901
Tel (517) 264-9153 *Founded/Ownrshp* 1946
Sales 333.3MM^E *EMP* 4,000
SIC 2434 Wood kitchen cabinets; Vanities, bathroom: wood
Pr: Karen L Strauss
**CFO:* Mike McCullough
VP: John Czerwonka
VP: Chuck Loudermilk
**VP:* W Jay Potter
**VP:* Michael Thompson
VP Mktg: Mark Ayers
Board of Directors: Raymond Kennedy, Richard G Mosteller

D-U-N-S 14-438-7198
■ **MASCO BUILDING PRODUCTS CORP**
(*Suby of* MASCO CORP) ★
21001 Van Born Rd, Taylor, MI 48180-1340
Tel (313) 274-7400 *Founded/Ownrshp* 1985
Sales 1.1MMM^E *EMP* 30,000
SIC 3429 3639 3644 Door locks, bolts & checks; Major kitchen appliances, except refrigerators & stoves; Outlet boxes (electric wiring devices)
Pr: Allan Barry
**VP:* Lebo Larry

D-U-N-S 09-997-0035 IMP/EXP
■ **MASCO CABINETRY LLC**
DENOVA
(*Suby of* MASCO CORP) ★
4600 Arrowhead Dr, Ann Arbor, MI 48105-2773
Tel (734) 205-4600 *Founded/Ownrshp* 2007
Sales 1.2MMM^E *EMP* 4,000
SIC 2434 Wood kitchen cabinets
Pr: Joe Gross
**Pr:* Jim Lind
COO: Donald Demarie Jr
**CFO:* Gordon Fournier
**CIO:* Viren Shah
VP Opers: Chris Winans
QI Cn Mgr: Mike Dugan

D-U-N-S 07-574-2361 IMP/EXP
■ **MASCO CABINETRY MIDDLEFIELD LLC**
(*Suby of* DENOVA) ★
15535 S State Ave, Middlefield, OH 44062
Tel (440) 632-5333 *Founded/Ownrshp* 2011
Sales 480.0MM^E *EMP* 3,022
SIC 2434 Wood kitchen cabinets; Vanities, bathroom: wood
Pr: Keith Scherzer
CFO: John Pederson
VP: Eugene A Gargaro
**VP:* Andrew Rattray
VP Sls: Roland Minogue

D-U-N-S 01-275-5930
■ **MASCO CONTRACTOR SERVICES EAST INC**
(*Suby of* MASCO CORP) ★
612 River Rd, Fair Haven, NJ 07704-3273
Tel (732) 933-4433 *Founded/Ownrshp* 1999
Sales 121.5MM^E *EMP* 5,000
SIC 1742 Insulation, buildings
Pr: Steven Raia
**CFO:* Tom Jarvis
**VP:* Dennis Raia

D-U-N-S 00-532-0924 IMP/EXP
▲ **MASCO CORP**
21001 Van Born Rd, Taylor, MI 48180-1300
Tel (313) 274-7400 *Founded/Ownrshp* 1929
Sales 7.1MMM *EMP* 25,000
Tkr Sym MAS *Exch* NYS
SIC 2434 3432 3088 3429 1742 Wood kitchen cabinets; Vanities, bathroom: wood; Faucets & spigots, metal & plastic; Plumbers' brass goods: drain cocks, faucets, spigots, etc.; Plastic plumbing fixture fittings, assembly; Plastics plumbing fixtures; Tubs (bath, shower & laundry), plastic; Bathroom fixtures, plastic; Hot tubs, plastic or fiberglass; Builders' hardware; Locks or lock sets; Acoustical & insulation work
Pr: Keith J Allman
Pr: Melonie Colaianne
Pr: W Timothy Yahhi
CFO: Brian Smith
CFO: John G Sznewajs
VP: Amit Bhargava
VP: Kenneth G Cole
VP: Chuck Greenwood
VP: Christopher K Kastner
VP: John P Lindow
VP: John Lindow
VP: Sharon Rothwell
VP: Gregory Wittrock
Exec: Edward Armstrong
Exec: Jai Shah
Board of Directors: Mark R Alexander, Dennis W Archer, J Michael Losh, Richard A Manoogian, Christopher A O'herlihy, Donald R Parfet, Lisa A Payne, John C Plant, Mary Ann Van Lokeren

D-U-N-S 09-201-2210 IMP/EXP
■ **MASCO CORP OF INDIANA**
(*Suby of* MASCO CORP) ★
55 E 111th St, Indianapolis, IN 46280-1071
Tel (317) 848-1812 *Founded/Ownrshp* 1973
Sales 342.8MM^E *EMP* 1,204
SIC 3432 Plumbing fixture fittings & trim; Faucets & spigots, metal & plastic; Plastic plumbing fixture fittings, assembly
CEO: Keith J Allman
**Pr:* John G Sznewajs
**Treas:* Rick Burkman
Ofcr: Pam Cunningham
**VP:* Amit Bhargava
VP: Jay Burnett
**VP:* Kenneth G Cole
**VP:* Richard G Hosteller
VP: John Kabbes

**VP:* Kevin A Kennedy
VP: Craig Selover
**VP:* Dana Severs
VP: Renee Straber

D-U-N-S 60-509-1115
■ **MASCOT PETROLEUM CO INC**
(*Suby of* SUNOCO INC) ★
1801 Market St Fl 10, Philadelphia, PA 19103-1610
Tel (215) 977-3000 *Founded/Ownrshp* 1976
Sales 1.4MMM^E *EMP* 2,046
SIC 4932 5411 Gas & other services combined; Convenience stores, independent
Pr: Robert Owens
**Treas:* Paul A Mulholland
**VP:* Bruce G Fischer
**VP:* John A Ruddy Jr

D-U-N-S 13-110-7625
MASER CONSULTING PA
331 Newman Springs Rd # 203, Red Bank, NJ 07701-5691
Tel (732) 383-1950 *Founded/Ownrshp* 1984
Sales 89.4MM *EMP* 620
Accts Withumsmith & Brown Pc Red B
SIC 8711 8742 8713 Engineering services; Management consulting services; Surveying services
CEO: Richard M Maser
COO: Kevin Haney
CFO: Tom Hinczynski
**Treas:* Raymond Walker
Exec: Allison Colantuoni
Dept Mgr: Thomas Bailey
Dept Mgr: Daniel W Busch
Dept Mgr: Dave Roberts
Dept Mgr: Ralph Tango
Dept Mgr: Chris Theodos
Sls&Mrk Ex: Robert Dibartolo

D-U-N-S 13-051-3414
MASERGY COMMUNICATIONS INC
2740 Dallas Pkwy Ste 260, Plano, TX 75093-4834
Tel (214) 442-5700 *Founded/Ownrshp* 2011
Sales 154.6MM^E *EMP* 250
SIC 4813
CEO: Chris Macfarland
**CFO:* Rob Bodnar
CFO: Steve Vannattan
**Sr VP:* CAM Anderson
**Sr VP:* John Dumbleton
**Sr VP:* Tim Naramore
**Sr VP:* Greg Nelson
VP: BJ Antweil
VP: Michael Bacich
VP: John Badillo
**VP:* Jeanne Baniewicz
VP: Tony Hertado
VP: Dean Manzoori
VP: Mel Melara
VP: Scott Nichols
VP: Irene Peterson
VP: Terry Traina
VP: Ray Watson
VP: Marilyn Zemba

D-U-N-S 79-179-3318
MASHANTUCKET PEQUOT TRIBAL NATION
FOXWOODS RESORT CASINO
2 Matts Path, Mashantucket, CT 06338-3804
Tel (860) 396-6500 *Founded/Ownrshp* 1983
Sales NA *EMP* 6,000^E
SIC 9131 Indian reservation;
Pr: Felix D Rappaport
**COO:* Todd Greenberg
**COO:* Felix Rappaport
**Chf Mktg O:* Rebecca G Carr
Ofcr: Hector Gonzalez
Sr VP: Franco Pilli
VP: Jessica A Baran
VP: Amy Diette
VP: Nelson N Parker
VP: Scott Rider
Exec: Edward Harris
**Int Pr:* William Sherlock

D-U-N-S 07-036-6489
MASHBURN CONSTRUCTION CO INC
1820 Sumter St, Columbia, SC 29201-2502
Tel (803) 400-1000 *Founded/Ownrshp* 1976
Sales 91.7MM^E *EMP* 110
SIC 1542 Commercial & office building, new construction; Shopping center construction; Institutional building construction
CEO: Harry Mashburn
**Pr:* Paul Mashburn
**Pr:* Lynn M Shealy
CFO: Robert Beebe
**CFO:* Robert Parsons
**Ex VP:* H Lee Mashburn Jr
**VP:* Jane C Andrews
VP: Danny Schaaf
Dir Bus: Bryan Stange
Sfty Dirs: Daniel Skinner
Sfty Mgr: Janeann Amick

D-U-N-S 78-042-1038 IMP
▲ **MASIMO CORP**
52 Discovery, Irvine, CA 92618-3105
Tel (949) 297-7000 *Founded/Ownrshp* 1989
Sales 630.1MM *EMP* 1,300
Tkr Sym MASI *Exch* NGS
SIC 3845 Patient monitoring apparatus; Phonocardiographs
Ch Bd: Joe Kiani
COO: Anand Sampath
CFO: Mark P De Raad
Ex VP: Raul Bennis
Ex VP: Paul Jansen
Ex VP: Yongsam Lee
Ex VP: Tom McClenahan
Sr VP: David Van Ramshorst
VP: Jim Beyer
VP: Mark Brinton
VP: Gerry Hammarth
VP: Carmen How
VP: Steve Jensen
VP: Daniel Rice
VP: Angela Wrolstad
Board of Directors: Sanford Fitch, Thomas Harkin, Adam Mikkelson, Craig Reynolds

MASLAND CARPETS & RUGS
See TDG OPERATIONS LLC

D-U-N-S 00-616-1962 IMP
MASON COMPANIES INC (WI)
1251 1st Ave, Chippewa Falls, WI 54729-1691
Tel (715) 720-4200 *Founded/Ownrshp* 1904, 1976
Sales 105.5MM^E *EMP* 415
SIC 5961 5661 Catalog sales; Shoe stores
CEO: Dan Hunt
**VP:* Joe Fesenmaier
VP: Sue Kern
CTO: Adam Stavn
IT Man: Jade Spangenberg
IT Man: George Wood
Web Dev: Carolyn Kranz
Ql Cn Mgr: Debra Lange
Mktg Dir: Darin Schemenauer
Mktg Mgr: Aaron Zwiefelhofer
Genl Couns: Timothy Scobie

D-U-N-S 05-730-7225
MASON COUNTY PUBLIC UTILITY DISTRICT NO 3
P U D
2621 E Johns Prairie Rd, Shelton, WA 98584-8231
Tel (360) 426-8255 *Founded/Ownrshp* 1934
Sales 91.3MM^E *EMP* 119^E
Accts Brian Sonntag Cgfm Olympia
SIC 4911 Generation, electric power
Off Mgr: Nancy Bolender
Telecom Mg: Ladonna Schuh
MIS Mgr: John Bennet

D-U-N-S 08-037-0553
MASON STREET OPCO LLC
FAIRMONT SAN FRANCISCO
950 Mason St, San Francisco, CA 94108-6000
Tel (415) 772-5000 *Founded/Ownrshp* 2015
Sales 112.0MM *EMP* 850
SIC 7011 Hotels & motels
Pr: Seung Geon Kim

D-U-N-S 07-662-3136
MASON TENDER DISTRICT COUNCIL TRUST FUND
MTDC WELFARE FUND
520 8th Ave Rm 600, New York, NY 10018-4196
Tel (212) 452-9700 *Founded/Ownrshp* 1947
Sales NA *EMP* 26
Accts Schultheis & Panettieri Llp H
SIC 6371 Union trust funds

D-U-N-S 07-523-7552
MASON TENDERS DISTRICT COUNCIL GREATER NEW YORK
520 8th Ave Rm 650, New York, NY 10018-6539
Tel (212) 452-9400 *Founded/Ownrshp* 1923
Sales 165.7MM *EMP* 3
Accts Schultheis & Panettieri Llp
SIC 8631 Labor unions & similar labor organizations
Pr: Pat Piscitelli
Counsel: Tamir Rosenblum

D-U-N-S 78-077-6188
MASON WELLS BUYOUT FUND II LIMITED PARTNERSHIP
411 E Wisconsin Ave, Milwaukee, WI 53202-4461
Tel (414) 727-6400 *Founded/Ownrshp* 1992
Sales 139.9MM^E *EMP* 500
SIC 3594 3492 3593 6211 Fluid power pumps; Control valves, fluid power: hydraulic & pneumatic; Fluid power cylinders, hydraulic or pneumatic; Investment firm, general brokerage
Pr: John Byrnes
CFO: Jim Domach
VP: Christopher Pummill
Mng Dir: Greg Myers

D-U-N-S 80-273-0218
MASON WELLS INC
411 E Wisconsin Ave # 1280, Milwaukee, WI 53202-4435
Tel (414) 727-6400 *Founded/Ownrshp* 1982
Sales 555.9MM *EMP* 990
SIC 6799 Investors
Pr: John T Byrnes
**CFO:* Jim Domach
**VP:* William Krugler
**VP:* Christopher Pummill
**VP:* Thomas Smith

MASONIC HOMES PA
See MASONIC VILLAGES OF GRAND LODGE OF PENNSYLVANIA

D-U-N-S 80-433-3771
MASONIC VILLAGES OF GRAND LODGE OF PENNSYLVANIA
MASONIC HOMES PA
1 Masonic Dr, Elizabethtown, PA 17022-2199
Tel (717) 367-1121 *Founded/Ownrshp* 1910
Sales 161.5MM *EMP* 2,000
SIC 8361 Home for the aged; Children's home
CEO: Joseph E Murphy
Treas: Ian Korman
VP: Douglas Policastro
Exec: Claudia J Stephens
Dir Lab: Stacy Piper
Ex Dir: Cris Dinsmore
Sls&Mrk Ex: Marybeth Meehan
Mktg Dir: Don Romberger

D-U-N-S 04-404-5826
MASONICARE CORP
22 Masonic Ave, Wallingford, CT 06492-3048
Tel (203) 679-5900 *Founded/Ownrshp* 1995
Sales 197.3MM^E *EMP* 2,500
SIC 8069 8082 8322 Geriatric hospital; Home health care services; Adult day care center
CEO: Darin M Spero
Pr: Tracey Lemay
**CEO:* Steven McPherson
VP: James Albert
Doctor: Gail Labadia

D-U-N-S 00-507-0578 IMP
■ **MASONITE CORP**
(*Suby of* MASONITE INTERNATIONAL CORP) ★
1 Tampa City Center 20, Tampa, FL 33602
Tel (813) 877-2726 *Founded/Ownrshp* 1925, 2001
Sales 1.6MMM^E *EMP* 4,928
SIC 2431 3469 Doors, wood; Doors & door parts & trim, wood; Stamping metal for the trade
Pr: Frederick J Lynch
**Treas:* Joanne Freiberger
Bd of Dir: Jonathan F Foster
Sr VP: Gail Auerbach
Sr VP: Robert Lewis
Sr VP: Chris Virostek
VP: John Kufner
VP: Dale Mayfield
VP: James Rabe
Creative D: Lorena Morales
Genl Mgr: Michael Hall

D-U-N-S 85-849-9569 IMP/EXP
MASONITE HOLDINGS INC
201 N Franklin St Ste 300, Tampa, FL 33602-5105
Tel (813) 877-2726 *Founded/Ownrshp* 1991
Sales 185.3MM^E *EMP* 11
SIC 2431 3442 Doors & door parts & trim, wood; Metal doors
Pr: Fred Lynch
Treas: Joanne Freiberger
Manager: Alan McDaniel

D-U-N-S 05-278-1353 IMP/EXP
▲ **MASONITE INTERNATIONAL CORP**
201 N Franklin St, Tampa, FL 33602-5182
Tel (813) 877-2726 *Founded/Ownrshp* 1925
Sales 1.8MMM *EMP* 10,200
Tkr Sym DOOR *Exch* NYS
SIC 2431 3442 Doors, wood; Metal doors
Pr: Frederick J Lynch
COO: Lawrence P Repar
CFO: Russell T Tiejema
Sr VP: Gail N Auerbach
Sr VP: Clare Doyle
Sr VP: Robert E Lewis
Exec: Rick Hunt
Board of Directors: Jody L Bilney, Robert J Byrne, Peter R Dachowski, Jonathan F Foster, George A Lorch, Rick J Mills, Francis M Scricco, John C Wills

D-U-N-S 00-799-7463 IMP
MASS ELECTRIC CONSTRUCTION CO
(*Suby of* KIEWIT INFRASTRUCTURE CO) ★
400 Totten Pond Rd # 400, Waltham, MA 02451-2051
Tel (781) 290-1000 *Founded/Ownrshp* 2005
Sales 263.7MM^E *EMP* 1,137^E
Accts Kpmg Llp Omaha Ne
SIC 1731 1623 General electrical contractor; Cable laying construction; Cable television line construction; Telephone & communication line construction; Transmitting tower (telecommunication) construction
Treas: Stephen S Thomas
Ex VP: Joseph A Forsythe
Ex VP: H Bryan Greene
Ex VP: Neal Parece
Ex VP: Alfredo E Sori
Ex VP: Frederick A Zambon
Sr VP: Tony Forsythe
Sr VP: Frederick A Hammel Jr
Sr VP: Shawn G Kelly
Sr VP: Jack E Oram Jr
Sr VP: Philip F Shepley
Sr VP: John Testa
VP: Howard L Barton Jr
VP: Bill Breen
VP: Rick Caramante
VP: Scott A Churill
VP: Greg Gzehoviak
VP: Michael J Piechoski
VP: Mark Steffen
VP: Thomas R Waltner
VP Bus Dev: Rick Duncan

D-U-N-S 06-641-0564 IMP
MASS MARKETING INC
SUPER S TRUE VALUE
401 Isom Rd Ste 210, San Antonio, TX 78216-5134
Tel (210) 314-7005 *Founded/Ownrshp* 1973
Sales 111.3MM^E *EMP* 1,400
SIC 5411

MASSACHSTTS SPREME JDICIAL CRT
See MASSACHUSETTS SUPREME JUDICIAL COURT

MASSACHUSETS EYE EAR INFERMERY
See LEILA A MANKARIOUS

D-U-N-S 10-224-7488
MASSACHUSETTS BAY COMMUTER RAILROAD CO LLC
MBCR
89 South St, Boston, MA 02111-2651
Tel (617) 222-8080 *Founded/Ownrshp* 2002
Sales 91.1MM^E *EMP* 1,700
SIC 4011 4111 Railroads, line-haul operating; Commuter bus operation; Commuter rail passenger operation
CFO: Jim Citro
Sr Cor Off: David Schevis
Genl Mgr: James F O Leary
Genl Mgr: Kevin Lydon

D-U-N-S 00-176-6260
MASSACHUSETTS BAY TRANSPORTATION AUTHORITY
(*Suby of* MASSACHUSETTS DEPARTMENT OF TRANSPORTATION) ★
Mbta 10 Park Plz Ste 3910, Boston, MA 02116
Tel (617) 222-3106 *Founded/Ownrshp* 1918, 2004
Sales NA *EMP* 6,100
Accts Kpmg Llp Boston Ma
SIC 9621 Transit system or authority: government, non-operating;
Ch: John R Jenkins
**Treas:* Wesley G Wallace Jr
Ofcr: Dorston R Bartlett
Ofcr: Raphael Cintron
Ofcr: Richard Donohue
Ofcr: Christine Lentini
Exec: Nancy Wallace
**Ex Dir:* Alan G Macdonald
**Genl Mgr:* Daniel A Grabauskas
Dir IT: Mark Saunders
Counsel: Julie Ciollo

D-U-N-S 05-524-9515
MASSACHUSETTS BOARD OF HIGHER EDUCATION SYSTEM
(*Suby of* EXECUTIVE OFFICE OF COMMONWEALTH OF MASSACHUSETTS) ★
1 Ashburton Pl Rm 1401, Boston, MA 02108-1518
Tel (617) 727-7785 *Founded/Ownrshp* 1981
Sales NA *EMP* 6,400
SIC 9411
IT Man: Clantha McCurdy

MASSACHUSETTS COLLEGE OF PHARM
See MCPHS UNIVERSITY

D-U-N-S 83-768-0198
MASSACHUSETTS COMMUNITY COLLEGES
(*Suby of* MASSACHUSETTS BOARD OF HIGHER EDUCATION SYSTEM) ★
15 Court Sq Ste 1100, Boston, MA 02108-2529
Tel (617) 542-2911 *Founded/Ownrshp* 1995
Sales 53.3MM^E *EMP* 6,000
SIC 8222 9199 Community college;
VP: Lorita Williams
Ex Dir: Betty Learned

D-U-N-S 87-850-9116
MASSACHUSETTS DEPARTMENT OF CHILDREN AND FAMILIES
(*Suby of* EOHHS) ★
600 Washington St, Boston, MA 02111-1704
Tel (617) 748-2000 *Founded/Ownrshp* 1980
Sales NA *EMP* 2,867
SIC 9111 Executive offices

D-U-N-S 09-096-2085
MASSACHUSETTS DEPARTMENT OF ENVIRONMENTAL PROTECTION
(*Suby of* OFFICE COASTAL ZONE MANAGEMENT) ★
1 Winter St, Boston, MA 02108-4747
Tel (617) 292-5500 *Founded/Ownrshp* 1980
Sales NA *EMP* 1,200
SIC 9511 Environmental agencies;
Off Mgr: Barbara Wyche
Netwrk Mgr: Rick Hawkins

D-U-N-S 82-484-8642
MASSACHUSETTS DEPARTMENT OF PUBLIC SAFETY
(*Suby of* EXECUTIVE OFFICE OF COMMONWEALTH OF MASSACHUSETTS) ★
1 Ashburton Pl Rm 2133, Boston, MA 02108-1518
Tel (617) 727-7775 *Founded/Ownrshp* 1969
Sales NA *EMP* 22,200
SIC 9221 9229 9223 State police; ; Public order & safety statistics centers; ; Correctional institutions;
Mktg Mgr: Susan Burgess-Chin

D-U-N-S 00-472-6456
MASSACHUSETTS DEPARTMENT OF REVENUE
(*Suby of* ADMINISTRATION AND FINANCE MASSACHUSETTS EXECUTIVE OFFICE FOR) ★
100 Cambridge St, Boston, MA 02114-2509
Tel (617) 626-2201 *Founded/Ownrshp* 1966
Sales NA *EMP* 2,200
SIC 9311 Finance, taxation & monetary policy;
Ofcr: Daniel Oconnell
Ofcr: Karen Rix
Creative D: Peter Olejnik

D-U-N-S 87-870-0798
MASSACHUSETTS DEPARTMENT OF STATE POLICE
(*Suby of* MASSACHUSETTS DEPARTMENT OF PUBLIC SAFETY) ★
470 Worcester Rd, Framingham, MA 01702-5309
Tel (508) 820-2350 *Founded/Ownrshp* 1865
Sales NA *EMP* 2,400^E
SIC 9221 State police;
Genl Mgr: Deborah Broderick

D-U-N-S 82-484-8659
MASSACHUSETTS DEPARTMENT OF TRANSPORTATION
(*Suby of* EXECUTIVE OFFICE OF COMMONWEALTH OF MASSACHUSETTS) ★
10 Park Plz Ste 4160, Boston, MA 02116-3979
Tel (857) 368-4636 *Founded/Ownrshp* 1969
Sales NA *EMP* 6,100^E
SIC 9621 Regulation, administration of transportation;
CEO: Stephanie Pollack
Genl Mgr: Paul Garrity
IT Man: Carol Sugerman

D-U-N-S 87-836-9362
MASSACHUSETTS DEPT OF MENTAL HEALTH
(*Suby of* EOHHS) ★
25 Staniford St, Boston, MA 02114-2503
Tel (617) 626-8000 *Founded/Ownrshp* 1900
Sales NA *EMP* 4,000
SIC 9431

D-U-N-S 87-865-1041
MASSACHUSETTS DEPT OF MENTAL RETARDATION
DMR METRO REGION
(*Suby of* EOHHS) ★
500 Harrison Ave Ste 1r, Boston, MA 02118-2439
Tel (617) 727-5608 *Founded/Ownrshp* 1987
Sales NA *EMP* 7,555
SIC 9431 Mental health agency administration, government;
**CFO:* Jeanette Maillet
CIO: Jack Coyne
IT Man: Henry Taylor

D-U-N-S 87-829-8900
MASSACHUSETTS DEPT OF PUBLIC HEALTH
(*Suby of* EOHHS) ★
250 Washington St, Boston, MA 02108-4603
Tel (617) 624-6000 *Founded/Ownrshp* 1975
Sales NA *EMP* 3,000
SIC 9431 Public health agency administration, government;
Ofcr: John Bernardo
Ofcr: Robert Locke
Assoc Dir: Beth English
Prgrm Mgr: Scott Calisti
Prgrm Mgr: Marisa Chiang
Genl Mgr: Sarah Cheung
Genl Mgr: Lourdes Ordinola
Plng Mgr: Paul Holloway
Genl Couns: Joel Buenaventura
Genl Couns: Alexandra Rubin
Pgrm Dir: Jennifer Bates

D-U-N-S 87-850-8167
MASSACHUSETTS DEPT OF TRANSITIONAL ASSISTANCE
(*Suby of* EOHHS) ★
600 Washington St Fl 5, Boston, MA 02111-1704
Tel (617) 348-8500 *Founded/Ownrshp* 1960
Sales NA *EMP* 3,250
SIC 9441 Administration of social & manpower programs;
Genl Mgr: Michael Cole
Genl Mgr: Mary Sheehan

D-U-N-S 94-757-9306
MASSACHUSETTS DEPT OF WORKFORCE DEVELOPMENT
(*Suby of* EXECUTIVE OFFICE OF COMMONWEALTH OF MASSACHUSETTS) ★
1 Ashburton Pl Rm 2112, Boston, MA 02108-1518
Tel (617) 626-7122 *Founded/Ownrshp* 1997
Sales NA *EMP* 2,239^E
SIC 9651 Labor regulatory agency
Prin: Jane C Edmonds

D-U-N-S 87-858-7658
MASSACHUSETTS EDUCATIONAL FINANCING AUTHORITY
M E F A
160 Federal St Fl 4, Boston, MA 02110-1721
Tel (617) 224-4800 *Founded/Ownrshp* 1981
Sales NA *EMP* 53
Accts Price Waterhouse Coopers
SIC 6111 Student Loan Marketing Association
Ex Dir: Thomas M Graf
Mng Pt: Neil Markson
**Ch Bd:* Joe Hunt
VP: Micheal Hogan
Exec: Greg Hargrave
**Ex Dir:* Thomas Graf

D-U-N-S 00-695-2626 IMP
MASSACHUSETTS ELECTRIC CO
NATIONAL GRID
(*Suby of* NATIONAL GRID USA) ★
40 Sylvan Rd, Waltham, MA 02451-1120
Tel (781) 907-1000 *Founded/Ownrshp* 1887
Sales 1.1MMM^E *EMP* 1,396
SIC 4911 Distribution, electric power; Generation, electric power; Transmission, electric power
Pr: Marcy L Reed
**Treas:* Malcolm Charles Cooper
**Ex VP:* Ellen Smith
**Sr VP:* Pat Hogan
**Sr VP:* Colin Owyang
**VP:* Ross Turrini
**VP:* Martin Wheatcroft
**VP:* Edward White
Board of Directors: Colin Owyang, Linda Claire Ryan, Ellen Smith

D-U-N-S 82-484-8451
MASSACHUSETTS EXECUTIVE OFFICE OF ENERGY & ENVIRONMENTAL AFFAIRS
OFFICE COASTAL ZONE MANAGEMENT
(*Suby of* EXECUTIVE OFFICE OF COMMONWEALTH OF MASSACHUSETTS) ★
100 Cambridge St Ste 900, Boston, MA 02114-2534
Tel (617) 626-1000 *Founded/Ownrshp* 1974
Sales NA *EMP* 2,657
SIC 9511 9512 9641 Air, water & solid waste management; ; Land, mineral & wildlife conservation; ; Regulation of agricultural marketing;

D-U-N-S 82-484-8477
MASSACHUSETTS EXECUTIVE OFFICE OF HEALTH AND HUMAN SERVICES
EOHHS
(*Suby of* EXECUTIVE OFFICE OF COMMONWEALTH OF MASSACHUSETTS) ★
1 Ashburton Pl Rm 1111, Boston, MA 02108-1518
Tel (617) 573-1600 *Founded/Ownrshp* 1975
Sales NA *EMP* 23,000
SIC 9431 9441 Administration of public health programs; ; Administration of social & manpower programs
**CFO:* Matthew Klitus

D-U-N-S 60-342-0563
MASSACHUSETTS EYE AND EAR ASSOCIATES INC
(*Suby of* MASSACHUSETTS EYE AND EAR INFIRMARY & PHYSICIAN STAFF INC) ★
243 Charles St, Boston, MA 02114-3002
Tel (617) 523-7900 *Founded/Ownrshp* 1986
Sales 106.0MM *EMP* 8^E
SIC 8011 Eyes, ears, nose & throat specialist: physician/surgeon
Pr: F Cortis Smith
Exec: Ramon Franco
Nurse Mgr: Maureen Martinez
Doctor: Robert Trotter

D-U-N-S 04-057-0892
MASSACHUSETTS EYE AND EAR INFIRMARY
(*Suby of* MASSACHUSETTS EYE AND EAR INFIRMARY & PHYSICIAN STAFF INC) ★
243 Charles St, Boston, MA 02114-3002
Tel (617) 573-3499 *Founded/Ownrshp* 1827
Sales 163.5MM *EMP* 1,550
SIC 8069 Eye, ear, nose & throat hospital
CEO: John Fernandez
**Pr:* Ephraim Friedman
Pr: Jennifer Street
**COO:* Jeff Pike M P H
**CFO:* Ken Holmes
CFO: Kenneth Holmes
**CFO:* Carrol Ann Williams
**Treas:* J Frank Gerrity
**VP:* Javier Balloffet
VP: Alan Long
**VP:* Debra Rogers
**VP:* Rachel Wasserstrom
Assoc Dir: Eric Pierce

D-U-N-S 07-382-5945
MASSACHUSETTS EYE AND EAR INFIRMARY & PHYSICIAN STAFF INC
243 Charles St, Boston, MA 02114-3002
Tel (617) 573-3499 *Founded/Ownrshp* 1988
Sales 221.6MM *EMP* 1,550
SIC 8069 8011 Eye, ear, nose & throat hospital; Plastic surgeon
Pr: John Fernandez
**CFO:* Peter Chinetti
**Treas:* William Darling
Prin: Anthony P Adamis
Prin: Saumil N Merchant
Doctor: Ramon A Franco Jr
Doctor: Janay L Wiggs MD
Board of Directors: Sheldon Buckler Phd

D-U-N-S 04-943-5415
MASSACHUSETTS FINANCIAL SERVICES CO
M F S
(*Suby of* SUN LIFE ASSURANCE COMPANY OF CANADA)
111 Huntington Ave, Boston, MA 02199-7610
Tel (617) 954-5000 *Founded/Ownrshp* 1969
Sales 797.4MM[E] *EMP* 1,700
SIC 6282 6211 6289 Investment advisory service; Mutual funds, selling by independent salesperson; Stock transfer agents
CEO: Robert J Manning
Pr: Don Carten
Pr: Fenn Duncan
Pr: Bob Landrigan
Pr: Mike W Roberge
Pr: Olympia Wheeler
Pr: Kevin Wiehn
COO: Robin Stelmach
CFO: Amrit Kawal
CFO: Amrit Konwal
Treas: W London
Chf Cred: Mary Scotten
Ex VP: Mark Leary
Sr VP: James Calmas
VP: Sal Barbagallo
VP: Paula Bartgis
VP: Aprile Burnes
VP: Thomas Connors
VP: Ann Costello
VP: Brian Curran
VP: Jennifer Danzi

D-U-N-S 07-313-0411 IMP
MASSACHUSETTS GENERAL HOSPITAL
GENERAL HOSPITAL, THE
(*Suby of* PARTNERS HEALTHCARE SYSTEM INC) ★
55 Fruit St, Boston, MA 02114-2696
Tel (617) 724-6454 *Founded/Ownrshp* 1811
Sales 2.4MMM *EMP* 10,156
SIC 8062 8011 General medical & surgical hospitals; Hospital, affiliated with AMA residency; Hospital, professional nursing school; Offices & clinics of medical doctors
CEO: David Torchiana
Chf Path: Robert B Colvin
**Pr:* Peter L Slavin
**CFO:* Laura Wysk
**Ch:* Cathy E Minehan
Treas: Michael Manning
**Treas:* Peter K Markell
Trst: Charles C Ames
Trst: John W Henry
Trst: Edward P Lawrence
Trst: W W McDougal Jr
Trst: Phillip A Sharp
Ofcr: Emily Parker
Sr VP: Jeff Davis
VP: Ronald Newbower
VP: Peggy Slasman
VP: James E Thompson
Exec: Samuel Thier
Assoc Dir: Carolyn Paul
Dir Rx: Meghan Kotarski

D-U-N-S 13-924-1389
MASSACHUSETTS GENERAL PHYSICIANS ORGANIZATION INC
(*Suby of* GENERAL HOSPITAL) ★
55 Fruit St 208, Boston, MA 02114-2621
Tel (617) 724-0578 *Founded/Ownrshp* 1983
Sales 44.4MM[E] *EMP* 1,000[E]
SIC 8011 Offices & clinics of medical doctors
Pr: Daniel A Ginsburg
**Pr:* Peter Slavin
Assoc Dir: Eric M Isselbacher
Adm Dir: Carol Milbury
Adm Dir: Dianne Moschella
Genl Mgr: Patricia McNamara
Doctor: Cheryl J Bunker
Snr Mgr: Ann Snow

D-U-N-S 03-081-1111
MASSACHUSETTS HIGHER EDUCATION ASSISTANCE CORP
AMERICAN STUDENT ASSISTANCE
100 Cambridge St Ste 1600, Boston, MA 02114-2518
Tel (617) 728-4507 *Founded/Ownrshp* 1956
Sales NA *EMP* 580
Accts Cbiz Tofias Boston Ma
SIC 6111 Student Loan Marketing Association
Pr: Paul C Combe
**Ch Bd:* Richard A Wiley
Pr: John Zurick
**CFO:* Michael F Finn
CFO: Barbara Matez
**V Ch Bd:* Patricia A McWade
**VP:* Susan Nathan
**VP:* Arnold Sammis
**VP:* Shelley Saunders
**VP:* Alexander Shapiro
VP: Mae St Julien
Exec: Trixi Pentick
Exec: Donna Shelby
Assoc Dir: Ann Brieck

D-U-N-S 00-142-5594
MASSACHUSETTS INSTITUTE OF TECHNOLOGY
MIT
77 Massachusetts Ave, Cambridge, MA 02139-4307
Tel (617) 253-1000 *Founded/Ownrshp* 1861
Sales 2.0MMM[E] *EMP* 12,000
SIC 8221 University
Pr: L Rafael Reif
**Ch:* Dana Mead
**Treas:* Israel Ruiz
Ofcr: Jim Doughty
Ex VP: Donald Rosenfield
Ex VP: Lianne Shields
VP: Joseph Beauregard
VP: Kathleen Hannan
VP: Charles G Jennings
**VP:* Kirk Kolendrander
VP: Julie Lucas
VP: John McDonald
VP: R G Morgan
VP: Nate Nickerson
VP: Meg Regan
VP: Kathryn Willmore
VP: David Woodruff
Exec: Edward Fields
Dir Pat Ca: Christine Ruzycki
Assoc Dir: Michael Myers
Assoc Dir: Rajeev J Ram

D-U-N-S 11-293-8055
MASSACHUSETTS LABORERS HEALTH AND WELFARE FUND
14 New England Exec Park, Burlington, MA 01803-5219
Tel (781) 238-0700 *Founded/Ownrshp* 1954
Sales NA *EMP* 30
SIC 6371 Union welfare, benefit & health funds
IT Man: James Morgan

D-U-N-S 07-535-7079
MASSACHUSETTS MEDICAL SOCIETY INC
NEW ENGLAND JOURNAL MEDICINE
860 Winter St, Waltham, MA 02451-1411
Tel (781) 893-4610 *Founded/Ownrshp* 1781
Sales 122.6MM *EMP* 700
Accts Cbiz Tofias Boston Ma
SIC 2721 8621 Trade journals: publishing & printing; Medical field-related associations
Pr: Dale Magee
VP: Charles Alagero
**VP:* Corinne Broderick
VP: Chris Lynch
Comm Dir: Frank Fortin
Ex Dir: Michael Farrell
Ex Dir: Bill Paige
DP Exec: Brian Stoughton
Dir IT: Leon Barzin
Dir IT: Julie Mock
Info Man: Jed Clifton

D-U-N-S 00-695-6049 IMP/EXP
MASSACHUSETTS MUTUAL LIFE INSURANCE CO
MASSMUTUAL
1295 State St, Springfield, MA 01111-0001
Tel (413) 788-8411 *Founded/Ownrshp* 1851
Sales NA *EMP* 27,091
SIC 6321 6324 6411 6282 Disability health insurance; Health insurance carriers; Group hospitalization plans; Pension & retirement plan consultants; Investment advice
Ch Bd: Roger W Crandall
Ch Bd: James Birle
V Ch: William F Glavin Jr
Pr: Judy Breault
Pr: Ken Brill
Pr: Shannon Caminiti
Pr: Don Carten
Pr: John Dunlop
Pr: Trista Fay
Pr: Gail Garvey
Pr: Geoff Gerow
Pr: Jill Hambley
Pr: Bernadette Harrigan
Pr: Chuck Higgins
Pr: Sean Jordan
Pr: Regan Klein
Pr: Craig Kronlund
Pr: Ellen M Milne
Pr: Trish Mueller
Pr: Ted Newton
Pr: Alethea Odonnell
Board of Directors: Karen Bechtel

D-U-N-S 87-824-9424
MASSACHUSETTS NATIONAL GUARD
(*Suby of* MASSACHUSETTS DEPARTMENT OF PUBLIC SAFETY) ★
2 Randolph Rd, Hanscom Afb, MA 01731-3001
Tel (339) 202-3832 *Founded/Ownrshp* 1996
Sales NA *EMP* 6,000
SIC 9711 National Guard;

D-U-N-S 00-176-6328 IMP
MASSACHUSETTS PORT AUTHORITY
MASSPORT
1 Harborside Dr Ste 200s, Boston, MA 02128-2905
Tel (617) 561-1600 *Founded/Ownrshp* 1956
Sales 118.6MM[E] *EMP* 1,102
Accts Pricewaterhousecoopers Llp Bo
SIC 4581 4491 6799 6512 4785 Airport terminal services; Waterfront terminal operation; Piers, incl. buildings & facilities: operation & maintenance; Investors; Commercial & industrial building operation; Toll bridge operation
CEO: Thomas P Glynn
**Ch Bd:* Mark Robinson
**CFO:* John Pranckevicius
Ofcr: Thomas Bessette
VP: Christine Donohoe
VP: George K Hertz
Prgrm Mgr: Richard Bessom
Snr Ntwrk: Joe Alves
MIS Dir: Lou Hinkley
IT Man: Stephanie Furfaro
Opers Supe: Nick Kline

D-U-N-S 36-070-5065
MASSACHUSETTS SUPREME JUDICIAL COURT
MASSACHSTTS SPREME JDICIAL CRT
(*Suby of* COMMONWEALTH OF MASSACHUSETTS) ★
1 Pemberton Sq Ste 2500, Boston, MA 02108-1717
Tel (617) 557-1020 *Founded/Ownrshp* 1628
Sales NA *EMP* 6,700
SIC 9211 State courts;

D-U-N-S 00-176-6278
MASSACHUSETTS TURNPIKE AUTHORITY
(*Suby of* MASSACHUSETTS DEPARTMENT OF TRANSPORTATION) ★
10 Park Plz Ste 5170, Boston, MA 02116-3980
Tel (617) 248-2800 *Founded/Ownrshp* 1952
Sales 45.7MM[E] *EMP* 1,200
SIC 4785 9199 Toll road operation; Tunnel operation, vehicular;
Ch Bd: John Cogliano
V Ch: Jordan Levy
CFO: Ann Journeay
CFO: Joe McCann
**CFO:* Joseph McCann
Bd of Dir: Matthew Amorello
Ex Dir: Allan Lebobidge
CIO: William Catina
DP Dir: Silvio Petratlia
Dir IT: Diane Nawrocki
Netwrk Eng: Tri Nguyen

D-U-N-S 07-916-1389
MASSACHUSETTS WATER RESOURCES AUTHORITY
MWRA
Charl Navy Yard 100 First, Boston, MA 02129
Tel (617) 788-4917 *Founded/Ownrshp* 1985
Sales 600.0MM *EMP* 1,200
SIC 1623 Water, sewer & utility lines
Ex Dir: Frederick Leskey

D-U-N-S 15-725-5522
MASSACHUSETTS WATER RESOURCES AUTHORITY
MWRA
(*Suby of* EXECUTIVE OFFICE OF COMMONWEALTH OF MASSACHUSETTS) ★
100 1st Ave, Boston, MA 02129-2043
Tel (617) 242-6000 *Founded/Ownrshp* 1972
Sales NA *EMP* 1,200
Accts Kpmg Llp Boston Ma
SIC 9511 Waste management program administration, government; Water control & quality agency, government
Ch: Richard K Sullivan Jr
**COO:* Michael Hornbrook
**CFO:* Rachel Madden
**Ex Dir:* Fred Laskey
Ex Dir: Frederick A Lskey
Genl Mgr: Evelyn Deleon
Pr Mgr: Leonard Cawley

MASSAPEQUA HIGH SCHOOL
See MASSAPEQUA UNION FREE SCHOOL DISTRICT

D-U-N-S 04-919-5720
MASSAPEQUA UNION FREE SCHOOL DISTRICT
MASSAPEQUA HIGH SCHOOL
4925 Merrick Rd, Massapequa, NY 11758-6201
Tel (516) 308-5900 *Founded/Ownrshp* 1800
Sales 51.8MM[E] *EMP* 1,000
Accts Rs Abrams & Co Llp Ronkonk
SIC 8211 Public senior high school
IT Man: Adrienne Gomez

D-U-N-S 94-867-7075
MASSASOIT COMMUNITY COLLEGE
1 Massasoit Blvd, Brockton, MA 02302-3996
Tel (508) 588-9100 *Founded/Ownrshp* 1965
Sales 35.9MM[E] *EMP* 1,203
Accts O Connor & Drew Pc Cpas Brai
SIC 8222 Community college
Pr: Charles Wall
**CFO:* William A Mitchell
CFO: Phillip Pergola
Sr VP: Ralph Kidder
**VP:* Barbara Finklestein
**VP:* David Tracey
Ex Dir: Linda Bean
Dir IT: John W Barrett
IT Man: Ray Inferrera

MASSEY COAL EXPORT COMPANY
See APPALACHIA HOLDING CO

D-U-N-S 03-262-7127 IMP
MASSEY SERVICES INC
GREENUP LAWN CARE
315 Groveland St, Orlando, FL 32804-4052
Tel (407) 645-2500 *Founded/Ownrshp* 1985
Sales 190.9MM *EMP* 1,318
SIC 7342 Exterminating & fumigating; Pest control in structures; Termite control
Ch Bd: Harvey L Massey
**Pr:* Anthony L Massey
**CFO:* Jean-Marie Grono
**Sr VP:* Andrea Massey-Farrell
**VP:* Jeff Buhler
**VP:* Gwyn Elias
**VP:* Eric Hernandez
**VP:* Adam Scheinberg
Board of Directors: Andrea Massey-Farrell, Steve Hatcher, Frank Sanderlin

D-U-N-S 08-014-1872
■ **MASSILLON HEALTH SYSTEM LLC**
(*Suby of* QUORUM HEALTH CORP) ★
400 Austin Ave Nw, Massillon, OH 44646-3554
Tel (330) 837-7200 *Founded/Ownrshp* 2016
Sales 128.9M[E] *EMP* 1,451
SIC 8062 General medical & surgical hospitals
Doctor: Bill Chandler
Doctor: Ranga Thalluri

D-U-N-S 62-012-5638 IMP/EXP
MASSIMO ZANETTI BEVERAGE USA INC
KAUAI COFFEE CO
(*Suby of* MASSIMO ZANETTI BEVERAGE GROUP SPA)
1370 Progress Rd, Suffolk, VA 23434-2148
Tel (757) 215-7300 *Founded/Ownrshp* 2005
Sales 486.0MM[E] *EMP* 375
SIC 0179 Coffee farm
CEO: John Boyle
**CEO:* Massimo Zanetti
**COO:* Larry Quier
**VP:* Chuck Gasstrom
**VP:* Ali Itani
Area Mgr: Marcie Waranch
Snr Ntwrk: Jeffrey Carden
Sls Dir: Mike Kusner

D-U-N-S 00-696-5982 IMP
MASSMAN CONSTRUCTION CO
4400 W 109th St Ste 300, Leawood, KS 66211-1319
Tel (913) 291-2600 *Founded/Ownrshp* 1908
Sales 134.3MM[E] *EMP* 250
SIC 1629 1622 Dam construction; Bridge construction
Pr: H J Massman IV
VP: Patrick Byrne
**VP:* Joseph T Kopp
**VP:* William G Praderio
**VP:* Paul D Scharmer
**VP:* Mark H Schnoebelen
**Prin:* Henry Massman IV
CIO: Irvin McCoy
Sfty Dirs: Danny R Moton
Opers Mgr: Steve Hayes

MASSMUTUAL
See MASSACHUSETTS MUTUAL LIFE INSURANCE CO

D-U-N-S 13-462-6667
MASSMUTUAL INTERNATIONAL LLC
(*Suby of* MASSMUTUAL) ★
1295 State St, Springfield, MA 01111-0001
Tel (413) 788-8411 *Founded/Ownrshp* 1983
Sales NA *EMP* 2,600[E]
SIC 6311 Life insurance carriers
**Pr:* Rodney J Dillman
VP: Michael Doshier

D-U-N-S 13-765-9280
MASSMUTUAL MORTGAGE FINANCE LLC
(*Suby of* MASSMUTUAL) ★
1295 State St, Springfield, MA 01111-0001
Tel (413) 788-8411 *Founded/Ownrshp* 1984
Sales 874.9MM[E] *EMP* 2,387
SIC 6531 Real estate managers
Pr: Gary E Wendlandt
**Treas:* Anne Isley

MASSPORT
See MASSACHUSETTS PORT AUTHORITY

D-U-N-S 05-345-8006 IMP/EXP
■ **MAST INDUSTRIES INC**
L BRANDS
(*Suby of* INTIMATE BRANDS HOLDING LLC) ★
2 Limited Pkwy, Columbus, OH 43230-1445
Tel (614) 415-7000 *Founded/Ownrshp* 2015
Sales 436.9MM[E] *EMP* 200
SIC 5137 5136 Women's & children's clothing; Men's & boys' clothing
CEO: Leslie H Wexner
**Pr:* James M Schwartz
**VP:* Stuart Burgdoerfer
VP: Danny McAtamney

D-U-N-S 02-845-8300 IMP
■ **MAST LOGISTICS SERVICES INC**
(*Suby of* L BRANDS) ★
2 Limited Pkwy, Columbus, OH 43230-1445
Tel (614) 415-7500 *Founded/Ownrshp* 1986
Sales 132.2MM[E] *EMP* 150
SIC 5113 Shipping supplies
Pr: Bruce Mosier
VP: Bernie Brown
Off Mgr: Debra Ausiello
Trfc Dir: Wanda Keil

D-U-N-S 00-692-4385 IMP
▲ **MASTEC INC**
800 S Douglas Rd Ste 1200, Coral Gables, FL 33134-3165
Tel (305) 599-1800 *Founded/Ownrshp* 1929
Sales 4.2MMM *EMP* 15,962
Tkr Sym MTZ *Exch* NYS
SIC 1623 8741 Water, sewer & utility lines; Cable television line construction; Transmitting tower (telecommunication) construction; Manhole construction; Construction management
CEO: Jose R Mas
Ch Bd: Jorge Mas
COO: Robert Apple
CFO: George Pita
Ex VP: Alberto De Cardenas
VP: Tony Brisco
VP: Robert Jackson
VP: John Miller
VP: Paul Miller
VP Bus Dev: Kevin Donnelly
Mtls Mgr: Yacer Morales
Board of Directors: C Robert Campbell, Ernst N Csiszar, Robert J Dwyer, Frank E Jaumot, Julia L

Johnson, Javier Palomarez, Jose S Sorzano, John Van Heuvelen

D-U-N-S 00-952-5802
■ MASTEC NETWORK SOLUTIONS LLC
(*Suby of* MASTEC INC) ★
806 S Douglas Rd Fl 11, Coral Gables, FL 33134-3157
Tel (866) 545-1782 *Founded/Ownrshp* 2008
Sales 242.6MM^E *EMP* 595^E
SIC 4812 7373 Radio telephone communication; Turnkey vendors, computer systems
Pr: Rick Suarez
CFO: Todd Smith
Ex VP: John Vento
VP: Moses Hardie
VP: Ramon Mas Sr

D-U-N-S 96-226-4532
■ MASTEC NETWORK SOLUTIONS LLC
(*Suby of* MASTEC INC) ★
806 S Douglas Rd Fl 11, Coral Gables, FL 33134-3157
Tel (866) 545-1782 *Founded/Ownrshp* 2008
Sales 204.7MM^E *EMP* 595^E
SIC 4812 7373 Radio telephone communication; Turnkey vendors, computer systems
Pr: Rick Suarez
**CFO:* Todd Smith
**Ex VP:* John Vento
**VP:* Moses Hardie
**VP:* Ramon Mas Sr

D-U-N-S 04-223-6278
■ MASTEC NORTH AMERICA INC (FL)
(*Suby of* MASTEC INC) ★
800 S Douglas Rd Ste 1200, Coral Gables, FL 33134-3165
Tel (305) 599-1800 *Founded/Ownrshp* 1998, 1999
Sales 2.6MMM^E *EMP* 7,250
SIC 1623 Water, sewer & utility lines
CEO: Jose Ramon Mas
**Pr:* Ray E Harris
**COO:* Robert Apple
**CFO:* C Robert Campbell
**VP:* Charles R Campbell
Board of Directors: Ernst N Csiszar, Robert J Dwyer, Frank E Jaumot, Julia L Johnson, Jorge Mas, Jose S Sorzano, John Van Heuvelen

D-U-N-S 82-487-6853
▲ MASTECH DIGITAL INC
1305 Cherrington Pkwy # 400, Moon Township, PA 15108-4355
Tel (412) 787-2100 *Founded/Ownrshp* 1986
Sales 123.4MM *EMP* 970^E
Tkr Sym MHH *Exch* ASE
SIC 7361 7371 Employment agencies; Custom computer programming services
Pr: Vivek Gupta
**Ch Bd:* Ashok Trivedi
**Ch Bd:* Sunil Wadhwani
CFO: John J Cronin Jr
Board of Directors: John Ausura, Brenda Galilee, Gerhard Watzinger

D-U-N-S 15-300-7948
■ MASTECH DIGITAL TECHNOLOGIES INC
(*Suby of* MASTECH DIGITAL INC) ★
1305 Cherrington Pkwy, Coraopolis, PA 15108-4355
Tel (412) 787-2100 *Founded/Ownrshp* 1986
Sales 105.1MM^E *EMP* 970
SIC 7371 Software programming applications; Custom computer programming services
CEO: Vivek Gupta
**Ch Bd:* Ashok Trivedi
**Ch Bd:* Sunil Wadhwani
**CFO:* Jack Cronin
VP: Denis Deet
VP: Risher Dumpit
Dir Bus: Madhup Malhotra
Mng Dir: Jeremy Pigott
Snr Sftwr: Heather McClure
Snr Sftwr: Harini Narayanagobbur
Snr Sftwr: Jason Novak

D-U-N-S 00-505-3616 IMP/EXP
MASTER CHEMICAL CORP (OH)
501 W Boundary St, Perrysburg, OH 43551-1200
Tel (419) 874-7902 *Founded/Ownrshp* 1951
Sales 98.1MM^E *EMP* 338
SIC 2992 3559 Cutting oils, blending: made from purchased materials; Oils & greases, blending & compounding; Recycling machinery
Ch Bd: Joe H Wright
CFO: Cary Glay
CFO: Cary R Glay
CFO: Jana Miller
CFO: Dan Witt
Ex Dir: Patrick Gouhin
Ex Dir: John Greene
Mng Dir: Petr Sterba
Dist Mgr: Michael Deel
Dist Mgr: Allen Jones
Genl Mgr: Garret Garcia

MASTER DISTRIBUTORS
See MASTER INTERNATIONAL CORP

MASTER HALCO
See MASTER-HALCO INC

MASTER IMPORTS
See GENERAL BEVERAGE SALES CO-MILWAUKEE

D-U-N-S 05-146-9039 IMP
MASTER INTERNATIONAL CORP
MASTER DISTRIBUTORS
1301 Olympic Blvd, Santa Monica, CA 90404-3725
Tel (310) 452-1229 *Founded/Ownrshp* 1966
Sales 214.3MM^E *EMP* 150
SIC 5065 Electronic parts
CEO: Ihsan Nizam
**Pr:* Jamill Nizam
Brnch Mgr: Rick Dale
Sls Mgr: Vanessa Gonzalez
Sls Mgr: Joanie Holland

D-U-N-S 05-410-5218 IMP
■ MASTER LOCK CO LLC
(*Suby of* FORTUNE BRANDS HOME & SECURITY INC) ★
137 W Forest Hill Ave, Oak Creek, WI 53154-2901
Tel (414) 444-2800 *Founded/Ownrshp* 2011
Sales 254.2MM^E *EMP* 700
SIC 3429 3462 Padlocks; Locks or lock sets; Door locks, bolts & checks; Iron & steel forgings
VP: Paul S Buskey
VP: Robert Rice Sr
IT Man: Joe Kaye
S&M/VP: Jeffrey Russell
Pgrm Dir: Don Gardner

MASTER PRINT
See VOMELA SPECIALTY CO

D-U-N-S 62-776-6645
MASTER PROTECTION HOLDINGS INC
(*Suby of* SIMPLEXTIME RECORDER LLC) ★
13050 Metro Pkwy Ste 1, Fort Myers, FL 33966-4800
Tel (239) 896-1680 *Founded/Ownrshp* 1990
Sales 16.7MM^E *EMP* 1,000
Accts Deloitte & Touche Llp New Yor
SIC 7389 1711 5999 Fire extinguisher servicing; Fire sprinkler system installation; Safety supplies & equipment
Pr: Dean De Buhr
**Ch Bd:* Wiliam R Berkley
VP: Gaylon R Claiborn
VP: Nickolas K Fisher
VP: Thomas L Kennedy
VP: John H Simon
Board of Directors: W R Berkley Jr, Catherine B James

D-U-N-S 04-609-8034 IMP
MASTER PUMPS & EQUIPMENT CORP (TX)
MASTER PUMPS & POWER
805 Port America Pl # 100, Grapevine, TX 76051-7670
Tel (817) 251-6745 *Founded/Ownrshp* 1993
Sales 84.8MM^E *EMP* 90
SIC 5084 7699 Pumps & pumping equipment; Compressors, except air conditioning; Pumps & pumping equipment repair; Compressor repair
Ch Bd: Donald W Moilan
**Ex VP:* James O'Donnell
VP: James Odonnell

MASTER PUMPS & POWER
See MASTER PUMPS & EQUIPMENT CORP

D-U-N-S 00-826-1620 IMP
MASTER-HALCO INC
MASTER HALCO
(*Suby of* ITOCHU INTERNATIONAL INC) ★
3010 Lbj Fwy Ste 800, Dallas, TX 75234-7770
Tel (972) 714-7300 *Founded/Ownrshp* 1977
Sales 626.4MM^E *EMP* 1,615
SIC 3315 5039 3496 3446 5031 1799 Chain link fencing; Fence gates posts & fittings: steel; Wire fence, gates & accessories; Miscellaneous fabricated wire products; Architectural metalwork; Lumber, plywood & millwork; Building materials, exterior; Fence construction
CEO: Ken Fishbein
**CFO:* Scott Suh
VP: Tim Obrien
VP: Jerry Short
Brnch Mgr: Mark Buchanan
Genl Mgr: Curt Cook
CIO: Tony Caesar
Netwrk Eng: Martin Straigis
Manager: Scott Wilhite
Sls Mgr: Mark Dukovich
Sls Mgr: Jay Housewright

D-U-N-S 14-478-6626
MASTER-TEC FLOORS INC
SIGN POST PROS
3109 N T St, Pensacola, FL 32505-5013
Tel (850) 454-0008 *Founded/Ownrshp* 2003
Sales 978.0MM *EMP* 3
SIC 1752 5713 Floor laying & floor work; Floor covering stores
CEO: Matthew S Kovach
**COO:* Martin D Cudlin
**CFO:* Brandy L Kovach
**VP:* Martin Cudlin

D-U-N-S 02-254-4501 IMP
■ MASTERBRAND CABINETS INC
HOMECREST
(*Suby of* FORTUNE BRANDS HOME & SECURITY INC) ★
1 Masterbrand Cabinets Dr, Jasper, IN 47546-2248
Tel (812) 482-2527 *Founded/Ownrshp* 1998
Sales 2.5MMM^E *EMP* 11,000
SIC 2434 Wood kitchen cabinets
Pr: David M Randich
Ex VP: Robert Foote
**Ex VP:* Gary Lautzehiser
Ex VP: Rob Mullally
VP: Brad Carpenter
VP: Greg Costello
VP: John Fogg
VP: David Goldblatt
VP: Robert Jacobs
VP: Kevin Mair
VP: Gordon McCance
VP: Roland Minogue
VP: Bill Schotanus
VP: Martin Vandoren
VP Bus Dev: Eric Skorge

D-U-N-S 08-376-4811 IMP
MASTERBUILT MANUFACTURING LLC (GA)
1 Masterbuilt Ct, Columbus, GA 31907-1313
Tel (706) 327-5622 *Founded/Ownrshp* 1985
Sales 109.9MM *EMP* 109
Accts Robinson Grimes & Company Pc
SIC 3631 3714 Household cooking equipment; Indoor cooking equipment; Motor vehicle parts & accessories
CEO: John McLemore
CFO: Lynne Jacobs
**CFO:* Glenn Scarborough
**Treas:* Lynne McLemore
**VP:* Nathan McGaan
Sys Mgr: Cristina Robinson
Plnt Mgr: Dan Baker
Natl Sales: Shaun McPhail
Mktg Dir: Keith Newton
Manager: Chad Underwood

D-U-N-S 11-856-9339
▲ MASTERCARD INC
2000 Purchase St, Purchase, NY 10577-2405
Tel (914) 249-2000 *Founded/Ownrshp* 1966
Sales 9.6MMM *EMP* 11,300^E
Accts Pricewaterhousecoopers Llp Ne
Tkr Sym MA *Exch* NYS
SIC 7389 Credit card service
Pr: Ajay S Banga
**Ch Bd:* Richard Haythornthwaite
V Ch: Walt W Macnee
**Pr:* Ajay Banga
Pr: Ann Cairns
Pr: Gilberto Caldart
Pr: Gary J Flood
Pr: Hai Ling
Pr: Raghu Malhorta
Pr: Cathy McCaul
Pr: Robert Reeg
Pr: ARI Sarker
Pr: Raj Seshadri
Pr: Kevin Stanton
Pr: Craig Vosburg
CFO: Martina Hund-Mejean
Chf Mktg O: Raja Rajamannar
Ofcr: Ronald E Garrow
Ofcr: Garry Lyons
Ofcr: Michael Miebach
Ex VP: Jon Briggs
Board of Directors: Silvio Barzi, David R Carlucci, Steven J Freiberg, Julius Genachowski, Merit E Janow, Nancy J Karch, Jose Octavio Reyes Lagunes, Rima Qureshi, Jackson Tai

D-U-N-S 05-048-3783
■ MASTERCARD INTERNATIONAL INC
MASTERCARD WORLDWIDE
(*Suby of* MASTERCARD INC) ★
2000 Purchase St, Purchase, NY 10577-2509
Tel (914) 249-2000 *Founded/Ownrshp* 1966
Sales 529.8MM^E *EMP* 3,000
SIC 7389 6099 Credit card service; Travelers' checks issuance; Automated teller machine (ATM) network
Pr: Ajay Banga
Pr: Ajay Bhalla
Pr: Javier Perez
Pr: Rob Reeg
**CEO:* Robert W Selander
**COO:* Alan Heuer
CFO: Frank Cotroneo
**CFO:* Chris McWilton
**Ch:* Stephanie Voquer
**Treas:* Sachin Mehra
Treas: Stephen Piccininni
**Chf Mktg O:* Alfredo Gangotena
Assoc VP: Souheil Yammine
Ex VP: Gary Flood
Ex VP: Australasia Grobler
Ex VP: Arthur Kranzley
Ex VP: Maria Polumbo
Sr VP: Aroon Maben
Sr VP: Steven Sklar
VP: Rob Barrale
VP: Geraldine Cooper

MASTERCARD WORLDWIDE
See MASTERCARD INTERNATIONAL INC

D-U-N-S 13-026-7685
MASTERCORP INC
3505 N Main St, Crossville, TN 38555-5417
Tel (931) 484-1752 *Founded/Ownrshp* 1973
Sales 166.8MM^E *EMP* 3,400
SIC 7349 7217 Building cleaning service; Cleaning service, industrial or commercial; Janitorial service, contract basis; Carpet & furniture cleaning on location
Pr: Alan Grindstaff
**COO:* David Goff
**CFO:* Kevin Swafford
**Sec:* Charlotte Grindstaff
**Sr VP:* Steve Hicks
**VP:* David Maier
VP: Len Wolin
Exec: Luz Gonzalez
Area Mgr: Shawn Williams
Genl Mgr: Toby Sweat
Dir IT: Jonathan Loveday

MASTERCRAFT
See MCBC HOLDINGS INC

D-U-N-S 05-266-2467 IMP/EXP
■ MASTERCRAFT BOAT CO LLC (TN)
(*Suby of* MASTERCRAFT) ★
100 Cherokee Cove Dr, Vonore, TN 37885-2129
Tel (423) 884-2221 *Founded/Ownrshp* 1968, 2000
Sales 213.8MM^E *EMP* 500
SIC 3799 Boat trailers
CEO: Terry McNew
COO: Terry Bell
**COO:* Shane Chittum
**CFO:* Tim Oxley
Bd of Dir: Mike Moberley
Sr VP: Carl Craig
**VP:* Jay S Povlin
**VP:* Greg Stanley
Dir Bus: Phil Walker
MIS Dir: David Kirkland
Dir IT: Travis Moye

D-U-N-S 07-384-6115 EXP
MASTERS GALLERY FOODS INC
328 Count Hwy Pp Pp, Plymouth, WI 53073-4143
Tel (920) 893-8431 *Founded/Ownrshp* 1991
Sales 800.0MM *EMP* 445
SIC 5143

D-U-N-S 84-492-0269
MASTERS INSURANCE AGENCY INC
ANICO
9785 Maroon Cir Ste 340, Englewood, CO 80112-5922
Tel (303) 814-1596 *Founded/Ownrshp* 1994
Sales NA *EMP* 200
SIC 6411 6331 6311 Insurance agents, brokers & service; Automobile insurance; Life insurance
Pr: Jeff Johnson

D-U-N-S 04-635-5827 IMP
MASTERS PHARMACEUTICAL INC
3600 Pharma Way, Lebanon, OH 45036-9479
Tel (513) 354-2690 *Founded/Ownrshp* 2000
Sales 207.0MM^E *EMP* 180^E
SIC 5122 Pharmaceuticals
Pr: Dennis Smith
**Pr:* Wayne A Corona
Pr: Christine Madden
CFO: Simon Clarke
**CFO:* Kevin Moore
VP: Brian Besse
VP: Darren Stepinski
Snr Sftwr: Josh Vega
IT Man: Lore Breetz
Natl Sales: Donna Johnson
Natl Sales: Kamiko Kahr

MASTHEAD HOSE & SUPPLY
See BRIDGESTONE HOSEPOWER LLC

MASTIC HM EXTERIORS BY PLY GEM
See MASTIC HOME EXTERIORS INC

D-U-N-S 00-423-9000 IMP
■ MASTIC HOME EXTERIORS INC
MASTIC HM EXTERIORS BY PLY GEM
(*Suby of* PLY GEM INDUSTRIES INC) ★
2600 Grand Blvd Ste 900, Kansas City, MO 64108-4626
Tel (816) 426-8200 *Founded/Ownrshp* 1990, 2006
Sales 357.7MM^E *EMP* 1,559
SIC 3081 3089 Plastic film & sheet; Siding, plastic
Ex VP: John Wayne
VP Mktg: Fred Vapenik
VP Sls: Frank G Riess

D-U-N-S 08-902-7924
MASTIN KIRKLAND BOLLING INC
MKB REALTORS
3801 Electric Rd, Roanoke, VA 24018-4510
Tel (540) 989-4555 *Founded/Ownrshp* 1972
Sales 100.0MM *EMP* 100
SIC 6531 Real estate brokers & agents
Pr: Betty Kirkland
COO: Elisha Walker
**Sec:* R Lee Mastin
**VP:* Ann Boldridge
VP: Chan W Bolling
**VP:* W Chan Bolling
**VP:* Stephen Hoover
Mktg Dir: Melissa Frost
Manager: John Walker
Sales Asso: Karin Colozza
Sales Asso: Sabrene Willis

MAT
See MIDWEST AIR TECHNOLOGIES INC

D-U-N-S 06-238-0318
MAT CONCESSIONAIRE LLC
860 Macarthur Cswy, Miami, FL 33132-1600
Tel (305) 929-0560 *Founded/Ownrshp* 2009
Sales 100.0MM *EMP* 9
SIC 5812 Concessionaire
CFO: Christophe Couallier

D-U-N-S 82-585-8470 IMP/EXP
MAT HOLDINGS INC
MAT-AUTOMOTIVE
6700 Wildlife Way, Long Grove, IL 60047
Tel (847) 821-9630 *Founded/Ownrshp* 1986
Sales 1.3MMM *EMP* 11,000
Accts Bdo Seidman Llp
SIC 2842 3714 3563 Specialty cleaning, polishes & sanitation goods; Motor vehicle parts & accessories; Air & gas compressors including vacuum pumps
CEO: Steve Wang
**Pr:* George Ruhl
CFO: Martin Beck
**CFO:* Greg Purse
VP: Darin Aprati
VP: Jay King
**VP:* Heather Korsvik
VP: Steven Rovtar
CIO: Edward Busse
IT Man: Manny Zavala
VP Mktg: Bryan Benson

D-U-N-S 80-949-3856 IMP/EXP
MAT INDUSTRIES LLC
(*Suby of* MAT-AUTOMOTIVE) ★
6700 Wildlife Way, Long Grove, IL 60047
Tel (847) 821-9630 *Founded/Ownrshp* 2004
Sales 107.1MM *EMP* 173
Accts Bdo Seidman Llp
SIC 3563 Air & gas compressors

MAT-AUTOMOTIVE
See MAT HOLDINGS INC

D-U-N-S 07-838-4474
▲ MATADOR RESOURCES CO
5400 Lbj Fwy Ste 1500, Dallas, TX 75240-1017
Tel (972) 371-5200 *Founded/Ownrshp* 1983
Sales 316.1MM *EMP* 151^E
Tkr Sym MTDR *Exch* NYS
SIC 1311 Crude petroleum & natural gas; Natural gas production; Oil shale mining
Ch Bd: Joseph Wm Foran
Pr: Matthew V Hairford
CFO: David E Lancaster
Treas: Kathryn L Wayne
Ex VP: Craig N Adams
Ex VP: Van H Singleton II
Sr VP: Billy E Goodwin
Sr VP: G Gregg Krug
Sr VP: Bradley M Robinson
VP: John Durham

VP: Robert T Macalik
VP: Matthew D Spicer

D-U-N-S 05-960-7275 IMP
MATAGRANO INC
440 Forbes Blvd, South San Francisco, CA 94080-2015
Tel (650) 829-4829 *Founded/Ownrshp* 1972
Sales 123.9MM^E *EMP* 175
SIC 5181 5149 Beer & other fermented malt liquors; Mineral or spring water bottling; Juices
Pr: Louis Matagrano
**CFO:* Trevor Bartlett
**CFO:* William Hill
**VP:* Tom Haas
**VP:* Frank Matagrano Jr
Opers Mgr: Bruce Davidson
Mktg Mgr: Dick Unsinn

D-U-N-S 96-705-5349
MATAN B SETER FOUNDATION INC
65 Livingston Ave, Roseland, NJ 07068-1725
Tel (973) 597-2510 *Founded/Ownrshp* 2011
Sales 88.9MM *EMP* 2
Accts Kpmg Llp New York Ny
SIC 8699 Charitable organization

D-U-N-S 07-782-6196
MATANDY STEEL & METAL PRODUCTS LLC
MATANDY STEEL SALES
1200 Central Ave, Hamilton, OH 45011-3825
Tel (513) 887-5274 *Founded/Ownrshp* 1987
Sales 129.4MM^E *EMP* 100
SIC 5051 3312 3444 3399 Metals service centers & offices; Sheet or strip, steel, cold-rolled: own hot-rolled; Studs & joists, sheet metal; Nails: aluminum, brass or other nonferrous metal or wire
Pr: Andrew Schuster
Genl Mgr: Aaron Higdon

MATANDY STEEL SALES
See MATANDY STEEL & METAL PRODUCTS LLC

D-U-N-S 04-133-8013 IMP
MATANUSKA ELECTRIC ASSOCIATION INC
M E A
163 E Industrial Way, Palmer, AK 99645-6703
Tel (907) 745-3231 *Founded/Ownrshp* 1941
Sales 120.9MM *EMP* 186
Accts Moss Adams Llp Portland Or
SIC 4911 Transmission, electric power; Distribution, electric power
Genl Mgr: Joe Griffith
**CFO:* Matt Reisterer
Treas: Peter Burchell
Bd of Dir: James Hermon
Genl Mgr: D Carmony
Mtls Mgr: Debra Affinito
Plnt Mgr: Robert C Drake

D-U-N-S 10-091-0306
MATANUSKA SUSITNA BOROUGH SCHOOL DISTRICT
MSBSD
501 N Gulkana St, Palmer, AK 99645-6147
Tel (907) 746-9255 *Founded/Ownrshp* 1964
Sales 68.8MM^E *EMP* 1,300
SIC 8211 Public elementary & secondary schools
Pr: Susan Pougher
VP: Marie Burton
**VP:* Erick Cordero
**VP:* Ole Larson

MATC
See MADISON AREA TECHNICAL COLLEGE DISTRICT

D-U-N-S 08-003-2474
■ **MATCH GROUP INC**
(*Suby of* IAC/INTERACTIVECORP) ★
8750 N Cntl Expy Ste 1400, Dallas, TX 75231
Tel (214) 576-9352 *Founded/Ownrshp* 2009
Sales 1.0MMM^E *EMP* 4,800
Tkr Sym MTCH *Exch* NGS
SIC 7299 7374 Dating service; Data processing & preparation
Ch Bd: Gregory R Blatt
CFO: Gary Swidler
Dir Sec: Amarnath Thombre
Board of Directors: Joseph Levin, Ann L McDaniel, Thomas J McInerney, Glenn H Schiffman, Pamela S Seymon, Alan G Spoon, Mark Stein, Gregg Winiarski

D-U-N-S 82-945-0634 IMP
■ **MATCO TOOLS CORP**
(*Suby of* FORTIVE CORP) ★
4403 Allen Rd, Stow, OH 44224-1096
Tel (330) 929-4949 *Founded/Ownrshp* 2016
Sales 283.5MM^E *EMP* 500
SIC 5251 5072 3469 3423 5013 Hardware; Hardware; Metal stampings; Hand & edge tools; Tools & equipment, automotive
Pr: Timothy J Gilmore
**Treas:* Raymond Michaud
VP: John C Green
VP: Eric Hagen
VP: Thomas M Hill
VP: Jeffrey J Peterson
VP: Jill Willis
Exec: John Capshaw
Dist Mgr: Mike McCaleb
Dist Mgr: David Miller
Dir IT: Dave Heffernan

D-U-N-S 96-542-2942
MATCON TRADING CORP
2020 Ponce De Leon Blvd # 1204, Coral Gables, FL 33134-4476
Tel (305) 442-6333 *Founded/Ownrshp* 1994
Sales 119.0MM *EMP* 5
SIC 6792 2951 Oil royalty traders; Asphalt paving mixtures & blocks
Pr: Jesus Iglesias
Treas: Ena Iglesias

D-U-N-S 06-173-4349
MATENAER CORP
810 Schoenhaar Dr, West Bend, WI 53090-2632
Tel (262) 338-0700 *Founded/Ownrshp* 1992
Sales 88.3MM^E *EMP* 115
SIC 5051 3452 Metals service centers & offices; Washers, metal
Pr: Chip Stringer
Off Mgr: Joan Williams

D-U-N-S 07-186-7774
MATER MISERICORDIAE HOSPITAL
MERCY MEDICAL CENTER MERCED
333 Mercy Ave, Merced, CA 95340-8319
Tel (209) 564-5000 *Founded/Ownrshp* 2006
Sales 305.6MM *EMP* 1,200
SIC 8062 General medical & surgical hospitals
CEO: David Dunham
COO: Chuck Kassis
CFO: Terry Bohlke
CFO: Doreen Hartmann
CFO: Michael Strasser
Dir Lab: Glen Bruss
Info Man: Cheryl Baijnauth
Mktg Dir: Paul Feltz
Pharmcst: Harwinder Sharma
HC Dir: Loretta Stuart-Edgerton

D-U-N-S 02-700-4043
MATERA PAPER CO INC
835 N Ww White Rd, San Antonio, TX 78219-2714
Tel (210) 892-5101 *Founded/Ownrshp* 1984
Sales 124.4MM^E *EMP* 182
SIC 5087 Janitors' supplies
Ch Bd: John Strieber
**Pr:* John Richardson
Treas: Steve Marshal
VP: Chris Goeschel
**VP:* B J Moore
**VP:* Barry Stevens
CIO: Terry Boehnke
Sls Mgr: Tammy Lovelady

D-U-N-S 12-631-6764
MATERIAL HANDLING SYSTEMS INC
MHS
3955 E Blue Lick Rd, Louisville, KY 40229-6047
Tel (502) 636-0690 *Founded/Ownrshp* 2004
Sales 260.0MM *EMP* 60
SIC 5084 Packaging machinery & equipment
Pr: Patrick Cowgill
COO: Mark Springstube
**CFO:* Brian Johnson
**VP Mktg:* Rush Fullerton
Mktg Dir: Anthony Holland
Snr PM: James Griffin

D-U-N-S 10-153-4209 IMP/EXP
MATERIAL IN MOTION INC
726 Palomar Ave, Sunnyvale, CA 94085-2914
Tel (650) 967-3300 *Founded/Ownrshp* 2001
Sales 85.0MM^E *EMP* 200
SIC 3571 Electronic computers
CEO: Ted Salah
IT Man: Rohit Kumar

D-U-N-S 01-975-3419
MATERIAL LOGISTICS & SERVICES LLC
(*Suby of* WSI) ★
1160 N Mayflower Dr, Appleton, WI 54913-9656
Tel (920) 830-5000 *Founded/Ownrshp* 2010
Sales 36.5MM^E *EMP* 1,200
SIC 4225 General warehousing
Pr: Robert Schroeder
CFO: Daniel Vandenheuvel
VP: Bill Lindeke
VP: Kevin Nixon
VP: Dan Sellers
Counsel: Ben Haupt

D-U-N-S 79-614-0556
MATERIAL PACKAGING CORP
ASH GROVE PACKAGING
(*Suby of* ASH GROVE CEMENT CO) ★
23018 S State Route 291, Harrisonville, MO 64701-4394
Tel (816) 380-4473 *Founded/Ownrshp* 1987
Sales 309.1MM^E *EMP* 2,500^E
SIC 3241 Cement, hydraulic
Pr: Jeff Sutton

D-U-N-S 06-457-2563 IMP
MATERIAL SCIENCES CORP
(*Suby of* ZINK ACQUISITION HOLDINGS INC.)
6855 Commerce Blvd, Canton, MI 48187-4458
Tel (734) 207-4444 *Founded/Ownrshp* 2014
Sales 129.3MM^E *EMP* 267
SIC 3479 3471 Painting of metal products; Coating of metals & formed products; Coating, rust preventive; Electroplating of metals or formed products
CEO: Pat Murley
**Pr:* Clifford D Nastas
**CFO:* James D Pawlak
**CFO:* Jim Todd
**Sr VP:* Steve Tatalovich
**VP:* Matthew M Murphy
VP: Robert Rocowski
**VP:* Michael R Wilson
Plnt Mgr: Bruce Woodward

D-U-N-S 96-413-4683
MATERIAL SCIENCES CORP
2250 Pratt Blvd, Elk Grove Village, IL 60007-5917
Tel (888) 603-1553 *Founded/Ownrshp* 1982
Sales 149.0MM^E *EMP* 567
SIC 3312 5051 Sheet or strip, steel, cold-rolled: own hot-rolled; Steel
CEO: Patrick Murley
**COO:* Michael Noble
**CFO:* James L Todd
**Sr VP:* Steve Tatalovich
**VP:* Michael E Noble

D-U-N-S 04-617-0577
MATERIAL SERVICE CORP
HANSON MATERIAL SERVICE
(*Suby of* SOUTHERN STAR CONCRETE) ★
2235 Entp Dr Ste 3504, Westchester, IL 60154
Tel (708) 731-2600 *Founded/Ownrshp* 2006
Sales 124.9MM^E *EMP* 600
SIC 1422 1442 Crushed & broken limestone; Construction sand mining; Gravel mining
Pr: Gerald Nagel
Pr: Dennis Dolan
Pr: Michael Stanczak
CFO: Walter Serwa
Sls Mgr: Darren Melvin
Counsel: David Ruben

D-U-N-S 79-100-2264
■ **MATERIAL SERVICE RESOURCES CORP**
(*Suby of* GENERAL DYNAMICS CORP) ★
222 N La Salle St # 1200, Chicago, IL 60601-1003
Tel (630) 325-7736 *Founded/Ownrshp* 1992
Sales 90.3MM^E *EMP* 2,188
SIC 1442 1221 Construction sand mining; Gravel mining; Bituminous coal & lignite-surface mining
Ch Bd: Lester Crown
Pr: Michael Stanczak

D-U-N-S 18-690-1377
MATERIAL SUPPLY INC
MSI HVAC
11700 Industry Ave, Fontana, CA 92337-6934
Tel (951) 727-2200 *Founded/Ownrshp* 1986
Sales 94.1MM^E *EMP* 250
SIC 3444 5075 7623 1711 Metal ventilating equipment; Warm air heating & air conditioning; Air filters; Ventilating equipment & supplies; Air conditioning repair; Heating & air conditioning contractors
CEO: Dion Quinn
**VP:* Bob Billiu
**VP:* Jon Dautrich
**VP:* Robert Hascall
Sls Mgr: Mark Seko

D-U-N-S 04-027-6248
MATERIALS PROCESSING INC
MPI
3500 Depauw Blvd, Indianapolis, IN 46268-1170
Tel (317) 803-3010 *Founded/Ownrshp* 1975
Sales 138.7MM^E *EMP* 800
SIC 6719 Investment holding companies, except banks
Pr: Clay Barnes
VP: Jason Brewer
**VP:* John A Firmani
VP: Kent Snyder
VP: Mike Winings
Dir Risk M: Elise Densborn

D-U-N-S 00-210-4875 IMP
■ **MATERION ADVANCED MATERIALS TECHNOLOGIES AND SERVICES INC** (NY)
(*Suby of* MATERION BRUSH INC) ★
2978 Main St, Buffalo, NY 14214-1004
Tel (800) 327-1355 *Founded/Ownrshp* 1912
Sales 113.0MM^E *EMP* 370
SIC 3339 Primary nonferrous metals
Pr: Donald Klinkowicz
VP: Bob Dixon
Rgnl Mgr: Sally James
Genl Mgr: Jeff Hazlett
Genl Mgr: Matthew Willson
IT Man: Patrick S Carpenter
IT Man: Richard W Sager
Mfg Dir: Jason Maher
Sfty Dirs: Robert Hanley
QC Dir: Eric Kissell
QC Dir: Derek Steele

D-U-N-S 00-421-2999 IMP
■ **MATERION BRUSH INC** (OH)
(*Suby of* MATERION CORP) ★
6070 Parkland Blvd Ste 1, Mayfield Heights, OH 44124-4191
Tel (216) 486-4200 *Founded/Ownrshp* 1931
Sales 259.3MM^E *EMP* 1,200
SIC 3351 3356 3264 3339 3341 3674 Copper & copper alloy sheet, strip, plate & products; Strip, copper & copper alloy; Plates, copper & copper alloy; Tubing, copper & copper alloy; Nickel & nickel alloy pipe, plates, sheets, etc.; Porcelain parts for electrical devices, molded; Beryllium metal; Secondary precious metals; Semiconductors & related devices
CFO: John D Grampa
**Sec:* Michael C Hasychak
VP: Mark J Asany
VP: Heiner Lichtenberger
Exec: Diane Ryan
Prin: B R Harman
Prin: E A Levine
Mng Dir: Tony Ong
CIO: Carl Cromer
Dir IT: William Chorman
Dir IT: Mark Jasany
Board of Directors: Charles Brush

D-U-N-S 01-560-3793
■ **MATERION CERAMICS INC**
(*Suby of* MATERION BRUSH INC) ★
6100 S Tucson Blvd, Tucson, AZ 85706-4520
Tel (520) 741-3411 *Founded/Ownrshp* 1930
Sales 70.0MM^E *EMP* 1,200
SIC 3351 3264 Copper & copper alloy sheet, strip, plate & products; Strip, copper & copper alloy; Plates, copper & copper alloy; Tubing, copper & copper alloy; Porcelain electrical supplies
Pr: John Scheatzle
Sfty Mgr: Richard Manes

D-U-N-S 62-291-3080 IMP/EXP
▲ **MATERION CORP**
6070 Parkland Blvd Ste 1, Mayfield Heights, OH 44124-4191
Tel (216) 486-4200 *Founded/Ownrshp* 1931
Sales 1.0MMM *EMP* 2,671
Accts Ernst & Young Llp Cleveland
Tkr Sym MTRN *Exch* NYS
SIC 3339 3351 3356 3341 3674 Beryllium metal; Copper & copper alloy sheet, strip, plate & products; Nickel & nickel alloy pipe, plates, sheets, etc.; Secondary precious metals; Semiconductors & related devices
Ch Bd: Richard J Hipple
Pr: Donald G Klimkowicz
CFO: Joseph P Kelley
VP: Nic Baloi
VP: Bob Canavan
VP: Gregory R Chemnitz
VP: Stephen Freeman
VP: David Gordon
VP: James Marrotte
VP: Walter G Maxwell
VP: John Scheatzle
VP: Ian Tribick
VP: Brent Van Scoik
VP Bus Dev: Matthew Willson
Board of Directors: Edward G Crawford, Joseph P Keithley, Vinod M Khilnani, William B Lawrence, M Mohan Reddy, Craig S Shular, Darlene J S Solomon, Robert B Toth, Geoffrey Wild

D-U-N-S 01-560-1664 IMP
■ **MATERION NATURAL RESOURCES INC**
(*Suby of* MATERION CORP) ★
10 Miles North Hwy 6, Delta, UT 84624
Tel (435) 864-2701 *Founded/Ownrshp* 2001
Sales 57.6MM^E *EMP* 1,862
SIC 1099 3339 Beryllium ore mining; Primary nonferrous metals
Opers Mgr: Dough Murpock
Snr Mgr: Debbie Watson

D-U-N-S 04-536-5541 IMP
■ **MATERION TECHNICAL MATERIALS INC**
(*Suby of* MATERION CORP) ★
5 Wellington Rd, Lincoln, RI 02865-4411
Tel (401) 333-1700 *Founded/Ownrshp* 1982
Sales 87.8MM^E *EMP* 200
SIC 3331 3339 3423 Primary copper smelter products; Nickel refining (primary); Hand & edge tools
Pr: Al Lubrano
**Treas:* M C Hasychak
**VP:* Robert Tavares
Prd Mgr: Greg Crandall
VP Sls: Ted Burdon
Sls Mgr: John Massoyan

D-U-N-S 15-412-5140
MATHEMATICA INC
600 Alexander Park # 100, Princeton, NJ 08540-6346
Tel (609) 799-3535 *Founded/Ownrshp* 1986
Sales 220.0MM *EMP* 1,000
Accts Parentebeard Llc Philadelphia
SIC 8732 Economic research
Pr: Paul Decker
**CFO:* Jay B Style
**Sr VP:* Barbara Devaney
**Sr VP:* Amy Johnson
**Sr VP:* Patrick Mooney
**Sr VP:* Mary T Moore
**Sr VP:* Craig Thornton
**Sr VP:* Judith Wooldridge
VP: Laura Eckly
VP: Murray Gillham
VP: Henrik Madsen
VP: Geraldine Mooney
VP: Buck Rodgers
VP: Jonathan Smith
**VP:* Pamela Tapscott
Assoc Dir: Daniel Shapiro

D-U-N-S 15-430-8522
MATHEMATICA POLICY RESEARCH INC
(*Suby of* MATHEMATICA INC) ★
600 Alexander Park, Princeton, NJ 08540-6346
Tel (609) 799-3535 *Founded/Ownrshp* 1986
Sales 145.9MM^E *EMP* 929
SIC 8732 Economic research
Pr: Paul Decker
Sr VP: Neil Clover
**Sr VP:* Barbara Devaney
**Sr VP:* Amy Johnson
**Sr VP:* Patrick Mooney
**Sr VP:* Mary Moore
**Sr VP:* Craig Thornton
**Sr VP:* Judith Wooldridge
**VP:* Alison Barger
VP: Randall Brown
VP: Adam Coyne
VP: Rob Glazier
VP: Harrison N Greene Jr
VP: Daniel Kasprzyk
VP: Chris Mayer
VP: Schochet Peter
VP: Margo L Rosenbach
VP: Allen Schirm
VP: Chris Trenholm
Exec: Chris Buchanan
Assoc Dir: Jeanne Bellotti

D-U-N-S 61-136-7715
MATHENA INC
(*Suby of* WEIR GROUP PLC(THE))
3900 S Hwy 81 Service Rd, El Reno, OK 73036-6808
Tel (405) 422-3600 *Founded/Ownrshp* 2012
Sales 89.0MM *EMP* 90
SIC 3699 3822 Security control equipment & systems; Surface burner controls, temperature
Pr: John Mathena
**VP:* Greg Cantrell
**VP:* David Mathena
**VP:* Harold Mathena
**VP:* Trebor Nall

D-U-N-S 17-909-2028 IMP/EXP
MATHESON TRI-GAS INC
(*Suby of* TAIYO NIPPON SANSO CORPORATION)
150 Allen Rd Ste 302, Basking Ridge, NJ 07920-2977
Tel (908) 991-9200 *Founded/Ownrshp* 1992
Sales 1.4MMM *EMP* 9,000
SIC 2813 5084 Industrial gases; Nitrogen; Oxygen, compressed or liquefied; Argon; Welding machinery & equipment; Safety equipment
Ch Bd: William J Kroll
**Pr:* Scott Kallman
VP: Jerry Girod
VP: Daniel Guerra
VP: Scott Kalman
VP: Kevin Lynch
Dir Bus: Lori McDowell
Genl Mgr: Brian Bisbocci
IT Man: C Guerra
Tech Mgr: Tim Brossard
Tech Mgr: Kavita Murthi

D-U-N-S 00-945-9660
MATHESON TRUCKING INC
9785 Goethe Rd, Sacramento, CA 95827-3559
Tel (916) 685-2330 *Founded/Ownrshp* 1964
Sales 412.6MM^E *EMP* 1,650
SIC 4213 4731 Trucking, except local; Less-than-truckload (LTL) transport; Freight transportation arrangement
Pr: Mark Matheson
**CEO:* Patricia Kepner
**Ofcr:* Charles J Mellor
**Ex VP:* Carole L Matheson
**VP:* Laurie Johnson
VP: Debra White
VP Bus Dev: Don Brocca
Exec: Shirley Curran
Rgnl Mgr: Dewey Adair
Area Mgr: Don Osness
Snr Ntwrk: Peter Evison

D-U-N-S 00-948-1672 EXP
MATHEUS LUMBER CO INC
15800 Woodinville Redmond, Woodinville, WA 98072-9059
Tel (206) 284-7500 *Founded/Ownrshp* 1985
Sales 280.0MM *EMP* 82
Accts Berntson Porter
SIC 5031 Lumber: rough, dressed & finished; Plywood
CEO: Gary Powell
**Pr:* Ben Powell
**CFO:* Dave Colley
**VP:* Dan Powell
**VP:* James Reynolds
**VP:* Larry Tommerup
Off Mgr: Dawn Rychlik
Opers Mgr: Jim Thompson

D-U-N-S 03-303-7193 IMP/EXP
MATHIS BROS OKLAHOMA CITY LLC
MATHIS BROTHERS
3434 W Reno Ave, Oklahoma City, OK 73107-6134
Tel (405) 943-3434 *Founded/Ownrshp* 1960
Sales 163.5MM^E *EMP* 1,500
Accts Grant Thornton
SIC 7991 Physical fitness clubs with training equipment
CEO: Larry Mathis
**Pr:* Bill Mathis
CFO: Sissy Holloway
**VP:* Calvin F Worth
VP: Calvin Worth
Genl Mgr: Robin Hood
Dir IT: Rich Mitton
Ql Cn Mgr: Jacob Durant
Advt Dir: Harry Fogarty
Mktg Mgr: Chad Wilson
Sales Asso: Kyle Willson

MATHIS BROTHERS
See MATHIS BROS OKLAHOMA CITY LLC

D-U-N-S 13-114-2747
MATHWORKS INC
3 Apple Hill Dr, Natick, MA 01760-2098
Tel (508) 647-7000 *Founded/Ownrshp* 1997
Sales 810.6MM^E *EMP* 1,800
SIC 7371 3823 8222 Computer software development & applications; Industrial instrmnts msrmnt display/control process variable; Junior colleges & technical institutes
Pr: Jack Little
Pt: Sari Germanos
Pr: Roy Lurie
**Treas:* Jeanne O'Keefe
VP: Bill Allison
VP: Mike Delucia
VP: Andy Grace
VP: Nevine Jacob
VP: Shirley Jeffreys
VP: Tom Kush
VP: Chris Law
VP: Leslie Mehrez
VP: Tanya Morton
VP Bus Dev: Peter Sandberg
Board of Directors: Cleve Moler

D-U-N-S 00-794-6221
MATHY CONSTRUCTION CO (WI)
DUNN BLACKTOP DIVISION
920 10th Ave N, Onalaska, WI 54650-2166
Tel (608) 783-6411 *Founded/Ownrshp* 1945, 1959
Sales 359.9MM^E *EMP* 476
SIC 1611 1771 1442 5171 General contractor, highway & street construction; Highway & street paving contractor; Resurfacing contractor; Blacktop (asphalt) work; Construction sand mining; Gravel mining; Petroleum bulk stations
Pr: Charles F Mathy
VP: Mark Carrk
**VP:* Steven C Mathy
VP: Tara Wetzel
Dist Mgr: Gary Ladick
Genl Mgr: Dana Fredrickson
Genl Mgr: Tony Tomashek
Genl Mgr: Kristi Whitehead
VP Opers: Tim Jones

D-U-N-S 02-393-3430
MATLET GROUP LLC
60 Delta Dr, Pawtucket, RI 02860-4556
Tel (401) 834-3007 *Founded/Ownrshp* 2005
Sales 144.4MM^E *EMP* 430
SIC 2759 Commercial printing
CEO: Gary Stiffler
**COO:* John Gaffney
Ex VP: Ed Wiegand
VP: Louis Simon
Sls Mgr: Ed Quinn

D-U-N-S 80-562-0437
MATLINPATTERSON ATA HOLDINGS LLC
520 Madison Ave Fl 35, New York, NY 10022-4350
Tel (212) 651-9500 *Founded/Ownrshp* 2005
Sales 57.3MM^E *EMP* 3,000
SIC 4581 Aircraft servicing & repairing
CFO: Lorence Titlebaum

D-U-N-S 10-152-6460
MATLINPATTERSON GLOBAL ADVISERS LLC
520 Madison Ave Fl 35, New York, NY 10022-4350
Tel (212) 651-9500 *Founded/Ownrshp* 2002
Sales 696.3M *EMP* 7,164
Accts Hymes & Associates Cpa Pc Bro
SIC 6733 Private estate, personal investment & vacation fund trusts
CFO: Larry Teiteldaum
VP: Catie Abrams
Dir Risk M: Robert Weiss

D-U-N-S 09-003-4471 IMP/EXP
MATOSANTOS COMMERCIAL CORP
Parque Industrial Ca, Vega Baja, PR 00693
Tel (787) 793-6900 *Founded/Ownrshp* 1940, 1983
Sales 101.4MM^E *EMP* 115
Accts Rsm Puerto Rico-Doris Barroso
SIC 5141 5113 5087 Groceries, general line; Industrial & personal service paper; Janitors' supplies
Pr: Manuel Matosantos Jr
**VP:* Geronimo Matosantos

D-U-N-S 79-169-8749
MATRIX ABSENCE MANAGEMENT INC
(*Suby of* DELPHI FINANCIAL GROUP INC) ★
2421 W Peoria Ave Ste 200, Phoenix, AZ 85029-4940
Tel (602) 866-2333 *Founded/Ownrshp* 1998
Sales NA *EMP* 416
SIC 6411 Insurance claim processing, except medical
CEO: Ivars Zvirbulis
**Pr:* Kenneth F Cope
**COO:* William Schutz
**CFO:* Michael Frederickson
VP: Marti Cardi
VP: Paul Dube
VP: Tim Rarick
VP: Bert Stone
**VP:* Suzanne Wilson
VP Bus Dev: Rick Bernstein
Opers Mgr: Cynthia Giordano

MATRIX BUSINESS TECHNOLOGIES
See MATRIX TELECOM LLC

D-U-N-S 11-151-9513
MATRIX HEALTHCARE SERVICES INC
MYMATRIXX
3111 W Dr Martin, Tampa, FL 33607
Tel (813) 247-2077 *Founded/Ownrshp* 2001
Sales NA *EMP* 150
Accts Warren Averett Llctampa Flo
SIC 6411 Insurance claim processing, except medical
CEO: Steven A Macdonald
**Pr:* Artemis Emslie
**CFO:* Thomas W Cardy
**Sr VP:* Mike Bunkley
**Sr VP:* Lindsay Rios
**Sr VP:* Alan P Walls
VP: Carlos Cordova
VP: Joel Playford
VP: Chuck Sweat
**CTO:* John S Kime
IT Man: Michael Moore
Board of Directors: Jason Beans

MATRIX INTEGRATED FACILITY MGT
See MATRIX LLC

D-U-N-S 07-730-6918
MATRIX LLC
MATRIX INTEGRATED FACILITY MGT
780 5th Ave Ste 115, King of Prussia, PA 19406-4065
Tel (607) 766-0700 *Founded/Ownrshp* 1996
Sales 45.1MM^E *EMP* 2,000
SIC 7349 Janitorial service, contract basis
CEO: James R Peduto
**Pr:* Peter R Criville
**Ex VP:* Thomas Niland

D-U-N-S 96-972-0957 IMP
MATRIX METALS HOLDINGS INC
NEPCO
(*Suby of* SANMAR GROUP)
126 Collins Rd, Richmond, TX 77469-3021
Tel (281) 633-4263 *Founded/Ownrshp* 2008
Sales 140.0MM^E *EMP* 691
SIC 3325 Alloy steel castings, except investment
CFO: Anthony Quinto

D-U-N-S 18-069-6247 IMP
MATRIX METALS LLC
KEOKUK STEEL CASTINGS CO
(*Suby of* NEPCO) ★
126 Collins Rd, Richmond, TX 77469-3021
Tel (281) 342-5511 *Founded/Ownrshp* 2001
Sales 140.0MM *EMP* 550
SIC 3325 Alloy steel castings, except investment
CEO: Robert Kukowski
**CFO:* Tony Quinto
**VP:* Al Kinnard
Sls Mgr: John Harvey

D-U-N-S 78-678-2508
■ **MATRIX NORTH AMERICAN CONSTRUCTION INC**
MATRIX SME, INC.
(*Suby of* MATRIX SERVICE CO) ★
5100 E Skelly Dr Ste 700, Tulsa, OK 74135-6577
Tel (918) 838-8822 *Founded/Ownrshp* 1985
Sales 118.4MM^E *EMP* 756
SIC 1731 1623 1629 Electrical work; Water, sewer & utility lines; Oil & gas pipeline construction; Oil & gas line & compressor station construction; Oil refinery construction
Pr: Matthew I Pettrizo
**Treas:* Jason W Turner
**VP:* James J Collins Jr

D-U-N-S 07-854-4784
■ **MATRIX PDM ENGINEERING INC**
(*Suby of* MATRIX SERVICE CO) ★
5100 E Skelly Dr Ste 800, Tulsa, OK 74135-6565
Tel (918) 624-6300 *Founded/Ownrshp* 2011
Sales 11.6MM^E *EMP* 2,000
SIC 1542 1623 8711 Nonresidential construction; Water, sewer & utility lines; Engineering services

VP: Kenneth L Erdmann

D-U-N-S 07-716-3350
MATRIX RESOURCES INC
1000 Abernathy Rd Ste 500, Atlanta, GA 30328-5605
Tel (770) 677-2400 *Founded/Ownrshp* 1982
Sales 186.5MM *EMP* 1,500
SIC 8742

D-U-N-S 11-510-5827 IMP/EXP
▲ **MATRIX SERVICE CO**
5100 E Skelly Dr Ste 700, Tulsa, OK 74135-6577
Tel (918) 838-8822 *Founded/Ownrshp* 1984
Sales 1.3MMM *EMP* 4,826
Tkr Sym MTRX *Exch* NGS
SIC 1542 1623 7349 8711 Nonresidential construction; Water, sewer & utility lines; Oil & gas line & compressor station construction; Oil & gas pipeline construction; Telephone & communication line construction; Building maintenance services; Engineering services
Pr: John R Hewitt
**Ch Bd:* Michael J Hall
COO: Joseph F Montalbano
CFO: Kevin S Cavanah
VP: Rick J Bennett
VP: Jack Frost
IT Man: Darrel Lutton
Sfty Mgr: Dale Horton
Snr PM: Jonathan Hoekstra
Board of Directors: John W Gibson, I Edgar Hendrix, Paul K Lackey, Tom E Maxwell, James H Miller, Jim W Mogg

D-U-N-S 78-012-8570 IMP
■ **MATRIX SERVICE INC**
(*Suby of* MATRIX SERVICE CO) ★
5100 E Skelly Dr Ste 700, Tulsa, OK 74135-6577
Tel (918) 838-8822 *Founded/Ownrshp* 1984
Sales 643.5MM^E *EMP* 1,738
SIC 1623 1629 1799 7699 Oil & gas pipeline construction; Chemical plant & refinery construction; Petroleum storage tanks, pumping & draining; Tank repair & cleaning services
Pr: James P Ryan
**CFO:* Kevin Cavanah
**VP:* Kevin A Durkin
**VP:* Bradley J Rinehart
**VP:* Alan Updyke
Exec: Karen Spradlin

MATRIX SME, INC.
See MATRIX NORTH AMERICAN CONSTRUCTION INC

D-U-N-S 78-437-6659
MATRIX TELECOM LLC
MATRIX BUSINESS TECHNOLOGIES
(*Suby of* IMPACT TELECOM LLC) ★
433 Las Colinas Blvd E # 500, Irving, TX 75039-5654
Tel (888) 411-0111 *Founded/Ownrshp* 2013
Sales 133.5MM^E *EMP* 276^E
SIC 4813 Telephone communication, except radio
CEO: Robert Beaty
**CEO:* Charles G Taylor Jr
Sr VP: Brian Gustas
**VP:* Brian D Gustas
Mktg Dir: Joey Alfred
Sls Mgr: Nathan Pyle

D-U-N-S 13-152-1809 IMP/EXP
■ **MATRIXX GROUP INC**
A. SCHULMAN
(*Suby of* CITADEL INTERMEDIATE HOLDINGS LLC) ★
15000 Highway 41 N, Evansville, IN 47725-9360
Tel (812) 421-3600 *Founded/Ownrshp* 2007
Sales 195.6MM^E *EMP* 153
SIC 5162 Plastics resins
CEO: Mike Huff
**Pr:* Jason Jimerson
**Pr:* Raymond Wright
**VP:* Kevin Andrews
**VP:* Kymberly Peters
VP: J Seymour
**VP:* Michael E Wright
Mtls Mgr: Bryan Farmer
Sls Mgr: Mike McLellan

D-U-N-S 19-283-9731
■ **MATSON ALASKA INC**
(*Suby of* MATSON NAVIGATION CO INC) ★
2550 W Tyvola Rd, Charlotte, NC 28217-4574
Tel (704) 973-7000 *Founded/Ownrshp* 2015
Sales 783.8MM^E *EMP* 1,621^E
SIC 4424 4731 4412 Deep sea domestic transportation of freight; Water transportation to noncontiguous territories, freight; Freight transportation arrangement; Deep sea foreign transportation of freight
CEO: Steven L Rubin
COO: William A Hamlin
CFO: Michael T Avara
CFO: Michael Avara
Ex VP: Michael F Zendan II
Dir IT: Jeffrey Yeager
Board of Directors: Jeffrey A Brodsky, Kurt M Cellar, James Lachance, Martin Tuchman, David N Weinstein

D-U-N-S 07-843-2469
▲ **MATSON INC**
1411 Sand Island Pkwy, Honolulu, HI 96819-4322
Tel (808) 848-1211 *Founded/Ownrshp* 2012
Sales 1.8MMM *EMP* 4,414
Tkr Sym MATX *Exch* NYS
SIC 4499 Water transportation cleaning services
CEO: Matthew J Cox
Ch Bd: Walter A Dods Jr
CFO: Joel M Wine
Sr VP: Vicente S Angoco Jr
Sr VP: Ronald J Forest
Sr VP: John P Lauer
Sr VP: Rusty K Rolfe
VP: Kenneth J Gill
Snr Mgr: Nuno Roberto
Board of Directors: W Blake Baird, Michael J Chun, Thomas B Fargo, Stanley M Kuriyama, Constance H Lau, Jeffrey N Watanabe

D-U-N-S 18-944-1561
■ **MATSON LOGISTICS INC**
(*Suby of* MATSON NAVIGATION CO INC) ★
1815 S Meyers Rd Ste 700, Oakbrook Terrace, IL 60181-5263
Tel (630) 203-3500 *Founded/Ownrshp* 1999
Sales 105.4MM^E *EMP* 382
SIC 4731 Agents, shipping
Pr: R K Rolfe
**Sec:* Paul Ito
VP: Grace Cerocke

D-U-N-S 00-691-2620 IMP/EXP
■ **MATSON NAVIGATION CO INC** (HI)
(*Suby of* MATSON INC) ★
555 12th St, Oakland, CA 94607-4046
Tel (510) 628-4000 *Founded/Ownrshp* 1882, 1980
Sales 822.0MM^E *EMP* 1,663
SIC 4424 4491 4492 Deep sea domestic transportation of freight; Marine cargo handling; Stevedoring; Marine terminals; Tugboat service
Pr: Matthew J Cox
**CFO:* Joel M Wine
**Treas:* Benedict J Bowler
Ex VP: Rusty Rolfe
Sr VP: Ronald Forest
**Sr VP:* Peter T Heilman
**Sr VP:* David L Hoppes
Sr VP: Kevin C O'Rourke
**Sr VP:* Kevin C O Rourke
VP: Vic Angoco
VP: John Dennen
**VP:* Paul Londynsky
VP: Doug Matthew
VP: Ku'uhaku Park
**VP:* Peter F Weis
Dir Risk M: Mary Tanios

D-U-N-S 00-828-6643 IMP/EXP
▲ **MATTEL INC**
333 Continental Blvd, El Segundo, CA 90245-5032
Tel (310) 252-2000 *Founded/Ownrshp* 1945
Sales 5.7MMM *EMP* 31,000
Tkr Sym MAT *Exch* NGS
SIC 3944 3942 Games, toys & children's vehicles; Dolls & stuffed toys; Dolls, except stuffed toy animals; Stuffed toys, including animals
Ch Bd: Christopher A Sinclair
Pr: Richard Dickson
CFO: Kevin M Farr
Ofcr: Richard R Gros
Ofcr: Geoffrey H Walker
Ex VP: Peter D Gibbons
VP: Michelle Charmello
VP: Jessica Dunne
VP: Mike Fulkerson
VP: Julia Jensen
VP: Joseph Johnson
VP: Nick Karamanos
VP: Jeff Korchek
VP: David Kosnoff
VP: Joe Lawandus
VP: Jon Marine
VP: Graciela Meibar
VP: Steve Sucher
VP: Michael Tsiakaros
VP: Evelyn Viohl
Board of Directors: Michael J Dolan, Trevor A Edwards, Frances D Fergusson, Ann Lewnes, Kathy White Loyd, Dominic Ng, Dean A Scarborough, Dirk Van De Put

D-U-N-S 03-978-3514 EXP
■ **MATTEL TOY CO**
(*Suby of* MATTEL INC) ★
333 Continental Blvd, El Segundo, CA 90245-5032
Tel (310) 252-2357 *Founded/Ownrshp* 1945
Sales 221.8MM^E *EMP* 1,900
SIC 5092 Toys & games
CEO: Robert Eckert
COO: Bruce L Stein

MATTERNS HATCHERY
See EMPIRE KOSHER POULTRY INC

D-U-N-S 83-133-5096
MATTHEW 25 MINISTRIES INC
11060 Kenwood Rd, Blue Ash, OH 45242-1816
Tel (513) 793-6256 *Founded/Ownrshp* 1991
Sales 158.8MM *EMP* 16
SIC 8399 Community development groups
Pr: Wendell Metty
**Pr:* Wendell Mettey
**Treas:* Don Olson
VP: Karen Otto

D-U-N-S 00-164-9789
MATTHEW BENDER & CO INC (NY)
LEXISNEXIS MATTHEW BENDER
(*Suby of* REED BUSINESS INFORMATION) ★
744 Broad St Fl 8, Newark, NJ 07102-3803
Tel (518) 487-3000 *Founded/Ownrshp* 1915, 1998
Sales 46.9MM^E *EMP* 1,214^E
SIC 2731 Books: publishing only
CEO: Andrew Prozes

D-U-N-S 14-153-4284
MATTHEW WARREN INC
MW INDUSTRIES
(*Suby of* MW INDUSTRIES INC) ★
9501 Tech Blvd Ste 401, Rosemont, IL 60018
Tel (847) 349-5760 *Founded/Ownrshp* 2011
Sales 385.5MM^E *EMP* 1,055
SIC 3493 Coiled flat springs; Cold formed springs; Helical springs, hot wound: railroad equipment etc.; Hot wound springs, except wire
CEO: William Marcum
Pr: Chris Thomas
**CFO:* Chester Kwasniak
Sr VP: Frank Szendrey
Sr VP: John Teeter
Genl Mgr: John Everette

D-U-N-S 00-434-1533
▲ **MATTHEWS INTERNATIONAL CORP** (PA)
2 N Shore Ctr Ste 200, Pittsburgh, PA 15212-5851
Tel (412) 442-8200 *Founded/Ownrshp* 1850
Sales 1.4MMM *EMP* 10,300

Accts Ernts & Young Llp Pittsburgh
Tkr Sym MATW *Exch* NGS
SIC 3366 1542 3569 3995 3953 2796 Bronze foundry; Mausoleum construction; Cremating ovens; Burial caskets; Marking devices; Platemaking services
Pr: Joseph C Bartolacci
**Ch Bd:* John D Turner
CFO: Steven F Nicola
VP: David F Beck
VP: Brian D Walters
CTO: Gregory S Babe
Board of Directors: Katherine E Dietze, Terry L Dunlap, Morgan K O'brien, John P O'leary Jr, Don W Quigley Jr, David A Schawk, Alvaro Garcia-Tunon, Jerry R Whitaker

D-U-N-S 12-534-8883 IMP/EXP
MATTHEY JOHNSON HOLDINGS INC
(*Suby of* JOHNSON MATTHEY PLC)
435 Devon Park Dr Ste 600, Wayne, PA 19087-1944
Tel (610) 971-3000 *Founded/Ownrshp* 1998
Sales 645.7MM[E] *EMP* 1,775[E]
SIC 3341 3339 3356 2834 3399 3714 Platinum group metals, smelting & refining (secondary); Gold smelting & refining (secondary); Silver smelting & refining (secondary); Platinum group metal refining (primary); Gold refining (primary); Silver refining (primary); Precious metals; Platinum group metals: rolling, drawing or extruding; Gold & gold alloy: rolling, drawing or extruding; Powders, pharmaceutical; Metal powders, pastes & flakes; Paste, metal; Exhaust systems & parts, motor vehicle
Pr: Robert Talley
**Treas:* Karil J Black
**VP:* Edward Ravert
**VP:* Edward H Ravert Jr
VP: A J Trifiletti

D-U-N-S 00-232-6734 IMP/EXP
MATTHEY JOHNSON INC
(*Suby of* MATTHEY JOHNSON HOLDINGS INC) ★
435 Devon Park Dr Ste 600, Wayne, PA 19087-1944
Tel (610) 971-3000 *Founded/Ownrshp* 1909
Sales 593.1MM[E] *EMP* 1,650
SIC 3341 3339 3356 2834 3399 3714 Platinum group metals, smelting & refining (secondary); Gold smelting & refining (secondary); Silver smelting & refining (secondary); Platinum group metal refining (primary); Gold refining (primary); Silver refining (primary); Precious metals; Platinum group metals: rolling, drawing or extruding; Gold & gold alloy: rolling, drawing or extruding; Silver & silver alloy: rolling, drawing or extruding; Powders, pharmaceutical; Metal powders, pastes & flakes; Paste, metal; Exhaust systems & parts, motor vehicle
CEO: Robert Macleod
COO: Richard Trout
**Ch:* Tim Stevenson
**Treas:* K J Black
Treas: Hai-Ying Chen
VP: David Cetola
**VP:* E H Ravert Jr
**Ex Dir:* Larry Pentz
Ex Dir: John Walker
Mng Dir: G P Otterman
Brnch Mgr: Bill Erickson
Board of Directors: P N Hawker, Roger M Kilburn, L C Pentz, F K Shefffy

MATTING PRODUCTS DIV
See RJF INTERNATIONAL CORP

D-U-N-S 01-848-6324
MATTINGLY FOODS INC
302 State St, Zanesville, OH 43701-3200
Tel (740) 454-0136 *Founded/Ownrshp* 1946
Sales 95.9MM[E] *EMP* 240
SIC 5149 5142 5141 Canned goods: fruit, vegetables, seafood, meats, etc.; Milk, canned or dried; Fruit juices, frozen; Vegetables, frozen; Fish, frozen: packaged; Meat, frozen: packaged; Groceries, general line
CEO: Rick Barnes
**Ch Bd:* Robert K Mattingly
**Pr:* Barbara Callahan
**CFO:* Rusty Deaton
**VP:* Andrew Hess
**VP:* Brandon Hess
Mktg Dir: Katie Coe

D-U-N-S 02-562-2416 IMP
MATTOON RURAL KING SUPPLY INC (IL)
4216 Dewitt Ave, Mattoon, IL 61938-6643
Tel (217) 254-6678 *Founded/Ownrshp* 1962
Sales 83.1MM[E] *EMP* 160[E]
SIC 5399

MATTRESS FIRM, THE
See MATTRESS FIRM INC

MATTRESS FIRM
See MATTRESS HOLDING CORP

D-U-N-S 96-726-0931
MATTRESS FIRM HOLDING CORP
(*Suby of* STEINHOFF INTERNATIONAL HOLDINGS N.V.)
10201 Main St, Houston, TX 77025-5229
Tel (713) 923-1090 *Founded/Ownrshp* 2016
Sales 2.5MMM *EMP* 10,552[E]
SIC 5712 Furniture stores
Pr: Kenneth E Murphy III
Ch Bd: R Stephen Stagner
CFO: Alexander S Weiss
Sr VP: Cathy Hauslein
Area Mgr: Richard Thompson
Store Mgr: Michael Archer
Board of Directors: Markus Johannes Jooste

D-U-N-S 08-108-8358 EXP
MATTRESS FIRM INC
MATTRESS FIRM, THE
(*Suby of* MATTRESS FIRM) ★
10201 Main St, Houston, TX 77025-5229
Tel (713) 923-1090 *Founded/Ownrshp* 2002
Sales 264.0MM[E] *EMP* 550
SIC 5712 Furniture stores
Ch: Gary Fazio
**Pr:* R Steven Stagner
**CEO:* Steve Stagner
**CFO:* James R Black
**Ex VP:* Ken Murphy
VP: Justin Cassell
VP: Tony Miller
VP: Joe Paviglianti
Exec: Gabe Dixon
Area Mgr: Fred Bethel
Area Mgr: Meagan Carroll

D-U-N-S 78-832-9589 IMP/EXP
MATTRESS GIANT CORP
(*Suby of* MATTRESS FIRM HOLDING CORP) ★
5815 Gulf Fwy, Houston, TX 77023-5341
Tel (713) 923-1090 *Founded/Ownrshp* 2012
Sales 127.0MM[E] *EMP* 1,005
SIC 5712 Bedding & bedsprings; Mattresses
Pr: Barrie Brown
CFO: Elaine D Crowley
CFO: Bob Pulciani
CFO: Steve Williams
**Sec:* Steven List
Sr Cor Off: Michael Glazer
VP: Luis Rechoni
VP: Terri Stevens
Brnch Mgr: Hava Zejnllahu
Dist Mgr: Steve Poertner
MIS Dir: Don Barker

D-U-N-S 16-233-9985 IMP
MATTRESS HOLDING CORP
MATTRESS FIRM
(*Suby of* MATTRESS FIRM HOLDING CORP) ★
5815 Gulf Fwy, Houston, TX 77023-5341
Tel (713) 923-1090 *Founded/Ownrshp* 2008
Sales 296.3MM[E] *EMP* 960
SIC 5712 Furniture stores; Bedding & bedsprings; Mattresses
Ch Bd: Gary Fazio
CEO: R Stephen Stagner
CFO: James R Black
Ex VP: Daniel McGuire
Area Mgr: Kris Nuno
VP Opers: Michael P Cannizzaro
Mktg Mgr: Bruce Kirby

MATTRESS WHSE SLEEP OUTFITTERS
See INNOVATIVE MATTRESS SOLUTIONS LLC

D-U-N-S 60-605-4476 IMP
MATTSON TECHNOLOGY INC
(*Suby of* BEIJING E-TOWN INTERNATIONAL INVESTMENT & DEVELOPMENT CO.,LTD)
47131 Bayside Pkwy, Fremont, CA 94538-6517
Tel (510) 657-5900 *Founded/Ownrshp* 2016
Sales 172.5MM *EMP* 297[E]
SIC 3559 Semiconductor manufacturing machinery
Pr: Fusen Chen
**COO:* J Michael Dodson
VP: Rene George
VP: Shannon Hart
Board of Directors: Richard Dyck, Scott Kramer, Scott Peterson, Thomas St Dennis

D-U-N-S 02-064-2625
MATURE SERVICES INC (OH)
415 S Portage Path, Akron, OH 44320-2327
Tel (330) 253-4597 *Founded/Ownrshp* 1975, 1978
Sales 12.4MM *EMP* 1,329
Accts Bober Markey Fedorovich & Co
SIC 8322 Geriatric social service
Pr: Linda Valentine
**Ch Bd:* Lee Walko
**V Ch Bd:* James Loveless
CTO: Dena Gilbert
IT Man: Dena Haswell
Board of Directors: David Barnhardt, Cynthia Bayer, Michael Demagall, Thomas Fuller, Pamela Hawkins, Richard Horak, Stephen Shamrock, Harvey Sterns, Barbara Venesy

MAU WORKFORCE SOLUTIONS
See MANAGEMENT ANALYSIS & UTILIZATION INC

D-U-N-S 07-860-2866
MAUI ACQUISITION CORP
13386 International Pkwy, Jacksonville, FL 32218-2383
Tel (904) 741-5400 *Founded/Ownrshp* 1998
Sales 804.0MM[E] *EMP* 2,280[E]
SIC 3069 2389 Life jackets, inflatable: rubberized fabric; Men's miscellaneous accessories
CEO: Warren B Kanders
**Pr:* Scott Obrien
**VP:* Gray Hudkins

MAUI DIVERS JEWELRY
See MAUI DIVERS OF HAWAII LIMITED

D-U-N-S 09-464-8862 IMP/EXP
MAUI DIVERS OF HAWAII LIMITED
MAUI DIVERS JEWELRY
1520 Liona St, Honolulu, HI 96814-2493
Tel (808) 946-7979 *Founded/Ownrshp* 1979
Sales 84.7MM[E] *EMP* 517[E]
SIC 3911 5944 5094

D-U-N-S 00-692-7164 IMP
■ **MAUI ELECTRIC CO LIMITED** (HI)
(*Suby of* HAWAIIAN ELECTRIC CO INC) ★
210 W Kamehameha Ave, Kahului, HI 96732-2253
Tel (808) 871-8461 *Founded/Ownrshp* 1921
Sales 258.5MM[E] *EMP* 312
SIC 4911
Pr: Sharon Suzuki
Sls&Mrk Ex: Eilene Wachi

MAUI JIM SUNGLASSES
See MAUI JIM USA INC

D-U-N-S 18-783-1508 IMP/EXP
MAUI JIM USA INC
MAUI JIM SUNGLASSES
1 Aloha Ln, Peoria, IL 61615-1871
Tel (309) 589-6158 *Founded/Ownrshp* 1980
Sales 190.5MM[E] *EMP* 500
SIC 5099 3851

D-U-N-S 04-078-6414
MAUI MEMORIAL MEDICAL CENTER
MMMC
(*Suby of* HHSC) ★
221 Mahalani St, Wailuku, HI 96793-2526
Tel (808) 244-9056 *Founded/Ownrshp* 2014
Sales 200.7MM *EMP* 1
SIC 8062 General medical & surgical hospitals
Prin: Neil Tamayo

D-U-N-S 17-365-1191
■ **MAUI OPERATING LLC**
WESTIN MAUI RESORT & SPA, THE
(*Suby of* STARWOOD HOTELS & RESORTS WORLDWIDE LLC) ★
2365 Kaanapali Pkwy, Lahaina, HI 96761-1900
Tel (808) 661-2588 *Founded/Ownrshp* 1998
Sales 84.0MM *EMP* 750
SIC 7011 7389 Hotels & motels; Restaurant reservation service
Genl Mgr: Greg Lundberg

D-U-N-S 03-321-7241 IMP/EXP
■ **MAUI PINEAPPLE CO LTD**
(*Suby of* MAUI LAND & PINEAPPLE COMPANY, INC.)
200 Village Rd, Lahaina, HI 96761-8723
Tel (808) 877-1624 *Founded/Ownrshp* 1969
Sales 1.3MMM[E] *EMP* 1,000
SIC 2033 Fruits: packaged in cans, jars, etc.
CEO: David Cole
Ch Bd: Richard Cameron
Ch Bd: Daniel Kest
CEO: Douglas R Schenk
Ex VP: James McCann
Ex VP: Paul Meyer
VP: Eduardo Chenchin
VP: L Douglas Maccluer
VP: Brian B Orlopp

D-U-N-S 83-501-0190
MAUI SCHOOL DISTRICT
(*Suby of* OFFICE OF SUPERINTENDENT) ★
54 S High St Fl 4, Wailuku, HI 96793-2102
Tel (808) 984-8001 *Founded/Ownrshp* 1880
Sales 97.3MM[E] *EMP* 2,400
SIC 8211 9411 Public elementary & secondary schools;

MAULDIN ROAD WRRF
See RENEWABLE WATER RESOURCES

MAURICE ELECTRICAL SUPPLY CO.
See ELECTRICAL WHOLESALERS METRO DC INC

D-U-N-S 00-198-8567 IMP/EXP
MAURICE SPORTING GOODS INC
1910 Techny Rd, Northbrook, IL 60062-5356
Tel (847) 715-1500 *Founded/Ownrshp* 1923
Sales 473.7MM[E] *EMP* 800
SIC 5091 Fishing equipment & supplies; Hunting equipment & supplies
Pr: Jory Katlin
MIS Mgr: Joe Peters

D-U-N-S 05-343-0419 IMP
■ **MAURICES INC**
(*Suby of* DRESS BARN INC) ★
425 W Superior St, Duluth, MN 55802-2095
Tel (218) 727-8431 *Founded/Ownrshp* 1977
Sales 414.7MM[E] *EMP* 3,000
SIC 5621 Ready-to-wear apparel, women's
CEO: David Jaffe
Pr: Tim McGrath
Pr: Traci Warren
**CFO:* George Goldfarb
**CFO:* Brian Thun
**Chf Mktg O:* Ali Wing
Ofcr: Brad Hartmann
Ex VP: Sue Ross
Ex VP: Erin Stern
Sr VP: Mike Herrick
Sr VP: Neil McPhail
VP: Gerard Darby
VP: Angela Sawyer
Exec: Craig Dykstra
Exec: Lynne Mihalik

D-U-N-S 07-916-7968
MAURICIO ESPINOSA
BURGEONING
3523 Division St, Los Angeles, CA 90065-3301
Tel (909) 253-9108 *Founded/Ownrshp* 2010
Sales 125.2MM *EMP* 5
SIC 7389 Personal service agents, brokers & bureaus
Prin: Mauricio Espinosa

D-U-N-S 07-979-8822
MAURY COUNTY PUBLIC SCHOOLS
501 W 8th St, Columbia, TN 38401-3182
Tel (931) 388-8403 *Founded/Ownrshp* 2015
Sales 87.8MM *EMP* 1,640[E]
SIC 8211 Public elementary & secondary schools

D-U-N-S 06-909-2286
MAURY REGIONAL HOSPITAL
MAURY REGIONAL MEDICAL CENTER
1224 Trotwood Ave, Columbia, TN 38401-4802
Tel (931) 381-1111 *Founded/Ownrshp* 1953
Sales 232.9MM *EMP* 2,100
SIC 8062 General medical & surgical hospitals
CEO: Alan Watson
**COO:* Paul Betz
CFO: Nick Swift
Chf Nrs Of: Jamie Davis
Adm Dir: Deborah Lumpkins
CIO: Jim Parcel
MIS Dir: Kyle Jones
QA Dir: Susan Pope
Dir IT: Bobby Ellis
Dir IT: Cindy Kington
IT Man: Warren Robinson

MAURY REGIONAL MEDICAL CENTER
See MAURY REGIONAL HOSPITAL

D-U-N-S 61-317-8701 IMP/EXP
MAUSER USA LLC
(*Suby of* MAUSER HOLDING INTERNATIONAL GMBH)
35 Cotters Ln, East Brunswick, NJ 08816-2032
Tel (732) 353-7100 *Founded/Ownrshp* 2006
Sales 480.3MM[E] *EMP* 1,000
SIC 3412 2655 Barrels, shipping: metal; Fiber cans, drums & containers
Treas: Elizabeth G Miller
VP: Michael Steubing
VP: Siegfried Weber
Dir IT: Christopher B Lind
Opers Mgr: George Guerrero
Plnt Mgr: David Busby
Plnt Mgr: Graeme Jones
Manager: Debbie Kirkland
Sls Mgr: Brandon Silver

MAVERICK ELECTRONICS
See HEILIND ELECTRONICS INC

D-U-N-S 02-517-0307
MAVERICK PUMP SERVICES LLC
9791 Titan Park Cir, Littleton, CO 80125-9345
Tel (303) 981-8349 *Founded/Ownrshp* 2008
Sales 500.0MM *EMP* 12
SIC 7389

MAVERICK QUICK SHOPS
See COX OIL CO INC

D-U-N-S 14-740-3930
■ **MAVERICK TECHNOLOGIES HOLDINGS LLC**
MAVERICK TECNOLOGIES
(*Suby of* ROCKWELL AUTOMATION INC) ★
265 Admiral Trost Rd, Columbia, IL 62236-2173
Tel (618) 281-9100 *Founded/Ownrshp* 2016
Sales 149.6MM[E] *EMP* 7[E]
SIC 8711 8748 1731 Consulting engineer; Business consulting; Electrical work
CEO: Paul J Galeski
Sr VP: John Mills
Sr VP: Suzanne Scrabis
VP: Paul Dunn
VP: Jim Huff
VP: Greg Millinger
VP: Larry Ray

D-U-N-S 13-376-4030
■ **MAVERICK TECHNOLOGIES LLC**
(*Suby of* MAVERICK TECNOLOGIES) ★
265 Admiral Trost Rd, Columbia, IL 62236-2173
Tel (618) 281-9100 *Founded/Ownrshp* 1999
Sales 148.4MM[E] *EMP* 400
SIC 8711 8748 1731 Consulting engineer; Business consulting; Electrical work
CEO: Paul J Galeski
CFO: Matt Johnson
Sr VP: Robert E Gellings
Sr VP: Kirk Norris
VP: Paul D Dunn
VP: Peter Esparrago
VP: Mark Hall
VP: Charles Judy
VP: Stephanie Maclean
VP: Larry Ray
VP: Bill Stew
VP: Wade Stewart

MAVERICK TECNOLOGIES
See MAVERICK TECHNOLOGIES HOLDINGS LLC

D-U-N-S 09-992-3310
MAVERICK TRANSPORTATION LLC
(*Suby of* MAVERICK USA INC) ★
13301 Valentine Rd, North Little Rock, AR 72117-9311
Tel (501) 955-1222 *Founded/Ownrshp* 1980
Sales 267.8MM[E] *EMP* 1,771
Accts Hudson & Cisne
SIC 4213 Building materials transport
Ch: Steven Williams
**COO:* Stephen Selig
**Ex VP:* Doug Richey
VP: Justin Brown
**VP:* Letha Haymes
Exec: Jim Paladino
Manager: Drew Allbritton

D-U-N-S 08-691-8398 IMP/EXP
MAVERICK TUBE CORP
TENARIS
(*Suby of* TENARIS SA)
2200 West Loop S Ste 800, Houston, TX 77027-3532
Tel (713) 767-4400 *Founded/Ownrshp* 1977
Sales 420.0MM[E] *EMP* 1,577
SIC 3317 Steel pipe & tubes; Welded pipe & tubes; Well casing, wrought: welded, lock joint or heavy riveted
CEO: Paolo Rocca
CFO: Edgardo Carlos
**CFO:* Chris North
Sls Mgr: Carolina Robledo
Board of Directors: Brad Lowe

D-U-N-S 83-297-6703
MAVERICK USA INC
13301 Valentine Rd, North Little Rock, AR 72117-9311
Tel (501) 945-6130 *Founded/Ownrshp* 1980
Sales 267.8MM[E] *EMP* 1,771[E]
SIC 4213 Building materials transport
Pr: Stephen Selig
**CEO:* Steve Williams
**CFO:* John A Culp
Ex VP: Kim Gary
VP: Debbie Mitchell
VP: Dean Newell
VP Opers: John Coppens

D-U-N-S 00-794-7997
MAVERIK INC
(*Suby of* FLYING J) ★
185 S State St Ste 800, Salt Lake City, UT 84111-1549
Tel (801) 936-9155 *Founded/Ownrshp* 1959, 2012
Sales 1.0MMM[E] *EMP* 2,900
SIC 5541 5411 Filling stations, gasoline; Convenience stores, chain
Pr: Mike Call

D-U-N-S 80-055-4896 IMP
MAVERIK LACROSSE LLC
(*Suby of* KOHLBERG SPORTS GROUP INC) ★
535 W 24th St Fl 5, New York, NY 10011-1140
Tel (516) 213-3050 *Founded/Ownrshp* 2010
Sales 231.9M^E *EMP* 5,019^E
SIC 3949 Lacrosse equipment & supplies, general

MAVIS DISCOUNT TIRE
See MAVIS TIRE SUPPLY LLC

D-U-N-S 01-291-5732 IMP
MAVIS TIRE SUPPLY LLC
MAVIS DISCOUNT TIRE
358 Saw Mill River Rd # 17, Millwood, NY 10546-1054
Tel (914) 984-2500 *Founded/Ownrshp* 1964, 1983
Sales 1.6MMM^E *EMP* 3,000
SIC 5014 5531 Automobile tires & tubes; Truck tires & tubes; Automotive tires
Brnch Mgr: Alberto Olaya

D-U-N-S 04-259-3343
MAX ARNOLD & SONS LLC
MAXFUEL C-STORES
702 N Main St, Hopkinsville, KY 42240-2790
Tel (270) 885-8488 *Founded/Ownrshp* 1961
Sales 231.1MM^E *EMP* 230
SIC 5171 5541 5411 5812 Petroleum bulk stations; Gasoline service stations; Convenience stores, chain; Delicatessen (eating places)
Pr: Bob Arnold
CFO: Gary Logan
* *Treas:* Doris Imogene Arnold
Ex VP: Gerald White
Off Mgr: Eddie Prevette
Plnt Mgr: Darin Stevens

D-U-N-S 01-235-8461 IMP
MAX FINKELSTEIN INC
2840 31st St, Astoria, NY 11102-2131
Tel (718) 274-8900 *Founded/Ownrshp* 1919
Sales 176.9MM^E *EMP* 150
SIC 5014 5531 Automobile tires & tubes; Truck tires & tubes; Automotive tires; Automobile & truck equipment & parts
Pr: Harold Finkelstein
* *VP:* Jerome Finkelstein
* *VP:* Scott Pattcoff
* *VP:* Howard Rosenthal
* *VP:* Ira Silver
Dir IT: Max Finkelstein
IT Man: Michael Sedlock

D-U-N-S 08-165-1150
MAX FOOTE CONSTRUCTION CO LLC
225 Antibes St W Ste 3, Mandeville, LA 70448-4793
Tel (985) 624-8569 *Founded/Ownrshp* 1979
Sales 96.1MM^E *EMP* 140
SIC 1629 Waste water & sewage treatment plant construction
CEO: Max F Foote Jr
* *Pr:* Roy Thompson
* *CEO:* Max E Foote Jr
* *VP:* David Brown
* *VP:* Dana B Bullard
* *VP:* Thomas Deville
* *VP:* Kenneth Emrick
VP: Bernie Isom
Off Mgr: Chris Sharp
Mtls Mgr: Ralph Holloway

D-U-N-S 14-717-6218 IMP
MAX GROUP CORP
17011 Green Dr, City of Industry, CA 91745-1800
Tel (626) 935-0050 *Founded/Ownrshp* 1985
Sales 88.6MM^E *EMP* 75^E
SIC 5045 Computer peripheral equipment; Disk drives; Keying equipment; Printers, computer
CEO: Su-Tzu Tsai
* *Pr:* Chung-Jen Tsai
Ofcr: Ellen Yi
Sales Asso: Vivi Veronica

MAX LEATHER
See GBG USA INC

D-U-N-S 09-945-7616 IMP
MAX LEON INC
MAX STUDIO.COM
3100 New York Dr, Pasadena, CA 91107-1524
Tel (626) 797-6886 *Founded/Ownrshp* 1979
Sales 124.0MM^E *EMP* 500
SIC 2339 5632 Sportswear, women's; Apparel accessories
Pr: Leon Max
Exec: Margaret Kessler
DP Exec: Matt Rich

D-U-N-S 62-163-7474 IMP
MAX RAVE LLC
(*Suby of* BCBG MAX AZRIA GROUP LLC) ★
2761 Fruitland Ave, Vernon, CA 90058-3607
Tel (201) 861-1416 *Founded/Ownrshp* 2006
Sales 216.2MM^E *EMP* 2,900
SIC 5621 Ready-to-wear apparel, women's
CEO: Max Azria

MAX STUDIO.COM
See MAX LEON INC

D-U-N-S 60-245-4944 IMP/EXP
MAXCESS INTERNATIONAL CORP
(*Suby of* MAXCESS INTERNATIONAL HOLDING CORP) ★
222 W Memorial Rd, Oklahoma City, OK 73114-2300
Tel (405) 755-1600 *Founded/Ownrshp* 1989
Sales 137.2MM^E *EMP* 690
SIC 3554 3565 6719 Paper industries machinery; Packaging machinery; Investment holding companies, except banks
CFO: Merlyn D Devries
VP: Sean Craig
VP: Marcel Hage
* *VP:* Tom Herold
Mng Dir: David Calhoun
Dist Mgr: Jan Gronewold
Dist Mgr: Thomas G Varner
Genl Mgr: Francesco Cristante
Genl Mgr: Robert Liu
Dir IT: Mike Schlosser
Mfg Dir: Karen Delong

D-U-N-S 07-925-8855
MAXCESS INTERNATIONAL HOLDING CORP
(*Suby of* WH ACQUISITIONS INC) ★
222 W Memorial Rd, Oklahoma City, OK 73114-2300
Tel (405) 755-1600 *Founded/Ownrshp* 2014
Sales 150.9MM^E *EMP* 690^E
SIC 3554 3565 6719 Paper industries machinery; Packaging machinery; Investment holding companies, except banks
CEO: Greg Jehlik
* *COO:* Doug Knudtson
CFO: Merlyn Devries
* *CFO:* Dave Hawkins
Off Admin: Holly Wernsing

D-U-N-S 06-884-9108 IMP
MAXCO SUPPLY INC (CA)
605 S Zediker Ave, Parlier, CA 93648-2033
Tel (559) 646-8449 *Founded/Ownrshp* 1972
Sales 178.6MM^E *EMP* 200
SIC 5113 2436 3554 Shipping supplies; Softwood veneer & plywood; Box making machines, paper
Pr: Max Flaming
* *COO:* David Bryant
VP: Kevin Martin
* *VP Mfg:* Robert Grote

MAXFUEL C-STORES
See MAX ARNOLD & SONS LLC

D-U-N-S 08-934-7736
■ MAXI DRUG INC
RITE AID
(*Suby of* RITE AID CORP) ★
30 Hunter Ln, Camp Hill, PA 17011-2400
Tel (717) 761-2633 *Founded/Ownrshp* 2007
Sales 71.8MM^E *EMP* 5,000
SIC 5912 Drug stores & proprietary stores
Ch Bd: John T Standley

MAXIFACIAL DENTAL SURGERY
See DARTMOUTH-HITCHCOCK MEDICAL CENTER

D-U-N-S 14-507-9708
MAXIFACIAL DENTAL SURGERY
MARY HITCHCOCK MEMORIAL HOSP
1 Medical Center Dr, Lebanon, NH 03756-1000
Tel (603) 650-5000 *Founded/Ownrshp* 1983
Sales 5.0MMM *EMP* 7,500
Accts Ernst & Young Us Llp Indian
SIC 8011 Cardiologist & cardio-vascular specialist
Pr: Nancy Formella
* *COO:* Daniel Jantzen
Ofcr: Thomas Corindia
Ofcr: Arthur Nichols
Dir Rad: Jocelyn D Chertoff
Dir Rad: Marc Seltzer
Off Mgr: Catherine I Garfield-Legare
Off Mgr: Donna Pourby
Mktg Mgr: Kathleen Barrell
Mktg Mgr: Rolf Olsen
Pathlgst: Nora R Atcliffe

D-U-N-S 36-218-2185
■ MAXIM CRANE WORKS HOLDINGS INC
(*Suby of* APOLLO GLOBAL MANAGEMENT LLC) ★
1225 Wash Pike Ste 100, Bridgeville, PA 15017-2844
Tel (412) 504-0200 *Founded/Ownrshp* 1998
Sales 302.4MM^E *EMP* 945^E
SIC 7353 7359 Heavy construction equipment rental; Equipment rental & leasing
VP: Don Goebel
* *CFO:* Jay Vanhorn
VP: John Werner
VP Admn: Richard Swartz

D-U-N-S 36-218-5451
■ MAXIM CRANE WORKS LP
(*Suby of* MAXIM CRANE WORKS HOLDINGS INC) ★
1225 Wash Pike Ste 100, Bridgeville, PA 15017-2844
Tel (412) 504-0200 *Founded/Ownrshp* 1994
Sales 302.4MM^E *EMP* 2,000
SIC 7353 Heavy construction equipment rental
CEO: Bryan Carlisle
Sr VP: Larry T Rettinger
VP: Don Goebel
VP: Joe Keefe
Off Mgr: Fawn Macey
Dir IT: Gary Perez
Dir IT: Sal Pirozzi
Trfc Dir: Jonathan Costa
Sfty Mgr: Thomas Lovel
Sfty Mgr: Mark Wetzel
Opers Mgr: Kenneth Lookingbill

MAXIM EGG FARMS
See MAXIM FARM EGG CO INC

D-U-N-S 05-030-8311
MAXIM FARM EGG CO INC
MAXIM EGG FARMS
580 Maxim Dr, Boling, TX 77420-0020
Tel (979) 657-2891 *Founded/Ownrshp* 1962
Sales 107.0MM^E *EMP* 45
SIC 5144 Eggs
CEO: Vincent J Reina
* *Pr:* Vincent Reina Jr
CFO: Michael Castleberry
* *VP:* Christofer Reina

D-U-N-S 13-184-2531
MAXIM GROUP LLC
405 Lexington Ave Fl 2, New York, NY 10174-0003
Tel (212) 895-3500 *Founded/Ownrshp* 2002
Sales 118.9MM^E *EMP* 350
SIC 6211 Brokers, security
CEO: Michael Rabinowitz
* *COO:* John Sergio
* *CFO:* Timothy G Murphy
Ofcr: Gerard McCarthy
Sr VP: Stephen Anderson
Sr VP: Daniel Balestra
Sr VP: John-Paul Cirigliano
Sr VP: John Conover
Sr VP: Paul Cooney
Sr VP: David Diaz
Sr VP: Kenneth Epstein
Sr VP: Keith Goodman
Sr VP: Peter Kaufman
Sr VP: Brian Kinstlinger
Sr VP: Jason Kolbert
Sr VP: Josh Levy
Sr VP: Kenneth McDonald
Sr VP: Anthony Musto
Sr VP: Dennis Nitka
Sr VP: Jason Sardo
Sr VP: Dirk Van Erp

MAXIM HEALTH CARE
See MAXIM HEALTH SYSTEMS LLC

D-U-N-S 15-288-6479
MAXIM HEALTH SYSTEMS LLC
MAXIM HEALTH CARE
(*Suby of* MAXIM HEALTHCARE SERVICES INC) ★
7227 Lee Deforest Dr, Columbia, MD 21046-3236
Tel (410) 910-1500 *Founded/Ownrshp* 1988
Sales 189.6MM^E *EMP* 4,150
SIC 8011 8099 Medical centers; Health screening service
CFO: Dave Franchak

D-U-N-S 60-629-0401
MAXIM HEALTHCARE SERVICES INC
7227 Lee Deforest Dr, Columbia, MD 21046-3236
Tel (410) 910-1500 *Founded/Ownrshp* 1988
Sales 1.2MMM *EMP* 35,000
Accts Pricewaterhousecoopers Llp Ba
SIC 8082 Home health care services
CEO: William Butz
COO: Chris Powell
COO: Christopher Powell
* *COO:* Paula Sotir
CFO: Raymond Carbone
Ofcr: Daniel V Fache
* *Ofcr:* Julie Judge
Sr VP: Melissa Fannin
Sr VP: Chery Nelson
* *VP:* Jacqueline Baratian
VP: Bart Kelly
* *VP:* W John Langley
* *VP:* Toni Jean Lisa
VP: Nancy Roy
VP: Lisa Toni-Jean
Dir Risk M: Eric Stieritz
Dir Bus: Paul Davis

D-U-N-S 10-211-2489 IMP
▲ MAXIM INTEGRATED PRODUCTS INC
160 Rio Robles, San Jose, CA 95134-1813
Tel (408) 601-1000 *Founded/Ownrshp* 1983
Sales 2.1MMM *EMP* 8,250
Accts Deloitte & Touche Llp San Jo
Tkr Sym MXIM *Exch* NGS
SIC 3674 Microcircuits, integrated (semiconductor)
Pr: Tunc Doluca
* *Ch Bd:* William P Sullivan
CFO: Bruce E Kiddoo
Sr VP: Edwin B Medlin
Sr VP: Edwin Medlin
Sr VP: Christopher J Neil
VP: David A Caron
VP: Randall Wollschlager
VP: Steve Yamasaki
Ex Dir: John Mutschink
Prgrm Mgr: Chris Hopwood
Board of Directors: Tracy Accardi, James R Bergman, Joseph R Bronson, Robert E Grady, B Kipling Hagopian, William D Watkins, A R Frank Wazzan, Maryann Wright

MAXIMUM QUALITY FD PPR & PLTY
See MAXIMUM QUALITY FOODS INC

D-U-N-S 07-817-5023
MAXIMUM QUALITY FOODS INC
MAXIMUM QUALITY FD PPR & PLTY
3351 Tremley Point Rd # 2, Linden, NJ 07036-3575
Tel (908) 474-0003 *Founded/Ownrshp* 1975
Sales 129.3MM^E *EMP* 100
SIC 5141 Groceries, general line
Pr: Gary Roccaro

D-U-N-S 36-422-1593
■ MAXIMUS FEDERAL SERVICES INC
(*Suby of* MAXIMUS INC) ★
1891 Metro Center Dr, Reston, VA 20190-5287
Tel (703) 251-8500 *Founded/Ownrshp* 2005
Sales 234.2MM^E *EMP* 1,350
SIC 8742 Hospital & health services consultant
Pr: Thomas Romeo

D-U-N-S 83-241-1727
MAXIMUS HOLDINGS INC
(*Suby of* SYMPHONY TECHNOLOGY GROUP LLC) ★
2475 Hanover St, Palo Alto, CA 94304-1114
Tel (650) 935-9500 *Founded/Ownrshp* 2009
Sales 214.5MM^E *EMP* 1,006^E
SIC 7372 Prepackaged software
CEO: Dominic Gallello
* *CFO:* Jim Johnson

D-U-N-S 08-234-7477
▲ MAXIMUS INC
1891 Metro Center Dr, Reston, VA 20190-5287
Tel (703) 251-8500 *Founded/Ownrshp* 1975
Sales 2.4MMM *EMP* 17,000
Tkr Sym MMS *Exch* NYS
SIC 8742 8741 Management consulting services; Management services
CEO: Richard A Montoni
* *Ch Bd:* Peter B Pond
* *Pr:* Bruce L Caswell
* *CFO:* Richard J Nadeau
CFO: David N Walker
Ofcr: Paul Mack
Ex VP: Gary Garofalo
Sr VP: Bruce Cowans
Sr VP: Harold Horton
Sr VP: Nora Paape
Sr VP: Steven Whitney
Sr VP: Chris Zitzow
VP: Kelly Blaschke
VP: Susan Boren
VP: Walt Carper
VP: Nelson Clugston
VP: John Donohue
VP: Viann Hardy
VP: Jana Jones
VP: Kevan McCallum
VP: Dan Miller
Board of Directors: Anne K Altman, Russell A Beliveau, John J Haley, Paul R Lederer, Raymond B Ruddy, Marilyn R Seymann, James R Thompson Jr Welli

D-U-N-S 00-535-7355 IMP
MAXION WHEELS
HAYES LEMMERZ INTERNATIONAL
(*Suby of* IOCHPE HOLDINGS LLC) ★
39500 Orchard Hill Pl # 500, Novi, MI 48375-5370
Tel (734) 737-5000 *Founded/Ownrshp* 2012
Sales 2.0MMM *EMP* 8,000
SIC 3714 Wheels, motor vehicle
CEO: Pieter Klinkers
Pr: Don Polk
COO: Michael Wood
CFO: Oscar Becker
Treas: Eric Moraw
VP: Steven Esau
VP: Kelly Knepley
VP: John A Salvette
Prin: Matt Gorman
Dir IT: Kai Kronenberg
IT Man: Steve Monroe

D-U-N-S 03-076-5429
MAXION WHEELS USA LLC
(*Suby of* HAYES LEMMERZ INTERNATIONAL) ★
39500 Orchard Hill Pl # 500, Novi, MI 48375-5370
Tel (734) 737-5000 *Founded/Ownrshp* 2012
Sales 680.8MM^E *EMP* 6,500
SIC 3714 Wheels, motor vehicle
CEO: Pieter Klinkers
* *Treas:* Eric Moraw
* *VP:* Steve Esau
* *VP:* John Salvette

D-U-N-S 08-851-3739
MAXIS HEALTH SYSTEM
(*Suby of* CATHOLIC HEALTH EAST) ★
3805 West Chester Pike # 100, Newtown Square, PA 19073-2329
Tel (570) 281-1000 *Founded/Ownrshp* 1998
Sales 19.5MM^E *EMP* 1,200
Accts Deloitte Tax Llp Philadelphia
SIC 8062 General medical & surgical hospitals
Pr: Mary Theresa Vautrinop
* *Pr:* Sister Jean Coughlin
* *CFO:* Richard Hager
VP: Ron Boldt
CTO: Joseph Casarella

D-U-N-S 17-876-5702 IMP
▲ MAXLINEAR INC
5966 La Place Ct Ste 100, Carlsbad, CA 92008-8830
Tel (760) 692-0711 *Founded/Ownrshp* 2003
Sales 300.3MM *EMP* 500
Tkr Sym MXL *Exch* NYS
SIC 3674 Semiconductors & related devices
Ch Bd: Kishore Seendripu
CFO: Adam C Spice
VP: Tim Gallagher
VP: Michael J Lachance
VP: Dana McCarty
VP: Raja Pullela
VP: Madhukar Reddy
VP: William G Torgerson
VP: Brendan Walsh
CTO: Curtis Ling
Mktg Dir: Stefan Szasz
Board of Directors: Steven C Craddock, Albert J Moyer, Thomas E Pardun, Donald E Schrock, Theodore Tewksbury

D-U-N-S 14-785-5340 IMP
MAXMARA USA INC
(*Suby of* MAX MARA FASHION GROUP SRL)
555 Madison Ave Fl 10, New York, NY 10022-3337
Tel (212) 536-6200 *Founded/Ownrshp* 1987
Sales 96.3MM^E *EMP* 300
SIC 5621 Women's clothing stores
Ch Bd: Luigi Maramotti
* *Pr:* Luigi Caroggio
* *Treas:* Gabriele D Agostino
* *VP:* Kristine Westerby

D-U-N-S 06-769-4315 EXP
■ MAXON FURNITURE INC
(*Suby of* HNI CORP) ★
2210 2nd Ave, Muscatine, IA 52761-5257
Tel (800) 876-4274 *Founded/Ownrshp* 2002
Sales 95.3MM^E *EMP* 450
SIC 2522 Panel systems & partitions, office: except wood
Pr: Woody Brooks

D-U-N-S 87-620-5774 IMP
MAXON LIFT CORP
11921 Slauson Ave, Santa Fe Springs, CA 90670-2221
Tel (562) 464-0099 *Founded/Ownrshp* 1957
Sales 221.8MM^E *EMP* 110
SIC 5084 3537 3534 Lift trucks & parts; Industrial trucks & tractors; Elevators & moving stairways
Pr: Casey Lugash
Ex VP: Lawerence Lugash
* *VP:* Brenda Leung
VP: Bill Moore
VP: John Teng
Exec: Lee Garrett
CIO: Roy Rubio
DP Dir: Arnold Kowal
QA Dir: Woody Woodrum
IT Man: Lorena Baltazar
Natl Sales: Darres Reeder

D-U-N-S 92-674-1893
MAXOR NATIONAL PHARMACY SERVICES LLC
MAXOR PHARMACIES
320 S Polk St Ste 900, Amarillo, TX 79101-1429
Tel (806) 324-5400 *Founded/Ownrshp* 1990
Sales 104.3MM^E *EMP* 481

Accts Brown Graham & Company Amaril
SIC 5912 Drug stores
CEO: John Ward
**Pr:* Carl Birdsong
**CFO:* Jerry Havard
**Ch:* Jerry Hodge
Treas: Cynthia Garner
**Sec:* Cynthia Carner
Sr VP: Steve Smith
VP: Heath Hodge
VP: Kendall Lynch
VP: Hanna Rubenzohl
VP: Allen D Sapp Jr
VP: Allen Sapp
VP: Angela Serioharney

MAXOR PHARMACIES
See MAXOR NATIONAL PHARMACY SERVICES LLC

D-U-N-S 79-202-9642
▲ MAXPOINT INTERACTIVE INC
3020 Carrington Mill Blvd, Morrisville, NC 27560-5432
Tel (800) 916-9960 *Founded/Ownrshp* 2006
Sales 140.1MM *EMP* 406E
Tkr Sym MXPT *Exch* NGM
SIC 7311 8711 Advertising agencies; Engineering services
Ch Bd: Joseph Epperson
COO: Gretchen Joyce
CFO: Brad Schomber
Genl Mgr: Amy Gittelman
CTO: Kurt Carlson
Snr Mgr: Kate Holmes
Board of Directors: Kevin Dulsky, Lynnette Frank, Len Jordan, Augustus Tai

D-U-N-S 17-766-7219 IMP
MAXTOR CORP
(*Suby of* SEAGATE TECHNOLOGY (US) HOLDINGS INC) ★
4575 Scotts Valley Dr, Scotts Valley, CA 95066-4517
Tel (831) 438-6550 *Founded/Ownrshp* 2007
Sales 418.7MME *EMP* 15,085
SIC 3572

D-U-N-S 07-981-1123
MAXUM ENTERPRISES LLC
PILOT THOMAS LOGISTICS
201 N Rupert St Ste 101, Fort Worth, TX 76107-1460
Tel (817) 877-8300 *Founded/Ownrshp* 2012
Sales 740.6MME *EMP* 110E
SIC 5171 5172 Petroleum terminals; Lubricating oils & greases; Engine fuels & oils; Gases, liquefied petroleum (propane)
CEO: Scott Prince
**VP:* Jeff Roberts
VP: Amit Walia

D-U-N-S 78-516-3291
MAXUM PETROLEUM INC
(*Suby of* PILOT FLYING J) ★
5508 Lonas Dr, Knoxville, TN 37909-3221
Tel (865) 588-7488 *Founded/Ownrshp* 2012
Sales 221.8MME *EMP* 399
SIC 5172 Crude oil; Engine fuels & oils; Diesel fuel; Gasoline
CEO: James A Haslan III
**Pr:* Michael Hughes
**COO:* George Ristevski
**Treas:* Paul H Runko
Sr VP: Michael A Brown
Sr VP: Steve Cross
Sr VP: Jeffrey Dill
VP: Mike McDonald
VP: Ryan A Secrist
Opers Supe: John R Cunningham

D-U-N-S 19-927-6960
MAXUS COMMUNICATIONS LLC
(*Suby of* WPP 2012 LIMITED)
498 Fashion Ave, New York, NY 10018-6798
Tel (212) 297-8300 *Founded/Ownrshp* 2005
Sales 103.5MME *EMP* 1,000
SIC 8999 Communication services
Pr: Louis Jones
Sr Pt: Jane Barasch
Sr Pt: Tara Cioffi
Sr Pt: Laura Lefever
Sr Pt: Tobias Wolf
CEO: Donna Triolo
COO: Carla Loffredo
CFO: Neil Sternberg
Ofcr: Jonathan Adams
Dir Bus: Karen Kaufman
Dir Bus: Andreas Rapp

D-U-N-S 82-636-9720
MAXWELL FOODS LLC
938 Millers Chapel Rd, Goldsboro, NC 27534-7772
Tel (919) 778-3130 *Founded/Ownrshp* 1989
Sales 51.6MME *EMP* 1,000
SIC 0213 Hogs
Pr: J L Maxwell III
CFO: Tom Howell
VP: Jere Walter Pelletier III
Genl Mgr: Robert Ivey

D-U-N-S 00-956-7942 IMP/EXP
▲ MAXWELL TECHNOLOGIES INC
3888 Calle Fortunada, San Diego, CA 92123-1825
Tel (858) 503-3200 *Founded/Ownrshp* 1965
Sales 167.3MM *EMP* 451E
Tkr Sym MXWL *Exch* NGS
SIC 3629 Capacitors & condensers; Capacitors, a.c., for motors or fluorescent lamp ballasts; Capacitors, fixed or variable; Power conversion units, a.c. to d.c.: static-electric
Pr: Franz Fink
CFO: David Lyle
Sr VP: Olaf Muller
VP Sls: Donald Patrician
Board of Directors: Richard Bergman, Steven Bilodeau, Jorg Buchheim, Robert Guyett, Roger Howsmon, Yon Yoon Jorden, David Schlotterbeck

D-U-N-S 00-690-8156
MAXXAM INC
1330 Post Oak Blvd # 2000, Houston, TX 77056-3058
Tel (832) 251-5960 *Founded/Ownrshp* 1955, 2011
Sales 72.6MME *EMP* 1,080E
SIC 6531 7948 Real estate agent, residential; Real estate agent, commercial; Jockey, horse racing
Ch Bd: Charles E Hurwitz
**Pr:* Shawn M Hurwitz
CFO: Emily Madison
VP: John T Laduc
VP: Joshua A Reiss
VP: Ronald L Reman
IT Man: Dave Clark

D-U-N-S 05-652-5152 IMP/EXP
MAXXIM REBUILD CO LLC
(*Suby of* ALPHA NATURAL RESOURCES LLC) ★
5703 Crutchfield Dr, Norton, VA 24273-3902
Tel (276) 679-7020 *Founded/Ownrshp* 1988
Sales 209.5MME *EMP* 2,000
SIC 1241 Coal mining services

D-U-N-S 00-527-9864
MAXYIELD COOPERATIVE
CENEX
313 3rd Ave Nw, West Bend, IA 50597-8572
Tel (515) 887-7211 *Founded/Ownrshp* 1915
Sales 324.0MM *EMP* 157
Accts Meriwether Wilson And Company
SIC 5153 5191 2999 0723 Grain elevators; Farm supplies; Coke (not from refineries), petroleum; Bean cleaning services
CEO: Keith Heim
**Pr:* Howard Haas
**CEO:* Keith Hime
**Sec:* Eric Marchand
**VP:* David Garrelts
Genl Mgr: Keith Hein

D-U-N-S 08-158-2637
MAY INSTITUTE INC
41 Pacella Park Dr, Randolph, MA 02368-1755
Tel (781) 440-0400 *Founded/Ownrshp* 1975
Sales 99.6MM *EMP* 2,000
Accts Feeley & Driscoll Pc Boston
SIC 8361 Rehabilitation center, residential: health care incidental
Ch Bd: Jory Berkwits
**Pr:* Walter P Christian PHD
**CEO:* Lauren C Solotar
**COO:* Ralph B Sperry
**Treas:* Michael Milczarek
Trst: Richard Wichmann
**Ex VP:* Aubrey Macfarlane
Sr VP: Janet Mercier
VP: Terese Brennan
VP: Jocelyn Lemaire
VP: Stephen D Merrill

D-U-N-S 00-985-9430
MAY TRUCKING CO
4185 Brooklake Rd Ne, Salem, OR 97303-9729
Tel (503) 393-7030 *Founded/Ownrshp* 1966
Sales 210.0MM *EMP* 900
SIC 4213 Contract haulers; Refrigerated products transport
CEO: C Marvin May
**Pr:* David M Daniels
CFO: Andrew Mantey
**CFO:* Dave Temple
Exec: Scott Smith
Comm Dir: Lisa Davis
Trfc Dir: Kelly Lee
Opers Mgr: Kory Knox
Manager: Mike McNeal
Snr Mgr: Boyd Puckett

D-U-N-S 83-248-3924
MAYA MANAGEMENT GROUP LLC
11411 Hillguard Rd, Dallas, TX 75243-5501
Tel (214) 751-2290 *Founded/Ownrshp* 2008
Sales 100.0MM *EMP* 60
SIC 8742 Management consulting services

D-U-N-S 00-507-1642
MAYBELLINE INC
(*Suby of* LOREAL USA PRODUCTS) ★
575 5th Ave Bsmt Fl, New York, NY 10017-2446
Tel (212) 885-1310 *Founded/Ownrshp* 1915
Sales 45.0ME *EMP* 4,118
SIC 2844 2841 Toilet preparations; Cosmetic preparations; Toilet preparations; Perfumes & colognes; Soap: granulated, liquid, cake, flaked or chip
Pr: John R Wendt
**Ch Bd:* Robert N Hiatt
**Pr:* Gerald C Beddall
Pr: Jack J Bucher
Pr: Daniel J Coffey Jr
**Pr:* R Heard Murphy
**Pr:* Bernard M O'Brien
**Pr:* Robert W Pierce
Pr: Rich Ullrich
Pr: Gary C Wilkerson
**Pr:* Catherine H Wills

D-U-N-S 78-706-8209 IMP
MAYCO INTERNATIONAL LLC
(*Suby of* P.I.M. MANAGEMENT COMPANY)
42400 Merrill Rd, Sterling Heights, MI 48314-3238
Tel (586) 803-6000 *Founded/Ownrshp* 2013
Sales 268.9MME *EMP* 910
SIC 3089 Injection molding of plastics
CFO: Al Grajek
Ex VP: Tom Eckhout

MAYCO PLASTICS
See STONEBRIDGE INDUSTRIES INC

D-U-N-S 01-029-1136
MAYER BROWN LLP
71 S Wacker Dr Ste 1000, Chicago, IL 60606-4716
Tel (312) 782-0600 *Founded/Ownrshp* 1881, 1940
Sales 584.8MME *EMP* 5,334
SIC 8111 General practice law office
Pt: Tyrone C Fahner
Pt: Scott A Anenberg
Pt: Joel Bertocchi
Pt: Edward S Best
Pt: Bruce Bettigole
Pt: Timothy S Bishop
Pt: Robert E Bloch
Pt: Cynthia Burch
**Pt:* Alan S Cohen
Pt: Barbara E Cohen
Pt: Marc R Cohen
Pt: Joseph P Collins
Pt: Pat Conti
**Pt:* Debora De Hoyos
Pt: Thomas J Delaney
Pt: Douglas A Doetsch
Pt: Robert M Dow Jr
Pt: John Ferrell
Pt: Eric John Finseth
Pt: Robert V Fitzsimmons
Pt: Joseph Goldstein
Board of Directors: David Staiano

D-U-N-S 00-690-0419
MAYER ELECTRIC SUPPLY CO INC
3405 4th Ave S, Birmingham, AL 35222-2300
Tel (205) 583-3500 *Founded/Ownrshp* 1979
Sales 811.4MM *EMP* 900
SIC 5063 5719 Electrical apparatus & equipment; Lighting fixtures, commercial & industrial; Lighting fixtures; Lighting, lamps & accessories
Ch Bd: Nancy Collat Goedecke
**Pr:* Glenn Goedecke
**Pr:* Wes Smith
**COO:* Charles A Collat Jr
VP: Sheila Dale
VP: Michael Likis
VP: Karen Rogers
Brnch Mgr: Mark Gorfuch
Brnch Mgr: Ken Swank
IT Man: Dionne Posey
Opers Mgr: Jason Cates

D-U-N-S 07-926-2349
MAYERLING GROUP INC
12065 Creekview Rd, Granada Hills, CA 91344-2021
Tel (323) 707-4748 *Founded/Ownrshp* 2014
Sales 100.0MM *EMP* 37
SIC 8742 Hospital & health services consultant
Pr: Abraham Abramian

D-U-N-S 07-775-2780
MAYFIELD CITY SCHOOL DISTRICT
1101 Som Center Rd, Cleveland, OH 44124-2006
Tel (440) 995-6800 *Founded/Ownrshp* 1903
Sales 83.0MM *EMP* 729
Accts Mary Taylor Cpa/Robert R Hin
SIC 8211 Public elementary school; Public junior high school; Public senior high school
VP: George Hughes
IT Man: Darcy Klimkowski
Pr Dir: Laurie Uhlir
HC Dir: Denise Cirino

D-U-N-S 00-333-7268 IMP
■ MAYFIELD DAIRY FARMS LLC (TN)
(*Suby of* DEAN HOLDING CO) ★
806 E Madison Ave, Athens, TN 37303-3858
Tel (423) 745-2151 *Founded/Ownrshp* 1930, 1990
Sales 253.8MM *EMP* 1,700
SIC 2026 2024 Milk processing (pasteurizing, homogenizing, bottling); Ice cream, packaged: molded, on sticks, etc.
Off Mgr: Pat Purdy
Plnt Mgr: Mark Howard
Mktg Mgr: Cindy Ward

D-U-N-S 00-607-0775 IMP/EXP
MAYLINE INVESTMENTS INC
555 Skokie Blvd, Northbrook, IL 60062-2812
Tel (847) 948-9340 *Founded/Ownrshp* 2007
Sales 97.0MME *EMP* 401
SIC 2522 2521 Office furniture, except wood; Office cabinets & filing drawers: except wood; Panel systems & partitions, office: except wood; Wood office furniture
Ch Bd: Charles Barancik
**Pr:* Paul Simons
**Treas:* Michael E Gronli
**Ex VP:* Chris Mc Namee
**Ex VP:* Eric Volcheff
**VP:* Don Clements

D-U-N-S 00-193-6533
MAYMEAD FARMS INC
1995 Roan Creek Rd, Mountain City, TN 37683-7022
Tel (423) 727-2000 *Founded/Ownrshp* 1976
Sales 100.0MME *EMP* 6E
SIC 0212 Beef cattle except feedlots
Pr: Wally B Roark
**Sec:* Mae Mount Roark
**VP:* Thomas G Purpur

D-U-N-S 00-337-8320
MAYMEAD INC (TN)
(*Suby of* MAYMEAD FARMS INC) ★
1995 Roan Creek Rd, Mountain City, TN 37683-7022
Tel (423) 727-2000 *Founded/Ownrshp* 1930
Sales 100.0MM *EMP* 81E
SIC 1611 2951 5032 5191 Highway & street paving contractor; Asphalt paving mixtures & blocks; Aggregate; Farm supplies
Pr: Wiley B Roark
**Pr:* Barton K Mount
**Sec:* Mae Mount Roark
Brnch Mgr: David Worley

D-U-N-S 86-722-0261
■ MAYNE PHARMA INC
(*Suby of* MAYNE PHARMA GROUP LIMITED)
1240 Sugg Pkwy, Greenville, NC 27834-9006
Tel (252) 752-3800 *Founded/Ownrshp* 2012
Sales 85.0MM *EMP* 350E
SIC 5122 2834 Pharmaceuticals; Pharmaceutical preparations
Pr: Stefan Cross
**CFO:* Wes Edwards
VP: Jeffrey Basham
Dir Bus: Gary Cantrell
Cmptr Lab: Anthony Pipho
QA Dir: Melanie Little
IT Man: Melissa Gardner
Ql Cn Mgr: Rodney Hill
Snr Mgr: Richard Vinson

MAYO CLINIC
See MAYO FOUNDATION FOR MEDICAL EDUCATION AND RESEARCH

D-U-N-S 00-647-1700
MAYO CLINIC (MN)
(*Suby of* MAYO CLINIC ROCHESTER) ★
200 1st St Sw, Rochester, MN 55905-0002
Tel (507) 284-2511 *Founded/Ownrshp* 1919
Sales 1.7MMM *EMP* 32,271
SIC 8011 8062 8071 8733 8221

D-U-N-S 16-714-1923 IMP
MAYO CLINIC
MAYO CLINIC ROCHESTER
200 1st St Sw, Rochester, MN 55905-0002
Tel (507) 284-2511 *Founded/Ownrshp* 1819
Sales 9.4MMM *EMP* 67,000
Accts Mcgladrey Llp Minneapolis Mi
SIC 8062 8733 8071 8011 General medical & surgical hospitals; Noncommercial research organizations; Medical laboratories; Offices & clinics of medical doctors
Pr: John H Noseworthy
**CFO:* Kedrick D Adkins Jr
CFO: Jeff Bolton
CFO: Bradley Schmidt
**VP:* Jeffrey W Bolton
**VP:* Wyatt W Decker
**VP:* William C Rupp
**Prin:* Denis A Cortese
**Prin:* Paul Haines
QA Dir: Stephen Swenson
IT Man: Shashi Dewan

D-U-N-S 15-366-5211 IMP
MAYO CLINIC ARIZONA
MAYO CLINIC HOSPITAL
(*Suby of* MAYO CLINIC ROCHESTER) ★
13400 E Shea Blvd, Scottsdale, AZ 85259-5499
Tel (480) 301-8000 *Founded/Ownrshp* 1986
Sales 263.8MME *EMP* 2,800
SIC 8011 Primary care medical clinic; Physicians' office, including specialists
Ch Bd: Wyatt W Decker MD
V Ch: Amy Vrable
CFO: Mike Vuhl
CFO: Boris Zavalkovskiy
CIO: Jonathan Torrens
CTO: Kenneth Bobis
Dir IT: Maureen Rector
IT Man: John Custer
Surgeon: Alyssa D Baliad Chapital
Ansthlgy: Froukje M Beynen
Ansthlgy: Andrew D Gorlin

D-U-N-S 02-549-5461
MAYO CLINIC HEALTH SYSTEM
MIDDLEFORT CLINIC
733 W Clairemont Ave, Eau Claire, WI 54701-6117
Tel (715) 838-6968 *Founded/Ownrshp* 1990
Sales 209.4MM *EMP* 1
SIC 8011 Offices & clinics of medical doctors
Prin: Jeffery Bartynski MD

D-U-N-S 07-149-5303
MAYO CLINIC HEALTH SYSTEM - RED WING
(*Suby of* MAYO CLINIC ROCHESTER) ★
701 Hewitt Blvd, Red Wing, MN 55066-2848
Tel (651) 267-5000 *Founded/Ownrshp* 2012
Sales 99.0MM *EMP* 760
SIC 8062 General medical & surgical hospitals
CEO: Tom Witt
**CFO:* Michael Larson
**Chf Mktg O:* Jack Alexander MD
**VP:* Jan Graner
**VP:* Judy Treharne
Sales Asso: Jessica Hinckley
Sales Asso: Brenda Stephens
Surgeon: Joshua Bodie
Opthamlgy: Christopher J McDevitt
Podiatrist: Jennifer L Granquist

D-U-N-S 17-019-1662
MAYO CLINIC HEALTH SYSTEM -ST JAMES
(*Suby of* MAYO CLINIC) ★
1025 Marsh St, Mankato, MN 56001-4752
Tel (507) 625-4031 *Founded/Ownrshp* 1984
Sales 30.8MME *EMP* 1,300
SIC 8082 Home health care services
Pr: Greg Kutcher
Ofcr: Jerome Crest
VP: Richard Grace
Dir Sec: Ken Combs
IT Man: Jen Conway
Info Man: Sarah Daniels
Pathlgst: Tina Carns
Pathlgst: Jose Crespo
Pathlgst: Dennis Gremel
Surgeon: Albert R Harris
Doctor: John Haley
Board of Directors: Bob Weiss

D-U-N-S 09-858-1689
MAYO CLINIC HEALTH SYSTEM IN WAYCROSS INC
(*Suby of* MAYO CLINIC ROCHESTER) ★
1900 Tebeau St, Waycross, GA 31501-6357
Tel (912) 283-3030 *Founded/Ownrshp* 2012
Sales 149.4MM *EMP* 1,300
SIC 8062 8051 General medical & surgical hospitals; Skilled nursing care facilities
CEO: Kenneth T Calamia
Ofcr: Robert Trimm
Genl Mgr: Amanda Baldwin
Genl Mgr: Kristie Eunice
Ansthlgy: Victor J Aranda
Pgrm Dir: Angela Jenkins-Jacobs

D-U-N-S 07-649-9565
MAYO CLINIC HEALTH SYSTEM—OWATONNA
(*Suby of* MAYO CLINIC ROCHESTER) ★
2200 Nw 26th St, Owatonna, MN 55060-5503
Tel (507) 451-1120 *Founded/Ownrshp* 2009

Sales 89.3MM *EMP* 350
SIC 8011 Clinic, operated by physicians
Pr: Brian Bunkers
Genl Mgr: James Tarasovitch
Surgeon: K Dean Olsen
Doctor: Kari E Bunkers MD
Doctor: Anthony F Chou MD
Doctor: Greg Jones
Doctor: Henry Krahn
Doctor: Kiernan J Minehan MD
Doctor: Vikas S Mittal MD
Doctor: Gerard Ohalloran
Doctor: Steven J Thompson MD

D-U-N-S 15-758-5043
MAYO CLINIC HEALTH SYSTEM-ALBERT LEA AND AUSTIN
(*Suby of* MAYO CLINIC) ★
404 W Fountain St, Albert Lea, MN 56007-2437
Tel (507) 373-2384 *Founded/Ownrshp* 2005
Sales 114.1MME *EMP* 1,200E
SIC 8062 8069 8051 8063 8011 General medical & surgical hospitals; Substance abuse hospitals; Skilled nursing care facilities; Psychiatric hospitals; Clinic, operated by physicians
CEO: Mark Ciota
CFO: Scott Rafferty
VP: Ronald Harmon
**VP:* Bruce Mairose

D-U-N-S 07-652-0667
MAYO CLINIC HEALTH SYSTEM-AUSTIN
(*Suby of* MAYO CLINIC) ★
1000 1st Dr Nw, Austin, MN 55912-2941
Tel (507) 433-7351 *Founded/Ownrshp* 2005
Sales 120.4MM *EMP* 778
SIC 8399 Health systems agency
Pr: David Agerter
CFO: Dick Graber
CFO: Kristen Johnson
CFO: Paula A Nelson
VP: Sarah Daniels
VP Opers: Laura Lowe
Nutrtnst: Tianna Bechly
Doctor: James Burke MD
Doctor: Sunil Khanna
Doctor: Waclaw Wedzina
Phys Thrpy: Debra Berg

D-U-N-S 02-329-6390
MAYO CLINIC HEALTH SYSTEM-EAU CLAIRE CLINIC INC (WI)
(*Suby of* MAYO CLINIC) ★
1400 Bellinger St, Eau Claire, WI 54703-5222
Tel (715) 838-5222 *Founded/Ownrshp* 1992
Sales 95.0MME *EMP* 4,000
Accts Wipfli Llp Eau Claire Wiscon
SIC 8062 General medical & surgical hospitals
CEO: Dr Randall Linton
Off Mgr: Janet Goodwin
Surgeon: Aundrea Rainville
Obsttrcn: Jennifer S Bantz
Obsttrcn: Blenda Yun
Ansthlgy: Xun Zhu
Doctor: Robert C Peck
Doctor: Matthew J Ritter

D-U-N-S 11-427-6769
MAYO CLINIC HEALTH SYSTEM-FRANCISCAN HEALTHCARE INC
(*Suby of* MAYO CLINIC) ★
700 West Ave S, La Crosse, WI 54601-4783
Tel (608) 785-0940 *Founded/Ownrshp* 1992
Sales 116.8M *EMP* 3,445
SIC 8062 8051 General medical & surgical hospitals; Convalescent home with continuous nursing care
CEO: Timothy Johnson MD
Dir Vol: Elaine George
**CEO:* Robert Nesse MD
**CFO:* Tom Tiggelaar
CFO: Tom Tiggelar
**VP:* Ron Paczkowski
Dir Lab: Gordon Triebs
Dir Rad: Jonathan Uy
Netwrk Mgr: Dean Kastenschmidt
Sfty Dirs: Phil Neimer
Ansthlgy: Steven C Borene

D-U-N-S 07-971-3459
MAYO CLINIC HEALTH SYSTEM-FRANCISCAN MEDICAL CENTER INC
700 West Ave S, La Crosse, WI 54601-4783
Tel (608) 785-0940 *Founded/Ownrshp* 1883
Sales 452.1MM *EMP* 3,300
SIC 8062 General medical & surgical hospitals
Pr: Robert Nesse
CFO: Mike Buhl
**CFO:* Thomas Tiggelaar

D-U-N-S 06-479-1809
MAYO CLINIC HEALTH SYSTEM-MANKATO
(*Suby of* MAYO CLINIC) ★
1025 Marsh St, Mankato, MN 56001-4752
Tel (507) 625-4031 *Founded/Ownrshp* 1968
Sales 319.4MM *EMP* 2,830E
SIC 8062 General medical & surgical hospitals
Pr: Gregory R Kutcher
CFO: Ryan Ashlando
VP: Jerome Crest
VP: Richard Grace
Pathlgst: Tina Carns
Pathlgst: Jose Crespo
Pathlgst: Eric Evans

D-U-N-S 06-815-7601
MAYO CLINIC HEALTH SYSTEM-NORTHWEST WISCONSIN REGION INC
EAU CLAIRE HOSPITAL
(*Suby of* MAYO CLINIC) ★
1221 Whipple St, Eau Claire, WI 54703-5200
Tel (715) 838-3311 *Founded/Ownrshp* 2002
Sales 259.9MM *EMP* 1,290E
SIC 8062 8011 General medical & surgical hospitals; Offices & clinics of medical doctors
Pr: Dr Randall Linton
Dir Vol: Victoria Zehms
Dir Rad: Gregory C Brickner
Dir Rad: Suzan Degan
VP Admn: Dennis Pope
Ex Dir: Patricia Pope
Doctor: Christine Blink

D-U-N-S 09-789-7045
MAYO CLINIC HEALTH SYSTEM-RED CEDAR INC
(*Suby of* MAYO CLINIC) ★
2415 Stout Rd, Menomonie, WI 54751-2344
Tel (715) 235-5531 *Founded/Ownrshp* 1976
Sales 88.8MM *EMP* 300
SIC 8062 General medical & surgical hospitals
CEO: Hank Simpson
**CFO:* Jeanie Lubinsky
Dir IT: Frank Wrogg
Dir Health: Kay Naatz

MAYO CLINIC HOSPITAL
See MAYO CLINIC ARIZONA

D-U-N-S 15-322-3151 IMP
MAYO CLINIC JACKSONVILLE (A NONPROFIT CORP)
MAYO CLINIC ROCHESTER
(*Suby of* MAYO CLINIC ROCHESTER) ★
4500 San Pablo Rd S, Jacksonville, FL 32224-1865
Tel (904) 953-2000 *Founded/Ownrshp* 1986
Sales 457.3MM *EMP* 5,500
SIC 8062 General medical & surgical hospitals
Ch Bd: Marilyn Carlson Nelson
**CEO:* William C Rupp
**CFO:* Mary J Hoffman
Dir IT: Paul Lanko
IT Man: Goutam Behera
IT Man: Carla Jerdee
Sys Mgr: Kevin Hoot
Doctor: Gerardo Colon-Otero MD

MAYO CLINIC ROCHESTER
See MAYO CLINIC JACKSONVILLE (A NONPROFIT CORP)

MAYO CLINIC ROCHESTER
See MAYO CLINIC

D-U-N-S 79-001-5101
MAYO FOUNDATION FOR MEDICAL EDUCATION AND RESEARCH
MAYO CLINIC
(*Suby of* MAYO CLINIC ROCHESTER) ★
200 1st St Sw, Rochester, MN 55905-0001
Tel (507) 284-2511 *Founded/Ownrshp* 1984
Sales 1.0MMM *EMP* 52,700
SIC 8741 Hospital management
Pr: William Litchy
COO: Gaile Hansen
Ofcr: Nikiki J Hager
Ofcr: Beth Knowles
Exec: Katina Bjorkstrand
Dir Lab: Nancy Moody
Dir Rad: Gerald Tabaka
Dir Rx: John Kranze
Dir Rx: Eric Nelson
Dir Rx: Kim Rux
Chf Nrs Of: Jan M Hofer

MAYOR
See TOWN OF STRATFORD

D-U-N-S 05-391-9510
MAYOR AND CITY COUNCIL OF OCEAN CITY
TOWN OF OCEAN CITY
301 N Baltimore Ave, Ocean City, MD 21842-3922
Tel (410) 289-8221 *Founded/Ownrshp* 1860
Sales NA *EMP* 1,385
Accts Sb & Company Llc Hunt Valley
SIC 9121 City council;

MAYOR'S OFFICE
See CITY OF CHICAGO

MAYOR'S OFFICE
See CITY OF DETROIT

MAYOR'S OFFICE
See CITY OF NEW ORLEANS

MAYOR'S OFFICE
See CITY OF COLUMBUS

MAYOR'S OFFICE
See CITY OF ALLENTOWN

MAYOR'S OFFICE
See CITY OF CORPUS CHRISTI

MAYOR'S OFFICE
See CITY OF PROVIDENCE

MAYOR'S OFFICE
See CITY OF SYRACUSE

MAYOR'S OFFICE
See CITY OF MIAMI

MAYOR'S OFFICE
See CITY OF SALT LAKE CITY

MAYOR'S OFFICE
See COUNTY OF SALT LAKE

MAYOR'S OFFICE
See COUNTY OF HAMILTON

MAYOR'S OFFICE
See CITY OF NIAGARA FALLS

D-U-N-S 09-814-9339 IMP/EXP
MAYS CHEMICAL CO INC
5611 E 71st St, Indianapolis, IN 46220-3920
Tel (317) 842-8722 *Founded/Ownrshp* 1980
Sales 95.0MM *EMP* 70
SIC 5169 4731 Industrial chemicals; Freight transportation arrangement
Pr: Kristin Corbitt
**Pr:* Kristin Mays-Corbitt
VP: Essie Fagen-Johnson
**VP:* Eric Gillispie
**VP:* George Hughes
VP: John Thompson
VP: Wilmer A West
Trfc Mgr: Mandy Ward
**S&M/VP:* Thomas Douglas
Mktg Dir: Kate Chargualas

MAYTAG APPLIANCES
See MAYTAG CORP

D-U-N-S 00-528-5689 IMP
■ MAYTAG CORP
MAYTAG APPLIANCES
(*Suby of* WHIRLPOOL CORP) ★
2000 N M 63, Benton Harbor, MI 49022-2632
Tel (269) 923-5000 *Founded/Ownrshp* 1893, 2006
Sales 6.0MMME *EMP* 60,000
SIC 3633 3631 3632 3639 3635 3581 Household laundry equipment; Laundry dryers, household or coin-operated; Gas ranges, domestic; Electric ranges, domestic; Household refrigerators & freezers; Dishwashing machines, household; Garbage disposal units, household; Household vacuum cleaners; Automatic vending machines
Ch Bd: Jeff M Fettig
Pr: William L Beer
Pr: Thomas A Briatico
Pr: Arthur B Learmonth
Pr: Henry Marcy
Pr: David R McConnaughey
Pr: Keith G Minton
Ex VP: David Binkley
Sr VP: Paul J Bognar
Sr VP: Kirsten Hewitt
Sr VP: Mark W Krivoruchka
VP: Blair Clark
VP: Ellen Dutton
VP: Stefan H Grunwald
VP: Al Holaday
VP: Thomas J Piersa
VP: Vitas A Stukas
Exec: Jeri Harris
Exec: Lori Saulsberry
Exec: Glenn Toughey

MAYVIEW CONVALESCENT CENTER
See MAYVIEW CONVALESCENT HOME INC

D-U-N-S 07-557-6405
MAYVIEW CONVALESCENT HOME INC
MAYVIEW CONVALESCENT CENTER
513 E Whitaker Mill Rd, Raleigh, NC 27608-2699
Tel (919) 828-2348 *Founded/Ownrshp* 1957
Sales 858.3MM *EMP* 165
SIC 8051 Skilled nursing care facilities
Pr: Travis H Tomlinson Jr
**Treas:* Travis H Tomlinson Sr
**VP:* W Parker Tomlinson

D-U-N-S 00-610-0630 EXP
MAYVILLE ENGINEERING CO INC
715 South St, Mayville, WI 53050-1823
Tel (920) 387-4500 *Founded/Ownrshp* 1946
Sales 513.2MME *EMP* 1,925
SIC 3469 Stamping metal for the trade
CEO: Robert D Kamphuis
CFO: Todd Butz
Ex VP: Ed Paradowski
VP: Jeff Pharris
VP: Cliff Sanderson
VP: Rick Torn
VP: Bob Wiedenhaft
Genl Mgr: Mike Janzer
Genl Mgr: Kyle Knous
CIO: Randall Hagedorn
MIS Dir: Duwayne Kuenzi
Board of Directors: Timothy L Christen

D-U-N-S 07-127-9798 IMP/EXP
MAZAK CORP
(*Suby of* YAMAZAKI MAZAK TRADING CORPORATION)
8025 Production Dr, Florence, KY 41042-3092
Tel (859) 342-1700 *Founded/Ownrshp* 1974
Sales 376.7MME *EMP* 750
SIC 3541 5084 Numerically controlled metal cutting machine tools; Metalworking machinery
Pr: Brian J Papke
**Ch Bd:* Teruyuki Yamazaki
CFO: Tetsuo Niwa
**Treas:* Kazunari Matsunami
**Treas:* Daniel Sweeney
**Ex VP:* Daniel Janka
Ex VP: Kelly Matsunmai
VP: Keith Henderson
VP: Richard Ware
Genl Mgr: Bruce Hill
MIS Dir: Bob Fuersich
Board of Directors: Yoshihiko Yamazaki

D-U-N-S 60-552-7923 IMP/EXP
MAZAK OPTONICS CORP
(*Suby of* YAMAZAKI MAZAK TRADING CORPORATION)
2725 Galvin Ct, Elgin, IL 60124-7956
Tel (847) 252-4500 *Founded/Ownrshp* 2005
Sales 89.8MME *EMP* 100
SIC 5084 Industrial machinery & equipment; Industrial machine parts
VP: Al Bohlen
**Pr:* William Citron
Treas: Hironori Yahata
Ex VP: Ken Nakashima
Genl Mgr: Nan Dibek
Genl Mgr: Mark Dilling
Genl Mgr: Kyle Uehara
IT Man: Mark Mercurio
Opers Mgr: Fran Spiekerman

D-U-N-S 60-128-4128 IMP/EXP
MAZDA MOTOR OF AMERICA INC
MAZDA NORTH AMERCN OPERATIONS
(*Suby of* MAZDA MOTOR CORPORATION)
7755 Irvine Center Dr, Irvine, CA 92618-2906
Tel (949) 727-1990 *Founded/Ownrshp* 1970
Sales 501.0MME *EMP* 948
SIC 5511 5531

MAZDA NORTH AMERCN OPERATIONS
See MAZDA MOTOR OF AMERICA INC

MAZELLA COMPANIES
See MAZZELLA HOLDING CO INC

D-U-N-S 96-894-0754
MAZZELLA HOLDING CO INC
MAZELLA COMPANIES
21000 Aerospace Pkwy, Cleveland, OH 44142-1072
Tel (513) 772-4466 *Founded/Ownrshp* 2011
Sales 109.1MME *EMP* 300E
SIC 5051 5085 5088 5072 Rope, wire (not insulated); Industrial supplies; Marine supplies; Builders' hardware
CEO: Tony Mazzella
**VP:* James J Mazzella
VP: Mark Shubel
Genl Mgr: Kenneth Wright
Opers Mgr: Trevor Shubel
Sls Mgr: Kent Richards

D-U-N-S 04-632-9058
MAZZIOS LLC
MAZZIO'S PIZZA
4441 S 72nd East Ave, Tulsa, OK 74145-4610
Tel (918) 663-8880 *Founded/Ownrshp* 1961
Sales 149.8MME *EMP* 3,780
SIC 5812 6794 Pizzeria, chain; Franchises, selling or licensing
Sr VP: Bradford J Williams
VP: Gregory Lippert
VP: Patrick Patterson
IT Man: Dale Southerland
VP Sls: Karen Lesiker
Mktg Dir: Mary-Anne Whisnant

MAZZIO'S PIZZA
See MAZZIOS LLC

D-U-N-S 08-013-2750
MB BARTER (USA) INC
3388 Sage Rd Unit 402e, Houston, TX 77056-7239
Tel (713) 505-1303 *Founded/Ownrshp* 2014
Sales 25.0MMM *EMP* 2
SIC 2821 Polymethyl methacrylate resins (plexiglass)
VP: Sunjoy Rai

D-U-N-S 06-036-4791
■ MB FINANCIAL BANK
(*Suby of* MB FINANCIAL BANK NA) ★
936 N Western Ave, Chicago, IL 60622-4616
Tel (773) 772-4500 *Founded/Ownrshp* 2004
Sales NA *EMP* 95
SIC 6035 Federal savings banks
Pr: Julian Kulas
Ch Bd: Paul Nadzikewycz
Pr: Paul Bandriwsky
COO: Harry Kucewicz
Ofcr: Suzon Lanz
Sr VP: Stewart Kapnick
VP: Mary Korb
VP: Irene Subota
Mng Dir: Michael Musselman
CIO: Andy Konchan
CTO: Jo Boylan

D-U-N-S 00-693-1463
■ MB FINANCIAL BANK NA (IL)
(*Suby of* MB FINANCIAL INC) ★
6111 N River Rd Ste 800, Rosemont, IL 60018-5111
Tel (847) 653-4800 *Founded/Ownrshp* 1933, 2001
Sales NA *EMP* 1,340
SIC 6021 National commercial banks
Ch: Ron Santo
**Pr:* Mitchell Feiger
Ofcr: Brian Bye
Ofcr: Thomas P Fitz Gibbon
Ofcr: Laura Labno
Ofcr: Mary Lapierre
**Ex VP:* Mark A Heckler
**Ex VP:* Michael J Morton
Sr VP: Elizabeth A Di Cola
Sr VP: Karen Perlman
Sr VP: Randy Perryman
Sr VP: John Sassaris
Sr VP: Sarah Willett
Sr VP: Jill York
VP: Emily Achtstatter
VP: Dustin Ackman
VP: Laurie Arnold
**VP:* Rosemarie Bouman
VP: Michael Bruce
**VP:* John Chang
VP: John Glass
Board of Directors: Stanley R Banas, Samuel M Budwig Jr, Charles F Clarke Jr, Allan J Dixon, Patrick Henry, Marshall S Leaf, Eugene Saywer, Richard M Wolff

D-U-N-S 92-887-5145
▲ MB FINANCIAL INC
800 W Madison St, Chicago, IL 60607-2630
Tel (888) 422-6562 *Founded/Ownrshp* 2001
Sales NA *EMP* 2,980E
Tkr Sym MBFI *Exch* NGS
SIC 6035 Savings institutions, federally chartered
Pr: Mitchell Feiger
**Ch Bd:* Thomas H Harvey
V Ch: Bruce Taylor
Pr: Andrea Bukacek
Pr: John Crouse
Pr: Nataliya Dovha
**Pr:* Mitchell Feige
Pr: Cindy Katsikas
Pr: Kelly Mathews
Pr: Guillermo Villagrana
COO: Tom Prothero
CFO: Randall T Conte
CFO: Jill E York
**V Ch Bd:* James N Hallene
Ofcr: Irene Miakush
Ex VP: Brian J Wildman
VP: Christina Bavery
VP: Melissa Bleiweis
VP: Michelle Christens
VP: Ellen Cook
VP: David Emerson
Board of Directors: David P Bolger, C Bryan Daniels, Sunil Garg, Charles J Gries, Richard J Holmstrom, Karen J May, Ronald D Santo, Jennifer W Steans, Renee Togher

D-U-N-S 00-344-7836
MB HAYNES CORP (NC)
H & M CONSTRUCTORS
187 Deaverview Rd, Asheville, NC 28806-1707
Tel (828) 254-6141 *Founded/Ownrshp* 1921, 1966
Sales 299.9MM^E *EMP* 440
SIC 1542 1623 1711 7382 Commercial & office building, new construction; Electric power line construction; Plumbing, heating, air-conditioning contractors; Security systems services
Pr: N Ellis Cannady III
**CFO:* R Faison Hester
**Ch:* N Ellis Cannady Jr
Treas: Samantha Ball
**Ex VP:* Brett P Cannady
**Sr VP:* Fred Lewis
VP: Tony Gentry
VP: Nat Harrison
VP: Steve Warner
Dir Risk M: Goerge Murphy
Genl Mgr: Shannon Fox

D-U-N-S 07-909-6120 IMP
MB INDUSTRIES INC
560 Salem Ave, Newfield, NJ 08344-9005
Tel (609) 970-1503 *Founded/Ownrshp* 2013
Sales 180.0MM *EMP* 23
SIC 5051 Steel
CEO: Nathan MA
**VP:* Barry Bernsten

D-U-N-S 92-641-2453
MBC HOLDINGS INC
1613 S Defiance St, Archbold, OH 43502-9488
Tel (419) 445-1015 *Founded/Ownrshp* 1944
Sales 154.2MM^E *EMP* 721
Accts Plante & Moran Pllc Toledo
SIC 1622 1611 Bridge construction; Highway & street paving contractor
Pr: Dean E Miller
**Sec:* Steven A Everhart
**VP:* Robert Miller

MBCR
See MASSACHUSETTS BAY COMMUTER RAILROAD CO LLC

D-U-N-S 07-846-2094
MBI ENERGY LOGISTICS LLC
M B I
(*Suby of* MBI ENERGY SERVICES) ★
12980 35th St Sw, Belfield, ND 58622-9703
Tel (701) 575-8242 *Founded/Ownrshp* 2011
Sales 91.0MM^E *EMP* 1,450^E
SIC 4731 Freight transportation arrangement
CEO: Jim Arthaud
**VP:* Jason Homiston

MBI ENERGY SERVICES
See MISSOURI BASIN WELL SERVICE INC

D-U-N-S 07-539-5921 IMP
MBI INC
DANBURY MINT
47 Richards Ave, Norwalk, CT 06857-0001
Tel (203) 853-2000 *Founded/Ownrshp* 1969
Sales 102.2MM^E *EMP* 600^E
SIC 5961 Toys & games (including dolls & models), mail order; Book club, mail order; Jewelry, mail order; Stamps, mail order
Ch: Theodore R Stanley
**Pr:* Peter Maglathlin
**CFO:* Michael Wilbur
**VP:* Russell Friedman
VP: Dave Macoy
VP: Jim Zulick
Exec: Robert Gabler
CTO: Tim Crispyn
QA Dir: Tara Feenan
IT Man: Dan Mastroianni
Mktg Mgr: Danny Debalsi

D-U-N-S 15-481-8223
▲ MBIA INC
1 Manhattanville Rd # 301, Purchase, NY 10577-2100
Tel (914) 273-4545 *Founded/Ownrshp* 1974
Sales NA *EMP* 170^E
Tkr Sym MBI *Exch* NYS
SIC 6351 Surety insurance
CEO: Joseph W Brown
**Ch Bd:* Charles R Rinehart
Pr: William C Fallon
CFO: Anthony McKiernan
Board of Directors: Maryann Bruce, Francis Y Chin, Keith D Curry, Steven J Gilbert, Lois A Scott, Theodore Shasta, Richard C Vaughan

D-U-N-S 07-915-0310
MBK-WI INC (WI)
FREEDOM GRAPHIC SYSTEMS
1101 S Janesville St, Milton, WI 53563-1838
Tel (608) 373-6500 *Founded/Ownrshp* 1987
Sales 121.0MM *EMP* 550
SIC 2752 Commercial printing, lithographic
Pr: Martin Liebert
**CFO:* Terrance Brady

MBM
See MEADOWBROOK MEAT CO INC

D-U-N-S 79-332-3007
■ MBNA MARKETING SYSTEMS INC
(*Suby of* FIA CARD SERVICES NATIONAL ASSOCIATION) ★
1100 N King St, Wilmington, DE 19884-0011
Tel (302) 456-8588 *Founded/Ownrshp* 1990
Sales 84.2MM^E *EMP* 1,484
SIC 7389 Telemarketing services
CEO: Bruce Hammonds
**Treas:* Vernon Wright

D-U-N-S 07-313-4553
■ MBNA TECHNOLOGY INC
(*Suby of* FIA CARD SERVICES NATIONAL ASSOCIATION) ★
16001 Dallas Pkwy, Addison, TX 75001-3311
Tel (972) 233-7101 *Founded/Ownrshp* 1990
Sales 98.4MM^E *EMP* 1,720
SIC 7374 6282 Data processing service; Investment advice
Ch Bd: Ronald W Davies
Pr: Douglas R Denton
Exec: John M Gala
Pr Mgr: Victoria Henrion

D-U-N-S 00-687-0711 IMP
MBS TEXTBOOK EXCHANGE INC
2711 W Ash St, Columbia, MO 65203-4613
Tel (573) 445-2243 *Founded/Ownrshp* 1909
Sales 2.0MMM^E *EMP* 1,125
SIC 5192 Books
CEO: Robert K Pugh
**Ch Bd:* Leonard Riggio
**Pr:* Dan M Schuppan
**CFO:* Andrew R Gingrich
VP: Juan Daniel
VP: Nelson Durk
VP: Dave Easton
VP: David Henderson
Comm Dir: Shane Lewis
Rgnl Mgr: Fred Green
CTO: Gordon Franck

MBSC DIV
See BUILDING MAINTENANCE SERVICE LLC

D-U-N-S 82-830-9570 IMP
MC ASSEMBLY HOLDINGS INC
425 North Dr, Melbourne, FL 32934-9209
Tel (321) 253-0541 *Founded/Ownrshp* 1984
Sales 243.1MM^E *EMP* 1,600
SIC 8734 3672 Testing laboratories; Printed circuit boards
Pr: George W Moore
Pr: Jorge Benedito
**COO:* Luis Ramirez
**CFO:* Mark McReynolds
**VP:* Tim Jameson
**VP:* Jake Kulp
**VP:* Carol McCauslin
**VP:* Jim Roche
**VP:* Tom Rossi

D-U-N-S 79-116-8367
MC ASSEMBLY INTERNATIONAL LLC
(*Suby of* M C ASSEMBLY) ★
425 North Dr, Melbourne, FL 32934-9209
Tel (321) 253-0541 *Founded/Ownrshp* 2004
Sales 86.7MM^E *EMP* 310
SIC 3825 1389 Test equipment for electronic & electrical circuits; Testing, measuring, surveying & analysis services
CEO: George Moore

D-U-N-S 18-533-9330
MC BRIDE & SON HOMES INC
(*Suby of* MCBRIDE & SON ENTERPRISES INC) ★
16091 Swingley Ridge Rd, Chesterfield, MO 63017-2056
Tel (636) 537-2000 *Founded/Ownrshp* 2000
Sales 179.7MM^E *EMP* 1,600
SIC 1521 New construction, single-family houses
Pr: John F Eilermann Jr
**Treas:* Michael D Arri
VP: Jeff Schindler
Sls Mgr: Amy Ameling
Sls Mgr: Joel Holtman
Sls Mgr: Kimberly Lamartina
Sls Mgr: Andy Mikula
Sls Mgr: Lori Vinciguerra
Sls Mgr: Paul Weber

D-U-N-S 17-566-9639
MC CARTY CORP
13494 Pond Springs Rd, Austin, TX 78729-4410
Tel (512) 331-1344 *Founded/Ownrshp* 1986
Sales 87.5MM^E *EMP* 250
SIC 1541 6411 Industrial buildings, new construction; Insurance agents, brokers & service
Pr: Mike Mc Carty
**VP:* James N McIntyre

MC CARTY-HULL
See MCCARTY-HULL CIGAR CO INC

D-U-N-S 08-486-1954
■ MC CLURE CO INC
(*Suby of* TALEN ENERGY CORP) ★
4101 N 6th St, Harrisburg, PA 17110-1617
Tel (717) 232-9743 *Founded/Ownrshp* 1998
Sales 88.5MM^E *EMP* 350
SIC 1711 Plumbing contractors; Warm air heating & air conditioning contractor; Process piping contractor; Ventilation & duct work contractor
Pr: Thomas F Brown Jr
**CFO:* Kevin T Bobb
**Ex VP:* Todd C Ray
**VP:* Jerry S Wills

D-U-N-S 04-320-3249 IMP
MC DEAN INC
22980 Indian Creek Dr, Sterling, VA 20166-6732
Tel (571) 262-8234 *Founded/Ownrshp* 1966
Sales 1.7MMM^E *EMP* 3,000
SIC 1731 General electrical contractor
Pr: William H Dean
**Treas:* Norman Douglas Cumins
**VP:* Daniel August
**VP:* James Brabham
VP: Tom Harpold
VP: Jalal Rahim
**VP:* Rhett Wade
Exec: Alyona Bragg
Div Mgr: Bob Link
Div Mgr: Glen McDean
Div Mgr: Scott Miller

MC DONALD WHOLESALE COMPANY
See MAJOR EAGLE INC

D-U-N-S 62-348-0100
MC DONALDS OF CALHOUN INC
MCDONALD'S
806 Columbia Ave W, Battle Creek, MI 49015-3030
Tel (269) 965-1402 *Founded/Ownrshp* 1993
Sales 25.8MM^E *EMP* 1,543
SIC 5812 8742 6794 Fast-food restaurant, chain; Management consulting services; Patent owners & lessors
Pr: H Jim Brasseur

D-U-N-S 09-333-6857
MC DOWELL COUNTY BOARD OF EDUCATION (INC)
MC DOWELL COUNTY SCHOOLS
334 S Main St, Marion, NC 28752-4527
Tel (828) 652-4535 *Founded/Ownrshp* 1890
Sales 43.1MM^E *EMP* 1,000
Accts Johnson Price & Sprinkle Pa
SIC 8211 School board
Ch Bd: Terry Frank
Dir Vol: Melanie Dunham
**V Ch:* Bob Brackett
Off Admin: Vershell Libow
IT Man: Kelly Combes
Pr Dir: Glenda Dean

MC DOWELL COUNTY SCHOOLS
See MC DOWELL COUNTY BOARD OF EDUCATION (INC)

D-U-N-S 11-534-2859
MC ELROY DEUTSCH MULVANEY & CARPERNTER LLP
MDM&C
1300 Mount Kemble Ave, Morristown, NJ 07960-8009
Tel (973) 993-8100 *Founded/Ownrshp* 1983
Sales 120.0MM *EMP* 550
SIC 8111 General practice law office
Mng Pt: Edward B Deutsch
Pt: Joseph P Lasala
Pt: James M Mulvaney
Mng Pt: Glen Laird
CFO: John A Dunlea
Off Mgr: Beth Devlin
IT Man: Jamie Howlett
Counsel: Robert Berta
Counsel: Richard Biedrzycki
Counsel: Kathleen Bornhorst
Counsel: Joseph Campbell

D-U-N-S 19-804-3841
MC INDUSTRIAL INC
(*Suby of* MCCARTHY HOLDINGS INC) ★
3117 S Big Bend Blvd, Saint Louis, MO 63143-3901
Tel (314) 646-4100 *Founded/Ownrshp* 2005
Sales 101.5MM *EMP* 261
Accts Rubinbrown Llp Saint Louis M
SIC 1541 Industrial buildings, new construction
Pr: Tom Felton
**CFO:* J Douglas Audiffred
**Treas:* Danel J Dillon
**Sr VP:* Robert Kohlburn

MC KENZIE TAXIDERMY SUPPLY
See MCKENZIE SPORTS PRODUCTS LLC

D-U-N-S 01-034-7144
MC KNIGHT FOUNDATION
710 S 2nd St Ste 400, Minneapolis, MN 55401-2290
Tel (612) 333-4220 *Founded/Ownrshp* 1953
Sales 113.1MM *EMP* 40
SIC 6732 Educational trust management
Pr: Kate Wolford
COO: Stephanie Duffy
Ofcr: Nora Bateman
Ofcr: Ron Kroese
Ofcr: Arleta Little
Ofcr: Sarah Lovan
Ofcr: Becky Monnens
Ofcr: Eric Muschler
Ofcr: Megan Powers
Ofcr: Brendon Slotterback
VP: Nan Jahnke

MC PHERSON OIL PRODUCTS
See MCPHERSON COMPANIES INC

D-U-N-S 02-041-3720
MC ROBERTS CORP
87 Nassau St, New York, NY 10038-3710
Tel (212) 425-2500 *Founded/Ownrshp* 1974
Sales 98.0MM^E *EMP* 3,800
SIC 7381 Detective & armored car services
CEO: Meredith McRoberts
**CFO:* Jeff Chludzinski
VP: Paul Bristow
IT Man: Michael Martone

MC SPORTS
See MICHIGAN SPORTING GOODS DISTRIBUTORS INC

MC SQUARE
See CREATIVE MANAGEMENT SERVICES LLC

D-U-N-S 07-994-2077
MC TIRES
538 Olive Ave Ste 304, Vista, CA 92083-3481
Tel (760) 846-5613 *Founded/Ownrshp* 2014
Sales 250.0MM *EMP* 2
SIC 5014 5531 Tires, used; Automotive tires
Owner: Rosa Calderon

D-U-N-S 95-711-7120
MC WIL GROUP LTD
WILMAC
209 N Beaver St, York, PA 17401-5321
Tel (717) 854-7857 *Founded/Ownrshp* 1995
Sales 100.5MM^E *EMP* 1,500
SIC 8059 8051 8069 6513 8742 6552 Convalescent home; Skilled nursing care facilities; Substance abuse hospitals; Apartment building operators; Hospital & health services consultant; Land subdividers & developers, commercial
Pr: Karen Mc Cormack
**VP:* Richard W Bricker
**VP:* D James Mc Cormack
**VP:* Ray A Wilson

D-U-N-S 00-401-3579
MCABEE CONSTRUCTION INC (AL)
5724 21st St, Tuscaloosa, AL 35401-2555
Tel (205) 349-2212 *Founded/Ownrshp* 1962
Sales 98.0MM *EMP* 800
Accts Jamisonmoneyfarmer Pc Tuscalo
SIC 1629 1791 1796 3443 3498 Industrial plant construction; Structural steel erection; Installing building equipment; Fabricated plate work (boiler shop); Fabricated pipe & fittings
CEO: Leroy McAbee
**Pr:* Gary Nichols
**Treas:* Ruth B McAbee
**VP:* Wendell McAbee
**VP:* Leah A Sexton
Genl Mgr: Kevin Shipp
Mtls Mgr: Matt Channell
Genl Couns: Tommy Nettles

D-U-N-S 60-620-5433
■ MCAFEE INC
(*Suby of* INTEL CORP) ★
2821 Mission College Blvd, Santa Clara, CA 95054-1838
Tel (408) 346-3832 *Founded/Ownrshp* 2011
Sales 1.3MMM^E *EMP* 7,852
SIC 7372 Prepackaged software; Application computer software; Business oriented computer software
Pr: Michael Decesare
Pr: Jean-Claude Broido
Pr: Tom Miglis
COO: Peter Watkins
CFO: Jonathan Chadwick
Bd of Dir: Kevin Jacobs
Chf Mktg O: Penny Baldwin
Chf Mktg O: David Milam
Ofcr: Mark Cochran
Ex VP: Bryan Reed Barney
Ex VP: Christopher Bolin
Ex VP: Michael Fey
Ex VP: Joseph Gabbert
Ex VP: Todd Gebhart
Ex VP: George Kurtz
Ex VP: Barry McPherson
Ex VP: Gerhard Watzinger
Sr VP: John Giamatteo
Sr VP: Rees Johnson
Sr VP: Stuart McClure
Sr VP: Marc Olesen

D-U-N-S 07-956-5058
■ MCAFEE SECURITY LLC
(*Suby of* MCAFEE INC) ★
2821 Mission College Blvd, Santa Clara, CA 95054-1838
Tel (866) 622-3911 *Founded/Ownrshp* 2006
Sales 98.4MM^E *EMP* 6,210
SIC 7372 Prepackaged software; Application computer software; Business oriented computer software
Pr: Michael Decesare
CFO: Bob Kelly
Sr VP: Edward Hayden
Sr VP: Louis Riley

MCALISTER'S DELI
See SAXTON GROUP INC

D-U-N-S 08-313-7620 IMP
MCALLEN INDEPENDENT SCHOOL DISTRICT
MCALLEN ISD
2000 N 23rd St, McAllen, TX 78501-6126
Tel (956) 618-6000 *Founded/Ownrshp* 1915
Sales 260.0MM *EMP* 3,500
Accts Long Chilton Llp Mcallen Te
SIC 8211 Public elementary school; Public junior high school; Public senior high school; Public special education school
Bd of Dir: Richard Moore
VP: Daniel Vela
Brnch Mgr: Eileen Davis
Cmptr Lab: Carmon Suentes
Software D: Florencio Perez
Teacher Pr: Aurora Zamora
Psych: Irene Neve
Psych: Amanda Sada
Psych: Edna Trevino
HC Dir: Adalia Del Bosque

MCALLEN ISD
See MCALLEN INDEPENDENT SCHOOL DISTRICT

D-U-N-S 15-009-6840 IMP
■ MCALLEN MEDICAL CENTER LP
SOUTH TEXAS HEALTH SYSTEM
(*Suby of* UNIVERSAL HEALTH SERVICES INC) ★
301 W Expressway 83, McAllen, TX 78503-3098
Tel (956) 632-4000 *Founded/Ownrshp* 1982
Sales 240.6MM^E *EMP* 2,500
SIC 8062 General medical & surgical hospitals
Pt: Doug Matney
Exec: Roxanna Godinez
Exec: Monique Maynez
Dir Lab: Grace Garza
Dir Rx: Lisa Ramirez
IT Man: Juan Juarez
Pr Dir: Lisa Killion
Doctor: Ana Gutierrez
Pharmcst: Biju Abraham

MCALLEN P&RS SERVICE CENTER
See GE ENGINE SERVICES - MCALLEN L P

D-U-N-S 00-698-7408
MCALLISTER BROTHERS INC
(*Suby of* MCALLISTER TOWING AND TRANSPORTATION CO INC) ★
17 Battery Pl Ste 1200, New York, NY 10004-1105
Tel (212) 269-3200 *Founded/Ownrshp* 1864, 1969
Sales 140.0MM *EMP* 350
SIC 4424 Coastwide transportation, freight
Pr: Brian McAllister
VP: Lawrence Lore
VP: Virginia Norfolk
Opers Mgr: Allen Aden
Sales Asso: Jessamy Woolley

D-U-N-S 07-860-9088
MCALLISTER TOWING AND TRANSPORTATION CO INC
17 Battery Pl Ste 1200, New York, NY 10004-1105
Tel (212) 269-3200 *Founded/Ownrshp* 1864
Sales 162.3MM^E *EMP* 700
SIC 4492

D-U-N-S 01-425-8495
MCANENY BROTHERS INC
470 Industrial Park Rd, Ebensburg, PA 15931-4114
Tel (814) 472-9800 *Founded/Ownrshp* 1978
Sales 125.8MM^E *EMP* 285
SIC 5141 5147 5148 5194 5113 5142

D-U-N-S 00-530-5412
MCANINCH CORP (IA)
4001 Delaware Ave, Des Moines, IA 50313-2543
Tel (515) 267-2500 *Founded/Ownrshp* 1959
Sales 154.6MM^E *EMP* 500
SIC 1623 1794 Sewer line construction; Water main construction; Excavation & grading, building construction
Ch Bd: Dwayne Mc Aninch
**Ch Bd:* Dwayne McAninch
**Pr:* Douglas McAninch
**CFO:* Chad Pohlmeier
**Ex VP:* Emery L Sanford
**VP:* David Manning
**VP:* Dave Stitz
**VP:* Mark Watkins

MCARTHUR DAIRY
See DEAN DAIRY HOLDINGS LLC

D-U-N-S 13-357-9446
■ **MCBC HOLDINGS INC**
MASTERCRAFT
(*Suby of* WAYZATA INVESTMENT PARTNERS LLC) ★
100 Cherokee Cove Dr, Vonore, TN 37885-2129
Tel (423) 884-2221 *Founded/Ownrshp* 2000
Sales 221.6MM *EMP* 510^E
Accts Bdo Usa Llp Memphis Tenness
Tkr Sym MCFT *Exch* NGM
SIC 3732 3799 Boat building & repairing; Jet skis; Motorboats, inboard or outboard: building & repairing; Boat trailers
Pr: Terry McNew
**Ch Bd:* Frederick A Brightbill
CFO: Timothy M Oxley
Board of Directors: Donald C Campion, Joseph M Deignan, Christopher Keenan, Peter G Leemputte

D-U-N-S 17-921-6239
MCBRIDE & SON ENTERPRISES INC
16091 Swingley Ridge Rd # 300, Chesterfield, MO 63017-2056
Tel (636) 537-2000 *Founded/Ownrshp* 1985
Sales 180.6MM^E *EMP* 1,700
SIC 1522 1542 Apartment building construction; Commercial & office building contractors
CEO: John F Eilermann Jr
**CFO:* Michael Arri

D-U-N-S 60-671-8679
MCBRIDE CLINIC ORTHOPEDIC HOSPITAL LLC
MCBRIDE ORTHOPEDIC HOSPITAL
9600 Broadway Ext, Oklahoma City, OK 73114-7408
Tel (405) 486-2515 *Founded/Ownrshp* 2002
Sales 123.8MM *EMP* 723^E
Accts Somerset Cpas Pc Indianapoli
SIC 8069 Specialty hospitals, except psychiatric
Ch Bd: Mark S Pascale
**CEO:* Mark Galliart
**CFO:* Greg Gisler
**VP:* Toni Young
Dir OR: Cathy Ramsay
Prin: Krista Reyna

MCBRIDE ORTHOPEDIC HOSPITAL
See MCBRIDE CLINIC ORTHOPEDIC HOSPITAL LLC

MCC
See MOBILE CLIMATE CONTROL CORP

D-U-N-S 11-897-2512
MCC GROUP L L C
3001 17th St, Metairie, LA 70002-3805
Tel (504) 833-8291 *Founded/Ownrshp* 1958
Sales 91.7MM^E *EMP* 700
SIC 1711 1542 1731 Mechanical contractor; Commercial & office building contractors; Electrical work
CEO: Joseph A Jaeger Jr
**Ex VP:* Philip Catanzaro
**Ex VP:* Philip Garcia Jr
**Sr VP:* Edward O'Connor
**VP:* Thomas W Boudreaux
Off Mgr: Vicki Sortino
Genl Couns: Andre Maillho
Board of Directors: Fred Esstopinal, D Waesche

D-U-N-S 19-758-2369 IMP
■ **MCC HOLDINGS INC**
CRANE CHEMPHARMA
(*Suby of* CRANE INTERNATIONAL HOLDINGS INC) ★
4526 Res Frest Dr Ste 400, The Woodlands, TX 77381
Tel (936) 271-6500 *Founded/Ownrshp* 1999
Sales 401.4MM^E *EMP* 2,276^E
SIC 3491 7699 Industrial valves; Valve repair, industrial
Pr: Alex Alcala
**Pr:* Louis V Pinkham
**COO:* Kevin Olsen
**CFO:* Kevin Burke
Genl Mgr: Augustus I Dupont
Opers Mgr: Glenn Harshman

D-U-N-S 00-578-0432
MCC INC (WI)
MURPHY CONSTRUCTION COMPANY
2600 N Roemer Rd, Appleton, WI 54911-8626
Tel (920) 749-3360 *Founded/Ownrshp* 1932
Sales 95.4MM^E *EMP* 335
SIC 3273 1442 1611 Ready-mixed concrete; Construction sand & gravel; Highway & street construction
Pr: Joe Murphy
**Treas:* Rick Kranzusch
**VP:* Brian Murphy
Genl Mgr: Dave Urban
IT Man: Michelle Sasman
Sfty Dirs: Dusty Adamson
Ql Cn Mgr: Scott Paque

MCCAFFERTY AUTO GROUP
See FORD MCCAFFERTY SALES INC

D-U-N-S 00-110-4736 IMP/EXP
MCCAIN FOODS USA INC (ME)
(*Suby of* MCCAIN USA INC) ★
2275 Cabot Dr, Lisle, IL 60532-3653
Tel (630) 955-0400 *Founded/Ownrshp* 1952
Sales 1.2MMM^E *EMP* 4,000
SIC 2037 Potato products, quick frozen & cold pack; Vegetables, quick frozen & cold pack, excl. potato products
Pr: Frank Finn
COO: Dirk Van De Put
**VP:* Michael Campbell
VP: Patrick Davis
VP: Richard Efting
VP: Doug Fraser
VP: Kurt Kinsey
VP: Keith Orchard
VP: Sherrie Osborn
VP: Ronald Pullsbury
VP: Robert H Thomas
Assoc Dir: Amanda Colgan

D-U-N-S 18-312-5970 IMP
MCCAIN INC
2365 Oak Ridge Way, Vista, CA 92081-8348
Tel (760) 727-8100 *Founded/Ownrshp* 2016
Sales 89.0MM^E *EMP* 600
SIC 5084 3444 3669 Industrial machinery & equipment; Sheet metalwork; Traffic signals, electric
CEO: Jeffrey L McCain
**COO:* Christine Jersey
Mng Dir: Felix Cuellar
VP Sls: Bill Brown

D-U-N-S 80-728-3650 EXP
MCCAIN USA INC
(*Suby of* MCCAIN FOODS LIMITED)
2275 Cabot Dr, Lisle, IL 60532-3653
Tel (800) 938-7799 *Founded/Ownrshp* 1985
Sales 1.2MMM^E *EMP* 4,100
SIC 2037 2038 5411 Potato products, quick frozen & cold pack; Fruit juices; Pizza, frozen; Grocery stores
Pr: Gilles Lessard
**Sec:* Randy A Myles
Genl Mgr: Jeff Anderson

D-U-N-S 00-334-4710 IMP/EXP
MCCALL FARMS INC (SC)
MARGARET HOLMES
6615 S Irby St, Effingham, SC 29541-3577
Tel (843) 662-2223 *Founded/Ownrshp* 1952, 1967
Sales 189.6MM^E *EMP* 700
SIC 2033 Vegetables: packaged in cans, jars, etc.
Pr: Marion Swink
**Pr:* Henry Swink
CFO: Mark Fornari
**VP:* Henry Mc Call Swink
**VP:* Mark Tarkenton

D-U-N-S 00-967-3559
MCCALL OIL AND CHEMICAL CORP
5480 Nw Front Ave, Portland, OR 97210-1198
Tel (503) 221-6400 *Founded/Ownrshp* 1983
Sales 180.0MM *EMP* 29^E
SIC 5172 Petroleum products
Ch Bd: Robert H McCall
**Pr:* Jim Charriere
**CFO:* Mike Walsh

D-U-N-S 03-600-3184
MCCALLION TEMPS INC (PA)
601 N Bthlhem Pike Bldg A, Montgomeryville, PA 18936
Tel (215) 855-8000 *Founded/Ownrshp* 1979, 1999
Sales 16.7MM^E *EMP* 1,000
SIC 7363 7361 Temporary help service; Employment agencies
CEO: James Mc Callion III
**Pr:* James McCallion
**VP:* Lisa McCallion

MCCANDLESS INTL TRCKS COLO
See MCCANDLESS TRUCK CENTER LLC

D-U-N-S 06-335-0854 EXP
■ **MCCANDLESS TRUCK CENTER LLC**
MCCANDLESS INTL TRCKS COLO
(*Suby of* NAVISTAR INC) ★
16704 E 32nd Ave, Aurora, CO 80011-1521
Tel (331) 332-5000 *Founded/Ownrshp* 1999
Sales 103.7MM^E *EMP* 182
SIC 5013 7538 5012 Truck parts & accessories; Truck engine repair, except industrial; Trucks, commercial
Pr: Scott McCandless
**Sec:* John Balnis
Sales Asso: Garrett Saye

D-U-N-S 78-442-4871 IMP/EXP
■ **MCCANN WORLDGROUP LLC**
(*Suby of* INTERPUBLIC GROUP OF COMPANIES INC) ★
622 3rd Ave Ste 3, New York, NY 10017-6707
Tel (646) 865-5000 *Founded/Ownrshp* 1997
Sales 749.4MM^E *EMP* 20,000
SIC 7311 7319 Advertising agencies; Media buying service
CEO: Nick Brien
Mng Pt: Paul Gardner
Ch Bd: Joyce King Thomas
Pr: Devika Bulchandani
Pr: Rob Doubal
Pr: Lori Feld
Pr: Yasuyuki Katagi
Pr: Bill Kolb
Pr: Luca Lindner
Pr: Chris Macdonald
Pr: Gustavo Martinez
Pr: John Mescall
Pr: Donnalyn Smith
Pr: Hank Summy
Pr: Laurence Thomson
CEO: Mark Lund
CEO: Michael McLaren
CEO: Ed Powers
CEO: Fred Schuster
COO: Murray Dudgeon
COO: Patrick Lafferty
Board of Directors: Susan Irwin

D-U-N-S 00-698-7416
■ **MCCANN-ERICKSON USA INC** (DE)
(*Suby of* INTERPUBLIC GROUP OF COMPANIES INC) ★
622 3rd Ave Fl 16, New York, NY 10017-6743
Tel (646) 865-2000 *Founded/Ownrshp* 1902, 1964
Sales 395.5MM^E *EMP* 1,700
SIC 8732 7311 Market analysis or research; Advertising agencies
Pr: Chris Macdonald
**Ch Bd:* Jonh Dooner
**Pr:* Luca Lindner
COO: Patrick Smith
**Ch:* Harris Diamond
**Ofcr:* Suzanne Power
Ex VP: Stewart Alter
Ex VP: Peggy Kelly
Ex VP: Dana Mansfield
Ex VP: Richard O'Leary
Sr VP: Julianna Bogdanski
Sr VP: Tammy Hwang
Sr VP: Jesse Johanson
Sr VP: Roger Kilmartin
Sr VP: Mike Medeiros
Sr VP: Kevin Scher
VP: Jonathan Armstrong
VP: Jeanne J Courtney
VP: James Dale
VP: Debbie Ebel
VP: Jan Franks

D-U-N-S 00-285-7860
■ **MCCARLS INC**
(*Suby of* TALEN ENERGY CORP) ★
1413 9th Ave, Beaver Falls, PA 15010-4106
Tel (724) 843-5660 *Founded/Ownrshp* 1946, 1999
Sales 184.3MM^E *EMP* 1,000
SIC 1711 Mechanical contractor; Process piping contractor; Ventilation & duct work contractor; Warm air heating & air conditioning contractor
Pr: Robert W Santillo
**VP:* William Cornell
VP: Paul Morrison
Site Mgr: Thomas Coleman
Mktg Dir: Dan Rains
Board of Directors: Gary L Banzhoff

D-U-N-S 04-073-1382
MCCARTER & ENGLISH LLP
2 Tower Center Blvd Fl 11, East Brunswick, NJ 08816-1100
Tel (732) 393-1900 *Founded/Ownrshp* 1844
Sales 221.0MM^E *EMP* 900
SIC 8111 General practice attorney, lawyer
Ch: Michael P Kelly
Pt: F Traynor Beck
Pt: Erik Belt
Pt: Richard A Beran
Pt: Howard M Berkower
Pt: Sarah B Biser
Pt: Lisa W S Bonsall
Pt: John B Brescher Jr
Pt: Gerard G Brew
Pt: William H Bright
Pt: Lee Bromberg
Pt: Joseph J Cherico
Pt: Patrick M Collins
Pt: Richard C Cooper
Pt: Joseph R Disalvo
Pt: Gary L Duescher
Pt: Alfred L Ferguson
Pt: Stephen M Fields
Pt: John E Flaherty
Pt: James J Freebery
Pt: Frederic J Giordano

D-U-N-S 00-195-1375 IMP
MCCARTHY BUILDING COMPANIES INC (MO)
(*Suby of* MCCARTHY HOLDINGS INC) ★
1341 N Rock Hill Rd, Saint Louis, MO 63124-1441
Tel (314) 968-3300 *Founded/Ownrshp* 1864, 1997
Sales 2.7MMM *EMP* 2,447
Accts Rubinbrown Llp Saint Louis M
SIC 1542 1541 Institutional building construction; Commercial & office building, new construction; Industrial buildings, new construction
CEO: Michael D Bolen
**Pr:* John Buescher
**Pr:* Robert H Calbert
**Pr:* Rich A Henry
**Pr:* Randy M Highland
**Pr:* Kevin Kuntz
**Pr:* Ray Sedey
Pr: Jim Stevenson
**Pr:* Scott Wittkop
CFO: Doug Audiffred
**CFO:* J Douglas Audiffred
Ex VP: Robert Betz
**Sr VP:* Matthew Lawson
VP: Charles Buescher
VP: Drew Jackson
VP: Ben Johanneman
VP: Mike Myers
VP: Mike Oster
VP: Jaime Perera
Dir Bus: Jennifer Abbott
Dir Bus: Jerry Schreiber

D-U-N-S 08-871-1643
MCCARTHY HOLDINGS INC
1341 N Rock Hill Rd, Saint Louis, MO 63124-1441
Tel (314) 968-3300 *Founded/Ownrshp* 1977
Sales 2.8MMM *EMP* 2,447^E
Accts Rubinbrown Llp Cpas Saint Lo
SIC 1542 1541 Institutional building construction; Commercial & office building, new construction; Industrial buildings, new construction
Ch Bd: Michael D Bolen
**Pr:* Scott Wittkop
**CFO:* J Douglas Audiffred
**Treas:* Danel Dillon
**Sr VP:* Matthew Lawson
Off Mgr: Flor Forson
Off Mgr: Luanne Santiago
Sfty Dirs: Travis Taylor
Ql Cn Mgr: Paul Tonner

D-U-N-S 07-867-7014
MCCARTHY STRAUB JV I
1341 N Rock Hill Rd, Saint Louis, MO 63124-1441
Tel (314) 646-4189 *Founded/Ownrshp* 2012
Sales 59.9MM^E *EMP* 2,874
SIC 1542 Nonresidential construction
VP: Scott Wittkop

D-U-N-S 01-511-5355 IMP
MCCARTHY TIRE SERVICE CO INC
340 Kidder St, Wilkes Barre, PA 18702-5688
Tel (570) 822-3151 *Founded/Ownrshp* 1926
Sales 232.0MM *EMP* 700
SIC 5014 5531

D-U-N-S 00-738-5578
■ **MCCARTY-HULL CIGAR CO INC**
MC CARTY-HULL
(*Suby of* MCLANE CO INC) ★
4714 Ne 24th Ave, Amarillo, TX 79107-5802
Tel (806) 383-1313 *Founded/Ownrshp* 1924
Sales 138.3MM *EMP* 79
SIC 5194 5145 Cigarettes; Chewing tobacco; Cigars; Candy; Fruits, fountain
Pr: Gordon Atkins
**Sr VP:* James L Kent
VP: Chuck Cota

MCCC
See MONTGOMERY COUNTY COMMUNITY COLLEGE

D-U-N-S 03-050-8928
MCCLAIN SONICS INC
SONIC DRIVE-IN
425 Christine Dr, Ridgeland, MS 39157-3437
Tel (601) 914-3401 *Founded/Ownrshp* 2000
Sales 34.1MM^E *EMP* 1,000
SIC 5812 Drive-in restaurant
Pr: Ronald G McClain
Treas: R Clark Spencer
VP: Cary L Harvey

MCCLAIN'S RV SUPERSTORES
See R V MCCLAINS INC

D-U-N-S 01-655-3971
▲ **MCCLATCHY CO**
2100 Q St, Sacramento, CA 95816-6816
Tel (916) 321-1846 *Founded/Ownrshp* 1857
Sales 1.0MMM *EMP* 5,600^E
Tkr Sym MNI *Exch* NYS
SIC 2711 Newspapers: publishing only, not printed on site
Pr: Patrick J Talamantes
**Ch Bd:* Kevin S McClatchy
CFO: Elaine Lintecum
Ex VP: James Calloway
VP: Terrance Geiger
VP: Anders Gyllenhaal
VP: Christian A Hendricks
VP: Andrew Pergam
VP: Mark Zieman
CTO: Arturo Huerta
Dir IT: Gary Pruitt
Board of Directors: Elizabeth Ballantine, Leroy Barnes Jr, Molly Maloney Evangelisti, Craig I Forman, William McClatchy, Clyde W Ostler, Frederick R Ruiz

D-U-N-S 07-932-4326
MCCLATCHY CO
2100 Q St, Sacramento, CA 95816-6816
Tel (916) 321-1941 *Founded/Ownrshp* 1998
Sales 72.8M^E *EMP* 10,000
SIC 8999

D-U-N-S 94-179-7990
MCCLATCHY MEDICAL CENTER
(*Suby of* METHODIST HEALTHCARE) ★
7235 Hacks Cross Rd, Olive Branch, MS 38654-4213
Tel (662) 893-7878 *Founded/Ownrshp* 2011
Sales 25.5MM^E *EMP* 1,696^E
SIC 8011 Medical centers
Prin: William Hardee McClatchy

D-U-N-S 00-918-2114 IMP/EXP
■ **MCCLATCHY NEWSPAPERS INC**
SACRAMENTO BEE
(*Suby of* MCCLATCHY CO) ★
2100 Q St, Sacramento, CA 95816-6899
Tel (916) 321-1000 *Founded/Ownrshp* 1998
Sales 970.3MM^E *EMP* 5,143
SIC 2711 2759 7375 Newspapers, publishing & printing; Commercial printing; On-line data base information retrieval
Ch Bd: Erwin Potts
**Treas:* James P Smith
VP: Dan Schaub
CTO: John Stark
Dir IT: Carol Vila
Sftwr Eng: Saul Moses
VP Opers: Robert Weil
VP Opers: Frank Whittaker
Sales Exec: Jim Paquette

MCCLEOD MED CENTER-DARLINGTON
See MCLEOD REGIONAL MEDICAL CENTER OF PEE DEE INC

D-U-N-S 83-098-7731
MCCLONE CONSTRUCTION CO
5170 Hillsdale Cir Ste B, El Dorado Hills, CA 95762-5774
Tel (916) 358-5495 *Founded/Ownrshp* 1993
Sales 149.8MM *EMP* 500
Accts Gallina Llp Roseville Califo
SIC 1771 1751 Concrete work; Carpentry work
CEO: Brett Steed
**Pr:* Tim Eble
**COO:* Grant Orr
**CFO:* Ted Hoffman
**VP:* Roy Cloud
VP: Travis Ferguson
**VP:* Mark McClone
**VP:* Kevin Miller
VP: Ken Ridens
**VP:* John Salluce
Rgnl Mgr: Chris Foster

D-U-N-S 19-857-8155
MCCLURE PROPERTIES LTD
WEST COST TOMATO
502 6th Ave W, Palmetto, FL 34221-5110
Tel (941) 722-4545 *Founded/Ownrshp* 1995
Sales 407.3MM^E *EMP* 12,000
SIC 0161 Rooted vegetable farms
**Pt:* Corrine A McClure
**Pt:* Daniel C McClure

D-U-N-S 02-532-0693
MCCOLLISTERS TRANSPORTATION GROUP INC
MCCOLLSTERS TRNSPRTION SYSTEMS
1800 N Route 130, Burlington, NJ 08016-3017
Tel (609) 386-0600 *Founded/Ownrshp* 1998
Sales 150.6MM^E *EMP* 647
SIC 4213 4212 Contract haulers; Household goods transport; Local trucking, without storage
Pr: Dan McCollister
COO: Ray Conlin
**CFO:* Gary Morgan
VP: Dj Warden
Dir Bus: Jack Ring
Genl Mgr: Jennifer Dolusic
VP Mktg: Dennis Mazar
Mktg Mgr: Gabrielle Sanson
Sls Mgr: Tony Avampato
Sls Mgr: Thomas Silva
Snr Mgr: Lynne Stewart

D-U-N-S 00-877-4788
MCCOLLISTERS TRANSPORTATION SYSTEMS OF NEW JERSEY
1344 N West Blvd, Vineland, NJ 08360-2270
Tel (800) 257-9595 *Founded/Ownrshp* 2007
Sales 100.0MM *EMP* 59
SIC 4213 4225 4214 Household goods transport; General warehousing; Local trucking with storage
Prin: H Daniel McCollister
**Prin:* Dale Traver McCollister

MCCOLLSTERS TRNSPRTION SYSTEMS
See MCCOLLISTERS TRANSPORTATION GROUP INC

MCCOLLY REAL ESTATE
See MCCOLLY REALTORS INC

D-U-N-S 11-492-0036
MCCOLLY REALTORS INC
MCCOLLY REAL ESTATE
850 Deer Creek Dr, Schererville, IN 46375-1352
Tel (219) 322-5508 *Founded/Ownrshp* 1974
Sales 750.0MM *EMP* 53
SIC 6531 Real estate brokers & agents
Pr: Ronald F McColly
**Pr:* Ronald F Mc Colly
**VP:* Martha Jane McColly

D-U-N-S 08-597-0036
MCCOMBS ENERGY LTD
5599 Saint Felipe St 12 # 1200, Houston, TX 77056
Tel (713) 621-0033 *Founded/Ownrshp* 1998
Sales 90.2MM *EMP* 12
SIC 1311 Crude petroleum production; Natural gas production
Pr: Bill Forney Jr
VP: Charles Forney
VP: Ricky Haikin
VP: Larry Wyont

D-U-N-S 04-361-4130 IMP/EXP
▲ MCCORMICK & CO INC
18 Loveton Cir, Sparks, MD 21152-9271
Tel (410) 771-7301 *Founded/Ownrshp* 1889
Sales 4.3MMM *EMP* 10,000
Accts Ernst & Young Llp Baltimore
Tkr Sym MKC *Exch* NYS
SIC 2099 2087 2038 2037 Spices, including grinding; Seasonings: dry mixes; Gravy mixes, dry; Sauces: dry mixes; Extracts, flavoring; Frozen specialties; French toast, frozen; Vegetables, quick frozen & cold pack, excl. potato products
Pr: Lawrence E Kurzius
Ch Bd: Alan D Wilson
CFO: Mike Smith
CFO: Gordon M Stetz Jr
Sr VP: Lisa Manzone
Sr VP: Nneka L Rimmer
Sr VP: Michael R Smith
VP: Martin Bazinet
VP: Darin Brewer
VP: Joyce Brooks
VP: Ron Daliara
VP: Stetz Gordon
VP: Harold Handley
VP: John Holmes
VP: Suzanne Levy
VP: Denise McCafferty
VP: Laura McGrath
VP: Christina M McMullen
VP: Cecile Parich
VP: Valentin Ramirez
VP: Alex Rizzuto
Board of Directors: Michael A Conway, J Michael Fitzpatrick, Freeman A Hrabowski III, Patricia Little, Michael D Mangan, Margaret M V Preston, Jacques Tapiero

D-U-N-S 16-014-1230
MCCORMICK & SCHMICK HOLDING CORP
(*Suby of* MCCORMICK & SCHMICKS SEAFOOD RESTAURANTS INC) ★
720 Sw Washington St # 550, Portland, OR 97205-3507
Tel (800) 552-6379 *Founded/Ownrshp* 1997
Sales 76.0MM^E *EMP* 4,300
SIC 5812 Seafood restaurants
Pr: William P Mc Cormick
**CFO:* Emanuel N Hilario
Genl Mgr: Jim Rooney
Sls&Mrk Ex: Gregg Le Le Blanc

D-U-N-S 12-238-2773
MCCORMICK & SCHMICK MANAGEMENT GROUP
(*Suby of* MCCORMICK & SCHMICKS SEAFOOD RESTAURANTS INC) ★
1510 West Loop S, Houston, TX 77027-9505
Tel (512) 836-0500 *Founded/Ownrshp* 1970
Sales 33.9MM^E *EMP* 1,000
SIC 5812 Restaurant, family: independent
Pr: William P McCormick

D-U-N-S 14-754-4642 IMP
MCCORMICK & SCHMICKS SEAFOOD RESTAURANTS INC
(*Suby of* LANDRYS SEAFOOD HOUSE) ★
1510 West Loop S, Houston, TX 77027-9505
Tel (800) 552-6379 *Founded/Ownrshp* 2012
Sales 130.5MM^E *EMP* 6,582^E
SIC 5812 Seafood restaurants
CEO: William T Freeman
CFO: Michelle M Lantow
Ex VP: Michael B Liedberg
VP: Kelly A B Gordon
VP: Christopher C Westcott
Rgnl Mgr: Kathryn Henderson
Genl Mgr: John Bremer
Genl Mgr: Greg Kerr
Genl Mgr: Daniel Shinaut
Board of Directors: Eric P Bauer, J Rice Edmonds, Elliott H Jurgensen Jr, James R Parish, Douglas L Schmick, Christine F Deputy Ott

D-U-N-S 05-180-3237
MCCORMICK INC
4000 12th Ave N, Fargo, ND 58102-2910
Tel (701) 277-1225 *Founded/Ownrshp* 1981
Sales 198.3MM *EMP* 500
Accts Eide Bailly Llp Fargo North
SIC 1611 1629 1623 General contractor, highway & street construction; Power plant construction; Land preparation construction; Water & sewer line construction
Pr: Stephen D McCormick
Pr: Steve McCormick
Treas: Bradley Ballweber
VP: John McCormick III
VP: Tom McCormick

D-U-N-S 00-807-9972
MCCORVEY SHEET METAL WORKS LP
DUCT DIRECT
8610 Wallisville Rd, Houston, TX 77029-1314
Tel (713) 672-7545 *Founded/Ownrshp* 1948
Sales 106.1MM^E *EMP* 500^E
SIC 3444 Sheet metalwork
Pr: Tony McCorvey
Ofcr: Courtney Petty
VP: Toni W McCorvey
Prin: Kristal Crites
Sls Mgr: Steven Longs

D-U-N-S 82-843-0913
MCCOURT CONSTRUCTION CO INC
60 K St, Boston, MA 02127-1617
Tel (617) 269-2330 *Founded/Ownrshp* 1976
Sales 110.1MM^E *EMP* 300^E
SIC 1611 1622 Highway & street construction; Bridge, tunnel & elevated highway
Pr: Richard McCourt
**COO:* Steven A Frick
**Treas:* Virginia R McCourt
**VP:* Jack Murphy
Genl Mgr: Regina Curran
Sfty Mgr: Scott Gorman
Sfty Mgr: Joshua Palen
VP Sls: Richard Roth

D-U-N-S 06-117-4769
MCCOY CORP (TX)
MCCOY'S BUILDING SUPPLY
1350 N Ih 35, San Marcos, TX 78666-7130
Tel (512) 353-5400 *Founded/Ownrshp* 1966
Sales 664.5MM^E *EMP* 2,200
SIC 5211 5251 5231

MCCOY ENTERPRISES
See MCCOY-ROCKFORD INC

D-U-N-S 10-672-4032
MCCOY GROUP INC
2099 Southpark Ct, Dubuque, IA 52003-8095
Tel (563) 556-3773 *Founded/Ownrshp* 1981
Sales 542.9MM^E *EMP* 1,596^E
SIC 5012 7538 4213 Trucks, commercial; Trailers for trucks, new & used; General truck repair; Contract haulers
Pr: Michael L Mc Coy
**VP:* John R McCoy

D-U-N-S 03-300-0837
MCCOY TREE SURGERY CO
3201 Broce Dr, Norman, OK 73072-2453
Tel (405) 579-6000 *Founded/Ownrshp* 1963
Sales 94.3MM^E *EMP* 500
SIC 0783 Tree trimming services for public utility lines
Pr: Bruce McCoy
**Sec:* Sam Batty
**VP:* Mark Kline

D-U-N-S 13-111-5669 IMP/EXP
MCCOY-ROCKFORD INC
MCCOY ENTERPRISES
6869 Old Katy Rd, Houston, TX 77024-2105
Tel (713) 862-4600 *Founded/Ownrshp* 1983
Sales 217.0MM^E *EMP* 275
Accts Pricewaterhousecoopers Llp Ho
SIC 5021 1799 Office furniture; Office furniture installation
Pr: Stan Bunting
**CFO:* David Barnett
**VP:* Wayne Cotton Carlson
VP: Amy H Lopez
VP: Gary Rust
VP: Kansas Sartin
Prd Mgr: Frank Minni
Mktg Mgr: Dustin Staiger
Snr PM: Joe Vega

MCCOY'S BUILDING SUPPLY
See MCCOY CORP

MCCRACKEN COUNTY BOARD EDUCATN
See MCCRACKEN COUNTY PUBLIC SCHOOLS

D-U-N-S 15-935-2442
MCCRACKEN COUNTY PUBLIC SCHOOLS
MCCRACKEN COUNTY BOARD EDUCATN
5347 Benton Rd, Paducah, KY 42003-0912
Tel (270) 538-4000 *Founded/Ownrshp* 1901
Sales 48.7MM^E *EMP* 1,000
SIC 8211 Public elementary & secondary schools
Treas: Taylor Holley
IT Man: Tony Burking

D-U-N-S 15-071-3766 IMP
MCCREARY MODERN INC
2564 S Us 321 Hwy, Newton, NC 28658-9349
Tel (828) 464-6465 *Founded/Ownrshp* 1985
Sales 123.4MM^E *EMP* 600
Accts Whisnant & Company Llp Hickor
SIC 2512 Upholstered household furniture
Pr: Bill Quirk
**Treas:* Jonell Harrison
**Ex VP:* Rick Coffee
Exec: Susan Shook
Dir IT: Dennis Baker
VP Mfg: Tommy Fox
Plnt Mgr: Mark Harris

MCCS
See MAINE COMMUNITY COLLEGE SYSTEM

MCCSC
See MONROE COUNTY COMMUNITY SCHOOL CORP

D-U-N-S 07-857-7352
MCCURLEY INTEGRITY DEALERSHIPS LLC
1325 N Autoplex Way, Pasco, WA 99301-3853
Tel (509) 547-5555 *Founded/Ownrshp* 2010
Sales 130.8MM *EMP* 166
SIC 5511 New & used car dealers
Sls Mgr: Beau Mohondro

D-U-N-S 00-279-9617
■ MCDANIEL TELEPHONE CO (WA)
TDS
(*Suby of* TDS TELECOMMUNICATIONS CORP) ★
160 Stowell Rd, Salkum, WA 98582
Tel (608) 831-1000 *Founded/Ownrshp* 1929
Sales 853.0MM *EMP* 99
SIC 4813 Telephone communication, except radio
Prin: David Wittwer
**Ch Bd:* Larry Boehmn
**Pr:* Mike Leavesseur

D-U-N-S 10-252-9930 IMP
■ MCDATA CORP
(*Suby of* BROCADE COMMUNICATIONS SYSTEMS INC) ★
4 Brocade Pkwy, Broomfield, CO 80021-8900
Tel (720) 558-8000 *Founded/Ownrshp* 1995
Sales 70.4MM^E *EMP* 1,297
SIC 3679 5045 3825 3577

D-U-N-S 10-225-9322
■ MCDATA SERVICES CORP
(*Suby of* MCDATA CORP) ★
4 Brocade Pkwy, Broomfield, CO 80021-8900
Tel (720) 558-8000 *Founded/Ownrshp* 2005
Sales 38.9MM^E *EMP* 1,008
SIC 7373 3572 Computer integrated systems design; Computer storage devices
Ch Bd: John A Kelley Jr
VP: Karen Niparko

MCDAVID, DAVID HONDA
See IRVING MCDAVID HONDA LP

D-U-N-S 05-014-6851
■ MCDAVID IRVING-HON LP
DAVID MCDAVID AUTO GROUP
(*Suby of* ASBURY AUTOMOTIVE SOUTHERN CALIFORNIA LLC) ★
3700 W Airport Fwy, Irving, TX 75062-5903
Tel (972) 790-6100 *Founded/Ownrshp* 1969
Sales 168.7MM^E *EMP* 694
SIC 5511 Automobiles, new & used
Genl Pt: B David McDavid Sr
Pt: Jimmy McDavid
VP: Allen Levenson
Genl Mgr: Selim Arisoy
IT Man: Jose Fores
Sls Dir: Travis Quadlander
Sls Mgr: Jason Burton
Sls Mgr: Paul Caudillo
Sls Mgr: David Henry
Sls Mgr: Ronnie Myers
Sls Mgr: Matt Volpi

D-U-N-S 12-269-1694 IMP/EXP
■ MCDERMOTT INC
(*Suby of* MCDERMOTT INTERNATIONAL INC) ★
757 N Eldridge Pkwy # 101, Houston, TX 77079-4526
Tel (281) 870-5000 *Founded/Ownrshp* 1985
Sales 1.5MMM^E *EMP* 5,000
SIC 1629 Marine construction
Sr VP: Gary L Carlson
Sr VP: Scott V Cummins
Sr VP: Perry L Elders
Sr VP: William R Robinson
VP: William L Soester
Opers Mgr: Virgil Akers
Snr PM: Stephen Whitcomb
Snr Mgr: Priscilla Lui-Sushitz

D-U-N-S 04-775-8503 IMP/EXP
▲ MCDERMOTT INTERNATIONAL INC
757 N Eldridge Pkwy, Houston, TX 77079-4527
Tel (281) 870-5000 *Founded/Ownrshp* 1959
Sales 3.0MMM *EMP* 10,600^E
Tkr Sym MDR *Exch* NYS
SIC 1389 1623 Construction, repair & dismantling services; Oil field services; Roustabout service; Servicing oil & gas wells; Pipeline construction
Pr: David Dickson
**Ch Bd:* Gary P Luquette
CFO: Stuart Spence
Bd of Dir: Mary Shafer-Malicki
Sr VP: Steve Allen
Sr VP: Liane Hinrichs
Sr VP: Jonathan Kennefick
Sr VP: Brian McLaughlin
VP: Linh Austin
VP: Hugh Cuthbertson
VP: Ricardo Davila
VP: Liane K Hinrichs
VP: Christopher A Krummel
VP: Scott Munro
Exec: Kenneth Smith
Board of Directors: John F Bookout III, Roger A Brown, Stephen G Hanks, Erich Kaeser, Mary L Shafer-Malicki, William H Schumann III, David A Trice

D-U-N-S 00-819-8731 IMP
■ MCDERMOTT INVESTMENTS LLC
(*Suby of* MCDERMOTT INTERNATIONAL INC) ★
757 N Eldridge Pkwy # 101, Houston, TX 77079-4526
Tel (281) 870-5000 *Founded/Ownrshp* 1946
Sales 485.3MM^E *EMP* 11,400
SIC 1629 Industrial plant construction
Ch Bd: Roger E Tetrault
CFO: Daniel R Gaubert
Ex VP: E Allen Womack Jr
Ex VP: James F Wood
Board of Directors: Richard E Woolbert

D-U-N-S 07-688-9054
MCDERMOTT WILL & EMERY LLP INC
M W E
227 W Monroe St Ste 4400, Chicago, IL 60606-5058
Tel (312) 372-2000 *Founded/Ownrshp* 1934
Sales 1.5MMM^E *EMP* 25,000
SIC 8111

D-U-N-S 06-675-3336 EXP
MCDEVITT TRUCKS INC
1 Mack Ave, Manchester, NH 03103-5916
Tel (800) 370-6225 *Founded/Ownrshp* 1973
Sales 100.0MM *EMP* 150
SIC 5012 5013 7538 Trucks, commercial; Truck parts & accessories; General truck repair
Pr: John J McDevitt Jr
CFO: David Citarelli
**Treas:* Kevin McDevitt
**Treas:* Joel Moran
Chf Mktg O: William McDevitt
Ofcr: Debra Barss
**Prin:* Jim Busby
**Prin:* Jim Conner

D-U-N-S 06-732-0804
MCDONALD AUTOMOTIVE GROUP LLC
MCDONALD VOLVO
6060 S Broadway, Littleton, CO 80121-8013
Tel (866) 775-9743 *Founded/Ownrshp* 2002
Sales 105.7MM^E *EMP* 310
SIC 5511 Automobiles, new & used
Pr: Douglas McDonald
VP: Michael McDonald
**Prin:* Tom Poole
**Prin:* Greg Shellabarger

MCDONALD FINANACIAL GROUP
See KEYBANC CAPITAL MARKETS INC

D-U-N-S 06-142-4917
MCDONALD OIL CO INC
MONEY BACK
1700 Lukken Indus Dr W, Lagrange, GA 30240-4004
Tel (706) 884-6191 *Founded/Ownrshp* 1972
Sales 91.3MM^E *EMP* 200
SIC 5541 5921 6519 Filling stations, gasoline; Liquor stores; Real property lessors
Pr: John A McDonald
VP: Scott Gordy

D-U-N-S 07-316-2695
MCDONALD TRANSIT ASSOCIATES INC
(*Suby of* RATP DEV USA LLC) ★
3800 Sandshell Dr Ste 185, Fort Worth, TX 76137-2441
Tel (817) 232-9551 *Founded/Ownrshp* 1978
Sales 94.7MM *EMP* 3,600
Accts Weaver And Tidwell Llp Fort
SIC 8742 Business consultant
Pr: Blaine Rigler
CFO: Fred E Crosley
Sr VP: Kenneth R Fischer
Sr VP: Kevin Kane
Sr VP: Stephen A Keiper
Sr VP: Tim Lett
Sr VP: Patrick May
Sr VP: John L Wilson
VP: John P Bartosiewicz
Opers Mgr: Andy Altenweg
Opers Mgr: Brent Black

MCDONALD VOLVO
See MCDONALD AUTOMOTIVE GROUP LLC

D-U-N-S 02-021-0361
MCDONALD WHOLESALE CO
2350 W Broadway, Eugene, OR 97402-2790
Tel (541) 345-8421 *Founded/Ownrshp* 2007
Sales 101.2MM *EMP* 118
Accts Isler Cpa Eugene Or
SIC 5141 Groceries, general line
Pr: Gary Thomsen
**Ch Bd:* Charles R Huey
**VP:* Jake Vanderveen
Board of Directors: Greg Betts, Greg Garn, Brian Huey, Charles R Huey, Kent Huey, Gary Thomsen, Jake Vanderveen

MCDONALD'S
See HEIDMAN INC

MCDONALD'S
See MELTON MANAGEMENT INC

MCDONALD'S
See BROS MANAGEMENT INC

MCDONALD'S
See PEZOLD MANAGEMENT ASSOCIATES INC

MCDONALD'S
See E E R INC

MCDONALD'S
See JTS ENTERPRISES OF TAMPA LIMITED

MCDONALD'S
See TREFZ CORP

MCDONALD'S
See RETZER RESOURCES INC

MCDONALD'S
See C L P CORP

MCDONALD'S
See REDARHCS INC

MCDONALD'S
See LPG ENTERPRISES INC

MCDONALD'S
See M & J MANAGEMENT CORP

MCDONALD'S
See MC DONALDS OF CALHOUN INC

MCDONALD'S
See HAVI GLOBAL SOLUTIONS LLC

D-U-N-S 04-153-4264 IMP/EXP
▲ MCDONALDS CORP
1 Mcdonalds Dr, Oak Brook, IL 60523-1911
Tel (630) 623-3000 *Founded/Ownrshp* 1940
Sales 25.4MMM *EMP* 420,000
Tkr Sym MCD *Exch* NYS
SIC 5812 6794 Fast-food restaurant, chain; Franchises, selling or licensing
Pr: Stephen J Easterbrook
Pr: Michael D Andres
Pr: Ian F Borden
Pr: Douglas M Goare
Pr: David L Hoffmann
CFO: Kevin M Ozan
Treas: Carlos E Teran
Ofcr: David O Fairhurst
Ofcr: Silvia Lagnado
Ex VP: Robert L Gibbs
Ex VP: Robert Gibbs
Ex VP: Christopher Kempczinski
Ex VP: Gloria Santona
Ex VP: Jim R Sappington
Ex VP: Jim Sappington
Sr VP: Brian J Mullens
VP: Catherine Adams
VP: Francesca Debiase
VP: Denise Horne
VP: Teresa Olson
VP: Greg Watson
Board of Directors: John W Rogers Jr, Lloyd H Dean, Miles D White, Robert A Eckert, Margaret H Georgiadis, Enrique Hernandez Jr, Jeanne P Jackson, Richard H Lenny, Walter E Massey, John J Mulligan, Sheila A Penrose

D-U-N-S 05-501-9277
■ MCDONALDS RESTAURANT OPERATIONS INC
(*Suby of* MCDONALDS CORP) ★
2111 Mcdonalds Dr, Oak Brook, IL 60523-5500
Tel (630) 623-3000 *Founded/Ownrshp* 1980
Sales 22.9MMM^E *EMP* 380,000
SIC 5812 8741 Fast-food restaurant, chain; Financial management for business
Pr: James Collins
Ex VP: Chris Kempczinski
Ex VP: Don Thompson
Sr VP: Frank Muschetto
VP: Bob Donovan
VP: Sharon Halsmer
VP: Phil Le-Brun
VP: Bob Marshall
VP: Robert Switzer
Prgrm Mgr: Deana Gelino
Prgrm Mgr: Jessica Rau

D-U-N-S 61-529-9281
■ MCDONALDS RESTAURANTS OF ALASKA INC
(*Suby of* MCDONALDS USA LLC) ★
2111 Mcdonalds Dr, Oak Brook, IL 60523-5500
Tel (630) 623-3000 *Founded/Ownrshp* 2006
Sales 28.7MM^E *EMP* 2,000^E
SIC 5812 Fast-food restaurant, chain
CEO: James A Skinner
CIO: David Weick

D-U-N-S 88-426-3468
■ MCDONALDS RESTAURANTS OF CALIFORNIA INC
(*Suby of* MCDONALDS USA LLC) ★
1 Mcdonalds Dr, Oak Brook, IL 60523-1911
Tel (630) 623-3000 *Founded/Ownrshp* 2006
Sales 131.7MM^E *EMP* 10,750
SIC 5812 Fast-food restaurant, chain
Ch Bd: James A Skinner
Treas: Windy Cavin
Treas: Nancy Custis
VP: Carl Dill

D-U-N-S 61-529-8168
■ MCDONALDS RESTAURANTS OF COLORADO INC
(*Suby of* MCDONALDS USA LLC) ★
1 Mcdonalds Dr, Oak Brook, IL 60523-1911
Tel (630) 623-3000 *Founded/Ownrshp* 2006
Sales 22.5MM^E *EMP* 2,000
SIC 5812 Fast-food restaurant, chain
CEO: James A Skinner

D-U-N-S 88-426-3807
■ MCDONALDS RESTAURANTS OF CONNECTICUT INC
(*Suby of* MCDONALDS USA LLC) ★
1 Mcdonalds Dr, Oak Brook, IL 60523-1911
Tel (630) 623-3000 *Founded/Ownrshp* 2006
Sales 28.5MM^E *EMP* 2,050
SIC 5812 Fast-food restaurant, chain
CEO: James A Skinner
**Pr:* Mike Roberts

D-U-N-S 78-068-0745
■ MCDONALDS RESTAURANTS OF DISTRICT OF COLUMBIA INC
(*Suby of* MCDONALDS USA LLC) ★
1 Mcdonalds Dr, Oak Brook, IL 60523-1911
Tel (630) 623-3000 *Founded/Ownrshp* 2006
Sales 18.4MM^E *EMP* 2,000
SIC 5812 Fast-food restaurant, chain
CEO: James A Skinner

D-U-N-S 88-426-3880
■ MCDONALDS RESTAURANTS OF FLORIDA INC
(*Suby of* MCDONALDS USA LLC) ★
1 Mcdonalds Dr, Hinsdale, IL 60523-1911
Tel (630) 623-3000 *Founded/Ownrshp* 1974
Sales 113.0MM^E *EMP* 6,650
SIC 5812 Fast-food restaurant, chain
CEO: James A Skinner
**Pr:* Edward Rensi
**VP:* Jack M Greenberg

D-U-N-S 14-835-1588
■ MCDONALDS RESTAURANTS OF GEORGIA INC
(*Suby of* MCDONALDS USA LLC) ★
1 Mcdonalds Dr, Oak Brook, IL 60523-1911
Tel (630) 623-3000 *Founded/Ownrshp* 1979
Sales 35.0MM^E *EMP* 2,500
SIC 5812 Fast-food restaurant, chain
CEO: James A Skinner
Pr: Edward H Rensi
VP: Robert J Doran
**VP:* George T Rummell
VP: W Robert Sanders
VP: Delbert H Wilson
**VP:* Shelby Yastrow

D-U-N-S 01-187-9665 IMP
■ MCDONALDS RESTAURANTS OF ILLINOIS INC
(*Suby of* MCDONALDS USA LLC) ★
21 Mcdonalds Dr, Oak Brook, IL 60523
Tel (630) 623-3000 *Founded/Ownrshp* 1980
Sales 42.3MM^E *EMP* 1,550
SIC 5812 Fast-food restaurant, chain
CEO: James A Skinner

D-U-N-S 09-718-2562
■ MCDONALDS RESTAURANTS OF INDIANA INC
(*Suby of* MCDONALDS USA LLC) ★
2111 Mcdonalds Dr, Oak Brook, IL 60523-5500
Tel (630) 623-3000 *Founded/Ownrshp* 1973
Sales 68.9MM^E *EMP* 3,000
SIC 5812 Fast-food restaurant, chain
CEO: James A Skinner
**Pr:* Mike Roberts
**VP:* Jack Greenberg
**VP:* Donald P Horowitz
**VP:* Gerald Newman
CIO: David Weick

D-U-N-S 12-654-3347
■ MCDONALDS RESTAURANTS OF MARYLAND INC
(*Suby of* MCDONALDS USA LLC) ★
1 Mcdonalds Dr, Oak Brook, IL 60523-1911
Tel (630) 623-3000 *Founded/Ownrshp* 1975
Sales 72.7MM^E *EMP* 4,700
SIC 5812 Fast-food restaurant, chain
CEO: James A Skinner
VP: Ken Barun
VP: Phyllis Fields
VP: Eric Leininger
CIO: David Grooms
CIO: Chris Millington

D-U-N-S 78-081-6059 IMP
■ MCDONALDS RESTAURANTS OF MASSACHUSETTS INC
(*Suby of* MCDONALDS USA LLC) ★
1 Mcdonalds Dr, Oak Brook, IL 60523-1911
Tel (630) 623-3000 *Founded/Ownrshp* 2006
Sales 30.3MM^E *EMP* 2,000
SIC 5812 Fast-food restaurant, chain
CEO: James A Skinner

D-U-N-S 88-445-3390 IMP
■ MCDONALDS RESTAURANTS OF MICHIGAN INC
(*Suby of* MCDONALDS USA LLC) ★
1 Mcdonalds Dr, Oak Brook, IL 60523-1911
Tel (630) 623-3000 *Founded/Ownrshp* 1972
Sales 140.1MM^E *EMP* 7,300
SIC 5812 Fast-food restaurant, chain
Ch Bd: James A Skinner
**Pr:* Allan Feldman
**Treas:* Carletond Pearl
**VP:* Matthew H Paull
**VP:* Edward H Rensi

D-U-N-S 09-525-9974
■ MCDONALDS RESTAURANTS OF MINNESOTA INC
(*Suby of* MCDONALDS USA LLC) ★
1 Mcdonalds Dr, Oak Brook, IL 60523-1911
Tel (630) 623-3000 *Founded/Ownrshp* 1980
Sales 50.4MM^E *EMP* 2,500
SIC 5812 Fast-food restaurant, chain
Genl Mgr: W Maney
**CEO:* James A Skinner

D-U-N-S 06-248-1288
■ MCDONALDS RESTAURANTS OF MISSOURI INC
(*Suby of* MCDONALDS USA LLC) ★
1 Mcdonalds Dr, Oak Brook, IL 60523-1911
Tel (630) 623-3000 *Founded/Ownrshp* 1980
Sales 29.0MM^E *EMP* 2,000
SIC 5812 Fast-food restaurant, chain
CEO: James A Skinner
**Pr:* Michael Quinlan
**Treas:* Robert Ryan
**VP:* Jack Greenberg
**VP:* Donald P Horowitz

D-U-N-S 88-445-5098 IMP
■ MCDONALDS RESTAURANTS OF NEVADA INC
(*Suby of* MCDONALDS USA LLC) ★
1 Mcdonalds Dr, Oak Brook, IL 60523-1911
Tel (630) 623-3000 *Founded/Ownrshp* 1980
Sales 19.3MM^E *EMP* 1,150
SIC 5812 Fast-food restaurant, chain
CEO: James A Skinner
**Pr:* Alan Feldman
**Treas:* Carleton Pearl

D-U-N-S 11-819-5346
■ MCDONALDS RESTAURANTS OF NEW JERSEY INC
(*Suby of* MCDONALDS USA LLC) ★
1 Mcdonalds Dr, Oak Brook, IL 60523-1911
Tel (630) 623-3000 *Founded/Ownrshp* 1971
Sales 13.1MM^E *EMP* 1,000
SIC 5812 Fast-food restaurant, chain
CEO: James A Skinner

D-U-N-S 09-525-9917
■ MCDONALDS RESTAURANTS OF NEW YORK INC
(*Suby of* MCDONALDS USA LLC) ★
1 Mcdonalds Dr, Oak Brook, IL 60523-1911
Tel (630) 623-3000 *Founded/Ownrshp* 1980
Sales 23.3MM^E *EMP* 1,250
SIC 5812 Fast-food restaurant, chain
CEO: James A Skinner
**Pr:* Edward H Rensi
**Treas:* Carleton D Pearl
VP: Michael L Conley
VP: G Lowell Dixon
**VP:* Jack M Greenberg
**VP:* Jerry R Lane
**VP:* Matthew Paull
**VP:* Shelby Yastrow
Board of Directors: G Lowell Dixon, George T Rummel, Gloria Santona

D-U-N-S 88-445-4216
■ MCDONALDS RESTAURANTS OF NORTH CAROLINA INC
(*Suby of* MCDONALDS USA LLC) ★
1 Mcdonalds Dr, Oak Brook, IL 60523-1911
Tel (630) 623-3000 *Founded/Ownrshp* 1995
Sales 33.1MM^E *EMP* 3,000
SIC 5812 Fast-food restaurant, chain
CEO: James A Skinner

D-U-N-S 07-235-7734
■ MCDONALDS RESTAURANTS OF OHIO INC
(*Suby of* MCDONALDS USA LLC) ★
1 Mcdonalds Dr, Oak Brook, IL 60523-1911
Tel (630) 623-3000 *Founded/Ownrshp* 1980
Sales 148.2MM^E *EMP* 7,604
SIC 5812 Fast-food restaurant, chain
CEO: James A Skinner
COO: Glen Steeves

D-U-N-S 88-445-5106
■ MCDONALDS RESTAURANTS OF OKLAHOMA INC
(*Suby of* MCDONALDS USA LLC) ★
1 Mcdonalds Dr, Oak Brook, IL 60523-1911
Tel (630) 623-3000 *Founded/Ownrshp* 1983
Sales 25.6MM^E *EMP* 2,300
SIC 5812 Fast-food restaurant, chain
CEO: James A Skinner

D-U-N-S 02-927-8967 IMP
■ MCDONALDS RESTAURANTS OF PENNSYLVANIA INC
(*Suby of* MCDONALDS USA LLC) ★
1 Mcdonalds Dr, Oak Brook, IL 60523-1911
Tel (630) 623-3000 *Founded/Ownrshp* 1979
Sales 20.4MMM *EMP* 4,250
SIC 5812 Fast-food restaurant, chain
Ch Bd: James A Skinner

D-U-N-S 78-081-5937
■ MCDONALDS RESTAURANTS OF SOUTH CAROLINA INC
(*Suby of* MCDONALDS USA LLC) ★
1 Mcdonalds Dr, Oak Brook, IL 60523-1911
Tel (630) 623-3000 *Founded/Ownrshp* 2006
Sales 19.5MM^E *EMP* 2,000
SIC 5812 Fast-food restaurant, chain
CEO: James A Skinner

D-U-N-S 88-445-5403
■ MCDONALDS RESTAURANTS OF TENNESSEE INC
(*Suby of* MCDONALDS USA LLC) ★
1 Mcdonalds Dr, Oak Brook, IL 60523-1911
Tel (630) 623-3000 *Founded/Ownrshp* 1976
Sales 19.9MM^E *EMP* 1,700^E
SIC 5812 Fast-food restaurant, chain
CEO: James A Skinner
**Pr:* Mike Roberts

D-U-N-S 61-530-3554
■ MCDONALDS RESTAURANTS OF TEXAS INC
(*Suby of* MCDONALDS USA LLC) ★
1 Mcdonalds Dr, Oak Brook, IL 60523-1911
Tel (630) 623-3000 *Founded/Ownrshp* 2006
Sales 49.5MM^E *EMP* 2,000
SIC 5812 Fast-food restaurant, chain
CEO: James A Skinner

D-U-N-S 10-318-4222
■ MCDONALDS RESTAURANTS OF VIRGINIA INC
(*Suby of* MCDONALDS USA LLC) ★
1 Mcdonalds Dr, Oak Brook, IL 60523-1911
Tel (630) 623-3000 *Founded/Ownrshp* 2000
Sales 2.1MM *EMP* 5,500
SIC 5812 Fast-food restaurant, chain
CEO: James A Skinner
**CEO:* James Askinner

D-U-N-S 88-445-5684
■ MCDONALDS RESTAURANTS OF WASHINGTON INC
(*Suby of* MCDONALDS USA LLC) ★
1 Mcdonalds Dr, Oak Brook, IL 60523-1911
Tel (630) 623-3000 *Founded/Ownrshp* 2006
Sales 36.2MM^E *EMP* 2,700
SIC 5812 8741 Fast-food restaurant, chain; Financial management for business
CEO: James A Skinner

D-U-N-S 11-819-5056
■ MCDONALDS RESTAURANTS OF WISCONSIN INC
(*Suby of* MCDONALDS USA LLC) ★
1 Mcdonalds Dr, Oak Brook, IL 60523-1911
Tel (630) 623-3000 *Founded/Ownrshp* 1972
Sales 35.0MM^E *EMP* 2,200
SIC 5812 Fast-food restaurant, chain
CEO: James A Skinner
**Pr:* Alan Feedman
**CEO:* Jack Greenberg
**Sr VP:* Mike Conley

D-U-N-S 78-059-2130 IMP/EXP
■ MCDONALDS USA LLC
(*Suby of* MCDONALDS CORP) ★
2111 Mcdonalds Dr, Oak Brook, IL 60523-5500
Tel (630) 623-3000 *Founded/Ownrshp* 2004
Sales 23.5MMM^E *EMP* 390,000
SIC 5812 Fast-food restaurant, chain
Pr: James Johannesen
VP: William Whitman

D-U-N-S 02-784-2363 IMP
MCDONOUGH HOLDINGS INC (FN)
MCDONOUGH MARINE SERVICE
21050 N Pima Rd Ste 100, Scottsdale, AZ 85255-6700
Tel (602) 544-5900 *Founded/Ownrshp* 2006
Sales 188.1MM^E *EMP* 1,043
SIC 2431 4449 2426 2421 Millwork; Staircases, stairs & railings; Moldings, wood: unfinished & prefinished; River transportation, except on the St. Lawrence Seaway; Hardwood dimension & flooring mills; Sawmills & planing mills, general
Pr: Brendan Riccobene
**CEO:* Dale Knight
**CFO:* Stan Hrnci
**Treas:* Larry Hillwig
**VP:* Matt Urrea

MCDONOUGH MARINE SERVICE
See MCDONOUGH HOLDINGS INC (FN)

D-U-N-S 79-431-2413 IMP
■ MCDOWELL RESEARCH CO INC
(*Suby of* ULTRALIFE CORPORATION)
2000 Technology Pkwy, Newark, NY 14513-2175
Tel (315) 332-7100 *Founded/Ownrshp* 2006
Sales 88.2MM^E *EMP* 800
SIC 3669 Intercommunication systems, electric
Pr: John D Kavazanjian
Chf Mktg O: Jeff Luke
**VP:* Julius Cirin

MCE CLEAN ENERGY
See MARIN CLEAN ENERGY

D-U-N-S 00-805-6475 IMP/EXP
MCELROY METAL MILL INC
1500 Hamilton Rd, Bossier City, LA 71111-3890
Tel (318) 747-8000 *Founded/Ownrshp* 1963
Sales 369.0MM^E *EMP* 750
SIC 3448 Prefabricated metal buildings
Ch: Tem McElroy
**Pr:* Ian McElroy
**VP:* Kenneth J Gieseke
Rgnl Mgr: Gary Lockart
Area Mgr: Beau Brown
Genl Mgr: Tommy Johnson
Off Admin: Ryan Alford
Off Admin: Wesley Bates
MIS Dir: Gloria Stahl
Tech Mgr: Jonathon Caraway
Opers Mgr: Gene Clark

MCEWEN LUMBER CO
See HOOD INDUSTRIES INC

MCFA
See MITSUBISHI CATERPILLAR FORKLIFT AMERICA INC

MCFARLAND CASCADE
See LD MCFARLAND CO LIMITED

D-U-N-S 15-535-7791
MCFARLAND CASCADE HOLDINGS INC
(*Suby of* STELLA-JONES INC)
1640 E Marc St, Tacoma, WA 98421
Tel (253) 572-3033 *Founded/Ownrshp* 1984
Sales 166.6MM^E *EMP* 352
SIC 2491 6552 6531 Poles & pole crossarms, treated wood; Wood products, creosoted; Land subdividers & developers, commercial; Real estate managers
Pr: Brian McManus
**Pr:* Wayne Wilkeson
**VP:* Greg D Mc Farland
Genl Mgr: Janet Allen

D-U-N-S 06-961-5482
MCFARLAND CLINIC PC
1215 Duff Ave, Ames, IA 50010-5469
Tel (515) 239-4400 *Founded/Ownrshp* 1946
Sales 126.2MM^E *EMP* 1,400
SIC 8011 Clinic, operated by physicians
CEO: Steve Koger
**Ch Bd:* Dr Michael Kitchell
CTO: David Meier
Dir IT: Stan Davis
Counsel: Jane Mathison

D-U-N-S 01-642-7858
MCFARLING FOODS INC
333 W 14th St, Indianapolis, IN 46202-2204
Tel (317) 687-6827 *Founded/Ownrshp* 1948
Sales 135.2MM^E *EMP* 195

SIC 5147 5149 5144 5146 Meats & meat products; Groceries & related products; Poultry products; Eggs; Fish & seafoods
Ch Bd: Donald P Mc Farling
**VP:* Mike Atwood
**VP:* Greg Clay
**VP:* Leonard I McFarling
**VP:* Robert E Mc Farling Jr
**VP:* Patrick J McCune
**VP:* Charles D McFarling
VP: Jerry Ward
Genl Mgr: Terry Yandl
IT Man: Anthony Descenzo
Sfty Dirs: David Ellis

D-U-N-S 00-213-4864 IMP/EXP
MCGARD LLC
3875 California Rd, Orchard Park, NY 14127-4198
Tel (716) 662-8980 *Founded/Ownrshp* 1964, 1959
Sales 113.0MM^E *EMP* 400^E
SIC 5072 Security devices, locks
CFO: David M Powers
**Ex VP:* Peter McCauley
VP: Jeff Sullivan
Comm Dir: Bill Turnage
CIO: Craig Alf
QA Dir: David Roy
Opers Supe: Gary McLouth
Plnt Mgr: Bob Wagner
Sls&Mrk Ex: John Mondo
VP Mktg: Christophe Smith
Manager: Serena Duminuco

D-U-N-S 07-904-6207
MCGEE BROTHERS CO INC
4608 Carriker Rd, Monroe, NC 28110-7490
Tel (704) 753-4582 *Founded/Ownrshp* 1971
Sales 101.3MM^E *EMP* 500^E
SIC 1741 1521 Masonry & other stonework; Single-family housing construction
Pr: Sam McGee
**Treas:* Mike R McGee
**VP:* Cletus Huntley

D-U-N-S 03-242-1349 EXP
MCGEE TIRE STORES INC
3939 Us Highway 98 S # 101, Lakeland, FL 33812-4248
Tel (863) 667-3347 *Founded/Ownrshp* 1974
Sales 146.3MM^E *EMP* 290
SIC 5531 7538 Automotive tires; General automotive repair shops
Pr: Michael J Mc Gee
**CFO:* Terry Borglund
**Sec:* Cynthia L McGee
**VP:* Terrance J McGee

D-U-N-S 00-690-3645
MCGEORGE CONTRACTING CO INC (AR)
GRANITE MOUNTAIN QUAR NUMBER 1
1501 Heartwood St, White Hall, AR 71602-4705
Tel (870) 534-7120 *Founded/Ownrshp* 1933
Sales 90.7MM^E *EMP* 252
SIC 1611 1423 General contractor, highway & street construction; Crushed & broken granite
Pr: Haskel L Dickinson II
**Ch Bd:* W Scott Mc George
**Sec:* Drew Atkinson
**VP:* Gerald Majors
**VP:* Wallace P Mc George III
Genl Mgr: Thomas Dickinson

MCGEORGE SCHOOL OF LAW
See UNIVERSITY OF PACIFIC

D-U-N-S 00-510-4138 IMP/EXP
■ MCGILL MANUFACTURING CO INC
(*Suby of* REGAL BELOIT AMERICA INC) ★
2300 Evans Ave, Valparaiso, IN 46383-4054
Tel (219) 465-2200 *Founded/Ownrshp* 1905, 2015
Sales 139.1MM^E *EMP* 510
SIC 3562 Ball & roller bearings; Roller bearings & parts
Pr: Tony Pajk
Sr Cor Off: Chuck Hibbett
Prgrm Mgr: Brian Esham
Genl Mgr: John Hickel
Genl Mgr: Jim Kovalcik
IT Man: Larry Pembelson

D-U-N-S 00-679-1313
MCGOUGH CONSTRUCTION CO INC
2737 Fairview Ave N, Saint Paul, MN 55113-1372
Tel (651) 633-5050 *Founded/Ownrshp* 1956
Sales 428.0MM^E *EMP* 809
SIC 1541 1542 Industrial buildings, new construction; Nonresidential construction
CEO: Thomas McGough Jr
**Ch Bd:* Lawrence J McGough
**Pr:* Thomas J McGough
**COO:* Michael Hangge
**Sec:* Richard Opitz
Ofcr: Paul Boespflug
Ex VP: Tim McGough
Sr VP: Bob Eno
VP: Dan Malecha
VP: Jeff Roundtree
**VP:* Keith Schuler

MCGRANN DIGITAL IMAGING
See MCGRANN PAPER CORP

D-U-N-S 08-516-6726 IMP
MCGRANN PAPER CORP
MCGRANN DIGITAL IMAGING
3800 Arco Corprt Dr # 350, Charlotte, NC 28273-4284
Tel (800) 240-9455 *Founded/Ownrshp* 1974
Sales 156.4MM^E *EMP* 65
SIC 5111 2752 Fine paper; Printing paper; Advertising posters, lithographed
Pr: Adam McGrann
CFO: Michael Antonishak
Mktg Dir: Keith Castle

D-U-N-S 02-205-2617
MCGRATH AUTOMOTIVE GROUP INC
MIKE MCGRATH AUTO CENTER
4610 Center Point Rd Ne, Cedar Rapids, IA 52402-2412
Tel (319) 688-2937 *Founded/Ownrshp* 1975
Sales 94.1MM^E *EMP* 225
SIC 5511 Automobiles, new & used
Pr: Patrick C McGrath
**Treas:* Rick Sayre
**VP:* Stan Cairy
**VP:* Michael P Mc Grath
**VP:* Patrick Mc Grath
Sls Mgr: Gavin McGrath

D-U-N-S 09-622-6253 IMP
▲ MCGRATH RENTCORP (CA)
5700 Las Positas Rd, Livermore, CA 94551-7806
Tel (925) 606-9200 *Founded/Ownrshp* 1979
Sales 404.5MM *EMP* 1,016^E
Accts Grant Thornton Llp San Jose
Tkr Sym MGRC *Exch* NGS
SIC 7359 5084 Equipment rental & leasing; Electronic equipment rental, except computers; Rental store, general; Measuring & testing equipment, electrical
Pr: Dennis C Kakures
**Ch Bd:* Ronald H Zech
COO: Joseph F Hanna
CFO: Keith E Pratt
Treas: John P Skenesky
Ofcr: Randle F Rose
VP: Susan Boutwell
VP: B Michael Buckland
VP: Philip B Hawkins
VP: Kristina Vantrease
VP: David M Whitney
VP: David Whitney
Dir Bus: Kristina Van Trease
Board of Directors: William J Dawson, Elizabeth A Fetter, Robert C Hood, M Richard Smith, Dennis P Stradford

D-U-N-S 03-708-5792
MCGRATHS PUBLICK FISH HOUSE LLC
1935 Davcor St Se, Salem, OR 97302-1146
Tel (503) 399-8456 *Founded/Ownrshp* 1980
Sales 37.1MM^E *EMP* 1,000
SIC 5812

D-U-N-S 18-170-5898
MCGRAW DAVISSON STEWART INC
MCGRAW DVSSON STEWART REALTORS
4105 S Rockford Ave, Tulsa, OK 74105-4205
Tel (918) 592-6000 *Founded/Ownrshp* 1965
Sales 800.0MM *EMP* 550
SIC 6531 Real estate brokers & agents
Pr: Joseph R McGraw
**Pr:* John Woolman
Sales Asso: Mickie Bingham
Sales Asso: Scott Coffman
Sales Asso: Maria Dickerson
Sales Asso: Jan Jackson
Sales Asso: Jenna Majors
Sales Asso: Mimi Sandberg
Sales Asso: Gary Smith
Sales Asso: Richard Taylor
Sales Asso: Mark Wojciehowski

MCGRAW DVSSON STEWART REALTORS
See MCGRAW DAVISSON STEWART INC

D-U-N-S 00-130-7248
MCGRAW-EDISON CO (DE)
(*Suby of* EATON ELECTRIC HOLDINGS LLC) ★
600 Travis St Ste 5400, Houston, TX 77002-3013
Tel (713) 209-8400 *Founded/Ownrshp* 1985, 2007
Sales 519.0MM^E *EMP* 13,144
SIC 3613 3641 3645 3646 Fuses & fuse equipment; Fuses, electric; Lamps, fluorescent, electric; Residential lighting fixtures; Fluorescent lighting fixtures, residential; Garden, patio, walkway & yard lighting fixtures: electric; Commercial indusl & institutional electric lighting fixtures; Fluorescent lighting fixtures, commercial
Pr: Terry A Klebe
**Treas:* Alan J Hill
**VP:* Diane K Schumacher

D-U-N-S 07-880-2466
MCGRAW-HILL GLOBAL EDUCATION HOLDINGS LLC
2 Penn Plz Fl 20, New York, NY 10121-2100
Tel (646) 766-2000 *Founded/Ownrshp* 2013
Sales 1.5MMM^E *EMP* 3,500^E
SIC 2731 Textbooks: publishing & printing
Pr: David Levin
Pr: Sally Shankland
**CFO:* Patrick Milano
**Ofcr:* Stephen J Laster
**Sr VP:* Teresa Martin-Retortillo
Sr VP: Heath Morrison
**Sr VP:* Maryellen Valaitis
**CIO:* David Wright

D-U-N-S 06-827-7348 IMP
MCGRAW-HILL GLOBAL EDUCATION LLC
MCGRAW-HILL HIGHER EDUCATION
(*Suby of* MCGRAW-HILL GLOBAL EDUCATION HOLDINGS LLC) ★
2 Penn Plz Fl 20, New York, NY 10121-2100
Tel (646) 766-2000 *Founded/Ownrshp* 2013
Sales 179.2MM^E *EMP* 3,500
SIC 8299 Educational services
Pr: David Levin
**CFO:* Patrick Milano
**Treas:* David Kraut
Ofcr: Stephen Laster
**Sr VP:* Teresa Martin-Retortillo
Sr VP: David Stafford
**Sr VP:* Maryellen Valaitis
Mktg Dir: Krista Bettino
Snr PM: Jack Arnett
Board of Directors: Nancy Lublin

MCGRAW-HILL HIGHER EDUCATION
See MCGRAW-HILL GLOBAL EDUCATION LLC

D-U-N-S 07-909-2445
MCGRAW-HILL SCHOOL EDUCATION HOLDINGS LLC
2 Penn Plz Fl 20, New York, NY 10121-2100
Tel (646) 766-2000 *Founded/Ownrshp* 2013
Sales 750.0MM *EMP* 2,000
SIC 2731 Books: publishing only
Pr: David Levin
**CFO:* Patrick Milano
**Sr VP:* Teresa Martin-Retortillo
**Sr VP:* David B Stafford
**Sr VP:* Maryellen Valaitis
**CIO:* David Wright

D-U-N-S 07-880-2474
MCGRAW-HILL SCHOOL EDUCATION LLC
(*Suby of* MCGRAW-HILL SCHOOL EDUCATION HOLDINGS LLC) ★
2 Penn Plz Fl 20, New York, NY 10121-2100
Tel (646) 766-2060 *Founded/Ownrshp* 2013
Sales 116.8MM^E *EMP* 599^E
SIC 2731 Book publishing; Books: publishing & printing
Pr: David Levin
CFO: Patrick Milano
Ofcr: Stephen J Laster
Sr VP: Teresa Martin-Retortillo
Sr VP: Maryellen Valaitis
CIO: David Wright

D-U-N-S 80-159-3823
MCGRAW/KOKOSING INC
(*Suby of* KOKOSING INC) ★
101 Clark Blvd, Westerville, OH 43081
Tel (614) 212-5700 *Founded/Ownrshp* 1992
Sales 116.9MM^E *EMP* 500
Accts Crowe Horwath Llp
SIC 1541 1542 Renovation, remodeling & repairs: industrial buildings; Industrial buildings, new construction; Nonresidential construction
Pr: Daniel B Walker
**CFO:* Tim Freed
CFO: Patti M Rye
**VP:* Chris A Bergs

MCGREEVER AND DANLEE VERY
See MORRIS NATIONAL INC

D-U-N-S 00-794-2303
MCGREGOR CO (WA)
TOMCO SEED
401 Colfax Airport Rd, Colfax, WA 99111-6002
Tel (509) 397-4355 *Founded/Ownrshp* 1882
Sales 182.4MM^E *EMP* 325
SIC 5191 3523 2874

D-U-N-S 04-563-1934 IMP
MCGRIFF INDUSTRIES INC
MCGRIFF TIRE CO.
86 Walnut St Ne, Cullman, AL 35055
Tel (256) 739-0780 *Founded/Ownrshp* 1955
Sales 110.0MM^E *EMP* 280
SIC 5531 7534 Automotive tires; Rebuilding & retreading tires
Ch Bd: Bertis McGriff
**Pr:* Barry McGriff
**VP:* Jeff McGriff
MIS Mgr: Vicky Carden
Plnt Mgr: Jim Osborne

D-U-N-S 07-210-2213
■ MCGRIFF SEIBELS & WILLIAMS INC
(*Suby of* BB&T INSURANCE HOLDINGS INC) ★
2211 7th Ave S, Birmingham, AL 35233-2340
Tel (205) 252-9871 *Founded/Ownrshp* 2004
Sales NA *EMP* 745
SIC 6411

MCGRIFF TIRE CO.
See MCGRIFF INDUSTRIES INC

D-U-N-S 00-691-0038
MCGUIRE AND HESTER
9009 Railroad Ave, Oakland, CA 94603-1245
Tel (510) 632-7676 *Founded/Ownrshp* 1926
Sales 119.5MM^E *EMP* 300^E
SIC 1623 7353 Underground utilities contractor; Heavy construction equipment rental
CEO: Michael R Hester
**Treas:* Louis Roessler
**Ex VP:* Robert Doud
Area Mgr: Kevin Hester
Div Mgr: Andrew Vasconi
Genl Mgr: Mabel Cater
Trfc Dir: Victor Camarillo
Trfc Dir: Ramon Gomez
Corp Couns: Kim Fisher
Snr Mgr: Matt Daley

MCGUIRE FURNITURE
See KOHLER INTERIORS FURNITURE CO

D-U-N-S 05-890-2008
MCGUIREWOODS LLP
800 E Canal St, Richmond, VA 23219-3956
Tel (804) 775-1000 *Founded/Ownrshp* 1952
Sales 396.6MM^E *EMP* 1,710
SIC 8111 General practice law office
Pt: Terrence M Bagley
**Pt:* Robert Couture
Pt: Peter J Covington
Pt: Robert H Patterson Jr
Pt: David P Pusateri
Pt: Ellen Ruff
Mng Pt: Jonathan Blank
Mng Pt: Thomas E Cabaniss
Mng Pt: Ava Lias-Booker
**Mng Pt:* Brian K Parker
COO: Eva Tashjian-Brown
CFO: Elizabeth Burke
Chf Mktg O: Tim Mullane
Ex VP: Matthew Monsour
Sr VP: Christopher R Nolen
VP: Joe Jaso
VP: Chris Lloyd
VP: Thomas Londrigan
VP: Christopher Nolen

D-U-N-S 83-105-0091
MCGUYER HOMEBUILDERS INC
PIONEER HOMES
7676 Woodway Dr Ste 104, Houston, TX 77063-1521
Tel (713) 952-6767 *Founded/Ownrshp* 1988
Sales 158.2MM^E *EMP* 375
SIC 1531 1521 Operative builders; Single-family housing construction
Ch Bd: Frank McGuyer
**Pr:* Mike Love
**Pr:* Gary R Tesch
Ex Dir: Charles H Phillips
Dir IT: Paul Piro

MCH
See MADERA COMMUNITY HOSPITAL

D-U-N-S 07-016-2144
MCHENRY COUNTY COLLEGE
COMMUNITY COLLEGE DST 528
(*Suby of* ILLINOIS COMMUNITY COLLEGE BD) ★
8900 Us Highway 14, Crystal Lake, IL 60012-2761
Tel (815) 455-3700 *Founded/Ownrshp* 1967
Sales 15.2MM *EMP* 1,000
Accts Sikich Llp Naperville Illin
SIC 8222 8221 9411 Community college; Colleges universities & professional schools; Administration of educational programs
Pr: Dr Vicky Smith
V Ch: Linda Liddell
**CFO:* Robert Tenuta
Treas: Ronald Ally
**Treas:* Larry West
**VP:* Laura Brown
VP: Al Butler
VP: Kate Midday
**VP:* Anthony Miksa
Assoc Dir: Geary Smith
Snr Sftwr: Janice Samsa

D-U-N-S 96-357-7502
MCHS - WEBSTER
750 W Texas Ave, Webster, TX 77598-3259
Tel (281) 332-3496 *Founded/Ownrshp* 2010
Sales 105.4MM *EMP* 10^E
SIC 8051 Skilled nursing care facilities

D-U-N-S 13-087-2773
MCHUGH ENTERPRISES INC
1737 S Michigan Ave, Chicago, IL 60616-1211
Tel (312) 986-8000 *Founded/Ownrshp* 1985
Sales 441.9MM^E *EMP* 1,000^E
SIC 1542 1522 1622 1771 1742 6552 Nonresidential construction; Multi-family dwelling construction; Bridge construction; Tunnel construction; Highway construction, elevated; Concrete work; Drywall; Subdividers & developers
Pr: James P McHugh
**Treas:* Patrick Seery

D-U-N-S 04-476-0643
■ MCI COMMUNICATIONS CORP
VERIZON BUSINESS
(*Suby of* VERIZON BUSINESS GLOBAL LLC) ★
22001 Loudoun County Pkwy, Ashburn, VA 20147-6105
Tel (703) 886-5600 *Founded/Ownrshp* 1968, 2006
Sales 7.3MMM^E *EMP* 39,000
SIC 4813 4812 4822 7372 Local & long distance telephone communications; Long distance telephone communications; Local telephone communications; Voice telephone communications; Cellular telephone services; Paging services; Cable, telegram & telex services; Facsimile transmission services; Telegram services; Telex services; Prepackaged software; Business oriented computer software
CEO: Gerald H Taylor
Pr: Timothy F Price
Tech Mgr: Pete Laverde
Counsel: Pat Escobedo
Board of Directors: Clifford L Alexander Jr, Judith Areen, Michael H Bader, Robert P Brace, Richard M Jones, Gordon S Macklin, Richard B Sayford, Judith Whittaker, John R Worthington

D-U-N-S 08-312-2643
■ MCI COMMUNICATIONS SERVICES INC
VERIZON BUSINESS
(*Suby of* VERIZON BUSINESS GLOBAL LLC) ★
22001 Loudoun County Pkwy, Ashburn, VA 20147-6105
Tel (703) 886-5600 *Founded/Ownrshp* 1992, 2006
Sales 577.5MM^E *EMP* 1,100^E
SIC 4813 Telephone communication, except radio
CEO: Michael Capellas

D-U-N-S 82-943-0458
■ MCI INTERNATIONAL INC
VERIZON BUSINESS
(*Suby of* VERIZON BUSINESS) ★
22001 Loudoun County Pkwy, Ashburn, VA 20147-6105
Tel (703) 886-5600 *Founded/Ownrshp* 1976
Sales 150.0MM^E *EMP* 955
SIC 4813 4812 4822 7372 Local & long distance telephone communications; Long distance telephone communications; Local telephone communications; Voice telephone communications; Cellular telephone services; Paging services; Cable, telegram & telex services; Facsimile transmission services; Telegram services; Telex services; Prepackaged software; Business oriented computer software
Pr: Robert A Toohey
**Chf Mktg O:* Anthony Recine
**Sr VP:* Martin Burvill
**Sr VP:* Christopher Formant

D-U-N-S 02-062-2762
■ MCI INTERNATIONAL SERVICES INC
VERIZON BUSINESS
(*Suby of* VERIZON BUSINESS) ★
22001 Loudoun County Pkwy, Ashburn, VA 20147-6105
Tel (703) 886-5600 *Founded/Ownrshp* 1974
Sales 150.0MM^E *EMP* 650
SIC 4813 Telephone communication, except radio
CEO: Michael D Cappellas
Ofcr: Grace Wong
VP: Troy Yenser
Mng Dir: Jesper Pedersen
Mng Dir: Simon Phoon
Admn Mgr: Cheryl U Ginyard-Jones
Snr Ntwrk: In Cho
Manager: Philip Mello
Snr Mgr: Erik Sherk

D-U-N-S 02-002-9971 IMP
MCI SERVICE PARTS INC
(*Suby of* MCII) ★
1700 E Golf Rd Fl 3, Schaumburg, IL 60173-5862
Tel (847) 285-2000 *Founded/Ownrshp* 1993
Sales 136.8MM^E *EMP* 325
SIC 5013 Automotive supplies & parts
Pr: Richard A Heller
COO: Janice Karijolic
**VP:* Pete Cotter

MCII
See MOTOR COACH INDUSTRIES INTERNATIONAL INC

D-U-N-S 14-780-9672
MCII HOLDINGS INC
(*Suby of* KPS CAPITAL PARTNERS LP) ★
1700 E Golf Rd, Schaumburg, IL 60173-5804
Tel (866) 624-2622 *Founded/Ownrshp* 1993
Sales 17.5MM^E *EMP* 1,500
SIC 6512 Nonresidential building operators
Pr: Thomas C Sorrells

D-U-N-S 07-498-2273
MCKAMISH INC
50 55th St, Pittsburgh, PA 15201-2311
Tel (412) 781-6262 *Founded/Ownrshp* 1975
Sales 109.8MM^E *EMP* 260
SIC 1711 Mechanical contractor
Pr: David H McKamish
**Sec:* Dennis R McKamish
VP: David Casciani
**VP:* Jamie A Clemente
Sfty Dirs: Ralph Natale
Mtls Mgr: Ed Idzakovich

D-U-N-S 60-715-6809
MCKEAN DEFENSE GROUP LLC
1 Crescent Dr Ste 400, Philadelphia, PA 19112-1015
Tel (215) 271-6108 *Founded/Ownrshp* 2006
Sales 121.3MM^E *EMP* 450^E
SIC 8711 Engineering services
CEO: Joseph L Carlini
**Pr:* Larry D Burrill
Sr VP: Don Lehner
VP: Jane Jennings
VP: Robert Pennoyer
**Prin:* Leonard F Destefano Jr
Prgrm Mgr: Bernie Disantis
Snr Ntwrk: Zachary Andrus
**CTO:* Rod Smith
MIS Dir: John Scipione
Software D: Rocco Aliberti
Board of Directors: Michael J Purcell

D-U-N-S 00-333-2723 EXP
MCKEE FOODS CORP
10260 Mckee Rd, Collegedale, TN 37315
Tel (423) 238-7111 *Founded/Ownrshp* 1934
Sales 1.7MMM^E *EMP* 6,000
SIC 2051 2052 2099 2043 Cakes, bakery: except frozen; Cookies; Food preparations; Cereal breakfast foods
Pr: Mike Kee
**CFO:* Barry Patterson
Ex VP: Deborah McKee-Fowler
VP: Lewis Belknap
**VP:* Joe Davis
Creative D: John Petticord
Snr Ntwrk: Joseph Mathew
VP Mfg: Roger Fiske
Opers Mgr: Gene Boyd
Plnt Mgr: Deris Bagli
Natl Sales: Danny Woodson

D-U-N-S 03-652-6122
MCKEE SHEPARD & GRIASKA MEDICAL ASSOCIATES
51 N 39th St Ste 1, Philadelphia, PA 19104-2640
Tel (215) 662-8978 *Founded/Ownrshp* 2001
Sales 429.9MM *EMP* 17
SIC 8011 General & family practice, physician/surgeon
Pr: Karen J Nichols MD

D-U-N-S 05-762-2227
MCKEESPORT AREA SCHOOL DISTRICT
3590 Oneil Blvd, McKeesport, PA 15132-1641
Tel (412) 664-3610 *Founded/Ownrshp* 1966
Sales 62.1MM^E *EMP* 1,257
SIC 8211 Public elementary school; Public junior high school; Public senior high school
Pr: Wayne Washowich
VP: Angie Kilbert
VP: Kim Potts
Pr Dir: Kristen Davis
Teacher Pr: James Humanic
Psych: Jennifer Pursh
Psych: David Stash

D-U-N-S 15-044-4966
MCKEEVER ENTERPRISES INC
PRICE CHOPPER
4216 S Hocker Dr, Independence, MO 64055-4754
Tel (816) 478-3095 *Founded/Ownrshp* 1985
Sales 118.1MM^E *EMP* 1,000
SIC 5411

D-U-N-S 11-334-2740
MCKENNA LONG & ALDRIDGE LLP
1900 K St Nw Ste Ll100, Washington, DC 20006-1102
Tel (202) 496-7145 *Founded/Ownrshp* 1995
Sales NA *EMP* 1,100
SIC 8111

D-U-N-S 00-389-5687
MCKENNEYS INC (GA)
(*Suby of* MCKENNEY'S MANAGEMENT CORPORATION)
1056 Moreland Indus Blvd, Atlanta, GA 30316-3296
Tel (404) 622-5000 *Founded/Ownrshp* 1943
Sales 186.9MM^E *EMP* 700
SIC 1711 8711

D-U-N-S 00-386-9062
MCKENZIE ELECTRIC COOPERATIVE INC (ND)
MEC
908 4th Ave Ne, Watford City, ND 58854-7608
Tel (701) 842-2311 *Founded/Ownrshp* 1947
Sales 129.6MM *EMP* 42
Accts Eide Bailly Llp Fargo Nd
SIC 4911 Distribution, electric power
CEO: John Skurupey
IT Man: Janice Koeser
Board of Directors: Glen Aamodt, Dennis Johnson, Earl Pelton, Ray Tescher, Travis Thompson

D-U-N-S 08-685-9741 IMP/EXP
MCKENZIE SPORTS PRODUCTS LLC
MC KENZIE TAXIDERMY SUPPLY
1910 Saint Luke Church Rd, Salisbury, NC 28146-7956
Tel (704) 279-7985 *Founded/Ownrshp* 2012
Sales 97.2MM^E *EMP* 540
SIC 3949 3423 Targets, archery & rifle shooting; Taxidermist tools & equipment
VP: Chad Davis

D-U-N-S 00-408-2145
MCKENZIE TANK LINES INC (FL)
1966 Commonwealth Ln, Tallahassee, FL 32303-3196
Tel (850) 576-1221 *Founded/Ownrshp* 1949, 1944
Sales 174.9MM^E *EMP* 819
SIC 4213 3715 3443 Liquid petroleum transport, non-local; Truck trailers; Fabricated plate work (boiler shop)
Pr: James C Shaeffer
Ch Bd: Joseph Audie
CFO: Robert Landrum
Sec: Robert G Landrum Jr
VP: Dana F Dudley
VP: Dana J Dudley
VP: Jack Faulkner
VP: John D Jackson
Dir Risk M: Josh Shelton
Area Mgr: Steve Johnson
Plnt Mgr: Donnie Alford
Board of Directors: S M Dyson, G M Landrum

MCKENZIE-WILLAMETTE HOSPITAL
See MCKINSEY WILLIAMETTE

MCKENZIE-WILLAMETTE MED CTR
See MCKENZIE-WILLAMETTE REGIONAL MEDICAL CENTER ASSOCIATES LLC

D-U-N-S 62-798-7407
■ **MCKENZIE-WILLAMETTE REGIONAL MEDICAL CENTER ASSOCIATES LLC**
MCKENZIE-WILLAMETTE MED CTR
(*Suby of* QUORUM HEALTH CORP) ★
1460 G St, Springfield, OR 97477-4112
Tel (541) 726-4400 *Founded/Ownrshp* 2016
Sales 136.5MM^E *EMP* 2,100
SIC 8062 General medical & surgical hospitals
CEO: Chad Campbell
Pr: Roy Orr
CFO: Steve Dougherty
CTO: Amy Lathrop
Anesthlgy: Barbara Coda
Anesthlgy: Daniel Hagengruber

MCKESSON AUTOMATION HEALTHCARE
See AESYNT INC

D-U-N-S 17-766-7227 IMP/EXP
▲ **MCKESSON CORP**
1 Post St Fl 18, San Francisco, CA 94104-5284
Tel (415) 983-8300 *Founded/Ownrshp* 1833
Sales 190.8MMM *EMP* 68,000
Accts Deloitte & Touche Llp San Fra
Tkr Sym MCK *Exch* NYS
SIC 5122 5047 5199 7372 Drugs, proprietaries & sundries; Pharmaceuticals; Proprietary (patent) medicines; Druggists' sundries; Medical equipment & supplies; First aid supplies; General merchandise, non-durable; Prepackaged software
Ch Bd: John H Hammergren
Pr: Patrick J Blake
Pr: Julie Coviello
Pr: Paul C Julian
CFO: James A Beer
Treas: Chris Edmonson
Chf Cred: Lori A Schechter
Ex VP: Jorge L Figueredo
Ex VP: Kathleen D McElligott
Ex VP: Bansi Nagji
VP: Chris Alverson
VP: Casey Antonson
VP: Bill Balaun
VP: Andy Birken
VP: Tim Boozan
VP: David Brown
VP: Deb Bulger
VP: Andy Burtis
VP: Gerardo Castaneda
VP: Mauricio Chavez
VP: David Didomenico
Board of Directors: Susan R Salka, Andy D Bryant, Wayne A Budd, N Anthony Coles, Alton F Irby III, M Christine Jacobs, Donald R Knauss, Marie L Knowles, David M Lawrence, Edward A Mueller

D-U-N-S 13-389-0736 IMP
■ **MCKESSON INFORMATION SOLUTIONS LLC**
MCKESSON TECH SOLUTIONS GROUP
(*Suby of* MCKESSON CORP) ★
5995 Windward Pkwy, Alpharetta, GA 30005-4184
Tel (404) 338-6000 *Founded/Ownrshp* 2003
Sales 173.9MM^E *EMP* 3,000
SIC 7373 Systems software development services

D-U-N-S 82-460-5141
■ **MCKESSON MEDICAL-SURGICAL HOLDINGS INC**
(*Suby of* MCKESSON MEDICAL-SURGICAL INC) ★
9954 Mayland Dr Ste 4000, Henrico, VA 23233-1484
Tel (804) 264-7500 *Founded/Ownrshp* 1997
Sales 219.5MM^E *EMP* 3,000
SIC 5047 Medical & hospital equipment; Medical equipment & supplies; Medical laboratory equipment; Surgical equipment & supplies
Pr: Emad Rizk
**Pr:* Paul Julian
**CFO:* Rene Gobeille
**Sr VP:* Carolyn J Wukitch
**VP:* Elaine Lemke
**VP:* John Leonard

D-U-N-S 02-390-4428 EXP
■ **MCKESSON MEDICAL-SURGICAL INC**
(*Suby of* MCKESSON CORP) ★
9954 Mayland Dr Ste 4000, Richmond, VA 23233-1484
Tel (804) 264-7500 *Founded/Ownrshp* 1980, 2010
Sales 2.4MMM^E *EMP* 3,000
SIC 5047 Medical & hospital equipment; Medical equipment & supplies; Medical laboratory equipment; Surgical equipment & supplies
Pr: McComb Stanton
**Pr:* Brian S Tyler
**CFO:* James Beer
Treas: Larry Burk
**Treas:* Nicholas A Loiacono
**Ex VP:* Patrick J Blake
**Ex VP:* John H Hammergren
**Sr VP:* Jerry E Neal
**VP:* Willie C Bogan
VP: Don Fauth
VP: Stephen Long
VP: Pat McClenaghan
VP: Doug Shaver
VP: Laraine Warner

D-U-N-S 02-047-7410
■ **MCKESSON MEDICAL-SURGICAL MEDIMART INC** (MN)
(*Suby of* MCKESSON CORP) ★
8121 10th Ave N, Minneapolis, MN 55427-4401
Tel (763) 595-6000 *Founded/Ownrshp* 1959, 1998
Sales 119.7MM^E *EMP* 750
SIC 5047 5999

D-U-N-S 83-050-0737
■ **MCKESSON PHARMACY SYSTEMS LLC**
(*Suby of* MCKESSON CORP) ★
30881 Schoolcraft Rd, Livonia, MI 48150-2010
Tel (734) 421-0260 *Founded/Ownrshp* 2008
Sales 93.4MM^E *EMP* 554
SIC 7372 5122 Prepackaged software; Pharmaceuticals
Pr: Emilie Ray
Pr: Brian Grobbel

D-U-N-S 87-757-7775
■ **MCKESSON SPECIALTY ARIZONA INC**
(*Suby of* MCKESSON CORP) ★
4343 N Scottsdale Rd # 370, Scottsdale, AZ 85251-3343
Tel (480) 663-4000 *Founded/Ownrshp* 1994
Sales 127.2MM^E *EMP* 700^E
SIC 5122 Druggists' sundries
Pr: Brian Tyler
**CFO:* Bill O Neill
VP: Pete Perron
**VP:* Peggy Yelinek
Exec: Rob Elwood
Off Mgr: Jacki Baldwin
Mktg Dir: Ronald Burnett
Snr PM: Vinayak Bhat
Snr Mgr: Mandy Wagner

MCKESSON TECH SOLUTIONS GROUP
See MCKESSON INFORMATION SOLUTIONS LLC

D-U-N-S 15-290-5089
■ **MCKESSON TECHNOLOGIES INC**
MEDAPHIS PHYSICIAN
(*Suby of* MCKESSON CORP) ★
11475 Great Oaks Way # 400, Alpharetta, GA 30022-2440
Tel (404) 338-6000 *Founded/Ownrshp* 2007
Sales 311.4MM^E *EMP* 5,100
SIC 7374 8741 8721 7322 7373 Computer processing services; Business management; Billing & bookkeeping service; Collection agency, except real estate; Systems integration services; Systems software development services
COO: Chris E Perkins
**CFO:* Jill Robinson
CFO: Stephen Scheppmann
Ex VP: Asif Ahmad
**Sr VP:* Paul J Quiner
VP: Rick Flynt
VP: Anne Law
CIO: Randall Spratt
CIO: Michael Wood
Genl Couns: Mike Missailidis

D-U-N-S 04-693-9948
MCKIM & CREED PA
1730 Varsity Dr Ste 500, Raleigh, NC 27606-2689
Tel (919) 233-8091 *Founded/Ownrshp* 1978
Sales 94.5MM^E *EMP* 284
SIC 8711 8713

D-U-N-S 60-714-7105
MCKINLEY INC
MCKINLEY PROPERTIES
320 N Main St Ste 200, Ann Arbor, MI 48104-1127
Tel (734) 769-8520 *Founded/Ownrshp* 1970
Sales 58.4MM^E *EMP* 1,600^E
SIC 6513 Apartment building operators
CEO: Albert Berriz
**COO:* Royal E Caswell III
COO: Royal Caswell
**Treas:* Jim Willet
VP: Garrett Hain
**VP:* Cheryl Rabbitt
Sls Mgr: Carmen Miller

MCKINLEY PROPERTIES
See MCKINLEY INC

D-U-N-S 02-611-3600
MCKINNEY DODGE INC
CHRYSLER JEEP DDGE CY MCKINNEY
321 N Central Expy # 240, McKinney, TX 75070-3503
Tel (972) 569-9650 *Founded/Ownrshp* 2013
Sales 88.9MM *EMP* 99
SIC 5511 Automobiles, new & used
Pr: Gus Rodriguez
**Sec:* Johnann McCain

D-U-N-S 00-793-5125 IMP
MCKINNEY DRILLING CO LLC
(*Suby of* KELLER FOUNDATIONS LLC) ★
7550 Teague Rd Ste 300, Hanover, MD 21076-1807
Tel (410) 874-1235 *Founded/Ownrshp* 2003
Sales 89.5MM^E *EMP* 450
SIC 1794 5082 Excavation & grading, building construction; Excavating machinery & equipment
Pr: Bill Maher
**CFO:* James Eikenberg
CFO: Philip Tannery
VP: Neal Howard
VP: Richard Rogers
Exec: Nicole Baldwin
Dist Mgr: Austin Pruitt

D-U-N-S 07-137-7600
MCKINNEY INDEPENDENT SCHOOL DISTRICT
MCKINNEY ISD
1 Duvall St, McKinney, TX 75069-3210
Tel (469) 302-4000 *Founded/Ownrshp* 1840
Sales 299.2MM *EMP* 1,130
Accts Evans Pingleton And Howard P
SIC 8211 Public elementary & secondary schools
Ofcr: Joseph Ayers
Exec: Jason Bird
Assoc Dir: Colin Wells
Off Mgr: Ardena Johnson
Off Mgr: Paula Martin
CIO: Allen McDaniel
Info Man: Shannon Evans
Pr Dir: Bobbi Hanna
Schl Brd P: Aimee Dangel
Psych: Janet Nelson
Snr Mgr: Kerry Roy

MCKINNEY ISD
See MCKINNEY INDEPENDENT SCHOOL DISTRICT

D-U-N-S 00-167-3920 IMP
MCKINSEY & CO INC (NY)
55 E 52nd St Fl 21, New York, NY 10055-0028
Tel (212) 446-7000 *Founded/Ownrshp* 1926
Sales 2.9MMM^E *EMP* 17,054
SIC 8742

D-U-N-S 78-947-2081
MCKINSEY WILLIAMETTE
MCKENZIE-WILLAMETTE HOSPITAL
1460 G St, Springfield, OR 97477-4112
Tel (541) 741-4600 *Founded/Ownrshp* 1992
Sales 166.2MM *EMP* 50
SIC 8011 8062 Occupational & industrial specialist, physician/surgeon; General medical & surgical hospitals
Prin: Richard Abraham
Chf Nrs Of: Kay Yanit
Sls&Mrk Ex: Rosemary Pryor
Anesthlgy: Robert A Bohanan
Doctor: Andrew Gilchrist

D-U-N-S 05-549-6004 IMP
MCKINSTRY CO LLC
5005 3rd Ave S, Seattle, WA 98134-2423
Tel (206) 762-3311 *Founded/Ownrshp* 1960
Sales 543.3MM^E *EMP* 1,300
SIC 1711 1623 3446 3444 Plumbing contractors; Ventilation & duct work contractor; Heating & air conditioning contractors; Pipeline construction; Architectural metalwork; Sheet metalwork
CEO: Dean Allen
CFO: Jim Chamberlin
**CFO:* Bill Teplicky
VP: Ash Awad
VP: Jamie Pedersen
Dir IT: Darren Borden
Sfty Dirs: John V Lossow
Opers Mgr: Paul Zasada

D-U-N-S 01-642-5522
MCL INC
M C L CAFETERIAS
2730 E 62nd St, Indianapolis, IN 46220-2958
Tel (317) 257-5425 *Founded/Ownrshp* 1985
Sales 48.2MM^E *EMP* 1,200
SIC 5812 Cafeteria
Pr: Craig Mc Gaughey
**COO:* Jesse Feil
**Treas:* Tony Hamlin
Dir Bus: Casey McGaughey
Sfty Mgr: Brent Brunnemer

D-U-N-S 00-433-0692 IMP/EXP
MCLANAHAN CORP
200 Wall St, Hollidaysburg, PA 16648-1637
Tel (814) 695-9807 *Founded/Ownrshp* 1835
Sales 119.6MM^E *EMP* 326
SIC 3532 3321 3599 3523 Crushers, stationary; Washers, aggregate & sand; Feeders, ore & aggregate; Screeners, stationary; Gray iron castings; Machine shop, jobbing & repair; Farm machinery & equipment
CEO: Sean McLanahan
**Pr:* George Sidney
CFO: Jay Nartatez
**Ch:* Michael McLanahan
**Treas:* Astride S Mc Lanahan
VP: James Carrieri
Rgnl Mgr: Stephen Shortsleeve
Div Mgr: Jerry Kauffman
Genl Mgr: Dan Ferguson
Genl Mgr: Mark Krause
IT Man: Tracy Kessling

D-U-N-S 00-983-0555 IMP/EXP
■ **MCLANE CO INC**
(*Suby of* BERKSHIRE HATHAWAY INC) ★
4747 Mclane Pkwy, Temple, TX 76504-4854
Tel (254) 771-7500 *Founded/Ownrshp* 1894
Sales 30.0MMM^E *EMP* 20,128
SIC 5141 5149 5311 5113 Groceries, general line; Specialty food items; Health foods; Department stores, discount; Towels, paper

Pr: William G Rosier
Pr: Tom Anderson
Pr: Grant Demers
**Pr:* Penny Echelberger
**Pr:* Mike Youngblood
**Pr:* Tom Zatina
**Ex VP:* James L Kent
**Sr VP:* Stuart Clark
Sr VP: Tom Sicola
VP: Ruel Athey
VP: Gary Bittner
VP: Julie Burns
VP: Tony Frankenberger
VP: Charles Freeman
VP: Hampton Inn
VP: Brad Kimbrough
**VP:* Kevin J Koch
**VP:* Len Mewhinney
VP: Julie Norris
VP: Jackie Palmer
VP: Jim Rueckert

D-U-N-S 19-868-1582
■ MCLANE FOODSERVICE INC
(*Suby of* MCLANE CO INC) ★
2085 Midway Rd, Carrollton, TX 75006-5063
Tel (972) 364-2000 *Founded/Ownrshp* 2000
Sales 6.4MMM *EMP* 3,618
SIC 8742 5141 5311 5113 Restaurant & food services consultants; Groceries, general line; Department stores; Industrial & personal service paper
**Ex VP:* Jim Kent
VP: Susan Adzick
VP: Gary Bittner
VP: Bill Larkin
VP: Syndee Stiles
VP: Max Wheeler
Prgrm Mgr: Helen Mejorado
Prgrm Mgr: Anne Speights
Prgrm Mgr: Atwell West
VP Opers: Cindy Stiles
Manager: Darren Crawford
Board of Directors: Russ Craddock, Charlie Gallagher, Lyn Harris, Jeff Hayes, Caroline Mann, Scott Mischnick, Celeste Walls

D-U-N-S 10-920-0436
■ MCLANE HIGH PLAINS INC
(*Suby of* MCLANE CO INC) ★
1717 E Loop 289, Lubbock, TX 79403-6501
Tel (806) 766-2900 *Founded/Ownrshp* 1982
Sales 142.8MM[E] *EMP* 335
SIC 5141 5142 5113 Groceries, general line; Packaged frozen goods; Industrial & personal service paper
CEO: William G Rosier
**Pr:* Mike Youngblood
**CFO:* Kevin Koch
**Ex VP:* Jim Kent
VP: Tim Paradoski
Sales Exec: Jay Warnick

D-U-N-S 12-034-8714
■ MCLANE MINNESOTA INC
(*Suby of* MCLANE CO INC) ★
1111 5th St W, Northfield, MN 55057-1602
Tel (507) 664-3000 *Founded/Ownrshp* 2002
Sales 183.9MM[E] *EMP* 435
SIC 5141 Groceries, general line
CEO: William G Rosier
**Pr:* Mike Youngblood
**Treas:* Kevin Koch
**Sr VP:* Jim Kent
VP: Jerry Kropman
VP: Andre McDonald

D-U-N-S 61-055-5695
■ MCLANE NEW JERSEY
(*Suby of* MCLANE CO INC) ★
742 Courses Landing Rd, Penns Grove, NJ 08069-2956
Tel (856) 351-6200 *Founded/Ownrshp* 2002
Sales 116.6MM[E] *EMP* 401
SIC 5141 5149 Groceries, general line; Groceries & related products
Pr: Jim Tidmore

D-U-N-S 96-683-4541
■ MCLANE/CAROLINA INC
(*Suby of* MCLANE CO INC) ★
7253 Nc 48, Battleboro, NC 27809-9183
Tel (252) 972-2500 *Founded/Ownrshp* 1996
Sales 221.8MM[E] *EMP* 558
SIC 5141 5142 5149 Groceries, general line; Packaged frozen goods; Health foods; Specialty food items
Pr: William G Rosier
**Pr:* Mike Youngblood
**CFO:* Kevin Koch
**Sr VP:* Jim Kent
VP: Jim Carpenter

D-U-N-S 10-893-3946
■ MCLANE/EASTERN INC
(*Suby of* MCLANE CO INC) ★
2828 Mclane Rd, Baldwinsville, NY 13027-1390
Tel (315) 638-7500 *Founded/Ownrshp* 1984
Sales 888.6MM[E] *EMP* 750
SIC 5141 Food brokers
Pr: Lee Cobb
**Pr:* Michael Youngblood
**Treas:* Kevin Koch
**Sr VP:* Jim Kent
Dir IT: Bob Smith

D-U-N-S 82-636-8060 IMP
■ MCLANE/MID-ATLANTIC INC
(*Suby of* MCLANE CO INC) ★
56 Mclane Dr, Fredericksburg, VA 22406-1147
Tel (540) 374-2000 *Founded/Ownrshp* 1992
Sales 221.8MM[E] *EMP* 659
SIC 5141 Groceries, general line
Pr: William G Rosier
Exec: Sam Bass
Opers Mgr: Ken Maddox
Snr Mgr: Ron Synan

D-U-N-S 60-395-2367 IMP
■ MCLANE/MIDWEST INC
(*Suby of* MCLANE CO INC) ★
3400 E Main St, Danville, IL 61834-9468
Tel (217) 477-7500 *Founded/Ownrshp* 1989
Sales 286.7MM[E] *EMP* 691
SIC 5141 Groceries, general line
Pr: William G Rosier
Pr: William Rosier
Pr: Michael Youngblood
CFO: Kevin Koch
Ex VP: Jim Kent
VP: Lee Cobb
VP Sls: Lynn Swanson

D-U-N-S 13-957-0956 IMP
■ MCLANE/PACIFIC INC
(*Suby of* MCLANE CO INC) ★
3876 E Childs Ave, Merced, CA 95341-9520
Tel (209) 725-2500 *Founded/Ownrshp* 1983
Sales 214.7MM[E] *EMP* 498
SIC 5141 Groceries, general line
CEO: William G Rosier
**Pr:* Mike Youngblood
**Treas:* Kevin Koch
**Ex VP:* Jim Kent

D-U-N-S 14-456-4965
■ MCLANE/SOUTHEAST
(*Suby of* MCLANE CO INC) ★
300 Highway 29 N, Athens, GA 30601-5556
Tel (706) 549-4520 *Founded/Ownrshp* 1980
Sales 160.3MM[E] *EMP* 462
SIC 5141 Groceries, general line
Pr: William G Rosier
Exec: Steve Parks

D-U-N-S 80-516-9315 IMP/EXP
■ MCLANE/SOUTHERN CALIFORNIA INC
(*Suby of* MCLANE CO INC) ★
4472 Georgia Blvd, Temple, TX 76504
Tel (909) 887-7500 *Founded/Ownrshp* 1992
Sales 193.4MM[E] *EMP* 398
SIC 5141 Groceries, general line
Pr: David Leach
**Pr:* Grady Rosier
**CEO:* William G Rosier
**CFO:* Kevin Koch
**Ex VP:* Jim Kent
Exec: Marcela Tropea

D-U-N-S 03-325-8518
■ MCLANE/SOUTHERN INC
(*Suby of* MCLANE CO INC) ★
2104 Mfrs Blvd Ne, Brookhaven, MS 39601
Tel (601) 833-6761 *Founded/Ownrshp* 1986
Sales 216.8MM[E] *EMP* 521
SIC 5141 Groceries, general line
CEO: William G Rosier
**Pr:* Mike Youngblood
**CFO:* Kevin Koch
**Ex VP:* Jim Kent

D-U-N-S 14-770-9802
■ MCLANE/SUNEAST INC
(*Suby of* MCLANE CO INC) ★
4747 Mclane Pkwy, Temple, TX 76504-4854
Tel (254) 771-7500 *Founded/Ownrshp* 1985
Sales 576.9MM[E] *EMP* 1,653
SIC 5141 Groceries, general line
CEO: William G Rosier
**Pr:* Mike Youngblood
**CFO:* Kevin J Koch
**Ex VP:* Jim Kent
**Sr VP:* James L Kent
VP: R D Harger

D-U-N-S 12-221-2863
■ MCLANE/SUNWEST INC
(*Suby of* MCLANE CO INC) ★
14149 W Mcdowell Rd, Goodyear, AZ 85395-2500
Tel (623) 935-7500 *Founded/Ownrshp* 1985
Sales 204.9MM[E] *EMP* 518
SIC 5141 Groceries, general line
Pr: Ken Mason
**Pr:* Mike Youngblood
**CFO:* Kevin Koch
**Sr VP:* Jim Kent
IT Man: Bobby Carlson

D-U-N-S 06-274-3646
■ MCLANE/WESTERN INC
(*Suby of* MCLANE CO INC) ★
2100 E Ken Pratt Blvd, Longmont, CO 80504-5280
Tel (303) 682-7500 *Founded/Ownrshp* 1972, 1976
Sales 200.6MM[E] *EMP* 523
SIC 5141 Groceries, general line
Pr: William G Rosier
**Treas:* Kevin Koch
**Ex VP:* Jim Kent
VP: Darryl Lyon
Exec: Karen Webb
Opers Mgr: Richard Davidson

MCLAREN FLINT
See MCLAREN REGIONAL MEDICAL CENTER

MCLAREN GREATER LANSING
See INGHAM REGIONAL MEDICAL CENTER

D-U-N-S 79-145-6056
MCLAREN HEALTH CARE CORP
G3235 Beecher Rd Ste B, Flint, MI 48532-3650
Tel (810) 342-1100 *Founded/Ownrshp* 1981
Sales 1.5MMM[E] *EMP* 10,003
SIC 8062 General medical & surgical hospitals
Pr: Philip A Incarnati
**COO:* Mark O'Halla
**CFO:* Dennis Kirzemkrski
VP: Michael P Lacusta
VP: Gregory Lane
**VP:* David Mazurkiewicz
Int Pr: Justin F Klamerus
VP Gov Rls: Deidra A Wilson
**CIO:* Ron Strachan
VP Opers: Susan Durst
VP Mktg: Kevin Tompkins

D-U-N-S 96-636-2761
MCLAREN LAPEER REGION
LAPEER REGION MEDICAL CENTER
(*Suby of* MCLAREN HEALTH CARE CORP) ★
1375 N Main St, Lapeer, MI 48446-1350
Tel (810) 667-5580 *Founded/Ownrshp* 2011
Sales 106.2MM *EMP* 1[E]
SIC 8069 Chronic disease hospital
CEO: Barton Buxton
CFO: Mary Callahan

D-U-N-S 07-930-1511
MCLAREN NORTHERN MICHIGAN
NORTHERN MICH REGIONAL HOSP
(*Suby of* MCLAREN HEALTH CARE CORP) ★
416 Connable Ave, Petoskey, MI 49770-2212
Tel (800) 248-6777 *Founded/Ownrshp* 1977
Sales 210.6MM *EMP* 1,003
SIC 8062 General medical & surgical hospitals
**COO:* Mary-Anne D Ponti
CFO: Timothy Joway
Treas: Nicole Lahaie
Off Mgr: Cindy Holman
MIS Dir: Mary Catton
Cmptr Lab: Kristen Holshoe
Nutrtnst: Janet Havens
Doctor: Tara Conti
Doctor: Patrick Maloney
Pgrm Dir: Rochelle Whitmore

D-U-N-S 01-087-0863
MCLAREN OAKLAND (MI)
POH MEDICAL CENTER
50 N Perry St, Pontiac, MI 48342-2217
Tel (248) 338-5000 *Founded/Ownrshp* 1952
Sales 152.6MM *EMP* 1,200
SIC 8062 Hospital, medical school affiliated with residency
CEO: Patrick Lamberti
Ch Bd: Leo Bowman
CFO: Thomas Schilling
Bd of Dir: Pat Lamberty
Exec: Mackenzee Carter
Doctor: K Buitkus
Board of Directors: Kenneth Lim Do, Clemon Pardelas Do, Joan Riley

D-U-N-S 06-883-6915
MCLAREN PORT HURON (MI)
1221 Pine Grove Ave, Port Huron, MI 48060-3511
Tel (810) 987-5000 *Founded/Ownrshp* 1880
Sales 167.2MM *EMP* 2,000
SIC 5912 Drug stores
Ch: Patrick Moran
Chf Path: Wendy Carter
**CEO:* Thomas Defaw
COO: Randall Wagner
CFO: Vernon Dencklau
**Sec:* David Whipple
Bd of Dir: Ross Green
Chf Mktg O: Michael Basha
Ofcr: Jim Lotts
Ofcr: Marcia Trenn
VP: Jennifer Montgomery
VP: Michael Tawney
Dir Risk M: Janet Bigelow
Dir Lab: Kathy Dupes
Dir Rad: Kanu B Dalal
Dir Rx: Michael Laeder
Dir Rx: Brian Shinavier

D-U-N-S 07-544-4281
MCLAREN REGIONAL MEDICAL CENTER
MCLAREN FLINT
(*Suby of* MCLAREN HEALTH CARE CORP) ★
401 S Ballenger Hwy, Flint, MI 48532-3638
Tel (810) 342-2000 *Founded/Ownrshp* 1984
Sales 410.0MM *EMP* 2,250
SIC 8062 Hospital, medical school affiliated with nursing & residency
CEO: Donald Kooy
Dir Lab: James M Nielsen
Dir Rad: Mark Camens
Pathlgst: Julio Badin
Pathlgst: Nader B Hanna
Pathlgst: Ernesto Quiachon
Opthamlgy: Walter Cukrowski
Opthamlgy: Edward Stack
Doctor: John Neumann

D-U-N-S 18-276-0900
MCLARNEY CONSTRUCTION INC
355 S Daniel Way, San Jose, CA 95128-5120
Tel (408) 246-8600 *Founded/Ownrshp* 1987
Sales 97.4MM *EMP* 46
Accts Robert Lee & Associates Llp
SIC 1542 Commercial & office building, new construction
Pr: Kevin M McLarney
**CFO:* Nicole Merriam
**VP:* Brett McLarney
Sales Exec: Lauren Doherty

D-U-N-S 00-695-0232
MCLEAN CONTRACTING CO
6700 Mclean Way, Glen Burnie, MD 21060-6480
Tel (410) 553-6700 *Founded/Ownrshp* 1933, 1903
Sales 149.4MM[E] *EMP* 300
Accts Mcgladrey & Pullen Llp Timon
SIC 1622 1623 1629 3449 Bridge construction; Sewer line construction; Pier construction; Miscellaneous metalwork
Pr: George Bosmajian III
COO: Bill Young
**Treas:* Cynthia Wray
**Ex VP:* Frederick W Rich
**VP:* Tyrus Fisher
**VP:* Cory Heisey
Exec: Pamela Herda
IT Man: Gregory Seidl

D-U-N-S 06-086-3032
MCLEAN COUNTY UNIT DISTRICT NO 5
1809 Hovey Ave, Normal, IL 61761-4315
Tel (309) 557-4000 *Founded/Ownrshp* 1948
Sales 72.5M *EMP* 1,117
SIC 8211 Public elementary & secondary schools
Teacher Pr: Bruce Weldy

D-U-N-S 04-651-4535
MCLEAN HOSPITAL CORP
(*Suby of* GENERAL HOSPITAL) ★
115 Mill St, Belmont, MA 02478-1048
Tel (617) 855-2000 *Founded/Ownrshp* 1993
Sales 116.4MM *EMP* 1,213
SIC 8063 Psychiatric hospitals
Ch: David Barlow
**Pr:* Scott Rauch
**CFO:* David A Lagasse
CFO: Cathy O'Connell
**Ex VP:* Michele L Gougeon
**Sr VP:* Catharine Cook
**Sr VP:* Philip G Levendusky
VP: Catharyn Gildesgame
VP: Philip Levendusky
Prgrm Mgr: Diane Davey
Admn Mgr: Sandra Pohlman

D-U-N-S 02-490-7388
MCLEAN IMPLEMENT INC (IL)
JOHN DEERE AUTHORIZED DEALER
793 Illinois Route 130, Albion, IL 62806-5209
Tel (618) 445-3676 *Founded/Ownrshp* 1964
Sales 96.9MM *EMP* 75
SIC 5083 Farm implements
Pr: Marilyn K Mason
Genl Mgr: Bob Mason
Off Mgr: Diane Buza
IT Man: Jackie Fewkes
Sls Mgr: Adam Bunting
**Sls Mgr:* Melinda Clark
Sls Mgr: Chad Nalley

MCLEAN THERMAL
See PENTAIR TECHNICAL PRODUCTS

D-U-N-S 02-739-8627 IMP
MCLENDON HARDWARE INC
MCLENDON HOME SERVICES
440 Rainier Ave S, Renton, WA 98057-2401
Tel (425) 264-1541 *Founded/Ownrshp* 1926
Sales 214.2MM[E] *EMP* 460
SIC 5031 5251 Lumber, plywood & millwork; Hardware
Pr: Gail McLendon
**Treas:* Debra Judd
**VP:* Michael McLendon
Store Mgr: Shelly Hoyt

MCLENDON HOME SERVICES
See MCLENDON HARDWARE INC

D-U-N-S 11-335-3341
MCLEOD EXPRESS LLC
5002 Cundiff Ct, Decatur, IL 62526-9627
Tel (217) 706-5045 *Founded/Ownrshp* 2001
Sales 86.7MM[E] *EMP* 425
SIC 4213 Trucking, except local
Genl Mgr: Tracy Black
Dir IT: Derek Agar
Mktg Dir: Kevin Bertsch
Sls Dir: Brian Firsick

D-U-N-S 96-631-9712
MCLEOD HEALTH
555 E Cheves St, Florence, SC 29506-2617
Tel (843) 777-2256 *Founded/Ownrshp* 2011
Sales 123.2MM *EMP* 2
Accts Deloitte Tax Lp Atlanta Ga
SIC 8099 Health & allied services
Prin: Suzanne Salhab
Chf Rad: Greg Cleveland
COO: Jennifer Smith
Chf Mktg O: Elvin Irvin
Ofcr: Debbie Locklair
VP: Teresa Anderson
VP: Edward Tinsley
Dir Inf Cn: Michelle Dore
Assoc Dir: Dennis Nobles
Ex Dir: Kelly Hughes
Dir Sec: Gregg Dewitt

D-U-N-S 78-142-2852 IMP/EXP
MCLEOD HEALTH SERVICES INC
(*Suby of* MCCLEOD MED CENTER-DARLINGTON) ★
555 E Cheves St, Florence, SC 29506-2617
Tel (843) 777-5146 *Founded/Ownrshp* 1990
Sales 121.3MM[E] *EMP* 5,000
SIC 8062 General medical & surgical hospitals
Pr: Robert L Colones
COO: Crystal Flowers
Trst: Steven Ross
Assoc VP: Wendy Hedrick
VP: Mark Cameron
VP: Tim Hess
VP: Robert Hinshelwood
VP: Jack Oconnor
Exec: Jeannette Glenn
Off Mgr: Debbie Goss
CIO: Jenean Blackmon

D-U-N-S 07-042-5793
MCLEOD PHYSICIAN ASSOCIATES INC (SC)
(*Suby of* MCLEOD HEALTH SERVICES INC) ★
555 E Cheves St, Florence, SC 29506-2617
Tel (843) 777-7000 *Founded/Ownrshp* 1997
Sales 101.3MM *EMP* 30
SIC 8011 General & family practice, physician/surgeon
**Sr VP:* Dr Charles Jordan
VP: Dane Ficco
**VP:* Mike Payne

MCLEOD REGIONAL MED CNTR OF
See SAINT EUGENE MEDICAL CENTER

D-U-N-S 07-370-9784
MCLEOD REGIONAL MEDICAL CENTER OF PEE DEE INC
MCCLEOD MED CENTER-DARLINGTON
555 E Cheves St, Florence, SC 29506-2617
Tel (843) 777-2000 *Founded/Ownrshp* 1930
Sales 607.8MM *EMP* 5,000
SIC 8062 Hospital, medical school affiliated with residency
Ch Bd: Ronnie Ward
Chf Rad: Cheney Meiere
**CEO:* Robert L Colones
CFO: Michael P Browning

CFO: H McCutcheon
VP: Mark Cameron
Dir Lab: Richard Ervin
Dir Lab: Louis Wright
CIO: Janice Fraley
Dir IT: Sabrina Muldrow
IT Man: Rick Bess

D-U-N-S 14-823-0746
■ **MCLEODUSA HOLDINGS INC**
(*Suby of* MCLEODUSA INC) ★
1770 Boyson Rd, Hiawatha, IA 52233-2342
Tel (319) 364-0000 *Founded/Ownrshp* 1991
Sales 110.1MM[E] *EMP* 1,547[E]
SIC 4813 4812 Telephone communication, except radio; Radio telephone communication
Ch Bd: Royce Holland
Mng Dir: Mary Greiner

D-U-N-S 80-886-2957
■ **MCLEODUSA INC**
(*Suby of* PAETEC HOLDING CORP) ★
6400 C St Sw, Cedar Rapids, IA 52404-7463
Tel (319) 364-0000 *Founded/Ownrshp* 2008
Sales 248.5MM[E] *EMP* 1,600
SIC 4813 4812 Telephone communication, except radio; Local telephone communications; Long distance telephone communications; Radio telephone communication
CEO: Royce Holland
**Pr:* Michael McDaniel
**CFO:* Joseph H Ceryanec
Bd of Dir: Jeffrey D Benjamin
**Ex VP:* Richard J Buyens
**VP:* Kurt O Langel
**VP:* Chris McFarland
VP: Cheri Roach
VP: Christopher Ryan

D-U-N-S 83-889-2842
MCM CAPITAL PARTNERS
25201 Chagrin Blvd # 360, Beachwood, OH 44122-5633
Tel (216) 514-1840 *Founded/Ownrshp* 1992
Sales 105.8MM[E] *EMP* 343[E]
SIC 6211 Security brokers & dealers
Mng Pt: Mark Mansour
Mng Pt: Fred Disanto
Bd of Dir: William M Weber
Ofcr: Lynette Biskis
VP: Robert Kingsbury
VP: Gregory Meredith
**Ex Dir:* James Poffenberger
**Ex Dir:* Steve Ross
**Ex Dir:* Gerry Weimann
Mktg Mgr: Kevin F Hayes

D-U-N-S 06-294-2453
MCM CONSTRUCTION INC
6413 32nd St, North Highlands, CA 95660-3001
Tel (916) 334-1221 *Founded/Ownrshp* 1973
Sales 150.0MM *EMP* 370
SIC 1622 Bridge construction
Pr: James A Carter
VP: H McGovern
**VP:* Harry D McGovern
VP: Kevin Wood
Exec: Dan Shaw
Sfty Mgr: Ed Orsi

D-U-N-S 09-157-0762
MCM CORP (NC)
702 Oberlin Rd Ste 300, Raleigh, NC 27605-1357
Tel (919) 833-1600 *Founded/Ownrshp* 1977, 2000
Sales NA *EMP* 175[E]
SIC 6331 Property damage insurance
Ch Bd: George E King
**CEO:* Stephen L Stephano
**CFO:* Kevin Ham
**VP:* Brenda Lewis
Netwrk Eng: Ryan Smith

D-U-N-S 00-693-1349 EXP
MCMASTER-CARR SUPPLY CO (IL)
600 N County Line Rd, Elmhurst, IL 60126-2081
Tel (630) 834-9600 *Founded/Ownrshp* 1901
Sales 347.2MM[E] *EMP* 200[E]
Accts Pricewaterhousecoopers Llp
SIC 5085 5075 Industrial supplies; Warm air heating & air conditioning
Pr: Robert Delaney
Pr: Dick Adams
Ofcr: John Francis
VP: Joann Callahan
VP: Paul Wiggin
Dir Soc: Mary Yonk
CIO: Edwin Whitlow
MIS Dir: Tracy Rourke
Dir IT: Jeff Puglielli
IT Man: Mike Delaney
IT Man: Pete Fitzpatrick

MCMC
See MID-COLUMBIA MEDICAL CENTER

D-U-N-S 87-757-2388
MCMC LLC
COLUMBIA MEDICAL CONSULTANTS
300 Crown Colony Dr # 203, Quincy, MA 02169-0929
Tel (617) 375-7700 *Founded/Ownrshp* 2002
Sales 83.0MM[E] *EMP* 506[E]
SIC 8742 Hospital & health services consultant
CEO: Michael Lindberg
Pr: Ron Williams
**CFO:* Pamela Ochs-Piasecki
Sr VP: Larry Brinton
**Sr VP:* Brenda Calia
Sr VP: Joe Lawless
VP: Nico Digioia
VP: Rhonda France
VP: Colleen Horiates
VP: Lawrence Reynolds
QA Dir: Trisha Hardee

D-U-N-S 02-957-4472
MCMENAMINS INC
ROCK CREEK RESTAURANT & TAVERN
430 N Killingsworth St, Portland, OR 97217-2441
Tel (503) 223-0109 *Founded/Ownrshp* 1983
Sales 192.1MM[E] *EMP* 1,400[E]
SIC 5813 5812 Drinking places; Eating places
Pr: Michael R McMenamin
**Pr:* Brian C McMenamin
Dir Soc: Cynthia Gonzalez
Genl Mgr: Blair Hampson
Genl Mgr: Rich Smith
Mktg Dir: Renee Rank
Mktg Dir: Mike Walker
Mktg Mgr: Kerry Beeaker

D-U-N-S 18-371-8212
MCMILLIN COMMUNITIES INC
MCMILLIN REALTY
2750 Womble Rd Ste 200, San Diego, CA 92106-6114
Tel (619) 561-5275 *Founded/Ownrshp* 1985
Sales 119.8MM[E] *EMP* 1,000[E]
SIC 6799 Investors
Pr: Mark McMillin
**Pr:* Kenneth Baumgartner
**CFO:* Gary Beason
**VP:* Bryce Jones
**Genl Mgr:* Joe W Shielly

MCMILLIN REALTY
See MCMILLIN COMMUNITIES INC

MCMM
See M C HOLDINGS INC

D-U-N-S 07-116-9130 IMP
MCMURRAY FABRICS INC
105 Vann Pl, Aberdeen, NC 28315-8612
Tel (910) 944-2128 *Founded/Ownrshp* 1968
Sales 134.1MM[E] *EMP* 514
SIC 2257 Weft knit fabric mills
Pr: Brian L McMurray
**VP:* Connie McMurray
Snr Sftwr: Ivan Lora
Dir IT: Paul Whitely
Ql Cn Mgr: Chris Williamson
Sls Mgr: Jim Curlee

MCN
See MICHCON PIPELINE CO

D-U-N-S 80-774-4995 IMP/EXP
MCN BUILD LLC
1214 28th St Nw, Washington, DC 20007-3315
Tel (202) 333-3424 *Founded/Ownrshp* 2007
Sales 120.0MM *EMP* 45
SIC 1541 1542 Industrial buildings & warehouses; School building construction; Commercial & office building, new construction; Institutional building construction; Religious building construction
CEO: Rudy Seikaly
Off Mgr: Anna Florence

D-U-N-S 60-200-3725
MCNATIONAL INC
502 2nd St E, South Point, OH 45680-9446
Tel (740) 377-4391 *Founded/Ownrshp* 1988
Sales 131.5MM[E] *EMP* 800[E]
SIC 3731 7699 4491 Barges, building & repairing; Cargo vessels, building & repairing; Aircraft & heavy equipment repair services; Marine cargo handling
Pr: Rick Griffith
**CEO:* Bruce D McGinnis
**Prin:* C Barry Gipson

MCNAUGHTON BOOK SERVICE
See BRODART CO

MCNAUGHTON-MCKAY ELECTRIC CO
See MCNAUGHTON-MCKAY SOUTHEAST INC

D-U-N-S 00-695-8474
MCNAUGHTON-MCKAY ELECTRIC CO
ADVANCE DISTRIBUTING COMPANY
1357 E Lincoln Ave, Madison Heights, MI 48071-4126
Tel (248) 399-7500 *Founded/Ownrshp* 1930
Sales 702.2MM *EMP* 760
Accts Kpmg Llp
SIC 5065 5063 Diskettes, computer; Antennas, receiving, satellite dishes
Pr: Donald D Slominski
COO: John R McNaughton
**CFO:* John D Kuczmanski
**Ex VP:* Richard Dahlstrom
**Ex VP:* Scott Sellers
**VP:* Greg Chun
VP: Gregory H Chun
**VP:* Kathleen M Gollin
VP: Ronald Hoff
VP: John Kuczmanski
VP: Richard S Miller

D-U-N-S 00-196-1317 IMP
MCNAUGHTON-MCKAY ELECTRIC CO OF OHIO INC (MI)
MCNAUGHTON-MCKAY ELECTRIC OHIO
(*Suby of* ADVANCE DISTRIBUTING CO) ★
2255 Citygate Dr, Columbus, OH 43219-3567
Tel (614) 476-2800 *Founded/Ownrshp* 1996
Sales 94.0MM[E] *EMP* 200
SIC 5063 Electrical apparatus & equipment; Motors, electric; Transformers, electric; Electrical supplies
CEO: Donald D Slominski Jr
**Sec:* Michael G Mimnaugh
**Ex VP:* Richard M Dahlstrom
**Ex VP:* John R McNaughton III
**VP:* Kathleen M Gollin
**VP:* John D Kuczmanski
**Genl Mgr:* William Parsons

MCNAUGHTON-MCKAY ELECTRIC OHIO
See MCNAUGHTON-MCKAY ELECTRIC CO OF OHIO INC

D-U-N-S 00-332-1320
MCNAUGHTON-MCKAY SOUTHEAST INC (NC)
MCNAUGHTON-MCKAY ELECTRIC CO
(*Suby of* ADVANCE DISTRIBUTING CO) ★
6685 Best Friend Rd, Norcross, GA 30071-2918
Tel (770) 825-8600 *Founded/Ownrshp* 1932
Sales 115.6MM[E] *EMP* 285
SIC 5063 Electrical supplies
Pr: Donald D Slominski Jr
Ex VP: Richard M Dahlstrom
Ex VP: John R McNaughton III
VP: David Beattie
VP: Kathleen M Gollin
VP: John D Kuczmanski

D-U-N-S 60-800-2416 IMP/EXP
■ **MCNEILUS COMPANIES INC**
(*Suby of* TOTAL MIXER TECHNOLOGIES LLC) ★
524 E Highway St, Dodge Center, MN 55927-9181
Tel (507) 374-6321 *Founded/Ownrshp* 1970
Sales 427.4MM[E] *EMP* 1,600
SIC 3713 Cement mixer bodies; Garbage, refuse truck bodies
Pr: Michael J Wuest
**CEO:* Charles Szews
VP: Gary Burgess
IT Man: Tyler Lermon
VP Opers: Gloria Georger
VP Opers: Tracy Timmerman
Sfty Mgr: Jeff Ditlevson

D-U-N-S 02-276-0326 IMP
MCNEILUS STEEL INC
702 2nd Ave Se, Dodge Center, MN 55927-8903
Tel (507) 374-6336 *Founded/Ownrshp* 1948
Sales 441.3MM *EMP* 475
Accts Mcgladrey Llp Rochester Min
SIC 5051 Structural shapes, iron or steel; Concrete reinforcing bars; Reinforcement mesh, wire
Pr: Leland P McNeilus
**CFO:* Daniel Blaisdell
Genl Mgr: Joel Furnari
Genl Mgr: Glenn Sylvester
Dir IT: Chuck Rhodes
IT Man: Darren Boeck
IT Man: Mark Dulaney
IT Man: Kory Kliner
Opers Mgr: Stephen Klomps
Ql Cn Mgr: Kevin Fettig
Sls Mgr: Ben Hansen
Board of Directors: Leland Patrick McNeilus

D-U-N-S 05-448-7756 IMP/EXP
■ **MCNEILUS TRUCK AND MANUFACTURING INC** (MN)
(*Suby of* MCNEILUS COMPANIES INC) ★
524 County Rd 34 E, Dodge Center, MN 55927
Tel (614) 868-0760 *Founded/Ownrshp* 1970
Sales 267.1MM[E] *EMP* 720
SIC 3713 3531 3537 3272 Cement mixer bodies; Garbage, refuse truck bodies; Concrete plants; Mixers, concrete; Industrial trucks & tractors; Concrete products
CEO: Charles Szews
Pr: Brad Nelson
CFO: Sonny Tara

D-U-N-S 00-294-7703 IMP/EXP
MCNICHOLS CO (OH)
2502 N Rocky Point Dr # 750, Rocky Point, FL 33607-1421
Tel (877) 884-4653 *Founded/Ownrshp* 1952
Sales 160.4MM[E] *EMP* 325
SIC 5051 Metals service centers & offices
CEO: Eugene McNichols
**Pr:* Scott McNichols
**COO:* John Farley
**CFO:* Craig A Stein
**Treas:* Larry F Jones
**Ex VP:* David Brenneman
**VP:* Jennifer McNichols
**VP:* Steven McNichols
VP: Bill Tuxhorn
Ex Dir: Katherine Woodrow
Brnch Mgr: Brad Hulse

MCP HAHNEMANN UNIVERSITY
See PHILADELPHIA HEALTH AND EDUCATION CORP

D-U-N-S 12-087-4599 IMP
MCP INDUSTRIES INC
MISSION RUBBER CO
708 S Temescal St Ste 101, Corona, CA 92879-2096
Tel (951) 736-1881 *Founded/Ownrshp* 1950
Sales 123.8MM[E] *EMP* 350
SIC 3069 3259 3089 Molded rubber products; Sewer pipe or fittings, clay; Injection molding of plastics
CEO: Walter N Garrett
**Sec:* Charlotte Garrett
**VP:* Owen Garrett
Sls&Mrk Ex: Kathy Kerecman

D-U-N-S 10-108-3173
MCPC INC
MCPC TECH PDTS & SOLUTIONS
1801 Superior Ave E # 300, Cleveland, OH 44114-2135
Tel (440) 238-0102 *Founded/Ownrshp* 2002
Sales 522.1MM[E] *EMP* 450
SIC 5045 Computers, peripherals & software
CEO: Michael Trebilcock
**Pr:* Lance Frew
**Pr:* Andy Jones
**CFO:* Rob Young
Ex VP: Peter Dimarco
**Ex VP:* Jason Taylor
VP: Mitch Breneman
VP: Brian Kinne
VP: Beth Svec
Snr Ntwrk: Larry Roberson
CIO: Ken Pratt

MCPC TECH PDTS & SOLUTIONS
See MCPC INC

D-U-N-S 06-926-5536
MCPHEE ELECTRIC LTD (CT)
(*Suby of* PHALCON LTD) ★
505 Main St, Farmington, CT 06032-2912
Tel (860) 677-9797 *Founded/Ownrshp* 1974, 2006
Sales 130.0MM *EMP* 500
Accts Blum Shapiro & Company Pc
SIC 1731 General electrical contractor
CEO: Michael Mc Phee
**Pr:* Marcus McPhee
**CEO:* Michael McPhee
**CFO:* John Conroy
Mng Dir: Bradley Pritchett
Brnch Mgr: Thomas Lombardo
Genl Mgr: Theresa Beck
Sfty Dirs: Steve Dauphinais
Opers Mgr: Steve Gesseck

D-U-N-S 05-721-2979 IMP
MCPHERSON COMPANIES INC
MC PHERSON OIL PRODUCTS
5051 Cardinal St, Trussville, AL 35173-1871
Tel (205) 661-2799 *Founded/Ownrshp* 1971
Sales 263.6MM[E] *EMP* 270
SIC 5171 5411 5541 Petroleum bulk stations; Convenience stores; Gasoline service stations
Ch Bd: Charles K Mc Pherson
**Pr:* Ken Mc Pherson

D-U-N-S 07-658-0695
MCPHS UNIVERSITY
MASSACHUSETTS COLLEGE OF PHARM
179 Longwood Ave, Boston, MA 02115-5804
Tel (617) 732-2132 *Founded/Ownrshp* 1852
Sales 292.2MM *EMP* 300
Accts Cbiz Tofias Boston Ma
SIC 8221 Service academy
Pr: Charles Monahan Jr
**CFO:* Richard J Lessard
Assoc Dir: Jodi Hanelt
Ex Dir: Karen Single
DP Dir: Carrie Glass
IT Man: Daniel Barbas
Doctor: Lindsay Fink
Genl Couns: Mary Tanona

MCPS
See MONTGOMERY COUNTY PUBLIC SCHOOLS

MCR
See MEDICAL CENTER OF ROCKIES

MCR SAFETY
See SHELBY GROUP INTERNATIONAL INC

D-U-N-S 05-456-1154
MCROBERTS PROTECTIVE AGENCY INC
(*Suby of* MC ROBERTS CORP) ★
42 Broadway Ste 1836, New York, NY 10004-3855
Tel (732) 886-0990 *Founded/Ownrshp* 1974
Sales 97.7MM[E] *EMP* 2,500
Accts Lawson Rescinio Schibell & A
SIC 7381 1731 Detective services; Protective services, guard; Security guard service; Fire detection & burglar alarm systems specialization
Ch Bd: Meredith McRoberts
**CFO:* Michael Lutz

D-U-N-S 60-573-0659
MCS & METROPLEX CONTROL SYSTEM
12903 Delivery, San Antonio, TX 78247-3476
Tel (210) 495-5245 *Founded/Ownrshp* 2005
Sales 108.1MM *EMP* 2[E]
SIC 1731 Access control systems specialization
Owner: Don Carr

MCS DESIGN
See MCS INDUSTRIES INC

D-U-N-S 09-787-8516 IMP/EXP
MCS INDUSTRIES INC
MCS DESIGN
2280 Newlins Mill Rd, Easton, PA 18045-7813
Tel (610) 253-6268 *Founded/Ownrshp* 1980
Sales 198.1MM[E] *EMP* 704
SIC 2499 3089 3499 3993 3231 Picture & mirror frames, wood; Injection molding of plastics; Picture frames, metal; Signs & advertising specialties; Products of purchased glass
CEO: Richard Master
**Pr:* Josh Macneel
**CEO:* Greg Yocco
CFO: Greg Yacco
VP: John Alvator
**VP:* Bob Goldfarb
VP: Anne M Plla
VP: Sandy Reiter
**VP:* Jim Scheyer
Ex Dir: Dianne Hockman
MIS Dir: Mike Kelley

MCS LIFE INSURANCE
See MEDICAL CARD SYSTEM INC

D-U-N-S 80-020-3580
MCS OF TAMPA INC
MISSION CRITICAL SOLUTION
8510 Sunstate St, Tampa, FL 33634-1312
Tel (813) 872-0217 *Founded/Ownrshp* 1988
Sales 99.9MM[E] *EMP* 280
SIC 1731 7373 4813 7378 Communications specialization; Computer integrated systems design; Telephone communication, except radio; Computer maintenance & repair
Pr: Gilbert T Gonzales
COO: Alice Mscaskil
**CFO:* Brian Calka
CFO: Kezele Duanes
CFO: Duane Kezele
CFO: Becky Walther
**Treas:* Kim Gonzales
**Ex VP:* David Dallmann
**Ex VP:* James V Slagle Jr
VP: James Slagle
Brnch Mgr: Chris Ruefer

D-U-N-S 12-232-5277
MCSHANE DEVELOPMENT CO LLC
MCSHANE WILLIAMS WAY MOB 1
9500 Bryn Mawr Ave, Rosemont, IL 60018-5211
Tel (847) 292-4300 *Founded/Ownrshp* 1984
Sales 113.5MM[E] *EMP* 300
SIC 6552 Land subdividers & developers, commercial
CEO: James McShane
**Pr:* Hunter Barrier
CFO: Melvin Meyer
Ex VP: Mathew R Dougherty
VP: Anthony Pricco
VP: Jeff Stringer
Prin: Molly McShane

MCSHANE WILLIAMS WAY MOB 1
See MCSHANE DEVELOPMENT CO LLC

D-U-N-S 03-872-6634
MCSI INC
2975 Northwoods Pkwy, Peachtree Corners, GA 30071-1537
Tel (770) 441-5263 *Founded/Ownrshp* 1981
Sales 91.0MM^E *EMP* 2,036
SIC 1731 5065 7359 Communications specialization; Communication equipment; Audio-visual equipment & supply rental
Pr: D Gordon Strickland
**Ch Bd:* Timothy R Chrisman
CFO: James R Vonier
Ofcr: Larry K Knipple
VP Opers: Mary A Stewart
VP Mktg: Joe Robinson
Mktg Mgr: Deborah Wilson
Board of Directors: Robert G Hecht, William D King, Henry Radcliffe

D-U-N-S 12-699-6230
MCV ASSOCIATED PHYSICIANS
MCV PHYSICIANS
830 E Main St Ste 1900, Richmond, VA 23219-2701
Tel (804) 358-6100 *Founded/Ownrshp* 1991
Sales 292.6MM *EMP* 1,337
Accts Kpmg Llp Mc Lean Va
SIC 8741 8721 Business management; Accounting, auditing & bookkeeping
Pr: John Ward
Genl Mgr: Keith Purcell

MCV PHYSICIANS
See MCV ASSOCIATED PHYSICIANS

MCWANE CAST IRON PIPE COMPANY
See MCWANE INC

D-U-N-S 00-400-1715 IMP/EXP
MCWANE INC
MCWANE CAST IRON PIPE COMPANY
2900 Highway 280 S # 300, Birmingham, AL 35223-2469
Tel (205) 414-3100 *Founded/Ownrshp* 1921, 1975
Sales 1.2MMM^E *EMP* 4,883
SIC 3491 1221 3321 3312 3494 Fire hydrant valves; Bituminous coal surface mining; Ductile iron castings; Coke oven products (chemical recovery); Valves & pipe fittings
Pr: G Ruffner Page Jr
**CFO:* Charles F Nowlin
**Sr VP:* Key Foster
**Sr VP:* Michael Keel
**Sr VP:* Jeff Otterstedt
**Sr VP:* James M Proctor II
**Sr VP:* Jitendra Radia
**VP:* Arne C Feyling
**VP:* Leon G McCullough
VP: Chris Nichols
VP: Andy Payant
VP: Gopi Ramanathan
**VP:* Kurt Winter
VP: Barb Wisniewski
**VP:* Barbara Wisniewski
Exec: Benida Slippo
Exec: Alvin Tucker

D-U-N-S 79-596-1650 IMP/EXP
MCWANE INC
TYLER PIPE COMPANY
(*Suby of* MCWANE CAST IRON PIPE CO) ★
11910 County Road 492, Tyler, TX 75706-5840
Tel (800) 527-8478 *Founded/Ownrshp* 2004
Sales 197.0MM^E *EMP* 600
SIC 3321 Sewer pipe, cast iron
Pr: Ruffner Page
VP: Rick Tatman
Rgnl Mgr: Sterling Bowman
Dir IT: Jerry Kirkley
IT Man: Debbie Hickman
Tech Mgr: Richard Bowman
Sfty Dirs: Jennie Shephard
Sfty Mgr: Ted Sweetman
Plnt Mgr: Bill Hoffman
Plnt Mgr: Dan Nelson
Plnt Mgr: Greg Simmons

D-U-N-S 04-889-1157
MD AUTO GROUP LLC
I-90 NISSAN
5013 Detroit Rd, Sheffield Village, OH 44054-2810
Tel (440) 934-6001 *Founded/Ownrshp* 2014
Sales 240.0MM *EMP* 35
SIC 5511 Automobiles, new & used

D-U-N-S 83-235-4042
MD INVESTORS CORP
METALDYNE
(*Suby of* ASP MD HOLDINGS INC) ★
47659 Halyard Dr, Plymouth, MI 48170-2429
Tel (734) 207-6200 *Founded/Ownrshp* 2012
Sales 1.2MMM^E *EMP* 6,500
SIC 6799 Investors
CEO: Thomas A Amato
CFO: Mark Blaufuss
**CFO:* Terry Iwasaki
Treas: Buddy Martin
VP: James Hug
VP: Richard Lefebvre
VP: Benjamin Schmidt
Prgrm Mgr: Tony Worth
Dir IT: Dick Lefabvre
Mfg Mgr: Tom Parrish
Opers Mgr: John Miller

MDA
See MUSCULAR DYSTROPHY ASSOCIATION INC

D-U-N-S 07-971-8473
MDA COMMUNICATIONS HOLDINGS LLC
3825 Fabian Way, Palo Alto, CA 94303-4604
Tel (650) 852-4000 *Founded/Ownrshp* 2015
Sales 144.8MM^E *EMP* 2,800
SIC 3663 Satellites, communications

D-U-N-S 07-858-7090
MDA INFORMATION SYSTEMS LLC
(*Suby of* MACDONALD, DETTWILER AND ASSOCIATES LTD)
820 W Diamond Ave Ste 300, Gaithersburg, MD 20878-1469
Tel (240) 833-8200 *Founded/Ownrshp* 2012
Sales 103.8MM *EMP* 198
Accts Kpmg Llp Mclean Va
SIC 7371 Custom computer programming services
CEO: Herbert Satterlee III

MDC
See MIAMI DADE COLLEGE

MDC DRYWALL
See MIDWEST DRYWALL CO INC

D-U-N-S 06-970-2181
▲ MDC HOLDINGS INC
4350 S Monaco St Ste 500, Denver, CO 80237-3400
Tel (303) 773-1100 *Founded/Ownrshp* 1972
Sales 1.8MMM *EMP* 1,225
Accts Ernst & Young Llp Irvine Cal
Tkr Sym MDC *Exch* NYS
SIC 1521 6162 7389 New construction, single-family houses; Mortgage bankers; Financial services
Ch Bd: Larry A Mizel
**Pr:* David D Mandarich
CFO: Robert N Martin
Sr VP: Michael Touff
IT Man: Jim Upchurch
Board of Directors: Raymond T Baker, Michael A Berman, David E Blackford, Herbert T Buchwald, Paris G Reece III, David Siegel

D-U-N-S 62-397-3968
▲ MDC PARTNERS INC
745 5th Ave Fl 19, New York, NY 10151-2003
Tel (646) 429-1800 *Founded/Ownrshp* 1986
Sales 1.3MMM *EMP* 5,690
Tkr Sym MDCA *Exch* NGS
SIC 7311 8748 Advertising agencies; Business consulting
Ch Bd: Scott L Kauffman
CFO: David B Doft
Chf Mktg O: Bob Kantor
Chf Mktg O: Ryan Linder
Sr VP: Alex Delanghe
Sr VP: Randy Duax
Sr VP: Amie Miller
Sr VP: David C Ross
VP: Tricia Benn
VP: Unai Ortega
Mng Dir: Stephanie Nerlich
Board of Directors: Clare R Copeland, Lawrence S Kramer, Anne Marie O'donovan, Irwin D Simon

MDC WALLCOVERINGS
See EPKO INDUSTRIES INC

MDEQ
See MICHIGAN DEPARTMENT OF ENVIRONMENTAL QUALITY

MDHHS
See MICHIGAN DEPARTMENT OF HEALTH & HUMAN SERVICES

MDHS FAMILY AND CHILDRENS SVCS
See MISSISSIPPI DEPARTMENT OF HUMAN SERVICES

MDI
See MARK DUNNING INDUSTRIES

D-U-N-S 16-878-5876
MDI HOLDINGS LLC
C/O COURT SQ CAPITL PARTNERS
399 Park Ave Fl 14, New York, NY 10022-4614
Tel (212) 559-1127 *Founded/Ownrshp* 2006
Sales 208.8MM^E *EMP* 2,900
SIC 2899 2842 2874 2992 2752 3577 Chemical preparations; Plating compounds; Rust resisting compounds; Stencil correction compounds; Cleaning or polishing preparations; Phosphates; Lubricating oils; Offset & photolithographic printing; Printers & plotters
Pr: Joseph M Silvestri
Mng Pt: John Weber

MDM&C
See MC ELROY DEUTSCH MULVANEY & CARPERNTER LLP

MDMC
See MISSOURI DELTA MEDICAL CENTER

MDOC
See DEPARTMENT OF CORRECTIONS MICHIGAN

MDOT
See MARYLAND DEPARTMENT OF TRANSPORTATION

D-U-N-S 07-525-8780
MDRC
16 E 34th St Fl 19, New York, NY 10016-4326
Tel (212) 532-3200 *Founded/Ownrshp* 1974
Sales 106.6MM *EMP* 225
Accts Grant Thornton Llp New York
SIC 8641 8733 Civic social & fraternal associations; Noncommercial social research organization
Pr: Gordon Berlin
**Sr VP:* Jesus M Amadeo
**Sr VP:* Robert Ivry
**VP:* Fred Doolittle
**VP:* Barbara Goldman
**VP:* Sharon Rowser
Exec: Janet Quint
CTO: John Hutchins
Opers Mgr: Michelle Ware

D-U-N-S 04-153-9784
MDS PHARMA SERVICES (US) INC
(*Suby of* NORDION INC)
2200 Rnpance Blvd Ste 400, King of Prussia, PA 19406
Tel (610) 239-7900 *Founded/Ownrshp* 1996
Sales 65.1MM^E *EMP* 3,042
SIC 8734 Testing laboratories
Pr: David Spaight
**CFO:* Rudy Howard
Ex VP: Alan Torrie
Sr VP: Robert Bland
Sr VP: Robert Breckon
**Sr VP:* Cameron T Hicks
**Sr VP:* James Mc Clurg
Sr VP: Teresa F Winslow
VP: James D Hulse
VP: Lori McDonald
VP: James Miskel
VP: Cinda Orr
VP: Vijay Vashi
**VP:* Peter D Winkley
Dir Bus: Judy Rubin
Dir Bus: Lorraine Rusch

D-U-N-S 78-065-6372
MDSA LLC
MIGHTY DISTRIBUTING SYS AMER
(*Suby of* GONHER, S.A. DE C.V.)
650 Engineering Dr, Norcross, GA 30092-2821
Tel (770) 448-3900 *Founded/Ownrshp* 2009
Sales 232.0MM *EMP* 180
SIC 5013 6794 Automotive supplies & parts; Franchises, selling or licensing
Pr: Kenneth S Voelker
**Ch Bd:* Thomas R Barry
Pr: Ron Ferguson
**Sr VP:* Gary Vann
Sr VP: Gerald Vann
**VP:* Brad Bradshaw
VP: Jesse A Bradshaw
VP: Scott Dees
VP: Barry Teagle
Comm Man: Rachel O Overby
Off Mgr: Gerry Smith

D-U-N-S 79-669-0993
MDSFEST INC
237 2nnd Ave S, Onalaska, WI 54650
Tel (608) 779-2720 *Founded/Ownrshp* 2005
Sales 70.7MM^E *EMP* 1,079^E
SIC 5411 Grocery stores
CFO: Kirk Stoa

D-U-N-S 09-029-0441
■ MDU CONSTRUCTION SERVICES GROUP INC
(*Suby of* MDU RESOURCES GROUP INC) ★
1150 W Century Ave, Bismarck, ND 58503-0942
Tel (701) 530-1000 *Founded/Ownrshp* 2003
Sales 1.9MMM^E *EMP* 4,030
SIC 4911 Generation, electric power; Transmission, electric power; Distribution, electric power
Pr: Jeff Thiede
**COO:* Craig Keller

D-U-N-S 00-696-2286 IMP/EXP
▲ MDU RESOURCES GROUP INC
1200 W Century Ave, Bismarck, ND 58503-0911
Tel (701) 530-1000 *Founded/Ownrshp* 1924
Sales 4.1MMM *EMP* 8,689
Accts Deloitte & Touche Llp Minnea
Tkr Sym MDU *Exch* NYS
SIC 4911 4924 4922 1221 1442 1311 Generation, electric power; Transmission, electric power; Distribution, electric power; Natural gas distribution; Pipelines, natural gas; Surface mining, lignite; Construction sand & gravel; Crude petroleum production; Natural gas production
Pr: David L Goodin
**Ch Bd:* Harry J Pearce
CFO: Doran N Schwartz
Treas: Jason L Vollmer
Bd of Dir: Jon Hunke
Chf Mktg O: Dawn Sackman
Ex VP: Dennis L Haider
VP: Cynthia J Norland
VP: Pat O'Bryan
Comm Dir: Cory Fong
CIO: Peggy A Link
Board of Directors: Thomas Everist, Karen B Fagg, Mark A Hellerstein, A Bart Holaday, Dennis W Johnson, William E McCracken, Patricia L Moss, John K Wilson

D-U-N-S 03-683-3952
MDWISE INC
1200 Madison Ave Ste 400, Indianapolis, IN 46225-1616
Tel (317) 630-2828 *Founded/Ownrshp* 1994
Sales NA *EMP* 43
Accts Crowe Horwath Llp Indianapoli
SIC 6324 Health maintenance organization (HMO), insurance only
Pr: Charlotte Macbeth
CFO: Terry Bright
**Sr VP:* Susan Overton
**VP:* Katherine Wentworth
CIO: Julie Sample
Pharmcst: Barbara Wilder

D-U-N-S 80-904-5859
ME DEPT OF BEHAVIORAL AND DEVELOPMENTAL SERVICES
(*Suby of* MAINE DEPARTMENT OF HEALTH AND HUMAN SERVICES) ★
40 State House Sta, Augusta, ME 04333-0040
Tel (207) 287-4200 *Founded/Ownrshp* 1981
Sales NA *EMP* 1,800
SIC 9431 Mental health agency administration, government;

D-U-N-S 06-686-2558 IMP
MEAD AND HUNT INC
2440 Deming Way, Middleton, WI 53562-1562
Tel (608) 273-6380 *Founded/Ownrshp* 1987
Sales 89.0MM *EMP* 530
SIC 8712 8711 Architectural engineering; Consulting engineer
CEO: Rajan I Sheth
**Pr:* Andrew Platz
**CFO:* Don Gotrik
**Treas:* Amy Squitieri
VP: Doug Green
**VP:* Richard Plymale
**VP:* Stephanie Ward
Off Admin: Vicky Valley
IT Man: Robert Halpop

D-U-N-S 36-271-7808
MEAD HOLDING CO INC
DO IT BEST
2218 11th St, Columbus, NE 68601-5777
Tel (402) 564-5225 *Founded/Ownrshp* 2003
Sales 248.4MM *EMP* 260
Accts Ketel Thorstenson Llp Rapid
SIC 6719 5211 Personal holding companies, except banks; Lumber & other building materials
CEO: Robert W Mead
**Pr:* Craig Bradshaw
**Sec:* Perry Mead

D-U-N-S 00-637-0092 EXP
■ MEAD JOHNSON & CO LLC
MEAD JOHNSON NUTRITION
(*Suby of* MEAD JOHNSON NUTRITION CO) ★
2400 W Lloyd Expy, Evansville, IN 47712-5095
Tel (812) 429-5000 *Founded/Ownrshp* 2009
Sales 376.8MM^E *EMP* 650^E
SIC 2099 2834 2032 Food preparations; Pharmaceutical preparations; Canned specialties
CEO: Peter Kasper Jakobsen
Sr VP: Sandy Mac Pherson
VP: William Cross
**VP:* Tom De Weerdt
VP: Leroy McBrien
VP: Roberto Moran
Dir Risk M: David Zaslavsky
Assoc Dir: Rama Donepudi
Assoc Dir: Sonja Garth
Assoc Dir: Thomas Giangrande
Assoc Dir: Ravi Ponnaganti
Assoc Dir: Kelly R Walsh
Assoc Dir: Richard Widup
Assoc Dir: Sara Wininger

MEAD JOHNSON NUTRITION
See MEAD JOHNSON & CO LLC

D-U-N-S 82-805-0877
▲ MEAD JOHNSON NUTRITION CO
2701 Patriot Blvd, Glenview, IL 60026-8039
Tel (847) 832-2420 *Founded/Ownrshp* 1905
Sales 4.0MMM *EMP* 7,660^E
Tkr Sym MJN *Exch* NYS
SIC 2023 2834 Baby formulas; Vitamin preparations
Pr: Peter Kasper Jakobsen
**Ch Bd:* James M Cornelius
Pr: Graciela Monteagudo
Pr: Christopher R Stratton
COO: Charles M Urbain
CFO: Michel Cup
Ofcr: Dirk Hondmann
Sr VP: James Jeffrey Jobe
Sr VP: Ian E Ormesher
Sr VP: Patrick M Sheller
Sr VP: James E Shiah
VP: Peter G Leemputte
VP: Christopher Perille
Exec: Regina Durlak
Assoc Dir: Corlis Smith
Assoc Dir: Vinson Wood

D-U-N-S 06-141-1880
■ MEAD PACKAGING INTERNATIONAL INC (OH)
(*Suby of* WESTROCK MWV LLC) ★
3423 Piedmont Rd Ne, Atlanta, GA 30305-1754
Tel (404) 875-2711 *Founded/Ownrshp* 1965, 2002
Sales 130.0MM *EMP* 125^E
SIC 6719 Personal holding companies, except banks

D-U-N-S 09-368-0502
MEAD SCHOOL DISTRICT #354
2323 E Farwell Rd, Mead, WA 99021-6011
Tel (509) 465-7480 *Founded/Ownrshp* 1890
Sales 70.3MM^E *EMP* 1,020
Accts Troy Kelley
SIC 8211 Public combined elementary & secondary school
Bd of Dir: Tom Hunt
Schl Brd P: Ron Farley
Teacher Pr: Keri Hutchins

MEADE DODGE
See MEADE GROUP INC

MEADE ELECTRIC CO
See L & H CO INC

D-U-N-S 00-693-1364
MEADE ELECTRIC CO INC
CONTRACTING & MATERIAL COMPANY
(*Suby of* MEADE ELECTRIC CO) ★
9550 W 55th St Ste A, Countryside, IL 60525-3641
Tel (708) 588-2500 *Founded/Ownrshp* 1980
Sales 173.3MM^E *EMP* 600
SIC 1731 General electrical contractor
Ch Bd: Joseph F Lizzadro
**Pr:* Frank J Lizzadro
VP: Charles Anderson
**VP:* Mike Kenutson
**VP:* Michael Knutson
**VP:* Perry Manago
**VP:* Bob Schacht
Div Mgr: Dan Plefka
Genl Mgr: David Leali
Off Mgr: Jan Labuhn
Sfty Dirs: Tim Swanson

D-U-N-S 02-844-8835
MEADE GROUP INC
MEADE DODGE
6951 19 Mile Rd, Sterling Heights, MI 48314-3209
Tel (586) 803-6250 *Founded/Ownrshp* 1982
Sales 87.5MM^E *EMP* 288
SIC 5511 Automobiles, new & used
Ch Bd: Kenneth G Meade
**Pr:* Barron Meade
**CFO:* Terry Tadlock
**Treas:* Stacy Weiler
Exec: Shane Taranto

D-U-N-S 08-085-5042
MEADOR STAFFING SERVICES INC
TEMPORARY STAFFING SERVICES
722a Fairmont Pkwy, Pasadena, TX 77504-2804
Tel (713) 941-0616 *Founded/Ownrshp* 1968
Sales 162.6MM[E] *EMP* 10,000
SIC 7361 7363 Placement agencies; Temporary help service; Industrial help service; Engineering help service
Pr: Ben F Meador Jr
VP: Linda Fields
**VP:* Darla Haygood
**VP:* Janice Meador
**VP:* Faye Smith
**VP:* Melinda Torrison
Sls&Mrk Ex: Gale Templeton

MEADOW VALLEY CONTRACTORS
See MEADOW VALLEY CORP

D-U-N-S 87-840-3500
MEADOW VALLEY CORP
MEADOW VALLEY CONTRACTORS
(*Suby of* MEADOW VALLEY HOLDINGS LLC) ★
3333 E Camelback Rd # 240, Phoenix, AZ 85018-2345
Tel (602) 437-5400 *Founded/Ownrshp* 1980
Sales 103.1MM[E] *EMP* 510[E]
SIC 1611 5032 General contractor, highway & street construction; Airport runway construction; Concrete mixtures
Ch: Ted W Beneski
Pr: Robert W Bottcher
Pr: L David Mathews
Pr: Robert A Terril
Treas: David D Doty
VP: Gary Burnell
VP: Kenneth D Nelson

D-U-N-S 83-121-9311
MEADOW VALLEY HOLDINGS LLC
(*Suby of* INSIGHT EQUITY ACQUISITION CO LLC) ★
4602 E Thomas Rd, Phoenix, AZ 85018-7710
Tel (602) 437-5400 *Founded/Ownrshp* 2008
Sales 103.2MM[E] *EMP* 510[E]
SIC 1611 5032 General contractor, highway & street construction; Airport runway construction; Concrete mixtures
Pr: Ted W Beneski
**CEO:* Bradley E Larson
**CFO:* David D Doty

MEADOWBROOK CLAIMS SERVICE
See MEADOWBROOK INC

D-U-N-S 94-853-6370
MEADOWBROOK GOLF GROUP INC
5385 Gateway Blvd Ste 12, Lakeland, FL 33811-1785
Tel (407) 589-7200 *Founded/Ownrshp* 1995
Sales 170.6MM[E] *EMP* 2,700
SIC 8742 8741 7992 5941 Management consulting services; Management services; Public golf courses; Sporting goods & bicycle shops
Pr: Ron E Jackson
**CFO:* Eric Burk
**CFO:* K Eric Burk
CFO: Calvin Sellers
**Ex VP:* Greg Plotner
**VP:* Scott Beasley

D-U-N-S 07-424-8923
MEADOWBROOK INC
MEADOWBROOK CLAIMS SERVICE
(*Suby of* MEADOWBROOK INSURANCE GROUP INC) ★
26255 American Dr, Southfield, MI 48034-6112
Tel (248) 358-1100 *Founded/Ownrshp* 1995
Sales NA *EMP* 929
SIC 6411 Insurance agents & brokers; Insurance information & consulting services; Loss prevention services, insurance
Ch Bd: Robert Naftaly
**Pr:* Robert S Cubbin
**CFO:* Caryn Spun
**Treas:* Josephine Duco
Sr VP: Mickey Fay
Sr VP: Heidi Langella

D-U-N-S 79-885-1069
MEADOWBROOK INSURANCE GROUP INC
(*Suby of* FOSUN INTERNATIONAL LIMITED)
26255 American Dr, Southfield, MI 48034-6112
Tel (248) 358-1100 *Founded/Ownrshp* 2015
Sales NA *EMP* 954[E]
SIC 6411 6211 Property & casualty insurance agent; Underwriters, security
Pr: Robert S Cubbin
CFO: Karen M Spaun
Ex VP: Christopher J Timm
Sr VP: Kenn R Allen
Sr VP: Kent R Allen
Sr VP: James M Mahoney
Sr VP: Archie S McIntyre
Sr VP: R Christopher Spring
Sr VP: Roger S Walleck
VP: Stephen Belden
VP: Dean Clemons
VP: Michael G Costello
VP: Michael Costello
VP: Steven Divine
VP: Tim Gordon
VP: Jeffrey Maltby
VP: Daniel Murphy
VP: Ron Scott

D-U-N-S 02-477-8391
■ **MEADOWBROOK MEAT CO INC** (NC)
MBM
(*Suby of* MCLANE CO INC) ★
2641 Meadowbrook Rd, Rocky Mount, NC 27801-9498
Tel (252) 985-7200 *Founded/Ownrshp* 1977, 2012
Sales 1.8MMM[E] *EMP* 3,000
SIC 5147 5113 5149 5142

D-U-N-S 14-927-5609
MEADOWGATE TECHNOLOGIES LLC
171 Jersey St Ste 1, Trenton, NJ 08611-2400
Tel (609) 393-3618 *Founded/Ownrshp* 2002
Sales 137.1MM *EMP* 14
SIC 5045 8711 Computers; Engineering services

Genl Mgr: Leslie Siskovic

D-U-N-S 02-284-2579
MEADOWLAND FARMERS COOP
25861 Us Highway 14, Lamberton, MN 56152-1146
Tel (507) 752-7335 *Founded/Ownrshp* 1905
Sales 186.3MM[E] *EMP* 84
SIC 5153 5191 0723 Grain elevators; Chemicals, agricultural; Fertilizer & fertilizer materials; Feed; Seeds: field, garden & flower; Crop preparation services for market
CEO: John D Valentin
**Sec:* Terry Quiring
**VP:* Steve Nelson
Sls Mgr: Pete Valentin

MEADOWLANDS HOSPITAL MED CTR
See MHA LLC

MEADOWS GOLF CLUB , THE
See GRAND VALLEY STATE UNIVERSITY

D-U-N-S 96-915-8224
MEADOWS HEALTHCARE ALLIANCE INC
MEADOWS REGIONAL MEDICAL CENTE
1 Meadows Pkwy, Vidalia, GA 30474-8759
Tel (912) 538-5866 *Founded/Ownrshp* 1992
Sales 2.5MM *EMP* 1,000
Accts Draffin & Tucker Llp Albany
SIC 8099 8062 Blood related health services; General medical & surgical hospitals
CEO: Alan Kent
**CFO:* John Cornell
Off Admin: Melissa Carnes
Sls Mgr: Ashley Collins
Pharmcst: Robin Britt

MEADOWS OFFICE FURNITURE
See MEADOWS OFFICE SUPPLY CO INC

D-U-N-S 04-155-5723 IMP
MEADOWS OFFICE SUPPLY CO INC
MEADOWS OFFICE FURNITURE
885 3rd Ave Fl 29, New York, NY 10022-4834
Tel (212) 741-0333 *Founded/Ownrshp* 1967
Sales 101.1MM[E] *EMP* 106
SIC 5021 Office furniture
Pr: Rosalie Edson
**CEO:* Sheri David
**CFO:* Stanley Fessler
**Mng Dir:* Pat Escobedo
Genl Mgr: Clint Barlow
Genl Mgr: Dina Radoncic

MEADOWS REGIONAL MEDICAL CENTE
See MEADOWS HEALTHCARE ALLIANCE INC

D-U-N-S 01-012-2257
MEADOWS REGIONAL MEDICAL CENTER INC
1703 Meadows Ln, Vidalia, GA 30474-8915
Tel (912) 537-8921 *Founded/Ownrshp* 1994
Sales 86.3MM[E] *EMP* 670[E]
SIC 8062 8051 General medical & surgical hospitals; Skilled nursing care facilities
CEO: Alan Kent
**CFO:* John Cornell
VP: Karen McColl
Dir Risk M: Melony Jacobs
Dir Rx: Michelle Cox
Sls Mgr: Diana Coursey
HC Dir: Joette Gay

D-U-N-S 06-874-8409
MEADVILLE MEDICAL CENTER
751 Liberty St, Meadville, PA 16335-2591
Tel (814) 333-5000 *Founded/Ownrshp* 1880
Sales 155.5MM *EMP* 995
Accts Bkd Llp Springfield/Joplin/B
SIC 8741 8062 8011 Hospital management; General medical & surgical hospitals; Offices & clinics of medical doctors
Pr: Anthony J De Fail
**Pr:* Tilit Pllgt
**CFO:* David A Poland
Bd of Dir: Walter Thomas
Ofcr: Sallie Frisina
Sr VP: Daniel Caplan
VP: Robert Concilus
VP: Valerie B Waid
VP: Anne White
Doctor: Sidney King
Doctor: James Macielak

MEAG POWER
See MUNICIPAL ELECTRIC AUTHORITY OF GEORGIA

MEALEY'S FURNITURE WARMINSTER
See K&D FUTURE INC

D-U-N-S 05-769-3145 IMP/EXP
MEANS INDUSTRIES INC
3715 E Washington Rd, Saginaw, MI 48601-9623
Tel (989) 754-1433 *Founded/Ownrshp* 1989
Sales 163.6MM[E] *EMP* 400
SIC 3714 3465 Transmission housings or parts, motor vehicle; Automotive stampings
Pr: D William Shaw
**Pr:* Bill Shaw
**VP:* Ed Shemanski
Exec: Joyce U Hynes
IT Man: Karen Esckelfon
IT Man: Bruce Gluski
Info Man: Karen Eckelson
Plnt Mgr: Ladd Irvine
VP Sls: Mark Willett
S&M/VP: Duane Barlow
Mktg Mgr: Cassie Saagman

D-U-N-S 08-556-2010
■ **MEARS GROUP INC**
(*Suby of* QUANTA SERVICES INC) ★
4500 N Mission Rd, Rosebush, MI 48878-8721
Tel (989) 433-2929 *Founded/Ownrshp* 2000
Sales 139.0MM[E] *EMP* 450
Accts Pricewaterhousecoopers Llp Ho
SIC 1623 8711 Oil & gas line & compressor station construction; Communication line & transmission tower construction; Engineering services

Pr: Scot Fluharty
**Treas:* Nicholas M Grindstaff
VP: Jonathan Bones
VP: David D Brittain
**VP:* William C Burdine
**VP:* John W Fluharty II
VP: James H Haddox
VP: Derrick A Jensen
VP: Peter Obrien
VP: Doug Waslen
**VP:* Steven J Wilhelm

MEASE HEALTH CARE
See TRUSTEES OF MEASE HOSPITAL INC

D-U-N-S 02-081-9236
MEASE HOSPITALS
(*Suby of* BAYCARE EDUCATION SERVICES) ★
601 Main St, Dunedin, FL 34698-5848
Tel (727) 734-6354 *Founded/Ownrshp* 1994
Sales 87.5MM *EMP* 30
SIC 8071 Medical laboratories
VP: John Couris
VP: Lisa Johnson
Ex Dir: Holly Duncan
Mktg Mgr: Susan Boydell

D-U-N-S 10-818-3682
MEASURED PROGRESS INC
100 Education Way, Dover, NH 03820-5816
Tel (603) 749-9102 *Founded/Ownrshp* 1983
Sales 93.7MM *EMP* 340
Accts William Steele & Associates Pc
SIC 8732 Educational research
Pr: Martin Borg
CFO: Wayne Agostino
**CFO:* Shelly Craig
**Sec:* Patti Ayer
**Founder:* Stuart Kahl
Sr VP: Timothy J Crockett
Sr VP: Rich Swartz
VP: Mike Russell
Exec: Chris Schuyler
Prgrm Mgr: Cherie Dudley
Prgrm Mgr: Dominique Parke
Board of Directors: Dan Caton, Karen Cowe, Mark Elgart, Alice Irby

D-U-N-S 03-715-9514
MEASUREMENT INC
M I
423 Morris St, Durham, NC 27701-2128
Tel (919) 683-2413 *Founded/Ownrshp* 1980
Sales 83.0MM *EMP* 407[E]
Accts Thomas Knight Trent King An
SIC 2752 8748 2791 2789 2759 Commercial printing, offset; Testing service, educational or personnel; Typesetting; Bookbinding & related work; Commercial printing
Pr: Henry H Scherich
VP: Nelson Androes
**VP:* Holly Baker
**VP:* Michael Bunch
VP: James A Henning
VP: Thomas Kelsh
**VP:* Kirk Ridge
Prgrm Mgr: Corey Palermo
Admn Mgr: Susan Kaney
Off Mgr: Kathleen Stapleton
Snr Sftwr: David Vaughn

D-U-N-S 02-935-1079 IMP/EXP
MEASUREMENT SPECIALTIES INC (NJ)
TE CONNECTIVITY
(*Suby of* TE CONNECTIVITY LTD.)
1000 Lucas Way, Hampton, VA 23666-1573
Tel (757) 766-1500 *Founded/Ownrshp* 1981, 2014
Sales 412.6MM *EMP* 3,721
SIC 3829 Measuring & controlling devices; Photopitometers; Pressure transducers; Vibration meters, analyzers & calibrators
Pr: Frank D Guidone
**COO:* Joe Gleeson
COO: Mark Long
**CFO:* Mark Thomson
**Ex VP:* Glen Macgibbon
**VP:* Mitch Thompson
VP Bus Dev: Caroline Tanton
Exec: Brenda Lawrence
Dir Bus: Randall Akers
Ex Dir: David Revels
Prgrm Mgr: Lee Fairchild

D-U-N-S 96-347-2787
MEAT AND SEAFOOD SOLUTIONS LLC
SOUTHERN FOODS
(*Suby of* P D C) ★
3500 Old Battleground Rd, Greensboro, NC 27410-2420
Tel (336) 545-3827 *Founded/Ownrshp* 2010
Sales 96.7MM[E] *EMP* 200
SIC 5146 5147 Fish & seafoods; Meats & meat products
CEO: Malcolm R Sullivan Jr
**Pr:* Bill Mutton
**COO:* Jim Cremins
VP: Sue James

D-U-N-S 07-448-9378
MEB GENERAL CONTRACTORS INC (VA)
4016 Holland Blvd, Chesapeake, VA 23323-1522
Tel (757) 487-5858 *Founded/Ownrshp* 1982
Sales 145.5MM[E] *EMP* 224[E]
SIC 1542 1629 1541 Commercial & office building contractors; Waste water & sewage treatment plant construction; Warehouse construction
Pr: George B Clarke IV
**Sec:* William A Paulette
**Sr VP:* Mark F Olmstead
**VP:* Thomas Atherton
**VP:* William R Blowe
**VP:* David M Ervin
VP: David Ervin
**VP:* Eric Keplinger
VP: Fred Wagner
CIO: Matt Weaver

D-U-N-S 18-873-4867
MEBILODDE OF PLYMOUTH
WESTTRAIL NURSING HOME
395 W Ann Arbor Trl, Plymouth, MI 48170-1641
Tel (734) 453-3983 *Founded/Ownrshp* 1983
Sales 352.1MM *EMP* 55
SIC 8051 Skilled nursing care facilities
Pr: Daniel M Abramson
**VP:* Louise Ann Padmos

MEC
See MCKENZIE ELECTRIC COOPERATIVE INC

MEC
See CENTER MANUFACTURING INC

D-U-N-S 07-684-3895
MECCA ELECTRONICS INDUSTRIES INC
1016 44th Dr, Long Island City, NY 11101-7014
Tel (718) 361-9001 *Founded/Ownrshp* 1974
Sales 153.8MM[E] *EMP* 25
Accts Billet Feit And Preis Pc
SIC 5092 Video games
Ch Bd: Raymond Aboody
**Sec:* Danny Mashal

D-U-N-S 82-866-9007
MECCANICA HOLDINGS USA INC
(*Suby of* LEONARDO - FINMECCANICA - SPA)
1625 I St Nw Fl 12, Washington, DC 20006-4073
Tel (202) 292-2620 *Founded/Ownrshp* 2008
Sales NA *EMP* 10,265
SIC 6719 Investment holding companies, except banks
CEO: Simone Bemporad

D-U-N-S 11-922-6660
MECHANICAL DYNAMICS & ANALYSIS LTD
RENEWAL PARTS MAINTENANCE
(*Suby of* MITSUBSHI PWR SYSTEMS AMERICAS) ★
19 British American Blvd, Latham, NY 12110
Tel (518) 399-3616 *Founded/Ownrshp* 2006
Sales 101.5MM[E] *EMP* 391
SIC 8711 7699

D-U-N-S 00-553-0951 IMP
MECHANICAL SERVANTS LLC
CONVENIENCE VALET
(*Suby of* WEINBERG CAPITAL GROUP INC) ★
2755 Thomas St, Melrose Park, IL 60160-2959
Tel (708) 486-1500 *Founded/Ownrshp* 2015
Sales 91.0MM[E] *EMP* 96
SIC 5122 Druggists' sundries
Pr: David A Baum
**COO:* Edward Edick
**CFO:* Barry Margolin
**Ex VP:* Jim Blosser
Ql Cn Mgr: Towana Elmore
Sales Exec: Jim Groves
VP Sls: Dave Arensdorf
VP Sls: Doug Steffen
Manager: Judy Esteppe
Sls Mgr: Mike Finke

D-U-N-S 00-691-0780
MECHANICS BANK (CA)
MECHANICS BANK ATM
(*Suby of* EB ACQUISITION CO LLC) ★
1111 Civic Dr Ste 333, Walnut Creek, CA 94596-3894
Tel (800) 797-6324 *Founded/Ownrshp* 1905
Sales NA *EMP* 650
SIC 6022 State commercial banks
Ch Bd: Carl Webb
Pr: Paula Allen
Pr: Nicholas Mellon
Pr: Thuy Nguyen
Pr: Suman Raj
CEO: Kenneth Russell
CFO: CJ Johnson
Treas: Douglas Pena
V Ch Bd: Micheal Banner
Chf Cred: Larry Cretan
Ofcr: Nathan Duda
Ofcr: Laura Hansen
Ofcr: Peggy Herzog
Ofcr: Peggy L Herzog-Mills
Ofcr: George Kerr
Ofcr: Jamie Ulibarri
Ofcr: Dena Villarreal
Ofcr: Krista Watson
Ex VP: Clinton Chew
Ex VP: Judy Ditchey
Ex VP: Debbie Kelley

MECHANICS BANK ATM
See MECHANICS BANK

D-U-N-S 02-255-8068 IMP/EXP
MECHOSHADE SYSTEMS INC
(*Suby of* SPRINGS WINDOW FASHIONS LLC) ★
4203 35th St, Long Island City, NY 11101-2301
Tel (718) 729-2020 *Founded/Ownrshp* 2015
Sales 125.3MM[E] *EMP* 500
SIC 2591 Window shades
Pr: Jan Berman
**CFO:* Norman Rathfelder
VP: Mel Byars
Rgnl Mgr: Jim Ashmore
Dir IT: Carolyn Gary
Dir IT: Kate Julisf
IT Man: Radu Negoescu
Natl Sales: Jesse Fried
VP Sls: Thompson Chau
Pr Dir: Richard Rosenbaum

D-U-N-S 04-436-8413
MED AMERICA HEALTH SYSTEMS CORP
1 Wyoming St, Dayton, OH 45409-2722
Tel (937) 223-6192 *Founded/Ownrshp* 1982
Sales 968.3MM *EMP* 4,700
SIC 8062 8741 8082 General medical & surgical hospitals; Management services; Home health care services
Pr: T G Breitenbach
**CFO:* Timothy Jackson

D-U-N-S 02-546-9426
MED ASSETS INC
5543 Legacy Dr, Plano, TX 75024-3502
Tel (800) 390-7459 Founded/Ownrshp 2010
Sales 109.2MM^E EMP 474^E
SIC 5099 Durable goods

MED EXPRESS URGENT CARE
See URGENT CARE HOLDINGS INC

D-U-N-S 11-938-7186
MED SERVICES INC
100 Knickerbocker Ave C, Bohemia, NY 11716-3127
Tel (631) 218-6450 Founded/Ownrshp 2005
Sales 155.0MM EMP 55
SIC 3845 7699 Electromedical equipment; Medical equipment repair, non-electric
Pr: Steven Cortese
Sr VP: Stefani Katz

MED TEC MEDICAL SERVICES
See MERCY MEDICAL SERVICES INC

MED, THE
See SHELBY COUNTY HEALTH CARE CORP

MED VET ASSOCIATES
See MEDVET ASSOCIATES INC

D-U-N-S 18-225-1553
MED-ACOUSTICS INC
E3 MED-ACOUSTICS
(Suby of E3 CAROLINA SALES & SERVICE) ★
1685 E Park Place Blvd, Stone Mountain, GA 30087-3447
Tel (770) 498-8075 Founded/Ownrshp 1987
Sales 437.3MM^E EMP 22^E
Accts Paul A Thomas Cpa
SIC 5047 1742 Medical & hospital equipment; Acoustical & insulation work
CEO: Don Williams
*Pr: Greg Ollick

D-U-N-S 18-670-8256
MED-CARE DIABETIC & MEDICAL SUPPLIES INC
901 Yamato Rd Ste 101, Boca Raton, FL 33431-4409
Tel (800) 407-0109 Founded/Ownrshp 2002
Sales 145.1MM^E EMP 300
Accts Glenn R Luisi Accountant Pa
SIC 5047 Medical equipment & supplies
Pr: Steven Silverman
*VP: Lorri Silverman
Off Mgr: Allen Wyle
Pharmcst: Max Lewis

D-U-N-S 88-376-0159
■ **MED3000 GROUP INC**
(Suby of MCKESSON CORP) ★
680 Andersen Dr Foster Pl, Pittsburgh, PA 15220
Tel (412) 937-8887 Founded/Ownrshp 2013
Sales 58.5MM^E EMP 1,100
Accts Schneider Downs & Co Incpi
SIC 8742 8721 Management consulting services; Billing & bookkeeping service
Ch Bd: Patrick V Hampson
Ex VP: Richard Schickler
Ex VP: Daniel Wiens
VP: Kevin Amos
VP: Ron Parker
VP: Scott Sanner
VP: David Sassano
VP: Pat Stroh
Exec: Margie Conley
Exec: Angela Hoffman
*Exec: Paul McLeod MD

MED3000 HEATLH SOLUTIONS
See MED3000 INVESTMENTS INC

D-U-N-S 16-506-5264
■ **MED3000 INVESTMENTS INC**
MED3000 HEATLH SOLUTIONS
(Suby of MED3000 GROUP INC) ★
680 Andersen Dr Ste 10, Pittsburgh, PA 15220-2759
Tel (412) 937-8887 Founded/Ownrshp 1987
Sales 13.4MM^E EMP 1,000
SIC 8071 Medical laboratories
CEO: Patrick Hampson
*CFO: David Dillon
*Sr VP: Stephen Ura
Board of Directors: Paul A McLeod

D-U-N-S 05-122-9602 IMP
MEDA PHARMACEUTICALS INC
(Suby of MEDA AB)
265 Davidson Ave Ste 400, Somerset, NJ 08873-4120
Tel (732) 564-2200 Founded/Ownrshp 2007
Sales 218.5MM^E EMP 747
SIC 2834 Pharmaceutical preparations
CEO: Maria Carell
*CFO: Jeffrey Hostler
*Treas: David Vernieri
Sr VP: Mark Spiers
VP: Charles Hoyt
Dist Mgr: Clark Lambert
Dist Mgr: Jarrid Spiegel
CIO: John Rupinski
IT Man: Diane Griswold
VP Sls: Anne M Fields
Manager: Ebby Sekulski

D-U-N-S 00-609-1334
■ **MEDALIST INDUSTRIES INC**
C-TECH SYSTEMS DIVISION
(Suby of ILLINOIS TOOL WORKS INC) ★
2700 Elmhurst Rd, Elk Grove Village, IL 60007-6315
Tel (847) 766-9000 Founded/Ownrshp 1954, 1996
Sales 126.0MM EMP 9
SIC 3452 Screws, metal; Bolts, metal; Nuts, metal; Washers, metal
Pr: James S Dahlke
Treas: James A Lathrop
VP: Michael Gregg
VP: James G Gumm
VP: William C O'Loughlin

MEDALLA DISTRIBUTORS PR
See C C 1 BEER DISTRIBUTORS INC

D-U-N-S 08-671-3372
MEDALLIA INC
395 Page Mill Rd Ste 100, Palo Alto, CA 94306-2066
Tel (650) 321-3000 Founded/Ownrshp 2000
Sales 86.5MM^E EMP 150
SIC 7372 8732 Business oriented computer software; Market analysis, business & economic research
CEO: Borge Hald
Pr: Fred Mondragon
*Pr: Amy Pressman-Hald
*CFO: Chris Watts
*Ofcr: Ken Fine
*VP: Alan Grebene
VP: Russell Haswell
VP: Krish Mantripragada
VP: Nelson Pascua
VP: David Reeses
VP: David Rice
VP: Dorian Stone
Dir Soc: Debby Courtney
Dir Bus: Carlton Osborne
Board of Directors: Frank Slootman

D-U-N-S 13-299-9603
■ **MEDALLION BANK**
(Suby of MEDALLION FINANCIAL CORP.)
1100 E 6600 S Ste 510, Salt Lake City, UT 84121-7422
Tel (801) 284-7065 Founded/Ownrshp 2002
Sales NA EMP 10^E
SIC 6029 Commercial banks
Pr: John M Taggart
VP: Kyle Brown
VP: Mike De Carlo
Natl Sales: George Demare
Sls&Mrk Ex: John Haymond

D-U-N-S 04-671-2626 EXP
MEDALLION CABINETRY INC
(Suby of NEPTUNE LIFETIME SINKS) ★
1 Medallion Way Ste 10501, Waconia, MN 55387-7000
Tel (952) 442-5171 Founded/Ownrshp 1993
Sales 150.6MM^E EMP 600
SIC 2434 Wood kitchen cabinets
CEO: Timothy J Jahnke
VP: Jim Koleski
Opers Mgr: Mark Storms
Plnt Mgr: Mark Storm
Ql Cn Mgr: Nancy Patterson
Natl Sales: Jim Haubenschild

MEDALLION HOMES
See RITZ-CRAFT CORP OF PENNSYLVANIA INC

MEDAPHIS PHYSICIAN
See MCKESSON TECHNOLOGIES INC

D-U-N-S 00-890-8758 IMP
MEDART INC (MO)
124 Manufacturers Dr, Arnold, MO 63010-4727
Tel (636) 282-2300 Founded/Ownrshp 1912
Sales 121.8MM^E EMP 158
SIC 5084 5088 Engines, gasoline; Marine supplies
Pr: J Michael Medart
*CFO: Dave Strubberg
*VP: J Scott Price
Genl Mgr: Steve White
IT Man: Mike Boyer
IT Man: Dwayne Upson
Sls Mgr: John Untereiner
Board of Directors: John Sulack

D-U-N-S 09-395-2070
MEDASSETS INC (GA)
(Suby of VIZIENT INC) ★
200 N Point Ctr E Ste 200, Alpharetta, GA 30022-8274
Tel (678) 323-2500 Founded/Ownrshp 1999, 2016
Sales 720.2MM^E EMP 3,350^E
SIC 8742 Hospital & health services consultant
CEO: R Halsey Wise
*Pr: Amy D Amick
Pr: Bryan Hardman
Pr: Christal Herbst
*CFO: Charles Garner
*Ofcr: Rand A Ballard
Ex VP: Jonathan H Glenn
*Sr VP: Richard Fitzgerald
Sr VP: Michael Gaddy
Sr VP: Joe Sfara
VP: Pedro Arellano
VP: Laurie Babin
VP: Kate Banks
VP: Patricia Bounds
VP: Claudia Chadwick
VP: Ravi Chinni
VP: Roseanne Cimo
VP: Noel Coppinger
VP: John Cunningham
VP: Kathi Deegan
VP: Beth Dengel

D-U-N-S 78-375-2298
MEDASSETS NET REVENUE SYSTEMS LLC
(Suby of MEDASSETS INC) ★
200 N Point Ctr E Ste 400, Alpharetta, GA 30022-8274
Tel (678) 248-8200 Founded/Ownrshp 1999
Sales 85.7MM^E EMP 1,100
SIC 8742 7371 Hospital & health services consultant; Computer software development
VP: Rand A Ballard
Software D: Mike Morgensen

MEDCARE
See GWINNETT HOSPITAL SYSTEM INC

D-U-N-S 02-111-5162
MEDCATH CORP (NC)
10800 Sikes Pl Ste 200, Charlotte, NC 28277-8139
Tel (704) 815-7700 Founded/Ownrshp 2001
Sales 318.8MM^E EMP 414^E
Accts Deloitte & Touche Llp Raleig
SIC 8099 8062 Medical services organization; General medical & surgical hospitals
Pr: Lora Ramsey
Pr: David Bussone
COO: Michael G Servais
CFO: Douglas Davenport
CFO: Kay Harrold
CFO: Jeffrey L Hinton
*Sr VP: Joan McCanless
*Sr VP: Paul Daniel Perritt
VP: Bill Greenfield
VP: Judy Littrell
VP: Larissa Spraker
VP: Brent White
Board of Directors: Pamela G Bailey, John T Casey, James A Deal, Robert S McCoy Jr, Jacque J Sokolov MD

D-U-N-S 60-816-1295
MEDCATH INC
(Suby of MEDCATH CORP) ★
10800 Sikes Pl Ste 200, Charlotte, NC 28277-8139
Tel (704) 815-7700 Founded/Ownrshp 1998
Sales 132.3MM^E EMP 2,975^E
SIC 8069 8093 8742 Specialty hospitals, except psychiatric; Specialty outpatient clinics; Hospital & health services consultant
Ch Bd: Stephen R Puckett
*Pr: Ed French
*CFO: Jeff Hinton
CFO: David Laird
CFO: James Parker
*Treas: Art Parker
VP: Gary Bryant
VP: Deanna Rutherford
VP: David Salix
VP: Jeff Sandene
VP: Doug Walkins

MEDCENTER ONE HEALTH SYSTEMS
See SANFORD BISMARCK

D-U-N-S 07-690-4705
MEDCENTRAL HEALTH SYSTEM
OHIOHEALTH MANSFIELD HOSPITAL
(Suby of OHIOHEALTH CORP) ★
335 Glessner Ave, Mansfield, OH 44903-2269
Tel (419) 526-8000 Founded/Ownrshp 1963
Sales 232.9MM EMP 2,700^E
SIC 8062 General medical & surgical hospitals
VP: Beth Hildreth
Bd of Dir: Adam Bihl
Bd of Dir: Ronald Kerst
VP: Brad Peffley
VP: Robert Wirtz
Exec: Carl Bartels
Dir Rad: Terry Baker
Dir Rx: Tom Arkwright
Dir Sec: Paul Johnson
Off Mgr: Rhonda Bentley
Off Mgr: Barb Cruse

MEDCO
See LIBERTY BELL EQUIPMENT CORP

MEDCO
See MARYLAND ECONOMIC DEVELOPMENT CORP

D-U-N-S 11-291-1839 EXP
■ **MEDCO HEALTH SOLUTIONS INC**
EXPRESS SCRIPTS HOLDING CO
(Suby of EXPRESS SCRIPTS HOLDING CO) ★
100 Parsons Pond Dr, Franklin Lakes, NJ 07417-2604
Tel (201) 269-3400 Founded/Ownrshp 2012
Sales 2.5MMM^E EMP 21,710^E
SIC 5961 Pharmaceuticals, mail order
Pr: George Paz
*Ch Bd: David B Snow Jr
Pr: Steven Fitzpatrick
*Pr: Kenneth O Klepper
Pr: George Serpikov
Pr: Timothy Wentworth
COO: Daniel Soper
CFO: Karen Obiso
*CFO: Richard J Rubino
Treas: Gary Tully
*Chf Mktg O: Jack A Smith
Chf Mktg O: Jack Smith
*Sr VP: Gabriel R Cappucci
Sr VP: Frank Sheehy
Sr VP: Daniel Tierney
VP: Bob Benson
VP: Mary Casale
VP: Felix Frueh
VP: Frank Gentilella
VP: Darren Gettings
VP: John Henderson
Board of Directors: Howard W Barker Jr, John L Cassis, Michael Goldstein, Charles M Lillis Phd, Myrtle S Potter, William L Roper MD, David D Stevens, Blenda J Wilson Phd

D-U-N-S 11-605-6490
MEDCOR INC
4805 Prime Pkwy, McHenry, IL 60050-7002
Tel (815) 363-9500 Founded/Ownrshp 1984
Sales 65.0MM^E EMP 1,000
SIC 8099 Medical services organization
Pr: Philip C Seeger
*CEO: Kais Salhut
*COO: Bennet W Petersen
*CFO: Cheryl Smith
*Ex VP: Curtis Smith
*VP: Robert Dooley
VP: Patrick Gannon
VP: Mike Gillen
*VP: Thomas Glimp
*VP: Peter Kleeburg
VP: Tim Sahori
*VP: Tim Sahouri
Exec: Paula Franklin

D-U-N-S 80-151-1999
MEDECINS SANS FRONTIERES USA INC
DOCTORS WITHOUT BORDERS USA
(Suby of MEDECINS SANS FRONTIERES (HK) LIMITED)
333 7th Ave Fl 2, New York, NY 10001-5089
Tel (212) 679-6800 Founded/Ownrshp 1987
Sales 344.6MM EMP 100^E
Accts Tait Weller & Baker Llp Phila
SIC 8399 7363 Advocacy group; Fund raising organization, non-fee basis; Medical help service
Pr: Deane Marchbein
*CFO: Maureen Burnley
Treas: John E Plum
Ofcr: Lauren Ford
*VP: Aditya Nadimpalli
VP: Christine Nadori
Exec: Lydia Elhassan
*Ex Dir: Sophie Delaunay
Ex Dir: Joelle Tanguy
Dir IT: Yon Lee

D-U-N-S 60-281-3511
MEDECISION INC
(Suby of BLUE CROSS AND BLUE SHIELD) ★
550 E Swedesford Rd # 220, Wayne, PA 19087-1620
Tel (484) 588-0102 Founded/Ownrshp 2008
Sales NA EMP 325^E
SIC 6324 7371 Hospital & medical service plans; Computer software development & applications
CEO: Deborah Gabe
Owner: Augusta Kairys
Ch Bd: Colleen Reitan
COO: Carole A Hodsdon
CFO: Kenneth Young
Ch: Terri Kline
Ofcr: Jennifer Ponski
Ex VP: William Gillespie
Ex VP: Andrew P Schuyler
Sr VP: Kathleen D'Amario
Sr VP: Larry Landau
Sr VP: Susan L Newton
Sr VP: Mary Sirois
Sr VP: Shelby Solomon
VP: Jerry Baker
VP: Ellen Donahue-Dalton
VP: Terri Gregorio
VP: Elay Lockwood
VP: Rick Meyer
VP: Susan Newton

D-U-N-S 87-781-8091 IMP
■ **MEDEGEN LLC**
(Suby of CAREFUSION CORP) ★
4501 E Wall St, Ontario, CA 91761-8143
Tel (909) 390-9080 Founded/Ownrshp 2010
Sales 121.4MM^E EMP 1,282
SIC 3089 Injection molded finished plastic products
CEO: Charles Stroupe

D-U-N-S 05-200-2029 IMP/EXP
MEDELA INC
(Suby of MEDELA AG)
1101 Corporate Dr, McHenry, IL 60050-7006
Tel (800) 435-8316 Founded/Ownrshp 1980
Sales 157.3MM^E EMP 300^E
SIC 5047 3596 Medical & hospital equipment; Scales & balances, except laboratory; Baby scales
Pr: Carolin Archibald
Pr: Karen Csech
CFO: Ruedi Temprpli
VP: Donald Alexander
VP: Patrik Bosshard
VP: Janet Gyger
VP: Mitch Odahowski
VP: Sean Pettibone
VP: Ruedi Temperli
Exec: Mike Adam
Genl Mgr: Bonnie Voigt
Board of Directors: Michael Larsson, Kurt Rudolph, Urs Tanner

D-U-N-S 07-640-1066
MEDFORD SCHOOL DISTRICT 549C
815 S Oakdale Ave, Medford, OR 97501-3531
Tel (541) 842-3621 Founded/Ownrshp 1885
Sales 68.9MM^E EMP 1,024
SIC 8211 Public elementary & secondary schools; Elementary school; High school, junior or senior
*CFO: Brad Earl
CFO: Cheryl Foote
*Prin: Terri Dahl
Genl Mgr: John Petach
IT Man: Keith Brabham
Netwrk Mgr: Jeff Bales

D-U-N-S 15-200-7423
MEDHOST OF TENNESSEE INC
MEDHOST SERVICES
(Suby of HEALTHTECH HOLDINGS INC) ★
6550 Carothers Pkwy # 100, Franklin, TN 37067-6693
Tel (615) 761-1000 Founded/Ownrshp 2000
Sales 84.1MM^E EMP 400
SIC 7371 Computer software development & applications
CEO: Bill Anderson
*Pr: Craig Herrod
*CFO: Kenneth Misch
VP: Steve Massey
VP: Chuck Steinmetz
VP: Kenneth Williamson
Exec: Cindy Meagher
Exec: Pat Murphy
Software D: Brian White
S&M/Mgr: Andrew Rittler
Board of Directors: Thomas E Givens, Phillip C Molner, Scott W Seelbach, Debbie Sudduth, Lisa Sullivan

MEDHOST SERVICES
See MEDHOST OF TENNESSEE INC

D-U-N-S 05-947-0927
■ **MEDI-PHYSICS INC**
GE HEALTHCARE
(Suby of GE HEALTHCARE LIMITED)
100 Results Way, Marlborough, MA 01752-3078
Tel (800) 526-3593 Founded/Ownrshp 2000
Sales 115.6MM^E EMP 25
SIC 5122 Medicinals & botanicals
CEO: Jeffrey R Immelt
Pr: Pascale Witz
CEO: Jeffery R Immelt
Treas: Vito Pulito
VP: Donald Quinn

MEDIA DISTRIBUTORS
See DISCOUNT MEDIA PRODUCTS LLC

D-U-N-S 80-565-4170
■ **MEDIA GENERAL COMMUNICATIONS INC**
(Suby of MGOC INC) ★
333 E Franklin St, Richmond, VA 23219-2213
Tel (804) 649-6000 Founded/Ownrshp 2010
Sales 317.5MM^E EMP 1,580^E
SIC 2711 Newspapers

Pr: George L Mahoney
CFO: James F Woodward
VP: Andrew C Carington

D-U-N-S 07-968-0912

▲ MEDIA GENERAL INC
333 E Franklin St, Richmond, VA 23219-2213
Tel (804) 887-5000 *Founded/Ownrshp* 1969
Sales 674.9MM *EMP* 5,300E
Tkr Sym MEG *Exch* NYS
SIC 4833 Television broadcasting stations
Pr: Vincent L Sadusky
COO: Deborah A McDermott
CFO: Kelly Pettijohn
CFO: James F Woodward
VP: Andrew C Carington
VP: Jim Carr
VP: James Conschafter
VP: Doug Forshey
VP: John O Lewis
Creative D: Ralph Mathes
Genl Mgr: Christine Riser
Board of Directors: Diana F Cantor, Royal W Carson III, H C Charles Diao, Dennis J Fitzsimons, Douglas W McCormick, John R Muse, Wyndham Robertson, Thomas J Sullivan

D-U-N-S 17-037-8066 IMP

■ MEDIA GENERAL OPERATIONS INC
VIRGINIA BUSINESS MAGAZINE
(*Suby of* MEDIA GENERAL COMMUNICATIONS INC) ★
333 E Franklin St, Richmond, VA 23219-2213
Tel (804) 887-5000 *Founded/Ownrshp* 2000
Sales 317.5MME *EMP* 1,580
SIC 2711 4833 Newspapers; Television broadcasting stations
Pr: George L Mahoney
COO: Reid O Ashe
Treas: John A Butler
* *Treas:* James F Woodward
Ex VP: Aaron Lorson
VP: Darby Greenhill

D-U-N-S 05-524-4347

MEDIA PLANNING GROUP USA LLC
M P G
(*Suby of* HAVAS MEDIA GROUP SPAIN SA.)
200 Hudson St, New York, NY 10013-1807
Tel (646) 587-5000 *Founded/Ownrshp* 2006
Sales 88.9MME *EMP* 382
SIC 7319 Media buying service
CEO: Shaun Holliday
Mng Pt: Marie Oldham
COO: John McLoughlin
Ex VP: Debi Kleiman
Sr VP: James Brickley
Sr VP: Melissa Keller
Sr VP: Christopher O'Connor
Sr VP: Geoffrey Summerville
Sr VP: Vanessa Watts
VP: Adam Cohen
VP: Erin Feeley
VP: Adriann Fonstein
VP: Jennifer Ford
VP: Gillian Greaves
VP: Lynn Martin
VP: Erin Obrien
Creative D: Lucas Zaiden

D-U-N-S 07-671-7503 IMP

■ MEDIA RECOVERY
MEDIA RECOVERY, INC.
(*Suby of* CAPITAL SOUTHWEST CORPORATION)
5501 L B Johnson Fwy 350, Dallas, TX 75240
Tel (800) 660-3586 *Founded/Ownrshp* 1997
Sales 130.6MME *EMP* 214E
SIC 7373 Computer system selling services
Pr: Gerry Smith
* *CFO:* David Chisum
Dir Soc: Sherry Pipkin
Mfg Dir: Angela Kerr

MEDIA RECOVERY, INC.
See MEDIA RECOVERY

MEDIA SOLUTIONS GROUP
See CLIFFORD PAPER INC

D-U-N-S 08-005-5924

■ MEDIABRANDS WORLDWIDE INC
INITIATIVE MEDIA
(*Suby of* INTERPUBLIC GROUP OF COMPANIES INC) ★
100 W 33rd St, New York, NY 10001-2900
Tel (212) 605-7000 *Founded/Ownrshp* 1994
Sales 167.6MME *EMP* 1,300
SIC 7319 7311 Media buying service; Advertising consultant
CEO: Jim Elms
Pr: Peter Mears
COO: Caroline Bivens
COO: Ed Powers
CFO: Jeff Lupinacci
CFO: Mark Sanders
CFO: Greg Walsch
CFO: Greg Walsh
Ex VP: Alain Damond
Ex VP: Janice Finkel-Greene
Ex VP: Sarah Ivey
Ex VP: Sarah Power
Sr VP: Teriann Link
VP: Marc Ducnuigeen
VP: Andrew Herreria
VP: Dab Nanus
VP: Greg Stimson
Exec: Loria Furay
Exec: Alec Jones
Assoc Dir: Michael Davis
Assoc Dir: Samira Ebrahim

D-U-N-S 78-598-2690

MEDIACOM BROADBAND LLC
(*Suby of* MEDIACOM COMMUNICATIONS CORP) ★
1 Mediacom Way, Mediacom Park, NY 10918-4810
Tel (845) 443-2600 *Founded/Ownrshp* 2001
Sales 982.3MM *EMP* 2,415E
Accts Pricewaterhousecoopers Llp N
SIC 4841 Cable & other pay television services; Subscription television services
CEO: Rocco B Commisso
* *CFO:* Mark E Stephan
* *Ex VP:* John G Pascarelli
* *Ex VP:* Italia Commisso Weinand
Sr VP: Italia Commissoweinand
* *Sr VP:* Brian M Walsh
* *Sr VP:* Joseph E Young

D-U-N-S 10-679-1739

MEDIACOM COMMUNICATIONS CORP
1 Mediacom Way, Mediacom Park, NY 10918-4850
Tel (877) 847-6221 *Founded/Ownrshp* 1999
Sales 2.5MMME *EMP* 4,520E
SIC 4841 4813 Cable & other pay television services; Cable television services; Closed circuit television services; Subscription television services;
CEO: Rocco B Commisso
CFO: Mark Stefan
CFO: Mark E Stephan
Ofcr: Weinand Italia
Ex VP: John G Pascarelli
Ex VP: Italia Commisso Weinand
Sr VP: David McNaughton
Sr VP: Edward S Pardini
Sr VP: Brian M Walsh
Sr VP: Joseph E Young
VP: Joseph Commisso
VP: Bruce Gluckman
VP: Paul Lalanne
VP: Dan Templin

D-U-N-S 94-776-9360

MEDIACOM LLC
(*Suby of* MEDIACOM COMMUNICATIONS CORP) ★
1 Mediacom Way, Mediacom Park, NY 10918-4810
Tel (845) 443-2600 *Founded/Ownrshp* 1995
Sales 738.7MM *EMP* 1,890E
SIC 4841 Cable & other pay television services
CEO: Rocco B Commisso
CFO: Mark E Stephan
Ex VP: John G Pascarelli
Sr VP: Brian M Walsh
Sr VP: Italia Commisso Weinand
Sr VP: Joseph E Young
Assoc Dir: Lauren Gottlieb
IT Man: Kenneth Kohrs

D-U-N-S 00-830-3807

MEDIACOM SOUTHEAST LLC
1104 N Westover Blvd, Albany, GA 31707-6625
Tel (229) 888-0242 *Founded/Ownrshp* 1997
Sales 242.6MME *EMP* 4,591
SIC 4841 4813 Cable & other pay television services; Telephone communication, except radio
Prin: Rocco Commisso
* *Pt:* Rocco B Commisso
* *Pt:* Mediacom LLC
Off Mgr: Jennifer Weeks

D-U-N-S 80-774-7220

MEDIAMATH INC
4 World Trade Ctr, New York, NY 10007-2366
Tel (646) 840-4200 *Founded/Ownrshp* 2007
Sales 185.8MME *EMP* 564E
SIC 7379
CEO: Joseph Zawadzki
* *Pr:* ARI Buchalter
* *Pr:* Michael Lamb
* *CFO:* Jeannie Mun
* *Chf Mktg O:* Joanna O'Connell
Ex VP: Steven Kaufman
Sr VP: Jeffrey Davis
* *Sr VP:* Dave Reed
* *Sr VP:* Dan Rosenberg
Sr VP: Wilfried Schobeiri
VP: Jake Engwerd
VP: Jake Engwerda
VP: Joey Hyche
VP: Kym Insana
VP: Michael Mullaney
VP: Ajit Thupil
VP: Chris Victory
* *VP:* Eric Wasserman
VP: Greg Williams
Board of Directors: Michael Barrett

D-U-N-S 78-782-4291

MEDIANEWS GROUP INC
DIGITAL FIRST MEDIA
(*Suby of* DIGITAL FIRST MEDIA LLC) ★
101 W Colfax Ave Ste 1100, Denver, CO 80202-5315
Tel (303) 954-6360 *Founded/Ownrshp* 2013
Sales 3.9MMME *EMP* 12,947
SIC 2711 Newspapers, publishing & printing
Pr: Steve Rossi
V Ch: Joel Robinson
Pr: Sandra Neely
* *CFO:* Michael Koren
Ex VP: Joseph Euteneuerer
Sr VP: Steve Hesse
Sr VP: Robert Jendusa
VP: Brock Berry
VP: David M Bessen
VP: Pat Eagan
VP: Michael Fluker
* *VP:* Guy Gilmore
VP: Doug Graham
VP: Dutch Greve
* *VP:* William Higginson
VP: Charles Kamen
* *VP:* Marc Katz
VP: Michael J Koren
* *VP:* Chris Loretto
VP: Tim Meredith
VP: Richard Michnick
Board of Directors: Heath Freeman, Eric Krauss, Bruce Schnelwar

D-U-N-S 01-868-2198

MEDIAOCEAN LLC
45 W 18th St, New York, NY 10011-4609
Tel (212) 633-8100 *Founded/Ownrshp* 2016
Sales 138.8MME *EMP* 400
SIC 7371 7311 Custom computer programming services; Advertising agencies
CEO: Bill Wise
* *CFO:* Nick Galassi
* *Ofcr:* Ramsey McGrory
* *Ex VP:* Gordon H Cohen
Sr VP: Ann-Marie Beals
Sr VP: Gordon Cohen
Sr VP: Stephanie Dorman
Sr VP: Regan Garrett
Sr VP: Maria Pousa
VP: Christian Arts
VP: David Bigler
VP: Steve Geller

D-U-N-S 78-933-8191

MEDICA HEALTH PLANS
401 Carlson Pkwy, Minnetonka, MN 55305-5359
Tel (952) 992-3056 *Founded/Ownrshp* 2001
Sales 118.4MME *EMP* 1,386
SIC 8011 Health maintenance organization
Pr: David Tilford
Pt: Eli Hazum
* *Chf Mktg O:* Charles Fazio
* *Ex VP:* Aaron Reynolds
* *Sr VP:* Glenn E Andis
VP: Geoff Bartsh
VP: Barbara Lynch
VP: Susan Pagel
* *VP:* Pennina Safer
Exec: Anton Dmytrenko
Dir Teleco: David Eckhardt

D-U-N-S 09-236-4462 IMP/EXP

■ MEDICAL ACTION INDUSTRIES INC
(*Suby of* OWENS & MINOR INC) ★
25 Heywood Rd, Arden, NC 28704-9302
Tel (631) 231-4600 *Founded/Ownrshp* 2014
Sales 287.8MM *EMP* 815E
SIC 3842 Applicators, cotton tipped; Bandages: plastic, muslin, plaster of paris, etc.; Adhesive tape & plasters, medicated or non-medicated; Bandages & dressings
CEO: Paul D Meringolo
* *Pr:* Paul Chapman
VP: Carmine Morello
Sfty Mgr: Gordon Collins
Board of Directors: Henry A Berling, William W Burke, Kenneth W Davidson, Pamela R Levy, Kenneth R Newsome

MEDICAL ASSISTANCE PROGRAMS
See MAP INTERNATIONAL (INC)

MEDICAL ASSOCIATES HEALTH CTRS
See PROHEALTH CARE MEDICAL ASSOCIATES INC

D-U-N-S 10-574-1268

MEDICAL CARD SYSTEM INC
MCS LIFE INSURANCE
Mcs Plaza 255 Ponce St Mcs Pla, San Juan, PR 00917
Tel (787) 758-2500 *Founded/Ownrshp* 1999
Sales NA *EMP* 135E
SIC 6411 Medical insurance claim processing, contract or fee basis
* *VP:* Jose D Ferrer
* *VP:* Guillermo Melendez
* *VP:* Domingo Rodriguez

D-U-N-S 80-967-6047

MEDICAL CEN
691 Cherry St Fl 5, Macon, GA 31201-7392
Tel (478) 633-6831 *Founded/Ownrshp* 2008
Sales 646.1MM *EMP* 2
SIC 8099 Health & allied services
Prin: A Don Faulk Jr

MEDICAL CENTER, THE
See BOWLING GREEN-WARREN COUNTY COMMUNITY HOSPITAL CORP

D-U-N-S 08-969-9508

MEDICAL CENTER
MEDICAL CENTER HOSPITAL
(*Suby of* COLUMBUS REGIONAL HEALTHCARE SYSTEM INC) ★
710 Center St, Columbus, GA 31901-1547
Tel (706) 660-6255 *Founded/Ownrshp* 1987
Sales 366.3MM *EMP* 1,500
Accts Dixon Hughes Goodman Llp Char
SIC 8062 General medical & surgical hospitals
Owner: James R Wheeler
Ofcr: Darlene Mitchell
* *VP:* Wayne Joyner
Dir Sec: Jeff Williams
IT Man: Pat McDougall
Netwrk Eng: Vernon Calcote
* *VP Opers:* Kevin Sass
VP Opers: Kevin SA
Surgeon: Timothy Henderson
Obsttrcn: Ehrman Eldridge
Ansthlgy: Rajesh Arora
Board of Directors: Lance Duke, Freda Stewart, Jeff Williams

D-U-N-S 07-375-8773

MEDICAL CENTER AT PRINCETON NEW JERSEY
UNIVERSITY MED CTR AT PRNCETON
1 Plainsboro Rd, Plainsboro, NJ 08536-1913
Tel (609) 497-4000 *Founded/Ownrshp* 1929
Sales 293.0MME *EMP* 2,343
SIC 8062 General medical & surgical hospitals
Pr: Barry A Rabner
* *CFO:* Bruce Traub
* *Ex VP:* Joesph Bonnano
* *VP:* Elizabeth Buff
* *VP:* Carol Norris
* *VP:* Joe Stampe
Dir Rad: Gerard A Compito
Off Mgr: Marie Porter
Nurse Mgr: Wendy Luca
CIO: Charles Schwenz
Dir IT: Ed Henry

MEDICAL CENTER CAMPUS
See PEACE HEALTH SOUTHWEST MEDICAL CENTER

MEDICAL CENTER HEALTH SYSTEM
See ECTOR COUNTY HOSPITAL DISTRICT

MEDICAL CENTER HOSPITAL
See MEDICAL CENTER

D-U-N-S 07-247-9710

MEDICAL CENTER OF CENTRAL GEORGIA INC (GA)
(*Suby of* NAVICENT HEALTH INC) ★
777 Hemlock St, Macon, GA 31201-2155
Tel (478) 633-1000 *Founded/Ownrshp* 1895, 1994
Sales 717.4MM *EMP* 3,750
SIC 8062 Hospital, medical school affiliated with residency
CEO: Ninfa M Saunders
* *COO:* Mike Gilstrap
* *CFO:* Virgil E Cooper Jr
* *CFO:* Rhonda S Perry
VP: Susan Lowery
Dir Rad: Paul W Chandler
Prin: David King
Dir Sec: Quinton Jude
Board of Directors: Oscar Battles, Kathy Bowen, Seth Bush, James Cunningham, Jim Doyle, Kay Lucia, Bernard Meyer Von Breme

D-U-N-S 02-607-6112

MEDICAL CENTER OF LOUISIANA AT NEW ORLEANS
CHARITY HOSPITAL
1532 Tulane Ave, New Orleans, LA 70112-2860
Tel (504) 903-3000 *Founded/Ownrshp* 1800
Sales 122.0ME *EMP* 4,000
SIC 8062 General medical & surgical hospitals
CFO: Bernie Hebert

D-U-N-S 79-056-5928

MEDICAL CENTER OF ROCKIES
MCR
(*Suby of* UNIVERSITY OF COLORADO HEALTH) ★
2500 Rocky Mountain Ave, Loveland, CO 80538-9004
Tel (970) 624-2500 *Founded/Ownrshp* 2002
Sales 403.5MM *EMP* 4,000
SIC 8062 General medical & surgical hospitals
CEO: George Hayes
* *Ex Dir:* Laurie Tuka

D-U-N-S 11-850-3395

MEDICAL CENTER OF SOUTHEAST TEXAS L P
MID-JEFFERSON HOSPITAL
(*Suby of* IASIS HEALTHCARE LLC) ★
2555 Jimmy Johnson Blvd, Port Arthur, TX 77640-2007
Tel (409) 724-7389 *Founded/Ownrshp* 2003
Sales 170.2MM *EMP* 765E
SIC 8062 General medical & surgical hospitals
CEO: Matt Roberts
* *CFO:* Terry Hohmann
* *Chf Cred:* Ruthie Robinson
Exec: Carol Hebert
Sales Exec: Tabby Deguia

MEDICAL CENTER OF TRINITY
See NEWPORT RICHEY HOSPITAL INC

MEDICAL CENTER PLANO
See COLUMBIA MEDICAL CENTER OF PLANO SUBSIDIARY LP

MEDICAL CITY DALLAS HOSPITAL
See MEDICAL CITY DALLAS IMAGING CENTER LLP

MEDICAL CITY DALLAS HOSPITAL
See COLUMBIA HOSPITAL AT MEDICAL CITY DALLAS SUBSIDIARY LP

D-U-N-S 61-038-7297

MEDICAL CITY DALLAS IMAGING CENTER LLP
MEDICAL CITY DALLAS HOSPITAL
7777 Forest Ln Ste C840, Dallas, TX 75230-2594
Tel (972) 566-7000 *Founded/Ownrshp* 2005
Sales 17.0MME *EMP* 2,700
SIC 8062 General medical & surgical hospitals
CEO: Troy Villareal
CFO: Mark Atchley
Chf Nrs Of: Carol Gregory
Surgeon: Brian Gogel
Obsttrcn: Kelli Culpepper
Obsttrcn: Amy Sigman
Plas Surg: Martin Lazar
Occ Thrpy: Angela Brown

MEDICAL COLLEGE OF VIRGINIA
See VCU HEALTH SYSTEM AUTHORITY

D-U-N-S 93-763-9060

MEDICAL COLLEGE OF WISCONSIN INC
8701 W Watertown Plank Rd, Milwaukee, WI 53226-3548
Tel (414) 456-8296 *Founded/Ownrshp* 1918
Sales 990.8MME *EMP* 4,700
Accts Pricewaterhousecoopers Llp Bo
SIC 8221 Colleges universities & professional schools
Pr: John R Raymond Sr
* *CFO:* Marjorie Spencer
* *Ex VP:* Joseph E Kerschner
VP: Daniel Wickeham
Dir Lab: Dani Didier
* *Prin:* T Michael Bolger
Off Mgr: Brad Schiereck
CIO: Terry Pouquette
Dir IT: Huoy-Jii Khoo
Dir IT: Kathy Lang
IT Man: Greg McQuestion

MEDICAL CTR SOUTHEASTERN OKLA
See DURANT HMA INC

D-U-N-S 07-474-5803

MEDICAL FACILITIES OF AMERICA VI AND XIII (LIMITED PARTNERSHIP)
VIRGINIA BEACH HEATHCARE & REH
2917 Penn Forest Blvd, Roanoke, VA 24018-4304
Tel (540) 989-3618 *Founded/Ownrshp* 1977
Sales 24.7MME *EMP* 1,083
SIC 8051 Skilled nursing care facilities
Pt: W Heywood Fralin

D-U-N-S 84-169-4974
MEDICAL FACULTY ASSOCIATES INC
GWU MEDICAL FACULTY ASSOCIATES
2150 Pennsylvania Ave Nw, Washington, DC 20037-3201
Tel (202) 741-3000 *Founded/Ownrshp* 2000
Sales 339.1MM *EMP* 1,600E
SIC 8011 Offices & clinics of medical doctors
CEO: Stephen L Badger
**Pr:* Alan Waserman MD
**CFO:* Kenneth W Marter
Pathlgst: Robert V Jones
Pathlgst: Donald S Karcher
Pathlgst: John F Keiser
Pathlgst: Sana O Tabbara
Obsttrcn: Anna Maria Gray
Doctor: John Larsen MD
Doctor: Sunila S Walia
Pharmcst: Edward Jennings

MEDICAL IMAGING EQUIPMENT
See PHILIPS MEDICAL SYSTEMS (CLEVELAND) INC

D-U-N-S 06-515-2530
MEDICAL INFORMATION TECHNOLOGY INC
Meditech Cir, Westwood, MA 02090
Tel (781) 821-3000 *Founded/Ownrshp* 1969
Sales 475.5MM *EMP* 4,000E
SIC 7372 Prepackaged software
Pr: Howard Messing
**Ch Bd:* A Neil Pappalardo
CFO: Jennifer Holland
CFO: Barbara A Manzolillo
**V Ch Bd:* Lawrence A Polimeno
Bd of Dir: Bernard Winston
Ex VP: Michelle O'Connor
Ex VP: Hoda Sayed-Friel
Sr VP: Christopher Anschuetz
Sr VP: Stuart N Lefthes
VP: David Anderson
VP: Rosalyn Elton
VP: Steven Koretz
VP: Myra Ng
VP: Melissa Rogers
Exec: James Lobban
Board of Directors: Roland L Driscoll, Edward B Roberts, L P Dan Valente

MEDICAL MAL PRACTICE
See TEXAS MEDICAL LIABILITY TRUST

D-U-N-S 19-674-8321
MEDICAL MANAGEMENT CONSULTANTS INC
MMC
8150 Beverly Blvd, Los Angeles, CA 90048-4513
Tel (310) 659-3835 *Founded/Ownrshp* 1982
Sales 71.4MME *EMP* 5,000
SIC 7363 8742 8748 8721 Help supply services; Hospital & health services consultant; Employee programs administration; Payroll accounting service
Pr: Mashi Rahmani
CTO: Crystal Obrien

D-U-N-S 82-722-9493
MEDICAL MANAGEMENT INTERNATIONAL INC
BANFIELD PET HOSPITAL
(*Suby of* MARS INC) ★
8000 Ne Tillamook St, Portland, OR 97213-6655
Tel (503) 922-5000 *Founded/Ownrshp* 1994
Sales 2.2MMME *EMP* 7,000
SIC 0742 5047 Veterinary services, specialties; Animal hospital services, pets & other animal specialties; Veterinarians' equipment & supplies
CEO: Tony Ueber
CFO: Phil Freeman
CFO: Margie Mendoza
Sr VP: Daniel Aja
Sr VP: Debbie Kujovich
**Sr VP:* Hugh B Lewis
Sr VP: Jeannine Taaffe
VP: John Bork
VP: Jeffrey Brant
VP: Jeffery Ellison
**VP:* John May
VP: Marta Monetti
VP: Andrea Sinnott

MEDICAL MANAGER
See EMDEON CORP

MEDICAL MISSION SISTER'S
See SOCIETY OF CATHOLIC MEDICAL MISSIONARIES INC

D-U-N-S 08-055-2359
MEDICAL MUTUAL LIABILITY INSURANCE SOCIETY OF MARYLAND
225 International Cir # 300, Hunt Valley, MD 21030-4358
Tel (410) 785-0050 *Founded/Ownrshp* 1975
Sales NA *EMP* 105
SIC 6351 Liability insurance
Ch Bd: George S Malouf Jr
Pt: John McCullough
V Ch: Mary Ellen
**Pr:* Jeffrey M Poole
**CEO:* Robert R Neall
Assoc VP: Elizabeth Svoysky
**Sr VP:* Wesley M Foster Jr
VP: William Ober
VP: Foster Wesley
Doctor: Malouf George
Doctor: Charles Mess

D-U-N-S 07-112-6262
MEDICAL MUTUAL OF OHIO
CONSUMERS LIFE INSURANCE CO
2060 E 9th St Frnt Ste, Cleveland, OH 44115-1355
Tel (216) 687-7000 *Founded/Ownrshp* 1945
Sales NA *EMP* 2,500
SIC 6324 Hospital & medical service plans; Dental insurance; Group hospitalization plans
CEO: Rick A Chiricosta
**CFO:* Ray Mueller
**Ofcr:* Kathy Golovan
Ex VP: Jared Chaney
**Ex VP:* Steffany Larkins
Ex VP: Kevin Sidon
Ex VP: Susan Tyler
VP: Carol Bushnell
VP: Mary Edwards
VP: Mark Hren
VP: Amber Hulme
VP: Dan Polk
VP: Renee Rupp
VP: Janice Santoll
VP: John Uhlir
VP: Richard Wallack
VP Bus Dev: Norm Steiner

D-U-N-S 11-885-2599
MEDICAL PROFESSIONAL MUTUAL INSURANCE CO
PRO MUTUAL
(*Suby of* COVERYS) ★
1 Financial Ctr Fl 13, Boston, MA 02111-2688
Tel (800) 225-6168 *Founded/Ownrshp* 1975
Sales NA *EMP* 385
SIC 6331 Fire, marine & casualty insurance
Pr: Gregg Hanson
Ch Bd: Dr Brandal Richardson
V Ch Bd: Brenda E Richardson
Prin: Kenneth A Heisler
Sys/Mgr: John Donehue
Sys/Mgr: Robert Gilmore
Board of Directors: Elizabeth Hartley Johnson

D-U-N-S 14-191-8958
MEDICAL PROPERTIES TRUST INC
1000 Urban Center Dr # 501, Vestavia, AL 35242-2225
Tel (205) 969-3755 *Founded/Ownrshp* 2004
Sales 312.5MM *EMP* 50E
SIC 6798 Real estate investment trusts
Ch Bd: Edward K Aldag Jr
COO: Emmett E McLean
**CFO:* R Steven Hamner
Board of Directors: G Steven Dawson, Robert E Holmes, Sherry A Kellett, William G McKenzie, Paul Sparks Jr, Michael G Stewart, C Reynolds Thompson

D-U-N-S 00-693-7171
■ **MEDICAL PROTECTIVE CO**
(*Suby of* MEDPRO GROUP INC) ★
5814 Reed Rd, Fort Wayne, IN 46835-3500
Tel (260) 485-9622 *Founded/Ownrshp* 1909
Sales NA *EMP* 275
SIC 6351 6411 Surety insurance; Insurance agents, brokers & service; Insurance agents; Property & casualty insurance agent
Pr: Timothy Kenesey
**Ch Bd:* Kaj Ahlmann
**Pr:* David E Rosendahl
Pr: Sue Shumaker
Treas: Anthony Bowser
**Treas:* Dan Landrigan
**Sr VP:* Timothy Beck
Sr VP: Robert Ignasiak
**Sr VP:* Mark Walthour
VP: Gregory G Chronis
**VP:* Robert L Ignasiak
VP: Kimberly Kem
**VP:* James D Kunce
VP: Timothy M Smith
VP: Joel Whitcraft
VP: Tim Wiggins
Exec: Jennifer Cheatham
Exec: Jeffrey Kitchens

D-U-N-S 86-797-9619
MEDICAL REHABILITATION CENTERS LLC
EXCEPTIONAL LIVING CENTERS
1050 Chinoe Rd Ste 300, Lexington, KY 40502-6571
Tel (859) 255-0075 *Founded/Ownrshp* 1992
Sales 125.9MME *EMP* 2,000
Accts Crowe Horwath Llp South Bend
SIC 8742 Management consulting services
Pr: C Lynn Redmond
**Treas:* Jim Johnson
Treas: Steven Wood
Sr VP: John Nabours
**VP:* Wayne Tush
Mng Ofcr: Tom Watts
Off Mgr: Janet Gillespie
CTO: Donna Williams
Board of Directors: Donna Williams

MEDICAL RES FOUNDATION ORE
See OREGON HEALTH & SCIENCE UNIVERSITY FOUNDATION INC

D-U-N-S 03-008-9726
MEDICAL SERVICES OF AMERICA INC
171 Monroe Ln, Lexington, SC 29072-3904
Tel (803) 957-0500 *Founded/Ownrshp* 1973
Sales 212.4MME *EMP* 3,000
Accts Scott And Company Llp Columbi
SIC 8082 8741 8011 8071 7352 5999 Home health care services; Hospital management; Cardiologist & cardio-vascular specialist; Medical laboratories; Medical equipment rental; Medical apparatus & supplies
Pr: Ronnie L Young
**VP:* James F Hardman
**VP:* John D Keim
Exec: Cheryl Brown
Exec: Sandra Gainey
Exec: Catherine Robins
Dir Rx: Joni Sane
Dir Bus: Bruce Goodman
Brnch Mgr: Bobbie Nuckols
CIO: Kenny Boggs
Dir IT: Diana Peck

D-U-N-S 15-360-8369 IMP
MEDICAL SPECIALTIES DISTRIBUTORS LLC
800 Technology Center Dr # 3, Stoughton, MA 02072-4721
Tel (781) 344-6000 *Founded/Ownrshp* 2013
Sales 451.5MME *EMP* 373
SIC 5047 7352 Medical equipment & supplies; Medical equipment rental
Pr: James Beck
**Ex VP:* Peter Huie
**Ex VP:* Richard Worthen

D-U-N-S 09-777-9912
MEDICAL TEAM INC
HOME CARE TEAM, THE
1902 Campus Commons Dr # 650, Reston, VA 20191-1589
Tel (703) 390-2300 *Founded/Ownrshp* 1978
Sales 51.6MME *EMP* 1,000
SIC 8082 Home health care services
Pr: Leslie Pembrook
**VP:* Nicolas Tzirimis

D-U-N-S 15-647-5279 EXP
MEDICAL TEAMS INTERNATIONAL
14150 Sw Milton Ct, Tigard, OR 97224-8024
Tel (503) 624-1000 *Founded/Ownrshp* 1984
Sales 165.0MM *EMP* 91
Accts Jones & Roth Pc Hillsboro
SIC 8099 8399 Blood related health services; Community development groups
Pr: Martha Newsome
**Ch:* Mark Dodson
**Treas:* Jeff Rideout
**VP:* Pamela Blikstad
**VP:* Bill Essig
VP: Doug Fountain
**VP:* Linda Ranz
**VP:* Steve Vickers
VP: Rachel Wolverton
VP: Bill Zook
Exec: Lindsey Card

D-U-N-S 01-291-8350
▲ **MEDICAL TRANSCRIPTION BILLING CORP**
MTBC
7 Clyde Rd, Somerset, NJ 08873-5049
Tel (732) 873-5133 *Founded/Ownrshp* 1999
Sales 23.0MM *EMP* 1,600
Tkr Sym MTBC *Exch* NAS
SIC 7372 Prepackaged software
Ch Bd: Mahmud Haq
Pr: Stephen A Snyder
CFO: Bill Korn
VP: Michael Menche
CIO: Ul Hadi

D-U-N-S 94-497-2322
MEDICAL TRANSPORTATION MANAGEMENT INC
M T M
16 Hawk Ridge Cir Ste 120, Lake Saint Louis, MO 63367-1861
Tel (636) 561-5686 *Founded/Ownrshp* 1995
Sales 111.4MME *EMP* 700
SIC 4119 Local passenger transportation
Ch Bd: Peg Griswold
**Pr:* Alaina Macia
**CFO:* Gary Richardson
**Ex VP:* Lynn Griswold
**Ex VP:* Donald Tiemeyer
VP: Kerri Schewe
VP: Phil Stalboerger
**VP:* Alison Whitelaw
Exec: Jacqueline Hodge
Dir Bus: Rhonda Hollingsworth
Admn Mgr: Melissa Workman

D-U-N-S 16-845-3525
MEDICAL UNIVERSITY HOSPITAL AUTHORITY
(*Suby of* DEPARTMENT OF PSYCHIATR) ★
169 Ashley Ave, Charleston, SC 29425-8905
Tel (843) 792-1414 *Founded/Ownrshp* 2000
Sales 337.7MME *EMP* 4,000E
Accts Kpmg Llp Atlanta Ga
SIC 8062 General medical & surgical hospitals
Ex Dir: Patrick Pawley
Surg Cl Rc: Patty Burn

D-U-N-S 07-756-1637
MEDICAL UNIVERSITY OF OHIO
3000 Arlington Ave, Toledo, OH 43614-2595
Tel (419) 383-4000 *Founded/Ownrshp* 2004
Sales 118.6MME *EMP* 3,200
SIC 8062 8221 Hospital, affiliated with AMA residency; College, except junior
Pr: Lloyd Jacobs
**VP:* Mark Chaftang
CIO: Melodie Rufener-Weedley
QA Dir: Margaret McFadden
Pathlgst: Kara Gatto-Weis
Pathlgst: Nurjehan A Quraisky
Surgeon: Jihad T Abbas
Surgeon: David C Allison
Surgeon: Douglas R Bowman
Surgeon: Krishma Malik
Surgeon: Abdul A Mustapha

D-U-N-S 06-931-6271
MEDICAL UNIVERSITY OF SOUTH CAROLINA (SC)
DEPARTMENT OF PSYCHIATR
(*Suby of* BUDGET & CTRL BD EXEC DIRS OFF) ★
171 Ashley Ave, Charleston, SC 29425-8908
Tel (843) 792-2123 *Founded/Ownrshp* 1824
Sales 781.7MM *EMP* 5,500
Accts Kpmg Llp Greensboro Nc
SIC 8062 8221 8069 Hospital, medical school affiliated with nursing & residency; University; Specialty hospitals, except psychiatric
Pr: David Cole
CFO: Janet Scarborough
**CFO:* Patrick Wamsley
CFO: Flora Zorn
Trst: Margret M Addison
Trst: Stanley C Baker
Trst: William H Bingham
Trst: Phillip D Fasser
Trst: Cotesworth P Fishburne
Trst: Donald R Johnson II
Trst: Robert C Lake Jr
Trst: Ed Conyers O' Briyan
Trst: Paula E Orr
Trst: Claudia W Peeples
Trst: Thomas C Rowland
Trst: Mark Sanford
Trst: Charles W Schulze
Trst: Allen E Stalvey
Trst: Robin M Tallon Jr
Trst: Charles B Thomas Jr
Trst: James E Wiseman

D-U-N-S 07-364-7849
MEDICAL WEST COMMUNITY HEALTH
BROOKS, CAROLYN E
444 Montgomery St, Chicopee, MA 01020-1969
Tel (413) 598-7440 *Founded/Ownrshp* 1999
Sales NA *EMP* 160
SIC 6324 Health maintenance organization (HMO), insurance only
CEO: Richard Shuman
Doctor: Emilio M Elchionna MD
Doctor: Michael R Soell MD
Doctor: Brian H Toole MD

D-U-N-S 14-190-3562
MEDICAL WEST RESPIRATORY SVCS LLC
9301 Dielman Indus Dr, Saint Louis, MO 63132-2204
Tel (314) 993-8100 *Founded/Ownrshp* 2003
Sales 97.0MME *EMP* 180
SIC 5047 8082 Medical & hospital equipment; Home health care services

D-U-N-S 05-071-4963
MEDICALODGES INC (KS)
201 W 8th St, Coffeyville, KS 67337-5807
Tel (620) 251-6700 *Founded/Ownrshp* 1961
Sales 108.2MM *EMP* 2,500
Accts Meara Welch Browne Pc Leaw
SIC 8051 Skilled nursing care facilities
Pr: Garen Cox
Pr: Travis McBride
**COO:* Fred Benjamin
COO: Fred B Fache
**COO:* Clifford Fischer
**CFO:* Scott L Hines
**Ch:* Richard Butler
Bd of Dir: Kathy Lantz
Bd of Dir: Diane Voss
VP: Helen Cherry
**VP:* Cathy Fisher
**VP:* Marilyn Peak
**VP:* J D Seller

D-U-N-S 78-367-0081
MEDICARE MUCHO MAS HOLDINGS INC
(*Suby of* INNOVACARE SERVICES CO LLC) ★
Torrechardon 350 Av Chard 350th Avenue, San Juan, PR 00918
Tel (787) 622-3000 *Founded/Ownrshp* 2004
Sales NA *EMP* 300
SIC 6324 Hospital & medical service plans
CEO: Val Dean
**Pr:* Timothy O'Donnell

MEDICAREY MUCHO MAS
See MMM HEALTHCARE LLC

D-U-N-S 04-086-1601
▲ **MEDICINES CO**
8 Sylvan Way, Parsippany, NJ 07054-3801
Tel (973) 290-6000 *Founded/Ownrshp* 1996
Sales 309.0MM *EMP* 614E
Accts Ernst & Young Llp Metropark
Tkr Sym MDCO *Exch* NGS
SIC 2834 Pharmaceutical preparations; Intravenous solutions
CEO: Clive A Meanwell
**Ch Bd:* Fred Eshelman
Pr: Tony Kingsley
CFO: William B O'Connor
Ex VP: Christopher Cox
Ex VP: Jeffrey Frazier
Ex VP: Nancye Green
Ex VP: Loretta Itri
Ex VP: Stephen Rodin
VP: Daniel Char
VP: Barbara Dawson
VP: Jeffrey Key
VP: William Knopf
VP: Alan Levy
VP: Mike McGuire
VP: Elaine Morten
VP: Jeri Thomas
Exec: Naomi David
Board of Directors: William W Crouse, Alexander J Denner, Robert J Hugin, John C Kelley, Armin M Kessler, Robert G Savage, Melvin K Spiegelman, Elizabeth Hs Wyatt

D-U-N-S 18-283-7492 IMP/EXP
MEDICIS PHARMACEUTICAL CORP
(*Suby of* VALEANT PHARMACEUTICALS INTERNATIONAL, INC)
700 Us Highway 202/206, Bridgewater, NJ 08807-1704
Tel (866) 246-8245 *Founded/Ownrshp* 2012
Sales 112.2MME *EMP* 646E
SIC 2834 Pharmaceutical preparations; Dermatologicals
CEO: Jonah Shacknai
**COO:* Jason D Hanson
**CFO:* Richard D Peterson
**Ex VP:* Seth Rodner
**Ex VP:* Mitchell Wortzman PHD
VP: Manuel Estrada
VP: Xiaoming Lin
VP: Tim Miller
Ex Dir: Robert Curwin
Admn Mgr: Janice Kopulos
Admn Mgr: Jamie Muhlenfeld

D-U-N-S 84-037-1087
▲ **MEDIDATA SOLUTIONS INC**
350 Hudson St Fl 9, New York, NY 10014-4535
Tel (212) 918-1800 *Founded/Ownrshp* 1999
Sales 392.5MM *EMP* 1,254
Tkr Sym MDSO *Exch* NGS
SIC 7372 Prepackaged software; Application computer software; Business oriented computer software
Ch Bd: Tarek A Sherif
**Pr:* Glen M De Vries
COO: Michael L Capone
CFO: Rouven Bergmann
Ex VP: Michael I Otner
Ex VP: Michael C Pinto
Ex VP: Eileen M Schloss

Sr VP: Steven I Hirschfeld
VP: Glenn Cahaly
VP: Susan Hailey
VP: Dan Klein
VP: Keta Lakdawala
VP: David Lee
VP: Nick Lucas
VP: Jeffrey Pease
VP: Dan Shannon
VP: Glenn Watt
Board of Directors: Carlos Dominguez, Neil M Kurtz, George W McCulloch, Lee A Shapiro, Robert B Taylor

D-U-N-S 36-288-6256
MEDIEVAL TIMES ENTERTAINMENT INC
(*Suby of* MEDIEVAL TIMES ENTERTAINMENT INC) ★
7662 Beach Blvd, Buena Park, CA 90620-1838
Tel (714) 523-1100 *Founded/Ownrshp* 2007
Sales 33.7MME *EMP* 1,907E
SIC 7041 7996 Membership-basis organization hotels; Theme park, amusement
Pr: Kenneth H Kim

D-U-N-S 93-214-0481
MEDIEVAL TIMES ENTERTAINMENT INC
6363 N State Highway 161 # 400, Irving, TX 75038-2269
Tel (214) 596-7600 *Founded/Ownrshp* 2001
Sales 148.6MME *EMP* 2,000E
SIC 8741 Restaurant management
CEO: Perico Montaner
Exec: Kristi Gill
Sls Mgr: Sinan Logan

D-U-N-S 00-228-8975 IMP
▲ MEDIFAST INC
3600 Crondall Ln, Owings Mills, MD 21117-2233
Tel (410) 581-8042 *Founded/Ownrshp* 1980
Sales 272.7MM *EMP* 425E
Tkr Sym MED *Exch* NYS
SIC 2099 2023 8093 Food preparations; Dietary supplements, dairy & non-dairy based; Weight loss clinic, with medical staff
Ch Bd: Michael C Macdonald
Pr: Mehrnaz Mona Ameli
**Pr:* Margaret E Sheetz
COO: Ashley Rombro
CFO: Timothy G Robinson
Bd of Dir: Donald F Reilly
Chf Mktg O: Brian Kagen
Ex VP: Donald Gould
**Ex VP:* Jason L Groves
Ex VP: Leo Williams
VP: Michael Decker
VP: Douglas Zimmermann
Board of Directors: Jeffrey J Brown, Kevin G Byrnes, Charles P Connolly, Constance J Hallquist, Carl E Sassano, Scott Schlackman, Glenn W Welling

D-U-N-S 02-183-0230
MEDIFAX-EDI LLC
(*Suby of* CHANGE HEALTHCARE HOLDINGS INC) ★
26 Century Blvd, Nashville, TN 37214-3685
Tel (615) 932-3226 *Founded/Ownrshp* 2010
Sales 606.8MME *EMP* 2,781E
SIC 7374 7389 Data processing & preparation; Financial services

D-U-N-S 07-888-0639 IMP
MEDIMA LLC
5727 Strickler Rd, Clarence, NY 14031-1372
Tel (716) 741-0400 *Founded/Ownrshp* 2008
Sales 425.0MM *EMP* 250
SIC 3339 3313 Silicon & chromium; Ferroalloys

D-U-N-S 96-738-4921
MEDIMMUNE BIOLOGICS INC
(*Suby of* ASTRAZENECA PLC)
1 Medimmune Way, Gaithersburg, MD 20878-2204
Tel (301) 398-0000 *Founded/Ownrshp* 2011
Sales 1.4MM *EMP* 3,000
SIC 8731 Biological research

D-U-N-S 19-063-9906 IMP
MEDIMMUNE LLC
(*Suby of* ASTRAZENECA PLC)
1 Medimmune Way, Gaithersburg, MD 20878-2204
Tel (301) 398-1200 *Founded/Ownrshp* 2007
Sales 1.8MMME *EMP* 6,030
SIC 2834 Pharmaceutical preparations
Pr: Tony Zook
Owner: Jonathan Klein-Evans
Pr: Barbara White
COO: Matthew Bell
CFO: Tim Gray
CFO: Timothey Pearson
Ofcr: Matt Bell
Ex VP: William C Bertrand Jr
Ex VP: Scott P Carmer
Ex VP: Max Donley
Ex VP: Bahija Jallal
Ex VP: Peter Kiener
Ex VP: Peter A Kiener
Ex VP: Bernardus Machielse
Ex VP: Andrew D Skibo
Ex VP: Andrew Skibo
Ex VP: Alexander Zukiwski
Sr VP: David Berman
Sr VP: Edward Bradley
Sr VP: Peter Greenleaf
Sr VP: Pamela J Lupien

D-U-N-S 78-838-8288
MEDIMPACT HEALTHCARE SYSTEMS INC
(*Suby of* MEDIMPACT HOLDINGS INC) ★
10181 Scripps Gateway Ct, San Diego, CA 92131-5152
Tel (858) 566-2727 *Founded/Ownrshp* 1989
Sales 16.0MM *EMP* 1,412
SIC 8621 Medical field-related associations
Ch Bd: Frederick Howe
CFO: James Gollaher
CFO: David Wheeler
Sr VP: Jerry Parker
Sr VP: John Treiman
VP: Karen Bates
VP: Adriana Cabre
VP: Ginny Carpenter
VP: Dave Daltorio
VP: Mike Lyon
VP: Jeanine Mc Bride
VP: William Nygard
VP: Aaron Roberts
VP: Tim Rourke
VP: Louis C Tripoli
VP: Roderick Wade
Dir Bus: Susan Glass
Dir Bus: Susie Veladi

D-U-N-S 96-871-5586
MEDIMPACT HOLDINGS INC
10181 Scripps Gateway Ct, San Diego, CA 92131-5152
Tel (858) 566-2727 *Founded/Ownrshp* 2010
Sales 92.5MME *EMP* 1,412E
SIC 6799 Investors
Prin: Frederick Howe
**CFO:* Jim Gollaher
VP: Debra Minich
Exec: Patience Stevens
Snr Sftwr: Jarek Kloda
Sftwr Eng: Jose Irigoyen

D-U-N-S 08-014-5238
MEDINA CITY SCHOOL DISTRICT
739 Weymouth Rd, Medina, OH 44256-2037
Tel (330) 725-8831 *Founded/Ownrshp* 1824
Sales 86.6MM *EMP* 755
Accts Dave Yost Columbus Ohio
SIC 8211 Public elementary school; Public junior high school; Public senior high school
**Treas:* David Chambers
Pr Dir: Amy Busby
Schl Brd P: Tom Cahalan

D-U-N-S 06-041-9181
MEDINA HOSPITAL
1000 E Washington St, Medina, OH 44256-2167
Tel (330) 725-1000 *Founded/Ownrshp* 1942
Sales 101.8MM *EMP* 900
SIC 8062

MEDIQ USA HOLDINGS
See BYRAM HEALTHCARE CENTERS INC

MEDISENSE
See ABBOTT DIABETES CARE INC

MEDISYS FAMILY CARE
See MEDISYS JAMAICA HOSPITAL & MEDICAL CENTER

D-U-N-S 13-267-1970
MEDISYS HEALTH NETWORK INC
JAMAICA HOSPITAL
8900 Van Wyck Expy, Jamaica, NY 11418-2832
Tel (718) 206-6000 *Founded/Ownrshp* 1995
Sales 232.8MME *EMP* 3,000
Accts Cohnreznick Llp New York Ny
SIC 8741 Hospital management
CEO: David P Rosen
**COO:* Bruce J Flanz
**CFO:* Mounir F Doss
IT Man: Patrick Rudden

D-U-N-S 10-525-4580 IMP
MEDISYS JAMAICA HOSPITAL & MEDICAL CENTER
MEDISYS FAMILY CARE
8900 Van Wyck Expy, Jamaica, NY 11418-2832
Tel (718) 206-6000 *Founded/Ownrshp* 1891
Sales 44.7MME *EMP* 3,000
SIC 8062 General medical & surgical hospitals
CEO: Bruce J Flanz
**Pr:* David Rosen
**COO:* William Lynch
**CFO:* Mounir F Doss

D-U-N-S 05-667-5853 IMP/EXP
MEDITERRANEAN SHIPPING CO (USA) INC
MEDITERRANEAN SHIPPING CRUISES
(*Suby of* MSC MEDITERRANEAN SHIPPING COMPANY HOLDING SA)
420 5th Ave Fl 8, New York, NY 10018-2709
Tel (212) 764-8280 *Founded/Ownrshp* 1989
Sales 338.1MME *EMP* 1,000
SIC 4731 Agents, shipping
Ch Bd: Claudio Bozzo
**Ch Bd:* Nicola Arena
**Sr VP:* John J Mullaney
Rgnl Mgr: Alastair Law
Area Mgr: Graham Dalzell
Genl Mgr: Denisse Jaime
Genl Mgr: Tony Manning
Genl Mgr: Lydia Miner

MEDITERRANEAN SHIPPING CRUISES
See MEDITERRANEAN SHIPPING CO (USA) INC

D-U-N-S 19-326-9789
■ MEDIVATION INC
XTANDI
(*Suby of* PFIZER INC) ★
525 Market St Fl 36, San Francisco, CA 94105-2747
Tel (415) 543-3470 *Founded/Ownrshp* 2016
Sales 943.2MM *EMP* 628E
SIC 2834 Pharmaceutical preparations; Adrenal pharmaceutical preparations; Drugs acting on the gastrointestinal or genitourinary system
Pr: David T Hung
COO: Marion McCourt
CFO: Jennifer Jarrett
Chf Mktg O: Mohammad Hirmand
Ofcr: Joseph Lobacki
VP: Elaine Wong
VP: Lily Yang
Assoc Dir: Lisa Arjes
Assoc Dir: Tong Lin
Assoc Dir: Iulia Tudor
Area Mgr: Dan Bransfield
Board of Directors: Kathryn E Falberg, Michael L King, C Patrick Machado, Dawn Svoronos, W Anthony Vernon, Wendy L Yarno

D-U-N-S 06-819-9363 IMP/EXP
■ MEDIVATORS INC (MN)
(*Suby of* CANTEL MEDICAL CORP) ★
14605 28th Ave N, Minneapolis, MN 55447-4822
Tel (763) 553-3300 *Founded/Ownrshp* 1974, 2001
Sales 138.9MME *EMP* 650
SIC 3841 3842 3845 3589 Surgical & medical instruments; Hemodialysis apparatus; Sterilizers, hospital & surgical; Surgical appliances & supplies; Electromedical equipment; Patient monitoring apparatus; Sewage & water treatment equipment
CEO: David C Hemink
**Ex VP:* Don Byrne
**Ex VP:* Paul E Helms
**Ex VP:* Javier Henao
**Sr VP:* Dennise A Baur
**Sr VP:* Kevin Finkle
**Sr VP:* Craig Smith
VP: Matt Conlon
VP: Kevin B Finkle
VP: Mary A Greenawalt
VP: Robert Mosher
VP: Michael Peterson
VP: John Piontkowski
**VP:* Mike Spicer
Dir Lab: Howard Nelson

D-U-N-S 17-724-0249
MEDIWARE INFORMATION SYSTEMS INC
11711 W 79th St, Lenexa, KS 66214-1497
Tel (913) 307-1000 *Founded/Ownrshp* 2012
Sales 113.5MME *EMP* 318E
SIC 7372 Prepackaged software
Ch Bd: Thomas Kelly Mann
Pr: Robert Tysall-Blay
**CFO:* Robert Watkins
Ex VP: Mike Crabtree
**Ex VP:* Robert C Weber
**Sr VP:* Alan Wittmer
VP: Todd Bransford
VP: Neil Moore
VP: Paul O'Toole
Prgrm Mgr: Maureen Macdonald
Snr Sftwr: Benjamin Turski

D-U-N-S 96-327-7400
MEDLEY CAPITAL CORP
375 Park Ave Fl 33, New York, NY 10152-0002
Tel (212) 759-0777 *Founded/Ownrshp* 2010
Sales 120.7MM *EMP* 3
Tkr Sym MCC *Exch* NYS
SIC 6726 Management investment funds, closed-end
Ch Bd: Brook Taube
CFO: Richard T Allorto Jr
Chf Cred: John D Fredericks
VP: Luba Romankevich

D-U-N-S 02-546-0908 IMP/EXP
MEDLINE INDUSTRIES INC (IL)
3 Lakes Dr, Northfield, IL 60093-2753
Tel (847) 949-5500 *Founded/Ownrshp* 1977, 1966
Sales 5.6MMME *EMP* 12,000
SIC 3841 5047 5999 Surgical & medical instruments; Instruments, surgical & medical; Medical apparatus & supplies
CEO: Charles N Mills
Pr: Dennis Devlin
Pr: Julia Downey
Pr: Pete Herbrand
**Pr:* Andrew Mills
Pr: Jeff Rubel
**COO:* Jim Abrams
CFO: Michael Fineberg
**CFO:* Kristofer Howard
**Ch:* James S Mills
**Ch:* Jon M Mills
Chf Mktg O: Sue Macinnes
Ex VP: Zach Pocklington
Sr VP: Michael Calogero
Sr VP: Dan Johnson
Sr VP: Richard H Lee
Sr VP: Dan O'Keefe
VP: Michael Carroll
VP: Debashish Chakravarthy
VP: Larry Corrigan
VP: Paul Dudzik

D-U-N-S 79-149-7431
▲ MEDNAX INC
1301 Concord Ter, Sunrise, FL 33323-2843
Tel (954) 384-0175 *Founded/Ownrshp* 1979
Sales 2.7MMM *EMP* 4,600E
Tkr Sym MD *Exch* NYS
SIC 8011 Specialized medical practitioners, except internal; Pediatrician; Physical medicine, physician/surgeon
Ch Bd: Cesar L Alvarez
Pr: Joseph M Calabro
Pr: Michael D Stanley
Pr: Karl B Wagner
**CEO:* Roger J Medel
COO: David A Clark
COO: William C Hawk
CFO: Vivian Lopez-Blanco
Bd of Dir: Stephanie Foster
Sr VP: Dominic J Andreano
Sr VP: Robert C Bryant
VP: Lim Beverly
VP: Bob Bryant
VP: James Evans
VP: Thomas Hawkins
VP: David Hoskinson
VP: Edison Humphries
VP: David Kanter
VP: Gail Lim
VP: Keith Meredith
VP: Cara Rhoads

D-U-N-S 08-039-0357
■ MEDPACE ACQUISITION INC
(*Suby of* MEDPACE HOLDINGS INC) ★
5375 Medpace Way, Cincinnati, OH 45227-1543
Tel (513) 579-9911 *Founded/Ownrshp* 2014
Sales 365.5MME *EMP* 1,969E
SIC 8741 Financial management for business
Pr: August Troendle

D-U-N-S 07-935-8069
▲ MEDPACE HOLDINGS INC
5375 Medpace Way, Cincinnati, OH 45227-1543
Tel (513) 579-9911 *Founded/Ownrshp* 1992
Sales 359.0MM *EMP* 2,300E
Tkr Sym MEDP *Exch* NGS
SIC 2834 8731 Pharmaceutical preparations; Commercial physical research; Biological research
Ch Bd: August J Troendle
COO: Jesse J Geiger
COO: Jesse Geiger
Sr VP: Susan E Burwig
VP: Penelope J Bucknell
VP: Yun Le

D-U-N-S 80-642-9424
■ MEDPACE INC
(*Suby of* MEDPACE INTERMEDIATECO INC) ★
5375 Medpace Way, Cincinnati, OH 45227-1543
Tel (513) 579-9911 *Founded/Ownrshp* 2014
Sales 365.5MME *EMP* 2,223
SIC 8731 5122 5047 Biotechnical research, commercial; Pharmaceuticals; Medical equipment & supplies
Pr: August Troendle
**COO:* Kurt Brykman
VP: Richard D Scheyer
VP: Franklin O Smith
VP: Dan Weng
Assoc Dir: Ross Ezzati
Assoc Dir: Gary Rickels
Dir Bus: Susan Grundy
Dir Bus: Eric C Hauser
Dir Bus: Stacie Wickliffe
Dir Bus: John Wynne

D-U-N-S 07-935-5790
■ MEDPACE INTERMEDIATECO INC
(*Suby of* MEDPACE ACQUISITION INC) ★
5375 Medpace Way, Cincinnati, OH 45227-1543
Tel (513) 579-9911 *Founded/Ownrshp* 2011
Sales 365.5MME *EMP* 1,967E
SIC 8741 Financial management for business
Pr: August Troendle

D-U-N-S 09-632-0473 IMP
MEDPLAST GROUP INC
7865 Northcourt Rd # 100, Houston, TX 77040-5615
Tel (480) 553-6400 *Founded/Ownrshp* 1999, 2016
Sales 342.0MME *EMP* 1,700
SIC 3089 Injection molded finished plastic products
Pr: David Amrhein
Mng Dir: Lee Bowen
Genl Mgr: Phil Matthews
Genl Mgr: Sk Tan
Sls Mgr: Gary Ahlschlager

D-U-N-S 83-312-0814
MEDPLAST LLC
405 W Geneva Dr, Tempe, AZ 85282-2003
Tel (480) 553-6400 *Founded/Ownrshp* 2007
Sales 94.7MME *EMP* 1,786E
SIC 6719 Personal holding companies, except banks
CEO: Harol Faig
Pr: Langton Matthew
CFO: James Doerr
Ex VP: Mike Farrell
VP: Phil Owens
VP: Keith Starks
Prgrm Mgr: Michele Kaminski
Genl Mgr: Matt Hallead
Dir IT: Dan Streufert
Mtls Mgr: Tanya Franks
Ql Cn Mgr: Brian Gathas

D-U-N-S 80-789-3441
■ MEDPRO GROUP INC
(*Suby of* COLUMBIA INSURANCE CO) ★
5814 Reed Rd, Fort Wayne, IN 46835-3568
Tel (800) 463-3776 *Founded/Ownrshp* 2005
Sales NA *EMP* 380
SIC 6351 Surety insurance
CEO: Tim Kenesey
**CFO:* Joe Svitek
**Ex VP:* Dan Landrigan
**Sr VP:* Trent Heinemeyer

D-U-N-S 01-538-5425
MEDQUEST INC
(*Suby of* MQ ASSOCIATES INC) ★
3480 Preston Ridge Rd # 500, Alpharetta, GA 30005-5460
Tel (678) 992-7200 *Founded/Ownrshp* 2002
Sales 60.4MME *EMP* 1,460
SIC 8071 X-ray laboratory, including dental; Ultrasound laboratory
CEO: Chris Winkle
COO: Dan Schaffer
COO: Michael Villa
CFO: Tod Andrews
CFO: Thomas Gentry
**Ch:* Gene Venesky
Software D: Jason Kelly
VP Opers: Alan Muir

D-U-N-S 83-676-3375
MEDRISK INC
2701 Renaissance Blvd, King of Prussia, PA 19406-2781
Tel (610) 768-5812 *Founded/Ownrshp* 1994
Sales NA *EMP* 230E
SIC 6411 Insurance agents, brokers & service
CEO: Shelley L Boyce
**Pr:* Michael Ryan
COO: Jerry Poole
**CFO:* Thomas Weir
Chf Mktg O: Ruth Estridge
Ex VP: Jamie Davis
Ex VP: Joseph McCullough
Ex VP: Roger Nelson
VP: Nancy Brennan
**VP:* Ruth Estrich
VP: Patricia Lairson
**VP:* Ed McBurnie

D-U-N-S 01-671-3716
MEDSOLUTIONS INC
EVICORE HEALTHCARE
(*Suby of* EVICORE HEALTHCARE) ★
730 Cool Springs Blvd # 250, Franklin, TN 37067-4643
Tel (615) 468-0600 *Founded/Ownrshp* 2014
Sales NA *EMP* 800
SIC 6324 8322 Dental insurance; Health maintenance organization (HMO), insurance only; Community center
Pr: John Arlotta
Pr: Melba Price
Pr: Joe Steele
CFO: David S Bassin

Ex VP: Roger Cheek
Sr VP: Susan Ott
VP: Ed Ernest
VP: Ken Van Cara
QA Dir: Julie Hester
QA Dir: Monica Williams
Telecom Mg: David Newlin

MEDSOURCE
See GRIFFIN HOSPITAL INC

D-U-N-S 05-888-9606
■ MEDSOURCE TECHNOLOGIES HOLDINGS LLC
(Suby of LAKE REGION MEDICAL) ★
100 Fordham Rd Bldg C, Wilmington, MA 01887-2168
Tel (978) 570-6900 Founded/Ownrshp 2004
Sales 54.6MM^E EMP 1,300
SIC 3841 8711 Surgical & medical instruments; Engineering services
Ch Bd: Richard Effress
**CFO:* Joseph Caffarelli
**CFO:* William J Kullback
**VP:* Daniel Croteau
**VP:* Jim Drill
VP: Douglas Woodruff

D-U-N-S 12-817-4427
MEDSPEED LLC
655 W Grand Ave Ste 320, Elmhurst, IL 60126-1065
Tel (630) 617-5050 Founded/Ownrshp 1999
Sales 85.5MM^E EMP 300
Accts Bnham Ichen & Knox Llp
SIC 4731 Transportation agents & brokers
CEO: Jake Crampton
COO: Tim O'Day
CFO: Don Parker
VP: Kathy Benn
VP: Wes Crampton
Mktg Mgr: Alison Huffines

MEDSTAR FRANKLIN SQ MED CTR
See FRANKLIN SQUARE HOSPITAL CENTER INC

D-U-N-S 07-886-1117
MEDSTAR GOOD SAMARITAN HOSPITAL
5601 Loch Raven Blvd, Baltimore, MD 21239-2945
Tel (443) 444-4100 Founded/Ownrshp 2012
Sales 291.2MM EMP 31^E
SIC 8062 8011 Hospital, affiliated with AMA residency; Physical medicine, physician/surgeon
Prin: Stephanie Schneider

D-U-N-S 36-151-6370
MEDSTAR HEALTH INC
MEDSTAR HEALTH VNA
5565 Sterrett Pl Ste 500, Columbia, MD 21044-2679
Tel (410) 772-6500 Founded/Ownrshp 1987
Sales 4.1MMM^E EMP 33,000
SIC 8741 8062 8082 8051 8011 Management services; Business management; General medical & surgical hospitals; Home health care services; Skilled nursing care facilities; Offices & clinics of medical doctors; Physical medicine, physician/surgeon; Physicians' office, including specialists
CEO: Kenneth A Samet
Pt: Paul B Fowler
**Ch Bd:* William R Roberts
Pr: Nancy Dibenedetto
Pr: Bonnie Levin
Pr: Debra Luffman
Pr: Govind Maheshwari
Pr: Rebekah Stewart
**CFO:* Michael J Curran
Treas: Bob Hall
V Ch Bd: William J Oetgen
Bd of Dir: James G Kane
Ofcr: Maureen P McCausland
Ex VP: M Joy Drass
Ex VP: Stephen R T Evans
Ex VP: Oliver M Johnson II
Ex VP: Carl J Schindelar
Ex VP: Christine M Swearingen
Ex VP: William L Thomas
Ex VP: Eric R Wagner
VP: Bruce Bartoo

MEDSTAR HEALTH VNA
See MEDSTAR-GEORGETOWN MEDICAL CENTER INC

MEDSTAR HEALTH VNA
See ST MARYS HOSPITAL OF SAINT MARYS COUNTY INC

MEDSTAR HEALTH VNA
See GOOD SAMARITAN HOSPITAL OF MD INC

MEDSTAR HEALTH VNA
See MONTGOMERY GENERAL HOSPITAL INC

MEDSTAR HEALTH VNA
See MEDSTAR SOUTHERN MARYLAND HOSPITAL CENTER INC

MEDSTAR HEALTH VNA
See MEDSTAR HEALTH INC

D-U-N-S 08-105-5154
MEDSTAR SOUTHERN MARYLAND HOSPITAL CENTER INC
MEDSTAR HEALTH VNA
(Suby of MEDSTAR HEALTH VNA) ★
7503 Surratts Rd, Clinton, MD 20735-3358
Tel (301) 868-8000 Founded/Ownrshp 1981
Sales 220.8MM EMP 3,000
SIC 8062 8011 General medical & surgical hospitals; Offices & clinics of medical doctors
Pr: Richard McAlee
**CFO:* Dan Feeley
VP: Yvette C Johnson-Threat
VP: Lou Mavromatis
VP: Reba McVay
VP: Andrew Sumner
Dir Lab: Michael Deabay
Dir Rx: Jack M Namara
Mktg Dir: Cheryl Richardson
Obsttrcn: Salem I Al-Naber
Obsttrcn: Raj B Samtani

MEDSTAR UNION MEMORIAL HOSP
See UNION MEMORIAL HOSPITAL

MEDSTAR WASHINGTON HOSP CTR
See WASHINGTON HOSPITAL CENTER CORP

D-U-N-S 01-502-6664
MEDSTAR-GEORGETOWN MEDICAL CENTER INC
MEDSTAR HEALTH VNA
(Suby of MEDSTAR HEALTH VNA) ★
3800 Reservoir Rd Nw, Washington, DC 20007-2113
Tel (202) 444-2000 Founded/Ownrshp 1898
Sales 774.5MM EMP 4,000
SIC 8062 8221 8069 General medical & surgical hospitals; Hospital, medical school affiliated with nursing & residency; Colleges universities & professional schools; Specialty hospitals, except psychiatric
Ex Dir: Joy Drass
Pr: Frances Baldwin
**CFO:* Pipper Williams
VP: Karen Alcorn
VP: Michael Sachtleben
Exec: Charlotte Dillis
Assoc Dir: Tammy Spellman
Dir Rx: Jeffrey Cox
Surgeon: John N Delahay
Ansthlgy: Joseph Myers
Doctor: Doreen Cunningham

D-U-N-S 96-206-9365
MEDSYNERGIES INC
909 Hidden Rdg Ste 300, Irving, TX 75038-3801
Tel (972) 791-1224 Founded/Ownrshp 1996
Sales 121.4MM^E EMP 700^E
SIC 8741 8742 8721 Management services; Hospital & health services consultant; Billing & bookkeeping service
Ch Bd: Joseph Boyd
**Pr:* Frank Marshall
**CEO:* John Robert Thomas
**COO:* Ellen Mahony
**CFO:* Doug Hansen
Ofcr: Nick Bohra
Sr VP: James Dye
VP: David Gregorio
VP: Tracy McLellan
VP: Richard Miksch
VP: Matthew Niebuhr
VP: Benito Orsini
VP: Chris Walker
VP: Al Wilson
Board of Directors: Britt Berrett

D-U-N-S 14-317-8577
MEDSYNERGIES NORTH TEXAS INC
PHYSERVE PHYSICIAN SERVICES
909 Hidden Rdg Ste 300, Irving, TX 75038-3801
Tel (972) 791-1224 Founded/Ownrshp 2010
Sales 72.3MM^E EMP 3,300
SIC 8741 Hospital management
CEO: Carl Soderstrom
Pr: Clay Heighten
Pr: Frank Marshall
CEO: John Thomas
COO: Ellen Mahony
CFO: Michael A Austin
CFO: Douglas Hansen
VP: Harold Simmons
Prin: Greg Benson
Prin: Bob Gay
Prin: Dave Halbert

D-U-N-S 00-479-5036 IMP
MEDTECH PUERTO RICO INC
Parque Industrial Carr Ca Que Industrial, Juncos, PR 00777
Tel (787) 561-2200 Founded/Ownrshp 2001
Sales 228.8MM^E EMP 2,400
SIC 3841 Surgical & medical instruments
Pr: Bill Hawkins
**VP:* Manuel Santiogo

D-U-N-S 09-113-3710 IMP/EXP
MEDTRONIC
COVIDIEN
(Suby of COVIDIEN LTD.)
201 Sabanetas Ind Pk, Ponce, PR 00716-4401
Tel (787) 844-4526 Founded/Ownrshp 2007
Sales 171.1MM^E EMP 1,400
Accts Deloitte & Touche Llp San Jua
SIC 3841 Surgical instruments & apparatus
Pr: Bryan Hanson
**Treas:* Gregory Andrulonis
**VP:* Richard G Brown
**VP:* Stephen C Carey
**VP:* Charles J Dockendorff
**VP:* Lisa K Golod
**VP:* Eric C Green
**VP:* Woodrow Howell
**VP:* John W Kapples
**VP:* Geoffrey Kupferschmid
**VP:* John H Masterson
**VP:* Matthew J Nicolella
**VP:* Lawrence T Weiss
Board of Directors: John W Kapples, Geoffrey Kupferschmid, Matthew J Nicolella

D-U-N-S 78-933-8969 IMP
MEDTRONIC CARDIOVASCULAR
3576 Unocal Pl, Santa Rosa, CA 95403-1774
Tel (707) 545-1156 Founded/Ownrshp 1999
Sales 394.1MM^E EMP 5,038
SIC 3841

D-U-N-S 00-626-1481 IMP
MEDTRONIC INC
(Suby of MEDTRONIC PUBLIC LIMITED COMPANY)
710 Medtronic Pkwy, Minneapolis, MN 55432-5604
Tel (763) 514-4000 Founded/Ownrshp 2015
Sales 20.0MMM^E EMP 49,000
SIC 3845 3842 3841 Electromedical equipment; Pacemaker, cardiac; Surgical appliances & supplies; Implants, surgical; Surgical & medical instruments; Blood transfusion equipment; Catheters; Medical instruments & equipment, blood & bone work
Ch Bd: Omar Ishrak
Pr: Bob Blankemeyer
Pr: Jean-Luc Butel
**Pr:* Michael J Coyle
Pr: Steve La Neve
Pr: Steve Laneve
Pr: Katie Szyman
Pr: Tom Tefft
**CFO:* Gary L Ellis
Ofcr: McDonnell Suzanne
Ex VP: Birdsall Matthew
Ex VP: Chris O'Connell
**Ex VP:* Christopher J O'Connell
Sr VP: Steven B Kelmar
**Sr VP:* Richard Kuntz
**Sr VP:* Rick Kuntz
**Sr VP:* Bradley E Lerman
Sr VP: Scott Solano
Sr VP: Keith Williams
VP: Penny Hunt
VP: William V Murray

D-U-N-S 06-775-9258 IMP
MEDTRONIC INTERVENTIONAL VASCULAR INC
(Suby of MEDTRONIC INC) ★
37a Cherry Hill Dr, Danvers, MA 01923-2565
Tel (978) 777-0042 Founded/Ownrshp 1989
Sales 94.3MM^E EMP 750
SIC 3841 Catheters
Prin: Mark Chartier
VP: John Mazzola
Opers Mgr: Chris Farrin

D-U-N-S 84-962-6338 IMP
MEDTRONIC MINIMED INC
(Suby of MEDTRONIC INC) ★
18000 Devonshire St, Northridge, CA 91325-1219
Tel (800) 646-4633 Founded/Ownrshp 2001
Sales 734.9MM^E EMP 3,500
SIC 3845 Electromedical equipment
Pr: Catherine Szyman
**VP:* Eric P Geismar
**VP:* Ron Lund
VP: John Mastrototaro
**VP:* George J Montague
Snr Sftwr: Linda Torres
QA Dir: Franklyn Adams
Dir IT: Pam Roller
Sales Exec: Greg Meehan
Sales Exec: Stephanie Meli
Snr Mgr: Jinghua Chen

D-U-N-S 09-045-2434
MEDTRONIC PUERTO RICO INC
(Suby of MEDTRONIC INC) ★
3 Carr 149 Km, Villalba, PR 00766-3401
Tel (787) 847-3500 Founded/Ownrshp 2001
Sales 126.1MM^E EMP 1,200^E
Accts Price Waterhouse Llp
SIC 3841 Surgical & medical instruments; Ultrasonic medical cleaning equipment; Inhalation therapy equipment; Medical instruments & equipment, blood & bone work
Prin: Olga Otero

D-U-N-S 10-629-3954 IMP/EXP
MEDTRONIC SOFAMOR DANEK USA INC
(Suby of MEDTRONIC INC) ★
1800 Pyramid Pl, Memphis, TN 38132-1703
Tel (901) 396-3133 Founded/Ownrshp 1999
Sales 222.0MM^E EMP 1,000
SIC 3842 8099 Implants, surgical; Blood related health services
Ch: Omar Ishrak
**CFO:* Gary Ellis
**Ex VP:* Michael J Coyle
**Ex VP:* Christopher J Oconnell
**Sr VP:* Katie Szyman
VP: CPA Michael Burrage
VP: Stephen Oesterle
VP: Caroline Stockdale
Area Mgr: Gregory Lande
Off Mgr: Cathy Martin
Mktg Dir: David Sharp

D-U-N-S 09-082-0309
MEDTRONIC SPINE LLC (DE)
(Suby of MEDTRONIC INC) ★
1221 Crossman Ave, Sunnyvale, CA 94089-1103
Tel (408) 548-6500 Founded/Ownrshp 2008
Sales 62.0MM^E EMP 1,090
SIC 3841 Surgical & medical instruments
Pr: Bill Hawkins
CFO: Robert Jordheim
VP: Karen D Talmadge
Dir IT: Jon Redick
Prd Mgr: Carrie Wolf

D-U-N-S 17-001-5171 IMP
MEDTRONIC USA INC
(Suby of MEDTRONIC PUBLIC LIMITED COMPANY)
710 Medtronic Pkwy, Minneapolis, MN 55432-5604
Tel (763) 514-4000 Founded/Ownrshp 2015
Sales 2.5MMM^E EMP 40,000
SIC 3841 5047 Surgical & medical instruments; Medical & hospital equipment
Pr: Omar Ishrak
**CFO:* Gary Ellis
**Treas:* Linda A Harty
Sr VP: Jean L Butel
Sr VP: Janet S Fiola
Sr VP: Stephen H Mahle
Sr VP: Stephen N Oesterle
Sr VP: Scott R Ward
Sr VP: Barry W Wilson
**VP:* Keyna Skeffington
Ex Dir: Mary Maida

D-U-N-S 18-809-2456
MEDTRONIC WORLD TRADE CORP
(Suby of MEDTRONIC INC) ★
710 Medtronic Pkwy, Minneapolis, MN 55432-5603
Tel (763) 574-4000 Founded/Ownrshp 2001
Sales 221.8MM^E EMP 2,500
SIC 5047 Medical & hospital equipment
CEO: Art Collins
VP: Penny Hunt
Prin: Michael Hegland
Software D: T Ryan

D-U-N-S 83-546-5063
MEDTRONIC XOMED INC
(Suby of MEDTRONIC INC) ★
6743 Southpoint Dr N, Jacksonville, FL 32216-6218
Tel (904) 296-9600 Founded/Ownrshp 1999
Sales 124.7MM^E EMP 1,000
SIC 3842 3841 Implants, surgical; Instruments, microsurgical: except electromedical
Pr: Mark J Fletcher
VP: Jerry Bussell
VP: Mike Darragh
**VP:* Gary L Ellis
**VP:* Cameron Findlay
**VP:* Jaime A Frias
**VP:* Doug A Hoekstra
**VP:* Jacob M Paul
Exec: Mike Nicoletta
**Prin:* Bob Blankemeyer
Mktg Dir: Janis Saunier

D-U-N-S 11-414-9008 IMP
MEDURI FARMS INC
12375 Smithfield Rd, Dallas, OR 97338-9587
Tel (503) 623-0308 Founded/Ownrshp 1984
Sales 176.1MM^E EMP 500
SIC 2035 Fruits, brined
Pr: Joseph J Meduri
Treas: Cynthia Meduri
Opers Mgr: Mario Meduri

MEDVED CADILLAC
See MEDVED CHEVROLET INC

D-U-N-S 03-188-7383
MEDVED CHEVROLET INC
MEDVED CADILLAC
11001 W I 70 Frontage Rd, Wheat Ridge, CO 80033-2186
Tel (303) 421-0100 Founded/Ownrshp 1988
Sales 122.6MM^E EMP 450
SIC 5511

D-U-N-S 84-804-3790
MEDVET ASSOCIATES INC
MED VET ASSOCIATES
300 E Wilson Bridge Rd # 100, Worthington, OH 43085-2300
Tel (614) 846-5800 Founded/Ownrshp 2009
Sales 90.7MM^E EMP 696
SIC 0742 Veterinary services, specialties
Pr: Eric Schertel
CFO: Denise Badgley
Treas: John Gordon
**Chf Mktg O:* Linda Lehmkuhl
Dir Bus: Matt Bennett
Prac Mgr: Heidi Hill
Surgeon: Karl Maritato

D-U-N-S 16-942-9086 IMP
MEE APPAREL LLC
MARC ECKO COLLECTION
501 10th Ave Fl 7, New York, NY 10018-1117
Tel (917) 262-1000 Founded/Ownrshp 2000
Sales NA EMP 1,000
SIC 2329

D-U-N-S 10-250-2994
MEEK LUMBER YARD INC
MEEKS
1311 E Woodhurst Dr, Springfield, MO 65804-4282
Tel (417) 521-2801 Founded/Ownrshp 1930
Sales 84.9MM^E EMP 384
SIC 5211 Lumber & other building materials
Pr: Terry O Meek

MEEKS
See MEEK LUMBER YARD INC

D-U-N-S 06-174-1880
MEETINGS & INCENTIVES WORLDWIDE INC
10520 7 Mile Rd, Caledonia, WI 53108-9652
Tel (262) 835-6710 Founded/Ownrshp 1967
Sales 84.7MM EMP 230
Accts Scribner Cohen & Company Sc
SIC 4724 8742 7389 Travel agencies; Business planning & organizing services; Trade show arrangement
Pr: Jean Johnson
**CFO:* Tina Madden
VP: Blake McKinney
Prgrm Mgr: Lesley Bartosek

D-U-N-S 06-204-7550 EXP
■ MEGA BRANDS AMERICA INC
ROSE ART INDUSTRIES
(Suby of MEGA BRANDS INC)
3 Ada Ste 200, Irvine, CA 92618-2322
Tel (949) 727-9009 Founded/Ownrshp 2005
Sales 182.0MM^E EMP 1,600
SIC 3944 Blocks, toy
CEO: Marc Bertrand
**CFO:* Vic Bertrand
Plnt Mgr: Steven Ferris
Natl Sales: Brenda Gaudenzi
Sls Dir: Roy Brunson

MEGA PICK N SAVE
See DITTO II LLC

D-U-N-S 83-044-6089
MEGACORP LOGISTICS LLC
7040 Wrightsville Ave, Wilmington, NC 28403-3683
Tel (910) 332-0820 Founded/Ownrshp 2009
Sales 100.0MM EMP 100
SIC 4731 Freight transportation arrangement
Rgnl Mgr: Brian Simpkins
Sfty Dirs: Diane Hack
Trfc Dir: Josh Gentry
Trfc Dir: April Rosenacker
Opers Mgr: Jill New
Natl Sales: Brad Colvin
Natl Sales: Elissa Pinter
Natl Sales: Charlie Rust
Natl Sales: Corey Smith
Natl Sales: David Wiesenberg

MEGAFOODS
See CONSUMERS COOPERATIVE ASSOCIATION OF EAU CLAIRE

D-U-N-S 83-310-3208
MEGAMEX FOODS LLC
333 S Anita Dr Ste 1000, Orange, CA 92868-3318
Tel (714) 385-4500 Founded/Ownrshp 2009
Sales 698.1MM^E EMP 670^E
SIC 5141 Food brokers

MEGAPATH
See GTT COMMUNICATIONS (MP) INC

D-U-N-S 07-986-0071
MEGAPATH CLOUD CO LLC
6800 Koll Center Pkwy, Pleasanton, CA 94566-7045
Tel (925) 201-2500 Founded/Ownrshp 2015
Sales 287.1MM^E EMP 300^E
SIC 4813 Data telephone communications
CEO: Donald Craig Young
*CFO: Paul Milley
*VP: Derek Heins

D-U-N-S 03-054-2161 IMP
MEGAPATH GROUP INC (DE)
(Suby of MEGAPATH CLOUD CO LLC) ★
2510 Zanker Rd, San Jose, CA 95131-1127
Tel (408) 952-6400 Founded/Ownrshp 1996
Sales 259.1MM^E EMP 2,093^E
SIC 4813 Voice telephone communications; Data telephone communications;
CEO: D Craig Young
*COO: Brett Flinchum
COO: Catherine Hemmer
*CFO: Jeffrey Bailey
CFO: Justin Spencer
Ofcr: Eric Weiss
Ex VP: Joseph Devich
Ex VP: John McDevitt
Ex VP: Frank C Thomas Jr
*Sr VP: Douglas A Carlen
VP: Stephan Derodeff
VP: Jake Heinz
VP: SAE Song
Exec: Karen Yan

D-U-N-S 13-776-0372
MEGAPATH INC
6800 Koll Center Pkwy # 200, Pleasanton, CA 94566-7045
Tel (877) 611-6342 Founded/Ownrshp 2000
Sales 5.0MM^E EMP 1,772
SIC 4813
Ch Bd: D Craig Young
*Pr: Dan Foster
COO: James Cragg
*COO: Mark Senda
*CFO: Paul Milley
Sr Cor Off: James Craig
Ofcr: Patrick Bennett
Ex VP: David McMorrow
*Sr VP: Steve Chisholm
Sr VP: Chris Gellos
VP: Eric Beller
VP: Sean Crandall
VP: Lester Espinoza
VP: Jay Lee
VP: Tom Valaski
VP: Scott Young

MEGAPLEX
See LARRY H MILLER THEATRES INC

D-U-N-S 08-013-2420
MEGGITT (ERLANGER) LLC
(Suby of MEGGITT POLYMERS & COMPOSITES) ★
1400 Jamike Ave, Erlanger, KY 41018-1040
Tel (859) 525-8040 Founded/Ownrshp 2015
Sales 144.4MM^E EMP 562^E
SIC 3369 Aerospace castings, nonferrous: except aluminum
Pr: David Horner
Treas: Richard Ramirez
Sr VP: Nick Bitter
Sr VP: Tom Little
VP: Eric G Lardiere

D-U-N-S 60-102-0951 IMP
MEGGITT (ROCKMART) INC
MEGGITT POLYMERS & COMPOSITES
(Suby of MEGGITT PLC)
669 Goodyear Ave, Rockmart, GA 30153-2554
Tel (770) 684-7855 Founded/Ownrshp 2013
Sales 165.0MM^E EMP 975
SIC 3728 Fuel tanks, aircraft
Pr: David Horner
*Sr VP: Tom Little
VP: Velma Brooks
VP: John Mlinchek
VP: Ian Noble
VP: Arsenault Richard
VP: David Sodders
*VP: Ann Theis
VP: Greg Williams
Dir Bus: Andrew Willcox
Dir IT: Paula Tucker

D-U-N-S 36-194-1875 IMP/EXP
MEGGITT AIRCRAFT BRAKING SYSTEMS CORP
MABSC
(Suby of MEGGITT PLC)
1204 Massillon Rd, Akron, OH 44306-4188
Tel (330) 796-4400 Founded/Ownrshp 2013
Sales 364.5MM^E EMP 1,100
SIC 3728 Brakes, aircraft; Wheels, aircraft
Pr: Luke Duardogan
CFO: Mark Taylor
Treas: Edward Clear
Ofcr: Carmen Yunker
VP: Gary Rimburger
Rgnl Mgr: Mario Andreou
Genl Mgr: Paul Robinson
Genl Mgr: Tim Rogers
IT Man: Dave Allison
IT Man: Paul Brown
IT Man: Jeremy Gallagher

MEGGITT CONTROL SYSTEMS
See MEGGITT SAFETY SYSTEMS INC

MEGGITT POLYMERS & COMPOSITES
See MEGGITT-USA INC

MEGGITT POLYMERS & COMPOSITES
See MEGGITT (ROCKMART) INC

D-U-N-S 10-832-8621 IMP
MEGGITT SAFETY SYSTEMS INC
MEGGITT CONTROL SYSTEMS
(Suby of MEGGITT PLC)
1785 Voyager Ave Ste 100, Simi Valley, CA 93063-3365
Tel (805) 584-4100 Founded/Ownrshp 2006
Sales 130.9MM^E EMP 500
SIC 3699 3724 3728 Betatrons; Exhaust systems, aircraft; Engine heaters, aircraft; Aircraft parts & equipment
Pr: Dennis Hutton
Treas: Jim Tarter
Sr VP: Brian Bondarenko
Sr VP: Ken Thrasher
VP: Alistair Burns
VP: Sims Doug
VP: Lisa Lawhorn
*VP: Dolores Watai
Prgrm Mgr: Scott Snelling
Prgrm Mgr: Robert Sutton
Admn Mgr: Sandy Russo

D-U-N-S 00-765-5863 IMP/EXP
MEGGITT TRAINING SYSTEMS INC (GA)
(Suby of MEGGITT POLYMERS & COMPOSITES) ★
296 Brogdon Rd, Suwanee, GA 30024-8615
Tel (678) 288-1090 Founded/Ownrshp 1996
Sales 110.0MM EMP 354
SIC 3699 Electronic training devices
CEO: Jeffrey Murphy
Ofcr: Darren Shavers
VP Bus Dev: Kevin Dietrick
Prgrm Mgr: Todd Meyers
Prgrm Mgr: John Olson
Genl Mgr: Amy Neighbors
Genl Mgr: Carol O'Neal
IT Man: Michelle McIntyre

D-U-N-S 17-814-6171 IMP
MEGGITT-USA INC
MEGGITT POLYMERS & COMPOSITES
(Suby of MEGGITT PLC)
1955 Surveyor Ave, Simi Valley, CA 93063-3369
Tel (805) 526-5700 Founded/Ownrshp 2005
Sales 436.1MM^E EMP 700^E
SIC 3728 3829 3679 Aircraft parts & equipment; Vibration meters, analyzers & calibrators; Electronic switches
Pr: Eric Lardiere
Pr: Diane Bird
Pr: Peter Stammers
*Treas: Robert W Soukup
Sr VP: Richard Hayden
Sr VP: Stuart Parker
VP: Robert Graham
Mng Dir: Stephen Salt
Prgrm Mgr: Mike Demario
Prgrm Mgr: Chris Fitzsimmons
Dir IT: Craig Feldman
Board of Directors: Michael A Stacey, Terry Twigger

D-U-N-S 14-846-6365 IMP/EXP
MEGLOBAL AMERICAS INC
(Suby of MEGLOBAL B.V.)
2150 Town Square Pl # 750, Sugar Land, TX 77479-1465
Tel (844) 634-5622 Founded/Ownrshp 2004
Sales 600.0MM EMP 15
SIC 5169 Industrial chemicals
Pr: Ramesh Ramachandran
*CFO: Niklaus Meier
*Treas: Sumit Pathak

D-U-N-S 17-683-8084 IMP
■ **MEGTEC SYSTEMS INC**
(Suby of BABCOCK & WILCOX CO) ★
830 Prosper St, De Pere, WI 54115-3104
Tel (920) 336-5715 Founded/Ownrshp 2014
Sales 289.9MM^E EMP 800
SIC 3822 3555 3567 3823 Auto controls regulating residntl & coml environmt & applncs; Printing trades machinery; Driers & redriers, industrial process; Thermal conductivity instruments, industrial process type
Pr: Mohit Uberoi
*CFO: Greg Linn
*Treas: James P Langelotti
Sr VP: Ken Zak
VP: Harald Bauer
VP: Pat Collins
VP: Gerald Norz
VP: Rodney Schwartz
VP: William Smith
CTO: David Evans
IT Man: Chris Mueller

D-U-N-S 04-143-8185
MEHARRY MEDICAL COLLEGE
1005 Dr Db Todd Jr Blvd, Nashville, TN 37208-3501
Tel (615) 327-6111 Founded/Ownrshp 1876
Sales 130.1MM EMP 1,100
SIC 8221 Colleges universities & professional schools
CEO: A Cherrie Epps
*Pr: Wayne J Riley
Ofcr: Alex Armstrong
Assoc VP: Jacqueline Gardner
*Ex VP: Frank S Royal Jr
*Sr VP: Lamel Bandy-Neal
VP: Osei Mevs
Exec: Stephanie McClure
Dir Lab: Tultul Nayyar
Prgrm Mgr: Rana Usmani
Off Mgr: Carla Jenkins

D-U-N-S 00-319-7340 IMP/EXP
MEHERRIN AGRICULTURAL & CHEMICAL CO (NC)
HAMPTON FARMS
413 Main St, Severn, NC 27877-9901
Tel (252) 585-1744 Founded/Ownrshp 1958
Sales 502.6MM^E EMP 1,000
Accts Dixon Hughes Pllc Greensboro
SIC 5159 5191 5145 Peanuts (bulk), unroasted; Chemicals, agricultural; Nuts, salted or roasted
CEO: G Dallas Barnes Jr
*CFO: William E McKeown
*CFO: Jeff Vinson
*Treas: George M Davis III
Board of Directors: G Barnes, Guy Fisher, Elbert Long

D-U-N-S 07-990-9925
MEHLVILLE R-IX SCHOOL DISTRICT
3120 Lemay Ferry Rd, Saint Louis, MO 63125-4416
Tel (314) 892-5000 Founded/Ownrshp 1951
Sales 105.5MM EMP 1,100
Accts Daniel Jones & Associates Pc
SIC 8211 Public elementary & secondary schools; School board
MIS Dir: Paul Westbrook
Schl Brd P: Ron Fedorchak
Schl Brd P: Venki Palamand
Teacher Pr: Mark Catalana

D-U-N-S 85-914-5658
MEI TECHNOLOGIES INC
18050 Saturn Ln Ste 300, Houston, TX 77058-4502
Tel (281) 283-6200 Founded/Ownrshp 1992
Sales 97.4MM EMP 721^E
Accts Whitley Penn Llp Houston Tex
SIC 8711 8733 Engineering services; Physical research, noncommercial
CEO: Ed Muniz
*CEO: David Cazes
CFO: Karen Todd
*VP: Alicia Muniz
*VP: Stephanie Murphy
Exec: Sherry Stewart
Dir Lab: Nathan Jarmon
Dir Lab: Nolandd Talley
Dir Bus: Bob Swanson
*Ex Dir: Richard Larson
Prgrm Mgr: Wilton Burwell

D-U-N-S 96-831-0412
MEI-GSR HOLDINGS LLC
GRAND SIERRA RESORT AND CASINO
2500 2nd St, Reno, NV 89595-1200
Tel (775) 789-2000 Founded/Ownrshp 2010
Sales 59.6MM^E EMP 1,500
SIC 7011 Casino hotel
VP Sls: Jessica Baran

D-U-N-S 02-492-7196
MEIER OIL SERVICE INC
405 N Second St, Ashkum, IL 60911-6033
Tel (815) 698-2343 Founded/Ownrshp 1947
Sales 139.7MM EMP 30
SIC 5171 5172 Petroleum bulk stations; Petroleum products
Pr: Michael Meier
*Sec: Troy Meier
Genl Mgr: Dan Tonton
Off Mgr: Larry Bretvelt

D-U-N-S 00-225-1478
MEIER SUPPLY CO INC
JOHNSON CONTRLS AUTHORIZED DLR
275 Broome Corporate Pkwy, Conklin, NY 13748-1511
Tel (607) 797-7700 Founded/Ownrshp 1957
Sales 88.2MM^E EMP 135
SIC 5075 5078 Air conditioning & ventilation equipment & supplies; Refrigeration equipment & supplies
CEO: Frank A Meier Jr
*VP: Micheal Meier
Brnch Mgr: Dennis Boback
Brnch Mgr: Lee Varrenti
Sales Asso: Dave Laliberte

D-U-N-S 15-192-8884 IMP
MEIJER COMPANIES LTD
2929 Walker Ave Nw, Grand Rapids, MI 49544-9428
Tel (616) 453-6711 Founded/Ownrshp 1987
Sales 15.3MMM^E EMP 65,000
Accts Ernst & Young Llp
SIC 5311 5411 5912 Department stores, discount; Supermarkets, chain; Drug stores
V Ch Bd: Mark A Murray
*Ch Bd: Douglas Meijer
*Ch Bd: Hank Meijer
*Pr: Rick Keyes
*CFO: Dan Webb
*Sr VP: Janet Kelley
CTO: Daniel Johnson

D-U-N-S 11-831-0700 IMP
MEIJER DISTRIBUTION INC
(Suby of MEIJER INC) ★
2929 Walker Ave Nw, Grand Rapids, MI 49544-9428
Tel (616) 453-6711 Founded/Ownrshp 1999
Sales 199.7MM^E EMP 500
SIC 5141 Groceries, general line
CEO: Hank Meijer
*Pr: Mark A Murray
*Co-Ch Bd: Douglas Meijer
*Treas: Daniel E Webb
Sr VP: Jim Postma
*VP: Janet Emerson
*VP: Rick Keyes
VP: Tim Lesneski
VP: Nat Love
VP: Michael Major
VP: Tom McCall
VP: Karen Mellema
VP: Tom Nakfoor

D-U-N-S 00-695-9555 IMP/EXP
MEIJER INC (MI)
(Suby of MEIJER COMPANIES LTD) ★
2929 Walker Ave Nw, Grand Rapids, MI 49544-9428
Tel (616) 453-6711 Founded/Ownrshp 1934
Sales 15.3MMM^E EMP 65,000
Accts Ernst & Young Llp
SIC 5411 5311 Supermarkets, chain; Department stores, discount
Co-Ch Bd: Hank Meijer
*Pr: Rick Keyes
Pr: Dave Perron
COO: Fred Silva
COO: Rose Zornes
CFO: James V Walsh
*CFO: Dan Webb
*Co-Ch Bd: Douglas Meijer
Bd of Dir: Pamela Carter
Bd of Dir: Barrie Loeks
Ex VP: William S Noakes
Ex VP: Robert Riley
Sr VP: Bob Jager
*Sr VP: Janet Kelley
Sr VP: Bill Stewart
VP: Jay Bayley
VP: Dave Clark
VP: Richard Dubnick
VP: Tim Lesneski
VP: Tom Nakfoor
VP: Joann Ogee

MEINEKE DISCOUNT MUFFLERS
See DRIVEN BRANDS INC

MEISNER DATACOM
See MEISNER ELECTRIC INC OF FLORIDA

D-U-N-S 14-778-2668
MEISNER ELECTRIC INC OF FLORIDA
MEISNER DATACOM
220 Ne 1st St, Delray Beach, FL 33444-3710
Tel (561) 278-8362 Founded/Ownrshp 1983
Sales 90.5MM^E EMP 345
SIC 1731 General electrical contractor
Pr: Tim Onnen
*COO: Todd Gurne
*CFO: Douglas Hutchison
*Ex VP: Kirsten Stanley
*VP: William Kale

D-U-N-S 14-453-2025 EXP
MEL STEVENSON & ASSOCIATES INC
SPEC ROOFING CONTRACTORS SUP
2840 Roe Ln, Kansas City, KS 66103-1543
Tel (913) 262-0505 Founded/Ownrshp 1985
Sales 387.9MM^E EMP 190
SIC 5033 5082 5023 Roofing & siding materials; Siding, except wood; General construction machinery & equipment; Window covering parts & accessories
Pr: Mel Stevenson
*CFO: John Ruhlman
*Sr VP: Steve Wright
*VP: Brook Benge
*VP: Shawn Gastner
Opers Mgr: Shawn Kelly

D-U-N-S 13-976-0102 IMP
MELALEUCA INC
MELALEUCA WELLNESS COMPANY
4609 W 65th S, Idaho Falls, ID 83402-6003
Tel (208) 522-0700 Founded/Ownrshp 1985
Sales 541.7MM^E EMP 2,000
SIC 2833 5122 2844 2841 2834 Vitamins, natural or synthetic: bulk, uncompounded; Drugs, proprietaries & sundries; Toilet preparations; Soap & other detergents; Pharmaceutical preparations
Pr: Frank L Vandersloot
COO: McKay Christensen
CFO: Thomas Knutson
Treas: John Burden
VP: Brian Carmack
VP: Paul Conley
VP: Mike Connaughton
VP: Michael Sackley
Exec: Angela Cook
Ex Dir: Linda Davenport
Rgnl Mgr: Rodney Pierce

MELALEUCA WELLNESS COMPANY
See MELALEUCA INC

MELART JEWELERS
See REEDS JEWELERS INC

D-U-N-S 60-943-8015 IMP/EXP
MELISSA & DOUG INC
141 Danbury Rd, Wilton, CT 06897-4411
Tel (203) 762-4500 Founded/Ownrshp 2006
Sales 99.4MM^E EMP 200^E
SIC 5092 Toys & hobby goods & supplies
Pr: Douglas Andrew Bernstein
COO: Ron Osher
VP: Chris Myers
*Prin: Melissa Landau

D-U-N-S 07-924-3274 IMP/EXP
MELISSA & DOUG LLC
141 Danbury Rd, Wilton, CT 06897-4411
Tel (203) 762-4500 Founded/Ownrshp 2007
Sales 162.1MM^E EMP 200^E
SIC 5092 Toys & hobby goods & supplies

D-U-N-S 02-855-6058
MELLANO & CO
MELLANO ENTERPRISES
766 Wall St, Los Angeles, CA 90014-2316
Tel (213) 622-0796 Founded/Ownrshp 1975
Sales 113.4MM^E EMP 275
SIC 5193 Flowers & florists' supplies
Pr: John Mellano
*Pr: Michael Matthew Mellano
*Sec: Battista Castellano
*VP: Michelle Castellano
*VP: Bob Mellano
*VP: H Mike Mellano Sr
Exec: Jason Valenzuela
Genl Mgr: Bob Showalter
VP Sls: Bruce Brady
Sales Asso: Amy Ha
Sales Asso: Kristin Sipe

MELLANO ENTERPRISES
See MELLANO & CO

D-U-N-S 14-632-3238
MELLANOX TECHNOLOGIES INC
(Suby of MELLANOX TECHNOLOGIES, LTD.)
350 Oakmead Pkwy, Sunnyvale, CA 94085-5400
Tel (408) 970-3400 Founded/Ownrshp 1999
Sales 658.1MM EMP 876^E
SIC 3674 Semiconductors & related devices
Ch Bd: Eyal Waldman
Pr: Chris Shea
COO: Shai Cohen
CFO: Michael Gray
CFO: Merle McClendon
VP: Ron Aghazarian
VP: Mehdi Asghari

VP: Eyal Babish
VP: Aviram Gutman
VP: Yaron Haviv
VP: Michael Kagan
VP: Deirling Kevin
VP: Evelyn Landman
VP: Yuval Leader
VP: Ronnen Lovinger
VP: Henning Lysdal
VP: Ayelet Margalit-Ilovich
VP: Yiftah Shahar
VP: Marc Sultzbaugh
Board of Directors: Dov Baharav, Glenda Dorchak, Irwin Federman, Thomas Weatherford

MELLING AUTOMOTIVE PRODUCTS
See MELLING TOOL CO

D-U-N-S 00-537-5217 IMP/EXP
MELLING TOOL CO (MI)
MELLING AUTOMOTIVE PRODUCTS
2620 Saradan Dr, Jackson, MI 49202-1258
Tel (517) 787-8172 Founded/Ownrshp 1956
Sales 267.6MM[E] EMP 600
SIC 3451 3714 3625 3568 3561 3494 Screw machine products; Oil pump, motor vehicle; Relays & industrial controls; Power transmission equipment; Pumps & pumping equipment; Valves & pipe fittings
Pr: Mark Melling
VP: Pat Richardson
Ql Cn Mgr: Michelle Kinch
VP Sls: Thomas Trosin

D-U-N-S 79-100-7516
■ **MELLON TRUST OF NEW ENGLAND NA**
(Suby of BNY MELLON) ★
1 Boston Pl Fl 8, Boston, MA 02108-4407
Tel (617) 722-7000 Founded/Ownrshp 2006
Sales 868.3MM EMP 1,960
SIC 6733 Trusts
Prin: Margerett Harrison

D-U-N-S 10-278-6019
MELLOY BROTHERS ENTERPRISES INC
MELLOY PARTS
7707 Lomas Blvd Ne, Albuquerque, NM 87110-7413
Tel (505) 265-8721 Founded/Ownrshp 1975
Sales 92.1MM[E] EMP 332[E]
SIC 5511 Automobiles, new & used; Pickups, new & used
Pr: Robert E Melloy
CFO: Bob Hayes
*VP: Patrick C Melloy

MELLOY PARTS
See MELLOY BROTHERS ENTERPRISES INC

MELMARK HOME
See MELMARK INC

D-U-N-S 07-948-1842
MELMARK INC
MELMARK HOME
2600 Wayland Rd, Berwyn, PA 19312-2307
Tel (610) 353-1726 Founded/Ownrshp 1966
Sales 80.8MM EMP 1,000[E]
Accts Rsm Us Llp Blue Bell Pennsyl
SIC 8211 8361 School for the retarded; School for physically handicapped; Self-help group home
Pr: Joanne Gillis-Donovan
*COO: George P Linke Jr
*CFO: Delyn Byerly
*Ch: Robert Marcus
*Treas: Michael Bradley
Ex VP: Peter Troy
*VP: Peter J Troy
*VP: Joseph Zakrzewski
Off Mgr: Monica Batchelor
CTO: Brian Haney
Mktg Dir: Michelle Bradsher

D-U-N-S 80-917-8833 IMP
MELODY FOODS INC
30777 Northwestern Hwy # 300, Farmington Hills, MI 48334-2594
Tel (248) 851-6990 Founded/Ownrshp 1993
Sales 130.0MM[E] EMP 509
Accts Follmer Rudzewicz Plc Southfi
SIC 5143 2026 5149 5145 Milk & cream, fluid; Ice cream & ices; Yogurt; Milk processing (pasteurizing, homogenizing, bottling); Juices; Snack foods
Prin: Michael J George
*Treas: Thomas A George
*VP: Robert T George

D-U-N-S 62-197-9723 IMP
MELR INC
(Suby of ONE JEANSWEAR) ★
250 Rittenhouse Cir, Bristol, PA 19007-1616
Tel (215) 785-4000 Founded/Ownrshp 2014
Sales 34.3MM[E] EMP 1,500
SIC 5621 Ready-to-wear apparel, women's
Ch Bd: Sidney Kimmel
*Pr: Howard Buerkle
*Treas: Wesley Card
VP: Patrick M Farrell
*VP: Herbert J Goodfriend

D-U-N-S 79-130-3592
MELROSE US 3 LLC
(Suby of MELROSE PLC)
2600 S Custer Ave, Wichita, KS 67217-1324
Tel (859) 887-6390 Founded/Ownrshp 2005
Sales 63.4MM[E] EMP 1,193
SIC 3089

D-U-N-S 03-448-7751
MELTON MANAGEMENT INC
MCDONALD'S
6342 Lantana Rd, Lake Worth, FL 33463-6606
Tel (561) 641-6717 Founded/Ownrshp 1986
Sales 28.4MM[E] EMP 1,400
SIC 5812 Fast-food restaurant, chain
Pr: Keith Melton

D-U-N-S 00-686-3419
MELTON TRUCK LINES INC (OK)
808 N 161st East Ave, Tulsa, OK 74116-4115
Tel (918) 234-1000 Founded/Ownrshp 1954
Sales 93.6MM[E] EMP 700
SIC 4213 Trucking, except local
Pr: Bob Peterson
*CFO: Robert Ragan
*Sr VP: Russ Elliott
*Sr VP: Randy Rhines
*Sr VP: Jeff Robinson
*Sr VP: Dan Taylor
*VP: Angie Buchanan
VP: Lawrence Daniels
*VP: Mike Dargel
*VP: Brice Peters
Board of Directors: Kyle Burchart, Lisa Mason, Elizabeth G Peterson, Jan Stone

D-U-N-S 07-779-4758
MELWOOD HORTICULTURAL TRAINING CENTER INC
5606 Dower House Rd, Upper Marlboro, MD 20772-3604
Tel (301) 599-8000 Founded/Ownrshp 1963
Sales 83.9MM EMP 1,800
Accts Rsm Us Llp Gaithersburg Md
SIC 8331 8322 Vocational training agency; Work experience center; Social services for the handicapped
Pr: Earl Copus Jr
*COO: Mary Buszuwski
Treas: George Watkins
VP: Richard Gallaher
VP: Scott Gibson
VP: Deborah Goins
VP: Robert Grom
VP: Jermaine Hunter
Prin: Douglas H Lemmonds
Dir IT: Chad Hebner
Pgrm Dir: James Akwarandu

D-U-N-S 07-839-1850
MELWOOD-WERNER HOUSING INC
6188 Oxon Hill Rd, Oxon Hill, MD 20745-3113
Tel (301) 982-6207 Founded/Ownrshp 2012
Sales 194.6M EMP 1,200
Accts Mcgladrey Llp Gaithersburg M
SIC 7021 Lodging house, except organization
CEO: Dana Stebbins
*Treas: Ronald Stubblefield
*VP: Jonathon Rondeau
*Prin: Donna Hurley

MEM CORPORATE
See MISSOURI EMPLOYERS MUTUAL INSURANCE CO

MEMBER WORKS
See VERTRUE LLC

D-U-N-S 09-788-1064
MEMBERS 1ST FEDERAL CREDIT UNION (PA)
5000 Louise Dr, Mechanicsburg, PA 17055-4899
Tel (717) 697-1161 Founded/Ownrshp 1950
Sales NA EMP 900
SIC 6061 Federal credit unions
CEO: Bob Marquette
*Ch Bd: Jackie Eakin
*Pr: Robert Marquette
Pr: Omar Shute
*V Ch Bd: Michael Whiteman
Ofcr: Melany Radel
*Ex VP: Craig Golfieri
*Ex VP: Kevin Lee
*Ex VP: Stephen Murray
Sr VP: Jason A Hicks
VP: Eric Bush
VP: Robb Keith
VP: Dave Kimmel
VP: Glenn Rambler

MEMBRANA - CHARLOTTE
See CELGARD LLC

D-U-N-S 92-677-5180
■ **MEMC SOUTHWEST INC**
(Suby of SUNEDISON INC) ★
6416 S Us Highway 75, Sherman, TX 75090-9493
Tel (903) 891-5000 Founded/Ownrshp 1995
Sales 95.3MM[E] EMP 1,400
SIC 3674 Silicon wafers, chemically doped
Pr: Jim Lang

MEMIC
See MAINE EMPLOYERS MUTUAL INSURANCE CO

MEMORIAL CAMPUS
See COLUMBIA UNITED PROVIDERS INC

MEMORIAL CARE MEDICAL CENTERS
See SADDLEBACK MEMORIAL MEDICAL CENTER

MEMORIAL CARE MEDICAL CENTERS
See MEMORIAL HEALTH SERVICES

MEMORIAL CENTER
See BAKERSFIELD MEMORIAL HOSPITAL

MEMORIAL HEALTH
See MEMORIAL HOSPITAL JACKSONVILLE INC

D-U-N-S 06-983-3697
MEMORIAL HEALTH CARE INC
GIFT SHOP
826 W King St, Owosso, MI 48867-2120
Tel (989) 725-8101 Founded/Ownrshp 1919
Sales 88.0MM EMP 71[E]
SIC 8641 5947 Civic social & fraternal associations; Gift shop
CEO: Brian L Long
Dir Lab: Margaret Noth
Telecom Mg: Todd Wyzynajtys
Opers Supe: Lisa Hasyn
Pathlgst: Wiemin Liu
Doctor: Michael Kramer
Doctor: Michael Schmidt
Nrsg Dir: Dean Schultz
Pgrm Dir: Angela Partridge

D-U-N-S 11-916-5301
MEMORIAL HEALTH CARE SYSTEM FOUNDATION INC
CHI MEMORIAL HOSPITAL
(Suby of CHI) ★
2525 De Sales Ave, Chattanooga, TN 37404
Tel (423) 495-2525 Founded/Ownrshp 1985
Sales 1.7MM EMP 5,000
Accts Lb Catholic Health Initiatives
SIC 8742 Hospital & health services consultant
CEO: Ruth Brinkley
*Pr: Debra L Moore
*COO: Deborah Moore
*VP: Michael Sutton

D-U-N-S 00-744-3109
MEMORIAL HEALTH CARE SYSTEM INC
CHI
(Suby of CHI) ★
2525 Desales Ave, Chattanooga, TN 37404-1161
Tel (423) 495-2525 Founded/Ownrshp 1985
Sales 527.1MM EMP 8,800
Accts Catholic Health Initiatives E
SIC 8082 Home health care services
Pr: James M Hobson
*Pr: Shawn Morrow
*CFO: Cheryl A Sadro
*Sr VP: Debra L Moore
*VP: Leigh Bertholf
*VP: Diona Brown
Off Mgr: Liz Browning

D-U-N-S 96-670-6280
MEMORIAL HEALTH INC
MEMORIAL UNIVERSITY MED CTR
4700 Waters Ave, Savannah, GA 31404-6220
Tel (912) 350-8000 Founded/Ownrshp 1955
Sales 42.1MM EMP 4,500
Accts Dixon Hughes Goodman Llp Ashe
SIC 8062 General medical & surgical hospitals
Pr: Margaret Gill
CFO: Suzanne Heck
Mktg Dir: Becky Bowden

D-U-N-S 60-208-4118
MEMORIAL HEALTH SERVICES
MEMORIAL CARE MEDICAL CENTERS
17360 Brookhurst St # 160, Fountain Valley, CA 92708-8003
Tel (714) 377-6748 Founded/Ownrshp 1937
Sales 215.9MM EMP 6,000[E]
Accts Pricewaterhousecoopers Llp L
SIC 8062 General medical & surgical hospitals
Pr: Barry Arbuckle
*CFO: Aaron Coley
*CFO: Karen Testman
*Treas: Rick Graniere
Ofcr: Wendy Dorchester
Sr VP: Judy Fix
VP: Regina Berman
VP: Devon Dougherty
VP: Deborah Eagle
VP: John Metcalf
VP: Gerald Russell
VP: Cheryl Sadro
VP: Wayne Sass
VP: Khalid Sheikh

D-U-N-S 07-619-4356
MEMORIAL HEALTH SERVICES - UNIVERSITY OF CALIFORNIA AT IRVINE CENTER FOR HEALTH EDUCATION
2801 Atlantic Ave, Long Beach, CA 90806-1701
Tel (562) 933-2000 Founded/Ownrshp 1974
Sales 324.0MM[E] EMP 10,000[E]
SIC 8062 8741 General medical & surgical hospitals; Management services
CEO: Edward Quilligan
*Pr: Diana Hendel
*Treas: Darrel Brownell
Sr VP: Wendy Dorchester
Dir IT: Ron Morte
HC Dir: Irene Rosales

MEMORIAL HEALTH SYSTEM
See MEMORIAL HOSPITAL CORP

D-U-N-S 14-840-1813
MEMORIAL HEALTH SYSTEM
701 N 1st St, Springfield, IL 62781-0001
Tel (217) 788-3000 Founded/Ownrshp 1981
Sales 84.9MM EMP 2,400[E]
SIC 8741 8062 Hospital management; General medical & surgical hospitals
Pr: Robert T Clarke
CEO: Edgar J Curtis
CFO: Barb Sullivan
Chf Mktg O: Robert Vautrain
VP: Andrea Ferrero-Violet
VP: Rajesh Govindaiah
Dir Rx: Alisa Groesch
Dir Bus: Drew Snyder
Adm Dir: Rebecca Anderson
Dir IT: Anthony Cogan
Dir IT: Steve Huffman

D-U-N-S 05-109-8184
MEMORIAL HEALTH SYSTEM OF EAST TEXAS
CHI ST. LUKE'S HEALTH MEMORIAL
1201 W Frank Ave, Lufkin, TX 75904-3357
Tel (936) 634-8111 Founded/Ownrshp 1944
Sales 121.8MM EMP 940
SIC 8062 General medical & surgical hospitals
Pr: Bryant H Krenek Jr
*Pr: Gary Looper
*COO: Peggy Mortensen
*CFO: Ken Miller
Treas: Floyd Dickens
Ex VP: Don Morris
VP: John Angstadt
VP: Tyane Dietz
*VP: Rick Hefner
VP: Mike Taylor
Exec: Melinda New
Dir Risk M: Cindi Reynolds
Dir Rx: Eric Ip

D-U-N-S 02-171-6881
MEMORIAL HEALTH SYSTEMS INC
FLORIDA HOSPITAL MEM MED CTR
301 Memorial Medical Pkwy, Daytona Beach, FL 32117-5167
Tel (386) 231-6000 Founded/Ownrshp 1961
Sales 49.1MM EMP 1,500
SIC 8062 General medical & surgical hospitals
Pr: Daryl Tol
*COO: Darwinda Copeland
*CFO: Debbie Thomas
*Chf Mktg O: Michelle Goeb-Burkett
Ofcr: Magie Epting
VP: Michele G Burkett
Nurse Mgr: Denise Duty
Nurse Mgr: Denise Halligan
CIO: Ruth Caldwell

D-U-N-S 11-075-2359
MEMORIAL HEALTH UNIVERSITY MEDICAL CENTER INC
4700 Waters Ave, Savannah, GA 31404-6283
Tel (912) 350-8000 Founded/Ownrshp 1984
Sales 466.1MM EMP 5,000
SIC 8062 8011 General medical & surgical hospitals; Offices & clinics of medical doctors
Pr: Magaret Gill
*COO: Mary Chatman
*Ch: J Curtis Lewis
*Treas: J Harry Haslam Jr
Treas: Karen B Panneil
Sr VP: David Byck
*Sr VP: Ramon V Meguiar
Sr VP: Don E Tomberlin
*VP: Ira P Berman
*VP: Rebecca Keightley
VP: Patty Lavely
*VP: Phoenicia Miracle
*VP: Robert M Tynan
Dir Rad: Barbara Brown

MEMORIAL HERMANN
See NORTHEAST HOSPITAL FOUNDATION

MEMORIAL HERMANN BAPTIST BEAUM
See BAPTIST HOSPITALS OF SOUTHEAST TEXAS

D-U-N-S 03-499-7192
MEMORIAL HERMANN BAPTIST BELMONT
MEMORIAL HERMANN BPTIST ORNGE
608 Strickland Dr, Orange, TX 77630-4717
Tel (409) 883-9361 Founded/Ownrshp 2001
Sales 47.2MM[E] EMP 1,600
SIC 8062 General medical & surgical hospitals
CEO: David Pirmer

D-U-N-S 01-079-1515
MEMORIAL HERMANN BAPTIST HOSPITAL
BAPTISTAL HOSPITAL OF SE TEXAS
3080 College St, Beaumont, TX 77701-4606
Tel (409) 212-5000 Founded/Ownrshp 1990
Sales 129.7MM[E] EMP 1,700
SIC 8062 General medical & surgical hospitals
CEO: David Parmer
CFO: Carol Moreen
CIO: William Toon
QA Dir: Julia Hyett
Telecom Mg: Jerry Frye
HC Dir: Betty Bullard

MEMORIAL HERMANN BPTIST ORNGE
See MEMORIAL HERMANN BAPTIST BELMONT

D-U-N-S 07-418-7949
MEMORIAL HERMANN HEALTH SYSTEM
MEMORIAL HERMANN MEM CY HOSP
(Suby of MEMORIAL HERMANN HEALTHCARE SYSTEM) ★
909 Frostwood Dr Fl 2, Houston, TX 77024-2307
Tel (713) 242-3000 Founded/Ownrshp 1982
Sales 3.7MM EMP 14,000
Accts Ernst & Young Llp Us Columbus
SIC 8062 8093 General medical & surgical hospitals; Specialty outpatient clinics
CEO: Daniel Styf
*COO: Chuck Stokes
CFO: Nancy Bennett
*CFO: Dennis Laraway
Dir Rad: Alla Vargo
IT Man: Joe Dickson
Mtls Mgr: Karen Cooper
Orthpdst: Carl L Cannon
Orthpdst: Brian T Chimenti
Orthpdst: Thomas O Clantn
Orthpdst: Plinio A Clder
Board of Directors: Roland Garcia Jr, James J Postl, Charlotte B Alexander, J Kevin Giglio, Stephen H Pouns, Joseph R Cali, David J Graham, George W Strake III, William J Campbell, Peter Huntsman, Willoughby C Williams Jr, Deborah M Cannon, Ralph D McBride, Daniel J Wolterman, Clarence P Cazalot Jr, Scott B McClelland, Robert G Croyle, Scott J McLean, William H Easter III, Gasper Mir III, Jason B Few, James R Montague, William F Galtney Jr, Melinda H Perrin

D-U-N-S 10-267-4629 IMP
MEMORIAL HERMANN HEALTHCARE SYSTEM
929 Gessner Rd, Houston, TX 77024-2515
Tel (713) 338-5555 Founded/Ownrshp 1982
Sales 14.6MMM[E] EMP 24,000
SIC 8059 8062 Convalescent home; General medical & surgical hospitals
Prin: Benjamin K Chu
Chf Rad: Terrance Oconner
*Pr: Benjamin K Chu
Pr: Emily Handwerk
Pr: Vicki Pellenz
*COO: Dale St Arnold
COO: Charles D Stokes
CFO: Carroll Aulbaugh
*CFO: Stacey Bevil
CFO: John Gay
CFO: Kevin Lovinggood
CFO: Larry Smith
*Treas: Carrol E Aubaugh
Chf Mktg O: Michael Davidson
Assoc VP: Perry Flowers

Assoc VP: James Polfreman
**VP:* David Bradshaw
VP: Frank Brown
VP: Ramona Cahn
VP: George Thomason
Exec: Robert Blake
Board of Directors: Benjamin K Chu

D-U-N-S 79-134-1832
MEMORIAL HERMANN KATY HOSPITAL
(*Suby of* MEMORIAL HERMANN MEM CY HOSP) ★
23900 Katy Fwy, Katy, TX 77494-1323
Tel (281) 644-7000 *Founded/Ownrshp* 1981
Sales 202.1MM *EMP* 275^E
SIC 8062 General medical & surgical hospitals
Pr: Jim Parisi
**COO:* John Kueven
CFO: Kevin Lovingood
Dir Lab: Kimmy Brown
Off Admin: Leilani Bell
DP Dir: Tina Harbert

D-U-N-S 96-961-0976
MEMORIAL HERMANN MEDICAL GROUP
909 Frostwood Dr Fl 2, Houston, TX 77024-2307
Tel (713) 448-5555 *Founded/Ownrshp* 2012
Sales 89.6MM *EMP* 50^E
SIC 8099 Health screening service
Prin: James A Faucett
CFO: Janet Smith

MEMORIAL HERMANN MEM CY HOSP
See MEMORIAL HERMANN HEALTH SYSTEM

MEMORIAL HERMANN MEMORIAL CITY
See INSTITUTE FOR REHABILITATION & RESEARCH

D-U-N-S 79-134-2319
MEMORIAL HERMANN TEXAS MEDICAL
(*Suby of* MEMORIAL HERMANN HEALTHCARE SYSTEM) ★
6411 Fannin St, Houston, TX 77030-1501
Tel (713) 704-4000 *Founded/Ownrshp* 2007
Sales 1.3MMM *EMP* 1
SIC 8062 General medical & surgical hospitals
CEO: Craig Cordola
Dir Risk M: Keith Askew
Dir Risk M: Steve Hartranft
Dir Rad: Jamile Y Alexander
Dir Rad: Jim Johnson
Dir Rx: Brian E Gulbis
Doctor: Chuck Cox MD

MEMORIAL HOSP & HLTH CARE CTR
See MEMORIAL HOSPITAL AND HEALTH CARE CENTER

MEMORIAL HOSPITAL
See YORK PENNSYLVANIA HOSPITAL CO LLC

MEMORIAL HOSPITAL
See PROTESTANT MEMORIAL MEDICAL CENTER INC

MEMORIAL HOSPITAL
See BEACON MEDICAL GROUP INC

D-U-N-S 06-052-2653
MEMORIAL HOSPITAL
ALBANY MEMORIAL HOSPITAL
600 Northern Blvd, Albany, NY 12204-1083
Tel (518) 471-3221 *Founded/Ownrshp* 1868
Sales 90.0MM *EMP* 1,110
Accts Pricewaterhousecooper Llp
SIC 8062 General medical & surgical hospitals
CEO: Norman Dascher
Chf Rad: Michael Gabor
COO: Karen Tossey
Exec: Norm Dasher
Dir Lab: Juan Patz
Chf Nrs Of: Margaret Sorenson
CIO: Robert Duthe
CIO: Lou Spychalski
Doctor: Hasan Atalay
Doctor: Ian Santoro
Doctor: Parag Shah

D-U-N-S 06-983-3523
MEMORIAL HOSPITAL
826 W King St, Owosso, MI 48867-2120
Tel (989) 723-5211 *Founded/Ownrshp* 1919
Sales 115.2MM *EMP* 1,000
Accts Plante & Moran Pllc East Lans
SIC 8062 General medical & surgical hospitals
Pr: James Full
**CFO:* Brian Long
VP: Tom Ogg
VP: Shirley Tate-Gibson
Dir Lab: Margaret Noth
Ex Dir: Lynda Beaton
Surgeon: Daniel Williams

D-U-N-S 06-985-2580
MEMORIAL HOSPITAL
MEMORIAL HOSPITAL RHODE ISLAND
(*Suby of* CARE NEW ENGLAND HEALTH SYSTEM INC) ★
111 Brewster St, Pawtucket, RI 02860-4474
Tel (401) 729-2000 *Founded/Ownrshp* 2013
Sales 133.5MM *EMP* 1,400
SIC 8062 6513 General medical & surgical hospitals; Apartment building operators
Pr: James Sanale MD
Trst Ofcr: William Kapos
VP: Robert Ackermann
VP: James Burke
VP: Shelly McDonald
VP: Thomas L Ross
VP: Michael Ryan
VP: Judy Van Tilburg
Genl Mgr: Nancy Lapham
Off Mgr: Gail Armstrong
QA Dir: Christine Rodrigues

D-U-N-S 86-859-9317
MEMORIAL HOSPITAL - WEST VOLUSIA INC
FLORIDA HOSPITAL DELAND
(*Suby of* ADVENTST HLTH SYSTM SUNBELT H) ★
701 W Plymouth Ave, Deland, FL 32720-3291
Tel (386) 943-4522 *Founded/Ownrshp* 1962
Sales 146.0MM *EMP* 1,000^E
SIC 8062 General medical & surgical hospitals
CEO: Tim Cook
Pr: Nancy Clark
**Pr:* Ed Noseworthy
**COO:* Hector De Jesus
**CFO:* Nigel Hinds
CFO: Debbie Thomas
Dir Teleco: Roy M Laughlin
Dir Rad: Wesley Harden
Dir Rx: David Moore
MIS Dir: Velma Songy
Opers Mgr: Saul Hollie

D-U-N-S 07-785-6029 EXP
MEMORIAL HOSPITAL AND HEALTH CARE CENTER
MEMORIAL HOSP & HLTH CARE CTR
800 W 9th St, Jasper, IN 47546-2514
Tel (812) 482-2345 *Founded/Ownrshp* 1951
Sales 191.1MM *EMP* 950
Accts Blue & Co Llc Indianapolis I
SIC 8062 General medical & surgical hospitals
Pr: Raymond W Snowden
COO: John Dillon
Bd of Dir: Adrian Davis
VP: Gary Light
VP: Ronald Salyk
Chf Nrs Of: Amy Weisman
IT Man: Sean Kluemper
Mktg Dir: Melanie Powell
Pharmcst: Jama Wallace
Cert Phar: Daniel Jenkins
Diag Rad: Timothy M McClure

MEMORIAL HOSPITAL AND MEDICAL
See MIDLAND COUNTY HOSPITAL DISTRICT

D-U-N-S 07-947-5109
MEMORIAL HOSPITAL AUXILIARY INC
4500 13th St, Gulfport, MS 39501-2515
Tel (228) 867-4000 *Founded/Ownrshp* 1946
Sales 399.3MM^E *EMP* 2,500
Accts Scott Niolet Pass Christian
SIC 8062 General medical & surgical hospitals
CEO: Gary G Marchand
**COO:* Kent Nicaud
**CFO:* Jennifer Dumal
**Ch:* Myrtis Franke
**Sec:* Edward O Reid
Ofcr: Linda Hebert
**VP:* Fred Gargiulo
VP: Melody Griffith
Mktg Mgr: Janet Stuart
Surgeon: Kristine Carter
Pharmcst: Harless Barber

MEMORIAL HOSPITAL CARBONDALE
See SOUTHERN ILLINOIS HOSPITAL SERVICES

D-U-N-S 07-576-1783
MEMORIAL HOSPITAL CORP
MEMORIAL HEALTH SYSTEM
1400 E Boulder St, Colorado Springs, CO 80909-5599
Tel (719) 365-5000 *Founded/Ownrshp* 1998
Sales 612.0MM *EMP* 2,438
SIC 8062 General medical & surgical hospitals
CEO: Mike Scialdone
COO: Bob Brazil
**COO:* Bill Mohon
CFO: Gary Flansburg
CFO: Elgin Glanzer
Treas: Margaret Carmack
VP: Oda Roozeboom
VP: Michael Sutton
VP: Mary Yantis
Dir Rx: Jim Lewis
Nurse Mgr: Cheryl Tate

D-U-N-S 61-007-3702
MEMORIAL HOSPITAL FLAGLER INC
FLORIDA HOSPITAL FLAGLER
60 Memorial Medical Pkwy, Palm Coast, FL 32164-5980
Tel (386) 586-2000 *Founded/Ownrshp* 1989
Sales 173.2MM *EMP* 218
SIC 8062 General medical & surgical hospitals
Pr: David Ottati
CFO: France Crunk
**CFO:* Valerie Ziesmer
**VP:* Joanne King
CIO: Mike Olsen
Mktg Dir: Lauren Dye
Mktg Dir: Lindsay Rew
Pathlgst: Karen Buchanan
Surgeon: Robert Martin
Pharmcst: Guy Wagner

D-U-N-S 07-682-8409
MEMORIAL HOSPITAL FOR CANCER AND ALLIED DISEASES
1275 York Ave, New York, NY 10065-6094
Tel (212) 639-2000 *Founded/Ownrshp* 1884
Sales 2.0MMM *EMP* 9,269
SIC 8069 Cancer hospital
CEO: Craig B Thompson MD
Pathlgst: Alice Ho

D-U-N-S 06-588-8422
■ **MEMORIAL HOSPITAL JACKSONVILLE INC**
MEMORIAL HEALTH
(*Suby of* HOSPITAL COPORATION OF AMERICA) ★
3625 University Blvd S, Jacksonville, FL 32216-4207
Tel (904) 399-6111 *Founded/Ownrshp* 1995
Sales 265.7MM^E *EMP* 1,380
SIC 8062 General medical & surgical hospitals
CEO: James O'Loughlin
Dir Rad: Mary Alderman
Dir Rad: Shannon Beardsley
Dir Rad: Michael J Borbely
Dir Rad: Richard Buxton
Dir Rad: James Caraway
Dir Rad: Timothy B Daniel
Dir Rx: Adrianne Schmidt
Off Mgr: Nancy Wilson
Opers Mgr: Sharon Viens
Pr Dir: Peter Moberg

D-U-N-S 07-491-9259
MEMORIAL HOSPITAL OF EASTON MD INC
219 S Washington St, Easton, MD 21601-2996
Tel (410) 822-1000 *Founded/Ownrshp* 1982
Sales 107.0MM^E *EMP* 1,241
SIC 8062 General medical & surgical hospitals
Pr: Joseph Ross
V Ch: Charles Lea Jr
Dir Soc: Lee Lewis
Nurse Mgr: Kim Billingslea
Dir QC: Donna Prahal
Ansthlgy: Kevin J Nebab
Diag Rad: David P Smith
HC Dir: Susan Walbridge

MEMORIAL HOSPITAL OF GARDENA
See GARDENA HOSPITAL LP

D-U-N-S 06-664-6183
MEMORIAL HOSPITAL OF GARDENA
(*Suby of* AVANTI HEALTH SYSTEM LLC) ★
4060 Woody Blvd, Los Angeles, CA 90023
Tel (323) 268-5514 *Founded/Ownrshp* 1960
Sales 117.0MM *EMP* 400
SIC 8062 General medical & surgical hospitals
CEO: Araceli Lonergan
**CFO:* Daniel Heckathorne
VP: Hector Hernandez
Pharmcst: Gary Fong
Pharmcst: Linh Nguyen
HC Dir: Tessie Meza

D-U-N-S 04-072-6275
MEMORIAL HOSPITAL OF LARAMIE COUNTY
CHEYENNE REGIONAL MEDICAL CTR
214 E 23rd St, Cheyenne, WY 82001-3748
Tel (307) 633-7667 *Founded/Ownrshp* 1919
Sales 279.4MM *EMP* 1,270
SIC 8062 Hospital, AMA approved residency
CEO: John Lucas MD
**CFO:* Kerry Warburton
Trst: Harmon Davis
Ofcr: Fran Cadez
Ofcr: Aimee Dendrinos
**VP:* Ashutosh Goel
VP: Debbie Nunley
VP: Kevin Stansbury
Exec: Sylvia Hackl
Dir Rx: Sarah A Blkely
Dir Rx: Cheyenne Cent
Dir Rx: Timothy Steffen

D-U-N-S 06-470-1261 IMP
MEMORIAL HOSPITAL OF SOUTH BEND INC
(*Suby of* MEMORIAL HOSPITAL SOUTH BEND) ★
615 N Michigan St, South Bend, IN 46601-1087
Tel (574) 647-7751 *Founded/Ownrshp* 2013
Sales 486.7MM *EMP* 158
SIC 8062 General medical & surgical hospitals; Hospital, medical school affiliated with nursing & residency
Pr: Kreg Gruber
Dir Rad: Diana Custer
Doctor: Michael J Hall
Doctor: Keith H Sherry

D-U-N-S 07-503-8703
MEMORIAL HOSPITAL OF UNION COUNTY
500 London Ave, Marysville, OH 43040-1594
Tel (937) 644-6115 *Founded/Ownrshp* 1952
Sales 90.6MM *EMP* 800
SIC 8062 Hospital, affiliated with AMA residency
Ch: Dennis Stone
**CEO:* Olas A Hubbs
COO: Laurie Whittington
**CFO:* Jeff Ehlers
Ex VP: Spence Fisher
VP: John R Evans
VP: Victor Trianfo
Exec: Julie Hamilton
Dir Lab: Eric Keifer
Dir Rad: Mareva Page
Dir Rx: Britt Cummins

MEMORIAL HOSPITAL RHODE ISLAND
See MEMORIAL HOSPITAL

MEMORIAL HOSPITAL SOUTH BEND
See BEACON HEALTH SYSTEM INC

MEMORIAL HOSPITAL WEST
See SOUTH BROWARD HOSPITAL DISTRICT

MEMORIAL MEDICAL CENTER
See SUTTER CENTRAL VALLEY HOSPITALS

MEMORIAL MEDICAL CENTER
See BON SECOURS-MEMORIAL REGIONAL MEDICAL CENTER INC

MEMORIAL MEDICAL CENTER
See PHC-LAS CRUCES INC

D-U-N-S 07-562-0179
MEMORIAL MEDICAL CENTER
701 N 1st St, Springfield, IL 62781-0001
Tel (217) 788-3000 *Founded/Ownrshp* 1981
Sales 699.2MM *EMP* 2,849
Accts Ernst & Young Llp St Louis
SIC 8062 General medical & surgical hospitals
Pr: Edgar J Curtis
**COO:* Douglas Rahn
CFO: Tim Schmidt
Ex VP: Rohn Douglas
VP: David C Chapman
VP: Kevin England
VP: Marsha A Prater
Dir Risk M: Barb Kline
Dir Rx: Les Ono
Adm Dir: Majorie Calvetti
CIO: David Graham

D-U-N-S 07-508-6520
MEMORIAL MEDICAL CENTER INC
2450 S Telshor Blvd, Las Cruces, NM 88011-5076
Tel (575) 522-8641 *Founded/Ownrshp* 1996
Sales 241.8MM *EMP* 1,450
SIC 8062

D-U-N-S 07-987-5249
MEMORIAL MEDICAL CENTER INC
2450 S Telshor Blvd, Las Cruces, NM 88011-5076
Tel (575) 522-8641 *Founded/Ownrshp* 2014
Sales 225.5MM *EMP* 36^E
Accts Kriegel Gray Shaw & Co Pc Las
SIC 8011 Medical centers
Prin: Brad McGrath
COO: Phil Rivera
Chf Nrs Of: Ann Debooy
CIO: Burt Stevens
Pathlgst: Margarita Topalovski
Plas Surg: Ravi Gorav
HC Dir: Sandra Saunders

D-U-N-S 07-456-4469
MEMORIAL MEDICAL CENTER-WOODSTOCK
3701 Doty Rd, Woodstock, IL 60098-7509
Tel (815) 334-3880 *Founded/Ownrshp* 1991
Sales 99.3MM^E *EMP* 3,000
SIC 8062 8051 General medical & surgical hospitals; Skilled nursing care facilities
CEO: Mike Eesley
Anesthlgy: Younan H Hamwi

D-U-N-S 78-618-6135
MEMORIAL NORTH PARK HOSPITAL
2151 Hamill Rd, Hixson, TN 37343-4028
Tel (423) 495-7100 *Founded/Ownrshp* 2006
Sales 74.0MM^E *EMP* 1,200^E
SIC 8062 General medical & surgical hospitals
Prin: Jim Hobson
COO: Jackie Jackson
VP: Lisa McCluskey
Pr Dir: Lisa M Culsky
Nrsg Dir: Diona Brown

D-U-N-S 96-912-9605
▲ **MEMORIAL PRODUCTION PARTNERS LP**
500 Dallas St Ste 1800, Houston, TX 77002-2067
Tel (713) 588-8300 *Founded/Ownrshp* 2011
Sales 358.1MM *EMP* 505^E
Accts Kpmg Llp Houston Texas
Tkr Sym MEMP *Exch* NGS
SIC 1311 Crude petroleum & natural gas production
Genl Pt: William J Scarff
Genl Pt: Memorial P LLC
Ch Bd: John A Weinzierl
COO: Larry R Forney
VP: Gregory M Robbins
VP: Robert L Stillwell
Sfty Mgr: Toby Nivens
Snr Mgr: John Deck

D-U-N-S 07-526-5157 IMP
MEMORIAL SLOAN-KETTERING CANCER CENTER
1275 York Ave, New York, NY 10065-6007
Tel (212) 639-2000 *Founded/Ownrshp* 1884
Sales 2.2MMM *EMP* 9,325
Accts Ernst & Young Us Llp Indianap
SIC 8069 Cancer hospital
Pr: Craig B Thompson
**Ch Bd:* Douglas A Warner III
V Ch: Richard R Barakat
V Ch: Yuman Fong
V Ch: William R Jarnagin
V Ch: David M Panicek
**COO:* Katherine Martin
**CFO:* Michael P Gutnick
**Treas:* Clifton S Robbins
Bd of Dir: Marie-Jos E Kravis
Ex VP: John R Gunn
Sr VP: Thomas J Fahey Jr
**Sr VP:* Jorge Lopez
**VP:* Kerry Bessey
**VP:* Murray F Brennan
**VP:* Eric Cottington
VP: Jason Klein
VP: Kathy Lewis
VP: Patricia C Skarulis
Assoc Dir: Anne-Marie Lesny
Dir Rad: Chester Mah

MEMORIAL UNIVERSITY MED CTR
See MEMORIAL HEALTH INC

D-U-N-S 05-538-6465 IMP
MEMORY CO LLC
25 Downing Dr, Phenix City, AL 36869-3342
Tel (334) 448-0708 *Founded/Ownrshp* 2000
Sales 89.5MM^E *EMP* 300
SIC 5199 Gifts & novelties
CEO: Charles D Sizemore
**Pr:* G Randy Brown
**VP:* Jennifer Freeman

D-U-N-S 80-948-7718
MEMPHIS CITY BOARD OF EDUCATIO
2597 Avery Ave, Memphis, TN 38112-4818
Tel (901) 416-5444 *Founded/Ownrshp* 2008
Sales 1.0MMM *EMP* 30^E
Accts Watkins Uiberall Pllc Memphis
SIC 8299 Educational services

MEMPHIS INTERNATIONAL AIRPORT
See MEMPHIS-SHELBY COUNTY AIRPORT AUTHORITY

D-U-N-S 05-256-3020
MEMPHIS-SHELBY COUNTY AIRPORT AUTHORITY
MEMPHIS INTERNATIONAL AIRPORT
2491 Winchester Rd # 113, Memphis, TN 38116-3851
Tel (901) 922-8000 *Founded/Ownrshp* 1969
Sales 113.4MM *EMP* 305
Accts Dixon Hughes Goodman Llp Memp
SIC 4581 Airport terminal services; Airport hangar rental
Pr: Larry D Cox
**Ch:* Arnold E Pearl

Ofcr: Jerry Brandon
Ofcr: Fred Hawkins
Ofcr: Rodger Murray
Ex VP: Scott A Brockman
**VP:* Scott Brockman
VP: Jim Covington
**VP:* Bob A Martin
VP: Richard White
Dir: James Hay
Comm Man: Clifford J Robinson

D-U-N-S 00-620-3210 IMP/EXP
MENARD INC (WI)
MIDWEST MANUFACTURING
5101 Menard Dr, Eau Claire, WI 54703-9604
Tel (715) 876-5911 *Founded/Ownrshp* 1962
Sales 15.7MMM^E^ *EMP* 40,000
SIC 2431 5211 Millwork; Lumber & other building materials
Pr: John Menard Jr
Pr: Frederic Masse
COO: Scott Collette
COO: Charlie Menard
**CFO:* Pete Liupakka
**Treas:* Jr Menard
Dir Bus: Marty Taube
Dept Mgr: Jeanette Lester
Brnch Mgr: Bart Coen
Genl Mgr: Troy Anderson
Genl Mgr: Chris Felice

D-U-N-S 00-607-3126 IMP/EXP
MENASHA CORP
1645 Bergstrom Rd, Neenah, WI 54956-9766
Tel (920) 751-1000 *Founded/Ownrshp* 1849
Sales 1.8MMM *EMP* 4,000
Accts Pricewaterhousecoopers Llp Mi
SIC 2631 2653 2679 3086 0811 Paperboard mills; Corrugated & solid fiber boxes; Paper products, converted; Packaging & shipping materials, foamed plastic; Timber tracts
Pr: James M Kotek
**Ch Bd:* Donald C Shepard
**CFO:* Thomas M Rettler
**Treas:* Lee Ann Hammen
Treas: Kevin Head
Ex VP: Jerry Hessel
VP: Jackie Barry
VP: Mark Gorzek
VP: Annette Groenink
VP: Lea A Hammen
VP: Evan Pritz
VP: Don Riviere

D-U-N-S 10-797-5224 IMP
MENASHA PACKAGING CO LLC
(*Suby of* MENASHA CORP) ★
1645 Bergstrom Rd, Neenah, WI 54956-9701
Tel (920) 751-1000 *Founded/Ownrshp* 2001
Sales 866.4MM^E^ *EMP* 2,200
SIC 2653 Sheets, corrugated: made from purchased materials
CEO: James M Kotek
**Pr:* Michael K Waite
**Sr VP:* Thomas M Rettler
VP: Tom Bender
VP: Gail A Constncio
**VP:* Rick J Fantini
VP: Jeff Krepline
**VP:* Evan S Pritz
Opers Mgr: Dennis Graf
Manager: Eric Phillippi
Sls Mgr: Jason Reu

D-U-N-S 60-737-6647
MENDELSON HOLDING CO LTD INC
8300 Pennsylvania Ave, Upper Marlboro, MD 20772-2610
Tel (301) 420-6400 *Founded/Ownrshp* 1989
Sales 94.4MM^E^ *EMP* 1,503
SIC 5411 Grocery stores
Prin: Ira Mendelsonchb
**Ch:* Ira Mendelson
**Treas:* Matthew Young

D-U-N-S 09-001-5694 IMP/EXP
MENDEZ & CO INC
Km 2/4 Mrtnez Nadal Rr 20, Guaynabo, PR 00969
Tel (787) 793-8888 *Founded/Ownrshp* 1912, 1940
Sales 229.7MM *EMP* 525^E^
Accts Llm&D Psc San Juan Puerto
SIC 5182 5141 Liquor; Groceries, general line
Ch Bd: Salustiano Alvarez
**Pr:* Jose A Alvarez Gallardo
**Treas:* Pablo Jose Alvarez
**VP:* Carlos Alvarez Jr
**VP:* Carlos Alvarez Mendez
Genl Mgr: Rafael Lopez Jr
IT Man: Sandra Rodriguez

D-U-N-S 01-936-7486
MENDOCINO FOREST PRODUCTS CO LLC
3700 Old Redwood Hwy # 200, Santa Rosa, CA 95403-5739
Tel (707) 620-2961 *Founded/Ownrshp* 1998
Sales 173.3MM^E^ *EMP* 400
SIC 5031 2421 Lumber, plywood & millwork; Sawmills & planing mills, general
CEO: Sandy Dean
Pr: John Russell
CEO: Bob Mertz
CFO: Jim Pelkey

D-U-N-S 61-000-5738
MENDOTA INSURANCE CO
(*Suby of* MIC HOLDINGS INC)
2805 Dodd Rd Ste 300, Eagan, MN 55121-2161
Tel (800) 422-0792 *Founded/Ownrshp* 2007
Sales NA *EMP* 230^E^
SIC 6331 Property damage insurance
Pr: Robert Zieper
Treas: Sandra Pappas
VP: Richard Slater
Trfc Dir: Tara Kittleson
Board of Directors: Norman Asplund Berg, Austin Chapman, Clarence George Frame, Robert England Grant, Edward Hersey Hamm

D-U-N-S 92-880-3352
MENLO HEALTH ALLIANCE
MENLO HEALTH CLINIC
1300 Crane St, Menlo Park, CA 94025-4260
Tel (650) 498-6640 *Founded/Ownrshp* 1988
Sales 164.6MM *EMP* 2
SIC 8011 Surgeon
Prin: Martin Bronk MD

MENLO HEALTH CLINIC
See MENLO HEALTH ALLIANCE

MENLO WORLDWIDE EXPEDITE
See MENLO WORLDWIDE FORWARDING INC

D-U-N-S 00-691-8577
■ **MENLO WORLDWIDE FORWARDING INC**
MENLO WORLDWIDE EXPEDITE
(*Suby of* UPS) ★
1 Lagoon Dr Ste 400, Redwood City, CA 94065-1564
Tel (650) 596-9600 *Founded/Ownrshp* 2002, 2004
Sales 126.2MM^E^ *EMP* 6,500^E^
SIC 4513 4215 4522 4731 6159 6351 Letter delivery, private air; Package delivery, private air; Parcel delivery, private air; Courier services, except by air; Package delivery, vehicular; Parcel delivery, vehicular; Flying charter service; Customhouse brokers; Freight forwarding; Equipment & vehicle finance leasing companies; Liability insurance
CEO: John H Williford

MENLO WORLDWIDE LOGISTICS
See XPO LOGISTICS WORLDWIDE INC

D-U-N-S 05-994-7952 IMP
MENNIES MACHINE CO
MMC ARMORY
Mennie Dr Rr 71, Mark, IL 61340
Tel (815) 339-2226 *Founded/Ownrshp* 1970
Sales 91.0MM^E^ *EMP* 260^E^
SIC 3544 8742 Special dies, tools, jigs & fixtures; Materials mgmt. (purchasing, handling, inventory) consultant
VP: David Mennie
**CFO:* Gary Hegland
**Treas:* Jennifer Smoode
VP: William Mennie
**VP:* Mark Stengel
Genl Mgr: Richard Cavaletto
Dir IT: Hubert J Mennie
VP Opers: Bill Mennie
Manager: Mark Mancini

D-U-N-S 09-018-0266 IMP/EXP
MENNONITE GENERAL HOSPITAL INC
Carr 14 Km 131 Sctor Lmas St Ca, Cayey, PR 00736
Tel (787) 535-1001 *Founded/Ownrshp* 1943
Sales 63.9MM^E^ *EMP* 1,172
Accts Parissi Psc San Juan Pr
SIC 8062 General medical & surgical hospitals
Pr: Victor Ortiz
**Pr:* Ruben Santos
**VP:* Jos E Rivera
**Ex Dir:* Domingo Torres

D-U-N-S 80-337-2069
MENORAH MEDICAL CENTER INC
5721 W 119th St, Overland Park, KS 66209-3753
Tel (913) 498-6000 *Founded/Ownrshp* 1989
Sales 107.0MM^E^ *EMP* 800
SIC 8011 8062 Clinic, operated by physicians; General medical & surgical hospitals
Pr: Steve Wilkinson
Pr: Ron Crabbs
CFO: Debra Gasford
Dir Lab: Sue Johnson
Dir Rx: Zack Mc Mahon
Dir QC: Annie Wehagezickwolf
Plas Surg: John Quinn
Doctor: Cindy C Chang MD
Doctor: Sam Weems
Pharmcst: Robert Province

D-U-N-S 07-691-5800
MENORAH PARK CENTER FOR SENIOR LIVING BET MOSHAV ZEKENIM HADATI
27100 Cedar Rd, Cleveland, OH 44122-1156
Tel (216) 831-6500 *Founded/Ownrshp* 1906
Sales 71.1MM *EMP* 1,096
Accts Mcgladrey Llp Cleveland Ohio
SIC 8051 6513 8322 Skilled nursing care facilities; Apartment building operators; Outreach program
Pr: Ira Kaplan
**Pr:* Enid Rosenberg
CFO: Robert S Matitia
CFO: Bob Schaefer
Exec: Michael Peterman
**Ex Dir:* Steven Raichilson
Off Mgr: Kris Christian
Off Mgr: Glenda Gamble
CIO: Richard Schwalberg
VP Mktg: Lisa Cullen
HC Dir: Lisa Cohen

D-U-N-S 06-510-1974 IMP
■ **MENS WEARHOUSE INC** (TX)
(*Suby of* TAILORED BRANDS INC) ★
6380 Rogerdale Rd, Houston, TX 77072-1649
Tel (281) 776-7000 *Founded/Ownrshp* 1973, 2016
Sales 3.5MMM *EMP* 26,100
Accts Deloitte & Touche Llp Houston
SIC 5611 5621 5632 5661 5699 Men's & boys' clothing stores; Suits, men's; Clothing accessories: men's & boys'; Tie shops; Women's clothing stores; Apparel accessories; Women's shoes; Uniforms & work clothing
CEO: Douglas S Ewert
Pr: Paul Fitzpatrick
**CFO:* Jon W Kimmins
**Chf Cred:* Gary G Ckodre
**Chf Mktg O:* Mary Beth Blake
Chf Mktg O: Diane Ridgwaycross
**Ofcr:* Ben Baum
Ex VP: Charlie Bresler
Ex VP: Eric J Lane
Ex VP: Scott Norris
Ex VP: Carole Souvenir
Ex VP: Jim Thorne
Sr VP: Theodore T Biele
Sr VP: Jeffrey Marshall
Sr VP: Susan G Neal
**Sr VP:* Brian T Vaclavik
VP: Mary Blake
VP: Bruce Hershey
VP: Suzi Madrid
Exec: Francesca Ramos
Exec: Eileen Ware

D-U-N-S 18-222-9567
MENTAL HEALTH CENTER OF DENVER
4141 E Dickenson Pl, Denver, CO 80222-6012
Tel (303) 504-6501 *Founded/Ownrshp* 1987
Sales 84.7MM *EMP* 570
Accts Cliftonlarsonallen Llp Greenw
SIC 8093 Mental health clinic, outpatient
CEO: Carl Clark
Pr: Barbara Shaw
**CFO:* Forrest Cason
Assoc Dir: Dawn Davenport
Prgrm Mgr: Terri Hamblen
Prgrm Mgr: Davis Schiele
Off Mgr: Priscilla Woodward
CTO: Christina Loetscher
IT Man: Karen Barritt
IT Man: Griff McClure
Sls Mgr: Oriana Sanchez

D-U-N-S 02-033-3597
MENTAL HEALTH MENTAL RETARDATION OF TARRANT COUNTY (TX)
MHMR OF TARRANT COUNTY
3840 Hulen St, Fort Worth, TX 76107-7277
Tel (817) 569-4300 *Founded/Ownrshp* 1969
Sales 137.2MM *EMP* 1,500
Accts Weaver And Tidwell Llp Fort
SIC 8093 8322 8361 Mental health clinic, outpatient; General counseling services; Home for the mentally retarded
CEO: Susan Garnett
**CEO:* James F Mc Dermott
Exec: Janelle Thurman
Prgrm Mgr: Stan Baker
Psych: Ricki Bickle

MENTAL HEALTH STATE OF MO DEPT
See MISSOURI DEPARTMENT OF MENTAL HEALTH

MENTOR BOARD OF EDUCATION
See MENTOR EXEMPTED VILLAGE SCHOOL DISTRICT

D-U-N-S 01-084-9602
MENTOR EXEMPTED VILLAGE SCHOOL DISTRICT
MENTOR BOARD OF EDUCATION
6451 Center St, Mentor, OH 44060-4109
Tel (440) 255-4444 *Founded/Ownrshp* 1953
Sales 103.9MM *EMP* 1,000
Accts Dave Yost Auditor Of State C
SIC 8211 Public elementary school; Public junior high school; Public senior high school
**Treas:* Daniel L Wilson
Psych: Faith Kover

D-U-N-S 03-137-4879
▲ **MENTOR GRAPHICS CORP** (OR)
8005 Sw Boeckman Rd, Wilsonville, OR 97070-7777
Tel (503) 685-7000 *Founded/Ownrshp* 1981
Sales 1.1MMM *EMP* 5,700^E^
Tkr Sym MENT *Exch* NGS
SIC 7373 Computer-aided system services
Ch Bd: Walden C Rhines
**Pr:* Gregory K Hinckley
**Sr VP:* Michael Ellow
**VP:* Brian Derrick
**VP:* Dean Freed
VP: Nafees Qureshy
VP: Subba Somanchi
Sls Dir: Keith Palmer
Sls Dir: Thomas Wagner
Mktg Mgr: Julie Fadling
Mktg Mgr: Della Felton
Board of Directors: Keith Barnes, Peter L Bonfield, Paul A Mascarenas, J Daniel McCranie, Cheryl L Shavers, Jeffrey M Stafeil

D-U-N-S 80-261-3138
MENTOR REM
(*Suby of* NMH INVESTMENT LLC) ★
9775 Rockside Rd Ste 200, Cleveland, OH 44125-6266
Tel (216) 642-5339 *Founded/Ownrshp* 2007
Sales 23.3MM^E^ *EMP* 5,013^E^
SIC 8211 Specialty education
Prin: Mary Kay Ziccardi

D-U-N-S 04-671-2931 IMP
■ **MENTOR WORLDWIDE LLC**
(*Suby of* ETHICON INC) ★
33 Technology Dr, Irvine, CA 92618-2346
Tel (800) 636-8678 *Founded/Ownrshp* 2009
Sales 274.0MM^E^ *EMP* 1,200
SIC 3842 3845 3841 Surgical appliances & supplies; Prosthetic appliances; Implants, surgical; Cosmetic restorations; Ultrasonic medical equipment, except cleaning; Medical instruments & equipment, blood & bone work
Pr: David Shepherd
V Ch: Stephen Bailey
Pr: Dean Freed
Sr VP: Eugene G Lover
VP: David J Adornetto
VP: Kathleen Beauchamp
VP: Warren Foust
VP: Lynn Hunt
VP: Loren McFarlnd
VP: Henry Potts
Exec: Vincent Monsaignon
Exec: Bryan Theobald

D-U-N-S 04-350-4588
MENU MAKER FOODS INC
GRAVES MENU MAKER FOODS
913 Big Horn Dr, Jefferson City, MO 65109-0336
Tel (573) 893-3000 *Founded/Ownrshp* 1968
Sales 88.6MM^E^ *EMP* 130
SIC 5141 5087 2011 5149 Groceries, general line; Cleaning & maintenance equipment & supplies; Meat packing plants; Groceries & related products
Pr: Dick Graves
**CEO:* Tracy Graves
Manager: Roy McConnell

D-U-N-S 14-001-4627
MENZIES AVIATION (TEXAS) INC
AMI
(*Suby of* JOHN MENZIES (108) LIMITED)
2520 W Airfield Dr, Dallas, TX 75261-4028
Tel (972) 929-1020 *Founded/Ownrshp* 1953
Sales 98.5MM^E^ *EMP* 1,600
SIC 4512 Air passenger carrier, scheduled
Pr: Larry Synder
**Treas:* Tristan Turnbull
**VP:* Todd Kilgore
VP: Clive Macmillan
**VP:* Mike Pattinson

MEPPI
See MITSUBISHI ELECTRIC POWER PRODUCTS INC

D-U-N-S 05-752-3423
MERA SOFTWARE SERVICES INC
2350 Mission College Blvd # 340, Santa Clara, CA 95054-1532
Tel (650) 703-7226 *Founded/Ownrshp* 2012
Sales 18.6MM *EMP* 1,300
SIC 7371 Computer software writing services
CEO: James Hymel
Pr: Bill Timm
**Ex VP:* Konstantin Nikashov
**VP:* Yury Menkov
**Prin:* Sergey Drozhilkin
Prin: Andrey Ladygin
Prin: Igor Piruyan
**Genl Mgr:* Dmitry Ponomarev

D-U-N-S 05-574-5996 IMP
MERCADO LATINO INC (CA)
245 Baldwin Park Blvd, City of Industry, CA 91746-1404
Tel (626) 333-6862 *Founded/Ownrshp* 1963
Sales 281.1MM^E^ *EMP* 350
SIC 5141 5148 Groceries, general line; Fresh fruits & vegetables
Pr: Graciliano Rodriguez
**CFO:* George Rodriguez
**Sr VP:* Richard Rodriguez

D-U-N-S 19-217-1791 IMP
MERCANTIL COMMERCEBANK HOLDING CORP
(*Suby of* MERCANTIL SERVICIOS FINANCIEROS, C.A.)
220 Alhambra Cir, Coral Gables, FL 33134-5174
Tel (305) 441-5555 *Founded/Ownrshp* 1987
Sales NA *EMP* 239
SIC 6021 7389 8721 National commercial banks; Financial services; Accounting, auditing & bookkeeping
Ch: Gustavo Vollmer A
Pr: Alberto Peraza
CEO: Millar Wilson
CFO: Alfonso Figueredo
Ofcr: Gonzalo Delgado
Ofcr: Cary Polanco
Ofcr: Frank Rodriguez
Ofcr: Evan Sicle
Ofcr: Peter H Smith
Top Exec: Rosa Costantino
Ex VP: Melanie Garman
Ex VP: Andres Sala
Sr VP: Carlos Lamourtte
Sr VP: Robert Lopez
Sr VP: Alexis Nahon
Sr VP: Francisco Roche
Sr VP: Laura Troszlair
VP: Brian Barroso
VP: Zachary Bennett
VP: Yvonne Boucugnani
VP: Luis Cabello

D-U-N-S 94-314-0426
MERCANTILE BANK
1560 Orange Ave Ste 300, Winter Park, FL 32789-5558
Tel (407) 622-3528 *Founded/Ownrshp* 2010
Sales NA *EMP* 1,015
SIC 6022 State commercial banks
Pr: Ernie Diaz
**CFO:* Ken Brewer
**Ex VP:* Charles B Lowe Jr
**Ex VP:* Theresa Spellings
Sr VP: Nadine Genet
VP: Grace Cook
VP: Terence Coyle
VP: Todd Labuzienski

D-U-N-S 09-680-9590
▲ **MERCANTILE BANK CORP** (MI)
310 Leonard St Nw, Grand Rapids, MI 49504-4224
Tel (616) 406-3000 *Founded/Ownrshp* 1997
Sales NA *EMP* 701^E^
Tkr Sym MBWM *Exch* NGS
SIC 6022 State commercial banks
Ch Bd: Michael H Price
COO: Robert B Kaminski Jr
CFO: Charles E Christmas
Board of Directors: David M Cassard, Edward J Clark, Jeff A Gardner, Edward B Grant, Thomas R Sullivan

D-U-N-S 36-429-3415
■ **MERCANTILE BANK OF MICHIGAN**
(*Suby of* MERCANTILE BANK CORP) ★
310 Leonard St Nw, Grand Rapids, MI 49504-4224
Tel (616) 406-3000 *Founded/Ownrshp* 1997
Sales NA *EMP* 250
SIC 6022 State commercial banks
CEO: Robert Kaminski Jr
**Pr:* Robert B Kaminski
**CFO:* Charles E Christmas
**Ch:* Michael H Price
Ofcr: Vicky Baker
Ofcr: Dan Quist
Sr VP: Wayne Smith

VP: Mark Conn
Brnch Mgr: Robert Staley

D-U-N-S 00-691-8684
■ MERCANTILE PENINSULA BANK
(*Suby of* PNC FINANCIAL SERVICES GROUP INC) ★
1 W Church St, Selbyville, DE 19975-2003
Tel (302) 436-8236 *Founded/Ownrshp* 2007
Sales NA *EMP* 374
SIC 6022 State commercial banks
Pr: Robert E Dickerson
Sr VP: D Brent Hurley
VP: James D Barr
VP: Russell D Brittingham
VP: Kenneth R Graham
VP: B Philip Lynch Jr
VP: Janet Mc Cabe
VP: Wayne C Morton
VP: Gerald Warren
Board of Directors: P Coleman Townsend Jr, Thurman Adams Jr, Eugene Bunting, R Carol Campbell, Robert E Dickerson, David C Doane, D Brent Hurley, Richard I Lewis, J C Murray, William O Murray

D-U-N-S 01-303-5779
MERCED CITY SCHOOL DISTRICT
444 W 23rd St, Merced, CA 95340-3723
Tel (209) 385-6600 *Founded/Ownrshp* 1905
Sales 78.8MM[E] *EMP* 1,500
SIC 8211 Public elementary school; Kindergarten
Exec: Sherry Munday
Teacher Pr: Doug Collins

D-U-N-S 04-846-3178
MERCED COUNTY OFFICE OF EDUCATION
632 W 13th St, Merced, CA 95341-5908
Tel (209) 381-6600 *Founded/Ownrshp* 1952
Sales 117.6MM *EMP* 900
Accts Vavrinek Trine Day & Co Ll
SIC 8211 Public elementary & secondary schools
Genl Mgr: Dominico Johnston
Genl Mgr: Lee Lor
Off Admin: Susan Butterman
Snr Ntwrk: Brian Yost
Netwrk Eng: Mark Mahacek
Pr Dir: Cindy Heaton
Schl Brd P: Rudy Albritton

D-U-N-S 00-598-2442
MERCED IRRIGATION DISTRICT
744 W 20th St, Merced, CA 95340-3601
Tel (209) 722-5761 *Founded/Ownrshp* 1919
Sales 113.6MM[E] *EMP* 164
Accts Burr Pilger Nayer Inc San Jos
SIC 4911 4971 Electric services; Water distribution or supply systems for irrigation
Pr: Tim Pellissier
**Treas:* Andre Urquidez
**VP:* Dave Long
Genl Mgr: Ted Selb
Genl Mgr: John Sweigard

D-U-N-S 01-423-3373
MERCED UNION HIGH SCHOOL DISTRICT CAPITAL FACILITIES CORP
3430 A St, Atwater, CA 95301-5100
Tel (209) 385-6400 *Founded/Ownrshp* 1919
Sales 82.0MM[E] *EMP* 1,050
SIC 8211 Public senior high school; Public adult education school
CEO: Sam Spangler
**VP:* Ida Johnson
Genl Mgr: Yvonne Eagle
Schl Brd P: Dave Honey

MERCEDES-BENZ
See R & H MOTOR CARS LTD

D-U-N-S 80-561-8399
MERCEDES-BENZ FINANCIAL SERVICES USA LLC
DAIMLER TRUCK FINANCIAL
(*Suby of* DAIMLER FINANCIAL SERVICES AG)
36455 Corporate Dr, Farmington Hills, MI 48331-3552
Tel (248) 991-6700 *Founded/Ownrshp* 2007
Sales NA *EMP* 400[E]
SIC 6159 Pari-mutuel totalizator equipment finance leasing & maint.
Pr: Klaus Entenmann
**Pr:* Peter Zieringer
**Ofcr:* Rodolfo Dominguez
VP: Steven Goodale
VP: Geoff Robinson
**VP:* Bryan Stevens
**VP:* Johan Swart
VP: Tobias Waldeck
CIO: Christel Plessers
Mktg Mgr: Kimberly Marks
Sls Mgr: Brian Braun

D-U-N-S 03-474-8897
MERCEDES-BENZ MANHATTAN INC
(*Suby of* MERCEDES-BENZ USA LLC) ★
770 11th Ave, New York, NY 10019-5007
Tel (212) 629-1600 *Founded/Ownrshp* 1981
Sales 88.0MM[E] *EMP* 250
SIC 5511 Automobiles, new & used
Pr: Claus Laugan
Sales Asso: Alejandro Villanueva

MERCEDES-BENZ OF CORAL GABLES
See BILL USSERY MOTORS BODY SHOP INC

MERCEDES-BENZ OF SAN FRANCISCO
See EUROMOTORS INC

MERCEDES-BENZ OF WILSONVILLE
See DON RASMUSSEN CO

D-U-N-S 82-483-9872 IMP/EXP
MERCEDES-BENZ US INTERNATIONAL INC
MERCEDES-BENZ USA
(*Suby of* DAIMLER AG)
1 Mercedes Dr, Vance, AL 35490-2900
Tel (205) 507-2252 *Founded/Ownrshp* 1994
Sales 1.1MMM[E] *EMP* 3,000[E]
SIC 3711 3714 Motor vehicles & car bodies; Motor vehicle parts & accessories
CEO: Markus Schaefer
**CEO:* Herbert Werner
COO: Roger Nielsen
VP: Michael Balke
VP: Jason Hoff
VP: Christian Treiber
VP: Armin Willy
Exec: Gavin Chan
Comm Man: Felyicia Jerald
Mng Dir: Ian Prophet
Prgrm Mgr: Kimberly Berg
Board of Directors: Markus Schaefer

MERCEDES-BENZ USA
See MERCEDES-BENZ US INTERNATIONAL INC

D-U-N-S 00-180-2511 IMP/EXP
MERCEDES-BENZ USA LLC (GA)
(*Suby of* MERCEDES-BENZ USA) ★
303 Perimeter Ctr N, Atlanta, GA 30346-3402
Tel (201) 573-0600 *Founded/Ownrshp* 2000
Sales 1.1MMM[E] *EMP* 1,400
SIC 5012 5013 7538 5511 Automobiles; Automotive supplies & parts; General automotive repair shops; Automobiles, new & used
Pr: Stephen Cannon
**CFO:* Harald Henn
**CFO:* John Ieronimo
Ch: Michael Bassermann
**Ex VP:* Sonja Bower
**VP:* Andrew McLaren
VP: Mark McNabb
**VP:* Drew Slaven
Prgrm Mgr: Julia Daniel
Genl Mgr: Astrid Fontaine
Genl Mgr: Mark Jackson

D-U-N-S 08-845-9540
■ MERCER (US) INC
(*Suby of* MERCER INC) ★
1166 Ave Of The Americ, New York, NY 10036-2708
Tel (212) 345-7000 *Founded/Ownrshp* 1975
Sales 907.1MM[E] *EMP* 15,643
SIC 8742 Compensation & benefits planning consultant; Personnel management consultant
CEO: Julio Portalatin
**Pr:* E Michael Caulfield
**Pr:* Patricia A Milligan
COO: Robert C Fox
CFO: Steve Mele
**CFO:* Terry Thompson
CFO: Tim Weininger
**Treas:* Daniel Percella
Ofcr: Mark Gilbert
VP: Lake Charles
VP: Kathy Mather
VP: Karen Pauley
VP: Shari Souza

D-U-N-S 06-814-0383
MERCER COUNTY BOARD OF EDUCATION (WV)
1403 Honaker Ave, Princeton, WV 24740-3065
Tel (304) 487-1551 *Founded/Ownrshp* 1934
Sales 66.6MM[E] *EMP* 1,398
SIC 8211 School board
Pr: Gilbert Bailey
**Treas:* Joy Hubbard

D-U-N-S 07-695-0807
MERCER COUNTY COMMUNITY COLLEGE
WEST WINDSOR CAMPUS
1200 Old Trenton Rd, Trenton, NJ 08690
Tel (609) 586-4800 *Founded/Ownrshp* 1966
Sales 52.1MM[E] *EMP* 1,500
SIC 8222 Junior college
Pr: Thomas Sepe
**Pr:* Dr Patricia C Donohue
**VP:* Jacob Eapen
**VP:* Donald Generals
**VP:* Dr Mellissia Zanjani
Assoc Dir: Jason Taylor
**Prin:* Lionel Frank
**Ex Dir:* Jose Fernandez
Ex Dir: Brian McCloskey
Netwrk Eng: Tonia Harrison
Mktg Dir: Lynn Holl
Board of Directors: Lionel Frank

D-U-N-S 07-979-8743
MERCER COUNTY PUBLIC SCHOOLS
1403 Honaker Ave, Princeton, WV 24740-3065
Tel (304) 487-1551 *Founded/Ownrshp* 2015
Sales 11.4MM[E] *EMP* 1,314[E]
SIC 8211 Public elementary & secondary schools
Teacher Pr: Kristal G Filipek

D-U-N-S 61-621-3125
■ MERCER HEALTH & BENEFITS LLC
(*Suby of* MERCER (US) INC) ★
1166 Ave Of The Americas, New York, NY 10036-2708
Tel (212) 345-7000 *Founded/Ownrshp* 2004
Sales 78.3MM[E] *EMP* 2,500
SIC 8742 Hospital & health services consultant
Pr: Bernard Morency
COO: Roy Gonella

D-U-N-S 18-292-2612
■ MERCER HUMAN RESOURCE CONSULTING OF MASSACHUSETTS INC
(*Suby of* MARSH & MCLENNAN COMPANIES INC) ★
99 High St, Boston, MA 02110-2320
Tel (617) 450-6000 *Founded/Ownrshp* 2005
Sales 107.4MM[E] *EMP* 500
SIC 8742 Human resource consulting services
Prin: Gerald Fazio
Treas: P R Mohan

D-U-N-S 94-882-5971
■ MERCER INC
(*Suby of* MARSH & MCLENNAN COMPANIES INC) ★
1166 Avenue Of The Americ, New York, NY 10036-2726
Tel (212) 345-7000 *Founded/Ownrshp* 1991
Sales 3.5MMM[E] *EMP* 15,758
SIC 8748 Economic consultant
Ch Bd: Peter Coster
Pr: David Anderson
Pr: Simon O'Regan
COO: Ken Haderer
CFO: Helen Shan
Chf Mktg O: Michelle Bottomley
Ex VP: Yves Roy
Prin: James Horrell
Prin: Dan Priga
Prin: Lisa Weber
Admn Mgr: Douglas Vander Linde

D-U-N-S 60-544-5980
■ MERCER INVESTMENT CONSULTING INC
(*Suby of* MERCER (US) INC) ★
1166 Ave Of The Americas, New York, NY 10036-2708
Tel (212) 345-7000 *Founded/Ownrshp* 1975
Sales 91.5MM[E] *EMP* 620
SIC 6282 Investment advice
Pr: Michelle Burns
COO: Roy Gonella
CFO: David Mahew
**CFO:* David L Mayhew
CFO: Joe Rotberg
CFO: Terri Thompson
Ofcr: Clare Collins-Newton
Ofcr: Steve Mele
Ofcr: Michael Sternklar
CIO: Ed Fenton
CIO: Darren James Lee

D-U-N-S 01-759-3112 EXP
MERCER LANDMARK INC (OH)
CW SERVICE
426 W Market St, Celina, OH 45822-2127
Tel (419) 628-3093 *Founded/Ownrshp* 1934
Sales 251.3MM[E] *EMP* 160
SIC 5153 5999 Grains; Feed & farm supply
Pr: Daren Deffenbaugh
**CFO:* Tim Weininger
Brnch Mgr: Ken Puthoff
CIO: Bob Barrett

D-U-N-S 08-675-9743
MERCER TRANSPORTATION CO INC
1128 W Main St, Louisville, KY 40203-1432
Tel (502) 584-2301 *Founded/Ownrshp* 1977
Sales 435.2MM *EMP* 312
SIC 4213

D-U-N-S 15-453-6817 IMP
MERCHANDISE MART PROPERTIES INC
(*Suby of* VORNADO REALTY TRUST) ★
222 Merchandise Mart Plz # 470, Chicago, IL 60654-1072
Tel (312) 527-4141 *Founded/Ownrshp* 1998
Sales 92.5MM[E] *EMP* 550
SIC 6531 Rental agent, real estate
CEO: Mark Falanga
**Sr VP:* John H Brennen
**Sr VP:* Randall Clark
Sr VP: Paul Heinen
Sr VP: John Jennings
Sr VP: Myron Maurer
Sr VP: Susan McCullough
Sr VP: Joan Ulrich
VP: Troy Durst
VP: Katherine Flaherty
VP: Susan Glick
VP: Steve Johnson
VP: Cheryl Longstreet
VP: Byron Martin
VP: Tim McGee
VP: Toni McIntosh
VP: Dick Norfolk
VP: Patti Stewart

D-U-N-S 17-190-9278
MERCHANDISING CORP OF AMERICA INC
M C A
11121 Carmel Commons Blvd # 455, Charlotte, NC 28226-4495
Tel (704) 944-4600 *Founded/Ownrshp* 1996
Sales 98.4MM[E] *EMP* 4,560
SIC 8748 Business consulting
Pr: Tom Palombo
VP: Donna Brockway
VP: Gentlesk Philip

D-U-N-S 16-631-7698
MERCHANDISING SOLUTIONS GROUP INC
MSG
260 Peachtree St Nw, Atlanta, GA 30303-1202
Tel (800) 417-1320 *Founded/Ownrshp* 2003
Sales 196.9MM[E] *EMP* 3,500
SIC 5199 1542 General merchandise, non-durable; Custom builders, non-residential
CEO: Rick Clark
**Pr:* Karen Reeves
**CFO:* Tanya Valera
**Dir Sec:* Shane Walker

D-U-N-S 36-063-9814
MERCHANT CASH AND CAPITAL LLC
BIZFI FUNDING
460 Park Ave S Fl 10, New York, NY 10016-7315
Tel (212) 545-3180 *Founded/Ownrshp* 2005
Sales NA *EMP* 225
SIC 6153 7389 Working capital financing; Financial services
CEO: John Donovan
Pr: Michael Ward
**CEO:* Jeff Beckwith
**COO:* Tomo Matsuo
**CFO:* Michael Kennedy
**Founder:* Stephen Sheinbaum
Ofcr: Bernie Lynch
Sr VP: Armstrong Lennox
VP: Michael Caronna
Software D: Kaif Memon

D-U-N-S 09-784-6828 IMP
MERCHANT OF TENNIS INC
US MERCHANT
8737 Wilshire Blvd, Beverly Hills, CA 90211-2701
Tel (310) 228-4000 *Founded/Ownrshp* 1984
Sales 143.9MM[E] *EMP* 1,400
SIC 5941 5621 5661 5961 5999 Sporting goods & bicycle shops; Dress shops; Shoe stores; Television, home shopping; Candle shops
CEO: Jeff Green
**Sec:* Marie Green
Sr VP: Bruce Carter

D-U-N-S 02-999-1395
MERCHANT SERVICES INC
1 S Van Ness Ave Fl 5, San Francisco, CA 94103-5416
Tel (817) 725-0900 *Founded/Ownrshp* 2014
Sales 34.0MM[E] *EMP* 1,000
SIC 7374 Data processing service
CEO: Lorraine Stimmell
**Sr VP:* Le Tran-Tl

D-U-N-S 10-723-6317
■ MERCHANTS AND FARMERS TELEPHONE CO
TDS
(*Suby of* TDS TELECOMMUNICATIONS CORP) ★
125 W Main St, Hillsboro, IN 47949-8111
Tel (765) 798-2145 *Founded/Ownrshp* 1999
Sales 853.0MM *EMP* 2,700
SIC 4813 Local & long distance telephone communications
Pr: David Wittwer
**Ofcr:* Noel Hutton

D-U-N-S 04-631-8887
MERCHANTS AUTOMOTIVE GROUP INC
MERCHANTS LEASING
1278 Hooksett Rd, Hooksett, NH 03106-1839
Tel (603) 669-4100 *Founded/Ownrshp* 1962
Sales 159.3MM[E] *EMP* 250[E]
Accts Baker Newman & Noyes Llp Manc
SIC 5521 7515 Automobiles, used cars only; Passenger car leasing
CEO: Phil Ryan
**Pr:* Stephen Singer
**CEO:* Glen Villano
**CFO:* Paul Barkworth
**Ofcr:* Jack Firriolo
**VP:* Alan Singer
Exec: Michael Rielly
Genl Mgr: Maria Neve
Genl Mgr: Adam Secore
CIO: Avery Finver
VP Sls: Tom Coffey

D-U-N-S 00-530-4845
MERCHANTS BONDING CO (MUTUAL)
6700 Westown Pkwy, West Des Moines, IA 50266-7754
Tel (515) 243-8171 *Founded/Ownrshp* 1933
Sales NA *EMP* 130
SIC 6351 Fidelity or surety bonding
Pr: Larry Taylor
Pr: Audrey Williams
**CFO:* Don Blum
**Ex VP:* Mike Foster
**Exec:* Stanley McCormick
Genl Mgr: Barbara Carlos

D-U-N-S 06-519-4920
MERCHANTS BUILDING MAINTENANCE CO
1190 Monterey Pass Rd, Monterey Park, CA 91754-3615
Tel (323) 881-6701 *Founded/Ownrshp* 1961
Sales 105.5MM[E] *EMP* 3,000[E]
SIC 7349 Building maintenance services
CEO: Theodore Haas
**Pr:* David Haas
**Treas:* Karen T Haas
VP: Wayne Eames
**VP:* Krista M Haas
Genl Mgr: Marco Ferrel
Opers Mgr: Eliseo Gutierrez
Opers Mgr: Margarita Pantcratz
Sls Dir: Ilza Waterman

D-U-N-S 00-818-4749
MERCHANTS CO
MERCHANTS FOODSERVICE
(*Suby of* TATUM DEVELOPMENT CORP) ★
1100 Edwards St, Hattiesburg, MS 39401-5511
Tel (601) 353-2461 *Founded/Ownrshp* 1983
Sales 788.3MM[E] *EMP* 500
Accts Mcarthur Thames Slay And Dew
SIC 5141 Groceries, general line
Pr: Andrew B Mercier
**Ch Bd:* Robert O Tatum
CFO: Allan Daglio
**CFO:* Jarrod Gray
VP: Scott Kliever
IT Man: Lee Walker
VP Sls: Ken Moore

D-U-N-S 00-699-6888 EXP
MERCHANTS DISTRIBUTORS LLC (NC)
M D I
(*Suby of* ALEX LEE INC) ★
5005 Alex Lee Blvd, Hickory, NC 28601-3395
Tel (828) 725-4424 *Founded/Ownrshp* 1931
Sales 221.8MM[E] *EMP* 1,300
SIC 5141 5142 5147 5148 5194 5122 Groceries, general line; Packaged frozen goods; Meats & meat products; Fresh fruits & vegetables; Tobacco & tobacco products; Cosmetics, perfumes & hair products; Toiletries
Pr: Bob McTeir
**Sr VP:* Donald Garvey
**VP:* Nick Carlino
**VP:* John Dollar
**VP:* John King
**VP:* Tim Markham
**VP Mktg:* Barry Bounds

MERCHANTS FOODSERVICE
See MERCHANTS CO

D-U-N-S 00-342-5949
MERCHANTS GROCERY CO INC (VA)
800 Maddox Dr, Culpeper, VA 22701-4156
Tel (540) 825-0786 *Founded/Ownrshp* 1917
Sales 138.9MM *EMP* 135
Accts Nicholas Jones & Company Plc
SIC 5194 5141 5145 Tobacco & tobacco products; Groceries, general line; Confectionery
Pr: Elvin V Smythers
CFO: Neal Deane
**Sec:* Michael G Hicks
**VP:* David G Cooper
Sales Exec: Bruce Davis

Mktg Mgr: Chris Smythers
Sls Mgr: William Beatley
Sls Mgr: Keith Sampson
Sales Asso: Tammy Zitz

D-U-N-S 02-379-6105
MERCHANTS INC
MERCHANT'S TIRE & AUTO CENTER
9073 Euclid Ave, Manassas, VA 20110-5306
Tel (703) 368-3171 *Founded/Ownrshp* 1999
Sales 178.2MM *EMP* 1,500
SIC 5014 7539 5531 Automobile tires & tubes; Automotive repair shops; Automotive tires
Pr: J Michael Riggan
Ch Bd: Carol K Bell
CFO: James R Cato
CFO: Jim Matthews
VP: James B Bull
VP: Carl Dunn Jr
VP: Carl Finamore
VP: Lee Fishkin
VP: George Lnoey
VP: John Seal
VP Admn: Bill Craig
Board of Directors: Linda Merchant Bell, Carol Merchant Kirby, Mae S Merchant, Wilson C Merchant III

D-U-N-S 13-168-7519
MERCHANTS INSURANCE GROUP
(*Suby of* AMERICAN EUROPEAN GROUP INC) ★
250 Main St, Buffalo, NY 14202-4104
Tel (716) 849-3333 *Founded/Ownrshp* 2007
Sales NA *EMP* 313
SIC 6331 Fire, marine & casualty insurance: stock; Property damage insurance; Fire, marine & casualty insurance & carriers
Pr: Brent D Baird
**Ch Bd:* Thomas E Kahn
Pr: Scott Behrent
**COO:* Robert M Zak
**CFO:* Kenneth J Wilson
Bd of Dir: Bob Perno
VP: Shad McKnight
**VP:* Edward M Murphy
VP: Ellen Willard
IT Man: Stephen Cross
Info Man: Greg Ball

MERCHANTS LEASING
See MERCHANTS AUTOMOTIVE GROUP INC

D-U-N-S 04-890-8180 IMP
MERCHANTS METALS LLC
ANCHOR DIE CAST
(*Suby of* ATLAS HOLDINGS LLC) ★
211 Perimeter Center Pkwy, Atlanta, GA 30346-1305
Tel (770) 741-0300 *Founded/Ownrshp* 2015
Sales 608.5MM^E *EMP* 1,593
SIC 3496 3446 5031 Fencing, made from purchased wire; Mesh, made from purchased wire; Concrete reinforcing mesh & wire; Fences, gates, posts & flagpoles; Fences or posts, ornamental iron or steel; Building materials, exterior; Fencing, wood
Pr: David Clarke
CFO: Gary Brandon
CFO: Terry Schillaci
CFO: Mike Singleton
Treas: Tammy R Hinkle
VP: Lyle D Bumgarner
VP: Robert L Burdette
VP: Tim Kelly
VP: Bill Ramsey
VP: William Stewart
**VP:* Robert N Tenczar
VP: Carl Wilkes

D-U-N-S 00-697-6757
MERCHANTS MUTUAL INSURANCE CO (NY)
240 Main St, Buffalo, NY 14202-4104
Tel (716) 849-3333 *Founded/Ownrshp* 1917
Sales NA *EMP* 250
SIC 6331 Property damage insurance; Fire, marine & casualty insurance: mutual
Pr: Robert Zak
**Treas:* Kenneth J Wilson
**Sr VP:* Fred Hildebrand
**VP:* Margaret Kafka

MERCHANT'S TIRE & AUTO CENTER
See MERCHANTS INC

D-U-N-S 12-182-0737 IMP/EXP
MERCHSOURCE LLC
THREESIXTY GROUP
15 Cushing, Irvine, CA 92618-4220
Tel (949) 900-0900 *Founded/Ownrshp* 2001
Sales 139.3MM^E *EMP* 46
SIC 5112 Stationery & office supplies
Mng Pt: Johann Clapp

D-U-N-S 05-455-4290 IMP/EXP
▲ MERCK & CO INC (NJ)
2000 Galloping Hill Rd, Kenilworth, NJ 07033-1310
Tel (908) 740-4000 *Founded/Ownrshp* 1928
Sales 39.5MMM *EMP* 68,000^E
Tkr Sym MRK *Exch* NYS
SIC 2834 2836 2844 5122 Pharmaceutical preparations; Druggists' preparations (pharmaceuticals); Drugs acting on the respiratory system; Drugs affecting parasitic & infective diseases; Vaccines; Veterinary biological products; Suntan lotions & oils; Animal medicines
Ch Bd: Kenneth C Frazier
CFO: Robert M Davis
Ofcr: Julie L Gerberding
Assoc VP: Nina Stuccio
Ex VP: Clark Golestani
Ex VP: Mirian M Graddick-Weir
Ex VP: Michael Rosenblatt
Sr VP: Rita A Karachun
VP: Patrick Bergstedt
VP: Stan Booth
VP: Arthur Burson
VP: John Carroll
VP: Beth Colnett
VP: Iain Dukes
VP: Yvette Espeleta
VP: Stephen Farrand
VP: Glen Firestone
VP: Raul Lacson
VP: Dorthe Mikkelsen
VP: James Philipson
VP: Geralyn Ritter
Board of Directors: Patricia F Russo, Leslie A Brun, Craig B Thompson, Thomas R Cech, Wendell P Weeks, Pamela J Craig, Peter C Wendell, Thomas H Glocer, William B Harrison Jr, C Robert Kidder, Rochelle B Lazarus, Carlos E Represas, Paul B Rothman

D-U-N-S 96-642-5733
MERCK AND CO INC EMPLOYEE BENEFITS TRUST
1 Merck Dr, Whitehouse Station, NJ 08889-3497
Tel (908) 423-1000 *Founded/Ownrshp* 2011
Sales NA *EMP* 2^E
Accts Buckconsultants Secaucus Nj
SIC 6411 Insurance agents, brokers & service

D-U-N-S 78-319-2800
■ MERCK HOLDINGS LLC
(*Suby of* MERCK SHARP & DOHME CORP) ★
1 Merck Dr, Whitehouse Station, NJ 08889-3497
Tel (908) 423-1000 *Founded/Ownrshp* 1884
Sales 196.1MM^E *EMP* 2,700
SIC 2834 6712 Proprietary drug products; Bank holding companies
Pr: Richard Henriques
**Pr:* Richard T Clark
**Treas:* Caroline Dorsa
**Sr VP:* Judy Lewent
VP: Bruno Strigini

D-U-N-S 96-688-6728
MERCK PATIENT ASSISTANCE PROGRAM INC
2 Clerico Ln Apt 201, Hillsborough, NJ 08844-1620
Tel (908) 423-1000 *Founded/Ownrshp* 2011
Sales 198.9MM *EMP* 2^E
SIC 8699

D-U-N-S 03-716-7426 IMP
■ MERCK SHARP & DOHME (IA) LLC
(*Suby of* MERCK HOLDINGS LLC) ★
1 Merck Dr, Whitehouse Station, NJ 08889-3497
Tel (908) 423-1000 *Founded/Ownrshp* 1949
Sales 98.7MM^E *EMP* 100
SIC 5122 Pharmaceuticals
Pr: Grey F Warner
Pr: Merri Baillargeon
**Sr VP:* Francis H Spiegel
VP: Rick Brasher
**VP:* Judy C Luwent

D-U-N-S 00-131-7601 IMP/EXP
■ MERCK SHARP & DOHME CORP (NJ)
(*Suby of* MERCK & CO INC) ★
2000 Galloping Hill Rd, Kenilworth, NJ 07033-1310
Tel (908) 740-4000 *Founded/Ownrshp* 1935
Sales 7.9MMM^E *EMP* 18,400
SIC 2834 8741 Pharmaceutical preparations; Druggists' preparations (pharmaceuticals); Drugs acting on the respiratory system; Drugs affecting parasitic & infective diseases; Management services
Ch Bd: Kenneth C Frazier
CFO: Robert M Davis
Ex VP: Sanat Chattopadhyay
Ex VP: Joseph Connors
Ex VP: Richard R Deluca Jr
Ex VP: Julie L Gerberding
Ex VP: Mirian M Graddick-Weir
Ex VP: Michael J Holston
Ex VP: Roger M Perlmutter
Ex VP: Adam H Schechter
VP: Richard Kinney

D-U-N-S 60-987-8343
MERCO GROUP INC
7711 N 81st St, Milwaukee, WI 53223-3847
Tel (414) 365-2600 *Founded/Ownrshp* 1989
Sales 111.4MM^E *EMP* 225
SIC 5199 5047

D-U-N-S 85-971-6677 EXP
MERCOM CORP
313 Commerce Dr, Pawleys Island, SC 29585-6052
Tel (843) 979-9957 *Founded/Ownrshp* 2000
Sales 105.8MM *EMP* 63
Accts Webster Rogers Llp Myrtle Bea
SIC 5999 Communication equipment
Pr: Stella Mercado
**CFO:* Jeff Miller
**VP:* Larry Mercado

D-U-N-S 04-319-0776 IMP
MERCURY AIR GROUP INC (NY)
MERCURY SERVICE
2780 Skypark Dr Ste 300, Torrance, CA 90505-7518
Tel (310) 602-3770 *Founded/Ownrshp* 1956, 2013
Sales 603.8MM^E *EMP* 1,200
SIC 5172 7389 4581 Aircraft fueling services; Brokers' services; Hangar operation; Airfreight loading & unloading services
Pr: Joseph A Czyzyk
CFO: Kent Rosenthal
CFO: Lawrence R Samuels
VP: Daniel K Barnard
VP: Carolina Gutierrez
VP: David Herbst Rejoins
IT Man: George Vaughn
Genl Couns: Kathryn M Schwertfeger

D-U-N-S 00-220-6639 IMP
MERCURY AIRCRAFT INC (NY)
8126 County Route 88, Hammondsport, NY 14840-9458
Tel (607) 569-4200 *Founded/Ownrshp* 1920
Sales 114.1MM^E *EMP* 600
SIC 3469 3444

D-U-N-S 07-530-6340
■ MERCURY CASUALTY CO
M C C
(*Suby of* MERCURY GENERAL CORP) ★
555 W Imperial Hwy, Brea, CA 92821-4802
Tel (323) 937-1060 *Founded/Ownrshp* 1979
Sales NA *EMP* 4,200
SIC 6331 6351 Automobile insurance; Warranty insurance, home
CEO: Gabriel Tirador
**CEO:* George Joseph
Ex VP: Gus Tepper
Snr Mgr: Hsin-Hsin Lee

D-U-N-S 01-885-6757
MERCURY FUEL SERVICE INC
43 Lafayette St, Waterbury, CT 06708-3897
Tel (203) 756-7284 *Founded/Ownrshp* 1947
Sales 116.8MM^E *EMP* 110
SIC 5172 5541 5411 5983 1711 2911 Gasoline; Fuel oil; Filling stations, gasoline; Convenience stores, chain; Fuel oil dealers; Warm air heating & air conditioning contractor; Petroleum refining
Pr: Michael Devino Jr
**Treas:* Martin F Devino
**VP:* David F Devino
Opers Mgr: George Strileckis
Sls Mgr: Jim Barone

D-U-N-S 07-530-0004
▲ MERCURY GENERAL CORP
4484 Wilshire Blvd, Los Angeles, CA 90010-3710
Tel (323) 937-1060 *Founded/Ownrshp* 1961
Sales NA *EMP* 4,300^E
Accts Kpmg Llp Los Angeles Califor
Tkr Sym MCY *Exch* NYS
SIC 6331 6411 Automobile insurance; Property damage insurance; Fire, marine & casualty insurance & carriers; Insurance agents, brokers & service
Pr: Gabriel Tirador
**Ch Bd:* George Joseph
CFO: Theodore R Stalick
Chf Inves: Christopher Graves
Ofcr: Robert Houlihan
Ofcr: Randall R Petro
Sr VP: Allan Lubitz
VP: Kenneth G Kitzmiller
VP: Heidi C Sullivan
VP: Charles Toney
VP: Judy A Walters
VP: David Yeager
Board of Directors: Donald R Spuehler, Bruce A Bunner, Michael D Curtius, James G Ellis, Christopher Graves, Richard E Grayson, Martha E Marcon, John G Nackel, Donald P Newell, Glenn S Schafer

D-U-N-S 09-600-7877
■ MERCURY INSURANCE CO
(*Suby of* MERCURY GENERAL CORP) ★
4484 Wilshire Blvd, Los Angeles, CA 90010-3710
Tel (323) 937-1060 *Founded/Ownrshp* 1972
Sales NA *EMP* 4,600
SIC 6331 Fire, marine & casualty insurance
CEO: Gabe Tirador
**CFO:* Ted Stalick
**Ch:* George Joseph
Sr VP: Allan Lubitz
VP: Hossein Abby
VP: Jason Owens
**VP:* Judith Walters
Exec: Heidi Sullivan
Dir IT: Art Coble

D-U-N-S 61-037-0210
■ MERCURY INSURANCE CO OF FLORIDA
(*Suby of* MERCURY GENERAL CORP) ★
1901 Ulmerton Rd Fl 6, Clearwater, FL 33762-2307
Tel (727) 561-4000 *Founded/Ownrshp* 2001
Sales NA *EMP* 300
SIC 6331 Automobile insurance

D-U-N-S 78-656-3010
■ MERCURY INSURANCE SERVICES LLC
(*Suby of* M C C) ★
4484 Wilshire Blvd, Los Angeles, CA 90010-3710
Tel (323) 937-1060 *Founded/Ownrshp* 2000
Sales NA *EMP* 4,000
SIC 6331 Fire, marine & casualty insurance; Property damage insurance
CEO: Gabriel Tirador

D-U-N-S 55-659-0040
■ MERCURY INTERACTIVE LLC
(*Suby of* HEWLETT PACKARD ENTERPRISE CO) ★
3000 Hanover St, Palo Alto, CA 94304-1112
Tel (650) 857-1501 *Founded/Ownrshp* 2015
Sales 80.4MM^E *EMP* 2,659
SIC 7372 Prepackaged software
Pr: Anthony Zingale
Pr: Moshe Egert
Treas: Jon E Flaxman
VP: Scott Bradley

D-U-N-S 79-881-4765 IMP/EXP
■ MERCURY MARINE INC
MERCURY MARINE INTERNATIONAL
(*Suby of* BRUNSWICK CORP) ★
W6250 W Pioneer Rd, Fond Du Lac, WI 54935-5636
Tel (920) 929-5000 *Founded/Ownrshp* 1939
Sales 1.3MMM^E *EMP* 4,100^E
SIC 3089 3535 Plastic boats & other marine equipment
Pr: John Pfeiffer
VP: Donald Anderson
VP: Stephan Cloutier
VP: Denise Devereaux
VP: Ray Donahue
VP: Mike Gyorog
VP: Terry Schroeder
Prgrm Mgr: Harry Classen
Prgrm Mgr: Rob Hackbarth
IT Man: Peter Brill
IT Man: Jackie Kottke

MERCURY MARINE INTERNATIONAL
See MERCURY MARINE INC

D-U-N-S 09-860-0984 EXP
MERCURY OVERSEAS INC
(*Suby of* HANNAN CHIKUSAN CO., LTD.)
830 Mission St, South Pasadena, CA 91030-3192
Tel (626) 799-9141 *Founded/Ownrshp* 1979
Sales 400.0MM *EMP* 9
SIC 5147 5146 Meats & meat products; Seafoods
Pr: Yutaka Nihira

D-U-N-S 16-130-7111 IMP
MERCURY PLASTICS INC
14825 Salt Lake Ave, City of Industry, CA 91746-3131
Tel (626) 369-8457 *Founded/Ownrshp* 1987
Sales 106.3MM^E *EMP* 550
SIC 2673 2759 3089 Plastic bags: made from purchased materials; Bags, plastic: printing; Plastic containers, except foam
CEO: Benjamin Deutsch
**CEO:* Mark Tao
**CFO:* Anna Rabchev
**Ex VP:* Andrew Deutsch
**VP:* Zachary Deutsch
**VP:* Kamyar Mirdamadi

D-U-N-S 00-525-8959 IMP
MERCURY PRODUCTS CORP (IL)
1201 Mercury Dr, Schaumburg, IL 60193-3513
Tel (847) 524-4400 *Founded/Ownrshp* 1946, 1995
Sales 90.0MM^E *EMP* 255
SIC 3465 3469 3714 Automotive stampings; Machine parts, stamped or pressed metal; Motor vehicle engines & parts; Exhaust systems & parts, motor vehicle
Pr: Bruce C Hael
**Pr:* Bruce Havel
CTO: Philip Haag
Plnt Mgr: Jack Ehlinger
Ql Cn Mgr: Ron Anderson

MERCURY SERVICE
See MERCURY AIR GROUP INC

D-U-N-S 10-676-0549 EXP
▲ MERCURY SYSTEMS INC
201 Riverneck Rd, Chelmsford, MA 01824-2820
Tel (978) 256-1300 *Founded/Ownrshp* 1981
Sales 270.1MM *EMP* 629
Tkr Sym MRCY *Exch* NGS
SIC 3672 7372 Printed circuit boards; Prepackaged software
Pr: Mark Aslett
Ch Bd: Vincent Vitto
Pr: Didier M C Thibaud
Chf Mktg O: Phil Juliano
Sr VP: Christopher C Cambria
VP: Darryl McKenney
VP: Jamie Ryan
VP: Charles A Speicher
VP Bus Dev: Mark Behrman
Exec: Diane Stacey
Dir Bus: John Procacci
Board of Directors: James K Bass, Michael A Daniels, George K Muellner, Mark S Newman, William K O'brien

MERCY ALLIANCE
See MERCY HEALTH SYSTEM CORP

MERCY BEHAVIORAL HEALTH
See MERCY LIFE CENTER CORP

D-U-N-S 10-231-9621
MERCY CARE MANAGEMENT INC
MERCY CARE NORTH
(*Suby of* MERCYCARE SERVICE CORP) ★
701 10th St Se, Cedar Rapids, IA 52403-1251
Tel (319) 398-6011 *Founded/Ownrshp* 1983
Sales 40.7MM *EMP* 2,200
SIC 8011 8741 8322 Freestanding emergency medical center; Management services; Individual & family services
Ch Bd: Lee Lui
**Treas:* Emmett Scherrman
Sr VP: Jeff Cash
VP: Phil Lasson

MERCY CARE NORTH
See MERCY CARE MANAGEMENT INC

MERCY CARE PLAN
See SOUTHWEST CATHOLIC HEALTH NETWORK CORP

D-U-N-S 82-716-1808
MERCY CATHOLIC MEDICAL CENTER OF SOUTHEASTERN PENNSYLVANIA
1 W Elm St, Conshohocken, PA 19428-4108
Tel (610) 567-6725 *Founded/Ownrshp* 2008
Sales 325.7MM *EMP* 80^E
Accts Deloitte Tax Llp Philadelphia
SIC 8062 General medical & surgical hospitals

D-U-N-S 07-306-7480
MERCY CHILDRENS HOSPITAL
2401 Gillham Rd, Kansas City, MO 64108-4619
Tel (816) 234-3000 *Founded/Ownrshp* 1897
Sales 978.1MM *EMP* 7,000
Accts Kpmg Llp Omaha Ne
SIC 8069 Children's hospital
Pr: Randall L O'Donnell PHD
Chf Rad: James C Brown
**CFO:* Dwight Hyde
Ch: Ed Connolly
**Co-COO:* Karen Cox
**Ex VP:* Sandra Aj Lawrence
**Ex VP:* Charles C Roberts
**Ex VP:* Jo Stueve
VP: Kimberly Brown
VP: Warren Dudley
VP: Michelle Overstreet
VP: Davoren Tempel
Dir Soc: Anoma Mullegama

D-U-N-S 96-238-9461
MERCY CLINIC OKLAHOMA COMMUNITIES INC
4300 W Memorial Rd, Oklahoma City, OK 73120-8304
Tel (405) 936-5213 *Founded/Ownrshp* 2009
Sales 178.4MM *EMP* 1
Accts Pleus And Company Llc Cheste
SIC 8011 Offices & clinics of medical doctors
Ex Dir: Diana Smalley
**Ex Dir:* Christopher Hahne

D-U-N-S 04-482-7764
MERCY COLLEGE
555 Broadway Frnt, Dobbs Ferry, NY 10522-1189
Tel (914) 455-2650 *Founded/Ownrshp* 1963
Sales 190.2MM *EMP* 500
Accts Marks Paneth Llp New York N
SIC 8221 College, except junior
Pr: Kimberly Cline
Pr: Margaret McGrail
Pr: Joseph Trentacoste
CFO: Dana Marrone
VP: Mary Lozina
Assoc Dir: Michael Agrest
Assoc Dir: Susana Briscoe-Alba
Assoc Dir: Nicholas Canzano
Dir Sec: Daniel Braccia
Off Admin: Elizabeth Dispenza
Dir IT: Donna F Bookin

D-U-N-S 17-679-0467
MERCY COLLEGE OF HEALTH SCIENCES
(*Suby of* MERCY MEDICAL CTR - DES MOINES) ★
928 6th Ave, Des Moines, IA 50309-1225
Tel (515) 643-3180 *Founded/Ownrshp* 1997
Sales 32.3MM^E *EMP* 2,222^E
Accts Deloitte Tax Llp Houston Tx
SIC 8221 Colleges universities & professional schools
Pr: Barb Decker
VP: Karen Anderson
VP: Steven Langdon
VP: Brian Tingleff
Sales Exec: Sue Zylstra
Nrsg Dir: Mildred Agena
Nrsg Dir: Dale Brown

MERCY CONTINUING CARE
See TRINITY SENIOR LIVING COMMUNITIES

D-U-N-S 13-417-0547 IMP/EXP
MERCY CORPS
45 Sw Ankeny St, Portland, OR 97204-3500
Tel (503) 796-6800 *Founded/Ownrshp* 1979
Sales 329.1MM *EMP* 450
SIC 8322 Refugee service
Pr: Neal L Keny-Guyer
CFO: Beth Dehamel
**Chf Mktg O:* Dara Royer
Ofcr: Prakash Basyal
Ofcr: Christy Delafield
Ofcr: Karissa Dunbar
Ofcr: Allison M Dworschak
Ofcr: Lily Frey
Ofcr: Sarah Halfman
Ofcr: Lynn Hector
Ofcr: Ben Melix
Ofcr: Terry Ndifuanja
Ofcr: Nathan Oetting
Ofcr: Angela Owen
Ofcr: Manasi Patwardhan
Ofcr: Jamey Pietzold
Ofcr: Carol Skowron
Ofcr: Tanya Sloan
Ofcr: Jeremy Snyder
Ofcr: Heidi Wagner
Ofcr: Luby Wind

D-U-N-S 80-466-9539
MERCY FITZGERALD HOSPITAL
MERCY HEALTH SYSTEM
(*Suby of* MERCY HEALTH SYSTEM) ★
1500 Lansdowne Ave Ste 1, Darby, PA 19023-1200
Tel (610) 237-4000 *Founded/Ownrshp* 1915
Sales 357.8M^E *EMP* 2,000
SIC 8062 General medical & surgical hospitals
CEO: Susan Croushore
**CFO:* Don Shenk
Comm Dir: Michael Bannon
Chf Nrs Of: Linda Kaufman
Ex Dir: Cathy Franklin
Dir Pat Ac: Mike Glitz
Dir IT: Jim Holmes
Telecom Mg: Mary Foster
QC Dir: Christine Frey
Pathlgst: Sandra E Harkavy
Pathlgst: Jung Shin

D-U-N-S 06-276-5425
MERCY FLOWERS & GIFTS (IA)
701 10th St Se, Cedar Rapids, IA 52403-1251
Tel (319) 398-6124 *Founded/Ownrshp* 1952
Sales 290.6MM *EMP* 7
SIC 5992 5947 Florists; Gift shop
**Prin:* Margaret Dunshee

D-U-N-S 83-877-2390
MERCY FRANCISCAN HOSPITAL MT AIRY
2446 Kipling Ave, Cincinnati, OH 45239-6650
Tel (513) 853-5101 *Founded/Ownrshp* 2004
Sales 117.3MM^E *EMP* 2,620
SIC 8741 8062 Hospital management; Nursing & personal care facility management; General medical & surgical hospitals
Pr: Rodney Reider
**VP:* Ruby Hemphil Crowford
**VP:* Judy Daleiden
Doctor: Mark Zoellner
Pharmcst: Mark Johnson

D-U-N-S 07-928-4725
MERCY GENERAL HEALTH PARTNERS
MERCY HEALTH
(*Suby of* CATHOLIC HEALTH EAST) ★
1500 E Sherman Blvd, Muskegon, MI 49444-1849
Tel (231) 728-4032 *Founded/Ownrshp* 1998
Sales 117.5MM^E *EMP* 2,000^E
SIC 8062 General medical & surgical hospitals
Pr: Roger Spoelman
**CFO:* Mary Boyd
Surgeon: Robert Schneeberger

D-U-N-S 13-380-6620
MERCY HAMILTON HOSPITAL
3000 Mack Rd, Fairfield, OH 45014-5335
Tel (513) 603-8600 *Founded/Ownrshp* 1800
Sales 231.3MM *EMP* 50
SIC 8062 General medical & surgical hospitals
Pr: Dave Ferrell
VP: Matt Eversole
VP: Mike Hibbard

Dir Inf Cn: Pamela Justice
Pathlgst: Joseph H Brandabur

MERCY HEALTH
See MERCY GENERAL HEALTH PARTNERS

D-U-N-S 04-766-8467
MERCY HEALTH
1701 Mercy Health Pl, Cincinnati, OH 45237-6147
Tel (513) 639-2800 *Founded/Ownrshp* 1986
Sales 4.2MMM *EMP* 35,000
Accts Ernst & Young Llp Cincinnati
SIC 8062 General medical & surgical hospitals
Pr: Michael D Connelly
Pr: Randy Curnow
COO: Brian Smith
CFO: Deborah Bloomfield
Ofcr: Anton Decker
Ex VP: David A Catalano
Sr VP: Donald E Casey
Sr VP: Rebecca Sykes
VP: Michele Napier
VP: Kristen H Wevers
Off Mgr: John Loughney

D-U-N-S 07-711-8982
MERCY HEALTH
SISTERS OF MERCY HEALTH SYSTEM
14528 South Outer 40 Rd # 100, Chesterfield, MO 63017-5743
Tel (314) 579-6100 *Founded/Ownrshp* 1986
Sales 1.5MMM^E *EMP* 8,800
Accts Ernst & Young Us Llp Clayton
SIC 8062 General medical & surgical hospitals
Pr: Lynn Britton
**COO:* Michael McCurry
COO: Andy Runge
CFO: Cheryl Matejka
**CFO:* Shannon Sock
Bd of Dir: Paul Bergant
Trst: Anita Desalvo
Ex VP: Donn Sorensen
Ex VP: Jon Vitiello
VP: James Britton
VP: Jennifer Laperre
VP: Mike Mc Creary
VP: Vance Moore
VP: Robert E Schimmel
VP: Stuart Stangeland
Exec: Michele Stewart
Dir Rx: Craig Campbell
Dir Rx: Gary Dipboye

D-U-N-S 07-757-4580
MERCY HEALTH - ST CHARLES HOSPITAL LLC
2600 Navarre Ave, Oregon, OH 43616-3207
Tel (419) 696-7200 *Founded/Ownrshp* 1953
Sales 133.5MM *EMP* 1,200^E
SIC 8062 General medical & surgical hospitals
**Pr:* Jacalyn Liebowitz
**CEO:* Jeffrey Dempseyn
**Prin:* F J Gallagher
**Prin:* Joseph W Rossler
**Prin:* Rolf H Scheidel

D-U-N-S 07-677-7275
MERCY HEALTH ANDERSON HOSPITAL
MERCY HOSPITAL ANDERSON
7500 State Rd, Cincinnati, OH 45255-2439
Tel (513) 624-4500 *Founded/Ownrshp* 1942
Sales 220.1MM *EMP* 823
SIC 8062 General medical & surgical hospitals
Pr: Patrica Shroer
VP: Julie Holt
Dir Risk M: Kristen Boggs

D-U-N-S 06-543-0712 IMP
MERCY HEALTH CENTER INC (OK)
(*Suby of* SISTERS OF MERCY HEALTH SYSTEM) ★
14528 South Outer 40 Rd # 100, Chesterfield, MO 63017-5743
Tel (405) 755-1515 *Founded/Ownrshp* 1947, 1974
Sales 207.9MM^E *EMP* 2,300
Accts Pleus And Company Llc Chester
SIC 8062 General medical & surgical hospitals
Pr: Jim R Gebhart
Doctor: Ann Parrington MD

D-U-N-S 08-012-3075
MERCY HEALTH CORP (IL)
2400 N Rockton Ave, Rockford, IL 61103-3655
Tel (815) 971-5000 *Founded/Ownrshp* 2014
Sales 1.3MMM *EMP* 2,200^E
SIC 8062 General medical & surgical hospitals
CEO: Javon R Bea

D-U-N-S 07-146-3590
MERCY HEALTH FOUNDATION OF SOUTHEASTERN PENNSYLVANIA
MERCY HEALTH SYSTEM
(*Suby of* CATHOLIC HEALTH EAST) ★
1 W Elm St Ste 100, Conshohocken, PA 19428-4108
Tel (610) 567-6000 *Founded/Ownrshp* 2014
Sales 94.4MM *EMP* 8,000
Accts Deloitte Tax Llp Philadelphia
SIC 8062 General medical & surgical hospitals
CEO: David Clark
Pr: Janet Borger
VP: Anthony Fanelli
VP: Michael McCreary
VP: Kathy Priest
VP: Elizabeth Riley-Wasserman
**VP:* Julie Topkis Scanlon
VP: Elizabeth Wasserman
VP: Gary Zimmer
Snr Ntwrk: Bill Brown
Dir IT: Tim Moore

D-U-N-S 09-835-6335
MERCY HEALTH NETWORK INC
CHI
(*Suby of* CHI) ★
1755 59th Pl, West Des Moines, IA 50266-7737
Tel (515) 247-3121 *Founded/Ownrshp* 1998
Sales 14.4MM *EMP* 7,500
SIC 8741 Hospital management
Pr: David Vellinga
COO: Sharon Phillips

Exec: Tracy Muhlenburg
Dir Rad: William Young
Dir IT: Jeffrey Wiese
Netwrk Mgr: Tracy Turner
Mktg Dir: Laura Vandenbosch
Doctor: Paul Babikian
Doctor: Mark Bissing
Doctor: Joel From
Doctor: Randall Hamilton

MERCY HEALTH PARTNERS
See HACKLEY HOSPITAL

D-U-N-S 01-579-6923
■ **MERCY HEALTH PARTNERS**
(*Suby of* COMMUNITY HEALTH SYSTEMS INC) ★
746 Jefferson Ave, Scranton, PA 18510-1624
Tel (570) 348-7100 *Founded/Ownrshp* 1997, 2011
Sales 67.2MM^E *EMP* 2,295
SIC 8062 General medical & surgical hospitals
CEO: Kevin Cook
IT Man: Frank Klassner
Genl Couns: Christine M Gubbiotti

D-U-N-S 05-830-0604
MERCY HEALTH PARTNERS
(*Suby of* MERCY HEALTH) ★
1701 Mercy Health Pl, Cincinnati, OH 45237-6147
Tel (513) 952-5000 *Founded/Ownrshp* 1982
Sales 349.6MM^E *EMP* 2,886
Accts Bkd Llp Cincinnati Oh
SIC 8062 General medical & surgical hospitals
Chf Rad: Scott T Welton
**CEO:* Tom Urban
Ofcr: Richard Schuster
Sr VP: Loretta L Lee
**Sr VP:* Kenneth C Page
Sr VP: Kenneth Page
VP: John Finley
VP: Hui Saldana
Off Mgr: Valerie Charles

D-U-N-S 07-409-7791
MERCY HEALTH PARTNERS - LOURDES INC
LOURDES HOSPITAL
(*Suby of* MERCY HEALTH) ★
1530 Lone Oak Rd Int24, Paducah, KY 42003-7901
Tel (270) 444-2444 *Founded/Ownrshp* 1962
Sales 185.1MM *EMP* 1,600
SIC 8062 General medical & surgical hospitals
CEO: Steven Grinnell
CFO: Edward W Miller
**CFO:* Mark Thomson
Ofcr: Jessica Toren
VP Bus Dev: Susan Schaefer
CIO: Carolyn Hansman
Mktg Dir: Kelly Nichols

D-U-N-S 17-586-1178
■ **MERCY HEALTH PARTNERS INC**
TENNOVA HEALTHCARE
(*Suby of* HMA) ★
900 E Oak Hill Ave, Knoxville, TN 37917-4505
Tel (865) 545-8000 *Founded/Ownrshp* 2011
Sales 447.8MM^E *EMP* 2,711
SIC 8062 General medical & surgical hospitals
CEO: Karen Metz
COO: Brett Flinchum
COO: Tiffany L Tomasso
Sr VP: Jerry Askew
VP: Carol Gray
VP Mktg: Pat McGee

D-U-N-S 15-397-9588
MERCY HEALTH PLAN INC
KEYSTONE MERCY HEALTH PLAN
200 Stevens Dr Ste 350, Philadelphia, PA 19113-1520
Tel (215) 937-8000 *Founded/Ownrshp* 1983
Sales NA *EMP* 470
SIC 6324 6321 Hospital & medical service plans; Accident & health insurance
Pr: Daniel J Hilferty
CFO: Alan Krigstein
Ex VP: Michael A Rashid
Sr VP: Christopher Drumm
VP: Amy Knapp
VP: Karen Michael
Comm Dir: Tracy Pou
CTO: Lorraine Garbarino
Sys Mgr: Paul Capper
Sys Mgr: Sean Fryatt
Web Dev: Daniel Eaker

D-U-N-S 88-372-1177
■ **MERCY HEALTH PLANS INC**
PREMIER HEALTH PLANS
(*Suby of* MHP, INC.)
14528 South Outer 40 Rd # 100, Chesterfield, MO 63017-5743
Tel (314) 214-2384 *Founded/Ownrshp* 2010
Sales NA *EMP* 390
SIC 6324 Hospital & medical service plans
CEO: Michael Murphy
COO: Eric Pianalto
**CFO:* George Schneider
Ex Dir: Barb Grayson
Ex Dir: Teresa Halloran
Dir IT: James Freeman
Dir IT: Shannon Williams
Sls Mgr: Carl Schultz

D-U-N-S 14-598-1945
MERCY HEALTH SERVICES-IOWA CORP
MERCY MEDICAL CENTER
(*Suby of* CATHOLIC HEALTH EAST) ★
20555 Victor Pkwy, Livonia, MI 48152-7031
Tel (734) 343-1000 *Founded/Ownrshp* 1993
Sales 665.5MM *EMP* 2,471
SIC 8011 Medical centers
CEO: Jack Weiner
**Pr:* Joseph Swevish
**Pr:* Daniel Varnum
**CFO:* James Peppiatt-Combes
Bd of Dir: Joellen Steil
Exec: Stephen Shivinsky
**Prin:* Scott Leighty
**Genl Couns:* Daniel G Hale

D-U-N-S 84-187-5040
MERCY HEALTH SPRINGFIELD COMMUNITIES
SAINT JHNS BHAVIORAL HLTH CARE
(*Suby of* SISTERS OF MERCY HEALTH SYSTEM) ★
1235 E Cherokee St, Springfield, MO 65804-2203
Tel (417) 885-2000 *Founded/Ownrshp* 1999
Sales 475.0MM *EMP* 6,300
Accts Ernst & Young Us Llp Saint Lo
SIC 8062 General medical & surgical hospitals
Pr: Jon D Swope
Dir Rx: Keith David
Dir Rx: C W Poell
Dir Rx: Mike Sieg

D-U-N-S 05-416-1948
MERCY HEALTH ST VINCENT MED LLC
ST. VINCENT HOSPITAL AND MEDIA
2213 Cherry St, Toledo, OH 43608-2603
Tel (419) 251-3232 *Founded/Ownrshp* 1875
Sales 467.2MM *EMP* 6,000
SIC 8062 General medical & surgical hospitals
Pr: Tim Koder
**Ch Bd:* Beverly J McBride
**Pr:* Steven Mickus
Pr: Jeffrey Peterson
**Treas:* Robert A Sullivan
Pathlgst: Shaheda R Ahmed
Pathlgst: Andrew J Britton
Surgeon: Gregory W Walker
Doctor: Alean Zeiler MD
Pharmcst: Debra Bakle
Pharmcst: Sooeun Williams

MERCY HEALTH SYSTEM
See MERCY SUBURBAN HOSPITAL

MERCY HEALTH SYSTEM
See NAZARETH HOSPITAL

MERCY HEALTH SYSTEM
See MERCY HEALTH FOUNDATION OF SOUTHEASTERN PENNSYLVANIA

MERCY HEALTH SYSTEM
See MERCY FITZGERALD HOSPITAL

D-U-N-S 95-914-3785
MERCY HEALTH SYSTEM - NORTHERN REGION
(*Suby of* MERCY HEALTH) ★
2200 Jefferson Ave, Toledo, OH 43604-7101
Tel (419) 251-1359 *Founded/Ownrshp* 1981
Sales 339.1MM^E *EMP* 7,200
Accts Bkd Llp Cincinnati Oh
SIC 8062 General medical & surgical hospitals
Pr: Steven Mickus
Pr: Christine Browning
Pr: Kathleen A Osborne
**CFO:* Samantha Platzke
CFO: Liz Snodgrass
VP: Joseph Sober
Doctor: Dick Evens

D-U-N-S 02-046-0788
MERCY HEALTH SYSTEM CORP
MERCY ALLIANCE
(*Suby of* MERCY HEALTH CORP) ★
1000 Mineral Point Ave, Janesville, WI 53548-2940
Tel (608) 741-6891 *Founded/Ownrshp* 2015
Sales 523.4MM *EMP* 2,200
Accts Wipfli Llp Milwaukee Wiscons
SIC 8062 General medical & surgical hospitals
CEO: Javon R Bea
Chf Path: Michael Strassman
Chf Rad: Allan Muraki
Ch Bd: Rowland J Mc Clellan
**CFO:* Joseph Nemeth
VP: Linda Hart
VP: Jennifer Laperre
Exec: Peter Kraemer
Dir Lab: Ruth Bythe
Dir Lab: Sheila Hillison
Dir Rad: Carol Barletta
Dir Rx: Don R Janczak
Dir Rx: Dale Miller

D-U-N-S 09-292-2137
MERCY HEALTH SYSTEM OF NORTHWEST ARKANSAS INC
MERCY HOSPITAL ST. LOUIS
(*Suby of* MERCY HOSPITAL ST LOUIS) ★
2710 S Rife Medical Ln, Rogers, AR 72758-1452
Tel (479) 338-8000 *Founded/Ownrshp* 1997
Sales 195.3MM *EMP* 1,650^E
Accts Ernst & Young Us Llp Clayton
SIC 8062 General medical & surgical hospitals
Pr: Eric Pianalto
VP: Cindy Carmichael
**Prin:* Steven Gus
Doctor: Robert Donnell
Doctor: Vernon O'Neil Tucker
Board of Directors: Dr Minh-Tah Dang, Dr Orlando Augliar-Guzman, Dr Richard Miles

D-U-N-S 78-530-0075
MERCY HEALTH SYSTEM OF SOUTHEASTERN PENNSYLVANIA
CHI
(*Suby of* CHI) ★
1 W Elm St Ste 100, Conshohocken, PA 19428-4108
Tel (610) 567-6000 *Founded/Ownrshp* 1982
Sales 88.3MM *EMP* 1^E
Accts Deloitte Tax Llp Philadelphia
SIC 8062 General medical & surgical hospitals
Ch Bd: Christine McCann
**CEO:* H Ray Welch
**CFO:* Joseph Bradley
Dir Risk M: Joyce H Taft

D-U-N-S 93-887-6661
MERCY HEALTH YOUNGSTOWN LLC
ST ELIZABETH HEALTH CENTER
(*Suby of* MERCY HEALTH) ★
1044 Belmont Ave, Youngstown, OH 44504-1006
Tel (330) 746-7211 *Founded/Ownrshp* 1996
Sales 309.7MM *EMP* 4,000
SIC 8062 8071 Hospital, affiliated with AMA residency; Ultrasound laboratory

Pr: Robert Shroder
*Pr: Genie Aubel
COO: James Davis
Sr VP: John Finicio
Sr VP: Thomas Kohl
Dir OR: Elaine Jones
Dir Risk M: Gordon Sanders
Dir Rx: Linda Lachman
*Prin: Sarah Quinn
Off Mgr: Anne Moss
Off Admin: Sandy Bascone-Jones

D-U-N-S 17-450-2682
MERCY HEALTHCARE SACRAMENTO
MERCY SAN JUAN HOSPITAL
(Suby of DIGNITY HEALTH) ★
3400 Data Dr, Rancho Cordova, CA 95670-7956
Tel (916) 379-2871 Founded/Ownrshp 1981
Sales 442.2MM^E EMP 6,131
SIC 8062 General medical & surgical hospitals
Pr: Michael Erne
*COO: William Hunt
*CFO: Richard Rothberger
*Chf Mktg O: Dan Ferguson
*Sr VP: John Chambers
*Sr VP: Scott Ideson

MERCY HOME CARE
See MERCY MEDICAL CENTER-CLINTON INC

D-U-N-S 07-610-1906
MERCY HOME SERVICES A CALIFORNIA LIMITED PARTNERSHIP
MERCY MEDICAL CENTER - REDDING
(Suby of DIGNITY HEALTH) ★
2175 Rosaline Ave Ste A, Redding, CA 96001-2549
Tel (530) 225-6000 Founded/Ownrshp 1987
Sales 446.3MM EMP 1,200
SIC 8062 General medical & surgical hospitals
CEO: George A Govier
CFO: Jill Belk
Dir Lab: Robert Folden
Dir Rad: Steve Buhler
IT Man: Wendy Scott
Ansthlgy: Gordon L Heminway
Plas Surg: Miguel A Mendez-Fernndez

D-U-N-S 07-173-2499
MERCY HOSPITAL
PORTLAND THORACIC SURGERY
(Suby of EMHS) ★
144 State St, Portland, ME 04101-3795
Tel (207) 879-3000 Founded/Ownrshp 2013
Sales 213.6MM EMP 1,200
SIC 8062 Hospital, affiliated with AMA residency
Pr: Eileen F Skinner
*COO: Robert Nutter
*CFO: Stephen McDonnell
*VP: Bette L Neville
*VP: Scott Rusk
Exec: William Clifford
Exec: Karen Newton
Dir Lab: Chris Murray
*Prin: Anthony Marple
Off Mgr: Catherine O'Bar
CIO: Patrick Grotten

D-U-N-S 02-004-7254
MERCY HOSPITAL AND MEDICAL CENTER
2525 S Michigan Ave, Chicago, IL 60616-2332
Tel (312) 567-2201 Founded/Ownrshp 1852
Sales 273.3MM EMP 1,550
SIC 8062 General medical & surgical hospitals
Pr: John McCarthy
Pr: Constance Murphy
CFO: Bob Diantonio
*CFO: Eric Krueger
CFO: Gary Zmrhal
*Ex VP: Richard Cerceo
VP: Ronald Arnone
VP: Carla Campbell
VP: Mary Caponigro
VP: Thomas Dohm
*VP: Susan Gallagher
VP: Tom Garvey
VP: Martin Hebda
VP: Eileen Knightly
VP: Maurice Raab
Dir Rad: Peter Jabeck

MERCY HOSPITAL ANDERSON
See MERCY HEALTH ANDERSON HOSPITAL

D-U-N-S 96-961-8235
MERCY HOSPITAL ARDMORE INC
1011 14th Ave Nw, Ardmore, OK 73401-1828
Tel (580) 223-5400 Founded/Ownrshp 2011
Sales 132.2MM EMP 47
Accts Pleus And Company Llc Chester
SIC 8062 General medical & surgical hospitals
Prin: Paul A Foster
CFO: Scott Calendar

D-U-N-S 06-962-0524
MERCY HOSPITAL CEDAR RAPIDS IOWA
MERCY MEDICAL CENTER
701 10th St Se, Cedar Rapids, IA 52403-1251
Tel (319) 398-6011 Founded/Ownrshp 1900
Sales 314.4MM EMP 2,375
Accts Rsm Us Llp Davenport Iowa
SIC 8062 General medical & surgical hospitals
Pr: Timothy L Charles
*CFO: Phil Peterson
VP: Ingrid Bishop
VP: Diane Stefani
Chf Nrs Of: James V Guliano
Chf Nrs Of: Nancy Hoyt
Dir Sec: Rod McCool
CIO: Jeff Cash
Info Man: Jeanne Brandes
Info Man: Duane Kellinger
Software D: Bindu Kalesan

D-U-N-S 07-566-1504
MERCY HOSPITAL FORT SMITH
SISTERS OF MERCY HEALTH SYSTEM
(Suby of SISTERS OF MERCY HEALTH SYSTEM) ★
7301 Rogers Ave, Fort Smith, AR 72903-4100
Tel (479) 314-6000 Founded/Ownrshp 1905
Sales 233.6MM EMP 1,553
Accts Ernst & Young Us Llp Saint Lo
SIC 8062 General medical & surgical hospitals
Pr: Ryan Gehrig
Chf Rad: David Diment
Chf Rad: Rick Nelson
*Sec: Greta Wilcher
Dir Rx: Gary Dipboye
Doctor: Norma Basinger
Doctor: Tamara Johnson
Doctor: Kurt Mehl MD

D-U-N-S 06-699-1902
MERCY HOSPITAL INC
(Suby of SISTERS PROVIDENCE HEALTH SYS) ★
271 Carew St, Springfield, MA 01104-2398
Tel (413) 748-9000 Founded/Ownrshp 1898
Sales 199.6MM^E EMP 1,635
SIC 8062 8071 8011 7219 8748 General medical & surgical hospitals; Medical laboratories; Offices & clinics of medical doctors; Laundry, except power & coin-operated; Employee programs administration
Pr: Vincent J McCorkle
*Pr: Daniel P Moen
*Treas: Arun R Adya
*Treas: Thomas Robert
Sr VP: Michael Stitcher
VP: Bette Neville
VP: Leonard Pansa
Dir: Susan Rouillard
Dir Rad: Parshant Puri
Dir Sec: Ann Carroll
IT Man: Claudine Schiro

D-U-N-S 07-387-2178
■ **MERCY HOSPITAL INC**
(Suby of PLANTATION GENERAL HOSPITAL LP) ★
3663 S Miami Ave, Miami, FL 33133-4237
Tel (305) 854-4400 Founded/Ownrshp 2012
Sales 150.7MM^E EMP 2,400
SIC 8062 General medical & surgical hospitals
CEO: Barbara J Simmons R N
Chf Rad: Mark Kravetz
*Pr: Howard Watts
CFO: Michael Heinrich
*CFO: Jerry Mashburn
*Ch: Joel M Jancko
*Treas: Linda V Wilford
Ofcr: Joseph Pino
VP: Francis Richardson
Exec: Maria Macias
Dir OR: Roger Grimshaw
Dir Lab: George Turell

D-U-N-S 07-350-0266
MERCY HOSPITAL IOWA CITY IOWA INC
500 E Market St, Iowa City, IA 52245-2689
Tel (319) 339-0300 Founded/Ownrshp 1873
Sales 136.0MM EMP 1,100
SIC 8062 8011 6512 8399

D-U-N-S 07-588-9337
MERCY HOSPITAL JEFFERSON (MO)
SISTERS OF MERCY HEALTH SYSTEM
(Suby of SISTERS OF MERCY HEALTH SYSTEM) ★
1400 Hwy 61 S, Crystal City, MO 63019
Tel (636) 933-1000 Founded/Ownrshp 1957, 2013
Sales 142.9MM EMP 1,200^E
Accts Pleus And Company Llc Chest
SIC 8062 General medical & surgical hospitals
CEO: Llyod Ford
*Pr: Bill McKenna
*CFO: Jim Meuhlhauser
CFO: James Muehlhaus
Treas: Ron Ravenscraft
VP: Beverly Johnson
Dir Rx: Ed Elder
*Prin: Amy McCally
Dir Sec: Andy Presti
Nurse Mgr: Theresa Thomas
QA Dir: Cathy Linhorst

D-U-N-S 07-626-2500 IMP/EXP
MERCY HOSPITAL JOPLIN
SISTERS OF MERCY HEALTH SYSTEM
(Suby of SISTERS OF MERCY HEALTH SYSTEM) ★
100 Mercy Way, Joplin, MO 64804-4524
Tel (417) 781-2727 Founded/Ownrshp 2009
Sales 165.8MM EMP 1,500
Accts Ernst & Young Us Llp Saint Lo
SIC 8062 General medical & surgical hospitals
CEO: Gary Pulsipher
*CFO: Shelly Hunter
Ofcr: Florence Lamberg
Ofcr: Michele Stewart
Ofcr: Marilyn Wylie
VP: Dave Goode
Dir Rad: Curtis S Hammerman
*Ex Dir: Robert Honeywell
IT Man: Debbie Francisco
Anesthlgy: Bradford Ramsey
Doctor: Eden Esguerra

D-U-N-S 04-012-7953
MERCY HOSPITAL LEBANON
100 Hospital Dr, Lebanon, MO 65536-9210
Tel (417) 533-6100 Founded/Ownrshp 1934
Sales 102.6MM EMP 400
Accts Ernst & Young Us Llp Clayton
SIC 8062 General medical & surgical hospitals
VP: Doug Hoban
VP: Karen Simpson

D-U-N-S 03-022-0727
MERCY HOSPITAL OF BUFFALO
CATHOLIC HEALTH
(Suby of CATHOLIC HEALTH SYSTEM INC) ★
565 Abbott Rd, Buffalo, NY 14220-2095
Tel (716) 826-7000 Founded/Ownrshp 1928
Sales 391.3MM EMP 2,000
SIC 8062 General medical & surgical hospitals
CEO: Charles J Urlaub
Pr: Karen Burger
*Pr: Nancy Sheehan
COO: Susan Kingston-Shack
*COO: Mark A Sullivan
*Treas: William K Buscaglia Jr
Ofcr: Michael Ebert
*Sr VP: Richard J Ruh
*Sr VP: John Stavros
*Prin: James R Boldt
Orthpdst: Daniel Wild

D-U-N-S 07-566-8418
MERCY HOSPITAL ROGERS
SAINT MARY'S HOSPITAL
2710 S Rife Medical Ln, Rogers, AR 72758-1452
Tel (479) 338-8000 Founded/Ownrshp 1995
Sales 211.7MM EMP 760
Accts Ernst & Young Us Llp Saint Lo
SIC 8062 General medical & surgical hospitals
Pr: Eric Pianalto

D-U-N-S 07-918-6011
MERCY HOSPITAL SCRANTON PENNSYLVANIA
REGIONAL HOSPITAL OF SCRANTON
746 Jefferson Ave, Scranton, PA 18510-1697
Tel (570) 348-7100 Founded/Ownrshp 1917
Sales 110.8MM^E EMP 1,485
SIC 8062 8051

D-U-N-S 07-625-6809
MERCY HOSPITAL SPRINGFIELD
1235 E Cherokee St, Springfield, MO 65804-2203
Tel (417) 820-2000 Founded/Ownrshp 1999
Sales 948.1MM EMP 4,400
SIC 8062 8011 General medical & surgical hospitals; Offices & clinics of medical doctors
CEO: Lynn Britton
Pr: John Swope
CEO: Kim Day
Ex VP: Michael McCurry
Ex VP: Shannon Sock
Off Mgr: Teri McMurry

MERCY HOSPITAL ST. LOUIS
See MERCY HOSPITALS EAST COMMUNITIES

MERCY HOSPITAL ST. LOUIS
See MERCY HEALTH SYSTEM OF NORTHWEST ARKANSAS INC

D-U-N-S 07-197-0222
MERCY HOSPITAL WASHINGTON
901 E 5th St Ste 222, Washington, MO 63090-3127
Tel (636) 239-8000 Founded/Ownrshp 1975
Sales 172.1MM EMP 576^E
SIC 8062 General medical & surgical hospitals
Pr: Terri L McLain
Chf Rad: Karl Lenzenhuber
*COO: Joan Frost
Dir Rad: Vicki Kriete
Dir Rx: Mark Pollock
Doctor: Emily Spear

D-U-N-S 07-195-8003
MERCY HOSPITALS EAST COMMUNITIES
MERCY HOSPITAL ST. LOUIS
615 S New Ballas Rd, Saint Louis, MO 63141-8221
Tel (417) 820-2000 Founded/Ownrshp 1891
Sales 940.6MM EMP 10,000
SIC 8062 General medical & surgical hospitals
Pr: Jeffrey Johnston
VP: Steven Bollin
*VP: Paul Hintze
Plas Surg: Brent Stromberg

D-U-N-S 10-906-7298
MERCY HOUSING INC
1999 Broadway Ste 1000, Denver, CO 80202-5704
Tel (303) 830-3300 Founded/Ownrshp 1981
Sales 13.0MM EMP 1,200
Accts Cohnreznick Llp Charlotte No
SIC 1522 6531 Apartment building construction; Real estate managers
Pr: Jane Graf
Pr: Jennifer Sakin
*Sr VP: Carol Breslau
Sr VP: Melissa Clayton
*Sr VP: Cindy Holler
Sr VP: Tina Lowe
*Sr VP: L Steven Spears
*VP: Vince Dodds
*VP: Michele Mamet
VP: Dave Mevis
Genl Mgr: Gary Ellefson

D-U-N-S 08-547-8241
MERCY INPATIENT MEDICAL ASSOCIATES INC
MERCY MEDICAL CENTER
271 Carew St Ste 106, Springfield, MA 01104-2377
Tel (413) 748-9000 Founded/Ownrshp 1988
Sales 272.7MM EMP 45
SIC 8011 8322 Internal medicine practitioners; Individual & family services
Pr: Daniel P Moen
Chf Rad: David B Mernoff
Dir Vol: Nancy Reilly
CFO: Thomas W Robert
*Treas: Thomas Robert
Ofcr: Paul H Oppenheimer
Sr VP: Mark M Fulco
VP: Sharon A Adams
VP: Diane Dukette
VP: Leonard F Pansa
VP: Stan Ragalski
*VP: Scott Wolf MD
Exec: Linda Reynolds
Dir Teleco: Sean Seslar
Dir Inf Cn: Kevin Sullivan
Dir Risk M: Janell Forget

D-U-N-S 00-210-1470
MERCY LIFE CENTER CORP
1200 Reedsdale St Ste 1, Pittsburgh, PA 15233-2109
Tel (412) 578-6675 Founded/Ownrshp 1983, 1988
Sales 90.3MM EMP 1,600
SIC 8322 Social service center
Pr: Susan Welsh
*CFO: Shelly Sullivan
Comm Dir: Jane Miller
Genl Mgr: Suzanne Saggio
Genl Mgr: Carol Seaseth

D-U-N-S 79-718-9719
MERCY LIFE CENTER CORP
MERCY BEHAVIORAL HEALTH
(Suby of MERCY LIFE CENTER CORP) ★
1200 Reedsdale St Ste 1, Pittsburgh, PA 15233-2109
Tel (412) 323-8026 Founded/Ownrshp 1988
Sales 41.8MM EMP 1,592
SIC 8093 Mental health clinic, outpatient
*Pr: Raymond Wolfe

D-U-N-S 07-967-9154
MERCY MARICOPA INTEGRATED CARE
4350 E Cotton Center Blvd D, Phoenix, AZ 85040-8852
Tel (602) 453-8308 Founded/Ownrshp 2014
Sales NA EMP 99
SIC 6324 Hospital & medical service plans
Prin: Eddy Broadway
*CEO: Broadway Eddy
*COO: Edge Angelo
*CFO: Dominguez Ramon

MERCY MEDICAL CENTER
See MERCY HOSPITAL CEDAR RAPIDS IOWA

MERCY MEDICAL CENTER
See MERCY INPATIENT MEDICAL ASSOCIATES INC

MERCY MEDICAL CENTER
See MERCY HEALTH SERVICES-IOWA CORP

D-U-N-S 06-592-6099
MERCY MEDICAL CENTER
(Suby of CATHOLIC HLTH SVCS LONG ISLAND) ★
1000 N Village Ave, Rockville Centre, NY 11570-1000
Tel (516) 562-6907 Founded/Ownrshp 1913
Sales 195.2MM EMP 1,610
SIC 8062 General medical & surgical hospitals
CEO: Dr Alan Guerci
*CFO: William Armstrong
*Ex VP: Nancy Simmons
Dir Lab: Louann Regensburg
Ex Dir: Annette Esposito
CIO: Jeff Cash
CIO: Joseph Perron
Dir IT: Rob Russell
IT Man: Ayana Bembry
Surgeon: Brian Donaldson

MERCY MEDICAL CENTER - REDDING
See MERCY HOME SERVICES A CALIFORNIA LIMITED PARTNERSHIP

D-U-N-S 80-815-6913
MERCY MEDICAL CENTER FOUNDATION - NORTH IOWA
CATHOLIC HEALTH EAST
(Suby of CATHOLIC HEALTH EAST) ★
1000 4th St Sw, Mason City, IA 50401-2800
Tel (641) 428-7000 Founded/Ownrshp 1993
Sales 3.1MM EMP 2,660
SIC 8062 General medical & surgical hospitals
Prin: Robert Lembke
*COO: Diane Fischels
*CFO: Rod Schlader
*Treas: Hal Johnson
*Sr VP: Teresa Mock
*VP: Jim Borgstrom
IT Man: Jill Malmin
Mktg Dir: Kris Kaiser
Snr Mgr: Emmy Fothergill

D-U-N-S 03-078-5042
MERCY MEDICAL CENTER INC
2700 Nw Stewart Pkwy, Roseburg, OR 97471-1214
Tel (541) 673-0611 Founded/Ownrshp 2006
Sales 190.7MM EMP 1,100
Accts Catholic Health Initiatives E
SIC 8062 General medical & surgical hospitals
Pr: Kelly C Morgan
*COO: Debbie Boswell
CFO: John Kasberger
*CFO: John Kasperger
*VP: Rhul Agarwal
Genl Mgr: Doug Klebe
CIO: Nancy Lancy
MIS Dir: Nancy Laney
Telecom Mg: Debbie Bertolino
IT Man: Ruth Verkuyl
Obsttrcn: Linda Sewell

D-U-N-S 07-494-3556
MERCY MEDICAL CENTER INC
345 Saint Paul St, Baltimore, MD 21202-2123
Tel (410) 332-9000 Founded/Ownrshp 1945
Sales 442.1MM EMP 2,139
Accts Dixon Hughes Goodman Llp Rock
SIC 8062 8011 General medical & surgical hospitals; Offices & clinics of medical doctors
Ch Bd: Sister Helen Amos
*CEO: Thomas R Mullen
*CFO: John E Topper
Ofcr: Luke Wiley
*Ex VP: Amy Freeman
*Sr VP: Dr Scott Spier
VP: Kathy Mucci
VP: Patrick Vizzard
Admn Mgr: Maureen Houston
Nurse Mgr: Cynthia Cohen
Mktg Dir: Sam Moskowitz

D-U-N-S 09-155-0256
MERCY MEDICAL CENTER INC
(Suby of SISTERS OF CHARITY OF ST AUGUSTINE HEALTH SYSTEM INC) ★
1320 Mercy Dr Nw, Canton, OH 44708-2641
Tel (330) 489-1000 Founded/Ownrshp 1908
Sales 298.2MM EMP 80
Accts Plante & Moran Pllc Columbus
SIC 8062 General medical & surgical hospitals
Pr: Thomas E Cecconi
Chf Rad: William Murphy
*COO: David D Cemate
*CFO: David K Stewart
Ofcr: Elaine Campbell
*VP: Sister Carolyn Capuano
*VP: David L Gormsen
*VP: Matthew A Heinle
VP: Matthew Heinle
VP: Jeffrey L Smith

VP: Thomas Turner
Dir Inf Cn: Pat Nelson
Dir Lab: Michael Doyle
Dir Lab: Anne Lovejoy
Dir Rx: John Feucht
Board of Directors: Suresh Patel

MERCY MEDICAL CENTER MERCED
See MATER MISERICORDIAE HOSPITAL

D-U-N-S 04-803-0985
MERCY MEDICAL CENTER OF OSHKOSH INC
AFFFINITY HEALTH SYSTEM
2700 W 9th Ave Ste 100, Oshkosh, WI 54904-7863
Tel (920) 223-2000 *Founded/Ownrshp* 1891
Sales 110.6MM *EMP* 1,400
SIC 8062 General medical & surgical hospitals
Pr: William Calhoun
**COO:* Cliff Lehman
**CFO:* Jeff Badger
Obsttrcn: Ginger Selle
Doctor: Michael Binder
Pgrm Dir: Jim Werner

D-U-N-S 10-738-8605
MERCY MEDICAL CENTER-CLINTON INC
MERCY HOME CARE
1410 N 4th St, Clinton, IA 52732-2940
Tel (563) 244-5555 *Founded/Ownrshp* 1982
Sales 95.7MM *EMP* 900
SIC 8062 8051 5122 Hospital, AMA approved residency; Extended care facility; Drugs, proprietaries & sundries
CEO: Donna Oliver
Treas: Dave Meade
VP: Amy Berentes
**VP:* Paul Mangin
Dir Rad: Laurel Brandeburg
**Prin:* Sean Williams
MIS Dir: Jannell Howard

MERCY MEDICAL CTR - DES MOINES
See CATHOLIC HEALTH INITIATIVES - IOWA CORP

D-U-N-S 15-312-6029
MERCY MEDICAL GROUP
12800 Corporate Hill Dr, Saint Louis, MO 63131-1845
Tel (888) 700-7171 *Founded/Ownrshp* 2004
Sales 229.5MM *EMP* 4^E
SIC 8011 Physicians' office, including specialists
Prin: Brenda Ryan
CIO: Dewey Freeman

D-U-N-S 78-780-0002
MERCY MEDICAL SERVICE INC
CAROLINA MEDICAL CENTER MERCY
(*Suby of* CAROLINAS HEALTHCARE SYSTEM) ★
2001 Vail Ave, Charlotte, NC 28207-1248
Tel (704) 379-5000 *Founded/Ownrshp* 1991
Sales 57.7MM^E *EMP* 1,000^E
SIC 8011 Clinic, operated by physicians
Pr: Curtis Copenhaver
**VP:* Janet Handy
Dir Teleco: Mason Blandford

D-U-N-S 13-973-9270
MERCY MEDICAL SERVICES INC
MED TEC MEDICAL SERVICES
(*Suby of* SISTERS OF MERCY HEALTH SYSTEM) ★
5401 Ellsworth Rd, Fort Smith, AR 72903-3219
Tel (479) 314-6060 *Founded/Ownrshp* 1983
Sales 580.4MM *EMP* 268
SIC 7363 Medical help service
Pr: John Hoffman

MERCY MEMORIAL HOSP SYSTEMS
See MERCY MEMORIAL HOSPITAL CORP

D-U-N-S 06-371-6542
MERCY MEMORIAL HOSPITAL CORP
MERCY MEMORIAL HOSP SYSTEMS
(*Suby of* PROMEDICA HEALTH SYSTEMS INC) ★
718 N Macomb St, Monroe, MI 48162-7815
Tel (734) 240-8400 *Founded/Ownrshp* 2015
Sales 153.3MM^E *EMP* 1,300
Accts Plante & Moran Pllc Southfiel
SIC 8062 General medical & surgical hospitals
Pr: Annette S Phillips
CFO: Thomas Schilling
Trst: Mark Worrell
Ex Dir: Cathy Osgood
Secur Mgr: John Williams
Pathlgst: Irving Hwang
Pharmcst: Prem Ghai

D-U-N-S 01-928-4160
MERCY METHODIST HOSPITAL
7500 Hospital Dr, Sacramento, CA 95823-5403
Tel (916) 423-6063 *Founded/Ownrshp* 1998
Sales 59.2MM^E *EMP* 1,043^E
Accts Deloitte & Touche Llp
SIC 8062 General medical & surgical hospitals
Orthpdst: Steven J Barad

D-U-N-S 17-416-0978
MERCY REGIONAL HEALTH CENTRE AUXILLIARY
ST MARY'S GIFT SHOP
1823 College Ave, Manhattan, KS 66502-3381
Tel (785) 776-2802 *Founded/Ownrshp* 1986
Sales 30.2MM^E *EMP* 1,000
SIC 5947 Gift shop
Treas: Chris Shank
VP: Debbi Elmore
VP: Lori Grubs
VP: Shelley Koltnow
VP: Sherrie String

MERCY RIVERSIDE
See BAPTIST HOSPITAL OF EAST TENNESSEE INC

MERCY SAN JUAN HOSPITAL
See MERCY HEALTHCARE SACRAMENTO

D-U-N-S 15-479-8891
MERCY SCRIPPS HOSPITAL
4077 5th Ave Mer35, San Diego, CA 92103-2105
Tel (619) 294-8111 *Founded/Ownrshp* 2004
Sales 750.4MM *EMP* 77^E
SIC 8062 General medical & surgical hospitals
Prin: Andrew C Ping
VP: David Shaw
Dir Risk M: Gayle Sandhu
Dir Rad: George Ochoa
Cmptr Lab: Wilda Mistura
IT Man: Steve Cornelius
Mtls Mgr: Eddye Coates
Secur Mgr: Anthony Roman
Mktg Dir: Tye Kennon
Surgeon: Paul Goldfarb
Surgeon: Bradford Hsu

D-U-N-S 19-419-1953
MERCY SERVICES IOWA CITY INC
(*Suby of* MERCY HOSPITAL IOWA CITY IOWA INC) ★
500 E Market St, Iowa City, IA 52245-2633
Tel (319) 339-3541 *Founded/Ownrshp* 1984
Sales 47.0MM^E *EMP* 1,100
SIC 8011 8082 Offices & clinics of medical doctors; Home health care services
Pr: Ronald Reed
**CFO:* Michael G Heinrich
**VP:* William A Watts
Doctor: Charles Carroll
Doctor: Christopher Scott

D-U-N-S 06-904-4386
MERCY SUBURBAN HOSPITAL
MERCY HEALTH SYSTEM
(*Suby of* MERCY HEALTH SYSTEM) ★
2701 Dekalb Pike, East Norriton, PA 19401-1820
Tel (215) 748-9000 *Founded/Ownrshp* 1944
Sales 104.1MM *EMP* 1,080
SIC 8062 General medical & surgical hospitals
CEO: Javon R Bea
Pr: Joy Hepkins
**CFO:* Peter Kenniff
Sr VP: Elizabeth Riley-Wasserman
Dir Inf Cn: Jim Hunter
**Prin:* Lifa Nallon
CIO: Christine Brutschea
IT Man: Chris Brutshea
Doctor: Jennifer Patterson
HC Dir: Diane Traver

D-U-N-S 06-875-9463
MERCY UPMC
UPMC HEALTH BENEFITS
(*Suby of* UPMC HEALTH BENEFITS) ★
1400 Locust St, Pittsburgh, PA 15219-5114
Tel (412) 232-8111 *Founded/Ownrshp* 2007
Sales 373.5MM *EMP* 2,010
SIC 8062 Hospital, medical school affiliated with nursing & residency
Pr: Will Cook
CFO: Eileen Simmons
Treas: Mark Scott
Trst: John R McGinley
Ofcr: Kathleen Broskin
VP: Joanne M Andiorio
VP: Linda Hogan
VP: Carolyn Schallenberger
Opthamlgy: Darren Hoover
Doctor: Hossein Noorbakhsh

D-U-N-S 10-734-6843
MERCYCARE SERVICE CORP
701 10th St Se, Cedar Rapids, IA 52403-1251
Tel (319) 398-6011 *Founded/Ownrshp* 1983
Sales 2.1MM *EMP* 2,500^E
SIC 8011 Medical centers
CEO: A J Tinker
**Pr:* Tim Charles
**Treas:* Emmett Scherman
CIO: Phil Wasson

D-U-N-S 09-951-9340
MERCYHURST UNIVERSITY
501 E 38th St, Erie, PA 16546-0002
Tel (814) 824-2000 *Founded/Ownrshp* 1926
Sales 87.1MM *EMP* 615
Accts Bkd Llp Cincinnati Ohio
SIC 8221 8243 8742 8299 College, except junior; Repair training, computer; Administrative services consultant; Educational service, nondegree granting: continuing educ.
Pr: Thomas Gamble
**Treas:* Jane Kelsey
Ofcr: Shawn Wroblewski
**VP:* Gary M Brown
VP: Caleb Pifer
Exec: Jim Tometsko
Assoc Dir: Guy Dipietro
Ex Dir: Kyle Foust
Opers Mgr: Barry Nuhfer
Pgrm Dir: Brett Johnson

D-U-N-S 00-527-9138 IMP
▲ MEREDITH CORP (IA)
1716 Locust St, Des Moines, IA 50309-3023
Tel (515) 284-3000 *Founded/Ownrshp* 1902
Sales 1.6MMM *EMP* 3,825
Accts Kpmg Llp Des Moines Iowa
Tkr Sym MDP *Exch* NYS
SIC 2721 2731 4833 Magazines: publishing & printing; Book publishing; Books: publishing only; Television broadcasting stations
Ch Bd: Stephen M Lacy
Pr: Georgine Anton
Pr: Thomas H Harty
Pr: Tom Harty
Pr: Paul A Karpowicz
Pr: Stan Pavlovsky
Pr: Tom Witschi
CFO: Joseph H Ceryanec
**V Ch Bd:* D Mell Meredith Frazier
Ofcr: Kim Martin
VP: Mom Chan
VP: Elise Contarsy
VP: Randy Stumbo
VP: Chris Susil
Creative D: Bernice Pfluger
Board of Directors: Donald A Baer, Donald C Berg, Mary Sue Coleman, Frederick B Henry, Joel W Johnson, Philip A Marineau, Elizabeth E Tallett

D-U-N-S 82-777-2443
MEREX TECHNOLOGY LEASING CORP
570 Lake Cook Rd Ste 300, Deerfield, IL 60015-5274
Tel (847) 940-1200 *Founded/Ownrshp* 1994
Sales NA *EMP* 516
SIC 6159 5045 Machinery & equipment finance leasing; Computers, peripherals & software
CEO: Ian J Pye
**Pr:* Brad V Ihlenfeld
**Treas:* Michael D Brannan
Treas: Michael Brannon
**Sr VP:* Rochelle Slater
Dir IT: Harvey Chebo
IT Man: Mike Kalis

D-U-N-S 18-111-6013
■ MERGE HEALTHCARE INC
(*Suby of* IBM) ★
71 S Wacker Dr Ste 2, Chicago, IL 60606-4716
Tel (312) 565-6868 *Founded/Ownrshp* 2015
Sales 212.3MM *EMP* 800^E
SIC 7373 3841 Computer integrated systems design; Diagnostic apparatus, medical
Pr: George Kotlarz
Pr: Todd Piccolo
Pr: Gary D Bowers
Pr: Jacques Cornet
Pr: Loris Sartor
Pr: Antonio Wells
Ex VP: Antonia Wells
Sr VP: Gary Bowers
VP: Mark Lombardo
Snr Sftwr: Anand Nair
Software D: Michael Bautista

D-U-N-S 06-154-2239 IMP
MERGENTHALER TRANSFER & STORAGE CO INC
AGENT FOR UNITED VAN LINES
1414 N Montana Ave, Helena, MT 59601-2998
Tel (406) 442-9470 *Founded/Ownrshp* 1974
Sales 85.5MM^E *EMP* 388
SIC 4213 4214 7538 Trucking, except local; Household goods transport; Local trucking with storage; Household goods moving & storage, local; General truck repair
Owner: Jerry Mergenthaler
**Pr:* Steve Mergenthaler
**VP:* Dave Gardner
**VP:* Mark Radwanski
Genl Mgr: Tim Evans
Genl Mgr: Marie Lewis
Genl Mgr: Alan Stacey
IT Man: Mark Dowdy
IT Man: Ronda Pekovitch
VP Sls: Michael Hastings
Sls Dir: Jan Caballero

MERGIS GROUP, THE
See SFN GROUP INC

D-U-N-S 79-964-1006 IMP/EXP
MERIAL INC
(*Suby of* AVENTIS INC) ★
3239 Satellite Blvd, Duluth, GA 30096-4640
Tel (678) 638-3000 *Founded/Ownrshp* 2001
Sales 511.0MM^E *EMP* 1,358
SIC 5122 Pharmaceuticals
CEO: Carsten Hellman
**CFO:* Christophe Hirtz
Ofcr: Thomas Zerzan
VP: Kate Morgan
Assoc Dir: Richard Jenkins
Ex Dir: Vaughn King
Dist Mgr: Michelle Everett
Dist Mgr: Renee Hall
Ql Cn Mgr: Chuck Maddox
Sls Mgr: Matthew Stinson
Snr PM: Jerome Claizergues

D-U-N-S 03-439-3582 EXP
MERIAL LIMITED
(*Suby of* MERIAL UK LLC) ★
3239 Satellite Blvd 500, Duluth, GA 30096-4640
Tel (678) 638-3000 *Founded/Ownrshp* 2002
Sales 128.1MM^E *EMP* 230
SIC 2836 Vaccines
Pr: Anthony Maunus
**CEO:* Rich Leiting
Treas: Joachim Hinzen
Bd of Dir: Cindy Apgar
Top Exec: Colin D'Cunha
Top Exec: Judy Jarecki-Black
**Sr VP:* Jose Barella
Sr VP: John Rivera
VP: Olivier Lecointre
VP: Jim May
Dir Bus: Marcus Remmers

D-U-N-S 05-421-9928 IMP/EXP
MERIAL SELECT INC
(*Suby of* MERIAL UK LLC) ★
1168 Airport Pkwy, Gainesville, GA 30501-6816
Tel (770) 536-8787 *Founded/Ownrshp* 1987
Sales 211.9MM^E *EMP* 300
SIC 5122 2836 Animal medicines; Vaccines
Pr: Keith Pritchard
**CFO:* Darrick Zink
Assoc Dir: Chuck Enslen
Dir IT: Kathy Jones
Snr Mgr: Charles Garriott

D-U-N-S 06-150-6796 IMP/EXP
MERIAL UK LLC
(*Suby of* MERIAL LIMITED)
3239 Satellite Blvd, Duluth, GA 30096-4640
Tel (678) 638-3000 *Founded/Ownrshp* 2001
Sales 763.3MM^E *EMP* 4,425
SIC 2836 2834 3841 Vaccines; Veterinary pharmaceutical preparations; Diagnostic apparatus, medical
Treas: Joachim Hinzen

D-U-N-S 00-810-6999 IMP/EXP
MERICHEM CO
5455 Old Spanish Trl, Houston, TX 77023-5013
Tel (713) 428-5000 *Founded/Ownrshp* 1965
Sales 108.0MM^E *EMP* 300
Accts Grant Thornton Llp Cpas Hous
SIC 2911 Petroleum refining
Ch Bd: Kenneth F Currie
Ch Bd: Kendra Lee
CEO: Patrick J Hickey
CFO: Bruce D Upshaw
Dir IT: Mike Ryan
Sys Mgr: Kenny Ware
Sales Exec: Eric Russo
Sls Dir: James Aiello
Genl Couns: Lou Flanz
Corp Couns: Brenda Landry
Snr PM: Tark Altintas

D-U-N-S 19-309-0925
MERIDEN PUBLIC SCHOOLS
22 Liberty St, Meriden, CT 06450-5609
Tel (203) 630-4171 *Founded/Ownrshp* 1970
Sales 51.8MM^E *EMP* 1,200
SIC 8211 9411 Public elementary & secondary schools; Administration of educational programs
Off Mgr: Kristin Culver
MIS Dir: Chris Sette
Psych: Samantha Boutin

MERIDIAN
See NY MCG INC

D-U-N-S 80-952-3579
▲ MERIDIAN BANCORP INC
67 Prospect St, Peabody, MA 01960-1604
Tel (617) 567-1500 *Founded/Ownrshp* 2014
Sales NA *EMP* 455^E
Tkr Sym EBSB *Exch* NGS
SIC 6035 Savings institutions, federally chartered; Federal savings & loan associations
Ch Bd: Richard J Gavegnano
COO: John A Carroll
CFO: Mark L Abbate
Bd of Dir: Richard Fernandez
Sr VP: Keith D Armstrong
Sr VP: Mary Hagen
Sr VP: James Morgan
Sr VP: Joseph Nash

D-U-N-S 09-281-5364
▲ MERIDIAN BIOSCIENCE INC (OH)
3471 River Hills Dr, Cincinnati, OH 45244-3023
Tel (513) 271-3700 *Founded/Ownrshp* 1976
Sales 196.0MM *EMP* 580^E
Tkr Sym VIVO *Exch* NGS
SIC 2835 2834 In vitro & in vivo diagnostic substances; Pharmaceutical preparations
Ch Bd: John A Kraeutler
**CFO:* Melissa A Lueke
Ofcr: Jared Schwartz
**Ex VP:* Lawrence J Baldini
Ex VP: Slava A Elagin
**Ex VP:* Vecheslav A Elagin
Ex VP: David Shardlow
Sr VP: Susan D Rolih
VP: James R Leroy
VP: Barb Maham
VP: Fred Rachford
VP: Frank Seurkamp

D-U-N-S 02-048-6429
MERIDIAN CITIZENS MUTUAL INSURANCE CO
2955 N Meridian St, Indianapolis, IN 46208-4714
Tel (317) 931-7000 *Founded/Ownrshp* 1914
Sales NA *EMP* 2,000
SIC 6331 Assessment associations: fire, marine & casualty insurance
Pr: Robert Restrepo

D-U-N-S 05-961-8694
MERIDIAN DRILLING CO LLC
11500 S Meridian Ave, Oklahoma City, OK 73173-8228
Tel (405) 691-1202 *Founded/Ownrshp* 2012
Sales 323.5MM^E *EMP* 140
SIC 1381 1799 5084

MERIDIAN GROUP
See MERIDIAN LEASING CORP

MERIDIAN GROUP
See MERIDIAN IT INC

D-U-N-S 96-254-1053
MERIDIAN GROUP INTERNATIONAL INC
(*Suby of* MEREX TECHNOLOGY LEASING CORP) ★
9 Parkway N Ste 500, Deerfield, IL 60015-2545
Tel (847) 940-1200 *Founded/Ownrshp* 1979
Sales 252.0MM^E *EMP* 499
SIC 8742 6159 Financial consultant; Machinery & equipment finance leasing
Pr: Brad Ihlenfeld
**Pr:* Mike Brannan
**Sr VP:* Rochelle Slater
**VP:* Bill Flaherty
**VP:* John O'Connor
VP: Steve Zogg
Rgnl Mgr: Victor M Munoz
Dir IT: Mike Calwas
Manager: Ed Restifo
Sls Mgr: Ben Baenen

MERIDIAN HOSPITAL
See HACKENSACK MERIDIAN HEALTH INC

D-U-N-S 96-540-8230
MERIDIAN HOSPITALS CORP
RIVERVIEW MEDICAL CENTER
(*Suby of* MERIDIAN HOSPITAL) ★
1945 Route 33, Neptune, NJ 07753-4859
Tel (732) 751-7500 *Founded/Ownrshp* 1996
Sales 674.2MM *EMP* 5,200^E
SIC 8062 General medical & surgical hospitals
Pr: Mark Lory
V Ch: Brian Erler
**Pr:* Timothy J Hogan
**Pr:* Marc Lory
**COO:* Jeff Brickman
**COO:* Joseph Miller
**CFO:* Bill Philips
Treas: James Bollerman
Ofcr: Alexander Lehrer
VP: Wayne Boatwright
VP: Anthony Cava
**VP:* Lori Colineri
VP: Frank Goldstein
VP: Marilyn Koczan

VP: Kathleen Murray
**VP:* Kelli O'Brien
**VP:* Joseph Reichman
VP: David Siegel
VP: Alvis Swinney

D-U-N-S 00-610-6959 IMP/EXP
MERIDIAN INDUSTRIES INC (WI)
MERIDIAN SPECIALTY YARN GROUP
735 N Water St Ste 630, Milwaukee, WI 53202-4104
Tel (414) 224-0610 *Founded/Ownrshp* 1943
Sales 367.4MM[E] *EMP* 2,000
SIC 3069 2843 2269 7389 Medical & laboratory rubber sundries & related products; Processing assistants; Dyeing: raw stock yarn & narrow fabrics; Packaging & labeling services
CEO: Bruce E Pindyck
V Ch: Mary Ellen Pindyck
CFO: Douglas C Miller
VP: Douglas J Arnold
VP: Frank C Deguire Jr

D-U-N-S 03-696-8949
MERIDIAN IT INC
MERIDIAN GROUP
(*Suby of* MERIDIAN GROUP) ★
9 Parkway N Ste 500, Deerfield, IL 60015-2545
Tel (847) 964-2664 *Founded/Ownrshp* 1992
Sales 172.8MM[E] *EMP* 113
SIC 5045 Computers, peripherals & software
CEO: Brad Ihlenfeld
**Pr:* Lisa Pettay
**CFO:* Mike Brannan
**Ex VP:* Steve Bickford
Sr VP: Robert Dickert
**Sr VP:* Rochelle Slater
VP: Sue Atwood
VP: Al Consena
VP: Chris Ellerman
**VP:* Bill Flaherty
VP: Tom Horan
VP: Dennis O'Connell
VP: Tim Patronik
VP: Bill Slaherty
VP: Steve Zogg

D-U-N-S 01-027-4405
MERIDIAN LEASING CORP (IL)
MERIDIAN GROUP
(*Suby of* MERIDIAN GROUP INTERNATIONAL INC) ★
9 Parkway N Ste 500, Deerfield, IL 60015-2545
Tel (847) 964-2700 *Founded/Ownrshp* 1979, 1994
Sales NA *EMP* 250
Accts Deloitte & Touche Llp Chicago
SIC 6159 Machinery & equipment finance leasing
CEO: Ian J Pye
**Pr:* Brad V Ihlenfeld
**CFO:* Michael D Brannan
Ex VP: Steve Bickford
Sr VP: John Adams
Sr VP: Robert Dickert
Sr VP: Thomas Horan
**Sr VP:* Rochelle Slater
**VP:* Bill Flaherty
VP: Tom Horan
VP: Mike Myers
VP: Dennis O'Connell
Exec: Fran Blumenfeld

D-U-N-S 04-950-4624
■ **MERIDIAN MEDICAL TECHNOLOGIES INC**
(*Suby of* PFIZER INC) ★
6350 Stevens Forest Rd, Columbia, MD 21046-3231
Tel (443) 259-7800 *Founded/Ownrshp* 2010
Sales 99.3MM[E] *EMP* 452
SIC 3841 Hypodermic needles & syringes
Pr: Dennis P O'Brien
**CEO:* James H Miller
CFO: Troy Brasfell
**Sr VP:* Gerald L Wannarka
DP Exec: Stan Hammond
IT Man: Paul Muma
IT Man: John Wittier
Tech Mgr: Dan Youker
Ql Cn Mgr: Dale W Warner
Snr PM: Kyal Hackett
Snr Mgr: Mitch Boyer

D-U-N-S 10-004-0013
MERIDIAN PUBLIC SCHOOL DISTRICT
1019 25th Ave, Meridian, MS 39301-4999
Tel (601) 483-6271 *Founded/Ownrshp* 1885
Sales 55.4MM[E] *EMP* 1,500
Accts Rea Shaw Giffin & Stuart Ll
SIC 8211 Public elementary school; Public junior high school; Public senior high school
Ofcr: Rebecca Stevens
HC Dir: Kelli Speed

D-U-N-S 61-911-8359 IMP
MERIDIAN RACK & PINION INC
6740 Cobra Way Ste 200, San Diego, CA 92121-4102
Tel (858) 587-8777 *Founded/Ownrshp* 1989
Sales 86.2MM[E] *EMP* 130
SIC 5013 5961 Automotive supplies & parts; Mail order house, order taking office only
CEO: Dara Greaney
**Pr:* Matt Glauber
**CFO:* Chris Struempler

MERIDIAN SPECIALTY YARN GROUP
See MERIDIAN INDUSTRIES INC

D-U-N-S 08-458-2428
MERIDIAN TITLE CORP
202 S Michigan St Ste 300, South Bend, IN 46601-2006
Tel (574) 232-5845 *Founded/Ownrshp* 1946
Sales NA *EMP* 242
SIC 6361 Real estate title insurance
Pr: Mark Myers
**CFO:* Renee Preniczny
**Ex VP:* Frank Antonovitz
Sales Exec: Amy Kintz
Counsel: Beau Dunfee

D-U-N-S 79-690-7181
■ **MERILLAT INDUSTRIES INC**
(*Suby of* MERILLAT LP) ★
865 Pilot Rd, Las Vegas, NV 89119-3726
Tel (702) 897-9800 *Founded/Ownrshp* 2007
Sales 75.6MM[E] *EMP* 2,028[E]
SIC 3999 Manufacturing industries
Plnt Mgr: Steve Johnson

D-U-N-S 96-364-2491 IMP
■ **MERILLAT LP**
(*Suby of* DENOVA) ★
5353 W Us Highway 223, Adrian, MI 49221-8901
Tel (517) 263-0771 *Founded/Ownrshp* 2011
Sales 197.9MM[E] *EMP* 3,210
SIC 2434 Wood kitchen cabinets
Genl Pt: Clay Kiefaber
Pt: Eugene A Gargaro Jr
Pt: Warren J Potter
COO: Keith Almond
Treas: Doug Austin
Treas: John Thurman
VP: Jerry Mollien
VP: Michael Thompson
Mng Dir: Jeff Park
Brnch Mgr: Mike Stickles
Div Mgr: John Jackson

D-U-N-S 07-552-9586
MERION LOWER SCHOOL DISTRICT INC
301 E Montgomery Ave, Ardmore, PA 19003-3338
Tel (610) 645-1983 *Founded/Ownrshp* 1936
Sales 85.2MM[E] *EMP* 1,600
Accts Rainer & Company Newtown Squa
SIC 8211 Public junior high school; Public senior high school; Public elementary school
Dir Sec: Dennis Witt
Pr Dir: Douglas Young
HC Dir: Terry Q Clampffer

D-U-N-S 80-120-5894 IMP/EXP
MERISANT CO
(*Suby of* FLAVORS HOLDINGS INC) ★
125 S Wacker Dr Ste 3150, Chicago, IL 60606-4414
Tel (312) 840-6000 *Founded/Ownrshp* 1999
Sales 150.0MM[E] *EMP* 437[E]
SIC 2869 Industrial organic chemicals
Pr: Paul Block
CFO: Ross Campbell
CFO: Julie Wool
VP: Brian Alsvig
VP: Dan Beck
VP: Jonathan W Cole
VP: Angelo Di Benedetto
VP: Yann Kervoern
VP: Carrie Murphy
VP: Hugues Pitre
CTO: Robin Hamerlinck

D-U-N-S 13-167-8406 IMP/EXP
MERISANT US INC
(*Suby of* MERISANT CO) ★
125 S Wacker Dr Ste 3150, Chicago, IL 60606-4414
Tel (312) 840-6000 *Founded/Ownrshp* 2000
Sales 150.0MM[E] *EMP* 436
SIC 2869 Sweeteners, synthetic
CEO: Albert Manzone
**CEO:* Albert Manzone
**CFO:* Trisha Rosado
**VP:* Brian Alsvig
VP: Jane Boyce
IT Man: Keith Halborsen
Board of Directors: Albert Manzone

D-U-N-S 02-193-1047 IMP/EXP
MERIT DISTRIBUTION GROUP LLC
LANCASTER
1310 Union St, Spartanburg, SC 29302-3342
Tel (864) 583-3011 *Founded/Ownrshp* 1953
Sales 812.0MM[E] *EMP* 590
SIC 5198 Paints; Varnishes; Paint brushes, rollers, sprayers
**CFO:* Jon Heard
VP Sls: Thomas Daniels
Manager: Dennis Fletcher
Sls Mgr: Pete Ahlstrom
Sls Mgr: Mike Bellerdine
Sls Mgr: Lou Duerinck
Sls Mgr: Sally Hanson
Sls Mgr: John Hardy
Sls Mgr: Roberta McKinney
Snr Mgr: Chris Bobo

D-U-N-S 60-547-0475 IMP
MERIT ENERGY CO LLC
13737 Noel Rd Ste 1200, Dallas, TX 75240-1335
Tel (972) 701-8377 *Founded/Ownrshp* 1989
Sales 556.2MM[E] *EMP* 640
SIC 1311 Crude petroleum production; Natural gas production
Ch Bd: William Gayden
**Pr:* Robert R Matejek
**Ex VP:* Thomas Porter Trimble
VP: Mike Markus
VP: Laura McElroy
VP Bus Dev: Jason Lindmark
Dir Risk M: Ann Mennel
Off Admin: Gloria Anderson
IT Man: John Stroud
IT Man: Dale Walters
Opers Mgr: Will Braud

MERIT HEALTH CENTRAL
See JACKSON HMA LLC

MERIT HEALTH RIVER REGION
See VICKSBURG HEALTHCARE LLC

D-U-N-S 14-591-8434
MERIT HEALTH SYSTEMS LLC
1033 Skokie Blvd Ste 360, Northbrook, IL 60062-4137
Tel (502) 753-0890 *Founded/Ownrshp* 2004
Sales 63.5MM[E] *EMP* 2,600
SIC 8741 Hospital management
CEO: Michael P Curran
Off Mgr: Erin Schaefer

D-U-N-S 05-138-4657
MERIT INTEGRATED LOGISTICS LLC
DROP LOT SERVICES
29122 Rancho Viejo Rd # 211, San Juan Capistrano, CA 92675-1039
Tel (949) 481-0685 *Founded/Ownrshp* 2013
Sales 40.0MM *EMP* 1,100
SIC 4731 Freight transportation arrangement

D-U-N-S 05-868-9951
■ **MERIT LIFE INSURANCE CO**
(*Suby of* SPRINGLEAF FINANCE CORP) ★
601 Nw 2nd St Unit 1, Evansville, IN 47708-1061
Tel (812) 424-8031 *Founded/Ownrshp* 1974
Sales NA *EMP* 107
Accts Ernst & Young Llp Indianapoli
SIC 6311 Life insurance
CEO: Daniel Leitch III
**Ch Bd:* James Turerff
**Pr:* Robert Womack
CFO: Donald R Breivogel Jr
**CFO:* Philip M Hanley
**Sr VP:* Wayne D Baker
Sr VP: Robert Cole
**Sr VP:* Bennie D Hendrix
**Sr VP:* James R Jerwers
**VP:* Larry R Klaholz
**VP:* Gary Smith
**VP:* Peter V Tuters

D-U-N-S 18-476-3290 IMP
▲ **MERIT MEDICAL SYSTEMS INC**
1600 W Merit Pkwy, South Jordan, UT 84095-2416
Tel (801) 253-1600 *Founded/Ownrshp* 1987
Sales 542.1MM *EMP* 3,889[E]
Tkr Sym MMSI *Exch* NGS
SIC 3841 Surgical & medical instruments
Ch Bd: Fred P Lampropoulos
Pr: Joseph C Wright
COO: Ronald A Frost
CFO: Bernard J Birkett
Ex VP: Justin J Lampropoulo
VP: Mark Flygare
VP: Tony Keaveney
VP: Peter Sutcliffe
Mng Dir: Rishat Gazizov
Genl Mgr: Camiel Peerlings
Off Mgr: Sheryl Matthews
Board of Directors: A Scott Anderson, Richard W Edelman, Nolan E Karras, Franklin J Miller, F Ann Millner, Kent W Stanger, Michael E Stillabower

D-U-N-S 82-693-1946
MERITAGE GROUP LP
The Embarcad Pier 5 St Pier, San Francisco, CA 94111
Tel (415) 399-5330 *Founded/Ownrshp* 2007
Sales 94.1MM[E] *EMP* 1,500
SIC 8741 Management services
Prin: Mark Mindich

D-U-N-S 19-690-5657
▲ **MERITAGE HOMES CORP**
8800 E Raintree Dr # 300, Scottsdale, AZ 85260-3966
Tel (480) 515-8100 *Founded/Ownrshp* 1988
Sales 2.5MMM *EMP* 1,409
Accts Deloitte & Touche Llp Phoeni
Tkr Sym MTH *Exch* NYS
SIC 1521 New construction, single-family houses
Ch Bd: Steven J Hilton
COO: Phillippe Lord
CFO: Larry W Seay
CFO: Hilla Sferruzza
Treas: Darin Rowe
Ofcr: Javier Feliciano
Ex VP: C Timothy White
Ex VP: Timothy White
CIO: Cindy Ketchelos
Mktg Mgr: Sherri Fastrich
Board of Directors: Peter L Ax, Dana C Bradford, Richard T Burke Sr, Gerald W Haddock, Deb Henretta, Michael R Odell, Raymond Oppel, Robert G Sarver

D-U-N-S 60-583-1895
■ **MERITAGE HOMES OF FLORIDA INC**
MONTEREY HOMES
(*Suby of* MERITAGE HOMES CORP) ★
8800 E Raintree Dr # 300, Scottsdale, AZ 85260-3966
Tel (480) 515-8500 *Founded/Ownrshp* 2004
Sales 93.1MM[E] *EMP* 1,200[E]
SIC 1521 Single-family housing construction
Ch Bd: Steven J Hilton
CFO: Larry Seay
Ex VP: Steve Davis
Ex VP: Sandi Karrmann
Ex VP: Tim White

D-U-N-S 15-136-7539
▲ **MERITAGE HOSPITALITY GROUP INC**
45 Ottawa Ave Sw Ste 600, Grand Rapids, MI 49503-4011
Tel (616) 776-2600 *Founded/Ownrshp* 1986
Sales 91.9MM *EMP* 1,700
Tkr Sym MHGU *Exch* OTO
SIC 5812 6794 Fast-food restaurant, chain; Franchises, selling or licensing
Ch Bd: Robert E Schermer Jr
**Pr:* Gary A Rose
COO: Alan Pruitt
**COO:* Roger L Zingle
VP: Robert Potts
**VP:* James R Saalfeld
Dist Mgr: Amanda Ramirez
Dir IT: Josiah Becker

MERITAGE II
See MERITAGE MIDSTREAM SERVICES II LLC

D-U-N-S 07-857-1828
MERITAGE MIDSTREAM SERVICES II LLC
MERITAGE II
1331 17th St Ste 1100, Denver, CO 80202-5819
Tel (303) 551-8150 *Founded/Ownrshp* 2012
Sales 200.0MM *EMP* 70
SIC 1389 Gas field services; Oil field services
Treas: William Champion
Off Mgr: Brook Kimber

D-U-N-S 15-738-2664
■ **MERITAIN HEALTH INC**
(*Suby of* PRODIGY HEALTH GROUP, INC.)
300 Corporate Pkwy 100s, Amherst, NY 14226-1272
Tel (716) 319-5500 *Founded/Ownrshp* 1986
Sales 92.3MM[E] *EMP* 1,300
SIC 8741 Hospital management; Nursing & personal care facility management
Pr: Elliot Cooperstone
Pr: Greg A Beloat
Pr: Jeffrey Diekema
Pr: Jennifer L Henry
Pr: Paul Knapp
Pr: John Pisarski
Pr: Ralph Reeves
Pr: Theresa Simonsen
Pr: Jennifer L Smith
**CFO:* Vincent Dimura
**Sr VP:* David C Parker
Sr VP: Christy Vago
VP: Kevin Conable
VP: Gena Joerger
VP: Lynn McCormick
VP: Kari Niblack

MERITCARE
See CULWELL HEALTH INC

D-U-N-S 15-731-3115
MERITER HEALTH SERVICES INC
UNITYPOINT HEALTH-MERITER
(*Suby of* UNITYPOINT HEALTH) ★
202 S Park St, Madison, WI 53715-1507
Tel (608) 417-5800 *Founded/Ownrshp* 2014
Sales 720.5MM *EMP* 3,330
Accts Kpmg Ll Milwaukee Wi
SIC 8741 Hospital management
Pr: Arthur Nizza
COO: Sue Erickson
CFO: Beth Erdman
Chf Mktg O: Pam Wetzel
VP: James Arnett
VP: Todd Burchill
VP: Mary Hansen
VP: Robert Turngren
Exec: Pat Grunwald

D-U-N-S 05-529-6529
MERITER HOSPITAL INC
202 S Park St, Madison, WI 53715-1596
Tel (608) 417-6000 *Founded/Ownrshp* 1898
Sales 434.0MM *EMP* 2,548
SIC 8062 General medical & surgical hospitals
Chf Path: Frank Zeller
**Pr:* Robert Turngren
**CEO:* James L Woodward
**CFO:* Kevin Boren
Bd of Dir: Susan Toth
**VP:* Sue Erickson
VP: Geoffrey Priest
Exec: Mary Grell
Exec: Layton Rikkers
Exec: Liz Sarafiny
Exec: Kristine Thome
Exec: Linda Vesterdahl
Dir Rad: Dave Childers

D-U-N-S 78-608-2092 IMP/EXP
▲ **MERITOR INC**
2135 W Maple Rd, Troy, MI 48084-7121
Tel (248) 435-1000 *Founded/Ownrshp* 1909
Sales 3.2MMM *EMP* 8,400
Accts Deloitte & Touche Llp Detroit
Tkr Sym MTOR *Exch* NYS
SIC 3714 3493 3625 3465 Motor vehicle parts & accessories; Drive shafts, motor vehicle; Axles, motor vehicle; Exhaust systems & parts, motor vehicle; Automobile springs; Actuators, industrial; Automotive stampings
Pr: Jeffrey A Craig
Pr: Tim Bowes
Pr: Pedro Ferro
Pr: Juan De La Riva
Pr: Joe Mejaly
Pr: Joe Plomin
Pr: Rakesh Sachdev
Pr: Rob Speed
CFO: James D Donlon
CFO: Kevin Nowlan
CFO: Kevin A Nowlan
Treas: Frank A Voltolina
Sr VP: Vernon G Baker
Sr VP: April Miller Boise
Sr VP: Sandra Quick
VP: Kent Barth
VP: Jeanne Booth
VP: Diane S Bullock
VP: Sergio Caravalho
VP: Sergio Carvalho
VP: Ernie Devincent
Board of Directors: Joseph B Anderson Jr, Victoria B Jackson Bridges, Rhonda L Brooks, Ivor J Evans, William J Lyons, William R Newlin, Thomas L Pajonas, Lloyd G Trotter

D-U-N-S 61-348-7834 IMP
MERITOR WABCO VEHICLE CONTROL SYSTEMS
2135 W Maple Rd, Troy, MI 48084-7121
Tel (248) 273-4698 *Founded/Ownrshp* 1990
Sales 100.6MM[E] *EMP* 150
SIC 5013 Automotive brakes; Truck parts & accessories
Genl Mgr: Jon Morrison
**Pr:* Matthew Stevenson
**Prin:* Carsten Duevell
**Prin:* Kurt Hall
**Prin:* Mark Melletat
Snr Sftwr: Susan Nickels
Sftwr Eng: Basil Asmar
Sls&Mrk Ex: Bonnie Gibson

D-U-N-S 78-055-7138
MERITUS HEALTH INC
11116 Medical Campus Rd, Hagerstown, MD 21742-6710
Tel (301) 790-8000 *Founded/Ownrshp* 1989
Sales NA *EMP* 3,105
SIC 6321

D-U-N-S 07-829-7314
MERITUS MEDICAL CENTER INC
11116 Medical Campus Rd, Hagerstown, MD 21742-6710
Tel (301) 797-2000 *Founded/Ownrshp* 1991
Sales 346.2MM *EMP* 2,400
SIC 8062 General medical & surgical hospitals
Pr: Joseph Ross
Bd of Dir: Philip Rohrer
**Sr VP:* Raymond Grahe
**Sr VP:* Deborah Addo Samuels
**VP:* Heather Lorenzo
**VP:* Carolyn Simonsen
Surgeon: Marc E Kross
Doctor: Scott Hamilton
Doctor: Joseph Reilly
Doctor: Christopher Vaccari
Nrsg Dir: Jesus Cepero

MERKLE COMPUTER SYSTEMS
See MERKLE GROUP INC

D-U-N-S 06-486-4507
MERKLE GROUP INC (MD)
MERKLE COMPUTER SYSTEMS
7001 Columbia Gateway Dr, Columbia, MD 21046-2289
Tel (443) 542-4000 *Founded/Ownrshp* 1971, 1977
Sales 202.8MM^E *EMP* 3,700
SIC 7331 Mailing list compilers
Ch Bd: David S Williams
Pr: Zhengda Z Shen
COO: Michael Komasinski
COO: Zhengda Shen
CFO: Sean Creamer
CFO: Rick Gross
Co-Pr: Tim Berry
Co-Pr: Patrick Hennessy
Chf Mktg O: Craig Dempster
Ex VP: Gil Anderson
Ex VP: George Gallate
Ex VP: Ryan Gibson
Ex VP: Tony Giordano
Ex VP: Michael McCoy
Sr VP: Eugene Becker
Sr VP: Deb Furey
Sr VP: Dale Hogg
Sr VP: Angie C Moore
Sr VP: Jason Reis
Sr VP: Colin Stewart
VP: Cyndie Beckwith

D-U-N-S 13-461-0331
MERKLE INC
(*Suby of* MERKLE COMPUTER SYSTEMS) ★
7001 Columbia Gateway Dr, Columbia, MD 21046-2289
Tel (443) 542-4000 *Founded/Ownrshp* 1998
Sales 147.3MM^E *EMP* 570^E
SIC 8742 Marketing consulting services
CEO: David S Williams
Pt: Shep Parke
Pt: Dan Schmerzler
Pt: Mathew Ward
Mng Pt: Peter Faber
**Pr:* Tim Berry
Pr: Tom Miller
**CFO:* Jean Holder
**Ch:* Robert N Frerichs
**Chf Mktg O:* Craig Dempster
**Ofcr:* Elizabeth Barden
**Ofcr:* Andy Fisher
**Ofcr:* Patrick Hounsell
**Ofcr:* Adam Lavelle
Ofcr: Angie Moore
Ex VP: Tony Steel
Sr VP: Andrew Hoeberichts
Sr VP: Glenn Lapidus
Sr VP: Paul Schottmiller
Sr VP: Colin Stewart
Sr VP: Ted Stites
Board of Directors: Robert N Frerichs

D-U-N-S 04-306-8944
MERLE WEST MEDICAL CENTER
DIABETES CARE LINK
2865 Daggett Ave, Klamath Falls, OR 97601-1106
Tel (541) 882-6311 *Founded/Ownrshp* 1998
Sales 447.9MM *EMP* 5
SIC 5912 Drug stores & proprietary stores
Off Mgr: Lenora Mueller
CTO: Dan Chancellor
CTO: Tom Drew
CTO: Kelly Thomas

D-U-N-S 07-853-5863
MERLIN ENTERTAINMENTS GROUP US LLC
MADAME TUSSAUDS NEW YORK
(*Suby of* MERLIN ENTERTAINMENTS GROUP LIMITED)
234 W 42nd St Frnt 4, New York, NY 10036-7215
Tel (212) 512-9604 *Founded/Ownrshp* 2007
Sales 420.5MM^E *EMP* 24,000
SIC 7996 Amusement parks
VP: Colin Armstrong
CFO: Andrew Carr
**VP:* Janine Di Gioacchino
**VP:* Donald Glen Erlham
**VP:* Sarah Reed
Ex Dir: Mark Fisher
Genl Mgr: Christopher Connors
Genl Mgr: Bret Pidgeon
Genl Mgr: Hayley Townsend
Opers Supe: Mark Woodland
Sfty Mgr: Heather Fitzpatrick

D-U-N-S 11-083-0072
MERRICK BANK CORP
(*Suby of* CARDWORKS INC) ★
10705 S Jordan Gtwy # 200, South Jordan, UT 84095-3977
Tel (801) 545-6600 *Founded/Ownrshp* 1996
Sales NA *EMP* 135
SIC 6021 National commercial banks
Ch: Robert Perro
**Pr:* Rickard Lake
**CFO:* David S Young
CFO: David Young
Sr VP: Tiffaney Johnston
Sr VP: Cami Mitchell
Sr VP: Jeff Smith
VP: Lane Delano
VP: Elise Ebert
VP: Jessica Fergus
VP: Todd Randall
VP: Scott Rose
VP: Mike Thomas
Dir Risk M: James Alberici

D-U-N-S 04-052-5263 IMP/EXP
MERRICK ENGINEERING INC
1275 Quarry St, Corona, CA 92879-1707
Tel (951) 737-6040 *Founded/Ownrshp* 1975
Sales 88.8MM *EMP* 600
Accts Moss Adams Llp Irvine Califo
SIC 3089 Injection molding of plastics
Pr: Abraham M Abdi
**CFO:* Katina Brown
VP: Francisco Castaneda
VP: Muna Vienna
Exec: Brown Patina
Brnch Mgr: Shannon Daugherty
Genl Mgr: Sadi Vahidy
Off Mgr: Maria Sonora
MIS Dir: Sivakumar Sethuraman
IT Man: Ali Jawady
IT Man: Sethuraman Kumar

D-U-N-S 04-427-5683 IMP
MERRICK NATURAL PETWORKS INC (TX)
101 Se 11th Ave Ste 200, Amarillo, TX 79101-3417
Tel (806) 322-2800 *Founded/Ownrshp* 1968
Sales 101.5MM^E *EMP* 500
SIC 2047

D-U-N-S 10-049-7952
MERRILL COMMUNICATIONS LLC
(*Suby of* MERRILL CORP) ★
1 Merrill Cir, Saint Paul, MN 55108-5267
Tel (651) 646-4501 *Founded/Ownrshp* 1999
Sales 412.0MM *EMP* 5,210
SIC 7374 7389 Data processing & preparation; Mailing & messenger services; Translation services
CEO: Rusty Wiley
**COO:* Rick R Atterbury
**COO:* Roy Gross
**COO:* Rodney D Johnson
**CFO:* Robert H Nazarian
**Ex VP:* Brenda J Vale
**Sr VP:* Katherine L Miller
**Genl Couns:* Lisa M Bilcik
Board of Directors: Joseph Bondi, John W Castro, James Continenza, Peter C J Harrison, Alfred Hurley, David Tanner, James R Wiley

D-U-N-S 07-867-9370 IMP/EXP
MERRILL CORP (MN)
1 Merrill Cir, Saint Paul, MN 55108-5264
Tel (651) 646-4501 *Founded/Ownrshp* 1968
Sales 579.3MM *EMP* 5,418
SIC 7389 8111 8999 Personal service agents, brokers & bureaus; Specialized legal services; Communication services
CEO: James R Wiley
**COO:* Rick R Atterbury
**COO:* Roy Gross
**COO:* Rodney D Johnson
**CFO:* Tom Donnelly
CFO: Robert H Nazarian
Chf Mktg O: Rhonda Sneed
**Ofcr:* Todd R Albright
**Ofcr:* Thomas Fredell
**Ofcr:* Hilary London
**Ofcr:* Katherine L Miller
**Ofcr:* Brenda J Vale
Assoc VP: Bhamathi Prakash
Ex VP: Scott Bernecker
Ex VP: William Guckien
Ex VP: Craig P Levinsohn
Sr VP: Doug Cullen
Sr VP: Jim Garippa
Sr VP: Raymond J Goodwin
Sr VP: Ken Lambert
Sr VP: Amy Reichenbach
Board of Directors: Joseph Bondi, John W Castro, James Continenza, Peter C J Harrison, Alfred Hurley, David Tanner, James R Wiley

D-U-N-S 80-605-8012
MERRILL GARDENS LLC
1938 Frview Ave E Ste 300, Seattle, WA 98102
Tel (206) 676-5300 *Founded/Ownrshp* 1890
Sales 85.5MM^E *EMP* 2,000
Accts Ernst & Young Seattle Washin
SIC 6531 Real estate agents & managers
Pr: Bill Pettit
**Pr:* William D Pettit
**Ch:* Charles Wright
**Ex VP:* Steve Delmore
**Sr VP:* Jason Childers
**Sr VP:* Morei Lingle
**Sr VP:* Doug Spear
VP: Reggie Mullis
Ex Dir: Peter Heck
Genl Mgr: Michael Fountain
Genl Mgr: Evelyn Mlitan

D-U-N-S 94-436-3795
■ **MERRILL LYNCH COMMODITIES INC**
(*Suby of* BANK OF AMERICA CORP) ★
20 Greenway Plz Ste 950, Houston, TX 77046-2008
Tel (832) 681-5904 *Founded/Ownrshp* 2015
Sales 181.8MM^E *EMP* 575
SIC 6211 6091 Brokers, security; Underwriters, security; Nondeposit trust facilities
CEO: Brian T Moynihan
Pr: Kuljinder Chase
VP: Charles Johansen

D-U-N-S 60-650-0635
■ **MERRILL LYNCH GROUP INC**
(*Suby of* BANK OF AMERICA CORP) ★
4 World Financial Ctr # 4, New York, NY 10080-0002
Tel (646) 855-5000 *Founded/Ownrshp* 1987
Sales 1.2MMM^E *EMP* 4,167
SIC 6282 6162 Investment advisory service; Mortgage bankers
Pr: Theresa Lang
Pr: Alan Ford
Sr VP: Jose Otero
VP: John Beauchamp
VP: Michael Bebawi
VP: Ken Brady
VP: Ed Darmiento
VP: Marc P Davis
VP: Craig Foreman
VP: Vincent Gamba
VP: Mark Gobble
VP: Hemanth Jayakumar
VP: Matthew M Kahn
VP: Jeffrey Kressen
VP: Lee McCauley
VP: Bart Mendez
VP: Mark Morasky
VP: Mark Nisbet
VP: Michael Parham
VP: James Parlapiano
VP: Jim Pell

D-U-N-S 14-464-6452
MERRILL LYNCH INSURANCE GROUP INC
(*Suby of* AEGON USA, INC.)
1700 American Blvd, Pennington, NJ 08534-4139
Tel (609) 274-5351 *Founded/Ownrshp* 2007
Sales NA *EMP* 302
SIC 6311 Life insurance
Mng Dir: Deborah Adlar
**CFO:* Joseph Justice
**Sr VP:* Barry Skolnick
VP: Nancy Hasson
VP: John Oleary
VP: Mike Omalley
VP: Matthew Pusak
VP: Paul St Amour
**Mng Dir:* John Carroll

D-U-N-S 82-957-2242
■ **MERRILL LYNCH INTERNATIONAL INC**
(*Suby of* BANK OF AMERICA CORP) ★
4 Wrld Fncl Ctr Fl 12, New York, NY 10281-1023
Tel (646) 855-5000 *Founded/Ownrshp* 2015
Sales 89.0MM^E *EMP* 274^E
SIC 6211 Security brokers & dealers
CEO: James B Quigley
Dir Bus: Gregory McGauley

D-U-N-S 14-464-6197
■ **MERRILL LYNCH INVESTMENT MANAGEMENT INC**
(*Suby of* BANK OF AMERICA CORP) ★
225 Liberty St Fl C1056, New York, NY 10281-1049
Tel (212) 449-1000 *Founded/Ownrshp* 1976
Sales 442.1MM^E *EMP* 7,000
SIC 6211 6282 Dealers, security; Investment advisory service
Ch Bd: Stan O'Neal
**CFO:* Ahmass Fakahany
Prin: John Fosina
IT Man: John Woolf
**Genl Couns:* Rosemary Berkery

D-U-N-S 00-892-0951
■ **MERRILL LYNCH PIERCE FENNER & SMITH INC**
(*Suby of* BANK OF AMERICA CORP) ★
111 8th Ave, New York, NY 10011-5201
Tel (800) 637-7455 *Founded/Ownrshp* 2015
Sales 14.7MMM^E *EMP* 46,000
SIC 6211 6411 Brokers, security; Dealers, security; Investment bankers; Insurance brokers
Ch Bd: Thomas Kell Montag
**V Ch:* Stephen L Hammerman
**Pr:* David H Komansky
**Treas:* Theresa Lang
Ofcr: Janine Rusch
**Ex VP:* Barry S Friedberg
**Ex VP:* Edward L Goldberg
**Ex VP:* Jerome P Kenney
**Ex VP:* Winthrop H Smith Jr
Sr VP: Casey Kavanaugh
**Sr VP:* Alan S Mann
Sr VP: Henry Pupke
Sr VP: Mandy Rofe
Sr VP: Marvin Waltuch
VP: Emily Arens
VP: Karen Bebee
VP: Joseph Corcoran
VP: Annette Fallmann
VP: Fred Graney
VP: Sam Hodgson
VP: Joseph Kasell

MERRILL TECHNOLOGIES GROUP
See MERRILL TOOL HOLDING CO

D-U-N-S 04-717-5245 IMP
MERRILL TOOL HOLDING CO
MERRILL TECHNOLOGIES GROUP
400 Florence St, Saginaw, MI 48602-1203
Tel (989) 791-6676 *Founded/Ownrshp* 1969
Sales 143.5MM^E *EMP* 400
SIC 3443 3599 8734 8711 3724 Fabricated plate work (boiler shop); Machine & other job shop work; Testing laboratories; Engineering services; Aircraft engines & engine parts
CEO: Robert Yackel
**CFO:* Michael E Beyer
**Ch:* Gary Yackel
**Sec:* Mary K Yackel
Ex VP: Jerry Artache
**VP:* Jeffery J Yackel
Exec: Kay Yackel
Dir IT: Jason Vardon
Mfg Mgr: Jeff North
Genl Couns: Michael Sauer

D-U-N-S 96-795-8419
MERRILL/GLOBAL INC
(*Suby of* MERRILL COMMUNICATIONS LLC) ★
1 Merrill Cir Ste 1433, Saint Paul, MN 55108-5267
Tel (651) 646-4501 *Founded/Ownrshp* 1997
Sales 17.2MM^E *EMP* 1,168^E
SIC 2759 2752 2791 Commercial printing; Commercial printing, lithographic; Typesetting

D-U-N-S 06-659-8673
MERRIMACK COLLEGE
315 Turnpike St, North Andover, MA 01845-5800
Tel (978) 837-5000 *Founded/Ownrshp* 1947
Sales 98.9MM *EMP* 600
Accts Grant Thornton Llp Boston Ma
SIC 8221 College, except junior
Pr: Christopher E Hopey
**Pr:* Joseph D Calderone
Pr: Sue Thorn
Sr VP: Charles Comegys
VP: Sara Brazda
VP Admn: Alexa Abowitz
Ex Dir: Tom Bourdon
Off Mgr: Rita Persichetti
Off Mgr: Katie Tavares
Mktg Dir: Zoe Cohen
Mktg Dir: Patrick Spiegel
Board of Directors: Robert Coppola

D-U-N-S 00-695-1354
MERRIMACK MUTUAL FIRE INSURANCE CO
STATE FIRE INSURANCE COMPANY
95 River Rd, Andover, MA 01810-1078
Tel (978) 475-3300 *Founded/Ownrshp* 1958
Sales NA *EMP* 240^E
SIC 6331 Fire, marine & casualty insurance; Property damage insurance
Pr: William E Nichols
**CEO:* Malcolm W Brawn
**VP:* Donald Vose
**VP:* Janet Wallace

D-U-N-S 00-122-1410
MERRIMACK PHARMACEUTICALS INC
1 Kendall Sq Ste B7201, Cambridge, MA 02139-1670
Tel (617) 441-1000 *Founded/Ownrshp* 1993
Sales 89.2MM *EMP* 426
Accts Pricewaterhousecoopers Llp B
Tkr Sym MACK *Exch* NGM
SIC 2834 Pharmaceutical preparations
Ch Bd: Gary L Crocker
CFO: Yasir Al-Wakeel
Sr VP: Fazal R Khan
Sr VP: Edward J Stewart
VP: Scott Lauder
VP: Istvan Molnar
Assoc Dir: Bart Hendriks
Assoc Dir: Marco Muda
Assoc Dir: Drew O'Brien
Assoc Dir: Anastasia Semienko
Genl Mgr: Venka Ramakrishnan
Board of Directors: John M Dineen, Vivian S Lee, John Mendelsohn, Michael E Porter, James H Quigley, Russell T Ray

D-U-N-S 13-333-8462
MERRITT HOSPITALITY LLC
(*Suby of* HEI HOTELS & RESORTS) ★
101 Merritt 7 Ste 14, Norwalk, CT 06851-1060
Tel (203) 849-8844 *Founded/Ownrshp* 2003
Sales 111.0MM^E *EMP* 1,915^E
SIC 8741 Hotel or motel management
Pr: Ted Darnall
**Ex VP:* Roger Aufieri
Sr VP: William J Scanlon
**Sr VP:* Glenn Tuckman
S&M/VP: Jacqueline Villamil

D-U-N-S 08-094-4747
MERRY LAND PROPERTIES LLC
209 7th St Ste 300, Augusta, GA 30901-1486
Tel (706) 722-6756 *Founded/Ownrshp* 1981
Sales 217.9MM *EMP* 785
SIC 6798 Realty investment trusts
Pr: W Tennent Houston
**COO:* Michael N Thompson
Sr VP: John W Gibson
VP: Joseph P Bailey III
VP: Ronald J Benton
VP: J Russ Davis Jr
VP: Dorrie Green
VP: Jay Simons
Board of Directors: Ben O Howell Sr, Boone A Knox Is Chairman O, Robert P Kirby, Hugh Long, Pierce Merry Jr, Paul S Simon

D-U-N-S 04-423-2932
■ **MERRY MAIDS LIMITED PARTNERSHIP**
(*Suby of* SERVICEMASTER CONSUMER SERVICES LIMITED PARTNERSHIP) ★
860 Ridge Lake Blvd Fl 3, Memphis, TN 38120-9422
Tel (901) 597-8100 *Founded/Ownrshp* 1988
Sales 171.3MM^E *EMP* 5,000
SIC 7349 Maid services, contract or fee basis
Pr: Mike Isakson
**COO:* Brent Armstrong
COO: Joe Chaves
COO: Sandy McCarrey
VP: Wes Jenkins
IT Man: John Browne
S&M/VP: Sherry Rose

D-U-N-S 07-944-9694
MERRY TECHNOLOGY INC
315 N Rverview St Apt 615, Wichita, KS 67203
Tel (316) 371-9533 *Founded/Ownrshp* 1998
Sales 110.0MM *EMP* 5
SIC 1521 1542

D-U-N-S 00-823-3355
MERRY X-RAY CHEMICAL CORP (CA)
M X R
4444 Viewridge Ave A, San Diego, CA 92123-1670
Tel (858) 565-4472 *Founded/Ownrshp* 1962, 1958
Sales 309.8MM^E *EMP* 390^E
SIC 5047 X-ray machines & tubes; X-ray film & supplies
Prin: Leo Zuckerman
**Pr:* Ted Sloan

D-U-N-S 05-413-1656
MERRY X-RAY CORP
4444 Viewridge Ave, San Diego, CA 92123-1670
Tel (858) 565-4472 *Founded/Ownrshp* 1958
Sales 114.5MM^E *EMP* 500
SIC 5047 Hospital equipment & furniture

Pr: Ted Sloan
CFO: Sandie Christensen
**VP:* Al Lewein
Off Mgr: Tracy Wilkson
Opers Mgr: Pam Hicks

D-U-N-S 07-196-5446
MERS LLC
ECONOMY BOAT STR CO-WOOD RIVER
(*Suby of* PILOT THOMAS LOGISTICS) ★
200 S Amoco Cutoff, Wood River, IL 62095
Tel (618) 254-4500 *Founded/Ownrshp* 2015
Sales 110.0MM[E] *EMP* 110
SIC 5172 Diesel fuel; Service station supplies, petroleum
Ch Bd: James F Barton Jr
**Pr:* Fred Barton
**CFO:* Walter Sheffield
Genl Mgr: Tom Zupan

D-U-N-S 05-694-6692
MERS/MISSOURI GOODWILL INDUSTRIES
1727 Locust St, Saint Louis, MO 63103-1703
Tel (314) 241-3464 *Founded/Ownrshp* 1917
Sales 156.1MM *EMP* 1,300
SIC 8331 Job training & vocational rehabilitation services
Pr: David Kutchback
Mng Pt: Jeffrey Haller
**CFO:* Dawayne Barnett
**VP:* Mark Arens
VP: Kristy Lance
**Ex Dir:* Lewis C Chartock
MIS Dir: Jeff Lawson
IT Man: Nate Sides

D-U-N-S 04-285-9876 IMP/EXP
MERSEN USA BN CORP
(*Suby of* MERSEN)
400 Myrtle Ave, Boonton, NJ 07005-1839
Tel (973) 334-0700 *Founded/Ownrshp* 1940
Sales 251.0MM[E] *EMP* 1,061
SIC 3624 Brushes & brush stock contacts, electric
Pr: Bernie Monsalvatge
CFO: Massimo Neri
Genl Mgr: Thierry Arnaud
Genl Mgr: Cedrick Fontes
Dir IT: Susan Forst
IT Man: Sean Crowe
Mtls Mgr: Pedro Melchor
Sfty Mgr: Colin McMurray
Opers Mgr: Claudio Clemente
Plnt Mgr: Doug Thomas

D-U-N-S 10-557-2155 IMP
■ **MERU NETWORKS INC**
(*Suby of* FORTINET INC) ★
894 Ross Dr, Sunnyvale, CA 94089-1403
Tel (408) 215-5300 *Founded/Ownrshp* 2015
Sales 108.5MM[E] *EMP* 419[E]
SIC 3669 Intercommunication systems, electric
CEO: Ken Xie
**Pr:* Michael Xie
**CFO:* Andrew Del Matto
Sr VP: Ajay Malik
Sr VP: Keith Matasci
VP: Peter Brant
VP: Ashok Chandran
VP: John Maddison
VP: Amanda Mallow
VP: Patrick Perche
VP: Manish Rai
VP: Kishore Reddy
VP: Michelle Spolver
VP: Sarosh Vesuna
VP: John Whittle

D-U-N-S 08-548-9271
MERUELO ENTERPRISES INC
9550 Firestone Blvd # 105, Downey, CA 90241-5560
Tel (562) 745-2300 *Founded/Ownrshp* 1986
Sales 293.7MM[E] *EMP* 501
SIC 1542 Nonresidential construction
CEO: Alex Meruelo
**CFO:* Al Stoller
**VP:* Joe Marchica

D-U-N-S 02-538-4637
MERVIS INDUSTRIES INC
MERVIS IRON & METAL DIV
3295 E Main St Ste C, Danville, IL 61834-9302
Tel (217) 442-5300 *Founded/Ownrshp* 1935
Sales 146.6MM[E] *EMP* 320
Accts Watermark Group Llc Indianap
SIC 5093 Metal scrap & waste materials; Plastics scrap; Waste paper
Ch Bd: Louis L Mervis
**Pr:* Adam Mervis
Treas: Richard George
**Treas:* Jennifer Kline
**VP:* Michael A Smith
Genl Mgr: George Matherly
VP Mfg: Steve Alberico
Prd Mgr: Bob Latham

MERVIS IRON & METAL DIV
See MERVIS INDUSTRIES INC

D-U-N-S 80-527-4727 IMP
MERYL DIAMOND LTD
M D L
1375 Broadway Fl 9, New York, NY 10018-7052
Tel (212) 730-0333 *Founded/Ownrshp* 1993
Sales 101.1MM *EMP* 60[E]
Accts Mayer Hoffman Mccann Cpa S Ne
SIC 2339 2389 Sportswear, women's; Men's miscellaneous accessories
Pr: Meryl Diamond

D-U-N-S 13-711-3929
MERZ NORTH AMERICA INC
NEOCUTIS
(*Suby of* MERZ PHARMA GMBH & CO. KGAA)
6501 Six Forks Rd, Raleigh, NC 27615-6515
Tel (919) 582-8000 *Founded/Ownrshp* 2003
Sales 93.7MM *EMP* 310
SIC 3841 Diagnostic apparatus, medical
Pr: William Humphries
**CFO:* John Donofrio
**Treas:* Rob Burgess
Sr VP: Adam Gridley
VP: Philippe Adams
VP: Matt Anderson
VP: Gregory B Bass
Exec: Victoria Winter
Assoc Dir: Wendy Jones
VP Mfg: Oliver Vogt
VP Opers: Matthew Anderson

D-U-N-S 05-815-3370
MESA AIR GROUP INC
410 N 44th St Ste 700, Phoenix, AZ 85008-7690
Tel (602) 685-4000 *Founded/Ownrshp* 1983
Sales 587.2MM[E] *EMP* 4,113
SIC 4512 4522 Air passenger carrier, scheduled; Air cargo carrier, scheduled; Flying charter service
Ch Bd: Jonathan G Ornstein
Pr: Michael J Lotz
Pr: Christopher J Pappaioanou
COO: Paul Foley
Ex VP: Brian S Gillman
Sr VP: David K Butler
Sr VP: David K Butler
Sr VP: Ed Wegel
VP: Kristen Sk Brookshire
VP: David Butler
VP: Sharon L Goddin
VP: Robert A Hornberg
VP: Chris Pappaioanou
Comm Dir: Marcia Scott
Board of Directors: Daniel J Altobello, Robert Beleson, Carlos E Bonilla, Joseph L Manson, Peter F Nostrand, Maurice A Parker, Richard R Thayer

D-U-N-S 12-610-7619
MESA AIRLINES INC
(*Suby of* MESA AIR GROUP INC) ★
410 N 44th St Ste 700, Phoenix, AZ 85008-7690
Tel (602) 685-4000 *Founded/Ownrshp* 1996
Sales 341.7MM[E] *EMP* 2,700
SIC 4512 4522 4581 Air passenger carrier, scheduled; Flying charter service; Aircraft servicing & repairing
Ch: Jonathan Ornstein
**Pr:* Michael Lotz
**COO:* Jorn Bates
**COO:* John Selvaggio
**CFO:* George Murmame III
Treas: Henri Vilaire
**Treas:* Darren Zapfe
Sr VP: Michael Ferverda
VP: Jeffrey Domrese
**VP:* Brian Gillman

D-U-N-S 05-582-7059
MESA COUNTY VALLEY SCHOOL DISTRICT 51 (INC)
2115 Grand Ave, Grand Junction, CO 81501-8007
Tel (970) 254-5100 *Founded/Ownrshp* 1951
Sales 195.2MM *EMP* 3,200[E]
Accts Chadwick Steinkirchner Davis
SIC 8211 Public elementary & secondary schools
Pr Dir: Emily Shockley
HC Dir: Marla Oppenheim

D-U-N-S 11-838-6309
■ **MESA ENERGY SYSTEMS INC**
EMCOR SERVICES
(*Suby of* EMCOR GROUP INC) ★
2 Cromwell, Irvine, CA 92618-1816
Tel (949) 460-0460 *Founded/Ownrshp* 1999
Sales 138.2MM[E] *EMP* 450
SIC 1711 7623 Warm air heating & air conditioning contractor; Refrigeration service & repair
Pr: Robert A Lake
**CFO:* Steve Hunt
**VP:* Kip Bagley
**VP:* Michael Ecshner
**VP:* Charles G Fletcher Jr
IT Man: Rob Wagner
Opers Mgr: Ted Stutz

MESA FOOD PRODUCTS
See MESA FOODS LLC

D-U-N-S 14-431-1255
MESA FOODS LLC
MESA FOOD PRODUCTS
(*Suby of* TEASDALE FOODS INC) ★
3701 W Magnolia Ave, Louisville, KY 40211-1635
Tel (502) 772-2500 *Founded/Ownrshp* 2016
Sales 95.3MM[E] *EMP* 275
SIC 2096 2045 2099 Tortilla chips; Pizza doughs, prepared: from purchased flour; Tortillas, fresh or refrigerated
Pr: Ted Longacre
VP: Steve Bright
Ql Cn Mgr: Tim Herndon

D-U-N-S 10-253-0326
▲ **MESA LABORATORIES INC**
12100 W 6th Ave, Lakewood, CO 80228-1252
Tel (303) 987-8000 *Founded/Ownrshp* 1982
Sales 84.6MM *EMP* 367[E]
Tkr Sym MLAB *Exch* NGM
SIC 3823 3841 Industrial instrmnts msrmnt display/control process variable; Flow instruments, industrial process type; Analyzers, industrial process type; Data loggers, industrial process type; Hemodialysis apparatus
Pr: Luke R Schmieder
Ch Bd: H Stuart Campbell
Pr: John J Sullivan
CFO: John V Sakys
Ofcr: Glenn E Adriance
Board of Directors: Michael T Brooks, Robert V Dwyer, Evan C Guillemin, David M Kelly, John B Schmieder

MESA MEDICAL GROUP
See MARSHALL PHYSICIAN SERVICES LLC

MESA PUBLIC SCHOOLS
See MESA UNIFIED SCHOOL DISTRICT 4

D-U-N-S 07-899-0504
MESA UNIFIED SCHOOL DISTRICT 4 (AZ)
MESA PUBLIC SCHOOLS
63 E Main St Ste 101, Mesa, AZ 85201-7422
Tel (480) 472-0000 *Founded/Ownrshp* 1890
Sales 531.3MM *EMP* 9,621
Accts Heinfeld Meech & Co Pc P
SIC 8211 Elementary & secondary schools
VP: Adam Risch
Exec: Russ Thompson
Ex Dir: Joe O'Reilly
Dir Sec: Allen R Moore
Dir IT: David Sanders
Mtls Mgr: Ken Polamalu
Site Mgr: Theresa Chucri
Psych: Carol Hoff
Psych: Julie Koehn
Psych: Anisia Palm
Doctor: Rachel Kruppa

D-U-N-S 62-083-6460
■ **MESABA AVIATION INC**
DELTA CONNECTION
(*Suby of* ENDEAVOR AIR INC) ★
1000 Blue Gentian Rd # 200, Eagan, MN 55121-1789
Tel (651) 367-5000 *Founded/Ownrshp* 2010
Sales 109.7MM[E] *EMP* 3,700
SIC 4512 Helicopter carrier, scheduled
Pr: John G Spanjers
CFO: John Stanjers
**VP:* Bill Donohue
**VP:* Bill Pal Freeman
**VP:* Tom Schmidt
Genl Couns: Max Shemesh

D-U-N-S 79-387-2180
MESCALERO APACHE HOUSING AUTHORITY
(*Suby of* CASINO APACHE TRAVEL CENTER) ★
101 Central Ave, Mescalero, NM 88340
Tel (575) 464-9245 *Founded/Ownrshp* 1852
Sales NA *EMP* 1,000
SIC 9531 Housing authority, non-operating: government
Ex Dir: Alvin Benally
**CFO:* Thomas Odell

D-U-N-S 07-761-8650
MESCALERO APACHE TRIBE
108 Old Mescalero Blvd, Mescalero, NM 88340
Tel (575) 464-4494 *Founded/Ownrshp* 1852
Sales NA *EMP* 2,000
SIC 9131 Indian reservation;
Pr: Carleton Palmer
**COO:* Brian Parrish
**CFO:* Lance Kintz
CFO: Bill Ramey
Ex Dir: Timothy Horan
IT Man: Adam Pepers

MESILLA VALLEY TRANSPORTATION
See MVT SERVICES LLC

D-U-N-S 15-453-7732
MESIROW FINANCIAL HOLDINGS INC
353 N Clark St Lowr Level, Chicago, IL 60654-5439
Tel (312) 595-6000 *Founded/Ownrshp* 1987
Sales 458.8MM[E] *EMP* 1,150
SIC 6211 6282 6531 6552 6411 Stock brokers & dealers; Bond dealers & brokers; Investment bankers; Investment advisory service; Real estate brokers & agents; Subdividers & developers; Insurance brokers
CEO: Richard S Price
Pr: Paul Meier
CFO: Kristie P Askvan
CFO: Kristie Paskvan
CFO: Eve Tyree
Ch: Howard M Rossman
Bd of Dir: Richard H Korengold
Bd of Dir: William A Maniscalco
Bd of Dir: Steven N Mesirow
Bd of Dir: Brian J Shevitz
Ofcr: Chris Helmetag
Ex VP: Thomas J Allison
Ex VP: Stephen C Jones
Ex VP: Peter Klingler
Ex VP: Larry H Lattig
Sr VP: Rux Currin
Sr VP: Thomas D Walsh
Sr VP: Mary Kay Wik
VP: Pedro Arellano
VP: Juan C Avila
VP: Jeffrey Bleiweis
Board of Directors: Ralph S Tuliano, Thomas E Galuhn, Julie E Vander Weele, Jeffrey A Golman, Stephen C Vogt, Ruth C Hannenberg, Bruce J Young, Martin B Kaplan, Gerald J Levin, Richard S Price, Paul E Rice, Howard M Rossman, Marc E Sacks

D-U-N-S 61-497-4475
MESIROW FINANCIAL INC
(*Suby of* MESIROW FINANCIAL HOLDINGS INC) ★
353 N Clark St Lowr Level, Chicago, IL 60654-5439
Tel (312) 595-6000 *Founded/Ownrshp* 1982
Sales 335.0MM[E] *EMP* 800
SIC 6211 Security brokers & dealers; Stock brokers & dealers; Bond dealers & brokers; Investment bankers
CEO: Richard S Price
**Pr:* Bruce Young
**CFO:* Kristie Paskvan
Sr VP: Rudy Betancourt
Sr VP: Daniel Goodmann
Sr VP: Tom Honn
Sr VP: Gain O Stein
VP: Jonathan Brandon
VP: Kerry Crandell
VP: Wendy Donaghue
VP: Wendy Evans
VP: Natalie Firestone
VP: Brian Gant
VP: Robert A Goshen
VP: Ryan D Johnson
VP: Ruth Jurkschat
VP: Luke Lau
VP: Patty Pappas
VP: Andrew Pataky
VP: Joseph Scheurich
VP: Jeff Sobczynski

D-U-N-S 11-303-3224
MESO SCALE DISCOVERY LLC
1601 Research Blvd, Rockville, MD 20850-3126
Tel (240) 314-2600 *Founded/Ownrshp* 2001
Sales 119.0MM[E] *EMP* 400[E]
SIC 3826 Analytical instruments
CEO: Jacob Wohlstadter
VP: Al Akowitz
VP: Belinda Patrick
VP: Lillian Quintero
Rgnl Mgr: Andrew Chow
Snr Sftwr: Mark Roush
IT Man: William Fefe
Web Dev: Edmund Wong
Software D: Jonathan Viccary
Sftwr Eng: Joshua Seltzer
VP Opers: Alan Kishbaugh

D-U-N-S 07-137-9846
MESQUITE INDEPENDENT SCHOOL DISTRICT
405 E Davis St, Mesquite, TX 75149-4701
Tel (972) 288-6411 *Founded/Ownrshp* 1901
Sales 414.6MM *EMP* 4,200
Accts Weaver And Tidwell Llp Da
SIC 8211 Public elementary & secondary schools
Pr: Robert Seward
Ofcr: Larry Brown
Ofcr: Debbie Gilbert
Ofcr: Judyann Robinson
**VP:* Phil Appenzeller
VP: Cheryl Gregory
VP: Joel Palmer
Adm Dir: Laura Jobe
Ex Dir: Randy Lewallyn
Dir Sec: Shelley Garrett
MIS Dir: Lance King

D-U-N-S 78-624-6624
MESQUITE SPECIALTY HOSPITAL
(*Suby of* ERNEST HEALTH INC) ★
1024 N Galloway Ave, Mesquite, TX 75149-2434
Tel (972) 216-2300 *Founded/Ownrshp* 2005
Sales 59.8MM[E] *EMP* 1,583[E]
SIC 8742 Hospital & health services consultant
CFO: Michael Exline

D-U-N-S 04-160-3499
MESSER CONSTRUCTION CO
5158 Fishwick Dr, Cincinnati, OH 45216-2216
Tel (513) 242-1541 *Founded/Ownrshp* 1975
Sales 1.1MMM *EMP* 900
Accts Deloitte & Touche Llp Cincinn
SIC 1542 1541 1522 Hospital construction; Commercial & office building, new construction; Commercial & office buildings, renovation & repair; School building construction; Industrial buildings & warehouses; Renovation, remodeling & repairs: industrial buildings; Warehouse construction; Hotel/motel, new construction; Multi-family dwellings, new construction
Ch Bd: Thomas M Keckeis
Pr: Matt Monnin
CFO: Chad Gagnon
**CFO:* E Paul Hitter Jr
**Sr VP:* C Allen Begley
**Sr VP:* Mark R Gillming
**Sr VP:* Mark S Luegering
**Sr VP:* Timothy J Steigerwald
**Sr VP:* Bernard P Suer
VP: Nick Apanius
VP: Steven M Bestard
VP: Daniel C France
VP: Stephen L Keckeis
VP: Thomas M Lampe
VP: Andrew R Lorenz
VP: David E Miller
VP: Bill Rutz
VP: William E Rutz
VP: Bernie Suer
VP: Robert E Verst Jr
VP: Robert Verst
Board of Directors: Edward D Diller, Charles S Mechem Jr, Nelson Schwab III, Peter S Strange, Robert L Wehling

D-U-N-S 07-119-7792
MESSIAH COLLEGE (PA)
1 College Ave Ste 3000, Mechanicsburg, PA 17055-6805
Tel (717) 766-2511 *Founded/Ownrshp* 1909
Sales 128.1MM *EMP* 800
SIC 8221 College, except junior
Pr: Kim S Phipps
**CFO:* David Walker
**VP:* Randall Basinger
**VP:* John Chopka
**VP:* Barry G Goodling
**Prin:* Eunice F Steinbrecher
MIS Dir: John Luft
**MIS Mgr:* William Strausbaugh

D-U-N-S 01-406-2350 EXP
MESSICK FARM EQUIPMENT INC (PA)
187 Merts Dr, Elizabethtown, PA 17022-8803
Tel (800) 222-3373 *Founded/Ownrshp* 1953
Sales 85.0MM[E] *EMP* 215
SIC 5083 5082 Farm equipment parts & supplies; Landscaping equipment; General construction machinery & equipment
Pr: Robert Messick
**VP:* Kenneth Messick

D-U-N-S 06-846-4874
MESSINA GROUP INC
BECO GROUP, THE
200 S Prospect Ave, Park Ridge, IL 60068-4037
Tel (847) 825-8000 *Founded/Ownrshp* 1956
Sales 60.4MM[E] *EMP* 2,662[E]
SIC 7361 7379 Employment agencies; Computer related consulting services

D-U-N-S 00-432-8225 IMP
MESTEK INC
DADANCO - MESTEK
260 N Elm St, Westfield, MA 01085-1614
Tel (413) 568-9571 *Founded/Ownrshp* 1898
Sales 438.2MM[E] *EMP* 2,584
Accts Mcgladrey Llp Boston Massach

SIC 3585 3634 3549 3542 3354 Heating equipment, complete; Air conditioning equipment, complete; Air conditioning units, complete: domestic or industrial; Heating units, electric (radiant heat): baseboard or wall; Metalworking machinery; Wiredrawing & fabricating machinery & equipment, ex. die; Coilers (metalworking machines); Cutting-up lines; Punching, shearing & bending machines; Shapes, extruded aluminum
CEO: Stuart B Reed
Treas: Stephen M Shea
Ofcr: Richard Allorto
Sr VP: Mark Albino
Sr VP: Robert G Dewey
VP: Greg Crosby
VP: Diana Jay
VP: Richard Kessler
Exec: Joanne Berwald
Prin: Bill Rafferty
Ex Dir: Ed Howell

MET-CON COMPANIES
See MET-CON CONSTRUCTION INC

D-U-N-S 08-767-9304
MET-CON CONSTRUCTION INC (MN)
MET-CON COMPANIES
15760 Acorn Trl, Faribault, MN 55021-7610
Tel (507) 332-2266 *Founded/Ownrshp* 1978
Sales 86.7MM^E *EMP* 250^E
SIC 1541 1542 5251 Industrial buildings & warehouses; Commercial & office building contractors; Hardware
CEO: Thomas Mc Donough
**Sec:* Sandra Mc Donough
**VP:* Scott Brown
**VP:* Randy McDonough
**VP:* Jim Roush
**VP:* Julie Teske
Sls Mgr: Joel Schafer

D-U-N-S 00-234-9280 EXP
■ **MET-PRO TECHNOLOGIES LLC**
(*Suby of* CECO ENVIRONMENTAL CORP) ★
460 E Swedesford Rd # 2030, Wayne, PA 19087-1821
Tel (215) 717-7909 *Founded/Ownrshp* 1966
Sales 92.9MM^E *EMP* 337^E
SIC 3564 Air cleaning systems; Air purification equipment; Filters, air: furnaces, air conditioning equipment, etc.
Ofcr: Bill Kelley
VP: Mark A Betchaver
VP: Karl Dean
VP: Sonja M Haggert
VP: Gregory Kimmer
VP: William Moffitt
VP: Bob Replogle
Genl Mgr: Thomas Walker
Dir IT: Robin Pmp
Ql Cn Mgr: Max Clouse
Sls&Mrk Ex: Jon Crane
Board of Directors: Michael J Morris, Stanley W Silverman, Judith A Spires, Robin L Wiessmann

D-U-N-S 82-735-0943
▲ **META FINANCIAL GROUP INC**
5501 S Broadband Ln, Sioux Falls, SD 57108-2253
Tel (605) 782-1767 *Founded/Ownrshp* 1993
Sales NA *EMP* 638^E
Tkr Sym CASH *Exch* NGM
SIC 6035 Federal savings banks
Ch Bd: J Tyler Haahr
**Pr:* Bradley C Hanson
COO: Cynthia M Smith
CFO: Glen W Herrick
**V Ch Bd:* Frederick V Moore
Sr VP: Sonja A Theisen

D-U-N-S 07-290-3990
■ **METABANK**
(*Suby of* META FINANCIAL GROUP INC) ★
121 E 5th St, Storm Lake, IA 50588-2339
Tel (712) 732-4117 *Founded/Ownrshp* 1954, 1955
Sales NA *EMP* 254
SIC 6035 Federal savings & loan associations
CEO: J Tyler Haar
**Pr:* Fred Hanson
CFO: David Leedom
**Ofcr:* John Hagy
**Ex VP:* Troy Moore
**Sr VP:* Jeff Gednalske
Sr VP: Troy Larson
Sr VP: Jeanni Stahl
Sr VP: Ian Stromberg
Sr VP: Sonja Theisen
VP: Greg Baker
VP: Lisa Binder
VP: Jeff Damman
VP: Tracee Dierenfield
VP: Petr Dvorak
VP: Kara Gerken
VP: Jeff Ketelhut
VP: Angela Ralston
VP: Karen Waller
Exec: Kathy Thorson

D-U-N-S 10-305-6594 IMP/EXP
METAGENICS INC
(*Suby of* ALTICOR INC) ★
25 Enterprise Ste 200, Aliso Viejo, CA 92656-2709
Tel (949) 366-0818 *Founded/Ownrshp* 2006
Sales 194.8MM^E *EMP* 386
Accts Grant Thornton Irvine Ca
SIC 5122 Vitamins & minerals; Medicinals & botanicals
Pr: Brent Eck
Pr: Jean M Bellin
CFO: Dave Tuit
Ofcr: John Troup
Ex VP: John Babish
VP: J Kuhlman
VP: Michael Kuhlman
VP: Deanna Minich
VP: Willy Pardinas
VP: Matthew L Tripp
Dist Mgr: Geoff Olsen

METAL ACESORIES
See DAYTON SUPERIOR CORP

METAL AIRE
See METAL INDUSTRIES INC

METAL CASTINGS CO
See ELECTRO-MECHANICAL CORP

D-U-N-S 06-691-0464 IMP/EXP
METAL CONTAINER CORP
(*Suby of* ANHEUSER-BUSCH COMPANIES LLC) ★
3636 S Geyer Rd Ste 400, Saint Louis, MO 63127-1237
Tel (314) 577-2000 *Founded/Ownrshp* 1973
Sales 302.6MM^E *EMP* 1,437
SIC 3411 Aluminum cans
Ch: Barry H Beracha
**Pr:* Joseph L Goltzman
VP: Todd A Brown
VP: James E Engelhuber
VP: William C Wilkenloh

METAL DEK GROUP
See CONSOLIDATED SYSTEMS INC

D-U-N-S 07-198-6160 IMP/EXP
METAL EXCHANGE CORP
PENNEX ALUMINUM COMPANY
111 West Port Plz Ste 350, Saint Louis, MO 63146-3013
Tel (314) 542-7250 *Founded/Ownrshp* 1980
Sales 246.5MM^E *EMP* 500
SIC 3334 5093 Aluminum ingots & slabs; Metal scrap & waste materials
Ch Bd: Mike Lefton
**Pr:* William J Aronson
**Pr:* Rick Merluzzi
**CFO:* Edward O Merz
**Ex VP:* Tom Akers
**VP:* Daryl Coleman
VP: Ea Craver
VP: Adrian Storey
IT Man: Dennis Allen
QC Dir: Tamara Koch
Sls Mgr: Richey Terry

D-U-N-S 04-841-0070 IMP
■ **METAL IMPROVEMENT CO LLC**
CURTISS-WRIGHT
(*Suby of* CURTISS-WRIGHT CORP) ★
80 E State Rt 4 Ste 310, Paramus, NJ 07652-2662
Tel (201) 843-7800 *Founded/Ownrshp* 1969
Sales 403.2MM^E *EMP* 1,800
SIC 3398 Metal heat treating; Shot peening (treating steel to reduce fatigue)
Pr: Gerald Nachman
**Ex VP:* Edward Bloom
**Sr VP:* J Daly
Sr VP: David Francis
**VP:* J Ruscin
Div Mgr: James Groark
IT Man: Peter Gerst
Prd Mgr: Todd Parish
Doctor: Dean Lunn Plumridge

D-U-N-S 00-408-7953 IMP/EXP
METAL INDUSTRIES INC (FL)
METAL AIRE
(*Suby of* J T WALKER INDUSTRIES INC) ★
1985 Carroll St, Clearwater, FL 33765-1909
Tel (727) 441-2651 *Founded/Ownrshp* 1949
Sales 425.6MM^E *EMP* 3,500
SIC 3585 Parts for heating, cooling & refrigerating equipment
CEO: Jay K Poppleton
**Pr:* Damian Macaluso
**CEO:* Peter Desoto
CFO: Dan Frankiewicz
**VP:* Janet L Fasenmyer
VP Mfg: David Hawkins

D-U-N-S 10-296-2370 IMP
METAL MANAGEMENT INC
SIMS METAL MANAGEMENT
(*Suby of* SIMS METAL MANAGEMENT LIMITED)
2500 S Paulina St, Chicago, IL 60608-5307
Tel (312) 645-0700 *Founded/Ownrshp* 2008
Sales 1.3MMM^E *EMP* 6,600
SIC 5093 1795 Metal scrap & waste materials; Demolition, buildings & other structures
CEO: Galvino Claro
**Ch Bd:* Daniel W Dienst
**Pr:* Robert A Kelman
CFO: Robert Larry
Ex VP: David Borg
Ex VP: Jimmie Buckland
**Ex VP:* Robert C Larry
Ex VP: Larry Snyder
VP: Brian Souza
Exec: Thomas Sansone
Ex Dir: Geoffrey Brunsdon

D-U-N-S 04-758-1335 IMP/EXP
METAL MANAGEMENT MIDWEST INC
SIMS METAL MANAGEMENT
(*Suby of* SIMS METAL MANAGEMENT) ★
2500 S Paulina St, Chicago, IL 60608-5307
Tel (773) 254-1200 *Founded/Ownrshp* 1965
Sales 154.0MM^E *EMP* 500^E
SIC 5093 Ferrous metal scrap & waste; Nonferrous metals scrap
Pr: Cristopher Dandror
**Pr:* Lewis H Ross

METAL MANAGEMENT SOUTHWEST
See PROLER SOUTHWEST INC

D-U-N-S 09-181-1232 IMP/EXP
METAL MASTERS FOODSERVICE EQUIPMENT CO INC
EAGLE FOODSERVICE
(*Suby of* EAGLE GROUP INC) ★
100 Industrial Blvd, Clayton, DE 19938-8900
Tel (302) 653-3000 *Founded/Ownrshp* 1978
Sales 104.9MM^E *EMP* 460
SIC 3589 3556 Commercial cooking & foodwarming equipment; Food products machinery
Pr: Larry N McAllister
**VP:* Betty McAllister
Netwrk Mgr: Debbie Wright
Manager: Lynda Donavon

D-U-N-S 15-822-9232
METAL ONE HOLDINGS AMERICA INC
(*Suby of* METAL ONE CORPORATION)
6250 N River Rd Ste 6055, Rosemont, IL 60018-4210
Tel (847) 318-0019 *Founded/Ownrshp* 2003
Sales 390.7MM^E *EMP* 419
SIC 5085 5051 Fasteners, industrial: nuts, bolts, screws, etc.; Wire
Pr: Ichiro Furuno
Pr: Tomohiro Kadokura
Treas: Nancy P Bryers

METAL PROCESSING
See BD VINTON LLC

D-U-N-S 07-864-4784 IMP/EXP
METAL TECHNOLOGIES OF INDIANA INC
1401 S Grandstaff Dr, Auburn, IN 46706-2664
Tel (260) 925-4717 *Founded/Ownrshp* 1999
Sales 284.8MM^E *EMP* 700
SIC 3321 3443 Gray & ductile iron foundries; Metal parts
CEO: Rick James
CFO: Greg Riker
**Sr VP:* Jeffrey L Turner
VP: John Neiger
Exec: Sara Brown
QA Dir: Mark Jagger
IT Man: Doug Spieth
Opers Mgr: Chad Jerrell
Sls Mgr: Craig Barkey

D-U-N-S 18-289-6670 IMP
METAL TRADERS INC
TRIAD METALS INTERNATIONAL
3480 Grand Ave, Pittsburgh, PA 15225-1508
Tel (412) 331-7772 *Founded/Ownrshp* 1987
Sales 415.0MM *EMP* 200
SIC 5051 Steel
Pr: Fred White
Ch Bd: Ronald J Hammond
VP Sls: Scott Lynch
Sls Mgr: Chris Albrecht
Sls Mgr: Chad Doublin

D-U-N-S 00-624-9668 IMP
METAL-MATIC INC (MN)
629 2nd St Se, Minneapolis, MN 55414-2109
Tel (612) 928-2856 *Founded/Ownrshp* 1951
Sales 102.2MM^E *EMP* 600
SIC 3317 Tubes, wrought: welded or lock joint
CEO: Gerald J Bliss
**Pr:* Thomas J Bliss
CFO: Thomas Jackson
**VP:* Gerald Bliss Jr
**VP:* James D Bliss
**VP:* Robert J Van Krevelen
Software D: Ben Brandt
Software D: Chris Herbst
Plnt Mgr: Jay Van Krevelen
Prd Mgr: Chad Klebs
Ql Cn Mgr: John Anderson

METALCOTE
See CHEMTOOL INC

D-U-N-S 05-290-7995 IMP
METALCRAFT OF MAYVILLE INC (WI)
SCAG POWER EQUIPMENT DIV
1000 Metalcraft Dr, Mayville, WI 53050-2354
Tel (920) 387-3150 *Founded/Ownrshp* 1970
Sales 195.0MM^E *EMP* 750
SIC 3523 3444 Grounds mowing equipment; Sheet metalwork
Pr: Jerry Bailey
CFO: Mike Bemis
**Ch:* Edwin A Gallun Jr
**VP:* Connie Quinn
VP: Tom Schraufnagel
Dir IT: Chris Frame
IT Man: Bob Struck
Tech Mgr: Pat Rohloff
VP Opers: Randy Gloede
Sfty Mgr: Kyle Gourlie
Mfg Mgr: Ron Lock

METALDYNE
See MPG

METALDYNE
See MD INVESTORS CORP

METALDYNE GLOBAL
See METALDYNE LLC

D-U-N-S 83-245-7977
■ **METALDYNE LLC**
METALDYNE GLOBAL
(*Suby of* METALDYNE PERFORMANCE GROUP INC) ★
47659 Halyard Dr, Plymouth, MI 48170-2429
Tel (734) 207-6200 *Founded/Ownrshp* 2009
Sales 1.2MMM^E *EMP* 6,500
SIC 3714 Motor vehicle parts & accessories
Pr: Doug Grimm
COO: Jeff Barringer
COO: Thomas V Chambers
**CFO:* Mark Blaufuss
CFO: Bill Lowe
VP: Jeff Burris
**VP:* Robert Defauw
**VP:* Christoph Guhe
VP: Michael Keflar
VP: Dave Manns
VP: Myra Moreland
VP: John Musat
**VP:* Ben Schmidt
VP: James Strahley
VP: George Thanopoulos
Exec: Thomas Crews

D-U-N-S 07-954-1112
▲ **METALDYNE PERFORMANCE GROUP INC**
1 Towne Sq Ste 550, Southfield, MI 48076-3710
Tel (248) 727-1800 *Founded/Ownrshp* 2005
Sales 3.0MMM *EMP* 12,690^E
Tkr Sym MPG *Exch* NYS
SIC 3714 Motor vehicle parts & accessories; Motor vehicle transmissions, drive assemblies & parts; Steering mechanisms, motor vehicle; Sanders, motor vehicle safety
CEO: George Thanopoulos
**Ch Bd:* Kevin Penn
Pr: Douglas Grimm
CFO: Mark Blaufuss
Ex VP: Russell Bradley
Ex VP: Tom Dono
VP: Gary Ford
Board of Directors: Nick Bhambri, Loren Easton, Michael Fisch, William Jackson, John Pearson Smith, Jeffrey Stafeil

D-U-N-S 06-365-4768 IMP/EXP
■ **METALDYNE SINTERED RIDGWAY LLC**
(*Suby of* METALDYNE GLOBAL) ★
1149 Rocky Rd, Ridgway, PA 15853-6427
Tel (814) 776-1141 *Founded/Ownrshp* 2009
Sales 100.0MM^E *EMP* 460
SIC 3399 3441 3462 Powder, metal; Fabricated structural metal; Automotive & internal combustion engine forgings
VP: Mark Farrell
IT Man: Janet Sauter
Plnt Mgr: Michael Sloff
Ql Cn Mgr: George Tahanopoulus

D-U-N-S 09-033-1737 IMP/EXP
METALICO INC
135 Dermody St, Cranford, NJ 07016-3217
Tel (908) 497-9610 *Founded/Ownrshp* 1999, 2015
Sales 476.0MM *EMP* 9
SIC 3449 Miscellaneous metalwork
Pr: Carlos E Aguero
**CFO:* Kevin Whalen
**Treas:* Eric W Finlayson
**Ex VP:* Michael J Drury
**Ex VP:* Arnold S Graber
VP: Steven M Alberico
VP: David Delbianco
VP: Joseph McGough
Genl Mgr: Mark Persichini

METALLGESELLSCHAFT
See GEA NORTH AMERICA INC

D-U-N-S 05-509-0815 IMP
METALLIX REFINING INC
59 Avenue At The Cmn # 201, Shrewsbury, NJ 07702-4806
Tel (732) 936-0050 *Founded/Ownrshp* 2006
Sales 90.0MM^E *EMP* 64
SIC 3339 Precious metals; Gold refining (primary); Platinum group metal refining (primary)
Pr: Eric Leiner
**Pr:* Pamela Rollins
**CFO:* Lynn Falk

D-U-N-S 10-593-9966
METALLURG HOLDINGS INC
(*Suby of* AMG ADVANCED METALLURGICAL GROUP N.V.)
435 Devon Park Dr Ste 200, Wayne, PA 19087-1937
Tel (610) 293-0838 *Founded/Ownrshp* 1997
Sales 249.5MM^E *EMP* 3,000^E
SIC 3313 1081 Alloys, additive, except copper: not made in blast furnaces; Ferrochromium; Ferromolybdenum; Ferrotitanium; Metal mining services
Pr: Heinz C Schimmelbusch
**Treas:* Arthur R Spector

D-U-N-S 00-137-4669
METALLURG INC
AMG ADVNCED MTLLRGCAL GROUP NV
(*Suby of* METALLURG HOLDINGS INC) ★
435 Devon Park Dr Ste 200, Wayne, PA 19087-1937
Tel (610) 293-2501 *Founded/Ownrshp* 1947
Sales 249.5MM^E *EMP* 3,000
SIC 3313 1081 Alloys, additive, except copper: not made in blast furnaces; Ferrochromium; Ferromolybdenum; Ferrotitanium; Metal mining services
Ch: Heinz Schimmelbusch
**Pr:* Eric E Jackson
**CFO:* Amy E Ard
**V Ch Bd:* Arthur R Spector
VP: Kevin Jones
VP: Dennis Shea

D-U-N-S 79-649-0634
METALMARK CAPITAL LLC
1177 Ave Of The Americas, New York, NY 10036-2714
Tel (212) 823-1900 *Founded/Ownrshp* 2004
Sales 260.6MM^E *EMP* 30
SIC 6726 Investment offices
CEO: Howard Hoffen
Mng Dir: Jefferson Siegal
IT Man: Assaf Rutenberg

METALS
See LYDALL THERMAL/ACOUSTICAL INC

D-U-N-S 03-244-1149 IMP
■ **METALS USA BUILDING PRODUCTS LP**
(*Suby of* METALS USA INC) ★
955 Columbia St, Brea, CA 92821-2923
Tel (713) 946-9000 *Founded/Ownrshp* 2001
Sales 329.1MM^E *EMP* 1,600
SIC 3355 5031 1542 Structural shapes, rolled, aluminum; Building materials, exterior; Commercial & office buildings, renovation & repair
Pt: Charles Canning
**Pt:* Robert McPherson
Mktg Mgr: Ronald Brown

METALS USA FLAT
See METALS USA SPECIALTY METALS NORTH-CENTRAL INC

D-U-N-S 62-669-9677
■ **METALS USA HOLDINGS CORP**
(*Suby of* RELIANCE STEEL & ALUMINUM CO) ★
2400 E Coml Blvd Ste 905, Fort Lauderdale, FL 33308
Tel (954) 202-4000 *Founded/Ownrshp* 2013
Sales 2.0MMM^E *EMP* 2,200^E
Accts Deloitte & Touche Llp Boca Ra

SIC 5051 3272 3354 Metals service centers & offices; Iron & steel (ferrous) products; Aluminum bars, rods, ingots, sheets, pipes, plates, etc.; Building materials, except block or brick: concrete; Aluminum extruded products
CEO: Robert C McPherson
*Sr VP: Roger Krohn
*Sr VP: William A Smith II
*VP: Danial L Henneke
Brnch Mgr: Tracy Bolton
Genl Mgr: Gary Macdonald
Plnt Mgr: James Pietruszka
Prd Mgr: Jesus Villicana
Ql Cn Mgr: Brian Kirkpatrick

D-U-N-S 15-780-8379 IMP/EXP
■ METALS USA INC
(Suby of FLAG INTERMEDIATE HOLDINGS CORP) ★
2400 E Coml Blvd Ste 905, Fort Lauderdale, FL 33308
Tel (954) 202-4000 Founded/Ownrshp 2005
Sales 1.3MMM[E] EMP 2,200
SIC 3441 Fabricated structural metal
CEO: Robert C McPherson III
*Ch Bd: C Lourenco Goncalves
*Pr: Roger Krohn
*CFO: Keith Koci
CFO: McPherson Robert
VP: Randy Sartain
VP: Samuel R Sciple
*VP: Joe Stewart
Dir IT: Debbie Cardoso
Dir IT: Charlton Williams
Info Man: Glenn Cortopassi

D-U-N-S 03-409-8736
■ METALS USA PLATES AND SHAPES NORTHEAST LP
(Suby of METALS USA INC) ★
50 Cabot Blvd E, Langhorne, PA 19047-1802
Tel (267) 580-2100 Founded/Ownrshp 2000
Sales 197.5MM[E] EMP 350
SIC 5051 Plates, metal
CEO: Robert C McPherson
Pt: Lorenco Boncalces
COO: Roger Krohn

D-U-N-S 18-570-5860 IMP/EXP
■ METALS USA PLATES AND SHAPES SOUTHCENTRAL INC
(Suby of METALS USA INC) ★
101 E Illinois Ave, Enid, OK 73701-7483
Tel (580) 233-0411 Founded/Ownrshp 1925
Sales 129.4MM[E] EMP 130
SIC 5051 Steel
Pr: David Martens
*Sr VP: Robert McPherson III

D-U-N-S 04-288-2076 IMP
■ METALS USA PLATES AND SHAPES SOUTHEAST INC (AL)
(Suby of METALS USA INC) ★
1251 Woodland Ave, Mobile, AL 36610-2559
Tel (251) 456-4531 Founded/Ownrshp 1966
Sales 174.8MM[E] EMP 300
SIC 5051 Steel
Pr: Mickey Marshall
*VP: Kim Calametti
*VP: Tim Calametti

D-U-N-S 00-693-0200 IMP
■ METALS USA SPECIALTY METALS NORTHCENTRAL INC
METALS USA FLAT
(Suby of METALS USA INC) ★
3000 Shermer Rd, Northbrook, IL 60062-7713
Tel (847) 291-2400 Founded/Ownrshp 1998
Sales 163.2MM[E] EMP 112
SIC 5051 Metals service centers & offices; Steel; Copper
COO: Russ Russell

D-U-N-S 96-610-0740 IMP
METALSA STRUCTURAL PRODUCTS INC
(Suby of METALSA, S.A. DE C.V.)
29545 Hudson Dr, Novi, MI 48377-1733
Tel (248) 669-3704 Founded/Ownrshp 2009
Sales 586.4MM[E] EMP 2,700
SIC 3714 Motor vehicle parts & accessories
CEO: Polo Cedillo
*Pr: Jose Jaime Salazar Reyes
*Treas: Laura Johnson
*VP: David Altemar Sanchez Hernande
Plnt Mgr: Luis Darroeta

D-U-N-S 02-173-8328 IMP
METALSA-ROANOKE INC
(Suby of GRUPO PROEZA, S.A.P.I. DE C.V.)
184 Vista Dr, Roanoke, VA 24019-8514
Tel (540) 966-5300 Founded/Ownrshp 1956
Sales 105.9MM[E] EMP 200
SIC 3713 Truck & bus bodies
Pr: Steven Helgeson
*CFO: Emmanuel Lopez Cazarez
*VP: Angel Loredo
*VP: Nicolas Villarreal
Mfg Mgr: Darrin Snay
Snr Mgr: Sean Fleming
Snr Mgr: Matt Sanders
Snr Mgr: David Spath

D-U-N-S 61-616-2756 IMP
METALTEK INTERNATIONAL INC
SOUTHERN CENTRIFUGAL DIV
905 E Saint Paul Ave, Waukesha, WI 53188-3804
Tel (262) 544-7777 Founded/Ownrshp 1890
Sales 260.9MM[E] EMP 1,000
SIC 3366 3443 3364 Copper foundries; Nuclear shielding, metal plate; Brass & bronze die-castings
Pr: Robert Smickley
*CFO: Richard Danning
*Treas: Richard Eshleman
Sr Cor Off: Andrew Cope
*VP: E J Kubick
VP: Jack Lilley
VP Opers: Todd Sternaman
Natl Sales: Rod Anderson

D-U-N-S 08-547-4690 IMP
METALWORKING LUBRICANTS CO
25 W Silverdome Indus Par, Pontiac, MI 48342-2994
Tel (248) 332-3500 Founded/Ownrshp 1952
Sales 170.9MM[E] EMP 243
SIC 5172 2869 2843 2992 Lubricating oils & greases; Phosphoric acid esters; Emulsifiers, except food & pharmaceutical; Cutting oils, blending: made from purchased materials; Rust arresting compounds, animal or vegetable oil base
Ch Bd: Robert F Tomlinson
*Treas: James P Tomlinson Jr
*VP: Adam Bujoll
*VP: Dr Nilda Grenier

D-U-N-S 05-692-5722
METALX LLC
295 S Commerce Dr, Waterloo, IN 46793-9437
Tel (260) 232-3000 Founded/Ownrshp 2012
Sales 150.0MM EMP 10
SIC 5093 Metal scrap & waste materials
Pr: Danny Rifkin
*Ex VP: Paul Everett
*Ex VP: Jim Ustian
*VP: Steve King
*VP: Jeff Rynearson
Opers Mgr: Dave Stage

D-U-N-S 80-037-6779
■ METAVANTE CORP
FIDELITY NATIONAL INFO SVCS
(Suby of METAVANTE HOLDINGS LLC) ★
4900 W Brown Deer Rd, Milwaukee, WI 53223-2422
Tel (904) 438-6000 Founded/Ownrshp 2007
Sales 630.1MM[E] EMP 5,500
SIC 7374 8742 6153 Data processing & preparation; Management consulting services; Short-term business credit
Pr: Frank Matire
Pr: Brian Dugan
Pr: Ed Hashek
Pr: Steve Taylor
Pr: Jon Young
*Ex VP: Debra Bronder
*Ex VP: Norrie Daroga
Ex VP: Mark Davey
*Ex VP: Jamie Geschke
*Ex VP: Don Layden
*Ex VP: Gary Nelson
*Ex VP: Steve Rathgaber
*Ex VP: Gary Refinski
Ex VP: James Susoreny
Sr VP: Marcia Danzeisen
VP: Jim Andracchi
VP: Jeff Bloedorn
VP: Chris Crone
VP: Jeff Erdmann
VP: David Kelly
VP: Janet Schaal

D-U-N-S 80-844-6632 EXP
■ METAVANTE HOLDINGS LLC
(Suby of FIS) ★
601 Riverside Ave, Jacksonville, FL 32204-2946
Tel (904) 438-6000 Founded/Ownrshp 2009
Sales 630.1MM[E] EMP 5,900
SIC 3578 5049 7374 Banking machines; Bank equipment & supplies; Data processing & preparation
Pr: Gary Norcross
VP: Michael Gravelle

D-U-N-S 78-703-2916 IMP/EXP
METAVATION LLC
(Suby of REVSTONE INDUSTRIES LLC) ★
900 Wilshire Dr Ste 270, Troy, MI 48084-1600
Tel (248) 351-1000 Founded/Ownrshp 2009
Sales 104.4MM[E] EMP 965
SIC 3714 Motor vehicle parts & accessories

D-U-N-S 06-659-7147
■ METCALF & EDDY INC
(Suby of AECOM) ★
1 Federal St Ste 800, Boston, MA 02110-2003
Tel (781) 246-5200 Founded/Ownrshp 2000
Sales 151.3MM[E] EMP 800
SIC 8711 Professional engineer
CEO: Robert Costello
*Pr: Steven Guttenplan
*CFO: Dennis Morrison
Genl Mgr: Paul Catanzano
IT Man: Ho Mandel
*Genl Couns: Michael Kolloway

METCARE
See METROPOLITAN HEALTH NETWORKS INC

D-U-N-S 96-465-5513
METDALSPI LLC
METHODIST HOSPITAL FOR SURGERY
17101 Dallas Pkwy, Addison, TX 75001-7103
Tel (469) 248-3900 Founded/Ownrshp 2010
Sales 102.7MM EMP 126[E]
SIC 8069 Specialty hospitals, except psychiatric
Ch: Robert Viere
*Ch Bd: Michael Schaefer
CFO: Kelly Hayes
*Treas: Scott Siemer
IT Man: Antwoine White

METED
See METROPOLITAN EDISON CO

D-U-N-S 07-935-3790
METER READINGS HOLDING LLC
945 Hornet Dr, Hazelwood, MO 63042-2309
Tel (561) 394-0550 Founded/Ownrshp 2014
Sales 5.1MMM[E] EMP 75,765[E]
SIC 3824 3825 3829 7371 7373 Mechanical & electromechanical counters & devices; Instruments to measure electricity; Measuring & controlling devices; Custom computer programming services; Computer integrated systems design
CEO: Marc Leder
*Pr: Allan Connolly
*CFO: Kurt R Bruenning
*Sr VP: Greg Bodehamer
*Sr VP: Michael R Garcia
*Sr VP: David F Hakala
*Sr VP: Kumi Premathilake
*Sr VP: Richard C Riccardi
*Sr VP: Greg Wilson

D-U-N-S 07-548-7660
METHACTON SCHOOL DISTRICT
1001 Kriebel Mill Rd, Norristown, PA 19403-1096
Tel (610) 489-5000 Founded/Ownrshp 1950
Sales 135.4MM EMP 825
Accts Major & Mastro Llc Montgomer
SIC 8211 Public elementary & secondary schools
Pr: Joyce Petrauskas
Teacher Pr: Robert Harney

D-U-N-S 36-409-2783 IMP
METHANEX METHANOL CO LLC
METHANEX USA SERVICES
(Suby of METHANEX CORPORATION)
5850 Granite Pkwy Ste 400, Plano, TX 75024-0047
Tel (972) 702-0909 Founded/Ownrshp 1989
Sales 156.9MM[E] EMP 44
SIC 5169 Alcohols
*Sr VP: John Floren

METHANEX USA SERVICES
See METHANEX METHANOL CO LLC

D-U-N-S 00-509-2135 IMP
▲ METHODE ELECTRONICS INC
7401 W Wilson Ave, Chicago, IL 60706-4548
Tel (708) 867-6777 Founded/Ownrshp 1946
Sales 809.1MM EMP 4,295
Tkr Sym MEI Exch NYS
SIC 3678 3674 3676 3672 3825 3643 Electronic connectors; Semiconductor circuit networks; Microcircuits, integrated (semiconductor); Resistor networks; Printed circuit boards; Wiring boards; Test equipment for electronic & electrical circuits; Current-carrying wiring devices; Bus bars (electrical conductors); Connectors & terminals for electrical devices
Pr: Donald W Duda
*Ch Bd: Walter J Aspatore
CFO: John Hrudicka
CFO: John R Hrudicka
Treas: Ronald L G Tsoumas
*V Ch Bd: Christopher J Hornung
VP: Timothy R Glandon
VP: Joseph E Khoury
VP: Theodore P Kill
VP: Douglas Koman
Mktg Mgr: Cecilia Ostberg
Board of Directors: Martha Goldberg Aronson, Warren L Batts, Darren M Dawson, Stephen F Gates, Isabelle C Goosse, Paul G Shelton, Lawrence B Skatoff

METHODIST CHILDRENS HOSPITAL
See METHODIST HEALTH GROUP INC

METHODIST DALLAS MED CENTRE
See METHODIST HOSPITALS OF DALLAS INC

D-U-N-S 10-545-9080 IMP
METHODIST HEALTH CARE SYSTEM
METHODIST HOSPITAL SYSTEM, THE
(Suby of METHODIST HOSPITAL SYSTEM) ★
6565 Fannin St D200, Houston, TX 77030-2703
Tel (713) 793-1602 Founded/Ownrshp 1984
Sales 1.2MMM EMP 30
Accts Grant Thornton Llp Dallas Tx
SIC 8011 Offices & clinics of medical doctors
Pr: Larry L Mathis
Chf Path: Abida Haque
Dir Vol: Margy Lohoff
V Ch: Ernest Cockrell
*Pr: Mauro Ferrari
COO: Jack Julius
CFO: Lowell E Stanton
CFO: Robert Zimmerli
Bd of Dir: Kelly Lange
Bd of Dir: Vidal Martinez
Bd of Dir: Stephen Wende
*VP: S Jeffrey Atcherman
VP: Carol Spang
VP: Stephen Spielman
Board of Directors: Tobias Samo

METHODIST HEALTH CENTER
See CAPITOL LAKES RETIREMENT COMMUNITY

D-U-N-S 05-295-2090
METHODIST HEALTH GROUP INC
METHODIST CHILDRENS HOSPITAL
(Suby of INDIANA UNIVERSITY HOSPITAL) ★
1701 Senate Blvd, Indianapolis, IN 46202-1239
Tel (317) 962-2000 Founded/Ownrshp 1899, 1997
Sales 185.1MM[E] EMP 5,967
SIC 8062 6321 General medical & surgical hospitals; Accident & health insurance
Pr: Dan Evans
Sr VP: Ron Stiver

D-U-N-S 84-845-7578
METHODIST HEALTH SERVICES CORP
(Suby of UNITYPOINT HEALTH) ★
221 Ne Glen Oak Ave, Peoria, IL 61636-0001
Tel (309) 672-5522 Founded/Ownrshp 1985
Sales 47.9M EMP 3,000
SIC 8062 General medical & surgical hospitals
CEO: Deborah Simon
*COO: Debbie Simon
CFO: Calvin Mackay

METHODIST HEALTHCARE
See METHODIST LE BONHEUR HEALTHCARE

D-U-N-S 01-979-0237
METHODIST HEALTHCARE MEMPHIS HOSPITALS
LE BONHEUR CHILDREN'S HOSPITAL
848 Adams Ave, Memphis, TN 38103-2816
Tel (901) 287-5437 Founded/Ownrshp 1902
Sales 36.5MM[E] EMP 1,830[E]
Accts Thompson Dunavant Plc Memphis
SIC 8069 8011 Children's hospital; Offices & clinics of medical doctors
Pr: CAM Welton
Pr: Phyllis Gatlin
Dir Case M: Kenneth Robertson

D-U-N-S 04-313-3859 IMP
METHODIST HEALTHCARE MEMPHIS HOSPITALS
1265 Union Ave, Memphis, TN 38104-3415
Tel (901) 516-7000 Founded/Ownrshp 1918
Sales 1.6MMM EMP 7,000
Accts Dixon Hughes Goodman Llp Ashe
SIC 8062 Hospital, AMA approved residency
CEO: David Baytos
*Pr: Meri Armour
Sr VP: Christopher McLean
VP: John Pehler
Exec: Sheila Troy
Exec: Steven W West
Genl Mgr: Cato Johnson
IT Man: Tim McGinnis
Opers Mgr: Alicia Smith
Plnt Mgr: William Troxel

D-U-N-S 01-986-8892
METHODIST HEALTHCARE MINISTRIES OF SOUTH TEXAS INC
M H M
4507 Medical Dr, San Antonio, TX 78229-4401
Tel (210) 692-0234 Founded/Ownrshp 1955
Sales 191.6MM EMP 250
Accts Ernst & Young Us Llp Fort Wor
SIC 8011 7363 Primary care medical clinic; Medical help service
CEO: Kevin C Moriarty
*COO: George Thomas
*CFO: Tony Lobasso
Bd of Dir: Joe Johnston
Sr VP: Peggy Cary
VP: Mark Holiday
IT Man: Vanessa M Adame
Ql Cn Mgr: Amanda Orahoske
Board of Directors: Alice H Gannon, Joe E Johnston, George N Ricks, Darrell Frank Smith, Shirley S Watkins, V Chm, V Chm

D-U-N-S 06-306-7326 IMP
■ METHODIST HEALTHCARE SYSTEM OF SAN ANTONIO LTD LLP
METHODIST HOSPITAL
(Suby of HOSPITAL COPORATION OF AMERICA) ★
8109 Fredericksburg Rd, San Antonio, TX 78229-3311
Tel (210) 575-8110 Founded/Ownrshp 1995
Sales 728.7M[E] EMP 5,400
SIC 8062 8011 General medical & surgical hospitals; Offices & clinics of medical doctors
CEO: John E Hornbeak
*CFO: Ed Vasquez
Ex VP: Michael Schaefer
VP: Palmira Arellano
Genl Mgr: Rhonda Magness
Off Mgr: Newton Courtney
Off Mgr: Jo Estrada
Snr Ntwrk: Talley Fritsch
CIO: Ron Hunsucker
MIS Dir: Michael Angelico
Dir IT: Jamie Cornell

METHODIST HOSP PAIN MGT CLINIC
See NEBRASKA METHODIST HOSPITAL INC

METHODIST HOSPITAL
See METHODIST HEALTHCARE SYSTEM OF SAN ANTONIO LTD LLP

D-U-N-S 07-417-2719 IMP
METHODIST HOSPITAL
METHODIST HOSPITAL SYSTEM, THE
6565 Fannin St, Houston, TX 77030-2892
Tel (713) 790-3311 Founded/Ownrshp 2010
Sales 3.4MMM EMP 15,000
SIC 8062 Hospital, affiliated with AMA residency
Pr: Marc L D
Chf Rad: King Li
*Ch Bd: John F Bookout
*Ch Bd: David M Underwood
V Ch: Connie M Dyer
Pr: Noel Rainey
*Pr: Ewing Werlein Jr
*CFO: Kevin Burns
CFO: Mick Cantu
CFO: John E Hagal
CFO: Linda Kulhanek
*Treas: Carlton Baucum
Bd of Dir: Kenneth R Levingston
Ex VP: Marc L Boom
Ex VP: Richard Gonzales
*Ex VP: Roberta Schwartz
Sr VP: Edward Etyrrell
*Sr VP: Edward L Tyrrell
VP: Steve Burns
VP: Thomas W Knight
Exec: Anne Eastman

D-U-N-S 07-960-3570
METHODIST HOSPITAL
7700 Floyd Curl Dr, San Antonio, TX 78229-3902
Tel (210) 575-4000 Founded/Ownrshp 2014
Sales 101.3MM[E] EMP 1,270[E]
SIC 8062 General medical & surgical hospitals
CEO: Gay Nord
COO: Michael Beaver
Treas: Scott Bryan
VP: Albert Zimmerli
Exec: Michelle Benoit
Dir Lab: Michael Davis
Chf Nrs Of: Wanda Gibbons
Dir Sec: Kevin Ritcher
Dir IT: Edward Cuellar
IT Man: Tricia Perez
Doctor: Wendell Schorlemer

D-U-N-S 83-880-0068
METHODIST HOSPITAL
BUILDING SERVICE DEPARTMENT
1900 N Capitol Ave Fl 3, Indianapolis, IN 46202
Tel (317) 962-2000 Founded/Ownrshp 1995
Sales 71.5MM[E] EMP 6,000
SIC 8062 General medical & surgical hospitals
Pr: Dan Evans
VP: Doug Morris

METHODIST HOSPITAL FOR SURGERY
See METDALSPI LLC

METHODIST HOSPITAL NORTHLAKE C
See METHODIST HOSPITALS INC

D-U-N-S 06-669-4803
METHODIST HOSPITAL OF SOUTHERN CALIFORNIA
300 W Huntington Dr, Arcadia, CA 91007-3402
Tel (626) 898-8000 *Founded/Ownrshp* 1903
Sales 300.0MM *EMP* 2,200
Accts Kpmg Llp Los Angeles Ca
SIC 8062 General medical & surgical hospitals
CEO: Dan F Ausman
Dir Recs: Bridgett Didier
CFO: Donald Deshotels
**Sr VP:* Clifford R Daniels
**Sr VP:* William E Grigg
**Sr VP:* Steven A Sisto
VP: Barry Burns
VP: Clifford Daniels
VP: Pamela Greenberg
Exec: Michele Benoit
Dir Inf Cn: Sharon Keehne
Dir Lab: Sonja Malgian
Dir Lab: Sonia Maljian
Dir Rad: Francis J Moorhead
Dir Rx: Dorothy Wong

METHODIST HOSPITAL SYSTEM, THE
See METHODIST HOSPITAL

METHODIST HOSPITAL SYSTEM, THE
See METHODIST HEALTH CARE SYSTEM

METHODIST HOSPITAL SYSTEM
See METHODIST WEST HOUSTON HOSPITAL

METHODIST HOSPITAL SYSTEM, THE
See SAN JACINTO METHODIST HOSPITAL

D-U-N-S 06-949-0670
METHODIST HOSPITALS INC
METHODIST HOSPITAL NORTHLAKE C
600 Grant St, Gary, IN 46402-6001
Tel (219) 886-4000 *Founded/Ownrshp* 1941
Sales 279.9MM *EMP* 3,260
SIC 8062 General medical & surgical hospitals; Hospital, AMA approved residency
Pr: Michael Davenport
Chf Path: Teresa Vazquez
**Pr:* James Burg
**Pr:* Ian E McFadden
COO: Steven Grant
**CFO:* John C Diehl
**CFO:* Matthew Doyle
**Ch:* Benjamin Luna
Treas: William Braman
**Treas:* Bruce Dahltorp
**VP:* Wright Alcorn
VP: James Kirchner
Assoc Dir: Jackie Ivankovic
Dir Rad: John A Scott
Dir Rad: Brian D White

D-U-N-S 07-485-3979
METHODIST HOSPITALS OF DALLAS INC
METHODIST DALLAS MED CENTRE
1441 N Beckley Ave, Dallas, TX 75203-1201
Tel (877) 637-4297 *Founded/Ownrshp* 1935
Sales 411.4MM *EMP* 4,804
SIC 8062 Hospital, medical school affiliation
Ch Bd: John Ford
Pr: Dwight Williams
**CEO:* Stephen L Mansfield
**CFO:* Michael J Schaefer
Ofcr: Barbara Odom
Ex VP: Kim N Hollo
**Ex VP:* Laura Irvine
**Ex VP:* Michael O Price
**Ex VP:* Pamela Stoyanoff
Sr VP: Pamela McNutt
VP: Deanna Kenard
VP: Harold Kolni
VP: Leslie Pierce

D-U-N-S 10-629-7500
METHODIST LE BONHEUR HEALTHCARE
METHODIST HEALTHCARE
1211 Union Ave Ste 700, Memphis, TN 38104-6600
Tel (901) 516-7000 *Founded/Ownrshp* 1981
Sales 150.7MM *EMP* 11,459
Accts Dixon Hughes Goodman Llp Ashe
SIC 8062 General medical & surgical hospitals
Pr: Gary S Shorb
COO: Kevin Spiegel
CFO: Hilder Peake
CFO: Kevin Todd
Ex VP: Dona Abbe
**Ex VP:* Donna Abney
**Sr VP:* Bill Breen
Sr VP: Steven T Miller
VP: Huss Antonio
VP: Michelle Collis
VP: Cynthia Davis
VP: Lenon Donahue
**VP:* Lynn M Field
VP: Larry Fogarty
VP: Donna Herrin
**VP:* Cato Johnson
VP: Alexander Macgrregor
VP: Stephen Miller
VP: Alastair Phillips
VP: Carol Spang
VP: Jim Summers

D-U-N-S 01-271-4593
METHODIST MEDICAL CENTER FOUNDATION
(*Suby of* METHODIST HEALTH SERVICES CORP) ★
221 Ne Glen Oak Ave, Peoria, IL 61636-0001
Tel (309) 672-4895 *Founded/Ownrshp* 1990
Sales 6.6MM *EMP* 2,150
SIC 8082 Home health care services
Pr: Kevin Vermeer
**COO:* Keith Knepp
**CFO:* Robert Quin
Board of Directors: Keith Knepp, Robert Quin, Deborah Simon

D-U-N-S 07-560-7689
METHODIST MEDICAL CENTER OF ILLINOIS
UNITYPOINT HEALTH - METHODIST
(*Suby of* METHODIST HEALTH SERVICES CORP) ★
221 Ne Glen Oak Ave, Peoria, IL 61636-0002
Tel (309) 672-5522 *Founded/Ownrshp* 1898
Sales 388.4MM *EMP* 2,400
SIC 8062 Hospital, medical school affiliated with nursing & residency
Pr: Debbie Simon
**COO:* Steve Brewer
CFO: Calvin M Kay
**CFO:* Rob Quin
Treas: R Younggren
**VP:* Rebekah Bourland
**VP:* Tammy Duvendack
VP: Gene Hoerr
**VP:* Keith Knepp
**VP:* Joy Ledbetter
**VP:* John Miller
**VP:* Roberta Parks
**VP:* Tony Schierbeck
**VP:* Jeanine Spain
**VP:* Terry Waters
VP: Steve Weaver

D-U-N-S 07-902-6738
METHODIST MEDICAL CENTER OF OAK RIDGE (TN)
(*Suby of* COVENANT HEALTH) ★
990 Oak Ridge Tpke, Oak Ridge, TN 37830-6942
Tel (865) 835-1000 *Founded/Ownrshp* 1959
Sales 154.3MM *EMP* 1,500[E]
SIC 8062 General medical & surgical hospitals
Pr: Mike Belbeck
Chf Rad: Steven Knight
CFO: Julie Utterback
VP: Rebekah Bourland
VP: Chad Clabough
VP: Jennifer Hanson
VP: Sue Harris
VP: Connie Martin
Dir Lab: Jackie Murray
Cmptr Lab: Scott Wing
QA Dir: Mitzi Thomas
Board of Directors: David Seay, H W Arrowsmith, Anne Travis, Ralph Aurin, Clement Block, David Compton MD, Gary Coxon, Greg Grimm, Sherry Hoppe, Francis Reid MD, Rev Gordon L Ridenour

D-U-N-S 84-972-6273
METHODIST MEDICAL CENTER OF OAK RIDGE
1420 Centerpoint Blvd C, Knoxville, TN 37932-1960
Tel (865) 374-6864 *Founded/Ownrshp* 2009
Sales 189.3MM *EMP* 6[E]
SIC 8011 Medical centers
Prin: Nancy Beck
CFO: Julie Utterback

D-U-N-S 95-991-4677
METHODIST WEST HOUSTON HOSPITAL
METHODIST HOSPITAL SYSTEM
18500 Katy Fwy, Houston, TX 77094-1110
Tel (832) 522-1000 *Founded/Ownrshp* 2011
Sales 201.7MM *EMP* 46[E]
SIC 8661 8062 Methodist Church; General medical & surgical hospitals
Pr: Sherene Thompson
Dir Vol: Laura Gomez
QC Dir: Sherry Nelson

D-U-N-S 01-965-9044 IMP/EXP
METHODS MACHINE TOOLS INC
65 Union Ave, Sudbury, MA 01776-2277
Tel (978) 443-5388 *Founded/Ownrshp* 1958
Sales 109.7MM[E] *EMP* 275
SIC 5084

METLIFE
See AMERICAN LIFE INSURANCE CO

METLIFE
See METROPOLITAN LIFE INSURANCE CO (INC)

METLIFE
See METROPOLITAN PROPERTY AND CASUALTY INSURANCE CO

METLIFE
See METROPOLITAN INSURANCE & ANNUITY CO

D-U-N-S 00-693-4053
■ **METLIFE AUTO & HOME INSURANCE AGENCY INC** (RI)
(*Suby of* METLIFE INC) ★
9797 Springboro Pike, Dayton, OH 45448-0001
Tel (815) 266-5301 *Founded/Ownrshp* 1915, 2002
Sales NA *EMP* 900
SIC 6411 Insurance agents & brokers
Ch Bd: Stephen Klingel
COO: Darla Fitchum
CFO: Patrick Thiele
Treas: Donald Swanson
Sr VP: Howard Dalton
Sr VP: Andrew Douglass
VP: Ruby Schroeder
Brnch Mgr: Tiffani Jackson
Brnch Mgr: Matthew Luedeke
Brnch Mgr: Shawn McAtee
Sales Asso: Thomas Nemeth

D-U-N-S 03-118-9345
■ **METLIFE GROUP INC**
(*Suby of* METLIFE INC) ★
1095 Ave Of The Americas, New York, NY 10036-6797
Tel (800) 638-5433 *Founded/Ownrshp* 2002
Sales NA *EMP* 282[E]
SIC 6411 Insurance agents & brokers
Prin: Richard Barquist
VP: Virginia Bartlett
VP: Robin Kidd
VP: Kareema Mejri
VP: Stephanie Miller
VP: Dinah Moore
VP: Sachin Shah
IT Man: Lakshmi Nanduri
VP Mktg: Joel Marlin
Advt Dir: Jennifer Cook
Mktg Dir: Ted Holcomb

D-U-N-S 01-290-2141
■ **METLIFE HOME LOANS LLC**
(*Suby of* METLIFE) ★
7880 Bent Branch Dr # 100, Irving, TX 75063-6046
Tel (214) 441-4000 *Founded/Ownrshp* 2008
Sales NA *EMP* 500
SIC 6162 Mortgage bankers & correspondents
Pr: Rodney Gayle
Pr: James Rose

D-U-N-S 11-215-8568
▲ **METLIFE INC**
200 Park Ave Fl 1200, New York, NY 10166-0188
Tel (212) 578-9500 *Founded/Ownrshp* 1863
Sales NA *EMP* 69,000
Tkr Sym MET *Exch* NYS
SIC 6311 6321 6331 Life insurance carriers; Accident & health insurance carriers; Disability health insurance; Fire, marine & casualty insurance: mutual; Property damage insurance
Pr: Steven A Kandarian
Pr: Yvette Bigornia
Pr: Doug Birkitt
Pr: Brian Bruneau
Pr: Jill Carmichael
Pr: Michel Khalaf
Pr: Paul Mattern
Pr: Christopher G Townsend
CEO: Gaurav Sharma
CFO: John C R Hele
Bd of Dir: Cheryl Gross
Bd of Dir: Marly Perou
Chf Mktg O: Esther Lee
Chf Inves: Steven J Goulart
Ofcr: Celina Ali
Ofcr: Frans Hijkoop
Ofcr: Lisa Rumph
Ofcr: Julia Sessa
Ex VP: Benjamin Alcid
Ex VP: Ricardo A Anzaldua
Ex VP: Todd Katz

D-U-N-S 00-691-7413
■ **METLIFE INSURANCE CO USA**
(*Suby of* METLIFE INC) ★
11225 N Community Hse Rd, Charlotte, NC 28277-4435
Tel (980) 949-3626 *Founded/Ownrshp* 1863, 2005
Sales NA *EMP* 65,000
Accts Deloitte & Touche Llp New Yor
SIC 6411 6321 6331 6324 Insurance agents & brokers; Medical insurance claim processing, contract or fee basis; Accident & health insurance; Accident insurance carriers; Health insurance carriers; Fire, marine & casualty insurance; Workers' compensation insurance; Hospital & medical service plans; Group hospitalization plans
Ch Bd: Eric T Steigerwalt
CFO: Stanley J Talbi
Ex VP: Peter M Carlson
Sr VP: Stuart L Baritz
Sr VP: Jay S Fishman
Sr VP: Elizabeth C Georgakopoulos
Sr VP: Russell H Johnson
Sr VP: Warren H May
Sys/Dir: Ronald Waid
Board of Directors: Elizabeth M Forget, Gene L Lunman

D-U-N-S 93-280-1343
■ **METLIFE INVESTORS DISTRIBUTION CO**
(*Suby of* METLIFE) ★
1 Met Life Plz, Long Island City, NY 11101-4018
Tel (212) 578-2211 *Founded/Ownrshp* 1987
Sales NA *EMP* 1[E]
SIC 6411 Insurance agents & brokers
Pr: Thomas P Lydon Jr
Sr VP: Robin Lenna
VP: Douglas Barone
VP: Bob Fratangelo
VP: Charles Miller
VP: Sean S Myles
VP: Robert Tarnok
IT Man: Bizz Anirudh
VP Sls: Curtis Wohlers
Mktg Mgr: Robert Chamerda
Genl Couns: Susan Flannery

D-U-N-S 04-878-8426 IMP
■ **METOKOTE CORP**
PPG-METOKOTE
(*Suby of* PPG INDUSTRIES INC) ★
1340 Neubrecht Rd, Lima, OH 45801-3120
Tel (419) 996-7800 *Founded/Ownrshp* 2016
Sales 688.1MM[E] *EMP* 2,000
SIC 3479 Painting, coating & hot dipping
Pr: Jeffrey J Oravitz

METRA COLUMBUS TRANSIT SYS
See CONSOLIDATED GOVERMENT OF GA INC

D-U-N-S 00-132-3807 IMP
METRA ELECTRONICS CORP
460 Walker St, Holly Hill, FL 32117-2653
Tel (386) 257-1186 *Founded/Ownrshp* 1949
Sales 116.9MM[E] *EMP* 501
SIC 3651 Audio electronic systems
Pr: William H Jones Jr
**CFO:* Anthony Guidice
**VP:* Bill Fornino
**VP:* Jan Jones
IT Man: Gary Lewis
Plnt Mgr: John Lelasher

METRA METROPOLITAN RAIL
See NORTHEAST ILLINOIS REGIONAL COMMUTER RAILROAD CORP

D-U-N-S 83-911-3438
■ **METRAHEALTH CARE MANAGEMENT CORP**
(*Suby of* UNITED HEALTHCARE INSURANCE CO) ★
9900 Bren Rd E, Minnetonka, MN 55343-9664
Tel (952) 936-1300 *Founded/Ownrshp* 1994
Sales NA *EMP* 10
SIC 6321 6311 Accident & health insurance; Life insurance
Pr: R Colby

D-U-N-S 79-825-3068
METRIC EQUIPMENT SALES INC
MICROLEASE
(*Suby of* MICROLEASE INC) ★
25841 Industrial Blvd # 200, Hayward, CA 94545-2991
Tel (510) 264-0887 *Founded/Ownrshp* 2013
Sales 97.7MM[E] *EMP* 70
SIC 5065 5084 7359 3825 Electronic parts & equipment; Measuring & testing equipment, electrical; Electronic equipment rental, except computers; Instruments to measure electricity
CEO: Nigel Brown
**CEO:* Mike Clark
**CFO:* Nathan Hurst
CFO: Robert Parker
**Sr VP:* David Sherve
**VP:* Gordon Curwen
IT Man: Teresa O'Connor
Sls Mgr: Richard Yanes

D-U-N-S 84-714-9247
METRICSTREAM INC
COMPLIANCEONLINE
2600 E Bayshore Rd, Palo Alto, CA 94303-3241
Tel (650) 620-2900 *Founded/Ownrshp* 1999
Sales 329.6MM[E] *EMP* 1,600
SIC 7372 Application computer software
CEO: Shellye Archambeau
**COO:* Gaurave Kapoor
**CFO:* Bert Clement
**Ch:* Gunjan Sinha
**Ex VP:* Venky Yerrapotu
VP: Kristin Gruaz
VP: Tim Schmutzler
Software D: Kumar Gaurav
Board of Directors: Ned Gilhuly

D-U-N-S 00-565-5360 IMP
METRIE INC
(*Suby of* METRIE CANADA LTD)
2200 140th Ave E Ste 600, Sumner, WA 98390-9672
Tel (253) 470-5050 *Founded/Ownrshp* 1999
Sales 258.2MM[E] *EMP* 500
SIC 5031 Building materials, exterior; Building materials, interior; Lumber: rough, dressed & finished
**VP:* William Sauder
Genl Mgr: Alan Dobie
Genl Mgr: Leo Pappas

METRO APPLIANCES AND MORE
See METRO BUILDERS SUPPLY INC

METRO ATLANTA YMCA
See YOUNG MENS CHRISTIAN ASSOCIATION OF METROPOLITAN ATLANTA INC

D-U-N-S 09-535-0802
METRO BANCORP INC
3801 Paxton St, Harrisburg, PA 17111-1418
Tel (888) 937-0004 *Founded/Ownrshp* 1999
Sales NA *EMP* 978
SIC 6022
Ch Bd: Gary L Nalbandian
V Ch: Harry D Madonna
COO: Percival B Moser III
CFO: Mark A Zody
Chf Cred: James R Ridd
Ofcr: Steven W Cribbs
Ofcr: Steven Cribbs
Ofcr: Adam L Metz
Sr VP: Victoria G Chieppa
Sr VP: Elisa M Cintron
CIO: Stephanie Morris
Board of Directors: Samir J Srouji, James R Adair, Douglas R Berry, John J Cardello, Douglas S Gelder, Alan R Hassman, J Rodney Messick, Jessica E Meyers, Michael A Serluco, Thomas F Smida

D-U-N-S 14-427-4701
METRO BANK
1249 Market St, Lemoyne, PA 17043-1419
Tel (717) 972-2875 *Founded/Ownrshp* 1999
Sales NA *EMP* 238
SIC 6022

D-U-N-S 07-864-2410
METRO BUILDERS SUPPLY INC (OK)
METRO APPLIANCES AND MORE
5313 S Mingo Rd, Tulsa, OK 74146-5736
Tel (918) 622-7692 *Founded/Ownrshp* 1974
Sales 103.1MM[E] *EMP* 300
SIC 5064 Electric household appliances
**CEO:* Nick Stavros
**Sec:* Jane E Stavros
**VP:* Todd Krauser
VP: Scott Tucker
Genl Mgr: Jon Anderson
Genl Mgr: Josh Beale
Genl Mgr: Brian Casey
Genl Mgr: Ann Howell
Genl Mgr: Christy Williams
Sls Mgr: Jay Baird
Sls Mgr: Tarah Duncan

D-U-N-S 15-531-6177 IMP
METRO BUSINESS SYSTEMS INC
11 Largo Dr S, Stamford, CT 06907-2337
Tel (203) 967-3435 *Founded/Ownrshp* 1986
Sales 106.4MM *EMP* 45
Accts Totilo & Company Llc
SIC 5045 Computers, peripherals & software
Pr: Frank Pelli
**COO:* Stellino Savarino
**Treas:* Ralph Boccuzzi
**VP:* Jeff Lorusso
Sales Exec: Nora Ballaro

D-U-N-S 05-703-1981
■ **METRO CARE CORP**
RURAL-METRO
(*Suby of* RURAL/METRO CORP) ★
8465 N Pima Rd, Scottsdale, AZ 85258-4489
Tel (800) 352-2309 *Founded/Ownrshp* 1990
Sales 99.1MM[E] *EMP* 2,000
SIC 4119 Ambulance service

Pr: Michael P Dimino
**Pr:* Michael Dimino
**Sr VP:* Mark A Lashley
**Sr VP:* Christopher R Yearout
Exec: Colin Williams
Comm Man: Shondra Young

METRO ELECTRIC
See ST LOUIS ELECTRIC SUPPLY INC

METRO HARDWOODS
See MIDWEST HARDWOOD CORP

METRO HEALTH HOSPITAL
See METROPOLITAN HOSPITAL

METRO LEASING COMPANY
See AMERICAN NATIONAL BANK

D-U-N-S 05-791-7536 IMP
■ METRO MACHINE CORP
GENERAL DYNAMICS NASSCO-NORFOLK
(*Suby of* GENERAL DYNAMICS CORP) ★
200 Ligon St, Norfolk, VA 23523-1000
Tel (757) 543-6801 *Founded/Ownrshp* 2011
Sales 286.5MM^E *EMP* 1,049
SIC 3731 Shipbuilding & repairing; Military ships, building & repairing
Pr: Frederick J Harris
**Treas:* David H Fogg
VP: Dave Carver
Genl Mgr: Dave Baker
Genl Mgr: Carleton Bryant
Genl Mgr: Steve Miley
Genl Mgr: Chris Obery
**Genl Mgr:* John Stram
IT Man: Nate Fowler
IT Man: Bonn Garrett

D-U-N-S 55-711-7702 IMP/EXP
METRO METALS NORTHWEST INC
5611 Ne Columbia Blvd, Portland, OR 97218-1237
Tel (503) 287-8861 *Founded/Ownrshp* 1991
Sales 144.1MM^E *EMP* 250
SIC 5093 Metal scrap & waste materials
Pr: Victor Winkler
Dir IT: Mike Wyant

D-U-N-S 08-268-9258 IMP
METRO NATIONAL CORP
METRONATIONAL COMMERCIAL LAND
945 Bunker Hill Rd # 400, Houston, TX 77024-1358
Tel (713) 973-6400 *Founded/Ownrshp* 1955
Sales 123.7MM^E *EMP* 600
SIC 6512 6531 6722 Nonresidential building operators; Real estate managers; Management investment, open-end
CEO: Roy F Johnson
**Pr:* David Kelley
**CFO:* Charles Delacey
**Ex VP:* Perry Hicks
**Sr VP:* William M Mosley Jr
**Sr VP:* Randy Nerren
VP: AIA Fuhrman

METRO NISSAN OF MONTCLAIR
See NEW AGE INVESTMENTS INC

D-U-N-S 96-327-4951
METRO PARKING CORP
PARKSAFE SYSTEMS
8300 Nw 7th Ave, North Miami Beach, FL 33160
Tel (305) 579-5300 *Founded/Ownrshp* 2010
Sales 200.0MM *EMP* 10
SIC 7521 4119 Automobile parking; Local passenger transportation
Pr: Elliot Alexander
**Pr:* Sao Mya Nwe
**VP:* Myat Maung
**VP:* Mario Nyat
Genl Mgr: Mario Maung

D-U-N-S 06-478-4051
METRO SALES INC
1640 E 78th St, Minneapolis, MN 55423-4636
Tel (612) 861-4000 *Founded/Ownrshp* 1969
Sales 139.1MM^E *EMP* 275
SIC 5044 5112 5065 7359 Office equipment; Duplicating machines; Typewriters; Stationery & office supplies; Computer & photocopying supplies; Facsimile equipment; Office machine rental, except computers
CEO: Jerry Mathwig
**VP:* Karen A Mathwig
Dir IT: Vincent Queau
Sls Mgr: Kevin Case
Sls Mgr: Karie Hamilton

D-U-N-S 07-995-6686
METRO WASTEWATER RECLAMATION DISTRICT
6450 York St, Denver, CO 80229-7407
Tel (303) 286-3000 *Founded/Ownrshp* 1966
Sales 240.4MM^E *EMP* 350
Accts Cliftonlarsonallen Llp Denve
SIC 4952 Sewerage systems
Dist Mgr: Cathy Gerali
Ofcr: Mark Barela
Ofcr: Leo Gengler
Ofcr: Lisa Hollander
Genl Mgr: Kathy Gerali
Cmptr Lab: Glen Jones
Cmptr Lab: Rich Macaltine

D-U-N-S 96-828-6153
METRO-GOLDWYN-MAYER INC
MGM
(*Suby of* MGM STUDIOS) ★
245 N Beverly Dr, Beverly Hills, CA 90210-5319
Tel (310) 449-3000 *Founded/Ownrshp* 2005
Sales 61.9MM^E *EMP* 1,440
SIC 7812 Motion picture production & distribution; Motion picture production & distribution, television; Television film production; Video production
CEO: Gary Barber
COO: Tricia Samuels
COO: Ken Schapiro
Treas: Doug Finberg
Ex VP: Peter Oillataguerre
Sr VP: Lori Silfen
VP: Maggie Adams
VP: Paul Bischoff
VP: Matt Dines
VP: Erik Ellner
VP: Simon Graty
VP: Cassidy Lange
VP: Michael Naud
VP: Shelley Reid
VP: Steve Stark

D-U-N-S 00-699-1624
METRO-GOLDWYN-MAYER STUDIOS INC (DE)
MGM
(*Suby of* MGM) ★
10250 Constellation Blvd, Los Angeles, CA 90067-6200
Tel (310) 449-3590 *Founded/Ownrshp* 1994, 1993
Sales 53.0MM^E *EMP* 1,000
SIC 7812

D-U-N-S 10-112-6142
METRO-NORTH COMMUTER RAILROAD CO INC
METRO-NORTH RAILROAD
(*Suby of* M T A) ★
420 Lexington Ave, New York, NY 10170-0002
Tel (212) 878-7000 *Founded/Ownrshp* 1983
Sales 298.8MM^E *EMP* 5,564
SIC 4013 4111 Switching & terminal services; Commuter rail passenger operation
Pr: Howard Permut
Pr: Marjorie Anders
**Treas:* Robert Maclagger
**Sr VP:* George Walker
VP: Seth J Cummins
**VP:* Kim Porcelain
Snr PM: James Robinson

METRO-NORTH RAILROAD
See METRO-NORTH COMMUTER RAILROAD CO INC

D-U-N-S 14-594-8860
METROGROUP CORP
(*Suby of* METROGROUP HOLDING LLC) ★
1805 E Washington St, Mount Pleasant, IA 52641-3206
Tel (319) 385-5135 *Founded/Ownrshp* 2008
Sales 98.4MM^E *EMP* 1,260
SIC 7331 7389 Direct mail advertising services; Printers' services: folding, collating
Pr: Glen Marder
**Pr:* James Russel
CFO: Albert Strausser
VP: Brian D Bomberger
**VP:* Don McKevitt
VP: Chad Spannaus
CIO: Thomas J McAlister
IT Man: George Johnson

D-U-N-S 80-716-8849
METROGROUP HOLDING LLC
1805 E Washington St, Mount Pleasant, IA 52641-3206
Tel (319) 385-5135 *Founded/Ownrshp* 2005
Sales 114.0MM^E *EMP* 1,260^E
SIC 6719 Personal holding companies, except banks
Pr: Albert Strausser

D-U-N-S 84-283-8161
METROHEALTH MEDICAL CENTER
METROHEALTH SYSTEM THE
2500 Metrohealth Dr, Cleveland, OH 44109-1900
Tel (216) 778-7800 *Founded/Ownrshp* 1837
Sales 782.2MM *EMP* 6,000^E
SIC 8062 General medical & surgical hospitals
CEO: Ekran Boutros
**Pr:* Akram Boutros
**CFO:* Nancy Fisher
**CFO:* Craig Richmond
Dir Rad: Sampath Alapati
**Prin:* Sharon Sobol Jordan
**Prin:* J B Silvers PHD
Dir Sec: Tom Miller
Doctor: James C Finley
Diag Rad: Howard Potash

METROHEALTH SYSTEM THE
See METROHEALTH MEDICAL CENTER

D-U-N-S 07-112-4291
METROHEALTH SYSTEM
2500 Metrohealth Dr, Cleveland, OH 44109-1900
Tel (216) 398-6000 *Founded/Ownrshp* 1953
Sales 859.8MM *EMP* 6,000
Accts Mcgladrey Llp Cleveland Ohio
SIC 8062 Hospital, affiliated with AMA residency
CEO: Akram Boutros
COO: Daniel K Lewis
**CFO:* Sharon Dougherty
CFO: Craig Richmond
Top Exec: Christopher McHenry
**Sr VP:* Elizabeth Heller Allen
**Sr VP:* Mavis Bechtle
**VP:* Karim Botros
**VP:* Kate Brown
**VP:* John Carroll
**VP:* Fusilero Jane Rn
**VP:* Vince Miller
VP: Donald Reichert
VP: Michael Stern
Dir Lab: Vicki Ingham
Dir Bus: Kathryn Milligan

D-U-N-S 07-105-8929 IMP
METROLINA GREENHOUSES INC
16400 Hntrsvle Concrd Rd, Huntersville, NC 28078-6650
Tel (704) 659-9400 *Founded/Ownrshp* 1972
Sales 89.3MM^E *EMP* 750^E
SIC 0181 Flowers: grown under cover (e.g. greenhouse production)
Pr: Art Van Wingerden
Pr: Tom Vanwingrden
**CFO:* Michael Colitti
Dir IT: Chris Long
Sfty Mgr: Kerry Krivanek
Mktg Dir: Abe Van Wingerden

D-U-N-S 04-862-0462 IMP
■ METROLOGIC INSTRUMENTS INC (NJ)
HONEYWELL
(*Suby of* HONEYWELL INTERNATIONAL INC) ★
534 Fellowship Rd, Mount Laurel, NJ 08054-3405
Tel (856) 228-8100 *Founded/Ownrshp* 1969
Sales 132.5MM^E *EMP* 1,400
SIC 3577 3699 Magnetic ink & optical scanning devices; Optical scanning devices; Laser systems & equipment
CEO: Benny A Noens
**Pr:* Dipanjan Deb
Pr: Mehul Patel
CFO: Kevin J Bratton
**CFO:* Michael Coluzzi
**Ex VP:* Joseph Sawitsky
**Ex VP:* Mark Schmidt
Sr VP: Mark C Shmidt
Sr VP: Jeffrey Yorsz
VP: Ed R Brown
VP: Leroy Dickinson
**VP:* Gregory Dinoia
**VP:* Bruce L Harrison
**VP:* Henri Juvanon
**VP:* Mark Ryan

D-U-N-S 00-698-7630
METROMEDIA CO
BENNIGAN'S
810 Seventh Ave Fl 29, New York, NY 10019-5871
Tel (212) 606-4437 *Founded/Ownrshp* 1955
Sales 339.2MM^E *EMP* 29,500
SIC 5812 6794 4813 4911

D-U-N-S 17-766-1394
METROMONT CORP
2802 White Horse Rd, Greenville, SC 29611-6119
Tel (804) 222-6770 *Founded/Ownrshp* 1997
Sales 150.3MM^E *EMP* 530
SIC 3272 Concrete stuctural support & building material
Ch Bd: Richard Pennell
**Pr:* Richard H Pennell Jr
**CFO:* James H Medders
**VP:* Harry A Gleich
**VP:* James H Knight

METRONATIONAL COMMERCIAL LAND
See METRO NATIONAL CORP

D-U-N-S 96-275-8574
METROPADIA HEALTH SYSTEM INC
HOSPITAL METROPOLITANO
2445 Las America Ave, Ponce, PR 00731
Tel (787) 848-5600 *Founded/Ownrshp* 2010
Sales 18.3MM^E *EMP* 2,050
SIC 8062 General medical & surgical hospitals
Pr: Eduardo Arteau

D-U-N-S 14-501-7203 IMP/EXP
METROPARK USA INC
5750 Grace Pl, Los Angeles, CA 90022-4121
Tel (323) 622-3600 *Founded/Ownrshp* 2003
Sales NA *EMP* 1,200
SIC 5632 5699

D-U-N-S 19-131-2321
METROPLEX ADVENTIST HOSPITAL INC
METROPLEX HOSPITAL
2201 S Clear Creek Rd, Killeen, TX 76549-4110
Tel (254) 526-7523 *Founded/Ownrshp* 1978
Sales 106.9MM *EMP* 779
SIC 8062 General medical & surgical hospitals
Prin: Carlyle Walton
**Pr:* Kenneth A Finch
**CFO:* Robert Brock
CFO: Penny Johnson
Obsttrcn: Arturo Romero
Doctor: Hemalkumar Ramani
Doctor: George Rebecca MD

D-U-N-S 79-034-5656
METROPLEX HOLDINGS INC
15 Commerce Dr S, Harriman, NY 10926-3100
Tel (845) 781-5000 *Founded/Ownrshp* 1988
Sales 172.9MM^E *EMP* 230
SIC 6512 5149 5087 Nonresidential building operators; Groceries & related products; Restaurant supplies
CEO: Peter R Grimm
**Ch Bd:* John Paterakis
**Pr:* Philip Praine

METROPLEX HOSPITAL
See METROPLEX ADVENTIST HOSPITAL INC

METROPLTAN COUNCIL ENVMTL SVCS
See METROPOLITAN COUNCIL MINNESOTA

D-U-N-S 83-551-5057
METROPLUS HEALTH PLAN INC
(*Suby of* NEW YORK CITY HLTH & HOSPITALS) ★
160 Water St Fl 3, New York, NY 10038-5009
Tel (212) 788-3648 *Founded/Ownrshp* 1994
Sales NA *EMP* 540
SIC 6324 Health maintenance organization (HMO), insurance only
COO: Phillip Passantino
**Chf Mktg O:* Talya Schwartz
Sr VP: Estelita Mastelero
Assoc Dir: Miriam Kelly
Assoc Dir: Kenya McCall
Mng Ofcr: Gail Smith
QA Dir: Cienciarley Stpaul
Dir IT: James Genesi
Info Man: Susan Sun

D-U-N-S 06-478-4267
METROPOLITAN AIRPORTS COMMISSION
MAC
6040 28th Ave S, Minneapolis, MN 55450-2701
Tel (612) 726-8100 *Founded/Ownrshp* 1943
Sales 307.4MM *EMP* 575
Accts Bkd Llp Indianapolis Indian
SIC 4581 Airport
CEO: Brian Ryks
**Ch:* Daniel Boivin
Bd of Dir: Rick Breezee
Ofcr: Bob Buth
Ofcr: Chidan Doobay
Ofcr: Jennifer Micek
Ofcr: Brad Wingate
VP: Roy Fuhrmann
Exec: David Ruch
Ex Dir: Janet Hielsen
Genl Mgr: Patricia Anderson

D-U-N-S 06-450-0903 IMP/EXP
METROPOLITAN ATLANTA RAPID TRANSIT AUTHORITY
2424 Piedmont Rd Ne, Atlanta, GA 30324-3311
Tel (404) 848-5000 *Founded/Ownrshp* 1965
Sales 157.1MM *EMP* 4,700
SIC 4111

D-U-N-S 00-959-6214 EXP
METROPOLITAN AUTOMOTIVE WAREHOUSE
AUTO VALUE
535 Tennis Court Ln, San Bernardino, CA 92408-1615
Tel (909) 885-2886 *Founded/Ownrshp* 1953
Sales 549.1MM^E *EMP* 700
SIC 5013 Automotive supplies & parts
CEO: John Spencer
COO: Richard Guyett
CFO: Chuck Siemer
VP: Pat Martin
Off Mgr: David Harlow
Sls Mgr: Erick Quiroz

METROPOLITAN COMMUNITY COLLEGE
See JUNIOR COLLEGE DISTRICT OF METROPOLITAN KANSAS CITY MISSOURI

D-U-N-S 12-053-2163
METROPOLITAN COMMUNITY COLLEGE
5300 N 30th St, Omaha, NE 68111-1610
Tel (402) 457-2400 *Founded/Ownrshp* 1977
Sales 19.5MM *EMP* 2,200
Accts Clifton Larson Allen Llp Tucs
SIC 8222 Community college
Pr: Jo Ann C McDowell
Ex Dir: Todd Hansen
Prac Mgr: Eastwood Boardman
Admn Mgr: Julie Langholp
IT Man: Lisa Bounds
Genl Couns: James Thibodeau

D-U-N-S 03-001-8576
METROPOLITAN COUNCIL MINNESOTA
METROPLTAN COUNCIL ENVMTL SVCS
(*Suby of* GOVERNORS OFFICE) ★
390 Robert St N, Saint Paul, MN 55101-1634
Tel (651) 602-1629 *Founded/Ownrshp* 1967
Sales NA *EMP* 1,234
Accts Rebecca Otto State Auditor S
SIC 9532 Urban planning & development commission, government; Rural planning & development agency, government;
Ch: Adam Duininck
V Ch: Katie Rodriguez
**CEO:* Tom Weaver
Ofcr: Richard Plato
Prin: Melba Hensel
Genl Couns: Ann Bloodhart
Snr Mgr: Richard Koop

D-U-N-S 04-918-2751
METROPOLITAN DISTRICT
WATER PLLUTION CTRL FACILITIES
555 Main St, Hartford, CT 06103-2915
Tel (860) 247-6487 *Founded/Ownrshp* 1985
Sales 107.5MM *EMP* 684
Accts Blum Shapiro & Company Pc
SIC 4941 4952 Water supply; Sewerage systems
CEO: M Steven Rhodes
**CEO:* Steven Rhodes
**COO:* Dominic Digangi
COO: Scott Jellison
CFO: John Zinzarella
**Treas:* Stephanie Russo
IT Man: Nelson Shick

D-U-N-S 00-791-6836
■ METROPOLITAN EDISON CO (PA)
METED
(*Suby of* FIRSTENERGY CORP) ★
76 S Main St, Akron, OH 44308-1812
Tel (800) 736-3402 *Founded/Ownrshp* 1922
Sales 410.0MM^E *EMP* 678^E
Accts Pricewaterhousecoopers Llp Cl
SIC 4911 Electric services; Generation, electric power; Distribution, electric power; Transmission, electric power
Pr: Charles E Jones
CFO: Mark T Clark
Treas: James F Pearson
Ex VP: Leila L Vespoli
VP: Harvey L Wagner

D-U-N-S 61-208-6392
METROPOLITAN FOODS INC
DRISCOLL FOODS
174 Delawanna Ave, Clifton, NJ 07014-1550
Tel (973) 672-9400 *Founded/Ownrshp* 1971
Sales 460.6MM^E *EMP* 400^E
SIC 5142 5149 2099 5141 Packaged frozen goods; Dried or canned foods; Food preparations; Food brokers
Pr: Tim Driscoll
**Pt:* Martin Rapport
Exec: Ralph Colombo
Exec: Nancy Cook
IT Man: Jeff McNally
VP Opers: Neal Russell
Opers Mgr: Keith Veltri
Sales Exec: Marty Eskow
Sales Exec: Lisa Smith
Mktg Dir: Jim Liakas
Sls Mgr: Edward Carey

D-U-N-S 07-821-7668
METROPOLITAN GOVERNMENT OF NASHVILLE & DAVIDSON COUNTY
NASHVILLE, CITY OF
100 Metro Courthouse, Nashville, TN 37201
Tel (615) 862-5000 *Founded/Ownrshp* 1784

Sales NA *EMP* 18,000
Accts Crosslin & Associates Nashvil
SIC 9111 Executive offices;
COO: May Bennett
COO: Marilyn Monk
CFO: Randy Pirtle
Bd of Dir: Peter Westerholm
Ofcr: Theresa Palmer
Assoc Dir: Jim Charles
Assoc Dir: Tom Cross
Dir Sec: Norman Robinson
Sfty Mgr: Thomas Mitchell
Snr Mgr: Wayne Denton

D-U-N-S 03-937-0598
■ METROPOLITAN GROUP PROPERTIES & CASUALTY
(*Suby of* METLIFE) ★
700 Quaker Ln, Warwick, RI 02886-6681
Tel (401) 827-2400 *Founded/Ownrshp* 1991
Sales NA *EMP* 1,350
SIC 6331 6351 Property damage insurance; Liability insurance
Pr: Catherine Rein
**Sr VP:* John S Lombardo

D-U-N-S 94-132-6076 IMP
■ METROPOLITAN HEALTH NETWORKS INC
METCARE
(*Suby of* HUMANA INC) ★
2900 N Military Trl, Boca Raton, FL 33431-6365
Tel (561) 805-8500 *Founded/Ownrshp* 2012
Sales 49.8MM^E *EMP* 1,140
SIC 8011 Health maintenance organization
CEO: John E Barger III
**Pr:* Bruce D Perkins
**CFO:* Robert J Sabo
**Chf Mktg O:* Luis H Izquierdo
**VP:* Joan O Lenahan III
Int Pr: Dan McCarthy
Off Mgr: Kathleen Bruscell

D-U-N-S 07-928-8601
METROPOLITAN HOSPITAL
METRO HEALTH HOSPITAL
5900 Byron Center Ave Sw, Wyoming, MI 49519-9606
Tel (616) 252-7200 *Founded/Ownrshp* 1941
Sales 277.4MM *EMP* 2,100
SIC 8062 8069

D-U-N-S 10-553-1164
METROPOLITAN HOSPITAL CENTER ASSOCIATION INC
(*Suby of* NEW YORK CITY HLTH & HOSPITALS) ★
1901 1st Ave, New York, NY 10029-7404
Tel (212) 423-6262 *Founded/Ownrshp* 1984
Sales 291.3MM^E *EMP* 3,000^E
SIC 8062 General medical & surgical hospitals
Ex Dir: Meryl Weinberg
**COO:* Elizabeth Guzman
Sr VP: Stanford A Roman Jr
Adm Dir: Matthew Taylor
**Ex Dir:* Dennis A Gowie
**Ex Dir:* Anthony Rajkunar
MIS Dir: Tamal Roy
Sfty Dirs: John Costello
Obsttrcn: Elmer C Agustin
Obsttrcn: Camille A Clare
Ansthlgy: Michael Girshin

D-U-N-S 18-755-5966
■ METROPOLITAN INSURANCE & ANNUITY CO
METLIFE
(*Suby of* METLIFE) ★
1 Madison Ave Lbby, New York, NY 10010-3687
Tel (212) 578-2211 *Founded/Ownrshp* 1976
Sales NA *EMP* 3,001
Accts Deloitte & Touche Llp
SIC 6411 Insurance agents & brokers
CEO: Robert Benmosche
Pr: Debbie Krautheim
Sr Cor Off: Allen Wheat
Ofcr: Mark A Schuman
Sr Ex VP: Lisa M Weber
Ex VP: Daniel Cavanaugh
Ex VP: John Dabek
Ex VP: William J Wheeler
Sr VP: William T Friedewald
Sr VP: Gene Lunman
Sr VP: David Monfried
VP: Bob Begun
VP: Linda Bloniarz
VP: Christopher C Clarke
**VP:* Susan Mary Ende
VP: Gary Fabian
VP: James Fago
VP: James J Kenny
VP: Liz Langone
VP: Theresa Maire
VP: Daniel M Mule

D-U-N-S 00-418-4896
METROPOLITAN JEWISH HEALTH SYSTEM INC (NY)
ALTIERI CAROL
6323 7th Ave Ste 2, Brooklyn, NY 11220-4742
Tel (718) 621-3600 *Founded/Ownrshp* 1995
Sales 71.9MM *EMP* 1,400
Accts Loeb & Troper Llp New York N
SIC 8322 Adult day care center
CEO: Eli S Feldman
COO: David Wagner
VP: Mary Wagner
Dir Bus: Susan Lage
Snr Ntwrk: Greg Koppenhoefer
Sls Mgr: Jian Li

D-U-N-S 96-782-4306
METROPOLITAN JEWISH HOME CARE INC
MJHS HOSPICE AND PALLIATIVE CA
6323 7th Ave Ste 2, Brooklyn, NY 11220-4742
Tel (718) 921-7742 *Founded/Ownrshp* 2003
Sales 136.1MM *EMP* 103
Accts Loeb & Troper Llp New York N
SIC 8082 Home health care services
CFO: Alexander Balko

D-U-N-S 00-698-7648 IMP
■ METROPOLITAN LIFE INSURANCE CO (INC) (NY)
METLIFE
(*Suby of* METLIFE INC) ★
2701 Queens Plz N Ste 1, Long Island City, NY 11101-4021
Tel (212) 578-2211 *Founded/Ownrshp* 2000
Sales NA *EMP* 46,000
SIC 6411 6324 6331 6321 6531 Insurance agents & brokers; Dental insurance; Fire, marine & casualty insurance: mutual; Property damage insurance; Health insurance carriers; Disability health insurance; Real estate brokers & agents
Ch Bd: C Robert Henrikson
**CFO:* William Wheeler
Ofcr: Jason Bloomfield
Ex VP: Steven Meyers
Sr VP: Daniel J Cavanagh
Sr VP: Ronald Chapin
Sr VP: David Findley
Sr VP: Steve Goulart
Sr VP: Anne E Hayden
VP: Ed Barrett
VP: William Bigelow
VP: Gordon Dinsmore
VP: John Geyer
VP: Toni Handler
VP: Judith Knight
VP: Diane Lund
VP: Salim Manzar
VP: Joe Massimo
VP: Paul Michael
**VP:* Catherine A Rein
VP: Hong Richard
Board of Directors: Hugh B Price, Curtis H Barnette, David Satcher, Burton A Dole Jr, William C Steere Jr, Cheryl W Grise, James R Houghton, R Glenn Hubbard, Harry P Kamen, Helene L Kaplan, John M Keane, Charles M Leighton

D-U-N-S 03-459-9779
METROPOLITAN LUMBER (NY)
METROPOLITAN LUMBER & HARDWARE
617 11th Ave, New York, NY 10036-2015
Tel (212) 246-9090 *Founded/Ownrshp* 1979
Sales 104.7MM^E *EMP* 200
SIC 5031 5211 5251 Lumber: rough, dressed & finished; Lumber products; Hardware
Ch Bd: Robert Gans
**VP:* Spencer Simon

METROPOLITAN LUMBER & HARDWARE
See METROPOLITAN LUMBER

D-U-N-S 13-721-4859
METROPOLITAN MARKET LLC
4025 Delridge Way Sw # 100, Seattle, WA 98106-1249
Tel (206) 284-2530 *Founded/Ownrshp* 1979
Sales 145.9MM^E *EMP* 850
SIC 5411 Grocery stores
CEO: Terry Robert Halverson
CFO: Brett Miller
**VP:* Gordon E Halverson
Genl Mgr: Jeff Baskett

D-U-N-S 04-177-9240
METROPOLITAN MECHANICAL CONTRACTORS INC
(*Suby of* API GROUP INC) ★
7450 Flying Cloud Dr, Eden Prairie, MN 55344-3582
Tel (952) 941-7010 *Founded/Ownrshp* 2011
Sales 200.9MM *EMP* 350
Accts Kpmg Llp Minneapolis Mn
SIC 1711 8711 Mechanical contractor; Warm air heating & air conditioning contractor; Plumbing contractors; Engineering services
Pr: Mark Anderson
VP: Tim Daly
VP: Robert Kaczke
Sales Exec: Mark Hill

METROPOLITAN MT PLTY & SEAFOOD
See MMSP INC

D-U-N-S 07-526-2949 IMP
METROPOLITAN MUSEUM OF ART
1000 5th Ave, New York, NY 10028-0198
Tel (212) 535-7710 *Founded/Ownrshp* 1870
Sales 379.5MM *EMP* 2,372
Accts Pricewaterhousecoopers Llp Ne
SIC 8412 5999 Museum; Art, picture frames & decorations
Ch Bd: James R Houghton
V Ch: Parker S Gilbert
**Sr VP:* Emily Kernan Rafferty
**VP:* J Nicholas Cameron
**VP:* Sharon H Cott
**VP:* Harold Holzer
**VP:* Philip T Venturino
Comm Man: Ann Bailis
Genl Mgr: Shadawn Smith
Software D: Chris Lees
Software D: Marina Tolkacheva

D-U-N-S 05-214-4318
METROPOLITAN NASHVILLE AIRPORT AUTHORITY
NASHVILLE INTERNATIONAL AIRPOR
1 Terminal Dr Ste 501, Nashville, TN 37214-4110
Tel (615) 275-1600 *Founded/Ownrshp* 1970
Sales 116.1MM *EMP* 275
Accts Dixon Hughes Goodman Llp Bre
SIC 4581 Airport
CEO: Raul L Regalado
**COO:* M O Burges

D-U-N-S 10-007-3253
METROPOLITAN NASHVILLE PUBLIC SCHOOLS
HUMAN CAPITAL
2601 Bransford Ave, Nashville, TN 37204-2811
Tel (615) 259-4636 *Founded/Ownrshp* 1800
Sales 584.4MM^E *EMP* 10,500
SIC 8211 Public elementary & secondary schools
Bd of Dir: Will Pinkston
Exec: Terry Shrader
Dir Sec: James Wheeler

Pr Dir: Olivia Brown
Pr Dir: Janel Lacy
Pr Dir: Woody McMillin
Instr Medi: Kelly McKinney
HC Dir: Nicole Proffitt
Snr PM: Brent Ostermiller

D-U-N-S 07-523-8840 IMP
METROPOLITAN OPERA ASSOCIATION INC
Lincoln Ctr, New York, NY 10023
Tel (212) 799-3100 *Founded/Ownrshp* 1936
Sales 335.3MM *EMP* 1,500^E
SIC 7922 Opera company
Pr: William Morris
CFO: Stewart Pearce
**Sec:* Kevin Kennedy
**VP:* Frayda Lindemann
**VP:* Mrs Ezra K Zilkha
Comm Dir: Lee Abrahamian
Mng Dir: Camille Labarre
Mng Dir: John Pennino
Genl Mgr: Peter Gelbas
Opers Mgr: Yefim Shnayder
Mktg Dir: Ronni Brown

D-U-N-S 05-434-3017
METROPOLITAN PIER AND EXPOSITION AUTHORITY
HYATT REGENCY MCCORMICK PLACE
301 Ecermak Rd Fl 5, Chicago, IL 60616
Tel (312) 791-7000 *Founded/Ownrshp* 1955
Sales 155.4MM *EMP* 2,500
SIC 7389 7999 7011 Convention & show services; Exposition operation; Hotels & motels
Pr: Julie Chavez
**Ch Bd:* Kelly Welsh
**CEO:* Leticia Davis
CFO: Martha Farrell
CFO: James Fricke
**Prin:* Dan Hynes
**Prin:* Roger J Kiley Jr
**Prin:* Carmen Lonstein
**Prin:* Ronald E Powell
Ex Dir: Michael Oconnor
Genl Mgr: David Causton
Board of Directors: John Ruel, William P Tuggle

METROPOLITAN POULTRY
See AM BRIGGS INC

D-U-N-S 07-569-9959
■ METROPOLITAN PROPERTY AND CASUALTY INSURANCE CO
METLIFE
(*Suby of* METLIFE INC) ★
700 Quaker Ln, Warwick, RI 02886-6681
Tel (401) 827-2400 *Founded/Ownrshp* 1982
Sales NA *EMP* 2,634
SIC 6411 Insurance agents & brokers
Pr: William Moore
Pr: Kevin A Raymond
Treas: John McSweeney
Ex VP: Mary Lovejoy
**VP:* Marvin A Beck
VP: Carol Stewart
Genl Mgr: Jeffrey Hebert
Advt Mgr: Greg Rosa

D-U-N-S 05-010-0130
METROPOLITAN SCHOOL DISTRICT OF LAWRENCE TOWNSHIP
6501 Sunnyside Rd, Indianapolis, IN 46236-9707
Tel (317) 423-8200 *Founded/Ownrshp* 1959
Sales 105.5MM^E *EMP* 2,500
SIC 8211 Public elementary & secondary schools
**CFO:* Robin Phelps
Treas: Dorothy Gaertner
Comm Dir: Caryn Goo
Ex Dir: Cori Korn
Genl Mgr: Michael Shreves
Off Admin: Debbie Reinking
Dir IT: Johnny McFarland
Psych: Beth Williams

D-U-N-S 05-010-0395
METROPOLITAN SCHOOL DISTRICT OF WARREN TOWNSHIP
975 N Post Rd, Indianapolis, IN 46219-5545
Tel (317) 869-4300 *Founded/Ownrshp* 1956
Sales 117.7MM^E *EMP* 1,400
SIC 8211 Public elementary & secondary schools
**Pr:* Julie A French
**CFO:* David Holt
**VP:* Anthony R Mendez
Ex Dir: Mary McKinley
Dir Sec: Emmit Carny
Sls Mgr: Lisa Hedge

D-U-N-S 07-204-1148
METROPOLITAN SCHOOL DISTRICT OF WAYNE TOWNSHIP
1220 S High School Rd, Indianapolis, IN 46241-3127
Tel (317) 988-8600 *Founded/Ownrshp* 1952
Sales 89.0MM^E *EMP* 2,200
SIC 8211 Public elementary & secondary schools; High school, junior or senior
Pr: Rachel Cravens
Pr: Matt Good
CFO: Dennis J Tackitt
Dir Sec: Doug Scheffel
Genl Mgr: Aaron Moss

D-U-N-S 07-207-1129
METROPOLITAN SCHOOL DISTRICT WASHINGTON TOWNSHIP
8550 Wdfld Xing Blvd, Indianapolis, IN 46240-2478
Tel (317) 845-9400 *Founded/Ownrshp* 1955
Sales 66.5MM^E *EMP* 1,294
SIC 8211 Public elementary & secondary schools
Exec: Victor Newsome
Teacher Pr: Thomas Oestreich

D-U-N-S 79-720-3932
METROPOLITAN SECURITY SERVICES INC
WALDEN SECURITY
100 E 10th St Ste 400, Chattanooga, TN 37402-4218
Tel (423) 702-8200 *Founded/Ownrshp* 1990
Sales 132.8MM^E *EMP* 2,500^E
Accts Lattimore Black Morgan & Cain

SIC 7381 Security guard service
CEO: Amy S Walden
**Pr:* Michael S Walden
Ofcr: Charles Condon
Ofcr: Mark Lavender
Ofcr: Alan Lewis
Ofcr: Mark Peek
Ofcr: Lewis Wright
**Sr VP:* Curtis Casey
**VP:* Dick Wong
Dir Sec: Sharon Dunn
Genl Mgr: Drew Burrows

METROPOLITAN SERVICES
See YMCA OF NORTHWEST NORTH CAROLINA

D-U-N-S 04-637-3312
METROPOLITAN ST LOUIS SEWER DISTRICT
MSD
2350 Market St Ste 300, Saint Louis, MO 63103-2555
Tel (314) 768-6200 *Founded/Ownrshp* 1954
Sales 260.0MM *EMP* 976
Accts Rubinbrown Llp Saint Louis M
SIC 4952 Sewerage systems
Ex Dir: Brian Hoelscher
Ch Bd: James Buford
Sec: Brenda Schaefer
Ofcr: Randy Belcher
Ofcr: Ken Lucas
Prgrm Mgr: Allen Muehlher
Tech Mgr: Jackie Weddington
Sfty Dirs: Joey Lech
Opers Supe: Joe Anselmo
Opers Supe: Tom Broaders
Opers Supe: Steve Hahn

D-U-N-S 05-909-4321 IMP
METROPOLITAN STATE UNIVERSITY OF DENVER
890 Auraria Pkwy, Denver, CO 80204-1806
Tel (303) 556-3030 *Founded/Ownrshp* 1965
Sales 148.0MM^E *EMP* 2,300
SIC 8221 Colleges universities & professional schools
Pr: Stephen Jordan
Ofcr: Judith Hilton
VP: Carrie A Besnette
VP: Kathleen A Mackay
VP: Carl R Powell
VP: Alberto Torres
VP: Jacob Welch
Dir Lab: Douglas Howey
Assoc Dir: Brooke Dilling
Assoc Dir: Marion Karanja
Assoc Dir: Daniel Parks
Assoc Dir: Chivonne Torres

D-U-N-S 09-483-4405 IMP
METROPOLITAN TRANSIT AUTHORITY OF HARRIS COUNTY
HOUSTON METRO TRNST AUTH
1900 Main St, Houston, TX 77002-8130
Tel (713) 635-4000 *Founded/Ownrshp* 1978
Sales 246.2MM^E *EMP* 3,700
Accts Kpmg Llp Austin Tx
SIC 4119 Local passenger transportation
Pr: Thomas C Lambert
CFO: Suzzane Bailey
Trst: Horace Marves
Ofcr: Ify Belonwu
Ofcr: Roger Salazar
Assoc VP: Danicel Whitaker
Ex VP: John M Sedlak
**Sr VP:* David W Couch
VP: M Helen Cavazos
VP: Terence Fontaine
**VP:* Raul Luzarraga
**VP:* Rocky Marrero
VP: Andrew Skabowski
VP: George F Smalley

D-U-N-S 04-544-5137 IMP/EXP
METROPOLITAN TRANSPORTATION AUTHORITY
M T A
2 Broadway Bsmt B, New York, NY 10004-3354
Tel (212) 878-7000 *Founded/Ownrshp* 1965
Sales 7.9MMM^E *EMP* 67,457
Accts Deloitte & Touche Llp New Yo
SIC 4111 Local & suburban transit
Ch Bd: Thomas F Predergast
**Pr:* Howard R Permut
CIO: Wael Hibri
Sftwr Eng: Will Ortiz
Sfty Mgr: Albert Albano
Snr PM: Patrick Charles

D-U-N-S 07-464-4501
METROPOLITAN TRANSPORTATION COMMISSION
M T C
375 Beale St, San Francisco, CA 94105-2066
Tel (510) 817-5700 *Founded/Ownrshp* 1970
Sales 237.8MM *EMP* 115^E
Accts Pricewaterhousecoopers Llp Sa
SIC 4111 Bus line operations
Ex Dir: Steve Hieminger
**CFO:* Brian Mayhew
**V Ch Bd:* Jake Mackenzie
Exec: Bond Counsel
**Ex Dir:* Therese McMillan
Prgrm Mgr: Stephen C Abbanat
IT Man: Mark Dinh

D-U-N-S 00-697-0321
METROPOLITAN UTILITIES DISTRICT
M U D
1723 Harney St, Omaha, NE 68102-1960
Tel (402) 554-6666 *Founded/Ownrshp* 1913
Sales 341.9MM *EMP* 852
Accts Kpmg Llp Lincoln Ne
SIC 4932 Gas & other services combined
Pr: Douglas R Clark
**Ch Bd:* Jack Frost
**Pr:* Daniel G Crouchley
**CFO:* Debra A Schneider
Ch: David J Friend
**Ch:* Michael W McGowan

Ex Ofcr: Kay Lange
**Sr VP:* Ron Bucher
Sls&Mrk Ex: Mike Corrigan

D-U-N-S 11-620-3001
METROPOLITAN WASHINGTON AIRPORTS AUTHORITY
DULLES INTERNATIONAL AIRPORT
1 Aviation Cir, Washington, DC 20001-6000
Tel (703) 417-8600 *Founded/Ownrshp* 1987
Sales 217.2MM[E] *EMP* 1,400
SIC 4581 4785 Airports, flying fields & services; Toll road operation
Ch: Frank Conner
**Pr:* John E Potter
**COO:* Margaret E McKeough
**CFO:* Andrew Rountree
Chf Inves: Michelle Watson
Ofcr: Katherine Ruhl
Ofcr: Angel Ruiz
VP: Leslie Berkowitz
**VP:* Quince T Brinkley
VP: Valerie Holt
VP: Goutam Kundu
VP: Paul Malendrino
VP: David Mould
VP: Roger Natsuhara
VP: Philip Sunderland
VP: Elmer Tippett
VP: Anthony Vegliante
Exec: Roger Atkins
Exec: Bob Curtin
Exec: Margo Horner

D-U-N-S 06-384-2975
METROPOLITAN WATER DISTRICT OF SOUTHERN CALIFORNIA
MWD
700 N Alameda St, Los Angeles, CA 90012-3352
Tel (213) 217-6000 *Founded/Ownrshp* 1928
Sales 1.5MMM *EMP* 2,000
SIC 4941

D-U-N-S 06-249-7441
METROPOLITAN WATER RECLAIMATION DISTRICT OF GREATER CHICAGO
MWRD
100 E Erie St, Chicago, IL 60611-2829
Tel (312) 751-5600 *Founded/Ownrshp* 1889
Sales NA *EMP* 2,259
Accts Baker Tilly Virchow Krause Ll
SIC 9511 Sanitary engineering agency, government;
Pr: Terrence J Obrien
Trst: Robert Regan
Ofcr: Allison Fore
Ofcr: Beverly Sanders
VP: Kathleen Meany
Dir Risk M: Ruth Joplin
Prin: Jeff Weber
QA Dir: John McNamara
Sfty Dirs: Jay Carlson
Sfty Dirs: Tim Delathouwer
Opers Supe: Stephen Haucke

D-U-N-S 09-962-9602
METROPOWER INC
ALBANY ELECTRIC COMPANY
(*Suby of* PPC PARTNERS INC) ★
798 21st Ave, Albany, GA 31701-1137
Tel (229) 432-7345 *Founded/Ownrshp* 1979
Sales 141.8MM[E] *EMP* 425
SIC 1731 Electrical work
CEO: Danny R Buck
**CFO:* Kayanne Blackwell
VP: Arnold Geeslin Jr
Dept Mgr: Tad Clark
Dept Mgr: Greg Greenway
Off Mgr: Glorianne Davies
Off Mgr: Debra West

METROSOUTH MEDICAL CENTER
See BLUE ISLAND HOSPITAL CO LLC

METROWEST MEDICAL CENTRE
See VHS ACQUISITION SUBSIDIARY NUMBER 9 INC

D-U-N-S 96-299-0284
METSO AUTOMATION
(*Suby of* METSO OYJ)
2425 Commerce Ave Ste 100, Duluth, GA 30096-8913
Tel (770) 476-3641 *Founded/Ownrshp* 2010
Sales 89.7MM[E] *EMP* 142[E]
SIC 5084 Industrial machinery & equipment
CEO: Matti Khknen
CFO: Neil Casale
**CFO:* Harri Nikunen
IT Man: Janice Powell
Sls Dir: Robert Guiler

D-U-N-S 10-489-5581 IMP
METSO FLOW CONTROL USA INC
(*Suby of* METSO USA INC) ★
44 Bowditch Dr, Shrewsbury, MA 01545-1719
Tel (508) 852-0200 *Founded/Ownrshp* 1954
Sales 116.4MM[E] *EMP* 420[E]
SIC 3592 Valves
Pr: John Quinlivan
Sr Cor Off: Jukka Tiitinen
Ex VP: Mike Mason
Ex VP: Robert Pape
Sr VP: Tuula Puhakka
Sr VP: Eeva-Liisa Virkkunen
VP: Paul Gannon
VP: Michael Hakovirta
VP: Mika Nissinen
VP: Jouni Pyatsia
Mng Dir: John Benson

D-U-N-S 18-284-6063 IMP/EXP
METSO MINERALS INDUSTRIES INC
(*Suby of* METSO USA INC) ★
20965 Crossroads Cir, Waukesha, WI 53186-4083
Tel (262) 798-3994 *Founded/Ownrshp* 1990
Sales 471.8MM[E] *EMP* 1,459
SIC 3321 3069 3561 3535 3532 Ductile iron castings; Linings, vulcanizable rubber; Hard rubber products; Pumps & pumping equipment; Bulk handling conveyor systems; Crushing, pulverizing & screening equipment
Pr: Matti Khknen
**Pr:* Perttu Louhiluoto
**Pr:* Mike Phillips
CFO: Juha Sepp L
Treas: Debbie Trost
Sr VP: Pekka Pohjoism Ki
VP: Raymond N Koper
VP: Robert Lindstr M
VP: Kelly McCue
VP: Yrj Norri
VP: Helmut Zeipelt

D-U-N-S 80-154-2994 IMP/EXP
METSO USA INC
(*Suby of* METSO OYJ)
133 Federal St Ste 302, Boston, MA 02110-1703
Tel (617) 369-7850 *Founded/Ownrshp* 1992
Sales 598.4MM[E] *EMP* 3,913
SIC 3554 5084 Paper industries machinery; Industrial machinery & equipment
Sr VP: Mike Phillips
**Treas:* Paul Gannon
VP: Jouko Kauppila
VP: Jack Marmet
VP: Scott McGlothlin
VP: Jerry Mitchell
VP: Pekka Pajalahti
VP: Richard Parker
VP: Jouko Yli-Kauppila
Genl Mgr: Ismo Vaiste
CIO: Thomas Smith

D-U-N-S 09-069-6071 IMP/EXP
▲ METTLER-TOLEDO INTERNATIONAL INC
1900 Polaris Pkwy Fl 6, Columbus, OH 43240-4055
Tel (614) 438-4511 *Founded/Ownrshp* 1991
Sales 2.4MMM *EMP* 13,500[E]
Accts Pricewaterhousecoopers Llp Co
Tkr Sym MTD *Exch* NYS
SIC 3596 3821 3826 3823 Industrial scales; Laboratory measuring apparatus; Balances, laboratory; Analytical instruments; Industrial instrmnts msrmnt display/control process variable
Pr: Olivier A Filliol
**Ch Bd:* Robert F Spoerry
CFO: Shawn P Vadala
Chf Mktg O: Martin Huber
Top Exec: Jennifer McCallum
Ex VP: William P Donnelly
Sftwr Eng: Jane Lin
Mktg Mgr: Tom Tait
Sls Mgr: Jane Riley
Sls Mgr: Piotr Witukiewicz
Snr Mgr: Geoff Bradford
Board of Directors: Francis A Contino, Connie L Harvey, Michael A Kelly, Hans Ulrich Maerki, George M Milne Jr, Thomas Salice

D-U-N-S 19-464-9323 IMP/EXP
■ METTLER-TOLEDO LLC
(*Suby of* METTLER-TOLEDO INTERNATIONAL INC) ★
1900 Polaris Pkwy Fl 6, Columbus, OH 43240-4055
Tel (614) 438-4511 *Founded/Ownrshp* 1986
Sales 882.7MM[E] *EMP* 9,500
SIC 3596 5049 7699 3821 3823 3826

D-U-N-S 06-663-1441 IMP
■ METTLER-TOLEDO RAININ LLC
(*Suby of* METTLER-TOLEDO INTERNATIONAL INC) ★
7500 Edgewater Dr, Oakland, CA 94621-3027
Tel (510) 564-1600 *Founded/Ownrshp* 2001
Sales 120.4MM[E] *EMP* 500
SIC 3821 3829 Laboratory apparatus & furniture; Pipettes, hemocytometer; Measuring & controlling devices
CEO: Olivier Filliol
COO: Henri Chahine
Dist Mgr: Robert Kum
Genl Mgr: Mark Jennings
**Genl Mgr:* Gerhard Keller
Genl Mgr: Sam Verdickt
QA Dir: Sophie Chang
QA Dir: Valerie Franco
Ql Cn Mgr: Eliseo Cuevas
Ql Cn Mgr: Anu Philip
VP Mktg: Murray Anderson

D-U-N-S 17-856-5565
■ METWEST INC
QUEST DIAGNOSTICS
(*Suby of* QUEST DIAGNOSTICS INC) ★
695 S Broadway, Denver, CO 80209-4003
Tel (303) 899-6000 *Founded/Ownrshp* 1990
Sales 33.6MM[E] *EMP* 1,000
SIC 8071 Medical laboratories
Pr: Christine Shlagor
Sfty Mgr: Patrick Jenkins

D-U-N-S 93-924-2020
METZ CULINARY MANAGEMENT INC
2 Woodland Dr, Dallas, PA 18612-9159
Tel (570) 675-8100 *Founded/Ownrshp* 1994
Sales 479.2MM[E] *EMP* 3,000
SIC 5461 Doughnuts
Ch: John C Metz Sr
Pr: Jim Dickson
Pr: Kathy Gonzalez
**Pr:* Jeffrey Metz
**CEO:* John C Metz
**COO:* Harold Leininger
VP: Grant Bennett
**VP:* John Geronimo
**VP:* Craig Phillips
**VP:* Greg Polk
Exec: Michele Pastorello

METZELER AUTO PROFILE SYSTEMS
See HENNIGES AUTOMOTIVE SEALING SYSTEMS NORTH AMERICA INC

MEUS
See MITSUBISHI ELECTRIC US INC

D-U-N-S 07-760-3595
MEWBOURNE HOLDINGS INC
3901 S Broadway Ave, Tyler, TX 75701-8716
Tel (903) 561-2900 *Founded/Ownrshp* 1965
Sales 344.3MM[E] *EMP* 176
SIC 1311 Crude petroleum production; Natural gas production
CEO: Curtis W Mewbourne
**COO:* Kenneth S Waits
**CFO:* J Roe Buckley
**CFO:* Roe Buckley
**Treas:* Alan Clark

D-U-N-S 04-783-9923
MEWBOURNE OIL CO
(*Suby of* MEWBOURNE HOLDINGS INC) ★
3620 Old Bullard Rd, Tyler, TX 75701-8644
Tel (903) 561-2900 *Founded/Ownrshp* 1991
Sales 344.1MM[E] *EMP* 175
SIC 1311 Crude petroleum production; Natural gas production
Pr: Curtis W Mewbourne
**CFO:* J Roe Buckley
**CFO:* Roe Buckley
VP: Jerry Lebo
**VP:* Joseph F Odom
**VP:* Monty Whetstone
Opers Mgr: Ronnie Howell

D-U-N-S 06-727-7947
MEXICAN RESTAURANTS INC
(*Suby of* WILLISTON HOLDINGS INC) ★
12000 Aerospace Ave # 400, Houston, TX 77034-5587
Tel (832) 300-5858 *Founded/Ownrshp* 2014
Sales 89.5MM[E] *EMP* 1,950[E]
SIC 5812 6794 5046 Mexican restaurant; Franchises, selling or licensing; Restaurant equipment & supplies
CEO: Marcus Jundt
COO: Loic M Porry
**CFO:* Andrew J Dennard
**CFO:* Douglas Hipskind
**CFO:* Lawrence Neumann
**Ofcr:* Perry Brush

MEXICHEM SHARED SERVICES
See DURA-LINE CORP

D-U-N-S 09-743-4484 IMP/EXP
MEXICHEM SPECIALTY COMPOUNDS INC
(*Suby of* MEXICHEM, S.A.B. DE C.V.)
170 Pioneer Dr, Leominster, MA 01453-3474
Tel (978) 537-8071 *Founded/Ownrshp* 2011
Sales 83.9MM[E] *EMP* 260
SIC 3087 2899 Custom compound purchased resins; Chemical preparations
Pr: Enrique Ramirez
Pr: William Temkin
**CFO:* Mike Funderburg
Mng Dir: Bob Gingue
Web Prj Mg: Mark Yankowskas
Opers Mgr: Terry Kimball

D-U-N-S 07-887-5792 IMP
MEXICHEM SPECIALTY RESINS INC
(*Suby of* MEXICHEM, S.A.B. DE C.V.)
33653 Walker Rd, Avon Lake, OH 44012-1044
Tel (440) 930-1435 *Founded/Ownrshp* 2013, 2014
Sales 96.7MM[E] *EMP* 300
SIC 2822 2821 Ethylene-propylene rubbers, EPDM polymers; Polymethyl methacrylate resins (plexiglass)
**Genl Mgr:* Frank Tomaselli

D-U-N-S 82-543-3266
MEXICO FOODS LLC
2600 Mccree Rd Ste 101, Garland, TX 75041-3901
Tel (972) 526-7200 *Founded/Ownrshp* 2007
Sales 265.5MM *EMP* 1,539
SIC 5411 Supermarkets
Pr: Salah Nafal
**Treas:* Marwan Nafal
**VP:* Khaled Nafal

D-U-N-S 00-632-1640 IMP
MEXICO PLASTIC CO (MO)
CONTINENTAL PRODUCTS
2000 W Boulevard St, Mexico, MO 65265-1209
Tel (573) 581-4128 *Founded/Ownrshp* 1964
Sales 85.7MM[E] *EMP* 200
SIC 2673 3089 2655 Plastic bags: made from purchased materials; Boxes, plastic; Fiber cans, drums & similar products
Pr: Carl Fuemmeler
CFO: Wilda Long
**VP:* Thad Fisher
**VP:* Vincent F Fuemmeler Jr
Sls Mgr: Bruce Leith

D-U-N-S 12-056-0417
MEYER & NAJEM CONSTRUCTION LLC
(*Suby of* MEYER & NAJEM INC) ★
11787 Lantern Rd Ste 100, Fishers, IN 46038-2801
Tel (317) 577-0007 *Founded/Ownrshp* 1999
Sales 189.7MM *EMP* 60
Accts Katz Sapper & Miller
SIC 1542 Nonresidential construction
Pr: Tim Russell
Ch Bd: Karl Meyer
CEO: Anthony Najem
CFO: Robert Lawyer
VP: Toby Holcomb
VP: Sam Mishelow
VP: Paul Toddy

D-U-N-S 18-053-7425
MEYER & NAJEM INC
11787 Lantern Rd Ste 100, Fishers, IN 46038-2801
Tel (317) 577-0007 *Founded/Ownrshp* 1987
Sales 189.7MM *EMP* 75
Accts Katz Sapper & Miller
SIC 1542 Commercial & office building, new construction; Commercial & office buildings, renovation & repair; Institutional building construction; Hospital construction
CEO: Karl Meyer
**Pr:* Anthony Najem
**CFO:* Robert Lawyer
**VP:* Sam Mishelow
**VP:* Tim Russell
VP: Paul Toddy

D-U-N-S 00-636-8914
MEYER DISTRIBUTING INC
560 E 25th St, Jasper, IN 47546-8117
Tel (812) 482-5102 *Founded/Ownrshp* 1937
Sales 196.6MM[E] *EMP* 600
SIC 5013 5012

D-U-N-S 00-425-0528 IMP/EXP
MEYER TOOL INC
3055 Colerain Ave, Cincinnati, OH 45225-1827
Tel (513) 681-7362 *Founded/Ownrshp* 1976
Sales 370.2MM[E] *EMP* 800
SIC 3724 3599 Aircraft engines & engine parts; Machine shop, jobbing & repair
Pr: Arlyn Easton
**VP:* Larry Allen
**VP:* Jerry Flyr
VP: Ed Mayer
DP Dir: Mike Johnson
VP Mfg: Gary McGuire
Mfg Mgr: Rob Menzer
Ql Cn Mgr: Penny Carr
Ql Cn Mgr: Andrew Levine
VP Sls: Rick Kowalski
Sls Dir: Joe Rowland

MEYERPT
See WBC GROUP LLC

D-U-N-S 13-163-8830
MEYERTONS HOOD KIVLIN KOWERT & GOETZEL P C
MHKK&G
1120 S Capital Of Texas, West Lake Hills, TX 78746-6464
Tel (512) 853-8800 *Founded/Ownrshp* 2002
Sales 250.0MM *EMP* 72
SIC 8011 Offices & clinics of medical doctors

MEYNE COMPANY DIV , THE
See BULLEY & ANDREWS LLC

D-U-N-S 96-501-6830
MF GLOBAL HOLDINGS LTD
142 W 57th St Ste 401, New York, NY 10019-3462
Tel (646) 568-8114 *Founded/Ownrshp* 2010
Sales 342.8MM[E] *EMP* 2,847[E]
SIC 6211 Security brokers & dealers
Pr: Bradley I Abelow
COO: Karel F Harbour
**CFO:* Henri J Steenkamp
**Ofcr:* Michael G Stockman
Top Exec: Edward V Garlich Jr
**Genl Couns:* Laurie R Ferber

D-U-N-S 05-059-3169
MF GLOBAL HOLDINGS USA INC
(*Suby of* MF GLOBAL HOLDINGS LTD) ★
717 5th Ave Fl 11, New York, NY 10022-8113
Tel (212) 589-6200 *Founded/Ownrshp* 2006
Sales 94.0MM[E] *EMP* 982
SIC 6211 Security brokers & dealers
Pr: Ira Polk
COO: Bradley Abelow
Ex VP: Tom Harte
Board of Directors: David P Bolger, David Gelber

MFA AGRI SERVICES
See MFA INC

D-U-N-S 13-372-5676
MFA FINANCIAL INC
350 Park Ave Fl 20, New York, NY 10022-6054
Tel (212) 207-6400 *Founded/Ownrshp* 1998
Sales 543.3MM *EMP* 53
Tkr Sym MFA *Exch* NYS
SIC 6798 Real estate investment trusts
CEO: William S Gorin
**Ch Bd:* George H Krauss
Pr: Craig L Knutson
CFO: Stephen D Yarad
Ex VP: Ronald A Freydberg
Sr VP: Kathleen A Hanrahan
Sr VP: Gudmundur Kristjansson
Sr VP: Terence B Meyers
Sr VP: Harold E Schwartz
Sr VP: Bryan Wulfsohn
Sr VP: Sunil Yadav
Board of Directors: Stephen R Blank, James A Brodsky, Richard J Byrne, Laurie Goodman, Alan L Gosule, Robin Josephs

D-U-N-S 00-696-5149
MFA INC
MFA AGRI SERVICES
201 Ray Young Dr, Columbia, MO 65201-3599
Tel (573) 874-5111 *Founded/Ownrshp* 1923
Sales 1.1MMM *EMP* 1,393
Accts Williams Keepers Llc Columbia
SIC 2875 2048 5191 5153 Fertilizers, mixing only; Prepared feeds; Farm supplies; Grains
CEO: Ernie Verslues
Treas: John Akridge
**Sr VP:* Janice Schuerman
**VP:* Craig Childs
**VP:* Bill Coen
VP: Bill Dunn
VP: Brian Griffith
**VP:* J Brian Griffith
VP: Dr Kent Haden
VP: Don Houston
VP: Cassy Landewee
VP: Joe Powell
**VP:* Alan Wessler
Exec: Joe Weydert
Comm Dir: Chuck Lay
Board of Directors: Don Mills, Phillip Becker, John Moffitt, Glen Cope, RT Sloan, Joe Dent, Harry Thompson, Tim Engemann, David Cottrill Vice Chb, Lester Evans Chb, Kendall Kircher, Tim Lichte, Randy Ludwig, William McClure

D-U-N-S 00-696-5123 IMP
MFA OIL CO (MO)
1 Ray Young Dr, Columbia, MO 65201-3506
Tel (573) 442-0171 *Founded/Ownrshp* 1929
Sales 800.3MM *EMP* 1,500

Accts Williams Keepers Llc Columbia
SIC 7549 5541 Lubrication service, automotive; Filling stations, gasoline
CEO: Jerry Taylor
Ch Bd: Benny Farrell
CFO: Robert Condron

MFCP
See MOTION AND FLOW CONTROL PRODUCTS INC

MFCP
See MOTION & FLOW CONTROL PRODUCTS INC

D-U-N-S 12-751-8855
MFG GALILEO COMPOSITES
(*Suby of* MOLDED FIBER GLASS COMPANIES) ★
18361 Galileo Dr, Opp, AL 36467-3774
Tel (334) 493-0014 *Founded/Ownrshp* 2003
Sales 80.6MM^E *EMP* 1,600^E
SIC 5731 3089 Antennas; Plastic processing
CEO: Richard Morrison
**CFO:* James G Irwin
IT Man: Alan Fletcher

D-U-N-S 02-316-4672
■ **MFI HOLDING CORP**
MICHAEL FOOD
(*Suby of* POST HOLDINGS INC) ★
301 Carlson Pkwy Ste 400, Minnetonka, MN 55305-5370
Tel (952) 258-4000 *Founded/Ownrshp* 2014
Sales 329.7MM^E *EMP* 3,596^E
SIC 6719 0252 Investment holding companies, except banks; Chicken eggs
Pr: Adrian M Jones

D-U-N-S 60-621-1977 IMP/EXP
▲ **MFRI INC**
6410 W Howard St, Niles, IL 60714-3302
Tel (847) 966-1000 *Founded/Ownrshp* 1993
Sales 122.7MM *EMP* 998^E
Accts Grant Thornton Llp Chicago I
Tkr Sym MFRI *Exch* NGM
SIC 3677 3564 3569 Filtration devices, electronic; Blowers & fans; Filters & strainers, pipeline
Pr: David J Mansfield
**Ch Bd:* David S Barrie
CFO: Karl J Schmidt
Ofcr: Wayne Bosch
IT Man: Emily Pintauro
Board of Directors: David B Brown, Jerome T Walker, Mark A Zorko

D-U-N-S 95-836-2212
MFS INVESTMENT MANAGEMENT FOUNDATION INC
(*Suby of* M F S) ★
111 Huntington Ave # 200, Boston, MA 02199-7632
Tel (800) 343-2829 *Founded/Ownrshp* 2000
Sales 275.0MM *EMP* 722^E
SIC 6722 Mutual fund sales, on own account
Pr: John Ballen
Sr Pt: Thomas Ward
Pr: Paula Chapman
Pr: Christopher Grant
Pr: Gaelen Yannetti
CFO: David A Antonelli
CFO: Amrit Kawal
**Ofcr:* Maria D Dwyer
Ofcr: Bob Emsing
Ofcr: Robyn Griffin
Ofcr: Stuart Lupton
Assoc VP: Gordon Forrest
Ex VP: Pat Zlotin
Sr VP: Robert Gandre
Sr VP: Mike Greene
Sr VP: David Rainville
Sr VP: John Riley
Sr VP: Brooks Taylor
Sr VP: Susan Unvarsky
VP: Bill A Allen
VP: Sal Barbagallo

MFS/YORK/STORMOR
See GLOBAL INDUSTRIES INC

D-U-N-S 78-882-7116
MG BUILDING MATERIALS LTD
MG TRUCK SALES
(*Suby of* GROTHUES BROTHERS HOLDINGS LTD) ★
2651 Sw Military Dr, San Antonio, TX 78224-1048
Tel (210) 924-8604 *Founded/Ownrshp* 2005
Sales 274.7MM^E *EMP* 780
SIC 2421 4212 5211 Sawmills & planing mills, general; Lumber (log) trucking, local; Lumber & other building materials
Pt: Allan Grothues
Sls Mgr: Gary Miller

D-U-N-S 08-273-1993
MG OIL CO (SD)
FLYING J TRAVEL PLAZA
1180 Creek Dr, Rapid City, SD 57703-4111
Tel (605) 342-0527 *Founded/Ownrshp* 1976
Sales 301.2MM *EMP* 450
Accts Ketel Thorstenson Llp Rapid
SIC 5172 5541 5411 Gasoline; Diesel fuel; Lubricating oils & greases; Filling stations, gasoline; Convenience stores, independent
Pr: Marlyn G Erickson
**VP:* Troy Erickson
Genl Mgr: Dave Kulish
IT Man: Tami Hellendoorn
Sls Mgr: Ken Hutton

MG TRUCK SALES
See MG BUILDING MATERIALS LTD

D-U-N-S 00-727-8641 IMP/EXP
■ **MG WALDBAUM CO**
(*Suby of* MICHAEL FOODS OF DELAWARE INC) ★
301 Carlson Pkwy Ste 400, Minnetonka, MN 55305-5370
Tel (952) 258-4000 *Founded/Ownrshp* 2007
Sales 375.4MM^E *EMP* 2,694
SIC 2015 5153 5191 Egg processing; Eggs, processed: frozen; Eggs, processed: desiccated (dried); Grains; Feed

Pr: Mark D Whitmer
**CFO:* Mark Westther

D-U-N-S 05-517-3959 IMP/EXP
MGA ENTERTAINMENT INC
16300 Roscoe Blvd Ste 150, Van Nuys, CA 91406-1257
Tel (818) 894-2525 *Founded/Ownrshp* 1980
Sales 435.6MM^E *EMP* 2,100
SIC 5092 Toys & games
Pr: Isaac Larian
VP: Lauren Conner
Snr Sftwr: David Roman
VP Mktg: AME Cameron
Snr Mgr: David Richter

D-U-N-S 10-820-2854
■ **MGA INSURANCE CO INC**
(*Suby of* GAINSCO AUTO INSURANCE) ★
3333 Lee Pkwy, Dallas, TX 75219-5111
Tel (972) 629-4301 *Founded/Ownrshp* 1989
Sales NA *EMP* 2
SIC 6331 Automobile insurance
Pr: Glenn Anderson
Treas: Daniel Coots
Ex VP: Carolyn Ray
VP: John Graham
VP: Joseph Pitts

MGC
See MITSUBISHI GAS CHEMICAL AMERICA INC

MGE ENERGY
See MADISON GAS AND ELECTRIC CO

D-U-N-S 12-237-1599
▲ **MGE ENERGY INC**
133 S Blair St, Madison, WI 53788-0001
Tel (608) 252-7000 *Founded/Ownrshp* 1896
Sales 564.0MM *EMP* 708^E
Tkr Sym MGEE *Exch* NGS
SIC 4939 4911 4924 Combination utilities; Electric services; Natural gas distribution
Ch Bd: Gary J Wolter
CFO: Jeffrey C Newman
Sr VP: Lynn K Hobbie
VP: Kristine Euclide
VP: Craig A Fenrick
VP: Gary Mathis
VP: Peter J Waldron
Ex Dir: Steve Schultz
Genl Mgr: Bob Stutz
CIO: James Bidlingmaier
Mktg Dir: Merl Banks
Board of Directors: Mark D Bugher, F Curtis Hastings, Regina M Millner, John R Nevin, Thomas R Stolper

D-U-N-S 07-834-2191 IMP
MGF SOURCING US LLC
(*Suby of* SYCAMORE PARTNERS MANAGEMENT LP) ★
4200 Regent St Ste 205, Columbus, OH 43219-6229
Tel (614) 904-3269 *Founded/Ownrshp* 2011
Sales 221.8MM^E *EMP* 825
SIC 5137 5136 Women's & children's clothing; Men's & boys' clothing
Pr: James Schwartz

D-U-N-S 62-337-4878
MGI HOLDINGS LP
(*Suby of* BLUE SAGE CAPITAL LP) ★
5912 Balcones Dr, Austin, TX 78731-4310
Tel (512) 459-4796 *Founded/Ownrshp* 2004
Sales 103.0MM^E *EMP* 800^E
SIC 5812 6794 Pizzeria, chain; Franchises, selling or licensing
CEO: Michael J Mrlik
Ch Bd: James D McBride
CFO: Steven B Burt

MGIC INVESTMENT
See MORTGAGE GUARANTY INSURANCE CORP

D-U-N-S 10-829-5650
▲ **MGIC INVESTMENT CORP**
250 E Kilbourn Ave, Milwaukee, WI 53202-3102
Tel (414) 347-6480 *Founded/Ownrshp* 1984
Sales NA *EMP* 800^E
Tkr Sym MTG *Exch* NYS
SIC 6351 6411 Mortgage guarantee insurance; Insurance information & consulting services
Pr: Patrick Sinks
**Ch Bd:* Curt S Culver
CFO: Timothy J Mattke
Ex VP: Jeffrey H Lane
Ex VP: Stephen C Mackey
Sr VP: Gregory A CHI
Sr VP: James J Hughes
Sr VP: James A Karpowicz
VP: Carla A Gallas
VP: Heidi Heyrmann
VP: Claudia Koehler
VP: Dan Stilwell
VP: Bernie Verhoeven
Board of Directors: Daniel A Arrigoni, Cassandra C Carr, C Edward Chaplin, Timothy A Holt, Kenneth M Jastrow II, Michael E Lehman, Gary A Poliner, Mark M Zandi

D-U-N-S 13-094-4361
MGL AMERICAS INC
1249 S River Rd Ste 102, Cranbury, NJ 08512-3633
Tel (609) 235-9632 *Founded/Ownrshp* 2001
Sales 37.4MM^E *EMP* 2,400
SIC 7379 7371 Computer related consulting services; Computer software development & applications
Ch: Sandy K Chandra
Ex Ofcr: Jaykar Krishnamurthy
S&M/Mgr: Amir Raza
S&M/Mgr: Ranga Sayee
Board of Directors: Sandy Chandra, Dr Nandu Thondavadi, Dr K S Vedantham

MGM
See METRO-GOLDWYN-MAYER STUDIOS INC

MGM
See NATIONAL GRANGE MUTUAL INSURANCE CO

MGM
See METRO-GOLDWYN-MAYER INC

D-U-N-S 08-491-8791
■ **MGM GRAND DETROIT LLC**
(*Suby of* MGM RESORTS INTERNATIONAL) ★
1777 3rd St, Detroit, MI 48226-2561
Tel (313) 465-1777 *Founded/Ownrshp* 1999
Sales 500.0MM *EMP* 3,000^E
SIC 7011 5812 7991 Casino hotel; Eating places; Spas
Ch: Jim Murren
**Pr:* Michael Neubecker
VP: Juliette Eboh
Info Man: Jeffrey Sauers
Sls&Mrk Ex: Daniela Cervenak
Advt Mgr: Tiffany Love
Mktg Mgr: Matt Buckley
Sls Mgr: Marie Etchells

MGM GRAND HOTEL & CASINO
See MGM GRAND HOTEL LLC

D-U-N-S 80-744-9095
■ **MGM GRAND HOTEL LLC**
MGM GRAND HOTEL & CASINO
(*Suby of* MGM RESORTS INTERNATIONAL) ★
3799 Las Vegas Blvd S, Las Vegas, NV 89109-4319
Tel (702) 891-1111 *Founded/Ownrshp* 2000
Sales 385.9MM^E *EMP* 9,000
SIC 7011 Casino hotel
Pr: Scot Sibella
**Pr:* Gamal Aziz
Sr Ex VP: Dave Cox
Ex VP: Mike Amie
**Ex VP:* Corey Sanders
Ex VP: Myrna Soto
**Sr VP:* Tom Peterman
VP: Jeff Ellis
**VP:* Mark Huntley
VP: Ann Krutchik
VP: Neil Lewis
VP: Patrick Lucas
VP: David McIntyre
VP: Cindy K Murphy
VP: Doug Seidenberg
VP: Richard Sturm
VP: David Vera

MGM HEALTHCARE
See MIDWEST GERIATRIC MANAGEMENT LLC

D-U-N-S 19-835-2564
MGM HOLDINGS II INC
MGM STUDIOS
(*Suby of* M G M) ★
245 N Beverly Dr, Beverly Hills, CA 90210-5319
Tel (310) 449-3000 *Founded/Ownrshp* 2005
Sales 68.1MM^E *EMP* 1,465
SIC 7812 Motion picture & video production
CEO: Daniel J Taylor
**CFO:* Steve Hendry
CFO: Tracy Reid
**Ex VP:* Charles Cohen
**Ex VP:* Scott Packman
VP: Cindy Wilford Perez

D-U-N-S 19-396-9248
MGM HOLDINGS INC
M G M
245 N Beverly Dr, Beverly Hills, CA 90210-5319
Tel (310) 449-3000 *Founded/Ownrshp* 2010
Sales 68.3MM^E *EMP* 1,482^E
SIC 7812 Motion picture production & distribution
CEO: Gary Barber
**COO:* Ken Schapiro
**CFO:* Kenneth Kay

D-U-N-S 17-578-1913
▲ **MGM RESORTS INTERNATIONAL**
3600 Las Vegas Blvd S, Las Vegas, NV 89109-4303
Tel (702) 693-7120 *Founded/Ownrshp* 1986
Sales 9.1MMM *EMP* 65,400
Tkr Sym MGM *Exch* NYS
SIC 7011 Hotels & motels; Casino hotel; Resort hotel
Ch Bd: James J Murren
Pr: William J Hornbuckle
COO: Corey I Sanders
CFO: Daniel J D'Arrigo
Ofcr: Robert H Baldwin
Sr Ex VP: Dave Cox
Ex VP: Paula Gentile
Ex VP: Phyllis A James
Ex VP: John M McManus
Ex VP: Robert C Selwood
Sr VP: Aaron Fischer
VP: Chris Baldizan
VP: Ondra L Berry
VP: John Bollen
VP: Chris Brophy
VP: Nancy Casey
VP: Carlos Castro
VP: Randy Dearborn
VP: Jeff Eisenhart
VP: Lance Evans
VP: Joseph Federici
Board of Directors: William A Bible, Mary Chris Gay, William W Grounds, Alexis M Herman, Roland Hernandez, Rose McKinney-James, Anthony Mandekic, Gregory M Spierkel, Daniel J Taylor

MGM STUDIOS
See MGM HOLDINGS II INC

MGMRESORTS
See MIRAGE RESORTS INC

D-U-N-S 04-833-1490
■ **MGOC INC**
(*Suby of* MEDIA GENERAL INC) ★
333 E Franklin St, Richmond, VA 23219-2213
Tel (804) 887-5000 *Founded/Ownrshp* 2014
Sales 674.9MM^E *EMP* 5,300^E
SIC 4833 4841 Television broadcasting stations; Cable television services
Pr: George L Mahoney
**CFO:* James F Woodward
**Ofcr:* John McCarus
**VP:* Andrew C Carington
VP: James R Conschafter

VP: John R Cottingham
**VP:* Robert E Macpherson
VP: Don Pratt

D-U-N-S 07-841-5272 IMP/EXP
▲ **MGP INGREDIENTS INC** (KS)
100 Commercial St, Atchison, KS 66002-2514
Tel (913) 367-1480 *Founded/Ownrshp* 1941
Sales 327.6MM *EMP* 293
Tkr Sym MGPI *Exch* NGS
SIC 2085 2041 Distillers' dried grains & solubles & alcohol; Flour & other grain mill products
Pr: Augustus C Griffin
**Ch Bd:* Karen L Seaberg
CFO: Thomas K Pigott
Ofcr: David E Rindom
VP: Michael R Buttshaw
VP: David E Dykstra
VP: Andrew Mansinne
VP Prd: Stephen J Glaser
Board of Directors: James L Bareuther, David J Colo, Terrence P Dunn, Anthony P Foglio, George W Page Jr, Daryl R Schaller, M Jeannine Strandjord

D-U-N-S 00-712-8218 IMP/EXP
■ **MGPI PROCESSING INC**
(*Suby of* MGP INGREDIENTS INC) ★
100 Commercial St, Atchison, KS 66002-2514
Tel (913) 367-1480 *Founded/Ownrshp* 1941
Sales 98.0MM^E *EMP* 192^E
Accts Kpmg Llp Kansas City Missour
SIC 2085 2041 Distilled & blended liquors; Flour & other grain mill products
Pr: Gus Griffin
**CFO:* Tom Pigott
**VP:* Scott B Phillips
**VP:* Randy M Schrick
Board of Directors: Michael Braude, John E Byom, Gary Gradinger, Linda E Miller, Daryl R Schaller Phd, Karen Seaberg, John R Speirs

D-U-N-S 03-629-4085 IMP/EXP
MGS GROUP NORTH AMERICA INC
TECXTAR
(*Suby of* MGS MFG GROUP INC) ★
W190n11701 Moldmakers Way, Germantown, WI 53022-2463
Tel (262) 250-2950 *Founded/Ownrshp* 1997
Sales 137.6MM^E *EMP* 425
SIC 3089 Plastic processing
CEO: Mark G Sellers
**Pr:* Craig Hall
**COO:* Raig Hall
**Ex VP:* Scott W Scampini
**VP:* Kevin P Christ
**VP:* Alan E Vick
Exec: Jeff Kolbow
VP Sls: Rudi Petrovic

D-U-N-S 03-628-7535 IMP/EXP
MGS MFG GROUP INC
W188n11707 Maple Rd, Germantown, WI 53022-2409
Tel (262) 255-5790 *Founded/Ownrshp* 2016
Sales 235.1MM^E *EMP* 1,316^E
SIC 3089 5047 2821 Molding primary plastic; Medical equipment & supplies; Molding compounds, plastics
CEO: Jeff Kolbow
Pr: Mark G Sellers
COO: Paul Manley
CFO: Lyle Meshberger
VP: John Hahn
Prgrm Mgr: Doug Hammond
Plng Mgr: Kimber Gedman
Off Admin: Sarah Cummins
Sls&Mrk Ex: Tanja Petrovic

MGWALGBAUMS
See MICHAEL FOODS INC

MH EBY TRAILERS
See M H EBY INC

D-U-N-S 02-574-3261 IMP
MH EQUIPMENT CO
(*Suby of* M H EQUIPMENT CO) ★
2001 Hartman, Chillicothe, IL 61523-9198
Tel (309) 579-8020 *Founded/Ownrshp* 2000
Sales 91.2MM^E *EMP* 140
SIC 5084 Industrial machinery & equipment; Materials handling machinery
Pr: John S Wieland
Brnch Mgr: Jeremy Burress
Brnch Mgr: Brian Michalec
Brnch Mgr: Ted Nime
Brnch Mgr: Ron Patterson
Brnch Mgr: Kevin Rodeman
Genl Mgr: Steve Rief
CTO: Mark Parker
Dir IT: James Gillis
IT Man: Matthew Lamb
Info Man: Margaret Zdanowski

D-U-N-S 96-502-3901
■ **MH INC**
(*Suby of* MGMRESORTS) ★
3950 Las Vegas Blvd S, Las Vegas, NV 89119-1005
Tel (702) 693-7120 *Founded/Ownrshp* 2010
Sales 12.5MM^E *EMP* 5,010^E
SIC 7011 Hotels & motels

D-U-N-S 13-555-7820 IMP
MH LOGISTICS CORP
M H EQUIPMENT COMPANY
2001 Hartman, Chillicothe, IL 61523-9198
Tel (309) 579-8030 *Founded/Ownrshp* 2000
Sales 238.6MM *EMP* 700
Accts Cliftonlarsonallen Llp Peoria
SIC 5084 Industrial machinery & equipment; Materials handling machinery
CEO: John S Wieland
**CFO:* Bradley W Barrow

D-U-N-S 04-074-2017
MHA LLC
MEADOWLANDS HOSPITAL MED CTR
55 Meadowlands Pkwy, Secaucus, NJ 07094-2977
Tel (201) 392-3200 *Founded/Ownrshp* 2010
Sales 498.8MM *EMP* 650

SIC 8062 General medical & surgical hospitals
Pr: Felicia Karsos
VP: Stanley Galichenko
Dir Rx: Rosemary Bab
Dir IT: Olga Konratev
Dir IT: William Regniault
Sfty Dirs: David Szatkiewicz
Opers Mgr: Robyn Maher
Mktg Dir: Sally Deering
Ansthlgy: Michael E Tawfellos
Pharmcst: Sonali Patel
Diag Rad: Vitaly Izgur

MHAS
See OHIO DEPARTMENT OF MENTAL HEALTH

D-U-N-S 07-465-5770
■ MHC INC
MIDAMERICAN
(*Suby of* MIDAMERICAN FUNDING LLC) ★
666 Grand Ave Ste 500, Des Moines, IA 50309-2511
Tel (515) 242-4300 *Founded/Ownrshp* 1996
Sales 3.5MMM^E *EMP* 3,500
Accts Deloitte & Touche Llp Des Moi
SIC 4924 4911 Natural gas distribution; Electric services
Ch Bd: David L Sokol
* *Pr:* Gregory E Abel
* *Treas:* Calvin D Haack
Netwrk Mgr: Solomon Egzi

MHC KENWORTH
See TEXAS KENWORTH CO

D-U-N-S 03-196-4653
MHC KENWORTH - KANSAS CITY
(*Suby of* MURPHY-HOFFMAN CO) ★
1524 N Corrington Ave, Kansas City, MO 64120-1944
Tel (816) 483-7035 *Founded/Ownrshp* 1986
Sales 161.7MM^E *EMP* 345
SIC 5012 Truck tractors
Pr: Tim Murphy
* *Ch Bd:* Reed F Murphy Jr
* *CFO:* Jeff Johnson
* *Ex VP:* Kenneth Hoffman
Ex VP: Mike Murphy
VP: David Douglas
VP: Todd Harrington
Brnch Mgr: Bill Haworth
Brnch Mgr: Jason Mc Gehe
Snr Ntwrk: Joe Evans
Dir IT: Scott Elliott

D-U-N-S 84-985-5788
■ MHC OPERATING LIMITED PARTNERSHIP
GOLF VISTA ESTATES
(*Suby of* EQUITY LIFESTYLE PROPERTIES INC) ★
2 N Riverside Plz Ste 800, Chicago, IL 60606-2682
Tel (312) 279-1400 *Founded/Ownrshp* 1996
Sales 74.8MM^E *EMP* 1,018
SIC 6515 6531 Mobile home site operators; Real estate agents & managers
Mng Pt: Howard Walker
CIO: Joe McAdams

MHI HOTELS
See MARYLAND HOSPITALITY INC

D-U-N-S 79-063-9843 IMP
MHI PARTNERSHIP LTD
PLANTATION HOMES
7676 Woodway Dr Ste 104, Houston, TX 77063-1521
Tel (713) 952-6767 *Founded/Ownrshp* 1991
Sales 485.0MM^E *EMP* 350
Accts Ernst & Young Llp Houston Tx
SIC 1531 Speculative builder, single-family houses
Ch Bd: Frank B McGuyer
Pr: Mike K Love
CFO: Gary Tesch
Ex Dir: Charles H Phillips

MHIA
See MITSUBISHI HEAVY INDUSTRIES AMERICA INC

MHKK&G
See MEYERTONS HOOD KIVLIN KOWERT & GOETZEL P C

D-U-N-S 09-534-7357 IMP
MHM SERVICES INC
1593 Spring Hill Rd # 600, Vienna, VA 22182-2245
Tel (703) 749-4600 *Founded/Ownrshp* 1981
Sales 100.8MM^E *EMP* 2,143
Accts Pricewaterhousecoopers Llp Mc
SIC 8093 8361 Mental health clinic, outpatient; Residential care
Pr: Steven H Wheeler
COO: David Lotocki
* *CFO:* John Campbell
CFO: Patrick Chunn
CFO: Susan Ritchey
VP: Deborah Crook
VP: Haddad Jane
VP: Renee Lipinski
VP: Bob May
VP: Gina Morris
Prgrm Mgr: Jeanne Jones

MHMR OF TARRANT COUNTY
See MENTAL HEALTH MENTAL RETARDATION OF TARRANT COUNTY

D-U-N-S 80-818-2559
■ MHN SERVICES
(*Suby of* HEALTH NET INC) ★
2370 Kerner Blvd, San Rafael, CA 94901-5546
Tel (415) 460-8300 *Founded/Ownrshp* 1988
Sales NA *EMP* 1,000
SIC 6324 8011 8742 8322 Hospital & medical service plans; Health maintenance organization; Management consulting services; Social service center
Pr: Juanell Hefner
Chf Mktg O: Ian Shaffer

MHRA
See PUBLIC HEALTH SOLUTIONS

MHS
See MATERIAL HANDLING SYSTEMS INC

D-U-N-S 00-128-7812
MI 2009 INC
4165 Half Acre Rd, Batavia, OH 45103-3247
Tel (513) 536-2000 *Founded/Ownrshp* 1884
Sales 30.6M^E *EMP* 3,350
SIC 3559 Plastics working machinery
CEO: Dennis Smith
CFO: John C Francy
Sr VP: Hugh C O'Donnell
VP: David J Bertke
VP: Hugh C Donnell
VP: William J Gruber
VP: Barbara G Kasting
VP: Jim Moore
VP: Gerold Schley
VP: James M Stergiopoulos
VP: Robert J Strickley
VP: Dale P Werle
Div/Sub He: Kyle Seymour

D-U-N-S 02-319-2268
MI METALS INC
(*Suby of* BEAM ASSOCIATES LLC) ★
301 Commerce Blvd, Oldsmar, FL 34677-2806
Tel (813) 855-5695 *Founded/Ownrshp* 1983
Sales 335.5MM^E *EMP* 350^E
SIC 3585 Refrigeration & heating equipment
Pr: Brook Massey
* *VP:* Kevin Sponsler

MI PUEBLO FOOD CENTER
See MI PUEBLO LLC

D-U-N-S 84-545-7063 IMP
MI PUEBLO LLC
MI PUEBLO FOOD CENTER
1775 Story Rd Ste 120, San Jose, CA 95122-1942
Tel (408) 928-1171 *Founded/Ownrshp* 1995
Sales 347.1MM^E *EMP* 1,500
SIC 5411 Grocery stores
Pr: Javier Ramirez
* *Ch Bd:* Juvenal Chavez
* *CFO:* Martin Cortes
* *VP:* Perla A Rodriguez
* *VP:* Hector Salas
Dir Risk M: Salvador Trejo
Dir IT: Tedd McCowan

D-U-N-S 00-829-7277 EXP
MI WINDOWS AND DOORS INC
650 W Market St, Gratz, PA 17030-9701
Tel (717) 365-3300 *Founded/Ownrshp* 2013
Sales 590.7MM^E *EMP* 2,500
SIC 3089 3442 Window frames & sash, plastic; Screens, window, metal
CEO: Peter Desoto
* *Pr:* Jay K Poppleton
* *CFO:* Sarah W Gutherie
* *Treas:* Stan Sullivan
* *VP:* Matt Desoto
VP: Jerry Meyer
IT Man: Troy Liddick
Tech Mgr: Brent Sitlinger
Prd Mgr: Brett Erdman

D-U-N-S 12-127-0024 IMP/EXP
MI-JACK PRODUCTS INC
(*Suby of* LANTECH LOGISTICS) ★
3111 167th St, Hazel Crest, IL 60429-0975
Tel (708) 596-5200 *Founded/Ownrshp* 1954
Sales 172.4MM^E *EMP* 450^E
SIC 3531 8711 Construction machinery; Designing: ship, boat, machine & product
Pr: Michael T Lanigan
* *Ch Bd:* John J Lanigan Sr
* *CFO:* Stephen J Bayers
Ex VP: Mike T Lanigan
Sr VP: Joe Belcastro
Sr VP: Dan Heraty
VP: Myron Glickman
VP: Michael Grace
VP: Aaron Newton
VP: Ray Tippit
VP: John Wepfer

D-U-N-S 06-324-2200 IMP/EXP
MI-T-M CORP (IA)
50 Mitm Dr, Peosta, IA 52068
Tel (563) 556-7484 *Founded/Ownrshp* 1971
Sales 172.3MM^E *EMP* 330
SIC 3569 Liquid automation machinery & equipment
CEO: Aj Spiegel
* *Pr:* Sam Humphrey
CFO: Tom Allendorf
CFO: Steve Cleary
* *VP:* Dana Schrack
Ql Cn Mgr: Brian Ruden

MIAMI BEACH CONVENTION CENTER
See CITY OF MIAMI BEACH

D-U-N-S 07-386-9471
■ MIAMI BEACH HEALTHCARE GROUP LTD
AVENTURA HOSPITAL AND MED CTR
(*Suby of* HOSPITAL CORPORATION OF AMERICA) ★
20900 Biscayne Blvd, Miami, FL 33180-1407
Tel (305) 682-7000 *Founded/Ownrshp* 1991
Sales 151.9MM^E *EMP* 1,100
SIC 8062 General medical & surgical hospitals
Pr: Dianne Goldenberg
Chf Rad: Reuven Porges
Chf Mktg O: Lester Eljack
Chf Mktg O: Alan Kutner
Dir Risk M: Patty Stover
Chf Nrs Of: Pam Hardesty
Doctor: Michael Bahrami
Doctor: Lawrence Berger
Doctor: Eugenio Bricio
Doctor: Henry Chua
Doctor: Aldo Coelho

D-U-N-S 07-312-9249
MIAMI DADE COLLEGE
MDC
300 Ne 2nd Ave Rm 3116, Miami, FL 33132-2204
Tel (305) 237-3000 *Founded/Ownrshp* 1960
Sales 243.3MM^E *EMP* 9,172
Accts William O Monroe Cpa/State Of
SIC 8222 9411 8221 Community college; Administration of educational programs; ; Colleges universities & professional schools
Pr: Eduardo J Padron
CFO: E H Lvring
Trst: Armando J Bucelo
Trst: Benjamin Le N
Ofcr: Charlotte Fulton
Ofcr: Karrigan Lawson
Comm Dir: Juan Mendieta
* *Prin:* Cathlene Rodregez
Prgrm Mgr: John Chin
Prgrm Mgr: Valerie Deangelis
Prgrm Mgr: Veronica Zayas

D-U-N-S 07-845-6712 IMP
MIAMI JEWISH HEALTH SYSTEMS INC
5200 Ne 2nd Ave, Miami, FL 33137-2706
Tel (305) 751-8626 *Founded/Ownrshp* 1945
Sales 70.8MM *EMP* 1,100
Accts Crowe Horwath Llp Dallas Tx
SIC 8051 Skilled nursing care facilities; Convalescent home with continuous nursing care; Extended care facility; Mental retardation hospital
Ch: Stephen H Cypen
* *CEO:* Jeffrey P Freimark
* *Treas:* Lisa J Desmarteau
Chf Mktg O: Wendie Nemeroff
VP: Cliff Bauer
* *VP:* Morris Funk
VP: Jack Kelleher
Dir Sec: Zoe Alvarez
CIO: David Wolff

MIAMI LAKER
See GRAHAM COMPANIES

D-U-N-S 04-106-5129
MIAMI UNIVERSITY
501 E High St, Oxford, OH 45056-1846
Tel (513) 529-1809 *Founded/Ownrshp* 1906
Sales 443.0MM *EMP* 4,925^E
Accts Mcgladrey Llp Cleveland Ohio
SIC 8221 University
Pr: David Hodge
Pr: Joe Bazeley
Pr: Troy Travis
Pr: Scott Walter
Top Exec: Belinda Barr
VP: Debra Allison
VP: Jayne Brownell
VP: Reid Christenberry
VP: Brenden Clinton
VP: David Creamer
VP: Alexis Debrunner
VP: Patricia Fagin
VP: Alan Ferrenberg
VP: Jeannine Fischer
VP: Valerie Garnett
VP: Daniel Johnson
VP: Barbara Jones
VP: Riley Kelly
VP: Carolyn Ledford
VP: Richard M Norman
VP: Beck Parker

MIAMI VALLEY
See PREMIER HEALTH PARTNERS

D-U-N-S 07-127-1951
MIAMI VALLEY HOSPITAL
1 Wyoming St, Dayton, OH 45409-2711
Tel (937) 208-8000 *Founded/Ownrshp* 1982
Sales 827.4MM *EMP* 6,000
SIC 8062 General medical & surgical hospitals
Pr: Bobbie Gerhart
* *Pr:* Mark Shaker
* *COO:* Barbara Johnson
* *CFO:* Lisa Bishop
Bd of Dir: Chris Snider
* *VP:* Makkie Clancy
VP: Deb Mals
VP: Diane Pleiman
Dir OR: David Kelly
Dir Risk M: Jennifer Theibert
Adm Dir: Vanessa Sandarusi

D-U-N-S 10-148-6280 EXP
MIAMI VALLEY STEEL SERVICE INC
201 Fox Dr, Piqua, OH 45356-9265
Tel (937) 773-7127 *Founded/Ownrshp* 2012
Sales 184.9MM^E *EMP* 140
SIC 5051 Metals service centers & offices
CEO: Louis Moran
CFO: Jill Kendall
* *CFO:* Jill Kindell
VP: Guy House
Exec: Susan Curtis
Dir Bus: Nick Straka
IT Man: Douglas Fenter
VP Opers: Ron Leak
Plnt Mgr: Chip Lameraue
Plnt Mgr: Chip Lamoreaux
VP Sls: Len Stahl

MIAMI WABASH PAPER
See MAFCOTE INC

D-U-N-S 82-587-7991
MIAMI-DADE COUNTY PUBLIC SCHOOLS-158
1450 Ne 2nd Ave, Miami, FL 33132-1308
Tel (305) 995-1000 *Founded/Ownrshp* 2008
Sales 1.9MMM^E *EMP* 40,000^E
SIC 8211 Elementary & secondary schools
V Ch: Martin Karp
Adm Dir: Dyann Rodriguez
Ex Dir: Victor Ferrante
Dir Sec: Ian Moffett
Off Mgr: Monica Santos
Pr Dir: Daisy Gonzalez-Diego
Pr Dir: John Schuster
Teacher Pr: Jose Dotres
Instr Medi: Richard Benvenuti
Psych: Laurel Taitt
HC Dir: Wilma Steiner

D-U-N-S 01-797-0443
MIAMI-LUKEN INC
PARAMOUNT CONFECTION CO
265 S Pioneer Blvd, Springboro, OH 45066-3307
Tel (937) 743-7775 *Founded/Ownrshp* 1994
Sales 277.6MM^E *EMP* 275
Accts Dohner Louis & Stephens Inc
SIC 5122 Drugs, proprietaries & sundries
CEO: Tony Rattini
* *Ch Bd:* Joseph Mastandrea
* *Prin:* Anthony V Rattini
IT Man: Charles Wilt
VP Mktg: Jim Barclay
VP Sls: Todd Hawkins
Board of Directors: Steve Fullarton, Cindy Willet

D-U-N-S 04-160-6869 IMP/EXP
MIAS FASHION MANUFACTURING CO INC
CALIFORNIA BASIC
12623 Cisneros Ln, Santa Fe Springs, CA 90670-3373
Tel (562) 906-1060 *Founded/Ownrshp* 1999
Sales 160.7MM *EMP* 252
Accts Kim & Lee Los Angeles Califo
SIC 5137 Women's & children's clothing
Pr: Peter D Anh
* *CFO:* Brian Song

D-U-N-S 15-842-4445
MIASOLE
2590 Walsh Ave, Santa Clara, CA 95051-1315
Tel (408) 919-5700 *Founded/Ownrshp* 2001
Sales 97.4MM^E *EMP* 315
SIC 3674

D-U-N-S 07-213-5692
MIB GROUP INC
50 Braintree Hill Park # 400, Braintree, MA 02184-8803
Tel (781) 751-6000 *Founded/Ownrshp* 1978
Sales NA *EMP* 150
SIC 6411 Information bureaus, insurance
Pr: Lee B Oliphant
Ch Bd: David P Wheeler
Pr: Jay Cook
Pr: Cliff Toplis
CFO: Linda Barnes
CFO: Linda Daines
Ex VP: Stacy J Gill
Ex VP: Jonathan W Sager
VP: Traci Davis
Snr Sftwr: Yong Wang
CIO: Bob Diangelo
Board of Directors: David Acselrod, Dean Del Vecchio, Thomas F English, Timothy A Walsh

D-U-N-S 03-806-8826 IMP
MIBA BEARINGS US LLC
(*Suby of* MITTERBAUER BETEILIGUNGS-AKTIENGESELLSCHAFT.)
5037 N State Route 60 Nw, McConnelsville, OH 43756-9218
Tel (740) 962-4242 *Founded/Ownrshp* 2001
Sales 100.4MM^E *EMP* 300
SIC 3799 Automobile trailer chassis
Ch Bd: F Peter Mitterbauer
CFO: Markus Hofer
Dir IT: Scott Roberts
Dir IT: Mike Starrett
Plnt Mgr: Bernie Anderson
Plnt Mgr: Ted Mc Mc Connell
Ql Cn Mgr: Marilyn Wampleman

MICCOSUKEE TRAIL RESTAURANT
See MICCOSUKEE TRIBE OF INDIANS OF FLORIDA

D-U-N-S 03-253-3754 EXP
MICCOSUKEE TRIBE OF INDIANS OF FLORIDA
MICCOSUKEE TRAIL RESTAURANT
Sw 8th St & Us Hwy 41, Miami, FL 33194
Tel (305) 223-8380 *Founded/Ownrshp* 1962
Sales 57.4MM^E *EMP* 1,500
SIC 5812 5331 8412 5947 4489 Indian/Pakistan restaurant; Variety stores; Museum; Gift shop; Airboats
Ch Bd: Colley Billie
* *CFO:* Mike Hernandez
* *Treas:* Max Billie
Exec: Risha Singh
Telecom Ex: Julio Martinez
DP Exec: Miguel Crispo
Dir IT: Miguel Crespo
Sls Mgr: Jodi Goldenberg

D-U-N-S 14-467-2060 IMP
MICHAEL & SON SERVICES INC
5740 General Wash Dr, Alexandria, VA 22312-2407
Tel (703) 658-3998 *Founded/Ownrshp* 1988
Sales 124.3MM^E *EMP* 140^E
SIC 1521 1731 5074 General remodeling, single-family houses; Electrical work; Plumbing & hydronic heating supplies
Pr: Basim Mansour
* *VP:* Joanna Mansour
Genl Mgr: Rami Sayegh
Genl Mgr: Chris Thompson
Genl Mgr: George Vogt
IT Man: Molly Ahelet
Trfc Dir: Barbara Coleman
Trfc Dir: Michele Copley
Trfc Dir: Norbert Rancke
Opers Mgr: Michael Seton
Sls Dir: Elias Moussa

D-U-N-S 09-808-0158
MICHAEL & SUSAN DELL FOUNDATION
4417 Westlake Dr, Austin, TX 78746-1437
Tel (512) 329-0799 *Founded/Ownrshp* 1999
Sales 111.4MM^E *EMP* 55
SIC 7389 Authors' agents & brokers
Ch Bd: Susan Dell
* *Prin:* Dr Alexander Dell
* *Prin:* Michael Dell
IT Man: Biplab Basu
IT Man: Ian Christopher

MICHAEL ANGELO'S GOURMET FOODS
See BOTTOM LINE FOOD PROCESSORS INC

D-U-N-S 00-791-6968
MICHAEL BAKER INTERNATIONAL HOLDCO CORP (PA)
(*Suby of* MICHAEL BAKER INTERNATIONAL LLC) ★
100 Airside Dr, Moon Township, PA 15108-4740
Tel (412) 269-6300 *Founded/Ownrshp* 1940, 2013
Sales 541.4MM[E] *EMP* 3,200[E]
SIC 8711 Civil engineering
CEO: Kurt C Bergman
**COO:* Jeffrey S Hill
CFO: Ryan Goodliffe
**CFO:* Brian Lutes
Treas: James Kempton
**Ofcr:* Samuel C Knoch
Ofcr: James McKnight
**Ofcr:* Michael J Ziemianski
Assoc VP: Peter Hankovszky
Ex VP: Joseph Bongiovi
**Ex VP:* John Kurgan
**Ex VP:* H James McKnight
Ex VP: James B Richards
Sr VP: Thomas J Zagorski
VP: Jeff Baker
VP: Ray Balentine
VP: Karen Ciccone
VP: Retta Gardner
**VP:* Jeremy N Gill
VP: Jeremy Gill
VP: Paul Gluck

D-U-N-S 07-917-1269
MICHAEL BAKER INTERNATIONAL LLC
500 Grant St Ste 5400, Pittsburgh, PA 15219-2523
Tel (412) 918-4000 *Founded/Ownrshp* 2012
Sales 592.9MM *EMP* 3,280[E]
Accts Mcgladrey Llp Mclean Virgini
SIC 8711 Civil engineering
Pr: Kurt Bergman
**COO:* John D Whiteford
**CFO:* Brian Lutes
VP: Louis Levner
Opers Mgr: Scott Vannoy
Mktg Mgr: Jennifer Riddle

D-U-N-S 09-733-6556
MICHAEL BEST & FRIEDRICH LLP
100 E Wisconsin Ave # 3300, Milwaukee, WI 53202-4108
Tel (414) 271-6560 *Founded/Ownrshp* 1997
Sales 96.5MM[E] *EMP* 500
SIC 8111 General practice law office
Mng Pt: Dave Krutz
Sr Pt: Tod B Linstroth
Mng Pt: Jos Olivieri
Mng Pt: Charles B Palmer
Ex Dir: Brian Wipperfurth
Off Mgr: Billie J Smith
CIO: Alan Ciochon
Dir IT: Tess Welch
Info Man: Roy La Budde
Counsel: Joseph R Filachek
Counsel: Richard Kaiser

D-U-N-S 05-152-6911 IMP
MICHAEL C FINA CO INC
3301 Hunters Point Ave, Long Island City, NY 11101-2528
Tel (212) 557-2500 *Founded/Ownrshp* 1969
Sales 297.8MM[E] *EMP* 325
SIC 5094 5947 Jewelry; Gifts & novelties
Pr: Ashley Fina
**Ch:* George Fina
VP: Bill Fina
**VP:* Jeffrey Fina
VP: Elliot Young
Exec: Jessica Geletez
Area Mgr: David Kovacovich
IT Man: Colville Cudjoe
Merch Mgr: Karen Y Lee

D-U-N-S 02-818-8076
MICHAEL CADILLAC INC
MICHAEL HUMMER
50 W Bullard Ave, Fresno, CA 93704-1700
Tel (559) 431-6000 *Founded/Ownrshp* 1985
Sales 106.8MM[E] *EMP* 340
SIC 5511 Automobiles, new & used; Pickups, new & used; Vans, new & used
CEO: Michael L Rosvold
Sls Dir: Dustin Felix

MICHAEL CASPERSON
See M CASPERSON ENTERPRISE LLC

MICHAEL FOOD
See MFI HOLDING CORP

MICHAEL FOODS
See PAPETTIS HYGRADE EGG PRODUCTS INC

D-U-N-S 36-155-3709
■ **MICHAEL FOODS GROUP INC**
(*Suby of* MFI MIDCO CORPORATION)
301 Carlson Pkwy Ste 400, Minnetonka, MN 55305-5370
Tel (952) 258-4000 *Founded/Ownrshp* 2011
Sales 1.9MMM[E] *EMP* 3,596
SIC 0252 2015 5144 5143 5148 6719 Chicken eggs; Egg processing; Eggs; Eggs: cleaning, oil treating, packing & grading; Cheese; Butter; Potatoes, fresh; Investment holding companies, except banks
Pr: James E Dwyer Jr
Treas: Mark Witmer
Sr VP: James G Mohr

D-U-N-S 01-807-6351 IMP/EXP
■ **MICHAEL FOODS INC**
MGWALGBAUMS
(*Suby of* POST HOLDINGS INC) ★
301 Carlson Pkwy Ste 400, Minnetonka, MN 55305-5370
Tel (507) 237-4600 *Founded/Ownrshp* 1928, 2015
Sales 690.1MM[E] *EMP* 3,596
SIC 0252 2015 5144 5143 5148 5499 Chicken eggs; Egg processing; Eggs; Eggs: cleaning, oil treating, packing & grading; Cheese; Butter; Potatoes, fresh; Eggs & poultry
Pr: James E Dwyer Jr
Pr: Mark Anderson
CFO: Mark W Westphal
Ex VP: Deborah Laue
Sr VP: Thomas J Jagiela
VP: Steve Bacon
VP: Kathy Brodhagen
VP: Deborah Cummings
VP: Carol Morgan
VP: Carolyn V Wolski
Exec: Matt E Smith
Board of Directors: Nicole V Agnew, Adrian M Jones, Leo F Mullin, Gregg A Ostrander, Oliver D Thymkent R Weldon

D-U-N-S 14-850-8716 EXP
■ **MICHAEL FOODS OF DELAWARE INC**
(*Suby of* MGWALGBAUMS) ★
301 Carlson Pkwy Ste 400, Minnetonka, MN 55305-5370
Tel (952) 258-4000 *Founded/Ownrshp* 1997
Sales 635.1MM[E] *EMP* 3,596
SIC 0252 2015 5144 5143 5148 2024 Chicken eggs; Egg processing; Eggs; Eggs: cleaning, oil treating, packing & grading; Cheese; Butter; Potatoes, fresh; Ice milk, bulk; Ice cream, bulk
CEO: James E Dwyer
VP: John D Reedy

MICHAEL HUMMER
See MICHAEL CADILLAC INC

D-U-N-S 84-976-6068
MICHAEL J FOX FOUNDATION FOR PARKINSONS RESEARCH
498 Fashion Ave, New York, NY 10018-6798
Tel (212) 509-0995 *Founded/Ownrshp* 2000
Sales 99.9MM *EMP* 34
Accts Eisner Amper Llp New York Ne
SIC 7389 Fund raising organizations
CEO: Todd Sherer
**Pr:* Deborah Brooks
Ofcr: Michelle Aquino
Ofcr: Alan Lee
Ofcr: Alyssa Reimer
VP: Sheila Kelly
VP: Karen Leies
VP: Todd Steiner
Assoc Dir: Jamie L Eberling
Assoc Dir: Stephanie Paddock
Assoc Dir: Stephanie Startz

MICHAEL KAIL
See STEPTOE & JOHNSON LLP

D-U-N-S 13-162-0630 IMP/EXP
MICHAEL KORS (USA) INC
(*Suby of* MICHAEL KORS HOLDINGS LIMITED)
11 W 42nd St Fl 20, New York, NY 10036-8002
Tel (212) 201-8100 *Founded/Ownrshp* 2002
Sales 528.9MM[E] *EMP* 400
SIC 5137 5651 5621 Women's & children's clothing; Family clothing stores; Women's clothing stores
CEO: John D Idol
Pr: Jennifer Grom
**Pr:* Michael Kors Hon
Pr: Jennifer Jordano
**CFO:* Joseph Parsons
**Sr VP:* Laura Lentini
VP: Akhil Bisaria
VP: Andrea Cahn
VP: Gerardo Figueroa
VP: Bob Hassen
VP: Ebrahim Hyder
VP: Ryan Jones
VP: Erin Kurpiewski
VP: Jeremy Levine
VP: Jack Needham
VP: Peter Nichols
VP: Carey Pontier
VP: Sundeep D Reddy
VP: Nathan Serphos
VP: Jung Yoon

D-U-N-S 00-512-0449 IMP/EXP
MICHAEL LEWIS CO
SIMON PRODUCTS CO
(*Suby of* SIMU LTD) ★
8900 W 50th St, Mc Cook, IL 60525-6005
Tel (708) 688-2200 *Founded/Ownrshp* 1933
Sales 421.9MM[E] *EMP* 250
Accts Lipschultz Levin & Gray Nort
SIC 5113 5141 5142 2782 2759 2621 Industrial & personal service paper; Groceries, general line; Packaged frozen goods; Looseleaf binders & devices; Menus: printing; Packaging paper
**Pr:* Craig Simon
**VP:* Sheldon L Rosen
Exec: Joe Bruzzino
Mng Dir: Bob Frye
Off Mgr: Donna Bryant
Mktg Dir: Frank Kunz

D-U-N-S 07-942-9778
▲ **MICHAELS COMPANIES INC**
8000 Bent Branch Dr, Irving, TX 75063-6023
Tel (972) 409-1300 *Founded/Ownrshp* 1983
Sales 4.9MMM *EMP* 50,000[E]
Tkr Sym MIK *Exch* NGS
SIC 5945 3999 2273 Arts & crafts supplies; Framed artwork; Mats & matting; Door mats: paper, grass, reed, coir, sisal, jute, rags, etc.
Ch Bd: Carl S Rubin
V Ch: Charles M Sonsteby
CFO: Denise Paulonis
Ex VP: Theodore J Bachmeier
Ex VP: Stephen J Carlotti
Ex VP: Dennis A Mullahy
Ex VP: Philo T Pappas
Ex VP: Michael J Veitenheimer
Board of Directors: Josh Bekenstein, Monte E Ford, Karen Kaplan, Lewis S Klessel, Matthew S Levin, John J Mahoney, James A Quella, Beryl B Raff, Peter F Wallace

D-U-N-S 10-912-9775
MICHAELS ENTERPRISES INC
IRVING MICHAELS & COMPANY
150 Mattatuck Heights Rd # 3, Waterbury, CT 06705-3861
Tel (203) 597-4942 *Founded/Ownrshp* 1885
Sales 84.2MM[E] *EMP* 120
Accts Blum Shapiro & Company Pc
SIC 5094 Jewelry
Pr: Paul Michaels
**Ch Bd:* John A Michaels
**VP:* Richard Michaels
**VP:* V Paul Michaels

D-U-N-S 07-947-7223
■ **MICHAELS FINCO HOLDINGS LLC**
(*Suby of* MICHAELS COMPANIES INC) ★
8000 Bent Branch Dr, Irving, TX 75063-6023
Tel (972) 409-1300 *Founded/Ownrshp* 2013
Sales 4.5MMM[E] *EMP* 50,600[E]
SIC 5945 Hobby, toy & game shops; Arts & crafts supplies
CEO: Carl S Rubin

D-U-N-S 07-940-2542
■ **MICHAELS FUNDING INC**
(*Suby of* MICHAELS FINCO HOLDINGS LLC) ★
8000 Bent Branch Dr, Irving, TX 75063-6023
Tel (972) 409-1300 *Founded/Ownrshp* 2013
Sales 4.5MMM[E] *EMP* 50,600[E]
SIC 5945 Hobby, toy & game shops; Hobby & craft supplies

D-U-N-S 18-051-7955
MICHAELS G L CONSTRUCTION INC
554 W Cedarwood Ave, West Terre Haute, IN 47885-8405
Tel (812) 478-3154 *Founded/Ownrshp* 1987
Sales 128.0MM *EMP* 10
SIC 1542 1541 Commercial & office building contractors; Industrial buildings, new construction
Pr: Gary Lasure
**Sec:* Kimberly Lasure

D-U-N-S 79-006-4567 IMP
MICHAELS HOLDINGS LLC
8000 Bent Branch Dr, Irving, TX 75063-6023
Tel (972) 409-1300 *Founded/Ownrshp* 2006
Sales 2.5MMM[E] *EMP* 89,000[E]
SIC 5945 5999 5949 5947 5199 5099 Hobby, toy & game shops; Art, picture frames & decorations; Needlework goods & supplies; Party favors; Gifts & novelties; Novelties, durable
Ofcr: Charles Sonsteby
Sr VP: Shawn Hearn

D-U-N-S 05-440-2896 IMP
■ **MICHAELS STORES INC**
(*Suby of* MICHAELS FUNDING INC) ★
8000 Bent Branch Dr, Irving, TX 75063-6023
Tel (972) 409-1300 *Founded/Ownrshp* 1962, 2013
Sales 4.5MMM *EMP* 50,600[E]
SIC 5945 5999 5949 5947 5199 5099 Hobby, toy & game shops; Hobby & craft supplies; Arts & crafts supplies; Hobbies; Art, picture frames & decorations; Artificial flowers; Picture frames, ready made; Artists' supplies & materials; Needlework goods & supplies; Bridal fabrics; Gift, novelty & souvenir shop; Artcraft & carvings; Novelties; Party favors; Gifts & novelties; Novelties, durable; Souvenirs
CEO: Carl S Rubin
Ofcr: Charles M Sonsteby
Ex VP: Theodore J Bachmeier
Ex VP: Thomas C Decaro
Ex VP: Philo T Pappas
Sr VP: Thomas Decaro
Sr VP: Shawn E Hearn
Sr VP: Shawn Hearn
Sr VP: Dennis A Mullahy
Sr VP: Michael J Veitenheimer
VP: Walter Asbury
VP: Mike Cairnes
VP: Michelle Eilers
VP: Chris Freeman
VP: Yvonne Freeman
VP: Rich Gartmann
VP: Mary Kuniski
VP: Michelle Ruocco
VP: Lance A Weibye
Exec: Tammy Park
Dir Soc: Douglas C Marker

D-U-N-S 93-787-3131
■ **MICHCON PIPELINE CO**
MCN
(*Suby of* DTE GAS CO) ★
500 Griswold St Fl 16th, Detroit, MI 48226-3480
Tel (313) 256-5505 *Founded/Ownrshp* 1995
Sales 325.0MM[E] *EMP* 4,576
SIC 4922 Pipelines, natural gas
Pr: Stephen E Ewing
**Pr:* Steven Kurmas
**Treas:* Howard Dow
IT Man: Tom Motsinger

D-U-N-S 04-469-1848 IMP/EXP
MICHELIN CORP (NY)
(*Suby of* MICHELIN NORTH AMERICA INC) ★
1 Parkway S, Greenville, SC 29615-5095
Tel (864) 458-5000 *Founded/Ownrshp* 1907, 1963
Sales 6.1MMM[E] *EMP* 23,000
SIC 5014

D-U-N-S 00-166-7161 IMP/EXP
MICHELIN NORTH AMERICA INC
(*Suby of* CIE GEN DES ETS MICHELIN)
1 Parkway S, Greenville, SC 29615-5095
Tel (864) 458-5000 *Founded/Ownrshp* 2000
Sales 9.3MMM[E] *EMP* 23,500
SIC 3011 Tires & inner tubes
Ch: Pete Selleck
COO: David Staffrod
CFO: Eric Le Le Corre
**CFO:* Thomas Praktish
**Ch:* Dick Wilkerson
**VP:* Scott Clark
VP: Michael Fanning
VP: Craig Macgibbon
Exec: Ronald Musgnug
Admn Mgr: Bob Willmerdinger
Genl Mgr: Shawn McCullough

D-U-N-S 00-580-9868 IMP/EXP
MICHELS CORP (WI)
MICHELS MID-AMERICA LINE CABLE
817 W Main St, Brownsville, WI 53006-1439
Tel (920) 583-3132 *Founded/Ownrshp* 1960
Sales 3.2MMM[E] *EMP* 5,000
Accts Grant Thornton Llp Appleton
SIC 1623 1771 1381 1629 3498 1794 Pipeline construction; Telephone & communication line construction; Foundation & footing contractor; Drilling oil & gas wells; Oil refinery construction; Fabricated pipe & fittings; Excavation work
Ch Bd: Ruth L Michels
**CEO:* Patrick D Michels
**CFO:* John Schroeder
**Ex VP:* Brian P Johnson
VP: Brad Eifert
VP: Tim McGuire
**VP:* Kevin Michels
**VP:* Tim Michels
VP: Troy Schneider
VP: Jack Westerman
VP: Bob Westphal
VP: Gary Ziehr

MICHELS MID-AMERICA LINE CABLE
See MICHELS CORP

D-U-N-S 02-758-7716 IMP
MICHELSEN PACKAGING CO OF CALIFORNIA
202 N 2nd Ave, Yakima, WA 98902-2625
Tel (509) 248-6270 *Founded/Ownrshp* 1964
Sales 96.3MM[E] *EMP* 175
SIC 5113 2653 Containers, paper & disposable plastic; Paper & products, wrapping or coarse; Pads, solid fiber: made from purchased materials
Pr: Dan Keck
**Ex VP:* Gary Gavin
Info Man: Dan Beddeson

D-U-N-S 60-636-0444 IMP/EXP
MICHIGAN AUTOMOTIVE COMPRESSOR INC
MACI
(*Suby of* TOYOTA INDUSTRIES CORPORATION)
2400 N Dearing Rd, Parma, MI 49269-9415
Tel (517) 622-7000 *Founded/Ownrshp* 1989
Sales 120.5MM[E] *EMP* 580[E]
SIC 3585 3714 3568 3563 Air conditioning, motor vehicle; Motor vehicle parts & accessories; Power transmission equipment; Air & gas compressors
Pr: Yuji Ishizaki
MIS Dir: Eric Chaney
QA Dir: Patrick Flahie
QA Dir: Jason Hoover
QA Dir: Matt Kunesh
QA Dir: Dawn Osullivan
Plnt Mgr: Gary Dods
Snr Mgr: Melissa Brodbeck

D-U-N-S 00-695-8524
■ **MICHIGAN BELL TELEPHONE CO**
AT&T MICHIGAN
(*Suby of* AT&T MIDWEST) ★
444 Michigan Ave, Detroit, MI 48226-2517
Tel (313) 223-9900 *Founded/Ownrshp* 1904
Sales 773.1MM[E] *EMP* 12,249
SIC 4813 8721 Local & long distance telephone communications; Local telephone communications; Billing & bookkeeping service
Pr: Gail Torreano

MICHIGAN CANCER FOUNDATION
See BARBARA ANN KARMANOS CANCER INSTITUTE

MICHIGAN CAT
See MACALLISTER MACHINERY CO INC

D-U-N-S 06-976-1146
MICHIGAN CITY AREA SCHOOLS
408 S Carroll Ave, Michigan City, IN 46360-5345
Tel (219) 873-2000 *Founded/Ownrshp* 1966
Sales 75.6MM[E] *EMP* 1,500
SIC 8211 Public elementary school; Public junior high school; Public senior high school
COO: Joan M Corick
**Treas:* Vincent Taylor
Prin: Richard Kirchner
Pr Dir: Wendel McCollum
HC Dir: Linda Bechinski

D-U-N-S 08-546-4295
MICHIGAN CONFERENCE OF TEAMSTERS WELFARE FUND
2700 Trumbull St, Detroit, MI 48216-1269
Tel (313) 964-2400 *Founded/Ownrshp* 1949
Sales NA *EMP* 96
Accts Plante & Moran Pllc Auburn Hi
SIC 6371 Union welfare, benefit & health funds
Ex Dir: Richard Burker
Dir IT: Sue Hamilton

D-U-N-S 36-205-1398
■ **MICHIGAN DAIRY LLC**
(*Suby of* KROGER CO) ★
29601 Industrial Rd, Livonia, MI 48150-2012
Tel (734) 367-5390 *Founded/Ownrshp* 1999
Sales 161.7MM[E] *EMP* 1[E]
SIC 5143 Dairy products, except dried or canned
IT Man: Matt Heywood

D-U-N-S 80-534-0056
MICHIGAN DEPARTMENT OF COMMUNITY HEALTH
201 Townsend St Fl 7, Lansing, MI 48933-1554
Tel (517) 241-1193 *Founded/Ownrshp* 1965
Sales NA *EMP* 4,000
SIC 9431

D-U-N-S 92-932-7880
MICHIGAN DEPARTMENT OF ENVIRONMENTAL QUALITY
MDEQ
(*Suby of* EXECUTIVE OFFICE OF STATE OF MICHIGAN) ★
525 W Allegan St, Lansing, MI 48933-1502
Tel (517) 284-6700 *Founded/Ownrshp* 1995
Sales NA *EMP* 1,100
SIC 9511 Air, water & solid waste management;

D-U-N-S 08-003-2707
MICHIGAN DEPARTMENT OF HEALTH & HUMAN SERVICES
MDHHS
(*Suby of* EXECUTIVE OFFICE OF STATE OF MICHIGAN) ★
201 Townsend St, Lansing, MI 48933-1551
Tel (517) 373-3740 *Founded/Ownrshp* 2015
Sales NA *EMP* 27,618^E
SIC 9431 9441 ; ; Administration of social & human resources

D-U-N-S 80-534-0163
MICHIGAN DEPARTMENT OF HUMAN SERVICES
235 S Grand Ave, Lansing, MI 48933-1805
Tel (517) 373-2000 *Founded/Ownrshp* 1965
Sales NA *EMP* 9,689
SIC 9441 8249

D-U-N-S 16-927-0662
MICHIGAN DEPARTMENT OF INFORMATION TECHNOLOGY
(*Suby of* EXECUTIVE OFFICE OF STATE OF MICHIGAN) ★
111 S Capitol Ave, Lansing, MI 48933-1555
Tel (517) 241-2000 *Founded/Ownrshp* 2003
Sales NA *EMP* 1,700
SIC 9111 City & town managers' offices;
Prin: Teri Takai
Dir IT: Kenneth D Theis

D-U-N-S 80-533-9439
MICHIGAN DEPARTMENT OF MILITARY AND VETERANS AFFAIRS
(*Suby of* EXECUTIVE OFFICE OF STATE OF MICHIGAN) ★
3411 N Martin Luther King, Lansing, MI 48906-2934
Tel (517) 481-8083 *Founded/Ownrshp* 1837
Sales NA *EMP* 14,500
SIC 9711 9451 National security; ; Administration of veterans' affairs;

D-U-N-S 80-533-9991
MICHIGAN DEPARTMENT OF NATURAL RESOURCES
(*Suby of* EXECUTIVE OFFICE OF STATE OF MICHIGAN) ★
525 W Allegan St, Lansing, MI 48933-1502
Tel (517) 284-5936 *Founded/Ownrshp* 1921
Sales NA *EMP* 1,800
SIC 9512

D-U-N-S 80-534-0247
MICHIGAN DEPARTMENT OF STATE POLICE
MICHIGAN STATE POLICE
(*Suby of* EXECUTIVE OFFICE OF STATE OF MICHIGAN) ★
7150 Harris Dr, Dimondale, MI 48821-5002
Tel (517) 241-1075 *Founded/Ownrshp* 1965
Sales NA *EMP* 2,600
SIC 9221 State police;
Ofcr: Monica Yesh
Genl Mgr: Doug Spitzley
Sys/Dir: Jime Cook
IT Man: Ramesh Devaram

D-U-N-S 80-534-0486
MICHIGAN DEPARTMENT OF TREASURY
(*Suby of* EXECUTIVE OFFICE OF STATE OF MICHIGAN) ★
430 W Allegan St, Lansing, MI 48933-1592
Tel (517) 373-3223 *Founded/Ownrshp* 1965
Sales NA *EMP* 1,200
SIC 9311 Finance, taxation & monetary policy;
Treas: Robert J Kleine
IT Man: Jana Therrian

D-U-N-S 08-832-7440
MICHIGAN EDUCATION SPECIAL SERVICES ASSOCIATION (MI)
1475 Kendale Blvd, East Lansing, MI 48823-2011
Tel (517) 332-2581 *Founded/Ownrshp* 1960
Sales NA *EMP* 325
SIC 6411 6321 Insurance agents, brokers & service; Accident & health insurance
Ex Dir: Cynthia Williams
* *Pr:* Sue Kelly
* *VP:* Jeff Nyquist
Ex Dir: Cynthia Irwin
Ex Dir: Cynthia Irwing

D-U-N-S 62-334-6095
MICHIGAN FARM BUREAU FINANCIAL CORP
(*Suby of* MICHIGAN FARM BUREAU)
7373 W Saginaw Hwy, Lansing, MI 48917-1124
Tel (517) 323-7000 *Founded/Ownrshp* 1990
Sales NA *EMP* 100
Accts Patrick H Blanchett Lansing
SIC 6311 6331 Life insurance; Automobile insurance; Property damage insurance
Pr: Wayne Wood
Mng Pt: Patrick Carpenter
* *Treas:* Thomas J Parker
* *Treas:* John Stindt

D-U-N-S 08-497-3748
MICHIGAN HEALTH ENDOWMENT FUND
330 Marshall St Ste 200, Lansing, MI 48912-2319
Tel (517) 374-0031 *Founded/Ownrshp* 2015
Sales 100.1MM *EMP* 2^E
SIC 8099 Health & allied services

CFO: Terry Gardner
Ofcr: Becky Cienki
Ofcr: Laurie Solotorow

D-U-N-S 00-538-2460
MICHIGAN MILK PRODUCERS ASSOCIATION
41310 Bridge St, Novi, MI 48375-1302
Tel (248) 474-6672 *Founded/Ownrshp* 1916
Sales 854.0MM *EMP* 200
Accts Cliftonlarsonallen Llp
SIC 5143 2023 2021 8611 2026 Milk & cream, fluid; Dried milk; Condensed milk; Creamery butter; Business associations; Fluid milk
CEO: John Dilland
* *Pr:* Kenneth Nobis
Treas: Eric Frahm
* *Treas:* C Velmar Green
* *VP:* Bob Kran

D-U-N-S 01-707-7355
■ **MICHIGAN OFFICE SOLUTIONS INC**
(*Suby of* GLOBAL IMAGING SYSTEMS INC) ★
2859 Walkent Dr Nw, Grand Rapids, MI 49544-1400
Tel (616) 459-1161 *Founded/Ownrshp* 2002
Sales 167.7MM^E *EMP* 215
SIC 5044 5045 7629 Office equipment; Computers, peripherals & software; Business machine repair, electric
Pr: Ralph Slider
* *CFO:* Charles Wooding
* *Ex VP:* Bill Orr III

D-U-N-S 05-205-2933 IMP
MICHIGAN PAVING AND MATERIALS CO
(*Suby of* OLDCASTLE MATERIALS GROUP) ★
2575 S Haggerty Rd # 100, Canton, MI 48188-2673
Tel (734) 397-2050 *Founded/Ownrshp* 1999
Sales 264.8MM^E *EMP* 600
SIC 1522 1541 2911 Residential construction; Industrial buildings, new construction; Asphalt or asphaltic materials, made in refineries
Pr: Dennis Rickard
COO: Allen Lindstrom
* *CFO:* Bill Brownell
* *CFO:* Gregg Campbell
* *VP:* Rick Becker
* *VP:* James Lindstrom
* *VP:* Robert Mayer
* *VP:* Andrew Schulz

D-U-N-S 06-587-9066
MICHIGAN PIZZA HUT INC
2053 Niles Rd, Saint Joseph, MI 49085-2505
Tel (269) 983-3888 *Founded/Ownrshp* 1970
Sales 45.6MM^E *EMP* 1,300
SIC 5812 Pizzeria, chain
Pr: Craig S Erickson
* *COO:* John C Brinker
* *VP:* Jeffrey White

D-U-N-S 12-131-1000 IMP/EXP
MICHIGAN SEAMLESS TUBE LLC
BLUE DIAMOND
(*Suby of* OPTIMA SPECIALTY STEEL INC) ★
400 Mcmunn St, South Lyon, MI 48178-1379
Tel (248) 486-0100 *Founded/Ownrshp* 2002
Sales 125.2MM^E *EMP* 280
SIC 3317 Tubes, seamless steel
* *Mng Pt:* Mark Hommel
CIO: Dick Doyle

D-U-N-S 01-709-3691 IMP
MICHIGAN SPORTING GOODS DISTRIBUTORS INC (MI)
MC SPORTS
3070 Shaffer Ave Se, Grand Rapids, MI 49512-1710
Tel (616) 942-2600 *Founded/Ownrshp* 1963, 1946
Sales 189.5MM^E *EMP* 1,300
SIC 5941 Sporting goods & bicycle shops
CEO: Bruce Ullery
VP: Ed Rix
VP: Rob Summerfield
VP: Dan Winchester
Store Mgr: Denise Ellshoff
Store Mgr: Chris Gilbert
Trfc Mgr: Karl Rinehart
Sls Mgr: John Mulligan

MICHIGAN STATE POLICE
See MICHIGAN DEPARTMENT OF STATE POLICE

D-U-N-S 05-334-3976 IMP
MICHIGAN STATE UNIVERSITY
426 Auditorium Rd Rm 301, East Lansing, MI 48824-2600
Tel (517) 355-5029 *Founded/Ownrshp* 1855
Sales 1.6MMM *EMP* 11,100
Accts Plante & Moran Pllc East Lans
SIC 8221 University
Ch: Joel I Ferguson
* *Pr:* Lou Anna K Simon
COO: Dunlap Jim
VP: Robert Groves
Exec: Kristin Anderson
Comm Dir: Stephanie Motschenbacher
Prin: Punyashloke Mishra
Ex Dir: Eric Doerr
Ex Dir: Irem Kiyak
Ex Dir: Barbara Sears
DP Exec: Gerry Felipe
Board of Directors: John Thelen

D-U-N-S 07-839-9219
MICHIGAN STATE UNIVERSITY FEDERAL CREDIT UNION
MSUFCU
3777 West Rd, East Lansing, MI 48823-8029
Tel (517) 333-2424 *Founded/Ownrshp* 1937
Sales NA *EMP* 371^E
Accts Crowe Horwath Llp Grand Rapid
SIC 6061 Federal credit unions
Pr: Patrick McPharlin
* *Ch Bd:* Thomas Scarlett
COO: April Clobes
* *Treas:* Thomas Dutch
* *V Ch Bd:* John Brick
Ofcr: Abby Dassance

Ofcr: Kristi Izzat
Ofcr: Jenny Smith
Ofcr: Jamie Zannini
VP: Ronda Bennett
VP: Sara Dolan
VP: Catherine Lynch
VP: Diana McFadden
VP: Al Scheffler

MICHIGAN SUGAR BEET GROWERS
See MICHIGAN SUGAR CO

D-U-N-S 10-320-4470 IMP
MICHIGAN SUGAR CO
MICHIGAN SUGAR BEET GROWERS
122 Uptown Dr Unit 300, Bay City, MI 48708-5627
Tel (989) 686-0161 *Founded/Ownrshp* 1906
Sales 600.0MM *EMP* 430
SIC 2063 Beet sugar
Pr: Mark Flegenheimer
* *CFO:* Brian Haraga
* *Ch:* Richard Gerstenberger
* *Treas:* Eugene Meylan
* *VP:* Charles Bauer
VP: Robert D Braem
* *VP:* Jerry Coleman
* *VP:* David Noble
* *VP:* Paul Pfenninger
* *VP:* James Ruhlman
* *VP:* Herb Wilson

D-U-N-S 06-545-3268
MICHIGAN TECHNOLOGICAL UNIVERSITY (MI)
1400 Townsend Dr, Houghton, MI 49931-1200
Tel (906) 487-1885 *Founded/Ownrshp* 1885
Sales 160.2MM *EMP* 1,939
Accts Rehmann Robson Llc Traverse C
SIC 8221 University
Pr: Glenn D Mroz
Pr: John Lehman
Pr: Beth Lunde
* *Pr:* Dr Glenn Dmroz
CFO: Daniel Greenlee
Ofcr: Ben Larson
Ofcr: Nathan Ruonavaara
Ofcr: Connie Scott
VP: Karla Aho
VP: Tim Beach
VP: David Dreed
VP: Dan Freiberg
VP: Nick Gravlin
VP: Kathy Halvorsen
VP: Josh Loukus
VP: Lesley Lovett-Doust
VP: Mariah Maggio
* *VP:* William J Mc Garry
VP: Helene Provost
VP: Gina Sayen
* *VP:* Max Seel

D-U-N-S 11-479-0210
MICHIGAN TURKEY PRODUCERS COOPERATIVE INC
2140 Chicago Dr Sw, Wyoming, MI 49519-1215
Tel (616) 245-2221 *Founded/Ownrshp* 1998
Sales 113.3MM^E *EMP* 575
SIC 2015 Turkey processing & slaughtering
Pr: Dan Lennon
* *CFO:* Brian Boerigter
QA Dir: Jason Hofman
Opers Mgr: Dave Heinrich

D-U-N-S 00-322-7188 EXP
MICKEY TRUCK BODIES INC (NC)
1305 Trinity Ave, High Point, NC 27260-8357
Tel (336) 882-6806 *Founded/Ownrshp* 1949, 1904
Sales 119.3MM^E *EMP* 400
SIC 3713 7532 3711 3715 Beverage truck bodies; Van bodies; Truck bodies (motor vehicles); Ambulance bodies; Body shop, trucks; Motor vehicles & car bodies; Truck trailers
Pr: H Dean Sink
* *CFO:* Greg Fisher
* *Ex VP:* Carl F Mickey Jr
VP: Wayne Childress
VP: Jim Hiatt
* *VP:* Kent Lapp
VP: Greg McLaughlin
Exec: Lisa Brunton
Exec: Bob Burdick
Rgnl Mgr: Dan Meyer
Genl Mgr: Sid Merrill

MICKY MART
See COLES ENERGY INC

MICON
See EARTH SUPPORT SERVICES INC

D-U-N-S 09-260-9585
MICREL INC
MICREL SEMICONDUCTOR
2180 Fortune Dr, San Jose, CA 95131-1815
Tel (408) 944-0800 *Founded/Ownrshp* 1978
Sales 247.5MM *EMP* 728^E
SIC 3674

D-U-N-S 07-995-3152
■ **MICREL LLC** (CA)
(*Suby of* MICROCHIP TECHNOLOGY INC) ★
2355 W Chandler Blvd, Chandler, AZ 85224-6199
Tel (480) 792-7200 *Founded/Ownrshp* 2015
Sales 92.4MM^E *EMP* 1,953^E
SIC 3674 Semiconductors & related devices
Pr: Steve Sanghi
COO: Ganesh Moorthy
CFO: J Eric Bjornholt
VP: Stephen V Drehobl
VP: Mitchell R Little
VP: Richard J Simoncic

MICREL SEMICONDUCTOR
See MICREL INC

MICRO CENTER
See MICRO ELECTRONICS INC

D-U-N-S 09-972-3066 IMP
MICRO ELECTRONICS INC
MICRO CENTER
4119 Leap Rd, Hilliard, OH 43026-1117
Tel (614) 850-3000 *Founded/Ownrshp* 1979
Sales 2.6MMM^E *EMP* 3,000
SIC 5045 5734 Computer peripheral equipment; Personal computers
Pr: Richard M Mershad
COO: Peggy Wolfe
CFO: John A Noble
VP: Kevin Hollingshead
Genl Mgr: Red Calub
Genl Mgr: Mark Hawes
Store Mgr: Jowayne Johnson
DP Exec: Chris Coneybeer
Merch Mgr: Scott Cortelletti
Sales Asso: Greg Wilson

D-U-N-S 04-076-0006
MICRO FOCUS (US) INC
(*Suby of* MICRO FOCUS INTERNATIONAL HOLDINGS LIMITED)
700 King Farm Blvd # 125, Rockville, MD 20850-5748
Tel (301) 838-5000 *Founded/Ownrshp* 2011
Sales 230.7MM^E *EMP* 400
SIC 7372 Business oriented computer software
Ch: Kevin Loosemore
CEO: Stephen Murdoch
COO: David Taylor
CFO: Mike Philips
Top Exec: Alison Baker
Sr VP: Luigi Bardelli
Sr VP: Mike Steinmetz
VP: Kenny Austin
VP: Joseph Bell
VP: Tom Bice
VP: Jim Bladich
VP: Seth Braverman
VP: Susan Drennan
VP: Bill Errico
VP: Chris Livesey
VP: Eric Pan
VP: Hugo Pullen
VP: Mike Sanford
VP: Michael Steinmetz
VP: Tod Tompkins
VP: Owen Williams

D-U-N-S 96-614-9887
MICRO HOLDING CORP
(*Suby of* HELLMAN & FRIEDMAN LLC) ★
1 Maritime Plz Fl 12, San Francisco, CA 94111-3502
Tel (415) 788-5111 *Founded/Ownrshp* 2010
Sales 182.3MM^E *EMP* 650
SIC 7374 7389 Computer graphics service; Advertising, promotional & trade show services
Pr: Warren Hellman

D-U-N-S 83-100-0021
MICRO METL CORP
3035 N Shadeland Ave # 300, Indianapolis, IN 46226-6281
Tel (800) 662-4822 *Founded/Ownrshp* 1965
Sales 87.9MM^E *EMP* 328
SIC 3444 Sheet metalwork
Pr: Gerald E Schultz
CFO: Mark Cohlman
CFO: Mark Kolmer
* *Prin:* Barbara E Schultz

D-U-N-S 06-729-5808 IMP/EXP
■ **MICRO MOTION INC**
(*Suby of* EECO INC) ★
7070 Winchester Cir, Boulder, CO 80301-3566
Tel (303) 530-8400 *Founded/Ownrshp* 1984
Sales 345.0MM^E *EMP* 1,023
SIC 3824 5084 Liquid meters; Industrial machinery & equipment
CEO: Andy Dudiak
VP: Ted Doering
VP: Andy Kolbeck
VP: Stanley Miller
VP: Jeff Nehr
VP: Paul Terry
VP: David Winder
CIO: Patrick Quinlan
Dir IT: Charles Stack
Tech Mgr: Geoffrey Lutz
Mktg Mgr: John Martin

MICRO P TECHNOLOGIES
See PCM SALES INC

D-U-N-S 00-514-2070 IMP
MICRO PLASTICS INC
111 Industry Ln, Flippin, AR 72634-8057
Tel (870) 453-8861 *Founded/Ownrshp* 1961
Sales 85.1MM^E *EMP* 400
SIC 3965 Fasteners
Pr: Tom Hill
* *Ex VP:* Marilyn H Hill
VP: Nueboch Vandermast
QC Dir: Jacki Due

MICRO SOLUTIONS ENTERPRISES
See WBI INC

MICROTECH
See STARKEY LABORATORIES INC

MICROAGE
See FRONTIER TECHNOLOGY LLC

D-U-N-S 04-819-2892
MICROBAC LABORATORIES INC
101 Bellevue Rd Ste 301, Pittsburgh, PA 15229-2132
Tel (412) 459-1060 *Founded/Ownrshp* 1969
Sales 161.7MM^E *EMP* 600
SIC 8734 Testing laboratories
Ch: J Trevor Boyce
* *CEO:* N Cabot Earle
* *COO:* Robert Crookston
VP: Ronald Sanders
Dir Lab: Nancy G Burnett
Dir Lab: Tom Zierenberg
Mng Dir: Rob Dermer
Prgrm Mgr: Chad Barnes
Div Mgr: Christine Pechacek

Div Mgr: Manish Shekhawat
Genl Mgr: Andrew Harris

D-U-N-S 18-691-7969 IMP
▲ MICROCHIP TECHNOLOGY INC
2355 W Chandler Blvd, Chandler, AZ 85224-6199
Tel (480) 792-7200 *Founded/Ownrshp* 1989
Sales 2.1MMM *EMP* 9,766
Accts Ernst & Young Llp Phoenix Ar
Tkr Sym MCHP *Exch* NGS
SIC 3674 Semiconductors & related devices
CEO: Steve Sanghi
**Pr:* Ganesh Moorthy
**CFO:* J Eric Bjornholt
Ex VP: Marcella Soloway
VP: Mathew Bunker
VP: Ron Cates
**VP:* Stephen V Drehobl
VP: Sudarshan Iyengar
VP: Bryan Liddiard
**VP:* Mitchell R Little
VP: Mitchell Little
VP: Gary Marsh
VP: Sumit K Mitra
VP: Mitch Obolsky
VP: Mark W Reiten
VP: Nawaz Sharif
**VP:* Richard J Simoncic
VP: Robert Williams
VP: Ian Yue
Dir Soc: Kristina Johnson
Board of Directors: Matthew W Chapman, L B Day, Esther L Johnson, Wade F Meyercord

D-U-N-S 00-118-9935 IMP/EXP
MICROFIBRES INC
124 Washington St Ste 101, Foxboro, MA 02035-1368
Tel (401) 725-4883 *Founded/Ownrshp* 1926
Sales 178.8MM^E *EMP* 1,080
SIC 2221 2295 5131 2262 Upholstery fabrics, manmade fiber & silk; Coated fabrics, not rubberized; Upholstery fabrics, woven; Printing: manmade fiber & silk broadwoven fabrics
Pr: James R McCulloch
COO: Bill Laird
**CFO:* Maryann Baron

D-U-N-S 12-215-3799 IMP
■ MICROGENICS CORP
(*Suby of* THERMO FISHER SCIENTIFIC INC) ★
46500 Kato Rd, Fremont, CA 94538-7310
Tel (510) 979-9147 *Founded/Ownrshp* 2006
Sales 433.4MM^E *EMP* 6,076
SIC 2834 Proprietary drug products
CEO: Seth H Hoogasian
**Pr:* David Rubinfien
VP: Azeem Syed

D-U-N-S 02-171-7962
MICROGROUP INC
ALL TUBE DIV
(*Suby of* K C P) ★
7 Industrial Park Rd, Medway, MA 02053-1732
Tel (508) 533-4925 *Founded/Ownrshp* 2005
Sales 135.8MM^E *EMP* 150
SIC 5051 3312 3498 3494 3492 3317 Metals service centers & offices; Tubes, steel & iron; Fabricated pipe & fittings; Valves & pipe fittings; Fluid power valves & hose fittings; Steel pipe & tubes
Pr: William J Bergen
**CFO:* Geoff Holczer
VP: Keith Miller
VP: Edward Perry
QA Dir: Tony Tran
IT Man: John Sorgert
VP Opers: Alex Magyar
Opers Mgr: Bob Donnelly
Ql Cn Mgr: John Slavin
Sales Asso: Nicole Nault

MICROLEASE
See METRIC EQUIPMENT SALES INC

D-U-N-S 08-940-0977
MICROLEASE INC
(*Suby of* MICROLEASE PLC)
9221 Globe Center Dr # 105, Morrisville, NC 27560-6205
Tel (866) 520-0200 *Founded/Ownrshp* 2001
Sales 97.7MM^E *EMP* 250
SIC 7359 Equipment rental & leasing
VP: Gordon Curwen
CEO: Michael E Clark
VP: Vince Petrecca
Natl Sales: Jim Carney
Manager: Nicole Crossman

D-U-N-S 62-673-2213
MICRON HOLDINGS INC
4436 Broadmoor Ave Se, Kentwood, MI 49512-5305
Tel (616) 698-0707 *Founded/Ownrshp* 2004
Sales 85.3MM^E *EMP* 2,612
SIC 3714 Motor vehicle parts & accessories
VP: John F X Daly
Pr: John C Kennedy
COO: John R Buchan
COO: Eduardo Renner De Castilho
COO: Jonathan B Degaynor
CFO: Warren A Veltman
VP: Jack Daly
VP: James A Hislop
VP: Adrian Jones
VP: Thomas K O'Mara
VP: Richard J Peters

D-U-N-S 03-648-0788 IMP
■ MICRON SEMICONDUCTOR PRODUCTS INC
(*Suby of* MICRON TECHNOLOGY INC) ★
8000 S Federal Way, Boise, ID 83716-9632
Tel (208) 368-4000 *Founded/Ownrshp* 1996
Sales 309.3MM^E *EMP* 550
SIC 5065 Semiconductor devices
Pr: Michael W Sadler
Pr: Brian Kalisek
Pr: Michael Knapp
COO: Mark Adams
Ex Dir: Dee K Mooney
Prgrm Mgr: Jennifer Glenday

Snr Sftwr: Tieniu LI
CIO: Dee Ogden
Dir IT: Tony Holden
Dir IT: Jeffrey King
IT Man: Dave Curtis

D-U-N-S 09-312-0871
▲ MICRON TECHNOLOGY INC
8000 S Federal Way, Boise, ID 83716-7128
Tel (208) 368-4000 *Founded/Ownrshp* 1978
Sales 12.4MMM *EMP* 31,800
Tkr Sym MU *Exch* NGS
SIC 3674 Semiconductors & related devices; Random access memory (RAM)
CEO: D Mark Durcan
**Ch Bd:* Robert E Switz
CFO: Ernest E Maddock
VP: Steven P Arnold
VP: Scott J Deboer
VP: Eric Endebrock
VP: Hideki Gomi
VP: Dean Klein
VP: Robert Peglar
VP: Joel L Poppen
VP: Brian M Shirley
VP: Steven L Thorsen Jr
Board of Directors: Robert L Bailey, Richard M Beyer, Patrick J Byrne, D Warren A East, Mercedes Johnson, Lawrence N Mondry

D-U-N-S 07-911-8736
MICROPORT ORTHOPEDICS INC
(*Suby of* SHANGHAI MICROPORT MEDICAL (GROUP) CO., LTD.)
5677 Airline Rd, Arlington, TN 38002-9501
Tel (866) 872-0211 *Founded/Ownrshp* 2014
Sales 243.3MM^E *EMP* 550^E
SIC 5047 Medical equipment & supplies; Orthopedic equipment & supplies
Pr: Yan Zhang
**CFO:* Hongbin Sun
Ofcr: John Knighton
**Sr VP:* Jonathan Chen
**Sr VP:* Kongrong Karl Pan
VP: Michael Carroll
VP: Ken Glatzer
VP: Todd Smith
VP: Eric Stookey
**VP:* Xu Yimin
CIO: Jimmy Berry

D-U-N-S 09-240-2726
■ MICROS SYSTEMS INC (MD)
(*Suby of* OC ACQUISITION LLC) ★
7031 Columbia Gateway Dr # 1, Columbia, MD 21046-2583
Tel (443) 285-6000 *Founded/Ownrshp* 1977, 2014
Sales 794.9MM^E *EMP* 6,506
SIC 7373 7372 3577 3578 Computer integrated systems design; Business oriented computer software; Computer peripheral equipment; Calculating & accounting equipment
Pr: Peter A Altabef
Ch Bd: A L Giannopoulos
CFO: Cynthia A Russo
Ofcr: Carlos Echalar
Ex VP: John E Gularson
Ex VP: Jennifer M Kurdle
Ex VP: Thomas L Patz
Ex VP: Stefan M Piringer
Ex VP: Peter J Rogers Jr
Sr VP: Ed Chapel
Sr VP: Jay Upchurch
VP: Russell Butler
VP: Christian Guinzburg
VP: Martin Hawkes
VP: Robin Layman
VP: Charles McGuire
VP: Michael P Russo
VP: Marc Schmalenberg
VP: James T Walsh
Exec: Michael Thummel
Dir Bus: Garrett Stom

D-U-N-S 05-155-0838
▲ MICROSEMI CORP
1 Enterprise, Aliso Viejo, CA 92656-2606
Tel (949) 380-6100 *Founded/Ownrshp* 1960
Sales 1.6MMM *EMP* 4,400
Accts Pricewaterhousecoopers Llp I
Tkr Sym MSCC *Exch* NGS
SIC 3674 Semiconductors & related devices; Rectifiers, solid state; Zener diodes; Diodes, solid state (germanium, silicon, etc.)
Ch Bd: James J Peterson
Pr: Paul H Pickle
CFO: John W Hohener
Ex VP: Steven G Litchfield
Sr VP: David Goren
Board of Directors: Kimberly Alexy, Thomas R Anderson, William E Bendush, Paul F Folino, William L Healey, Dennis R Leibel, Matthew E Massengill

D-U-N-S 80-772-8431
■ MICROSEMI CORP - ANALOG MIXED SIGNAL GROUP
LINFINITY MICROELECTRONICS
(*Suby of* MICROSEMI CORP) ★
11861 Western Ave, Garden Grove, CA 92841-2119
Tel (714) 898-8121 *Founded/Ownrshp* 1999
Sales 252.9MM^E *EMP* 1,300^E
SIC 3674 Semiconductor circuit networks
CEO: James Peterson
**COO:* Paul Pickle
**CFO:* John Hohener
**Ex VP:* Russ Garcia
**Dir Sec:* Steve Litchfield
**CTO:* Jim Aralis

D-U-N-S 00-824-8593 IMP
■ MICROSEMI FREQUENCY AND TIME CORP
(*Suby of* MICROSEMI CORP) ★
3870 N 1st St, San Jose, CA 95134-1702
Tel (408) 428-6993 *Founded/Ownrshp* 2001
Sales 197.0MM^E *EMP* 544
SIC 3625 7372 Timing devices, electronic; Business oriented computer software

CEO: Steven G Litchfield
**CEO:* Liz Fetter
Ex VP: Bill Minor
Ex VP: Daniel L Scharre
Genl Mgr: Heera Lee
Sftwr Eng: Manika Goyal
Sftwr Eng: Jay Inamdar

D-U-N-S 14-822-2045 IMP
■ MICROSEMI SOC CORP
(*Suby of* MICROSEMI CORP) ★
3870 N 1st St, San Jose, CA 95134-1702
Tel (408) 643-6000 *Founded/Ownrshp* 1985
Sales 111.6MM^E *EMP* 550^E
SIC 3674 7371 Microcircuits, integrated (semiconductor); Computer software development
CEO: James J Peterson
**CFO:* John W Hohener
**Sr VP:* Esmat Z Hamdy
**Sr VP:* Fares N Mubarak
VP: Rich Brossart
**VP:* David L Van De Hey
VP: David De Hey
VP: Doug Goodyear
VP: Dennis Nye
VP: Mike Pardini
VP Mktg: Richard Kapusta

D-U-N-S 10-276-5476
■ MICROSEMI STORAGE SOLUTIONS INC
(*Suby of* MICROSEMI CORP) ★
1380 Bordeaux Dr, Sunnyvale, CA 94089-1005
Tel (408) 239-8000 *Founded/Ownrshp* 2016
Sales 525.6MM *EMP* 1,442^E
SIC 3674 Semiconductors & related devices; Modules, solid state; Microcircuits, integrated (semiconductor)
Pr: Paul Pickle
CFO: John W Hohener
VP: Alinka Flaminia
VP: Ken Wagner
Sftwr Eng: John Lloyd
Mktg Mgr: Rachel Lin
Mktg Mgr: Dinsmore Michael
Snr Mgr: Daniel Chan
Snr Mgr: Alex Cochran
Snr Mgr: Radjendirane Codandaramane
Snr Mgr: Calvin Hass

D-U-N-S 08-146-6849
▲ MICROSOFT CORP (WA)
1 Microsoft Way, Redmond, WA 98052-8300
Tel (425) 882-8080 *Founded/Ownrshp* 1975
Sales 85.3MMM *EMP* 114,000
Tkr Sym MSFT *Exch* NGS
SIC 7372 7371 3577 7375 Prepackaged software; Operating systems computer software; Business oriented computer software; Application computer software; Computer software development; Computer peripheral equipment; Information retrieval services
CEO: Satya Nadella
**Ch Bd:* John W Thompson
Pr: Jean-Philippe Courtois
CFO: Amy E Hood
Chf Mktg O: Christopher C Capossela
Ex VP: Kathleen T Hogan
Ex VP: Margaret L Johnson
VP: Sue Bevington
VP: Cesar Cernuda
VP: Chuck Chan
VP: Arthur De Haan
VP: Kurt Delbene
VP: Brian Macdonald
VP: Jack Martin
VP: Joe Matz
VP: Shaun M McCarthy
VP: Tuula Rytil
VP: Gaurav Sareen
VP: Bharat Shah
VP: Frank Shaw
VP: Michael Tremblay

D-U-N-S 83-695-4123 IMP
■ MICROSOFT NETWORK L L C
(*Suby of* MICROSOFT CORP) ★
1 Microsoft Way, Redmond, WA 98052-8300
Tel (425) 538-2948 *Founded/Ownrshp* 1996
Sales 3.9MMM^E *EMP* 2,852^E
SIC 4813 ;
Top Exec: Frank Shaw
Ex VP: Sarah Kennedy
VP: David Kubelka
Dir Sec: Ned Curic
Prgrm Mgr: Eric Fitzgerald
Prgrm Mgr: Diego Tamburini
Prgrm Mgr: Russell Wilson
CTO: Bryce Cogswell
Mktg Mgr: Justin Rice

D-U-N-S 62-289-5613
▲ MICROSTRATEGY INC
1850 Towers Crescent Plz # 700, Tysons Corner, VA 22182-6231
Tel (703) 848-8600 *Founded/Ownrshp* 1989
Sales 529.8MM *EMP* 1,947
Tkr Sym MSTR *Exch* NGS
SIC 7372 7371 Prepackaged software; Application computer software; Computer software systems analysis & design, custom
Ch Bd: Michael J Saylor
CFO: Phong Q Le
Ex VP: Paul Zolfaghari
VP: Flavio Bolieiro
VP: Stephen Bruggers
VP: Doug Everhart
VP: Tim Lang
VP: Brian Reitenauer
VP: Glen Schulenburg
VP: Bob Sharman
Exec: Timothy E Lang
Exec: David J Rennyson
Exec: W Ming Shao
Exec: Michael S Tae
Board of Directors: Robert H Epstein, Stephen X Graham, Jarrod M Patten, Carl J Rickertsen

D-U-N-S 14-545-4182
MICROTECHNOLOGIES LLC
8330 Boone Blvd Ste 600, Vienna, VA 22182-2658
Tel (703) 891-1073 *Founded/Ownrshp* 2004

Sales 95.1MM *EMP* 425
SIC 7379 Computer related consulting services
Pr: Anthony R Jimenez
CFO: David A Hinson
CFO: Lynn Wasylina
Ex VP: Rusty Lingenfelter
Ex VP: Steve Truitt
Sr VP: Rod McKinley

D-U-N-S 18-857-7050 IMP/EXP
■ MICROTEK MEDICAL HOLDINGS INC
(*Suby of* ECOLAB INC) ★
13000 Drfeld Pkwy Ste 300, Alpharetta, GA 30004
Tel (678) 896-4400 *Founded/Ownrshp* 2007
Sales 202.2MM^E *EMP* 1,863
SIC 3842 Surgical appliances & supplies; Surgical appliances & supplies; Sterilizers, hospital & surgical; Cotton & cotton applicators
CEO: Martha Goldberg Aronson
COO: Mark J Alvarez
CFO: Ching Meng Chew
CFO: Roger G Wilson
Bd of Dir: Ronald Smorada
VP: Amy Levinson
VP: Peter Schmitt
VP: David Velmosky
Prin: Timothy Mulhere
Board of Directors: Kenneth F Davis, Michael E Glasscock III, Gene R McGrevin, Marc R Sarni, Ronald L Smorada

D-U-N-S 10-690-8437 IMP/EXP
■ MICROTEK MEDICAL INC
(*Suby of* MICROTEK MEDICAL HOLDINGS INC) ★
512 N Lehmberg Rd, Columbus, MS 39702-4464
Tel (662) 327-1863 *Founded/Ownrshp* 1996
Sales 222.2MM^E *EMP* 1,087
SIC 3841 Surgical & medical instruments
Pr: Dan R Lee
COO: Mark J Alverez
VP: Tico Capote
VP: Robin Humble
VP: Gary Moses
VP: Debbie Wooley
Plng Mgr: Bert Rector
Natl Sales: Mark Gardner
Mktg Dir: Mary Ann Whitlock
Snr Mgr: Carol Pack-Walden

MICROUNITED DIVISION
See ESSENDANT CO

D-U-N-S 00-326-3105 IMP
MICROVENTION INC
MICROVENTION TERUMO
(*Suby of* TERUMO AMERICAS HOLDING INC) ★
1311 Valencia Ave, Tustin, CA 92780-6447
Tel (714) 258-8001 *Founded/Ownrshp* 1997, 2006
Sales 233.8MM^E *EMP* 737^E
SIC 3841 Surgical & medical instruments
Pr: Richard Cappetpa
**COO:* William R Hughes
**Sr VP:* Glenn Latham
**VP:* Rob Green
VP: Rob Greene
**VP:* Philip Harvey
**VP:* Cherie Henket
**VP:* Jun Hoshino
VP: Todd Zive
Exec: Bill Hughes
Genl Mgr: Linn Pearce

MICROVENTION TERUMO
See MICROVENTION INC

MID AM
See MID-AM BUILDING SUPPLY INC

D-U-N-S 11-811-7522
MID AMERICA CORP
BURGER KING
2812 N Broadway St, Knoxville, TN 37917-3834
Tel (865) 524-3477 *Founded/Ownrshp* 1982
Sales 22.9MM^E *EMP* 1,000
SIC 5812 Fast-food restaurant, chain
Pr: Merritt C Fore Jr
**Sec:* Gene B Camp
**VP:* Russ Seus

MID ATLANTIC CARS
See BROWN AUTOMOTIVE GROUP LTD

D-U-N-S 18-854-7145
■ MID ATLANTIC MEDICAL SERVICES LLC
(*Suby of* UNITEDHEALTH GROUP INC) ★
800 King Farm Blvd # 600, Rockville, MD 20850-5979
Tel (301) 990-3844 *Founded/Ownrshp* 2004
Sales NA *EMP* 3,315
SIC 6324 Health maintenance organization (HMO), insurance only
Ch Bd: Mark D Groban MD
Pr: Thomas Barbera
Sr VP: Debbie J Hulen
Exec: Robert E Foss

D-U-N-S 11-550-3448
MID CITY MEDICAL CENTER
3600 Florida Blvd, Baton Rouge, LA 70806-3842
Tel (225) 387-7000 *Founded/Ownrshp* 1999
Sales 14.1MM^E *EMP* 3,000
SIC 8062 General medical & surgical hospitals
Pr: William Holman
**Ex VP:* Dionne Viator

MID COAST HEALTH SERVICES
See MID COAST-PARKVIEW HEALTH

D-U-N-S 07-173-2523
MID COAST HOSPITAL
123 Medical Center Dr, Brunswick, ME 04011-2652
Tel (207) 373-6000 *Founded/Ownrshp* 1907
Sales 147.3MM *EMP* 1,000^E
SIC 8062 General medical & surgical hospitals
CEO: Herbert Paris
Chf Path: Ramesh Gaindh
Chf Rad: Jaime Kline
CFO: Robert McCue
Dir Inf Cn: Lorna Mackinnon
Dir Rx: Sue Fraser
Prac Mgr: Marcia A Smith

Off Mgr: Leeann Smith
Dir QC: Carolyn Koepke
Mtls Dir: Rita Renaud
Surgeon: Mia H Marietta

D-U-N-S 18-068-1488
MID COAST-PARKVIEW HEALTH
MID COAST HEALTH SERVICES
123 Medical Center Dr G, Brunswick, ME 04011-2652
Tel (207) 729-0181 *Founded/Ownrshp* 1987
Sales 8.0M *EMP* 1,500
Accts Baker Newman & Noyes Portland
SIC 8062 8082 8051 General medical & surgical hospitals; Home health care services; Skilled nursing care facilities
Pr: Herbert Paris
VP: Joe Grant
**VP:* Robert McCue
**VP:* Philip Ortolani
VP: Lois Skillings
Dir Bus: Sue Frasier
**Prin:* Kathy Arsenault
Prac Mgr: Fran Fontanez
Prac Mgr: Celeste Moreau
Off Mgr: Leeann Smith
Mtls Dir: Rita Renaud

MID CONTINENT CABINETRY
See NORCRAFT COMPANIES LP

MID CONTINENT WAREHOUSE CO
See LUIGINOS INC

D-U-N-S 02-202-1315
MID IOWA COOPERATIVE
201 S Main St, Conrad, IA 50621-7757
Tel (641) 366-2740 *Founded/Ownrshp* 1907
Sales 108.3MM^E *EMP* 60
Accts Meriwether Wilson And Company
SIC 5153 5191 2048 Grains; Seeds: field, garden & flower; Feed; Fertilizer & fertilizer materials; Prepared feeds
Pr: Hank Miller
**CFO:* Shane Coughenour
**Ex Dir:* Cliss Kitzman

MID NEBRASKA LUBRICANTS
See COOPERATIVE PRODUCERS INC

D-U-N-S 10-412-2408
MID OAKS INVESTMENTS LLC
750 W Lake Cook Rd # 460, Buffalo Grove, IL 60089-2090
Tel (847) 215-3475 *Founded/Ownrshp* 1997
Sales 710.7MM^E *EMP* 1,655
SIC 6726 3089 Investment offices; Plastic kitchenware, tableware & houseware
CEO: Wayne C Kocourek
**Pr:* Michael A Kocourek
**CFO:* David A Boyle
VP: Christopher Willis
**Mng Dir:* David L Crouch

D-U-N-S 16-908-4790 EXP
■ MID PAC PETROLEUM LLC
PAR HAWAII
(*Suby of* KOKO OHA INVESTMENTS INC) ★
1132 Bishop St Ste 2500, Honolulu, HI 96813-2864
Tel (808) 535-5999 *Founded/Ownrshp* 2003
Sales 110.4MM^E *EMP* 650^E
SIC 5984 5172 Liquefied petroleum gas dealers; Gases, liquefied petroleum (propane)
Dir Bus: Keith Yoshida
Sls Mgr: Russell Whang

D-U-N-S 12-464-9232
MID SOUTH LUMBER INC
1115 C St, Meridian, MS 39301-5436
Tel (601) 483-4389 *Founded/Ownrshp* 1999
Sales 600.0MM *EMP* 150
SIC 2411 Logging
CEO: Ross York

D-U-N-S 03-551-5162
MID SOUTH SALES INC (AR)
BULK WAREHOUSE
243 County Road 414, Jonesboro, AR 72404-7508
Tel (870) 933-6457 *Founded/Ownrshp* 1962, 2012
Sales 156.6MM *EMP* 95
Accts Mayer Hoffman Mccann Pc Mem
SIC 5172 Petroleum products
Pr: Murray Benton Jr
**CFO:* Allen Crisp
Brnch Mgr: Chuck Preslar
Genl Mgr: Victoria Livingston
Off Mgr: Leonard Sharp
Plnt Mgr: Thomas Handy
Sls Mgr: Jim Sugg

D-U-N-S 04-700-3165
■ MID STATE AUTOMOTIVE DISTRIBUTORS INC
THE PARTS DIVISION
(*Suby of* OREILLY AUTO PARTS) ★
485 Craighead St, Nashville, TN 37204-2333
Tel (615) 383-8566 *Founded/Ownrshp* 2001
Sales 58.7MM^E *EMP* 1,000
SIC 5013 5531 Automotive supplies & parts; Automotive parts
CEO: David O'Reilly
**Ch Bd:* Lawrence P O'Reilly
**CFO:* James R Batten
IT Man: Cliff Dunn

D-U-N-S 10-340-2608
MID VALLEY AGRICULTURAL SERVICES INC
16401 E Highway 26, Linden, CA 95236-9746
Tel (209) 931-7600 *Founded/Ownrshp* 1983
Sales 208.4MM^E *EMP* 125
Accts Croce & Company Stockton Cal
SIC 5191 Chemicals, agricultural
Pr: Larry Beck
**VP:* Pete Bulthuis
Opers Mgr: Randy Northcutt
Opers Mgr: Gene Silveria

D-U-N-S 15-508-4028
MID VALLEY HEALTH SYSTEM
1401 E 8th St, Weslaco, TX 78596-6640
Tel (956) 969-5112 *Founded/Ownrshp* 1996
Sales 109.5MM *EMP* 1,000
Accts Bkd Llp Houston Tx
SIC 6719 Investment holding companies, except banks
Pr: Robert W Vanderveer
**CFO:* Curtis Haley

MID VALLEY I P A
See MID VALLEY IPA INC

D-U-N-S 83-138-3443
MID VALLEY IPA INC
MID VALLEY I P A
2995 Ryan Dr Se Ste 200, Salem, OR 97301-5157
Tel (503) 371-7701 *Founded/Ownrshp* 1976
Sales 245.4MM *EMP* 200
SIC 8011 Primary care medical clinic
Pr: Steven Paulissen
**CFO:* Dean Andretta

MID VALLEY PRODUCTS
See EURPAC SERVICE INC

MID WEST HOLDINGS
See MIDAMERICA DIVISION INC

MID WEST RAILROAD TIE SALES
See NATIONAL SALVAGE & SERVICE CORP

D-U-N-S 02-991-7945 IMP/EXP
MID-AM BUILDING SUPPLY INC
MID AM
1615 Omar Bradley Rd, Moberly, MO 65270-9406
Tel (660) 263-2140 *Founded/Ownrshp* 1967
Sales 258.9MM^E *EMP* 400
SIC 5031 Building materials, exterior; Building materials, interior; Millwork
Pr: Joseph F Knaebel
CFO: John Rakers
Treas: James Deresinski
VP: Lilly Elliott
VP: Alan Knaebel
Sales Asso: Keene Saxon
Sales Asso: Tom Scarborough
Sales Asso: Brian Wilson

D-U-N-S 08-953-5694
▲ MID-AMERICA APARTMENT COMMUNITIES INC
MAA
6584 Poplar Ave, Memphis, TN 38138-3687
Tel (901) 682-6600 *Founded/Ownrshp* 1977
Sales 1.0MMM *EMP* 1,949^E
Tkr Sym MAA *Exch* NYS
SIC 6798 Real estate investment trusts
Ch Bd: H Eric Bolton Jr
COO: Thomas L Grimes Jr
CFO: Albert M Campbell III
Sr Cor Off: Rebecca Wade
Ex VP: Robert J Delpriore
Ex VP: Ed Wright
VP: Rick Barton
VP: Jon King
VP: Tilea Terry
VP: Cynthia Thompson
VP: Leslie Wolfgang
Board of Directors: Alan B Graf Jr, James K Lowder, Thomas H Lowder, Monica McGurk, Claude B Nielsen, Philip W Norwood, W Reid Sanders, William B Sansom, Gary Shorb

D-U-N-S 05-341-4877
■ MID-AMERICA APARTMENTS LP
(*Suby of* MAA) ★
6584 Poplar Ave, Germantown, TN 38138-3687
Tel (866) 620-1130 *Founded/Ownrshp* 1993
Sales 363.3MM^E *EMP* 1,949^E
Accts Securities And Exchange Commis
SIC 6798 Real estate investment trusts
Genl Pt: Mid-America Apartment Communit

D-U-N-S 10-762-8158 IMP
MID-AMERICA OVERSEAS INC
M A O
650 E Devon Ave Ste 150, Itasca, IL 60143-1265
Tel (630) 285-9083 *Founded/Ownrshp* 1976
Sales 93.6MM^E *EMP* 200^E
SIC 4731 Foreign freight forwarding; Customhouse brokers
CEO: Minte Stienstra
**Pr:* Burkard Schmitt
**CFO:* Michael Mierwinski
Brnch Mgr: Milo Ott
Brnch Mgr: Resa Silcox
Brnch Mgr: Vickie Slotuik

D-U-N-S 14-523-7876
MID-AMERICA PIPELINE CO LLC
(*Suby of* ENTERPRISE PRODUCTS CO) ★
1100 La St Ste 1000, Houston, TX 77002
Tel (713) 880-6500 *Founded/Ownrshp* 2002
Sales 105.2MM^E *EMP* 250^E
SIC 4922 Pipelines, natural gas
Pr: J M Collingsworth
Treas: Bryan F Bulawa
Sr VP: Michael J Knesek
Plnt Mgr: David Zaffuto

D-U-N-S 84-850-5582
■ MID-AMERICA TELEPHONE INC
TDS
(*Suby of* TDS TELECOMMUNICATIONS CORP) ★
110 W 5th St, Stonewall, OK 74871
Tel (608) 831-1000 *Founded/Ownrshp* 1992
Sales 853.0MM *EMP* 2,700
SIC 4813 Data telephone communications
Pr: David Wittwer
Sec: Debbie Meier

D-U-N-S 96-834-7281
MID-ATLANTIC HEALTH CARE LLC
1922 Greenspring Dr Ste 3, Lutherville Timonium, MD 21093-7603
Tel (410) 308-2300 *Founded/Ownrshp* 2003
Sales 937.2MM^E *EMP* 2,521^E
SIC 8062 General medical & surgical hospitals
CFO: Scott D Potter

D-U-N-S 80-497-3295
MID-ATLANTIC HOME HEALTH NETWORK INC
25 Winchester St, Warrenton, VA 20186-2825
Tel (540) 347-4901 *Founded/Ownrshp* 1982
Sales 25.7MM^E *EMP* 2,000
SIC 8082 Home health care services
Ch Bd: Phillip Warman
CFO: Chich Gilpin

MID-ATLNTIC CONVENIENCE STORES
See UPPYS CONVENIENCE STORES INC

D-U-N-S 00-379-3239
MID-CAROLINA ELECTRIC COOPERATIVE INC (SC)
254 Longs Pond Rd, Lexington, SC 29071
Tel (803) 749-6400 *Founded/Ownrshp* 1940
Sales 120.5MM *EMP* 143
Accts Mcnair Mclemore Midd Ebrooks &
SIC 4911 Distribution, electric power
CEO: B Robert Paulling
**CFO:* Theresa Crepes
**VP:* Lee Ayers
**VP:* Troy Simpson
**VP:* Keith Sturkie
**VP:* Bobby Wilbur
Board of Directors: J Carey Bedenbaugh Jr, Eddie C Best Jr, Kenneth V Frick, Lavenia D Hentz, J Allan Risinger, Clifford B Shealy, Marvin W Sox, Justin B Watts

D-U-N-S 84-948-0293
MID-CITY TRUCK DRIVING ACADEMY INC
AUTOMBILE DRIVING INSTRUCTIONS
6740 W Belmont Ave, Chicago, IL 60634-4649
Tel (773) 725-3000 *Founded/Ownrshp* 2007
Sales 12.7MM^E *EMP* 2,007
SIC 8299 5511 Automobile driving instruction; Trucks, tractors & trailers: new & used
Pr: Jan Nikos

D-U-N-S 04-627-4452
MID-COAST ELECTRIC SUPPLY INC
1801 Stolz St, Victoria, TX 77901-6299
Tel (361) 575-6311 *Founded/Ownrshp* 1980
Sales 99.2MM^E *EMP* 95
SIC 5063 Electrical supplies
Pr: Steve Barker
**VP:* Thomas C Barker
Sls Dir: Glen Jamerson
Sales Asso: Melissa Adcox
Sales Asso: Frank Bettencourt
Sales Asso: Carolyn Hamilton
Sales Asso: Monica Huddleston
Sales Asso: Modesto Paradero
Sales Asso: Colt Roberts

D-U-N-S 05-097-2314
MID-COLUMBIA MEDICAL CENTER
MCMC
1700 E 19th St, The Dalles, OR 97058-3398
Tel (541) 296-1111 *Founded/Ownrshp* 1944
Sales 109.7MM *EMP* 944
SIC 8062 8011 Hospital, affiliated with AMA residency; Offices & clinics of medical doctors
Pr: Duane W Francis
Ex VP: Dianne Storby
**VP:* Don Arbon
VP: Erick Larson
VP: Randy Skov
Dir Rad: Michael Capek
Dir Rx: Robert Pollard
CTO: Marsha Davis
IT Man: Tom Cunningham
Pathlgst: Hahn Huang

D-U-N-S 96-908-0204
▲ MID-CON ENERGY PARTNERS LP
2431 E 61st St Ste 850, Tulsa, OK 74136-1261
Tel (972) 479-5980 *Founded/Ownrshp* 2011
Sales 96.2MM *EMP* 90^E
Accts Grant Thornton Llp Tulsa Okl
Tkr Sym MCEP *Exch* NGM
SIC 1311 Crude petroleum & natural gas
CEO: Jeffery R Olmstead
Genl Pt: Mid-Con Energy GP
CFO: Michael D Peterson
CFO: Michael Peterson

D-U-N-S 00-790-7678
■ MID-CONTINENT CASUALTY CO
OKLAHOMA SURETY COMPANY
(*Suby of* GREAT AMERICAN INSURANCE CO) ★
1437 S Boulder Ave # 200, Tulsa, OK 74119-3693
Tel (918) 587-7221 *Founded/Ownrshp* 1947
Sales NA *EMP* 280
SIC 6331 Fire, marine & casualty insurance; Automobile insurance
Pr: Michael Coon
**CFO:* Greg Jones
CFO: Gregg Jones
Sr VP: Kirby Pancoast
**VP:* Todd Bazata
**VP:* Jim Davis
VP: John Gant
VP: Bob Martin
**VP:* Kirby Tancoast
Admn Mgr: Brian Garrett
**VP Mktg:* John Gent

D-U-N-S 03-106-9412
MID-CONTINENT PAPER AND DISTRIBUTING CO INC
11809 Borman Dr, Saint Louis, MO 63146-4112
Tel (314) 989-0894 *Founded/Ownrshp* 1993
Sales 88.1MM^E *EMP* 65
SIC 5113 Paperboard & products
Pr: Robert S Grommet
**VP:* Cathy Grommet
VP: Darren Schmiemeier

MID-DEL SCHOOL SYSTEM
See MIDWEST CITY PUBLIC SCHOOLS I-52

MID-FLORIDA MATERIALS DIVISION
See HUBBARD CONSTRUCTION CO

D-U-N-S 10-895-0312
MID-FLORIDA MEDICAL SERVICES INC
WINTER HEAVEN HOSPITAL
200 Avenue F Ne, Winter Haven, FL 33881-4131
Tel (863) 297-1895 *Founded/Ownrshp* 1983
Sales 254.7MM *EMP* 2,300
Accts Mcgladrey Llp Fort Lauderdale
SIC 8741 8062 8082 Hospital management; General medical & surgical hospitals; Home health care services
Pr: Lance W Anastasio

MID-JEFFERSON HOSPITAL
See MEDICAL CENTER OF SOUTHEAST TEXAS L P

D-U-N-S 00-713-5395
MID-KANSAS COOPERATIVE ASSOCIATION
MKC
307 W Cole St, Moundridge, KS 67107-7533
Tel (620) 345-6328 *Founded/Ownrshp* 1965
Sales 458.6MM *EMP* 250
Accts Lindburg Vogel Pierce Faris H
SIC 5153 5191 Grain elevators; Farm supplies; Chemicals, agricultural; Fertilizer & fertilizer materials
Pr: Dave Christiansen
CFO: Danny Porch
**CFO:* Danny Posch
Sls&Mrk Ex: Liz McKim

D-U-N-S 17-596-3524
MID-MISSOURI ENERGY LLC
MME GRAIN
15311 N Saline 65 Hwy, Malta Bend, MO 65339-1310
Tel (660) 595-0144 *Founded/Ownrshp* 2001
Sales 150.0MM *EMP* 45
SIC 2869 Ethyl alcohol, ethanol
Pr: Ryland Utlaut
**CEO:* Chris Wilson
CFO: Art Madden
**Treas:* Ronald T Linneman
**VP:* Mark Casner
CIO: Matthew Endicott
Plnt Mgr: Tyler Edmundson

D-U-N-S 07-488-6771 IMP
MID-MOUNTAIN FOODS INC
MISTY MOUNTAIN SPRING WATER CO
(*Suby of* FOOD CITY) ★
26331 Hillman Hwy, Abingdon, VA 24210
Tel (276) 623-5000 *Founded/Ownrshp* 1974
Sales 221.8MM^E *EMP* 500
SIC 5141 Groceries, general line
Pr: Jessee A Lewis
**Ch:* Dozier J Perry
**Treas:* Donald E Lay
**VP:* K Sutton Rigg
Sfty Dirs: Jimmy Asbury

D-U-N-S 03-753-2314
MID-OHIO FOODBANK
3960 Brookham Dr, Grove City, OH 43123-9741
Tel (614) 317-9400 *Founded/Ownrshp* 1980
Sales 89.0MM *EMP* 118
Accts Hemphill & Associates Inc Col
SIC 8322 Meal delivery program
Pr: Mathew Habash
**COO:* Lyn Hang
**CFO:* Sharon Grunwell
VP: Bridget Decrane
**VP:* Marilyn Tomasi
**VP:* Greg Winslow
**Prin:* Kimberly Dorniden
Dir IT: John Grunwell

D-U-N-S 00-440-2301 IMP
MID-SOUTH INDUSTRIES INC (AL)
2620 E Meighan Blvd, Gadsden, AL 35903-1924
Tel (256) 492-8997 *Founded/Ownrshp* 1962
Sales 141.6MM^E *EMP* 1,474
SIC 3672 3089 3824 3714

D-U-N-S 04-179-1617
■ MID-STATE TELEPHONE CO
TDS TELECOMMUNICATIONS
(*Suby of* TDS TELECOMMUNICATIONS CORP) ★
7902 Chapin Dr Ne, New London, MN 56273-8538
Tel (320) 354-7805 *Founded/Ownrshp* 1972
Sales 258.7MM^E *EMP* 2,700
SIC 4813 Telephone communication, except radio
Pr: David A Wittwer

D-U-N-S 00-621-2369 IMP
MID-STATES DISTRIBUTING CO INC (ND)
1370 Mendota Hts Rd, Mendota, MN 55150
Tel (651) 280-4300 *Founded/Ownrshp* 1954
Sales 484.8MM^E *EMP* 51^E
SIC 5072 5013 5191 5091 5092 5136 Hardware; Automotive supplies & parts; Farm supplies; Sporting & recreation goods; Toys & games; Men's & boys' clothing
CEO: Thomas Mahlke
CFO: Barbara Townsend
Off Mgr: Pam Nord
Sales Exec: Greg Mann

MID-STATES SUPPLY COMPANY INC
See MSS LIQUIDATION CORP

D-U-N-S 05-814-8305
MID-VALLEY HEALTHCARE INC
LEBANON COMMUNITY HOSPITAL
525 N Santiam Hwy, Lebanon, OR 97355-4363
Tel (541) 258-2101 *Founded/Ownrshp* 1950
Sales 96.3MM *EMP* 740
SIC 8062 8051 8011 8082 General medical & surgical hospitals; Skilled nursing care facilities; Offices & clinics of medical doctors; Home health care services
CEO: Larry Mullins
**Pr:* Bud Laurent
Dir Risk M: Kathy Guthrie
Dir Soc: Sandra Taylor
Doctor: Leslie Pliskin
HC Dir: Charlene Hayden

D-U-N-S 02-579-9586
MID-WEST DAIRYMENS CO
4313 W State St, Rockford, IL 61102-1339
Tel (815) 968-0504 *Founded/Ownrshp* 1924
Sales 115.5MM *EMP* 6E
SIC 5143 Milk & cream, fluid
CEO: Dennis Tonak
*Ch Bd: Daruis Simler

D-U-N-S 03-941-7696
MID-WEST FERTILIZER INC
1105 Baptiste Dr, Paola, KS 66071-1344
Tel (913) 294-5555 *Founded/Ownrshp* 1980
Sales 91.9MME *EMP* 48
SIC 5191 Fertilizer & fertilizer materials
*Pr: John Kershner

D-U-N-S 10-239-2925 IMP
MID-WEST HOSE & SPECIALTY INC
MIDWEST HOSE
3312 S I 35 Service Rd, Oklahoma City, OK 73129-6762
Tel (405) 670-6718 *Founded/Ownrshp* 1983
Sales 140.0MME *EMP* 267
SIC 5085 Hose, belting & packing; Rubber goods, mechanical
Pr: W Harvey Sparkman
Brnch Mgr: Daniel Utchel
Store Mgr: Caleb Dirks
IT Man: Scotty Sparkman
Sls Mgr: Andy Benson

D-U-N-S 83-083-6321
MID-WEST INSTITUTIONAL FOOD DISTRIBUTORS INC
MIDWEST FOODS
3100 W 36th St, Chicago, IL 60632-2304
Tel (773) 927-8870 *Founded/Ownrshp* 1997
Sales 110.9MME *EMP* 150
SIC 5142 5143 5144 5147 5148 Packaged frozen goods; Dairy products, except dried or canned; Poultry & poultry products; Meats & meat products; Fresh fruits & vegetables
Pr: Erin Fitzgerald

D-U-N-S 04-067-6348 IMP/EXP
MID-WEST TEXTILE CO
1600 E San Antonio Ave, El Paso, TX 79901-1726
Tel (915) 351-0231 *Founded/Ownrshp* 1988
Sales 146.7MME *EMP* 270
SIC 5093 5137 5136 Waste rags; Women's & children's clothing; Men's & boys' clothing
Pr: James Maxfield
Treas: Tom Clark
VP: Sunny Hull
VP: John Paben
Dir IT: Sergio Pacheco

D-U-N-S 15-209-5840
MIDAMERICA CARE FOUNDATION INC
HILLSBORO REHABILITATI
7611 State Line Rd, Kansas City, MO 64114-6801
Tel (816) 444-0900 *Founded/Ownrshp* 1983
Sales 57.9MM *EMP* 2,500
SIC 8051 8052 Skilled nursing care facilities; Intermediate care facilities
Pr: Mike Machaud

D-U-N-S 18-467-3775
MIDAMERICA DIVISION INC
MID WEST HOLDINGS
903 E 104th St Ste 500, Kansas City, MO 64131-3464
Tel (816) 508-4000 *Founded/Ownrshp* 1996
Sales 345.8MME *EMP* 15,040E
SIC 8741 Hospital management
Pr: ML Lagarde
Pr: David Carnes
COO: Phil Buttell Fache
COO: Donald King III
COO: James Strieby
COO: Greg Udiak
*CFO: Clifton Mills
VP: Corrine Everson
*VP: Patrick Patterson
Dir Risk M: Jennifer Cross
Dir Rad: Tracy Miller

D-U-N-S 04-636-9930
MIDAMERICA HOTELS CORP (MO)
HOLIDAY INN
105 S Mount Auburn Rd, Cape Girardeau, MO 63703-4915
Tel (573) 334-0546 *Founded/Ownrshp* 1968
Sales 60.6MME *EMP* 1,000
SIC 5812 Fast-food restaurant, chain
Pr: Daniel M Drury
*Treas: Harold G Hale
*VP: John A Drury
VP: Diane Edwards
Exec: Larry Nelson
Genl Mgr: John Echimovich
Dir IT: Carl Archer
IT Man: Shawn Lowery
VP Opers: Joel Neikirk
Mktg Dir: Karla Drury
Sls Mgr: Monica Adams

MIDAMERICAN
See MHC INC

D-U-N-S 88-471-8768
■ **MIDAMERICAN ENERGY CO**
(*Suby of* MIDAMERICAN) ★
666 Grand Ave Ste 500, Des Moines, IA 50309-2511
Tel (515) 242-4300 *Founded/Ownrshp* 1996
Sales 3.7MMM *EMP* 2,100
Accts Deloitte & Touche Llp Des Moi
SIC 4931 Electric & other services combined
Pr: William J Fehrman
*CFO: Thomas B Specketer
Ofcr: Mark A Hewett
Ex VP: Doug Anderson
*Sr VP: Steven R Weiss
VP: Sara Schillinger
Dir Risk M: Vu Nguyen
IT Man: Ann Boucher
Software D: Thomas Dohman
Sftwr Eng: David Ogden
Site Mgr: Brady Evans

D-U-N-S 09-950-3943
■ **MIDAMERICAN FUNDING LLC**
(*Suby of* BERKSHIRE HATHAWAY ENERGY CO) ★
666 Grand Ave Ste 500, Des Moines, IA 50309-2511
Tel (515) 242-4300 *Founded/Ownrshp* 1999
Sales 3.7MMM *EMP* 3,600E
SIC 4911 4924 Electric services; Distribution, electric power; Generation, electric power; Transmission, electric power; Natural gas distribution
Pr: William J Fehrman
Sr VP: David Levy
VP: Thomas B Specketer

D-U-N-S 00-812-8394 IMP
MIDAS INC
MIDAS MUFFLER
(*Suby of* TBC CORP) ★
4300 Tbc Way, Palm Beach Gardens, FL 33410-4281
Tel (630) 438-3000 *Founded/Ownrshp* 2012
Sales 109.8MME *EMP* 940
SIC 7533 6794 Muffler shop, sale or repair & installation; Franchises, selling or licensing
Pr: Alan D Feldman
*CFO: William M Guzik
*Chf Mktg O: Frederick W Dow Jr
Ofcr: Ronald J McEvoy
Sr VP: James D Hamrick
Sr VP: D Bruce Hutchison
Sr VP: Gerard M Klaisle
*Sr VP: Alvin K Marr
VP: Carl R Daniels Jr
*VP: Michael J Gould
VP: James M Haeger Jr
VP: David C Perrin
VP: Wendell Province
Board of Directors: Thomas L Bindley, Archie R Dykes, Diane L Routson, Robert R Schoeberl

D-U-N-S 83-155-8924
▲ **MIDAS MEDICI GROUP HOLDINGS INC**
445 Park Ave Frnt 5, New York, NY 10022-8603
Tel (212) 792-0920 *Founded/Ownrshp* 2009
Sales 89.6MM *EMP* 347
Tkr Sym MMED *Exch* OTO
SIC 7372 Prepackaged software
Ch Bd: Nana Baffour
*Pr: Johnson M Kachidza
*Ofcr: Frank Asante-Kissi
*Ex VP: Robert F McCarthy
VP: Ricardo Giudice
VP: Mitch Lemons

MIDAS MUFFLER
See MIDAS INC

D-U-N-S 09-656-3689
MIDATLANTIC FARM CREDIT
45 Aileron Ct, Westminster, MD 21157-3022
Tel (410) 848-1033 *Founded/Ownrshp* 2000
Sales NA *EMP* 210
SIC 6159

D-U-N-S 03-340-0029
MIDCO COMMUNICATIONS INC
(*Suby of* MIDCONTINENT MEDIA INC) ★
3901 N Louise Ave, Sioux Falls, SD 57107-0112
Tel (605) 334-1200 *Founded/Ownrshp* 1982
Sales 171.4MM *EMP* 1,200
SIC 8748 5961 7389 4812 Telecommunications consultant; Mail order house, order taking office only; Telephone answering service; Paging services
Pr: Scott Anderson
Pr: Joseph H Floyd
Treas: Mark S Niblick
VP: Dick Busch
Genl Mgr: Tom Simmons
Tech Mgr: N Bentson
Tech Mgr: Mark Niblick
Mtls Dir: Joe Mauss
Opers Mgr: Nishanth Kannan
Mktg Mgr: Pat Johnson
Sls Mgr: Mark Powell

D-U-N-S 07-886-4088
■ **MIDCOAST ENERGY PARTNERS LP**
(*Suby of* ENBRIDGE ENERGY PARTNERS LP) ★
1100 La St Ste 3300, Houston, TX 77002
Tel (713) 821-2000 *Founded/Ownrshp* 2013
Sales 2.8MMM *EMP* 13
Tkr Sym MEP *Exch* NYS
SIC 1311 4923 Crude petroleum & natural gas; Gas transmission & distribution
Pr: C Gregory Harper
Genl Pt: Midcoast Holdings
Sr VP: Mark A Maki

D-U-N-S 05-841-7374
■ **MIDCOAST OPERATING LP**
(*Suby of* ENBRIDGE ENERGY PARTNERS LP) ★
1100 La St Ste 3300, Houston, TX 77002
Tel (713) 821-2000 *Founded/Ownrshp* 1999
Sales 345.0MME *EMP* 500E
SIC 5172 1389 Gases, liquefied petroleum (propane); Processing service, gas; Gas field services
CEO: Curtis J Dufour
Pr: Dan Tutcher
VP: Mark A Maki
VP: Terry L McGill
Genl Mgr: Trey Hall

D-U-N-S 07-933-8582
MIDCON FUEL SERVICES LLC
8401 Lindsey Rd, Little Rock, AR 72206-3835
Tel (501) 708-2000 *Founded/Ownrshp* 2013
Sales 150.0MM *EMP* 7
SIC 5172 Engine fuels & oils
Pr: David Hightower

D-U-N-S 93-002-3630
MIDCON INVESTORS INC
401 S Boston Ave Ste 3600, Tulsa, OK 74103-4020
Tel (918) 587-7325 *Founded/Ownrshp* 2000
Sales 172.2MME *EMP* 701
SIC 5084 Hydraulic systems equipment & supplies; Pneumatic tools & equipment
Pr: Ian H Hill

D-U-N-S 01-773-4562
MIDCONTINENT COMMUNICATIONS
3600 Minnesota Dr Ste 700, Minneapolis, MN 55435-7918
Tel (952) 844-2600 *Founded/Ownrshp* 2000
Sales 293.7MME *EMP* 1,015
SIC 4841 4813 Cable & other pay television services; Telephone communication, except radio;
Pt: Patrick McAdaragh
*Pt: Richard Busch
*Pt: Steven Grosser
CFO: Steven E Grosser
Sr VP: Tom Simmons
IT Man: Kyle Norberg
Pgrm Dir: Wynne Haakenstad

D-U-N-S 15-894-4798
MIDCONTINENT INDEPENDENT SYSTEM OPERATOR INC
MISO
720 City Center Dr, Carmel, IN 46032-3826
Tel (317) 249-5400 *Founded/Ownrshp* 1998
Sales 305.6MM *EMP* 700E
Accts Ernst & Young Llp Indianapoli
SIC 4911 Distribution, electric power; Generation, electric power; Transmission, electric power
CEO: John R Bear
Treas: Kevin Vannoy
Sr Cor Off: J Evans
*Ex VP: Richard Doying
*Ex VP: Clair Moeller
*Sr VP: John Goode
*VP: Robert Berntsen
*VP: Jo Biggers
VP: Michael Chiasson
*VP: Jennifer Curran
VP: Michael J Gahagan
VP: Michael Gahagan
*VP: Joseph Gardner
VP: Amy L Headdy
*VP: Todd Hillman
VP: Daniel L Jones
*VP: Stephen G Kozey
VP: Keith Mitchell
*VP: Greg Powell
*VP: Todd Ramey
*VP: Wayne Schug

D-U-N-S 00-792-0457
MIDCONTINENT MEDIA INC
3600 Minnesota Dr Ste 700, Minneapolis, MN 55435-7918
Tel (952) 844-2600 *Founded/Ownrshp* 1990
Sales 493.6MME *EMP* 1,300
SIC 4841 Cable television services
Ch Bd: Mark S Niblick
*Pr: Patrick McAdaragh
*COO: Richard Busch
CFO: Steven Grosser
*Sr VP: Tom Simmons
VP: Steven Schuster
IT Man: Amy Lingbeck
Netwrk Eng: Dustin Beare
Mtls Dir: Joe Mauss
Sls Mgr: Nancy Graham
Genl Couns: Scott Anderson

MIDCONTINENT PUBLIC LIBRARY
See CONSOLIDATED LIBRARY DISTRICT NO 3

D-U-N-S 17-842-4854
MIDCOUNTRY BANK
(*Suby of* MIDCOUNTRY FINANCIAL CORP) ★
Investors Bldg 7 Ste 103, Minneapolis, MN 55402
Tel (952) 843-5200 *Founded/Ownrshp* 1933
Sales NA *EMP* 1,200
SIC 6035 Savings institutions, federally chartered
Pr: Steve Meads
*COO: Maureen O'Brien Wieser
CFO: Greg Christensen
CFO: David Soukup
Chf Cred: Greg Christianson
Sr VP: Tom Naughtin
*Sr VP: Robin Roberts
*VP: Bob Calander
*VP: Karen Conrad
VP: Trevor Johnson
VP: Todd Streed
Dir Risk M: Sandra L Laughlin

D-U-N-S 14-481-4006
MIDCOUNTRY FINANCIAL CORP
201 2nd St Ste 950, Macon, GA 31201-8259
Tel (478) 746-8222 *Founded/Ownrshp* 2002
Sales 342.8MME *EMP* 1,490E
SIC 7389 Financial services
Pr: Robert F Hatcher
CFO: David L Hall
Ofcr: Christopher Leckrone
Ex VP: Charles G Davis
Ex VP: Richard A Hills
Ex VP: Marian M Mackle
Ex VP: Lee B Murphey
Ex VP: Hills Richard
Dir Risk M: Sandra Laughlin
Dir IT: Monica Cole
Board of Directors: Richard W Carpenter, James L Clayton, C Lee Ellis, R Kirby Godsey, Robert F Hatcher, Robert F Hatcher Jr, Carol A Jackson, Sherry A Kellett, Jerry A Newby

D-U-N-S 05-396-4680
■ **MIDDENDORF MEAT CO LLC**
MIDDENDORF QUALITY FOODS
(*Suby of* P F G) ★
3737 N Broadway, Saint Louis, MO 63147-3496
Tel (314) 241-4800 *Founded/Ownrshp* 2002
Sales 83.4MME *EMP* 200
SIC 5147 5141 5148 5146 5113 2011 Meats, fresh; Groceries, general line; Fresh fruits & vegetables; Fish, frozen, unpackaged; Industrial & personal service paper; Meat packing plants
Pr: Orville Middendorf
*Treas: Jeffery W Fender
VP: Donald Middendorf
Genl Mgr: Jerry Jones
Manager: Tom Maertz
Manager: Paul Witwer

MIDDENDORF QUALITY FOODS
See MIDDENDORF MEAT CO LLC

D-U-N-S 10-124-2022 IMP/EXP
MIDDLE ATLANTIC PRODUCTS INC
DATATEL
(*Suby of* LEGRAND HOLDING INC) ★
300 Fairfield Rd, Fairfield, NJ 07004-1932
Tel (973) 839-1011 *Founded/Ownrshp* 2011
Sales 94.3MME *EMP* 339
SIC 3444 Casings, sheet metal
CEO: Bob Schluter
*Pr: Michael L Baker
*Treas: James Laperriere
*VP: Robert Julian
VP Opers: William Fuchs
Prd Mgr: Okan Esendemir
Mktg Mgr: Megan Knedler
Manager: Matthew Curtin
Sales Asso: Justin Smith

D-U-N-S 01-374-8132
MIDDLE ATLANTIC WAREHOUSE DISTRIBUTOR INC
20 Hazelwood Dr Ste 100, Amherst, NY 14228-2200
Tel (716) 531-9200 *Founded/Ownrshp* 1963
Sales 139.9MME *EMP* 1,600
SIC 5013

D-U-N-S 07-750-9438
MIDDLE COUNTRY CENTRAL SCHOOL DISTRICT
8 43rd St, Centereach, NY 11720-2325
Tel (631) 285-8000 *Founded/Ownrshp* 1930
Sales 222.3MM *EMP* 1,600
Accts Rs Abrams & Co Llp Island
SIC 8211 Public elementary & secondary schools
Dir IT: Enrico Crocetti

D-U-N-S 13-839-3819
MIDDLE EAST BROADCASTING NETWORKS INC
MIDDLE EAST TELEVISION NETWORK
7600 Boston Blvd, Springfield, VA 22153-3136
Tel (703) 852-9000 *Founded/Ownrshp* 2003
Sales 107.1MM *EMP* 624
Accts Gelman Rosenberg & Freedman B
SIC 4841 4832 Cable & other pay television services; Direct broadcast satellite services (DBS); Radio broadcasting stations
Pr: Brian T Conniff
*Treas: Kelley Sullivan
VP: Daniel Nassif
CTO: Vijaykumar Mirchandani
Dir IT: Vivek Chopra
IT Man: Ross Castle
IT Man: Dean Cowan
Snr Mgr: Jim Schoonmaker

MIDDLE EAST TELEVISION NETWORK
See MIDDLE EAST BROADCASTING NETWORKS INC

D-U-N-S 87-903-2654
MIDDLE GEORGIA STATE UNIVERSITY
(*Suby of* GEORGIA BOARD OF REGENTS) ★
100 University Pkwy, Macon, GA 31206-5100
Tel (478) 471-2700 *Founded/Ownrshp* 1973
Sales 99.9MME *EMP* 1,125
Accts Russell W Hinton State Audit
SIC 8221 University
Pr: Chris Blake
*Ex VP: Nancy Stroud
VP: Melanie Hatch
*VP: Martha Venn
Dir IT: Charles Warren
Opers Mgr: Alice Jane

MIDDLE RIVER AIRCRAFT SYSTEMS
See MRA SYSTEMS INC

MIDDLE SCHOOLS EDUCATION OFF
See HILLSBOROUGH COUNTY SCHOOL DISTRICT

D-U-N-S 96-388-9063
MIDDLE TENNESSEE MEDICAL CENTER
1700 Medical Center Pkwy, Murfreesboro, TN 37129-2245
Tel (615) 396-4100 *Founded/Ownrshp* 1927
Sales 253.9MM *EMP* 9E
Accts Deloitte Tax Llp Cincinnati
SIC 8062 General medical & surgical hospitals
Pr: Gordon B Ferguson
COO: Elizabeth Lemons
VP: Dr Andy Brown
Prin: Carol Bragdon
Prin: Kelly Miles

D-U-N-S 00-792-2321
MIDDLE TENNESSEE ELECTRIC MEMBERSHIP CORP
555 New Salem Hwy, Murfreesboro, TN 37129-3390
Tel (615) 890-9762 *Founded/Ownrshp* 1936
Sales 549.9MM *EMP* 410
Accts Winnett Associates Pllc Shelb
SIC 4911 Distribution, electric power
Pr: Chris Jones
*Ch Bd: Michael Woods
*V Ch: Tom Purkey
*COO: Tom Suggs
*CFO: Bernie Steen
*Sec: Steve Seger
*Sr VP: Brad Gibson
VP: Gray Bateman
VP: John Florida
*VP: Keith Thomason
Dist Mgr: Ron Washington

D-U-N-S 07-764-8780
MIDDLE TENNESSEE STATE UNIVERSITY
1301 E Main St, Murfreesboro, TN 37132-0002
Tel (615) 898-2300 *Founded/Ownrshp* 1972
Sales 182.9MM *EMP* 2,610
SIC 8221 University
Pr: Sidney A McPhee
Pr: Kathy I Musselman
COO: John Schmidt
VP: John W Cothern
VP: Evan Lester

VP: Courtney Lynch
VP: Tom Wallace
Exec: Terri Ferrell
Assoc Dir: Will Pritchett
Ex Dir: Amanda Toney
Ex Dir: Tom Tozer

MIDDLEBY COOKING SYSTEMS GROUP
See MARSHALL MIDDLEBY INC

D-U-N-S 08-893-2108
▲ MIDDLEBY CORP
1400 Toastmaster Dr, Elgin, IL 60120-9274
Tel (847) 741-3300 Founded/Ownrshp 1888
Sales 1.8MMM EMP 7,800
Accts Ernst & Young Llp Chicago I
Tkr Sym MIDD Exch NGS
SIC 3556 3589 Food products machinery; Ovens, bakery; Mixers, commercial, food; Commercial cooking & foodwarming equipment; Cooking equipment, commercial; Food warming equipment, commercial
Ch Bd: Selim A Bassoul
COO: David Brewer
CFO: Timothy J Fitzgerald
Treas: Martin M Lindsay
QA Dir: Ivan Lopez

MIDDLEFORT CLINIC
See MAYO CLINIC HEALTH SYSTEM

D-U-N-S 07-844-2222
MIDDLESEX BANCORP MHC
6 Main St, Natick, MA 01760-4506
Tel (508) 653-0300 Founded/Ownrshp 2012
Sales NA EMP 547E
SIC 6036 Savings institutions, not federally chartered
CEO: John Heerwagen
Chf Inves: Brian Stewart
Ex VP: Brian Lanigan
Ex VP: Bill Wilkinson
Sr VP: Cheryl Corman
Sr VP: Robert Lavelle
VP: Michael Hart
VP: Kevin Kane
VP: Henry Liu
VP: Doug Rosenau
VP: Bill Whelton

D-U-N-S 06-218-5517
MIDDLESEX CORP (MA)
1 Spectacle Pond Rd, Littleton, MA 01460-1128
Tel (978) 742-4400 Founded/Ownrshp 1973
Sales 223.5MME EMP 500
SIC 1611 1794 1622 General contractor, highway & street construction; Excavation work; Bridge, tunnel & elevated highway
Pr: Robert Pereira II
*Pr: Alfred S Aponas
*Pr: Robert L Mabardy
*CFO: Robert N Jacobson
Ex VP: Robert Mabardy
*Sr VP: David Skerrett
*Sr VP: David Socci

D-U-N-S 06-870-7801 IMP
MIDDLESEX COUNTY COLLEGE
2600 Woodbridge Ave, Edison, NJ 08837-3675
Tel (732) 548-6000 Founded/Ownrshp 1964
Sales 35.8MME EMP 1,014
SIC 8222 9111 8221 8211 Community college; County supervisors' & executives' offices; Colleges universities & professional schools; Elementary & secondary schools
Pr: Joann La Perla-Morales
VP: Laura Cahill
*VP: Ronald Goldfarb
*VP: Karen Hays
*VP: Susan Perkins
Assoc Dir: Ronald Balint
Assoc Dir: Daniel Fuchs
Ex Dir: K Katt
Ex Dir: Karen Katt
Psych: Lafayette Smith

D-U-N-S 07-313-3100
MIDDLESEX COUNTY OF (INC) (NJ)
75 Bayard St, New Brunswick, NJ 08901-2112
Tel (732) 745-3000 Founded/Ownrshp 1682
Sales NA EMP 2,100E
Accts Hodulik & Morrison Pa High
SIC 9111 Executive offices;
COO: John Ferguson
CFO: Albert Kuchinskas
Treas: Jim Phillips
Exec: Vanessa Young
Genl Mgr: Kathy Borgen

MIDDLESEX COUNTY TREASURER
See COUNTY OF MIDDLESEX

D-U-N-S 07-041-2812
MIDDLESEX COUNTY UTILITIES AUTHORITY INC
2571 Main St, Sayreville, NJ 08872-1478
Tel (732) 721-3800 Founded/Ownrshp 1950
Sales 114.0MME EMP 185
Accts Parentebeard Llc Clark New J
SIC 4952 Sewerage systems
Ch: Ted Light
V Ch: John Pantalone
*Treas: Margaret M Brennan
Treas: William Burns
Exec: Robert Burner
Exec: Kathleen Guss
*Ex Dir: Richard Fitamant
*Dist Mgr: John F Wiley
Off Mgr: Theresa Gallagher
Cmptr Lab: Stephen Fincham
Software D: Diane Leonik

D-U-N-S 96-676-1152
MIDDLESEX HEALTH SYSTEM INC
28 Crescent St, Middletown, CT 06457-3654
Tel (860) 358-6000 Founded/Ownrshp 1985
Sales 1.1MM EMP 2,665E
Accts Saslow Lufkin & Buggy Llp Wea
SIC 8062 General medical & surgical hospitals
Pr: Vincent G Capece Jr
VP: Ludwig Johnson
*VP: Susan Martin
MIS Dir: Karen Kohler

D-U-N-S 06-925-7152
MIDDLESEX HOSPITAL FOUNDATION INC (CT)
(Suby of MIDDLESEX HEALTH SYSTEM INC) ★
28 Crescent St, Middletown, CT 06457-3654
Tel (860) 358-6000 Founded/Ownrshp 1895
Sales 366.5MM EMP 2,632
Accts Saslow Lufkin & Buggy Llp Ha
SIC 8062 Hospital, medical school affiliation
Ch Bd: Arthur Mc Dowell III
*Pr: Robert Kiely
COO: Kathleen Russo
COO: Barbara Thompson
*CFO: Vincent G Capece Jr
VP: David Giuffrida
VP: Ludwig Johnson
VP: Arthur McDowell
VP: David J Miner
VP: Geg Nokes
Dir Risk M: Jeffrey Lemkin
Dir Lab: Jack Boehme
Dir Lab: Nancy Goodwin
Dir Rx: Ann Calamari

D-U-N-S 00-695-5181
MIDDLESEX SAVINGS BANK
(Suby of MIDDLESEX BANCORP MHC) ★
6 Main St, Natick, MA 01760-4534
Tel (508) 653-0300 Founded/Ownrshp 1835
Sales NA EMP 464
SIC 6036 Savings institutions, not federally chartered
CEO: John R Heerwagen
*Pr: James A Lavoie
*COO: Brian D Lanigan
COO: Patricia Slaney
*CFO: Brian D Stewart
*CFO: Paul M Totino
Ofcr: Mitchell Hryckowian
Ofcr: Carla Stover
Ex VP: Charles R Bauer
Ex VP: Karen M Curtis
Ex VP: Falwell David
Ex VP: Michael G McAuliffe
Ex VP: Dana M Neshe
Sr VP: David Shorey
VP: Paul Adams
VP: Antonio Battista
VP: David Bennett
VP: Dennis A Carlson
VP: Patricia K Conry
VP: Susan T Dunnigan
VP: Timothy Fahey

D-U-N-S 00-697-5122
▲ MIDDLESEX WATER CO (NJ)
1500 Ronson Rd, Iselin, NJ 08830-3020
Tel (732) 634-1500 Founded/Ownrshp 1896
Sales 126.0MM EMP 293E
Tkr Sym MSEX Exch NGS
SIC 4941 1623 Water supply; Water, sewer & utility lines
Ch Bd: Dennis W Doll
Pr: Gerard L Esposito
COO: Richard M Risoldi
CFO: A Bruce O'Connor
Bd of Dir: John Cutting
VP: Jay L Kooper
VP: Bruce O'Connor
VP: Bernadette M Sohler
Netwrk Eng: Ignat Sitnikov
Board of Directors: James F Cosgrove Jr, Kim C Hanemann, Kim C Hanemann, Steven M Klein, Amy B Mansue, John R Middleton, Walter G Reinhard, Jeffries Shein

D-U-N-S 04-019-6354
MIDDLETON BRATRUD INSURANCE BROKERS INC
BRATRUD MIDDLETON INSURANCE
1201 Pacific Ave Ste 1000, Tacoma, WA 98402-4321
Tel (253) 759-2200 Founded/Ownrshp 1996
Sales NA EMP 175
SIC 6411 Insurance brokers
Pr: Kurt Carlson
*Pr: Charles Miller
*CFO: Stephen Feltus
CFO: Peter M Hendrick
VP: Cory Corye
VP: Kathy Fraley
VP: Nancy Frost
VP: Kyle Howat
Mng Dir: Sandi Paschall
Sales Exec: Jim Baker
Sales Exec: Allen Bergstrom

D-U-N-S 09-302-6367
MIDDLETON-CROSS PLAINS-AREA SCHOOL DISTRICT
7106 South Ave, Middleton, WI 53562-3263
Tel (608) 829-9000 Founded/Ownrshp 1968
Sales 80.4MM EMP 1,100
Accts Johnson Block And Company Inc
SIC 8211 Public elementary & secondary schools; Secondary school; High school, junior or senior
Bd of Dir: Anne Bauer
HC Dir: Blanche Baker-Vlask
Snr Mgr: Cathy Patton
Snr Mgr: Aaron Stutz

D-U-N-S 06-869-7705
MIDDLETOWN TOWNSHIP BOARD OF EDUCATION
834 Leonardville Rd Fl 2, Leonardo, NJ 07737-1751
Tel (732) 671-3850 Founded/Ownrshp 1900
Sales 129.6MME EMP 1,000
SIC 8211 School board
Pr: James Cody
*VP: Bob Banta
MIS Dir: Jay Attiya

D-U-N-S 07-979-9779
MIDDLETOWN TOWNSHIP SCHOOL DISTRICT
MIDDLTOWN TOWNSHIP PUB SCHOOLS
834 Leonardville Rd, Middletown, NJ 07748
Tel (732) 671-3850 Founded/Ownrshp 2015
Sales 34.4MME EMP 1,165E
SIC 8211 Public elementary & secondary schools

MIDDLTOWN TOWNSHIP PUB SCHOOLS
See MIDDLETOWN TOWNSHIP SCHOOL DISTRICT

D-U-N-S 04-620-3444
MIDDOUGH INC
1901 E 13th St Ste 400, Cleveland, OH 44114-3542
Tel (216) 367-6000 Founded/Ownrshp 1950
Sales 136.6MME EMP 700
SIC 8711 8712 Consulting engineer; Architectural engineering
Pr: Ronald Ledin
*CFO: Anthony Donofrio
*Sr VP: Joseph S Cardile
*Sr VP: Charles Dietz
*VP: George Hlavacs
*VP: Charles L Krzysiak
*VP: Donald Majba

D-U-N-S 12-395-7524
MIDFIRST BANK
(Suby of MIDLAND GROUP) ★
501 Nw Grand Blvd, Oklahoma City, OK 73118-6037
Tel (405) 767-7000 Founded/Ownrshp 1982
Sales NA EMP 1,336
SIC 6035 Federal savings & loan associations
Ch Bd: G Jeffrey Records Jr
Owner: Ashley Grigsby
Mng Pt: Nicholas Powell
*CFO: Todd Dobson
*Ofcr: David G Goodall
Sr Ex VP: Garland Wilkinson
Ex VP: Roger Disalvatore
Ex VP: Randy Roper
Sr VP: Ed Fariss
*Sr VP: Ralph Farrar Jr
Sr VP: H James Holloman
Sr VP: Mary Przybyla
*Sr VP: Betty L Rodgers
Sr VP: Tim Schneider
Sr VP: Marc Short
Sr VP: Tim Tackett
Sr VP: Chris Wertzberger
Sr VP: Scot Williams
VP: Daniel Adams
VP: Seth Bertram
VP: Marisa Bradanini

D-U-N-S 07-947-4270
MIDHUDSON REGIONAL HOSPITAL OF WESTCHESTER MEDICAL CENTER
(Suby of WESTCHESTER MEDICAL CENTER) ★
241 North Rd, Poughkeepsie, NY 12601-1154
Tel (845) 483-5000 Founded/Ownrshp 2014
Sales 37.6MME EMP 1,700E
SIC 8062 8322 General medical & surgical hospitals; Individual & family services
Pr: Arthur Nizza
*Pr: Mark Foster
*CFO: Kristin Cash-Holland
*Chf Mktg O: Keith Festa
*VP: Joline Frey
*VP: Barbara Naru
*VP: George Prisco
Dir Rx: David Schaff
*CIO: Joseph McCann
Snr Mgr: Joseph Fulton

D-U-N-S 06-316-6094
MIDJERSEY DISPOSAL INC
WASTE MANAGEMENT
1298 Industrial Way, Toms River, NJ 08755-4814
Tel (732) 341-6100 Founded/Ownrshp 1984
Sales 479.1MME EMP 130
SIC 4212 4953

D-U-N-S 09-306-4731
MIDJIT MARKET INC
GREEN VALLEY GROCERY
1580 S Jones Blvd, Las Vegas, NV 89146-1237
Tel (702) 216-2154 Founded/Ownrshp 1978
Sales 123.6MME EMP 350
SIC 5541 5141 Filling stations, gasoline; Groceries, general line
Pr: Richard Crawford
CFO: Mike Flinspach
Dist Mgr: Rhonda Knapp
Store Mgr: Dennis Capuno

D-U-N-S 04-661-6918
■ MIDLAND CO
(Suby of MUNICH-AMERICAN HOLDING CORP) ★
7000 Midland Blvd, Amelia, OH 45102-2646
Tel (513) 947-5503 Founded/Ownrshp 2008
Sales NA EMP 1,200
SIC 6331 4449 Property damage insurance; Fire, marine & casualty insurance: stock; Intracoastal (freight) transportation
Pr: John W Hayden
*Ch Bd: Joseph P Hayden III
*CFO: W Todd Gray
Treas: Matthew McConnell
Bd of Dir: W Gray
*Ex VP: Paul T Brizzolara
*Ex VP: John I Von Lehman
Ex VP: John Lehman
Sr VP: Larry Compton
VP: Patrick Law
VP: Kevin Morreale

D-U-N-S 07-314-9411
MIDLAND COUNTY HOSPITAL DISTRICT
MEMORIAL HOSPITAL AND MEDICAL
400 R Redfern Grover Pkwy, Midland, TX 79701
Tel (432) 685-1111 Founded/Ownrshp 1942
Sales 264.0MM EMP 1,700
Accts Bkd Llp Waco Texas
SIC 8062 Hospital, affiliated with AMA residency
Pr: Russell Meyers
CFO: Steven Bowerman
CFO: Lawrence Sanz
Ofcr: Michelle Pendergrass
VP: Robert Dent
VP: Cory Edmondson
Exec: Ann Carter
Exec: Maria McAllister
Exec: Brian Middlebrook
Dir Case M: Barbara Wallace
Dir Lab: Denise Kemp
Dir Lab: Kerry Noormohamed
Assoc Dir: Tricia Cobb
Board of Directors: Robert Dimit, Pete Holder, Leigh Ann Lane, David Orr DDS, Jess Parrish, Jay Reynolds, Oral Williams

D-U-N-S 03-979-1061
■ MIDLAND CREDIT MANAGEMENT INC
(Suby of ENCORE CAPITAL GROUP INC) ★
3111 Camino Del Rio N, San Diego, CA 92108-5720
Tel (877) 240-2377 Founded/Ownrshp 1953
Sales NA EMP 1,800
SIC 6153 Short-term business credit
CEO: Kenneth A Vecchione
*Pr: Carl Gregory
Sr VP: Olivier Baudoux
*Sr VP: Robin Pruitt
Sr VP: Manu Rikhye
Sr VP: Christopher Trepel
VP: Andrew Asch
Div Mgr: Katie Merrill
Corp Couns: Simona Clark
Corp Couns: Gregory Gerkin
Corp Couns: Kelly Macbeth

D-U-N-S 00-477-3149
MIDLAND ENTERPRISES INC
(Suby of INGRAM INDUSTRIES INC) ★
4400 Harding Pike, Nashville, TN 37205-2204
Tel (615) 298-8200 Founded/Ownrshp 1917
Sales 38.1MME EMP 1,400
SIC 4449 4492 3731 4491 River transportation, except on the St. Lawrence Seaway; Intracoastal (freight) transportation; Marine towing services; Tugboat service; Shipbuilding & repairing; Barges, building & repairing; Waterfront terminal operation
Ch Bd: Orrin H Ingram
Pr: Kaj Shah
CFO: Mary K Cavarra
Treas: R C Agricola
Ex VP: Eleanor McDonald
Board of Directors: Mary K Cavarra, Orrin H Ingram, Eleanor McDonald

D-U-N-S 11-536-6270
MIDLAND FINANCIAL CO
MIDLAND GROUP, THE
501 Nw Grand Blvd Ste 180, Oklahoma City, OK 73118-6037
Tel (405) 840-7600 Founded/Ownrshp 1981
Sales NA EMP 1,421
SIC 6035 6162 6531 Federal savings & loan associations; Mortgage bankers; Real estate brokers & agents; Real estate managers
Ch Bd: George J Records
Pr: John Gassen
Pr: Robin Perry
*COO: Robert F Dilg Jr
*CFO: Todd A Dobson
*Sr VP: Betty L Rodgers
VP: Brian Gage
VP: Donny Hector
VP: Nichole Lipps
VP: Cynthia Pearson
*Prin: Marion C Bauman

D-U-N-S 61-728-8766
MIDLAND FOOD SERVICES LLC
6200 Rockside Woods Blvd # 315, Independence, OH 44131-2333
Tel (216) 524-2251 Founded/Ownrshp 2012
Sales 69.6MME EMP 3,800
SIC 5812 Pizzeria, chain
CFO: Christopher Flocken
Ex Dir: Carol McMakin

MIDLAND GROUP, THE
See MIDLAND FINANCIAL CO

MIDLAND HOSPITAL
See MIDMICHIGAN MEDICAL CENTER-MIDLAND

D-U-N-S 08-108-5391
MIDLAND INDEPENDENT SCHOOL DISTRICT
MIDLAND ISD
615 W Missouri Ave, Midland, TX 79701-5017
Tel (432) 689-1000 Founded/Ownrshp 1893
Sales 222.4MM EMP 2,760
Accts Weaver And Tidwell Llp Mi
SIC 8211 Public elementary school; Public junior high school; Public senior high school
*Ch Bd: Jay Issacs
*CFO: David Garcia
Bd of Dir: Karen Fullen
Bd of Dir: Angel Hernandez
VP: Karen Nicholson
Exec: Nicole Gabriel
Comm Dir: Woodrow Bailey
Ex Dir: Sylvia Garza
Ex Dir: Ann McClarty
Ex Dir: Jane Rambo
IT Man: Elise Kail

MIDLAND ISD
See MIDLAND INDEPENDENT SCHOOL DISTRICT

D-U-N-S 01-220-0585
■ MIDLAND LOAN SERVICES A DIVISION OF PNC BANK NATIONAL ASSOCIATION
(Suby of PNC FINANCIAL SERVICES GROUP INC) ★
10851 Mastin St Ste 700, Overland Park, KS 66210-1687
Tel (913) 253-9000 Founded/Ownrshp 1998
Sales NA EMP 475
SIC 6162 Mortgage bankers & correspondents
Pr: Steven W Smith
Ex VP: Jeff Johnson
*Sr VP: Vince E Beckett
Sr VP: Sherry Ducarme
Sr VP: Bob Wright
VP: Jeremy Davis
VP: Michael Hall
VP: Chad Milbrant
VP: Karen Mills
VP: Kevin Semon
Dir IT: John Bauer

D-U-N-S 00-694-2783
MIDLAND MARKETING CO-OP INC
219 E 9th St, Hays, KS 67601-4415
Tel (785) 625-5138 *Founded/Ownrshp* 1915
Sales 89.8MM *EMP* 2[E]
Accts Lindburg Vogel Pierce Faris H
SIC 5153 5191 5541 5171 4221 Grains; Feed; Chemicals, agricultural; Fertilizer & fertilizer materials; Filling stations, gasoline; Petroleum bulk stations; Grain elevator, storage only

D-U-N-S 11-910-0670
MIDLAND MEMORIAL HOSPITAL
400 Rosalind Rdfrn Grovr, Midland, TX 79701-6499
Tel (432) 221-1111 *Founded/Ownrshp* 1950
Sales 264.0MM *EMP* 2[E]
SIC 8049 Speech pathologist
Pr: Russell Meyers

D-U-N-S 87-310-1307
MIDLAND MEMORIAL HOSPITAL & MEDICAL CENTER
2200 W Illinois Ave, Midland, TX 79701-6407
Tel (432) 685-1111 *Founded/Ownrshp* 1969
Sales 11.7MM[E] *EMP* 1,300
SIC 8062 General medical & surgical hospitals
Pr: Russel Meyers

D-U-N-S 00-792-0531
MIDLAND NATIONAL LIFE INSURANCE CO (IA)
(*Suby of* SAMMONS ENTERPRISES INC) ★
1 Sammons Plz, Sioux Falls, SD 57193-1001
Tel (605) 335-5700 *Founded/Ownrshp* 1906
Sales NA *EMP* 683
SIC 6311 Life insurance carriers
Pr: Steven C Palmitier
Pr: Theresa Hagedorn
Pr: Theresa Kuiper
Pr: Richard Lee
COO: Shawn Frederiksen
**CFO:* John J Craig II
CFO: Thomas M Eyer
CFO: Tom Myer
Treas: Alan H Spencer
**Ofcr:* Kevin Paulson
**Sr VP:* Esfandyar Dinshaw
Sr VP: John E Fromlt
**Sr VP:* Gary J Gaspar
**Sr VP:* Stephen P Horvat Jr
**Sr VP:* Donald J Lyons
**Sr VP:* Brian P Rohr
VP: Bob Coscarelli
VP: David Everett
**VP:* Jeff Hugunin
VP: Dan Kiefer
VP: Justin Rafferty

D-U-N-S 00-798-0329 IMP/EXP
MIDLAND PAPER CO (IL)
PAPERS UNLIMITED
101 E Palatine Rd, Wheeling, IL 60090-6512
Tel (847) 777-2700 *Founded/Ownrshp* 1907
Sales 897.4MM[E] *EMP* 400
SIC 5111 Printing paper
Pr: E Stanton Hooker III
**COO:* Michael Graves
**CFO:* Ralph Deletto
Chf Mktg O: John Millen
Ex VP: Frank Morley
VP: Hume Crawford
VP: Jim O'Toole
VP: Patti Rank
VP: Michael Ratcliff
VP: Tom Wolven
Genl Mgr: Wally Haglund

D-U-N-S 07-424-7305
MIDLAND PUBLIC SCHOOL DISTRICT
600 E Carpenter St, Midland, MI 48640-5417
Tel (989) 923-5001 *Founded/Ownrshp* 1900
Sales 66.1MM[E] *EMP* 1,396
Accts Yeo & Yeo Pc Saginaw Michig
SIC 8211 Public adult education school; Public combined elementary & secondary school
Dir IT: Steve Tacey
Schl Brd P: Gerald Wasserman
Teacher Pr: Brian Brutyn
Teacher Pr: Cynthia Marchese

D-U-N-S 62-339-5068
▲ **MIDLAND STATES BANCORP INC**
1201 Network Centre Dr, Effingham, IL 62401-4677
Tel (217) 342-7321 *Founded/Ownrshp* 1988
Sales NA *EMP* 700
Tkr Sym MSBI *Exch* NAS
SIC 6022 State commercial banks
Pr: Leon J Holschbach
**Ch Bd:* John M Schultz
CFO: Jeffrey G Ludwig
CFO: Kevin L Thompson
Treas: Michael Karibian
Chf Inves: John Culhane
Sr VP: Douglas J Tucker
VP: Eric Forguson
VP: Linda L Perry
VP: Jan Woodward
Exec: Scott Snavely
Board of Directors: Deborah A Golden, Jerry L McDaniel, Jeffrey M McDonnell, Dwight A Miller, Richard T Ramos, Laurence A Schiffer, Robert F Schultz, Thomas D Shaw, Jeffrey C Smith

D-U-N-S 00-798-1616
■ **MIDLAND STATES BANK**
(*Suby of* MIDLAND STATES BANCORP INC) ★
1201 Network Centre Dr, Effingham, IL 62401-4677
Tel (217) 342-2141 *Founded/Ownrshp* 1881, 1989
Sales NA *EMP* 125
SIC 6022 State commercial banks
Pr: Randall S Dempsey
Treas: Michael Karibian
Chf Cred: Jeff Brunoehler
VP: Scott Denton
VP: Eric R Forguson
VP: Ben Malsch
Exec: Ken Spaeth
Mng Ofcr: Pat Hartke
Rgnl Mgr: Doug Noble
IT Man: Jeff McDevitt
Board of Directors: Richard T Ramos, Thomas D Shaw

D-U-N-S 07-674-6999
■ **MIDLAND TITLE SECURITY INC**
FIRST AMRCN TTLE MIDLAND TITLE
(*Suby of* FIRST AMERICAN TITLE INSURANCE CO) ★
1111 Superior Ave E # 700, Cleveland, OH 44114-2540
Tel (216) 241-6045 *Founded/Ownrshp* 1986
Sales NA *EMP* 500
SIC 6361 Title insurance
Pr: James Stipanovich
CFO: Norman Romansky
VP: Michael Koors
VP: Jeff Myers

D-U-N-S 05-443-6118
■ **MIDLAND-GUARDIAN CO** (OH)
(*Suby of* MIDLAND CO) ★
7000 Midland Blvd, Amelia, OH 45102-2646
Tel (513) 943-7100 *Founded/Ownrshp* 1952, 1988
Sales NA *EMP* 1,080
SIC 6311 6331 Life insurance carriers; Fire, marine & casualty insurance: stock
**CFO:* Todd Gray
**Treas:* Matt McConnell
Ex VP: John Von Lehman

D-U-N-S 61-681-5122
■ **MIDLANDS MANAGEMENT CORP**
(*Suby of* PMA CAPITAL) ★
3817 Nw Expwy Ste 1000, Oklahoma City, OK 73112-1469
Tel (405) 840-0074 *Founded/Ownrshp* 1990
Sales NA *EMP* 190[E]
SIC 6411 6331 6321 Insurance agents & brokers; Fire, marine & casualty insurance; Accident & health insurance
Pr: Charles Caldwell
**Sec:* Dennis Ottis
Sr Cor Off: Mark Davis
**VP:* Sheryl Case
VP Mktg: Jake Harris
Manager: Bill Seal

D-U-N-S 06-932-9753
MIDLANDS TECHNICAL COLLEGE FOUNDATION
316 Beltline Blvd, Columbia, SC 29205-3624
Tel (803) 738-8324 *Founded/Ownrshp* 1974
Sales 2.2MM *EMP* 1,186
Accts Jackson Braswell Mullins & Bai
SIC 8222 8221 Technical institute; Colleges universities & professional schools
Ch Bd: Mary H Wilkins
**Treas:* R Scott McClelland
Assoc VP: Diane Carr
Assoc VP: Deborah Tirado
VP: Ron Drayton
**VP:* Van Gunter
**VP:* Sandy Oliver
**VP:* Starnell Williams
Assoc Dir: Allyson Porter
Genl Mgr: Jessica Booth
Pgrm Dir: Elaine Evans

MIDLOTHIAN HERITAGE HIGH SCHL
See MIDLOTHIAN INDEPENDENT SCHOOL DISTRICT

D-U-N-S 93-197-7417
MIDLOTHIAN INDEPENDENT SCHOOL DISTRICT
MIDLOTHIAN HERITAGE HIGH SCHL
100 Walter Stephenson Rd, Midlothian, TX 76065-3418
Tel (972) 723-6290 *Founded/Ownrshp* 1989
Sales 86.8MM *EMP* 618
Accts Hankins Eastup Deaton Tonn
SIC 8211 Public senior high school
Trst: Heather Prather
Dir Sec: Rhonda Welch
IT Man: Julie Wood
Pr Dir: Jana Pongratz
Schl Brd P: Wayne Shuffield
Instr Medi: Nancy Bergvall
Psych: Andra Chapman
HC Dir: Diane Gossett

D-U-N-S 00-503-6025 IMP/EXP
MIDMARK CORP (OH)
60 Vista Dr, Versailles, OH 45380-9310
Tel (937) 526-3662 *Founded/Ownrshp* 1915
Sales 390.0MM[E] *EMP* 1,530
SIC 3648 3842 3843 2542 3841 Lighting equipment; Stretchers; Dental equipment & supplies; Partitions & fixtures, except wood; Operating tables
Pr: Anne E D
**COO:* Greg Blackmore
**CFO:* Anthony Borzillo
**CFO:* Robert Morris
VP: Anne Eiting Klamar
VP: Dick Moorman
VP: Eric Shirley
Genl Mgr: Joe Rothstein
QA Dir: Denny Gerling
Mktg Mgr: Tom Gorman
Mktg Mgr: Beth Marshall

D-U-N-S 18-335-4877
MIDMICHIGAN HEALTH
4000 Wellness Dr, Midland, MI 48670-2000
Tel (989) 839-3000 *Founded/Ownrshp* 1983
Sales 677.9MM *EMP* 6,500[E]
SIC 8741 Hospital management
Pr: Terence F Moore
**Pr:* Richard M Reynolds
CFO: Francine Cadcagette
Trst: Robert Lofiego
VP: James Frye
VP: Dennis Knoss
Info Man: Gerald Wilhelm
Sls Dir: Shelli Wood
Psych: Lynn Simons
Surgeon: Jeffrey Bonacci
Opthamlgy: Thomas Claringbold

D-U-N-S 10-929-8471
MIDMICHIGAN HEALTH SERVICES
HOUGHTON LAKE HEALTH PARK
9249 W Lake City Rd, Houghton Lake, MI 48629-9602
Tel (989) 422-5148 *Founded/Ownrshp* 1977
Sales 8.9MM *EMP* 1,404
SIC 8011 Clinic, operated by physicians
**V Ch:* Jim Bischoff
**Ch:* Tom Moreau
**Sec:* Bev Budzynski
**Med Dir:* Jeffrey Strickler

D-U-N-S 07-259-4997
MIDMICHIGAN MEDICAL CENTER-GRATIOT (MI)
GRATIOT COMMUNITY HOSPITAL
300 E Warwick Dr, Alma, MI 48801-1014
Tel (989) 463-1101 *Founded/Ownrshp* 1953
Sales 90.8MM *EMP* 1,000
Accts Andrews Hooper Pavlik Plc Sag
SIC 8062 General medical & surgical hospitals
CEO: Marc Bush
**CFO:* Scott Currie
VP: Carol Goffnett
Dir Lab: Larry Lashuay
CIO: Mike Larson

D-U-N-S 10-687-3698
MIDMICHIGAN MEDICAL CENTER-MIDLAND
MIDLAND HOSPITAL
(*Suby of* HOUGHTON LAKE HEALTH PARK) ★
4000 Wellness Dr, Midland, MI 48670-2000
Tel (989) 839-3000 *Founded/Ownrshp* 1940
Sales 348.9MM *EMP* 1,404
Accts Andrews Hooper Pavlik Plc Sag
SIC 8062 General medical & surgical hospitals
Chf Rad: Rick Ohle
**CFO:* Scott Currie
CFO: Deb Mills
VP: Cindy Fredrich
**VP:* Sandy Hermann
VP: Tom Lind
**VP:* Francine Padgett
**VP:* Greg Rogers
Dir Lab: Randy Wise
Dir Rad: Katie Mostek
Dir Sec: Chris Warczynski

D-U-N-S 10-651-8517
MIDNITE AIR CORP
MNX
(*Suby of* RIVERSIDE CO) ★
2132 Michelson Dr, Irvine, CA 92612-1304
Tel (310) 330-2300 *Founded/Ownrshp* 2000
Sales 97.2MM[E] *EMP* 230
SIC 4513 Air courier services
CEO: Paul Martins
**COO:* Thomas Belmont
**CFO:* Sergio Palad
**Treas:* Steve Stubitz
Genl Mgr: Ed Rochat
Board of Directors: Renzo Dicarlo Matt Dailey, Renzo Dicaro, Marty Graul, Joseph Kolshak, Paul Martins, Steven Stubitz, Peter Tsang

MIDOCEAN PARTNERS
See MIDOCEAN US ADVISOR LP

D-U-N-S 13-325-4438
MIDOCEAN US ADVISOR LP
MIDOCEAN PARTNERS
320 Park Ave Fl 16, New York, NY 10022-6815
Tel (212) 497-1400 *Founded/Ownrshp* 2003
Sales 397.5MM[E] *EMP* 9,185
SIC 8742 Financial consultant
CEO: Ted Virtue
COO: Deborah Hodges
Ofcr: Candice Richards
VP: Barrett Gilmer
VP: Andrew Kuan
VP: Jonathan Marlow
VP: Daniel Penn
Mng Dir: Mike Apfel
Mng Dir: Christopher Cichella
Mng Dir: Frank Schiff

D-U-N-S 79-610-5930
MIDREX TECHNOLOGIES INC
(*Suby of* KOBE STEEL USA HOLDINGS INC) ★
2725 Water Ridge Pkwy # 100, Charlotte, NC 28217-4580
Tel (704) 373-1600 *Founded/Ownrshp* 1992
Sales 89.5MM[E] *EMP* 215[E]
SIC 8711 Engineering services
Pr: James D McClaskey
**CFO:* David Hamilton
**Ex VP:* Hiroshi Ishikawa
**Ex VP:* Akihiro Al Sawada
**VP:* Stephen Montague
VP: Eberhard Neumann
**VP:* Daniel J Sanford
VP: Masahiko Tetsumoto
Genl Mgr: Russell Howell
IT Man: Bill Keiger
Tech Mgr: Antonio Elliot

D-U-N-S 15-660-0710
▲ **MIDSOUTH BANCORP INC**
102 Versailles Blvd, Lafayette, LA 70501-6700
Tel (337) 237-8343 *Founded/Ownrshp* 1984
Sales NA *EMP* 536[E]
Tkr Sym MSL *Exch* NYS
SIC 6021 National commercial banks
Pr: Clive R Cloutier
**Ch Bd:* Will Charbonnet Sr
CFO: James R McLemore
Chf Cred: Jeffery L Blum
Exec: Troy Cloutier
Board of Directors: Leonard Q Abington, James R Davis Jr, Jake Delhomme, Milton B Kidd III, Timothy J Lemoine, R Glenn Pumpelly, William M Simmons, Joseph V Tortorice Jr

D-U-N-S 13-122-3273
■ **MIDSOUTH BANK NA**
(*Suby of* MIDSOUTH BANCORP INC) ★
102 Versailles Blvd # 100, Lafayette, LA 70501-6703
Tel (337) 237-8343 *Founded/Ownrshp* 1985
Sales NA *EMP* 600
SIC 6021 National commercial banks
Pr: Troy Cloutier
Pr: Lynn Fowler
Pr: Gary W Junek
Pr: David Locke
Pr: Blake McCaskill
Pr: John Wattinger
COO: Karen Hail
CFO: Terri Stelley
Chf Cred: John Nichols
Ofcr: Carolyn Lay
Ex VP: Donnie Landry
Sr VP: Jennifer Fontenot
Sr VP: Jem Fountenol
Sr VP: Teri Stelly
VP: David Bussell
VP: Ken Freeman
VP: Heather Hebert
VP: Lee F Hertel
VP: Adam Phillips
VP: Janice Savoie
Exec: Nell Britner
Board of Directors: Jake Delhomme

MIDSOUTH RFID
See RESOURCE LABEL GROUP LLC

D-U-N-S 06-925-6618
MIDSTATE MEDICAL CENTER
RADIOLOGY ASSOCIATES
(*Suby of* HARTFORD HEALTHCARE CORP) ★
435 Lewis Ave, Meriden, CT 06451-2101
Tel (203) 694-8200 *Founded/Ownrshp* 1885
Sales 212.3MM *EMP* 900
SIC 8062 Hospital, medical school affiliation
Pr: Lucille A Janatka
**CFO:* Ralph Becker
**VP:* Kenneth Cesca
VP: Harold P Kaplan
**VP:* Cindy Russo

D-U-N-S 07-839-8142
▲ **MIDSTATES PETROLEUM CO INC**
321 S Boston Ave Ste 1000, Tulsa, OK 74103-3322
Tel (918) 947-8550 *Founded/Ownrshp* 2011
Sales 365.1MM *EMP* 287
Tkr Sym MPO *Exch* ASE
SIC 1311 Crude petroleum & natural gas
CEO: Frederic F Brace
**Ch Bd:* Thomas C Knudson
COO: Mark E Eck
CFO: Nelson M Haight
Ex VP: Mitchell G Elkins

D-U-N-S 15-211-8477
MIDSTATES VIDEO CORP
1022 E Adams St, Springfield, IL 62703-1028
Tel (217) 544-8433 *Founded/Ownrshp* 1985
Sales 307.4MM[E] *EMP* 5,000
SIC 7389 7841 Coffee service; Video disk/tape rental to the general public
CEO: Charles R Hoogland
**Pr:* Keith Hoogland
Pr: Bob Kording
CFO: Craig Hartner
**Treas:* Charles Eric Hoogland
Dist Mgr: Andra L Morrissey

D-U-N-S 08-395-8371
MIDTEX OIL LP
PIT STOP FOOD MART
3455 Ih 35 S, New Braunfels, TX 78132-5270
Tel (830) 625-4214 *Founded/Ownrshp* 1986
Sales 101.4MM[E] *EMP* 220
SIC 5541 5171 Filling stations, gasoline; Petroleum bulk stations
CEO: Maurice D Fischer
Pr: Rodney Fischer
CFO: Scott Schwind
VP: Russell Fischer
IT Man: Matt Curtis
Mktg Mgr: Katie Perera

MIDTOWN ATHLETIC CLUBS
See TENNIS CORP OF AMERICA

D-U-N-S 00-693-1133
MIDVALE INDEMNITY CO (IL)
6000 American Pkwy, Madison, WI 53783-0001
Tel (847) 320-2000 *Founded/Ownrshp* 1912
Sales NA *EMP* 9,000
Accts Kpmg Llp
SIC 6331 8099 Workers' compensation insurance; Automobile insurance; Fire, marine & casualty insurance & carriers; Property damage insurance; Medical services organization
Pr: Douglas Andrews
**CFO:* Frederick T Griffith
Treas: Clark H Roberts
IT Man: Mike Gibbs
Board of Directors: John T Chain Jr, Peter B Hamilton, George R Lewis, Arthur J Massolo, David B Mathis

MIDWAY CAR RENTAL
See MIDWAY RENT A CAR INC

D-U-N-S 03-591-5149
MIDWAY CHEVROLET CO
MIDWAY ISUZU
2323 W Bell Rd, Phoenix, AZ 85023-3298
Tel (602) 866-0102 *Founded/Ownrshp* 1966
Sales 88.6MM[E] *EMP* 255[E]
SIC 5511 Automobiles, new & used
Pr: Larry Van Tuyl
**CFO:* John Bhatt
**Sec:* Allan M Cady
**VP:* Patricia Van Tuyl
Sls Mgr: Richie Levingston

D-U-N-S 00-694-3476
MIDWAY CO-OP ASSOCIATION
MIDWAY COOP
210 W Harrison St, Osborne, KS 67473-1500
Tel (785) 346-5451 *Founded/Ownrshp* 1908
Sales 130.2MM *EMP* 90
Accts Lindburg Vogel Pierce Faris H
SIC 5153 5171 Grains; Petroleum bulk stations & terminals
Genl Mgr: Dell Princ
Sales Exec: Kenneth A Otte

MIDWAY COOP
See MIDWAY CO-OP ASSOCIATION

MIDWAY ENERGY SERVICES
See MIDWAY OILFIELD CONSTRUCTORS INC

D-U-N-S 03-129-4283
MIDWAY FORD TRUCK CENTER INC (DE)
7601 Ne 38th St, Kansas City, MO 64161-9409
Tel (816) 455-3000 *Founded/Ownrshp* 1961, 1973
Sales 116.8MM^E *EMP* 235
SIC 5511 7538 Trucks, tractors & trailers: new & used; General automotive repair shops
CEO: Donald C Ahnger
**Pr:* Trey Meyer
**CFO:* Michael Doran
Ofcr: Mike Goebel
**Ex VP:* Michael Gaskill
**Ex VP:* Danny Warner
VP: John Miller
VP: Larry Pasquini
VP: Dwight A Potts
**VP:* Terry Tyrrell
Exec: Kathy Mandacina
Board of Directors: Mark Graves

D-U-N-S 61-185-1627 IMP
MIDWAY IMPORTING INC
1807 Brittmoore Rd, Houston, TX 77043-2213
Tel (713) 802-9363 *Founded/Ownrshp* 1989
Sales 126.7MM^E *EMP* 230
SIC 5122 Cosmetics, perfumes & hair products
Pr: Christopher D Hartmann
**CFO:* Thomas J Schifanella Jr
Exec: Kathy Collins

D-U-N-S 10-261-3940
MIDWAY INDEPENDENT SCHOOL DISTRICT
13885 Woodway Dr, Woodway, TX 76712-7621
Tel (254) 761-5610 *Founded/Ownrshp* 1947
Sales 60.2MM *EMP* 1,060
Accts Pattillom Brown & Hill Llp W
SIC 8211 Public elementary school; Public junior high school; Public senior high school

MIDWAY ISUZU
See MIDWAY CHEVROLET CO

D-U-N-S 06-797-2349
MIDWAY OILFIELD CONSTRUCTORS INC (TX)
MIDWAY ENERGY SERVICES
12627 State Highway 21 E, Midway, TX 75852-2833
Tel (936) 348-3721 *Founded/Ownrshp* 1981
Sales 289.7MM^E *EMP* 650
SIC 1389 1623 Oil field services; Oil & gas pipeline construction
Pr: Billy A Smith Sr
VP: Jake Cain
Exec: Ginger Barger
Dir Bus: Landon Martin
Opers Mgr: Mil Clute
Opers Mgr: Ryan Payne

D-U-N-S 87-423-2465
MIDWAY PRODUCTS GROUP INC
1 Lyman E Hoyt Dr, Monroe, MI 48161
Tel (734) 241-7242 *Founded/Ownrshp* 1991
Sales 190.9MM^E *EMP* 352
SIC 8741 3469 Management services; Metal stampings
Pr: James E Hoyt
**VP:* Lloyd A Miller
Prgrm Mgr: Lou Achille
Prgrm Mgr: Robert Bazner
Prgrm Mgr: Dan Bolster
Prgrm Mgr: Ken Gove
Mfg Dir: Bob Prucka
Opers Mgr: David Clawson
Plnt Mgr: Erik Brodin
Ql Cn Mgr: Sandy Dillon

D-U-N-S 80-855-4992
MIDWAY RENT A CAR INC
MIDWAY CAR RENTAL
4751 Wilshire Blvd # 120, Los Angeles, CA 90010-3827
Tel (323) 692-4000 *Founded/Ownrshp* 1977
Sales 90.0MM *EMP* 400
SIC 5511 7515 5521 4119 7513

MIDWAY TECHNOLOGY SOLUTIONS
See HUNT ELECTRIC CORP

D-U-N-S 13-937-4680 IMP/EXP
MIDWEST AIR TECHNOLOGIES INC
MAT
(*Suby of* MAT-AUTOMOTIVE) ★
6700 Wildlife Way, Long Grove, IL 60047
Tel (847) 821-9630 *Founded/Ownrshp* 1984
Sales 137.8MM^E *EMP* 75
Accts Bdo Seidman Llp
SIC 5072 5191 5063 5051 5031 Hardware; Garden supplies; Electrical apparatus & equipment; Nails; Fencing, wood
Pr: George Ruhl
CFO: Gregory R Puse
VP: Grace Chang
VP: Doug Hale
VP: Steven Rovtar
VP: Charles Walker
Dir IT: Kevin Balster
Opers Mgr: Patty Cate

D-U-N-S 03-941-2275
MIDWEST AIR TRAFFIC CONTROL SERVICE INC
7285 W 132nd St Ste 340, Overland Park, KS 66213-1164
Tel (913) 782-7082 *Founded/Ownrshp* 1978
Sales 89.2MM *EMP* 12
SIC 4581 Airport control tower operation, except government
Pr: Shane Cordes
**CFO:* Greg Schoofs

D-U-N-S 00-506-6873 IMP/EXP
MIDWEST CANVAS CORP (IL)
4635 W Lake St, Chicago, IL 60644-2798
Tel (773) 287-4400 *Founded/Ownrshp* 1947, 1960
Sales 108.5MM^E *EMP* 300^E
SIC 3081 3089 Plastic film & sheet; Laminating of plastic
Pr: Barry A Handwerker
IT Man: Steve Rosen
Plnt Mgr: Scott Kramer
Sls Dir: Paul Winn

D-U-N-S 05-209-8345
MIDWEST CASE MANAGEMENT INC
MIDWEST VOCATIONAL MANAGEMENT
2905 Lucerne Dr Se # 102, Grand Rapids, MI 49546-7160
Tel (616) 957-7796 *Founded/Ownrshp* 1988
Sales 900.0MM^E *EMP* 8
SIC 8331 Job training & vocational rehabilitation services
Pr: Nicole Phillips-Smith
Genl Mgr: Michele Korponai

D-U-N-S 10-006-6190
MIDWEST CITY PUBLIC SCHOOLS I-52
MID-DEL SCHOOL SYSTEM
7217 Se 15th St, Oklahoma City, OK 73110-5235
Tel (405) 737-4461 *Founded/Ownrshp* 1944
Sales 95.0MM *EMP* 1,700
Accts Murrel Hall Mcintosh & Co
SIC 8211 Public elementary & secondary schools
**CFO:* Kay Medcals
Software D: April Barney
Psych: Becky Worth

D-U-N-S 07-625-2659
■ **MIDWEST DIVISION RMC LLC**
RESEARCH COLLEGE OF NURSING
(*Suby of* HOSPITAL COPORATION OF AMERICA) ★
2316 E Meyer Blvd, Kansas City, MO 64132-1136
Tel (816) 276-4000 *Founded/Ownrshp* 2003
Sales 354.1MM *EMP* 2,400
SIC 8062 General medical & surgical hospitals
Dir Rx: Robert Bub
CIO: Kent McAllister
Dir IT: William Schwab
Pathlgst: Larry Lawson

D-U-N-S 05-996-6986
MIDWEST DRYWALL CO INC
MDC DRYWALL
1351 S Reca Ct Ste 101, Wichita, KS 67209-1815
Tel (316) 722-9559 *Founded/Ownrshp* 1972
Sales 135.5MM^E *EMP* 800
SIC 1742 Drywall; Acoustical & ceiling work; Plastering, plain or ornamental
Pr: Steven A Nienke
**CFO:* Denis Dieker

D-U-N-S 04-237-9594
MIDWEST ENERGY INC
1330 Canterbury Dr, Hays, KS 67601-2708
Tel (785) 625-3437 *Founded/Ownrshp* 1979
Sales 205.8MM *EMP* 274
Accts Bkd Llp Oklahoma City Oklah
SIC 4911 8611 Generation, electric power; Business associations
Pr: Earnest A Lehman
**Treas:* Chuck Moore
VP: Rhiannon Corn
**VP:* Bill Dowling
**VP:* Sharon Dreher
**VP:* Tim Flax
VP: Phil Goodell
VP: Lynn Horner
**VP:* Tom Meis
Opers Mgr: Brett Albert
Opers Mgr: Michael Stremel

D-U-N-S 18-340-3674
MIDWEST EXPRESS INC
(*Suby of* HONDA LOGISTICS NORTH AMERICA INC) ★
11590 Township Road 298, East Liberty, OH 43319-9450
Tel (937) 642-0335 *Founded/Ownrshp* 2008
Sales 175.6MM^E *EMP* 1,183
SIC 4226 Special warehousing & storage
Pr: Tamaki Hashimoto
Treas: Akio Nabuto
**VP:* Ed Allison
VP: Brian Blair
**VP:* Robert Overbaugh
**Prin:* Tadao Endo
Tech Mgr: Tonya Wright
Opers Mgr: Jacqueline Wheeler

MIDWEST FARMERS COOP
See GREENWOOD FARMERS COOPERATIVE

D-U-N-S 00-486-9442
MIDWEST FARMERS COOPERATIVE
304 S 3rd St, Elmwood, NE 68349-6114
Tel (402) 994-2585 *Founded/Ownrshp* 1919
Sales 170.7MM *EMP* 150
Accts Gardiner Thomsen Cpa Lincoln
SIC 5153 5191 5541 Grains; Fertilizer & fertilizer materials; Feed; Filling stations, gasoline
Pr: Dale Piper
**CFO:* Tim Junge
CFO: Tim Piper
IT Man: Gayln Boesiger

D-U-N-S 62-352-6840
MIDWEST FOOD BANK NFP
1703 S Veterans Pkwy, Bloomington, IL 61701-7019
Tel (309) 663-5350 *Founded/Ownrshp* 2003
Sales 89.4MM *EMP* 2^E
Accts Phillips & Salmi Associates Ll
SIC 8322 Individual & family services
Pr: David Kieser
**Treas:* Dave Hodel
**VP:* John Feit

MIDWEST FOODS
See MID-WEST INSTITUTIONAL FOOD DISTRIBUTORS INC

D-U-N-S 12-711-2931
■ **MIDWEST GENERATION EME LLC**
(*Suby of* EDISON MISSION ENERGY) ★
440 Suth La Salle St 3500, Chicago, IL 60605
Tel (312) 583-6000 *Founded/Ownrshp* 1999
Sales 1.6MMM^E *EMP* 1,000
SIC 4911 Electric services
Rgnl VP: Charles Parnell
VP: Mark Clarke
VP: John Deshong
Dir IT: Jacqueline Trapp

D-U-N-S 11-446-6571 IMP
■ **MIDWEST GENERATION LLC**
(*Suby of* NRG ENERGY INC) ★
529 E Romeo Rd, Romeoville, IL 60446-1538
Tel (609) 524-4526 *Founded/Ownrshp* 2013
Sales 360.7MM^E *EMP* 586
SIC 4911 Electric services; Distribution, electric power; Generation, electric power; Transmission, electric power
Pr: Douglas R McFarlan
CFO: Maria Rigatti
Ofcr: David Knox
VP: John C Kennedy
VP: Fred W McCluskey
VP: Daniel D McDevitt

D-U-N-S 07-934-7612
MIDWEST GERIATRIC MANAGEMENT LLC
MGM HEALTHCARE
477 N Lindbergh Blvd # 310, Saint Louis, MO 63141-7856
Tel (314) 631-3000 *Founded/Ownrshp* 2011
Sales 1.2MMM^E *EMP* 134
SIC 8741 Management services; Nursing & personal care facility management
Pr: Judah Bienstock
**Prin:* Emily Baxter

MIDWEST GLOVES AND GEAR
See MIDWEST QUALITY GLOVES INC

D-U-N-S 00-691-9476 IMP/EXP
MIDWEST HARDWOOD CORP
METRO HARDWOODS
9540 83rd Ave N, Maple Grove, MN 55369-4567
Tel (763) 425-8700 *Founded/Ownrshp* 1981
Sales 145.0MM^E *EMP* 385
SIC 5031 2421 Lumber: rough, dressed & finished; Plywood; Particleboard; Molding, all materials; Sawmills & planing mills, general; Kiln drying of lumber; Custom sawmill
Pr: Michael D Flynn
COO: Michael Mallin
CIO: Chris Olson
Sls Mgr: Joyce Wilson

MIDWEST HAYWOOD
See HAYWOOD REGIONAL MEDICAL CENTER

MIDWEST HOSE
See MID-WEST HOSE & SPECIALTY INC

MIDWEST KENWORTH
See OZARK KENWORTH INC

D-U-N-S 10-677-0980
MIDWEST LOGISTICS SYSTEMS LTD
7021 State Route 703, Celina, OH 45822-2777
Tel (419) 584-1414 *Founded/Ownrshp* 1998
Sales 87.3MM^E *EMP* 389
SIC 4213 4212 Trucking, except local; Local trucking, without storage
Pr: F Edward Voelker
Trst: Andrew Roettger
Trst: Bill Russell
**VP:* Ellen Welker
**Prin:* James Duvall
Oper/Mgr: Floyd Sheaks

MIDWEST MANUFACTURING
See MENARD INC

D-U-N-S 07-950-1758 IMP/EXP
MIDWEST MANUFACTURING INC
(*Suby of* MIDWEST MANUFACTURING) ★
5311 Kane Rd, Eau Claire, WI 54703-9822
Tel (715) 876-5555 *Founded/Ownrshp* 1983
Sales 151.9MM^E *EMP* 200^E
SIC 5033 5031 3965 Roofing & siding materials; Building materials, exterior; Fasteners
Pr: John Menard
Plnt Mgr: Brett Leith
Prd Mgr: Mike Grant

D-U-N-S 05-396-8590 IMP/EXP
MIDWEST MEDICAL SUPPLY CO LLC
MMS, A MEDICAL SUPPLY COMPANY
(*Suby of* SENECA MEDICAL) ★
13400 Lakefront Dr, Earth City, MO 63045-1516
Tel (314) 291-2900 *Founded/Ownrshp* 2016
Sales 291.8MM^E *EMP* 440
SIC 5047 Medical equipment & supplies
Pr: Gary Reeve
**Ex VP:* Tom Harris
Sr VP: Dan Rieman
VP: Spencer King
VP: Kelly Siebert
VP: Tom Tenhula
Genl Mgr: Richard Hawkins
Genl Mgr: Gina Marchese
QA Dir: Pam Scherrer
IT Man: George Kellner
VP Opers: Kevin McDonnell

D-U-N-S 00-386-8213
MIDWEST MOTOR EXPRESS INC (ND)
(*Suby of* MME, INC.)
5015 E Main Ave, Bismarck, ND 58501-9301
Tel (701) 223-1880 *Founded/Ownrshp* 1938
Sales 92.8MM *EMP* 695
SIC 4212 Local trucking, without storage
CEO: John T Roswick
Pr: Marlin Kling
CFO: Jodi Kary
VP: Joe Greenstein
Brnch Mgr: Ken Loken
Genl Mgr: Ron Martin
IT Man: Jim Sullivan
Opers Mgr: Chapman Law
Opers Mgr: Craig C Ramsay
Trfc Mgr: Keith Becker
Trfc Mgr: Frieze Sheri

D-U-N-S 01-790-6231 IMP
MIDWEST MOTOR SUPPLY CO
KIMBALL MIDWEST
4800 Roberts Rd, Columbus, OH 43228-9791
Tel (800) 233-1294 *Founded/Ownrshp* 1955
Sales 152.5MM^E *EMP* 670
SIC 3965 3399 8742 Fasteners; Metal fasteners; Materials mgmt. (purchasing, handling, inventory) consultant
Pr: Patrick J McCurdy Jr
**CFO:* Robert McCurdy
**VP:* Charles McCurdy
**Prin:* A Glenn McClelland
Manager: Dale Tinkham
Sales Asso: Chris Ryan

D-U-N-S 02-027-4804
MIDWEST OPERATING ENGINEERS FRINGE BENEFIT FUND
6150 Joliet Rd, Countryside, IL 60525-3994
Tel (708) 482-0589 *Founded/Ownrshp* 1963
Sales NA *EMP* 80
SIC 6371 Union welfare, benefit & health funds

D-U-N-S 96-164-0682
MIDWEST OPERATING ENGINEERS WELFARE FUND
6150 Joliet Rd, Countryside, IL 60525-3994
Tel (708) 482-7300 *Founded/Ownrshp* 2010
Sales 331.0MM *EMP* 2
Accts Graff Ballauer & Blanski Pc N
SIC 6722 Management investment, open-end
Prin: David Bodley

D-U-N-S 03-106-9941
MIDWEST PETROLEUM CO (MO)
6760 Southwest Ave, Saint Louis, MO 63143-2624
Tel (314) 647-5550 *Founded/Ownrshp* 1938
Sales 159.4MM^E *EMP* 450
Accts Bkd Llp St Louis Mo
SIC 5541 Gasoline service stations
Pr: Don McNutt
COO: Walter Vance
**VP:* Bernard Levin
**VP:* Mike McNutt
Dist Mgr: Gary Masters
Dist Mgr: Ken Nill
Dir IT: Paul Jeffries
Dir IT: Marty O'Brien

D-U-N-S 04-899-5484 IMP
MIDWEST POULTRY SERVICES LP
MIDWEST PULLET FARM
9951 W State Road 25, Mentone, IN 46539-9131
Tel (574) 353-7232 *Founded/Ownrshp* 1993
Sales 174.9MM *EMP* 350
Accts Haines Isenbarger & Skiba Ll
SIC 0751 2015 Poultry services; Egg processing
CEO: Robert Krouse
Genl Mgr: Dan Krouse
Sfty Mgr: Stacey Harsh
Sls Mgr: Mike Krouse
Sls Mgr: Jennifer Taylor

MIDWEST PRO SERV
See PULMUONE FOODS USA INC

MIDWEST PULLET FARM
See MIDWEST POULTRY SERVICES LP

D-U-N-S 11-893-0577 IMP
MIDWEST QUALITY GLOVES INC
MIDWEST GLOVES AND GEAR
835 Industrial Rd, Chillicothe, MO 64601-3218
Tel (660) 646-2165 *Founded/Ownrshp* 1984
Sales 99.4MM^E *EMP* 215
Accts Bkd Llp Kansas City Missour
SIC 5199 3151 Leather goods, except footwear, gloves, luggage, belting; Leather gloves & mittens; Gloves, leather: work
Pr: Stephen J Franke
**COO:* Karen Nichols
Exec: Elizabeth Fechtig

D-U-N-S 14-826-7313
■ **MIDWEST REGIONAL MEDICAL CENTER LLC**
(*Suby of* HMA) ★
2825 Parklawn Dr, Midwest City, OK 73110-4201
Tel (405) 610-4411 *Founded/Ownrshp* 1961
Sales 183.5MM *EMP* 1,205
SIC 8011 8062 Medical centers; Hospital, affiliated with AMA residency
CEO: Damon Brown
Dir Risk M: Bernadette Burns
Dir Rx: Luann Young

MIDWEST RESEARCH INSTITUTE
See MRIGLOBAL

D-U-N-S 62-332-7434 IMP
MIDWEST SCRAP MANAGEMENT INC
4501 Packers Ave, Saint Joseph, MO 64504-3532
Tel (816) 214-9204 *Founded/Ownrshp* 1996
Sales 125.0MM *EMP* 35^E
SIC 5093 Metal scrap & waste materials
CEO: Kenneth A Burgess Jr
**Sec:* Shirley Butcher

D-U-N-S 02-304-6501
MIDWEST SIGN & SCREEN PRINTING SUPPLY CO INC
45 Maryland Ave E, Saint Paul, MN 55117-4610
Tel (651) 489-9999 *Founded/Ownrshp* 1977
Sales 122.0MM^E *EMP* 187
SIC 5084 5063 Printing trades machinery, equipment & supplies; Electrical supplies
CEO: Nancy J Peterson Anderson
VP: Craig Anderson
VP: Lyle Hanzal
VP: Russel May
VP: Roger Olson
Opers Mgr: Bob Dalpe
Sales Asso: Becky Chambers

D-U-N-S 19-807-2506
MIDWEST STAFFING GROUP INC
162 Pennsylvania Ave W, Saint Paul, MN 55103-1893
Tel (651) 641-0442 *Founded/Ownrshp* 1988
Sales 29.9MM^E *EMP* 4,018
SIC 7363 Temporary help service
Pr: Joseph Thoemke
**CFO:* Anna Marie Theissen
Dir Bus: Dan Iannazzo

D-U-N-S 60-408-2701
MIDWEST STEEL INC
2525 E Grand Blvd, Detroit, MI 48211-2001
Tel (313) 873-2220 *Founded/Ownrshp* 1989
Sales 130.0MM *EMP* 500
SIC 3441 1791 Fabricated structural metal; Structural steel erection
Pr: Gary R Broad
CFO: Ken Crismore
Sls Dir: Mike Adkins
Snr Mgr: Jeff Curley

D-U-N-S 60-733-1498 IMP
MIDWEST TAPE LLC
1417 Timber Wolf Dr, Holland, OH 43528-8302
Tel (419) 868-9370 *Founded/Ownrshp* 2004
Sales 105.7MM^E *EMP* 330
SIC 7822 5099 8741 7389 5961 7374 Video tapes, recorded: wholesale; Motion picture distribution; Video cassettes, accessories & supplies; Administrative management; Packaging & labeling services; ; Data processing service
VP: Brad Rose
Exec: Jeff Jankowski
Genl Mgr: Gerald Bascuk
Genl Mgr: Sue Bascuk

D-U-N-S 04-756-5866 EXP
MIDWEST TRANSIT EQUIPMENT INC
146 W Issert Dr, Kankakee, IL 60901-7134
Tel (815) 933-2412 *Founded/Ownrshp* 1991
Sales 185.9MM^E *EMP* 100
SIC 5012 Buses; Trucks, commercial
Pr: Barry Huebner
**Ch Bd:* James Bridgewater Sr
**Sec:* James R Bridgewater Jr
Opers Mgr: Jeff Burlison
Opers Mgr: Mario Tafoya
Manager: Sam Day
Sls Mgr: Jerod Collins
Sls Mgr: Joe Crabtree

D-U-N-S 04-921-1089
MIDWEST TRANSPORT INC
11385 N Trimble Rd, Robinson, IL 62454-7206
Tel (618) 544-3399 *Founded/Ownrshp* 2003
Sales 103.5MM^E *EMP* 700
Accts Kemper Cpa Group Llc
SIC 4213 Trucking, except local
Pr: Mitch Ferree
**CFO:* Brian Garrard
Genl Couns: John Elmore

D-U-N-S 02-780-4421
MIDWEST UNDERGROUND TECHNOLOGY INC
MUTI
(*Suby of* SABRE COMMUNICATIONS) ★
2626 Midwest Ct, Champaign, IL 61822-8929
Tel (217) 819-3040 *Founded/Ownrshp* 2013
Sales 103.4MM^E *EMP* 400^E
SIC 1731 1623 Fiber optic cable installation; Water, sewer & utility lines
Pr: Darrin M Peters
VP: Geoff Bennett
VP: Scott Kisting
VP: Doug Poe
Sftwr Eng: Marshall Quick

D-U-N-S 10-053-7096
MIDWEST UNITED ENERGY LLC
(*Suby of* MIDWEST ENERGY INC) ★
12687 W Cedar Dr Ste 200, Lakewood, CO 80228-2014
Tel (303) 989-7165 *Founded/Ownrshp* 2000
Sales 117.2MM *EMP* 7
Accts Ghp Horwath Pc
SIC 5172 Gases

D-U-N-S 02-292-0821
MIDWEST VETERINARY SUPPLY INC
21467 Holyoke Ave, Lakeville, MN 55044-7303
Tel (952) 894-4350 *Founded/Ownrshp* 1960
Sales 311.0MM^E *EMP* 260
SIC 5122 5047 Animal medicines; Veterinarians' equipment & supplies
Pr: Guy G Flickinger
CFO: Janice Halvorsen
**Ex VP:* Cheryl Peterson
**VP:* Thomas Wheeler
Dir Bus: Pam Koopman
Dir IT: Stefan Lindberg
Dir IT: Brad Peterson
Manager: Larry Rustand
Sls Mgr: Gwen Dunn
Sls Mgr: Alane Halley
Sls Mgr: Rebecca Nankervis

MIDWEST VOCATIONAL MANAGEMENT
See MIDWEST CASE MANAGEMENT INC

D-U-N-S 07-459-0969
MIDWESTERN REGIONAL MEDICAL CENTER INC
(*Suby of* CTCA) ★
2501 Emmaus Ave, Zion, IL 60099
Tel (847) 731-1364 *Founded/Ownrshp* 1975
Sales 84.3MM^E *EMP* 1,021
SIC 8069 Cancer hospital
CEO: Scott Jones
**Ch Bd:* Richard J Stephenson
Pr: Elizabeth Maribito
Ofcr: Janet Cheek
Ofcr: Sharon Day
Sr VP: Jacklynn Lesniak
Dir Rx: Gregg Helm
**Prin:* Anne Meisner
Acupntre: Stephen Ray

D-U-N-S 18-177-8846
MIDWESTERN UNIVERSITY
555 31st St, Downers Grove, IL 60515-1235
Tel (630) 515-7300 *Founded/Ownrshp* 1985
Sales 380.2MM *EMP* 1,300
Accts Ernst & Young Llp Chicago Il
SIC 8221 University
Pr: Kathleen H Goeppinger
V Ch: Mary Kliethermes
**CFO:* Gregory J Gaus
**VP:* Karen D Johnson
**VP:* Mary Lee
VP: Dean Malon
**VP:* Dean Malone
**VP:* Angela Marty
**Exec:* Arthur G Dobbelaere
Comm Dir: Dana Fay
Dir Rx: Susan R Winkler

D-U-N-S 62-709-4675
▲ MIDWESTONE FINANCIAL GROUP INC
102 S Clinton St, Iowa City, IA 52240-4065
Tel (319) 356-5800 *Founded/Ownrshp* 1983
Sales NA *EMP* 374^E
Accts Rsm Us Llp Cedar Rapids Iowa
Tkr Sym MOFG *Exch* NGS
SIC 6022 6331 State commercial banks; Assessment associations: fire, marine & casualty insurance
Pr: Charles N Funk
**Ch Bd:* Kevin W Monson
COO: Susan R Evans
CFO: Gary J Ortale
Ofcr: James M Cantrell
Ofcr: Holly Hankins
Ofcr: Kent L Jehle
Ofcr: Marcia McKeag
VP: Allen Schneider
VP: Jason Swestka
Exec: Ron Haines
Exec: Kathy Simon

D-U-N-S 11-856-2412 IMP
MIECO INC
(*Suby of* MARUBENI CORPORATION)
301 E Ocean Blvd Ste 1100, Long Beach, CA 90802-4832
Tel (562) 435-0085 *Founded/Ownrshp* 1984
Sales 157.3MM^E *EMP* 50
SIC 5172 4925 Petroleum brokers; Mixed natural & manufactured gas, distribution
**CEO:* Tomonari Sano
COO: Bettie Claxton
VP: Doug Jeter
VP: Bruce Shapiro
Dir Risk M: Kristin Seawright
Genl Mgr: Dave Engbrock

D-U-N-S 11-534-8054 IMP/EXP
MIELE INC
MIELE PROFESSIONAL PRODUCTS
(*Suby of* MIELE & CIE. KG)
9 Independence Way, Princeton, NJ 08540-6621
Tel (609) 419-9898 *Founded/Ownrshp* 1984
Sales 88.9MM^E *EMP* 275
SIC 5064 Electric household appliances
Pr: Nick Ord
VP: Jeremy Jones
VP: Peggy Kotlarz
Exec: Ellie Jocham
Dir Soc: Vicki Robb
Rgnl Mgr: Justin Wagner
Genl Mgr: Lisa Choplo
Genl Mgr: Stephanie Dickerson
CTO: Ned Brigham
IT Man: Carol McDonald
IT Man: Aixa Saez-Ferry

MIELE PROFESSIONAL PRODUCTS
See MIELE INC

MIGHTY DISTRIBUTING SYS AMER
See MDSA LLC

MIGHTY GOOD
See H & S BAKERY INC

D-U-N-S 11-857-5422 IMP
■ MIKASA INC
(*Suby of* LIFETIME BRANDS INC) ★
1 Century Way, Secaucus, NJ 07094-2532
Tel (866) 645-2721 *Founded/Ownrshp* 2008
Sales 168.6MM^E *EMP* 1,048
SIC 5023 5099 5719 Home furnishings; China; Glassware; Stainless steel flatware; Crystal goods; Kitchenware
Pr: Raymond B Dingman Jr
**Ch Bd:* George T Aratani
VP: Enrique Bernal
VP: Shannon M Erson
VP: James B Linsalata
VP: Shannon Merson
**VP:* Anthony F Santarelli
Creative D: Robert T Wheale
Mktg Mgr: Julie Lien

D-U-N-S 15-345-6488
MIKE CAMPBELL & ASSOCIATES LTD
MIKE CAMPBELL ASSOC LOGICTICS
13031 Temple Ave, City of Industry, CA 91746-1418
Tel (626) 369-3981 *Founded/Ownrshp* 1983
Sales 123.0MM^E *EMP* 1,000
SIC 4222 4225 4214 4213 Storage, frozen or refrigerated goods; General warehousing & storage; Local trucking with storage; Trucking, except local
CEO: Vickie J Campbell
**Pr:* James Heermans
**Pr:* Paul Trump
Mktg Dir: Ryan Campbell

MIKE CAMPBELL ASSOC LOGICTICS
See MIKE CAMPBELL & ASSOCIATES LTD

D-U-N-S 00-190-8086 IMP/EXP
■ MIKE HALL CHEVROLET INC
AUTONATION CHEVROLET HIGHWAY 6
(*Suby of* AUTONATION ENTERPRISES INC) ★
8100 Highway 6 S, Houston, TX 77083-5701
Tel (281) 561-9900 *Founded/Ownrshp* 1998
Sales 1.6MMM^E *EMP* 8,000
SIC 5511 Automobiles, new & used
**Pr:* David Casto
**Treas:* Ian Swartz
**VP:* Ed Bailey
Genl Mgr: Aaron Harrison
Off Mgr: Amy Konstantin

D-U-N-S 96-695-3387
MIKE KELLY FOUNDATION FOR ARTS
7019 N Figueroa St, Los Angeles, CA 90042-1247
Tel (323) 257-7853 *Founded/Ownrshp* 2011
Sales 86.6MM *EMP* 2^E
Accts Regina Chinweze Accountancy Co
SIC 8699 Charitable organization
Prin: Antonio G Martires

MIKE MCGRATH AUTO CENTER
See MCGRATH AUTOMOTIVE GROUP INC

D-U-N-S 94-107-0864
MIKE ROVNER CONSTRUCTION INC
MRC
5400 Tech Cir, Moorpark, CA 93021-1792
Tel (805) 584-5961 *Founded/Ownrshp* 1991
Sales 131.3MM^E *EMP* 300
Accts Mayer Hoffman Mccann Pc Oxn
SIC 1522 Remodeling, multi-family dwellings
Pr: Mike Rovner
VP: Dave Holland
Dir Bus: Thomas McBride
IT Man: Stephen Parks

D-U-N-S 02-322-8224 IMP
MIKE SHANNON AUTOMOTIVE INC
HOLIDAY MAZDA
321 N Rolling Meadows Dr, Fond Du Lac, WI 54937-9726
Tel (920) 921-8898 *Founded/Ownrshp* 1979
Sales 144.5MM^E *EMP* 175
SIC 5511 Automobiles, new & used
Pr: Michael Shannon
**COO:* Rob Beane
**Sec:* Pat McCullough
VP: Bill Agnew
Sls Mgr: Chad Guell

D-U-N-S 15-424-1967
MIKE STUART ENTERPRISES INC
LAKELAND PHARMACY
18565 Business 13, Branson West, MO 65737-9659
Tel (417) 272-8064 *Founded/Ownrshp* 1998
Sales 140.3MM^E *EMP* 100
SIC 5122 Pharmaceuticals
Pr: Mike Stuart
Off Mgr: Dan Priest
IT Man: Jim Parten
Cert Phar: Anne Lafferty
Cert Phar: Brenda Smith
Cert Phar: Heather Sutherland

D-U-N-S 96-502-9366
MIKEN SPECIALTIES LTD
BROCK GROUP, THE
(*Suby of* ATLANTIC HOLDINGS II INC) ★
10343 Sam Houston Park Dr, Houston, TX 77064-4656
Tel (979) 265-9599 *Founded/Ownrshp* 2008
Sales 56.7MM^E *EMP* 1,054
SIC 1721 1799 Industrial painting; Fireproofing buildings; Insulation of pipes & boilers
Pt: Mike Scarborough
Pt: Robert Hardy
Mtls Mgr: Dan Holy

D-U-N-S 04-668-6622 IMP
MIKRON INDUSTRIES INC
1034 6th Ave N, Kent, WA 98032-2991
Tel (253) 854-8020 *Founded/Ownrshp* 2004
Sales NA *EMP* 1,000
SIC 3089

D-U-N-S 04-600-2572 IMP
MIKUNI AMERICAN CORP
M A C
(*Suby of* MIKUNI CORPORATION)
8910 Mikuni Ave, Northridge, CA 91324-3403
Tel (310) 676-0522 *Founded/Ownrshp* 1968
Sales 129.1MM^E *EMP* 214
SIC 5013 5088 Automotive hardware; Aircraft engines & engine parts; Aircraft & parts
Pr: Satoshi Fujimori
**CFO:* Hirokazu Masahashi
**Ch:* Masaki Ikuta
**VP:* Shigeru Ikuta
Genl Mgr: Hiroyuki Ono
Dir IT: Charlie Zhao
Sls Mgr: Steve Webb

D-U-N-S 16-157-9735
MIL CORP
4000 Mitchellville Rd R, Bowie, MD 20716-3104
Tel (301) 805-8500 *Founded/Ownrshp* 1980
Sales 105.0MM^E *EMP* 560
SIC 7371 7373 7374 7375 7376 8711 Computer software systems analysis & design, custom; Computer integrated systems design; Data processing & preparation; Information retrieval services; Computer facilities management; Engineering services
Pr: Maurice I Long
CFO: Michael Means
CFO: Brenda Pridgen
Ex VP: Jim McIntyre

Sr VP: William Dunkin
Sr VP: Dave Larson
VP: Martha Bailey
VP: Tom Clark
VP: David Galway
VP: Harvil Jenkins
VP: Peg Kendra
VP: Harvey Weiner

D-U-N-S 07-979-3814
▲ MILACRON HOLDINGS CORP
10200 Alliance Rd Ste 200, Blue Ash, OH 45242-4716
Tel (513) 487-5000 *Founded/Ownrshp* 1860
Sales 1.1MMM *EMP* 5,551^E
Tkr Sym MCRN *Exch* NYS
SIC 3544 Industrial molds; Forms (molds), for foundry & plastics working machinery
Pr: Tom J Goeke
**Ch Bd:* Ira G Boots
CFO: Bruce Chalmers

D-U-N-S 07-984-3362
■ MILACRON INTERMEDIATE HOLDINGS INC
(*Suby of* MILACRON HOLDINGS CORP) ★
3010 Disney St, Cincinnati, OH 45209-5028
Tel (513) 536-2000 *Founded/Ownrshp* 2015
Sales 1.7MMM^E *EMP* 4,718^E
SIC 5962 8741 Merchandising machine operators; Industrial management

D-U-N-S 83-226-5602 IMP
■ MILACRON LLC
(*Suby of* MILACRON INTERMEDIATE HOLDINGS INC) ★
10200 Alliance Rd Ste 200, Blue Ash, OH 45242-4716
Tel (513) 487-5000 *Founded/Ownrshp* 2012
Sales 1.7MMM^E *EMP* 4,718
SIC 3549 2899 Metalworking machinery; Correction fluid
CEO: Tom Goeke
**COO:* John Gallagher
**COO:* Ron Krisanda
CFO: Ross A Anderson
**CFO:* Bruce Chalmers
Sr VP: Hugh O Donnell
VP: Brian Bish
VP: Shirish Divgi
Exec: Erwin Miller
Dist Mgr: John Sherman
Off Mgr: Lynn Townsend

D-U-N-S 83-186-0494 IMP/EXP
■ MILACRON MARKETING CO LLC
WEAR TECHNOLOGY
(*Suby of* MILACRON LLC) ★
4165 Half Acre Rd, Batavia, OH 45103-3247
Tel (513) 536-2000 *Founded/Ownrshp* 2009
Sales 702.7MM^E *EMP* 4,700^E
SIC 3541 Machine tools, metal cutting type
CEO: Tom Goeke
**CFO:* John Francy
Exec: Roy Schweiger

D-U-N-S 83-226-5859 IMP
■ MILACRON PLASTICS TECHNOLOGIES GROUP LLC
(*Suby of* MILACRON LLC) ★
4165 Half Acre Rd, Batavia, OH 45103-3247
Tel (513) 536-2000 *Founded/Ownrshp* 2009
Sales 235.4MM *EMP* 777
SIC 3544 Forms (molds), for foundry & plastics working machinery
CEO: Tom Goeke
Pr: Dave Lawrence
COO: Ron Krisanda
CFO: John C Francy
VP: Mark Dixon
VP: Richard A Oleary
IT Man: Gary Smith

MILAGRO MEZZ
See MILAGRO OIL & GAS INC

D-U-N-S 96-814-8523
MILAGRO OIL & GAS INC
MILAGRO MEZZ
(*Suby of* MILAGRO HOLDINGS LLC)
1301 Mckinney St Ste 500, Houston, TX 77010-3089
Tel (713) 750-1600 *Founded/Ownrshp* 1997
Sales 135.5MM *EMP* 19
Accts Deloitte & Touche Llp Houston
SIC 1382

D-U-N-S 01-726-1579
MILAN SUPPLY CO
7125 E Pickard Rd, Mount Pleasant, MI 48858-7423
Tel (989) 773-9938 *Founded/Ownrshp* 1962
Sales 83.5MM^E *EMP* 50
SIC 5082 Wellpoints (drilling equipment)
Pr: John Gall
VP: Marty Derocco
**VP:* Dean Dubay
**VP:* Daniel Milan

D-U-N-S 96-017-4795
MILBANK INSURANCE CO
518 E Broad St, Columbus, OH 43215-3901
Tel (614) 464-5000 *Founded/Ownrshp* 2014
Sales NA *EMP* 2^E
SIC 6411 Insurance agents, brokers & service
Prin: Robert S Pein

D-U-N-S 00-712-6378 IMP/EXP
MILBANK MANUFACTURING CO
4801 Deramus Ave, Kansas City, MO 64120-1180
Tel (816) 483-5314 *Founded/Ownrshp* 1913
Sales 141.6MM^E *EMP* 600
SIC 3825 3444 Meters: electric, pocket, portable, panelboard, etc.; Energy measuring equipment, electrical; Sheet metalwork
Pr: Brad Skinner
**Ch Bd:* Warren Weaver
**CFO:* James A Fitts
**Sr VP:* Lezlie Ensor
VP: Eric M Kirchbaum
**VP:* John Siglock
**VP:* Doug Ubel

Exec: Larry Minnix
Dir IT: Kyle Bachtel
Dir IT: Jeff Caudle
* *VP Mfg:* Shelley Jaderborg

D-U-N-S 07-526-0034
MILBANK TWEED HADLEY & MCCLOY LLP
28 Liberty St Fl 47, New York, NY 10005-1413
Tel (212) 530-5000 *Founded/Ownrshp* 1999
Sales 138.2MM^E *EMP* 900
SIC 8111 General practice law office
Pt: Trayton Davis
* *Pt:* Matthew S Barr
* *Pt:* Elizabeth A Besio
* *Pt:* Bruce Kale
CFO: Steven M Gacsik
CFO: Steven M Gamcsic
Ex VP: Ronald Freydberg
Dir Bus: Robert Gero
Mng Dir: Mel M Iergut
IT Man: Heather Flaherty

MILE HI FROZEN FOODS
See ROCKY QCD MOUNTAIN LLC

MILE HI VALET SERVICE
See CIRI - STROUP INC

D-U-N-S 00-743-4608 IMP/EXP
MILE HIGH EQUIPMENT LLC
ICE-O-MATIC
(*Suby of* SCOTSMAN OF LOS ANGELES) ★
11100 E 45th Ave, Denver, CO 80239-3029
Tel (303) 576-2940 *Founded/Ownrshp* 1982, 2012
Sales 133.2MM^E *EMP* 260
SIC 3585 Ice making machinery; Ice boxes, industrial
* *CFO:* Meg Collins
CIO: Robert D Crane
Mtls Dir: Nancy Roberts
Mktg Dir: Scott Deshetler
Manager: David Swille

MILE ONE
See ATLANTIC AUTOMOTIVE CORP

D-U-N-S 13-007-5179
MILENDER WHITE CONSTRUCTION CO
MWCC
12655 W 54th Dr, Arvada, CO 80002-1343
Tel (303) 216-0420 *Founded/Ownrshp* 1997
Sales 131.6MM *EMP* 110^E
Accts Bauerle And Company Pc Den
SIC 1542 1522 Nonresidential construction; Residential construction
Pr: Bryon White
* *Pr:* Mike Milender
* *VP:* Shane Fobes
* *VP:* Darren Hinton
VP: Adam Mack
* *VP:* John Milender
Genl Mgr: Matt Joens
Snr PM: Jeff Hall
Snr PM: Dave McCall
Board of Directors: Brian Shelton

D-U-N-S 07-828-5491
MILES & STOCKBRIDGE PC
100 Light St Fl 5, Baltimore, MD 21202-1153
Tel (410) 385-3671 *Founded/Ownrshp* 1993
Sales 91.7MM^E *EMP* 600
SIC 8111 General practice attorney, lawyer
CEO: John Frisch
Pr: Michelle Hunt
Pr: Amanda Palma
VP: Patrick Smith
Prin: David B Eberhardt
* *Prin:* John H Murray
Off Admin: Mari B Moulton
IT Man: Tim Rodgers
Mktg Dir: Ryan Burruss
Counsel: Katherine Lawler
Counsel: Adam Treiber

D-U-N-S 12-135-4435
MILES HEALTH CARE INC
COVES EDGE
(*Suby of* LINCOLNHEALTH GROUP)
35 Miles St, Damariscotta, ME 04543-4047
Tel (207) 563-1234 *Founded/Ownrshp* 1981
Sales 1.0MMM *EMP* 800
SIC 8741 Hospital management; Nursing & personal care facility management
CEO: James Donavan

MILES JENNINGS INDUSTRIAL SUP
See DILLON SUPPLY CO

D-U-N-S 07-948-0707
MILES MARINE INC
(*Suby of* VIGOR INDUSTRIAL LLC) ★
5555 N Channel Ave, Portland, OR 97217-7655
Tel (503) 247-1777 *Founded/Ownrshp* 2010
Sales 152.6MM^E *EMP* 1,110
SIC 3731 Shipbuilding & repairing; Combat vessels, building & repairing; Military ships, building & repairing; Commercial cargo ships, building & repairing
Pr: Frank J Foti
* *COO:* David R Whitcomb
* *CFO:* Lon V Leneve

D-U-N-S 00-948-0278
MILES SAND & GRAVEL CO
CONCRETE NOR'WEST DIVISION
400 Valley Ave Ne, Puyallup, WA 98372-2516
Tel (253) 833-3705 *Founded/Ownrshp* 1964
Sales 96.7MM^E *EMP* 300
SIC 3273 5032 Ready-mixed concrete; Sand, construction; Gravel
Pr: Walter Miles
* *VP:* Lisa Kittilsby
* *VP:* Frank Miles
Genl Mgr: Jerry Trudeau
Dir IT: Jarud Pierson
Sls Mgr: Jeff Kushmaul
Sls Mgr: Bob Thompson

D-U-N-S 08-611-5946 IMP
MILESTONE AV TECHNOLOGIES LLC
CHIEF
(*Suby of* PRITZKER GROUP- CHICAGO LLC) ★
6436 City West Pkwy, Eden Prairie, MN 55344-3245
Tel (952) 236-7231 *Founded/Ownrshp* 2013
Sales 187.3MM^E *EMP* 427
SIC 3669 Intercommunication systems, electric
Pr: Scott Gill
CFO: Troy Peifer
* *CFO:* Troy Pfeiffer
VP: Greg Andrews
VP: Keith T Pribyl
Exec: Patricia McConnell
Comm Man: Katie Sillanpa
CTO: Rich Haddad
Dir IT: Josh Barber
Dir IT: Ron Jensen
Ql Cn Mgr: Olivia Oliver

D-U-N-S 00-604-8912
MILESTONE CONTRACTORS LP
5950 S Belmont Ave, Indianapolis, IN 46217-9757
Tel (317) 788-6885 *Founded/Ownrshp* 1994
Sales 186.0MM^E *EMP* 300
SIC 1611 Highway & street paving contractor; Surfacing & paving
Pt: Ted Lucas
VP: Jim Delk
VP: Ralph Simpson
VP Opers: John Waechter
Sfty Mgr: Russell Randle
Plnt Mgr: Ron Terrel
Prd Mgr: Mark McGaughey
Ql Cn Mgr: Brad Cruea
Mktg Mgr: Mark Blade
Sls Mgr: Brad Mc Call

D-U-N-S 82-745-1162
MILESTONE MANAGEMENTS LLC
5429 Lyndon B Johnson Fwy # 800, Dallas, TX 75240-2607
Tel (214) 561-1200 *Founded/Ownrshp* 2002
Sales 28.6MM^E *EMP* 1,100
SIC 6513 Apartment building operators
Pr: John B Bartling
* *Pr:* Steve T Lamberti
* *CFO:* Ryan Newberry
* *CFO:* Christopher A Phillips
* *Ch:* David B Deniger
* *VP:* Monica Blankenship
* *VP:* Jeffrey L Sherman
Ex Dir: Robert Honstein

D-U-N-S 01-816-9727
MILESTONE PARTNERS MANAGEMENT CO LP
MARINER FINANCE
555 E Lancaster Ave, Radnor, PA 19087-5158
Tel (610) 526-2700 *Founded/Ownrshp* 1994
Sales 99.5MM^E *EMP* 300^E
SIC 6799 Investors
Pt: W Scott Warren
Pt: Robert G Levine
Pt: John P Shoemaker
Prin: Patrick Hanaraty

D-U-N-S 00-520-2754
MILESTONE TECHNOLOGIES INC
3101 Skyway Ct, Fremont, CA 94539-5910
Tel (510) 651-2454 *Founded/Ownrshp* 1997
Sales 156.1MM^E *EMP* 900^E
SIC 7373 7374 Computer integrated systems design; Data processing & preparation
CEO: Prem Chand
CFO: James Schultz
VP: Aaron Belansky
VP: Gary Bilovesky
VP: Kristi H Ledwein
VP: Tony Silveira
CTO: Lou Noble
IT Man: Ken Caffrey
Sftwr Eng: Michael Moody
Netwrk Eng: Chris Tate

D-U-N-S 36-108-6684
■ MILFORD ANESTHESIA ASSOCIATES LLC
(*Suby of* EMCARE INC) ★
111 Continental Dr # 412, Newark, DE 19713-4332
Tel (203) 783-1831 *Founded/Ownrshp* 2010
Sales 47.5MM^E *EMP* 3,769^E
SIC 8011 Anesthesiologist
Off Mgr: Nancy Ferguson
Ansthlgy: Ko Chan
Ansthlgy: Terence Gray
Ansthlgy: Scott Switzer

MILFORD BOARD OF EDUCATION
See MILFORD EXEMPTED VILLAGE SCHOOL DISTRICT

D-U-N-S 09-650-9641
MILFORD EXEMPTED VILLAGE SCHOOL DISTRICT
MILFORD BOARD OF EDUCATION
777 Garfield Ave, Milford, OH 45150-1607
Tel (513) 576-4175 *Founded/Ownrshp* 1900
Sales 62.5MM^E *EMP* 1,000^E
Accts Plattenburg & Associates Inc
SIC 8211 Public elementary & secondary schools; High school, junior or senior; Elementary school
Psych: Corbin M Beth

MILFORD MEMORIAL HOSPITAL
See KENT GENERAL HOSPITAL

MILFORD PIPE AND SUPPLY
See MPS ENTERPRISES INC

D-U-N-S 04-868-9637
MILFORD REGIONAL HEALTHCARE FOUNDATION INC
14 Prospect St, Milford, MA 01757-3003
Tel (508) 473-1190 *Founded/Ownrshp* 1984
Sales 187.7MM *EMP* 1,777^E
Accts Feeley & Driscoll Boston Ma
SIC 6733 8082 8011 Trusts; Visiting nurse service; Physicians' office, including specialists
CEO: Francis M Saba
* *Pr:* Edward J Kelly
* *CFO:* Jeanne Lynskey
* *Ch:* Roger Calarese
* *Treas:* John Armstrong
CIO: Lawrence Fraize

D-U-N-S 07-534-6940
MILFORD REGIONAL MEDICAL CENTER INC
MILFORD RGNAL HLTHCARE FNDTION
(*Suby of* MILFORD REGIONAL HEALTHCARE FOUNDATION INC) ★
14 Prospect St, Milford, MA 01757-3003
Tel (508) 473-1190 *Founded/Ownrshp* 1903
Sales 195.2MM *EMP* 1,159
SIC 8062 8082 General medical & surgical hospitals; Visiting nurse service
Pr: Ed Kelly
V Ch: Harold Gould
* *CFO:* Jeanne Lynskey
Treas: John Armstrong
Dir Rad: Brian Coolbaugh
Secur Mgr: Bryan Bailey
Doctor: Gregory Begin
Doctor: Mark M Mangano
Doctor: Christopher S Moore
Diag Rad: Michael J Thompson
Snr PM: Shiraz Fagan

MILFORD RGNAL HLTHCARE FNDTION
See MILFORD REGIONAL MEDICAL CENTER INC

D-U-N-S 00-925-5068 IMP
■ MILGARD MANUFACTURING INC
MILGARD WINDOWS
(*Suby of* MASCO CORP) ★
1010 54th Ave E, Fife, WA 98424-2793
Tel (253) 922-6030 *Founded/Ownrshp* 2001
Sales 422.0MM^E *EMP* 2,037
SIC 3089 3442 Windows, plastic; Sash, door or window: metal
Pr: Gary Gessel
* *VP:* Kenneth Cole
VP: Beth Galliher-Ponce
* *VP:* Lawrence Leaman
* *VP:* David Maki
VP: Rick McCurdy
* *VP:* Stephen Moore
* *VP:* Mark Sturgis
Mtls Mgr: Scott Krause
Sls Mgr: Rick Wilson

MILGARD WINDOWS
See MILGARD MANUFACTURING INC

D-U-N-S 96-910-8844
MILITARY DELI & BAKERY SERVICES INC
10600 N Trademark Pkwy, Rancho Cucamonga, CA 91730-5936
Tel (909) 373-1344 *Founded/Ownrshp* 1996
Sales 22.5MM^E *EMP* 1,000
SIC 5812 Commissary restaurant
Pr: Timothy I Howard

MILITARY DEPARTMENT ARKANSAS
See ARKANSAS DEPARTMENT OF NATIONAL GUARD

D-U-N-S 80-748-1148
MILITARY DEPARTMENT CONNECTICUT
ADJUTANT GENERAL
(*Suby of* GOVERNORS OFFICE STATE OF CONNECTICUT) ★
360 Broad St, Hartford, CT 06105-3706
Tel (860) 524-4953 *Founded/Ownrshp* 1788
Sales NA *EMP* 5,000
SIC 9711 National security;
Prin: Thad Martin

D-U-N-S 80-985-0050
MILITARY DEPARTMENT MISSISSIPPI
EXECUTIVE OFFICE OF THE STATE
(*Suby of* EXECUTIVE OFFICE OF STATE OF MISSISSIPPI) ★
1410 Riverside Dr, Jackson, MS 39202-1271
Tel (601) 313-6209 *Founded/Ownrshp* 1817
Sales NA *EMP* 1,853
SIC 9711
Pr: Harold Cross

D-U-N-S 00-501-1544
MILITARY DIVISION OF STATE OF IDAHO
(*Suby of* EXECUTIVE OFFICE OF STATE OF IDAHO) ★
4040 W Guard St Bldg 600, Boise, ID 83705-5004
Tel (208) 422-5507 *Founded/Ownrshp* 1893
Sales NA *EMP* 3,681
SIC 9711 National security;
Genl Mgr: Gary Sayler

MILITARY PARK FIRE DISTRICT
See COUNTY OF PALM BEACH

D-U-N-S 05-968-3727
MILITARY PERSONNEL SERVICES CORP
6066 Leesburg Pike # 900, Falls Church, VA 22041-2234
Tel (571) 481-4000 *Founded/Ownrshp* 1998
Sales NA *EMP* 1,550
SIC 9451 Administration of veterans' affairs
Pr: Ross B Deblois
* *COO:* Jonathan Tipa
* *Treas:* Stanley Rubinstein
* *VP:* Jeff Christi
* *VP:* Duane Jahner
* *VP:* Jackie Livingston

MILITARY SPEC PACKAGING
See TRI-W GROUP INC

D-U-N-S 14-694-4855
■ MILITARY SURFACE DEPLOYMENT & DISTRIBUTION COMMAND
(SDDC)
(*Suby of* UNITED STATES DEPARTMENT OF THE ARMY) ★
200 Stovall St Fl 18, Alexandria, VA 22332-4013
Tel (703) 428-2753 *Founded/Ownrshp* 2015
Sales NA *EMP* 1,700
SIC 9711 Army;
Prin: Edna Lewis
Snr Mgr: Stephen Chadwick
Snr Mgr: Eric Scheper

D-U-N-S 04-962-1519
MILK INDUSTRY MANAGEMENT CORP
BALFORD FARMS
4 Manhattan Dr, Burlington, NJ 08016-4120
Tel (609) 747-9542 *Founded/Ownrshp* 1969
Sales 244.8MM^E *EMP* 170
SIC 5143 Dairy products, except dried or canned; Milk & cream, fluid; Ice cream & ices
Pr: Laurance Bowes
* *Ch Bd:* George H Baldwin Sr
* *Pr:* John F Baldwin
* *CFO:* Robert Venafra
* *Ex VP:* George H Baldwin Jr
Ex VP: Daniel Smith
Exec: David W Buys
Board of Directors: Marc N Levin, David Menard

D-U-N-S 11-571-5930 IMP/EXP
MILK SPECIALTIES CO
MILK SPECIALTIES GLOBAL
7500 Flying Cloud Dr # 500, Eden Prairie, MN 55344-3703
Tel (952) 942-7310 *Founded/Ownrshp* 2016
Sales 100.1MM^E *EMP* 100
SIC 2026 2834 5149 Fermented & cultured milk products; Vitamin, nutrient & hematinic preparations for human use; Health foods
CEO: David Lenzmeier
* *Pr:* Eddie Wells
Sr Cor Off: Garrett Dawes
Dir Risk M: Shane Reynolds
QA Dir: Amy Bolton
QA Dir: Cheryl Jeske
Dir IT: Chuck Langdon
Opers Mgr: Tamara McDonnell
Plnt Mgr: Mike Artery
Plnt Mgr: Todd Spykstra
Prd Mgr: John Gravito

MILK SPECIALTIES GLOBAL
See MILK SPECIALTIES CO

D-U-N-S 01-954-8853
MILK TRANSPORT SERVICES LP
910 Shelton Dr, Cabool, MO 65689-6310
Tel (417) 962-2373 *Founded/Ownrshp* 1998
Sales 31.0MM^E *EMP* 1,000
SIC 4213 4212 Trucking, except local; Local trucking, without storage
Pt: Regina Garrabrant
Pt: David Jones

D-U-N-S 00-893-3400 IMP
MILL CREEK LUMBER & SUPPLY CO INC
6974 E 38th St, Tulsa, OK 74145-3203
Tel (405) 671-3540 *Founded/Ownrshp* 1934
Sales 183.3MM^E *EMP* 500
SIC 3442 1771 5031 5211 Casements, aluminum; Flooring contractor; Lumber, plywood & millwork; Building materials, exterior; Building materials, interior; Lumber: rough, dressed & finished; Lumber & other building materials; Millwork & lumber; Doors, wood or metal, except storm; Windows, storm: wood or metal
Pr: Jeffrey T Dunn
COO: Kyle Brewer
COO: Arrington Tom
* *VP:* Jim Cavanaugh
* *VP:* James D Dunn
Dir IT: Matt Sloan

MILL PRODUCTS DIVISION
See TC INDUSTRIES INC

D-U-N-S 17-510-7965 IMP/EXP
MILL SERVICES CORP
(*Suby of* WELLSPRING CAPITAL MANAGEMENT LLC) ★
12 Monongahela Ave, Glassport, PA 15045-1315
Tel (412) 678-6141 *Founded/Ownrshp* 2004
Sales 108.5MM^E *EMP* 1,109^E
SIC 3295 1422 8742 3341 Slag, crushed or ground; Cement rock, crushed & broken-quarrying; Public utilities consultant; Secondary nonferrous metals
CEO: Michael Coslov
Genl Mgr: Tim Carmack

D-U-N-S 09-612-8418
MILL-RUN TOURS INC
424 Madison Ave Fl 12, New York, NY 10017-1161
Tel (212) 486-9840 *Founded/Ownrshp* 1975
Sales 179.0MM *EMP* 82
SIC 4724 4725 Travel agencies; Tourist agency arranging transport, lodging & car rental; Arrangement of travel tour packages, wholesale
Ch Bd: Issam N Sawaya
* *Ofcr:* Pierre Azzi
* *Ofcr:* Jalal Jafri
* *Ofcr:* Abel Nunez
* *VP:* Maricruz Sawaya
Sls Mgr: Philip Badu

D-U-N-S 07-403-6476
MILLARD FILLMORE HOSPITALS
100 High St D1-588, Buffalo, NY 14203-1126
Tel (716) 859-5960 *Founded/Ownrshp* 1872
Sales 26.4MM^E *EMP* 1,605
SIC 8062 General medical & surgical hospitals
CEO: Carol Cassell
CFO: Anthony F Zito
* *Treas:* Bryant H Prentice III
Prin: Maria Falbo
Ansthlgy: Daxin Chen

D-U-N-S 02-523-1747
MILLARD GROUP INC (IL)
MILLARD METAL MAINTENANCE CO.
7301 N Cicero Ave, Lincolnwood, IL 60712-1613
Tel (847) 674-4100 *Founded/Ownrshp* 1920, 1958
Sales 235.6MM^E *EMP* 4,600
SIC 7349 Janitorial service, contract basis; Window cleaning
Pr: Lawrence B Kugler
Rgnl Mgr: Jim English
CTO: Kendra Cunningham

D-U-N-S 00-749-6193
MILLARD LUMBER INC
DO IT BEST
12900 I St, Omaha, NE 68137-1600
Tel (402) 896-2800 *Founded/Ownrshp* 1948
Sales 180.3MM^E *EMP* 220
SIC 5031 5211 Building materials, exterior; Building materials, interior; Millwork & lumber; Home centers
Pr: G Richard Russell
**VP:* David M Anderson
**VP:* Don Rowe
**VP:* Joel R Russell
VP: Jeff D Taake
Genl Mgr: Eric Briggs
Genl Mgr: Luke Wiesen
Sfty Dirs: Bob Walters
Opers Mgr: Matt Polito
Sales Asso: Dick Skaggs

MILLARD METAL MAINTENANCE CO.
See MILLARD GROUP INC

D-U-N-S 08-021-3259
MILLARD PUBLIC SCHOOLS
SCHOOL DISTRICT 17
5606 S 147th St, Omaha, NE 68137-2647
Tel (402) 715-8200 *Founded/Ownrshp* 1938
Sales 225.1MM *EMP* 2,500
Accts Hsmc Orizon Llc Omaha Nebras
SIC 8211 Public elementary & secondary schools; High school, junior or senior
**Treas:* Patrick Ricketts
Bd of Dir: Nolan Beyer
Bd of Dir: Paul Meyer
**VP:* Linda Poole
Exec: Cindi Alberico
Exec: Peggy Silva
Prin: Connie Heinen
Prin: Mark Smith
Prin: Janet Wilson
Genl Mgr: Christopher Hughes
Genl Mgr: Jennifer Smith

D-U-N-S 04-124-4153 IMP/EXP
MILLARD REFRIGERATED SERVICES LLC
13030 Pierce St, Omaha, NE 68144-1123
Tel (402) 896-6600 *Founded/Ownrshp* 2014
Sales NA *EMP* 2,000
SIC 4222

D-U-N-S 15-037-4135
MILLBRAE WCP HOTEL I LLC
WESTIN SFO
(*Suby of* ULTIMA HOSPITALITY LLC) ★
335 Powell St, San Francisco, CA 94102-1804
Tel (415) 397-7000 *Founded/Ownrshp* 2013
Sales 30.2MM^E *EMP* 1,000
SIC 7011 Hotels & motels
Pr: Marc Swerdlow
**COO:* Mark Zettl
Exec: Richard Horshington

D-U-N-S 00-625-4387 IMP
MILLBROOK DISTRIBUTION SERVICES INC (DE)
UNFI SPECIALTY DIST SERICES
88 Huntoon Memorial Hwy, Leicester, MA 01524
Tel (508) 892-8171 *Founded/Ownrshp* 2007
Sales NA *EMP* 1,300
SIC 5122 5023 5072 5112 5049 5199

D-U-N-S 92-796-7448
MILLCRAFT GROUP LLC
DELTACRAFT
6800 Grant Ave, Cleveland, OH 44105-5628
Tel (216) 441-5500 *Founded/Ownrshp* 1995
Sales 127.3MM^E *EMP* 275
SIC 5111 5113 2679 Printing & writing paper; Industrial & personal service paper; Paper products, converted
Ch Bd: Kay Mlakar
Ch Bd: Katherine Mlakar
Pr: Travis Mlakar
CFO: David Hegeman
VP: Mike Davoran
VP: Bill Desantis
VP: Greg Lovensheimer
VP: John Orlando
VP: M Ortman
VP: Nicolas Piszko
Div Mgr: Mark Hephner

D-U-N-S 00-790-0988 IMP
MILLCRAFT PAPER CO
6800 Grant Ave, Cleveland, OH 44105-5628
Tel (216) 441-5505 *Founded/Ownrshp* 1967
Sales 400.1MM^E *EMP* 250^E
SIC 5111 5113 Printing paper; Industrial & personal service paper
Pr: Travis Mlakar
Ex VP: Peter Vogel Jr
**VP:* Mike Davoran
**VP:* Eric Michel
VP: Alastair Mitchell
**VP:* John Orlando
VP: John Shoup
Div Mgr: Jack Oldiges
IT Man: Rick Zizak
S&M/VP: Russ James
Sales Asso: Tiffany Hawes

D-U-N-S 06-068-8975
MILLCREEK TOWNSHIP SCHOOL DISTRICT
3740 W 26th St, Erie, PA 16506-2039
Tel (814) 835-5300 *Founded/Ownrshp* 1955
Sales 72.8MM^E *EMP* 1,152
Accts Felix And Gloekler Pc Erie
SIC 8211 9111 Public elementary & secondary schools; Mayors' offices
Teacher Pr: Liz Detich

D-U-N-S 01-004-4000
■ **MILLENNIAL MEDIA INC**
(*Suby of* AOL INC) ★
2400 Boston St Ste 300, Baltimore, MD 21224-4781
Tel (410) 522-8705 *Founded/Ownrshp* 2006, 2015
Sales 296.1MM *EMP* 636^E
SIC 7319 7371 Display advertising service; Computer software development & applications
CEO: Michael G Barrett
Pr: Jason Kelly
COO: Ernie Cormier
CFO: Michael Avon
CFO: Andrew Jeanneret
Ex VP: Mark Connon
Sr VP: Eric Hastings
Sr VP: Michael Kocorowski
Sr VP: Jeff Tennery
VP: Jim Butler
VP: Patrick McCormack
Creative D: Sarah Jennings
Dir Bus: Marcy Stone

MILLENNIUM
See CRISTAL USA INC

D-U-N-S 01-197-1939
MILLENNIUM ENGINEERING AND INTEGRATION CO
1400 Crystal Dr Ste 800, Arlington, VA 22202-4153
Tel (703) 413-7750 *Founded/Ownrshp* 1995, 2005
Sales 114.4MM^E *EMP* 400
SIC 8711 8731 Engineering services; Commercial physical research
CEO: Patrick Murphy
**CFO:* Dante Reeves
VP: Alfred Wassel

D-U-N-S 01-478-2231
MILLENNIUM HEALTH LLC
16981 Via Tazon Ste F, San Diego, CA 92127-1645
Tel (877) 451-3534 *Founded/Ownrshp* 2007
Sales 133.6MM^E *EMP* 258^E
SIC 8734 Testing laboratories
CEO: Ronald A Rittenmeyer
**Pr:* Howard Appel
**COO:* David Cohen
**COO:* Mark A Winham
**CFO:* Michael Keane
**CFO:* Timothy C Kennedy
**Chf Cred:* Darrell W Contreras
**Chf Mktg O:* Nikhil A Nayak
Chf Mktg O: Nikhil Nayak
**Ofcr:* Thomas W Arnst
**Ofcr:* Angela Huskey
Ex VP: Josh Benner
Sr VP: Rami Ben-Joseph
**Sr VP:* Charles Mikel
**Sr VP:* Janna Sipes
VP: Michael Burnett
VP: Michael E Flowers
VP: Brent Gibbs
VP: Lisa Rhodes
Assoc Dir: Craig Davis
Board of Directors: Eugene I Davis, Jeffrey D Goldberg, Joan B Stafslien

MILLENNIUM HOTELS & RESORTS
See RICHFIELD HOLDINGS INC

MILLENNIUM HOTELS & RESORTS
See M&C HOTEL INTERESTS INC

D-U-N-S 00-505-0463 IMP/EXP
MILLENNIUM INDUSTRIES CORP (MI)
(*Suby of* TI GROUP AUTOMOTIVE SYSTEMS LLC) ★
925 N Main St, Ligonier, IN 46767-2060
Tel (260) 894-3163 *Founded/Ownrshp* 1990, 2016
Sales 130.0MM *EMP* 400
SIC 3469 Metal stampings
Pr: William Kozyra

D-U-N-S 61-195-5852 IMP
MILLENNIUM PARTNERS SPORTS CLUB MANAGEMENT LLC
SPORTS CLUB LA, THE
7 Water St Ste 200, Boston, MA 02109-4106
Tel (617) 476-8910 *Founded/Ownrshp* 2005
Sales 21.7MM^E *EMP* 1,500
SIC 7991 Athletic club & gymnasiums, membership
CEO: Smaiyra Million

D-U-N-S 80-414-8757
MILLENNIUM PHARMACEUTICALS INC
(*Suby of* TAKEDA PHARMACEUTICAL COMPANY LIMITED)
40 Landsdowne St, Cambridge, MA 02139-4234
Tel (617) 679-7000 *Founded/Ownrshp* 2008
Sales 280.3MM^E *EMP* 947
SIC 8731 Biological research
Pr: Deborah Dunsire
COO: Sherry Reynolds
**CFO:* Marsha H Fanucci
**Treas:* Todd Shegog
Ofcr: Joseph B Bolen
Ofcr: Joel Goldberg
Ofcr: Liz Lewis
**Ex VP:* Christophe Bianchi
**Sr VP:* Stephen M Gansler
Sr VP: Paul Hamelin
Sr VP: David Schenkein
Sr VP: Claire Thom
Sr VP: Susan J Ward
VP: Lisa Adler
VP: Janet Bush
VP: Alan Crane
VP: Daniel Curran
VP: Sandra Dicesare
VP: Sandy Dicesare
VP: Dixie-Lee Esseltine
VP: John Ferguson

D-U-N-S 10-564-9466
■ **MILLENNIUM PHARMACY SYSTEMS LLC**
MILLENNIUM PHRM SYSTEMS INC
(*Suby of* PHARMERICA CORP) ★
100 E Kensinger Dr # 500, Cranberry Township, PA 16066-3557
Tel (724) 940-2490 *Founded/Ownrshp* 2014
Sales 104.6MM^E *EMP* 500^E
SIC 5912 Drug stores
Pr: Philip J Keough IV
**CFO:* J Chris Luthin
Chf Cred: A Jeffrey Newell
Ex VP: George Hepburn
**Ex VP:* Lena Sturgeon
Sr VP: Stephen Duvall
Sr VP: Anthony Gerardi
Sr VP: Gaile M Omori
VP: Thomas A Caneris
Dist Mgr: Elissa Heck

MILLENNIUM PHRM SYSTEMS INC
See MILLENNIUM PHARMACY SYSTEMS LLC

D-U-N-S 00-285-2747 IMP
MILLER & LONG CO INC
4824 Rugby Ave, Bethesda, MD 20814-3019
Tel (301) 657-8000 *Founded/Ownrshp* 1947
Sales 306.8MM^E *EMP* 3,000
SIC 1771

MILLER & SMITH
See MILLER AND SMITH INC

D-U-N-S 02-255-1667
MILLER AND SMITH INC
MILLER & SMITH
8401 Greensboro Dr # 450, Mc Lean, VA 22102-5113
Tel (703) 821-2500 *Founded/Ownrshp* 2008
Sales 187.0MM *EMP* 130
SIC 1799 1531 Building mover, including houses;
Ch: Gordon V Smith
**Ch Bd:* Alvin D Hall
**Pr:* Doug Smith
**Sr VP:* Richard J North
**Sr VP:* Spencer R Stouffer
**Sr VP:* Charles Stuart Jr
MIS Mgr: L Reed
Corp Couns: Allyson McCarron

D-U-N-S 78-535-5439 IMP
■ **MILLER AUTOMOTIVE GROUP INC**
MILLER NISSAN
(*Suby of* GROUP 1 AUTOMOTIVE INC) ★
5425 Van Nuys Blvd, Sherman Oaks, CA 91401-5628
Tel (818) 787-8400 *Founded/Ownrshp* 2002
Sales 141.9MM^E *EMP* 650
SIC 5511 7538 5521 Automobiles, new & used; General automotive repair shops; Automobiles, used cars only
Ch Bd: Fred Miller
**Pr:* Michael Miller
**CFO:* Doug Stewart
**VP:* Mark Miller

D-U-N-S 14-939-0416
■ **MILLER BREWERIES EAST INC**
(*Suby of* MILLERCOORS LLC) ★
3939 W Highland Blvd, Milwaukee, WI 53208-2816
Tel (414) 931-2000 *Founded/Ownrshp* 2004
Sales 248.3M *EMP* 2,889
SIC 2082 Beer (alcoholic beverage)
Pr: Gavin Hattersley
VP: Gary Booher
VP: Thomas J Cardella
VP: Kevin Doyle
VP: Bill Dreger
VP: Erv Frederick
VP: David Goulet
VP: Paul Hansen
VP: Jeffrey Hembrock
VP: John C Radi
VP: Stephen D Rogers
VP: Jim Scheey
VP: Jerry Schiedt
VP: Jeffrey Schouten
VP: Denise Smith
VP: Charlie Teal
VP: David Zini

MILLER CANFIELD
See MILLER CANFIELD PADDOCK AND STONE PLC

D-U-N-S 07-635-2012
MILLER CANFIELD PADDOCK AND STONE PLC
MILLER CANFIELD
150 W Jefferson Ave # 2500, Detroit, MI 48226-4416
Tel (313) 963-6420 *Founded/Ownrshp* 1934
Sales 99.5MM^E *EMP* 700
SIC 8111 General practice law office
CEO: Michael P McGee
CFO: David Hoin
Counsel: Michael Allen
Counsel: Bob Baksi
Counsel: Bruce D Birgbauer
Counsel: Troy Harris
Counsel: Loren M Opper
Counsel: Loretta Stoyka

MILLER CHILDREN'S HOSPITAL
See LONG BEACH MEMORIAL MEDICAL CENTER

D-U-N-S 00-287-4006
MILLER ELECTRIC CO (NE)
2501 Saint Marys Ave, Omaha, NE 68105-1696
Tel (402) 341-6479 *Founded/Ownrshp* 1912, 1977
Sales 150.7MM *EMP* 800
Accts Lutz & Company Pc Omaha Ne
SIC 1731 General electrical contractor
Pr: Ray Bruegman
**Treas:* William Henrichs
**VP:* Jeff Allen
**VP:* Ron Kohlmieer
Dir IT: Monte Watembach
IT Man: Jason Tagge
Sales Exec: Don Fitzpatrick
Snr PM: Jeff Boots
Snr PM: Roger Knobbe Sr
Snr PM: Craig Langfeldt Sr

D-U-N-S 00-583-4205
MILLER ELECTRIC CO (FL)
2251 Rosselle St, Jacksonville, FL 32204-3125
Tel (904) 388-8000 *Founded/Ownrshp* 1928, 1966
Sales 260.5MM *EMP* 691
Accts Bishop And Draper Cpa Jackso
SIC 1731 General electrical contractor
CEO: Henry K Brown
Pr: Thomas D Long
CFO: Sandra Miller
CFO: Susan A Walden
Sr VP: David Long
Sr VP: Ed Witt Jr
VP: Daniel Brown
VP: Donnie Smith
VP: Edward Witt
CTO: Jonathan Matulevich
Site Mgr: Richard Dion

D-U-N-S 00-612-6379 IMP/EXP
■ **MILLER ELECTRIC MFG CO** (WI)
(*Suby of* ILLINOIS TOOL WORKS INC) ★
1635 W Spencer St, Appleton, WI 54914-4911
Tel (920) 734-9821 *Founded/Ownrshp* 1935, 1995
Sales 469.3MM^E *EMP* 1,500
SIC 3548 3621 Welding apparatus; Gas welding equipment; Arc welders, transformer-rectifier; Armatures, industrial
Pr: Michael Weller
VP: Kenneth Escoe
VP: Bill Henrichs
Rgnl Mgr: Keith Rzucidlo
Dist Mgr: Scott Wright
Genl Mgr: Jeff Schroeder
Snr Sftwr: Jeremy Erdmann
CTO: Steve Clark
Dir IT: Keith King
Dir IT: Roy Miller
Sftwr Eng: Jeremy Overesch

D-U-N-S 07-578-8851
MILLER ENVIRONMENTAL GROUP INC (NY)
M E G
538 Edwards Ave, Calverton, NY 11933-1636
Tel (631) 369-4900 *Founded/Ownrshp* 1971
Sales 105.2MM^E *EMP* 145
SIC 4959 Oil spill cleanup
CEO: Mark Miller
CFO: Tom Horyczun
**VP:* George Wallace III
Brnch Mgr: Mark Lucy
IT Man: Dave Bender

D-U-N-S 78-320-8130
MILLER ENVIRONMENTAL SERVICES LLC
401 Navigation Blvd, Corpus Christi, TX 78408-2747
Tel (361) 289-9800 *Founded/Ownrshp* 2014
Sales 86.0MM^E *EMP* 110
SIC 4953 7375 Hazardous waste collection & disposal; Data base information retrieval
Pr: Charles K Miller Jr
IT Man: Vincent Cotton

D-U-N-S 61-738-5208 IMP/EXP
▲ **MILLER INDUSTRIES INC**
8503 Hilltop Dr, Ooltewah, TN 37363-6841
Tel (423) 238-4171 *Founded/Ownrshp* 1990
Sales 540.9MM *EMP* 990
Tkr Sym MLR *Exch* NYS
SIC 3713 Truck & bus bodies
Co-CEO: Jeffrey I Badgley
**Ch Bd:* William G Miller
CFO: J Vincent Mish
Ex VP: Frank Madonia
VP: Deborah Whitmire
Board of Directors: Theodore H Ashford III, A Russell Chandler III, Richard H Roberts

D-U-N-S 07-904-2511
■ **MILLER INDUSTRIES TOWING EQUIPMENT INC**
(*Suby of* MILLER INDUSTRY) ★
8503 Hilltop Dr, Ooltewah, TN 37363-6841
Tel (423) 238-4171 *Founded/Ownrshp* 1987
Sales 107.2MM^E *EMP* 425
SIC 3799 Towing bars & systems
Ch Bd: William G Miller
**Pr:* Jeffrey Badgley
**Pr:* Will Miller
**CFO:* J Vincent Mish
**VP:* Randy Olson

MILLER INDUSTRY
See CENTURY HOLDINGS INC

D-U-N-S 05-904-0923
MILLER INSULATION CO INC
3520 E Century Ave, Bismarck, ND 58503-0739
Tel (701) 258-4323 *Founded/Ownrshp* 1984
Sales 94.6MM^E *EMP* 515
SIC 1742 1542 Insulation, buildings; Nonresidential construction
Pr: Brad Miller
**VP:* Dwight Miller
CTO: Curt Heiser

MILLER LITTLE GIANT
See MILLER MANUFACTURING CO

D-U-N-S 04-671-2097 IMP
MILLER MANUFACTURING CO
MILLER LITTLE GIANT
(*Suby of* FRANDSEN CORP) ★
2910 Waters Rd Ste 150, Eagan, MN 55121-1654
Tel (651) 982-5100 *Founded/Ownrshp* 1996
Sales 87.4MM^E *EMP* 150
SIC 1542 5199 Farm building construction; Pet supplies
CEO: Dan Frandsen
**Pr:* Tom Botten
VP: Ron Barsalou
VP: Dan Gorowsky
VP: Jason Wildung
**VP Sls:* James Thompson

MILLER MARTS
See MILLER OIL CO INC

MILLER MEAT POULTRY
See CRYSTAL VALLEY FARMS LLC

MILLER NISSAN
See MILLER AUTOMOTIVE GROUP INC

D-U-N-S 08-629-2513 IMP
MILLER OIL CO INC (VA)
MILLER MARTS
1000 E City Hall Ave, Norfolk, VA 23504-4214
Tel (757) 623-6600 *Founded/Ownrshp* 1977
Sales 121.9MM^E *EMP* 550
SIC 5411 5172 5983 7549 Convenience stores, chain; Petroleum products; Fuel oil dealers; Lubrication service, automotive
CEO: Augustus C Miller
**Pr:* Jeffrey G Miller

*Sec: Deanne Miller
Ex Dir: Lindsay Pryor
Ex Dir: Carrie Short
Dist Mgr: Ron Reed

D-U-N-S 00-902-6659
MILLER PAINT CO INC
12812 Ne Whitaker Way, Portland, OR 97230-1110
Tel (503) 255-0190 Founded/Ownrshp 1890
Sales 98.7MM[E] EMP 370
SIC 2851 5231 Paints: oil or alkyd vehicle or water thinned; Paints, waterproof; Wood stains; Paint; Paint brushes, rollers, sprayers & other supplies; Wallpaper
Pr: Stephen L Dearborn
*CFO: Bill Cameron
CFO: Steve Cowan
*Sr VP: Paul Sawyer
*VP: Steve Serra
Store Mgr: John Curtis
Sales Asso: Brian Brown

D-U-N-S 00-287-9294
■ MILLER PIPELINE LLC
(Suby of VECTREN CORP) ★
8850 Crawfordsville Rd, Indianapolis, IN 46234-1559
Tel (317) 293-0278 Founded/Ownrshp 1995
Sales 369.3MM[E] EMP 2,000
SIC 1623 Pipeline construction
CEO: Douglas S Banning Jr
*Pr: Kevin Miller
COO: Robert McCormick
CFO: Banning Douglas
*CFO: Daniel Short
*Sec: Nina Mann
*Ex VP: Dale Anderson
VP: Frank Bracht
VP: Greg Frazier
VP: Mark Hallett
VP: Ralph Miller
VP: Dave Tucker
Dir Risk M: Mark Benson

D-U-N-S 05-202-0176
■ MILLER SPRINGS MATERIALS LLC
(Suby of JAMES CONSTRUCTION GROUP LLC) ★
6218 State Highway 317, Belton, TX 76513-5397
Tel (254) 780-9959 Founded/Ownrshp 2010
Sales 119.1MM[E] EMP 716[E]
SIC 5085 5999 Springs; Rock & stone specimens
Pr: Danny L Hester
CFO: Donald B Bonaventure
Off Mgr: Josey Taylor

D-U-N-S 00-385-1409
MILLER TRANSPORTATION SERVICES INC (MS)
(Suby of DEWEY CORP) ★
5500 Highway 80 W, Jackson, MS 39209-3507
Tel (601) 856-6526 Founded/Ownrshp 1942, 1964
Sales 101.9MM EMP 1,000
Accts Horne Llp Ridgeland Mississ
SIC 4231 Trucking terminal facilities
Pr: Lee Miller
Ex VP: Hal Miller
Sfty Dirs: Ray Riley

D-U-N-S 10-788-3126
MILLER TRANSPORTERS EMPLOYEES
5500 Highway 80 W, Jackson, MS 39209-3507
Tel (601) 922-8331 Founded/Ownrshp 1950
Sales NA EMP 2
Accts Securities And Exchange Commis
SIC 6141 Personal credit institutions
Pr: Scott Miller
*Treas: James Smith

D-U-N-S 07-914-1630
MILLER TRANSPORTERS INC
(Suby of MILLER TRANSPORTATION SERVICES INC) ★
5500 Highway 80 W, Jackson, MS 39209-3507
Tel (601) 922-8331 Founded/Ownrshp 1942
Sales 110.0MM EMP 204[E]
SIC 4731 Truck transportation brokers
*Ex VP: Hal Miller
*VP: Joe Hegi

MILLER VALENTIN CONSTRUCTION
See MV COMMERCIAL CONSTRUCTION LLC

MILLER VALENTINE GROUP
See MILLER-VALENTINE OPERATIONS INC

D-U-N-S 00-615-0023 IMP
MILLER WASTE MILLS INC
RTP COMPANY
580 E Front St, Winona, MN 55987-4256
Tel (507) 454-6906 Founded/Ownrshp 1927
Sales 345.3MM[E] EMP 650
SIC 3087 2821 Custom compound purchased resins; Thermoplastic materials
CEO: Hugh L Miller
*CFO: Brian Evenson
*Sec: Jonathan Miller
*Ex VP: Joe Kluck
VP: Brian K Evenson
*VP: Steve Maki
Exec: Jamey Erickson
Exec: Lance Sebo
Genl Mgr: Rolf Dahl
Genl Mgr: Kevin Jennings
Genl Mgr: Don Mueller

D-U-N-S 03-354-4917 IMP/EXP
MILLER ZELL INC
(Suby of ISD HOLDINGS INC) ★
6100 Fulton Indus Blvd Sw, Atlanta, GA 30336-2853
Tel (404) 691-7400 Founded/Ownrshp 1999
Sales 127.5MM[E] EMP 400
Accts Pricewaterhousecoopers Llp
SIC 7389 2542 2759 2752 Design services; Fixtures, store: except wood; Screen printing; Commercial printing, offset
CEO: Harmon Miller IV
*Pr: Paul R Papantonis
*CEO: Harmon B Miller III
*CFO: David Seem
VP: Dave Feem
VP: Dave Seem
VP: Larry Wolfson
Creative D: Paul Wolski
Dept Mgr: Devin Nutter
DP Dir: Larry Watkins
IT Man: Mike Colbaugh

D-U-N-S 02-516-5359
MILLER-VALENTINE OPERATIONS INC
MILLER VALENTINE GROUP
137 N Main St Ste 900, Dayton, OH 45402-1846
Tel (937) 293-0900 Founded/Ownrshp 2004
Sales 153.0MM EMP 800
SIC 6552 6531 Subdividers & developers; Real estate managers
CEO: Bill Krul
*CFO: Edward Blake
CFO: Al Schneider
*Ex VP: Jack Goodwin
Sr VP: Denny Whitehead
VP: Gerry Smith
VP: Kevin Werner
Dir Bus: Peter Horton
Off Mgr: Lois Smith
Dir IT: Mark Flannery
Software D: Bob Cannata

D-U-N-S 00-618-6415
MILLERBERND MANUFACTURING CO (MN)
622 6th St S, Winsted, MN 55395-7721
Tel (320) 485-2111 Founded/Ownrshp 1933, 1914
Sales 121.3MM[E] EMP 320
SIC 3312 Stainless steel; Structural shapes & pilings, steel
Pr: Trevor S Millerbernd
*VP: Stephen A Millerbernd
IT Man: Tad William
Sfty Dirs: Bill Krause
Mktg Mgr: Cody Cuhel
Mktg Mgr: Mike Wendolek
Sls Mgr: Mitch Gaida
Snr Mgr: Alan Barfknecht

D-U-N-S 00-609-5251 IMP/EXP
■ MILLERCOORS LLC
(Suby of MOLSON COORS BREWING CO) ★
250 S Wacker Dr Ste 800, Chicago, IL 60606-5888
Tel (312) 496-2700 Founded/Ownrshp 2016
Sales 2.0MMM[E] EMP 4,500
SIC 2082 Beer (alcoholic beverage)
CEO: Gavin Hattersley
V Ch: Alan Clark
*CFO: Tracey Joubert
Div Pres: Tom Cardella
Div Pres: Ed McBrien
*Chf Mktg O: David Kroll
Ofcr: Cornell Boggs III
Ofcr: Karen Ripley
Ofcr: Jim Sheeran
*Ex VP: Fernando Palacios
Ex VP: Fernando J Palacios
Exec: Tim Maly

D-U-N-S 80-018-8141
MILLERS ALE HOUSE INC
(Suby of ALE HOUSE MANAGEMENT INC) ★
5750 Major Blvd Ste 400, Orlando, FL 32819-7971
Tel (407) 547-1120 Founded/Ownrshp 1988
Sales 68.1MM[E] EMP 1,223[E]
SIC 5812 Restaurant, family: chain
CEO: Phil Hickey
VP: Bruce Belskey
VP: Doug Jackson
Rgnl Mgr: Vince Caci
Genl Mgr: AMR Sallam

D-U-N-S 60-684-7523
MILLERS HEALTH SYSTEMS INC
MILLER'S MERRY MANOR
1690 S County Farm Rd, Warsaw, IN 46580-8248
Tel (574) 267-7211 Founded/Ownrshp 1964
Sales 120.5MM[E] EMP 3,000
SIC 8052 8051 8361 Intermediate care facilities; Skilled nursing care facilities; Residential care
Pr: Patrick H Boyle
COO: Greg Spaulding
Sr VP: Mike Forgey
Sr VP: Debbie Hale
VP: Krista Lickey
Exec: Tammy Fritzel
Exec: Julie Steele
Off Mgr: Barbara Green
Off Mgr: Cathy Rademaker
MIS Dir: Brad Harris
IT Man: Brian Holdrread
Board of Directors: Brad Harris

D-U-N-S 03-136-9135
MILLERS INC
610 E Jefferson St, Pittsburg, KS 66762-5913
Tel (620) 231-8050 Founded/Ownrshp 1939
Sales 139.0MM EMP 380
SIC 7384 Film developing & printing
Ch Bd: Richard G Miller
*Pr: Todd R Coleman
*CFO: Marcia Sorrick
*VP: H Richard Coleman
CIO: Mark Ripley
IT Man: Travis Bonine
IT Man: Paul Olsen
Mktg Mgr: Paul Rogger

MILLER'S MERRY MANOR
See MILLERS HEALTH SYSTEMS INC

MILLERS SUPPLIES AT WORK
See MILLERS SUPPLIES AT WORK INC

D-U-N-S 05-860-5775
MILLERS SUPPLIES AT WORK INC
MILLERS SUPPLIES AT WORK
8600 Cinder Bed Rd, Lorton, VA 22079-1470
Tel (703) 644-2200 Founded/Ownrshp 1974
Sales 113.2MM[E] EMP 115[E]
SIC 5112 5044 5021 Office supplies; Office equipment; Furniture
Pr: Patricia Miller
*Ex VP: Wayne Stillwagon
Opers Mgr: Scott George

D-U-N-S 79-690-1205
MILLERSVILLE UNIVERSITY OF PENNSYLVANIA
STATE SYSTEM OF HGHR
(Suby of STATE SYSTEM HIGHER EDUCATN PA) ★
1 S George St, Millersville, PA 17551
Tel (717) 872-3011 Founded/Ownrshp 1983
Sales 131.8MM[E] EMP 1,040[E]
SIC 8221 9411 University; Administration of educational programs;
Pr: Francine G McNairy
Pr: Carol Y Phillips
VP: Chip German
Genl Mgr: Robert Slabinski
Store Mgr: Lisa Schorr
Dir IT: Sandy Robertson
Pr Mgr: Steven Diguiseppe

D-U-N-S 00-194-5971
MILLIE AND SEVERSON INC (NV)
(Suby of SEVERSON GROUP INC) ★
3601 Serpentine Dr, Los Alamitos, CA 90720-2440
Tel (562) 493-3611 Founded/Ownrshp 1945, 1990
Sales 288.6MM EMP 75
SIC 1541 Industrial buildings, new construction; Renovation, remodeling & repairs: industrial buildings; Steel building construction; Warehouse construction
Pr: Scott Feest
*Sr VP: Robert E Wissmann
*VP: John Grossman
*VP: Mark Huber
Sfty Mgr: Richard Wroble
Corp Couns: Clark Severson
Snr PM: Dave Kutnyak

D-U-N-S 00-201-7440 IMP/EXP
MILLIKEN & CO
MILLIKEN LIBRARY
920 Milliken Rd, Spartanburg, SC 29303-4995
Tel (864) 503-2020 Founded/Ownrshp 1865
Sales 2.8MMM[E] EMP 9,140
SIC 2221 2211 2231 2273 2821 4911

MILLIKEN LIBRARY
See MILLIKEN & CO

D-U-N-S 01-693-0976 IMP
MILLIKEN MILLWORK INC (MI)
6361 Sterling Dr N, Sterling Heights, MI 48312-4553
Tel (586) 264-0950 Founded/Ownrshp 1953
Sales 99.8MM[E] EMP 400
SIC 5031 Lumber, plywood & millwork; Millwork; Door frames, all materials; Doors
Ch Bd: Mary Lou Milliken
*COO: Kevin T Milliken
*CFO: Timothy Milliken
*Sec: Maureen A Adams
*VP: Keith M Milliken
*VP: Terrance P Milliken
Genl Mgr: Paul Williams
Dir IT: Jerrod Rothey
Opers Mgr: Steve Saddler
Plnt Mgr: Jay Portmess
Mktg Dir: Jordan Buschmohle

D-U-N-S 07-183-5995
MILLIMAN INC
1301 5th Ave Ste 3800, Seattle, WA 98101-2635
Tel (206) 624-7940 Founded/Ownrshp 1947
Sales 828.2MM EMP 3,000
SIC 8742 8999 7389

MILLIPORE SIGMA
See ALDRICH CHEMICAL CO LLC

MILLIPORE SIGMA
See SIGMA-ALDRICH CORP

D-U-N-S 06-048-1090
MILLIS TRANSFER INC
121 Gebhardt Rd, Black River Falls, WI 54615-9111
Tel (715) 284-4384 Founded/Ownrshp 1936
Sales 120.3MM[E] EMP 750
SIC 4213 4231 4212 Contract haulers; Trucking terminal facilities; Local trucking, without storage
Pr: David Millis
*VP: Steve Millis

D-U-N-S 00-687-0703
MILLMAN LUMBER CO (MO)
FOREST PRODUCTS SUPPLY
9264 Manchester Rd, Saint Louis, MO 63144-2636
Tel (314) 961-6195 Founded/Ownrshp 1946
Sales 258.0MM EMP 80
Accts Randolph L Russo Cpa
SIC 5031 Lumber: rough, dressed & finished; Millwork; Plywood; Building materials, interior
Ch Bd: Robert L Millman
*Pr: Richard G Millman
*Treas: Kenneth G Mains
Genl Mgr: Dave Worthington
Dir IT: Mike Henson
Sales Exec: Patrick Sinclair

D-U-N-S 07-392-9002
MILLS COLLEGE
5000 Macarthur Blvd, Oakland, CA 94613-1000
Tel (510) 430-2255 Founded/Ownrshp 1852
Sales 92.4MM EMP 211[E]
Accts Grant Thornton Lp San Francis
SIC 8221 College, except junior
Pr: Alecia A Decoudreaux
*Pr: Janet Holmgren
CFO: Peter Michell
Bd of Dir: Kristine Kaes
Trst: Kathleen Burke
Trst: Alexandra Moses
Trst: Clare Springs
Trst: Barbara Wolfe
Assoc VP: David Gin
Assoc VP: Judith Silva
Ex VP: Joan Braun
VP: Christi Chapman
Exec: Angela Gonsalves
Exec: Gayle Hall
Exec: Thea Hillman

D-U-N-S 08-350-3631
MILLS CORP
(Suby of SPG-FCM VENTURES LLC) ★
5425 Wisconsin Ave # 300, Chevy Chase, MD 20815-3581
Tel (301) 968-6000 Founded/Ownrshp 2007
Sales 127.1MM[E] EMP 1,150
SIC 6798 Real estate investment trusts
Pr: Mark S Ordan
*CFO: Richard J Nadeau
*Ex VP: Gordon Glenn
VP: Norman Finbloom
VP: Bill Gilliland
CTO: Nelson Shimon
Dir IT: Sean Curran
Dir IT: Thomas Furness
Dir IT: Troy Sachs
Dir IT: Sylvie Williams
Info Man: Brent Pasanen

MILLS FLEET FARM
See FLEET WHOLESALE SUPPLY CO LLC

MILLS GILBANE
See GILBANE BUILDING CO

D-U-N-S 00-371-8203
MILLS PENINSULA HOSPITAL INC
1635 Rollins Rd, Burlingame, CA 94010-2301
Tel (650) 652-3807 Founded/Ownrshp 2010
Sales 609.8MM EMP 9[E]
SIC 8099 Health & allied services
Prin: Don McMahon

D-U-N-S 07-876-9643
MILLS-PENINSULA HEALTH SERVICES
MILLS-PENINSULA HOSPITALS
1501 Trousdale Dr, Burlingame, CA 94010-4506
Tel (650) 696-5400 Founded/Ownrshp 1998
Sales 609.8MM EMP 2,200
SIC 8062

MILLS-PENINSULA HOSPITALS
See MILLS-PENINSULA HEALTH SERVICES

D-U-N-S 07-612-9477 IMP
■ MILLSTONE COFFEE INC
(Suby of J M SMUCKER CO) ★
1 Procter And Gamble Plz, Cincinnati, OH 45202-3315
Tel (513) 983-1100 Founded/Ownrshp 2008
Sales 82.2MM[E] EMP 1,169
SIC 2095 Coffee roasting (except by wholesale grocers)
Pr: R Kerry Clark
*Pr: G W Pric
*VP: Clayton C Daley Jr
*VP: S P Donovan Jr
*VP: H J Kangis
*VP: Alan G Lafley
*VP: D R Walker

MILLSTONE POWER STATION
See DOMINION NUCLEAR CONNECTICUT INC

D-U-N-S 07-376-1355
MILLVILLE BOARD OF EDUCATION
110 N 3rd St, Millville, NJ 08332-3302
Tel (856) 293-2000 Founded/Ownrshp 1800
Sales 69.3MM[E] EMP 1,100
SIC 8211 School board
Pr: Charles Flickinger
Pr: William Herman
Prin: Michael Calareso
Prin: Jennifer Lookabaugh
Prin: Fred Setser
Prin: William Sheridan
Prin: Harry Tillotson
IT Man: Linda Woodson

D-U-N-S 55-658-0843
MILLVILLE PUBLIC SCHOOLS
110 N 3rd St, Millville, NJ 08332-3302
Tel (856) 293-2000 Founded/Ownrshp 1980
Sales 1.2MM[E] EMP 1,100[E]
SIC 8211 Public elementary & secondary schools
MIS Dir: Daniel Wright

D-U-N-S 01-029-8628
MILLWARD BROWN LLC
(Suby of W P P) ★
11 Madison Ave Ste 1200, New York, NY 10010-3696
Tel (212) 548-7200 Founded/Ownrshp 1975
Sales 186.1MM[E] EMP 1,632
SIC 8732 Market analysis or research
CEO: Mary Ann Packo
Sr Pt: Nick Cooper
*Pr: Eileen Cantbell
Pr: Stephen Dimarco
Pr: Scott Megginson
CFO: Elizabeth Brownhill
CFO: Dave Sandberg
*CFO: David Sandberg
Ofcr: Deepender Rana
Ex VP: Jeff Cox
Ex VP: Nick Findlay
Ex VP: Brian Jacobs
Sr VP: Thomas O Neuman
Sr VP: Ali Rana
Sr VP: Douglas Scott
Sr VP: Eric Villain
VP: Jim Carbone
VP: Ken Clark
VP: Jeremy Coen
VP: Bob Coppola
VP: Jeremy Doyle

D-U-N-S 94-850-4337 IMP
MILLWOOD INC
3708 International Blvd, Vienna, OH 44473-9796
Tel (330) 393-4400 Founded/Ownrshp 1993
Sales 413.6MM[E] EMP 1,400
SIC 3565 4731 Packaging machinery; Freight transportation arrangement
Pr: Steven J Miller
*Pr: Lionel W Trebilcock
*CFO: Craig Gretter
*Ex VP: Ronald C Ringness
Brnch Mgr: Edwin Melendez
Genl Mgr: Kirk Ambrose
*CIO: Tim Light

*VP Opers: Brad Arnold
Plnt Mgr: Michael Cusack
Plnt Mgr: Emad Mana
Plnt Mgr: Peter Wendt

D-U-N-S 17-443-1601
MILNER INC
5125 Peachtree Indus Blvd, Norcross, GA 30092-3027
Tel (770) 458-0999 Founded/Ownrshp 1981
Sales 85.0MM^E EMP 228
SIC 7372 5999 7389 5065 5049 5044 Prepackaged software; Business machines & equipment; Microfilm recording & developing service; Facsimile equipment; Engineers' equipment & supplies; Duplicating machines
Pr: Gene W Milner Jr
CFO: Jason Black
*Treas: Eric W Daly
*VP: Charles M Gibson
*VP: Robert L Haverstick
VP: Tom Hintz
Snr Ntwrk: Juan Velasquez
Ql Cn Mgr: Jay Monson
Manager: Brett Aks
Sls Mgr: Gary Hinchcliffe

MILNER MILLING
See GRAIN CRAFT INC

D-U-N-S 09-497-3922
MILPITAS UNIFIED SCHOOL DISTRICT
1331 E Calaveras Blvd, Milpitas, CA 95035-5707
Tel (408) 635-2600 Founded/Ownrshp 1969
Sales 67.6MM^E EMP 1,133
SIC 8211 Public elementary & secondary schools
*Pr: Daniel Bobay
Trst: Chris Norwood
*VP: Marsha Grilli
VP: Bob Nunez
Prin: Rita Scott
Dir IT: Richard Rose
Dir IT: Chin Song
Opers Mgr: Sucheta Gehani
Pr Dir: Tabitha Kappeler-Horle
Schl Brd P: Danny Lau

D-U-N-S 07-862-2802 IMP
■ **MILSCO MANUFACTURING CO**
(Suby of JASON INDUSTRIES INC) ★
9009 N 51st St, Milwaukee, WI 53223-2483
Tel (414) 354-0500 Founded/Ownrshp 2014
Sales 139.3MM^E EMP 905^E
SIC 2531 Vehicle furniture
VP: Tom Amherdt
Ql Cn Mgr: Jamie H Hodgson

D-U-N-S 06-979-5110
MILTON HERSHEY SCHOOL
1201 Homestead Ln, Hershey, PA 17033-8818
Tel (717) 520-2000 Founded/Ownrshp 1909
Sales 105.4MM^E EMP 2,267
SIC 8211 Private combined elementary & secondary school
Pr: Anthony Colistra
*Pr: Peter G Gurt
*Ch: Robert F Cavanaugh
*Sec: Robert C Vowler
VP: Steve Hanzelman
Div/Sub He: Robert Fehrs
VP Admn: Elliott Robinson
Ex Dir: Beth Shaw
Snr Ntwrk: Dave Gattens
Cmptr Lab: Robert Johnston
IT Man: John Grab

D-U-N-S 96-685-2670
MILTON HERSHEY SCHOOL & SCHOOL TRUST
711 Crest Ln, Hershey, PA 17033-8903
Tel (717) 520-1100 Founded/Ownrshp 2011
Sales 386.3MM EMP 12^E
Accts Pricewaterhousecoopers Llp Ph
SIC 8211 Elementary & secondary schools
Owner: Milton Hershey

D-U-N-S 05-077-2557 EXP
MILTON J WOOD CO
3805 Faye Rd, Jacksonville, FL 32226-2394
Tel (904) 353-5527 Founded/Ownrshp 1969
Sales 85.8MM^E EMP 300
SIC 1711 1542 Mechanical contractor; Commercial & office building contractors
CEO: Zarko Ognjenovic
*Ch Bd: Mark S Wood
*Pr: David W Tankersley
*CFO: Annmarie M Nemeth
Area Mgr: Steven Raney
IT Man: Justin Macdonald

MILTON ROY AMERICAS
See MILTON ROY LLC

D-U-N-S 00-409-7309 IMP
MILTON ROY LLC
MILTON ROY AMERICAS
(Suby of ACCUDYNE INDUSTRIES LLC) ★
201 Ivyland Rd, Ivyland, PA 18974-1706
Tel (215) 441-0800 Founded/Ownrshp 1936
Sales 154.8MM^E EMP 330
SIC 3561 3586 3826 Pumps & pumping equipment; Measuring & dispensing pumps; Spectroscopic & other optical properties measuring equipment; Mass spectrometers; Photometers
Pr: Chris Krieps
CFO: James Englund
CFO: Jean-Louis Favre-Bully
*Treas: Charles Gilstrap
*Ex VP: Elmer Doty
*VP: Kevin McGlinchey
Dir IT: Dolores Forliano
Dir IT: Justin Foster
IT Man: Mike Connors
VP Sls: Miriam Clements

D-U-N-S 79-037-5088
MILTON S HERSHEY MEDICAL CENTER
PENN STATE HERSHEY MEDICAL CTR
(Suby of PENN STATE) ★
500 University Dr, Hershey, PA 17033-2390
Tel (717) 531-8521 Founded/Ownrshp 2000
Sales 77.1MM^E EMP 9,000^E
SIC 8011 Medical centers
Ex Dir: Alan L Brechbill
*COO: Robin Wittenstein
*Sr VP: A Craig Hillemeier
*VP: Lisa Abbott
*VP: Kelly A Altland
Off Mgr: Deborah Null

MILWAKEE AREA TCHNICAL COLLEGE
See MILWAKEE AREA TECHNICAL COLLEGE FOUNDATION INC

D-U-N-S 04-118-8830
MILWAKEE AREA TECHNICAL COLLEGE FOUNDATION INC
MILWAKEE AREA TCHNICAL COLLEGE
(Suby of WISCONSIN TECHNICAL COLLEGE SYSTEM BOARD) ★
700 W State St, Milwaukee, WI 53233-1419
Tel (414) 297-6792 Founded/Ownrshp 1970
Sales 7.0MM EMP 2,800
Accts Baker Tilly Virchow Krause Llp
SIC 8222 8221 Technical institute; Colleges universities & professional schools
Pr: Michael L Burke
VP: Wilma Bonaparte
Genl Mgr: Cheralyn Randall
Pgrm Dir: Patti Winters

D-U-N-S 04-113-0779
MILWAUKEE COUNTY BEHAVORIAL HEALTH DIVISION
9455 W Watertown Plank Rd, Milwaukee, WI 53226-3559
Tel (414) 257-6995 Founded/Ownrshp 1998
Sales 63.4MM^E EMP 1,000
SIC 8063 Psychiatric hospitals
COO: Cheryl Schloegl
Opers Mgr: James Tietjen
Psych: Sara K Coleman
Psych: Steven P Dykstra
Psych: Shelly T Silfven
Psych: Gary J Stark

MILWAUKEE COUNTY TRANSIT SYS
See MILWAUKEE TRANSPORT SERVICES INC

D-U-N-S 00-609-4908 IMP/EXP
MILWAUKEE ELECTRIC TOOL CORP
MILWAUKEE TOOL
(Suby of TTI) ★
13135 W Lisbon Rd, Brookfield, WI 53005-2550
Tel (800) 729-3878 Founded/Ownrshp 1924
Sales 550.9MM^E EMP 2,000
SIC 3546 3425 Power-driven handtools; Saw blades for hand or power saws
Pr: Steven P Richman
Sr VP: Harry Peterson
VP: Jamie Christian
VP: Scott Ertl
VP: Steven Hachey
VP: Shad Hansen
VP: William Hughes
VP: John Rushmer
*VP: Joseph Smith
Area Mgr: Micheal Perko
Software D: Scott Davis

MILWAUKEE JOURNAL/SENTINEL
See JOURNAL SENTINEL INC

D-U-N-S 07-613-7892
MILWAUKEE PUBLIC SCHOOLS (INC)
M P S
5225 W Vliet St, Milwaukee, WI 53208-2698
Tel (414) 475-8393 Founded/Ownrshp 1846
Sales 732.3MM^E EMP 14,154
Accts Baker Tilly Virchow Krause Ll
SIC 8211 Public elementary & secondary schools
*COO: Gerald Pace
Prin: Deborah Bell
Prin: Daniel J Donder
Prin: Jewell Riano
Prin: Martha Wheeler-Fair
Psych: Melannie Litscher
Psych: Christopher Nyman
HC Dir: Linda Williams

D-U-N-S 01-985-7153
MILWAUKEE SCHOOL OF ENGIINEERING
MSOE
1025 N Broadway, Milwaukee, WI 53202-3109
Tel (414) 277-6763 Founded/Ownrshp 2008
Sales 140.9MM EMP 144^E
Accts Baker Tilly Virchow Krause Ll
SIC 8221 Colleges & universities

D-U-N-S 00-643-3452
MILWAUKEE SCHOOL OF ENGINEERING (WI)
1025 N Broadway, Milwaukee, WI 53202-3109
Tel (414) 277-7300 Founded/Ownrshp 1903
Sales 130.8MM EMP 600^E
Accts Baker Tilly Virchow Krause Llp
SIC 8221 University
Pr: Hermann Viets
V Ch: Thomas Hauske
*CFO: Mr Armund Janto
*Ch: John Mellowes
VP: Fred Berry
*VP: Roger Frankowski
*VP: Mr Frank Habib
Genl Mgr: Janda Timmerman
IT Man: James Blank
IT Man: Thomas Dazey
Sftwr Eng: Dan Fischer

MILWAUKEE TOOL
See MILWAUKEE ELECTRIC TOOL CORP

D-U-N-S 08-048-5402
MILWAUKEE TRANSPORT SERVICES INC
MILWAUKEE COUNTY TRANSIT SYS
1942 N 17th St, Milwaukee, WI 53205-1652
Tel (414) 344-6711 Founded/Ownrshp 1975
Sales 70.4MM^E EMP 1,130
SIC 4131 Intercity & rural bus transportation
Pr: Anita Connelly

MILWAUKEE TRUCK SALES
See KRIETE TRUCK CENTER MILWAUKEE INC

D-U-N-S 00-609-5616 IMP
MILWAUKEE VALVE CO INC (WI)
HAMMOND
16550 W Stratton Dr, New Berlin, WI 53151-7301
Tel (262) 432-2800 Founded/Ownrshp 1901, 1959
Sales 90.1MM^E EMP 450
SIC 3494 3492 3432 Valves & pipe fittings; Fluid power valves & hose fittings; Plumbing fixture fittings & trim
Ch Bd: Herschel L Seder
Pr: Rick Giannini
VP: Elias Rizk
Rgnl Mgr: Brian Crowe
Rgnl Mgr: Mike McKeever
Rgnl Mgr: Todd M Miller
Rgnl Mgr: Ryan OHM
Rgnl Mgr: Chris Tarantello
Dist Mgr: Bob Rudman
Genl Mgr: Jim Sauer
Sls Mgr: Jerry Radomski

D-U-N-S 02-046-1125
MILWAUKEE WORLD FESTIVAL INC
SUMMERFEST
114 N Jackson St, Milwaukee, WI 53202-6205
Tel (414) 273-2680 Founded/Ownrshp 1965
Sales 38.8MM EMP 1,200
Accts Lb Wipfli Llp Milwaukee Wi
SIC 7999 Festival operation
Ch Bd: Howard Schnoll
*Pr: Don Fimley
CFO: Sue Landry
*Treas: Wally Mores
*VP: Ann Minahan
*VP: Howard Sosoff
Ex Dir: Donald Smiley
Genl Mgr: Steve Kosbau

D-U-N-S 87-648-5496
▲ **MIMEDX GROUP INC**
1775 W Oak Commons Ct, Marietta, GA 30062-2254
Tel (770) 651-9100 Founded/Ownrshp 2008
Sales 187.3MM EMP 550^E
Tkr Sym MDXG Exch NAS
SIC 3842 3841 Surgical appliances & supplies; Surgical & medical instruments
Ch Bd: Parker H Petit
*Pr: William C Taylor
CFO: Rebeccah Brown
CFO: Michael J Senken
Ex VP: Brent Miller
VP: Mike Carlton
VP: John E Cranston
VP: Jim Dozier
VP: Roberta McCaw
Exec: Charly Albin
Exec: Donovan Schmidt
Board of Directors: Joseph G Blesser, J Terry Dewberry, Charles R Evans, Bruce L Hack, Charles E Koob, Larry W Papasan, Neil S Yeston

D-U-N-S 07-610-2602
MIMEO.COM INC
3 Park Ave Fl 22, New York, NY 10016-5909
Tel (212) 847-3000 Founded/Ownrshp 1998
Sales 247.9MM^E EMP 425^E
SIC 2759 Commercial printing
CEO: Adam Slutsky
*COO: John Delbridge
COO: Chuck Gehman
*COO: Nicole P Haughey
Sr Cor Off: Scott Klemm
Ofcr: Nancy Ramirez
Ex VP: Wilfred Busby
Ex VP: Skip Trevathan
Sr VP: Andrew Nied
VP: Mike Barker
VP: Andy Berman
*VP: Oliver Doughtie
VP: Adam Ferguson
VP: Robert A Krauss
VP Bus Dev: Paul Baker
Creative D: Douglas Jung

MIN
See TREASURE ISLAND RESORT AND CASINO

D-U-N-S 79-962-8730
MINACS GROUP USA INC
(Suby of MINACS GROUP INC,THE)
34115 W 12 Mile Rd, Farmington Hills, MI 48331-3368
Tel (248) 553-8355 Founded/Ownrshp 1997
Sales 303.8MM^E EMP 2,600
SIC 7389 8742 Telephone services; Management consulting services; Marketing consulting services
Pr: Anil Bhalla
*CFO: Ramesh Kamath
*Sec: Kaveena Barretto
Creative D: Mary Lebrato
Sales Exec: Dave Livingway

D-U-N-S 09-637-0655
MINACT INC
5220 Keele St, Jackson, MS 39206-4302
Tel (601) 362-1631 Founded/Ownrshp 1978
Sales 93.4MM EMP 1,100
Accts Carr Riggs & Ingram Llc Ridge
SIC 8331 8742 Job training services; Management consulting services
Ch: Reuben V Anderson
*V Ch: Robert Smith
*Pr: Booker T Jones
Ex VP: Sam Devore
VP: Jacqueline Beasley
VP: Mark Brantley
Ex Dir: Gwendolyn Antoine
Ex Dir: Brenda Banks
Ex Dir: Creston Burse
Ex Dir: Darlene Garavelli
Ex Dir: David Grier

D-U-N-S 00-647-8093 IMP
MINCO PRODUCTS INC (MN)
7300 Commerce Ln Ne, Minneapolis, MN 55432-3177
Tel (763) 571-3121 Founded/Ownrshp 1956
Sales 144.1MM^E EMP 655
SIC 3672 3823 3829

D-U-N-S 78-441-0263
▲ **MINDBODY INC**
4051 Broad St Ste 220, San Luis Obispo, CA 93401-8723
Tel (877) 755-4279 Founded/Ownrshp 2001
Sales 101.3MM EMP 1,226
Tkr Sym MB Exch NGM
SIC 7372 8741 Business oriented computer software; Business management
Ch Bd: Richard L Stollmeyer
COO: Brett White
Sr VP: Kimberly Lytikainen
Sr VP: Alexander Mahernia
Dir Sec: Bradford L Wills
Software D: Christopher Ellwood
Sftwr Eng: Barbara Wong
Manager: Gia Derose
Sales Asso: Ej Furgison
Sales Asso: Jennifer Risk
Snr Mgr: Julia Arellano
Board of Directors: Katherine Blair Christie, Gail Goodman, Cipora Herman, Jeremy Levine, Eric Liaw, Graham Smith

D-U-N-S 17-241-8605
MINDLANCE INC
1095 Morris Ave Unit 101a, Union, NJ 07083-7143
Tel (201) 386-5400 Founded/Ownrshp 1999
Sales 116.4MM EMP 225^E
SIC 8742 Human resource consulting services
VP: Vikram Kalra
Ex VP: Sumit Seth
*VP: Rajad Dhall
Exec: Raja Yalamanchi

D-U-N-S 82-629-3776 IMP
MINDRAY DS USA INC
MINDRAY NORTH AMERICA
(Suby of SHENZHEN MINDRAY BIO-MEDICAL ELECTRONICS CO., LTD.)
800 Macarthur Blvd, Mahwah, NJ 07430-2001
Tel (201) 995-8000 Founded/Ownrshp 2008
Sales 228.8MM^E EMP 4,050
SIC 3845 2835 3841 Electromedical equipment; Patient monitoring apparatus; In vitro diagnostics; Surgical & medical instruments
Pr: George Solomon
*Treas: Frank Gutworth
VP: Michael Thompson
Dir IT: Olivia Delmonico
Tech Mgr: Frank Rocco
VP Mktg: James Fidacaro
VP Sls: Wayne Quinn

MINDRAY NORTH AMERICA
See MINDRAY DS USA INC

MINDSHARE INTERACTION
See MINDSHARE USA LLC

D-U-N-S 84-397-5165
MINDSHARE USA LLC
MINDSHARE INTERACTION
(Suby of GROUPM) ★
498 Fashion Ave, New York, NY 10018-6798
Tel (212) 297-7000 Founded/Ownrshp 2003
Sales 116.0MM^E EMP 630
SIC 7319 Media buying service
CEO: Kelly Clark
Sr Pt: Kelly Foster
Sr Pt: Brent McKay
Sr Pt: Stacie Medley
Sr Pt: Susan Noble
Sr Pt: Laura Powers
Mng Pt: Duncan Coates
Mng Pt: Paul Gibbins
Mng Pt: Brian Hughes
Mng Pt: Gary Jones
Mng Pt: Luigi Sorrentino
Mng Pt: Benjamin Spiegel
Mng Pt: Gera Sulinska
CEO: Jennie Caormina
*COO: Anthony Young
*CFO: Joseph Scangamor
Chf Mktg O: David Adelman
VP: Don Anderson
Assoc Dir: Jessica Brown
Assoc Dir: Matthew Denerstein
Assoc Dir: Howard Gross

D-U-N-S 78-510-4832 IMP
MINDSINSYNC INC
(Suby of MINDSINSYNC LIMITED)
276 5th Ave Rm 505, New York, NY 10001-4527
Tel (212) 228-1828 Founded/Ownrshp 2006
Sales 169.5MM EMP 50
SIC 5023 Sheets, textile
Pr: Iain Scorgie
COO: Paul Cuthbertson
CFO: Antony Pereira
VP: Angus Davidson
VP: Jacqui Hatcher
VP: Larry Wilkins

D-U-N-S 00-803-6191
■ **MINDSPEED TECHNOLOGIES INC**
MACOM
(Suby of MACOM TECHNOLOGY SOLUTIONS HOLDINGS INC) ★
4000 Macarthur Blvd, Newport Beach, CA 92660-2558
Tel (949) 579-3000 Founded/Ownrshp 2002, 2013
Sales 200.7MM^E EMP 554^E
SIC 3674 Semiconductors & related devices
CEO: Raouf Y Halim
*CFO: Stephen N Ananias
*Sr VP: Abdelnaser M Adas
Sr VP: Naser Adas
*Sr VP: Najabat H Bajwa
*Sr VP: Gerald J Hamilton
*Sr VP: Allison K Musetich

Sr VP: Thomas A Stites
Sr VP: Thomas Stites
Sr VP: Preet Virk
**Sr VP:* Preetinder S Virk
**VP:* Brandi R Steege
VP: Yasuyuki Tanaka
VP: Kevin Thornber
VP: Kevin Trosian
VP: James Watkins
Exec: Robert Wood
Board of Directors: Robert J Conrad, Dwight W Decker, Michael T Hayashi, Ming Louie, Thomas A Madden, Jerre L Stead

D-U-N-S 87-820-6838
■ MINE SAFETY AND HEALTH ADMINISTRATION
(*Suby of* UNITED STATES DEPARTMENT OF LABOR) ★
201 12th St S Ste 401, Arlington, VA 22202-5414
Tel (202) 693-9899 *Founded/Ownrshp* 1978
Sales NA *EMP* 2,419
SIC 9651 Inspection for labor standards & safety, government;
**Prin:* David J McAteer
**Prin:* Merrifield Neal

D-U-N-S 00-432-1865 IMP
■ MINE SAFETY APPLIANCES CO LLC (PA)
(*Suby of* MSA SAFETY INC) ★
1000 Cranberry Woods Dr, Cranberry Township, PA 16066-5296
Tel (724) 776-8600 *Founded/Ownrshp* 1914, 2014
Sales 1.1MMM *EMP* 5,000
SIC 3842 3826 3823 3648 3829 Personal safety equipment; Gas masks; Radiation shielding aprons, gloves, sheeting, etc.; Respiratory protection equipment, personal; Environmental testing equipment; Industrial process control instruments; Lighting equipment; Gas detectors
Pr: William M Lambert
**CFO:* Stacy McMahan
**Chf Cred:* Joseph Bigler
VP: J M Barendt
VP: B V Demaria
VP: Ronald N Herring
**VP:* Douglas K McClaine
**VP:* Markus H Weber
Dir IT: Brian Cythert

D-U-N-S 95-939-4750
MINER CORP
(*Suby of* MINER HOLDING CO INC) ★
11827 Tech Com Rd Ste 115, San Antonio, TX 78233-6015
Tel (210) 655-8600 *Founded/Ownrshp* 1994
Sales 182.9MM[E] *EMP* 250
SIC 5084 Industrial machinery & equipment
CEO: Phillip T Miner III
**Pr:* Matt Dirienzo
Pr: Benjie Hunt
**CFO:* Steve Weaver
VP: Bob Flecken
**VP:* Sue Ellen Miner
VP: Fred Renteria
VP: Rick Upton
Genl Mgr: Colette Criss
CIO: Mirza Chughtai
Dir IT: Justin Steen

D-U-N-S 94-187-9715
MINER HOLDING CO INC
11827 Tech Com Rd Ste 115, San Antonio, TX 78233-6015
Tel (830) 627-8600 *Founded/Ownrshp* 2009
Sales 184.6MM[E] *EMP* 250[E]
SIC 1799 6719 Parking facility equipment & maintenance; Personal holding companies, except banks
Pr: Phillip T Miner III
Mktg Dir: Melissa Albright

MINER TECHNOLOGIES
See SANDEN NORTH AMERICA INC

D-U-N-S 79-692-9313 IMP
▲ MINERALS TECHNOLOGIES INC
MTI
622 3rd Ave Fl 38, New York, NY 10017-6729
Tel (212) 878-1800 *Founded/Ownrshp* 1968
Sales 1.8MMM *EMP* 3,868
Accts Kpmg Llp New York New York
Tkr Sym MTX *Exch* NYS
SIC 3295 2819 3274 1411 3281 5032 Minerals, ground or treated; Minerals, ground or otherwise treated; Talc, ground or otherwise treated; Calcium compounds & salts, inorganic; Quicklime; Limestone & marble dimension stone; Limestone, cut & shaped; Limestone
Ch Bd: Joseph C Muscari
CFO: Douglas T Dietrich
Chf Cred: Thomas J Meek
Bd of Dir: Donald Winter
Sr VP: Gary L Castagna
Sr VP: D Randy Harrison
Sr VP: Jonathan J Hastings
Sr VP: Douglas W Mayger
Sr VP: W Rand Mendez
VP: Brett Argirakis
VP: Patrick Carpenter
VP: Michael A Cipolla
VP: Richard Hasselbusch
VP: Joel Henley
VP: Andrew Jones
VP: Andrew M Jones
VP: Alexander Masetti
VP: Dj Monagle
VP: Lisa D Russ
VP: Todd Tannehill
Board of Directors: Joseph C Breunig, John J Carmola, Robert L Clark, Duane R Dunham, Marc E Robinson, Barbara Smith, Donald C Winter

D-U-N-S 02-280-6665
MINERS INC
COUNTY MARKET
5065 Miller Trunk Hwy, Hermantown, MN 55811-1442
Tel (218) 729-5882 *Founded/Ownrshp* 1957
Sales 530.6MM *EMP* 2,300
Accts Mcgladrey Llp Duluth Minneso
SIC 5411 Supermarkets, chain
Pr: James A Miner Sr
**Treas:* Theresa Lorentz
VP: Jim Miner
Store Mgr: Mark McKenna
Merch Mgr: Roger Nordby
Genl Couns: Bruce Anderson

D-U-N-S 03-354-5054
MINGLEDORFFS INC
JOHNSON CONTRLS AUTHORIZED DLR
6675 Jones Mill Ct, Norcross, GA 30092-4394
Tel (770) 446-6311 *Founded/Ownrshp* 1945
Sales 182.2MM[E] *EMP* 290
SIC 5075 Air conditioning equipment, except room units; Furnaces, warm air
Ch Bd: Robert M Kesterton
**Pr:* Lindy B Mingledorff
**CEO:* David R Kesterton
**CFO:* Matthew Ranstead
**Ch:* Bob Kesterton
VP: Ed Eckles
VP Bus Dev: Jim Feczko
Dir Soc: Carol Caldwell
Brnch Mgr: Jeff Vetter
Genl Mgr: Bill Hallenberg
Genl Mgr: Mike Harrison

D-U-N-S 86-948-0405
MINGS RESOURCE CORP
3316 47th Ave, Sacramento, CA 95824-2434
Tel (916) 421-5054 *Founded/Ownrshp* 2009
Sales 125.0MM *EMP* 25
Accts Gallina Llp Roseville Ca
SIC 4953 Recycling, waste materials
Pr: Kenny Eric Luong
**CFO:* Kevin Luong

D-U-N-S 06-406-0452
■ MINI MART INC
LOAF 'N JUG
(*Suby of* KROGER CO) ★
442 Keeler Pkwy, Pueblo, CO 81001-4813
Tel (719) 948-3071 *Founded/Ownrshp* 1986
Sales 189.8MM[E] *EMP* 1,600
SIC 5411 Convenience stores
Pr: Arthur Stawski
**CFO:* James Shiner
**VP:* Robert Moeder
IT Man: Vicky Hart
Site Mgr: Dave Wenger

MINI U STORAGE
See DAHN CORP

MINI-CIRCUITS
See SCIENTIFIC COMPONENTS CORP

D-U-N-S 07-933-8949
MINIAT COMPANIES INC
16250 Vincennes Ave, South Holland, IL 60473-1260
Tel (708) 589-2400 *Founded/Ownrshp* 2013
Sales 269.4MM[E] *EMP* 184[E]
SIC 5147 5144 Meats & meat products; Poultry & poultry products
Pr: David J Miniat
**VP:* Sam Colson

D-U-N-S 07-953-8416
MINIAT HOLDINGS LLC
(*Suby of* MINIAT COMPANIES INC) ★
16250 Vincennes Ave, South Holland, IL 60473-1260
Tel (708) 589-2400 *Founded/Ownrshp* 2014
Sales 269.4MM[E] *EMP* 179[E]
SIC 5147 5144 Meats & meat products; Poultry & poultry products
Pr: David J Miniat

D-U-N-S 06-351-5605 IMP
MINIATURE PRECISION COMPONENTS INC
820 Wisconsin St, Walworth, WI 53184-9516
Tel (262) 275-5791 *Founded/Ownrshp* 1974
Sales 551.6MM[E] *EMP* 1,700
SIC 3089 Injection molded finished plastic products; Molding primary plastic
Ch: Jay Brost
**Pr:* Dennis Konkol
**CEO:* James Brost
**CFO:* Nish Patel
**Prin:* Dan Brost
Prgrm Mgr: Brian Czapla
Prgrm Mgr: Matt Spittle
CIO: Bob Kamin
CTO: Rick Traeger
VP Opers: Vadim Yakubov
Plnt Mgr: Jose Maldonado

MINING JOY MACHINERY
See JOY GLOBAL UNDERGROUND MINING LLC

D-U-N-S 15-731-6381
MINISTRY HEALTH CARE INC
(*Suby of* ASCENSION HEALTH ALLIANCE) ★
400 W River Woods Pkwy, Milwaukee, WI 53212-1060
Tel (414) 359-1060 *Founded/Ownrshp* 2013
Sales 190.2MM *EMP* 5,000
Accts Deloitte Tax Llp Milwaukee W
SIC 8011 8051 Offices & clinics of medical doctors; Convalescent home with continuous nursing care
Pr: Nicholas F Desien
CFO: Steve Umland
Treas: Michael Schumitsch
Ofcr: Jeffrey Francis
Ex VP: Theresa Richards
**Sr VP:* Sister Lois Bush
VP: Jerry Burke
VP: Dennis Kepchar
VP: Kenlyn Kibler
VP: Ronald Mohorek
VP: Douglas Shew
VP: Jennifer Wagner-Mauk
Dir Rad: Mike Debay
Dir Rx: Mike Bushko

D-U-N-S 36-102-3489
MINISTRY MEDICAL GROUP
2251 N Shore Dr Ste 200, Rhinelander, WI 54501-6712
Tel (715) 361-4700 *Founded/Ownrshp* 2005
Sales 113.0MM *EMP* 100
SIC 8011 Physicians' office, including specialists
Prin: Mike Jones
Doctor: Judith S Pagano MD

D-U-N-S 96-233-1596
MINISTRY MEDICAL GROUP INC
11925 W Lake Park Dr, Milwaukee, WI 53224-3002
Tel (414) 359-1060 *Founded/Ownrshp* 2010
Sales 125.1MM *EMP* 4
Accts Deloitte Tax Llp Milwaukee W
SIC 8011 Offices & clinics of medical doctors
Pr: Donald Fasoli
Doctor: Steven Brown

MINISTRY SAINT CLARES HOSPITAL
See SAINT CLARES HOSPITAL OF WESTON INC

MINKA GROUP
See MINKA LIGHTING INC

D-U-N-S 10-312-3956 IMP/EXP
MINKA LIGHTING INC
MINKA GROUP
1151 Bradford Cir, Corona, CA 92882-7166
Tel (951) 735-9220 *Founded/Ownrshp* 1982
Sales 91.5MM[E] *EMP* 250
SIC 5063 Lighting fixtures
CEO: Marian Tang
**Prin:* Kurt Schulzman
Dir IT: Jason Yu
VP Opers: Dan Hitzeman
S&M/VP: Tim Flannery

D-U-N-S 06-653-2086 EXP
MINN-DAK FARMERS COOPERATIVE INC
7525 Red River Rd, Wahpeton, ND 58075-9698
Tel (701) 642-8411 *Founded/Ownrshp* 1972
Sales 260.0MM *EMP* 455[E]
SIC 2099 Sugar; Yeast
Pr: Kurt Wickstrom
CFO: Rick Kasper
VP: Thomas D Knudsen
VP: Tom Knudsen
VP: Richard Richter
VP: Parker Thilmony
VP: Ofelia Wegley
VP: John Wieser
Counsel: Simone Sandberg
Board of Directors: Dennis Butenhoff, Douglas Etten, Dennis Klosterman, C Kevin Kutzer, Russell Mauch, Charles Steiner

D-U-N-S 07-179-2303
MINNEAPOLIS FOUNDATION
80 S 8th St Ste 800, Minneapolis, MN 55402-2115
Tel (612) 672-3878 *Founded/Ownrshp* 1915
Sales 89.1MM *EMP* 20
Accts Cliftonlarsonallen Llp Minnea
SIC 6732 Charitable trust management
Pr: Sandra Vargas
Ofcr: Kevin Murray
Ofcr: Robyn Schein
Sr VP: Beth Halloran
VP: Jean Adams
VP: William Sternberg
Snr Mgr: Kent Swanson

D-U-N-S 02-050-4114
MINNEAPOLIS PUBLIC SCHOOL DISTRICT
MINNEAPOLIS PUBLIC SCHOOLS
1250 W Broadway Ave, Minneapolis, MN 55411-2533
Tel (612) 668-0200 *Founded/Ownrshp* 1894
Sales 685.2MM *EMP* 9,000
Accts Larson Allen Llp Minneapolis
SIC 8211 Public elementary & secondary schools; Public junior high school; Public senior high school; Public adult education school
Bd of Dir: Elizabeth Glidden
Bd of Dir: Lydia Lee
Exec: Sue Mortonsen
Exec: Vernon Rowe
Dir Sec: Jason Matlock
Off Mgr: Melissa Burns
IT Man: Linda Bartling
IT Man: Jeffrey Carlson
Netwrk Mgr: Ben Lander
Pr Dir: Gail Plewacki
Teacher Pr: Steve Barrett

MINNEAPOLIS PUBLIC SCHOOLS
See MINNEAPOLIS PUBLIC SCHOOL DISTRICT

D-U-N-S 96-954-5032
MINNESOTA AVIATION LLC
805 Enterprise Dr E Ste H, Belle Plaine, MN 56011-2345
Tel (651) 681-3900 *Founded/Ownrshp* 2011
Sales 389.2MM *EMP* 1,501[E]
SIC 6719 Investment holding companies, except banks
Sec: Thomas James Ward

MINNESOTA CENTRAL SCHOOL BUS
See ILLINOIS CENTRAL SCHOOL BUS LLC

MINNESOTA COMMUNITY FOUNDATION
See SAINT PAUL FOUNDATION INC

D-U-N-S 80-483-2640
MINNESOTA DEPARTMENT OF EMPLOYMENT AND ECONOMIC DEVELOPMENT
DEED
(*Suby of* GOVERNORS OFFICE) ★
332 Minnesota St Ste E200, Saint Paul, MN 55101-1349
Tel (651) 259-7114 *Founded/Ownrshp* 2003
Sales NA *EMP* 1,700
SIC 9441 Administration of social & manpower programs;
CFO: Cindy Farrell
CIO: Henry May

D-U-N-S 80-389-4203
MINNESOTA DEPARTMENT OF HUMAN SERVICES
(*Suby of* GOVERNORS OFFICE) ★
540 Cedar St, Saint Paul, MN 55164
Tel (651) 431-2000 *Founded/Ownrshp* 1953
Sales NA *EMP* 35,217
Accts Tautges Redpath Ltd White B
SIC 9441 Administration of social & manpower programs;
**Prin:* Lucinda Jesson

D-U-N-S 80-488-6869
MINNESOTA DEPARTMENT OF NATURAL RESOURCES
D N R
(*Suby of* GOVERNORS OFFICE) ★
500 Lafayette Rd N, Saint Paul, MN 55155-4002
Tel (651) 296-6157 *Founded/Ownrshp* 1931
Sales NA *EMP* 3,800
SIC 9512 Conservation & stabilization agency, government;
**CIO:* Robert Maki
MIS Dir: Michael Hager
Dir IT: Linda Randolph
Info Man: David Lent
Snr Mgr: Susan Sylvester

D-U-N-S 80-488-6729
MINNESOTA DEPARTMENT OF PUBLIC SAFETY
MINNESOTA DEPT -PUBLIC SAFETY
(*Suby of* GOVERNORS OFFICE) ★
445 Minnesota St, Saint Paul, MN 55101-2190
Tel (651) 201-7000 *Founded/Ownrshp* 1970
Sales NA *EMP* 1,800
SIC 9229 Public order & safety statistics centers;

D-U-N-S 80-483-2327
MINNESOTA DEPARTMENT OF TRANSPORTATION
(*Suby of* GOVERNORS OFFICE) ★
395 John Ireland Blvd, Saint Paul, MN 55155-1800
Tel (651) 296-3000 *Founded/Ownrshp* 1976
Sales NA *EMP* 4,900
SIC 9621 Regulation, administration of transportation;
VP: Wayne Brede
Exec: Dean Shaklee
Prgrm Mgr: Susan Mulvihill
Genl Mgr: Randy Christensen
IT Man: Michael Barnes
Netwrk Mgr: Lowell Schafer
Info Man: Tim Henkel
Info Man: Jeffrey Johnson

MINNESOTA DEPT -PUBLIC SAFETY
See MINNESOTA DEPARTMENT OF PUBLIC SAFETY

D-U-N-S 78-006-2605
■ MINNESOTA ENERGY RESOURCES CORP
(*Suby of* WEC ENERGY GROUP INC) ★
2665 145th St W, Rosemount, MN 55068-4927
Tel (651) 322-8900 *Founded/Ownrshp* 2015
Sales 107.9MM[E] *EMP* 450
SIC 4924 Natural gas distribution
Pr: Barbara Nick
**Pr:* Charles A Cloninger

MINNESOTA LIFE INSURANCE CO
See SECURIAN FINANCIAL GROUP INC

D-U-N-S 00-696-3375 IMP/EXP
MINNESOTA LIFE INSURANCE CO (MN)
SECURIAN
(*Suby of* MINNESOTA LIFE INSURANCE CO) ★
400 And 401 Robert St N, Saint Paul, MN 55101
Tel (478) 314-3189 *Founded/Ownrshp* 1880
Sales NA *EMP* 2,000
Accts Kpmg Llp Minneapolis Mn
SIC 6311 Mutual association life insurance
Pr: Randy F Wallake
Pr: Richard Manke
**CEO:* Christopher Michael Hilger
**CFO:* Warren Zaccaro
**Sr VP:* Dwayne Radel
VP: Dean Czarnetzki
VP: Peter Hobart
VP: Kathleen Pinkett
VP: Vicki Shawn
VP: Adam Swartz
Dir: Mary Streed

D-U-N-S 04-119-7369
MINNESOTA LIMITED LLC
18640 200th St Nw, Big Lake, MN 55309-2118
Tel (763) 262-7000 *Founded/Ownrshp* 1966
Sales 226.1MM[E] *EMP* 350
SIC 1623 Oil & gas pipeline construction
**Pr:* Reuben Leines
**VP:* Chris Leines
Sfty Mgr: Anthony Abbott

D-U-N-S 01-963-4836 IMP
MINNESOTA MUNICIPAL POWER AGENCY
MMPA
220 S 6th St Ste 1300, Minneapolis, MN 55402-4525
Tel (612) 349-6868 *Founded/Ownrshp* 1992
Sales 106.1MM *EMP* 5[E]
Accts Kpmg Llp Minneapolis Minneso
SIC 4911 Generation, electric power
Ch Bd: Steve Schmidt
**Prin:* Derick O Dahlen
**Prin:* Oncu H Er
**Prin:* Joseph V Fulliero
**Prin:* David W Niles
Snr PM: Randall W Porter

D-U-N-S 78-647-7278
MINNESOTA MUTUAL COMPANIES INC
400 Robert St N Ste A, Saint Paul, MN 55101-2099
Tel (651) 665-3500 *Founded/Ownrshp* 1998
Sales NA *EMP* 2,500
SIC 6311 Life insurance carriers
CEO: Robert L Senkler
Treas: Margaret Milosevich
Sr VP: Charles M Peterson
VP: George C Fremder

D-U-N-S 00-696-3383
MINNESOTA PIPE LINE CO LLC
(Suby of KOCH INDUSTRIES INC) ★
4111 E 37th St N, Wichita, KS 67220-3203
Tel (316) 828-5500 Founded/Ownrshp 1953
Sales 101.5MM EMP 48
SIC 4612 Crude petroleum pipelines
Pr: Dave Stecher

D-U-N-S 96-914-8795
MINNESOTA PUBLIC RADIO AMERICAN PUBLIC MEDIA
480 Cedar St, Saint Paul, MN 55101-2230
Tel (651) 290-1446 Founded/Ownrshp 2011
Sales 91.1MM EMP 217
Accts Mcgladrey Llp Minneapolis Mn
SIC 4832 Radio broadcasting stations
Prin: Doug Roderick
CFO: Douglas Roderick
VP: Mike Reszler
Dir Soc: Elena See

MINNESOTA RUBBER & PLASTICS CO
See QUADION LLC

D-U-N-S 08-491-6654
MINNESOTA SOYBEAN PROCESSORS (MN)
121 Zeh Ave, Brewster, MN 56119-3009
Tel (507) 842-6677 Founded/Ownrshp 2003
Sales 500.0MM EMP 80
SIC 5153 2075 Soybeans; Soybean oil, cake or meal
Ch Bd: Jim Sallstrom
*CEO: Taryl Enderson
VP: Brad Louwagie
Dir Lab: Lyle Oberloh
Genl Mgr: Scott Austin
Plnt Mgr: Wayne Faulkner

D-U-N-S 80-678-2330
MINNESOTA STATE COLLEGES AND UNIVERSITIES
ST. CLOUD STATE UNIVERSITY
(Suby of GOVERNORS OFFICE) ★
720 4th Ave S, Saint Cloud, MN 56301-4442
Tel (320) 308-0121 Founded/Ownrshp 1869
Sales 100.9MM EMP 1,583
Accts Cliftonlarsonallen Minneapoli
SIC 8221 9199 Colleges universities & professional schools;
Pr: Earl H Potter III
Dir Recs: Susan Bayer
Pr: Melissa M Krause
CFO: Nancy Anwary
CFO: Anne Chelin-Anderson
Treas: Nic Greer
Sr VP: Derrick Silvestri
VP: Nicolette Deason
VP: Greg Rosten
Dir Lab: Dien D Phan
Assoc Dir: Tyler Knudson

D-U-N-S 80-719-1432
MINNESOTA STATE COLLEGES AND UNIVERSITIES
GOVERNOR'S OFFICE
(Suby of GOVERNORS OFFICE) ★
30 7th St E Ste 350, Saint Paul, MN 55101-4812
Tel (651) 296-8012 Founded/Ownrshp 1975
Sales 38.0MM EMP 15,000
Accts Cliftonlarsonallen Llp Minnea
SIC 8221 9411 Colleges universities & professional schools; Administration of educational programs;
Pr: Devinder Malhotra
CFO: Laura M King
VP: Sharon Lacomb
Comm Man: Amy Yerkes
Ex Dir: R Dickhudt
Prgrm Mgr: Kent Dirks
Prgrm Mgr: James Morgan
Prgrm Mgr: Jeanne Qualley
Prgrm Mgr: Mary Rothchild
Web Dev: Neal Dawson
Corp Couns: Gail Olson

D-U-N-S 05-342-3133
MINNESOTA STATE UNIVERSITY MANKATO
(Suby of GOVERNORS OFFICE) ★
620 South Rd, Mankato, MN 56001-7013
Tel (507) 389-1866 Founded/Ownrshp 2004
Sales 2.7MM^E EMP 1,310
SIC 8221 9199 College, except junior;
Pr: Richard Davenport
Ofcr: Paulette Kimber
Ofcr: Seth Whalen
VP: Mike Gustafson
VP: Rebecca McQuiston
Assoc Dir: Torin Akey
Dir Sec: Suzie Dugan
Genl Mgr: Deborah Sinning
Genl Mgr: Steven Smith
Off Mgr: Carol Alfson
Off Mgr: Patricia Davis

D-U-N-S 07-134-1358
MINNETONKA INDEPENDENT SCHOOL DISTRICT 276
5621 County Road 101, Minnetonka, MN 55345-4214
Tel (952) 401-5000 Founded/Ownrshp 1860
Sales 144.8MM EMP 16,000
Accts Cliftonlarsonallen Llp Minnea
SIC 8211 Public elementary & secondary schools
Dir Sec: Jim McCann
Pr Dir: Janet Swiecichowski
Instr Medi: Dave Eisenmann

MINNIELAND ACADEMY
See MINNIELAND PRIVATE DAY SCHOOL INC

D-U-N-S 07-830-3435
MINNIELAND PRIVATE DAY SCHOOL INC
MINNIELAND ACADEMY
4300 Prince William Pkwy, Woodbridge, VA 22192-5361
Tel (703) 680-2548 Founded/Ownrshp 1972
Sales 45.1MM^E EMP 1,200
SIC 8351 8211 Child day care services; Private elementary school
Pr: Jacqueline M Leopold
*VP: Charles W Leopold

D-U-N-S 00-699-8082 IMP
MINNKOTA POWER COOPERATIVE INC
SQUARE BUTTE ELECTRIC COOPS
1822 Mill Rd, Grand Forks, ND 58203-1536
Tel (701) 795-4000 Founded/Ownrshp 1940
Sales 159.4MM EMP 355
Accts Brady Martz & Associates Pc
SIC 4911 Distribution, electric power; Generation, electric power
CEO: Robert McLennan
*Sec: Jeffrey Folland
VP: Wally Lang
*VP: Russell Okeson
VP: David Sogard
Sfty Mgr: Jason Uhlir

D-U-N-S 78-439-1948
MINNWEST CORP
14820 Highway 7 Ste 200, Minnetonka, MN 55345-4576
Tel (952) 230-9800 Founded/Ownrshp 1986
Sales NA EMP 356
SIC 6022 State commercial banks
Pr: T Todd McVay
*Ch Bd: M D McVay
*CFO: Lannon Brown
*Chf Cred: Russ Bushman
VP: Greg Czerwinski
*VP: Mary McVay
Off Mgr: Joyce Coulter

MINOLTA BUSINESS SYSTEMS
See KONICA MINOLTA BUSINESS SOLUTIONS USA INC

D-U-N-S 10-227-1384
MINOT PUBLIC SCHOOLS
215 2nd St Se, Minot, ND 58701-3924
Tel (701) 420-7503 Founded/Ownrshp 1890
Sales 79.7MM^E EMP 1,400
SIC 8211 Public elementary & secondary schools
MIS Dir: Billy Boyeff

MINOVA AMERICAS
See ORICA GROUND SUPPORT INC

D-U-N-S 13-038-2588 IMP
MINOVA HOLDING INC
(Suby of ORICA US SERVICES INC) ★
150 Carley Ct, Georgetown, KY 40324-9303
Tel (502) 863-6800 Founded/Ownrshp 2003
Sales 175.2MM^E EMP 532^E
SIC 2821 3564 2439 Plastics materials & resins; Epoxy resins; Blowers & fans; Structural wood members
CEO: Rory Harris
Opers Mgr: Mark Canapa

D-U-N-S 04-009-1885 IMP
MINTED LLC
747 Front St Ste 200, San Francisco, CA 94111-1917
Tel (415) 399-1100 Founded/Ownrshp 2007
Sales 1.0MMM^E EMP 2,014^E
SIC 5112 Social stationery & greeting cards
CEO: Mariam Naficy
*Pr: Melissa Kim
Pr: Jordan Zamir
*VP: Vlad Kuznetsov
*VP: Namrata Patel
*VP: Brady Wood
Sftwr Eng: John Wang

D-U-N-S 79-727-1186 IMP
■ **MINTEQ INTERNATIONAL INC**
(Suby of MTI) ★
35 Highland Ave, Bethlehem, PA 18017-9482
Tel (724) 794-3000 Founded/Ownrshp 1992
Sales 302.7MM^E EMP 1,800
SIC 3297 Nonclay refractories
Ch Bd: Joseph C Muscari
*CFO: Douglas Dietrick
VP: Rick Honey
*VP: Johannes Schut
VP: Brian J Seelig
*Mng Dir: Han Schut

D-U-N-S 02-292-2207
■ **MINTER-WEISMAN CO**
(Suby of CORE-MARK INTERNATIONAL INC) ★
1035 Nathan Ln N Ste A, Minneapolis, MN 55441-5028
Tel (763) 545-3706 Founded/Ownrshp 2004
Sales 108.4MM^E EMP 320^E
SIC 5194 5149 5145 5013 5122 Cigarettes; Groceries & related products; Candy; Automotive supplies & parts; Cosmetics, perfumes & hair products
CEO: J Michael Walsh
VP: Audrey Fujimoto
VP: Paul Siegel
MIS Dir: Ron Vetch
Dir IT: Mark Jordan
VP Sls: Gary Christensen

MINTZ LEVIN COHN
See MINTZ LEVIN COHN FERRIS GLOVSKY AND POPEO PC

D-U-N-S 07-380-4361
MINTZ LEVIN COHN FERRIS GLOVSKY AND POPEO PC
MINTZ LEVIN COHN
1 Financial Ctr Fl 39, Boston, MA 02111-2657
Tel (617) 348-4951 Founded/Ownrshp 1960
Sales 190.6MM^E EMP 1,100
SIC 8111 General practice law office
Ch: R R Popeo Jr
Owner: Pedro Suarez
COO: David A Ballinger
COO: Robert D Kubic
CFO: John Palmer
Bd of Dir: Patrick Donnelly
Bd of Dir: Rick Macdonald
Bd of Dir: Danielle Mackinnon
Bd of Dir: Erin Manganello
Bd of Dir: Brian Pirri
Bd of Dir: Brendan Sheehan
Bd of Dir: Blake E Stuart
Bd of Dir: Shaun Thompson
Bd of Dir: Janet Tighe
Bd of Dir: John M Williams
Chf Inves: Mitch Dynan
Sr VP: Gary E Bacher
Sr VP: David L O'Connor
Sr VP: Paul Scapicchio
Sr VP: Nancy J Sterling
VP: Bachergary E Bacher

D-U-N-S 08-042-3315
MINUTE TRANSFER INC
1055 Westlakes Dr Ste 300, Berwyn, PA 19312-2410
Tel (215) 987-3711 Founded/Ownrshp 2011
Sales 135.0MM^E EMP 40
SIC 7629 Telecommunication equipment repair (except telephones)
CEO: Anurag Jain
CTO: Ajay Goyal

D-U-N-S 83-173-2735
■ **MINUTECLINIC DIAGNOSTIC MEDICAL GROUP OF SAN DIEGO INC**
(Suby of CVS HEALTH CORP) ★
1 Cvs Dr, Woonsocket, RI 02895-6146
Tel (401) 765-1500 Founded/Ownrshp 2009
Sales 38.6MM^E EMP 1,801^E
SIC 5912 Drug stores & proprietary stores

D-U-N-S 87-843-4752
MINWAX GROUP INC
10 Montinview Rd Ste N300, Upper Saddle River, NJ 07458
Tel (201) 818-7500 Founded/Ownrshp 1994
Sales 113.5MM^E EMP 990
SIC 2851 Stains: varnish, oil or wax
Pr: Peter Black
*Pr: Stewart D Bill
*Pr: Ridgely W Harrison III
*CFO: Brian C Harriss
*Treas: John C Zoephel
*VP: Ann Allard
*VP: Paul Gaynor
*VP: Hank Holtermann
Board of Directors: Richard Mayer, Michael A Miles

MINYARD GROUP
See ACQUISITION VEHICLE TEXAS II LLC

D-U-N-S 96-455-4401
MIQ HOLDINGS INC
11501 Outlook St Ste 500, Overland Park, KS 66211-1808
Tel (913) 696-7363 Founded/Ownrshp 2010
Sales 377.4MM^E EMP 1,300
Accts Ernst & Young Llp Kansas City
SIC 4225 4731 8741 General warehousing & storage; Freight transportation arrangement; Management services
Pr: John Carr
*CFO: Brenda Stasiulis
*Sr VP: Dan Bentzinger
*VP: Mike Collins

D-U-N-S 11-641-9818
MIQ LOGISTICS LLC
(Suby of MIQ HOLDINGS INC) ★
11501 Outlook St Ste 500, Overland Park, KS 66211-1808
Tel (913) 696-7100 Founded/Ownrshp 2010
Sales 389.5MM^E EMP 1,300
SIC 4731 8741 Freight transportation arrangement; Management services
Pr: John E Carr
COO: Reid Schultz
CFO: Brenda Stasiulis
Ex VP: Valerie Bonebrake
Sr VP: Michael W Collins
Sr VP: Clint Dvorak
VP: Tina Jansen
Dir Bus: Kimberly Duca
Dir Bus: Rochelle Wilson
Snr Sftwr: Kevin Tresenriter
Snr Sftwr: MEI Wong

D-U-N-S 06-394-1827
MIRABILE INVESTMENT CORP
POPEYES CHICKEN & BISCUITS
1900 Whitten Rd, Memphis, TN 38133-7026
Tel (901) 873-1187 Founded/Ownrshp 1978
Sales 66.4MM^E EMP 2,000
SIC 5812 Fast-food restaurant, chain
Pr: Joseph W Mirabile
*VP: J J Mc Nelis
*VP: Vivian Vaccaro
Mktg Dir: Kim Sabino

MIRABITO FUEL GROUP
See MIRABITO HOLDINGS INC

D-U-N-S 05-265-4006
MIRABITO HOLDINGS INC
MIRABITO FUEL GROUP
49 Court St Ste 1, Binghamton, NY 13901-4640
Tel (607) 561-2700 Founded/Ownrshp 1927
Sales 949.8MM^E EMP 765
SIC 5172 4925 5541 5411 5983 Petroleum products; Gas production and/or distribution; Gasoline service stations; Convenience stores, chain; Fuel oil dealers
Ch Bd: William C Craine
*Ch Bd: Joseph P Mirabito
*Pr: Richard R Mirabito
CFO: Jerry Canny
*VP: John Fitzsimmons
*VP: Denny Mirabito
Rgnl Mgr: John Kennedy
Dist Mgr: Scott Lee
*CIO: Ross Mirabito
Site Mgr: Kristie Lacey
Sls Dir: Kevin Quinton

D-U-N-S 04-724-9925
MIRACLE-EAR INC
(Suby of AMPLIFON (USA) INC) ★
5000 Cheshire Pkwy N # 1, Minneapolis, MN 55446-3729
Tel (763) 268-4000 Founded/Ownrshp 1948
Sales 194.0MM^E EMP 800
SIC 5999 Hearing aids
Pr: Heinz Ruch
*CFO: Mario Riemma
Treas: Shawn McDonald
Treas: Ester Porter
Exec: Kevin Fitzgerald
Brnch Mgr: Doug Rice
Off Mgr: Paul Damico
Dir IT: Atul Dua

D-U-N-S 60-322-9261
■ **MIRAGE CASINO-HOTEL**
(Suby of MGM RESORTS) ★
3400 Las Vegas Blvd S, Las Vegas, NV 89109-8923
Tel (702) 791-7111 Founded/Ownrshp 1986
Sales 230.7MM^E EMP 6,000
SIC 7011 Casino hotel
Prin: Trevor Scherrer
*CFO: Debbie Hottenson
*Treas: Daniel J Darrigo
*VP: Christopher Nordling
Exec: Celina Navarro
Ex Dir: Clint O'Brien

D-U-N-S 00-697-0883
■ **MIRAGE RESORTS INC**
MGMRESORTS
(Suby of MGM RESORTS INTERNATIONAL) ★
3400 Las Vegas Blvd S, Las Vegas, NV 89109-8923
Tel (702) 791-7111 Founded/Ownrshp 1949
Sales 484.3MM^E EMP 25,900
SIC 7011 Casino hotel
Pr: James J Murren
Pr: Felix Rappaport
Pr: Frank P Visconti
CFO: Bobby Baldwin
Treas: Daniel J D Arrigo
Sr VP: Bryan Wright
VP: Paul Garcia
VP: Brian Hardee
VP: Franz Kallao
VP: Laura Lee
VP: Bruce A Levin
VP: Gary Mayo
VP: James E Pettis
VP: James M Powers
VP: Mark Russell
VP: John Schadler
VP: Robert C Selwood
VP: Joshua Soliz
VP: Kenneth R Wynn
Exec: Milorad Cerovina
Exec: Chase Connolly

D-U-N-S 80-774-3963
MIRAMED GLOBAL SERVICES INC
255 W Michigan Ave, Jackson, MI 49201-2218
Tel (866) 544-6647 Founded/Ownrshp 2006
Sales 98.4MM^E EMP 2,000
SIC 8742 Hospital & health services consultant
Pr: Tony Mira
*COO: Sue Mira
*CFO: Alan Sugerman
*Ex VP: Greg Fleckenstein
*Ex VP: Joe Miserendino
VP: Angela M Hickman
Ansthlgy: Selma M Velilla

D-U-N-S 06-390-2704
MIRIAM HOSPITAL
164 Summit Ave, Providence, RI 02906-2894
Tel (401) 793-2500 Founded/Ownrshp 2010
Sales 388.5MM EMP 1,928^E
SIC 8062 General medical & surgical hospitals
CEO: Dr Timothy Babineau
*CEO: Timothy J Babineau
*CFO: Mary A Wakefield
*VP: Paul Pierannunzi
Dir Inf Cn: Nancy Vallande
Dir Risk M: Joan Flynn
*Ex Dir: Arthur Sampson
CTO: David Hemingder
Doctor: James M Atkinson
Doctor: Sandra Cheng
Doctor: Bradley J Collins

D-U-N-S 78-871-2318
MIRION TECHNOLOGIES INC
3000 Executive Pkwy # 518, San Ramon, CA 94583-4355
Tel (925) 543-0800 Founded/Ownrshp 2015
Sales 174.5MM^E EMP 1,290
SIC 3829 Measuring & controlling devices
CEO: Thomas Logan
*CFO: Maggie S Yuen
*Ex VP: Mike Brumbaugh
*Ex VP: Seth Rosen
VP: Louis Biacchi
Off Mgr: Judy Sims
CTO: Jukka Kahilainen
QA Dir: Rachel Ronquillo
Dir IT: Craig Yurosko
Web Dev: Yong Lee
Sftwr Eng: Neil Young
Board of Directors: Brian S Graff

D-U-N-S 00-280-9804
MIRON CONSTRUCTION CO INC (WI)
1471 Mcmahon Rd, Neenah, WI 54956-6305
Tel (920) 969-7000 Founded/Ownrshp 1918, 1979
Sales 750.0MM EMP 1,200
SIC 1542 1541 1796

MISA
See MARUBENI-ITOCHU STEEL AMERICA INC

D-U-N-S 00-790-3073 IMP
MISA METALS INC
J R METALS
(Suby of MISA) ★
9050 Centre Pointe Dr, West Chester, OH 45069-4874
Tel (212) 660-6000 Founded/Ownrshp 2001
Sales 230.6MM^E EMP 400
SIC 5051 Steel; Structural shapes, iron or steel
CEO: Takeshi Mitomi
*VP: John Hritz
*VP: Jason Jamieson
VP: David Pratt
*VP: Ronald P Roemer
VP: John Wallace

*VP: Larry Wells
Netwrk Mgr: Stephen Pate

MISD
See MACOMB INTERMEDIATE SCHOOL DISTRICT

MISENER MARINE CONSTRUCTION
See ORION MARINE CONSTRUCTION INC

MISERICORDIA HEART OF MERCY CE
See MISERICORDIA HOME

D-U-N-S 19-390-4265 IMP
MISERICORDIA HOME
MISERICORDIA HEART OF MERCY CE
6300 N Ridge Ave, Chicago, IL 60660-1099
Tel (773) 973-6300 Founded/Ownrshp 1921
Sales 94.6MM EMP 950E
Accts Deloitte Tax Llp Chicago Il
SIC 8052 Home for the mentally retarded, with health care
Ex Dir: SIS Rosemary Connelly
CFO: Mark Moran
Exec: Maureen Meter
Dir IT: Timothy Campbell
Dir IT: Aj Grauer
Dir IT: Jane Guptill
Dir IT: Aj Mahadevan
Dir IT: Ronald Masterson
Dir IT: Hilda White
Telecom Mg: Jim Ahlfeld
IT Man: Marge Murphy

D-U-N-S 06-564-6341 IMP
MISERICORDIA UNIVERSITY
301 Lake St, Dallas, PA 18612-7752
Tel (570) 674-6400 Founded/Ownrshp 1924
Sales 88.7MM EMP 503E
Accts Baker Tilly Virchow Krause Llp
SIC 8221 University
Pr: Thomas J Botzman
*Pr: Michael A Mac Dowell
Treas: Dave Martin
*Treas: John Risboskin
VP: Jennifer Delmar
VP: Susan Helwig
Exec: Pam Parsnik
Assoc Dir: Linda Ross
Assoc Dir: Christine Somers
Dir: Barbara Merdiushev
Store Mgr: Diana Morreale

MISO
See MIDCONTINENT INDEPENDENT SYSTEM OPERATOR INC

MISS ME
See SWEET PEOPLE APPAREL INC

MISSION ARCH CENTER
See PEAK MEDICAL ROSWELL LLC

MISSION BAY AQUATIC CENTER
See ASSOCIATED STUDENTS OF SAN DIEGO STATE UNIVERSITY

D-U-N-S 12-065-5977
MISSION BROADCASTING INC
30400 Detroit Rd Ste 304, Westlake, OH 44145-1855
Tel (440) 526-2227 Founded/Ownrshp 1998
Sales 88.1MM EMP 38
Accts Pricewaterhousecoopers Llp Da
SIC 4833 Television broadcasting stations
Pr: Dennis Thatcher
*Ch Bd: Nancie J Smith

MISSION COMMUNITY HOSPITAL
See DEANCO HEALTHCARE LLC

D-U-N-S 01-053-1739
MISSION CONSOLIDATED INDEPENDENT SCHOOL DISTRICT
1201 Bryce Dr, Mission, TX 78572-4311
Tel (956) 323-5500 Founded/Ownrshp 1908
Sales 115.8MME EMP 2,000
Accts Reyna & Garza Pllc Edinburg
SIC 8211 Public elementary school; Public junior high school; Public senior high school
Dir Sec: Sylvia Cruz
IT Man: Luis Rocha
Schl Brd P: Patricia Olivarez
Schl Brd P: Sonia Trevino
HC Dir: Magda L Sauceda
Board of Directors: Oscar Rodirguez Sup

MISSION CRITICAL SOLUTION
See MCS OF TAMPA INC

D-U-N-S 08-932-6453
■ MISSION ENERGY HOLDING CO
(Suby of EDISON MISSION GROUP INC) ★
2600 Michelson Dr # 1700, Irvine, CA 92612-1550
Tel (949) 752-5588 Founded/Ownrshp 2001
Sales NA EMP 1,890
SIC 6719 Personal holding companies, except banks
CEO: Mark C Clarke
Pr: Thomas R McDaniel
CFO: W James Scilacci
Board of Directors: Jacob A Bouknight Jr

MISSION FOODS
See GRUMA CORP

D-U-N-S 06-256-8209
MISSION HEALTH SYSTEM INC
509 Biltm Ave Aka Hwy 25, Asheville, NC 28801
Tel (828) 213-1111 Founded/Ownrshp 1998
Sales 578.9MME EMP 5,500
SIC 8062 General medical & surgical hospitals
CEO: Ronald A Paulus MD
CFO: Charles Aysques
Treas: Carol Goodrun
Chf Mktg O: William R Hathaway
Sr VP: Sonya B Greck
Sr VP: Marc B Westle
VP: Monica Collins
VP: Melody Dunlop
VP: Dale Fell
VP: Tara Lewis
Chf Nrs Of: Mark D Johnson

D-U-N-S 96-635-3505
MISSION HEALTH SYSTEM INC
400 Ridgefield Ct, Asheville, NC 28806-2213
Tel (828) 257-7004 Founded/Ownrshp 1981
Sales 85.1MM EMP 26E
Accts Grant Thornton Llp Charlotte
SIC 8062 General medical & surgical hospitals
Pr: Ronald A Paulus

D-U-N-S 01-272-2138
MISSION HOSPITAL INC (TX)
MISSION REGIONAL MEDICAL CENTE
900 S Bryan Rd, Mission, TX 78572-6613
Tel (956) 323-9000 Founded/Ownrshp 1954
Sales 102.1MM EMP 1,100
Accts Bkd Llp Houston Texas
SIC 8062 General medical & surgical hospitals
CEO: Javier Iruegas
*CFO: Timothy McVey
CFO: Sandra Yanez
Chf Mktg O: Desi Canad
Exec: Martha Carbajal
Dir Lab: Carlos Gonzalez
Dir Lab: Isardo Resendez
Dir Rx: Imelda Ochoa
Chf Nrs Of: Cheryl Nail
Mng Dir: Laura Cavazos
Dir IT: Emundo Ortega

D-U-N-S 07-452-6690 IMP
MISSION HOSPITAL INC
509 Biltmore Ave, Asheville, NC 28801-4601
Tel (828) 213-1111 Founded/Ownrshp 1951
Sales 1.0MMM EMP 5,400E
SIC 8062 General medical & surgical hospitals
Pr: Joseph Damore
*CEO: Ronald A Paulus
COO: Bryan Astin
Ex VP: Paul Thomas
*Sr VP: Charles F Ayscue
VP: Kathy Guyette
VP: John Maher
VP: Ann Young
Dir Rad: Michael R Boene
Dir Rx: Elizabeth Michalet
Dir Rx: Mollie A Scott

D-U-N-S 06-445-7005
MISSION HOSPITAL REGIONAL MEDICAL CENTER INC
27700 Medical Center Rd, Mission Viejo, CA 92691-6426
Tel (949) 364-1400 Founded/Ownrshp 1941
Sales 516.2MM EMP 2,600
Accts Ernst & Young Us Llp San Dieg
SIC 8062 General medical & surgical hospitals
CEO: Kenn Nicfaralnd
CFO: Eileen Haubl
Dir Lab: Don White
Ex Dir: Connie Gagliardo
Genl Mgr: Paul Gausman
MIS Dir: Marsha Defrofierf
Pathlgst: Alireza Tafazzoli
Obsttrcn: Bruce A Hgdorn
Obsttrcn: Marvin Posner
Doctor: Hitomi Momose
Nrsg Dir: Karen Cronk

MISSION INDUSTRIES
See MISSION OF NEVADA INC

MISSION LINEN & UNIFORM SVC
See MISSION LINEN SUPPLY

D-U-N-S 03-494-6574 IMP
MISSION LINEN SUPPLY
MISSION LINEN & UNIFORM SVC
717 E Yanonali St, Santa Barbara, CA 93103-3235
Tel (805) 730-3620 Founded/Ownrshp 1973
Sales 186.8MME EMP 3,000
SIC 7218 7213 Industrial launderers; Linen supply
CEO: John Ross
*CFO: Anne Wilson
*Ex VP: Nick Katzenstein
*Ex VP: Joe Plowman
*VP: Mark Whitten
Genl Mgr: Dennis Pieper
Info Man: Mike Daymude

D-U-N-S 00-289-7333
MISSION OF NEVADA INC
MISSION INDUSTRIES
1 W Mayflower Ave, North Las Vegas, NV 89030-3951
Tel (702) 639-2500 Founded/Ownrshp 1995
Sales 23.4MME EMP 2,100
SIC 7213 Linen supply
Pr: Grover W Ferguson
*Pr: D W Doc Wiener
*CFO: Andrew Zimmerman
*Ch: James B Page

D-U-N-S 00-811-7095 IMP/EXP
MISSION PHARMACAL CO
10999 W Interstate 10 # 1000, San Antonio, TX 78230-1300
Tel (210) 696-8400 Founded/Ownrshp 1946
Sales 138.3MM EMP 495
Accts Ernst & Young Llp San Antonio
SIC 2834 Vitamin preparations
Ch Bd: Neill B Walsdorf Sr
*Pr: Neill B Walsdorf Jr
*CFO: Tom Dooley
*Treas: Beverly A Walsdorf
Ofcr: Marshall Hayward
Ofcr: Anita Scott
VP: Jim Mazurek
VP: Johnny Taylor
Exec: Eric White
Ex Dir: Jonathan Retano
Dist Mgr: Miguel Vela

D-U-N-S 10-304-6736 IMP/EXP
MISSION PRODUCE INC
2500 E Vineyard Ave # 300, Oxnard, CA 93036-1377
Tel (805) 981-3650 Founded/Ownrshp 1983
Sales 185.4MME EMP 300
SIC 5148

MISSION REGIONAL MEDICAL CENTE
See MISSION HOSPITAL INC

MISSION RESTAURANT SUPPLY CO
See SOUTHWEST TEXAS EQUIPMENT DISTRIBUTORS INC

MISSION RUBBER CO
See MCP INDUSTRIES INC

D-U-N-S 01-060-5464
MISSION SUPPORT ALLIANCE LLC
MSA
2490 Garlick Blvd, Richland, WA 99354-1786
Tel (509) 376-6770 Founded/Ownrshp 2009
Sales 98.4MME EMP 1,945
SIC 8741 Business management
Pr: William Johnson
Genl Mgr: Jennifer Jahner
Genl Mgr: Mary Skelton
Tech Mgr: Richard Grantham

MISSION SUPPORT SERVICES
See PRESBYTERIAN CHURCH (USA) A CORP

MISSION VIEW HEALTH CENTER
See COMPASS HEALTH INC

D-U-N-S 06-311-5372
MISSION WEST PROPERTIES INC
10050 Bandley Dr, Cupertino, CA 95014-2102
Tel (408) 725-0700 Founded/Ownrshp 1969
Sales 104.8MM EMP 6E
SIC 6798

D-U-N-S 07-945-8287
MISSISSIPPI ACTION FOR PROGRESS INC
HEAD START SCHOOL
1751 Morson Rd, Jackson, MS 39209-6546
Tel (601) 923-4100 Founded/Ownrshp 1966
Sales 41.8MM EMP 1,250
Accts Watkins Ward & Stafford Pllc
SIC 8099 8211 Health screening service; Preparatory school
Ex Dir: Bobby E Brown
*Prin: Hodding Carter III
*Prin: Owen Cooper
*Prin: Leroy Percy
*Ex Dir: Dorothy S Foster

D-U-N-S 04-574-9256
MISSISSIPPI AG CO
JOHN DEERE AUTHORIZED DEALER
441 Haley Barbour Pkwy, Yazoo City, MS 39194-9412
Tel (662) 746-6208 Founded/Ownrshp 2004
Sales 178.2MME EMP 240
SIC 5083 Farm implements; Tractors, agricultural
Pr: G Leyden Pugh
*Sec: Gus Pugh
*VP: Frank Pugh
Store Mgr: Don Arensman

D-U-N-S 07-764-6446
MISSISSIPPI BAND OF CHOCTAW INDIANS
101 Industrial Rd, Choctaw, MS 39350-4224
Tel (601) 650-1845 Founded/Ownrshp 1945
Sales NA EMP 8,500
SIC 9131 Indian reservation
CFO: Lawrene J Kovneh
*Treas: Lola Parkerson

D-U-N-S 06-954-0123
MISSISSIPPI BAPTIST HEALTH SYSTEMS INC
1225 N State St Ofc, Jackson, MS 39202-2069
Tel (601) 968-1000 Founded/Ownrshp 2008
Sales 76.5MM EMP 3,000
Accts Bkd Llp Jackson Ms
SIC 8741 8721 8069 Hospital management; Accounting, auditing & bookkeeping; Specialty hospitals, except psychiatric
CEO: Mark F Slyter
*Pr: Mark Slider
*CFO: Russell York
VP: William Grete
Dir Inf Cn: Erica Payne
Dir Lab: Pat Herrington
*Prin: Eric McVey
QA Dir: Karlene Cooper
Doctor: Michael R Byers MD
Doctor: Luther H Fulcher MD
Doctor: Robert McGee

D-U-N-S 01-038-4659
MISSISSIPPI BAPTST MEDICAL CENTER INC
(Suby of MISSISSIPPI BAPTIST HEALTH SYSTEMS INC) ★
1225 N State St, Jackson, MS 39202-2064
Tel (601) 968-1000 Founded/Ownrshp 1912
Sales 396.3MM EMP 3,000
SIC 8062 8069 8051

MISSISSIPPI BRAVES
See ATLANTA NATIONAL LEAGUE BASEBALL CLUB INC

D-U-N-S 00-705-3556
MISSISSIPPI COUNTY ELECTRIC COOPERATIVE INC (AR)
510 N Broadway St, Blytheville, AR 72315-2732
Tel (870) 763-4563 Founded/Ownrshp 1938
Sales 160.6MM EMP 16
SIC 4911 Distribution, electric power
Pr: Larry Hellums
*Sec: Steve West

D-U-N-S 80-939-9918
MISSISSIPPI DEPARTMENT OF HUMAN SERVICES
MDHS FAMILY AND CHILDRENS SVCS
(Suby of EXECUTIVE OFFICE OF STATE OF MISSISSIPPI) ★
750 N State St, Jackson, MS 39202-3033
Tel (601) 359-5131 Founded/Ownrshp 1989
Sales NA EMP 4,000
SIC 9441 Administration of social & manpower programs;
Ex Dir: Richard Berry

D-U-N-S 80-939-9926
MISSISSIPPI DEPARTMENT OF MENTAL HEALTH
(Suby of EXECUTIVE OFFICE OF STATE OF MISSISSIPPI) ★
239 N Lamar St Ste 1101, Jackson, MS 39201-1325
Tel (601) 359-1288 Founded/Ownrshp 1974
Sales NA EMP 8,800
SIC 9431 Mental health agency administration, government;
Ex Dir: Edwin Legrand G III
*CFO: Glynn Kegley
Ofcr: Jackie Bailey
Ofcr: Leslie Smith

D-U-N-S 80-985-0076
MISSISSIPPI DEPARTMENT OF PUBLIC SAFETY
STATE HIGHWAY PATROL
(Suby of EXECUTIVE OFFICE OF STATE OF MISSISSIPPI) ★
1900 E Woodrow Wilson Ave, Jackson, MS 39216-5118
Tel (601) 987-1212 Founded/Ownrshp 1938
Sales NA EMP 1,014
SIC 9229 9221 Public order & safety statistics centers; Police protection
Ch: Robert Latham
Genl Mgr: Kimberly Proctor

D-U-N-S 80-939-4067
MISSISSIPPI DEPARTMENT OF TRANSPORTATION
TRANSPORTATION COMMISSION
(Suby of EXECUTIVE OFFICE OF STATE OF MISSISSIPPI) ★
401 N West St, Jackson, MS 39201-1010
Tel (601) 359-7001 Founded/Ownrshp 1916
Sales NA EMP 3,300
SIC 9621 Regulation, administration of transportation;
Ex Dir: Larry L Brown
Genl Mgr: Alison Brown
MIS Dir: John M Sipson
Opers Mgr: Denise Jones
Opers Mgr: Sherry Milner

D-U-N-S 02-102-1431
MISSISSIPPI FARM BUREAU MUTUAL INSURANCE CO
FARM BUREAU INSURANCE
6311 Ridgewood Rd, Jackson, MS 39211-2035
Tel (601) 957-3200 Founded/Ownrshp 1952
Sales NA EMP 325
SIC 6331 Fire, marine & casualty insurance: mutual
Pr: David W Waide
*Sec: Robert Arnold
Genl Couns: Kent Bloodworth

D-U-N-S 07-944-8973
MISSISSIPPI GULF COAST COMMUNITY COLLEGE
PERKINSTON CAMPUS
51 Main St, Perkinston, MS 39573-3374
Tel (601) 928-5211 Founded/Ownrshp 1915
Sales 117.0MM EMP 980
Accts Culumber Fletcher Harvey & A
SIC 8222 Community college
Pr: Willis H Lott
VP: Jay Allen
VP: Mary Graham
VP Admn: Billy Stewart
Dir IT: David Beascon
Netwrk Mgr: Raymond Hutton
Pr Mgr: Brenda Donahoe

MISSISSIPPI INSTITUTIONS OF HL
See BOARD OF TRUSTEES OF STATE INSTITUTIONS OF HIGHER LEARNING

D-U-N-S 00-628-5225 IMP/EXP
MISSISSIPPI LIME CO
FALCO LIME COMPANY
3870 S Lindbergh Blvd # 200, Saint Louis, MO 63127-1398
Tel (314) 543-6300 Founded/Ownrshp 1907
Sales 248.5MME EMP 750
SIC 3274 2819 2879 1422 Quicklime; Industrial inorganic chemicals; Agricultural chemicals; Limestones, ground
CEO: William H Ayers
*CFO: Don Roberts
Sr Cor Off: Harry Mathews
*VP: Bruce L Baggio
VP: Kris Schuster
VP Sls: Eric V Rens
Sls Mgr: Mark Free
Snr Mgr: Thomas French

D-U-N-S 62-308-2963 IMP
MISSISSIPPI PHOSPHATES CORP
601 Industrial Rd, Pascagoula, MS 39581-3233
Tel (228) 762-3210 Founded/Ownrshp 1990
Sales 126.7MME EMP 225
SIC 2874

D-U-N-S 00-696-4118 IMP
■ MISSISSIPPI POWER CO
(Suby of SOUTHERN CO) ★
2992 W Beach Blvd, Gulfport, MS 39501-1907
Tel (228) 864-1211 Founded/Ownrshp 1972
Sales 1.1MMM EMP 1,344
SIC 4911 Electric services; Distribution, electric power; Generation, electric power
Pr: G Edison Holland Jr
CFO: Moses H Feagin
CFO: A Southern
Bd of Dir: Carl J Chaney
Bd of Dir: Jeff Harrison
Ofcr: Michelle Kinsey
VP: John W Atherton
VP: Jeff G Franklin
VP: Don E Mason
VP: Don Mason
VP: R Allen Reaves
VP: Emile Troxclair
Board of Directors: Carl J Chaney, L Royce Cumbest,

Thomas A Dews, Mark D Kleemum, L Pickering, Philip J Terrel, Marion L Waters

D-U-N-S 07-947-1580
MISSISSIPPI SILICON LLC (OH)
80 County Road 210, Burnsville, MS 38833-9529
Tel (662) 696-2600 *Founded/Ownrshp* 2010
Sales 100.0MM *EMP* 130
SIC 3339 Silicon, pure
Pr: David Tuten
Ch: Ricardo Vicintin

D-U-N-S 07-546-1814
MISSISSIPPI STATE UNIVERSITY
245 Barr Ave Mcrthur Hl Mcarthur Hall, Mississippi State, MS 39762
Tel (662) 325-2302 *Founded/Ownrshp* 1878
Sales 392.8MM *EMP* 8,000
SIC 8221 University
Pr: Mark E Keenum
COO: Raymond Brooks
Top Exec: Bill Epperson
VP: Brad Carter
Dir Soc: Artis Ford
Ex Dir: Jonathan Adams
Ex Dir: Adam Thigpen
Dir IT: Tom Ritter
Web Dev: Cindy Callahan
Snr Mgr: Ronald Tiffin

D-U-N-S 15-204-8682
MISSISSIPPI VALLEY BANCSHARES INC
13205 Manchester Rd, Saint Louis, MO 63131-1733
Tel (314) 543-3512 *Founded/Ownrshp* 1984
Sales NA *EMP* 50
SIC 6022 6712 State commercial banks; Bank holding companies
Ch Bd: Andrew N Baur
**Pr:* Linn H Bealke
CFO: Paul M Strieker
Sec: Carol B Dolenz
Assoc VP: Paula Evans
Sr VP: Daniel Fridrich
VP: Dennis Hunter
VP: Steve Sanden
Board of Directors: G Watts Humphrey Jr, John Baumstark, Donna D Lambert, Andrew S Baur, Michael D Latta, Andrew N Baur, Louis B Shipley, Alice C Behan, William H T Bush, Franklin J Cornwell Jr, Theodore P Desloge Jr, Louis N Goldring, Richard T Grote, Frederick O Hanser

D-U-N-S 04-591-3787
MISSOULA COUNTY PUBLIC SCHOOLS
215 S 6th St W, Missoula, MT 59801-4081
Tel (406) 728-2400 *Founded/Ownrshp* 1910
Sales 32.2MM[E] *EMP* 1,500
SIC 8299 8211 Educational service, nondegree granting: continuing educ.; School board
Trst: Dupree Debbie
Ofcr: Dave Hayden
Genl Mgr: Sam Cole
Pr Dir: Hatton Littman
Teacher Pr: David Rott
Psych: Janet M Metcalf
Psych: Gene Oliver
Psych: Marit Waldum
Psych: Erica Zins

D-U-N-S 07-588-6358
MISSOURI BAPTIST MEDICAL CENTER
3015 N Ballas Rd, Saint Louis, MO 63131-2374
Tel (314) 996-5000 *Founded/Ownrshp* 1890
Sales 511.3MM *EMP* 1,670
SIC 8062 General medical & surgical hospitals
Pr: Joan Magruder
Chf Rad: John Niemeyer
**CFO:* Gary McLaughlin
CFO: Tony Noronha
**VP:* Douglas Black
**VP:* Tim Mislan
**VP:* Timothy Ranney
**VP:* Sandra Young
Dir Lab: Cynthia M Kling
Dir Rad: Dennis Balfe
Dir Rad: Gene Davis
Dir Rad: Lawrence Kotner
Dir Rad: Maxwell Lazinger
Dir Rad: Christine Menias
Dir Rad: Vivian Prinster
Dir Rad: Vijay Sadhu
Dir Rx: Tom Hall

D-U-N-S 05-297-1405
MISSOURI BASIN WELL SERVICE INC
MBI ENERGY SERVICES
12980 35th St Sw, Belfield, ND 58622-9703
Tel (701) 575-8242 *Founded/Ownrshp* 1981
Sales 237.4MM[E] *EMP* 1,900
SIC 4213 1389 Contract haulers; Servicing oil & gas wells
CEO: James Arthaud
**CFO:* David Wanner
**Treas:* Bob Arthaud
**VP:* Don Hecker
Dir IT: Brent Pringle
Opers Mgr: Rachel Wiedmer

D-U-N-S 07-313-4231
MISSOURI CITY OF KANSAS CITY
414 E 12th St Ste 105, Kansas City, MO 64106-2705
Tel (816) 513-1313 *Founded/Ownrshp* 1853
Sales NA *EMP* 8,000
Accts Bkd Llp Kansas City Missour
SIC 9111 City & town managers' offices;
CFO: Jeffrey A Yates
Sr Cor Off: Ronnell Simpson Sr
Ofcr: Mary Charles
Ex Dir: Ron Goold

D-U-N-S 80-985-9010
MISSOURI CONSOLIDATED HEALTH CARE PLAN
832 Weathered Rock Ct, Jefferson City, MO 65101-1824
Tel (573) 751-8881 *Founded/Ownrshp* 1994
Sales NA *EMP* 78
SIC 6321 Health insurance carriers
Ex Dir: Ron Meyer

D-U-N-S 07-195-6247
MISSOURI DELTA MEDICAL CENTER
MDMC
1008 N Main St, Sikeston, MO 63801-5044
Tel (573) 471-1600 *Founded/Ownrshp* 1968
Sales 90.5MM *EMP* 750
SIC 8062 General medical & surgical hospitals
Pr: Jason Schrumps
**CFO:* Greg Carda
Ofcr: Linda Culbertson
**Sr VP:* Jim Henson
VP: John Runastedler
VP: Earl Sisk
Dir OR: Libby Klipfel
Genl Mgr: James Henson
Off Mgr: Amanda Lewis
Off Mgr: Marsha Roberts
Psych: Terri Burton

D-U-N-S 87-901-6764
MISSOURI DEPARTMENT OF CONSERVATION
(*Suby of* EXECUTIVE OFFICE OF STATE OF MISSOURI) ★
2901 W Truman Blvd, Jefferson City, MO 65109-4999
Tel (573) 751-4115 *Founded/Ownrshp* 1937
Sales NA *EMP* 1,550
SIC 9512 Conservation & stabilization agency, government;
**CFO:* Margie Miller
Sr Cor Off: Jim Price
**Prin:* Robert Zeihmer
Off Mgr: Kimberly Devine
Off Mgr: Geanna Gettys
Off Mgr: Megan Halford
Snr Mgr: Jeff Leftwich
Snr Mgr: Mike Schroer

D-U-N-S 87-901-4686
MISSOURI DEPARTMENT OF ECONOMIC DEVELOPMENT
(*Suby of* EXECUTIVE OFFICE OF STATE OF MISSOURI) ★
301 W High St, Jefferson City, MO 65101-1517
Tel (573) 751-4962 *Founded/Ownrshp* 1821
Sales NA *EMP* 1,000
SIC 9611 Economic development agency, government;
Brnch Mgr: Mike Downing
**Prin:* Jay Nixon

D-U-N-S 87-901-6624
MISSOURI DEPARTMENT OF ELEMENTARY AND SECONDARY EDUCATION
(*Suby of* EXECUTIVE OFFICE OF STATE OF MISSOURI) ★
205 Jefferson St, Jefferson City, MO 65101-2901
Tel (573) 751-4212 *Founded/Ownrshp* 1821
Sales NA *EMP* 1,693
SIC 9411 State education department;
**CFO:* Andrea Beck
Pr Dir: Sarah Potter

D-U-N-S 87-809-2600
MISSOURI DEPARTMENT OF HEALTH AND SENIOR SERVICES
(*Suby of* EXECUTIVE OFFICE OF STATE OF MISSOURI) ★
920 Wildwood Dr, Jefferson City, MO 65109-5796
Tel (573) 751-6014 *Founded/Ownrshp* 1821
Sales NA *EMP* 1,200
SIC 9431

D-U-N-S 87-814-3742
MISSOURI DEPARTMENT OF MENTAL HEALTH
MENTAL HEALTH STATE OF MO DEPT
(*Suby of* EXECUTIVE OFFICE OF STATE OF MISSOURI) ★
1706 E Elm St, Jefferson City, MO 65101-4130
Tel (573) 751-4122 *Founded/Ownrshp* 1972
Sales NA *EMP* 8,000
SIC 9431 Mental health agency administration, government;
Genl Mgr: Dan Haug
Dir IT: Larry Bradley
Dir IT: Virginia Rowe

D-U-N-S 87-814-4757
MISSOURI DEPARTMENT OF NATURAL RESOURCES
(*Suby of* EXECUTIVE OFFICE OF STATE OF MISSOURI) ★
1101 Riverside Dr, Jefferson City, MO 65101-4272
Tel (573) 751-3443 *Founded/Ownrshp* 1974
Sales NA *EMP* 1,800
SIC 9512 Land, mineral & wildlife conservation;

D-U-N-S 87-804-7364
MISSOURI DEPARTMENT OF PUBLIC SAFETY
(*Suby of* EXECUTIVE OFFICE OF STATE OF MISSOURI) ★
1101 Riverside Dr 4w, Jefferson City, MO 65101-4272
Tel (573) 751-4905 *Founded/Ownrshp* 1821
Sales NA *EMP* 4,971
SIC 9229 Criminal justice statistics center, government;
**Prin:* Jay Nixon

D-U-N-S 87-804-8008
MISSOURI DEPARTMENT OF SOCIAL SERVICES
(*Suby of* EXECUTIVE OFFICE OF STATE OF MISSOURI) ★
221 W High St Ste 240, Jefferson City, MO 65101-1516
Tel (573) 751-4815 *Founded/Ownrshp* 1999
Sales NA *EMP* 9,216
SIC 9441 8322

D-U-N-S 02-528-0335
MISSOURI DEPARTMENT OF TRANSPORTATION
(*Suby of* EXECUTIVE OFFICE OF STATE OF MISSOURI) ★
105 W Capitol Ave, Jefferson City, MO 65101-6811
Tel (573) 751-2551 *Founded/Ownrshp* 1821
Sales NA *EMP* 6,295
Accts Bkd Llp Springfield Mo
SIC 9621 Bureau of public roads

D-U-N-S 87-792-8002
MISSOURI EMPLOYERS MUTUAL INSURANCE CO
MEM CORPORATE
101 N Keene St, Columbia, MO 65201-6619
Tel (573) 499-9714 *Founded/Ownrshp* 1994
Sales NA *EMP* 250
SIC 6331 Workers' compensation insurance
Pr: Jim Owen
COO: Timothy D Jackman
COO: Dina Schultz
CFO: Doug Phillips
VP: Jennifer Barth
VP: David Fischhoff
VP: Robert Gibson
VP: Timothy D Jackman
VP: Timothy Jackman
VP: Michael Kravchick
VP: Kevin T Miller
VP: Steven Millikan
VP: Jennifer Peck

D-U-N-S 10-517-4846
MISSOURI FOUNDATION FOR HEALTH
415 S 18th St Ste 400, Saint Louis, MO 63103-2269
Tel (314) 345-5500 *Founded/Ownrshp* 2000
Sales 140.7MM *EMP* 43
SIC 8399 Health systems agency
Ch Bd: Wentzville J Brown
**Pr:* Dr Jim Kimmey
**Treas:* Jay D Auner
Ofcr: Amy Stringer Heffel
VP: Martha Gragg

D-U-N-S 80-972-7399
■ **MISSOURI GAMING CO**
ARGOSY RIVERSIDE CASINO
(*Suby of* PENN NATIONAL GAMING INC) ★
777 Nw Argosy Pkwy, Riverside, MO 64150-1512
Tel (816) 746-3171 *Founded/Ownrshp* 2013
Sales 31.7MM[E] *EMP* 1,000
Accts Ernst & Young Llp Kansas City
SIC 7999 7011 Gambling & lottery services; Casino hotel
Ch Bd: Peter Carlino
**Pr:* Tim Wilmott
**VP:* Robert Ippolito
Sfty Dirs: Kim Linneen

D-U-N-S 18-939-6138
MISSOURI HIGHER EDUCATION LOAN AUTHORITY
MOHELA
633 Spirit Dr, Chesterfield, MO 63005-1243
Tel (636) 733-3700 *Founded/Ownrshp* 1981
Sales NA *EMP* 550
SIC 6111 Student Loan Marketing Association
Ex Dir: Raymond Bayer Jr
**CFO:* Scott Gailes
VP: Susan Crump
CIO: Don Bertier

D-U-N-S 62-520-4854
MISSOURI JOINT MUNICIPAL ELECTRIC UTILITY COMMISSION
MOPEP ENRGY SCHEDULING TAGGING
1808 Interstate 70 Dr Sw, Columbia, MO 65203-1032
Tel (573) 445-3279 *Founded/Ownrshp* 1983
Sales 352.2MM *EMP* 29
SIC 4911
CEO: Duncan Kincheloe
**CFO:* Michael Loethen

MISSOURI OFFC OF STATE CRT ADM
See JUDICIARY COURTS OF STATE OF MISSOURI

D-U-N-S 87-804-6036
MISSOURI OFFICE OF ADMINISTRATION
EXECUTIVE OFFICE OF THE STATE
(*Suby of* EXECUTIVE OFFICE OF STATE OF MISSOURI) ★
201 W Capitol Ave Rm125, Jefferson City, MO 65101-1556
Tel (573) 751-1851 *Founded/Ownrshp* 2000
Sales NA *EMP* 1,100
SIC 9199 General government administration;
Prin: Barb Shimmens

D-U-N-S 02-150-6878
MISSOURI PETROLEUM PRODUCTS CO LLC
(*Suby of* LIONMARK CNSTR COMPANIES) ★
1620 Woodson Rd, Saint Louis, MO 63114-6179
Tel (314) 219-7305 *Founded/Ownrshp* 1932
Sales 141.7MM[E] *EMP* 334
SIC 5033 1611 2951 Asphalt felts & coating; Highway & street maintenance; Asphalt paving mixtures & blocks
**VP:* Henry Schmitt
Ex Dir: Teresa Gier
Genl Mgr: Stan Burris
Off Mgr: Debbie Novak

D-U-N-S 07-625-5876
MISSOURI STATE UNIVERSITY
901 S National Ave, Springfield, MO 65897-0001
Tel (417) 836-5000 *Founded/Ownrshp* 1905
Sales 215.3MM *EMP* 2,066
Accts Bkd Llp Springfield Missour
SIC 8221 8211 University; Elementary & secondary schools
Pr: Clif Smart
Treas: Lenord McGownd
Ofcr: Stacie Mulso
Top Exec: April Reno
VP: Thomas Allen
VP: Jim Baker
VP: Ken McClure
VP: Ken McLure
VP: Steve Robinette
VP: Kent Thomas
Ex Dir: Julie Ebersold

D-U-N-S 80-386-5369
MISSOURI VALLEY LINE CONTRUCTORS
7505 Nw Tffany Sprng Pkwy, Kansas City, MO 64153-1386
Tel (816) 891-9066 *Founded/Ownrshp* 2001
Sales 187.8MM *EMP* 3
SIC 8742 8631 Labor & union relations consultant; Trade union

D-U-N-S 12-513-6015
MISSOURI VALLEY PETROLEUM INC
1722 Mandan Ave, Mandan, ND 58554-2203
Tel (701) 663-5091 *Founded/Ownrshp* 1978
Sales 321.9MM *EMP* 200
Accts Eide Bailly Llp Bismarck Nor
SIC 5172 3443 Gasoline; Diesel fuel; Lubricating oils & greases; Gases, liquefied petroleum (propane); Tank towers, metal plate
Pr: Dave Froelich
**CFO:* Lance Olson
**Sec:* Kathy Nilles
**VP:* Jim Froelich

D-U-N-S 01-064-8814
MISSOURI WESTERN STATE UNIVERSITY
4525 Downs Dr, Saint Joseph, MO 64507-2246
Tel (816) 271-4464 *Founded/Ownrshp* 1969
Sales 35.3MM *EMP* 1,300
Accts Cliftonlarsonallen Llp St Lo
SIC 8221 College, except junior
CEO: Robert Vartabedian
VP: Ronald Olinger
Off Admin: Jamie Willis
Art Dir: Nathanael May

MISTER CAR WASH
See CAR WASH PARTNERS INC

D-U-N-S 93-983-2494
MISTRAL EQUITY PARTNERS LP
650 5th Ave Fl 31, New York, NY 10019-6108
Tel (212) 616-9600 *Founded/Ownrshp* 2008
Sales 129.8MM[E] *EMP* 871[E]
SIC 6211 Investment bankers
Mng Pt: Andrew Heyer
Mng Dir: Jeff Ginsberg

D-U-N-S 93-261-7434
▲ **MISTRAS GROUP INC**
195 Clarksville Rd Ste 2, Princeton Junction, NJ 08550-5392
Tel (609) 716-4000 *Founded/Ownrshp* 1978
Sales 719.1MM *EMP* 5,700
Tkr Sym MG *Exch* NYS
SIC 8711 7372 3829 3825 Engineering services; Prepackaged software; Measuring & controlling devices; Instruments to measure electricity
Ch Bd: Sotirios J Vahaviolos
CFO: Jonathan H Wolk
**V Ch Bd:* Michael J Lange
Ex VP: Dennis Bertolotti
Ex VP: Mark F Carlos
Ex VP: Michael C Keefe
Mng Dir: Kelly S Siemens
Rgnl Mgr: Chuck Johnson
Genl Mgr: Steve Diamond
Genl Mgr: Steven Fey
Genl Mgr: Jon Rice
Board of Directors: Nicholas Debenedictis, James J Forese, Richard H Glanton, Manuel N Stamatakis, W Curtis Weldon

MISTY MOUNTAIN SPRING WATER CO
See MID-MOUNTAIN FOODS INC

D-U-N-S 07-884-8218
MISUMI INVESTMENT USA CORP
(*Suby of* MISUMI GROUP INC.)
500 Progress Rd, Dayton, OH 45449-2326
Tel (937) 859-5111 *Founded/Ownrshp* 2013
Sales 106.2MM *EMP* 1,402
SIC 6719 3544 Investment holding companies, except banks; Die sets for metal stamping (presses)
Pr: Ryusei Ono

D-U-N-S 18-722-2559 IMP
MISUMI USA INC
(*Suby of* MISUMI GROUP INC.)
1717 N Penny Ln Ste 200, Schaumburg, IL 60173-5627
Tel (800) 681-7475 *Founded/Ownrshp* 1988
Sales 87.7MM[E] *EMP* 180[E]
SIC 5084 Machine tools & metalworking machinery
Pr: Nobu Ashida
VP: Jim B Browning

D-U-N-S 80-839-7137
MISYS INTERNATIONAL BANKING SYSTEMS INC
(*Suby of* MISYS LIMITED)
1180 Avenue Of The Amer, New York, NY 10036-8401
Tel (914) 428-7200 *Founded/Ownrshp* 1997
Sales 88.6MM[E] *EMP* 350
SIC 7378 7372 Computer maintenance & repair; Prepackaged software
Ch Bd: Richard Salk
**Pr:* Edward Ho
**CEO:* Nadeem Syed
**Ex VP:* M H Herskovits
**VP:* Shaye Mozes

MIT
See MASSACHUSETTS INSTITUTE OF TECHNOLOGY

D-U-N-S 00-784-5555
MITCHELL & STARK CONSTRUCTION CO INC
170 W 1st St, Medora, IN 47260
Tel (812) 966-2151 *Founded/Ownrshp* 1955, 1986
Sales 86.1MM[E] *EMP* 250
Accts Kb Parrish & Co Llp Indian

SIC 1623 1629 Water & sewer line construction; Waste water & sewage treatment plant construction
Pr: Fred C Harrison
*VP: Brian R Penner
Exec: Connie Sparks

D-U-N-S 07-944-7331
MITCHELL BEVERAGE OF MARYLAND LLC
CHESAPEAKE BEVERAGE
(Suby of MITCHELL COMPANIES) ★
7001 Quad Ave, Baltimore, MD 21237-2441
Tel (410) 646-5500 Founded/Ownrshp 2014
Sales 182.9MM[E] EMP 225[E]
SIC 5181 5182 Beer & other fermented malt liquors; Liquor
CEO: Manny Mitchell
*Pr: Evan Athanas

MITCHELL COMPANIES
See MITCHELL DISTRIBUTING CO INC

D-U-N-S 07-912-5449 IMP
MITCHELL DISTRIBUTING CO INC
MITCHELL COMPANIES
100 James E Chaney Dr, Meridian, MS 39307-6720
Tel (601) 482-6161 Founded/Ownrshp 1972
Sales 208.3MM[E] EMP 390
SIC 5181 Beer & ale
Pr: John Mitchell Jr
CFO: Kent Davis
VP: Melanie M Mitchell
Dir IT: Wes Robbins

MITCHELL GOLD BOB WILLIAMS
See MITCHELL GOLD CO

D-U-N-S 05-793-1024 IMP/EXP
MITCHELL GOLD CO (NC)
MITCHELL GOLD BOB WILLIAMS
135 One Comfortable Pl, Taylorsville, NC 28681-3783
Tel (828) 632-9200 Founded/Ownrshp 1989
Sales 265.2MM[E] EMP 750[E]
SIC 2512 Upholstered household furniture
Ch Bd: Mitchell Gold
*Pr: George Ackerman
Pr: Eloise Goldman
CFO: John Bannons
CFO: John Bounous
*CFO: Bob Williams
VP: Garrett Barr
VP: Marjorie Hall
VP: Charley Holt
VP: Lewis Kohnle
VP: Jerry Mitchell
Comm Dir: Mindy Drucker

D-U-N-S 03-146-7350
MITCHELL GROCERY CORP
FOODLAND ALBERTVILLE
550 Railroad Ave, Albertville, AL 35950-1485
Tel (256) 878-4211 Founded/Ownrshp 1965
Sales 139.1MM[E] EMP 550
SIC 5411 Grocery stores
CEO: Jack Mitchell
*Pr: David Mitchell
CFO: Jennifer Amos
*Sec: Bill Woodham
Exec: Gary Cameron
IT Man: Glenda Kilpatrick
IT Man: Eileen Walls
Mktg Dir: Kirk Clark

D-U-N-S 15-537-6916
■ **MITCHELL INTERNATIONAL INC**
(Suby of KKR & CO LP) ★
6220 Greenwich Dr, San Diego, CA 92122-5913
Tel (858) 368-7000 Founded/Ownrshp 2013
Sales 954.7MM[E] EMP 1,094[E]
SIC 7371 Computer software development & applications
V Ch Bd: James Lindner
Pr: Jack Farnan
Pr: Alex Sun
CFO: Arthur J Long
CFO: Elias Olmeta
Ex VP: Jesse Herrera
Ex VP: Arthur Long
Ex VP: Nina Smith-Garmon
VP: Scott Baierl
VP: Michael Bishop
VP: Michael Cwynar
VP: Vidya Dinamani
VP: Todd Fleming
VP: Mike Goggins
VP: Tom Herndon
VP: Eric Johannsen
VP: W McCraken
VP: Kristen Morrison
VP: Pauline Mulvey
VP: Uma Palepu
VP: Keith Peterson

D-U-N-S 12-108-0287
MITCHELL MANOR CONVALESCENT HOME INC
315 W Electric Ave, McAlester, OK 74501-3600
Tel (918) 423-4661 Founded/Ownrshp 1974
Sales 251.4MM EMP 60
SIC 8051 8059 Skilled nursing care facilities; Convalescent home with continuous nursing care; Convalescent home
VP: Joe Wayne-Mitchell

D-U-N-S 08-951-0234
MITCHELLS OILFIELD SERVICE INC
(Suby of JOHN WOOD GROUP P.L.C.)
409 N Central Ave, Sidney, MT 59270-4219
Tel (406) 482-4927 Founded/Ownrshp 2012
Sales 185.4MM[E] EMP 135
Accts Chms Pc Sidney Montana
SIC 1389 3273 Oil field services; Haulage, oil field; Ready-mixed concrete
Pr: Todd Appel
*CFO: Patrick Sameulson
*Treas: Andrea Davidson
*VP: Dan Boulds
*VP: Duane Mitchell

D-U-N-S 00-413-0415
■ **MITEK INDUSTRIES INC**
(Suby of BERKSHIRE HATHAWAY INC) ★
16023 Swinly Rdg, Chesterfield, MO 63017
Tel (314) 434-1200 Founded/Ownrshp 2001
Sales 739.9MM[E] EMP 1,500
SIC 8711 8748 Engineering services; Systems analysis & engineering consulting services
Ch Bd: Eugene M Toombs
*CFO: Ronald S Burkhardt
VP: Joseph Arr
*VP: Joseph C Carr Jr

D-U-N-S 84-999-5725
■ **MITEK USA INC**
(Suby of MITEK INDUSTRIES INC) ★
16023 Swingley Ridge Rd, Chesterfield, MO 63017-2052
Tel (314) 434-1200 Founded/Ownrshp 1987
Sales 465.6MM[E] EMP 740
SIC 3443 3429 3542 8711 5051 5085 Truss plates, metal; Metal fasteners; Presses: hydraulic & pneumatic, mechanical & manual; Consulting engineer; Steel; Industrial supplies
CEO: Thomas Manenti
Ex VP: Gene Toombs
*VP: Joseph C Carr Jr
VP: Richard Marriott
VP: Terry McGrath
VP: Norman McKenna
VP: David A McQuinn
VP: David McQuinn
Exec: Joseph Carr
Mng Dir: Greg Mason
IT Man: Nancy Dahl

D-U-N-S 04-838-4143
MITEL (DELAWARE) INC
(Suby of MITEL US HOLDINGS, INC)
1146 N Alma School Rd, Mesa, AZ 85201-3000
Tel (480) 449-8900 Founded/Ownrshp 2007
Sales 569.4MM[E] EMP 1,949
SIC 3661 5045 4813 5065 1731 7359 Telephone & telegraph apparatus; Telephones & telephone apparatus; PBX equipment, manual or automatic; Computer software; Long distance telephone communications; Telephone equipment; Telephone & telephone equipment installation; Equipment rental & leasing
CEO: Richard McBee
*Pr: Craig W Rauchle
*CFO: Kurt R Kneip
*CFO: Steve Spooner
*Ex VP: Graham Bevington
*Ex VP: Joe Vitalone
*Ex VP: Ron Wellard
*Sr VP: Jeffrey T Ford
*Sr VP: John L Gardner
Software D: Mark Strickland
VP Opers: Todd West

D-U-N-S 60-317-1658
MITEL MOBILITY INC
(Suby of BAYART DAVID)
1700 Intl Pkwy Ste 200, Richardson, TX 75081
Tel (469) 916-4393 Founded/Ownrshp 2015
Sales 190.0MM[E] EMP 700
Accts Bdo Usa Llp Dallas Texas
SIC 4813 Voice telephone communications
CEO: Pardeep Kohli
*Ch Bd: Ben Scott
*CFO: Terry Hungle
*Ex VP: Bahram Jalalizadeh
VP: Bejoy Pankajakshan
Dir Bus: Gagan Bhalla
Off Mgr: Stacy Priddy
*CTO: Terence McCabe
Tech Mgr: Manish Srivastava
VP Sls: Bethe A Strickland
Sls Dir: Juan Tan

D-U-N-S 03-869-7942 IMP
MITEL NETWORKS INC
(Suby of MITEL NETWORKS LIMITED)
1146 N Alma School Rd, Mesa, AZ 85201-3000
Tel (480) 961-9000 Founded/Ownrshp 2001
Sales 405.3MM[E] EMP 2,000
SIC 3661 7359 1731 7373 Telephones & telephone apparatus; Switchboards, telephone or telegraph; PBX equipment, manual or automatic; Electronic equipment rental, except computers; Telephone & telephone equipment installation; Systems integration services
CEO: Richard McBee
CFO: Souglas McCarthy
*CFO: Steve Spooner
VP: Robert Anderson
*VP: Tim Gaines
VP: Doug Michaelides
*VP: Charles Oakley
VP: John Uehling
*VP: Joe Vitalon
Exec: Bob Darmody
Exec: Mark Donnelly
Exec: Brad Ross

D-U-N-S 10-348-4783
MITEL TECHNOLOGIES INC
(Suby of MITEL (DELAWARE) INC) ★
1146 N Alma School Rd, Mesa, AZ 85201-3000
Tel (480) 449-8900 Founded/Ownrshp 1989
Sales 198.1MM[E] EMP 1,900
SIC 5065 Electronic parts & equipment
Pr: Martyn Etherington
CFO: Kurt Kneip
*Treas: Paul Ciaramitaro
Treas: Susan K Sherman
*VP: Steven E Spooner

D-U-N-S 00-787-2690 IMP
MITRE CORP (DE)
202 Burlington Rd, Bedford, MA 01730-1420
Tel (781) 271-2000 Founded/Ownrshp 1958
Sales 1.4MMM EMP 7,000
SIC 8733 8711 Noncommercial research organizations; Engineering services
CEO: Alfred Grasso
*Ch Bd: John Hamre
*Treas: Mark Kontos
Trst: Nicholas M Donofrio
Trst: Jane C Garvey
Trst: Edmund P Giambastiani Jr
Trst: John J Hamre
Trst: Elizabeth J Keefer
Trst: Donald M Kerr
Trst: Cleve L Killingsworth Jr
Trst: Montgomery C Meigs
Trst: Cathy E Minehan
*VP: Julie Bowen
*VP: Richard Byrne
*VP: Jmaes Cook
*VP: Greg Crawford
*VP: Julie Gravallese
VP: Jane Hall
VP: Stephen D Huffman

D-U-N-S 15-403-2585 IMP/EXP
MITSUBA BARDSTOWN INC
AMERICAN MITSUBA
(Suby of MITSUBA CORPORATION)
901 Withrow Ct, Bardstown, KY 40004-2672
Tel (502) 348-1409 Founded/Ownrshp 2007
Sales 129.2MM EMP 200
Accts Plante & Moran Pllc Auburn Hi
SIC 3714 Motor vehicle parts & accessories
Pr: Toshifumi Kohno
*Pr: Yoshimasa Nmn Kimura
*COO: Tetsuya Nmn Onai
*Treas: Yosuke Hashimoto
*Sec: Kenneth W Shelver
*VP: Atsushi Katakai
*VP: Masayoshi Nmn Shirato
*VP: David Stevens
*Plnt Mgr: Michael Ballard
Board of Directors: Michael Ballard, David Stevens

D-U-N-S 79-045-1231 IMP/EXP
MITSUBISHI CATERPILLAR FORKLIFT AMERICA INC
MCFA
(Suby of MITSUBISHI NICHIYU FORKLIFT CO.,LTD.)
2121 W Sam Houston Pkwy N, Houston, TX 77043-2305
Tel (713) 365-1000 Founded/Ownrshp 1992
Sales 257.5MM[E] EMP 1,100
SIC 3537 5084 Forklift trucks; Lift trucks & parts
Pr: Hiroshi Nagai
*Treas: Michiaki Nakamura
Ofcr: Robert Lafley
*Ex VP: Hiroki Oikawa
*VP: Kent E Eudy
*VP: Jack Sipola
*VP: Michael Veillete
*VP Admn: John Hansen
Genl Mgr: Perry Ardito
Genl Mgr: David Mackinnon
Software D: Kushal Paudyal
Board of Directors: Richard A Benson

D-U-N-S 19-607-2334 IMP
MITSUBISHI CEMENT CORP
(Suby of MITSUBISHI MATERIALS CORPORATION)
151 Cassia Way, Henderson, NV 89014-6616
Tel (702) 932-3900 Founded/Ownrshp 1988
Sales 135.7MM[E] EMP 619
SIC 3297 5032 Cement refractories; Cement
Pr: Kimball P McCloud
*Treas: H Kubota
*Treas: Naoki Shigeta
*VP: Lndaro Galeg
*VP: Michael Jasberg
*VP: William Mein

D-U-N-S 07-834-6382 IMP
MITSUBISHI CORP (AMERICAS)
(Suby of MITSUBISHI CORPORATION)
655 3rd Ave, New York, NY 10017-5621
Tel (212) 605-2000 Founded/Ownrshp 2012
Sales 1.3MMM[E] EMP 810
SIC 5051 5172 5141 5153 5169 5084 Ferrous metals; Nonferrous metal sheets, bars, rods, etc.; Steel; Petroleum products; Crude oil; Fuel oil; Gasoline; Groceries, general line; Grains; Industrial chemicals; Alkalines; Synthetic rubber; Aromatic chemicals; Industrial machinery & equipment
Pr: Seiei Ono
Sr VP: Hiroshi Kizaki
Sr VP: Yu Sato
Dept Mgr: Shunji Aritake

MITSUBISHI ELECT ELECTRNCS USA
See MITSUBISHI ELECTRIC US HOLDINGS INC

D-U-N-S 18-311-7860 IMP
MITSUBISHI ELECTRIC AUTOMOTIVE AMERICA INC
(Suby of MITSUBISHI ELECT ELECTRNCS USA) ★
4773 Bethany Rd, Mason, OH 45040-8344
Tel (513) 573-6614 Founded/Ownrshp 2005
Sales 186.7MM[E] EMP 754
SIC 3694 3651 3714 Motors, starting: automotive & aircraft; Alternators, automotive; Household audio & video equipment; Motor vehicle parts & accessories
Pr: Takeo Sasaki
Pr: Richard Krieger
*Ex Dir: Dave Stone
IT Man: Dana Keish
Opers Mgr: Scott Lennig
Ql Cn Mgr: Josiah Coleman
Sls&Mrk Ex: Bill Mondillo

D-U-N-S 15-374-7456 IMP/EXP
MITSUBISHI ELECTRIC POWER PRODUCTS INC
MEPPI
(Suby of MITSUBISHI ELECT ELECTRNCS USA) ★
530 Keystone Dr, Warrendale, PA 15086-7537
Tel (724) 772-2555 Founded/Ownrshp 2005
Sales 246.0MM[E] EMP 700
SIC 3613 Power circuit breakers
Pr: Brian Herry
Pr: Ben Steiner
*CFO: Bruce J Hampton
VP: Michael Doak
VP: Brian Heery
VP: Tammy Savoie
VP: Noah Tai
VP: Sally Wade
Exec: Keijiro Hora
Genl Mgr: Phil Bolin
Genl Mgr: George Danbury

D-U-N-S 06-779-2481 EXP
MITSUBISHI ELECTRIC US HOLDINGS INC
MITSUBISHI ELECT ELECTRNCS USA
(Suby of MITSUBISHI ELECTRIC CORPORATION)
5900 Katella Ave Ste A, Cypress, CA 90630-5019
Tel (714) 220-2500 Founded/Ownrshp 2002
Sales 1.3MMM[E] EMP 3,900
SIC 5065 5045 3651 3663 Electronic parts & equipment; Semiconductor devices; Computer peripheral equipment; Television receiving sets; Cellular radio telephone
Pr: Katsuya Takamiya
Pr: Kyle Martin
*Treas: Hiroshi Ishikawa
*Ex VP: Alan Olschwang
Exec: Dan Roth
Area Mgr: George Carrera
Sales Exec: Mike Corbo
Sls&Mrk Ex: Brice McKendry
Snr Mgr: Gail Kato

D-U-N-S 09-141-8897 IMP/EXP
MITSUBISHI ELECTRIC US INC
MEUS
(Suby of MITSUBISHI ELECT ELECTRNCS USA) ★
5900 Katella Ave Ste A, Cypress, CA 90630-5019
Tel (714) 220-2500 Founded/Ownrshp 2000, 2002
Sales 519.6MM[E] EMP 750
SIC 5065 5045 1796 3534 Electronic parts & equipment; Semiconductor devices; Computer peripheral equipment; Elevator installation & conversion; Escalators, passenger & freight
CEO: Kiyoshi Furukawa
*Treas: Makoto Kono
*Ex VP: Perry Pappous
*VP: Jared Baker
VP: Don Lee
*VP: Yuri Nakagawa
Comm Man: Cayce Blanchard
Genl Mgr: Mike Corbo
Genl Mgr: Mark Foster
QA Dir: Steve Guyton
Snr Mgr: Scott Coughlin

D-U-N-S 17-511-4909 IMP
MITSUBISHI GAS CHEMICAL AMERICA INC
MGC
(Suby of MITSUBISHI GAS CHEMICAL COMPANY,INC.)
655 3rd Ave Fl 24, New York, NY 10017-9105
Tel (212) 687-9030 Founded/Ownrshp 1984
Sales 231.1MM EMP 18
Accts Kiso & Tanaka Llp New York
SIC 5169 8742 Chemicals & allied products; Marketing consulting services
Ch Bd: Kinji Hiramoto
*CFO: Shuichi Murai
*Treas: Hajime Fujaita
*Ex VP: Tracy Austin
VP: Yoshikazu Nose
Tech Mgr: Yusuke Yamataka

MITSUBISHI HEAVY INDS AMER
See PRIMETALS TECHNOLOGIES USA HOLDINGS INC

D-U-N-S 14-785-2636 IMP/EXP
MITSUBISHI HEAVY INDUSTRIES AMERICA INC
MHIA
(Suby of MITSUBISHI HEAVY INDUSTRIES, LTD.)
20 Greenway Plz Ste 830, Houston, TX 77046-2027
Tel (346) 308-8800 Founded/Ownrshp 1979
Sales 591.4MM EMP 300
Accts Ernst & Young Llp New York
SIC 5084 Industrial machinery & equipment; Petroleum industry machinery; Machine tools & metalworking machinery; Engines & transportation equipment
Pr: Kiyoshi Okazoe
*Treas: Masato Shibata
*Ex VP: Shoichiro Asada
*Ex VP: Jun Fukuda
*VP: Robert Allen Evers
VP: Ichiro Hagiwara
Opers Mgr: Dick Reinke
Counsel: Michael Bacon
Board of Directors: Jun Fukuda

D-U-N-S 60-913-3744 IMP
MITSUBISHI HITACHI POWER SYSTEMS AMERICA-ENERGY AND ENVIRONMENT LTD
HPSA
645 Martinsville Rd, Basking Ridge, NJ 07920-4701
Tel (908) 542-9101 Founded/Ownrshp 2005
Sales 150.0MM EMP 100
SIC 8711

D-U-N-S 02-792-7958 IMP
MITSUBISHI HITACHI POWER SYSTEMS AMERICAS INC
MITSUBSHI PWR SYSTEMS AMERICAS
(Suby of MITSUBISHI HITACHI POWER SYSTEMS,LTD.)
400 Colonial Center Pkwy # 400, Lake Mary, FL 32746-7682
Tel (407) 688-6100 Founded/Ownrshp 2014
Sales 447.9MM[E] EMP 600
SIC 5084 1796 Industrial machinery & equipment; Petroleum industry machinery; Machine tools & metalworking machinery; Engines & transportation equipment; Power generating equipment installation
CEO: Henry E Bartoli
*Pr: Koji Hasegawa
*CFO: Arunava Mitra
*Treas: Tomonari Takahashi
*Ex VP: Tanc King
*Ex VP: Mani Seshamani
*Sr VP: William Buffa
*Sr VP: Rick Inskeep
*VP: David Brozek

VP: Chris Jensen
VP: Shinichi Ueki

D-U-N-S 00-698-7770 IMP/EXP
MITSUBISHI INTERNATIONAL CORP
M I C
(*Suby of* MITSUBISHI CORP (AMERICAS)) ★
655 3rd Ave Ste 800, New York, NY 10017-9122
Tel (212) 605-2000 *Founded/Ownrshp* 2000
Sales 1.0MMM^E *EMP* 752
SIC 5051 5172 5141 5153 5169 5084 Ferrous metals; Nonferrous metal sheets, bars, rods, etc.; Steel; Petroleum products; Crude oil; Fuel oil; Gasoline; Groceries, general line; Grains; Industrial chemicals; Alkalines; Synthetic rubber; Aromatic chemicals; Industrial machinery & equipment
Ch Bd: Seiei Ono
Ch Bd: Hidemoto Mizuhara
CFO: Yoichi Tamagawa
CFO: Naoki Tsuruta
Ex VP: Katsuhiko Hiyama
Ex VP: Osamu Tanaka
Ex VP: Kazumi Yashimora
Sr VP: Jil Galloway
Sr VP: Koji Hamano
Sr VP: Jason Stevens
VP: Kazuki Haginoya
VP: Hironori Kobayashi
VP: Bill Ono
VP: Fernando Puliti
VP: Takatoshi Wako

D-U-N-S 16-855-1443 IMP/EXP
MITSUBISHI INTERNATIONAL FOOD INGREDIENTS INC
(*Suby of* MITSUBISHI CORP (AMERICAS)) ★
5080 Tuttle Crossing Blvd, Dublin, OH 43016-3540
Tel (614) 652-1111 *Founded/Ownrshp* 2004
Sales 150.0MM *EMP* 83
SIC 5169 Food additives & preservatives
COO: Gerry McKiernan
**CFO:* Montgomery Emmanuel

D-U-N-S 80-701-9070 IMP/EXP
MITSUBISHI INTERNATIONAL POLYMERTRADE CORP
M I P
(*Suby of* M I C) ★
2 Penn Plz E Fl 11, Newark, NJ 07105-2251
Tel (732) 357-2000 *Founded/Ownrshp* 2003
Sales 800.0MM^E *EMP* 60
Accts Deloitte & Touche Llp New Yor
SIC 5169 Chemicals & allied products
Pr: Motoi Azumi
Sls Mgr: Takanori Ishii
Snr Mgr: Tetsuya Misawa

D-U-N-S 36-136-1462 IMP/EXP
MITSUBISHI KAGAKU IMAGING CORP
FUTURE GRAPHICS
(*Suby of* MITSUBISHI CHEMICAL CORPORATION)
655 N Central Ave # 1550, Glendale, CA 91203-1451
Tel (818) 837-8100 *Founded/Ownrshp* 2010
Sales 250.3MM^E *EMP* 277
SIC 5044 3699 Office equipment; Laser systems & equipment
Pr: Hiromitsu Takayama
**Pr:* Yoshinobu Ikeda
**Ex VP:* Jimmy Simba

D-U-N-S 05-817-8583 IMP/EXP
MITSUBISHI MOTORS NORTH AMERICA INC
MMNA
(*Suby of* MITSUBISHI MOTORS CORPORATION)
6400 Katella Ave, Cypress, CA 90630-5208
Tel (714) 799-4730 *Founded/Ownrshp* 1981
Sales 1.5MMM^E *EMP* 3,600
SIC 5511 5013 6159 6512 Automobiles, new & used; Motor vehicle supplies & new parts; Automobile finance leasing; Truck finance leasing; Nonresidential building operators
Ch: Gayu Uesugi
**COO:* Jerry Berwanger
**Ex VP:* Takashi Kawasaki
Ex VP: Daniel P Kuhnert
VP: Shalini Lahoty
VP: Vijay Maheshwari
VP: John McElroy
VP: Dick Rinehimer
VP: Gary Shultz
**Exec:* Dan Booth
Comm Dir: Dan Irvin
Board of Directors: Dan Booth, Richard Gilligan, Hiroshi Harunari, Takashi Kawasaki

D-U-N-S 09-411-9133 IMP/EXP
MITSUBISHI POLYESTER FILM INC
(*Suby of* MITSUBISHI PLASTICS,INC.)
2001 Hood Rd, Greer, SC 29650-1014
Tel (864) 879-5000 *Founded/Ownrshp* 1999
Sales 228.8MM^E *EMP* 500
SIC 3081 2671 Unsupported plastics film & sheet; Packaging paper & plastics film, coated & laminated
VP: Bill Wells
COO: Dennis Trice
**CFO:* Rick Mizuno
**Treas:* Dave Etherington
VP: Bill Radlein
Genl Mgr: Steven Yurich
IT Man: Jimmy Deyoung
Mfg Mgr: Ted Higgins

D-U-N-S 92-858-6312 IMP
MITSUBISHI RAYON AMERICA INC
(*Suby of* MITSUBISHI RAYON CO., LTD.)
655 3rd Ave Fl 15, New York, NY 10017-9135
Tel (212) 223-3043 *Founded/Ownrshp* 1983
Sales 131.1MM^E *EMP* 187
SIC 5169 Chemicals & allied products
Ch Bd: Hakaru Inaokam
**Ch Bd:* Hakaru Inaoka
**Pr:* Hiroyuki Sugao
**Treas:* D Ohyama
VP: Ryozo Nishioka
VP: Ward Urban
Mktg Mgr: Tats Iwai
Mktg Mgr: Mark Vassar

MITSUBSHI PWR SYSTEMS AMERICAS
See MITSUBISHI HITACHI POWER SYSTEMS AMERICAS INC

D-U-N-S 00-166-4523 IMP
MITSUI & CO (USA) INC (NY)
(*Suby of* MITSUI & CO., LTD.)
200 Park Ave Fl 35, New York, NY 10166-3599
Tel (212) 878-4000 *Founded/Ownrshp* 1966
Sales 2.9MMM *EMP* 1,000
Accts Deloitte & Touche Llp New Yor
SIC 5051 5094 5084 5153 5172 5169 Ferrous metals; Nonferrous metal sheets, bars, rods, etc.; Steel; Bullion, precious metals; Industrial machinery & equipment; Machine tools & accessories; Grains; Petroleum products; Crude oil; Gases, liquefied petroleum (propane); Industrial chemicals
CEO: Yasushi Takahashi
Sr VP: Kenichi Hori
Sr VP: Katagiri Susumu
VP: Phil Demarest
VP: Keith Ewing
VP: Yuji Kawase
VP: Daiji Kojima
VP: David Matsushita
VP: Egoshi Shozo
Exec: Keiichi Furihata
Exec: Kazumi Furukawa
Exec: Fuminobu Kawashima

D-U-N-S 62-730-4108 IMP/EXP
MITSUI CHEMICALS AMERICA INC
(*Suby of* MITSUI CHEMICALS,INC.)
800 Westchester Ave N607, Rye Brook, NY 10573-1328
Tel (914) 253-0777 *Founded/Ownrshp* 1988
Sales 284.3MM^E *EMP* 830
SIC 2821 2865 3082 8731 5169 6159 Plastics materials & resins; Plasticizer/additive based plastic materials; Cyclic crudes & intermediates; Unsupported plastics profile shapes; Computer (hardware) development; Chemical additives; Loan institutions, general & industrial
Pr: Naoto Tani
**Treas:* Tsuneo Shibacaki
Ex VP: Toshikazu Tanaka
VP: Furukawa Manabu
Mng Dir: Keiichi Sano

D-U-N-S 05-666-7983 IMP
MITSUI FOODS INC
M F I
(*Suby of* MITSUI & CO (USA) INC) ★
35 Maple St, Norwood, NJ 07648-2003
Tel (201) 750-0500 *Founded/Ownrshp* 1972
Sales 95.0MM^E *EMP* 140
SIC 5142 5149 5499

D-U-N-S 19-536-4260 IMP/EXP
MITSUI PLASTICS INC
(*Suby of* MITSUI & CO (USA) INC) ★
11 Martine Ave Ste 1175, White Plains, NY 10606-4026
Tel (914) 287-6800 *Founded/Ownrshp* 1988
Sales 116.6MM *EMP* 62
Accts Deloitte & Touche Llp Stamfor
SIC 5162 Plastics materials
Pr: Fumitaka Tasaka
**CFO:* Kevi Siladi
**Ex VP:* David Matsushita

D-U-N-S 12-365-1817
MITSUI SUMITOMO INSURANCE CO OF AMERICA
(*Suby of* MSIG HOLDINGS (AMERICAS) INC) ★
560 Lexington Ave Fl 20, New York, NY 10022-6828
Tel (212) 446-3600 *Founded/Ownrshp* 2002
Sales NA *EMP* 24^E
SIC 6331 Fire, marine & casualty insurance
Prin: Tetsuro Kihara

D-U-N-S 88-440-8956
MITSUI SUMITOMO INSURANCE CO OF AMERICA
MSIG
(*Suby of* MSIG HOLDINGS (AMERICAS) INC) ★
15 Independence Blvd 1100a, Warren, NJ 07059-2713
Tel (908) 604-2900 *Founded/Ownrshp* 2001
Sales NA *EMP* 197
SIC 6331 Fire, marine & casualty insurance
Pr: Koji Yoshida
Treas: Joseph L Farrell
Treas: Hisatoshi Saito
Ofcr: Robert B Miller

D-U-N-S 06-665-5614 IMP
MITSUWA CORP
MITSUWA MARKETPLACE
(*Suby of* KAMEI CORPORATION)
21515 S Western Ave, Torrance, CA 90501-3048
Tel (310) 782-6800 *Founded/Ownrshp* 1998
Sales 86.2MM^E *EMP* 652
SIC 5411 Grocery stores, chain
CEO: Takeshi Izuma
**CFO:* Kazuhiko Hori
VP: Noriyoshi Miyata
Store Mgr: Yasuaki Kishimoto

MITSUWA MARKETPLACE
See MITSUWA CORP

MITTAL STEEL -IHW- 3 SP
See ARCELORMITTAL MINORCA MINE INC

D-U-N-S 00-527-5870
MITTERA GROUP INC
ROCK COMMUNICATIONS
1312 Locust St Ste 202, Des Moines, IA 50309-2920
Tel (515) 343-5353 *Founded/Ownrshp* 1992
Sales 174.8MM^E *EMP* 410
SIC 2752 7319 Commercial printing, offset; Transit advertising services
Pr: Jon Troen
Creative D: Darby Oppold
Dir IT: Jeremy Witte
IT Man: Rich May
Genl Couns: Thomas Slaughter

D-U-N-S 00-185-4892 IMP/EXP
MITUTOYO AMERICA CORP (NY)
(*Suby of* MITUTOYO CORPORATION)
965 Corporate Blvd, Aurora, IL 60502-9176
Tel (630) 820-9666 *Founded/Ownrshp* 1963
Sales 144.8MM *EMP* 250
SIC 5084 7373 Measuring & testing equipment, electrical; Computer systems analysis & design
Pr: Shigeyuki Sasaki
VP: Doug Atkins
VP: Matt Dye
VP: Nobuo Suga
Dir IT: Bob Brown
IT Man: Brent Hayashi
Manager: Joseph Thompson
Sls Mgr: Robert Dillon
Sales Asso: Kay McQueen

D-U-N-S 18-107-2521 IMP/EXP
MITY-LITE INC
(*Suby of* M L E HOLDINGS INC) ★
1301 W 400 N, Orem, UT 84057-4442
Tel (801) 224-0589 *Founded/Ownrshp* 2000
Sales 89.2MM^E *EMP* 392
Accts Deloitte & Touche Llp Salt La
SIC 2531 2522 7359 Public building & related furniture; Tables, office: except wood; Dishes, silverware, tables & banquet accessories rental
Pr: John Dudash
**COO:* Brian Bowers
**CFO:* Jim Yostrum
**Ex VP:* Dennis Claspell
**Ex VP:* Brandon Ross
VP: Mark Hoffman

MITZEL'S AMERICAN KITCHENS
See ELMERS RESTAURANTS INC

MIU MIU
See PRADA USA CORP

D-U-N-S 79-037-1269
MIX HOLDINGS INC
(*Suby of* HALLMARK CARDS INC) ★
2501 Mc Gee Traffic Way, Kansas City, MO 64108
Tel (816) 274-5111 *Founded/Ownrshp* 2000
Sales 927.6MM^E *EMP* 5,650^E
SIC 3952 3951 3295 3944 Lead pencils & art goods; Crayons: chalk, gypsum, charcoal, fusains, pastel, wax, etc.; Chalk: carpenters', blackboard, marking, tailors', etc.; Paints, except gold & bronze: artists'; Markers, soft tip (felt, fabric, plastic, etc.); Clay, ground or otherwise treated; Games, toys & children's vehicles; Craft & hobby kits & sets
Ofcr: Tim Malcomvetter
VP: Michael Goodwin
Dir IT: Danyel Bischof-Forsyth
IT Man: Ken Cameron
IT Man: Steve Eikos
IT Man: Jerry Wolfe
IT Man: Joel Zigelstein

D-U-N-S 04-895-1842 IMP
MIZAR HOLDING CO INC
BERNINA OF AMERICA
(*Suby of* BERNINA INTERNATIONAL AG)
3702 Prairie Lake Ct, Aurora, IL 60504-3135
Tel (630) 978-2500 *Founded/Ownrshp* 2002
Sales 96.2MM^E *EMP* 425
SIC 5064 Sewing machines, household: electric
Ch Bd: H P Ueltschi
**Pr:* Paul Ashworth
**Pr:* Michael Perich
CFO: Mike Parish
VP: Hermann Kuhn
Prgrm Mgr: Judy Hahner
Mktg Dir: Amy Gutierrez
Mktg Mgr: Gayle Schliemann
Mktg Mgr: Alice Voss

D-U-N-S 18-505-0002 IMP/EXP
MIZKAN AMERICA HOLDINGS INC
NAKANO FOODS
(*Suby of* MIZKAN J PLUS HOLDINGS CO.,LTD.)
1661 Feehanville Dr # 300, Mount Prospect, IL 60056-6087
Tel (847) 590-0059 *Founded/Ownrshp* 1982
Sales 156.1MM^E *EMP* 350
SIC 2099 Vinegar
Pr: Hiroyasu Nakano
VP: Jayne Hoover
**VP:* Kenji Sano
**VP:* Ichiro Suzuki
Ex Dir: Dave Rotunno
Off Admin: Shawanda Cobb
QA Dir: Debbie Lukenbill
Plnt Mgr: Darren James
QI Cn Mgr: Charles Goodson
Natl Sales: Tim Marvin
Sls Dir: Akashi Matsuno

D-U-N-S 06-832-6164 IMP/EXP
MIZKAN AMERICA INC
NAKANO FOODS
(*Suby of* NAKANO FOODS) ★
1661 Feehanville Dr # 200, Mount Prospect, IL 60056-6087
Tel (847) 590-0059 *Founded/Ownrshp* 1902, 1987
Sales 202.2MM^E *EMP* 350
SIC 2099 2035 Vinegar; Dressings, salad: raw & cooked (except dry mixes); Mustard, prepared (wet)
CEO: Koichi Yuki
Pr: Kevin Ponticelli
Pr: Craig Smith
CFO: Tommy Isshiki
CFO: Mark Majewski
CFO: Michael McGuire
Ex VP: Mike Smith
Sr VP: Matt Moore
VP: Peter Marsing
Ex Dir: Mohammad Adnan
QA Dir: John Gonzales

D-U-N-S 06-020-3957
MIZUHO BANK LTD
(*Suby of* MIZUHO BANK, LTD.)
1251 Ave Of The Americas, New York, NY 10020-1104
Tel (212) 282-3000 *Founded/Ownrshp* 2002
Sales NA *EMP* 500^E
SIC 6022 6082 7359 State commercial banks; Foreign trade & international banking institutions; Equipment rental & leasing
Ex Dir: Masathuga Nagato
CFO: Koji Mimura
Treas: Ashok Kapoor
Ofcr: Luis Baltodano
Ofcr: Hikaru Morita
Ofcr: Hiroe Nikaido
Ofcr: Shuran Szalapski
Sr VP: Raffi Dawson
Sr VP: Daniel Guevara
Sr VP: Christian Hammerbeck
Sr VP: Eileen Hodgkins
Sr VP: Kevin Holmes
Sr VP: Masatoshi Imaeda
Sr VP: David McCarthy
Sr VP: Michael Meiss
Sr VP: Jun Nozaki
Sr VP: Noel Purcell
Sr VP: Ko Saito
Sr VP: Takayuki Shimizu
Sr VP: Bertram Tang
Sr VP: Harvey Tieh

D-U-N-S 08-308-6298
MIZUHO SECURITIES USA INC
(*Suby of* MIZUHO SECURITIES CO., LTD.)
320 Park Ave Fl 12, New York, NY 10022-6848
Tel (212) 282-3000 *Founded/Ownrshp* 1979, 2007
Sales 188.1MM^E *EMP* 290
SIC 6211 Traders, security
CEO: Jerry Rizzieri
**Ch Bd:* Bernard Jensen
COO: Patrick Fay
Bd of Dir: Hidetaka Kawakita
Bd of Dir: Hidefumi Kobayashi
Bd of Dir: Masaru Ono
Bd of Dir: Hajime Saito
Ofcr: Brendan Daly
VP: Vanessa Goodger
VP: Mark Guthrie
VP: Jim Jenkinson
VP: Erica Miolla
VP: Bob Nicholson
VP: Yoko Omori
VP: Charles Reinholtz
VP: Thomas Smith
VP: Kevin Takarada
VP: Steven Williams

D-U-N-S 88-341-8378
MJ HARRIS CONSTRUCTION SERVICES LLC
1 Riverchase Rdg Ste 300, Hoover, AL 35244-2910
Tel (205) 380-6800 *Founded/Ownrshp* 2012
Sales 106.6MM^E *EMP* 135
SIC 1542 Commercial & office building contractors
Pr: Michael J Harris
**CFO:* Robbie Egan
**Sec:* Bobby J Harris
**Sr VP:* Tommy Yeager
VP: Blair Hayes
**Exec:* Robert Lambe
Telecom Ex: Deborah Wiliams
Dir IT: Chris Baswell
VP Opers: Matt Hall
Snr PM: Ralph Crumpton

D-U-N-S 05-182-5347 IMP/EXP
■ **MJ SOFFE LLC**
COTTON EXCHANGE, THE
(*Suby of* DELTA APPAREL INC) ★
1 Soffe Dr, Fayetteville, NC 28312-5262
Tel (910) 435-3138 *Founded/Ownrshp* 2003
Sales 68.3MM^E *EMP* 1,190
SIC 2339 2329 2369 2321 Athletic clothing: women's, misses' & juniors'; Athletic (warmup, sweat & jogging) suits: men's & boys'; Girls' & children's outerwear; Men's & boys' furnishings
Pr: Steve Cochran
VP: Tony Augustine
**VP:* Keith Bilyeu
Genl Mgr: Genie William
IT Man: Lori Herring
MIS Mgr: Carla Autry
QC Dir: Teresa Jones
Natl Sales: Ryan Crosby
VP Sls: Elisa Palefsky
S&M/VP: Steve Wheeler
Mktg Dir: Paul Anderson

D-U-N-S 04-324-2606 IMP
MJB WOOD GROUP INC (TX)
MJB WORLD TRADE DIVISION
2201 W Royal Ln Ste 250, Irving, TX 75063-3210
Tel (972) 401-0005 *Founded/Ownrshp* 1998
Sales 250.0MM *EMP* 165
SIC 5031 Lumber, plywood & millwork
CEO: Joe A Caldwell
Pt: Mitch Bradham
Pt: Larry Gaskey
Pt: Ruben Trujillo
**Pr:* Jeffrey L Messick
**CFO:* Charles A Little
CFO: Pete Little
**VP:* Amy G Quaid
VP: Amy Quaid
Div Mgr: William Corbo
Div Mgr: Steve Daugherty

MJB WORLD TRADE DIVISION
See MJB WOOD GROUP INC

MJHS HOSPICE AND PALLIATIVE CA
See METROPOLITAN JEWISH HOME CARE INC

D-U-N-S 09-286-5679
MJKL ENTERPRISES LLC
5210 S Priest Dr, Tempe, AZ 85283-1431
Tel (480) 897-7777 *Founded/Ownrshp* 2000
Sales 50.8MM^E *EMP* 1,200
SIC 5812 Eating places
CEO: Jason Levecke

MKB REALTORS
See MASTIN KIRKLAND BOLLING INC

MKC
See MID-KANSAS COOPERATIVE ASSOCIATION

MKMG
See CAREMOUNT MEDICAL PC

D-U-N-S 00-105-3982 IMP/EXP
▲ MKS INSTRUMENTS INC (MA)
2 Tech Dr Ste 201, Andover, MA 01810-2434
Tel (978) 645-5500 *Founded/Ownrshp* 1961
Sales 813.5MM *EMP* 4,661
Tkr Sym MKSI *Exch* NGS
SIC 3823 3491 3494 Pressure measurement instruments, industrial; Flow instruments, industrial process type; Industrial valves; Pressure valves & regulators, industrial; Valves & pipe fittings
Pr: Gerald G Colella
**COO:* John T C Lee
**CFO:* Seth H Bagshaw
Treas: William Donlan
**Sr VP:* John R Abrams
**Sr VP:* Brian C Quirk
VP: Kathleen Burke
VP: Wayne Cole
VP: Derek D'Antilio
VP: John Ippolito
Dist Mgr: Shayne Gillin

D-U-N-S 07-998-9822
MKTG INC
32 Avenue Of The Americas # 20, New York, NY 10013-2473
Tel (212) 366-3481 *Founded/Ownrshp* 2015
Sales 33.0MM[E] *EMP* 6,000
SIC 8742 Marketing consulting services
Pr: Rachelle McDonough

D-U-N-S 83-569-5453
MKTG INC
(*Suby of* AEGIS LIFESTYLE INC) ★
32 Avenue Of The Americas # 20, New York, NY 10013-2473
Tel (212) 366-3400 *Founded/Ownrshp* 2014
Sales 139.0MM[E] *EMP* 6,840[E]
SIC 7311 7389 8743 Advertising agencies; Advertising, promotional & trade show services; Sales promotion
Ch Bd: Charles Horsey
Pr: Dave Wein
CFO: Paul Trager
Ex VP: Patty Hubbard
VP: Leslie Brennan
VP: Marlena Edwards
VP: Kerry Lange
Exec: Peter Rozie
Dir Soc: Mischelle Maurer
Creative D: Michelle Heller
CTO: Rose Zory

D-U-N-S 07-867-7609
ML INDUSTRIES INC
605 W Austin St, Fredericksburg, TX 78624-3211
Tel (956) 279-8678 *Founded/Ownrshp* 2008
Sales 64.1MM[E] *EMP* 3,850
SIC 7549 Automotive maintenance services
Pr: Mickey T Dunn
CFO: Gary Dunham

D-U-N-S 00-767-3671
MLB ADVANCED MEDIA LP
M L B
(*Suby of* M L B) ★
75 9th Ave Fl 5, New York, NY 10011-7076
Tel (212) 485-3444 *Founded/Ownrshp* 2001
Sales 147.0MM[E] *EMP* 300[E]
SIC 4841 7313 7929 Subscription television services; Electronic media advertising representatives; Entertainment service
CEO: Robert Bowman
**CFO:* Edward Weber Jr
Bd of Dir: David James
Sr VP: Tony Santomauro
VP: George Brett
VP: Andy Butters
VP: John Fisher
VP: Joe Inzerillo
VP: Anne Occi
VP: Charles Osborne
VP: Laurel Pried
VP: Keith Stoler
Exec: Ronald Conway
Exec: Bill Morningstar
Assoc Dir: Aleksandar Kolundzija

D-U-N-S 07-887-7191
■ MLIM LLC
(*Suby of* TRONC INC) ★
350 Camino De La Reina, San Diego, CA 92108-3003
Tel (619) 299-3131 *Founded/Ownrshp* 2011
Sales 177.1MM[E] *EMP* 766[E]
SIC 2711 Newspapers
Ch: Douglas Manchester
**CEO:* John Lynch
**CFO:* Ryan Kiesel

D-U-N-S 05-073-6644
■ MLT VACATIONS LLC (GA)
(*Suby of* DELTA AIRLINES) ★
700 S Central Ave, Atlanta, GA 30354-1923
Tel (651) 289-8500 *Founded/Ownrshp* 1969, 1989
Sales 630.0MM[E] *EMP* 500
SIC 4725 Arrangement of travel tour packages, wholesale
Pr: John Caldwell
**CEO:* James J Cron
Sr VP: Tina Iglio
VP: Ava Pratte
VP: Terry Williams
Dir Soc: Erin Buye
IT Man: Kim Boesen
Mktg Mgr: Cathy Zheng
Sales Asso: Melissa Horner

D-U-N-S 05-141-1130
MM USA HOLDINGS LLC
780 Township Line Rd, Yardley, PA 19067-4200
Tel (267) 685-2300 *Founded/Ownrshp* 1976
Sales 477.2MM[E] *EMP* 1,500
SIC 2741 8732 Miscellaneous publishing; Market analysis or research
CEO: William Goldberg
**CFO:* Puneet Sapra
Ex VP: Sue Lewis
Sr VP: Sean P Wagner
VP: Sharon Aquaro
VP: Earlene Biggs
VP: Camm Epstein
VP: Mary Hurley
VP: Jodie McVan
Exec: Christopher Labarthe
Exec: Laurie Telsey
Creative D: Sean Kelly
Creative D: David Senior

MMC
See MARSH RISK & INSURANCE SERVICES INC

MMC
See MEDICAL MANAGEMENT CONSULTANTS INC

MMC ARMORY
See MENNIES MACHINE CO

D-U-N-S 00-716-8214
MMC CONTRACTORS NATIONAL INC (MO)
(*Suby of* MMC CORP) ★
13800 Wyandotte St, Kansas City, MO 64145-1518
Tel (816) 215-3422 *Founded/Ownrshp* 1932
Sales 131.0MM[E] *EMP* 500
SIC 1711 Mechanical contractor
CEO: William F McDermott
CFO: David Cimpl
Treas: Michael J Teahan
**Treas:* Michael J Tehan
**VP:* Keith E Andrews
VP: Michael Chick
VP: Keith Flowers
VP: David Leibowitz
Dir IT: Jim Scales
VP Opers: Brent Hawley
Sfty Dirs: Bob Knudsen

D-U-N-S 62-221-1712
MMC CORP
10955 Lowell Ave Ste 350, Overland Park, KS 66210-2408
Tel (913) 469-0101 *Founded/Ownrshp* 1990
Sales 427.4MM[E] *EMP* 790
SIC 1542 1711 Commercial & office building contractors; Mechanical contractor
Pr: Tim Chadwick
**Pr:* Bill McDermott
**CFO:* Dave Cimpl
Ex VP: Keith E Andrews
**VP:* Robin Broder
**VP:* Erica Jones
**VP:* Harold Mitts
**VP:* Craig Woodson

D-U-N-S 00-817-7180
MMC MATERIALS INC (MS)
(*Suby of* DUNN INVESTMENT CO) ★
1052 Highland Colony Pkwy # 201, Ridgeland, MS 39157-8764
Tel (601) 898-4000 *Founded/Ownrshp* 1927
Sales 84.9MM[E] *EMP* 450
SIC 3273 Ready-mixed concrete
Pr: James Overstreet Jr
**Pr:* Rodney Grogan
**VP:* Butch Bailess
VP: Eliza Henderson
**VP:* Chris Hoyt
**VP:* J Shane Huff
**VP:* Shane Huff
Area Mgr: Rocky McBride
Genl Mgr: Brian McDonald
CIO: Jeff Sinclair
Dir IT: Ben Knight

D-U-N-S 80-848-2983
MMC PRECISION HOLDINGS CORP
1021 W Birchwood St, Morton, IL 61550-9617
Tel (309) 266-7176 *Founded/Ownrshp* 2006
Sales 110.5MM[E] *EMP* 1,370[E]
SIC 3449 Miscellaneous metalwork
Pr: Frank C Lukacs

MME GRAIN
See MID-MISSOURI ENERGY LLC

D-U-N-S 78-321-1035
MMETRO.COM LLC
THRILLIST.COM
568 Broadway Rm 507, New York, NY 10012-3225
Tel (646) 786-1938 *Founded/Ownrshp* 2006
Sales 136.2MM[E] *EMP* 113[E]
SIC 7371 Custom computer programming services
CFO: Jeff Farnath
VP: Marjorie Ajero
Exec: Kevin Alexander
Creative D: Benjamin Gelinas
Off Admin: Claire Colmar
Advt Dir: Jody Rones
Corp Couns: Dave Ugelow
Assoc Ed: Carrie Dennis

D-U-N-S 07-173-8629
MMG INSURANCE CO
MAINE MUTUAL GROUP
44 Maysville Rd, Presque Isle, ME 04769-3220
Tel (207) 764-6611 *Founded/Ownrshp* 1897
Sales NA *EMP* 201
SIC 6331

D-U-N-S 01-501-9255
MMH AMERICAS INC
(*Suby of* MORRIS MATERIAL HANDLING) ★
4401 Gateway Blvd, Springfield, OH 45502-9339
Tel (414) 764-6200 *Founded/Ownrshp* 1998
Sales 135.0MM[E] *EMP* 350
SIC 3536 5084 6719 Hoists, cranes & monorails; Cranes, overhead traveling; Boat lifts; Materials handling machinery; Cranes, industrial; Investment holding companies, except banks
Pr: Tom Sothard
**Treas:* Steve Mayes
VP: Ross Smith
Sfty Mgr: Bob Kotecki

D-U-N-S 02-515-7061 IMP/EXP
MMH HOLDINGS INC
MORRIS MATERIAL HANDLING
(*Suby of* KONECRANES INC) ★
4401 Gateway Blvd, Springfield, OH 45502-9339
Tel (937) 525-5533 *Founded/Ownrshp* 2006
Sales 150.0MM[E] *EMP* 350
SIC 3536 5084 Hoists, cranes & monorails; Cranes, overhead traveling; Boat lifts; Materials handling machinery; Cranes, industrial
Pr: Tom Sothard
CFO: Fran Kelch
**Treas:* Steve Mayes
VP: Peter A Kerrick
Brnch Mgr: John Snyder
Genl Mgr: Bob Locasale
Sfty Mgr: Bob Kotecki
Prd Mgr: Kenneth Lindstrom
Sales Exec: Kim Hall
Sales Exec: Joe Manis
VP Mktg: Ed Romaine

D-U-N-S 07-193-7437
MMI HOTEL GROUP INC
1000 Red Fern Pl, Jackson, MS 39232-8879
Tel (601) 936-3666 *Founded/Ownrshp* 1965
Sales 59.7MM[E] *EMP* 1,627
SIC 7011 Hotels & motels; Motel, franchised
Ch Bd: Earle F Jones
**Pr:* Gaines P Sturdivant
**Treas:* Michael J Hart
Dist Mgr: Cynde Houston

D-U-N-S 36-444-5312
MMIC GROUP INC
7701 France Ave S Ste 500, Minneapolis, MN 55435-3201
Tel (952) 838-6700 *Founded/Ownrshp* 1988
Sales 138.3MM *EMP* 120[E]
Accts Ernst & Young Llp Minneapolis
SIC 6719 Investment holding companies, except banks
CEO: David P Bounk
COO: Bill McDonough
**CFO:* Niles Cole
CFO: Harvatine John
VP: Gerald Connell
VP: Woodward John
**VP:* Elizabeth Lincoln
VP: Debra McBride
**VP:* Jerry O'Connell
VP: Jeff Pearson
**VP:* Julie Stafford
**VP:* Peggy Warner
**VP:* Jerry Zeitlin
Exec: Rachel St Moritz
Dir Risk M: Steven Dubois
Dir Bus: Robert Thompson

D-U-N-S 11-927-3667
MMM HEALTHCARE LLC
MEDICARE Y MUCHO MAS
(*Suby of* MEDICARE MUCHO MAS HOLDINGS INC) ★
350 Ave Carlos Chardon # 500, San Juan, PR 00918-2124
Tel (787) 622-3000 *Founded/Ownrshp* 2004
Sales NA *EMP* 280
SIC 6324 Health maintenance organization (HMO), insurance only
Pr: Val Dean
VP: Javier Andino
VP: David Scanavino

MMMC
See MAUI MEMORIAL MEDICAL CENTER

MMMM
See 4M BUILDING SOLUTIONS INC

MMNA
See MITSUBISHI MOTORS NORTH AMERICA INC

D-U-N-S 96-685-9188
MMODAL INC
M MODAL
(*Suby of* LEGEND PARENT, INC.)
5000 Meridian Blvd # 200, Franklin, TN 37067-6668
Tel (888) 840-4050 *Founded/Ownrshp* 2012
Sales 692.2MM *EMP* 12,000
SIC 7374 Data processing & preparation
CEO: Scott Mackenzie
**Pr:* Michael Finke
**COO:* Ronald L Scarboro
**CFO:* David Woodworth
**Sr VP:* William J Donovan
Sr VP: Matt Jenkins
VP: Eric Carraux
Ex Dir: Agnelo Rodrigues
Genl Mgr: Valerie Beale
Snr Sftwr: Bret Bailey
Snr Sftwr: Paul Harrison
Board of Directors: William Allen, Eugene Davis, Jeffrey Goldberg, Michael O'boyle

D-U-N-S 01-643-9999
MMODAL SERVICES INC
(*Suby of* M MODAL) ★
5000 Meridian Blvd # 200, Franklin, TN 37067-6668
Tel (615) 261-1500 *Founded/Ownrshp* 2008
Sales 288.5MM[E] *EMP* 5,382[E]
SIC 7372 7371 Prepackaged software; Custom computer programming services
CIO: Kevin Piltz
Pr: Adell Bareato
**COO:* Anthony D James
CFO: Ethan Cohen
**Sr VP:* Michael F Clark
**Sr VP:* Alan Gold
VP: Frank Digiambattista
VP: Toni Maldonado
VP: Chris Spring
Ex Dir: Quirino Micua
Ex Dir: Colin Obrien
Board of Directors: Robert Aquilina, Frank Baker, Peter E Berger, John F Jastrem, Colin J O'brien, Warren E Pinckert II, Michael Seedman, Andrew E Vogel

D-U-N-S 04-716-7556
MMODAL SERVICES LTD INC
(*Suby of* MMODAL SERVICES INC) ★
5000 Meridian Blvd # 200, Franklin, TN 37067-6667
Tel (800) 233-3030 *Founded/Ownrshp* 1965
Sales 204.8MM[E] *EMP* 5,000
SIC 8999 Communication services
Pr: Michael Finke
**COO:* Ronald L Scarboro
**CFO:* David Woodworth
**Ex VP:* Mike Etue
CIO: Kevin M Piltz

MMPA
See MINNESOTA MUNICIPAL POWER AGENCY

MMR CONSTRUCTORS
See MMR GROUP INC

D-U-N-S 14-450-1798
MMR CONSTRUCTORS INC
MMR OFFSHORE SERVICES
(*Suby of* MMR CONSTRUCTORS) ★
15961 Airline Hwy, Baton Rouge, LA 70817-7412
Tel (225) 756-5090 *Founded/Ownrshp* 1985
Sales 513.2MM *EMP* 2,500
Accts Maddox & Associates Apc Bato
SIC 1731 Computerized controls installation; General electrical contractor
Pr: James B Rutland
**CFO:* Donald Fairbanks
VP: Thomas B Rutland
**VP:* Tom Welborn

D-U-N-S 84-720-7057 EXP
MMR GROUP INC
MMR CONSTRUCTORS
15961 Airline Hwy, Baton Rouge, LA 70817-7412
Tel (225) 756-5090 *Founded/Ownrshp* 1985
Sales 585.1MM *EMP* 2,500
Accts Maddox & Associates Apc Bato
SIC 1731 Computerized controls installation; General electrical contractor
Pr: James B Rutland
CFO: Donald Fairbanks
**Sec:* Donald W Fairbanks
**VP:* Thomas O Welborn

MMR OFFSHORE SERVICES
See MMR CONSTRUCTORS INC

MMS, A MEDICAL SUPPLY COMPANY
See MIDWEST MEDICAL SUPPLY CO LLC

D-U-N-S 79-111-1854
MMS USA HOLDINGS INC
(*Suby of* PUBLICIS GROUPE S A)
35 W Wacker Dr, Chicago, IL 60601-1723
Tel (800) 933-3622 *Founded/Ownrshp* 2002
Sales 249.7MM[E] *EMP* 1,740[E]
SIC 8742 Marketing consulting services
Pr: John Betley
**CEO:* Monica Gasby
**COO:* Jose Rosario
**Prin:* Maurice Levy
Mng Dir: St Phane Buisseret
Board of Directors: Maurice Levy

D-U-N-S 80-187-7952
MMS USA INVESTMENTS INC
(*Suby of* PUBLICIS GROUPE S A)
41 Madison Ave, New York, NY 10010-2202
Tel (212) 463-2000 *Founded/Ownrshp* 2001
Sales 44.1MM[E] *EMP* 1,000
SIC 7311 Advertising agencies
CEO: Kevin Roberts
CFO: Johann Xavier
Ex VP: Vaughan Emsley
Ex VP: Kevin Honey
Ex VP: Ed Nathan
Sr VP: Jim Cartwright
VP: Dan Gonda
VP: Nicole Lobkowicz
VP: Debbie Marsico
VP: Carol Plunkett
VP: April Portner
VP: Tina Sperber
Exec: Stacey Kelley
Assoc Dir: Anna Binninger
Dir: Tom Lanktree
Creative D: Erich Funke
Creative D: Leslie Long
Creative D: Ted Monnin
Creative D: John Payne
Creative D: Mark Reichard

MMSD
See MADISON METROPOLITAN SCHOOL DISTRICT

D-U-N-S 02-426-1323 IMP
MMSP INC
METROPOLITAN MT PLTY & SEAFOOD
1920 Stanford Ct, Landover, MD 20785-3219
Tel (301) 773-2175 *Founded/Ownrshp* 1944
Sales 96.0MM[E] *EMP* 175
SIC 5143 5144 5146 5147

D-U-N-S 79-649-1244
MMTF LOGISTICS LLC
8080 Beckett Center Dr, West Chester, OH 45069-5026
Tel (513) 860-2871 *Founded/Ownrshp* 2006
Sales 145.0MM *EMP* 2
SIC 4731 Transportation agents & brokers
Pr: Craig Leonard

D-U-N-S 11-437-0096
MN AIRLINES LLC
SUN COUNTRY AIRLINES
(*Suby of* MINNESOTA AVIATION LLC) ★
1300 Corporate Ctr Curv, Eagan, MN 55121-2589
Tel (651) 681-3900 *Founded/Ownrshp* 2011
Sales 389.2MM *EMP* 1,500
SIC 4512 Air passenger carrier, scheduled
Pr: Zarir Erani
VP: Jim Olsen
VP: Tim Wise
Exec: Katie Bellows
Admn Mgr: Madison Fri
MIS Dir: Mark Osterberg

Dir IT: Gary Elwood
IT Man: Jae Ljiyode
Mktg Mgr: Pete Heunisch
Board of Directors: Robert R Fafinski Jr, Michael J Opat

D-U-N-S 04-252-6087
MNI ENTERPRISES INC
NICHOLAS HOMES
8080 E Gelding Dr Ste 108, Scottsdale, AZ 85260-6983
Tel (480) 505-4600 *Founded/Ownrshp* 1965
Sales 110.8MM^E *EMP* 500
SIC 1521 Single-family housing construction
Pr: Michael G Nicholas
CEO: Christopher Lombardi
CFO: Harry Griffith
VP: Ken Christopherson
VP: Bob Dalton
Dir IT: Sean Wegele
Sls Mgr: Karen Smith

D-U-N-S 10-797-8954
MNJTECHNOLOGIES DIRECT INC
1025 Busch Pkwy, Buffalo Grove, IL 60089-4504
Tel (847) 634-0700 *Founded/Ownrshp* 2002
Sales 103.8MM *EMP* 78^E
SIC 5734 5045 7373 Personal computers; Printers & plotters: computers; Modems, monitors, terminals & disk drives: computers; Printers, computer; Value-added resellers, computer systems
Pr: Susan Kozak
Mng Pt: David Pfau
**VP:* Paul Kozak
VP: Dillon Pletsch
Off Mgr: Michael Garner
Dir IT: Jim Brice
IT Man: Martin Guerrero
IT Man: Vincent Yarmoska
Sales Exec: Brian Ford
Sales Exec: Bob Kerr
VP Sls: Diane Bierman

D-U-N-S 07-029-9268 IMP
MNP CORP
STEEL AND WIRE
44225 Utica Rd, Utica, MI 48317-5464
Tel (586) 254-1320 *Founded/Ownrshp* 1970
Sales 192.3MM *EMP* 1,000
Accts Baker Tilly Virchow Krause Llp
SIC 3452 5051 5072 3714 Bolts, metal; Screws, metal; Washers, metal; Steel; Wire; Bolts; Screws; Washers (hardware); Miscellaneous fasteners; Motor vehicle parts & accessories
CEO: Terri Chapman
**Pr:* Thomas Klein
**CFO:* Craig L Stormer
VP: Randy Allison
**VP:* Chad Clifford
**VP:* David Cronovich
VP: Floyd J Cushman
VP: Janice Kelin
Dir Bus: Gerald Lorenz
Genl Mgr: Randy Feger
IT Man: Brian Krupa

D-U-N-S 03-319-6387 IMP/EXP
MNS LTD
ABC STORES
766 Pohukaina St, Honolulu, HI 96813-5307
Tel (808) 591-1063 *Founded/Ownrshp* 1949
Sales 198.6MM^E *EMP* 700
SIC 5099

MNX
See MIDNITE AIR CORP

D-U-N-S 00-680-1369
MO-VAC SERVICE CO (TX)
3721 S Mccoll Rd, Edinburg, TX 78539-9618
Tel (956) 682-6381 *Founded/Ownrshp* 1960
Sales 265.6MM^E *EMP* 315
SIC 1389 4959 Mud service, oil field drilling; Environmental cleanup services
Pr: Glynn Andrews
Genl Mgr: Arnold Perez
Opers Mgr: Mike Flanagan
Opers Mgr: Erick McLaughlin

D-U-N-S 02-992-7662 IMP
MOARK LLC
(*Suby of* LAND OLAKES INC) ★
28 Under The Mountain Rd, North Franklin, CT 06254-1421
Tel (951) 332-3300 *Founded/Ownrshp* 2000
Sales 773.9MM^E *EMP* 1,000
SIC 5144 2048 0252 2015 Eggs; Poultry feeds; Chicken eggs; Started pullet farm; Poultry slaughtering & processing
CFO: Craig Wells
VP: Donald Brown
VP: Nyle McAnally

D-U-N-S 07-522-6498 IMP/EXP
■ **MOBIL CORP** (DE)
(*Suby of* EXXONMOBIL) ★
5959 Las Colinas Blvd, Irving, TX 75039-4202
Tel (972) 444-1000 *Founded/Ownrshp* 1976, 1999
Sales 2.8MMM^E *EMP* 41,500
SIC 2911 5171 4612 4613 1311 Petroleum refining; Petroleum bulk stations & terminals; Crude petroleum pipelines; Refined petroleum pipelines; Crude petroleum production; Natural gas production
Pr: F A Risch
Exec: Lynnette Jordan

D-U-N-S 80-377-8034
■ **MOBIL EXPLORATION & PRODUCING US INC**
(*Suby of* MOBIL CORP) ★
22777 Sprngwoods Vlg Pkwy, Spring, TX 77389-1425
Tel (281) 288-4545 *Founded/Ownrshp* 1987
Sales 297.5MM^E *EMP* 2,800
SIC 5541 Petroleum refining
Pr: P J Hoenmans
CFO: Mohammed Ghannam

D-U-N-S 18-311-0840 IMP/EXP
■ **MOBIL INTERNATIONAL PETROLEUM CORP**
(*Suby of* L & S AVIATION LUBRICANTS) ★
22777 Sprngwoods Vlg Pkwy, Spring, TX 77389-1425
Tel (281) 288-4545 *Founded/Ownrshp* 1935
Sales 135.0MM^E *EMP* 343
SIC 2911 Petroleum refining
Pr: Eugene A Renna
**Treas:* George Broadhead
**VP:* R H Gardner
**VP:* Joe B Hinton
**VP:* Paul J Hoenmans
VP: N S Kyburg
**VP:* Robert J Mc Cool
**VP:* Robert O Swanson
Sls Dir: Tim Hinchman
Manager: Mohamed Elgarhy

D-U-N-S 06-492-7486 IMP
■ **MOBIL PETROLEUM CO INC**
(*Suby of* EXXONMOBIL) ★
22777 Sprngwoods Vlg Pkwy, Spring, TX 77389-1425
Tel (703) 846-3000 *Founded/Ownrshp* 1960
Sales 350.5MM^E *EMP* 597^E
SIC 2911 Petroleum refining
CEO: Rex Tillerson
**Pr:* W M Colton
Treas: Hartwell Gardner
**Treas:* David Levy
Sr VP: Harold Kramer
VP: Rob Franklin
VP: Edward Galante
**VP:* H H Hubble
VP: T F Lemons Jr
VP: Senior Vice Stuart
Telecom Mg: Kevin Citizen

D-U-N-S 03-776-6813
■ **MOBIL PRODUCING TEXAS AND NEW MEXICO INC**
(*Suby of* EXXONMOBIL) ★
9 Greenway Plz 2700, Houston, TX 77046-0905
Tel (713) 871-5000 *Founded/Ownrshp* 2014
Sales 30.9MM^E *EMP* 2,400
SIC 1311 Crude petroleum & natural gas
Pr: Fines F Martin

D-U-N-S 05-666-5136 IMP/EXP
■ **MOBIL RESEARCH AND DEVELOPMENT CORP**
(*Suby of* L & S AVIATION LUBRICANTS) ★
600 Billingsport Rd, Paulsboro, NJ 08066-1034
Tel (856) 224-2134 *Founded/Ownrshp* 1967
Sales 210.8MM^E *EMP* 2,300
SIC 2911 Petroleum refining
Pr: J E Crawford
**VP:* R H Gardner
**VP:* J R Green
**VP:* J R Katzer
**VP:* K D Kroupa
**VP:* R J McGowan
**VP:* A J Silvestri
**VP:* J J Wise
IT Man: Rick Burns
IT Man: Steve Goldman

MOBILE AREA WATER & SEWER SYS
See BOARD OF WATER AND SEWER COMMISSIONERS OF CITY OF MOBILE

D-U-N-S 03-128-3187 IMP
MOBILE CLIMATE CONTROL CORP
MCC
(*Suby of* MOBILE CLIMATE CONTROL GROUP HOLDING AB)
17103 State Road 4, Goshen, IN 46528-6674
Tel (574) 534-1516 *Founded/Ownrshp* 1987, 2008
Sales 87.5MM^E *EMP* 117
SIC 5075 3714 Compressors, air conditioning; Air conditioner parts, motor vehicle
CEO: Clas Genneberg
Board of Directors: Timothy Hested

D-U-N-S 07-979-8929
MOBILE COUNTY PUBLIC SCHOOLS
1 Magnum Pass, Mobile, AL 36618-3412
Tel (251) 221-4394 *Founded/Ownrshp* 2015
Sales 64.4MM^E *EMP* 7,015^E
SIC 8211 Public elementary & secondary schools

D-U-N-S 00-690-1094
■ **MOBILE GAS SERVICE CORP**
(*Suby of* ENERGYSOUTH INC) ★
2828 Dauphin St, Mobile, AL 36606-2493
Tel (251) 476-2720 *Founded/Ownrshp* 2008
Sales 156.2MM^E *EMP* 259^E
SIC 4924 5722 Natural gas distribution; Gas household appliances
Pr: Mike Fine
**Pr:* John Davis
**CEO:* Gregory H Welch
CFO: Faith McInnis
VP: Susan Stringer
Genl Mgr: Russell Kendrick
IT Man: Suzanne Hunt
Mktg Mgr: Courtney Coward
Mktg Mgr: Rick Schaffer

MOBILE HOSE AND HYDRAULIC SUP
See CONTROLLED MOTION SOLUTIONS INC

D-U-N-S 07-260-8367
MOBILE INFIRMARY ASSOCIATION
MOBILE INFIRMARY MEDICAL CTR
5 Mobile Infirmary Cir, Mobile, AL 36607-3513
Tel (251) 435-2400 *Founded/Ownrshp* 1910
Sales 413.6MM *EMP* 2,938
SIC 8062 General medical & surgical hospitals
Ch Bd: David Cooper
Ofcr: Katherine Shiver
VP: Donald J Kirby
Exec: William J McLaughlin Jr
Dir Lab: Sandra Lozano
Off Mgr: Barry Sanders
Doctor: Chandler E Bramitt
Pharmcst: John Childs
Pharmcst: Bill Perry
Pharmcst: Michael Predmore

MOBILE INFIRMARY MEDICAL CTR
See MOBILE INFIRMARY ASSOCIATION

D-U-N-S 11-806-2157
▲ **MOBILE MINI INC**
4646 E Van Buren St # 400, Phoenix, AZ 85008-6927
Tel (480) 894-6311 *Founded/Ownrshp* 1983
Sales 530.7MM *EMP* 1,982
Tkr Sym MINI *Exch* NGS
SIC 4225 3448 3441 3412 7359 Miniwarehouse, warehousing; Buildings, portable: prefabricated metal; Fabricated structural metal; Drums, shipping: metal; Shipping container leasing
Pr: Erik Olsson
**Ch Bd:* Michael L Watts
COO: Kelly Williams
CFO: Mark E Funk
Sr VP: Christopher J Miner
VP: Chad Ainsworth
Brnch Mgr: Chad Devries
Brnch Mgr: Andrew Gums
Off Mgr: Christina Minjarez
Manager: Robby Fountain
Sales Asso: Lindsey Taylor
Board of Directors: Sara R Dial, Jeffrey S Goble, James J Martell, Stephen A McConnell, Frederick G McNamee III, Kimberly J McWaters, Lawrence Trachtenberg

D-U-N-S 00-816-3115 IMP/EXP
MOBILE PAINT MANUFACTURING CO OF DELAWARE INC
B L P MOBILE PAINT STORES
4775 Hamilton Blvd, Theodore, AL 36582-8509
Tel (251) 443-6110 *Founded/Ownrshp* 1921
Sales 91.5MM^E *EMP* 240
Accts Wilkins Miller Hieronymus Llc
SIC 2851 5198 5231 Paints & allied products; Paints; Varnishes; Lacquers; Enamels; Paint & painting supplies; Wallcoverings
CFO: John Wilson
**Pr:* William Miles Tunno
Ex VP: Louis Petit
Plnt Mgr: Curtis Polk
VP Sls: Tony McDonald

D-U-N-S 62-005-9766 EXP
■ **MOBILE STORAGE GROUP INC**
A BETTER MOBILE STORAGE
(*Suby of* MOBILE MINI INC) ★
7420 S Kyrene Rd Ste 101, Tempe, AZ 85283-4610
Tel (480) 894-6311 *Founded/Ownrshp* 2008
Sales 94.2MM^E *EMP* 700^E
SIC 5999 7359 Packaging materials: boxes, padding, etc.; Shipping container leasing
Pr: Douglas A Waugaman
Ch Bd: Ronald F Valenta
Treas: Allan A Villegas

D-U-N-S 02-562-6944
▲ **MOBILEIRON INC**
415 E Middlefield Rd, Mountain View, CA 94043-4005
Tel (650) 919-8100 *Founded/Ownrshp* 2007
Sales 149.3MM *EMP* 843^E
Tkr Sym MOBL *Exch* NGS
SIC 7372 Prepackaged software
Pr: Barry Mainz
**Ch Bd:* Tae Hea Nahm
CFO: Simon Biddiscombe
Chf Cred: Laurel Finch
Sr VP: Daniel Fields
VP: Damian Artt
VP: Carter Busse
VP: John Morgan
VP: John Spencer
CTO: Suresh Batchu
QA Dir: Mansu Kim
Board of Directors: Matthew Howard, Kenneth R Klein, Frank Marshall, Robert Tinker, James Tolonen

D-U-N-S 08-033-6678
MOBILESOFT TECHNOLOGY INC
100 Washington Ave S, Minneapolis, MN 55401-2110
Tel (612) 460-4700 *Founded/Ownrshp* 2016
Sales 100.0MM *EMP* 8
SIC 7371 Computer software development

D-U-N-S 87-285-1568
MOBILEUM INC
2880 Lakeside Dr Ste 135, Santa Clara, CA 95054-2830
Tel (408) 844-6600 *Founded/Ownrshp* 2016
Sales 94.7MM^E *EMP* 180^E
SIC 4899 7373 Data communication services; Computer systems analysis & design
CEO: Bobby Srinivasan
**CFO:* Andrew Warner
**Chf Mktg O:* James Doyle
VP: Bishal Bisht
VP: John Curtis
VP: Richard Grohot
VP: Sudhir Kadam
VP: Rob McMillen
Genl Mgr: Pablo Maffei
**CTO:* Avnish Chauhan
Genl Couns: Kirk Williams
Board of Directors: Craig Ehrlich, Scott Fox, David Kaplan, Rob Theis, Mohan Uttarwar

MOBILITYWORKS
See WMK LLC

D-U-N-S 13-098-1710 IMP
MOBIS ALABAMA LLC
GEORGIA PLANT
(*Suby of* MOBIS AMERICA INC) ★
1395 Mitchell Young Rd, Montgomery, AL 36108-5818
Tel (334) 387-4800 *Founded/Ownrshp* 2002
Sales 401.6MM^E *EMP* 1,655
SIC 3714 Motor vehicle body components & frame
CEO: Chul SOO
**CFO:* Beom Seo Koo
QA Dir: Shakerha Sturdivant
Ql Cn Mgr: Robert Hanson

D-U-N-S 62-129-7691 IMP
MOBIS AMERICA INC
(*Suby of* HYUNDAI MOBIS CO., LTD.)
1395 Mitchell Young Rd, Montgomery, AL 36108-5818
Tel (334) 387-4840 *Founded/Ownrshp* 2006
Sales 401.6MM^E *EMP* 950^E
SIC 3714 Motor vehicle body components & frame
CEO: Chul SOO Kim

D-U-N-S 16-397-6512 IMP
MOBIS NORTH AMERICA LLC
MOBIS PARTS DETRIOT
(*Suby of* HYUNDAI MOBIS CO., LTD.)
46501 Commerce Dr, Plymouth, MI 48170
Tel (248) 426-5577 *Founded/Ownrshp* 2004
Sales 266.5MM^E *EMP* 62^E
SIC 5013 8731 Automotive supplies; Commercial physical research
Pr: James Lee

D-U-N-S 16-426-2656 IMP
MOBIS PARTS AMERICA LLC
(*Suby of* HYUNDAI MOBIS CO., LTD.)
10550 Talbert Ave Fl 4, Fountain Valley, CA 92708-6031
Tel (786) 515-1101 *Founded/Ownrshp* 2015
Sales 221.2MM^E *EMP* 300
SIC 5012 Automobiles & other motor vehicles

MOBIS PARTS DETRIOT
See MOBIS NORTH AMERICA LLC

D-U-N-S 09-767-2182
MOBLEY INDUSTRIAL SERVICES INC
(*Suby of* SAFWAY GROUP HOLDING LLC) ★
1220 Miller Cut Off Rd, La Porte, TX 77571-9799
Tel (281) 470-9120 *Founded/Ownrshp* 1979
Sales 143.0MM^E *EMP* 1,400
SIC 1721 1799 5033 Residential painting; Fireproofing buildings; Insulation of pipes & boilers; Sandblasting of building exteriors; Scaffolding construction; Insulation materials
Pr: Chuck Mobley
**Sec:* Bernice L Mobley
VP: Paul Carter
VP: Charles Mobley
**VP:* Kirk Mobley
**VP:* Bob Yates
**VP:* Blake Young
IT Man: Justin Meeks
Psych: Ron Roth

MOBLEY OILFIELD SERVICES
See TERVITA LLC

D-U-N-S 08-179-3945 EXP
MOC PRODUCTS CO INC
AUTO EDGE SOLUTIONS
12306 Montague St, Pacoima, CA 91331-2279
Tel (818) 794-3500 *Founded/Ownrshp* 1975
Sales 177.4MM^E *EMP* 250
SIC 5169 7549 Chemicals & allied products; Automotive maintenance services
CEO: Mark Waco
Sec: Nadelin Waco
VP: Dave Waco
Opers Mgr: Anthony Camacho
Manager: Monty Skinner
Genl Couns: Marta Stitcher

D-U-N-S 03-419-4845
MOCKLER BEVERAGE CO
MOCKLER BEVERAGE/BUDWEISER
11811 Reiger Rd, Baton Rouge, LA 70809-4925
Tel (225) 408-4283 *Founded/Ownrshp* 1988
Sales 91.0MM *EMP* 156
SIC 5181 5921 Beer & other fermented malt liquors; Beer (packaged)
Pt: Gary W Mockler
**Pt:* Michael A Coon
**Pt:* Douglas F Mackey
**Pt:* Patrick E Mockler
**Pt:* William C Ruiz
VP: Mary Lewis
IT Man: Keith Dahlgreen
Natl Sales: Michael Taylor
VP Sls: Chris Davis
Snr Mgr: Dan Palmer

MOCKLER BEVERAGE/BUDWEISER
See MOCKLER BEVERAGE CO

D-U-N-S 95-990-7411
MODA HEALTH PLAN INC
ODS COMPANIES
(*Suby of* ODS COMPANIES) ★
601 Sw 2nd Ave, Portland, OR 97204-3199
Tel (503) 228-6554 *Founded/Ownrshp* 1984
Sales NA *EMP* 741^E
SIC 6321 Accident & health insurance
Pr: William Johnson
IT Man: Jerry Beagle
Sls Mgr: C J McLeod

D-U-N-S 09-603-2545
MODEC INTERNATIONAL INC
(*Suby of* MODEC,INC.)
15011 Katy Fwy Ste 500, Houston, TX 77094-0010
Tel (281) 529-8100 *Founded/Ownrshp* 1999, 2008
Sales 495.2MM^E *EMP* 2,500
SIC 8711 2499 3731 Professional engineer; Floating docks, wood; Commercial cargo ships, building & repairing
Pr: Toshiro Miyazaki
**COO:* Shigeru Usami
**CFO:* Bruce John Beever
CFO: Bruce Beever
Ex VP: John Gremp
VP: Katsuyuki Imaizumi
Exec: Jeffrey Carr
Dir Risk M: Michael Lipowski
**Prin:* Norihisa Fukuda
**Prin:* Ricky Alan Hall
**Prin:* Takashi Nashino

MODEC SOFEC
See SOFEC INC

D-U-N-S 03-495-4131
■ MODEL DAIRY LLC
(*Suby of* DEAN FOODS CO) ★
500 Gould St, Reno, NV 89502-1466
Tel (775) 788-7900 *Founded/Ownrshp* 1996
Sales 92.3MM[E] *EMP* 324
SIC 2026 5143 Fluid milk; Dairy products, except dried or canned
Sls Mgr: Dave Demars

D-U-N-S 15-124-9971 IMP
MODEL MODEL HAIR FASHION INC
83 Harbor Rd, Port Washington, NY 11050-2535
Tel (516) 944-7777 *Founded/Ownrshp* 2004
Sales 90.5MM *EMP* 24[E]
SIC 5087 Beauty parlor equipment & supplies
Ch Bd: Kim Bokhwa

MODELL'S SPORTING GOODS
See HENRY MODELL & CO INC

D-U-N-S 00-806-8603
MODERN AG PRODUCTS LTD
DRAGON ESP
1655 Louisiana St, Beaumont, TX 77701-1120
Tel (409) 833-2665 *Founded/Ownrshp* 1963
Sales 306.4MM[E] *EMP* 1,900
SIC 7359 6792 0161 Equipment rental & leasing; Oil royalty traders; Artichoke farm
CEO: Will Crenshaw
Pr: Casey Crenshaw
CFO: Brian Balmer
VP Sls: Johnny Tennison

D-U-N-S 15-133-7201
MODERN BUILDERS SUPPLY INC
POLARIS TECHNOLOGIES
302 Mcclurg Rd, Youngstown, OH 44512-6401
Tel (330) 729-2690 *Founded/Ownrshp* 1986
Sales 361.4MM[E] *EMP* 750
SIC 5032 3089 3446 3442 Brick, stone & related material; Windows, plastic; Doors, folding: plastic or plastic coated fabric; Architectural metalwork; Metal doors, sash & trim
CEO: Kevin Leggett
**Ch Bd:* Larry Leggett
**Treas:* G Taylor Evans III
**VP:* Eric Leggett
**VP:* Jack Marstellar
VP: Tony Puntel
Genl Mgr: Kevin Buchholtz
Opers Mgr: Alan Murphy
Manager: Dale Sorrell

D-U-N-S 05-181-7682
MODERN DISPOSAL SERVICES INC
4746 Model City Rd, Model City, NY 14107-9800
Tel (716) 692-1272 *Founded/Ownrshp* 1964
Sales 130.1MM[E] *EMP* 177[E]
SIC 4953 Refuse collection & disposal services
Ch: Sonia Washuta
**Pr:* Richard Washuta
CFO: Brendan McCafferty
**Sec:* Lorie Washuta
**VP:* Gary Smith
CTO: Kevin Doyle

D-U-N-S 02-418-4525
MODERN DISTRIBUTORS INC (KY)
817 W Columbia St, Somerset, KY 42501-1729
Tel (606) 679-1178 *Founded/Ownrshp* 1961, 1965
Sales 97.7MM[E] *EMP* 170
SIC 5194 5962 5145 5064 Cigarettes; Cigarettes vending machines; Sandwich & hot food vending machines; Candy; Electrical entertainment equipment
Pr: Gerald D Ray
**Sec:* Robert Mickey Ray
IT Man: J C Meece

D-U-N-S 05-074-5876 IMP/EXP
MODERN GROUP LTD
2501 Durham Rd, Bristol, PA 19007-6999
Tel (215) 943-9100 *Founded/Ownrshp* 2003
Sales 224.7MM[E] *EMP* 570
SIC 5084 7353 7699 Industrial machinery & equipment; Materials handling machinery; Heavy construction equipment rental; Earth moving equipment, rental or leasing; Industrial equipment services
Pr: Dave Griffith
Pr: Paul Farrell
Ex VP: George S Wilkinson
Sr VP: Thomas Callahan
VP: Nancy Lee
VP: Stephen Seminack
VP: Eric Walker
Genl Mgr: John McClure
VP Mktg: Don Sherow
Sales Asso: Shirley Patterson

D-U-N-S 93-272-0139 IMP
MODERN GROUP LTD
1655 Louisiana St, Beaumont, TX 77701-1120
Tel (800) 231-8198 *Founded/Ownrshp* 1980
Sales 302.8MM[E] *EMP* 1,500
SIC 7359 3441 Equipment rental & leasing; Fabricated structural metal
CEO: Will Crenshaw
Pr: Casey Crenshaw

D-U-N-S 00-232-2071 IMP
MODERN HANDLING EQUIPMENT CO (PA)
(*Suby of* MODERN GROUP LTD) ★
2501 Durham Rd Ste G, Bristol, PA 19007-6923
Tel (215) 943-9100 *Founded/Ownrshp* 1955, 1979
Sales 187.8MM[E] *EMP* 203
SIC 5084 7353 Materials handling machinery; Cranes & aerial lift equipment, rental or leasing
Pr: Paul Farrell
**CFO:* Stephen Seminack
**Treas:* George S Wilkinson
**VP:* Thomas P Callahan
VP: Lawrence Norton
**Prin:* Gerald Couch
IT Man: Nancy Lee
Board of Directors: Steve Lecatsas, John F Smith

D-U-N-S 04-837-9077 IMP
MODERN INDUSTRIES INC
4747 E Beautiful Ln, Phoenix, AZ 85044-5318
Tel (602) 267-7248 *Founded/Ownrshp* 1969
Sales 104.5MM[E] *EMP* 380
SIC 3599 3769 Machine shop, jobbing & repair; Guided missile & space vehicle parts & auxiliary equipment
CEO: Andrew W Yahraus
**Pr:* Daniel L Yahraus
COO: Timothy Sweny
CFO: Tom Feeney
CFO: Michael Knowles
**Treas:* Jean A Lashinske
Exec: Melody Goswick
Dir Bus: Steven Cropper
Div Mgr: Darrin Smiley
Ql Cn Mgr: Denise Elliott
Ql Cn Mgr: Sisto Tarquino

MODERN JEWELER MAGAZINE
See CYGNUS BUSINESS MEDIA INC

D-U-N-S 00-585-4070 IMP/EXP
MODERN MACHINERY CO INC
(*Suby of* WASHINGTON COMPANIES) ★
101 International Dr, Missoula, MT 59808-1549
Tel (406) 523-1100 *Founded/Ownrshp* 1944
Sales 213.0MM[E] *EMP* 450
SIC 5082 Construction & mining machinery; General construction machinery & equipment; Mining machinery & equipment, except petroleum; Logging equipment & supplies
Pr: Brian Sheridan
**Sec:* Paul W Keiper
**Sec:* Helen B Miller
**VP:* William G Brandall
VP: Chris Johnson
IT Man: Leora Kautzman
Sls Mgr: Dan Kipp
Sls Mgr: Mark Parsons
Sales Asso: Karl Lechner

D-U-N-S 80-745-4640
MODERN TECHNOLOGY SOLUTIONS INC
MTSI
5285 Shawnee Rd Ste 400, Alexandria, VA 22312-2328
Tel (703) 564-3800 *Founded/Ownrshp* 1993
Sales 109.0MM *EMP* 615
Accts Cherry Bekaert Llp Tysons Cor
SIC 8711 8742 8731 7379 Engineering services; Management consulting services; Commercial physical research; Computer related maintenance services
Pr: Kevin M Robinson
**Ch Bd:* Phil Soucy
COO: Angel Garcia
Treas: Valerie Underhill
Prgrm Mgr: Greg Green
Prgrm Mgr: Michael Hague
Prgrm Mgr: Kevin Haldeman
Prgrm Mgr: Sean Hayes
Prgrm Mgr: Kevin Steffenson
Genl Mgr: Molly James
Snr Sftwr: Mark Krutz
Board of Directors: Frank Backes, Pamela Little, Tom McMahan, Kevin Robinson, Phil Soucy

D-U-N-S 00-637-0712
MODERN WELDING CO INC (KY)
2880 New Hartford Rd, Owensboro, KY 42303-1321
Tel (270) 685-4400 *Founded/Ownrshp* 1932, 1946
Sales 99.3MM[E] *EMP* 430
SIC 3443 5051 3441 5085

D-U-N-S 06-104-8450
MODERN WOODMEN OF AMERICA
1701 1st Ave, Rock Island, IL 61201-8779
Tel (309) 793-5537 *Founded/Ownrshp* 1883
Sales NA *EMP* 480
SIC 6311 Life insurance
Pr: W Kenneth Massey
Mng Pt: Michael R Farris
Mng Pt: Jarrett Glosson
Mng Pt: Bradley Turner
**Treas:* Nick S Coin
Chf Cred: Pamela Fritz
Ofcr: Marsha Mayfield
VP: Crewe Chamber
Exec: Tom Haertjens
Brnch Mgr: Clay Hull
Dist Mgr: Lee S Arellano

D-U-N-S 83-887-2377
■ MODERNHEALTH SPECIALTY (PX) LLC
PX DRUG STORE
(*Suby of* KROGER SPECIALTY PHARMACY HOLDINGS I INC) ★
7373 Lincoln Way, Garden Grove, CA 92841-1428
Tel (818) 769-0313 *Founded/Ownrshp* 2012
Sales 115.0MM *EMP* 70
SIC 5912 Drug stores & proprietary stores
CEO: Dominic Meffe
CFO: Vincent Cook

D-U-N-S 03-022-9542
MODERNIZING MEDICINE INC
3600 Fau Blvd Ste 202, Boca Raton, FL 33431-6474
Tel (561) 544-0906 *Founded/Ownrshp* 2010
Sales 90.5MM[E] *EMP* 500[E]
SIC 7372 Application computer software
Pr: Daniel Cane
COO: Karen Obyrne
CFO: Karen Byrne
Chf Mktg O: Michael Sherling
Sr VP: Maria Hernandez
VP: Mark Fleisher
VP: Thom Schildmeyer
Exec: Brad Rennick
Dir Risk M: Rick Von Pusch
Dir Bus: Scott Ponder
Off Admin: Serena Reno
Board of Directors: Mark Delaar

D-U-N-S 07-937-0968
MODEST BILLIONAIRES LLC
3815 Martha Ln, Dallas, TX 75229-6126
Tel (972) 672-0755 *Founded/Ownrshp* 2014
Sales 1.0MMM *EMP* 3
SIC 7374 7371 7389 Computer graphics service; Computer software development & applications;
Pr: Thomas Richard

D-U-N-S 06-012-5051
MODESTO CITY OF (INC)
1010 10th St Ste 2100, Modesto, CA 95354-0861
Tel (209) 577-5200 *Founded/Ownrshp* 1884
Sales NA *EMP* 1,200
Accts Brown Armstrong Bakersfield
SIC 9111 City & town managers' offices;
Ofcr: Adam Foster
VP: Kay Maksoud
Exec: Joanne Azevedo
Exec: Tina Rocha
Comm Man: Cheryl Detmar
Comm Man: Firoz Vohra
Ex Dir: Regan Wilson
Plng Mgr: Patrick Kelly
CTO: Kathy Espinoza
Sales Exec: Rafael Rodriguez
Mktg Dir: Brent Sinclair

D-U-N-S 07-467-5844
MODESTO CITY SCHOOL DISTRICT
MODESTO CITY SCHOOLS
426 Locust St, Modesto, CA 95351-2631
Tel (209) 576-4011 *Founded/Ownrshp* 1871
Sales 333.6MM *EMP* 3,000
Accts Vavrinek Trine Day & Co Ll
SIC 8211 Public elementary & secondary schools
CEO: Pamela Able
**Pr:* Cindy Marks
Bd of Dir: David Allan
Bd of Dir: Jordan Dickson
Bd of Dir: Steven Grenbeaux
**VP:* Amy Elliott Neumann
Exec: Becky Fortuna
Prgrm Mgr: John Blackman
MIS Dir: Cindy Minter
Teacher Pr: Craig Rydquist
HC Dir: Mark Herbst

MODESTO CITY SCHOOLS
See MODESTO CITY SCHOOL DISTRICT

D-U-N-S 04-131-9419
MODESTO IRRIGATION DISTRICT (INC)
1231 11th St, Modesto, CA 95354-0701
Tel (209) 526-7337 *Founded/Ownrshp* 1887
Sales 425.0MM *EMP* 440
Accts Baker Tilly Madison Wi
SIC 4911 4971 ; Water distribution or supply systems for irrigation
Pr: Allen Short
Bd of Dir: Angela Cartisano
Bd of Dir: Roger Vanhoy
Dir Risk M: Scott Vuren
CTO: Erick Davis
Tech Mgr: Toxie Burris
Sfty Mgr: Craig Castro
Sfty Mgr: Jeff Fairbanks
Sfty Mgr: Dave Willard
Plnt Mgr: Richard Smith
VP Mktg: Tracy Herbeck

D-U-N-S 00-609-2555 IMP/EXP
▲ MODINE MANUFACTURING CO INC (WI)
1500 Dekoven Ave, Racine, WI 53403
Tel (262) 636-1200 *Founded/Ownrshp* 1916
Sales 1.3MMM *EMP* 7,100[E]
Tkr Sym MOD *Exch* NYS
SIC 3443 3714 3433 3585 Heat exchangers, condensers & components; Heat exchangers: coolers (after, inter), condensers, etc.; Air coolers, metal plate; Air conditioner parts, motor vehicle; Radiators & radiator shells & cores, motor vehicle; Heating equipment, except electric; Refrigeration & heating equipment; Heating equipment, complete; Air conditioning equipment, complete; Refrigeration equipment, complete
Pr: Thomas A Burke
COO: Thomas F Marry
CFO: Michael B Lucareli
VP: Scott L Bowser
VP: Margaret C Kelsey
VP: Matthew J McBurney
VP: Holger Schwab
VP: Scott D Wollenberg
Mtls Mgr: Erin Wilson
Board of Directors: David J Anderson, David G Bills, Charles P Cooley, Suresh V Garimella, Larry O Moore, Christopher W Patterson, Marsha C Williams, Christine Y Yan

D-U-N-S 00-553-7469
MODINEER CO (MI)
2190 Industrial Dr, Niles, MI 49120-1233
Tel (269) 683-2550 *Founded/Ownrshp* 1940
Sales 126.1MM[E] *EMP* 500
SIC 3469 3599 3544 Stamping metal for the trade; Machine shop, jobbing & repair; Special dies & tools
Ch: Michael J Dreher
**CFO:* Roger Kluge
**VP:* Gary Dreher
Prgrm Mgr: Jason Hamilton
Off Mgr: Patti Wolf
CIO: Todd Kankel

D-U-N-S 19-660-8905
MODIS INC
(*Suby of* ADECCO TECHNICAL) ★
10151 Deerwood Pkwy Bldg, Jacksonville, FL 32256
Tel (904) 360-2300 *Founded/Ownrshp* 1994
Sales 661.7MM[E] *EMP* 9,000
SIC 7371 Computer software systems analysis & design, custom
Pr: John P Pcoo Cullen
**Pr:* Jack Cullen
**CEO:* Theron Ceod Gilliam
CFO: Robert Crouch
Ofcr: Keenan Field
Exec: Amy Herron
Mng Dir: Jana Bergman
Mng Dir: Clyde Bouler
Mng Dir: Brian Hofbauer
Mng Dir: Rod Laver
Mng Dir: Michael Leacy

MODSPACE
See MODULAR SPACE CORP

D-U-N-S 16-951-3108 EXP
MODULAR SPACE CORP
MODSPACE
1200 W Swedesford Rd Fl 2, Berwyn, PA 19312-1172
Tel (610) 232-1200 *Founded/Ownrshp* 1986
Sales 298.2MM[E] *EMP* 680
SIC 7359 1542 Equipment rental & leasing; Nonresidential construction
Pr: Charles R Paquin
**CFO:* Craig Burns
**Sr VP:* Marc Boily
**VP:* Jon Ryan
**VP:* Ron Wagner
Prgrm Mgr: Beth Kelly
CIO: Jane Somes
IT Man: Clifford Lamason
Manager: JP Farster
Sales Asso: Joseph Zernhelt

D-U-N-S 17-852-5879
■ MODUSLINK CORP
(*Suby of* MODUSLINK GLOBAL SOLUTIONS INC) ★
1601 Trapelo Rd Ste 170, Waltham, MA 02451-7353
Tel (781) 663-5000 *Founded/Ownrshp* 2004
Sales 532.4MM[E] *EMP* 2,900
SIC 7379 7389 5045 Computer related maintenance services; Telemarketing services; Telephone answering service; Computers, peripherals & software
CEO: James R Henderson
Pr: Bill McLennan
COO: Matt Farber
COO: Barbara Simeon
CFO: Lorraine Buffman
**CFO:* Steven G Crane
CFO: Paula McFarland
**Treas:* Brian O'Donnell
**Ofcr:* Scott D Smith
**Ex VP:* Peter L Gray
Ex VP: Peter Gray
Sr VP: Pat Ring
VP: Eric Ammon
VP: Thomas Collins
VP: Phil Stathas
Board of Directors: Anthony J Bay, Virginia Bonker, Francis J Jules, Jonathan A Kraft, Michael J Mardy, David S Wetherell

D-U-N-S 13-620-6000
▲ MODUSLINK GLOBAL SOLUTIONS INC
1601 Trapelo Rd Ste 170, Waltham, MA 02451-7353
Tel (781) 663-5000 *Founded/Ownrshp* 1986
Sales 459.0MM *EMP* 2,500[E]
Tkr Sym MLNK *Exch* NGS
SIC 7379 Computer related consulting services
CEO: Louis J Belardi
**Ch Bd:* Warren G Lichtenstein
CFO: Bram Barendregt
**Ofcr:* Glen M Kassan
Ex VP: Michael Mortson
Ex VP: Scott D Smith
Sr VP: Alan R Cormier
VP: Kathleen V Betts
Snr Ntwrk: Ken Clifford
CIO: Neil Hampshire
Dir IT: Charlie Tempeski
Board of Directors: Anthony Bergamo, Jeffrey J Fenton, Philip E Lengyel, Jeffrey S Wald

D-U-N-S 07-936-9610
▲ MOELIS & CO
399 Park Ave Fl 5, New York, NY 10022-4416
Tel (212) 883-3800 *Founded/Ownrshp* 2007
Sales 518.7MM *EMP* 550[E]
Tkr Sym MC *Exch* NYS
SIC 6282 Investment advice
Ch Bd: Kenneth Moelis
Mng Pt: Rick Leaman
**Pr:* Navid Mahmoodzadegan
**Pr:* Jeffrey Raich
COO: Elizabeth Crain
CFO: Joseph Simon
Chf Cred: Osamu R Watanabe
Sr VP: Matthew Ahearn
Sr VP: Julian Biggins
Sr VP: Ramy Ibrahim
Sr VP: Robert Roeder
VP: Ashish Ajmera
VP: Azad Badakhsh
VP: Coleen Hoy
VP: Ko Kobayashi
VP: Paul Mann
VP: Demetra Stellas
VP: Will Sun
VP: Sabrina Tamraz
VP: Suraj Tolani
VP: Adam Waldman
Board of Directors: John A Allison IV, Eric Cantor, Yvonne Greenstreet, J Richard Leaman III, Jeffrey Raich, Kenneth L Shropshire

MOELIS & COMPANY INTERNATIONAL
See MOELIS & CO LLC

D-U-N-S 80-781-9565
■ MOELIS & CO LLC
MOELIS & COMPANY INTERNATIONAL
(*Suby of* MOELIS & CO) ★
399 Park Ave Fl 5, New York, NY 10022-4416
Tel (212) 883-3800 *Founded/Ownrshp* 2007
Sales 181.6MM[E] *EMP* 470
SIC 6733 6282 Private estate, personal investment & vacation fund trusts; Investment advisory service
Ofcr: Elizabeth Crain
Mng Pt: Kurt Larsen
CFO: Joseph W Simon
Sr VP: Timothy Dahms
Sr VP: Andrew Haber
Sr VP: Gavin Kolt
Sr VP: Mark Laoun
Sr VP: Frank Sellman
VP: Christopher Callesano
VP: Barak Klein
VP: Jane MA

D-U-N-S 96-179-0529
MOELIS CAPITAL PARTNERS LLC
399 Park Ave Fl 5, New York, NY 10022-4416
Tel (212) 883-3800 *Founded/Ownrshp* 2007
Sales 96.5MM *EMP* 1,535
SIC 6726 Investment offices
VP: Andrew Goldfarb

D-U-N-S 00-539-0083 IMP
MOELLER MFG CO LLC
(*Suby of* AE INDUSTRIAL PARTNERS LLC) ★
30100 Beck Rd, Wixom, MI 48393-2827
Tel (248) 960-3999 *Founded/Ownrshp* 1963, 2016
Sales 97.9MM^E *EMP* 550
SIC 3724 3728

D-U-N-S 04-006-7670 IMP
MOET HENNESSY USA INC
(*Suby of* LVMH MOET HENNESSY LOUIS VUITTON)
85 10th Ave Fl 2, New York, NY 10011-4753
Tel (212) 888-7575 *Founded/Ownrshp* 1980
Sales 499.3MM^E *EMP* 3,442
SIC 0172 2844 6153 5182 5122 Grapes; Perfumes, natural or synthetic; Short-term business credit; Wine; Neutral spirits; Perfumes
Pr: James Clerkin
Ex VP: Jon Potter
VP: Tex McCarthy
VP: Tim Norris
VP: Gene Robinson
VP: Rodney Williams
Exec: John Baer
Exec: Robert Gilroy
Exec: Cassondra Hall
Genl Mgr: Victoria Maitland
Mktg Mgr: Jenay Alejandro

D-U-N-S 05-486-0010 IMP
MOFFATT & NICHOL
3780 Kilroy Arprt Way, Long Beach, CA 90806-2457
Tel (562) 590-6500 *Founded/Ownrshp* 1946
Sales 200.3MM^E *EMP* 450
SIC 8711 Structural engineering; Civil engineering; Mechanical engineering; Marine engineering
CEO: Eric Nichol
**CFO:* Olie Abbamonto
Assoc VP: Russell Boudreau
VP: Kerry Simpson
Brnch Mgr: Thomas McCollough
Genl Mgr: Vishal Chugani
Genl Mgr: Nhan Truong
Snr PM: Pekka Ranta
Snr Mgr: Janet Sedlak
Board of Directors: Mark Faeth, Pierce Homer, Michael Johnson, Ralph Larison, Eric Nichol, Richard Steinke

MOFO
See MORRISON & FOERSTER LLP

MOGAN DAVID WINE
See WINE GROUP INC

D-U-N-S 00-279-3438
MOHAVE ELECTRIC CO-OPERATIVE INC (AZ)
928 Hancock Rd, Bullhead City, AZ 86442-5159
Tel (928) 763-4115 *Founded/Ownrshp* 1946
Sales 83.3MM *EMP* 80
Accts Dreyer & Kelso Pc Pa Mission
SIC 4911 1731 Distribution, electric power; Electrical work
Pr: Lyn R Opalka
**Treas:* Carlos Tejeda
**VP:* John B Nelssen
Opers Mgr: Bob Hancock

MOHAWK
See ALADDIN MANUFACTURING CORP

D-U-N-S 13-384-7512
■ **MOHAWK CARPET DISTRIBUTION INC**
(*Suby of* MOHAWK INDUSTRIES INC) ★
160 S Industrial Blvd, Calhoun, GA 30701-3030
Tel (706) 695-9743 *Founded/Ownrshp* 2001
Sales 115.5MM^E *EMP* 500
SIC 2273 Carpets & rugs
CEO: Frank H Boykin
**CEO:* Jeff Lorberbaum
**CFO:* James Brunk

D-U-N-S 96-947-5516 IMP/EXP
■ **MOHAWK CARPET LLC**
(*Suby of* MOHAWK INDUSTRIES INC) ★
160 S Industrial Blvd, Calhoun, GA 30701-3030
Tel (706) 629-7721 *Founded/Ownrshp* 1995
Sales 2.9MMM^E *EMP* 20,431
SIC 2273 Finishers of tufted carpets & rugs; Smyrna carpets & rugs, machine woven
VP: Antony Patti

D-U-N-S 80-792-2935 IMP/EXP
MOHAWK CUSTOMS & SHIPPING CORP
MOHAWK GLOBAL LOGISTICS
123 Air Cargo Rd, North Syracuse, NY 13212-3917
Tel (315) 455-3003 *Founded/Ownrshp* 1993
Sales 101.0MM *EMP* 117
SIC 4731

D-U-N-S 00-207-0076 IMP
MOHAWK FINE PAPERS INC (NY)
465 Saratoga St, Cohoes, NY 12047-4626
Tel (518) 237-1740 *Founded/Ownrshp* 1876, 1986
Sales 251.1MM^E *EMP* 725
SIC 2672 2621 Coated & laminated paper; Paper mills; Uncoated paper
Ch Bd: Thomas D O'Connor
**Pr:* John F Haren
**COO:* Kevin P Richard
Treas: John Macy
**V Ch Bd:* Walter Duignan
Sr VP: George Milner
VP: Paul Bourgeois
VP: John O'Connor
Exec: Paul Strobell
Software D: Vincent Brower
Mill Mgr: Sean Reilly

D-U-N-S 00-958-1103 IMP
■ **MOHAWK FLUSH DOORS**
(*Suby of* MASONITE CORP) ★
980 Point Township Dr, Northumberland, PA 17857-8886
Tel (570) 473-3557 *Founded/Ownrshp* 1951
Sales 190.6MM^E *EMP* 1,699^E
SIC 2431 Doors & door parts & trim, wood; Door trim, wood; Door frames, wood; Doors, wood
Prin: Gary Willow
Plnt Mgr: Bill Freeman

MOHAWK GLOBAL LOGISTICS
See MOHAWK CUSTOMS & SHIPPING CORP

D-U-N-S 61-275-7070 IMP/EXP
▲ **MOHAWK INDUSTRIES INC**
160 S Industrial Blvd, Calhoun, GA 30701-3030
Tel (706) 629-7721 *Founded/Ownrshp* 1988
Sales 8.0MMM *EMP* 34,100
Accts Kpmg Llp Atlanta Georgia
Tkr Sym MHK *Exch* NYS
SIC 2273 3253 Carpets & rugs; Finishers of tufted carpets & rugs; Smyrna carpets & rugs, machine woven; Ceramic wall & floor tile
Ch Bd: Jeffrey S Lorberbaum
Pr: Brian M Carson
Pr: Bernard P Thiers
Pr: John C Turner Jr
**Pr:* W Christopher Wellborn
CFO: Frank H Boykin
Ofcr: Connie Layson
Sr VP: Karen R Mendelsohn
VP: Philip Brown
VP: Kenneth Durning
VP: Frank Endrenyi
VP: Carley Ferguson
VP: Dan Flowers
VP: Randy Gardner
VP: Chip Gillen
VP: Neil Hegwood
VP: Kelly Moore
VP: Bob Nichols
VP: Allen Parker
VP: R David Patton
VP: James Quist
Board of Directors: Karen A Smith Bogart, Bruce C Bruckmann, Frans De Cock, Richard C Ill, Joseph A Onorato, William Henry Runge III

D-U-N-S 80-269-4455
MOHAWK VALLEY HEALTH SYSTEM
MOHAWK VALLEY NETWORK
1656 Champlin Ave, Utica, NY 13502-4830
Tel (315) 624-5116 *Founded/Ownrshp* 1991
Sales 293.0MM^E *EMP* 3,015
SIC 8062 General medical & surgical hospitals
Pr: Scott Perra
**Pr:* Keith Fenstemacher
Ofcr: Nancy Ricci
Sr VP: Patricia Roach

MOHAWK VALLEY NETWORK
See MOHAWK VALLEY HEALTH SYSTEM

MOHEGAN SUN CASINO
See MTIC LLC

D-U-N-S 07-994-6033
MOHEGAN SUN CASINO
MOHEGAN TRIBAL GAMING AUTH
1 Mohegan Sun Blvd, Uncasville, CT 06382-1372
Tel (888) 226-7711 *Founded/Ownrshp* 1996
Sales 5.3MM^E *EMP* 7,000
SIC 7011 Casino hotel

MOHEGAN TRIBAL GAMING AUTH
See MOHEGAN SUN CASINO

D-U-N-S 00-897-7480
MOHEGAN TRIBAL GAMING AUTHORITY
(*Suby of* MOHEGAN SUN CASINO) ★
1 Mohegan Sun Blvd, Uncasville, CT 06382-1355
Tel (860) 862-0777 *Founded/Ownrshp* 1995
Sales 1.2MMM *EMP* 9,220^E
SIC 7011 Casino hotel
CEO: Mitchell Grossinger Etess
COO: Thomas P Burke
**CFO:* Mario C Kontomerkos
**Ch:* Kevin P Brown
VP Mktg: Donald Chapman
Board of Directors: Bruce S Bozsum, Mark F Brown, Ralph James Gessner Jr, Kathleen M Reagan-Pyne, William Quidgeon, Mark M Sperry, Cheryl A Todd

MOHELA
See MISSOURI HIGHER EDUCATION LOAN AUTHORITY

MOHR ENGINEERING DIVISION
See STRESS ENGINEERING SERVICES INC

MOJO
See STRATASYS INC

D-U-N-S 61-146-1153 IMP/EXP
MOL (AMERICA) INC
(*Suby of* MITSUI O.S.K. LINES, LTD.)
700 E Bttrfeld Rd Ste 250, Lombard, IL 60148
Tel (630) 424-3480 *Founded/Ownrshp* 1991
Sales 104.4MM^E *EMP* 389
SIC 4731 7373 4412 Agents, shipping; Railroad freight agency; Truck transportation brokers; Computer integrated systems design; Deep sea foreign transportation of freight
Pr: Richard Craig
Ex Ofcr: Akihiko Ono
Chf Cred: Richard Hiller
Bd of Dir: Akimitsu Ashida
Bd of Dir: Tomonobu Hada
Bd of Dir: Yoshinori Hama
Bd of Dir: Hidehiro Harada
Bd of Dir: Kentaro Hino
Bd of Dir: Tokinao Hojo
Bd of Dir: Noriaki Hori
Bd of Dir: Tsutomu Iizuka
Bd of Dir: Kazuo Iwamoto
Bd of Dir: Makoto Iwata
Bd of Dir: Toshifumi Kato
Bd of Dir: Tsuneo Kawahara
Bd of Dir: Saburo Koide
Bd of Dir: Kazuaki Konishi
Bd of Dir: Makoto Kuroishi
Bd of Dir: Kenji Machino
Bd of Dir: Kazuki Mori
Bd of Dir: Chikanobu Nomura

D-U-N-S 06-052-3156 IMP/EXP
MOLD-RITE PLASTICS LLC
(*Suby of* IRVING PLACE CAPITAL LLC) ★
30 N La Salle St Ste 2425, Chicago, IL 60602-3361
Tel (518) 561-1812 *Founded/Ownrshp* 2010
Sales 124.9MM^E *EMP* 481^E
SIC 3089 Closures, plastic
**CFO:* Tom Recny
Sr VP: Dennis Houpt
VP: Barry Daggett
VP: Bhojraj Naveen
Dept Mgr: Mark Lucas
Telecom Ex: Bud Durland
Opers Mgr: Keith Kelble
Ql Cn Mgr: Kim Desch
Ql Cn Mgr: Chris McLear
VP Sls: Jeff Titherington
Mktg Dir: Aimee Weber

D-U-N-S 78-469-8250
MOLDED ACOUSTICAL PRODUCTS OF EASTON INC
MAP OF EASTON
3 Danforth Dr, Easton, PA 18045-7821
Tel (610) 253-7135 *Founded/Ownrshp* 1973
Sales 89.7MM^E *EMP* 400
SIC 3296

D-U-N-S 04-841-4098 EXP
MOLDED FIBER GLASS COMPANIES
2925 Mfg Pl, Ashtabula, OH 44004-9445
Tel (440) 997-5851 *Founded/Ownrshp* 1946
Sales 644.1MM^E *EMP* 1,917
SIC 3089 Molding primary plastic; Boxes, plastic; Injection molding of plastics
CEO: Richard Morrison
**Pr:* Dave Denny
**COO:* Greg Tilton
**CFO:* Darren Schwede
Sr VP: Peter Emrich
Sr VP: David M Giovannini
**Sr VP:* Carl Lafrance
Exec: Perry Bennett
Genl Mgr: Mike Leonard
Genl Mgr: Wesley Shamp
Genl Mgr: Joe Wilk

MOLDED PARTS DIVISION
See PREMIX INC

MOLDED PRODUCTS DIVISION
See COOPER CROUSE- HINDS LLC

D-U-N-S 06-623-7736 IMP/EXP
MOLDEX-METRIC INC (CA)
10111 Jefferson Blvd, Culver City, CA 90232-3509
Tel (310) 837-6500 *Founded/Ownrshp* 1960
Sales 136.1MM^E *EMP* 500
SIC 3842 Personal safety equipment; Ear plugs
CEO: Mark Magidson
COO: Claudia Berblinger
Exec: Richard Barriere
CIO: Carlos Acosta
Sales Exec: David Taylor
Mktg Dir: Craig Smidet
Sls Dir: Dave Schuck
Mktg Mgr: Craig Smidt
Manager: Moira Brennan
Sls Mgr: Fred Moeller
Sls Mgr: Mark Rohde

D-U-N-S 02-353-9876
MOLDING ACQUISITION CORP
ROTOPLAS
(*Suby of* GRUPO ROTOPLAS, S.A. DE C.V.)
2651 Cooper Ave, Merced, CA 95348-4315
Tel (209) 723-5000 *Founded/Ownrshp* 2013
Sales 6.0MM *EMP* 4,000
SIC 2822 Polyethylene, chlorosulfonated (hypalon)

MOLDING PRODUCTS
See INTERPLASTIC CORP

D-U-N-S 09-148-7140 IMP/EXP
■ **MOLECULAR BIOPRODUCTS INC**
(*Suby of* FISHER SCIENTIFIC INTERNATIONAL LLC) ★
9389 Waples St, San Diego, CA 92121-3903
Tel (858) 453-7551 *Founded/Ownrshp* 2006
Sales 310.6MM^E *EMP* 470
SIC 4953 Medical waste disposal
CEO: Seth H Hoogasian
**VP:* Verner Andersen

D-U-N-S 12-512-3125 IMP
■ **MOLECULAR DEVICES LLC**
(*Suby of* DANAHER CORP) ★
1311 Orleans Dr, Sunnyvale, CA 94089-1136
Tel (408) 747-1700 *Founded/Ownrshp* 2011
Sales 141.1MM^E *EMP* 543
SIC 3826 3841 Analytical instruments; Surgical & medical instruments
Pr: Kevin Chance
VP: Gillian Humphries
VP: Gillian M Huphries
VP: Bart Sanford
VP: Poonam Taneja
VP: Igor Zeltzer
Dir Bus: Suzanne Corkins
Genl Mgr: Sungjun Han
Genl Mgr: Shawn Laymon
IT Man: Danica Fryhling
IT Man: Robert Scheuermann

D-U-N-S 00-524-6673 IMP
MOLEX LLC
(*Suby of* KOCH INDUSTRIES INC) ★
2222 Wellington Ct, Lisle, IL 60532-1682
Tel (630) 969-4550 *Founded/Ownrshp* 2013
Sales 11.1MMM^E *EMP* 42,600
SIC 3679 3643 3357 Antennas, receiving; Electronic circuits; Connectors & terminals for electrical devices; Communication wire; Fiber optic cable (insulated)
CEO: Martin P Slark
Pr: Graham Brock
COO: Liam McCarthy
CFO: Travis George
CFO: David D Johnson
Div Pres: J Michael Nauman
Ex VP: Gary J Matula
VP: Todd Hester
VP: Brian Krause
Sls Dir: Damien Boras

D-U-N-S 08-015-2294
MOLEX PREMISE NETWORKS INC
2222 Wellington Ct, Lisle, IL 60532-1682
Tel (866) 733-6659 *Founded/Ownrshp* 1994
Sales 126.8MM^E *EMP* 10,001
SIC 3679 3643 3357 Antennas, receiving; Electronic circuits; Connectors & terminals for electrical devices; Communication wire; Fiber optic cable (insulated)
Pr: Liam McCarthy

D-U-N-S 19-476-1490
MOLEX U S INC
(*Suby of* MOLEX LLC) ★
2222 Wellington Ct, Lisle, IL 60532-1682
Tel (630) 969-4550 *Founded/Ownrshp* 1986
Sales 144.7MM^E *EMP* 2,200^E
SIC 3678 3679 3643 3357 Electronic connectors; Electronic switches; Electronic circuits; Connectors & terminals for electrical devices; Communication wire
Pr: John H Krehbiel Jr
Ex VP: James Fleischhacker
Ex VP: Charles Graham

D-U-N-S 11-017-5023
▲ **MOLINA HEALTHCARE INC**
200 Oceangate Ste 100, Long Beach, CA 90802-4317
Tel (562) 435-3666 *Founded/Ownrshp* 1980
Sales 14.1MMM *EMP* 10,500
Tkr Sym MOH *Exch* NYS
SIC 8011 6324 Health maintenance organization; Hospital & medical service plans; Health maintenance organization (HMO), insurance only
Ch Bd: J Mario Molina
Pr: Craig Bass
Pr: Richard Chambers
Pr: Russ Fendley
Pr: Norman Nichols
Pr: Scott Sherratt
Pr: Betty Thomas
Pr: Jesse L Thomas
Pr: Chad Westover
CEO: Ann Wehr
**COO:* Terry P Bayer
COO: Amy S Clubbs
**CFO:* John C Molina
**Chf Mktg O:* Keith Wilson
Ofcr: Daniel Barzman
Ofcr: Stephen Harris
**Ofcr:* Joseph W White
Assoc VP: Kay Anders
Assoc VP: Kristine Macrae
Assoc VP: Jennifer Rasmussen
Ex VP: Martha M Bernadett
Board of Directors: Daniel Cooperman, Charles Z Fedak, Steven G James, Frank E Murray, Steven J Orlando, Ronna E Romney, Richard M Schapiro, Dale B Wolf

D-U-N-S 83-228-0973
■ **MOLINA HEALTHCARE OF CALIFORNIA PARTNER PLAN INC**
(*Suby of* MOLINA HEALTHCARE INC) ★
200 Oceangate Ste 100, Long Beach, CA 90802-4317
Tel (562) 435-3666 *Founded/Ownrshp* 1980
Sales NA *EMP* 2,800
SIC 6321 8011 Health insurance carriers; Clinic, operated by physicians
CEO: Richard Chambers
**Pr:* Dr J Mario Molina
**COO:* Terry Bayer
**Ofcr:* Dr James Howatt

D-U-N-S 80-377-7671
■ **MOLINA HEALTHCARE OF WASHINGTON INC**
(*Suby of* MOLINA HEALTHCARE INC) ★
21540 30th Dr Se Ste 400, Bothell, WA 98021-7015
Tel (425) 424-1100 *Founded/Ownrshp* 2000
Sales 600.0MM *EMP* 320
SIC 8011 Health maintenance organization
CEO: Dael Ahlskog
Pr: Bela Biro
Pr: Janeen Tarrow
Ofcr: John Robinson
Assoc VP: Claudia Stclair
VP: Julie Lindberg
VP: Michael Siegel
Dir Rx: Shea Wilson
IT Man: Alberto Laveaga
VP Mktg: Jeannie Koontz
Pharmcst: Holly McClure

D-U-N-S 03-550-1633
MOLINA INFORMATION SYSTEMS LLC
200 Oceangate Ste 100, Long Beach, CA 90802-4317
Tel (562) 435-3666 *Founded/Ownrshp* 2010
Sales 7.2MM^E *EMP* 1,022
SIC 8011 Medical insurance plan

D-U-N-S 96-582-6865
■ **MOLINA INFORMATION SYSTEMS LLC**
MOLINA MEDICAL SOLUTIONS
(*Suby of* MOLINA HEALTHCARE INC) ★
200 Oceangate Ste 100, Long Beach, CA 90802-4317
Tel (916) 561-8540 *Founded/Ownrshp* 2011
Sales NA *EMP* 1,200^E
SIC 6411 Medical insurance claim processing, contract or fee basis

MOLINA MEDICAL SOLUTIONS
See MOLINA INFORMATION SYSTEMS LLC

D-U-N-S 08-038-5788
■ MOLINA PATHWAYS LLC
(*Suby of* MOLINA HEALTHCARE INC) ★
200 Oceangate Ste 100, Long Beach, CA 90802-4317
Tel (562) 491-5773 *Founded/Ownrshp* 2011
Sales 80.2MM^E *EMP* 3,577^E
SIC 8011 Health maintenance organization
CEO: Craig Bass

D-U-N-S 04-730-0363
MOLINE DISPATCH PUBLISHING CO
ROCK ISLAND ARGUS
(*Suby of* JOURNAL) ★
1720 5th Ave, Moline, IL 61265-7907
Tel (309) 764-4344 *Founded/Ownrshp* 1983
Sales 72.6MM^E *EMP* 1,000
SIC 2711 2752 Newspapers, publishing & printing; Commercial printing, lithographic
Exec: Stephanie Hoffstatter
Advt Dir: Nick Norman

D-U-N-S 09-875-0813
MOLINE-COAL VALLEY COMMUNITY UNIT SCHOOL DISTRICT 40
1619 11th Ave, Moline, IL 61265-3143
Tel (309) 743-1600 *Founded/Ownrshp* 1871
Sales 88.8MM *EMP* 1,000
Accts Mcgladrey Llp Davenport Iowa
SIC 8211 School board
Ofcr: Rick Sanchez
VP: Keith Lindbloom
MIS Dir: Craig Reid
Snr Mgr: Angie Curnyn

D-U-N-S 82-677-6684
MOLLER INVESTMENT GROUP INC
6591 Collins Dr Ste E11, Moorpark, CA 93021-1493
Tel (805) 299-8200 *Founded/Ownrshp* 1991
Sales 115.5MM *EMP* 120
SIC 5541 Filling stations, gasoline
Ch: John Moller
**Treas:* Christian Driscoll

MOLLER SUPPLY SERVICES
See ATLANTIC PACIFIC MARINE CORP

MOLLIE STONE'S MARKET
See ALBECO INC

D-U-N-S 07-239-0198
MOLLOY COLLEGE
1000 Hempstead Ave Unit 1, Rockville Centre, NY 11570-1135
Tel (516) 678-5733 *Founded/Ownrshp* 1955
Sales 117.3MM *EMP* 700^E
SIC 8221 Colleges universities & professional schools
Pr: Drew Bogner
**Ch Bd:* Daniel T Henry
**Treas:* Michael A McGovern
Bd of Dir: Janet Knipfing
Bd of Dir: Lynne Nordone
Bd of Dir: Susan Pickering
Bd of Dir: Chris Sedlacek
Trst: Jeff Massey
**VP:* Valerie Collins
VP: Robert C Houlihan
VP: Jackie Meli-Rizzo
VP: Edward Thompson

D-U-N-S 16-530-1032 IMP
MOLNLYCKE HEALTH CARE US LLC
(*Suby of* MOLNLYCKE HEALTH CARE AB)
5550 Peachtree Pkwy # 500, Norcross, GA 30092-2825
Tel (678) 250-7900 *Founded/Ownrshp* 2004
Sales 125.7MM^E *EMP* 230
SIC 5047 Surgical equipment & supplies
Genl Mgr: Nicholas Gossett
IT Man: Delano Francis
IT Man: Jeff Wynia
Manager: Christina Colson
Manager: Rose Ventress
Sls Mgr: Emily DOE

D-U-N-S 00-705-7342 EXP
▲ MOLSON COORS BREWING CO
1801 Calif St Ste 4600, Denver, CO 80202-2664
Tel (303) 927-2337 *Founded/Ownrshp* 1873
Sales 3.5MMM *EMP* 9,100
Accts Pricewaterhousecoopers Llp De
Tkr Sym TAP *Exch* NYS
SIC 2082 Malt beverages; Beer (alcoholic beverage); Near beer; Malt liquors
Ch Bd: Geoffrey E Molson
V Ch: Peter H Coors
Pr: Mark R Hunter
Pr: Pat Porach
CFO: Tracey Joubert
CFO: Mauricio Restrepo
Ofcr: Brenda Davis
Ofcr: Celso L White
Sr VP: William H Weintraub
VP: Bart Alexander
VP: Scott Gordon
VP: David Lamb
VP: Betsy Walker

D-U-N-S 00-129-4719 IMP
▲ MOLYCORP INC
5619 Denver Tech Ste, Greenwood Village, CO 80111
Tel (303) 843-8040 *Founded/Ownrshp* 2010
Sales 475.6MM *EMP* 2,650^E
Accts Kpmg Llp Toronto Canada
Tkr Sym MCPIQ *Exch* OTC
SIC 1099 Rare-earth ores mining; Zirconium ore mining
Pr: Geoffrey R Bedford
**Ch Bd:* Constantine E Karayannopoulos
CFO: Michael F Doolan
Ex VP: Kevin W Johnson
Ex VP: Shannon Y Song
Sr VP: Kevin D Morris
VP: Carl Hassler
VP: Doug Jackson
VP: Robert Noll
Mng Dir: Doug McInnes
Snr Mgr: Arnold Wasser
Board of Directors: Russell D Ball, Brian T Dolan, John Graell, Charles R Henry, James J Jackson, Mark S Kristoff, Alec Machiels, Michael Schwarzkopf

D-U-N-S 00-625-4312 IMP/EXP
■ MOM BRANDS CO LLC
POST CONSUMER BRANDS
(*Suby of* POST HOLDINGS INC) ★
20802 Kensington Blvd, Lakeville, MN 55044-8052
Tel (952) 322-8000 *Founded/Ownrshp* 2015
Sales 416.2MM^E *EMP* 400
SIC 2043 Cereal breakfast foods; Oatmeal: prepared as cereal breakfast food; Oats, rolled: prepared as cereal breakfast food; Corn flakes: prepared as cereal breakfast food
CEO: Christopher J Neugen
CFO: John A Gappa
**CFO:* Tim Rossini
Ofcr: Mike Ahrens
VP: Aaron Jackson
Exec: Gene Pagel
Comm Dir: Linda Fisher
IT Man: David Aman
IT Man: Raymond Picl
VP Opers: Richard Dahl
Sfty Mgr: Jimmy Johnson

MOMA
See MUSEUM OF MODERN ART

D-U-N-S 11-795-5422
▲ MOMENTA PHARMACEUTICALS INC
675 W Kendall St, Cambridge, MA 02142-1110
Tel (617) 491-9700 *Founded/Ownrshp* 2002
Sales 89.6MM *EMP* 258^E
Tkr Sym MNTA *Exch* NGS
SIC 2834 Pharmaceutical preparations
Pr: Craig A Wheeler
Ch Bd: James R Sulat
COO: Matthew P Ottmer
CFO: Richard P Shea
Ofcr: James M Roach
Sr VP: John E Bishop
Sr VP: Ganesh V Kaundinya
Sr VP: Bruce A Leicher
Snr Mgr: Terri Deangelo
Snr Mgr: Scott McKinney
Board of Directors: Bruce L Downey, Marsha H Fanucci, Corey N Fishman, Georges Gemayel, Steven C Gilman, Thomas P Koestler, Jose Carlos Gutierrez-Ramo, Elizabeth Stoner

MOMENTIVE
See MPM SILICONES LLC

D-U-N-S 96-219-2279
MOMENTIVE PERFORMANCE MATERIALS HOLDINGS INC
MOMENTIVE PRFMCE MTLS HOLDINGS
(*Suby of* MOMENTIVE PERFORMANCE MATERIALS INC) ★
22 Corporate Woods Blvd, Albany, NY 12211-2374
Tel (518) 533-4600 *Founded/Ownrshp* 2010
Sales 461.8M^E *EMP* 9,270
SIC 2869 3479 Silicones; Coating of metals with silicon
Ch Bd: Bradley J Bell
CFO: Bill Carter
CFO: Anthony S Colatrella
Treas: Geroge Knight
Treas: Gregory Rustowicz
Ex VP: Mark Brammer
Ex VP: Douglas Johns
VP: David Rusinko
CIO: Ellen Kaufman
IT Man: Steve Dorn
Tech Mgr: David Dilworth

D-U-N-S 78-999-4014 IMP/EXP
MOMENTIVE PERFORMANCE MATERIALS INC
(*Suby of* MPM INTERMEDIATE HOLDINGS INC) ★
260 Hudson River Rd, Waterford, NY 12188-1910
Tel (518) 237-3330 *Founded/Ownrshp* 2014
Sales 2.2MMM *EMP* 4,600
Accts Pricewaterhousecoopers Llp Co
SIC 2869 3479 3679 Silicones; Coating of metals with silicon; Electronic crystals; Quartz crystals, for electronic application
Pr: John G Boss
**CFO:* Brian D Berger
**Ex VP:* Nathan E Fisher
Sr VP: John Moran
**VP:* Craig R Branchfield
CIO: Mike Lamantia
Mfg Dir: Cliff Hardaway
Mktg Mgr: Robert Frye
Mktg Mgr: James Papa
Snr Mgr: David Minor
Snr Mgr: Gerardo Rocha

D-U-N-S 96-521-4146 EXP
MOMENTIVE PERFORMANCE MATERIALS INC
180 E Broad St, Columbus, OH 43215-3707
Tel (614) 986-2495 *Founded/Ownrshp* 2006
Sales 2.6MMM^E *EMP* 10,000^E
SIC 2821 2869 Thermosetting materials; Silicones
CEO: Craig O Morrison
**Pr:* Dale N Plante
**CFO:* William H Carter
Treas: George F Knight
Top Exec: Deepak Kumar
Ex VP: Nathan E Fisher
Ex VP: Anthony B Greene
Ex VP: Kevin W McGuire
**Ex VP:* Judith A Sonnett
Sr VP: Raymond Baran
VP: Colette Barricks
VP: Nancy Brown
VP: Bill Floyd
VP: Peter F Loscocco
Board of Directors: Robert T Seminara, Kenneth Cordell, Jordan C Zaken, Robert J Duffy, Joshua J Harris, William H Joyce, Scott M Kleinman, Stan Parker, Jonathan Rich, David B Sambur, Marvin O Schlanger

MOMENTIVE PRFMCE MTLS HOLDINGS
See MOMENTIVE PERFORMANCE MATERIALS HOLDINGS INC

D-U-N-S 16-160-7460 IMP/EXP
MOMENTUM TEXTILES LLC
TEXTUS GROUP
(*Suby of* RIVERSIDE CO) ★
17811 Fitch, Irvine, CA 92614-6001
Tel (949) 833-8886 *Founded/Ownrshp* 2011
Sales 92.6MM^E *EMP* 140
SIC 5131 2221 Upholstery fabrics, woven; Broadwoven fabric mills, manmade
Pr: John Wilkinson
**CFO:* Joanne Corrao
VP: Roger Arciniega
VP: Kathy Gowdy
VP: Anita Lee
Sls Mgr: Margarita Ocampo
Art Dir: J Kennedy

MOMENTUM WORLDWIDE
See MOMENTUM-NA INC

D-U-N-S 10-802-4191
■ MOMENTUM-NA INC
MOMENTUM WORLDWIDE
(*Suby of* INTERPUBLIC GROUP OF COMPANIES INC) ★
250 Hudson St Fl 2, New York, NY 10013-1413
Tel (646) 638-5400 *Founded/Ownrshp* 1998
Sales 95.3MM^E *EMP* 520
SIC 8743 7311 8732 Sales promotion; Advertising consultant; Commercial nonphysical research
CEO: Chris Weil
CFO: Philippe Touzot
Chf Cred: Omid Farhang
Sr VP: Bill Burnes
VP: Seth Freed
VP: Elena Klau
VP: Phil Koutsis
VP: Alexander Liss
VP: Caitlin O'Connell
Creative D: Laurie Ahrens
Creative D: Heather Bettis
Creative D: David Chamberlain
Creative D: Julie Clark
Creative D: Jeff Gould
Creative D: Tj Rapach

D-U-N-S 60-413-6119
MOMI PALI MEDICAL CENTER
(*Suby of* HAWAII PACIFIC HEALTH) ★
98-1079 Moanalua Rd # 680, Aiea, HI 96701-4725
Tel (808) 486-6000 *Founded/Ownrshp* 1989
Sales 198.6MM *EMP* 618
SIC 8011 Medical centers
CEO: Jen Chahanovich
Dir Vol: Betty Karratti
VP: Terry Long
VP: Herbert Uesara
Dir Rx: Lois Nash
Sfty Dirs: Susan Ohlson
Sfty Mgr: Tony Miranda
Doctor: Jeffrey Killeen
Doctor: Marsh Paul

MOM'S MEALS
See PURFOODS LLC

MON GENERAL HOSPITAL
See MONONGALIA HEALTH SYSTEM INC

MON POWER
See MONONGAHELA POWER CO

MON VALLEY HOSPITAL
See MONONGAHELA VALLEY HOSPITAL INC

D-U-N-S 15-652-1221
MON-VALE HEALTH RESOURCES INC
1163 Country Club Rd, Monongahela, PA 15063-1013
Tel (724) 258-1000 *Founded/Ownrshp* 1982
Sales 161.9MM *EMP* 1,024^E
Accts Carbis Walker Llp New Castle
SIC 8062 General medical & surgical hospitals
Pr: Louis Panza Jr
Sr VP: Daniel Simmons
VP: Lawrence J Rusnock
Genl Mgr: Veronica Vamivakas
Sls Mgr: Silver Hawk

D-U-N-S 61-921-9736
MONA ELECTRIC GROUP INC
7915 Malcolm Rd Ste 400w, Clinton, MD 20735-1768
Tel (301) 868-8400 *Founded/Ownrshp* 1966
Sales 99.2MM^E *EMP* 400
SIC 1731 Electrical work
Ch Bd: Vincent P Mona
CFO: Barbara Gordon
VP: Al Dimuzio

D-U-N-S 07-062-2592
MONARCH
350 Pee Dee Ave Ste 101, Albemarle, NC 28001-4945
Tel (704) 986-1500 *Founded/Ownrshp* 1958
Sales 76.6MM *EMP* 1,200
Accts Davidson Holland Whitesell &
SIC 8322 8049 8331 8052 Association for the handicapped; Psychotherapist, except M.D.; Vocational rehabilitation agency; Home for the mentally retarded, with health care
CEO: Dr Peggy S Terhune
**COO:* James Kelley
CFO: Cindy Jones
Treas: Brenda Hinson
IT Man: Troy Connell
Opers Mgr: Elizabeth Randle
Pgrm Dir: Relena Hair

D-U-N-S 05-331-9740
MONARCH BANK
1435 Crossways Blvd, Chesapeake, VA 23320-2896
Tel (757) 222-2100 *Founded/Ownrshp* 1998
Sales NA *EMP* 52
SIC 6029

D-U-N-S 01-643-0407 IMP
MONARCH BEVERAGE CO INC
WORLD CLASS BEVERAGE DIV
9347 Pendleton Pike, Indianapolis, IN 46236-2768
Tel (317) 612-1310 *Founded/Ownrshp* 1983
Sales 139.9MM^E *EMP* 360
SIC 5181 5182 Beer & other fermented malt liquors; Wine
Pr: Edwin T French Jr
CFO: Fred Dufor
**VP:* Phil Terry
Mng Dir: Wayne Miller
Area Mgr: Paige Codalata
Area Mgr: Jeff Zabel
Dist Mgr: Nick Vores
Genl Mgr: Jason Pfister
Genl Mgr: John E Xnos
VP Sls: Scott Shipley
Mktg Mgr: Amanda Uhles

D-U-N-S 80-755-0280
▲ MONARCH CASINO & RESORT INC
3800 S Virginia St, Reno, NV 89502-6005
Tel (775) 335-4600 *Founded/Ownrshp* 1972
Sales 202.2MM *EMP* 2,100^E
Tkr Sym MCRI *Exch* NGS
SIC 7011 Hotels & motels; Casino hotel; Resort hotel
Ch Bd: John Farahi
**Ch Bd:* Bob Farahi
COO: David Farahi
Treas: Richard L Cooley
Board of Directors: Paul Andrews, Yvette E Landau, Craig F Sullivan

D-U-N-S 00-714-4884 IMP/EXP
▲ MONARCH CEMENT CO
449 1200th St, Humboldt, KS 66748-1785
Tel (620) 473-2222 *Founded/Ownrshp* 1913
Sales 147.0MM *EMP* 510
Tkr Sym MCEM *Exch* OTC
SIC 3241 3273 Portland cement; Ready-mixed concrete
Ch Bd: Walter H Wulf Jr
CFO: Debbie Roe
CFO: Debra P Roe
Treas: Byron K Radcliff
VP: Robert M Kissick
VP: Rick Rush
Telecom Ex: Karen Emerson
DP Exec: Karen Jarred
Opers Mgr: Dennis Osborn
Board of Directors: Jack R Callahan, Ronald E Callaway, David L Deffner, Gayle C McMillen, Byron J Radcliff, Michael R Wachter, Walter H Wulf III

D-U-N-S 94-570-4823
MONARCH DENTAL CORP
(*Suby of* BRIGHT NOW DENTAL) ★
7989 Belt Line Rd Ste 90, Dallas, TX 75248-5728
Tel (972) 720-9017 *Founded/Ownrshp* 2003
Sales 51.6MM^E *EMP* 2,300
SIC 8021 Dental clinics & offices
Pr: Steven Bilt
CFO: Bradley Schmidt
Ofcr: Roy D Smith III DDS
VP: Dennis Fratt
Opers Mgr: Rachel Petty
Board of Directors: Glenn E Hemmerle, Allan S Huston, John E Maupin Jr DDS, Warren F Melamed DDS

D-U-N-S 78-961-7029
MONARCH FINANCIAL HOLDINGS INC
1435 Crossways Blvd, Chesapeake, VA 23320-2896
Tel (757) 389-5111 *Founded/Ownrshp* 2006
Sales NA *EMP* 631^E
SIC 6022

MONARCH WINDOW
See WINDSOR WINDOW CO

D-U-N-S 61-341-3934 IMP/EXP
MONAVIE LLC
(*Suby of* JEUNESSE GLOBAL HOLDINGS LLC) ★
10855 S River Front Pkwy # 100, South Jordan, UT 84095-5763
Tel (801) 748-3100 *Founded/Ownrshp* 2015
Sales 84.6MM^E *EMP* 400^E
SIC 5963 Direct selling establishments
Pr: Mauricio Bellora
**COO:* Dell Brown
**COO:* Walter Noot
**CFO:* James Marsh
**Ch:* Randy Larsen
**Ch:* Henry Marsh
**Chf Mktg O:* Paul Muehlmann
VP: Katy Holt-Larsen

D-U-N-S 07-860-5713 IMP
■ MONDELEZ GLOBAL LLC
(*Suby of* MONDELEZ INTERNATIONAL INC) ★
3 Parkway N Ste 300, Deerfield, IL 60015-2565
Tel (847) 943-4000 *Founded/Ownrshp* 2012
Sales 5.7MMM^E *EMP* 14,430
SIC 2052 2066 3999 2067 2022 2087 Crackers, dry; Biscuits, dry; Chocolate; Candles; Chewing gum; Cheese, natural & processed; Beverage bases

D-U-N-S 87-714-7228 IMP/EXP
▲ MONDELEZ INTERNATIONAL INC
3 Parkway N Ste 300, Deerfield, IL 60015-2565
Tel (847) 943-4000 *Founded/Ownrshp* 2000
Sales 29.6MMM *EMP* 99,000
Tkr Sym MDLZ *Exch* NGS
SIC 2022 2013 2095 2043 2035 2087 Processed cheese; Natural cheese; Spreads, cheese; Dips, cheese-based; Sausages & other prepared meats; Bacon, side & sliced: from purchased meat; Frankfurters from purchased meat; Luncheon meat from purchased meat; Coffee roasting (except by wholesale grocers); Freeze-dried coffee; Instant coffee; Cereal breakfast foods; Dressings, salad: raw & cooked (except dry mixes); Powders, drink
Ch Bd: Irene B Rosenfeld
Pr: Gustavo H Abelenda
Pr: Maurizio Brusadelli
Pr: Lawrence Macdougall
Pr: Roberto De Oliveira Marques
Pr: Doug Skeoch
Pr: Hubert Weber
COO: George Zoghbi
CFO: Brian T Gladden
Chf Cred: Mark A Clouse
Ofcr: Timothy P Cofer
Ex VP: Robin S Hargrove
Ex VP: Karen J May

Ex VP: Daniel P Myers
Ex VP: Gerhard W Pleuhs
VP: Jennifer Fox
VP: Jack Hewitt
VP: Kim Jones
VP: Mary Oyama
VP: Jean Spence
Assoc Dir: Nancy Abrams-Rivera
Board of Directors: Patrick T Siewert, Stephen F Bollenbach, Ruth J Simmons, Lewis W K Booth, Lois D Juliber, Mark D Ketchum, Jorge S Mewquita, Joseph Neubauer, Nelson Peltz, Fredric G Reynolds, Christiana S Shi

D-U-N-S 09-003-6302 IMP/EXP
■ MONDELEZ PUERTO RICO LLC
KRAFT FOODS
(*Suby of* MONDELEZ INTERNATIONAL INC) ★
9615 Ave Los Romeros # 801, San Juan, PR 00926-7036
Tel (787) 522-9810 *Founded/Ownrshp* 1959, 2012
Sales 83.5MM^E *EMP* 150
SIC 5141 Groceries, general line

D-U-N-S 07-950-3347
MONDI BAGS USA LLC
(*Suby of* MONDI FRANTSCHACH GMBH)
281 Hemphill Blvd, Eastman, GA 31023-8293
Tel (478) 374-7032 *Founded/Ownrshp* 2014
Sales 255.0MM^E *EMP* 2,000
SIC 2393 2621 Textile bags; Paper mills
Pr: Allen Ennis
**COO:* Thomas Ott

D-U-N-S 07-980-0940
MONDI BAGS USA LLC
MONDI PAPER SALES NORTH AMER
1200 Abernathy Rd Ste 450, Atlanta, GA 30328-5678
Tel (770) 243-5410 *Founded/Ownrshp* 2002
Sales 553.1MM *EMP* 1,288
SIC 2621 Packaging paper
CEO: David Hathorn
**CFO:* Andrew King
Mktg Mgr: Mark Fournier

D-U-N-S 61-162-6524 IMP/EXP
MONDI JACKSON LLC
(*Suby of* MONDI GRONAU GMBH)
14591 State Highway 177, Jackson, MO 63755-8309
Tel (573) 335-4900 *Founded/Ownrshp* 2014
Sales 188.2MM^E *EMP* 415
SIC 2671 Plastic film, coated or laminated for packaging; Wrapping paper, waterproof or coated
Pr: Kevin Young
**COO:* Thomas Ott
**VP:* David Gonzales
VP: Patrick Kaelin
Exec: Andreas Picolin
Ex Dir: Fred Himpelmann
**Genl Mgr:* Paul Ortiz
**Genl Mgr:* Shawn Somerday
CIO: Chris Davis
Web Dev: Jim Ostergaard
VP Sls: Joe Fiore

MONDI PAPER SALES NORTH AMER
See MONDI BAGS USA LLC

D-U-N-S 86-781-4444 IMP/EXP
■ MONESSEN HEARTH SYSTEMS CO
VERMONT CASTINGS GROUP
(*Suby of* HNI CORP) ★
149 Cleveland Dr, Paris, KY 40361-9782
Tel (859) 987-0740 *Founded/Ownrshp* 2014
Sales 105.9MM^E *EMP* 500
SIC 3433 Logs, gas fireplace; Room & wall heaters, including radiators
Pr: Ricardo Leon
**CFO:* Jacob Reuben
CTO: Pat Kelly
Dir IT: Patrick Miller

D-U-N-S 87-980-5299
MONETARY MANAGEMENT OF CA INC
MONEY MART
(*Suby of* DOLLAR FINANCIAL GROUP INC) ★
1436 Lancaster Ave, Berwyn, PA 19312-1200
Tel (610) 296-3400 *Founded/Ownrshp* 1990
Sales NA *EMP* 510
SIC 6099 Check cashing agencies
Pr: Gary Wheihart
**Ch Bd:* Randy Underwood
**CFO:* Jeffrey Weiss

MONEY BACK
See MCDONALD OIL CO INC

D-U-N-S 01-023-6532
MONEY MANAGEMENT INTERNATIONAL INC
M M I
14141 Southwest Fwy # 1000, Sugar Land, TX 77478-3493
Tel (713) 923-2227 *Founded/Ownrshp* 1997
Sales 54.5MM *EMP* 1,100
Accts Tax Resource Group Galveston
SIC 7389 Financial services
Pr: Ivan L Hand Jr
**Ch Bd:* Scot Sheldon
**CFO:* David Juengel
Ex VP: Ann Morris
**VP:* Chuck Stanley
IT Man: Kim Vance
VP Opers: Kandee Jahns
S&M/VP: Alan Olinger

MONEY MART
See MONETARY MANAGEMENT OF CA INC

MONEYGRAM INTERNATIONAL
See MONEYGRAM PAYMENT SYSTEMS INC

D-U-N-S 14-579-1997
▲ MONEYGRAM INTERNATIONAL INC
2828 N Harwood St Fl 15, Dallas, TX 75201-1518
Tel (214) 999-7552 *Founded/Ownrshp* 1940
Sales NA *EMP* 2,820^E
Tkr Sym MGI *Exch* NGS
SIC 6099 Electronic funds transfer network, including switching; Money order issuance
Ch Bd: Pamela H Patsley
**CEO:* W Alexander Holmes
CFO: Lawrence Angelilli
CFO: Alexander Holmes
Chf Mktg O: Juan Agualimpia
Ofcr: Phyllis J Skene-Stimac
Ofcr: Alvaro Velez
Ex VP: Francis Aaron Henry
Ex VP: W Alexander Hoffmann
Ex VP: Grant A Lines
Ex VP: Wayne F McGurk
Ex VP: Peter E Ohser
Ex VP: Steven Piano
Sr VP: R Lee Furnival
VP: Ann Knapp
VP: Craig McDonald
VP: Jeff Shonty
VP: John D Stoneham
Board of Directors: J Coley Clark, Victor W Dahir, Antonio O Garza, Seth W Lawry, Michael P Rafferty, W Bruce Turner, Peggy Vaughan

D-U-N-S 00-645-4151
■ MONEYGRAM PAYMENT SYSTEMS INC
MONEYGRAM INTERNATIONAL
(*Suby of* MONEYGRAM INTERNATIONAL INC) ★
1550 Utica Ave S Ste 100, Minneapolis, MN 55416-5300
Tel (952) 591-3000 *Founded/Ownrshp* 1940, 2004
Sales NA *EMP* 1,650
SIC 6099 7389 Money order issuance; Electronic funds transfer network, including switching; Financial services
CEO: Alex Holmes
**Pr:* Philip Milne
**Pr:* Pamela H Patsley
**COO:* Anthony Ryan
Chf Mktg O: Juan Agualimpia
Ofcr: Deb Guertin
Ex VP: David Albright
Ex VP: Timothy C Everett
Ex VP: Teresa H Johnson
Ex VP: Daniel J Omalley
VP: Massimo Canovi
VP: Michael Daugherty
VP: Keith Fulton
VP: Robert W Glaus
VP: Jeff Gorsuch
VP: Joe Steiger
VP: J Wimer
Exec: Eleni Chanioti
Board of Directors: Robert H Bohannon, Ronald G Nelson

D-U-N-S 10-288-4194
MONEYTREE INC
6720 Fort Dent Way # 230, Tukwila, WA 98188-8508
Tel (888) 516-6643 *Founded/Ownrshp* 1983
Sales NA *EMP* 750
SIC 6099 Check cashing agencies
Pr: Agartha Sylvia Clark
**CEO:* Dennis Bassford
COO: Chris Kiely
**CFO:* Rob Grover
CFO: Tom King
Treas: Sara Bassford
**Ex VP:* David Bassford
VP: Mark Lewington
Brnch Mgr: Jose Alarcon
Dist Mgr: Brent Davis
Dist Mgr: Brianne Sullivan

D-U-N-S 79-689-2362
MONGOLIAN OPERATING CO LLC
BD'S MONGOLIAN GRILL
200 E Travelers Trl # 235, Burnsville, MN 55337-4192
Tel (952) 288-2363 *Founded/Ownrshp* 1992
Sales 62.5MM^E *EMP* 2,950^E
SIC 5812 6794 Buffet (eating places); Franchises, selling or licensing
CFO: William T Downs III
COO: Todd Pahl

D-U-N-S 10-218-7408
MONICAL PIZZA CORP
530 N Kinzie Ave, Bradley, IL 60915-1225
Tel (815) 937-1890 *Founded/Ownrshp* 1982
Sales 53.4MM^E *EMP* 1,000
SIC 5812 6794 Pizza restaurants; Franchises, selling or licensing
Pr: Janelle L Reents
**Pr:* Harry Bond
CFO: Alvey Pat
CTO: Todd Hallberg
MIS Dir: Dawn Savoie
IT Man: Mike Pelletier
Opers Mgr: Doug Davis

MONITOR, THE
See AIM MEDIA TEXAS OPERATING LLC

D-U-N-S 19-645-7873
■ MONITRONICS INTERNATIONAL INC
(*Suby of* ASCENT CAPITAL GROUP INC) ★
1990 Wittington Pl, Dallas, TX 75234-1904
Tel (972) 243-7443 *Founded/Ownrshp* 2010
Sales 563.3MM *EMP* 923^E
Accts Kpmg Llp Dallas Texas
SIC 7382 1731 Burglar alarm maintenance & monitoring; Electrical work
Pr: Mike Haislip
**CFO:* Michael Meyers
**Treas:* David Verret
Ex VP: William Niles
**VP:* Darin Anderson
VP: Rick Hudson
VP: Rick L Hudson
**VP:* Frank McGhee
VP: John Mejia
**VP:* Bruce Mungiguerra
VP: Robert N Sherman
VP: Phyllis Turner

MONMOUTH COUNTY
See COUNTY OF MONMOUTH

D-U-N-S 04-987-5636
MONMOUTH MEDICAL CENTER INC
300 2nd Ave, Long Branch, NJ 07740-6395
Tel (732) 222-5200 *Founded/Ownrshp* 1889
Sales 375.9MM *EMP* 2,400
SIC 8062 Hospital, AMA approved residency
Ex Dir: Frank Vozos
Pr: James Alexander
**CFO:* David McClung
CFO: Gerald Tofani
VP: Bill Arnold
VP: Patricia Keating
VP: Tara Kelly
Dir Rad: Patricia Derosa
Dir Rx: Julie Saleh
Adm Dir: Shirley S Hwang
CIO: Kathryn Collins

MONMOUTH PARK RACETRACK
See NEW JERSEY SPORTS & EXPOSITION AUTHORITY

D-U-N-S 36-186-7088
MONMOUTH UNIVERSITY
400 Cedar Ave, West Long Branch, NJ 07764-1898
Tel (732) 571-3400 *Founded/Ownrshp* 1948
Sales 171.1MM *EMP* 1,000^E
Accts Kpmg Llp Short Hills Nj
SIC 8221 Colleges universities & professional schools
Pr: Paul G Gaffney II
V Ch: Alfred J Schiavetti
**Pr:* Paul Brown PHD
Trst: Monica M Sweeney
Ofcr: Tracy Turner
Exec: Barbara Growney
Admn Mgr: Nikki Reed
DP Exec: Barbara Nitzberg
Dir IT: Fred Del Guercio

D-U-N-S 78-101-2005
MONOGRAM FOOD SOLUTIONS LLC
530 Oak Court Dr Ste 400, Memphis, TN 38117-3735
Tel (901) 685-7167 *Founded/Ownrshp* 2004
Sales 419.2MM *EMP* 790
Accts Mayer Hoffman Mccann Pc Mem
SIC 5142 2013 5147 Packaged frozen goods; Pigs' feet, cooked & pickled: from purchased meat; Beef, dried: from purchased meat; Snack sticks, including jerky: from purchased meat; Meats & meat products
CFO: Joey Stoner
VP: Don Ephgrave
IT Man: Jeff Ketchum
Mktg Dir: Sheri Gardner

D-U-N-S 96-736-6969
MONOGRAM RESIDENTIAL TRUST INC
5800 Gran Pkwy Ste 1000, Plano, TX 75024
Tel (469) 250-5500 *Founded/Ownrshp* 2006
Sales 238.0MM *EMP* 370^E
Accts Deloitte & Touche Llp Dallas
SIC 6798 Real estate investment trusts
Pr: Mark T Alfieri
**Ch Bd:* E Alan Patton
CFO: Howard S Garfield
Assoc VP: Derrick Cranor
Ex VP: Margaret M Daly
Ex VP: Bob Poynter
Ex VP: Robert T Poynter
Sr VP: James Fadley
Sr VP: Jim McGinley
Sr VP: Ross Odland
Sr VP: Daniel J Rosenberg
VP: Rob Hodge
Board of Directors: Sami S Abbasi, Robert S Aisner, Roger D Bowler, David D Fitch, Tammy K Jones, Jonathan L Kempner, Murray J McCabe

D-U-N-S 83-202-9651
MONOGRAM SNACKS MARTINSVILLE LLC
(*Suby of* MONOGRAM FOOD SOLUTIONS LLC) ★
200 Knauss Dr, Martinsville, VA 24112-1958
Tel (901) 685-7167 *Founded/Ownrshp* 2009
Sales 272.7MM^E *EMP* 514
SIC 5147 Meats & meat products

MONOGRAM SYSTEMS
See MAG AEROSPACE INDUSTRIES INC

D-U-N-S 79-996-8680
▲ MONOLITHIC POWER SYSTEMS INC
79 Great Oaks Blvd, San Jose, CA 95119-1311
Tel (408) 826-0600 *Founded/Ownrshp* 1997
Sales 333.0MM *EMP* 1,200^E
Accts Deloitte & Touche Llp San Jos
Tkr Sym MPWR *Exch* NGS
SIC 3674 8711 Semiconductors & related devices; Engineering services
Pr: Michael R Hsing
Pr: Deming Xiao
CFO: Bernie Blegen
Sr VP: Maurice Sciammas
VP: Saria Tseng
Area Mgr: Roger Straight
Mktg Mgr: Zhihong Yu
Manager: Patrick Lim
Manager: Kevin Ronk
Manager: Dan Tanoury
Sls Mgr: John Bagatelos
Board of Directors: Karen A Smith Bogart, Herbert Chang, Eugen Elmiger, Victor K Lee, James C Moyer, Jeff Zhou

D-U-N-S 60-194-4072
MONOMOY CAPITAL PARTNERS LLC
142 W 57th St Fl 17, New York, NY 10019-3300
Tel (212) 699-4000 *Founded/Ownrshp* 2005
Sales NA *EMP* 780
SIC 6371 Pension, health & welfare funds

D-U-N-S 79-106-7080
MONOMOY CAPITAL PARTNERS LP
142 W 57th St Fl 17, New York, NY 10019-3300
Tel (212) 699-4000 *Founded/Ownrshp* 2005
Sales 822.9MM^E *EMP* 3,775
SIC 6799 Venture capital companies
Genl Pt: Stephen Presser
Pt: Kareem Aktar
Pt: Andrea Cipriani
Pt: Daniel Collin
Pt: Justin Hillenbrand
Pt: Nathan Richey
Pt: Loren Roseman
Pt: Earl Dos Santos
Pt: Mayank Singh
Pt: Philip Von Burg
VP: Keith Motelson
VP: Lauren Mulholland
Board of Directors: Scot Duncan, Jaime McKenzie

D-U-N-S 95-861-1774
■ MONONA HOLDINGS LLC
(*Suby of* CVG) ★
1952 Mc Dowell Rd Ste 207, Naperville, IL 60563-6506
Tel (630) 946-0630 *Founded/Ownrshp* 2005
Sales 175.6MM^E *EMP* 1,200
SIC 3694 5063 Harness wiring sets, internal combustion engines; Wire & cable
MIS Mgr: Dan Hurley

D-U-N-S 04-856-2664
■ MONONA WIRE CORP
(*Suby of* MONONA HOLDINGS LLC) ★
301 W Spruce St, Monona, IA 52159-8035
Tel (563) 539-2012 *Founded/Ownrshp* 2002
Sales 176.6MM^E *EMP* 1,100
SIC 3679 3694 Harness assemblies for electronic use: wire or cable; Harness wiring sets, internal combustion engines
CFO: Timothy Trenary
VP: Kevin Frailey

D-U-N-S 00-794-4812
■ MONONGAHELA POWER CO (OH)
MON POWER
(*Suby of* FIRSTENERGY CORP) ★
1310 Fairmont Ave, Fairmont, WV 26554-3526
Tel (800) 686-0022 *Founded/Ownrshp* 1924, 2012
Sales 2.4MMM^E *EMP* 4,000
SIC 4911 Generation, electric power; Distribution, electric power; Transmission, electric power
Ch Bd: Paul J Evanson
**Pr:* David E Flitman
**CFO:* Jeffrey David Serkes
**VP:* Philip L Goulding
**VP:* Hyun Park
CTO: Keith March
Mktg Dir: Trent Smith

D-U-N-S 06-872-8773
MONONGAHELA VALLEY HOSPITAL INC
MON VALLEY HOSPITAL
1163 Country Club Rd, Monongahela, PA 15063-1095
Tel (724) 258-1000 *Founded/Ownrshp* 1982
Sales 133.6MM *EMP* 1,200
Accts Arnett Carbis Toothman Llp N
SIC 8062 8063 8069 General medical & surgical hospitals; Psychiatric hospitals; Specialty hospitals, except psychiatric
CEO: Anthony M Lombardi
CFO: Anthony Lombardi
CFO: Daniel Simmons
**Treas:* John G Schaeffer
VP: Donna Ramusivich
VP: Sara Schumacher
Exec: Renee Hurley
Dir Lab: Betty Ritzer
Comm Dir: Corinne Laboon
Dir Rad: Jan Forlini
Ex Dir: Walter Young

D-U-N-S 01-179-9830
MONONGALIA COUNTY BOARD OF EDUCATION (WV)
13 S High St, Morgantown, WV 26501-7546
Tel (304) 291-9210 *Founded/Ownrshp* 1933
Sales 104.7MM^E *EMP* 1,400
SIC 8211 School board
Pr: Barbara Parsons
**Treas:* William T Hawkins
Board of Directors: Jean Schmalzried

D-U-N-S 07-748-3154 IMP
MONONGALIA COUNTY GENERAL HOSPITAL CO
MONONGALIA GENERAL HOSPITAL
1200 J D Anderson Dr, Morgantown, WV 26505-3494
Tel (304) 598-1200 *Founded/Ownrshp* 1943
Sales 251.8MM *EMP* 1,100
SIC 8062 General medical & surgical hospitals
Pr: Thomas J Senker
**Pr:* Darryl Duncan
**COO:* Linda Ollis
**CFO:* Nicholas Grubbs
**Treas:* Sister Nancy White
**Ex VP:* Robert P Ritz
VP: Linda Allen
VP: Steven A Mariner
**VP:* Daris Rosencrance
Nurse Mgr: Cynthia Cox
Nurse Mgr: Linda Felton

MONONGALIA GENERAL HOSPITAL
See MONONGALIA COUNTY GENERAL HOSPITAL CO

D-U-N-S 15-377-1936
MONONGALIA HEALTH SYSTEM INC
MON GENERAL HOSPITAL
1200 J D Anderson Dr, Morgantown, WV 26505-3494
Tel (304) 598-1200 *Founded/Ownrshp* 1982
Sales 5.3MM *EMP* 1,500
Accts Dixon Hughes Goodman Llp Morg
SIC 8062 8011 General medical & surgical hospitals; Offices & clinics of medical doctors
Pr: Daris Rosencrance
CFO: Nick Grubbs
CFO: Daris Rosencran
**Sec:* Terry Shaffer
Dir Risk M: Denice Myers
Nurse Mgr: Linda Felton
CTO: Ellison Ponzurak
VP Opers: Steve Mariner

D-U-N-S 14-950-4917 IMP/EXP
MONOPRICE INC
MONOPRICE.COM
(*Suby of* YFC-BONEAGLE ELECTRIC CO., LTD.)
11701 6th St, Rancho Cucamonga, CA 91730-6030
Tel (909) 989-6887 *Founded/Ownrshp* 2016
Sales 153.3MM^E *EMP* 160
SIC 5099 Video & audio equipment
CEO: John Clendening
VP: Julie Hong
VP: Jeovahna Vazquez
Exec: Larry Chong
IT Man: Andy Park
Software D: Brandi Bailes
Opers Mgr: Eric Han
Natl Sales: Darin Stout
VP Mktg: Luke Grant
Mktg Mgr: Nelson Fisher
Mktg Mgr: Diana Toldoya

MONOPRICE.COM
See MONOPRICE INC

D-U-N-S 80-704-5732
▲ MONOTYPE IMAGING HOLDINGS INC
600 Unicorn Park Dr, Woburn, MA 01801-3376
Tel (781) 970-6000 *Founded/Ownrshp* 2005
Sales 192.4MM *EMP* 494^E
Tkr Sym TYPE *Exch* NGS
SIC 7371 7372 Custom computer programming services; Prepackaged software
Pr: Scott E Landers
**Ch Bd:* Robert L Lentz
Ex VP: Janet M Dunlap
Ex VP: Steven R Martin
Ex VP: John L Seguin
Ex VP: Benjamin W L Semmes III
Sr VP: Mark S Brown
Sr VP: Daniel T Gerron
Sr VP: Lisa A Landa
Sr VP: John H McCallum
Sr VP: Jennifer H Peterson
Sr VP: Christopher J Roberts
Sr VP: Joseph G Roberts
Sr VP: Brett S Zucker
Board of Directors: Gay W Gaddis, Roger J Heinen Jr, Pamela F Lenehan, Douglas J Shaw, Peter J Simone, Timothy B Yeaton

D-U-N-S 01-313-5058 IMP
▲ MONRO MUFFLER BRAKE INC
200 Holleder Pkwy, Rochester, NY 14615-3808
Tel (585) 647-6400 *Founded/Ownrshp* 1957
Sales 943.6MM *EMP* 6,725
Tkr Sym MNRO *Exch* NGS
SIC 7539 7533 7534 7549 Wheel alignment, automotive; Powertrain components repair services; Automotive brake lining, installation; Shock absorber replacement; Muffler shop, sale or repair & installation; Tire retreading & repair shops; Emissions testing without repairs, automotive; Inspection & diagnostic service, automotive
Pr: John W Van Heel
**Ch Bd:* Robert G Gross
CFO: Catherine D'Amico
Ex VP: Joseph Tomarchio Jr
Sr VP: Craig L Hoyle
VP: Brian D'Ambrosia
VP: Ed Mullen
Genl Mgr: Robert Hannan
Sftwr Eng: Adam Nowak
Sls Mgr: Dave Rudd
Board of Directors: Frederick M Danziger, Donald Glickman, Stephen C McCluski, Robert E Mellor, Peter J Solomon, James R Wilen, Elizabeth A Wolszon

D-U-N-S 14-105-7385
MONROE 1 BOCES EDUCATIONAL FOUNDATION INC
41 Oconnor Rd, Fairport, NY 14450-1327
Tel (585) 377-4660 *Founded/Ownrshp* 2000
Sales 1.3MM *EMP* 2,000
Accts John C Bott Cpa Rochester Ny
SIC 8299 Educational services
Pr: Eugene Kinney
Treas: Elizabeth Hartley
**Treas:* Sheila Wallenhorst
**VP:* Frederick Shippey
Genl Mgr: Nancy Moore
Psych: Doreen Massie
Snr Mgr: Derrick Mitchell

MONROE 2-ORLEANS BOCES
See BOARD OF COOP EDUC SERVICES OF 2ND SUPERVISORY DISTRICT OF MONROE & ORLEANS COUNTIES

MONROE CAROL JR CHILDREN HOSPT
See VANDERBILT CHILDRENS HOSPITAL

MONROE CITY SCHOOL BOARD
See MONROE CITY SCHOOLS INC

D-U-N-S 02-032-8662
MONROE CITY SCHOOLS INC
MONROE CITY SCHOOL BOARD
2006 Tower Dr, Monroe, LA 71201-5036
Tel (318) 325-0601 *Founded/Ownrshp* 1900
Sales 81.2MM^E *EMP* 1,405
SIC 8211 Public elementary & secondary schools
Teacher Pr: Phedra Brantley

D-U-N-S 07-115-3951
MONROE CLINIC INC
515 22nd Ave, Monroe, WI 53566-1598
Tel (608) 324-2775 *Founded/Ownrshp* 1963
Sales 176.5MM *EMP* 1,100
Accts Wipfli Llp Milwaukee Wiscons
SIC 8062 8011 General medical & surgical hospitals; Offices & clinics of medical doctors
Pr: Michael Sanders
V Ch: Bill Oemichen
**CFO:* James Nemeth
Ofcr: Julie Allemagne
VP: Paula Elmer
VP: Jane Monahan
VP: Karen Thomas
VP: Jane Weldon
Off Admin: Jill Devries
Off Admin: Ann Kloepping
CTO: Dana Truttmann

D-U-N-S 06-792-1585 IMP
MONROE COMMUNITY COLLEGE (NY)
(*Suby of* SUNY ADMINISTRATION) ★
1000 E Henrietta Rd, Rochester, NY 14623-5780
Tel (585) 292-2000 *Founded/Ownrshp* 1962
Sales 68.9MM *EMP* 1,800
Accts Bonadio & Co Llp Pittsford
SIC 8222 9411 Community college; Administration of educational programs;
Pr: Anne M Kress
**Pr:* Thomas Flynn
VP: Andrea Wade
Snr Mgr: Todd Garnier

D-U-N-S 06-791-0356
MONROE COMMUNITY HOSPITAL (INC)
(*Suby of* COUNTY OF MONROE) ★
435 E Henrietta Rd, Rochester, NY 14620-4684
Tel (585) 760-6500 *Founded/Ownrshp* 1933
Sales 68.7MM *EMP* 1,000
SIC 8051 Skilled nursing care facilities
Ex Dir: Todd Spring
Pr: Dixie Schaedel
**CFO:* Tom Anderson
Ofcr: Linda Vanvilet
Assoc Dir: Gary Griffin
Dir Rx: Julie Olschewski
DP Dir: Richmond Dyes
Dir IT: Joel Snider
Mfg Dir: Mary Quinn
Pharmcst: Amy Burke

D-U-N-S 07-206-2342
MONROE COUNTY COMMUNITY SCHOOL CORP
MCCSC
315 E North Dr, Bloomington, IN 47401-6595
Tel (812) 330-7700 *Founded/Ownrshp* 1968
Sales 65.6MM *EMP* 2,300
SIC 8211 Public elementary & secondary schools; Elementary school
Bd of Dir: Chris Gaal
Bd of Dir: Jim Muehling
Dir Sec: Jim Witmer
Pr Dir: Andrew Clampitt
Teacher Pr: Vick Chambers

D-U-N-S 79-115-4185
MONROE COUNTY SCHOOL DISTRICT
241 Trumbo Rd, Key West, FL 33040-6684
Tel (305) 293-1400 *Founded/Ownrshp* 2007
Sales 73.5MM^E *EMP* 1,000
SIC 8211 Public elementary & secondary schools
**CFO:* Michael Kinneer
Off Mgr: Zulema Pradas-Bergnes
MIS Dir: David Richardson

D-U-N-S 07-852-2170 IMP/EXP
■ MONROE ENERGY LLC
(*Suby of* DELTA AIRLINES) ★
4101 Post Rd, Trainer, PA 19061-5052
Tel (610) 364-8000 *Founded/Ownrshp* 2012
Sales 228.8MM^E *EMP* 445
SIC 2911 Petroleum refining
Pr: Jeffrey Warmann
VP: Rodney Smith
VP: Coby Stweart
QA Dir: Sharon Watkins
Sfty Dirs: Mike McClure
Opers Mgr: Edward Ernst
Snr Mgr: Adam Gattuso
Snr Mgr: Brian McTiernan
Snr Mgr: Mark Schuck

D-U-N-S 00-699-7076 IMP
MONROE HARDWARE CO INC
101 N Sutherland Ave, Monroe, NC 28110-3601
Tel (704) 289-3121 *Founded/Ownrshp* 1968
Sales 105.4MM^E *EMP* 220
SIC 5072 5083 Shelf or light hardware; Farm implements
Ch Bd: Carl G Belk
**Pr:* James G Allred
Exec: Agnes Frodge
Mktg Dir: Keith Driscoll
Mktg Mgr: Brooks Gornto
Sales Asso: Todd Burr

D-U-N-S 07-829-1396
MONROE L BRFHH L C
UNIVERSITY HEALTH CONWAY
4864 Jackson St, Monroe, LA 71202-6400
Tel (318) 330-7000 *Founded/Ownrshp* 2013
Sales 92.1MM *EMP* 61^E
SIC 8062 General medical & surgical hospitals
CEO: John F George Jr
**CFO:* James Dean

MONROE MANNOR
See GRAND UNION HEALTHCARE LLC

D-U-N-S 08-275-0571
MONROE PLAN FOR MEDICAL CARE INC
1120 Pittsford Victor Rd, Pittsford, NY 14534-3818
Tel (585) 244-5550 *Founded/Ownrshp* 1970
Sales NA *EMP* 180
Accts Robinson & Gordon Cpas Pc Roc
SIC 6324 Hospital & medical service plans
CEO: Dennis Graziano
CFO: Michael Messier
Dir IT: Scott Ferris

D-U-N-S 01-806-4845
MONROE REGIONAL HEALTH SYSTEM
131 Sw 15th St, Ocala, FL 34471-6529
Tel (352) 351-7200 *Founded/Ownrshp* 1996
Sales 340.6MM *EMP* 2,500
SIC 8011 Medical centers
Prin: R Cyrus Huffman
VP: Carl Candullo Jr
VP: Sharon Jones
Ex Dir: Sharon Stuckey

D-U-N-S 19-249-6990
MONROE STAFFING SERVICES LLC
35 Nutmeg Dr Ste 250, Trumbull, CT 06611-5451
Tel (203) 268-8624 *Founded/Ownrshp* 2010
Sales 66.0MM^E *EMP* 1,700
SIC 7361 Employment agencies
Pr: Matt Briand
**CFO:* Steve Miller
Treas: Sophia H Huang
Sr VP: Michelle Crispino
**VP:* Paul Polito
**VP:* Erik Schwartz
**VP:* Steve Thompson
IT Man: Michael Clifford
Opers Mgr: Melissa Franklin
Manager: Josh Iadarola

D-U-N-S 02-077-7785
MONROE TOWNSHIP BOARD OF EDUCATION (NJ)
423 Buckelew Ave, Monroe Township, NJ 08831-2976
Tel (732) 521-2111 *Founded/Ownrshp* 1895
Sales 107.3MM^E *EMP* 900
SIC 8211 Public elementary & secondary schools
Pr: Doug Poye
VP: Tom Nothstein

D-U-N-S 01-272-3128 IMP
MONROE TRACTOR & IMPLEMENT CO INC (NY)
1001 Lehigh Station Rd, Henrietta, NY 14467-9311
Tel (585) 334-3867 *Founded/Ownrshp* 1951
Sales 88.2MM^E *EMP* 200
SIC 5082 5083 7353

D-U-N-S 00-608-1863 IMP/EXP
MONROE TRUCK EQUIPMENT INC (WI)
M T E
1051 W 7th St, Monroe, WI 53566-9100
Tel (608) 328-8127 *Founded/Ownrshp* 1958
Sales 271.9MM^E *EMP* 678
SIC 5013 3441 3599 Truck parts & accessories; Fabricated structural metal for bridges; Building components, structural steel; Machine & other job shop work; Machine shop, jobbing & repair; Custom machinery
Pr: David Quade
**Treas:* Richard Rufenacht
**VP:* Gregory Krahenbuhl
VP: Dan Nommensen
Off Mgr: Lisa Smith
Dir IT: Teresa Johnson
Ql Cn Mgr: Gary Hess
Sls Mgr: Max Hawkins
Sls Mgr: Noah Martin
Sls Mgr: Shawn Steinmann
Sales Asso: Steve Broge

D-U-N-S 01-495-8797
MONROE-WOODBURY CENTRAL SCHOOL DISTRICT
278 Route 32, Central Valley, NY 10917-3226
Tel (845) 460-6200 *Founded/Ownrshp* 1951
Sales 51.4MM^E *EMP* 1,200
Accts Nugent & Haeussler Pc Mont
SIC 8211 Public elementary & secondary schools; High school, junior or senior
**Pr:* Michael J Digeronimo
Treas: Sandra Clohessy
Treas: Mike Henry
VP: Lorraine Carroll
**VP:* Erich Tusch
Schl Brd P: John Huberth
Psych: Christine Ricker

MONROVIA GROWES
See MONROVIA NURSERY CO

D-U-N-S 00-690-4049 IMP
MONROVIA NURSERY CO
MONROVIA GROWES
817 E Monrovia Pl, Azusa, CA 91702-6297
Tel (626) 334-9321 *Founded/Ownrshp* 1926
Sales 487.5MM^E *EMP* 2,000
SIC 0181 5193 5261 Nursery stock, growing of; Flowers & florists' supplies; Nurseries & garden centers
CEO: Miles R Rosedale
Pr: William B Usrey
Pr: Richard Van Landinghan
VP: Dennis Conner
VP: Greg Schaan
Exec: Sylvia Lopez
Genl Mgr: Rick Wells
Dir IT: Michael Scannell
VP Sls: Phil Harley
Sls Mgr: Gregory Estes
Sls Mgr: Nicholas Staddon
Board of Directors: Harry E Rosedale Jr Direc, Lance H Rosedale, Miles R Rosedale, Martin W Usrey

D-U-N-S 16-842-8287 IMP/EXP
▲ MONSANTO CO
800 N Lindbergh Blvd, Saint Louis, MO 63167-0001
Tel (314) 694-1000 *Founded/Ownrshp* 2000
Sales 13.5MMM *EMP* 22,500
Tkr Sym MON *Exch* NYS
SIC 2879 0181 Agricultural chemicals; Seeds, vegetable: growing of
Ch Bd: Hugh Grant
Pr: Brett D Begemann
CFO: Pierre Courduroux
Bd of Dir: Joni Barron
Bd of Dir: Ray Drachenberg
Bd of Dir: David Somers
Ex VP: Robert T Fraley
Ex VP: Michael Scallan
Ex VP: David F Snively
Sr VP: Sarah S Hull
VP: Scott Baucum
VP: Melissa Bharper
VP: Steven Bierschenk
VP: Stefan Bledig
VP: Jayme Collins
VP: Nanci Daesch
VP: Francisco Diaz
VP: Natalie Dinicola
VP: Mike Edgerton
VP: Steven Engeberg
VP: Jerry Glover
Board of Directors: Jon R Moeller, Mitch Barns, William U Parfet, Gregory H Boyce, George H Poste, David L Chicoine, Robert J Stevens, Janice L Fields, Patricia Verduin, Arthur H Harper, Laura K Ipsen, Gwendolyn S King, Marcos M Lutz, C Steven McMillan

MONSIEUR HENRI WINE
See SAZERAC CO INC

D-U-N-S 04-941-9682 IMP
MONSON COMPANIES INC
(*Suby of* AZELIS AMERICAS INC) ★
154 Pioneer Dr, Leominster, MA 01453-3474
Tel (978) 840-7007 *Founded/Ownrshp* 1987
Sales 96.1MM^E *EMP* 76
SIC 5169 5172 2899 2842 Industrial chemicals; Antifreeze compounds; Lubricating oils & greases; Chemical preparations; Specialty cleaning, polishes & sanitation goods
Pr: Charles P Walkovich
**Pr:* Steven Barney
COO: Holly Daley
Genl Mgr: Kevin Kelly
Genl Mgr: Retta-Jo Madore
VP Opers: Hal Chevalier

D-U-N-S 62-543-7488 IMP/EXP
■ MONSTER BEVERAGE 1990 CORP
(*Suby of* MONSTER BEVERAGE CORP) ★
1 Monster Way, Corona, CA 92879-7101
Tel (951) 739-6200 *Founded/Ownrshp* 1985
Sales 2.2MMM^E *EMP* 2,001^E
SIC 2086 Bottled & canned soft drinks; Carbonated beverages, nonalcoholic: bottled & canned; Iced tea & fruit drinks, bottled & canned
Ch Bd: Rodney C Sacks
Ch Bd: Dennis Quinn
Pr: Hilton H Schlosberg
COO: Nick R Gagliardi
Sr VP: Thomas J Kelly
VP: Carl Willis
CIO: Kate Webb
Mktg Dir: Jerry Wood
Mktg Mgr: Allison Erfort
Mktg Mgr: Ryan Lujan
Mktg Mgr: Howard Rosner
Board of Directors: Norman C Epstein, Gary P Fayard, Mark J Hall, Benjamin M Polk, Sydney Selati, Harold C Taber Jr, Mark S Vidergauz, Kathy N Waller

D-U-N-S 07-992-4394
▲ MONSTER BEVERAGE CORP
1 Monster Way, Corona, CA 92879-7101
Tel (951) 739-6200 *Founded/Ownrshp* 1985
Sales 2.7MMM *EMP* 2,214^E
Tkr Sym MNST *Exch* NGS
SIC 2086 Bottled & canned soft drinks; Carbonated beverages, nonalcoholic: bottled & canned
Ch Bd: Rodney C Sacks
**V Ch:* Hilton H Schlosberg
Ofcr: Mark J Hall
Sr VP: Thomas J Kelly
VP: Alan Clark
VP: Marc De Beffort
Board of Directors: Norman C Epstein, Gary P Fayard, Mark J Hall, Benjamin M Polk, Sydney Selati, Harold C Taber Jr, Mark S Vidergauz, Kathy N Waller

D-U-N-S 79-310-6956 EXP
■ MONSTER ENERGY CO
(*Suby of* MONSTER BEVERAGE 1990 CORP) ★
1 Monster Way, Corona, CA 92879-7101
Tel (951) 739-6200 *Founded/Ownrshp* 1992
Sales 1.0MMM^E *EMP* 1,000^E
SIC 5149 Juices; Soft drinks
CEO: Rodney C Sacks
Pr: Ray La Rue
**V Ch Bd:* Hilton H Scholsberg
Sr VP: Gareth Bowen
VP: John Beasley
VP: Michael A Cucchiara
VP: Paul Dechary
VP: Steve Edgar
VP: Rich Frediani
VP: Greg Hall
VP: Heidi Hand
VP: Ron Kane
VP: Tom Kelly
VP: Carl Willis
Exec: Kristen Purdy

D-U-N-S 08-452-9171 IMP/EXP
MONSTER INC
MONSTER PRODUCTS
455 Valley Dr, Brisbane, CA 94005-1209
Tel (415) 840-2000 *Founded/Ownrshp* 1978
Sales 290.3MM^E *EMP* 700
SIC 5099 4841 3679 Video & audio equipment; Cable & other pay television services; Headphones, radio
CEO: Noel Lee
COO: Nora Considine
CFO: Leo Lin
**VP:* Irene Baron
VP: Chaka Zulu
Creative D: Leeroy Francisco
VP Opers: David Tognotti
Natl Sales: Eliana Robleto
Mktg Mgr: Ryan Chennault

MONSTER PRODUCTS
See MONSTER INC

D-U-N-S 05-047-1754
MONSTER WORLDWIDE INC
(*Suby of* RANDSTAD NORTH AMERICA INC) ★
133 Boston Post Rd, Weston, MA 02493-2525
Tel (978) 461-8000 *Founded/Ownrshp* 2016
Sales 666.9MM *EMP* 3,700
Accts Bdo Usa Llp New York New Yo
SIC 7311 7361 Advertising agencies; Employment agencies
CEO: Mark Stoever
Ofcr: Patrick W Manzo
Ex VP: Andrea Bertone
Ex VP: Mark Conway

Ex VP: Steven M Cooker
Ex VP: Paul Forte
Ex VP: Michael C Miller
Ex VP: Kimberly Mullaney
Ex VP: Matthew Mund
Sr VP: Phillip Bond
Sr VP: Jeffrey Fleischman
Sr VP: Susan J Hayden
Sr VP: Kathy Paladino
Sr VP: Linda Soldatos

D-U-N-S 02-151-3820 IMP/EXP
MONTACHEM INTERNATIONAL INC
200 S Andrews Ave Ste 702, Fort Lauderdale, FL 33301-2066
Tel (954) 385-9908 *Founded/Ownrshp* 2004
Sales 186.6MM[E] *EMP* 41
SIC 5169 Synthetic resins, rubber & plastic materials
CEO: Murcia Jerry
**Pr:* Liston Steve
**Treas:* Valentina Webel
**Prin:* Steven Liston
**Genl Mgr:* Juan Carlos Avila

D-U-N-S 12-285-5120
MONTAGE HOTELS & RESORTS LLC
MONTAGE LAGUNA BEACH
1 Ada Ste 250, Irvine, CA 92618-5340
Tel (949) 715-5002 *Founded/Ownrshp* 2002
Sales 430.9MM[E] *EMP* 1,770
SIC 6531 Real estate managers
CEO: Alan Fuerstman
**Pr:* Jason Herthel
**VP:* Iqbal Bashir
**VP:* James D Bermingham
**VP:* Bill Claypool
**VP:* Monica Digilio
VP: Edgar Gasparyan
**VP:* Greg Villeneuve
Exec: Yolanda Jimenez
Mng Dir: Rick Riess
Dir Sec: Chad Pohle

MONTAGE LAGUNA BEACH
See MONTAGE HOTELS & RESORTS LLC

D-U-N-S 94-962-6444
MONTANA DEPARTMENT OF PUBLIC HEALTH AND HUMAN SERVICES
(*Suby of* EXECUTIVE OFFICE OF STATE OF MONTANA) ★
111 N Sanders St Rm 6, Helena, MT 59601-4520
Tel (406) 444-4228 *Founded/Ownrshp* 1930
Sales NA *EMP* 2,900
SIC 9431

D-U-N-S 80-979-1320
MONTANA DEPARTMENT OF TRANSPORTATION
(*Suby of* EXECUTIVE OFFICE OF STATE OF MONTANA) ★
2701 Prospect Ave, Helena, MT 59601-9746
Tel (406) 444-6201 *Founded/Ownrshp* 1991
Sales NA *EMP* 1,725
SIC 9621 Regulation, administration of transportation;
Comm Dir: Casey Kyler-West
Prgrm Mgr: Alice Flesch
Prgrm Mgr: Kathy Terrio
Off Mgr: Larry Murolo

D-U-N-S 80-958-8726
MONTANA DEPT OF JUSTICE
(*Suby of* EXECUTIVE OFFICE OF STATE OF MONTANA) ★
215 N Sanders St, Helena, MT 59601-4522
Tel (406) 444-2026 *Founded/Ownrshp* 2000
Sales NA *EMP* 1,124
SIC 9222 Attorney General's office;
Prin: Mike McGrath
Plnt Mgr: CT Reap
**Counsel:* Chris Tweeten

D-U-N-S 18-063-0378
MONTANA RAIL LINK INC
M R L
101 International Dr, Missoula, MT 59808-1598
Tel (406) 523-1500 *Founded/Ownrshp* 2015
Sales 132.8MM[E] *EMP* 1,150
SIC 4011 Railroads, line-haul operating
Pr: Tom Walsh
Bd of Dir: Rick Shelley
VP: David Koerner
Exec: Clint Hammer
Genl Mgr: Michelle Watt
Telecom Ex: Trish Anderson
CTO: Steve Larance
Sls Dir: Jim Lewis

D-U-N-S 07-884-8042
MONTANA STATE FUND
855 Front St, Helena, MT 59601-3842
Tel (406) 444-6500 *Founded/Ownrshp* 1990
Sales NA *EMP* 287
SIC 6331 Workers' compensation insurance
Pr: Laurence Hubbard
Snr Sftwr: Darren Munson
CIO: Maura Fleetwood
CTO: Pam Byers

MONTANA STATE UNIV - BOZEMAN
See MONTANA STATE UNIVERSITY INC

D-U-N-S 06-556-9048 IMP
MONTANA STATE UNIVERSITY INC
MONTANA STATE UNIV - BOZEMAN
(*Suby of* MONTANA UNIVERSITY SYSTEM) ★
901 W Garfield St, Bozeman, MT 59717
Tel (406) 994-4361 *Founded/Ownrshp* 1893
Sales 349.6MM *EMP* 2,500[E]
Accts Cindy Jorgenson Cpa Helena
SIC 8221 University
Pr: Waded Cruzado
**Treas:* Laura Humberger
Top Exec: Christopher Jenkins
VP: Brittany Nickolay
VP: Craig Oloff

D-U-N-S 07-971-3608
MONTANA STATE UNIVERSITY-BILLINGS (MT)
CITY COLLEGE
(*Suby of* MONTANA STATE UNIV - BOZEMAN) ★
1500 University Dr, Billings, MT 59101-0245
Tel (406) 657-2011 *Founded/Ownrshp* 1927
Sales 35.4MM *EMP* 1,109
Accts Cindy Jorgensen Helena Mt
SIC 4832 5942 8221 Radio broadcasting stations; Book stores; Colleges & universities
Pr: Tim Schruth
**Treas:* Curt Starr
**VP:* Bobby Anner-Hughes
**Prin:* Dean John Cech
Sfty Mgr: Patrick Schenck
Psych: Doxey Hatch
Psych: Judith McLaughlin
Psych: Matthew McMullen

D-U-N-S 07-960-2596
MONTANA UNIVERSITY SYSTEM (MT)
2500 E Broadway St, Helena, MT 59601-4901
Tel (406) 444-6570 *Founded/Ownrshp* 1994
Sales 544.6MM[E] *EMP* 2,500[E]
SIC 8221 University
Assoc Dir: Mary Lachenbruch
Nrsg Dir: Sandra Sacry

D-U-N-S 94-868-6894 IMP
MONTAPLAST OF NORTH AMERICA INC
(*Suby of* MONTAPLAST GESELLSCHAFT MIT BESCHRANKTER HAFTUNG)
2011 Hoover Blvd, Frankfort, KY 40601-8213
Tel (502) 695-7766 *Founded/Ownrshp* 1992
Sales 91.1MM[E] *EMP* 284[E]
SIC 3714 3089 Motor vehicle parts & accessories; Plastic processing
Pr: Christian A Stulz
**CFO:* Holger Ramcke
VP: Dave Burnett
VP: Karlheinz Poehlmann
VP: Sanford Roth
**Prin:* Albert Stulz Jr
Prgrm Mgr: Randy Boehm
Prgrm Mgr: Pat Herman
Prgrm Mgr: Derek Johnson
Genl Mgr: Oliver Dahl
QC Dir: Tom Nimrick
Board of Directors: John Phillips

D-U-N-S 04-073-1119
MONTCLAIR BOARD OF EDUCATION (INC)
22 Valley Rd, Montclair, NJ 07042-2709
Tel (973) 509-4000 *Founded/Ownrshp* 1890
Sales 101.7MM *EMP* 1,100
SIC 8211 School board
Pr: Jessica Dekoninck
VP: Wilford Adkins
IT Man: Abagale Adams
IT Man: Samantha Morra

D-U-N-S 83-854-9392
MONTCLAIR HOTELS MB LLC
6600 Mannheim Rd, Rosemont, IL 60018-3625
Tel (847) 457-3900 *Founded/Ownrshp* 1995
Sales 32.0MM[E] *EMP* 1,500
SIC 7011 Hotels & motels

D-U-N-S 07-979-9162
MONTCLAIR PUBLIC SCHOOLS
22 Valley Rd, Montclair, NJ 07042-2709
Tel (973) 509-4000 *Founded/Ownrshp* 2015
Sales 13.4MM[E] *EMP* 1,176[E]
SIC 8211 Public elementary & secondary schools
Bd of Dir: Eve Robinson
Teacher Pr: Felice H Crawford

D-U-N-S 05-350-6184 IMP
MONTCLAIR STATE UNIVERSITY
825 8th Ave Fl 14, New York, NY 10019-7416
Tel (973) 655-4000 *Founded/Ownrshp* 1908
Sales 280.3MM *EMP* 2,000
Accts O Connonr Davies Llp Paramus
SIC 8221 University
Ch: George Hiltzik
**Pr:* Susan Cole
**V Ch Bd:* Dougla Kennedy
Ex VP: James Wassel
**VP:* Willard Gingerich
Ex Dir: Julie Adams
Prd Mgr: Jeffrey Rosolen
Psych: Doris V Reavis

MONTE CARLO HOTEL AND CASINO
See VICTORIA PARTNERS

MONTEBELLO COMMUNITY DAY SCHL
See MONTEBELLO UNIFIED SCHOOL DISTRICT PROTECTIVE LEAGUE

D-U-N-S 07-694-9197
MONTEBELLO UNIFIED SCHOOL DISTRICT PROTECTIVE LEAGUE
MONTEBELLO COMMUNITY DAY SCHL
123 S Montebello Blvd, Montebello, CA 90640-4729
Tel (323) 887-7900 *Founded/Ownrshp* 1933
Sales 296.9MM *EMP* 4,000
Accts Vasquez & Company Llp Los Ang
SIC 8211 Public senior high school; Public junior high school
CEO: Howard Stuckey Commander
**Pr:* David Bela
**Pr:* Edwin Chau
Genl Mgr: Kim Tran
Off Admin: Dorene Carrillo
Off Admin: Martha Gallegos
Off Admin: Renata Hernandez
Off Admin: Leticia Jimenez
Off Admin: Vanessa Munoz
Off Admin: Liya Yang
CIO: Bob Geiger

MONTEBELLO WELLNESS CENTER
See OAKBEND MEDICAL CENTER

D-U-N-S 00-492-9288 IMP/EXP
MONTEBIANCO USA LLC (FL)
(*Suby of* MONTEBIANCO SPA)
2315 Nw 107th Ave Ste 75, Doral, FL 33172-2132
Tel (305) 597-8248 *Founded/Ownrshp* 2001
Sales 300.0MM *EMP* 5
SIC 5143 Dairy products, except dried or canned; Frozen dairy desserts

D-U-N-S 78-877-6685
MONTEFIORE HEALTH SYSTEM INC
MONTIFIORE NORTH MEDICAL CTR
555 S Broadway, Tarrytown, NY 10591-6301
Tel (718) 920-8239 *Founded/Ownrshp* 2004
Sales 4.1MM *EMP* 13,295[E]
Accts Ernst & Young Us Llp New York
SIC 8062 General medical & surgical hospitals
Pr: Steven M Safyer
**CFO:* Colleen M Blye
**CFO:* Philip O Ozuah
**Ex VP:* Joel A Perlman
**Sr VP:* Alfredo Cabrera
**Sr VP:* Richard T Celiberti
Pathlgst: Lucia Wolgast
Obsttrcn: Cassandra E Henderson
Obsttrcn: Kristin Patzkowsky
Ansthlgy: Shafiq A Bazaz
Podiatrist: Bijou M Dennis-Nfor

D-U-N-S 04-158-1026 IMP
MONTEFIORE MEDICAL CENTER
111 E 210th St, Bronx, NY 10467-2401
Tel (718) 920-4321 *Founded/Ownrshp* 1884
Sales 2.5MMM *EMP* 11,000
SIC 8062 General medical & surgical hospitals
CEO: Steven M Safyer MD
COO: Susan Green
**COO:* Philip O Ozuah
**CFO:* Joel A Perlman
Treas: Tammi Reel
Ofcr: Kristin Wller-Donovan
**Sr VP:* Alfredo Cabrera
Sr VP: Andrew D Racine
**Sr VP:* Lynn Richmond
VP: Marjory Karlin
VP: Joanne Ritter-Teitel
Assoc Dir: Ronald Walsh
Comm Dir: Stephen Stafford

D-U-N-S 07-923-0105
MONTEFIORE NEW ROCHELLE HOSPITAL
(*Suby of* MONTEFIORE MEDICAL CENTER) ★
16 Guion Pl, New Rochelle, NY 10801-5502
Tel (914) 632-5000 *Founded/Ownrshp* 2013
Sales 124.6MM[E] *EMP* 1,200[E]
SIC 8062 General medical & surgical hospitals
Pr: Steven M Safyer
**COO:* Philip O Ozuah
**CFO:* Joel A Perlman

D-U-N-S 07-499-7545
MONTEFIORE UNIVERSITY HOSPITAL
(*Suby of* UPMC HEALTH BENEFITS) ★
3459 5th Ave, Pittsburgh, PA 15213-3236
Tel (412) 647-2345 *Founded/Ownrshp* 1990
Sales 247.3MM[E] *EMP* 1,500
SIC 8062 General medical & surgical hospitals
Pr: Jeffrey A Romoff
CFO: Robert Demichiei
Doctor: T C Gamblin MD

MONTENAY POWER
See VEOLIA ES WASTE-TO-ENERGY INC

MONTEREY BOATS
See SEABRING MARINE INDUSTRIES INC

MONTEREY HOMES
See MERITAGE HOMES OF FLORIDA INC

D-U-N-S 08-859-5186 IMP
MONTEREY MUSHROOMS INC
260 Westgate Dr, Watsonville, CA 95076-2452
Tel (831) 763-5300 *Founded/Ownrshp* 1988
Sales 759.8MM[E] *EMP* 3,500
SIC 0182 Mushrooms grown under cover
Pr: Shah Kazemi
**CFO:* Robert V Jenkins
VP: Joe Caldwell
VP: Michael O'Brien
Exec: Terry Marler
Exec: Edward Stoll
Genl Mgr: Wayne Bautista
CTO: Laurie Heath
IT Man: Michael Matelli
IT Man: David Reed

D-U-N-S 07-718-6302
MONTEREY PENINSULA UNIFIED SCHOOL DISTRICT
700 Pacific St, Monterey, CA 93940-2815
Tel (831) 392-3915 *Founded/Ownrshp* 1933
Sales 60.2MM[E] *EMP* 1,400
SIC 8211 Public elementary & secondary schools
Trst: Bettye Lusk
Dir IT: Gerardo Z Ceja
Dir IT: Antonio Navarro
Site Mgr: Sylvia Covarrubias
Site Mgr: Amanda Newman
Site Mgr: Paya Vang
Pr Dir: Marci McFadden
Pgrm Dir: Robin McCall

MONTERREY THE NATURAL CHOICE
See MPCI HOLDINGS INC

D-U-N-S 15-839-0158
MONTERREY SECURITY CONSULTANTS INC
2232 S Blue Island Ave, Chicago, IL 60608-4412
Tel (773) 843-0434 *Founded/Ownrshp* 1999
Sales 98.4MM[E] *EMP* 1,150
SIC 8742 Management consulting services
Pr: Juan Gaytan
COO: Anthony G Casa
Dir Sec: Daniel Ramos
Secur Mgr: Mitch Cohen

MONTGMERY HOSP PHYSCN RFERRALS
See MONTGOMERY HOSPITAL

D-U-N-S 08-000-0273
MONTGOMERY CAPITAL INC
7111 Valley Green Rd, Fort Washington, PA 19034-2207
Tel (877) 836-8300 *Founded/Ownrshp* 1999
Sales 109.1MM[E] *EMP* 295[E]
SIC 8322 Settlement house
Ch Bd: Alan Beurger
**Pr:* Constance Beurger
VP: Reid Beurger

D-U-N-S 07-482-0978
MONTGOMERY COLLEGE
MONTGOMERY COMMUNITY COLLEGE
900 Hungerford Dr, Rockville, MD 20850-1728
Tel (240) 567-5000 *Founded/Ownrshp* 1982
Sales 91.6MM *EMP* 3,600
Accts Cliftonlarsonallen Llp Balti
SIC 8222 Community college
Pr: Derionne Pollard
**Sr VP:* Janet Wormack
Genl Mgr: Patrick Johnson
Pgrm Dir: Liliana Arango
Snr Mgr: Michelle Santiago

MONTGOMERY COMMUNITY COLLEGE
See MONTGOMERY COLLEGE

MONTGOMERY COUNTY BD EDUCATN
See MONTGOMERY PUBLIC SCHOOLS

D-U-N-S 06-988-6679
MONTGOMERY COUNTY COMMUNITY COLLEGE
MCCC
340 Dekalb Pike, Blue Bell, PA 19422-1412
Tel (215) 641-6300 *Founded/Ownrshp* 1964
Sales 3.3MM *EMP* 2,000[E]
SIC 8222

D-U-N-S 07-482-1505 EXP
MONTGOMERY COUNTY PUBLIC SCHOOLS
MCPS
850 Hungerford Dr Rm 149, Rockville, MD 20850-1718
Tel (301) 279-3617 *Founded/Ownrshp* 1858
Sales 2.6MMM *EMP* 11,500
SIC 8211

D-U-N-S 61-723-2236
MONTGOMERY COUNTY PUBLIC SCHOOLS
850 Hungerford Dr, Rockville, MD 20850-1718
Tel (301) 517-5099 *Founded/Ownrshp* 1998
Sales 1.3MM *EMP* 1,900[E]
SIC 8621 8741 Education & teacher association; Management services

D-U-N-S 94-321-5830
MONTGOMERY COUNTY PUBLIC SCHOOLS
750 Imperial St, Christiansburg, VA 24073-5309
Tel (540) 382-5100 *Founded/Ownrshp* 1929
Sales 101.8MM[E] *EMP* 1,700[E]
SIC 8211 Public elementary & secondary schools
Bd of Dir: Penny Franklin
Bd of Dir: Wendell Jones
Prgrm Mgr: Larry Lowe
Off Mgr: Lisa Radford
MIS Dir: Harvey Goodwin
Netwrk Eng: Nelson Gravely
Pr Dir: Brenda Drake
Teacher Pr: Joe Makolandra
Teacher Pr: Roberta Snelling
Psych: Kathleen Decker
HC Dir: Joni Underwood

D-U-N-S 07-780-6669 IMP
MONTGOMERY GENERAL HOSPITAL INC
MEDSTAR HEALTH VNA
(*Suby of* MEDSTAR HEALTH VNA) ★
18101 Prince Philip Dr, Olney, MD 20832-1512
Tel (301) 774-8882 *Founded/Ownrshp* 1984
Sales 147.5MM *EMP* 1,500
Accts Kpmg Llp Mc Lean Va
SIC 8062 General medical & surgical hospitals
Pr: Peter W Monge
COO: Robert Gancayco
COO: Frederick Guckes
COO: Adele Henderson
COO: Michelle Kosci
COO: Samuel Maller
COO: Curtis Ollayos
CFO: David Havrilla
Sr VP: Kiersten Henry
VP: Roger Leonard
VP: Kevin Mell
VP: Harold Pickett
VP: Betty Anne Secrist
VP: Connie Stone
VP: Linda Winger
Exec: Karen Hardart
Exec: Owen Horne
Exec: Rong Huang
Exec: Julia Kariya
Exec: Alberto Rotsztain
Exec: Annemarie Steetin

D-U-N-S 07-365-8981
MONTGOMERY HOSPITAL
MONTGOMERY HOSP PHYSCN RFERRALS
(*Suby of* ALBERT EINSTEIN HEALTHCARE NETWORK) ★
559 W Germantown Pike, East Norriton, PA 19403-4250
Tel (215) 456-7890 *Founded/Ownrshp* 1874
Sales 64.4MM[E] *EMP* 1,200[E]
SIC 8062 General medical & surgical hospitals; Hospital, affiliated with AMA residency
Pr: Tim Casey
Dir Lab: Paul Belser

MONTGOMERY IRON & METAL
See SABEL STEEL SERVICE INC

MONTGOMERY MEDICAL EQUIPMENT
See QMES LLC

D-U-N-S 08-206-5442
MONTGOMERY PUBLIC SCHOOLS
MONTGOMERY COUNTY BD EDUCATN
307 S Decatur St, Montgomery, AL 36104-4305
Tel (334) 223-6873 *Founded/Ownrshp* 1910
Sales 197.8MM^E *EMP* 4,500
SIC 8211 Public elementary & secondary schools
Ex VP: Anna Willis
VP: Carol Doucet
**Prin:* Gary Adams
**Prin:* Ronald Glover
**Prin:* Michael Lenhart
**Prin:* Deborah Thomas
Genl Mgr: Carlinda Percell
Dir IT: Drew Douglas
Dir IT: Gaynelle Harris-Jackson
IT Man: Ron Glover
IT Man: Vance Mason

D-U-N-S 09-355-8864 IMP
■ **MONTGOMERY REGIONAL HOSPITAL INC**
COLUMBIA HCA
(*Suby of* HOSPITAL COPORATION OF AMERICA) ★
3700 S Main St, Blacksburg, VA 24060-7081
Tel (540) 951-1111 *Founded/Ownrshp* 1995
Sales 99.3MM *EMP* 437
SIC 8062 General medical & surgical hospitals
CEO: Scott Hill
**Pr:* Samuel N Hazen
**Sr VP:* Donald W Stinnett
**VP:* David G Anderson
VP: Gege Beall
**VP:* Dora A Blackwood
**VP:* John M Franck II
CTO: Maggie Ratcliff
IT Man: George Snyder
Obsttrcn: Robert J Young
Doctor: Edwin J Wilder MD

MONTIFIORE NORTH MEDICAL CTR
See MONTEFIORE HEALTH SYSTEM INC

MONTPELIER STEELWORKS
See SSAB IOWA INC

MONTRAIL
See MOUNTAIN HARDWEAR INC

D-U-N-S 01-063-3667
MONTROSE MEMORIAL HOSPITAL INC
800 S 3rd St, Montrose, CO 81401-4212
Tel (970) 249-2211 *Founded/Ownrshp* 1951
Sales 84.8MM *EMP* 514
SIC 8062 8011 General medical & surgical hospitals; Offices & clinics of medical doctors
CEO: Dave Hample
CFO: Connie Pruitt
VP: Patricia Dickinson
VP: Burt Hatter
Pathlgst: Nicholas Radovich

D-U-N-S 00-966-4247 IMP/EXP
MONUMENT CHEMICAL KENTUCKY LLC
2450 Olin Rd, Brandenburg, KY 40108-9508
Tel (270) 422-2101 *Founded/Ownrshp* 2013
Sales 171.3MM^E *EMP* 182^E
SIC 2911 Fractionation products of crude petroleum, hydrocarbons
IT Man: Kaye Redmon

D-U-N-S 03-207-9105
MONUMENT OIL CO
GO FER FOOD
560 Colorado Ave, Grand Junction, CO 81501-2606
Tel (970) 245-3440 *Founded/Ownrshp* 1963
Sales 94.8MM *EMP* 60
SIC 5172 Diesel fuel; Gasoline
CEO: Cullen R Brown
**Pr:* C Paul Brown

MONUMENTAL SPORTS & ENTRMT
See WASHINGTON SPORTS & ENTERTAINMENT LIMITED PARTNERSHIP

MONUMENTAL SPORTS & ENTRMT
See LINCOLN HOLDINGS LLC

D-U-N-S 04-231-6997
■ **MONY GROUP INC**
(*Suby of* AXA FINANCIAL INC) ★
1740 Broadway Ste 202, New York, NY 10019-4315
Tel (212) 708-2000 *Founded/Ownrshp* 2004
Sales NA *EMP* 2,288
SIC 6411 Insurance agents, brokers & service
CEO: Michael I Roth
Pr: Samuel J Foti
CFO: Richard Daddario
Ex VP: Kenneth M Levine
Sr VP: Bart R Schwartz
VP: Eileen Forrest

D-U-N-S 00-698-7960
MONY LIFE INSURANCE CO (NY)
(*Suby of* PROTECTIVE LIFE INSURANCE CO) ★
1740 Broadway, New York, NY 10019-4315
Tel (800) 487-6669 *Founded/Ownrshp* 1843, 2013
Sales NA *EMP* 1,900
SIC 6411 6321 6211 6282 6531 Insurance agents, brokers & service; Accident insurance carriers; Health insurance carriers; Disability health insurance; Distributors, security; Mutual funds, selling by independent salesperson; Investment advisory service; Manager of mutual funds, contract or fee basis; Real estate managers
Pr: Samuel J Foti
CFO: Richard Daddario
Treas: Tamara Bronson
Ex VP: Kenneth M Levine
Ex VP: Steven G Orluck
Sr VP: Stephen J Hall
Sr VP: Thomas McCahill
Sr VP: Evelyn L Peos
Sr VP: Ernest P Rogers
Sr VP: Bart Schwartz
Sr VP: Michael Slipowitz
Sr VP: Robert O Wright Jr
VP: Debbie Udicious
Board of Directors: Daniel G Kaye, Kristi A Matus

D-U-N-S 07-872-4681
MOOD MEDIA CORP
1703 W 5th St Ste 600, Austin, TX 78703-4894
Tel (800) 345-5000 *Founded/Ownrshp* 2013
Sales 494.0MM *EMP* 2,000^E
SIC 7319 7389 Media buying service; Music & broadcasting services
CEO: Steve Richards
**COO:* Ken Eissing
**CFO:* Dodd Haynes
**Ex VP:* Jim McFelea
Ex VP: Randal Rudniski
**Sr VP:* Trey Courtney
VP: John Sheehan
VP: John Walker
Mng Dir: Mick Bennett
Mktg Dir: Anne Zavorskas
Manager: Maryanne Baker

D-U-N-S 08-508-1268
MOOD MEDIA NORTH AMERICA LIMITED
(*Suby of* MOOD MEDIA CORPORATION)
1703 W 5th St Ste 600, Austin, TX 78703-4894
Tel (512) 380-8500 *Founded/Ownrshp* 2011
Sales 351.5MM^E *EMP* 950
SIC 6794 7389 Franchises, selling or licensing; Music & broadcasting services
CEO: Stephen P Richards
CFO: Dodd Haynes
**CFO:* R Dodd Haynes
Ex VP: Tom Garrett
VP: Troy Cooper
Off Admin: Yvonne Helfer
Mktg Dir: Mike Kelly
Manager: Tony Franklin
Corp Couns: Marshall Eudy

D-U-N-S 00-175-2252 IMP/EXP
MOODY BIBLE INSTITUTE OF CHICAGO (IL)
820 N La Salle Dr, Chicago, IL 60610-3263
Tel (312) 329-4000 *Founded/Ownrshp* 1886
Sales 123.5MM *EMP* 605
Accts Crowe Horwath Llp Chicago Il
SIC 8661 8299 8221 4832 2731 Religious organizations; Bible school; Professional schools; Radio broadcasting stations; Books: publishing only
Pr: Paul Nyquist
Ch Bd: Jerry Jenkins
Pr: Christine Gorz
CFO: Kenneth D Heulitt
CFO: Delmar Mohler
Treas: Eleanor Ehresman
Ex VP: Steven Mogck
VP: Elizabeth Brolon
VP: Elizabeth Brown
VP: Larry Davidhizer
VP: John Jelinek
VP: Colin Lambert
VP: Janet Steven
VP: Gregory Thornton
Dir Soc: Ruth Dinwiddie

D-U-N-S 17-758-6880
MOODY GARDENS INC
PALM BEACH AT MOODY GARDENS
1 Hope Blvd, Galveston, TX 77554-8928
Tel (409) 744-4673 *Founded/Ownrshp* 1986
Sales 103.3MM *EMP* 650
Accts Pannell Kerr Forster Of Texas
SIC 8412 8422 7999 7011 Museum; Arboreta & botanical or zoological gardens; Golf services & professionals; Hotels
Ch: E Douglas McLeod
Pr: Phillip Miller
**Treas:* John Peterson Jr

D-U-N-S 03-418-8052
MOODY-PRICE LLC
18320 Petroleum Dr, Baton Rouge, LA 70809-6123
Tel (225) 751-7001 *Founded/Ownrshp* 1954, 1985
Sales 99.7MM^E *EMP* 90
SIC 5084 Industrial machinery & equipment; Instruments & control equipment
Treas: Danny Daniel Jr
Genl Mgr: Mike Leggett
Dir IT: Kendall Ducote
S&M/VP: Kenneth Lebleu
Sls Dir: Jimmy Sandifer

D-U-N-S 61-964-8199
■ **MOODYS ANALYTICS INC**
(*Suby of* MOODYS CORP) ★
250 Greenwich St 7w, New York, NY 10007-2140
Tel (415) 874-6368 *Founded/Ownrshp* 1994
Sales 277.7MM^E *EMP* 9,900^E
SIC 7323 Credit reporting services
CEO: Mark E Almeida
Treas: Randolph Roy
**Ex VP:* Geoff Fite
VP: Trevor Pijper
Snr Sftwr: Ryan Wibawa
Software D: Andrew Terekhov
Sls Dir: Linda Wong

D-U-N-S 04-997-7473
▲ **MOODYS CORP**
250 Greenwich St, New York, NY 10007-2140
Tel (212) 553-0300 *Founded/Ownrshp* 1900
Sales 3.4MMM *EMP* 10,400^E
Tkr Sym MCO *Exch* NYS
SIC 7323 6282 Credit reporting services; Investment advisory service
Ch Bd: Henry A McKinnell Jr
V Ch: Michel Madelain
Pr: Mark E Almeida
Pr: Ardavan Amini
Pr: Dany Castiglione
Pr: Becky Chen
Pr: John Dunlea
Pr: Liam Gibbon
Pr: Carole Gintz
Pr: Martha Graybow
Pr: Rebekah Irion
Pr: Cristin Jacoby
Pr: Essence Liburd
Pr: Raymond W McDaniel Jr
Pr: Ryan McKillop
Pr: Suzanne Miller
Pr: Oliver Moldenhauer
Pr: Alonso Rosario
Pr: Yuri Sarkisyan
Pr: Heidi Schmid
Pr: Pushkar Suri

D-U-N-S 00-192-2178
■ **MOODYS INVESTORS SERVICE INC**
(*Suby of* MOODYS CORP) ★
250 Greenwich St, New York, NY 10007-2140
Tel (212) 553-0300 *Founded/Ownrshp* 1900, 1962
Sales 127.4MM^E *EMP* 1,950
SIC 7323 Credit reporting services
CEO: Raymond McDaniel
Pr: Betty Ng
COO: Michel Madelain
Treas: Jeff Hare
Chf Mktg O: Sherry Rashkovsky
Ofcr: James Bodovitz
Assoc VP: Sarah Glendon
Sr VP: Alex Altshuler
Sr VP: Kent Becker
Sr VP: James Hempstead
Sr VP: Robert Jankowitz
Sr VP: Algis Remeza
VP: Scott Bosch
VP: Heidi Bridle
VP: Manoj Chadha
VP: Diane Debenedictus
VP: Dennis Gephardt
VP: Jessica Gladstone
VP: John J Goggins
VP: Lisa Heller
VP: Janice Hofferber
Board of Directors: Clifford L Alexander Jr

D-U-N-S 00-210-3166 IMP/EXP
▲ **MOOG INC** (NY)
400 Jamison Rd Plant26, Elma, NY 14059-9497
Tel (716) 652-2000 *Founded/Ownrshp* 1951
Sales 2.4MMM *EMP* 10,691
Tkr Sym MOGA *Exch* NYS
SIC 3812 3492 3625 3769 3728 3841 Aircraft control systems, electronic; Fluid power valves for aircraft; Relays & industrial controls; Actuators, industrial; Guided missile & space vehicle parts & auxiliary equipment; Aircraft parts & equipment; Surgical & medical instruments
Ch Bd: John R Scannell
**CFO:* Donald R Fishback
**V Ch Bd:* Richard A Aubrecht
VP: Joseph Bell
VP: Sasidhar Eranki
VP: Gary A Szakmary
Genl Mgr: Dave Fijas
IT Man: Terry Skelton
Ql Cn Mgr: Bruce Faso
Sls&Mrk Ex: Paul Bement
VP Mktg: Sunil Murthy

MOON MOUNTAIN FARMS
See MOON VALLEY NURSERY INC

D-U-N-S 93-850-8215
MOON VALLEY NURSERY INC
MOON MOUNTAIN FARMS
18047 N Tatum Blvd, Phoenix, AZ 85032-1506
Tel (602) 493-0403 *Founded/Ownrshp* 1995
Sales 237.4MM^E *EMP* 365
SIC 5193 5261 Flowers & florists' supplies; Nurseries
Pr: Les Blake
VP: John Marshall

MOONLIGHT COMPANIES
See MOONLIGHT PACKING CORP

D-U-N-S 84-786-0939
MOONLIGHT PACKING CORP
MOONLIGHT COMPANIES
17719 E Huntsman Ave, Reedley, CA 93654-9205
Tel (559) 638-7799 *Founded/Ownrshp* 1992
Sales 539.7MM^E *EMP* 2,000
SIC 5148 4783 Fruits, fresh; Packing & crating
Pr: Russell Tavlan
**CFO:* Ty Tavlan

D-U-N-S 09-920-8444
MOOR INNOVATIVE TECHNOLOGIES LLC
4812 64th St E, Tacoma, WA 98443-2345
Tel (253) 343-2216 *Founded/Ownrshp* 2000
Sales 100.0MM *EMP* 2^E
SIC 2326 Work uniforms

D-U-N-S 09-546-1141
MOORE & VAN ALLEN PLLC
100 N Tryon St Ste 4700, Charlotte, NC 28202-4003
Tel (704) 331-1000 *Founded/Ownrshp* 1933
Sales 109.7MM^E *EMP* 575
SIC 8111 General practice law office
Pt: W B Hawfield
**Pt:* Hal A Levinson
**Pt:* Peter J McGrath
**Pt:* Randel E Phillips
Ex Dir: Matthew F Gillespie
Mng Dir: Walter S Price
Off Admin: Kay Mangum
Telecom Ex: Marc Suttle
IT Man: Kevin Benjamin
Netwrk Eng: Jeff Elliott
Mktg Mgr: Shelly Hefner

D-U-N-S 00-119-9926 IMP/EXP
MOORE CO (RI)
36 Beach St, Westerly, RI 02891-2771
Tel (401) 596-2816 *Founded/Ownrshp* 1909
Sales 243.1MM^E *EMP* 1,000
Accts Mayer Hoffman Mccann Providen
SIC 2258 2241 3069 3061 2821 Fabric finishing, warp knit; Manmade fiber narrow woven fabrics; Tape, pressure sensitive: rubber; Thread, rubber; Appliance rubber goods (mechanical); Molding compounds, plastics
Pr: Dana Barlow
**Pr:* Alexandra Moore
Treas: Janet Robidoux
VP: Jim Oconnor
Dir IT: Chuck Pease
IT Man: George Watts
Board of Directors: Lee Judd, Nicholas Moore, Peter Moore, Thomas F Moore, James Murphy

D-U-N-S 06-030-6917
MOORE COUNTY BOARD OF EDUCATION
5227 Us 15 501 Hwy, Carthage, NC 28327-8665
Tel (910) 947-2976 *Founded/Ownrshp* 2004
Sales 109.7MM^E *EMP* 415^E
Accts Dixon Hughes Goodman Llp Pine
SIC 8211 Public elementary & secondary schools
Ch: Bruce Cunningham
**VP:* Ed Dennison

D-U-N-S 07-979-8903
MOORE COUNTY SCHOOLS
5277 Hwy 15 501 S, Carthage, NC 28327
Tel (910) 947-2976 *Founded/Ownrshp* 2015
Sales 63.8MM^E *EMP* 1,478^E
SIC 8211 Public elementary & secondary schools

D-U-N-S 02-070-7881
MOORE INDEPENDENT SCHOOL DISTRICT NO 2
MOORE SCHOOL FOOD SERVICE
1500 Se 4th St, Moore, OK 73160-8266
Tel (405) 735-4200 *Founded/Ownrshp* 1908
Sales 106.6MM^E *EMP* 2,000
Accts Sanders Bledsoe & Hewett Cpa
SIC 8211 Public elementary school; Public junior high school; Public senior high school; Specialty education
VP: Pauline Caldwell
Adm Dir: Kerry Cooter
Off Admin: Gina Henry
Mtls Mgr: Heather Azbell
Mtls Mgr: Virginia Shepherd
Board of Directors: Larry Leemaster

D-U-N-S 05-142-0107 EXP
■ **MOORE MEDICAL LLC**
(*Suby of* MCKESSON MEDICAL-SURGICAL INC) ★
1690 New Britain Ave A, Farmington, CT 06032-3361
Tel (860) 826-3600 *Founded/Ownrshp* 1949
Sales 103.2MM^E *EMP* 305
SIC 5047 5122 Medical equipment & supplies; Surgical equipment & supplies; Instruments, surgical & medical; Physician equipment & supplies; Pharmaceuticals
Pr: J Richard Frey
**VP:* Tim Bidwell
VP: Rick Frey
VP Inf Sys: Michelle Solomon
IT Man: Jeff Jakiel
Snr Mgr: Brad Csuka

MOORE REGIONAL HOSPITAL
See FIRSTHEALTH OF CAROLINAS INC

D-U-N-S 07-156-2060
MOORE REGIONAL HOSPITAL
20 Page Dr, Pinehurst, NC 28374-8847
Tel (910) 295-7888 *Founded/Ownrshp* 1929
Sales 468.1MM *EMP* 1,400
SIC 8062 General medical & surgical hospitals
Ch Bd: Walker Morris
**Treas:* Norris L Hodgins Jr

MOORE SCHOOL FOOD SERVICE
See MOORE INDEPENDENT SCHOOL DISTRICT NO 2

D-U-N-S 05-923-5333
MOOREFIELD CONSTRUCTION INC
600 N Tustin Ave Ste 210, Santa Ana, CA 92705-3781
Tel (714) 972-0700 *Founded/Ownrshp* 1957
Sales 112.7MM *EMP* 52
Accts Gelman Llp Santa Ana Califor
SIC 1542 Shopping center construction
CEO: Ann Moorefield
**Pr:* Mike Moorefield
**VP:* Hal Moorefield
Mktg Dir: Fred Stephenson

D-U-N-S 15-121-6371
MOORES ELECTRICAL & MECHANICAL CONSTRUCTION INC
101 Edgewood Ave, Altavista, VA 24517-1051
Tel (434) 369-4374 *Founded/Ownrshp* 1985
Sales 85.1MM *EMP* 275
Accts Shelton & Company Cpas Pc L
SIC 1731 1711 General electrical contractor; Plumbing, heating, air-conditioning contractors
Pr: Dale Moore
**Treas:* Linnie W Barr
**VP:* Michael Booth
**VP:* George J Coleman Jr
VP: Susan Foster
VP: Buzz Layne
**VP:* Troy Shelton
Exec: Fred Huckstep
Dir IT: Alan Adams
Opers Mgr: Bruce Canterbury
Mktg Dir: Barry Herstein

D-U-N-S 15-430-6534
MOORES SERVICE CENTER LLC
82 Winfield Rd, Saint Albans, WV 25177-1558
Tel (304) 722-1175 *Founded/Ownrshp* 1974
Sales 350.4MM *EMP* 4
SIC 7538 General automotive repair shops

D-U-N-S 78-848-8518
■ **MOORESVILLE HOSPITAL MANAGEMENT ASSOCIATES LLC**
LAKENORMAN REGIONAL MED CTR
(*Suby of* HMA) ★
170 Medical Park Rd # 208, Mooresville, NC 28117-8540
Tel (704) 660-4000 *Founded/Ownrshp* 1986
Sales 136.1MM *EMP* 900^E
SIC 8062 General medical & surgical hospitals
CEO: Jill Gibson
**COO:* Todd Dixson
COO: Jaylene Fultz
**CFO:* Jamie Stoner
Sr VP: Glenn Silverman
Dir Sec: Chuck Ball
MIS Dir: Brian Bissonnette
Web Dev: Isabell Spidel
Mktg Dir: Leigh Whitfield
Doctor: Sylvia Whitmire

D-U-N-S 18-385-5089 IMP/EXP
MOORIM USA INC
RAINIER PAPER CO
(*Suby of* MOORIM PAPER CO., LTD.)
3700 Crestwood Pkwy Nw, Duluth, GA 30096-5599
Tel (303) 770-8809 *Founded/Ownrshp* 2007
Sales 170.0MM *EMP* 10
SIC 5111 Printing & writing paper; Printing paper
Pr: Jay Kim

MOPAC
See JBS SOUDERTON INC

MOPEP ENRGY SCHEDULING TAGGING
See MISSOURI JOINT MUNICIPAL ELECTRIC UTILITY COMMISSION

D-U-N-S 05-658-7512 IMP
MOR FURNITURE FOR LESS INC
8996 Miramar Rd Ste 300, San Diego, CA 92126-4463
Tel (858) 547-1616 *Founded/Ownrshp* 1987
Sales 135.6MM^E *EMP* 600
SIC 5712 Furniture stores
CEO: Richard D Haux
**Ch Bd:* Rick Haux Sr
**Pr:* Jeff Haux
Pr: George Meier
Genl Mgr: Jeffrey Allen
Genl Mgr: Derek Riedlinger
Genl Mgr: Nick Wilkin
Dir IT: Jim Sanford
Site Mgr: Jenna Rivera
VP Sls: Harold Linebarger
**S&M/VP:* Robert Kelley

D-U-N-S 13-473-5294
■ **MOR PPM INC**
(*Suby of* EMCOR GROUP INC) ★
1127 S Main St, Society Hill, SC 29593-8990
Tel (843) 378-4700 *Founded/Ownrshp* 2008
Sales 158.5MM^E *EMP* 1,000
SIC 1731 General electrical contractor
Pr: Henry B Moree
**VP:* Hank Moree
**VP:* Bobby L Ollis

D-U-N-S 14-298-0478 IMP
MORADA PRODUCE CO LP
500 N Jack Tone Rd, Stockton, CA 95215-9725
Tel (209) 546-0426 *Founded/Ownrshp* 2003
Sales 57.6MM^E *EMP* 1,500
SIC 0723 Fruit (fresh) packing services; Vegetable packing services
Pt: Henry Foppiano

D-U-N-S 06-620-8398
MORAINE VALLEY COMMUNITY COLLEGE
COMMUNITY COLLEGE DST 524
9000 W College Pkwy, Palos Hills, IL 60465-2478
Tel (708) 974-4300 *Founded/Ownrshp* 1967
Sales 40.0MM *EMP* 1,200
Accts Crowe Horwath Llp Oak Brook
SIC 8222 Community college
CEO: Dr Sylvia Jenkins
IT Man: Jack Lifel
Secur Mgr: John Wagrowski

D-U-N-S 07-884-9062
MORALE WELFARE RECREATION ACTIVITY
MARINE CORPS COMMUNITY SVCS
1401 West Rd, Camp Lejeune, NC 28547-2539
Tel (910) 451-2861 *Founded/Ownrshp* 1989
Sales 71.8MM^E *EMP* 2,500
SIC 5311 5812 8322 7999 9711 Department stores; Eating places; Individual & family services; Recreation center;
Prin: Michael Smith

D-U-N-S 09-548-4572 EXP
■ **MORAN FOODS LLC**
(*Suby of* SUPERVALU HOLDINGS INC) ★
100 Corporate Office Dr, Earth City, MO 63045-1511
Tel (314) 592-9100 *Founded/Ownrshp* 1992
Sales 2.4MMM^E *EMP* 5,000
SIC 5141 5411 Groceries, general line; Grocery stores
Pr: Bill Shaner
Pr: Brian Thiemann
**CFO:* Rob Anderson

D-U-N-S 96-353-6003
MORAVIAN SPRINGS HEALTH CENTER
175 W North St, Nazareth, PA 18064-1410
Tel (610) 746-1000 *Founded/Ownrshp* 2010
Sales 1.3MMM *EMP* 9^E
SIC 8051 Skilled nursing care facilities
Owner: Susan C Drabic

D-U-N-S 19-558-6185 IMP/EXP
MORBARK LLC
8507 S Winn Rd, Winn, MI 48896
Tel (989) 866-2381 *Founded/Ownrshp* 1988
Sales 106.4MM^E *EMP* 414
SIC 3599 3553 3549 3523 Machine shop, jobbing & repair; Woodworking machinery; Metalworking machinery; Farm machinery & equipment
CEO: Dan Ruskin
**Treas:* Debra Lehmann
**VP:* Miland Robinson
**Exec:* Larry H Noch

D-U-N-S 02-145-8018
MORC REHABILITATION SERVICES
16200 19 Mile Rd, Clinton Township, MI 48038-1103
Tel (586) 739-5792 *Founded/Ownrshp* 2001
Sales 198.2MM *EMP* 8
SIC 8322 Rehabilitation services

D-U-N-S 85-926-0317 IMP
■ **MOREDIRECT INC**
CONNECTION
(*Suby of* PC CONNECTION INC) ★
1001 Yamato Rd Ste 200, Boca Raton, FL 33431-4403
Tel (561) 237-3300 *Founded/Ownrshp* 2002
Sales 497.4MM^E *EMP* 316
SIC 5045 7373 7376 Computers; Computer software; Systems software development services; Computer facilities management
Pr: John Thomas
**VP:* Kerri Chiappone
**VP:* Carlos Covarrubias
VP: Sylvia Diamant
VP: Paul Geiss
**VP:* Sylvia Johe
Dir Bus: Kay Childs
Dir Bus: George Hartlein
Genl Mgr: Michael Staal
IT Man: Sigrid Acagua
IT Man: John Madden

D-U-N-S 04-195-7010
MOREHEAD STATE UNIVERSITY
207 Hal Mcdowell, Morehead, KY 40351-1683
Tel (606) 783-2053 *Founded/Ownrshp* 1922
Sales 77.5MM *EMP* 1,200
Accts Dean Doiton Allen Ford Pllc
SIC 8221 University
Pr: Wayne D Andrews
**Assoc VP:* Gary Holeman
Sr VP: Teresa Judd
VP: Brenda Porter

D-U-N-S 07-887-7419
MOREHOUSE BIOENERGY LLC
7070 Carl Rd, Bastrop, LA 71220-6584
Tel (770) 743-4300 *Founded/Ownrshp* 2012
Sales 100.0MM *EMP* 50
SIC 2493 Reconstituted wood products
Treas: Tamara Richards
Board of Directors: Charles Davis

D-U-N-S 07-586-1773
MOREHOUSE COLLEGE (INC)
830 Westview Dr Sw, Atlanta, GA 30314-3776
Tel (404) 681-2800 *Founded/Ownrshp* 1867
Sales 114.3MM *EMP* 700^E
Accts Kpmg Llp Greensboro Nc
SIC 8221 College, except junior
CEO: John Silvanus Wilson Jr
**Pr:* Robert Franklin
COO: Maurice Washington
**CFO:* Shelia B Jacobs
**CFO:* Gwendolyn Sykes
**Treas:* John Whllace
Trst: Garrett Auzenne
Trst: Susan Buffett
Trst: Dawud Crooms
Trst: Chester Davenport
Trst: Michael Garrett
Trst: Walter E Massey
Trst: Phillip H McCall Jr
Trst: Otis Moss
Ofcr: Ralph Johnson
Ofcr: Sheryl Spivey
VP: Andr Bertrand
VP: Nashon Hornsby
VP: Willis B Sheftall Jr
VP: Shytall Willis
VP: Gary Wright

D-U-N-S 10-200-5451
MOREHOUSE SCHOOL OF MEDICINE INC
720 Westview Dr Sw, Atlanta, GA 30310-1458
Tel (404) 752-1500 *Founded/Ownrshp* 1980
Sales 140.5MM *EMP* 700^E
Accts Bdo Usa Llp Atlanta Ga
SIC 8322 8221 Drug abuse counselor, nontreatment; College, except junior
Pr: John E Maupin Jr
Pr: Rajagopala Sridaran
Ofcr: Brian Byars
Ofcr: Lonon Norwood
Ofcr: Howard Rodgers
Ofcr: Daphine Seay
Exec: Saunder Reid
Div/Sub He: Sisi Arango
Prgrm Mgr: Jaques Ellis
Prgrm Mgr: Sheakeena K Lamb
Off Mgr: Demarlo I West

MORENO PETROLEUM
See STURDY OIL CO

D-U-N-S 08-913-9257 IMP
MORENO VALLEY UNIFIED SCHOOL DISTRICT
25634 Alessandro Blvd, Moreno Valley, CA 92553-4916
Tel (951) 571-7500 *Founded/Ownrshp* 1962
Sales 16.4MM *EMP* 3,500
Accts Jeanette L Garcia & Asso Fate
SIC 8211 Public elementary & secondary schools; High school, junior or senior
VP: Cleveland Johnson
Admn Mgr: Tammy Guzzetta
IT Man: Abdul Kamara
Psych: Diane Hansen

D-U-N-S 83-539-8538
■ **MOREQUITY INC**
(*Suby of* SPRINGLEAF FINANCE CORP) ★
7116 Eagle Crest Blvd, Evansville, IN 47715-8152
Tel (800) 345-0187 *Founded/Ownrshp* 1994
Sales NA *EMP* 125
SIC 6162 Mortgage bankers
Pr: George D Roach
Assoc Dir: Darell Pennington

MORET GROUP, THE
See JACQUES MORET INC

D-U-N-S 00-215-4607 IMP
MORETRENCH AMERICAN CORP (NJ)
FREEZ WALL
100 Stickle Ave, Rockaway, NJ 07866-3146
Tel (262) 652-4444 *Founded/Ownrshp* 1911
Sales 130.0MM^E *EMP* 600
SIC 1629

D-U-N-S 16-196-2428 IMP
MOREYS SEAFOOD INTERNATIONAL LLC
742 Decatur Ave N, Minneapolis, MN 55427-4323
Tel (763) 541-0129 *Founded/Ownrshp* 1998
Sales 194.5MM^E *EMP* 400
SIC 5146 2091 Fish, cured; Fish, fresh; Fish, frozen, unpackaged; Seafoods; Fish, smoked; Fish, cured; Fish, pickled; Seafood products: packaged in cans, jars, etc.
Ex VP: Heyman Justin
CIO: Ann Walstrom
Dir IT: Tom Pfluger
VP Mktg: Tracy Wiese
Mktg Dir: Paul Clemensen
Mktg Mgr: Lauren Hesser

D-U-N-S 61-782-5468
MORGAN & MORGAN PA
20 N Orange Ave Ste 1607, Orlando, FL 32801-4645
Tel (407) 420-1414 *Founded/Ownrshp* 1988
Sales 97.2MM^E *EMP* 400
SIC 8111 General practice law office
Pr: John B Morgan
Pr: Mary Graves
Pr: Stacy Smith
**VP:* Scott H Bates
IT Man: David McKeon

D-U-N-S 00-415-5347 IMP
MORGAN ADHESIVES CO LLC
MACTAC
4560 Darrow Rd, Stow, OH 44224-1898
Tel (330) 688-1111 *Founded/Ownrshp* 2014
Sales 657.3MM^E *EMP* 1,600
SIC 2891 3565 2672 2823 Adhesives; Labeling machines, industrial; Adhesive papers, labels or tapes: from purchased material; Cellulosic manmade fibers
Pr: Ed T Laforge
**CFO:* Jerry S Krempa
**VP:* Sheri S Edison
Comm Man: Sandy Syme
Genl Mgr: Clarence Chan
Genl Mgr: Ingrid V Cluyzen
Genl Mgr: Brian Kady
Mktg Mgr: Kim Hensley

D-U-N-S 78-708-5901 IMP
MORGAN ADVANCED CERAMICS INC
M C
(*Suby of* MORGANITE INDUSTRIES INC) ★
2425 Whipple Rd, Hayward, CA 94544-7807
Tel (510) 491-1100 *Founded/Ownrshp* 1991
Sales 84.1MM^E *EMP* 572
SIC 2899 3251 3264

MORGAN ADVANCED MATERIALS
See THERMAL CERAMICS INC

D-U-N-S 80-823-5373
MORGAN BROSUPPLY INC
7559 W Gulf To Lake Hwy, Crystal River, FL 34429-7804
Tel (386) 255-2200 *Founded/Ownrshp* 1980
Sales 91.3MM^E *EMP* 75
SIC 5074 Plumbing & hydronic heating supplies
Pr: Peter Morgan
Sales Exec: Robert Stephenson
Sls Mgr: Richard Formel
Sls Mgr: Sonny Peterson
Sales Asso: Dave Turner

MORGAN CORPORATION
See MORGAN TRUCK BODY LLC

D-U-N-S 05-591-6241
MORGAN CORP (SC)
1800 E Main St, Duncan, SC 29334-9785
Tel (864) 433-8800 *Founded/Ownrshp* 1970
Sales 184.6MM^E *EMP* 508
SIC 1629

D-U-N-S 07-210-5547
MORGAN COUNTY BOARD OF EDUCATION (INC)
302 Fourth Ave, Decatur, AL 35601
Tel (256) 309-2100 *Founded/Ownrshp* 1910
Sales 75.0MM *EMP* 1,000
Accts Ronald L Jones Montgomery A
SIC 8211 School board
Pr: Karen Duke
Prin: William Ellinger
Ex Dir: George Crawford
IT Man: Sharey Adams
HC Dir: Brenda Caudle
Board of Directors: Gary Cobb, Tom Earwood, Kenneth Henson, Kevin Murphy, Carolyn Wallace, Dora Woodard

D-U-N-S 07-839-1318
MORGAN COUNTY SCHOOLS FOUNDATION
235 Highway 67 S, Decatur, AL 35603-5438
Tel (256) 309-2100 *Founded/Ownrshp* 2012
Sales 26.7MM^E *EMP* 1,220^E
SIC 8211 Public elementary & secondary schools
Teacher Pr: Ann Knowlton

D-U-N-S 03-055-6674
MORGAN DISTRIBUTING INC
3425 N 22nd St, Decatur, IL 62526-2107
Tel (217) 877-3570 *Founded/Ownrshp* 1976
Sales 83.3MM *EMP* 67
Accts May Cocagne & King Pc Decat
SIC 5171 Petroleum bulk stations
CEO: Gary R Morgan
**Pr:* Daniel E Butler
**CFO:* Beverly D Evitt
IT Man: Kim Grant
Opers Mgr: Joe Hodge
Manager: Rebekah Miller
Manager: Jim Potthast
Manager: Jeff Wehner
Sls Mgr: Matt Macintosh
Sls Mgr: Beth Medlen

MORGAN FINANCIAL
See WJ BRADLEY MORTGAGE CAPITAL LLC

D-U-N-S 00-638-6809 IMP
MORGAN FOODS INC
90 W Morgan St, Austin, IN 47102-1741
Tel (812) 794-1170 *Founded/Ownrshp* 1901
Sales 204.3MM^E *EMP* 550
SIC 2032 Soups, except seafood: packaged in cans, jars, etc.
Ch Bd: John S Morgan
**VP:* Lawrence M Higdon
Sfty Dirs: Dwayne Bratcher
Sls Mgr: Mike Mullaney

D-U-N-S 78-237-3344 IMP
MORGAN INDUSTRIAL INC
OMEGA MORGAN MACHINERY MOVING
23810 Nw Huffman St, Hillsboro, OR 97124-5987
Tel (503) 647-7474 *Founded/Ownrshp* 1991
Sales 83.1MM^E *EMP* 250^E
SIC 1796 4213 Machine moving & rigging; Machinery dismantling; Heavy machinery transport
CEO: Greg Tansey
**Ch Bd:* Vic Petroff
VP: Troy Tallent
Board of Directors: Erik Krieger, Jeff Morgan, Vic Petroff, Dennis Pixton, Peter Stott

MORGAN LEWIS
See MORGAN LEWIS & BOCKIUS LLP

D-U-N-S 06-886-6292
MORGAN LEWIS & BOCKIUS LLP
(*Suby of* MORGAN LEWIS) ★
1 Market St Ste 500, San Francisco, CA 94105-1306
Tel (415) 393-2000 *Founded/Ownrshp* 2014
Sales 92.7MM^E *EMP* 696
SIC 8111 General practice law office
Pt: Donn Pickett
Pt: Dale Barnes
Pt: Michael Begert
Pt: Charles Crompton
Pt: Anne Deibert
Pt: Debra Fischer
Pt: Matthew Fisher
Pt: David Heilbron
Pt: Stephen Hibbard
Pt: Holly House
Pt: Mary Huser
Pt: Karen Kennard
Pt: Anne Knowles
Pt: James Rockett
Pt: R Raymond Rothman
Pt: Stephen Ryan
Pt: Neil Shapiro
Pt: Cecily Talbert

D-U-N-S 07-695-9279
MORGAN LEWIS & BOCKIUS LLP
MORGAN LEWIS
1701 Market St Ste Con, Philadelphia, PA 19103-2987
Tel (215) 963-5000 *Founded/Ownrshp* 1873
Sales 848.5MM^E *EMP* 3,100
SIC 8111 General practice law office
Ch: Jami Wintz McKeon
Pt: Paul Huey- Burns
Pt: Steven M Cohen
Pt: J Gordon Cooney Jr
Pt: Bonnie L Dixon
Pt: Mark P Edwards
Pt: Brady L Green
Pt: J Pat Heptig
Pt: Stephen A Jannetta
Pt: Thomas P Lemke
Pt: Morgan Lewis
Pt: Edward S Mazurek
Pt: John J McAleese
Pt: Carol Merchasin
Pt: John M Ramsay
Pt: Mari M Shaw
Pt: David A Sirignano
Pt: Lawrence Slattery
Pt: Randall B Sunberg
Pt: Larry L Turner
Pt: Gary B Wilcox

MORGAN MURPHY MEDIA
See TELEVISION WISCONSIN INC

D-U-N-S 13-577-2668 IMP/EXP
MORGAN OLSON LLC
(*Suby of* J B POINDEXTER & CO INC) ★
1801 S Nottawa St, Sturgis, MI 49091-8723
Tel (269) 659-0200 *Founded/Ownrshp* 2003
Sales 228.7MM^E *EMP* 500
SIC 3713 Truck bodies (motor vehicles)
Pr: Michael Ownbey
Pr: Robert Zeaton
**CFO:* Greg Pairitz
VP: David Halladay
VP: Steve Hart
Sfty Dirs: Larry York
Plnt Mgr: Eugene Yoder
Mktg Mgr: Kenn Klein
Manager: Nick Harker
Manager: Jim Killion
Sales Asso: Lauren Roberts

D-U-N-S 06-118-2234
■ **MORGAN SOUTHERN INC** (GA)
(*Suby of* ROADRUNNER TRANSPORTATION SYSTEMS INC) ★
700 Westpark Dr Ste 250, Peachtree City, GA 30269-3554
Tel (404) 366-1345 *Founded/Ownrshp* 1982, 2011
Sales 87.0MM^E *EMP* 350
SIC 4213 Trucking, except local
CEO: Benjamin G Kirkland
**CFO:* Mark Diblasi
**VP:* Jim Morgan
**VP:* Lance Spencer
**VP Sls:* Jeff Hershey

D-U-N-S 10-114-7130
▲ **MORGAN STANLEY**
1585 Broadway, New York, NY 10036-8200
Tel (212) 761-4000 *Founded/Ownrshp* 1924
Sales 37.9MMM *EMP* 56,218
Accts Deloitte & Touche Llp New Yor
Tkr Sym MS *Exch* NYS
SIC 6211 6282 Security brokers & dealers; Investment advice
Ch Bd: James P Gorman
V Ch: Thomas R Nides
COO: James A Rosenthal
COO: Clare Woodman
CFO: Jonathan M Pruzan

Bd of Dir: Larry Ferdig
Ofcr: Jeffrey S Brodsky
Ex VP: Keishi Hotsuki
Ex VP: Jerry Shea
VP: Desiree Ally
VP: Paul Attwater
VP: David Bartoli
VP: Dick Breining
VP: Anthony Brock
VP: Ralph Colo
VP: Lee Corey
VP: Robert Curry
VP: Steven Esposito
VP: Mark Fisher
VP: Richard French
VP: Julie Gulla
Board of Directors: Rayford Wilkins Jr, Erskine B Bowles, Alistair Darling, Thomas H Glocer, Robert H Herz, Klaus Kleinfeld, Dennis M Nally, Donald T Nicolaisen, James W Owens, Perry M Traquina

D-U-N-S 00-698-7879 IMP/EXP
■ MORGAN STANLEY & CO LLC
(*Suby of* MORGAN STANLEY) ★
1585 Broadway, New York, NY 10036-8200
Tel (212) 761-4000 *Founded/Ownrshp* 1935
Sales 10.0MMM^E *EMP* 27,838
SIC 6211 Brokers, security; Dealers, security; Investment bankers
Ch Bd: Richard B Fisher
**Pr:* Peter Karches
**CEO:* James P Gorman
**Treas:* Eileen K Murray
Chf Inves: Edward Kerschner
Sr VP: David Sherman
VP: Mike P Bouros
VP: Angela Di Martino
Ex Dir: Sergio Alvarez-Mena
Ex Dir: Rebecca Doede
Ex Dir: John Grassia

D-U-N-S 36-155-5282
■ MORGAN STANLEY BANK
(*Suby of* STANLEY MORGAN DOMESTIC HOLDINGS INC) ★
680 W 10000 S Fl 2, South Jordan, UT 84095-3970
Tel (212) 761-4000 *Founded/Ownrshp* 1990
Sales NA *EMP* 38^E
SIC 6022 State commercial banks
Ch Bd: James P Gorman
**Pr:* Robert D Myrick
**Prin:* Michael Salmon
Mktg Mgr: Karyn Dobin

D-U-N-S 13-019-8013
■ MORGAN STANLEY CAPITAL GROUP INC
(*Suby of* MORGAN STANLEY) ★
1585 Broadway, New York, NY 10036-8200
Tel (212) 761-4000 *Founded/Ownrshp* 1984
Sales 325.9MM^E *EMP* 749
SIC 6221 Commodity dealers, contracts
Pr: John A Shapiro
Ch Bd: Simon T W Greenshields
VP: Ralph Pellecchio

D-U-N-S 18-337-2721
■ MORGAN STANLEY DEAN WITTER & CO
(*Suby of* MORGAN STANLEY) ★
1585 Broadway Lowr B, New York, NY 10036-8293
Tel (212) 761-4000 *Founded/Ownrshp* 1997
Sales 278.3MM^E *EMP* 4,500
SIC 6211 Brokers, security; Dealers, security
CEO: Phillip Purcell
**Ch Bd:* Richard B Fisher
Ex Dir: Bruce Sandberg

D-U-N-S 17-725-5320
■ MORGAN STANLEY INVESTMENT MANAGEMENT INC
(*Suby of* MORGAN STANLEY) ★
1585 Broadway, New York, NY 10036-8200
Tel (888) 454-3965 *Founded/Ownrshp* 1997
Sales 381.6MM^E *EMP* 870
SIC 6282 Investment advisory service
Ch: Barton Biggs
**Pr:* James M Allwin
**Pr:* Gregory J Fleming
Ex VP: Christina Carroll
Exec: A Smith
Sls Mgr: Kenneth M Deregt

MORGAN STANLEY MORTGAGE
See SAXON CAPITAL INC

D-U-N-S 12-157-0758
■ MORGAN STANLEY MORTGAGE CAPITAL HOLDINGS LLC
(*Suby of* MORGAN STANLEY) ★
1585 Broadway Lowr B, New York, NY 10036-8200
Tel (212) 761-4000 *Founded/Ownrshp* 1997
Sales NA *EMP* 1,627
SIC 6162 Mortgage bankers & correspondents
Prin: Robert Scott
**VP:* James R Gross

D-U-N-S 96-908-3323
■ MORGAN STANLEY SMITH BARNEY HOLDINGS LLC
(*Suby of* MORGAN STANLEY) ★
1585 Broadway, New York, NY 10036-8200
Tel (212) 761-4000 *Founded/Ownrshp* 2009
Sales 968.9MM^E *EMP* 16,044^E
SIC 6211 Security brokers & dealers
Pr: Joseph B Parrish

D-U-N-S 83-261-4502
■ MORGAN STANLEY SMITH BARNEY LLC
(*Suby of* MORGAN STANLEY SMITH BARNEY HOLDINGS LLC) ★
2000 Westchester Ave, Purchase, NY 10577-2530
Tel (914) 225-5510 *Founded/Ownrshp* 2009
Sales 968.7MM^E *EMP* 16,000^E
SIC 6211 Security brokers & dealers
Pr: Gregory Fleming
**CEO:* James P Gorman
**COO:* Jim Rosenthal
**CFO:* Ruth Porat

Chf Inves: Jeffrey M Applegate
VP: Angus Miller
VP: Sarah Tan

D-U-N-S 87-994-1318
MORGAN STATE UNIVERSITY
1700 E Cold Spring Ln, Baltimore, MD 21251-0002
Tel (443) 885-3015 *Founded/Ownrshp* 1970
Sales 100.1MM *EMP* 1,500
Accts Sb & Company Llc Hunt Valley
SIC 8221 University
VP: George I Glenn
VP: Tanya V Rush
VP: Ken Xavier
Prgrm Mgr: Levi Lipscomb
Off Mgr: Patricia Burgess
Off Mgr: Merlyn R Morgan
Off Admin: Chanelle Goods
Off Admin: Wanda Hedgepeth
DP Exec: Joyce Wilkins
IT Man: Duane Jackson

MORGAN TECHNICAL CERAMICS
See CERTECH INC

D-U-N-S 05-845-2814 IMP
MORGAN TIRE & AUTO LLC
TEAM TIRES PLUS
2021 Sunnydale Blvd, Clearwater, FL 33765-1202
Tel (727) 441-3727 *Founded/Ownrshp* 2007
Sales 248.3MM^E *EMP* 6,500
SIC 7539 5531 5014

D-U-N-S 00-236-0485 IMP
MORGAN TRUCK BODY LLC
MORGAN CORPORATION
(*Suby of* J B POINDEXTER & CO INC) ★
111 Morgan Way, Morgantown, PA 19543-7714
Tel (610) 286-5025 *Founded/Ownrshp* 1952, 1990
Sales 242.6MM^E *EMP* 600
SIC 3713 7532 5013 5084 Truck bodies (motor vehicles); Body shop, trucks; Truck parts & accessories; Materials handling machinery
Chf Mktg O: Steve Vajda
VP: Cathy Clark
VP: Lisa Owens
Div/Sub He: Peter Hunt
Genl Mgr: Paul Jarossy
Dir IT: Michael McPhee
IT Man: John Kachel
IT Man: Bill Quillen
VP Opers: Harold E Holm Jr
Sfty Mgr: Doug Sanders
Opers Mgr: Doug Andresko

MORGAN-KELLER CONSTRUCTION
See MORGAN-KELLER INC

D-U-N-S 04-101-4598
MORGAN-KELLER INC
MORGAN-KELLER CONSTRUCTION
70 Thomas Johnson Dr # 200, Frederick, MD 21702-4306
Tel (301) 663-0626 *Founded/Ownrshp* 1981
Sales 116.6MM^E *EMP* 225
SIC 1542 1541 Institutional building construction; Commercial & office building, new construction; Commercial & office building, renovation & repair; Industrial buildings & warehouses; Industrial buildings, new construction
Pr: Bradley C Guyton
**Pr:* Charlie Clark
**Ch:* Gail T Guyton
**Treas:* Joy A Watt
**Ex VP:* Jerry L Bowman
**VP:* Darrell Guyton
**VP:* Karl Morris
VP: Bob Rininger
VP: Joy Watt
VP: Andy Woolard
Genl Mgr: Dina Davis

D-U-N-S 00-893-6460 IMP/EXP
MORGANITE INDUSTRIES INC
(*Suby of* MORGAN ADVANCED MATERIALS PLC)
4000 Westchase Blvd # 170, Raleigh, NC 27607-3971
Tel (919) 821-1253 *Founded/Ownrshp* 1979
Sales 606.2MM^E *EMP* 3,260
SIC 3674 3255 3699 3264 3299 3624 Semiconductors & related devices; Clay refractories; Electrical equipment & supplies; Porcelain electrical supplies; Ceramic fiber; Carbon & graphite products
Pr: Fred Wollman

D-U-N-S 00-446-9771
MORGANS FOODS INC
(*Suby of* APEX RESTAURANT MANAGEMENT INC) ★
4829 Galaxy Pkwy Ste S, Cleveland, OH 44128-5955
Tel (216) 359-9000 *Founded/Ownrshp* 2014
Sales 50.1MM^E *EMP* 1,495
SIC 5812 Fast-food restaurant, chain; Family restaurants; Pizza restaurants
Pr: James J Liguori
**CFO:* Kenneth L Hignett
VP: Ramesh J Gursahaney
VP: Bob McLaughlin
VP: Vincent J Oddi
VP Opers: Ramesh Gursahaney

D-U-N-S 61-910-1608
▲ MORGANS HOTEL GROUP CO
475 10th Ave Fl 11, New York, NY 10018-9716
Tel (212) 277-4100 *Founded/Ownrshp* 2005
Sales 219.9MM *EMP* 2,700^E
Tkr Sym MHGC *Exch* NGM
SIC 7011 Hotels & motels; Hotels
CEO: Richard T Szymanski
**Ch Bd:* Howard M Lorber
COO: Chadi Farhat
Ex VP: Meredith L Deutsch

D-U-N-S 93-189-1725 IMP
MORGANS HOTEL GROUP MANAGEMENT LLC
(*Suby of* MORGANS HOTEL GROUP CO) ★
475 10th Ave Fl 11, New York, NY 10018-9716
Tel (212) 277-4100 *Founded/Ownrshp* 1997
Sales 100.9MM^E *EMP* 2,000
SIC 7011 Hotels

CEO: Jason Kalisman
**CEO:* Michael Gross
Sls Mgr: Taylor Deutsch

D-U-N-S 07-774-8663
MORGANS RESTAURANT OF PENNSYLVANIA INC
KFC
(*Suby of* MORGANS FOODS INC) ★
24200 Chagrin Blvd # 126, Cleveland, OH 44122-5550
Tel (216) 360-7500 *Founded/Ownrshp* 1977
Sales 27.2MM^E *EMP* 1,200
SIC 5812 Fast-food restaurant, chain
Pr: James J Ligouri
**Ch Bd:* Leonard Stein-Sapir
COO: James J Liguori
**CFO:* Kenneth Hignett
**VP:* Ramesh Gursahaney
**VP:* Vincent Oddi

D-U-N-S 08-176-6636 IMP
MORGENTHALER MANAGEMENT PARTNERS VI LLC
MORGENTHALER MGT PARTNERS
50 Public Sq Ste 2700, Cleveland, OH 44113-2236
Tel (216) 416-7500 *Founded/Ownrshp* 1999
Sales 178.6MM^E *EMP* 2,324
SIC 1731 5065 7622 7373 5999 Telephone & telephone equipment installation; Telephone & telegraphic equipment; Communication equipment repair; Local area network (LAN) systems integrator; Telephone & communication equipment
Pr: David T Morgenthaler
Pt: Hank Plain

MORGENTHALER MGT PARTNERS
See MORGENTHALER MANAGEMENT PARTNERS VI LLC

D-U-N-S 00-713-5387 IMP/EXP
MORIDGE MANUFACTURING INC (KS)
GRASS HOPPER COMPANY
105 Old Us Highway 81, Moundridge, KS 67107-7110
Tel (620) 345-6301 *Founded/Ownrshp* 1958
Sales 128.5MM^E *EMP* 290
SIC 3524 3523 Lawnmowers, residential: hand or power; Driers (farm): grain, hay & seed
Pr: E Guyer
**Treas:* Dwayne Guyer
Exec: Donald Moore
Sfty Dirs: Ryan Wiebe

MORINDA BIOACTIVES
See MORINDA HOLDINGS INC

D-U-N-S 16-175-6643
MORINDA BIOACTIVES INC
(*Suby of* MORINDA BIOACTIVES) ★
737 E 1180 S, American Fork, UT 84003-3395
Tel (801) 234-1000 *Founded/Ownrshp* 1997
Sales 138.3MM^E *EMP* 1,150
SIC 6719 Investment holding companies, except banks
Pr: Kerry Asay
Mng Dir: Carl Aure
VP Opers: Joel Neilsen
Plnt Mgr: Larry Knight
Mktg Dir: Adam Olsen
Sls Mgr: Jonathan Hallstrom
Snr Mgr: Julie Seamons
Snr Mgr: John Williams

D-U-N-S 95-792-6140 IMP/EXP
MORINDA HOLDINGS INC
MORINDA BIOACTIVES
737 E 1180 S, American Fork, UT 84003-3395
Tel (801) 234-1000 *Founded/Ownrshp* 1996
Sales 287.1MM^E *EMP* 1,164
SIC 5149 8099 3999 Health foods; Nutrition services; Bleaching & dyeing of sponges
Pr: Kerry O Asay
**Treas:* Randall N Smith
**VP:* Kim S Asay
VP: Kelly Olsen
**VP:* Stephen P Story
Rgnl Mgr: Shane Greer
Plnt Mgr: Larry Knight
Mktg Dir: Bruce Call

D-U-N-S 06-424-2977
MORITZ PARTNERS LP
DISCOUNT MOTORS
2111 N Collins St Ste 323, Arlington, TX 76011-2810
Tel (817) 461-9222 *Founded/Ownrshp* 2002
Sales 94.6MM^E *EMP* 300^E
SIC 5511 Automobiles, new & used

D-U-N-S 11-857-5000
MORLEY BUILDERS INC
BENCHMARK CONTRACTORS
3330 Ocean Park Blvd # 101, Santa Monica, CA 90405-3240
Tel (310) 399-1600 *Founded/Ownrshp* 1984
Sales 166.0MM^E *EMP* 350
SIC 1541 1522 1542 1771

D-U-N-S 07-386-3946
MORLEY COMPANIES INC
MORLEY TRAVEL
1 Morley Plz, Saginaw, MI 48603-1363
Tel (989) 791-2550 *Founded/Ownrshp* 1982
Sales 148.6MM^E *EMP* 1,200
SIC 8742 4724 Marketing consulting services; Travel agencies
CEO: Paul W Furlo
**Ch Bd:* Louis J Furlo Sr
**CFO:* Richard Mott
**VP:* Thomas C Fay
**VP:* Christopher J Furlo
**VP:* Louis J Furlo Jr
**VP:* Robert Reindel
VP: Dale Walk
Prgrm Mgr: Monica Guerra
Prgrm Mgr: Mara Hetzner
Prgrm Mgr: Steve Mulvaney
Board of Directors: John Armstrong, cass Ferris

MORLEY TRAVEL
See MORLEY COMPANIES INC

MORMON HANDICRAFT
See DESERET BOOK CO

MORNING CALL, INC., THE
See MORNING CALL LLC

D-U-N-S 00-239-4666
■ MORNING CALL LLC
MORNING CALL, INC., THE
(*Suby of* TRONC INC) ★
101 N 6th St, Allentown, PA 18101-1480
Tel (610) 820-6500 *Founded/Ownrshp* 1905, 2012
Sales 203.0MM^E *EMP* 878
SIC 2752 2711 Commercial printing, lithographic; Newspapers, publishing & printing

D-U-N-S 00-427-7034 IMP
■ MORNING PRIDE MFG LLC
HONEYWELL FIRST RESPONDER PDTS
(*Suby of* HONEYWELL INTERNATIONAL INC) ★
1 Innovation Ct, Dayton, OH 45414-3967
Tel (937) 264-2662 *Founded/Ownrshp* 2008
Sales 277.7MM^E *EMP* 1,042
SIC 3842 2326 Respirators; Men's & boys' work clothing
Pr: William L Grilliot
Pr: Cathy Black
QA Dir: John Hodac
IT Man: Marcus Grams
IT Man: Ron Stone
Plnt Mgr: Craig Barnes
Sls&Mrk Ex: Gary Mc Evoy
Mktg Mgr: Alechia Brown
Mktg Mgr: Tammy Wells

MORNING STAR
See MANAGEMENT SENIOR LLC MORNINGSTAR

MORNING STAR COMPANY THE
See LIBERTY PACKING CO LLC

MORNING SUN
See BALTIMORE SUN CO

D-U-N-S 12-147-7160
▲ MORNINGSTAR INC
22 W Washington St # 600, Chicago, IL 60602-1607
Tel (312) 696-6000 *Founded/Ownrshp* 1984
Sales 788.8MM *EMP* 3,930^E
Tkr Sym MORN *Exch* NGS
SIC 6282 6722 7375 Investment advice; Management investment, open-end; Money market mutual funds; Information retrieval services; Data base information retrieval; On-line data base information retrieval
Ch Bd: Joe Mansueto
Pr: Kunal Kapoor
Pr: Daniel E Needham
CFO: Stephane Biehler
Chf Mktg O: Rob Pinkerton
Ofcr: James Rhodes
Ex VP: Davide Frattini
VP: Brian Alan
VP: Eric Baker
VP: Greg Beek
VP: Matthew Felix
VP: Adam Grabow
VP: Mike Hogan
VP: Scott Mackenzie
VP: James Mahoney
VP: David Nathanson
VP: Dermot O'Mahony
VP: Vincent Piskorski
VP: Hal Ratner
VP: John Rekenthaler
VP: Celeste Stinson

D-U-N-S 02-329-8912
MOROCH HOLDINGS INC
MOROCH PARTNERS
3625 N Hall St Ste 1100, Dallas, TX 75219-5113
Tel (214) 520-9700 *Founded/Ownrshp* 1981
Sales 114.7MM^E *EMP* 580
SIC 7311 Advertising agencies
Founder: Tom Moroch
Sr Pt: Jim Larivee
Sr Pt: Scott Manning
Sr Pt: Lyndsay Van Brunt
CEO: Rob Boswell
COO: Melinda Yoder
CFO: Laura Keene
Bd of Dir: Jose Ortega
Chf Mktg O: Jack Phifer
Ofcr: Brad B McCormick
VP: Cathy Beath
VP: Julie Bebey
VP: Carol Dodson
VP: Michael Dugat
VP: Chip Gorman
VP: Dustin Taylor
Exec: Joseph Salazar
Exec: Laura Theut
Creative D: Thomas Hripko
Creative D: Ray Sturdivant
Creative D: Kathleen Torres

MOROCH PARTNERS
See MOROCH HOLDINGS INC

D-U-N-S 92-843-4117
MORONGO UNIFIED SCHOOL DISTRICT
PRESCHOOL
5715 Utah Trl, Twentynine Palms, CA 92277-6917
Tel (760) 367-9191 *Founded/Ownrshp* 1914
Sales 73.2MM^E *EMP* 1,000
SIC 8211 Public elementary school
Genl Mgr: Lynn Lee
MIS Dir: Troy Slayden
Sfty Mgr: Donna Wendt
HC Dir: Kathi Papp

D-U-N-S 62-392-4651 IMP
MORPHO DETECTION LLC
(*Suby of* SAFRAN)
7151 Gateway Blvd, Newark, CA 94560-1012
Tel (510) 739-2400 *Founded/Ownrshp* 2014
Sales 376.4MM^E *EMP* 1,009
SIC 3812 Detection apparatus: electronic/magnetic field, light/heat
Pr: Karen Bomba

*Treas: Linda Hildebrant
Ex VP: Brad Buswell
VP: Monty Lutzker
Snr Sftwr: Alexei Kireev
IT Man: Dan Fanucchi
IT Man: Mike Patterson
Software D: Natarajan Subramanian
Sftwr Eng: Clement Lan
Sftwr Eng: Kelly Roosevelt
Mfg Mgr: Vandana Chellani

D-U-N-S 14-855-3712 IMP
MORPHOTRAK LLC
SAFRAN
(Suby of SAFRAN IDENTITY & SECURITY)
5515 E La Palma Ave # 100, Anaheim, CA 92807-2116
Tel (714) 238-2000 Founded/Ownrshp 2014
Sales 108.3MM^E EMP 400
SIC 7373 Computer integrated systems design
CEO: Celeste Thomasson
CFO: Florian Hebras
VP: Clark Nelson
VP: Hieu Tran
Sys Mgr: Stephen Talbert

D-U-N-S 96-905-5321
MORPHOTRUST USA LLC
(Suby of SAFRAN)
296 Concord Rd Ste 300, Billerica, MA 01821-3487
Tel (978) 215-2400 Founded/Ownrshp 1996
Sales 604.9MM EMP 1,100^E
SIC 7374 8711 Data entry service; Electrical or electronic engineering
CEO: Robert Eckel
*Treas: Greg Magoon
Chf Mktg O: Joseph Paresi
*VP: Scott Boylan
VP: Alex Quinonez
Prgrm Mgr: Kevin Brown
Prgrm Mgr: Joel Perez
Snr Sftwr: Tyrone Jones
CIO: John May
Sys Mgr: Gary Chan
Software D: Olga Svet

D-U-N-S 01-742-3997 IMP/EXP
MORRELL INC
3333 Bald Mountain Rd, Auburn Hills, MI 48326-1808
Tel (248) 373-1600 Founded/Ownrshp 1979
Sales 95.6MM^E EMP 325
SIC 5084 5065 3621 3643 3559 3357 Hydraulic systems equipment & supplies; Electronic parts; Motors & generators; Power line cable; Metal finishing equipment for plating, etc.; Nonferrous wiredrawing & insulating
Pr: Steven L Tallman
*VP: James E Cook
Dir IT: Matt Endres
IT Man: Ruthanne Dudley
Sales Exec: Brett Sevon
Mktg Dir: Dawn Hall
Sls Mgr: Ty Huser

D-U-N-S 19-946-8179
MORRELL INTERNATIONAL INC
14901 S Heritagecrest Way, Riverton, UT 84065-4894
Tel (801) 495-3111 Founded/Ownrshp 2005
Sales 106.9MM^E EMP 370
SIC 4213 4226 5039 Trucking, except local; Special warehousing & storage; Structural assemblies, prefabricated: non-wood
CEO: Paul Jeffries
*Ch Bd: Phil Morrell
*CFO: Neil Vos

D-U-N-S 00-521-3772 IMP/EXP
MORRELL JOHN & CO
(Suby of SMITHFIELD FOODS INC) ★
805 E Kemper Rd, Cincinnati, OH 45246-2515
Tel (513) 782-3800 Founded/Ownrshp 1957, 1995
Sales 145.0MM EMP 6,565
SIC 2011 Meat packing plants; Pork products from pork slaughtered on site; Bacon, slab & sliced from meat slaughtered on site; Hams & picnics from meat slaughtered on site
Pr: Joseph B Sebring
VP: Terry Wendt
*Prin: Mark Dorsey
IT Man: Russ Dokken

D-U-N-S 00-799-5079 IMP
MORRIS & DICKSON CO LLC
410 Kay Ln, Shreveport, LA 71115-3611
Tel (318) 797-7900 Founded/Ownrshp 1918
Sales 697.1MM^E EMP 120^E
SIC 5122 Drugs & drug proprietaries
Pr: Markham A Dickson
*VP: C Markham Dickson Jr
CIO: Eileen Ferguson
Mktg Dir: Russell Henry

D-U-N-S 05-730-1764 IMP
MORRIS COMMUNICATIONS CO LLC (GA)
BESTREADGUIDE.COM
(Suby of SHIVERS TRADING & OPERATING CO) ★
725 Broad St, Augusta, GA 30901-1336
Tel (706) 724-0851 Founded/Ownrshp 1970, 2011
Sales 573.0MM^E EMP 2,000
SIC 2711 5199 2721 2731 Newspapers; Newspapers, publishing & printing; Advertising specialties; Periodicals; Books: publishing only
Ch: William S Morris III
*CEO: William S Morris IV
CFO: Trimble Carol
*CFO: Steve K Stone
Sr Cor Off: Raymond Dallman
Sr Cor Off: Amelia Patrie
Ex VP: James Currow
Ex VP: Gay Ketchum
Ex VP: Haines Wilkerson
*Sr VP: Craig S Mitchell
VP: Bob Auhar
VP: Susie Baker
VP: John Bock
VP: Dick Cheney
VP: Frank Denton
VP: Steven R Guchawka
VP: Jeffrey Hartley
*VP: Derek May
VP: Morris May
VP: Martha McHaney
VP: Patti Ruesch

D-U-N-S 01-797-1540 IMP
MORRIS FURNITURE CO INC
MORRIS HOME FURNISHING
2377 Commerce Center Blvd, Fairborn, OH 45324-6377
Tel (937) 874-7100 Founded/Ownrshp 1998
Sales 86.6MM^E EMP 450^E
SIC 5731 5722 5712

D-U-N-S 80-117-7523 IMP
MORRIS GROUP INC
910 Day Hill Rd, Windsor, CT 06095-5727
Tel (860) 687-3300 Founded/Ownrshp 2004
Sales 142.3MM^E EMP 337
SIC 5084 Industrial machinery & equipment
Ch: Lee B Morris
*Pr: Bradley Morris
*CFO: John B Bowen

MORRIS GROUP INTERNATIONAL
See ACORN ENGINEERING CO

D-U-N-S 05-534-4097
MORRIS HOLDINGS INC
SUBWAY
1650 County Road 210 W, Jacksonville, FL 32259-2011
Tel (904) 829-3946 Founded/Ownrshp 1971
Sales 93.3MM EMP 350
Accts Erwin Fountain & Jackson Pa
SIC 5541 5812 5411 Truck stops; Filling stations, gasoline; Eating places; Grocery stores; Convenience stores, independent
Pr: George R Morris
Sls Dir: Geoffrey Willoughby

MORRIS HOME FURNISHING
See MORRIS FURNITURE CO INC

MORRIS HOSP & HEALTHCARE CTRS
See MORRIS HOSPITAL

D-U-N-S 07-559-9308
MORRIS HOSPITAL
MORRIS HOSP & HEALTHCARE CTRS
150 W High St, Morris, IL 60450-1497
Tel (815) 942-2932 Founded/Ownrshp 1906
Sales 137.8MM EMP 525
SIC 8011 8062 Offices & clinics of medical doctors; General medical & surgical hospitals
Pr: Mark Steadham
Dir Recs: Joan Naines
CFO: Kathy Rink
Ofcr: Cassandra Reynolds
VP Bus Dev: Cindy Dupler
Dir Risk M: Linda Petrick
Dir Rad: Liz Bates
Off Mgr: Sandra Pierce
Software D: John Bolden
Plnt Mgr: Byron Gillespie
Pathlgst: Beatriz Setrini

MORRIS MATERIAL HANDLING
See MMH HOLDINGS INC

D-U-N-S 11-551-9188 IMP/EXP
MORRIS MATERIAL HANDLING INC
(Suby of PHMH HOLDING CO) ★
4401 Gateway Blvd, Springfield, OH 45502-9339
Tel (937) 525-5520 Founded/Ownrshp 1998
Sales 135.0MM^E EMP 350
SIC 3625 3443 7699 Crane & hoist controls, including metal mill; Crane hooks, laminated plate; Construction equipment repair
Pr: Tom Sothard
*Treas: Steve Mayes
*VP: Bernard D'Ambrosi Jr
*VP: Keith King
*VP: Steve Kosir
*VP: Kim Sullivan
*Prin: Tom Berringer
IT Man: Doug Weber

D-U-N-S 05-102-9890
MORRIS MULTIMEDIA INC
27 Abercorn St, Savannah, GA 31401-2715
Tel (912) 233-1281 Founded/Ownrshp 1970
Sales 308.1MM^E EMP 1,005
SIC 4833 2752 Television broadcasting stations; Lithographing on metal
Pr: Charles H Morris
COO: Bobby Berry
*VP: Alden M Maier
Dir IT: Charles Joiner

D-U-N-S 07-299-5681
MORRIS MURDOCK LLC
MORRIS MURDOCK TRAVEL
101 S 200 E Ste 100, Salt Lake City, UT 84111-3107
Tel (801) 483-6441 Founded/Ownrshp 2000
Sales 99.0MM EMP 125
SIC 4724 Travel agencies
Pr: Becky Potts
CFO: BJ Mendenhall
VP: Dick Jensen
Exec: Kathy Hirst

MORRIS MURDOCK TRAVEL
See MORRIS MURDOCK LLC

D-U-N-S 10-703-5404 IMP/EXP
MORRIS NATIONAL INC
MCGREEVER AND DANLEE VERY
(Suby of MORRIS NATIONAL INC)
760 N Mckeever Ave, Azusa, CA 91702-2349
Tel (626) 385-2000 Founded/Ownrshp 1950
Sales 193.4MM^E EMP 330
Accts Ernst & Young Llp Toronto C
SIC 5145 5149 Confectionery; Chocolate
CEO: Gerry Morris Zubatoff
*Pr: Gerald Morris
*CFO: David Pistole
VP: Al Herpt
Exec: Alejandra Jaytan

D-U-N-S 14-125-0188
MORRIS PUBLISHING GROUP LLC
(Suby of MPG NEWSPAPER HOLDING LLC) ★
725 Broad St, Augusta, GA 30901-1336
Tel (706) 724-0851 Founded/Ownrshp 2009
Sales 225.2MM EMP 1,722^E
SIC 2711 Newspapers; Newspapers, publishing & printing
Pr: William S Morris IV
CFO: Delinda Fogel
*Treas: Craig S Mitchell
Ex VP: Derek J May
Sr VP: Steve K Stone
VP: James Currow
VP: Robert J Kuhar
Dir IT: Tilden Leigh
Sls Mgr: Lindsay Randall
Board of Directors: William S Morris III

D-U-N-S 00-180-0770 IMP/EXP
MORRIS ROTHENBERG & SON INC (NY)
ROTHCO
3015 Veterans Mem Hwy, Ronkonkoma, NY 11779-7612
Tel (631) 585-9446 Founded/Ownrshp 1953
Sales 98.0MM^E EMP 165
SIC 5199 5091 5139 5136 General merchandise, non-durable; Camping equipment & supplies; Shoes; Men's & boys' clothing
Ch Bd: Milton Somberg
*Pr: Howard Somberg
*CFO: Richard Fleishman
Ofcr: Fran Vecchio
QA Dir: Rocky Lalumia
Dir IT: Anthony Prossi
Mktg Dir: Hans Blechschmidt
Mktg Mgr: Kristy Dineen
Sls Mgr: Chuck Moore
Sls Mgr: Ted Statharos

D-U-N-S 02-459-5951 IMP/EXP
MORRISETTE PAPER CO INC
5925 Summit Ave, Browns Summit, NC 27214-9704
Tel (336) 375-1515 Founded/Ownrshp 1962
Sales 108.0MM EMP 200
Accts Dmj & Co Pllc Greensboro N
SIC 5113 5111 5087 Industrial & personal service paper; Printing & writing paper; Janitors' supplies
*Pr: William Morrisette Jr
*Ex VP: Marie Morrisette Sartin
*VP: Jim Dawson
*VP: Henry B Harwell
Brnch Mgr: Randy Butler
Brnch Mgr: Betsy Futrelle
Brnch Mgr: Rick Gilliam
Off Mgr: Gina Clark
Dir IT: James Cass

D-U-N-S 09-039-3260
MORRISON & FOERSTER LLP
MOFO
425 Market St Fl 30, San Francisco, CA 94105-2482
Tel (415) 268-7000 Founded/Ownrshp 1883
Sales 1.0MMM EMP 2,000
SIC 8111 Legal services
Ch: Larren Nashelsky
Pt: Jay Baris
Pt: Paul T Friedman
Pt: Craig D Martin
Pt: Eric J Piesner
Pt: Tessa J Schwartz
Mng Pt: Eric J Coffill
Mng Pt: Charles C Comey
Mng Pt: David A Gold
Mng Pt: Gregory B Koltun
Mng Pt: Anna White
COO: Pat Cavaney
COO: Patrick Cavaney
COO: Cathy Flight
Bd of Dir: Lmasetti Martin
VP: Reema Abdelhamid

D-U-N-S 00-693-7577
MORRISON CONSTRUCTION CO INC
1834 Summer St, Hammond, IN 46320-2236
Tel (219) 932-5036 Founded/Ownrshp 1925, 1948
Sales 128.2MM^E EMP 300
SIC 1541 Industrial buildings & warehouses
CEO: James M Morrison
*Pr: Daniel Sharpe
*VP: Mark Winter
Exec: Yvonne Goodrich
Div Mgr: Mark Kallay
IT Man: John Ray Jr

D-U-N-S 92-810-0259
MORRISON ENERGY GROUP
16285 Park Ten Pl, Houston, TX 77084-5070
Tel (281) 616-8405 Founded/Ownrshp 2011
Sales 20.6MM^E EMP 1,000
SIC 1389 Oil field services
Pr: Chad Morrison

D-U-N-S 00-656-6376
MORRISON INDUSTRIES INC (MI)
HI-LIFT OF MICHIGAN COMPANY
1825 Monroe Ave Nw, Grand Rapids, MI 49505-6240
Tel (616) 447-3838 Founded/Ownrshp 1953
Sales 101.5MM^E EMP 350
SIC 5084 7699 7359 Materials handling machinery; Compressor repair; Industrial truck rental
CEO: Roger Troost
*Pr: Richard G Morrison
*CEO: Roger Troost
*VP: Dale Monticello

D-U-N-S 93-753-4295
MORRISON MANAGEMENT SPECIALISTS INC
(Suby of EUREST DINING SERVICES) ★
5801 Pachtree Dunwoody Rd, Atlanta, GA 30342-1503
Tel (404) 845-3330 Founded/Ownrshp 2001
Sales 239.3MM^E EMP 4,000
SIC 8099 Nutrition services
CEO: Scott Maclellan
*Pr: Tim Pierce
CFO: Jerry D Underhill
Sr VP: Gary L Gaddy
*Sr VP: Jim Rathburn
*VP: John E Fountain
VP: Chip Kent
VP: Richard Roberson
Exec: Michael Traynor
Genl Mgr: Jon Ramallo
Dir IT: Kia Oneill

D-U-N-S 00-417-2888 EXP
MORRISON PRODUCTS INC
16900 S Waterloo Rd, Cleveland, OH 44110-3895
Tel (216) 486-4000 Founded/Ownrshp 1923
Sales 87.8MM EMP 420
SIC 3564

D-U-N-S 00-792-9938 IMP
MORRISON SUPPLY CO
(Suby of MORSCO INC) ★
311 E Vickery Blvd, Fort Worth, TX 76104-1385
Tel (817) 336-0451 Founded/Ownrshp 1995, 2011
Sales 366.7MM^E EMP 300
SIC 5074 Plumbing & hydronic heating supplies
*Pr: Stan Allen
*CEO: Chip Hornsby
*COO: Kevin Moore
*CFO: Kerry Warren
Bd of Dir: Eddie Brown
VP: Charlie Allen
VP: Ron Bohannon
VP: Dan Filler
VP: Mark Kirby
*VP: Joe Lacik
VP: Phil Osborn

MORRISTOWN MEMORIAL HOSPITAL
See AHS HOSPITAL CORP

MORRISTOWN POWER SYSTEM
See MORRISTOWN UTILITY COMMISSION

D-U-N-S 06-671-7992
MORRISTOWN UTILITY COMMISSION
MORRISTOWN POWER SYSTEM
441 W Main St, Morristown, TN 37814-4615
Tel (423) 317-8845 Founded/Ownrshp 1901
Sales 104.8MM^E EMP 105
Accts Coulter & Justus Pc Knoxville
SIC 4931 Electric & other services combined
CEO: Joseph Wigington
*Ch: George B Mc Guffin
*Sec: Harold Nichols
Genl Mgr: Clark Rucker

D-U-N-S 00-969-4779
MORROW-MEADOWS CORP
CHERRY CITY ELECTRIC
231 Benton Ct, City of Industry, CA 91789-5213
Tel (858) 974-3650 Founded/Ownrshp 1964
Sales 309.9MM^E EMP 1,200
SIC 1731 General electrical contractor
CEO: Karen V Price
*Ch Bd: Elizabeth Meadows
*CFO: Timothy D Langley
*Ch: J Robert Meadows
VP: Bob Atkinson
VP: Gary Deadmon
VP: Rick Jarvis
*VP: Robert E Meadows
VP: Ed Slingluff
Exec: Ken Freeman
Exec: Dan Gleason
Exec: Olivia Scherer
Dir Risk M: Norberto Enriquez
Dir Risk M: Michael Kirley

D-U-N-S 07-991-1315
MORSCO INC
100 E 15th St Ste 200, Fort Worth, TX 76102-6567
Tel (877) 709-2227 Founded/Ownrshp 1917
Sales 386.4MM^E EMP 300^E
SIC 5074 1711 Plumbing & hydronic heating supplies; Plumbing, heating, air-conditioning contractors; Heating & air conditioning contractors
CEO: Chip Hornsby
*CFO: Kerry Warren
*Chf Mktg O: Darren Taylor
VP: Dan Filler
VP: Mark Kirby
*VP: Joe Lacik
VP: Philip K Osborn

D-U-N-S 78-450-8897 IMP
MORSE AUTOMOTIVE CORP
MORSE HEAVY DUTY
750 W Lake Cook Rd # 480, Buffalo Grove, IL 60089-2074
Tel (773) 843-9000 Founded/Ownrshp 1992
Sales 116.2MM^E EMP 1,500
SIC 3714 Motor vehicle brake systems & parts
CEO: Peter Morse
*CFO: Robert Kurasz
CFO: Robert Murasz
Bd of Dir: Joe Delarhim
Bd of Dir: Michael Kuzma
Bd of Dir: Ron Moskal
*Ex VP: Jay McCrory
CIO: John Giardina

D-U-N-S 00-783-4914
MORSE ELECTRIC INC (IL)
500 W South St, Freeport, IL 61032-6836
Tel (815) 266-4200 Founded/Ownrshp 1944, 1977
Sales 95.1MM^E EMP 400
SIC 1731 General electrical contractor
CEO: Donald Morse
*Pr: Lou Rotello
COO: Melissa Crippen
CFO: Janey Morse
*Treas: Brian Scott
*Ex VP: David Morse
Sfty Mgr: Mike Daniel
Opers Mgr: Chuck Sudberry
Mktg Dir: Bill Morrow
Board of Directors: Jane Morse

D-U-N-S 82-947-1312
MORSE GROUP INC
500 W South St, Freeport, IL 61032-6836
Tel (815) 266-4200 Founded/Ownrshp 2007
Sales 112.6MM^E EMP 500
SIC 1731 Electrical work

Pr: Lou Rotello
**Treas:* Brian Scott

MORSE HEAVY DUTY
See MORSE AUTOMOTIVE CORP

D-U-N-S 04-546-6083 EXP
MORSE OPERATIONS INC
ED MORSE AUTOMOTIVE GROUP
2850 S Federal Hwy, Delray Beach, FL 33483-3216
Tel (561) 276-5000 *Founded/Ownrshp* 1960
Sales 1.1MMM *EMP* 1,295
Accts Crowe Horwath Llp Fort Lauder
SIC 5511 Automobiles, new & used
Pr: Edward J Morse
**CEO:* Edward Ted Morse Jr
Ofcr: Craig Davis
**VP:* Elizabeth A Beaver
**VP:* Richard Beaver Sr
**VP:* Carmine Colella
VP: Beaver Richard
Creative D: Scott Reynolds
Web Prj Mg: Vic Parra
MIS Mgr: C Roth
Sls Mgr: Tommy Davis

D-U-N-S 02-127-0269
MORSTAN GENERAL INSURANCE AGENCY INC
GMAC INSURANCE
600 Community Dr, Manhasset, NY 11030-3802
Tel (516) 488-4747 *Founded/Ownrshp* 1980
Sales NA *EMP* 250
SIC 6411

D-U-N-S 06-204-6149 IMP
MORTARA INSTRUMENT INC (WI)
7865 N 86th St, Milwaukee, WI 53224-3431
Tel (414) 354-1600 *Founded/Ownrshp* 1982
Sales 84.8MM^E *EMP* 180^E
SIC 8731 3845 Medical research, commercial; Electrocardiographs
CEO: Justin Mortara
Pr: Maurizio Fumagalli
Pr: Maurizio Fumigalli
**Pr:* David W Mortara
COO: Paul Andress
COO: Frank Schmidt
**CFO:* Brian Brenegan
Sr VP: Chuck Webster
VP: Joe Austin
VP: Merat Bagha
VP: Ted Johnston
VP: Mark Mentzer
VP: Michael Schulz
Exec: Robert G Pierdzioch

MORTENSON CONSTRUCTION
See M A MORTENSON CO

D-U-N-S 07-316-1317 IMP
MORTEX PRODUCTS INC
SUMMIT
501 Terminal Rd, Fort Worth, TX 76106-1954
Tel (817) 624-0820 *Founded/Ownrshp* 1963
Sales 113.1MM^E *EMP* 300
SIC 3585 3433 1711 3999 Parts for heating, cooling & refrigerating equipment; Heating equipment, except electric; Heating & air conditioning contractors; Atomizers, toiletry
CEO: Terrell J Small III
**Pr:* Joe McCorkle
Exec: Michelle Dye

D-U-N-S 10-829-5718
■ **MORTGAGE GUARANTY INSURANCE CORP**
MGIC INVESTMENT
(*Suby of* MGIC INVESTMENT CORP) ★
270 E Kilbourn Ave, Milwaukee, WI 53202-3199
Tel (414) 347-6480 *Founded/Ownrshp* 1985
Sales NA *EMP* 877^E
SIC 6351 Mortgage guarantee insurance
CEO: Curt S Culver
Pr: Chris Burns
**Pr:* Patrick Sinks
CEO: Chuck Wilson
**COO:* Heidi A Heyrman
**CFO:* J Michael Lauer
CFO: Timothy J Mattke
Chf Mktg O: Carolyn Omelina
**Ofcr:* Kurt Thomas
Ex VP: Stephen Mackey
**Ex VP:* Lawrence J Pierzchalski
**Sr VP:* Gregory CHI
Sr VP: Sean Dilweg
**Sr VP:* Jeffrey H Lane
VP: Gail Andrich
VP: Gary Antonovich
VP: Mark Conrad
VP: Geoffrey Cooper
VP: Stephen M Dempsey
VP: Sandra Dunst
VP: Ted Durant
Board of Directors: C Edward Chaplin

D-U-N-S 14-995-4224
■ **MORTGAGE GUARANTY REINSURANCE CORP**
(*Suby of* MGIC INVESTMENT CORP) ★
250 E Kilbourn Ave 270, Milwaukee, WI 53202-3102
Tel (414) 347-6480 *Founded/Ownrshp* 1985
Sales NA *EMP* 1,093
SIC 6351 Mortgage guarantee insurance
CEO: Curt Culver
Mktg Mgr: Kyle Bensen

D-U-N-S 78-675-2048
MORTGAGE INFORMATION SERVICES INC
4877 Galaxy Pkwy Ste I, Cleveland, OH 44128-5952
Tel (216) 514-7480 *Founded/Ownrshp* 1990
Sales NA *EMP* 320
Accts Deloitte & Touche Llp
SIC 6361 6531 Title insurance; Appraiser, real estate
Ch Bd: Leonard R Stein-Sapir
CFO: Todd Rossman
**Treas:* Kenneth Hignett
VP: Dawn Podobnik
VP: Brian Schorr
VP: Dawn Wolf
Exec: Amy Cilik
CIO: Ryan Falkofsky
CTO: Scott Crawford
Sftwr Eng: Adrian Wenzel
Sales Exec: Shannon Kallay

D-U-N-S 00-541-8306
MORTGAGE INVESTORS CORP (OH)
AMERIGROUP
6090 Central Ave, Saint Petersburg, FL 33707-1622
Tel (727) 347-1930 *Founded/Ownrshp* 1938
Sales NA *EMP* 1,200
Accts Grant Thornton Llp Tampa Fl
SIC 6162 Mortgage bankers
Ch Bd: William L Edwards
**Pr:* Jeffrey Crilley
**CFO:* David L Lattner
Ofcr: Tom Carpenter
Sr VP: Jesse Lehn
MIS Dir: Dan Smith
Dir IT: Andrew Cleaveland
Dir IT: Andrew Clevland
VP Sls: John King

MORTGAGE MASTER
See CALM INC

D-U-N-S 12-236-8942
MORTGAGE SOURCE LLC
600 Old Country Rd Rm 210, Garden City, NY 11530-2011
Tel (516) 487-3111 *Founded/Ownrshp* 2002
Sales NA *EMP* 70
SIC 6162 Mortgage bankers & correspondents

D-U-N-S 00-516-3753
MORTON BUILDINGS INC (IL)
252 W Adams St, Morton, IL 61550-1804
Tel (309) 263-7474 *Founded/Ownrshp* 1903
Sales 490.8MM^E *EMP* 1,800
SIC 2452

D-U-N-S 05-994-7317
MORTON COMMUNITY BANK INC
721 W Jackson St, Morton, IL 61550-1537
Tel (309) 263-8126 *Founded/Ownrshp* 1961
Sales NA *EMP* 132
SIC 6022 6021 State commercial banks; National commercial banks
Pr: James Mamer
CFO: Bob Dittmer
Ofcr: Bill Anderson
Ofcr: Kandice Finch
Ofcr: Doug Shull
Sr VP: Cliff Haelbacher
**Sr VP:* Clifford Hasselbacher
Sr VP: Donna Meyering
Sr VP: Joe Schmidgall
VP: Steve Freeze
VP: Lynn Losey
VP: Anita Oberle
VP: Joe Peterson
VP: Jim Williams

D-U-N-S 80-189-7505 IMP
MORTON GROVE PHARMACEUTICALS INC
(*Suby of* WOCKHARDT LIMITED)
6451 Main St, Morton Grove, IL 60053-2633
Tel (847) 967-5600 *Founded/Ownrshp* 2007
Sales 149.0MM^E *EMP* 300
SIC 2834 Pharmaceutical preparations
Pr: Sunil Khera
Sr Cor Off: Prakash Chainani
Prd Mgr: Scott Starbuck

D-U-N-S 16-134-7315
MORTON HOSPITAL AND MEDICAL CENTER INC
CARITAS CHRISTI HEALTH CARE
(*Suby of* CARITAS CHRISTI HEALTH CARE) ★
88 Washington St, Taunton, MA 02780-2499
Tel (508) 828-7000 *Founded/Ownrshp* 2011
Sales 115.3MM *EMP* 14,000^E
SIC 6733 8062 Trusts; General medical & surgical hospitals
Ch Bd: Joseph Quinn
**Pr:* Kim Bassett
**COO:* Donna L Maher
**CFO:* Carmen Acker
**CFO:* Richard Jeffcote
Treas: Lawrence Seck
**VP:* Kelly Hoye
**VP:* Harvey Kowaloff
Dir Rx: Joseph Andrade
MIS Dir: Jeanne Fallon
QA Dir: William Gass

D-U-N-S 00-520-3828 IMP
MORTON INDUSTRIAL GROUP INC (GA)
(*Suby of* MMC PRECISION HOLDINGS CORP) ★
1021 W Birchwood St, Morton, IL 61550-9617
Tel (309) 266-7176 *Founded/Ownrshp* 1998
Sales 110.5MM^E *EMP* 1,370
SIC 3449 Miscellaneous metalwork
Pr: Frank C Lukacs
**Ch Bd:* William D Morton
**Sr VP:* Brian Doolittle
**Sr VP:* Brian Geiger
**Sr VP:* Daryl R Lindemann
IT Man: Robert Johnson
Board of Directors: Patrick K McGee

D-U-N-S 02-566-1075 IMP
MORTON INDUSTRIES LLC
(*Suby of* NELSON GLOBAL PRODUCTS INC) ★
70 Commerce Dr, Morton, IL 61550-9198
Tel (309) 263-2590 *Founded/Ownrshp* 2011
Sales 99.3MM^E *EMP* 400
SIC 3498 Fabricated pipe & fittings
CFO: Jan Christiansan
QI Cn Mgr: Brandon Frampton

D-U-N-S 03-646-1556 IMP/EXP
MORTON INTERNATIONAL LLC
MORTON SALT
(*Suby of* K+S AG)
123 N Wacker Dr Ste 2400, Chicago, IL 60606-1760
Tel (312) 807-2696 *Founded/Ownrshp* 2009
Sales 639.6MM^E *EMP* 2,900
SIC 2891 2851 2822 1479 2899 Adhesives; Lacquers, varnishes, enamels & other coatings; Polysulfides (thiokol); Salt & sulfur mining; Salt
Pr: Mark L Roberts
COO: James Swanson
**CFO:* Andrew J Kotlarz
Treas: Charlie Thacker
Dir IT: Kurt Berghofer
Dir IT: Chris Carbaugh
Dir IT: Ben Caruso
Dir IT: Brian Cook
Dir IT: Grooms David
Dir IT: Keven Longfellow
Dir IT: Tom Lusha

D-U-N-S 11-550-0191
MORTON PLANT HOSPITAL ASSOCIATION INC
(*Suby of* MORTON PLANT MEASE HEALTH CARE INC) ★
300 Pinellas St, Clearwater, FL 33756-3892
Tel (727) 462-7000 *Founded/Ownrshp* 1914
Sales 598.3MM *EMP* 3,000
Accts Ernst & Young Us Llp Atlanta
SIC 8062 8051 General medical & surgical hospitals; Skilled nursing care facilities
Pr: Phil Beauchant
CFO: David O"neil
CFO: Dave Oneil
**VP:* Hal Ziecheck
Dir Lab: Pam Pound
Dir Rad: Craig A Bnull
Dir Rad: Barbara J Bourland
CIO: Neal Brown
Pathlgst: Michael Linden
Pathlgst: Jason Savell
Surgeon: Michael Rothberg

D-U-N-S 60-247-7192
MORTON PLANT MEASE HEALTH CARE INC
(*Suby of* BAYCARE EDUCATION SERVICES) ★
300 Pinellas St, Clearwater, FL 33756-3804
Tel (727) 462-7777 *Founded/Ownrshp* 1983
Sales 69.4MM *EMP* 3,950
SIC 8741 8721 Hospital management; Billing & bookkeeping service
Pr: Philip K Beauchamp
Doctor: William C Brown MD

MORTON SALT
See MORTON INTERNATIONAL LLC

D-U-N-S 96-477-8299 IMP/EXP
MORTON SALT INC
CHICAGO SALT SERVICE
(*Suby of* K+S SALT LLC) ★
123 N Wacker Dr Fl 24, Chicago, IL 60606-1760
Tel (800) 725-8847 *Founded/Ownrshp* 2010
Sales 1.1MMM^E *EMP* 2,900
SIC 2891 2851 2822 1479 2899 Adhesives & sealants; Paints & allied products; Synthetic rubber; Salt & sulfur mining; Chemical preparations
CEO: Christian Herrmann
CFO: Andrew J Kotlarz
CFO: Andy Totlerz
Bd of Dir: Walt Bryant
VP: Robert Alberico
VP: Matt Beliveau
VP: Guy Leblanc
VP: Betsey Nohe
VP: Elizabeth Nohe
VP: Carol Panozzo
VP: Wallace Shayn
VP: Chad E Walker
VP: Lisa Zumbach

MORTONS OF CHICAGO
See MORTONS OF CHICAGO/BOCA RATON INC

D-U-N-S 04-687-4277
MORTONS OF CHICAGO/BOCA RATON INC
MORTONS OF CHICAGO
(*Suby of* LANDRYS SEAFOOD HOUSE) ★
350 W Hubbard St, Chicago, IL 60654-5798
Tel (713) 850-1010 *Founded/Ownrshp* 1989
Sales 86.2MM^E *EMP* 3,950
SIC 5812 Steak restaurant
V Ch Bd: Klaus Fritsch
**Pr:* Edi Ames
**Pr:* John T Bettin
**CFO:* Ronald M Dinella
Sr VP: Jim Kirkpatrick
VP: Kate Shehan
**VP:* E Nichols Wagner

D-U-N-S 19-982-4822
MORTONS RESTAURANT GROUP INC
MORTON'S THE STEAKHOUSE
(*Suby of* LANDRYS SEAFOOD HOUSE) ★
1510 West Loop S, Houston, TX 77027-9505
Tel (713) 850-1010 *Founded/Ownrshp* 2012
Sales 65.2MM^E *EMP* 4,154^E
SIC 5812 Steak restaurant; Family restaurants; Italian restaurant
Pr: Christopher Artinian
CFO: Ronald M Dinella
Ofcr: Nilam Patel
Sr VP: Roger J Drake
Sr VP: James W Kirkpatrick
Sr VP: Scott D Levin
Exec: Tara Ball
Exec: Laura Richards
Genl Mgr: Thomas Allen
Genl Mgr: Jon Barkell
Genl Mgr: Jeff Bueche

MORTON'S THE STEAKHOUSE
See MORTONS RESTAURANT GROUP INC

D-U-N-S 16-911-0165 IMP/EXP
■ **MOS HOLDINGS INC**
MOSAIC COMPANY
(*Suby of* MOSAIC CO) ★
3033 Campus Dr Ste E490, Plymouth, MN 55441-2655
Tel (763) 577-2700 *Founded/Ownrshp* 2004
Sales 1.6MMM^E *EMP* 7,700
SIC 2874 1475 2819 1094 1481 Phosphatic fertilizers; Phosphate rock; Sulfuric acid, oleum; Uranium ore mining; Nonmetallic mineral services
CEO: Joc O Rourke
Pr: James T Prokopanko
CFO: Lawrence W Stranghoener
Ex VP: Bruce Bodine
Ex VP: Richard L Mack
Sr VP: Mark J Isaacson
Sr VP: Stephen P Malia
Sr VP: Richard N McLellan
Sr VP: Corrine D Ricard
VP: Norman Beug
VP: Anthony T Brausen
VP: Jeff Clyne
VP: Laura C Gagnon
VP: Mark E Kaplan
VP: Mark Kaplan
VP: Karen Swager
Board of Directors: David T Seaton, Phyllis E Cochran, Steven M Seibert, William R Graber, Emery N Koenig, Robert L Lumpkins, Harold H Mackay, David B Mathis, William T Monahan, James L Popowich, Sergio Rial

D-U-N-S 07-804-1035
MOSAIC (NE)
4980 S 118th St, Omaha, NE 68137-2200
Tel (402) 896-3884 *Founded/Ownrshp* 1912, 2002
Sales 242.6MM *EMP* 5,000
Accts Seim Johnson Llp Omaha Nebra
SIC 8361 8741 Home for the mentally handicapped; Administrative management
CEO: Linda Timmons
**COO:* Raul Saldivar
**CFO:* Cindy Schroeder
**Treas:* Cynthia L Schroeder
**Sr VP:* Keith Schmode
**Sr VP:* Donna Werner
VP: Paula Burton
VP: David Defreese
VP: Yvette Gillett
VP: Kristin Rossow
VP: Brenda Solomon
Assoc Dir: Michelle McFadden
Assoc Dir: Paul Weber
Comm Dir: Tracie Klassen

MOSAIC COMPANY
See MOS HOLDINGS INC

D-U-N-S 96-955-3820 IMP/EXP
▲ **MOSAIC CO**
3033 Campus Dr Ste E490, Plymouth, MN 55441-2655
Tel (800) 918-8270 *Founded/Ownrshp* 2004
Sales 8.9MMM *EMP* 8,900^E
Tkr Sym MOS *Exch* NYS
SIC 2874 1475 Phosphatic fertilizers; Phosphate rock
Pr: James C O'Rourke
**Ch Bd:* Robert L Lumpkins
CFO: Richard L Mack
Sr VP: Bruce Bodine
Sr VP: Gary N Davis
Sr VP: Mark J Isaacson
Sr VP: Mark E Kaplan
Sr VP: Richard N McLellan
Sr VP: Walter F Precourt III
Sr VP: Corrine D Ricard
VP: Laura Gagnon
VP: Joe Kline
VP: Dennis Orke
Board of Directors: Kelvin Westbrook, Nancy E Cooper, Gregory L Ebel, Timothy S Gitzel, Denise C Johnson, Emery N Koenig, William T Monahan, James L Popowich, David T Seaton, Steven M Seibert

D-U-N-S 78-933-4422
MOSAIC COMMUNITY SERVICES INC
DULANEY STATION
1925 Greenspring Dr, Lutherville Timonium, MD 21093-4128
Tel (410) 453-9553 *Founded/Ownrshp* 1984
Sales 37.6MM *EMP* 1,100
Accts Sc&H Tax & Advisory Services L
SIC 8322 8093 Individual & family services; Mental health clinic, outpatient
Ex Dir: Jeff Richardson
CFO: Donald Biles
**CFO:* Janet Deal
**Treas:* Rob Williams
Ofcr: Spencer Gear
**VP:* Ellen Callegary

D-U-N-S 00-892-2187
■ **MOSAIC CROP NUTRITION LLC**
(*Suby of* MOSAIC CO) ★
3033 Campus Dr, Minneapolis, MN 55441-2651
Tel (763) 577-2700 *Founded/Ownrshp* 2004
Sales 98.1MM^E *EMP* 831
SIC 2874 1474 Phosphatic fertilizers; Potash, soda & borate minerals
CFO: Lawrence W Stranghoener

D-U-N-S 06-469-6107 IMP/EXP
■ **MOSAIC FERTILIZER LLC**
(*Suby of* MOSAIC CO) ★
13830 Circa Crossing Dr, Lithia, FL 33547-3953
Tel (813) 500-6300 *Founded/Ownrshp* 2004
Sales 782.1MM^E *EMP* 1,300
SIC 2874 Phosphatic fertilizers
CEO: James T Prokopanko
**Ex VP:* Richard L Mack
**Sr VP:* Gary Davis
**VP:* Mark E Kaplan
**Prin:* Jason Vanvleet
IT Man: Hugh Hensley
IT Man: Maureen Ryan

D-U-N-S 17-765-7095
■ **MOSAIC GLOBAL HOLDINGS INC**
(*Suby of* MOSAIC CO) ★
3033 Campus Dr Ste E490, Minneapolis, MN 55441-2655
Tel (763) 577-2700 *Founded/Ownrshp* 2004
Sales 624.1MM^E *EMP* 5,017
SIC 2874 1474 1475 2875 2819 Phosphatic fertilizers; Potash mining; Phosphate rock; Fertilizers, mixing only; Chemicals, high purity: refined from technical grade

CFO: Lawrence Stranghoener
CFO: Lawrence W Stranghoener

D-U-N-S 13-676-0811
MOSAIC SALES SOLUTIONS US OPERATING CO LLC
(*Suby of* ACOSTA SALES & MARKETING) ★
220 Las Colinas Blvd E, Irving, TX 75039-5500
Tel (972) 870-4800 *Founded/Ownrshp* 2012
Sales 472.9MM[E] *EMP* 8,000
SIC 8742 8743 7374 Merchandising consultant; Sales promotion; Computer graphics service
Pr: Aidan Tracey
**Pr:* Brian Kava
**CFO:* Kelly Parsons
CFO: Bob Vesely
**Sr VP:* Dick Doyle
Sr VP: Tim Hauser
**Sr VP:* Ed Slavin
Sr VP: Jeff Stelmach
VP: Chad Grenier
Exec: Tracie Carter
Creative D: Ivan Druzic

D-U-N-S 60-866-1083
MOSBY HOLDINGS CORP
(*Suby of* REED BUSINESS INFORMATION) ★
125 Park Ave, New York, NY 10017-5529
Tel (212) 309-8100 *Founded/Ownrshp* 1998
Sales 106.8MM[E] *EMP* 2,000[E]
SIC 2741 8999 Technical manuals: publishing only, not printed on site; Writing for publication
Pr: Ron Mobed

D-U-N-S 80-813-3925
MOSCOW CAMDEN AND SAN AUGUSTINE RAILROAD LLC
(*Suby of* GEORGIA-PACIFIC WOOD PRODUCTS SOUTH LLC) ★
133 Peachtree St Ne, Atlanta, GA 30303-1804
Tel (404) 652-4000 *Founded/Ownrshp* 2007
Sales 49.1MM[E] *EMP* 1,723[E]
SIC 2656 Paper cups, plates, dishes & utensils

D-U-N-S 00-833-7545 IMP
MOSELEY ASSOCIATES INC
82 Coromar Dr, Santa Barbara, CA 93117-3024
Tel (805) 968-9621 *Founded/Ownrshp* 1977
Sales 96.5MM[E] *EMP* 350[E]
SIC 3663 Radio & TV communications equipment
Pr: Jamal N Hamdani
**CFO:* Bruce Tarr
Tech Mgr: Matthew Coon

D-U-N-S 80-617-8468
MOSES CONE-WESLEY LONG COMMUNITY HEALTH FOUNDATION INC
CONE HEALTH FOUNDATION
1200 N Elm St, Greensboro, NC 27401-1004
Tel (336) 832-9555 *Founded/Ownrshp* 1996
Sales 4.2MM *EMP* 2,105[E]
SIC 8699 Charitable organization
Pr: Susan Fitzgibbon Shumaker
COO: Terrence Akin
Ex VP: Bob Goldstein
Ex VP: Jim Roskelly
VP: Andy Barrow
**VP:* Sandra Welch Boren
VP: Cindy Farrand
VP: Debbie Green
VP: Skip Hislop
VP: John Jenkins
VP: Anne Macner
VP: Grace Moffitt
VP: William Porter
**VP:* Antonia Reaves
VP: Brian Romig
VP: Melissa Shearer
VP: Annette Smith
VP: Cheryl Somers

D-U-N-S 05-703-6071
MOSES H CONE MEMORIAL HOSPITAL
ANNIE PENN HOSPITAL
1200 N Elm St, Greensboro, NC 27401-1020
Tel (336) 832-7000 *Founded/Ownrshp* 1911
Sales 1.5MMM *EMP* 12,000
SIC 8062 General medical & surgical hospitals
CEO: Terry Akin
V Ch: Craven E Williams
**COO:* Judy Schanel
**CFO:* Jeff Jones
Trst: Dwight M Davidson
Trst: Lily Kelly-Radford
Trst: William V Nutt
Trst: Henry W Smith
Trst: William R Soles
VP: Noel Burt
Dir Case M: Marjorie Jenkins

D-U-N-S 83-209-7336
MOSES H CONE MEMORIAL HOSPITAL OPERATING CORP
CONE HEALTH
(*Suby of* ANNIE PENN HOSPITAL) ★
1200 N Elm St, Greensboro, NC 27401-1020
Tel (336) 832-7000 *Founded/Ownrshp* 1985
Sales 1.6MMM *EMP* 393[E]
Accts Pricewaterhousecoopers Llp Gr
SIC 8062 General medical & surgical hospitals
Ex Dir: R Timothy Rice
COO: Tim Rice

MOSES LAKE HIGH SCHOOL
See MOSES LAKE SCHOOL DIST 161

D-U-N-S 10-008-0795
MOSES LAKE SCHOOL DIST 161
MOSES LAKE HIGH SCHOOL
920 W Ivy Ave, Moses Lake, WA 98837-2047
Tel (509) 766-2650 *Founded/Ownrshp* 1935
Sales 65.3MM[E] *EMP* 1,000
SIC 8211 Elementary & secondary schools; High school, junior or senior
Pr: Kevin Donovan
MIS Dir: Marlin Howell
Teacher Pr: Patty Laughery

MOSES LAKES FARMS
See WILLAMETTE EGG FARMS LLC

MOSES TAYLOR HOSPITAL
See QUINCY SCRANTON HOSPITAL LLC

D-U-N-S 00-606-1576
MOSEY MANUFACTURING CO INC
262 Fort Wayne Ave, Richmond, IN 47374-2392
Tel (765) 983-8800 *Founded/Ownrshp* 1946
Sales 84.1MM[E] *EMP* 450
SIC 3541 Machine tools, metal cutting type
Pr: George N Mosey
**Ex VP:* Stephen A Mosey
**VP:* Dan Kindley
**VP:* Kenneth L Mackey

D-U-N-S 00-479-8443
■ MOSINEE TELEPHONE CO LLC
TDS
(*Suby of* TDS TELECOMMUNICATIONS CORP) ★
410 4th St, Mosinee, WI 54455-1199
Tel (715) 693-2622 *Founded/Ownrshp* 1947
Sales 853.0MM *EMP* 2,700
Accts Kiesling Associates Llp
SIC 4813 Local telephone communications
Pr: David Wittwer
**Ofcr:* Noel Hutton
VP: Jack Koss
**VP:* William J Megan

D-U-N-S 00-682-2324
MOSITES CONSTRUCTION CO (PA)
4839 Campbells Run Rd, Pittsburgh, PA 15205-1386
Tel (412) 923-2255 *Founded/Ownrshp* 1959
Sales 143.1MM[E] *EMP* 250
SIC 1542 1611 Commercial & office building contractors; Highway & street construction
Pr: Steven T Mosites
**CFO:* Joe Pazicni
**Treas:* Donald A Mosites
VP: Mark Edgar
**VP:* M Dean Mosites
VP: David N Rubis
Exec: Mark Minnerly
Dir IT: Benjamin Winkworth
VP Opers: Joe Wattick
Sfty Dirs: Jason P Malatak
Sfty Mgr: Jason Malatok

D-U-N-S 14-123-6237 IMP/EXP
MOSS & ASSOCIATES LLC
2101 N Andrews Ave, Wilton Manors, FL 33311-3946
Tel (954) 524-5678 *Founded/Ownrshp* 2004
Sales 271.8MM[E] *EMP* 350[E]
SIC 1542 Nonresidential construction; Commercial & office building, new construction; Commercial & office buildings, renovation & repair; Hospital construction
Pr: Bob L Moss
**Pr:* Scott Moss
**Ex VP:* Ted Adams
**Ex VP:* Joe Harris
**Ex VP:* Mike Little
**Ex VP:* Bruce Moldow
Ex VP: W Trethewey
**Sr VP:* Chad Moss
Sr VP: Anderson Russell
VP: Steven McNeely
VP: Brad Wilson
Exec: Jason Sizemore
Exec: Randy Spicer

D-U-N-S 07-573-4889 IMP
MOSS ADAMS LLP
999 3rd Ave Ste 2800, Seattle, WA 98104-4057
Tel (206) 302-6500 *Founded/Ownrshp* 1913
Sales 284.4MM[E] *EMP* 1,280
SIC 8721 Certified public accountant
CEO: Chris Schmidt
Pt: Rick Anderson
Pt: Carol Suruki
Mng Pt: Wayne Brown
Mng Pt: Paul Farkas
Mng Pt: Randy Fenich
Mng Pt: Dick Fohn
Mng Pt: Kerry Gordon
Mng Pt: Jeff Green
Mng Pt: Rob Greenspan
Mng Pt: Bob Hinton
Mng Pt: Joe Karas
Mng Pt: Steve Keene
Mng Pt: Ed Kitrosser
Mng Pt: Tom Krippaehne
Mng Pt: Mike Lynch
Mng Pt: Tony Maki
Mng Pt: Curtis Matthews
Mng Pt: Ty Pforsich
Mng Pt: Bob Ryker
Mng Pt: David W Schilling

D-U-N-S 00-315-0893
MOSS SUPPLY CO (NC)
5001 N Graham St, Charlotte, NC 28269-4826
Tel (704) 596-8717 *Founded/Ownrshp* 1961
Sales 86.1MM[E] *EMP* 350
SIC 3442 Screen & storm doors & windows
CEO: Robert Moss Jr
**Pr:* Gregory B Smith
**Pr:* Ralph Wearsch
**CFO:* Gregory Smith
**Sec:* Cassandra Nott
Opers Mgr: Vance Almonde

D-U-N-S 06-370-7699
MOSSER CONSTRUCTION INC
(*Suby of* MOSSER GROUP) ★
122 S Wilson Ave, Fremont, OH 43420-2725
Tel (419) 334-3801 *Founded/Ownrshp* 1974
Sales 121.1MM *EMP* 200
SIC 1541 1542

MOSSER GROUP, THE
See WMOG INC

D-U-N-S 62-608-0915
MOSSY HOLDING CO INC
MOSSY OLDSMOBILE
12150 Old Katy Rd, Houston, TX 77079
Tel (281) 558-9970 *Founded/Ownrshp* 1946
Sales 354.4MM[E] *EMP* 1,090
SIC 5511 6159 7532 Automobiles, new & used; Pickups, new & used; Vans, new & used; Automobile finance leasing; Body shop, automotive
Ch Bd: Wiley Mossy
**Pr:* David Mossy
**Pr:* Philip Mossy
CFO: Amy Gladys

MOSSY NISSAN KEARNY MESA
See NISSAN MOSSY INC

MOSSY OLDSMOBILE
See MOSSY HOLDING CO INC

D-U-N-S 03-427-9948 IMP/EXP
MOTCO INC (FL)
7900 Sw 57th Ave Ste 10, South Miami, FL 33143-5545
Tel (305) 662-8814 *Founded/Ownrshp* 1975
Sales 89.7MM[E] *EMP* 424
SIC 5182 5122 5199 Liquor; Toiletries; Gifts & novelties
Pr: Harold M Rifas
**Treas:* Mary Crawley
**VP:* David Granick

MOTEL 6
See G6 HOSPITALITY LLC

D-U-N-S 15-277-2463
MOTEL 6 OPERATING LP
(*Suby of* MOTEL 6) ★
4001 Intl Pkwy Ste 500, Carrollton, TX 75007
Tel (972) 360-9000 *Founded/Ownrshp* 2012
Sales 141.2MM[E] *EMP* 2,000
SIC 7011 Hotels & motels
CEO: Jim Amorosia
**Genl Pt:* Emmett Gossen
Ofcr: Jeff Winslow
Genl Mgr: Jack Gillinghan

D-U-N-S 04-074-6430
MOTHER FRANCES HOSPITAL REGIONAL HEALTH CARE CENTER
800 E Dawson St, Tyler, TX 75701-2093
Tel (903) 593-8441 *Founded/Ownrshp* 1937
Sales 618.6MM *EMP* 2,747
Accts Bkd Llp Houston Tx
SIC 8062 General medical & surgical hospitals
Pr: Lindsey Bradely
Chf Rad: Robert Sanchez
**CFO:* William Bellenfant
**CFO:* Joyce Hester
VP: Chris Gleeney
**VP:* Ray Thompson
IT Man: Robert Hilliard
Obsttrcn: Ann H Abrameit
Obsttrcn: Randall Howerton
Obsttrcn: John H Sum
Obsttrcn: James Wasson

D-U-N-S 62-803-6600
MOTHER LODE HOLDING CO
189 Fulweiler Ave, Auburn, CA 95603-4507
Tel (530) 887-2410 *Founded/Ownrshp* 1987
Sales NA *EMP* 480
SIC 6361 6531 7389 Title insurance; Escrow agent, real estate; Courier or messenger service
CEO: Jerry Adams
**Pr:* Marsha Emmett
**CFO:* David Philipp
Ofcr: Marty Erickson
VP: Nancy Nardini-Hanson
IT Man: Jason Thomson

D-U-N-S 13-026-0826 IMP
MOTHER PARKERS TEA & COFFEE USA LTD
MOTHER PARKER'S TEA AND COFFEE
(*Suby of* MOTHER PARKER'S TEA & COFFEE INC)
7800 Will Rogers Blvd, Fort Worth, TX 76140-6026
Tel (817) 551-5500 *Founded/Ownrshp* 1912
Sales 106.5MM[E] *EMP* 155
SIC 5149 2095 2099 Coffee & tea; Roasted coffee; Food preparations
Mng Pt: Paul Higgins
**Pt:* Michael Higgins
VP: Dennis Paynter
Natl Sales: Don Scott
Mktg Mgr: Brian Reilly
Manager: Carolyn Bowers

MOTHER PARKER'S TEA AND COFFEE
See MOTHER PARKERS TEA & COFFEE USA LTD

D-U-N-S 07-997-3530
MOTION & FLOW CONTROL PRODUCTS INC
MFCP
7941 Shaffer Pkwy, Littleton, CO 80127-3734
Tel (303) 666-2183 *Founded/Ownrshp* 2006
Sales 110.0MM *EMP* 285
SIC 5085 Industrial supplies
Pr: Darrel Saban

D-U-N-S 03-879-4762
MOTION AND FLOW CONTROL PRODUCTS INC
MFCP
7941 Shaffer Pkwy, Littleton, CO 80127-3734
Tel (303) 762-8012 *Founded/Ownrshp* 2006
Sales 109.2MM[E] *EMP* 285
SIC 5085 5074 Industrial supplies; Plumbing & hydronic heating supplies
Pr: Darrell Sabin
Brnch Mgr: Matt Lopezi
Genl Mgr: Steve Bohn
Mktg Mgr: Mike Robinson

D-U-N-S 00-796-0446 IMP/EXP
■ MOTION INDUSTRIES INC
(*Suby of* GENUINE PARTS CO) ★
1605 Alton Rd, Birmingham, AL 35210-3770
Tel (205) 956-1122 *Founded/Ownrshp* 1946
Sales 3.8MMM[E] *EMP* 5,200
SIC 5085 Industrial supplies; Bearings; Power transmission equipment & apparatus
Pr: Timothy P Breen
**Ch Bd:* William J Stevens
Pr: Chris Brewer
Pr: Pamela Sims
**COO:* Bob Summerlin
**Treas:* Michael D Harper
Sr VP: Randall P Breaux
Sr VP: Ellen H Holladay
VP: Austin Amos
VP: Donald Bland
VP: Tony Cefalu
**VP:* G Harold Dunaway
VP: Zahir Hameer
VP: Billy Hamilton
VP: Grady Harper
**VP:* Ellen Holladay
**VP:* Wayne Law
**VP:* Joe Limbaugh
VP: Rulon Ramsey
VP: Jon Tart
VP: Phil Taylor

D-U-N-S 96-658-7797
MOTION PICTURE INDUSTRY HEALTH PLAN
11365 Ventura Blvd, Studio City, CA 91604-3148
Tel (818) 769-0007 *Founded/Ownrshp* 2011
Sales NA *EMP* 19[E]
Accts Miller Kaplan Arase Llp North
SIC 6371 Pension, health & welfare funds
Prin: David Wescoe
CFO: Theodore Friesen

D-U-N-S 18-760-0259
MOTION PICTURE INDUSTRY PENSION & HEALTH PLANS
11365 Ventura Blvd # 300, Studio City, CA 91604-3148
Tel (818) 769-0007 *Founded/Ownrshp* 1954
Sales NA *EMP* 150
SIC 6371 Pension, health & welfare funds
CEO: David Wescoe
**CFO:* Chuck Killian
Bd of Dir: Ronald Kutak
Trst: Krysten Brennan
Exec: Thomas Zimmerman
CIO: Joel Manfredo
Dir IT: Patrick Carmona
Snr Mgr: Celso Perez

D-U-N-S 02-383-8670 IMP
MOTIVA ENTERPRISES LLC
MOTIVA SALES TERMINAL
500 Dallas St, Houston, TX 77002-4800
Tel (713) 241-6161 *Founded/Ownrshp* 1998
Sales 1.6MMM[E] *EMP* 3,000
SIC 2911 5541
CEO: Dan Romasko
**CEO:* Robert W Pease
CFO: Ronald Langan
**CFO:* Marcel P Luijten
**Treas:* James B Castles
Dir Risk M: Chen Chiang
Genl Mgr: Gerry Jackson
Genl Mgr: Don Jasperson
Genl Mgr: Bryan Schorzman
MIS Dir: Frank Doyle
**VP Mfg:* Tom Purves

MOTIVA SALES TERMINAL
See MOTIVA ENTERPRISES LLC

MOTIVE NATION
See ROCKVIEW DAIRIES INC

D-U-N-S 11-475-9124 IMP/EXP
■ MOTIVEPOWER INC
(*Suby of* WABTEC) ★
4600 S Apple St, Boise, ID 83716-5505
Tel (208) 947-4800 *Founded/Ownrshp* 1972
Sales 170.3MM[E] *EMP* 750
SIC 3743 Railroad car rebuilding
Pr: Albert J Neupaver
**COO:* Raymond T Betler
**Ex VP:* Alvaro Garcia-Tunon
**Sr VP:* Patrick D Dugan
**Sr VP:* Charles F Kovac
**VP:* Robert C Bourg
**VP:* Mark Warner

MOTOMART CONVENIENCE STORES
See FKG OIL CO

MOTOMCO
See BELL LABORATORIES INC

D-U-N-S 07-311-5065
■ MOTOR CARGO
(*Suby of* UPS GROUND FREIGHT INC) ★
845 W Center St, North Salt Lake, UT 84054-2916
Tel (801) 936-1111 *Founded/Ownrshp* 2005
Sales 67.0MM[E] *EMP* 1,726
SIC 4213 Contract haulers
Co-Pr: Pete Morrow
Co-Pr: Lynn H Wheeler
Sr VP: Marvin Friedland
Netwrk Mgr: Jared Roper

D-U-N-S 00-481-7490 IMP
MOTOR CITY ELECTRIC CO (MI)
9440 Grinnell St, Detroit, MI 48213-1151
Tel (313) 567-5300 *Founded/Ownrshp* 1952
Sales 172.6MM[E] *EMP* 500
SIC 1731 General electrical contractor; Lighting contractor; Telephone & telephone equipment installation
Pr: Dale Wieczorek
**Ex VP:* Steve Frantz
Ex VP: Denise Hodgins
**Ex VP:* Thomas McGrail
**Sr VP:* Paul Gillespie
**VP:* Dick Martin
Exec: Denise Hodgens
Exec: Courteney Zagacki

D-U-N-S 00-594-3873
MOTOR COACH INDUSTRIES INC
VERIZON BUSINESS
(*Suby of* MCII) ★
552 W Stutsman St, Pembina, ND 58271-4308
Tel (701) 825-6234 *Founded/Ownrshp* 1962
Sales 218.9MM[E] *EMP* 600

SIC 3711 Motor buses, except trackless trolleys, assembly of
Pr: Steven Clough
CFO: Sandra Morrison
Ex Dir: Carlos Godinez
Sfty Mgr: Rick Anderson
Manager: Robert Lessor

D-U-N-S 79-819-4171
MOTOR COACH INDUSTRIES INTERNATIONAL INC
MCII
(*Suby of* NEW FLYER INDUSTRIES INC)
200 E Oakton St, Des Plaines, IL 60018-1948
Tel (847) 285-2000 *Founded/Ownrshp* 2015
Sales 414.2MM[E] *EMP* 1,500
SIC 3713 3711 3714 Bus bodies (motor vehicles); Buses, all types, assembly of; Motor vehicle parts & accessories
Pr: Paul Soubry
CFO: Horst O Sieben
Treas: William M Murray
Ex VP: Mario Gonzalez
VP: Timothy J Nalepka
VP: Allan D Swanson
VP: Peter Tully
VP: Tom Wagner
VP: Patricia Ziska
Tech Mgr: David Mailhot
Opers Mgr: John Ellsworth

MOTOR STATE DISTRIBUTING
See LANE AUTOMOTIVE INC

MOTOR WERKS OF BARRINGTON
See MOTOR WERKS PARTNERS LP

D-U-N-S 05-784-6966
MOTOR WERKS PARTNERS LP
MOTOR WERKS OF BARRINGTON
1475 S Barrington Rd, Barrington, IL 60010-5205
Tel (847) 842-1352 *Founded/Ownrshp* 1981
Sales 124.7MM[E] *EMP* 308
SIC 5511 7515 Automobiles, new & used; Passenger car leasing
Pt: Paul D Tamraz
**Pt:* Nick Pontikes
VP: Tom U Martin
Genl Mgr: Chase Hawkins
Genl Mgr: James Hub
Off Mgr: Sheryl Kohnert
IT Man: Brian Farruggio

D-U-N-S 04-447-7123 IMP/EXP
▲ MOTORCAR PARTS OF AMERICA INC
MPA
2929 California St, Torrance, CA 90503-3914
Tel (310) 212-7910 *Founded/Ownrshp* 1968
Sales 368.9MM *EMP* 2,663
Accts Ernst & Young Llp Los Angeles
Tkr Sym MPAA *Exch* NGS
SIC 3714 3694 3625 5013 Motor vehicle parts & accessories; Alternators, automotive; Starter, electric motor; Motor vehicle supplies & new parts
Ch Bd: Selwyn Joffe
COO: Steve Kratz
CFO: David Lee
Chf Mktg O: Doug Schooner
VP: Michael Umansky
Admn Mgr: Maria Gonzalez
IT Man: Hector Novelo
Board of Directors: Scott J Adelson, Rudolph J Borneo, David Bryan, Joseph Ferguson, Philip Gay, Duane Miller, Jeffrey Mirvis

MOTORCITY CASINO & HOTEL
See DETROIT ENTERTAINMENT LLC

D-U-N-S 07-135-1233
MOTORISTS COMMERCIAL MUTUAL INSURANCE CO
MOTORISTS INSURANCE GROUP
471 E Broad St Bsmt, Columbus, OH 43215-3852
Tel (614) 225-8211 *Founded/Ownrshp* 1899
Sales NA *EMP* 32
SIC 6331 Fire, marine & casualty insurance: mutual
Ch Bd: John J Bishop
**Pr:* David L Kaufman
**CFO:* Susan E Haack
Board of Directors: Charles Stapleton, John Bishop, Michael Wiseman, Larry Forrester, Robert Western, Susan Haack, Sandra Harbrecht, David Kaufman, David Lemon, Robert McCracken, Thomas Ogg, Robert Smith

MOTORISTS INSURANCE GROUP
See MOTORISTS MUTUAL INSURANCE CO

MOTORISTS INSURANCE GROUP
See MOTORISTS LIFE INSURANCE CO

MOTORISTS INSURANCE GROUP
See MOTORISTS COMMERCIAL MUTUAL INSURANCE CO

D-U-N-S 05-285-8636
MOTORISTS LIFE INSURANCE CO
MOTORISTS INSURANCE GROUP
(*Suby of* MOTORISTS INSURANCE GROUP) ★
471 E Broad St Ste 200, Columbus, OH 43215-3842
Tel (614) 225-8211 *Founded/Ownrshp* 1965
Sales NA *EMP* 48
SIC 6311 Life insurance
CEO: David Kaufman
Ch Bd: John Bishop
Pr: Michael Agan
CFO: Susan Haack
Bd of Dir: Michael Wiseman
Board of Directors: Yvette McGee Brown, Larry Forrester, Susan Haack, Sandra Harbrecht, David Kaufman, Charles Stapleton, Michael Wiseman, Johnykessler L

D-U-N-S 00-790-2018
MOTORISTS MUTUAL INSURANCE CO
MOTORISTS INSURANCE GROUP
471 E Broad St Ste 200, Columbus, OH 43215-3805
Tel (614) 225-8211 *Founded/Ownrshp* 1928
Sales NA *EMP* 736
SIC 6331 Fire, marine & casualty insurance: mutual; Automobile insurance; Property damage insurance; Burglary & theft insurance
Ch Bd: John Bishop
Pr: Drew Bright
Pr: Larry Conner
Pr: Jeanne Gibbons
Pr: Teresa M King
Pr: Austin Slattery
**CEO:* David Kaufman
**CFO:* Susan Haack
**CFO:* Michael L Wiseman
Sr VP: John Kessler
VP: Michael J Agan
VP: Daniel L Crawford
VP: Charles R Gaskill
VP: John Huey
VP: Dan Jeffers
VP: Rick Stelzer
VP: Pete Weisenberger
Board of Directors: Yvette McGee Brown, Sandra Harbrecht, Robert McCracken, Thomas Ogg, Robert Smith, Michael Wiseman

D-U-N-S 96-342-0638 IMP
MOTOROLA MOBILITY HOLDINGS LLC
(*Suby of* LENOVO GROUP LIMITED)
222 Merchandise Mart Plz, Chicago, IL 60654-1103
Tel (800) 668-6765 *Founded/Ownrshp* 2014
Sales 2.6MMM[E] *EMP* 20,500[E]
SIC 3663 Radio & TV communications equipment; Mobile communication equipment
Pr: Rick Osterloh
**Pr:* Daniel M Moloney
**CEO:* Dennis Woodside
**CFO:* Vanessa Wittman
CFO: Vanessa A Wittman
Chf Mktg O: Bill Ogle
**Sr VP:* Iqbal Arshad
Sr VP: Adrienne Hayes
Sr VP: Steve Horowitz
**Sr VP:* Kouji Kodera
Sr VP: Bill Morgan
**Sr VP:* D Scott Offer
Sr VP: Scott Offer
Sr VP: Geoff Roman
**Sr VP:* Geoffrey S Roman
VP: John Bucher
VP: Nick Hackett
VP: Nadim Halabi
VP: Jeff Miller
VP: Michael Pencek
VP: Don Wolfe

D-U-N-S 96-342-7765 IMP
MOTOROLA MOBILITY LLC
(*Suby of* MOTOROLA MOBILITY HOLDINGS LLC) ★
222 Merchandise Mart Plz, Chicago, IL 60654-1103
Tel (800) 866-6765 *Founded/Ownrshp* 2007
Sales 706.3MM[E] *EMP* 1,996
SIC 3663 4812 Mobile communication equipment; Cellular telephone services
Pr: Rick Osterloh
**Pr:* Sanjay Jha
**CFO:* Sanjay Vanjani
**Sr VP:* Iqbal Arshad
**Sr VP:* Kouji Kodera
**Sr VP:* Mark Randall
**VP:* Magnus Ahlqvist
**VP:* Sergio Buniac
**VP:* Seang Chau
**VP:* Jeff Millerv
Snr Sftwr: Xiaofei MA

D-U-N-S 02-951-8649
MOTOROLA SATELLITE COMMUNICATIONS INC
(*Suby of* MOTOROLA MOBILITY LLC) ★
2900 S Diablo Way, Tempe, AZ 85282-3201
Tel (480) 732-2000 *Founded/Ownrshp* 1998, 2011
Sales 54.5MM[E] *EMP* 1,650
SIC 3674 Semiconductors & related devices
Pr: Christopher B Galvin

D-U-N-S 00-132-5463 IMP/EXP
▲ MOTOROLA SOLUTIONS INC
500 W Monroe St, Chicago, IL 60661-3671
Tel (847) 576-5000 *Founded/Ownrshp* 1928
Sales 5.7MMM *EMP* 14,405
Tkr Sym MSI *Exch* NYS
SIC 3663 3661 Radio & TV communications equipment; Mobile communication equipment; Pagers (one-way); Cellular radio telephone; Modems; Multiplex equipment, telephone & telegraph
Ch Bd: Gregory Q Brown
CFO: Gino A Bonanotte
Ofcr: Mark S Hacker
Ex VP: Bruce W Brda
Ex VP: Bruce Brda
Ex VP: John P Molloy
Sr VP: Eduardo F Conrado
VP: Michael Annes
VP: Rishi Bhaskar
VP: Frederic Bismuth
VP: Nadalie Bosse
VP: Tom Collins
VP: Sue Conatser
VP: Laura Davis
VP: Dan Delaney
VP: Randy Johnson
VP: Ed McCabe
VP: Greg Meyers
VP: James Munro
VP: James Niewiara
VP: Derek Phipps
Board of Directors: Kenneth C Dahlberg, Egon P Durban, Michael V Hayden, Clayton M Jones, Judy C Lewent, Gregory K Mondre, Anne R Pramaggiore, Samuel C Scott III

D-U-N-S 00-552-7247 IMP/EXP
■ MOTOROLA SOLUTIONS SALES AND SERVICES
(*Suby of* MOTOROLA SOLUTIONS INC) ★
1303 E Algonquin Rd, Schaumburg, IL 60196-1079
Tel (847) 576-1000 *Founded/Ownrshp* 1952
Sales 396.3MM[E] *EMP* 2,500
SIC 5065 Electronic parts; Mobile telephone equipment
**Pr:* Edward Fitzpatrick
**CEO:* Greg Brown
**CFO:* David Devonshire
**Treas:* Garth Milne
**Ex VP:* Gino A Bonanotte
**Ex VP:* Mark Moon
**Sr VP:* Eduardo Conrado
**Sr VP:* Mark S Hacker
Snr Sftwr: Frank Wong
Opers Mgr: Reggie Barnes
Snr Mgr: Craig Wess

D-U-N-S 05-455-0371
■ MOTORS INSURANCE CORP
MIC
(*Suby of* GMAC) ★
300 Galleria Officentre # 201, Southfield, MI 48034-8461
Tel (248) 263-6000 *Founded/Ownrshp* 2008
Sales NA *EMP* 2,260
SIC 6331

D-U-N-S 05-249-9873
MOTORSPORT AFTERMARKET GROUP INC
(*Suby of* LDI LTD LLC) ★
17771 Mitchell N Ste A, Irvine, CA 92614-6028
Tel (949) 440-5500 *Founded/Ownrshp* 2014
Sales 930.6MM[E] *EMP* 1,150
SIC 3751 Motorcycle accessories
CEO: J A Lacy
**Pr:* Brian Etter

D-U-N-S 07-194-5906 IMP/EXP
MOTOSPORT INC
15353 Sw Sequoia Pkwy # 140, Portland, OR 97224-7283
Tel (503) 783-5600 *Founded/Ownrshp* 2005
Sales 85.7MM[E] *EMP* 200
SIC 5571 Motorcycle parts & accessories
Dir: Ian Griffith
Sftwr Eng: Andy Manliguez

D-U-N-S 00-193-9826
MOTT CHARLES STEWART FOUNDATION INC (MI)
503 S Saginaw St Ste 1200, Flint, MI 48502-1807
Tel (810) 238-5651 *Founded/Ownrshp* 1926
Sales 106.7MM *EMP* 106
SIC 6732 Charitable trust management
Ch Bd: William S White
Ch Bd: William S Flint
Ofcr: Maggie Potter
VP: Maureen H Flint
VP: Marilyn Stein Lefeber
**VP:* Phillip Peters
**VP:* Maureen Smyth
**VP:* Robert E Swaney Jr
Pgrm Dir: Sam Passmore

MOTTS
See MOTTS LLP

D-U-N-S 06-987-1200 IMP/EXP
■ MOTTS LLP
MOTTS
(*Suby of* DR PEPPER SNAPPLE GROUP INC) ★
55 Hunter Ln, Elmsford, NY 10523-1334
Tel (972) 673-8088 *Founded/Ownrshp* 2008
Sales 228.8MM[E] *EMP* 1,000
SIC 2033 5149 2087 Fruit juices: packaged in cans, jars, etc.; Apple sauce: packaged in cans, jars, etc.; Beverage concentrates; Cocktail mixes, nonalcoholic
MIS Dir: Jeff Morgan
**Genl Couns:* Jim Baldwin

MOTUS INTEGRATED TECHNOLOGIES
See MOTUS LLC

D-U-N-S 07-921-5669
MOTUS LLC
MOTUS INTEGRATED TECHNOLOGIES
(*Suby of* MOTUS US HOLDING B.V.)
88 E 48th St, Holland, MI 49423-9307
Tel (616) 422-7479 *Founded/Ownrshp* 2013, 2014
Sales 265.9MM[E] *EMP* 760
SIC 3465 Body parts, automobile: stamped metal
Treas: Beth Haseley
VP: Stacy Spondike
Tech Mgr: Chad Krusniak

D-U-N-S 96-301-6535
MOUNDS VIEW PUBLIC SCHOOL DISTRICT
350 Highway 96 W, Shoreview, MN 55126-1951
Tel (651) 621-6017 *Founded/Ownrshp* 1952
Sales 298.8M *EMP* 1,500[E]
SIC 8211 Elementary & secondary schools
CEO: Dan Hooverman
CFO: Carol Neilsen

MOUNDS VIEW SCHOOL DISTRICT 62
See IND SCHOOL DIST 621

D-U-N-S 07-381-2125
MOUNT AUBURN HOSPITAL
(*Suby of* CAREGROUP INC) ★
330 Mount Auburn St, Cambridge, MA 02138-5597
Tel (617) 492-3500 *Founded/Ownrshp* 1871
Sales 316.1MM *EMP* 1,700
SIC 8062 General medical & surgical hospitals
CEO: Jeanette G Clough
**CFO:* Peter Semaneza
Dir Sec: Norman Colling
MIS Dir: Eric Flint
MIS Dir: Robert Todd
QA Dir: Margaret Martello
Info Man: Andrew Gardner
Info Man: Doug Weil
Mktg Dir: Michael Oconnell
Pathlgst: John Perry
Obsttrcn: Esther M Yun

D-U-N-S 95-884-2643
MOUNT CARMEL EAST HOSPITAL
(*Suby of* NIAGARA HEALTH CORP) ★
6001 E Broad St, Columbus, OH 43213-1570
Tel (614) 234-6000 *Founded/Ownrshp* 1995
Sales 145.4MM[E] *EMP* 1,100
SIC 8062 General medical & surgical hospitals
CEO: Joseph Calvaruso
Exec: Beth Waite
QA Dir: Katie Barga
Surgeon: Melinda K Jack
Surgeon: Aaron D Kulwicki
Doctor: Thomas Brady
Doctor: Timothy J Wynn
HC Dir: Tiffany Anderson

D-U-N-S 07-504-0121
MOUNT CARMEL HEALTH
(*Suby of* NIAGARA HEALTH CORP) ★
793 W State St, Columbus, OH 43222-1551
Tel (614) 234-5000 *Founded/Ownrshp* 1995
Sales 260.9MM[E] *EMP* 3,507
SIC 8062 General medical & surgical hospitals; Hospital, professional nursing school
Prin: Marcia Ladue
COO: Sloan A Fache
CFO: Jackie Prineau
VP: Larry Swanner MD
Mktg Dir: Robyn Morton
Orthpdst: James A Sides
Doctor: Laurie M Chevalier MD

D-U-N-S 07-975-8372
MOUNT CARMEL HEALTH PLAN MEDIG
6150 E Broad St, Columbus, OH 43213-1574
Tel (614) 546-3138 *Founded/Ownrshp* 2013
Sales 423.5MM *EMP* 3[E]
SIC 8099 Health & allied services

D-U-N-S 04-912-6871
MOUNT CARMEL HEALTH SYSTEM
MOUNT CARMEL WEST HOSPITAL
(*Suby of* CATHOLIC HEALTH EAST) ★
793 W State St, Columbus, OH 43222-1551
Tel (614) 234-5000 *Founded/Ownrshp* 2010
Sales 707.2MM *EMP* 1[E]
SIC 8062 General medical & surgical hospitals
Sr VP: Barbara Hahl
VP: Bruce Lucas
VP: Brian Smith
Exec: Tonya Globnik
Dir Risk M: Billie Watson
Dir Lab: Randy Clark
Ex Dir: Joy Parker
Prgrm Mgr: Lori A Cropper
Off Mgr: Christie Schlaegel
Software D: Jodi Doherty
Sfty Dirs: Gina Birko

D-U-N-S 04-965-3066
MOUNT CARMEL HEALTH SYSTEM
CATHOLIC HEALTH EAST
(*Suby of* CATHOLIC HEALTH EAST) ★
6150 E Broad St, Columbus, OH 43213-1574
Tel (614) 234-6000 *Founded/Ownrshp* 1995
Sales 1.2MMM *EMP* 8,000
SIC 8062 General medical & surgical hospitals
CEO: Claus Von Zychlin
**Pr:* Douglas H Stine
Treas: Michael Cooney
Ofcr: Marsha Newkirk
VP: Christine Aucreman
VP: Tessa Burke
VP: David Cozier
VP: Lyn Flanagan
VP: Bob Waldeck
Software D: Catherine Bock
Software D: Cramblit Debbie

D-U-N-S 96-489-7487
MOUNT CARMEL NEW ALBANY SURGICAL HOSPITAL
7333 Smiths Mill Rd, New Albany, OH 43054-9291
Tel (614) 775-6600 *Founded/Ownrshp* 2010
Sales 113.5MM *EMP* 37[E]
SIC 8062 General medical & surgical hospitals
Chf Nrs Of: Lynda Yonker
Occ Thrpy: Mary Zappa

MOUNT CARMEL WEST HOSPITAL
See MOUNT CARMEL HEALTH SYSTEM

D-U-N-S 07-635-7946
MOUNT CLEMENS REGIONAL MEDICAL CENTER
PLUMBROOK FAMILY MEDICINE
(*Suby of* MCLAREN FLINT) ★
1000 Harrington St, Mount Clemens, MI 48043-2920
Tel (586) 493-8000 *Founded/Ownrshp* 1944
Sales 285.0MM[E] *EMP* 2,249
SIC 8062 General medical & surgical hospitals
CEO: Thomas M Brisse
Pr: Mark O'Halla
Off Mgr: Bridget Berlin
VP Opers: Susan Durst
Sfty Dirs: Bruce Anderson

D-U-N-S 06-238-6883 IMP
MOUNT FRANKLIN FOODS LLC (TX)
ELAMF
1800 Northwestern Dr, El Paso, TX 79912-1122
Tel (915) 877-4079 *Founded/Ownrshp* 1914, 2006
Sales 475.2MM[E] *EMP* 980
SIC 5145 2068 2064

D-U-N-S 00-783-6462
MOUNT NITTANY HEALTH SYSTEM
1800 E Park Ave, State College, PA 16803-6709
Tel (814) 231-7040 *Founded/Ownrshp* 2011
Sales 354.1M *EMP* 1,321[E]
SIC 8062 General medical & surgical hospitals
Pr: Steven Brown
Owner: Robert Foust

D-U-N-S 06-979-6241 IMP
MOUNT NITTANY MEDICAL CENTER
(*Suby of* MOUNT NITTANY HEALTH SYSTEM) ★
1800 E Park Ave, State College, PA 16803-6797
Tel (814) 231-7000 *Founded/Ownrshp* 1902
Sales 331.0MM *EMP* 902
Accts Baker Tilly Virchow Krause Llp
SIC 8062 General medical & surgical hospitals
CEO: Richard Wisniewski
CFO: Richard Wiesensky
Bd of Dir: Julie Charnosky
Ofcr: Steven Brown
Ofcr: Scott Kaufman

**Ex VP:* David B Peterson
**Sr VP:* Janet Schachtner
Comm Dir: Maureen Karstetter
Dir Rad: Jenny Foreman
Dir Rad: Dana Miller
Dir Rx: John Rossi

D-U-N-S 00-318-3902 IMP
MOUNT OLIVE PICKLE CO INC (NC)
THAT'S PICKLICIOUS
1 Cucumber Blvd, Mount Olive, NC 28365-1210
Tel (919) 658-2535 *Founded/Ownrshp* 1926
Sales 198.6MM[E] *EMP* 600
SIC 2035 Pickles, vinegar; Relishes, vinegar
Pr: William H Bryan
**VP:* Richard D Bowen
**VP:* A Douglas Brock
**VP:* Robert D Frye Jr
Manager: Debbie Jones

D-U-N-S 04-708-3662
MOUNT PLEASANT INDEPENDENT SCHOOL DISTRICT
2230 N Edwards Ave, Mount Pleasant, TX 75455-2036
Tel (903) 575-2000 *Founded/Ownrshp* 1851
Sales 54.2MM *EMP* 1,050
Accts Arnold Walker Arnold & Co
SIC 8211 Public elementary & secondary schools
Pr Dir: Judi Saxton
Psych: Lela Elliott
Psych: Sarah Long
HC Dir: Debra Malone

MOUNT SAINT MARY'S SEMINARY
See MOUNT SAINT MARYS UNIVERSITY INC

D-U-N-S 07-495-0254
MOUNT SAINT MARYS UNIVERSITY INC
MOUNT SAINT MARY'S SEMINARY
16300 Old Emmitsburg Rd, Emmitsburg, MD 21727-7702
Tel (301) 447-3723 *Founded/Ownrshp* 1808
Sales 124.2MM[E] *EMP* 890
Accts Mcgladrey Llp Gaithersburg M
SIC 8221 College, except junior
Pr: Simon Newman
Ofcr: Matthew Lewis
Ofcr: Tracy Reagan
**VP:* Robert Brennan
**VP:* William Davies
**VP:* Pauline Engelstater
**VP:* David Rehm
**VP:* Paula Whetsel-Ribeau
**Int Pr:* Timothy Trainor
IT Man: Kathy Fissel
IT Man: Lynn Ott

D-U-N-S 94-645-9583
MOUNT SINAI HEALTH SYSTEM INC
150 E 42nd St Bsmt 2, New York, NY 10017-5642
Tel (646) 605-4750 *Founded/Ownrshp* 2013
Sales 2.0MMM[E] *EMP* 20,000
SIC 8011 Health maintenance organization; Group health association
Pr: Kenneth L Davis
Doctor: Rica Arnon

MOUNT SINAI HOSPITAL
See SINAI CHILDRENS HOSPITAL

MOUNT SINAI HOSPITAL, THE
See ICAHN SCHOOL OF MEDICINE AT MOUNT SINAI

D-U-N-S 05-830-2266 IMP
MOUNT SINAI HOSPITAL
(*Suby of* MOUNT SINAI HEALTH SYSTEM INC) ★
1 Gustave L Levy Pl Fl 12, New York, NY 10029-6574
Tel (212) 241-6500 *Founded/Ownrshp* 1852
Sales 2.0MMM *EMP* 12,559
SIC 8062 General medical & surgical hospitals
Pr: Kenneth L Davis
Chf Mktg O: Deborah Marin
VP: Diane Adams
VP: Mark Delaney
VP: Colin Lahiff
VP: Randy Numbers
VP: Robin Solomon
Assoc Dir: Jeffery Beck
Dir Rad: Josef Machac
Dir Rx: Ravi Iyengar
Dir Bus: Sean Healy

D-U-N-S 07-443-3046 IMP
MOUNT SINAI HOSPITAL MEDICAL CENTER OF CHICAGO
FRIENDS OF SINAI CHILDREN
1501 S California Ave, Chicago, IL 60608-1732
Tel (773) 542-2000 *Founded/Ownrshp* 1918
Sales 280.7MM *EMP* 1,700
SIC 8062 Hospital, AMA approved residency
Pr: Alan Channing
**CFO:* Charles Weis
Treas: Linda Manning
**Ex VP:* Rachel Dvorken
**VP:* David Berkey
VP: Peter Ingram
Phys Thrpy: Brenda Koverman

D-U-N-S 04-602-5144
MOUNT SINAI MEDICAL CENTER OF FLORIDA INC
4300 Alton Rd, Miami Beach, FL 33140-2948
Tel (305) 674-2121 *Founded/Ownrshp* 1946
Sales 533.0MM *EMP* 3,225[E]
SIC 8062 8741 General medical & surgical hospitals; Management services
Pr: Steven Sonenreich
**Ch Bd:* Wayne Chaplain
**CFO:* Alex Mendez
Ofcr: Caesar Nunez
Sr VP: Robert Goldszer
VP: Wayne Chukan
VP: Charles Koch
**VP:* Angel Pallin
VP: Amy Perry
VP: Mike Phillips
Exec: Morton Robinson
Dir Teleco: Allison Grabin
Dir Lab: Robert Poppiti

Assoc Dir: Albert Golebiowski
Dir Rad: Karin Knesaurek
Dir Rx: Mukush Shah

MOUNT ST MARY'S HOSPITAL AND H
See MOUNT ST MARYS HOSPITAL OF NIAGARA FALLS

D-U-N-S 07-147-4316
MOUNT ST MARYS HOSPITAL OF NIAGARA FALLS
MOUNT ST MARY'S HOSPITAL AND H
5300 Military Rd, Lewiston, NY 14092-1903
Tel (716) 297-4800 *Founded/Ownrshp* 1909
Sales 91.1MM *EMP* 832
SIC 8062 Hospital, medical school affiliated with nursing & residency
Pr: Judith A Maness
**Pr:* Judy Maness
**CFO:* Michael Ickowski
VP: Barbara Bucci
**VP:* Deborah Serafin
CIO: Dick Witkowski

D-U-N-S 00-308-2203 IMP/EXP
MOUNT VERNON MILLS INC (MD)
(*Suby of* R B PAMPLIN CORP) ★
503 S Main St, Mauldin, SC 29662-2204
Tel (864) 688-7100 *Founded/Ownrshp* 1847, 1982
Sales 393.8MM[E] *EMP* 2,700
SIC 2211 2221 2281

MOUNTAIN AMERICA CREDIT UNION
See MOUNTAIN AMERICA FEDERAL CREDIT UNION

D-U-N-S 07-311-5537
MOUNTAIN AMERICA FEDERAL CREDIT UNION
MOUNTAIN AMERICA CREDIT UNION
7181 S Campus View Dr, West Jordan, UT 84084-4312
Tel (801) 325-6228 *Founded/Ownrshp* 1952
Sales NA *EMP* 1,033
SIC 6062 State credit unions, not federally chartered
Pr: Sterling Nielsen
**CFO:* Chad Curtis
Ofcr: John M Holt
Ofcr: Nicole Persons
Ofcr: Torri Rydalch
Sr VP: Dennis Bromley
Sr VP: Pamela Lewis
Sr VP: Tony Rasmussen
Sr VP: Jason Rogers
Sr VP: Catherine Smoyer
Sr VP: Michael Turner
VP: Jade Beckman
VP: Jonathan Brouse
VP: Tammy Bryant
VP: David Glod
VP: Jared Johnstone
VP: Chad Waddoups
VP: Christy Zaudke
Exec: Marshall Paepke

D-U-N-S 03-467-6981
MOUNTAIN EMPIRE OIL CO
ROADRUNNER MARKETS
282 Christian Church Rd, Johnson City, TN 37615-4475
Tel (423) 928-7241 *Founded/Ownrshp* 1977
Sales 131.4MM[E] *EMP* 450
SIC 5541 5411 Filling stations, gasoline; Convenience stores
Pr: Ryan Broyles
**Sec:* Ralph Fellars
**VP:* John Kelly

D-U-N-S 80-884-5473 IMP
■ **MOUNTAIN HARDWEAR INC**
MONTRAIL
(*Suby of* COLUMBIA SPORTSWEAR USA CORP) ★
1414 Harbour Way S, Richmond, CA 94804-3694
Tel (510) 558-3000 *Founded/Ownrshp* 1993
Sales 8.2MM[E] *EMP* 1,500
SIC 2399 2394 5651

D-U-N-S 01-079-2922
MOUNTAIN RANGE RESTAURANTS LLC
825 S 48th St, Tempe, AZ 85281-5101
Tel (480) 829-5090 *Founded/Ownrshp* 2001
Sales 51.8MM[E] *EMP* 2,500
SIC 5812 Restaurant, family: chain

D-U-N-S 06-318-9898
MOUNTAIN STATES HEALTH ALLIANCE
400 N State Of Frnklin Rd, Johnson City, TN 37604-6035
Tel (423) 431-6111 *Founded/Ownrshp* 1945
Sales 707.3MM *EMP* 5,978
SIC 8741 Management services
Pr: Dennis Vonderfecht
Pr: Melissa Carr
**CFO:* Marvin Eichorn
Ofcr: Patricia Niday
VP: Bill Alton
VP: Tony Benton
VP: William C Fache
Exec: Charles Dugger
Comm Man: Teresa Hicks
Prac Mgr: Kimberly Hunt
Plng Mgr: Allison Rogers

D-U-N-S 62-139-6514
MOUNTAIN STATES HEALTH ALLIANCE
JOHNSON CITY MEDICAL CENTER
(*Suby of* MOUNTAIN STATES HEALTH ALLIANCE) ★
400 N State Of Frnklin Rd, Johnson City, TN 37604-6035
Tel (423) 431-6111 *Founded/Ownrshp* 1978
Sales 280.1MM[E] *EMP* 2,300
SIC 8062 General medical & surgical hospitals
**Sr VP:* Marvin Eichorn
VP: Ed Herbert
VP: Kenneth E Marshall
Dir Rx: Trish Tanner
Psych: Grace Pereira
Pharmcst: Richard Mackin

D-U-N-S 18-208-6835
MOUNTAIN STATES STEEL INC
325 S Geneva Rd Ste 1, Lindon, UT 84042-1698
Tel (801) 785-5085 *Founded/Ownrshp* 1987
Sales 83.1MM[E] *EMP* 170
Accts Squire & Company Orem Utah
SIC 3441 Fabricated structural metal for bridges; Building components, structural steel
Pr: J Chris Olsen
VP: Chris Olsen
**VP:* Jack Olsen
Exec: Brad Olsen
Genl Mgr: Geaniel Rowley
QC Dir: Jeff Perry

D-U-N-S 07-298-2929
MOUNTAIN STATES TUMOR INSTITUTE INC
190 E Bannock St, Boise, ID 83712-6241
Tel (208) 381-2222 *Founded/Ownrshp* 1969
Sales 116.5MM *EMP* 80
SIC 8093 Specialty outpatient clinics
**Treas:* Clarence Pomeroy
**VP:* Gary Fletcher

D-U-N-S 00-634-8890
MOUNTAIN VALLEY SPRING CO LLC
283 Mountain Vly Wtr Pl, Hot Springs Village, AR 71909-9559
Tel (501) 623-6671 *Founded/Ownrshp* 2002
Sales 494.7MM[E] *EMP* 2,600
SIC 5084 Industrial machinery & equipment
Ch: James Speed
VP Opers: Mike Eccles
Ql Cn Mgr: Karen Malone
Ql Cn Mgr: Jo Russell-Price
VP Sls: Don Simmons
Manager: Kelly Davidson

D-U-N-S 18-850-7974
MOUNTAIN VALLEY SPRING CO LLC
CLEAR MTN NATURAL SPRING WTR
283 Mountain Vly Wtr Pl, Hot Springs, AR 71909-9559
Tel (501) 624-7329 *Founded/Ownrshp* 2014
Sales 107.1MM[E] *EMP* 148
SIC 5149 5499 Mineral or spring water bottling; Water: distilled mineral or spring
CEO: Breck Speed
**CFO:* Brad Frieberg
**VP:* John Speed
Sls Dir: Speed Stodghill

D-U-N-S 82-550-6756
MOUNTAIN VIEW AG SERVICES INC
13281 Avenue 416, Orosi, CA 93647-9405
Tel (559) 528-6004 *Founded/Ownrshp* 2009
Sales 6.2MM *EMP* 1,200
SIC 0761 Farm labor contractors
Pr: Leonard Hutchinson
**Sec:* Sonya Hutchinson

D-U-N-S 16-873-5116
MOUNTAIN VIEW CO-OP
2200 Old Havre Hwy, Black Eagle, MT 59414-1043
Tel (406) 453-5900 *Founded/Ownrshp* 2002
Sales 91.3MM[E] *EMP* 175[E]
SIC 5541 5153 2875 5191 Filling stations, gasoline; Grain elevators; Fertilizers, mixing only; Farm supplies
Pr: Del Styren
**VP:* Terry Allen
Sfty Mgr: Dan Sieler

D-U-N-S 07-526-8318
MOUNTAIN VIEW ELEMENTARY SCHOOL DISTRICT
MOUNTAIN VIEW SCHOOL DISTRICT
3320 Gilman Rd, El Monte, CA 91732-3201
Tel (626) 652-4000 *Founded/Ownrshp* 1898
Sales 56.1MM[E] *EMP* 1,013
Accts Vicenti Lloyd & Stutzman Llp
SIC 8211 Public elementary school
**Pr:* Patsy Sutley
**CFO:* Steve Thomas
Bd of Dir: Robert Griffith
Exec: Michele Earle
Rgnl Mgr: George Schonborn
Genl Mgr: Lisa Loop
Genl Mgr: Deo Persaud

D-U-N-S 12-115-6983
MOUNTAIN VIEW HOSPITAL LLC
READYCARE
2325 Coronado St, Idaho Falls, ID 83404-7407
Tel (208) 557-2700 *Founded/Ownrshp* 1999
Sales 136.7MM *EMP* 420[E]
SIC 8062 General medical & surgical hospitals
Pr: Jeffery L Sayer
Brnch Mgr: Scott Nelson

MOUNTAIN VIEW SCHOOL DISTRICT
See MOUNTAIN VIEW ELEMENTARY SCHOOL DISTRICT

D-U-N-S 78-476-1780
MOUNTAIN VISTA MEDICAL CENTER LP
(*Suby of* IASIS HEALTHCARE CORP) ★
1301 S Crismon Rd, Mesa, AZ 85209-3767
Tel (480) 358-6100 *Founded/Ownrshp* 2015
Sales 164.2MM *EMP* 600
SIC 8062 General medical & surgical hospitals
CEO: Anthony R Marinello
CFO: Darryl Linnington
Dir Rx: Kal Stiles

D-U-N-S 04-610-0065
MOUNTAIN VISTA SURGICAL SPECIALISTS
(*Suby of* IASIS HEALTHCARE LLC) ★
10238 E Hampton Ave # 402, Mesa, AZ 85209-3319
Tel (480) 354-3200 *Founded/Ownrshp* 2010
Sales 674.9M[E] *EMP* 1,994[E]
SIC 8011 General & family practice, physician/surgeon

D-U-N-S 13-234-5120 EXP
MOUNTAIN WEST LLC
4212 S Highway 191, Rexburg, ID 83440-4251
Tel (208) 359-5640 *Founded/Ownrshp* 1999
Sales 98.7MM[E] *EMP* 150
SIC 1429 Basalt, crushed & broken-quarrying
Treas: David Wolfe
Sales Exec: Lyle Jeppesen

D-U-N-S 11-274-6458
MOUNTAINEER GAS CO
501 56th St Se, Charleston, WV 25304-2323
Tel (888) 420-4427 *Founded/Ownrshp* 1957
Sales 251.7MM[E] *EMP* 489[E]
SIC 4924 Natural gas distribution
Pr: Tom M Tylor
**Treas:* Scott F Klemm
**VP:* Danny Chandler
**VP:* Michael N Trusty
VP Admn: Moses Skaff
Genl Mgr: Gary Barnard

MOUNTAINEER RACE TRACK RESORT
See PARK MOUNTAINEER INC

MOUNTAINSIDE HOSPITAL
See HACKENSACKUMC MOUNTAINSIDE

D-U-N-S 83-817-7129
MOUNTAINVIEW HOSPITAL INC
SUNRISE MOUNTAIN VIEW HOSPITAL
3100 N Tenaya Way, Las Vegas, NV 89128-0436
Tel (702) 255-5000 *Founded/Ownrshp* 1996
Sales 127.3MM[E] *EMP* 1,051
SIC 8062 8011 4119 General medical & surgical hospitals; Offices & clinics of medical doctors; Ambulance service
CEO: Chris Mowan
**COO:* JD Melchiode
COO: J D Melchioe
COO: Tad Morley
**CFO:* Steve Killian
Chf Mktg O: Linda Erwin
Dir IT: Donna Forrester
Sls&Mrk Ex: Louise Colwill

MOUNTAINVIEW REGIONAL MED CTR
See LAS CRUCES MEDICAL CENTER LLC

D-U-N-S 11-112-9115
MOUNTAINVIEW THOROUGHBRED RACING ASSOCIATION LLC
HOLLYWOOD CASINO
777 Hollywood Blvd, Grantville, PA 17028-9237
Tel (717) 469-2211 *Founded/Ownrshp* 1986
Sales 52.5MM[E] *EMP* 1,100
SIC 7999 Off-track betting
Pr: Peter Carlino
**CFO:* Tim Ebling
VP: Garlon Banks
**VP:* Frank Quigley
Exec: Ken Shapiro

D-U-N-S 00-634-3958 IMP/EXP
MOUNTAIRE CORP (AR)
1901 Napa Valley Dr, Little Rock, AR 72212-3913
Tel (501) 372-6524 *Founded/Ownrshp* 1964
Sales 1.3MMM[E] *EMP* 6,079
SIC 2015 Poultry slaughtering & processing
Pr: Ronald M Cameron
**CFO:* Dabbs Cavin
CFO: Alan H Duncan
**Treas:* Gina Risberg
**Ex VP:* Dee Ann Landreth
**VP:* Alan Duncan
Genl Mgr: Andrew Cobb

D-U-N-S 09-181-2669 IMP/EXP
MOUNTAIRE FARMS INC
(*Suby of* MOUNTAIRE CORP) ★
1901 Napa Valley Dr, Little Rock, AR 72212-3913
Tel (501) 372-6524 *Founded/Ownrshp* 1980
Sales 1.0MMM[E] *EMP* 4,100
SIC 2015 Poultry slaughtering & processing
Pr: Paul Downes
**Ch Bd:* Ronald Cameron
**CFO:* Dabbs Cavin
**Treas:* Gina Risberg
**VP:* Alan Duncan
**VP:* Dee A Landreth
QA Dir: Elizabeth Krushinskie

D-U-N-S 00-101-8816 EXP
MOUNTAIRE FARMS OF DELAWARE INC
(*Suby of* MOUNTAIRE CORP) ★
1901 Napa Valley Dr, Little Rock, AR 72212-3913
Tel (501) 372-6524 *Founded/Ownrshp* 2000
Sales 34.3MM[E] *EMP* 1,500
SIC 0751 Poultry services
Pr: Paul Downes
**Ch Bd:* Ronald Cameron
**CFO:* Dabbs Cavin
**Treas:* Gina Risberg
**Sr VP:* Dee Ann Landreth
**VP:* Alan H Duncan

D-U-N-S 01-250-1922 IMP/EXP
MOUNTAIRE FARMS OF DELAWARE INC
(*Suby of* MOUNTAIRE CORP) ★
29005 John J Williams Hwy, Millsboro, DE 19966-4095
Tel (302) 934-1100 *Founded/Ownrshp* 2000
Sales 321.5MM[E] *EMP* 1,699
SIC 2015 Poultry slaughtering & processing
CEO: Paul Downs
**Ch Bd:* Ronald Cameron
**CFO:* Dabbs Cavin
**Ex VP:* Dee Ann English
VP: Dan Bailey
**VP:* Phil Plylar
VP: Beth B Sise
Dir IT: Bill Saulsbury
IT Man: Chad Elliott
IT Man: Lollita Ramcharran
IT Man: Michael Taylor

D-U-N-S 08-869-8097
MOUNTRAIL-WILLIAMS ELECTRIC COOPERATIVE
218 58th St W, Williston, ND 58801
Tel (701) 577-3765 *Founded/Ownrshp* 1944
Sales 211.5MM *EMP* 86[E]
SIC 4911 Distribution, electric power

IT Man: Cole Arndt
IT Man: Jay Lux

D-U-N-S 00-330-8558 IMP/EXP
MOUNTVILLE MILLS INC (GA)
ANDRESON COMPANY, THE
1729 S Davis Rd, Lagrange, GA 30241-6172
Tel (706) 882-2961 *Founded/Ownrshp* 1963
Sales 132.2MM^E *EMP* 500
SIC 2273 2211 2221 Door mats: paper, grass, reed, coir, sisal, jute, rags, etc.; Broadwoven fabric mills, cotton; Broadwoven fabric mills, manmade
CEO: Emmett David Jr Hart
**Ch Bd:* David Hart
**CFO:* Susan H Ekkebus
VP: Bud Paulk
**VP:* David Watterson
VP Admn: Anna Turner
Off Admin: Brenda Toney
Dir IT: Michael Eastman
IT Man: Artie Todd
Web Dev: Jennifer Smith
Sftwr Eng: Caleb Duncan

D-U-N-S 16-119-4410 IMP
■ MOUSER ELECTRONICS INC
MOUSER TRONICS
(*Suby of* TTI INC) ★
1000 N Main St, Mansfield, TX 76063-1514
Tel (817) 804-3800 *Founded/Ownrshp* 1964
Sales 814.3MM^E *EMP* 500
SIC 5065 Electronic parts
Ch Bd: Paul Andrews
**Ch Bd:* Warren Buffett
**CEO:* Glenn Smith
Sr VP: Jeff Newell
VP: Kevin Hess
VP: Andy Kerr
VP: Hayne Shumate
VP: Stephanie Sorrell
VP: Dan Troutt
Telecom Ex: Scott Williams
IT Man: Bruce Jamilkowski

MOUSERTRONICS
See MOUSER ELECTRONICS INC

D-U-N-S 04-619-5103 IMP
▲ MOVADO GROUP INC
650 From Rd Ste 375, Paramus, NJ 07652-3556
Tel (201) 267-8000 *Founded/Ownrshp* 1881
Sales 594.9MM *EMP* 1,100^E
Tkr Sym MOV *Exch* NYS
SIC 3873 3915 7631 Watches, clocks, watchcases & parts; Jewel preparing: instruments, tools, watches & jewelry; Watch repair
Ch Bd: Efraim Grinberg
Pr: Ricardo Quintero
CFO: Sallie A Demarsilis
Chf Mktg O: Mary Leach
**Sr VP:* Alex Grinberg
Sr VP: Frank A Morelli
Sr VP: Mitchell C Sussis
VP: Scott Gregory
Rgnl Mgr: Craig Massa
Store Mgr: Cheryl Doucet
CTO: Valerio Gambino
Board of Directors: Margaret Hayes Adame, Peter A Bridgman, Richard J Cote, Alan H Howard, Richard Isserman, Nathan Leventhal, Maurice Reznik

D-U-N-S 03-535-7768
■ MOVE INC
(*Suby of* NEWS CORP) ★
3315 Scott Blvd Ste 250, Santa Clara, CA 95054-3139
Tel (408) 558-7100 *Founded/Ownrshp* 2014
Sales 227.0MM *EMP* 913
SIC 6531 Real estate listing services; Multiple listing service, real estate
CEO: Steven H Berkowitz
Pr: Sunil Mehrotra
Pr: Eric Thorkilsen
**CFO:* Bryan Charap
**CFO:* Rachel C Glaser
**Chf Mktg O:* Nate Johnson
**Ofcr:* Vineet Singh
**Ex VP:* James S Caulfield
Ex VP: Luke Glass
Ex VP: Marcy Greenberg
Ex VP: Jeremy R Lent
Ex VP: Ray Picard
Sr VP: M Jeffrey Charney
Sr VP: Hahn Lee
Sr VP: Suzanne Zinn Mueller
VP: Michael Douglas
VP: Julie Karafiath
VP: Janice McDill
VP: Anthony Perry
VP: Celeste Starchild

D-U-N-S 86-945-2177 IMP/EXP
MOVIE GALLERY INC
9275 Sw Peyton Ln, Wilsonville, OR 97070-9200
Tel (503) 570-1700 *Founded/Ownrshp* 1994
Sales 575.2MM^E *EMP* 36,250
SIC 7841 5735 Video tape rental; Film or tape rental, motion picture; Video tapes, prerecorded; Video discs, prerecorded
Pr: Clarence J Gabriel Jr
**CFO:* Lucinda M Baier
**Chf Mktg O:* Wes Sand
**Chf Mktg O:* Clifford Torng
Ex VP: Guy Marsala
**Ex VP:* Craig J Miller
Ex VP: Pamela R Schneide
**Ex VP:* Pamela R Schneider
VP: Sherif J Mityas
Dist Mgr: Karen Osborn
Dist Mgr: Mel Phillips
Board of Directors: Robert Fiorella, Mark E Holliday, Thomas B McGrath, Steven D Scheiwe, Richard L Shorten Jr, Neil S Subin

MOVIE STAR
See FREDERICKS OF HOLLYWOOD INC

MOVIE STAR
See FOH GROUP INC

D-U-N-S 82-585-2189
MOWAT CONSTRUCTION CO
20210 142nd Ave Ne, Woodinville, WA 98072-4477
Tel (425) 398-0205 *Founded/Ownrshp* 1994
Sales 90.0MM^E *EMP* 180
Accts Moss Adams Llp Everett Washi
SIC 1611 General contractor, highway & street construction
Ch Bd: Mark Mowat
**Pr:* John Sandstrom
VP: Janifer Hays
**VP:* Doug Smith
Board of Directors: Mark Mowat

MOXEE RANCH
See ZIRKLE FRUIT CO

D-U-N-S 01-458-8107 EXP
MOYER & SON INC
113 E Reliance Rd, Souderton, PA 18964-1308
Tel (215) 799-2000 *Founded/Ownrshp* 1869
Sales 121.6MM^E *EMP* 240
SIC 5191 5983 2875 0782 1711 Animal feeds; Fuel oil dealers; Fertilizers, mixing only; Lawn care services; Plumbing, heating, air-conditioning contractors
Pr: John Moyer
**VP:* Jon Clemmer
**VP:* David A Moyer
Div Mgr: Lori Klinger
Opers Mgr: John Haley

D-U-N-S 02-436-3376
MOYLE PETROLEUM CO (SD)
COMMON CENTS STORES
2504 W Main St, Rapid City, SD 57702-2424
Tel (605) 343-1966 *Founded/Ownrshp* 1957
Sales 136.3MM^E *EMP* 400
SIC 5541 5411 Filling stations, gasoline; Convenience stores
CEO: Gilbert D Moyle III
**Pr:* Gilbert D Moyle
**Treas:* E Steve Mentele
**VP:* Clark Moyle
Exec: Jack Sullivan
Telecom Ex: Derek Budahl
IT Man: Andy Foster
Mktg Dir: Darcy Paluch

D-U-N-S 08-027-2476 EXP
MOZA LLC
101 Church St Ofc 5, Moscow, PA 18444-9115
Tel (570) 848-7926 *Founded/Ownrshp* 2009
Sales 200.0MM^E *EMP* 4
SIC 5141 7389 Food brokers;

D-U-N-S 05-112-2146 IMP
MP DIRECT INC
TALK2US
4800 126th Ave N, Clearwater, FL 33762-4709
Tel (727) 572-8443 *Founded/Ownrshp* 2000
Sales 84.9MM^E *EMP* 530
SIC 5094 5944 5091 Clocks, watches & parts; Clock & watch stores; Golf equipment
Pr: Kenneth W Byers

D-U-N-S 62-278-9923
MP ENVIRONMENTAL SERVICES INC
3400 Manor St, Bakersfield, CA 93308-1451
Tel (800) 458-3036 *Founded/Ownrshp* 1991
Sales 117.3MM^E *EMP* 225
SIC 4953 4213 8748 7699 Hazardous waste collection & disposal; Radioactive waste materials, disposal; Trucking, except local; Environmental consultant; Tank repair & cleaning services
Pr: Dawn Calderwood
Opers Mgr: Shawn Calderwood

D-U-N-S 12-960-8126 IMP
MP NEXLEVEL LLC
500 County Road 37, Maple Lake, MN 55358-2864
Tel (320) 963-2400 *Founded/Ownrshp* 2002
Sales 233.6MM^E *EMP* 600^E
Accts Larsonallen Llp Minneapolis
SIC 1623 Gas main construction; Cable television line construction; Electric power line construction
Pr: Larry Pribyl
CFO: Mike Aydt
**VP:* Robbi Pribyl
**VP:* Timothy Pribyl
Sls Dir: Derek Groth

MPA
See MOTORCAR PARTS OF AMERICA INC

MPA
See MARINE PRESERVATION ASSOCIATION INC

D-U-N-S 00-108-2908 IMP
■ MPB CORP
TIMKEN SUPER PRECISION
(*Suby of* TIMKEN CO) ★
7 Optical Ave, Keene, NH 03431-4348
Tel (603) 352-0310 *Founded/Ownrshp* 1941, 1990
Sales 269.3MM^E *EMP* 1,820
SIC 3562 6061 Ball bearings & parts; Roller bearings & parts; Federal credit unions
Pr: Erik Paulhardt
**Treas:* John Ted Mihaila
**VP:* Phillip Fracassa
Exec: Bill Kellher
Genl Mgr: Cengiz Kurkcu
Genl Mgr: Gerald Levesque
Dir IT: Eric Gibson
Mktg Mgr: Maureen Curtiss

D-U-N-S 00-545-1240 IMP/EXP
■ MPC PRODUCTS CORP (IL)
WOODWARD MPC, INC.
(*Suby of* WOODWARD INC) ★
6300 W Howard St, Niles, IL 60714-3406
Tel (847) 673-8300 *Founded/Ownrshp* 1962, 2008
Sales 171.0MM *EMP* 963^E
SIC 3728 3621 3676 3812 3625 Aircraft body & wing assemblies & parts; Aircraft assemblies, subassemblies & parts; Motors & generators; Electronic resistors; Aircraft/aerospace flight instruments & guidance systems; Relays & industrial controls
CEO: Thomas Gendron
**Pr:* Martin Glass
**CFO:* Robert Webber Jr
Sls Mgr: Jeffrey Brown

D-U-N-S 06-447-8381 IMP
MPCI HOLDINGS INC (CA)
MONTERREY THE NATURAL CHOICE
7850 Waterville Rd, San Diego, CA 92154-8219
Tel (619) 294-2222 *Founded/Ownrshp* 1972
Sales 178.2MM^E *EMP* 130^E
SIC 5147 5143 5148 5113 Meats, fresh; Cheese; Fresh fruits & vegetables; Disposable plates, cups, napkins & eating utensils; Boxes & containers
Pr: Thomas Luke Abbott
VP: Colleen Goodloe

D-U-N-S 17-350-2824
MPD INC
316 E 9th St, Owensboro, KY 42303-3513
Tel (270) 685-6200 *Founded/Ownrshp* 1997
Sales 149.2MM^E *EMP* 897
SIC 3671 3829 3812 3663 3643 3053 Electron tubes; Breathalyzers; Radar systems & equipment; Radio & TV communications equipment; Current-carrying wiring devices; Gaskets, packing & sealing devices
Pr: Gary J Braswell
**CFO:* Michael D Robinson
**Treas:* Randy L Roos
**VP:* Janice Tomblinson
VP: Robert White
IT Man: David Blythe
MIS Mgr: Terry Horn
Board of Directors: Anthony Lewis, John P Olson, Frederick S Perry, David A York

D-U-N-S 11-926-9827 IMP/EXP
MPG
METALDYNE
(*Suby of* METALDYNE) ★
47659 Halyard Dr, Plymouth, MI 48170-2429
Tel (734) 207-6200 *Founded/Ownrshp* 2009
Sales 1.2MMM^E *EMP* 6,500
SIC 3499 Aerosol valves, metal; Aquarium accessories, metal; Doors, safe & vault: metal
Pr: Thomas V Chambers
Pr: George Thomas
COO: Witkow Edward
COO: Tina Kozak
COO: Beverly Mathews
**CFO:* Takao Yoshida
Treas: Sandra Galac
**Ex VP:* Logan Robinson
Ex VP: Jeff Stafeil
VP: Denis Bardou
VP: Dennis Cutright
VP: Robert J Defauw
VP: Juergen Depp
VP: James Hudak
VP: Jim Hudak
VP: George Lanni
VP: Myra Moreland
VP: Joanne Ryan
VP: Ben Schmidt
VP: Roseann Stevens

D-U-N-S 00-446-1042 IMP/EXP
MPG GEAR TECHNOLOGIES (OH)
7800 Ball Rd, Fort Smith, AR 72908-8424
Tel (479) 646-1662 *Founded/Ownrshp* 1920, 2006
Sales 237.9MM^E *EMP* 1,031
SIC 3714 3568 3399 Gears, motor vehicle; Sprockets (power transmission equipment); Powder, metal
Ch: Malcolm R Myers
**Pr:* Trevor Myers
CTO: Lance Davis

D-U-N-S 83-133-8616
MPG NEWSPAPER HOLDING LLC
(*Suby of* SHIVERS TRADING & OPERATING CO) ★
725 Broad St, Augusta, GA 30901-1336
Tel (706) 724-0851 *Founded/Ownrshp* 2009
Sales 225.2MM^E *EMP* 2,500^E
SIC 2711 Newspapers; Newspapers, publishing & printing
Pr: William S Morris IV

D-U-N-S 08-717-2532
MPG OFFICE TRUST INC
355 S Grand Ave Ste 3300, Los Angeles, CA 90071-1592
Tel (213) 626-3300 *Founded/Ownrshp* 2003
Sales 231.1MM *EMP* 70^E
SIC 6798

D-U-N-S 82-710-9005
MPG PIPELINE CONTRACTORS LLC
16770 Imperial Valley Dr # 105, Houston, TX 77060-3422
Tel (713) 904-1168 *Founded/Ownrshp* 2008
Sales 200.7MM *EMP* 40^E
SIC 1623 Pipeline construction
CEO: Jimmy L Fontenot
**COO:* Kenneth M McDougall Jr
**COO:* Aaron Simon
**VP:* Francis A Simon
Opers Mgr: Bruce Ainsworth

D-U-N-S 04-780-9350
MPHASIS CORP
(*Suby of* MPHASIS LIMITED)
460 Park Ave S Rm 1101, New York, NY 10016-7315
Tel (212) 686-6655 *Founded/Ownrshp* 1998
Sales 459.4MM^E *EMP* 2,000
SIC 7371 Custom computer programming services
Pr: Vikas Gurugunti
**CFO:* Ganesh Murthy
Top Exec: Michelle Kumar
Assoc VP: Sunil Jain
Assoc VP: Subrato Mozumdar
Assoc VP: Vinod Nair
Sr VP: Ajay Jotwani
VP: Krishna Banda
VP: Sudeep Nadkarni
VP: Rekha Vijayalakshmi
Dir Risk M: Murali Soundar
Comm Man: Daphne Jacob

MPI
See MATERIALS PROCESSING INC

D-U-N-S 83-736-3605
MPI RESEARCH INC
54943 N Main St, Mattawan, MI 49071-8353
Tel (269) 668-3336 *Founded/Ownrshp* 1995
Sales 231.3MM^E *EMP* 1,300
SIC 8731 Commercial research laboratory
COO: Andy Dumpis
CFO: Paul R Sylvester
Ex VP: James Lavaglia
Sr VP: David G Serota
VP: Ed Amat
VP: Roger Hayes
VP Bus Dev: Randall Guthrie
Assoc Dir: Steve Denham
Assoc Dir: Thomas Stahl
Dir Bus: Gary Oliff
Dir IT: Murali Krishnan

D-U-N-S 07-854-2035
▲ MPLX LP
200 E Hardin St, Findlay, OH 45840-4963
Tel (419) 672-6500 *Founded/Ownrshp* 2012
Sales 703.0MM *EMP* 2,200^E
Tkr Sym MPLX *Exch* NYS
SIC 4612 4613 Crude petroleum pipelines; Refined petroleum pipelines
Ch Bd: Gary R Heminger
Genl Pt: Mplx GP LLC
V Ch: Frank M Semple
Pr: Donald C Templin
COO: Gregory S Floerke
COO: John C Mollenkopf
CFO: Nancy K Buese
Ex VP: Randy S Nickerson
VP: John S Swearingen

D-U-N-S 07-974-6031
MPM HOLDINGS INC
260 Hudson River Rd, Waterford, NY 12188-1910
Tel (518) 237-3330 *Founded/Ownrshp* 2014
Sales 2.2MMM^E *EMP* 4,605
SIC 2869 3479 3679 Silicones; Coating of metals with silicon; Electronic crystals; Quartz crystals, for electronic application
Pr: John G Boss
CFO: Erick R Asmussen
**CFO:* Brian D Berger
**Ex VP:* Douglas A Johns
**Sr VP:* John D Moran
**VP:* George F Knight
**Genl Couns:* Stephen J Psutka

D-U-N-S 07-974-6051
MPM INTERMEDIATE HOLDINGS INC
(*Suby of* MPM HOLDINGS INC) ★
260 Hudson River Rd, Waterford, NY 12188-1910
Tel (518) 237-3330 *Founded/Ownrshp* 2014
Sales 2.2MMM^E *EMP* 4,602
SIC 2869 3479 3679 Silicones; Coating of metals with silicon; Electronic crystals; Quartz crystals, for electronic application
Pr: John G Boss
**CFO:* Brian D Berger

D-U-N-S 82-585-6151
MPM SILICONES LLC
MOMENTIVE
(*Suby of* MOMENTIVE PERFORMANCE MATERIALS INC) ★
260 Hudson River Rd, Waterford, NY 12188-1910
Tel (518) 233-3330 *Founded/Ownrshp* 2000
Sales 223.9MM^E *EMP* 4,600
SIC 2869 Silicones
CFO: Brian D Berger
Snr Mgr: Chris Powhida

D-U-N-S 96-700-1801 IMP
MPOWER COMMUNICATIONS CORP
(*Suby of* TELEPACIFIC COMMUNICATIONS) ★
515 S Flower St, Los Angeles, CA 90071-2201
Tel (213) 213-3000 *Founded/Ownrshp* 1996
Sales 136.9MM^E *EMP* 750
SIC 4813 Telephone communication, except radio
Ch Bd: Rolla P Huff
Pr: Joseph M Wetzel
CFO: S Gregory Clevenger
CFO: Tim Medina
Treas: Michael J Tschiderer
Sr VP: Russell I Zuckerman
VP: Dan Blank
VP: Gary Durbin
VP: Kent F Heyman
VP: Mark Magarian
VP: Linda Sunbury

D-U-N-S 05-886-8811
MPS ENTERPRISES INC (NM)
MILFORD PIPE AND SUPPLY
1224 W Broadway Pl, Hobbs, NM 88240-5568
Tel (432) 563-3332 *Founded/Ownrshp* 1967, 2011
Sales 116.5MM^E *EMP* 60
SIC 5169 Polyurethane products
CEO: Shawn Beard
**CFO:* Scott Brown
**VP:* Cody Tippy

D-U-N-S 09-660-2008
MPS GROUP INC
ADO STAFFING
10151 Deerwood Park Blvd 200-400, Jacksonville, FL 32256-0557
Tel (904) 360-2000 *Founded/Ownrshp* 2010
Sales 470.6MM^E *EMP* 9,000
SIC 7363 8742 7361

D-U-N-S 82-705-3773
■ MPS HOLDCO INC
JOHN HENRY HOLDINGS, INC.
(*Suby of* MULTI PACKAGING SOLUTIONS INC) ★
5800 W Grand River Ave, Lansing, MI 48906-9111
Tel (517) 886-2526 *Founded/Ownrshp* 2004
Sales 431.2MM^E *EMP* 2,100^E
SIC 6719 Investment holding companies, except banks
CEO: Marc Shore

*Pr: Dennis Kalpman
*Treas: Ed Gasper
Sr VP: Tim Schultz
VP: Ray Wheelan
QA Dir: Brian Angell
IT Man: David Diehl
Web Dev: Jeannette McGarry
Opers Supe: Cathy Coggins

D-U-N-S 07-955-8265
■ MPS INTERNATIONAL LTD
(Suby of MONOLITHIC POWER SYSTEMS INC) ★
79 Great Oaks Blvd, San Jose, CA 95119-1311
Tel (408) 826-0660 Founded/Ownrshp 2014
Sales 238.0MM EMP 1,000
SIC 3674 Semiconductors & related devices
CEO: Michael R Hsing
Snr Mgr: Wingfield Liu

D-U-N-S 79-560-2890
MPT OPERATING PARTNERSHIP LP
(Suby of MEDICAL PROPERTIES TRUST INC) ★
3500 Colonnade Pkwy # 540, Birmingham, AL 35243-8300
Tel (205) 969-3755 Founded/Ownrshp 2003
Sales 312.5MM EMP 6,000E
SIC 6798 Real estate investment trusts
Pt: Edward K Aldag Jr

D-U-N-S 03-126-8464
MPW INDUSTRIAL SERVICES GROUP INC (OH)
9711 Lancaster Rd, Hebron, OH 43025-9764
Tel (740) 927-8790 Founded/Ownrshp 1972
Sales 221.6MME EMP 2,000E
SIC 7349 8744 3589 Cleaning service, industrial or commercial; Facilities support services; Commercial cleaning equipment
CEO: Monte R Black
Pr: Jared Black
COO: Robert Valentine
CFO: Sarah D Pemberton
Area Mgr: John Bergin
Area Mgr: Darci Huth
Genl Mgr: Adam Black
Off Mgr: Susan Williams
Dir IT: Randy Keefer
Dir IT: John Kirjowa
Dir IT: Mike McCormick
Board of Directors: Pete A Klisares, Timothy A Walsh

D-U-N-S 07-503-7747
MPW INDUSTRIAL SERVICES INC
(Suby of MPW INDUSTRIAL SERVICES GROUP INC) ★
9711 Lancaster Rd, Hebron, OH 43025-9764
Tel (800) 827-8790 Founded/Ownrshp 1997
Sales 160.3MME EMP 1,200
SIC 7349 Building maintenance services
CEO: Monte Black
VP: Kristen Hargus
Mktg Dir: Bryan Whitehead

D-U-N-S 92-890-3699 IMP
MQ ASSOCIATES INC
(Suby of LAKESIDE FAMILY PHYSICIANS) ★
3480 Preston Ridge Rd # 600, Alpharetta, GA 30005-2028
Tel (770) 300-0101 Founded/Ownrshp 2007
Sales 66.3MME EMP 1,604
SIC 8099 Physical examination & testing services
CEO: Chris Winkle
*Ch Bd: Donald C Tomasso
*COO: Daniel J Schaefer
COO: Jennifer Swearinger
COO: Michael A Vill
*CFO: Todd Andrews
Board of Directors: John R Belk, Benjamin B Edmands, Anthony R Masso, Stephen P Murray

D-U-N-S 36-061-6817 IMP
MR CHIPS INC
1380 Gateway Dr Ste 7, Elgin, IL 60124-7891
Tel (847) 468-9000 Founded/Ownrshp 1988
Sales 893.7M EMP 1,013
SIC 5092 5047 Bingo games & supplies; Board games; Medical equipment & supplies
Pr: Natalia Kovari
Treas: Natasha Kovari
*VP: Andrew J Kovari

MR CLEAN MAINTENANCE SYSTEMS
See CHIRO INC

D-U-N-S 96-593-3455
■ MR COPY INC
MRC, SMARTTECH SOLUTIONS
(Suby of GLOBAL IMAGING SYSTEMS INC) ★
5657 Copley Dr, San Diego, CA 92111-7903
Tel (858) 573-6300 Founded/Ownrshp 2009
Sales 113.4MME EMP 120
SIC 5044 Office equipment; Photocopy machines
Pr: Bob Leone
CFO: Kevin McCarty

D-U-N-S 07-443-8078 IMP/EXP
MR DAVIDS FLOORING INTERNATIONAL LLC
MR. DAVID'S FLOORING INTL
865 W Irving Park Rd, Itasca, IL 60143-2021
Tel (847) 250-4600 Founded/Ownrshp 1976
Sales 90.7MME EMP 500
SIC 1752 Carpet laying
CEO: Leonard Zmijewski
*Co-Ownr: David Zmijewski
Mktg Dir: Peter Standish

MR. DAVID'S FLOORING INTL
See MR DAVIDS FLOORING INTERNATIONAL LLC

MR FUEL
See AROGAS INC

D-U-N-S 04-701-6787
MR GATTIS LP
GATTI'S PIZZA
(Suby of MGI HOLDINGS LP) ★
5912 Balcones Dr Ste 200, Austin, TX 78731-4202
Tel (512) 459-4796 Founded/Ownrshp 2015
Sales 103.0MME EMP 500
SIC 6794 5812 Franchises, selling or licensing; Pizzeria, chain
Pr: Michael Poates
CFO: Steven B Burt
Board of Directors: James D McBride III

MR. GREEN PRODUCE
See FLORIDA VEG INVESTMENTS LLC

D-U-N-S 09-008-0649 IMP/EXP
MR SPECIAL SUPERMARKETS INC
SUPERMERCADOS MR SPECIAL
620 Ave Sta Tresa Journet, Mayaguez, PR 00682-1342
Tel (787) 834-2695 Founded/Ownrshp 1999
Sales 282.0MM EMP 1,707
Accts Rodriguez Rivera & Toro Psc
SIC 5411 Supermarkets, 55,000-65,000 square feet (superstore)
Pr: Santos Alonso
Treas: Iris Alonso
VP: Edwin Alonso
Mktg Dir: Debbie Alonso
Mktg Dir: Victor Caban

D-U-N-S 00-509-5000
■ MRA SYSTEMS INC
MIDDLE RIVER AIRCRAFT SYSTEMS
(Suby of GE AIRCRAFT ENGINES HOLDINGS INC) ★
103 Chesapeake Park Plz, Baltimore, MD 21220-4201
Tel (410) 682-1500 Founded/Ownrshp 1997
Sales 241.2MME EMP 700E
SIC 3728 Aircraft assemblies, subassemblies & parts
Pr: David Joyce
*CFO: William Heskett
*Ex VP: Michael Chanatry
*Ex VP: William Fritzgerald
*VP: Pupinder Bhutiani
*VP: Bernard Grossman
*VP: Doug Mallon
*VP: Christopher Wright

MRC
See MIKE ROVNER CONSTRUCTION INC

D-U-N-S 85-843-7221 IMP
MRC BEARINGS INC
SKF AEROENGINE NORTH AMERICA
1 Maroco St, Falconer, NY 14733-9705
Tel (716) 661-2600 Founded/Ownrshp 1933
Sales 124.2MME EMP 700
SIC 3562

D-U-N-S 00-794-4580 IMP/EXP
■ MRC GLOBAL (US) INC
(Suby of MRC GLOBAL INC) ★
1301 Mckinney St Ste 2300, Houston, TX 77010-3035
Tel (877) 294-7574 Founded/Ownrshp 2007
Sales 405.3MME EMP 280
SIC 5051 5085 Pipe & tubing, steel; Industrial supplies; Valves & fittings
Ch Bd: Andrew Lane
*Ex VP: James E Braun
Sr VP: Mike Chamberlain
Sr VP: James Dionisio
Sr VP: David A Fox
VP: Stuart Bailey
VP: Grant Bates
VP: Brenda Combs
VP: Ft Graff
Brnch Mgr: Tim Fish
Brnch Mgr: Kathryn Maines

D-U-N-S 82-871-0348 IMP
▲ MRC GLOBAL INC
1301 Mckinney St Ste 2300, Houston, TX 77010-3035
Tel (877) 294-7574 Founded/Ownrshp 2006
Sales 4.5MMM EMP 4,100E
Tkr Sym MRC Exch NYS
SIC 5051 5085 Pipe & tubing, steel; Industrial supplies; Valves & fittings
Pr: Andrew R Lane
*Ch Bd: Rhys J Best
CFO: James E Braun
Ofcr: Gary Ittner
Ex VP: Daniel J Churay
Sr VP: Steinar Aasland
Sr VP: Grant Bates
Sr VP: Elton Bond
Sr VP: John Bowhay
Sr VP: Scott A Hutchinson
Sr VP: Tod Moss
Sr VP: Robert Stein
Sr VP: Karl Witt
VP: Tommy Bruns
VP: Don Stepp
VP Bus Dev: Joe Barnes
Board of Directors: Leonard M Anthony, Barbara J Duganier, Craig Ketchum, Gerard P Krans, Cornelis A Linse, John A Perkins, H B Wehrle III, Robert L Wood

MRC, SMARTTECH SOLUTIONS
See MR COPY INC

MRD SERVICES
See MUELLER ROOFING DISTRIBUTORS INC

D-U-N-S 06-604-4827
MRI SOFTWARE LLC
28925 Fountain Pkwy, Solon, OH 44139-4356
Tel (800) 327-8770 Founded/Ownrshp 2015
Sales 111.4MME EMP 408E
SIC 7374 7371 6531 Data processing & preparation; Computer software development; Real estate managers
CEO: Patrick Ghilani
CFO: Michael Vantusko
Ofcr: Brian Zrimsek
VP: Marc Dicapua
VP: Chuck McDowell
VP: Oren Rosen
VP: Helene Slosarik
VP: Phil Trudeau
Snr Sftwr: Jason Buffin
Snr Sftwr: Doug Obojski
CTO: Joshua Amick

D-U-N-S 00-717-3453
MRIGLOBAL (MO)
MIDWEST RESEARCH INSTITUTE
425 Volker Blvd, Kansas City, MO 64110-2241
Tel (816) 753-7600 Founded/Ownrshp 1943
Sales 466.8MM EMP 2,547
Accts Kpmg Llp Kansas City Missour
SIC 8731 6794 Commercial physical research; Patent owners & lessors
Pr: Thomas M Sack
Ch Bd: Tom Bowser
CFO: R Thomas Fleener
CFO: Sandra Lawrence
Trst: Jonathan Kemper
Ofcr: Matthew O'Callaghan
Ofcr: Lisa Read
Ex VP: Dan Arvizu
VP: John Barsa
VP: Jerry Bellows
VP: Robert P Casillas
VP: Robert A Conklin
VP: Linda D Evans
VP: David Franz
VP: Roger Harris
VP: Steve Phillips
Board of Directors: David B Dillon, David Field Oliver

D-U-N-S 96-456-0309
MRRC HOLD CO
382 Greenwich Ave Apt 1, Greenwich, CT 06830-6501
Tel (203) 987-3500 Founded/Ownrshp 2010
Sales 188.0MME EMP 3,800E
SIC 5812 Mexican restaurant
Pr: Scott P Scharfman

D-U-N-S 02-001-7286 IMP
MRS BAIRDS BAKERIES BUSINESS TRUST (DE)
(Suby of BIMBO BAKERIES USA INC) ★
14401 Statler Blvd, Fort Worth, TX 76155-2861
Tel (817) 864-2500 Founded/Ownrshp 1997
Sales 228.8MME EMP 7,000
SIC 2051 Bread, cake & related products
Pr: Reynaldo Reyna
*Sr VP: Jim Brennan
*Sr VP: Joe Dangelmaier
*Sr VP: Andy Lang
*VP: H Darrell Miller
*VP: Greg Stehr
Dir IT: Natalie Newby
Sls&Mrk Ex: Reid Stinnett

D-U-N-S 13-615-3553
MRS FIELDS COMPANIES INC
FAMOUS BRANDS INTERNATIONAL
8001 Arista Pl Unit 600, Broomfield, CO 80021-4135
Tel (720) 599-3374 Founded/Ownrshp 2001
Sales 724.5MME EMP 6,614
SIC 6794 5461 Franchises, selling or licensing; Cookies
Pr: James Zenni
Pr: Greg Berglund
CFO: Gregory K Barber
CFO: Michael Chao
Ex VP: Michael Ward
Sr VP: David Bloom
VP: Belinda Oakley
Prin: Jon M Biotti
Prin: Alexander Coleman
Prin: John D Collins
Prin: George N Fugelsang
Board of Directors: Jon M Biotti, Alexander Coleman, John D Collins, George N Fugelsang, Peter W Mullin, Don Rice, John D Shafer, Christopher Wright

D-U-N-S 96-213-0472
MRS FIELDS HOLDING CO INC
FAMOUS BRANDS
(Suby of FAMOUS BRANDS INTERNATIONAL) ★
8001 Arista Pl Unit 600, Broomfield, CO 80021-4135
Tel (720) 599-3350 Founded/Ownrshp 1996
Sales 114.2MME EMP 2,326
Accts Kpmg Llp Salt Lake City Ut
SIC 5461 6794 Cookies; Franchises, selling or licensing
Pr: Stephen Russo
*Ch: Herbert S Winokur Jr
*Sr VP: Garry Remington
VP: John Lauck
*VP: Michael R Ward
Board of Directors: Richard Ferry, Debbi Fields, Nat Gregory, Walker Lewis, Peter Mullin, Gilbert Osnos

MRS GOOCHES
See WHOLE FOODS MARKET SOPAC

D-U-N-S 19-202-1608 IMP
▲ MRV COMMUNICATIONS INC
20520 Nordhoff St, Chatsworth, CA 91311-6113
Tel (818) 773-0900 Founded/Ownrshp 1988
Sales 88.2MM EMP 268E
Tkr Sym MRVC Exch NAS
SIC 3674 Semiconductors & related devices; Integrated circuits, semiconductor networks, etc.
Pr: Mark J Bonney
*Ch Bd: Kenneth H Traub
CFO: Stephen Krulik
*V Ch Bd: Robert M Pons
Snr Sftwr: Deby Laufer
Snr Sftwr: Raymond Ng
Board of Directors: Brian J Bellinger, Jeannie H Diefenderfer, Jeffrey Tuder

D-U-N-S 79-110-1413
MS AEROSPACE INC
13928 Balboa Blvd, Sylmar, CA 91342-1086
Tel (818) 833-9095 Founded/Ownrshp 1992
Sales 105.3MME EMP 302
SIC 3452 3728 Bolts, nuts, rivets & washers; Aircraft parts & equipment
CEO: Michel Szostak
*CFO: Jerome Taieb
*VP: Jim Cole
Prd Mgr: Adrien Szsostak
Genl Couns: Charles McLean

D-U-N-S 09-210-9222
■ MS CARRIERS INC
(Suby of SWIFT TRANSPORTATION CO) ★
1940 E Brooks Rd Ste 20, Memphis, TN 38116-3645
Tel (901) 332-2500 Founded/Ownrshp 2001
Sales 88.2MME EMP 3,336
SIC 4213 Trucking, except local
Pr: Michael S Starnes
*Treas: M J Barrow
*Sr VP: James W Welch
VP: John M Hudson
*VP: Robert P Hurt
VP: Azmi B Ujang

MS COMPANIES
See ABC EMPLOYMENT HOLDINGS LLC

MS ENERGY SERVICES
See MULTI-SHOT LLC

D-U-N-S 78-266-6895
MS PAWN LIMITED PARTNERSHIP
1901 Capital Pkwy, Austin, TX 78746-7613
Tel (512) 314-3400 Founded/Ownrshp 1989
Sales 276.2MME EMP 7,500
SIC 5932 6141 Pawnshop; Personal credit institutions
Prin: Jason Duma

D-U-N-S 36-070-4613
MS SUPREME COURT
(Suby of STATE OF MISSISSIPPI) ★
450 High St Ste 300, Jackson, MS 39201-1082
Tel (601) 359-3694 Founded/Ownrshp 1817
Sales NA EMP 1,050
SIC 9211 State courts;
Genl Mgr: Joey Craft

MSA
See MISSION SUPPORT ALLIANCE LLC

D-U-N-S 07-935-8187
▲ MSA SAFETY INC
1000 Cranberry Woods Dr, Cranberry Township, PA 16066-5207
Tel (724) 776-8600 Founded/Ownrshp 2014
Sales 1.1MMM EMP 5,000E
Tkr Sym MSA Exch NYS
SIC 3842 3826 3823 3648 3829 Surgical appliances & supplies; Personal safety equipment; Environmental testing equipment; Industrial process control instruments; Lighting equipment; Gas detectors
Ch Bd: William M Lambert
CFO: Kenneth D Krause
CFO: Stacy McMahan
Sr VP: Kerry M Bove
VP: Anne Herman
VP: Douglas K McClaine
VP: Paul R Uhler
VP: Markus H Weber
VP: Markus Weber

MSBSD
See MATANUSKA SUSITNA BOROUGH SCHOOL DISTRICT

D-U-N-S 93-261-9265 IMP
▲ MSC INDUSTRIAL DIRECT CO INC
75 Maxess Rd, Melville, NY 11747-3151
Tel (516) 812-2000 Founded/Ownrshp 1941
Sales 2.8MMM EMP 6,642
Tkr Sym MSM Exch NYS
SIC 5084 5085 5063 5072 Industrial machinery & equipment; Machine tools & metalworking machinery; Measuring & testing equipment, electrical; Safety equipment; Industrial supplies; Abrasives & adhesives; Fasteners & fastening equipment; Electrical apparatus & equipment; Hardware
Pr: Erik Gershwind
CFO: Rustom Jilla
Treas: John G Chironna
Bd of Dir: Robert Davis
Ofcr: Kari D Heerdt
Ex VP: Douglas Jones
Sr VP: Ross Anker
Sr VP: Steve Armstrong
Sr VP: Charles Bonomo
VP: Shelley M Boxer
VP: John Chironna
VP: David Collier
VP: Steve Gettleman
VP: Greg Polli
Board of Directors: Jonathan Byrnes, Roger Fradin, Louise Goeser, Mitchell Jacobson, Michael Kaufmann, Denis Kelly, Steven Paladino, Philip Peller

D-U-N-S 80-809-5793
▲ MSCI INC
250 Greenwich St Fl 49, New York, NY 10007-2340
Tel (212) 804-3900 Founded/Ownrshp 1969
Sales 1.0MMM EMP 2,754E
Accts Pricewaterhousecoopers Llp Ne
Tkr Sym MSCI Exch NYS
SIC 7389 7371 6282 8742 Financial services; Software programming applications; Investment advice; Management consulting services; Business consultant
Ch Bd: Henry A Fernandez
COO: C D Baer Pettit
CFO: Kathleen A Winters
Treas: Laurasusana Boren
Chf Cred: Laurent Seyer
Ofcr: Scott A Crum
VP: Dana Brubaker
VP: Lisa Clarke
VP: Douglas Cogan
VP: Seth Corwin
VP: Jay Dermody
VP: Harsh Deshpande
VP: Ernesto Guridi
VP: Deepak Kaul
VP: Gabor Kiss
VP: Adam Kraidin
VP: Larry Lawrence
VP: Jerry S Lettieri
VP: Yang Liu
VP: Russ Maile
VP: Tom Mulry
Board of Directors: Rodolphe M Vallee, Robert G Ashe, Benjamin F Dupont, Wayne Edmunds, Alice W

Handy, Catherine R Kinney, Wendy E Lane, Linda H Riefler, George W Siguler, Patrick Tierney

D-U-N-S 00-965-3148
MSCSOFTWARE CORP
(*Suby of* MAXIMUS HOLDINGS INC) ★
4675 Macarthur Ct Ste 900, Newport Beach, CA 92660-1845
Tel (714) 540-8900 *Founded/Ownrshp* 1963, 2009
Sales 214.5MM[E] *EMP* 1,006
SIC 7372 Prepackaged software
Pr: Dominic Gallello
Pr: Douglas Lubben
CFO: Kevin Rubin
Sr VP: Kais Bouchiba
Sr VP: Douglas W Peterson
VP: Mohan Barbela
VP: Leslie Bodnar
VP: Stephen Bodnar
VP: Chris Brecher
VP: Peter Dodd
VP: Jeffrey Graff
VP: John Howaniec
VP: John Janevic
VP: Bert Knops
VP: Michael Lambert
VP: Doug Neill
VP: Himanshu Shah
Board of Directors: Frank Cappuccio

MSD
See METROPOLITAN ST LOUIS SEWER DISTRICT

MSD PERFORMANCE
See MSDP GROUP LLC

D-U-N-S 07-969-4557
MSDP GROUP LLC
MSD PERFORMANCE
(*Suby of* HOLLEY PERFORMANCE PRODUCTS INC) ★
1350 Pullman Dr Dr14, El Paso, TX 79936-7737
Tel (915) 857-5200 *Founded/Ownrshp* 2013, 2015
Sales 87.1MM[E] *EMP* 300[E]
SIC 3694 Ignition systems, high frequency
CEO: Rick Ruebusch

D-U-N-S 80-674-1851 IMP/EXP
MSEAFOOD CORP
17934 Point Sur St, Fountain Valley, CA 92708-5042
Tel (714) 842-7900 *Founded/Ownrshp* 2001
Sales 101.4MM *EMP* 5[E]
SIC 5146 Fish & seafoods
Prin: Quang Van Le

MSG
See MERCHANDISING SOLUTIONS GROUP INC

D-U-N-S 83-283-1999
▲ **MSG NETWORKS INC**
11 Penn Plz, New York, NY 10001-2006
Tel (212) 465-6400 *Founded/Ownrshp* 1879
Sales 658.2MM *EMP* 1,009[E]
Tkr Sym MSGN *Exch* NYS
SIC 4841 7922 7941 4832 Cable & other pay television services; Television program, including commercial producers; Entertainment promotion; Sports clubs, managers & promoters; Sports
Pr: Andrea Greenberg
**Ch Bd:* James L Dolan
CFO: Donna M Coleman
CFO: Bret Richter
Ex VP: Lawrence J Burian
Ex VP: John P Caparella Jr
Ex VP: Joel Fisher
Ex VP: Scott Henry
Ex VP: Sandra P Kapell
Ex VP: Ron Skotarczak
Ex VP: Barry Watkins
Sr VP: Dawn Darino-Gorski
VP: Andrew Karson
VP: Michael Lehr
VP: Jacob Pariseau
Board of Directors: Brian G Sweeney, William J Bell, John L Sykes, Eugene F Demark, Charles F Dolan, Paul J Dolan, Quentin F Dolan, Thomas C Dolan, Wilt Hildenbrand, Joel M Litvin, Hank J Ratner

D-U-N-S 08-004-9921
MSG SPORTS & ENTERTAINMENT LLC
MADISON SQUARE GARDEN COMPANY
2 Penn Plz Fl 15, New York, NY 10121-1700
Tel (212) 465-6000 *Founded/Ownrshp* 2015
Sales 4.3MMM *EMP* 1,020[E]
SIC 7941 Stadium event operator services; Sports field or stadium operator, promoting sports events
CEO: David O'Connor
Pr: Mikyl Cordova
Pr: Kai Haasler
Pr: Kristin Herring
Pr: Stephanie Jacqueney
CFO: Donna Coleman
Treas: Robert Lynn
Ex VP: Lawrence Burian
Ex VP: Michael Guth
Ex VP: Jonathan Hochwald
Ex VP: Timothy Schmidt
Sr VP: Jeremiah Bosgang
**Sr VP:* Rich Claffey
Sr VP: Maritza Evans
Sr VP: Joel Fisher
Sr VP: Kristina Heney
Sr VP: Michael Magee
Sr VP: Gregg Palesky
Sr VP: John Schultz
Sr VP: Larry Sedwick
Sr VP: Bob Shea

D-U-N-S 83-553-4694 IMP
■ **MSGN HOLDINGS LP**
NEW YORK KNICKS
(*Suby of* MSG NETWORKS INC) ★
4 Penn Plz, New York, NY 10121-0078
Tel (212) 465-6000 *Founded/Ownrshp* 2011
Sales 204.8MM[E] *EMP* 500
SIC 4832 7922 Sports; Television program, including commercial producers; Entertainment promotion
Genl Pt: James Dolan
Pr: Al Coates
Ex VP: Seth Abrham
Ex VP: David Clark
Ex VP: Joe Gangone
Ex VP: Howard Handler
Ex VP: Robert Pollichino
Sr VP: Sean Barror
Sr VP: Mark Cresitello
Sr VP: John Cudmore
Sr VP: Glen Grunwald
Sr VP: Chris Moseley
Sr VP: Jerry Passaro
Sr VP: Lewis Sherr
Sr VP: Art Ventura
VP: Joseph Ali
VP: Lisa Banbury
VP: Adam Campbell
VP: John Carr
VP: Matt Doherty
VP: Joe Favorito

D-U-N-S 07-977-7755
MSHC INC
SERVICE LOGIC
12005 E 45th Ave, Denver, CO 80239-3111
Tel (303) 455-2825 *Founded/Ownrshp* 2006
Sales 200.0MM *EMP* 1,000[E]
SIC 8741 Administrative management
CEO: Craig A Steinke
**COO:* Timothy Ridel
**CFO:* Matthew W Austin
Genl Mgr: Levi Reeves

MSI
See MANAGEMENT SYSTEMS INTERNATIONAL INC

MSI
See M S INTERNATIONAL INC

MSI HVAC
See MATERIAL SUPPLY INC

MSI MERCHANT SERVICES
See CREDIT CARD PROCESSING USA INC

MSIG
See MITSUI SUMITOMO INSURANCE CO OF AMERICA

D-U-N-S 80-998-8764
MSIG HOLDINGS (AMERICAS) INC
(*Suby of* MITSUI SUMITOMO INSURANCE COMPANY, LIMITED)
560 Lexington Ave Fl 20, New York, NY 10022-6828
Tel (212) 446-3600 *Founded/Ownrshp* 1988
Sales 399.4MM[E] *EMP* 600
SIC 8741 6331 Administrative management; Fire, marine & casualty insurance
Ch Bd: Tetsuro Kihara
**Treas:* Shinichiro Nakayama

D-U-N-S 07-836-3630
MSIP-SSCC HOLDINGS LLC
1585 Broadway, New York, NY 10036-8200
Tel (270) 852-5000 *Founded/Ownrshp* 2005
Sales 216.1MM[E] *EMP* 498[E]
SIC 4923 Gas transmission & distribution
Pr: Jerry L Morris

MSOE
See MILWAUKEE SCHOOL OF ENGIINEERING

MSOUTH EQUITY PARTNERS
See EQUITY MSOUTH PARTNERS L P

D-U-N-S 03-346-8583
■ **MSR HOTELS & RESORTS INC**
CNL HOSPITALITY PROPERTIES
(*Suby of* MORGAN STANLEY) ★
450 S Orange Ave, Orlando, FL 32801-3383
Tel (407) 650-1000 *Founded/Ownrshp* 2007
Sales 89.4MM[E] *EMP* 2,640
SIC 7011 Hotels & motels
CEO: John R Klopp
**Ch Bd:* James N Seneff Jr
**Pr:* John A Griswold
**Co-CEO:* Thomas J Hutchison III
Chf Invest: Sean McLaughlin
**Ex VP:* C Brian Strickland
VP: Pj Behr
VP: Brian Brooks
VP: Ron Olstad
VP: Tommy Trimble
VP: Ted Watson
VP: Patrick Willis

D-U-N-S 13-160-5636 IMP
MSR PUBLIC POWER AGENCY
1231 11th St, Modesto, CA 95354-0701
Tel (209) 526-7473 *Founded/Ownrshp* 1980
Sales 87.8MM *EMP* 4
Accts Pricewaterhousecoopers Llp Sa
SIC 4911 Generation, electric power
Genl Mgr: Merchant Hopper
**Treas:* Lou Hampel

MSRC
See MARINE SPILL RESPONSE CORP

D-U-N-S 00-385-4478 IMP
MSS LIQUIDATION CORP (MO)
MID-STATES SUPPLY COMPANY INC
1716 Guinotte Ave, Kansas City, MO 64120-1424
Tel (816) 842-4290 *Founded/Ownrshp* 1956
Sales 380.8MM[E] *EMP* 450
SIC 5085 3545

MSSS
See MANAGEMENT SSS INC

D-U-N-S 09-869-4649
MSTC INC
(*Suby of* ICOV INC)
10900 Pump House Rd Ste B, Annapolis Junction, MD 20701-1208
Tel (240) 280-8064 *Founded/Ownrshp* 1978
Sales 968.2MM *EMP* 5
SIC 8742 8748 Industry specialist consultants; Automation & robotics consultant; Business consulting
Pr: Steven Hartung

MSUFCU
See MICHIGAN STATE UNIVERSITY FEDERAL CREDIT UNION

MSX AMERICAS
See MSX INTERNATIONAL INC

D-U-N-S 13-947-0009
MSX INTERNATIONAL INC
MSX AMERICAS
500 Woodward Ave Ste 2150, Detroit, MI 48226-3417
Tel (248) 829-6300 *Founded/Ownrshp* 1997
Sales 500.0MM *EMP* 6,000
SIC 8748 7363 8742 8711 Test development & evaluation service; Labor resource services; Management consulting services; Engineering services
Pr: Frederick K Minturn
**CFO:* Sam Del Mar
VP: Jim Bazner
VP: Leslie Cooney
VP: Shawn Coyle
VP: David Graff
VP: Frederick Minturn
**VP:* Michael Muraske
VP: Craig Schmelzer
VP: Andrea Sorrenti
**VP:* Margaret Turner
Board of Directors: Richard Puricelli

D-U-N-S 08-616-6576
MT DIABLO UNIFIED SCHOOL DISTRICT
1936 Carlotta Dr, Concord, CA 94519-1358
Tel (925) 682-8000 *Founded/Ownrshp* 1948
Sales 330.5MM *EMP* 3,800
Accts Christy White Associates San
SIC 8211 Public elementary & secondary schools
Pr: Richard Nicoll
**CFO:* Bryan Richards
Off Mgr: Val Bostwick
Off Mgr: Teresa Poindexter
IT Man: Michael Holmes
Psych: Debbie Lindstrom

MT EPHRAIM DODGE
See FOULKE MANAGEMENT CORP

D-U-N-S 05-096-4063
MT HOOD COMMUNITY COLLEGE DISTRICT FOUNDATION INC
26000 Se Stark St, Gresham, OR 97030-3300
Tel (503) 491-6422 *Founded/Ownrshp* 1966
Sales 1.3MM *EMP* 1,100
SIC 8222 8221 Community college; Colleges universities & professional schools
Pr: Nancy Jaksich
CFO: Jay Crowthers
VP: Jennifer Dement
Exec: Barbara Howell
Assoc Dir: Russell Johnson
Assoc Dir: Sheri A Mosher
**Prin:* William Becker
IT Man: Marcia Graves

D-U-N-S 06-874-8078
MT LEBANON SCHOOL DISTRICT
7 Horsman Dr, Pittsburgh, PA 15228-1107
Tel (412) 344-2077 *Founded/Ownrshp* 1912
Sales 70.7MM[E] *EMP* 1,269
Accts Maher Duessel Pittsburgh Pen
SIC 8211 Public elementary & secondary schools; High school, junior or senior
Ex Dir: Alyssa Beluca
Bd of Dir: Marc Allemang
Bd of Dir: Beth Evans
Bd of Dir: Nora Nealon
Bd of Dir: Thomas Peterson
Bd of Dir: Karen Wolowski
VP: Donna Dinardo
VP: Cliff Luke
VP: Robert Mallery
Dir Bus: Janice Klien
Prin: David Zolkowski

D-U-N-S 00-896-4835 IMP
■ **MT MANSFIELD CO INC**
STOWE MOUNTAIN RESORT
(*Suby of* NATIONAL UNION FIRE INSURANCE CO OF PITTSBURGH PA) ★
5781 Mountain Rd, Stowe, VT 05672-4803
Tel (802) 253-7311 *Founded/Ownrshp* 1973
Sales NA *EMP* 400
SIC 6331 5812 5813 Fire, marine & casualty insurance; Eating places; Drinking places
Pr: C Robert McEleney
**Ch Bd:* M R Greenberg
**Pr:* Henry Lundi
Pr: Scott Reeves
**V Ch Bd:* Thomas J Amidon
**VP:* Barry Pius
Exec: Gary Crouse
Dir Risk M: Joshua Klevans
Comm Dir: Jeff Weis
Off Mgr: Patti Spence
Dir IT: Ric Schaaf

MT RUSHMORE BLACK HILLS GOLD
See RIDDLES GROUP INC

MT SAN ANTONIO COLLEGE
See MT SAN ANTONIO COMMUNITY COLLEGE DISTRICT

D-U-N-S 10-298-5108
MT SAN ANTONIO COMMUNITY COLLEGE DISTRICT
MT SAN ANTONIO COLLEGE
(*Suby of* CALIFORNIA COMMUNITY COLLEGES SYSTEM) ★
1100 N Grand Ave, Walnut, CA 91789-1341
Tel (909) 594-5611 *Founded/Ownrshp* 1946
Sales 93.6MM[E] *EMP* 1,500
SIC 8222 Community college
Pr: William Scroggins
**Pr:* Rosa Royce
**CFO:* Michael D Gregoryk
**Bd of Dir:* Manuel Baca
**Bd of Dir:* Rosanne Bader
**Bd of Dir:* Fred Chyr
**Bd of Dir:* Judy Chen Haggerty
**Bd of Dir:* Dr David K Hall
**VP:* James Czaja
**VP:* Irene Malmgren
**VP:* Dr Audrey Yamagata-

D-U-N-S 18-126-1439
■ **MT SUPPLY INC**
MACHINE TOOLS SUPPLY
(*Suby of* WILSON EXPORTS) ★
3505 Cadillac Ave Ste K2, Costa Mesa, CA 92626-1432
Tel (714) 434-4748 *Founded/Ownrshp* 2015
Sales 185.8MM[E] *EMP* 163
SIC 5085 5084 Industrial supplies; Materials handling machinery
CEO: George H Ponce Jr
Treas: David Herman
Prin: Joseph Custer
Prin: Steve Gurley
Prin: Steve Pixley
Brnch Mgr: Richard Botkin
Brnch Mgr: Mike Hodges
IT Man: Andrea Pixley
IT Man: Victor Santiago
Site Mgr: Jill Grochala
Sls Mgr: Kevin Dohner

D-U-N-S 07-095-4904
MT VERNON CITY SCHOOL DISTRICT
165 N Columbus Ave, Mount Vernon, NY 10553-1101
Tel (914) 665-5000 *Founded/Ownrshp* 1894
Sales 98.4MM[E] *EMP* 1,951
SIC 8211 Public elementary & secondary schools
**Treas:* Shaji Zacharia
Ofcr: Alice Patterson
VP: Serigne Gningue
Schl Brd P: Adriane Saunders
Psych: Francine Silvestri

MT VERNON NRSING RHBLTTION CTR
See EXTENDICARE HEALTH SERVICES INC

MT&L CARD PRODUCTS
See MAGNETIC TICKET & LABEL CORP

D-U-N-S 05-973-8255
MTA DEVELOPMENT INC
3222 E Autumn Ln, Eagle Mountain, UT 84005-4230
Tel (801) 647-3247 *Founded/Ownrshp* 2011
Sales 729.0MM *EMP* 25
SIC 8741 Management services
Pr: Mike Aagard

MTA LEASING
See FORD MONTROSE INC

MTA LONG ISLAND RAIL ROAD
See LONG ISLAND RAIL ROAD CO

MTBC
See MEDICAL TRANSCRIPTION BILLING CORP

D-U-N-S 09-191-9394 IMP
MTC DIRECT INC
17837 Rowland St, City of Industry, CA 91748-1122
Tel (626) 839-6800 *Founded/Ownrshp* 1989
Sales 90.7MM[E] *EMP* 106[E]
SIC 5045 Computers, peripherals & software
CEO: Roy Han
VP Sls: Brian Wang

D-U-N-S 00-886-0967
MTC DISTRIBUTING (CA)
4900 Stoddard Rd, Modesto, CA 95356-9389
Tel (209) 523-6449 *Founded/Ownrshp* 1921
Sales 148.2MM[E] *EMP* 200
SIC 5194 5145 5149 Tobacco & tobacco products; Candy; Groceries & related products
Dir IT: Billy Williams
IT Man: Robert Bettencourt
Opers Mgr: Herb Rodgriguez
VP Mktg: Roe Edwards
Mktg Dir: Tom Kennedy
Sls Dir: Noel Chavez
Sls Mgr: John Esquivel

D-U-N-S 07-870-9924 EXP
MTD CONSUMER GROUP INC
5965 Grafton Rd, Valley City, OH 44280-9329
Tel (330) 225-2600 *Founded/Ownrshp* 1999
Sales 174.4MM[E] *EMP* 660[E]
SIC 3524 Lawn & garden equipment
Prin: Steven E Pryatel

D-U-N-S 18-408-2118 EXP
MTD HOLDINGS INC
5965 Grafton Rd, Valley City, OH 44280-9329
Tel (330) 225-2600 *Founded/Ownrshp* 2002
Sales 2.6MMM[E] *EMP* 6,000
SIC 3524 3544 3469 6141 Lawn & garden equipment; Lawnmowers, residential: hand or power; Special dies & tools; Metal stampings; Financing: automobiles, furniture, etc., not a deposit bank
Ch Bd: Curtis E Moll
**Treas:* Jeff Deuch

D-U-N-S 00-419-6515 IMP/EXP
MTD PRODUCTS INC
(*Suby of* MTD HOLDINGS INC) ★
5965 Grafton Rd, Valley City, OH 44280-9329
Tel (330) 225-2600 *Founded/Ownrshp* 1932, 2002
Sales 2.6MMM[E] *EMP* 5,614
SIC 3524 Lawn & garden equipment; Lawnmowers, residential: hand or power
CEO: Robert T Moll
**Pr:* Jean Hlay
CFO: Craig Boyd
**CFO:* Jeffery C V Deuch
CFO: David Duckhouse
**Treas:* Mike Griffith
Ex VP: Gary Lobaza
Ex VP: James Milinsky
Comm Man: Rachel Rice
Prgrm Mgr: Pete Sadosky
Rgnl Mgr: Ian Rogers

D-U-N-S 08-066-8163 IMP/EXP
MTD SOUTHWEST INC
(*Suby of* MTD CONSUMER GROUP INC) ★
9235 S Mckemy St, Tempe, AZ 85284-2938
Tel (480) 961-1002 *Founded/Ownrshp* 2000
Sales 174.4MM[E] *EMP* 650

SIC 3524 3546 3423 Lawn & garden equipment; Blowers & vacuums, lawn; Hedge trimmers, electric; Power-driven handtools; Hand & edge tools
Pr: Jean H Hlay
**Treas:* Michael Griffith
Genl Mgr: Gene Elefane
Genl Mgr: Randy Parrish
Board of Directors: Robert T Moll

MTDC WELFARE FUND
See MASON TENDER DISTRICT COUNCIL TRUST FUND

D-U-N-S 08-008-4059
MTG ACQUISITIONS LLC
DAV EL WOLDWIDE
69 Norman St, Everett, MA 02149-1951
Tel (800) 922-0343 *Founded/Ownrshp* 2002
Sales 13.8MM^E *EMP* 2,500
SIC 4789 Transportation services
Ch: David Marcu
**VP Sls:* Steve Patel

D-U-N-S 96-807-9017
▲ MTGE INVESTMENT CORP
2 Bethesda Metro Ctr # 14, Bethesda, MD 20814-6319
Tel (301) 968-9220 *Founded/Ownrshp* 2011
Sales 222.7MM *EMP* 395^E
Accts Ernst & Young Mclean Virgini
Tkr Sym MTGE *Exch* NGS
SIC 6798 Real estate investment trusts
CEO: Gary Kain
**Ch Bd:* Alvin N Puyear
**CFO:* John R Erickson
CFO: Peter J Federico
**Ex VP:* Samuel A Flax
Sr VP: Christopher J Kuehl
Sr VP: Aaron Pas

MTI
See MINERALS TECHNOLOGIES INC

D-U-N-S 87-282-3109
MTIC LLC
MOHEGAN SUN CASINO
1 Mohegan Sun Blvd, Uncasville, CT 06382-1355
Tel (860) 862-6100 *Founded/Ownrshp* 1995
Sales 1.3MMM^E *EMP* 10,745^E
SIC 7011 Hotels & motels; Casino hotel
Ch Bd: Marilynn Malerba
**Ch Bd:* Kevin Brown
CFO: Leo Chupaska
VP: George Galinsky
Dir Sec: Donna Haney
Sls Mgr: Kelly Connors

D-U-N-S 00-693-1653
MTL INSURANCE CO
MUTUAL TRUST FINANCIAL GROUP
1200 Jorie Blvd Ste 100, Oak Brook, IL 60523-2274
Tel (630) 990-1000 *Founded/Ownrshp* 1904
Sales NA *EMP* 144
SIC 6311

MTM
See MANITOWOC TOOL AND MACHINING LLC

D-U-N-S 12-664-0981
MTM OLDCO INC
MAINE SUNDAY TELEGRAM
1 City Ctr Fl 5, Portland, ME 04101-4070
Tel (207) 791-6650 *Founded/Ownrshp* 2009
Sales 125.1MM^E *EMP* 720
SIC 2711 Newspapers, publishing & printing
CEO: Charles Cochrane
Mktg Dir: Pamela Cassidy

D-U-N-S 06-544-6577 IMP
MTM RECOGNITION CORP
3201 Se 29th St, Oklahoma City, OK 73115-1605
Tel (405) 609-6900 *Founded/Ownrshp* 1971
Sales 96.1MM^E *EMP* 500
SIC 3911 3873 2499 2389 3499 2791 Jewelry, precious metal; Watches, clocks, watchcases & parts; Trophy bases, wood; Men's miscellaneous accessories; Trophies, metal, except silver; Typesetting
Owner: Dave Smith
**Pr:* Roger Mashore
**CFO:* Mark Landes
**Treas:* Linda Smith
**VP:* Darrel Davis
**VP:* Monica Finley
**VP:* Guy Manley
**VP:* Molly Martin
**VP:* David Smith Jr
**VP:* Bob Thomas
Software D: Joe Young

D-U-N-S 15-772-7991
MTM TECHNOLOGIES INC
(*Suby of* FIRSTMARK CAPITAL LLC) ★
4 High Ridge Park Ste 102, Stamford, CT 06905-1325
Tel (203) 588-1981 *Founded/Ownrshp* 1986
Sales 135.1MM^E *EMP* 250
SIC 5045 7379 Computers, peripherals & software; Computer peripheral equipment; Computers & accessories, personal & home entertainment; Computer software; Computer related consulting services
Pr: Marcus Holloway
Pr: Jerry Mattey
Pr: Shawn Patterson
CFO: John W Braukman
CFO: Michael El-Hillow
CFO: Michael Elhillow
**CFO:* Rosemarie Milano
Bd of Dir: Howard A Pavony
Ex VP: Steven Rothman
Sr VP: Yvonne Gluck
**Sr VP:* Stephen Hicks
VP: Gary Bernstein
**VP:* Jason Bernstein
VP: Rodney Callum
VP: John Cross
VP: Greg Galanos
VP: Steve Hartenstein
VP: Chris Harvey
VP: Dean J Maire
VP: Michael Ritchken
VP: Richard Roux

D-U-N-S 62-522-5946
MTPCS LLC
CELLULAR ONE
1170 Devon Park Dr # 104, Wayne, PA 19087-2128
Tel (610) 688-1334 *Founded/Ownrshp* 2005
Sales 207.5MM^E *EMP* 500
SIC 4812 Cellular telephone services
VP: Kevin Marshall
VP: Angela Tufte
Genl Couns: Julia Tanner

D-U-N-S 18-200-0430
■ MTR GAMING GROUP INC
(*Suby of* ELDORADO RESORTS INC) ★
Hc 2 Box S, Chester, WV 26034
Tel (304) 387-8000 *Founded/Ownrshp* 2014
Sales 351.8MM *EMP* 2,600^E
SIC 7011 7948 Casino hotel; Horse race track operation
Ch Bd: Gary L Carano
**Pr:* Thomas R Reeg
COO: Joseph L Billhimer Jr
COO: William Robinson
CFO: Robert M Jones
Ex VP: John W Bittner
Ex VP: Anthony L Carano
VP: Chris Kern
Genl Couns: Thomas Diehl

D-U-N-S 13-177-1446 IMP
■ MTS MEDICATION TECHNOLOGIES INC
(*Suby of* OMNICELL INC) ★
2003 Gandy Blvd N Ste 800, Saint Petersburg, FL 33702-2167
Tel (727) 576-6311 *Founded/Ownrshp* 1986
Sales 95.5MM^E *EMP* 271
SIC 3565 3089 Packaging machinery; Blister or bubble formed packaging, plastic
CEO: Todd E Siegel
**Pr:* William G Shields
**COO:* Michael D Stevenson
**Sec:* Matthew C Hicks
Sr VP: Dennis H Ayo
**VP:* Robert A Martin
VP: Ronald M Rosenbaum
Mng Dir: Peter A Williams
QA Dir: Brett Smith
IT Man: Sandra Beiter
IT Man: Rick Maher

D-U-N-S 00-645-2312 IMP/EXP
▲ MTS SYSTEMS CORP
14000 Technology Dr, Eden Prairie, MN 55344-2247
Tel (952) 937-4000 *Founded/Ownrshp* 1966
Sales 563.9MM *EMP* 3,315
Tkr Sym MTSC *Exch* NGS
SIC 3829 3825 Measuring & controlling devices; Testing equipment: abrasion, shearing strength, etc.; Stress, strain & flaw detecting/measuring equipment; Vibration meters, analyzers & calibrators; Instruments to measure electricity
Ch Bd: David J Anderson
**Pr:* Jeffrey A Graves
**CFO:* Jeffrey P Oldenkamp
**Chf Cred:* Catherine S Powell
**Sr VP:* William E Bachrach
**Sr VP:* John V Emholz
Sr VP: Mark D Losee
Sr VP: Steven G Mahon
VP: Bill Bachrach
VP: Kelly Donaldson
VP: Bill Hardy
VP: Doug Mielke

MTSI
See MODERN TECHNOLOGY SOLUTIONS INC

D-U-N-S 02-001-6718 IMP
MTU AMERICA INC
(*Suby of* MTU FRIEDRICHSHAFEN GMBH)
39525 Mackenzie Dr, Novi, MI 48377-1602
Tel (248) 560-8000 *Founded/Ownrshp* 1978
Sales 181.3MM^E *EMP* 518
SIC 3519 Diesel, semi-diesel or duel-fuel engines, including marine
Pr: Thomas Koenig
Treas: Anke Lorscheid
Prgrm Mgr: Larry Benedict
Genl Mgr: Joe Lewis
Genl Mgr: Joanna Vardas
Sls Mgr: Dave Brunette
Sls Mgr: Duane Warden
Snr Mgr: Jennifer Riley

D-U-N-S 00-617-5954 IMP/EXP
MTU ONSITE ENERGY CORP (MN)
(*Suby of* ROLLS-ROYCE POWER SYSTEMS AG)
100 Power Dr, Mankato, MN 56001-4790
Tel (507) 625-7973 *Founded/Ownrshp* 1952, 2007
Sales 92.1MM^E *EMP* 300
SIC 3621 Power generators
CEO: Todd Riemann
**CFO:* Markus Hentschel
Genl Mgr: William Gernentz
Mtls Mgr: John Griebel
Ql Cn Mgr: Paul Mehltretter
Mktg Mgr: Jennifer Heimer
Sls Mgr: Keith Burg

MTV NETWORKS
See VIACOM NETWORKS

D-U-N-S 19-586-0770 IMP
■ MTV NETWORKS INC
(*Suby of* VIACOM INC) ★
1515 Broadway Fl 31, New York, NY 10036-5797
Tel (212) 258-8000 *Founded/Ownrshp* 2006
Sales 148.3MM^E *EMP* 329
SIC 4833 Television broadcasting stations
CEO: Judy McGrath
V Ch: Herb Scannell
Pr: Sean Atkins
Pr: Hank Close
Pr: Larry Divney
Pr: Kevin Kay
Pr: Mika Salmi
COO: Long Ellis
COO: Alex Ferrari
COO: Sarah Levy
CFO: Jacques Tortoroli
Treas: George S Smith Jr
Ofcr: Colleen Fahey Rush
Ex VP: Gideon Bierer
Ex VP: Houser Catherine
Ex VP: Colette Chestnut
Ex VP: Denise D Dahldorf
Ex VP: Rich Eigendorff
Ex VP: Sahar Elhabashi
Ex VP: Scott Guthrie
Ex VP: Douglas Herzog

D-U-N-S 79-681-2233
MU SIGMA INC
3400 Dundee Rd Ste 160, Northbrook, IL 60062-2333
Tel (847) 919-0445 *Founded/Ownrshp* 2004
Sales 104.6MM^E *EMP* 360
SIC 7378 7374 Computer & data processing equipment repair/maintenance; Data processing & preparation
Pr: Dhiraj C Rajaram
VP: Mukund Raghunath
Genl Mgr: Vinay Kastak
Snr Mgr: Sumit Bajaj

D-U-N-S 04-448-9110 IMP
MUBEA INC
(*Suby of* MUHR UND BENDER KG)
6800 Industrial Rd, Florence, KY 41042-3090
Tel (859) 746-5300 *Founded/Ownrshp* 1981
Sales 417.6MM^E *EMP* 1,300
SIC 3493 3312 3495 3429 3714 Automobile springs; Bar, rod & wire products; Wire springs; Clamps & couplings, hose; Motor vehicle parts & accessories
CEO: Byrd Douglas Cain III
Pr: Juan Dominguez
**Pr:* Dr Thomas Muhr
CFO: Doug Cain
VP: Peter Lohage
**VP:* Rudolph Muhr
Genl Mgr: Frederick Klein PHD
Genl Mgr: Travis Walker
IT Man: Johnny Ju
Plnt Mgr: Rainer Blankenburg
Ql Cn Mgr: Jason Salensky

D-U-N-S 07-665-5851
MUCKLESHOOT INDIAN TRIBE
MUCKLESHOOT TRIBAL ENTERPRISES
39015 172nd Ave Se, Auburn, WA 98092-9763
Tel (253) 333-8741 *Founded/Ownrshp* 1934
Sales NA *EMP* 2,000
SIC 9131 Indian reservation;
Ch: Louie Ungaro
**Ch Bd:* John Daniels Jr
Treas: Marcie Elkins
Ex Dir: Isabel Tinoco
Prgrm Mgr: Wendy Burdette
Brnch Mgr: Judith Zelter
Genl Mgr: Jeff Songster
Dir IT: Pius Oleskey
Pr Mgr: Linda Freed

MUCKLESHOOT TRIBAL ENTERPRISES
See MUCKLESHOOT INDIAN TRIBE

D-U-N-S 00-589-3029 IMP/EXP
MUEHLSTEIN INTERNATIONAL LTD (NY)
(*Suby of* POLYMERLINE) ★
10 Westport Rd Ste 200, Wilton, CT 06897-4548
Tel (203) 855-6000 *Founded/Ownrshp* 1959
Sales 236.1MM^E *EMP* 115^E
SIC 5169 5162 Synthetic rubber; Plastics materials & basic shapes
CEO: Fernando Montenegro
**Pr:* James Duffy
**CFO:* Ron Restivo
**Treas:* Ronald J Nardozzi
**VP:* Jerrold Johnston
**VP:* Mark Lux
**VP:* Oscar Novo

D-U-N-S 00-535-7504 IMP
■ MUELLER BRASS CO (MI)
MUELLER BRASS PRODUCTS
(*Suby of* MUELLER BRASS HOLDING CO INC) ★
8285 Tournament Dr # 150, Memphis, TN 38125-1745
Tel (901) 753-3200 *Founded/Ownrshp* 1917, 1930
Sales 208.8MM^E *EMP* 740
SIC 3351 3463 3354 3494 Copper rolling & drawing; Copper pipe; Pipe, brass & bronze; Tubing, copper & copper alloy; Nonferrous forgings; Plumbing fixture forgings, nonferrous; Aluminum extruded products; Valves & pipe fittings; Plumbing & heating valves
Pr: Steffen Sigloch
**Treas:* Kent A McKee

D-U-N-S 82-894-7783
■ MUELLER BRASS HOLDING CO INC
(*Suby of* MUELLER INDUSTRIES INC) ★
8285 Tournament Dr # 150, Memphis, TN 38125-1745
Tel (901) 753-3200 *Founded/Ownrshp* 2007
Sales 209.4MM^E *EMP* 1,942^E
SIC 3351 3463 3494 Copper rolling & drawing; Copper pipe; Pipe, brass & bronze; Tubing, copper & copper alloy; Nonferrous forgings; Plumbing fixture forgings, nonferrous; Valves & pipe fittings; Plumbing & heating valves
Pr: Gregory Christopher

MUELLER BRASS PRODUCTS
See MUELLER BRASS CO

D-U-N-S 00-516-2102 IMP
■ MUELLER CO LLC
(*Suby of* MUELLER WATER PRODUCTS INC) ★
633 Chestnut St Ste 1200, Chattanooga, TN 37450-1202
Tel (423) 209-4800 *Founded/Ownrshp* 1857, 2008
Sales 745.8MM^E *EMP* 2,685
SIC 3823 3533 7699 Flow instruments, industrial process type; Drilling tools for gas, oil or water wells; Pumps & pumping equipment repair
Pr: Greg Rogowski
**Treas:* Walt Smith
VP: Mark Gingerich
**Prin:* Vann Beeker
VP Opers: John Van Gerwen

D-U-N-S 00-433-5519 IMP
■ MUELLER COPPER TUBE PRODUCTS INC
(*Suby of* MUELLER INDUSTRIES INC) ★
8285 Tournament Dr # 150, Memphis, TN 38125-1743
Tel (901) 753-3200 *Founded/Ownrshp* 1998
Sales 400.6MM^E *EMP* 3,925
SIC 3351 Tubing, copper & copper alloy
CEO: Gregory L Christopher
**Ex VP:* Brian Caufield
**VP:* Kent McKee

D-U-N-S 09-469-5314 IMP/EXP
■ MUELLER GROUP LLC
(*Suby of* MUELLER WATER PRODUCTS INC) ★
1200 Abernathy Rd, Atlanta, GA 30328-5662
Tel (770) 206-4200 *Founded/Ownrshp* 2005
Sales 1.1MMM^E *EMP* 4,015
SIC 3823 3321 3533 7699 Flow instruments, industrial process type; Gray & ductile iron foundries; Drilling tools for gas, oil or water wells; Pumps & pumping equipment repair

D-U-N-S 62-203-1748
▲ MUELLER INDUSTRIES INC
8285 Tournament Dr # 150, Memphis, TN 38125-1743
Tel (901) 753-3200 *Founded/Ownrshp* 1917
Sales 2.1MMM *EMP* 4,104
Tkr Sym MLI *Exch* NYS
SIC 3463 3494 3089 Nonferrous forgings; Aluminum forgings; Valves & pipe fittings; Plumbing & heating valves; Fittings for pipe, plastic
Ch Bd: Gregory L Christopher
CFO: Jeffrey A Martin
VP: James Brown
VP: Bob Cook
VP: Daniel R Corbin
VP: Daniel Corbin
VP: Richard W Corman
VP: Jack Mueller
VP: Gary C Wilkerson
Admn Mgr: Chris Hu
Plnt Mgr: Joe Beaujean
Board of Directors: Paul J Flaherty, Gennaro J Fulvio, Gary S Gladstein, Scott J Goldman, John B Hansen, Terry Hermanson

D-U-N-S 01-762-2770
MUELLER ROOFING DISTRIBUTORS INC (OH)
MRD SERVICES
327 E Wyoming Ave, Cincinnati, OH 45215-3027
Tel (513) 679-8540 *Founded/Ownrshp* 1977
Sales 168.7MM^E *EMP* 120
SIC 5033 5099 Roofing & siding materials; Containers: glass, metal or plastic
CEO: Herbert J Mueller
CFO: Brad Schwartz
**Ex VP:* Terry J Powell
**VP:* Robert P Marini
Brnch Mgr: Donna Mueller

D-U-N-S 00-504-5898
MUELLER SERVICES INC
63 Main St, Tonawanda, NY 14150-2133
Tel (716) 691-4344 *Founded/Ownrshp* 1998
Sales NA *EMP* 200
SIC 6331 Fire, marine & casualty insurance
Ch Bd: John F Noe
Pr: John Armstrong
**Pr:* Thomas R Noe
CFO: Phillip Arp
CFO: Chad Mize
VP: Ken Clark
VP: Mat Huftalen
QA Dir: Brett Barber
QA Dir: Jessica Jobe
Software D: Eric Small
Mktg Mgr: Lindsay Buckley

D-U-N-S 00-804-0743 IMP
MUELLER SUPPLY CO INC (TX)
1913 Hutchins Ave, Ballinger, TX 76821-4401
Tel (325) 365-3555 *Founded/Ownrshp* 1936, 2014
Sales 206.9MM^E *EMP* 359
SIC 3448 3496 5039 Prefabricated metal components; Miscellaneous fabricated wire products; Metal buildings
Pr: Morris B Davenport
CFO: Phillip Arp
**VP:* Nyle T Davenport
VP: James Syzdek
Brnch Mgr: Ben Albarado
Brnch Mgr: Rudy Fuentes
Brnch Mgr: Andy Gallant
Brnch Mgr: Tyler Jones
Brnch Mgr: Eddy Torres
Brnch Mgr: Frank Trevino
Brnch Mgr: Jeffrey Wisner

D-U-N-S 00-350-1079
▲ MUELLER WATER PRODUCTS INC (GA)
1200 Abernathy Rd # 1200, Atlanta, GA 30328-5670
Tel (770) 206-4200 *Founded/Ownrshp* 2005
Sales 1.1MMM *EMP* 4,100^E
Accts Ernst & Young Llp Atlanta Ge
Tkr Sym MWA *Exch* NYS
SIC 3491 3492 3494 3443 3321 3823 Industrial valves; Fluid power valves & hose fittings; Valves & pipe fittings; Pipe, standpipe & culverts; Gray & ductile iron foundries; Industrial flow & liquid measuring instruments
Ch Bd: Gregory E Hyland
CFO: Evan L Hart
Chf Cred: Keith L Belknap
Sr VP: Keith Belknap
Sr VP: Robert P Keefe
Sr VP: Marietta Edmunds Zakas
VP: Tim Holcombe
VP: Greg Hollod
VP: Jim Lambert
VP: Kevin G McHugh
VP: Steve Mead
Board of Directors: Shirley C Franklin, Thomas J Hansen, Jerry W Kolb, Joseph B Leonard, Mark J O'brien, Bernard G Rethore, Lydia W Thomas,

Michael T Tokarz

D-U-N-S 00-691-1770 IMP
MUFG AMERICAS HOLDINGS CORP (CA)
(*Suby of* BANK OF TOKYO-MITSUBISHI UFJ, LTD., THE)
1251 Ave Of The Americas, New York, NY 10020-1104
Tel (212) 782-5911 *Founded/Ownrshp* 1996, 2008
Sales NA *EMP* 12,550E
Accts Deloitte & Touche Llp San Fr
SIC 6021 National commercial banks
Pr: Masashi Oka
**Pr:* Katsumi Hatao
CFO: John F Woods
CFO: Johannes H Worsoe
Ofcr: Donna Dellosso
Ofcr: Arthur G Smith
Ofcr: Annemieke Van Der Werff
Ex VP: Mary A Curran
Ex VP: Ronald H Kendrick
Ex VP: Joseph M Petitti
Ex VP: Michael A C Spilsbury
Sr VP: Mark L Stevenson
Board of Directors: Michael D Fraizer, Christine Garvey, Ann F Jaedicke, Henry R Keizer, Takashi Morimura, Barbara L Rambo, Dean A Yoost

D-U-N-S 00-691-1754 IMP
MUFG UNION BANK NA
(*Suby of* MUFG AMERICAS HOLDINGS CORP) ★
400 California St, San Francisco, CA 94104-1302
Tel (212) 782-6800 *Founded/Ownrshp* 1864
Sales NA *EMP* 9,676
SIC 6021 National commercial banks
Pr: Norimichi Kanari
**Ch Bd:* Kyota Omori
**V Ch:* Mark W Midkiff
**V Ch:* Timothy H Wennes
**COO:* Philip B Flynn
**CFO:* Johannes H Worsoe
Ch: Patrick M Fahey
**Ch:* Takashi Morimura
Bd of Dir: Richard Farman
Bd of Dir: Standley Farrar
Bd of Dir: Michael Gillfillan
Bd of Dir: Steven Glaser
Bd of Dir: Ronald Havner
Bd of Dir: Carl Robertson
**Chf Mktg O:* Arthur G Smith
Ofcr: Tammie Klink
**Ofcr:* Annemieke Van Der Werff
**Ex VP:* Linda Betzer
Ex VP: John M Edmonston
Ex VP: Morris W Hirsch
**Ex VP:* John H McGuckin Jr

D-U-N-S 04-735-2836
MUHLENBERG COLLEGE
2400 Chew St, Allentown, PA 18104-5586
Tel (484) 664-3100 *Founded/Ownrshp* 1864
Sales 142.9MM *EMP* 758E
SIC 8221 Colleges & universities
Ch Bd: Richard Bruekner
**Pr:* Peyton R Helm
**CFO:* Kent A Dyer
Top Exec: Marcia A Teeno
VP: Michael Krouse
Exec: Jeffrey Rudski
Assoc Dir: Patrick Fligge
Assoc Dir: Laura A Garland
Genl Mgr: Joe Swanson
Off Mgr: Anitra Witkowski
CTO: Clif Kussmaul

D-U-N-S 07-753-9708
MUHLENBERG REGIONAL MEDICAL CENTER INC
JFK MEDICAL CENTER
(*Suby of* JFK MEDICAL CENTER) ★
Park Ave & Randolph Rd, Plainfield, NJ 07060
Tel (908) 668-2000 *Founded/Ownrshp* 1997
Sales 657.6M *EMP* 1,400E
Accts Parente Beard Llc Clark New
SIC 8062 General medical & surgical hospitals
Pr: John McGee
Dir Rad: Fred Wishner
Phys Thrpy: Lynn Stallworth

D-U-N-S 09-288-5516
MUKILTEO SCHOOL DISTRICT
9401 Sharon Dr, Everett, WA 98204-2699
Tel (425) 356-1274 *Founded/Ownrshp* 1952
Sales 101.3MME *EMP* 1,800
SIC 8211 Public elementary school; Public junior high school; Public senior high school
Off Admin: Karen Ebel
Pr Dir: Andy Muntz
Teacher Pr: Joan Steiner
HC Dir: Lisa Pitsh

D-U-N-S 60-680-2445
MULBERRY CHILD CARE CENTERS INC
(*Suby of* KINDERCARE LEARNING CENTERS LLC) ★
990 Washington St Ste 104, Dedham, MA 02026-6715
Tel (781) 320-9222 *Founded/Ownrshp* 2001
Sales 25.4MME *EMP* 2,100
SIC 8351 Preschool center
VP: Deann Besch
Doctor: Roderick Fletcher

D-U-N-S 03-027-3697
MULBERRY CHILDCARE CENTERS INC
KINDERCARE
650 Ne Holladay St # 1400, Portland, OR 97232-2045
Tel (503) 872-1300 *Founded/Ownrshp* 2001
Sales 47.8MME *EMP* 2,000
SIC 8351 Child day care services
Pr: Tom Heymann
Treas: Dan R Jackson
**Sr VP:* Edward Brewington
**Sr VP:* Eva Kripalani
**Sr VP:* Bruce Walters
**VP:* David Benedict
VP: Lauren Klein
Ex Dir: Mary K Travis

MULCOA
See C-E MINERALS INC

D-U-N-S 79-746-4810
MULESOFT INC
77 Geary St Fl 400, San Francisco, CA 94108-5707
Tel (415) 229-2009 *Founded/Ownrshp* 2003
Sales 191.1MME *EMP* 500E
SIC 7371 Computer software development
Pr: Greg Schott
Pr: James Donelan
Pr: Chris Erickson-King
Pr: Andy Shorkey
Pr: Terry Tripp
Pr: Nick Trombetta
**Pr:* Ken Yagen
**CFO:* Matt Langdon
**Ofcr:* Mark Dao
**Sr VP:* Simon Parmett
**VP:* Ed Dubrawski
**VP:* Jim Emerich
VP: Brent Grimes
VP: Stephen Hallowell
VP: Brent Hayward
VP: Sarvesh Jagannivas
VP: Matthew Kilguss
**VP:* Ross Mason
VP: Laura Merkl
**VP:* Chris Purpura
VP: Mike Randall
Board of Directors: Michael Capellas, Steve Collins

D-U-N-S 02-214-5767
MULGREW OIL CO
PERFECTION OIL
10314 Silverwood Dr, Dubuque, IA 52003-8477
Tel (563) 583-7386 *Founded/Ownrshp* 1955
Sales 199.6MM *EMP* 48
SIC 5171 5172 5541

D-U-N-S 05-773-0764 IMP/EXP
MULLER MARTINI CORP
MULLER MARTINI HOLDING AG
(*Suby of* GRAPHA-HOLDING AG)
456 Wheeler Rd, Hauppauge, NY 11788-4343
Tel (631) 582-4343 *Founded/Ownrshp* 1967
Sales 86.5MME *EMP* 150
SIC 5084 7699 Industrial machinery & equipment; Industrial machinery & equipment repair
Pr: Werner Naegeli
CFO: Richard Slattery
Ex Dir: Kris Organ
Div Mgr: Douglas Stryker
Off Mgr: Tom Duckett
CTO: Carrington Herbert
Dir IT: Elie Saliba
IT Man: David Brown
Info Man: Daniel Denue
Plnt Mgr: Fred Jones
VP Sls: Wolfgang Hanzl
Board of Directors: Kasper F Meier

MULLER MARTINI HOLDING AG
See MULLER MARTINI CORP

D-U-N-S 84-883-2663
■ **MULLINTBG INSURANCE AGENCY SERVICES LLC**
MULLINTBG
(*Suby of* PRUDENTIAL INSURANCE CO OF AMERICA) ★
100 N Sepulveda Blvd, El Segundo, CA 90245-4359
Tel (310) 203-8770 *Founded/Ownrshp* 2008
Sales NA *EMP* 260
SIC 6411 Insurance agents, brokers & service
CEO: Michael R Shute
**Pr:* Michael Glickman
Ex VP: Anne Fitzgerald
Sr VP: Yong Lee
VP: Matthew Cobb
VP: Carl Greene
VP: Harry Levitt
VP: Geoff Nathanson
VP: Felicia Smith
VP: Erik Speed
Mng Dir: Scott Striegel

D-U-N-S 08-286-8423 IMP
MULLINIX PACKAGES INC (IN)
(*Suby of* SABERT CORP) ★
3511 Engle Rd, Fort Wayne, IN 46809-1117
Tel (260) 747-3149 *Founded/Ownrshp* 1984, 2016
Sales 103.1MME *EMP* 350E
SIC 3089 Plastic containers, except foam
Pr: Gene Gentili
CFO: Belinda Glenn
VP: Luther Gross
VP: Robert Inlow
VP: Timothy Love
VP: Victor Rimkevicius
VP: German Valdez
Ql Cn Mgr: Douglas Dark

D-U-N-S 00-512-5786
MULLINS FOOD PRODUCTS INC
2200 S 25th Ave, Broadview, IL 60155-4584
Tel (708) 344-3224 *Founded/Ownrshp* 1957
Sales 143.8MME *EMP* 405
SIC 2033 2035 Tomato products: packaged in cans, jars, etc.; Barbecue sauce: packaged in cans, jars, etc.; Catsup: packaged in cans, jars, etc.; Dressings, salad: raw & cooked (except dry mixes)
Pr: Jeanne Gannon
**COO:* Michael Mullins
**CFO:* Arthur Clausen
Genl Mgr: Ed Mullins
QA Dir: Jamie Krystofiak
Dir IT: Joe Sands
IT Man: Nelson Powell
Sfty Dirs: Gary Saatkamp
Sfty Dirs: Rich Vlach
Opers Mgr: Mike Mazur
Opers Mgr: Terry McCarthy

MULLINTBG
See MULLIN TBG INSURANCE AGENCY SERVICES LLC

D-U-N-S 11-950-0101 IMP
MULTEK FLEXIBLE CIRCUITS INC
(*Suby of* FLEXTRONICS INTL LATIN AMER) ★
1150 Sheldahl Rd, Northfield, MN 55057-9444
Tel (507) 663-8000 *Founded/Ownrshp* 2004
Sales 131.0MME *EMP* 450
SIC 3672 Printed circuit boards
CEO: Franck Lize
Bd of Dir: Stewart Auerbach
Bd of Dir: Kenneth Roering
**VP:* Jim Drass
VP: Alex Liew
CIO: Matt Hoffa
IT Man: Tim Seitz
IT Man: Paul Watterson
Ql Cn Mgr: Taylor Kendall
Ql Cn Mgr: Paul Laughlin
Ql Cn Mgr: Sherrie Thibodeau

D-U-N-S 14-368-3832
MULTI GROUP LOGISTICS INC
10900 Belmont Ave Ste 400, Franklin Park, IL 60131-1416
Tel (847) 621-3333 *Founded/Ownrshp* 2004
Sales 88.7MME *EMP* 550
SIC 4213

D-U-N-S 79-128-9742 IMP/EXP
■ **MULTI PACKAGING SOLUTIONS INC**
(*Suby of* MULTI PACKAGING SOLUTIONS INTERNATIONAL LIMITED) ★
150 E 52nd St Ste 2800, New York, NY 10022-6240
Tel (646) 885-0005 *Founded/Ownrshp* 2004
Sales 1.1MMME *EMP* 2,415
SIC 2759 2731 2761 3089 5092 2671 Commercial printing; Screen printing; Letterpress printing; Tags: printing; Books: publishing & printing; Continuous forms, office & business; Identification cards, plastic; Arts & crafts equipment & supplies; Packaging paper & plastics film, coated & laminated
CEO: Marc Shore
**Pr:* Dennis Kaltman
Pr: Nancy Smith
**CFO:* William Hogan
Ex VP: Arthur Kern
**Ex VP:* Rick Smith
Sr VP: Keith Kiedinger
Sr VP: Tim Klewicki
**Sr VP:* Tim Whitfield
Sr VP: Marty Zarett
VP: Jim Ferrel

D-U-N-S 07-989-1229
▲ **MULTI PACKAGING SOLUTIONS INTERNATIONAL LIMITED**
150 E 52nd St Fl 28, New York, NY 10022-6017
Tel (646) 885-0005 *Founded/Ownrshp* 2005
Sales 1.6MMM *EMP* 8,700E
Tkr Sym MPSX *Exch* NYS
SIC 2657 Folding paperboard boxes
CEO: Marc Shore
Pr: Dennis Kaltman
CFO: William H Hogan
Ex VP: Rick Smith

D-U-N-S 96-479-8508 IMP
■ **MULTI-CHEM GROUP LLC**
(*Suby of* HALLIBURTON CO) ★
424 S Chadbourne St, San Angelo, TX 76903-6926
Tel (325) 223-8200 *Founded/Ownrshp* 2011
Sales 372.3MME *EMP* 1,024
SIC 1389 Oil field services; Servicing oil & gas wells
Pr: David J Lesar
**Treas:* Jon Grottis
**VP:* James Archer
VP: Thane Schaffer
Plnt Mgr: Randy Harris

D-U-N-S 12-129-8590 IMP
▲ **MULTI-COLOR CORP**
4053 Clough Woods Dr, Batavia, OH 45103-2587
Tel (513) 381-1480 *Founded/Ownrshp* 1985
Sales 870.8MM *EMP* 5,000
Accts Grant Thornton Llp Cincinnati
Tkr Sym LABL *Exch* NGS
SIC 2759 2679 2672 Labels & seals: printing; Labels, paper: made from purchased material; Labels (unprinted), gummed: made from purchased materials
Pr: Nigel A Vinecombe
**Pr:* Vadis A Rodato
COO: Floyd E Needham
CFO: Sharon E Birkett
Dir IT: Larry Morgan

D-U-N-S 05-964-1266
MULTI-CRAFT CONTRACTORS INC
AIRWORKS
2300 N Lowell Rd, Springdale, AR 72764-1842
Tel (479) 751-4330 *Founded/Ownrshp* 1986
Sales 87.6MME *EMP* 392
SIC 1711 3441 1731

MULTI-FINANCIAL
See PLASTIPAK PACKAGING INC

D-U-N-S 13-184-4185
MULTI-FINELINE ELECTRONIX INC
(*Suby of* SUZHOU DONGSHAN PRECISION MANUFACTURING CO.,LTD.)
8659 Research Dr, Irvine, CA 92618-4291
Tel (949) 453-6800 *Founded/Ownrshp* 2016
Sales 636.6MM *EMP* 5,560
SIC 3672 Printed circuit boards
Pr: Reza Meshgin
CFO: Tom Kampfer
CFO: Thomas Liguori
Ex VP: Christine Besnard
Ex VP: Thomas Lee
Mng Dir: Larry L Longden
Mng Dir: Leif Ottosson
CIO: Neil Liu
IT Man: Franklin Tay
Counsel: Dean Matheson

D-U-N-S 09-754-0397 IMP/EXP
MULTI-PLASTICS INC
7770 N Central Dr, Lewis Center, OH 43035-9404
Tel (740) 548-4894 *Founded/Ownrshp* 1979
Sales 231.1MME *EMP* 300
SIC 5162 Plastics film
Pr: John R Parsio
**CFO:* Michael T Hickey
**Ex VP:* John Parsio Jr
**VP:* Wesley Hall
**VP:* Steven Parsio
Exec: Kim Chalmers
Info Man: Steve Lindquist
Mfg Dir: Juan Escobar
Plnt Mgr: Larry Wright
Mktg Dir: Cheryl Caudill
Sls Mgr: Robert Weber

D-U-N-S 83-570-2127
MULTI-SHOT LLC
MS ENERGY SERVICES
3335 Pollok Dr, Conroe, TX 77303-5702
Tel (936) 441-6630 *Founded/Ownrshp* 2004
Sales 390.6MME *EMP* 468E
SIC 1389 1381 Servicing oil & gas wells; Drilling oil & gas wells
CFO: Scot Bork
Exec: Lantier Don
Exec: Ken McCorkle
Exec: Steve McCoy
Dir IT: Chris Darlen
IT Man: Chris Darland
Opers Mgr: Charles Curtis
Sales Exec: Chris Snow
VP Sls: David Cudd

D-U-N-S 00-463-8750
MULTI-VIEW INC (TX)
7701 Las Colinas Rdg, Irving, TX 75063-8081
Tel (972) 402-7070 *Founded/Ownrshp* 2000
Sales 130.3MME *EMP* 700E
SIC 7313 Electronic media advertising representatives
CEO: Scott Bedford
COO: Cathy Breden
**COO:* Steve Fullbright
COO: Edward F Haye
**CFO:* Omar Choucair
**Chf Mktg O:* Todd Ebert
**VP:* Colby Horton
**VP:* Brandon Webb
Exec: Andrew Harvot
Comm Man: Callie Cady
**Prin:* Mark Colodny

D-U-N-S 03-001-6992
MULTIBAND CORP
(*Suby of* GOODMAN NETWORKS INC) ★
2801 Network Blvd Ste 300, Frisco, TX 75034-1881
Tel (763) 504-3000 *Founded/Ownrshp* 2013
Sales 1.0MMME *EMP* 3,612E
SIC 4841 4813 Cable & other pay television services; Cable television services;
CEO: James Mandel
**COO:* Kent Whitney
**CFO:* Steven M Bell
VP: J B Mattingly
VP: Don Synder
**CIO:* David Ekman

D-U-N-S 19-512-8640
MULTICARE HEALTH SYSTEM
ALLENMORE HOSPITAL
316 M L King Jr Way # 314, Tacoma, WA 98405-4260
Tel (253) 403-1000 *Founded/Ownrshp* 1986
Sales 1.0MMME *EMP* 6,510
Accts Kpmg Llp Seattle Washington
SIC 8062 8093 8069 General medical & surgical hospitals; Specialty outpatient clinics; Children's hospital
Pr: William G Robertson
Mng Pt: Andrea L Hartley
**Pr:* Theresa M Boyle
CFO: Anna Loomis
**CFO:* Vince Schmitz
CFO: Vincent Schmitz
Ofcr: Claire Spain-Remy
**Ex VP:* Florence Chang
**Sr VP:* Sarah M Horsman
**Sr VP:* Lois I Bernstein
VP: Sara Long
VP: Harold Moscho
VP: Erik Rasmussen
VP: Lester Reed
Exec: Kate Bechtold
Exec: Ginger Fraley
Exec: Pamela A Hannah

D-U-N-S 88-406-9915 IMP
MULTIEXPORT FOODS INC
AQUAFARMS INTERNATIONAL
703 Nw 62nd Ave Ste 510, Miami, FL 33126-4688
Tel (305) 364-0009 *Founded/Ownrshp* 1994
Sales 194.0MM *EMP* 15
SIC 5146 Seafoods
CEO: Jose Ramon Gutierrez
**VP:* Andres Lyon
**VP:* Jason Paine

MULTIFAB
See MULTILINK INC

D-U-N-S 10-786-2732 IMP/EXP
MULTILINK INC
MULTIFAB
580 Ternes Ln, Elyria, OH 44035-6252
Tel (440) 366-6966 *Founded/Ownrshp* 1983
Sales 147.4MME *EMP* 140
SIC 5063 3829 Wire & cable; Cable testing machines
Pr: Steven Kaplan
COO: Bernadette Golas
Sr VP: Mike French
**VP:* Kathy Kaplan
VP: Will Lundstrom
VP: Michael Shaw
QA Dir: Chris Slivka
VP Sls: Matt Ternes
Manager: Mike Walsh

D-U-N-S 07-301-9465
MULTIPLAN INC
115 5th Ave Fl 7, New York, NY 10003-1004
Tel (212) 780-2000 *Founded/Ownrshp* 2014
Sales 314.8MME *EMP* 506
SIC 8742 Hospital & health services consultant
CEO: Mark Tabak
V Ch: Rubin Shelly
Pr: Rudy Gontek
**CFO:* David Redmond
**Ex VP:* Marcy Feller

**Ex VP:* Michael Ferrante
**Ex VP:* Dale White
VP: Adam Aitkin
VP: Frank Budzisz
VP: Andrea Buford
VP: Leeann Christ
VP: Mike Clericuzio
VP: Kurt Fullmer
VP: Andrew Hoffmann
VP: Steven Jolie
VP: Arthur Klein
VP: Dave Manning
VP: Michael McEttrick
VP: Alok Sanghvi
VP: Jim Sherry
VP: Andrea Spooner

D-U-N-S 06-089-5679 IMP/EXP
MULTIQUIP INC
(*Suby of* ITOCHU INTERNATIONAL INC) ★
18910 Wilmington Ave, Carson, CA 90746-2820
Tel (310) 537-3700 *Founded/Ownrshp* 1973
Sales 276.0MM^E *EMP* 383
SIC 5063 5082 3645 Generators; General construction machinery & equipment; Garden, patio, walkway & yard lighting fixtures: electric
CEO: Tom Yasuda
**Pr:* Gary Moskovitz
**CFO:* Jim Henehan
**Sr VP:* Bob Graydon
**Sr VP:* Mike Howlett
VP: Michael Ferguson
VP: Michael Hanken
Rgnl Mgr: Ken Bartelli
Rgnl Mgr: Todd Jones
Ql Cn Mgr: Preston Adams

D-U-N-S 00-211-3744 IMP/EXP
MULTISORB TECHNOLOGIES INC (NY)
325 Harlem Rd, Buffalo, NY 14224-1893
Tel (716) 824-8900 *Founded/Ownrshp* 1961
Sales 95.3MM^E *EMP* 500
SIC 2819

MULTNOMAH COUNTY
See COUNTY OF MULTNOMAH

D-U-N-S 00-639-7566
MULZER CRUSHED STONE INC
TELL CITY CONCRETE SUPPLY
534 Mozart St, Tell City, IN 47586-2446
Tel (812) 547-7921 *Founded/Ownrshp* 1939
Sales 544.6MM^E *EMP* 450
SIC 1422 3273 5191 5085 Crushed & broken limestone; Ready-mixed concrete; Limestone, agricultural; Industrial supplies
Pr: Kenneth Mulzer Jr
IT Man: Patty Hawhoose
Mtls Mgr: Don Gengelbach
Sfty Mgr: Matthew Bunner
Opers Mgr: Kennneth Mulzer Jr
Mktg Dir: Natalie Maasberg
Sls Mgr: Ed Donnelly
Sales Asso: Carlyn Greene

D-U-N-S 07-206-1641
MUNCIE COMMUNITY SCHOOLS
2501 N Oakwood Ave, Muncie, IN 47304-2399
Tel (765) 747-5205 *Founded/Ownrshp* 1958
Sales 74.9MM^E *EMP* 1,600
SIC 8211 Public senior high school; Public junior high school; Public elementary school
CFO: Deborah Williams
Ex Dir: Julie A Bailey

MUNDI WESTPORT GROUP
See WESTPORT CORP

MUNDY COMPANY
See MUNDY PLANT MAINTENANCE INC

D-U-N-S 18-602-1093
MUNDY CONTRACT MAINTENANCE INC
11150 S Wilcrest Dr # 300, Houston, TX 77099-4388
Tel (281) 530-8711 *Founded/Ownrshp* 1985
Sales 38.1MM^E *EMP* 1,200
SIC 7349 Building maintenance services
Pr: David A Mundy
**VP:* John Mundy

D-U-N-S 04-034-2321
MUNDY PLANT MAINTENANCE INC
MUNDY COMPANY
11150 S Wilcrest Dr # 300, Houston, TX 77099-4388
Tel (281) 530-8711 *Founded/Ownrshp* 1955
Sales 345.9M *EMP* 2,725
SIC 7699 Industrial equipment services
Pr: David Mund
**Pr:* Shane Burden
**Pr:* David Mundy
**Sr VP:* Scott Bratton
**Sr VP:* Sydney McDavid

D-U-N-S 05-620-2625
■ **MUNICH AMERICAN REASSURANCE CO PAC INC**
MARC LIFE
(*Suby of* MUNICH-AMERICAN HOLDING CORP) ★
56 Perimeter Ctr E # 200, Atlanta, GA 30346-2290
Tel (770) 350-3200 *Founded/Ownrshp* 1995
Sales NA *EMP* 230
SIC 6331 Fire, marine & casualty insurance & carriers
Pr: Michael G Dekoning
Pr: David Bruggeman
Pr: Leo Tinkham
COO: James Sweeney
CFO: Michael W Farley
Treas: Steven K Thompson
Sr VP: Paige S Freeman
Sr VP: ARI J Lindner
Sr VP: Michael Taht
Sr VP: Michael S Taht
Sr VP: Michael Taht
VP: Andrew Carroll
VP: Dieter S Gaubatz
VP: Dieter Gaubatz
VP: Scott Gilliam
VP: Mike Happold
VP: D Hintz
VP: Robert Lund
VP: Emily Roman
VP: Ron Schaber
VP: Meg Schultz

D-U-N-S 96-274-5555
■ **MUNICH HEALTH NORTH AMERICA INC**
(*Suby of* MUNICH-AMERICAN HOLDING CORP) ★
555 College Rd E, Princeton, NJ 08540-6616
Tel (609) 243-4200 *Founded/Ownrshp* 2010
Sales NA *EMP* 4^E
SIC 6331 Fire, marine & casualty insurance & carriers
Pr: Juan Serrano
Pr: Scott Machut
Pr: Travis Micucci
Sr VP: Michael Shevlin
Rgnl Mgr: Mike Reisinger
Rgnl Mgr: Gary Stropoli

D-U-N-S 15-737-8407
■ **MUNICH RE AMERICA BROKERS INC**
(*Suby of* MUNICH-AMERICAN HOLDING CORP) ★
685 College Rd E, Princeton, NJ 08540-6625
Tel (609) 243-4900 *Founded/Ownrshp* 1994
Sales NA *EMP* 1,100
SIC 6321 6311 Reinsurance carriers, accident & health; Life insurance
CEO: John Phelan
**Pr:* Anthoney Kuczinski
**Pr:* George Roberts
**Ch:* Edward J Noonan
VP: Denise M Ambrogio
VP: David R Clark
**VP:* Donald F Merkel Jr
Rgnl Mgr: Dominic J Adesso
VP Mktg: Joseph Stuhl
VP Mktg: John K Tracey

D-U-N-S 79-689-0044
■ **MUNICH RE AMERICA CORP**
(*Suby of* MUNICH-AMERICAN HOLDING CORP) ★
555 College Rd E, Princeton, NJ 08540-6616
Tel (609) 243-4200 *Founded/Ownrshp* 1991
Sales NA *EMP* 1,450
SIC 6331 Fire, marine & casualty insurance & carriers
CEO: Anthony J Kuczinski
**Pr:* Pina C Albo
Pr: James B Couch
Pr: Blaine Desmond
Pr: Joe Dintrone
Pr: John Vasturia
Pr: Peter J Walker
COO: Michael McMonagle
COO: Kari Parker
COO: Donna Peterson
COO: Nick Young
CFO: Mike Farley
CFO: Anthony Kuczinski
CFO: George Oshaughnessey
CFO: Herma Pohlchristoph
Ofcr: Charlie Shamieh
**Ex VP:* Albert J Beer
**Ex VP:* Wolfgang Engshuber
Sr VP: Ashish Agarwal
Sr VP: Jill Beggs
Sr VP: Stefan Birkel

D-U-N-S 00-698-0031
■ **MUNICH REINSURANCE AMERICA INC**
MUNICH-AMERICA GLOBAL SERVICES
(*Suby of* MUNICH RE AMERICA CORP) ★
555 College Rd E, Princeton, NJ 08540-6616
Tel (609) 243-4200 *Founded/Ownrshp* 1917, 1996
Sales NA *EMP* 1,200
SIC 6331 6311 Fire, marine & casualty insurance & carriers; Life insurance
Pr: Steven Levy
Pr: Anthony J Kuczinski
Pr: John Vasturia
CFO: M Steven Levy
Treas: Ray Cox
Ex VP: Robert Burgess
Ex VP: Wolfgang Engshuber
Sr VP: Jill Beggs
Sr VP: Lucy Crawford
Sr VP: Daniel Fisher
Sr VP: Oliver Frase
Sr VP: Edward Lang
Sr VP: David O'Keefe
Sr VP: Alden Provost
Sr VP: Nicholas Signoretta
Sr VP: John K Tracey
Sr VP: Robin Willcox
VP: Rich Dlugosb
VP: Peter Doyle
VP: Michelle Glass
VP: David Grimley

MUNICH-AMERICA GLOBAL SERVICES
See MUNICH REINSURANCE AMERICA INC

D-U-N-S 12-887-3671
■ **MUNICH-AMERICAN HOLDING CORP**
(*Suby of* MUNCHENER RUCKVERSICHERUNGS-GESELLSCHAFT AG IN MUNCHEN)
555 College Rd E, Princeton, NJ 08540-6616
Tel (609) 243-4876 *Founded/Ownrshp* 2000
Sales NA *EMP* 3,912
SIC 6331 Fire, marine & casualty insurance & carriers
Pr: John P Phelan
VP: Raymond Cox
VP: Michael Davis
VP: Gary Greene
VP: Eric Herbst
VP: Brian McCormick
VP: Stephen Morello
VP: Douglas Paige
VP: Joseph Peppelman
VP: Edward Ryan
VP: Michael Shevlin
VP: Howard Taylor

D-U-N-S 07-683-8143
MUNICIPAL CREDIT UNION
2 Lafayette St Frnt D, New York, NY 10007-1353
Tel (212) 238-3300 *Founded/Ownrshp* 1917
Sales NA *EMP* 430
SIC 6062 State credit unions, not federally chartered
CEO: William Porter
**COO:* Norman Kohn
CFO: Shirley Laliberte
**CFO:* Kam Wong
Treas: Mick Lamedola
Bd of Dir: S Osei-Bonsu
Ofcr: Eric Gong
Ofcr: Timothy Wheeler
Sr VP: Carole Porter
VP: John Beeson
VP: Richard Casamassa
VP: Katherine Dugmore
VP: Corey Fernandes
VP: Willie James
VP: Latosha McCoy
VP: Vincent Miller
VP: Leon S Smith
VP: Jean Suffak

D-U-N-S 08-282-4566
MUNICIPAL ELECTRIC AUTHORITY OF GEORGIA
MEAG POWER
1470 Riveredge Pkwy, Atlanta, GA 30328-4640
Tel (770) 563-0300 *Founded/Ownrshp* 1975
Sales 642.9MM *EMP* 150
Accts Pricewaterhousecoopers Llp At
SIC 1623 Electric power line construction
Pr: James E Fuller
**Treas:* Steve A Rentfrow
VP: Gary Schaeff
**VP:* William J Yearta
Rgnl Mgr: Holly Bisig
Rgnl Mgr: Scott Miller
Telecom Ex: Doug Lego
Dir IT: Ron King

D-U-N-S 04-816-7923
MUNICIPAL EMERGENCY SERVICES INC
7 Poverty Rd Ste 85h, Southbury, CT 06488-2273
Tel (203) 364-0620 *Founded/Ownrshp* 2001
Sales 192.3MM^E *EMP* 330
SIC 5087 Firefighting equipment
CEO: Thomas Hubregsen
**VP:* Jeff Johnson
**VP:* John Skaryak
Sls Mgr: Brian Alsup

D-U-N-S 01-441-1420
MUNICIPAL EMPLOYEES RETIREMENT SYSTEM OF MICHIGAN
1134 Municipal Way, Lansing, MI 48917-7886
Tel (517) 703-9030 *Founded/Ownrshp* 1996
Sales NA *EMP* 126
SIC 6371 Pension funds
CEO: Anne Wagner
**CFO:* Luke Huelskamp
**VP:* Jeb Burns
VP: Judith Jarvis
Comm Dir: Lisa B Brewer
CIO: Bob Luedeman
CTO: Kim Rhead
Dir IT: Chris Neff
Dir IT: Scott Thompson
Software D: David Ehnis

D-U-N-S 17-550-3770
MUNICIPAL ENERGY AGENCY OF NEBRASKA (INC)
M E A N
8377 Glynoaks Dr, Lincoln, NE 68516-6304
Tel (402) 474-4759 *Founded/Ownrshp* 1981
Sales 125.0MM *EMP* 50
Accts Bkd Llp Lincoln Nebraska
SIC 4911 Distribution, electric power; Generation, electric power; Transmission, electric power
CEO: J Gary Stauffer
**COO:* Tim Sutherland
Genl Mgr: Larry Marquis

D-U-N-S 18-390-9514
MUNICIPAL GAS AUTHORITY OF GEORGIA
PUBLIC GAS PARTNERS
104 Townpark Dr Nw, Kennesaw, GA 30144-5556
Tel (770) 590-1000 *Founded/Ownrshp* 1987
Sales 390.1MM *EMP* 50
Accts Ernst & Young Llp Atlanta Ge
SIC 5172 Petroleum products
Pr: Arthur C Corbin
Treas: Carter Crawford

D-U-N-S 79-430-7686
MUNICIPAL UTILITIES BOARD OF DECATUR MORGAN COUNTY ALABAMA
DECATUR UTILITIES
1002 Central Pkwy Sw, Decatur, AL 35601-4848
Tel (256) 552-1440 *Founded/Ownrshp* 1938
Sales 141.0MM *EMP* 170^E
Accts Alexander Thompson Arnold Pllc
SIC 4911 Distribution, electric power
Ch: Neal Holland
**CFO:* Steve Pirkle

D-U-N-S 09-109-0266
MUNICIPIO DE ARECIBO
Jose De Diego St, Arecibo, PR 00612
Tel (787) 879-1561 *Founded/Ownrshp* 1616, 1898
Sales NA *EMP* 1,480
SIC 9199 Personnel agency, government

D-U-N-S 09-058-4798
MUNICIPIO DE BAYAMON
Road 2 Km 11 Hm 3 St Ro, Bayamon, PR 00959
Tel (787) 780-5552 *Founded/Ownrshp* 1772
Sales NA *EMP* 3,300
SIC 9111 Mayors' offices;

D-U-N-S 13-497-2710
MUNICIPIO DE MAYAGUEZ
Betances St Crnr Mckinley Corner Mckinley, Mayaguez, PR 00680
Tel (787) 834-8585 *Founded/Ownrshp* 1760
Sales NA *EMP* 1,555^E
SIC 9111 Mayors' offices;

D-U-N-S 09-112-7365
MUNICIPIO DE PONCE
Calle Comercio Frente, Ponce, PR 00731
Tel (787) 284-4141 *Founded/Ownrshp* 1692
Sales NA *EMP* 3,000
SIC 9111 City & town managers' offices
Pr: Francisco Zayas Seijo
Pr: Rafael Santiago

D-U-N-S 09-036-2773
MUNICIPIO DE SAN JUAN
SAN JUAN CITY HALL
1306 Ave Fernandez Juncos, San Juan, PR 00909-2521
Tel (787) 724-7171 *Founded/Ownrshp* 1898
Sales NA *EMP* 3,171^E
SIC 9111 Executive offices
Pr: Laura Del Carmen
**Prin:* Carlos A Acevedo

D-U-N-S 13-922-0714
MUNICIPIO DE SAN JUAN
EMPRESAS MUNICIPALES DEPT.
(*Suby of* SAN JUAN CITY HALL) ★
1205 Ave Ponce De Leon, San Juan, PR 00907-3916
Tel (787) 289-0310
Sales NA *EMP* 2,854^E
SIC 9611

D-U-N-S 09-111-3944
MUNICPALITY OF GUAYNABO
Jose De Diego St Final, Guaynabo, PR 00969
Tel (787) 720-4040 *Founded/Ownrshp* 1912
Sales NA *EMP* 2,577^E
SIC 9111 Mayors' offices;

D-U-N-S 11-860-4537 IMP
MUNILLA CONSTRUCTION MANAGEMENT LLC
M C M
6201 Sw 70th St Fl 2, South Miami, FL 33143-4718
Tel (305) 541-0000 *Founded/Ownrshp* 1983
Sales 250.9MM *EMP* 255
Accts Cherry Bekaert Llp Coral Gab
SIC 1622 1542 Bridge, tunnel & elevated highway; Commercial & office building, new construction
VP: Brian McDonald

D-U-N-S 06-213-9076 IMP
MUNRO & CO INC (AR)
LAKE CATHERINE FOOTWEAR CO
3770 Malvern Rd, Hot Springs, AR 71901-6744
Tel (501) 262-6000 *Founded/Ownrshp* 1971, 1972
Sales 53.5MM^E *EMP* 1,200
SIC 3144 3149 Women's footwear, except athletic; Children's footwear, except athletic; Sandals, except rubber or plastic: children's
Pr: Buddy Eoff
**CFO:* Jane Adams
**Ex VP:* Mollie Munro
CIO: David Swan
Natl Sales: Ron Dillehay

D-U-N-S 07-998-9869
MUNROE REGIONAL MEDICAL CENTER INC (FL)
1500 Sw 1st Ave, Ocala, FL 34471-6559
Tel (352) 351-7200 *Founded/Ownrshp* 1927
Sales 384.2MM^E *EMP* 2,179
SIC 8062 General medical & surgical hospitals
CEO: Richard D Mutarelli
**Sr VP:* Paul Clark
Sr VP: Lon Mc Pherson
**Sr VP:* Lon H McPherson
**Sr VP:* Marc J Miller
VP: Beth NC Call
VP: Cy Huffman
VP: Rich Muteralli
Dir Rad: Ralf Barckhausen
Ex Dir: Rosalee Coyner
Ex Dir: Cynthia Preuit

D-U-N-S 15-193-0278
MUNSON HEALTHCARE
MUNSON HOSPICE HOUSE
1105 Sixth St, Traverse City, MI 49684-2349
Tel (800) 252-2065 *Founded/Ownrshp* 1985
Sales 8.0MM *EMP* 4,000
SIC 8062 General medical & surgical hospitals
CEO: Ed Ness
**Pr:* Al Pilong
COO: Derk Pronger
**Ch:* John Pelizzari
**Ch:* Dan Wolf
**Treas:* Connie Deneweth
**Treas:* Christina Macinnes
**Treas:* Dan McDavid
Ofcr: Rochelle Steimel
Sr VP: Mark R Anthony
VP: Tim Binder
VP: Cristen Dingman
VP: Kenneth Eike
VP: David S McGreaham
Exec: Ruth Bloomer
Exec: Barbara Platts
Dir: Heidi Gustine

MUNSON HOSPICE HOUSE
See MUNSON HEALTHCARE

D-U-N-S 06-017-9595 IMP
MUNSON MEDICAL CENTER
(*Suby of* MUNSON HOSPICE HOUSE) ★
1105 Sixth St, Traverse City, MI 49684-2386
Tel (231) 935-6000 *Founded/Ownrshp* 1985
Sales 510.9MM *EMP* 3,100
SIC 8062 General medical & surgical hospitals
CEO: Edwin A Ness
Pr: Paul Shirilla
**COO:* Derk Pronger
**CFO:* Edward Carlson
Ofcr: Kathy Warnes
VP: Eugene Lyons
Dir Rad: Frederick J Brodeur
Dir Rad: Charlie Dziedzic
Chf Nrs Of: Kathleen Glaza
CIO: Christopher Podges
MIS Dir: William Chung

D-U-N-S 06-949-0167
MUNSTER MEDICAL RESEARCH FOUNDATION INC
COMMUNITY HOSPITAL
901 Macarthur Blvd, Munster, IN 46321-2901
Tel (219) 836-1600 *Founded/Ownrshp* 1985
Sales 495.2MM *EMP* 2,000
Accts Ernst & Young Us Llp Indianap
SIC 8062 General medical & surgical hospitals
Pr: Donald S Powers
CFO: Maryann Schalett
CFO: Marianne Shacklett
* *Ch:* Frankie L Fesko
* *Treas:* George E Watson
* *Treas:* David E Wickland
* *VP:* Joseph Morrow
Dir Lab: Arist Sgouroudis
Dir Rx: Tim Gardiner
* *Prin:* James J Richards
Off Mgr: Sandy Sonaty

MUNTERS CARGOCAIRE
See MUNTERS USA INC

D-U-N-S 95-799-6341 IMP
MUNTERS CORP
(*Suby of* MUNTERS AB)
79 Monroe St, Amesbury, MA 01913-3204
Tel (978) 241-1100 *Founded/Ownrshp* 1965
Sales 163.6MM^E *EMP* 500
SIC 3585 3822 3569 3564 Humidifiers & dehumidifiers; Air flow controllers, air conditioning & refrigeration; Filters, general line: industrial; Blowers & fans
Pr: Maj Britt Hallmark
* *VP:* Mark Collins
IT Man: Michael Rabkin
Netwrk Mgr: Don Blaney
Mtls Mgr: Mike Lyonnais
Ql Cn Mgr: Dwayne Hill
Sales Exec: Scott Gagliostro
Mktg Mgr: Kathy Arbelo
Manager: Tyler Fawber
Manager: Mike Sadosky

D-U-N-S 04-416-8888 IMP
MUNTERS USA INC
MUNTERS CARGOCAIRE
(*Suby of* MUNTERS AB)
79 Monroe St, Amesbury, MA 01913-3204
Tel (978) 241-1100 *Founded/Ownrshp* 1978
Sales 83.4MM^E *EMP* 700
SIC 3585 Refrigeration & heating equipment
Pr: Lennart Lindquist
CFO: Don Driscoll
Dist Mgr: Andrew Cook
Dir IT: Michael Rabkin
Netwrk Mgr: Josh Currier
Mtls Mgr: Mike Lyonnais
Natl Sales: Russ Brown

D-U-N-S 02-478-0061 IMP
MURAKAMI MANUFACTURING USA INC (KY)
(*Suby of* MURAKAMI CORPORATION)
575 Watertower Byp, Campbellsville, KY 42718-8693
Tel (270) 469-3939 *Founded/Ownrshp* 2000
Sales 84.0MM *EMP* 275
SIC 3231 Mirrors, truck & automobile: made from purchased glass
CEO: Masaharu Okuno
* *Pr:* Michael Rodenberg
Sr VP: Toru Komatsu
Genl Mgr: Eric Thompson
IT Man: Masaki Suzuki
Ql Cn Mgr: Dana Mattingly
Ql Cn Mgr: Naoto Yoshimura

D-U-N-S 05-080-6447 IMP
MURANAKA FARM
11018 E Los Angeles Ave, Moorpark, CA 93021
Tel (805) 529-6692 *Founded/Ownrshp* 1966
Sales 148.6MM^E *EMP* 250
SIC 5148 Vegetables, fresh
Ch Bd: Roy Muranaka
* *CEO:* Harry Muranaka
* *Ex VP:* Charles Muranaka
* *Prin:* Carolyn Muranaka
Prin: Frank Saltzman

D-U-N-S 06-258-7324 IMP
MURATA ELECTRONICS NORTH AMERICA INC (GA)
(*Suby of* MURATA MANUFACTURING CO.,LTD.)
2200 Lake Park Dr Se, Smyrna, GA 30080-7604
Tel (770) 436-1300 *Founded/Ownrshp* 1973
Sales 357.1MM^E *EMP* 1,200
SIC 5065 3675 3679 Electronic parts; Electronic capacitors; Electronic circuits
Pr: David Kirk
* *Pr:* Hiroshi Jozuka
* *Treas:* Hidekazu Tachikawa
Treas: Toshiyuki Yasutaka
* *Ex VP:* Tom Yamamoto
* *VP:* Tony Coalson
* *VP:* John F Denslinger
* *VP:* David McGinnis
IT Man: Tony Garcia
Opers Supe: Delphine Claggion
Mktg Mgr: Yong Fang

D-U-N-S 12-673-9320 IMP/EXP
MURATA MACHINERY USA HOLDINGS INC
MURATATEC
(*Suby of* MURATA MACHINERY,LTD.)
2120 Queen City Dr, Charlotte, NC 28208-2709
Tel (704) 394-8331 *Founded/Ownrshp* 2002
Sales 116.9MM^E *EMP* 220^E
SIC 3542 3552 5065 Punching & shearing machines; Textile machinery; Facsimile equipment
Pr: Masahiko Hattori

D-U-N-S 60-620-4030 IMP
MURATA MACHINERY USA INC
MURATEC
(*Suby of* MURATATEC) ★
2120 Queen City Dr, Charlotte, NC 28208-2709
Tel (704) 875-9280 *Founded/Ownrshp* 2002
Sales 100.7MM^E *EMP* 220
SIC 5084 5085 3542 Textile & leather machinery; Metal refining machinery & equipment; Clean room supplies; Punching & shearing machines
Pr: Masahiko Hattori
* *CFO:* Dale R Mitchell
Sr VP: Charlie Cutting
VP: Jim Cicora
Exec: Matt Herd
Exec: Threse Scott
Rgnl Mgr: Gabe Morelli
Snr Sftwr: Craig Strong
QA Dir: Travis James
Natl Sales: Lloyd Keller
Mktg Mgr: Alisa Criswell

MURATATEC
See MURATA MACHINERY USA HOLDINGS INC

MURATEC
See MURATA MACHINERY USA INC

D-U-N-S 00-265-9688
MURDOCH CENTER FOUNDATION INC
1600 E C St, Butner, NC 27509-2530
Tel (919) 575-1000 *Founded/Ownrshp* 1957
Sales 32.4M *EMP* 1,700
SIC 8699 Charitable organization

MURDOCH'S RANCH & HOME SUPPLY
See RANCH AND HOME SUPPLY LLC

D-U-N-S 16-142-9253 EXP
MUREX LLC
7160 Dallas Pkwy Ste 300, Plano, TX 75024-7112
Tel (972) 702-0018 *Founded/Ownrshp* 2012
Sales 2.0MMM *EMP* 35
SIC 5172 Petroleum products
Pr: Robert Wright
* *CFO:* Rick Bartel
* *CFO:* Richard J Patel
* *Sec:* Charles E Senn
* *VP:* Chris Wall

D-U-N-S 82-505-9280 EXP
MURFIN DRILLING CO INC
250 N Water St Ste 300, Wichita, KS 67202-1299
Tel (316) 267-3241 *Founded/Ownrshp* 1991
Sales 176.9MM^E *EMP* 303
SIC 1381 1382 5082 6512 6514 Directional drilling oil & gas wells; Aerial geophysical exploration oil & gas; General construction machinery & equipment; Commercial & industrial building operation; Dwelling operators, except apartments
Pr: David Murfinis
* *CFO:* Richard Koll
* *Treas:* Robert D Young
* *VP:* Jerry Abels
* *VP:* David Doyel
* *VP:* Leon Rodak
Sfty Dirs: Hans Krohn

D-U-N-S 12-436-1783
MURFREESBORO CITY SCHOOLS
2552 S Church St Ste 100, Murfreesboro, TN 37127-7135
Tel (615) 893-2313 *Founded/Ownrshp* 1968
Sales 65.3MM^E *EMP* 1,000
SIC 8211 Elementary & secondary schools; School board
Ex Dir: Linda Gilbert
* *Treas:* Golena Bell
Top Exec: Aaron Thompson
Pr Dir: Lisa Trail
Teacher Pr: Ralph Ringstaff
Board of Directors: Phil Huddleson

D-U-N-S 62-513-7716 IMP
MURPHY CO
MURPHY PLYWOOD
2350 Prairie Rd, Eugene, OR 97402-9742
Tel (541) 461-4545 *Founded/Ownrshp* 1986
Sales 95.8MM^E *EMP* 450
SIC 2435 2436 Hardwood veneer & plywood; Softwood veneer & plywood
Pr: John Murphy
CFO: Kimball Charlie
CFO: Charlie Kimball
* *VP:* John Jr Murphy
Board of Directors: John Murphy

D-U-N-S 00-383-3365 IMP
MURPHY CO MECHANICAL CONTRACTORS AND ENGINEERS (MO)
1233 N Price Rd, Saint Louis, MO 63132-2303
Tel (314) 997-6600 *Founded/Ownrshp* 1907
Sales 212.2MM *EMP* 550
Accts Rubin Brown Llp Saint Louis
SIC 1711 Mechanical contractor; Plumbing contractors; Warm air heating & air conditioning contractor
Ch Bd: James J Murphy Jr
Pr: Patrick J Murphy Jr
COO: Donald D Hardin
CFO: Rob Koester
CFO: Robert L Koester
Treas: Kent Decker
Sr VP: Lawrence Dicicco
Sr VP: Michael J Knapp
Sr VP: Robert Mathisen
VP: Edward Becker
VP: Mark L Bengard
VP: Mark Bengard
VP: Dave Book
VP: David Book
VP: Bob Breth
VP: Christopher Carter
VP: Kevin Cook
VP: Tim Dace
VP: Greg Hackl
VP: Thomas Hegger
VP: Christopher Hiemenz

MURPHY CONSTRUCTION COMPANY
See MCC INC

D-U-N-S 87-954-0193
MURPHY ENERGY CORP
2250 E 73rd St Ste 600, Tulsa, OK 74136-6835
Tel (918) 743-7979 *Founded/Ownrshp* 1991
Sales 184.4MM^E *EMP* 129^E
SIC 5172 Petroleum products
CEO: Matthew J Murphy
* *Pr:* Carter Simmons
Ofcr: Ed Paitsel
* *Ex VP:* Gregory A Westfall
* *VP:* Patrick Johndrow
* *VP:* Glen Smith
Dir Risk M: Tim McLeod
IT Man: Sarah Habiger

D-U-N-S 00-885-1479 IMP
■ **MURPHY EXPLORATION & PRODUCTION CO - USA**
(*Suby of* MURPHY OIL CORP) ★
9805 Katy Fwy Ste G200, Houston, TX 77024-1269
Tel (281) 599-8145 *Founded/Ownrshp* 1953
Sales 852.8MM^E *EMP* 611
Accts Kpmg By Fax On September 20 2
SIC 1382 1311 Oil & gas exploration services; Crude petroleum & natural gas production
Pr: R W Jenkins
* *Treas:* Miendy K West
VP: Steven A Coss
Pr Dir: Nancy Perkins

D-U-N-S 06-529-1981
MURPHY FARMS LLC
CHIEF FEED MILL
(*Suby of* SMITHFIELDS HOG PRODUCTION DIV) ★
600 Rte Hwy A, Rose Hill, NC 28458
Tel (910) 289-6439 *Founded/Ownrshp* 1962
Sales 57.6MM^E *EMP* 2,100
SIC 0213 Hogs
Pr: Dr M Terry Coffey

MURPHY FOODSERVICE
See BADGER FARMS INC

D-U-N-S 10-891-7493 IMP
▲ **MURPHY OIL CORP**
300 E Peach St, El Dorado, AR 71730-5838
Tel (870) 862-6411 *Founded/Ownrshp* 1950
Sales 3.0MMM *EMP* 1,258
Tkr Sym MUR *Exch* NYS
SIC 1311 1382 2911 Crude petroleum & natural gas; Crude petroleum & natural gas production; Crude petroleum production; Natural gas production; Oil & gas exploration services; Petroleum refining
Pr: Roger W Jenkins
CFO: John W Eckart
Treas: John B Gardner
Ex VP: Eugene T Coleman
Ex VP: Walter K Compton
Ex VP: Michael K McFadyen
Sr VP: Keith Caldwell
Sr VP: Keith S Caldwell
Sr VP: Kelli M Hammock
Sr VP: K Todd Montgomery
VP: E Ted Botner
VP: Tim F Butler
VP: Barry F R Jeffery
VP: Allan J Misner
VP: Kelly L Whitley
Exec: Leona Ralph

D-U-N-S 00-805-3712
■ **MURPHY OIL USA INC**
MURPHY USA
(*Suby of* MURPHY USA INC) ★
200 E Peach St, El Dorado, AR 71730-5836
Tel (870) 862-6411 *Founded/Ownrshp* 2013
Sales 17.2MMM *EMP* 7,350
Accts Kpmg Llp Houston Texas
SIC 8742 2911 1311 4213 Industry specialist consultants; Gasoline; Liquefied petroleum gases, LPG; Crude petroleum production; Liquid petroleum transport, non-local
Pr: R Andrew Clyde
Treas: Kevin Fitzgerald
Sr VP: Henry J Heithaus
VP: Ijaz Iqbal
Genl Mgr: Gil Reath
VP Mfg: Kevin Melnyk
Opers Mgr: Sharolyn Givens
Snr Mgr: Tom Holt

MURPHY PLYWOOD
See MURPHY CO

D-U-N-S 06-293-6075 IMP/EXP
MURPHY TRACTOR & EQUIPMENT CO INC
JOHN DEERE AUTHORIZED DEALER
(*Suby of* MURFIN DRILLING CO INC) ★
5375 N Deere Rd, Park City, KS 67219-3307
Tel (855) 246-9124 *Founded/Ownrshp* 1982
Sales 122.5MM^E *EMP* 300
SIC 5082 General construction machinery & equipment
Pr: Thomas A Udland
* *Sec:* Robert D Young
Area Mgr: Curtis Christiansen
Area Mgr: Chris Seta
Brnch Mgr: Ken Geoghegan
Mktg Mgr: Candace Jindra
Manager: Bill Boyer
Manager: Darrell Dupree
Manager: Christopher Grimes
Manager: Greg Kozisek
Manager: Thomas McKee

MURPHY USA
See MURPHY OIL USA INC

D-U-N-S 96-566-6824
▲ **MURPHY USA INC**
200 E Peach St, El Dorado, AR 71730-5836
Tel (870) 875-7600 *Founded/Ownrshp* 2013
Sales 12.7MMM *EMP* 9,800^E
Tkr Sym MUSA *Exch* NYS
SIC 5531 5541 Automotive & home supply stores; Gasoline service stations
Pr: R Andrew Clyde
* *Ch Bd:* R Madison Murphy
CFO: Mindy K West
Sr VP: Marn K Cheng
Sr VP: John A Moore
VP: Donald Smith
Board of Directors: Claiborne P Deming, Thomas M Gattle Jr, Fred L Holliger, Christoph Keller III, James W Keyes, Diane N Landen, David B Miller, Jack T Taylor

D-U-N-S 03-905-5368 IMP
MURPHY-BROWN LLC
SMITHFIELDS HOG PRODUCTION DIV
(*Suby of* SMITHFIELD FOODS INC) ★
2822 W Nc 24 Hwy, Warsaw, NC 28398-7952
Tel (910) 293-3434 *Founded/Ownrshp* 2001
Sales 2.1MMM^E *EMP* 5,000
SIC 0213 Hogs
Pr: Gregg Schmidt
Dir IT: Dan Murphy

D-U-N-S 15-559-0128
MURPHY-HOFFMAN CO
11120 Tomahawk Creek Pkwy, Leawood, KS 66211-2695
Tel (816) 483-6444 *Founded/Ownrshp* 1985
Sales 873.9MM^E *EMP* 1,998
SIC 5012 7513 7538 6159 5511 Truck tractors; Truck leasing, without drivers; General truck repair; Truck finance leasing; Pickups, new & used
Pr: Timothy R Murphy
* *CFO:* Jeff Johnson
* *Treas:* Reed F Murphy Jr
* *Ex VP:* Kenneth A Hoffman
Ex VP: David Stroop
VP: Robert Barnicle
VP: Jay Lang
Brnch Mgr: Kevin Eberenz
Brnch Mgr: Lance Miller
Snr Ntwrk: Joe Evans
Sales Exec: Richard Rush

D-U-N-S 12-095-7097 IMP
■ **MURRAY BISCUIT CO LLC**
(*Suby of* KELLOGGS) ★
1550 Marvin Griffin Rd, Augusta, GA 30906-3853
Tel (706) 798-8600 *Founded/Ownrshp* 2001
Sales 119.9MM^E *EMP* 1,000
SIC 2052 2051 Cookies; Crackers, dry; Saltine crackers; Cakes, pies & pastries
Pr: William G Bayer
CFO: Byron Russell
VP: Jerry Cavitt
VP: Gerald Defalco

MURRAY COMPANY
See MURRAY PLUMBING AND HEATING CORP

D-U-N-S 04-799-7501
MURRAY COUNTY SCHOOLS
1006 Green Rd, Chatsworth, GA 30705-2012
Tel (706) 695-4531 *Founded/Ownrshp* 2010
Sales 43.2MM^E *EMP* 1,000^E
SIC 8211 Public elementary & secondary schools
Psych: Misty Donahoo

D-U-N-S 79-044-2649 IMP/EXP
MURRAY EDGEN CORP
(*Suby of* EDGEN GROUP INC) ★
18444 Highland Rd, Baton Rouge, LA 70809-6105
Tel (225) 756-9868 *Founded/Ownrshp* 2007
Sales 295.6MM^E *EMP* 280
SIC 5051 Iron & steel (ferrous) products
Ch Bd: Daniel J O'Leary
* *Pr:* Craig S Kiefer
* *CFO:* Erika Fortenberry
Sr VP: Douglas J Daly
* *Sr VP:* Daniel Keaton
* *VP:* Graeme Cad
* *VP:* Craig Doel
* *VP:* Rob Fishbein
* *VP:* David Kemp
* *VP:* John Nicholas
CIO: Randy Harless

D-U-N-S 82-855-8978
MURRAY EDGEN II L P
(*Suby of* EDGEN GROUP INC) ★
18444 Highland Rd, Baton Rouge, LA 70809-6105
Tel (225) 756-9868 *Founded/Ownrshp* 2007
Sales 165.9MM^E *EMP* 1,038
Accts Kpmg Llp Baton Rouge Louisia
SIC 5051 Iron & steel (ferrous) products
CEO: Daniel J O Leary
Pr: Craig S Kiefer
CFO: David L Laxton III
Sr VP: Dan Keaton
Sr VP: Daniel D Keaton
VP: Graeme Cadger
VP: David Mullaney
VP: John Nicholas
Dist Mgr: Perry Luigs
Dist Mgr: Tom Watson
IT Man: Randy Harlis

D-U-N-S 11-487-0509
MURRAY ENERGY CORP
46226 National Rd W, Saint Clairsville, OH 43950-8742
Tel (740) 338-3100 *Founded/Ownrshp* 2003
Sales 4.0MMM^E *EMP* 3,000
SIC 1222 Bituminous coal-underground mining
CEO: Robert E Murray
* *COO:* Robert D Moore
* *Treas:* Michael Loiacono
* *Ex VP:* Moore Robert D
Sr VP: Michael O McKwn
* *Sr VP:* McKown Michael O
* *VP:* Cornelius BJ
* *VP:* Murray Ryan
* *Prin:* Paul Piccolini

D-U-N-S 03-479-7860
MURRAY GUARD INC
58 Murray Guard Dr, Jackson, TN 38305-3625
Tel (731) 668-3400 *Founded/Ownrshp* 1968
Sales 68.8MM^E *EMP* 2,030
Accts Horne Cpas Jackson Tn
SIC 7381 Protective services, guard; Security guard service
Ch Bd: Roger G Murray Jr
* *Pr:* Gerald P Ferguson Jr
* *Ex VP:* James L Exum
* *Ex VP:* James A Ward
* *VP:* Bruce K Burch
VP: John Carter
* *VP:* David Harris

*VP: Claude Kelly
VP: Claude H Kelly Jr
*VP: Blair Ross
*VP: Rick Shackleford
VP: David Tremblay

D-U-N-S 06-624-6133
MURRAY PLUMBING AND HEATING CORP
MURRAY COMPANY
18414 S Santa Fe Ave, E Rncho Dmngz, CA 90221-5612
Tel (310) 637-1500 Founded/Ownrshp 1972
Sales 134.3MM^E EMP 500^E
SIC 1711 Plumbing contractors; Warm air heating & air conditioning contractor
CEO: Kevan Steffey
*Pr: Jim Deflavio
*Pr: John Odom
CFO: Barbara Braymajor
Brnch Mgr: Douglas Orban
Genl Mgr: Jenee Dixon
Dir IT: Peter Cheng

D-U-N-S 04-198-0632
MURRAY STATE UNIVERSITY
102 Curris Ctr, Murray, KY 42071-3369
Tel (270) 809-3774 Founded/Ownrshp 1922
Sales 122.1MM EMP 1,250
Accts Rubin Brown Llp Saint Louis
SIC 8221 University
Pr: Robert Davies
Bd of Dir: Stephanie REA
Ofcr: Gay Rollins
VP: Bonnie Higginson
Assoc Dir: Alison Marshall
Opers Mgr: Scott Thile
Pr Dir: Dana Starnes

MURRAY-CALLOWAY COUNTY HOSPITA
See MURRAY-CALLOWAY COUNTY PUBLIC HOSPITAL CORP

D-U-N-S 07-965-1162
MURRAY-CALLOWAY COUNTY PUBLIC HOSPITAL CORP (KY)
MURRAY-CALLOWAY COUNTY HOSPITA
803 Poplar St, Murray, KY 42071-2432
Tel (270) 762-1100 Founded/Ownrshp 1948
Sales 106.8MM EMP 1,110
SIC 8062 General medical & surgical hospitals
Pr: Keith Bailey
Chf Path: Dewey L Dean
Chf OB: Charles G Cook
Chf Rad: Henry C Hines
*CFO: Brad Bloemer
CFO: Vicki H Parks
Chf Mktg O: Richard Crouch
Ofcr: Don Futrell
VP: Sandra Dick
*VP: Lisa Ray
*VP: Keith Travis
*VP: John Wilson
Dir OR: Jill Asher
Dir Lab: Linda Cavitt
Dir Rad: Heidi Hordyk
Dir Rx: Sheila Walker
Dir Env Sv: Mark Torsak

MURRAY'S AUTO PART
See MURRAYS DISCOUNT AUTO STORES INC

D-U-N-S 05-880-1507 IMP
■ **MURRAYS DISCOUNT AUTO STORES INC**
MURRAY'S AUTO PART
(Suby of CSK AUTO CORP) ★
8080 Haggerty Rd, Belleville, MI 48111-1643
Tel (734) 957-8080 Founded/Ownrshp 2005
Sales 278.2MM^E EMP 2,200
SIC 5531 Automotive parts; Automotive accessories
Pr: Thomas McFall
CFO: Fred Tinfey
VP: Jim Mangiapane
VP: George Sutherland
VP: Brian Woodworth
VP Admn: John Broses

D-U-N-S 61-693-8809
MURRIETA VALLEY UNIFIED SCHOOL DISTRICT
41870 Mcalby Ct, Murrieta, CA 92562-7036
Tel (951) 696-1600 Founded/Ownrshp 1989
Sales 103.5MM^E EMP 2,000
Accts Vavrinek Trine Day & Co Ll
SIC 8211 Public elementary & secondary schools
Dir Sec: Dale Velk
Genl Mgr: Dawn Cherry
Teacher Pr: Faythe Mutchnick-Jayx
HC Dir: Cathy Owens

D-U-N-S 06-119-0187
MURRYS OF MARYLAND INC
(Suby of MURRY'S, INC.)
7852 Walker Dr Ste 420, Greenbelt, MD 20770-3262
Tel (888) 668-7797 Founded/Ownrshp 1948
Sales 94.4MM^E EMP 800
SIC 5421 Food & freezer plans, meat
Ch Bd: Ira Mendelson
*Treas: Matthew Young
Bd of Dir: Richard Meyer
*VP: Gary Gold

D-U-N-S 02-850-0007 IMP
MUSASHI AUTO PARTS MICHIGAN INC
TECHNICAL AUTO PARTS
(Suby of MUSASHI SEIMITSU INDUSTRY CO., LTD.)
195 Brydges Dr, Battle Creek, MI 49037-7340
Tel (269) 965-0057 Founded/Ownrshp 1980
Sales 88.7MM^E EMP 330
SIC 3714 Motor vehicle transmissions, drive assemblies & parts
Pr: Mr Takayuki Miyata

D-U-N-S 04-748-5495
MUSCATINE COMMUNITY SCHOOL DISTRICT
2900 Mulberry Ave, Muscatine, IA 52761-2757
Tel (563) 263-7223 Founded/Ownrshp 1900
Sales 54.3MM^E EMP 1,000
SIC 8211 Public elementary & secondary schools
*Pr: Penny Jones
VP: Michael McGrory
*VP: Mary Wildermuth
Teacher Pr: Jill Bourkquin

D-U-N-S 06-104-4160
MUSCATINE POWER & WATER (INC)
MACHLINK-MUSCATINE POWER & WTR
3205 Cedar St, Muscatine, IA 52761-2287
Tel (563) 263-2631 Founded/Ownrshp 1900
Sales 117.9MM EMP 302
SIC 4911 4941 Electric services; Water supply
CEO: D Scott Ingstad
*Pr: Doyle D Tubandt
CFO: Kathy Griffin
*Ch: Warren Heidbreder
*VP: Tracy McGinnis
*Genl Mgr: Salvatore L Lobianco
Sfty Mgr: Jeff Hedrington
Opers Mgr: Jay Freese
Snr Mgr: Dennis Riedel

MUSCLE & FITNESS FLEX M&F HERS
See WEIDER PUBLICATIONS LLC

D-U-N-S 82-968-0276 EXP
▲ **MUSCLEPHARM CORP**
4721 Ironton St Unit A, Denver, CO 80239-2422
Tel (303) 396-6100 Founded/Ownrshp 2006
Sales 166.8MM EMP 248^E
Tkr Sym MSLP Exch OTO
SIC 2023 Dietary supplements, dairy & non-dairy based
Ch Bd: Ryan Drexler
CFO: John Price
Sr VP: Brian Cavanaugh
VP: Brent Baker
VP: Mark Miller
Mng Dir: John Mills
VP Opers: Jon Heussner
Snr Mgr: Gary Davis
Board of Directors: William Bush, Michael J Doron, Richard F Estalella, Stacey Jenkins, Noel Thompson

D-U-N-S 00-526-4718
MUSCO CORP (IA)
MYCRO GROUP CO
100 1st Ave W, Oskaloosa, IA 52577-3244
Tel (641) 676-1746 Founded/Ownrshp 1978, 1988
Sales 175.1MM^E EMP 672
SIC 7359 3648 3646 3641 3545 3423 Sound & lighting equipment rental; Area & sports luminaries; Commercial indusl & institutional electric lighting fixtures; Electric lamps; Machine tool accessories; Hand & edge tools
Pr: Joe P Crookham
*Treas: Christopher K Hyland
VP: Mike Dahlhauser
VP: Louann Ferreira
*VP: Myron K Gordin
Exec: Greg Gilley
VP Admn: Diane Crookham
Admn Mgr: Terri Petty
CTO: Dave McCumber
MIS Dir: Brenda Landers
QA Dir: Kevin Yerington

D-U-N-S 13-525-9000 IMP/EXP
MUSCO SPORTS LIGHTING LLC
(Suby of MYCRO GROUP CO) ★
100 1st Ave W, Oskaloosa, IA 52577-3244
Tel (641) 673-0411 Founded/Ownrshp 1988
Sales 162.7MM^E EMP 550
SIC 3648 Lighting equipment
Mktg Dir: Joe P Crookham
Genl Mgr: Karyl Thomas
Dir IT: Tony Rivera
Dir IT: Jane Ryder
IT Man: Dave McCumber
Mktg Mgr: Kelly Wheeler
Manager: Jeff Omer
Sls Mgr: Tim Imhoff
Sls Mgr: Mike Marchetti
Sls Mgr: Doug Miller

MUSCOGEE COUNTY
See COLUMBUS GEORGIA CONSOLIDATED GOVERNMENT

D-U-N-S 07-812-5408
MUSCOGEE COUNTY SCHOOL DISTRICT
2960 Macon Rd, Columbus, GA 31906-2204
Tel (706) 748-2000 Founded/Ownrshp 1950
Sales 215.6MM^E EMP 6,000
Accts Robinson Grimes & Company P
SIC 8211 Public elementary & secondary schools
VP: John Barge
MIS Dir: Andy Canady
Pr Dir: Don Hall
Schl Brd P: Mary S Polleys

D-U-N-S 07-240-6150
MUSCOGEE CREEK NATION
AGRI-BUSINESS COMPLEX DIVISION
1008 E Eufaula St, Okmulgee, OK 74447-7939
Tel (918) 756-8700 Founded/Ownrshp 1907
Sales NA EMP 1,200
Accts Finance Office Of Muscogee (Cr
SIC 9131 Executive & legislative combined
CEO: Perry Beaver
*Prin: Susanna Barnett
*Prin: George Tiger
Off Mgr: Ryan Logan
IT Man: Cindy Freiling

D-U-N-S 07-324-9625 IMP
MUSCULAR DYSTROPHY ASSOCIATION INC
MDA
222 S Riverside Plz # 1500, Chicago, IL 60606-6000
Tel (520) 529-2000 Founded/Ownrshp 1950
Sales 139.7MM EMP 950
Accts Bdo Usa Llp Phoenix Arizona
SIC 8733 Medical research
Pr: Steven M Derks
Sr Pt: Alfred Schrader
CFO: Julie Faber
CFO: Bruce Neufeld
Ch: R Rodney Howell
*Treas: Suzanne Lowden
Ex VP: Valerie Cwik
Ex VP: Steven G Ford
Ex VP: Rob Grinsfelder
Ex VP: Ann McNamara
Sr VP: Ronald Schenkenberger
VP: Louis Benzak
VP: John F Crowley
VP: Brenda Davis
VP: Stephen P Evans
VP: Patricia A Laus
VP: Amy Mitchell
VP: Kristin Stephenson
Dir Bus: Danielle Etter
Board of Directors: Maureen McGovern, Stanley H Appel, Ed McMahon, Robert M Bennett, Olin F Morris, Leon I Charash MD, Christopher J Rosa Phd, Bart Conner, Jeanne Y Russell, Harold C Crump, Charles D Schoor, Joseph S Dimartino, Lois R West, Daniel G Fries, David L Hutton, Suzanne L Lowden

D-U-N-S 18-756-0545 IMP
MUSCULOSKELETAL TRANSPLANT FOUNDATION INC
MTF
125 May St, Edison, NJ 08837-3264
Tel (732) 661-0202 Founded/Ownrshp 1987
Sales 404.8MM EMP 1,000
SIC 8099 Organ bank
Pr: Bruce W Stroever
Pr: Marc Jacobs
*CFO: Michael J Kawas
*Ch: William Tomford
*Ex VP: Martha Anderson
*Ex VP: Mark Spilker
Ex VP: Joseph Yaccarino
VP: Hans Burchardt
*VP: Michael Schuler
Dir Soc: Laura Dey
Dir IT: Pio Egan

D-U-N-S 83-137-4892
MUSEUM ASSOCIATES
LA COUNTY MUSEUM OF ART
5905 Wilshire Blvd, Los Angeles, CA 90036-4504
Tel (323) 857-6172 Founded/Ownrshp 1938
Sales 103.2MM EMP 400
Accts Singerlewak Llp Los Angeles
SIC 8412 Museum
CEO: Michael Gavin
Ofcr: Mark Mitchell
Ofcr: Diana Vesga
IT Man: CHI-Young Kim

D-U-N-S 11-085-7039
MUSEUM CO INC
695 Us Highway 46 Ste 400, Fairfield, NJ 07004-1592
Tel (973) 575-4446 Founded/Ownrshp 2006
Sales 23.0MM^E EMP 1,000
SIC 5947 Gifts & novelties
Ch: Joel Kier

D-U-N-S 07-856-9897 IMP/EXP
MUSEUM OF BIBLE INC
7507 Sw 44th St, Oklahoma City, OK 73179-4312
Tel (405) 996-4900 Founded/Ownrshp 2012
Sales 163.0MM EMP 5
Accts Rsm Us Llp Oklahoma City Okl
SIC 8412 Museum
Pr: Cary Summers
*Ch: Steven Green
*VP: Steven Bickley
*VP: Allen Quine
*VP: Jeff Schneider

D-U-N-S 07-658-0638 IMP
MUSEUM OF FINE ARTS
465 Huntington Ave, Boston, MA 02115-5597
Tel (617) 369-3861 Founded/Ownrshp 1867
Sales 151.0MM EMP 1,000
Accts Cbiz Tofias Boston Ma
SIC 8412 5961 8299 Museum; Clothing, mail order (except women's); Art school, except commercial
Ch Bd: Richard Lubin
CFO: Peter Gerondeau
Trst: Roger Servison
Ofcr: Lesley Gaughan
VP: John B Adams
*VP: Bettina Burr
Ex Dir: John Schroder
Ex Dir: Richard Woodward
Genl Mgr: Jordana Weiss
Snr Ntwrk: Sergey Koren
MIS Dir: Jon Hallis

D-U-N-S 07-415-5219 IMP
MUSEUM OF FINE ARTS OF HOUSTON
GLASSELL SCHOOL OF ART
1001 Bissonnet St, Houston, TX 77005-1896
Tel (713) 639-7300 Founded/Ownrshp 1913
Sales 215.6MM EMP 494
Accts Deloitte Tax Llp Houston Tx
SIC 8412 5999 Museum; Architectural supplies
CFO: Eric Anyah
Assoc Dir: Willard Holmes
Ex Dir: Gwen Goffee
Web Dev: Anthony Reynolds
Sales Asso: Shelby Rodriguez

D-U-N-S 01-925-6627
MUSEUM OF FLIGHT FOUNDATION (WA)
9404 E Marginal Way S, Tukwila, WA 98108-4097
Tel (206) 764-5720 Founded/Ownrshp 1965
Sales 115.5MM EMP 156
Accts Clark Nuber Ps Bellevue Wa
SIC 8412 Museum
CEO: Douglas R King
*CFO: Edward Waale
*Treas: James Farmer
*VP: Michael Hallman
VP: Trip Switzer
IT Man: Rosemarie Gran
Sls Dir: Richard Rime
S&M/Mgr: Bill Hayes

D-U-N-S 07-327-3559 IMP/EXP
MUSEUM OF MODERN ART
MOMA
11 W 53rd St, New York, NY 10019-5497
Tel (212) 708-9400 Founded/Ownrshp 1929
Sales 321.2MM^E EMP 825
SIC 8412 5942

MUSIC & ARTS CENTERS
See GUITAR CENTER STORES INC

D-U-N-S 08-046-9140
MUSICIANS LIVEORG
MUSICIANS PRACTICE GLOVE
77 Brookfield Dr, Elizabethtown, PA 17022-8828
Tel (717) 413-3265 Founded/Ownrshp 2016
Sales 10.0M EMP 2,016
SIC 5736 5961 7389 Musical instrument stores; Catalog & mail-order houses;
Owner: Donald J Grabowski

MUSICIANS PRACTICE GLOVE
See MUSICIANS LIVEORG

D-U-N-S 62-607-4066 IMP
MUSKET CORP
LOVE'S TRVL STOPS CNTRY STORES
(Suby of LOVES TRAVEL STOPS & COUNTRY STORES INC) ★
10601 N Pennsylvania Ave, Oklahoma City, OK 73120-4108
Tel (713) 332-5726 Founded/Ownrshp 1964
Sales 489.9MM^E EMP 64
SIC 5172 Gasoline
Pr: Frank Love
*Ch Bd: Tom E Love
Pr: Roger Griffin
*Treas: Doug Stussi
*Ex VP: Gregory M Love
*VP: Brad Jenkins
Exec: Dave Coburn
*Prin: Daniel P Kavanaugh
*Prin: Judith M Love
MIS Mgr: Reg Kennerty
Mktg Mgr: Noah Contreras

D-U-N-S 07-241-0111
MUSKOGEE REGIONAL MEDICAL CENTER LLC
EASTAR HEALTH SYSTEM
300 Rockefeller Dr, Muskogee, OK 74401-5075
Tel (918) 682-5501 Founded/Ownrshp 2007
Sales 120.4MM EMP 1,003
SIC 8062 General medical & surgical hospitals
CEO: Kevin Fowler
Chf OB: David Whatley
*COO: James Davidson
*CFO: Matthew Romero
Chf Mktg O: Gary Lambert
Chf Nrs Of: Diane Feder
Doctor: Evan Cole
Doctor: Jewell Daniels
Doctor: Jason Dansby
Doctor: Jackie Dean
Doctor: Lori Ford

MUSTANG CAT
See MUSTANG MACHINERY CO LTD

D-U-N-S 15-396-6721
MUSTANG ENGINEERS AND CONSTRUCTORS LP
(Suby of WOOD GROUP MUSTANG INC) ★
16001 Park Ten Pl, Houston, TX 77084-5135
Tel (713) 215-8000 Founded/Ownrshp 2000
Sales NA EMP 3,500
SIC 1542 1541 Commercial & office building contractors; Industrial buildings & warehouses
VP: Meg Lassart

D-U-N-S 15-202-5045 IMP
MUSTANG FUEL CORP
9800 N Oklahoma Ave, Oklahoma City, OK 73114-7406
Tel (405) 884-2092 Founded/Ownrshp 1969
Sales 186.3MM^E EMP 124
Accts Grant Thornton Llp Oklahoma
SIC 1311 4923 Crude petroleum production; Natural gas production; Gas transmission & distribution
Ch Bd: Carey Joullian IV
Ch Bd: E Carey Joullian IV
CFO: Scott M Chapline
Sr VP: Rand Phipps
VP: Paul Belflower
VP: Thomas Bennett
VP: Carrie Brower
VP: Carrie Buchanan
Exec: Eric Rice

D-U-N-S 78-507-1882
MUSTANG HEAVY HAUL LLC
LATSHAW DRILLING
(Suby of LATSHAW DRLG CO) ★
4905 S Perkins Rd, Stillwater, OK 74074-7554
Tel (405) 743-0085 Founded/Ownrshp 2012
Sales 57.0MM^E EMP 1,100
SIC 1381 Drilling oil & gas wells
COO: Mike Brown
CFO: Rich Goode
Ofcr: Roff Duke
VP: Steve Owen
Opers Mgr: Jason Burke

D-U-N-S 00-793-2163 IMP/EXP
MUSTANG MACHINERY CO LTD (TX)
MUSTANG CAT
12800 Northwest Fwy, Houston, TX 77040-6302
Tel (713) 861-1440 Founded/Ownrshp 1952
Sales 902.0MM^E EMP 1,340
SIC 5082 5084 General construction machinery & equipment; Industrial machinery & equipment; Engines & transportation equipment
Pr: Bradford Tucker
Sr Cor Off: Steve Ross
*Ex VP: Douglas R Fisk
Off Mgr: Peggy Gexler
Mtls Mgr: Roy Escamilla
Sales Exec: Guy Chason
Mktg Mgr: Scott Bowen

Sls Mgr: Ken Rickett
Sls Mgr: Sam Tucker
Sales Asso: Cody Odell
Sales Asso: Daryl Wingo

D-U-N-S 87-426-3036
MUSTANG PROCESS AND INDUSTRIAL INC
(*Suby of* WOOD GROUP MUSTANG INC) ★
30 Patewood Dr Ste 200, Greenville, SC 29615-6812
Tel (864) 288-3009 *Founded/Ownrshp* 2008
Sales 98.4MM^E *EMP* 4,500
SIC 8741 Management services
Pr: Steve Knowles
Sr VP: Christopher Barton
*Prin: Gordon Gibson
Sfty Mgr: Ron Kinder

D-U-N-S 09-614-8267
MUSTANG PUBLIC SCHOOLS
906 S Heights Dr, Mustang, OK 73064-3542
Tel (405) 376-2461 *Founded/Ownrshp* 1923
Sales 59.9MM^E *EMP* 1,000
SIC 8211 Public combined elementary & secondary school; Public elementary school; Public junior high school
Ofcr: Toni Pearson
IT Man: Carol Scott
*Schl Brd P: Chad Fulton
Teacher Pr: Tracy Skinner
HC Dir: Karen Wilson

MUTI
See MIDWEST UNDERGROUND TECHNOLOGY INC

D-U-N-S 19-536-7669 IMP
MUTSUTECH LTD
(*Suby of* MUTSUKI ELECTRIC CO., LTD.)
3130 Bonita Rd Ste 107, Chula Vista, CA 91910-3263
Tel (619) 691-7056 *Founded/Ownrshp* 1988
Sales 223.9MM^E *EMP* 700
SIC 5064 5013 Electrical appliances, major; Automotive supplies & parts
CEO: Nobutoshi Mutsuki
*Pr: Hiro Hamamatsu

MUTUAL BENEFIT GROUP
See MUTUAL BENEFIT INSURANCE CO

D-U-N-S 07-283-7677
MUTUAL BENEFIT INSURANCE CO
MUTUAL BENEFIT GROUP
409 Penn St, Huntingdon, PA 16652-1601
Tel (814) 643-3000 *Founded/Ownrshp* 1908
Sales NA *EMP* 160
SIC 6331 Fire, marine & casualty insurance
Pr: Steven C Sliver
Pr: Peggy Abbott
*CFO: John Coursen
CFO: Joseph L Soan
*Treas: Joseph L Sloan
VP: Beverly Skopic
Dir IT: Steven J Phillips

MUTUAL DISTRIBUTING COMPANY
See BJT INC

MUTUAL DRUG
See NORTH CAROLINA MUTUAL WHOLESALE DRUG CO

D-U-N-S 36-462-6515 IMP
MUTUAL INDUSTRIES NORTH INC
BILT-RITE MASTEX
707 W Grange Ave Ste 1, Philadelphia, PA 19120-2298
Tel (215) 927-6000 *Founded/Ownrshp* 1910
Sales 90.6MM^E *EMP* 300
SIC 3842 2221 Personal safety equipment; Broadwoven fabric mills, manmade
CEO: Edmund Dunn
*Pr: Andrew Dunn

D-U-N-S 78-337-2709
MUTUAL OF AMERICA CORP
(*Suby of* MUTUAL OF AMERICA LIFE INSURANCE CO) ★
320 Park Ave Fl 5, New York, NY 10022-6839
Tel (212) 224-1147 *Founded/Ownrshp* 1985
Sales NA *EMP* 1,000
SIC 6311 7389 Life insurance; Financial services
Ch Bd: William J Flynn
Pr: Thomas Kelly
Pr: James Tiensvold
*CFO: Manfred Altstadt
Sr Ex VP: Frida Maiorana
Ex VP: Jared Gutman
Ex VP: Andrew Heiskell
Ex VP: Scott Rothstein
Sr VP: Jeffrey Angelo
Sr VP: Katherine Cannizzaro
Sr VP: John Corrigan
Sr VP: Chris Festog
Sr VP: Harold Gannon
*Sr VP: Edward J T Kenney
Sr VP: Nicole Lanni
Sr VP: Paul Ohara
Sr VP: Robert Ruane
Sr VP: John Terwilliger
VP: Hal Bacharach
VP: Miro Beverin
VP: David Block

D-U-N-S 07-330-0337
MUTUAL OF AMERICA LIFE INSURANCE CO
320 Park Ave Fl 5, New York, NY 10022-6839
Tel (212) 224-1600 *Founded/Ownrshp* 1945
Sales NA *EMP* 1,100
Accts Kpmg Llp New York New York
SIC 6311 Mutual association life insurance
Pr: John R Greed
*Ch Bd: William J Flynn
*COO: William S Conway
*CFO: Manfred Altstadt
*CFO: Thomas Gilliam
Treas: Chris W Festog
Ofcr: Jared Gutman
Ex VP: Jeffrey M Angelo
Ex VP: Diane M Aramony
*Ex VP: Jeremy J Brown
Ex VP: John J Corrigan
Ex VP: William A Demilt
Ex VP: Robert Giaquinto
Ex VP: Thomas E Gilliam
Ex VP: Theodore L Herman
Ex VP: Daniel J Lesaffre
Ex VP: Kathryn Lu
Ex VP: George L Medlin
*Ex VP: James J Roth
Ex VP: Scott H Rothstein
Ex VP: Sonia Samuels
Board of Directors: Wayne A I Frederick

D-U-N-S 07-664-0028
MUTUAL OF ENUMCLAW INSURANCE CO
1460 Wells St, Enumclaw, WA 98022-3098
Tel (360) 825-2591 *Founded/Ownrshp* 1898
Sales NA *EMP* 573
SIC 6331 6311 Fire, marine & casualty insurance: mutual; Automobile insurance; Burglary & theft insurance; Property damage insurance; Life insurance carriers
Pr: Gerald P Schmidt
*Ch Bd: Vance O Fredrickson
*Treas: Larry Edlund
Chf Inves: Anthony Baruffi
Sr VP: Eric Nelson
VP: John Engel
VP: Rich Hundven
VP: Matthew L Picinich
Software D: Brian Doner
Software D: Jason Ellison
Software D: Samuel Gates

D-U-N-S 09-468-4107
MUTUAL OF OMAHA BANK
(*Suby of* OMAHA FINANCIAL HOLDINGS, INC.)
3333 Farnam St Ste 10, Omaha, NE 68131-3406
Tel (402) 351-5118 *Founded/Ownrshp* 1927, 2007
Sales NA *EMP* 200
SIC 6035 Savings institutions, federally chartered
CEO: Jeffrey R Schmid
Pr: John Clark
Pr: Carl Hamm
*CEO: Marjorie J Heller
*Chf Cred: Tod R Ellis
Ofcr: Phil Koentges
Ofcr: Joel Risser
Ofcr: Bob Thomas
Trst Ofcr: Sharon Schock
Ex VP: Kevin C Hale
Ex VP: Barry S Major
Sr VP: Jeff Barnett
Sr VP: Karen Cenovic
Sr VP: Tate Fitzgerald
Sr VP: Mike Lechtenberger
Sr VP: Craig Lefler
Sr VP: Richard Morgan
Sr VP: Kevin Naughton
Sr VP: Ronald Watkins
VP: April Ahrendsen
VP: Erin Bowen

D-U-N-S 02-398-6156
MUTUAL OF OMAHA HEALTH PLANS INC
(*Suby of* MUTUAL OF OMAHA INSURANCE CO) ★
3301 Dodge St, Omaha, NE 68131-3416
Tel (402) 342-7600 *Founded/Ownrshp* 1994
Sales NA *EMP* 354
SIC 6411 Insurance agents & brokers
Pr: Dan Neary
Treas: James T Blackledge

D-U-N-S 00-697-0347
MUTUAL OF OMAHA INSURANCE CO
Mutual Of Omaha Plaza, Omaha, NE 68175-0001
Tel (402) 342-7600 *Founded/Ownrshp* 1909
Sales NA *EMP* 5,392
SIC 6311 6211 8748 Life insurance carriers; Mutual funds, selling by independent salesperson; Business consulting
CEO: Daniel P Neary
Owner: Rachelle Bruning
Pr: James T Blackledge
Pr: Jeffrey R Schmid
CFO: David A Diamond
CFO: Tommy Thomason
Treas: Tommie D Thompson
Ofcr: Richard Leeberg
Ofcr: James Schema
Ex VP: Richard C Anderl
Ex VP: Richard L Frederick
Ex VP: James L Hanson
Ex VP: Randall C Horn
Ex VP: Richard Hrabchak
Ex VP: Daniel P Martin
Ex VP: Stacy A Scholtz
Sr VP: Devon Fischer
Sr VP: Gil Peers
Sr VP: Mark Prauner
Sr VP: Anthony J Principi
VP: Mary Bachle
Board of Directors: Samuel L Foggie Sr, Carol B Hallett, Jeffrey M Heller, Hugh W Hunt, Derek R McClain, James G McFarlane, Richard W Mies, Anthony J Principi

D-U-N-S 55-654-0920
MUTUAL OF OMAHA MARKETING CORP
(*Suby of* MUTUAL OF OMAHA INSURANCE CO) ★
3301 Dodge St, Omaha, NE 68131-3416
Tel (402) 342-7600 *Founded/Ownrshp* 1987
Sales 87.7MM^E *EMP* 600
SIC 6722 Management investment, open-end
MIS Mgr: William Harrold

D-U-N-S 12-173-5955 IMP
MUTUAL PHARMACEUTICAL CO INC
URL PHARMA
(*Suby of* SUN PHARMACEUTICAL INDUSTRIES INC) ★
1100 Orthodox St, Philadelphia, PA 19124-3199
Tel (215) 288-6500 *Founded/Ownrshp* 2012
Sales 108.5MM^E *EMP* 520^E
SIC 2834 Pharmaceutical preparations
Sr VP: Donald L Evans
*Treas: Whitney K Stearns Jr
*Ex VP: Kurt R Nielsen
Sr VP: Nicholas J Hart
*Sr VP: Gerald E Monigle
*VP: Scott Delancy
*VP: Richard P Foster
*VP: Brendan Magrab
Ql Cn Mgr: Adnan Wasim
Mktg Mgr: Nicole M Bailey

D-U-N-S 02-856-3443 IMP/EXP
MUTUAL TRADING CO INC
M T C
431 Crocker St, Los Angeles, CA 90013-2180
Tel (213) 626-9458 *Founded/Ownrshp* 1963
Sales 86.1MM^E *EMP* 181
SIC 5149 5141 5023 Groceries & related products; Groceries, general line; Home furnishings
CEO: Kosei Yamamoto
Pr: Noritoshi Kanai
VP: Seicho Fujikawa
Prin: Kotaro Hoshizaki
Dir IT: Keita Yagai
Sls&Mrk Ex: Atsuko Kanai
Counsel: Nakamura Tetsujiro

MUTUAL TRUST FINANCIAL GROUP
See MTL INSURANCE CO

D-U-N-S 06-327-5176 EXP
MUTZ MOTORS LTD PARTNERSHIP
LAKELAND AUTO MALL
1430 W Memorial Blvd, Lakeland, FL 33815-1231
Tel (863) 682-1100 *Founded/Ownrshp* 1967
Sales 105.4MM^E *EMP* 240
SIC 5511 7538 7532 7515 5531 5521 Automobiles, new & used; General automotive repair shops; Top & body repair & paint shops; Passenger car leasing; Automotive & home supply stores; Used car dealers
Pt: Oscar Mutz
Pt: Marsey Wickenkamp
CFO: Cory Neupauer
Genl Mgr: Robert Aguinaga
Off Mgr: Peggy Chambers
IT Man: Nelson Moreles
Sales Asso: Ken Ramka

MUVICO ENTERTAINMENT
See MUVICO THEATERS INC

D-U-N-S 80-228-0024
MUVICO THEATERS INC
MUVICO ENTERTAINMENT
2929 E Coml Blvd Ste 408, Fort Lauderdale, FL 33308
Tel (954) 564-6550 *Founded/Ownrshp* 1984
Sales 36.9MM^E *EMP* 1,200
SIC 7832 8741 Motion picture theaters, except drive-in; Management services
Pr: Neil F Bretan
*Pr: Michael Melvin
COO: Hank Linghstone
CFO: Dennis Jones
*Ch: Joseph Amaturo
*VP: Alan Rainbeau
*Exec: Mary Ann Majni
Admn Mgr: Irene Pierpont

D-U-N-S 07-870-0753
MUY HAMBURGER PARTNERS LLC
WENDY'S
17890 Blanco Rd Ste 401, San Antonio, TX 78232-1031
Tel (210) 408-2400 *Founded/Ownrshp* 2012
Sales 37.6MM^E *EMP* 1,064^E
SIC 5812 Fast-food restaurant, chain

D-U-N-S 05-932-8922
MUZAK LLC
(*Suby of* MOOD MEDIA CORPORATION)
3318 Lakemont Blvd, Fort Mill, SC 29708-8309
Tel (803) 396-3000 *Founded/Ownrshp* 2011
Sales 132.3MM^E *EMP* 950
SIC 7389 6794 Music & broadcasting services; Franchises, selling or licensing
CEO: Stephen Villa
Pr: Dan Kath
*COO: Thomas Gantert
*CFO: Dodd Hynes
Ex VP: Robert Finigan
Ex VP: Christopher Williams
*VP: Michael F Zendan II
VP: Paul Ziegler
CIO: Bob Gingras
*CTO: David Moore
IT Man: Beth Langford

D-U-N-S 03-992-6311
MV COMMERCIAL CONSTRUCTION LLC
MILLER VALENTIN CONSTRUCTION
137 N Main St Ste 900, Dayton, OH 45402-1846
Tel (937) 293-0900 *Founded/Ownrshp* 2000
Sales 125.0MM *EMP* 125
SIC 1541 Industrial buildings & warehouses
Pr: Christopher Knueven
VP: Nick Beach

D-U-N-S 82-521-0958
MV RESIDENTIAL CONSTRUCTION INC
9349 Waterstone Blvd # 200, Cincinnati, OH 45249-8325
Tel (513) 588-1000 *Founded/Ownrshp* 1963
Sales 120.3MM^E *EMP* 750
SIC 1522 Residential construction
CEO: Mike Green
*Pr: Randy Humbert

D-U-N-S 10-418-3132
MV TRANSPORTATION INC
5910 N Cntrl Expy # 1145, Dallas, TX 75206-5146
Tel (972) 391-4600 *Founded/Ownrshp* 1978
Sales 2.5MMM^E *EMP* 12,389
SIC 4111 Local & suburban transit
CEO: Brian Kibby
*Pr: Kevin A Klika
Pr: Chris Ruhig
*CFO: David B Brown
CFO: Van J Heavrin
CFO: Bob Pagorek
Sr VP: John Calame
Sr VP: Thomas Greufe
VP: Fran Coyne
VP: Thomas Hand
VP: Mike Kopaczewski
VP: Gary Richardson
Board of Directors: John Monson

D-U-N-S 79-128-4602
▲ MVB FINANCIAL CORP
301 Virginia Ave, Fairmont, WV 26554-2777
Tel (304) 363-4800 *Founded/Ownrshp* 2004
Sales NA *EMP* 371
Tkr Sym MVBF *Exch* OTO
SIC 6022 State commercial banks
Pr: Larry F Mazza
*Ch Bd: Stephen R Brooks
CFO: Donald T Robinson
CFO: Eric Tichenor
*V Ch Bd: David B Alvarez

D-U-N-S 04-306-5825 IMP/EXP
MVP GROUP INTERNATIONAL INC (KY)
TLC
(*Suby of* PRIMACY INDUSTRIES LIMITED)
1031 Legrand Blvd, Charleston, SC 29492-7673
Tel (843) 216-8380 *Founded/Ownrshp* 1998
Sales 448.5MM^E *EMP* 900
SIC 3999 5122 Candles; Perfumes
CEO: Mary V Propes
*Pr: Troy R Propes
Pr: Scott Wehrs
VP: Tom Begg
VP: Susan Fisher
VP: Tuck McConnell
VP: Tanya Rose
VP: Katherine Vermette
Creative D: Joyce Barbati
Mfg Dir: Josh Cox
VP Sls: Aaron Galloway

MVP HEALTH CARE
See MVP HEALTH PLAN INC

MVP HEALTH CARE
See HUDSON HEALTH PLAN INC

D-U-N-S 10-868-9787
MVP HEALTH PLAN INC
MVP HEALTH CARE
625 State St, Schenectady, NY 12305-2260
Tel (518) 370-4793 *Founded/Ownrshp* 1982
Sales 1.6MMM^E *EMP* 1,500
Accts Pricewaterhousecoopers Llp Ha
SIC 8011 Health maintenance organization
Pr: David Oliker
*Pr: Patrick Glavey
*Pr: Denise Gonick
Pr: Dale Hockel
*CFO: Mark Fish
Bd of Dir: Jon Jarrett
Bd of Dir: Jeff Kuberka
*Ex VP: Karla Austen
Ex VP: Scott W Averill
Ex VP: Christopher Delvecchio
*Ex VP: Allen J Hinkle
Ex VP: Allen J Hinkle
VP: Dennis L Allen
VP: Daniel Drislane
VP: Kathleen Fish
VP: James Hester
VP: Margaret Hetherington
VP: James Hopsicker
VP: Dawn Jablonski
VP: Augusta Martin
VP: Vijaya Saduvu

D-U-N-S 07-974-6886
MVP HOLDINGS LLC
8301 E 21st St N Ste 370, Wichita, KS 67206-2955
Tel (316) 262-2819 *Founded/Ownrshp* 2013
Sales 3.0MMM *EMP* 50
SIC 6719 Investment holding companies, except banks

D-U-N-S 15-295-6504
MVT SERVICES LLC
MESILLA VALLEY TRANSPORTATION
3590 W Picacho Ave, Las Cruces, NM 88007-4725
Tel (915) 791-4000 *Founded/Ownrshp* 1981
Sales 201.4MM^E *EMP* 850
SIC 4213 Trucking, except local
CFO: Dean Rigg
*VP: Jimmy Ray
Sftwr Eng: Colleen Barnitz
Sftwr Eng: Kim C Hayes
Netwrk Eng: Jason Gaume
Natl Sales: Arminda Neyland
Sls&Mrk Ex: Dennis Sherman
Sls Dir: John Kelley
Genl Couns: Todd H Silberman
Snr Mgr: Noemi Aldana

D-U-N-S 78-436-8982
MW BUILDERS GROUP INC
(*Suby of* MMC CORP) ★
10955 Lowell Ave Ste 350, Shawnee Mission, KS 66210-2408
Tel (913) 345-0007 *Founded/Ownrshp* 2002
Sales 174.8MM^E *EMP* 700
SIC 1542 Nonresidential construction
Pr: William McDermott
Treas: David A Burt
*Sec: David Cimpl
*VP: Harold W Mitts Jr

D-U-N-S 10-671-7353
MW BUILDERS INC
(*Suby of* MW BUILDERS GROUP INC) ★
1701 N General Bruce Dr, Temple, TX 76504-2474
Tel (254) 778-4241 *Founded/Ownrshp* 2001
Sales 91.7MM^E *EMP* 140
SIC 1542 Nonresidential construction
CEO: William McDermott
*Pr: Tim Chadwick
*Pr: R Jason Evelyn
*VP: David Burt
*VP: Todd Winnerman
VP: Craig Woodson
Off Mgr: Allison Laird
Sfty Mgr: John Francis
Opers Mgr: Sparky Campbell
Opers Mgr: Greg Herriott
Mktg Dir: Erica Jones

MW INDUSTRIES
See HELIX ACQUISITION HOLDINGS INC

MW INDUSTRIES
See MATTHEW WARREN INC

D-U-N-S 08-015-7922
MW INDUSTRIES INC
(*Suby of* MWI HOLDINGS INC) ★
9501 Tech Blvd Ste 401, Rosemont, IL 60018
Tel (847) 349-5760 *Founded/Ownrshp* 2011
Sales 26.1MMᴱ *EMP* 1,055ᴱ
SIC 6719 5085 Investment holding companies, except banks; Fasteners, industrial: nuts, bolts, screws, etc.; Fasteners & fastening equipment
CEO: William Marcum
CFO: Chester Kwasniak
Sales Exec: Greg Hazard
Mktg Mgr: Sarah Kosar

D-U-N-S 13-054-0719 IMP
■ **MW MANUFACTURERS INC**
(*Suby of* PLY GEM INDUSTRIES INC) ★
433 N Main St, Rocky Mount, VA 24151-1165
Tel (540) 483-0211 *Founded/Ownrshp* 2004
Sales 204.9MMᴱ *EMP* 1,600
SIC 2431 Window frames, wood; Window sashes, wood; Window trim, wood; Doors, wood
Pr: Art Steinhafel
* *Treas:* Shawn K Poe
* *Prin:* Lynn Morstad

MWCC
See MILENDER WHITE CONSTRUCTION CO

MWD
See METROPOLITAN WATER DISTRICT OF SOUTHERN CALIFORNIA

D-U-N-S 04-523-2204
MWH AMERICAS INC
(*Suby of* MWH GLOBAL INC) ★
370 Interlocken Blvd, Broomfield, CO 80021-8009
Tel (303) 410-4000 *Founded/Ownrshp* 1992
Sales 493.8MM *EMP* 3,000
SIC 8711 Engineering services
CEO: Alan Krause
* *Pr:* Daniel McConville
* *CFO:* David Barnes
* *Treas:* Thomas Payne
VP: Greg Clark
VP: Lori Peterson
Brnch Mgr: Kevin Kelly

D-U-N-S 87-863-5176
MWH CONSTRUCTORS INC
(*Suby of* MWH GLOBAL INC) ★
370 Interlocken Blvd # 300, Broomfield, CO 80021-8012
Tel (303) 439-2800 *Founded/Ownrshp* 1993
Sales 134.0MMᴱ *EMP* 330
Accts Deloitte & Touche Llp Denver
SIC 8711 1629 Pollution control engineering; Waterway construction
Pr: Blair Lavoie
* *Ch Bd:* Alan Krause
* *CFO:* David Barnes
* *Treas:* Thomas Payne
VP: Joseph Willich Jr
Dir IT: Chris Chri

D-U-N-S 80-192-7492
MWH GLOBAL INC
(*Suby of* STANTEC INC)
370 Interlocken Blvd # 300, Broomfield, CO 80021-8009
Tel (303) 533-1900 *Founded/Ownrshp* 2016
Sales 1.3MMM *EMP* 6,700
Accts Deloitte & Touche Llp Denver
SIC 8711 8741 Civil engineering; Management services
CEO: Alan J Krause
Pr: Greg Clark
Pr: Finis Mario
* *CFO:* David G Barnes
Sr Cor Off: Vic Gualas
* *Ofcr:* Jeffrey D'Agosta
* *Ofcr:* David A Smith
Ex VP: Michael Bruen
VP: Bob Armstrong
VP: Edwin Cryer
VP: Norman Gadzinski
VP: Raymond Hartley
VP: Jonathan Hersey
VP: Rob Hunter
VP: Joseph Jacangelo
VP: Glenn Jaffe
VP: Ed Kimura
VP: Eugene Minnick
VP: Khalid Nazeer
VP: Bob Parent
VP: Bill Pisano

D-U-N-S 55-556-7721 IMP
■ **MWI ANIMAL HEALTH**
(*Suby of* AMERISOURCEBERGEN CORP) ★
3041 W Pasadena Dr, Boise, ID 83705-4776
Tel (208) 955-8930 *Founded/Ownrshp* 2015
Sales 1.2MMMᴱ *EMP* 1,732ᴱ
SIC 5047 5149 Veterinarians' equipment & supplies; Pet foods
Pr: James F Cleary Jr
* *CFO:* Richard Dubois
Treas: Joshua Ingram
Sr VP: Mary Patricia B Thompson
VP: John L Francis
VP: John J Francis
* *VP:* Alden J Sutherland
Info Man: Joseph Bond
VP Opers: Bryan P Mooney
Opers Mgr: Joe Bond
Opers Mgr: Phillip Buch

D-U-N-S 93-200-5473
MWI HOLDINGS INC
(*Suby of* MW INDUSTRIES) ★
9501 Tech Blvd Ste 401, Rosemont, IL 60018
Tel (847) 349-5760 *Founded/Ownrshp* 2011
Sales 97.6MMᴱ *EMP* 1,055
SIC 6719 Investment holding companies, except banks
CEO: William Marcum
* *Pr:* Daniel Sebastian
* *CFO:* Chet Kwasniak
* *VP:* James Callaghan

D-U-N-S 01-992-6120 IMP
■ **MWI VETERINARY SUPPLY CO** (ID)
(*Suby of* MWI ANIMAL HEALTH) ★
3041 W Pasadena Dr, Boise, ID 83705-4776
Tel (208) 955-8930 *Founded/Ownrshp* 1981, 2002
Sales 720.5MMᴱ *EMP* 558
SIC 5047 2834 2835 2836 Veterinarians' equipment & supplies; Veterinary pharmaceutical preparations; Veterinary diagnostic substances; Vaccines
Ch Bd: John F McNamara
* *Pr:* James Cleary
* *CFO:* Mary Patricia Thompson
* *Treas:* Tracy Huettl
Treas: Tracy Tucker
VP Admn: John L Francis
* *CIO:* James S Hay
Sls Mgr: Eric Scott
Board of Directors: William Robison

MWRA
See MASSACHUSETTS WATER RESOURCES AUTHORITY

MWRA
See MASSACHUSETTS WATER RESOURCES AUTHORITY

MWRD
See METROPOLITAN WATER RECLAIMATION DISTRICT OF GREATER CHICAGO

D-U-N-S 01-617-9272
■ **MWSTAR WASTE HOLDINGS CORP**
F/K/A VEOLIA ES SOLID WASTE
(*Suby of* ADVANCED DISPOSAL SERVICES INC) ★
90 Fort Wade Rd Ste 200, Ponte Vedra, FL 32081-5112
Tel (904) 737-7900 *Founded/Ownrshp* 1992
Sales 1.4MMMᴱ *EMP* 5,704ᴱ
SIC 1629 4953 Waste disposal plant construction; Hazardous waste collection & disposal
CEO: Richard Burke
* *CFO:* Steven Carn
* *VP:* Jaime Marini
Off Mgr: John Perugia

D-U-N-S 60-522-8592
MWW GROUP LLC
1 Meadowlands Plz Ste 600, East Rutherford, NJ 07073-2232
Tel (201) 507-9500 *Founded/Ownrshp* 1986
Sales 86.0MMᴱ *EMP* 253
SIC 8743

D-U-N-S 83-006-6721
MX HOLDINGS US
153 Technology Dr Ste 200, Irvine, CA 92618-2461
Tel (949) 727-3277 *Founded/Ownrshp* 1997
Sales 400.9MMᴱ *EMP* 1,790
SIC 1711 1731 5999 Fire sprinkler system installation; Fire detection & burglar alarm systems specialization; Fire extinguishers
CEO: Klaus Hoffmann

D-U-N-S 05-386-2777 IMP/EXP
MXD GROUP INC
(*Suby of* PLATINUM EQUITY LLC) ★
7795 Walton Pkwy Ste 400, New Albany, OH 43054-8246
Tel (614) 895-1959 *Founded/Ownrshp* 2013
Sales 329.8MMᴱ *EMP* 800
SIC 4214 4213 Local trucking with storage; Household goods transport
CEO: Terry Solvedt
* *Pr:* David Vieira
* *CFO:* Renee Albarano
Sr VP: W T Thompson
VP: Mike Agey
VP: Frank Gaura
VP: Marvin T Larger
Dir Bus: Kim Banton
Genl Mgr: Allison Ramer
Snr PM: Jack Catlin

MXR SOURCEONE
See SOURCEONE HEALTHCARE TECHNOLOGIES INC

MY DIAMOND STORY
See HK DESIGNS INC

MY GOODS MARKET
See EAGLE CANYON CAPITAL LLC

MYCLEARWATER
See CITY OF CLEARWATER

D-U-N-S 10-315-7442 EXP
■ **MYCOGEN CORP**
(*Suby of* ROFAN SERVICES INC) ★
9330 Zionsville Rd, Indianapolis, IN 46268-1053
Tel (317) 337-3000 *Founded/Ownrshp* 1998
Sales 209.2MMᴱ *EMP* 300
SIC 5191 2879 0721 8731 Seeds & bulbs; Seeds: field, garden & flower; Agricultural chemicals; Crop protecting services; Crop disease control services; Crop related entomological services (insect control); Agricultural research
Pr: Jerome Periberie
Treas: Geoffrey E Merszer
VP: W Pete Siggelko
VP: William W Wales

D-U-N-S 13-911-8306 IMP
■ **MYCOGEN PLANT SCIENCE INC**
(*Suby of* MYCOGEN CORP) ★
9330 Zionsville Rd, Indianapolis, IN 46268-1053
Tel (317) 337-3000 *Founded/Ownrshp* 2004
Sales 190.2MMᴱ *EMP* 324ᴱ
SIC 5191 Seeds: field, garden & flower
Pr: Jerome Peribere

D-U-N-S 00-464-0715
MYCOM NORTH AMERICA INC (GA)
(*Suby of* MYCOM INTERNATIONAL INC)
1080 Holcomb Bridge Rd # 200210, Roswell, GA 30076-4348
Tel (770) 776-0000 *Founded/Ownrshp* 2000
Sales 90.0MMᴱ *EMP* 250
SIC 4899 Data communication services
Pr: Richard Hessler
* *VP:* Brian Arabi
IT Man: Gilbert Fong
IT Man: Brett Ullman
Board of Directors: Brian Arabi, Richard Hessler

D-U-N-S 18-410-7845
MYCON GENERAL CONTRACTORS INC
208 E La St Ste 200, Mc Kinney, TX 75069
Tel (972) 529-2444 *Founded/Ownrshp* 1987
Sales 140.2MM *EMP* 47
SIC 1542

D-U-N-S 01-476-9301 IMP
MYCONE DENTAL SUPPLY CO INC
KEYSTONE INDUSTRIES
480 S Democrat Rd, Gibbstown, NJ 08027-1239
Tel (856) 663-4700 *Founded/Ownrshp* 1983
Sales 116.3MMᴱ *EMP* 250
SIC 5047 3843 2844 Dental equipment & supplies; Dental equipment & supplies; Toilet preparations
Ch Bd: Fred Robinson
* *Pr:* Cary Robinson
CFO: Tim Cryan
Exec: John Fetterolf
Dir IT: John Deppen

MYCRO GROUP CO
See MUSCO CORP

D-U-N-S 96-202-0090
MYERS & SONS CONSTRUCTION LP
4600 Northgate Blvd # 100, Sacramento, CA 95834-1121
Tel (916) 283-9950 *Founded/Ownrshp* 2010
Sales 144.8MM *EMP* 250
Accts Grant Thornton Llp Houston T
SIC 1611 Highway & street construction
Pt: Clinton C Myers
Pt: Clinton W Myers

D-U-N-S 04-498-6685
MYERS AND STAUFFER LC
700 W 47th St Ste 1100, Kansas City, MO 64112-2050
Tel (816) 945-5300 *Founded/Ownrshp* 1995
Sales 116.7MM *EMP* 720
SIC 8721 Accounting, auditing & bookkeeping
VP: Jeanne Tomisser
Genl Mgr: Amy Schuman
Genl Mgr: Lisa Stevenson
DP Dir: Donald Byrd
DP Dir: Charles Schreiner

D-U-N-S 07-922-3882
MYERS AUTO GROUP LLC
PALM BEACH MOTOR CARS
915 S Dixie Hwy, West Palm Beach, FL 33401-6401
Tel (561) 659-6206 *Founded/Ownrshp* 1979
Sales 120.0MM *EMP* 53
SIC 5511 New & used car dealers

MYERS FSI
See MYERS POWER PRODUCTS INC

D-U-N-S 01-744-0715 IMP/EXP
MYERS GROUP L L C
SOGIMEX
74 Blanchard Rd, South Orange, NJ 07079-1341
Tel (973) 761-6414 *Founded/Ownrshp* 2005
Sales 87.0MM *EMP* 1,380
SIC 3111 Tanneries, leather
VP: Benjamin Myers
Sls Dir: Ted Salomon

D-U-N-S 00-195-0849 IMP/EXP
▲ **MYERS INDUSTRIES INC**
1293 S Main St, Akron, OH 44301-1339
Tel (330) 253-5592 *Founded/Ownrshp* 1933
Sales 601.5MM *EMP* 2,360
Tkr Sym MYE *Exch* NYS
SIC 3089 3086 3069 3052 5013 5014 Pallets, plastic; Stock shapes, plastic; Boxes, plastic; Blow molded finished plastic products; Plastics foam products; Packaging & shipping materials, foamed plastic; Insulation or cushioning material, foamed plastic; Padding, foamed plastic; Rubber automotive products; Automobile hose, rubber; Tools & equipment, automotive; Tire & tube repair materials
Pr: R David Banyard
* *Ch Bd:* F Jack Liebau Jr
COO: David Smith
CFO: Kevin L Brackman
Bd of Dir: Richard Johnston
VP: Kevin Brackman
VP: Ray Cunningham
VP: Mike Smith
VP: Alex Williamson
Brnch Mgr: Ben Pryor
Genl Mgr: Cindy Dawson
Board of Directors: Sarah R Coffin, John B Crowe, William A Foley, Daniel R Lee, Bruce M Lisman, Jane Scaccetti, Robert A Stefanko

D-U-N-S 06-122-0583 IMP
MYERS POWER PRODUCTS INC
MYERS FSI
2950 E Philadelphia St, Ontario, CA 91761-8545
Tel (909) 923-1800 *Founded/Ownrshp* 2003
Sales 118.6MMᴱ *EMP* 305
SIC 3629 Inverters, nonrotating: electrical
CEO: Diana Grootonk
COO: Raymond Swinger
CFO: Jose Cudal
Genl Mgr: Bruce Steigerwald
S&M/VP: Chris Boehm
Snr Mgr: John Pantaleo

D-U-N-S 03-970-5343 EXP
■ **MYERS TIRE SUPPLY DISTRIBUTION INC**
MYERS TIRE SUPPLY INTL
(*Suby of* MYERS INDUSTRIES INC) ★
1293 S Main St, Akron, OH 44301-1302
Tel (330) 253-5592 *Founded/Ownrshp* 1999
Sales 128.8MMᴱ *EMP* 410
SIC 5531 Automotive & home supply stores
CEO: R David Banyard
* *CFO:* Matteo Anversa
* *VP:* Kevin Gehrt
* *VP:* Monica Vinay
Brnch Mgr: Larry Nester
Genl Mgr: Todd Smith
Sls Mgr: Patrick Bell
Sls Mgr: Michael Smith

MYERS TIRE SUPPLY INTL
See MYERS TIRE SUPPLY DISTRIBUTION INC

D-U-N-S 02-796-7793 IMP
MYGRANT GLASS CO INC
3271 Arden Rd, Hayward, CA 94545-3901
Tel (510) 785-4360 *Founded/Ownrshp* 1971
Sales 217.9MMᴱ *EMP* 600
SIC 5013 Automobile glass
CEO: Michael Mygrant
Treas: Cathy Mygrant
Sec: Kathy Mygrant
Genl Mgr: Tom Higginbottom

D-U-N-S 05-929-8141 IMP
MYLAN INC
(*Suby of* MYLAN N.V.)
1000 Mylan Blvd, Canonsburg, PA 15317-5853
Tel (724) 514-1800 *Founded/Ownrshp* 2015
Sales 10.0MMMᴱ *EMP* 30,000
SIC 2834 Pharmaceutical preparations; Analgesics; Antibiotics, packaged; Tranquilizers or mental drug preparations
CEO: Heather Bresch
* *Ch Bd:* Robert J Coury
* *Pr:* Rajiv Malik
CFO: Daniel Caron
* *V Ch Bd:* Rodney L Piatt
Ex VP: John Sheehan
VP: Anil Amin
VP: Christopher Basar
VP: Kim Cauchy
VP: Andrew Cuneo
VP: Nina Devlin
VP: Paul Feuerman
VP: Dan Ford
VP: Sinead Griffiths
VP: Tim Harris
VP: Sherry Korczynski
VP: Maribel Marin
VP: Satish Medakkar
VP: Brian Roman
VP: Brian Stone
VP: Kenton Walker

D-U-N-S 05-929-5980 IMP/EXP
MYLAN PHARMACEUTICALS INC
(*Suby of* MYLAN INC) ★
781 Chestnut Ridge Rd, Morgantown, WV 26505-2772
Tel (304) 599-2595 *Founded/Ownrshp* 1961
Sales 1.4MMMᴱ *EMP* 7,500ᴱ
SIC 2834 Proprietary drug products; Druggists' preparations (pharmaceuticals)
Pr: Robert Tighe
V Ch: Rodney L Piatt
* *COO:* John Deiriggi
COO: Harry A Korman
CFO: Gary E Sphar
* *Treas:* Colleen Ostrowski
Bd of Dir: Prasad Nimmagadda
* *Ex VP:* Mark Fitch
* *VP:* John P O'Donnell
* *VP:* Brian Roman
* *VP:* Alan R Weiner
Assoc Dir: Sarat Chattaraj

D-U-N-S 19-477-5557 IMP
MYLAN SPECIALTY LP
(*Suby of* MYLAN INC) ★
781 Chestnut Ridge Rd, Morgantown, WV 26505-2772
Tel (304) 554-4519 *Founded/Ownrshp* 2007
Sales 106.0MMᴱ *EMP* 1,000
SIC 2834 8731 Drugs acting on the respiratory system; Commercial physical research
Pr: Roger Graham
* *Pt:* Imtiaz Chaundry
VP: David Jones
Snr Mgr: James Lugo
Snr Mgr: Deendayal Reddy

MYMATRIXX
See MATRIX HEALTHCARE SERVICES INC

D-U-N-S 11-269-9025 IMP
MYOFFICEPRODUCTS INC
(*Suby of* HITOUCH BUSINESS SERVICES LLC) ★
22 Century Blvd Ste 420, Nashville, TN 37214-3724
Tel (615) 507-3515 *Founded/Ownrshp* 2010
Sales 650.6MMᴱ *EMP* 359
SIC 5112 5943 Stationery & office supplies; Office forms & supplies
CEO: Michael Brown
* *Pr:* John Frisk
COO: Jason Palmer
* *CFO:* Jeff Sammons
* *Ch:* Howard Brown
* *Ex VP:* Joseph Aiello
* *Ex VP:* Anthony Cavalieri
* *Ex VP:* Earlis Johnson Jr
* *Ex VP:* Michael Palmer
VP: Dwayne Deal
VP: Brian Kaffee
VP: Debbie Lafferty
VP: Lane Thomas
Exec: Lenny Morella

D-U-N-S 04-534-8588
▲ **MYR GROUP INC**
1701 Golf Rd Ste 3-1012, Rolling Meadows, IL 60008-4210
Tel (847) 290-1891 *Founded/Ownrshp* 1891
Sales 1.0MMM *EMP* 4,075ᴱ
Tkr Sym MYRG *Exch* NGS

SIC 1623 1731 Electric power line construction; General electrical contractor
Pr: William A Koertner
COO: Richard S Swartz Jr
CFO: Betty R Johnson
Sr VP: Tod M Cooper
Opers Mgr: Larry Baker
Opers Mgr: Don Egan

D-U-N-S 79-757-1668
▲ MYRIAD GENETICS INC
320 S Wakara Way, Salt Lake City, UT 84108-1214
Tel (801) 584-3600 *Founded/Ownrshp* 1991
Sales 753.8MM *EMP* 2,206ᴱ
Accts Ernst & Young Llp Salt Lake C
Tkr Sym MYGN *Exch* NGS
SIC 2835 8731 In vitro & in vivo diagnostic substances; In vitro diagnostics; In vivo diagnostics; Biological research; Biotechnical research, commercial
Pr: Mark C Capone
**Ch Bd:* John T Henderson
Pr: Alexander Ford
Pr: Ralph L McDade
Pr: Bernard F Tobin
**CFO:* R Bryan Riggsbee
**V Ch Bd:* Walter Gilbert
Bd of Dir: Lynne Daugirda
**Chf Mktg O:* Richard J Wenstrup
Ex VP: Richard M Arsh
Ex VP: Gary A King
**Ex VP:* Richard M Marsh
Ex VP: Chip Parkinson
Ex VP: Ronald Rogers
VP: Kirsten Timms
Dir Lab: Debbie Dinardo
Board of Directors: Lawrence C Best, Dennis H Langer, S Louise Phanstiel

MYRLEN
See EP BOLLINGER LLC

D-U-N-S 00-200-2228 IMP/EXP
MYRON CORP
205 Maywood Ave, Maywood, NJ 07607-1000
Tel (201) 843-6464 *Founded/Ownrshp* 1949
Sales 355.2MMᴱ *EMP* 700
SIC 5199 Advertising specialties
Ch: Myron Adler
**Pr:* Hal Korman
**CEO:* Donald J Adler
COO: David Chun
**CFO:* William Byrne
Treas: Robert Lack
Ex VP: Jim Odowd
VP: Edward Hohnecker
VP: Mark Pepin
VP: Andrew Perelson
VP: John Rolleri
Board of Directors: Jackie Ward

D-U-N-S 78-723-0051
MYRON GREEN CORP
TREAT AMERICA FOOD SERVICES
8500 Shawnee Mission Pkwy, Merriam, KS 66202-2967
Tel (913) 384-4900 *Founded/Ownrshp* 2001
Sales 84.7MMᴱ *EMP* 900
Accts Mayer Hoffman Mccann Pc Lea
SIC 5962 Food vending machines; Beverage vending machines
CEO: John Mitchell Sr
**CFO:* Mike Meurer
CFO: Larry Weinstein
Exec: Conrad Caguimbal

D-U-N-S 85-858-3404
MYRTLE BEACH FARMS CO INC
(*Suby of* BURROUGHS & CHAPIN CO INC) ★
8820 Marina Pkwy, Myrtle Beach, SC 29572-8101
Tel (843) 448-5123 *Founded/Ownrshp* 1990
Sales 165.1MMᴱ *EMP* 1,000ᴱ
SIC 6552 7996 6512 Subdividers & developers; Theme park, amusement; Commercial & industrial building operation
Pr: Douglas P Wendell
Ch Bd: James Egerton Burroughs
Pr: Jim Rosenburg
CFO: Barry Spivey
Sr VP: Tanya Greenlee
Sr VP: William F Pritchard
VP: Mary E Basden
VP: Tony Cox
VP: Franklin J Long

MYSTIC APPAREL COMPANY
See MYSTIC APPAREL LLC

D-U-N-S 13-596-1774 IMP/EXP
MYSTIC APPAREL LLC
MYSTIC APPAREL COMPANY
1333 Broadway Fl 6, New York, NY 10018-7268
Tel (212) 279-2466 *Founded/Ownrshp* 2003
Sales 120.0MM *EMP* 19ᴱ
SIC 5021 5137 Household furniture; Women's & children's clothing

MYSTIC LAKE CASINO
See SMSC GAMING ENTERPRISE

D-U-N-S 01-335-8002
MYTHICS INC
1439 N Great Neck Rd, Virginia Beach, VA 23454-1347
Tel (757) 965-6756 *Founded/Ownrshp* 2000
Sales 387.8MMᴱ *EMP* 222ᴱ
SIC 5045 Computers
CEO: Robert S Larose
**Pr:* Gary Newman
CFO: Barbara Darr
**CFO:* Rick Welborn
VP: Dale Darr
**VP:* Sloan Frey
VP: Robert Jones
**VP:* Chris Richards
**VP:* Brent Seaman
Prgrm Mgr: Ben Butler
CIO: Mark Sunday

D-U-N-S 01-192-2176 IMP
MZ BERGER & CO INC (NY)
ELGIN WATCH
2976 Northern Blvd Fl 4, Long Island City, NY 11101-2829
Tel (718) 472-7500 *Founded/Ownrshp* 1963, 1950
Sales 84.5MMᴱ *EMP* 135
SIC 5094 3873 Watches & parts; Watches, clocks, watchcases & parts
CFO: Patrick Carlsen
VP: Stefanie Barone
VP: Jackie Leathem
CIO: Rudy Adametz

N

N & S SUPPLY
See CENTRAL PURCHASING CORP

D-U-N-S 83-173-0382
■ N A BANKUNITED
(*Suby of* BANKUNITED INC) ★
14817 Oak Ln, Miami Lakes, FL 33016-1517
Tel (305) 231-6400 *Founded/Ownrshp* 2009
Sales NA *EMP* 1,100
SIC 6035 6163 6111 Federal savings & loan associations; Loan brokers; Federal National Mortgage Association
CEO: John A Kanas
Pr: Thomas M Cornish
Pr: Lisa Min
**Pr:* Ramiro A Ortiz
Pr: Dan Overbey
**COO:* Rajinder P Singh
**CFO:* Leslie Lunak
**CFO:* Douglas J Pauls
Ex VP: Mark Bagnoli
Ex VP: Frank Fernandez
**Ex VP:* Felix M Garcia
**Ex VP:* Robert Green
**Ex VP:* Abel L Iglesias
**Ex VP:* Randy R Melbym
Ex VP: Gladys Reed
**Ex VP:* Clay Wilson
Sr VP: Andrew Ashby
Sr VP: Vanessa Civalero
Sr VP: Dean Couluris
Sr VP: Steven Demarest
**Sr VP:* Mary Harris
Board of Directors: Sue Cobb

N A C
See NORTH AMERICAN COMMUNICATIONS INC

N A S
See NATIONAL ACADEMY OF SCIENCES OF UNITED STATES OF AMERICA

N A S
See NORTH AMERICAN STAINLESS

N A S S
See NATIONAL AGRICULTURAL STATISTICS SERVICE

D-U-N-S 04-203-5485 EXP
N A SUEZ
UNITED WATER SERVICES INC.
(*Suby of* SUEZ)
461 From Rd Ste F, Paramus, NJ 07652-3524
Tel (201) 767-9300 *Founded/Ownrshp* 1964, 1997
Sales 853.1MMᴱ *EMP* 1,154
SIC 4941 Water supply
Pr: Douglas D Reichlin
COO: Robert Iacullo
CFO: Philippe Dartienne
**Treas:* Michael Algranati
VP: Edmund Deveaux
**VP:* Rick Farnham
VP: Jim Glozzy
VP: Steve Mahan
VP: Matthew Mahoney
VP: Rui Sobral
Exec: John Dyksen
Comm Dir: Erika Berlinghof
Comm Dir: Deb Rizzi

N B A
See NATIONAL BASKETBALL ASSOCIATION INC

N BT
See NBT INC

N BT BANK
See NBT BANK NA

N C B
See NATIONAL CONSUMER COOPERATIVE BANK

D-U-N-S 04-439-7156
N C B SAVINGS BANK FSB
(*Suby of* N C B) ★
139 S High St Ste 1, Hillsboro, OH 45133-1442
Tel (937) 393-4246 *Founded/Ownrshp* 1890, 1988
Sales NA *EMP* 125ᴱ
SIC 6035 Federal savings banks
Pr: Deb Shoemaker
Pr: Chris Goettke

N C C
See NEW COMMUNITY CORP

N C FARM BUREAU MUTUAL INSUR
See NORTH CAROLINA FARM BUREAU INSURANCE AGENCY INC

D-U-N-S 79-708-8627 IMP
N C MACHINERY CO
CATERPILLAR AUTHORIZED DEALER
(*Suby of* HARNISH GROUP INC) ★
17025 W Valley Hwy, Tukwila, WA 98188-5552
Tel (425) 251-9800 *Founded/Ownrshp* 2000
Sales 353.5MMᴱ *EMP* 1,000
SIC 5082 5013 5083 Construction & mining machinery; Tractors, construction; Front end loaders; Graders, motor; Automotive engines & engine parts; Agricultural machinery & equipment; Tractors, agricultural; Cultivating machinery & equipment; Planting machinery & equipment
Pr: John Harnish
Genl Mgr: Adam Hirstein
CTO: Dale Buzitis
Mtls Mgr: Scott Jensen
Mktg Mgr: Scott Field

N C PARTNERSHIP FOR CHILDREN
See NORTH CAROLINA PARTNERSHIP FOR CHILDREN INC

D-U-N-S 79-708-8734 IMP
N C POWER SYSTEMS CO
CATERPILLAR AUTHORIZED DEALER
(*Suby of* HARNISH GROUP INC) ★
17900 W Valley Hwy, Tukwila, WA 98188-5533
Tel (425) 251-5877 *Founded/Ownrshp* 1999
Sales 86.7MMᴱ *EMP* 200
SIC 5013 5082 5083 Automotive engines & engine parts; Construction & mining machinery; Agricultural machinery & equipment
Pr: John Harnish
**VP:* Richard Bellin
**VP:* Joseph Huley
Exec: Sally Hausken
Brnch Mgr: William Ring
Sls Mgr: Warren Hull
Sls Mgr: Don King

N C R A
See CHS MCPHERSON REFINERY INC

N D C
See NDCHEALTH CORP

N D C
See NITINOL DEVICES AND COMPONENTS INC

N E A
See NATIONAL EDUCATION ASSOCIATION OF UNITED STATES

D-U-N-S 15-448-0859
N E WHERE TRANSPORT INC
3808 E Dr M L King Jr Blv Martin Luther, Tampa, FL 33610
Tel (813) 363-0959 *Founded/Ownrshp* 1983
Sales 320.0MM *EMP* 13
SIC 4212 Delivery service, vehicular
Pr: John E Amato
**VP:* Lenore L Amato

N F A
See NATIONAL FUTURES ASSOCIATION (INC)

N F I B
See NATIONAL FEDERATION OF INDEPENDENT BUSINESS

N F L
See NATIONAL FOOTBALL LEAGUE INC

N F R
See NATIONAL FIELD REPRESENTATIVES INC

D-U-N-S 11-738-2457 IMP
N F SMITH & ASSOCIATES LP
5306 Hollister St, Houston, TX 77040-6120
Tel (713) 430-3000 *Founded/Ownrshp* 1984
Sales 516.1MM *EMP* 400
SIC 5065

N G A
See NATIONAL GEOSPATIAL-INTELLIGENCE AGENCY

N G I
See NEVELL GROUP INC

N G L
See NETWORK GLOBAL LOGISTICS LLC

D-U-N-S 00-301-5489
N GLANTZ & SON LLC (TX)
(*Suby of* GLANTZ HOLDINGS INC) ★
2501 Constant Comment Pl, Louisville, KY 40299-6324
Tel (502) 426-4473 *Founded/Ownrshp* 1988
Sales 163.2MMᴱ *EMP* 156
SIC 5046 Neon signs
CEO: Davey Glantz
Ch: Joe Hartman
VP Opers: Thomas Morrison
Opers Supe: Ed Haddick
Opers Supe: Ted Mayfield
VP Mktg: Beth Wolf
Manager: John Johnston

N H
See NORTHSIDE HOSPITAL - CHEROKEE INC

N H A
See NEIGHBORHOOD HOUSE ASSOCIATION

N H A
See NATIONAL HERITAGE ACADEMIES INC

D-U-N-S 10-469-8720
N H C O P L P
100 E Vine St, Murfreesboro, TN 37130-3734
Tel (615) 890-2020 *Founded/Ownrshp* 1997
Sales 144.5MMᴱ *EMP* 3,000
SIC 8051 Skilled nursing care facilities
Pr: W Andrew Adams

N H L
See NHL ENTERPRISES INC

N I H
See NATIONAL INSTITUTES OF HEALTH

D-U-N-S 09-163-5623
N J PROTOCALL INC
1 Mall Dr Ste 100, Cherry Hill, NJ 08002-2102
Tel (856) 667-9003 *Founded/Ownrshp* 1965
Sales 118.5MMᴱ *EMP* 7,000
SIC 7363 Temporary help service
Pr: Janis Le Bude
CFO: Francis McGlynn
VP: Roy Fazio
VP: Lois Weidhaas

D-U-N-S 02-577-0264
N KOHL GROCER CO (IL)
KOHL WHOLESALE
130 Jersey St, Quincy, IL 62301-3831
Tel (217) 222-5000 *Founded/Ownrshp* 1873
Sales 194.9MM *EMP* 383
SIC 5141 5113 5046 Groceries, general line; Industrial & personal service paper; Restaurant equipment & supplies
Pr: R A Ehrhart
**Treas:* Richard Ehrhart
**VP:* Mark J Ehrhart
Mktg Mgr: Greg Whitney

N L C
See NATIONS LENDING CORP

D-U-N-S 00-131-7577
▲ N L INDUSTRIES INC (NJ)
5430 Lbj Fwy Ste 1700, Dallas, TX 75240-2620
Tel (972) 233-1700 *Founded/Ownrshp* 1891
Sales 108.9MM *EMP* 2,792ᴱ
Accts Pricewaterhousecoopers Llp Da
Tkr Sym NL *Exch* NYS
SIC 2819 3572 3699 Industrial inorganic chemicals; Computer storage devices; Security devices
Pr: Robert D Graham
**Ch Bd:* Steven L Watson
CFO: Gregory M Swalwell
Treas: John A St Wrba
Ex VP: Kelly D Luttmer
Ex VP: Bobby D O'Brien
VP: Tim C Hafer
VP: A Andrew R Louis
VP: Andrew B Nace
VP: Courtney J Riley
Board of Directors: Keith R Coogan, Loretta J Feehan, Cecil H Moore Jr, Thomas P Stafford, Terry N Worrell

N MT
See NATIONAL MATERIAL TRADING LLC

D-U-N-S 12-818-7221
▲ N MODEL INC
1600 Seaport Blvd Ste 400, Redwood City, CA 94063-5564
Tel (650) 610-4600 *Founded/Ownrshp* 1999
Sales 106.9MM *EMP* 721ᴱ
Accts Pricewaterhousecoopers Llp Sa
Tkr Sym MODN *Exch* NYS
SIC 7371 Custom computer programming services; Computer software development & applications
Ch Bd: Zack Rinat
CFO: Mark Tisdel
Ofcr: Christopher Larsen
Sr VP: Mark Anderson
Sr VP: Eric Carrasquilla
Sr VP: David Miller
Assoc Dir: Samuel Kim
Mng Dir: Paul Beckham
Off Mgr: Narsimha Viriyala
Snr Sftwr: Duy Diep
Sls Mgr: Bruce Birtwistle
Board of Directors: Tim Adams, David Bonnette, Melissa Fisher, Mark Garrett, Alan Henricks, Mark Leslie, Charles Robel

N O V E C
See NORTHERN VIRGINIA ELECTRIC COOPERATIVE

N P P
See NORTHERN PIPE PRODUCTS INC

N P R
See NATIONAL PUBLIC RADIO INC

N P S SERVICES
See DAY & ZIMMERMANN NPS INC

N R H
See NATIONAL REHABILITATION HOSPITAL INC

N R I
See NATIONAL REFRIGERANTS INC

N R S
See NATIONAL RETAIL SYSTEMS INC

D-U-N-S 06-380-2151 IMP
N S INTERNATIONAL LTD
(*Suby of* NIPPON SEIKI CO.,LTD.)
600 Wilshire Dr, Troy, MI 48084-1625
Tel (248) 251-1600 *Founded/Ownrshp* 1977
Sales 83.0MMᴱ *EMP* 174ᴱ
SIC 5013 Automotive supplies & parts; Motorcycle parts
CEO: Teruyuki Matsui
Prgrm Mgr: John Ogger
Prgrm Mgr: Yuka Pearl
Div Mgr: Kenichiro Onuma
Dir IT: Jim Aiello
Opers Mgr: Therissa Allen

N S M G
See NORTHSTAR MEMORIAL GROUP LLC

NT G
See NOLAN TRANSPORTATION GROUP LLC

D-U-N-S 04-826-0418 IMP
N W ELECTRIC POWER COOPERATIVE INC
1001 W Grand Ave, Cameron, MO 64429-1116
Tel (816) 632-2121 *Founded/Ownrshp* 1949
Sales 99.2MM *EMP* 60
SIC 4911 Transmission, electric power
Genl Mgr: Donald R McQuitty
Sr VP: Susan Wood
Genl Mgr: Kent Brown
Genl Mgr: Jennifer Hill
Genl Mgr: R McQuitty
Sfty Mgr: Gerald Mathews

D-U-N-S 00-428-9864 EXP
N WASSERSTROM & SONS INC (OH)
WASSERSTROM MARKETING DIVISION
(*Suby of* NATIONAL SMALLWARES) ★
2300 Lockbourne Rd, Columbus, OH 43207-6111
Tel (614) 737-8543 *Founded/Ownrshp* 1933
Sales 125.6MMᴱ *EMP* 460

SIC 3556 5046 3444 Food products machinery; Restaurant equipment & supplies; Sheet metalwork
Pr: William Wasserstrom
Sr VP: John H Mc Cormick
VP: Craig Dietz
Mktg Dir: Adam Caltrider
Sls Dir: Eric Wasserstrom
Board of Directors: Leonard Wasserstrom, Stanley Wasserstrom

NY B
See NEW YORK BLOWER CO

D-U-N-S 78-321-2772
■ NY MCG INC
MERIDIAN
(*Suby of* SANTANDER HOLDINGS USA INC) ★
1 Battery Park Plz Fl 26, New York, NY 10004-1432
Tel (212) 972-3600 *Founded/Ownrshp* 1991
Sales NA *EMP* 124
SIC 6163 Mortgage brokers arranging for loans, using money of others
Pr: J Jay Lobell
**VP:* Tara Heal
VP: Reuven Hellman
**VP:* Marcia Larson
**VP:* Gaffar Mohamed
**VP:* Tal Savariego
**VP:* Matthew Texler
**Prin:* Aaron Birnbaum
**Prin:* Ralph Herzka
**Prin:* Jeffrey Weinberg
**Prin:* Abraham Weinstock

D-U-N-S 87-795-0295
NY STEAMSTER HEALTH PENSION & RETIREMENT FUND
151 Northern Concourse, Syracuse, NY 13212-4065
Tel (315) 455-9790 *Founded/Ownrshp* 1994
Sales 192.8MM *EMP* 3
SIC 8631 Labor unions & similar labor organizations

NY U
See NEW YORK UNIVERSITY

NY U
See NYU HOSPITALS CENTER

N-STAR
See NORTHSTAR REALTY FINANCE CORP

N9305-192
See WELLS FARGO FOUNDATION MINNESOTA

NAACP
See NATIONAL ASSOCIATION FOR ADVANCEMENT OF COLORED PEOPLE

D-U-N-S 95-969-2984 IMP
NAARTJIE CUSTOM KIDS INC
3676 W Ca Ave Ste D100, Salt Lake City, UT 84104-6516
Tel (801) 973-7988 *Founded/Ownrshp* 2001
Sales 84.8MM[E] *EMP* 870[E]
SIC 5641 Children's & infants' wear stores
Pr: Glenn Wood

D-U-N-S 00-635-9277
NABHOLZ CONSTRUCTION CORP (AR)
NABHOLZ CONSTRUCTION-OZARK DIV
612 Garland St, Conway, AR 72032-4418
Tel (501) 505-5800 *Founded/Ownrshp* 1949
Sales 509.9MM[E] *EMP* 900
SIC 1541

NABHOLZ CONSTRUCTION-OZARK DIV
See NABHOLZ CONSTRUCTION CORP

NABHOLZ CRANES & RIGGINGS
See NABHOLZ INC

D-U-N-S 09-341-4555
NABHOLZ INC (AR)
NABHOLZ CRANES & RIGGINGS
612 Garland St, Conway, AR 72032-4418
Tel (501) 505-5800 *Founded/Ownrshp* 1951
Sales 105.4MM[E] *EMP* 410
SIC 5084 7359

D-U-N-S 07-888-8322
NABI BUS LLC
(*Suby of* NEW FLYER INDUSTRIES INC)
106 National Dr, Anniston, AL 36207-8339
Tel (888) 452-7871 *Founded/Ownrshp* 2013
Sales 193.8MM[E] *EMP* 633
SIC 3713 5012 Bus bodies (motor vehicles); Automobiles & other motor vehicles

NABORS
See C&J WELL SERVICES INC

D-U-N-S 04-569-6499
NABORS ALASKA DRILLING INC
(*Suby of* NABORS INDUSTRIES INC) ★
2525 C St Ste 200, Anchorage, AK 99503-2632
Tel (907) 263-6000 *Founded/Ownrshp* 1980
Sales 270.2MM[E] *EMP* 800[E]
SIC 1381 Drilling oil & gas wells
Pr: Anthony G Petrello
**Pr:* Jerry C Shanklin
**Treas:* Jenia Jarrett
**VP:* Ben Kent
**Genl Mgr:* David Hebert
CIO: SRI Vallaru
Dir IT: Dan Hammocker
Opers Mgr: Norm Haynes

NABORS DRILLING INTERNATIONAL
See NABORS INTERNATIONAL INC

D-U-N-S 00-790-7603 IMP/EXP
NABORS DRILLING USA LP
(*Suby of* NABORS INDUSTRIES INC) ★
515 W Greens Rd Ste 1200, Houston, TX 77067-4536
Tel (281) 874-0035 *Founded/Ownrshp* 1911, 1990
Sales 2.4MMM[E] *EMP* 1,637
SIC 1381 Directional drilling oil & gas wells
Pt: Joe Hudson
Pr: Larry Heidt
VP: Randy Clark
VP: Joey Husband
VP: Ernie Nelson
VP: Saj Shapiro
Exec: Bob Wilder
IT Man: Michelle Brown
IT Man: Robert Wexler
Sfty Dirs: David Darling
Snr PM: Bob Turner
Board of Directors: James H Denney

D-U-N-S 07-887-4351 IMP
NABORS INDUSTRIES INC
(*Suby of* NABORS INDUSTRIES LTD.)
515 W Greens Rd Ste 1200, Houston, TX 77067-4599
Tel (281) 874-0035 *Founded/Ownrshp* 1987
Sales 8.9MMM[E] *EMP* 16,847
SIC 1381 1389 Drilling oil & gas wells; Servicing oil & gas wells
CEO: Eugene M Isenberg
**Ch Bd:* Anthony G Petrello
Pr: Tyler Byers
COO: Jerry Shanklin
CFO: Bruce P Koch
CFO: Kevin White
Sr VP: Ronnie Witherspoon
VP: G Arms
VP: Kevin Brown
**VP:* Jose S Cadena
**VP:* Laura W Doerre
VP: Ron Morrison
VP: Earney White
Assoc Dir: William Conroy

D-U-N-S 00-691-5748 IMP/EXP
NABORS INTERNATIONAL INC (DE)
NABORS DRILLING INTERNATIONAL
(*Suby of* NABORS INDUSTRIES INC) ★
515 W Greens Rd Ste 600, Houston, TX 77067-4510
Tel (281) 874-0035 *Founded/Ownrshp* 1947
Sales 2.5MMM[E] *EMP* 1,689
SIC 1381 7353 Drilling oil & gas wells; Oil well drilling equipment, rental or leasing
CEO: Anthony G Petrello
**CFO:* William Restrepo
**VP:* Jose Cadena
**VP:* Derryl W Cleaveland
**VP:* Christopher Papouras
**VP:* Bob Supopin

D-U-N-S 96-988-0012 IMP
NABORS OFFSHORE CORP
(*Suby of* NABORS INDUSTRIES INC) ★
515 W Greens Rd Ste 1200, Houston, TX 77067-4536
Tel (281) 874-0406 *Founded/Ownrshp* 1996
Sales 342.8MM[E] *EMP* 700
SIC 1381 1389 Reworking oil & gas wells; Directional drilling oil & gas wells; Servicing oil & gas wells; Oil field services
Pr: Jerry C Shanklin
**VP:* Ronnie L Gaspard
**VP:* Daniel McLachlin
**VP:* Lonnie Mills
**VP:* Earney White
Board of Directors: Jose Cadena, Anthony G Petrello

NABORS OIL TOOLS
See NABORS WELL SERVICES CO

D-U-N-S 00-571-7228 IMP
NABORS WELL SERVICES CO
NABORS OIL TOOLS
(*Suby of* NABORS INDUSTRIES INC) ★
515 W Greens Rd Ste 1000, Houston, TX 77067-4536
Tel (281) 874-0035 *Founded/Ownrshp* 1999
Sales 2.1MMM[E] *EMP* 4,740
SIC 1389 Oil field services
Ch: Eugene M Isenberg
**CEO:* Anthony G Petrello
**CFO:* William Restrepo
VP: Jim Denney
VP: Frank Labrenz
VP: Ron Morrison
Telecom Ex: Jill Gregory

D-U-N-S 18-273-0440
NABORS WELL SERVICES LTD
(*Suby of* NABORS OIL TOOLS) ★
515 W Greens Rd Ste 1200, Houston, TX 77067-4536
Tel (281) 874-0035 *Founded/Ownrshp* 1987
Sales 594.5MM[E] *EMP* 1,668
SIC 1389 7353 Servicing oil & gas wells; Oil equipment rental services
Ch Bd: Anthony G Petrello
Pr: Nicholas Petronio

D-U-N-S 01-020-3842 IMP
NABTESCO AEROSPACE INC (WA)
(*Suby of* NABTESCO CORPORATION)
12413 Willows Rd Ne, Kirkland, WA 98034-8766
Tel (425) 602-8400 *Founded/Ownrshp* 1976
Sales 90.0MM *EMP* 48
SIC 3728 3812 3593 Aircraft parts & equipment; Search & navigation equipment; Fluid power cylinders & actuators
Pr: Isao Ohashi

NAC MECHANICAL & ELEC SVCS
See NORTHERN AIR CORP

D-U-N-S 03-233-0909
NACA HOLDINGS INC
DIRECT CONTAINER LINE
5000 Arprt Plz Dr Ste 200, Long Beach, CA 90815
Tel (650) 872-0800 *Founded/Ownrshp* 2000
Sales 232.2MM *EMP* 685
SIC 4731 Freight consolidation
CEO: Charles Brennan
**CFO:* J Thurso Barendse
Treas: Jeff Alinsangan
**VP:* Therese Groff

D-U-N-S 14-720-4127
▲ NACCO INDUSTRIES INC
5875 Landerbrook Dr # 300, Cleveland, OH 44124-4069
Tel (440) 229-5151 *Founded/Ownrshp* 1913
Sales 915.8MM *EMP* 1,900
Tkr Sym NC *Exch* NYS
SIC 3634 1221 5719 3631 Electric household cooking appliances; Toasters, electric: household; Irons, electric: household; Coffee makers, electric: household; Surface mining, lignite; Kitchenware; Cookware, except aluminum; Household cooking equipment; Microwave ovens, including portable: household
Ch Bd: Alfred M Rankin Jr
CFO: Elizabeth I Loveman
Sr VP: J C Butler Jr
VP: Jennifer Langer
VP: John D Neumann
QA Dir: Walter Massie
QA Dir: Stacy Whitehurst
Counsel: Jesse L Adkins
Counsel: Miles B Haberer
Counsel: Mary D Maloney
Board of Directors: Scott S Cowen, John P Jumper, Dennis W Labarre, Richard De J Osborne, James A Ratner, Britton T Taplin, David F Taplin, David B H Williams

NADEL & GUSSMAN ANADARKO
See NADEL AND GUSSMAN LLC

D-U-N-S 00-790-7744
NADEL AND GUSSMAN LLC
NADEL & GUSSMAN ANADARKO
15 E 5th St Ste 3300, Tulsa, OK 74103-4340
Tel (918) 583-3333 *Founded/Ownrshp* 2000
Sales 254.6MM[E] *EMP* 110
SIC 1311 Crude petroleum production; Natural gas production
Pr: James F Adelson
CFO: Wayne Hamilton
Genl Mgr: Stephen Heyman

D-U-N-S 79-084-8464
NADONAH MEDICAL SUPPLY
5021 Columbia Way, Quartz Hill, CA 93536-3010
Tel (661) 718-3870 *Founded/Ownrshp* 2014
Sales 213.6MM *EMP* 4
SIC 5999 Medical apparatus & supplies
CEO: Donald Nnamdi Iwuagwu

D-U-N-S 05-044-4603
NAES CORP
(*Suby of* ITOCHU INTERNATIONAL INC) ★
1180 Nw Maple St Ste 200, Issaquah, WA 98027-8106
Tel (425) 961-4700 *Founded/Ownrshp* 2001
Sales 617.5MM *EMP* 2,534
Accts Pricewaterhousecoopers Llp Se
SIC 4911 Electric services
Pr: Robert E Fishman
**COO:* Thomas Bartolomei
COO: John Meyer
COO: John Stender
**Sr VP:* Glen Canavera
**Sr VP:* Norman Escover
**Sr VP:* Andrew Gay
**Sr VP:* George Wackerhagen
VP: Robert C Faull
**VP:* Susan George

NAF BUSINESS AND SUPPORT SVCS
See BUSINESS AND SUPPORT SERVICES

NAFI
See NORTH AMERICAN FAMILY INSTITUTE INC

D-U-N-S 14-759-6477 IMP/EXP
NAG LLC
1260 Andes Blvd, Saint Louis, MO 63132-1702
Tel (314) 214-2700 *Founded/Ownrshp* 1999
Sales 1.3MMM[E] *EMP* 2,300
SIC 5149 Dried or canned foods
Pr: Doug Albrecht
**CFO:* Russ Willey
Treas: John T Connell
VP: Alexander Lee
VP: Michael Leland
VP: Russ Wiley
Exec: Jim Theiss
Dir IT: Harry Lohse
Dir IT: Kerif Shannon
IT Man: Shayne Bean
IT Man: Rob Stangl

D-U-N-S 00-220-5727
NAGARRO INC
PROJISTICS
2001 Gateway Pl Ste 100w, San Jose, CA 95110-1046
Tel (408) 436-6170 *Founded/Ownrshp* 1999
Sales 51.2MM[E] *EMP* 2,000[E]
SIC 7373 Computer-aided system services
Pr: Vikram Sehgal
Pr: Manmohan Gupta
**Off Mgr:* Aurora Jorge
IT Man: Punit Sachan

D-U-N-S 07-326-5449 IMP
NAGASE AMERICA CORP
(*Suby of* NAGASE & CO., LTD.)
546 5th Ave Fl 16, New York, NY 10036-5000
Tel (212) 703-1340 *Founded/Ownrshp* 1971
Sales 98.7MM[E] *EMP* 96
SIC 5169 5162 5122 5065 5047 Industrial chemicals; Plastics materials & basic shapes; Pharmaceuticals; Electronic parts & equipment; Medical equipment & supplies
Pr: Gen Hirao
**Ch:* Ryuichi Uchida
**Treas:* Keiichiro Yamashita
**Sr VP:* Kazuyuki Sato
**Sr VP:* Takuya Tomomura
Genl Mgr: Masao Hidaka
Sales Exec: Jeremy Smith
Sls Mgr: Mitsuaki Murashige
Snr Mgr: Gary Goble
Board of Directors: Jessica Chan

D-U-N-S 00-621-4464 IMP
NAHAN PRINTING INC (MN)
7000 Saukview Dr, Saint Cloud, MN 56303-0814
Tel (320) 217-7700 *Founded/Ownrshp* 1972
Sales 157.8MM[E] *EMP* 505
SIC 2759 2752 Commercial printing; Commercial printing, lithographic; Commercial printing, offset
CEO: Michael Nahan
Pr: Kurt Brintlinge
Pr: Dan Sand
**COO:* Kent Gilmore
CFO: Marty Kaufman
Sr VP: Alicia Andres
VP: Daniel Carlo
**VP:* Steve Kirk
**VP:* Dale Kopel
**VP:* Tim Wolfe
IT Man: Eric Becker

NAHC
See SOUTH CENTRAL FS INC

D-U-N-S 96-464-2586 IMP/EXP
NAHI LLC
NORTH AMERICAN HYDROLICS
(*Suby of* FLODRAULIC GROUP INC) ★
3539 N 700 W, Greenfield, IN 46140-8272
Tel (317) 890-3700 *Founded/Ownrshp* 2010
Sales 2.5MMM *EMP* 30
SIC 5084 Industrial machinery & equipment

NAI
See NATURAL ALTERNATIVES INTERNATIONAL INC

D-U-N-S 01-864-5625
NAI GROUP LLC
7975 N Hayden Rd Ste D105, Scottsdale, AZ 85258-3247
Tel (480) 556-6066 *Founded/Ownrshp* 2002
Sales 292.9MM[E] *EMP* 1,500[E]
Accts Bdo Usa Llp Phoenix Az
SIC 3679 Harness assemblies for electronic use: wire or cable
CEO: Preston Speers
**CFO:* Kevin Dye
**Ex VP:* Wayne Harrison

NAIC
See NATIONAL ASSOCIATION OF INSURANCE COMMISSIONERS

D-U-N-S 80-197-9340
NAJAFI COMPANIES LLC
2525 E Camelback Rd, Phoenix, AZ 85016-4219
Tel (602) 476-0600 *Founded/Ownrshp* 2003
Sales 489.7MM[E] *EMP* 2,335
SIC 3695 Magnetic disks & drums
CEO: Jahm Najafi
CFO: Tina Rhodes

D-U-N-S 14-469-3561 IMP/EXP
NAJARIAN FURNITURE CO INC
ITALIAN CONCEPTS
265 N Euclid Ave, Pasadena, CA 91101-1594
Tel (626) 839-8700 *Founded/Ownrshp* 1986
Sales 200.0MM *EMP* 100
SIC 5021 5023 Household furniture; Home furnishings
Pr: Antranik Najarian
**Pr:* Mike Najarian
**VP:* George Najarian
VP Sls: Michael Lawrence
Board of Directors: Michael Lawrence

D-U-N-S 19-327-5641 IMP
NAKANISHI MANUFACTURING CORP
(*Suby of* NAKANISHI METAL WORKS CO.,LTD.)
1225 Voyles Rd, Winterville, GA 30683-2510
Tel (706) 353-0006 *Founded/Ownrshp* 1987
Sales 111.4MM[E] *EMP* 150
SIC 5085 3562 Bearings; Ball & roller bearings
Pr: Junji Tokuume
**Ch Bd:* Tatsuo Nakanishi
**CFO:* Naoshi Shimamura
**VP:* Hirotaka Nakanishi
Ex Dir: Shuji Miwa
Opers Mgr: Mitsu Takimoto
Board of Directors: Kazuo Nakanishi

NAKANO FOODS
See MIZKAN AMERICA INC

NAKANO FOODS
See MIZKAN AMERICA HOLDINGS INC

NALC
See NATIONAL ASSOCIATION OF LETTER CARRIERS

NALCO CHAMPION - AN ECOLAB CO
See NALCO CO LLC

D-U-N-S 00-802-4580 IMP/EXP
■ NALCO CHAMPION LLC
(*Suby of* ECOLAB INC) ★
7705 Highway 90a, Sugar Land, TX 77478-2121
Tel (713) 627-3303 *Founded/Ownrshp* 1953, 2013
Sales 989.5MM[E] *EMP* 2,500
SIC 2819 Industrial inorganic chemicals
CEO: Tom Amonett
**CFO:* Christopher Johnson
**Ch:* Steven J Lindley
Dir IT: Scott Knutson
Dir IT: Siva K Tanuku
IT Man: Shane Roberts
Ql Cn Mgr: Elena Senkina
Sls&Mrk Ex: Rick Martinez
Genl Couns: Peter Olasky

D-U-N-S 00-496-2403 IMP/EXP
■ NALCO CO LLC
NALCO CHAMPION - AN ECOLAB CO
(*Suby of* ECOLAB INC) ★
1601 W Diehl Rd, Naperville, IL 60563-1198
Tel (630) 305-1000 *Founded/Ownrshp* 1928, 2011
Sales 4.6MMM[E] *EMP* 10,560
SIC 3559 2899 2992 2891 Chemical machinery & equipment; Corrosion preventive lubricant; Lubricating oils; Adhesives
Ch: Douglas M Baker
Pr: Daniel Fee
COO: William Roe
CFO: Bradley Bell
VP: Christopher C Boyd
VP: Jim Chew
VP: Gary Cooper
VP: Jeff Dickens

VP: Jeannie Shimer
Dist Mgr: Bruce Barker
Dist Mgr: Gary Frank

D-U-N-S 86-815-9013 IMP/EXP
■ NALCO ENERGY SERVICES LP
(*Suby of* NALCO CHAMPION - AN ECOLAB CO) ★
7705 Highway 90a, Sugar Land, TX 77478-2121
Tel (281) 263-7000 *Founded/Ownrshp* 1994
Sales 374.8MM^E *EMP* 1,500
SIC 2899 Chemical preparations
Pt: Mark L Bosanko
Pt: Gary Aman
Pt: David Johnson
Pt: Bruno Lavandier
Pt: Steve Taylor
Bd of Dir: Chinh E Chu
Bd of Dir: Joshua J Harris
Bd of Dir: Sanjeev K Mehra
Bd of Dir: Paul H O'Neill
Bd of Dir: Daniel S Sanders
Ex VP: William J Roe
VP: Lisa Curran
VP: Michael Gibson
VP: John L Gigerich
VP: Deborah C Hockman
VP: Mary T Manupella
VP: Manian Ramesh
Exec: Dave Larson

D-U-N-S 16-707-5113
■ NALCO HOLDING CO
(*Suby of* ECOLAB INC) ★
1601 W Diehl Rd, Naperville, IL 60563-1198
Tel (630) 305-1000 *Founded/Ownrshp* 2003
Sales 2.3MMM^E *EMP* 12,400^E
SIC 2899 2992 Chemical preparations; Corrosion preventive lubricant; Water treating compounds; Lubricating oils & greases
Ch Bd: J Erik Fyrwald
Pr: David E Flitman
Pr: Terrence M Gallagher
CFO: Kathryn A Mikells
Treas: Todd Hacker
Chf Mktg O: Mary Kay Kaufmann
Ofcr: Lori F Arnold
Ex VP: David Johnson
Ex VP: John Macleod
Ex VP: Scott Mason
Ex VP: Eric G Melin
Sr VP: R J Allain
VP: Richard A Bendure
VP: Lisa Curran
VP: C Deborah
VP: Matthew Knight
VP: Stephen N Landsman
VP: Chris Moore
VP: Pete Nassos
VP: Mark Stoll
Dir Risk M: James Smaga

D-U-N-S 15-442-9620 IMP
■ NALCO HOLDINGS LLC
(*Suby of* NALCO HOLDING CO) ★
1601 W Diehl Rd, Naperville, IL 60563-1198
Tel (630) 305-1000 *Founded/Ownrshp* 2004
Sales 479.6MM^E *EMP* 11,590
SIC 2899 2992 3559 Corrosion preventive lubricant; Water treating compounds; Antiscaling compounds, boiler; Lubricating oils; Chemical machinery & equipment
Ch: J Eric Fyrwald
Pr: Richard Bendure
Pr: David Flitman
Pr: David Johnson
Pr: Eric Melin
Pr: Steve Taylor
CFO: Kathryn Mikells
Bd of Dir: Richard B Marchese
Chf Mktg O: Mary Kay Kaufmann
Sr VP: Daniel M Harker
Snr Ntwrk: Eugene Dvoretsky
Board of Directors: Carl M Casale, Paul J Norris, Douglas A Pertz, Daniel S Sanders

D-U-N-S 19-408-2517 IMP/EXP
■ NALGE NUNC INTERNATIONAL CORP
(*Suby of* FISHER SCIENTIFIC INTERNATIONAL LLC) ★
75 Panorama Creek Dr, Rochester, NY 14625-2303
Tel (585) 586-8800 *Founded/Ownrshp* 1995
Sales 265.3MM^E *EMP* 1,519
SIC 3089 3949 3821 3085 3083 Plastic processing; Plastic & fiberglass tanks; Sporting & athletic goods; Laboratory apparatus & furniture; Plastics bottles; Laminated plastics plate & sheet
Prin: Michaeline Reed
Creative D: John Staton
VP Opers: Ken Bunn

NALLEY MOTOR TRUCKS
See ASBURY AUTOMOTIVE ATLANTA LLC

NAL.SYNCREON
See SYNCREON TECHNOLOGY (USA) LLC

D-U-N-S 16-014-2055 EXP
NAMASTE LABORATORIES LLC
(*Suby of* DABUR INDIA LIMITED)
310 S Racine Ave Fl 8, Chicago, IL 60607-2841
Tel (708) 824-1393 *Founded/Ownrshp* 2011
Sales 88.2MM^E *EMP* 90
SIC 2844 Hair preparations, including shampoos
CEO: Clarisa Wilson
COO: Clyde Burks
* *Sls Dir:* Vikram Bali

NAMCO
See NORTH AMERICAN MARKETING CORP

NAMCO
See NORTH ATLANTIC CORP

D-U-N-S 00-122-6943
NAMDAR INC (NY)
(*Suby of* GRISTEDES SUPERMARKETS) ★
800 3rd Ave Fl 5, New York, NY 10022-7655
Tel (212) 956-5770 *Founded/Ownrshp* 1946, 1984
Sales 102.1MM^E *EMP* 1,700^E
SIC 5411 Supermarkets
Ch Bd: John Catsimatidis

NAMEBRAND OUTLET
See DOWNEAST OUTFITTERS INC

D-U-N-S 02-964-6478
NAMPA SCHOOL DISTRICT 131
619 S Canyon St, Nampa, ID 83686-6634
Tel (208) 468-4600 *Founded/Ownrshp* 1900
Sales 107.9MM *EMP* 1,800
SIC 8211 Public elementary & secondary schools
Prin: Nancy Chopko
Prin: William Deakins
Prin: John Emerson
Prin: Vicki McNeal
Teacher Pr: Rachelle Armstrong

NAMPAC
See NORTH AMERICA PACKAGING CORP

NAMSA
See NORTH AMERICAN SCIENCE ASSOCIATES INC

D-U-N-S 62-161-0278 IMP/EXP
NAN INC
OCEAN HOUSE BUILDERS
636 Laumaka St, Honolulu, HI 96819-2312
Tel (808) 842-4929 *Founded/Ownrshp* 1995
Sales 240.0MM^E *EMP* 350
SIC 1542 Commercial & office buildings, renovation & repair
Pr: Fooney Freestone
* *VP:* Ryan Nakaima
* *VP:* Frank Okimoto
Off Mgr: Jocelyn Peralta

D-U-N-S 61-812-4507 IMP/EXP
NANYA PLASTICS CORP AMERICA
(*Suby of* NAN YA PLASTICS CORPORATION)
9 Peach Tree Hill Rd, Livingston, NJ 07039-5702
Tel (973) 992-1775 *Founded/Ownrshp* 1989
Sales 1.1MMM *EMP* 1,300
SIC 2824 2869 3083 Polyester fibers; Ethylene glycols; Laminated plastics plate & sheet
Ch: William Wong
* *Pr:* Chia-Chau Wu
* *Treas:* David Lin

D-U-N-S 08-062-5106 IMP
NANYA PLASTICS CORP USA
(*Suby of* NAN YA PLASTICS CORPORATION)
9 Peach Tree Hill Rd, Livingston, NJ 07039-5702
Tel (973) 992-1775 *Founded/Ownrshp* 1979
Sales 120.2MM *EMP* 1,300
SIC 3081 Vinyl film & sheet
Pr: Chia-Chau Wu
* *Ch Bd:* William Wong
* *Treas:* David Lin
IT Man: Brian Chen

NANA CORPORATE SERVICES
See NANA MANAGEMENT SERVICES LLC

D-U-N-S 07-925-6996
NANA DEVELOPMENT CORP
(*Suby of* NANA REGIONAL CORP INC) ★
909 W 9th Ave, Anchorage, AK 99501-3322
Tel (907) 265-4100 *Founded/Ownrshp* 1974
Sales 1.9MMM^E *EMP* 3,000^E
Accts Kpmg Llp Anchorage Ak
SIC 7381 1389 Security guard service; Oil field services
Pr: Helvi Sandvik
* *Ch Bd:* Lester Hadley
* *Pr:* Sandvik Helvi K
* *Ch:* Luke Sampson
* *Treas:* Henry Horner
Bd of Dir: Levi Cleveland
Bd of Dir: Rosa Horner
Sr VP: Barry Coleman
* *Sr VP:* Stan Fleming
* *Sr VP:* Jacquelyn R Luke
* *Sr VP:* David W Mrquez
* *Sr VP:* Lawrence Mucciarelli
Sr VP: David Springgate
* *VP:* Thomas Kevin E
* *VP:* Charles J Greene
* *VP:* Selina Moose
* *VP:* Kornfield Robin
Comm Dir: Blythe Campbell

D-U-N-S 09-782-6176
NANA MANAGEMENT SERVICES LLC
NANA CORPORATE SERVICES
(*Suby of* NANA DEVELOPMENT CORP) ★
800 E Dimond Blvd 3-450, Anchorage, AK 99515-2059
Tel (907) 273-2400 *Founded/Ownrshp* 1978
Sales 89.2MM^E *EMP* 2,234
SIC 5812 7349 7021 7033 7381

D-U-N-S 07-925-3761
NANA REGIONAL CORP INC
3150 C St Ste 150, Kotzebue, AK 99752
Tel (907) 442-3301 *Founded/Ownrshp* 1972
Sales 2.0MMM^E *EMP* 4,650
SIC 7011 Hotels & motels
* *CEO:* Marie Green
* *COO:* Lori Henry
CFO: Marsh Gross
* *Prin:* Kevin Thomas
VP Admn: Sandy Shroyer
Mktg Dir: Carol Richards

D-U-N-S 09-950-0944 IMP
NANDANSONS INTERNATIONAL INC
NN
55 Mayfield Ave, Edison, NJ 08837-3820
Tel (908) 561-2400 *Founded/Ownrshp* 1979
Sales 105.3MM^E *EMP* 48
SIC 5122 Perfumes
CEO: Ajay Gupta
* *Pr:* Ankur Gupta
* *CFO:* Ankit Gupta
* *Sec:* Nutan Gupta
* *Genl Couns:* Anuj Gupta

D-U-N-S 07-630-3858 IMP
▲ NANOMETRICS INC
1550 Buckeye Dr, Milpitas, CA 95035-7418
Tel (408) 545-6000 *Founded/Ownrshp* 1975
Sales 187.3MM *EMP* 518^E
Tkr Sym NANO *Exch* NGS
SIC 3829 3559 Measuring & controlling devices; Geophysical or meteorological electronic equipment; Semiconductor manufacturing machinery
Pr: Timothy J Stultz
* *Ch Bd:* Bruce C Rhine
CFO: Jeffrey Andreson
Sr VP: S Mark Borowicz
Sr VP: Kevin Heidrich
Snr Sftwr: Raj Sinnadurai
Genl Couns: Janet Taylor
Board of Directors: J Thomas Bentley, Edward J Brown Jr, Christopher A Seams, Christine A Tsingos

D-U-N-S 96-340-6652
NANTICOKE HEALTH SERVICES INC
801 Middleford Rd, Seaford, DE 19973-3636
Tel (302) 629-6611 *Founded/Ownrshp* 1985
Sales 138.0MM *EMP* 950^E
Accts Cliftonlarsonallen Llp Plymo
SIC 8099 Medical services organization
Prin: E Hancock
CFO: Douglas Connell
DP Exec: Susan Godesky
Dir IT: Susan Godeski
Sls&Mrk Ex: Tom Brown
Doctor: Robert Ferber
Doctor: Anthony M Policastro

D-U-N-S 07-162-0025
NANTICOKE MEMORIAL HOSPITAL INC (DE)
(*Suby of* NANTICOKE HEALTH SERVICES INC) ★
801 Middleford Rd, Seaford, DE 19973-3636
Tel (302) 629-6611 *Founded/Ownrshp* 1945
Sales 139.8MM *EMP* 706
SIC 8062

D-U-N-S 07-831-1051
▲ NANTWORKS LLC
9920 Jefferson Blvd, Culver City, CA 90232-3506
Tel (310) 405-7539 *Founded/Ownrshp* 2011
Sales 87.3MM^E *EMP* 864^E
SIC 7373 Computer-aided system services

NAPA AUTO PARTS
See BARNES MOTOR & PARTS CO INC

NAPA AUTO PARTS
See BROOKS AUTO PARTS INC

NAPA BALKAMP
See BALKAMP INC

NAPA VALLEY MEDICAL CENTER
See QUEEN OF VALLEY MEDICAL CENTER

D-U-N-S 07-653-0807
NAPA VALLEY UNIFIED SCHOOL DISTRICT
2425 Jefferson St, NAPA, CA 94558-4931
Tel (707) 253-3715 *Founded/Ownrshp* 1965
Sales 428.1M *EMP* 1,800
SIC 8211 Public elementary & secondary schools
Dir Sec: Ken Spencer
Off Mgr: Teri Ellicock
MIS Dir: Elizabeth Emett

D-U-N-S 05-497-9125
▲ NAPCO SECURITY TECHNOLOGIES INC
333 Bayview Ave, Amityville, NY 11701-2801
Tel (631) 842-9400 *Founded/Ownrshp* 1969
Sales 82.5MM *EMP* 1,013^E
Tkr Sym NSSC *Exch* NGS
SIC 3669 3699 3429 1731 7373 Emergency alarms; Fire alarm apparatus, electric; Security control equipment & systems; Door locks, bolts & checks; Safety & security specialization; Systems software development services
Ch Bd: Richard L Soloway
* *Treas:* Kevin S Buchel
Sr VP: Michael Carrieri
Sr VP: Jorge Hevia
VP: Byron Thurmond
Board of Directors: Paul Stephen Beeber, Randy B Blaustein, Arnold Blumenthal, Donna A Soloway, Andrew J Wilder

NAPERVILLE COLLEGE
See NORTH CENTRAL COLLEGE

D-U-N-S 07-442-5547
NAPERVILLE COMMUNITY UNIT SCHOOL DISTRICT 203
203 W Hillside Rd, Naperville, IL 60540-6500
Tel (630) 420-6300 *Founded/Ownrshp* 1972
Sales 309.4MM *EMP* 2,000
Accts Klein Hall Cpas Aurora Illin
SIC 8211 Public elementary & secondary schools
Bd of Dir: Jim Dennison
Bd of Dir: Mike Jaensch
Bd of Dir: Jackie Romberg
Bd of Dir: Terry Tamblyn
Trst: Debbie Shipley
VP: Susan Crotty
DP Exec: Josh Mika
MIS Dir: Jill Hlavasek
IT Man: Lisa Dalton
Pr Dir: Michelle Fregoso
Schl Brd P: Suzyn Price

NAPI
See NAVAJO AGRICULTURAL PRODUCTS INDUSTRY

D-U-N-S 07-847-2818
NAPLES COMMUNITY HOSPITAL INC
NCH HEALTHCARE SYSTEM
350 7th St N, Naples, FL 34102-5754
Tel (239) 436-5000 *Founded/Ownrshp* 1956
Sales 443.4MM *EMP* 3,300
SIC 8062 General medical & surgical hospitals
Ch: Carl E Westman
* *Pr:* Allen S Weiss MD
COO: Gail Dolan
* *CFO:* Vicki Hale
* *Sec:* Edwin Stedem
Chf Mktg O: Aurora Estevez
Mtls Mgr: David Mobley
Doctor: Karen M Henrichsen
Doctor: Marchelle K Hofeldt MD
Doctor: Obayedur R Khan
Dir Health: Carol White
Board of Directors: Daniel Baer, Jay Baker

D-U-N-S 00-119-3655
NARRAGANSETT ELECTRIC CO (RI)
(*Suby of* NATIONAL GRID USA) ★
280 Melrose St, Providence, RI 02907-2157
Tel (401) 784-7000 *Founded/Ownrshp* 1926, 1969
Sales 423.4MM^E *EMP* 800
SIC 4911 Generation, electric power; Transmission, electric power; Distribution, electric power
Pr: Timothy F Horan
* *Treas:* Malcolm Charles Cooper
* *Ex VP:* Ellen Smith
* *Sr VP:* James B Howe
* *Sr VP:* Colin Owyang
VP: Tim Horan
VP: Charles Meunier
VP: Sharon Partridge
VP: Jeffrey Polucha
* *VP:* Michael F Ryan
* *VP:* Martin Wheatcroft
VP: Ed White
Exec: Lynda Scannell
Board of Directors: James B Howe, Thomas B King, Paul R Renaud, Michael F Ryan, Ellen Smith

NARS
See INTEGRITY SOLUTION SERVICES INC

D-U-N-S 83-736-3571 IMP
NARS COSMETICS INC
(*Suby of* SHISEIDO COSMETICS) ★
900 3rd Ave Fl 6, New York, NY 10022-4792
Tel (212) 941-0890 *Founded/Ownrshp* 1994
Sales 152.1MM^E *EMP* 390
SIC 5122 Cosmetics
CEO: Masahiko Uotani
* *Ch:* Suichi Tanaka
* *Ch:* Kuninori Veno
* *VP:* Barbara Calcagni

NASA
See NATIONAL AERONAUTICS AND SPACE ADMINISTRATION

NASA
See JOHN F KENNEDY SPACE CENTER

D-U-N-S 16-486-2935 IMP/EXP
NASA ELECTRONICS CORP
2330 Nw 102nd Pl, Doral, FL 33172-2517
Tel (305) 716-7706 *Founded/Ownrshp* 2002
Sales 100.0MM *EMP* 8
SIC 5065 Electronic parts & equipment
Owner: Hussein M Alawieh
* *Pr:* Mohammad I Ghaddar
* *Pr:* Diya Salame
* *VP:* Mohammad Hteit

D-U-N-S 00-452-3320
■ NASA GLENN RESEARCH CENTER
(*Suby of* NASA) ★
21000 Brookpark Rd, Cleveland, OH 44135-3191
Tel (216) 433-4000 *Founded/Ownrshp* 1941
Sales NA *EMP* 3,359^E
SIC 9661 Space flight operations, government; Space research & development, government;
Prin: Arlene Holbert
Exec: Monica Palivoda
Assoc Dir: Howard Ross
Adm Dir: Victoria Anzalone
Adm Dir: Linda Yavoich
IT Man: Mark D Kankam
IT Man: Allison Walker
Sftwr Eng: Keith G Marsteller
Netwrk Eng: Brian Frantz
Netwrk Eng: Joseph A Ishac
Netwrk Eng: Michael A Mackin

D-U-N-S 02-761-3459
■ NASA LANGLEY RESEARCH CENTER
(*Suby of* NASA) ★
11 Langley Blvd, Hampton, VA 23681-2143
Tel (757) 864-1000 *Founded/Ownrshp* 1917
Sales NA *EMP* 4,000^E
SIC 9661 Space flight operations, government; Space research & development, government;
Ofcr: Les Kagey
Ofcr: John Rogers
Top Exec: Stanley Cole
Top Exec: William Cooke
Top Exec: William Edwards
Top Exec: Gary Gibson
Top Exec: Larry Leavitt
Top Exec: William Winfree
VP: Farzin Amzajerdian
VP: Marian Clayton
VP: Richard Ferrare
VP: Steve Harrah
VP: Phil Schaffner
Assoc Dir: Frank Jones

D-U-N-S 01-945-3930
■ NASA/GEORGE C MARSHALL SPACE FLIGHT CENTER
(*Suby of* NASA) ★
George C Marsha, Huntsville, AL 35812
Tel (256) 544-8620 *Founded/Ownrshp* 1994
Sales NA *EMP* 3,000
SIC 9661 Space flight operations, government; Space research & development, government;
Assoc Dir: Neil Rodgers
Genl Mgr: Don Beckmeyer
Dir IT: Lisa Roberts
Info Man: Roberta Allen
Sftwr Eng: Rodney Grubbs
Netwrk Eng: Ron Newby
Netwrk Eng: Mike Tankersley

D-U-N-S 00-496-8611
■ NASA/GODDARD SPACE FLIGHT CENTER
(Suby of NASA) ★
8800 Greenbelt Rd, Greenbelt, MD 20771-0002
Tel (301) 286-2000 Founded/Ownrshp 2002
Sales NA EMP 7,000E
SIC 9661 Space flight operations, government; Space research & development, government;
*CFO: Nancy Abell
Ofcr: Josef Wonsever
Assoc Dir: Preston Burch
Assoc Dir: Eric Isaac
Assoc Dir: Azita Valinia
Prgrm Mgr: Kenneth Anderson
Genl Mgr: Dan Andrews
Off Admin: Bruce Gentry
IT Man: Mark McInerney
IT Man: Jeannine Shirley
Netwrk Eng: Earnestine Smart

D-U-N-S 06-037-5672
■ NASA/JET PROPULSION LABORATORY INC
(Suby of NASA) ★
4800 Oak Grove Dr, La Canada Flintridge, CA 91011
Tel (818) 354-4321 Founded/Ownrshp 2003
Sales NA EMP 5,000
SIC 9661 Space flight operations, government
Assoc Dir: Thomas Gavin
Prgrm Mgr: Larry Bergman
Prgrm Mgr: Fuk Li
Genl Mgr: Cara Dawn
Snr Sftwr: Tim Canham
CIO: Tom Soderstrom
Dir IT: Diane Evans
Sftwr Eng: Edith Parrott
Genl Couns: Harry Yohalem
Snr Mgr: Timothy Corn
Snr Mgr: Jonathan Pettus

D-U-N-S 03-700-9581
▲ NASB FINANCIAL INC
12498 S Us Highway 71, Grandview, MO 64030-1733
Tel (816) 765-2200 Founded/Ownrshp 1998
Sales NA EMP 463E
Accts Bkd Llp Kansas City Missour
Tkr Sym NASB Exch OTO
SIC 6035 Savings institutions, federally chartered
CEO: Paul L Thomas
*Ch Bd: David H Hancock
CFO: Rhonda Nyhus
Ofcr: Cheryl Thompson
Ofcr: Jason Zook
Ex VP: Bruce J Thielen
Ex VP: Bruce Thielen
VP: Roger Campbell
VP: Pat Cox
VP: Wade Hall
VP: Jennie Harris
VP: Lisa Lillard
VP: Luke Miller
VP: Dan Morton
VP: Paul Thomas
VP: Lori West
VP: Donna Williams
Board of Directors: Frederick V Arbanas, Barrett Brady, Laura Brady, Linda S Hancock, W Russell Welsh

NASC
See NAVMAR APPLIED SCIENCES CORP

D-U-N-S 15-117-9603 IMP/EXP
NASCO HEALTHCARE INC
(Suby of GENEVE CORP) ★
901 Janesville Ave, Fort Atkinson, WI 53538-2497
Tel (920) 568-5600 Founded/Ownrshp 1986
Sales 271.0MME EMP 900E
SIC 3999 Education aids, devices & supplies
CEO: Craig Johnson
*VP: Anup Bagaria
*VP: Rohan Rai
*VP: Todd Weisbrod
Ex Dir: Margaret Cianci
Dir IT: Kevin Walter
Advt Dir: Ken Parks
Sls Dir: Judi Boyd

D-U-N-S 16-276-3820 IMP
NASCOTE INDUSTRIES INC
(Suby of MAGNA INTERNATIONAL INC)
18310 Enterprise Ave, Nashville, IL 62263-1619
Tel (618) 327-3286 Founded/Ownrshp 2006
Sales 254.4MME EMP 800
SIC 3714 Bumpers & bumperettes, motor vehicle
Pr: Andrew Barban
*Pr: Alan J Power
Prgrm Mgr: Todd Schneider
CIO: Brian Mense

NASDA
See NATIONAL ASSOCIATION OF STATE DEPARTMENTS OF AGRICULTURE INC

D-U-N-S 07-916-4212
■ NASDAQ CORPORATE SOLUTIONS LLC
(Suby of NASDAQ INC) ★
1 Liberty Plz Ste 4900, New York, NY 10006-1400
Tel (212) 231-5369 Founded/Ownrshp 2013
Sales 139.3MME EMP 2,009E
SIC 6231 Security exchanges
VP: Demetrios Skalkotos

D-U-N-S 12-655-4732
▲ NASDAQ INC
1 Liberty Plz Ste 4900, New York, NY 10006-1400
Tel (212) 401-8700 Founded/Ownrshp 1971
Sales 3.4MMM EMP 3,824E
Tkr Sym NDAQ Exch NGS
SIC 6231 8742 Security & commodity exchanges; Financial consultant
CEO: Robert Greifeld
Pr: Daniel Carrigan
Pr: Adena T Friedman
Pr: Branden Jones
Pr: John O'Boyle
Pr: Matthew Rafter
CFO: Michael Ptasznik
Top Exec: Apollo Otika
Assoc VP: Mario Jimenez
Assoc VP: Mike Pelliccia
Assoc VP: Matthew Savarese
Assoc VP: Jim Wee
Ex VP: Anna M Ewing
Ex VP: Edward S Knight
Ex VP: Bradley J Peterson
Ex VP: Michael S Ptasznik
Ex VP: Lars Ottersg Rd
Ex VP: Bjorn Sibbern
Ex VP: Stacie Swanstrom
Sr VP: Ann M Dennison
Sr VP: Frank Hatheway
Board of Directors: Charlene T Begley, Steven D Black, Borje E Ekholm, Glenn F Hutchins, Thomas A Kloet, Ellyn A McColgan, Michael R Splinter, Lars R Wedenborn

NASDAQ OMX
See OMX (US) INC

D-U-N-S 00-232-3087
■ NASDAQ OMX PHLX LLC
(Suby of NASDAQ INC) ★
1900 Market St Fl 2, Philadelphia, PA 19103-3510
Tel (215) 496-5000 Founded/Ownrshp 1790, 2008
Sales 328.6MM EMP 130E
Accts Ernst & Young Llp New York N
SIC 6231 Security & commodity exchanges
Pr: Thomas Wittman
Treas: Tom Kelly
Ofcr: Charles Roger
Ex VP: William N Briggs
Ex VP: Edward Knight
Ex VP: Lanny Schwartz
VP: Lynda Caravello
VP: Joseph Cusick
VP: Bernie Donnally
VP: Robert Grant
VP: Amy Kitzen
VP: Ken Meaden
VP: Richard Rudolph
VP: Walt Smith
VP: Tom Wittman

D-U-N-S 07-925-1912
NASGTENNESSEE NORTH 2 LLC (TN)
(Suby of TENNESSEE STAMPINGS PORTLAND) ★
160 Kirby Dr, Portland, TN 37148-2003
Tel (615) 323-0500 Founded/Ownrshp 2013, 2014
Sales 202.5MME EMP 165
SIC 3465 Automotive stampings
Ch: Jana Haughey
CFO: David Hannah

NASH GENERAL HOSPITAL
See NHCS INC

D-U-N-S 80-386-1186
NASH HEALTH CARE SYSTEMS
2460 Curtis Ellis Dr, Rocky Mount, NC 27804-2237
Tel (252) 962-8000 Founded/Ownrshp 1983
Sales 147.1MME EMP 1,850E
SIC 8011 8741 Clinic, operated by physicians; Management services
Ch: Vincent C Andracchio II
*Pr: Larry Chewning
*Pr: Mary Chewning
*COO: Bradd Weisner
*CFO: Leslie Hall
*CFO: Al Hooks
*Treas: James Lilley
*Sr VP: CAM Blalock
VP: Brian Agan
VP: Michelle Cosimeno
Exec: Pam Owens
Dir Inf Cn: Wanda Lamm

D-U-N-S 83-076-2576
NASH HOLDINGS LLC
1403 Hamlin St Ne, Washington, DC 20017-2944
Tel (202) 334-6727 Founded/Ownrshp 2013
Sales 1.7MMME EMP 10,000E
SIC 2711 2721 Newspapers, publishing & printing; Periodicals: publishing & printing

D-U-N-S 00-319-9692 IMP/EXP
NASH JOHNSON & SONS FARMS INC
3385 S Us Highway 117, Rose Hill, NC 28458-8493
Tel (910) 289-3113 Founded/Ownrshp 1950
Sales 1.0MMM EMP 6,000
SIC 2015 0254 0253 0251 2048 Poultry, slaughtered & dressed; Poultry hatcheries; Turkey farm; Broiler, fryer & roaster chickens; Poultry feeds
CEO: Robert C Johnson
*Ch Bd: E Marvin Johnson
*COO: Don Taber
VP Sls: Robert Johnson

D-U-N-S 13-110-7757
NASH KENSEY CORP
DSM BIOMEDICAL
(Suby of KONINKLIJKE DSM N.V.)
735 Pennsylvania Dr, Exton, PA 19341-1130
Tel (484) 713-2100 Founded/Ownrshp 2012
Sales 90.4MME EMP 307E
SIC 3841 Surgical & medical instruments
Ch Bd: Walter Maupay Jr
Pr: Holly Harrity
*Pr: Joseph W Kaufmann
*COO: Douglas G Evans
*CFO: Michael Celano
VP: Donald Bond
VP: Kevin Carouge
VP: Donald L Daveer
VP: Don Daveler
*VP: Todd W Dewitt
VP: William Fiehler
VP: Tom Maguire
*VP: John E Nash
VP: Joan Reihardt
Dir Bus: Jediah White

D-U-N-S 00-696-2294 IMP
■ NASH-FINCH CO
(Suby of SPARTANNASH CO) ★
7600 France Ave S Ste 200, Minneapolis, MN 55435-5920
Tel (952) 832-0534 Founded/Ownrshp 1885, 2013
Sales 20.1MME EMP 8,134
SIC 5141 5148 5142 5147 5411 Groceries, general line; Fruits, fresh; Vegetables, fresh; Packaged frozen goods; Meats, fresh; Meats, cured or smoked; Supermarkets, chain
CEO: Dennis Eidson
Pr: Roger Nelson
*COO: David M Staples
*CFO: Christopher Meyers
Ex VP: Jeffrey E Poore
Sr VP: Terri Belene
Sr VP: Paul Bischel
Sr VP: Edward L Brunot
Sr VP: Lori Cramer
Sr VP: Keith Erickson
Sr VP: Steve Freehauf
Sr VP: Scott Gentzler
Sr VP: Charles McCown
Sr VP: Tom Swanson
Sr VP: Judy Welter
Sr VP: Denise M Wilson
Sr VP: Dave Wolfgang
VP: Jason Burnett
VP: Dan Davidson
VP: Terry Littrell
Exec: Steve Brougham

D-U-N-S 80-832-8306
NASH-ROCKY MOUNT SCHOOLS
NRMS
930 Eastern Ave, Nashville, NC 27856-1716
Tel (252) 459-5220 Founded/Ownrshp 1992
Sales 91.8MME EMP 2,670
SIC 8211 Public elementary & secondary schools
VP: Jim Albright
MIS Dir: Lisa Ballance
IT Man: Sharon Braswell
Pr Dir: Patricia Hollingsworth
Schl Brd P: Evelyn Bullock
Instr Medi: Danny Plyler

D-U-N-S 61-021-0622 EXP
NASHTEC LLC
4633 Hwy 361, Gregory, TX 78359
Tel (361) 777-2280 Founded/Ownrshp 2004
Sales 200.0MM EMP 22
SIC 2819 Industrial inorganic chemicals
Pr: Robert Barnes

D-U-N-S 00-107-9433 EXP
■ NASHUA CORP
NASHUA SPECIALTY COATED PDTS
(Suby of CENVEO INC) ★
59 Daniel Webster Hwy A, Merrimack, NH 03054-4831
Tel (603) 880-1100 Founded/Ownrshp 2009
Sales 181.5MME EMP 761
SIC 2672 2754 2679 2621 2782 Thermoplastic coated paper: made from purchased materials; Adhesive papers, labels or tapes: from purchased material; Gummed paper: made from purchased materials; Labels (unprinted), gummed: made from purchased materials; Tickets: gravure printing; Tags & labels, paper; Specialty papers; Receipt, invoice & memorandum books
Pr: Thomas G Brooker
*Pr: Robert G Burton Sr
*CFO: Scott Goodwin
*CFO: John L Patenaude
*Treas: David Jacoboski
VP: William Todd McKeown
Sls Mgr: Helen Duquette

D-U-N-S 17-673-1412
■ NASHUA HOLLIS CVS INC
(Suby of CVS HEALTH CORP) ★
1 Cvs Dr, Woonsocket, RI 02895-6146
Tel (401) 765-1500 Founded/Ownrshp 1989
Sales 385.5MME EMP 3,195
SIC 5912 Drug stores & proprietary stores
Prin: Thomas Ryan

D-U-N-S 10-005-0327
NASHUA SCHOOL DISTRICT
(Suby of SAU 42) ★
141 Ledge St, Nashua, NH 03060-3073
Tel (603) 966-1000 Founded/Ownrshp 1853
Sales 99.7MME EMP 2,000
SIC 8211 Public elementary & secondary schools
Dir Vol: Ginger Snogles

NASHUA SPECIALTY COATED PDTS
See NASHUA CORP

D-U-N-S 07-930-1304
NASHVILLE AUTOMOTIVE LLC
SERRA CHEVROLET BUICK GMC
2340 Gallatin Pike N, Madison, TN 37115-2008
Tel (615) 851-8000 Founded/Ownrshp 2013
Sales 100.0MM EMP 138
SIC 5511 Automobiles, new & used
Pr: Joseph O Serra
VP: Barry K Carver

NASHVILLE, CITY OF
See METROPOLITAN GOVERNMENT OF NASHVILLE & DAVIDSON COUNTY

NASHVILLE ELECTRIC SERVICE
See ELECTRIC POWER BOARD OF METROPOLITAN GOVERNMENT OF NASHVILLE & DAVIDSON COUNTY

NASHVILLE INTERNATIONAL AIRPOR
See METROPOLITAN NASHVILLE AIRPORT AUTHORITY

D-U-N-S 00-403-5168 IMP
NASHVILLE WIRE PRODUCTS MFG CO (TN)
199 Polk Ave, Nashville, TN 37210-4629
Tel (615) 743-2500 Founded/Ownrshp 1934, 2009
Sales 150.0MM EMP 800
SIC 3496 3471 3643 Miscellaneous fabricated wire products; Plating & polishing; Lightning protection equipment
CEO: Steven Rollins
Pr: Dwayne Smith
*CFO: Brad Hunter
VP: Kent Rollins
Exec: Cindy Tilson
Genl Mgr: Kara Oberlander
Plnt Mgr: Nick Phy
VP Sls: Geof Wigner
Manager: Gunner Pendleberry

D-U-N-S 95-972-6555
NASSAU ASSOCIATION FOR HELP OF RETARDED CHILDREN INC
189 Wheatley Rd, Glen Head, NY 11545-2641
Tel (516) 626-1000 Founded/Ownrshp 2002
Sales 9.6MME EMP 1,500
SIC 8093 8322 Mental health clinic, outpatient; Child related social services
Pr: Jack Garofalo

D-U-N-S 05-497-9992
NASSAU BOCES SCHOOL DISTRICT
71 Clinton Rd Ste 100, Garden City, NY 11530-4728
Tel (516) 396-2500 Founded/Ownrshp 1967
Sales 183.5MME EMP 3,059
Accts Rs Abrams And Co Llp Island
SIC 8211 Public elementary & secondary schools
Pr: Eric B Schultz
*Treas: Charles Carollo
Ofcr: Barbara Meskill
Ex Dir: Lucinda Hurley
Ex Dir: Tracey Nekulak
Schl Brd P: Stephen Witt

D-U-N-S 83-982-4992
NASSAU BROADCASTING PARTNERS LP
619 Alexander Rd Ste 300, Princeton, NJ 08540-6000
Tel (609) 452-9696 Founded/Ownrshp 1995
Sales 91.8MME EMP 500
SIC 4832 Radio broadcasting stations
Pr: Louis F Mercatanti Jr
VP: Tim Gatz
Ex Dir: Laurena Gilbert
Dir IT: Man Chan
Sls Mgr: Stacey Geelan
Pgrm Dir: Dave McKay

D-U-N-S 10-120-6456 IMP/EXP
NASSAU CANDY DISTRIBUTORS INC
NASSAU CANDY SPECIALTY
(Suby of NASSAU-SOSNICK DISTRIBUTION CO LLC) ★
530 W John St, Hicksville, NY 11801-1039
Tel (516) 433-7100 Founded/Ownrshp 1984
Sales 148.4MM EMP 600
SIC 5145 Candy
Pr: Lesley Stier
*Pr: Barry Rosenbaum
*CFO: Joe Vanella
Treas: Michael Pritchett
VP: Michael Cohen
VP: Randy S Goldbaum
VP: Guastella Maryann
Off Mgr: Jennifer Collins
IT Man: Pat Chiapuzzi
VP Mfg: Torben Hansen
Mfg Dir: Garrett Stier

NASSAU CANDY SPECIALTY
See NASSAU CANDY DISTRIBUTORS INC

D-U-N-S 13-926-7728
NASSAU COMMUNITY COLLEGE
NCC
(Suby of SUNY ADMINISTRATION) ★
1 Education Dr, Garden City, NY 11530-6793
Tel (516) 572-7501 Founded/Ownrshp 1959
Sales 201.4MME EMP 2,965
Accts Deloitte & Touche Llp New Yor
SIC 8222 9411 Community college; Administration of educational programs;
Pr: Dr W Hubert Keen
Assoc VP: Lynette Brown
Assoc VP: Dennis Gai
VP: Janice Grackin
Exec: James F Peluso
Off Admin: Joan Iovane
DP Exec: Les Frimerman
Sls&Mrk Ex: Martin Lomonaco

D-U-N-S 06-593-9225
NASSAU COUNTY A H R C
AHRC-NASSAU COUNTY CHAPTER
(Suby of NYSARC INC) ★
189 Wheatley Rd, Glen Head, NY 11545-2641
Tel (516) 626-1000 Founded/Ownrshp 1948
Sales 1.1MME EMP 1,225
SIC 8331 8322 Vocational training agency; Individual & family services
Pr: Terrence Ullrich
*Pr: Paul Giordano
*CFO: Will Derr
*Treas: Kenneth Fpulick
*Ex Dir: Michael Mascari

D-U-N-S 19-304-6778
NASSAU COUNTY SCHOOL DISTRICT
NASSAU DISTRICT SCHOOL BOARD
1201 Atlantic Ave, Fernandina Beach, FL 32034-3403
Tel (904) 491-9900 Founded/Ownrshp 1869
Sales 103.8MM EMP 1,500
SIC 8211 Public combined elementary & secondary school; Kindergarten
Ch: Donna Martin
Treas: Laurye Ray
*Ex Dir: Edward Turvey
Netwrk Mgr: Dana Whicker
Opers Mgr: Tim Groat
Pr Dir: Mark Eurham
Teacher Pr: Suzanne J Davis
Snr Mgr: James Schreiber

NASSAU DISTRICT SCHOOL BOARD
See NASSAU COUNTY SCHOOL DISTRICT

D-U-N-S 01-112-5825
NASSAU HEALTH CARE CORP
NASSAU UNIVERSITY MEDICAL CTR
2201 Hempstead Tpke, East Meadow, NY 11554-1859
Tel (516) 572-0123 Founded/Ownrshp 1999
Sales 363.3MM EMP 3,500
SIC 8062 General medical & surgical hospitals
Pr: Arthur A Gianelli
COO: Michael M Deluca

*CFO: John Maher
*CFO: Richard Perrotti
Ofcr: Megan Ryan
*Ex VP: Robert S Heatley
Ex VP: Robert Heatley
*Ex VP: Larry I Slatky
*Ex VP: Steven J Walerstein
*Sr VP: Kathy Skarka
VP: James Capoziello
VP: Guy Courbois
VP: Kevin Mannle
VP: Sharon Popper
*VP: Ronald Tomo
Dir Lab: Adele Wilson
Dir Rad: Shari Lobel
Dir Rx: Martine Eliconte
Dir Rx: Marcelle Santoror
Board of Directors: Arthur Gianelli

D-U-N-S 05-061-7893 IMP
NASSAU LENS CO INC
NASSAU VISION GROUP
(Suby of OMEGA DALLAS) ★
160 Legrand Ave, Northvale, NJ 07647-2484
Tel (201) 767-8033 Founded/Ownrshp 1932
Sales 172.8MM^E EMP 440
SIC 5048 Frames, ophthalmic; Lenses, ophthalmic
Pr: Francois Bezberc
*CFO: Irwin Kaufman
Genl Mgr: Kim Carrera
Sales Asso: Joe Lombardo

NASSAU UNIVERSITY MEDICAL CTR
See NASSAU HEALTH CARE CORP

NASSAU VISION GROUP
See NASSAU LENS CO INC

D-U-N-S 08-004-2284
NASSAU-SOSNICK DISTRIBUTION CO LLC
258 Littlefield Ave, South San Francisco, CA 94080-6922
Tel (650) 952-2226 Founded/Ownrshp 2015
Sales 148.4MM^E EMP 603^E
SIC 5149 5145 5182 Groceries & related products; Candy; Wine
CEO: Jeff Sosnick
*Pr: Martin Sosnick
*VP: Wayne Sosnick

NASSCO
See NATIONAL STEEL & SHIPBUILDING CO

D-U-N-S 60-206-5989 IMP
■ **NASSCO HOLDINGS INC**
(Suby of GENERAL DYNAMICS CORP) ★
2798 Harbor Dr, San Diego, CA 92113-3650
Tel (619) 544-3400 Founded/Ownrshp 1998
Sales 452.2MM^E EMP 3,500
SIC 3731 Shipbuilding & repairing
Pr: Frederick J Harris
*CFO: Eric Murray
*VP: Michael Askew
*VP: Tom Brown
*VP: David J Carver
*VP: William Cuddy
*VP: Kevin M Graney
Exec: Jenie Farotte
IT Man: Teresa Duberg
Opers Mgr: Andy Jenkins

D-U-N-S 13-051-7287
NASSER CO INC
NASSER COMPANY OF ARIZONA
22720 Savi Ranch Pkwy, Yorba Linda, CA 92887-4614
Tel (714) 279-2100 Founded/Ownrshp 1984
Sales 128.9MM^E EMP 150
SIC 5141 Food brokers
Pr: Burhan Nasser
Pr: Bill Arink
CFO: Bruce Nye
Ch: Ken Darienzo
*Sec: Mary Beth Nasser
VP: Dean Sandello
*VP Admn: Becky Salazar
MIS Dir: Gregory Dapkus
Dir IT: Jan Hornstrom
Sls&Mrk Ex: Michael Girard
Sls&Mrk Ex: Linda Jones

NASSER COMPANY OF ARIZONA
See NASSER CO INC

D-U-N-S 09-946-9488
NASSIRI INC
2035 Helm Dr, Las Vegas, NV 89119-3909
Tel (702) 837-7332 Founded/Ownrshp 1966
Sales 98.3MM^E EMP 45
Accts Grobstein Horwath & Company L
SIC 5136 5137 Sportswear, men's & boys'; Sportswear, women's & children's
Pr: Fred Nassiri

NAT
See NORTH AMERICAN TITLE CO INC

NATCO
See CAMERON SOLUTIONS INC

D-U-N-S 60-563-2884 IMP
NATCO GROUP INC
(Suby of CAMERON INTERNATIONAL CORP) ★
11210 Equity Dr Ste 100, Houston, TX 77041-8239
Tel (713) 849-7500 Founded/Ownrshp 2009
Sales 443.7MM^E EMP 2,100^E
SIC 3533 1389 Oil & gas field machinery; Gas field machinery & equipment; Oil field machinery & equipment; Oil field services; Gas field services
Pr: Les Hiller
Sr VP: Byron J Eiermann
VP: Elizabeth Evans
VP: Scott Thompson
Sfty Mgr: Jim Leblanc
Opers Mgr: Philip Hamilton
Plnt Mgr: Charlie Gordon

D-U-N-S 05-666-7231
NATCO INDUSTRIES INC DEL
150 Thorn Hill Rd, Warrendale, PA 15086-7528
Tel (724) 776-4857 Founded/Ownrshp 1991
Sales 97.1MM EMP 7
SIC 6799 Investors
Ch Bd: Jay Schottenstein
*Ex VP: Joseph E Kerin
*Ex VP: Thomas Kettler

D-U-N-S 00-119-8522 IMP
NATCO PRODUCTS CORP
155 Brookside Ave, West Warwick, RI 02893-3800
Tel (401) 828-0300 Founded/Ownrshp 1923
Sales 171.1MM^E EMP 580
SIC 3996 2273 5023 Asphalted-felt-base floor coverings: linoleum, carpet; Carpets, textile fiber; Mats & matting; Rugs
Ch Bd: Robert T Galkin
*Pr: Michael Litner
*V Ch Bd: Warren B Galkin
*Ex VP: Alan Ross
VP Sls: Norm Chabot

NATEL
See EPIC TECHNOLOGIES LLC

D-U-N-S 07-624-4789 IMP
NATEL ENGINEERING CO INC
NEOTECH
9340 Owensmouth Ave, Chatsworth, CA 91311-6915
Tel (818) 734-6523 Founded/Ownrshp 1975
Sales 1.4MMM^E EMP 2,334
SIC 3674 3679 Semiconductors & related devices; Antennas, receiving
Pr: Sudesh K Arora
*COO: Kunal Sharma
CFO: John W Lorey
*CFO: Laura Siegal
VP: Todd Baggett
VP: Will Bolinger
VP: James Campbell
VP: Henry Magdy
*VP: Victor Yamauchi
Prgrm Mgr: Tracy Hille
Prgrm Mgr: Katherine Siordia

D-U-N-S 01-896-2756
▲ **NATERA INC**
201 Industrial Rd Ste 410, San Carlos, CA 94070-2396
Tel (650) 249-9090 Founded/Ownrshp 2003
Sales 190.3MM EMP 716
Tkr Sym NTRA Exch NGS
SIC 8071 2835 Testing laboratories; In vitro diagnostics
Ch Bd: Matthew Rabinowitz
CFO: Herm Rosenman
VP: Darrin Crisitello
VP: Matthew Hill
Dir Bus: Marin Markov
Off Mgr: Robin McElroy
*CTO: Jonathan Sheena
Tech Mgr: Susan Lin
Manager: Donnie Purto
Sls Mgr: Jason Steiner
Counsel: Jonathan Rabin
Board of Directors: Todd Cozzens, Edward C Driscoll Jr, James I Healy, John Steuart

D-U-N-S 96-923-0788
NATH COMPANIES INC
900 American Blvd E # 300, Minneapolis, MN 55420-1392
Tel (952) 853-1400 Founded/Ownrshp 1996
Sales 173.5MM^E EMP 900
SIC 5812 Fast-food restaurant, chain
Pr: Mahendra Nath
CFO: Patty Smith
Sec: Asha Nath
Area Mgr: Doug Bartholomew
Genl Mgr: Mike Meyers
Genl Mgr: Barbara Newberry
Opers Mgr: Scott Henning
Mktg Dir: Jodi Schoenauer

D-U-N-S 55-694-4163
NATH MINNESOTA FRANCHISE GROUP INC
(Suby of NATH COMPANIES INC) ★
900 E 79th St Ste 300, Minneapolis, MN 55420-1393
Tel (952) 853-1400 Founded/Ownrshp 1991
Sales 160.0MM EMP 1,300
SIC 5812 8741 Fast-food restaurant, chain; Management services
CEO: Mahendra Nath
*COO: Ashok Mehta
*CFO: Patti Porteous
*VP: Asha Nath

D-U-N-S 18-763-7913
■ **NATHAN & LEWIS SECURITIES INC**
(Suby of NL HOLDING CORP (DEL)) ★
260 Madison Ave Ste 11, New York, NY 10016-2412
Tel (212) 413-4553 Founded/Ownrshp 1998
Sales 115.0MM EMP 130
Accts Ernst & Young Llp
SIC 6211 Brokers, security; Dealers, security
Pr: Jay L Lewis
CFO: Michael Caska
*VP: Tom Wirtshafter
Netwrk Mgr: Mohammad Akbar

D-U-N-S 06-054-1570
NATHAN LITTAUER HOSPITAL ASSOCIATION
NATHAN LTTAUER HOSP NURSING HM
99 E State St, Gloversville, NY 12078-1293
Tel (518) 725-8621 Founded/Ownrshp 1891
Sales 95.6MM EMP 918
SIC 8051 8062 8011

NATHAN LTTAUER HOSP NURSING HM
See NATHAN LITTAUER HOSPITAL ASSOCIATION

D-U-N-S 01-260-6737
▲ **NATHANS FAMOUS INC**
1 Jericho Plz Fl 2, Jericho, NY 11753-1680
Tel (516) 338-8500 Founded/Ownrshp 1916
Sales 100.8MM EMP 237
Tkr Sym NATH Exch NGM
SIC 5812 6794 Fast-food restaurant, chain; Franchises, selling or licensing
CEO: Eric Gatoff
*Ch Bd: Howard M Lorber
CFO: Ronald G Devos
Ex VP: Scott Harvey
VP: Leigh Platte
VP: Donald P Schedler
VP: Randy K Watts
Sls Mgr: Barbara Freitas
Board of Directors: Robert J Eide, Brian S Genson, Barry Leistner, Wayne Norbitz, Attilio F Petrocelli, Charles Raich

D-U-N-S 01-230-8128 IMP/EXP
NATHEL & NATHEL INC
NATHEL INTERNATIONAL
357 Nyc Term Mkt C, Bronx, NY 10474-7403
Tel (718) 991-6050 Founded/Ownrshp 1971
Sales 104.8MM^E EMP 125^E
SIC 5148 Fresh fruits & vegetables
Ch Bd: Ira Nathel
*Pr: Sheldon Nathel
*CFO: Richard Byllott
CFO: Ken Cohen
Exec: Wanda Lopez
Ex Dir: Angel Helck

NATHEL INTERNATIONAL
See NATHEL & NATHEL INC

NATIO COUN ON COMP INSU
See NCCI HOLDINGS INC

NATION PIZZA AND FOODS
See NATION PIZZA PRODUCTS LP

D-U-N-S 62-513-2535
NATION PIZZA PRODUCTS LP
NATION PIZZA AND FOODS
601 E Algonquin Rd, Schaumburg, IL 60173-3803
Tel (847) 397-3320 Founded/Ownrshp 1991
Sales 176.8MM^E EMP 700
SIC 2038 2045 2033 Pizza, frozen; Pizza doughs, prepared: from purchased flour; Pizza sauce: packaged in cans, jars, etc.
Co-CEO: Marshall Bauer
*Pr: Richard Auskalnis
*CFO: Joe Giglio
*Co-CEO: Jay Bauer
*VP: Jack Campolo
*VP: Keith Ohlsen
MIS Dir: Bruce Waid
Mtls Mgr: Aaron Brown
Sfty Mgr: Mirta Perez

NATION WIDE SECURITY
See NATION WIDE SERVICES INC

D-U-N-S 04-569-0224
NATION WIDE SERVICES INC
NATION WIDE SECURITY
223 Sequoyah Rd, Loudon, TN 37774-2885
Tel (248) 355-0500 Founded/Ownrshp 1996
Sales 12.2MM^E EMP 1,200
SIC 7381 Security guard service; Detective services
Pr: John Montville
VP: William M Foster
*VP: Craig Michalski
Brnch Mgr: Robert Bradberry

D-U-N-S 04-196-4057
NATIONAL ACADEMY OF SCIENCES OF UNITED STATES OF AMERICA
N A S
2101 Constitution Ave Nw, Washington, DC 20418-0006
Tel (202) 334-2000 Founded/Ownrshp 1863
Sales 343.9MM EMP 1,175
SIC 8733 8999 8748

D-U-N-S 00-325-9074
■ **NATIONAL AERONAUTICS AND SPACE ADMINISTRATION**
NASA
(Suby of EXECUTIVE OFFICE OF UNITED STATES GOVERNMENT) ★
300 E St Sw Ste 5r30, Washington, DC 20546-0002
Tel (202) 358-0000 Founded/Ownrshp 1958
Sales NA EMP 17,749
SIC 9661 Space flight operations, government; Space research & development, government;
CFO: Alethea Mack
Bd of Dir: Bill Garner
Ofcr: James Becker
Ofcr: Patti Stockman
VP: Sang Choi
VP: Carol Grunsfeld
VP: Paul Keller
VP: Glen King
VP: Parimal Kopardekar
VP: Deborah Kromis
VP: Christina Moats
VP: Compton Tucker
VP: Woody Turner
VP: Kanitra Tyler
Assoc Dir: David B King
Dir Soc: Timothy Honeycutt

D-U-N-S 92-933-2310
■ **NATIONAL AGRICULTURAL STATISTICS SERVICE**
N A S S
(Suby of U S D A) ★
1400 Independence Ave Sw, Washington, DC 20250-0002
Tel (202) 720-2707 Founded/Ownrshp 1816
Sales NA EMP 1,100
SIC 9641 Regulation of agricultural marketing;
Top Exec: Craig Flynn
Top Exec: Chris Mertz
MIS Dir: Phill Zellers

D-U-N-S 78-373-0641
NATIONAL AIR CARGO HOLDINGS INC
5955 T G Lee Blvd Ste 200, Orlando, FL 32822-4423
Tel (716) 631-0011 Founded/Ownrshp 1990
Sales 97.8MM^E EMP 410
SIC 4731

D-U-N-S 82-937-0134
▲ **NATIONAL AMERICAN UNIVERSITY HOLDINGS INC**
5301 S Highway 16 Ste 200, Rapid City, SD 57701-8931
Tel (605) 721-5220 Founded/Ownrshp 1941
Sales 96.1MM EMP 740^E
Tkr Sym NAUH Exch NGM
SIC 8221 6531 1531 Colleges universities & professional schools; University; Rental agent, real estate; Condominium developers
Pr: Ronald L Shape
*Ch Bd: Robert D Buckingham
Pr: Michael Buckingham
Pr: Robert A Paxton
CFO: David K Heflin
*V Ch Bd: Jerry L Gallentine
CIO: Anthony Deangelis
Board of Directors: Jeffrey B Berzina, Edward Buckingham, Therese K Crane, Richard L Halbert, James A Rowan, Thomas D Saban

NATIONAL AMMONIA DIV
See TANNER INDUSTRIES INC

D-U-N-S 04-942-2439 IMP/EXP
▲ **NATIONAL AMUSEMENTS INC**
C B S
846 University Ave, Norwood, MA 02062-2631
Tel (781) 461-1600 Founded/Ownrshp 1959
Sales 13.9MMM^E EMP 133,269
SIC 7832 7833 4832 4833 4841 Motion picture theaters, except drive-in; Drive-in motion picture theaters; Radio broadcasting stations; Television broadcasting stations; Cable & other pay television services
Ch Bd: Sumner M Redstone
Pr: Shari E Redstone
Pr: Patricia P Reeser
Pr: John Shahbazian
CFO: Michael Kszystyniak
Treas: Jerome Magner
Ex VP: Tad Jankowski
Sr VP: Bill Leclair
Sr VP: Joe Mollo
VP: James Hughes
VP: Thaddeus P Jankowski
VP: William Leclair
VP: George Levitt
VP: Elaine U Purdy
VP: Duncan Short
VP: Stephen Sohles
VP: Amber Stepper
VP: Shawn Sullivan
VP: Mark Walukevich
Dir Risk M: Roy Murphy
Board of Directors: Brandon Korff

D-U-N-S 10-467-1235 IMP
■ **NATIONAL ARCHIVES AND RECORDS ADMINISTRATION**
(Suby of EXECUTIVE OFFICE OF UNITED STATES GOVERNMENT) ★
8601 Adelphi Rd Ste 4200, College Park, MD 20740-6001
Tel (301) 837-2000 Founded/Ownrshp 1934
Sales NA EMP 2,907
SIC 9199 General government administration;
COO: William J Bosanko
Dir Recs: Warren Finch
*Ofcr: Laurence Brewer
Ofcr: Nancy Davis
Ofcr: Rick Morgan
Exec: Tony Clark
Adm Dir: Ann Baker
Adm Dir: Vurniece Jackson
Adm Dir: Kelley Yackley
CIO: Martha Morphy
CTO: Vivek Navale

D-U-N-S 07-280-5328 IMP
NATIONAL ASSOCIATION FOR ADVANCEMENT OF COLORED PEOPLE
NAACP
4805 Mount Hope Dr, Baltimore, MD 21215-3206
Tel (410) 358-8900 Founded/Ownrshp 1909
Sales 31.0MM EMP 2,300
Accts Bert Smith & Co Washington D
SIC 8641 Social associations
Pr: Ben Jealous
Pt: Marvin Beatty
Pr: Rose Joshua
COO: Nelson B Rivers
COO: Claudia A Withers
CFO: Roger Vann
Ch: Roslyn M Brock
Treas: Jesse H Turner Jr
Bd of Dir: Bishop Graves
Bd of Dir: David L Lewis
Bd of Dir: Joe Madison
Ex VP: Virgil E Ecton
Ex VP: Peter M Williams
Sr VP: Hilary O Shelton
VP: Stephen Jackson
VP: Tonya Jones
VP: Leila McDowell
VP: Jesse Milan

D-U-N-S 07-383-8377
NATIONAL ASSOCIATION OF INSURANCE COMMISSIONERS
NAIC
1100 Walnut St Ste 1500, Kansas City, MO 64106-2277
Tel (816) 842-3600 Founded/Ownrshp 1871
Sales 94.5MM EMP 491
Accts Rsm Us Llp Kansas City Misso
SIC 8621 Professional membership organizations
CEO: Andrew Beal
CFO: Richard Ford
CFO: Brady Kelley
Sr Cor Off: Catherine Weatherford
Off Mgr: Wanda Carlson
Mktg Mgr: Julie Fritz
Genl Couns: Ross S Myers
Counsel: Sarah Heidenreich

D-U-N-S 07-480-4501
NATIONAL ASSOCIATION OF LETTER CARRIERS
NALC
100 Indana Ave Nw Ste 709, Washington, DC 20001
Tel (202) 393-4695 *Founded/Ownrshp* 1775
Sales 1.4MMM *EMP* 5,000
Accts Bond Beebe Pc Bethesda Md
SIC 8631 Labor union
Pr: Fredric V Rolando
**Treas:* Jane E Broendell
Off Mgr: Steven Harrell

D-U-N-S 04-757-9214
NATIONAL ASSOCIATION OF REALTORS
REALTOR MAGAZINE
430 N Michigan Ave Lowr 2, Chicago, IL 60611-4088
Tel (800) 874-6500 *Founded/Ownrshp* 2005
Sales 208.7MM *EMP* 623
Accts Crowe Horwath Llp Chicago Il
SIC 8611 2721 8299 Trade associations; Periodicals: publishing & printing; Educational service, nondegree granting: continuing educ.
CEO: Dale Stinton
**Pr:* Steve Brown
**Pr:* Maurice Veissi
**Treas:* William J Armstrong III
Bd of Dir: Catherine Dickinson
Ex VP: Terrence M McDermott
VP: Scott Louser
VP: Dj Snapp
**Prin:* John Pierpoint
**CTO:* Mark Lesswing

D-U-N-S 09-777-8104
NATIONAL ASSOCIATION OF STATE DEPARTMENTS OF AGRICULTURE INC
NASDA
4350 Fairfax Dr Ste 910, Arlington, VA 22203-1619
Tel (202) 296-9680 *Founded/Ownrshp* 1996
Sales 39.5MM *EMP* 3,339
Accts Gelman Rosenberg & Freedman
SIC 8611 Trade associations
Ex Dir: Stephen Haterius

D-U-N-S 07-313-5808
NATIONAL AUDUBON SOCIETY INC
225 Varick St Fl 7, New York, NY 10014-4396
Tel (212) 979-3000 *Founded/Ownrshp* 1905
Sales 88.9MM *EMP* 600
Accts O Connor Davies Lp Harrison
SIC 8641 2721 Environmental protection organization; Magazines: publishing only, not printed on site
Pr: David Yarnold
COO: Susan Lunden
COO: Bob Perciasepe
CFO: Mary Beth Henson
Ch: David B Ford
VP: Diane Clifford
VP: Mike Daulton
VP: Mark Jannot
VP: Stephen Kress
VP: Gary Langham
VP: Joe Ryan
VP: Marc Scollo
VP: Chandra Taylor Smith
Assoc Dir: Sarah Porter
Board of Directors: Karim Al-Khafaji, Jane Alexander, Stephanie Little, Jon Anda, Alexis Maybank, Susan Bell, Hector E Morales Jr, A Cary Brown, David Roux, Michele Crist, Hugh Simmons, Joseph H Ellis, Jack Stewart, Jeffrey Goodby, Lili Taylor, James C Greenwood, Doug Varley, Constance Holsinger, Maggie Walker

D-U-N-S 17-518-8176
NATIONAL AUTOMATIC SPRINKLER INDUSTRY WELFARE FUND
(*Suby of* NATIONAL AUTOMATIC SPRINKLER INDUSTRY)
8000 Corporate Dr, Landover, MD 20785-2239
Tel (301) 577-1700 *Founded/Ownrshp* 1953
Sales 208.6MM *EMP* 50
SIC 8741 6371 Administrative management; Union welfare, benefit & health funds

D-U-N-S 96-302-3408
▲ NATIONAL BANK HOLDINGS CORP
7800 E Orchard Rd Ste 300, Greenwood Village, CO 80111-2549
Tel (720) 529-3336 *Founded/Ownrshp* 2009
Sales NA *EMP* 1,056ᴱ
Accts Kpmg Llp Denver Colorado
Tkr Sym NBHC *Exch* NYS
SIC 6021 National commercial banks
Ch Bd: G Timothy Laney
CFO: Brian F Lilly
Ofcr: Zsolt Besska
Ofcr: Zsolt K Bessko
Dir Risk M: Richard U Newfield Jr

D-U-N-S 00-792-2081
■ NATIONAL BANK OF COMMERCE (TN)
(*Suby of* SUNTRUST BANKS INC) ★
1 Commerce Sq, Memphis, TN 38103-2514
Tel (901) 523-3434 *Founded/Ownrshp* 1873
Sales NA *EMP* 5,194
SIC 6021 6211 7374 6712 National commercial banks; Investment bankers; Data processing service; Bank holding companies
Ch Bd: Ernest C Roessler
**Ch Bd:* William Reed
**Pr:* William Minkel
**V Ch Bd:* Lewis Holland
Ofcr: Ken Milman
**Ex VP:* Gus B Denton
**Ex VP:* Dick Grantham
**Ex VP:* Ron Reddin
**Ex VP:* John Womble
VP: John Mistretta

D-U-N-S 14-162-2253
NATIONAL BANKRUPTCY SERVICES LLC
NBS
14841 Dallas Pkwy Ste 300, Dallas, TX 75254-7883
Tel (972) 643-6600 *Founded/Ownrshp* 2012
Sales 101.5MMᴱ *EMP* 610
SIC 7389 Financial services
CEO: Lawrence J Buckley
COO: Brad Cloud
Ex VP: Luke Madole
CIO: Chris Lundquist

D-U-N-S 07-525-5729 IMP
NATIONAL BASKETBALL ASSOCIATION INC
N B A
100 Plaza Dr Fl 3, Secaucus, NJ 07094-3766
Tel (212) 407-8000 *Founded/Ownrshp* 1969
Sales 98.3MMᴱ *EMP* 865
SIC 7941 Professional & semi-professional sports clubs; Basketball club
Pr: Joel M Litvin
**COO:* Russell T Granik
CFO: Carol Sawdye
Chf Mktg O: Fred Nangione
Assoc VP: Amy McCarthy
Ex VP: Mitch Kupchak
Ex VP: Gregg Winik
**Sr VP:* Michael T Allen
Sr VP: Timothy P Andree
VP: Phil Horn
VP: Rachel Jacobson
VP: Kurt Rambis
Creative D: Ryan Flaherty
Creative D: Henry Moore
Creative D: Emilie Rainsberry

D-U-N-S 60-302-5933 IMP
NATIONAL BEDDING CO LLC
SERTA MATTRESS COMPANY
(*Suby of* SERTA SIMMONS BEDDING LLC) ★
2600 Forbs Ave, Hoffman Estates, IL 60192-3723
Tel (847) 645-0200 *Founded/Ownrshp* 1931
Sales 622.3MMᴱ *EMP* 2,400
SIC 2515 Box springs, assembled
Ch Bd: Norman Axelrod
Ch Bd: Richard E Yulman
CFO: Brian Callaham
Sr VP: Barbara Bradford
VP: Charissa Dillard
VP: Thomas Wenholz
VP Mfg: Jay Patel

D-U-N-S 82-988-8952 IMP
■ NATIONAL BEEF LEATHERS LLC
(*Suby of* NATIONAL BEEF PACKING CO LLC) ★
205 Florence Rd, Saint Joseph, MO 64504-1069
Tel (816) 236-1603 *Founded/Ownrshp* 2009
Sales 228.8MMᴱ *EMP* 1,113
SIC 3111 Leather tanning & finishing

D-U-N-S 14-795-0794 IMP/EXP
■ NATIONAL BEEF PACKING CO LLC
(*Suby of* LEUCADIA NATIONAL CORP) ★
12200 N Ambassador Dr # 101, Kansas City, MO 64163-1201
Tel (800) 449-2333 *Founded/Ownrshp* 2011
Sales 1.8MMMᴱ *EMP* 8,900
SIC 2011 Beef products from beef slaughtered on site
CEO: Timothy M Klein
V Ch: Terry Ryan
**COO:* Terry L Wilkerson
**CFO:* Simon McGee
**Ex VP:* David Grosenheider
**Ex VP:* Carey Hoskinson
**Ex VP:* Monte E Lowe
Ex VP: Steve Rhodes
Ex VP: Terry Wilkerson
VP: Brian McMullen
VP: Mike Pawela
VP: Bret G Wilson

D-U-N-S 10-340-2343 IMP/EXP
▲ NATIONAL BEVERAGE CORP
8100 Sw 10th St Ste 4000, Plantation, FL 33324-3224
Tel (954) 581-0922 *Founded/Ownrshp* 1985
Sales 704.7MM *EMP* 1,200ᴱ
Tkr Sym FIZZ *Exch* NGS
SIC 2086 Bottled & canned soft drinks; Carbonated beverages, nonalcoholic: bottled & canned; Water, pasteurized: packaged in cans, bottles, etc.; Fruit drinks (less than 100% juice): packaged in cans, etc.
Ch Bd: Nick A Caporella
**Pr:* Joseph G Caporella
Ex VP: George R Bracken
Sr VP: Dean A McCoy
VP: Gregory P Cook
VP: Robert Spindler
Netwrk Mgr: Danny Graham
Board of Directors: Cecil D Conlee, Samuel C Hathorn Jr, Stanley M Sheridan

NATIONAL BEVPAK
See SHASTA BEVERAGES INC

D-U-N-S 06-184-0328
NATIONAL BOARD OF MEDICAL EXAMINERS OF UNITED STATES OF AMERICA
3750 Market St, Philadelphia, PA 19104-3102
Tel (215) 590-9500 *Founded/Ownrshp* 1915
Sales 154.3MM *EMP* 300
Accts Mitchell & Titus Philadelphia
SIC 8748 Testing service, educational or personnel
Ch: Lewis R First
COO: Kathleen Kilkenny
**Treas:* Suzanne T Anderson
Ofcr: Brent Pierce
Assoc VP: Elizabeth Azari
Assoc VP: Kenny Yu
Sr VP: Frank Bilotta
**VP:* Lynn M Cleary
Assoc Dir: DOT Horber
Dir Soc: Kate Vangraafeiland
**Prin:* Joseph P Grande

D-U-N-S 62-198-8732 IMP
NATIONAL BOOK NETWORK INC
(*Suby of* ROWMAN & LITTLEFIELD PUBLISHING GROUP INC) ★
4501 Forbes Blvd Ste 200, Lanham, MD 20706-4346
Tel (301) 459-8020 *Founded/Ownrshp* 1986
Sales 136.7MMᴱ *EMP* 450ᴱ
SIC 5192 Books, periodicals & newspapers
Ch: Stanley Plotnick
**Pr:* James Lyons
VP: Marianne Bohr
VP: Ron Powers
Assoc Ed: Nick Johns

D-U-N-S 09-036-4662
NATIONAL BUILDING MAINTENANCE CORP
(*Suby of* GCA SERVICES GROUP INC) ★
855 Ave Hostos, Ponce, PR 00716-1105
Tel (787) 290-7020 *Founded/Ownrshp* 1969, 2003
Sales 32.6MMᴱ *EMP* 2,189
SIC 7349 5169 Building maintenance, except repairs; Industrial chemicals
Pr: Helcias Bermudez
**Treas:* Provines Torres
**VP:* Mildred Aviles De Bermudez

D-U-N-S 07-616-4771 IMP/EXP
NATIONAL BUSINESS FURNITURE LLC
(*Suby of* TAKKT AMERICA HOLDING INC) ★
770 S 70th St, Milwaukee, WI 53214-3109
Tel (414) 276-8511 *Founded/Ownrshp* 2005
Sales 138.1MMᴱ *EMP* 500
SIC 5021 Office furniture
Pr: Kent Anderson
**CFO:* Eileen Baus
**Ch:* Felix Zimmerman

D-U-N-S 19-228-0915
NATIONAL BUSINESS GROUP INC
NATIONAL TUBE & STEEL
15319 Chatsworth St, Mission Hills, CA 91345-2040
Tel (818) 221-6000 *Founded/Ownrshp* 1985
Sales 108.2MMᴱ *EMP* 1,000
SIC 7353 5039 7359 3496 7519 Earth moving equipment, rental or leasing; Wire fence, gates & accessories; Garage facility & tool rental; Fencing, made from purchased wire; Utility trailer rental
Pr: James Mooneyham

D-U-N-S 92-675-3919
NATIONAL CANCER COALITION LLC
225 Hillsborough St # 280, Raleigh, NC 27603-1767
Tel (919) 821-2182 *Founded/Ownrshp* 2007
Sales 140.3MM *EMP* 2ᴱ
SIC 8099 Medical services organization
Pr: Robert Landry
CFO: Hall C Overall
CFO: Hall Overall

D-U-N-S 61-511-3982
NATIONAL CATASTROPHE ADJUSTERS INC
NCA GROUP
9725 Windermere Blvd, Fishers, IN 46037-9015
Tel (317) 915-8888 *Founded/Ownrshp* 1984
Sales NA *EMP* 246
SIC 6411 Insurance adjusters
Prin: James Pearl President
**Prin:* David Ross

D-U-N-S 02-031-6568
NATIONAL CAUCUS AND CENTER ON BLACK AGING INC
1220 L St Nw Ste 800, Washington, DC 20005-4023
Tel (202) 637-8400 *Founded/Ownrshp* 1974
Sales 21.7MM *EMP* 2,300
Accts Bert Smith & Co Washington
SIC 8322 8641 Geriatric social service; Civic social & fraternal associations
Pr: Karyne Jones
**Pr:* Karyne Conley

D-U-N-S 06-712-7068 IMP
NATIONAL CEMENT CO INC
(*Suby of* VICAT)
15821 Ventura Blvd # 475, Encino, CA 91436-2935
Tel (818) 728-5200 *Founded/Ownrshp* 1920, 1974
Sales 402.2MMᴱ *EMP* 1,100
SIC 3241 3273 Portland cement; Ready-mixed concrete
Ch Bd: James E Rotch
CFO: Daniel Yukelson
IT Man: Stuart Haddock
Trfc Mgr: David Ollis

D-U-N-S 92-725-8350
■ NATIONAL CEMETERY ADMINISTRATION
(*Suby of* UNITED STATES DEPT OF VETERANS AFFAIRS) ★
810 Vrmont Ave Nw Ste 427, Washington, DC 20420-0001
Tel (800) 827-1000 *Founded/Ownrshp* 1862
Sales 54.7MMᴱ *EMP* 1,400
SIC 6553 9451 Cemetery subdividers & developers;

NATIONAL CENTER FOR ATMOSPHERI
See UNIVERSITY CORP FOR ATMOSPHERIC RESEARCH

NATIONAL CHOICE BAKERY
See TWIN CITY BAGEL INC

D-U-N-S 85-938-3130
NATIONAL CHRISTIAN CHARITABLE
11625 Rainwater Dr # 500, Alpharetta, GA 30009-8678
Tel (404) 252-0100 *Founded/Ownrshp* 2008
Sales 665.6MM *EMP* 2
Accts Capin Crouse Llp Atlanta Ge
SIC 8699 Charitable organization
Prin: Terra Parker
**Treas:* David D Johnson
Ex VP: Mardi Mountford
**VP:* George Cox
VP: Roger Sandberg
**VP:* Marsha Walker
Ex Dir: Lyston Peebles
Mng Dir: Pam Chumley
CIO: Wesley Barlow
**CIO:* Amy Garrett

D-U-N-S 07-942-3323
NATIONAL CHURCH RESIDENCES
2333 N Bank Dr, Columbus, OH 43220-5423
Tel (614) 451-2151 *Founded/Ownrshp* 1961
Sales 47.1MM *EMP* 1,500
SIC 6531 6513 8051 8059 Real estate agents & managers; Real estate managers; Apartment building operators; Apartment hotel operation; Retirement hotel operation; Skilled nursing care facilities; Convalescent home with continuous nursing care; Convalescent home; Nursing home, except skilled & intermediate care facility
Pr: Thomas W Slemmer
**COO:* Jerry B Kuyoth
**CFO:* Joseph R Kasberg
**Treas:* Doug Vesey
Bd of Dir: Ginny Barney
Sr VP: Jacci Nickell
Sr VP: Jeff Wolf
VP: Teresa D Allton
VP: Colleen Bain
**VP:* David A Kayuha
VP: Kathy Locke
VP: Kathleen McDonnell
VP: Pamela Monroe
VP: Christine Nocar
VP: John Whitlock

D-U-N-S 79-649-4222
▲ NATIONAL CINEMEDIA INC
NCM
9110 E Nichols Ave # 200, Centennial, CO 80112-3450
Tel (303) 792-3600 *Founded/Ownrshp* 2007
Sales 446.5MM *EMP* 634ᴱ
Tkr Sym NCMI *Exch* NGS
SIC 7311 7389 Advertising agencies; Advertising, promotional & trade show services
CEO: Andrew J England
**Ch Bd:* Scott N Schneider
Pr: Clifford E Marks
COO: Alfonso P Rosabal
CFO: Katherine L Scherping
CFO: Katie Scherping
Ex VP: Ralph E Hardy
Board of Directors: Peter B Brandow, Lawrence A Goodman, David R Haas, Stephen L Lanning, Thomas F Lesinski, Paula Williams Madison, Lee Roy Mitchell, Craig R Ramsey

D-U-N-S 19-773-2162
■ NATIONAL CINEMEDIA LLC
(*Suby of* NCM) ★
9110 E Nichols Ave # 200, Centennial, CO 80112-3450
Tel (303) 792-3600 *Founded/Ownrshp* 2005
Sales 446.5MM *EMP* 150
Accts Deloitte & Touche Llp Denver
SIC 7311 Advertising agencies
Pr: Laurie Lundquist
Ex VP: David Giesler
Ex VP: Ralph E Hardy
Ex VP: Al Rosabal
Sr VP: Chris Helm
Sr VP: Vinny Saavedra
VP: Jill Bergeson
VP: Cathy Breen
VP: Michael Eaton
VP: Mike Fenne
VP: David Murray
VP: Stuart Walker
Exec: Cliff Marks
Dir Soc: Meghan Berry

NATIONAL CITY BANK
See PNC BANK NATIONAL ASSOCIATION

D-U-N-S 07-128-9128
■ NATIONAL CITY MORTGAGE INC
(*Suby of* PNC FINANCIAL SERVICES GROUP INC) ★
3232 Newmark Dr, Miamisburg, OH 45342-5433
Tel (937) 910-1200 *Founded/Ownrshp* 1955, 2008
Sales NA *EMP* 5,800
Accts Ernst & Youngs Llp Cleveland
SIC 6162 Mortgage bankers & correspondents
Ch Bd: Leo E Knight Jr
**Pr:* Rick A Smalldon
**Treas:* Steven M Scheid
Ex VP: James Bell
**Ex VP:* Jack Case
**Ex VP:* Gregory A Davis
Ex VP: Jon Gorney
**Ex VP:* Todd A Householder
Sr VP: Steve Atwood
Sr VP: Edward R Metzger
Sr VP: Theodore W Tozer
VP: Brad Belcher
**VP:* John D Bollman
VP: Jeff Crothers
VP: Alex Laufersweiler
VP: Dave Menker
Exec: Jon McBride
Board of Directors: Bernadine Healy, Jeffrey D Kelly

D-U-N-S 96-938-3327
NATIONAL COALITION OF CERTIFICATION CENTERS
4940 88th Ave, Kenosha, WI 53144-7467
Tel (262) 914-1515 *Founded/Ownrshp* 2009
Sales 714.3Mᴱ *EMP* 2,016
SIC 8734 Calibration & certification
Ex Dir: Roger Tadajewski
**Treas:* Tom Friedemann
Board of Directors: Dr John Richman

D-U-N-S 96-776-7216 IMP
NATIONAL COATINGS & SUPPLIES INC
4900 Falls Of Neuse Rd, Raleigh, NC 27609-5388
Tel (919) 573-2900 *Founded/Ownrshp* 2008
Sales 390.5MMᴱ *EMP* 766ᴱ
SIC 5013 Automotive supplies & parts
Pr: Wayne Lavrack
**CFO:* Curtis Beeson
VP: Harry Hall
Store Mgr: Steve Goff
Store Mgr: Amanda Panchyshyn
Opers Mgr: Bill Walters
Opers Mgr: April Whitted
VP Sls: Kevin Nelson
Manager: Matthew Mann
Manager: Jeff Peck
Manager: Leslee Waters

D-U-N-S 07-625-3095
NATIONAL COLLEGIATE ATHLETIC ASSOCIATION
NCAA
700 W Washington St, Indianapolis, IN 46204-2710
Tel (317) 917-6222 *Founded/Ownrshp* 1906
Sales 906.1MM *EMP* 508
Accts Deloitte Tax Llp Indianapolis
SIC 8699 Athletic organizations
Pr: Mark A Emmert
Ex VP: Donald Remy
VP: Dan Dutcher
Assoc Dir: Eric Hartung
Assoc Dir: Maritza Jones
Comm Man: Susan Dunlap
Netwrk Mgr: Kim Johnson
Sls Mgr: Jason Bolden
Board of Directors: Karl Eller

D-U-N-S 05-475-7612
NATIONAL CONSTRUCTION ENTERPRISES INC
5075 Carpenter Rd, Ypsilanti, MI 48197-9601
Tel (734) 434-1600 *Founded/Ownrshp* 1978
Sales 81.2MM^E *EMP* 1,000
Accts Crowe Horwath South Bend In
SIC 8741 Construction management
CEO: Pino Mancina
Ex VP: Jerry Stakhiv
* *VP:* Don Quinn
Board of Directors: James R Markiewicz, Robert C Walrich

D-U-N-S 06-666-9995 IMP/EXP
NATIONAL CONSTRUCTION RENTALS INC
(*Suby of* NATIONAL TUBE & STEEL) ★
15319 Chatsworth St, Mission Hills, CA 91345-2040
Tel (818) 221-6000 *Founded/Ownrshp* 1991
Sales 108.2MM^E *EMP* 900
SIC 7353 Heavy construction equipment rental
Pr: James R Mooneyham
* *Pr:* W Robert Mooneyham
Dir IT: Joseph Young

D-U-N-S 09-777-8633
NATIONAL CONSUMER COOPERATIVE BANK
N C B
2001 Penn Ave Nw Ste 625, Washington, DC 20006-1878
Tel (202) 349-7444 *Founded/Ownrshp* 1982
Sales NA *EMP* 248
SIC 6021 National commercial banks
Pr: Charles E Snyder
Pr: Karen Barerra
* *COO:* Kathleen H Luzik
* *CFO:* Richard L Reed
* *Ofcr:* Mark W Hiltz
Sr VP: Shawn Brenneman
* *Sr VP:* Patrick N Connealy
* *Sr VP:* Casey Fannon
Sr VP: Robert Jenkens
VP: Jim Bethea
VP: Earl Carson
VP: Brendan Gale
VP: Cecil Green
VP: Isaac Holt
VP: Jeremy Morgan
VP: Michael Novak
VP: Patricia Poznanski
VP: Stan Sherfy
Board of Directors: Stuart M Saft, Roger B Collins, Walden Swanson, Peter A Conrad, Nguyen Van Hanh Phd, Irma Cota, Judy Ziewacz, Steven F Cunningham, Jane Garcia, William F Hampel, Janis Herschkowitz, Alfred A Plamann, Kenneth Rivkin

D-U-N-S 18-741-6540 IMP/EXP
NATIONAL CONSUMER OUTDOORS CORP
BRINKMANN PET
4215 Mcewen Rd, Dallas, TX 75244-5202
Tel (972) 716-4200 *Founded/Ownrshp* 1994
Sales 107.1MM^E *EMP* 292
SIC 3999 2399 2394 3732

D-U-N-S 02-663-0269
■ **NATIONAL CONVENIENCE STORES INC**
STOP N GO
(*Suby of* DIAMOND SHAMROCK REFINING AND MARKETING CO) ★
6000 N Loop 1604 W, San Antonio, TX 78249-1100
Tel (830) 995-4303 *Founded/Ownrshp* 2002
Sales 91.7MM^E *EMP* 1,000
SIC 5411 5812 Convenience stores, chain; Fast food restaurants & stands
Ch Bd: Jean Gaulin
CFO: H Pete Smith
Treas: Steven A Blank
Ex VP: Timothy J Fretthold
Ex VP: William R Klesse
Sr VP: W Paul Eisman
Sr VP: Christopher Havens

D-U-N-S 96-819-6100
NATIONAL CONVENTION SERVICES LLC
145 W 30th St Rm 200, New York, NY 10001-4039
Tel (212) 947-8255 *Founded/Ownrshp* 2002
Sales 17.3MM *EMP* 2,500
Accts Dominic Loguidice Cpa Yonker
SIC 7389 Exhibit construction by industrial contractors
VP Sls: Salvatore Longhitano

D-U-N-S 00-591-2589 IMP
NATIONAL COUNCIL OF YOUNG MENS CHRISTIAN ASSOCIATIONS OF UNITED STATES OF AMERICA
YMCA OF THE USA
101 N Wacker Dr Ste 1600, Chicago, IL 60606-7310
Tel (312) 977-0031 *Founded/Ownrshp* 1982
Sales 114.2MM *EMP* 350^E
Accts Grant Thornton Llp Chicago I
SIC 7997 8399 8322 Membership sports & recreation clubs; Community action agency; Individual & family services
Pr: Neil J Nicoll
* *Ch Bd:* Sharon L Allen
COO: Gary Clarke
CFO: Jim Mellor
CFO: Jody Shaffer
Bd of Dir: Jay Alexander
Bd of Dir: Eunice Azzani
Bd of Dir: Barbara M Barron
Bd of Dir: Andrew Boninti
Bd of Dir: James C Bourke
Bd of Dir: Henry E Brown
Bd of Dir: Mary C Carroll
Bd of Dir: Michael A Colling
Bd of Dir: Michael A Corfield
Bd of Dir: Barbara Dingfield
Bd of Dir: Cindy Doyle
Bd of Dir: Ron Edele
Bd of Dir: David Epperson
Bd of Dir: Anne M Fawcett
Bd of Dir: Lillian G Frank
Bd of Dir: Matthew H Gauck
Board of Directors: John G Conley, Curt Hazelbaker, Christopher A Padilla, Derrick Stewart, Janice Reals Ellig

D-U-N-S 13-219-9873
NATIONAL COUNCIL ON COMPENSATION INSURANCE INC
NATIONAL WORKERS COMPENSATION
(*Suby of* NATIO COUN ON COMP INSU) ★
901 Peninsula Corp Cir, Boca Raton, FL 33487-1339
Tel (561) 893-1000 *Founded/Ownrshp* 2000
Sales NA *EMP* 800
SIC 6331 Workers' compensation insurance
CEO: Stephen Klingel
CFO: Guerra Alfedo
* *CFO:* Alfredo Guerra
Counsel: Adam Levell

D-U-N-S 01-843-2612
NATIONAL DAIRY LLC
(*Suby of* BORDEN DAIRY COMPANY)
8750 N Central Expy # 400, Dallas, TX 75231-6417
Tel (469) 587-0190 *Founded/Ownrshp* 2009
Sales 2.8MMM^E *EMP* 3,800^E
SIC 5143 Milk; Milk & cream, fluid
VP: Diego Rosenfledt

D-U-N-S 11-619-9142
NATIONAL DAIRY PROMOTION AND RESEARCH BOARD
10255 W Higgins Rd # 900, Rosemont, IL 60018-5638
Tel (847) 803-2000 *Founded/Ownrshp* 1984
Sales 85.7MM *EMP* 15
SIC 8611 Trade associations
Pr: Thomas Gallagher

D-U-N-S 80-560-8762 EXP
NATIONAL DCP LLC
DUNKIN' DONUTS
3805 Crestwood Pkwy Nw, Duluth, GA 30096-7164
Tel (770) 369-8600 *Founded/Ownrshp* 2005
Sales 319.9MM^E *EMP* 1,100^E
SIC 5461 Doughnuts

D-U-N-S 02-635-6225 EXP
NATIONAL DELI LLC
7250 Nw 35th Ter Tce, Miami, FL 33122-1356
Tel (305) 592-0300 *Founded/Ownrshp* 2001
Sales 95.0MM^E *EMP* 130
SIC 5147
Ex VP: Joey Bonomo
VP: Richie Fives
VP: Nestor Martinez
VP: Bert Patterson
VP Opers: Charlie Hart
S&M/VP: Chris Marriott
Sls Mgr: Tim Petrilak

D-U-N-S 11-030-9622
NATIONAL DEMOCRATIC INSTITUTE FOR INTERNATIONAL AFFAIRS
455 Mdcchstts Ave Nw Fl 8, Washington, DC 20001
Tel (202) 728-5500 *Founded/Ownrshp* 1983
Sales 135.3MM *EMP* 1,300
Accts Bdo Usa Llp Bethesda Md
SIC 8651 Political action committee
Pr: Kenneth Wollack
Ofcr: Jesper Frant
Ofcr: Francis Madugu
Ofcr: Kellen Nahumbya
Ofcr: Daniel Reilly
Ofcr: Lindsay Robinson
Ofcr: Angela Vance
* *VP:* Shari Bryan
VP: Isabel Emerson
VP: Aminata Kasse
Prgrm Mgr: Jared Ford

D-U-N-S 05-531-2342
NATIONAL DENTEX CORP
(*Suby of* GEODIGM CORP) ★
11601 Kew Gardens Ave, Palm Beach Gardens, FL 33410-2852
Tel (877) 942-5871 *Founded/Ownrshp* 2010
Sales 90.4MM^E *EMP* 1,745
SIC 8072 Crown & bridge production; Denture production; Orthodontic appliance production
CEO: Steven E Casper
* *CFO:* Mark Brockelman
CFO: Wayne M Coll
CFO: Micheal Schantz
VP: Lynn D Dine
VP: James F Dodd III

D-U-N-S 00-884-7105 IMP
NATIONAL DISTRIBUTING CO INC (GA)
1 National Dr Sw, Atlanta, GA 30336-1631
Tel (404) 696-1681 *Founded/Ownrshp* 1935, 1946
Sales 546.8MM^E *EMP* 1,000
SIC 5182 5181 Liquor; Wine; Beer & other fermented malt liquors
Ch Bd: Jay Davis
* *CEO:* Jay M Davis
* *CFO:* John A Carlos
Ofcr: Jerry Rosenberg
* *Ex VP:* Chris Carlos
VP: Leon Cikota
Comm Dir: Elizabeth Barkan
Area Mgr: Henry Castellana
Dist Mgr: Kevin England
Snr Sftwr: Shiva Boothalingam
MIS Dir: Bobby Heid

D-U-N-S 09-077-1676
NATIONAL DISTRIBUTION CENTERS LP
NFI DISTRIBUTION
(*Suby of* NFI INDUSTRIES INC) ★
1515 Burnt Mill Rd, Cherry Hill, NJ 08003-3637
Tel (856) 691-7000 *Founded/Ownrshp* 1993
Sales 186.7MM^E *EMP* 805
SIC 4225 Warehousing, self-storage
Pt: Sidney R Brown
Pt: Irwin Brown

D-U-N-S 09-599-5809 IMP
NATIONAL DIVERSIFIED SALES INC
A D P
(*Suby of* NORMA GROUP SE)
21300 Victory Blvd # 215, Woodland Hills, CA 91367-2525
Tel (559) 562-9888 *Founded/Ownrshp* 2014
Sales 175.6MM^E *EMP* 500
SIC 3089 Plastic hardware & building products; Fittings for pipe, plastic
CEO: David Silver
* *Pr:* Michael Gummeson
* *CFO:* Randall Stott
Ofcr: Mark Peterson
VP: Michael Fallon
VP: Barry McHone
Sfty Mgr: Alex Rodriguez
Sls Mgr: Darren Bridges

D-U-N-S 78-532-6286
NATIONAL ECOLOGICAL OBSERVATORY NETWORK INC
BATTELLE ECOLOGY
1685 38th St Ste 100, Boulder, CO 80301-2735
Tel (720) 746-4844 *Founded/Ownrshp* 2005
Sales 97.2MM *EMP* 40
Accts Eidebailly Llp Golden Colora
SIC 8733 Scientific research agency
* *CEO:* Richard Leonard
Sftwr Eng: Wilson Yang

D-U-N-S 06-677-8044
NATIONAL EDUCATION ASSOCIATION OF UNITED STATES
N E A
1201 16th St Nw, Washington, DC 20036-3290
Tel (202) 833-4000 *Founded/Ownrshp* 1857
Sales 384.2MM *EMP* 735
SIC 8631 Labor union
Pr: Reg Weaver
* *CFO:* Mike McPherson
* *Treas:* Lily Eskelsen
* *VP:* Dennis Vanroekel
* *Ex Dir:* John Wilson
Dist Mgr: Ruben Cedeno
Sales Exec: Patricia Penna

D-U-N-S 08-919-4211
NATIONAL ELECTRICAL BENEFIT FUND
NEBF
2400 Res Blvd Ste 500, Rockville, MD 20850
Tel (301) 556-4300 *Founded/Ownrshp* 1946
Sales NA *EMP* 160
Accts Calibre Cpa Group Pllc Bethes
SIC 6371 Pension funds
Ex Dir: Lawrence J Bradley
Exec: Crystal Davis
Ex Dir: Terry Moloznik
IT Man: Cathy Clark

D-U-N-S 60-420-2184 IMP/EXP
NATIONAL ELECTRONICS INC
500 Smith St, Farmingdale, NY 11735-1115
Tel (631) 683-8000 *Founded/Ownrshp* 1989
Sales 152.0MM *EMP* 20
Accts Marks Paneth Llp New York Ne
SIC 5065 Mobile telephone equipment
CEO: Abdulrahman S Khwaja
Treas: Nadia Khwaja

D-U-N-S 13-936-4426
NATIONAL ELECTRONICS WARRANTY LLC
22894 Pacific Blvd, Sterling, VA 20166-6722
Tel (703) 375-8100 *Founded/Ownrshp* 1983
Sales NA *EMP* 6,000
Accts Pricewaterhousecoopers Llp Fr
SIC 6411 Insurance agents, brokers & service
CEO: Anthony P Nader
Ch Bd: Fredrick D Schaufeld
Exec: Danny Hourigan
Exec: Kevin Porter
Snr Mgr: Brian Dwinnell

D-U-N-S 96-775-0030
NATIONAL ELEVATOR INDUSTRY HEALTH BENEFIT PLAN
19 Campus Blvd Ste 200, Newtown Square, PA 19073-3288
Tel (610) 325-9100 *Founded/Ownrshp* 2012
Sales NA *EMP* 2^E
Accts Daniel A Winters & Company Cpa
SIC 6411 Hospital & medical service plans; Union welfare, benefit & health funds
Prin: Robert O Betts

D-U-N-S 13-227-9084
NATIONAL ENDOWMENT FOR DEMOCRACY INC
1025 F St Nw Ste 800, Washington, DC 20004-1432
Tel (202) 378-9700 *Founded/Ownrshp* 1983
Sales 134.0MM *EMP* 99^E
Accts Mcgladrey Llp Vienna Va
SIC 8399 Social change association
Pr: Carl Gershman
* *Ch Bd:* Martin Frost
Bd of Dir: Igor Blazevic
Bd of Dir: Francesca Bomboko
Bd of Dir: Yuri Dzhibladze
Bd of Dir: Paul Graham
Bd of Dir: Jana Hybaskova
Bd of Dir: George Mathew
Bd of Dir: Inna Pidluska
Bd of Dir: Yevgeniy Zhovtis
Snr Ntwrk: Chris French
Board of Directors: Barry Jackson, Jayne M Kurzman, Ellen O Tauscher, Robert B Zoellick

D-U-N-S 00-230-9511 IMP
NATIONAL ENTERTAINMENT COLLECTIBLES ASSOCIATION INC
NECA
603 Sweetland Ave, Hillside, NJ 07205-1799
Tel (908) 686-3300 *Founded/Ownrshp* 1996
Sales 94.4MM^E *EMP* 200^E
SIC 5199 Gifts & novelties
Ch: Joel Weinshanker
CFO: Michael Sosidka

D-U-N-S 19-608-3869 IMP
NATIONAL ENTERTAINMENT NETWORK LLC
SUGARLOAF CREATIONS
(*Suby of* NEN HOLDINGS INC) ★
325 Interlocken Pkwy B, Broomfield, CO 80021-3497
Tel (303) 444-2559 *Founded/Ownrshp* 2009
Sales 135.7MM^E *EMP* 750
SIC 5046 5962 Commercial equipment; Novelty vending machines
CEO: Ed Flaherty
CFO: Peter Jacobson
Chf Mktg O: Randy Chilton

D-U-N-S 00-753-8473
NATIONAL EQUIPMENT SERVICES INC
(*Suby of* NES RENTALS HOLDINGS INC) ★
8420 W Bryn Mawr Ave, Chicago, IL 60631-3479
Tel (773) 695-3999 *Founded/Ownrshp* 1996
Sales 90.2MM^E *EMP* 1,100
SIC 7359 Equipment rental & leasing
Pr: Andrew P Studdert
* *CFO:* Michael D Milligan
VP: Rick Juster

D-U-N-S 95-913-2622
NATIONAL EQUITY TITLE AGENCY INC
NETCO
415 N La Salle Dr Ste 202, Chicago, IL 60654-2730
Tel (312) 782-4290 *Founded/Ownrshp* 1991
Sales NA *EMP* 500
SIC 6361 Real estate title insurance
Pr: John Baumgart
* *CFO:* Thomas Evans
* *VP:* Edward Cook

D-U-N-S 05-650-7037 IMP
NATIONAL EWP INC
500 Main St, Woodland, CA 95695-3434
Tel (530) 419-2117 *Founded/Ownrshp* 2010
Sales 110.2MM^E *EMP* 100
SIC 1081 Metal mining exploration & development services
Pr: Jeffrey D Morgan
* *CFO:* Michael Paris

D-U-N-S 10-759-0002
NATIONAL EXCHANGE CARRIER ASSOCIATION
NECA
80 S Jefferson Rd Ste 1, Whippany, NJ 07981-1049
Tel (800) 228-8398 *Founded/Ownrshp* 1983
Sales 84.7MM^E *EMP* 427
SIC 7389 8611 Telephone answering service; Regulatory associations
Pr: Bill Hegmann
* *CFO:* Peter Dunbar
* *VP:* James W Frame
* *VP:* Regina McNeil Gc
VP: Peter Tyrrell
Dept Mgr: Joe Chang
Netwrk Mgr: Laurie Debeer
Snr Mgr: Glen Ramcharan

D-U-N-S 82-706-0026
NATIONAL EXPRESS LLC
NEC
(*Suby of* NATIONAL EXPRESS GROUP PLC)
4300 Weaver Pkwy Ste 100, Warrenville, IL 60555-3920
Tel (800) 950-0485 *Founded/Ownrshp* 1998
Sales 897.3MM^E *EMP* 10,151^E
SIC 4119 Vanpool operation
CEO: David A Duke
Pr: Rick Klaus
Pr: Andrew Ptak
* *CFO:* Judith Crawford
* *Sr VP:* John Elliott Jr
* *Sr VP:* Mike Goddard
* *Sr VP:* Daryl Hendricks
Sr VP: Cristen Kogl
VP: David Brabender
VP: John Lebens
VP: Carey Paster
VP: Michael Settle
VP: Andrew Tarman
Exec: Elsie Hernandez
Dir Bus: Justin Grygiel
Dir Bus: Mark Herington

NATIONAL FARMERS ORGANIZATION
See NFO INC

D-U-N-S 86-791-2511
NATIONAL FARMERS ORGANIZATION
(*Suby of* NATIONAL FARMERS ORGANIZATION) ★
528 Billy Sunday Rd # 100, Ames, IA 50010-8087
Tel (515) 292-2000 *Founded/Ownrshp* 1991
Sales 600.0MM *EMP* 90
SIC 8631 Collective bargaining unit
Pr: Paul Olson
CFO: Micheal Miller
VP: Paul Riniker
Board of Directors: Dale Depies, Bill Goettemoeller, Brian Harris, Ernest Muhlenkamp, Mark Rubin, Dan Sorenson, Ed Tvrdy, Leander Wagner

D-U-N-S 00-923-8221
NATIONAL FEDERATION OF INDEPENDENT BUSINESS
N F I B
53 Century Blvd Ste 250, Nashville, TN 37214-4618
Tel (615) 872-5800 *Founded/Ownrshp* 1943
Sales 100.0MM *EMP* 825

Accts Kpmg Llp Nashville Tn
SIC 8611 Business associations
Pr: Dan Danner
**CFO:* Tammy Boehms
CFO: Tammy S Boehms
**Sr VP:* Mary Blasinsky
Sr VP: Brad Close
**Sr VP:* John Lanier
**Sr VP:* David Silverman
**Sr VP:* Steve Woods
VP: Amanda Austin
**VP:* Jannet Connor
**VP:* Susan Eckerly
VP: Tim Franke
**VP:* Roger Geiger
**VP:* Lisa Goeas
**VP:* Jeff Koch
**VP:* Susan Ridge
VP: Beverly Shea
Dir Soc: Desiree Richard
Comm Dir: Andy Patterson

D-U-N-S 78-334-2504
NATIONAL FIELD REPRESENTATIVES INC
N F R
136 Maple Ave, Claremont, NH 03743-2938
Tel (603) 543-5210 *Founded/Ownrshp* 1989
Sales 120.0MM *EMP* 250
SIC 7389 1799 Building inspection service; Building board-up contractor
Pr: Steve Cossingham
**Treas:* Eduard Hristache
VP: Douglas Brecht
**VP:* Deborah Cossingham
VP: Henry Cossingham
**VP:* Doug Drecht
VP: Mary Jane Masaro
VP Admn: Vickie Page

D-U-N-S 09-628-4047 IMP
NATIONAL FINANCIAL SERVICES LLC (MA)
(*Suby of* FIDELITY INVESTMENTS) ★
200 Seaport Blvd Ste 630, Boston, MA 02210-2031
Tel (800) 471-0382 *Founded/Ownrshp* 1978
Sales 2.8MMM[E] *EMP* 36,000
SIC 6211 6411 6282 Security brokers & dealers; Brokers, security; Dealers, security; Investment firm, general brokerage; Insurance agents; Investment advisory service
Ofcr: Denisa Kirchoff
VP: Patrick H McEvoy
Prgrm Mgr: Michael Leynor

D-U-N-S 00-787-4191
■ **NATIONAL FIRE INSURANCE CO OF HARTFORD** (CT)
(*Suby of* CNA INSURANCE) ★
Cna Plz, Chicago, IL 60604
Tel (312) 822-5000 *Founded/Ownrshp* 1869, 2008
Sales NA *EMP* 2,000
SIC 6331 Fire, marine & casualty insurance
Prin: Brian Hartford

NATIONAL FIRE SUPPRESSION
See WESTERN STATES FIRE PROTECTION CO INC

D-U-N-S 17-517-2527
NATIONAL FISH & WILDLIFE FOUNDATION
1133 15th St Nw Fl 11, Washington, DC 20005-2708
Tel (202) 857-0166 *Founded/Ownrshp* 1984
Sales 185.6MM *EMP* 85
Accts Grant Thornton Llp Mc Lean V
SIC 8641 Environmental protection organization
Ch Bd: Don J McGrath
**CEO:* Jeff Trandahl
**CFO:* Robert Menzi
Ex VP: Jennifer C Simpson
VP: Eric Schwaab
Pgrm Dir: Michelle Pico
Pgrm Dir: Andrew Purkey
Board of Directors: Charles McCrary, R King Milling, Edwin R Rodriquez Jr, Thomas L Strickland

D-U-N-S 09-744-7403 IMP/EXP
NATIONAL FISH AND SEAFOOD INC
(*Suby of* PACIFIC ANDES INTERNATIONAL HOLDINGS LIMITED)
11 15 Parker St, Gloucester, MA 01930
Tel (978) 282-7880 *Founded/Ownrshp* 1997
Sales 176.8MM[E] *EMP* 253
SIC 5146 2092 Fish, frozen, unpackaged; Fresh or frozen packaged fish
Pr: Jack A Ventola
VP: Richard Reeder
Sfty Mgr: Jack Duarte
Trfc Mgr: Ernie Viens
VP Mktg: Nancy Peterson
Manager: Danielle Gauthier
Doctor: Dick Pandolfo
Doctor: Todd Provost

D-U-N-S 02-745-8009 IMP/EXP
NATIONAL FOOD CORP
808 134th St Sw Ste 116, Everett, WA 98204-2300
Tel (425) 349-4257 *Founded/Ownrshp* 1956
Sales 168.6MM[E] *EMP* 500
SIC 0252 Chicken eggs
Pr: Brian Bookkey
CFO: Shaun McCann
**Sec:* Dean Fox
**VP:* Roger Deffner
Genl Mgr: Noelle Heideman
CTO: Debra Straub
IT Man: Debra Dreger

D-U-N-S 78-349-5005 IMP
NATIONAL FOOD GROUP INC
C S V SALES
46820 Magellan Dr Ste A, Novi, MI 48377-2454
Tel (734) 453-4544 *Founded/Ownrshp* 1990
Sales 96.4MM[E] *EMP* 72[E]
SIC 5142 Packaged frozen goods
Pr: Sean Zecman
**Sec:* Vaughn H Zecman
Off Admin: Nick Crivac

D-U-N-S 07-828-6530
NATIONAL FOOTBALL LEAGUE INC
N F L
345 Park Ave Bsmt Lc1, New York, NY 10154-0017
Tel (212) 450-2000 *Founded/Ownrshp* 1920
Sales 265.0MM[E] *EMP* 1,795
SIC 7941 Football club
Pr: Eric P Grubman
COO: Kim Williams
CFO: Adrian Bracy
**CFO:* Anthony Noto
CFO: Bill Prescott
**Chf Mktg O:* Dawn Hudson
Ex VP: Ray Anderson
Ex VP: Steve Bornstein
Ex VP: Robert Gulliver
**Ex VP:* Jeff Pash
VP: Joel Bussert
VP: Anthony Cardillo
VP: Ken Fiore
VP: Chris Fuller
VP: Eyal Gutentag
VP: Scott Hagel
VP: Christopher Halpin
VP: Chris Hardart
VP: Frank Hawkins
VP: Natara Holloway
VP: Rick Kay

D-U-N-S 07-483-9218
NATIONAL FOOTBALL LEAGUE PLAYERS ASSOCIATION (VA)
1133 20th St Nw Frnt 1, Washington, DC 20036-3449
Tel (202) 756-9100 *Founded/Ownrshp* 1969
Sales 84.8MM *EMP* 89
Accts Calibre Cpa Group Pllc Bethes
SIC 7941 Football club
Pr: Domonique Foxworth
**VP:* Drew Brees
**VP:* Brian Dawkins
**VP:* Scott Fujita
Prgrm Mgr: Caryl Banks
Genl Mgr: Mary Moran
Dir IT: Heather McPhee
Dir IT: Leslie Satchell
Dir IT: Mike Shehan
Counsel: Sean Sansiveri
Snr Mgr: Doug Airel

D-U-N-S 00-248-3659
NATIONAL FREIGHT INC (NJ)
NFI TRANSPORTATION
(*Suby of* NFI INDUSTRIES INC) ★
1515 Burnt Mill Rd, Cherry Hill, NJ 08003-3637
Tel (856) 691-7000 *Founded/Ownrshp* 1932, 2012
Sales 249.5MM[E] *EMP* 1,526
SIC 7513 4213 Truck rental & leasing, no drivers; Trucking, except local
Ch Bd: Sidney Brown
COO: Josiah Knapp
CFO: Gary Nichols
**V Ch Bd:* Jeffrey Brown
VP: Craig Bollinger
Brnch Mgr: Ed Deal
CIO: Scott Bentom
CIO: Scott Denton
VP Opers: Mark Morrison
VP Sls: Marc Earl

D-U-N-S 00-926-2064 IMP/EXP
NATIONAL FROZEN FOODS CORP
PAC/GRO AND ASSOCIATES
1600 Frview Ave E Ste 200, Seattle, WA 98102
Tel (206) 322-8900 *Founded/Ownrshp* 1912
Sales 202.5MM *EMP* 1,009
SIC 2037 Vegetables, quick frozen & cold pack, excl. potato products
Pr: Richard Grader
**Treas:* Celeste Gazarek
**VP:* Robert Ashmun
VP: John Bafus
**VP:* Jonathan Bafus
**VP:* Edward Rosenbach
Admn Mgr: Judy Barron
Genl Mgr: Bill Obryan
Off Mgr: Judi Rang
IT Man: Peter Larsen
IT Man: Bill Wagoner

D-U-N-S 00-306-2684
NATIONAL FRUIT PRODUCT CO INC
550 Fairmont Ave, Winchester, VA 22601-3931
Tel (540) 662-3401 *Founded/Ownrshp* 1908
Sales 197.1MM[E] *EMP* 550
SIC 0723 2033 2035 2099

D-U-N-S 00-698-8059
▲ **NATIONAL FUEL GAS CO** (NY)
6363 Main St, Williamsville, NY 14221-5887
Tel (716) 857-7000 *Founded/Ownrshp* 1902
Sales 1.4MMM *EMP* 2,125[E]
Accts Pricewaterhousecoopers Llp Bu
Tkr Sym NFG *Exch* NYS
SIC 4924 4922 1311 1382 Natural gas distribution; Pipelines, natural gas; Storage, natural gas; Natural gas production; Oil & gas exploration services
Pr: Ronald J Tanski
**Ch Bd:* David F Smith
COO: John P McGinnis
COO: John R Pustulka
CFO: David P Bauer
VP: Paula Ciprich
VP: Jay Lesch
VP: Robert Sauer
VP: Ann Wegrzyn
Ex Dir: Kevin Cotter
Genl Mgr: Ray Boy
Board of Directors: Thomas E Skains, Philip C Ackerman, David C Carroll, R Don Cash, Stephen E Ewing, Joseph N Jaggers, Ronald W Jibson, Craig G Matthews, Rebecca Ranich, Jeffrey W Shaw

D-U-N-S 00-697-6666
■ **NATIONAL FUEL GAS DISTRIBUTION CORP** (NY)
(*Suby of* NATIONAL FUEL GAS CO) ★
6363 Main St, Williamsville, NY 14221-5887
Tel (716) 857-7000 *Founded/Ownrshp* 1973
Sales 696.3MM[E] *EMP* 1,267[E]
SIC 4925 Gas production and/or distribution
Pr: Anna M Cellino
**Ch Bd:* Rj Tanski
Genl Mgr: Patricia Galbo
Plnt Mgr: Jennifer Schaller
Snr Mgr: Ruth Friedrich-Alf

D-U-N-S 00-791-2959
■ **NATIONAL FUEL GAS SUPPLY CORP** (PA)
(*Suby of* NATIONAL FUEL GAS CO) ★
6363 Main St, Williamsville, NY 14221-5887
Tel (716) 857-7000 *Founded/Ownrshp* 1902, 1974
Sales 189.1MM *EMP* 312
SIC 4924 Natural gas distribution
Pr: Ronald J Tanski
**Ch:* David F Smith
**VP:* Matthew D Cabell
**VP:* John R Pustulka
**VP:* James D Ramsdell
Genl Mgr: Patricia Galbo

D-U-N-S 05-321-9924
NATIONAL FUNDING INC
9820 Towne Centre Dr # 200, San Diego, CA 92121-1944
Tel (888) 576-4685 *Founded/Ownrshp* 1999
Sales NA *EMP* 135
SIC 6153 6159 7389

D-U-N-S 79-180-3885 IMP
NATIONAL FURNITURE LIQUIDATORS I LLC
NFL OFFICEWORKS
2865 Log Cabin Dr Se, Atlanta, GA 30339-1568
Tel (404) 872-7280 *Founded/Ownrshp* 1992
Sales 137.5MM[E] *EMP* 50
SIC 5021 5712 5932 Furniture; Office furniture; Furniture stores; Office furniture; Office furniture, secondhand
Pr: Rick Robillard
**CEO:* William Jones
**VP:* Tim Butler

D-U-N-S 05-239-4764
NATIONAL FUTURES ASSOCIATION (INC)
N F A
300 S Riverside Plz # 1800, Chicago, IL 60606-6615
Tel (312) 781-1300 *Founded/Ownrshp* 1982
Sales 92.5MM *EMP* 500
Accts Grant Thornton Llp Chicago I
SIC 8611 Regulatory associations
Pr: Daniel Roth
**COO:* Daniel Driscoll
**Ch:* Christopher Hehmeyer
**Treas:* David Hawrysz
Assoc Dir: Tom Sexton
Snr Mgr: Tracey Hunt

D-U-N-S 02-187-0837 IMP
■ **NATIONAL GALLERY OF ART**
(*Suby of* EXECUTIVE OFFICE OF UNITED STATES GOVERNMENT) ★
6th And Cnsttution Ave Nw, Washington, DC 20565-0001
Tel (202) 737-4215 *Founded/Ownrshp* 1941
Sales 146.8MM *EMP* 1,000
Accts Kpmg Llp Washington Dc
SIC 5942 8412 Book stores; Art gallery, noncommercial
Ch: John Wilmerding
**Pr:* Victoria P Sant
**Pr:* Robert H Smith
Ofcr: Naomi Remes
Off Mgr: Susanne Cook
Off Mgr: Carol Koelemay
CIO: Greg Swift
IT Man: Chris Caldwell
IT Man: Barbara McNair
IT Man: Kristhian Senzano
Netwrk Eng: Ward Meier

D-U-N-S 12-818-3725
NATIONAL GALVANIZING LP
1500 Telb St, Monroe, MI 48162-2572
Tel (734) 243-1882 *Founded/Ownrshp* 1983
Sales 174.4MM[E] *EMP* 1,000
SIC 3312 3316 3471 3341 5051 Sheet or strip, steel, hot-rolled; Strip steel, cold-rolled: from purchased hot-rolled; Plating & polishing; Secondary nonferrous metals; Metals service centers & offices
Prin: Mike Robinson

NATIONAL GARDEN WHOLESALE
See SUNLIGHT SUPPLY INC

D-U-N-S 96-191-8468
▲ **NATIONAL GENERAL HOLDINGS CORP**
59 Maiden Ln Fl 38, New York, NY 10038-4502
Tel (212) 380-9500 *Founded/Ownrshp* 2009
Sales NA *EMP* 7,083[E]
Tkr Sym NGHC *Exch* NGM
SIC 6411 Insurance agents, brokers & service; Fire insurance underwriters' laboratories; Patrol services, insurance
Pr: Barry S Karfunkel
Ch Bd: Barry Zyskind
COO: Peter Rendall
CFO: Michael Weiner
Chf Mktg O: Robert Karfunkel
Ofcr: George Hall
Ex VP: Brenda Castellano
Ex VP: Doug Hanes
VP: Susan Eylward
CIO: Leslie Leb
Board of Directors: Ephraim Brecher, Donald T Decarlo, Patrick Fallon, Barbara Paris, Barry Zyskind

D-U-N-S 07-942-0838
NATIONAL GENERAL INSURANCE
59 Maiden Ln Fl 38, New York, NY 10038-4502
Tel (212) 380-9477 *Founded/Ownrshp* 2014
Sales NA *EMP* 500[E]
SIC 6411 Insurance agents, brokers & service; Insurance agents & brokers
Prin: Kevin Bailey
Prin: Matthew Milner
Netwrk Mgr: Jeff Richterkessing
VP Sls: Brian Macias

D-U-N-S 61-031-8763
■ **NATIONAL GENERAL LENDER SERVICES INC**
QBE FINANCIAL INSTITUTION
(*Suby of* NATIONAL GENERAL HOLDINGS CORP) ★
210 Interstate N Pkwy, Atlanta, GA 30339-2230
Tel (770) 690-8400 *Founded/Ownrshp* 2015
Sales 211.4MM[E] *EMP* 1,356
SIC 6719 Investment holding companies, except banks
CEO: David Duclos
CFO: John Fitzgerald
Ex VP: Matthew Freeman
Sr VP: John Anderson
VP: Eric Laton
VP: John Tomko
Prin: C D Davies

D-U-N-S 15-029-8131
■ **NATIONAL GENERAL MANAGEMENT CORP**
GMAC INSURANCE
(*Suby of* NATIONAL GENERAL HOLDINGS CORP) ★
5630 University Pkwy, Winston Salem, NC 27105-1312
Tel (336) 435-3164 *Founded/Ownrship* 2010
Sales NA *EMP* 400
SIC 6411 Insurance agents, brokers & service
Pr: Gary Kusumi
**VP:* Don Bolar
**VP:* George Hall
VP: Renee Kero
VP: Rick Pierce
Brnch Mgr: Sandra Mason
IT Man: Tom McKinney
IT Man: Rusty Whiteheart
Netwrk Eng: Chip Durham
Sls Dir: Rob Owen
Sls Mgr: Nicole Luciano

NATIONAL GEOGRAPHIC CHANNEL
See NATIONAL GEOGRAPHIC SOCIETY

D-U-N-S 00-324-7756 IMP/EXP
NATIONAL GEOGRAPHIC SOCIETY (DC)
NATIONAL GEOGRAPHIC CHANNEL
1145 17th St Nw, Washington, DC 20036-4707
Tel (202) 857-7000 *Founded/Ownrshp* 1888
Sales 593.1MM[E] *EMP* 1,700
SIC 2721

D-U-N-S 61-480-8681
■ **NATIONAL GEOSPATIAL-INTELLIGENCE AGENCY**
N G A
(*Suby of* OFFICE OF THE SECRETARY OF DEFENSE) ★
4600 Sangamore Rd, Bethesda, MD 20816-5004
Tel (703) 262-4316 *Founded/Ownrshp* 1947
Sales NA *EMP* 8,500
SIC 9711 National security;
Exec: Robert Murrett
COO: Ellen E McCarthy
CIO: Robert H Laurine
IT Man: James Stephens
Snr Mgr: Patricia Curtis
Snr Mgr: Don Self

D-U-N-S 80-844-5803
NATIONAL GOLF PROPERTIES LLC
2951 28th St Ste 3000, Santa Monica, CA 90405-2987
Tel (310) 664-4000 *Founded/Ownrshp* 2003
Sales 13.9MM[E] *EMP* 1,040
SIC 6519 8111 Real property lessors; Legal services
Pr: Charles S Paul
CFO: Keith Brown

D-U-N-S 80-789-9653
■ **NATIONAL GOVERNMENT SERVICES INC**
(*Suby of* BLUE CROSS) ★
8115 Knue Rd, Indianapolis, IN 46250-1936
Tel (317) 841-4400 *Founded/Ownrshp* 1991
Sales 157.2MM[E] *EMP* 2,200
SIC 8099 Medical services organization
Ch Bd: Angela Braley
**Pr:* Michael Kapp
**CFO:* Jim Maguire
**Treas:* R David Kretschmer
**VP:* Jeff Hannah
**VP:* Mary Ludden
**VP:* Dave Marshall
**VP:* Tim Masheck
**VP:* Wendy Perkins
**CIO:* Frank Lasota
Snr PM: Tracy Lynch

D-U-N-S 79-115-2312
NATIONAL GRANGE MUTUAL INSURANCE CO
MGM
(*Suby of* MAIN STREET AMERICA GROUP) ★
55 West St, Keene, NH 03431-3348
Tel (603) 358-6517 *Founded/Ownrshp* 2007
Sales NA *EMP* 227[E]
SIC 6411 Insurance agents, brokers & service
CEO: Thomas M Van Berkel

D-U-N-S 00-194-0758 IMP/EXP
NATIONAL GRAPE CO-OPERATIVE ASSOCIATION INC
80 State St, Westfield, NY 14787
Tel (716) 326-5200 *Founded/Ownrshp* 1945
Sales 608.4MM *EMP* 1,325
Accts Kpmg Llp Boston Ma
SIC 2033 2037 Fruit juices: packaged in cans, jars, etc.; Fruit juices: concentrated, hot pack; Tomato juice: packaged in cans, jars, etc.; Jams, jellies & preserves: packaged in cans, jars, etc.; Frozen fruits & vegetables; Fruit juices, frozen; Fruit juice concentrates, frozen
Pr: Randolph Graham
Trst Ofcr: Craig Bardwell
**VP:* Joseph C Falcone
**VP:* Harold Smith

NATIONAL GRID
See MASSACHUSETTS ELECTRIC CO

NATIONAL GRID
See NIAGARA MOHAWK POWER CORP

NATIONAL GRID
See KEYSPAN GAS EAST CORP

D-U-N-S 84-474-9010 IMP
NATIONAL GRID CORPORATE SERVICES LLC
KEYSPAN ENERGY
(*Suby of* KEYSPAN CORP) ★
175 E Old Country Rd, Hicksville, NY 11801-4257
Tel (718) 403-2000 *Founded/Ownrshp* 2007
Sales 6.1MMM[E] *EMP* 9,594
SIC 4924 4911 1311 4922 Natural gas distribution; Distribution, electric power; Generation, electric power; Transmission, electric power; Crude petroleum & natural gas; Natural gas transmission; Pipelines, natural gas; Storage, natural gas
Ch: Peter Gershon Cbe
CEO: Steve Holliday Freng
Ex VP: John A Caroselli
Ex VP: Ellen Smith
Sr VP: James Madej
Sr VP: Colin Owyang
VP: Robert Demarinis
VP: Brian Noone
VP: Nereida Perez
VP: Martin Wheatcroft
IT Man: Kenneth Mackin
Board of Directors: Colin Owyang

D-U-N-S 83-041-0150
NATIONAL GRID ENERGY CORP
(*Suby of* KEYSPAN CORP) ★
1 Metrotech Ctr Fl 1, Brooklyn, NY 11201-3850
Tel (718) 403-2000 *Founded/Ownrshp* 2009
Sales 490.0MM[E] *EMP* 500
SIC 8748 Business consulting
VP: Michael Nilsen

D-U-N-S 08-617-3403 IMP
NATIONAL GRID GENERATION LLC
(*Suby of* KEYSPAN CORP) ★
175 E Old Country Rd, Hicksville, NY 11801-4257
Tel (631) 755-6650 *Founded/Ownrshp* 1998
Sales 87.3MM[E] *EMP* 200
SIC 4924 Natural gas distribution
Pr: John Gregory Cochrane
**Treas:* Malcolm Charles Cooper
**VP:* Robert Teetz
Board of Directors: Colin Owyang

D-U-N-S 09-004-7122
NATIONAL GRID SERVICES INC (NY)
(*Suby of* NATIONAL GRID ENERGY CORP) ★
1 Metrotech Ctr Fl 1, Brooklyn, NY 11201-3850
Tel (718) 403-2000 *Founded/Ownrshp* 1998
Sales 377.2MM[E] *EMP* 450
SIC 4924 Natural gas distribution
Ch Bd: John G Cochrane
**CEO:* Wallace P Parker Jr
VP: Elaine Weinstein
IT Man: Chris Hantzschel
Software D: Philip Lembo
Sftwr Eng: Kwok Chow

D-U-N-S 82-993-7965
NATIONAL GRID USA
(*Suby of* NATIONAL GRID PLC)
40 Sylvan Rd, Waltham, MA 02451-1120
Tel (781) 907-1000 *Founded/Ownrshp* 1999
Sales 19.4MMM[E] *EMP* 18,100[E]
SIC 4911 Transmission, electric power
CEO: John Pettigrew
Pr: Kenneth Daly
**Pr:* Thomas B King
**Pr:* Dean Seavers
**COO:* Ellen Smith
**CFO:* Linda Claire Ryan
**Treas:* Malcolm Charles Cooper
**Chf Cred:* David Lodemore
Ofcr: Ray Schlaff
**Ex VP:* John A Caroselli
VP: Stan Blazewicz
VP: Elisabeth Coleman
**VP:* Christopher McConnachie
VP: Brian Noone
VP: David Way
Board of Directors: Lisa Crutchfield, Thomas King, Colin Owyang, Andrew Sloey, Ellen Smith, Nickolas Stavropoulos

D-U-N-S 00-695-2840 IMP
NATIONAL GRID USA SERVICE CO INC
(*Suby of* NATIONAL GRID USA) ★
40 Sylvan Rd, Waltham, MA 02451-1120
Tel (800) 260-0054 *Founded/Ownrshp* 1926
Sales 9.9MMM[E] *EMP* 18,100
SIC 4911 1311 Generation, electric power; Transmission, electric power; Distribution, electric power; Crude petroleum production; Natural gas production
Pr: Thomas B King
Pr: Vivienne Bracken
CFO: Kenneth D Daly
Treas: Malcolm Charles Cooper
Treas: Lorraine Lynch
Ex VP: John A Caroselli
Sr VP: William J Akley
Sr VP: Colin Owyang
VP: Sue Mais
VP: Martin Wheatcroft
VP: Bradley White

NATIONAL GRINDING WHEEL
See RADIAC ABRASIVES INC

NATIONAL GUARD
See WEST VIRGINIA DEPARTMENT OF MILITARY AFFAIRS AND PUBLIC SAFETY

NATIONAL GUARD & ADJUTANT GEN
See NORTH DAKOTA DEPARTMENT OF MILITARY AFFAIRS

D-U-N-S 78-958-8191
NATIONAL GUARD DELAWARE
ARMY NATIONAL GUARD, DELAWARE
(*Suby of* EXECUTIVE OFFICE OF GOVERNOR OF DELAWARE) ★
250 Airport Rd, New Castle, DE 19720-1502
Tel (302) 326-7160 *Founded/Ownrshp* 1787
Sales NA *EMP* 2,000
SIC 9711 National Guard;

D-U-N-S 09-748-2470
NATIONAL GUARD NORTH CAROLINA
(*Suby of* NORTH CAROLINA DEPARTMENT OF PUBLIC SAFETY) ★
1636 Gold Star Dr, Raleigh, NC 27607-3371
Tel (919) 664-6000 *Founded/Ownrshp* 1975
Sales NA *EMP* 11,500[E]
SIC 9711 National Guard;

NATIONAL GUARD OF NEW MEXICO
See NEW MEXICO DEPT OF MILITARY AFFAIRS

D-U-N-S 08-109-9710
NATIONAL GUARD UTAH
(*Suby of* EXECUTIVE OFFICE OF STATE OF UTAH) ★
12953 S Minuteman Dr, Draper, UT 84020-9286
Tel (801) 432-4439 *Founded/Ownrshp* 1763
Sales NA *EMP* 6,381
SIC 9711 National Guard;
Genl Mgr: Karma Bentson

D-U-N-S 00-794-6379
NATIONAL GUARDIAN LIFE INSURANCE CO (INC) (WI)
2 E Gilman St Stop 1, Madison, WI 53703-1480
Tel (608) 257-5611 *Founded/Ownrshp* 1909
Sales NA *EMP* 270[E]
SIC 6311 Mutual association life insurance
Pr: John D Larson
Pr: Tracy Fritz
Pr: Mike Wiley
COO: Jessica Oehrlein
CFO: Brian J Hogan
**Treas:* Robert A Mucci
Ofcr: John Egan
Ofcr: Jerie Olson
VP: Joseph Freitas
VP: Walter Lethem
**VP:* Timothy J Nicholson
**VP:* Mark Solverud
VP: Casey Wolfe

NATIONAL GYPSUM COMPANY
See NEW NGC INC

NATIONAL HEADQUARTERS
See CIVIL AIR PATROL INC

D-U-N-S 93-187-3004
NATIONAL HEALTH CARE AFFILIATES INC
(*Suby of* HAMISTER GROUP LLC) ★
10 Lafayette Sq Ste 1900, Buffalo, NY 14203-1801
Tel (716) 839-4000 *Founded/Ownrshp* 1997
Sales 16.7MM[E] *EMP* 2,500
SIC 8082 8052 Home health care services; Intermediate care facilities
Pr: Jack Turesky
Ch Bd: Mark Hamister
IT Man: Craig Adams
IT Man: Carl Yost

D-U-N-S 86-100-8035
NATIONAL HEALTH CARE ASSOCIATES INC
NHCA
20 E Sunrise Hwy Unit 1, Valley Stream, NY 11581-1256
Tel (516) 705-4800 *Founded/Ownrshp* 1984
Sales 326.1MM[E] *EMP* 5,500[E]
SIC 8741 Hospital management; Nursing & personal care facility management
Pr: Marvin Ostreicher
VP: Barry Bokow
VP: Trish Thomas
Comm Dir: Tim Brown
Rgnl Mgr: Nunzio Incorvaia
Off Mgr: Andrew Wildman
IT Man: Uuan Grant
Mktg Dir: Jennifer Kennedy
Mktg Dir: Suzanne Plourde
Pr Dir: Elza Augustin
Nrsg Dir: Janet Azulay
Board of Directors: Susan Ostreicher

D-U-N-S 02-690-0068
■ **NATIONAL HEALTH INDUSTRIES INC**
(*Suby of* ALMOST FAMILY INC) ★
9510 Ormsby Station Rd # 300, Louisville, KY 40223-4081
Tel (502) 448-5862 *Founded/Ownrshp* 1991
Sales 49.4MM[E] *EMP* 2,200
SIC 8082 Home health care services
Pr: William B Yarmuth
**CFO:* C Steven Guenthner
**Sr VP:* Todd Lyles
**Sr VP:* Rick Pritchard
**Sr VP:* Mary A Yarmuth

NATIONAL HEALTH INFO NETWRK
See PDX INC

D-U-N-S 78-813-4542
▲ **NATIONAL HEALTH INVESTORS INC**
NHI
222 Robert Rose Dr, Murfreesboro, TN 37129-6346
Tel (615) 890-9100 *Founded/Ownrshp* 1991
Sales 228.9MM *EMP* 12
Tkr Sym NHI *Exch* NYS
SIC 6798 Real estate investment trusts
Pr: D Eric Mendelsohn
**Ch Bd:* W Andrew Adams
Chf Cred: Kristin S Gaines
Ex VP: John L Spaid

D-U-N-S 06-910-0097
▲ **NATIONAL HEALTHCARE CORP** (TN)
100 E Vine St, Murfreesboro, TN 37130-3734
Tel (615) 890-2020 *Founded/Ownrshp* 1971
Sales 906.6MM *EMP* 13,225[E]
Tkr Sym NHC *Exch* ASE
SIC 8051 8082 Skilled nursing care facilities; Home health care services
Ch Bd: Robert G Adams
Pr: Stephen F Flatt
Pr: Dinsie Hale
COO: Michael Ussery
Treas: Charlotte A Swafford
Sr VP: Donald K Daniel
Sr VP: John K Lines
IT Man: Carolyn Hempfner
Board of Directors: J Paul Abernathy, W Andrew Adams, Ernest G Burgess III, Emil E Hassan, Richard F Laroche Jr, Lawrence C Tucker

D-U-N-S 36-123-6847
■ **NATIONAL HEALTHCARE OF CLEVELAND INC**
SKYRIDGE MEDICAL CENTER
(*Suby of* COMMUNITY HEALTH SYSTEMS INC) ★
4000 Meridian Blvd, Franklin, TN 37067-6325
Tel (423) 339-4100 *Founded/Ownrshp* 1986
Sales 52.6MM[E] *EMP* 1,000
SIC 8062 General medical & surgical hospitals
CFO: Coleman Foss
CFO: Bill Zeismer
Exec: Kristine Godfrey

D-U-N-S 96-074-2484
NATIONAL HERITAGE ACADEMIES INC
N H A
3850 Broadmoor Ave Se # 201, Grand Rapids, MI 49512-3975
Tel (877) 223-6402 *Founded/Ownrshp* 1995
Sales 357.9MM[E] *EMP* 4,500
SIC 8211 8741 Private elementary & secondary schools; Management services
Pr: Brian Britton
Pt: Robert J Bellafiore
**Ch Bd:* J C Huizenga
**Pr:* Harry Hurlburt III
**CFO:* Stephen Conley
VP: Mark Dehaan
VP: Nick Paradiso
VP: Thea Reigler
Dir IT: Susan Mills
IT Man: Jim Hines

D-U-N-S 17-655-3402
■ **NATIONAL HOLDINGS CORP**
(*Suby of* FORTRESS BIOTECH, INC.)
410 Park Ave Fl 14, New York, NY 10022-9442
Tel (212) 417-8000 *Founded/Ownrshp* 2016
Sales 163.0MM *EMP* 352[E]
Tkr Sym NHLD *Exch* NAS
SIC 6719 Investment holding companies, except banks
CEO: Robert Fagenson
CFO: Alan B Levin
Chf Cred: Kay Johnson

D-U-N-S 11-543-5935
NATIONAL HOME HEALTH CARE CORP
(*Suby of* A G HOME HEALTH LLC) ★
700 White Plains Rd Ste 2, Scarsdale, NY 10583-5013
Tel (914) 722-9000 *Founded/Ownrshp* 2007
Sales 78.2MM[E] *EMP* 3,680
SIC 8082 7361 Home health care services; Employment agencies
CEO: Stan Dennis
**CFO:* Robert P Heller
CTO: Jason Pickman

D-U-N-S 07-412-2078
NATIONAL HOT ROD ASSOCIATION
NHRA
2035 E Financial Way, Glendora, CA 91741-4602
Tel (626) 914-4761 *Founded/Ownrshp* 1951
Sales 99.2MM *EMP* 220
Accts Moss Adams Llp Stockton Ca
SIC 7948 2711 2741 Automotive race track operation; Newspapers: publishing only, not printed on site; Miscellaneous publishing
V Ch: Harvey Palash
Pr: Tom Compton
CFO: Peter Clifford
Treas: Kurt Wolfe
Sr VP: Gary Darcy
VP: Glen Gray
VP: Linda Louie
VP: Brian Tracy
Opers Mgr: Pete Chipana
Mktg Dir: Lori Bollas
Mktg Mgr: Michael Rau

NATIONAL HOT WATER
See NATIONAL WHOLESALE SUPPLY INC

D-U-N-S 00-697-0354
■ **NATIONAL INDEMNITY CO (INC)** (NE)
(*Suby of* BERKSHIRE HATHAWAY INC) ★
1314 Douglas St Ste 1400, Omaha, NE 68102-1944
Tel (402) 916-3000 *Founded/Ownrshp* 1940, 1967
Sales NA *EMP* 650
SIC 6331 6411 6311 Fire, marine & casualty insurance: stock; Insurance agents, brokers & service; Property & casualty insurance agent; Insurance claim processing, except medical; Life insurance
Ch Bd: Marc Hamberg
Pr: Rodney Rathbun
**Pr:* Donald F Wurster
**V Ch Bd:* Michael A Goldberg
VP: Lori Cleary
VP: Phillip Wolf
VP: Tom Young
Dir IT: Dennis Halloran
IT Man: Doug Deden
Snr Mgr: Kevin Trojan

D-U-N-S 03-203-9724 IMP
NATIONAL INDUSTRIAL CONCEPTS INC
NIC GLOBAL
23518 63rd Ave Se, Woodinville, WA 98072-8664
Tel (425) 489-4300 *Founded/Ownrshp* 2000
Sales 95.0MM[E] *EMP* 350
SIC 3444 Sheet metalwork
Pr: Bridget Brewer
Treas: William King
VP: Michael Ryan
VP: Troy Wood

D-U-N-S 05-545-8350
NATIONAL INFORMATION SOLUTIONS COOPERATIVE INC
NISC
1 Innovation Cir, Lake Saint Louis, MO 63367-2649
Tel (636) 755-2300 *Founded/Ownrshp* 2000
Sales 150.0MM *EMP* 850
SIC 7374 Data processing service
Pr: Vern Dosch
**COO:* Dan Wilbanks
**CFO:* Tracy Porter
VP: David Bonnett
**VP:* Todd Eisenhauer
VP: Wally Goulet
**VP:* Doug Remboldt
**VP:* Ed Wolff
Snr Sftwr: Rebekah Morales
Snr Sftwr: Dawn Schumacher
CTO: Sean Wiese

D-U-N-S 92-933-2385
■ **NATIONAL INSTITUTE OF FOOD AND AGRICULTURE**
NIFA
(*Suby of* U S D A) ★
1400 Independence Ave Sw, Washington, DC 20250-0002
Tel (202) 720-4276 *Founded/Ownrshp* 1914
Sales NA *EMP* 5,743[E]
SIC 9641 Regulation of agricultural marketing;

D-U-N-S 92-995-6050 IMP
■ **NATIONAL INSTITUTE OF STANDARDS & TECHNOLOGY**
NIST
(*Suby of* US DOC) ★
100 Bureau Dr Stop 1070, Gaithersburg, MD 20899-0003
Tel (301) 975-6478 *Founded/Ownrshp* 1901
Sales NA *EMP* 3,000
SIC 9611
CFO: George E Jenkins
Exec: Joseph W Hodges
Assoc Dir: Kent Rochford
Assoc Dir: Mary H Saunders
Assoc Dir: Phillip Singerman
Adm Dir: Susan Loar
Admn Mgr: Herb Jones
CIO: Daniel Benigni
CIO: Delwin Brockett
CIO: Thomas Chung
CIO: Charles L Eater

D-U-N-S 92-764-5168 IMP
■ **NATIONAL INSTITUTES OF HEALTH**
N I H
(*Suby of* UNITED STATES DEPARTMENT OF HEALTH & HUMAN SERVICES) ★
9000 Rockville Pike # 1, Bethesda, MD 20892-0001
Tel (301) 496-4000 *Founded/Ownrshp* 1954
Sales 2.8MMM[E] *EMP* 19,000
SIC 8062 9431 General medical & surgical hospitals;
Dir Recs: Tricia Coffey
Pr: David Lisle
Ofcr: Marsha Hennings
Exec: Valery Gheen
Assoc Dir: Mark Chavez
Assoc Dir: Jason Paragas
Adm Dir: Virginia Betson
Adm Dir: Darlene Blocker
Adm Dir: Mitzi Diley
Adm Dir: Lisa Freeny
Adm Dir: Kathleen Grillo

D-U-N-S 07-048-7657
▲ **NATIONAL INSTRUMENTS CORP**
11500 N Mopac Expy, Austin, TX 78759-3563
Tel (512) 338-9119 *Founded/Ownrshp* 1976
Sales 1.2MMM *EMP* 7,441
Tkr Sym NATI *Exch* NGS
SIC 7372 Prepackaged software; Application computer software
Ch Bd: James J Truchard
COO: Alexander M Davern
Ex VP: Eric H Starkloff
Sr VP: Scott A Rust
VP: Rick Bush
VP: David Fuller
VP: Matthew Viele
Snr Sftwr: Shawn Ebert
Snr Sftwr: Ciro Nishiguchi
Snr Sftwr: Bobby Thurman
Snr Sftwr: Nicolas Vazquez
Board of Directors: John M Berra, Donald M Carlton, Gerhard P Fettweis, Jeffrey L Kodosky, Michael E McGrath, Charles J Roesslein

NATIONAL INTERAD
See COBALT GROUP INC

D-U-N-S 62-607-6707
■ **NATIONAL INTERSTATE CORP**
(*Suby of* AMERICAN FINANCIAL GROUP INC) ★
3250 Interstate Dr, Richfield, OH 44286-9000
Tel (330) 659-8900 *Founded/Ownrshp* 2016
Sales NA *EMP* 715[E]
SIC 6331 6411 Fire, marine & casualty insurance; Property & casualty insurance agent
Pr: Anthony J Mercurio
CFO: Julie A McGraw
Sr VP: Arthur J Gonzales
Sr VP: Terry E Phillips
VP: Gary N Monda

D-U-N-S 36-462-4205
■ **NATIONAL INTERSTATE INSURANCE CO**
(*Suby of* NATIONAL INTERSTATE CORP) ★
3250 Interstate Dr, Richfield, OH 44286-9000
Tel (330) 659-8900 *Founded/Ownrshp* 1989
Sales NA *EMP* 310
Accts Ernst & Young Llp Cleveland
SIC 6331 Fire, marine & casualty insurance
Ch: Alan R Spachman
**Pr:* David W Michelson
**Treas:* Arthur M Kraus

VP: Arthur Gonzales
VP: Julie McGraw
Dir IT: Vicki L Rockwell
Dir IT: Ron Steiger
Netwrk Mgr: Angelo Fortunato
Corp Couns: Thomas King

NATIONAL INVESTIGATION & PROTE
See ST JAMES SECURITY SERVICES INC

D-U-N-S 07-644-3019
NATIONAL JEWISH HEALTH
1400 Jackson St, Denver, CO 80206-2762
Tel (303) 388-4461 *Founded/Ownrshp* 2005
Sales 161.8MM *EMP* 1,500^E
SIC 8062

D-U-N-S 00-228-3547 IMP
NATIONAL LABEL CO
2025 Joshua Rd, Lafayette Hill, PA 19444-2426
Tel (610) 825-3250 *Founded/Ownrshp* 1914
Sales 187.1MM^E *EMP* 285
SIC 2672 2679 2759 2671 Labels (unprinted), gummed: made from purchased materials; Tape, pressure sensitive: made from purchased materials; Paper products, converted; Commercial printing; Packaging paper & plastics film, coated & laminated
Prin: Jim H Shacklett III
**COO:* Dean R Shacklett
**Prin:* Jim H Shacklett III
Sls Dir: Joseph Bird

D-U-N-S 00-325-6633
■ NATIONAL LABOR RELATIONS BOARD
(*Suby of* EXECUTIVE OFFICE OF UNITED STATES GOVERNMENT) ★
1015 Half St Se, Washington, DC 20003-3654
Tel (202) 273-3884 *Founded/Ownrshp* 1935
Sales NA *EMP* 1,800
SIC 9651 Labor-management negotiations board, government;
Ch: Mark Gaston Pierce
Admn Mgr: Annette Burrelaao
Sales Exec: Sydney Lee

D-U-N-S 05-783-0879
■ NATIONAL LIABILITY & FIRE INSURANCE CO
(*Suby of* BERKSHIRE HATHAWAY INC) ★
3024 Harney St, Omaha, NE 68131-3535
Tel (402) 536-3000 *Founded/Ownrshp* 1958
Sales NA *EMP* 30
SIC 6411 Insurance agents, brokers & service
Pr: Donald F Wurster
**Treas:* Dale Geistkemper
**VP:* Leslie J Baller
**VP:* J Michael Gottschalk
**VP:* Forrest N Krutter
**VP:* Philip M Wolf
Dir IT: Ty Reil
Board of Directors: Warren E Buffett, Michael A Goldberg, Ajit Jain, Barry L Kroll, Forrest N Krutter, Charles B Montgomery, Robert D O'connell, Lloyd E Williams Jr, Donald F Wurster

NATIONAL LIFE GROUP
See NATIONAL LIFE HOLDING CO

D-U-N-S 17-641-0939
NATIONAL LIFE HOLDING CO
NATIONAL LIFE GROUP
1 National Life Dr, Montpelier, VT 05604-1000
Tel (802) 229-3333 *Founded/Ownrshp* 1998
Sales NA *EMP* 850
SIC 6311 6321 Mutual association life insurance; Accident insurance carriers; Health insurance carriers
CEO: Mehran Assadi
**Ch Bd:* Thomas H Mac Leay
Pr: Chris Graff
Pr: Christina Johnson
**Treas:* Donald P Messier
**Sr VP:* Tom Anfuso
Sr VP: Gregory Woodworth
VP: Graff Chris
VP: Stephen Farr
VP: Michelle Jones
VP: Tammy King
VP: Eric Lopez
VP: Elizabeth Macgowan
VP: Angela McCraw
VP: Vicki McDonald
VP: Beth Rusnock
VP: David Soccodato
VP: Andrew Speirs

D-U-N-S 00-793-9572
NATIONAL LIFE INSURANCE CO
NATIONAL LIFE OF VERMONT
(*Suby of* NATIONAL LIFE GROUP) ★
1 National Life Dr, Montpelier, VT 05604-0001
Tel (802) 229-3333 *Founded/Ownrshp* 1850, 1999
Sales NA *EMP* 850
SIC 6311 Life insurance
Pr: Mehran Assadi
**Ch Bd:* Thomas H Macleay
Pr: Jim Carroll
Pr: Mike Duncan
**CFO:* Edward Bonach
**Treas:* Robert Cotton
**Treas:* Mary Eileen Vongal
Ofcr: Mary M Lee
Ofcr: Eddie Rousse
Assoc VP: Mike Carter
**Ex VP:* Wade Mayo
**Ex VP:* Ruth B Smith
Ex VP: Ruth Smith
**Ex VP:* Christian Thwaites
Sr VP: Pamela Blalock
**Sr VP:* Thomas H Brownell
Sr VP: Jay Bugg
Sr VP: Matthew Desantos
**Sr VP:* Allen N Hanson
**Sr VP:* Richard Pederson
**Sr VP:* Gregory D Woodworth

NATIONAL LIFE OF VERMONT
See NATIONAL LIFE INSURANCE CO

D-U-N-S 00-503-8336
NATIONAL LIME AND STONE CO
551 Lake Cascade Pkwy, Findley, OH 45840-1388
Tel (419) 422-4341 *Founded/Ownrshp* 1903
Sales 4.0MMM^E *EMP* 320
SIC 1422 1442 3273 1423 1499

D-U-N-S 06-848-8626
NATIONAL LOUIS UNIVERSITY
122 S Michigan Ave # 600, Chicago, IL 60603-6162
Tel (312) 261-3599 *Founded/Ownrshp* 1886
Sales 69.0MM *EMP* 2,300
SIC 8221 8211

D-U-N-S 00-257-7732 IMP/EXP
NATIONAL LUMBER CO
DO IT BEST
245 Oakland St, Mansfield, MA 02048-1554
Tel (508) 337-8020 *Founded/Ownrshp* 1955
Sales 124.5MM^E *EMP* 400
SIC 5211 2431 Millwork & lumber; Insulation material, building; Siding; Roofing material; Millwork
CEO: Marjorie Kaitz
**CEO:* Steven Kaitz
**CFO:* Louis Kaitz
**VP:* John Intravaia
**VP:* Michael McDole
**VP:* Marc Osborne Mr
VP: Mark Osborn
**VP:* David M Pelletier
Exec: Bob Nickerson
CIO: Marc Osborne
Dir IT: Ted Pensfield

D-U-N-S 04-811-2213 IMP
NATIONAL MACHINE CO
NMG AEROSPACE
(*Suby of* ELECTROMOTIVE INC) ★
4880 Hudson Dr, Stow, OH 44224-1799
Tel (330) 688-6494 *Founded/Ownrshp* 1967
Sales 158.3MM^E *EMP* 400
Accts Bober Markey Fedorovich Co
SIC 3599 3492 Machine shop, jobbing & repair; Control valves, fluid power: hydraulic & pneumatic
Ch: Peter Piglia
**Pr:* Bill Anop
Pr: Brian Fakler
**CEO:* Michael Piglia
**CFO:* Jeffrey Bissell
VP: Jesse Dolan
VP: Tracy Konjovic
Dir Bus: Jeremy Earley
Genl Mgr: Tracey Bognar
Sfty Mgr: Jenni Ticer
Plnt Mgr: David Kubala

D-U-N-S 04-103-5788 IMP/EXP
NATIONAL MACHINERY LLC
(*Suby of* NM GROUP GLOBAL LLC) ★
161 Greenfield St, Tiffin, OH 44883-2471
Tel (419) 447-5211 *Founded/Ownrshp* 2002
Sales 104.4MM^E *EMP* 386
SIC 3542 Headers; High energy rate metal forming machines; Mechanical (pneumatic or hydraulic) metal forming machines
COO: John Bolte

D-U-N-S 00-526-3124 IMP/EXP
■ NATIONAL MANUFACTURING CO
STANLEY NATIONAL HARDWARE
(*Suby of* STANLEY BLACK & DECKER INC) ★
19701 Da Vinci, Foothill Ranch, CA 92610-2622
Tel (800) 346-9445 *Founded/Ownrshp* 1901, 2014
Sales 7.6MM^E *EMP* 1,660
SIC 3429

D-U-N-S 79-694-8487 IMP/EXP
NATIONAL MARINE SUPPLIERS INC
2800 Sw 2nd Ave, Fort Lauderdale, FL 33315-3120
Tel (954) 462-3131 *Founded/Ownrshp* 1990
Sales 117.0MM^E *EMP* 95
SIC 5088 Marine supplies
Pr: Dean Dutoit
CFO: Rita Dutoit
Store Mgr: Ivan Caro
IT Man: Anthony Nickel
Mktg Dir: Tom Rowe
Sales Asso: Ana Averza
Sales Asso: Gordon Demary
Sales Asso: Scott Dodgin

D-U-N-S 62-322-5737
NATIONAL MARROW DONOR PROGRAM INC
BE THE MATCH
500 N 5th St, Minneapolis, MN 55401-1206
Tel (612) 627-5800 *Founded/Ownrshp* 1987
Sales 397.6MM *EMP* 800^E
Accts Lb Eide Bailly Llp Minneapoli
SIC 8099 8742 Medical services organization; Management consulting services
CEO: Jeffrey W Chell
COO: Karen Dodson
CFO: Amy Ronneberg
Ofcr: Michael Boo
Sr VP: Tracy Schmidt
Prgrm Mgr: Nicole Haskins
Dir IT: Kyle Nelson
Dir IT: Ericka Wheeler
IT Man: Mary Frey
Opers Mgr: Kristin Naruko
Mktg Mgr: Michelle Kolb

D-U-N-S 18-329-5195 IMP/EXP
NATIONAL MATERIAL LP
NMLP
1965 Pratt Blvd, Elk Grove Village, IL 60007-5905
Tel (847) 806-7200 *Founded/Ownrshp* 1988
Sales 590.4MM^E *EMP* 2,500
SIC 5051 3469 3354 5093 4911 4924

D-U-N-S 80-925-5420 IMP
NATIONAL MATERIAL TRADING LLC
N M T
(*Suby of* NMLP) ★
1965 Pratt Blvd, Elk Grove Village, IL 60007-5905
Tel (847) 806-0990 *Founded/Ownrshp* 2005
Sales 11.2MM^E *EMP* 1,428^E
SIC 5051 Steel

D-U-N-S 83-157-5548
NATIONAL MEDICAL CARE INC
(*Suby of* FRESENIUS MEDICAL CARE NORTH) ★
920 Winter St Ste A, Waltham, MA 02451-1519
Tel (781) 699-9000 *Founded/Ownrshp* 1984
Sales 287.4MM *EMP* 16,761
SIC 8092 Kidney dialysis centers
CEO: Ronald Kuerbitz
**Pr:* Simon Castellanos
**Pr:* William J Valle
**CFO:* Angelo Moesslang
**Treas:* Mark Fawcett
**VP:* Jolene Varney

D-U-N-S 13-624-6043
NATIONAL MENTOR HOLDINGS INC
313 Congress St Fl 5, Boston, MA 02210-1218
Tel (617) 790-4800 *Founded/Ownrshp* 1980
Sales 1.2MMM *EMP* 20,200^E
SIC 8082 8361 Home health care services; Home for the mentally handicapped
CEO: Edward M Murphy
**Ch Bd:* Gregory T Torres
Pr: Bruce F Nardella
CFO: Denis M Holler
VP: Patti Maguire
CIO: Jeffrey M Cohen
Board of Directors: Chris A Durbin, James L Elrod Jr, Patrick M Gray, Pamela F Lenehan, Kevin A Mundt, Guy Sansone

D-U-N-S 15-779-2052
NATIONAL MENTOR INC
NEURORESTORATIVE
(*Suby of* NATIONAL MENTOR HOLDINGS INC) ★
313 Congress St Fl 5, Boston, MA 02210-1218
Tel (617) 790-4800 *Founded/Ownrshp* 2001
Sales 71.6MM^E *EMP* 1,655
SIC 8361 Residential care
Pr: Gregory Torres
COO: Bill Duffy
**Treas:* Donald Monack
Ex VP: Juliette Fay
**VP:* John Gillespie

NATIONAL MORTGAGE & FINANCE CO
See ISLAND HOLDINGS INC

D-U-N-S 07-105-0462
NATIONAL MULTIPLE SCLEROSIS SOCIETY (NY)
M S
733 3rd Ave Fl 3, New York, NY 10017-3211
Tel (212) 463-9791 *Founded/Ownrshp* 1946
Sales 105.7MM *EMP* 1,200
Accts Grant Thornton Llp New York
SIC 8322 Association for the handicapped
CEO: Cyndi Zagieboylo
Dir Vol: Sandra Baldi
Pt: Patti Radzik
**Ch Bd:* Neal S Grunstra
**Ch Bd:* Tom Kuhn
**Pr:* Joyce Nelson
**CFO:* Tami Caesar
CFO: Lisa Iris
**Treas:* Earl K Chism
Bd of Dir: Peter G Tarricone
Assoc VP: David Sobel
**Ex VP:* Bruce Bebo
**Ex VP:* Kathleen Costello
**Ex VP:* Sherri Giger
Ex VP: Linda Guiod
VP: Terry Bell
VP: Kristina Fransel
VP: Kristin Hesse
VP: Becca Kornfeld
VP: Shawn Oneail
VP: Traci Sassak
Board of Directors: Lori Leidholm, Chuck Riley, Mindy B Alpert, Thomas P Leist, Loren A Rolak, Donald Barone, Clyde Markowitz, Barbara Travis, Michael Brady, Bernadine Munley, Timothy L Vollmer, Kim Corna, Beth Norviel, Bill Whitaker, Jim Coulson, Elizabeth Pelley, Jacquelyn Dezort, J T Phillips Jr, Pamela Gray, Katherine S Ploessel, John Hall, Cynthia Pritchard, David Jones, Elizabeth Reeves

D-U-N-S 77-997-2033
NATIONAL MUSIC RACK INC
440a Boulevard Apt 1, Hasbrouck Heights, NJ 07604-1534
Tel (201) 641-8188 *Founded/Ownrshp* 1990
Sales 116.7MM^E *EMP* 1,000
SIC 5099 Phonograph records
Pr: Jeffrey Bitensky

D-U-N-S 94-708-2095 EXP
NATIONAL OAK DISTRIBUTORS INC
6529 Southern Blvd Ste 6, West Palm Beach, FL 33413-1735
Tel (561) 478-2711 *Founded/Ownrshp* 2000
Sales 287.6MM^E *EMP* 290
SIC 5013 5198 Automotive supplies & parts; Automotive servicing equipment; Automotive supplies; Paints, varnishes & supplies
Pr: Geoffrey S Peckham
Pr: Chuck Vanslaars
CFO: Greg Laffey
CFO: Marc Noland
**CFO:* Zachery Tapp
Rgnl Mgr: Edward Gross
Dir IT: Steve West
Opers Mgr: Brian Bronson
Sales Exec: Larry Ryan
Manager: George Hattaway
Manager: Mark Maves

D-U-N-S 16-003-6091
■ NATIONAL OCEAN SERVICE
(*Suby of* NATIONAL OCEANIC AND ATMOSPHERIC ADMINISTRATION) ★
1305 E West Hwy, Silver Spring, MD 20910-3278
Tel (301) 713-3074 *Founded/Ownrshp* 1970
Sales NA *EMP* 1,000^E
SIC 9511 Water control & quality agency, government;
CFO: Peter Gibson
CIO: Hugh Johnson

D-U-N-S 78-476-9085
■ NATIONAL OCEANIC AND ATMOSPHERIC ADMINISTRATION
(*Suby of* US DOC) ★
1305 Ew Hwy Fl 10, Silver Spring, MD 20910
Tel (301) 713-3155 *Founded/Ownrshp* 1970
Sales NA *EMP* 1,225^E
SIC 9611
**CFO:* Maureen Wylie
Ofcr: Elizabeth McLanahan
Creative D: Charles Rasak
Ex Dir: Jawed Hameedi
Admn Mgr: Kenneth Batty
Admn Mgr: Aubry Bhattarai
Admn Mgr: Scott Broo
Admn Mgr: Pam Bussey
Admn Mgr: Yi Chen
Admn Mgr: Caroline Corvington
Admn Mgr: Jenny Dissen

D-U-N-S 13-913-7611 IMP/EXP
■ NATIONAL OFFICE FURNITURE INC
(*Suby of* KIMBALL FURNITURE GROUP LLC) ★
1610 Royal St, Jasper, IN 47549-0001
Tel (812) 482-1600 *Founded/Ownrshp* 1969
Sales 168.0MM^E *EMP* 1,200^E
SIC 5712 Office furniture
Pr: Kevin McCoy
**VP:* Don Banwinkle
VP: Richard Farr
**VP:* Richard Fassar
VP: Michael Roch
VP: Don Vanwinkle
Area Mgr: Mike Dekemper
Dist Mgr: Jessica Barrios
Dist Mgr: Linda Barry
Dist Mgr: Halina Blaszkowiak
Dist Mgr: Jay Cole

D-U-N-S 16-168-1044 IMP/EXP
▲ NATIONAL OILWELL VARCO INC
NOV
7909 Parkwood Circle Dr, Houston, TX 77036-6757
Tel (713) 346-7500 *Founded/Ownrshp* 1982
Sales 14.7MMM *EMP* 50,197
Tkr Sym NOV *Exch* NYS
SIC 3533 3594 5084 Oil & gas field machinery; Oil & gas drilling rigs & equipment; Gas field machinery & equipment; Oil field machinery & equipment; Pumps, hydraulic power transfer; Motors: hydraulic, fluid power or air; Petroleum industry machinery
Ch Bd: Clay C Williams
Pr: Isaac H Joseph
Pr: Joseph W Rovig
CFO: Jose A Bayardo
Sr VP: Craig L Weinstock
VP: Grant Almond
VP: Craig Ballinger
VP: Brent A Benoit
VP: Oddleon Bjerga
VP: David Cardellini
VP: Bob Cooke
VP: Howard Davis
VP: Bruce Dawson
VP: Scott K Duff
VP: David W Granderson
VP: Hege Kvernland
VP: Sungwoo Lee
VP: Todd Lee
VP: Kevin McDonough
VP: Jaehwa Park
VP: John Roche
Board of Directors: Greg L Armstrong, Ben A Guill, James T Hackett, David D Harrison, Roger L Jarvis, Eric L Mattson, William R Thomas

D-U-N-S 08-339-5843 IMP/EXP
■ NATIONAL OILWELL VARCO LP
(*Suby of* NOV) ★
1530 W Sam Houston Pkwy N, Houston, TX 77043-3113
Tel (713) 960-5100 *Founded/Ownrshp* 1996
Sales 299.9MM^E *EMP* 700
SIC 3533 5082 5084 Oil field machinery & equipment; Oil field equipment; Industrial machinery & equipment
Pt: Joel Staff
Pt: Merrill Miller
Pt: Dan Molinaro
Pt: Frederick Pheasey
VP: Craig Goss
Opers Mgr: Jim Cirone
Sales Exec: Randy L Scates
Mktg Mgr: Ryan Fox

D-U-N-S 06-951-2291
NATIONAL OPINION RESEARCH CENTER
NORC
1155 E 60th St, Chicago, IL 60637-2799
Tel (773) 753-7500 *Founded/Ownrshp* 1941
Sales 209.7MM^E *EMP* 1,200
SIC 8732

D-U-N-S 07-834-1328 IMP
NATIONAL OUTDOOR LEADERSHIP SCHOOL
NOLS
284 Lincoln St, Lander, WY 82520-2848
Tel (800) 710-6657 *Founded/Ownrshp* 1965
Sales 37.6MM *EMP* 1,000
Accts Mcgee Hearne & Paiz Llp Che
SIC 8299 5941 Survival school; Camping equipment
Ch: Katherine Gunness Williams
**CFO:* Jeff Buchanan
**Treas:* Jonathan Kleisner
Ofcr: Katie Price
VP: Steve Smith
Dir Risk M: Drew Leemon
**Ex Dir:* John Gans
Ex Dir: Liz Tuohy
Prgrm Mgr: Atila Rego-Monteiro
Off Mgr: Gabi Jackson
Telecom Mg: Don Webber

NATIONAL PACKING SUPPLY
See REAL REEL CORP

NATIONAL PARK MEDICAL CENTER
See HOT SPRINGS NATIONAL PARK HOSPITAL HOLDINGS LLC

D-U-N-S 92-618-0977 IMP/EXP
■ NATIONAL PARK SERVICE
(*Suby of* UNITED STATES DEPARTMENT OF INTERIOR) ★
1849 C St Nw, Washington, DC 20240-0001
Tel (202) 208-6843 *Founded/Ownrshp* 1916
Sales NA *EMP* 20,000ᴱ
SIC 9512 Land, mineral & wildlife conservation;
**Pr:* John L Nau III
Ofcr: Jeffrey A Shaffer
Ofcr: Diana Shiba
Adm Dir: Anne Ashe
Adm Dir: Vicki Boyce
Adm Dir: Tisha Langfitt
Area Supr: Mike Stewart

D-U-N-S 11-977-7428
NATIONAL PASTEURIZED EGGS INC
2963 Bernice Rd Ste 1, Lansing, IL 60438-1285
Tel (708) 418-8500 *Founded/Ownrshp* 2001
Sales 113.4MMᴱ *EMP* 125
SIC 5144 Eggs
Pr: Gregory M West
**CFO:* Michael Smith
**VP:* Joseph Berglind
**VP:* Hector Lara
**Prin:* Marvin Aardema
**Prin:* Brian Boomsma
Natl Sales: Chip Baxter
Mktg Mgr: Deborah Rayhab
Manager: Zach Just
Manager: Jim Schlindwein

NATIONAL PEN COMPANY
See NATIONAL PEN CO LLC

D-U-N-S 05-988-3975 IMP/EXP
NATIONAL PEN CO LLC
NATIONAL PEN COMPANY
12121 Scripps Summit Dr # 200, San Diego, CA 92131-4609
Tel (866) 388-9850 *Founded/Ownrshp* 2012
Sales 260.7MMᴱ *EMP* 1,250
SIC 3951 3993 Pens & mechanical pencils; Advertising novelties
CEO: David F Thompson
CFO: Kathy McDermont
**CFO:* Richard N Obrigawitch
Sr Cor Off: Kathy McDermott
**Sr VP:* Ron Childs
**Sr VP:* Gregg Kornfeld
VP: Annette Williams
VP: Laurent Yung
Web Prj Mg: Eliot Kaagan
VP Mfg: Bill Owen

D-U-N-S 80-708-1638 IMP
NATIONAL PEN CORP
12121 Scripps Summit Dr # 200, San Diego, CA 92131-4609
Tel (858) 675-3000 *Founded/Ownrshp* 1966
Sales 156.9MMᴱ *EMP* 1,929
SIC 5961 Educational supplies & equipment, mail order
CEO: Dave Thompson
**Pr:* Gregg Kornfeld
**CFO:* Rich Obrigawitch
**Sr VP:* Ron Childs
**Sr VP:* Laurent Yung
VP: Mike Green
VP: Bill Owen
VP: Jason Pierce
Creative D: Christopher Coats
Genl Mgr: Eric Miller
CIO: Allen Dedman

D-U-N-S 07-937-3247
NATIONAL PENN BANCSHARES INC
645 Hamilton St Ste 1100, Allentown, PA 18101-2188
Tel (800) 822-3321 *Founded/Ownrshp* 1982
Sales NA *EMP* 3,505
Accts Kpmg Llp Philadelphia Pennsy
SIC 6331
Pr: Scott V Fainor
CFO: Michael J Hughes
Ofcr: Bridget Keretz
Ofcr: Amy Lyng
Ofcr: Debra Wetzel
Ex VP: Dawn Hamm
Ex VP: Tito L Lima
Sr VP: Stephen C Lyons
Sr VP: Michele Melcher
VP: Nancy Gigler-Smith
VP: Debra Hippensteel
VP: Debbie Nowak
VP: Carl Walbert
Exec: Sandra L Bodnyk
Exec: David B Kennedy
Board of Directors: Thomas A Beaver, Jeffrey P Feather, Donna D Holton, Thomas L Kennedy, Patricia L Langiotti, Christian F Martin IV, R Chadwick Paul Jr, C Robert Roth, Wayne R Weidner

D-U-N-S 00-790-9914 IMP/EXP
■ NATIONAL PENN BANK
(*Suby of* BB&T) ★
645 Hamilton St Ste 900, Allentown, PA 18101-2198
Tel (610) 705-9101 *Founded/Ownrshp* 1874
Sales NA *EMP* 1,768
SIC 6021 National trust companies with deposits, commercial
CEO: Glenn E Moyer
CEO: Pam Koeshartanto
**Ch:* Wayne Weidner
Ofcr: Debbie Johnson
Ofcr: Mary Lorah
Ofcr: Tracy Smithnosky
Ofcr: Jennifer Snyder
Ex VP: Peter Gray
Sr VP: Doug Denlinger
Sr VP: Jim Ferry
Sr VP: Scott Herald
Sr VP: Stephen C Lyons
Sr VP: Sharon McMichael
Sr VP: Andrew Melzer
Sr VP: Richard Montevidoni
Sr VP: Colette Price
Sr VP: Michael L Spotts
Sr VP: Dan Wiekrykas
VP: Adam Althouse
VP: Joe Andrews
VP: James Aten

D-U-N-S 17-044-4371
NATIONAL PHILANTHROPIC TRUST
165 Township Line Rd # 1200, Jenkintown, PA 19046-3594
Tel (215) 277-3010 *Founded/Ownrshp* 1996
Sales 670.3MM *EMP* 19
SIC 7389 Fund raising organizations
Pr: Eileen Heisman
CEO: John Canady
Assoc VP: Helen Picher
VP: Donna Pulini
Assoc Dir: Erin Hoyes
Prin: Patricia Patrizi
CTO: Christopher Adams

D-U-N-S 96-670-6764 IMP/EXP
NATIONAL PIPE & PLASTICS INC
NPPI
3421 Vestal Rd, Vestal, NY 13850-2188
Tel (607) 729-9381 *Founded/Ownrshp* 2004
Sales 92.9MMᴱ *EMP* 280
SIC 3084 Plastics pipe
CEO: David J Culbertson
**Treas:* Michelle Suer
**VP:* Charles E Miller
VP: Matt Siegel
Admn Mgr: Jackie Christens
CIO: Karen Krouse
MIS Dir: Bill Scott
IT Man: Dave Kunkel
QC Dir: Eric Paugh
Plnt Mgr: Michael Westover
Ql Cn Mgr: John Brooks

D-U-N-S 09-031-2765
NATIONAL PORK BOARD (IA)
1776 Nw 114th St, Des Moines, IA 50325-7000
Tel (515) 223-2600 *Founded/Ownrshp* 1986
Sales 89.1MMᴱ *EMP* 75
Accts Mcgladrey & Pullen Llp Des M
SIC 5147 Meats, fresh
CEO: Chris Novak
**CFO:* Calvin Van Dekrol
**Ex VP:* Jim Meimann
Tech Mgr: Charles Cozad
Art Dir: Chris Oldt

D-U-N-S 07-122-5155
NATIONAL POSTAL MAIL HANDLERS UNION
1101 Conn Ave Nw Ste 500, Washington, DC 20036-4325
Tel (202) 833-9095 *Founded/Ownrshp* 1920
Sales 60.5MMᴱ *EMP* 1,100
SIC 8631 Labor union
Pr: John F Hegarty
**Sec:* Mark A Gardner
**VP:* Paul Hogrogian
Dir IT: Robin Daniels

D-U-N-S 00-619-6174
▲ NATIONAL PRESTO INDUSTRIES INC
3925 N Hastings Way, Eau Claire, WI 54703-3703
Tel (715) 839-2121 *Founded/Ownrshp* 1905
Sales 427.6MM *EMP* 1,090ᴱ
Accts Bdo Usa Llp Milwaukee Wisco
Tkr Sym NPK *Exch* NYS
SIC 2211 3483 3634 Diaper fabrics; Ammunition components; Housewares, excluding cooking appliances & utensils
Ch Bd: Maryjo Cohen
**CFO:* Randy F Lieble
VP Sls: Spencer W Ahneman
Snr Mgr: Lisa Nelson
Board of Directors: Richard N Cardozo, Patrick J Quinn, Joseph G Stienessen

D-U-N-S 94-417-2816
NATIONAL PROCESSING CO
RETRIEVER PAYMENTS SYSTEMS
(*Suby of* FAIRMOUNT FOOD GROUP INC)
20405 State Highway 249 # 700, Houston, TX 77070-3815
Tel (281) 376-3399 *Founded/Ownrshp* 2007
Sales 221.8MMᴱ *EMP* 546
SIC 5065 Electronic parts & equipment
Pr: Thomas A Wimsett
**Ch Bd:* William H Higgins
**Pr:* Adam Coyle
**CFO:* Steve Stevenson
Treas: Tim Cooper
**Ex VP:* James Oberman

D-U-N-S 15-427-6521
■ NATIONAL PROJECTS INC
(*Suby of* AECOM ENERGY & CONSTRUCTION INC) ★
720 E Park Blvd, Boise, ID 83712-7758
Tel (208) 386-5000 *Founded/Ownrshp* 1985
Sales 73.8MMᴱ *EMP* 1,162
SIC 1629 1542 1541 Dam construction; Commercial & office building, new construction; Industrial buildings & warehouses
Pr: Stephen G Hanks
**Ch:* Dennis Washington

D-U-N-S 05-338-7221
NATIONAL PUBLIC RADIO INC
N P R
1111 N Capitol St Ne, Washington, DC 20002-7502
Tel (202) 513-2000 *Founded/Ownrshp* 1970
Sales 204.2MM *EMP* 741
Accts Bdo Usa Llp Bethesda Md
SIC 8611 Business associations
CEO: Jarl Mohn
**CFO:* Debbie Cullen
**Chf Mktg O:* Emma Carrasco
Dir Soc: Terry Gross
Dir Soc: Peter Sagal

D-U-N-S 07-885-9701
NATIONAL RADIO ASTRONOMY OBSERVATORY
NRAO
520 Edgemont Rd, Charlottesville, VA 22903-2454
Tel (434) 296-0211 *Founded/Ownrshp* 2013
Sales 101.7MM *EMP* 1,299
SIC 8731 Commercial physical research
Prin: Andrea Gianopoulos
Ofcr: Brian Bell
Ofcr: Anthony Thompson
Exec: Charles Blue
Prgrm Mgr: Joyce Johnson
Prgrm Mgr: Mary Mayo
Prgrm Mgr: Michael Shannon
Prgrm Mgr: Lory Wingate
Web Dev: Davis Murphy
Sftwr Eng: Pamela Ford
Sftwr Eng: Andy Hale

D-U-N-S 05-442-7745 IMP
■ NATIONAL RAILROAD PASSENGER CORP (DC)
AMTRAK
(*Suby of* UNITED STATES DEPARTMENT OF TRANSPORTATION) ★
60 Massachusetts Ave Ne, Washington, DC 20002-4285
Tel (202) 906-3741 *Founded/Ownrshp* 1970
Sales 4.2MMMᴱ *EMP* 18,650
SIC 4011 4013 Interurban railways; Railroad terminals
Pr: Joseph H Boardman
Ch Bd: Anthony R Coscia
COO: William Crosby
COO: William Cry
CFO: William H Campbell
Sr Cor Off: Wade Jones
Sr Cor Off: David Smith
V Ch Bd: Jeffrey R Moreland
Act CFO: Dale M Stein
Bd of Dir: Robert Hunter
Ofcr: Magdy El-Sibaie
Ofcr: Dennis Henry
Ofcr: James Rusbarsky
Assoc VP: Floyd L Kemerer
Ex VP: Karen Seibert
Sr VP: James T Lloyd
VP: Eleanor D Acheson
VP: Sandy J Brown
VP: Roy Deitchman
VP: Donald G Gentry
VP: Anne W Hoey
Board of Directors: Christopher R Beall, Joseph H Boardman, Yvonne Brathwaite Burke, Thomas C Carper, Anthony R Coscia, Albert Diclemente, Anthony Foxx, Jeffrey R Moreland

D-U-N-S 10-319-3751 IMP/EXP
NATIONAL RAILWAY EQUIPMENT CO
NREC
1100 Shawnee St, Mount Vernon, IL 62864-5454
Tel (618) 242-6590 *Founded/Ownrshp* 1980
Sales 274.5MMᴱ *EMP* 810
SIC 5088 3743

D-U-N-S 15-774-8914
NATIONAL RAILWAY EQUIPMENT CO
(*Suby of* NREC) ★
1300 Kentucky Ave, Paducah, KY 42003-1961
Tel (270) 444-4555 *Founded/Ownrshp* 1994
Sales 100.6MMᴱ *EMP* 950
SIC 3743 Mining locomotives & parts, electric or nonelectric; Railroad locomotives & parts, electric or nonelectric
Pr: Robert A Pedersen
**Sr VP:* Charles E Marshall
**VP:* Burton Lamont

NATIONAL RAISIN COMPANY
See SUNSHINE RAISIN CORP

D-U-N-S 10-143-9925 IMP/EXP
NATIONAL REFRIGERANTS INC
N R I
11401 Roosevelt Blvd, Philadelphia, PA 19154-2197
Tel (215) 698-6620 *Founded/Ownrshp* 1983
Sales 135.6MMᴱ *EMP* 100
SIC 5169 Chemicals & allied products
Pr: John H Reilly Jr
CFO: Nick Hope
**Treas:* Hope V Nicholas
**VP:* John H Reilly III

D-U-N-S 19-558-2853 IMP
NATIONAL REFRIGERATION & AIR CONDITIONING PRODUCTS INC
NATIONAL REFRIGERATION PDTS
539 Dunksferry Rd, Bensalem, PA 19020-5908
Tel (215) 244-1400 *Founded/Ownrshp* 1988
Sales 111.1MMᴱ *EMP* 230
SIC 3585 5075 Refrigeration equipment, complete; Air conditioning equipment, complete; Warm air heating & air conditioning
**Pr:* Michael Coyle
**CEO:* John H Reilly
CFO: John Haselbarth
**Treas:* Carmen Carosella
**Treas:* William Hawkins
**VP:* Nicholas V Hope
Sfty Dirs: Mike Coyle
Mktg Mgr: Faith Bamka
Sls Mgr: Kevin Brown
Sls Mgr: Grant Price
Sales Asso: Kenny Ford

NATIONAL REFRIGERATION PDTS
See NATIONAL REFRIGERATION & AIR CONDITIONING PRODUCTS INC

D-U-N-S 07-736-6664
NATIONAL REHABILITATION HOSPITAL INC
N R H
102 Irving St Nw, Washington, DC 20010-2921
Tel (202) 877-1000 *Founded/Ownrshp* 1983
Sales 118.2MM *EMP* 900
Accts Kpmg Llp Mc Lean Va
SIC 8069 Specialty hospitals, except psychiatric
Ch: Jimmy V Reyes
**Pr:* Edward Eckenhoff
**CFO:* Michael Bammel
**Treas:* Robert B Ourisman
VP: Pamela Ashby
Exec: Casey Yazel
CIO: Anjoo Marchant

NATIONAL RENT A CAR
See NATIONAL RENTAL (US) INC

D-U-N-S 80-700-1628
NATIONAL RENTAL (US) INC
NATIONAL RENT A CAR
(*Suby of* VANGUARD CAR RENTAL USA INC.)
6929 N Lakewood Ave # 100, Tulsa, OK 74117-1824
Tel (918) 401-6000 *Founded/Ownrshp* 2003
Sales 175.0MMᴱ *EMP* 4,957ᴱ
SIC 7514 Rent-a-car service
Pr: Greg Stubblefield
Pr: Rob Connors
Treas: Brenda Miller
Ex VP: Thomas C Kennedy
Sr VP: Tyler Best
Sr VP: Thomas Kennedy
VP: Gary Cunningham
VP: Wesley C Fredenburg
VP: Mark Friedman
VP: Jim Wood
Dir Bus: Dick Hunt

D-U-N-S 05-085-7788
▲ NATIONAL RESEARCH CORP (WI)
NRC
1245 Q St Ste 100, Lincoln, NE 68508-1454
Tel (402) 475-2525 *Founded/Ownrshp* 1981
Sales 102.3MM *EMP* 375ᴱ
Tkr Sym NRCIA *Exch* NGS
SIC 8732 Market analysis or research
CEO: Michael D Hays
Pr: Steven D Jackson
COO: Jona Raasch
CFO: Kevin R Karas
Ofcr: Kimberle Hall
VP: Helen Hrdy
Sftwr Eng: Lanny Boswell
Sftwr Eng: Eric Faust
Advt Dir: Justin Kubick
Pgrm Dir: Ryan Donohue
Board of Directors: Donald M Berwick, Joann M Martin, Barbara J Mowry, John N Nunnelly, Gail L Warden

D-U-N-S 79-738-4252 EXP
NATIONAL RESPONSE CORP
3500 Sunrise Hwy, Great River, NY 11739-1001
Tel (631) 224-9141 *Founded/Ownrshp* 2012
Sales 127.4MM *EMP* 700
SIC 4959 8999 Oil spill cleanup; Earth science services
Pr: Paul Taveira
**CFO:* Sal Sacco
**Sr VP:* Neil Challis
**Sr VP:* Mike Reese
**Sr VP:* Todd Roloff
VP: Michael Reese

D-U-N-S 01-216-1568
NATIONAL RESTAURANTS MANAGEMENT INC
RIESE ORGANIZATION
560 5th Ave Fl 3, New York, NY 10036-5005
Tel (212) 563-7440 *Founded/Ownrshp* 1961
Sales 71.1MMᴱ *EMP* 2,500
SIC 5812 6531 Eating places; Real estate agents & managers
CEO: Dennis Riese
**Ex VP:* Larry Abrams
**VP:* Ann Martinez
VP: James Rosenzweig
VP: Mark Stempel
Dist Mgr: Lisa Dibello

D-U-N-S 16-649-7644
NATIONAL RESTAURANTS MANAGEMENT INC
RIESE ORGANIZATION
(*Suby of* RIESE ORGANIZATION) ★
604 5th Ave Fl 5, New York, NY 10020-2304
Tel (212) 563-7440 *Founded/Ownrshp* 1961
Sales 50.4MMᴱ *EMP* 2,400
SIC 5812 Eating places
Pr: Dennis Riese
**CFO:* John Dunne

D-U-N-S 10-915-1175
▲ NATIONAL RETAIL PROPERTIES INC
450 S Orange Ave Ste 900, Orlando, FL 32801-3339
Tel (407) 265-7348 *Founded/Ownrshp* 1984
Sales 482.9MM *EMP* 62ᴱ
Tkr Sym NNN *Exch* NYS
SIC 6798 Real estate investment trusts
Ch Bd: Craig Macnab
Pr: Julian E Whitehurst
CFO: Kevin B Habicht
Ex VP: Paul E Bayer
Ex VP: Stephen A Horn Jr
Ex VP: Michelle Miller
Ex VP: Christopher P Tessitore
VP: Mike Iannone
VP: Russell Shelton

D-U-N-S 13-047-6831
NATIONAL RETAIL SYSTEMS INC
N R S
2820 16th St, North Bergen, NJ 07047-1541
Tel (201) 330-1900 *Founded/Ownrshp* 1983
Sales 255.8MMᴱ *EMP* 1,500
SIC 7363 Truck driver services
Pr: Raymond Wisniewski
CFO: Paul Hennesy
VP: Irene Kneeter
VP: Lou Piscitelli
Sfty Dirs: Joe Torres

D-U-N-S 09-926-3725 IMP
NATIONAL RETAIL TRANSPORTATION INC
(*Suby of* N R S) ★
2820 16th St, North Bergen, NJ 07047-1541
Tel (201) 866-0462 *Founded/Ownrshp* 1979
Sales 203.2MM^E *EMP* 1,040
SIC 4213 Trucking, except local
Pr: Raymond Wisniewski
**CFO:* Paul K Hennessy

D-U-N-S 00-325-6500
NATIONAL RIFLE ASSOCIATION OF AMERICA (NY)
INSTITUTE FOR LGSLATIVE ACTION
11250 Waples Mill Rd # 1, Fairfax, VA 22030-9400
Tel (703) 267-1000 *Founded/Ownrshp* 1997
Sales 310.4MM *EMP* 500
Accts Mcgladrey Llp Mc Lean Va
SIC 8699 Amateur sports promotion
Pr: Porter II James W
**Pr:* John C Sigler
**CFO:* Wilson H Phillips
**Treas:* Phillips Jr Wilson H
Treas: H P Wilson
Bd of Dir: Dolores R Gresham
**VP:* Cors Allan D
**VP:* David Keene
**VP:* Lapierre Jr Wayne
**VP:* Brownell Pete
VP: James W Porter II
**VP:* Ronald L Schmeits
Comm Man: Monica Huie

D-U-N-S 04-549-7427
NATIONAL RURAL ELECTRIC COOPERATIVE ASSOCIATION
NRECA
4301 Wilson Blvd Ste 1, Arlington, VA 22203-1867
Tel (703) 907-5500 *Founded/Ownrshp* 1942
Sales 230.4MM *EMP* 885
Accts Bdo Usa Llp Bethesda Md
SIC 8611 Trade associations
CEO: Glenn L English Jr
**CEO:* Joann Emerson
**Sec:* Curtis Wynn
Ofcr: Cathy Windfield-Jones
VP: Kirk Johnson
VP: Tom Stangroom
Exec: Kim Jewell
Prgrm Mgr: Craig Miller
Prgrm Mgr: Brian Sloboda
Brnch Mgr: Tom Montgomery
CTO: Karen Ford

D-U-N-S 07-483-3401
NATIONAL RURAL UTILITIES COOPERATIVE FINANCE CORP
CFC
20701 Cooperative Way, Dulles, VA 20166-6691
Tel (703) 467-1800 *Founded/Ownrshp* 1969
Sales NA *EMP* 243^E
Accts Kpmg Llp Mclean Va
SIC 6141 6159 Personal credit institutions; Loan institutions, general & industrial
CEO: Sheldon C Petersen
**Pr:* R Grant Clawson
COO: John T Evans
CFO: J Andrew Don
**Sec:* Harry N Park
Sr VP: Joel Allen
Sr VP: Roberta B Aronson
Sr VP: John M Borak
Sr VP: Brad L Captain
Sr VP: Graceann D Clendenen
Sr VP: Steven M Kettler
Sr VP: Robin C Reed
Sr VP: Gregory Starheim
**VP:* Mike Campbell
VP: John Suter
Board of Directors: Jimmy A Lafoy, Patrick L Bridges, Debra L Robinson, Robert Brockman, Bradley J Schardin, Phillip A Carson, Mark D Snowden, Mel Coleman, Dean R Tesch, Kent D Farmer, Kirk A Thompson, Roman E Gillen, Stephen C Vail, Doyle Jay Hanson, Todd P Ware, Thomas L Hayes, Alan W Wattles, Robert M Hill, Gregory D Williams

D-U-N-S 19-739-5551
NATIONAL SALVAGE & SERVICE CORP
MID WEST RAILROAD TIE SALES
6755 S Old State Road 37, Bloomington, IN 47401-8918
Tel (812) 339-8437 *Founded/Ownrshp* 1988
Sales 85.5MM^E *EMP* 130^E
Accts Katz Sapper & Miller Indiana
SIC 5088 1629 1795 5099 5093 Railroad equipment & supplies; Railroad & railway roadbed construction; Wrecking & demolition work; Demolition, buildings & other structures; Timber products, rough; Scrap & waste materials
Pr: Curtis C Schopp
**Pr:* Victoria E Schopp
**Sec:* Catherine Ruf
IT Man: Keri Decker
Trfc Dir: Chantel Faultless
Sls Dir: David Ralston
Sls Mgr: Rachel Strong

D-U-N-S 07-873-0983
NATIONAL SCHOOL DISTRICT
1500 N Ave, National City, CA 91950-4827
Tel (619) 336-7500 *Founded/Ownrshp* 1871
Sales 200.7MM^E *EMP* 6,000
SIC 8211 School board
Dir Sec: Meghann O'Connor
Psych: Raz Gibson
Psych: Susie Rico

D-U-N-S 07-481-1803
■ **NATIONAL SCIENCE FOUNDATION**
NSF
(*Suby of* EXECUTIVE OFFICE OF UNITED STATES GOVERNMENT) ★
4201 Wilson Blvd Ste 1205, Arlington, VA 22230-0002
Tel (703) 292-5050 *Founded/Ownrshp* 1950
Sales NA *EMP* 1,300^E
SIC 9199 9111

D-U-N-S 78-847-7305
NATIONAL SEATING & MOBILITY INC
320 Premier Ct S Ste 220, Franklin, TN 37067-8252
Tel (615) 595-1115 *Founded/Ownrshp* 1989
Sales 381.2MM^E *EMP* 750
SIC 3842 5999 Wheelchairs; Convalescent equipment & supplies
CEO: William Mixon
Pr: Doug McDaniel
Pr: Tom Strickland
**COO:* Sandi Neiman
**CFO:* Tim Maddox
**Ch:* Mike Ballard
Ofcr: Staci L Brockwell
**Sr VP:* Bill Noelting
**VP:* John Bertone
VP: David Catoe
**VP:* Kevin Harmon
**VP:* Charles Sargeant

D-U-N-S 79-134-2194 IMP
■ **NATIONAL SEATING CO**
C V G
(*Suby of* CVG) ★
7800 Walton Pkwy, New Albany, OH 43054-8233
Tel (219) 872-7295 *Founded/Ownrshp* 1976
Sales 99.3MM^E *EMP* 66^E
SIC 2392 Chair covers & pads: made from purchased materials
Pr: Mervin Dunn
Opers Mgr: Bill Stimel
Ql Cn Mgr: Jeremy Mosley

D-U-N-S 55-606-9110
▲ **NATIONAL SECURITY GROUP INC**
661 Davis St E, Elba, AL 36323-1621
Tel (334) 897-2273 *Founded/Ownrshp* 1947
Sales NA *EMP* 1,591^E
Accts Warren Averett Llc Birmingha
Tkr Sym NSEC *Exch* NGM
SIC 6311 6331 Life insurance; Fire, marine & casualty insurance
Pr: William L Brunson Jr
**Ch Bd:* Winfield Baird
CFO: Brian R McLeod
VP: Gary Slater
Mktg Mgr: Eddie Vaughan
Genl Couns: Douge Martin

D-U-N-S 19-519-4779
NATIONAL SECURITY TECHNOLOGIES LLC
NSTEC
2621 Losee Rd, North Las Vegas, NV 89030-4129
Tel (702) 295-1000 *Founded/Ownrshp* 2005
Sales 584.5MM^E *EMP* 2,543
SIC 8711 1629 Civil engineering; Industrial plant construction
Pr: Raymond Juzaicis
CFO: Jack Stumpf
VP: Terry Marotta
IT Man: Kevin Forcade
Web Dev: Bev Larson
Sftwr Eng: Ryan Bellow
Opers Supe: William Colucci
Sls&Mrk Ex: Shari Morrison

D-U-N-S 18-143-5236
NATIONAL SENIOR CARE INC
1 Ravinia Dr Ste 1500, Atlanta, GA 30346-2115
Tel (678) 443-7000 *Founded/Ownrshp* 2004
Sales 4.1MMM^E *EMP* 35,000
SIC 5912 8051 8093 8741 8062 3443 Drug stores & proprietary stores; Extended care facility; Rehabilitation center, outpatient treatment; Industrial management; General medical & surgical hospitals; Chambers & caissons
Pr: Harry Grunstein

D-U-N-S 88-399-3698
NATIONAL SERVICES GROUP INC
COLLEGE WORKS PAINTING
1682 Langley Ave, Irvine, CA 92614-5620
Tel (714) 564-7900 *Founded/Ownrshp* 1999
Sales 93.2MM^E *EMP* 685
SIC 1721

NATIONAL SLEEP PRODUCTS
See PACIFIC COAST FEATHER CO

D-U-N-S 03-724-3987
NATIONAL SLOVAK SOCIETY OF USA INC
351 Valley Brook Rd, Mc Murray, PA 15317-3337
Tel (724) 731-0094 *Founded/Ownrshp* 1890
Sales NA *EMP* 11
SIC 6311 Fraternal life insurance organizations
Pr: David Blazek
**Treas:* Paul Payerchin
**VP:* Dean A Burns
**Prin:* Paul Good

NATIONAL SMALLWARES
See WASSERSTROM CO

NATIONAL SPINE AND PAIN CTRS
See CENTER FOR PAIN MANAGEMENT LLC

D-U-N-S 00-160-3570 IMP/EXP
NATIONAL SPINNING CO INC
1481 W 2nd St, Washington, NC 27889-4157
Tel (252) 975-7111 *Founded/Ownrshp* 1900, 1919
Sales 182.8MM^E *EMP* 650
SIC 2281 Wool yarn, spun; Acrylic yarn, spun: made from purchased staple; Polyester yarn, spun: made from purchased staple
Pr: James W Chesnutt
**Ch Bd:* Morgan Miller
**Pr:* Jim Booterbaugh
**CFO:* Linda Fanton
**Ch:* Joseph N Leff
Treas: Thomas Markey
**Ex VP:* Bob Millere
Sr VP: Bob Miller
**VP:* Robert Miller
Plnt Mgr: Ed Atkins
Plnt Mgr: Buford Hutchins

NATIONAL STARCH AND CHEMICAL
See INDOPCO INC

D-U-N-S 15-428-8666 EXP
■ **NATIONAL STARCH AND CHEMICAL HOLDING CORP**
(*Suby of* INGREDION INC) ★
10 Finderne Ave, Bridgewater, NJ 08807-3365
Tel (908) 685-5000 *Founded/Ownrshp* 1978
Sales 241.8MM^E *EMP* 6,000
Accts Coopers & Lybrand
SIC 2891 2046 2869 Adhesives & sealants; Wet corn milling; Industrial organic chemicals; Vinyl acetate
Pr: Ned W Bandler
CFO: Tim Brownly
VP: Herbert J Baumgarten
VP: Tony Delio
Board of Directors: Robert B Albert

NATIONAL STEAK & POULTRY
See NATIONAL STEAK PROCESSORS INC

D-U-N-S 09-444-0328
NATIONAL STEAK PROCESSORS INC
NATIONAL STEAK & POULTRY
301 E 5th Ave, Owasso, OK 74055-3450
Tel (918) 274-8787 *Founded/Ownrshp* 1980
Sales 104.2MM^E *EMP* 325
SIC 2013 2015 Prepared beef products from purchased beef; Poultry slaughtering & processing
CEO: Dave Albright
**Pr:* Steven A Kormondy
VP: Chuck Rogers
Dir IT: Joe Johnson
Sfty Mgr: James Reitz
Opers Mgr: Tanta Ward
Manager: Eric Dinkel

D-U-N-S 00-915-8932 IMP/EXP
■ **NATIONAL STEEL & SHIPBUILDING CO**
NASSCO
(*Suby of* GENERAL DYNAMICS CORP) ★
2798 Harbor Dr, San Diego, CA 92113-3650
Tel (619) 544-3400 *Founded/Ownrshp* 1989
Sales 589.0MM^E *EMP* 3,000^E
SIC 3731 Military ships, building & repairing; Commercial cargo ships, building & repairing
Pr: Frederick J Harris
**Ch Bd:* Michael Toner
Pr: Timothy P McCue
CFO: Eric Murray
**Treas:* D H Fogg
**Ex VP:* Phebe Novakoviz
VP: Steve Clarey
VP: Richard Danehy
VP: Steven Davison
VP: Janice Grace
VP: Matthew Luxton
VP: Lane McVey

D-U-N-S 07-980-8768
NATIONAL STORAGE AFFILIATES TRUST
5200 Dtc Pkwy Ste 200, Greenwood Village, CO 80111-2715
Tel (720) 630-2600 *Founded/Ownrshp* 2013
Sales 133.9MM *EMP* 13
SIC 6798 Real estate investment trusts
Pr: Arlen D Nordhagen
CFO: Tamara D Fischer
Sr VP: Steven B Treadwell

D-U-N-S 04-222-9328 IMP/EXP
NATIONAL STORES INC (CA)
FALLAS-PAREDES
15001 S Figueroa St, Gardena, CA 90248-1721
Tel (310) 324-9962 *Founded/Ownrshp* 1961
Sales 943.9MM^E *EMP* 4,000
SIC 5651 Family clothing stores
CEO: Michael Fallas
CFO: Sandy Menichelli
Sr VP: Dwane Huesers
VP: Rob Langer
Site Mgr: Jake Kogan
Mktg Dir: Helene Wagner

NATIONAL SUPPLY
See CWI INC

D-U-N-S 00-691-2752
NATIONAL SURETY CORP
(*Suby of* FIREMANS FUND INSURANCE CO) ★
1465 N Mcdowell Blvd # 100, Petaluma, CA 94954-6516
Tel (415) 899-2000 *Founded/Ownrshp* 1954
Sales NA *EMP* 1,000
SIC 6351 Surety insurance
CEO: Lori D Fouche
Board of Directors: Lauren R Bailey, Douglas E Franklin, John F Huddleston Jr, Jeffery F Johnson, Sally B Narey, Frank A Sapio, D Andrew Torrance, Kevin E Walker, David M Zona

D-U-N-S 17-356-5529
NATIONAL SURGICAL HOSPITALS INC
250 S Wacker Dr Ste 500, Chicago, IL 60606-5897
Tel (312) 627-8400 *Founded/Ownrshp* 1998
Sales 291.3MM^E *EMP* 3,100
Accts E&Y Chicago Il
SIC 8062 8093 General medical & surgical hospitals; Specialty outpatient clinics
CEO: David Crane
**Pr:* Bryan Fisher
**Pr:* Donna Worsham
**CFO:* David N T Watson
Ofcr: Rob Guenthner
**Ex VP:* James T Grant
**Sr VP:* Scott B Clark
**Sr VP:* Dennis D Solheim
VP: Cathy Borst
VP: Donna Giles
VP: Charlie Smith
Dir Lab: Michelle Cornstubble
Dir Rad: Kevin Bassett
Dir Rx: Emilio Bethencourt

NATIONAL SWAGE
See CROSBY GROUP LLC

D-U-N-S 06-381-8587 IMP
NATIONAL TECHNICAL SYSTEMS INC
NTS
(*Suby of* NEST PARENT INC) ★
24007 Ventura Blvd # 200, Calabasas, CA 91302-1430
Tel (818) 591-0776 *Founded/Ownrshp* 1996
Sales 231.0MM *EMP* 1,162
SIC 8711 Engineering services
Pr: William McGinnis
Pr: Dan Coleman
Pr: Bruce Irwin
**Pr:* Vicki Panhuise
**COO:* Derek Coppinger
**CFO:* Michael El-Hillow
**Sr VP:* Douglas Briskie
VP: Tammy Buckly
VP: Wesley Furrh
VP: Marvin Hoffman
VP: Loren Isley
VP: Chuck Lamarca
VP: Dave Mann
VP: Barry Peter
VP: Sara Philippi
VP: Jim Pinyan
VP: Austin Schaffter

D-U-N-S 07-483-0720
NATIONAL TELECOMMUNICATIONS COOPERATIVE ASSOCIATION
NTCA RURAL BROADBAND ASSN
4121 Wilson Blvd Ste 1000, Arlington, VA 22203-4145
Tel (703) 351-2000 *Founded/Ownrshp* 1954
Sales 294.2MM^E *EMP* 136
Accts Cliftonlarsonallen Llp Arling
SIC 8611 8741 Trade associations; Management services
CEO: Shirley Bloomfield
**Pr:* Force Terry
**Treas:* Ronald Laudner
VP: Shary Denes
**VP:* Lisa I Schweitzer
**VP:* Donald D Miller
Counsel: Gregory Whiteaker

NATIONAL TELEVISION BOOK CO
See NTVB MEDIA INC

NATIONAL TITLE SOURCE
See TITLE SOURCE INC

NATIONAL TRCK PARTS OF MIDWEST
See CCC PARTS CO

D-U-N-S 19-550-3263
NATIONAL TRUCK PARTS OF MIDWEST INC
TRUCK PARTS SPECIALIST
(*Suby of* CCI CORP) ★
1901 N Sheridan Rd, Tulsa, OK 74115-3602
Tel (918) 836-0151 *Founded/Ownrshp* 1983
Sales 180.2MM^E *EMP* 1,150
SIC 5531 Truck equipment & parts
Pr: Joseph M Klein
**VP:* D M Hardin

NATIONAL TUBE & STEEL
See NATIONAL BUSINESS GROUP INC

D-U-N-S 62-048-7637 IMP
NATIONAL TUBE SUPPLY CO
(*Suby of* SICAM SOCIETA' ITALIANA COMMERCIO ACCIAI E METALLI SPA)
925 Central Ave, University Park, IL 60484-3143
Tel (708) 534-2700 *Founded/Ownrshp* 1990
Sales 226.7MM^E *EMP* 170
SIC 5051 Tubing, metal
Pr: Gary Chess
COO: Brian Kluge
VP: Marc Biolchin
Dir IT: Sean Tomei
IT Man: Michele L Markowski
Opers Mgr: Dan Rusnak
VP Sls: Jim Manser
Sales Asso: Chuck Holmer
Sales Asso: Bryan Wiesemann

D-U-N-S 04-361-4098
■ **NATIONAL UNION FIRE INSURANCE CO OF PITTSBURGH PA**
(*Suby of* CHARTIS US INC) ★
70 Pine St Fl 50, New York, NY 10005-1522
Tel (631) 692-4545 *Founded/Ownrshp* 1973
Sales NA *EMP* 1,000
SIC 6331 Property damage insurance; Fire, marine & casualty insurance: stock
Pr: John Q Doyle
Pr: Tracy Johnson
CFO: Robert Jacobson
VP: Michael Castelli

D-U-N-S 07-334-7809
NATIONAL UNIVERSITY
11355 N Torrey Pines Rd, La Jolla, CA 92037-1013
Tel (858) 642-8000 *Founded/Ownrshp* 1971
Sales 263.7MM *EMP* 1,954
Accts Moss Adams Llp San Diego Ca
SIC 8221 University
Treas: Maheba Merhi
VP: Thomas Green
VP: Vernon Taylor
Prgrm Mgr: Kimberleigh Kopp
MIS Dir: Mark Sotelo
VP Mktg: Patricia Potter
Mktg Dir: Julie L Bandy
Pr Dir: David Neville

D-U-N-S 15-782-6058
NATIONAL VETERINARY ASSOCIATES INC
29229 Canwood St Ste 100, Agoura Hills, CA 91301-1503
Tel (805) 777-7722 *Founded/Ownrshp* 1997
Sales 708.1MM^E *EMP* 1,900^E
SIC 0742 Veterinary services, specialties
CEO: Greg Hartmann
**COO:* Thomas Sawicki
**CFO:* R James Woloshyn
Bd of Dir: Craig Frances
Chf Mktg O: Carol Henry
Prac Mgr: Amy Cole
Rgnl Mgr: Shannon Zemlock

Dir IT: Patrick Hong
Dir IT: Adam Zilberman
Opers Mgr: Brad Schuch
Mktg Mgr: Marla Katz

D-U-N-S 61-874-5954 IMP
NATIONAL VISION INC
2435 Commerce Ave # 2200, Duluth, GA 30096-4980
Tel (770) 822-3600 *Founded/Ownrshp* 1990
Sales 1.2MMM^E *EMP* 5,000
SIC 5995 8042 Optical goods stores; Eyeglasses, prescription; Contact lenses, prescription; Contact lense specialist optometrist
Pr: Reade Fahs
* *Pr:* Bruce J Steffey
COO: Jay Bruce Steffey
* *CFO:* Paul A Criscillis Jr
Treas: Timothy W Renney
* *Sr VP:* Chuck Criscillis
* *Sr VP:* Mitchell Goodman
VP: Chris Beasley
VP: Michelle Berger
VP: Renee Himel
VP: Alex Louw
VP: Robert E Schnelle
Dir Lab: Chris Conrad
Dir Lab: Michael Gibson
Board of Directors: L Reade Fahs, D Randolph Peeler

D-U-N-S 06-950-6236
■ NATIONAL WASTE SERVICE INC
ALLIED WASTE SERVICES
(*Suby of* ALLIED WASTE INDUSTRIES INC) ★
2608 S Damen Ave, Chicago, IL 60608-5209
Tel (773) 579-3600 *Founded/Ownrshp* 1992
Sales 92.1MM^E *EMP* 205
SIC 4953 Refuse systems
Pr: Thomas Van Weelden
* *VP:* Richard Van Hattem

D-U-N-S 92-995-9153
■ NATIONAL WEATHER SERVICE
NATIONAL WEATHER SERVICE OHD1
(*Suby of* NATIONAL OCEANIC AND ATMOSPHERIC ADMINISTRATION) ★
1325 E West Hwy, Silver Spring, MD 20910-3280
Tel (609) 261-6600 *Founded/Ownrshp* 1870
Sales NA *EMP* 1,225
SIC 9611 Administration of general economic programs;
Ofcr: Kathleen Oleary

NATIONAL WEATHER SERVICE OHD1
See NATIONAL WEATHER SERVICE

D-U-N-S 00-787-5206
▲ NATIONAL WESTERN LIFE INSURANCE CO
850 E Anderson Ln, Austin, TX 78752-1602
Tel (512) 836-1010 *Founded/Ownrshp* 1956
Sales NA *EMP* 279^E
Accts Bkd Little Rock Arkansas
Tkr Sym NWLI *Exch* NGS
SIC 6311 Life insurance; Life insurance carriers
Ch Bd: Robert L Moody
Pr: Fabiola Best
* *Pr:* Ross R Moody
Pr: K Kennedy Nelson
CFO: Brian M Pribyl
Treas: Wil Ross
Chf Mktg O: S Christopher Johnson
Sr VP: Paul D Facey
Sr VP: James P Payne
Sr VP: Robert Sweeney
VP: Daniel Calderon
VP: Mark Gulas
VP: Riad Hasan
VP: Jo Morris
VP: Rey Perez
VP: Lawrence Scott
VP: Bruce E Wood
Board of Directors: Frances A Moody-Dahlberg, Stephen E Glasgow, E Douglas McLeod, Charles D Milos, Ann M Moody, Russell S Moody, Louis E Pauls Jr, E J Pederson

NATIONAL WHOLESALE LIQUIDATORS
See NWL HOLDINGS INC

D-U-N-S 11-178-1279
NATIONAL WHOLESALE SUPPLY INC
NATIONAL HOT WATER
1972 Cal Crossing Rd, Dallas, TX 75220-7006
Tel (972) 331-7770 *Founded/Ownrshp* 2002
Sales 104.0MM^E *EMP* 130
SIC 5074 Plumbing fittings & supplies
Pr: Charles Reynolds

D-U-N-S 00-385-4189 IMP
NATIONAL WINE & SPIRITS INC
ALLEN PRODUCTS COMPANY
733 S West St, Indianapolis, IN 46225-1253
Tel (317) 636-6092 *Founded/Ownrshp* 1935
Sales 355.3MM^E *EMP* 1,600
SIC 5182 Wine & distilled beverages
Ch Bd: James E Lacrosse
* *COO:* John J Baker
* *Treas:* Patrick A Trefun
* *Ex VP:* Gregory J Mauloff
* *VP:* Dwight Deming
Dist Mgr: Bill Brown
* *VP Sls:* Catherine M Lacrosse
Board of Directors: James R Beck, Vaughn D Bryson, William M Cockrum, David W Goodrich, Norma M Johnston, Stephen E Lacrosse, Mitchell T Stoltz

NATIONAL WINE & SPIRITS MICH
See NWS MICHIGAN INC

D-U-N-S 12-121-7087 IMP
NATIONAL WOOD PRODUCTS INC
2705 S 600 W, Salt Lake City, UT 84115-2967
Tel (801) 977-1171 *Founded/Ownrshp* 1984
Sales 95.4MM^E *EMP* 160
SIC 5031 Lumber: rough, dressed & finished; Plywood
Pr: Donald L Meyer
* *Sec:* Donald A Eichler
Bd of Dir: Chad Bingham
VP: Kurt Mitek
* *VP:* Kurt Winn

NATIONAL WORKERS COMPENSATION
See NATIONAL COUNCIL ON COMPENSATION INSURANCE INC

D-U-N-S 96-974-9758
NATIONAL YMCA EMPLOYEE BENEFITS TRUST
101 N Wacker Dr Ste 1500, Chicago, IL 60606-7380
Tel (312) 977-0031 *Founded/Ownrshp* 2011
Sales 90.3MM *EMP* 3
Accts Grant Thornton Chicago Il
SIC 8641 Youth organizations
Pr: Michael Bright

D-U-N-S 00-506-9257 IMP
NATIONAL-STANDARD LLC
(*Suby of* HEICO COMPANIES L L C) ★
1631 Lake St, Niles, MI 49120-1270
Tel (269) 683-9902 *Founded/Ownrshp* 2008
Sales 97.5MM^E *EMP* 300^E
SIC 3315 3496 Wire & fabricated wire products; Wire, ferrous/iron; Wire products, ferrous/iron: made in wiredrawing plants; Miscellaneous fabricated wire products; Wire cloth & woven wire products

NATIONALEASE
See AMERIQUEST BUSINESS SERVICES INC

NATIONALEASE
See SALEM LEASING CORP

NATIONALEASE
See AIM LEASING CO

D-U-N-S 92-692-2758
NATIONS BROADBAND INC
NATIONS TEL
15455 Dallas Pkwy Ste 600, Addison, TX 75001-6760
Tel (972) 851-7851 *Founded/Ownrshp* 1993
Sales 25.0MM *EMP* 2,500
SIC 4813 Telephone communication, except radio
Pr: Eric Green
* *VP:* Robert Green

D-U-N-S 13-732-0961
NATIONS LENDING CORP
N L C
4 Summit Park Dr Ste 200, Independence, OH 44131-2583
Tel (440) 842-4817 *Founded/Ownrshp* 2003
Sales NA *EMP* 100
SIC 6162 6163 Mortgage bankers; Mortgage brokers arranging for loans, using money of others
CEO: Jeremy E Sopko
Pr: George Chapin
* *CFO:* William Lee Osborne Jr
Chf Mktg O: Dave Scilabro
Exec: Dale Phelps
* *Brnch Mgr:* Stephen Anderson
Brnch Mgr: Jeremy McClure
Brnch Mgr: Timothy Moore

D-U-N-S 78-785-5001
NATIONS ROOF CENTRAL LLC
AFFILIATED WITH NATIONS ROOF
2914 Lawing Ln, Rowlett, TX 75088-7514
Tel (972) 278-9200 *Founded/Ownrshp* 2006
Sales 87.4MM *EMP* 600
SIC 1761 Roofing, siding & sheet metal work

D-U-N-S 36-209-5775
NATIONS ROOF EAST LLC
AFFILIATE OF NATIONS ROOF
255 Lake Ave, Yonkers, NY 10701-5705
Tel (914) 423-6171 *Founded/Ownrshp* 2004
Sales 87.4MM *EMP* 600
SIC 1761 Roofing contractor; Siding contractor

D-U-N-S 60-301-2373
NATIONS ROOF LLC
NATIONS ROOF NORTH
1633 Blairs Bridge Rd, Lithia Springs, GA 30122-3118
Tel (678) 567-1533 *Founded/Ownrshp* 2004
Sales 276.5MM^E *EMP* 600
SIC 1761 Roofing contractor
CEO: Richard Nugent
CFO: Sue Kimble
VP: James Nugen

NATIONS ROOF NORTH
See NATIONS ROOF LLC

D-U-N-S 18-486-2204
NATIONS ROOF NORTH LLC
(*Suby of* NATIONS ROOF NORTH) ★
901 Sentry Dr, Waukesha, WI 53186-5964
Tel (262) 542-0002 *Founded/Ownrshp* 2004
Sales 87.4MM *EMP* 600
SIC 1761 Roofing contractor; Siding contractor
Pr: David Hinkley

D-U-N-S 15-687-8543
NATIONS ROOF OF CONNECTICUT LLC
NATIONS ROOF OF NEW ENGLAND
1400 Honeyspot Road Ext, Stratford, CT 06615-7142
Tel (203) 335-8109 *Founded/Ownrshp* 2004
Sales 87.4MM *EMP* 600
SIC 1761 Roofing contractor

D-U-N-S 55-721-8158
NATIONS ROOF OF FLORIDA LLC
(*Suby of* NATIONS ROOF NORTH) ★
1313 E Landstreet Rd, Orlando, FL 32824-7926
Tel (407) 649-1333 *Founded/Ownrshp* 2005
Sales 87.4MM *EMP* 600
SIC 1761 Roofing contractor; Siding contractor
Pr: Burt Logan
Off Mgr: Wendy Allman

NATIONS ROOF OF NEW ENGLAND
See NATIONS ROOF OF CONNECTICUT LLC

D-U-N-S 16-855-9909
NATIONS ROOF OF NEW YORK LLC
AFFILIATES OF NATIONS ROOF
70 Saint Casimir Ave, Yonkers, NY 10701-3304
Tel (914) 509-7020 *Founded/Ownrshp* 2004
Sales 87.4MM *EMP* 600
SIC 1761 Roof repair

D-U-N-S 78-223-5415
NATIONS ROOF OF OHIO LLC
AFFILIATE OF NATIONS ROOF
275 S Pioneer Blvd, Springboro, OH 45066-1180
Tel (937) 439-4160 *Founded/Ownrshp* 2006
Sales 87.4MM *EMP* 50
SIC 1761 Roofing contractor; Siding contractor
Pr: Chuck Painter
VP: Andrew Strauser
Off Mgr: Karen Wagner
Sls Mgr: Jennifer Dunaway

NATIONS TEL
See NATIONS BROADBAND INC

D-U-N-S 06-677-3326
■ NATIONSBANK NA (INC)
(*Suby of* BANK OF AMERICA CORP) ★
100 S Charles St Ste 207, Baltimore, MD 21201-2735
Tel (410) 605-5000 *Founded/Ownrshp* 1993
Sales NA *EMP* 802
SIC 6021 6531 National commercial banks; Real estate managers
Pr: R Eugene Taylor
VP: Kevin J Kelley
VP: Lee Martinec
VP: Kathryn C Swain
VP: John B Wood II
VP: Regina M Zussman

NATIONSCHOICE MORTGAGE
See FISHER FINANCIAL GROUP INC

D-U-N-S 02-814-1186
■ NATIONSTAR CAPITAL CORP
(*Suby of* NATIONSTAR MORTGAGE HOLDINGS INC) ★
350 Highland Dr, Lewisville, TX 75067-4177
Tel (469) 549-2000 *Founded/Ownrshp* 2010
Sales NA *EMP* 4,100^E
SIC 6162 Mortgage bankers & correspondents; Bond & mortgage companies
Prin: Jay Bray

D-U-N-S 07-841-9794
▲ NATIONSTAR MORTGAGE HOLDINGS INC
8950 Cypress Waters Blvd, Coppell, TX 75019-4620
Tel (469) 549-2000 *Founded/Ownrshp* 1994
Sales NA *EMP* 6,740^E
Tkr Sym NSM *Exch* NYS
SIC 6162 Mortgage bankers & correspondents; Bond & mortgage companies
Ch Bd: Jay Bray
CFO: Robert D Stiles
Ex VP: Anthony L Ebers
Ex VP: Ramesh Lakshminarayanan
Ex VP: Michael R Rawls
Ex VP: Anthony W Villani
Board of Directors: Robert H Gidel, Roy A Guthrie, Brett Hawkins, Michael D Malone

D-U-N-S 11-048-5328
■ NATIONSTAR MORTGAGE LLC
(*Suby of* NATIONSTAR MORTGAGE HOLDINGS INC) ★
8950 Cypress Waters Blvd, Coppell, TX 75019-4620
Tel (469) 549-2000 *Founded/Ownrshp* 2006
Sales NA *EMP* 2,599^E
SIC 6162 Mortgage bankers & correspondents
CEO: Jay Bray
* *Pr:* Harold Lewis
Pr: Jason McRonal
* *CFO:* David C Hisey
Ex VP: Robert Appel
Ex VP: John Butler
Ex VP: Steve Mix
Ex VP: Shawn Stone
* *Ex VP:* Anthony W Villani
VP: Jon Hodge
VP: Binni Skariah
VP: Sam Wilson
Board of Directors: Anthony H Barone, Peter Smith

D-U-N-S 04-059-6434 IMP/EXP
NATIONWIDE ARGOSY SOLUTIONS LLC
NWAS
2764 Bingle Rd, Houston, TX 77055-1135
Tel (713) 961-4700 *Founded/Ownrshp* 1998
Sales 210.2MM^E *EMP* 469^E
SIC 2759 Commercial printing
CEO: Carl L Norton
* *Pr:* Jerry L Hyde
Software D: Richard Figueras

D-U-N-S 14-561-4181
NATIONWIDE BANK
(*Suby of* NATIONWIDE FINANCIAL SERVICES INC) ★
3 Nationwide Plz, Columbus, OH 43215-2410
Tel (800) 882-2822 *Founded/Ownrshp* 1998
Sales NA *EMP* 300
SIC 6035 Federal savings banks
Pr: Steven J Rose

D-U-N-S 04-643-0013 IMP/EXP
NATIONWIDE CHILDRENS HOSPITAL
700 Childrens Dr, Columbus, OH 43205-2639
Tel (614) 722-3040 *Founded/Ownrshp* 1892
Sales 1.3MMM *EMP* 6,000
SIC 8069 Children's hospital
CEO: Steve Allen
* *COO:* Rick Miller
* *CFO:* Timothy Robinson
CFO: Timothy C Robinson
Trst: Theodore L Adams
Trst: Ann I Wolfe
Trst: Pamela T Farber
Trst: James H Gilmour
Trst: Lawrence A Hilsheimer
Trst: William G Jurgensen
Trst: James A Rutherford
Trst: Barbara C Trueman
Ofcr: Stephen A Koff
Ofcr: Linda Stoverock
VP: Lauren Bakaletz
VP: Luke Brown
VP: Jack Clark
VP: Karen Heiser
VP: Michael Hester
VP: William Long
VP: Jamie Phillips

D-U-N-S 00-790-2026
NATIONWIDE CORP (OH)
(*Suby of* NATIONWIDE MUTUAL INSURANCE CO) ★
1 Nationwide Plz, Columbus, OH 43215-2226
Tel (614) 249-7111 *Founded/Ownrshp* 1947
Sales NA *EMP* 6,523
SIC 6411 6321 Insurance agents, brokers & service; Accident insurance carriers; Health insurance carriers
Prin: Henry S Ballard
Pr: Thomas Hickey
Pr: Damon R McFerson
CEO: Steve Rasmussen
CFO: Robert J Bobien
CFO: John Helmsdoerfer
CFO: Robert A Oakley
Treas: David Diamond
Ofcr: George Lombardo
Ofcr: James Rabenstine
Assoc VP: Susan Gueli
Assoc VP: Jerri Lybarger
Assoc VP: Gus Martinez
Assoc VP: Betsy Radley
Assoc VP: John Reese
Ex VP: Donna A James
Ex VP: Michael Keller
Ex VP: Robert Rusholt
Sr VP: Philip C Gath
Sr VP: Patricia Hatler
Sr VP: Keith I Milner
Board of Directors: Keith W Eckel, David O Miller, James F Patterson, Arden L Shisler

D-U-N-S 10-199-0398
NATIONWIDE CREDIT INC
NCI
(*Suby of* ALTISOURCE SOLUTIONS INC) ★
1225 W Washington St # 300, Tempe, AZ 85281-1239
Tel (800) 456-4729 *Founded/Ownrshp* 1990
Sales 38.4MM^E *EMP* 2,000
Accts Deloitte & Touche Llp Atlanta
SIC 7322 Collection agency, except real estate
CEO: Vivek Bhandari
* *Pr:* Arindam Bose
* *CFO:* John P Barrack
CFO: Jeff Estep
Treas: Tim Farmer
Treas: Alfred Norris
* *VP:* David Albers
* *VP:* Arindam Ghosh
VP: Kay Staggs

D-U-N-S 79-044-2230
NATIONWIDE FINANCIAL INSTITUTION DISTRIBUTORS AGENCY INC
(*Suby of* NATIONWIDE CORP) ★
1 W Nationwide Blvd 2-0501, Columbus, OH 43215-2752
Tel (614) 249-6825 *Founded/Ownrshp* 1990
Sales 127.3MM^E *EMP* 60^E
SIC 6211 Mutual funds, selling by independent salesperson
Pr: David L Giertz
* *Pr:* Richard Karas
* *CEO:* Mark R Thresher
CIO: Carol Dimonda
CIO: James Korcykoski
CTO: Shekhar Mahajan
CTO: Guru Vasudeva

D-U-N-S 96-641-8220
NATIONWIDE FINANCIAL SERVICES INC
(*Suby of* NATIONWIDE CORP) ★
1 Nationwide Plz, Columbus, OH 43215-2226
Tel (614) 249-7111 *Founded/Ownrshp* 1996
Sales NA *EMP* 4,644^E
SIC 6311 6411 8742 Life insurance; Pension & retirement plan consultants; Life insurance agents; Advisory services, insurance; Banking & finance consultant
Pr: Mark R Thresher
Pr: Vince Antonucci
Pr: Rob Bilo
Pr: Eric Freud
Pr: Patrick Gill
* *CFO:* Timothy G Frommeyer
* *Treas:* Harry H Hallowell
Bd of Dir: James Bachmann
Ofcr: Michael Keller
Ofcr: James Rabenstine
Assoc VP: Bobbi Allan
Assoc VP: Claudia Comtois
Assoc VP: Stephen Farley
Assoc VP: Mark Poeppelman
* *Ex VP:* Stephen S Rasmussen
Ex VP: Kathleen D Ricord
Sr VP: David A Diamond
Sr VP: Philip C Gath
Sr VP: Donna A James
VP: Michael Benson
VP: Vince Centineo

D-U-N-S 04-830-6294
NATIONWIDE FOODS INC
BROOKFIELD FARMS
700 E 107th St, Chicago, IL 60628-3806
Tel (773) 787-4900 *Founded/Ownrshp* 1969
Sales 125.0MM *EMP* 500
SIC 2013 5142 5147 Corned beef from purchased meat; Meat, frozen: packaged; Meats, fresh
Ch Bd: Frank Swan
Pr: Dennis Gleason
Exec: David Peterson
MIS Mgr: Patrick Keable

D-U-N-S 05-464-0649
NATIONWIDE HOMES INC
1100 London Bridge Rd G102, Lake Havasu City, AZ 86404-2421
Tel (928) 453-6600 *Founded/Ownrshp* 1993
Sales 100.0MM *EMP* 35
SIC 1521 6531 New construction, single-family houses; Real estate agents & managers
Pr: Maureen M Tate
CFO: Ema Roquin
* *VP:* Arthur W Tate
Sales Asso: Lorelei Tuss

D-U-N-S 16-198-2108
NATIONWIDE INSURANCE CO OF FLORIDA
(*Suby of* NATIONWIDE MUTUAL INSURANCE CO) ★
2 Nationwide Plz, Columbus, OH 43215-2534
Tel (614) 249-7111 *Founded/Ownrshp* 1998
Sales NA *EMP* 29^E
SIC 6411 Insurance agents, brokers & service; Insurance information & consulting services
Prin: David Meyer

D-U-N-S 12-366-9116
NATIONWIDE LIFE AND ANNUITY INSURANCE CO
(*Suby of* NATIONWIDE MUTUAL INSURANCE CO) ★
1 W Nationwide Blvd # 100, Columbus, OH 43215-2752
Tel (614) 249-7111 *Founded/Ownrshp* 1982
Sales NA *EMP* 9^E
SIC 6411 Insurance agents, brokers & service
Prin: Philip Gath

D-U-N-S 00-790-2034
NATIONWIDE LIFE INSURANCE CO
(*Suby of* NATIONWIDE FINANCIAL SERVICES INC) ★
1 Nationwide Plz, Columbus, OH 43215-2226
Tel (877) 669-6877 *Founded/Ownrshp* 1929
Sales NA *EMP* 691^E
SIC 6411 Insurance agents, brokers & service; Pension & retirement plan consultants
Pr: Kirt A Walker
* *CFO:* Timothy G Frommeyer
* *Ex VP:* Mark Berven
Ex VP: Patricia Hatler
* *Ex VP:* Matt Jauchius
Ex VP: Michael Keller
* *Ex VP:* Gale V King
Ex VP: Melanie Kolp
VP: David Arango
VP: Dan Mahlum
Sls Mgr: Patrick Swenson

D-U-N-S 00-791-4641
NATIONWIDE LIFE INSURANCE CO OF AMERICA
(*Suby of* NATIONWIDE FINANCIAL SERVICES INC) ★
1000 Chesterbrook Blvd, Berwyn, PA 19312-1084
Tel (610) 407-1717 *Founded/Ownrshp* 1865, 2002
Sales NA *EMP* 1,500
SIC 6411 6211 6719 Insurance agents, brokers & service; Brokers, security; Investment holding companies, except banks
Pr: Gary D McMahan
* *CFO:* Mary Lynn Finelli
* *Treas:* Rosanne Gatta
* *Ex VP:* James G Potter Jr
* *Ex VP:* Joan Tucker
* *Sr VP:* Sarah Coxe Lange
* *VP:* Jim Benson

D-U-N-S 00-790-2042
NATIONWIDE MUTUAL FIRE INSURANCE CO
(*Suby of* NATIONWIDE MUTUAL INSURANCE CO) ★
1 W Nationwide Blvd # 100, Columbus, OH 43215-2752
Tel (614) 249-7111 *Founded/Ownrshp* 1934
Sales NA *EMP* 46^E
SIC 6411 Insurance agents, brokers & service
Ch Bd: Dimon R Mc Ferson
* *Pr:* Richard D Crabtree
CFO: Robert A Oakley
Treas: Harry H Hallowell
Ex VP: Gordon E Mc Cutchan
Ex VP: Robert J Woodward Jr
VP: Duane M Campbell

NATIONWIDE MUTUAL INSURANCE
See FARMLAND MUTUAL INSURANCE CO INC

D-U-N-S 00-790-2059
NATIONWIDE MUTUAL INSURANCE CO
1 Nationwide Plz, Columbus, OH 43215-2226
Tel (614) 249-7111 *Founded/Ownrshp* 1925
Sales NA *EMP* 34,417
SIC 6331 6311 6321 6531 Fire, marine & casualty insurance: mutual; Property damage insurance; Automobile insurance; Life insurance carriers; Accident insurance carriers; Health insurance carriers; Real estate agents & managers
CEO: Steve Rasmussen
Pr: Anne Arvia
Pr: Larry Hilsheimer
CFO: Robert A Rosholt
CFO: Mark R Thresher
Ofcr: Kirk Herath
Ofcr: Mark S Howard
Ofcr: Michael W Mahaffey
Ofcr: Jennifer L Marshalek
Assoc VP: Lynn Carnes
Assoc VP: Oyauma Garrison
Assoc VP: Travis Hodges
Assoc VP: Lisa Hodkinson
Assoc VP: Lori Pierson
Ex VP: Mark Berven
Ex VP: Michael C Keller
Ex VP: Gale V King
Ex VP: Syed Rizvi
Ex VP: Terrance Williams
Sr VP: Harry H Hallowell
VP: Joe Case
Board of Directors: M Diane Koken, Lewis J Alphin, Lydia M Marshall, James B Bachmann, Terry W McClure, Arthur I Bell, Barry J Nalebuff, Timothy J Corcoran, Ralph M Paige, Yvonne M Curl, Brent Porteus, Kenneth D Davis, Jeffrey W Zellers, Keith W Eckel, Fred C Finney, Daniel T Kelley

D-U-N-S 04-531-0430 IMP/EXP
NATIONWIDE OF CHICAGO-FOOD BROKERS INC
915 Harger Rd Ste 110, Oak Brook, IL 60523-1400
Tel (630) 286-1500 *Founded/Ownrshp* 1963
Sales 174.6MM^E *EMP* 12^E
SIC 5142 Packaged frozen goods; Fruits, frozen; Fruit juices, frozen
Pr: Ian Rahal
* *VP:* Jordan D Rahal
Brnch Mgr: Markus Farnleitner
IT Man: Mark Smith

D-U-N-S 00-246-2448 IMP
NATIONWIDE PRECISION PRODUCTS CORP (NY)
HN PRECISION-NY
200 Tech Park Dr, Rochester, NY 14623-2445
Tel (585) 272-7100 *Founded/Ownrshp* 1999, 2015
Sales 109.9MM^E *EMP* 425
SIC 3356 Nonferrous rolling & drawing
CEO: Dan Nash
* *CFO:* Paul Ainsworth
* *VP:* Dan Brooks
* *VP:* Rick Menaldino
* *VP:* Sharon Pierce
IT Man: Greg Gillete

D-U-N-S 06-381-4255
NATIONWIDE THEATRES CORP
(*Suby of* DECURION CORP) ★
120 N Robertson Blvd Fl 3, Los Angeles, CA 90048-3115
Tel (310) 657-8420 *Founded/Ownrshp* 1966
Sales 45.4MM^E *EMP* 3,000
SIC 7833 7832 Drive-in motion picture theaters; Motion picture theaters, except drive-in
Pr: Christopher Forman
* *COO:* Nora Dashwood

D-U-N-S 79-109-8270
NATIONWIDE TITLE CLEARING INC
2100 Alt 19, Palm Harbor, FL 34683-2620
Tel (727) 771-4000 *Founded/Ownrshp* 1992
Sales NA *EMP* 150
SIC 6162 6541 Bond & mortgage companies; Title reconveyance companies
Pr: Jim Stewart
* *Sr VP:* John Hillman
Sr VP: Arta Lavaie
Sr VP: Dave Pearson
Sr VP: Jeremy Pomerantz
* *Sr VP:* Alan Turbin
VP: Debbie Lastoria
* *VP:* Edward E Marsh
VP: Shawn Sorensen
VP: Michael Verneuille
Exec: Sean Hunt
Comm Dir: Donna Jones

D-U-N-S 79-038-1425
NATIVE OILFIELD SERVICES LLC
7900 S Interstate 35 W, Alvarado, TX 76009-7297
Tel (817) 783-3636 *Founded/Ownrshp* 2006
Sales 96.3MM^E *EMP* 75^E
SIC 1389 Oil field services

D-U-N-S 07-170-2745
NATIVIDAD HOSPITAL INC
OCCUPATIONAL MEDICINE
1441 Constitution Blvd, Salinas, CA 93906-3100
Tel (831) 755-4111 *Founded/Ownrshp* 1950
Sales 151.4MM *EMP* 659
SIC 8062 8011 8093 General medical & surgical hospitals; Offices & clinics of medical doctors; Specialty outpatient clinics
Pr: William Foley

D-U-N-S 13-166-5358
NATIXIS GLOBAL ASSET MANAGEMENT LP
(*Suby of* NATIXIS GLOBAL ASSET MANAGEMENT)
399 Boylston St, Boston, MA 02116-3305
Tel (617) 449-2100 *Founded/Ownrshp* 1997
Sales 542.5MM^E *EMP* 1,425
SIC 6282 8742 Investment advisory service; Investment counselors; Financial consultant
Pt: Pierre Servant
Pt: Beverly Bearden
Pt: Philip Bertram
Pt: Jeffrey D Plunkett
Pt: Neal Ryland
Pr: David Giunta
Ofcr: Pascal Delaunay
Ex VP: Beverly Beardon
Ex VP: Joshua Bogen
Ex VP: Coleen Dinneen
Ex VP: Mark Doyle
Ex VP: Robert Hussey
Ex VP: Beatriz Pinasmith
Ex VP: Sharon Wratchford
Sr VP: Matthew Garzone
Sr VP: Kathryn Karazia
Sr VP: Michael Kardok
Sr VP: Ted Leclair
Sr VP: Anthony Loureiro
Sr VP: Cynthia Lyons
Sr VP: Rosa Mailloux

NAT'L ASSN FOR HISPANIC ELDERL
See LA ASOCIACION NACIONAL PRO PERSONAS MAYORES

D-U-N-S 10-000-7541
NATOMAS UNIFIED SCHOOL DISTRICT
1901 Arena Blvd, Sacramento, CA 95834-3721
Tel (916) 567-5400 *Founded/Ownrshp* 1952
Sales 55.6MM^E *EMP* 1,000
SIC 8211 Public elementary & secondary schools; High school, junior or senior
Pr: Susan Heredia
* *VP:* Scott Dosick
Dir IT: Karen Whitlock
Schl Brd P: Susane Heredia
Schl Brd P: Scott Sosick

D-U-N-S 07-970-4682
NATROL LLC
(*Suby of* AUROBINDO PHARMA USA INC) ★
21411 Prairie St, Chatsworth, CA 91311-5829
Tel (818) 739-6000 *Founded/Ownrshp* 2015
Sales 110.0MM *EMP* 212^E
SIC 5122 2099 Drugs, proprietaries & sundries; Food preparations
Cmptr Lab: Edgar Rodriguez
Dir IT: Mirrella Jolicoeur
Prd Mgr: German Miranda
Ql Cn Mgr: Dieng Bui
Natl Sales: Tom Lane
Natl Sales: Joseph Mullan
VP Sls: Richard Yoder
Mktg Mgr: Stacy Dill
Mktg Mgr: Thomas Hart
Sls Mgr: Tiffany Hutson
Art Dir: Eli McIntyre

D-U-N-S 07-575-8540
NATRONA COUNTY SCHOOL DISTRICT
NATRONA COUNTY SCHOOL DST 1
970 N Glenn Rd, Casper, WY 82601-1635
Tel (307) 253-5200 *Founded/Ownrshp* 1900
Sales 106.4MM^E *EMP* 1,500
Accts Porter Muirhead Cornia & How
SIC 8211 Public elementary school; Public junior high school; Public senior high school
Off Mgr: Paulette Moore
MIS Dir: Drew Walker
Teacher Pr: Mike Jenning
HC Dir: Andrea Nester

NATRONA COUNTY SCHOOL DST 1
See NATRONA COUNTY SCHOOL DISTRICT

D-U-N-S 05-479-3658 IMP
▲ NATURAL ALTERNATIVES INTERNATIONAL INC
NAI
1535 Faraday Ave, Carlsbad, CA 92008-7319
Tel (760) 744-7340 *Founded/Ownrshp* 1980
Sales 114.2MM *EMP* 177
Tkr Sym NAII *Exch* NGM
SIC 2833 Vitamins, natural or synthetic: bulk, uncompounded
Ch Bd: Mark A Ledoux
Pr: Kenneth E Wolf
CFO: Michael E Fortin
Board of Directors: Joe E Davis, Alan G Dunn, Alan J Lane, Lee G Weldon

NATURAL CHOICE
See NUTRO CO

D-U-N-S 04-111-8100 IMP
NATURAL COUNTRY FARMS INC
(*Suby of* COUNTRY PURE FOODS INC) ★
681 W Waterloo Rd, Akron, OH 44314-1547
Tel (330) 753-2293 *Founded/Ownrshp* 1995
Sales 229.0MM *EMP* 180
SIC 2033 2037 2086 Fruit juices: fresh; Fruit juice concentrates, frozen; Pasteurized & mineral waters, bottled & canned
CEO: Raymond Lee
Sr VP: Tom Kolb
Sr VP: Paul E Sukalich

D-U-N-S 00-693-1794
■ NATURAL GAS PIPELINE CO OF AMERICA LLC
(*Suby of* KMI) ★
1001 Louisiana St, Houston, TX 77002-5089
Tel (713) 369-9000 *Founded/Ownrshp* 1950, 1930
Sales 233.7MM^E *EMP* 1,747
SIC 4922 1311 8741 Pipelines, natural gas; Storage, natural gas; Natural gas production; Management services
Pr: David Devine
* *CFO:* Jim Saunders
* *Ex VP:* Steve Kean

D-U-N-S 06-851-7171
▲ NATURAL GAS SERVICES GROUP INC
508 W Wall St Ste 550, Midland, TX 79701-5079
Tel (432) 262-2700 *Founded/Ownrshp* 1998
Sales 95.9MM *EMP* 263^E
Tkr Sym NGS *Exch* NYS
SIC 7353 3563 Oil field equipment, rental or leasing; Air & gas compressors
Ch Bd: Stephen C Taylor
CFO: G Larry Lawrence
Board of Directors: David L Bradshaw, John W Chisholm, Charles G Curtis, William F Hughes Jr

D-U-N-S 08-043-0290
NATURAL GAS SUPPLY LLC
TEXAS GAS TRANSPORT
9233 Denton Dr Ste 300, Dallas, TX 75235-1807
Tel (469) 305-1508 *Founded/Ownrshp* 2016
Sales 100.0MM^E *EMP* 5
SIC 4212 Petroleum haulage, local

D-U-N-S 07-854-0211
▲ NATURAL GROCERS BY VITAMIN COTTAGE INC
12612 W Alameda Pkwy, Lakewood, CO 80228-2824
Tel (303) 986-4600 *Founded/Ownrshp* 1955
Sales 705.5MM *EMP* 2,830^E
Tkr Sym NGVC *Exch* NYS
SIC 5411 5499 Grocery stores; Grocery stores, chain; Health & dietetic food stores
Pr: Zephyr Isely
* *Ch Bd:* Kemper Isely
CFO: Sandra Buffa
* *Ex VP:* Elizabeth Isely
* *Ex VP:* Heather Isely
Board of Directors: Michael T Campbell, Edward Cerkovnik, Richard Halle

D-U-N-S 61-301-3580
▲ NATURAL HEALTH TRENDS CORP
609 Deep Valley Dr # 390, Rllng HLS Est, CA 90274-3629
Tel (310) 541-0888 *Founded/Ownrshp* 1988
Sales 264.8MM *EMP* 133
Tkr Sym NHTC *Exch* NAS
SIC 5122 5961 Cosmetics, perfumes & hair products; Vitamins & minerals; Pharmaceuticals, mail order; Cosmetics & perfumes, mail order
Pr: Chris T Sharng
* *Ch Bd:* Randall A Mason
CFO: Timothy S Davidson

D-U-N-S 07-917-6973
NATURAL MARKETS FOOD GROUP
PLANET ORGANIC MARKET
1 Bridge St Ste 2, Irvington, NY 10533-1552
Tel (914) 472-7900 *Founded/Ownrshp* 1992
Sales 139.3MM^E *EMP* 1,200
SIC 5499 Health foods
CFO: Brian Shelton
CEO: Pallavi Moorthy
* *Ofcr:* John Boyle
* *Sr VP:* Sherry Nolan-Schultz
Off Mgr: Curt Avallone

D-U-N-S 06-080-1813
▲ NATURAL RESOURCE PARTNERS LP
1201 La St Ste 3400, Houston, TX 77002
Tel (713) 751-7507 *Founded/Ownrshp* 2002
Sales 488.8MM *EMP* 313^E
Tkr Sym NRP *Exch* NYS
SIC 1221 1474 Bituminous coal & lignite-surface mining; Soda ash (natural) mining
Ch Bd: Corbin J Robertson Jr
Genl Pt: Nrp LP
Pr: Wyatt L Hogan
VP: David Hensley

D-U-N-S 19-603-5430
■ NATURAL RESOURCES CONSERVATION SERVICE
USDA NRCS
(*Suby of* U S D A) ★
1400 Independence Ave Sw, Washington, DC 20250-0002
Tel (202) 720-7246 *Founded/Ownrshp* 1935
Sales NA *EMP* 12,000
SIC 9512 Soil conservation services, government;
CFO: Joseph D O'Leska Jr

D-U-N-S 07-861-5580
NATURAL RESOURCES DEFENSE COUNCIL INC
NRDC
40 W 20th St, New York, NY 10011-4211
Tel (212) 727-2700 *Founded/Ownrshp* 1970
Sales 121.6MM *EMP* 500
Accts Lb Grant Thornton Llp New Yor
SIC 8641 Environmental protection organization
CEO: Daniel R Tishman
* *Pr:* Frances G Beinecke
CFO: Judith Keefer
CFO: Lawrence Levine
* *Treas:* Joy Covey
Ofcr: Alexandra Hernandez
Sr VP: Jennifer Alley
VP: Sonah Allie
VP: Sevi Glekas
VP: Albert Huang
VP: Matthew Perrin
VP: Roseann Rock
Exec: Laura Wright
Comm Dir: Matt Howes

D-U-N-S 80-938-8713
NATURAL RESOURCES VIRGINIA
(*Suby of* OFFICE OF GOVERNOR) ★
1111 E Broad St, Richmond, VA 23219-1934
Tel (804) 786-0044 *Founded/Ownrshp* 1986
Sales NA *EMP* 1,680
SIC 9511 9512 Air, water & solid waste management; ; Land, mineral & wildlife conservation;
Bd of Dir: Mac McArthur-Fox
Bd of Dir: Sandy Hermann

D-U-N-S 04-210-1360 IMP
■ NATURALLY FRESH INC (GA)
(*Suby of* TREEHOUSE FOODS INC) ★
1000 Naturally Fresh Blvd, Atlanta, GA 30349-2909
Tel (404) 765-9000 *Founded/Ownrshp* 1966
Sales 184.8MM^E *EMP* 340
SIC 2035 2099 Dressings, salad: raw & cooked (except dry mixes); Maple syrup; Dips, except cheese & sour cream based; Sauces: dry mixes
CEO: Edward J Greene
* *Ch Bd:* Coby G Brooks
* *Pr:* Jerry Greene
* *CFO:* Pete Rostad
* *VP:* Patricia B Frederick
Dir IT: Ted Young

D-U-N-S 08-690-0578 EXP
NATURE AMERICA INC
NATURE PUBLISHING GROUP
(*Suby of* MACMILLAN MAGAZINES LIMITED)
1 New York Plz Ste 4500, New York, NY 10004-1562
Tel (212) 726-9200 *Founded/Ownrshp* 1979
Sales 300.0MM *EMP* 440
SIC 2721 Magazines: publishing only, not printed on site
Pr: Steven Inchcoombe
COO: John Carroll
Ex VP: Peter Honig
Sr VP: Nick Kemp
VP: John Elduff
VP: Richard Lalonde
Assoc Dir: Pankaj Jay
Mng Dir: Christian Dorbrandt
Genl Mgr: Muctar Ibrahim
Mktg Dir: Della Sar
Mktg Mgr: Nazly De La Rosa

NATURE BAKE
See AVB INC

D-U-N-S 07-265-6630
NATURE CONSERVANCY
4245 Fairfax Dr Ste 100, Arlington, VA 22203-1650
Tel (703) 841-5300 *Founded/Ownrshp* 1951
Sales 949.9MM *EMP* 3,400
SIC 8641 Environmental protection organization
Ch: Teresa Beck
* *Pr:* Mark Tercek

COO: Lois E Quam
**CFO:* Stephen Howell
Treas: Lara Rainbolt
**Treas:* Muneer Satter
Bd of Dir: John Randall
Ofcr: Brian McPeek
Ofcr: Claudia Sherman
Ex VP: Mark Burget
VP: Tim Barnett
VP: Karen Berky
VP: Donna Geluso
VP: Laurel Mayer
VP: Barbara Olin
VP: Francis Quitazol
VP: Rebecca Stowe
Exec: Doug Ladd
Exec: Stephanie McNamara
Exec: Barton Thompson
Assoc Dir: Christina Cheatham

NATURE NATE'S
See NORTH DALLAS HONEY CO LP

NATURE PUBLISHING GROUP
See NATURE AMERICA INC

NATURE SWEET TOMATOES
See NATURESWEET LTD

NATURE'S BAKERY
See BELLA FOUR BAKERY INC

D-U-N-S 07-952-5954
NATURES BEST DISTRIBUTION LLC (CA)
(*Suby of* KEHE SOLUTIONS) ★
6 Pointe Dr Ste 300, Brea, CA 92821-6323
Tel (714) 255-4600 *Founded/Ownrshp* 2014
Sales 177.9MM^E *EMP* 125^E
SIC 5149 Health foods
CEO: James Beck
VP Sls: Amy Kirtland
Sls Mgr: Shelly Bell
Sls Mgr: Eric Kawamoto

D-U-N-S 36-150-7622 IMP
■ **NATURES BOUNTY INC**
(*Suby of* ARCO PHARMACEUTICAL) ★
2100 Smithtown Ave, Ronkonkoma, NY 11779-7347
Tel (631) 580-6137 *Founded/Ownrshp* 1995
Sales 637.6MM^E *EMP* 6,000
SIC 2834 Vitamin preparations
Ch Bd: Scott Rudolph
**Ch Bd:* Michael Collins
**Pr:* Harvey Kamil
Sr VP: Jim Flaherty
VP: Kristine Urea
Web Dev: Yulia Fedotov

NATURES EAT
See TEXAS STAR NUT AND FOOD CO INC

D-U-N-S 18-328-2862 IMP/EXP
NATURES PRODUCTS INC
(*Suby of* WELLNEXT LLC) ★
1301 Sawgrs Corp Pkwy, Sunrise, FL 33323-2813
Tel (954) 233-3300 *Founded/Ownrshp* 1986
Sales 192.2MM^E *EMP* 244
SIC 5122 5499 Vitamins & minerals; Health & dietetic food stores
Pr: Jose Minski
CFO: George Daulerio
**Sr Cor Off:* Meyer Minski
VP: Lianne Demoya
**VP:* Ruben Minski
VP Opers: Randy Clark
Opers Mgr: Dave Cohen MBA
Plnt Mgr: Felipe Garay

D-U-N-S 08-183-2388 IMP/EXP
▲ **NATURES SUNSHINE PRODUCTS INC**
2500 W Executive Pkwy # 100, Lehi, UT 84043-3857
Tel (801) 341-7900 *Founded/Ownrshp* 1972
Sales 324.7MM *EMP* 901^E
Tkr Sym NATR *Exch* NAS
SIC 2834 Pharmaceutical preparations; Vitamin, nutrient & hematinic preparations for human use; Vitamin preparations
Ch Bd: Gregory L Probert
Pr: Paul E Noack
COO: Susan M Armstrong
CFO: Joseph W Baty
**V Ch Bd:* Kristine F Hughes
Chf Cred: Richard D Strulson
Dir IT: Justin Swapp
Snr Mgr: Clair Talbot
Board of Directors: Albert R Dowden, Robert B Mercer, Mary Beth Springer, Rebecca L Steinfort, J Christopher Teets, Jeffrey D Watkins

D-U-N-S 13-180-5707
NATURES TREES INC
SAVE A TREE
(*Suby of* GLENWOOD TREE EXPERTS) ★
550 Bedford Rd, Bedford Hills, NY 10507-1605
Tel (914) 241-4999 *Founded/Ownrshp* 2013
Sales 151.1MM^E *EMP* 310
SIC 0783 0782 0781 1629 Ornamental shrub & tree services; Arborist services; Lawn & garden services; Landscape counseling & planning; Irrigation system construction
Pr: Daniel Van Starrenburg
**CFO:* Jon Cervoni
**VP:* Rich Anda
**VP:* Donald Becker
**VP:* Ralph J Robbins
VP: Ralph Robbins
Exec: Ryan Moore
Brnch Mgr: Jim Kiely
Brnch Mgr: Kevin Kraft
Off Mgr: Nikki Nasr
Off Mgr: Emily Niemczyk

NATURE'S WAY PRODUCTS
See SCHWABE NORTH AMERICA INC

D-U-N-S 78-320-9281 IMP
NATURESWEET LTD
NATURE SWEET TOMATOES
2338 N Loop 1604 W, San Antonio, TX 78248-4521
Tel (210) 408-8500 *Founded/Ownrshp* 1999
Sales 216.9MM^E *EMP* 830^E
SIC 0161 Tomato farm
Pr: Bryant Ambelang
CFO: Armando C Lanes
CFO: Armando Llanes
CFO: Bo Meissner
VP: Adrian Almeida
VP: Kathryn Ault
VP: Manolo Reyes
VP: Dave Shaver
Software D: Pat Gomez

D-U-N-S 09-249-3501 IMP/EXP
NATUREX INC
NATUREX ULTMATE BTNCAL BNEFITS
(*Suby of* NATUREX)
375 Huyler St, South Hackensack, NJ 07606-1532
Tel (201) 440-5000 *Founded/Ownrshp* 2005
Sales 158.2MM^E *EMP* 185
Accts Prager Metis Cpas Llc Baskin
SIC 2833 Botanical products, medicinal: ground, graded or milled
Ch Bd: Thierry Lambert
**CEO:* Olivier Rigaud
**COO:* Maxime Angeluccim
**CFO:* Francois De Gantes
**CFO:* Thierr Bertrand Lambert
**CFO:* Gaetan Sourceau
**VP:* Stephane Ducroux
IT Man: Gustavo Lopez
Sls Dir: Amandine Guidi
Sls Dir: Guillaume Levade

NATUREX ULTMATE BTNCAL BNEFITS
See NATUREX INC

D-U-N-S 11-292-5144
▲ **NATUS MEDICAL INC**
6701 Koll Center Pkwy # 150, Pleasanton, CA 94566-8060
Tel (925) 223-6700 *Founded/Ownrshp* 1987
Sales 375.8MM *EMP* 1,067^E
Tkr Sym BABY *Exch* NGS
SIC 3845 Electromedical equipment
Ch Bd: Robert A Gunst
**Pr:* James B Hawkins
**CFO:* Jonathan Kennedy
VP: Christopher Chung
**VP:* D Christopher Chung
**VP:* Austin F Noll III
VP: Marybeth Smith
**VP:* Kenneth M Traverso
Snr Sftwr: Terry Henning
Sls Dir: Jeff Shields
Mktg Mgr: Leslie Snyder
Board of Directors: Doris E Engibous, Kenneth E Ludlum, William M Moore, Barbara R Paul

D-U-N-S 14-463-0597 IMP
NATUZZI AMERICAS INC
(*Suby of* NATUZZI SPA)
130 W Commerce Ave, High Point, NC 27260-4906
Tel (336) 887-8300 *Founded/Ownrshp* 1959
Sales 116.7MM *EMP* 65
SIC 5021 Furniture
Pr: Joseph Mussallem
COO: David Jacobstein
CFO: Ian Mocori
**Treas:* Karen Skinner
**Ex VP:* Gaetano De Cataldo
Sr VP: Christian Schwab
Off Mgr: Cheryllel Deal

D-U-N-S 79-696-2868
NAU COUNTRY INSURANCE CO
QBE THE AMERICAS
(*Suby of* QBE AMERICAS) ★
7333 Sunwood Dr Nw, Ramsey, MN 55303-5119
Tel (763) 323-0175 *Founded/Ownrshp* 2010
Sales NA *EMP* 25^E
SIC 6331 Fire, marine & casualty insurance & carriers; Property damage insurance
CFO: James R Korin
VP: Hope Floberg
VP: John Fremoire
VP: Rollin Grefsrud
VP: Randy Hinders
VP: Elliot Konschak
VP: John Wienstroer
VP: Bill Wilson
**Prin:* James D Deal
Rgnl Mgr: Rick Guestin
Genl Mgr: James Korin

D-U-N-S 00-901-0562
NAUMANN/HOBBS MATERIAL HANDLING CORP II INC (AZ)
4335 E Wood St, Phoenix, AZ 85040-2045
Tel (602) 437-1331 *Founded/Ownrshp* 1949, 1968
Sales 90.0MM *EMP* 325
SIC 5084 Industrial machinery & equipment
Pr: Tom Hobbs
**CFO:* Keith Sawottke
VP: Ray Hammerich
VP: Karen A Hobbs
Genl Mgr: Eric Bailey
IT Man: Peter Kingsley
IT Man: James Ryan
**VP Opers:* Scott Simmons
Sfty Mgr: Brock Brockelsby
Opers Mgr: Keith Jaeger
Manager: Ted Repella

D-U-N-S 02-768-1485 EXP
NAUMES INC
2 W Barnett St, Medford, OR 97501-3666
Tel (541) 772-6268 *Founded/Ownrshp* 1946
Sales 184.5MM^E *EMP* 700
SIC 0175 0723 4222 Deciduous tree fruits; Fruit crops market preparation services; Warehousing, cold storage or refrigerated
Pr: Michael D Naumes
CFO: Annie Geffel
**VP:* Laura F Naumes
Genl Mgr: Dave Bridge
IT Man: Jessie Sanchez

D-U-N-S 87-283-4080
NAUTIC PARTNERS LLC
100 Westminster St # 1220, Providence, RI 02903-2395
Tel (401) 278-6770 *Founded/Ownrshp* 2000
Sales 534.5MM^E *EMP* 1,797
SIC 6799 7629 Real estate investors, except property operators; Electrical equipment repair services; Telecommunication equipment repair (except telephones)
VP: Allan Petersen
Mng Dir: Douglas Hill

D-U-N-S 87-737-4140 IMP
■ **NAUTICA RETAIL USA INC**
(*Suby of* NAUTICA VF) ★
40 W 57th St Fl 3, New York, NY 10019-4001
Tel (212) 541-5990 *Founded/Ownrshp* 1992
Sales 110.8MM^E *EMP* 1,250
SIC 5611 Clothing, sportswear, men's & boys'
CEO: David Lawner
**Pr:* Karen Murray
Dir Soc: Carlie Brown
Rgnl Mgr: John Mosier
Off Mgr: Tracy Lier
Mktg Mgr: Alexandra List

NAUTICA VF
See VF SPORTSWEAR INC

D-U-N-S 02-059-5299
NAUTILUS GROUP
NEW YORK LIFE
15305 Dallas Pkwy Ste 950, Addison, TX 75001-6755
Tel (972) 720-6600 *Founded/Ownrshp* 1993
Sales NA *EMP* 38
SIC 6411 Insurance agents & brokers
CEO: Walter Ridlon

D-U-N-S 15-766-1877 IMP/EXP
▲ **NAUTILUS INC**
17750 Se 6th Way, Vancouver, WA 98683-7565
Tel (360) 859-2900 *Founded/Ownrshp* 1986
Sales 335.7MM *EMP* 470
Tkr Sym NLS *Exch* NYS
SIC 3949 Sporting & athletic goods; Gymnasium equipment
CEO: Bruce M Cazenave
**Ch Bd:* M Carl Johnson III
COO: William B McMahon
CFO: Sidharth Nayar
Sr VP: Wayne M Bolio
VP: Jeffery L Collins
VP: Dennis H Lee
VP: Robert O Murdock
Genl Mgr: Lou Pollino
IT Man: Ted McClure
Tech Mgr: Gary Nichols
Board of Directors: Ronald P Badie, Richard A Horn, Anne G Saunders, Marvin G Siegert

D-U-N-S 00-405-7816 EXP
NAUTIQUE BOAT CO INC (FL)
NAUTIQUES
14700 Aerospace Pkwy, Orlando, FL 32832-7100
Tel (407) 855-4141 *Founded/Ownrshp* 1925
Sales 125.0MM *EMP* 360^E
SIC 3799 3732 Boat trailers; Boats, fiberglass: building & repairing
CEO: Bill Yeargin
**CFO:* Sean Marrero
Treas: Gilbert Paul
**VP:* Angela R Pilkington
Exec: Matt Tierney
**Prin:* Yeargin William E
**Prin:* Marrero Sean
VP Admn: Angela Pilkington
CIO: Thomas Bates
Dir IT: Matt F McGinnis
Opers Mgr: Robin Karaffa

NAUTIQUES
See NAUTIQUE BOAT CO INC

D-U-N-S 07-576-0850
NAVAJO AGRICULTURAL PRODUCTS INDUSTRY
NAPI
10086 Nm Hwy 371, Farmington, NM 87499
Tel (505) 326-2730 *Founded/Ownrshp* 1976
Sales 57.6MM^E *EMP* 1,200
SIC 0191 General farms, primarily crop
CEO: Tsosie Lewis
**CFO:* Darryl Multine
Sr Cor Off: Lewis Tsosie
Genl Mgr: Lorenzo Baten
Genl Mgr: T Sosie Lewis

D-U-N-S 02-682-5757
NAVAJO ENGINEERING & CONSTRUCTION AUTHORITY
1 Uranium Blvd, Shiprock, NM 87420
Tel (505) 368-5151 *Founded/Ownrshp* 1973
Sales 106.8MM^E *EMP* 490
SIC 1611 1623 Highway & street construction; Water, sewer & utility lines
Genl Mgr: William C Brouthton
IT Man: James Henry
Mtls Mgr: Shoni Shorthair

NAVAJO EXPRESS
See NAVAJO SHIPPERS INC

D-U-N-S 03-098-3712
NAVAJO EXPRESS INC
(*Suby of* NAVAJO EXPRESS) ★
1400 W 64th Ave, Denver, CO 80221-2430
Tel (303) 287-3800 *Founded/Ownrshp* 1990
Sales 117.0MM^E *EMP* 527
SIC 4213 Refrigerated products transport
Pr: Don Digby
**Pr:* Don Digby Jr
**CFO:* Chris Kelly
**Ex VP:* Becky Mackintosh
VP: Chris Parson
**VP:* Jim Schram
**VP:* George Snyder
VP Opers: Steve Lusty
Sfty Dirs: Allen Lowry
Opers Mgr: Ron Hooper
Mktg Dir: Collin Varner

D-U-N-S 02-776-5099
NAVAJO NATION GAMING ENTERPRISE
249 E Nm State Hwy 118, Church Rock, NM 87311
Tel (505) 905-7100 *Founded/Ownrshp* 2006
Sales 123.5MM^E *EMP* 1,400^E
SIC 8748 Business consulting
CEO: Derrick Watchman

D-U-N-S 00-900-1702
NAVAJO NATION TRIBAL GOVERNMENT
2 Miles N Of Hwy 264, Window Rock, AZ 86515
Tel (928) 871-6352 *Founded/Ownrshp* 1923
Sales NA *EMP* 5,000
SIC 9131 Indian reservation;
Pr: Ben Shelly
Comm Dir: George Hardeen
**Prin:* Joe Shirley Jr
Netwrk Mgr: Alex Largie

NAVAJO REFINING COMPANY LLC
See HOLLYFRONTIER NAVAJO REFINING LLC

D-U-N-S 02-026-4248
NAVAJO SHIPPERS INC
NAVAJO EXPRESS
1400 W 64th Ave, Denver, CO 80221-2430
Tel (303) 287-3800 *Founded/Ownrshp* 1980
Sales 120.1MM^E *EMP* 700
SIC 4213 Refrigerated products transport; Less-than-truckload (LTL) transport; Contract haulers
Pr: Don Digby
**CFO:* Chris Kelly
Top Exec: Jim Schram
**VP:* George Synder
Off Mgr: Rebeca Mackintosh
MIS Dir: Ackbar Mirmortazavi

D-U-N-S 80-002-1990
NAVAJO TRIBAL UTILITY AUTHORITY
NTUA
(*Suby of* NAVAJO NATION TRIBAL GOVERNMENT) ★
Hwy 12 N, Fort Defiance, AZ 86504
Tel (928) 729-5721 *Founded/Ownrshp* 1959
Sales 110.0MM *EMP* 619^E
SIC 4939 4924 4911 Combination utilities; Natural gas distribution; Electric services
Genl Mgr: Sidney Dietz II
CFO: Dennis Carter
**CFO:* Thomas Nelson
Bd of Dir: Sonny Clark
Ofcr: Jackson Yazzie
Prgrm Mgr: Larry Ahasteen
Dist Mgr: Vircynthia Charley
Dist Mgr: Rubianne Dugi
Dist Mgr: Justin Paul
Genl Mgr: Gerard Curley
**Genl Mgr:* Walter W Haase

D-U-N-S 19-017-1467
■ **NAVAL POSTGRADUATE SCHOOL**
(*Suby of* UNITED STATES DEPARTMENT OF THE NAVY) ★
1 University Cir Rm M10, Monterey, CA 93943-5019
Tel (831) 656-7893 *Founded/Ownrshp* 1970
Sales 126.8MM^E *EMP* 1,100
SIC 8221 9711 University; Navy;
**Pr:* Ronald Route
Ex VP: Leonard Ferrari
Assoc Dir: Deborah Shifflett
Ex Dir: Christine Cermak
Genl Mgr: Jennifer Watson
Dir IT: Joe Lopiccolo
Sfty Mgr: Michael Berry
HC Dir: Susan Dooley

D-U-N-S 02-006-0658
■ **NAVAL RESEARCH LABORATORY**
NRL
(*Suby of* UNITED STATES DEPARTMENT OF THE NAVY) ★
4555 Overlook Ave Sw, Washington, DC 20375-0001
Tel (202) 767-2370 *Founded/Ownrshp* 1999
Sales NA *EMP* 3,300^E
SIC 9661
Ofcr: Mark Bruington
Top Exec: David Abe
Sr VP: Paul Natishan
VP: Matthew Carey
VP: Olle G Heinonen
IT Man: Amey Peltzer
Sftwr Eng: Alexander Velazquez

D-U-N-S 96-421-5979
NAVAPACHE REGIONAL MEDICAL CENTER
2200 E Show Low Lake Rd, Show Low, AZ 85901-7800
Tel (928) 537-4375 *Founded/Ownrshp* 2010
Sales 134.1MM *EMP* 18^E
SIC 8011 Offices & clinics of medical doctors
CEO: Leigh Cox
Chf Mktg O: Terrence J Cavanaugh
Dir Rad: Grant Berges
Dir Rad: Kenneth A Giles
Dir Rad: Linda Michel
Mktg Dir: Kim Mayfield
Mktg Dir: Mitzi Melero
Pr Dir: Kim Mayfeild
Opthamlgy: Daryl Pfister
Opthamlgy: Jack Sipperley
Doctor: Mike Dunlap

D-U-N-S 09-493-0963 IMP/EXP
■ **NAVARRO DISCOUNT PHARMACIES LLC** (FL)
NAVARRO DISCOUNT PHARMACY
(*Suby of* CVS HEALTH CORP) ★
9675 Nw 117th Ave 202, Medley, FL 33178-1228
Tel (305) 805-1076 *Founded/Ownrshp* 2006, 2014
Sales 242.2MM^E *EMP* 1,300
SIC 5912 Drug stores
**CEO:* Juan Ortiz
**Chf Mktg O:* Cristina Leon-Rivero
**Ex VP:* Albert Garcia
**VP:* Manuel Leon
**VP:* Vicente A Urrutia
Exec: Christina Rivero

*CIO: Sergio Campos
Pharmcst: Nancy Arrascaeta

NAVARRO DISCOUNT PHARMACY
See NAVARRO DISCOUNT PHARMACIES LLC

D-U-N-S 07-986-0350
NAVARRO MIDSTREAM SERVICES LLC
(Suby of LEWIS ENERGY GROUP LP) ★
10101 Reunion Pl Ste 1000, San Antonio, TX 78216-4157
Tel (956) 728-6000 Founded/Ownrshp 1983
Sales 19.7MM^E EMP 1,500
SIC 1382 Oil & gas exploration services
Pr: Craig Rosenstein

NAVCO SECURITY SYSTEMS
See NORTH AMERICAN VIDEO CORP

D-U-N-S 13-518-5606
NAVEX GLOBAL INC
ETHICS POINT
5500 Meadows Rd Ste 500, Lake Oswego, OR 97035-3626
Tel (971) 250-4100 Founded/Ownrshp 2014
Sales 99.8MM^E EMP 230
SIC 8748 Business consulting
CEO: Bob Conlin
*COO: Luis Ramos
CFO: Todd Henne
*CFO: Craig Stoehr
*Chf Cred: Carrie Penman
Ex VP: Doug Coblens
*Sr VP: Roger Akers
*Sr VP: Stephen Chapman
*Sr VP: Tom McNamara
*Sr VP: Chris Morton
*Sr VP: Jennifer Sherman
VP: Jeff Angtuaco
VP: Gary Borchart
VP: Steve Chapman
VP: Nick Ciancio
VP: Rhonda McNally
VP: Edward Petry
Creative D: Jeffrey Berman

D-U-N-S 94-322-9435
NAVICENT HEALTH INC
777 Hemlock St, Macon, GA 31201-2102
Tel (478) 633-1000 Founded/Ownrshp 1994
Sales 61.7MM EMP 3,900
Accts Lb Draffin & Tucker Llp Atlan
SIC 8741 Management services
CEO: Ninfa Saunders
*CEO: A Donald Faulk Jr
*CFO: Rhonda S Perry
VP: Holly Amerson
VP: William Avenell
CIO: Rick Schooler

D-U-N-S 00-713-9199 IMP
NAVICO INC
LOWRANCE SMRAD B G GFREE BRNDS
(Suby of ALTOR 2003 GP LIMITED)
4500 S 129th East Ave # 200, Tulsa, OK 74134-5885
Tel (918) 437-6881 Founded/Ownrshp 2006
Sales 529.8MM^E EMP 1,500
SIC 3812 Navigational systems & instruments
Pr: Leif Ottosson
*COO: John Scott
*CFO: Marcel Crince
CFO: Rodney Hyde
*CFO: Paul C Murphy
*Ex VP: Lucinda Abood
*Ex VP: Jim Brailey
*Ex VP: Louis Chemi
*Ex VP: Tom Edvardsen
*Ex VP: Jose Herrero
*Ex VP: Greg Konig
*Ex VP: Ronald G Weber
Sr VP: Robert Earnest
*Sr VP: Larry B Toering
VP: John Bay
VP: Anita Hatherley
*VP: Jane M Kaiser

D-U-N-S 01-624-2890
▲ NAVIENT CORP
123 S Justison St Ste 300, Wilmington, DE 19801-5363
Tel (302) 283-8000 Founded/Ownrshp 2013
Sales 5.2MMM EMP 7,300^E
Tkr Sym NAVI Exch NGS
SIC 6211 6163 Security brokers & dealers; Loan brokers
Pr: Jack Remondi
*Ch Bd: William M Diefenderfer III
Pr: John Kane
Pr: Jeff Whorley
CFO: Somsak Chivavibul
VP: Kurt Slawson
VP: Kerry Trahan
Dir Risk M: Timothy Hynes
Genl Couns: Rachel Keene
Snr Mgr: Penny Nasuti
Board of Directors: John K Adams Jr, Anna Escobedo Cabral, Diane Suitt Gilleland, Katherine A Lehman, Linda Mills, Barry A Munitz, Jane J Thompson, Laura S Unger, Barry L Williams

D-U-N-S 07-264-6094
■ NAVIENT SOLUTIONS INC (VA)
(Suby of NAVIENT CORP) ★
2001 Edmund Halley Dr, Reston, VA 20191-3436
Tel (703) 810-3000 Founded/Ownrshp 1972, 1997
Sales NA EMP 6,000
SIC 6111 Student Loan Marketing Association
Pr: Jack Remondi
CEO: John F Remondi
COO: Jon Mello
CFO: Chivavibul Somsak
Trst Ofcr: Letitia Reyna
Sr VP: John Kane
Sr VP: Steve Kirkpatrick
Sr VP: Timothy Morrison
VP: Debby Bragg
VP: Ameri Christian
VP: Doug Maurer
VP: Mark Perrault
Exec: Patricia McCarthy

D-U-N-S 02-258-2428
▲ NAVIGANT CONSULTING INC
30 S Wacker Dr Ste 3550, Chicago, IL 60606-7481
Tel (312) 573-5600 Founded/Ownrshp 1996
Sales 919.4MM EMP 5,507
Accts Kpmg Llp Chicago Illinois
Tkr Sym NCI Exch NYS
SIC 8742 Management consulting services
Ch Bd: Julie M Howard
Pr: Kenneth Swain
*CFO: Stephen R Lieberman
CFO: Stephen Lieberman
Bd of Dir: Bruce Hamilton
Ex VP: Adam Kreczko
*Ex VP: Lee A Spirer
*Ex VP: Monica M Weed
VP: Jennifer Hutchins
VP: Michael O'Keefe
VP: Catherine Rosenberg
Assoc Dir: Katie Jensen
Assoc Dir: Amy Lawless
Assoc Dir: Detlef Westphalen

D-U-N-S 79-902-1279
NAVIGATION CAPITAL PARTNERS INC
3060 Peachtree Rd Nw, Atlanta, GA 30305-2234
Tel (404) 504-4070 Founded/Ownrshp 2006
Sales 103.4MM^E EMP 716
SIC 6726 Investment offices
CEO: Lawrence E Mock
CFO: Darlene Clott
*Sec: John Richardson
VP: Zuri Briscoe
*VP: David Panton
*Prin: Mark Downs
*Prin: Eerik Giles

D-U-N-S 05-493-3502 IMP
NAVIGATORS
GLEN EYRIE CHRSTN CNFRENCE CTR
3820 N 30th St, Colorado Springs, CO 80904-5000
Tel (719) 598-1212 Founded/Ownrshp 1933
Sales 115.3MM EMP 1,750
SIC 8661 7032 5942

D-U-N-S 14-463-8251
▲ NAVIGATORS GROUP INC
400 Atlantic St Fl 8, Stamford, CT 06901-3512
Tel (203) 905-6090 Founded/Ownrshp 1982
Sales NA EMP 675^E
Tkr Sym NAVG Exch NGS
SIC 6331 6351 Fire, marine & casualty insurance; Liability insurance
Pr: Stanley A Galanski
*Ch Bd: Robert V Mendelsohn
Pr: Michael J Casella
Pr: Stephen R Coward
Pr: Jeff L Saunders
Pr: Vincent C Tizzio
CFO: Ciro M Defalco
Chf Mktg O: Loriann Lowery-Biggers
Ofcr: R Scott Eisdorfer
Ofcr: Denise M Lowsley
Ofcr: Colin D Sprott
Sr VP: H Clay Bassett Jr
Sr VP: Emily B Miner
VP: Kathleen Boswell
VP: Dustin Grande
VP: Roger Horvath
Board of Directors: Saul L Basch, H J Mervyn Blakeney, Terence N Deeks, Geoffrey E Johnson, David M Platter, Patricia H Roberts, Janice C Tomlinson, Marc M Tract

NAVILLUS CONTRACTING
See NAVILLUS TILE INC

D-U-N-S 19-853-6898
NAVILLUS TILE INC
NAVILLUS CONTRACTING
633 3rd Ave Fl 17, New York, NY 10017-8113
Tel (212) 750-1808 Founded/Ownrshp 1987
Sales 131.2MM^E EMP 400
Accts Grassi & Co Cpas Pc Jerich
SIC 1741 1771 1743 Masonry & other stonework; Concrete work; Tile installation, ceramic
Pr: Donald Sullivan
Genl Mgr: Mina Asaad

D-U-N-S 80-969-9023 IMP
■ NAVILYST MEDICAL INC
(Suby of ANGIODYNAMICS INC) ★
10 Glens Fls Technical Pa, Glens Falls, NY 12801
Tel (800) 833-9973 Founded/Ownrshp 2012
Sales 188.6MM^E EMP 670
SIC 3841 Surgical & medical instruments

NAVISITE INTERNET SERVICES
See NAVISITE LLC

D-U-N-S 96-994-1806
■ NAVISITE LLC
NAVISITE INTERNET SERVICES
(Suby of TIME WARNER) ★
400 Minuteman Rd, Andover, MA 01810-1093
Tel (978) 682-8300 Founded/Ownrshp 2011
Sales 85.6MM^E EMP 83
SIC 4813
Sr VP: Chris Cordom
Pr: Kenneth Drake
CFO: John Gavin
CFO: James W Pluntze
CFO: Jim Pluntze
Treas: David Flynn
Treas: Kenneth Hale
Bd of Dir: James Dennedy
*Chf Mktg O: Claudine Bianchi
*Ofcr: Allen Allison
Ex VP: John Muleta
*Sr VP: Mark Clayman
Sr VP: Christopher Cordom
*Sr VP: Michael Poole
*Sr VP: Sumeet Sabharwal
*Sr VP: Roger Schwanhausser
VP: Jim Ciampaglio
VP: Paul Cioni
VP: Katie Hamler
VP: Bernd Leger
VP: Staci Lyons

D-U-N-S 00-521-4200 IMP/EXP
■ NAVISTAR INC
(Suby of NAVISTAR INTERNATIONAL CORP) ★
2701 Navistar Dr, Lisle, IL 60532-3637
Tel (331) 332-5000 Founded/Ownrshp 1965
Sales 661.1MM^E EMP 1,696
Accts Miller Cooper & Co Ltd Deerfi
SIC 3711 3714 3519 6153 6159 6331 Motor vehicles & car bodies; Chassis, motor vehicle; Motor vehicle parts & accessories; Engines, diesel & semi-diesel or dual-fuel; Financing of dealers by motor vehicle manufacturers organ.; Purchasers of accounts receivable & commercial paper; Buying of installment notes; Truck finance leasing; Finance leasing, vehicles: except automobiles & trucks; Property damage insurance; Fire, marine & casualty insurance: stock
CEO: Troy A Clarke
Pr: Bill Kozek
Pr: Persio V Lisboa
Pr: Persio Lisboa
Pr: Rudi Von Meister
COO: Jack Allen
CFO: Walter G Borst
CFO: Andrew J Cederoth
Treas: Karen Kalejs
Treas: Jim Moran
Chf Cred: James K Spangler
Chf Mktg O: Al Saltiel
Sr VP: Steven K Covey
Sr VP: Greg W Elliott
Sr VP: Pamela J Hamilton
Sr VP: James M Moran
Sr VP: Richard C Tarapchak
Sr VP: Pamela J Turbeville
VP: Annette Freund
VP: Jonathan Peisner
VP: Brian B Whalen

D-U-N-S 07-927-0694 IMP
NAVISTAR INC
Caller Service 59010, Knoxville, TN 37950
Tel (865) 558-1904 Founded/Ownrshp 1965
Sales 83.9MM^E EMP 54^E
SIC 5085 Industrial supplies
Pr: Troy A Clarke

D-U-N-S 16-198-4646 IMP/EXP
▲ NAVISTAR INTERNATIONAL CORP
2701 Navistar Dr, Lisle, IL 60532-3637
Tel (331) 332-5000 Founded/Ownrshp 1993
Sales 10.1MMM EMP 14,400
Tkr Sym NAV Exch NYS
SIC 3711 3714 3713 3519 6159 Truck & tractor truck assembly; Chassis, motor vehicle; Motor homes, self-contained, assembly of; Motor vehicle parts & accessories; Truck & bus bodies; Engines, diesel & semi-diesel or dual-fuel; Automobile finance leasing
Pr: Troy A Clarke
*Ch Bd: James H Keyes
Pr: William R Kozek
Pr: William V McMenamin
CFO: Walter G Borst
Sr VP: Steven K Covey
Sr VP: Samara A Strycker
VP: Rob Henry
VP: Joe Kory
VP: Michael Lynch
VP: Bob Mann
VP: Peter O'Hara
VP: Mark Stasell
VP: Samara Strycker
VP Bus Dev: Mike Sandfort
Exec: Deirdre McClarin
Board of Directors: Dennis D Williams, Jose Maria Alapont, Stephen R D'arcy, Michael N Hammes, Vincent J Intrieri, Stanley A McChrystal, Samuel J Merksamer, Mark H Rachesky, Michael Sirignano, Dennis A Suskind

D-U-N-S 03-964-2017
NAVITAS INC
TAKE
502 Carnegie Ctr Ste 100, Princeton, NJ 08540-6289
Tel (609) 720-1002 Founded/Ownrshp 2000
Sales 168.9MM^E EMP 1,100
SIC 7379 Computer related maintenance services
CEO: Tara Baer
*CEO: Ram Yeleswarapu
CFO: D V Rai
Sr VP: Vijay Gnanaraj
VP: Anil Kodali
Exec: Jagan Devendran
Ex Dir: Mohamed Ibrahim
Genl Mgr: Reji Nair
Snr Sftwr: Mark Araas
Dir IT: Dayasan Swaminathan

D-U-N-S 62-717-0546
NAVITOR INC
COSCO INDUSTRIES
(Suby of TAYLOR CORP) ★
1725 Roe Crest Dr, North Mankato, MN 56003-1807
Tel (507) 625-2828 Founded/Ownrshp 2005
Sales 332.8MM^E EMP 1,657
SIC 2759 Commercial printing
CEO: Thomas C Ninneman
*Treas: Thomas Johnson
*VP: Suzanne Spellacy
Off Mgr: Wendy Trandahl
Software D: Jim Blare
Software D: Dale Looft
VP Mktg: Brian Hilt
Mktg Mgr: Vicki Rudenick
Sls Mgr: Amy Schmidt

D-U-N-S 09-527-5343
NAVMAR APPLIED SCIENCES CORP
NASC
65 W Street Rd Ste C, Warminster, PA 18974-3225
Tel (215) 675-4900 Founded/Ownrshp 1977
Sales 210.1MM EMP 460
Accts Frank Dzara Feasterville Pa
SIC 8731 8711 Commercial physical research; Engineering services
Pr: Thomas Fenerty
Ex VP: Harold Cody
*VP: Robert Bauder

VP: Carl Engelbert
Prgrm Mgr: Butch Snead
Genl Mgr: Karen Gallelli
IT Man: Nick Defrancesco
Mktg Dir: Daniel Fenerty

D-U-N-S 03-730-7469
NAVY ARMY COMMUNITY CREDIT UNION
2730 Rodd Field Rd, Corpus Christi, TX 78414-3146
Tel (361) 986-4500 Founded/Ownrshp 1976
Sales NA EMP 330
SIC 6061 Federal credit unions
Pr: Wayne Vann
COO: Dana Sisk
*Treas: Oran Chapman
Treas: Vicki Gonzales
Ex VP: Sarah Brien
Ex VP: Louise Foreman
Ex VP: Sarah O'Brien
*VP: Sarah O Brien
Brnch Mgr: Linda Roberts
Genl Mgr: Clare Green
CTO: Shannon SRP

D-U-N-S 00-170-7694 IMP/EXP
■ NAVY EXCHANGE SERVICE COMMAND
NEXCOM
(Suby of UNITED STATES DEPARTMENT OF DEFENSE) ★
3280 Virginia Beach Blvd, Virginia Beach, VA 23452-5799
Tel (757) 631-3696 Founded/Ownrshp 1946
Sales 2.8MMM^E EMP 14,000
Accts Kpmg Llp Norfolk Va
SIC 5399 9711 Army-Navy goods; Navy;
CEO: Robert J Bianchi
*COO: Michael P Good
*CFO: Laurie P Hasten
*Treas: Thomas McDonald
Treas: Stephen P Rodgers
VP: Gary King
VP: Thomas Williams
Netwrk Mgr: Tim Anthony
VP Mktg: Michael Conner
Snr Mgr: Kristen Garfole

D-U-N-S 06-926-9975 EXP
NAVY FEDERAL CREDIT UNION
820 Follin Ln Se, Vienna, VA 22180-4907
Tel (703) 255-8000 Founded/Ownrshp 1933
Sales NA EMP 6,037
SIC 6061 Federal credit unions
Pr: Cutler Dawson
Pr: Jacob Talton
CFO: Brady Cole
Treas: Brian McDonnell
Ofcr: Kevin Torres
VP: Nancy Astorga
VP: Debby Carter
VP: Paul Lough
VP: Joel Polster
VP: John Sherman
VP: Dana Sisk
Exec: Pat McNichol

D-U-N-S 07-264-6888
NAVY MUTUAL AID ASSOCIATION
Henderson Hall, 29, Arlington, VA 22212-0001
Tel (703) 945-1440 Founded/Ownrshp 1879
Sales 250.6MM EMP 75
Accts Lb Johnson Lambert Llp Raleig
SIC 8641 6411 Veterans' organization; Insurance agents, brokers & service
Pr: Philip Coady
COO: Stephen Pietropaoli
Assoc VP: Tom Edwareds
VP: John McVeigh

D-U-N-S 00-713-9952
NAVY PIER INC (IL)
600 E Grand Ave Ste 134, Chicago, IL 60611-6335
Tel (312) 595-5333 Founded/Ownrshp 2011
Sales 118.4MM EMP 68^E
Accts Bdo Usa Llp Chicago Il
SIC 6519 7999 Real property lessors; Sub-lessors of real estate; Exhibition operation; Carnival operation
Ch: William J Brodsky
*Pr: Andrea Zopp
*CEO: James R Reilly
COO: Brian Murphy
CFO: Ralph Leslie
Ex VP: Dan Blondin
Dir Risk M: Gina Kirchner
Dir Soc: Aloni Farmer
Dir Soc: Lyndsey Van Wyk
Admn Mgr: Margaret Murray
Genl Mgr: Chris Hayes

NAYLOR ASSOCIATION SOLUTIONS
See NAYLOR LLC

D-U-N-S 84-549-2701
NAYLOR LLC
NAYLOR ASSOCIATION SOLUTIONS
5950 Nw 1st Pl, Gainesville, FL 32607-6060
Tel (800) 369-6220 Founded/Ownrshp 2013
Sales 139.8MM^E EMP 420
SIC 2759 7374 Publication printing; Computer graphics service
Pr: Alex Debarr
*CFO: Tim Hedke
*Ex VP: Chris Caldwell
*Ex VP: Robert S Ingraham
*VP: Tara Ericson
VP: Craig Judt
*VP: Jon Meurlott
VP: Charles Popper
Exec: Douglas Pratt
Dir Soc: Dan Gardner
Advt Mgr: Ray Goodwin

D-U-N-S 06-987-3958
NAZARETH HOSPITAL
MERCY HEALTH SYSTEM
(Suby of MERCY HEALTH SYSTEM) ★
2601 Holme Ave, Philadelphia, PA 19152-2096
Tel (215) 335-6000 Founded/Ownrshp 1995
Sales 147.5MM EMP 1,230
SIC 8062 General medical & surgical hospitals
Pr: Susan Croushore

Pr: Jamal Ahmad
CEO: Lynn Odonneoo
**CFO:* Dave Wajda
VP: Mary Ellen Cockerham
Dir Lab: Geralyn Fattore
Dir Soc: Elaine March' McDonald
Dir Rx: Richard Centafonte
Dir Env Sv: Kelly Brennan
**Prin:* Cristina Fitzpatrick
Nurse Mgr: Kathy Pries
Board of Directors: Mike Murphy

D-U-N-S 00-523-3960 IMP/EXP
NAZDAR CO
NAZDAR SOURCE ONE
(*Suby of* THRALL ENTERPRISES INC) ★
8501 Hedge Lane Ter, Shawnee, KS 66227-3289
Tel (913) 422-1888 *Founded/Ownrshp* 1995
Sales 140.5MM[E] *EMP* 470
SIC 2893 Screen process ink
CEO: J Jeffrey Thrall
**Pr:* Mike Fox
CFO: Tom Muldan
**Ch:* Stanley D Christianson
**Treas:* Nancy G Haller
Ofcr: Leslie Parsons
**VP:* Richard Bowles
VP: Randy Thrall
Plnt Mgr: Tony Goodson
Plnt Mgr: David Henderson
Sls Dir: Patrick Wong
Board of Directors: Jerome A Thrall

NAZDAR SOURCE ONE
See NAZDAR CO

D-U-N-S 00-522-9448 IMP
NB COATINGS INC (IL)
(*Suby of* NIPPON PAINT AMERICA) ★
2701 E 170th St, Lansing, IL 60438-1107
Tel (800) 323-3224 *Founded/Ownrshp* 1945, 2006
Sales 107.8MM[E] *EMP* 400
SIC 2851 2865 Plastics base paints & varnishes; Coating, air curing; Color pigments, organic
Sec: Hidefumi Morita
**CEO:* Kristina Nelson
**Ch:* Mitsuo Yamada
**Ex VP:* Takashi Tohi
Exec: Kent Burich
Exec: Sam Giarraputo
Dir IT: Tracy Juno
Dir IT: Hector Sims
Tech Mgr: Mike Arias
Tech Mgr: Yutaro Kawasaki
Tech Mgr: Hans Neubeck

D-U-N-S 13-850-6162
NB VENTURES INC
GEP
100 Walnut Ave Ste 304, Clark, NJ 07066-1247
Tel (732) 382-6565 *Founded/Ownrshp* 2000
Sales 66.0MM[E] *EMP* 1,200
SIC 8742 Management consulting services
CEO: Subhash Makhija
**Pr:* Roopa Makhija
Pr: Reva Modi
**COO:* Jagadish Turimella
VP: Joel Goldhammer
VP: Joshua House
VP: David Medvedeff
**VP:* Neha Shah
Exec: Chris Martoglio
Assoc Dir: Gopinath Bharathi
Assoc Dir: Amit Kadam

D-U-N-S 04-302-5915
NBBJ LP
223 Yale Ave N, Seattle, WA 98109-5430
Tel (206) 223-5555 *Founded/Ownrshp* 1961
Sales 107.4MM[E] *EMP* 700
Accts Moss-Adams Llp Seattle Washi
SIC 8712 Architectural services
Pt: William J Bain Jr
**Pt:* Mackenzie L Skene AIA
**Pt:* Richard F Dallam
**Pt:* Helen Dimoff
**Pt:* John J F Halleran
**Pt:* Timothy J Johnson
**Pt:* David Lewis
**Pt:* Robert C Mankin
**Pt:* Aj Montero
**Pt:* Ryan Mullenix
**Pt:* William J Nichols
**Pt:* R Douglas Parris
**Pt:* Joan L Saba
**Pt:* Thomas Sieniewicz
**Pt:* Jonathan R Ward
**Pt:* Scott W Wyatt
**Pt:* David Yuan
Mng Pt: Steven R McConnell
**CEO:* R Steven McConnell
**COO:* Juli Cook
COO: Jim Jonasson

D-U-N-S 83-817-5081
NBC ACQUISITION CORP
(*Suby of* NBC HOLDINGS CORP) ★
4700 S 19th St, Lincoln, NE 68512-1216
Tel (402) 421-7300 *Founded/Ownrshp* 2004
Sales 154.0MM[E] *EMP* 2,700
SIC 5192 5942 Books; Book stores
CEO: Mark W Oppegard
Pr: Barry S Major
CFO: Alan G Siemek
Board of Directors: Mark L Bono

D-U-N-S 82-933-2548
NBC HOLDINGS CORP
(*Suby of* WESTON PRESIDIO CAPITAL MANAGEMENT II LP) ★
4700 S 19th St, Lincoln, NE 68512-1216
Tel (402) 421-7300 *Founded/Ownrshp* 1990
Sales 248.9MM[E] *EMP* 3,000[E]
SIC 5192 6719 Books; Investment holding companies, except banks
CEO: Mark W Oppegard
**Pr:* Barry Major
**CFO:* Alan Siemeck

D-U-N-S 62-006-2281
■ **NBC INTERNATIONAL LTD**
(*Suby of* NBC SUBSIDIARY 18 INC)
30 Rockefeller Plz Fl 2, New York, NY 10112-0037
Tel (212) 664-4444 *Founded/Ownrshp* 1970
Sales 13.3MM[E] *EMP* 2,026[E]
SIC 7822 Motion picture & tape distribution
CEO: Robert C Wright
**Ch Bd:* Gerard Petry
**Pr:* Fedrick Huntsberry
VP: Richard Westcott

D-U-N-S 07-887-2526
■ **NBC NEWS WORLDWIDE LLC**
(*Suby of* NBCUNIVERSAL) ★
30 Rockefeller Plz Fl 2, New York, NY 10112-0037
Tel (212) 664-4444 *Founded/Ownrshp* 1969
Sales 1.5MM[E] *EMP* 5,237[E]
SIC 4832 4833 4841 6021 6531 7383 Radio broadcasting stations; Television broadcasting stations; Cable television services; National commercial banks; Real estate brokers & agents; News syndicates
Ch: Patricia Fili-Krushel
CEO: Stephen B Burke
Ch: Robert Greenblatt
Ex VP: Matt Bond
Ex VP: Cesar Conde
Sr VP: Charles Fournier
Sr VP: David Mazza
Sr VP: Maureen Murphy
Sr VP: Ron Suter
VP: Craig Lau
VP: Art Lopez
VP: Frank Morano

D-U-N-S 60-713-0762
NBC STUDIOS INC
100 Universal City Plz, Universal City, CA 91608-1002
Tel (818) 777-1000 *Founded/Ownrshp* 1961
Sales 1.1MM[E] *EMP* 1,000
SIC 7922

D-U-N-S 00-698-8034 IMP
■ **NBC UNIVERSAL LLC**
(*Suby of* NECN) ★
1221 Avenue Of The Americ, New York, NY 10020-1001
Tel (212) 664-4444 *Founded/Ownrshp* 1987
Sales 7.3MM *EMP* 6,152
SIC 4833 8111 Television broadcasting stations; Legal services
Pr: Andrew R Lack
Pr: Christopher Baker
Pr: Adriane Berman
Pr: Neil Braun
**Pr:* Steve Capus
Pr: Mike McCarley
**Pr:* Scott M Sassa
**Pr:* Pamela Thomas-Graham
**CEO:* William Bolster
**CEO:* Stephen B Burke
COO: Beth Roberts
**CFO:* Stuart J Epstein
Ch: Mark Lazarus
**Ex VP:* Mark W Begor
**Ex VP:* Richard Cotton
Ex VP: Chris McCumber
**Ex VP:* Edward L Scanlon
Sr VP: Scot Chastain
**Sr VP:* Stephen Doerr
VP: Christina M Bailey
**VP:* Krishan Bhatia
Board of Directors: Barbara Scott Preiskel, D W Calloway, Frank Rhodes, Silas S Cathcart, Keith Sherrin, Dennis D Dammerman, Andrew C Sigler, Claudio X Gonzalez, Douglas A Warner III, Robert E Mercer, Gertrude G Michelson, Sam Nunn, John D Opie, Roger Penske

D-U-N-S 96-770-1769
■ **NBC UNIVERSITY LLC**
NBCUNIVERSAL
(*Suby of* COMCAST CORP) ★
30 Rockefeller Plz Fl 51, New York, NY 10112-0015
Tel (212) 664-4444 *Founded/Ownrshp* 2011
Sales 12.1MMM[E] *EMP* 53,000
SIC 4832 4833 4841 6021 6531 7383 Radio broadcasting stations; Television broadcasting stations; Cable television services; National commercial banks; Real estate brokers & agents; News syndicates
CEO: Stephen B Burke
Pr: Linda Yaccarino
CFO: Stuart Epstein
CFO: Anand Kini
CFO: Earl Marshall
Ofcr: Craig Robinson
Ex VP: Henry Ahn
Ex VP: Krishan Bhatia
Ex VP: Matt Bond
Ex VP: Cesar Conde
Ex VP: Darren Feher
Ex VP: Patricia Fili-Krushel
Ex VP: Lisa Hsia
Ex VP: Juliette Morris
Ex VP: John Shea
Sr VP: Catherine Balsam-Schwaber
Sr VP: Phil Cara
Sr VP: Kathy Kelly-Brown
Sr VP: James Kreckler
Sr VP: Tom Stevens
Sr VP: Maggie McLean Suniewick

NBCUNIVERSAL
See NBC UNIVERSITY LLC

D-U-N-S 60-713-0036 IMP
■ **NBCUNIVERSAL MEDIA LLC**
NECN
(*Suby of* COMCAST CORP) ★
30 Rockefeller Plz Fl 2, New York, NY 10112-0037
Tel (212) 664-4444 *Founded/Ownrshp* 2013
Sales 28.4MMM *EMP* 53,000
SIC 4841 4833 7812 7996 Cable television services; Television broadcasting stations; Motion picture production & distribution; Amusement parks
Pr: Stephen B Burke
Pr: Mark Lund
COO: Salil Mehta
CFO: Megan Canavan
CFO: Jeff Fleeher
Chf Mktg O: John Miller
Ofcr: Michael J Cavanagh
Ofcr: George Kliavkoff
Ofcr: Lawrence J Salva
Ofcr: Vivian Schiller
Ex VP: Henry Ahn
Ex VP: Meredith Ahr
Ex VP: Cameron Blanchard
Ex VP: Jay Bockhaus
Ex VP: Marianne Gambelli
Ex VP: Robert Hayes
Ex VP: Richard Licata
Sr VP: Cori Abraham
Sr VP: Meredith A Baker
Sr VP: Alyssa Corcoran
Sr VP: Salil Dalvi

D-U-N-S 07-313-1377
■ **NBD SERVICE CORP**
(*Suby of* JPMORGAN CHASE & CO) ★
1235 E Big Beaver Rd, Troy, MI 48083-1905
Tel (248) 680-2600 *Founded/Ownrshp* 1998
Sales 19.6MM[E] *EMP* 1,000
SIC 7389 Credit card service
Pr: Leonard E Ciokajlo
**Treas:* Robert E Allison
Board of Directors: Fred M Adams Jr, James E Barlett, Gerald K Hanson, Richard J McCullen

D-U-N-S 00-890-7461
■ **NBH BANK**
BANK MIDWEST
(*Suby of* NATIONAL BANK HOLDINGS CORP) ★
1111 Main St Ste 100, Kansas City, MO 64105-2114
Tel (816) 471-9800 *Founded/Ownrshp* 2010
Sales NA *EMP* 986
SIC 6022 State commercial banks
Pr: Thomas M Metzger
Pr: Sheri L Ramirez
**CEO:* G Timothy Laney
**CFO:* Dennis P Ambroske
**CFO:* Brian Lilly
Ofcr: Amy Prater
Ex VP: Kevin Kramer
Ex VP: Marvin Schutte
Ex VP: Gary L Sims
Sr VP: Joseph Arnone
Sr VP: Whitney Bartelli
Sr VP: John Baxter
**Sr VP:* Margaret Bosley
Sr VP: Amy H Crcm
Sr VP: Harold C Goldback
Sr VP: Kathy Hunter
Sr VP: Brandi Myers
**Sr VP:* Eugene J Twellman
VP: Bob Clark
VP: Shelly Cloutier
VP: Dave Coons

NBHCC'S
See NORTHEAST BEHAVIORAL HEALTH CARE CONSORTIUM

D-U-N-S 07-986-5084
■ **NBL TEXAS LLC**
(*Suby of* NOBLE ENERGY INC) ★
1001 Noble Energy Way, Houston, TX 77070-1435
Tel (281) 872-3100 *Founded/Ownrshp* 2015
Sales 454.4MM[E] *EMP* 253[E]
SIC 1311 Crude petroleum production
CEO: Charles J Rimer

NBS
See NATIONAL BANKRUPTCY SERVICES LLC

D-U-N-S 36-225-0391
▲ **NBT BANCORP INC**
52 S Broad St, Norwich, NY 13815-1646
Tel (607) 337-2265 *Founded/Ownrshp* 1986
Sales NA *EMP* 1,721
Accts Kpmg Llp Albany New York
Tkr Sym NBTB *Exch* NGS
SIC 6021 National commercial banks
Ch Bd: Martin A Dietrich
Pr: Bryan Green
CFO: Michael J Chewens
Ex VP: Timothy L Brenner
Ex VP: Catherine M Scarlett
Ex VP: Joseph R Stagliano
VP: Robert Hill
VP: Peter Kain
VP: Jim Terry
Brnch Mgr: Ellen Bouchard

D-U-N-S 00-699-3364
■ **NBT BANK NA**
N B T BANK
(*Suby of* NBT BANCORP INC) ★
52 S Broad St, Norwich, NY 13815-1699
Tel (607) 337-2265 *Founded/Ownrshp* 1986
Sales NA *EMP* 1,472
SIC 6021 National commercial banks
CEO: Martin A Dietrich
Treas: Rita Demarko
Chf Inves: John Cook
Ofcr: Kathy L Black
Ofcr: Paul J Ward
**Trst Ofcr:* Timothy Handy
Ex VP: Timothy L Brenner
Ex VP: Lance Mattingly
Sr VP: John F Buffa
**Sr VP:* Michael J Chewens
Sr VP: George Doherty
**Sr VP:* Timothy J Handy
Sr VP: Elizabeth Reynolds
Sr VP: Joseph A Stagliano
Sr VP: Patrick Ward
VP: Bradford Adams
VP: Deb Barker
VP: Deb Curriere
VP: Florence Dollar
VP: Florence Doller
VP: Brian Gladwin

D-U-N-S 03-550-3403
NBT INC (TN)
N B T
813 Ridge Lake Blvd, Memphis, TN 38120-9403
Tel (901) 818-3309 *Founded/Ownrshp* 1995
Sales NA *EMP* 70
SIC 6153 Short-term business credit
Pr: Dudley Boyd
**CFO:* Jeff Rose
**VP:* Mark Burgan

D-U-N-S 05-279-0318 IMP/EXP
■ **NBTY INC**
ARCO PHARMACEUTICAL
(*Suby of* ALPHABET HOLDING CO INC) ★
2100 Smithtown Ave, Ronkonkoma, NY 11779-7347
Tel (631) 200-2000 *Founded/Ownrshp* 1971, 2010
Sales 3.2MMM *EMP* 1,500
Accts Pricewaterhousecoopers Llp Ne
SIC 2833 5122 5499 5961 Vitamins, natural or synthetic: bulk, uncompounded; Vitamins & minerals; Health & dietetic food stores; Vitamin food stores; Health foods; Dietetic foods; Pharmaceuticals, mail order
CEO: Jeffrey A Nagel
Pr: Andre Branch
**Pr:* Glenn Schneider
Pr: Kevin Warren
**CFO:* Michael Collins
**CFO:* Stephen J Conboy
**CFO:* Dipak Golechha
**V Ch Bd:* Harvey Kamil
**Ofcr:* Andrew Archambault
Ofcr: Bernard O'Keefe
Ofcr: Matthew Roberts
Sr VP: Christopher S Brennan
Sr VP: Barry Drucker
**Sr VP:* James P Flaherty
VP: Paul Bittinger
VP: Diann Botelho
VP: Mike Collier
VP: Glenn Davis
VP: William Doherty
VP: William Dougherty
VP: Ali Ezzeddine

D-U-N-S 07-979-9010
NC HEALTH AND HUMAN SERVICES
3006 Mail Service Ctr, Raleigh, NC 27699-3000
Tel (252) 208-4000 *Founded/Ownrshp* 2015
Sales 19.5MM[E] *EMP* 1,743[E]
SIC 8211 Public elementary & secondary schools

D-U-N-S 01-666-8188
NC INC
WHOLESALE BUILDING MTLS CO
1023 Main St, Vincennes, IN 47591-2915
Tel (812) 886-4412 *Founded/Ownrshp* 1933
Sales 90.4MM[E] *EMP* 180
SIC 5031 5211 Lumber: rough, dressed & finished; Home centers
CEO: Bernard G Niehaus
**Pr:* Bernard F Niehaus
**VP:* David Niehaus
Sls Mgr: Todd Donovan

D-U-N-S 13-985-7549
NC MEDICAL SOCIETY HEALTH
700 Spring Forest Rd # 400, Raleigh, NC 27609-9124
Tel (919) 878-7513 *Founded/Ownrshp* 2003
Sales 104.7MM *EMP* 2
SIC 8621 Health association

NCA GROUP
See NATIONAL CATASTROPHE ADJUSTERS INC

NCAA
See NATIONAL COLLEGIATE ATHLETIC ASSOCIATION

NCC
See NASSAU COMMUNITY COLLEGE

D-U-N-S 06-023-0794
NCCI HOLDINGS INC
NATIO COUN ON COMP INSU
901 Peninsula Corp Cir, Boca Raton, FL 33487-1362
Tel (561) 893-1000 *Founded/Ownrshp* 1919
Sales NA *EMP* 950
SIC 6331 Workers' compensation insurance
CEO: Stephen J Klingel
**CFO:* Alfredo T Guerra
CFO: Alfredo Guerra
CFO: Alfredo Tguerra
**Treas:* Craig Ehrnst
Ofcr: Cheryl Budd
VP: Laura B Hall
CIO: Michael S Orourke
CIO: Ali A Subaihin
QA Dir: Wayne Lehmann
IT Man: Jeffrey Carlsen
Board of Directors: David H Long, Susan Rivera

NCDEQ
See NORTH CAROLINA DEPARTMENT OF ENVIRONMENTAL QUALITY

NCDOT
See NORTH CAROLINA DIVISION OF HIGHWAYS

NCE
See NORTH COAST ELECTRIC CO

NCEMC
See NORTH CAROLINA ELECTRIC MEMBERSHIP CORP

NCFE
See NORTH CENTRAL FARMERS ELEVATOR

NCFI
See BARNHARDT MANUFACTURING CO

NCH
See NORTHWEST COMMUNITY HOSPITAL FOUNDATION

D-U-N-S 00-896-3910 IMP/EXP
NCH CORP
CHEMSEARCH DIVISION
2727 Chemsearch Blvd, Irving, TX 75062-6454
Tel (972) 438-0211 *Founded/Ownrshp* 1919
Sales 2.1MMM^E *EMP* 8,500
Accts Deloitte & Touche Llp Dallas
SIC 2842 2899 3432 3548 3429 Specialty cleaning preparations; Sanitation preparations, disinfectants & deodorants; Water treating compounds; Fluxes: brazing, soldering, galvanizing & welding; Plumbing fixture fittings & trim; Welding & cutting apparatus & accessories; Electrodes, electric welding; Soldering equipment, except hand soldering irons; Metal fasteners
Pr: Irvin Levy
CFO: Iris Ho
**CFO:* Christopher T Sortwell
CFO: Jim Warnker
**Treas:* Irena Ki
Treas: Susan Sullivan
Ex VP: Don Carafiol
Ex VP: James R Fiedbeg
**Ex VP:* Levy John
Ex VP: John I Levy
Ex VP: Joe Osullivan
VP: John Currie
VP: Garland Edgell
VP: Joe Farrier
**VP:* Donald L Jones
VP: John Larsson
VP: Ann Levy
VP: James Marshall
VP: Dan Mason
VP: Earl Nicholson
VP: John Roheim
Board of Directors: Mike Benton

NCH DOWNTOWN NAPLES HOSPITAL
See NCH HEALTHCARE SYSTEM INC

NCH HEALTHCARE SYSTEM
See NAPLES COMMUNITY HOSPITAL INC

D-U-N-S 15-130-6057
NCH HEALTHCARE SYSTEM INC
NCH DOWNTOWN NAPLES HOSPITAL
350 7th St N, Naples, FL 34102-5754
Tel (239) 624-5000 *Founded/Ownrshp* 1983
Sales 385.4MM^E *EMP* 3,500^E
Accts Pricewaterhousecoopers Llp Ph
SIC 8062 General medical & surgical hospitals
Pr: Allan Weiss
V Ch: Mariann T Macdonald
V Ch: Stephen Schwartz
COO: Gail A Doln
Trst: Melody Kappauf
Trst: Robert D Landon
Trst: Raymond F Pettit
Trst: Raymond E Rilly
Trst: Howard Willner
Ofcr: Kelly Daly
VP: Sue Facteau
VP: Dora Krauss

D-U-N-S 93-321-0734
NCH MARKETING SERVICES INC
(*Suby of* VALASSIS COMMUNICATIONS INC) ★
155 N Pfingsten Rd # 200, Deerfield, IL 60015-4961
Tel (847) 317-9039 *Founded/Ownrshp* 2003
Sales 130.6MM^E *EMP* 3,300
SIC 7389 Coupon redemption service
Pr: Brian Husselbee
COO: Wan Ling
**CFO:* Maria Rosselli
Ofcr: Pearl Fields
Sr VP: David G Johnson
**VP:* Javier Acosta
VP: Laura Czekala
**VP:* Maureen Greene
VP: Timothy Halfmann
**VP:* Michelle Carey Jones
VP: Neil McManus
Exec: Julie Smykowski

NCI
See NATIONWIDE CREDIT INC

D-U-N-S 13-023-4529 IMP
▲ NCI BUILDING SYSTEMS INC
10943 N Sam Huston Pkwy W, Houston, TX 77064-5758
Tel (281) 897-7788 *Founded/Ownrshp* 1984
Sales 1.5MMM *EMP* 5,326
Accts Ernst & Young Llp Houston Te
Tkr Sym NCS *Exch* NYS
SIC 3448 3444 3442 1542 1541 7389 Prefabricated metal buildings; Prefabricated metal components; Metal roofing & roof drainage equipment; Rolling doors for industrial buildings or warehouses, metal; Nonresidential construction; Steel building construction; Drafting service, except temporary help
Ch Bd: Norman C Chambers
Pr: Don Riley
Pr: Donald R Riley
Pr: Bradley D Robeson
COO: William M Young
CFO: Mark E Johnson
Ex VP: Eric J Brown
Ex VP: Todd R Moore
VP: Charles W Dickinson
VP: Jime Garza
VP: Mark Golladay
VP: Jerome Kelleher
VP: Dan Ronchetto
VP: Fred Schubert
VP: Mark Shearer
VP: Jerry Williams
Board of Directors: Jonathan L Zrebiec, Kathleen J Affeldt, George L Ball, James G Berges, Matthew J Espe, Gary L Forbes, John J Holland, Lawrence J Kremer, George Martinez, Nathan K Sleeper

D-U-N-S 06-071-3047 EXP
■ NCI GROUP INC
M B C I
(*Suby of* NCI BUILDING SYSTEMS INC) ★
10943 N Sam Huston Pkwy W, Houston, TX 77064-5758
Tel (281) 897-7500 *Founded/Ownrshp* 1998
Sales 498.1MM^E *EMP* 2,364
SIC 3448 3446 Prefabricated metal buildings; Prefabricated metal components; Architectural metalwork
CEO: Norman C Chambers
**Pr:* John L Kuzdal
**Pr:* Donald R Riley
**Ex VP:* Eric J Brown
**Ex VP:* Mark E Johnson
Ex VP: Todd Moore
**VP:* Katy K Theroux
Rgnl Mgr: Mike Trogler
Dist Mgr: Trey Ohl
Natl Sales: Steve Stone
Sls Mgr: Chuck Glady

D-U-N-S 19-531-3866
▲ NCI INC
11730 Plaza America Dr # 700, Reston, VA 20190-4764
Tel (703) 707-6900 *Founded/Ownrshp* 1989
Sales 333.1MM *EMP* 2,000^E
Tkr Sym NCIT *Exch* NGS
SIC 7373 8711 Computer integrated systems design; Engineering services
Pr: Paul A Dillahay
**Ch Bd:* Charles K Narang
COO: Marco F De Vito
CFO: Lucas J Narel
CFO: Lucas Narel
Sr VP: Michele R Cappello
VP: John Heim
VP: John Simpson
Prgrm Mgr: Sarah Turner
Prgrm Mgr: Powell Wilson
MIS Dir: Richard Bjornaas
Board of Directors: James P Allen, Paul V Lombardi, Cindy E Moran, Austin J Yerks, Daniel R Young

D-U-N-S 62-086-4504
■ NCI INFORMATION SYSTEMS INC
(*Suby of* NCI INC) ★
11730 Plaza America Dr # 700, Reston, VA 20190-4764
Tel (703) 707-6900 *Founded/Ownrshp* 1989
Sales 229.8MM^E *EMP* 1,380^E
Accts Ernst & Young Llp Mclean Va
SIC 7373 Computer integrated systems design
Ch Bd: Charles K Narang
**Pr:* Terry W Glasgow
**CFO:* Judith L Bjornaas
CFO: Gerard Parker
Ex VP: Amorette Jones
Sr VP: Tom McDermott
VP: Maureen Boyette
VP: David Gardner
VP: Dave Goodman
VP: Carol Miller
VP: Sharyn Pensmith
Board of Directors: Stephen L Waechter

D-U-N-S 82-824-9073
■ NCL (BAHAMAS) LTD A BERMUDA CO
NORWEGIAN CRUISE LINE
(*Suby of* NORWEGIAN CRUISE LINE) ★
7665 Corporate Center Dr, Miami, FL 33126-1201
Tel (305) 436-4000 *Founded/Ownrshp* 1966
Sales 91.1MM^E *EMP* 1,800
SIC 4729 Transportation ticket offices
CEO: Frank J Del Rio
**CFO:* Wendy Beck
**VP:* Daniel Farkas

D-U-N-S 17-539-2547
■ NCL CORP LTD
NORWEGIAN CRUISE LINE
(*Suby of* NORWEGIAN CRUISE LINE HOLDINGS LTD) ★
7665 Corporate Center Dr, Miami, FL 33126-1201
Tel (305) 436-4000 *Founded/Ownrshp* 1966
Sales 4.3MMM *EMP* 24,900
Accts Pricewaterhousecoopers Llp Mi
SIC 4481 Deep sea passenger transportation, except ferry
Pr: Frank J Del Rio
Pr: Robert J Binder
Pr: Jason M Montague
Pr: Andrew Stuart
CFO: Wendy A Beck
Sr VP: Daniel S Farkas
Board of Directors: David M Abrams, Adam M Aron, John Chidsey, Kevin Crowe, Steve Martinez, Karl Peterson, Walter L Revell, F Robert Salerno, Robert Seminara

NCM
See NATIONAL CINEMEDIA INC

D-U-N-S 82-699-3011
NCP 2 LP
3060 Peachtree Rd Nw # 780, Atlanta, GA 30305-2234
Tel (404) 504-4080 *Founded/Ownrshp* 1997
Sales 94.4MM^E *EMP* 570
SIC 6211 Investment firm, general brokerage
Pt: John Richardson
Pt: Lawrence E Mock
Pt: David Panton

D-U-N-S 01-910-8872
NCP SOLUTIONS LLC
(*Suby of* HARLAND CLARKE CORP) ★
5200 E Lake Blvd, Birmingham, AL 35217-3546
Tel (205) 849-5200 *Founded/Ownrshp* 2013
Sales 95.6MM^E *EMP* 400
SIC 7374 Data processing service; Data verification service
Pr: Steven D Greenwalt
**CFO:* Russell McEwen
Treas: Ivanka Zovko
**Sr VP:* Tim Cooper
**Sr VP:* Dave Erwin
**Sr VP:* Kris Ness
**VP:* Jeff Booker
VP: Laura Cain
**VP:* Forrest Cook
**VP:* Mark Frechette
Snr Sftwr: Adam Fines

NCPA
See NORTHERN CALIFORNIA POWER AGENCY

D-U-N-S 00-131-6090 IMP
▲ NCR CORP
3097 Satellite Blvd # 100, Duluth, GA 30096-1293
Tel (937) 445-5000 *Founded/Ownrshp* 1884
Sales 6.3MMM *EMP* 32,600
Tkr Sym NCR *Exch* NYS
SIC 3575 3578 7379 7374 7371 Computer terminals; Point-of-sale devices; Computer related maintenance services; Data processing & preparation; Custom computer programming services; Software programming applications
Ch Bd: William R Nuti
Pr: Michael B Bayer
Pr: Mark D Benjamin
Pr: Andrew S Heyman
CFO: Robert P Fishman
Ofcr: Andrea L Ledford
Ex VP: Frederick Marquardt
Ex VP: Frederick J Marquardt
Sr VP: Edward R Gallagher
Sr VP: Eli Rosner
VP: Susan Boyrne
VP: Luc Brusselaers
VP: Mark Davies
VP: Ken Fabian
VP: Rick Holt
VP: John Kinney
VP: Greta Krupetsky
VP: Sylvia Lake
VP: Ralph Lamphere
VP: David Lewis
VP: Todd Michaud
Board of Directors: Gregory R Blank, Edward Boykin, Richard L Clemmer, Gary J Daichendt, Robert P Derodes, Kurt P Kuehn, Linda Fayne Levinson

D-U-N-S 09-262-9427
NCS HEALTHCARE INC
3201 Entp Pkwy Ste 220, Cleveland, OH 44122
Tel (216) 514-3350 *Founded/Ownrshp* 2003
Sales NA *EMP* 2,640
SIC 5122 8093 8049 8082 8742 5912

D-U-N-S 11-505-1877
NCS MULTISTAGE LLC
19450 State Highway 249 # 200, Houston, TX 77070-1553
Tel (281) 453-2222 *Founded/Ownrshp* 2014
Sales 200.0MM *EMP* 200
SIC 5084 Machine tools & metalworking machinery
CEO: Marty Stromquist
**Ch Bd:* Robert Nipper
**COO:* Tim Willems
**CFO:* Wade Bitter
**VP:* John Ravensberger
**VP:* Wes Stephens
Exec: Lyle Laun
Dist Mgr: Eric Duckett
**CTO:* Don Getzlaf

D-U-N-S 04-385-6723 IMP/EXP
NCS PEARSON INC
(*Suby of* PEARSON EDUCATION INC) ★
5601 Green Valley Dr # 220, Minneapolis, MN 55437-1187
Tel (952) 681-3000 *Founded/Ownrshp* 2000
Sales 1.7MMM^E *EMP* 6,981
SIC 3577 7372 7374 8748 7379 Optical scanning devices; Application computer software; Tabulating service; Optical scanning data service; Testing service, educational or personnel; Computer related maintenance services
CEO: John Fallon
**COO:* Eileen Youds
**CFO:* Robin Freestone
**Ch:* Glen Moreno
VP: Clive Hay-Smith
Counsel: Mary Lany

D-U-N-S 82-972-8141
NCU HOLDINGS LLC
10000 E University Dr, Prescott Valley, AZ 86314-2336
Tel (928) 541-7777 *Founded/Ownrshp* 2008
Sales 21.8MM^E *EMP* 1,000^E
SIC 6719 Investment holding companies, except banks
Assoc Dir: Linda Bloomberg

D-U-N-S 07-839-5803 IMP
ND INDUSTRIES INC
ND TECHNOLOGIES
1000 N Crooks Rd, Clawson, MI 48017-1003
Tel (248) 288-0000 *Founded/Ownrshp* 1992
Sales 97.0MM^E *EMP* 400
SIC 3452 2851 5072 2891 3479 Bolts, nuts, rivets & washers; Paints & allied products; Miscellaneous fasteners; Adhesives & sealants; Coating of metals & formed products
Pr: Richard Wallace
**CFO:* Bonnie M Spanke
**VP:* Michael Garofalo
**Prin:* Tracy Haase
Genl Mgr: Jim Count
Genl Mgr: Tom Pennington
Dir IT: Joe Gutowski
Dir IT: Joe Gutowstk
QC Dir: James Barr
Prd Mgr: Andrew Bryers
Ql Cn Mgr: Humberto Avila

D-U-N-S 15-242-8103
ND PROPERTIES INC
(*Suby of* TEACHERS INSURANCE AND ANNUITY ASSOCIATION OF AMERICA) ★
730 3rd Ave Ste 15485, New York, NY 10017-3206
Tel (800) 842-2252 *Founded/Ownrshp* 1990
Sales 427.5MM *EMP* 1
Accts Agh Llc Atlanta Georgia
SIC 6512 Commercial & industrial building operation
Prin: Mark L Serlen

ND TECHNOLOGIES
See ND INDUSTRIES INC

NDC MEDICAL CENTER
See SENTARA MEDICAL GROUP

D-U-N-S 04-297-8528
■ NDCHEALTH CORP
N D C
(*Suby of* MEDAPHIS PHYSICIAN) ★
1564 Northeast Expy Ne, Brookhaven, GA 30329-2071
Tel (404) 728-2000 *Founded/Ownrshp* 1967, 2006
Sales 63.1MM^E *EMP* 1,100
SIC 7374 8742 Data processing service; Data verification service; Industry specialist consultants
Pr: Philip M Pead
Pr: Art Keegan
COO: Thomas M Dunn
CFO: Gordon Campbell
**CFO:* Chris E Perkins
**Sr VP:* Philip J Jordan
**Sr VP:* Paul J Quiner
VP: David Shenk
Genl Mgr: William C McCahan
Snr Ntwrk: Scott Lokey
Sales Asso: Kim Cleary

NDF
See NEWPARK DRILLING FLUIDS LLC

NDGA
See BANDAI NAMCO ENTERTAINMENT AMERICA INC

NDOT
See NEVADA DEPARTMENT OF TRANSPORTATION

D-U-N-S 95-969-1940 IMP/EXP
■ NDS SURGICAL IMAGING LLC
(*Suby of* NOVANTA INC) ★
5750 Hellyer Ave, San Jose, CA 95138-1000
Tel (408) 776-0085 *Founded/Ownrshp* 2013
Sales 85.8MM^E *EMP* 215
Accts Deloitte & Touche Llp San Jos
SIC 5047 Patient monitoring equipment
Pr: Karim Khadr
**CFO:* Sam Brown
CFO: Deborah Young
Bd of Dir: Katia Bejan
**VP:* Dave Cantin
**VP:* Rainer Scholl
**VP:* Darko Spoljaric
VP: Daniel Webster
CTO: Stephen Tomei
QC Dir: An Nguyen
Ql Cn Mgr: David Tsai

D-U-N-S 07-392-1897
NE COLORADO CELLULAR INC
VIAERO WIRELESS
1224 W Platte Ave, Fort Morgan, CO 80701-2949
Tel (970) 467-3137 *Founded/Ownrshp* 1991
Sales 251.7MM^E *EMP* 370^E
SIC 4812 Cellular telephone services
Pr: Frank Dirico
Pr: Arnold Agcaoili
**VP:* Mike Felicissimo
Genl Mgr: Jon Becker
Store Mgr: Leslie Aeby
Store Mgr: Reuben Heikkinen
Opers Mgr: Dan Meininger
Sls Dir: Oliver Lei
Genl Couns: Eric Preston
Snr Mgr: Dennis Garza

D-U-N-S 15-980-6079
NE FOODS INC
1640 Freeport Rd, North East, PA 16428-1963
Tel (814) 725-4835 *Founded/Ownrshp* 2003
Sales 153.0MM^E *EMP* 570^E
SIC 2038 Frozen specialties; Pizza, frozen
Pr: Christopher R Miller
**Sr VP:* Richard Steele

NE KIDS
See NEW ENERGY INC

D-U-N-S 00-103-2358
NE MEDIA GROUP INC (MA)
135 Wlliam T Mrrssey Blvd, Boston, MA 02125-3310
Tel (617) 929-2000 *Founded/Ownrshp* 1989, 2013
Sales 558.0MM^E *EMP* 2,300
SIC 2711 Newspapers, publishing & printing
CEO: Michael J Sheehan
**Pr:* Christopher Mayer
**Pr:* Kenneth Arichieri
**Treas:* Laurena L Emhoff
**Treas:* Christopher Pircio
**VP:* R Anthony Benten
Exec: J P Giuggio
Div Mgr: Kathryn Colafemina
Dir IT: Dan Bunker
Netwrk Eng: Ron Briggs
Opers Mgr: Frank Foley

D-U-N-S 96-487-1730
NEA - ALASKA HEALTH PLAN TRUST FUND
4003 Iowa Dr, Anchorage, AK 99517-2539
Tel (907) 274-7526 *Founded/Ownrshp* 2010
Sales 112.4MM *EMP* 2^E
Accts Hemming Morse San Frandisco
SIC 8099 Health & allied services
Prin: Teri Burke

D-U-N-S 02-754-0607
NEA BAPTIST CLINIC
3024 Red Wolf Blvd, Jonesboro, AR 72401-7415
Tel (870) 972-7000 *Founded/Ownrshp* 2009
Sales 102.9MM *EMP* 91^E
SIC 8011 Medical centers
CEO: Brad Parsons
COO: Kara Cooper
**CFO:* Kyle Sanders

NEACE LUKENS
See ASSURED NL INSURANCE AGENCY INC

NEACE, MUSSELMAN & MAYFIELD
See NL OF KY INC

NEAD ELECTRIC
See NEAD ORGANIZATION INC

D-U-N-S 36-230-6151
NEAD ELECTRIC INC
(*Suby of* NEAD ELECTRIC) ★
187 E Union Ave, East Rutherford, NJ 07073-2123
Tel (201) 460-5200 *Founded/Ownrshp* 1987
Sales 85.5MM *EMP* 200
Accts Saxbst Llp Clifton New Jerse
SIC 1731 General electrical contractor
CEO: Robert Marziotto
* *COO:* Robert J Marziotto
* *CFO:* Joseph Gusera
Snr PM: Mike Cirlincione
Snr Mgr: Maria Cucalon

D-U-N-S 85-841-2497
NEAD ORGANIZATION INC
NEAD ELECTRIC
187 E Union Ave, East Rutherford, NJ 07073-2123
Tel (201) 460-5200 *Founded/Ownrshp* 1993
Sales 95.0MM[E] *EMP* 550
Accts Saxbst Llp Clifton New Jerse
SIC 1731 Electrical work; Communications specialization
Co-Pr: Robert Marziotto
* *Co-Pr:* Dorothy Marziotto
Snr PM: Marco Totaro

NEAL MAST & SONS GREENHOUSE
See NEAL MAST AND SON INC

D-U-N-S 08-887-1181 IMP
NEAL MAST AND SON INC
NEAL MAST & SONS GREENHOUSE
1780 4 Mile Rd Nw, Grand Rapids, MI 49544-9702
Tel (616) 784-3323 *Founded/Ownrshp* 1985
Sales 111.3MM[E] *EMP* 165
SIC 5193 Flowers & nursery stock
Owner: James Mast
* *Owner:* James Raterink
IT Man: Doug Maurer
Prd Mgr: Steve Raterink

NEAL TIRE & AUTO SERVICE
See BEN TIRE DISTRIBUTORS LTD

D-U-N-S 08-879-5091 IMP
NEAPCO COMPONENTS LLC
(*Suby of* NEAPCO HOLDINGS LLC) ★
740 Queen St, Pottstown, PA 19464-6008
Tel (610) 323-6000 *Founded/Ownrshp* 2006
Sales 434.7MM[E] *EMP* 2,200
SIC 3714 3568 Transmission housings or parts, motor vehicle; Motor vehicle transmissions, drive assemblies & parts; Power transmission equipment
CEO: Kenneth L Hopkins
* *Pr:* Keith Sanford
* *COO:* Gerald Coster

D-U-N-S 96-832-9347 IMP/EXP
NEAPCO HOLDINGS LLC
(*Suby of* WANXIANG GROUP CO., LTD.)
6735 Haggerty Rd, Belleville, MI 48111-5271
Tel (734) 447-1380 *Founded/Ownrshp* 2010
Sales 500.0MM *EMP* 2,530
SIC 3568 3714 6719 6799 Power transmission equipment; Transmission housings or parts, motor vehicle; Investment holding companies, except banks; Investment clubs
CEO: Kenneth Hopkins
* *COO:* Gerald Coster
* *CFO:* Gregory Anderson
VP: Ray Adamckyz
VP: Patrick Flanagan
Genl Mgr: Neil Wasylewski

NEAR NORTH INSURANCE BROKERAGE
See NEAR NORTH NATIONAL GROUP INC

D-U-N-S 01-842-2670
NEAR NORTH NATIONAL GROUP INC
NEAR NORTH INSURANCE BROKERAGE
875 N Michigan Ave # 3100, Chicago, IL 60611-1803
Tel (312) 867-0064 *Founded/Ownrshp* 1991
Sales NA *EMP* 739[E]
SIC 6411 Insurance agents
Pr: William Bartholomay
* *COO:* John Harney
* *CFO:* Maggie Mastensen
* *Ch:* Fred Foreman
* *VP:* Elizabeth O Simer

D-U-N-S 11-623-6597 IMP
NEATON AUTO PRODUCTS MANUFACTURING INC
(*Suby of* NIHON PLAST CO.,LTD.)
975 S Franklin St, Eaton, OH 45320-9400
Tel (937) 456-7103 *Founded/Ownrshp* 1984
Sales 111.6MM[E] *EMP* 427[E]
SIC 3714 Motor vehicle parts & accessories; Steering mechanisms, motor vehicle
Pr: Naoki Horikawa
* *Ex VP:* David Gulling
* *VP:* Kazuhiro Watanabe
VP: Aki Yokoyama
Exec: Angela Jones
Exec: Cheryl White
Dir Lab: William Schommer
Cmptr Lab: Kevin Gadd
Dir IT: Rodney Reynolds
IT Man: John Norton
IT Man: Donna Perin

D-U-N-S 78-657-5147
NEB CORP
130 S Main St, Fond Du Lac, WI 54935-4210
Tel (920) 921-7700 *Founded/Ownrshp* 1974
Sales NA *EMP* 315[E]
SIC 6029 Commercial banks
Pr: Peter E Stone

NEBCO
See AMWINS GROUP BENEFITS INC

D-U-N-S 00-725-9179
NEBCO INC (NE)
REIMERS-KAUFMAN CONCRETE PDTS
1815 Y St, Lincoln, NE 68508-1233
Tel (402) 434-1212 *Founded/Ownrshp* 1922, 1908
Sales 165.0MM[E] *EMP* 1,000
SIC 5999 3273 3272 3271 1442 4013 Concrete products, pre-cast; Ready-mixed concrete; Concrete products, precast; Concrete block & brick; Construction sand & gravel; Railroad switching
* *Treas:* Charles D Meyer
VP: Ted Butler
VP: Dale Kisling
* *VP:* J Ross Mc Cown
* *VP:* Robert E Miller
IT Man: Trent Heiser
Sfty Mgr: Dan Brock
Opers Mgr: Terry Landen
Plnt Mgr: Mike Mueller
Mktg Mgr: Adam Burmood

NEBF
See NATIONAL ELECTRICAL BENEFIT FUND

D-U-N-S 07-300-3360
NEBO SCHOOL DISTRICT
350 S Main St, Spanish Fork, UT 84660-2408
Tel (801) 354-7400 *Founded/Ownrshp* 1915
Sales 236.7MM *EMP* 2,000
Accts Gilbert & Stewart Cpa Pc Pr
SIC 8211 Public elementary school; Public junior high school; Public senior high school
Bd of Dir: Randy Boothe
Bd of Dir: Denise Ray
* *VP:* Rod Oldroyd
Dir Risk M: Dave Gneiting
Prgrm Mgr: Eileen Quintana
Store Mgr: Cheryl Davis
IT Man: Chris Loveless
Netwrk Eng: Robert Schmoyer
Opers Mgr: Steve Maughan
Schl Brd P: Rick Ainge
Psych: Joy Benson

D-U-N-S 87-713-4908 EXP
NEBRASKA BEEF LTD
4501 S 36th St, Omaha, NE 68107-1330
Tel (402) 734-6823 *Founded/Ownrshp* 1994
Sales 224.1MM[E] *EMP* 900
SIC 2011 Meat packing plants
Pt: William Hughes
Pt: Marvin Schrack
Pt: Mike Thatcher
VP Admn: Jake Timmerman
Mktg Dir: Ann M Bosshamer

D-U-N-S 06-864-0457 IMP/EXP
NEBRASKA BOOK CO INC
(*Suby of* NEBRASKA BOOK INTERMEDIATE HOLDINGS INC) ★
4700 S 19th St, Lincoln, NE 68512-1216
Tel (402) 421-7300 *Founded/Ownrshp* 2012
Sales 407.3MM[E] *EMP* 2,600[E]
SIC 5942 5192 5961 College book stores; Books; Educational supplies & equipment, mail order
Pr: Benjamin Riggsby
Mng Pt: Rick Reeble
CFO: John Macieo
Sr Cor Off: Noreen Manfield
Chf Mktg O: Barry Major
Sr VP: Nathan D Rempe
VP: Bill Allen
VP: John A Callahan
VP: Bill Edmonds
VP: Kenneth Jirovsky
VP: Art Joyner
VP: Nate Rempe
VP: Bill Zeuch

D-U-N-S 07-925-5689
NEBRASKA BOOK HOLDINGS INC
4700 S 19th St, Lincoln, NE 68512-1216
Tel (402) 421-0500 *Founded/Ownrshp* 2012
Sales 431.7MM[E] *EMP* 2,600[E]
SIC 6719 5942 5192 5961 Investment holding companies, except banks; College book stores; Books; Educational supplies & equipment, mail order
Pr: Benjamin Riggsby
* *CFO:* Jay Amond
* *CFO:* John Macieo
Sr VP: Kara Bunde-Dunn
* *VP:* Nathan Rempe

D-U-N-S 02-461-9149
NEBRASKA BOOK INTERMEDIATE HOLDINGS INC
(*Suby of* NEBRASKA BOOK HOLDINGS INC) ★
4701 S 19th St, Lincoln, NE 68512
Tel (402) 421-7300 *Founded/Ownrshp* 2012
Sales 184.3MM[E] *EMP* 2,600[E]
SIC 6719 5942 5192 5961 Investment holding companies, except banks; College book stores; Books; Educational supplies & equipment, mail order
Pr: Benjamin Riggsby
* *CFO:* John Macieo
* *VP:* Nathan Rempe

D-U-N-S 80-882-0054
NEBRASKA DEPARTMENT OF ADMINISTRATIVE SERVICES
(*Suby of* EXECUTIVE OFFICE OF THE STATE OF NEBRASKA)
1526 K St Ste 250, Lincoln, NE 68508-2732
Tel (402) 471-2331 *Founded/Ownrshp* 1965
Sales NA *EMP* 1,357[E]
SIC 9199 General government administration;

D-U-N-S 04-557-6279
NEBRASKA ELECTRIC GENERATION & TRANSMISSION COOPERATIVE INC
2472 18th Ave, Columbus, NE 68601-2604
Tel (402) 564-8142 *Founded/Ownrshp* 1956
Sales 247.5MM *EMP* 4
SIC 4911 Generation, electric power; Transmission, electric power
Pr: Mike Siefken
Genl Mgr: Bruce Pontow

D-U-N-S 00-787-5040 IMP
■ **NEBRASKA FURNITURE MART INC**
(*Suby of* BERKSHIRE HATHAWAY INC) ★
700 S 72nd St, Omaha, NE 68114-4697
Tel (402) 397-6100 *Founded/Ownrshp* 1937
Sales 830.2MM[E] *EMP* 2,614
SIC 5712 5713 5722 5731 5734 5946 Furniture stores; Floor covering stores; Household appliance stores; Radio, television & electronic stores; Television sets; Video recorders, players, disc players & accessories; Video cameras & accessories; Computer & software stores; Camera & photographic supply stores
CEO: Irv Blumkin
Pr: Ronald Blumkin
CFO: Doug Hamlin
CFO: Brian Koenig
Treas: April Jackson
VP: Ryan Blumkin
VP: Brian Hoppe
VP: Ed Lipsett
Store Dir: Jeff Lind
Genl Mgr: Jim Cahill
CIO: David Bash

D-U-N-S 17-195-6568
NEBRASKA INDUSTRAIL COMPETITIVENESS SERVICE
SENIOR INDEPENDENCE ADULT DAY
(*Suby of* STATE OF NEBRASKA) ★
8800 O St, Lincoln, NE 68520-1227
Tel (402) 437-2535 *Founded/Ownrshp* 1997
Sales NA *EMP* 5,004[E]
SIC 9199 General government administration;

D-U-N-S 04-353-1607
NEBRASKA MEDICAL CENTER (NE)
NEBRASKA MEDICINE
987400 Nebraska Med Ctr, Omaha, NE 68198-0001
Tel (402) 552-2000 *Founded/Ownrshp* 1903, 1997
Sales 1.0MMM *EMP* 9,100
Accts Kpmg Llp Omaha Ne
SIC 8062 Hospital, professional nursing school with AMA residency
CEO: William S Dinsmoor
Chf Rad: Craig Walker
* *Ch Bd:* Harlan J Noddle
CFO: Bill Dinsmoor
* *Treas:* Bruce E Grewcock
* *Treas:* Bruce R Lauritsen
* *V Ch Bd:* Kenneth E Stinson
Ofcr: Leslie A Spethman
Sr VP: Michael Ash
VP: Jennifer Graber
Ex Dir: Crista Latham

NEBRASKA MEDICINE
See NEBRASKA MEDICAL CENTER

D-U-N-S 11-507-2787
NEBRASKA METHODIST HEALTH SYSTEM INC
8511 W Dodge Rd, Omaha, NE 68114-3403
Tel (402) 354-2176 *Founded/Ownrshp* 1981
Sales 50.2MM *EMP* 5,200
SIC 8062

D-U-N-S 06-152-9418 IMP
NEBRASKA METHODIST HOSPITAL INC
METHODIST HOSP PAIN MGT CLINIC
(*Suby of* NEBRASKA METHODIST HEALTH SYSTEM INC) ★
8303 Dodge St, Omaha, NE 68114-4108
Tel (402) 354-4540 *Founded/Ownrshp* 1981
Sales 511.7MM *EMP* 2,635
SIC 8062 General medical & surgical hospitals
Pr: John M Fraser
Chf Rad: Kevin Nelson
* *CFO:* Linda K Burt
* *VP:* Mark A Burmester
* *Prin:* Steven Zuber
Genl Mgr: Megan Harris
Pathlgst: Gene N Herbek
Doctor: Thomas Brennan

D-U-N-S 14-729-7126
NEBRASKA ORTHOPAEDIC HOSPITAL LLC
2808 S 143rd Plz, Omaha, NE 68144-5611
Tel (402) 637-0600 *Founded/Ownrshp* 2004
Sales 85.8MM *EMP* 240
SIC 8069 Orthopedic hospital
CEO: Thomas C Macy
* *COO:* Mark Longacre
* *CFO:* Anna E McCaslin

D-U-N-S 00-729-5272 IMP
NEBRASKA PUBLIC POWER DISTRICT
NUCLEAR FACILITY
1414 15th St, Columbus, NE 68601-5226
Tel (402) 564-8561 *Founded/Ownrshp* 1939
Sales 1.1MMM *EMP* 2,003
Accts Pricewaterhousecoopers Llp St
SIC 4911 Generation, electric power; Transmission, electric power; Distribution, electric power
Pr: Pat Pope
Pr: Elaine Kuta
* *COO:* Tom Kent
* *CFO:* Traci Bender
Treas: Christine Pillen
Bd of Dir: Jerry Cholopek
VP: Michael Culjat
* *VP:* Ken Curry
* *VP:* Oscar Limpias
* *VP:* John McClure
VP: William Merrill
VP: Patrick Pope
VP: Dave Rich
VP: Roy Steiner
Exec: Stan Clouse
Board of Directors: Ed Schrock, Jerry Chlopek, Gary Thompson, Fred Christensen, Barry Dekay, Virgil Froehlich, Mary Harding, Thomas Hoff, Ken Kunze, Ron Larsen, Larry Linstrom

D-U-N-S 03-499-0374
NEBRASKA-IOWA SUPPLY CO INC
CONWAY OIL COMPANY
1160 Lincoln St, Blair, NE 68008-2163
Tel (402) 426-2171 *Founded/Ownrshp* 1985
Sales 119.6MM *EMP* 95
Accts Masimore Magnuson & Associate
SIC 5172 Gasoline; Crude oil; Lubricating oils & greases
* *Pr:* Mark T Lippincott
CFO: John Borchardt
* *Treas:* John P Borchardt
Treas: Celeste Lux
* *VP:* Janice Lippincott
Genl Mgr: Luke Wiese

D-U-N-S 61-484-1625 IMP
NEBRASKALAND INC
355 Food Center Dr Ste G4, Bronx, NY 10474-7580
Tel (718) 842-0700 *Founded/Ownrshp* 1989
Sales 223.9MM[E] *EMP* 200[E]
SIC 5147 Meats & meat products
Pr: Richard Romanoff
COO: Barbara Sarner
Ex VP: Daniel Romanoff
VP Sls: Lucia Tejeda
Sls Mgr: Marc Greenberg

NEBRASKALAND TIRE CO OF NORTH
See NEBRASKALAND TIRE INC

D-U-N-S 07-012-0985
NEBRASKALAND TIRE INC
NEBRASKALAND TIRE CO OF NORTH
Hwy 283 & Hwy I 80, Lexington, NE 68850
Tel (308) 324-2338 *Founded/Ownrshp* 1974
Sales 89.3MM *EMP* 340
Accts Bkd Llp Wichita Ks
SIC 5531 5541 5411 Automotive tires; Truck stops; Convenience stores, independent
Pr: Gary K Wright
* *Treas:* Scott Samway
* *Sec:* Nancy Wright

NEBS
See NEW ENGLAND BUSINESS SERVICE INC

NEC
See NATIONAL EXPRESS LLC

D-U-N-S 14-725-5405 IMP
NEC CORP OF AMERICA
(*Suby of* NEC CORPORATION)
3929 W John Carpenter Fwy, Irving, TX 75063-2909
Tel (214) 262-6000 *Founded/Ownrshp* 2004
Sales 1.4MMM[E] *EMP* 3,000
SIC 5045 5065 Computers, peripherals & software; Electronic parts & equipment
CEO: Shinsuke Takahashi
* *Pr:* Nobuhiro Endo
COO: Pierre Richer
CFO: Yoshio Kakishita
CFO: Hiroyuki Matsukura
CFO: Glenn Means
Treas: Michael Arterberry
Treas: Yoshihiro Mori
* *Treas:* Ed Welch
Ex VP: Gordon Chapple
* *Ex VP:* Harumi Ikeda
* *Ex VP:* Toshiyuki Mineno
Sr VP: Brian Archer
Sr VP: Iwao Fuchigami
Sr VP: Kazumasa Fujie
Sr VP: Kevin Hooper
* *Sr VP:* Kenichi Kanazu
Sr VP: Kazuhiko Kobayashi
* *Sr VP:* Takashi Niino
* *Sr VP:* Kuniaki Okada
Sr VP: Phil Scarfo

NECA
See NATIONAL ENTERTAINMENT COLLECTIBLES ASSOCIATION INC

NECA
See NATIONAL EXCHANGE CARRIER ASSOCIATION

D-U-N-S 01-230-2230
NECA IBEW FAMILY MEDICAL CARE PLAN
410 Chickamauga Ave # 301, Rossville, GA 30741-1349
Tel (877) 937-9602 *Founded/Ownrshp* 2005
Sales NA *EMP* 4[E]
Accts Calibre Cpa Group Pllc Bethes
SIC 6371 Union trust funds
Ex Dir: Lawrence J Bradley

D-U-N-S 11-477-0654
NECA IBEW WELFARE TRUST FUND
2120 Hubbard Ave, Decatur, IL 62526-2871
Tel (800) 765-4239 *Founded/Ownrshp* 1955
Sales 146.9MM *EMP* 40
SIC 8631 Labor unions & similar labor organizations

NECN
See NBCUNIVERSAL MEDIA LLC

D-U-N-S 60-424-5170
NECTAR ACQUISITION CORP
(*Suby of* TNS GROUP HOLDINGS LIMITED)
410 Horsham Rd Frnt, Horsham, PA 19044-2041
Tel (215) 442-9000 *Founded/Ownrshp* 2003
Sales 25.2MM[E] *EMP* 1,301
SIC 8732 Market analysis or research
Pr: Kenneth M Freeman
Treas: Brian Haveson
VP: Thomas C Mattick

NEDCO SUPPLY
See PHILCOR TV & ELECTRONIC LEASING INC

D-U-N-S 10-229-1309
NEDELCO INC
HAMILTON TELECOMMUNICATIONS
1001 12th St, Aurora, NE 68818-2004
Tel (402) 694-5101 *Founded/Ownrshp* 1963
Sales 165.0MM[E] *EMP* 800[E]
SIC 4813 Local telephone communications; Long distance telephone communications;
Pr: Phillip C Nelson
* *Sec:* Betty A Van Luchene
VP: Dan Molliconi
* *VP:* John Nelson
Genl Mgr: Pat Shaw
Off Mgr: Ronni Harvey
Sftwr Eng: Keo Sabell
Mktg Mgr: Gary Lewien
Sls Mgr: Bob Mazza

D-U-N-S 01-950-5056
■ **NEEDHAM ELECTRIC SUPPLY CORP** (MA)
NESCO
(Suby of WESCO DISTRIBUTION INC) ★
5 Shawmut Rd, Canton, MA 02021-1408
Tel (781) 828-9494 Founded/Ownrshp 1958, 1960
Sales 146.2MM[E] EMP 250
SIC 5063 3648

D-U-N-S 96-809-1202
NEEDLE HOLDINGS INC
5555 Darrow Rd, Hudson, OH 44236-4011
Tel (330) 656-2600 Founded/Ownrshp 2010
Sales 520.0MM[E] EMP 22,000[E]
SIC 5945 Arts & crafts supplies
Pr: Darrell Webb

D-U-N-S 94-606-6396
NEEDLER ENTERPRISES INC
FRESH ENCOUNTER
317 W Main Cross St, Findlay, OH 45840-3314
Tel (419) 422-8090 Founded/Ownrshp 1985
Sales 154.4MM[E] EMP 1,371
SIC 5411 Grocery stores
Ch Bd: Michael S Needler
COO: John Holbrook
CFO: Dale Hoffman
*CFO: Ken Williams
*Sr VP: Mark Gephart
MIS Dir: Chris Groman

D-U-N-S 14-772-1229
NEEL-SCHAFFER INC
125 S Congress St # 1100, Jackson, MS 39201-3395
Tel (601) 948-3071 Founded/Ownrshp 1983
Sales 91.4MM[E] EMP 350
SIC 8711

D-U-N-S 09-313-9947
NEELY COBLE CO
(Suby of NEELY COBLE CO INC) ★
319 Fesslers Ln, Nashville, TN 37210-2905
Tel (615) 244-8900 Founded/Ownrshp 1977
Sales NA EMP 172
SIC 6159 Truck finance leasing
Ch Bd: Neely B Coble Jr
*Pr: Neely Coble III
*Ex VP: William R Foster
*VP: G William Coble

D-U-N-S 00-405-2734
NEELY COBLE CO INC (TN)
319 Fesslers Ln, Nashville, TN 37210-2905
Tel (615) 244-8900 Founded/Ownrshp 1951
Sales 88.0MM[E] EMP 172
SIC 5012 5013 Trucks, commercial; Automotive supplies & parts
Pr: Neely B Coble III
*Ch Bd: Neely B Coble Jr
CFO: John Carroll
*CFO: William R Foster
*VP: G W Coble III
Exec: Pam Kittrell
Genl Mgr: Tracy Linville
Manager: Kirk Scott
Sls Mgr: Dudley Smith
Sales Asso: Myles Baldwin
Sales Asso: Edward Coble

D-U-N-S 02-387-6381
▲ **NEENAH ENTERPRISES INC**
2121 Brooks Ave, Neenah, WI 54956-4756
Tel (920) 725-7000 Founded/Ownrshp 2010
Sales 409.5MM[E] EMP 1,650[E]
Tkr Sym NNHE Exch OTO
SIC 3272 3312 Cast stone, concrete; Axles, rolled or forged: made in steel mills
Pr: Thomas J Riordan
*CFO: Thomas Adrians
VP: Mark Steine
Exec: Lori Spangenberg
Netwrk Eng: Michael Hoeppner

NEENAH FOUNDERY
See NFC CASTINGS INC

D-U-N-S 19-471-8961 IMP/EXP
■ **NEENAH FOUNDRY CO**
(Suby of NEENAH FOUNDERY) ★
2121 Brooks Ave, Neenah, WI 54956-4700
Tel (920) 725-7000 Founded/Ownrshp 2006
Sales 409.5MM[E] EMP 1,650
Accts Ernst & Young Llp Milwaukee
SIC 3321 3315 Ductile iron castings; Gray iron castings; Steel wire & related products
CEO: Thomas J Riordan
*CFO: Thomas Adrians
CFO: Bob Thompson
*VP: Robert Spence
VP: Joseph Varkoly
Ex Dir: Scott Harper
Rgnl Mgr: A J Mann
Brnch Mgr: Mark Larson
CTO: Julie Vandenacker
QA Dir: Dave Kutchenriter
Netwrk Eng: Henry Etteldorf
Board of Directors: Tim Bernlohr, James Chapman, John Forsgren, Walter Jones, Ted Lodge, Mark Richards, Thomas Riordan

D-U-N-S 14-523-5615 IMP/EXP
■ **NEENAH NORTHEAST LLC**
FIBERMARK NORTH AMERICA
(Suby of NEENAH PAPER INC) ★
70 Front St, West Springfield, MA 01089-3113
Tel (413) 533-0699 Founded/Ownrshp 1861
Sales 188.8MM[E] EMP 494
SIC 2631 Pressboard
CEO: Anthony Pd Maclaurin
Treas: Matthew Levine
VP: Eric Schondorf
VP: Craig Thiel

D-U-N-S 79-293-6353 IMP/EXP
■ **NEENAH PAPER FR LLC**
(Suby of NEENAH PAPER INC) ★
1376 Kimberly Dr, Neenah, WI 54956-1641
Tel (800) 558-8327 Founded/Ownrshp 2010
Sales 275.8MM[E] EMP 775
SIC 2679 2621 Paper products, converted; Paper mills
Ch: Robert C Buchanan
VP: Robert M McDonald
VP: Lyle H Richter
Dir IT: Lynn Asten
Board of Directors: Richard W Gygi

D-U-N-S 17-598-4137 EXP
▲ **NEENAH PAPER INC**
3460 Preston Ridge Rd # 150, Alpharetta, GA 30005-2064
Tel (678) 566-6500 Founded/Ownrshp 2004
Sales 887.7MM EMP 2,340
Tkr Sym NP Exch NYS
SIC 2621 2741 Paper mills; Specialty or chemically treated papers; Book, bond & printing papers; Stationery, envelope & tablet papers; Technical manual & paper publishing
Pr: John P O'Donnell
*Ch Bd: Sean T Erwin
Pr: Julie A Schertell
CFO: Bonnie C Lind
Sr VP: Steven S Heinrichs
Sr VP: James R Piedmonte
Sr VP: Armin S Schwinn
VP: Larry N Brownlee
VP: Chris Simard
S&M/VP: Julie Schertell
Advt Mgr: Thomas Wright
Board of Directors: William M Cook, Margaret S Dano, Timothy S Lucas, John F McGovern, Philip C Moore, Stephen M Wood

D-U-N-S 04-071-5013
NEENAN CO LLLP
3325 S Timberline Rd # 100, Fort Collins, CO 80525-2903
Tel (970) 493-8747 Founded/Ownrshp 1973
Sales 83.7MM[E] EMP 140
SIC 1542 Commercial & office building, new construction; Commercial & office buildings, renovation & repair
Ch Bd: David G Neenan
Pr: Randolph Myers
Treas: Ryan Dellos
Exec: Jason Brown
Ex Dir: Dave Spencer
IT Man: Russell Anderson

D-U-N-S 08-994-1496
NEESER CONSTRUCTION INC
2501 Blueberry Rd Ste 100, Anchorage, AK 99503-2656
Tel (907) 276-1058 Founded/Ownrshp 1970
Sales 128.0MM[E] EMP 250
Accts Bernston Porter & Co Pllc B
SIC 1542 Commercial & office building, new construction; Commercial & office buildings, renovation & repair
Pr: Gerald Neeser
*CEO: Jerry Neeser
Ofcr: John Stallone
VP: Natalie Neeser
Dir Bus: Denise Tousignant
IT Man: Rusty Myrick
Snr PM: Neal Bhargava

NEFAB COMPANIES
See NEFAB PACKAGING NORTH EAST LLC

D-U-N-S 07-838-4841 IMP
NEFAB COMPANIES INC
(Suby of NEFAB AB)
204 Airline Dr Ste 100, Coppell, TX 75019-4602
Tel (866) 332-4425 Founded/Ownrshp 1870, 2010
Sales 133.5MM[E] EMP 550
SIC 2448 2449 2441 Pallets, wood & wood with metal; Skids, wood & wood with metal; Rectangular boxes & crates, wood; Nailed wood boxes & shook
Pr: Wade Mullis
*Pr: Brian Bulatao
*Pr: Kenneth Wilson

D-U-N-S 15-088-1852 IMP/EXP
NEFAB PACKAGING NORTH EAST LLC
NEFAB COMPANIES
(Suby of NEFAB COMPANIES INC) ★
204 Airline Dr Ste 100, Coppell, TX 75019-4602
Tel (469) 444-5264 Founded/Ownrshp 2011
Sales 123.5MM[E] EMP 550
SIC 2448 2449 2441 Pallets, wood & wood with metal; Skids, wood & wood with metal; Rectangular boxes & crates, wood; Nailed wood boxes & shook
Pr: Rodney W Mullus
*Pr: Rodney W Mullis
*CFO: Frank Slovacek
*VP: Koen Adams
DP Exec: Carlos Miranda

D-U-N-S 04-823-4074 EXP
NEFCO CORP (CT)
NORTHEASTERN FASTENERS
411 Burnham St, East Hartford, CT 06108-1157
Tel (860) 290-9044 Founded/Ownrshp 1981
Sales 118.0MM[E] EMP 106
SIC 5085 5072 Industrial supplies; Fasteners & fastening equipment; Fasteners, industrial: nuts, bolts, screws, etc.; Hardware
Pr: David Gelles
*CFO: Tom Drennen
*VP: Ronald L Cipriano
VP: Skip Maxfield
Sls Dir: Bruce Keaton

D-U-N-S 07-962-6838
▲ **NEFF CORP**
NEFF RENTAL
3750 Nw 87th Ave Ste 400, Doral, FL 33178-2433
Tel (305) 513-3350 Founded/Ownrshp 2014
Sales 371.9MM EMP 1,100[E]
Tkr Sym NEFF Exch NYS
SIC 7359 Equipment rental & leasing
CEO: Graham Hood
*Ch Bd: James Continenza
COO: Westley Parks
CFO: Mark Irion
VP: Henry Lawson
Prin: Brian Kwait
Area Mgr: Joe Yetter
Brnch Mgr: Mike Doyle
Brnch Mgr: Shawn Heath
Brnch Mgr: Ronald Riding
Board of Directors: Joseph Deignan, Gerard E Holthaus, Michael Sileck, Robert Singer

D-U-N-S 00-427-8446
NEFF PACKAGING SOLUTIONS INC (OH)
10 Kingbrook Pkwy, Simpsonville, KY 40067-5625
Tel (502) 722-5020 Founded/Ownrshp 1959
Sales 107.2MM[E] EMP 346
SIC 2657 Folding paperboard boxes
Ch Bd: Robert D Neff
*VP: James M Younkin
Sfty Mgr: John Rulander
Natl Sales: Laurie Haefner
Snr Mgr: Eddie Bischoff

NEFF RENTAL
See NEFF CORP

D-U-N-S 11-118-2189 IMP/EXP
NEH INC
Airport Ofc Pk Bl 2 400 R, Coraopolis, PA 15108
Tel (412) 299-7200 Founded/Ownrshp 2000
Sales 91.0MM[E] EMP 359
SIC 3313 6719 Electrometallurgical products; Investment holding companies, except banks
Pr: Geir I Kvernmo
*CFO: Al Woodrich

NEI
See UNICOM ENGINEERING INC

D-U-N-S 07-939-1435
■ **NEIGHBORCARE HOLDINGS INC**
(Suby of NEIGHBORCARE INC) ★
201 E 4th St Ste 900, Cincinnati, OH 45202-4160
Tel (513) 719-2600 Founded/Ownrshp 2014
Sales 402.1MM[E] EMP 3,488[E]
SIC 8741 Nursing & personal care facility management

D-U-N-S 13-108-8833
■ **NEIGHBORCARE INC**
(Suby of OMNICARE HOLDING COMPANY)
201 E 4th St Ste 900, Cincinnati, OH 45202-4160
Tel (513) 719-2600 Founded/Ownrshp 2005
Sales 402.1MM[E] EMP 3,000
SIC 5122 5912 5047 7389 Pharmaceuticals; Drug stores & proprietary stores; Medical equipment & supplies; Purchasing service
Pr: Elizabeth A Haley
*COO: Robert A Smith
CFO: Richard W Hunt
*Ex VP: John L Kordash
*Sr VP: John F Gaither Jr
Sr VP: Kirk Popeo
VP: Laurence F Lane
VP: James W Tabak
Exec: Tracey Crandell

D-U-N-S 78-938-1873
■ **NEIGHBORCARE PHARMACY SERVICES INC**
(Suby of NEIGHBORCARE SERVICES CORP) ★
201 E 4th St Ste 900, Cincinnati, OH 45202-4160
Tel (513) 719-2600 Founded/Ownrshp 1998
Sales 401.2MM[E] EMP 3,480[E]
SIC 5912 Drug stores
Pr: Elizabeth A Haley
*Treas: Regis T Robbins

D-U-N-S 07-862-6571
■ **NEIGHBORCARE SERVICES CORP**
(Suby of NEIGHBORCARE HOLDINGS INC) ★
201 E 4th St Ste 900, Cincinnati, OH 45202-4160
Tel (513) 719-2600 Founded/Ownrshp 1989
Sales 401.2MM[E] EMP 3,483[E]
SIC 5122 Pharmaceuticals
CEO: John L Workman

D-U-N-S 07-303-2765
NEIGHBORHOOD CENTERS INC
WORK SOURCE
4500 Bissonnet St Ste 200, Bellaire, TX 77401-3113
Tel (713) 667-9400 Founded/Ownrshp 1907
Sales 228.2MM EMP 1,000
Accts Lb Blazek & Vetterling Housto
SIC 8351 8322 Child day care services; Neighborhood center
Pr: Angela Blanchard
CFO: Kirk Rummel
Treas: Nancy W Mitchell
*Sr VP: Ray Chung
*Sr VP: Emelda Douglas
Sr VP: Christina Rodriguez
*Sr VP: Claudia Vasquez
VP: Ann Hilbig
Ex Dir: Joseph Britt
Ex Dir: Brian Loring
CIO: Thomas R Comella

D-U-N-S 88-309-6299
■ **NEIGHBORHOOD HEALTH PARTNERSHIP INC**
(Suby of UNITED HEALTHCARE OF FLORIDA INC) ★
7600 Nw 19th St Ste 100, Miami, FL 33126-1219
Tel (305) 715-2200 Founded/Ownrshp 2005
Sales NA EMP 421
SIC 6324 6321 Health maintenance organization (HMO), insurance only; Accident & health insurance
CEO: Joseph Papa
CFO: Mercy C Kirk
*CFO: Mercy Kirkpatrick
*Ex VP: John Fries
*Sr VP: Charles Ricevuto
CIO: Thomas Packert
Dir IT: Gary Kalin

D-U-N-S 18-117-4434
NEIGHBORHOOD HEALTH PLAN
NHP
(Suby of PARTNERS HEALTHCARE SYSTEM INC) ★
253 Summer St Fl 5, Boston, MA 02210-1120
Tel (617) 772-5500 Founded/Ownrshp 2012
Sales 1.7MMM EMP 340[E]
SIC 8011 Health maintenance organization
Pr: Deborah Enos
*CFO: Garrett Parker
CFO: Doug Thompson
*Ofcr: Katie Catlender
*VP: Jill D Arbeloff
*VP: Carla Bettano
VP: Deb Bonin
VP: Marilyn Daly
Tech Mgr: Daniel Wilson
Opers Mgr: Natasha Volf
Mktg Dir: Sandra Roberts

D-U-N-S 87-450-3998
NEIGHBORHOOD HEALTH PLAN OF RHODE ISLAND
299 Promenade St, Providence, RI 02908-5720
Tel (401) 459-6000 Founded/Ownrshp 1995
Sales NA EMP 150
Accts Ernst & Young Llp Boston Ma
SIC 6411 Insurance agents
Ch: Merrill Thomas
*CEO: James A Hooley
COO: Raymond M Sessler
CFO: Debbie Greve
CFO: Scott F Ogorman
CFO: Clark Phillip
*CFO: T Clark Phillip Jr
CFO: Thomas Clark Phillip Jr
CFO: Gregory J Young
*Treas: Peter Walsh
Dir Rx: Peter Vargas

D-U-N-S 07-333-7461
NEIGHBORHOOD HOUSE ASSOCIATION
N H A
5660 Copley Dr, San Diego, CA 92111-7902
Tel (858) 715-2642 Founded/Ownrshp 1914
Sales 42.7MM[E] EMP 1,000
SIC 8322 Neighborhood center
CEO: Rudolph A Johnson III
COO: Michael Kemp
CFO: Kim Peck
Treas: Derek Brown
VP: Norma Johnson

D-U-N-S 09-636-3700
NEIGHBORHOOD REINVESTMENT CORP
NEIGHBORWORKS OF AMERICA
999 N Capitol St Ne # 900, Washington, DC 20002-4684
Tel (202) 760-4000 Founded/Ownrshp 1978
Sales 261.2MM EMP 260
Accts Lb Bdo Usa Llp Washington Dc
SIC 8611 Community affairs & services
Pr: Chuck Wehrwein
*Ch Bd: Sarah Bloom Raskin
V Ch: Rodney E Hood
V Ch: Rodney Hood
*CEO: Paul Weech
*COO: Tom Chabolla
COO: Margo Kelly
CFO: Michael L Forster
*CFO: Leonard Williams
Treas: Jeff Marshall
*V Ch Bd: Debbie Matz
Bd of Dir: Terry Cunningham
Bd of Dir: Stacey Epperson
Bd of Dir: Randall S Kroszner
Bd of Dir: Paul Lopez
Bd of Dir: Vickie McGinnis
Bd of Dir: Jon Murakami
VP: Richard Berliner
VP: Rose Coleman
VP: Damodar Konda
VP: Christina McHenry
Board of Directors: Nani Coloretti, Craig Gilmore, Bonnie Gilovich, Connie Lindsey, Brian Montgomery, Frank Pagura, Andre Payten

D-U-N-S 86-945-9180 IMP
NEIGHBORHOOD RESTAURANTS INC
601 Main St Ste 102, Hazard, KY 41701-1382
Tel (606) 436-0736 Founded/Ownrshp 1991
Sales 75.7MM[E] EMP 2,000
SIC 5812 Fast-food restaurant, chain
Pr: Theresa Johnson
*Treas: Marty Johnson

D-U-N-S 02-257-7506
NEIGHBORS STORES INC
ACTION OUTDOOR ADVERTISING
1314 Old Highway 601, Mount Airy, NC 27030-7211
Tel (336) 789-5561 Founded/Ownrshp 1982
Sales 102.3MM EMP 130
SIC 5541 5411 Filling stations, gasoline; Grocery stores, independent
Pr: Gary York
*CFO: Donna Draughn

NEIGHBORWORKS OF AMERICA
See NEIGHBORHOOD REINVESTMENT CORP

NEIL
See NUCLEAR ELECTRIC INSURANCE LIMITED

D-U-N-S 04-973-3777 IMP
NEILL CORP
SALONBIZ
303 S Pine St, Hammond, LA 70403-4133
Tel (985) 345-1085 Founded/Ownrshp 1968
Sales 134.5MM[E] EMP 550
SIC 5087 5999 Barber shop equipment & supplies; Hair care products
CEO: Edwin H Neill III
*Ch Bd: Debra Neill
VP: Donna Dixon
*VP: Roger Doody
Ex Dir: Valerie Daniel
Ex Dir: Candice Hoz
MIS Dir: Keith Stokes
Dir IT: Bill Curry

D-U-N-S 10-915-9405
NEIMAN ENTERPRISES INC
RUSHMORE FOREST PRODUCTS
51 State Highway 112, Hulett, WY 82720-9657
Tel (307) 467-5252 Founded/Ownrshp 1958
Sales 98.9MM^E EMP 400
SIC 2421 Lumber: rough, sawed or planed; Kiln drying of lumber; Planing mills
Pr: James S Neiman
*COO: Tom Shaffer
*CFO: Chad Voyles
*VP: Jim D Neiman

D-U-N-S 07-918-1478
NEIMAN MARCUS GROUP INC
1618 Main St, Dallas, TX 75201-4748
Tel (214) 743-7600 Founded/Ownrshp 2013
Sales 4.9MMM^E EMP 16,500^E
SIC 5311 5961 Department stores; Catalog & mail-order houses
Pr: Karen Katz
COO: Donald T Grimes
Sr VP: Wanda Gierhart
Sr VP: Michael R Kingston

D-U-N-S 17-909-7431 IMP/EXP
NEIMAN MARCUS GROUP LLC
(Suby of NEIMAN MARCUS GROUP LTD LLC) ★
1618 Main St, Dallas, TX 75201-4748
Tel (214) 741-6911 Founded/Ownrshp 2005
Sales 2.3MMM^E EMP 14,400
SIC 5311 Department stores, non-discount
CFO: James E Skinner
CFO: Michael Wirkkala
Treas: Marie Lewis
Ex VP: Karen Katz
Sr VP: Nelson A Bangs
Sr VP: Gerald Barnes
Sr VP: Steven Dennis
Sr VP: Marita O'Dea
VP: Mackay Boynton
VP: Mary Carroll
VP: Kevin Garvin
VP: Terry Gradidge
VP: Gail Mann
VP: Cynthia Marcus
VP: Ariela Shani
Board of Directors: David A Barr, Ron Beegle, Jonathan Coslet, James Coulter, John G Danhakl, Sidney Lapidus, Carrie Wheeler

D-U-N-S 60-731-5137
NEIMAN MARCUS GROUP LTD LLC
(Suby of MARIPOSA INTERMEDIATE HOLDINGS LLC) ★
1618 Main St, Dallas, TX 75201-4748
Tel (214) 743-7600 Founded/Ownrshp 2013
Sales 4.9MMM EMP 15,100^E
Accts Ernst & Young Llp Dallas Tex
SIC 5311 5961 Department stores; Catalog & mail-order houses
Pr: Karen W Katz
Pr: John E Koryl
Pr: Joshua G Schulman
COO: Donald T Grimes
Treas: Stacie R Shirley
Chf Mktg O: Wanda M Gierhart
Ofcr: Joseph N Weber
Sr VP: Michael R Kingston
Sr VP: Thomas J Lind
Sr VP: Tracy M Preston
Sr VP: T Dale Stapleton

NEIMAN-REED LUMBER CO
See LUMBER CITY CORP

D-U-N-S 10-237-0426
NEISEWANDER ENTERPRISES INC
RAYNOR GARAGE DOOR
1101 E River Rd, Dixon, IL 61021-3252
Tel (815) 288-1431 Founded/Ownrshp 1944
Sales 269.9MM^E EMP 1,800
SIC 3442 2431 3429 Garage doors, overhead: metal; Garage doors, overhead: wood; Manufactured hardware (general)
Pr: Ray H Neisewander III

D-U-N-S 78-329-6023
▲ NEKTAR THERAPEUTICS
455 Mission Bay Blvd S, San Francisco, CA 94158-2158
Tel (415) 482-5300 Founded/Ownrshp 1990
Sales 230.7MM EMP 425
Tkr Sym NKTR Exch NGS
SIC 2834 Pharmaceutical preparations
Pr: Howard W Robin
*Ch Bd: Robert B Chess
COO: John Nicholson
CFO: Gil M Labrucherie
Chf Mktg O: Ivan P Gergel
Sr VP: Stephen K Doberstein
Sr VP: Maninder Hora
Sr VP: Jillian B Thomsen
VP: Stephen Doberstein
Assoc Dir: Rebecca Cazares
Assoc Dir: Sherwin Sy
Board of Directors: R Scott Greer, Joseph J Krivulka, Christopher A Kuebler, Lutz Lingnau, Roy A Whitfield, Dennis L Winger

D-U-N-S 07-853-8991
NEKTOVA GROUP LIMITED LIABILITY CO
534 Whitesville Rd, Jackson, NJ 08527-5044
Tel (732) 835-2303 Founded/Ownrshp 2012
Sales 85.0MM EMP 28
SIC 5065 Electronic parts

NELLCOR PURITAN BENNETT INC
See NELLCOR PURITAN BENNETT LLC

D-U-N-S 05-465-2201 IMP
NELLCOR PURITAN BENNETT LLC
NELLCOR PURITAN BENNETT INC
(Suby of COVIDIEN LP) ★
15 Hampshire St, Mansfield, MA 02048-1113
Tel (508) 261-8000 Founded/Ownrshp 2012
Sales 289.7MM^E EMP 4,000
SIC 3845 3841 Patient monitoring apparatus; Automated blood & body fluid analyzers, except laboratory; Respiratory analysis equipment, electromedical; Electromedical apparatus; Surgical & medical instruments

NELL'S FAMILY MARKET
See NK LIQUIDATION INC

D-U-N-S 04-741-9627 IMP
NELLSON NUTRACEUTICAL INC
5801 Ayala Ave, Irwindale, CA 91706-6216
Tel (626) 812-6522 Founded/Ownrshp 2002
Sales 83.2MM^E EMP 297
SIC 2064 Candy bars, including chocolate covered bars
CEO: Scott Greenwood
*Pr: Ben Muhlenkamp
*CEO: Jeff Moran
*Sr VP: Paul Hanson
*VP: Bart Child
*VP: Raymond Collins
*VP: Jeremy Ivie
QA Dir: Evelyn Reher

D-U-N-S 80-957-7716
NELLSON NUTRACEUTICAL LLC
5801 Ayala Ave, Irwindale, CA 91706-6216
Tel (626) 812-6522 Founded/Ownrshp 2013
Sales 153.9MM^E EMP 400^E
SIC 5499 Health foods
CEO: James Better
*COO: Jean Filion
*CFO: Manuel Martinez
CFO: Maribel Quinones
*Sr VP: Bart Child
*VP: Raymond Collins
VP: Paul Hanson
*VP: Jeremy Ivie
Dir Soc: Jeff Dias
Plnt Mgr: Joe Mogilewsky
Prd Mgr: Mike Winn

D-U-N-S 13-496-0447
▲ NELNET INC
121 S 13th St Ste 100, Lincoln, NE 68508-1904
Tel (402) 458-2370 Founded/Ownrshp 1977
Sales NA EMP 3,400^E
Tkr Sym NNI Exch NYS
SIC 6141 7389 Personal credit institutions; Financial services
CEO: Jeffrey R Noordhoek
*Ch Bd: Michael S Dunlap
Pr: Timothy A Tewes
COO: Terry J Heimes
CFO: James D Kruger
*V Ch Bd: Stephen F Butterfield
Ex VP: Tim Sabo
Ex VP: Jennifer Termaat
VP: Amit Mittal
IT Man: John Swanborg
Netwrk Eng: Andrew Musgrave
Board of Directors: James P Abel, William R Cintani, Kathleen A Farrell, David S Graff, Thomas E Henning, Kimberly K Rath, Michael D Reardon

D-U-N-S 06-809-6275
■ NELNET STUDENT LOAN CORP-1
UNION FINANCIAL SERVICES
(Suby of NELNET INC) ★
121 S 13th St Ste 301, Lincoln, NE 68508-1904
Tel (402) 458-2370 Founded/Ownrshp 1996
Sales NA EMP 1
SIC 6111 Student Loan Marketing Association
CEO: Steven Butterfield

NELSON & ASSOCIATES
See NELSON WORLDWIDE INC

NELSON A TAYLOR CO
See TAYLOR MADE GROUP HOLDINGS INC

D-U-N-S 06-367-1234 IMP
NELSON BROTHERS INC
820 Shades Creek Pkwy # 2000, Birmingham, AL 35209-4528
Tel (205) 414-2900 Founded/Ownrshp 1980
Sales 132.9MM^E EMP 300
SIC 2892 5169 Explosives; Nitromannitol (explosive); Chemicals & allied products
CEO: William H Nelson III
*Pr: Charles A Nelson
*CFO: Ralph M Hymer
*VP: Gary L Self

D-U-N-S 82-907-1906
NELSON BROTHERS LLC
ORICA
820 Shades Creek Pkwy # 2000, Birmingham, AL 35209-4528
Tel (205) 414-2900 Founded/Ownrshp 2000
Sales 94.8MM^E EMP 400^E
SIC 2892 Explosives
CEO: William Nelson
*Ex VP: Ralph Hymer
Genl Mgr: Philip Hudson

D-U-N-S 96-802-1886 IMP
NELSON GLOBAL PRODUCTS INC
1560 Williams Dr, Stoughton, WI 53589-3336
Tel (608) 719-1800 Founded/Ownrshp 2010
Sales 960.7MM^E EMP 3,000
SIC 3714 3317 Mufflers (exhaust), motor vehicle; Steel pipe & tubes
CEO: Steve Scgalski
*Pr: Sergio L Carvalho
*CFO: Kris Radhakrishnan
VP: Robert Bass
VP: Joseph Freeman

NELSON INDUSTRIES DIVISION
See NELSON INDUSTRIES INC

D-U-N-S 00-610-5944
■ NELSON INDUSTRIES INC
NELSON INDUSTRIES DIVISION
(Suby of CUMMINS INC) ★
1801 Us Highway 51 & 138, Stoughton, WI 53589-1909
Tel (608) 873-4200 Founded/Ownrshp 1939
Sales 228.8MM^E EMP 2,200
SIC 3714 3519 3569 Mufflers (exhaust), motor vehicle; Motor vehicle electrical equipment; Exhaust systems & parts, motor vehicle; Filters: oil, fuel & air, motor vehicle; Parts & accessories, internal combustion engines; Filters
Pr: Trevor Passmore
Bd of Dir: Greg Anderson
VP: Doug Benham
IT Man: Paula Quella
Sls Dir: Brian Kahl

D-U-N-S 15-166-3234
NELSON LABORATORIES INC
(Suby of STERIGENICS INTERNATIONAL LLC) ★
6280 S Redwood Rd, Salt Lake City, UT 84123-6600
Tel (801) 290-7500 Founded/Ownrshp 2016
Sales 85.7MM^E EMP 415
SIC 8734 Testing laboratories
Pr: Jeff Nelson
*Ch: Lynda Nelson
*Sec: Jerry R Nelson
VP: Jeff Hone

D-U-N-S 08-471-1993
NELSON MULLINS RILEY & SCARBOROUGH LLP
1320 Main St Ste 1700, Columbia, SC 29201-3268
Tel (803) 799-2000 Founded/Ownrshp 1898
Sales 161.0MM^E EMP 1,000
SIC 8111 General practice attorney, lawyer
Mng Pt: James C Gray Jr
*Pt: Bianca Brazell
*Pt: Valorie M Songer
*Pt: David N Worth
Mng Pt: David E Duks
Mng Pt: William T Hogan III
Mng Pt: Michael E Hollingsworth
Mng Pt: Amy Mandragouras
Mng Pt: Kenneth L Millwood
Mng Pt: Marvin Quattlebaum
Mng Pt: Jonathan H Talcott
Mng Pt: George B Wolfe
V Ch: Ron Thomas
V Ch: Thad Westbrook
*CFO: Douglas M Webb
Bd of Dir: S Hutto

D-U-N-S 00-446-6199 IMP/EXP
NELSON STUD WELDING INC
(Suby of DONCASTERS 456 LIMITED)
7900 W Ridge Rd, Elyria, OH 44035-1952
Tel (440) 329-0400 Founded/Ownrshp 2000, 2007
Sales 202.8MM^E EMP 351^E
SIC 3452 3548 Bolts, nuts, rivets & washers; Welding apparatus
Pr: Ken Caratelli
CFO: Johnathan Chrzanowski
*VP: David Bubar
*VP: Debbie Hunnel
VP: Jim King
Genl Mgr: Linda Loosli
IT Man: Nick Hullums
IT Man: Diana Virgei
Opers Mgr: John Garmon
Opers Mgr: Doug Shantz
Plnt Mgr: Cornel Irimies

D-U-N-S 09-683-8701
NELSON WORLDWIDE INC (PA)
NELSON & ASSOCIATES
222-230 Walnut St, Philadelphia, PA 19106
Tel (215) 925-6562 Founded/Ownrshp 1978
Sales 113.0MM^E EMP 425
SIC 7389 Interior decorating
CEO: John Nelson Jr
*CFO: Tony Manuelli
*Ex VP: Jill Hackenmueller
VP: Daniel Nelson
Genl Mgr: Cherryl Wardwell
Dir IT: Harvey Mindel
Dir IT: Marcus Weidner

D-U-N-S 02-334-1597 IMP
NELSON-JAMESON INC
2400 E 5th St, Marshfield, WI 54449-4661
Tel (715) 387-1151 Founded/Ownrshp 1947
Sales 137.8MM EMP 175
SIC 5084 Food industry machinery; Dairy products manufacturing machinery
Ch Bd: John E Nelson
*Pr: Jerry Lippert
CFO: Brian Lautenschlag
IT Man: Fritz Buss
IT Man: Adam Nelson
Web Dev: David Hayakawa
Natl Sales: David Anderson
Mktg Dir: Murray Smith
Pr Dir: Donald Koch
Pr Dir: Sue Krings
Manager: Amanda Sasse

D-U-N-S 00-386-7710
NEMAHA COUNTY COOPERATIVE ASSOCIATION
223 E Main St, Seneca, KS 66538-1946
Tel (785) 336-6153 Founded/Ownrshp 1936
Sales 108.6MM EMP 88
SIC 5153 5191 5541 Grains; Grain elevators; Feed; Fertilizer & fertilizer materials; Chemicals, agricultural; Filling stations, gasoline
CEO: Bobby Martin
*V Ch Bd: Kent Heinen

D-U-N-S 01-887-4284
NEMAK AUTOMOTIVE CASTINGS INC
J.L. FRENCH AUTO CASTINGS INC
(Suby of NEMAK MEXICO, S.A.)
3101 S Taylor Dr, Sheboygan, WI 53081-8424
Tel (920) 458-7724 Founded/Ownrshp 1997
Sales 698.6MM^E EMP 3,599
SIC 3341 3363 8711 Aluminum smelting & refining (secondary); Aluminum die-castings; Designing: ship, boat, machine & product
Ch Bd: Tom Musgrave
CFO: James A Amodeo
Sr Cor Off: John Falcon
Sr Cor Off: Tim Price
*VP: Joe Heady
*VP: Timothy R Kadeabek
Prgrm Mgr: Kirk Nick
CTO: Jerry Palmer
*CTO: Charles Waldon
VP Opers: Tim Kadarafic
Mfg Mgr: Warren Hacker

NEMAK TENNESSEE
See NEMAK USA INC

D-U-N-S 17-433-0365 IMP
NEMAK USA INC
NEMAK TENNESSEE
(Suby of NEMAK, S.A.B. DE C.V.)
1635 Old Columbia Rd, Dickson, TN 37055-7705
Tel (615) 446-8110 Founded/Ownrshp 2007
Sales 14.6MM^E EMP 1,097
SIC 3363 3714 Aluminum die-castings; Cylinder heads, motor vehicle
Pr: Armando Tamez

D-U-N-S 07-940-9914
NEMERA BUFFALO GROVE LLC
(Suby of NEMERA US HOLDING INC) ★
600 Deerfield Pkwy, Buffalo Grove, IL 60089-7050
Tel (847) 541-7900 Founded/Ownrshp 2014
Sales 86.9MM^E EMP 300
SIC 3841 Surgical & medical instruments

D-U-N-S 07-989-7056
NEMERA US HOLDING INC
(Suby of NEMERA LA VERPILLIERE)
600 Deerfield Pkwy, Buffalo Grove, IL 60089-7050
Tel (847) 325-3620 Founded/Ownrshp 2015
Sales 90.5MM^E EMP 318^E
SIC 3841

NEMF
See NEW ENGLAND MOTOR FREIGHT INC

D-U-N-S 03-692-7204
NEMOURS CHILDRENS HOSPITAL
ALFRED I DUPONT HOSPITAL FOR C
(Suby of ALFRED I DUPONT HOSPITAL FOR) ★
13535 Nemours Pkwy, Orlando, FL 32827-7402
Tel (407) 567-4000 Founded/Ownrshp 2010
Sales 100.6MM EMP 143^E
SIC 8069 Children's hospital
Pr: David J Bailey
*Ex VP: Roy Proujansky
*Sr VP: Steven Sparks
*VP: Gina Altieri

D-U-N-S 03-729-3792
NEMOURS FOUNDATION
ALFRED I DUPONT HOSPITAL FOR
10140 Centurion Pkwy N, Jacksonville, FL 32256-0532
Tel (904) 697-4100 Founded/Ownrshp 1974
Sales 226.5MM EMP 4,400
Accts Kpmg Llp Jacksonville Fl
SIC 8069 8093 Children's hospital; Specialty outpatient clinics
Ch Bd: John S Lord
*Ch Bd: Brian P Anderson
*Pr: David J Bailey
COO: Michelle Arnold
CFO: Kimberly Englert
Treas: Bill Higginbotham
Sec: Stacie Lynne Pack
*V Ch Bd: Richard T Christopher
Chf Mktg O: David West
VP: Robert Bridges
VP: Jay Cummings
VP: Norma Everett
VP: Bradley Robinson
VP: Theresa Young
Exec: Linda Favorite
Board of Directors: John S Lord

D-U-N-S 07-924-3752
NEMOURS FOUNDATION PENSION PLAN
10140 Centurion Pkwy N, Jacksonville, FL 32256-0532
Tel (904) 697-4100 Founded/Ownrshp 2014
Sales NA EMP 581^E
SIC 6371 Pensions
VP: Karen Hartis
Exec: Wanda Heavner
Off Mgr: Linda Krawczuk
Nurse Mgr: Amber Degrenier
Off Admin: Carmen Moore
CIO: Bernie Rice
Web Dev: Gerald Murray
Mktg Mgr: Karen Kent
Ansthlgy: Jack Bairamian
Pharmcst: Thao Dinh
Snr Mgr: Floyd Livingston

D-U-N-S 83-192-1692 IMP
NEN HOLDINGS INC
397 S Taylor Ave, Louisville, CO 80027-3027
Tel (303) 444-2559 Founded/Ownrshp 2009
Sales 135.7MM^E EMP 750^E
Accts Brock And Company Cpas Pc
SIC 5962 Merchandising machine operators
Pr: Kevin J Wall

NEO TECH
See ONCORE MANUFACTURING LLC

NEO TECH NATEL EPIC ONCORE
See ONCORE MANUFACTURING SERVICES INC

NEOCUTIS
See MERZ NORTH AMERICA INC

D-U-N-S 06-955-0929 IMP
▲ NEOGEN CORP
620 Lesher Pl, Lansing, MI 48912-1509
Tel (517) 372-9200 Founded/Ownrshp 1982
Sales 321.2MM EMP 1,062^E
Tkr Sym NEOG Exch NGS

SIC 2835 3841 2836 In vitro & in vivo diagnostic substances; Veterinary diagnostic substances; Veterinarians' instruments & apparatus; Veterinary biological products
Ch Bd: James L Herbert
Pr: Richard E Calk Jr
CFO: Steven J Quinlan
Bd of Dir: William Boehm
VP: Edward L Bradley
VP: Joseph A Corbett
VP: Jason W Lilly
VP: Terri A Morrical
VP: Mark A Mozola
VP: Jennifer A Rice
VP: Dwight E Schroedter
Board of Directors: William T Boehm, Ronald D Green, G Bruce Papesh, Jack C Parnell, Thomas H Reed, Clayton K Yeutter

D-U-N-S 11-300-7301
▲ NEOGENOMICS INC
12701 Commwl Dr Ste 9, Fort Myers, FL 33913
Tel (239) 768-0600 *Founded/Ownrshp* 2001
Sales 99.8MM *EMP* 850
Tkr Sym NEO *Exch* NAS
SIC 8734 8071 Testing laboratories; Testing laboratories
Ch Bd: Douglas M Vanoort
CFO: George A Cardoza
CFO: Gabriel Melamed
**Chf Cred:* Steven C Jones
Chf Mktg O: Maher Albitar
Ofcr: Steven Brodie
Ofcr: Robert J Shovlin
VP: Mark A Machulcz
VP: Jack Spitz
CIO: Steven A Ross
CTO: Steve Hoyt
Board of Directors: Bruce K Crowther, Alison L Hannah, Raymond R Hipp, Kevin C Johnson, Kieran P Murphy, William J Robison, Lynn A Tetrault

D-U-N-S 07-910-6979
NEOGENOMICS LABORATORIES INC
12701 Commwl Dr Ste 9, Fort Myers, FL 33913
Tel (239) 768-0600 *Founded/Ownrshp* 2001
Sales 99.8MM[E] *EMP* 400[E]
SIC 8071 Medical laboratories; Testing laboratories
CEO: Douglas M Vanoort

D-U-N-S 07-870-9787
NEOLPHARMA INC
99 Calle Jardines, Caguas, PR 00725-3382
Tel (787) 286-4000 *Founded/Ownrshp* 2013
Sales 179.0MM[E] *EMP* 240
SIC 5122 Pharmaceuticals
Pr: Efren Ocampo
**CFO:* Marco A Monrouzeau Bonilla

D-U-N-S 96-825-0977 IMP
▲ NEOPHOTONICS CORP
2911 Zanker Rd, San Jose, CA 95134-2125
Tel (408) 232-9200 *Founded/Ownrshp* 1996
Sales 339.4MM *EMP* 2,304
Accts Deloitte & Touche Llp San Jos
Tkr Sym NPTN *Exch* NYS
SIC 3674 Semiconductors & related devices
Ch Bd: Timothy S Jenks
CFO: Cal R Hoagland
CFO: Clyde Raymond Wallin
CFO: Ray Wallin
Ofcr: CHI Yue Cheung
Sr VP: Benjamin L Sitler
Sr VP: Wupen Yuen
VP: Milind Gokhale
VP: Bandy Wu
Prgrm Mgr: Frans Kusnadi
IT Man: Ikram Lakhani
Board of Directors: Charles J Abbe, Michael J Sophie, Lee Sen Ting

D-U-N-S 08-070-8241 IMP
NEOPOST USA INC
(*Suby of* NEOPOST FRANCE)
478 Wheelers Farms Rd, Milford, CT 06461-9105
Tel (203) 301-3400 *Founded/Ownrshp* 1992
Sales 339.5MM[E] *EMP* 1,017
SIC 3579 7359 7629 Postage meters; Business machine & electronic equipment rental services; Business machine repair, electric
Pr: Dennis P Lestrange
COO: Bill Quinn
CFO: Kenneth Kocher
Ex VP: Alain Fairise
Sr VP: Tara Whitmore
VP: Fabrice Assous
**VP:* Christopher M Obrien
Brnch Mgr: Robert Szehner
Dir IT: Bastien S Cantos
Dir IT: Sam Lavanaway
Dir IT: Catlin Roman

D-U-N-S 01-065-3751
NEORIS USA INC
703 Waterford Way Ste 700, Miami, FL 33126-4689
Tel (305) 728-6000 *Founded/Ownrshp* 2000
Sales 250.4MM[E] *EMP* 1,200
SIC 4813 Telephone communication, except radio
CEO: Claudio Muruzabal
Pr: Sam Elfawal
CFO: Rubio Guillermo
Ofcr: Jairo Fern Ndez
VP: Carlos Castilla
VP: Stephen Hitchings
VP: Martin Mendez
VP: Greg Reynolds
VP: Ray Russ
Dir Rx: Fernando Aguirre
Mng Dir: Omar Daz

NEOSTRATA
See TRISTRATA INC

D-U-N-S 60-575-4829 IMP
NEOSTRATA CO INC
(*Suby of* NEOSTRATA) ★
307 College Rd E, Princeton, NJ 08540-6608
Tel (609) 520-0715 *Founded/Ownrshp* 1994
Sales 128.1MM[E] *EMP* 85[E]
SIC 5122 Cosmetics
CEO: Mark D Steele

NEOTECH
See NATEL ENGINEERING CO INC

D-U-N-S 05-703-1854
NEOVIA LOGISTICS SERVICES LLC
6363 N State Highway 161 # 700, Irving, TX 75038-2262
Tel (469) 513-7000 *Founded/Ownrshp* 1999
Sales 125.3MM[E] *EMP* 75[E]
SIC 4789 5082 Cargo loading & unloading services; Construction & mining machinery
CEO: Jos Opdeweegh
**CFO:* Joe Tomczak
**Chf Cred:* Carey Falcone
**Ofcr:* Zach Green
**CTO:* Tim Oglesby

D-U-N-S 07-908-7702
NEOVIA LOGISTICS SERVICES LLC
(*Suby of* PLATINUM EQUITY LLC) ★
2001 Bttrfeld Rd Ste 1400, Downers Grove, IL 60515
Tel (469) 513-7000 *Founded/Ownrshp* 1987
Sales 184.1MM[E] *EMP* 499[E]
SIC 6719 Investment holding companies, except banks
CEO: Jozef J Opdeweegh
COO: Dan Spellman
CFO: Joe Tomczak
VP: Kris Paquin

NEP
See NOBLE ENVIRONMENTAL POWER LLC

D-U-N-S 19-478-4096
NEPC LLC
255 State St Ste 600, Boston, MA 02109-2657
Tel (617) 314-3176 *Founded/Ownrshp* 1986
Sales NA *EMP* 218
Accts Kpmg Peat Marwick
SIC 6411 6282 Pension & retirement plan consultants; Investment advice
Pr: Richard Charlton
Mng Pt: Joseph Breitfelder
Ofcr: William Bogle
**Prin:* Mike Manning
Off Mgr: Terri Sacramone
IT Man: John Shanklin
MIS Mgr: Eric Hill

NEPCO
See MATRIX METALS HOLDINGS INC

D-U-N-S 78-390-5201 IMP
NEPHRON PHARMACEUTICALS CORP
4121 Sw 34th St, Orlando, FL 32811-6475
Tel (407) 246-1389 *Founded/Ownrshp* 1991
Sales 122.5MM[E] *EMP* 560[E]
SIC 2834 Chlorination tablets & kits (water purification)
Pr: Lou W Kennedy
Pr: Joey Russell
**COO:* John Petta
Ex VP: Alexander Borsoi
Ex VP: William Dudley
**VP:* Ashley Whitner
**Dir Sec:* Jerry Webb
Rgnl Mgr: Gregg Polacek
QA Dir: Roy Camp
Manager: Michael McGowan

D-U-N-S 00-120-0781 IMP/EXP
■ NEPTCO INC (RI)
(*Suby of* CHASE CORP) ★
30 Hamlet St, Pawtucket, RI 02861-2827
Tel (401) 722-5500 *Founded/Ownrshp* 1953
Sales 106.1MM[E] *EMP* 500
SIC 3496 3083 2672 Woven wire products; Laminated plastic sheets; Coated & laminated paper
CEO: Guy Marini
**VP:* Frank Conti
**VP:* Ken Feroldi
VP: Charles Glue
**VP:* Joel Gruhn
**VP:* Lois Kilsey
Exec: David Blythe
IT Man: Stephen Wan
Natl Sales: Steve Dumas

NEPTUNE FOODS
See FISHERMANS PRIDE PROCESSORS INC

D-U-N-S 08-034-3364
NEPTUNE HOLDING US CORP
ALTICE USA
6 Corporate Center Dr, Melville, NY 11747-3845
Tel (516) 803-2265 *Founded/Ownrshp* 2015
Sales 88.0MM[E] *EMP* 17,000
SIC 7313 7929 Electronic media advertising representatives; Entertainment service
CEO: Dexter Goei
COO: Hakim Boubazine
CFO: Charles Stewart
V Ch Bd: Lisa Rosenblum
Ex VP: David Connolly

NEPTUNE LIFETIME SINKS
See ELKAY MANUFACTURING CO INC

D-U-N-S 00-909-9537 IMP/EXP
■ NEPTUNE TECHNOLOGY GROUP INC
(*Suby of* ROPER TECHNOLOGIES INC) ★
1600 Al Highway 229 S, Tallassee, AL 36078-1714
Tel (334) 283-6555 *Founded/Ownrshp* 2001, 2004
Sales 164.7MM[E] *EMP* 500[E]
SIC 3824 Water meters
Pr: Charles C Dilaura
VP: Mike Berg
VP: Don Deemer
VP: Kent Murray
**VP:* Lawrence Russo
VP: David Stoddart
Dir IT: Margie West
IT Man: Bob Brown
Netwrk Mgr: John David
Sftwr Eng: Burt Carter
Sftwr Eng: Taylor Jackson

D-U-N-S 85-849-5443
NERIS BAKERY PRODUCTS INC
31 Pearl St 37, Port Chester, NY 10573-4610
Tel (914) 937-3235 *Founded/Ownrshp* 1990
Sales 106.1MM[E] *EMP* 200
SIC 5149 5461 2051 Bakery products; Bakeries; Bread, cake & related products
**VP:* Paul Neri

D-U-N-S 62-501-3409
NES ASSOCIATES LLC
6400 Beulah St Ste 100, Alexandria, VA 22310-2628
Tel (703) 224-2600 *Founded/Ownrshp* 2006
Sales 94.2MM *EMP* 365[E]
Accts Matthews Carter & Boyce Cpas
SIC 7373 Local area network (LAN) systems integrator
CEO: Andrew Gomer
COO: Tim Murray
CFO: Dan Rice

D-U-N-S 10-421-3785
NES GLOBAL LLC
(*Suby of* NES GLOBAL LIMITED)
800 Gessner Rd Ste 310, Houston, TX 77024-4599
Tel (713) 551-4444 *Founded/Ownrshp* 2000
Sales 183.9MM *EMP* 35
SIC 1799 Athletic & recreation facilities construction
CEO: Neil Tregarthen
Dir Bus: Brandon Blume

D-U-N-S 83-862-2256
NES HOLDINGS INC
39 Main St, Belvedere Tiburon, CA 94920-2507
Tel (415) 435-4591 *Founded/Ownrshp* 1994
Sales 100.0MM *EMP* 196
SIC 7363 Medical help service
Ch Bd: Allan H Rappaport MD
CFO: Dave Ulrich
**VP:* Thomas Botts
**Prin:* William H Warren
Counsel: Sanford Pomerantz

D-U-N-S 05-270-8745
■ NES INVESTMENT CO
(*Suby of* JOY GLOBAL INC) ★
6140 Parkland Blvd, Cleveland, OH 44124-6142
Tel (440) 461-6000 *Founded/Ownrshp* 2000, 2008
Sales 73.7MM[E] *EMP* 1,431
SIC 5065 5085 5169 5013 Security control equipment & systems; Fasteners, industrial: nuts, bolts, screws, etc.; Industrial chemicals; Automotive supplies & parts
Pr: Robert J Tomsich
VP: Patrick Brainard
Counsel: David Sweeny

D-U-N-S 15-077-1959
NES RENTALS HOLDINGS INC
(*Suby of* DIAMOND CASTLE HOLDINGS LLC) ★
8420 W Bryn Mawr Ave # 310, Chicago, IL 60631-3479
Tel (773) 695-3999 *Founded/Ownrshp* 2006
Sales 347.0MM *EMP* 1,100
Accts Kpmg Llp Chicago Illinois
SIC 7359 7699 5082 Equipment rental & leasing; Industrial machinery & equipment repair; Construction & mining machinery
Pr: Andrew P Studdert
**CFO:* Michael D Milligan
**Sr VP:* Christopher Bowers
**VP:* Ananda Rakhit
VP Bus Dev: Andrew Cho
Brnch Mgr: Jim Anderson
Off Mgr: Don Lonard
VP Opers: Brent Mumford
VP Mktg: Mike Disser
Sales Asso: Randy Johnson

D-U-N-S 60-258-0771
NESBITT BURNS SECURITIES INC
(*Suby of* BMO FINANCIAL CORP) ★
115 S La Salle St Ste 20w, Chicago, IL 60603-3801
Tel (312) 461-6220 *Founded/Ownrshp* 1993
Sales 256.0MM[E] *EMP* 7,000
SIC 6211 Security brokers & dealers
CEO: Jeff Orr
**Ch Bd:* James K Beqaj
**Pr:* Aubrey W Baillie
Mng Dir: John Dillon

NESCO
See NEEDHAM ELECTRIC SUPPLY CORP

D-U-N-S 05-551-5076 IMP/EXP
NESCO INC
NESCO RESOURCE
6140 Parkland Blvd # 110, Cleveland, OH 44124-6106
Tel (440) 461-6000 *Founded/Ownrshp* 1988
Sales 684.8MM[E] *EMP* 5,000
SIC 3535 3541 3544 8711 6531 Conveyors & conveying equipment; Machine tools, metal cutting type; Special dies, tools, jigs & fixtures; Engineering services; Real estate managers
Pr: Robert Tomsich
**CFO:* Frank Rzicznek
VP: Michael Gallagher
Area Mgr: Tom Villhard
Brnch Mgr: Jerry Arena
Brnch Mgr: Justin Brake
Brnch Mgr: Christy Fee
Brnch Mgr: Camaran Jones
Brnch Mgr: Linda Levandoski
Brnch Mgr: John Maimone
Brnch Mgr: Nancy McIntyre

NESCO RESOURCE
See NESCO INC

D-U-N-S 07-710-7696
NESHAMINY SCHOOL DISTRICT
2001 Old Lincoln Hwy, Langhorne, PA 19047-3240
Tel (215) 809-6562 *Founded/Ownrshp* 1925
Sales 89.0MM[E] *EMP* 1,200
Accts Maillie Falconiero & Company
SIC 8211 Public combined elementary & secondary school
**Pr:* Ritchie Webb
**Treas:* Barbara Markowitz
**VP:* Scott E Congdon
Dir Sec: Cliff Fiedler
Admn Mgr: Alexander Menio
Dir IT: Vickie Kerr
IT Man: Lynn Duminiak

D-U-N-S 96-902-8351
NESHER PHARMACEUTICALS (USA) LLC
(*Suby of* CADILA HEALTHCARE LIMITED)
13910 St Charles Rock Rd, Bridgeton, MO 63044-3826
Tel (314) 209-4700 *Founded/Ownrshp* 2011
Sales 315.2MM *EMP* 120[E]
SIC 2834 Pharmaceutical preparations
Pr: Vince Kaiman
QA Dir: Sumeer Bhargava
VP Opers: Frank Harmon
Opers Mgr: Phil Biles

D-U-N-S 79-466-1801 IMP/EXP
NESPRESSO USA INC
(*Suby of* NESTLE HOLDINGS INC) ★
2401 44th Rd Fl 12, Long Island City, NY 11101-4605
Tel (800) 562-1465 *Founded/Ownrshp* 1990
Sales 168.2MM[E] *EMP* 400
SIC 5149 5046 5499 Coffee, green or roasted; Coffee brewing equipment & supplies; Coffee
Pr: Fredrick Levy
Off Mgr: Danielle Diaz
IT Man: Yezid Acosta

D-U-N-S 02-292-5051 IMP
NESS ELECTRONICS INC
1800 E 121st St, Burnsville, MN 55337-6801
Tel (651) 251-5700 *Founded/Ownrshp* 1999
Sales 450.0MM *EMP* 28
SIC 5065 Electronic parts
Pr: Michael Ness
**VP:* Arlene Ness

D-U-N-S 02-774-2758
NESS HOLDING CO
KOOL PAK
4550 Kruse Way Ste 350, Lake Oswego, OR 97035-3588
Tel (503) 240-0400 *Founded/Ownrshp* 1968
Sales 92.2MM[E] *EMP* 345
SIC 5141 Groceries, general line; Food brokers
Pr: Steven A Ness
CFO: Marie Dolan
**CFO:* Wade J Palmer
VP: Bill Knechtel
Board of Directors: Brian Hart

D-U-N-S 13-472-0544
NESS TECHNOLOGIES INC
300 Frank W Burr Blvd, Teaneck, NJ 07666-6704
Tel (201) 488-7222 *Founded/Ownrshp* 2013
Sales 419.1MM[E] *EMP* 7,710[E]
SIC 7371 Computer software development
CEO: Paul Lombardo
CFO: Zachi Hadad
CFO: Manny Malkan
Chf Mktg O: Amber Blaha
Ofcr: Satyajit Bandyopadhyay
Ofcr: Mark Lister
Ofcr: Kuruvilla Mathew
Ofcr: Narayanan Nair
Ofcr: Rajeev Sharma
Top Exec: Rohit Jayaswal
Top Exec: Narayan Parameswaran
Assoc VP: Kelly S Cook
VP: Matthew Lee
VP: Shannon Shirk

D-U-N-S 07-921-9939
NEST PARENT INC
10877 Wilshire Blvd, Los Angeles, CA 90024-4341
Tel (310) 551-0101 *Founded/Ownrshp* 2012
Sales 209.0MM[E] *EMP* 1,165[E]
SIC 6719 Personal holding companies, except banks
Prin: Gerald L Parsky
**Prin:* John T Mapes

D-U-N-S 06-656-3859 IMP/EXP
NESTLE DREYERS ICE CREAM CO
HAAGEN-DAZS
(*Suby of* DREYERS GRAND ICE CREAM HOLDINGS INC) ★
5929 College Ave, Oakland, CA 94618-1325
Tel (510) 594-9466 *Founded/Ownrshp* 2003
Sales 283.0MM[E] *EMP* 5,000
SIC 5812 2024 Ice cream stands or dairy bars; Ice cream & frozen desserts
CEO: Michael Mitchell
**CFO:* Steven P Barbour
CFO: Doug Holdt
Ex VP: William Rolden
VP: Sam Donsing
VP: Rosanna Neagle
VP: Jeffrey Vogt
Dir IT: David Mack
VP Mfg: Paul Dibartolo
Sfty Mgr: Chris Duffield
Opers Mgr: Gary Amundson

D-U-N-S 00-624-7332 IMP/EXP
NESTLE HEALTHCARE NUTRITION INC
(*Suby of* NESTLE S.A.)
12 Vreeland Rd Fl 2, Florham Park, NJ 07932-1521
Tel (952) 848-6000 *Founded/Ownrshp* 2007
Sales 124.1MM[E] *EMP* 488[E]
SIC 2099 2032 Food preparations; Canned specialties
CEO: Greg Behar
**Pr:* David Yates
COO: Mark Sponsler
VP: Diana Bryan
VP: Steve Drozda
Corp Couns: Mary Prentnieks

D-U-N-S 13-148-1657 IMP/EXP
NESTLE HOLDINGS INC
(*Suby of* NESTLE S.A.)
800 N Brand Blvd, Glendale, CA 91203-1245
Tel (818) 549-6000 *Founded/Ownrshp* 1983
Sales 11.4MMM[E] *EMP* 25,000
Accts Kpmg Llp Los Angeles Ca

SIC 2023 2032 2038 2033 2064 2026 Dry, condensed, evaporated dairy products; Canned specialties; Soups & broths: canned, jarred, etc.; Beans & bean sprouts, canned, jarred, etc.; Italian foods: packaged in cans, jars, etc.; Frozen specialties; Fruits & fruit products in cans, jars, etc.; Vegetables & vegetable products in cans, jars, etc.; Jams, jellies & preserves: packaged in cans, jars, etc.; Tomato products: packaged in cans, jars, etc.; Candy & other confectionery products; Fluid milk
Ch Bd: Brad Alford
CFO: Mario Corti
CFO: Dana Sherman
**Treas:* Don Gosline
**Sr VP:* John Gatlin

D-U-N-S 12-731-2358 IMP
NESTLE ICE CREAM CO
(*Suby of* DREYERS GRAND ICE CREAM HOLDINGS INC) ★
7301 District Blvd, Bakersfield, CA 93313-2042
Tel (661) 398-3500 *Founded/Ownrshp* 1993
Sales 221.8MM^E *EMP* 1,920
SIC 5143 5451 Ice cream & ices; Ice cream (packaged)
CEO: James L Dintaman
Brnch Mgr: Paul Stanberry

NESTLE INFANT NUTRITION
See GERBER PRODUCTS CO

D-U-N-S 07-113-0868 IMP
NESTLE PREPARED FOODS CO
(*Suby of* STOUFFER CORP) ★
5750 Harper Rd, Solon, OH 44139-1831
Tel (440) 248-3600 *Founded/Ownrshp* 1969
Sales 1.5MMM^E *EMP* 8,610
SIC 2038 5411 2037 Dinners, frozen & packaged; Soups, frozen; Pizza, frozen; Grocery stores; Vegetables, quick frozen & cold pack, excl. potato products
Pr: C Wayne Partin
**Ch Bd:* David H Jennings
**VP:* James M Biggar
**VP:* Charles Werner

NESTLE PROFESSIONAL VITALITY
See VITALITY FOODSERVICE INC

NESTLE PURINA FACTORY
See NESTLE PURINA PETCARE CO

D-U-N-S 00-626-6811 IMP/EXP
NESTLE PURINA PETCARE CO (MO)
NESTLE PURINA FACTORY
(*Suby of* NESTLE HOLDINGS INC) ★
901 Chouteau Ave, Saint Louis, MO 63102-1009
Tel (314) 982-1000 *Founded/Ownrshp* 1894, 2001
Sales 2.2MMM^E *EMP* 8,000
SIC 2047 Dog & cat food
Pr: W Patrick McGinnis
Pr: Thomas Blair
**CFO:* Rock Foster
Ex VP: Bill Kumke
Plnt Mgr: Terence E Block

D-U-N-S 00-825-6224 IMP/EXP
NESTLE USA INC
WONKA BAMBOOZLE
(*Suby of* NESTLE HOLDINGS INC) ★
800 N Brand Blvd, Glendale, CA 91203-3213
Tel (818) 549-6000 *Founded/Ownrshp* 1920
Sales 3.5MMM^E *EMP* 25,000
SIC 2023 2033 2064 2047 2099 2032

D-U-N-S 10-133-6568 IMP/EXP
NESTLE WATERS NORTH AMERICA HOLDINGS INC
(*Suby of* NESTLE WATERS)
900 Long Ridge Rd Bldg 2, Stamford, CT 06902-1140
Tel (203) 531-4100 *Founded/Ownrshp* 1992
Sales 4.6MMM^E *EMP* 8,500
SIC 5149 Mineral or spring water bottling
CEO: Tim Brown
**CFO:* William J Pearson
**Treas:* Don W Gosline
**Ex VP:* Dave Muscato
**Ex VP:* Heidi Paul
Sr VP: Dennis Crumbine
**VP:* Charles D Broll
**Exec:* Bill Pearson

D-U-N-S 84-744-9121 IMP/EXP
NESTLE WATERS NORTH AMERICA INC
PERRIER WATER
(*Suby of* NESTLE WATERS NORTH AMERICA HOLDINGS INC) ★
900 Long Ridge Rd Bldg 2, Stamford, CT 06902-1140
Tel (203) 531-4100 *Founded/Ownrshp* 2009
Sales 4.6MMM *EMP* 4,817
SIC 5149 Mineral or spring water bottling
CEO: Tim Brown
CFO: Rick Croarken
**CFO:* Rick Croarkin
**CFO:* Bill Pearson
**Ex VP:* Dave Muscato
Ex VP: Antonio Sciuto
**VP:* Charlie Broll
**VP:* David Colville
**VP:* Heidi Paul
**VP:* Nelson Switzer
**Prin:* Thomas Muttitt

D-U-N-S 06-469-5190 IMP
■ **NESTOR SALES LLC**
AIM SUPPLY CO
(*Suby of* MICROUNITED DIVISION) ★
7337 Bryan Dairy Rd, Largo, FL 33777-1507
Tel (727) 544-6114 *Founded/Ownrshp* 1971
Sales 153.8MM^E *EMP* 270
SIC 5013 5085 Tools & equipment, automotive; Industrial supplies
Pr: Peter Hofbauer
**CFO:* Barry Katz
Exec: Karen Bowser
Rgnl Mgr: Mike Willis
Genl Mgr: Leslie Beck
IT Man: Michael Huling
Mktg Dir: Kevin Amico

NET WEST
See WESTERN PAPER DISTRIBUTORS INC

D-U-N-S 80-205-4742
▲ **NETAPP INC**
495 E Java Dr, Sunnyvale, CA 94089-1125
Tel (408) 822-6000 *Founded/Ownrshp* 1992
Sales 6.1MMM *EMP* 12,810
Tkr Sym NTAP *Exch* NGS
SIC 3572 7373 7372 Computer storage devices; Computer integrated systems design; Systems software development services; Computer system selling services; Prepackaged software
Pr: George Kurian
Ch Bd: T Michael Nevens
CFO: Ron Pasek
CFO: Ronald J Pasek
Treas: Dan Chilton
Bd of Dir: Robert Wall
Ofcr: Jean English
Ex VP: Tom Gerstenberger
Ex VP: Jeff Hall
Ex VP: David Hitz
Ex VP: James Lau
Ex VP: Joel Reich
Ex VP: Henri Richard
Sr VP: Matthew K Fawcett
VP: J Ahn
VP: Brian Bakstran
VP: Jim Bampos
VP: Randy Blatt
VP: Steve Blaz
VP: Walt Blomquist
VP: Derek Bomar
Board of Directors: Jeffry R Allen, Alan L Earhart, Gerald Held, Kathryn M Hill, George T Shaheen, Steve Smith, Robert T Wall, Richard P Wallace

NETCO
See NATIONAL EQUITY TITLE AGENCY INC

D-U-N-S 18-645-7552
NETCO INC (IL)
EQUITY TITLE COMPANY AMERICA
7501 Lemont Rd Ste 305, Woodridge, IL 60517-2687
Tel (312) 782-4290 *Founded/Ownrshp* 1994
Sales NA *EMP* 370
SIC 6361 Title insurance
CEO: John Baumgart
**Pr:* Mark Schlueter
**CFO:* Thomas Evans
**Ex VP:* Edward Cook

D-U-N-S 84-907-0701
NETCRACKER TECHNOLOGY CORP
(*Suby of* NEC CORPORATION)
95 Sawyer Rd, Waltham, MA 02453-3464
Tel (781) 419-3300 *Founded/Ownrshp* 2008
Sales 282.6MM^E *EMP* 1,000^E
SIC 7372 Prepackaged software
Pr: Andrew Feinberg
**Treas:* Toshio Takahashi
VP: Ganesh Balasubramanian
VP: Dmitry Belous
VP: Joe Dooley
VP: Rick Frizalone
VP: Sanjeev Patel
VP: Angela Pinette
VP: Juergen Reinhardt
Exec: Susan Douglas-Precobb
Dir IT: Doug Witsken

D-U-N-S 96-562-8746
NETECH CORP
6355 E Paris Ave Se, Caledonia, MI 49316-9139
Tel (212) 324-4398 *Founded/Ownrshp* 2016
Sales 104.0MM^E *EMP* 275
SIC 7379

D-U-N-S 79-964-6716 IMP
▲ **NETFLIX INC**
100 Winchester Cir, Los Gatos, CA 95032-1815
Tel (408) 540-3700 *Founded/Ownrshp* 1997
Sales 6.7MMM *EMP* 3,700
Accts Ernst & Young Llp San Jose C
Tkr Sym NFLX *Exch* NGS
SIC 2741 7841 Miscellaneous publishing; Video tape rental; Video disk/tape rental to the general public
Ch Bd: Reed Hastings
CFO: David Wells
Bd of Dir: Timothy Haley
Bd of Dir: Reed Hasting
Chf Mktg O: Kelly Bennett
Ofcr: Tawni Cranz
Ofcr: Jonathan Friedland
Ofcr: Greg Peters
Ofcr: Ted Sarandos
VP: Kevin McEntee
VP: Larry Tanz
VP: Hilary Ware
VP: Jerret West
VP: Mark Yurechko
VP Bus Dev: Bill Holmes
Dir Rx: Bryony Gagan
Board of Directors: Richard N Barton, A George Battle, Timothy M Haley, Jay C Hoag, Leslie Kilgore, Ann Mather, Brad Smith, Anne M Sweeney

D-U-N-S 94-576-6863 IMP/EXP
▲ **NETGEAR INC**
350 E Plumeria Dr, San Jose, CA 95134-1911
Tel (408) 907-8000 *Founded/Ownrshp* 1996
Sales 1.3MMM *EMP* 963
Tkr Sym NTGR *Exch* NGS
SIC 3661 3577 Modems; Carrier equipment, telephone or telegraph; Computer peripheral equipment
Ch Bd: Patrick C S Lo
CFO: Christine M Gorjanc
Bd of Dir: Timothy Godwin
Sr VP: Patrick J Collins III
Sr VP: Michael F Falcon
Sr VP: David J Henry
Sr VP: Andrew W Kim
Sr VP: John P McHugh
Sr VP: Tamesa T Rogers
Sr VP: Michael A Werdann
VP: Tom Babula
VP: Scott Bachinski
VP: Richard Jonker
VP: Jim Kirkpatrick

Board of Directors: Ralph E Faison, Jef T Graham, Jocelyn E Carter-Miller, Gregory J Rossmann, Barbara V Scherer, Julie A Shimer, Grady K Summers, Thomas H Waechter

D-U-N-S 17-558-8826
NETHERLANDS INSURANCE CO
(*Suby of* LIBERTY MUTUAL GROUP INC) ★
62 Maple Ave, Keene, NH 03431-1625
Tel (603) 352-3221 *Founded/Ownrshp* 2005
Sales NA *EMP* 8^E
SIC 6411 Insurance agents, brokers & service
Pr: Gary R Gregg

D-U-N-S 94-130-1624
NETIQ CORP
(*Suby of* ATTACHMATE WRQ) ★
515 Post Oak Blvd # 1000, Houston, TX 77027-9435
Tel (713) 548-1700 *Founded/Ownrshp* 2006
Sales 147.8MM^E *EMP* 857
SIC 7372 7371 Prepackaged software; Computer software development & applications
Ch: Jeff Hawn
**Pr:* Jay Gardner
**COO:* Marc B Andrews
Sr VP: Flint Brenton
Sr VP: Daniel J Meub
Sr VP: Richard J Pleczko
VP: James Barth
**VP:* Edwin Bowman
**VP:* John Delk
**VP:* Ron Hardy
**VP:* Boris Ivancic
**VP:* Luann Johnson
**VP:* Bill Koehl
**VP:* Ron Milton
**VP:* Somesh Singh
VP: Will Smith
Dir: Steve Latham

D-U-N-S 05-993-4919
■ **NETJETS AVIATION INC**
(*Suby of* NETJETS INC) ★
4111 Bridgeway Ave, Columbus, OH 43219-1882
Tel (614) 239-5500 *Founded/Ownrshp* 1998
Sales 167.1MM^E *EMP* 2,500
SIC 4522

D-U-N-S 60-622-2552 IMP/EXP
■ **NETJETS INC**
(*Suby of* BERKSHIRE HATHAWAY INC) ★
4111 Bridgeway Ave, Columbus, OH 43219-1882
Tel (614) 239-5500 *Founded/Ownrshp* 1998
Sales 3.8MMM *EMP* 6,157
SIC 4522 5088 7359 Flying charter service; Aircraft & parts; Aircraft rental
CEO: Adam Johnson
**Pr:* Bill Noe
**COO:* Robert Molsbergen
CFO: Peter S Richards
**CFO:* Brent Smith
**Sr VP:* Colleen Nissl
Sr VP: Sean Silver
VP: Diego Briani
VP: Douglas Clarke
VP: Knight Culver
VP: Craig Dufresne
VP: Bobbie Fenske
VP: Tom Hoyt
VP: Steve Kulesa
VP: Marta De La Rocha
VP: John McCormick
VP: Richard Meikle
VP: Sheridan Root
VP: Gail Victor
VP: Seth Zlotkin

D-U-N-S 06-358-3397
■ **NETJETS SALES INC**
(*Suby of* NETJETS INC) ★
4111 Bridgeway Ave, Columbus, OH 43219-1882
Tel (614) 239-5500 *Founded/Ownrshp* 1998
Sales 97.8MM^E *EMP* 200
SIC 5088 4522 Aircraft & parts; Air transportation, nonscheduled
Pr: Bill Noe
**Treas:* Lesha Thorpe
QA Dir: Rick Montgomery
Board of Directors: Marc Hamburg, Jordan Hansell, Bill Noe, Brent Smith

D-U-N-S 00-958-5113
NETLINK SOFTWARE GROUP AMERICA INC (MI)
999 Tech Row, Madison Heights, MI 48071-4680
Tel (248) 204-8803 *Founded/Ownrshp* 1999
Sales 113.7MM^E *EMP* 300
SIC 7379 7371 Computer related consulting services; Computer software development
CEO: Dilip Dubey
**Pr:* Anurag Shrivastava
COO: Ahmet Corapcioglu
CFO: Sharma Ajoy
**CFO:* Ajoy Sharma
Ofcr: Toyai Hayward
Ex VP: Russ Miller
VP: Sam George
**VP:* Greg Hacias
VP: Amit Horton
VP: Amit Soni

D-U-N-S 92-918-3630
NETLOGIC MICROSYSTEMS LLC
BROADCOM
(*Suby of* BROADCOM CORP) ★
3975 Freedom Cir Ste 900, Santa Clara, CA 95054-1255
Tel (408) 454-3000 *Founded/Ownrshp* 2011
Sales 88.8MM^E *EMP* 645
Accts Pricewaterhousecoopers Llp Sa
SIC 3674 Integrated circuits, semiconductor networks, etc.
CEO: Ronald S Jankov
Pr: Scott A McGregor
CFO: Michael Tate
Ex VP: Behrooz Abdi
Ex VP: Eric K Brandt
Ex VP: Arthur Chong
Sr VP: Ibrahim Korgav

VP: Roland Cortes
Prin: Norman Godinho
Plng Mgr: Angelito Vasquez
Snr Sftwr: Parineeth Reddy

D-U-N-S 14-795-1230 IMP
▲ **NETSCOUT SYSTEMS INC**
310 Littleton Rd, Westford, MA 01886-4105
Tel (978) 614-4000 *Founded/Ownrshp* 1984
Sales 955.4MM *EMP* 3,144
Tkr Sym NTCT *Exch* NGS
SIC 7373 3577 Computer integrated systems design; Computer peripheral equipment
Ch Bd: Anil Singhal
COO: Michael Szabados
CFO: Jean Bua
Sr VP: John W Downing
VP: Ashwani Singhal
Exec: Anthony Lalli
Rgnl Mgr: Dominique Audoin
Sftwr Eng: Jeff Hauk
Sales Exec: Ted Richardson
Sales Asso: Jeremy Nix
Board of Directors: Victor A Demarines, Robert E Donahue, John R Egan, Joseph G Hadzima Jr, James A Lico, Vincent J Mullarkey, Christopher Perretta

D-U-N-S 10-516-2312 IMP
NETSHAPE TECHNOLOGIES INC
(*Suby of* NST HOLDINGS GROUP INC) ★
3620 Paoli Pike Ste 8, Floyds Knobs, IN 47119-9787
Tel (812) 248-9273 *Founded/Ownrshp* 2015
Sales 171.0MM^E *EMP* 500
SIC 3339 Antimony refining (primary)
CEO: Dax Whitehouse
COO: Ric Wrye
CFO: Patty Burkland
Tech Mgr: Robert Doyle
Opers Mgr: Rhett Luecke
Sales Exec: Don Leonard

D-U-N-S 80-791-8628
NETSMART TECHNOLOGIES INC
4950 College Blvd, Overland Park, KS 66211-1612
Tel (913) 327-7444 *Founded/Ownrshp* 1992
Sales 276.7MM^E *EMP* 790
SIC 7371 7372 Custom computer programming services; Prepackaged software
CEO: Michael Valentine
CFO: Anthony F Grisanti
**Ex VP:* Kevin Scalia
**Ex VP:* Alan B Tillinghast
VP: Jim Bartunek
VP: Jason Burritt
VP: Kevin Davidson
VP: Timothy Donovan
VP: Jason Douthit
VP: Jay Golonka
VP: Leordina Lew
VP: Kevin Mallot
VP: Tom Stucke
VP: Justin Sturgeon
VP: Liz Vasti
Exec: John Blanchett
Dir Rx: Michael Littman
Board of Directors: Paul Black, Francis J Calcagno, Joseph G Sicinski, John ST Gallagher

D-U-N-S 13-029-9568
▲ **NETSOL TECHNOLOGIES INC**
24025 Park Sorrento # 410, Calabasas, CA 91302-4018
Tel (818) 222-9195 *Founded/Ownrshp* 1997
Sales 64.5MM *EMP* 1,630^E
Tkr Sym NTWK *Exch* NAS
SIC 7372 7373 7299 Prepackaged software; Computer integrated systems design; Personal document & information services
Ch Bd: Najeeb Ghauri
CFO: Roger Almond
Sr VP: Patti L W McGlasson
Board of Directors: Eugen Beckert, Mark Caton

D-U-N-S 06-981-1862
■ **NETSPEND CORP**
(*Suby of* NETSPEND HOLDINGS INC) ★
701 Brazos St, Austin, TX 78701-3258
Tel (512) 532-8200 *Founded/Ownrshp* 1999
Sales NA *EMP* 300^E
SIC 6091 Nondeposit trust facilities
CEO: Daniel R Henry
Pt: Lisa Henken
Pr: Chuck Harris
COO: Frank Cotroneo
CFO: Adam Chibib
CFO: George W Gresham
CFO: Jim Sargent
Ex VP: Anh Vazquez
Sr VP: James De Voglaer
Sr VP: Roger Kidwell
VP: James Devoglaer
VP: Paige Ellis
VP: Scott Gardner
VP: Joe Silva
VP: Trent Sorbe

D-U-N-S 96-225-7395
■ **NETSPEND HOLDINGS INC**
(*Suby of* TSYS) ★
701 Brazos St Ste 1300, Austin, TX 78701-2674
Tel (512) 532-8200 *Founded/Ownrshp* 2013
Sales NA *EMP* 484^E
SIC 6153 Credit card services, central agency collection
CEO: Daniel R Henry
**Pr:* Charles J Harris
**CFO:* George W Gresham
**Ex VP:* Steven F Coleman
**Ex VP:* James Devoglaer

D-U-N-S 11-639-3195
■ **NETSUITE INC**
(*Suby of* OC ACQUISITION LLC) ★
2955 Campus Dr Ste 100, San Mateo, CA 94403-2539
Tel (650) 627-1000 *Founded/Ownrshp* 2016
Sales 741.1MM *EMP* 4,603^E
SIC 7372 Prepackaged software
Pr: Dorian Daley
Pr: Peter Daffern
Treas: Gregory Hilbrich

Ex VP: Jason Maynard
Sr VP: Mike Arntz
Sr VP: Frank Iannotti
Sr VP: Harvey North
Sr VP: Lee Thompson
VP: Zakir Ahmed
VP: Laura Brumage
VP: Sanjay Bulchandani
VP: Lauretta Carbray
VP: Jeff Davidson
VP: Brian Enright
VP: Chip Erickson
VP: Guido Haarmans
VP: Sandra Lapedis
VP: Sam Levy
VP: Tomoyuki Nakanishi
VP: Douglas Solomon
Board of Directors: Brian S Higgins

D-U-N-S 82-989-6666
NETVERSANT SOLUTIONS LLC
(*Suby of* PATRIARCH PARTNERS LLC) ★
9750 W Sam Houston Pkwy N # 100, Houston, TX 77064-5552
Tel (800) 540-2739 *Founded/Ownrshp* 2009
Sales 109.7MM^E *EMP* 541
SIC 7373 8999 7381 Local area network (LAN) systems integrator; Communication services; Security guard service
CEO: Charles Sweet
**CFO:* Ronald E Hale Jr
**Ex VP:* Reagan S Busbee
**Ex VP:* Robert N Feldman
VP: Andrew Dipasquale

NETWORK 180
See KENT COUNTY OF (INC)

NETWORK 180
See KENT COUNTY CMH AUTHORITY

D-U-N-S 02-038-0747
NETWORK ASSOCIATES INC
CLEANWISE
1100 E Wdfield Rd Ste 200, Schaumburg, IL 60173
Tel (847) 803-4888 *Founded/Ownrshp* 1968
Sales 1.0MMM *EMP* 140^E
SIC 8742 5113 Business consultant; Industrial & personal service paper
Pr: Tracy Evatt
**CFO:* Bob Mtchum
**Sr VP:* Walter Dethlefsen
**VP:* Cheryl Gilbert
Board of Directors: Paul Weyand, David Brown, Leonard Green, James Jackson, Fred Kfoury Jr, Brooks Lammey, John Miller, Matthew Moore, Steve Morris, Herb Sedler

D-U-N-S 01-014-9230 IMP/EXP
NETWORK COMMUNICATIONS INC (GA)
2 Sun Ct Ste 300, Norcross, GA 30092-2865
Tel (678) 346-9300 *Founded/Ownrshp* 2005
Sales 177.6MM^E *EMP* 800
SIC 2731 2721

D-U-N-S 62-709-1184
NETWORK FOB INC
6622 Sthpint Dr S Ste 210, Jacksonville, FL 32216
Tel (651) 256-1000 *Founded/Ownrshp* 1987
Sales 105.0MM^E *EMP* 150
SIC 4731 Freight forwarding
Ch Bd: Timothy Taylor
**Pr:* Jim Handoush
**CFO:* Alan Unger
**Ofcr:* Bill Sandberg

D-U-N-S 12-996-9809
NETWORK FOR GOOD INC
GROUNDSPRING
1140 Conn Ave Nw Ste 700, Washington, DC 20036-4011
Tel (202) 627-1600 *Founded/Ownrshp* 2001
Sales 230.8MM *EMP* 20^E
SIC 4813
CEO: Bill Strathmann
Pr: Jing Gu
Ch: Meredith Maples
Bd of Dir: Ted Cahall Jr
VP: Louise Felton
VP: Stacie Mann
VP: Caryn Stein
Cust Svc D: Annie Olmsted
Sls Mgr: Patrick Drago
Sales Asso: Michael Garceau
Sales Asso: Velma Hutchins

D-U-N-S 07-190-3819
NETWORK GLOBAL LOGISTICS LLC
N G L
320 Interlocken Pkwy # 100, Broomfield, CO 80021-3475
Tel (866) 938-1870 *Founded/Ownrshp* 2005
Sales 211.3MM^E *EMP* 610
SIC 4731 Freight transportation arrangement
CEO: John Labrie
**Ch Bd:* Raymond J Garcia
**CFO:* Forrest Kragten
Genl Mgr: Betty Pearce
IT Man: Ranjit Thaker
Opers Supe: Christopher Cobb

NETWORK HEALTH PLAN
See NETWORK PLAN OF WISCONSIN INC

D-U-N-S 08-281-7073
NETWORK HEALTH SYSTEM INC
(*Suby of* AFFINITY HEALTH SYSTEM) ★
1165 Appleton Rd, Menasha, WI 54952-1905
Tel (920) 831-8920 *Founded/Ownrshp* 1998
Sales 239.5MM^E *EMP* 1,020
SIC 8011 Offices & clinics of medical doctors
CEO: Kevin Nolan
**COO:* Sheila Jenkins

D-U-N-S 92-688-3844 IMP/EXP
NETWORK IMAGING SOLUTIONS INC
NIS
242 E 90th St, Davenport, IA 52806-7341
Tel (563) 285-6123 *Founded/Ownrshp* 1995
Sales 90.7MM *EMP* 220
Accts Reiser Jennings & Co Pc
SIC 4225 General warehousing & storage
Pr: Michael R Strajack
**Pr:* Randall J McDonald
Prd Mgr: Doug Vranek
Ql Cn Mgr: Bill Hopkins

D-U-N-S 08-188-1617
NETWORK PLAN OF WISCONSIN INC
NETWORK HEALTH PLAN
(*Suby of* NETWORK HEALTH SYSTEM INC) ★
1570 Midway Pl, Menasha, WI 54952-1165
Tel (920) 720-1200 *Founded/Ownrshp* 1982
Sales NA *EMP* 300
SIC 6324 Health maintenance organization (HMO), insurance only
Pr: Sheila Jenkins
Pt: Orlando Ayala
VP: Tom Laabs
VP: Penny Ransom
Dir IT: Jennifer L Resch

NETWORK SERVICES
See TALKAMERICA INC

D-U-N-S 08-294-1204 IMP
NETWORK SERVICES CO
(*Suby of* CLEANWISE) ★
1100 E Wdfield Rd Ste 200, Schaumburg, IL 60173
Tel (847) 803-4888 *Founded/Ownrshp* 1975
Sales 1.0MMM^E *EMP* 140
SIC 5113

D-U-N-S 09-636-1225
■ **NETWORK SOLUTIONS LLC**
(*Suby of* WEB.COM GROUP INC) ★
13861 Sunrise Valley Dr # 300, Herndon, VA 20171-6124
Tel (703) 668-4600 *Founded/Ownrshp* 2011
Sales 128.3MM^E *EMP* 900
SIC 7375 7389 4813 7374 Information retrieval services; Credit card service; ; Computer graphics service
CEO: David L Brown
Sr VP: Donald N Telage
VP Bus: Harry Lalor
Exec: Ana Rossi
Dir Bus: Brigette Dega
Dir Bus: Sherry Monday
Prgrm Mgr: Jeff Cooke
Snr Sftwr: Jigar Parikh
CIO: Rick Walsh
Dir IT: Matthew Price

D-U-N-S 09-095-6129
NEUBERGER & BERMAN PARTNERS FUND INC
605 3rd Ave Fl 21, New York, NY 10158-2199
Tel (212) 476-8800 *Founded/Ownrshp* 1967
Sales 44.0MM^E *EMP* 1,000
SIC 6722 Management investment, open-end
Pr: Lawrence Zicklin
VP: Alex Easton

D-U-N-S 83-176-6113
NEUBERGER BERMAN GROUP LLC
605 3rd Ave Fl 21, New York, NY 10158-2199
Tel (212) 476-9000 *Founded/Ownrshp* 2009
Sales 786.9MM^E *EMP* 1,649^E
SIC 6282 6211 6722 Investment advice; Security brokers & dealers; Management investment, open-end
Ch Bd: George H Walker IV
**Pr:* Joseph V Amato
**COO:* Andrew Komaroff
**Chf Inves:* Erik Knutzen
Assoc VP: Vl Decaro
**Ex VP:* Heather Zuckerman
Sr VP: Jolie Cornelius
VP: Peter Andjelkovich
Mktg Dir: Barbara Bresnahan
Board of Directors: Steven A Kandarian

D-U-N-S 08-464-3803
NEUBERGER BERMAN LLC
(*Suby of* NEUBERGER BERMAN GROUP LLC) ★
605 3rd Ave Fl 21, New York, NY 10158-2199
Tel (212) 476-9000 *Founded/Ownrshp* 2003
Sales 710.6MM^E *EMP* 1,200
SIC 6282 6211 6722 Investment advice; Security brokers & dealers; Management investment, open-end
Pr: Joseph V Amato
Pr: Alexander Botkhin
Pr: Peter Janczewski
Pr: Bala Muthuswamy
COO: Bob Matza
COO: Amir Nooriala
COO: Matthew S Stadler
CFO: Philip Ambrosio
CFO: Matthew S Tadler
Ofcr: Andrew Allard
Ofcr: Gary Jansen
Ofcr: Erik L Knutzen
Ofcr: Brad Tank
Ex VP: Steve Kwong
Ex VP: Peter E Sundman
Sr VP: Jonathan Cohen
Sr VP: Patrick Heffernan
Sr VP: Ilich Martinez
Sr VP: Ralph D Sinsheimer
VP: Arlene Adler
VP: Anthony Desantis

D-U-N-S 02-524-4161
NEUCO INC (IL)
5101 Thatcher Rd, Downers Grove, IL 60515-4072
Tel (630) 960-3800 *Founded/Ownrshp* 1970
Sales 133.5MM^E *EMP* 85
SIC 5075 Air conditioning & ventilation equipment & supplies
Pr: Paul J Neustadt
VP: Brian Neustadt
VP: Tim Stelzer
CIO: Gregg Skala
Web Dev: Jason Stelzer

D-U-N-S 12-239-6356
NEUDESIC LLC
100 Spectrum Center Dr # 1200, Irvine, CA 92618-4962
Tel (949) 754-4500 *Founded/Ownrshp* 2002
Sales 83.6MM^E *EMP* 300
SIC 7379 Computer related consulting services
CEO: Parsa Rohani
Exec: Steve Oprian
Genl Mgr: Jason Noble
Genl Mgr: Marty Wasznicky
VP Opers: Mike Collins
Mktg Mgr: Katie Danielson

D-U-N-S 14-874-9497
▲ **NEULION INC**
1600 Old Country Rd, Plainview, NY 11803-5013
Tel (516) 622-8300 *Founded/Ownrshp* 2003
Sales 94.0MM *EMP* 638^E
Tkr Sym NEUL *Exch* OTO
SIC 4841 7372 Cable & other pay television services; Prepackaged software
Pr: Roy E Reichbach
**Ch Bd:* Nancy Li
CFO: Trevor Renfield
Software D: Jordan Montpetit
Mktg Dir: William Frantz
Board of Directors: John R Anderson, Gabriel A Battista, Robert E Bostrom, John A Coelho, James R Hale, Shirley Strum Kenny, David Kronfeld

NEURORESTORATIVE
See NATIONAL MENTOR INC

D-U-N-S 11-240-3295
▲ **NEUSTAR INC**
21575 Ridgetop Cir, Sterling, VA 20166-6505
Tel (571) 434-5400 *Founded/Ownrshp* 1996
Sales 1.0MMM *EMP* 2,125^E
Tkr Sym NSR *Exch* NYS
SIC 7375 4899 Information retrieval services; Data base information retrieval; Remote data base information retrieval; On-line data base information retrieval; Data communication services
Pr: Lisa A Hook
**Ch Bd:* James G Cullen
CFO: Paul S Lalljie
Ofcr: Nick Hulse
Sr VP: Steven J Edwards
Sr VP: Leonard J Kennedy
Sr VP: Edward M Prince Jr
Sr VP: Ivor Sequeira
Sr VP: Hank Skorny
VP: Steve Boyce
VP: Mark F Bregman
VP: Randy Buffenbarger
VP: John Caldwell
VP: Sean Corcoran
VP: Mark Foster
VP: Reynold Harbin
VP: Steve Johnson
VP: John Keaveney
VP: John Kelly
VP: Robert May
VP: Ryan McGavran
Board of Directors: Paul D Ballew, Gareth C C Chang, Joel P Friedman, Mark N Greene, Ross K Ireland, Paul A Lacouture, Deborah D Rieman, Michael J Rowny

D-U-N-S 96-504-3388
NEV HOLDINGS LLC
3211 Internet Blvd # 200, Frisco, TX 75034-1948
Tel (972) 731-1100 *Founded/Ownrshp* 2010
Sales 194.8MM^E *EMP* 3,401
SIC 2677 Envelopes

D-U-N-S 00-697-0925
■ **NEVADA BELL TELEPHONE CO** (NV)
AT&T NEVADA
(*Suby of* AT&T INC) ★
645 E Plumb Ln B128, Reno, NV 89502-3595
Tel (775) 333-3124 *Founded/Ownrshp* 1913, 2006
Sales 16.0MMM *EMP* 860
SIC 4813 Local telephone communications; Long distance telephone communications
Prin: Marsha Lindsey
**Pr:* Sivia Samano
**Treas:* R W Wohlert
Software D: Mary Evans

D-U-N-S 00-968-8599
NEVADA BEVERAGE CO (NV)
ALTERNATIVE BEVERAGE
3940 W Tropicana Ave, Las Vegas, NV 89103-5516
Tel (702) 739-9998 *Founded/Ownrshp* 1943
Sales 162.2MM^E *EMP* 280
SIC 5181 Beer & other fermented malt liquors
Pr: Pat Clark

NEVADA CANCER INSTITUTE
See REGENTS OF UNIVERSITY OF CALIFORNIA

NEVADA COUNTY PUBLISHING CO
See SWIFT COMMUNICATIONS INC

D-U-N-S 03-289-4342
NEVADA DEPARTMENT OF CORRECTIONS
(*Suby of* EXECUTIVE OFFICE OF STATE OF NEVADA) ★
5500 Snyder Ave Bldg 89, Carson City, NV 89701-6752
Tel (775) 887-3285 *Founded/Ownrshp* 1977
Sales NA *EMP* 2,600^E
SIC 9223 Prison, government;
**CFO:* Lorraine Pagwell
**Prin:* Darell Wreck

D-U-N-S 80-988-8266
NEVADA DEPARTMENT OF HEALTH AND HUMAN SERVICES
DIRECTOR'S OFFICE
(*Suby of* EXECUTIVE OFFICE OF STATE OF NEVADA) ★
4126 Tech Way Ste 100, Carson City, NV 89706
Tel (775) 684-4000 *Founded/Ownrshp* 1963
Sales NA *EMP* 5,374
SIC 9431 Administration of public health programs;
Ofcr: Michael Torvinen

D-U-N-S 80-988-8399
NEVADA DEPARTMENT OF MOTOR VEHICLES
(*Suby of* EXECUTIVE OFFICE OF STATE OF NEVADA) ★
555 Wright Way, Carson City, NV 89711-0001
Tel (775) 684-4549 *Founded/Ownrshp* 1957
Sales NA *EMP* 1,030
SIC 9621 Motor vehicle licensing & inspection office, government;

D-U-N-S 14-786-0105
NEVADA DEPARTMENT OF PUBLIC SAFETY
(*Suby of* EXECUTIVE OFFICE OF STATE OF NEVADA) ★
555 Wright Way, Carson City, NV 89701-5229
Tel (775) 684-4556 *Founded/Ownrshp* 2001
Sales NA *EMP* 1,600
SIC 9229 Public safety bureau, government;
Ex Ofcr: Kathalie Koche

D-U-N-S 82-469-5720
NEVADA DEPARTMENT OF TRANSPORTATION
NDOT
(*Suby of* EXECUTIVE OFFICE OF STATE OF NEVADA) ★
1263 S Stewart St, Carson City, NV 89712-0001
Tel (775) 888-7440 *Founded/Ownrshp* 1982
Sales NA *EMP* 1,604
SIC 9621 Regulation, administration of transportation;

D-U-N-S 09-901-2221
▲ **NEVADA GOLD & CASINOS INC**
NG CASINOS
133 E Warm Springs Rd # 102, Las Vegas, NV 89119-4122
Tel (702) 685-1000 *Founded/Ownrshp* 1977
Sales 70.3MM *EMP* 1,280^E
Tkr Sym UWN *Exch* ASE
SIC 7011 Casino hotel
CEO: Michael P Shaunnessy
**Ch Bd:* William J Sherlock
CFO: James D Meier
VP: Ernest E East
VP: Victor H Mena
Board of Directors: Frank Catania, William G Jayroe, Francis M Ricci, Wayne H White

D-U-N-S 96-294-9983
NEVADA MEZZ 1 LLC
60 Wall St, New York, NY 10005-2836
Tel (702) 314-3265 *Founded/Ownrshp* 2008
Sales 9.1MM^E *EMP* 4,187
SIC 7011 Resort hotel; Casino hotel
CEO: John Unwin

D-U-N-S 00-697-0891 IMP
■ **NEVADA POWER CO**
NV ENERGY
(*Suby of* NV ENERGY INC) ★
6226 W Sahara Ave, Las Vegas, NV 89146-3060
Tel (702) 402-5000 *Founded/Ownrshp* 1998
Sales 2.3MMM *EMP* 1,524
Accts Deloitte & Touche Llp Las Veg
SIC 4911 Electric services; Distribution, electric power; Generation, electric power; Transmission, electric power
Pr: Paul J Caudill
**Ch Bd:* Philip G Satre
Pr: Paul J Kaleta
COO: Dilek L Samil
CFO: Kevin Bethel
CFO: Jonathan S Halkyard
Treas: Mohammed N Mughal
Chf Cred: Ryan Hampton
Ofcr: Eskil Elmer
Ex VP: Paul Kaleta
VP: E Kevin Bethel
Exec: Wayne Baca
Exec: James Doubek
Exec: Linda Garver
Exec: Mark Shank
Board of Directors: Joseph B Anderson Jr, Glenn C Christenson, Susan F Clark, Stephen E Frank, Brian J Kennedy, Maureen T Mullarkey, John F O'reilly, Donald D Snyder

D-U-N-S 82-894-7601
NEVADA PROPERTY 1 LLC
COSMOPOLITAN OF LAS VEGAS, THE
(*Suby of* BRE SPADE VOTECO LLC) ★
3708 Las Vegas Blvd S, Las Vegas, NV 89109-4309
Tel (702) 698-7000 *Founded/Ownrshp* 2014
Sales 528.5MM^E *EMP* 4,400^E
SIC 7011 Resort hotel; Casino hotel
CEO: John Unwin
**Ch Bd:* Enrico Sanna
COO: Thomas McCartney
**CFO:* Ronald G Eidell
Chf Mktg O: Lisa Marchese
Ofcr: Anthony Pearl
VP: John Anstey
VP: Daniel Espino
VP: Ken Hoff
VP: Simon Pettigrew
Exec: Jeff Walter
Exec: Duane Welch
Assoc Dir: Lori Foit

D-U-N-S 00-697-0909
NEVADA STATE BANK
750 E Warm Springs Rd # 240, Las Vegas, NV 89119-4383
Tel (702) 855-4575 *Founded/Ownrshp* 1985
Sales NA *EMP* 922
SIC 6022

D-U-N-S 04-165-4195 IMP
NEVADA SYSTEM OF HIGHER EDUCATION
NSHE
(*Suby of* EXECUTIVE OFFICE OF STATE OF NEVADA) ★
2601 Enterprise Rd, Reno, NV 89512-1666
Tel (775) 784-4901 *Founded/Ownrshp* 1864

Sales 671.6MME EMP 8,000
SIC 8221 9411 University; Administration of educational programs;
CEO: Daniel Klaich
Ofcr: Vic Redding
CTO: Steven Zink
Board of Directors: Howard Rosenberg, Mark Alden, Steve Sisolak, Dr Stavros Anthony Phd, Bret Whipple, Michael Wixom Chair, Cedric Crear, Thalia M Dondero, Dorothy S Gallagher, Jason Geddes, Ron Knecht, James Dean Leavitt

D-U-N-S 04-622-9720
NEVADA YELLOW CAB CORP
5225 W Post Rd, Las Vegas, NV 89118-4331
Tel (702) 873-8012 Founded/Ownrshp 1980
Sales 74.4MME EMP 1,500
SIC 4121 Taxicabs
Pr: David Willden
CFO: Gene Auffert
*Sec: Harry Eliades
*VP: Milton I Schwartz
Genl Couns: Marc Gordon

D-U-N-S 00-743-4615 IMP/EXP
NEVAMAR CO LLC
NEVAMAR DISTRIBUTORS
(Suby of PANOLAM SURFACE SYSTEMS) ★
20 Progress Dr, Shelton, CT 06484-6216
Tel (203) 925-1556 Founded/Ownrshp 2002
Sales 133.6MME EMP 1,000
SIC 3089 5162 Panels, building: plastic; Plastics materials & basic shapes
Mtls Mgr: Donna Gohagan

NEVAMAR DISTRIBUTORS
See NEVAMAR CO LLC

D-U-N-S 12-978-0537
NEVELL GROUP INC
N G I
3001 Enterprise St # 200, Brea, CA 92821-6210
Tel (714) 579-7501 Founded/Ownrshp 2002
Sales 108.2MME EMP 350
Accts Jlk Partners Llp Tustin Cali
SIC 1542 Commercial & office building, new construction
Pr: Michael J Nevell
*CFO: Bryan Bodine
*Ex VP: Therese Belisle
*Sr VP: Bruce Pasqua
*VP: Greg Thomas

D-U-N-S 02-230-3726 IMP
NEW 5-7-9 AND BEYOND INC
(Suby of RAINBOW SHOPS) ★
1000 Pennsylvania Ave, Brooklyn, NY 11207-8417
Tel (718) 485-3000 Founded/Ownrshp 1999
Sales 150.0MM EMP 165
SIC 5621 Ready-to-wear apparel, women's
CEO: Joseph Chehebar
*Pr: Albert Chehebar
*COO: Martin Stein
*Treas: Jacob Chehebar
VP: Johnathan Appel
*VP: Isaac Chehebar

D-U-N-S 62-387-5114
NEW AFFIRMATIVE LLC
4450 Sojourn Dr Ste 500, Addison, TX 75001-5094
Tel (972) 728-6300 Founded/Ownrshp 2005
Sales NA EMP 1,269
SIC 6331 Automobile insurance
Ch Bd: Kevin R Callahan

D-U-N-S 10-313-3211
NEW AGE INVESTMENTS INC
METRO NISSAN OF MONTCLAIR
9440 Autoplex St, Montclair, CA 91763-2300
Tel (909) 625-8990 Founded/Ownrshp 1970
Sales 112.9MME EMP 366
SIC 5511 Automobiles, new & used
CEO: David A Marvin
CFO: Michelle Lowe
*Sec: Susie Mc Nutt
Dir IT: Naveen Kathuria
Dir IT: Shane Powell

D-U-N-S 07-406-5061
NEW ALBANY FLOYD COUNTY CONSOLIDATED SCHOOL CORP
2813 Grant Line Rd, New Albany, IN 47150-2457
Tel (812) 949-4200 Founded/Ownrshp 1956
Sales 75.6MME EMP 1,800
SIC 8211

D-U-N-S 17-423-1746 EXP
NEW ALBERTSONS INC
JEWEL-OSCO
(Suby of ALBERTSONS) ★
150 E Pierce Rd Ste 200, Itasca, IL 60143-1224
Tel (630) 948-6000 Founded/Ownrshp 2014
Sales 747.2MME EMP 1E
SIC 5411 5912 5331 Grocery stores; Supermarkets; Drug stores; Variety stores
CEO: Robert Miller

D-U-N-S 78-014-8537 IMP
NEW ALBERTSONS INC
ACME
(Suby of ALBERTSONS) ★
250 E Parkcenter Blvd, Boise, ID 83706-3940
Tel (208) 395-6200 Founded/Ownrshp 2008
Sales 4.8MMME EMP 36,822
SIC 5411 Grocery stores
Pr: Michael L Jackson
*CFO: Pamela K Knous
*Ex VP: David L Boehnen
VP: Yolanda Scharton
Off Mgr: Samuel Stockdale

D-U-N-S 12-170-8747
NEW ALTERNATIVES INC
3589 4th Ave, San Diego, CA 92103-4912
Tel (619) 543-0293 Founded/Ownrshp 1978
Sales 46.5MM EMP 1,000
SIC 8322 Child related social services
Ex Dir: Michael Bruich

NEW AMEREN ENERGY RESOURCES
See ILLINOIS POWER RESOURCES LLC

NEW AMERICAN FUNDING
See BROKER SOLUTIONS INC

D-U-N-S 13-518-1993
NEW APPLE INC
APPLEBEE'S
170 Wind Chime Ct, Raleigh, NC 27615-6433
Tel (919) 870-0513 Founded/Ownrshp 2000
Sales 31.4MME EMP 1,500
SIC 5812 Restaurant, family: chain
Pr: Michael Olander

D-U-N-S 07-929-3442
NEW ASURION CORP
648 Grassmere Park, Nashville, TN 37211-3663
Tel (615) 837-3000 Founded/Ownrshp 2008
Sales NA EMP 11,019E
SIC 6331 Property damage insurance
CEO: Bret Comolli

D-U-N-S 08-014-3520
■ **NEW AVON LLC**
(Suby of CERBERUS CAPITAL MANAGEMENT LP) ★
777 3rd Ave Fl 8, New York, NY 10017-1307
Tel (212) 282-8500 Founded/Ownrshp 2016
Sales 656.1MME EMP 2,500
SIC 2844 5122 5999 Toilet preparations; Cosmetics; Cosmetics
Pr: Betty Palm
Pr: Anjana Srivastava
*Ofcr: Helene F Rutledge

D-U-N-S 05-888-5963 IMP/EXP
NEW BALANCE ATHLETICS INC
DUNHAM BOOTMAKERS
(Suby of NEW BALANCE INC) ★
100 Guest St Fl 5, Boston, MA 02135-2088
Tel (617) 783-4000 Founded/Ownrshp 1972
Sales 586.1MME EMP 2,200
SIC 8699 Charitable organization
CEO: Robert Demartini
V Ch: Anne Davis
Pr: Barry Gutwillig
*CFO: John K Withee
*Ch: James S Davis
*Treas: Kevin Doyle
Treas: Alan Rosen
Ex VP: David Crosier
Ex VP: Alan Hed
Ex VP: Chris Quinn
Ex VP: John Wilson
VP: Ken Benser
VP: Edward Haddad
VP: Kevin Holian
VP: Perry Miroballi
VP: Martin Walter

D-U-N-S 01-795-3639 IMP
NEW BALANCE INC
100 Guest St, Brighton, MA 02135-2088
Tel (617) 783-4000 Founded/Ownrshp 1972
Sales 1.8MMME EMP 4,000
SIC 5139 Footwear, athletic
CEO: Robert T Demartini
Pr: Barry Gutwillig
*CFO: Bill Hayden
*Sec: James S Davis
*Ex VP: Anne Davis
*Ex VP: John Withee
VP: Christine Madigan
VP: David Nelligan
VP: Joseph Preston
Dir: Jodie Saracco
Store Mgr: Vanessa Ellis

D-U-N-S 07-571-9187
NEW BEDFORD CITY OF (INC)
133 William St Unit 208, New Bedford, MA 02740-6113
Tel (508) 979-1400 Founded/Ownrshp 1787
Sales NA EMP 3,657
Accts Hague Sahady & Co Pc
SIC 9111 Mayors' offices;
*Treas: Renee Fernandes-Abbott
Dir IT: Maria Pina-Rocha
Dir IT: Robert Tetreault

NEW BEGINNINGS WEIGHT LOSS PRO
See VIRTUA HEALTH INC

D-U-N-S 78-220-5611 IMP
NEW BELGIUM BREWING CO INC
500 Linden St, Fort Collins, CO 80524-2457
Tel (970) 221-0524 Founded/Ownrshp 1990
Sales 91.3MME EMP 210E
Accts Ehrhardt Keefe Steiner & Hottm
SIC 2082 Beer (alcoholic beverage)
Ch Bd: Kimberly Jordan
CFO: Danielle McLamon
CFO: David McMahon
CFO: Jennifer Vervier-Orgolini
Bd of Dir: Paul Hudnut
Creative D: Melyssa Mead
Mng Dir: Dick Knight
Area Mgr: Geoffrey Becker
Area Mgr: Joe Kurz
Genl Mgr: Nate Turner
QA Dir: Mandy Miller
Board of Directors: Peter Bouckaert, Floris Delee, Jeff Lebesch, Greg Owsley, Nate Turner

D-U-N-S 03-834-6169
NEW BRAUNFELS UTILITIES (TX)
263 Main Plz, New Braunfels, TX 78130-5135
Tel (830) 608-8867 Founded/Ownrshp 1942
Sales 155.0MME EMP 210E
Accts Holtman Wagner & Company Llp
SIC 4911 4941 4952 Distribution, electric power; Water supply; Sewerage systems
CEO: Paula J Difonzo
Trst: John Harrell
Exec: Janice Jessen
Ex Dir: Douglas Draeger
*Ex Dir: Al Kaufmann
Div Mgr: Trino Pedraza
Dir IT: Kurt Knettel

D-U-N-S 02-077-6910
NEW BRUNSWICK PUBLIC SCHOOLS
268 Baldwin St, New Brunswick, NJ 08901-2947
Tel (732) 745-5300 Founded/Ownrshp 1900
Sales 85.0MME EMP 1,352
SIC 8211 Public elementary & secondary schools; High school, junior or senior
Dir IT: Del Kunert

NEW BURGH ENLARGED CY SCHL DST
See NEWBURGH CITY SCHOOL DISTRICT

D-U-N-S 07-219-7676
NEW CANEY INDEPENDENT SCHOOL DISTRICT
21580 Loop 494, New Caney, TX 77357-8239
Tel (281) 577-8600 Founded/Ownrshp 1937
Sales 75.7MME EMP 1,250
SIC 8211 Public elementary school; Public junior high school; Public senior high school; Public special education school
*CFO: Clisty Vaden
Ofcr: Sherri Kreg
Admn Mgr: Janet Adare
MIS Dir: Dan Casteel
Dir IT: Susan Hoisington
Pr Dir: Scott Powers
Pr Dir: Cindy Reynolds
Schl Brd P: Curt Joslin
Psych: Carrie Shaver
HC Dir: Christina Nunez

NEW CASTLE BUILDING PRODUCTS
See S & K DISTRIBUTION LLC

D-U-N-S 60-908-8059 IMP
■ **NEW CASTLE CORP**
EXCALIBUR HOTEL & CASINO
(Suby of MANDALAY BAY RESORT AND CASINO) ★
3850 Las Vegas Blvd S, Las Vegas, NV 89109-4324
Tel (702) 597-7777 Founded/Ownrshp 2005
Sales 71.8MME EMP 4,200
SIC 5812 7011 Eating places; Casino hotel
Ch Bd: Jim Murran
*Pr: Rene West
VP: Michelle Borgel
Exec: Concepcion Delgado
Exec: Yvonne Godert
Mng Dir: Lorenzo Herrera
Advt Mgr: Dana Emberley
Sls Mgr: Linda Lang
Sls Mgr: Robin Walker

D-U-N-S 95-915-7652
NEW CASTLE HOTELS LLC
2 Corporate Dr Ste 154, Shelton, CT 06484-6253
Tel (203) 925-8370 Founded/Ownrshp 1994
Sales 153.8MME EMP 4,200
SIC 7011 8741 8742 Hotel, franchised; Hotel or motel management; Industry specialist consultants
*COO: Gerry Chase
VP: Lisa Blank
VP: Bryan Woodhouse
VP: Alan Zaccario
Admn Mgr: Lisa Besescheck
Genl Mgr: Angela Steeves
Genl Mgr: Jim Wefers

D-U-N-S 79-115-2713
■ **NEW CASTLE TELEPHONE CO**
TDS
(Suby of TDS TELECOMMUNICATIONS CORP) ★
320 Salem Ave, New Castle, VA 24127-8501
Tel (608) 831-1000 Founded/Ownrshp 1990
Sales 853.0MM EMP 99
SIC 4813 Telephone communication, except radio
Pr: David Wittwer
*Treas: Paul Abraham
*VP: G Ronnie Barnes
*VP: Jerry Harms

D-U-N-S 82-957-8132
NEW CENTAUR LLC
CENTAUR GAMING
(Suby of CENTAUR HOLDINGS LLC) ★
10 W Market St Ste 2700, Indianapolis, IN 46204-2982
Tel (317) 656-8787 Founded/Ownrshp 2011
Sales 38.0MME EMP 1,010
SIC 8741 Administrative management
CEO: Roderick J Ratcliff
*CFO: Kurt E Wilson
Ex VP: Kurt Wilson

D-U-N-S 10-999-9636
NEW CENTURY TRANSPORTATION INC
45 E Park Dr, Mount Holly, NJ 08060-5123
Tel (609) 265-1110 Founded/Ownrshp 2000
Sales NA EMP 1,713
SIC 4213

D-U-N-S 13-059-8238 IMP
■ **NEW CINGULAR WIRELESS SERVICES INC**
AT&T MOBILITY
(Suby of AT&T MOBILITY LLC) ★
7277 164th Ave Ne, Redmond, WA 98052-7823
Tel (425) 827-4500 Founded/Ownrshp 1987
Sales 13.8MMME EMP 31,000
SIC 4812 Cellular telephone services; Paging services
Pr: Michael G Keith
*Pr: Paul Roth
*CFO: Joseph McCabe Jr
CFO: Peter Ritcher
*Treas: Jonathan P Klug
*Ex VP: William Hague
Ex VP: Jane Marvin
*Ex VP: Brian Shay
Sr VP: Steven L Elfman
Sr VP: Kendra Vandermeulen
*VP: Sean P Foley

D-U-N-S 02-235-4377
NEW CO-OPERATIVE INC
2626 1st Ave S, Fort Dodge, IA 50501-4381
Tel (515) 955-2040 Founded/Ownrshp 1973
Sales 611.2MME EMP 226
SIC 5153 5191 Grain elevators; Grains; Feed; Seeds: field, garden & flower; Fertilizer & fertilizer materials; Chemicals, agricultural
Opers Mgr: Robert Koestern
Sls Mgr: Dennis Habben
Sls Mgr: Tony Hilbert

D-U-N-S 13-858-3161
NEW CO-OPERATIVE INC
MAPS
(Suby of NEW CO-OPERATIVE INC) ★
2626 1st Ave S, Fort Dodge, IA 50501-4381
Tel (515) 955-2040 Founded/Ownrshp 1924
Sales 611.2MME EMP 225
SIC 5153 Grains
Prin: Dennis Knight
Treas: Dale Seehusen
VP: Jon Larson
IT Man: Terry Panbecker
Sales Asso: Christopher Bro
Sales Asso: Daniel Foth
Sales Asso: Chuck Lundquist
Sales Asso: Ken Rasmussen

D-U-N-S 12-214-4645
NEW COMMUNITY CORP
N C C
233 W Market St, Newark, NJ 07103-2713
Tel (973) 623-2800 Founded/Ownrshp 1968
Sales 19.6MM EMP 1,200E
Accts Withumsmithbrown Pc New Bruns
SIC 8399 Community development groups
Pr: Arthur L Wilson
*CEO: Richard Rohrman
*CFO: Elizabeth Mbakaya
*Treas: Edgar Nemorin
Assoc Ed: Angela Stewart
Board of Directors: Maida Avellanet, Barry Baker, Elma Bateman, Patrick Duff, Edgar Nemorin, Desmond O'connell, Felix Roig, Madge Wilson

D-U-N-S 18-175-7659
NEW COUNTRY MOTOR CAR GROUP INC
358 Broadway Ste 403, Saratoga Springs, NY 12866-3190
Tel (518) 583-4896 Founded/Ownrshp 1983
Sales 181.6MME EMP 234
SIC 8741 5511 Business management; Automobiles, new & used
Ch Bd: Michael Cantanucci
*VP: Chris Mackey

D-U-N-S 03-693-1215
NEW CUSTOMER SERVICE COMPANIES INC
(Suby of NEW ASURION CORP) ★
22894 Pacific Blvd, Sterling, VA 20166-6722
Tel (703) 318-7700 Founded/Ownrshp 2015
Sales 95.7MME EMP 1,200E
SIC 8748 Business consulting
Ch Bd: Fredrick Schaufeld
*Pr: Tony Nader
*COO: David Bosserman
*Sr VP: Ray Zukowski
VP: Mark Malnati
IT Man: Jill Gundlach
Prd Mgr: Saundra Ellis

D-U-N-S 08-027-5653
NEW DALTON FOUNDRY LLC
1900 E Jefferson St, Warsaw, IN 46580-3761
Tel (574) 267-8111 Founded/Ownrshp 2016
Sales 104.4MME EMP 300E
SIC 3321 Gray iron castings

D-U-N-S 03-092-8543
NEW DISTRIBUTING CO INC
FUEL EXPRESS
4102 Us Highway 59 N, Victoria, TX 77905-5592
Tel (361) 575-1981 Founded/Ownrshp 1959
Sales 92.1MM EMP 25E
SIC 5171 Petroleum bulk stations
Pr: Jon R New
Genl Mgr: Mike Ross
Sls Mgr: Larry Surratt
Sales Asso: Larry McDowell
Sales Asso: Tiffany Williams

D-U-N-S 02-476-8194
NEW DIXIE OIL CORP (NC)
1501 Marshall St, Roanoke Rapids, NC 27870-4415
Tel (252) 537-4118 Founded/Ownrshp 1962
Sales 100.4MM EMP 195
Accts Mcgladrey & Pullen Llp Rocky
SIC 5983 Fuel oil dealers
Pr: Timothy Scott Aman
*Sec: Renee L Aman
Sales Exec: John Elam
Board of Directors: Barbara Aman, Carey Wallace Aman Charim

NEW ENERGY
See CONSTELLATION NEWENERGY INC

D-U-N-S 01-305-7500 IMP
NEW ENERGY INC (VA)
NE KIDS
2300 Prospect Dr, Christiansburg, VA 24073-2561
Tel (540) 382-7377 Founded/Ownrshp 1979
Sales 140.0MM EMP 26
SIC 5021

D-U-N-S 96-337-3530
NEW ENGLAND ALLIANCE FOR HEALTH LLC
(Suby of DARTMOUTH-HITCHCOCK) ★
1 Medical Center Dr, Lebanon, NH 03756-1000
Tel (603) 653-1223 Founded/Ownrshp 2008
Sales 69.0MME EMP 3,719E
SIC 8742 Hospital & health services consultant
Prin: Stephen Leblanc
CFO: Richard Showalter
Doctor: Julia Burdick
Doctor: Heather Gray
Doctor: Christian Hallowell
Doctor: Jeffrey Harnsberger
Doctor: Douglas Marks

Doctor: Christine Rosenwasser
Doctor: Eric Shulman

D-U-N-S 07-661-8883 IMP/EXP
NEW ENGLAND BAPTIST HOSPITAL INC
125 Parker Hill Ave Ste 2, Boston, MA 02120-2865
Tel (617) 754-5000 *Founded/Ownrshp* 1996
Sales 227.2MM^E *EMP* 1,200
SIC 8062 General medical & surgical hospitals
CEO: Joe Dioniso
**Pr:* Raymond C McAfoose
COO: Arnold Scheller
**CFO:* Tom Gerangalli
CFO: Robert Kelly
CFO: John Szum
**Treas:* Edward Fraioli
Ofcr: Sandra Gaston
Ofcr: Maureen Tringale
Assoc VP: Scott W Anderson
Assoc VP: Valerie J Giordano
**VP:* Thomas J Gheringhelli
VP: Val Giordano
VP: Diane Gulczynski
VP: Mary S Smith
VP: Linda Thompson
Dir Rad: Damon Spitz

D-U-N-S 00-142-0686 EXP
■ NEW ENGLAND BUSINESS SERVICE INC (DE)
NEBS
(*Suby of* DELUXE CORP) ★
500 Main St, Groton, MA 01471-0001
Tel (978) 448-6111 *Founded/Ownrshp* 1952, 2004
Sales 344.5MM^E *EMP* 3,611^E
SIC 2759 2771 5045 2653 3089 3069 Commercial printing; Business forms: printing; Stationery: printing; Labels & seals: printing; Greeting cards; Computer software; Corrugated & solid fiber boxes; Boxes, corrugated: made from purchased materials; Boxes, solid fiber: made from purchased materials; Plastic containers, except foam; Tape, pressure sensitive: rubber
Pr: Richard H Rhoads
**Sec:* Paul F Robinson
Sr VP: Joel Hughes
Sr VP: Robert D Warren
VP: Tim Althof
VP: Timothy Althof
**VP:* Barbara Baklund
VP: David Foster
VP: Robert H Glaudel
Counsel: Ellen Grant

D-U-N-S 06-933-7186
NEW ENGLAND CONTROLS INC
9 Oxford Rd, Mansfield, MA 02048-1126
Tel (508) 339-5522 *Founded/Ownrshp* 1966
Sales 118.5MM^E *EMP* 115
SIC 5085 Industrial supplies
Pr: Thomas A Ramundo
Ofcr: Jacob Yany
**VP:* Tim Alosi
**VP:* Jenn Azar
**VP:* Ed Browne
**VP:* Mike Stajduhar
IT Man: Scott Hayden
Sales Asso: Pete Plucinski

D-U-N-S 15-518-5903
NEW ENGLAND DEACONESS HOSPITAL CORP
1 Deaconess Rd, Boston, MA 02215-5321
Tel (814) 777-4805 *Founded/Ownrshp* 1984
Sales 17.0MM *EMP* 2,521
Accts Deloitte & Touche Llp Boston
SIC 8062 General medical & surgical hospitals
Pr: Robert Norton
**CFO:* Cheryl A Hoffman
Doctor: Benjamin W White MD

D-U-N-S 95-604-9571
NEW ENGLAND DEVELOPMENT INC
75 Park Plz Ste 3, Boston, MA 02116-3934
Tel (617) 965-8700 *Founded/Ownrshp* 1985
Sales 183.1MM^E *EMP* 140^E
SIC 6552 Subdividers & developers
Pr: Stephen R Karp
Pr: Jerold Rutberg
**CEO:* Steven S Fischman
COO: Dolly Lau
CFO: Michelle Parven
**Ex VP:* Armen D Aftandilian
Ex VP: Michael Dicosola
**Ex VP:* Bruce Herman
Ex VP: Bruce M Herman
Sr VP: Bill Cronin
Sr VP: James Fischer
VP: Michael Barelli
**VP:* Douglass E Karp
VP: Tad Lee
**VP:* Greg Murphy

NEW ENGLAND ELECTRIC SYSTEM
See NEW ENGLAND ELECTRIC TRANSMISSION CORP

D-U-N-S 15-236-5102
NEW ENGLAND ELECTRIC TRANSMISSION CORP
NEW ENGLAND ELECTRIC SYSTEM
(*Suby of* NATIONAL GRID USA) ★
25 Research Dr, Westborough, MA 01581-3680
Tel (617) 322-3091 *Founded/Ownrshp* 1981
Sales 2.4MM *EMP* 9,000
SIC 4911 Transmission, electric power
Pr: Richard Sergel
**VP:* Christopher E Root
**VP:* Masheed H Rosenqvist

NEW ENGLAND FINANCIAL
See NEW ENGLAND LIFE INSURANCE CO

D-U-N-S 06-004-3812
NEW ENGLAND ICE CREAM CORP
555 Constitution Dr, Taunton, MA 02780-7365
Tel (508) 824-0500 *Founded/Ownrshp* 1988
Sales 103.9MM^E *EMP* 170
SIC 5084 Food industry machinery
CEO: Bruce C Ginsberg
**Pr:* Stephen W Beck
**COO:* Robert Frotten
**Treas:* Jamey Lagor
Dir Surg: Mike Dinatale

NEW ENGLAND JOURNAL MEDICINE
See MASSACHUSETTS MEDICAL SOCIETY INC

D-U-N-S 18-809-0732
■ NEW ENGLAND LIFE INSURANCE CO
NEW ENGLAND FINANCIAL
(*Suby of* METLIFE) ★
501 Boylston St Ste 1, Boston, MA 02116-3738
Tel (617) 578-2000 *Founded/Ownrshp* 1980
Sales NA *EMP* 2,400
SIC 6411 Life insurance agents
Pr: Robert A Shafto
Mng Pt: Michael Amine
Pr: Tony Gandito
**Pr:* Rob Henrickson
CFO: Philippe Bertrand
CFO: Bill Lampley
Treas: Frank Nesvet
Ofcr: Jack Boland
Ofcr: Donna Degennaro
Ofcr: Nidal Hamameh
Ofcr: Ross Leonard
Ofcr: Dale McNabb
Sr VP: Breneman Brian
Sr VP: Gordon Mackay
Sr VP: Donald R Shepherd
VP: Terri Eilers
VP: James Medeiros
VP: Joseph Naselli
VP: Douglas D Ramos
VP: Nathan R Wentworth
Exec: Ingrid Wood

D-U-N-S 06-134-2879 IMP/EXP
NEW ENGLAND MOTOR FREIGHT INC
NEMF
1-71 North Ave E, Elizabeth, NJ 07201-2958
Tel (908) 965-0100 *Founded/Ownrshp* 1972
Sales 860.8MM^E *EMP* 3,200
SIC 4213 Less-than-truckload (LTL) transport
Ch Bd: Myron P Shevell
COO: Rich Cabral
**CFO:* Craig Eisenberg
**VP:* Nancy Shevell Blakeman
VP: Rick Bowden
VP: Kenneth Ditmars
**VP:* Ernest Hardy
Sales Exec: Rose Cirne
Sales Asso: Michael Lamberth

NEW ENGLAND OFFICE SUPPLY
See W B MASON CO INC

D-U-N-S 96-676-3443 IMP
NEW ENGLAND PETROLEUM LIMITED PARTNERSHIP
6 Kimball Ln Ste 400, Lynnfield, MA 01940-2685
Tel (617) 660-7400 *Founded/Ownrshp* 1994
Sales 1.0MMM *EMP* 25
Accts Pricewaterhousecoopers Llp B
SIC 5172 Petroleum products
Pt: Gary Kaneb

D-U-N-S 00-695-2881
NEW ENGLAND POWER CO
(*Suby of* NATIONAL GRID USA) ★
25 Research Dr, Westborough, MA 01581-3680
Tel (315) 460-3981 *Founded/Ownrshp* 1916
Sales 476.4MM^E *EMP* 842
SIC 4911 Electric services
Pr: Rudolph L Wynter
Genl Couns: Francis J Murphy

D-U-N-S 00-194-3869
NEW ENTERPRISE STONE & LIME CO INC
BUFFALO CRUSHED STONE
3912 Brumbaugh Rd, New Enterprise, PA 16664-9137
Tel (814) 224-6883 *Founded/Ownrshp* 1924
Sales 651.9MM *EMP* 3,500
SIC 1422 1611 Crushed & broken limestone; Highway & street paving contractor
Ch Bd: Paul I Detwiler Jr
Pr: Paul Detwiler III
COO: Robert J Schmidt
COO: Tim Servello
COO: James Van Buren
CFO: Paul Detwiller
CFO: Albert L Stone
Treas: Thomas G Frye
**V Ch Bd:* Donald L Detwiler
Sr VP: Steven B Detwiler
VP: Ransom Roberts
VP: Randal Van Scyoc
Board of Directors: Steven B Detwiler, James W Van Buren

D-U-N-S 05-661-2773 IMP
NEW ERA CAP CO INC
160 Delaware Ave, Buffalo, NY 14202-2404
Tel (716) 604-9000 *Founded/Ownrshp* 1920
Sales 433.1MM^E *EMP* 1,388
SIC 2353 Uniform hats & caps; Baseball caps
Ch Bd: Christopher Koch
**Pr:* Peter M Augustine
COO: Jim Patterson
CFO: Kevin Wilson
**Sec:* Valerie Koch
Sr VP: Gerry Matos
VP: Josh Creasman
VP: Lorenz Gan
VP: Paul Gils
VP: Paul McAdam
VP: Matthew Reeves
VP: Howard Smith

D-U-N-S 03-250-4553
NEW ERA REALTY INC
2441 Eliot St, Denver, CO 80211-4707
Tel (303) 248-3519 *Founded/Ownrshp* 2005
Sales 100.0MM *EMP* 3
SIC 6531 Real estate agent, residential
Pr: John Stegner
**Pr:* Brian Leahnerz
Off Mgr: Laura Apodaca

NEW FLYER
See AFTERMARKET PARTS CO LLC

D-U-N-S 62-188-7959
NEW FLYER OF AMERICA INC
(*Suby of* NEW FLYER INDUSTRIES CANADA ULC)
6200 Glenn Carlson Dr, Saint Cloud, MN 56301-8852
Tel (320) 203-0576 *Founded/Ownrshp* 1990
Sales 333.0MM^E *EMP* 990^E
SIC 3713 3711 Truck & bus bodies; Buses, all types, assembly of
Pr: Paul Soubry
**CFO:* Glenn Asham
**Ex VP:* Wayne Joseph
**Ex VP:* Ian Smart
**Ex VP:* Paul Smith
**Ex VP:* David White
VP: Joe Gibson
Exec: Loretta Berg
**Prin:* John Marinucci
MIS Dir: Greg Gowryluk
IT Man: Darrin Smith

D-U-N-S 01-601-7102
NEW FRENCH BAKERY INC
(*Suby of* LE PETIT PAIN HOLDINGS LLC) ★
2325 Pine St, San Francisco, CA 94115-2714
Tel (415) 440-0356 *Founded/Ownrshp* 1996
Sales 21.2MM^E *EMP* 1,200
SIC 5461 Bakeries
CEO: Clifford Burrows

D-U-N-S 55-710-5608 IMP
■ NEW GALVESTON CO
(*Suby of* CULLEN/FROST BANKERS INC) ★
100 W Houston St, San Antonio, TX 78205-1414
Tel (210) 220-4011 *Founded/Ownrshp* 1981
Sales NA *EMP* 3,132
SIC 6712 Bank holding companies
Ch Bd: T C Frost
**Treas:* Phillip D Green

D-U-N-S 00-108-6321 IMP
NEW HAMPSHIRE BALL BEARINGS INC (NH)
NHBB
(*Suby of* NMB TECH) ★
175 Jaffrey Rd, Peterborough, NH 03458-1767
Tel (603) 924-3311 *Founded/Ownrshp* 1946, 1985
Sales 264.0MM *EMP* 1,250
SIC 3562 Ball bearings & parts
Pr: Dan Lemieux
Treas: Yasunari Kuwano
VP: Rich Bargellini
VP: Jim Geary
VP: James Petersen
Genl Mgr: Sue Broderick
IT Man: Mike Hanley
IT Man: Tammy Kirouac
Mktg Mgr: Robyn Nattila
Sls Mgr: Diane Mazejka

D-U-N-S 09-936-9308
NEW HAMPSHIRE CATHOLIC CHARITIES INC
CATHOLIC CHARITIES NH
215 Myrtle St, Manchester, NH 03104-4354
Tel (603) 669-3030 *Founded/Ownrshp* 1945
Sales 74.4MM *EMP* 1,000
Accts Howe Riley & Howe Pllc Manch
SIC 8322 8059 8331 8661 8361 Individual & family services; Social service center; General counseling services; Adoption services; Nursing home, except skilled & intermediate care facility; Community service employment training program; Religious organizations; Children's home
Pr: Thomas E Blonski
**COO:* Dominique Rust
**VP:* Michael D Lehrman
VP: Lisa Merrill-Burzak
Opers Mgr: Marylou Thompson

D-U-N-S 80-859-1697
NEW HAMPSHIRE DEPARTMENT OF TRANSPORTATION
(*Suby of* OFFICE OF ECONOMIC STIMULUS) ★
7 Hazen Dr, Concord, NH 03301-6502
Tel (603) 271-3734 *Founded/Ownrshp* 1985
Sales NA *EMP* 6,354^E
SIC 9621 Regulation, administration of transportation;

D-U-N-S 87-798-5119
NEW HAMPSHIRE DEPT OF CORRECTIONS
(*Suby of* OFFICE OF ECONOMIC STIMULUS) ★
105 Pleasant St Fl 4, Concord, NH 03301-3852
Tel (603) 271-4053 *Founded/Ownrshp* 1995
Sales NA *EMP* 1,000
SIC 9223 Prison, government;
Dir IT: Ronald Cormier

D-U-N-S 80-859-0954
NEW HAMPSHIRE DEPT OF HEALTH AND HUMAN SERVICES
DHHS
(*Suby of* OFFICE OF ECONOMIC STIMULUS) ★
129 Pleasant St, Concord, NH 03301-3857
Tel (603) 271-4688 *Founded/Ownrshp* 1983
Sales NA *EMP* 3,000
SIC 9431 9441 Administration of public health programs; ; Administration of social & manpower programs;
Ofcr: Irvin Heth
IT Man: Laurie Snow

D-U-N-S 00-881-9492
NEW HAMPSHIRE ELECTRIC COOPERATIVE INC
579 Tenney Mountain Hwy, Plymouth, NH 03264-3147
Tel (603) 536-8824 *Founded/Ownrshp* 1939
Sales 139.0MM *EMP* 199
SIC 4911 Distribution, electric power
Pr: Steven Camerino
CFO: Theresa Muzzey
Ex VP: William R Gosney
VP: Dina Deluca
VP: Dena Delucca
VP: Judy Gove
Exec: David Talbot
Prgrm Mgr: Joe Lajewski
IT Man: Dave Lague
IT Man: Lynne Uhlman
QI Cn Mgr: Guy Ford

D-U-N-S 00-697-1345
■ NEW HAMPSHIRE INSURANCE CO
(*Suby of* CHARTIS US INC) ★
70 Pine St Fl 23, New York, NY 10005-1522
Tel (212) 770-7000 *Founded/Ownrshp* 1869
Sales NA *EMP* 1,279
SIC 6331 Fire, marine & casualty insurance & carriers
Treas: Robert S Schimek
**Sr VP:* Robert P Jacobson
VP: Charles H Dangelo
VP: Gary Whitehead

D-U-N-S 80-859-1572
NEW HAMPSHIRE STATE POLICE
(*Suby of* OFFICE OF ECONOMIC STIMULUS) ★
33 Hazen Dr, Concord, NH 03305-0011
Tel (603) 223-8500 *Founded/Ownrshp* 1961
Sales NA *EMP* 1,175
SIC 9221 9229 State police; ; Public order & safety statistics centers;

D-U-N-S 10-066-4572
NEW HANOVER COUNTY BLACK LEADERSHIP CONFERENCE
6410 Carolina Beach Rd, Wilmington, NC 28412-2908
Tel (910) 763-5431 *Founded/Ownrshp* 1937
Sales 88.0MM^E *EMP* 3,600^E
SIC 8211 School board
Trfc Dir: Diane Blanton

D-U-N-S 82-633-8506
NEW HANOVER COUNTY SCHOOLS
NHCS
6410 Carolina Beach Rd, Wilmington, NC 28412-2908
Tel (910) 254-4206 *Founded/Ownrshp* 2008
Sales 223.7MM *EMP* 3,500^E
Accts Cherry Bekaert Llp Raleigh N
SIC 8211 Public elementary & secondary schools
CFO: Donna Rossers
**CFO:* Mary Hazel Small
Treas: Linda Kirby
**Prin:* Jeannette S Nichols
Dir Sec: Dave Spencer
IT Man: Bev Haley
IT Man: Danielle McIntosh
Info Man: Pat Campbell
Netwrk Eng: George Best
Pr Dir: Valita Quattlebaum
Teacher Pr: Norma Trant

NEW HANOVER REGIONAL MED CTR
See COASTAL REHABILITATION HOSPITAL

D-U-N-S 07-202-9143 IMP
NEW HANOVER REGIONAL MEDICAL CENTER INC
2131 S 17th St, Wilmington, NC 28401-7407
Tel (910) 343-7001 *Founded/Ownrshp* 1967
Sales 246.6MM *EMP* 3,692
SIC 8062 General medical & surgical hospitals
CEO: Jack Barto
Chf Rad: Fred Scialabba
CEO: Kathy Batchelor
COO: John Gizdic
COO: Matthew Haewood
COO: Sharon Timmons
CFO: Ed Ollie
Trst: Carl D Brown
Trst: Robert G Greer
Trst: David B Sims
Ofcr: Stephania Bloodworth
Sr VP: Susan Phillips
VP: Donna B Fache
VP: Alice Reynolds
Dir Rad: Steven T Crawford
Dir Rad: Nguyen Evans
Comm Man: Iris Baker

D-U-N-S 00-551-7814
NEW HAVEN PUBLIC SCHOOLS
54 Meadow St Fl 1, New Haven, CT 06519-1719
Tel (203) 946-8501 *Founded/Ownrshp* 2007
Sales 129.1MM^E *EMP* 3,290^E
SIC 8211 Public elementary & secondary schools
CEO: Reginald Mayo
**COO:* William F Clark
**CFO:* Victor De La Paz
**Prin:* Glen Worthy
Dir Sec: Lt D Ware
Genl Mgr: Laura Benevento
MIS Dir: Kevin Moriarty
Prd Mgr: David Prescott
Pr Dir: Mercy Quaye
Instr Medi: Robin Metaj
HC Dir: Susan Peters

D-U-N-S 08-184-7113
NEW HAVEN UNIFIED SCHOOL DISTRICT
34200 Alvarado Niles Rd, Union City, CA 94587-4402
Tel (510) 471-1100 *Founded/Ownrshp* 1954
Sales 56.0MM^E *EMP* 1,201
Accts Vavrinek Trine Day & Company
SIC 8211 Public elementary & secondary schools; Public elementary school; Public junior high school; Public senior high school
Pr: Michelle Matthews
Exec: Nancy George
Adm Dir: Jill Ahnen
Dir IT: Raymond Mar
Opers Supe: Sandy Vaughn
Teacher Pr: Derek McNamara
HC Dir: Sara Kappler
HC Dir: Carol Williams

NEW HOLLAND FORD ISUZU
See BEANS-CLASS FORD MERCURY INC

D-U-N-S 15-136-2431 IMP/EXP
NEW HOLLAND NORTH AMERICA INC
(*Suby of* FIAT ALLIS NORTH AMERICA INC)
300 Diller Ave, New Holland, PA 17557-1631
Tel (717) 355-1121 *Founded/Ownrshp* 1991

Sales 648.3MM[E] *EMP* 3,840
SIC 3523 Farm machinery & equipment
Pr: A R Rider
**CFO:* W T Kennedy
**VP:* M D Jack
**VP:* Gary L Tessitore
Netwrk Mgr: Michael McElravy
Natl Sales: Ron Shaffer
Mktg Dir: Franco Invernizzi
Mktg Mgr: Bob Bledsoe
Mktg Mgr: Frederik Klein
Sls Mgr: Ben Demange
Sls Mgr: Greg Kiesewetter
Board of Directors: Richard E Cook, Bruno Doria, Horace G McCarty, Mario Rosso, Bert Urrunaga

D-U-N-S 07-887-6973
▲ NEW HOME CO INC
85 Enterprise Ste 450, Aliso Viejo, CA 92656-2680
Tel (949) 382-7800 *Founded/Ownrshp* 2009
Sales 430.1MM *EMP* 272[E]
Tkr Sym NWHM *Exch* NYS
SIC 1531 Operative builders
Ch Bd: H Lawrence Webb
COO: Tom Redwitz
CFO: John M Stephens
VP: Mark Kawanami
VP: John Sherwood
VP: Douglas Woodward
**CIO:* Wayne Stelmar
Board of Directors: Sam Bakhshandehpour, Michael Berchtold, David Berman, Paul Heeschen, Gregory P Lindstrom, Cathey S Lowe, Douglas C Neff, Nadine Watt, William A Witte

NEW HORIZON CHILD CARE
See NEW HORIZON ENTERPRISES INC

D-U-N-S 78-267-1648
NEW HORIZON ENTERPRISES INC
NEW HORIZON CHILD CARE
3405 Annapolis Ln N # 100, Minneapolis, MN 55447-5342
Tel (763) 557-1111 *Founded/Ownrshp* 1976
Sales 36.6MM[E] *EMP* 2,300
SIC 8351 Child day care services
Ch Bd: William M Dunkley
**Sec:* Lorraine Dunkley
**VP:* Susan Dunkley

D-U-N-S 15-126-4512
NEW HORIZONS BAKING CO INC
211 Woodlawn Ave, Norwalk, OH 44857-2276
Tel (419) 668-8226 *Founded/Ownrshp* 1995
Sales 94.0MM *EMP* 350
SIC 2051 Buns, bread type: fresh or frozen; Breads, rolls & buns
Pr: Ronald Jones
**VP:* Trina Bediako
**VP:* Robert Creighton
**VP:* Mark Duke
**VP:* Mike Porter
**VP:* John Widman
Opers Mgr: Jim McFadden

D-U-N-S 06-314-1063
NEW HORIZONS WORLDWIDE INC
100 4 Falls Corporate Ctr # 408, Conshohocken, PA 19428-2950
Tel (888) 236-3625 *Founded/Ownrshp* 1988
Sales 795.8MM *EMP* 3,500
SIC 6794 8243 Franchises, selling or licensing; Software training, computer
Pr: Mark A Miller
Mng Pt: Robert J Hussey
Pr: Earl Pratt
Genl Mgr: Dave Butterfield
Genl Mgr: Kristin Catlett
CIO: Howard Mark
MIS Dir: Adam Gordon
Dir IT: Adam Goodman
Board of Directors: William H Heller, Donald W Hughes, Robert Orleyand Curtis Lee, David L Warnock, Arnold M Jacob,mark Miller

D-U-N-S 96-870-3467
NEW ILC DOVER INC
1 Moonwalker Rd, Frederica, DE 19946-2080
Tel (302) 335-3911 *Founded/Ownrshp* 2008
Sales 90.6MM[E] *EMP* 475[E]
SIC 3842 Personal safety equipment
Pr: William Wallach

D-U-N-S 84-190-0124
■ NEW INSPIRATION BROADCASTING CO INC
(*Suby of* SALEM MEDIA GROUP INC) ★
4880 Santa Rosa Rd, Camarillo, CA 93012-5190
Tel (805) 987-0400 *Founded/Ownrshp* 1982
Sales 39.5MM[E] *EMP* 1,457
SIC 4832 2731 Radio broadcasting stations; Book publishing
CEO: Edward G Atsinger III
**Ch Bd:* Stuart Epperson
**Pr:* David Evans
**CFO:* Evan Masyr
**VP:* Christopher Henderson

D-U-N-S 60-407-0198
NEW JERNBERG SALES INC
(*Suby of* KPS CAPITAL PARTNERS LP) ★
39475 W 13 Mile Rd # 105, Novi, MI 48377-2359
Tel (248) 479-2699 *Founded/Ownrshp* 2005
Sales 170.0MM *EMP* 8
SIC 5051 Steel
Pr: George Phanopoulos

D-U-N-S 18-481-4317
■ NEW JERSEY AMERICAN WATER CO
(*Suby of* AMERICAN WATER WORKS CO INC) ★
131 Woodcrest Rd, Cherry Hill, NJ 08003-3620
Tel (856) 310-2206 *Founded/Ownrshp* 1988
Sales 199.4MM[E] *EMP* 565
SIC 4941 Water supply
CEO: Jeffry Sterba
**Pr:* John R Bigelow
**Sr VP:* Susan N Story
**Sr VP:* Mark Strauss
VP: Kevin Kirwan
VP: Karl Kyriss
VP: William Pearce
**VP:* Edward D Vallejo
VP: Bill Walsh
VP: Howard Woods

NEW JERSEY CARPENTERS FUNDS
See NEW JERSEY CARPENTERS PENSION FUND

D-U-N-S 08-920-4788
NEW JERSEY CARPENTERS PENSION FUND
NEW JERSEY CARPENTERS FUNDS
91 Fieldcrest Ave, Edison, NJ 08837-3627
Tel (732) 417-3900 *Founded/Ownrshp* 1958
Sales NA *EMP* 72
SIC 6371 Pension funds
Admn Mgr: George R Laufenberg
VP: Phillip E Cooney

D-U-N-S 08-728-1531
NEW JERSEY CITY UNIVERSITY
NJCU
2039 Kennedy Blvd, Jersey City, NJ 07305
Tel (201) 200-2000 *Founded/Ownrshp* 1927
Sales 92.9MM[E] *EMP* 900[E]
SIC 8221 College, except junior
Pr: Sue Henderson
**Ch Bd:* Rafael Perez
Pr: Daniel P Elwell
VP: Jan Aguilos
VP: Maria Lynn
VP: John Melendez
Exec: Harris Hordon
Exec: Robert Piaskowsky
Assoc Dir: Mohammad I Sheikh
Assoc Dir: Devan Salem
Assoc Dir: Ritu Shastri

D-U-N-S 80-665-6682
NEW JERSEY COMMISSION ON HIGHER EDUCATION
(*Suby of* EXECUTIVE OFFICE OF STATE OF NEW JERSEY) ★
20 W State St Fl 7, Trenton, NJ 08608-1206
Tel (609) 292-4310 *Founded/Ownrshp* 1967
Sales NA *EMP* 16,641
SIC 9411 Administration of educational programs;

D-U-N-S 80-632-7268
NEW JERSEY DEPARTMENT OF ENVIRONMENTAL PROTECTION
(*Suby of* EXECUTIVE OFFICE OF STATE OF NEW JERSEY) ★
401 E State St, Trenton, NJ 08608-1501
Tel (609) 292-2885 *Founded/Ownrshp* 1970
Sales NA *EMP* 2,800
SIC 9512 9511 Land, mineral & wildlife conservation; Air, water & solid waste management;

D-U-N-S 80-641-8075
NEW JERSEY DEPARTMENT OF HEALTH
(*Suby of* EXECUTIVE OFFICE OF STATE OF NEW JERSEY) ★
369 S Warren St, Trenton, NJ 08608-2308
Tel (609) 292-6915 *Founded/Ownrshp* 1948
Sales NA *EMP* 1,508
SIC 9431 Administration of public health programs;

D-U-N-S 80-641-8257
NEW JERSEY DEPARTMENT OF HUMAN SERVICES
(*Suby of* EXECUTIVE OFFICE OF STATE OF NEW JERSEY) ★
222 S Warren St, Trenton, NJ 08608-2306
Tel (609) 292-3717 *Founded/Ownrshp* 1976
Sales NA *EMP* 19,000
SIC 9441 Public welfare administration: non-operating, government
Ofcr: Ellen Lovejoy
Off Mgr: Julie Culliton
**CIO:* Douglas Mc Grugher
IT Man: Lou Marino

D-U-N-S 80-641-8430
NEW JERSEY DEPARTMENT OF LABOR AND WORKFORCE DEVELOPMENT
(*Suby of* EXECUTIVE OFFICE OF STATE OF NEW JERSEY) ★
1 John Fitch Plz Fl 13, Trenton, NJ 08611-1760
Tel (609) 292-2323 *Founded/Ownrshp* 1948
Sales NA *EMP* 4,214
SIC 9651 Labor regulatory agency;
**Prin:* Marilyn Davis
IT Man: Bob Schisler

D-U-N-S 80-747-7898
NEW JERSEY DEPARTMENT OF TREASURY
(*Suby of* EXECUTIVE OFFICE OF STATE OF NEW JERSEY) ★
125 W State St, Trenton, NJ 08608-1101
Tel (609) 292-6748 *Founded/Ownrshp* 1948
Sales NA *EMP* 3,500
SIC 9311 Treasurers' office, government
Treas: Andrew P Sidamon-Eristoff
Treas: Bradley Abelow
CTO: George Kelly

D-U-N-S 80-641-7143
NEW JERSEY DEPT OF COMMUNITY AFFAIRS
(*Suby of* EXECUTIVE OFFICE OF STATE OF NEW JERSEY) ★
101 S Broad St, Trenton, NJ 08608-2401
Tel (609) 292-6420 *Founded/Ownrshp* 1966
Sales NA *EMP* 1,100
SIC 9441 Administration of social & manpower programs;

D-U-N-S 80-665-6781
NEW JERSEY DEPT OF LAW & PUBLIC SAFETY
OFFICE OF THE ATTORNEY GENERAL
(*Suby of* EXECUTIVE OFFICE OF STATE OF NEW JERSEY) ★
25 Market St Fl 8, Trenton, NJ 08611-2148
Tel (609) 292-4925 *Founded/Ownrshp* 1948
Sales NA *EMP* 7,500[E]
SIC 9222 9221 Attorney General's office; ; Police protection
Prin: John Jay Hoffman
IT Man: Fred Gmitter

D-U-N-S 80-665-7177
NEW JERSEY DEPT OF TRANSPORTATION
(*Suby of* EXECUTIVE OFFICE OF STATE OF NEW JERSEY) ★
1035 Parkway Ave Fl 2, Ewing, NJ 08618-2309
Tel (609) 530-3855 *Founded/Ownrshp* 1966
Sales NA *EMP* 3,400
SIC 9621 Regulation, administration of transportation;
CFO: Gary Brune
Ex Dir: William S Beetle
Genl Mgr: David Kuhn
Genl Mgr: Jim Vari

NEW JERSEY DIVISION
See ELIZABETHTOWN GAS CO

D-U-N-S 07-146-4515
NEW JERSEY EDUCATION ASSOCIATION INC
NJEA
180 W State St, Trenton, NJ 08608-1104
Tel (609) 599-4561 *Founded/Ownrshp* 1853
Sales 129.6MM *EMP* 257
Accts Novak Francella Llc Bala Cynw
SIC 8621 Professional membership organizations
Ex Dir: Vince Giordan
Treas: Anne Simon
**Sec:* Marie Blistan
**VP:* Barbara Keshishian
**VP:* Wendell Steinhauer
Assoc Dir: Howard Bookin
Assoc Dir: Martha Deblieu
Assoc Dir: Janet Morrison
Ex Dir: Vincent Giordano
Genl Mgr: Joyce Powell

NEW JERSEY HEART INSTITUTE
See OUR LADY OF LOURDES MEDICAL CENTER INC

D-U-N-S 04-735-5839
NEW JERSEY HERALD
(*Suby of* QUINCY BRDCAST PRINT INTRCTIVE) ★
2 Spring St, Newton, NJ 07860-2077
Tel (973) 383-1500 *Founded/Ownrshp* 1991
Sales 43.0MM[E] *EMP* 1,000
SIC 2711 Newspapers, publishing & printing
Pr: Thomas Oakley
CFO: David Oakley
VP: Tony Rose
Dist Mgr: Leland Bonelli
Genl Mgr: James Collins

D-U-N-S 09-925-4682
NEW JERSEY HOUSING AND MORTGAGE FINANCE AGENCY CJ
(*Suby of* EXECUTIVE OFFICE OF STATE OF NEW JERSEY) ★
637 S Clinton Ave, Trenton, NJ 08611-1811
Tel (609) 278-7400 *Founded/Ownrshp* 1984
Sales NA *EMP* 250
Accts Cliftonlarsonallen Llp Baltim
SIC 6162 9199 Mortgage bankers & correspondents;
Ex Dir: Marge D Vecchia
**CFO:* David Bonomo
Ofcr: Beverly Drago
Prin: Dawn Parreott
**Ex Dir:* Anthony L Marchetta
Ex Dir: Anthony Marchetta
Opers Mgr: Linda Gargiulo
Mktg Mgr: Joseph Kuzemka
Snr Mgr: Annie Bowser

D-U-N-S 07-516-2990
NEW JERSEY INSTITUTE OF TECHNOLOGY (INC)
NJIT
323 Dr Martin Luth, Newark, NJ 07102
Tel (973) 596-3000 *Founded/Ownrshp* 1928
Sales 220.5MM *EMP* 1,047
Accts Grant Thornton Llp Edison N
SIC 8221 University
Pr: Joel S Bloom
Pr: Ed Bishof
CFO: Anthony Tomandel
Treas: Tworischuk Assistant
Ex VP: Jarry Paris
Sr VP: Henry A Mauermeyer
VP: Joel Bloom
VP: Andrew P Christ
VP: Matthew Golden
VP: Theodore Johnson
VP: Kathryn Kelly
VP: Mojgan Mohtashami
VP: Gale Spak
VP: Nancy Steffen-Fluhr
Assoc Dir: James McHugh

D-U-N-S 00-697-4851
NEW JERSEY MANUFACTURERS INSURANCE CO
NJM INSURANCE GROUP
301 Sullivan Way, Ewing, NJ 08628-3406
Tel (609) 883-1300 *Founded/Ownrshp* 1913
Sales NA *EMP* 2,500
SIC 6331 Workers' compensation insurance; Fire, marine & casualty insurance: mutual; Automobile insurance
Pr: Bernard M Flynn
**CFO:* Charles A Prall
CFO: Charles A Prall
Ofcr: Thomas J Defalco
**Ex VP:* Robert H Vetterstrom
Ex VP: Robert H Zetterstrom
VP: Katie Cavallo
VP: Karen Danjolell
**VP:* Neil Delaney
VP: Neil J Delaney
VP: Mark Lynch
VP: Anna McLaren
VP: Diane Taylor
VP: Michael Van Wagner

D-U-N-S 06-184-3553
■ NEW JERSEY NATURAL GAS CO
(*Suby of* NEW JERSEY RESOURCES CORP) ★
1415 Wyckoff Rd, Wall Township, NJ 07727-3940
Tel (732) 938-1000 *Founded/Ownrshp* 1982
Sales 636.7MM[E] *EMP* 750
SIC 4924 Natural gas distribution
Ch Bd: Lawrence M Downes
**COO:* Kathleen T Ellis
**Sr VP:* Oleta J Harden
**Sr VP:* Thomas J Kononowitz
**VP:* Francis X Colford
VP: Joseph J Marazzo
VP: Thomas J Massaro
VP: Thomas Massaro
VP: Ginger Richman
VP: Mark Sperduto
Mng Dir: Stephen D Westhoven
Board of Directors: Bruce Coe, Warren R Haas, Lester Johnson, Dorothy Light

D-U-N-S 15-377-1662
NEW JERSEY PROPERTY LIABILITY INSURANCE GUARANTY ASSOCIATION
222 Mount Airy Rd, Basking Ridge, NJ 07920-2335
Tel (908) 953-9533 *Founded/Ownrshp* 1975
Sales NA *EMP* 22
Accts Eisneramper Llp Bridgewater
SIC 6411 Insurance agents
Ex Dir: Holly C Bakke

D-U-N-S 06-004-0953
NEW JERSEY RE-INSURANCE CO
(*Suby of* NJM INSURANCE GROUP) ★
301 Sullivan Way, Ewing, NJ 08628-3406
Tel (609) 883-1300 *Founded/Ownrshp* 1977
Sales NA *EMP* 9
SIC 6311 6331 Life reinsurance; Automobile insurance; Property damage insurance; Workers' compensation insurance
CEO: Anthony G Dickson
**CFO:* Thomas A Meyers
Treas: Steven P Kerner Jr

D-U-N-S 00-697-1592
▲ NEW JERSEY RESOURCES CORP
1415 Wyckoff Rd, Wall Township, NJ 07727-3940
Tel (732) 938-1480 *Founded/Ownrshp* 1981
Sales 1.8MMM *EMP* 991[E]
Accts Deloitte & Touche Llp Parsipp
Tkr Sym NJR *Exch* NYS
SIC 4924 Natural gas distribution
Ch Bd: Laurence M Downes
COO: Kathleen T Ellis
CFO: Glenn C Lockwood
CFO: Patrick Migliaccio
Treas: Timothy C Hearne
Ofcr: Amanda Mullan
Sr VP: Mariellen Dugan
Sr VP: Thomas J Kononowitz
Sr VP: Thomas J Massaro Jr
Sr VP: Kevin A Moss
Sr VP: Wayne K Tarney
Sr VP: Debbie Zilai
VP: Jacqueline K Shea
VP: George Smith
VP: Mark Sperduto
VP: Stephen D Westhoven
Board of Directors: George R Zoffinger, Lawrence R Codey, Donald L Correll, Robert B Evans, M William Howard Jr, Jane M Kenny, Alfred C Koeppe, J Terry Strange, Sharon C Taylor, David A Trice

NEW JERSEY SCHOOL CONSTRUCTION
See NEW JERSEY SCHOOLS DEVELOPMENT AUTHORITY

D-U-N-S 13-389-1650
NEW JERSEY SCHOOLS DEVELOPMENT AUTHORITY
NEW JERSEY SCHOOL CONSTRUCTION
32 E Front St, Trenton, NJ 08608-2106
Tel (609) 943-5955 *Founded/Ownrshp* 2007
Sales 87.2MM[E] *EMP* 256[E]
SIC 1542 School building construction
CEO: Charles McKenna
VP: Donald R Guarriello Jr
VP: Andrew Yosha

D-U-N-S 06-427-5316
NEW JERSEY SPORTS & EXPOSITION AUTHORITY
MONMOUTH PARK RACETRACK
1 Dekorte Park Plz, Lyndhurst, NJ 07071
Tel (201) 460-1700 *Founded/Ownrshp* 1971
Sales 88.1MM[E] *EMP* 3,500
SIC 8641 7941 6512

D-U-N-S 00-697-3200
NEW JERSEY TRANSIT BUS OPERATIONS INC
(*Suby of* NJ TRANSIT) ★
1 Penn Plz E, Newark, NJ 07105-2245
Tel (973) 491-7000 *Founded/Ownrshp* 1928
Sales 194.0MM[E] *EMP* 10,000
SIC 4131 4111 Intercity bus line; Subway operation
CFO: Charlie Wedel
Ex Dir: George D Warrington
IT Man: Daryl Gibson

D-U-N-S 03-848-5140
NEW JERSEY TRANSIT CORP
NJ TRANSIT
1 Penn Plz E, Newark, NJ 07105-2245
Tel (973) 491-7000 *Founded/Ownrshp* 1979
Sales 848.5MM[E] *EMP* 10,000
Accts Ernst & Young Llp Iselin New

SIC 4111 4131 Commuter rail passenger operation; Intercity bus line
Ex Dir: Richard Sarles
**Ch Bd:* Stephen Dilts
CFO: H Charles Wedel
VP: Leo Sanders
**Ex Dir:* William Crosbie
Ex Dir: Shirley A Delibero
Ex Dir: Veronique Hakim
Prgrm Mgr: John Clark
Prgrm Mgr: Lou Ellis
Prgrm Mgr: Bernie Pattay
CIO: Debbie Pemberton

D-U-N-S 95-791-5986
NEW JERSEY TRANSPORTATION TRUST FUND AUTHORITY
(*Suby of* STATE OF NEW JERSEY) ★
1035 Parkway Ave, Ewing, NJ 08618-2309
Tel (609) 530-2035 *Founded/Ownrshp* 1920
Sales 934.3MM *EMP* 724[E]
Accts Mercadien Pc Princeton Nj
SIC 8611 Business associations

D-U-N-S 00-177-4736
NEW JERSEY TURNPIKE AUTHORITY INC
581 Mack Cali Bldg Main, Woodbridge, NJ 07095
Tel (732) 750-5300 *Founded/Ownrshp* 1948
Sales 1.5MMM *EMP* 2,400
SIC 4785 Toll road operation
Ch Bd: Jamie Fox
**CEO:* Ronald Gravino
**COO:* John F O Hern
CFO: Catherine A Coryat
**Treas:* Michael R Dupont
Treas: Gary Lewis
VP: John Lewis
Dir: Mary Ruotolo
**Ex Dir:* Veronique Hakim
Genl Mgr: Dawn Iacobelli
Sfty Mgr: Edward Marsh

D-U-N-S 93-250-3394
NEW LEXINGTON CLINIC PSC
1221 S Broadway, Lexington, KY 40504-2701
Tel (859) 258-4950 *Founded/Ownrshp* 1994
Sales 111.8MM[E] *EMP* 1,075
SIC 8011 Medical centers; Primary care medical clinic
CEO: Andrew Henderson MD
**CFO:* Randall K Lemay
Dept Mgr: Cale Jacobs
Off Mgr: Sharon Baker
Pathlgst: Mary O'Daniel-Pierce
Pathlgst: Joan E Simpson
Surgeon: Joseph Fine
Surgeon: Karl M Larsen
Doctor: William Camp
Doctor: Jeniffer Huhn
Doctor: Stephen Monnig
Board of Directors: Dr John Collins, John Dineen, Michael Eden, Dr David Gammon, Andrew Henderson, Michael McKinney, Dr Henry Tutt, Dr Pell Wardrop, Dr Paul Warfield

D-U-N-S 07-302-2683
NEW LIBERTY HOSPITAL DISTRICT OF CLAY COUNTY MISSOURI
2525 Glenn Hendren Dr, Liberty, MO 64068-9625
Tel (816) 781-7200 *Founded/Ownrshp* 1974
Sales 179.6MM *EMP* 1,700[E]
Accts Paige Cooper
SIC 8062 8051 General medical & surgical hospitals; Skilled nursing care facilities
Pr: David Feess
Dir Vol: Carmella Kovach
CFO: Erin Parde
Ofcr: Joanie Peterson
**Prin:* Richard Boswell
**Prin:* Dennis L Carter
**Prin:* William Christian Sizemore
**Prin:* Jim Streu
Ansthlgy: Michael G Ivancic
Doctor: Neal Anson
Doctor: Brent S Carlson

NEW LIFE PUBLICATIONS
See CAMPUS CRUSADE FOR CHRIST INC

NEW LIFE TRANSPORT PARTS CTR
See JOMAR INVESTMENTS INC

D-U-N-S 80-776-4340
NEW LIFECARE HOSPITALS OF MILWAUKEE LLC
LIFECARE HOSPITALS WISCONSIN
(*Suby of* LIFECARE FAMILY OF HOSPITALS) ★
2400 Golf Rd, Pewaukee, WI 53072-5590
Tel (262) 524-2600 *Founded/Ownrshp* 2008
Sales 75.3MM[E] *EMP* 1,140[E]
SIC 8062 General medical & surgical hospitals
CEO: Phillip B Douglas
**VP:* Maegan Bowman
**VP:* Stephanie Carpenter
Dir Rx: Lori Breckheimer

D-U-N-S 78-972-9019
NEW MANHEIM AUTO AUCTIONS LIMITED (INC)
COX MEDIA GROUP
(*Suby of* MANHEIM INVESTMENTS INC) ★
6205 Pachtree Dunwoody Rd, Atlanta, GA 30328-4524
Tel (678) 645-0000 *Founded/Ownrshp* 1993
Sales 212.4MM[E] *EMP* 1,000
SIC 5012 Automobiles & other motor vehicles
Pr: Dean H Eisner
Sr VP: Ralph M Liniado
VP: Mark Brunn
VP: Brian Cooper
VP: Leon Levitt
VP: Tim Lott
VP: Jay Oconnor
**VP:* Jamie D Porter
Comm Dir: James Cox
Comm Dir: Bob Jimenez
Dir Bus: Matthew Nelson
Dir Bus: Derek Robinson

D-U-N-S 07-920-5441
▲ NEW MEDIA INVESTMENT GROUP INC
1345 Avenue Of The Americ, New York, NY 10105-0014
Tel (212) 479-3160 *Founded/Ownrshp* 2014
Sales 1.2MMM *EMP* 8,322
Tkr Sym NEWM *Exch* NYS
SIC 2711 7373 Newspapers, publishing & printing; Systems integration services
CEO: Michael E Reed
**Ch Bd:* Wesley R Edens
**COO:* Kirk Davis
**CFO:* Gregory W Freiberg
CIO: Paul Ameden
Board of Directors: Theodore P Janulis, Kevin M Sheehan, Laurence Tarica

NEW MEXICO COFFEE COMPANY
See TRILLIANT FOOD AND NUTRITION LLC

D-U-N-S 80-856-1823
NEW MEXICO DEPARTMENT OF CHILDREN YOUTH AND FAMILIES
(*Suby of* GOVERNORS OFFICE NEW MEXICO) ★
1120 Paseo De Peralta, Santa Fe, NM 87501-2747
Tel (505) 827-7602 *Founded/Ownrshp* 1992
Sales NA *EMP* 2,161
SIC 9441 Administration of social & manpower programs;
CIO: Crawford Spooner

D-U-N-S 80-856-1567
NEW MEXICO DEPARTMENT OF FINANCE & ADMINISTRATION
(*Suby of* GOVERNORS OFFICE NEW MEXICO) ★
Bataan Memorial Bldg 180, Santa Fe, NM 87501
Tel (505) 827-4985 *Founded/Ownrshp* 1957
Sales NA *EMP* 1,000
SIC 9311 Finance, taxation & monetary policy;

D-U-N-S 80-838-9274
NEW MEXICO DEPARTMENT OF HEALTH
(*Suby of* GOVERNORS OFFICE NEW MEXICO) ★
1190 S Saint Francis Dr, Santa Fe, NM 87505-4173
Tel (505) 827-2613 *Founded/Ownrshp* 1991
Sales NA *EMP* 4,000
SIC 9431 Administration of public health programs;
Prin: Retta Ward SEC
Off Mgr: Jeanne Alano
CIO: Mike Mier
CIO: Elisa Storie
Netwrk Mgr: Rod Skiver
Snr Mgr: Lawrence White

D-U-N-S 83-771-0722
NEW MEXICO DEPARTMENT OF HUMAN SERVICES
(*Suby of* GOVERNORS OFFICE NEW MEXICO) ★
2009 S Pacheco St, Santa Fe, NM 87505-5473
Tel (505) 827-7750 *Founded/Ownrshp* 2001
Sales NA *EMP* 1,535
SIC 9441 Administration of social & human resources;

D-U-N-S 80-838-9357
NEW MEXICO DEPARTMENT OF PUBLIC SAFETY
(*Suby of* GOVERNORS OFFICE NEW MEXICO) ★
4491 Cerrillos Rd, Santa Fe, NM 87507-9721
Tel (505) 827-9000 *Founded/Ownrshp* 1987
Sales NA *EMP* 1,200
SIC 9229 Public order & safety statistics centers;
Ofcr: Jeanelle Lerouge
Brnch Mgr: Stephen Libicer
Dir IT: David Keys
Snr Mgr: Ron Burton
Snr Mgr: Darrell Graham
Snr Mgr: Laura Romero

D-U-N-S 80-838-9233
NEW MEXICO DEPARTMENT OF TAXATION AND REVENUE
(*Suby of* GOVERNORS OFFICE NEW MEXICO) ★
1100 S Saint Francis Dr, Santa Fe, NM 87505-4147
Tel (505) 827-0700 *Founded/Ownrshp* 1978
Sales NA *EMP* 1,304
SIC 9311 Taxation department, government;
Treas: Jim Burleson
Doctor: Rand Tilton

D-U-N-S 80-838-9407
NEW MEXICO DEPARTMENT OF TRANSPORTATION
(*Suby of* GOVERNORS OFFICE NEW MEXICO) ★
1120 Cerrillos Rd, Santa Fe, NM 87505-1842
Tel (505) 827-5100 *Founded/Ownrshp* 1903
Sales NA *EMP* 2,600
Accts Meyners & Company Llc Albaqu
SIC 9621 Regulation, administration of transportation;
CFO: Bridgette Long
Exec: Don Graham
Exec: Jackie Padilla
Exec: Mary Segura

D-U-N-S 86-740-6639
NEW MEXICO DEPT OF MILITARY AFFAIRS
NATIONAL GUARD OF NEW MEXICO
(*Suby of* GOVERNORS OFFICE NEW MEXICO) ★
47 Bataan Blvd, Santa Fe, NM 87508-4695
Tel (505) 474-1200 *Founded/Ownrshp* 1996
Sales NA *EMP* 4,000
SIC 9711 National Guard;
Genl Mgr: Lorenzo Gurule

D-U-N-S 82-524-4697
NEW MEXICO GAS CO
(*Suby of* NEW MEXICO GAS INTERMEDIATE INC) ★
7120 Wyoming Blvd Ne # 20, Albuquerque, NM 87109-4887
Tel (505) 697-3803 *Founded/Ownrshp* 2008
Sales 375.8MM *EMP* 729[E]
SIC 4924 4922 Natural gas distribution; Pipelines, natural gas
Pr: Ryan Shell
**Pr:* Annette Gardiner
**Ch:* William Real
**VP:* Douglas Arney
**VP:* Thomas Domme
**VP:* Kenneth Oostman Jr
**VP:* Aaron Roberson
**VP:* Tommy Sanders
IT Man: Janelle Callahan
IT Man: Shelly Gordon
IT Man: Lisa Griffith

D-U-N-S 07-954-8183
NEW MEXICO GAS INTERMEDIATE INC
(*Suby of* TECO ENERGY INC) ★
7201 Wyoming Blvd Ne, Albuquerque, NM 87109-4814
Tel (505) 697-3827 *Founded/Ownrshp* 2014
Sales 375.8MM[E] *EMP* 740[E]
SIC 4924 Natural gas distribution
VP: Thomas M Domme

D-U-N-S 04-135-8904
NEW MEXICO INSTITUTE OF MINING AND TECHNOLOGY
NEW MEXICO TECH
801 Leroy Pl, Socorro, NM 87801-4750
Tel (575) 835-5312 *Founded/Ownrshp* 1981
Sales 120.0MM *EMP* 1,000
Accts Atkinson & Co Ltd Albuquer
SIC 8221 University
Pr: Daniel H Lopez
CFO: Chris Armstrong
Assoc VP: Daniel Walsh
VP: Brian Borchers
**VP:* Melissa Jaramillo-Fleming
**VP:* Lonnie Marquez
VP: Van Romero
VP: Leyla Sedillo
Prgrm Mgr: Patricia Mills
Genl Mgr: Brad Smith
Off Mgr: Griego Patricia

D-U-N-S 55-628-5120
NEW MEXICO MUTUAL CASUALTY CO
3900 Singer Blvd Ne, Albuquerque, NM 87109-5817
Tel (800) 788-8851 *Founded/Ownrshp* 1991
Sales NA *EMP* 145
SIC 6331 Workers' compensation insurance
CEO: Chris Krahling
**Ch Bd:* Evangeline Tinajero
**Pr:* Warren D Smalley
Bd of Dir: Samuel Baca
VP: Nick Franklin
**VP:* Beverly Jornigan
**VP:* Patricia McCarthy
VP: Lou Volk
VP: Dwight Ward
Exec: Amyann F Baker
Admn Mgr: Ronda Merrill

D-U-N-S 86-136-7373 IMP
NEW MEXICO STATE UNIVERSITY
NMSU
2850 Weddell St Rm 210, Las Cruces, NM 88003-1245
Tel (575) 646-0111 *Founded/Ownrshp* 1888
Sales 324.9MM *EMP* 5,000
Accts Moss Adams Llp Albuquerque N
SIC 8221 University
Pr: Garrey Carruther
Pr: Ken Ramsey
Pr: Deborah Widger
CEO: Andy Burke
Top Exec: Edward Pines
Ex VP: Kim Rumford
VP: Kevin Boberg
VP: Olga Conter
VP: Robert Franklin
VP: Nellie Quezada-Aragon
VP: Michael L Rickenbaker
VP: Angela Throneberry
Dir Lab: Willis Fedio
Assoc Dir: Angela Velasco
Dir Rx: John Landrum

D-U-N-S 96-353-0436
NEW MEXICO STATE VETERANS HOME
922 S Broadway St, T or C, NM 87901-3198
Tel (575) 894-4200 *Founded/Ownrshp* 2009
Sales 281.2MM *EMP* 33[E]
SIC 8051 Skilled nursing care facilities

NEW MEXICO TECH
See NEW MEXICO INSTITUTE OF MINING AND TECHNOLOGY

D-U-N-S 05-237-1981
NEW MOUNTAIN CAPITAL I LLC
787 7th Ave Fl 49, New York, NY 10019-6018
Tel (212) 720-0300 *Founded/Ownrshp* 1999
Sales 2.2MMM[E] *EMP* 5,527[E]
SIC 6726 Management investment funds, closed-end
COO: John R Kline
CFO: David M Cordova
Ofcr: Adam B Weinstein
VP: Matthew S Holt
VP: Lars Johansson
**Mng Dir:* Pete Masucci
Mng Dir: James W Stone III

D-U-N-S 83-320-1317
NEW MOUNTAIN CAPITAL LLC
787 7th Ave Fl 49, New York, NY 10019-6018
Tel (212) 720-0300 *Founded/Ownrshp* 2005
Sales 457.1MM[E] *EMP* 7,603
SIC 6726 Investment offices
CEO: Steven B Klinsky
VP: Trish Belfiore
VP: Krish Daftary
VP: Josh Hirschhorn
VP: Matt Holt
VP: Karrie Jerry
VP: Lars Johansson
VP: Kyle B Peterson
Mng Dir: Michael Ajouz
Mng Dir: Peter Masucci
Opers Mgr: Michael McCarthy

D-U-N-S 07-878-0198
NEW MOUNTAIN FINANCE CORP
787 7th Ave Fl 48, New York, NY 10019-6018
Tel (212) 720-0300 *Founded/Ownrshp* 2010
Sales 153.8MM *EMP* 6
Accts Deloitte & Touche Llp New Yor
Tkr Sym NMFC *Exch* NYS
SIC 6726 Management investment funds, closed-end
CEO: Robert A Hamwee
**Ch Bd:* Steven B Klinsky
Pr: John R Kline
CFO: David Cordova
Chf Cred: Paula A Bosco
Bd of Dir: Alfred Hurley
**Ofcr:* Adam B Weinstein
Mng Dir: James Stone

D-U-N-S 80-856-7940
NEW MOUNTAIN LAKE HOLDINGS LLC
4080 Jenkins Rd, Chattanooga, TN 37421-1174
Tel (423) 510-3000 *Founded/Ownrshp* 2007
Sales 1.2MMM[E] *EMP* 10,885
SIC 4213 4731 Trucking, except local; Freight transportation arrangement
CEO: Max L Fuller
Pr: Lisa M Pate

D-U-N-S 80-883-6894 IMP/EXP
NEW NGC INC
NATIONAL GYPSUM COMPANY
(*Suby of* DELCOR INC) ★
2001 Rexford Rd, Charlotte, NC 28211-3415
Tel (704) 365-7300 *Founded/Ownrshp* 1993
Sales 618.8MM[E] *EMP* 2,100
SIC 2679 Wallboard, decorated: made from purchased material
Ch Bd: Thomas C Nelson
CFO: George Beckwith
CFO: Richard Parkhurst
Sr VP: Craig Weisbruch
VP: John C Corsi
VP: Craig Robertson
VP: Craig C Robertson
VP: Samual A Schiffman
Genl Mgr: Cory Farris
Off Mgr: Bob Jarman
Off Admin: Sheryl Naulty

D-U-N-S 80-558-3353
NEW OMAHA HOLDINGS LP
9 W 57th St Ste 4200, New York, NY 10019-2707
Tel (212) 750-8300 *Founded/Ownrshp* 2007
Sales NA *EMP* 29,010
SIC 6712 Bank holding companies

D-U-N-S 04-072-1577
NEW OPTICS USA INC
510 W Main St, El Centro, CA 92243-2900
Tel (760) 547-7136 *Founded/Ownrshp* 2013
Sales 396.9MM *EMP* 2[E]
Accts Kim Yoo Jang Llp San Diego C
SIC 5048 Lenses, ophthalmic
CEO: Jigon Jeong

D-U-N-S 08-042-7959
NEW OPTICS USA INC
653 W Main St Ste 1, El Centro, CA 92243-2958
Tel (760) 996-9067 *Founded/Ownrshp* 2013
Sales 396.9MM *EMP* 3[E]
Accts Kim Yoo Jang Llp San Diego C
SIC 5048 Ophthalmic goods
Pr: Jimmy Jong
CFO: Harris Jong

D-U-N-S 11-299-0452
NEW PARTNERS INC
PARTNERS IN CARE
(*Suby of* VISITING NURSE SERVICE OF NEW YORK) ★
1250 Broadway Fl 10, New York, NY 10001-3746
Tel (212) 609-7700 *Founded/Ownrshp* 1983
Sales 213.0MM *EMP* 4,400
Accts Kpmg Llp Albany Ny
SIC 8082 Home health care services
Ch Bd: Richard Flender
Exec: Jacci Obrien

D-U-N-S 08-045-0022
■ NEW PDS CORP
(*Suby of* BORGWARNER PDS (INDIANA) INC) ★
600 Corporation Dr, Pendleton, IN 46064-8610
Tel (800) 372-3555 *Founded/Ownrshp* 2014
Sales 2.1MMM[E] *EMP* 6,605[E]
SIC 3694 3714 Battery charging alternators & generators; Motor vehicle engines & parts; Motor vehicle transmissions, drive assemblies & parts; Motor vehicle electrical equipment
Pr: Ronald T Hundzinski

D-U-N-S 80-699-4153
NEW PENN FINANCIAL LLC
(*Suby of* SHELLPOINT PARTNERS LLC) ★
4000 Chemical Rd Ste 200, Plymouth Meeting, PA 19462-1708
Tel (484) 594-1000 *Founded/Ownrshp* 2015
Sales NA *EMP* 346
Accts St Clair Cpa S Pc Coshohocke
SIC 6162 Mortgage bankers & correspondents
Pr: Jerry Schiano
Pr: Patrica Peirce
**COO:* Brian Simon
CFO: Daniel Egan
Sr VP: Charles Dipino
VP: Mercedes Dotter
VP: Tony Hale
VP: Robert Johnson
VP: Mark Lebrett
VP Opers: Todd Stiverson
Sls Mgr: Alexandria Saloman

D-U-N-S 00-893-6759 IMP/EXP
■ NEW PENN MOTOR EXPRESS LLC
(*Suby of* ROADWAY LLC) ★
625 S 5th Ave, Lebanon, PA 17042-7715
Tel (800) 285-5000 *Founded/Ownrshp* 1957, 2014
Sales 270.0MM *EMP* 1,800
SIC 4213 4231 Less-than-truckload (LTL) transport; Trucking terminal facilities
Pr: Steven D Gast
Pr: Don Foust
Treas: Cornelius J Keim
VP: Terry L Gerrond
VP: Anthony Nicosia
VP: Daniel Schmidt

Genl Mgr: Gordy Ackers
DP Exec: John Boesch
Dir IT: Tim Luce
IT Man: Randy Croce
Trfc Dir: James Hartman

NEW PHASE TECHNOLOGIES
See BAKER PETROLITE LLC

D-U-N-S 96-260-4104
■ NEW PORT RICHEY HOSPITAL INC
COMMUNITY HOSPITAL
(*Suby of* HOSPITAL COPORATION OF AMERICA) ★
1 Park Plz, Nashville, TN 37203-6527
Tel (727) 848-1733 *Founded/Ownrshp* 1978
Sales 34.0MM^E *EMP* 1,007
SIC 8062 General medical & surgical hospitals
CFO: Glenn Romig
Dir Rx: Matthew Mc Neill
Doctor: Joel Frazier
Doctor: James Rosacker
Doctor: Houshang Seradge
Doctor: Glenn Smith
Doctor: Cheng SOO
Pharmcst: George Bopp
Pharmcst: Louis Passannante
Pharmcst: Phillip Yeh

D-U-N-S 15-218-2473
NEW PRIME INC
2740 N Mayfair Ave, Springfield, MO 65803-5084
Tel (800) 321-4552 *Founded/Ownrshp* 1986
Sales 1.1MMM^E *EMP* 5,000
Accts Abacus Cpas Llc Springfield
SIC 4213 Refrigerated products transport
**CFO:* Dean Hoedl
Treas: Lawana L Low
VP: Jim Owen
Prgrm Mgr: Stan Kasterke
IT Man: Brianne Calvert
Trfc Dir: August Newberry
Trfc Dir: Vincent Snider
Opers Mgr: Stan Auman
Opers Mgr: Troy Rich
Manager: Richard Sarkissian
Genl Couns: Steve Crawford

D-U-N-S 06-803-1376
NEW PROCESS STEEL HOLDING CO INC
5800 Westview Dr, Houston, TX 77055-5495
Tel (713) 686-9631 *Founded/Ownrshp* 1977
Sales 88.5MM^E *EMP* 500
SIC 5051 Steel
Pr: Richard E Fant
**Sec:* Phil O Kelley

D-U-N-S 05-826-5513 IMP/EXP
NEW PROCESS STEEL LP
1322 N Post Oak Rd, Houston, TX 77055-5406
Tel (713) 686-9631 *Founded/Ownrshp* 1999
Sales 266.3MM^E *EMP* 375
SIC 5051 3469 Sheets, metal; Steel; Sheets, galvanized or other coated; Stamping metal for the trade
Pr: Richard E Fant
**COO:* Robert L Proch
VP: Bill Williams
Div Mgr: David Bowman
Dir IT: Jim Wilson
Sales Exec: Tammy Rasmussen

D-U-N-S 82-589-7833
▲ NEW RELIC INC
188 Spear St Ste 1200, San Francisco, CA 94105-1750
Tel (650) 777-7600 *Founded/Ownrshp* 2007
Sales 181.3MM *EMP* 936^E
Tkr Sym NEWR *Exch* NYS
SIC 7372 Prepackaged software; Application computer software
CEO: Lewis Cirne
**Ch Bd:* Peter Fenton
Pr: Hilarie Koplow-Mcadams
Pr: Bill Lapcevic
COO: Mark Sachleben
Ex VP: Erica Schultz
Sr VP: John Gray
VP: Jay Fry
VP: Shaun Gordon
VP: Steve McElfresh
VP: Robin J Schulman
Board of Directors: Sarah Friar, Adam Messinger, Dan Scholnick, James R Tolonen

D-U-N-S 07-874-2068
▲ NEW RESIDENTIAL INVESTMENT CORP
1345 Ave Americas, New York, NY 10105-0302
Tel (212) 798-3150 *Founded/Ownrshp* 2011
Sales 687.1MM *EMP* 3^E
Tkr Sym NRZ *Exch* NYS
SIC 6798 Real estate investment trusts
Ch Bd: Michael Nierenberg
CFO: Nicola Santoro Jr

D-U-N-S 00-307-8532
NEW RIDGE ASSOCIATES INC (MD)
HIGH'S
2700 Loch Raven Rd, Baltimore, MD 21218-4729
Tel (410) 859-3636 *Founded/Ownrshp* 1929, 2015
Sales 118.8MM^E *EMP* 968
SIC 5411 Convenience stores, chain
Pr: Brian Darnell
**VP:* Briana Darnell
**VP:* Ben Jatlow
VP: Benjamin Jatlow
Site Mgr: Tracy Paine
Site Mgr: Dawn Roark
Site Mgr: Belinda Slate

D-U-N-S 00-979-7416 IMP/EXP
NEW RIVER ELECTRICAL CORP
15 Cloverdale Pl, Cloverdale, VA 24077-3124
Tel (540) 966-1650 *Founded/Ownrshp* 1984
Sales 271.8MM *EMP* 900
Accts Kennett & Kennett Pc Roanoke
SIC 1731 1623 Electrical work; Electric power systems contractors; Fire detection & burglar alarm systems specialization; General electrical contractor; Electric power line construction
Pr: Thomas M Wolden
**Ex VP:* Richard C Furr II
**Sr VP:* Robert B Arritt Jr
**Sr VP:* John E Swim
VP: R C Furr II
**VP:* Terry M Garrett
**VP:* John E Lanning
VP: Frank R Mille
**VP:* Frank R Miller
**VP:* Barry S Murray
**VP:* John F Ney
VP: Christopher J Whitely
Board of Directors: Robert Arritt Jr, Terry Garrett, John Lanning, Jeffrey Leinard, Barry Murray, John Ney, Thomas Wolden

D-U-N-S 17-559-7137 IMP
NEW SABINA INDUSTRIES INC
(*Suby of* NIPPON SEIKI CO.,LTD.)
12555 Us Highway 22 And 3, Sabina, OH 45169-9463
Tel (937) 584-2433 *Founded/Ownrshp* 1986
Sales 120.1MM^E *EMP* 500
SIC 3714 Instrument board assemblies, motor vehicle
Pr: Kazu Kishi
VP: Carol Engle
VP: Ryan Higgins
Exec: Pat McGreevy
Plnt Mgr: Stuart Lohrum

D-U-N-S 07-888-9449
NEW SBARRO INTERMEDIATE HOLDINGS INC
1328 Dublin Rd, Columbus, OH 43215-1054
Tel (614) 769-9911 *Founded/Ownrshp* 2013
Sales 227.7MM^E *EMP* 1,396^E
SIC 6719 Investment holding companies, except banks
Pr: David Karam
Pr: Tony Missano
**CFO:* Carolyn Spatafora
**Treas:* Stuart Steinberg

D-U-N-S 07-103-0969
NEW SCHOOL (NY)
66 W 12th St, New York, NY 10011-8871
Tel (212) 229-5600 *Founded/Ownrshp* 1919
Sales 370.0MM *EMP* 855
Accts Kpmg Llp New York Ny
SIC 8221 Colleges universities & professional schools
Pr: David Van Zandt
COO: Melanie Hiner
**COO:* Tim Marshall-Provost
Treas: Mary Dixon
Bd of Dir: Baillie Aaron
Bd of Dir: Apryl A Alexander
Bd of Dir: Timothy Allen
Bd of Dir: Zhanna Bagdasarov
Bd of Dir: Marcelle Bartolo-Abela
Bd of Dir: Stacie Bigelow
Bd of Dir: Todd Bishop
Bd of Dir: Rebecca Blais
Bd of Dir: Chloe G Bland
Bd of Dir: Stefanie Boswell
Bd of Dir: Markus Burrell
Bd of Dir: Jason Cantone
Bd of Dir: Jennifer Carusone
Bd of Dir: Sungkun Cho
Bd of Dir: Alin Coman
Bd of Dir: Guyla Davis
Bd of Dir: John Denboer

D-U-N-S 11-441-2468 IMP
NEW SEASONS MARKET LLC
1300 Se Stark St Ste 401, Portland, OR 97214-2473
Tel (503) 292-1987 *Founded/Ownrshp* 1999
Sales 131.5MM^E *EMP* 620
SIC 5411 Grocery stores
Pt: Lisa Sedlar
**Pt:* Joanne Morrissey
**Pt:* Brian Rohter
CFO: Jeremy Fogle
Chf Mktg O: Dina Keenan
IT Man: Ezra Hunt

D-U-N-S 07-944-7890
NEW SENIOR INVESTMENT GROUP INC
1345 Avenue Of The Americ, New York, NY 10105-0014
Tel (212) 479-3140 *Founded/Ownrshp* 2014
Sales 388.4MM *EMP* 3^E
Accts Ernst & Young Llp New York
Tkr Sym SNR *Exch* NYS
SIC 6726 Investment offices
CEO: Susan Givens
**CFO:* Justine Cheng

NEW SMYRNA DAILY JOURNAL
See NEWS-JOURNAL CORP

D-U-N-S 07-872-3658
NEW SOURCE ENERGY PARTNERS LP
300 Delaware Ave Ste 1100, Wilmington, DE 19801-1670
Tel (405) 272-3028 *Founded/Ownrshp* 2012
Sales 165.6MM *EMP* 136
SIC 1311 1389
Ch Bd: Kristian B Kos
Genl Pt: New Source Energy GP LLC
Pr: Dikran Tourian

D-U-N-S 05-528-4368 EXP
NEW SOUTH COMPANIES INC
(*Suby of* CANFOR CORPORATION)
3700 Claypond Rd Ste 6, Myrtle Beach, SC 29579-7330
Tel (843) 236-9399 *Founded/Ownrshp* 2006
Sales 239.4MM^E *EMP* 700
SIC 2421 2491 2431 Lumber: rough, sawed or planed; Wood chips, produced at mill; Sawdust & shavings; Piles, foundation & marine construction: treated wood; Structural lumber & timber, treated wood; Millwork
Pr: Douglas J Warstler
Off Mgr: Debbie Robinson

D-U-N-S 62-101-4000
NEW SOUTH CONSTRUCTION CO INC
1180 W Peachtree St Nw # 70, Atlanta, GA 30309-3407
Tel (404) 443-4000 *Founded/Ownrshp* 1993
Sales 136.5MM^E *EMP* 185
SIC 1541 8741 Industrial buildings & warehouses; Construction management
Pr: Douglas C Davidson
**CFO:* Dan Smith
**Ex VP:* Huntly Gordon
**Ex VP:* Tom Troutman
VP: Rob Dunn
Genl Mgr: Dan Hobson
Off Mgr: Kelley Thomas
Sfty Mgr: Bryan Fowler
Sfty Mgr: Brad Ketner
Mktg Dir: Theresa Smith
Snr PM: David Martin

D-U-N-S 05-205-0585 EXP
NEW SOUTH LUMBER CO INC
(*Suby of* NEW SOUTH COMPANIES INC) ★
3700 Claypond Rd Ste 6, Myrtle Beach, SC 29579-7330
Tel (843) 236-9399 *Founded/Ownrshp* 2006
Sales 234.0MM^E *EMP* 600
SIC 2421 Lumber: rough, sawed or planed
Pr: Fred Stimpson
**Treas:* Ken Thomas
**VP:* Keith McGreggor

D-U-N-S 00-300-2060 IMP
NEW STANDARD CORP (PA)
74 Commerce Way, York, PA 17406-8038
Tel (717) 757-9450 *Founded/Ownrshp* 1909, 1940
Sales 140.7MM^E *EMP* 450
SIC 3469 3465 Metal stampings; Automotive stampings
CEO: Morton F Zifferer Jr
Pr: Dave Meckley
COO: Todd Musso
CFO: Mark Wheeler
Treas: Tom McEvoy
VP: Dave Porter
Sls Mgr: Bill Schenck
Snr Mgr: Tim Pate

D-U-N-S 80-907-1470
■ NEW STAR HOLDINGS INTERNATIONAL INC
(*Suby of* MIDDLEBY COOKING SYSTEMS GROUP) ★
10 Sunnen Dr, Saint Louis, MO 63143-3800
Tel (800) 264-7827 *Founded/Ownrshp* 2008
Sales 93.0MM^E *EMP* 614
SIC 3589 Commercial cooking & foodwarming equipment
Pr: Frank Ricchio

NEW TIMES WEEKLY
See VILLAGE VOICE MEDIA HOLDINGS LLC

D-U-N-S 05-410-1944
NEW TRIBES MISSION INC (FL)
NEW TRIBES MISSION INSTITUTE
1000 E 1st St, Sanford, FL 32771-1487
Tel (407) 323-3430 *Founded/Ownrshp* 1942
Sales 38.9MM^E *EMP* 1,055
Accts Batts Morrison Wales And Lee
SIC 8661 Religious organizations
COO: Kirk Rogers
**Treas:* Tim Meisel
Chf Mktg O: Dan Stokes
**Ex Dir:* Paul Wyma
Off Mgr: Terresa Hiebert
Nurse Mgr: Susan Russell
Dir IT: Alan Foster
Dir IT: Jeffrey Porter
Software D: David Burson

NEW TRIBES MISSION INSTITUTE
See NEW TRIBES MISSION INC

D-U-N-S 10-297-0571 IMP/EXP
NEW UNITED MOTOR MANUFACTURING INC
NUMMI
45500 Fremont Blvd, Fremont, CA 94538-6326
Tel (510) 498-5500 *Founded/Ownrshp* 1983
Sales NA *EMP* 5,000^E
SIC 3714 3711

D-U-N-S 96-212-6541
NEW VENTURE FUND
1201 Conn Ave Nw Ste 300, Washington, DC 20036-2656
Tel (202) 595-1061 *Founded/Ownrshp* 2010
Sales 179.4MM *EMP* 3
Accts Cliftonlarsonallen Llp Arling
SIC 7389 Fund raising organizations
Pr: Eric Kessler

D-U-N-S 03-905-2704
NEW VISION CO-OP
38438 210th St, Brewster, MN 56119-2017
Tel (507) 842-2001 *Founded/Ownrshp* 1998
Sales 154.5MM^E *EMP* 73
SIC 5153 Grain elevators
CEO: Frank McDowell

D-U-N-S 04-854-7946 IMP/EXP
NEW VISION DISPLAY INC
1430 Blue Oaks Blvd # 100, Roseville, CA 95747-5156
Tel (916) 786-8111 *Founded/Ownrshp* 1986
Sales 113.0MM *EMP* 3,007
SIC 3679 Liquid crystal displays (LCD)
CEO: Jeff Olyniec
**Ch Bd:* Owen Chen
**CFO:* Alan M Lefko

D-U-N-S 84-890-1062
NEW WATER STREET CORP
55 Water St Ste Conc6, New York, NY 10041-0033
Tel (212) 422-1320 *Founded/Ownrshp* 1993
Sales 141.5MM *EMP* 10
Accts Carr Riggs & Ingram Llc Montg
SIC 6531 Real estate agent, commercial

NEW WAVE COMMUNICATION
See TELECOMMUNICATIONS MANAGEMENT LLC

D-U-N-S 78-850-2573
NEW WAVE TECHNOLOGIES INC
4635 Wedgewood Blvd # 107, Frederick, MD 21703-3300
Tel (301) 624-5300 *Founded/Ownrshp* 1992
Sales 103.8MM^E *EMP* 64
SIC 5045 Computers, peripherals & software
Pr: William Cordell
**Pt:* Frank Lee
Pr: Thomas Boyle
**VP:* Lenny Martin
IT Man: Dale Andrews
Software D: Carol Dorsey
Mfg Dir: Joel Pont
Mfg Dir: Bobbi Stackman
Opers Mgr: Tim Voigt
Natl Sales: Matt Cornell
Mktg Dir: Cathy Nieves

D-U-N-S 80-558-2892
NEW WERNER HOLDING CO INC
93 Werner Rd, Greenville, PA 16125-9434
Tel (724) 588-2000 *Founded/Ownrshp* 2007
Sales 535.1MM^E *EMP* 1,804
SIC 3499 3355 3089 3446 2499 6512 Ladders, portable: metal; Extrusion ingot, aluminum: made in rolling mills; Synthetic resin finished products; Scaffolds, mobile or stationary: metal; Stepladders, wood; Nonresidential building operators
Pr: William T Allen
Pr: Dave Plotner
**CFO:* Larry Friend
CFO: Marc L Werner
**VP:* Edward Gericke
MIS Dir: Lee Easton
Dir IT: Howard Solot

D-U-N-S 15-097-9230 IMP
NEW WINCUP HOLDINGS INC
(*Suby of* WINCUP INC) ★
4640 Lewis Rd, Stone Mountain, GA 30083-1004
Tel (770) 938-5281 *Founded/Ownrshp* 1962
Sales 285.3MM^E *EMP* 1,000^E
SIC 3086 Cups & plates, foamed plastic
CEO: Jack Brucker
**Pr:* Glenn Wredenhagen
**Pr:* George W Wurtz III
**CFO:* Scott Haftmann
**CFO:* Mark Thomas
**Treas:* Evan Hardin
**Sr VP:* Mike Revier
**Sr VP:* Michael Winters
Sls Mgr: Henry Bowen

D-U-N-S 04-874-5165 IMP
NEW WORLD PASTA CO
(*Suby of* EBRO FOODS, SA)
85 Shannon Rd, Harrisburg, PA 17112-2787
Tel (717) 526-2200 *Founded/Ownrshp* 1996
Sales 233.2MM^E *EMP* 800
SIC 2098 Macaroni & spaghetti
CEO: Bastiaan De Zeeuw
**COO:* Peter E Cotter
**CFO:* Edward J Lyons
**CFO:* Horst O Sieben
**Sr VP:* Brett Beckfield
**Sr VP:* Douglas W Ehrenkranz
**Sr VP:* Gerard Ferguson
**Sr VP:* Lawrence C Kleinman
**Sr VP:* Gregory Richardson
**VP:* Joseph Marelli Jr
VP: Cary Metz

NEW WORLD SALES
See STEVE SELVIN ASSOCIATES INC

NEW WORLD TRADING
See NWT WORLD ARTS INC

NEW WORLD VAN LINES CALIFORNIA
See NEW WORLD VAN LINES INC

D-U-N-S 05-775-9276 IMP/EXP
NEW WORLD VAN LINES INC
NEW WORLD VAN LINES CALIFORNIA
5875 N Rogers Ave, Chicago, IL 60646-5953
Tel (773) 685-3399 *Founded/Ownrshp* 1982
Sales 94.9MM^E *EMP* 500
SIC 4213

D-U-N-S 14-918-6442 IMP/EXP
▲ NEW YORK & CO INC
330 W 34th St Fl 9, New York, NY 10001-2406
Tel (212) 884-2000 *Founded/Ownrshp* 1918
Sales 950.1MM *EMP* 6,282
Tkr Sym NWY *Exch* NYS
SIC 5621 Women's clothing stores
CEO: Gregory J Scott
Mng Pt: Peggy Allicock
**Ch Bd:* Grace Nichols
Pr: John M Worthington
CFO: Sheamus Toal
Ex VP: Chau Banks
Ex VP: Faeth Bradley
Ex VP: Kevin Finnegan
Ex VP: Michelle Pearlman
VP: Neil Beckerman
VP: Alison Eichner
VP: Kelly Radford
VP: Adam Ratner
VP: Jeanette Reed
VP: Linda Vilaikeo
Exec: Mila Rabkana
Dir: Michael Dalton
Creative D: Darryl Powlus
Board of Directors: David H Edwab, James O Egan, Lori H Greeley, Christy Haubegger, John D Howard, Arthur E Reiner

D-U-N-S 92-957-4168
■ NEW YORK - NEW YORK HOTEL & CASINO LLC
(*Suby of* MGM RESORTS INTERNATIONAL) ★
3790 Las Vegas Blvd S, Las Vegas, NV 89109-4338
Tel (702) 740-6969 *Founded/Ownrshp* 1997
Sales 93.5MM^E *EMP* 2,300
SIC 7011 7996 Casino hotel; Theme park, amusement
Pr: Cynthia Kiser Murphey
COO: David Cacci

*CFO: William Basborg
Exec: Barbara Barnot
Comm Man: Tina Rushton
Ex Dir: Michelle Borgel
Ex Dir: Marcia Perna
Dir Sec: Greg Goll
Brnch Mgr: Mark Slesser
Secur Mgr: Glenn Nulle
VP Mktg: Cathryn Schmit

NEW YORK AIR BRAKE
See KNORR BRAKE TRUCK SYSTEMS CO

D-U-N-S 01-272-9476 IMP
NEW YORK AND PRESBYTERIAN HOSPITAL
NEWYORK-PRESBYTERIAN HOSPITAL
525 E 68th St, New York, NY 10065-4870
Tel (212) 746-5454 Founded/Ownrshp 1998
Sales 4.2MMM EMP 15,078
SIC 8062 8011 General medical & surgical hospitals; Offices & clinics of medical doctors
Ch Bd: John J Mack
*Pr: Herbert Pardes
*COO: Steven J Corwin MD
COO: Laura L Forese
*CFO: Phyllis R Lantos
Treas: Ed Cleveland
Bd of Dir: Mathew Eapen
Bd of Dir: Wendy Goldstein
Bd of Dir: Judy Graham
Bd of Dir: Roger Greene
Trst: Roger C Altman
Trst: Raymond J McGuire
Trst: Daniel S Och
Trst: Sanford I Weill
Trst: Ivan G Seidenberg
*Ofcr: Maxine Fass
Ofcr: Maxine Frank
Ofcr: William Greene
Ofcr: Wilhelmina Manzano
Ofcr: Carol Silk
Sr VP: Andria Castellanos

D-U-N-S 07-327-1827
NEW YORK BLOOD CENTER INC
LONG ISLAND BLOOD SERVICES
310 E 67th St, New York, NY 10065-6273
Tel (212) 570-3010 Founded/Ownrshp 1959
Sales 320.2MM EMP 1,600
Accts Kpmg Llp New York Ny
SIC 8099 2836 Blood bank; Blood donor station; Blood derivatives
CEO: Christopher D Hillyer
CFO: Beth Gibson
*CFO: Lawrence Hannigan
Treas: Christine Foran
*Sr VP: Elizabeth C Gibson
*Sr VP: Elizabeth J McQuail
*Sr VP: Michael J Monahan
VP: Ollie Cheatham
VP: Doriane Gloria
VP: Charles Grossenbacher
VP: Frederick W Hill
VP: Donald Kender
VP: Eva Maurer
VP: Michael Monahan
VP: John R Mullen
VP: Pablo Rubinstein
VP: Harvey Schaffler
Dir Soc: Rolf Kovenetsky

D-U-N-S 00-506-9414 IMP/EXP
NEW YORK BLOWER CO
NY B
7660 S Quincy St, Willowbrook, IL 60527-5596
Tel (630) 794-5700 Founded/Ownrshp 1889
Sales 83.2MM^E EMP 350
SIC 3564

D-U-N-S 07-325-0946 IMP
NEW YORK BOTANICAL GARDEN
2900 Southern Blvd, Bronx, NY 10458-5153
Tel (718) 817-8779 Founded/Ownrshp 1891
Sales 89.0MM EMP 500^E
Accts Deloitte & Touche Llp Jericho
SIC 8422 8299 Botanical garden; Educational services
Pr: Gregory R Long
Assoc VP: Dale Brooks
Assoc VP: Jerry Eng
Assoc VP: Margaret Falk
Assoc VP: Todd Forrest
Assoc VP: Kristin Schleiter
*Sr VP: J V Cossaboom
VP: Francisca Coelho
VP: Coelho Francisca
VP: Karl Lauby
*VP: Dennis Stevenson
Assoc Dir: Terry Skoda

D-U-N-S 00-243-0072
NEW YORK CENTRAL MUTUAL FIRE INSURANCE CO (NY)
NYCM INSURANCE
1899 Central Plz E, Edmeston, NY 13335-1828
Tel (607) 965-8321 Founded/Ownrshp 1899
Sales NA EMP 850
SIC 6331 Fire, marine & casualty insurance
Ch Bd: Vanness D Robinson
Pr: Michael Perrino
*Pr: D Daniel Robinson II
Pr: Robert Snyder
*CFO: Albert Pylinski Jr
Treas: Jeremy Robinson
Sr VP: Doughlas Franklin
Sr VP: John E Holdorf
Sr VP: James R Slosek
Sr VP: Timothy Trueworth
VP: William Couperthwait

D-U-N-S 07-816-3383 IMP
NEW YORK CITY BOARD OF EDUCATION
DEPARTMENT OF EDUCATION
52 Chambers St Ste 320, New York, NY 10007-1222
Tel (212) 374-5141 Founded/Ownrshp 1900
Sales 0.0 EMP 135,000^E
SIC 8211

D-U-N-S 80-046-9715
NEW YORK CITY DEPT OF EDUCATION
NYC EMPOWERMENT SCHOOLS
52 Chambrs St Twd Crthse Tweed Courthouse, New York, NY 10007
Tel (212) 374-6000 Founded/Ownrshp 2007
Sales 157.3MM^E EMP 1,215^E
SIC 8732 Educational research
*COO: Veronica Conforme
CFO: Raymond Orlando
*Prin: Kemi Akinsanya-Rose
Ex Dir: Roger Platt
Software D: Muthuraja Pillai

D-U-N-S 07-995-4994
NEW YORK CITY GEOGRAPHIC DISTRICT 1
166 Essex St, New York, NY 10002-1502
Tel (212) 353-2948 Founded/Ownrshp 2015
Sales 14.9MM^E EMP 1,630^E
SIC 8211 Public elementary & secondary schools

D-U-N-S 07-980-6893
NEW YORK CITY GEOGRAPHIC DISTRICT 10
1 Fordham Plz Rm 835, Bronx, NY 10458-5871
Tel (718) 741-5852 Founded/Ownrshp 2015
Sales 29.9MM^E EMP 6,587^E
SIC 8211 Public elementary & secondary schools

D-U-N-S 07-995-5108
NEW YORK CITY GEOGRAPHIC DISTRICT 12
1970 W Farms Rd, Bronx, NY 10460-6024
Tel (718) 328-2310 Founded/Ownrshp 2015
Sales 67.4MM^E EMP 2,544^E
SIC 8211 Public elementary & secondary schools

D-U-N-S 07-980-6891
NEW YORK CITY GEOGRAPHIC DISTRICT 13
355 Park Pl, Brooklyn, NY 11238-4001
Tel (718) 636-3204 Founded/Ownrshp 2015
Sales 15.1MM^E EMP 2,548^E
SIC 8211 Public elementary & secondary schools

D-U-N-S 95-643-1373
NEW YORK CITY GEOGRAPHIC DISTRICT 14
215 Heyward St, Brooklyn, NY 11206-2966
Tel (718) 302-7600 Founded/Ownrshp 1999
Sales 30.6MM^E EMP 2,894^E
SIC 8211 Public elementary & secondary schools

D-U-N-S 07-995-5120
NEW YORK CITY GEOGRAPHIC DISTRICT 15
131 Livingston St Rm 301, Brooklyn, NY 11201-5105
Tel (718) 935-4317 Founded/Ownrshp 2015
Sales 19.6MM^E EMP 2,878^E
SIC 8211 Public elementary & secondary schools

D-U-N-S 07-976-7516
NEW YORK CITY GEOGRAPHIC DISTRICT 17
1224 Park Pl, Brooklyn, NY 11213-2703
Tel (718) 221-4372 Founded/Ownrshp 1900
Sales 34.2MM^E EMP 4,173^E
SIC 8211 Public elementary & secondary schools

D-U-N-S 07-980-6898
NEW YORK CITY GEOGRAPHIC DISTRICT 19
335 Adams St, Brooklyn, NY 11201-3752
Tel (718) 923-5124 Founded/Ownrshp 2015
Sales 22.9MM^E EMP 2,944^E
SIC 8211 Public elementary & secondary schools

D-U-N-S 07-980-6914
NEW YORK CITY GEOGRAPHIC DISTRICT 2
333 7th Ave Fl 7, New York, NY 10001-5119
Tel (212) 356-3815 Founded/Ownrshp 2015
Sales 27.4MM^E EMP 5,109^E
SIC 8211 Public elementary & secondary schools

D-U-N-S 04-530-3065
NEW YORK CITY GEOGRAPHIC DISTRICT 20
415 89th St, Brooklyn, NY 11209-5905
Tel (718) 759-3942 Founded/Ownrshp 2010
Sales 24.2MM^E EMP 3,852^E
SIC 8211 Public elementary & secondary schools

D-U-N-S 07-980-6916
NEW YORK CITY GEOGRAPHIC DISTRICT 21
501 West Ave, Brooklyn, NY 11224-4220
Tel (718) 714-2502 Founded/Ownrshp 2015
Sales 482.5M^E EMP 3,829^E
SIC 8211 Public elementary & secondary schools

D-U-N-S 07-859-9455
NEW YORK CITY GEOGRAPHIC DISTRICT 22
5619 Flatlands Ave, Brooklyn, NY 11234-2501
Tel (718) 968-6117 Founded/Ownrshp 2012
Sales 1.5MM^E EMP 3,791^E
SIC 8211 Elementary & secondary schools
Prin: Mary Bosco

D-U-N-S 06-107-5229
NEW YORK CITY GEOGRAPHIC DISTRICT 23
1665 Saint Marks Ave, Brooklyn, NY 11233-4813
Tel (718) 922-4794 Founded/Ownrshp 2011
Sales 14.2MM^E EMP 1,880^E
SIC 8211 Public elementary & secondary schools

D-U-N-S 03-271-4159
NEW YORK CITY GEOGRAPHIC DISTRICT 24
9850 50th Ave, Corona, NY 11368-2757
Tel (718) 592-3357 Founded/Ownrshp 2011
Sales 171.3MM^E EMP 5,411^E
SIC 7336 Commercial art & graphic design

D-U-N-S 07-980-6903
NEW YORK CITY GEOGRAPHIC DISTRICT 26
6115 Oceania St, Bayside, NY 11364-2139
Tel (718) 631-6982 Founded/Ownrshp 2015
Sales 19.1MM^E EMP 2,541^E
SIC 8211 Public elementary & secondary schools

D-U-N-S 11-038-6526
NEW YORK CITY GEOGRAPHIC DISTRICT 27
8201 Rockaway Blvd, Ozone Park, NY 11416-1213
Tel (718) 642-5861 Founded/Ownrshp 2002
Sales 839.1M^E EMP 3,500^E
SIC 8211 Public elementary & secondary schools

D-U-N-S 04-530-3461
NEW YORK CITY GEOGRAPHIC DISTRICT 28
9027 Sutphin Blvd Rm 24, Jamaica, NY 11435-3647
Tel (718) 557-2618 Founded/Ownrshp 2010
Sales 22.2MM^E EMP 3,289^E
SIC 8211 Public elementary & secondary schools
Prin: Beverly Ffolkes-Bryant

D-U-N-S 04-530-3416
NEW YORK CITY GEOGRAPHIC DISTRICT 29
22214 Jamaica Ave, Hollis, NY 11423
Tel (718) 217-7740 Founded/Ownrshp 2010
Sales 25.3MM^E EMP 3,005^E
SIC 8211 Public elementary & secondary schools

D-U-N-S 07-995-5013
NEW YORK CITY GEOGRAPHIC DISTRICT 3
501 W 165th St, New York, NY 10032-4206
Tel (212) 678-5857 Founded/Ownrshp 2015
Sales 13.1MM^E EMP 2,325^E
SIC 8211 Public elementary & secondary schools

D-U-N-S 04-812-4719
NEW YORK CITY GEOGRAPHIC DISTRICT 30
2811 Queens Plz N, Long Island City, NY 11101-4008
Tel (718) 391-8323 Founded/Ownrshp 1900
Sales 90.6MM^E EMP 3,569^E
SIC 8211 Public elementary & secondary schools

D-U-N-S 07-995-5135
NEW YORK CITY GEOGRAPHIC DISTRICT 31
715 Ocean Ter Rm 129, Staten Island, NY 10301-4542
Tel (718) 420-5667 Founded/Ownrshp 2015
Sales 132.8MM^E EMP 5,818^E
SIC 8211 Public elementary & secondary schools

D-U-N-S 07-980-6920
NEW YORK CITY GEOGRAPHIC DISTRICT 4
319 E 117th St, New York, NY 10035-4902
Tel (212) 831-4981 Founded/Ownrshp 2015
Sales 14.1MM^E EMP 1,654^E
SIC 8211 Public elementary & secondary schools

D-U-N-S 07-980-6901
NEW YORK CITY GEOGRAPHIC DISTRICT 5
425 W 123rd St, New York, NY 10027-5002
Tel (212) 769-7500 Founded/Ownrshp 2015
Sales 14.2MM^E EMP 2,001^E
SIC 8211 Public elementary & secondary schools

D-U-N-S 07-980-6904
NEW YORK CITY GEOGRAPHIC DISTRICT 6
4360 Broadway Rm 527, New York, NY 10033-2409
Tel (212) 521-3757 Founded/Ownrshp 2015
Sales 22.4MM^E EMP 2,932^E
SIC 8211 Public elementary & secondary schools

D-U-N-S 07-995-5036
NEW YORK CITY GEOGRAPHIC DISTRICT 7
501 Courtland Ave, Bronx, NY 10451
Tel (718) 742-6500 Founded/Ownrshp 2015
Sales 60.3MM^E EMP 2,479^E
SIC 8211 Public elementary & secondary schools

D-U-N-S 07-995-5080
NEW YORK CITY GEOGRAPHIC DISTRICT 8
601 Stickball Blvd, Bronx, NY 10473-2624
Tel (718) 828-6653 Founded/Ownrshp 2015
Sales 86.3MM^E EMP 3,285^E
SIC 8211 Public elementary & secondary schools

D-U-N-S 04-945-8580
NEW YORK CITY GEOGRAPHIC DISTRICT 9
250 E 164th St, Bronx, NY 10456-6201
Tel (718) 741-3157 Founded/Ownrshp 2010
Sales 1.9MM^E EMP 3,618^E
SIC 8211 Public elementary & secondary schools

NEW YORK CITY HEALTH AND HOSPI
See LINCOLN MEDICAL AND MENTAL HEALTH CENTER

NEW YORK CITY HEALTH AND HOSPI
See HARLEM HOSPITAL CENTER

D-U-N-S 06-496-1261 IMP
NEW YORK CITY HEALTH AND HOSPITALS CORP
NEW YORK CITY HLTH & HOSPITALS
125 Worth St Rm 514, New York, NY 10013-4006
Tel (212) 788-3321 Founded/Ownrshp 1970
Sales 694.5MM EMP 35,700
SIC 8062 8069 8093 General medical & surgical hospitals; Chronic disease hospital; Specialty outpatient clinics
Pr: Ramanathan Raju
Dir Vol: Luisa Hernandez
Ch Bd: Stephen Raynis
Pr: Robert Kee
Pr: Roslyn Weinstein
COO: Antonio Martin
CFO: Marlene Zurack
Ch: Ross Wilson
Ofcr: Joanne Lischin
Sr Inv Off: John Merseburg
Ex VP: Ramanathan Raju MD
Sr VP: Laray Brown
Sr VP: Caroline M Jacobs
Sr VP: Tony Martin
Sr VP: Cynthia Murray
Sr VP: Joanna OMI
Sr VP: Carlos Perez
Sr VP: Norberto Robles
Sr VP: Anne Marie Sullivan
Sr VP: William P Walsh
VP: Richard Levy
Board of Directors: Edwin Mendez-Santiago, Ruth Bloom, Edwin Mendez-Santiago, Josephine Bolus, Lloyd I Sederer MD, Marcia R Brown MD, Marc V Shaw, Verna Eggleston, Bruce J Teitelbaum, Thomas R Frieden, Rev Diane E Lacey Winley, John R Maese MD, Cecilia E Norat, Daniel D Ricciardi, Bernard Rosen

NEW YORK CITY HLTH & HOSPITALS
See NEW YORK CITY HEALTH AND HOSPITALS CORP

D-U-N-S 00-167-2062
NEW YORK CITY HOUSING AUTHORITY
250 Broadway, New York, NY 10007-2516
Tel (212) 306-3000 Founded/Ownrshp 1934
Sales NA EMP 11,605
SIC 9531 Housing authority, non-operating: government
Ch Bd: Shola Olatoye
CFO: Richard Couch
Ofcr: Jean Weinberg
Ex VP: David Farber
Ex VP: Melanie Hart
Ex VP: Cathy Pennington
Ex VP: Raymond A Ribeiro
Ex VP: Natalie Y Rivers
Sr VP: Brian Clarke
Sr VP: Luis Ponce
VP: Bill Crawley
VP: Anne-Marie Flatley
VP: Deidra Gilliard
VP: Rudolph Kurkjian
VP: Celeste Morgan
VP: Michael Rosen
VP: John Saggese
Dir Surg: Joan Lebow

D-U-N-S 13-975-4332
NEW YORK CITY SCHOOL CONSTRUCTION AUTHORITY
3030 Thomson Ave Fl 3, Long Island City, NY 11101-3045
Tel (718) 472-8000 Founded/Ownrshp 1988
Sales 2.1MMM EMP 600
Accts Pricewaterhousecooper Llp Ne
SIC 1542 School building construction
Pr: Loraine Grillo
CFO: Juanita Rosillo
Ofcr: Bassam Abdu
Ofcr: Haytham Awad
Ofcr: Robert Bowers
Ofcr: Michael Gonzalez
Ofcr: Michael Ogbutor
Ofcr: Aslam Qureshi
Ofcr: Jacobie S Ricard
Ofcr: Eric Tiedemann
*Ex VP: Ross J Holden
VP: Bruce Barrett
VP: Maryann Egri
VP: George Toma

D-U-N-S 00-970-2853
NEW YORK CITY TRANSIT AUTHORITY
PUBLIC TRANSPORTATION
(Suby of M T A) ★
2 Broadway, New York, NY 10004-3357
Tel (718) 330-1234 Founded/Ownrshp 1955
Sales 2.0MMM^E EMP 47,956
Accts Pricewaterhousecoopers Llp Ne
SIC 4111 Subway operation; Bus transportation
*Pr: Lawrence G Reuter
*Ex VP: Barbara Spencer
IT Man: Josiane Codio

D-U-N-S 60-698-7808
■ **NEW YORK COMMERCIAL BANK**
ATLANTIC BANK DIVISION
(Suby of NEW YORK COMMUNITY BANCORP INC) ★
615 Merrick Ave, Westbury, NY 11590-6607
Tel (800) 535-2269 Founded/Ownrshp 2005
Sales NA EMP 509
SIC 6022 State commercial banks
Ch Bd: Joseph Ficalora
*CFO: Thomas Buonaiuto
*V Ch Bd: Frank J Esposito
*V Ch Bd: John C Tsunis
*Ofcr: James T Burns
*Ofcr: Kevin Hennessy
*Ofcr: Scott Swain
*Ofcr: Mel Vizzini
*Ex VP: Kenneth M Scheriff
*Sr VP: James Jsperanza
VP: Charles Baker
VP: Judith Guarino
VP: Mike Pesce
VP: Kevin Wolfe
Board of Directors: Lawrence Rosano Jr, Lawrence J Savares

D-U-N-S 80-914-3217
▲ **NEW YORK COMMUNITY BANCORP INC**
615 Merrick Ave, Westbury, NY 11590-6607
Tel (516) 683-4100 Founded/Ownrshp 1993
Sales NA EMP 3,448^E
Tkr Sym NYCB Exch NYS
SIC 6036 State savings banks, not federally chartered
Pr: Joseph R Ficalora
*Ch Bd: Dominick Ciampa
*COO: Robert Wann
CFO: Thomas R Cangemi
Ex VP: John J Pinto
VP: Thomas Graziano
VP: Marquita Guerra
VP: Howard Henderson
VP: Ronald Lehrer
VP: Michele Reid
VP: Jeff Roe
Board of Directors: Maureen E Clancy, Leslie D Dunn,

James J O'donovan, Lawrence Rosano Jr, Ronald A Rosenfeld, Lawrence J Savarese, John M Tsimbinos

D-U-N-S 00-699-3018
■ **NEW YORK COMMUNITY BANK**
(Suby of NEW YORK COMMUNITY BANCORP INC) ★
615 Merrick Ave, Westbury, NY 11590-6607
Tel (516) 203-0010 Founded/Ownrshp 1859, 1993
Sales NA EMP 2,550
SIC 6036 State savings banks, not federally chartered
Ch Bd: Joseph R Ficalora
*CFO: Thomas R Cangemi
*Ex VP: Michael J Lincks
*Ex VP: John J Pinto
*Sr VP: Russ Dibenedetto
*Sr VP: James J O'Donovan
*Sr VP: Robert Wann
VP: Robert Brown
Dir IT: Dwayne Pringle

D-U-N-S 05-935-0421
NEW YORK COMMUNITY HOSPITAL
2525 Kings Hwy, Brooklyn, NY 11229-1705
Tel (718) 692-5300 Founded/Ownrshp 1945
Sales 93.1MM EMP 400
SIC 8062 General medical & surgical hospitals
Ch Bd: George Weinberger
*Pr: Lin H MO
*V Ch Bd: Richard Goldberg
VP: Vincent Desantis
VP Admn: Stephen Meyers
CIO: Edward Stolyar
MIS Dir: Alex Litvinov

NEW YORK COMMUNITY TRUST
See COMMUNITY FUNDS INC

D-U-N-S 06-823-6686
NEW YORK COMMUNITY TRUST AND COMMUNITY FUNDS INC
LONG ISLAND COMMUNITY FOUNDATI
909 3rd Ave Fl 22, New York, NY 10022-4752
Tel (212) 686-0010 Founded/Ownrshp 1923
Sales 304.5MM EMP 65
Accts Kpmg Llp New York Ny
SIC 6732 Trusts: educational, religious, etc.
Pr: Lorie A Slutsky
Ofcr: Roderick Jenkins
*Sr VP: Joyce Bove
*VP: Robert V Edgar
*VP: Mercedes M Leon
VP: Gay Young
Pgrm Dir: Pat Jenny

D-U-N-S 05-456-7326
NEW YORK CONVENTION CENTER OPERATING CORP
JACOB K JAVITS CONVENTION CTR
655 W 34th St, New York, NY 10001-1114
Tel (212) 216-2000 Founded/Ownrshp 1980
Sales 190.9MM EMP 3,500
Accts Uhy Llp New York New York
SIC 7389 Convention & show services; Tourist information bureau
Pr: Alan E Steel
*Ch Bd: Henry Silverman
*CFO: Melanie McManus
*Chf Cred: Tony Sclafani
Sr VP: Doreen Guerin
Sr VP: Kenneth Sanchez
*Sr VP: Bradley Siciliano
*Sr VP: Mark Sims
VP: Kenneth Dixon
VP: Vincent Michello
VP: Margaret Tobin

NEW YORK DAILY NEWS
See DAILY NEWS LP

D-U-N-S 80-678-0573
NEW YORK DEPARTMENT OF CORRECTIONS AND COMMUNITY SUPERVISION
NYS DPRTMENT CORRECTIONAL SVCS
(Suby of EXECUTIVE OFFICE OF STATE OF NEW YORK) ★
1220 Washngtn Ave Bldg 2, Albany, NY 12226-1799
Tel (518) 457-8126 Founded/Ownrshp 1788
Sales 929.2MM^E EMP 30,000
SIC 8322 9223 Offender rehabilitation agency; Prison, government;
Genl Mgr: David Aziz

D-U-N-S 80-678-0912
NEW YORK DEPARTMENT OF ENVIRONMENTAL CONSERVATION
(Suby of EXECUTIVE OFFICE OF STATE OF NEW YORK) ★
625 Broadway, Albany, NY 12207-2942
Tel (518) 402-8545 Founded/Ownrshp 1970
Sales NA EMP 3,400
SIC 9512 Land, mineral & wildlife conservation;
VP: Joshua Clague

D-U-N-S 80-678-1340
NEW YORK DEPARTMENT OF HEALTH
(Suby of EXECUTIVE OFFICE OF STATE OF NEW YORK) ★
Empire State Plaza, Albany, NY 12237-0001
Tel (518) 474-2011 Founded/Ownrshp 1901
Sales NA EMP 17,226
SIC 9431 Administration of public health programs;
*Ch: Larita R Boren
Ex Dir: Bob Reed

D-U-N-S 83-542-2064
NEW YORK DEPARTMENT OF TRANSPORTATION
NYS DEPARTMENT TRANSPORTATION
(Suby of EXECUTIVE OFFICE OF STATE OF NEW YORK) ★
50 Wolf Rd Ste 5, Albany, NY 12205-2645
Tel (518) 457-4445 Founded/Ownrshp 1960
Sales NA EMP 2,600
SIC 9621 Transportation department: government, non-operating;
Prin: Joan McDonald
MIS Dir: Don Wells

D-U-N-S 04-477-6024
NEW YORK DIVISION OF MILITARY AND NAVAL AFFAIRS
(Suby of EXECUTIVE OFFICE OF STATE OF NEW YORK) ★
330 Old Niskayuna Rd, Latham, NY 12110-3514
Tel (518) 786-4500 Founded/Ownrshp 1985
Sales NA EMP 3,538
SIC 9711 National security;
Prin: Patrick A Murphy
Genl Mgr: Thomas Halabuda
Genl Mgr: Jane Sherwood
IT Man: Roger Townsend

D-U-N-S 07-886-9807
NEW YORK DOWNTOWN HOSPITAL
170 William St, New York, NY 10038-2649
Tel (212) 312-5000 Founded/Ownrshp 1979
Sales NA EMP 1,400
SIC 8062

NEW YORK DST CNL CPTRS BFT FD
See CARPENTERS WELFARE BENEFIT FUND OF NEW YORK CITY (INC)

NEW YORK EYE & EAR INFIRMARY
See NEW YORK EYE AND EAR INFIRMARY IPA INC

D-U-N-S 07-102-4277
NEW YORK EYE AND EAR INFIRMARY IPA INC (NY)
NEW YORK EYE & EAR INFIRMARY
310 E 14th St, New York, NY 10003-4201
Tel (212) 979-4000 Founded/Ownrshp 1822
Sales 156.8MM EMP 850
Accts Ernst & Young Us Llp Indianap
SIC 8069 Eye, ear, nose & throat hospital
CEO: D McWilliams Kessler
Chf Path: Steven Mc Cormick
*Pr: James Itsai MD
*CFO: Charles Figliozzi
Trst: Jay Wisnicki
Dir Soc: Geraldine Capanong
Dir Rx: Sui L Ho
Dir Rx: William Stratis
Prac Mgr: Michelle Morris
Off Mgr: Kim Garcia-Kreppein
Nurse Mgr: Teresita Ignacio

D-U-N-S 07-100-8221
NEW YORK FOUNDLING HOSPITAL
590 Ave Of The Americas # 1, New York, NY 10011-2022
Tel (212) 633-9300 Founded/Ownrshp 1869
Sales 120.8MM EMP 1,500
Accts Bdo Usa Llp New York Ny
SIC 8361 8399 Group foster home; Community development groups
Ch Bd: Kenneth R Horner
Pr: Beth Stellato
*CEO: Bill Baccaglini
*COO: Bethany Lampland
*CFO: Kenneth Klum
*Treas: Carol A Barnes
Treas: Rita Meaney
*Sec: Sister Rita Meaney
*V Ch Bd: Robert J Farrell
VP: Jennifer Apple
Assoc Dir: Carmen Rivera

D-U-N-S 07-995-5102
NEW YORK GEOGRAPHIC DISTRICT 11
2750 Throop Ave, Bronx, NY 10469-5327
Tel (718) 519-2620 Founded/Ownrshp 2015
Sales 78.4MM^E EMP 4,688^E
SIC 8211 Public elementary & secondary schools

D-U-N-S 07-995-5127
NEW YORK GEOGRAPHIC DISTRICT 18
1106 E 95th St, Brooklyn, NY 11236-3735
Tel (718) 566-6008 Founded/Ownrshp 2015
Sales 45.1MM^E EMP 2,300^E
SIC 8211 Public elementary & secondary schools

D-U-N-S 10-367-0485 IMP
▲ **NEW YORK HEALTH CARE INC**
20 E Sunrise Hwy Ste 201, Valley Stream, NY 11581-1257
Tel (718) 375-6700 Founded/Ownrshp 1983
Sales 145.9MM^E EMP 1,462
Tkr Sym BBAL Exch OTO
SIC 2834 8082

D-U-N-S 60-531-2412
NEW YORK HOTEL TRADES COUNCIL & HOTEL ASSOC OF NEW YORK
305 W 44th St, New York, NY 10036-5402
Tel (212) 586-6400 Founded/Ownrshp 1949
Sales 112.6MM EMP 825
Accts Armao Llp Garden City Ny
SIC 8011 Medical centers
Ch Bd: Joseph E Spinnato
*Pr: Peter Ward
*CEO: Robert Greenstan
*CFO: Harry Veras
CIO: John Driscoe

D-U-N-S 96-630-5356
NEW YORK HOTEL TRADES COUNCIL AND HOTEL ASSOC OF NYC INC HEALTH BENEFITS FUND
305 W 44th St, New York, NY 10036-5498
Tel (212) 586-6400 Founded/Ownrshp 2011
Sales 355.0MM EMP 19^E
Accts Armao Costa & Ricciardi Cpa S
SIC 8631 Labor unions & similar labor organizations
Prin: Marisol Suarez

D-U-N-S 08-227-3269
NEW YORK INDEPENDENT SYSTEM OPERATOR INC
NYISO
10 Krey Blvd, Rensselaer, NY 12144-9681
Tel (518) 356-6000 Founded/Ownrshp 1997
Sales 174.3MM EMP 500
SIC 4911 Electric services
Pr: Stephen G Whitley
Pr: Karen Antion
Pr: James V Mahoney
COO: Rick Gonzales
COO: Jr Thomas F Ryan
CFO: Kevin Jones
CFO: Mary McGarvey
CFO: Christopher Russell
Ofcr: Jean Dergurahian
Ofcr: Susan Disco
VP: Rana Mukerji
Exec: John Buechler
*Int Pr: Robert A Hiney
Board of Directors: Alfred F Boschulte, Richard J Grossi, Erland E Kailbourne, Thomas F Ryan, Harold N Scherer, Richard E Schuler

D-U-N-S 05-059-4019
NEW YORK INSTITUTE OF TECHNOLOGY INC
NYIT
Northern Blvd, Old Westbury, NY 11568
Tel (516) 686-7530 Founded/Ownrshp 1950
Sales 276.9MM EMP 2,000
Accts Kpmg Llp New York Ny
SIC 8221 Professional schools
Pr: Edward Guiliano PHD
CFO: Leonard Aubrey
VP: Richard Pizer
Assoc Dir: Lisa Moore
Ex Dir: Mohamed Hussein
Off Admin: Josephine Spinelli

D-U-N-S 14-247-1494
NEW YORK INTERCONNECT L L C
(Suby of CABLEVISION) ★
530 5th Ave Fl 6, New York, NY 10036-5119
Tel (212) 382-5300 Founded/Ownrshp 2004
Sales 22.8MM^E EMP 1,889^E
SIC 7311 Advertising agencies
Prin: E Renicker
Mktg Dir: Amy Friedland

NEW YORK KNICKS
See MSGN HOLDINGS LP

NEW YORK LAW JOURNAL
See ALM MEDIA LLC

NEW YORK LIFE
See NAUTILUS GROUP

D-U-N-S 00-698-8307 IMP
NEW YORK LIFE INSURANCE CO
51 Madison Ave Bsmt 1b, New York, NY 10010-1655
Tel (212) 576-7000 Founded/Ownrshp 1845
Sales NA EMP 12,150
SIC 6311 6321 6282 Life insurance carriers; Health insurance carriers; Investment advice
Ch Bd: Ted Mathas
V Ch: Phillip Hluebrand
Pr: Galina Ksendzov
COO: Christopher O Blunt
COO: Paul T Pasteris
COO: Paul Pasteris
CFO: Chris Ashe
CFO: David G Bedard
CFO: Stephen Devito
CFO: John Fleurant
CFO: Mark Grass
CFO: Michael E Sproule
Treas: Jay S Calhoun
Treas: Richard J Witterschein
V Ch Bd: Gary Wendlandt
Bd of Dir: Stephen Carrillo
Bd of Dir: Osbert Hood
Ofcr: David J Castellani
Ofcr: Joel Steinberg
Assoc VP: Robert Tabick
Assoc VP: Aaron Zachko
Board of Directors: Ronald Pressman, Edward D Shirley

NEW YORK LIFE INV MGT GROUP
See NEW YORK LIFE INVESTMENT MANAGEMENT LLC

D-U-N-S 83-565-7966
NEW YORK LIFE INVESTMENT MANAGEMENT LLC
NEW YORK LIFE INV MGT GROUP
(Suby of NEW YORK LIFE INSURANCE CO) ★
30 Hudson St, Jersey City, NJ 07302-4600
Tel (973) 394-3000 Founded/Ownrshp 2000
Sales 254.5MM^E EMP 1,500^E
SIC 6799 Real estate investors, except property operators
Pr: John Kim
*CFO: David G Bedard
CFO: William Gibson
*Ch: Gary Wendlandt
Chf Inves: Jerrold Senser
*Ofcr: Don Salama
Rgnl VP: Nancy Lavin
Rgnl VP: Cheryl Potter
Rgnl VP: Frances Rogell
Rgnl VP: Matthew Silver
Ex VP: Pamela Conroy
Ex VP: Gary Maurer
Ex VP: Paula Rogers
VP: William Anglyn
VP: Robert W Baker
VP: Benjamin Bielawski
VP: Kevin Bopp
VP: Barry Branch
VP: Michael Breyel
VP: Jim Byrne
VP: Michael Citrano

D-U-N-S 14-200-9575
NEW YORK MEDIA LLC
75 Varick St, New York, NY 10013-1917
Tel (212) 508-0700 Founded/Ownrshp 2004
Sales 87.2MM^E EMP 250
SIC 2721 Periodicals
*COO: Katharine Taylor
CFO: Adelina Pepenella
Ex Dir: Leslie Farrand
Ex Dir: Marisa Woocher
Genl Mgr: Michael Silberman
CTO: Larry Chevres
Sftwr Eng: Victor Alvarez
Sftwr Eng: Colin Flanagan
Prd Dir: Ann Amrhein
Prd Mgr: Kaitlin Butz
Prd Mgr: Ruth Monsanto

D-U-N-S 04-190-7486
NEW YORK MEDICAL COLLEGE (INC)
(Suby of TOURO COLLEGE) ★
40 Sunshine Cottage Rd, Valhalla, NY 10595-1524
Tel (914) 594-4100 Founded/Ownrshp 2011
Sales 132.9MM EMP 1,100
SIC 8221 Professional schools
CEO: Edward C Halperin
*Pr: Allan Kadish
*Pr: George Nestler
*CFO: Stephen Piccolo Jr
*VP: Robert W Amler MD
VP: Adam Hammerman
VP: Julie A Kubaska
VP: Madlena Pesheva
VP: Brieyona Reaves
VP: Michael Rogovin
Assoc Dir: Kellie Elson
Assoc Dir: Luis Montes
Assoc Dir: Chao-CHI Tien

D-U-N-S 04-525-5478
■ **NEW YORK MERCANTILE EXCHANGE INC**
NYMEX
(Suby of CME GROUP INC) ★
1 N End Ave Frnt, New York, NY 10282-1101
Tel (212) 299-2000 Founded/Ownrshp 2008
Sales 108.7MM^E EMP 635
SIC 6221 Commodity traders, contracts
Ch Bd: Terrence Duffy
*CEO: Frank Donnahill
Treas: Bruce Rubin
Sr VP: Madeline Boyd
Sr VP: Thomas Lasala
VP: Richard Daniele
VP: John Higgins
Mng Dir: Henrik Hasselknippe
CIO: Sean Carrington
CIO: David Keller
MIS Dir: Elizabeth Venute

D-U-N-S 05-281-0801
NEW YORK METHODIST HOSPITAL (NY)
506 6th St, Brooklyn, NY 11215-3609
Tel (718) 780-3000 Founded/Ownrshp 1881
Sales 732.8MM EMP 3,185
SIC 8062 General medical & surgical hospitals
Ch Bd: John E Carrington
*Pr: Mark J Mundy
*CFO: Edward Zaidberg
*Treas: Robert Rodgers Jr
VP: Lyn Hill
VP: Lauren Yedvab
Dir Teleco: Laura Maturano
Assoc Dir: Myriam Soto
Chf Nrs Of: Lamarcia Parkin
Mtls Dir: Jennele Sinckler
Doctor: Gerardo C Chiricolo

D-U-N-S 16-368-3498
NEW YORK MORTGAGE TRUST INC
275 Madison Ave Fl 32, New York, NY 10016-1116
Tel (212) 792-0107 Founded/Ownrshp 2004
Sales 382.6MM EMP 7^E
Accts Grant Thornton Llp New York
SIC 6798 6163 Real estate investment trusts; Mortgage investment trusts; Mortgage brokers arranging for loans, using money of others
Ch Bd: Steven R Mumma
CFO: Kristine R Nario
VP: Nathan R Reese

D-U-N-S 04-238-0167
NEW YORK OFFICE OF ALCOHOLISM & SUBSTANCE ABUSE SERVICES
(Suby of EXECUTIVE OFFICE OF STATE OF NEW YORK) ★
1450 Western Ave, Albany, NY 12203-3539
Tel (518) 457-2061 Founded/Ownrshp 1999
Sales NA EMP 1,000
SIC 9431 Administration of public health programs;
CEO: Arlene Gonzlez Snchez
*Prin: Jackie Reider

D-U-N-S 80-678-1860
NEW YORK OFFICE OF TEMPORARY & DISABILITY ASSISTANCE
(Suby of EXECUTIVE OFFICE OF STATE OF NEW YORK) ★
40 N Pearl St Ste 100, Albany, NY 12207-2729
Tel (518) 426-2950 Founded/Ownrshp 1922
Sales NA EMP 2,500
SIC 9441 Administration of social & human resources;

NEW YORK PALACE HOTEL, THE
See LOTTE HOTEL NEW YORK PALACE LLC

D-U-N-S 09-883-1530
NEW YORK PAVING INC
3718 Railroad Ave, Long Island City, NY 11101-2033
Tel (718) 482-0780 Founded/Ownrshp 1976
Sales 83.2MM^E EMP 308^E
SIC 1611 Surfacing & paving
Pr: Anthony Bartone
*Treas: Mike Bartone

NEW YORK POST
See NYP HOLDINGS INC

D-U-N-S 07-525-2098 IMP/EXP
NEW YORK POWER AUTHORITY
POWER AUTH OF THE STATE NY
123 Main St, White Plains, NY 10601-3104
Tel (914) 681-6200 Founded/Ownrshp 1914
Sales 2.6MMM EMP 1,700
Accts Kpmg Llp New York Ny
SIC 4911 Generation, electric power; Transmission, electric power
Pr: Gil C Quiniones
*Pr: Rocco Iannarelli

*COO: Edward A Welz
*CFO: Robert F Lurie
*Ofcr: Soubhagya Parija
*Ex VP: Justin E Driscoll
*Sr VP: Jill C Anderson
*Sr VP: Jennifer Faulkner
*Sr VP: James F Pasquale
*Sr VP: Kristine Pizzo
Software D: Arun Alla

D-U-N-S 00-273-8115
NEW YORK PRESBYTERIAN HOSPITAL WEILL CORNELL UNIVERSITY MEDICAL CENTER
525 E 68th St, New York, NY 10065-4870
Tel (212) 746-1754 Founded/Ownrshp 1998
Sales 4.5MMM EMP 5
Accts Ernst & Young Us Llp Indianap
SIC 8011 Offices & clinics of medical doctors
Owner: Lewis Drusin MD
VP: Anita R Golbey
Prac Mgr: Diego Arias
IT Man: Michael Paizzi
Web Prj Mg: Peter Guida
Anesthlgy: Andrew Kim
Plas Surg: Lloyd B Gayle
Doctor: Karen S Carlson
Doctor: Neal Flomenbaum
Genl Couns: Janice K Lunde

D-U-N-S 04-543-3919 IMP
NEW YORK PUBLIC LIBRARY
5th Ave & 42nd St, New York, NY 10018
Tel (212) 592-7400 Founded/Ownrshp 1895
Sales 139.5MM^E EMP 3,645
SIC 8231 Libraries
CEO: Anthony Marx
Treas: Ralph E Hansmann
VP: Jeffrey Roth
Assoc Dir: Greg Cram
*Prin: Davi Offensent
Prin: Kathleen Riegelhaupt
CTO: David M Stur
Pr Dir: Joan Harris
Counsel: Daniel Dex

D-U-N-S 96-958-8149
NEW YORK PUBLIC LIBRARY ASTOR LENOX AND TILDEN FOUNDATIONS
188 Madison Ave, New York, NY 10016-4314
Tel (212) 592-7403 Founded/Ownrshp 2011
Sales 305.0MM EMP 71^E
Accts Kpmg Llp New York Ny
SIC 8231 General public libraries
Dir Sec: Salvatore Magaddino
Opers Mgr: Anne Lehmann
Merch Mgr: Elana Sinsabaugh
Counsel: Bridget Smith

D-U-N-S 01-998-4908
NEW YORK RACING ASSOCIATION INC
11000 Rockaway Blvd Ste 1, South Ozone Park, NY 11420-1004
Tel (718) 641-4700 Founded/Ownrshp 1955
Sales 41.0MM^E EMP 1,400
SIC 7948 Horse race track operation
CFO: Michael Lagamma
*Pr: Charles E Hayward

D-U-N-S 96-269-4787
NEW YORK REIT INC
NYRT
405 Park Ave Fl 14, New York, NY 10022-9406
Tel (212) 415-6500 Founded/Ownrshp 2011
Sales 155.5MM EMP 3
SIC 6531 Selling agent, real estate
Pr: Michael A Happel
*Ch Bd: William M Kahane
COO: Gregory W Sullivan

D-U-N-S 07-101-2413 IMP
NEW YORK SHIPPING ASSOCIATION INC
333 Thornall St Ste 3a, Edison, NJ 08837-2220
Tel (732) 452-7800 Founded/Ownrshp 1939
Sales 263.9MM EMP 40^E
SIC 8611 Shipping & steamship company association
Pr: John Nardi
CFO: Daniel Massaro
Ex VP: Charles Darrell
Off Admin: Lesley Krause
Board of Directors: O A Sweedlund, James A Capo, William A Trok, V Carreras, C De Zego, J Gebhardt, R F Gronda, S Y Kuo, M B Maher, J W Millard, J F Reardon

D-U-N-S 00-393-7364 IMP
NEW YORK SOCIETY FOR RELIEF OF RUPTURED AND CRIPPLED MAINTAINING HOSPITAL FOR
HOSPITAL FOR SPECIAL SURGERY
535 E 70th St, New York, NY 10021-4823
Tel (212) 606-1000 Founded/Ownrshp 1987
Sales 811.8MM EMP 3,350
SIC 8069 Specialty hospitals, except psychiatric; Orthopedic hospital
CEO: Louis Shapiro
V Ch: Emil Mosbacher
Trst: Charles P Coleman
Trst: Henry U Harris
Trst: Charlton Reynders
Trst: Henry A Wilmerding
Trst: Kendrick R Wilson
*Ex VP: Lisa A Goldstein
*Ex VP: Stacey L Malakof
Assoc Dir: Rebekah Grote
Adm Dir: Mary McDermott

NEW YORK SPORTS CLUB
See TOWN SPORTS INTERNATIONAL INC

NEW YORK STATE ASSEMBLY
See LEGISLATIVE OFFICE STATE OF NY

D-U-N-S 87-923-0431
NEW YORK STATE CATHOLIC HEALTH PLAN INC
FIDELIS CARE NEW YORK
9525 Queens Blvd Fl 8, Rego Park, NY 11374-4511
Tel (888) 343-3547 Founded/Ownrshp 1993
Sales 5.3MMM EMP 1,625
Accts Lb Deloitte Tax Llp Jericho
SIC 8011 Health maintenance organization
Pr: Mark Lane
*Pr: Rev Patrick J Frawley
Pr: Maryjean Valigorsky
*COO: Father Patrick Frawley
*CFO: Thomas Halloran
CFO: Ronald Weingartner
*Ex VP: David P Thomas
Dir IT: Don Martin
IT Man: Dave Walters
Mktg Mgr: George Rodriguez
Mktg Mgr: Chris White

D-U-N-S 94-791-2531
NEW YORK STATE COURT OFFICERS ASSOCIATION SECURITY BENEFIT FUND
321 Broadway Ste 600, New York, NY 10007-3636
Tel (212) 608-1124 Founded/Ownrshp 1994
Sales NA EMP 1,600
Accts Gould Kobrick & Schlapp Pc Ne
SIC 6371 Union funds
Pr: Dennis Quirk

D-U-N-S 80-678-0730
NEW YORK STATE DEPARTMENT OF MOTOR VEHICLES
(Subsy of EXECUTIVE OFFICE OF STATE OF NEW YORK) ★
6 Empire State Plz Rm 321, Albany, NY 12223-1000
Tel (518) 474-0835 Founded/Ownrshp 1960
Sales NA EMP 3,482
SIC 9621 Regulation, administration of transportation;

D-U-N-S 78-087-5423
NEW YORK STATE DIVISION OF CRIMINAL JUSTICE SERVICES
(Subsy of EXECUTIVE OFFICE OF STATE OF NEW YORK) ★
80 S Swan St, Albany, NY 12210-8001
Tel (518) 457-9896 Founded/Ownrshp 2013
Sales NA EMP 1,987^E
SIC 9211
Genl Mgr: Ron Dickens

D-U-N-S 12-412-2123
NEW YORK STATE DIVISION OF HOUSING AND COMMUNITY RENEWAL
(Subsy of EXECUTIVE OFFICE OF STATE OF NEW YORK) ★
38-40 State St, Albany, NY 12207-2837
Tel (518) 473-2517 Founded/Ownrshp 2002
Sales NA EMP 1,056^E
SIC 9531 Housing programs;
Snr Mgr: Paul Fuller

D-U-N-S 04-186-6497
NEW YORK STATE ELECTRIC & GAS CORP
18 Link Dr, Binghamton, NY 13904-3222
Tel (607) 762-7200 Founded/Ownrshp 2015
Sales 1.6MMM^E EMP 2,648
SIC 4911 4924 4923

D-U-N-S 07-328-9634
NEW YORK STATE ENVIRONMENTAL FACILITIES CORP
625 Broadway, Albany, NY 12207-2942
Tel (518) 486-9267 Founded/Ownrshp 2005
Sales 528.7MM EMP 12^E
Accts Uhy Llp Albany New York
SIC 8742 Compensation & benefits planning consultant
Pr: David Sterman

D-U-N-S 15-086-6374
NEW YORK STATE INDUSTRIES FOR DISABLED INC
NYSID
11 Columbia Cir, Albany, NY 12203-5156
Tel (518) 463-9706 Founded/Ownrshp 1975
Sales 214.8MM EMP 50
Accts Uhy Advisors Ny Inc Albany
SIC 8322 Association for the handicapped
CEO: Ronald P Romano
*Pr: Larry Barker
*Ch: James Flannagan
*Ch: Edward Lokomski
Treas: Henry Cohen
*Treas: Jack Manganello
*V Ch Bd: Tim Gieselsman
VP: Tim Mott
VP: Mary Shaheen
IT Man: Frank Heuer
Board of Directors: Frank Coco, Kevin Crosley, Mary Jo Thorn, Carolina Cordero Dyer, Donaldrsiegel

D-U-N-S 80-678-0623
NEW YORK STATE OFFICE OF MENTAL HEALTH
(Subsy of EXECUTIVE OFFICE OF STATE OF NEW YORK) ★
44 Holland Ave, Albany, NY 12208-3411
Tel (518) 474-4403 Founded/Ownrshp 1978
Sales NA EMP 17,000
SIC 9431 Mental health agency administration, government;
CFO: Martha Schaefer
*CFO: Martha Schefer
Exec: Roberto Cerda
Dir: Jeremy Darman
Dir Rx: Gerald M Engel
Admn Mgr: Rose Celestin
Genl Mgr: Susan Penn
Genl Mgr: Lee Vanapeldorn
IT Man: Conrad Dalton
IT Man: Tim Shaer
Pr Dir: Leesa Rademacher

D-U-N-S 80-678-2033
NEW YORK STATE OFFICE OF STATE COMPTROLLER
COMPTROLLER OF THE STATE OF NY
(Subsy of EXECUTIVE OFFICE OF STATE OF NEW YORK) ★
110 State St, Albany, NY 12207-2027
Tel (518) 474-4044 Founded/Ownrshp 1797
Sales NA EMP 2,131
SIC 9311 Controllers' office, government;
Pr: Alan G Hevesi
Ofcr: Jane Hall

D-U-N-S 13-818-7539 IMP
NEW YORK STATE UNITED TEACHERS
NYSUT
(Subsy of N E A) ★
800 Troy Schenectady Rd, Latham, NY 12110-2424
Tel (518) 213-6000 Founded/Ownrshp 1972
Sales 152.8MM EMP 550
Accts Bonadio & Co Llp Albany Ny
SIC 8631 Labor unions & similar labor organizations
Pr: Richard C Iannuzzi
*Sec: Lee Cutler
Bd of Dir: Mary Schneider
*Ex VP: Andrew Pallotta
*VP: Kathleen M Donahue
*VP: Maria Neira
Ex Dir: Thomas Anapolis
CIO: Ralph Watson
Netwrk Eng: Anthony Kovel
Mktg Dir: Sheryl Allen
Pr Dir: Michelle Di Benedetto

D-U-N-S 79-119-5311
■ **NEW YORK STOCK EXCHANGE LLC**
(Subsy of NYSE GROUP INC) ★
11 Wall St Fl 6, New York, NY 10005-1905
Tel (212) 656-3000 Founded/Ownrshp 2005
Sales 577.6MM^E EMP 1,503^E
SIC 6231 Security & commodity exchanges
CEO: Duncan L Niederauer

D-U-N-S 00-131-5613 IMP
▲ **NEW YORK TIMES CO** (NY)
WIRECUTTER, THE
620 8th Ave, New York, NY 10018-1618
Tel (212) 556-1234 Founded/Ownrshp 1896
Sales 1.5MMM EMP 3,560^E
Tkr Sym NYT Exch NYS
SIC 2711 4832 4833 7383 7375 Newspapers, publishing & printing; Radio broadcasting stations; Television broadcasting stations; News feature syndicate; Information retrieval services
Pr: Mark Thompson
Ch Bd: Arthur Sulzberger Jr
Pr: Scott Heekin-Canedy
Pr: Mary Jacobus
Pr: David Vail
CFO: James M Follo
Ch: Arthur O Sulzberger
V Ch Bd: Michael Golden
Chf Mktg O: Alyse Myers
Ofcr: Danny Hakim
Ex VP: Kenneth A Richieri
Grp VP: Virginia French
Sr VP: R Anthony Benten
Sr VP: Yasmin Namini
Sr VP: Martin A Nisenholtz
Sr VP: David K Norton
Sr VP: John M Obrien
Sr VP: Tracy Raiser
Sr VP: Dennis L Stern
VP: Alexis Buryk
VP: Jay Fogarty
Board of Directors: Rebecca Van Dyck, Raul E Cesan, Robert E Denham, Steven B Green, Carolyn D Greenspon, Dara Khosrowshahi, James A Kohlberg, Ellen R Marram, Brian P McAndrews, Doreen A Toben

D-U-N-S 00-110-7176
■ **NEW YORK TIMES REGIONAL NEWSPAPER GROUP** (DE)
(Subsy of WIRECUTTER) ★
2339 Beville Rd, Daytona Beach, FL 32119-8720
Tel (212) 556-4673 Founded/Ownrshp 1878, 2011
Sales 89.1MM^E EMP 2,900
SIC 2711 Newspapers
Pr: Lynn Matthews
*CFO: Stephen Dewitt
*Ex VP: P Steven Ainsley

D-U-N-S 04-196-8306 IMP
NEW YORK UNIVERSITY
N Y U
70 Washington Sq S, New York, NY 10012-1019
Tel (212) 998-1212 Founded/Ownrshp 1831
Sales 8.2MMM^E EMP 21,000^E
Accts Pricewaterhousecoopers Llp Ne
SIC 8221 University
Pr: John Sexton
*Ch Bd: Richard Foley
V Ch: William R Bekley
V Ch: Kenneth G Lanone
Trst: Eric J Gleacher
Trst: Norman Goodman
Trst: Charles Kushner
Trst: Henry R Silveman
Trst: John L Vogestein
Trst: Martin J Wygod
Trst: Mariuccia Zerilli-Marim
Trst: Mortimer B Zuckerman
Top Exec: Paula De Stefano
*Ex VP: Bob Berne
*Ex VP: Martin S Dorph
Ex VP: Carolyn Keller
*Ex VP: Alison Leary
Ex VP: Jacob J Lew
Ex VP: Reginald Odom
Sr VP: Bonnie S Brier
VP: Ashlee Ford

D-U-N-S 82-999-9213
NEW YORK UNIVERSITY
NYU COLLEGE OF NURSING
(Subsy of N Y U) ★
250 Park Ave S Fl 6, New York, NY 10003-1402
Tel (212) 998-5813 Founded/Ownrshp 2009
Sales 5.9MMM EMP 30
Accts Pricewaterhousecoopers Llp Ne
SIC 8621 Nursing association
Pr: John Sexton
Dir Opers: Barbara Bricoli
Doctor: Jacqueline E Friedman MD

D-U-N-S 17-282-1936
NEW YORK UNIVERSITY MEDICAL CENTER
NYU LANGONE MEDICAL CENTER
550 1st Ave, New York, NY 10016-6402
Tel (646) 929-7870 Founded/Ownrshp 1980
Sales 206.1MM^E EMP 30,000
SIC 8011 General & family practice, physician/surgeon
CEO: Robert I Grossman
Bd of Dir: Priyanka Chugh
VP: Kevin Kirchen
Dir Rad: Andrew Litt
Dir Rad: John Loh
*Prin: Itzhak Kronzon
Orthpdst: Judith Brook
Anesthlgy: Wanda A Chin
Anesthlgy: Kevin Gingrich
Anesthlgy: Jung Kim
Anesthlgy: Daniel O'Neill

NEW YORK ZOOLOGICAL SOCIETY
See WILDLIFE CONSERVATION SOCIETY

D-U-N-S 96-452-8231
NEW YORK-PRESBYTERIAN FUND INC
525 E 68th St, New York, NY 10065-4870
Tel (212) 297-4356 Founded/Ownrshp 2010
Sales 385.5MM EMP 4^E
Accts Ernst & Young Us Llp New Yo
SIC 8011 Medical centers
CEO: Phyllis Lantos

D-U-N-S 82-564-0097 IMP
NEW YUNG WAH TRADING LLC
311 Richardson St, Brooklyn, NY 11222-5709
Tel (718) 388-3322 Founded/Ownrshp 1993
Sales 107.0MM EMP 52
Accts Siew And Company Llc Brookly
SIC 5141 Groceries, general line
Genl Mgr: Jessi Zheng

D-U-N-S 60-426-2311
NEW-CELL LLC
CELLCOM
(Subsy of NSIGHTTELESERVICES) ★
1580 Mid Valley Dr, De Pere, WI 54115-8193
Tel (920) 617-7800 Founded/Ownrshp 1986
Sales 97.4MM^E EMP 370
SIC 4812 Cellular telephone services
Pr: Patrick Riordan
*Ex VP: Robert H Riordan
VP: Dan Fabry
Comm Man: Jodi Delahaut
IT Man: Bubb Lidke
Mktg Dir: Al Dummer
Sls Dir: Judy Maki
Snr Mgr: Corey O'Connell

D-U-N-S 14-416-1841
NEW-COM INC
6600 Amelia Earhart Ct B, Las Vegas, NV 89119-3535
Tel (702) 642-3331 Founded/Ownrshp 1984
Sales 98.0MM^E EMP 340
SIC 7353 Heavy construction equipment rental
Pr: Greg Jpaulk
CFO: Janell Cassell
*Sec: Brady Stevens

NEW-INDY CONTAINERBOARD
See NEW-INDY ONTARIO LLC

NEW-INDY CONTAINERBOARD
See NEW-INDY OXNARD LLC

D-U-N-S 07-852-4909
NEW-INDY ONTARIO LLC
NEW-INDY CONTAINERBOARD
(Subsy of NEW-INDY CONTAINERBOARD LLC)
5100 Jurupa St, Ontario, CA 91761-3618
Tel (909) 390-1055 Founded/Ownrshp 2012
Sales 345.0MM EMP 110
SIC 2621 Paper mills
CEO: Richard Hartman
*VP: Mike Conkey

D-U-N-S 07-852-4922 IMP
NEW-INDY OXNARD LLC
NEW-INDY CONTAINERBOARD
(Subsy of NEW-INDY CONTAINERBOARD LLC)
5936 Perkins Rd, Oxnard, CA 93033-9044
Tel (805) 986-3881 Founded/Ownrshp 2012
Sales 345.0MM EMP 224
SIC 2621 Paper mills
CEO: Richard Hartman
*VP: Mike Conkey
Plnt Mgr: Rudy Rehbein

D-U-N-S 07-118-3214
NEWARK BETH ISRAEL MEDICAL CENTER INC
CHILDREN'S HOSPITAL OF NEW JER
201 Lyons Ave, Newark, NJ 07112-2027
Tel (973) 926-7000 Founded/Ownrshp 1996
Sales 542.0MM EMP 3,000^E
Accts Withumsmithbrown Pc Morristow
SIC 8062 General medical & surgical hospitals
Pr: Paul Mertz
*COO: Kenneth Tyson
*CFO: Veronica Zichner
VP: Bruce Brener
Dir Rx: Craig Dolan
Mng Dir: Jennifer L Costello
Dir Sec: Tom Adams
Off Mgr: Rhonda Lubin
CIO: Nina Diquollo
CIO: Angelo Schittone
IT Man: Joyce Longo

D-U-N-S 96-935-2140
NEWARK CITY SCHOOLS
621 Mount Vernon Rd, Newark, OH 43055-4615
Tel (740) 670-7000 Founded/Ownrshp 2011

Sales 10.2MM[E] *EMP* 1,046[E]
Accts Kennedy Cottrell Richard Gaha
SIC 8211 Public elementary & secondary schools
Bd of Dir: Michael Blowers
Bd of Dir: Warren Weber
VP: Tim Carr
Pr Dir: Seth Roy
Teacher Pr: Barbara Quackenbush

D-U-N-S 11-471-2842 IMP/EXP
■ NEWARK CORP
NEWARK ELEMENT14
(*Suby of* NEWARK ELECTRONICS CORP) ★
300 S Riverside Plz # 2200, Chicago, IL 60606-6765
Tel (773) 784-5100 *Founded/Ownrshp* 1970
Sales 525.1MM *EMP* 834
SIC 5065 Electronic parts & equipment
Pr: Dan Hill
Treas: Paul M Barlak
Sr VP: Barry Litwin
VP: Paul Buckley
VP: Colin Campbell
VP: John Campbell
VP: Joseph R Daprile
VP: Dianne Kibbey
VP: David Macaluso
VP: Paula Manley
VP: Thomas Mayfield
**VP:* Steven Webb

D-U-N-S 01-924-1129 IMP
■ NEWARK ELECTRONICS CORP
(*Suby of* PREMIER FARNELL CORP) ★
300 S Riverside Plz, Chicago, IL 60606-6613
Tel (773) 784-5100 *Founded/Ownrshp* 1995
Sales 525.1MM *EMP* 834
SIC 5065 5063 5961 Electronic parts & equipment; Electrical apparatus & equipment; Catalog & mail-order houses
Pr: Dan Hill
Treas: Paul M Barlak
Ofcr: Larisa Miles
Sr VP: Susan Fischer
Sr VP: Paula Manley
Sr VP: Patrick Milbourne
**VP:* Jospeh R Daprile
VP: Thomas Mayfield
**VP:* Steven Webb
Genl Mgr: Jaya Farnela
CTO: Jim Ure

NEWARK ELEMENT14
See NEWARK CORP

D-U-N-S 08-565-3186 IMP/EXP
NEWARK GROUP INC
NEWARK RCYCLED PPRBD SOLUTIONS
20 Jackson Dr, Cranford, NJ 07016-3609
Tel (908) 276-4000 *Founded/Ownrshp* 2015
Sales 694.9MM[E] *EMP* 1,700
SIC 2679 2631

D-U-N-S 00-218-7342
NEWARK MORNING LEDGER CO
SUNDAY STAR LEDGER
(*Suby of* ADVANCE PUBLICATIONS, INC.)
1 Gateway Ctr Ste 1100, Newark, NJ 07102-5323
Tel (973) 392-4141 *Founded/Ownrshp* 1916
Sales 196.7MM[E] *EMP* 1,200
SIC 2711 Newspapers, publishing & printing
Pr: Donald E Newhouse
Pr: Patrick Riccio
VP: Brad Young
Exec: James Loughlin
Genl Mgr: John Dennan
Genl Mgr: Mark Newhouse
Dir IT: Gene Rizzo
Netwrk Eng: Michael Montenegro
Assoc Ed: Tom Curran
Board of Directors: Samuel I Newhouse Jr

D-U-N-S 04-074-0334
NEWARK PUBLIC SCHOOLS
2 Cedar St Ste 1, Newark, NJ 07102-3015
Tel (973) 733-7333 *Founded/Ownrshp* 1995
Sales 493.2MM[E] *EMP* 8,061
SIC 8211 Public elementary & secondary schools
Bd of Dir: Rashon Hasan
Ex Dir: Rita Salley
CIO: Alejandro Echevarria
Sfty Dirs: Manuel Quinones
Teacher Pr: Laurette Asante

NEWARK RCYCLED PPRBD SOLUTIONS
See NEWARK GROUP INC

D-U-N-S 07-367-0689
NEWARK-WAYNE COMMUNITY HOSPITAL
(*Suby of* ROCHESTER GENERAL HEALTH SYSTEM) ★
1200 Driving Park Ave, Newark, NY 14513-1090
Tel (315) 332-2022 *Founded/Ownrshp* 2005
Sales 95.5MM *EMP* 800
Accts Fust Charles Chambers Llp Syr
SIC 8062 General medical & surgical hospitals
Pr: Annette Leahy
Ofcr: Mark Klyczek
Dir Rad: Yvonne Mactaggart
Dir Pat Ac: John Midolo

D-U-N-S 08-469-1781 IMP/EXP
NEWAY PACKAGING CORP
1973 E Via Arado, Rancho Dominguez, CA 90220-6102
Tel (602) 454-9000 *Founded/Ownrshp* 1977
Sales 84.7MM[E] *EMP* 89
SIC 5113 5084 Shipping supplies; Packaging machinery & equipment
Pr: Russell E Freebury
**VP:* Sarah D Giles-Bell
Brnch Mgr: Susan Freebury
Opers Mgr: Susan McCarthy
Sales Exec: Robert Hayward

NEWAYS
See MAPLE MOUNTAIN GROUP INC

D-U-N-S 15-349-1329
NEWBAY MEDIA LLC
(*Suby of* WICKS GROUP OF COMPANIES LLC (DE CORP)) ★
28 E 28th St Fl 12, New York, NY 10016-7959
Tel (212) 378-0400 *Founded/Ownrshp* 2006
Sales 89.0MM[E] *EMP* 165
SIC 4833 Television broadcasting stations
CEO: Steve Palm
**CFO:* Paul Mastronardi
**Ex VP:* Adam Goldstein
**Ex VP:* Carmel King
VP: Robert Ames
VP: Ed Hecht
VP: John Morr
**VP:* Eric Trabb
Exec: Dade Hayes
Mng Dir: Mark Burton
IT Man: Ileana Vega

D-U-N-S 01-256-7822
NEWBERRY COUNTY SCHOOL DISTRICT
3419 Main St, Newberry, SC 29108-4145
Tel (803) 321-2600 *Founded/Ownrshp* 1889
Sales 66.8MM *EMP* 1,000
Accts Greene Finney & Horton Llp
SIC 8211 Public elementary & secondary schools; Vocational high school
Dir Sec: Wesley Palmore
Psych: Christy Lantz

NEWBERRY TECHNICAL SERVICES
See NTS INC

D-U-N-S 79-119-3428
■ NEWBEVCO INC
(*Suby of* NATIONAL BEVERAGE CORP) ★
1 N University Dr, Plantation, FL 33324-2038
Tel (954) 581-0922 *Founded/Ownrshp* 1996
Sales 704.7MM[E] *EMP* 1,200
SIC 2086 Bottled & canned soft drinks
Pr: Nick A Caporella
**Pr:* Joseph G Caporella

D-U-N-S 10-348-6486
NEWBRIDGE BANCORP
1501 Highwoods Blvd # 400, Greensboro, NC 27410-2050
Tel (336) 369-0900 *Founded/Ownrshp* 1982
Sales NA *EMP* 449
SIC 6022
Pr: Pressley A Ridgill
CFO: Ramsey K Hamadi
Ofcr: David P Barksdale
Ofcr: William W Budd Jr
Ofcr: Brenda M Houser
Ex VP: Robin S Hager
Sr VP: Coretta J Bigelow
Sr VP: Craig L Call
Sr VP: Ronald E Coleman
Sr VP: Nicholas A Daves
Sr VP: Philip G Gibson
Sr VP: Andrew G McDowell
Sr VP: Charles N Reynolds
Sr VP: Kathy V Richardson
Sr VP: Ronald W Sink
Sr VP: Edward C Sopp
Sr VP: Pamela J Varela
Sr VP: Joseph T Wallace
VP: Marcus Smith
Exec: Linda Maynard
Board of Directors: E Reid Teague, Michael S Albert, Richard A Urquhart III, Robert A Boyette, G Alfred Webster, C Arnold Britt, Julius S Young Jr, Robert C Clark, J David Branch, Alex A Diffey Jr, Donald P Johnson, Joseph H Kinnaney, Michael S Patterson, Mary E Rittling

D-U-N-S 07-158-0971
NEWBRIDGE BANK
(*Suby of* NEWBRIDGE BANCORP) ★
1501 Highwoods Blvd, Greensboro, NC 27410-2050
Tel (336) 248-6500 *Founded/Ownrshp* 1949, 1983
Sales NA *EMP* 385
SIC 6022

D-U-N-S 09-948-6847
NEWBURGH CITY SCHOOL DISTRICT
NEW BURGH ENLARGED CY SCHL DST
124 Grand St, Newburgh, NY 12550-7301
Tel (845) 563-3400 *Founded/Ownrshp* 1825
Sales 120.6MM[E] *EMP* 3,356[E]
SIC 8211 Public elementary & secondary schools; Public elementary school; Public junior high school; Public senior high school
Pr: Dawn M Fucheck
**VP:* Pamela R Freeman-Resc
Off Mgr: Dale Salisbury

D-U-N-S 62-608-6342
■ NEWBURYPORT HOLDINGS INC
DEXTRYS
(*Suby of* EPAM SYSTEMS INC) ★
4 Middle St Ste 226, Newburyport, MA 01950-2766
Tel (781) 246-8234 *Founded/Ownrshp* 2016
Sales 85.8MM[E] *EMP* 1,277
SIC 7371 Computer software development
Pr: William A Murphy
CFO: Joseph Hartnett
VP: Rajesh Bashyam

D-U-N-S 09-414-7266
NEWCASTLE CAPITAL MANAGEMENT LP
200 Crescent Ct Ste 1400, Dallas, TX 75201-7826
Tel (317) 704-6000 *Founded/Ownrshp* 1999
Sales 108.0MM[E] *EMP* 700[E]
SIC 6799 Investors
Ch Bd: Mark E Schwarz

D-U-N-S 78-426-1401
▲ NEWCASTLE INVESTMENT CORP
1345 Avenue Of America Flr 46, New York, NY 10105
Tel (212) 798-6100 *Founded/Ownrshp* 1998
Sales 95.8MM *EMP* 4,600[E]
Tkr Sym NCT *Exch* NYS
SIC 6798 Real estate investment trusts
Pr: Sarah L Watterson
**Ch Bd:* Wesley R Edens
COO: Sara A Yakin
CFO: Lawrence A Goodfield Jr
Doctor: William Gadsden

D-U-N-S 36-447-0294
NEWCOMB ENTERPRISES INC JOHN
BURGER KING
910 Triangle St, Blacksburg, VA 24060-7716
Tel (540) 552-7718 *Founded/Ownrshp* 1989
Sales 28.1MM[E] *EMP* 1,000
SIC 5812 Fast-food restaurant, chain
Pr: John W Newcomb

D-U-N-S 05-000-6196
NEWCOMB OIL CO LLC
FIVE STAR FOOD MART
901 Withrow Ct, Bardstown, KY 40004-2672
Tel (502) 348-3961 *Founded/Ownrshp* 1924
Sales 140.0MM[E] *EMP* 850
SIC 5411 5171 Convenience stores, chain; Petroleum bulk stations
Prin: William D Newcomb
Dist Mgr: Robert Bouland
Opers Mgr: Janet Osborne
Mktg Mgr: Ruth Seward
Sls Mgr: Kenny Fletcher

D-U-N-S 00-535-7769
NEWCOR INC
BAY CITY DIVISION
715 South Blvd E Ste 101, Rochester Hills, MI 48307-5362
Tel (248) 537-0014 *Founded/Ownrshp* 2003
Sales 104.3MM[E] *EMP* 750
SIC 3714 Motor vehicle transmissions, drive assemblies & parts; Gears, motor vehicle; Drive shafts, motor vehicle; Transmission housings or parts, motor vehicle
CEO: David Segal

D-U-N-S 16-966-9616 IMP/EXP
NEWEGG INC
NEWEGG.COM
17560 Rowland St, City of Industry, CA 91748-1114
Tel (626) 271-9700 *Founded/Ownrshp* 2005
Sales 2.5MMM *EMP* 1,072
SIC 5734 Computer & software stores; Computer peripheral equipment
CEO: Danny Lee
V Ch: Fred Chang
Pr: Bob Bellack
COO: Edison Chih
COO: James Wu
COO: Jing Wu
CFO: David King
Ofcr: Soren A Mills
Ex VP: Craig Hayes
Ex VP: Shih C Lee
VP: Ron L Bester
VP: Robert Chang
VP: Jonathan Han
VP: Grace Hsiao
Exec: Cathy Lee
Exec: Rick Quiroga

NEWEGG.COM
See NEWEGG INC

NEWELL BRANDS
See JARDEN CORP

D-U-N-S 16-140-3852 IMP
▲ NEWELL BRANDS INC
221 River St, Hoboken, NJ 07030-5891
Tel (201) 610-6600 *Founded/Ownrshp* 1903
Sales 5.9MMM *EMP* 17,200
Tkr Sym NWL *Exch* NYS
SIC 3089 3469 2591 3951 3999 3546 Plastic kitchenware, tableware & houseware; Household cooking & kitchen utensils, porcelain enameled; Household cooking & kitchen utensils, metal; Drapery hardware & blinds & shades; Pens & mechanical pencils; Markers, soft tip (felt, fabric, plastic, etc.); Hair & hair-based products; Power-driven handtools
CEO: Michael B Polk
**Ch Bd:* Michael T Cowhig
Pr: Mark S Tarchetti
CFO: Ralph Nicoletti
Ofcr: Richard B Davies
Ex VP: William A Burke
Sr VP: James L Cunningham III
Board of Directors: Steven J Strobel, Ian G H Ashken, Michael A Todman, Thomas E Clarke, Raymond G Viault, Kevin C Conroy, Scott S Cowen, Domenico De Sole, Martin E Franklin, Jose Ignacio Perez-Lizaur, Cynthia A Montgomery, Christopher D O'leary

D-U-N-S 00-523-8183 IMP/EXP
■ NEWELL OPERATING CO
(*Suby of* NEWELL BRANDS INC) ★
29 E Stephenson St, Freeport, IL 61032-4235
Tel (815) 235-4171 *Founded/Ownrshp* 1903
Sales 783.2MM[E] *EMP* 9,800
SIC 3365 3991 3089 2591 3965 3596 Cooking/kitchen utensils, cast aluminum; Paint rollers; Paint brushes; Trays, plastic; Shade, curtain & drapery hardware; Shade pulls, window; Window shade rollers & fittings; Needles, hand or machine; Hooks, crochet; Bathroom scales
Pr: Mark D Ketchum
**Pr:* William A Burke III
CFO: Danniel Connel
**VP:* Dale L Matschullat
Sls Mgr: Jesus Cital

NEWELL PAPER CO OF COLUMBUS
See JACKSON PAPER CO

D-U-N-S 96-921-4782 EXP
NEWELL RECYCLING OF ATLANTA LLC
1359 Central Ave, Atlanta, GA 30344-4946
Tel (404) 766-1621 *Founded/Ownrshp* 1995
Sales 142.1MM[E] *EMP* 240
SIC 4953

D-U-N-S 06-066-8837
NEWFIELD CONSTRUCTION INC (CT)
225 Newfield Ave, Hartford, CT 06106-3635
Tel (860) 953-1477 *Founded/Ownrshp* 1976, 1977
Sales 83.9MM *EMP* 50
Accts Whittlesey & Hadley Pc Har
SIC 1541 1542 Industrial buildings, new construction; Renovation, remodeling & repairs: industrial buildings; Commercial & office building, new construction; Commercial & office buildings, renovation & repair
Pr: Damien T Davis
**VP:* Paul W Davis
VP Opers: Peter Etzel

D-U-N-S 19-706-7267 IMP
▲ NEWFIELD EXPLORATION CO
4 Waterway Square Pl # 100, The Woodlands, TX 77380-2764
Tel (281) 210-5100 *Founded/Ownrshp* 1988
Sales 1.5MMM *EMP* 1,111
Tkr Sym NFX *Exch* NYS
SIC 1311 Crude petroleum production; Natural gas production
Ch Bd: Lee K Boothby
COO: Gary D Packer
CFO: Lawrence S Massaro
Sr VP: George T Dunn
Sr VP: John H Jasek
VP: Stephen C Campbell
VP: Eric A Hillerman
VP: Joseph B Johnson
VP: Valerie A Mitchell
VP: Matthew R Vezza
VP: James T Zernell
Board of Directors: Pamela J Gardner, Steven W Nance, Roger B Plank, Thomas G Ricks, Juanita M Romans, John W Schanck, J Terry Strange, James Kent Wells

D-U-N-S 12-237-5892
■ NEWFIELD EXPLORATION GULF COAST INC
(*Suby of* NEWFIELD EXPLORATION CO) ★
363 N Sam Houston Pkwy E # 2020, Houston, TX 77060-2424
Tel (713) 243-3100 *Founded/Ownrshp* 2002
Sales 40.5MM[E] *EMP* 1,500
SIC 1311 Crude petroleum production; Natural gas production
Ch Bd: Thomas M Hamilton
**Pr:* Lee K Boothby
**COO:* David R Henderson
**CFO:* Richard S Langdon
**Treas:* Susan G Riggs
**Ex VP:* Larry S Massaro
**Ex VP:* Gary D Packer
**Sr VP:* George T Dunn
VP: Tracey E Coats

D-U-N-S 02-080-2802
■ NEWFIELD EXPLORATION MID-CONTINENT INC
(*Suby of* NEWFIELD EXPLORATION CO) ★
101 E 2nd St, Tulsa, OK 74103-3203
Tel (918) 582-2690 *Founded/Ownrshp* 2001
Sales 231.0MM[E] *EMP* 327
SIC 1311 Crude petroleum production; Natural gas production
CEO: Lee K Boothby
**Ex VP:* Larry S Massaro
**Ex VP:* Gary D Packer
**Ex VP:* Terry W Rathert
**Sr VP:* George T Dunn
Board of Directors: Lee K Boothby

D-U-N-S 08-836-2330
■ NEWFIELD PRODUCTION CO
(*Suby of* NEWFIELD EXPLORATION CO) ★
1001 17th St Ste 2000, Denver, CO 80202-2035
Tel (303) 893-0102 *Founded/Ownrshp* 2004
Sales 169.8MM[E] *EMP* 486[E]
SIC 1311 Crude petroleum & natural gas
CEO: Lee K Boothby
**Pr:* Stephen C Campbell
**Pr:* Daryll T Howard
**COO:* Gary D Packer
**CFO:* Larry S Massaro
**Ex VP:* Terry W Rathert
**Sr VP:* George T Dunn
VP: William War
Board of Directors: Lee K Boothby

D-U-N-S 96-343-7418
NEWGISTICS INC
(*Suby of* LITTLEJOHN & CO LLC) ★
2700 Via Fortuna Ste 300, Austin, TX 78746-7996
Tel (512) 225-6000 *Founded/Ownrshp* 2013
Sales 151.3MM[E] *EMP* 479
SIC 4731 Freight transportation arrangement
CEO: William Razzouk
COO: Trent Brown
**COO:* Todd Everett
**CFO:* Michael Twomey
CFO: Ben Wade
**Sr VP:* Ken Johnson
Sr VP: Benoit Robinot
Sr VP: Edward Stashluk
VP: Brandie Clevenger
VP: Mike Stevens
Exec: Richard Baun
Exec: Paul Gates
Board of Directors: Robert Rosenblatt, Andrea Weiss

D-U-N-S 01-727-1313 IMP
NEWKIRK ELECTRIC ASSOCIATES INC
1875 Roberts St, Muskegon, MI 49442-6094
Tel (231) 722-1691 *Founded/Ownrshp* 1972
Sales 108.5MM *EMP* 400
Accts Rehmann Robson Llc Muskegon
SIC 1731 1629 8711 Electrical work; Power plant construction; Engineering services
Pr: Theodore Anton
**VP:* Jim Anton
Div Mgr: Mark Lengyel

D-U-N-S 02-436-3517
NEWKIRK HOLDING CO INC
ACE HARDWARE
320 West Blvd, Rapid City, SD 57701-2671
Tel (605) 342-4840 *Founded/Ownrshp* 1928, 1978
Sales 88.1MM[E] *EMP* 500

SIC 5251 Hardware
Ch Bd: Robert Mead
**Pr:* Craig Bradshaw
Genl Mgr: Wallace Bork
Genl Mgr: Bryan Rice

D-U-N-S 00-514-3987 IMP/EXP
NEWLY WEDS FOODS INC
4140 W Fullerton Ave, Chicago, IL 60639-2198
Tel (773) 489-7000 *Founded/Ownrshp* 1932
Sales 2.0MM *EMP* 3,100
SIC 2099 Bread crumbs, not made in bakeries; Sugar powdered from purchased ingredients; Seasonings & spices
Pr: Charles T Angell
CFO: Brian Johnson
CFO: John Seely
Sr VP: Kent Bergene
**Sr VP:* John J Seely
**VP:* Sharon Angell
VP: Donald Harr
VP: Bruce Leshinski
VP: Chris Swain
Genl Mgr: Jack Conway
Genl Mgr: John Norton

D-U-N-S 03-331-7785 IMP
NEWMAN LUMBER CO
11367 Reichold Rd, Gulfport, MS 39503-6022
Tel (228) 604-2178 *Founded/Ownrshp* 1947
Sales 111.7MME *EMP* 800
SIC 5031 Lumber: rough, dressed & finished
Pr: Dug Newman
**CEO:* Cynthia N Bergin
**CFO:* Roianne Gutierrez
Treas: N Gutierrez
**VP:* Douglas Newman
Exec: Roy Newman

D-U-N-S 07-302-3939
NEWMAN MEMORIAL HOSPITAL FOUNDATION
NEWMAN REGIONAL HEALTH
1201 W 12th Ave, Emporia, KS 66801-2504
Tel (620) 343-6800 *Founded/Ownrshp* 1922
Sales 89.2MME *EMP* 575
Accts Wendling Noe Nelson Johnson Ll
SIC 8062 5047 8011 Hospital, medical school affiliated with nursing & residency; Medical & hospital equipment; Hospital equipment & supplies; Clinic, operated by physicians
CEO: Robert Wright
Ch Bd: Deanne Korsak
**CEO:* John Rossseld
**CFO:* Holly French
**Treas:* William O Barnes
Bd of Dir: Jodi Heermann
Dir Inf Cn: Jami White
Dir Lab: Barb Haag
Assoc Dir: Kevin Stock
Chf Nrs Of: Denisa Ketterman
**Prin:* Nancy Wells

NEWMAN REGIONAL HEALTH
See NEWMAN MEMORIAL HOSPITAL FOUNDATION

D-U-N-S 61-426-4752 IMP
NEWMAN TECHNOLOGY INC
(*Suby of* SANKEI GIKEN CO.,LTD.)
100 Cairns Rd, Mansfield, OH 44903-8990
Tel (419) 525-1856 *Founded/Ownrshp* 1987
Sales 224.1MME *EMP* 1,200E
SIC 3714 3751 Motor vehicle parts & accessories; Mufflers (exhaust), motor vehicle; Motorcycle accessories
Pr: Shigeyuki Handa
**Ex VP:* Yukihisa Murata
**Sr VP:* Dick Pacelli
**Sr VP:* Stephen Rourke
Admn Mgr: Bill Nagel
CIO: Dennis Laffey
Ql Cn Mgr: Mike Blevins
Ql Cn Mgr: Paul Harper
Snr Mgr: Tim Berry

D-U-N-S 10-235-6888
NEWMAR CORP
355 Delaware St, Nappanee, IN 46550-9453
Tel (574) 773-7791 *Founded/Ownrshp* 1968
Sales 293.0MME *EMP* 1,840
SIC 3716 3792 Motor homes; Travel trailers & campers
Pr: Mahlon Miller
**VP:* Mahlon A Miller
VP: Michael O'Connell
VP: Phil Stilley
**Prin:* Richard Parks
VP Admn: Gary Shuder
Dir IT: Kevin Bogan
Sfty Dirs: Dennis Ramer
S&M/VP: John Sammut
Mktg Mgr: Shannon Stover
Manager: Jeff Lake

D-U-N-S 07-684-9009
■ NEWMARK & CO REAL ESTATE INC
NEWMARK GRUBB KNIGHT FRANK
(*Suby of* BGC PARTNERS INC) ★
125 Park Ave, New York, NY 10017-5529
Tel (212) 372-2000 *Founded/Ownrshp* 2011
Sales 1.0MMM *EMP* 2,250
SIC 6531 Real estate brokers & agents
CEO: Barry M Gosin
V Ch: Arthur Rosenbloom
V Ch: Brian Waterman
Pr: David A Falk
**Pr:* James D Kuhn
Pr: Carol Miles
Pr: Don Roberts
Pr: Andrew G Tracey
**COO:* Joseph I Rader
**CFO:* Michael J Rispoli
**Ch:* Jeffrey R Gural
Bd of Dir: Tom McChesney
Assoc VP: Mark F Gleason
Ex VP: Steven Adamczyk
Ex VP: Michael Arnold
Ex VP: William Cohen
Ex VP: Bradford H Fletcher
Ex VP: Mitch Friedel
Ex VP: Phil Giunta
Ex VP: Jay Luchs
Ex VP: Doug Nicholson

NEWMARK GRUBB KNIGHT FRANK
See NEWMARK & CO REAL ESTATE INC

D-U-N-S 15-222-7067 IMP/EXP
▲ NEWMARKET CORP
330 S 4th St, Richmond, VA 23219-4350
Tel (804) 788-5000 *Founded/Ownrshp* 2004
Sales 2.1MMM *EMP* 1,979E
Tkr Sym NEU *Exch* NYS
SIC 2869 2899 2841 2865 Industrial organic chemicals; Corrosion preventive lubricant; Oil treating compounds; Soap & other detergents; Cyclic crudes & intermediates
Ch Bd: Thomas E Gottwald
CFO: Brian D Paliotti
Treas: Cameron D Warner Jr
Ofcr: Bruce R Hazelgrove III
Sr VP: Newton Perry
VP: Jim Leary
VP: M Rudolph West
Exec: Steven Mayer
Dir IT: Stephen Petersen
S&M/VP: Rob Shama
Board of Directors: Phyllis L Cothran, Mark M Gambill, Bruce C Gottwald, Patrick D Hanley, H Hiter Harris III, James E Rogers

NEWMARKET INTERNATIONAL, INC.
See AMADEUS HOSPITALITY AMERICAS INC

D-U-N-S 04-278-6921
■ NEWMONT GOLD CO
(*Suby of* NEWMONT MINING CORP) ★
6363 S Fiddlers Green Cir, Greenwood Village, CO 80111-5011
Tel (303) 863-7414 *Founded/Ownrshp* 2001
Sales NA *EMP* 3,600
SIC 1041 Gold ores mining
CEO: Gary J Goldberg
**Ch Bd:* Ronald C Cambre

NEWMONT MINING
See NEWMONT USA LIMITED

D-U-N-S 00-698-8414 IMP
▲ NEWMONT MINING CORP
6363 S Fiddlers Green Cir # 800, Greenwood Village, CO 80111-5011
Tel (303) 863-7414 *Founded/Ownrshp* 1921
Sales 7.7MMM *EMP* 15,600
Tkr Sym NEM *Exch* NYS
SIC 1041 1021 Gold ores mining; Gold ores processing; Copper ore milling & preparation
Pr: Gary J Goldberg
Ch Bd: Vincent A Calarco
COO: Chris J Robison
CFO: Nancy K Buese
Treas: Thomas Mahoney
Ex VP: Elaine Dorward-King
Ex VP: John A Dow
Ex VP: Randy Engel
Ex VP: Stephen P Gottesfeld
Ex VP: Brian Hill
Ex VP: Guy Lansdown
Ex VP: Scott P Lawson
Ex VP: William N Macgowan
Sr VP: Carlos S Cruz
Sr VP: Glenn Culpepper
Sr VP: Tom Palmer
Sr VP: Grigore Simon
Sr VP: Trent Tempel
VP: Michael Byrne
VP: Mary Donnelly
VP: Rich Herold
Board of Directors: Gregory H Boyce, Bruce R Brook, J Kofi Bucknor, Joseph A Carrabba, Noreen Doyle, Veronica M Hagen, Jane Nelson, Julio M Quintana

D-U-N-S 12-250-2870
■ NEWMONT USA LIMITED
NEWMONT MINING
(*Suby of* NEWMONT MINING CORP) ★
6363 Sout Fidd Gree Cir, Greenwood Village, CO 80111
Tel (303) 863-7414 *Founded/Ownrshp* 2000
Sales 57.6MME *EMP* 1,000
SIC 1041 1021 Gold ores mining; Copper ore mining & preparation
Treas: Thomas Mahoney
**CFO:* Russell D Ball
Ofcr: Debbie Robinson
VP: Thomas Enos
Exec: David Grander
Dir Surg: John Gundersen
Comm Dir: Michie Ogura-Huerta
Prgrm Mgr: Alex Young
Genl Mgr: Scott Santti
CIO: John Huber

NEWPAGE
See LUKE PAPER CO

D-U-N-S 19-753-3446 IMP/EXP
■ NEWPAGE CORP
(*Suby of* VERSO CORP) ★
8540 Gander Creek Dr, Miamisburg, OH 45342-5439
Tel (877) 855-7243 *Founded/Ownrshp* 2014
Sales 593.8MME *EMP* 1,500
SIC 2621 2611 Fine paper; Uncoated paper; Pulp manufactured from waste or recycled paper
CEO: Mike Jackson
CFO: Jay A Epstein
Ch: Mark A Angelson
Treas: Timothy Nusbaum
Ofcr: Daniel A Clark
Ex VP: James C Tyrone
Sr VP: J Mark Lukacs
Sr VP: Barry Nelson
Sr VP: David L Santez
VP: Mike Entz
VP: Michael L Marziale
VP: Moller Palmi
VP: Randal Romberio
VP: Russ Wanke
VP: Paul Yearling

D-U-N-S 79-892-9514 EXP
NEWPAGE ENERGY SERVICES LLC
8540 Gander Creek Dr, Miamisburg, OH 45342-5439
Tel (877) 855-7243 *Founded/Ownrshp* 2004
Sales 228.8MME *EMP* 6,000
SIC 2672 2621 2611 Coated & laminated paper; Paper mills; Uncoated paper; Pulp mills

D-U-N-S 82-619-3612
■ NEWPAGE GROUP INC
(*Suby of* CERBERUS CAPITAL MANAGEMENT LP) ★
8540 Gander Creek Dr, Miamisburg, OH 45342-5439
Tel (937) 242-9500 *Founded/Ownrshp* 2007
Sales 3.5MMME *EMP* 6,000E
SIC 2671 Packaging paper & plastics film, coated & laminated
Pr: George F Martin
**Ch:* Chan W Galbato
Treas: Tim Nusbaum
Treas: Randal Spence
**Ex VP:* James C Tyrone
**Sr VP:* Daniel A Clark
**Sr VP:* Douglas K Cooper
**Sr VP:* Jay A Epstein
Exec: Randal Romberio

D-U-N-S 60-273-9877
■ NEWPAGE HOLDING CORP
(*Suby of* NEWPAGE GROUP INC) ★
8540 Gander Creek Dr, Miamisburg, OH 45342-5439
Tel (877) 855-7243 *Founded/Ownrshp* 2011
Sales 680.4MME *EMP* 6,000
SIC 2621 2672 2611 Fine paper; Coated & laminated paper; Pulp mills
Pr: George F Martin
CFO: Matthew L Jesch
**CFO:* David J Prystash
**Ex VP:* James C Tyrone
**Sr VP:* Daniel A Clark
**Sr VP:* Laszlo M Lukacs
**VP:* Douglas K Cooper
**VP:* Jay A Epstein
**VP:* David L Santez
CIO: Christine Walroth
IT Man: Jon Lafreniere
Board of Directors: Robert M Armstrong, Chan W Galbato, Ronald C Kesselman, Julian Markby, Robert L Nardelli, Lenard B Tessler, Raymond H Wechsler, Alexander M Wolf, George J Zahringer III

D-U-N-S 94-554-3770 IMP/EXP
NEWPAGE WISCONSIN SYSTEM INC
111 W Jackson St, Wisconsin Rapids, WI 54495
Tel (715) 422-3111 *Founded/Ownrshp* 2000
Sales NA *EMP* 1,200
SIC 2621 2611 2653 7011

D-U-N-S 60-660-2175 IMP
■ NEWPARK DRILLING FLUIDS LLC
NDF
(*Suby of* NEWPARK RESOURCES INC) ★
21920 Merchants Way, Katy, TX 77449-6834
Tel (281) 754-8600 *Founded/Ownrshp* 2007
Sales 293.9MME *EMP* 860
SIC 5169 5172 4953 Drilling mud; Petroleum products; Refuse systems
Pr: Bruce C Smith
**Treas:* Brian M Feldott
**VP:* Mark J Airola
VP: Tim Armand
**VP:* Joseph L Gocke
**VP:* Gregg S Piontek
**VP:* Pravin Tampi
**VP:* Phil Vollands
**VP:* Doug White
CIO: Sergio Juan
Dir IT: Larry Douglas
Board of Directors: Paul L Howes, Bruce C Smith

D-U-N-S 00-287-6977
■ NEWPARK MATS & INTEGRATED SERVICES LLC (TX)
(*Suby of* NEWPARK RESOURCES INC) ★
9320 Lkeside Blvd Ste 100, The Woodlands, TX 77381
Tel (281) 362-6800 *Founded/Ownrshp* 2007
Sales 102.5MME *EMP* 300
SIC 1389 Construction, repair & dismantling services; Excavating slush pits & cellars; Oil field services
CEO: Paul L Howes
**Pr:* Jeff L Juergens
**CFO:* Gregg Piontek
Ex VP: Bruce C Smith
**Sr VP:* Mark J Airola
VP: WT Ballantine
VP: Eric Wingerter
Tech Mgr: David Spencer
Opers Mgr: Brent Barnard

D-U-N-S 00-697-0982 IMP
▲ NEWPARK RESOURCES INC
9320 Lkeside Blvd Ste 100, The Woodlands, TX 77381
Tel (281) 362-6800 *Founded/Ownrshp* 1932
Sales 676.8MM *EMP* 1,980
Accts Deloitte & Touche Llp Houston
Tkr Sym NR *Exch* NYS
SIC 1389 4959 4953 2273 Construction, repair & dismantling services; Excavating slush pits & cellars; Testing, measuring, surveying & analysis services; Cleaning wells; Environmental cleanup services; Non-hazardous waste disposal sites; Recycling, waste materials; Mats & matting
Pr: Paul L Howes
Pr: William D Moss
CFO: Gregg S Piontek
Ex VP: Bruce C Smith
Sr VP: Mark J Airola
VP: Frank Lyon
Exec: JW Cross
Dir Risk M: Veronica C Mozell
Genl Mgr: Carlos Bianconi
Snr Ntwrk: Duane Street
IT Man: Nanda Kumar
Board of Directors: David C Anderson, Anthony J Best, G Stephen Finley, Roderick A Larson, James W McFarland, Gary L Warren

NEWPORT BRASS
See BRASSTECH INC

D-U-N-S 13-580-1467 IMP/EXP
NEWPORT CH INTERNATIONAL LLC
1100 W Town And Country R, Orange, CA 92868-4662
Tel (714) 572-8881 *Founded/Ownrshp* 2003
Sales 187.6MME *EMP* 50
SIC 5093 Waste paper
VP: Clark Hahne
CFO: Mike Milby

D-U-N-S 00-914-5814 IMP/EXP
■ NEWPORT CORP
(*Suby of* MKS INSTRUMENTS INC) ★
1791 Deere Ave, Irvine, CA 92606-4814
Tel (949) 863-3144 *Founded/Ownrshp* 1938, 2016
Sales 602.6MM *EMP* 2,480E
Accts Deloitte & Touche Llp Costa M
SIC 3821 3699 3827 3826 Worktables, laboratory; Laser systems & equipment; Optical instruments & lenses; Mirrors, optical; Prisms, optical; Analytical optical instruments; Laser scientific & engineering instruments
Pr: Robert Phillippy
VP: Christopher Palmer
Netwrk Mgr: Mark Carroll
Snr Mgr: Sudheer Kota
Snr Mgr: Scott White

NEWPORT HARBOR HIGH SCHOOL
See NEWPORT MESA UNIFIED SCHOOL DISTRICT

D-U-N-S 79-180-3158
NEWPORT HEALTH CARE CORP
NEWPORT HOSPITAL
11 Friendship St, Newport, RI 02840-2209
Tel (401) 846-6400 *Founded/Ownrshp* 1983
Sales 90.8MM *EMP* 700E
Accts Kpmg Llp Providence Rhode Is
SIC 8062 6531 6732 General medical & surgical hospitals; Real estate agents & managers; Charitable trust management
CEO: Timothy J Babineau
**Pr:* Arthur Sampson
CFO: Frank Burn
CFO: Ann Kashmanian
**Ex VP:* Cathy Duquette
**Sr VP:* Kenneth E Arnold
**Sr VP:* Carole M Cotter
**Sr VP:* Richard J Goldberg
VP: Lynn Francis
VP: M Francis
Dir Rx: Paul Parchesky

NEWPORT HOSPITAL
See NEWPORT HEALTH CARE CORP

D-U-N-S 07-567-8177
NEWPORT HOSPITAL
11 Friendship St Ste 1, Newport, RI 02840-2299
Tel (401) 846-6400 *Founded/Ownrshp* 2004
Sales 90.8MM *EMP* 700
Accts Kpmg Llp Boston Ma
SIC 8062 General medical & surgical hospitals
Pr: Arthur Sampson

D-U-N-S 08-117-3080
NEWPORT MESA UNIFIED SCHOOL DISTRICT
NEWPORT HARBOR HIGH SCHOOL
2985 Bear St Ste A, Costa Mesa, CA 92626-4300
Tel (714) 424-5000 *Founded/Ownrshp* 1966
Sales 93.2M *EMP* 3,000
Accts E Wayne Lytle Dba Pay Oll
SIC 8211 Public combined elementary & secondary school
Pr: Dana Black
Bd of Dir: Dave Brooks
Bd of Dir: Walt Davenport
Bd of Dir: Judy A Franco
Bd of Dir: Karen Yelsey
Trst: Judy Franco
Exec: Brenda Quinn
Off Mgr: Erik Pannizzo
Off Mgr: Denise Potterton
Off Admin: Christine Holguin
Off Admin: Elizabeth Sachs

D-U-N-S 19-307-5876
NEWPORT NEWS PUBLIC SCHOOL DISTRICT
12465 Warwick Blvd, Newport News, VA 23606-3041
Tel (757) 591-4500 *Founded/Ownrshp* 1898
Sales 315.7MM *EMP* 4,300
Accts Cherry Bekaert Llp Richmond
SIC 8211 Public elementary & secondary schools
Ch: Jeff Stodghill
**Ch:* Carlton Ashby
Dir Sec: Jeff Nelson
Psych: Amanda Levoy
Snr Mgr: Margaret Owens

NEWPORT NEWS SHIPBUILDING
See NORTHROP GRUMMAN NEWPORT NEWS INC

D-U-N-S 00-212-3871
NEWPORT RICHEY HOSPITAL INC (FL)
MEDICAL CENTER OF TRINITY
9330 State Road 54, Trinity, FL 34655-1808
Tel (727) 834-4000 *Founded/Ownrshp* 1972, 2002
Sales 180.3MM *EMP* 111E
SIC 8011 Medical centers
CEO: Leigh Massenpill
**CFO:* Alex Romanchik

D-U-N-S 01-418-5499
NEWPORT TELEVISION LLC
460 Nichols Rd Ste 250, Kansas City, MO 64112-2047
Tel (816) 751-0200 *Founded/Ownrshp* 2007
Sales 48.9MME *EMP* 2,000E
SIC 7922 Television program, including commercial producers
Sls Dir: David Diprosa

D-U-N-S 02-450-8000
■ NEWQUEST LLC
(*Suby of* HEALTHSPRING INC) ★
44 Vantage Way Ste 300, Nashville, TN 37228-1550
Tel (615) 291-7000 *Founded/Ownrshp* 2000
Sales NA *EMP* 1,749E

SIC 6321 Health insurance carriers
CEO: Herbert Fritch

NEWS & SUN SENTINEL COMPANY
See SUN-SENTINEL CO INC

D-U-N-S 06-196-3567
■ NEWS AMERICA MARKETING IN-STORE SERVICES LLC (ID)
SMART SOURCE
(*Suby of* NEWS CORP) ★
20 Westport Rd Ste 320, Wilton, CT 06897-4550
Tel (203) 563-6600 *Founded/Ownrshp* 1971, 2013
Sales 210.9MM^E *EMP* 20,000
SIC 7319 Display advertising service
COO: Gene Klein
Ex VP: Steve Ross
VP: Christopher Blanco
VP: Kathy McNamara
Natl Sales: Patrick Reynolds
Sls Mgr: Kayleigh Walls

D-U-N-S 00-319-4875 IMP
■ NEWS AND OBSERVER PUBLISHING CO (NC)
GOLD LEAF PUBLISHERS
(*Suby of* SACRAMENTO BEE) ★
215 S Mcdowell St, Raleigh, NC 27601-2929
Tel (919) 829-4500 *Founded/Ownrshp* 1894, 1995
Sales 115.3MM^E *EMP* 1,000
SIC 2711 2741 2721 2752 Newspapers, publishing & printing; Commercial printing & newspaper publishing combined; Job printing & newspaper publishing combined; Shopping news: publishing & printing; Magazines: publishing & printing; Commercial printing, lithographic
Pr: Orage Quarles III
* *VP:* George McCanless
IT Man: Mark Williams
Web Dev: Alexandra Porter
Opers Mgr: Deborah Jackson
Prd Mgr: Matt Long
Sales Exec: Pam Corey

D-U-N-S 07-882-6673
▲ NEWS CORP
1211 Ave Of The Americas, New York, NY 10036-8701
Tel (212) 416-3400 *Founded/Ownrshp* 2012
Sales 8.2MMM *EMP* 25,000^E
Tkr Sym NWS *Exch* NGS
SIC 2711 2731 7375 Newspapers; Newspapers, publishing & printing; Book publishing; On-line data base information retrieval
CEO: Robert J Thomson
* *Ch Bd:* K Rupert Murdoch
* *Ch Bd:* Lachlan K Murdoch
CFO: Bedi Ajay Singh
Chf Cred: David B Pitofsky
Bd of Dir: James R Murdoch
Ex VP: James E Kennedy
VP: Aashish Chandarana
VP: Joanne Dowdell
VP: Robert Ennis
VP: Lou Ermilio
VP: Marc Heller
VP: Raju Narisetti
VP: Trista Reiser
VP: Linden Slaugh
VP: Paula Wardynski
Board of Directors: Jose Maria Aznar, Natalie Bancroft, Peter L Barnes, Elaine L Chao, John Elkann, Joel I Klein, James R Murdoch, Ana Paula Pessoa

NEWS GROUP THE
See GREAT PACIFIC NEWS CO INC

D-U-N-S 94-238-2433
NEWS GROUP INC
LONE STAR PERIODICALS
5130 Comm Pkwy, San Antonio, TX 78218
Tel (210) 226-9333 *Founded/Ownrshp* 2005
Sales 90.8MM^E *EMP* 140
SIC 5192 5994 Books, periodicals & newspapers; Magazine stand
CEO: Michael Korenberg
* *Pr:* John Seebach
* *VP:* Rod Bergen
VP: Mike Cullingham
Off Mgr: Joy Neimer
CTO: Mike Manero

NEWS GROUP-SOUTHEAST, THE
See GREAT ATLANTIC NEWS LLC

D-U-N-S 85-903-0512
NEWS MEDIA CORP
211 E Il Route 38, Rochelle, IL 61068-2303
Tel (815) 562-2061 *Founded/Ownrshp* 1979
Sales 90.9MM^E *EMP* 570
SIC 2711 Newspapers
Pr: John C Tompkins
* *Treas:* R Michael Tompkins
* *VP:* Bret Yager
Div Mgr: Keith Cerny
Genl Mgr: Amy Bartlett
Sls&Mrk Ex: Pat Duffy

D-U-N-S 00-522-4126
■ NEWS PUBLISHING CO INC
(*Suby of* MCCLATCHY CO) ★
600 W Main St, Fort Wayne, IN 46802-1408
Tel (260) 461-8444 *Founded/Ownrshp* 1917, 1904
Sales 113.3MM^E *EMP* 601
SIC 2711 Newspapers
Pr: Scott Mc Gehee
CFO: John Kovatch

D-U-N-S 08-167-4830 IMP
NEWS WORLD COMMUNICATIONS INC
WASHINGTON TIMES NEWSPAPER
(*Suby of* ONE UP ENTERPRISES INC) ★
3600 New York Ave Ne, Washington, DC 20002-1947
Tel (202) 636-3000 *Founded/Ownrshp* 1977
Sales 106.9MM^E *EMP* 1,000
SIC 2711 Newspapers, publishing & printing
Pr: Thomas McDevitt
* *Treas:* Keith Cooperrider
Mktg Dir: Tom McDevitt

D-U-N-S 00-406-6585 IMP
NEWS-JOURNAL CORP
NEW SMYRNA DAILY JOURNAL
901 6th St, Daytona Beach, FL 32117-8099
Tel (386) 252-1511 *Founded/Ownrshp* 1927
Sales 111.5MM^E *EMP* 875
SIC 2711 Newspapers
Pr: Herbert M Davidson Jr
* *Treas:* Marc L Davidson
Sr VP: Leween Jones
* *VP:* Georgia M Kaney
* *VP:* David R Kendall
Off Mgr: Patricia Winston
CIO: Karen M Coy
Advt Dir: Kathy Coughlin
Sls Mgr: Jamie Brown

D-U-N-S 00-713-4190
NEWS-PRESS & GAZETTE CO INC (MO)
NPG NEWSPAPERS
825 Edmond St, Saint Joseph, MO 64501-2737
Tel (816) 271-8500 *Founded/Ownrshp* 1951
Sales 166.6MM^E *EMP* 1,025
SIC 2711

D-U-N-S 07-925-2140
NEWSCYCLE SOLUTIONS INC
7900 Intl Dr Ste 800, Minneapolis, MN 55425
Tel (651) 639-0662 *Founded/Ownrshp* 2013
Sales 133.2MM^E *EMP* 555^E
SIC 7371 Computer software development & applications
CEO: Preston McKenzie
COO: Scott Roessler
CFO: Lynn Danko
VP: Carsten B Pedersen
Dir Risk M: Dan Paulus
CTO: Talin Bingham
VP Mktg: Peter G Marsh

D-U-N-S 05-278-2497
NEWSDAY LLC
NEWSDAY MEDIA GROUP
(*Suby of* CABLEVISION) ★
235 Pinelawn Rd, Melville, NY 11747-4250
Tel (631) 843-4050 *Founded/Ownrshp* 1940, 2008
Sales 269.1MM^E *EMP* 1,228
SIC 2711 Newspapers, publishing & printing
Pr: Patrick Dolan
Treas: Richard Jones
VP: Edward Bushey
VP: David Kniffin
VP: Paul Likins
Brnch Mgr: Patricia Burne
IT Man: Andrew R McCaffey
Opers Mgr: Ed Bushey
Sls&Mrk Ex: Liza Burby
Doctor: David Laffer
Assoc Ed: Bill McTernan

NEWSDAY MEDIA GROUP
See NEWSDAY LLC

D-U-N-S 05-020-6288 IMP
NEWSMAX MEDIA INC
750 Park Of Commerce Dr # 100, Boca Raton, FL 33487-3650
Tel (561) 686-1165 *Founded/Ownrshp* 1998
Sales 103.5MM *EMP* 275
Accts Daszkal Bolton Llp Sunrise F
SIC 2721 2741 Periodicals; Miscellaneous publishing
Pr: Christopher Ruddy
* *COO:* Brian Todd
VP: Kevin Byrnes
QI Cn Mgr: Michelle Baker

NEWSOUTH COMMUNICATIONS
See NUVOX INC

D-U-N-S 00-434-1434
NEWSPAPER HOLDING INC
JOHNSTOWN TRIBUNE DEMOCRAT
(*Suby of* COMMUNITY NEWSPAPER HOLDINGS INC) ★
425 Locust St, Johnstown, PA 15901-1817
Tel (814) 532-5102 *Founded/Ownrshp* 1902, 1999
Sales 262.3MM^E *EMP* 2,150
SIC 2711 Newspapers, publishing & printing
Pr: Donna Barrett
* *Treas:* Mike Reed
* *VP:* Keith Blevins

D-U-N-S 16-891-7552
▲ NEWSTAR FINANCIAL INC
500 Boylston St Ste 1250, Boston, MA 02116-3891
Tel (617) 848-2500 *Founded/Ownrshp* 2004
Sales NA *EMP* 122^E
Tkr Sym NEWS *Exch* NGS
SIC 6162 Mortgage bankers & correspondents; Loan correspondents; Mortgage bankers
Ch Bd: Timothy J Conway
CFO: John K Bray
Treas: John J Frishkopf
Chf Inves: Daniel D McCready
VP: David Teszler
Mng Dir: Mark Four
Board of Directors: Charles N Bralver, Bradley E Cooper, Brian L P Fallon, Frank R Noonan, Maureen P O'hara, Richard E Thornburgh

D-U-N-S 01-473-3005
▲ NEWTEK BUSINESS SERVICES INC
SMALL BUSINESS AUTHORITY, THE
1981 Marcus Ave Ste C130, New Hyde Park, NY 11042-2030
Tel (212) 356-9500 *Founded/Ownrshp* 1998
Sales NA *EMP* 337^E
Tkr Sym NEWT *Exch* NGM
SIC 6153 7374 4813 Working capital financing; Data processing service;
Ch Bd: Barry Sloane
Pr: William Bayer
Pr: Joe Canul
Pr: Harold Gartner
Pr: Bruce Hopkins
Pr: Richard Rebetti
Pr: Gary T Taylor
CFO: Dave Hertz
CFO: Michael Holden
Treas: Dean Choksi
* *Chf Cred:* Matthew G Ash
Ofcr: Joseph Delap
* *Ofcr:* Peter Downs
* *Ofcr:* Michael A Schwartz
* *Ex VP:* Craig J Brunet
* *Ex VP:* Jennifer Eddelson
Ex VP: Timothy C Ihlefeld
Sr VP: Dian F Gamble
Sr VP: Neil Wolfe
VP: Talisa Barnes
VP: Camille Bastian
Board of Directors: Sam Kirschner, Salvatore Mulia, Richard J Salute

D-U-N-S 08-037-6530
NEWTON BIOFUELS LLC
127 Crystal Ave, Newport Beach, CA 92662-1311
Tel (949) 697-3088 *Founded/Ownrshp* 2016
Sales 294.0MM *EMP* 6
SIC 2911 Diesel fuels
CEO: Geoffrey Hirson

D-U-N-S 07-593-7110
NEWTON COUNTY BOARD OF EDUCATION
NEWTON COUNTY SCHOOLS
2109 Newton Dr Ne, Covington, GA 30014-2459
Tel (770) 787-1330 *Founded/Ownrshp* 1972
Sales 85.2MM^E *EMP* 2,500
Accts Russell W Hinton Cpa Cgfm
SIC 8211 Public elementary & secondary schools
Psych: Marge Paz

NEWTON COUNTY SCHOOLS
See NEWTON COUNTY BOARD OF EDUCATION

D-U-N-S 07-989-3881
NEWTON COUNTY SCHOOLS
2109 Newton Dr Ne, Covington, GA 30014-2459
Tel (770) 787-1330 *Founded/Ownrshp* 2015
Sales 93.0MM^E *EMP* 2,355^E
SIC 8211 Public elementary & secondary schools
Treas: Craig Dinn
Dir IT: Geveva Guthrie
Pr Dir: Sherri Davis-Vineyard
Schl Brd P: Abigail Coggins
Teacher Pr: Nyree Sanders
Psych: Janelle McClasky
HC Dir: Darren Berry

D-U-N-S 06-857-2544 EXP
NEWTON MEMORIAL HOSPITAL INC
(*Suby of* MORRISTOWN MEMORIAL HOSPITAL) ★
175 High St, Newton, NJ 07860-1099
Tel (973) 383-2121 *Founded/Ownrshp* 1985
Sales 106.6MM^E *EMP* 805^E
Accts Parentebeard Llc Wilkesbarre
SIC 8062 General medical & surgical hospitals
Pr: Tom Senker
Pr: Catherine Enright
* *COO:* Sean O'Rourke
CFO: Robert Ragona
Treas: Robert E McCrackn
Exec: Sean Mulch
Exec: Joe Zweig
Dir OR: Sharon Sefcik
Dir Risk M: Stephanie Dubanowitz
Mng Dir: Daya Nadarajah
CIO: Charles Schwenz

D-U-N-S 09-219-1428
NEWTON PUBLIC SCHOOL DISTRICT
100 Walnut St, Newton, MA 02460-1314
Tel (617) 559-6000 *Founded/Ownrshp* 1858
Sales 77.6MM^E *EMP* 1,900^E
SIC 8211 Public elementary & secondary schools; Public elementary school; Public junior high school; Public senior high school
Genl Mgr: Elaine Sterzin
MIS Dir: Eileen Keane
IT Man: Susan Dzikowski
Psych: Lindsey Hogan
Psych: Betsy Juarez

D-U-N-S 07-658-1768
NEWTON WELLESLEY HOSPITAL CORP
(*Suby of* PARTNERS HEALTHCARE SYSTEM INC) ★
2014 Washington St, Newton, MA 02462-1607
Tel (617) 243-6000 *Founded/Ownrshp* 1981
Sales 422.9MM *EMP* 2,500^E
SIC 8062 General medical & surgical hospitals
Pr: Kerry Russell Watson
Chf Path: Dennis J Feen
* *Pr:* Patrick Jordan
CFO: Dan Gross
CFO: Marlene Ward
Treas: Michael Jellinek
Sr VP: Edward D Mueller
VP: Joan Archer
VP: Elaine Bridge
VP: Brian Odea
Dir OR: Susan Duffy-Smith
Dir Lab: Robert Page

D-U-N-S 12-101-4658
NEWTON-WELLESLEY HEALTH CARE SYSTEM INC
2014 Washington St, Newton, MA 02462-1607
Tel (617) 243-6000 *Founded/Ownrshp* 2006
Sales 173.5MM *EMP* 31
SIC 8741 7374 6512 Hospital management; Data processing & preparation; Commercial & industrial building operation
Pr: John P Bihldorff
Treas: Ronald E Bartlett
Ofcr: Martha Farrell
CIO: Scott Maclean
Dir QC: Paulette Diangi

D-U-N-S 02-992-5488
NEWTRON BEAUMONT LLC
(*Suby of* NEWTRON HOLDINGS LLC) ★
1905 Industrial Park Rd, Nederland, TX 77627-3125
Tel (409) 727-6344 *Founded/Ownrshp* 2011
Sales 101.4MM *EMP* 600
SIC 1731 Electrical work
Pr: Mike Defee

D-U-N-S 10-719-2858
NEWTRON GROUP L L C
8183 W El Cajon Dr, Baton Rouge, LA 70815-8093
Tel (225) 927-8921 *Founded/Ownrshp* 1982
Sales 436.3MM *EMP* 2,000^E
Accts Hannis T Bourgeois Llp Baton
SIC 1731 Electrical work
CEO: Newton B Thomas
Pr: John Schempf
CFO: Tami H Misuraca
Rgnl Mgr: Mark Richardson
Off Mgr: Monai Ruppert
Site Mgr: Kevin Ganucheau
VP Mktg: Duff Schempf

D-U-N-S 07-920-0732
NEWTRON HOLDINGS LLC
(*Suby of* NEWTRON GROUP L L C) ★
8183 W El Cajon Dr, Baton Rouge, LA 70815-8093
Tel (225) 927-8921 *Founded/Ownrshp* 2013
Sales 130.9MM *EMP* 800^E
Accts Hannis T Bourgeois Llp Baton
SIC 1731 Electrical work
CFO: Tami H Misuraca

NEWYORK-PRESBYTERIAN HOSPITAL
See NEW YORK AND PRESBYTERIAN HOSPITAL

D-U-N-S 07-274-4592
NEWYORK-PRESBYTERIAN/QUEENS
5645 Main St, Flushing, NY 11355-5045
Tel (718) 670-2000 *Founded/Ownrshp* 1992
Sales 669.9MM *EMP* 2,380
Accts Lb Ernst & Young Us Llp India
SIC 8062 General medical & surgical hospitals
Pr: Stephen S Mills
* *CFO:* Kevin Ward
Assoc VP: Adam Weinstein
* *Ex VP:* Stephen Rimar
* *Ex VP:* John E Sciortino
* *Sr VP:* Kevin J Ward
* *Sr VP:* Michaelle Williams
Doctor: Stephen Lee
Pharmcst: Sandra Chang

NEX-TECH
See RURAL TELEPHONE SERVICE CO INC

D-U-N-S 94-316-9482 IMP/EXP
NEXAIR LLC
1385 Corporate Ave, Memphis, TN 38132-1723
Tel (901) 396-5050 *Founded/Ownrshp* 1940
Sales 277.7MM^E *EMP* 314^E
Accts Thompson Dunavant Plc Memphis
SIC 5169 5084 7699 7359 Industrial gases; Industrial machinery & equipment; Welding equipment repair; Equipment rental & leasing
CEO: M Kevin McEniry
CFO: Scott Heppel
CFO: Milton Lovell
Treas: John Coker
Bd of Dir: Mike Dlugach
Ex VP: Steve Atkins
VP: Larry Odom
VP: Becky Reed
IT Man: Jeff Corkran
IT Man: Angie Garbuzinski
Opers Mgr: Marcus Adcock

D-U-N-S 01-072-7712 IMP/EXP
NEXANS USA INC
(*Suby of* NEXANS PARTICIPATIONS)
39 2nd St Nw, Hickory, NC 28601-6104
Tel (828) 323-2660 *Founded/Ownrshp* 2000
Sales 198.5MM^E *EMP* 850
SIC 3357 3661 3678 Communication wire; Telephones & telephone apparatus; Electronic connectors
Pr: Stephen Hall
* *Pr:* Yvon Raak
* *Treas:* Kevin Stinson
Genl Mgr: Carlos Sanchez

D-U-N-S 11-956-0824
NEXANT INC
101 2nd St Ste 1000, San Francisco, CA 94105-3651
Tel (415) 369-1000 *Founded/Ownrshp* 1999
Sales 146.9MM^E *EMP* 610
SIC 8748 Energy conservation consultant
CEO: Basam Y Sarandah
* *Pr:* Basam Sarandah
CFO: Michael Alvarez
* *Ch:* Arjun Gupta
Bd of Dir: Richard Balzhiser
Sr VP: Bruce Burke
VP: Michael Alexander
VP: Jonathan Bourne
VP: Marcos Cesar
VP: Gerald Choi
VP: John Dirkman
VP: Ella Duval
VP: Clive Gibson
VP: Oton Iskarpatyoti
VP: Sarah Yarger Kienzle
VP: Peter Noland
VP: Virgil Rose
Exec: Bill O'Riordan
Comm Dir: Heatheryn Higgins

NEXCOM
See NAVY EXCHANGE SERVICE COMMAND

D-U-N-S 94-779-7650
NEXCYCLE INC
5221 N O Connor Blvd # 850, Irving, TX 75039-3714
Tel (972) 506-7200 *Founded/Ownrshp* 1994
Sales 143.9MM^E *EMP* 570
SIC 4953 Recycling, waste materials
CEO: Alex Rankin

D-U-N-S 07-834-6156
■ NEXEO SOLUTIONS HOLDINGS LLC
(*Suby of* NEXEO SOLUTIONS INC) ★
3 Waterway Square Pl # 1000, The Woodlands, TX 77380-3487
Tel (281) 297-0700 *Founded/Ownrshp* 2016
Sales 3.9MMM *EMP* 2,300
SIC 5169 5162 Industrial chemicals; Plastics materials & basic shapes
Pr: David A Bradley

CFO: Ross J Crane
Treas: Michael L Everett
Ex VP: Lisa P Britt
Ex VP: David L Chapman
Sr VP: Henry E Harrell III
Sr VP: Ronald J Labuschewsky
Sr VP: Alberto J Machado
Sr VP: Shawn D Williams
VP: Kristina A Smith
Sls Mgr: Richard Darnell

D-U-N-S 07-940-1259
▲ NEXEO SOLUTIONS INC
3 Waterway Square Pl # 1000, The Woodlands, TX 77380-3488
Tel (281) 297-0700 *Founded/Ownrshp* 2014
Sales 1.0MMM *EMP* 2,400E
Tkr Sym NXEO *Exch* NAS
SIC 6799 Investors
Pr: David A Bradley
**Ch Bd:* Wilbur L Ross Jr
CFO: Michael J Gibbons
Sr VP: Brian Herington
Sr VP: Wendy L Teramoto

D-U-N-S 96-641-0859 IMP/EXP
■ NEXEO SOLUTIONS LLC
ARPOL
(*Suby of* NEXEO SOLUTIONS HOLDINGS LLC) ★
3 Waterway Square Pl # 1000, The Woodlands, TX 77380-3487
Tel (281) 297-0700 *Founded/Ownrshp* 2010
Sales 3.3MMM *EMP* 2,450E
Accts Pricewaterhousecoopers Llp
SIC 5169 5162 2821 Industrial chemicals; Plastics materials & basic shapes; Plastics materials & resins
Pr: David A Bradley
**Pr:* Michael B Farnell Jr
**CFO:* Ross Crane
**Treas:* Michael Everett
**Ex VP:* Lisa P Britt
**Ex VP:* David Chapman
Sr VP: Claudia Chike
**Sr VP:* Alberto Machado
VP: Dirk Martin
VP: Steven Seelig
Dist Mgr: Greg Bermosk

D-U-N-S 18-538-4328 EXP
NEXFOR (USA) INC
FRASER PAPERS
(*Suby of* NORBORD INC)
82 Bridge Ave, Madawaska, ME 04756-1229
Tel (207) 728-3321 *Founded/Ownrshp* 1987
Sales 133.1MME *EMP* 1,000
SIC 2621 2493 Paper mills; Fiberboard, other vegetable pulp; Waferboard
Pr: Bert Martin
QC Dir: Roger Bergeron
Opers Mgr: Richard Arnold

NEXGEN BUILDING SUPPLY
See NEXGEN ENTERPRISES INC

NEXGEN BUILDING SUPPLY
See HWZ DISTRIBUTION GROUP LLC

D-U-N-S 00-184-6203
NEXGEN ENTERPRISES INC (OH)
NEXGEN BUILDING SUPPLY
3274 Spring Grove Ave, Cincinnati, OH 45225-1338
Tel (513) 618-0300 *Founded/Ownrshp* 1920
Sales 174.5MME *EMP* 320
Accts Barnes Dennig & Company Ltd C
SIC 5032 Brick, stone & related material
CEO: Robert Hoge
**Pr:* Richard C Wolgemuth
**CFO:* Bruce J Fahey
**Sr VP:* Bruce Kirchhofer
**VP:* Richard J Hoge

NEXICOR
See SENCO BRANDS INC

D-U-N-S 01-268-2295
NEXION HEALTH INC
6937 Warfield Ave, Sykesville, MD 21784-7454
Tel (410) 552-4800 *Founded/Ownrshp* 2000
Sales 145.9MME *EMP* 5,000
SIC 8051 Skilled nursing care facilities
Pr: Fran Kirley
**CFO:* Bretton Bolt
**Treas:* Keith Mutschler
VP: Ayanna Tasby
Genl Mgr: Heidi Biden
Mktg Dir: Kimberly Howard
Mktg Dir: Ronda Marsh

D-U-N-S 07-876-3974
NEXIUS SOLUTIONS INC
2595 Dallas Pkwy Ste 300, Frisco, TX 75034-8530
Tel (703) 650-7777 *Founded/Ownrshp* 2010
Sales 217.5MME *EMP* 464
SIC 5045 Computers, peripherals & software
Pr: Mark Baysinger
VP: Rolf Lumpe
VP: Emily Mountford
VP: Richard Statler
VP Mktg: Julia Pitlik
Snr Mgr: Kimberly Camm

D-U-N-S 16-730-1675 IMP/EXP
NEXLINK COMMUNICATIONS LLC
3355 Bald Mountain Rd # 10, Auburn Hills, MI 48326-4312
Tel (248) 409-2511 *Founded/Ownrshp* 2004
Sales 124.0MM *EMP* 200E
SIC 5065 Communication equipment
Pr: Jeffrey Messano
**VP:* Steve Cosgrove
Sls Mgr: Andy Griglio

D-U-N-S 05-816-8001
▲ NEXSTAR BROADCASTING GROUP INC
545 E John Carpenter Fwy # 700, Irving, TX 75062-3932
Tel (972) 373-8800 *Founded/Ownrshp* 1997
Sales 896.3MM *EMP* 4,422
Tkr Sym NXST *Exch* NGM
SIC 4833 Television broadcasting stations
Ch Bd: Perry A Sook
COO: Timothy C Busch
COO: Brian Jones
CFO: Thomas E Carter
Sr VP: Todd A Porch
Sr VP: Julie Pruett
Sr VP: Elizabeth Ryder
Sr VP: William Sally
VP: Albert Gutierrez
VP: Craig Marrs
VP: Dione Rigsby
VP: Jon Skorburg
VP: Randy Stone
Exec: Ethan Miller
Dir Soc: Larry Krauck
Board of Directors: Geoff Armstrong, Jay M Grossman, C Thomas McMillen, Lisbeth McNabb, Dennis A Miller, I Martin Pompadur

D-U-N-S 86-109-6816 IMP
NEXT DAY BLINDS CORP
8251 Preston Ct Ste B, Jessup, MD 20794-9369
Tel (240) 568-8800 *Founded/Ownrshp* 1993
Sales 86.6MME *EMP* 400
SIC 5023 2591 5719 1799 Window furnishings; Drapery hardware & blinds & shades; Window furnishings; Window treatment installation
Pr: Steve Freishtat
**Ex VP:* Fred Alladin
Dist Mgr: Lyn Gooden
Genl Mgr: Mark Hartman
CIO: Mike Schmitt
IT Man: Jamie Patel
Web Dev: Stephen Blades
Site Mgr: Sue Russ
Site Mgr: Clinton Sietz
Sls Dir: Debbie Smith

D-U-N-S 10-545-7746
NEXT PHASE INC
COMFORT KEEPERS
1410 S Main St, Roswell, NM 88203-5568
Tel (575) 624-9999 *Founded/Ownrshp* 2001
Sales 3.7MM *EMP* 2,400
SIC 8082 Home health care services
Pr: Cindy Lewis

D-U-N-S 08-409-8042
NEXTCARE HOLDINGS INC
1138 N Alma School Rd # 120, Mesa, AZ 85201-3003
Tel (480) 924-8382 *Founded/Ownrshp* 2008
Sales 61.4MME *EMP* 1,000
SIC 8093 8741 8011 Specialty outpatient clinics; Management services; Medical centers
Pr: John Julian
COO: Larry Crist Jr
CFO: Rex T Clevenger
Ofcr: Laura Becker
Ofcr: Ken Walsh
Sr VP: Jeffrey R Gerlach
Sr VP: Keith Marple
VP: Joleen Haxton

D-U-N-S 94-735-0922
NEXTCARE INC
(*Suby of* NEXTCARE HOLDINGS INC) ★
2550 N Thunderbird Cir # 303, Mesa, AZ 85215-1214
Tel (480) 924-8382 *Founded/Ownrshp* 1993
Sales 59.3MM *EMP* 1,000
SIC 8093 8741 Specialty outpatient clinics; Management services
Pr: John Julian
**Ch Bd:* John J Shufeldt
Ex VP: Kellyann Kimble
Off Mgr: Bernie Gunia
Doctor: Rhea Cole
Doctor: Paraag Kumar
Doctor: Fedelia Maez
Doctor: Robin Shaver

D-U-N-S 80-962-2322 IMP
NEXTEER AUTOMOTIVE CORP
(*Suby of* PACIFIC CENTURY MOTORS INC.)
1272 Doris Rd, Auburn Hills, MI 48326-2617
Tel (989) 757-5000 *Founded/Ownrshp* 2008
Sales 674.9MM *EMP* 4,647
SIC 3714 Motor vehicle parts & accessories
Ch: Guibin Zhao
CFO: Peter Gong
Sr VP: Mike Richardson
VP: Matt Beaver
Exec: Mark Decker
Mng Dir: Georgia LI
IT Man: Keshav Hegde
Opers Mgr: James Burghardt
Opers Mgr: Manuel Grimaldo
Plnt Mgr: Jill Dralle
Ql Cn Mgr: Leroy Ward

D-U-N-S 17-821-9796
■ NEXTEL COMMUNICATIONS INC
(*Suby of* SPRINT COMMUNICATIONS INC) ★
12502 Sunrise Valley Dr, Reston, VA 20191-3438
Tel (703) 433-4000 *Founded/Ownrshp* 2004
Sales 4.5MMME *EMP* 19,000
SIC 4812 Radio telephone communication
CEO: Paul Saleh
**COO:* Thomas N Kelly Jr
VP: Kevin Gleason
Genl Couns: Len Kennedy
Board of Directors: Paul Saleh, James Hance Jr Chb

D-U-N-S 60-401-2294
■ NEXTEL FINANCE CO
(*Suby of* SPRINT CORP) ★
2001 Edmund Halley Dr, Reston, VA 20191-3436
Tel (703) 433-4000 *Founded/Ownrshp* 1997
Sales 1.1MMME *EMP* 7,000
SIC 4812 6719 Radio telephone communication; Investment holding companies, except banks
Pr: Timothy Donahue
**CFO:* Steven Shindler
**Treas:* John Brittain
**Ex VP:* William G Arendt
**VP:* Deanne Campbell
**VP:* Thomas J Sidman

D-U-N-S 79-064-5188
■ NEXTEL OF CALIFORNIA INC
SPRINT
(*Suby of* SPRINT CORP) ★
6200 Sprint Pkwy, Overland Park, KS 66251-6117
Tel (866) 505-2385 *Founded/Ownrshp* 1991
Sales 685.5MME *EMP* 966
SIC 4812 Cellular telephone services
Sr Cor Off: Mike Egan
Exec: David Kellogg
Genl Mgr: Amy Edwards
VP Opers: Dennis Lombardi
VP Opers: Randy Shaneyfelt
Sls&Mrk Ex: Gary Godbout

D-U-N-S 80-940-8545
■ NEXTEL OF NEW YORK INC
(*Suby of* NEXTEL FINANCE CO) ★
565 Taxter Rd Ste 450, Elmsford, NY 10523-2341
Tel (914) 421-2800 *Founded/Ownrshp* 1991
Sales 53.1MME *EMP* 1,200
SIC 4812 Radio telephone communication
Pr: Jerry Reynolds

D-U-N-S 05-187-3040
■ NEXTEL OF TEXAS INC (TX)
(*Suby of* NEXTEL FINANCE CO) ★
8911 N Capital Of Texas, Austin, TX 78759-7247
Tel (512) 342-3800 *Founded/Ownrshp* 1987
Sales 99.0MME *EMP* 1,700
SIC 4812 Radio telephone communication
Pr: Tim Donahue

D-U-N-S 12-495-9987
■ NEXTEL PARTNERS INC
(*Suby of* SPRINT COMMUNICATIONS INC) ★
4500 Carillon Pt, Kirkland, WA 98033-7342
Tel (425) 576-3600 *Founded/Ownrshp* 2006
Sales 987.0ME *EMP* 2,905
SIC 4812 Cellular telephone services
Pr: John Chapple
**COO:* James Ryder
**CFO:* Barry Rowan
**VP:* David Aas
**VP:* Donald Manning

D-U-N-S 05-850-0716
■ NEXTEL PARTNERS OPERATING CORP
(*Suby of* SPRINT COMMUNICATIONS INC) ★
6200 Sprint Pkwy, Overland Park, KS 66251-6117
Tel (800) 829-0965 *Founded/Ownrshp* 1998
Sales 823.7MME *EMP* 6,002E
SIC 4812 Radio telephone communication
Pr: John Chapple
**Treas:* John D Thompson

D-U-N-S 82-484-2520
■ NEXTEL SOUTH CORP
(*Suby of* NEXTEL FINANCE CO) ★
6575 The Corners Pkwy, Norcross, GA 30092-3312
Tel (703) 592-7422 *Founded/Ownrshp* 1996
Sales 219.0MME *EMP* 1,555
SIC 4812 Radio telephone communication
Pr: Dan Hesse

D-U-N-S 60-886-2546
■ NEXTEL WEST CORP
(*Suby of* NEXTEL FINANCE CO) ★
10545 Willows Rd Ne # 100, Redmond, WA 98052-2505
Tel (253) 924-8545 *Founded/Ownrshp* 1995
Sales 173.9MME *EMP* 2,616
SIC 4812 Radio telephone communication
CEO: Tim Donahue

D-U-N-S 14-980-7000
■ NEXTERA ENERGY CAPITAL HOLDINGS INC
(*Suby of* NEXTERA ENERGY INC) ★
700 Universe Blvd, Juno Beach, FL 33408-2657
Tel (561) 694-6311 *Founded/Ownrshp* 1985
Sales 4.3MMME *EMP* 1,465E
SIC 6799 Investors
Pr: James Robo

D-U-N-S 12-272-3174 IMP/EXP
▲ NEXTERA ENERGY INC
700 Universe Blvd, Juno Beach, FL 33408-2657
Tel (561) 694-4000 *Founded/Ownrshp* 1984
Sales 17.4MMM *EMP* 13,800
Accts Deloitte & Touche Llp Boca R
Tkr Sym NEE *Exch* NYS
SIC 4911 Electric services; Distribution, electric power; Generation, electric power; Transmission, electric power
Ch Bd: James L Robo
Pr: Manoochehr K Nazar
Pr: Armando Pimentel Jr
Pr: Eric E Silagy
CFO: John W Ketchum
CFO: John Ketchum
Treas: Paul I Cutler
Ex VP: Miguel Arechabala
Ex VP: Deborah H Caplan
Ex VP: Joseph T Kelliher
Ex VP: Charles E Sieving
Ex VP: William L Yeager
VP: Lakshman Charanjiva
VP: Max Guinn
VP: Ron Reagan
Comm Man: Stephanie Eberline

D-U-N-S 05-908-6145 IMP
■ NEXTERA ENERGY OPERATING SERVICES LLC
(*Suby of* NEXTERA ENERGY INC) ★
700 Universe Blvd, Juno Beach, FL 33408-2657
Tel (561) 691-7171 *Founded/Ownrshp* 1998
Sales 141.6MME *EMP* 335
SIC 4911 Distribution, electric power; Generation, electric power; Transmission, electric power
Pr: C O Woody
**Treas:* Peter D Boylan
**VP:* John W Stanton

D-U-N-S 07-941-1676
▲ NEXTERA ENERGY PARTNERS LP
700 Universe Blvd, Juno Beach, FL 33408-2657
Tel (561) 694-4000 *Founded/Ownrshp* 1989
Sales 471.0MM *EMP* 7E
Tkr Sym NEP *Exch* NYS
SIC 4911 Electric services; Generation, electric power
Ch Bd: James L Robo
Genl Pt: Nextera E GP
Pr: Armando Pimentel Jr

D-U-N-S 80-800-7962
■ NEXTERA ENERGY POINT BEACH LLC
POINT BEACH NUCLEAR PLANT
(*Suby of* NEXTERA ENERGY INC) ★
6610 Nuclear Rd, Two Rivers, WI 54241-9516
Tel (920) 755-7705 *Founded/Ownrshp* 2006
Sales 599.5MME *EMP* 1,418E
SIC 4911 ; Generation, electric power
CEO: Eric Silagy

D-U-N-S 05-448-1341 IMP
■ NEXTERA ENERGY POWER MARKETING LLC
(*Suby of* NEXTERA ENERGY INC) ★
700 Universe Blvd, Juno Beach, FL 33408-2657
Tel (561) 691-7171 *Founded/Ownrshp* 1998
Sales 304.0MME *EMP* 719E
SIC 4911 Distribution, electric power
Pr: Thomas Sutton
**CEO:* James L Robo
**CFO:* Moray P Dewhurst
**Ex VP:* Maria V Fogarty
**Ex VP:* Joseph T Kelliher
**Ex VP:* Charles E Sieving

D-U-N-S 05-900-6937 IMP/EXP
■ NEXTERA ENERGY RESOURCES LLC
(*Suby of* NEXTERA ENERGY CAPITAL HOLDINGS INC) ★
700 Universe Blvd, Juno Beach, FL 33408-2657
Tel (561) 691-7171 *Founded/Ownrshp* 1997
Sales 4.3MMME *EMP* 4,700
SIC 4911 Generation, electric power
Pr: Armando Pimentel
**CEO:* James L Robo
**CEO:* Eric Silagy
**Ex VP:* John Ketchum
**Ex VP:* Charles E Sieving
Opers Mgr: Jeffrey Plew

D-U-N-S 13-517-1630 IMP
■ NEXTERA ENERGY SEABROOK LLC
(*Suby of* NEXTERA ENERGY RESOURCES LLC) ★
626 Lafayette Rd, Seabrook, NH 03874-4213
Tel (603) 474-3808 *Founded/Ownrshp* 2002
Sales 3.4MMME *EMP* 750
SIC 4911 ; Generation, electric power

D-U-N-S 60-216-9265
NEXTERA ENERGY SERVICES HOLDINGS LLC
(*Suby of* ESI ENERGY LLC) ★
700 Universe Blvd, Juno Beach, FL 33408-2657
Tel (561) 691-7171 *Founded/Ownrshp* 2005
Sales 88.3MME *EMP* 99E
SIC 4911 Electric services
Pr: Michael L Leighton
**Treas:* Mark R Sorensen
**VP:* Bryan J Fennell
**VP:* Michael O'Sullivan

D-U-N-S 60-217-7193
NEXTERA ENERGY SERVICES LLC
(*Suby of* NEXTERA ENERGY SERVICES HOLDINGS LLC) ★
700 Universe Blvd, Juno Beach, FL 33408-2657
Tel (561) 691-7171 *Founded/Ownrshp* 2005
Sales 88.3MME *EMP* 92E
SIC 4911 Electric services
CEO: Armando Pimentel
**Pr:* Michael Leighton
**Treas:* Mark R Sorensen
**VP:* S Mitchell Davidson
**VP:* Charles J Muoio
**VP:* Michael O'Sullivan
**VP:* Ronald L Scheirer

D-U-N-S 61-193-0590
NEXTGEAR CAPITAL INC
(*Suby of* COX AUTOMOTIVE INC) ★
11799 N College Ave, Carmel, IN 46032-5605
Tel (317) 571-3721 *Founded/Ownrshp* 2005
Sales NA *EMP* 215
SIC 6159 Automobile finance leasing
Pr: Brian Geitner
**Pr:* Marty McFarland
**COO:* Shane Odell
**CFO:* David Horan
VP: Joe Carusella
**VP:* Rich Coutu
VP: Patrick Inks
Dir Risk M: Tom Quackenbush
Sales Exec: Eve Burton
Sales Exec: Renee Kimbrell
Natl Sales: Nate Marine

D-U-N-S 78-645-7689
■ NEXTIRAONE FEDERAL LLC
BLACK BOX NETWORK SERVICES
(*Suby of* BLACK BOX CORP) ★
510 Spring St Ste 200, Herndon, VA 20170-5148
Tel (703) 885-7900 *Founded/Ownrshp* 2006
Sales 110.1MME *EMP* 450
SIC 5065

D-U-N-S 06-867-2153
■ NEXTIRAONE LLC
(*Suby of* BLACK BOX CORP) ★
5050 Lincoln Dr Ste 300, Minneapolis, MN 55436-1179
Tel (952) 352-4410 *Founded/Ownrshp* 1997
Sales 847.5MME *EMP* 3,464

SIC 5065 7629 1731 5999 4813 4841 Telephone equipment; Communication equipment; Telecommunication equipment repair (except telephones); Telephone & telephone equipment installation; Telephone equipment & systems; Telephone communication, except radio; Long distance telephone communications; Cable television services
Pr: Dale Booth
**CFO:* Bob Buhay
CFO: J R ME An
VP: Jean-Jacques Berthelon
Mng Dir: Foucault De La Roch RE
Prgrm Mgr: Christine Howard
Genl Mgr: Larry Underwood

D-U-N-S 03-230-9028
NEXTMED HOLDINGS LLC
6339 E Speedway Blvd, Tucson, AZ 85710-1147
Tel (520) 323-8732 *Founded/Ownrshp* 1999
Sales NA *EMP* 150[E]
SIC 6324 Hospital & medical service plans
Pr: Chris Gleason
COO: Matt Lyden
**CFO:* Jeff Gerwin
**VP:* Matt Gleason
**VP:* Todd Pierce
Sls Dir: Scott Hallett

D-U-N-S 00-257-7927
NEXTMEDIA OPERATING INC
6312 S Fiddlers Green Cir # 2, Greenwood Village, CO 80111-4943
Tel (303) 694-9118 *Founded/Ownrshp* 2000
Sales 124.6MM[E] *EMP* 1,020
SIC 4832 Radio broadcasting stations
Pr: Jim Donahoe
**CFO:* Sean Stover
VP: Eric Neumann
Genl Mgr: John Leathers

D-U-N-S 07-919-3017 EXP
NEXTRAN CORP
NEXTRAN TRCK CNTR-JACKSONVILLE
1986 W Beaver St, Jacksonville, FL 32209-7540
Tel (904) 354-3721 *Founded/Ownrshp* 1992
Sales 265.8MM[E] *EMP* 480
SIC 5511 5531 7538 Trucks, tractors & trailers: new & used; Truck equipment & parts; General truck repair
Ch Bd: Marvin H Pritchett
Pr: Mike Maddox
**CEO:* Jon W Pritchett
**CFO:* Steve F Perez
Brnch Mgr: Vicki Coy
Opers Mgr: Don Cox
Mktg Dir: Denis Abromavage
Sls Mgr: Eric Schmidt

NEXTRAN TRCK CNTR-JACKSONVILLE
See NEXTRAN CORP

D-U-N-S 13-414-2988
NEXTSOURCE INC
1040 Avenue Of The Americ, New York, NY 10018-3726
Tel (212) 736-5870 *Founded/Ownrshp* 2009
Sales 159.6MM[E] *EMP* 3,500
SIC 7363 8741 Labor resource services; Management services
Ch Bd: Joseph Musacchio
COO: Janet Cross
**CFO:* Fern Swiss
Dir IT: Melissa Alexander
Web Dev: Richard Couzzi

D-U-N-S 07-026-8545
NEXUS (MN)
505 Highway 169 N Ste 500, Plymouth, MN 55441-6447
Tel (763) 551-8640 *Founded/Ownrshp* 1974, 1981
Sales 43.5MM *EMP* 1,000
Accts Messerli & Schadow Pllp Minn
SIC 8322 8361 Individual & family services; Group foster home
Pr: David Hutchinson
Pr: Jack Ewing
**COO:* Brock Wolff
**CFO:* Alan K Nordby
Creative D: Nancy Baldrica
IT Man: Tyson Schumacher

D-U-N-S 07-940-1791
NEXUS BIOENERGY INC
3026 Castle Peak Ave, Superior, CO 80027-6067
Tel (720) 318-2339 *Founded/Ownrshp* 2015
Sales 367.3MM[E] *EMP* 4,939
SIC 4939 7389 8731 Combination utilities; ; Energy research
Pr: Syed Reza

D-U-N-S 83-269-7093 EXP
NEXUS DX INC
(*Suby of* SAMSUNG ELECTRONICS CO., LTD.)
6759 Mesa Ridge Rd, San Diego, CA 92121-4902
Tel (858) 410-4600 *Founded/Ownrshp* 2009
Sales 83.4MM[E] *EMP* 480
SIC 3841 Surgical & medical instruments
CEO: Nam Shin
**Pr:* Joseph M Nemmers Jr
**VP:* Jim P McMenamy
**VP:* Gordon Sangster
Assoc Dir: Dan Johnson
Off Mgr: Ann Collins
Opers Supe: Spencer Baker

D-U-N-S 14-718-4969
NEXXAR GROUP INC
580 Sylvan Ave Ste Ma, Englewood Cliffs, NJ 07632-3105
Tel (201) 477-6045 *Founded/Ownrshp* 2004
Sales NA *EMP* 900
SIC 6099 Check clearing services
Pr: Frank J Petrilli
**CFO:* Eric Eaton
Board of Directors: Colin Vickerie

D-U-N-S 02-257-6560
NEXXLINX CORP INC
3565 Piedmont Rd Ne 2-104, Atlanta, GA 30305-8210
Tel (877) 747-0658 *Founded/Ownrshp* 1998
Sales 674.0M[E] *EMP* 1,200
Accts Rc Financials Services Decatu
SIC 7389 8742
CEO: Craig Mento
**COO:* William I Coffeen II
**CFO:* Neil Quarterman
**Ex VP:* William J Hadel
VP: Stephen Smith
**CIO:* Robert Hornbuckle

D-U-N-S 01-823-1480
NEY OIL CO INC
145 S Water St, Ney, OH 43549-9624
Tel (419) 658-2324 *Founded/Ownrshp* 1927
Sales 84.8MM *EMP* 100
Accts Donald A Hohenbrink Ottawa
SIC 5171 Petroleum bulk stations
Pr: Lynn Bergman
**Treas:* Barbara Vance
**VP:* Jerry Bergman

NEZ FOODS
See NORTHWESTERN SELECTA INC

D-U-N-S 05-068-6633 IMP
NFA CORP
HOPE GLOBAL DIV
50 Martin St, Cumberland, RI 02864-5335
Tel (617) 232-6060 *Founded/Ownrshp* 1982
Sales 9.5MM *EMP* 1,000
SIC 5012 2241 Automobiles; Narrow fabric mills
Pr: Lee Casty
**Ex VP:* Emil Bernsten
VP Mktg: Jack Wacksman

D-U-N-S 00-924-3887
■ NFC CASTINGS INC
NEENAH FOUNDERY
(*Suby of* NEENAH ENTERPRISES INC) ★
2121 Brooks Ave, Neenah, WI 54956-4756
Tel (920) 725-7000 *Founded/Ownrshp* 2010
Sales 418.5MM[E] *EMP* 1,650[E]
SIC 3325 3321 Steel foundries; Gray & ductile iron foundries
CEO: Thomas Riordan
**CFO:* Thomas Arians

NFI DISTRIBUTION
See NATIONAL DISTRIBUTION CENTERS LP

D-U-N-S 15-092-4439 IMP
NFI INDUSTRIES INC
1515 Burnt Mill Rd, Cherry Hill, NJ 08003-3637
Tel (856) 691-7000 *Founded/Ownrshp* 1985
Sales 1.3MMM[E] *EMP* 2,100
SIC 4213 4212 8741 4225 4214 4783 Trucking, except local; Local trucking, without storage; Management services; General warehousing & storage; Local trucking with storage; Packing & crating
CEO: Sidney Brown
**Pr:* Jeffrey Brown
COO: Joe Roeder
Ex VP: Rob Barron
Ex VP: Frank Raschilla
Sr VP: Susanne Batchelor
VP: Bill Bliem
VP: Scott Brucker
VP: Brian Gillmore
VP: Adam Greenberg
VP: Bob Knowles
VP: John Krauser
VP: Carolina Montes
VP: Jon Sandeen
VP: Tom Scandura
Dir Risk M: Ross Ennis

D-U-N-S 87-911-2063
NFI INTERACTIVE LOGISTICS LLC
NFI LOGISTICS
1515 Burnt Mill Rd, Cherry Hill, NJ 08003-3637
Tel (856) 857-1324 *Founded/Ownrshp* 2005
Sales 85.6MM[E] *EMP* 123
SIC 4731 8742 Transportation agents & brokers; Materials mgmt. (purchasing, handling, inventory) consultant
CEO: Sidney Brown
COO: Josiah Knapp
CFO: Frank Raschilla
**Treas:* Jeffrey Brown
Sr VP: Tj Lynch

NFI LOGISTICS
See NFI INTERACTIVE LOGISTICS LLC

NFI TRANSPORTATION
See NATIONAL FREIGHT INC

NFISD
See NORTH FOREST INDEPENDENT SCHOOL DISTRICT

NFL OFFICEWORKS
See NATIONAL FURNITURE LIQUIDATORS I LLC

D-U-N-S 04-219-0942
NFO INC (IA)
NATIONAL FARMERS ORGANIZATION
528 Billy Sunday Rd # 100, Ames, IA 50010-8089
Tel (515) 292-2000 *Founded/Ownrshp* 1955
Sales 610.7MM[E] *EMP* 90
SIC 8631 Collective bargaining unit
Ch Bd: Paul D Olson
**Treas:* Michael D Miller
VP: Tom Dieringer
**VP:* Paul Riniker
Genl Mgr: Scott Benedict
Genl Mgr: Jack Leis
Genl Mgr: Terry Nelson
Genl Mgr: Brad Rock
Genl Mgr: Jim Steier

NFP ADVISORS
See NFP CORP

D-U-N-S 08-207-0892
NFP CORP
NFP ADVISORS
(*Suby of* PATRIOT INTERMEDIATE HOLDINGS B CORP) ★
340 Madison Ave Fl 21, New York, NY 10173-0401
Tel (212) 301-4000 *Founded/Ownrshp* 2013
Sales NA *EMP* 2,837
SIC 6411 7389 6282 Insurance agents, brokers & service; Financial services; Investment advice
CEO: Douglas Hammond
CEO: Terrence Scali
COO: Michael Goldman
Ex VP: Stancil E Barton
Ex VP: Kim Davis
Sr VP: Suzanne Spradley
VP: Daniel Agus
VP: Eric Boester
VP: Chase Cannon
VP: Ford Darger
VP: Ed Kroell
VP: Stephen Lishnoff
VP: Sal Lundy
VP: Veronica Moo
VP: Jason Sickle
VP: Claire Steinberg

D-U-N-S 80-680-7186
NFRASTRUCTURE TECHNOLOGIES LLC
(*Suby of* ZONES INC) ★
5 Enterprise Ave, Halfmoon, NY 12065-3423
Tel (518) 664-3899 *Founded/Ownrshp* 2016
Sales 88.9MM[E] *EMP* 225
SIC 7373 Systems software development services
CEO: Daniel Pickett III
**Pr:* Jim Pascarell
**COO:* Stephen L Miller
**CFO:* Gerald Anderson
**Ofcr:* Kevin O'Neil
**Ex VP:* Bill Morrissey
VP: Gerald Goff
**CIO:* Michael Martin
Netwrk Eng: Jeff Lawson
VP Opers: Jennifer Perrotta

NG CASINOS
See NEVADA GOLD & CASINOS INC

NGC INDUSTRIES, INC.
See NGC INDUSTRIES LLC

D-U-N-S 94-198-4312
NGC INDUSTRIES LLC
NGC INDUSTRIES, INC.
(*Suby of* NATIONAL GYPSUM CO) ★
2001 Rexford Rd, Charlotte, NC 28211-3415
Tel (704) 365-7300 *Founded/Ownrshp* 1996
Sales 136.6MM[E] *EMP* 2,100
SIC 2679 Wallboard, decorated: made from purchased material
CEO: Thomas C Nelson
**CFO:* George Beckwith
**Treas:* Richard G Parkhurst
**VP:* Gerald P Carroll
**VP:* John Mixson
**VP:* Samuel A Schiffman
**VP Mfg:* John Corsi
**VP Sls:* Craig Weisbruch
Snr Mgr: John Lewis

NGI CONSTRUCTION
See NOVA GROUP INC

D-U-N-S 19-475-5534 IMP/EXP
NGK NORTH AMERICA INC
(*Suby of* NGK INSULATORS, LTD.)
1105 N Market St Ste 1300, Wilmington, DE 19801-1241
Tel (302) 654-1344 *Founded/Ownrshp* 2005
Sales 136.1MM[E] *EMP* 820
SIC 3714 5013 3264 5063 Motor vehicle parts & accessories; Automotive supplies & parts; Insulators, electrical: porcelain; Insulators, electrical
Pr: Susumu Sakabe
**Treas:* Tomokazu Asai
VP: Josh Niwa
**Genl Mgr:* Yutaka Yonekura

D-U-N-S 60-382-1062 IMP/EXP
NGK SPARK PLUGS (USA) HOLDING INC
(*Suby of* NGK SPARK PLUG CO., LTD.)
1011 Centre Rd, Wilmington, DE 19805-1267
Tel (302) 288-0131 *Founded/Ownrshp* 1995
Sales 188.2MM[E] *EMP* 750[E]
SIC 3643 3264 Current-carrying wiring devices; Porcelain parts for electrical devices, molded; Spark plugs, porcelain
Pr: Shin Odo
IT Man: John Morici

D-U-N-S 04-522-2874 IMP
NGK SPARK PLUGS (USA) INC
NGK SPARK PLUGS USA
(*Suby of* NGK SPARK PLUGS (USA) HOLDING INC) ★
46929 Magellan, Wixom, MI 48393-3699
Tel (248) 926-6900 *Founded/Ownrshp* 1995
Sales 169.7MM[E] *EMP* 600
SIC 3643 3264 Current-carrying wiring devices; Porcelain parts for electrical devices, molded
CEO: Goro Ogawa
**Pr:* Shin Odo
VP: Michael Schwab
VP: Mike Vanca
Exec: Steven Burgett
Mng Dir: Kazuho Kociszewski
Dist Mgr: Chris Hillestad
Genl Mgr: Mark Pratt
VP Mfg: Robert Pepper
Opers Mgr: Ann Nelson
Prd Mgr: Tak Shigehara

D-U-N-S 87-851-6160 IMP
NGK SPARK PLUGS (USA) INC
(*Suby of* NGK SPARK PLUGS USA) ★
1 Ngk Dr, Sissonville, WV 25320-9546
Tel (304) 988-0060 *Founded/Ownrshp* 1936
Sales 169.7MM[E] *EMP* 450
SIC 5013 3694 Automotive engines & engine parts; Ignition apparatus & distributors
CEO: Norihiko Adachi
CFO: Yosnitaka Nakita
Ofcr: Hiraoki Hiraoka
Ex VP: Larry Magee
**VP:* Richard Sullivan
Exec: Rosanna Gahran
IT Man: Davey Perdue
Sls Mgr: John Edlund

NGK SPARK PLUGS USA
See NGK SPARK PLUGS (USA) INC

D-U-N-S 96-885-1126
NGL CROSSTEX MARKETING L P
2501 Cedar Springs Rd, Dallas, TX 75201-1409
Tel (214) 754-4752 *Founded/Ownrshp* 2005
Sales 175.3MM[E] *EMP* 560
SIC 5172 Petroleum products
Pt: William W Davis
Pt: Crosstex Energy Services GP

D-U-N-S 82-747-6230
■ NGL CRUDE LOGISTICS LLC
(*Suby of* NGL ENERGY PARTNERS LP) ★
1299 Farnam St Ste 120, Omaha, NE 68102-1880
Tel (402) 889-4000 *Founded/Ownrshp* 2013
Sales 724.4MM[E] *EMP* 600
SIC 6221 5153 Commodity contracts brokers, dealers; Grain & field beans
Pr: Greg Heckman
**COO:* Jim Anderson
**COO:* Greg Piper
**CFO:* John Neppl
**Ofcr:* Robert Jones
**VP:* Dana Wright
**CIO:* Gary Acromite
VP Opers: Dennis Stieren

D-U-N-S 96-546-5086
▲ NGL ENERGY PARTNERS LP
6120 S Yale Ave Ste 805, Tulsa, OK 74136-4233
Tel (918) 481-1119 *Founded/Ownrshp* 2010
Sales 11.7MMM *EMP* 3,200
Accts Grant Thornton Llp Tulsa Okl
Tkr Sym NGL *Exch* NYS
SIC 5172 5984 Petroleum products; Gases, liquefied petroleum (propane); Propane gas, bottled
CEO: H Michael Krimbill
Genl Pt: NGL Energy Holdings LLC
Pr: James J Burke
CFO: Robert W Karlovich III
VP: Patrice Armbruster
VP: Donald Jensen
VP: Sharra Straight
VP Bus Dev: Bradley Atkinson
Mktg Mgr: Cole Carrigan
Snr Mgr: Lynette Biers

D-U-N-S 15-352-4541
■ NGL SUPPLY LLC
(*Suby of* NGL ENERGY PARTNERS LP) ★
6120 S Yale Ave Ste 805, Tulsa, OK 74136-4233
Tel (918) 481-1119 *Founded/Ownrshp* 2010
Sales 109.8MM[E] *EMP* 119
SIC 5172 Gases, liquefied petroleum (propane)
CEO: Stephen D Tuttle
**Pr:* Brian K Pauling
**CFO:* Craig S Jones
Sr VP: Stan Perry
VP: Stan A Bugh
VP: Mark McGinty
Sls Dir: Bryan Lehman

D-U-N-S 00-697-1170
NGM INSURANCE CO
MAIN STREET AMERICA GROUP, THE
4601 Touchton Rd E # 3400, Jacksonville, FL 32246-4486
Tel (904) 380-7282 *Founded/Ownrshp* 1923
Sales NA *EMP* 1,000
Accts Ernst & Young Llp Boston Ma
SIC 6331 Fire, marine & casualty insurance
CEO: Tom Van Berkel
**Pr:* William Mc Kenna
**Ex VP:* Ed Kuhl
**Sr VP:* Doug Eden
**Sr VP:* Susan E Mack

D-U-N-S 02-109-8538
NGS AMERICAN INC
(*Suby of* CORESOURCE INC) ★
27575 Harper Ave, Saint Clair Shores, MI 48081-1923
Tel (586) 552-4656 *Founded/Ownrshp* 2006
Sales NA *EMP* 380
SIC 6411 8741 Medical insurance claim processing, contract or fee basis; Administrative management
Pr: Kimberly A Gunter
VP: Susan Darga

NHBB
See NEW HAMPSHIRE BALL BEARINGS INC

NHCA
See NATIONAL HEALTH CARE ASSOCIATES INC

NHCS
See NEW HANOVER COUNTY SCHOOLS

D-U-N-S 07-554-9139
NHCS INC
NASH GENERAL HOSPITAL
2416 Professional Dr, Rocky Mount, NC 27804-2253
Tel (252) 962-8585 *Founded/Ownrshp* 1966
Sales 155.1MM[E] *EMP* 1,653
Accts Deloitte & Touche Llp Charlot
SIC 8062 8063 General medical & surgical hospitals; Psychiatric hospitals
Pr: Larry Chewning
V Ch: Wilmer Brantley
COO: Bradford Weiner
**CFO:* Claude Allen Hooks
DP Exec: David Hinkle
Surgeon: J Gregory Nelson
Doctor: Sudhir Prasada
Doctor: Shalendra Varma

NHI
See NATIONAL HEALTH INVESTORS INC

D-U-N-S 83-821-7701
NHK INTERNATIONAL CORP
(*Suby of* NHK SPRING CO., LTD.)
46855 Magellan Dr Ste 200, Novi, MI 48377-2451
Tel (248) 926-0111 *Founded/Ownrshp* 1976
Sales 894.4MM *EMP* 200
Accts Ernst & Young Llp Louisville
SIC 8711 Engineering services
Pr: Yosei Morioka

Sr Cor Off: Ko Masuda
IT Man: James Green
Sales Asso: Mark Sakata

D-U-N-S 13-808-4298 IMP
NHL ENTERPRISES INC
N H L
1185 Ave Of The Americas, New York, NY 10036-2601
Tel (212) 789-2000 *Founded/Ownrshp* 1967
Sales 124.3MM *EMP* 200
Accts Ernst & Young Us Llp Indianap
SIC 7941 Sports clubs, managers & promoters
Pt: Gary B Bettman
Pt: Joseph Desousa
Pt: Craig C Harnett
Pt: Brian Jennings
Pt: Mary McCarthy
Pr: Olivia Pietrantonio
COO: Bill Daly
CFO: Art McCarthy
Sr Ex VP: Colin Campbell
Ex VP: Hicks Thomas
Ex VP: David Zimmerman
Sr VP: Perry Cooper
VP: Jim Bednarek
VP: Dennis Cunningham
VP: Carol Duncanson
VP: Julie Grand
VP: Ruth Gruhin
VP: Russell Levine
VP: Bernadette Mansur
VP: Ken Martin
VP: Dean Matsuzaki

D-U-N-S 78-128-8688
NHM COMMUNITY COLLEGE DISTRICT
5000 Research Forest Dr, Spring, TX 77381-4356
Tel (832) 813-6500 *Founded/Ownrshp* 1972
Sales 11.0MM^E *EMP* 1,400
SIC 8222 Community college
Prin: John Pickleman

NHP
See NEIGHBORHOOD HEALTH PLAN

D-U-N-S 78-684-7640 IMP/EXP
NHR NEWCO HOLDINGS LLC
6500 Hollister Ave # 210, Santa Barbara, CA 93117-3011
Tel (800) 230-6638 *Founded/Ownrshp* 1986
Sales 364.0MM^E *EMP* 645
SIC 5045 5065 7379 Computers, peripherals & software; Telephone equipment; Computer related maintenance services
CEO: Mike Sheldon
**COO:* Sachi Thompson
**CFO:* Thomas Pickett
**VP:* Mark Kelly
**VP:* Holger Peters
**VP:* Jeff Zanardi
Comm Man: Katie Mowery
Sales Exec: Murali Lambotharan
Sls Dir: Wes Clanton
Pr Mgr: Sarah Main

NHRA
See NATIONAL HOT ROD ASSOCIATION

D-U-N-S 05-719-1876
NHS HUMAN SERVICES INC
620 Germantown Pike, Lafayette Hill, PA 19444-1810
Tel (610) 260-4600 *Founded/Ownrshp* 1981
Sales 44.3MM *EMP* 6,500
SIC 8093 8059 8082 Mental health clinic, outpatient; Alcohol clinic, outpatient; Drug clinic, outpatient; Rehabilitation center, outpatient treatment; Home for the mentally retarded, exc. skilled or intermediate; Visiting nurse service
CEO: M Joseph Rocks
COO: Brian Baxter
**CFO:* Kevin W McClure
VP: Terri Close
VP: Karen Markle
VP: Tom Morgan
VP: John Scheck
Ex Dir: Rayni Brindley
Prac Mgr: Dana Schaffer
Netwrk Mgr: Drew Yang
VP Opers: Becki Fassl

D-U-N-S 04-972-7332
NHS MANAGEMENT LLC
931 Fairfax Park, Tuscaloosa, AL 35406-2805
Tel (205) 391-3600 *Founded/Ownrshp* 1981
Sales 255.5MM^E *EMP* 5,000
SIC 8082 8059 Home health care services; Nursing home, except skilled & intermediate care facility
Pr: J Norman Estes
COO: Robert Sprague
CFO: Claude Lee
Nrsg Dir: Marian Peeples

D-U-N-S 96-939-2146
NHS PENNYLVANIA
620 Germantown Pike, Lafayette Hill, PA 19444-1810
Tel (610) 238-4403 *Founded/Ownrshp* 2011
Sales 149.6MM *EMP* 2^E
SIC 8699 8299 Charitable organization; Educational services

D-U-N-S 11-837-0142 IMP/EXP
NIAGARA BOTTLING LLC
2560 E Philadelphia St, Ontario, CA 91761-7768
Tel (909) 230-5000 *Founded/Ownrshp* 1998
Sales 335.7MM^E *EMP* 445
SIC 2086 Water, pasteurized: packaged in cans, bottles, etc.
**VP:* Brian Hess
Snr Ntwrk: Kevin Crocker
QA Dir: Octavia Ferrell
Netwrk Eng: Wilson Shiao
Sfty Mgr: Chris Aznar
Opers Mgr: Geoffrey Kamansky
Opers Mgr: Carlos Valencia
Manager: Brian Fluke
Prd Mgr: Adam Johnson
Prd Mgr: Lupe Munoz
Prd Mgr: Juan Zepeda

NIAGARA CHOCOLATES
See SWEETWORKS INC

NIAGARA FALLS BOARD OF EDUCATI
See CITY SCHOOL DISTRICT OF CITY OF NIAGARA FALLS

D-U-N-S 07-993-4667
NIAGARA FALLS MEMORIAL MEDICAL CENTER INC (NY)
621 10th St, Niagara Falls, NY 14301-1813
Tel (716) 278-4000 *Founded/Ownrshp* 1895
Sales 82.6MM *EMP* 1,105
SIC 8062 General medical & surgical hospitals
CEO: Joseph Ruffalo
CFO: Chris D Frauenhofer
CFO: Phillip Johnson
CFO: Raj Mehta
Treas: Charles Rader
Ofcr: Laureen Jacobs
Ex VP: Maryanne Wooley
VP: Vijay Bojedla
VP: Marnie Lavigne
Dir Rad: Les Mackenzie
Dir Rx: Jack Koford

D-U-N-S 03-022-3663
NIAGARA FRONTIER HOCKEY LP
BUFFALO SABRES
111 Eight Ave, Buffalo, NY 14203
Tel (716) 855-4160 *Founded/Ownrshp* 2000
Sales 51.3MM^E *EMP* 1,587
SIC 7941 Ice hockey club
Genl Mgr: Darcy Regier
MIS Dir: Ken Bass

D-U-N-S 05-661-5677
NIAGARA FRONTIER TRANSPORTATION AUTHORITY
BUFFALO NIAGARA INTL ARPRT
181 Ellicott St Ste 1, Buffalo, NY 14203-2298
Tel (716) 855-7300 *Founded/Ownrshp* 1967
Sales 155.2MM^E *EMP* 1,500
Accts Kpmg Llp Buffalo Ny
SIC 4111 4581 Bus line operations; Subway operation; Airport
Ch: Sister Denise A Roche
COO: Peter Deglopper
**CFO:* John Cox
**Treas:* Bonita R Durand
**Ex Dir:* Kimberley A Minkel
IT Man: Darren Kempner
Mktg Mgr: James Lynch
Counsel: Mary Perla

D-U-N-S 62-055-7355
NIAGARA HEALTH CORP
(*Suby of* CATHOLIC HEALTH EAST) ★
6150 E Broad St, Columbus, OH 43213-1574
Tel (614) 898-4000 *Founded/Ownrshp* 1988
Sales 408.5MM^E *EMP* 8,000
SIC 8741 8062 Hospital management; General medical & surgical hospitals
Prin: Randall E Moore
Dir IT: Les Boyer
Mktg Mgr: Jessica Amendolare
Mktg Mgr: Brandi Pennington

D-U-N-S 78-788-4381
■ NIAGARA HOLDINGS INC
(*Suby of* CARLYLE GROUP L P) ★
300 Lindenwood Dr, Malvern, PA 19355-1740
Tel (610) 651-4200 *Founded/Ownrshp* 2007
Sales 43.1MM^E *EMP* 1,300
SIC 2819 3231 Sodium & potassium compounds, exc. bleaches, alkalies, alum.; Sodium hyposulfite, sodium hydrosulfite; Potassium compounds or salts, except hydroxide or carbonate; Products of purchased glass
Pr: Michael R Boyce
Pr: Michael R Imbriani
Pr: Scott Randolph
CFO: James P Cox
Ofcr: William Sichko

D-U-N-S 15-478-1579 IMP
NIAGARA LASALLE CORP
(*Suby of* OPTIMA SPECIALTY STEEL INC) ★
1412 150th St, Hammond, IN 46327-1743
Tel (219) 853-6000 *Founded/Ownrshp* 2011
Sales 340.7MM^E *EMP* 1,000
SIC 3316 Bars, steel, cold finished, from purchased hot-rolled
CEO: Mordechai Korf
VP: Michael Ivetich
Exec: Mike Flood
Genl Mgr: Michael Burchwell

D-U-N-S 05-454-2779
NIAGARA MOHAWK HOLDINGS INC (NY)
(*Suby of* NATIONAL GRID USA) ★
300 Erie Blvd W, Syracuse, NY 13202-4201
Tel (315) 474-1511 *Founded/Ownrshp* 1998, 2002
Sales 2.7MM *EMP* 3,950
SIC 4911 4924 Generation, electric power; Transmission, electric power; Distribution, electric power; Natural gas distribution
CEO: Thomas B King
Pr: Albert J Budney Jr
CFO: William F Edwards
Treas: Arthur Roos
Sr VP: David J Arrington
VP: Theresa Flaim
VP: William Flynn
VP: Nabil Hitti
VP: Michael Kelleher
VP: Steven W Tasker
VP: David Walsh

D-U-N-S 00-699-4735
NIAGARA MOHAWK POWER CORP
NATIONAL GRID
(*Suby of* NIAGARA MOHAWK HOLDINGS INC) ★
300 Erie Blvd W, Syracuse, NY 13202-4250
Tel (315) 474-1511 *Founded/Ownrshp* 1937, 2002
Sales 3.2MM^E *EMP* 3,950
SIC 4911 4924 Generation, electric power; Transmission, electric power; Distribution, electric power; Natural gas distribution
CEO: Kenneth Daly
**Pr:* Thomas B King
**Treas:* Malcolm Charles Cooper
**Sr VP:* James B Howe
**VP:* Susan M Crossett
VP: T Flaim
VP: Timothy Small
**VP:* Martin Wheatcroft
Prin: Greg Hunter
Prin: Doug Newton
Prgrm Mgr: Patrick Cody

D-U-N-S 03-022-5734
NIAGARA UNIVERSITY
5795 Lewiston Rd, Niagara University, NY 14109-9809
Tel (716) 285-1212 *Founded/Ownrshp* 1856
Sales 117.3MM *EMP* 500^E
Accts Bonadio & Co Llp Buffalo Ny
SIC 8221 University
Pr: Rev Joseph Levesque
**Ex VP:* Bonnie Rose
VP: Timothy Downs
VP: Kevin Hearn
**VP:* Michael S Jaszka
Dir Soc: Susan Clements
Ex Dir: Sara Capen
Ex Dir: Jill Shuey
Off Admin: Mark Gabriele

D-U-N-S 00-506-7616 IMP/EXP
NIBCO INC
1516 Middlebury St, Elkhart, IN 46516-4740
Tel (574) 295-3000 *Founded/Ownrshp* 1909
Sales 500.0MM *EMP* 2,420
Accts Bdo Usa Llp Grand Rapids Mi
SIC 3494 3491 3089 Valves & pipe fittings; Pipe fittings; Plumbing & heating valves; Industrial valves; Plastic hardware & building products; Fittings for pipe, plastic
Ch Bd: Rex Martin
V Ch: Alice A Martin
Pr: Steven E Malm
VP: Kenneth J Eme Jr
VP: David Goodling
VP: Cody Huffines
VP: Todd A Nowicki
Genl Mgr: Randy Doering
VP Mfg: David L Goodling
Mktg Mgr: Rebecca Foletta
Board of Directors: Howard L Clark Jr, Arthur J Decio, William C Kunkler, Richard E Newsted

NIC GLOBAL
See NATIONAL INDUSTRIAL CONCEPTS INC

D-U-N-S 08-922-8477 IMP
NIC HOLDING CORP
225 Brd Hllow Rd Ste 212w, Melville, NY 11747
Tel (631) 753-4200 *Founded/Ownrshp* 2000
Sales 5.2MMM *EMP* 60
SIC 5172 Petroleum products
Ch Bd: Jay H Bernstein
COO: Peter Ripp
Software D: Antonio Correra

D-U-N-S 07-081-6710
▲ NIC INC
25501 W Valley Pkwy # 300, Olathe, KS 66061-8474
Tel (877) 234-3468 *Founded/Ownrshp* 1991
Sales 292.3MM *EMP* 859
Tkr Sym EGOV *Exch* NGS
SIC 7371 Custom computer programming services; Computer software development & applications
Ch Bd: Harry H Herington
COO: Robert W Knapp Jr
CFO: Stephen M Kovzan
Sr VP: Ron E Thornburgh
VP: Robert Chandler
VP: Chris Neff
VP: Ron Thornburgh
Dir Sec: Jayne Friedland Holland
Genl Mgr: Russell Castagnaro
Genl Mgr: Sandi Miller
Genl Mgr: Sloane Wright
Board of Directors: Art N Burtscher, Karen S Evans, Ross C Hartley, C Brad Henry, Alexander C Kemper, William M Lyons, Pete Wilson

D-U-N-S 13-794-4992
NICA INC
1451 E Lincoln Ave, Madison Heights, MI 48071-4136
Tel (248) 586-3300 *Founded/Ownrshp* 1998
Sales 158.0MM^E *EMP* 1,300^E
SIC 2396 Automotive trimmings, fabric
Ch Bd: Jorge Morales

D-U-N-S 09-990-0136
NICE N EASY GROCERY SHOPPES INC
7840 Oxbow Rd, Canastota, NY 13032-4665
Tel (315) 397-2802 *Founded/Ownrshp* 1980
Sales 145.0MM^E *EMP* 650
Accts Bowers & Company Cpas Pllc Sy
SIC 5411 5541 Convenience stores; Filling stations, gasoline
CEO: John Macdougall

D-U-N-S 01-452-1947
NICE SYSTEMS INC
(*Suby of* NICE LTD)
461 From Rd Ste 103, Paramus, NJ 07652-3526
Tel (201) 964-2600 *Founded/Ownrshp* 1989
Sales 310.8MM^E *EMP* 537
SIC 7372 7382 1731 8741

D-U-N-S 00-377-8198 IMP/EXP
NICE-PAK PRODUCTS INC (NY)
2 Nice Pak Park, Orangeburg, NY 10962-1376
Tel (845) 365-2772 *Founded/Ownrshp* 1955
Sales 438.2MM^E *EMP* 1,000
SIC 2621 7389 2676 Towels, tissues & napkins: paper & stock; Sanitary tissue paper; Packaging & labeling services; Sanitary paper products
Pr: Robert Julius
Pr: John Culligan
Pr: Jon Kupperman
**Sr VP:* William E Dwan
VP: Wallis Brooks
VP: Jeffrey Hurley
VP: Matt Marshhouser
VP: Kevin Tully
Creative D: Lisa Meyers
CTO: Steven Carter
MIS Dir: Irene Clements

D-U-N-S 03-537-5757 IMP
NICHOLAS & CO INC
5520 W Harold Gatty Dr, Salt Lake City, UT 84116-3725
Tel (801) 531-1100 *Founded/Ownrshp* 1939
Sales 508.0MM *EMP* 555
SIC 5046 5141 5142 Restaurant equipment & supplies; Groceries, general line; Packaged frozen goods
Ch Bd: William N Mouskondis
Sr Pt: Walter E Rogers Jr
**Pr:* Peter Mouskondis
CFO: Jeffrey May
**Treas:* Bill Athens
Ex VP: Dave Robbins
VP: Ken Adams
Exec: George Adondakis
CIO: Joseph Wood
Dir IT: Michael Kattelman
Dir IT: Tony Sansone

D-U-N-S 79-071-7292
▲ NICHOLAS FINANCIAL INC
2454 N Mcmullen Booth Rd, Clearwater, FL 33759-1353
Tel (727) 726-0763 *Founded/Ownrshp* 2008
Sales NA *EMP* 280
Tkr Sym NICK *Exch* NGS
SIC 6141 Financing: automobiles, furniture, etc., not a deposit bank
Pr: Ralph T Finkenbrink
**Sr VP:* Kevin D Bates
Board of Directors: Kevin D Bates, Scott Fink, Robin J Hastings, Todd B Pfister

NICHOLAS HOMES
See MNI ENTERPRISES INC

D-U-N-S 82-500-3494
NICHOLS ALUMINUM LLC
DAVENPORT ROLLING MILL
(*Suby of* ALERIS ROLLED PRODUCTS INC) ★
25825 Science Park Dr # 400, Beachwood, OH 44122-7392
Tel (216) 910-3400 *Founded/Ownrshp* 2014
Sales 159.0MM^E *EMP* 542
SIC 3355 3354

D-U-N-S 19-758-1853
■ NICHOLS INSTITUTE REFERENCE LABORATORIES
(*Suby of* QUEST DIAGNOSTICS NICHOLS INSTITUTE) ★
33608 Ortega Hwy, San Juan Capistrano, CA 92675-2042
Tel (949) 728-4000 *Founded/Ownrshp* 1971
Sales 13.3MM^E *EMP* 1,000
SIC 8071 Testing laboratories
Pr: Douglas Harrington
**CFO:* Charles Olson
**Treas:* Jolene Kahn
**VP:* Michael O'Gorman
**VP:* Murugan R Pandian
**VP Sls:* Chuck Miller
S&M/Mgr: Robert Menna

D-U-N-S 01-727-1339
NICHOLS PAPER & SUPPLY CO
1391 Judson Rd, Norton Shores, MI 49456-9691
Tel (231) 799-2120 *Founded/Ownrshp* 1976
Sales 112.1MM^E *EMP* 90
SIC 5113 5087 Industrial & personal service paper; Shipping supplies; Cleaning & maintenance equipment & supplies; Carpet & rug cleaning equipment & supplies, commercial
CEO: Michael K Olthoff
**COO:* Kevin Rahrig
CFO: Will Kelderhouse
VP: Richard Billadeau
Sls Mgr: Hal Grossman
Snr Mgr: Chris Caird

D-U-N-S 08-020-8299
NICHOLS PORTLAND LLC
2400 Congress St, Portland, ME 04102-1949
Tel (207) 774-6121 *Founded/Ownrshp* 2016
Sales 87.1MM^E *EMP* 348
SIC 3714 8711 Motor vehicle parts & accessories; Engineering services
Pr: Richard Izor
CIO: Marty Cunningham

NICHOLS SUPER THRIFT
See G L N INC

NICHOLSON
See APEX TOOL GROUP LLC

D-U-N-S 00-450-4684 IMP/EXP
NICHOLSON CONSTRUCTION CO (PA)
(*Suby of* BACHY SOLETANCHE LIMITED)
2400 Ansys Dr Ste 303, Canonsburg, PA 15317-0403
Tel (412) 221-4500 *Founded/Ownrshp* 1955, 1969
Sales 142.0MM *EMP* 250
Accts Scheider Downs & Co Inc Pi
SIC 1629 1771 1799 Pile driving contractor; Foundation & footing contractor; Grouting work; Shoring & underpinning work
VP: John D Wise
**VP:* Richard Deschamps
**VP:* Laurent Lefebvre
Dist Mgr: Ron Hall
Off Mgr: Nayma Aguila
Netwrk Mgr: Chris Jankowiak
Opers Mgr: Paul Krumm

NICKELS PERFORMANCE
See TRANSTAR INDUSTRIES INC

NICKLAUS CHILDREN'S HOSPITAL
See VARIETY CHILDRENS HOSPITAL

D-U-N-S 07-831-4636
NICOLE CRAFTS LLC
14 Sbar Blvd, Moorestown, NJ 08057-1057
Tel (856) 234-8220 Founded/Ownrshp 2011
Sales 500.0MM^E EMP 4,400^E
SIC 5092 Arts & crafts equipment & supplies
Prin: Nicole McGuigan

D-U-N-S 09-858-2505 IMP/EXP
NICOLON CORP
TENCATE NICOLON
(Suby of ROYAL TEN CATE (USA) INC) ★
365 S Holland Dr, Pendergrass, GA 30567-4625
Tel (706) 693-2226 Founded/Ownrshp 1979
Sales 171.8MM EMP 402^E
SIC 2221 5949 Polypropylene broadwoven fabrics; Polyester broadwoven fabrics; Sewing, needlework & piece goods
Pr: Lee Bryan
Treas: Joseph Averette
CIO: Scott Gleeson
Sls Mgr: Brett Ayers

NICOR ENERGY SERVICES COMPANY
See NICOR SERVICES

NICOR GAS COMPANY
See NORTHERN ILLINOIS GAS CO

D-U-N-S 62-366-1019
■ **NICOR SERVICES**
NICOR ENERGY SERVICES COMPANY
(Suby of OTTAWA ACQUISITION LLC) ★
1751 W Diehl Rd Ste 200, Naperville, IL 60563-4843
Tel (630) 718-2707 Founded/Ownrshp 2011
Sales 58.0MM^E EMP 1,475^E
SIC 4924 Natural gas distribution
Pr: Daniel Dodge
VP: Gerald O'Connor
Genl Mgr: Dale Larkin

D-U-N-S 07-864-5628
NIDEC AMERICAS HOLDING CORP
(Suby of NIDEC CORPORATION)
8050 W Florissant Ave, Saint Louis, MO 63136-1414
Tel (314) 595-8000 Founded/Ownrshp 2012
Sales 890.6MM^E EMP 2,849^E
SIC 3625 3594 6719 Motor controls, electric; Fluid power pumps & motors; Investment holding companies, except banks
Pr: Shigenobu Nagamori
*Pr: Patrick Murphy
*CFO: Masuo Yoshimatsu
*VP: Motoyoshi Hanaoka

D-U-N-S 00-503-5969 IMP/EXP
NIDEC MINSTER CORP (OH)
(Suby of NIDEC-SHIMPO CORPORATION)
240 W 5th St, Minster, OH 45865-1065
Tel (419) 628-2331 Founded/Ownrshp 1901, 2012
Sales 124.1MM EMP 517^E
SIC 3542 3568

D-U-N-S 96-500-4240 IMP/EXP
NIDEC MOTOR CORP
HURST MANUFACTURING DIVISION
(Suby of NIDEC AMERICAS HOLDING CORP) ★
8050 W Florissant Ave, Saint Louis, MO 63136-1414
Tel (314) 595-8000 Founded/Ownrshp 2010
Sales 890.6MM^E EMP 1,900
SIC 3625 3594 Motor controls, electric; Fluid power pumps & motors
Pr: Kei Y Pang
CFO: Michael Briggs
Treas: Elizabeth Miller
VP: Austin Bonnett
VP: Mark Weisheit
Dir Bus: Tom Aloor
Prgrm Mgr: Andrew Poag
Dist Mgr: Mike Gardiner
Natl Sales: Jim D'Angelo
Mktg Mgr: Gregg Young
Manager: Brian Wolek

D-U-N-S 13-180-8081 EXP
NIDERA US LLC
(Suby of NIDERA B.V.)
195 Danbury Rd Ste 240, Wilton, CT 06897-4075
Tel (203) 834-5700 Founded/Ownrshp 2010
Sales 531.4MM^E EMP 50
Accts Dbh & Associates Llc Normal
SIC 5153 Grain elevators; Grains
VP: Barry Schechtman
*Pr: Hugh Niven

D-U-N-S 00-942-8681
■ **NIELS FUGAL SONS CO LLC**
(Suby of DYCOM INDUSTRIES INC) ★
1005 S Main St, Pleasant Grove, UT 84062-3509
Tel (801) 785-3152 Founded/Ownrshp 1924
Sales 100.1MM^E EMP 325
SIC 1623 Underground utilities contractor
Pr: Gary McQueen
*VP: Ray Fugal
*VP: Boyd J Holdaway
Div Mgr: Brad Mills
IT Man: Kaystan Drew
Sfty Dirs: Kevin Lebaron
Opers Mgr: David McDonald
Sls Mgr: Erik Sundstrom

D-U-N-S 08-940-5539 IMP/EXP
NIELSEN & BAINBRIDGE LLC
PINNACLE FRAMES & ACCENTS
12303 Tech Blvd Ste 950, Austin, TX 78727
Tel (512) 506-8844 Founded/Ownrshp 1999
Sales 330.4MM^E EMP 1,155
SIC 2499 5023 Picture & mirror frames, wood; Frames & framing, picture & mirror
Pr: Scott Slater
Mng Pt: Dave Gereau
Mng Pt: Mort Madison
COO: Terry Cole
CFO: Gary Golden
VP: Randy Faltesek
VP: Peter Tamuzza
MIS Dir: Michael Morrison
IT Man: Mike Latimer
VP Sls: Tim Charon
Mktg Mgr: Gretchen Faltesek

D-U-N-S 06-677-8036
NIELSEN AUDIO INC
7000 Columbia Gateway Dr # 200, Columbia, MD 21046-1572
Tel (410) 312-8000 Founded/Ownrshp 2013
Sales 160.3MM^E EMP 1,443
SIC 8732 7372 Market analysis or research; Survey service: marketing, location, etc.; Application computer software
CEO: David Calhoun
Pr: Pierre Bouvard
Pr: Owen Charlebois
COO: Brian West
Ofcr: Delores L Cody
Ofcr: Debra Delman
Ex VP: Manish Bhatia
Ex VP: Mark Blake
Ex VP: Katie Burke
Ex VP: Paul Donato
Ex VP: Itzhak Fisher
Ex VP: Robert F Henrick
Ex VP: Vaughan S Henry
Ex VP: Mary Lou Legge
Ex VP: Gregg Lindner
Ex VP: Steven M Smith
Sr VP: Carol Hanley
Sr VP: William J McKenna
VP: Joseph Alisa
VP: Gary Marince
VP: John Poche

D-U-N-S 80-045-7801
NIELSEN CO
85 Broad St Bsmt, New York, NY 10004-2781
Tel (646) 654-5000 Founded/Ownrshp 1924
Sales 5.5MMM^E EMP 30,000
SIC 7389

D-U-N-S 95-973-8261
NIELSEN CO US LLC
NIELSEN MEDIA RESEARCH
(Suby of TNC (US) HOLDINGS INC) ★
85 Broad St, New York, NY 10004-2434
Tel (646) 654-5000 Founded/Ownrshp 1999
Sales 3.2MMM^E EMP 34,730
SIC 8732

NIELSEN MEDIA RESEARCH
See NIELSEN CO US LLC

D-U-N-S 00-910-0348
NIELSON CONSTRUCTION AND MATERIALS
825 N Loop Rd, Huntington, UT 84528
Tel (435) 687-2494 Founded/Ownrshp 1946
Sales 91.3MM^E EMP 280
SIC 1611 Highway & street construction
Ch: Wayne L Nielson
*Pr: John Wayne Nielson
*COO: Steve Ogden
*CFO: Gary Miyasaki
Mtls Mgr: Shawn Ward

D-U-N-S 02-577-1635
NIEMANN FOODS FOUNDATION
COUNTY MARKET
923 N 12th St, Quincy, IL 62301-2129
Tel (217) 221-5600 Founded/Ownrshp 1917
Sales 156.4M EMP 5,000^E
SIC 5411 5541 Grocery stores; Supermarkets; Gasoline service stations
CEO: Richard H Niemann
*Pr: Richard H Niemann II
*CFO: Christopher Niemann
*VP: James Cox
*Prin: Connie Roberts
Genl Mgr: Scott Mounce

NIES ARTCRAFT COMPANIES
See NIES/ARTCRAFT INC

D-U-N-S 01-284-8847
■ **NIES/ARTCRAFT INC**
NIES ARTCRAFT COMPANIES
(Suby of RR DONNELLEY) ★
3049 Chouteau Ave, Saint Louis, MO 63103-2900
Tel (314) 951-0400 Founded/Ownrshp 2006
Sales 83.2MM^E EMP 364
SIC 2752 Commercial printing, offset
CEO: James W Finger II
VP: Tom Hedrick
VP: John Kruszka
Exec: Carol Schallert
Dept Mgr: John Geisler
Sales Exec: Catherine McGavin
Snr Mgr: Brendan Delong

NIFA
See NATIONAL INSTITUTE OF FOOD AND AGRICULTURE

D-U-N-S 00-742-1712 IMP
NIFCO AMERICA CORP
(Suby of NIFCO INC.)
8015 Dove Pkwy, Canal Winchester, OH 43110-9697
Tel (614) 920-6800 Founded/Ownrshp 1996
Sales 210.7MM^E EMP 650
SIC 3089 Automotive parts, plastic
Pr: Toshiyuki Yamamoto
*CFO: John Kosik
*VP: Tom Day

D-U-N-S 14-586-5304
NIGHTINGALE HOLDINGS LLC
4700 Ashwood Dr Ste 200, Blue Ash, OH 45241-2424
Tel (513) 489-7100 Founded/Ownrshp 2000
Sales 8.7MM^E EMP 1,000^E
SIC 8051 Skilled nursing care facilities
Pr: Steve Rosedale
IT Man: Ann Trimble

D-U-N-S 10-626-5668
NIGHTINGALE NURSING SERVICE INC
CONSUMER DIRECT SERVICES
3301 Great Northrn Ave203 Ste 203, Missoula, MT 59808
Tel (406) 541-1700 Founded/Ownrshp 1996
Sales 24.3MM^E EMP 1,000^E
SIC 8082 Home health care services
Pr: William F Woody
IT Man: Ron Dunbar

D-U-N-S 83-756-8609 IMP
▲ **NII HOLDINGS INC**
1875 Explorer St Ste 800, Reston, VA 20190 6023
Tel (703) 390-5100 Founded/Ownrshp 1995
Sales 529.4MM^E EMP 2,875
Tkr Sym NIHD Exch NGS
SIC 4812 Cellular telephone services
CEO: Steven M Shindler
*Ch Bd: Kevin L Beebe
Pr: Francisco Tosta Valim Filho
CFO: Daniel E Freiman
CFO: Gokul V Hemmady
Ex VP: Gary D Begeman
VP: Shana C Smith
Plng Mgr: David Grados
CTO: Bernardo Sanabria
Mktg Mgr: Adriana Weber
Snr Mgr: Mary Mireles
Board of Directors: James V Continenza, Howard S Hoffmann, Ricardo Knoepfelmacher

D-U-N-S 14-945-7454
NIIT TECHNOLOGIES INC
(Suby of NIIT TECHNOLOGIES LIMITED)
1050 Crown Pinte Pkwy 5th # 5, Atlanta, GA 30338
Tel (770) 551-9494 Founded/Ownrshp 2004
Sales 140.0MM EMP 55
SIC 7379 7371 Computer related consulting services; Software programming applications
Pr: Lalit Kumardhingra
*Pr: C N Madhusudan
Sr VP: Milind Gurjar
VP: Georgy Mathews
Exec: Antara Das
Exec: Pia N Gaurav
Exec: Ashit Madhok
Dir Bus: Gaurav Bhatia
Dir Bus: Sarvesh Bhatnagar
Prgrm Mgr: Arvind Kanaujia
Prgrm Mgr: Ashwani Saxena

D-U-N-S 05-095-7364 IMP/EXP
▲ **NIKE INC**
1 Sw Bowerman Dr, Beaverton, OR 97005-0979
Tel (503) 671-6453 Founded/Ownrshp 1964
Sales 32.3MMM EMP 62,612
Tkr Sym NKE Exch NYS
SIC 3021 2329 2339 5139 5661 5136 Rubber & plastics footwear; Athletic (warmup, sweat & jogging) suits: men's & boys'; Athletic clothing: women's, misses' & juniors'; Footwear, athletic; Shoes; Footwear, athletic; Men's & boys' sportswear & work clothing
Pr: Mark G Parker
Pr: Trevor A Edwards
Pr: Michael Spillane
COO: Eric D Sprunk
CFO: Donald W Blair
CFO: Angie Laroche
Bd of Dir: Nico Harrison
Ofcr: Hilary K Krane
Ex VP: David J Ayre
Ex VP: Keith Crawford
Ex VP: Reham Habib
Ex VP: John F Slusher
VP: Mark Allen
VP: Gina Arndt
VP: Dermott Cleary
VP: Ralph Dilorio
VP: Archie McEachern
VP: Sarah Mensah
VP: Jeff Perkins
VP: David Schriber
VP: Hans Vanalebeek
Board of Directors: John R Thompson Jr, Elizabeth J Comstock, Phyllis M Wise, John G Connors, Timothy D Cook, John J Donahoe II, Alan B Graf Jr, Travis A Knight, John C Lechleiter, Michelle A Peluso, Johnathan A Rodgers

D-U-N-S 05-432-4207 EXP
■ **NIKE INTERNATIONAL LTD**
(Suby of NIKE INC) ★
1 Sw Bowerman Dr, Beaverton, OR 97005-0979
Tel (503) 671-6750 Founded/Ownrshp 1981
Sales 154.0MM^E EMP 291
SIC 5139 5136 5137 Shoes; Sportswear, men's & boys'; Sportswear, women's & children's
CEO: Philip H Knight
*Pr: Thomas E Clarke
*VP: David Kottkamp
Brnch Mgr: Ron Quering

D-U-N-S 62-069-1147 EXP
■ **NIKE RETAIL SERVICES INC**
(Suby of NIKE INC) ★
1 Sw Bowerman Dr, Beaverton, OR 97005-0979
Tel (503) 671-6453 Founded/Ownrshp 1985
Sales 90.5MM^E EMP 1,100
SIC 5661 5699 Footwear, athletic; Sports apparel
Pr: Mark G Parker
VP: Charles Denson

D-U-N-S 62-387-3473 IMP/EXP
■ **NIKE USA INC**
(Suby of NIKE INC) ★
1 Sw Bowerman Dr, Beaverton, OR 97005-0979
Tel (503) 671-6453 Founded/Ownrshp 1998
Sales 168.1MM^E EMP 10,000^E
SIC 7941 Sports clubs, managers & promoters
Pr: Mark G Parker

D-U-N-S 60-280-1870 IMP/EXP
NIKKEN INTERNATIONAL INC
2 Corporate Park Ste 100, Irvine, CA 92606-5103
Tel (949) 789-2000 Founded/Ownrshp 2001
Sales 99.9MM EMP 480^E
Accts Bdo Usa Llp Costa Mesa Ca
SIC 5199 General merchandise, non-durable
Ch Bd: Toshizo Watanabe
*Pr: Doug Beaun
*CEO: Kurt H Fulle
*VP: Larry Proffitm

D-U-N-S 92-923-2478 IMP
NIKON AMERICAS INC
(Suby of NIKON CORPORATION)
1300 Walt Whitman Rd Fl 2, Melville, NY 11747-3064
Tel (631) 547-4200 Founded/Ownrshp 1981
Sales 425.7MM^E EMP 750
SIC 5043 5084 Photographic equipment & supplies; Industrial machinery & equipment
Ch Bd: Notio Hashizume
*Pr: Atsuo Nakada
Sr VP: Peter J Moleski
Snr Mgr: Chris Marshall

D-U-N-S 00-196-2976 IMP/EXP
NIKON INC (NY)
(Suby of NIKON AMERICAS INC) ★
1300 Walt Whitman Rd Fl 2, Melville, NY 11747-3064
Tel (631) 547-4200 Founded/Ownrshp 1960, 1981
Sales 188.3MM^E EMP 335
SIC 5043 5049 Photographic equipment & supplies; Optical goods
Pr: Nobuyoshi Gokyu
Pr: Tom Hedges
Treas: Nick Farno
*Treas: Peter Moleski
*Sr VP: David C Lee
VP: John P Browne
VP: Joseph J Carfora
Assoc Dir: Mike Boyle
Dir: Megan Lambdin
Comm Man: Anna Marie Bakker
Comm Man: Jillian Cutrone

D-U-N-S 11-508-1903 IMP
NIKON PRECISION INC
(Suby of NIKON AMERICAS INC) ★
1399 Shoreway Rd, Belmont, CA 94002-4107
Tel (650) 508-4674 Founded/Ownrshp 1982
Sales 190.7MM^E EMP 600
SIC 5084 5065 Industrial machinery & equipment; Electronic parts & equipment
CEO: Toyohiro Takamine
*Pr: Takao Naito
Sr VP: Tom Novak
Assoc Dir: Bill Cole
Cmptr Lab: David Mahan

D-U-N-S 00-624-9338 IMP/EXP
NILFISK INC (MN)
EURO CLEAN
(Suby of NILFISK A/S)
9435 Winnetka Ave N, Brooklyn Park, MN 55445-1618
Tel (800) 334-1083 Founded/Ownrshp 1910, 1925
Sales 261.6MM^E EMP 598
SIC 3589 5087 Floor washing & polishing machines, commercial; Service establishment equipment
CEO: Christian C Knudsen
*Pr: Jeff Barna
*CFO: Morten Johansen
Mng Dir: Don Galley
Genl Mgr: Christina Barthel
Genl Mgr: Susanne Jansen
Genl Mgr: Wade Reitmeier
Genl Mgr: Anton Soerensen
CIO: Jason Banick
IT Man: Shelley Frederickson
IT Man: Peter Stahlmann

D-U-N-S 94-144-9142 IMP/EXP
NILIT AMERICA INC
(Suby of NILIT B.V.)
420 Industrial Park Rd, Ridgeway, VA 24148-4439
Tel (276) 638-2434 Founded/Ownrshp 1969
Sales 110.9MM^E EMP 210
SIC 5199 2299 5531 Industrial yarns; Fibers, textile: recovery from textile mill waste & rags; Automotive accessories
Ch Bd: Michael P Levi
IT Man: Fried Sandy
Prd Mgr: Jimmy Cockram

D-U-N-S 01-993-7709
▲ **NIMBLE STORAGE INC**
211 River Oaks Pkwy, San Jose, CA 95134-1913
Tel (408) 432-9600 Founded/Ownrshp 2007
Sales 322.2MM EMP 1,104^E
Tkr Sym NMBL Exch NYS
SIC 3572 Computer storage devices
Ch Bd: Suresh Vasudevan
CFO: Anup Singh
CFO: Anup V Singh
VP: Rod Bagg
VP: Aparna Bawa
VP: Carolyn Crandall
VP: Leonard Iventosch
VP: Praniti Lakhwara
VP: Dan Leary
VP: Eric Mann
VP: Denis Murphy
VP: Mark Stevens
VP: Mike Wallerstedt
Board of Directors: Frank Calderoni, James J Goetz, William D Jenkins Jr, Bob Kelly, Jerry M Kennelly, Ping Li, William J Schroeder

D-U-N-S 06-101-5889
NIMED CORP
(Suby of CENTEGRA HEALTH SYSTEM) ★
4201 W Medical Center Dr, McHenry, IL 60050-8409
Tel (815) 344-5555 Founded/Ownrshp 1982
Sales 590.5M EMP 1,500
SIC 8062 General medical & surgical hospitals
Pr: Paul Laudick
*Ch Bd: Ernest Rich
*Sec: James F Frasor
*V Ch Bd: Ronald Bykowski

NINE ENERGY SERVICE
See CDK PERFORATING LLC

D-U-N-S 01-978-5303
NINE ENERGY SERVICE INC
16945 Northchase Dr, Houston, TX 77060-2135
Tel (281) 730-5100 Founded/Ownrshp 2013
Sales 264.4MM^E EMP 300^E
SIC 5211 1382 Energy conservation products; Oil & gas exploration services
CEO: Paul Butero
CFO: Ann G Fox
Sr VP: Rocky Seale

D-U-N-S 14-493-0922 IMP
NINE WEST FOOTWEAR CORP
1411 Broadway Fl 20, New York, NY 10018-3471
Tel (800) 999-1877 Founded/Ownrshp 1933
Sales 34.6MM^E EMP 6,000
SIC 3144 3171 5661 5632 5139 Women's footwear, except athletic; Boots, canvas or leather: women's; Dress shoes, women's; Sandals, women's; Women's handbags & purses; Handbags, women's; Purses, women's; Shoe stores; Women's shoes; Women's boots; Apparel accessories; Handbags; Footwear
Pr: Rick Paterno
CFO: John T McClain
Ofcr: Whitney Alan
VP: Ira Dansky
VP: Stacy Lastina
VP: Dora Thagouras
Creative D: Fred Allard
Creative D: Mark Kucharski
Brnch Mgr: Beth Romanelli
Dir IT: Thomas Murray
IT Man: Peter Caracciolo

D-U-N-S 00-586-1955 IMP/EXP
NINE WEST HOLDINGS INC
ONE JEANSWEAR
180 Rittenhouse Cir, Bristol, PA 19007-1618
Tel (215) 785-4000 Founded/Ownrshp 1997, 2015
Sales 2.6MMM^E EMP 4,100^E
SIC 2337 Women's & misses' suits & coats
Pr: Ralph A Schipani
*Treas: Joseph T Donnalley
Ofcr: Christopher R Cade
Ex VP: Ira M Dansky
Snr Mgr: Sheri Getts

D-U-N-S 06-769-5015 IMP
NINTENDO OF AMERICA INC (WA)
(Suby of NINTENDO CO., LTD.)
4600 150th Ave Ne, Redmond, WA 98052-5115
Tel (425) 882-2040 Founded/Ownrshp 1980
Sales 697.3MM^E EMP 955
SIC 5092 Video games
Pr: Reggie Fils-Aime
*Ex VP: John Bauer
Ex VP: Cammie Dunaway
Ex VP: Reginald Fils-Aime
*Ex VP: Mike Fukuda
Ex VP: Don James
Ex VP: Matt Kasson
*Ex VP: Peter Main
*Ex VP: Phillip Rogers
*Ex VP: Jacqualee Story
*Sr VP: Rick Flamm
*Sr VP: George Harrison
*Sr VP: Flip Morse
Sr VP: Duncan Orrell-Jones
Sr VP: Sara Rades
*Sr VP: Rob Thompson
VP: Robert Champagne
*VP: Leon Feuerberg
*VP: Ken Frost
VP: Cynthia Gordon
VP: Andy Hieke

D-U-N-S 82-879-4193
NINTEX USA LLC
(Suby of NINTEX GROUP PTY LTD)
10900 Ne 8th St Ste 230, Bellevue, WA 98004-4453
Tel (425) 324-2455 Founded/Ownrshp 2006
Sales 20.0MMM^E EMP 68^E
SIC 5734 Computer software & accessories
CEO: John Burton
*CFO: Eric Johnson
*Founder: Brett Campbell
*Ofcr: Russ Mann
Sr VP: Christian Smith
VP: Kim Albrecht
VP: Justin Donato
*VP: Ryan Duguid
VP: Baran Erkel
*VP: Steve Heaney
*VP: Alberto Sutton
VP: Josh Waldo
Board of Directors: Steve Largent, Brian V Turner, Mark Woodward

NIPCO
See NORTHWEST IOWA POWER COOPERATIVE

D-U-N-S 04-682-4090
NIPPON EXPRESS USA INC
(Suby of NIPPON EXPRESS CO., LTD.)
2401 44th Rd Fl 14, Long Island City, NY 11101-4605
Tel (212) 758-6100 Founded/Ownrshp 1962
Sales 860.5MM^E EMP 1,500
SIC 4731 4225 Foreign freight forwarding; General warehousing & storage
CEO: Kenji Fujii
VP: Joanna Ferrell
VP: Norman Sawanobori
Admn Mgr: Dianne Palmar
Genl Mgr: Toshikzu Kitai
Genl Mgr: Kunihiko Shimizu
Genl Mgr: Hideki Takami

D-U-N-S 78-761-2795 IMP
NIPPON PAINT (USA) INC
NIPPON PAINT AMERICA
(Suby of NIPPON PAINT HOLDINGS CO., LTD.)
300 Frank W Burr Blvd # 10, Teaneck, NJ 07666-6726
Tel (201) 692-1111 Founded/Ownrshp 1990
Sales 180.9MM^E EMP 560
SIC 2851 Paints & allied products
CEO: Hiroaki Ueno
*Pr: Hidefumi Morita
COO: Jeffrey M Yordon
CFO: Joan P Daniels

NIPPON PAINT AMERICA
See NIPPON PAINT (USA) INC

D-U-N-S 00-170-9302 IMP
NIPPON STEEL & SUMITOMO METAL USA INC
(Suby of NIPPON STEEL & SUMITOMO METAL CORPORATION)
1251 Ave Of The Ave Fl 23, New York, NY 10020
Tel (212) 486-7150 Founded/Ownrshp 1972
Sales 160.0MM^E EMP 757
SIC 5051 5084 Steel; Pipe & tubing, steel; Printing trades machinery, equipment & supplies
Pr: Nobuhiko Ikura
*Treas: Takeshi Uchida
*Exec: Yuki Ishii

D-U-N-S 07-662-7934 IMP/EXP
NIPPON SUISAN (USA) INC
(Suby of NIPPON SUISAN KAISHA,LTD.)
15400 Ne 90th St 100, Redmond, WA 98052-3507
Tel (425) 869-1703 Founded/Ownrshp 1974
Sales 331.4MM^E EMP 1,003
SIC 5146 Seafoods
Pr: Volker Kuntzsch
*Sec: Kazuo Kozakai
*VP: Hiroyuki Hamano

NIPPON YUSEN KABUSHIKI
See NYK LINE (NORTH AMERICA) INC

NIPRO DIAGNOSTICS
See TRIVIDIA HEALTH INC

D-U-N-S 79-737-2554 IMP/EXP
NIPRO MEDICAL CORP
(Suby of NIPRO CORPORATION)
3150 Nw 107th Ave, Doral, FL 33172-2135
Tel (305) 599-7174 Founded/Ownrshp 1992
Sales 299.3MM EMP 24^E
SIC 5047 Medical equipment & supplies
Pr: Goichi Miyazumi
*Pr: Luis Candelario
*Treas: Seiyi Ishida
VP: Jessica Oswald
*VP: Minuro Sano
IT Man: Nelson Flores
VP Sls: Omar Valenzuela
Mktg Dir: Mauro Arguello

D-U-N-S 96-937-0464 IMP/EXP
NIPRO PHARMAPACKAGING AMERICAS CORP
(Suby of NIPRO CORPORATION)
1200 N 10th St, Millville, NJ 08332-2032
Tel (856) 825-1400 Founded/Ownrshp 2011
Sales 150.1MM^E EMP 350^E
SIC 3221 Vials, glass
Pr: Kurt Van Dal
Prd Mgr: John Birdsall

NIS
See NETWORK IMAGING SOLUTIONS INC

D-U-N-S 86-723-6358
NISA INVESTMENT ADVISORS INC
101 S Hanley Rd Ste 1700, Saint Louis, MO 63105-3487
Tel (314) 721-1900 Founded/Ownrshp 1994
Sales 97.4MM^E EMP 210
SIC 6722 6282 Management investment, open-end; Investment advice
Prin: Jess Yawitz
CFO: Mark Folkins
Ofcr: Marianne O'Doherty
Ofcr: Alex Shipp
*Prin: William Marshall
CTO: Donald Pinkard
IT Man: Richard Benduski
IT Man: Stephan Guilford
Software D: Matt Freiburg
Genl Couns: Bella Sanevich
Counsel: Joyce Lafontain

NISC
See NATIONAL INFORMATION SOLUTIONS COOPERATIVE INC

D-U-N-S 06-536-9365
■ **NISCAYAH INC**
HAMILTON PACIFIC
(Suby of STANLEY BLACK & DECKER INC) ★
2400 Commerce Ave Ste 500, Duluth, GA 30096-8920
Tel (678) 474-1720 Founded/Ownrshp 2011
Sales 89.0MM^E EMP 605
SIC 5065 Security control equipment & systems
Pr: Martin Schnurr
CFO: Kevin M Lobdell
VP: Thomas Benson
VP: Marty Guay
Brnch Mgr: Dagostin Tina
Brnch Mgr: Joe Zulli
Opers Mgr: Kyle Harris
Manager: Marshall Pinnix

NISCO
See NISHIKAWA COOPER LLC

D-U-N-S 18-198-9807 IMP
NISHIBA INDUSTRIES CORP
(Suby of NISHIBA INDUSTRY CO., LTD.)
2360 Marconi Ct, San Diego, CA 92154-7241
Tel (619) 661-8866 Founded/Ownrshp 1987
Sales 120.9MM^E EMP 650
SIC 3089 3544 5162 Plastic hardware & building products; Special dies, tools, jigs & fixtures; Plastics materials & basic shapes
Pr: Yoshiaki Nishiba
Opers Mgr: Daniel Bosco

D-U-N-S 14-707-9123 IMP
NISHIKAWA COOPER LLC
NISCO
(Suby of NISHIKAWA OF AMERICA INC) ★
324 Morrow St, Topeka, IN 46571-9076
Tel (260) 593-2156 Founded/Ownrshp 1987
Sales 228.7MM^E EMP 923
Accts Ernst & Young Llp Indianapoli
SIC 3069 Weather strip, sponge rubber
Pr: Futoshi Higashida
VP: Chad Klopfenstein
*VP: Michael Talaga
Plnt Mgr: Tony Baker
Sls Mgr: Jason Allen
Snr Mgr: Linda Herendeen

D-U-N-S 60-535-3267 IMP
NISHIKAWA OF AMERICA INC
(Suby of NISHIKAWA RUBBER CO.,LTD.)
324 Morrow St, Topeka, IN 46571-9076
Tel (260) 593-2156 Founded/Ownrshp 1989
Sales 228.7MM^E EMP 923
SIC 3069 Weather strip, sponge rubber
Pr: Bunji Yamamoti
Pt: Jol Vanatti
*VP: Bill Burga

D-U-N-S 01-988-4712
■ **NISOURCE CORPORATE SERVICES CO**
(Suby of NISOURCE INC) ★
801 E 86th Ave, Merrillville, IN 46410-6272
Tel (219) 647-4222 Founded/Ownrshp 1933
Sales 833.0MM^E EMP 1,700
SIC 8741 Business management
Pr: Robert C Skaggs Jr
*CFO: Stephen Smith
*VP: Gary Pottorff
IT Man: Christine Butcher
Counsel: Christine Morace

D-U-N-S 18-565-4076
▲ **NISOURCE INC**
801 E 86th Ave, Merrillville, IN 46410-6272
Tel (877) 647-5990 Founded/Ownrshp 1987
Sales 4.6MMM EMP 7,596^E
Tkr Sym NI Exch NYS
SIC 4939 4922 Combination utilities; Pipelines, natural gas
Pr: Joseph Hamrock
*Ch Bd: Richard L Thompson
CEO: Eileen O'Neill Odum
COO: Jim L Stanley
CFO: Donald E Brown
Bd of Dir: Keith Schafer
Ex VP: Michael O'Donnell
Ex VP: Eileen O'Neill
Ex VP: Stephen Smith
Sr VP: Karl Brack
VP: Richard Bond
VP: Karl Eckweiler
VP: Larry Francisco
VP: Joel Hoelzer
VP: Dick James
VP: Julie McElmurry
VP: Barbara McKay
VP: Joe Mulpas
VP: Joseph W Mulpas
VP: Shawn Patterson
VP: Cassandra Pullin
Board of Directors: Richard A Abdoo, Aristides S Candris, Wayne S Deveydt, Deborah A Henretta, Michael E Jesanis, Kevin T Kabat, Carolyn Y Woo

D-U-N-S 96-796-1632
■ **NISSAN CONYERS INC**
(Suby of PENSKE AUTOMOTIVE GROUP INC) ★
1420 Iris Dr, Morrow, GA 30260
Tel (770) 922-7600 Founded/Ownrshp 2005
Sales 58.1MM^E EMP 1,112^E
SIC 5511 Automobiles, new & used
Pr: Terry Tayllor
Genl Mgr: Pat Zill
Sales Exec: Alfonzo Osborne
Sls Mgr: Eddie Card
Sls Mgr: Ryan Martin
Sls Mgr: Jake Meissner
Sls Mgr: Carl Whipple

NISSAN FORKLIFT
See UNICARRIERS AMERICAS CORP

D-U-N-S 79-551-8398
NISSAN GRUBBS MID-CITIES LTD
BEDFORD RENT A CAR
310 Airport Fwy, Bedford, TX 76022-6404
Tel (817) 268-1000 Founded/Ownrshp 2000
Sales 115.0MM EMP 85
SIC 5511

D-U-N-S 03-226-4368
NISSAN MOSSY INC
MOSSY NISSAN KEARNY MESA
(Suby of MOSSY OLDSMOBILE) ★
4625 Brinnell St, San Diego, CA 92111-2301
Tel (619) 474-7011 Founded/Ownrshp 1982
Sales 308.3MM^E EMP 1,000
SIC 5511 Automobiles, new & used
Pr: Philip Mossy
*CFO: John Epps
*VP: Peter Mossy
Genl Mgr: Matt Seamark

D-U-N-S 06-138-0739
NISSAN MOTOR ACCEPTANCE CORP
INFINITI FINANCIAL SERVICE
(Suby of NISSAN NORTH AMERICA INC) ★
1 Nissan Way, Franklin, TN 37067-6367
Tel (615) 725-1000 Founded/Ownrshp 1982
Sales NA EMP 700
SIC 6141 Financing: automobiles, furniture, etc., not a deposit bank
Pr: Carlos Ghosn
Pr: Rebecca Vest
Sr VP: Carla Bailo
VP: Brian Carolin
VP: William J Krueger
VP: Motohiro Matsumura
VP: Mark McNabb
VP: Mark Stout
VP: Tsuyoshi Yamaguchi
Mktg Dir: Nat Mason
Snr Mgr: Kevin Cullum

D-U-N-S 00-960-2533 IMP/EXP
NISSAN NORTH AMERICA INC
(Suby of NISSAN MOTOR CO.,LTD.)
1 Nissan Way, Franklin, TN 37067-6367
Tel (615) 725-1000 Founded/Ownrshp 2014
Sales 8.7MMM^E EMP 13,000
SIC 5012 8711 8734 6141 8741 3711 Commercial vehicles; Designing: ship, boat, machine & product; Product testing laboratories; Automobile proving & testing ground; Financing: automobiles, furniture, etc., not a deposit bank; Financial management for business; Automobile assembly, including specialty automobiles; Trucks, pickup, assembly of
Pr: Carlos Ghosn
V Ch: Jim Morton Jr
Pr: Jack Wilkerson
CFO: Matt Loader
Chf Mktg O: Tom F Smith
Ofcr: Alfred Gloddeck
Ex VP: Hidetoshi Imazu
Ex VP: Bill Krueger
Ex VP: Jos Muoz
Ex VP: Elias Najjar
Ex VP: Hiroto Saikawa
Sr VP: Doug Betts
Sr VP: John Martin
Sr VP: Dominique Thormann
Sr VP: Mitsuhiko Yamashita
VP: Eric Anderson
VP: Scott E Becker
VP: Carla Bobadilla
VP: Alan J Buddendeck
VP: Fred M Diaz
VP: Bryan Dumais

D-U-N-S 61-056-0971
NISSAN ROBBINS INC
ROBBINS NISSAN-OLDS
18711 Highway 59 N, Humble, TX 77338-4223
Tel (281) 446-3181 Founded/Ownrshp 1989
Sales 84.7MM EMP 80
SIC 5511 Automobiles, new & used; Pickups, new & used; Vans, new & used
Pr: William Robbins
Genl Mgr: Alicia Lopez

D-U-N-S 15-772-3578
NISSAN SMITHTOWN INC
535 Middle Country Rd, Saint James, NY 11780-3203
Tel (631) 361-9696 Founded/Ownrshp 1988
Sales 134.1MM EMP 99^E
SIC 5511 New & used car dealers
Ch Bd: Joseph Oscar Rubio
*Pr: Thomas Rubio

D-U-N-S 15-136-1854 IMP/EXP
NISSAN TRADING CORP AMERICAS
NISSAN TRADING CORP U.S.A.
(Suby of NISSAN TRADING CO., LTD.)
1974 Midway Ln, Smyrna, TN 37167-5872
Tel (615) 220-7100 Founded/Ownrshp 1984
Sales 179.7MM^E EMP 150
SIC 5013 5012 5051 5084 Automotive supplies & parts; Automobiles; Aluminum bars, rods, ingots, sheets, pipes, plates, etc.; Machine tools & metalworking machinery
Pr: Mamoru Kawahara
*VP: Taichi Matsuda

NISSAN TRADING CORP U.S.A.
See NISSAN TRADING CORP AMERICAS

D-U-N-S 96-859-9626
NISSHIN HOLDING INC
(Suby of NISSHIN STEEL CO., LTD.)
1701 Golf Rd, Rolling Meadows, IL 60008-4227
Tel (847) 290-5100 Founded/Ownrshp 2011
Sales 384.3MM^E EMP 192^E
SIC 8742 Management consulting services

D-U-N-S 19-840-1259 IMP
NISSIN BRAKE OHIO INC
(Suby of NISSIN KOGYO CO., LTD.)
1901 Industrial Dr, Findlay, OH 45840-5442
Tel (419) 420-3800 Founded/Ownrshp 1988
Sales 143.9MM^E EMP 677
SIC 3714 Motor vehicle brake systems & parts
Pr: Itsuo Miyake
*Treas: Hiro Sato
VP: Ron Hall
VP: Ken Lee
*VP: Wilson J Schroeder
Dir IT: Deiter Jennifer
Opers Supe: Jim Gove
Ql Cn Mgr: Ann Lasater
Ql Cn Mgr: Jeff Marok
Ql Cn Mgr: Brandon Peterson

D-U-N-S 05-924-5753 IMP/EXP
NISSIN FOODS (USA) CO INC (CA)
(Suby of NISSIN FOODS HOLDINGS CO.,LTD.)
2001 W Rosecrans Ave, Gardena, CA 90249-2994
Tel (310) 327-8478 Founded/Ownrshp 1970
Sales 124.5MM^E EMP 350
SIC 2098 2038 Noodles (e.g. egg, plain & water), dry; Ethnic foods, frozen
CEO: Hiroyuki Yoshida
Pr: Evelyn Jareno
CFO: Toshio Shigete
*VP: Takahiro Enomoto
VP: Eiichi Yamakawa
Genl Mgr: Susumu Nakagawa
Snr Sftwr: Masa Rushing
CIO: Koji Hiramoto
Dir IT: Ruben Haritoonian
IT Man: Fumi Mimami
Sfty Dirs: Osman Molina

D-U-N-S 07-292-4640
NISSIN INTERNATIONAL TRANSPORT USA INC
(Suby of NISSIN CORPORATION)
1540 W 190th St, Torrance, CA 90501-1121
Tel (310) 222-8500 Founded/Ownrshp 1973
Sales 205.4MM^E EMP 540
SIC 4731 Domestic freight forwarding
CEO: Yasushi Ihara
COO: Masahiro Ugai
*CFO: Mitsugu Matsusaka
VP: Mark Sclafani
VP: Dave Thompson
Brnch Mgr: Hiro Kawano
Brnch Mgr: Tak Kono
Brnch Mgr: Tetsuya Taga

Brnch Mgr: Kazuhiko Usami
Genl Mgr: Linda Kwok
Sls Mgr: John Leverett

NIST
See NATIONAL INSTITUTE OF STANDARDS & TECHNOLOGY

NITCO
See NORTHLAND INDUSTRIAL TRUCK CO INC

D-U-N-S 96-192-6073 IMP/EXP
NITINOL DEVICES AND COMPONENTS INC
N D C
47533 Westinghouse Dr, Fremont, CA 94539-7463
Tel (510) 683-2000 *Founded/Ownrshp* 2007
Sales 114.4MM[E] *EMP* 525
SIC 3841 5047 Surgical & medical instruments; Medical & hospital equipment
CEO: Dean Schauer
**Pr:* Tom Duerig
**VP:* Craig Bonsignore
VP: John Dicello
**VP:* Chuck Faris
**VP:* David Johnston
**Prin:* Mark Lemma
Mng Dir: Kaiya Duerig
IT Man: Danette Ondi
Prd Mgr: Roberto Carvajal
Ql Cn Mgr: Angel Ruiz
Board of Directors: Dan Lemaitre

NITRO STEEL
See GERDAU MACSTEEL INC

NITTANY MINITMART
See NITTANY OIL CO INC

D-U-N-S 93-346-3556
NITTANY OIL CO INC
NITTANY MINITMART
1540 Martin St, State College, PA 16803-3058
Tel (814) 237-4859 *Founded/Ownrshp* 1994
Sales 98.6MM[E] *EMP* 250
SIC 5171 1711 Petroleum bulk stations; Plumbing, heating, air-conditioning contractors
Pr: Jart V Martin
**Sec:* John Martin
**Sec:* James W Scott
**VP:* Sharon S Martin
**Prin:* James O Martin

D-U-N-S 00-466-6330 IMP/EXP
NITTO AMERICAS INC
PERMACEL-AUTOMOTIVE
(*Suby of* NITTO DENKO CORPORATION)
48500 Fremont Blvd, Fremont, CA 94538-6579
Tel (510) 445-5400 *Founded/Ownrshp* 1968
Sales 358.0MM[E] *EMP* 1,050
SIC 2672 3589 5162 5065 Tape, pressure sensitive: made from purchased materials; Water treatment equipment, industrial; Plastics products; Electronic parts
Ch Bd: Toru Takeuchi
**Pr:* Yoichiro Sakuma
**CFO:* Steve Evans
Sales Asso: Julie Pacheco

D-U-N-S 78-401-1566
NITYO INFOTECH CORP
666 Plainsboro Rd Ste 210, Plainsboro, NJ 08536-3004
Tel (609) 799-5959 *Founded/Ownrshp* 2005
Sales 60.2MM[E] *EMP* 1,000
SIC 7379 Computer related consulting services
Pr: Naveen Kumar
**CFO:* Baskar Nathan
Exec: Savita Dedha
Genl Mgr: Karunjit Dhir

D-U-N-S 92-965-7497
NITYO INFOTECH CORP
2652 Hidden Valley Rd # 103, Pittsburgh, PA 15241-3915
Tel (412) 894-9054 *Founded/Ownrshp* 2005
Sales 55.1MM[E] *EMP* 1,000
SIC 7379 Computer related consulting services
Pr: Naveen Kumar
**CFO:* Bhaskar Nathan

NIX HEALTH CARE SYSTEM
See ACCORD MEDICAL MANAGEMENT LP

NIX HEALTHCARE SYSTEM
See NIX HOSPITALS SYSTEM LLC

D-U-N-S 07-868-0042
NIX HOSPITALS SYSTEM LLC (TX)
NIX HEALTHCARE SYSTEM
414 Navarro St Ste 600, San Antonio, TX 78205-2541
Tel (210) 271-1800 *Founded/Ownrshp* 2011
Sales 99.6MM[E] *EMP* 950[E]
SIC 8062 General medical & surgical hospitals
Pr: John F Strieby
**CFO:* Lester E Surrock
Sr VP: Annette Burns
VP: Jennifer Murphy
CTO: Cynthia Cruz
Doctor: Mario Hernandez

D-U-N-S 07-969-5506
NIXON PEABODY LLP
1300 Clinton Sq, Rochester, NY 14604-1707
Tel (585) 263-1000 *Founded/Ownrshp* 1875
Sales 233.7MM[E] *EMP* 1,300
SIC 8111 General practice law office
Genl Pt: Richard F Langan Jr
**Pt:* James Curley
**Pt:* Karen Greenbaum
**Pt:* Carolyn S Kaplan
Pt: Jennifer Kuenster
**Pt:* Nestor M Nicholas
Pt: Philip B Taub
**Pt:* Harry P Trueheart III
Pt: Stephen D Zubiago
Mng Pt: Arnaud De Senilhes
Mng Pt: Kevin M Fitzgerald
Mng Pt: Richard Jones
Mng Pt: Cheng Lam
Mng Pt: Jeffrey S Lesk
Mng Pt: Neal J McNamara
Mng Pt: Gary Oberstein
Mng Pt: Gregory Ohara
Mng Pt: Denise D Pursley
Mng Pt: Susan C Roney
Mng Pt: Andrew C Rose
Mng Pt: Arthur J Rosner

NIXON POWER SERVICES COMPANY
See NIXON POWER SERVICES LLC

D-U-N-S 96-748-4325 IMP
NIXON POWER SERVICES LLC
NIXON POWER SERVICES COMPANY
5038 Thoroughbred Ln, Brentwood, TN 37027-4225
Tel (615) 309-5823 *Founded/Ownrshp* 2003
Sales 194.5MM[E] *EMP* 200
SIC 5063 4911 Generators; Generation, electric power
CEO: Ronald M Stanley Jr
Pr: Bryant Phillips
CFO: Kevin W Mann
Sls Mgr: Paul Grebel

D-U-N-S 96-912-0398
NJ CARPENTERS CATASTROPHIC HEALTH FUND
P.O. Box 7818 (08818-7818)
Tel (732) 417-3900 *Founded/Ownrshp* 2011
Sales 133.9MM *EMP* 3[E]
SIC 8631 Trade union

D-U-N-S 80-641-7549
NJ DEPARTMENT OF CORRECTIONS
(*Suby of* EXECUTIVE OFFICE OF STATE OF NEW JERSEY) ★
Stuyvsant Av Whttlesey Rd Whittlesey, Trenton, NJ 08618
Tel (609) 292-2162 *Founded/Ownrshp* 1976
Sales NA *EMP* 10,000[E]
SIC 9223

D-U-N-S 10-258-9082
NJ MALIN & ASSOCIATES LLC
(*Suby of* RAYMOND CORP) ★
15870 Midway Rd, Addison, TX 75001-4279
Tel (972) 458-2680 *Founded/Ownrshp* 2011
Sales 136.0MM[E] *EMP* 400
SIC 5046 5084

NJ TRANSIT
See NEW JERSEY TRANSIT CORP

NJCU
See NEW JERSEY CITY UNIVERSITY

NJDWSC
See NORTH JERSEY DISTRICT WATER SUPPLY COMMISSION

NJEA
See NEW JERSEY EDUCATION ASSOCIATION INC

NJIT
See NEW JERSEY INSTITUTE OF TECHNOLOGY (INC)

NJM INSURANCE GROUP
See NEW JERSEY MANUFACTURERS INSURANCE CO

D-U-N-S 02-571-5165
■ **NJR ENERGY SERVICES CO**
(*Suby of* NEW JERSEY RESOURCES CORP) ★
1415 Wyckoff Rd, Belmar, NJ 07719
Tel (732) 938-1273 *Founded/Ownrshp* 1996
Sales 86.0MM[E] *EMP* 100
SIC 4924 Natural gas distribution;
**COO:* Joseph P Shields
**Sr VP:* Stephen Westhoven
**VP:* Ginger Richman
Off Mgr: Kathy Cassey

D-U-N-S 00-838-5903
NJVC LLC
(*Suby of* CHENEGA CORP) ★
14295 Park Meadow Dr, Chantilly, VA 20151-2220
Tel (703) 429-9000 *Founded/Ownrshp* 2001
Sales 313.0MM *EMP* 1,300
Accts Rsm Us Llp Frederick Marylan
SIC 7379
Pr: Chris Andersen
VP: Jennifer IAMS
VP: Charles McGaugh
VP: Fredrick Turman
Dir Bus: Van Henderson
Prgrm Mgr: Denise Droneburg
Prgrm Mgr: Patti Oliver
Genl Mgr: Jeff Bongianino
Snr Sftwr: Daniel Gilbert
Snr Sftwr: Rob Hoffmann
Snr Ntwrk: Rik Koenig

D-U-N-S 01-404-2147
NK LIQUIDATION INC
NELL'S FAMILY MARKET
(*Suby of* C&S WHOLESALE PRODUCE) ★
600 Arsenal Rd, York, PA 17402-2127
Tel (717) 854-1505 *Founded/Ownrshp* 1983
Sales 121.2MM[E] *EMP* 1,000
SIC 5411 Supermarkets
VP: J Warren Weaver
**Sec:* Thomas Teeter

D-U-N-S 61-274-3997 IMP/EXP
NK PARTS INDUSTRIES INC
(*Suby of* NIKKON HOLDINGS CO., LTD.)
777 S Kuther Rd, Sidney, OH 45365-8861
Tel (937) 498-4651 *Founded/Ownrshp* 1987
Sales 175.9MM[E] *EMP* 1,060
SIC 5013 1796 4731

D-U-N-S 82-888-0075
NK STEEL LLC
31731 Northwstrn Hwy 15 Ste 157 W, Farmington Hills, MI 48334
Tel (248) 865-9000 *Founded/Ownrshp* 2008
Sales 100.0MM *EMP* 12
SIC 5051

D-U-N-S 61-783-5244
■ **NL HOLDING CORP (DEL)**
(*Suby of* NEW ENGLAND FINANCIAL) ★
260 Madison Ave Ste 11, New York, NY 10016-2412
Tel (212) 354-8800 *Founded/Ownrshp* 1998
Sales 115.0MM[E] *EMP* 170[E]
SIC 6211 6411 Brokers, security; Dealers, security; Insurance agents; Insurance brokers
Ch: James Benson
**Pr:* Jay L Lewis
**Exec:* Thomas Wirtshafter

D-U-N-S 78-723-7668
NL OF KY INC
NEACE, MUSSELMAN & MAYFIELD
(*Suby of* ASSUREDPARTNERS INC) ★
2305 River Rd, Louisville, KY 40206-1010
Tel (502) 894-2100 *Founded/Ownrshp* 2013
Sales NA *EMP* 434
SIC 6411 Insurance agents & brokers
Pr: John F Neace
**Pr:* Louis M Berman
**Pr:* Scott R Heiser
**Pr:* Alan J Jones
**Pr:* Joseph T Lukens
**Pr:* Douglas A Stough
Sr VP: Daniel Rossen
**VP:* Gerald B Budde

D-U-N-S 00-772-4095
NLFH ACCT PAYABLE BILL CH
541 N Fairbanks Ct Fl 16, Chicago, IL 60611-3319
Tel (312) 926-2094 *Founded/Ownrshp* 2011
Sales 666.8M[E] *EMP* 7,000
SIC 8721 Accounting, auditing & bookkeeping
Off Mgr: Sue Davis-Bilbo

D-U-N-S 79-981-1646 IMP
NLIGHT INC
5408 Ne 88th St Ste E, Vancouver, WA 98665-0990
Tel (360) 566-4460 *Founded/Ownrshp* 2000
Sales 152.6MM[E] *EMP* 549
SIC 3674 3699 Semiconductors & related devices; Laser systems & equipment
CEO: Scott Keeney
**CFO:* David Schaezler
**VP:* Jake Bell
**VP:* Mike Boston
**VP:* Joe Debartolo
**VP:* Mark Devito
**VP:* Rob Martinsen
VP: Joseph Sauvageau
Genl Mgr: Ed Gillespie
Dir IT: Todd Brainard
Dir IT: Sandra Garcia
Board of Directors: Doug Carlisle, Bill Ericson, Jeff Grant, Scott Keeney, Ray Link, Dave Osborne

D-U-N-S 60-973-2979 IMP
NLMK INDIANA LLC
(*Suby of* NLMK, PAO)
6500 S Boundary Rd, Portage, IN 46368-1334
Tel (219) 787-8200 *Founded/Ownrshp* 2008
Sales 150.1MM[E] *EMP* 380
SIC 3312 Hot-rolled iron & steel products
Pr: Robert Miller
**CFO:* Corinn Grossetti
VP: Jack Drapp
**VP:* Alexander Tseitline
Genl Mgr: Ken Crain

D-U-N-S 04-679-8059 IMP
NLMK PENNSYLVANIA LLC
15 Roemer Blvd, Farrell, PA 16121-2201
Tel (724) 983-6464 *Founded/Ownrshp* 2011
Sales 93.1MM *EMP* 500
SIC 3316 3356 3312 Cold finishing of steel shapes; Nonferrous rolling & drawing; Blast furnaces & steel mills
Pr: Robert Miller
**CEO:* Benedict Sciortino
**COO:* James Banker
**VP:* Jason Adams
Area Supr: Kevin Szolek
Genl Mgr: Scott Bishop
Ql Cn Mgr: Paul Harpst
Sls Dir: Frank Fonner

D-U-N-S 08-795-0056
NLV FINANCIAL CORP
(*Suby of* NATIONAL LIFE OF VERMONT) ★
1 National Life Dr, Montpelier, VT 05604-1000
Tel (802) 229-3333 *Founded/Ownrshp* 2006
Sales NA *EMP* 850
Accts Pricewaterhousecoopers Llp B
SIC 6311 6321 Mutual association life insurance; Accident insurance carriers; Health insurance carriers
Pr: Mehran Assadi
**Treas:* Robert E Cotton
Ex VP: Thomas H Brownell

D-U-N-S 09-532-3213
NM GROUP GLOBAL LLC
161 Greenfield St, Tiffin, OH 44883-2499
Tel (419) 447-5211 *Founded/Ownrshp* 2002
Sales 127.2MM[E] *EMP* 490
SIC 3542 3599 6799 Forging machinery & hammers; Custom machinery; Investors

D-U-N-S 07-989-8886
NM Z PARENT INC
787 7th Ave Fl 49, New York, NY 10019-6018
Tel (212) 720-0300 *Founded/Ownrshp* 2015
Sales 920.6MM[E] *EMP* 2,300[E]
SIC 6726 2841 2879 2842 Investment offices; Soap & other detergents; Pesticides, agricultural or household; Degreasing solvent
CEO: Steven B Klinsky

D-U-N-S 11-749-5838 IMP/EXP
NMB (USA) INC
NMB TECH
(*Suby of* MINEBEA CO., LTD.)
9730 Independence Ave, Chatsworth, CA 91311-4323
Tel (818) 709-1770 *Founded/Ownrshp* 1983
Sales 353.3MM[E] *EMP* 2,800
SIC 3562 5063 5084 3728 5065

NMB TECH
See NMB (USA) INC

N.M.C
See NUCLEAR MANAGEMENT CO LLC

D-U-N-S 00-696-9919 IMP/EXP
NMC GROUP INC (NE)
NMC POWER SYSTEMS
11002 Sapp Brothers Dr, Omaha, NE 68138-4812
Tel (402) 891-8600 *Founded/Ownrshp* 1938
Sales 150.3MM[E] *EMP* 150[E]
SIC 5082 5084 Construction & mining machinery; Road construction equipment; Graders, motor; Pavers; Lift trucks & parts
Pr: Nick Mizaur
**Treas:* Jay M Samuelson
Ex Dir: Brad Foster
Brnch Mgr: Dwight McDermott
Brnch Mgr: Aaron Rubesh
IT Man: England Tristan
Sfty Mgr: Michael Walters
Sls Mgr: Mark Anderson
Snr Mgr: Ryan Craven

NMC POWER SYSTEMS
See NMC GROUP INC

NMCOV
See ORO VALLEY HOSPITAL LLC

NMG AEROSPACE
See NATIONAL MACHINE CO

D-U-N-S 83-304-0657
NMH INVESTMENT LLC
313 Congress St Fl 5, Boston, MA 02210-1218
Tel (617) 790-4800 *Founded/Ownrshp* 2006
Sales 84.8MM[E] *EMP* 19,000
SIC 8361 Residential care

D-U-N-S 13-859-3913
NMHG HOLDING CO
HYSTER AND YALE
650 Ne Holladay St # 1600, Portland, OR 97232-2045
Tel (503) 721-6000 *Founded/Ownrshp* 1999
Sales 3.7MMM[E] *EMP* 7,800
SIC 3537 5084

NMLP
See NATIONAL MATERIAL LP

NMSU
See NEW MEXICO STATE UNIVERSITY

D-U-N-S 83-035-0372
NMTI HOLDINGS INC
75 Nh Ave, Portsmouth, NH 03801-2864
Tel (603) 427-5794 *Founded/Ownrshp* 2007
Sales 129.3MM *EMP* 380
SIC 7371 Computer software development
CEO: Sean O'Neill
**Pr:* Jeff Hiscox
**CFO:* Kenneth Smaha

NN
See NANDANSONS INTERNATIONAL INC

D-U-N-S 03-790-5247 IMP
▲ **NN INC**
207 Mockingbird Ln Ste 10, Johnson City, TN 37604-3137
Tel (423) 743-9151 *Founded/Ownrshp* 1980
Sales 667.2MM *EMP* 4,741
Tkr Sym NNBR *Exch* NGS
SIC 3562 Ball bearings & parts; Roller bearings & parts
Pr: Richard D Holder
**Ch Bd:* G Ronald Morris
CFO: Thomas C Burwell Jr
Ofcr: William C Kelly Jr
Sr VP: Matthew S Heiter
Sr VP: L Jeffery Manzagol
Sr VP: John A Manzi
Sr VP: Warren Veltman
Sr VP: James R Widders
VP: Will Kelly

NNA INSURANCE SERVICES
See NNA SERVICES LLC

D-U-N-S 07-798-3690
NNA SERVICES LLC
NNA INSURANCE SERVICES
9350 De Soto Ave, Chatsworth, CA 91311-4926
Tel (818) 739-4071 *Founded/Ownrshp* 2012
Sales NA *EMP* 204
SIC 6411 Insurance agents, brokers & service
Ch Bd: Milton G Valera
**CEO:* Thomas A Heymann
**CFO:* Robert A Clarke
**Ex VP:* Deborah M Thaw
VP: Deborah Valera
Exec: Kelly Rush
Board of Directors: Deborah M Thaw, Milton G Valera

D-U-N-S 36-218-9388
NNE PHARMAPLAN INC
NNE PHARMERPAN
(*Suby of* NNE PHARMAPLAN A/S)
3005 Carrington Mill Blvd, Morrisville, NC 27560-8885
Tel (919) 481-3765 *Founded/Ownrshp* 1967
Sales 175.3MM[E] *EMP* 1,700
SIC 8711 Consulting engineer
CEO: Morten Nielsen
**Pr:* Bob Brown Petersen
COO: Julie Jallad
**CFO:* Soren Jelert
Ql Cn Mgr: Emily Nelson

NNE PHARMERPAN
See NNE PHARMAPLAN INC

D-U-N-S 06-247-1537
NNR GLOBAL LOGISTICS USA INC
(*Suby of* NISHI-NIPPON RAILROAD CO.,LTD.)
450 E Devon Ave Ste 260, Itasca, IL 60143-1262
Tel (630) 773-1490 *Founded/Ownrshp* 1971
Sales 252.3MM *EMP* 340
Accts Ernst & Young Llp Chicago I
SIC 4731 Foreign freight forwarding

Pr: Kenji Oki
Opers Supe: Brad Jordan
Board of Directors: John Beggin, John Beggin, Andrew Hadley, Akira Nokuo

D-U-N-S 11-869-4629
NO FRILLS SUPERMARKETS INC OF OMAHA
11163 Mill Valley Rd, Omaha, NE 68154-3933
Tel (402) 399-9244 *Founded/Ownrshp* 1955
Sales NA *EMP* 1,300
SIC 5411

NO KIDDING
See HIS INTERNATIONAL CORP

NO LIMITS
See WRIGHT & FILIPPIS INC

NO NONSENSE
See KAYSER-ROTH CORP

D-U-N-S 02-823-9689
NOB HILL GENERAL STORE INC
SUPPORT CENTER
(*Suby of* BEL AIR MARKETS) ★
500 W Capitol Ave, West Sacramento, CA 95605-2624
Tel (916) 373-3333 *Founded/Ownrshp* 1998
Sales 400.4MM *EMP* 1,645
SIC 5411 5961 Supermarkets, chain; Pharmaceuticals, mail order
CEO: Michael Teel

D-U-N-S 60-945-7494
■ NOBEL BIOCARE USA LLC
(*Suby of* NOBEL BIOCARE AB)
22715 Savi Ranch Pkwy, Yorba Linda, CA 92887-4609
Tel (714) 282-4800 *Founded/Ownrshp* 2004
Sales 290.0MM *EMP* 500
SIC 3843 Dental equipment & supplies
Pr: Thomas Olsen
Ch: Ken Darienzo
* *Treas:* Frederick Walther
Sr VP: Mike Thompson
VP: Dan Hinkle
Dir IT: Tim Cronin
Sftwr Eng: Vanessa Simon
Ql Cn Mgr: John Sharobiem
Mktg Dir: Julie Ficke
Mktg Mgr: Teresa Heyne
Mktg Mgr: Linda Jones

D-U-N-S 11-261-9762
NOBEL LEARNING COMMUNITIES INC
(*Suby of* ACADEMIC ACQUISITION CORP) ★
1615 W Chester Pike # 200, West Chester, PA 19382-6223
Tel (484) 947-2000 *Founded/Ownrshp* 2011
Sales 333.2MM^E *EMP* 4,700^E
SIC 8211 8299 Private elementary & secondary schools; Specialty education; Educational services
Pr: George H Bernstein
* *COO:* Patricia B Miller
* *CFO:* Thomas Frank
* *Sr VP:* G Lee Bohs
* *Sr VP:* Jeanne Marie Welsko
Ex Dir: Susanne Bernard
CIO: Jada Hightower
CIO: Folake Odunlami
CIO: Scott Witmoyer
IT Man: Steven Ballios
Snr Mgr: Gigi Garcia

D-U-N-S 07-915-3423
▲ NOBILIS HEALTH CORP
11700 Katy Fwy Ste 300, Houston, TX 77079-1218
Tel (713) 355-8614 *Founded/Ownrshp* 2007
Sales 229.2MM *EMP* 715^E
Tkr Sym HLTH *Exch* ASE
SIC 8011 Offices & clinics of medical doctors; Clinic, operated by physicians
CEO: Harry Fleming
Ch Bd: Steve Ozonian
Pr: Kenneth Efird
CFO: Kenneth Klein
VP: Michael Nelson
Board of Directors: Richard Ganley, Jennifer Hauser, Donald Kramer

D-U-N-S 96-788-8330 IMP/EXP
NOBLE AMERICAS CORP
(*Suby of* NOBLE GROUP LIMITED)
107 Elm St Fl 1, Stamford, CT 06902-3834
Tel (203) 324-8555 *Founded/Ownrshp* 2008
Sales 1.4MMM^E *EMP* 630
SIC 5052 1311 Coal & other minerals & ores; Coal & coke; Natural gas production
Ch Bd: Richard Samuel Elman
* *Pr:* Richard Di Donna
* *Ch:* Edward Rubin
Treas: Connie M Grossman
* *Treas:* Christina Reynolds
* *Treas:* Eric B Twombly
* *Ex VP:* Williams Coonin
* *Ex VP:* Theodore W Robinson
* *Ex VP:* Robert Jan Van Der Zalm
Sr VP: Thomas Silva
VP: Jeffrey Huber
VP: Minghai Liu
* *VP:* Ram Patel
* *VP:* Thomas F Reich

NOBLE AMERICAS ENRGY SOLUTIONS
See CALPINE ENERGY SOLUTIONS LLC

D-U-N-S 78-628-2756 IMP
NOBLE DRILLING (US) INC
(*Suby of* NOBLE DRILLING CORP) ★
13135 Dry Ashfd 800, Sugar Land, TX 77478
Tel (281) 276-6100 *Founded/Ownrshp* 1990
Sales 191.3MM^E *EMP* 400
SIC 1381 Drilling oil & gas wells
Pr: James C Day
* *Treas:* Michael Lamb
* *VP:* William C Hofman

D-U-N-S 00-790-7785 IMP/EXP
NOBLE DRILLING CORP
(*Suby of* NOBLE HOLDING (US) CORP) ★
13135 Dairy Ashford Rd # 700, Sugar Land, TX 77478-3685
Tel (281) 276-6100 *Founded/Ownrshp* 1921
Sales 1.0MMM^E *EMP* 500
SIC 1381 8711 Drilling oil & gas wells; Petroleum engineering
Ch Bd: James C Day
* *Pr:* Mark A Jackson
* *CFO:* Tom Mitchell
* *Treas:* Mike Lamb
* *Sr VP:* Robert D Campbell
* *Sr VP:* Julie J Robertson
* *Sr VP:* David Williams
VP: Kevin D Roche

D-U-N-S 83-169-8779
NOBLE DRILLING HOLDING LLC
(*Suby of* NOBLE CORPORATION PLC)
13135 Dairy Ashford Rd # 700, Sugar Land, TX 77478-3685
Tel (281) 276-6100 *Founded/Ownrshp* 2002
Sales 124.2MM^E *EMP* 262^E
SIC 1381 Drilling oil & gas wells
Ch: David W Williams
COO: Mark Jackson
Sr VP: William Turcotte

D-U-N-S 78-388-1956 IMP/EXP
NOBLE DRILLING SERVICES INC
(*Suby of* NOBLE DRILLING CORP) ★
13135 Dairy Ashford Rd # 800, Sugar Land, TX 77478-3698
Tel (281) 276-6100 *Founded/Ownrshp* 1990
Sales 225.2MM^E *EMP* 500
SIC 3541 Drilling & boring machines
Pr: David W Williams
* *Pr:* James C Day
* *Pr:* Dennis J Lubojacky
COO: Greg Broussard
* *VP:* Bob Campbell
VP: Robert Campbell
VP: Jeffrey Chastain
VP: Kara Freshwater
Dir IT: Tom O'Rourke
Dir IT: Dora Thompson
IT Man: Sam Denman

NOBLE ENERGY
See SAMEDAN OIL CORP

D-U-N-S 05-287-7586
▲ NOBLE ENERGY INC
1001 Noble Energy Way, Houston, TX 77070-1435
Tel (281) 872-3100 *Founded/Ownrshp* 1932
Sales 3.1MMM *EMP* 2,395^E
Tkr Sym NBL *Exch* NYS
SIC 1311 Crude petroleum production; Natural gas production
Ch Bd: David L Stover
CFO: Kenneth M Fisher
Ex VP: Susan M Cunningham
Ex VP: Gary W Willingham
Sr VP: J Keith Elliott
Sr VP: Terry R Gerhart
Sr VP: Louis Gregory
Sr VP: Arnold J Johnson
Sr VP: John T Lewis
Sr VP: Charles J Rimer
Sr VP: A Lee Robison
VP: Lawson Freeman
VP: Sebastian Kristof
Exec: Michael W Putnam
Exec: Niv Sarne
Board of Directors: Molly K Williamson, Jeffrey L Berenson, Michael A Cawley, Edward F Cox, James E Craddock, Thomas J Edelman, Eric P Grubman, Kirby L Hedrick, Scott D Urban, William T Van Kleef

D-U-N-S 19-286-9142
NOBLE ENVIRONMENTAL POWER LLC
NEP
6 Main St Ste 121, Centerbrook, CT 06409-1094
Tel (860) 581-5010 *Founded/Ownrshp* 2008
Sales 99.7MM^E *EMP* 120
SIC 4911 Generation, electric power
Sr VP: Kay C Mann
* *VP:* Robert Depalermo
VP: Neil Dyment
VP: Jeffrey Nelson
VP: Michael J Palmieri
VP: Sandra L Dykstra Sayyeau
VP: Harry Silton
VP: Francis R Stone
VP: Pamela Sutton-Hall
Off Mgr: Tiffany Leonard
Off Mgr: Linda Weller
Board of Directors: Christopher C Behrens, Stephen P Murray, John M Warner

D-U-N-S 11-916-6556 IMP/EXP
NOBLE HOLDING (US) CORP
(*Suby of* NOBLE CORPORATION)
3135 S Dairy Ashford Ste 800, Sugar Land, TX 77478
Tel (281) 276-6100 *Founded/Ownrshp* 2002
Sales 3.3MMM *EMP* 3,744
Accts Pricewaterhousecoopers Llp H
SIC 1381 Drilling oil & gas wells
VP: Ross W Gallup
VP: Mike Lowther
VP: John T Rynd

D-U-N-S 92-614-9659
NOBLE HOUSE HOTELS & RESORTS LTD
600 6th St S, Kirkland, WA 98033-6716
Tel (425) 827-8737 *Founded/Ownrshp* 1984
Sales 110.5MM *EMP* 2,000
SIC 7011 Resort hotel
CEO: John M Donoghue
Pr: Michael Benecke
Pr: Sean Mullen
COO: Chris Gautier
CFO: Patricia Handjaja
Ch: Patrick R Colee
VP: Darrell Stark

D-U-N-S 93-339-8075
NOBLE INTERNATIONAL LTD
840 W Long Lake Rd # 601, Troy, MI 48098-6356
Tel (248) 519-0700 *Founded/Ownrshp* 1993
Sales 146.7MM^E *EMP* 2,700
SIC 3714 Motor vehicle body components & frame
CEO: Andrew J Tav
Ch Bd: Richard P McCracken
CEO: Andrew J Tavi
COO: David J Fallon
CFO: Jay J Hansen
V Ch Bd: Jean-Francois Crancee
VP: Craig S Parsons
VP: Thomas D Talboys
VP Opers: Larry W Garretson
Board of Directors: Philippe Landron, Gerard Picard, James R Thomas

D-U-N-S 55-724-1945
NOBLE INVESTMENT GROUP LLC
3424 Peachtree Rd Ne # 2000, Atlanta, GA 30326-1147
Tel (404) 262-9660 *Founded/Ownrshp* 2003
Sales 103.0MM^E *EMP* 195
SIC 6726 Investment offices
* *CFO:* Jim Conley
Ex VP: Steve Nicholas
* *Sr VP:* Roy Croop
VP: Kevin Grass
VP: Michael Quinlan
Exec: Stephen Baldwin
Exec: Chris Weydig
Genl Mgr: Brian Cole
Genl Mgr: Marcel Girard
Genl Mgr: Bill Gmaz

D-U-N-S 19-892-6060
NOBLE NETWORK OF CHARTER SCHOOLS
NOBLE STREET CHARTER SCHOOL
1 N State St Fl 7, Chicago, IL 60602-3311
Tel (773) 278-6895 *Founded/Ownrshp* 1998
Sales 134.9MM *EMP* 85^E
Accts Ostrow Reisin Berk & Abrams Lt
SIC 8211 Elementary & secondary schools
CEO: Michael Milky
* *Pt:* John Harris
* *Ch Bd:* Allan Muchin
Genl Mgr: Sara Kandler

NOBLE STREET CHARTER SCHOOL
See NOBLE NETWORK OF CHARTER SCHOOLS

D-U-N-S 62-214-1299
NOBLE SYSTEMS CORP
1200 Ashwood Pkwy Ste 300, Atlanta, GA 30338-4747
Tel (404) 851-1331 *Founded/Ownrshp* 2006
Sales 122.5MM^E *EMP* 400
SIC 3661 Telephone dialing devices, automatic
CEO: James K Noble Jr
Pr: Mark Moore
* *CFO:* Martin D Kidder
CFO: Bruce Reese
CFO: Michael Sturdivan
Sr VP: Kevin Ball
Sr VP: Ellwood Neuer
VP: Patrick McDaniel
VP: Tom Miller
VP: Michaele Rose
Exec: Katie Shafer
Dir Bus: Reddy Annapureddy

NOBLE WORLDWIDE FLA CITRUS SLS
See G ROE WM & SONS INC

D-U-N-S 17-323-0426
NOBLESSE OBLIGE INC
EIGHT STAR EQUIPMENT
2015 Silsbee Rd, El Centro, CA 92243-9671
Tel (760) 353-3336 *Founded/Ownrshp* 1985
Sales 21.2MM^E *EMP* 1,200
SIC 0722 Combining services; Cotton, machine harvesting services; Hay, machine harvesting services; Vegetables & melons, machine harvesting services
Pr: Alex Abatti Jr
CFO: Tim Castelli
* *CFO:* David Wells

D-U-N-S 93-290-2364
NOBLIS INC
3150 Fairview Park Dr, Falls Church, VA 22042-4504
Tel (703) 610-2000 *Founded/Ownrshp* 1995
Sales 320.1MM *EMP* 804
Accts Grant Thornton Llp Mclean Va
SIC 8733 8748 Noncommercial research organizations; Business consulting
Pr: AMR A Elsawy
* *CFO:* Mark A Simione
Trst: John McLaughlin
VP: Drew Cohen
VP: Ernie Giuffriday
VP: Gail Hogan
VP: Edward Preston
Prin: Luis Rose
Ex Dir: Alan F Dowling
Ex Dir: Steven Pomerantz
Prgrm Mgr: Walter Berger

D-U-N-S 83-124-3857
NOCO INC
2440 Sheridan Dr Ste 202, Tonawanda, NY 14150-9416
Tel (716) 833-6626 *Founded/Ownrshp* 1999
Sales 403.2MM^E *EMP* 900
Accts Bonadio & Co Llp Pittsford
SIC 2992 6719 5172 4924 Lubricating oils & greases; Investment holding companies, except banks; Petroleum products; Natural gas distribution
Ch Bd: James D Newman
* *Ch Bd:* R J Stapell
* *CFO:* Michael L Bradley
* *Ex VP:* Michael Newman

D-U-N-S 80-675-0449
NOCO NATURAL GAS LLC
2440 Sheridan Dr, Tonawanda, NY 14150-9416
Tel (716) 614-1152 *Founded/Ownrshp* 2006
Sales 111.5MM^E *EMP* 620
SIC 5171 Petroleum bulk stations

D-U-N-S 00-892-6081
NODAK ELECTRIC COOPERATIVE INC
4000 32nd Ave S, Grand Forks, ND 58201-5944
Tel (701) 746-4461 *Founded/Ownrshp* 1939
Sales 94.3MM *EMP* 64
SIC 4911 Distribution, electric power
Pr: George Berg
* *Prin:* Mylo Einarson

D-U-N-S 04-302-5212
NOEL CORP
PEPSICO
1001 S 1st St, Yakima, WA 98901-3403
Tel (509) 248-4545 *Founded/Ownrshp* 1934
Sales 110.5MM^E *EMP* 255
SIC 2086 7389 4212 6512 4225 5962 Soft drinks: packaged in cans, bottles, etc.; Interior designer; Local trucking, without storage; Nonresidential building operators; General warehousing & storage; Merchandising machine operators
Pr: Roger Noel
* *Treas:* Cindy Zimmerman
* *VP:* Justin Noel
Exec: Tamara Kline
IT Man: Ken Persson
Plnt Mgr: Sam Brackney
Sls Mgr: William Dalton

D-U-N-S 05-799-0017
NOEL GROUP LLC
501 Nmc Dr, Zebulon, NC 27597-2762
Tel (919) 269-6500 *Founded/Ownrshp* 1996
Sales 95.5MM^E *EMP* 442
SIC 3086 Plastics foam products

D-U-N-S 62-129-4412 IMP
NOGALES PRODUCE INC
8220 Forney Rd, Dallas, TX 75227-4212
Tel (214) 275-3500 *Founded/Ownrshp* 1990
Sales 84.8MM^E *EMP* 240
SIC 5148

D-U-N-S 07-854-0854
NOKIA INC
(*Suby of* NOKIA OYJ)
6363 N State Highway 161 # 800, Irving, TX 75038-2262
Tel (214) 496-0329 *Founded/Ownrshp* 2012
Sales 100.0MM^E *EMP* 179^E
SIC 3663

D-U-N-S 10-664-8322 IMP
NOKIA INC
200 S Mathilda Ave, Sunnyvale, CA 94086-6135
Tel (408) 530-7600 *Founded/Ownrshp* 1992
Sales NA *EMP* 2,500
SIC 3663 5065 3661 3577

D-U-N-S 79-406-4571 IMP
NOKIA SOLUTIONS AND NETWORKS US LLC
(*Suby of* NOKIA SOLUTIONS AND NETWORKS BRANCH OPERATIONS OY)
6000 Connection Dr, Irving, TX 75039-2600
Tel (972) 374-3000 *Founded/Ownrshp* 2008
Sales 1.8MMM^E *EMP* 4,000
SIC 3663 5999 4813 Radio broadcasting & communications equipment; Telephone & communication equipment; Telephone communication, except radio
Sr Cor Off: Bodhisattwa Gangopadhyay
VP Sls: Reggie Perry
Snr Mgr: Fadi Hakim

D-U-N-S 02-347-0896 IMP
NOKIAN TYRES INC
(*Suby of* NOKIAN RENKAAT OYJ)
1945 Main St, Colchester, VT 05446-7652
Tel (800) 852-5222 *Founded/Ownrshp* 1997
Sales 123.6MM^E *EMP* 120
SIC 5014 Tires & tubes
CEO: ARI Lehtoranta
VP: Bob Hepp

D-U-N-S 60-690-7603
NOLAN TRANSPORTATION GROUP LLC
N T G
85 Mill St Ste 214, Roswell, GA 30075-4955
Tel (770) 509-9611 *Founded/Ownrshp* 2005
Sales 114.9MM *EMP* 135
SIC 4731 Freight transportation arrangement
Opers Mgr: Christopher Graham
Manager: Hamilton Schuler

D-U-N-S 00-794-0604 IMP/EXP
NOLAND CO (VA)
GREENVILLE NOLAND
(*Suby of* WSS- DAYTON) ★
3110 Kettering Blvd, Moraine, OH 45439-1924
Tel (937) 396-7980 *Founded/Ownrshp* 1915, 2005
Sales 235.0MM^E *EMP* 600
SIC 5074 5075 5063 5085 Plumbing & hydronic heating supplies; Air conditioning equipment, except room units; Electrical supplies; Industrial supplies
Pr: Arjay Hoggard
* *COO:* James H Adcox
COO: John W Simmons
* *Treas:* David E Metzger
Treas: James E Sykes
VP: Ron K Binger
VP: Paul H Donarum
VP: Steven B Edwards
VP: Roger E Gibbs
VP: Robert C Guiney
VP: Arthur P Henderson
* *VP:* Jack W Johnston
* *VP:* Monte L Salsman
VP: Aaron Stanley

D-U-N-S 19-820-5622
NOLAND HEALTH SERVICES INC
600 Corporate Pkwy # 100, Birmingham, AL 35242-5451
Tel (205) 321-5373 *Founded/Ownrshp* 2001
Sales 130.8MM *EMP* 1,100^E
Accts Dixon Hughes Goodman Llp Asha
SIC 8051 Skilled nursing care facilities
Pr: Gary M Glasscock

**Ch:* Leon C Hamrick Sr
Chf Cred: Marta Bardonner
**Ex VP:* R Gary Goff
VP: John Heffner
VP: Pam Nichols
CIO: Joey Sestili
Sys Mgr: Jason Rosolowski
Nrsg Dir: Janet Langford

NOLI INDIAN SCHOOL
See SOBOBA BAND OF LUISENO INDIANS

NOLS
See NATIONAL OUTDOOR LEADERSHIP SCHOOL

D-U-N-S 00-693-5345 IMP/EXP
NOMACORC LLC (NC)
400 Vintage Park Dr, Zebulon, NC 27597-3803
Tel (919) 460-2200 *Founded/Ownrshp* 1998
Sales 125.1MM[E] *EMP* 400
SIC 3089 Caps, plastic
VP: Malcolm Thompson
Area Mgr: Mark Coleman
Genl Mgr: Eric Dunkelberg
Prd Mgr: Don Ellis
Prd Mgr: Todd Lee
Ql Cn Mgr: Christophe Robert
Mktg Dir: Jeff Slater
Board of Directors: Jason Glass, Kevin Mohan, Mark Noel

D-U-N-S 61-293-6385
NOMURA HOLDING AMERICA INC
(*Suby of* NOMURA HOLDINGS, INC.)
309 W 49th St, New York, NY 10019-9102
Tel (212) 667-9300 *Founded/Ownrshp* 1989
Sales 541.2MM[E] *EMP* 1,600
SIC 6211 Dealers, security
Ch Bd: David Findlay
**CEO:* Hideyuki Takahashi
CFO: Jonathan Lewis
**Treas:* Ray Carli
VP: Deepesh Bhandari
VP: Noel Carrero
VP: Ann Caruso
VP: Rajat Goel
VP: Sudhir Gokhale
VP: Michael Kirshenbaum
VP: Elizabeth Nicklas
VP: Rakesh Petel
VP: Roger Petho
VP: Joseph Petruccelli
VP: Syed Rizvi
VP: Roman Shnayder
VP: Christine Tsu
VP: Xiaobo Xie
Comm Dir: Thomas Salatte

D-U-N-S 04-361-3520
NOMURA SECURITIES INTERNATIONAL INC
(*Suby of* NOMURA HOLDING AMERICA INC) ★
Worldwide Plaza 309 W 49t, New York, NY 10019
Tel (212) 667-9000 *Founded/Ownrshp* 1989
Sales 516.0MM[E] *EMP* 1,581
SIC 6211 Dealers, security
Ch Bd: Hideyuki Takahashi
**Ch Bd:* David Findlay
Pr: Bhaskar Desai
Pr: Derek Leung
Pr: Igor Reznikovsky
**Pr:* Joseph R Schmuckler
Pr: Harsha Shah
**CFO:* Larry Wagner
Treas: Mary Langevin
Treas: Patrick Lewis
Ex VP: Jeff Zorek
VP: Sal Azzarelli
VP: Tarun Bahadur
VP: Danielle Chaikin
VP: Irene Chen
VP: George Chernenko
VP: Ada Cheung
VP: George Daqui
VP: Fabien Dusseaux
VP: Oleg Farberov
VP: Michael Flynn

NONE
See PLYMOUTH TUBE CO

NONE
See BLEVINS INC

D-U-N-S 12-720-2187 IMP/EXP
NONGSHIM AMERICA INC
(*Suby of* NONGSHIM CO., LTD.)
12155 6th St, Rancho Cucamonga, CA 91730-6115
Tel (909) 481-3698 *Founded/Ownrshp* 1994
Sales 248.0MM[E] *EMP* 300
SIC 5141 2098 Groceries, general line; Noodles (e.g. egg, plain & water), dry
CEO: Dong Y Shin
CFO: Kevin Chang
**Prin:* Chris Gepford
IT Man: John Seo
Ql Cn Mgr: Abel Escalante

NONNI'S
See NONNIS FOODS LLC

D-U-N-S 96-717-9966
NONNIS FOODS LLC
NONNI'S
3920 E Pine St, Tulsa, OK 74115-5126
Tel (918) 621-1200 *Founded/Ownrshp* 2011
Sales 84.4MM[E] *EMP* 250[E]
SIC 2052 2053 Bakery products, dry; Frozen bakery products, except bread
CEO: Dave Bere
CFO: Rod Liddle
Ex VP: John Bischoff
VP: Pete Hetrick
Opers Mgr: Mark Swim
Manager: Brent Dilonardo
Plnt Mgr: Tom McCarthy
VP Sls: Jan R Grywczynski

D-U-N-S 06-797-6340 IMP/EXP
NONPAREIL CORP (ID)
411 W Collins Rd, Blackfoot, ID 83221-5664
Tel (208) 785-5880 *Founded/Ownrshp* 1945
Sales 102.9MM[E] *EMP* 485[E]
SIC 2099 Packaged combination products: pasta, rice & potato
Pr: Chris Abend
**CFO:* John Fullmer
CFO: Jace Katseanes
**Sec:* Tracy Fullmer
**VP:* Walter Gay
**VP:* Howard Phillips
Genl Mgr: Patti Callison
Trfc Mgr: Rulon Robinson
Snr Mgr: Fran Taylor

D-U-N-S 95-621-2542
▲ NOODLES & CO
520 Zang St Ste D, Broomfield, CO 80021-8239
Tel (720) 214-1900 *Founded/Ownrshp* 1995
Sales 455.4MM *EMP* 10,600
Tkr Sym NDLS *Exch* NGS
SIC 5812 Eating places
CEO: Dave Boennighausen
**Ch Bd:* Robert Hartnett
COO: Victor R Heutz
COO: Keith Kinsey
Ex VP: Jason Gallelli
Ex VP: Mark Mears
Ex VP: Mark A Mears
Ex VP: Phil Petrilli
Ex VP: Paul Strasen
Ex VP: Paul A Strasen
VP: David Lehn
VP: Kathy Lockhart
VP: Bill Long
Exec: Mary Orlando
Board of Directors: Scott Dahnke, Francois Dufresne, Jeffrey Jones, Johanna Murphy, James Rand, Andrew Taub

D-U-N-S 88-375-9565
NOONAN BROTHERS PETROLEUM PRODUCTS INC
415 West St, West Bridgewater, MA 02379-1030
Tel (508) 588-8026 *Founded/Ownrshp* 1994
Sales 142.9MM *EMP* 14
Accts Nicholas P Dinatale Cpa Sto
SIC 5172 Petroleum products
Pr: J Peter Noonan Sr
**Treas:* J Timothy Noonan

D-U-N-S 62-199-2288
NOOTER CONSTRUCTION CO
(*Suby of* NOOTER CORP) ★
1500 S 2nd St, Saint Louis, MO 63104-4513
Tel (314) 621-6000 *Founded/Ownrshp* 1981
Sales 173.4MM[E] *EMP* 300
SIC 1541 Industrial buildings & warehouses
Pr: Bernard C Wicklein
VP: Chris Cimarolli
VP: Jim Woodward
**VP:* David Zach
Ql Cn Mgr: Thomas Moslander

D-U-N-S 00-627-4385 IMP
NOOTER CORP (MO)
(*Suby of* CIC GROUP INC) ★
1500 S 2nd St, Saint Louis, MO 63104-4513
Tel (314) 421-7200 *Founded/Ownrshp* 1896
Sales 348.0MM[E] *EMP* 811
SIC 3443 3479 1796 8711 7699 1542 Tanks, standard or custom fabricated: metal plate; Pressurizers or auxiliary equipment, nuclear: metal plate; Columns (fractioning, etc.): metal plate; Towers (bubble, cooling, fractionating, etc.): metal plate; Coating of metals & formed products; Hot dip coating of metals or formed products; Machinery installation; Pollution control equipment installation; Energy conservation engineering; Heating & ventilation engineering; Tank repair; Tank truck cleaning service; Nonresidential construction
Pr: Michael W Bytnar
**Ch Bd:* Ross G Osiek
**Pr:* John A Drehor
**Pr:* Vernon L Eriksen
Sec: Derek Falb
**Sr VP:* Ronald C Zinzer
VP: Don Majchrowski
VP Admn: David J Zach
IT Man: William Robinson
VP Opers: Bernard Wicklein
Sfty Mgr: Tony Templet

D-U-N-S 16-152-0994 IMP
NOOTER/ERIKSEN INC
(*Suby of* CIC GROUP INC) ★
1509 Ocello Dr, Fenton, MO 63026-2406
Tel (636) 651-1000 *Founded/Ownrshp* 1987
Sales 250.7MM[E] *EMP* 280[E]
SIC 5075 Warm air heating equipment & supplies
Pr: Tim Peterson

D-U-N-S 00-911-3374 EXP
NOR-CAL BEVERAGE CO INC
2150 Stone Blvd, West Sacramento, CA 95691-4049
Tel (916) 372-0600 *Founded/Ownrshp* 1937
Sales 257.0MM[E] *EMP* 574
SIC 5181 2086 Beer & ale; Soft drinks: packaged in cans, bottles, etc.; Fruit drinks (less than 100% juice): packaged in cans, etc.
Pr: Shannon Deary-Bell
**Ch Bd:* Donald Deary
**Pr:* Grant Deary
**CFO:* Mike Montroni
**CFO:* Michael Motroni
**VP:* Roy Grant Deary III
**VP:* Timothy Deary
Sales Exec: Larry Buban

D-U-N-S 08-947-6410
NOR-SON INC
7900 Hastings Rd, Baxter, MN 56425-8465
Tel (218) 828-1722 *Founded/Ownrshp* 1978
Sales 89.2MM[E] *EMP* 190
SIC 1521 1542 1541 New construction, single-family houses; Commercial & office building, new construction; Commercial & office buildings, renovation & repair; Industrial buildings, new construction; Renovation, remodeling & repairs: industrial buildings
**Pr:* Brooke Silvernail
Exec: Don Hines

D-U-N-S 16-831-6557 IMP/EXP
NORANDA ALUMINA LLC
(*Suby of* NORANDA ALUMINUM HOLDING CORP) ★
1111 E Airline Hwy Us61, Gramercy, LA 70052-6302
Tel (225) 869-2100 *Founded/Ownrshp* 2009
Sales 228.8MM[E] *EMP* 500
SIC 3334 Primary aluminum
**CFO:* Dale Boyles
**VP:* Mike Fox
**VP:* John Habisreitinger
Opers Mgr: Eddie Bowden

D-U-N-S 80-137-2686
NORANDA ALUMINUM HOLDING CORP
801 Crescent Cntre Dr 6 Ste 600, Franklin, TN 37067
Tel (615) 771-5700 *Founded/Ownrshp* 2007
Sales 1.2MMM *EMP* 2,200
Accts Ernst & Young Llp Nashville
SIC 3334 2819 3353 Primary aluminum; Ingots (primary), aluminum; Bauxite, refined; Flat rolled shapes, aluminum
Pr: Layle K Smith
Ch Bd: Richard B Evans
CFO: Dale W Boyles
Ofcr: Gail E Lehman
VP: Greg North
IT Man: Brent Koenig
VP Mfg: Michael J Griffin
Board of Directors: William H Brooks, Pasquale Fiore, Thomas R Miklich, Carl J Rickertsen, Ronald S Rolfe, Elliot G Sagor, Alan H Schumacher

D-U-N-S 07-198-4652 IMP
NORANDA ALUMINUM INC
(*Suby of* NORANDA ALUMINUM HOLDING CORP) ★
St Jude Industrial Park, New Madrid, MO 63869
Tel (573) 643-2361 *Founded/Ownrshp* 2007
Sales 501.0MM[E] *EMP* 2,350
SIC 3353 3354 3334 3714 Flat rolled shapes, aluminum; Aluminum extruded products; Primary aluminum; Wheels, motor vehicle
Pr: Scott M Croft
**Pr:* William H Brooks
**Pr:* Mike Griffin
**Pr:* Wayne Hale
**CEO:* Layle K Kip Smith
**CFO:* Dale Boyles
**Treas:* Mark J Walker
**VP:* Richard J Anderson
**VP:* Devonne Canady
**VP:* Chris Roepe
**VP:* Ronald Rowe
**VP:* Joe Smith

D-U-N-S 80-139-8079
NORANDA INTERMEDIATE HOLDING CORP
(*Suby of* NORANDA ALUMINUM HOLDING CORP) ★
801 Crescent Centre Dr, Franklin, TN 37067-6224
Tel (615) 771-5700 *Founded/Ownrshp* 2008
Sales 228.8MM[E] *EMP* 2,350
SIC 3353 3334 3714 3354 Flat rolled shapes, aluminum; Primary aluminum; Wheels, motor vehicle; Aluminum extruded products
CEO: Layle K Smith
VP: Thomas Harris

D-U-N-S 09-379-0277 IMP
NORANDAL USA INC
801 Crescent Centre Dr # 600, Franklin, TN 37067-7202
Tel (615) 778-2000 *Founded/Ownrshp* 1978
Sales 222.5MM[E] *EMP* 565
SIC 3353

D-U-N-S 04-571-4342 IMP
NORANDEX BUILDING MATERIALS DISTRIBUTION INC
NORANDEX BUILDING MTLS DIST
300 Executive Park Ste 100, Hudson, OH 44236
Tel (330) 656-8924 *Founded/Ownrshp* 1997
Sales 647.8MM[E] *EMP* 1,000
SIC 5033 5031

NORANDEX BUILDING MTLS DIST
See NORANDEX BUILDING MATERIALS DISTRIBUTION INC

NORBORD TEXAS LIMITED
See NORBORD TEXAS LP

D-U-N-S 09-191-9022 IMP/EXP
NORBORD TEXAS LP
NORBORD TEXAS LIMITED
(*Suby of* NORBORD INC)
500 Nexfor Blvd, Jefferson, TX 75657-1055
Tel (936) 568-8009 *Founded/Ownrshp* 2002
Sales 138.9MM[E] *EMP* 1,000
SIC 2493 Reconstituted wood products
Genl Pt: Norbord Georgia
CEO: Peter C Wijnbergen
Exec: Michael Weekes

NORC
See NATIONAL OPINION RESEARCH CENTER

D-U-N-S 09-255-8741
NORCAL MUTUAL INSURANCE CO INC
560 Davis St Fl 2, San Francisco, CA 94111-1974
Tel (415) 397-9703 *Founded/Ownrshp* 1975
Sales NA *EMP* 325
SIC 6411 6331 Insurance agents, brokers & service; Fire, marine & casualty insurance
CEO: Theodore Scott Diener
Pr: Jim Sunsari
COO: Scott Diener
Assoc VP: Bradley Ignasiak
Assoc VP: Michael Roque
Assoc VP: Lucy Sam
Assoc VP: Kevin Smith
Sr VP: Mark Johnson
Sr VP: Ronald Rumin
VP: John McClain
VP: Dustin Shaver
VP: Neil Simons
Exec: Alicia Low
Creative D: Max Malloy

D-U-N-S 04-369-4645
NORCO INC
1125 W Amity Rd, Boise, ID 83705-5412
Tel (208) 336-1643 *Founded/Ownrshp* 1989
Sales 568.4MM[E] *EMP* 1,070
SIC 5084 5169 7352 5999 3548 2813 Welding machinery & equipment; Safety equipment; Industrial gases; Medical equipment rental; Medical apparatus & supplies; Welding apparatus; Industrial gases
Pr: Ned Pontious
**CFO:* Mike Sabin
**Ch:* James Kissler
Ofcr: Brian Anderson
VP: Brent Seward
VP: Greg Stanley
Brnch Mgr: Preston Rizzuto
CTO: Christopher Dominiak
Sys/Mgr: Francis Kissler
Opers Mgr: Larry Aarsby
Sales Exec: Jason Whitehead

D-U-N-S 07-920-8258
NORCO INC
3030 Hoyt Ave, Everett, WA 98201-4005
Tel (425) 205-4200 *Founded/Ownrshp* 2000
Sales 35.7MM[E] *EMP* 1,150
SIC 7352 Medical equipment rental
CEO: James Ross

D-U-N-S 07-920-8277
NORCO INC
101 E Stuart Rd, Bellingham, WA 98226-8196
Tel (360) 746-0826 *Founded/Ownrshp* 2013
Sales 39.0MM[E] *EMP* 1,150
SIC 7352 Medical equipment rental
CEO: James Ross

D-U-N-S 96-811-9974 IMP
NORCOLD INC
(*Suby of* THETFORD CORP) ★
600 S Kuther Rd, Sidney, OH 45365-8840
Tel (937) 497-3080 *Founded/Ownrshp* 1997
Sales 103.4MM[E] *EMP* 380
SIC 3632 Refrigerators, mechanical & absorption: household
CEO: Michael Harris
COO: Michael Larime
VP: Dave Roberts

NORCRAFT CABINETARY
See NORCRAFT HOLDINGS LP

D-U-N-S 05-191-6638
■ NORCRAFT COMPANIES INC
(*Suby of* FORTUNE BRANDS HOME & SECURITY INC) ★
950 Blue Gentian Rd # 200, Saint Paul, MN 55121-3486
Tel (800) 297-0661 *Founded/Ownrshp* 2015
Sales 246.7MM[E] *EMP* 2,234
SIC 2434 Wood kitchen cabinets; Vanities, bathroom: wood
CEO: Mark Buller
Pr: John Swedeen
Pr: Kurt Wanninger
CFO: Leigh Ginter

D-U-N-S 07-762-7594 IMP/EXP
■ NORCRAFT COMPANIES LP
MID CONTINENT CABINETRY
(*Suby of* FORTUNE BRANDS HOME & SECURITY INC) ★
950 Blue Gentian Rd # 200, Saint Paul, MN 55121-3486
Tel (651) 234-3300 *Founded/Ownrshp* 2015
Sales 288.7MM[E] *EMP* 1,892
SIC 2434 Wood kitchen cabinets; Vanities, bathroom: wood
Pr: Mark Buller
**CFO:* Leigh Ginter
VP: Betty Hitchcock
VP: Jack Laninga
VP: John Loucks
Genl Mgr: Scott Raschke
IT Man: Rod Brewer
Tech Mgr: Darin Wipf
Mtls Mgr: Amy Carpenter
Sfty Mgr: Joey Lecy
Plnt Mgr: Kevin Andersen

D-U-N-S 16-845-4135 IMP/EXP
NORCRAFT HOLDINGS LP
NORCRAFT CABINETARY
950 Blue Gentian Rd, Eagan, MN 55121-1576
Tel (800) 297-0661 *Founded/Ownrshp* 2003
Sales 400.0MM *EMP* 2,500[E]
SIC 2434 Wood kitchen cabinets; Vanities, bathroom: wood
CEO: Kurt Wanninger
CFO: Leigh Ginter
Plnt Mgr: Justin Hopper
Mktg Dir: Jennifer Thom
Sls Mgr: Darrill Andries
Sls Mgr: Jason Clark
Sls Mgr: Chad Larson

D-U-N-S 88-488-0998 IMP
NORCROSS SAFETY PRODUCTS LLC
HONEYWELL SAFETY PRODUCTS
900 Douglas Pike Ste 100, Smithfield, RI 02917-1879
Tel (800) 430-5490 *Founded/Ownrshp* 2008
Sales NA *EMP* 2,700
SIC 3842 3021 3469

D-U-N-S 08-595-7876 IMP/EXP
NORDAM GROUP INC (CA)
NORDAM REPAIR DIVISION
6911 Whirlpool Dr, Tulsa, OK 74117-1306
Tel (918) 878-4000 *Founded/Ownrshp* 1969
Sales 710.1MM[E] *EMP* 2,413
SIC 3728 3724 Aircraft parts & equipment; Bodies, aircraft; Aircraft engines & engine parts

Ch: Paul Kenneth Lackey Jr
**Ch Bd:* Ken Lackey
**CEO:* Meredith Siegfried
Ex VP: Basil Barimo
Sr VP: Dave Whitten
VP: Mike Bunney
VP: Mark Ferrari
VP: Daryl Hartzell
VP: Parker James
VP: James Parker
VP: Alain Poupin
VP: Meredith R Siegfried
VP: Raymond H Siegfried
VP: Basil Walsh
Board of Directors: Bill Peacher, Mike Shonka

NORDAM REPAIR DIVISION
See NORDAM GROUP INC

D-U-N-S 07-860-4521
NORDFAB LLC
(*Suby of* NEDERMAN HOLDING AB)
150 Transit Ave, Thomasville, NC 27360-8927
Tel (336) 821-0829 *Founded/Ownrshp* 2011
Sales 400.0MM *EMP* 200
SIC 3443 Ducting, metal plate
Pr: Pear Erickson

NORDIC
See PHYSICIANS INSURANCE A MUTUAL CO

D-U-N-S 05-020-8045
NORDIC CORP
TACO BELL
11019 Mccormick Rd # 320, Hunt Valley, MD 21031-8670
Tel (410) 771-1880 *Founded/Ownrshp* 1997
Sales 19.9MM^E *EMP* 1,000
SIC 5812 Fast-food restaurant, chain
Pr: Kurt Aarsand
**Sec:* Krista Bedford

D-U-N-S 62-220-9179
NORDIC GROUP OF COMPANIES LTD
715 Lynn Ave Ste 100, Baraboo, WI 53913-2744
Tel (608) 356-7303 *Founded/Ownrshp* 1988
Sales 342.8MM *EMP* 2,500
Accts Baker Tilly Virchow Krause Ll
SIC 8742 8111 5561 Management consulting services; Legal services; Recreational vehicle parts & accessories
Ch: William R Sauey
**CFO:* Bill Hans
**Treas:* Todd L Sauey
IT Man: Allan Freuller

D-U-N-S 00-462-3695 IMP/EXP
NORDIC LOGISTICS AND WAREHOUSING LLC (GA)
4300 Pleasantdale Rd, Atlanta, GA 30340-3526
Tel (770) 448-7400 *Founded/Ownrshp* 2000, 2011
Sales 105.3MM^E *EMP* 500
SIC 4222 Warehousing, cold storage or refrigerated
Pr: Don Schoenl

NORDIC WARE
See NORTHLAND ALUMINUM PRODUCTS INC

D-U-N-S 00-416-6005 IMP/EXP
▲ NORDSON CORP (OH)
28601 Clemens Rd, Westlake, OH 44145-1119
Tel (440) 892-1580 *Founded/Ownrshp* 1935
Sales 1.8MMM *EMP* 6,232
Accts Ernst & Young Llp Cleveland
Tkr Sym NDSN *Exch* NGS
SIC 3563 Spraying outfits: metals, paints & chemicals (compressor); Robots for industrial spraying, painting, etc.
Pr: Michael F Hilton
**Ch Bd:* Joseph P Keithley
CFO: Gregory A Thaxton
Treas: Raymond Cushing
Ofcr: Jacquelyn Hayden
Sr VP: Robert A Dunn
Sr VP: John J Keane
Sr VP: Gregory P Merk
VP: Douglas C Bloomfield
VP: James E Devries
VP: Ken Forden
VP: Stephen P Lovass
VP: James W Messerly
VP: Shelly M Peet
VP: George Porter
VP: Owen Sit
VP: Herman Turner
VP: Robert E Veillette
VP: Greg Wood
Board of Directors: Lee C Banks, Randolph W Carson, Arthur L George Jr, Frank M Jaehnert, Michael J Merriman Jr, Mary G Puma, Victor L Richey Jr

D-U-N-S 04-661-2776 IMP
■ NORDSON EFD LLC
E F D
(*Suby of* NORDSON CORP) ★
40 Catamore Blvd, East Providence, RI 02914-1206
Tel (401) 434-1680 *Founded/Ownrshp* 2000
Sales 102.5MM^E *EMP* 350
SIC 3548 3586 3699 Welding apparatus; Measuring & dispensing pumps; Electrical equipment & supplies
VP: Jeff Pembroke
**Pr:* Michael F Hilton
**Sr VP:* Gregory A Thaxton
**VP:* David Guiot
**VP:* John J Keane
VP: Virginia Lacy
VP: Steve Lord
VP: Francis Moreau
VP: Roman Skonieczny
Dir Lab: Kevin Gaugler
Ex Dir: Wil Vandenboogaard

D-U-N-S 00-246-1812 IMP
■ NORDSON XALOY INC
(*Suby of* NORDSON CORP) ★
1399 County Line Rd, New Castle, PA 16101-2955
Tel (724) 656-5600 *Founded/Ownrshp* 1929, 2012
Sales 203.1MM^E *EMP* 580
SIC 3544 Forms (molds), for foundry & plastics working machinery
CEO: Michael F Hilton
Treas: Keith E Young
VP: Myron Marsh
VP: Steven Purcell
Telecom Ex: Tom Woolaway
CTO: Timothy W Womer
QI Cn Mgr: Wayne Harris
Sales Exec: Fred Scocchera
Manager: Shannon Abts
Manager: Brad Casale

D-U-N-S 00-794-2915 IMP
▲ NORDSTROM INC (WA)
1617 6th Ave, Seattle, WA 98101-1707
Tel (206) 628-2111 *Founded/Ownrshp* 1901
Sales 14.4MMM *EMP* 72,500^E
Accts Deloitte & Touche Llp Seattl
Tkr Sym JWN *Exch* NYS
SIC 5651 5661 5632 5611 5641 5961 Family clothing stores; Shoe stores; Women's accessory & specialty stores; Men's & boys' clothing stores; Children's & infants' wear stores; Children's wear; Catalog sales
Ch Bd: Enrique Hernandez Jr
Pr: Kevin Knight
**Pr:* Blake W Nordstrom
Pr: Jamie Nordstrom
**Pr:* Peter E Nordstrom
Pr: Ken Worzel
CFO: Michael G Koppel
Treas: James A Howell
Ex VP: Teri Bariquit
Ex VP: Jammie A Baugh
Ex VP: Kirk M Beardsley
Ex VP: Linda Finn
Ex VP: Kristin Frossmo
Ex VP: Gemma Lionello
Ex VP: Daniel F Little
Ex VP: Scott A Meden
Ex VP: Margaret Myers
Ex VP: Erik Nordstorm
Ex VP: Robert B Sari
Ex VP: Tricia D Smith
Ex VP: Loretta Soffe
Board of Directors: B Kevin Turner, Phyllis J Campbell, Robert D Walter, Tanya L Domier, Alison A Winter, Michelle M Ebanks, Enrique Hernandez Jr, Robert G Miller, Philip G Satre, Brad D Smith, Gordon A Smith, Bradley D Tilden

D-U-N-S 07-866-0127
■ NORESCO INC
(*Suby of* UNITED TECHNOLOGIES CARRIER) ★
1 Research Dr Ste 400c, Westborough, MA 01581-3963
Tel (508) 614-1000 *Founded/Ownrshp* 2001
Sales 131.0MM^E *EMP* 525^E
SIC 8711 8741 8748 4911 4924 Energy conservation engineering; Construction management; Energy conservation consultant; ; Natural gas distribution
Pr: Neil Petchers
Pr: Britta Macintosh
Pr: Gopal Shiddapur
VP: Wade Carleton
VP: Randy Clark
VP: Bill Foster
VP: David Mannherz
VP: Gerard Reilley
VP: Ian Roth
Exec: Ruth Gaccetta
Rgnl Mgr: Leonard Bernard

D-U-N-S 60-672-7402
■ NORESCO LLC
(*Suby of* NORESCO INC) ★
1 Research Dr Ste 400c, Westborough, MA 01581-3963
Tel (508) 614-1000 *Founded/Ownrshp* 2008
Sales 108.3MM^E *EMP* 525
SIC 8711 8741 8744 8748 4911 4924 Energy conservation engineering; Construction management; Facilities support services; Energy conservation consultant; ;
Pr: Neil Petchers
Pr: Michael Beccaria
Pr: Randall Clark
Pr: Britta Macintosh
**CFO:* David G Mannherz
CFO: Jack Martin
**VP:* Paul Pimentel
Brnch Mgr: Paul Ravenelle
Dir IT: Christopher Johnston
Sls Mgr: Chuck Coyne
Counsel: Kenneth Mattern

D-U-N-S 03-325-1401 IMP/EXP
NORFALCO LLC
(*Suby of* GLENCORE LTD) ★
301 Tresser Blvd, Stamford, CT 06901-3250
Tel (416) 775-1400 *Founded/Ownrshp* 2015
Sales 182.6MM^E *EMP* 10
SIC 2819 Sulfuric acid, oleum
Pr: Paul Shaw

D-U-N-S 00-794-1644
■ NORFOLK AND WESTERN RAILWAY CO (INC)
(*Suby of* NORFOLK SOUTHERN RAILWAY CO) ★
3 Commercial Pl, Norfolk, VA 23510-2108
Tel (757) 629-2600 *Founded/Ownrshp* 1896, 1982
Sales 2.0MMM *EMP* 9
SIC 4011 Railroads, line-haul operating
Ch Bd: David R Goode
Treas: Ronald E Sink
**VP:* James C Bishop Jr
**VP:* L I Prillaman
**VP:* Stephen C Tobias

D-U-N-S 05-098-9532 IMP
NORFOLK DREDGING CO
110 Centerville Tpke N, Chesapeake, VA 23320-3004
Tel (757) 547-9391 *Founded/Ownrshp* 1999
Sales 91.3MM^E *EMP* 180
SIC 1629 Dredging contractor
Pr: G Dudley Ware
**Sec:* James M Brady
**Sec:* Judith C Stultz
**Ex VP:* Mike B Haverty
**Ex VP:* F Graham Payne
**VP:* Paul C Knowles
VP: Paul Knowles
**VP:* Stephen M Newton

NORFOLK PUBLIC SCHOOLS
See SCHOOL BOARD OF CITY OF NORFOLK

D-U-N-S 80-076-6136
NORFOLK PUBLIC SCHOOLS
800 E City Hall Ave # 1201, Norfolk, VA 23510-2723
Tel (757) 628-3830 *Founded/Ownrshp* 2007
Sales 157.3MM^E *EMP* 6,950^E
SIC 8211 Public elementary & secondary schools
MIS Dir: Thomas Etheridge
Teacher Pr: Vandrig Billops

D-U-N-S 04-918-4690 IMP
▲ NORFOLK SOUTHERN CORP
3 Commercial Pl Ste 1a, Norfolk, VA 23510-2108
Tel (757) 629-2680 *Founded/Ownrshp* 1980
Sales 10.5MMM *EMP* 30,456
Accts Kpmg Llp Norfolk Virginia
Tkr Sym NSC *Exch* NYS
SIC 4011 Railroads, line-haul operating
Ch Bd: James A Squires
Pr: Patti Carroll
Pr: Robert C Fort
Pr: Mark Wolf
COO: Michael J Wheeler
CFO: Marta R Stewart
Bd of Dir: Thomas Bell
Chf Mktg O: Alan H Shaw
Ex VP: James A Hixon
Ex VP: Kitty Vollbrecht
VP: Dave Becker
VP: James Carter
VP: Joseph C Dimino
VP: Timothy J Drake
VP: Cindy C Earhart
VP: Fred Ehlers
VP: Fredric M Ehlers
VP: Terry Evans
VP: Bob Fort
VP: Donald D Graab
VP: Thomas E Hurlbut
Board of Directors: Amy E Miles, Thomas D Bell Jr, Martin H Nesbitt, Erskine B Bowles, John R Thompson, Robert A Bradway, Wesley G Bush, Daniel A Carp, Mitchell E Daniels Jr, Karen N Horn, Steven F Leer, Michael D Lockhart

D-U-N-S 00-692-0417 IMP
■ NORFOLK SOUTHERN RAILWAY CO
(*Suby of* NORFOLK SOUTHERN CORP) ★
3 Commercial Pl Ste 1a, Norfolk, VA 23510-2108
Tel (757) 629-2680 *Founded/Ownrshp* 1894
Sales 3.4MMM^E *EMP* 28,057
SIC 4011 Railroads, line-haul operating
CEO: Charles W Moorman
Treas: Judith K Sublett
Ofcr: Joey Shirley
VP: Fredric Ehlers
VP: Terry N Evans
VP: Tim Heilig
VP: John P Rathbone
VP: James A Squires
VP: Marta R Stewarte
Off Mgr: Darlene Nipper
QA Dir: Stephen Skelley
Board of Directors: L I Prillaman, Stephen C Tobias

D-U-N-S 07-475-4805
NORFOLK STATE UNIVERSITY
(*Suby of* STATE COUNCIL OF HIGHER EDUCATION FOR VIRGINIA) ★
700 Park Ave, Norfolk, VA 23504-8090
Tel (757) 823-8600 *Founded/Ownrshp* 1935
Sales 112.7MM^E *EMP* 1,095
SIC 8221 9411 University; Administration of educational programs;
Int Pr: Eddie N Moore Jr
COO: Kim Luckes
CFO: Marry Weaver
Ofcr: Shelley M Thomas
Top Exec: Carray Banks
VP: Philip Adams
VP: Nuria Cuevas
VP: Anton Kashiri
VP: Alvin Schexnider
VP: Edward M Willis
VP: Julia B Wingard
Assoc Dir: John Francis
Assoc Dir: Dennis Montgomery
Assoc Dir: Terricita Sass

D-U-N-S 00-705-9439 IMP/EXP
NORGREN INC
IMI PRECISION ENGINEERING
(*Suby of* IMI AMERICAS INC) ★
5400 S Delaware St, Littleton, CO 80120-1698
Tel (303) 794-5000 *Founded/Ownrshp* 1972
Sales 160.0MM^E *EMP* 673
SIC 3492 Control valves, fluid power: hydraulic & pneumatic
Pr: Robert Guerra
**CFO:* Matt Drosendahl
VP: Richard Fish
VP: Donald McMahan
VP: Robin Papadimitrio
CTO: Michael Karol
Dir IT: Jim Wilson
Tech Mgr: Michael Suman
Sls&Mrk Ex: O'Dell Byron
Mktg Mgr: Steve Nagy
Snr Mgr: Jeff Andersen

D-U-N-S 13-001-2599
NORIDIAN HEALTHCARE SOLUTIONS LLC
(*Suby of* BLUE CROSS BLUE SHIELD ND) ★
900 42nd St S, Fargo, ND 58103-2119
Tel (701) 277-6500 *Founded/Ownrshp* 2002
Sales NA *EMP* 1,909
SIC 6324 Hospital & medical service plans
Pr: Tom McGraw
**CFO:* Richard Haugen
**Sr VP:* Kevin Erickson
**Sr VP:* Paul O'Donnell
**Sr VP:* Emy Stenerson
VP: Jeanne Narum
VP: Mark Tschider
Doctor: Monique Eva

D-U-N-S 07-313-0601
NORIDIAN MUTUAL INSURANCE CO
BLUE CROSS BLUE SHIELD ND
4510 13th Ave S, Fargo, ND 58121-0002
Tel (701) 282-1100 *Founded/Ownrshp* 1940
Sales 1.2MMM^E *EMP* 16,000
SIC 8399 6321 6324 Advocacy group; Health insurance carriers; Hospital & medical service plans; Group hospitalization plans
Pr: Tim Huckle
Pr: Jack Easton
Pr: Steven Rodvold
Bd of Dir: Deb Selland
Ofcr: Rebecca Nichol
VP: Bradley Bartle
**VP:* Dane Breuer
VP: Craig Campbell
VP: Dan Conrad
VP: John Dixon
VP: Sharon Fletcher
VP: Gail Richter
VP: Mark Tschider
**VP:* Judd Wagner
VP: Jacquelyn Walsh
Exec: Pat Bellmore
Exec: Corey Burnett

D-U-N-S 09-642-3819 IMP/EXP
NORITSU AMERICA CORP (CA)
(*Suby of* NORITSU KOKI CO., LTD.)
6900 Noritsu Ave, Buena Park, CA 90620-1372
Tel (714) 521-9040 *Founded/Ownrshp* 1978
Sales 110.0MM^E *EMP* 310
SIC 5043 Photographic processing equipment
CEO: Michiro Niikura
**Ch Bd:* Kanichi Nishimoto
Pr: Rick Voutour
VP: Frank Morrow
VP: Patrik Norrby
VP: Tim Ohlson
VP: Patrick Todd
VP: David Warburton
**Prin:* Akihiko Kuwabara
CIO: Edwin Trinh
IT Man: Gilbert Siongco

D-U-N-S 04-530-8830
NORKOL INC
11650 W Grand Ave, Northlake, IL 60164-1300
Tel (708) 531-1000 *Founded/Ownrshp* 1985
Sales 126.5MM^E *EMP* 175
SIC 2679 Book covers, paper
Pr: Denise M Callahan
**Ch Bd:* Lawrence Kolinski
**CFO:* Dominick Fashoda
**Sec:* Mary E Kolinski
**VP:* James Lindquist
**Exec:* Ellen Rehm
Genl Mgr: Eric Holzer

D-U-N-S 01-127-5468
NORKUS ENTERPRISES INC
FOODTOWN
505 Richmond Ave, Point Pleasant Beach, NJ 08742-2552
Tel (732) 899-8485 *Founded/Ownrshp* 1935
Sales 129.7MM^E *EMP* 1,000
SIC 5411 Supermarkets, independent
Pr: Gerard K Norkus
**VP:* Mark F Norkus

NORM REEVES HONDA SUPERSTORE
See NORM REEVES INC

D-U-N-S 09-786-9218
NORM REEVES INC
NORM REEVES HONDA SUPERSTORE
18500 Studebaker Rd, Cerritos, CA 90703-5337
Tel (562) 402-3844 *Founded/Ownrshp* 1995
Sales 129.7MM^E *EMP* 325
SIC 5511 5521 Automobiles, new & used; Used car dealers
CEO: David M Conant
**Sec:* Marlene Lewis
**VP:* Lee Stacey
Genl Mgr: John Dalpe
Sls Mgr: Jeff Aoki
Sls Mgr: Allen Nouri
Sls Mgr: Susanna Yim

D-U-N-S 06-344-3949 IMP/EXP
NORM THOMPSON OUTFITTERS INC
SAHALIE
(*Suby of* BEDFORD FAIR APPAREL) ★
35 Village Rd Ste 500, Middleton, MA 01949-1236
Tel (503) 614-4600 *Founded/Ownrshp* 1981
Sales 93.1MM^E *EMP* 500
SIC 5961 Catalog sales; Clothing, mail order (except women's); Gift items, mail order; Women's apparel, mail order
Pr: Martin McClanan
CFO: Bill Stanners
**V Ch Bd:* Rebecca L Jewett
Ofcr: Chris Navigato
**Sr VP:* William J Stanner Jr
VP: Adrienne Cote
VP: Kristin Fisch
VP: Louisa Van Eepoel
VP: Louise Walczak
VP: Dave Walde
Exec: Ellis Fox
Board of Directors: Patrick J Connolly, Al W Emrick Jr, Larry B Gordon, Amy James, Derek Smith

D-U-N-S 03-185-3240 IMP
NORMA PENNSYLVANIA INC
BREEZE INDUSTRIAL PRODUCTS
(*Suby of* NORMA GROUP HOLDING GMBH)
3582 Tunnelton Rd, Saltsburg, PA 15681-3305
Tel (724) 639-3571 *Founded/Ownrshp* 2007
Sales 145.7MM^E *EMP* 465
SIC 3429 Clamps & couplings, hose
CEO: Werner Deggim
**Pr:* Tim Jones
**Pr:* Mike Russel
**COO:* John Stephenson

*CFO: Othmar Belker
*Sec: Durg Kumar
Sr VP: Lynnette Kinter
Sls Mgr: John Seifert

NORMAL LIFE OF SHERIDAN
See TRANSITIONAL HEALTH PARTNERS

D-U-N-S 02-795-7695 IMP/EXP
NORMAN INDUSTRIAL MATERIALS INC
INDUSTRIAL METAL SUPPLY CO
8300 San Fernando Rd, Sun Valley, CA 91352-3222
Tel (818) 729-3333 Founded/Ownrshp 1945
Sales 179.1MM[E] EMP 300
SIC 5051 3441 3449 Metals service centers & offices; Fabricated structural metal; Miscellaneous metalwork
CEO: Eric Steinhauer
*COO: David Pace
*CFO: David Berkey
Genl Mgr: Aaron Brown
Sfty Mgr: Julio Galvez
Ql Cn Mgr: Diana Rising
Sls Mgr: Jack Costella
Sls Mgr: Mike Reihl

D-U-N-S 00-417-5147
NORMAN NOBLE INC (OH)
5507 Avion Park Dr, Highland Heights, OH 44143-1921
Tel (216) 761-5387 Founded/Ownrshp 1962
Sales 94.1MM[E] EMP 400
SIC 3599 Machine shop, jobbing & repair
Pr: Lawrence Noble
*VP: Chris Noble
*VP: Dan Stefano
Genl Mgr: Rick Link
Dir IT: Rebecca Noble
Sales Asso: Barry Sobole

NORMAN PUBLIC SCHOOLS
See INDEPENDENT SCHOOL DISTRICT I-29

D-U-N-S 07-427-8896 IMP
NORMAN REGIONAL HOSPITAL AUTHORITY
901 N Porter Ave, Norman, OK 73071-6482
Tel (405) 307-1000 Founded/Ownrshp 1927
Sales 360.2MM EMP 2,900
Accts Bkd Llp Tulsa Oklahoma
SIC 8062 General medical & surgical hospitals
CEO: Richie Splitt
V Ch: Tom Clote
Bd of Dir: Carol Anderson
*Sr VP: Greg Terrell
*VP: Nancy A Brown
VP: Nancy Brown
*VP: Meegan Carter
VP: Ryan Gehrig
*VP: Ken Hopkins
*Exec: Melvin Alexander
Dir Rx: Darin Smith
Board of Directors: Robin Wiens Campbell, Terry J Garrett

D-U-N-S 10-283-8588
NORMAN S WRIGHT MECHANICAL EQUIPMENT CORP
99 S Hill Dr Ste A, Brisbane, CA 94005-1282
Tel (415) 467-7600 Founded/Ownrshp 1906
Sales 159.0MM[E] EMP 115
SIC 5075 Warm air heating equipment & supplies; Air conditioning & ventilation equipment & supplies
Pr: Richard F Leao
*Ex VP: Robert L Beyer
*Ex VP: Salvatore M Giglio

D-U-N-S 14-005-9549 EXP
NORMAN W FRIES INC
CLAXTON POULTRY FARMS
8816 Us Highway 301, Claxton, GA 30417-5428
Tel (912) 739-1158 Founded/Ownrshp 1958
Sales 228.8MM[E] EMP 1,700
SIC 2015 Chicken slaughtering & processing
CEO: Doris Fries
*Pr: Jerry Lane
CFO: Greg Finch
Sfty Dirs: David Moore
Sales Exec: Tom Scarborough

D-U-N-S 07-933-1007
NORMAN YORK INTERNATIONAL
JCI
5005 York Dr, Norman, OK 73069-9504
Tel (405) 364-4040 Founded/Ownrshp 2005
Sales 330.0MM EMP 600
SIC 5075 Warm air heating & air conditioning
Snr Mgr: Michael Millwee

NORMANDY TERRACE NURSING REHAB
See SENIOR MANAGEMENT SERVICES OF NORMANDY AT SAN ANTONIO INC

D-U-N-S 02-889-9748 EXP
NORMANS NURSERY INC
8665 Duarte Rd, San Gabriel, CA 91775-1139
Tel (626) 285-9795 Founded/Ownrshp 1949
Sales 17.78MM[E] EMP 620
SIC 5193 0181 Nursery stock; Nursery stock, growing of
Pr: Charles Norman
*Treas: Caroline Norman
VP: Nancy Webb

NORMS
See NORMS RESTAURANTS

D-U-N-S 05-240-2450
NORMS RESTAURANTS
NORMS
17844 Lakewood Blvd, Bellflower, CA 90706-6414
Tel (562) 925-4026 Founded/Ownrshp 1949
Sales 44.0MM[E] EMP 1,100
SIC 5812 American restaurant
CEO: Philip H Singerman
*Pr: Sterling Bogart
*VP: Janice Derowen

NORPAC
See NORTH PACIFIC PAPER CO LLC

D-U-N-S 00-905-8561 IMP/EXP
NORPAC FOODS INC (OR)
3225 25th St Se, Salem, OR 97302-1133
Tel (503) 480-2100 Founded/Ownrshp 1924
Sales 878.7MM[E] EMP 4,000
SIC 2037 2033 2038 Fruits, quick frozen & cold pack (frozen); Vegetables, quick frozen & cold pack, excl. potato products; Fruits: packaged in cans, jars, etc.; Vegetables: packaged in cans, jars, etc.; Soups, frozen
Pr: George Smith
*CFO: Jon Greeley
VP: Steve Cerri
VP: Manuel Silveira
Genl Mgr: Walter Smith
Dir IT: Sam Borg
Dir IT: Barry Brown
Dir IT: Joe Vondrachek
*VP Opers: Bill Burich
Sfty Mgr: Ray Noble
Opers Mgr: Jim Gill

D-U-N-S 01-210-7459 IMP
NORPLAS INDUSTRIES INC
MAGNA
(Suby of DECOMA ADMARK) ★
7825 Caple Blvd, Northwood, OH 43619-1070
Tel (419) 662-3317 Founded/Ownrshp 1997
Sales 313.6MM[E] EMP 1,000[E]
SIC 3469 Metal stampings
CEO: Donald J Walker
*VP: Graham Burrow

D-U-N-S 05-750-4599
NORQUIST SALVAGE CORP INC
THRIFTTOWN
2151 Prof Dr Ste 200, Roseville, CA 95661
Tel (916) 787-1070 Founded/Ownrshp 1972
Sales 100.4MM[E] EMP 700
SIC 5932

NORRIS FOOD SERVICES
See CONSTANCE FOOD GROUP INC

NORRIS PRODUCTION SOLUTIONS
See DOVER ARTIFICIAL LIFT INTERNATIONAL LLC

NORSE DAIRY SYSTEMS
See INTERBAKE FOODS LLC

NORSHIPCO
See BAE SYSTEMS NORFOLK SHIP REPAIR INC

D-U-N-S 06-819-6054
■ **NORSTAN COMMUNICATIONS INC** (MN)
BLACK BOX NETWORK SERVICES
(Suby of NORSTAN INC) ★
5050 Lincoln Dr Ste 300, Minneapolis, MN 55436-1179
Tel (952) 935-9002 Founded/Ownrshp 1974
Sales 226.2MM[E] EMP 1,090
SIC 5065 1731 7629 Telephone equipment; Telephone & telephone equipment installation; Telecommunication equipment repair (except telephones)
Ch Bd: Paul Baszucki
*Pr: Scott Christian
*Treas: Alice Vazquez

D-U-N-S 05-341-7945
■ **NORSTAN INC**
(Suby of BLACK BOX CORP) ★
5050 Lincoln Dr Ste 300, Minneapolis, MN 55436-1179
Tel (952) 352-4000 Founded/Ownrshp 2005
Sales 266.6MM[E] EMP 1,090
SIC 7389 3661 8748 7379 Telephone services; Teleconferencing services; Telephone answering service; Telephones & telephone apparatus; Electronic secretary; Message concentrators; Telecommunications consultant; Computer related consulting services
Pr: Scott G Christian
Pr: Jeffery Lusenhop
Ex VP: Peter Stilson
*Sr VP: Steven D Anderson
*Sr VP: Roger D Van Beusekom
*Sr VP: Donna M Warner
VP: Richard A Camuso
VP: Kenneth R Croken
VP: Kim Keller
VP: Kenneth Larson
VP: Jeffery Mattson
VP: Larry Schmidt
VP: Jack White

D-U-N-S 79-469-4166 IMP/EXP
NORSTAR OFFICE PRODUCTS INC
BOSS
5353 Jillson St, Commerce, CA 90040-2115
Tel (323) 262-1919 Founded/Ownrshp 1999
Sales 251.2MM[E] EMP 2,367
SIC 2521 2522 Chairs, office: padded, upholstered or plain: wood; Chairs, office: padded or plain, except wood
Pr: William W Huang

D-U-N-S 19-516-3600
NORSTAR PIPELINE CO INC
ENSTAR NATURAL GAS
(Suby of SEMCO ENERGY INC) ★
3000 Spenard Rd, Anchorage, AK 99503-3606
Tel (907) 277-5551 Founded/Ownrshp 2001
Sales 109.9MM[E] EMP 143[E]
SIC 4922 Natural gas transmission
Ch Bd: Jared Green
*CFO: Mark A Moses
*VP: John Sims
*VP: Moira Smith
IT Man: Ray Anderson
*VP Opers: John Lau
Snr Mgr: Travis Renk

NORSUN
See DICKINSON FROZEN FOODS INC

D-U-N-S 01-042-9728 EXP
▲ **NORTECH SYSTEMS INC**
7550 Meridian Cir N # 150, Maple Grove, MN 55369-4932
Tel (952) 345-2244 Founded/Ownrshp 1981
Sales 115.1MM EMP 841
Tkr Sym NSYS Exch NAS
SIC 3674 3679 Semiconductors & related devices; Integrated circuits, semiconductor networks, etc.; Electronic circuits
CEO: Richard G Wasielewski
*Ch Bd: Michael J Degen
CFO: Paula M Graff
Ofcr: Curtis J Steichen
Ql Cn Mgr: Keith Gadacz
Board of Directors: Kathleen Iverson, Michael Kennedy, David B Kunin, Kenneth Larson, Richard W Perkins

D-U-N-S 08-909-0534 IMP
NORTEK AIR SOLUTIONS LLC
(Suby of NORTEK INC) ★
13200 Pioneer Trl Ste 150, Eden Prairie, MN 55347-4125
Tel (952) 358-6600 Founded/Ownrshp 1977
Sales 465.3MM[E] EMP 2,100
SIC 3585 Air conditioning equipment, complete; Heating equipment, complete
Pr: Eric Roberts
*CFO: Brian Smith
VP: Susan Snyder
CIO: Mike Murphy
IT Man: John Clayton
Mktg Dir: Chris Sackrison

D-U-N-S 00-632-3034 IMP
NORTEK GLOBAL HVAC LLC
INTERTHERM
(Suby of NORTEK INC) ★
8000 Phoenix Pkwy, O Fallon, MO 63368-3827
Tel (636) 561-7300 Founded/Ownrshp 1985
Sales 509.6MM[E] EMP 2,300
SIC 3585 3567 3433 Heating & air conditioning combination units; Industrial furnaces & ovens; Heating equipment, except electric
Pr: David J Legrand
VP: Michael Nix
VP: Steven Wu
Mng Dir: Mohd Rahman
Brnch Mgr: John Saffeels
Genl Mgr: Amit K Mondal
Dir IT: Wade Bestgen
IT Man: Tom T Ho
Tech Mgr: Keith A Skipper
Opers Mgr: Doug Rowe
Ql Cn Mgr: Glen McKee
Board of Directors: Richard L Bready, Richard J Harris

D-U-N-S 61-533-2900 IMP/EXP
NORTEK INC
(Suby of MELROSE INDUSTRIES PLC)
500 Exchange St, Providence, RI 02903-2630
Tel (401) 751-1600 Founded/Ownrshp 2016
Sales 2.5MMM EMP 11,400
SIC 3585 3444 3634 3699 2434 Refrigeration & heating equipment; Heating equipment, complete; Air conditioning equipment, complete; Air conditioning units, complete: domestic or industrial; Metal ventilating equipment; Hoods, range: sheet metal; Electric housewares & fans; Fans, exhaust & ventilating, electric: household; Electrical equipment & supplies; Security control equipment & systems; Door opening & closing devices, electrical; Chimes, electric; Wood kitchen cabinets; Vanities, bathroom: wood
Pr: Michael J Clarke
*Ch Bd: J David Smith
Sr VP: Timothy J Burling
Sr VP: Kevin W Donnelly
VP: Michael Botelho
VP: Rob Halligan
CIO: Mark Rafferty
Board of Directors: Joseph A Arcuri, Jeffrey C Bloomberg, John T Coleman, James B Hirshorn, Daniel C Lukas, Chris A McWilton, Bennett Rosenthal

D-U-N-S 82-931-6269
NORTEL NETWORKS HPOCS INC
(Suby of NORTEL NETWORKS CORPORATION)
725 Cool Springs Blvd # 600, Franklin, TN 37067-2702
Tel (800) 684-2228 Founded/Ownrshp 2001
Sales 116.4MM[E] EMP 2,024[E]
SIC 3661 Telephone & telegraph apparatus

D-U-N-S 03-010-4025
NORTH ADVOCATE SIDE HEALTH NETWORK (IL)
(Suby of ADVOCATE HEALTH CARE NETWORK) ★
836 W Wellington Ave, Chicago, IL 60657-5147
Tel (773) 296-5699 Founded/Ownrshp 1981
Sales 471.4MM EMP 1,600
SIC 8741 8721 Hospital management; Accounting, auditing & bookkeeping
CEO: Kenneth J Rojek
Opers Mgr: Paul Mangura

D-U-N-S 07-215-9288
NORTH ALLEGHENY SCHOOL DISTRICT
200 Hillvue Ln Ste 1, Pittsburgh, PA 15237-5391
Tel (412) 369-5484 Founded/Ownrshp 1948
Sales 136.6MM EMP 1,019
SIC 8211 Public elementary & secondary schools
Recvr: Brian Austin
Bd of Dir: Karen Boujoukos
VP: Linda Bishop
VP: Diane Feliciani
Genl Mgr: Lynn Reaghard
Teacher Pr: Laura Jowelter
Psych: Stephanie Marshall
Psych: Terry Valentino
HC Dir: Charity Istone

D-U-N-S 18-283-8516 EXP
NORTH AMERICA PACKAGING CORP
NAMPAC
(Suby of BWAY CORP) ★
1515 W 22nd St Ste 550, Oak Brook, IL 60523-8742
Tel (630) 203-4100 Founded/Ownrshp 2004
Sales 209.5MM[E] EMP 1,200
SIC 3089 Plastic containers, except foam
Pr: Tom Linton
*VP: Danny Byrne

D-U-N-S 06-625-6842
NORTH AMERICA SEKISUI HOUSE LLC
(Suby of SEKISUI HOUSE, LTD.)
2001 Jefferson Davis Hwy, Arlington, VA 22202-3603
Tel (703) 740-0229 Founded/Ownrshp 2010
Sales 200.0MM EMP 1[E]
SIC 6719 Investment holding companies, except banks
COO: Satoshi Yoshimura

D-U-N-S 62-309-5718
■ **NORTH AMERICAN ASSET DEVELOPMENT CORP**
(Suby of NORTH AMERICAN TITLE GROUP INC) ★
1855 Gateway Blvd Ste 650, Concord, CA 94520-8454
Tel (925) 935-5599 Founded/Ownrshp 1998
Sales NA EMP 1,001[E]
SIC 6361 6531 Title insurance; Escrow agent, real estate
Pr: Dan R Wentzel
*CFO: Jeff Wright

D-U-N-S 87-651-5172
NORTH AMERICAN BANCARD LLC
ADVANCED PAYMENT SOLUTIONS
250 Stephenson Hwy, Troy, MI 48083-1117
Tel (800) 226-2273 Founded/Ownrshp 1991
Sales NA EMP 600[E]
Accts Doeren Mayhew Troy Michigan
SIC 6153 Working capital financing
Pr: Marc Gardner
*COO: Terri Harwood
COO: Gary Rutledge
*CFO: Kirk Haggarty
CFO: Howard Morof
VP: Scott Addyman
VP: Rita Feldman
VP: Scott Fessler
VP: Jamie Hamilton
VP: Richard Parrott
VP: Robert Seward
VP: David Tepoorten
VP: Scott Webb

D-U-N-S 82-978-2445 EXP
NORTH AMERICAN BREWERIES INC
NORTHAMERICAN BREWERIES
(Suby of FLORIDA BEBIDAS SA)
445 Saint Paul St, Rochester, NY 14605-1726
Tel (585) 546-1030 Founded/Ownrshp 2012
Sales 310.6MM[E] EMP 1,043
SIC 2082 Beer (alcoholic beverage)
Ch Bd: Richard Lozyniak
*Pr: Raquel Vargas
*CEO: Kris Sirchio
CIO: Paul Yarnot
Sls Dir: Bill Gillespie
Manager: Douglas Smith

D-U-N-S 06-949-6867
NORTH AMERICAN CO FOR LIFE & HEALTH INSURANCE
(Suby of SAMMONS FINANCIAL GROUP INC) ★
525 W Van Buren St # 1200, Chicago, IL 60607-3820
Tel (312) 648-7600 Founded/Ownrshp 1986
Sales NA EMP 350
SIC 6311 6321 Life insurance carriers; Accident insurance carriers; Health insurance carriers
Pr: Steven C Palmitier
Sr Pt: Steppe Gregory
Sr Pt: Beucler Lykens
*Treas: John J Craig
Ofcr: Brent Mardis
*Ex VP: Edward Turner
VP: Norma Davis
VP: Curtis Foody
VP: C Haley
VP: Gary Helder
VP: Robert Kaufman
VP: Bill Keffer
VP: William Keffer
VP: Barbara Murray
VP: Robert Tekolste
VP: Heath Williams
Exec: Michael Masterson
Board of Directors: Gary Gaspar, Steve Horvat, Brian Rohr

D-U-N-S 00-790-1085 IMP
■ **NORTH AMERICAN COAL CORP**
(Suby of NACCO INDUSTRIES INC) ★
5340 Legacy Dr Ste 300, Plano, TX 75024-3141
Tel (972) 448-5400 Founded/Ownrshp 1986
Sales 723.0MM[E] EMP 1,500
Accts Ernst & Young Llp Richmond V
SIC 1221 Bituminous coal & lignite-surface mining
Ch: Alfred M Rankin
*Pr: Bob Benson
*CEO: JC Butler Jr
*CFO: Bob D Carlton
*Treas: K Donald Grischow
VP: Robert Benson
*VP: Michael J Gregory
*VP: Thomas Andrew Koza
IT Exec: Bruce Daves

D-U-N-S 06-763-0582
NORTH AMERICAN COMMUNICATIONS INC
N A C
7 Edgemont Rd, Katonah, NY 10536-1503
Tel (914) 273-8620 Founded/Ownrshp 1982
Sales 66.2MM[E] EMP 1,000
SIC 7331 Direct mail advertising services
CEO: Nicholas D Robinson
*Pr: Robert Herman
*Ch: Michael Herman
Ql Cn Mgr: Stacey Burket

D-U-N-S 14-915-4614 IMP
NORTH AMERICAN COMPOSITES CO
(Suby of MOLDING PRODUCTS) ★
300 Apollo Dr, Circle Pines, MN 55014-3018
Tel (651) 766-6892 Founded/Ownrshp 1999
Sales 125.9MM[E] EMP 150
SIC 5162 Plastics materials
Pr: James D Wallenfelsz
VP: David Engelsgaard

*VP: Richard Rodriguez
Rgnl Mgr: Douglas Kennedy
Dist Mgr: Bern Brody
Dist Mgr: Steve Hewson
Opers Mgr: Tina Anderson

D-U-N-S 04-295-3810
NORTH AMERICAN CONTAINER CORP
1811 W Oak Pkwy Ste D, Marietta, GA 30062-2279
Tel (770) 431-4858 Founded/Ownrshp 1967
Sales 171.6MM[E] EMP 600
SIC 3443 Containers, shipping (bombs, etc.): metal plate
CEO: John Grigsby Jr
*CFO: Michael Grigsby
VP: Charles Grigsby
Opers Mgr: Harold Briner
Plnt Mgr: Paul Burkart
Plnt Mgr: David Peters
Plnt Mgr: Ken Wilson
Sls Mgr: Steve Rollins

D-U-N-S 02-524-7354
NORTH AMERICAN CORP OF ILLINOIS (IL)
2101 Claire Ct, Glenview, IL 60025-7634
Tel (847) 832-4000 Founded/Ownrshp 1919
Sales 273.2MM[E] EMP 330
SIC 5113 5169 Industrial & personal service paper; Chemicals & allied products
Pr: John A Miller
*CFO: Rosemarie Egan
*CFO: Matt Zimmermann

NORTH AMERICAN DRAGER
See DRAEGER INC

D-U-N-S 96-319-3404 IMP/EXP
NORTH AMERICAN FABRICATORS LLC
LASHIP
367 Dickson Rd, Houma, LA 70363-7310
Tel (985) 917-2000 Founded/Ownrshp 1996
Sales 96.7MM[E] EMP 300
SIC 3731 Offshore supply boats, building & repairing; Cargo vessels, building & repairing; Crew boats, building & repairing

D-U-N-S 19-645-6917
NORTH AMERICAN FAMILY INSTITUTE INC
NAFI
300 Rosewood Dr Ste 101, Danvers, MA 01923-1685
Tel (978) 538-0286 Founded/Ownrshp 1974
Sales 98.4MM EMP 1,600
Accts Kpmg Llp Boston Ma
SIC 8322 Child related social services; Family counseling services
Pr: Yitzhak Bakal
CFO: Pamela Bruce
*Treas: Hildegarde Paris
Off Mgr: Jeannine Pelkey
CTO: Karley Root
Dir IT: Christian Tirella
Opers Supe: Martha Adams
Pgrm Dir: Carlos Agudelo
Pgrm Dir: Jill Dichiara
Pgrm Dir: Ted Holmes

D-U-N-S 04-027-8889 IMP
■ **NORTH AMERICAN FOREST PRODUCTS LIQUIDATION INC**
(Suby of CANA) ★
27263 May St, Edwardsburg, MI 49112-8680
Tel (269) 663-8500 Founded/Ownrshp 1989
Sales 90.0MM[E] EMP 220
SIC 2421 5031 Resawing lumber into smaller dimensions; Lumber: rough, sawed or planed; Building & structural materials, wood; Lumber: rough, dressed & finished
Pr: John Robert Wiley II
*Pr: Bob Wiley
*COO: Andrew Clark
VP: Brett Lamont
Sfty Mgr: Mike Chaffee

D-U-N-S 00-884-1058
■ **NORTH AMERICAN GALVANIZING & COATINGS INC**
AZZ GALVANIZING SERVICES
(Suby of AZZ INC) ★
3100 W 7th St Ste 500, Fort Worth, TX 76107-8701
Tel (817) 810-0095 Founded/Ownrshp 1955, 2010
Sales 468.8M[E] EMP 1,156
SIC 7539 3312 Electrical services; Iron & steel: galvanized, pipes, plates, sheets, etc.
CEO: Tom Ferguson
VP: Mike Echebarria
*VP: Deanna Perry
Dir IT: Tom Morgan
IT Man: Brad Smith
Opers Mgr: Alvin Love
S&M/VP: Joseph Langemeier
Mktg Mgr: Kevin Irving
Sls Mgr: Steve Cessna
Sls Mgr: Randy Straight
Sls Mgr: Tim Welch

NORTH AMERICAN GROUP
See NORTH AMERICAN INSURANCE AGENCY INC

D-U-N-S 19-667-1416 IMP/EXP
NORTH AMERICAN HOGANAS CO
(Suby of HOGANAS AB)
111 Hoganas Way, Hollsopple, PA 15935-6416
Tel (814) 479-3500 Founded/Ownrshp 2001
Sales 213.7MM EMP 355
SIC 3399 Metal powders, pastes & flakes
Pr: Avinash Gore
Pr: Sydney Foulkes-Arnold
Pr: Sydney Luk
Pr: Luk Sydney
Chf Mktg O: Beth Walker
*VP: Terry Henrich
*VP: Ronald Solomon
Genl Mgr: James Cordek
IT Man: Debra Gindlesperger
Opers Mgr: Matthew Smith
Plnt Mgr: Donald Bowman

D-U-N-S 09-016-0008 IMP/EXP
NORTH AMERICAN HOGANAS HOLDINGS INC (DE)
(Suby of HOGANAS AB)
111 Hoganas Way, Hollsopple, PA 15935-6416
Tel (814) 479-2551 Founded/Ownrshp 1999
Sales 84.7MM[E] EMP 360
SIC 3462 Ornamental metal forgings, ferrous
Pr: Avinash Gore
VP: Perry Heinrich
*VP: Dean Howard
VP: Sydney Luk
*VP: Sydney Luke
VP: Ronald Soloman
*VP: Ronald Solomon
Plnt Mgr: Donald Bowman

NORTH AMERICAN HYDROLICS
See NAHI LLC

D-U-N-S 84-988-3392
NORTH AMERICAN INDUSTRIAL SERVICES INC
1240 Saratoga Rd, Ballston Spa, NY 12020-3500
Tel (518) 885-1820 Founded/Ownrshp 1994
Sales 98.1MM[E] EMP 400
SIC 7349 Cleaning service, industrial or commercial; Demonstration service; Excavation & grading, building construction
Pr: Frank Zilka
CFO: Christopher Scaringe
Genl Mgr: Chris Boulden
Genl Mgr: Chris Spain
Opers Mgr: James Lehrke

D-U-N-S 07-732-7013
NORTH AMERICAN INSURANCE AGENCY INC
NORTH AMERICAN GROUP
5101 Classen Cir, Oklahoma City, OK 73118-4424
Tel (405) 523-2100 Founded/Ownrshp 1959
Sales NA EMP 369
SIC 6411 Insurance agents, brokers & service; Insurance agents
Ch Bd: Bill Durrett
*Pr: Mike Ross
VP: John Hester
*VP: Gary Jarmon
Brnch Mgr: Mark Heyne
CIO: Jeff Nickles
IT Man: Mike Ro
IT Man: Todd West

D-U-N-S 12-507-3432 IMP
NORTH AMERICAN INTERCONNECT LLC
(Suby of NAI GROUP LLC) ★
7975 N Hayden Rd Ste D105, Scottsdale, AZ 85258-3247
Tel (480) 556-6066 Founded/Ownrshp 2002
Sales 292.9MM[E] EMP 1,100
SIC 2298 Cable, fiber
CEO: Preston Spears
Snr Sftwr: Harjinder Kaur
Ql Cn Mgr: Carlos Tellez
VP Sls: Bill Mills
Snr Mgr: Judith Lopez

D-U-N-S 01-846-8756
NORTH AMERICAN KIOSK LLC
AKM
3930 Howard Hughes Pkwy # 500, Las Vegas, NV 89169-0948
Tel (702) 691-2948 Founded/Ownrshp 1998
Sales 97.9MM[E] EMP 1,350
SIC 8741 Business management
CEO: Linda Johansen-James
*Pr: Linda Johensen
*COO: Scott Jackson
*CFO: Kenneth E Jones
*VP: Patricia Adame
*VP: Joe Lecak
*VP: Nicole Lloyd

D-U-N-S 11-580-5228 IMP
NORTH AMERICAN LIGHTING INC
(Suby of KOITO MANUFACTURING CO., LTD.)
2275 S Main St, Paris, IL 61944-2963
Tel (217) 465-6600 Founded/Ownrshp 1998
Sales 666.7MM[E] EMP 2,200
SIC 3647 Automotive lighting fixtures
CEO: Takashi Ohtake
*Pr: Jun Toyota
*Sec: Kirk Gadberry
*VP: Kishore Ahuja
*VP: Kem Cooley
*VP: Naoshi Misawa
Prgrm Mgr: Kevin Blatnik
Prgrm Mgr: Cindy Bunkelman
Prgrm Mgr: Mark Green
Prgrm Mgr: Wade Haggstrom
Prgrm Mgr: Rick Pumphrey

D-U-N-S 01-869-1303 IMP
NORTH AMERICAN MARKETING CORP (CT)
NAMCO
30 Waterchase Dr, Rocky Hill, CT 06067-2110
Tel (860) 649-3666 Founded/Ownrshp 1962
Sales 250.2MM[E] EMP 1,012[E]
SIC 5999 Swimming pools, hot tubs & sauna equipment & supplies; Swimming pool chemicals, equipment & supplies
Pr: Stephen Radocchia
*CFO: Stephen Park
VP: Robert Prosser
VP: Rod Wiggins
Dir IT: Bill Cooney
Netwrk Mgr: Domingo Serrano

NORTH AMERICAN PET PRODUCTS
See PET PARTNERS INC

D-U-N-S 83-246-1086
NORTH AMERICAN POWER AND GAS LLC
20 Glover Ave Ste 1, Norwalk, CT 06850-1234
Tel (203) 893-4196 Founded/Ownrshp 2009
Sales 270.0MM EMP 113
SIC 4931 Electric & other services combined
Ch: Kerry Breitbart
*Pr: Bill Kinneary

*CEO: Deryl Brown
*COO: Taff Tschamlar
*CFO: Keith Schwartz
*CIO: Jim Crysdale

D-U-N-S 09-390-2542 IMP/EXP
NORTH AMERICAN REFRACTORIES CO
1305 Cherrington Pkwy # 100, Coraopolis, PA 15108-4355
Tel (412) 375-6600 Founded/Ownrshp 2013
Sales 118.6MM[E] EMP 835[E]
SIC 3297 3255

D-U-N-S 80-720-0902 EXP
NORTH AMERICAN ROOFING SERVICES INC
41 Dogwood Rd, Asheville, NC 28806-2208
Tel (828) 687-7767 Founded/Ownrshp 1993
Sales 117.6MM[E] EMP 500
SIC 1761 Roofing contractor
Pr: Brian Verble
*CFO: Timothy Sparrow
*Ex VP: Kelly Wade

D-U-N-S 06-271-5214
■ **NORTH AMERICAN SAVINGS BANK FSB**
(Suby of NASB FINANCIAL INC) ★
12498 S Us Highway 71, Grandview, MO 64030-1782
Tel (816) 765-2200 Founded/Ownrshp 1923, 1997
Sales NA EMP 314
SIC 6035 Federal savings & loan associations
CEO: Paul L Thomas
*Ch Bd: David H Hancock
Pr: Keith B Cox
CFO: Rhonda Nyhus
Bd of Dir: Linda Hancock
Ofcr: Tom Wagers
Sr VP: Brad Lee
Sr VP: John Nesselrode
Sr VP: Bruce Thielen
VP: Mark Bitteker
VP: Michael P Braman
VP: Jerry Brown
VP: Phil Craven
VP: Sherrie Eimer
VP: Jesseka Endecott
VP: Cathleen Gwin
VP: Scott Haase
VP: Jeff Jackson
VP: Lisa M Reynolds
VP: Ron Stafford
VP: Drake Vidrine

D-U-N-S 06-372-2102
NORTH AMERICAN SCIENCE ASSOCIATES INC
NAMSA
6750 Wales Rd, Northwood, OH 43619-1012
Tel (419) 666-9455 Founded/Ownrshp 1967
Sales 142.2MM[E] EMP 533
SIC 8731 8734 Commercial physical research; Testing laboratories
Pr: John J Gorski
*CFO: Scott Sellick
*VP: Jane A Kervin
*VP: Dennis Nevins
VP: Chris Pulling
*VP: Gina Skolmowski
Dir Bus: Sheri Bibins
Genl Mgr: Jean Boutrand
Genl Mgr: An Liu
Dir IT: Steve Napier
Snr PM: Don Pohl

D-U-N-S 06-951-8868 IMP
NORTH AMERICAN SHIPBUILDING LLC
800 Industrial Park Rd, Larose, LA 70373-5147
Tel (985) 693-4072 Founded/Ownrshp 1974
Sales 102.5MM[E] EMP 550
SIC 3731 Offshore supply boats, building & repairing; Cargo vessels, building & repairing; Crew boats, building & repairing
Prin: Gary J Chouest
*CFO: Charles Comeaux
*Prin: Dino Chouest
Sfty Dirs: Rene Stewart

D-U-N-S 62-081-9318 IMP/EXP
NORTH AMERICAN STAINLESS
NAS
(Suby of ACERINOX, SA)
6870 Us Highway 42 E, Ghent, KY 41045-8451
Tel (502) 347-6000 Founded/Ownrshp 2005
Sales 400.5MM[E] EMP 1,375[E]
SIC 3316 3312 Cold finishing of steel shapes; Blast furnaces & steel mills
CEO: Cristobal Fuentes

D-U-N-S 13-211-7636
NORTH AMERICAN STAMPING GROUP LLC
TENNESSEE STAMPINGS PORTLAND
119 Kirby Dr, Portland, TN 37148-2004
Tel (615) 323-0500 Founded/Ownrshp 1968
Sales 255.6MM[E] EMP 558[E]
SIC 3469 6719 Metal stampings; Investment holding companies, except banks

D-U-N-S 14-873-3053
NORTH AMERICAN TIE & TIMBER LLC
6406 N Santa Fe Ave Ste B, Oklahoma City, OK 73116-9117
Tel (405) 848-1800 Founded/Ownrshp 2003
Sales 480.0MM EMP 43
SIC 5099 Timber products, rough

D-U-N-S 10-341-1757
■ **NORTH AMERICAN TITLE CO INC**
NAT
(Suby of NORTH AMERICAN ASSET DEVELOPMENT CORP) ★
1855 Gateway Blvd Ste 600, Concord, CA 94520-8474
Tel (925) 935-5599 Founded/Ownrshp 1983
Sales NA EMP 1,000
SIC 6361 6531 Title insurance; Escrow agent, real estate
Pr: Linda L Reed
*CEO: Anita Demmon

*CFO: Jeffrey Wright
Sr VP: Richard Lundbeck

D-U-N-S 02-818-2074
■ **NORTH AMERICAN TITLE GROUP INC** (FL)
(Suby of LENNAR FINANCIAL SERVICES LLC) ★
700 Nw 107th Ave Ste 300, Miami, FL 33172-3139
Tel (305) 552-1102 Founded/Ownrshp 1984
Sales NA EMP 1,050
SIC 6361 Title insurance
Pr: Linda L Reed
*CFO: Clotilde C Keller
*Treas: Donnis Benson
*Ex VP: Emilio Fernandez
Ex VP: Nancy A Kminsky
*Sr VP: Richard K Kasunick
*VP: Carol Burgin
*VP: Alex Kidd
Dir Bus: Loni Andal

D-U-N-S 15-065-2923
NORTH AMERICAN TRUCK & TRAILER INC
4500 N Cliff Ave, Sioux Falls, SD 57104-0553
Tel (605) 332-7112 Founded/Ownrshp 1989
Sales 92.2MM[E] EMP 240
SIC 5012 7538

D-U-N-S 00-693-7197 IMP/EXP
NORTH AMERICAN VAN LINES INC (TX)
(Suby of SIRVA WORLDWIDE INC) ★
5001 Us Highway 30 W, Fort Wayne, IN 46818-9799
Tel (260) 429-1682 Founded/Ownrshp 1933
Sales 230.7MM[E] EMP 1,382
SIC 4213 4731 4214 6331 7389 4212 Trucking, except local; Household goods transport; Freight forwarding; Furniture moving & storage, local; Assessment associations: fire, marine & casualty insurance; Property damage insurance; Relocation service; Local trucking, without storage
CEO: Michael T Wolfe
*Sr VP: John M Dupuy
*Sr VP: Eryk J Spytek
VP: Dennis Koziol
VP: Richard Omlor
Exec: Joe Steen
Genl Mgr: O Neil
Sales Exec: Tammy Smith
Board of Directors: Robert W Tieken, Kathleen Affeldt, Frederick Brace, Robert J Dellinger, Laban P Jackson Jr, Gen Sir Jeremy Mackenzie, James Roger, Richard Schnall, Joseph A Smialowski, Carl Stocker

D-U-N-S 07-659-2187 IMP/EXP
NORTH AMERICAN VIDEO CORP
NAVCO SECURITY SYSTEMS
1041 N Pacificenter Dr, Anaheim, CA 92806-2126
Tel (714) 779-7499 Founded/Ownrshp 1979
Sales 114.5MM[E] EMP 115
SIC 5065 3812 Video equipment, electronic; Security control equipment & systems; Acceleration indicators & systems components, aerospace
CEO: Jason Oakley
*Ch Bd: Margaret Groves
*Pr: William Groves
*Treas: Debra Laberge
*Prin: William Augustus Groves
Natl Sales: Casey Knapp
Sls Mgr: Ali Nik

D-U-N-S 83-230-2322
NORTH ARKANSAS REGIONAL MEDICA
620 N Main St, Harrison, AR 72601-2911
Tel (870) 365-2000 Founded/Ownrshp 2009
Sales 95.7MM EMP 35[E]
Accts Bkd Llp Little Rock Ar
SIC 8011 Medical centers
Owner: Timothy A Gannon
Off Mgr: Lucia Gonzalez

D-U-N-S 14-473-5198
NORTH ARKANSAS REGIONAL MEDICAL CENTER
620 N Main St, Harrison, AR 72601-2911
Tel (870) 414-4000 Founded/Ownrshp 1996
Sales 93.5MM EMP 700
Accts Bkd Llp Little Rock Ar
SIC 8062 General medical & surgical hospitals
CEO: Vincent Leist
COO: Richard McBride
*COO: Richard McBryde
*CFO: Bebbie Henry
*CFO: Debbie Henry
VP: Sammie Cribbs
VP: Ronnie McAlister
Dir Risk M: Jeanette Milligan
Dir Lab: Vincent List
Dir Rx: Jean Senn
Genl Mgr: Krissy Pierce

D-U-N-S 80-342-1296 IMP
NORTH ATLANTIC CORP
NAMCO
1255 Grand Army Hwy, Somerset, MA 02726-1203
Tel (508) 324-7700 Founded/Ownrshp 1992
Sales 108.2MM[E] EMP 180
SIC 5031 Doors; Door frames, all materials
Pr: Peter Humphrey
*Treas: Irving D Humphrey
*VP: I Gary Fox

D-U-N-S 94-507-2676
■ **NORTH ATLANTIC ENERGY CORP**
(Suby of FPL) ★
626 Lafayette Rd, Seabrook, NH 03874-4213
Tel (603) 474-9521 Founded/Ownrshp 2002
Sales 844.2MM[E] EMP 1,000
SIC 4911 Electric services
Pr: Bruce D Kenyon
*Treas: David McHale
*Ofcr: Ted C Feigenbaum
*VP: John J Roman

D-U-N-S 14-426-3340
■ **NORTH ATLANTIC ENERGY SERVICE CORP**
SEABROOK NUCLEAR POWER PROJECT
(*Suby of* EVERSOURCE ENERGY) ★
626 Lafayette Rd, Seabrook, NH 03874-4213
Tel (603) 474-9521 *Founded/Ownrshp* 1992
Sales 368.8MM[E] *EMP* 800
SIC 4924 Natural gas distribution
Ch Bd: Michael Morris
**Pr:* Bruce Kenyonn
**CFO:* John Forsgren
**Ofcr:* Ted C Feigenbaum

D-U-N-S 00-289-8182 IMP
■ **NORTH ATLANTIC TRADING CO INC**
(*Suby of* TURNING POINT BRANDS INC) ★
5201 Interchange Way, Louisville, KY 40229-2184
Tel (502) 778-4421 *Founded/Ownrshp* 1997
Sales 180.2MM *EMP* 299[E]
Accts Mcgladrey Llp Greensboro No
SIC 2131 Chewing & smoking tobacco
Pr: Lawrence S Wexler
**Ch Bd:* Thomas F Helms Jr
**CFO:* Brian C Harris
**V Ch Bd:* Jack Africk
**Sr VP:* James W Dobbins
**Sr VP:* James M Murray
Board of Directors: Gregory H A Baxter, Geoffrey J F Gorman

D-U-N-S 07-982-3233
NORTH BABYLON UNION FREE SCHOOL DISTRICT
5 Jardine Pl, Babylon, NY 11703-4203
Tel (631) 321-3209 *Founded/Ownrshp* 1932
Sales 45.0MM[E] *EMP* 1,000
SIC 8211 8741 Public combined elementary & secondary school; Management services

D-U-N-S 00-843-4465
NORTH BAKERSFIELD TOYOTA SCION
19651 Industry Parkway Dr, Bakersfield, CA 93308-9442
Tel (661) 615-1100 *Founded/Ownrshp* 2007
Sales 83.6MM *EMP* 125
SIC 5511 Automobiles, new & used
Pr: Steven Downs
Genl Mgr: Larry Puryear
Sls Mgr: Alex Ayyoub

NORTH BALDWIN INFIRMARY
See GULF HEALTH HOSPITALS INC

D-U-N-S 08-988-1114
NORTH BAY DEVELOPMENTAL DISABILITIES SERVICES INC (CA)
NORTH BAY REGIONAL CENTER
10 Executive Ct Ste A, NAPA, CA 94558-6267
Tel (707) 256-1224 *Founded/Ownrshp* 1972
Sales 157.1MM *EMP* 160
Accts Thompson Noble Company Llp Sa
SIC 8331 8322 Job training services; Individual & family services
Ex Dir: Nancy Gardner
CFO: David Johnson

D-U-N-S 78-423-9485 IMP/EXP
NORTH BAY PRODUCE INC
1771 N Us Highway 31 S, Traverse City, MI 49685-8748
Tel (231) 946-1941 *Founded/Ownrshp* 1991
Sales 180.5MM *EMP* 25
Accts Dennis Gartland & Niergarth
SIC 5148 Fruits; Vegetables
Ch Bd: George Wright
**Pr:* Mark Girardin
**Sec:* Ken Schwallier
**V Ch Bd:* Tom Gee
**VP:* Richard L Bogard
Mktg Mgr: Victor Cotner
Sls Mgr: Eric Olshove

NORTH BAY REGIONAL CENTER
See NORTH BAY DEVELOPMENTAL DISABILITIES SERVICES INC

NORTH BROOKLYN HEALTH NETWORK
See WOODHULL MEDICAL & MENTAL HEALTH CENTER AUXILIARY INC

D-U-N-S 07-225-2703
NORTH BROWARD HOSPITAL DISTRICT
BROWARD HEALTH MEDICAL CENTER
1800 Nw 49th St, Fort Lauderdale, FL 33309-3092
Tel (954) 473-7010 *Founded/Ownrshp* 1951
Sales 931.1MM[E] *EMP* 7,000
SIC 8062 General medical & surgical hospitals
CEO: Nabil El Sanadi
**COO:* Paul Echelard
**CFO:* Robert Martin
Sr VP: Joseph S Rogers
Rgnl Mgr: Janice Benggio
Rgnl Mgr: Amos Linton
Rgnl Mgr: Denise Mansfield
Off Mgr: Linda Neira
Nurse Mgr: Barbara Ensign
Nurse Mgr: Tonya Royster
CTO: Tom Kester
Board of Directors: Paul Echelard, Robert Martin, Nabil El Sanadi

D-U-N-S 80-181-2801
NORTH BROWARD HOSPITAL DISTRICT FEDERAL CREDIT UNION
303 Se 17th St Ste 106, Fort Lauderdale, FL 33316-2523
Tel (954) 355-4400 *Founded/Ownrshp* 1994
Sales NA *EMP* 11
SIC 6061 Federal credit unions
Ex Dir: Kevin Hall
CFO: Kathy Cameron
CIO: Steve Benson
QA Dir: Beverly Beyerlein
QA Dir: Deborah Williams

D-U-N-S 10-380-5370
NORTH BRUNSWICK TOWNSHIP BOARD OF EDUCATION
NORTH BRUNSWICK TWP SCHL DST
300 Old Georges Rd, North Brunswick, NJ 08902-4800
Tel (732) 289-3000 *Founded/Ownrshp* 1917
Sales 105.1MM *EMP* 800
SIC 8211 Public elementary school; Public junior high school; Public senior high school
Pr Dir: Vincent Delucia

NORTH BRUNSWICK TWP SCHL DST
See NORTH BRUNSWICK TOWNSHIP BOARD OF EDUCATION

NORTH CAMPUS
See LUCY LEE HOSPITAL INC

NORTH CAROLINA A&T STATE UNIV
See NORTH CAROLINA AGRICULTURAL AND TECHNICAL STATE UNIVERSITY

D-U-N-S 07-157-6482
NORTH CAROLINA AGRICULTURAL AND TECHNICAL STATE UNIVERSITY
NORTH CAROLINA A&T STATE UNIV
(*Suby of* OFFICE OF PRESIDENT) ★
1601 E Marke St Dowdy Bld, Greensboro, NC 27411-0001
Tel (336) 334-7684 *Founded/Ownrshp* 1891
Sales 302.5MM[E] *EMP* 3,600
SIC 8221 University
Exec: Harold L Martin
CFO: Willie Ellis
Top Exec: John C Teleha
Dir Lab: Charles Wilson
Info Man: Wilsonia Carter
Pgrm Dir: D C Lofton

D-U-N-S 07-202-6321
NORTH CAROLINA CENTRAL UNIVERSITY
(*Suby of* OFFICE OF PRESIDENT) ★
1801 Fayetteville St, Durham, NC 27707-3129
Tel (919) 530-6100 *Founded/Ownrshp* 1923
Sales 109.9MM[E] *EMP* 1,100
SIC 8221 Colleges universities & professional schools
Exec: Frank Lloyd
Prgrm Mgr: Eva Marmon-Halm
Off Mgr: Brenda Atwater
Off Mgr: Kristy Caldwell

D-U-N-S 80-978-4648
NORTH CAROLINA COMMUNITY COLLEGE SYSTEM
(*Suby of* NORTH CRLINA OFFICE OF GVERNOR) ★
200 W Jones St, Raleigh, NC 27603-1378
Tel (919) 807-7100 *Founded/Ownrshp* 1963
Sales 7.7MM *EMP* 1,000
SIC 8222 9411 Community college; Administration of educational programs;
Pr: Scott Ralls
Assoc VP: Kimberly Sepich
Assoc VP: Debra Smith
Sr VP: Lisa Chapman
VP: Lynda Wilkins
QA Dir: Suzanne Baker
Dir IT: Arthur Hohnsbehn

D-U-N-S 80-978-4580
NORTH CAROLINA DEPARTMENT OF AGRICULTURE & CONSUMER SERVICES
(*Suby of* STATE OF NORTH CAROLINA) ★
2 W Edenton St, Raleigh, NC 27601-1020
Tel (919) 707-3000 *Founded/Ownrshp* 1877
Sales NA *EMP* 1,400[E]
SIC 9641 Regulation of agricultural marketing;
Ofcr: Terri Butler
Ofcr: Towanda Jackson
Ofcr: Jen Kendrick
Exec: Jen Nixon

D-U-N-S 80-978-4762
NORTH CAROLINA DEPARTMENT OF CRIME CONTROL AND PUBLIC SAFETY
(*Suby of* NORTH CRLINA OFFICE OF GVERNOR) ★
512 N Salisbury St, Raleigh, NC 27604-1170
Tel (919) 825-2720 *Founded/Ownrshp* 1977
Sales NA *EMP* 2,800
SIC 9221 Police protection
Board of Directors: Doug Phillips

D-U-N-S 80-978-5280
NORTH CAROLINA DEPARTMENT OF ENVIRONMENTAL QUALITY
NCDEQ
(*Suby of* NORTH CRLINA OFFICE OF GVERNOR) ★
217 W Jones St Ste 5103, Raleigh, NC 27603-2396
Tel (877) 623-6748 *Founded/Ownrshp* 1784
Sales NA *EMP* 5,344
SIC 9512 Land, mineral & wildlife conservation;
Prin: Donald Van Der Vaart
Sfty Dirs: Chuck Stanfill
Snr Mgr: Erica Green
Board of Directors: Donald Van Der Vaart

D-U-N-S 80-978-5363
NORTH CAROLINA DEPARTMENT OF HEALTH & HUMAN SERVICES
(*Suby of* NORTH CRLINA OFFICE OF GVERNOR) ★
2025 Mail Service Ctr, Raleigh, NC 27699-2000
Tel (919) 733-4534 *Founded/Ownrshp* 1972
Sales NA *EMP* 17,697
SIC 9441 Administration of social & manpower programs;

D-U-N-S 80-978-5934
NORTH CAROLINA DEPARTMENT OF JUSTICE
DOJ
(*Suby of* NORTH CRLINA OFFICE OF GVERNOR) ★
114 W Edenton St, Raleigh, NC 27603-1712
Tel (919) 779-8213 *Founded/Ownrshp* 1789
Sales NA *EMP* 1,140
SIC 9222 Attorney General's office;
**CFO:* Nels Roseland
Bd of Dir: Bubba Summerlin
Exec: Noelle Talley
Sfty Dirs: Linda Sherrard

D-U-N-S 80-978-4721
NORTH CAROLINA DEPARTMENT OF PUBLIC SAFETY
(*Suby of* NORTH CRLINA OFFICE OF GVERNOR) ★
512 N Salisbury St, Raleigh, NC 27604-1170
Tel (919) 733-2126 *Founded/Ownrshp* 1975
Sales NA *EMP* 18,000
SIC 9223 Prison, government;
VP: Teresa Jordan

D-U-N-S 80-958-1879
NORTH CAROLINA DEPARTMENT OF REVENUE
(*Suby of* NORTH CRLINA OFFICE OF GVERNOR) ★
501 N Wilmington St, Raleigh, NC 27604-8002
Tel (877) 252-3052 *Founded/Ownrshp* 1921
Sales NA *EMP* 1,400
SIC 9311 Finance, taxation & monetary policy;
Ofcr: Lisa Travis

D-U-N-S 80-958-1937
NORTH CAROLINA DEPARTMENT OF TRANSPORTATION
(*Suby of* NORTH CRLINA OFFICE OF GVERNOR) ★
1 S Wilmington St, Raleigh, NC 27601-1494
Tel (919) 707-2500 *Founded/Ownrshp* 1971
Sales NA *EMP* 14,000
SIC 9621 Regulation, administration of transportation;

D-U-N-S 94-913-6527
NORTH CAROLINA DIVISION OF ADULT PROBATION AND PAROLE
(*Suby of* NORTH CAROLINA DEPARTMENT OF PUBLIC SAFETY) ★
4000 Wake Forest Rd, Raleigh, NC 27609-6879
Tel (919) 850-2900 *Founded/Ownrshp* 1996
Sales NA *EMP* 2,188
SIC 9223 Prison, government;

D-U-N-S 00-273-5517
NORTH CAROLINA DIVISION OF HIGHWAYS
NCDOT
(*Suby of* NORTH CAROLINA DEPARTMENT OF TRANSPORTATION) ★
1 S Wilmington St, Raleigh, NC 27601-1453
Tel (919) 733-7384 *Founded/Ownrshp* 2000
Sales NA *EMP* 2,293[E]
SIC 9621 Regulation, administration of transportation;

D-U-N-S 94-901-1902
NORTH CAROLINA DIVISION OF PRISONS
(*Suby of* NORTH CAROLINA DEPARTMENT OF PUBLIC SAFETY) ★
831 W Morgan St, Raleigh, NC 27603-1658
Tel (919) 838-4000 *Founded/Ownrshp* 1974
Sales NA *EMP* 10,000
SIC 9223 Prison, government;

D-U-N-S 10-587-2147
NORTH CAROLINA EASTERN MUNICIPAL POWER AGENCY
1427 Meadow Wood Blvd, Raleigh, NC 27604-1532
Tel (919) 760-6000 *Founded/Ownrshp* 1976
Sales 696.5MM *EMP* 100[E]
Accts Cherry Bekaert Llp Raleigh
SIC 4911 Distribution, electric power
CEO: Jesse C Tilton III
COO: Roy Jones
**CFO:* Al Conyers
IT Man: Caroline Casey
Secur Mgr: Matt Schull
Mktg Mgr: Robert Tugwell

D-U-N-S 07-555-0962
NORTH CAROLINA ELECTRIC MEMBERSHIP CORP
NCEMC
3400 Sumner Blvd, Raleigh, NC 27616-2950
Tel (919) 872-0800 *Founded/Ownrshp* 1949
Sales 1.1MMM *EMP* 150[E]
Accts Deloitte Tax Llp Atlanta Ga
SIC 4911 Electric services
CEO: Joe Brannon
COO: Robert B Schwentker
CFO: Lark James
Sr VP: Lewis Hovson
VP: Tim Eisel
VP: Bob Goodson
VP: Liberache Harris
VP: Joy Hart
VP: Lee Ragsdale
Exec: Lauren Liles
Creative D: Tara Verna

D-U-N-S 04-895-8995
NORTH CAROLINA FARM BUREAU INSURANCE AGENCY INC
N C FARM BUREAU MUTUAL INSUR
5301 Glenwood Ave, Raleigh, NC 27612-3244
Tel (919) 782-1705 *Founded/Ownrshp* 1953
Sales NA *EMP* 750
Accts A T Allen & Company Llp Cpas
SIC 6331 6411 6311 Property damage insurance; Fire, marine & casualty insurance & carriers; Insurance agents, brokers & service; Life insurance
Pr: Larry Wooten
Pr: Misty Smith
**CFO:* Ronald Medeiros
**Treas:* Perry Crutchfield
**Ex VP:* Steve Carrol
**VP:* J M Wright Jr
Exec: Steve Brinn
Exec: Bryan Crook
CTO: Phillips Ian
Dir IT: Lawrence B Wooten
IT Man: Ellen Squires

D-U-N-S 15-393-2066
NORTH CAROLINA INSURANCE UNDERWRITING ASSOCIATION
5651 Dillard Dr, Cary, NC 27518-9226
Tel (919) 821-1299 *Founded/Ownrshp* 1969
Sales NA *EMP* 65
Accts Ncjua-Nciua Cary Nc
SIC 6331 Fire, marine & casualty insurance
Genl Mgr: Dewey Meshaw

D-U-N-S 00-687-1743
NORTH CAROLINA MUTUAL WHOLESALE DRUG CO
MUTUAL DRUG
816 Ellis Rd, Durham, NC 27703-6019
Tel (919) 596-2151 *Founded/Ownrshp* 1952
Sales 179.7MM[E] *EMP* 160
Accts Thomas Knight Trent King An
SIC 5122 Drugs & drug proprietaries; Druggists' sundries
CEO: David S Moody
**Pr:* Thomas P Davis
**VP:* Hal Harrison
Board of Directors: Dave Marley

D-U-N-S 95-678-3849
NORTH CAROLINA PARTNERSHIP FOR CHILDREN INC
N C PARTNERSHIP FOR CHILDREN
1100 Wake Forest Rd, Raleigh, NC 27604-1354
Tel (919) 821-7999 *Founded/Ownrshp* 1993
Sales 102.6MM *EMP* 48
Accts Blackman & Sloop Cpas Pa Chap
SIC 8399 Social change association
Pr: Stephanie Fanjul
**Treas:* Leslie Karlsson
IT Man: James Dodson

D-U-N-S 04-209-2122 IMP
NORTH CAROLINA STATE UNIVERSITY
(*Suby of* OFFICE OF PRESIDENT) ★
2701 Sullivan Dr Ste 240, Raleigh, NC 27695-0001
Tel (919) 515-2011 *Founded/Ownrshp* 1987
Sales 750.0MM *EMP* 2,560[E]
SIC 8221 University
Pr: Randy Woodsen
V Ch: Robert B Jordan
Trst: Bob L Mattocks
Trst: Burley B Mitchell Jr
Ofcr: Erin Folk
Adm Dir: Gwen Bell
Adm Dir: Helen Crane
Adm Dir: Susan Davis
Ex Dir: Randy Thomson
DP Exec: Valerie Oti
Doctor: Derek Foster

D-U-N-S 06-965-0179
NORTH CASTLE PARTNERS LLC
183 E Putnam Ave, Greenwich, CT 06830-5613
Tel (203) 485-0216 *Founded/Ownrshp* 1997
Sales 170.2MM[E] *EMP* 3,510
SIC 7299 6794 5149 5499 Diet center, without medical staff; Franchises, selling or licensing; Diet foods; Dietetic foods
Mng Dir: Alison Minter

D-U-N-S 06-857-7667
NORTH CENTRAL COLLEGE
NAPERVILLE COLLEGE
30 N Brainard St, Naperville, IL 60540-4690
Tel (630) 637-5100 *Founded/Ownrshp* 1861
Sales 87.7MM *EMP* 699[E]
Accts Crowe Horwath Llp Chicago Il
SIC 8221 College, except junior
Pr: Troy D Hammond
**VP:* Paul H Loscheider
**VP:* R Devadoss Pandian
**VP:* Martin Sauer
**VP:* Kimberly Sluis
VP: Rick Spencer
**Prin:* Harold R Wilde

D-U-N-S 00-798-8009
NORTH CENTRAL COOPERATIVE
221 4th Ave Nw, Clarion, IA 50525-1035
Tel (515) 532-2881 *Founded/Ownrshp* 1907
Sales 189.8MM *EMP* 96
SIC 5153 5191 5172 Grain elevators; Feed; Seeds: field, garden & flower; Fertilizer & fertilizer materials; Petroleum products
Genl Mgr: Mike Nail
Dir IT: Tully Waddingham

D-U-N-S 00-694-0209
NORTH CENTRAL COOPERATIVE INC
2025 S Wabash St, Wabash, IN 46992-4124
Tel (800) 992-3495 *Founded/Ownrshp* 1927
Sales 331.8MM *EMP* 280
Accts Blue & Co Llc Seymour Indi
SIC 5172 5153 5191 Petroleum products; Diesel fuel; Gasoline; Lubricating oils & greases; Grain elevators; Farm supplies; Fertilizer & fertilizer materials; Chemicals, agricultural; Seeds: field, garden & flower
Pr: J Mark Tullis
**CFO:* Doug Bible
Plnt Mgr: Ronald Holcomb
Sales Exec: Ron Pettet
VP Sls: John Scicluna

D-U-N-S 16-236-2995
NORTH CENTRAL EQUITY LLC
60 S 6th St Ste 2535, Minneapolis, MN 55402-4406
Tel (612) 465-0260 *Founded/Ownrshp* 2004
Sales 105.6MM[E] *EMP* 262
SIC 6799 4813 Venture capital companies; Long distance telephone communications
CEO: Elam Baer
**COO:* Laura Carlson
**VP:* Bernie Coyle
**VP:* Daniel Hogan
**VP:* Peter Jacobson
**VP:* Ron Jost
**VP:* Greg Wilmes
Off Mgr: Elizabeth Husman
Genl Couns: Drew S Backstrand

D-U-N-S 02-433-4674
NORTH CENTRAL FARMERS ELEVATOR (SD)
NCFE
12 5th Ave, Ipswich, SD 57451
Tel (605) 426-6021 *Founded/Ownrshp* 1915
Sales 574.0MM^E *EMP* 200
Accts Eide Bailly Llp Aberdeen Sou
SIC 5153 5191 5171 5541 Grain elevators; Farm supplies; Chemicals, agricultural; Fertilizer & fertilizer materials; Petroleum bulk stations; Gasoline service stations
Pr: Rick Osterday
**Sec:* Quentin Larson
**VP:* Mike Clements
VP: Kevin Stark
**VP:* Larry Vetch
Comm Dir: Subrena Green
Genl Mgr: Mike Nickolas

NORTH CLACKAMAS SCHOOL DST 12
See NORTH CLACKAMAS SCHOOLS

D-U-N-S 05-596-3722
NORTH CLACKAMAS SCHOOLS
NORTH CLACKAMAS SCHOOL DST 12
12400 Se Freeman Way # 100, Milwaukie, OR 97222-4620
Tel (503) 353-6001 *Founded/Ownrshp* 1971
Sales 202.9MM *EMP* 1,857
Accts Pauly Rogers And Co Pc Tig
SIC 8211 Public elementary school; Public junior high school; Public senior high school; Vocational high school
**V Ch:* Rein Vaga
CFO: Mary Knigge
Assoc Dir: Jonathan Fost
Teacher Pr: Mark Moser

D-U-N-S 06-878-9833 EXP
NORTH COAST ELECTRIC CO
NCE
2450 8th Ave S Ste 200, Seattle, WA 98134-2005
Tel (206) 442-9898 *Founded/Ownrshp* 1990
Sales 607.4MM^E *EMP* 650
SIC 5063 Electrical construction materials; Lighting fixtures
Ch: Peter Lemman
**Pr:* Michael Miller
CFO: Ronald Stewart
VP: Alexander Hickethier
VP: Doug Lafrance
Brnch Mgr: Dave Evans
MIS Mgr: Lester J Johnson
Opers Supe: Rebekah Peoples
Opers Mgr: Renee Haworth

D-U-N-S 92-771-1911
NORTH COAST MORTGAGE CO
80 E Sir Francis Drake Bl, Larkspur, CA 94939-1709
Tel (415) 461-2070 *Founded/Ownrshp* 1994
Sales NA *EMP* 20
SIC 6162 Mortgage bankers & correspondents
Pr: Christopher Solle

D-U-N-S 04-858-4817
NORTH COLONIE CENTRAL SCHOOL DISTRICT (NY)
91 Fiddlers Ln, Latham, NY 12110-5343
Tel (518) 785-8591 *Founded/Ownrshp* 1950
Sales 106.9MM *EMP* 1,200
Accts Marvin And Company Pc Lath
SIC 8211 Public elementary & secondary schools
**Treas:* Kathleen Caulfield
**Treas:* Steve Zautner
Bd of Dir: Nancy Hooley
Bd of Dir: Marie Oppedisano
Exec: Djoseph Corr
Pr Dir: Taryn Kane
Pr Dir: Stephen King
Teacher Pr: Jenna Bongermino

D-U-N-S 60-877-6824
NORTH COLORADO MEDICAL CENTER
(*Suby of* BKRY PHYSICIAN GROUP INC) ★
1801 16th St, Greeley, CO 80631-5199
Tel (970) 352-4121 *Founded/Ownrshp* 2006
Sales 372.6MM *EMP* 12
SIC 8011 Offices & clinics of medical doctors
CEO: Gene O'Hara
Dir Rx: Richard Einhellig
QA Dir: Elaine Obleness
Sfty Dirs: Paul Reimer
Doctor: Gary Bauerle

D-U-N-S 07-341-0839
NORTH COLORADO MEDICAL CENTER FOUNDATION INC
BANNER HEALTH
1801 16th St, Greeley, CO 80631-5154
Tel (970) 356-9020 *Founded/Ownrshp* 1975
Sales 3.2MM *EMP* 1,902
Accts Eks&H Lllp Denver Co
SIC 8062 Hospital, affiliated with AMA residency
CEO: Gene O'Hara
Dir Recs: Tami Figal
**Pr:* Chris Kiser
CFO: Mike Lewis
Assoc Dir: Gloria Mawson
Dir Rx: Don McNemar
Dir Rx: John Placko
Off Admin: Judy Dunlap
Dir IT: Steve Rains
Sls Mgr: Donna Crane
Doctor: Erin Rose

D-U-N-S 88-308-9492
NORTH COUNTRY ASSOCIATES INC
HALL-DALE MANOR
179 Lisbon St Ste 3, Lewiston, ME 04240-7248
Tel (207) 786-3554 *Founded/Ownrshp* 1986
Sales 65.4MM^E *EMP* 1,500
SIC 8361 Residential care
Pr: John Orestis
VP: Tamra Deering
VP Opers: Douglas Gardner

NORTH CRLINA OFFICE OF GVERNOR
See EXECUTIVE OFFICE OF STATE OF NORTH CAROLINA

D-U-N-S 19-159-9971
NORTH CYPRESS MEDICAL CENTER OPERATING CO GP LLC
21214 Northwest Fwy, Cypress, TX 77429-3373
Tel (832) 912-3500 *Founded/Ownrshp* 2004
Sales 301.3MM *EMP* 200^E
SIC 8062 General medical & surgical hospitals
CEO: Robert A Behar
COO: Jimmy W C Lee
CFO: Robert Martel

D-U-N-S 80-274-3534
NORTH DAKOTA DEPARTMENT OF HUMAN SERVICES
(*Suby of* EXECUTIVE OFFICE OF STATE OF NORTH DAKOTA) ★
600 E Boulevard Ave # 325, Bismarck, ND 58505-0250
Tel (701) 872-2081 *Founded/Ownrshp* 1982
Sales NA *EMP* 2,100
SIC 9441 Administration of social & manpower programs;
Ex Dir: Maggie D Anderson
IT Man: Debra McDermott

D-U-N-S 80-274-9242
NORTH DAKOTA DEPARTMENT OF MILITARY AFFAIRS
NATIONAL GUARD & ADJUTANT GEN
(*Suby of* EXECUTIVE OFFICE OF STATE OF NORTH DAKOTA) ★
30 Fraine Barracks Ln, Bismarck, ND 58504-5222
Tel (701) 333-2079 *Founded/Ownrshp* 1891
Sales NA *EMP* 1,000
SIC 9711 National security;
Prin: Keith D Bjerke

D-U-N-S 80-274-2742
NORTH DAKOTA DEPT OF TRANSPORTATION
(*Suby of* EXECUTIVE OFFICE OF STATE OF NORTH DAKOTA) ★
608 E Boulevard Ave, Bismarck, ND 58505-0606
Tel (701) 328-2500 *Founded/Ownrshp* 1989
Sales NA *EMP* 1,015
SIC 9621 Regulation, administration of transportation;
Netwrk Eng: Doug Hay

D-U-N-S 00-616-1665 IMP/EXP
NORTH DAKOTA MILL & ELEVATOR ASSOCIATION INC
1823 Mill Rd, Grand Forks, ND 58203-1535
Tel (701) 795-7000 *Founded/Ownrshp* 1922
Sales 216.1MM *EMP* 120
Accts Robert R Peterson Fargo Nor
SIC 2052 2041 Bakery products, dry; Wheat flour
Pr: Vance Taylor
Brnch Mgr: Kevin Anderson

D-U-N-S 80-388-2299
NORTH DAKOTA STATE UNIVERSITY
1919 University Dr N # 102, Fargo, ND 58102-1843
Tel (701) 231-7015 *Founded/Ownrshp* 1890
Sales 252.2MM *EMP* 4,500
SIC 8221 University
Pr: Dean Bresciani
Ex VP: Corey McIntire
CIO: Thomas Moberg
CIO: Randall Thursby
Software D: Eric Christeson
Manager: Bob Mecklenburg
Nutrtnst: Laura Penovich
**Counsel:* Matthew Hammer
Pgrm Dir: Matthew Kirkwood
Pgrm Dir: Mary Siverson

D-U-N-S 07-150-3784
NORTH DAKOTA UNIVERSITY SYSTEM
2000 44th St S Ste 301, Fargo, ND 58103-7434
Tel (701) 231-6326 *Founded/Ownrshp* 2011
Sales 676.9MM *EMP* 12^E
Accts Robert R Peterson State Audi
SIC 8221 University

D-U-N-S 80-450-1732
NORTH DAKOTA UNIVERSITY SYSTEM FOUNDATION
600 E Boulevard Ave # 215, Bismarck, ND 58505-0601
Tel (701) 328-2960 *Founded/Ownrshp* 1939
Sales 676.9MM *EMP* 252
Accts Robert R Peterson Fargo Nort
SIC 8221 Colleges universities & professional schools
Prin: Hamid Augustine Shirvani
V Ch: Dennis Cooley
V Ch: Kathleen Neset
**Pr:* Kirsten Diederich
CFO: Tammy Dolan
Ofcr: Kirsten Franzen
Ofcr: Karol Riedman
**VP:* Terry Hjelmstad
Off Mgr: Janine Trowbridge
Sftwr Eng: Andrew Jocobson
Opers Mgr: Rebecca Hellman

D-U-N-S 96-880-3106
NORTH DALLAS HONEY CO LP
NATURE NATE'S
2910 Nature Nate Farms, McKinney, TX 75071-6815
Tel (214) 642-9367 *Founded/Ownrshp* 1997
Sales 90.6MM^E *EMP* 535^E
SIC 5149 Honey
Pr: Nathan H Sheets
CFO: Brantley Walch

D-U-N-S 07-692-3283
NORTH EAST INDEPENDENT SCHOOL DISTRICT
NORTH EAST ISD
8961 Tesoro Dr, San Antonio, TX 78217-6226
Tel (210) 407-0359 *Founded/Ownrshp* 1950
Sales 737.1MM *EMP* 10,000^E
Accts Abip Pc San Antonio Texas
SIC 8211 Public elementary & secondary schools
**Pr:* Beth Plummer
Ofcr: Wilson An
Ofcr: Powell Booker
Ofcr: Langley Charles
Ofcr: Andres De Leon
Ofcr: Sandoval Javier
Ofcr: Bieszk Kenneth
Ofcr: Alonzo Mario
Ofcr: Gauthier Raymond
Ofcr: Anderson Stephen
**VP:* Susan Galindo

NORTH EAST ISD
See NORTH EAST INDEPENDENT SCHOOL DISTRICT

D-U-N-S 09-255-8063
NORTH EAST MEDICAL SERVICES
1520 Stockton St, San Francisco, CA 94133-3354
Tel (415) 391-9686 *Founded/Ownrshp* 1968
Sales 94.2MM *EMP* 120
SIC 8011

D-U-N-S 84-826-7951
NORTH ELECTRIC INC
2438 W Robin Rd, Scottsburg, IN 47170-6860
Tel (812) 752-4804 *Founded/Ownrshp* 1990
Sales 93.9MM^E *EMP* 8
SIC 1731 General electrical contractor
Pr: Jerry North

NORTH FLORIDA REGIONAL HOSP
See NORTH FLORIDA REGIONAL MEDICAL CENTER INC

D-U-N-S 92-857-7410
■ **NORTH FLORIDA REGIONAL MEDICAL CENTER INC**
NORTH FLORIDA REGIONAL HOSP
(*Suby of* HOSPITAL COPORATION OF AMERICA) ★
6500 W Newberry Rd, Gainesville, FL 32605-4309
Tel (352) 333-4100 *Founded/Ownrshp* 1994
Sales 358.0MM^E *EMP* 2,000
SIC 8062 8093 8011 8082 8069 General medical & surgical hospitals; Rehabilitation center, outpatient treatment; Offices & clinics of medical doctors; Home health care services; Specialty hospitals, except psychiatric
Pr: Brian T Cook
**Pr:* Samuel N Hazen
**COO:* Matt Davis
**VP:* John M Franck
**VP:* Keith M Giger
**VP:* Ronald L Grubbs
**VP:* Donald W Stinnett
Dir Rad: Donald E Jackson
Doctor: Greg Imperi MD

D-U-N-S 05-554-3672 IMP
NORTH FOOD GROUP INC (TX)
EVERSPRING ENTERPRISES
1245 W Royal Ln, Dallas, TX 75261
Tel (972) 445-3322 *Founded/Ownrshp* 1981, 2006
Sales 86.8MM *EMP* 120
SIC 5146 5147 5149 5113 Fish & seafoods; Meats & meat products; Groceries & related products; Industrial & personal service paper; Disposable plates, cups, napkins & eating utensils
Pr: Hanhue Wang
**VP:* Patrick Pang
**VP:* Hong Xue

D-U-N-S 07-843-9528
NORTH FOREST INDEPENDENT SCHOOL DISTRICT
NFISD
4400 W 18th St, Houston, TX 77092-8501
Tel (713) 633-1600 *Founded/Ownrshp* 1936
Sales 84.3MM *EMP* 1,091
Accts Walter D Davis Cpa Houston
SIC 8211 Public elementary & secondary schools; Finishing school, secondary; High school, junior or senior
Prin: William Jones

D-U-N-S 61-797-0777
NORTH FOREST ISD
4400 W 18th St, Houston, TX 77092-8501
Tel (713) 633-1600 *Founded/Ownrshp* 2008
Sales 84.3MM *EMP* 1,420
SIC 8211 Public elementary & secondary schools
Treas: Billy Hall
VP: Samuel Julian

NORTH FORK EQUIPMENT LEASING
See ALL POINTS CAPITAL CORP

D-U-N-S 13-231-0160 IMP
NORTH FULTON MEDICAL CENTER VOLUNTEER SERVICES ORGANIZATION INC
NORTH MEDICAL HOSPITAL
(*Suby of* WELLSTAR HEALTH SYSTEM INC) ★
3000 Hospital Blvd, Roswell, GA 30076-4915
Tel (770) 751-2500 *Founded/Ownrshp* 2016
Sales 178.2MM *EMP* 1,010
SIC 8062 General medical & surgical hospitals
Pr: Lynn Lommer
MIS Dir: Linda Musgrave
Sls&Mrk Ex: June Meltzer
Doctor: Cynthia Griggs

NORTH GA ELECTRIC MEMB
See NORTH GEORGIA ELECTRIC MEMBERSHIP FOUNDATION INC

D-U-N-S 08-436-2896
NORTH GEORGIA CONFERENCE OF METHODIST CHURCH INC
159 Ralph Mcgill Blvd Ne, Atlanta, GA 30308-3343
Tel (706) 548-6616 *Founded/Ownrshp* 1866
Sales NA *EMP* 1,400
SIC 8661

D-U-N-S 00-692-5978
NORTH GEORGIA ELECTRIC MEMBERSHIP FOUNDATION INC
NORTH GA ELECTRIC MEMB
1850 Cleveland Hwy, Dalton, GA 30721-8315
Tel (706) 259-9441 *Founded/Ownrshp* 1936
Sales 249.1MM *EMP* 192
Accts Henderson Hutcherson & Mccullo
SIC 4911 Distribution, electric power
CEO: Bill Scott
**CFO:* Mary Whittington
Bd of Dir: Dean Smith
**Genl Mgr:* Ron Hutchins
CTO: Edwin Parker
Sls Mgr: Allison Crossen

D-U-N-S 80-466-5990
NORTH HIGHLAND CO LLC
3333 Piedmont Rd Ne # 1000, Atlanta, GA 30305-1843
Tel (404) 233-1015 *Founded/Ownrshp* 1989
Sales 277.5MM *EMP* 2,300
SIC 8742 7379 Management consulting services; Computer related consulting services
CEO: Dan Reardon
**Ch Bd:* Marsha Evans
CFO: Oliver Colling
**CFO:* Kirk Hancock
**CFO:* Beth Schiavo
CFO: Trish Young-Thompson
**Chf Mktg O:* Matthew Klein
**Chf Mktg O:* Ricardo Martinez
**Ofcr:* Mary Slaughter
Ex VP: Christy Thomas
**VP:* Greg Bradley
VP: Marty Brennan
VP: Doug Condidorio
VP: Anna Danegger
VP: Scott Demorest
VP: Tony Doocey
VP: Tina Ehrig
VP: Steve Frenz
VP: Michael Hollar
**VP:* Hunter Holliday
VP: Ashley Horne

D-U-N-S 07-832-7457
NORTH HIGHLAND HOLDING CO INC
3333 Piedmont Rd Ne # 1000, Atlanta, GA 30305-1843
Tel (404) 233-1015 *Founded/Ownrshp* 2009
Sales 327.8MM *EMP* 1
Accts Grant Thornton Llp Atlanta G
SIC 8742 Management consulting services
CEO: Daniel D Reardon
**CFO:* J Kirk Hancock
**Prin:* Loretta Penn

D-U-N-S 07-932-5874
NORTH JERSEY DISTRICT WATER SUPPLY COMMISSION
NJDWSC
1 F A Orechio Dr, Wanaque, NJ 07465-1517
Tel (973) 831-6212 *Founded/Ownrshp* 1928
Sales 117.8MM^E *EMP* 174
Accts Mcenerney Brady & Company Ll
SIC 4971 4941 Irrigation systems; Water supply
Ch: Charles P Shotmeyer
**CFO:* John Blonski
**Prin:* Carmen A Orechio
**Ex Dir:* Todd R Caliguire
**Ex Dir:* Colleen Destefano
Dir Sec: Bill Mullanaphy
Genl Mgr: Jerry Notte
CIO: Charles Billings
IT Man: Charlie Billins

D-U-N-S 78-850-4512
NORTH JERSEY HEALTH CARE CORP
175 High St, Newton, NJ 07860-1004
Tel (973) 383-2121 *Founded/Ownrshp* 1985
Sales 2.0MM *EMP* 1,350
SIC 8741 Hospital management; Nursing & personal care facility management
Pr: Dennis Collette
**Ch Bd:* Tom Digby MD
**Ch Bd:* H Alden Welch
**Pr:* Thomas J Senker
**COO:* Sean O'Rourke
CFO: David Richolas

D-U-N-S 00-215-5869 IMP
NORTH JERSEY MEDIA GROUP INC
NORTH JRSEY MDIA GROUP FNDTION
(*Suby of* MACROMEDIA INC) ★
1 Garret Mountain Plz # 201, Woodland Park, NJ 07424-3318
Tel (201) 646-4000 *Founded/Ownrshp* 1964
Sales 299.8MM^E *EMP* 1,431
SIC 2711 4813 Newspapers, publishing & printing;
Ch Bd: Malcolm A Borg
**Pr:* Stephen A Borg
CFO: Charles Gibney
**CFO:* Thomas G Heffernan
CFO: Thomas Heffernan
**VP:* Susan Beard
VP: Glenn Garvie
VP: Bob Konig
**VP:* Robert Konig
VP: Richard A Ndeu
Dir IT: Greg Hoffmann

NORTH JRSEY MDIA GROUP FNDTION
See NORTH JERSEY MEDIA GROUP INC

NORTH KANSAS CITY
See HENRY WURST INC

D-U-N-S 19-799-6163
NORTH KANSAS CITY HOSPITAL
BOARD OF TRUSTEE NORTH KANSAS
2800 Clay Edwards Dr, North Kansas City, MO 64116-3220
Tel (816) 691-2000 *Founded/Ownrshp* 2005
Sales 462.9MM *EMP* 6,200
SIC 8062 General medical & surgical hospitals
CEO: Peggy Schmitt
**COO:* Jody Abbott
**CFO:* Jim McNey
VP: Matt Foresman DDS
VP: Beverly Johnston
VP: Ric Slanczka
Dir OR: April Patten
Dir Inf Cn: Becky Smith
Dir Risk M: Michele Asher
Dir Case M: Debbie Beauchamp
Dir Rad: Joe Strano

D-U-N-S 01-065-4168 IMP
NORTH KANSAS CITY SCHOOL DISTRICT NO 74
2000 Ne 46th St, Kansas City, MO 64116-2042
Tel (816) 413-5000 Founded/Ownrshp 1913
Sales 255.8MM EMP 3,100
Accts Marr And Company Pc Kansas
SIC 8211 Public elementary school; Public junior high school; Public senior high school
*CFO: Paul Harrell
Exec: Janessa Dyer
Ex Dir: Mark Maus
Off Mgr: Vickie Freese
Dir IT: Eric Sipes
IT Man: Joann Pearson
Site Mgr: Ray Killion
Site Mgr: Judy Spunaugle
Pr Dir: Michelle Cronk
Teacher Pr: Deborah Delsemme
Psych: Laine Guerry

D-U-N-S 61-004-9157
NORTH LA COUNTY REGIONAL CENTER INC
15400 Sherman Way Ste 170, Van Nuys, CA 91406-4272
Tel (818) 778-1900 Founded/Ownrshp 1974
Sales 345.9MM EMP 350
Accts Lautze & Lautze San Francisco
SIC 8748 Test development & evaluation service
Ex Dir: George Stevens
CFO: Ellen Stein
Bd of Dir: K Jennifr
Ex Dir: Thompson Kelly
Prgrm Mgr: Shannon Murphy
Pgrm Dir: Diane Ambrose

D-U-N-S 83-272-0879
NORTH LIME HOLDINGS CORP
120 N Lime St, Lancaster, PA 17602-2923
Tel (717) 397-3633 Founded/Ownrshp 2006
Sales 246.7MM^E EMP 1,736
Accts Baker Tilly Virchow Krause Ll
SIC 1799 Coating, caulking & weather, water & fire-proofing; Insulation of pipes & boilers; Fireproofing buildings
Pr: W K Liddell
*Sec: Lori A Pickell
VP: Gale Blefko
Ex Dir: Phyllis Burkholder

D-U-N-S 62-102-9693
NORTH LITTLE ROCK SCHOOL DISTRICT
2700 N Poplar St, North Little Rock, AR 72114-2332
Tel (501) 771-8000 Founded/Ownrshp 1913
Sales 89.3MM^E EMP 1,532
SIC 8211 Public elementary & secondary schools
*CFO: Denise Drennan
Teacher Pr: Gregg Thompson

NORTH MEDICAL HOSPITAL
See NORTH FULTON MEDICAL CENTER VOLUNTEER SERVICES ORGANIZATION INC

D-U-N-S 07-136-3634 IMP
NORTH MEMORIAL HEALTH CARE (MN)
NORTH MEMORIAL MEDICAL CENTER
3300 Oakdale Ave N, Minneapolis, MN 55422-2900
Tel (763) 520-5200 Founded/Ownrshp 1940
Sales 777.6MM EMP 5,180
Accts Deloitte & Touche Llp Minneap
SIC 8062 8011 General medical & surgical hospitals; Medical centers
Pr: Loren Taylor
Chf OB: Sherry Paulson
*COO: David W Cress
*CFO: Patrick Boran
CFO: Todd Ostendorf
Treas: Ryan Johnson
VP: Laramie Anderson
VP: Aaron Bloomquist
*VP: M Kaye Foley
VP: Andrew Houlton
VP: Lisa H Job
VP: Tracy Kirby
VP: Cory Olson
VP: Mike Parrish
VP: Melissa Smith
VP: Thomas E Timmons
VP: Kelly White
Dir Inf Cn: Joanne Ferguson
Dir Rx: Tony Kausenberg
Dir Rx: Paul Krogh

NORTH MEMORIAL MEDICAL CENTER
See NORTH MEMORIAL HEALTH CARE

D-U-N-S 11-526-9813
NORTH MISSISSIPPI HEALTH SERVICES INC
HOSPITAL-NORTH MISS MED CTR
830 S Gloster St, Tupelo, MS 38801-4934
Tel (662) 377-3000 Founded/Ownrshp 1981
Sales 860.0MM EMP 6,000
SIC 8741 Hospital management; Nursing & personal care facility management
Ch Bd: Jim Kelley
Pr: John Heer
CEO: Shane Spees
Treas: Joe Reppert
VP Inf Sys: Tommy Bozeman
Netwrk Mgr: Rachel Hill
Doctor: Robert Stewart
Board of Directors: A E Bland, Henry Brevard, Dr James Cooper, Dr Roger Lowrey, Aubrey Patterson, John Smith, Travis Staub, Billy Wheeler

D-U-N-S 07-350-6487
NORTH MISSISSIPPI MEDICAL CENTER INC
(Suby of HOSPITAL-NORTH MISS MED CTR) ★
830 S Gloster St, Tupelo, MS 38801-4934
Tel (662) 377-3000 Founded/Ownrshp 1935
Sales 627.4MM EMP 6,000
SIC 8062 8051 8082 General medical & surgical hospitals; Skilled nursing care facilities; Home health care services
Pr: Steve Altmiller
Chf Path: Mark Huffman
Chf Rad: Doug Clark
VP: Daniel Cotton
Dir Rad: James Boyd
Dir Rx: William Calhoon
Dir Rx: Bill Calhoun
Chf Nrs Of: Donna Lewis
CIO: Tony Bozeman
Ansthlgy: Kevin L Hitt
Ansthlgy: Brad Womack

NORTH OAKS HEALTH SYSTEM
See HOSPITAL SERVICE DISTRICT NO 1 OF TANGIPAHOA PARISH

D-U-N-S 62-382-4013
NORTH OAKS HEALTH SYSTEM FOUNDATION
15790 Paul Vega Md Dr, Hammond, LA 70403-1434
Tel (985) 345-2700 Founded/Ownrshp 2003
Sales 263.9MM^E EMP 2,000
SIC 6733 Trusts
CFO: Shirley Hsing
Chf Rad: Michael Doner
Pathlgst: Joan T Hoffpauir

NORTH OKALOOSA MEDICAL CENTER
See CRESTVIEW HOSPITAL CORP

D-U-N-S 02-821-7743
NORTH ORANGE COUNTY COMMUNITY COLLEGE DISTRICT
CYPRESS COLLEGE
1830 W Romneya Dr, Anaheim, CA 92801-1819
Tel (714) 808-4500 Founded/Ownrshp 1964
Sales 92.5MM^E EMP 2,567
Accts Vavrinek Trine Day & Co Llp
SIC 8222 Community college
VP: Molly McClanahan
Dist Mgr: Fred Rocha
Genl Mgr: Rodrigo Garcia
IT Man: Kashu Vyas

D-U-N-S 05-497-0769
NORTH PACIFIC INSURANCE CO
(Suby of LIBERTY NORTHWEST INSURANCE CORP) ★
1 Liberty Ctr, Portland, OR 97232-2030
Tel (503) 239-5800 Founded/Ownrshp 2002
Sales NA EMP 350
SIC 6331 Automobile insurance; Fire, marine & casualty insurance & carriers; Burglary & theft insurance
Pr: Larry Becker
*CFO: Jim McKittrick
*VP: Mark Backstrom
*VP: Tom Becker
*VP: John Shaw
*VP: Jim Vavrek

D-U-N-S 04-195-6012 IMP/EXP
NORTH PACIFIC PAPER CO LLC
NORPAC
(Suby of NP PAPER CO LLC) ★
3001 Indl Way, Longview, WA 98632
Tel (360) 636-6400 Founded/Ownrshp 2016
Sales 477.0MM^E EMP 410
SIC 2621 5084 3554 Paper mills; Newsprint paper; Paper manufacturing machinery; Paper mill machinery: plating, slitting, waxing, etc.
CEO: Craig Anneberg

D-U-N-S 05-835-3525 IMP/EXP
NORTH PACIFIC SEAFOODS INC
ALASKA PACIFIC SEAFOOD
(Suby of MARUBENI CORPORATION)
4 Nickerson St Ste 400, Seattle, WA 98109-1699
Tel (206) 726-9900 Founded/Ownrshp 2005
Sales 296.4MM^E EMP 1,200
SIC 2091 Canned & cured fish & seafoods
CEO: Masayuki Yano
*Pr: John Garner
*Pr: Tomonobu Miki
*VP: Jeff Backlund
*VP: Leauri Moore
*VP: Roberto Torres
Genl Mgr: Slim Jorgensen
Sls&Mrk Ex: Jeff U Backlund

NORTH PARK
See PARK NORTH LINCOLN-MERCURY INC

NORTH PARK LEXUS
See KAHLIG MOTOR CO

D-U-N-S 06-996-3312
NORTH PARK UNIVERSITY
2543 W Cullom Ave, Chicago, IL 60618-1501
Tel (773) 244-6200 Founded/Ownrshp 1891
Sales 89.7MM EMP 375
SIC 8221 College, except junior; Theological seminary
Pr: David G Horner
*Pr: David Parkyn
Ofcr: Tracy Byerly
Ofcr: Charisma Eaglin
Ofcr: Michael Flynn
Ofcr: Roby Geevarghese
Ofcr: Phillip Lapalermo
Ofcr: Russell Mueller
Ofcr: Steven Murphy
Ofcr: Zachary Rubald
Ofcr: Raymond Schalk
Ofcr: Marshall Schultz
Ofcr: Timothy Tannehill
Ofcr: Paul Tasch
*VP: Carl E Balsam
VP: Jodi Koslow
Assoc Dir: Judson Curry
Board of Directors: Alfred Johnson

D-U-N-S 14-818-6844
■ **NORTH PITTSBURGH SYSTEMS INC**
(Suby of CONSOLIDATED COMMUNICATIONS HOLDINGS INC) ★
4008 Gibsonia Rd, Gibsonia, PA 15044-9311
Tel (724) 443-9600 Founded/Ownrshp 2007
Sales 155.3MM^E EMP 357
SIC 4813 5065 Telephone communication, except radio; ; Telephone equipment
Pr: Harry R Brown
CFO: Allen P Kimble
Treas: David Doedtman
Treas: Matthew D Poleski
VP: N William Barthlow
VP: Frank A McEfe
VP: Mark Steward
IT Man: Albert W Weigand
VP Sls: Frank A Macefe

D-U-N-S 02-017-3340
NORTH PLATTE NEBRASKA HOSPITAL CORP
GREAT PLAINS HEALTH
601 W Leota St, North Platte, NE 69101-6525
Tel (308) 534-9310 Founded/Ownrshp 1975
Sales 180.7MM EMP 900^E
Accts Seim Johnson Llp Omaha Nebr
SIC 8062 8082 General medical & surgical hospitals; Home health care services
CEO: Melvin McNea
Dir Surg: Michael Feagler
Dir Sec: Tom Didier
Pharmcst: Andrew Sokoloski

D-U-N-S 62-387-8035
NORTH PUGET SOUND CENTER FOR SLEEP DISORDERS LLC
ASSOCIATE EVERETT CLINIC PS
1728 W Marine View Dr, Everett, WA 98201-2094
Tel (425) 339-5460 Founded/Ownrshp 2004
Sales 18.7MM^E EMP 2,500^E
SIC 8011 Oncologist
COO: Jeff Bissey

NORTH READING TRANSPORTATION
See NRT BUS INC

NORTH RIDGE HEALTH AND REHAB
See NORTH RIDGE SKILLED LLC

D-U-N-S 01-033-1726
NORTH RIDGE SKILLED LLC
NORTH RIDGE HEALTH AND REHAB
5430 Boone Ave N, Minneapolis, MN 55428-3615
Tel (763) 592-3000 Founded/Ownrshp 1966
Sales 85.2MM^E EMP 1,000^E
SIC 6513 8051 Retirement hotel operation; Skilled nursing care facilities
Sr VP: Tina Thomas
*CEO: Eric Neetenbeek
Off Mgr: Mee Xiong
Dir IT: Debbie Deutsch

D-U-N-S 07-930-9233
NORTH RIVER INSURANCE CO (NJ)
(Suby of CRUM & FORSTER INC) ★
305 Madison Ave, Morristown, NJ 07960-6117
Tel (973) 490-6600 Founded/Ownrshp 1822, 1993
Sales NA EMP 400
SIC 6331 Property damage insurance
Pr: Nikolas Antonopoulos
Bd of Dir: Diana Cossetti
Sr VP: Martha Van Hise
Mktg Mgr: Pam Gaddy

NORTH ROCKLAND CENTRAL SCHOOL
See HAVERSTRAW STONY POINT CENTRAL SCHOOL DISTRICT INC

D-U-N-S 05-998-0441 IMP/EXP
NORTH SAFETY PRODUCTS LLC
2000 Plainfield Pike, Cranston, RI 02921-2012
Tel (401) 943-4400 Founded/Ownrshp 2008
Sales NA EMP 1,050^E
SIC 3842

D-U-N-S 06-937-7468
NORTH SAINT PAUL MAPLEWOOD & OAKDALE SCHOOL DISTRICT 622
2520 12th Ave E, Saint Paul, MN 55109-2420
Tel (651) 748-7420 Founded/Ownrshp 2002
Sales 145.0MM EMP 69
Accts Malloy Montague Karnowski R
SIC 8211 Public elementary & secondary schools
Psych: Debra Biddick

NORTH SHORE ARC
See NORTHEAST ARC INC

NORTH SHORE COMMUNITY BNK & TR
See WINTRUST BANK

D-U-N-S 00-693-6306
■ **NORTH SHORE GAS CO** (IL)
(Suby of PEOPLES ENERGY LLC) ★
200 E Randolph St # 2200, Chicago, IL 60601-6433
Tel (312) 240-4000 Founded/Ownrshp 1963
Sales 161.4MM^E EMP 335
SIC 4924 Natural gas distribution
CEO: Lawrence T Borgard
*Pr: Willard S Evans Jr
*CFO: Joseph P O Leary
CFO: Joseph Oleary
Treas: Douglas M Ruschau
*VP: Diane L Ford
VP: Thomas Nardi
*VP: James F Schott
Genl Couns: Theodore R Tetzlaff
Board of Directors: Thomas P Meinz, Phillip M Mikulsky, Charles A Schrock

NORTH SHORE LIJ
See FRANKLIN HOSPITAL

D-U-N-S 10-787-5007
NORTH SHORE LIJ HEALTH SYSTEM FEDERAL CREDIT UNION
NSLIJHSFCU
350 Jericho Tpke Ste 103, Jericho, NY 11753-1317
Tel (516) 301-3040 Founded/Ownrshp 1972
Sales NA EMP 23
SIC 6061 Federal credit unions
CEO: Joann Doyle
*Ch: Gary Leonard
VP: John Kane
VP: Brian McKenna
Assoc Dir: Melissa Devlin
Assoc Dir: Kelly Treacy
Doctor: Dorene Marinese
Doctor: Jules Winokur
Pgrm Dir: Paul Crespi
Snr Mgr: Sharlene Bronstorph
Snr Mgr: Daniel Levitt

D-U-N-S 07-846-2611 EXP
■ **NORTH SHORE MEDICAL CENTER INC**
(Suby of TENET HEALTHCARE CORP) ★
1100 Nw 95th St, Miami, FL 33150-2038
Tel (305) 835-6000 Founded/Ownrshp 1952
Sales 134.3MM^E EMP 1,100^E
SIC 8062 General medical & surgical hospitals
CEO: Manny Linares
Chf OB: Carlos Szajnert
V Ch: Alan Silbert
COO: Leonard Freehauf
COO: Patricia Sechia
*COO: Joshua Tetillio
*CFO: Alex Fernandes
Dir OR: Maria Ruiz
Dir Inf Cn: Veronica Torres
Dir QC: Isis Zambrana
Doctor: Steve Klein

D-U-N-S 62-065-5746
NORTH SHORE MEDICAL CENTER INC
NSMC SALEM HOSPITAL
(Suby of PARTNERS HEALTHCARE SYSTEM INC) ★
81 Highland Ave, Salem, MA 01970-2768
Tel (978) 741-1200 Founded/Ownrshp 1997
Sales 403.9MM EMP 5,000^E
SIC 8062 General medical & surgical hospitals
Ch: Terence McGinnis
*Pr: Robert G Norton
*Treas: John V Gandolfo
*V Ch Bd: Richard Osgood
VP: Beatrice Thibedeau
Dir Rx: Ralph McHatton
CTO: Christopher Maccarini
QA Dir: Karen Conti
QA Dir: Virginia Dolan-Horgan
Pathlgst: Bruce A Beckwith
Pathlgst: Linnea W Garcia

D-U-N-S 96-661-0854
NORTH SHORE PHYSICIANS GROUP INC
81 Highland Ave, Salem, MA 01970-2714
Tel (617) 724-9841 Founded/Ownrshp 2011
Sales 96.0MM EMP 4
SIC 8011 Primary care medical clinic
Prin: Steven E Kapfhammer

NORTH SHORE STEEL
See NORTH SHORE SUPPLY CO INC

D-U-N-S 02-663-1770 IMP/EXP
NORTH SHORE SUPPLY CO INC
NORTH SHORE STEEL
1566 Miles St, Houston, TX 77015-6319
Tel (713) 453-3533 Founded/Ownrshp 1955
Sales 123.4MM^E EMP 217
SIC 5051 5085 3441 Pipe & tubing, steel; Steel; Valves & fittings; Fabricated structural metal
Pr: Buzzy Bluestone
*Pr: Burton L Bluestone
VP: Tim Dodson
VP: Cindy Howard
*VP: Stanley D Katz
Genl Mgr: Byron Cooper
Genl Mgr: Bradley Lazard
Dir IT: George Wynne
Sls Mgr: Serena Martin
Sales Asso: Mac Cannon
Sales Asso: Jay Muscovalley
Board of Directors: Lou Beth Nemzin

D-U-N-S 06-241-5290
NORTH SHORE UNIVERSITY HEALTH SYSTEM
2650 Ridge Ave, Evanston, IL 60201-1718
Tel (847) 570-2640 Founded/Ownrshp 2011
Sales 1.4MMM EMP 3
SIC 8011 Offices & clinics of medical doctors
Prin: Steven Swiryn
VP: Nicole Fernandez
Exec: Rosemary Kelly
Adm Dir: Holly Hawes
Adm Dir: Pamela Schwartz
Dir QC: Mick Meiselman
QI Cn Mgr: Dawn Futris
QI Cn Mgr: Hannah Whitney
Obsttrcn: Hani J Saleh
Ansthlgy: Steven Greenberg
Ansthlgy: Arthur Tokarczyk

D-U-N-S 07-236-4490
NORTH SHORE UNIVERSITY HOSPITAL
(Suby of NSLIJ) ★
300 Community Dr, Manhasset, NY 11030-3876
Tel (516) 562-0100 Founded/Ownrshp 1946
Sales 1.6MMM EMP 5,000
SIC 8062 8011 General medical & surgical hospitals; Medical centers
Pr: Michael J Dowling
Mng Pt: Scott Christensen
V Ch: Gary Giangola
Ex VP: Mark Solazzo
Sr VP: John Bosco
VP: Frank Danza
VP: Dorothy Feldman
VP: Catherine Galla
VP: Mark Jarrett
VP: Jeffrey A Kraut
VP: Phyllis McCready
VP: Elaine Page
Dir Lab: Leonard Kahn
Assoc Dir: Shifra Atik
Dir Rad: Edward Wind
Dir Rx: Sanjai Singh
Comm Man: Denise Hall

D-U-N-S 96-777-5094
NORTH SHORE-LONG ISLAND JEWISH HEALTH CARE
972 Brush Hollow Rd 5th, Westbury, NY 11590-1740
Tel (516) 876-6611 Founded/Ownrshp 2011
Sales 719.4MM EMP 2
SIC 8099 Health & allied services
Prin: Filippo Petti
Nurse Mgr: Meredith Colon

D-U-N-S 83-041-4798
NORTH SHORE-LONG ISLAND JEWISH HEALTH SYSTEM LABORATORIES
10 Nevada Dr, New Hyde Park, NY 11042-1114
Tel (516) 719-1000 *Founded/Ownrshp* 1997
Sales 247.2MM *EMP* 99
SIC 8734 Testing laboratories
Pr: Richard Tesoriero

D-U-N-S 07-924-8290
NORTH SLOPE BOROUGH (AK)
1274 Agvik St, Barrow, AK 99723
Tel (907) 852-2611 *Founded/Ownrshp* 1972
Sales NA *EMP* 1,027
Accts Kpmg Llp Achorage Ak
SIC 9111 City & town managers' offices;
Pr: Grace Rosa
Bd of Dir: Jess McCoy
Exec: Kristine Hilderbrand
Div Mgr: Max Ahgeak
Div Mgr: Maria Esparza
Div Mgr: Roberta Oviok
Genl Mgr: Andrew Mack
Snr Mgr: Othniel Oomittuk

D-U-N-S 60-601-9750 IMP/EXP
NORTH SOUTH FOODS GROUP INC
3373 Sterling Ridge Ct, Longwood, FL 32779-3183
Tel (407) 805-9075 *Founded/Ownrshp* 1981
Sales 184.2MM[E] *EMP* 7
Accts Kittell Branagan & Sargent St
SIC 5144 5147 5146 Poultry & poultry products; Meats & meat products; Meat brokers
Pr: Ron Bateman
**Treas:* Brad Bateman
**VP:* Karen Bateman

NORTH STAR BUMPER
See KEYSTONE AUTOMOTIVE INDUSTRIES MN INC

NORTH STAR DISTRIBUTING
See ICE CREAM SPECIALTIES INC

D-U-N-S 93-752-5236
NORTH STAR GENERAL INSURANCE CO
(*Suby of* NORTH STAR MUTUAL INSURANCE CO INC) ★
269 Barstad Rd S, Cottonwood, MN 56229
Tel (507) 423-6262 *Founded/Ownrshp* 1991
Sales NA *EMP* 55
SIC 6411 Insurance agents, brokers & service
Pr: Jeff Mauland
**VP:* Joe Hoff
VP: Melinda Smith

D-U-N-S 00-644-7775
NORTH STAR MUTUAL INSURANCE CO INC
269 Barstad Rd S, Cottonwood, MN 56229
Tel (507) 423-6262 *Founded/Ownrshp* 1920
Sales NA *EMP* 197
SIC 6411 Insurance agents, brokers & service
Pr: Jeffrey L Mauland
COO: Carol Myhre
**Sec:* Joe E Hoff
**Sr VP:* Terry Timm
Genl Mgr: Terry Davis
Genl Mgr: Pete Hellie

D-U-N-S 07-971-7740
NORTH STAR RESOURCE GROUP
2701 University Ave Se # 300, Minneapolis, MN 55414-3236
Tel (612) 617-6000 *Founded/Ownrshp* 2009
Sales NA *EMP* 275
SIC 6411 Insurance agents, brokers & service
CEO: Edward G Deutschlander
Sr Pt: Joseph P Fox
Sr Pt: David Johnson
Sr Pt: Eric Seybert
**Ch Bd:* Phillip C Richards
**Pr:* David Vasos
Ofcr: Amy Bertle
Ofcr: Emily Nelson
Sr VP: Schoeller Don
Sr VP: Gary H Schwartz
Sr VP: Diane Yohn
VP: Cheryl L Marks
VP: Tim White

D-U-N-S 84-070-5847
NORTH STAR UTILITIES GROUP INC
(*Suby of* SALTCHUK RESOURCES INC) ★
420 L St Ste 101, Anchorage, AK 99501-1976
Tel (206) 792-0077 *Founded/Ownrshp* 2008
Sales 110.7MM[E] *EMP* 5[E]
SIC 5172 Petroleum products
Prin: Brian Bogen

D-U-N-S 00-478-9645
NORTH STATE COMMUNICATIONS LLC (NC)
111 Hayden Pl, High Point, NC 27260-4928
Tel (336) 886-3600 *Founded/Ownrshp* 1895, 2004
Sales 131.4MM[E] *EMP* 400[E]
SIC 4813 Telephone communication, except radio
CEO: J Patrick Harman
Pr: Royster Tucker III
CFO: Jonathan M Cage
Ex VP: Royster M Tucker III
VP: James D McCarson
IT Man: Herbert Lyle
IT Man: Dan Nicholson
S&M/VP: Jim Cortes

NORTH STATE FLEXIBLES
See NS FLEXIBLES LLC

D-U-N-S 60-344-8770
NORTH STATE GROCERY INC
HOLIDAY QUALITY FOODS
20803 Front St, Cottonwood, CA 96022
Tel (530) 347-4621 *Founded/Ownrshp* 1988
Sales 187.3MM[E] *EMP* 1,070
SIC 5411 Supermarkets, independent
Pr: Richard E Morgan Jr
Dir IT: Steve Kasper
Snr Mgr: Michel Leclerc

NORTH STATE PYROPHYLLITE
See RESCO PRODUCTS INC

D-U-N-S 03-323-1916
NORTH STATE TELECOMMUNICATIONS CORP
111 N Main St, High Point, NC 27260-5007
Tel (336) 472-6048 *Founded/Ownrshp* 1895
Sales 102.9MM[E] *EMP* 400
SIC 4813 Local telephone communications; Long distance telephone communications
Ch Bd: J Patrick Harman
**Pr:* Jonathan M Cage
**Pr:* Royster M Tucker III
Sr VP: Hayden C Mkenzie
**VP:* James D Mc Carson

D-U-N-S 00-699-6912
NORTH STATE TELEPHONE CO (NC)
(*Suby of* NORTH STATE TELECOMMUNICATIONS CORP) ★
111 N Main St, High Point, NC 27260-5007
Tel (336) 886-3660 *Founded/Ownrshp* 1905
Sales 98.0MM[E] *EMP* 400
SIC 4813 Local telephone communications; Long distance telephone communications
Ch: J Patrick Harman
**CEO:* Hayden McKenzie
**CEO:* Royster M Tucker III
**CFO:* Jonathan Cage
**VP:* Jonathan M Cage
**VP:* Mark Dula
**VP:* James D McCarson
**VP:* Richard Worden
Board of Directors: David L Harman, Lizbeth W Privette

D-U-N-S 07-160-2254
NORTH SYRACUSE CENTRAL SCHOOL DISTRICT
5355 W Taft Rd, North Syracuse, NY 13212-2796
Tel (315) 218-2100 *Founded/Ownrshp* 1930
Sales 165.5MM *EMP* 1,400
Accts Grossman St Amour Cpa Syrac
SIC 8211 Public elementary & secondary schools
**Pr:* Pat V Carbone
**VP:* Robert Crabtree
MIS Dir: Donna Norton
IT Man: Alan Verrette
Psych: Sean Kesselring

D-U-N-S 07-259-7966
NORTH TEXAS FOOD BANK (TX)
4500 S Cockrell Hill Rd, Dallas, TX 75236-2028
Tel (214) 330-1396 *Founded/Ownrshp* 1981
Sales 112.2MM *EMP* 150
Accts Bkd Llp Dallas Tx
SIC 8322 Meal delivery program
CEO: Jan Pruitt
**COO:* Colleen Hager
CFO: Bill Alorn
Dir: Colleen Brinkmann
IT Man: Lori Kachner
Opers Mgr: Geoff Slaymaker
Snr Mgr: Brad Wendling

D-U-N-S 07-760-8933 IMP
NORTH TEXAS MUNICIPAL WATER DISTRICT
NTMWD
505 E Brown St, Wylie, TX 75098-4406
Tel (972) 442-5405 *Founded/Ownrshp* 1951
Sales 338.5MM[E] *EMP* 670
Accts Weaver And Tidwell Llp Dalla
SIC 4953 4941 Refuse collection & disposal services; Water supply
Pr: Darwin Whiteside
Ofcr: Russell Moody
**VP:* Joe Joplin
VP: Lynn Shuyler
**Ex Dir:* Tom Kula
IT Man: David Collins
IT Man: Ronnie Rowell
Sfty Dirs: Dan Dalton
Opers Mgr: Bobby J Reeves

D-U-N-S 05-549-2565 IMP
NORTH WEST HANDLING SYSTEMS INC
1100 Sw 7th St, Renton, WA 98057-2939
Tel (425) 255-0500 *Founded/Ownrshp* 1971
Sales 112.9MM[E] *EMP* 240
SIC 5084 7699 Materials handling machinery; Industrial machinery & equipment repair
Pr: James Franck
Exec: Erik Gordon

NORTH WIND GROUP
See CIRI DEVELOPMENT CORP

NORTHAMERICAN BREWERIES
See NORTH AMERICAN BREWERIES INC

D-U-N-S 06-856-9870
NORTHAMPTON COMMUNITY COLLEGE
NORTHAMPTON COUNTY AREA
3835 Green Pond Rd, Bethlehem, PA 18020-7599
Tel (610) 861-5300 *Founded/Ownrshp* 1967
Sales 52.3MM[E] *EMP* 1,582
Accts Kreischer Miller Horsham Pen
SIC 8222 Community college
Pr: Arthur Scott
**Pr:* Mark H Erickson
VP: Carolyn Bortz
**VP:* James Dunleavy
VP: Krista Freeh
VP: Kassie Hilgert
**VP:* Susan Kubik
VP: Michael Mc Govern
VP: Paul Pierpoint
VP: Susan M Salvador
Prgrm Mgr: Jay Dieter

NORTHAMPTON COUNTY AREA
See NORTHAMPTON COMMUNITY COLLEGE

D-U-N-S 07-365-4121
■ **NORTHAMPTON HOSPITAL CORP**
EASTON HOSPITAL
(*Suby of* COMMUNITY HEALTH SYSTEMS INC) ★
250 S 21st St, Easton, PA 18042-3851
Tel (610) 250-4000 *Founded/Ownrshp* 1890, 2001
Sales 177.5MM *EMP* 1,425
SIC 8062 General medical & surgical hospitals
CEO: Brian Finestein
**CFO:* Steven Murassky
VP: Lorry Ofner
VP: Om Sharma
Dir Risk M: Georgiann Gerlach
IT Man: Wayne Bruch
QC Dir: Cristine Biege
Surgeon: Abdul S Badr
Surgeon: Monzur Haque
Surgeon: Michael McCoy
Surgeon: Robert P McEvoy

D-U-N-S 07-654-6829
NORTHBAY HEALTHCARE GROUP
NORTHBAY MEDICAL CENTER
1200 B Gale Wilson Blvd, Fairfield, CA 94533-3552
Tel (707) 646-5000 *Founded/Ownrshp* 1995
Sales 460.5MM *EMP* 1,200
Accts Moss Adams Llp San Francisco
SIC 8062 General medical & surgical hospitals
CEO: Deborah Sugiyama
CFO: Gallen Gorman
CFO: George Stock
Dir OR: Susan Gornall
Chf Nrs Of: Traci Duncan
Doctor: David A Ehrenfeld
Doctor: Craig L Gillespie
Doctor: Alina Hongsakaphadana
Doctor: Robert R Klingman
Doctor: Jonathan D Lopez
Doctor: Steven R Tolkan

NORTHBAY MEDICAL CENTER
See NORTHBAY HEALTHCARE GROUP

D-U-N-S 00-380-1800
NORTHCENTRAL MISSISSIPPI ELECTRIC POWER ASSOCIATION (INC)
4600 Northcentral Way, Olive Branch, MS 38654-5097
Tel (800) 325-8925 *Founded/Ownrshp* 1950
Sales 93.3MM *EMP* 61
Accts Williams Pitts & Beard Pllc H
SIC 4911 Distribution, electric power
Pr: Pat Woods
**VP:* Robert F Williams
Mktg Dir: Mike Bellipanni

D-U-N-S 84-850-6580
NORTHCOTT HOSPITALITY INTERNATIONAL LLC
PERKINS FAMILY RESTAURANT
250 Lake Dr E, Chanhassen, MN 55317-9364
Tel (952) 294-5100 *Founded/Ownrshp* 2000
Sales 110.9MM[E] *EMP* 1,900[E]
SIC 7011 5812 Hotels & motels; Restaurant, family: chain
COO: Paul Kirwin
**CFO:* Joe Martin
**CFO:* Brian Schwen
**Sr VP:* Nasir H Raja
**VP:* Howard Anderson
VP: Mark A Clarey
VP: Jeannine Momchilovich
**VP:* Mark S Nicpon
**VP:* Robin L Oneill
**VP:* Julie R Roettger
Rgnl Mgr: Char Davis-Menda

D-U-N-S 04-082-5473
NORTHDALE OIL INC
448 Main Ave, Neche, ND 58265-4005
Tel (218) 773-4345 *Founded/Ownrshp* 1977
Sales 85.8MM *EMP* 130
Accts Brady Martz & Associates Pc
SIC 5171 Petroleum bulk stations
Pr: Scott Reck
**Sec:* Missy Reck

NORTHEAST ALA REGIONAL MED CTR
See REGIONAL MEDICAL CENTER BOARD

D-U-N-S 07-658-0760
NORTHEAST ARC INC
NORTH SHORE ARC
64 Holten St, Danvers, MA 01923-1973
Tel (978) 762-4878 *Founded/Ownrshp* 1956
Sales 171.3MM *EMP* 1,000
Accts Cbiz Tofias Boston Ma
SIC 8361 8322 8331 Home for the mentally retarded; Family counseling services; General counseling services; Vocational training agency
CEO: Gerard L McCarthy
**Pr:* Tim Brenton
**Pr:* Jeffrey Musnan
**COO:* Joanne Plourde
**CFO:* Gary Penninam
**Treas:* Stephen Johnson
Treas: Rob Rainer
**VP:* Julie Cunnings
MIS Dir: Peter Cabral
Art Dir: Fariba O'Donald

D-U-N-S 84-881-1142
NORTHEAST BEHAVIORAL HEALTH CARE CONSORTIUM
NBHCC'S
72 Glenmaura Nat Blvd, Moosic, PA 18507-2133
Tel (570) 344-9618 *Founded/Ownrshp* 2002
Sales 117.4MM *EMP* 4
SIC 8082 Home health care services
Prin: Steve Arnone
Ofcr: Ed McCarthy

D-U-N-S 10-234-4355
NORTHEAST COMMUNICATIONS OF WISCONSIN INC
NSIGHT TELESERVICES
450 Security Blvd, Green Bay, WI 54313-9705
Tel (920) 617-7000 *Founded/Ownrshp* 1982
Sales 244.3MM[E] *EMP* 1,154
SIC 4812 4813 Cellular telephone services; Local telephone communications
Pr: Patrick Riordan
COO: Dan Fabry
**CFO:* Mark Naze
**Ex VP:* Robert H Riordan
VP: Amy Demeny
**VP:* Lloyd Wielgus
Dir IT: Bruce Lenoble
Dir IT: Lee Thibaudeau

NORTHEAST DELTA DENTAL
See DELTA DENTAL PLAN OF NEW HAMPSHIRE INC

NORTHEAST ELECTRICAL DISTRS
See SONEPAR DISTRIBUTION NEW ENGLAND INC

D-U-N-S 08-056-3745
NORTHEAST FOODS INC
AUTOMATIC ROLLS OF NEW YORK
601 S Caroline St, Baltimore, MD 21231-2814
Tel (410) 276-7254 *Founded/Ownrshp* 1976
Sales 364.0MM[E] *EMP* 850
SIC 2051 5149 Bread, cake & related products; Bread, all types (white, wheat, rye, etc): fresh or frozen; Rolls, bread type: fresh or frozen; Bakery products
Ch Bd: John Paterakis
**Pr:* Steven Paterakis
**VP:* William Paterakis
Genl Mgr: John Lyons
Plnt Mgr: Andy Black
Plnt Mgr: Charlie Podolak

NORTHEAST GA INPATIENT SVCS
See LONGSTREET CLINIC P C

D-U-N-S 11-720-6677
■ **NORTHEAST GENERATION SERVICES CO**
(*Suby of* NU ENTERPRISES INC) ★
301 Hammer Mill Rd, Rocky Hill, CT 06067-3784
Tel (860) 810-1700 *Founded/Ownrshp* 1999
Sales 130.6MM[E] *EMP* 300
SIC 4911 Electric services
Pr: Bruce Kenyon
**VP:* Bill Nadeau
VP: Erick Pelletier
VP Opers: Dennis Brown

D-U-N-S 06-450-2057
NORTHEAST GEORGIA HEALTH SYSTEM INC
743 Spring St Ne, Gainesville, GA 30501-3715
Tel (770) 219-9000 *Founded/Ownrshp* 1986
Sales 50.3MM *EMP* 7,000
Accts Lb Pershing Yoakley & Associat
SIC 8062 General medical & surgical hospitals
Pr: James E Gardner
**COO:* Carol Burrell
**CFO:* Tony Herdener
Ofcr: Kenneth McMillan
VP: Sam Johnson
VP: Sonja McLendon
Adm Dir: Bryan Jones
CIO: Allana Cummings
Dir IT: Dan McDaniel
Dir IT: Chris Paravate
Surgeon: Thomas Abbruzzese

D-U-N-S 62-088-3603
NORTHEAST GEORGIA MEDICAL CENTER INC
(*Suby of* NORTHEAST GEORGIA HEALTH SYSTEM INC) ★
743 Spring St Ne, Gainesville, GA 30501-3715
Tel (770) 219-9000 *Founded/Ownrshp* 1951
Sales 892.1MM *EMP* 3,053
SIC 8062 General medical & surgical hospitals
CEO: Carol Burrell
**CFO:* Anthony M Herdener
CFO: Tony Herdener
**VP:* Tracy Vardeman
**VP:* Paul Vervalin
**VP:* Anthony Williamson
Dir Risk M: Jerry McConnell
Dir Rad: Brett C Baudin
Dir Rad: Steven E Black
Dir Rad: Colby T Chasain
Dir Rad: Richard C Ory

D-U-N-S 94-669-8008
NORTHEAST HEALTH
NORTHEAST HEALTH REHABILITATIO
600 Northern Blvd, Albany, NY 12204-1004
Tel (518) 471-3229 *Founded/Ownrshp* 1867
Sales 396.9MM *EMP* 2,000
SIC 8741 Hospital management; Nursing & personal care facility management
CFO: Lori Santos
**CEO:* Norman Dascher
**COO:* Karen Passey
Exec: Joe Brodzinski
CIO: Jay Wilcox
Doctor: Gregory Bishop
Doctor: Joseph Fay
Doctor: Kyle Flik
Doctor: Leonard Goldstock
Doctor: Alice Kim
Doctor: William Montgomery

D-U-N-S 96-587-3763
NORTHEAST HEALTH INC
315 S Manning Blvd, Albany, NY 12208-1707
Tel (518) 292-6200 *Founded/Ownrshp* 1995
Sales 844.5M *EMP* 4,000
Accts Deloitte Tax Llp Philadelphia
SIC 8059 8322 Personal care home, with health care; Senior citizens' center or association
Pr: James Reed
**VP:* Robert Ducey
Exec: Susan Moran
Dir Risk M: Robert Allen
Dir Rad: Robert Arsenault
Ex Dir: Donnamarie Martocci
Prgrm Mgr: Cheryl Articola
CIO: Patrick J Clark
MIS Dir: Sammie Brinson
IT Man: Glen Eddy
Web Prj Mg: Peter Dobler

NORTHEAST HEALTH REHABILITATIO
See NORTHEAST HEALTH

D-U-N-S 10-118-3184
NORTHEAST HEALTH SYSTEMS INC
BEVERLY HOSPITAL
85 Herrick St, Beverly, MA 01915-1777
Tel (978) 922-3000 *Founded/Ownrshp* 1994
Sales 10.8MM *EMP* 5,100
Accts Pricewaterhousecoopers Llp Bo
SIC 8741 Hospital management; Nursing & personal care facility management
Prin: Philip M Cormier
**Ch Bd:* Henry Rameni
**Pr:* Steven Defossez
**CEO:* Dennis S Conroy
COO: Wendy Beesley
**COO:* Philip Cormier
COO: Philip M Cormier
CFO: Katharine Irvine
CFO: Michael Stefanowicz
Treas: Frederick Kauders
Treas: Peter Simonds
Trst: Joseph Haley
Sr VP: Jody Fleit
Sr VP: Michael Valantine
**VP:* Greg Bird
VP: Elliot Cohen
**VP:* William E Donaldson
VP: Denis Gallagher
VP: Barbara McCarthy
VP: Lisa Nevling
VP: Paul Oshea

NORTHEAST HOSPICE SERVICE
See NORTHEAST MEDICAL CENTER HOSPITAL

D-U-N-S 07-380-9121
NORTHEAST HOSPITAL CORP
BEVERLY HOSPITAL
(*Suby of* BEVERLY HOSPITAL) ★
85 Herrick St, Beverly, MA 01915-1790
Tel (978) 922-3000 *Founded/Ownrshp* 1893
Sales 341.1MM *EMP* 2,800
Accts Pricewaterhousecoopers Llp Bo
SIC 8062 Hospital, AMA approved residency
CEO: Philip M Cormier
**Pr:* Robert Tufts
COO: Linda Cancellieri
**CFO:* Gary P Marlow
**VP:* Cynthia Cafasso Donaldson
**VP:* Rebecca Imperiali
**VP:* Althea Lyons
**VP:* Lisa Neveling
Dir OR: Mary Jenkins
Nurse Mgr: Candace Sklarz
Doctor: Elise Campagnolo

D-U-N-S 08-348-1168
NORTHEAST HOSPITAL FOUNDATION
MEMORIAL HERMANN
18951 N Memorial Dr, Humble, TX 77338-4217
Tel (281) 540-7817 *Founded/Ownrshp* 1977
Sales 236.6MM *EMP* 900
SIC 8062 Hospital, affiliated with AMA residency
Pr: Norman Funderburk
Chf Rad: Scott Allison
COO: Sean Henderson
CFO: David Glassburn
**Sec:* Mary Lea Layton
Ofcr: Dan Peterson
**VP:* Barbara Reischmann MD
Dir Lab: Rita Glass
Dir Sec: Joshua Phipps
CIO: Louis Smith
Mktg Dir: Tom Broad

D-U-N-S 05-227-2150
NORTHEAST ILLINOIS REGIONAL COMMUTER RAILROAD CORP
METRA METROPOLITAN RAIL
547 W Jackson Blvd Ste 1, Chicago, IL 60661-5768
Tel (312) 322-6900 *Founded/Ownrshp* 1981
Sales 404.0MM[E] *EMP* 2,800
Accts Crowe Chizek And Company Llc
SIC 4111 4011 Commuter rail passenger operation; Railroads, line-haul operating
Ch: Jeffrey R Ladd
COO: Vaughn L Stoner
CFO: Frank Racibozynski
Ex Dir: Philip A Pagano
Genl Couns: Michael Noland
Board of Directors: Lowell A Anderson, Larry A Huggins, Jeffrey R Ladd, W Warren Nugent, Gerald L Porter, Joseph A Tecson, Donald A Udsten

D-U-N-S 05-180-7121
NORTHEAST INVESTORS TRUST
125 High St Ste 1801, Boston, MA 02110-2749
Tel (857) 263-8100 *Founded/Ownrshp* 1950
Sales 133.0MM *EMP* 18
SIC 6722 Mutual fund sales, on own account
Pr: William A Oates Jr
**Ch Bd:* Ernest E Monrad
**Treas:* Gordon Barrett
**Trst:* Robert B Minturn Jr
**Trst:* Bruce Monrad

D-U-N-S 87-814-3692
NORTHEAST IOWA COMMUNITY COLLEGE FOUNDATION
1625 Highway 150, Calmar, IA 52132-7606
Tel (563) 562-3263 *Founded/Ownrshp* 1967
Sales 40.6MM *EMP* 1,514
Accts Hacker Nelson & Co Pc Deco
SIC 8222 Junior college
Pr: Mark Downhowe
**Sec:* John Noel
**VP:* Jim Anderson
VP: Kathy Nacos-Burds
**Prin:* Dr Liang Chee Wee
Prgrm Mgr: Terry Jenkins
Prgrm Mgr: Carolyn Olberding
Genl Mgr: Heidi Herold
Tech Mgr: Lora Hannan
Mktg Dir: Shea Herbst
Psych: Kathryn Davis

NORTHEAST MEDICAL CENTER
See CAROLINAS MEDICAL CENTER NORTHEAST

D-U-N-S 94-205-8439
NORTHEAST MEDICAL CENTER HOSPITAL
NORTHEAST HOSPICE SERVICE
(*Suby of* MEMORIAL HERMANN HEALTHCARE SYSTEM) ★
9813 Memorial Blvd Ste H, Humble, TX 77338-4253
Tel (281) 540-7167 *Founded/Ownrshp* 2007
Sales 1.0MM[E] *EMP* 1,000
SIC 8062 General medical & surgical hospitals
CEO: Hiath Rushing

D-U-N-S 93-869-9444
NORTHEAST MEDICAL GROUP INC
99 Hawley Ave Fl 3, Bridgeport, CT 06606-5038
Tel (203) 339-6499 *Founded/Ownrshp* 1991
Sales 199.3MM *EMP* 30[E]
Accts Lb Ernst & Young Us Llp India
SIC 8011 Offices & clinics of medical doctors
COO: Amit Rastogi

D-U-N-S 05-253-7933
■ **NORTHEAST NUCLEAR ENERGY CO**
(*Suby of* EVERSOURCE ENERGY) ★
107 Selden St, Berlin, CT 06037-1616
Tel (860) 665-5000 *Founded/Ownrshp* 1950
Sales 92.2MM[E] *EMP* 200
SIC 4911 Generation, electric power
Pr: Bruce D Kenyon
**Ch Bd:* Michael G Morris
**Treas:* John B Keane
**Ex VP:* John H Forsgen
**VP:* John Stack

D-U-N-S 07-455-4098
NORTHEAST OHIO REGIONAL SEWER DISTRICT
3900 Euclid Ave, Cleveland, OH 44115-2506
Tel (216) 881-6600 *Founded/Ownrshp* 1972
Sales 280.4MM *EMP* 623
Accts Ciuni & Panichi Llc Clevelan
SIC 4959 Sanitary services
Pr: Darnell Brown
VP: Nichole Pinson
**VP:* Ronald D Sulik
Exec: Allan Velez
Comm Man: Kim Jones
**Ex Dir:* Julius Ciaccia
Ex Dir: Julius Ciaccia
Plng Mgr: Devona Marshall
IT Man: Frank Greenland
Genl Couns: Marlene Sundheimer
Snr Mgr: Jeff Huang

D-U-N-S 80-423-7477
■ **NORTHEAST RECYCLING CORP**
WASTE MANAGEMENT
(*Suby of* WM) ★
1198 Prospect Ave, Westbury, NY 11590-2723
Tel (516) 937-0900 *Founded/Ownrshp* 1991
Sales 93.8MM[E] *EMP* 300
SIC 4953 4212 Refuse systems; Local trucking, without storage
Dist Mgr: Rich Geisser

D-U-N-S 79-689-4392
NORTHEAST REMSCO CONSTRUCTION INC
JAG COMPANIES
(*Suby of* JAG COMPANIES INC) ★
1433 State Route 34 Ste 6, Wall Township, NJ 07727-1613
Tel (732) 557-6100 *Founded/Ownrshp* 2011
Sales 176.7MM[E] *EMP* 450
SIC 1623 1622 1629 1611 Water, sewer & utility lines; Bridge construction; Land clearing contractor; General contractor, highway & street construction
Ch: Juan Gutierrez
**Pr:* Rolando E Acosta
**CFO:* Marcelo Afonso
VP: Alberto Solana
Dir Bus: Marc Dodeman
IT Man: Dan Alvarado

D-U-N-S 14-502-3529
NORTHEAST TEXAS ELECTRIC COOPERATIVE INC
2221 H G Mosley Pkwy # 100, Longview, TX 75604-3670
Tel (903) 757-3282 *Founded/Ownrshp* 1972
Sales 225.1MM *EMP* 3
SIC 4911 Generation, electric power
Pr: John Dugen
Genl Mgr: Rick Tyler

NORTHEAST UTILITIES
See EVERSOURCE ENERGY SERVICE CO

D-U-N-S 07-479-7739
NORTHEAST WISCONSIN TECHNICAL COLLEGE DISTRICT
NWTC
(*Suby of* WISCONSIN TECHNICAL COLLEGE SYSTEM BOARD) ★
2740 W Mason St, Green Bay, WI 54303-4966
Tel (920) 498-5400 *Founded/Ownrshp* 1911
Sales 131.5MM[E] *EMP* 2,200
Accts Wipfli Llp Rhinelander Wisco
SIC 8221 8222 Colleges universities & professional schools; Technical institute
Pr: Dr Jeffrey Rafin
Pt: Kellian Collins
CFO: Jim Blumreich
Mktg Dir: Erica Plaza

NORTHEASTERN FASTENERS
See NEFCO CORP

NORTHEASTERN HEALTH SYSTEM
See TAHLEQUAH HOSPITAL AUTHORITY

D-U-N-S 87-933-1445
NORTHEASTERN ILLINOIS UNIVERSITY
RONALD WILLIAMS LIBRARY
5500 N Saint Louis Ave, Chicago, IL 60625-4699
Tel (773) 442-4000 *Founded/Ownrshp* 1961
Sales 84.5MM *EMP* 1,500
SIC 8221

D-U-N-S 10-109-3847
NORTHEASTERN PENNSYLVANIA CENTER FOR INDEPENDENT LIVING INC
1142 Sanderson Ave, Scranton, PA 18509-2623
Tel (570) 344-7211 *Founded/Ownrshp* 1987
Sales 115.8MM *EMP* 84
Accts Joneskohanski & Co Pc Moosi
SIC 8322 Individual & family services
Ex Dir: Timothy Moran
CIO: Mike Masters

D-U-N-S 15-213-9887
NORTHEASTERN PENNSYLVANIA HEALTH CORP
LEHIGH VALLEY HEALTH NETWORK
(*Suby of* LEHIGH VALLEY HEALTH NETWORK INC) ★
700 E Broad St, Hazleton, PA 18201-6835
Tel (570) 501-4000 *Founded/Ownrshp* 2013
Sales 109.1MM *EMP* 1,000[E]
SIC 8062 General medical & surgical hospitals
Pr: John Fletcher
**CFO:* William C Bauer
Dir Risk M: James Nelson
Dir Rad: William Reppy
Dir Rx: Ray Bernardi
Plnt Mgr: Mike Kempchinsky

NORTHEASTERN REMC
See NORTHEASTERN RURAL ELECTRIC MEMBERSHIP CORP

D-U-N-S 80-893-1138
NORTHEASTERN REMC
4901 E Park Dr Fl 30, Columbia City, IN 46725
Tel (260) 625-3700 *Founded/Ownrshp* 2007
Sales 89.3MM *EMP* 2
SIC 4911 Electric services
CEO: Gregg Kiess
Exec: Keith Sievers
VP Mktg: Michael Defreeuw

D-U-N-S 00-693-6587
NORTHEASTERN RURAL ELECTRIC MEMBERSHIP CORP
NORTHEASTERN REMC
4901 E Park 30 Dr, Columbia City, IN 46725-8885
Tel (260) 625-3700 *Founded/Ownrshp* 1936
Sales 111.0MM *EMP* 35
SIC 4911 Distribution, electric power
Pr: Gregg L Kiess
**Treas:* Doug Schrader
**VP:* Gene Donaghy
**VP:* Curt Irven
**VP:* Marjorie Kennedy
**VP:* Richard R Smith

D-U-N-S 07-240-0500
NORTHEASTERN STATE UNIVERSITY
NSU
600 N Grand Ave, Tahlequah, OK 74464-2301
Tel (918) 456-5511 *Founded/Ownrshp* 2008
Sales 45.5MM *EMP* 1,031
Accts Arledge & Associates Pc Ed
SIC 8221 University
Pr: Steve Turner
**Pr:* Dr Steve Turner
**VP:* Dr Laura Boren
**VP:* Dr Pam Fly
**VP:* Tim Foutch
**VP:* David Koehn
VP: James Pate
**VP:* William Rugg
Comm Dir: Nancy Garber
Off Mgr: Janie Polk
IT Man: Susan Evans
Board of Directors: Dr Steve Turner

D-U-N-S 02-249-2987 EXP
NORTHEASTERN SUPPLY INC
8323 Pulaski Hwy, Baltimore, MD 21237-2941
Tel (410) 574-0010 *Founded/Ownrshp* 1971
Sales 162.9MM[E] *EMP* 285
Accts Ellin & Tucker Chartered Bal
SIC 5074 Plumbing & hydronic heating supplies
Pr: Stephen D Cook
**Sec:* Cheryl Cook-Boyle
**VP:* Mike Cornbrooks
VP: Russ Everson
VP: Rick Tomaschefsky
Brnch Mgr: Laura Caviness
Brnch Mgr: Rick Foxwell
Brnch Mgr: Dwayne Graham
Manager: Alan Cowan
Sales Asso: Allen Brown
Sales Asso: Dave Gibas

D-U-N-S 00-142-3631
NORTHEASTERN UNIVERSITY
360 Huntington Ave, Boston, MA 02115-5000
Tel (617) 373-2000 *Founded/Ownrshp* 1916
Sales 1.0MMM[E] *EMP* 4,175
Accts Pricewaterhousecoopers Llp B
SIC 8221 University
Pr: Joseph Aoun
CFO: Jennifer Tonneson
Treas: Rodelio Mandawe
**Treas:* Thomas Nedell
Sr VP: Ahmed T Abdelal
**Sr VP:* Michael Armini
**Sr VP:* James Bean
**Sr VP:* Diane Macgillivray
**Sr VP:* Philomena Mantella
Sr VP: Philomena V Mantella
**Sr VP:* Ralph Martin
Sr VP: Laurence F Mucciolo
Sr VP: Mark Putnam
Sr VP: Carol Scheman
Sr VP: George Triantaris
VP: Ahmed Abdelal
VP: Amelia Brizicky
VP: Jane Brown
VP: Nanette Callihan
VP: William J Cotter
VP: Robert Gittens

NORTHERN NEW ENGLAND CARPENT
See NORTHERN NEW ENGLAND DISTRICT COUNCIL OF CARPENTERS INC

D-U-N-S 13-072-9189
NORTHERN AIR CORP
NAC MECHANICAL & ELEC SVCS
1001 Labore Industrial Ct B, Saint Paul, MN 55110-5168
Tel (651) 490-9868 *Founded/Ownrshp* 1985
Sales 134.1MM[E] *EMP* 320
SIC 1711 Warm air heating & air conditioning contractor; Ventilation & duct work contractor; Refrigeration contractor
Pr: Lynn Bishop
**VP:* Steve Anderson
VP: Bill Zellmer
Sfty Dirs: Mike Heinze
Sls Mgr: David Carlson

D-U-N-S 15-366-5070
NORTHERN ARIZONA HEALTHCARE CORP
1200 N Beaver St, Flagstaff, AZ 86001-3118
Tel (928) 779-3366 *Founded/Ownrshp* 1985
Sales 61.4MM *EMP* 2,500
Accts Ernst & Young Us Llp Phoenix
SIC 8741 8062 8399 4119 Hospital management; Nursing & personal care facility management; General medical & surgical hospitals; Fund raising organization, non-fee basis; Ambulance service
CEO: Chris Bavasi
**Pr:* Bill Bradeo
**CFO:* Gregory D Kuzma
Ofcr: Jack Dempsey
Ex VP: Gundrun Moll
Ex VP: Dixie Morrison
VP: Marilynn Black
VP: Jennnifer Brewer
VP: Roger Dewalt
VP: Alice Gagnaire
VP: Ginamarie Harris
VP: Darlene Lewis
VP: Kai McSwain
VP: Sandra Milligan
VP: James Paris
VP: Cindy Sanders
VP: Madelyn Szep
VP: Thomas Ziffer
Exec: Greg Kouzma
Dir Lab: Gwin Filleman
Dir Lab: Karen McMullin

D-U-N-S 80-634-5542
NORTHERN ARIZONA UNIVERSITY
601 S Knoles Dr Rm 220, Flagstaff, AZ 86011-7034
Tel (928) 523-9011 *Founded/Ownrshp* 1899
Sales 308.8MM *EMP* 3,863[E]
Accts Debbie Davenport Phoenix Ari
SIC 8221 Colleges universities & professional schools
Pr: Dr Rita Cheng
COO: David Richardson
Chf Mktg O: Piper Jameson
Assoc VP: Betsy Mennell
Sr VP: Mary Ellen C Williams
Dir Lab: Janelle Bauerle
IT Man: Peter Gomersall
Software D: Kevin Labranche
Psych: Stanley Clark
Doctor: Tanya Mure
Pgrm Dir: Emily McCarthy

D-U-N-S 88-494-8985 IMP/EXP
NORTHERN BEEF INDUSTRIES INC
719 S Shoreline Blvd # 204, Corpus Christi, TX 78401-3548
Tel (361) 654-6180 *Founded/Ownrshp* 1995
Sales 90.0MM *EMP* 9
SIC 5147 Meats & meat products
Pr: David Hausman
**VP:* Laura Hausman

D-U-N-S 02-163-2583
NORTHERN BORDER PIPELINE CO
TRANSCANADA KEYSTONE PIPELINE
700 Louisiana St Ste 700, Houston, TX 77002-2873
Tel (832) 320-5000 *Founded/Ownrshp* 1978
Sales 112.8MM[E] *EMP* 135[E]
Accts Kpmg Llp
SIC 4922 Pipelines, natural gas
VP: Dean Ferguson
Treas: Rhonda Amundson

D-U-N-S 05-163-6017
NORTHERN CALIFORNIA CONFERENCE OF SEVENTH-DAY ADVENTISTS
401 Taylor Blvd, Pleasant Hill, CA 94523-2146
Tel (925) 685-4300 *Founded/Ownrshp* 1911
Sales 77.1MM[E] *EMP* 1,150
SIC 8211 8661 Elementary school; Seventh Day Adventist Church
CEO: James E Pedersen
**CFO:* John Rasmussen

D-U-N-S 08-290-0564
NORTHERN CALIFORNIA POWER AGENCY
NCPA
651 Commerce Dr, Roseville, CA 95678-6411
Tel (916) 781-3636 *Founded/Ownrshp* 1968
Sales 126.1MM[E] *EMP* 166
Accts Moss-Adams Llp Portland Oreg
SIC 4911 Transmission, electric power; Generation, electric power
Treas: Ute Woodall
Bd of Dir: Karen England
Bd of Dir: Diane Morgan
Dir Risk M: Rui Dai
Genl Mgr: Vicki Cichocki
Off Admin: Victoria Nguyen
Opers Mgr: Peter Hill

D-U-N-S 13-066-6642
NORTHERN CALIFORNIA TPG INC
PERFORMANCE GROUP
6673 Owens Dr, Pleasanton, CA 94588-3335
Tel (925) 556-0512 *Founded/Ownrshp* 2002
Sales 135.0MM *EMP* 25
SIC 5141 Food brokers
Pr: Phil Costello
Sls Mgr: Tony Metz

D-U-N-S 79-703-2190 IMP/EXP
NORTHERN CONTOURS INC
1355 Mendota Heights Rd # 100, Saint Paul, MN 55120-1112
Tel (651) 695-1698 *Founded/Ownrshp* 1992
Sales 110.7MM[E] *EMP* 500
SIC 3083 1751 2435 Plastic finished products, laminated; Cabinet & finish carpentry; Hardwood veneer & plywood
CEO: John A Goebe
**CFO:* James Moe
**VP:* Duaine Miranowski
Rgnl Mgr: David Estilow
VP Sls: Larry Skow
Mktg Mgr: Melissa Sjerben
Mktg Mgr: Missy Sjerven
Sls Mgr: Jason Kirchgatter

D-U-N-S 02-066-1757
NORTHERN DUTCHESS HOSPITAL
(*Suby of* HEALTH QUEST SYSTEMS INC) ★
6511 Spring Brook Ave, Rhinebeck, NY 12572-3709
Tel (845) 876-3001 *Founded/Ownrshp* 1924
Sales 92.6MM *EMP* 320
Accts Pricewaterhousecoopers Llp N
SIC 8062 General medical & surgical hospitals
Pr: Dennis George
Chf Rad: Judy Zaho
**CFO:* Alan Mossoff
Dir OR: Gail Richardson
Ex Dir: Deborah Breen
Pathlgst: Uma Medapati

D-U-N-S 10-252-9166
NORTHERN ELECTRIC INC
12789 Emerson St, Thornton, CO 80241-3396
Tel (303) 428-6969 *Founded/Ownrshp* 2001
Sales 158.5MM[E] *EMP* 275
SIC 1731 Electrical work
Pr: Orville J Fleming
CFO: Tyler Fleming
**Treas:* Joseph Dopler
**VP:* Albert Fisher
Snr PM: Dennis Kreutz
Snr PM: Brian Pallissard

D-U-N-S 09-709-2266 IMP
NORTHERN ENGRAVING CORP
(*Suby of* LAWRENCE HOLDING INC) ★
803 S Black River St, Sparta, WI 54656-2221
Tel (608) 269-6911 *Founded/Ownrshp* 2012
Sales 120.0MM *EMP* 1,200
SIC 3469 3544 3089 Stamping metal for the trade; Special dies, tools, jigs & fixtures; Automotive parts, plastic
CEO: Jeff Xu
COO: Geroge Murray
CFO: Arnold Olson
VP: Mike Mulvaney
Prgrm Mgr: Seth Jacobson
Ql Cn Mgr: Ken Schmidt

NORTHERN EXPLORATION SERVICES
See SAEXPLORATION INC

D-U-N-S 01-780-8684
NORTHERN FROZEN FOODS INC
NORTHERN HASEROT
21500 Alexander Rd, Cleveland, OH 44146-5511
Tel (440) 439-0600 *Founded/Ownrshp* 1966
Sales 209.7MM[E] *EMP* 200
SIC 5142 5149 5147 Packaged frozen goods; Canned goods: fruit, vegetables, seafood, meats, etc.; Meats, fresh
Pr: Douglas Kern
Pr: Joe Canfield
**Sec:* Bruce Kern
**VP:* Richard C Speicher
Exec: Jason Baliman
IT Man: Bruce Schaeffer
IT Man: Bruce Shaffner
Opers Mgr: Drew Benson
Natl Sales: Yachanin John
Natl Sales: John Yachanin
VP Sls: Robert McKechnie

D-U-N-S 00-490-4686 EXP
NORTHERN FRUIT CO (WA)
220 2nd St Ne, East Wenatchee, WA 98802-4851
Tel (509) 884-6651 *Founded/Ownrshp* 1924, 1928
Sales 89.9MM *EMP* 30
Accts Homchick Smith & Associates P
SIC 0723 Fruit (fresh) packing services
Pr: Doug Pauly

D-U-N-S 04-395-4192
NORTHERN GROWERS LLC
48416 144th St, Big Stone City, SD 57216-5406
Tel (605) 862-7902 *Founded/Ownrshp* 2002
Sales 142.0MM *EMP* 51
SIC 6719 Investment holding companies, except banks
Pdt Mgr: Gail Street
Board of Directors: Ronald Anderson, Dennis Fleming, Robert Metz, Robert Narem, Brent Olson, Greg Toben, Bill Whipple, Robert Wittnebel

NORTHERN HASEROT
See NORTHERN FROZEN FOODS INC

NORTHERN HOSPITILITY
See SAULT SAINTE MARIE TRIBE OF CHIPPEWA INDIANS

D-U-N-S 10-871-6408
NORTHERN ILLINOIS FOOD BANK
273 Dearborn Ct, Geneva, IL 60134-3587
Tel (630) 443-6910 *Founded/Ownrshp* 1982
Sales 135.1MM *EMP* 97
Accts Plante & Moran Pllc Chicago
SIC 8322 Individual & family services
Pr: Julie Yurko
**CFO:* Dianne Korizon
**VP:* Leon Goins
Exec: Eric Albrecht
Genl Mgr: Rita Trallis
CTO: Eugene Maule
Software D: Corinne Boyd

D-U-N-S 00-692-7792
■ **NORTHERN ILLINOIS GAS CO** (IL)
NICOR GAS COMPANY
(*Suby of* OTTAWA ACQUISITION LLC) ★
1844 W Ferry Rd, Naperville, IL 60563-9600
Tel (630) 983-8676 *Founded/Ownrshp* 1954, 2011
Sales 1.7MMM[E] *EMP* 2,050[E]
SIC 4924 4922 Natural gas distribution; Natural gas transmission; Storage, natural gas
Ch Bd: Henry P Linginfelter
Pr: Melvin D Williams
CFO: Andrew W Evans
Ex VP: Paul R Shlanta
Ex VP: Peter Tumminello
Sr VP: Bryan E Seas
VP: Kevin W Kirby
Genl Mgr: Paul Delacey
Genl Mgr: James Jerozal
Genl Mgr: Patrick Whiteside
Genl Mgr: Chris Ziemba
Board of Directors: John Somerhalder II

D-U-N-S 14-478-2570
NORTHERN ILLINOIS HEALTH PLAN
773 W Lincoln St Ste 402, Freeport, IL 61032-4980
Tel (815) 599-7050 *Founded/Ownrshp* 1984
Sales 34.1MM[E] *EMP* 1,200
SIC 8741 8721 Hospital management; Nursing & personal care facility management; Accounting, auditing & bookkeeping
Pr: Dennis L Hamilton
**Ch Bd:* Woodruff A Burt
**Sec:* Richard Zimmerman
Board of Directors: Harold Fenton

D-U-N-S 07-456-1432
NORTHERN ILLINOIS MEDICAL CENTER (IL)
4201 W Medical Center Dr, McHenry, IL 60050-8499
Tel (815) 344-5000 *Founded/Ownrshp* 1956
Sales 242.8MM *EMP* 1,200
Accts Kpmg Llp Columbus Oh
SIC 8062 General medical & surgical hospitals
Pr: Michael S Eesley
**Pr:* Jason Sciarro
**CFO:* David L Tomlinson
**Treas:* Eric Zornow
**Sr VP:* Aaron Shepley
Doctor: Archana Reddy
Doctor: Prashant Sura

D-U-N-S 00-174-5512
NORTHERN ILLINOIS UNIVERSITY ALUMNI ASSOCIATION (IL)
1425 W Lincoln Hwy, Dekalb, IL 60115-2828
Tel (815) 753-9500 *Founded/Ownrshp* 1895
Sales 672.3MM[E] *EMP* 8,500
Accts Ec Ortiz & Co Llp Chicago
SIC 8221 University
Pr: Douglas Baker
Mng Pt: Cindy Kubasiak
Ofcr: Devon Buckle
Assoc VP: Joseph Matty
Ex VP: Lisa C Freeman
VP: Anne Arne
VP: Brad Bond
VP: Tracey Brill
VP: Cara Carlson
VP: John Cheney
VP: Sien Deng
VP: Diane Docking
VP: John Dzuryak
VP: Linda Faivre
VP: Bonni Feltz
VP: Sean Frazier
VP: Steven Gorski
VP: Aaron Kushner
VP: Carolyn Law
VP: Beth Metzler
VP: Tabitha Sims

D-U-N-S 03-181-8289
NORTHERN IMPROVEMENT CO
(*Suby of* MCCORMICK INC) ★
4000 12th Ave N, Fargo, ND 58102-2910
Tel (701) 277-1225 *Founded/Ownrshp* 1959
Sales 177.9MM *EMP* 125
Accts Eide Bailly Llp Fargo North
SIC 1611 1629 Highway & street paving contractor; Airport runway construction; Power plant construction
Pr: Thomas McCormick
**CFO:* Jay Kjos
**Ex VP:* Steve McCormick
**VP:* Brad Ballweber
VP: Kim Conlon
Area Mgr: Keith Reiss
Mtls Mgr: Christopher Mathern

D-U-N-S 00-693-7585 IMP
■ **NORTHERN INDIANA PUBLIC SERVICE CO**
(*Suby of* NISOURCE INC) ★
801 E 86th Ave, Merrillville, IN 46410-6271
Tel (877) 647-5990 *Founded/Ownrshp* 1912, 1988
Sales 1.5MMM[E] *EMP* 3,096
SIC 4924 4911 Natural gas distribution; Generation, electric power
Pr: Kathleen O'Leary
**CFO:* Pete Disser
Sr VP: Guy Ausmus
**Sr VP:* Timothy A Dehring
**VP:* Gary W Pottorff
**VP:* Jon D Veurink
Ex Dir: Karl Stanley

D-U-N-S 07-287-9760
NORTHERN KENTUCKY UNIVERSITY
Nunn Dr, Newport, KY 41099-0001
Tel (859) 572-5100 *Founded/Ownrshp* 1970
Sales 143.7MM *EMP* 1,600
Accts Bkd Llp Cpas & Advisors Cinc
SIC 8221 University
Pr: Geoffrey S Mearns
COO: Larry Terrell
Bd of Dir: Jim Hilgefort
Ofcr: Bobby Pate
Ofcr: Becky Roberts
Assoc Dir: Sarah Mann
Dir IT: Doug J Wells
IT Man: Kim Baker

D-U-N-S 05-529-6479 IMP/EXP
NORTHERN LABS INC
5800 West Dr, Manitowoc, WI 54220-8367
Tel (920) 684-7137 *Founded/Ownrshp* 1986
Sales 128.1MM[E] *EMP* 250
SIC 2842 2841 Automobile polish; Detergents, synthetic organic or inorganic alkaline
Pr: James D Culea
CFO: N Weigarth
CFO: N Weingarth

NORTHERN MICH REGIONAL HOSP
See MCLAREN NORTHERN MICHIGAN

D-U-N-S 07-313-5634
NORTHERN MICHIGAN UNIVERSITY
1401 Presque Isle Ave, Marquette, MI 49855-2818
Tel (906) 227-1000 *Founded/Ownrshp* 1899
Sales 101.3MM[E] *EMP* 981
Accts Rehmann Robson Llc Traverse C
SIC 8221 College, except junior
Ch Bd: Sook Wilkson
**Pr:* Dr Fritz Erickson
Treas: Patrick Lakenen
Ofcr: Julie Genore
Top Exec: Courtney Case
Ex VP: Alfred Joyal
VP: Fred Joyal
VP: Betsy Lehman
VP: Ken Reindel
Assoc Dir: Bridget Berube
Assoc Dir: Jolene Klumpp
Board of Directors: Deanna Hemmila, Carol Carr, Amy Hubinger, Alison Crowley, Gina Lombardini, Gerri Daniels, Cindy L Paavola, Allison Erickson, Kathy Richards, Kristi Evans, Robyn Stille, Kathy Frazier, Jane Surrell, Sheri Giordana, Scott Thum, Brad Hamel, Dan Truckey, Martha Haynes

D-U-N-S 78-415-8214
■ **NORTHERN NATURAL GAS CO**
(*Suby of* BERKSHIRE HATHAWAY ENERGY CO) ★
1111 S 103rd St, Omaha, NE 68124-1072
Tel (877) 654-0646 *Founded/Ownrshp* 2002
Sales 224.1MM[E] *EMP* 1,055
SIC 4226 4922 4923 4925 Special warehousing & storage; Oil & gasoline storage caverns for hire; Natural gas transmission; Pipelines, natural gas; Gas transmission & distribution; Gas production and/or distribution
CEO: Greg Abel
**Pr:* Mark A Hewett
Treas: Leanne Meyer
VP: Joe Lillo
VP: Joseph M Lillo
VP: Paul Maakestad
VP: Mary Miller
VP: J G Porter
Comm Man: Toby Kuehl
Dir IT: Hasan Kedwaii
IT Man: Joanne Bisbee

D-U-N-S 79-161-8499
■ **NORTHERN NEVADA MEDICAL CENTER LP**
(*Suby of* UNIVERSAL HEALTH SERVICES INC) ★
2375 E Prater Way, Sparks, NV 89434-9665
Tel (775) 331-7000 *Founded/Ownrshp* 1989
Sales 89.6MM *EMP* 505
SIC 8062 8093 8071 8049 8011 General medical & surgical hospitals; Rehabilitation center, outpatient treatment; X-ray laboratory, including dental; Speech pathologist; Freestanding emergency medical center
CEO: Alan Olive
Pt: Wayne Allen
Pt: Gina Anderson
Pt: Meg Cleary
Pt: James R Pagels
COO: Tiffany Meert
CFO: Ryan Heit
Chf Mktg O: Ira Pauly
Dir Inf Cn: Beth Wilmer
CIO: Harry McQueen
Doctor: Timothy Bray

D-U-N-S 07-397-1608
NORTHERN NEW ENGLAND BENEFIT TRUST
51 Goffstown Rd Ste 2, Manchester, NH 03102-2746
Tel (603) 669-4771 *Founded/Ownrshp* 1965
Sales NA *EMP* 8
Accts Howe Riley & Howe Pllc Manche
SIC 6371 Pension, health & welfare funds
Ex Dir: Robert Gibbons
**Trst:* William Clifford
**Trst:* Gerard Cole
**Trst:* Bob Gibbons
**Trst:* Robert Homes

D-U-N-S 06-098-6858
NORTHERN NEW ENGLAND DISTRICT COUNCIL OF CARPENTERS INC
NORTHERN NEW ENGLAND CARPENT
350 Fordham Rd, Wilmington, MA 01887-2174
Tel (800) 383-2759 *Founded/Ownrshp* 1974
Sales 129.4MM *EMP* 3
Accts Daniel A Winters & Company Cpa
SIC 8631 Labor unions & similar labor organizations
Pr: Bruce King

D-U-N-S 82-477-6749
NORTHERN NEW ENGLAND ENERGY CORP
(*Suby of* GAZ METRO INC)
85 Swift St, South Burlington, VT 05403-7306
Tel (802) 658-6555 *Founded/Ownrshp* 2008
Sales 787.9MM[E] *EMP* 192[E]
SIC 4911 Electric services
Pr: Sophie Brochu

D-U-N-S 82-985-9615
NORTHERN OIL AND GAS INC
315 Manitoba Ave Ste 200, Wayzata, MN 55391-1660
Tel (952) 476-9800 *Founded/Ownrshp* 2007
Sales 275.0MM *EMP* 20
Tkr Sym NOG *Exch* ASE
SIC 1311 Crude petroleum & natural gas
CEO: Thomas W Stoelk
**Ch Bd:* Richard Weber
Ex VP: Brandon R Elliott
Ex VP: Erik J Romslo

D-U-N-S 82-991-0848
NORTHERN PARTNERS COOPERATIVE
1000 6th Ave, Mendota, IL 61342-1736
Tel (815) 539-6772 *Founded/Ownrshp* 1915
Sales 100.6MM *EMP* 70
SIC 5153 Grain & field beans
CEO: Eric Anderson
**CFO:* Alan Zehr
Off Mgr: Kim Higgins
Plnt Mgr: Cory Davidson

D-U-N-S 80-563-9960 IMP
■ **NORTHERN PIPE PRODUCTS INC**
N P P
(*Suby of* OTTER TAIL CORP) ★
1302 39th St N, Fargo, ND 58102-2808
Tel (701) 282-7655 *Founded/Ownrshp* 1995
Sales 107.8MM[E] *EMP* 90
SIC 3084 Plastics pipe
Pr: Steve Laskey
**CEO:* John Abbott
**CFO:* Lyle Ganyo
**Treas:* Kevin G Moug
**VP:* Ken Doggett
**VP:* Vic Weigel

D-U-N-S 02-300-9996
NORTHERN RESOURCES COOPERATIVE
1504 Center St W, Roseau, MN 56751-1915
Tel (218) 463-1805 *Founded/Ownrshp* 1933
Sales 83.7MM[E] *EMP* 70
SIC 5191 5172 5251 5541 Fertilizer & fertilizer materials; Chemicals, agricultural; Petroleum products; Gases, liquefied petroleum (propane); Hardware; Gasoline service stations
Pr: Steve Dahl
**CEO:* Kelly Christianson
**Sec:* Roger Falk
Genl Mgr: Kelly Christiansen

NORTHERN SAFETY AND INDUSTRIAL
See NORTHERN SAFETY CO INC

D-U-N-S 10-774-1878 IMP/EXP
NORTHERN SAFETY CO INC
NORTHERN SAFETY AND INDUSTRIAL
(*Suby of* WURTH INDUSTRY NORTH AMERICA LLC)
232 Industrial Park Dr, Frankfort, NY 13340-4748
Tel (315) 793-4900 *Founded/Ownrshp* 2015
Sales 241.3MM[E] *EMP* 400
SIC 5099

D-U-N-S 03-541-8987 IMP
NORTHERN SALES CO INC
KETCHIKAN NORTHERN SALES
15022 Puyallup St E # 101, Sumner, WA 98390-2401
Tel (253) 299-0500 *Founded/Ownrshp* 2006
Sales 87.9MM[E] *EMP* 270
SIC 5145 5149 5194 5141 Snack foods; Potato chips; Soft drinks; Tobacco & tobacco products; Groceries, general line
Pr: Lance Crosby
**CFO:* Rose Treutel
**VP:* Darrin Erdahl
Dir IT: Andrew Greco
Sls Mgr: Rich Sjoroos

NORTHERN SECURITY INSURANCE CO
See VERMONT MUTUAL INSURANCE CO

D-U-N-S 08-964-3501
NORTHERN SERVICES GROUP INC
2000 Fountainview Dr, Monsey, NY 10952-2875
Tel (845) 356-9880 *Founded/Ownrshp* 2000
Sales 0.1 *EMP* 1,100
Accts Abbate Demarinis Llp Garden C
SIC 8059 Nursing home, except skilled & intermediate care facility
CEO: Morris Klein
Ofcr: Michael T Nowicki

D-U-N-S 36-157-7687 IMP/EXP
NORTHERN STAMPING CO
6600 Chapek Pkwy, Cleveland, OH 44125-1049
Tel (216) 883-8888 *Founded/Ownrshp* 2009
Sales 316.9MM[E] *EMP* 1,700
SIC 3465 3469 Automotive stampings; Metal stampings
Ch Bd: Matthew S Friedman
**CFO:* Ian Hessel
**VP:* Scott Sheffield
Dir IT: Tom Benedict
Board of Directors: Mady Friedman, Matthew S Friedman, Ian B Hessel

D-U-N-S 96-835-0715
NORTHERN STAR GENERATION LLC
2929 Allen Pkwy Ste 2200, Houston, TX 77019-7112
Tel (713) 580-6300 *Founded/Ownrshp* 2004
Sales 227.0MM[E] *EMP* 250[E]
SIC 4911 Generation, electric power
Pr: Jack F Browder
**CFO:* Vincent Schager
**Ofcr:* David A Kellermeyer
**VP:* Joe M Evans Jr
**VP:* David R Roth
Off Mgr: Ellen Roeth
Plnt Mgr: Doug Jensen
Plnt Mgr: Jim Murray

D-U-N-S 14-862-9848
NORTHERN STAR GENERATION SERVICES LLC
(*Suby of* NORTHERN STAR GENERATION LLC) ★
2929 Allen Pkwy Ste 2200, Houston, TX 77019-7112
Tel (713) 580-6300 *Founded/Ownrshp* 2007
Sales 125.9MM[E] *EMP* 220[E]
SIC 4911 Generation, electric power
CEO: Jack Browder
CFO: Wincent Scager
**VP:* Scott M Churbock
**VP:* David R Roth

*VP: Robert W Schima
*VP: David M Sims

D-U-N-S 02-372-5617 IMP/EXP
NORTHERN STAR VENTURES LLC
WORLDS BEST CHEESECAKE
10440 Leadbetter Rd, Ashland, VA 23005-3415
Tel (804) 368-0747 *Founded/Ownrshp* 2004
Sales 117.3MM^E *EMP* 90
SIC 5149 5461 Bakery products; Bakeries
CEO: John D Fernandez
VP: Woody Vickery

D-U-N-S 00-696-2419 IMP
■ **NORTHERN STATES POWER CO** (MN)
XCEL ENERGY
(*Suby of* XCEL ENERGY INC) ★
414 Nicollet Mall, Minneapolis, MN 55401-1927
Tel (612) 330-5500 *Founded/Ownrshp* 2000
Sales 4.7MMM *EMP* 3,793
SIC 4931 Electric & other services combined;
Ch Bd: Ben Fowke
*Pr: Christopher B Clark
CFO: Richard Kelly
*CFO: Teresa S Madden
Sr VP: Jeffrey S Savage

D-U-N-S 00-794-5868
■ **NORTHERN STATES POWER CO** (WI)
XCEL ENERGY
(*Suby of* XCEL ENERGY INC) ★
1414 W Hamilton Ave, Eau Claire, WI 54701-7252
Tel (715) 839-2625 *Founded/Ownrshp* 1901, 2000
Sales 956.5MM *EMP* 570
SIC 4931 Electric & other services combined;
Pr: Mark E Stoering
*Ch Bd: Benjamin G S Fowke III
*CFO: Teresa S Madden
Sr VP: Jeffrey S Savage
Netwrk Eng: Mark Larsen
Board of Directors: Marvin E McDaniel Jr

D-U-N-S 96-535-5766
■ **NORTHERN TIER ENERGY LLC**
(*Suby of* NORTHERN TIER ENERGY LP) ★
38c Grove St Ste 5, Ridgefield, CT 06877-4667
Tel (203) 244-6550 *Founded/Ownrshp* 2010
Sales 4.6MMM *EMP* 10^E
Accts Pricewaterhousecoopers Llp Ho
SIC 1311 Crude petroleum & natural gas production
CEO: David Lamp
Treas: Oscar Rodriguez
VP: Peter T Gelfman
VP: Chester J Kuchta
Store Mgr: Brian Goodwin
Dir IT: Michelle Gutwein

D-U-N-S 07-844-6962
■ **NORTHERN TIER ENERGY LP**
(*Suby of* WESTERN REFINING INC) ★
1250 W Washington St # 101, Tempe, AZ 85281-1794
Tel (602) 302-5450 *Founded/Ownrshp* 2016
Sales 3.4MMM *EMP* 2,896^E
SIC 2911 Petroleum refining
Pr: Dave L Lamp
CFO: Karen B Davis
Ex VP: Melissa M Buhrig
Sr VP: Scott L Stevens
VP: Jason Akey
VP: Rick Hastings
VP: Jack A Helmick
Opers Mgr: Ryan McNellis

D-U-N-S 82-521-0263 IMP
NORTHERN TOOL & EQUIPMENT CATALOG CO INC
NORTHERN TOOL EQUIPMENT
(*Suby of* GREAT PLAINS) ★
2800 Southcross Dr W, Burnsville, MN 55306-6936
Tel (952) 894-9510 *Founded/Ownrshp* 1994
Sales 199.8MM^E *EMP* 1,600
SIC 5961 Tools & hardware, mail order
CEO: Donald L Kotula
*Pr: Charles Albrecht

D-U-N-S 09-979-1493 IMP/EXP
NORTHERN TOOL & EQUIPMENT CO INC
GREAT PLAINS
2800 Southcross Dr W, Burnsville, MN 55306-6936
Tel (952) 894-9510 *Founded/Ownrshp* 1980
Sales 749.2MM^E *EMP* 2,000
SIC 5961 5251 Tools & hardware, mail order; General merchandise, mail order; Hardware
CEO: Donald L Kotula
Ch Bd: Julie Gathern
*Pr: Charles Albrecht
COO: Todd Gulbranson
*CFO: Tom Ericson
Sr VP: Mark Kauffman
VP: John Bakke
VP: Jay Berlin
VP: Scott Carlson
VP: Al Kotula
VP: Bill Perizzo
VP: John Rose
VP: Dennis Shockro
Exec: Chris Erath
Exec: Nathan Miller
Dir Soc: Eric Randa

NORTHERN TOOL EQUIPMENT
See NORTHERN TOOL & EQUIPMENT CATALOG CO INC

D-U-N-S 00-693-1968 IMP
■ **NORTHERN TRUST CO** (DE)
(*Suby of* NORTHERN TRUST CORP) ★
50 S La Salle St, Chicago, IL 60603-1003
Tel (312) 630-6000 *Founded/Ownrshp* 1984
Sales NA *EMP* 8,000
SIC 6021 National commercial banks
Pr: J C Goodall Jr
Pr: Robert Baillie
Pr: Ken Jatczak
Pr: Frederick H Waddell
CFO: Steven L Fradkin
Treas: William R Dodds Jr
Ofcr: Laura Doggett
Trst Ofcr: Frank E Loomis
Ex VP: Sherry S Barrat
Ex VP: David C Blowers
Ex VP: S Biff Bowman
Ex VP: Penelope J Briggs
Ex VP: Jeffrey D Cohodes
Ex VP: Marianne G Doan
Ex VP: James Draths
Ex VP: John Jeffrey Kauffman
Ex VP: Wilson Leech
Ex VP: Connie L Lindsey
Ex VP: Lyle L Logan
Ex VP: Hugh R Magill
Ex VP: R Hugh Magill
Board of Directors: William D Smithburg, Linda Walker Bynoe, Enrique J Sosa, Nicholas D Chabraja, Charles A Tribbett III, Susan Crown, Frederick H Waddell, Arthur L Kelly, Robert C McCormack, Edward J Mooney, William A Osborn, John W Rowe, Harold B Smith

D-U-N-S 05-943-9083 IMP
▲ **NORTHERN TRUST CORP**
50 S La Salle St, Chicago, IL 60603-1003
Tel (312) 630-6000 *Founded/Ownrshp* 1971
Sales NA *EMP* 16,200
Tkr Sym NTRS *Exch* NGS
SIC 6022 State commercial banks
Ch Bd: Frederick H Waddell
Pr: Jonathan Hershman
Pr: Lori Lewis
Pr: Vivek Menon
Pr: William L Morrison
COO: Jana R Schreuder
CFO: S Biff Bowman
CFO: Stephen B Bowman
Chf Cred: Debra Mairs
Chf Inves: James Grinney
Chf Inves: Richard Pell
Ofcr: Deborah Smith
Trst Ofcr: Lloyd Sebastian
Trst Ofcr: Susie Torres
Assoc VP: Andrea Jenkins
Ex VP: Penny Biggs
Ex VP: Aileen B Blake
Ex VP: James Brand
Ex VP: Robert P Browne
Ex VP: Danny Carpenter
Ex VP: Peter B Cherecwich
Board of Directors: Donald Thompson, Linda Walker Bynoe, Charles A Tribbett III, Susan Crown, Dean M Harrison, Jay L Henderson, Jose Luis Prado, Thomas E Richards, John W Rowe, Martin P Slark, David H B Smith Jr

D-U-N-S 07-299-8032
■ **NORTHERN UTAH HEALTHCARE CORP**
ST MARK'S HOSPITAL
(*Suby of* HOSPITAL COPORATION OF AMERICA) ★
1200 E 3900 S, Salt Lake City, UT 84124-1300
Tel (801) 268-7111 *Founded/Ownrshp* 1994
Sales 341.7MM *EMP* 1,600
SIC 8062 8082 8011 General medical & surgical hospitals; Home health care services; Neurologist
CEO: John Hanshaw
Chf Rad: Ronald Miller
*Pr: Samuel N Hazen
*CFO: Brian McKenley
VP: Jesse Cordova
VP: Kathy Watt
Exec: Peggy Hanover
Dir Risk M: Pauline Parker
Dir Lab: Suzanne Wade
Dir Rx: Dennis Long
CIO: Bruk Kammerman

D-U-N-S 15-368-0277 IMP
NORTHERN VIDEO SYSTEMS INC
TRI-ED/NORTHERN VIDEO
(*Suby of* TRI-ED/NORTHERN VIDEO) ★
135 Cronyways Park Dr Ste 101, Woodbury, NY 11797
Tel (516) 941-2800 *Founded/Ownrshp* 1986
Sales 114.0MM^E *EMP* 260
SIC 5065 Closed circuit television; Video equipment, electronic; Security control equipment & systems; Radio receiving & transmitting tubes
CEO: Steven Roth
*Pr: Mark Haney
*CFO: Paul Haney
*Ex VP: James Rothstein

D-U-N-S 00-794-0356
NORTHERN VIRGINIA ELECTRIC COOPERATIVE (VA)
N O V E C
10323 Lomond Dr, Manassas, VA 20109-3113
Tel (703) 335-0500 *Founded/Ownrshp* 1976, 1983
Sales 433.0MM *EMP* 275
SIC 4911 8611 8741 4939 Distribution, electric power; Business associations; Management services; Combination utilities
Pr: Stanley C Feuerberg
*CFO: Wilbur Rollins
VP: Patti Neal
VP: Wilber Rollin
VP: Wilber Rollins
VP Bus Dev: Mike Dailey
Exec: Marlane Parsons
Prgrm Mgr: Abbas Kazmi
Dir IT: Howard M Spinner
Info Man: Mark Gayda
Mtls Mgr: Kent R Cassell

D-U-N-S 96-162-0643
NORTHERN VIRGINIA SURGERY CENTER II LLC
(*Suby of* INOVA FAIRFAX HOSPITAL) ★
3620 Joseph Siewick Dr # 406, Fairfax, VA 22033-1761
Tel (703) 766-6960 *Founded/Ownrshp* 2002
Sales 71.7MM^E *EMP* 2,247^E
SIC 8011 Ambulatory surgical center
Ofcr: Mary Lindsay

D-U-N-S 07-780-8087
NORTHERN VIRGINIA TRANSPORTATION COMMISSION
2300 Wilson Blvd Ste 620, Arlington, VA 22201-5426
Tel (703) 524-3322 *Founded/Ownrshp* 1964
Sales 178.6MM *EMP* 9
Accts Pbgh Llp Hrrisonburg Va
SIC 4111 Bus line operations
Pr: Richard K Taube

D-U-N-S 07-871-6123 IMP
NORTHERN WESTCHESTER HOSPITAL ASSOCIATION (NY)
400 E Main St, Mount Kisco, NY 10549-3477
Tel (914) 666-1200 *Founded/Ownrshp* 1916
Sales 250.6MM *EMP* 1,000^E
SIC 8062 General medical & surgical hospitals
Pr: Joel Seligman
Ofcr: Brian Blaufeux
*Sr VP: Marla Koroly
*Sr VP: John Partenza
*Sr VP: Lauraine Szekely
VP: Teresa Alongi
*VP: Michael Caruso
VP: Mike Caruso
VP Bus: Sue Etkin
Exec: Carlos Forcade
Dir OR: Stephanie Vogel-Rosenthal
Dir Inf Cn: Kristine Goldstein
Dir Risk M: Kathryn Griffin
Dir Rx: Anthony Luppino

D-U-N-S 80-040-7178
▲ **NORTHFIELD BANCORP INC**
581 Main St, Woodbridge, NJ 07095-1148
Tel (732) 499-7200 *Founded/Ownrshp* 2010
Sales NA *EMP* 326^E
Accts Kpmg Llp Short Hills New Jer
Tkr Sym NFBK *Exch* NGS
SIC 6035 Savings institutions, federally chartered; Federal savings & loan associations; Federal savings banks
Ch Bd: John W Alexander
*Pr: Steven M Klein
CFO: William R Jacobs
Ofcr: Kenneth J Doherty
Ex VP: Robin Lefkowitz
Ex VP: Michael J Widmer
Sr VP: Denny John
VP: Judith Calabrese
VP: Jim Castelletti
VP: Douglas Doerr
VP: Angela Ho
VP: Angelo Verrone

D-U-N-S 14-057-8548
NORTHFIELD HOSPITAL & SKILLED NURSING
2000 North Ave, Northfield, MN 55057-1498
Tel (507) 646-1000 *Founded/Ownrshp* 1910
Sales 87.6MM *EMP* 500^E
SIC 8062 General medical & surgical hospitals
Pr: Mary Crow
QA Dir: Ann Reuter
Opers Supe: Melissa Neil
Pharmcst: Beth Alexander

D-U-N-S 19-543-0103
■ **NORTHFIELD INSURANCE CO**
(*Suby of* NORTHLAND INSURANCE CO) ★
385 Washington St, Saint Paul, MN 55102-1309
Tel (651) 310-4100 *Founded/Ownrshp* 2007
Sales NA *EMP* 25
SIC 6331 Property damage insurance
Pr: Randall Dean Jones
VP: Robert Northrop Billings
VP: Kenneth Lee Brendle
VP: David Joseph Brick
VP: David Edward Byrne
VP: Larry Burton Colburn
VP: Weston Stanley Day
VP: Gregory Kevin Erickson
VP: Cheryl Olga Peters
VP: David Lee Pickard
VP: Dennis Merton Sager
VP: Robert Bruce Spanfelner
VP: Allen Jon Stendahl
VP: Barbara Lou Sutherland
VP: Daniel John Zaborsky

D-U-N-S 02-057-2459
NORTHFIELD SAVINGS BANK
(*Suby of* NSB HOLDING CORP)
1731 Victory Blvd, Staten Island, NY 10314-3511
Tel (718) 448-1000 *Founded/Ownrshp* 1887
Sales NA *EMP* 127
SIC 6036 State savings banks, not federally chartered
Ch Bd: John Alexander
*CFO: Stephen Klein
*Ex VP: Kenneth Doherty
Sr VP: William Jacobs
*Sr VP: Robin Lefkowitz
Sr VP: Kevin McCloskey
*Sr VP: Jeffrey Schnorbus
Sr VP: Michael Widmer
VP: Maureen Deangelo
VP: Irene Greenman
VP: Richard Maida
VP: Angie Tsirkas

D-U-N-S 04-873-6425 IMP
NORTHGATE GONZALEZ INC
CORPORATE OFFICE
1201 N Magnolia Ave, Anaheim, CA 92801-2609
Tel (714) 778-3784 *Founded/Ownrshp* 1980
Sales 266.7MM^E *EMP* 900
SIC 5411 Grocery stores, independent
Pr: Miguel Gonzalez Jr
Sr VP: Carl Middleton
*VP: Jose Gonzalez
Store Dir: Alex Diaz
Store Dir: Irma Salcido
QA Dir: Robert Maldonado
Dir IT: Brenda Austin

D-U-N-S 79-649-7456 IMP
NORTHGATE GONZALEZ LLC
NORTHGATE MARKET
1201 N Magnolia Ave, Anaheim, CA 92801-2609
Tel (714) 778-3784 *Founded/Ownrshp* 2006
Sales 71.8MM^E *EMP* 4,000
SIC 5411 Grocery stores

NORTHGATE HLTH RHBLITATION CTR
See SSC SAN ANTONIO NORTHGATE OPERATING CO LLC

NORTHGATE MARKET
See NORTHGATE GONZALEZ LLC

NORTHHAMPTON CROSSING
See RRERF REGENCY PARK LLC

D-U-N-S 00-624-8868 IMP
NORTHLAND ALUMINUM PRODUCTS INC
NORDIC WARE
5005 Highway 7, Minneapolis, MN 55416-2274
Tel (952) 924-8505 *Founded/Ownrshp* 1962
Sales 159.4MM^E *EMP* 350
SIC 3089 3479 Kitchenware, plastic; Coating of metals & formed products
CEO: David Dalquist
*CFO: Dave Hopkins
*Ch: Dorothy Dalquist
VP: Gene Karlson
CTO: Jamie Aker
Dir IT: Linda Olson
Plnt Mgr: Ron Jansen
Sls&Mrk Ex: Nate Burgau
Mktg Mgr: Dana Norsten
Sales Asso: Christine Cook

D-U-N-S 00-194-6482
■ **NORTHLAND CO**
NORTHLAND INSURANCE
(*Suby of* TRAVELERS INSURANCE) ★
385 Washington St, Saint Paul, MN 55102-1309
Tel (800) 328-5972 *Founded/Ownrshp* 1937, 2000
Sales NA *EMP* 15,000
SIC 6331 6162 6531 Fire, marine & casualty insurance & carriers; Mortgage bankers; Real estate managers
Ch Bd: Edward H Hamm
*Pr: Gene G Gopon
*Treas: William C Peterson
Board of Directors: Norman Berg, Clarence G Frame, Robert E Grant

D-U-N-S 10-584-9798 IMP
NORTHLAND INDUSTRIAL TRUCK CO INC
NITCO
6 Jonspin Rd, Wilmington, MA 01887-4408
Tel (978) 658-5900 *Founded/Ownrshp* 1983
Sales 101.7MM^E *EMP* 265
SIC 5084 7699 7359

NORTHLAND INSURANCE
See NORTHLAND CO

D-U-N-S 00-787-3409
■ **NORTHLAND INSURANCE CO**
(*Suby of* JUPITER HOLDINGS INC) ★
385 Washington St, Saint Paul, MN 55102-1309
Tel (651) 310-4100 *Founded/Ownrshp* 2000
Sales NA *EMP* 247
SIC 6331 Property damage insurance
Pr: Brian Maclean
*CFO: Jay Benet
*Treas: Mario Olivo
Ofcr: Robert Long
Mng Dir: Steve Perovich
Mng Dir: Robert D Taylor
Genl Mgr: Carmela Garlow
QA Dir: Samantha Lycha
VP Mktg: Scott Schaefers
Snr Mgr: Sandy Schwan

D-U-N-S 06-661-8125
NORTHLAND INVESTMENT CORP
2150 Washington St # 300, Newton, MA 02462-1443
Tel (617) 965-7100 *Founded/Ownrshp* 1970
Sales 320.9MM^E *EMP* 425
Accts Metis Group Cpas Llc New Yor
SIC 6799 6411 6531 Real estate investors, except property operators; Advisory services, insurance; Real estate managers
Ch: Lawrence Gottesdiener
Pr: Robert Gatof
CEO: Steven P Rosenthal
CFO: AMI Fatula
CFO: Terence McNally
Sr VP: Kevin Bell
Sr VP: Suzanne M Bonito
VP: Bruce Noland
VP: Brad Swinnerton
Sys/Dir: Willow Cunningham

D-U-N-S 15-147-0317
NORTHLAND TELECOMMUNICATIONS CORP
101 Stewart St Ste 700, Seattle, WA 98101-2449
Tel (206) 621-1351 *Founded/Ownrshp* 1985
Sales 99.3MM^E *EMP* 450
SIC 4841 7371 Cable television services; Computer software development
Ch Bd: John S Whetzell
*Treas: Richard I Clark

D-U-N-S 07-841-0262
NORTHPOINT DEVELOPMENT LLC
4825 Nw 41st St Ste 500, Riverside, MO 64150-7806
Tel (816) 888-7380 *Founded/Ownrshp* 2004
Sales 100.0MM *EMP* 50
SIC 6552 6531 Land subdividers & developers, commercial; Real estate agent, commercial
CEO: Nathaniel Hagedorn
COO: Chad Meyer
CFO: Brett Grady
VP: Brent Miles
Off Mgr: Rene Halterman

NORTHPOINT FORD
See ASBURY AUTOMOTIVE ARKANSAS DEALERSHIP HOLDINGS LLC

D-U-N-S 61-429-9993
NORTHPOINT MORTGAGE CORP
10002 101st Ave, Ozone Park, NY 11416-2609
Tel (718) 641-7000 *Founded/Ownrshp* 2000
Sales NA *EMP* 3
SIC 6162 Mortgage brokers, using own money

Pr: Attique Rehman
Off Mgr: Stephania Renz

D-U-N-S 01-033-0969
NORTHPOINT PROPERTY MANAGEMENT LLC
55 Lake St Ste 4, Nashua, NH 03060-4516
Tel (603) 594-2300 *Founded/Ownrshp* 2008
Sales 128.0MM *EMP* 23
SIC 8641 6531 Condominium association; Condominium manager

D-U-N-S 62-250-5659
▲ NORTHRIM BANCORP INC
3111 C St, Anchorage, AK 99503-3901
Tel (907) 562-0062 *Founded/Ownrshp* 1990
Sales NA *EMP* 297[E]
Accts Moss Adams Llp Portland Oreg
Tkr Sym NRIM *Exch* NGS
SIC 6022 6282 State commercial banks; Investment advisory service
Pr: Joseph M Beedle
**Ch Bd:* R Marc Langland
COO: Joseph M Schierhorn
CFO: Latosha M Frye
Ex VP: Steven L Hartung
Ex VP: Michael Martin
Sr VP: Ramona Evers
Sr VP: Camilla Forstner
Sr VP: Debra Shannon
Sr VP: Suzanne Whittle
VP: Leonard F Horst
Board of Directors: Larry S Cash, Mark G Copeland, Anthony Drabek, Karl L Hanneman, David W Karp, David J McCambridge, John C Swalling, Linda C Thomas, David G Wight

D-U-N-S 96-735-6127
▲ NORTHROP GRUMMAN CORP
2980 Fairview Park Dr, Falls Church, VA 22042-4511
Tel (703) 280-2900 *Founded/Ownrshp* 1939
Sales 23.5MMM *EMP* 65,000[E]
Accts Deloitte & Touche Llp Mclean
Tkr Sym NOC *Exch* NYS
SIC 3812 Search & navigation equipment
Ch Bd: Wesley G Bush
Pr: Kenneth Bedingfield
COO: Gloria A Flach
CFO: Kenneth L Beddingfield
CFO: Kenneth L Bedingfield
Treas: Precious Haines
Ofcr: Denise M Peppard
Ofcr: Doreen Schefer
VP: Patrick M Antkowiak
VP: M Sidney Ashworth
VP: Jaime Bohnke
VP: Mark A Caylor
VP: Sheila C Cheston
VP: Jerry Dodd
VP: Carol Erikson
VP: Monty Frahm
VP: Gene Fraser
VP: Brad Furukawa
VP: Michael A Hardesty
VP: Michael Hinkey
VP: Christopher T Jones
Board of Directors: Gary Roughead, Marianne C Brown, Thomas M Schoewe, Victor H Fazio, James S Turley, Donald E Felsinger, Mark A Welsh III, Ann Marie Fudge, Bruce S Gordon, William H Hernandez, Madeleine A Kleiner, Karl J Krapek, Richard B Myers

D-U-N-S 00-690-3900
■ NORTHROP GRUMMAN ENTERPRISE MANAGEMENT SERVICES CORP (DE)
(*Suby of* NORTHROP GRUMMAN TECHNICAL SERVICES INC) ★
2340 Dulles Corner Blvd, Herndon, VA 20171-3400
Tel (703) 713-4000 *Founded/Ownrshp* 2011
Sales 42.1MM[E] *EMP* 3,000
SIC 8741 8744 4731 8331 7349 Business management; Facilities support services; Foreign freight forwarding; Skill training center; Building cleaning service
Pr: George R Petteys
**Pr:* Patricia Parrish
**Treas:* Edward L Bennardo
**Treas:* James L Sanford
**VP:* Alan R Cocks
**VP:* Marsha A Klontz
**VP:* Gary W McKenzie
**VP:* Edward Shedlick
**VP:* William A Warren
**VP:* Kathleen A Weigand

NORTHROP GRUMMAN INFO SYSTEMS
See NORTHROP GRUMMAN INFORMATION TECHNOLOGY INC

D-U-N-S 62-148-6781
■ NORTHROP GRUMMAN INFORMATION TECHNOLOGY GLOBAL CORP
DEFENSE
(*Suby of* NORTHROP GRUMMAN SYSTEMS CORP) ★
7575 Colshire Dr, Mc Lean, VA 22102-7508
Tel (703) 556-3187 *Founded/Ownrshp* 2009
Sales 37.2MM[E] *EMP* 1,000
SIC 8733 Scientific research agency
CEO: Jim O'Neill
**Pr:* Kent Schneider
**VP:* Mark Gagen
VP: Michele Toth
VP: Carol Zierhoffer

D-U-N-S 05-227-2044
■ NORTHROP GRUMMAN INFORMATION TECHNOLOGY INC
NORTHROP GRUMMAN INFO SYSTEMS
(*Suby of* NORTHROP GRUMMAN SYSTEMS CORP) ★
7575 Colshire Dr, Mc Lean, VA 22102-7508
Tel (703) 556-1000 *Founded/Ownrshp* 1978
Sales 972.6MM[E] *EMP* 24,000
SIC 7373 7372 8733 Computer integrated systems design; Prepackaged software; Scientific research agency
Pr: Linda Amills
**Pr:* Herb W Anderson
Pr: Jay Grove
**CFO:* Steve Movius
**VP:* Nils Ericson
VP: John Huff
VP: Catherine Kuenzel
**VP:* James Mmyers
**VP:* David Lryan
VP: Zaki Saleh
**VP:* Michael Rtwyman
**VP:* Kathy Warden
**VP:* Karen Awilliams
Dir Risk M: Andrew S Harasim

D-U-N-S 60-229-5933 IMP
■ NORTHROP GRUMMAN MARITIME SYSTEMS
(*Suby of* TITAN II INC) ★
1070 Seminole Trl, Charlottesville, VA 22901-2827
Tel (434) 974-2000 *Founded/Ownrshp* 2002
Sales 97.0MM[E] *EMP* 500[E]
SIC 5088 Marine propulsion machinery & equipment
VP: Michael S Dunn
COO: Dhanvant Goradia
CFO: Ron Pugh
**Treas:* Steven D Spiegel
**VP:* Rudolph L Linde
VP: Matthew Mulherin
Exec: Carl Miller

D-U-N-S 14-989-9957 IMP/EXP
■ NORTHROP GRUMMAN NEWPORT NEWS INC
NEWPORT NEWS SHIPBUILDING
(*Suby of* TITAN II INC) ★
4101 Washington Ave, Newport News, VA 23607-2734
Tel (757) 380-2000 *Founded/Ownrshp* 2001
Sales 35.3M[E] *EMP* 18,000
SIC 3731 Shipbuilding & repairing; Submarines, building & repairing; Military ships, building & repairing; Tankers, building & repairing
Pr: Mike Petters
CFO: Linda Leukhardt
Treas: James Sanford
Ex VP: Daniel Arczynski
Ex VP: Matthew Mulherin
**VP:* Bharat Amin
**VP:* Ray Bagley
VP: Bill Bell
VP: Marty Chanik
VP: Stephen Clarkson
VP: Jerri Dickseski
VP: William Ebbs
VP: Irwin Edenzon
VP: Bill Ermatinger
VP: Jerri Fuller
VP: Bruce Hawthorne
VP: Jimmie Haygood
VP: Danny Hunley
VP: Doug Lounsberry
VP: Frank Martin
VP: John Mazach

D-U-N-S 00-417-9453 IMP/EXP
■ NORTHROP GRUMMAN SPACE & MISSION SYSTEMS CORP
(*Suby of* NORTHROP GRUMMAN CORP) ★
6377 San Ignacio Ave, San Jose, CA 95119-1200
Tel (703) 280-2900 *Founded/Ownrshp* 1901, 2011
Sales 1.6MMM[E] *EMP* 12,000
SIC 7373 3663 3661 3812 3761 Computer integrated systems design; Radio & TV communications equipment; Telephone & telegraph apparatus; Defense systems & equipment; Guided missiles & space vehicles
Pr: Robert M Hamje
Pr: Jeanne Usher
Ex VP: William K Maciven
Sr VP: Nick Barnes
VP: Ron Foudray
VP: Elizabeth D Iversen
VP: John Jadik
VP: S Lunn
VP: Daniel J McClain
VP: Steven McCoy
VP: George R Petteys
VP: G C Roman
VP: David Rosener
VP: Joe G Taylor
VP: Scott Winship
VP: Sandra Wright

D-U-N-S 00-825-5408 IMP/EXP
■ NORTHROP GRUMMAN SYSTEMS CORP
(*Suby of* NORTHROP GRUMMAN CORP) ★
2980 Fairview Park Dr, Falls Church, VA 22042-4511
Tel (703) 280-2900 *Founded/Ownrshp* 1985
Sales 9.1MMM[E] *EMP* 40,000[E]
SIC 3721 3761 3728 3812 3825 4581 Airplanes, fixed or rotary wing; Research & development on aircraft by the manufacturer; Guided missiles, complete; Guided missiles & space vehicles, research & development; Fuselage assembly, aircraft; Wing assemblies & parts, aircraft; Research & dev by manuf., aircraft parts & auxiliary equip; Inertial guidance systems; Gyroscopes; Warfare counter-measure equipment; Search & detection systems & instruments; Test equipment for electronic & electrical circuits; Aircraft servicing & repairing
CEO: Wesley G Bush
**Pr:* Mark Rabinowitz
CFO: James L Sanford
Treas: Albert F Myers
Treas: Ronald P Vargo
VP: Robert Brammer
VP: Rosanne Brien
VP: James L Cameron
VP: Gary W Ervin
VP: T A Gasparini
VP: Ed Halibozek
VP: C T Harvie
**VP:* Gary W McKenzie
VP: Linda A Mills
VP: C Michael Peters
VP: James F Pitts
VP: W A Warren
VP: Kathleen A Weigand
VP: Carol Zierhoffer

D-U-N-S 05-906-9211
■ NORTHROP GRUMMAN TECHNICAL SERVICES INC
(*Suby of* NORTHROP GRUMMAN CORP) ★
2340 Dulles Corner Blvd, Herndon, VA 20171-3400
Tel (703) 713-4096 *Founded/Ownrshp* 1973
Sales 492.9MM[E] *EMP* 4,745
SIC 4581 7699 Aircraft maintenance & repair services; Aircraft servicing & repairing; Aircraft & heavy equipment repair services
CEO: Wes Bush
**Pr:* Gregory J Donley
**Pr:* Thomas E Vice
**Treas:* Mark Rabinowitz
Ofcr: Marty Kirwan
**VP:* Sid Ashworth
**VP:* Mark Caylor
**VP:* Sheila C Cheston
**VP:* Martin Clark
**VP:* Gloria A Flach
**VP:* David Harvey
**VP:* Stephen Movius
**VP:* Edgar Smith
**VP:* Louise Ussery

NORTHRUP SUPPLY
See IRR SUPPLY CENTERS INC

D-U-N-S 60-355-7687 EXP
■ NORTHSHORE MINING CO
CLIFFS
(*Suby of* CLIFFS NATURAL RESOURCES INC) ★
1100 Superior Ave E # 1500, Cleveland, OH 44114-2544
Tel (216) 694-5700 *Founded/Ownrshp* 1994
Sales 425.4MM[E] *EMP* 500
SIC 1011 4931 Iron ore mining; Iron ore preparation; Electric & other services combined
VP: Donald R Prahl
Area Mgr: Ralland W Hess
Area Mgr: Peter Judd
Area Mgr: Conor M McCue
Area Mgr: Matthew W REA
Snr Mgr: Gabe Johnson

D-U-N-S 08-148-0964
NORTHSHORE SCHOOL DISTRICT
3330 Monte Villa Pkwy, Bothell, WA 98021-8972
Tel (425) 408-6000 *Founded/Ownrshp* 1958
Sales 266.1MM *EMP* 2,312
Accts Troy Kelley Olympia Wa
SIC 8211 Public elementary & secondary schools; Public senior high school; Public junior high school; Public elementary school
Bd of Dir: Sheila Guard
Ex Dir: Carmin Dalziel
Dir Sec: Robert Noll
Genl Mgr: Angie Brown
Genl Mgr: Lydia Sellie
Off Mgr: Stacia Miller
Off Mgr: Judy Mitchell
IT Man: Rose Hertzog
Opers Mgr: Jon Wiederspan
Pr Dir: Casey Henry
Schl Brd P: Janet Quinn

D-U-N-S 80-702-8451
NORTHSHORE SCHOOL DST 112
1936 Green Bay Rd, Highland Park, IL 60035-3112
Tel (224) 765-3000 *Founded/Ownrshp* 1993
Sales 95.4MM *EMP* 618
Accts Baker Tilly Virchow Krause Ll
SIC 8211 Public elementary school; Public junior high school
**CFO:* Mohsin Dada

D-U-N-S 06-949-0621
NORTHSHORE UNIVERSITY HEALTHSYSTEM
EVANSTON HOSPITAL
1301 Central St, Evanston, IL 60201-1613
Tel (847) 570-5295 *Founded/Ownrshp* 1891
Sales 1.8MMM[E] *EMP* 9,000
SIC 5912 Drug stores
Pr: Mark R Neaman
V Ch: Gregory K Jones
**Pr:* Raymond Grady
COO: JP Gallagher
**COO:* Jeffrey Hillebrand
CFO: Sue Allan
Ch: Julian E Bailes
**Chf Cred:* Harry Jones Sr
VP: Gina Cialoni
VP: Brian Washa
Adm Dir: Sally Faulkner

D-U-N-S 79-074-3140
■ NORTHSIDE HOSPITAL
HCA
(*Suby of* HOSPITAL COPORATION OF AMERICA) ★
6000 49th St N, Saint Petersburg, FL 33709-2145
Tel (727) 521-4411 *Founded/Ownrshp* 1976
Sales 160.1MM *EMP* 340
SIC 8031 8011 8069 8062 Offices & clinics of osteopathic physicians; Offices & clinics of medical doctors; Specialty hospitals, except psychiatric; General medical & surgical hospitals
CEO: Dia Nichols
**CEO:* Stephen J Daugherty
**COO:* Jayme Chancellor
**CFO:* Gary Searls
IT Man: Kirk Hendricks
Doctor: Catherine A Phillips MD
Pharmcst: Sally Daoul
Pharmcst: Eliza Hoernle
Pharmcst: Lo-An Pham

D-U-N-S 06-918-9801
NORTHSIDE HOSPITAL - CHEROKEE INC (GA)
N H
(*Suby of* NORTHSIDE HOSPITAL-ATLANTA) ★
201 Hospital Rd, Canton, GA 30114-2408
Tel (770) 720-5100 *Founded/Ownrshp* 1997
Sales 184.9MM *EMP* 575
SIC 8062 General medical & surgical hospitals
CEO: William M Hayes
Chf Path: Richard E Fingerle
Pr: Leah Allen
COO: Cynthia Foust
**CFO:* Steve Hudson
CFO: Brian Jennette
Dir Inf Cn: Sybil Gayton
Dir Case M: Jodi Ochler
Dir Lab: Sue Tidwell
CIO: Bill Dunford
Pharmcst: Robert Allen

D-U-N-S 08-969-7395
NORTHSIDE HOSPITAL INC
NORTHSIDE HOSPITAL-ATLANTA
1000 Johnson Ferry Rd, Atlanta, GA 30342-1611
Tel (404) 851-8000 *Founded/Ownrshp* 1970
Sales 1.7MMM *EMP* 8,000
SIC 8062 General medical & surgical hospitals
CEO: Robert T Quattrocchi
**CFO:* Debbie Mitcham
CFO: Debbie Mitchum
Ofcr: Cynthia Bennett
VP: Chuck Dalton
VP: Lee Echols
VP: Doug Macdonald
Nurse Mgr: Simone Cambridge
Snr Ntwrk: Mario Eury
Dir IT: Kirk Hendrick
IT Man: Sarah Brown

NORTHSIDE HOSPITAL-ATLANTA
See NORTHSIDE HOSPITAL INC

D-U-N-S 06-945-0716
NORTHSIDE INDEPENDENT SCHOOL DISTRICT
5900 Evers Rd, San Antonio, TX 78238-1606
Tel (210) 397-8770 *Founded/Ownrshp* 1949
Sales 1.0MMM *EMP* 13,698
Accts Weaver And Tidwell Llp Austi
SIC 8211 Public elementary & secondary schools; Public elementary school; Public junior high school; Public senior high school
**Pr:* Robert Blount Jr
CFO: Alisa Thienpont
Bd of Dir: Randall H Fields
VP: David Halbert
**VP:* Katie N Reed
Prin: Ellen Sutton
Genl Mgr: Patrick Garcia
MIS Dir: Erika Foester
Dir IT: Kellye Halpern
IT Man: John King
Teacher Pr: Cecil Tatum

NORTHSTAR AEROSPACE CHICAGO
See HELIGEAR ACQUISITION CO

D-U-N-S 07-942-0909
▲ NORTHSTAR ASSET MANAGEMENT GROUP INC
399 Park Ave Fl 18, New York, NY 10022-4968
Tel (212) 547-2600 *Founded/Ownrshp* 2014
Sales 435.8MM *EMP* 383[E]
Tkr Sym NSAM *Exch* NYS
SIC 8741 6531 6282 Management services; Real estate managers; Investment advice
Pr: Albert Tylis
CFO: Debra A Hess
Ch: David T Hamamoto
Ofcr: Daniel R Gilbert
Ex VP: Ronald J Lieberman
Board of Directors: Stephen E Cummings, Judith A Hannaway, Oscar Junquera, Justin Metz, Wesley D Minami, Louis J Paglia

D-U-N-S 06-636-5263
NORTHSTAR BANK OF TEXAS
(*Suby of* CARLILE BANCSHARES INC) ★
1300 S University Dr # 100, Fort Worth, TX 76107-5737
Tel (940) 591-1200 *Founded/Ownrshp* 2011
Sales NA *EMP* 500
SIC 6022 State commercial banks
CEO: Tom Nichols
**Pr:* Tony Clark
Pr: Matthew Steward
CFO: Randy Fahm
**Treas:* Judy Leveridge
Ofcr: Caitlin Brule
Ofcr: Lupe Ramirez
Ofcr: Christopher Rios
Ofcr: Mark Stuart
Ofcr: Melanie Vowell
Ofcr: Lisa Waters
Ex VP: Terry Almon
Ex VP: Greg Studer
Sr VP: William Bachino
**Sr VP:* Rita Bennett
Sr VP: Angela Duwe
Sr VP: Trenna Ezzell
Sr VP: Chris Farmer
Sr VP: Debbie Irby
Sr VP: Ralph Ramsey
Sr VP: Randal Sahm

D-U-N-S 01-033-6530 IMP/EXP
NORTHSTAR BATTERY CO LLC (MO)
4000 E Continental Way, Springfield, MO 65803-8801
Tel (417) 575-8200 *Founded/Ownrshp* 2000
Sales 170.0MM *EMP* 458
SIC 3692 Primary batteries, dry & wet
Pr: Jerry Hoffman
**COO:* Joel Gibson
**CFO:* Hans AF Silln
VP: John Semeniuk
**VP:* Thierry Tardivent
IT Man: David Leclaire
Sfty Dirs: Tom Price
Ql Cn Mgr: Carlos Estrada
Ql Cn Mgr: Michael Rossi
Natl Sales: Ray Goodearl
Sls Mgr: Grant Bell

D-U-N-S 19-855-6276
NORTHSTAR DEMOLITION AND REMEDIATION LP
(*Suby of* NORTHSTAR GROUP SERVICES INC) ★
404 N Berry St, Brea, CA 92821-3104
Tel (714) 672-3500 *Founded/Ownrshp* 2014
Sales 201.6MM[E] *EMP* 708

SIC 1795 1799 8744 Wrecking & demolition work; Decontamination services;
Genl Mgr: Jose Alonso
Pr: Subhas Khara
CFO: Duane Kerr
VP: Joseph Delahunty
VP: Trent Michaels
VP: Charles J Myers
VP: Philip Truedinger
Dir Bus: John Estrada
Brnch Mgr: Donald B McGlamery
IT Man: Sharon Katsiroumbas

D-U-N-S 07-959-5753
NORTHSTAR GROUP HOLDINGS LLC
370 7th Ave Ste 1803, New York, NY 10001-3969
Tel (212) 951-3660 Founded/Ownrshp 2014
Sales 371.8MM^E EMP 3,500
SIC 1795 Demolition, buildings & other structures
CEO: Scott E State
*Pr: Gregory G Dicarlo
*Pr: Subhas Kahara
*CFO: Paul S Cutrone
Board of Directors: Tim Bernardez, Richard Ferrucci, Gerald Girardi, Robert Hogan, Michael Nibarger, Jason Scheir, Brian Simmons, Irene Wang

D-U-N-S 18-140-5994 IMP
NORTHSTAR GROUP SERVICES INC
(Suby of LVI PARENT CORP) ★
370 7th Ave Ste 1803, New York, NY 10001-3969
Tel (212) 951-3660 Founded/Ownrshp 1986
Sales 565.7MM^E EMP 2,630
SIC 1795 1799 Demolition, buildings & other structures; Asbestos removal & encapsulation
CFO: Paul Cutrone
*Pr: Scott E State
*CFO: Paul S Cutrone
*VP: Gregory G Dicarlo
*VP: John Leonard
*VP: Kamal Sookram
*VP: Gary Thibodeaux
VP Sls: Teresa Felder

D-U-N-S 07-861-3674
NORTHSTAR HEALTHCARE INCOME INC
399 Park Ave Fl 18, New York, NY 10022-4968
Tel (212) 547-2600 Founded/Ownrshp 2012
Sales 111.2MM EMP 2
Accts Grant Thornton Llp New York
SIC 6798 Real estate investment trusts
CEO: Ronald J Jeanneault
Ch Bd: Daniel R Gilbert
V Ch Bd: James F Flaherty III
Exec: Cameron Groah
Exec: John Mielke
Exec: Owen Mulvaney
Exec: Courtney Rosepink
Exec: Ted Yeo

D-U-N-S 80-360-1165
NORTHSTAR MEMORIAL GROUP LLC
N S M G
1900 Saint James Pl # 300, Houston, TX 77056-4128
Tel (713) 979-9690 Founded/Ownrshp 2007
Sales 146.7MM^E EMP 550^E
SIC 8748 Business consulting
Sr VP: Detlef Taylor
Sr VP: Donna Wagner
Genl Mgr: John Bokas
Genl Mgr: John Roemmelt
Off Mgr: Tessa Armbrister
Off Mgr: Jo Green
Off Mgr: Cindy Gruber
Off Mgr: Lara Lefebvre
CIO: Michael Zislis
VP Opers: David Jenkins
VP Opers: David Salove

D-U-N-S 07-991-8577
NORTHSTAR REALTY EUROPE CORP
399 Park Ave Fl 18, New York, NY 10022-4968
Tel (212) 547-2600 Founded/Ownrshp 2015
Sales 120.5MM EMP 4
Accts Pricewaterhousecoopers Societ
Tkr Sym NRE Exch NYS
SIC 6798 Real estate investment trusts
Pr: Mahbod Nia
*Ch Bd: David T Hamamoto
CFO: Debra A Hess

D-U-N-S 17-122-0192
NORTHSTAR REALTY FINANCE CORP
399 Park Ave Fl 18, New York, NY 10022-4968
Tel (212) 319-8801 Founded/Ownrshp 2004
Sales 634.7MM EMP 12^E
SIC 6798

D-U-N-S 78-450-8223
▲ NORTHSTAR REALTY FINANCE CORP
N-STAR
399 Park Ave Fl 18, New York, NY 10022-4968
Tel (212) 547-2600 Founded/Ownrshp 2003
Sales 2.0MMM EMP 25^E
Tkr Sym NRF Exch NYS
SIC 6798 Real estate investment trusts
Pr: Jonathan A Langer
*Ch Bd: David T Hamamoto
CFO: Debra A Hess
Ex VP: Ronald J Lieberman
VP: Michelle Montenegro
Genl Mgr: Luigi Spiridigliozzi

D-U-N-S 06-726-3181
NORTHSTAR TRAVEL MEDIA LLC
100 Lighting Way Ste 200, Secaucus, NJ 07094-3681
Tel (201) 902-2000 Founded/Ownrshp 2016
Sales 252.6MM^E EMP 1,012
SIC 2721 4789 4724 Periodicals; Cargo loading & unloading services; Travel agencies
CEO: Tom Kemp
CFO: Lisa Cohen
Treas: Nadine Godwin
Sr VP: Janine L Bavoso
VP: Bernie Schraer
VP: Megan Sheekey
VP Bus Dev: Sheila Rice
Dir Soc: Susan Brooks
Dir Soc: Debbie Cortese

Snr Sftwr: Jijie Song
Dir IT: Rich Mastropietro

D-U-N-S 04-983-3163
NORTHTOWN AUTOMOTIVE COMPANIES INC
NORTHTOWN WORLD AUTO CENTER
1135 Millersport Hwy, Amherst, NY 14226-1722
Tel (716) 836-4600 Founded/Ownrshp 1969
Sales 110.6MM^E EMP 336
SIC 5511 Automobiles, new & used
Pr: Norman Schreiber
CFO: Harold Erbacher
*VP: Joseph Calabrese
VP: Larry Schreiber
*VP: Craig Schreiber
Sales Asso: Joshua Lange

NORTHTOWN WORLD AUTO CENTER
See NORTHTOWN AUTOMOTIVE COMPANIES INC

D-U-N-S 07-634-2203
NORTHVILLE PUBLIC SCHOOL DISTRICT
501 W Main St, Northville, MI 48167-1576
Tel (248) 349-3400 Founded/Ownrshp 1867
Sales 97.2MM EMP 850
Accts Plante & Moran Pllc Auburnvi
SIC 8211 Public elementary school; Public junior high school; Public senior high school; Public special education school
IT Man: Richard Tabor
Schl Brd P: James Mazurek
HC Dir: Nadine Harris

D-U-N-S 80-792-0368
NORTHWELL HEALTH INC
NSLIJ
2000 Marcus Ave, New Hyde Park, NY 11042-1069
Tel (516) 321-6000 Founded/Ownrshp 1997
Sales 5.4MMM^E EMP 60,000
SIC 8082 8062 Home health care services; Hospital, medical school affiliation
Pr: Kevin F Lawlor
*Pr: Michael J Dowling
*COO: Mark J Solazzo
*CFO: Robert Shapiro
CFO: Robert S Shapiro
Trst: Aim E Merszei
Ex VP: Lawrence G Smith
*Sr VP: David L Battinelli MD
Sr VP: Howard Gold
*Sr VP: Arthur Klein MD
Sr VP: Jeff Kraut
*Sr VP: Keith Thompson
VP: Donna Armellino
VP: Jeremy Boal
VP: John Bosco
VP: Jeffrey A Kraut
VP: Karen Nelson
VP: Eugene Tangney
VP: Maureen White
Exec: Arthur A Klein

D-U-N-S 07-665-2262
NORTHWEST ADMINISTRATORS INC
2323 Eastlake Ave E, Seattle, WA 98102-3305
Tel (206) 329-4900 Founded/Ownrshp 1958
Sales NA EMP 400
SIC 6371 Pension, health & welfare funds
Pr: Christopher R Hughes
*Ofcr: Gayle Bushnell
*Sr VP: Robert H Gies
*VP: James Baker
VP: Mark Coles
VP: Don Ditter
VP: Arlyn Escalona
VP: Bob Gies
VP: Aleksandra Gluhcheva
*VP: John Hughes Jr
VP: Jeannine Madrigal
VP: Michael Sander

D-U-N-S 00-696-3508 IMP/EXP
NORTHWEST AIRLINES INC (MN)
7500 Airline Dr, Minneapolis, MN 55450-1101
Tel (404) 715-2600 Founded/Ownrshp 2009
Sales 706.5MM^E EMP 26,000
SIC 4512 4513 4522

D-U-N-S 82-745-7586
NORTHWEST BANCORP MHC
100 Liberty St, Warren, PA 16365-2411
Tel (814) 728-7260 Founded/Ownrshp 2001
Sales NA EMP 1,967^E
SIC 6036 Savings institutions, not federally chartered
Ch Bd: William J Wagner

D-U-N-S 88-346-0958
NORTHWEST BANCORP INC
(Suby of NORTHWEST BANCORP MHC) ★
100 Liberty St, Warren, PA 16365-2411
Tel (814) 726-2140 Founded/Ownrshp 2001
Sales NA EMP 1,964^E
SIC 6036 Savings institutions, not federally chartered
Ch Bd: William J Wagner
Pr: Chip Pfohl
CFO: William W Harvey Jr
Chf Cred: Myra Sletson
Ofcr: Weikel I Dean
Trst Ofcr: Ellen B Allison
Ex VP: Gregory C Larocca
Sr VP: Ben Jamieson
Sr VP: Roger Mosby
Sr VP: Robert A Ordiwy
Sr VP: Thomas Ziacik
VP: Kurt Bevan
VP: Michael Doherty
VP: Drew Ecklund
VP: Norman Ewing
VP: Ken Faulconbridge
VP: Mark Gdog
VP: Jodie Guiffre
VP: Braden R Jones
VP: Regina Lutz
VP: Julie A Mrsco

D-U-N-S 83-228-2375
▲ NORTHWEST BANCSHARES INC
100 Liberty St, Warren, PA 16365-2411
Tel (814) 726-2140 Founded/Ownrshp 2009
Sales NA EMP 2,231^E
Accts Kpmg Llp Pittsburgh Pennsylv
Tkr Sym NWBI Exch NGS
SIC 6021 National commercial banks
Ch Bd: William J Wagner
COO: David E Westerburg
CFO: William W Harvey Jr
Ofcr: Michael G Smelko
Ofcr: Thomas J Townsend
Ex VP: Gregory Larocca
Ex VP: Richard K Laws
Ex VP: Julia W McTavish
Ex VP: Andrew C Young
Sr VP: Gerald J Ritzert

D-U-N-S 07-401-3749
NORTHWEST BANK
(Suby of NORTHWEST BANCORP INC) ★
100 Liberty St, Warren, PA 16365-2411
Tel (814) 723-9696 Founded/Ownrshp 1994
Sales NA EMP 1,963
SIC 6035 Federal savings banks
Pr: William J Wagner
Pr: Peter Bower
Pr: Steven Carman
Pr: James E Martin
Treas: Donald E Reed
Ofcr: Barb Demontier
*Ofcr: Timothy A Huber
Trst Ofcr: Laura Ahl
*Ex VP: Steven G Fisher
*Ex VP: Wayne W Harvey
*Ex VP: Robert A Ordiway
Sr VP: Julia McTavish
*Sr VP: Richard F Seibel
*Sr VP: James E Vecellio
VP: Mark Buchek
VP: Hall Carol
VP: Joseph J Colosimo
VP: Karen Cummings
VP: Jodie Guiffre
VP: James Holding
VP: Robert Krzeminski
Board of Directors: A Paul King, Joseph F Long

NORTHWEST BUILDING MATERIALS
See NORTHWEST BUILDING SUPPLY INC

D-U-N-S 13-106-2473
NORTHWEST BUILDING SUPPLY INC
NORTHWEST BUILDING MATERIALS
5535 Nw 5th St, Oklahoma City, OK 73127-5811
Tel (405) 946-0500 Founded/Ownrshp 1985
Sales 104.5MM^E EMP 100^E
SIC 5033 5031 5211 Roofing & siding materials; Building materials, interior; Building materials, exterior; Doors & windows; Millwork; Lumber & other building materials; Roofing material; Lumber products; Millwork & lumber
Pr: Cliff Stockton

D-U-N-S 80-565-0058
NORTHWEST CAPITAL APPRECIATION INC
1200 Westlake Ave N # 310, Seattle, WA 98109-3543
Tel (206) 689-5615 Founded/Ownrshp 1992
Sales 83.2MM^E EMP 1,871
SIC 2611 Pulp produced from wood base
Co-Pr: Brad Creswell
*Co-Pr: E Perot Bissell

D-U-N-S 02-969-5053
NORTHWEST CASCADE INC
HONEYBUCKETS
10412 John Bananola Way E, Puyallup, WA 98374-9333
Tel (253) 848-2371 Founded/Ownrshp 1985
Sales 163.3MM^E EMP 300
Accts Sutor Krystad & Rosenfeld Pl
SIC 1623 7359 7699 3272 1711 Underground utilities contractor; Portable toilet rental; Septic tank cleaning service; Septic tanks, concrete; Septic system construction
Pr: Carl Liliequest
COO: Ron Inman
*CFO: Greg Potts
*Ch: Mark Perry
VP: Tom Rogers

D-U-N-S 07-209-3172 IMP
NORTHWEST CO LLC
WILMINGTON PRODUCTS USA
49 Bryant Ave, Roslyn, NY 11576-1123
Tel (516) 484-6996 Founded/Ownrshp 2007
Sales 150.0MM EMP 160
Accts Mayer Hoffman Mccann Cpas
SIC 2211 Blankets & blanketings, cotton
Pr: Ross Auerbach
*COO: Marc Friedman
*CFO: Robert Jolson
*Ex VP: Glenn Auerbach
VP: Kim Rizzardi
Creative D: Elizabeth Gilmore
VP Mktg: Stanley Mieszkowski
VP Sls: Brian Horchler
Sls Dir: Ann Willis
Mktg Mgr: Katherine Knarr

NORTHWEST COMMUNITY HLTH SVCS
See NORTHWEST COMMUNITY HOSPITAL INC

D-U-N-S 12-148-1832
NORTHWEST COMMUNITY HOSPITAL FOUNDATION
NCH
800 W Central Rd, Arlington Heights, IL 60005-2349
Tel (847) 618-1000 Founded/Ownrshp 1981
Sales 158.9MM^E EMP 4,000
SIC 8062 General medical & surgical hospitals
CEO: Stephen O Scogna
*Pr: Bruce K Crowther
*VP: Marsha Liu
VP: Connie Yuska
Dir Rad: Patricia Stack
CIO: Karen Bruns
CIO: Carl Cornell
CTO: Glen Malan
IT Man: Mike Degraff
IT Man: Beth Rawski
Surgeon: Khalid Husain

D-U-N-S 04-232-9615
NORTHWEST COMMUNITY HOSPITAL INC
NORTHWEST COMMUNITY HLTH SVCS
800 W Central Rd, Arlington Heights, IL 60005-2349
Tel (847) 618-1000 Founded/Ownrshp 1953
Sales 432.8MM EMP 2,800
SIC 8062 Hospital, AMA approved residency
CEO: Stephen Scogna
Chf OB: Kristen Stone-Mulhern
Dir Recs: Ron Tapnio
COO: Mike Hartke
*CFO: John Skeans
*CFO: Michael Zenn
VP: Bob Klasek
VP: Jane D Mass
VP: Ann Patrick
VP: Melissa Smith
VP: Angie Stefaniu
VP: David Ungurean
Dir Lab: Demi Callias
Dir Rad: Daniel B Crane
Dir Rad: Carl L Kabhen
Dir Rad: Anthony J Malone
Dir Rx: Paul Zega
Comm Man: Laurice Knox

D-U-N-S 11-850-0649 IMP/EXP
NORTHWEST DAIRY ASSOCIATION
1130 Rainier Ave S, Seattle, WA 98144-2842
Tel (206) 284-7220 Founded/Ownrshp 1916
Sales 1.4MMM^E EMP 1,300
SIC 8611 Manufacturers' institute
CEO: Jim Werkhoven
Pr: James Wegner
Treas: Sherman Polinder
Sec: Randy Lindley
VP: Tim McMillan
VP: Steve Rowe

D-U-N-S 60-653-5177
NORTHWEST EVALUATION ASSOCIATION
NWEA
121 Nw Everett St, Portland, OR 97209-4049
Tel (503) 624-1951 Founded/Ownrshp 1977
Sales 119.3MM EMP 600
Accts Clark Nuber Ps Bellevue Wa
SIC 8299 8748 Educational services; Educational consultant
Pr: Matt Chapman
*CFO: Geri Cohen
*Ex VP: Jeff Strickler
*Sr VP: Mark Campillo
*Sr VP: Toni Jaffe
*Sr VP: Jan Larocca
*Sr VP: Brent Lieberman
*Sr VP: Fred McDaniel
*Sr VP: Jason Mendenhall
*Sr VP: Katie Topping
*Sr VP: Raymond Yeagley
Board of Directors: Jim Angermeyr, Ronald Blocker, Deborah Delisle, Steve Fleischman, Patricia Smith, Joseph Wise, Kenneth Wong

NORTHWEST FARM CR SVCS FLCA
See NORTHWEST FARM CREDIT SERVICES

D-U-N-S 06-958-5933
NORTHWEST FARM CREDIT SERVICES
NORTHWEST FARM CR SVCS FLCA
2001 S Flint Rd, Spokane, WA 99224-9198
Tel (509) 838-2429 Founded/Ownrshp 1985
Sales NA EMP 500
Accts Pricewaterhousecoopers Llp S
SIC 6111 Federal & federally sponsored credit agencies
CEO: Phil Dipofi
Pr: Rhonda Baglien
Pr: Sophie Conley
Pr: Jessi Dressen
Pr: Zack Wolf
CFO: Tom Nakano
Ofcr: Stephanie Rennie
Ex VP: Roger Calhoun
Ex VP: Fred Depell
Ex VP: Joan E Haynes
Ex VP: Bill Johnson
Ex VP: Daniel Stainbrook
Ex VP: Thomas Tracy
VP: David Barbieri
VP: Don Bellamy
VP: Rich Fehringer
VP: Karen Goens
VP: Gary Hutchens
VP: Alan Kirpes
VP: Amy Kraft
VP: Gary A Smith

D-U-N-S 96-857-3399 IMP/EXP
NORTHWEST HARDWOODS INC
(Suby of LITTLEJOHN & CO LLC) ★
820 A St Ste 500, Tacoma, WA 98402-5297
Tel (253) 568-6800 Founded/Ownrshp 2014
Sales 870.6MM^E EMP 2,000
SIC 2426 5031 Lumber, hardwood dimension; Lumber, plywood & millwork; Lumber: rough, dressed & finished
Pr: Tony Rosengarth
*CFO: Frederic Jung
*Sec: Jeffrey Steed
*VP: Christopher Bennett
*VP: Stan Edme
*VP: Brian Narramore
VP: Jeffrey Gornev Steed
*VP: David Weyerhaeuser

D-U-N-S 07-567-0463
■ NORTHWEST HEALTH SYSTEM INC
NORTHWEST MED CTR WASH CNTY
(Suby of COMMUNITY HEALTH SYSTEMS INC) ★
609 W Maple Ave, Springdale, AR 72764-5335
Tel (479) 751-5711 Founded/Ownrshp 2001
Sales 284.1MM^E EMP 1,400
SIC 8062 General medical & surgical hospitals
CEO: Dan McKay
Chf Rad: James Cherry
COO: Mark Bethell
*COO: Donnie Frederick
*CFO: Sean Barnett
CFO: Pamela Hill
Dir OR: Angela Cox

Dir OR: Bryon Taylor
CIO: Holly Hamilton-Haynie
**CIO:* Shannon Williams
Cmptr Lab: Jessica Estepp

NORTHWEST HOSPITAL & MEDICAL C
See UW MEDICINE/NORTHWEST

D-U-N-S 11-896-8684
NORTHWEST HOSPITAL & MEDICAL CENTER
1550 N 115th St, Seattle, WA 98133-8498
Tel (206) 364-0500 *Founded/Ownrshp* 1981
Sales 281.7MM *EMP* 1,600^E
Accts Clark Nuber Ps Bellevue Wa
SIC 8741 8062 Hospital management; Nursing & personal care facility management; General medical & surgical hospitals
CEO: Cynthia Hecker
**Pr:* Bill Schneider
CFO: Bob Steiegmeyer
Ofcr: Cynthia Coronel
VP: Gregory Schroedl
Netwrk Mgr: Michael Dipietro
Ansthlgy: Jorg Dziersk
Ansthlgy: Rajninder Jutla
Ansthlgy: Richard Nguyen
Podiatrist: Kelly Hall
Doctor: Keiko Aikawa

D-U-N-S 06-936-9791 IMP
NORTHWEST HOSPITAL CENTER INC (MD)
5401 Old Court Rd, Randallstown, MD 21133-5103
Tel (410) 521-2200 *Founded/Ownrshp* 1984
Sales 226.3MM *EMP* 981
SIC 8062 General medical & surgical hospitals
Ch: Harold Weiss
Chf Path: Michael S Ballo
Dir Recs: Jennifer Marrujo
**Pr:* Erik Wexler
**Pr:* Brian White
**Sr VP:* David Krajewski
**VP:* Brian Cawley
VP: Julie Cox
VP: Christine Deangelis
**VP:* Ron Ginsberg
VP: Ronald L Ginsberg
**VP:* Candy Hamner
**VP:* Sue Jalbert
Dir OR: Sepi Gharanfoli
Dir Inf Cn: Betsy Addis
Dir Inf Cn: Mary Wallace
Dir Lab: Paul Griffey
Dir Rad: Rodney Hopkins
Dir Rad: Karen Steinhist
Dir Rx: Ken Mercer

D-U-N-S 10-007-6025
NORTHWEST INDEPENDENT SCHOOL DISTRICT
2001 Texan Dr, Justin, TX 76247-8791
Tel (817) 215-0000 *Founded/Ownrshp* 1952
Sales 202.4MM *EMP* 2,000
Accts Haynes And Associates Pc Roa
SIC 8211 Public elementary & secondary schools; School board
Bd of Dir: Russell Neal
Bd of Dir: Jennifer Wigant
VP: Mark Schluter
Comm Dir: Lesley Weaver
Prin: Ron Andres
Dir Sec: Mike Conklin
MIS Dir: Cara Carter
Pr Dir: Rob Ludwig

D-U-N-S 94-269-6451
NORTHWEST INSURANCE NETWORK INC
515 N State St Ste 2100, Chicago, IL 60654-7066
Tel (312) 427-1777 *Founded/Ownrshp* 1995
Sales NA *EMP* 122
SIC 6411 Insurance agents, brokers & service
Pr: Martin Joseph
Brnch Mgr: Amelia Siddiqui

NORTHWEST IOWA HOSPITAL
See UNITY POINT HEALTH ST LUKE

D-U-N-S 07-698-3055
NORTHWEST IOWA HOSPITAL CORP
ST. LKES REGIONAL MEDICAL CENT
2800 Pierce St Ste 410, Sioux City, IA 51104-3759
Tel (712) 279-3500 *Founded/Ownrshp* 1996
Sales 152.6MM *EMP* 1,200^E
SIC 8062 8051 General medical & surgical hospitals; Skilled nursing care facilities
Pr: Peter Thoreen
**CFO:* Mark Johnson
**VP:* Jim Gobell
**VP:* Richard Hildebrand
**VP:* Chad Markham
**VP:* Lynn Wold
Pathlgst: Thomas J Carroll Jr
Doctor: Roger Heath
Pharmcst: Paula Emerson
Pharmcst: Marce Wagner
Pharmcst: Howard White

D-U-N-S 00-986-2053
NORTHWEST IOWA POWER COOPERATIVE
NIPCO
31002 C38, Le Mars, IA 51031-8197
Tel (712) 546-4141 *Founded/Ownrshp* 1949
Sales 87.4MM *EMP* 50
Accts Eide Bailly Llp Sioux Falls
SIC 4911 Transmission, electric power
Genl Mgr: Kent Pauling
**CFO:* Matt Washburn
**Treas:* Louis Reed
IT Man: William Wolf
VP Opers: Steve Vermulm

D-U-N-S 04-302-1880
NORTHWEST KIDNEY CENTERS
700 Broadway, Seattle, WA 98122-4302
Tel (206) 292-2771 *Founded/Ownrshp* 1961
Sales 106.8MM *EMP* 550
Accts Clark Nuber Ps Bellevue Wa
SIC 8092 Kidney dialysis centers
Pr: Joyce Jackson
**CFO:* Scott Strandgord

Trst: Jean Rolfe
VP: Connie Anderson
Nurse Mgr: Cindy Black
Nurse Mgr: Ed Stauffer
Pr Mgr: Linda Sellers
Nutrtnst: Katy Wilkens
Doctor: Leanna Tyshler
Cert Phar: Judy Ngo

D-U-N-S 36-427-4670
NORTHWEST LOCAL SCHOOL DISTRICT
3240 Banning Rd, Cincinnati, OH 45239-5207
Tel (513) 923-1000 *Founded/Ownrshp* 1924
Sales 71.7MM^E *EMP* 1,300
SIC 8211 Public elementary & secondary schools
**Pr:* David Denny
CFO: Randy Bertram
**VP:* Pam Detzel
CIO: David Plotts
IT Man: Scott Fortkamp
Pr Dir: Matt Fisher
Teacher Pr: Steffaniy Kessling
Instr Medi: Eric Lorta
Psych: Julie Martini
Nrsg Dir: Jean Wimmer
HC Dir: Shonda Moore

NORTHWEST MED CTR WASH CNTY
See NORTHWEST HEALTH SYSTEM INC

D-U-N-S 18-791-9907
■ **NORTHWEST MEDICAL CENTER**
(*Suby of* COMMUNITY HEALTH SYSTEMS INC) ★
6200 N La Cholla Blvd, Tucson, AZ 85741-3529
Tel (520) 742-9000 *Founded/Ownrshp* 1997
Sales 287.8MM *EMP* 1,100
SIC 8062 General medical & surgical hospitals
CEO: Kevin Stockton
Chf Path: Matthew A Baptista
Chf Path: Michael Lynch
Chf Rad: Mark Yoshino
COO: David Schultz
**CFO:* Ronald Patrick
Dir Case M: Rebecca Grisson
Dir Rx: Ferena Salek
Telecom Ex: Don Kuhn
CTO: Dana Carreras
Mtls Mgr: Daniel Galpin

D-U-N-S 00-790-8916
▲ **NORTHWEST NATURAL GAS CO** (OR)
NW NATURAL
220 Nw 2nd Ave, Portland, OR 97209-3991
Tel (503) 226-4211 *Founded/Ownrshp* 1859
Sales 723.7MM *EMP* 1,076^E
Tkr Sym NWN *Exch* NYS
SIC 4924 Natural gas distribution
Pr: David H Anderson
**Ch Bd:* Tod R Hamachek
CFO: Gregory C Hazelton
Treas: Steve Feltz
Treas: C Alex Miller
Chf Mktg O: Kimberly A Heiting
Ofcr: Lea Anne Doolittle
Sr VP: Margaret D Kirkpatrick
Sr VP: Mardilyn Saathoff
Sr VP: Grant M Yoshihara
VP: Shawn M Filippi
VP: Thomas J Imeson
VP: Ngoni Murandu
VP: David R Williams
Board of Directors: Timothy P Boyle, Martha L Byorum, John D Carter, Mark S Dodson, C Scott Gibson, Jane L Peverett, Kenneth Thrasher, Malia H Wasson

D-U-N-S 05-429-7247
NORTHWEST NEWS CO INC (MT)
BENJAMIN NEWS GROUP
1701 Rankin St, Missoula, MT 59808-1629
Tel (406) 721-7801 *Founded/Ownrshp* 1971, 1996
Sales 292.9MM^E *EMP* 300
SIC 5192 Magazines; Books; Periodicals
Pr: Paul Benjamin
**Treas:* John Benjamin
**Genl Mgr:* Ray Anderson

D-U-N-S 00-399-3060 IMP/EXP
▲ **NORTHWEST PIPE CO**
5721 Se Columbia Way # 200, Vancouver, WA 98661-5991
Tel (360) 397-6250 *Founded/Ownrshp* 1966
Sales 236.6MM *EMP* 676
Accts Pricewaterhousecoopers Llp P
Tkr Sym NWPX *Exch* NGS
SIC 3317 3443 Steel pipe & tubes; Welded pipe & tubes; Pipes, wrought: welded, lock joint or heavy riveted; Tubes, wrought: welded or lock joint; Industrial vessels, tanks & containers; Tanks, standard or custom fabricated: metal plate; Vessels, process or storage (from boiler shops): metal plate
Pr: Scott J Montross
**Ch Bd:* Richard A Roman
CFO: Robin Gantt
Ex VP: Martin Dana
Ex VP: William Smith
Opers Mgr: Shane Zeeman
Board of Directors: Michelle G Applebaum, James E Declusin, Harry L Demorest, Michael Franson, Keith R Larson

D-U-N-S 00-456-5222
NORTHWEST PIPELINE LLC
(*Suby of* WILLIAMS PARTNERS OPERATING LLC) ★
295 S Chipeta Way Fl 4, Salt Lake City, UT 84108-1285
Tel (801) 583-8800 *Founded/Ownrshp* 1965
Sales 472.9MM *EMP* 2^E
Accts Ernst & Young Llp Houston Te
SIC 4923 Gas transmission & distribution
CEO: Allison G Bridges
CFO: Ted T Timmermans
Ofcr: Donald R Chappel

D-U-N-S 14-440-5826
NORTHWEST RESTAURANTS INC
KFC
(*Suby of* KFC) ★
18815 139th Ave Ne Ste C, Woodinville, WA 98072-3565
Tel (425) 486-6336 *Founded/Ownrshp* 1980

Sales 40.6MM^E *EMP* 1,000
SIC 5812 Fast-food restaurant, chain
Pr: Sam Sibert

D-U-N-S 19-132-6438
NORTHWEST STAFFING RESOURCES INC
RESOURCE STAFFING GROUP
851 Sw 6th Ave Ste 300, Portland, OR 97204-1310
Tel (503) 323-9190 *Founded/Ownrshp* 1985
Sales 140.2MM^E *EMP* 6,700
SIC 7363 7361 Temporary help service; Employment agencies
Pr: Frank Dulcich
CFO: Mary Sauer
**Genl Mgr:* Molly Kalomiris

D-U-N-S 94-935-0441
■ **NORTHWEST TEXAS HEALTHCARE SYSTEM INC**
NORTHWEST TEXAS HOSPITAL
(*Suby of* UNIVERSAL HEALTH SERVICES INC) ★
1501 S Coulter St, Amarillo, TX 79106-1770
Tel (806) 354-1000 *Founded/Ownrshp* 1996
Sales 270.5MM *EMP* 1,798
SIC 8062 8063 8051 8049 General medical & surgical hospitals; Psychiatric hospitals; Skilled nursing care facilities; Physical therapist
CEO: Moody Chisholm
**Pr:* Marvin Pember
**CEO:* Mark Crawford
CFO: Ray Greiner
CFO: James D Taylor
**Treas:* Steve Filton
VP: Becky McGaughy
Mng Dir: Nick Hughey
CTO: Mark Tarty
Dir IT: Tim Taylor
Mktg Mgr: Caytie Martin

NORTHWEST TEXAS HOSPITAL
See NORTHWEST TEXAS HEALTHCARE SYSTEM INC

D-U-N-S 05-290-2744
NORTHWEST VISTA COLLEGE
(*Suby of* SAN ANTONIO COLLEGE) ★
3535 N Ellison Dr, San Antonio, TX 78251-4217
Tel (210) 706-9291 *Founded/Ownrshp* 2000
Sales 54.5MM^E *EMP* 1,200
SIC 8222 8221 Junior college; Colleges universities & professional schools
Pr: Jacqueline Claunch
Brnch Mgr: Mike Keiscer
Pr Dir: Jerry Arellano
Snr Mgr: Mohamed Basiouny

D-U-N-S 00-792-0291
▲ **NORTHWESTERN CORP**
NORTHWESTERN ENERGY
3010 W 69th St, Sioux Falls, SD 57108-5613
Tel (605) 978-2900 *Founded/Ownrshp* 1923
Sales 1.2MMM *EMP* 1,608^E
Accts Deloitte & Touche Llp Minneap
Tkr Sym NWE *Exch* NYS
SIC 4911 4924 Generation, electric power; Distribution, electric power; Natural gas distribution
Pr: Robert C Rowe
**Ch Bd:* E Linn Draper Jr
CFO: Brian B Bird
VP: Michael R Cashell
VP: Patrick R Corcoran
VP: Heather H Grahame
VP: John D Hines
VP: Kendall Kliewer
VP: Crystal D Lail
VP: Curtis T Pohl
VP: Bobbi L Schroeppel
Board of Directors: Stephen P Adik, Dorothy M Bradley, Dana J Dykhouse, Jan R Horsfall, Julia L Johnson, Denton Louis Peoples

NORTHWESTERN ENERGY
See NORTHWESTERN CORP

D-U-N-S 80-040-1064
NORTHWESTERN ENERGY
11 E Park St, Butte, MT 59701-1711
Tel (406) 497-3000 *Founded/Ownrshp* 2002
Sales 328.5MM^E *EMP* 170^E
SIC 4911 Electric services
CFO: Brian Bird
CFO: Kipp Orme
Ofcr: Michael Cashell
Ofcr: John Hines
VP: Patrick Corcoran
VP: Miggie Cramblit
VP: David G Gates
VP: Heather Grahame
VP: Kendall Kliewer
VP: Curtis Pohl
VP: Jana Quam
VP: Bobbi Schroeppel
VP: Bart Thielbar

D-U-N-S 13-502-1934
■ **NORTHWESTERN ENERGY CORP**
(*Suby of* NORTHWESTERN ENERGY) ★
3010 W 69th St, Sioux Falls, SD 57108-5613
Tel (605) 978-2900 *Founded/Ownrshp* 1996
Sales 389.6MM^E *EMP* 580^E
SIC 4911 4924 Electric services; Natural gas distribution
**CFO:* Brian B Bird
**Treas:* Paul Evans
VP: Michael R Cashell
VP: Miggie E Cramblit
**VP:* Glen R Herr
**VP:* Curtis T Pohl
**VP:* Bobbi L Schroeppel
VP Opers: Curt Pohl
Plnt Mgr: Ray Lee

D-U-N-S 07-458-8492
NORTHWESTERN LAKE FOREST HOSPITAL
WOMENS AUX OF LK FOREST HOSP
(*Suby of* NORTHWESTERN MEMORIAL HEALTHCARE) ★
660 N Westmoreland Rd, Lake Forest, IL 60045-1696
Tel (847) 234-0945 *Founded/Ownrshp* 2010

Sales 156.3MM^E *EMP* 1,700
SIC 8062 5947 5932 5812 Hospital, medical school affiliated with nursing & residency; Gift shop; Novelties; Used merchandise stores; Coffee shop
Pr: Matthew J Flynn
**CEO:* Dean Harrison
**Ex VP:* Peter McCanna
**VP:* Michael G Ankin
**VP:* Jane C Griffin
**VP:* Kimberly A Nagy
Mng Dir: Harold Chin
Prgrm Mgr: Shanel Martens
Nurse Mgr: Susan Balling
Obsttrcn: Karen Mass
Ansthlgy: Erica Noel

NORTHWESTERN MEDIA
See UNIVERSITY OF NORTHWESTERN - ST PAUL

D-U-N-S 06-052-5748
NORTHWESTERN MEDICAL CENTER INC
133 Fairfield St, Saint Albans, VT 05478-1726
Tel (802) 524-5911 *Founded/Ownrshp* 1977
Sales 97.8MM *EMP* 600
SIC 8062 General medical & surgical hospitals
CEO: Jill Berry Bowen
Chf Rad: Luis F Gonzalez III
**Pr:* John Casavant
CFO: Dawn Bugbee
CFO: Ted Sirotta
**Treas:* Harold Hebert
**VP:* Judy Ashley-Mclaughlin
VP: Joel Benware
VP: Johnathan Bilings
VP: Jonathan Billings
VP: Jane Catton
VP: Joel Heiser
VP: John Minadeo
Dir Risk M: Nilda French
Dir Rad: Jim Block

D-U-N-S 10-683-9707
NORTHWESTERN MEDICAL FACULTY FOUNDATION INC
NORTHWESTERN MEDICAL GROUP
680 N Lake Shore Dr Ste 1, Chicago, IL 60611-4546
Tel (312) 926-2630 *Founded/Ownrshp* 1980
Sales 800.0MM *EMP* 3,000
SIC 8011

NORTHWESTERN MEDICAL GROUP
See NORTHWESTERN MEDICAL FACULTY FOUNDATION INC

D-U-N-S 10-333-5733 IMP
NORTHWESTERN MEMORIAL HEALTHCARE
251 E Huron St Ste 3-710, Chicago, IL 60611-2908
Tel (312) 926-2000 *Founded/Ownrshp* 1981
Sales 421.3MM *EMP* 20,000
Accts Ernst & Young Us Llp Indianap
SIC 8082 6513 7389 8099 Home health care services; Apartment building operators; Fund raising organizations; Medical services organization
Pr: Dean Harrison
Ch Bd: Carol L Bernick
COO: Cynthia Hall
**Ex VP:* Peter McCanna
VP: Gina Weldy
Dir Risk M: Scott Stanley
Dir Rx: Neal Grosshans
Ex Dir: Judy Wood
Prac Mgr: Andrew Powers
Prac Mgr: Steven Thill
Snr Ntwrk: Myles Gehrke

D-U-N-S 05-945-7150
NORTHWESTERN MEMORIAL HOSPITAL
(*Suby of* NORTHWESTERN MEMORIAL HEALTHCARE) ★
251 E Huron St, Chicago, IL 60611-3055
Tel (312) 755-0604 *Founded/Ownrshp* 1867
Sales 1.3MMM *EMP* 5,800
SIC 8062 General medical & surgical hospitals
CEO: Dean Harrison
Ch Bd: William J Brodsky
Pr: Richard J Gannotta
COO: Hank Moya
COO: Dennis Murphy
CFO: Peter McCanna
Bd of Dir: Reeve Waud
Sr VP: Julie Creamer
VP: Stephen C Falk
VP: Ira Goldstone
Dir Risk M: Laura Lingl
Dir Rad: Cynthia K Broos

D-U-N-S 00-794-7146
NORTHWESTERN MUTUAL LIFE INSURANCE CO
720 E Wisconsin Ave, Milwaukee, WI 53202-4703
Tel (414) 271-1444 *Founded/Ownrshp* 1857
Sales NA *EMP* 6,662
Accts Pricewaterhousecoopers Llp
SIC 6311 6321 7389 Life insurance carriers; Disability health insurance; Financial services
CEO: John E Schlifske
**Ch Bd:* James D Ericson
**Pr:* Gregory C Oberland
**Pr:* Gary A Poliner
**COO:* John M Bremer
COO: Daniel Riedl
**CFO:* Michael G Carter
CFO: Wallace Fischer
Ofcr: Derek Petersen
**Ofcr:* Sarah E Schott
Ofcr: Adam Selden
Ofcr: Aaron Simpson
Ofcr: Michael Zielinski
Ex VP: Rebekah Barsch
Ex VP: Jordan Fenchel
Ex VP: Ronald P Joelson
**Ex VP:* Todd M Schoon
**Sr VP:* Joann M Eisenhart
**Sr VP:* John M Grogan
Sr VP: Marcia Rimai
VP: Carmen Allen

D-U-N-S 80-560-3763
NORTHWESTERN MUTUAL WEALTH MANAGEMENT CO
(*Suby of* NORTHWESTERN MUTUAL LIFE INSURANCE CO) ★
611 E Wisconsin Ave, Milwaukee, WI 53202-4695
Tel (206) 623-8801 *Founded/Ownrshp* 2007
Sales NA *EMP* 25
SIC 6411 Insurance agents, brokers & service
Prin: Mark J McLennon
Ofcr: James Chavez
Ofcr: John Grogan Jr
Ofcr: Jack Kincannon
Ofcr: Alexander Lewis
Ofcr: Lauren Schoenberger
VP: Steve Radke
VP: William H Taylor
Mng Dir: Paul Hoerrner
Sls Dir: Brian Wilson

D-U-N-S 09-113-2589 IMP/EXP
NORTHWESTERN SELECTA INC
NEZ FOODS
796 Calle C M Julia Indst, San Juan, PR 00920
Tel (787) 781-1950 *Founded/Ownrshp* 1980
Sales 167.3MM *EMP* 300
Accts Kevane Grant Thornton Llp San
SIC 5147 5146 5142 Meats, fresh; Fish & seafoods; Meat, frozen: packaged; Fish, frozen: packaged
Pr: Elpidio Nunez III
* *VP:* Rafael Flores
* *VP Admn:* Miguel Portillo

D-U-N-S 12-730-9172
■ **NORTHWESTERN SERVICES LLC**
(*Suby of* NORTHWESTERN ENERGY) ★
600 Market St W, Huron, SD 57350-1510
Tel (605) 353-7478 *Founded/Ownrshp* 1925
Sales 359.8MM^E *EMP* 450
SIC 4911 4924 Electric services; Natural gas distribution

D-U-N-S 00-543-6803 IMP
NORTHWESTERN UNIVERSITY (IL)
633 Clark St, Evanston, IL 60208-0001
Tel (847) 491-3741 *Founded/Ownrshp* 1851
Sales 2.3MMM^E *EMP* 5,954
Accts Pricewaterhousecoopers Llp Ch
SIC 8221 University
Pr: Morton Schapiro
Pr: Bruce Lewis
* *Pr:* Schapiro Morton
Chf Mktg O: Tom Hayden
* *Ex VP:* Nim Ehinniah
VP: Thomas G Cline
VP: Thomas Cline
VP: Lynn Hunsberger
VP: Donna Jurdy
VP: Will McLean
VP: Catherine Schwanke
VP: Ingrid S Stafford
VP: Jeffrey Strauss
VP: Margaret Sullivan
VP: Joseph T Walsh
VP: Michael Weston
Assoc Dir: Todd Murphy

D-U-N-S 16-105-2329
NORTHWESTERN UNIVERSITY INFORMATION TECHNOLOGIES
1800 Sherman Ave Ste 7, Evanston, IL 60201-3496
Tel (847) 467-1766 *Founded/Ownrshp* 1850
Sales 1.5MMM *EMP* 250
SIC 4813 7374 4812 Local & long distance telephone communications; Data processing & preparation; Radio telephone communication
VP: Patricia Todus

D-U-N-S 09-295-4130
NORTHWIND INVESTMENTS INC
BURGER KING
109 E Broadway St, Mount Pleasant, MI 48858-2312
Tel (989) 772-2600 *Founded/Ownrshp* 1978
Sales 35.8MM^E *EMP* 1,100
SIC 5812 Fast-food restaurant, chain
Pr: Kevin Egnatuk
* *Sec:* Greg Johnroe
* *VP:* Bob Spalding

NORTHWOOD HOMES
See NORTHWOOD INVESTMENTS CORP

D-U-N-S 62-709-8288
NORTHWOOD INVESTMENTS CORP
NORTHWOOD HOMES
59948 Downs Rd, La Grande, OR 97850-5295
Tel (541) 962-6274 *Founded/Ownrshp* 1991
Sales 89.4MM^E *EMP* 350^E
SIC 3792 Travel trailers & campers
CEO: Jim Jones
* *Pr:* Ronald L Nash
* *CFO:* Craig Orton
* *VP:* Ernest P Lewis

D-U-N-S 92-710-7722
NORTHWOOD MANUFACTURING INC
(*Suby of* NORTHWOOD HOMES) ★
59948 Downs Rd, La Grande, OR 97850-5295
Tel (541) 962-6274 *Founded/Ownrshp* 1993
Sales 89.0MM *EMP* 350
Accts Delap Llp Lake Oswego Or
SIC 3792 Travel trailers & campers
CEO: James Jones
* *Pr:* Ronald L Nash
* *CFO:* Craig Orton
Exec: Cerise Smallwood
Dir IT: Noel Beden
Sls Dir: Donald Cochran
Sls Mgr: Jim Baehmann
Sls Mgr: Scott Richgruber
Sls Mgr: Clint Williams

D-U-N-S 07-422-5566
NORTHWOOD UNIVERSITY (MI)
4000 Whiting Dr, Midland, MI 48640-2398
Tel (800) 622-9000 *Founded/Ownrshp* 1959, 1960
Sales 103.4MM *EMP* 500
SIC 8221 Colleges universities & professional schools
Pr: Keith A Pretty
Pr: Sue Nowicki
Treas: Donald E Hunkins
Treas: John Malone
VP: David Long
Assoc Dir: Ron Browne
Assoc Dir: Emily Yeager
Brnch Mgr: Tracy Graham
Off Mgr: Jerri Pelletier
Off Mgr: Ann Salva
Dir IT: Julie Becker-Myers

D-U-N-S 16-802-4144
NORTON AUDUBON HOSPITAL
(*Suby of* NORTON HOSPITALS INC) ★
1 Audubon Plaza Dr, Louisville, KY 40217-1318
Tel (502) 636-7111 *Founded/Ownrshp* 1998
Sales 141.5MM^E *EMP* 1,242
SIC 8062 General medical & surgical hospitals
Pr: Thomas D Kmetz
VP: Heather Cote
Dir Case M: Sharon Higdon
Dir Bus: Lee Greenwell
Dir QC: Shirley Schilling
IT Man: Damon Yeary
Ql Cn Mgr: Kathy Jenkins
Podiatrist: Walter M Butler
Doctor: Vincent Degeare
Doctor: Kent Morris
Doctor: Jacob Nunamaker

NORTON DOOR CONTROL
See YALE SECURITY INC

NORTON DRILLING
See PATTERSON-UTI DRILLING SERVICES LP LLLP

D-U-N-S 85-917-3585
NORTON HEALTHCARE FOUNDATION INC
(*Suby of* NORTON HEALTHCARE INC) ★
4967 Us Highway 42 # 100, Louisville, KY 40222-6363
Tel (502) 629-8000 *Founded/Ownrshp* 1962
Sales 85.5M *EMP* 9,000
Accts Ernst & Young Llp Louisville
SIC 7389 Fund raising organizations
VP: Mary M Corbett
VP: Steve Hester
Diag Rad: Stewart C Hoertz
Diag Rad: Brian C Jones
Diag Rad: Lawrence R Kelly
Diag Rad: Nancy S Pile
Diag Rad: Greg S Walton

D-U-N-S 14-779-2105
NORTON HEALTHCARE INC
200 E Chestnut St, Louisville, KY 40202-1831
Tel (502) 629-8000 *Founded/Ownrshp* 1983
Sales 1.8MMM^E *EMP* 9,300
SIC 8741 8062 Hospital management; General medical & surgical hospitals
Pr: Stephen A Williams
Chf Rad: Sean Owens
Pr: Christopher Watkins
COO: Russell F Cox
CFO: Shirley Miller
* *Treas:* Gordon King
Trst: Maria L Bouvette
Trst: Carolyn J Gatz
Trst: Craig D Grant
Trst: Raymond K Guillaume
Trst: Kevin J Hable
Trst: Mitch Nichols
Trst: Joseph A Paradis
Trst: Alton H Roberts
Trst: Donald H Robinson
Trst: William J Schultz
Trst: Richard S Wolf
Trst: Wendell P Wright
Assoc VP: Jon Cooper
* *Sr VP:* Michael W Gough
Sr VP: Steven T Hester

D-U-N-S 16-802-2031
NORTON HOSPITAL
(*Suby of* NORTON HOSPITALS INC) ★
200 E Chestnut St Frnt, Louisville, KY 40202-1800
Tel (502) 629-8159 *Founded/Ownrshp* 2001
Sales 1.5MMM *EMP* 1,242
SIC 8062 General medical & surgical hospitals

D-U-N-S 16-816-4643
NORTON HOSPITALS INC
(*Suby of* NORTON HEALTHCARE INC) ★
200 E Chestnut St, Louisville, KY 40202-1831
Tel (502) 629-8000 *Founded/Ownrshp* 1969
Sales 1.5MMM *EMP* 1,500
SIC 8062 8011 8093 8071 General medical & surgical hospitals; Physicians' office, including specialists; Specialty outpatient clinics; Ultrasound laboratory
Pr: Steven A Williams
* *Treas:* Michael W Gough
Trst: Richard Wolf
* *VP:* Russell F Cox
Chf Nrs Of: Heather R Cote
Netwrk Mgr: Diana Wetterer
Obsttrcn: Susan E Hagan
Doctor: Rodney Miguel
Doctor: Michele G Phipps MD
Doctor: Johanna Pope
HC Dir: Susan Kerry

D-U-N-S 12-715-0956
NORTON LILLY INTERNATIONAL INC
KERR NORTON STRACHAN AGENCY
1 Saint Louis St Ste 5000, Mobile, AL 36602-3929
Tel (251) 431-6335 *Founded/Ownrshp* 1999
Sales 129.9MM^E *EMP* 402
SIC 4731 Agents, shipping
Ch: Hw Thurber III
* *Pr:* Alejandro Barthold
* *CFO:* Raul Moreira
Ex VP: Paul Carlton
Ex VP: Dwain Denniston
Ex VP: Dinesh Deogaonkar
Ex VP: Steve Haverstock
Sr VP: Ira Rudnick
VP: Barry Germain
VP: Norton Lilly
Rgnl Mgr: Patrick Cavan
Board of Directors: Rachel Allen, Alejandro Barthold, Raul Moreira

NORTON METALS
See RUSSEL JMS METALS CORP

D-U-N-S 07-220-3987
NORTON ROSE FULBRIGHT US LLP
1301 Mckinney St Ste 5100, Houston, TX 77010-3095
Tel (713) 651-5151 *Founded/Ownrshp* 1919
Sales 347.7MM^E *EMP* 1,900
SIC 8111

D-U-N-S 01-018-9223
NORTON SOUND HEALTH CORP
NORTON SOUND REGIONAL HOSPITAL
790 Lower St, Turner, ME 04282-3925
Tel (907) 443-3311 *Founded/Ownrshp* 1970
Sales 106.0MM *EMP* 521
Accts Elgee Rehfeld Mertz Llc Junea
SIC 8062 8051 8069 8093 8011 General medical & surgical hospitals; Skilled nursing care facilities; Specialty hospitals, except psychiatric; Substance abuse hospitals; Specialty outpatient clinics; Offices & clinics of medical doctors
CEO: Angie Gorn
* *Pr:* Deven Pralakar
Dir Inf Cn: Barbara Collino
Dir Env Sv: Mike Tall

NORTON SOUND REGIONAL HOSPITAL
See NORTON SOUND HEALTH CORP

D-U-N-S 11-958-3164 IMP
■ **NORTRAX INC**
(*Suby of* DEERE & CO) ★
4042 Park Oaks Blvd # 200, Tampa, FL 33610-9538
Tel (813) 635-2300 *Founded/Ownrshp* 2003
Sales 248.3MM^E *EMP* 1,125
SIC 5082 General construction machinery & equipment
CEO: Timothy J Murphy
* *Treas:* Michael J Mack
VP: Peter Marsh
VP: Eric Mason
* *VP:* Ben Richmond
Brnch Mgr: Tiffani Folles
Genl Mgr: Bill Lopas
Off Admin: Rhonda Poirier

D-U-N-S 06-358-4643
■ **NORTRU LLC**
(*Suby of* PSC ENVIRONMENTAL SERVICES LLC) ★
515 Lycaste St, Detroit, MI 48214-3473
Tel (313) 824-5840 *Founded/Ownrshp* 2000
Sales 169.3MM^E *EMP* 500
SIC 4953 5169 Recycling, waste materials; Industrial chemicals

D-U-N-S 07-689-3635
NORWALK AREA HEALTH SYSTEMS INC
272 Benedict Ave, Norwalk, OH 44857-2374
Tel (419) 668-8101 *Founded/Ownrshp* 1985
Sales 1.5MM *EMP* 1,000
SIC 8062 8051 General medical & surgical hospitals; Skilled nursing care facilities
Pr: Patrick J Martin
VP: Duane Woods

D-U-N-S 07-539-7190
NORWALK HOSPITAL ASSOCIATION
34 Maple St, Norwalk, CT 06850-3894
Tel (203) 852-2000 *Founded/Ownrshp* 2004
Sales 355.5MM *EMP* 1,660^E
SIC 8062 Hospital, medical school affiliated with nursing & residency
CEO: Daniel Debarba Jr
Sr Pt: David Lehn
* *Ch Bd:* Diane M Allison
* *Pr:* Jeffrey Cole
* *Treas:* Andrew J Whittingham
Sr VP: Patrick McCabe
VP: Daniel D Barba
VP: Damon Dechamplain
VP: Jamie M Mooney
VP: Mary Nolan
Adm Dir: Robert Bepko

D-U-N-S 07-797-7072
NORWALK LA MIRADA UNIFIED SCHOOL DISTRICT
12820 Pioneer Blvd, Norwalk, CA 90650-2875
Tel (562) 868-0431 *Founded/Ownrshp* 1965
Sales 215.6MM *EMP* 4,200
SIC 8211

D-U-N-S 79-603-9949
NORWALK PUBLIC SCHOOL DISTRICT
125 East Ave, Norwalk, CT 06851-5702
Tel (203) 852-9874 *Founded/Ownrshp* 1970
Sales 82.8MM^E *EMP* 1,500
SIC 8211 9111 Public elementary & secondary schools; Mayors' offices
IT Man: Armand Madeo
IT Man: John Silbert
Pr Dir: Brenda Wilcox-William
Teacher Pr: Cherese Chery
Teacher Pr: Bruce Morris

D-U-N-S 00-379-3338
■ **NORWAY TELEPHONE CO INC** (SC)
TDS
(*Suby of* TDS TELECOMMUNICATIONS CORP) ★
8432 Savannah Hwy, Norway, SC 29113-9120
Tel (608) 831-1000 *Founded/Ownrshp* 1944
Sales 853.0MM *EMP* 2,700
SIC 4813 Local telephone communications
Pr: David Wittwer

D-U-N-S 06-745-8018
NORWEGIAN AMERICAN HOSPITAL INC
1044 N Francisco Ave, Chicago, IL 60622-2743
Tel (773) 278-8800 *Founded/Ownrshp* 1894
Sales 109.8MM *EMP* 800
Accts Plante & Moran Pllc Elgin I
SIC 8062 General medical & surgical hospitals
CEO: Jose R Sanchez
Chf Path: Rafael Campanini
VP: Tim Egan
Exec: Deborah Bielanski
Exec: Latisha Williams
Dir Risk M: Tricia McVicker
Dir Rx: Shawn M McGhee-Paratore
Dir Sec: Scott McManus
Nurse Mgr: Elona Lundstrom
CIO: Stephen Depooter
Dir IT: Kristen Moody

NORWEGIAN CRUISE LINE
See NCL CORP LTD

NORWEGIAN CRUISE LINE
See NCL (BAHAMAS) LTD A BERMUDA CO

D-U-N-S 07-872-7129
▲ **NORWEGIAN CRUISE LINE HOLDINGS LTD**
7665 Corp Ctr Dr, Miami, FL 33126
Tel (305) 436-4000 *Founded/Ownrshp* 1966
Sales 4.3MMM *EMP* 26,500^E
Tkr Sym NCLH *Exch* NGS
SIC 4481 Deep sea passenger transportation, except ferry
Pr: Frank J Del Rio
* *Ch Bd:* Walter L Revell
CFO: Wendy A Beck
Ex VP: Wendy Beck
Ex VP: Victor Gonzalez
Ex VP: T Robin Lindsay
Ex VP: Howard Sherman
Ex VP: Harry Sommer
Sr VP: Faye L Ashby
Sr VP: Daniel S Farkas
VP: Wayne Castellon
VP: George Chesney
VP: Alvin Dennis
VP: Howard Flanders
VP: Meg Lee
VP: John McGirl
VP: Karl Muhlberger
VP: Steve Riester
VP: Andrew Stuart
VP: Mark Warren
Board of Directors: David M Abrams, Adam M Aron, John W Chidsey, Russell W Galbut, Chad A Leat, Steve Martinez, F Robert Salerno

D-U-N-S 00-792-0481
■ **NORWEST BANK SOUTH DAKOTA NATIONAL ASSOCIATION** (SD)
WELLS FARGO
(*Suby of* WELLS FARGO & CO) ★
101 N Phillips Ave Ste A, Sioux Falls, SD 57104-6714
Tel (605) 575-4900 *Founded/Ownrshp* 1921
Sales NA *EMP* 1,322
SIC 6021 National trust companies with deposits, commercial
Pr: Terry Baloun

NORWEST EQUITY PARTNERS
See NORWEST VENTURE CAPITAL MANAGEMENT INC

D-U-N-S 14-851-4995 IMP/EXP
■ **NORWEST VENTURE CAPITAL MANAGEMENT INC**
NORWEST EQUITY PARTNERS
(*Suby of* WELLS FARGO & CO) ★
80 S 8th St Ste 3600, Minneapolis, MN 55402-2213
Tel (612) 215-1600 *Founded/Ownrshp* 1961
Sales 314.7MM^E *EMP* 1,220
SIC 6799 Venture capital companies
Genl Pt: Tim Devries
Pt: Brian Allingham
Ch: John Lindahl
Treas: John Chatley III
Bd of Dir: Paula J Hanson
VP: Jerry Lester
Genl Couns: Chuck Moorse

NORWICH MANUFACTURING DIVISION
See FELCHAR MANUFACTURING CORP

D-U-N-S 06-991-2962
NORWICH UNIVERSITY
VERMONT COLLEGE
158 Harmon Dr, Northfield, VT 05663-1035
Tel (802) 485-2000 *Founded/Ownrshp* 1819
Sales 103.7MM *EMP* 510
Accts Cliftonlarsonallen Llp Bosto
SIC 8221 College, except junior
Pr: Richard W Schneider
Dir Vol: Nicole Didomenico
V Ch: Rowland Brucken
V Ch: Reina Pennington
CFO: Ann Luis
* *CFO:* Richard E Rebmann
* *Sr VP:* David Whaley
VP: William Clements
VP: Diane Scolaro
VP: Frank Vanecek
Div/Sub He: Cathy Frey
Assoc Dir: Elizabeth Kennedy
Assoc Dir: Meghan Oliver
Assoc Dir: Nu Ski

D-U-N-S 07-949-8804
NORWOOD CO
375 Technology Dr, Malvern, PA 19355-1306
Tel (610) 240-4400 *Founded/Ownrshp* 1975
Sales 96.9MM *EMP* 80
Accts Fegley & Associates Pc Ply
SIC 1541 1542 8741 Industrial buildings, new construction; Renovation, remodeling & repairs: industrial buildings; Pharmaceutical manufacturing plant construction; Warehouse construction; Commercial & office building, new construction; Commercial & office buildings, renovation & repair; Hospital construction; Construction management
Pr: John E Farrell
* *CFO:* William J Burke
* *Sr VP:* Joseph Mitchell Jr
* *VP:* James Goshow
* *VP:* Timothy Kelly
* *VP:* Robert Risnychok
* *VP:* Eric Urbanski
Snr PM: Gregory Kratz

NORWOOD HOSPITAL, A CARITAS FA
See STEWARD NORWOOD HOSPITAL INC

D-U-N-S 62-308-6725
NOS COMMUNICATIONS INC
INTERNATIONAL PLUS
250 Pilot Rd Ste 300, Las Vegas, NV 89119-3514
Tel (702) 547-8000 *Founded/Ownrshp* 1989
Sales 3.6MM *EMP* 1,150
Accts Buchbinder Tunick & Company Ll
SIC 8748 4813 Fiber optic cable (insulated)
CEO: Joseph Koppy
CFO: Andrea Zingo
Board of Directors: Raymond Perea

D-U-N-S 00-516-2680 IMP
NOSCO INC
(*Suby of* HOLDEN INDUSTRIES INC) ★
651 S Ml King Jr Ave, Waukegan, IL 60085-7500
Tel (847) 336-4200 *Founded/Ownrshp* 1980
Sales 130.3MM^E *EMP* 509
SIC 2752 2657 Commercial printing, lithographic; Folding paperboard boxes
Pr: Russell S Haraf
**CFO:* Michael J Biesboer
**VP:* Joseph S Haas
Exec: Brooks Townsend
MIS Dir: Kevin Maule
QA Dir: Peter Kleinheinz
Prd Mgr: Rick Potochnik
Ql Cn Mgr: Kurt Smith
VP Mktg: Joe Tenhagan
VP Sls: Craig Curran

D-U-N-S 96-269-8085
NOT FOR PROFIT HOSPITAL CORP
UNITED MEDICAL CENTER
1310 Southern Ave Se, Washington, DC 20032-4623
Tel (202) 574-6024 *Founded/Ownrshp* 2008
Sales 100.3MM *EMP* 3
SIC 6732 Trusts: educational, religious, etc.
Ch: Charles Hudson Jr

D-U-N-S 87-931-6255
NOT YOUR AVERAGE JOES INC
2 Granite Ave Ste 300, Milton, MA 02186-4377
Tel (774) 213-2800 *Founded/Ownrshp* 1999
Sales 40.3MM^E *EMP* 1,000
SIC 5812 Eating places
Pr: Steven Silverstein
**CFO:* Joe McGuire
Rgnl Mgr: Tony White

D-U-N-S 96-189-5948
NOT-FOR-PROFIT HOSPITAL CORP
UNITED MEDICAL CENTER
1310 Southern Ave Se, Washington, DC 20032-4623
Tel (202) 574-6000 *Founded/Ownrshp* 2007
Sales 94.2MM *EMP* 900
SIC 8062 General medical & surgical hospitals
CEO: Frank Delisi
**CFO:* Derrick Hollings
CFO: Anne Ibekwe
CFO: Robert Schneider
VP: Serah Davis
Dir Teleco: Bee McCarthy
Chf Nrs Of: Jean Thaire
**Prin:* David Small
Pathlgst: Morteza Moussavi
Pharmcst: Sidney Wabara

D-U-N-S 10-674-6597 IMP/EXP
NOTIONS MARKETING CORP
1500 Buchanan Ave Sw, Grand Rapids, MI 49507-1613
Tel (616) 243-8424 *Founded/Ownrshp* 1970
Sales 221.8MM^E *EMP* 250
SIC 5131 5199 5092 Piece goods & notions; Fabrics, yarns & knit goods; Artists' materials; Toys & hobby goods & supplies
Ch Bd: Herbert D Lantinga
**Pr:* Jay Klein
CFO: John Dyke
**Treas:* John Van Dyke
**VP:* Sharon Lantinga
Exec: Terry Hare
Exec: Mark Rendel
CTO: Baughman Donna
Sls Dir: Jayne Owles
Snr Mgr: Stan Laffrey

D-U-N-S 00-890-4427 IMP
NOTT CO
4480 Round Lake Rd W, Arden Hills, MN 55112-1961
Tel (651) 415-3400 *Founded/Ownrshp* 1879
Sales 196.4MM^E *EMP* 200
SIC 5084 5085 3492 3053 Materials handling machinery; Industrial supplies; Fluid power valves & hose fittings; Gaskets, packing & sealing devices
CEO: Ed Davis
**CFO:* Darrell Babcock
CFO: Dave Lindberg
CTO: Roy Horton
Mktg Dir: Christy Nelson
Sls Mgr: Ross Taflin
Board of Directors: Duane J Solem

D-U-N-S 18-324-1538
NOUVEAU ELEVATOR INDUSTRIES INC
4755 37th St, Long Island City, NY 11101-1803
Tel (718) 349-4700 *Founded/Ownrshp* 1987
Sales 100.0MM *EMP* 390
SIC 7699 1796 Elevators: inspection, service & repair; Elevator installation & conversion
Pr: Donald Speranza Sr
CFO: Fred Sheinblum
**Ex VP:* Yolanda Speranza
**VP:* Dean Speranza
**VP:* Donald Speranza Jr
**VP:* Robert Speranza

D-U-N-S 80-774-7493
NOUVEAU VERRE HOLDINGS INC
(*Suby of* PORCHER INDUSTRIES)
3802 Robert Porcher Way, Greensboro, NC 27410-2190
Tel (336) 545-0011 *Founded/Ownrshp* 2004
Sales 252.7MM^E *EMP* 864^E
SIC 2221 3624 2241 2295 Glass broadwoven fabrics; Fibers, carbon & graphite; Glass narrow fabrics; Mats, varnished glass
CEO: Phillipe Porcher
**CFO:* Philippe R Dorier
Chf Mktg O: Robert Dunnagan
Ofcr: James R Henderson

NOV
See NATIONAL OILWELL VARCO INC

NOV
See TUBOSCOPE INC

D-U-N-S 07-061-7139 IMP
NOVA BIOMEDICAL CORP (MA)
200 Prospect St, Waltham, MA 02453-3465
Tel (781) 894-0800 *Founded/Ownrshp* 1976
Sales 310.4MM^E *EMP* 900
SIC 2833 3826 Medicinals & botanicals; Blood testing apparatus
Pr: Francis Manganaro
Pr: Eileen Konik
**CFO:* Luciano A Borrelli
VP: Jeff Chien
VP: Heraldo Couto
VP: Thomas Larkin
VP: John McHale
VP: James Sidwell
VP: Nicholas Theodore
Exec: Tony Yu
Prgrm Mgr: John Balsavich

NOVA BUS LFS, A DIVISION OF PR
See PREVOST CAR US INC

D-U-N-S 07-912-6143
NOVA CAPITAL MANAGEMENT USA LLC
(*Suby of* NOVA CAPITAL MANAGEMENT LIMITED)
401 N Michigan Ave # 1200, Chicago, IL 60611-4255
Tel (312) 822-3380 *Founded/Ownrshp* 2004
Sales 102.2MM^E *EMP* 405^E
SIC 6799 Investors

D-U-N-S 10-400-0625 IMP/EXP
NOVA CHEMICALS INC
(*Suby of* NC HOLDINGS USA INC.)
400 Frankfort Rd, Monaca, PA 15061-2212
Tel (412) 490-4560 *Founded/Ownrshp* 2016
Sales 1.2MMM^E *EMP* 2,131^E
SIC 2821 Polyethylene resins; Polystyrene resins
CEO: Todd D Karran
**Sr VP:* Chris Bezaire
**Sr VP:* Bill Greene
**Sr VP:* Grant Thomson
**Prin:* Randy G Woelfel
CTO: Todd Carrin
Board of Directors: Laurie Brlas, Pierre Choquette, John E Feick, Charles W Fischer, John Kuziak, Brian F Olson, Janice Rennie

NOVA CM
See NOVA CORP INC

D-U-N-S 09-384-3118 EXP
NOVA CORP INC
NOVA CM
1 Main St, Nyack, NY 10960-3231
Tel (201) 567-4404 *Founded/Ownrshp* 1979
Sales 98.4MM^E *EMP* 50
SIC 1541 8748 Industrial buildings & warehouses; Business consulting
Pr: Mark Di Stefano
**CFO:* Edward Bohn
**Ex VP:* Brian Fleury
Ex VP: Michael Maldari
Ex VP: Sue Massaro
**Ex VP:* Robert Pappas
**VP:* Judith Florio
VP: Brian Fluery
Assoc Dir: Paul Drew

D-U-N-S 06-609-9219
NOVA GROUP INC
NGI CONSTRUCTION
185 Devlin Rd, NAPA, CA 94558-6255
Tel (707) 265-1100 *Founded/Ownrshp* 1957
Sales 101.1MM^E *EMP* 200
SIC 1629 1623 1622 5172 Marine construction; Waterway construction; Underground utilities contractor; Tunnel construction; Aircraft fueling services
Pr: Ronald M Fedrick
**Pr:* Scott R Victor
**VP:* Carole Bionda
**VP:* Walter Birdsall
**VP:* Dee Fedrick
**VP:* Chris Mathies
VP: Walt Schwartz
VP: Scott Victor
Mng Dir: Ross Preston
Ql Cn Mgr: Kurt Kuha

D-U-N-S 06-116-2675
▲ NOVA LIFESTYLE INC (NV)
6565 E Washington Blvd, Commerce, CA 90040-1821
Tel (323) 888-9999 *Founded/Ownrshp* 2011, 2009
Sales 109.8MM *EMP* 522
Accts Crowe Horwath (Hk) Cpa Limited
Tkr Sym NVFY *Exch* NGM
SIC 2511 2512 Wood household furniture; Upholstered household furniture; Chairs: upholstered on wood frames
Ch Bd: Tawny Lam
CFO: Sammy Ho
**CFO:* Yuen Ching Ho
VP Mktg: Mark Chapman
VP Mktg: Ah Wan Wong

D-U-N-S 79-726-4009
NOVA MANAGEMENT INC
660 Camino Aguajito # 300, Monterey, CA 93940-3654
Tel (831) 373-4544 *Founded/Ownrshp* 1992
Sales 50.0MM *EMP* 1,800
SIC 8711 7361 Engineering services; Executive placement
Pr: Charles Tope

D-U-N-S 60-334-6529
NOVA MUD INC
IDA
5800 Nova, Hobbs, NM 88240-1328
Tel (575) 393-8786 *Founded/Ownrshp* 1989
Sales 115.8MM^E *EMP* 155
SIC 5169 Drilling mud
CEO: David Chu
**Pr:* Ken Bromley
**Treas:* C Dean Graves
**VP:* Scott Bromley
**VP:* Ruth L Greenstein
**VP:* Philip L Major
**VP:* Bill Smith

D-U-N-S 00-297-1240
NOVA SOUTHEASTERN UNIVERSITY INC
3301 College Ave, Davie, FL 33314-7796
Tel (954) 262-7300 *Founded/Ownrshp* 1964
Sales 678.1MM *EMP* 2,500
Accts Kpmg Llp Greensboro Nc
SIC 8221 8211 University; Elementary & secondary schools
Ch: Robert Steele
V Ch: Barry J Silverman
**Pr:* Dr George Larbury
COO: Jacqueline A Travisano
CFO: Henry Del Riego
CFO: Bibi Haddad
CFO: David Heron
CFO: Henry D Reigo
**CFO:* Alyson Silva
Trst: Mitchell W Berger
Trst: Keith A Brown
Trst: Rick Case
Trst: Andrew J Dibattista
Trst: Arthur J Falcone
Trst: Silvia M Flores
Trst: David W Horvitz
Trst: Royal F Jonas
Trst: Milton Jones
Trst: Alan B Levan
Trst: Nell M Lewis
Trst: Joseph R Millsaps

D-U-N-S 00-893-0755
NOVA USA INC
(*Suby of* FRUTAS CONCENTRADAS, S.A.P.I. DE C.V.)
500 W Overland Ave # 300, El Paso, TX 79901-1085
Tel (915) 594-1618 *Founded/Ownrshp* 1999
Sales 176.0MM *EMP* 230
SIC 6719 Investment holding companies, except banks
CEO: Luis Fernandez

D-U-N-S 09-946-4695 IMP
■ NOVACAP LLC
(*Suby of* KNOWLES CORP) ★
25111 Anza Dr, Valencia, CA 91355-3478
Tel (661) 295-5920 *Founded/Ownrshp* 1987
Sales 94.6MM^E *EMP* 280
SIC 3675 Electronic capacitors
CEO: Mark Skoog
Genl Mgr: Dee Akers
Plnt Mgr: John Sanders
Manager: Heather White
Sls Mgr: Joe Elias

D-U-N-S 96-221-6503 IMP
NOVAE CORP
I-69 TRAILER CENTER
1 Novae Pkwy, Markle, IN 46770-9087
Tel (260) 758-9800 *Founded/Ownrshp* 1995
Sales 87.8MM^E *EMP* 280^E
SIC 5084 3524 Trailers, industrial; Lawn & garden mowers & accessories
CEO: Steve Bermes
**COO:* Christopher Storie
CFO: Chris Story
**VP:* Mike Bermes
Dir Bus: Mark Yde
Off Mgr: Marty Westbrook
Snr Sftwr: Kal Govindu
Mtls Mgr: Chad Williams
Plnt Mgr: Chad Ousley
Sls Mgr: Shaun Davis

NOVAMEX
See TIPP DISTRIBUTORS INC

NOVANT HEALTH BRUNSWICK MEDICA
See BRUNSWICK NOVANT MEDICAL CENTER

D-U-N-S 07-960-5926
NOVANT HEALTH INC
3333 Silas Creek Pkwy, Winston Salem, NC 27103-3013
Tel (336) 718-5000 *Founded/Ownrshp* 1983
Sales NA *EMP* 256^E
SIC 6324 Hospital & medical service plans
Pr: Jeffrey T Lindsay
**COO:* Denise Mihal
VP: Chad Setliff
Dir Rx: Timothy Williams
Chf Nrs Of: Cathy Lewis
Off Mgr: Leonora Halen
Off Mgr: Birdie M Jackson
Off Mgr: Jan Wagoner
Info Man: Miranda Dicello
Mktg Dir: Kyle Norman
Mktg Dir: Leslie Robbins

D-U-N-S 15-973-5711
NOVANT HEALTH INC
LAKESIDE FAMILY PHYSICIANS
2085 Frontis Plaza Blvd, Winston Salem, NC 27103-5614
Tel (336) 277-1120 *Founded/Ownrshp* 1981
Sales 2.4MMM^E *EMP* 13,800
SIC 8062 General medical & surgical hospitals
CEO: Carl S Armato
COO: Richard Belden
COO: Denise Mihal
CFO: Dennis Bolin
CFO: Fred Hargett
CFO: Fred M Hargett
Treas: Ann Lampron
Bd of Dir: Sue Smith
Ofcr: Jesse Cureton
Ex VP: Jacque Daniels
Ex VP: Sallye A Liner
Ex VP: Stephen L Wallenhaupt
Sr VP: James Tobalski
VP: Yele Aluko
VP: Steven Burke
VP: Joe Carroll
VP: Tom Elmore
VP: Kathy Johnson
VP: Sean Keyser
VP: Janet Smith-Hill
VP Bus Dev: Derek Goldin

NOVANT HEALTH PRESBT MED CTR
See PRESBYTERIAN HOSPITAL

D-U-N-S 79-882-5634
NOVANT MEDICAL GROUP INC
(*Suby of* LAKESIDE FAMILY PHYSICIANS) ★
200 Hawthorne Ln, Charlotte, NC 28204-2515
Tel (704) 384-4966 *Founded/Ownrshp* 1998
Sales 97.2MM^E *EMP* 3,000
SIC 8011 Medical centers
Pr: Carl Armato

D-U-N-S 04-376-9173 IMP
■ NOVANTA CORP
GSI GROUP
(*Suby of* NOVANTA INC) ★
125 Middlesex Tpke, Bedford, MA 01730-1409
Tel (781) 266-5700 *Founded/Ownrshp* 1989
Sales 373.6MM *EMP* 1,355^E
Accts Pricewaterhousecoopers Llp Bo
SIC 3699 Laser systems & equipment
CEO: John A Roush
**Pr:* Jamie B Bader
**Pr:* Matthijs Glastra
**CFO:* Robert Buckley
**VP:* Peter Chang
**VP:* Deborah A Mulryan
**VP:* Brian Young
Genl Mgr: Robert Hyman
Genl Mgr: Matthew Reghitto
Sftwr Eng: John Crabtree
Corp Couns: Patrick Rykhus
Board of Directors: Stephen W Bershad, Harry Bosco, Dennis J Fortino, Ira J Lamel, Dominic Romeo, John A Roush, Thomas Secor

D-U-N-S 78-780-3761
▲ NOVANTA INC
125 Middlesex Tpke, Bedford, MA 01730-1409
Tel (781) 266-5700 *Founded/Ownrshp* 1968
Sales 373.6MM *EMP* 1,355^E
Tkr Sym NOVT *Exch* NGS
SIC 3699 3845 Laser systems & equipment; Laser welding, drilling & cutting equipment; Laser systems & equipment, medical
CEO: Matthijs Glastra
Ch Bd: Stephen W Bershad
CFO: Robert Buckley
Board of Directors: Harry L Bosco, Dennis J Fortino, Ira J Lamel, Dominic A Romeo, Thomas N Secor

D-U-N-S 02-049-2982
NOVARIA GROUP LLC
6300 Ridglea Pl Ste 800, Fort Worth, TX 76116-5708
Tel (817) 381-3810 *Founded/Ownrshp* 2011
Sales 109.4MM^E *EMP* 367^E
SIC 6726 Investment offices
Pr: Bryan D Perkins
VP: Mike Wagner

NOVARTIS ANIMAL HEALTH US INC
See ELANCO US INC

NOVARTIS CONSUMER HEALTH, INC.
See GSK CONSUMER HEALTHCARE

D-U-N-S 00-122-1845 IMP/EXP
NOVARTIS CORP (NY)
(*Suby of* NOVARTIS INTERNATIONAL AG)
520 White Plains Rd, Tarrytown, NY 10591-5102
Tel (212) 307-1122 *Founded/Ownrshp* 1903
Sales 49.4MMM^E *EMP* 30,186
SIC 2834 2879 2032 2865 Pharmaceutical preparations; Drugs acting on the cardiovascular system, except diagnostic; Drugs acting on the central nervous system & sense organs; Veterinary pharmaceutical preparations; Agricultural chemicals; Canned specialties; Cyclic crudes & intermediates
Ch Bd: Christi Shaw
**CFO:* Harry Kirsch
Treas: Kenneth J Schuster
Treas: Kenneth Schuster
VP: Susan Damico
VP: Deborah Dunshire
VP: Carole Grabowski
VP: Charles Koen
VP: Farryn Melton
VP: Robert Shearin
VP: Robert L Thompson Jr
Exec: Debra Burdick
Exec: Randy Perez
Assoc Dir: John Green
Assoc Dir: Karin Hunziker
Assoc Dir: John Jacques
Assoc Dir: John Robinson
Assoc Dir: David Speck

D-U-N-S 00-214-7023 IMP
NOVARTIS PHARMACEUTICALS CORP
NPS
(*Suby of* NOVARTIS CORP) ★
1 Health Plz, East Hanover, NJ 07936-1016
Tel (862) 778-8300 *Founded/Ownrshp* 1919
Sales 49.4MMM *EMP* 7,000
SIC 3826 Analytical instruments
Pr: Paulo Costa
Pr: Anna Frable
**Pr:* Gary E Rosenthal
**Pr:* Andre Wyss
**COO:* Alex Gorsky
**CFO:* Helen Boudreau
CFO: Paolo Tombesi
**Chf Mktg O:* Nancy Lurker
Ex VP: Bill Hinshaw
VP: Joan Antokol
VP: Scot Harper
VP: Robert Heinrich
VP: Kenny Hood

*VP: Julie Kane
VP: Dan Lopuch
VP: Brenda Luckritz
VP: Carol Lynch
VP: Kelli Moran
*VP: Yves Teirlynck
Assoc Dir: Jason Brown
Assoc Dir: Wenhua Deng

D-U-N-S 04-686-6463 IMP
NOVARTIS VACCINES AND DIAGNOSTICS INC
(Suby of GLAXOSMITHKLINE PLC)
350 Massachusetts Ave, Cambridge, MA 02139-4182
Tel (617) 871-7000 Founded/Ownrshp 2015
Sales 1.0MMM^E EMP 5,500
SIC 2834 2835 2836 Pharmaceutical preparations; Drugs affecting parasitic & infective diseases; In vitro & in vivo diagnostic substances; Vaccines & other immunizing products
CEO: Joerg Reinhardt
Natl Sales: Graham Thoms
Corp Couns: Suzanne Suppa
Board of Directors: Dr Daniel Vasella

D-U-N-S 12-487-7361
■ **NOVASTAR MORTGAGE LLC**
(Suby of NFI HOLDING CORPORATION)
2114 Central St Ste 600, Kansas City, MO 64108-2098
Tel (816) 237-7000 Founded/Ownrshp 1996
Sales NA EMP 1,600
SIC 6162 Mortgage bankers
*Pr: W Lance Anderson
*CFO: Rodney Schwatken

D-U-N-S 01-548-9406
NOVATECH HOLDINGS CORP
(Suby of WEIR SPM) ★
8388 C F Hawn Fwy, Dallas, TX 75217-7009
Tel (214) 398-1491 Founded/Ownrshp 2012
Sales 90.0MM^E EMP 1,220
SIC 3491 Pressure valves & regulators, industrial
Pr: Jack Rogers
*VP: Dave Warnick

D-U-N-S 11-102-3727 IMP
▲ **NOVATEL WIRELESS INC**
9645 Scranton Rd Ste 205, San Diego, CA 92121-1764
Tel (858) 812-3400 Founded/Ownrshp 1996
Sales 220.9MM EMP 1,330
Tkr Sym INSG Exch NGS
SIC 3661 7371 Modems; Computer software development & applications; Computer software development
Ch Bd: Sue Swenson
CFO: Michael Newman
Ex VP: Stephen Sek
Sr VP: Lance Bridges
VP: Jutta Gebauer
Manager: Rod Macleod
Board of Directors: Philip Falcone, James Ledwith, Robert Pons, David Werner

D-U-N-S 79-351-8643 IMP
NOVEL LABORATORIES INC
(Suby of LUPIN PHARMACEUTICALS INC) ★
400 Campus Dr, Somerset, NJ 08873-1145
Tel (908) 603-6000 Founded/Ownrshp 2016
Sales 84.1MM^E EMP 175
SIC 2834 Pharmaceutical preparations
Pr: Veerappan Subramanian
QA Dir: Irina Shnayder
Prd Mgr: Lakshmi Nammalzar
Genl Couns: Anand Natarajan
Snr Mgr: Sita Nuti

NOVEL WRITING WORKSHOP
See F+W MEDIA INC

D-U-N-S 00-699-9676
NOVELART MANUFACTURING CO
TOPICZ
2121 Section Rd, Cincinnati, OH 45237-3509
Tel (513) 351-7700 Founded/Ownrshp 1903
Sales 361.7MM EMP 160
Accts Pitcher Enders & Drohan Cinc
SIC 5141 5145 5194 Groceries, general line; Confectionery; Tobacco & tobacco products
Pr: Marvin H Schwartz
Genl Mgr: Dan Sunderhaus
CIO: Bob Reckers
Dir IT: Bob Schilling

D-U-N-S 61-349-8067
NOVELION THERAPEUTICS INC
AEGERION PHARMACEUTICALS
(Suby of QLT INC)
1 Main St 800, Cambridge, MA 02142-1531
Tel (877) 764-3131 Founded/Ownrshp 2016
Sales 239.8MM EMP 12^E
SIC 2834 Pharmaceutical preparations
CEO: Mary Szela
Ofcr: Roger Louis
Ofcr: Remi Menes
Ofcr: Gregory Perry
Ex VP: John Orloff
Ex VP: John J Orloff
Sr VP: Linda Buono
Genl Couns: Ben Harshberger

D-U-N-S 00-150-4935 EXP
NOVELIS CORP (TX)
ADITYA BIRLA GROUP
(Suby of NOVELIS INC) ★
3560 Lenox Rd Ne Ste 2000, Atlanta, GA 30326-4271
Tel (404) 760-4000 Founded/Ownrshp 1960, 2007
Sales 1.1MMM^E EMP 3,000
SIC 3353 Aluminum sheet, plate & foil; Foil, aluminum
CEO: Marco Palmieri
*CEO: Thomas Walpole
*CFO: Tracy Tan
*Treas: Glen Gurnan
*Ofcr: Erwin Mayr
*VP: Charles R Aley
*VP: Brenda Pulley
Ql Cn Mgr: Kara Dinatale
Ql Cn Mgr: Jennifer Sater
Snr Mgr: Tom Granbois

D-U-N-S 96-325-8483 IMP/EXP
NOVELIS INC
(Suby of HINDALCO INDUSTRIES LIMITED)
3560 Lenox Rd Ne Ste 2000, Atlanta, GA 30326-4271
Tel (404) 760-4000 Founded/Ownrshp 2004
Sales 11.1MMM EMP 11,560^E
SIC 3355 Aluminum rolling & drawing; Aluminum ingot
Pr: Steve Fisher
Ch Bd: Kumar Mangalam Birla
Pr: Shashi Maudgal
Pr: Erwin Mayr
Pr: Antonio Tadeu Coelho Nardocci
Pr: Marco Palmieri
CFO: Devinder Ahuja
CFO: Steven Pohl
Treas: Randal P Miller
V Ch Bd: D Bhattacharya
Ofcr: Leslie Joyce
Sr VP: Jack Clark
Sr VP: Leslie J Parrette Jr
VP: Bill Devine
VP: Steve Fehling
VP: Michael Hahne
VP: Bob Nelson
VP: Robert Nelson
VP: Stephanie Rauls
VP: Karen Renner
VP: Eddreania Roan
Board of Directors: Clarence J Chandran, Satish Pai, Donald A Stewart

D-U-N-S 03-778-7298
NOVELL INC
1800 Novell Pl, Provo, UT 84606-6101
Tel (801) 861-4272 Founded/Ownrshp 2011
Sales 575.3MM^E EMP 3,400
SIC 7372 Prepackaged software
Pr: Jeff Hawn
Ch Bd: Gerard Van Kemmel
*Pr: Bob Flynn
Pr: Rhonda O'Donnell
Pr: Tim Wolfe
*CFO: Dana C Russell
*CFO: Charles Sanbury
*Treas: Jim Beck
*Chf Mktg O: John K Dragoon
Sr VP: Jim Ebzery
Sr VP: Carl S Ledbetter
*Sr VP: Russell C Poole
*Sr VP: Scott N Semel
Sr VP: John J Slitz Jr
VP: Jos Almandoz
*VP: Juan Carlos Cerrutti
VP: Ronalda De Jong
VP: Boris Ivancic
VP: Ron Milton
VP: Sergio Toshio Mituiwa
VP: Katherine Tate

D-U-N-S 05-378-4232
■ **NOVELLA CLINICAL INC**
(Suby of QUINTILES INC) ★
1700 Perimeter Park Dr, Morrisville, NC 27560-8404
Tel (919) 484-1921 Founded/Ownrshp 2013
Sales 87.5MM^E EMP 670
SIC 8731 Medical research, commercial
Pr: W Richard Staub III
*COO: Robert King
*CFO: Charles R Lambert
*Chf Mktg O: Frank Santoro
Ex VP: Nick Dyer
Ex VP: Wingate Elaine
*Ex VP: Krystyna Kowalczyk
*Ex VP: Rob Stallings
Ex VP: Elaine Wingate
VP: Jane Bentley
VP: Elizabeth Edwards
VP: Kimberly Hunsicker
VP: Rob Murray
VP: David Novotny
VP: Stan Patterson
VP: Cathy White
Assoc Dir: Elli Ganas
Assoc Dir: Stacey King
Assoc Dir: Nathan Landon
Assoc Dir: Stephanie Love

D-U-N-S 11-330-3416
NOVELLUS SYSTEMS INC
4000 N 1st St, San Jose, CA 95134-1568
Tel (408) 943-9700 Founded/Ownrshp 2012
Sales NA EMP 2,855^E
SIC 3559

D-U-N-S 14-858-5441 IMP
NOVEN PHARMACEUTICALS INC
(Suby of HISAMITSU PHARMACEUTICAL CO INC) ★
11960 Sw 144th St, Miami, FL 33186-6109
Tel (305) 964-3393 Founded/Ownrshp 2009
Sales 137.2MM^E EMP 586
SIC 2834 Pharmaceutical preparations
CEO: Jeff Mihm
*CFO: John Choi
CFO: William Pecora
Bd of Dir: Melinda Downs
Bd of Dir: Bryan Foughty
Bd of Dir: Julie Pomerantz
*Ofcr: Ralph Lipp
*Ex VP: Joel Lippman
Ex VP: Grace Lopez
*VP: Peter Amanatides
VP: Peter G Amanatides
*VP: Brian J Board
VP: Jason Bone
VP: Carrie Bowers
VP: Anthony De Padova
*VP: Steven M Dinh
VP: Bruce Friedman
*VP: Patrick Gallagher
*VP: Richard Gilbert
*VP: Michael Greene
*VP: Joseph C Jones

D-U-N-S 96-929-1306
NOVETTA SOLUTIONS LLC
7921 Jones Branch Dr # 500, Mc Lean, VA 22102-3354
Tel (571) 282 3000 Founded/Ownrshp 2012
Sales 119.7MM^E EMP 430^E
SIC 7373 Systems engineering, computer related
CEO: Peter Lamontagne
Pr: Scott Gessay
CFO: Richard Sawcahk
Chf Mktg O: Richard Clements
Sr VP: Raj Navavati
VP: Kim Bartoe
VP: Keith Dill
VP: Mark Procaccini
Prgrm Mgr: Judith Renaud
Snr Sftwr: Kathleen Romanik
Snr Sftwr: Lauren Sandbek

D-U-N-S 18-109-8997
NOVINGER GROUP INC
1441 Stoneridge Dr, Middletown, PA 17057-5977
Tel (717) 930-0300 Founded/Ownrshp 1987
Sales 129.2MM^E EMP 351
SIC 1742 1799 5032 5033 5039 Drywall; Plastering, plain or ornamental; Fireproofing buildings; Drywall materials; Insulation, thermal; Ceiling systems & products
Pr: James D Novinger
COO: Bob Myers

D-U-N-S 13-430-6138
NOVINIUM INC
22820 Russell Rd, Kent, WA 98032-4892
Tel (253) 288-7100 Founded/Ownrshp 2003
Sales 109.8MM^E EMP 240
SIC 1521 General remodeling, single-family houses
*CFO: David L Lewis
*VP: Richard K Brinton
*VP: Kurt Wangenheim
Area Mgr: Matthew Thomas

D-U-N-S 07-976-8050
NOVIPAX LLC
(Suby of ATLAS HOLDINGS LLC) ★
2215 York Rd Ste 504, Oak Brook, IL 60523-2379
Tel (630) 686-2735 Founded/Ownrshp 2015
Sales 127.5MM^E EMP 671
SIC 2821 2299 Polystyrene resins; Padding & wadding, textile
CEO: Bob Larson
CFO: Jeffrey Williams

D-U-N-S 78-598-5354
NOVITAS SOLUTIONS INC
(Suby of GUIDEWELL SOURCE) ★
2020 Tech Pkwy Ste 100, Mechanicsburg, PA 17050
Tel (717) 526-3459 Founded/Ownrshp 2012
Sales NA EMP 791^E
SIC 6321 Accident & health insurance
CEO: Sandra Coston
*Treas: Thomas Hickson
VP: Carolyn Cridlersmith
Genl Mgr: Samantha Bailor
Genl Mgr: Joanne Grier
Genl Mgr: Gayeta Porter
IT Man: Christopher Moir
VP Opers: David Vaughan

D-U-N-S 12-173-3018
NOVITEX ENTERPRISE SOLUTIONS INC
300 First Stamford Pl # 2, Stamford, CT 06902-6765
Tel (844) 668-4839 Founded/Ownrshp 2013
Sales 478.3MM^E EMP 2,850^E
SIC 7334 8741 Photocopying & duplicating services; Management services
CEO: John Visentin
*Pr: Irina Novoselsky
*COO: Joe Trost
*CFO: Robert G Rooney
VP: Dawn Marie Weimer
Opers Mgr: Milton Otey
Snr Mgr: Beth Allison
Snr Mgr: Howard Vermonth

D-U-N-S 04-961-0942
NOVITEX GOVERNMENT SOLUTIONS LLC
(Suby of NOVITEX ENTERPRISE SOLUTIONS INC) ★
8401 Corporate Dr Ste 420, Landover, MD 20785-2277
Tel (301) 731-4595 Founded/Ownrshp 2012
Sales 77.7MM^E EMP 1,400
SIC 8744 Facilities support services
Pr: Irina Novoselsky
Exec: Theresa Mohan

D-U-N-S 01-031-3018
NOVO 1 INC
(Suby of DIALOGDIRECT INC) ★
4301 Cambridge Rd, Fort Worth, TX 76155-2627
Tel (817) 355-8909 Founded/Ownrshp 2016
Sales 114.9MM^E EMP 2,500^E
SIC 7389 Telemarketing services
CEO: Mary Murcott
*COO: Eric Rothert
*CFO: John Sykstus
*Chf Mktg O: Jack Wilkie
Sr VP: Rosemary Bennett
Dir Rx: Christopher Wade
*CTO: Mitchell Swindell
Dir IT: Bob Gardner
Opers Mgr: Michelle Wilson

D-U-N-S 06-571-2247
NOVO CONSTRUCTION INC
1460 Obrien Dr, Menlo Park, CA 94025-1432
Tel (650) 701-1500 Founded/Ownrshp 2000
Sales 553.8MM EMP 155
SIC 1542 Commercial & office building contractors
CEO: James C Fowler
*Pr: Jim Fowler
Exec: Doug Ballou
Exec: Chuck Flynn
Exec: Tom Smoll
Off Mgr: Jennifer Hampson
Sfty Dirs: Thomas Allison
Snr PM: Mike Bank
Snr PM: Noel Howard
Snr PM: Curtis Ikemoto
Snr PM: Yudice Sean

D-U-N-S 94-209-2466
NOVO FOUNDATION
535 5th Ave Fl 33, New York, NY 10017-3665
Tel (212) 808-5400 Founded/Ownrshp 1999
Sales 157.2MM EMP 5
SIC 8641 Civic social & fraternal associations
Off Mgr: Kelly Merryman

D-U-N-S 01-217-7531 IMP/EXP
NOVO NORDISK INC
(Suby of NOVO-NORDISK OF NORTH AMERICA INC) ★
800 Scudders Mill Rd, Plainsboro, NJ 08536-1606
Tel (609) 987-5800 Founded/Ownrshp 1989
Sales 257.3MM^E EMP 390^E
SIC 2834 Pharmaceutical preparations
Pr: Jesper Hiland
*Pr: Martin Soeters
Sr Cor Off: Claus Jordan
*Chf Mktg O: Alan C Moses
Ex VP: Lars Almblom
*Sr VP: Andrew Ajello
*Sr VP: Lars Green
Sr VP: Camille Lee
*VP: Philip Fornecker
VP: Peter Haahr
VP: Eddie Li
VP: Fill Niels
VP: Karin Nielsen
VP: Curtis G Oltmans
VP: Andrew J Purcell
VP: Henrik Rasmussen
VP: Jackie Scanlan
VP: Hanne Schou-Rode
VP: Michael Shalmi
Exec: Jerzy Gruhn
Assoc Dir: Craig Delarge

D-U-N-S 62-292-0320 IMP/EXP
NOVO NORDISK PHARMACEUTICAL INDUSTRIES INC
(Suby of NOVO NORDISK INC) ★
3612 Powhatan Rd, Clayton, NC 27527-9217
Tel (919) 550-2200 Founded/Ownrshp 1991
Sales 152.2MM^E EMP 390
SIC 2833 Insulin: bulk, uncompounded
Prin: David W Bright
VP: Birgitte Rassing
VP: Joann Sufalko
*VP: Palle Thorsen
VP: Per Valstorp
Exec: Stefan Daugaard
Assoc Dir: David Kamenir
Dist Mgr: Nathaniel Lewey
Genl Mgr: Douglas Tharp
QA Dir: Paul Nelson
IT Man: Amy Hill

D-U-N-S 19-680-1849 IMP
NOVO-NORDISK OF NORTH AMERICA INC
(Suby of NOVO NORDISK A/S)
800 Scudders Mill Rd, Plainsboro, NJ 08536-1606
Tel (609) 987-5800 Founded/Ownrshp 1976
Sales 257.3MM^E EMP 1,200
SIC 8741 8733 5122 2833 2834 Management services; Medical research; Drugs, proprietaries & sundries; Insulin: bulk, uncompounded; Pharmaceutical preparations
Ex VP: Jerzy Gruhn
Pr: Lars Jrgensen
VP: Per Lundgren
IT Man: Jennifer Holmes
Ql Cn Mgr: Rene Pedersen
Ql Cn Mgr: Bill Quinn
Ql Cn Mgr: Xu Yang
Snr Mgr: Matthew Ford

NOVOLEX
See HERITAGE BAG CO

NOVOLEX
See HILEX POLY CO LLC

D-U-N-S 07-978-7120
NOVOLEX HOLDINGS INC
101 E Carolina Ave, Hartsville, SC 29550-4213
Tel (843) 857-4800 Founded/Ownrshp 2009
Sales 2.2MMM^E EMP 5,000
SIC 2673 2674 Plastic bags: made from purchased materials; Paper bags: made from purchased materials
Pr: Stanley B Bikulege
*CFO: Paul Palmisano
*Sr VP: Mark Daniels
*VP: Joyce A Foster

D-U-N-S 05-209-0909 IMP/EXP
NOVOZYMES NORTH AMERICA INC
(Suby of NOVOZYMES A/S)
77 Perry Chapel Church Rd, Franklinton, NC 27525-9677
Tel (919) 494-2014 Founded/Ownrshp 1969
Sales 167.9MM^E EMP 400^E
SIC 2869 Enzymes
Ch Bd: Adam Monroe
*Pr: Steen Riisgaard
CFO: John Gaebler
*CFO: Benny D Loft
*VP: Per Falholt
VP: Claus C Fuglsang
*VP: Thomas Nagy
Rgnl Mgr: Christopher Kruszewski
Mktg Mgr: Daniel Evanson

D-U-N-S 62-652-1264 IMP/EXP
NOVUS INTERNATIONAL INC
(Suby of MITSUI & CO (USA) INC) ★
20 Research Park Dr, Saint Charles, MO 63304-5633
Tel (314) 576-8886 Founded/Ownrshp 1991
Sales 212.8MM^E EMP 350
SIC 0752 Grooming services, pet & animal specialties
CEO: Francois Fraudeau
Pr: Gasperoni Giovanni
*Pr: Jeff Klopfenstein
*CFO: John C Wade
VP: Yuhei Saito
Exec: Olivia Lindsey
Tech Mgr: Omar Gutierrez
Mktg Dir: Ted Estwan
Sls Dir: Scott Moore
Mktg Mgr: Daniela Prestes
Sls Mgr: Jorge Gonzalez

D-U-N-S 06-747-2530 IMP/EXP
NOW HEALTH GROUP INC
NOW NATURAL FOODS
244 Knollwood Dr Ste 300, Bloomingdale, IL 60108-2288
Tel (630) 545-9098 *Founded/Ownrshp* 1962
Sales 379.0MM[E] *EMP* 985
SIC 2834 Vitamin, nutrient & hematinic preparations for human use
Ch Bd: Elwood Richard
**Pr:* Albert Powers
Ofcr: Angela H Marte
VP: Dan Scoles
Genl Mgr: Dave Reczek
Genl Mgr: Dan Richard
CTO: Marria Newman
QA Dir: Azad Lakhani
VP Opers: Jim Emme
Mfg Mgr: Michael Utech
Ql Cn Mgr: David Laureano

D-U-N-S 07-933-0215
▲ NOW INC
7402 N Eldridge Pkwy, Houston, TX 77041-1902
Tel (281) 823-4700 *Founded/Ownrshp* 2013
Sales 3.0MMM *EMP* 5,000[E]
Tkr Sym DNOW *Exch* NYS
SIC 5084 Industrial machinery & equipment; Petroleum industry machinery
Pr: Robert R Workman
Ch Bd: Merrill A Miller Jr
CFO: Daniel L Molinaro
VP: Raymond W Chang
VP: David A Cherechinsky
VP: David Cherechinsky
Board of Directors: Richard Alario, Terry Bonno, Galen Cobb, James Crandell, Rodney Eads, Michael Frazier, J Wayne Richards

NOW NATURAL FOODS
See NOW HEALTH GROUP INC

D-U-N-S 00-308-2997 IMP
■ NOXELL CORP
PROCTER & GAMBLE COSMETICS
(*Suby of* P&G) ★
11050 York Rd, Hunt Valley, MD 21030-2098
Tel (410) 785-7300 *Founded/Ownrshp* 1912
Sales 183.1MM[E] *EMP* 1,509
SIC 2844 Cosmetic preparations; Perfumes & colognes; Toilet preparations
Pr: Marc S Pritchard
VP: Robert Blanchard
VP: Carroll A Bodie
VP: Clayton C Daley Jr
VP: James J Hoskins
VP: Richard G Pease
VP: Valarie Sheppard
VP Admn: Stanley Boric
Snr Mgr: Eric S Beyer

D-U-N-S 08-045-7529
NP PAPER CO LLC
(*Suby of* ONE ROCK CAPITAL PARTNERS LLC) ★
3001 Industrial Way, Longview, WA 98632
Tel (360) 636-6400 *Founded/Ownrshp* 2016
Sales 477.0MM[E] *EMP* 410[E]
SIC 2621 Newsprint paper
Prin: Tony W Lee

D-U-N-S 07-912-8769
■ NPC GROUP INC
(*Suby of* VANTIV INC) ★
5100 Interchange Way, Louisville, KY 40229-2160
Tel (312) 627-6000 *Founded/Ownrshp* 2013
Sales 24.8MM[E] *EMP* 2,493
SIC 7389 Credit card service
CEO: Charles D Drucker

D-U-N-S 00-433-9727
NPC INC (PA)
13710 Dunnings Hwy, Claysburg, PA 16625-7802
Tel (814) 239-8787 *Founded/Ownrshp* 1931
Sales 95.3MM[E] *EMP* 450
SIC 2752 2789 2759 Commercial printing, offset; Bookbinding & related work; Commercial printing
Ch Bd: Mark N Barnhart
Pr: Mark Kelly
Ofcr: Joe Bieniek
Ex VP: Tim McCarthy
VP: Joshua E Barnhart
VP: Ed Detwiler
VP: Chip W Gallaher
VP: Robert R Latoche
VP: Timothy P McCarthy
CTO: Chip Gallaher
IT Man: Mark Gallaher
Board of Directors: Mark Gallaher, Thomas E Schwartz

D-U-N-S 07-835-5793
NPC INTERNATIONAL HOLDINGS INC
7300 W 129th St, Overland Park, KS 66213-2631
Tel (913) 327-3109 *Founded/Ownrshp* 2011
Sales 1.2MMM[E] *EMP* 29,000[E]
SIC 5812 Pizzeria, chain
Ch Bd: James K Schwartz

D-U-N-S 07-626-4456 IMP
NPC INTERNATIONAL INC
PIZZA HUT
(*Suby of* NPC RESTAURANT HOLDINGS LLC) ★
7300 W 129th St, Overland Park, KS 66213-2631
Tel (913) 632-0300 *Founded/Ownrshp* 2006
Sales 916.2MM[E] *EMP* 25,000[E]
SIC 5812 Pizzeria, chain
Ch: James K Schwartz
COO: J Hedrick
CFO: Troy D Cook
Sr VP: Marty Couk
VP: L Bruce Sharp
VP: D Blayne Vaughn
VP: Michael J Woods
VP Mktg: Linda L Sheedy
Mktg Dir: Michelle Mandley
Mktg Dir: Janis Speaks
Board of Directors: Brandon K Barnholt, Christopher J Birosak, Robert F End, Charles W Peffer

D-U-N-S 80-847-1796
NPC RESTAURANT HOLDINGS LLC
(*Suby of* NPC INTERNATIONAL HOLDINGS INC) ★
7300 W 129th St, Overland Park, KS 66213-2631
Tel (913) 327-5555 *Founded/Ownrshp* 2011
Sales 1.2MMM *EMP* 29,000
Accts Kpmg Llp Kansas City Missour
SIC 5812 6794 Pizzeria, chain; Fast-food restaurant, chain; Franchises, selling or licensing
Ch Bd: James K Schwartz
CFO: Troy D Cook
Sr VP: Linda L Sheedy
Sr VP: D Blayne Vaughn

NPC SALES
See BA MERCHANT SERVICES

D-U-N-S 06-593-6890
NPD GROUP INC
900 W Shore Rd, Port Washington, NY 11050-4663
Tel (516) 625-0700 *Founded/Ownrshp* 1966
Sales 300.0MM *EMP* 1,447
SIC 8732 Market analysis or research
Pr: Tod Johnson
Pr: Tim Bush
**COO:* Karyn Schoenbart
CFO: Sonia Cox
**CFO:* Tom Lynch
Sr VP: John Deputato
Sr VP: Chris Kyriacou
Sr VP: Lisa Schultz
VP: Allan Baldinger
VP: Harry Balzer
VP: Bob Brien
VP: Stephen Costello
VP: Luis Delahoz
VP: Isabelle Grenet
VP: Christine Miserandino
VP: Mike Oak
VP: Patricia Riehl
VP: Warren Solochek
VP: Mark Truss
VP: Jane A Zimmy

NPG NEWSPAPERS
See NEWS-PRESS & GAZETTE CO INC

D-U-N-S 17-524-9432
NPI PROPERTY MANAGEMENT CORP
(*Suby of* AIMCO PROPERTIES LP) ★
55 Beattie Pl, Greenville, SC 29601-2165
Tel (864) 239-1000 *Founded/Ownrshp* 1994
Sales 102.3MM[E] *EMP* 1,474[E]
SIC 6798 Real estate investment trusts
Pr: David Robertson

D-U-N-S 04-230-0384
■ NPL CONSTRUCTION CO
(*Suby of* SOUTHWEST GAS CORP) ★
2355 W Utopia Rd, Phoenix, AZ 85027-4167
Tel (623) 582-1235 *Founded/Ownrshp* 1967
Sales 1.1MMM[E] *EMP* 2,219
SIC 1623 Oil & gas pipeline construction
Pr: James P Kane
Ofcr: Dan Weaklend
**VP:* Mark S Wambach
Area Mgr: Brian Hallan
Off Admin: Jessica Dawson
Dir IT: Mike McConnell
Sfty Mgr: Manuel Collazo
Mktg Mgr: Jessica Franklin

D-U-N-S 16-917-5382
NPP LLC
4860 33rd Ave, Columbus, NE 68601-1662
Tel (402) 564-9464 *Founded/Ownrshp* 2007
Sales 100.0MM *EMP* 350
SIC 0213 Hogs
**CFO:* Jim Rasmussen

NPPI
See NATIONAL PIPE & PLASTICS INC

D-U-N-S 10-107-0238
NPPI INTERMEDIATE INC
106 E 6th St Ste 300, Austin, TX 78701-3661
Tel (512) 476-7100 *Founded/Ownrshp* 2001
Sales 361.8MM *EMP* 35
SIC 3086 Insulation or cushioning material, foamed plastic; Ice chests or coolers (portable), foamed plastic; Cups & plates, foamed plastic
Ch Bd: Michael Stakias
CFO: James Gunning
**CFO:* Gary Kofnovec
**Treas:* Mike Derrick
VP: Debra Garrett
VP: Gary Haley
VP: Paul W Larson
VP: Kevin Poirier
**VP:* David Rogalski
Mktg Mgr: James Preston

NPS
See NOVARTIS PHARMACEUTICALS CORP

NRAO
See NATIONAL RADIO ASTRONOMY OBSERVATORY

NRC
See NATIONAL RESEARCH CORP

D-U-N-S 03-377-0956
NRD HOLDINGS LLC (FL)
625 Dekalb Ste 100, Decatur, GA 30033
Tel (404) 499-1960 *Founded/Ownrshp* 2010
Sales NA *EMP* 1,200
SIC 6719 Investment holding companies, except banks
Pr: Aziz Hashim

NRDC
See NATURAL RESOURCES DEFENSE COUNCIL INC

NREC
See NATIONAL RAILWAY EQUIPMENT CO

NRECA
See NATIONAL RURAL ELECTRIC COOPERATIVE ASSOCIATION

D-U-N-S 06-184-9881 IMP
NRF DISTRIBUTORS INC
485 Old Belgrade Rd, Augusta, ME 04330-8061
Tel (207) 622-4744 *Founded/Ownrshp* 1973
Sales 126.9MM *EMP* 310
SIC 5023

NRG
See GENON ENERGY INC

D-U-N-S 79-342-2213 IMP
▲ NRG ENERGY INC
804 Carnegie Ctr, Princeton, NJ 08540-6023
Tel (609) 524-4500 *Founded/Ownrshp* 1989
Sales 14.6MMM *EMP* 10,468
Accts Kpmg Llp Philadelphia Pennsy
Tkr Sym NRG *Exch* NYS
SIC 4911 Electric services; Distribution, electric power; Generation, electric power; Transmission, electric power
Pr: Mauricio Gutierrez
**Ch Bd:* Howard E Cosgrove
CFO: Kirkland B Andrews
**V Ch Bd:* Edward R Muller
Chf Mktg O: Sicily Dickenson
Ex VP: John Chillemi
Ex VP: David R Hill
Ex VP: Elizabeth Killinger
Sr VP: Donna Benefield
Sr VP: Chris Moser
VP: Nahla Azmy
VP: John X Bates
VP: Kevin Boudreaux
VP: David Callen
VP: Don Claybaugh
VP: Bill Clayton
VP: Steve Corneli
VP: Mark Herrmann
VP: Lee McFalls
VP: Chad Plotkin
VP: Susan Rogers
Board of Directors: E Spencer Abraham, Lawrence S Coben, Terry G Dallas, William E Hantke, Paul W Hobby, Anne C Schaumburg, Evan J Silverstein, Thomas H Weidemeyer, Walter R Young

D-U-N-S 02-550-3157
NRG MANUFACTURING INC
11311 Holderrieth Rd # 100, Tomball, TX 77375-7385
Tel (281) 320-2525 *Founded/Ownrshp* 2001
Sales 109.8MM[E] *EMP* 140
SIC 3449 3441 Miscellaneous metalwork; Fabricated structural metal
Pr: Mark Terry
**Sec:* James Cauble
**VP:* Tom Giles
**VP:* Rachael Terry
VP Opers: Tim Rodabough
Opers Mgr: Jason Neel
VP Sls: David Leiper
Pgrm Dir: Robert Chevalier

D-U-N-S 12-468-6408
NRG MEDIA LLC
2875 Mount Vernon Rd Se, Cedar Rapids, IA 52403-3553
Tel (319) 862-0300 *Founded/Ownrshp* 2002
Sales 197.8MM[E] *EMP* 749
SIC 4832 Radio broadcasting stations
Exec: Dallas Nau
Genl Mgr: Mary Harris
Genl Mgr: Kurt Luchs
IT Man: Charlie Johnson
Prd Mgr: Gary Douglas
Mktg Dir: Brooke Schulz
Sls Dir: Aleese Fielder
Sls Mgr: Stacie McElligott
Pgrm Dir: Andrew Mihm

D-U-N-S 15-588-4732
■ NRG NORTHEAST GENERATING LLC
(*Suby of* NRG ENERGY INC) ★
211 Carnegie Ctr, Princeton, NJ 08540-6299
Tel (609) 524-4500 *Founded/Ownrshp* 2000
Sales 328.1MM[E] *EMP* 363
SIC 4911
Opers Mgr: Robert Hemperley

D-U-N-S 02-825-5979 IMP
■ NRG POWER MARKETING LLC
(*Suby of* NRG ENERGY INC) ★
804 Carnegie Ctr, Princeton, NJ 08540-6023
Tel (609) 524-4500 *Founded/Ownrshp* 2000, 2007
Sales 187.3MM[E] *EMP* 245
SIC 4911 4924 Distribution, electric power; Natural gas distribution
Sr VP: John Chillemi
Treas: Clint Freeland
**Ex VP:* Kirkland Andrews
**Ex VP:* Anne M Cleary
**Ex VP:* Lee Davis
**Prin:* Jeffrey Baudier
**Prin:* M Hoffmann
**Prin:* J Murphy
Board of Directors: Jeffrey Baudier, M Hoffmann, J Murphy

D-U-N-S 96-497-4310
■ NRG REMA LLC
(*Suby of* NRG ENERGY INC) ★
1000 Main St, Houston, TX 77002-6336
Tel (713) 497-3000 *Founded/Ownrshp* 1998
Sales 2.2MMM[E] *EMP* 860[E]
SIC 4911 Electric services
Pr: William Lee Davis
**VP:* Daniel M Keane
**VP:* Judith Lagano
**VP:* Christopher S Moser
**VP:* Phil Williamson

D-U-N-S 17-277-4379
■ NRG TEXAS LLC
(*Suby of* NRG ENERGY INC) ★
521 5th Ave Fl 30, New York, NY 10175-3001
Tel (713) 795-6000 *Founded/Ownrshp* 2006
Sales 647.3MM[E] *EMP* 2,015
SIC 4911 Generation, electric power; Transmission, electric power

D-U-N-S 07-849-8291
■ NRG TEXAS POWER LLC
(*Suby of* NRG ENERGY INC) ★
1301 Mckinney St Ste 2300, Houston, TX 77010-3035
Tel (713) 537-3000 *Founded/Ownrshp* 2012
Sales 2.3MMM[E] *EMP* 7,786
SIC 3621 Motors & generators

D-U-N-S 07-887-0121
■ NRG YIELD INC
(*Suby of* NRG ENERGY INC) ★
804 Carnegie Ctr, Princeton, NJ 08540-6023
Tel (609) 524-4500 *Founded/Ownrshp* 2012
Sales 869.0MM *EMP* 6[E]
Tkr Sym NYLD *Exch* NYS
SIC 4911 Electric services; Distribution, electric power; Generation, electric power; Transmission, electric power
CEO: Mauricio Gutierrez
**Pr:* Christopher S Sotos
CFO: Chad Plotkin
Ex VP: David R Hill
VP: David Callen

D-U-N-S 85-845-1784
NRHMC INC
SOUND SHORE MEDICAL CENTER
16 Guion Pl, New Rochelle, NY 10801-5502
Tel (914) 632-5000 *Founded/Ownrshp* 1983
Sales 179.1MM[E] *EMP* 1,232
SIC 8062 8721 General medical & surgical hospitals; Hospital, AMA approved residency; Accounting, auditing & bookkeeping
Pr: John R Spicer
**Ch Bd:* Lawrence Ruisi
**COO:* Douglas O Landy
**CFO:* Thomas M Daly
**Treas:* James Millstein
**V Ch Bd:* Thomas M McEvoy
Plnt Mgr: Carey Laramore
Obsttrcn: Edward Amelemah
Ansthlgy: Michael Whang
Opthamlgy: Robert Baker
Opthamlgy: Rajendra Bansal

D-U-N-S 07-266-3750
NRI INC
NRI STAFFING RESOURCES
1015 18th St Nw Ste 710, Washington, DC 20036-5206
Tel (202) 466-4670 *Founded/Ownrshp* 1972
Sales 9.5MM *EMP* 2,740
SIC 7363 7361 Temporary help service; Executive placement
Pr: Robert Mulberger
**Treas:* Robert McClimans
Founder: Les Meil
Dist Mgr: Ernie Lorandeau

NRI STAFFING RESOURCES
See NRI INC

NRL
See NAVAL RESEARCH LABORATORY

NRMS
See NASH-ROCKY MOUNT SCHOOLS

D-U-N-S 93-186-8376
NRP CONTRACTORS LLC
5309 Transportation Blvd, Cleveland, OH 44125-5333
Tel (216) 475-8900 *Founded/Ownrshp* 1995
Sales 95.8MM[E] *EMP* 100
Accts Ss & G Financial Sources Inc
SIC 1521 1522 Single-family housing construction; Hotel/motel & multi-family home construction
CFO: Andrew Tanner

D-U-N-S 14-658-9440
NRP HOLDINGS LLC
5309 Transportation Blvd, Cleveland, OH 44125-5333
Tel (216) 475-8900 *Founded/Ownrshp* 2002
Sales 100.0MM *EMP* 150
Accts Ss & G Financial Services Inc
SIC 1531 Townhouse developers

D-U-N-S 78-099-2384
NRT BUS INC
NORTH READING TRANSPORTATION
55 Hampshire Rd, Methuen, MA 01844-1112
Tel (978) 681-4100 *Founded/Ownrshp* 1988
Sales 83.2MM[E] *EMP* 600
SIC 4151 School buses
Pr: John McCarthy

D-U-N-S 96-925-6445 IMP/EXP
■ NRT COMMERCIAL UTAH LLC
COLDWELL BANKER
(*Suby of* REALOGY GROUP LLC) ★
175 Park Ave, Madison, NJ 07940-1123
Tel (973) 407-6880 *Founded/Ownrshp* 1997
Sales 930.2MM[E] *EMP* 9,000
SIC 6531

D-U-N-S 17-603-6499 IMP
NS FLEXIBLES LLC
NORTH STATE FLEXIBLES
(*Suby of* EMBALLAGE ST-JEAN LTEE)
2619 Phoenix Dr, Greensboro, NC 27406-6320
Tel (336) 292-9911 *Founded/Ownrshp* 2012
Sales 86.6MM[E] *EMP* 190
SIC 2671 7336 2759 Packaging paper & plastics film, coated & laminated; Package design; Commercial printing
**Genl Mgr:* Tim Mage
**Genl Mgr:* Tim Mages
CTO: Mark Powell
IT Man: Pam Davis

D-U-N-S 04-854-7681 IMP
NSA INDUSTRIES LLC
210 Pierce Rd, Saint Johnsbury, VT 05819-8343
Tel (802) 748-5007 *Founded/Ownrshp* 1982
Sales 95.2MM[E] *EMP* 250
SIC 3444 1799 1796 Sheet metalwork; Coating of metal structures at construction site; Machinery installation
CEO: James Moroney
**VP:* Matt Smith

*VP: Ed Stanley
Genl Mgr: Emery Noyes
Sfty Dirs: Jason Edmunds
Ql Cn Mgr: Carl Sirois

NSF
See NATIONAL SCIENCE FOUNDATION

D-U-N-S 06-880-1992 IMP
NSF INTERNATIONAL
789 N Dixboro Rd, Ann Arbor, MI 48105-9723
Tel (734) 769-8010 Founded/Ownrshp 1944
Sales 135.2MM^E EMP 456
Accts Deloitte Tax Lp Detroit Mi
SIC 8731 8734 Commercial research laboratory; Testing laboratories
Pr: Kevan P Lawlor
Ofcr: Heather Wade
*Sr VP: Lori Bestervelt
VP: Tom Chestnut
*VP: Elizabeth Jones
VP: David Richardson
VP: Pierre Sbabo
Exec: Cheryl Luptowski
Dir Bus: Dan Fone
Dir Bus: Peter Langlais
Mng Dir: Tarik Bellahcene

D-U-N-S 07-910-5775
NSF INTERNATIONAL HOLDINGS
789 N Dixboro Rd, Ann Arbor, MI 48105-9723
Tel (734) 769-8010 Founded/Ownrshp 2013
Sales 250.0MM EMP 2
SIC 6799 Investment clubs
Pr: Kevin Lawler

NSHE
See NEVADA SYSTEM OF HIGHER EDUCATION

NSIGHT TELESERVICES
See NORTHEAST COMMUNICATIONS OF WISCONSIN INC

D-U-N-S 80-837-9460 IMP
NSK AMERICAS INC
(Suby of NSK LTD.)
4200 Goss Rd, Ann Arbor, MI 48105-2799
Tel (734) 913-7500 Founded/Ownrshp 1973
Sales 515.6MM^E EMP 2,618
SIC 3714 5013 5085 Steering mechanisms, motor vehicle; Automotive supplies & parts; Industrial supplies
Pr: Brian Lindsay
*CFO: Brian Parsons
Treas: John Ellis
VP: David Schoewe
Prgrm Mgr: Desmond Weaver
Genl Mgr: Tony Martell
Ql Cn Mgr: Adam Coolich
Sls Dir: Paul Eifel
Sls Mgr: Angus Pate
Sls Mgr: Scott Richter
Sls Mgr: Doug Turacy

D-U-N-S 06-417-2703 IMP/EXP
NSK CORP
NSK CORPORATION HQ
(Suby of NSK AMERICAS INC) ★
4200 Goss Rd, Ann Arbor, MI 48105-2799
Tel (734) 913-7500 Founded/Ownrshp 1997
Sales 166.2MM^E EMP 1,181
SIC 3714 5013 3594 3568 3562

NSK CORPORATION HQ
See NSK CORP

D-U-N-S 19-371-1702 IMP
NSK STEERING SYSTEMS AMERICA INC
NSSA HQ
(Suby of NSK AMERICAS INC) ★
4200 Goss Rd, Ann Arbor, MI 48105-2799
Tel (734) 913-7500 Founded/Ownrshp 2007
Sales 125.0MM^E EMP 1,112
SIC 3714 Steering mechanisms, motor vehicle
Pr: Michael Rivenburgh
Ex VP: Tsutomu Komori
Ex VP: Masahide Matsubara
Ex VP: Naoki Mitsue
Ex VP: Toshihiro Uchiyama
VP: David Bradshaw

NSLIJ
See STATEN ISLAND UNIVERSITY HOSPITAL

NSLIJ
See NORTHWELL HEALTH INC

NSLIJ-SOUTHSIDE HOSPITAL
See SOUTHSIDE HOSPITAL

NSLIJHSFCU
See NORTH SHORE LIJ HEALTH SYSTEM FEDERAL CREDIT UNION

D-U-N-S 96-661-1720
NSMC HEALTHCARE INC
(Suby of PARTNERS HEALTHCARE SYSTEM INC) ★
81 Highland Ave, Salem, MA 01970-2714
Tel (978) 354-2575 Founded/Ownrshp 2011
Sales 423.1M^E EMP 1,884^E
SIC 8099 Health & allied services
Pr: James E Kraus Jr

NSMC SALEM HOSPITAL
See NORTH SHORE MEDICAL CENTER INC

NSSA HQ
See NSK STEERING SYSTEMS AMERICA INC

D-U-N-S 00-540-4729
NST HOLDINGS GROUP INC
3620 Paoli Pike Ste 8, Floyds Knobs, IN 47119-9787
Tel (812) 248-9273 Founded/Ownrshp 2008
Sales 171.0MM^E EMP 500
SIC 6289 Security holders protective committee
CEO: Dax Whitehouse

D-U-N-S 00-552-4256
■ **NSTAR ELECTRIC & GAS CORP**
(Suby of NSTAR LLC) ★
800 Boylston St Ste 1700, Boston, MA 02199-8108
Tel (617) 424-2000 Founded/Ownrshp 1999
Sales 1.6MMM^E EMP 3,000
SIC 4922 4911 Natural gas transmission; Distribution, electric power
Ch Bd: Thomas J May
Pr: Lawrence Gelbien
Treas: Don Anastasia
*Treas: Philip J Lembo
VP: Joan Hurley
Prgrm Mgr: David Olivier
Dir IT: Domenic Gugliotti
Dir IT: Andrew Kasznaj
Sftwr Eng: Stephen Morelli
Genl Couns: Samuel Lee
Counsel: Mary Grover

D-U-N-S 00-695-1552
■ **NSTAR ELECTRIC CO**
EVERSOURCE ENERGY
(Suby of NSTAR LLC) ★
800 Boylston St Ste 1700, Boston, MA 02199-8108
Tel (617) 424-2000 Founded/Ownrshp 1886
Sales 2.6MMM EMP 2,194^E
SIC 4911 4924 Distribution, electric power; Generation, electric power; Transmission, electric power; Natural gas distribution
CEO: Leon J Olivier
*Ch Bd: Thomas J May
*CEO: Werner J Schweiger
COO: Thomas Glynn
*CFO: James J Judge
*Sr VP: Gregory B Butler
Sr VP: Christine M Carmody
VP: Jay S Buth
Exec: William Beament
VP Sls: Joseph Nolan

D-U-N-S 08-757-1431 IMP
■ **NSTAR LLC**
(Suby of EVERSOURCE ENERGY) ★
800 Boylston St Ste 1700, Boston, MA 02199-8108
Tel (617) 424-2000 Founded/Ownrshp 2012
Sales 4.3MMM^E EMP 3,000^E
SIC 4911 4924 Distribution, electric power; Transmission, electric power; Natural gas distribution
Treas: Philip Lembo
Ex VP: David McHale
VP: Gregory Butler
VP: Christine M Carmody
VP: Penelope Conner
VP: Philip Martin
Prin: Gary L Countryman
Prin: Thomas G Dignan Jr
Prin: James S Distasio
Prin: Charles K Gifford
Prin: Matina S Horner
Board of Directors: Gary L Countryman, Thomas G Dignan Jr, James S Distasio, Charles K Gifford, Paul A La Camera, William C Van Faasen, Gerald L Wilson

NSTEC
See NATIONAL SECURITY TECHNOLOGIES LLC

NSU
See NORTHEASTERN STATE UNIVERSITY

D-U-N-S 96-936-3337 IMP
NTA PRECISION AXLE CORP
(Suby of NTN CORPORATION)
795 Kimberly Dr, Carol Stream, IL 60188-9407
Tel (630) 690-6300 Founded/Ownrshp 2010
Sales 120.0MM EMP 260
SIC 3714 Bearings, motor vehicle

NTCA RURAL BROADBAND ASSN
See NATIONAL TELECOMMUNICATIONS COOPERATIVE ASSOCIATION

D-U-N-S 61-729-5246
■ **NTELOS HOLDINGS CORP**
SHENTEL
(Suby of SHENTEL) ★
1154 Shenandoah Vlg Dr, Waynesboro, VA 22980-9253
Tel (540) 946-3500 Founded/Ownrshp 2016
Sales 362.6MM EMP 854^E
SIC 4813 4812 Telephone communication, except radio; ; Cellular telephone services
Prin: Christopher French
*COO: Earle Mackenzie
*CFO: Adele Skolits
*Sr VP: Edward McKay
*Sr VP: Thomas Whitaker
VP: Richard Baughman
VP: Brian Brooks
VP: Kevin Folk
VP: Christopher Kyle
VP: Raymond Ostroski
VP: Angela Washington

D-U-N-S 80-120-9375
■ **NTELOS INC**
(Suby of SHENTEL) ★
1154 Shenandoah Vlg Dr, Waynesboro, VA 22980-9253
Tel (540) 946-3500 Founded/Ownrshp 1988
Sales 405.5MM^E EMP 955
SIC 4899 Communication signal enhancement network system
CEO: Rod Dir
*CEO: James A Hyde
CFO: Michael B Moneymaker
*Ex VP: Stebbins B Chandor Jr
*Ex VP: Conrad D Hunter
*Sr VP: Brian J O'Neil
Snr Ntwrk: Harris Duncan
Snr Ntwrk: Jonathan Lee

D-U-N-S 19-688-6592
■ **NTELOS NET LLC**
(Suby of SHENTEL) ★
1 Lumos Plz, Waynesboro, VA 22980-4549
Tel (540) 946-3500 Founded/Ownrshp 2003
Sales 407.6MM^E EMP 960^E
SIC 4813 Telephone communication, except radio
Pr: James S Quarforth
*Pr: David R Maccarelli
*Pr: Carl A Rosberg
*CFO: Michael B Moneymaker
CFO: Suzan Sweet
*Sr VP: Mary McDermott

D-U-N-S 78-112-3211
NTH GENERATION COMPUTING INC
17055 Camino San Bernardo, San Diego, CA 92127-5709
Tel (858) 451-2383 Founded/Ownrshp 1988
Sales 119.4MM^E EMP 96
SIC 5045 Computer peripheral equipment; Computer software
CEO: Janis I Baldwin
VP: Todd Burkhard
VP: Todd Burkhardt
Prin: Liane Komagome
*Dir Sec: Richard Baldwin
CIO: Jorge Mata
CTO: Joel Manfredo
CTO: Alex Ryals
Mktg Dir: Jeri Egbert

D-U-N-S 83-607-2918
NTHRIVE SOLUTIONS
CAPITAL MT
1275 Drummers Ln Ste 200, Wayne, PA 19087-1571
Tel (610) 688-2464 Founded/Ownrshp 2015
Sales 75.1MM^E EMP 1,200
SIC 8742 Management consulting services
CEO: Christopher A Powell
*CFO: James Matas
*Ofcr: Pamela Goans
VP: Bonnie S Cassidy
VP: Cindy Doyon
VP: Paul Flanagan
VP: Karen Heisler
VP: Thomas Ormondroyd
VP: Emilie Pasternoster
Natl Sales: Chris Skiffington

D-U-N-S 07-854-5025
NTHRIVE SOLUTIONS INC
1275 Drummers Ln Ste 200, Wayne, PA 19087-1571
Tel (800) 555-2311 Founded/Ownrshp 2008
Sales 273MM^E EMP 1,200
SIC 8099 Blood related health services

NTMWD
See NORTH TEXAS MUNICIPAL WATER DISTRICT

D-U-N-S 04-391-0256 IMP
NTN BEARING CORP OF AMERICA (NY)
(Suby of NTN USA CORP) ★
1600 Bishop Ct, Mount Prospect, IL 60056-6055
Tel (847) 298-7500 Founded/Ownrshp 1963, 1990
Sales 131.2MM^E EMP 369
SIC 5085 Bearings
Pr: Pete Eich
VP: Laura Kearns
VP: Dennis Tanrikulu
CTO: John Husemann
Dir IT: Hirosha Kawakami
IT Man: David Malmquist
Ql Cn Mgr: Greg Keller
Sls Dir: Paul Tervo
Mktg Mgr: Cheryl Loew
Genl Couns: Craig Dunn
Board of Directors: H Morii

D-U-N-S 60-816-7276 IMP
NTN DRIVESHAFT INC
(Suby of NTN USA CORP) ★
8251 S International Dr, Columbus, IN 47201-9329
Tel (812) 342-5414 Founded/Ownrshp 1989
Sales 228.8MM^E EMP 1,000
SIC 3568 Joints & couplings
Pr: Tohru Tomiyama
*Pr: Nobuo Satoh
*Sec: Hidekazu Asaba
VP: Douglas Evers
*VP: Tom Fowler
VP Admn: Barry Parkhurst
QA Dir: Roy Baker
QA Dir: Chris Graburn
QA Dir: Joe Winters
Dir IT: Chris Paugh
IT Man: Chris Elmore

D-U-N-S 62-143-0610 EXP
NTN USA CORP
(Suby of NTN CORPORATION)
1600 Bishop Ct, Mount Prospect, IL 60056-6055
Tel (847) 298-4652 Founded/Ownrshp 1990
Sales 749.1MM^E EMP 3,500^E
SIC 5085 3562 3568 Bearings; Ball bearings & parts; Roller bearings & parts; Joints, swivel & universal, except aircraft & automotive
Pr: Masaaki Ayano

D-U-N-S 14-735-1092 IMP
NTN-BOWER CORP
(Suby of NTN USA CORP) ★
711 Bower Rd, Macomb, IL 61455-2511
Tel (309) 837-0440 Founded/Ownrshp 1990
Sales 172.0MM EMP 873^E
SIC 3562 Roller bearings & parts
Pr: Kunio Kamo
Sfty Mgr: Tammy Dalbello
Opers Mgr: Mike Lawson

D-U-N-S 06-343-6463 IMP
■ **NTP DISTRIBUTION INC**
(Suby of KEYSTONE AUTOMOTIVE OPERATIONS INC) ★
27150 Sw Kinsman Rd, Wilsonville, OR 97070-8246
Tel (503) 570-2154 Founded/Ownrshp 2011
Sales 100.0MM EMP 400
SIC 5013 Trailer parts & accessories
Ch: Robert L Mortier
*Pr: Greg Boyd
*Pr: Edward H Orszetti
*COO: Steven M Whitrock
VP Sls: Jon White
Mktg Dir: Donna Martin
Sales Asso: John Donaghe

D-U-N-S 78-437-8189 IMP
NTP MARBLE INC
COLONIAL MARBLE & GRANITE
201 W Church Rd Ste 300, King of Prussia, PA 19406-3241
Tel (610) 994-2222 Founded/Ownrshp 2006
Sales 542.2MM^E EMP 125^E
SIC 5032 Marble building stone; Granite building stone
Pr: Nikolaos Papadopoulos
VP: Angelo Bekas
Opers Mgr: Steve Basdekis
Sls Dir: Cleanthes Papadopoulos
Sls Mgr: Demetrios Proios
Sales Asso: Gus Repici
Sales Asso: Anthony Tartaglia

NTS
See NATIONAL TECHNICAL SYSTEMS INC

D-U-N-S 03-620-3818
NTS COMMUNICATIONS INC
(Suby of NTS INC) ★
1220 Brdwy, Lubbock, TX 79401
Tel (806) 791-0687 Founded/Ownrshp 2008
Sales 106.4MM^E EMP 231
SIC 4813 Long distance telephone communications;
Pr: Guy Nissenson
Pr: Dawn Ambrose
Pr: Barbara Baldwin
*CEO: Cyrus Driver
COO: Brad Worthington
CFO: Jerry E Hoover
Sec: Niv Krikov
Ex VP: Tal Sheynfeld
VP: John Baldwin
VP: Roberto Chang
VP: Milton Schober Jr

NTS, INC.
See NTS INC

D-U-N-S 06-717-5609
NTS INC (NV)
NTS, INC.
(Suby of T3 NORTH INTERMEDIATE HOLDINGS, INC.)
1220 Broadway Ste 100, Lubbock, TX 79401-3202
Tel (806) 771-5212 Founded/Ownrshp 2000, 2014
Sales 120.1MM^E EMP 376^E
SIC 4813 Telephone communication, except radio
Pr: Cyrus Driver
*Pr: Guy Nissenson
*COO: Brad Worthington
*CFO: Niv Krikov
*VP: Roberto Chang
*VP: Nathan Hasse
*VP: Wendy J Lee
*VP: Aaron Peters
*VP: Priscilla Rivas
*VP: Tal Sheynfeld
*VP: Daniel Wheeler

D-U-N-S 13-094-9873
NTS INC
NEWBERRY TECHNICAL SERVICES
8200 Stockdale Hwy Ste M, Bakersfield, CA 93311-1029
Tel (661) 588-8514 Founded/Ownrshp 2001
Sales 136.3MM^E EMP 425
SIC 1623 1541 1771

D-U-N-S 09-354-4323 IMP
NTT AMERICA INC
(Suby of NTT COMMUNICATIONS CORPORATION)
757 3rd Ave Ste 1400, New York, NY 10017-2054
Tel (212) 661-0810 Founded/Ownrshp 1987, 2006
Sales 280.0MM^E EMP 500
SIC 4813 Telephone communication, except radio
Pr: Tetsuro Yamaguchi
*COO: Kazuhiro Gomi
Bd of Dir: Miwa Matsushita
Bd of Dir: Patricia Nickens
*Ofcr: Michael Devito
Ex VP: Christopher P Eldredge
VP: Pete Bell
VP: Eiri Fujikawa
VP: Don Goodwin
VP: Rich Harper
*VP: Tomoyoshi Kosugi
VP: Chris Lathrop
VP: Douglas Smith
VP: Fang Wu

D-U-N-S 07-170-7764
NTT DATA INC
(Suby of NTT DATA INTERNATIONAL LLC) ★
5601 Gran Pkwy Ste 1000, Plano, TX 75024
Tel (800) 745-3263 Founded/Ownrshp 1986
Sales 178.3MM^E EMP 200
SIC 7373 7372 7379 Computer integrated systems design; Systems software development services; Prepackaged software; Computer related consulting services
Pr: John W McCain
Pr: Aurora Coya
Pr: Barry Severns
COO: Ted Armstead
CFO: David Croxville
Treas: Andrea Romoli
Treas: Lawrence D Whelan
Rgnl VP: Charles Mears
Ex VP: Bob Gray
Ex VP: Jim Milde
Ex VP: Marv Mouchawar
Ex VP: Pam Silver
Ex VP: Michael Thomas
Sr VP: John Flavin
Sr VP: Donald Hiller
Sr VP: Bill Kelly
Sr VP: Raymond Paris
VP: William Baver
VP: William Butler
VP: Raissa Carvatta
VP: John Coupland

D-U-N-S 80-436-5083
NTT DATA INTERNATIONAL LLC
(*Suby of* NTT DATA CORPORATION)
45 W 36th St Fl 7, New York, NY 10018-7634
Tel (212) 355-5585 *Founded/Ownrshp* 2000
Sales 178.5MM[E] *EMP* 355
SIC 7374 Data processing service
Pr: Takashi Enomoto
COO: Fran Convery
Sr VP: Patrick Branagan
VP: Bob Dority
VP: Joseph A Gulli
VP: Dan Peet
VP: Mel Takata
Prgrm Mgr: Hana Taha
Genl Mgr: Shigenari Oketani
CIO: Phil Christofalor

D-U-N-S 80-999-1912
NTT DATA INTERNATIONAL SERVICES INC
(*Suby of* NTT DATA CORPORATION)
100 City Sq, Boston, MA 02129-3721
Tel (800) 745-3263 *Founded/Ownrshp* 1993
Sales 1.3MMM[E] *EMP* 18,000
SIC 7371 7372 Custom computer programming services; Computer software development; Prepackaged software
CEO: John W McCain
COO: Mark Keane
**CFO:* David Kaminsky
**Ex VP:* Tim Conway
**Ex VP:* John M Dick
**Ex VP:* Amir Durrani
**Ex VP:* Robert W Gray
**Ex VP:* James T Milde
Ex VP: Marv Mouchawar
Sls Dir: Dan Keane

D-U-N-S 17-534-4753
■ **NTT DATA SERVICES FEDERAL GOVERNMENT INC**
DELL SVCS FDRAL GOVERNMENT INC
(*Suby of* DELL COMPUTER) ★
13880 Dulles Corner Ln, Herndon, VA 20171-4685
Tel (703) 289-8000 *Founded/Ownrshp* 2009
Sales 291.6MM[E] *EMP* 1,504
SIC 8711 7373 7374 Engineering services; Systems integration services; Data processing & preparation
Pr: George Newstrom
**VP:* Mike Kauffman
**VP:* Neil Seiden
Dir IT: Michael Stark
IT Man: Vaughn Chamberland
IT Man: Jamie Kerner

NTUA
See NAVAJO TRIBAL UTILITY AUTHORITY

D-U-N-S 01-132-1635
NTVB MEDIA INC
NATIONAL TELEVISION BOOK CO
209 Park Dr, Troy, MI 48083-2726
Tel (248) 583-4190 *Founded/Ownrshp* 1981
Sales 136.4MM[E] *EMP* 285
SIC 2752 Commercial printing, offset
Pr: Andrew V De Angelis
**CFO:* Larry Mackenzie
Off Mgr: Alex Park

D-U-N-S 03-927-1064
■ **NU ENTERPRISES INC**
(*Suby of* EVERSOURCE ENERGY) ★
107 Selden St, Berlin, CT 06037-1616
Tel (860) 665-5000 *Founded/Ownrshp* 1998
Sales 184.4MM[E] *EMP* 400
SIC 4911 Electric services
Pr: Charles W Shivery

D-U-N-S 07-724-5942 IMP
■ **NU HORIZONS ELECTRONICS CORP**
(*Suby of* ARROW ELECTRONICS INC) ★
70 Maxess Rd, Melville, NY 11747-3102
Tel (631) 396-5000 *Founded/Ownrshp* 2011
Sales 185.8MM[E] *EMP* 650
SIC 5065 Electronic parts & equipment; Semiconductor devices; Diodes; Transistors
Pr: Martin Kent
Pr: Wendell Boyd
Pr: Chris O'Brien
Pr: Rich Schuster
**CFO:* Kurt Freudenberg
Sr VP: Michael McGuire
Sr VP: Ken Sykes
VP: John Borusheski
VP: Joseph Clutter
VP: Bruce Haskin
VP: Gregg Scott
VP: Roberta Valencia

D-U-N-S 96-681-7975 IMP/EXP
▲ **NU SKIN ENTERPRISES INC**
75 W Center St, Provo, UT 84601-4432
Tel (801) 345-1000 *Founded/Ownrshp* 1984
Sales 2.2MMM *EMP* 26,800
Tkr Sym NUS *Exch* NYS
SIC 2844 5122 Toilet preparations; Cosmetic preparations; Hair coloring preparations; Cosmetics; Vitamins & minerals
Pr: M Truman Hunt
**Ch Bd:* Steven J Lund
Pr: Ryan S Napierski
CFO: Ritch N Wood
Ex VP: Joseph Y Chang
VP: Ruth Todd
Dir IT: Lance Broderick
IT Man: Ennio Fraiponts
Mktg Dir: Nate Jackson
Board of Directors: Nevin N Andersen, Daniel W Campbell, Andrew D Lipman, Neil H Offen, Thomas R Pisano, Edwina D Woodbury

D-U-N-S 01-397-9955
■ **NU SKIN ENTERPRISES UNITED STATES INC**
(*Suby of* NU SKIN ENTERPRISES INC) ★
75 W Center St, Provo, UT 84601-4432
Tel (801) 377-6056 *Founded/Ownrshp* 1998
Sales 115.6MM[E] *EMP* 1,271
SIC 5122 Drugs, proprietaries & sundries
CEO: Blake M Roney
**Pr:* Steven J Lund

D-U-N-S 14-475-1849 IMP
■ **NU SKIN INTERNATIONAL INC**
PHARMANEX DIVISION
(*Suby of* NU SKIN ENTERPRISES INC) ★
75 W Center St, Provo, UT 84601-4432
Tel (801) 345-1000 *Founded/Ownrshp* 1984
Sales 197.3MM[E] *EMP* 1,414
SIC 2844 Toilet preparations
Ch Bd: Steven J Lund
**Pr:* Truman Hunt
COO: John Fralick
COO: Lester Packer
CFO: Wood Rich
**CFO:* Rich Wood
Ch: Blake M Roney
Sr VP: Sandy N Tillotson
VP: Jodi Durrant
VP: Brooke B Roney
Exec: Sam Holoviak

D-U-N-S 00-633-4122 IMP
NU WAY CONCRETE FORMS INC (MO)
4190 Hoffmeister Ave, Saint Louis, MO 63125-2298
Tel (573) 893-8786 *Founded/Ownrshp* 1955
Sales 95.1MM[E] *EMP* 160
SIC 5032 5051 5072 7359 Masons' materials; Rods, metal; Hand tools; Tool rental
Pr: Gerald A Rhomberg
Pt: Dave Pazdernik
**Treas:* Daphne Rhomberg
**VP:* Arthur Rhomberg
Genl Mgr: Joe Wibbenmeyer
Sls Mgr: Mike Townsend

D-U-N-S 08-024-2845
NU WAY COOPERATIVE (INC)
440 Highway 4 S, Trimont, MN 56176-4002
Tel (507) 639-2311 *Founded/Ownrshp* 1937
Sales 97.1MM *EMP* 75
Accts Carlosn Highland Cpa New Ulm
SIC 5191 5171 5541 2875 Chemicals, agricultural; Fertilizer & fertilizer materials; Petroleum bulk stations & terminals; Gasoline service stations; Fertilizers, mixing only
Pr: Kevin Jones
Genl Mgr: Kevin M Jones

NU WORLD
See NU-WORLD CORP

D-U-N-S 09-638-3633 IMP/EXP
NU-FOAM PRODUCTS INC (TN)
1101 Wisdom St, Chattanooga, TN 37406-1756
Tel (423) 698-6911 *Founded/Ownrshp* 1989
Sales NA *EMP* 1,200
SIC 3086

D-U-N-S 00-785-9580
NU-LITE ELECTRICAL WHOLESALERS LLC
850 Edwards Ave, Harahan, LA 70123-3123
Tel (504) 733-3300 *Founded/Ownrshp* 1950, 1987
Sales 126.4MM[E] *EMP* 130
SIC 5063 Electrical apparatus & equipment
Genl Mgr: Joseph Impastato
VP Opers: Gary Corales
Sls Mgr: Lenny Lassus
Sales Asso: Jeff Pierre

D-U-N-S 16-088-8582
NU-WEST INDUSTRIES INC
(*Suby of* AGRIUM US INC) ★
3010 Conda Rd, Soda Springs, ID 83276-5301
Tel (208) 547-4381 *Founded/Ownrshp* 1995
Sales 98.2MM[E] *EMP* 300[E]
SIC 2874 Phosphates
Pr: Mike Wilson
**CFO:* Mark R Sanders
**Treas:* Patrick Freeman
**Ex VP:* H Alan Dahlbach
**VP:* Don G Larue
Sfty Mgr: Katrina Miller
**Genl Couns:* Leslie O Donohue

D-U-N-S 62-804-5858 IMP
NU-WORLD CORP
NU WORLD
300 Milik St, Carteret, NJ 07008-1113
Tel (732) 541-6300 *Founded/Ownrshp* 1991
Sales 85.9MM[E] *EMP* 250[E]
Accts Bederson & Company Llc West O
SIC 2844 Cosmetic preparations
CEO: Jonathan Rosenbaum
**Pr:* Stuart Dolleck
COO: Peter Greene
**CFO:* Stuart Mont
Sr VP: Joe Moreno
VP: Dianna Ruth
Creative D: Ilyse Davis
Dir Sec: Richard Kuohn
Dir IT: Robert Russell
IT Man: Craig Dykes
Sales Exec: David Dourson

D-U-N-S 79-740-7517
▲ **NUANCE COMMUNICATIONS INC**
1 Wayside Rd, Burlington, MA 01803-4609
Tel (781) 565-5000 *Founded/Ownrshp* 1992
Sales 1.9MMM *EMP* 13,524
Tkr Sym NUAN *Exch* NGS
SIC 7372 Prepackaged software
Ch Bd: Paul A Ricci
V Ch: Robert Stewart
Pr: Trace Devanny
Pr: Vanessa Richter
CFO: Daniel D Tempesta
CFO: Daniel D Tempesta
Treas: Thomas Chagnon
Bd of Dir: Jeanne Nauman
Chf Mktg O: Steven G Chambers
Ofcr: Kenneth M Siegel
Ex VP: A Bruce Bowden
Ex VP: Bruce Bowden
Ex VP: Frederik Brabant
Ex VP: Thomas T Brown IV
Ex VP: Satish R Maripuri
Ex VP: Robert McDonough
Ex VP: Bill Nelson
Ex VP: Brett Phaneuf
Ex VP: Michael R Rich
Ex VP: William Robbins
Ex VP: Bob Schassler
Board of Directors: Robert Finocchio, Robert J Frankenberg, Brett Icahn, William H Janeway, Mark R Laret, Katharine A Martin, Mark B Myers, Philip J Quigley, David S Schechter

D-U-N-S 61-310-5402
■ **NUANCE TRANSCRIPTION SERVICES INC**
TRANSCEND SERVICES, INC.
(*Suby of* NUANCE COMMUNICATIONS INC) ★
1 Glenlake Pkwy Ste 800, Atlanta, GA 30328-3494
Tel (800) 205-7047 *Founded/Ownrshp* 2012
Sales 87.9MM[E] *EMP* 3,211[E]
SIC 7338 Word processing service
Pr: Thomas L Beaudoin
COO: David Murphy
Ex VP: Alex Munoz
Sr VP: Jeff Felshaw

D-U-N-S 02-668-3723
NUBO BOTTLE CO LLC
3700 Nw 124th Ave Ste 109, Coral Springs, FL 33065-2431
Tel (954) 283-9057 *Founded/Ownrshp* 2010
Sales 780.0MM *EMP* 7
SIC 2086 Water, pasteurized: packaged in cans, bottles, etc.
Pr: Abraham K Kohl
**Treas:* Kirsten Kohl

D-U-N-S 62-650-0276
NUCLEAR ELECTRIC INSURANCE LIMITED
NEIL
1201 N Market St Ste 1100, Wilmington, DE 19801-1805
Tel (302) 888-3000 *Founded/Ownrshp* 1973
Sales NA *EMP* 60
Accts Deloitte & Touche Llp Philade
SIC 6331 Property damage insurance
Pr: Bruce A Sassi
**CEO:* Dave Ripsom
**VP:* Gregory J Blackburn
**VP:* Michael W Kolodner
**VP:* Kenneth C Manne
**VP:* Harry J Phillips
**VP:* Thomas G Tannion

NUCLEAR FACILITY
See NEBRASKA PUBLIC POWER DISTRICT

D-U-N-S 55-622-6108
■ **NUCLEAR LOGISTICS INC**
(*Suby of* AZZ INC) ★
7410 Pebble Dr, Fort Worth, TX 76118-6961
Tel (817) 284-0077 *Founded/Ownrshp* 2012
Sales 145.2MM[E] *EMP* 155
SIC 5065 8711 Electronic parts & equipment; Engineering services
Ofcr: Kim Tomlinson
VP: Archie Bell
Off Mgr: Kathy Baker
CTO: Scott Dauphin
QA Dir: Tracy Bolt
VP Mktg: Craig Irish

D-U-N-S 11-373-8889
■ **NUCLEAR MANAGEMENT CO LLC**
N.M.C
(*Suby of* XCEL ENERGY) ★
414 Nicollet Mall, Minneapolis, MN 55401-1927
Tel (612) 330-5500 *Founded/Ownrshp* 1999
Sales 61.4MM[E] *EMP* 2,460
SIC 8741 8999 Management services; Nuclear consultant
VP: Karen Miller

D-U-N-S 04-053-5809
■ **NUCLEAR REGULATORY COMMISSION UNITED STATES**
U.S.NRC
(*Suby of* EXECUTIVE OFFICE OF UNITED STATES GOVERNMENT) ★
11555 Rockville Pike, Rockville, MD 20852-2746
Tel (800) 368-5642 *Founded/Ownrshp* 1975
Sales NA *EMP* 4,000
SIC 9631 Nuclear energy inspection & regulation office, government;
Ch: Dra Allison M Macfarlane
**CFO:* Jesse Funches
VP: William Webster
**Ex Dir:* William D Travers
**CIO:* Dave Nelson
**CIO:* Stewart Reiter
Genl Couns: Margaret M Doane
Snr Mgr: Kristin Davis
Snr Mgr: Jose Diaz

NUCLEAR SYSTEMS GROUP
See SIEMENS MEDICAL SOLUTIONS USA INC

D-U-N-S 10-768-8822
■ **NUCO2 INC**
(*Suby of* PRAXAIR INC) ★
2800 Se Market Pl, Stuart, FL 34997-4965
Tel (772) 221-1754 *Founded/Ownrshp* 2013
Sales 377.2MM[E] *EMP* 700
SIC 5169 Carbon dioxide
Pr: Kevin Foti
COO: Scott W Wade
**Ex VP:* Keith Gordon
**Sr VP:* Randy Gold
**Sr VP:* Peter Green
**Sr VP:* Nancy Pawlowski
VP: John Scollard
Dist Mgr: David Mitchell
IT Man: Chad Ray
Manager: Benjamin Fletcher
Manager: Seth Flowers

D-U-N-S 00-344-6796 IMP/EXP
▲ **NUCOR CORP**
1915 Rexford Rd Ste 400, Charlotte, NC 28211-3888
Tel (704) 366-7000 *Founded/Ownrshp* 1940
Sales 16.4MMM *EMP* 23,920
Accts Pricewaterhousecoopers Llp Ch
Tkr Sym NUE *Exch* NYS
SIC 3312 3441 3448 3452 5093 Blast furnaces & steel mills; Primary finished or semifinished shapes; Bar, rod & wire products; Plate, sheet & strip, except coated products; Building components, structural steel; Joists, open web steel: long-span series; Prefabricated metal buildings; Prefabricated metal components; Bolts, metal; Screws, metal; Ferrous metal scrap & waste; Nonferrous metals scrap
Ch Bd: John J Ferriola
CFO: James D Frias
Ofcr: Mike Heine
Ex VP: James R Darsey
Ex VP: Ladd R Hall
Ex VP: Raymond S Napolitan Jr
Ex VP: R Joseph Stratman
Ex VP: Dave Sumoski
Ex VP: Chad Utermark
VP: Bill Abbey
VP: Allen Behr
VP: Elizabeth Bowers
VP: Michael D Keller
VP: Paige Okelley
VP: D Ryan
VP: Tammy Willis
Exec: Rhonda Miller
Board of Directors: Harvey B Gantt, Gregory J Hayes, Victoria F Haynes, Bernard L Kasriel, Christopher J Kearney, Laurette T Koellner, Raymond J Milchovich, John H Walker

D-U-N-S 02-630-8620 IMP
■ **NUCOR STEEL AUBURN INC**
(*Suby of* NUCOR CORP) ★
25 Quarry Rd, Auburn, NY 13021-1146
Tel (315) 253-4561 *Founded/Ownrshp* 2001
Sales 117.8MM[E] *EMP* 290
SIC 3312 Blast furnaces & steel mills
Ch: Dan Dimicco
Genl Mgr: Mary E Slate
Genl Mgr: Dave Smith
Dir IT: Diane Schillawski
Software D: Maria Starr
Sfty Mgr: Luke Scott
Plnt Mgr: Ed Wolf
Mktg Mgr: Sharon Farrelly
Snr Mgr: Clara Van Aswegen

D-U-N-S 12-432-6476 IMP
■ **NUCOR STEEL BIRMINGHAM INC**
(*Suby of* NUCOR CORP) ★
2301 Fl Shuttlesworth Dr, Birmingham, AL 35234-1335
Tel (866) 862-4796 *Founded/Ownrshp* 2002
Sales 96.1MM[E] *EMP* 250
SIC 3312 Bars & bar shapes, steel, cold-finished: own hot-rolled
Pr: Daniel R Dimicco
**CFO:* James Rias
**Ex VP:* James Darsey
**Genl Mgr:* Franky Riggs
Dir IT: Sharon Rogers
Sales Exec: Gary Young
Sls Mgr: Del Benzenhafer
Sls Mgr: Matt Isbell

D-U-N-S 11-889-9371 IMP
■ **NUCOR STEEL DECATUR LLC**
(*Suby of* NUCOR CORP) ★
4301 Iverson Blvd, Trinity, AL 35673-6642
Tel (256) 301-3500 *Founded/Ownrshp* 2002
Sales 228.8MM[E] *EMP* 696
SIC 3312 Blast furnaces & steel mills
CEO: Dan Dimicco
VP: Peter Campbell
VP: Michael Lee
IT Man: Dave Kirkland
Ql Cn Mgr: Shawna Starks
Sls Mgr: John Sacco

D-U-N-S 11-490-0934 IMP/EXP
■ **NUCOR STEEL JACKSON INC**
(*Suby of* NUCOR CORP) ★
3630 Fourth St, Flowood, MS 39232-2000
Tel (601) 939-1623 *Founded/Ownrshp* 2002
Sales 107.2MM[E] *EMP* 265
SIC 3312 Blast furnaces & steel mills
Pr: Daniel R Dimicco
VP: Don Barney
**VP:* Gim Shebel
Ql Cn Mgr: Heather Poschel

D-U-N-S 11-487-4865 IMP
■ **NUCOR STEEL KANKAKEE INC**
(*Suby of* NUCOR CORP) ★
1 Nucor Way, Bourbonnais, IL 60914-3213
Tel (815) 937-3131 *Founded/Ownrshp* 2002
Sales 121.8MM[E] *EMP* 330
SIC 3312 3547 3449 Blast furnaces & steel mills; Rolling mill machinery; Miscellaneous metalwork
CEO: John J Fierrola
**Pr:* James Darsey
**Pr:* Alex Weisselberg
**CFO:* Jim Frias
**Prin:* Matthew Brooks
**Prin:* Bill Vorderer
Genl Mgr: Johnny Jacobs
Dir IT: Peggy Hutnick
Sls Mgr: Ken Walls

D-U-N-S 15-322-5821 IMP/EXP
■ **NUCOR STEEL MEMPHIS INC**
(*Suby of* NUCOR CORP) ★
3601 Paul R Lowry Rd, Memphis, TN 38109-3007
Tel (901) 786-5837 *Founded/Ownrshp* 2002
Sales 220.6MM[E] *EMP* 420
SIC 3312 3441 3448 3452 Blast furnaces & steel mills; Primary finished or semifinished shapes; Bar, rod & wire products; Plate, sheet & strip, except coated products; Building components, structural steel; Joists, open web steel: long-span series; Prefabricated metal buildings; Bolts, metal; Screws, metal
Genl Mgr: Dave Smith

D-U-N-S 13-116-5714 IMP/EXP
■ **NUCOR STEEL TUSCALOOSA INC**
(*Suby of* NUCOR CORP) ★
1700 Holt Rd Ne, Tuscaloosa, AL 35404-1046
Tel (205) 556-1310 *Founded/Ownrshp* 2006
Sales 181.6MM[E] *EMP* 345
SIC 3312 Blast furnaces & steel mills; Plate, steel
Ch Bd: Harold Homer
**COO:* Jim Lewis
VP: Jan Mass
**VP:* Randey Skagen
Ql Cn Mgr: Conor Bentley
Sales Asso: Emily Watkins
Snr Mgr: Aundrea Lollar

D-U-N-S 18-109-2545 IMP/EXP
■ **NUCOR-YAMATO STEEL CO (LIMITED PARTNERSHIP)**
(*Suby of* NUCOR CORP) ★
5929 E State Highway 18, Blytheville, AR 72315-7429
Tel (870) 762-5500 *Founded/Ownrshp* 1987
Sales 1.3MMM[E] *EMP* 800
Accts Pricewaterhousecooper Llp Cha
SIC 3312 3441 Structural shapes & pilings, steel; Fabricated structural metal
Genl Mgr: D Chad Utermark
CFO: Chuck Ryan
**Treas:* Donald K Prevost
VP: Leon Topalian
Prin: Elizabeth W Bowers
**Genl Mgr:* Doug Jellison
Dir IT: Jason Carter
Dir IT: Tom Wallis
IT Man: Kenneth Baker
Sfty Dirs: April Bentley
Sfty Mgr: William Kent

D-U-N-S 82-811-4764
NUCOURSE DISTRIBUTION INC
22342 Avenida Empresa # 200, Rcho STA Marg, CA 92688-2148
Tel (866) 655-4366 *Founded/Ownrshp* 2008
Sales 89.0MM *EMP* 55
SIC 5065
CEO: Nicholas Troy Seedorf
**VP:* Brandon Seedorf

D-U-N-S 00-524-5717 IMP
NUFARM AMERICAS INC
NUFARM NORTH AMERICAN OFFICE
(*Suby of* NUFARM LIMITED)
11901 S Austin Ave Ste A, Alsip, IL 60803-6013
Tel (708) 377-1330 *Founded/Ownrshp* 1999
Sales 120.5MM[E] *EMP* 177
SIC 2869 2879 Industrial organic chemicals; Agricultural chemicals
Pr: Brendan Deck
CFO: Gary Barber
VP: Keith Moon
Exec: Mike Miller
Comm Man: Sherry Mitchell
Genl Mgr: Dale Mellody
IT Man: John Calderon
VP Opers: Thomas Lyons
Mfg Dir: Tom Butera
Sls Dir: Tra Huddleston
Mktg Mgr: Jerome Kovar

NUFARM NORTH AMERICAN OFFICE
See NUFARM AMERICAS INC

D-U-N-S 93-073-9987
■ **NUGEN ENERGY LLC**
(*Suby of* REX AMERICAN RESOURCES CORP) ★
27283 447th Ave, Marion, SD 57043-5100
Tel (605) 648-2100 *Founded/Ownrshp* 2009
Sales 323.0MM *EMP* 50
Accts Deloitte & Touche Llp Cincin
SIC 0139 1731 5211 Food crops; Energy management controls; Energy conservation products
Pr: Aaron Riedell

NUGGET, THE
See NUGGET MARKET INC

D-U-N-S 02-966-2145
NUGGET MARKET INC
NUGGET, THE
168 Court St, Woodland, CA 95695-3113
Tel (530) 669-3300 *Founded/Ownrshp* 1968
Sales 263.6MM[E] *EMP* 1,300
SIC 5411 Co-operative food stores
Ch Bd: Eugene N Stille
**Pr:* Eric Stille
Store Dir: Dave Welch
Dept Mgr: Trevor Cummings
Dist Mgr: Lorna Parton

D-U-N-S 83-020-1237 IMP/EXP
■ **NUK USA LLC**
(*Suby of* NEWELL BRANDS) ★
728 Booster Blvd, Reedsburg, WI 53959-2123
Tel (608) 524-4343 *Founded/Ownrshp* 2008
Sales 131.5MM[E] *EMP* 260
SIC 2676 Infant & baby paper products
Pr: Douglas Gillespie
VP: Greg Gomez
Exec: Steve Lundin

D-U-N-S 17-329-1675 IMP
NUKOTE INC
(*Suby of* BLACK CREEK HOLDINGS LTD) ★
2400 Dallas Pkwy Ste 230, Plano, TX 75093-4371
Tel (972) 398-7100 *Founded/Ownrshp* 2006
Sales 59.5MM[E] *EMP* 1,300
SIC 3955 3861 Ribbons, inked: typewriter, adding machine, register, etc.; Carbon paper for typewriters, sales books, etc.; Toners, prepared photographic (not made in chemical plants)
Ch: John Rochon
**Pr:* C Ronald Baiocchi
**Ex VP:* Steven Baiocchi
**Sr VP:* Alan S Lockwood
VP: Cindy Hutchinson
Board of Directors: C Ronald Baiocchi, Nick G Bouras, Alan S Lockwood, John P Rochon

D-U-N-S 79-870-0324 IMP
NUMARK INDUSTRIES LP
200 Scenic View Dr, Cumberland, RI 02864-1847
Tel (401) 658-3131 *Founded/Ownrshp* 1992
Sales 300.0MM[E] *EMP* 120
SIC 5736 Musical instrument stores
CEO: John E O Donnell
**COO:* Paul Antrop
**CFO:* Paul Stansky
Ex VP: Richard Seymour
IT Man: Mark Sciola
Sls Mgr: Keith Stewart

D-U-N-S 07-860-4632 IMP
NUMBER HOLDINGS INC
99 CENT ONLY STORE
4000 Union Pacific Ave, Commerce, CA 90023-3202
Tel (323) 980-8145 *Founded/Ownrshp* 2011
Sales 2.0MMM[E] *EMP* 15,000[E]
SIC 5331 5199 Variety stores; General merchandise, non-durable
CFO: Frank J Schools

D-U-N-S 82-675-1232
▲ **NUMEREX CORP**
400 Interstate North Pkwy, Atlanta, GA 30339-7214
Tel (770) 693-5950 *Founded/Ownrshp* 1992
Sales 89.4MM *EMP* 190[E]
Tkr Sym NMRX *Exch* NGM
SIC 3669 7371 Intercommunication systems, electric; Computer software development & applications
CEO: Marc Zionts
**Ch Bd:* Stratton J Nicolaides
CFO: Richard Flynt
CFO: Kenneth L Gayron
Chf Mktg O: Shu Gan
VP: Eugene Hyun
Dir Risk M: Vin Costello
Prgrm Mgr: Chris Napoletano
Genl Mgr: Ed Kourany
Off Mgr: Elizabeth Keeler
CTO: Sridhar Ramachandran
Board of Directors: Tony G Holcombe, Brian Igoe, Sherrie G McAvoy, Jerry A Rose, Andrew J Ryan, Eric Singer

D-U-N-S 08-441-3293
NUMERICA CREDIT UNION
14610 E Sprague Ave, Spokane Valley, WA 99216-2146
Tel (509) 535-7613 *Founded/Ownrshp* 1937
Sales NA *EMP* 280
Accts Moss-Adams Llp Spokane Wash
SIC 6062 State credit unions, not federally chartered
Pr: Carla Altepeter
**Ch Bd:* David Schriver
**CFO:* Cindy Leaver
**V Ch Bd:* Joseph Day
**Ex VP:* Jennifer Lehn

D-U-N-S 96-808-1088
NUMIT LLC
15415 Shelbyville Rd, Louisville, KY 40245-4137
Tel (502) 245-2110 *Founded/Ownrshp* 2010
Sales 408.0MM[E] *EMP* 1,672[E]
SIC 3316 Cold-rolled strip or wire; Strip steel, cold-rolled: from purchased hot-rolled; Sheet, steel, cold-rolled: from purchased hot-rolled

NUMMI
See NEW UNITED MOTOR MANUFACTURING INC

NUMOTION
See ASSISTIVE TECHNOLOGY GROUP INC

NUMOTION
See UNITED SEATING & MOBILITY LLC

NUMOTION
See ATG / USM HOLDINGS LLC

NUMOTION
See ATG HOLDINGS INC

D-U-N-S 96-213-7162
NURSECORE MANAGEMENT SERVICES LLC
NURSECORE OF AMARILLO
2201 Brookhollow Plaza Dr # 450, Arlington, TX 76006-7482
Tel (817) 649-1166 *Founded/Ownrshp* 1996
Sales 201.6MM[E] *EMP* 4,200
SIC 8742 8082 Hospital & health services consultant; Home health care services
CEO: Deborah Lollar

NURSECORE OF AMARILLO
See NURSECORE MANAGEMENT SERVICES LLC

D-U-N-S 04-519-7803
■ **NURSEFINDERS LLC**
(*Suby of* AMN HEALTHCARE SERVICES INC) ★
12400 High Bluff Dr, San Diego, CA 92130-3077
Tel (858) 314-7427 *Founded/Ownrshp* 1975
Sales 91.5MM[E] *EMP* 1,400
SIC 7361 8082 7363 8049 Employment agencies; Home health care services; Help supply services; Temporary help service; Nurses, registered & practical
CEO: Susan Salka
Pr: Ralph S Henderson
Sr VP: Denise L Jackson
Pdt Mgr: Michele Colbert

D-U-N-S 00-181-9572 IMP/EXP
NURSERY SUPPLIES INC
1415 Orchard Dr, Chambersburg, PA 17201-4810
Tel (717) 263-7780 *Founded/Ownrshp* 1966
Sales 89.9MM[E] *EMP* 550
SIC 3089

D-U-N-S 12-124-9734
NURSES UNLIMITED INC
NURSES UNLIMITED MANAGED CARE
511 N Lincoln Ave, Odessa, TX 79761-4429
Tel (432) 580-2085 *Founded/Ownrshp* 1983
Sales 58.8MM *EMP* 3,400
SIC 8049 Nurses, registered & practical
CEO: Bobby Laughry
**CFO:* David Nelson
**Ch:* Patsy Gerron
**Sec:* Jim Gerron DDS
Off Mgr: Sandra Rowe
IT Man: Rod Valenzuela

NURSES UNLIMITED MANAGED CARE
See NURSES UNLIMITED INC

D-U-N-S 78-161-8355 EXP
NURTURE INC
HAPPY FAMILY BRANDS
(*Suby of* DANONE NORTH AMERICA LLC) ★
40 Fulton St Fl 17, New York, NY 10038-1850
Tel (212) 374-2779 *Founded/Ownrshp* 2013
Sales 126.0MM *EMP* 70
SIC 5137 Baby goods
CEO: Shazi Visram
**COO:* Jessica Rolph
**CFO:* Shauna Grob
Sr VP: Sebastian Erdociain
Sr VP: Robert Zimmerman
VP: Anne Laraway
Off Mgr: Marykate Maher
QC Dir: Mark Fairgrieve
VP Mktg: Molly Breiner
VP Sls: Bob Zimmerman
Mktg Dir: Helen Bernstein

D-U-N-S 09-901-3328 IMP/EXP
NUSIL TECHNOLOGY LLC
1050 Cindy Ln, Carpinteria, CA 93013-2906
Tel (805) 684-8780 *Founded/Ownrshp* 1970
Sales 103.4MM[E] *EMP* 500
SIC 3069

D-U-N-S 09-841-9567 EXP
NUSS TRUCK GROUP INC
NUSS TRUCKS-ROCHESTER
6500 Highway 63 S, Rochester, MN 55904-8429
Tel (507) 288-9488 *Founded/Ownrshp* 1973
Sales 132.3MM[E] *EMP* 240
SIC 5511 5531 Trucks, tractors & trailers: new & used; Truck equipment & parts
Pr: Robert Nuss
**VP:* Bradley Nuss
Ex Dir: Michael Sweeney
Brnch Mgr: Mark Nygaard
Genl Mgr: Clyde Jacobsen
Off Mgr: Teresa Clark
Off Mgr: Cindy Jackson
Off Mgr: Joyce Jacobs
Off Mgr: Brittany Jorgensen
Off Mgr: Mary Romie
Off Mgr: Holly Schlueter

NUSS TRUCKS-ROCHESTER
See NUSS TRUCK GROUP INC

NUSTAR
See AXEON REFINING LLC

D-U-N-S 84-811-0701 IMP/EXP
▲ **NUSTAR ENERGY LP**
19003 W Ih 10, San Antonio, TX 78257-9518
Tel (210) 918-2000 *Founded/Ownrshp* 1999
Sales 2.0MMM *EMP* 1,251
Tkr Sym NS *Exch* NYS
SIC 4612 4613 4226 Crude petroleum pipelines; Refined petroleum pipelines; Special warehousing & storage
Pr: Bradley C Barron
Genl Pt: Riverwalk Logistics
CFO: Thomas R Shoaf
Bd of Dir: Leticia Holbert
Ofcr: Pam Schmidt
Ex VP: Mary Brown
Sr VP: James R Bluntze
Sr VP: Manish Kapoor
Sr VP: Mary Morgan
Sr VP: Daniel S Oliver
Sr VP: Amy L Perry
Sr VP: Karen M Thompson
Sr VP: Mike Truby
VP: Brad Barron
VP: Kent Brewer
VP: Michael Burgett
VP: James Calvert
VP: Bill Greehey
VP: Steve Hays
VP: Greg Kaneb
VP: Terence Keogh

D-U-N-S 78-243-6005
▲ **NUSTAR GP HOLDINGS LLC**
19003 W Ih 10, San Antonio, TX 78257-9518
Tel (210) 918-2000 *Founded/Ownrshp* 2000
Sales 79.6MM *EMP* 1,251[E]
Accts Kpmg Llp San Antonio Texas
Tkr Sym NSH *Exch* NYS
SIC 4612 4613 Crude petroleum pipelines; Refined petroleum pipelines
Pr: Bradley C Barron
**Ch Bd:* William E Greehey
CFO: Thomas R Shoaf
Ofcr: Mary Rose Brown
Sr VP: Jorge A Del Alamo
Sr VP: Amy L Perry
Sr VP: Karen M Thompson

D-U-N-S 14-537-1543
■ **NUSTAR GP LLC**
(*Suby of* NUSTAR GP HOLDINGS LLC) ★
19003 W Interstate 10, San Antonio, TX 78257-9518
Tel (210) 370-2000 *Founded/Ownrshp* 2002
Sales 78.2MM[E] *EMP* 1,228[E]
SIC 3533 Oil & gas field machinery
CEO: Curtis V Anastasio
**CFO:* Steven A Blank
**VP:* James R Bluntzer
**VP:* Clayton E Killinger
**VP:* Jerry D McVicker
**VP:* Rodney L Reese

D-U-N-S 14-240-3430
■ **NUSTAR LOGISTICS LP**
(*Suby of* NUSTAR ENERGY LP) ★
19003 W Interstate 10, San Antonio, TX 78257-9518
Tel (210) 918-2000 *Founded/Ownrshp* 1999
Sales 509.5MM[E] *EMP* 1,172
SIC 1311 Crude petroleum & natural gas production
Pr: Brad Barron

D-U-N-S 78-176-6308
■ **NUSTAR PIPELINE PARTNERS LP**
(*Suby of* NUSTAR ENERGY LP) ★
2435 N Central Expy Ste 7, Richardson, TX 75080-2753
Tel (972) 899-4062 *Founded/Ownrshp* 1989
Sales 47.3MM[E] *EMP* 1,114
SIC 4613 Refined petroleum pipelines
Pt: Edward D Doherty
Pt: Michael Rose
Pt: Ronald D Scoggins
Pt: Howard C Wadsworth

D-U-N-S 07-857-9212
■ **NUSTAR SUPPLY & TRADING LLC**
(*Suby of* NUSTAR LOGISTICS LP) ★
19003 W Interstate 10, San Antonio, TX 78257-9518
Tel (210) 918-2000 *Founded/Ownrshp* 2012
Sales 134.7MM[E] *EMP* 1,000
SIC 5172 Crude oil
CEO: Brad Barron
CFO: Steven A Blank
Treas: Chris Russell
Ex VP: Mary Rose Brown
Prin: Curtis V Anastasio

D-U-N-S 96-185-9605
▲ **NUTANIX INC**
1740 Tech Dr Ste 150, San Jose, CA 95110
Tel (408) 216-8360 *Founded/Ownrshp* 2009
Sales 241.4MM *EMP* 1,980
Accts Deloitte & Touche Llp San Jos
Tkr Sym NTNX *Exch* NGS
SIC 7373 Systems engineering, computer related
Ch Bd: Dheeraj Pandey
**Pr:* Sudheesh Nair Vadakkedath
**CFO:* Duston M Williams
Ofcr: Sunil Potti
**Ofcr:* Howard Ting
**Ex VP:* David Sangster
Sr VP: Rajiv Mirani
VP: Andres Hurtado
VP: Wayne Neich
Dir IT: Shawn Chen
Mktg Dir: Lionel Marks
Board of Directors: Steven J Gomo, John McAdam, Ravi Mhatre, Jeffrey T Parks, Michael P Scarpelli

NUTEC METAL JOINING PRODUCTS
See PRINCE & IZANT CO

D-U-N-S 02-034-6458 IMP/EXP
NUTRA BLEND LLC (MO)
NUTRA-BLEND
(*Suby of* LAND O'LAKES INC) ★
3200 2nd St, Neosho, MO 64850-7738
Tel (417) 451-6111 *Founded/Ownrshp* 1975, 1979
Sales 89.1MM[E] *EMP* 200[E]
SIC 2048 Feed supplements; Mineral feed supplements
CEO: Mike Osborne
CFO: Scott Cooper
VP: Jennifer Spencer
**MIS Dir:* Chris Enloe
QA Dir: Monica Culina
Trfc Dir: Tammy Goswick
**VP Sls:* Randy Shanks
Manager: Shawn Atkins
Manager: Eric Lonnevik

NUTRA-BLEND
See NUTRA BLEND LLC

D-U-N-S 00-725-7355 IMP/EXP
■ **NUTRA-FLO CO**
NUTRA-FLO EQUIPMENT CO
(*Suby of* FLO KAY INDUSTRIES INC) ★
200 S Derby Ln, North Sioux City, SD 57049-3031
Tel (712) 277-2011 *Founded/Ownrshp* 1928
Sales 179.3MM[E] *EMP* 380
SIC 2873 2816 2048 Nitrogenous fertilizers; Zinc pigments: zinc oxide, zinc sulfide; Feed supplements
Pr: Raun D Lohry
**Treas:* Royal Q Lohry
IT Man: Tim Doring
Board of Directors: Dirk Lohry

NUTRA-FLO EQUIPMENT CO
See NUTRA-FLO CO

NUTRABOLT
See WOODBOLT DISTRIBUTION LLC

D-U-N-S 88-349-2720 IMP
■ **NUTRACEUTICAL CORP**
(*Suby of* NUTRACEUTICAL INTERNATIONAL CORP) ★
1400 Kearns Blvd Ste 200, Park City, UT 84060-7228
Tel (435) 655-6000 *Founded/Ownrshp* 1995
Sales 180.8MM[E] *EMP* 706
SIC 2834 Vitamin preparations
Pr: Bruce Hough
Pr: Jason Jones
**CFO:* Cory McQueen
Ex VP: Jeffrey Hinrichs
Ex VP: Gary M Hume
VP: Vern Christensen
VP: Kim Heward
VP: Tim Hinrichs
VP: Margo Ochs
VP: Cary Roberts
VP: John Russo
VP: Joel Tippets
Creative D: Joe Arrigo

D-U-N-S 00-512-7654 IMP/EXP
▲ **NUTRACEUTICAL INTERNATIONAL CORP**
1400 Kearns Blvd Fl 2, Park City, UT 84060-7228
Tel (435) 655-6106 *Founded/Ownrshp* 1993
Sales 232.9MM *EMP* 845[E]
Tkr Sym NUTR *Exch* NGS
SIC 2833 Vitamins, natural or synthetic: bulk, uncompounded
Ch Bd: Frank W Gay II
Pr: Bruce R Hough
**COO:* Jeffrey A Hinrichs
CFO: Cory J McQueen
Ex VP: Gary M Hume

VP: Jason D Jones
VP: Daren P Peterson
VP: Stanley E Soper
VP: Matthew A Vance
VP Mktg: Christopher B Neuberger
Board of Directors: Gregory M Benson, Michael D Burke, J Kimo Esplin, James D Stice

D-U-N-S 05-374-5811 IMP
NUTRAMED INC
(*Suby of* ELITE ONE SOURCE NUTRISCIENCES INC) ★
1001 S 3rd St W, Missoula, MT 59801-2337
Tel (406) 273-5493 *Founded/Ownrshp* 1998
Sales 127.6MM^E *EMP* 200
SIC 5149 Specialty food items
Pr: Manu Patolia
**VP:* Dana Patolia

NUTRI-FORCE NUTRITION
See FDC VITAMINS LLC

NUTRI-FORCE NUTRITION
See VS HERCULES LLC

NUTRILITE
See ACCESS BUSINESS GROUP INTERNATIONAL LLC

NUTRILITE
See ACCESS BUSINESS GROUP LLC

D-U-N-S 13-263-0448
▲ NUTRISYSTEM INC
600 Office Center Dr, Fort Washington, PA 19034-3232
Tel (215) 706-5300 *Founded/Ownrshp* 1972
Sales 462.6MM *EMP* 451
Tkr Sym NTRI *Exch* NGS
SIC 5961 Food, mail order
Pr: Dawn M Zier
**Ch Bd:* Michael J Hagan
CFO: Michael P Monahan
Chf Mktg O: Keira Krausz
Exec: Jane Boudreaux
Software D: Michelle Odonnell
Board of Directors: Robert F Bernstock, Paul Guyardo, Jay Herratti, Michael D Mangan, Brian P Tierney, Andrea M Weiss

D-U-N-S 07-749-1330
NUTRITION INC
580 Wendel Rd Ste 100, Irwin, PA 15642-5001
Tel (724) 978-2100 *Founded/Ownrshp* 1975
Sales 69.1MM^E *EMP* 1,800
Accts Bielau Tierney Coon & Compan
SIC 5812 2099 Contract food services; Food preparations
Pr: Gerald Moore
**Pr:* Edward W Caswell
COO: Tammy Murphy
**Sec:* Donald Baker
VP: Patrick D Davis
Rgnl Mgr: Fletcher Vollmer

NUTRITION TRANSPORTATION SVCS
See PROVIMI NORTH AMERICA INC

D-U-N-S 00-833-8345 IMP/EXP
NUTRO CO
NATURAL CHOICE
(*Suby of* MARS INC) ★
1550 W Mcewen Dr Ste 100, Franklin, TN 37067-1770
Tel (888) 607-4081 *Founded/Ownrshp* 1985
Sales 110.6MM^E *EMP* 450
SIC 2047 0742 Dog food; Cat food; Veterinary services, specialties
CEO: Rodolfo Spielmann
**Ch Bd:* David Traitel
CFO: Sandip Grewal
IT Man: Christopher Coughlan

D-U-N-S 05-395-0783 IMP
▲ NUVASIVE INC
7475 Lusk Blvd, San Diego, CA 92121-5707
Tel (858) 909-1800 *Founded/Ownrshp* 1997
Sales 811.1MM *EMP* 1,600
Tkr Sym NUVA *Exch* NGS
SIC 3841 Surgical & medical instruments
Ch Bd: Gregory T Lucier
Pr: Jason D Hanson
CFO: Quentin S Blackford
CFO: Quentin Blackford
Ex VP: Carol Cox
Ex VP: Scott Durall
Ex VP: Peter Leddy
Ex VP: Tyler P Lipschultz
Ex VP: Mike Paolucci
Ex VP: Russell Powers
Ex VP: Stephan Siemers
Ex VP: Joan Stafslien
Sr VP: Jeffrey Rydin
VP: Jason Hannan
VP: Ed Mayadag
VP: Pat Miles
VP: Mark Ojeda
VP: Jonathan D Spangler
Board of Directors: Daniel J Wolterman, Jack R Blair, Vickie L Capps, Peter C Farrell, Robert F Friel, Lesley H Howe, Pat Miles, Leslie V Norwalk, Mike O'halleran, Donald J Rosenberg

D-U-N-S 78-949-4374
NUVEEN INVESTMENTS INC
(*Suby of* TIAA-CREF) ★
333 W Wacker Dr, Chicago, IL 60606-1220
Tel (312) 917-7700 *Founded/Ownrshp* 2014
Sales 696.8MM^E *EMP* 828^E
SIC 6282 6211 Manager of mutual funds, contract or fee basis; Investment bankers; Underwriters, security; Bond dealers & brokers; Mutual funds, selling by independent salesperson
Pr: John P Amboian
Pr: Julie Evinger
Pr: Joseph Marks
COO: Glenn Richter
Sr Cor Off: Allen Williamson
Chf Mktg O: Stephen Ban
Ex VP: John Maccarthy
Sr VP: Walter Kelly
VP: Sandra Alvarenga
VP: Chip Bailey
VP: Christopher Barron
VP: Bruce Bedford
VP: Greg Bottjer
VP: Susi Budiman
VP: Jae H Chung
VP: Thomas Eggen
VP: Anthony Eichler
VP: Mark Flynn
VP: Thomas Griffith
VP: Todd M Heine
VP: Steven Krupa

D-U-N-S 04-252-9396
NUVEEN JOHN & CO INC (DEL) (IL)
(*Suby of* NUVEEN INVESTMENTS INC) ★
333 W Wacker Dr Fl 33, Chicago, IL 60606-2203
Tel (312) 917-7700 *Founded/Ownrshp* 1898, 1992
Sales 131.3MM^E *EMP* 610
SIC 6211 8742 Mutual funds, selling by independent salesperson; Business consultant
Ch Bd: Timothy R Schwertfeger
Pr: John Amboian
Chf Mktg O: Alan Brown
Sr VP: Alan Berkshire
VP: Jeff Kratz
Mng Dir: Frank Maiorano

NUVERRA
See THERMO FLUIDS INC

D-U-N-S 92-950-4533
▲ NUVERRA ENVIRONMENTAL SOLUTIONS INC
14624 N Scottsdale Rd, Scottsdale, AZ 85254-2753
Tel (602) 903-7802 *Founded/Ownrshp* 2007
Sales 356.7MM *EMP* 1,365^E
Accts Kpmg Llp Phoenix Arizona
Tkr Sym NESC *Exch* OTC
SIC 1389 4953 Servicing oil & gas wells; Liquid waste, collection & disposal
Ch Bd: Mark D Johnsrud
Pr: Mark Ridgley
V Ch Bd: Robert B Simonds Jr
Ex VP: Joseph M Crabb
Dir Risk M: Ken Davis
CTO: Lawrence Strohmaier
Software D: Christopher Ryhal
Board of Directors: William M Austin, Edward A Barkett, Tod C Holmes, R Dan Nelson, Alfred E Osborne Jr, J Danforth Quayle

D-U-N-S 07-940-4755
NUVI GLOBAL CORP
8423 Rochester Ave # 101, Rancho Cucamonga, CA 91730-3995
Tel (844) 740-6938 *Founded/Ownrshp* 2014
Sales 900.0MM *EMP* 20
SIC 5122 Vitamins & minerals
CEO: Eva Zamora
**CEO:* Victor H Chavez
Genl Mgr: Jessica Hernandez

D-U-N-S 14-608-7841
■ NUVOX INC
NEWSOUTH COMMUNICATIONS
(*Suby of* WINDSTREAM SERVICES LLC) ★
2 N Main St, Greenville, SC 29601-4874
Tel (864) 672-5000 *Founded/Ownrshp* 2010
Sales 365.8MM^E *EMP* 1,800
SIC 4813 Local & long distance telephone communications
CEO: James W Akerhielm
**Pr:* Michael Gallagher
COO: Bruce Cameron
CFO: Ron Harold
**CFO:* David Solomon
Sr Cor Off: Robert Rogers
Ex VP: Tracy Cooper
Ex VP: Edward Terrell
Sr VP: Ricky El-Mogazi
**VP:* Matt Blocha
VP: Susan Butler
VP: Lawrence Dubow
VP: Rob Gage
VP: Joe Jefferson
VP: Jake Jennings
VP: Gwen Jordan
VP: Max Major
VP: Michele Marckini
VP: Linda Obrien
VP: Vincent Oddo
VP: Kash Patel

NV ENERGY
See NEVADA POWER CO

NV ENERGY
See SIERRA PACIFIC POWER CO

D-U-N-S 12-180-9347 IMP
■ NV ENERGY INC
(*Suby of* BERKSHIRE HATHAWAY ENERGY CO) ★
6226 W Sahara Ave, Las Vegas, NV 89146-3060
Tel (702) 402-5000 *Founded/Ownrshp* 2013
Sales 3.2MMM^E *EMP* 2,699^E
SIC 4911 4924 Generation, electric power; Transmission, electric power; Distribution, electric power; Natural gas distribution
Pr: Paul Caudill
**COO:* Dilek L Samil
**CFO:* Jonathan S Halkyard
Bd of Dir: Leo Wong
**Ex VP:* Paul J Kaleta
Sr VP: Tony F Sanchez
**VP:* E Kevin Bethel
VP: Kevin Bethel
VP: Alice Cobb
VP: James Doubek
VP: Star Lacy
VP: Gary L Lavey
VP: John Owens
VP: Tony Sanchez
VP: Mary Simmons
VP: John Williams
VP: Tracey Yancey
Exec: Max Kuniansky

D-U-N-S 07-848-2872
▲ NV5 GLOBAL INC
200 S Park Rd Ste 350, Hollywood, FL 33021-8798
Tel (954) 495-2112 *Founded/Ownrshp* 1949
Sales 154.6MM *EMP* 975^E
Tkr Sym NVEE *Exch* NAS
SIC 8711 8748 Engineering services; Business consulting
Ch Bd: Dickerson Wright
**Pr:* Alexander A Hockman
CFO: Michael P Rama
Ofcr: Maryjo O'Brien
**Ex VP:* Donald C Alford
Ex VP: Richard Tong
Board of Directors: Jeffrey A Liss, William D Pruitt, Gerald J Salontai, Francois Tardan

D-U-N-S 96-191-5761
■ NV5 INC
VERTICAL V, INC.
(*Suby of* NV5 GLOBAL INC) ★
200 S Park Rd Ste 350, Hollywood, FL 33021-8798
Tel (954) 495-2112 *Founded/Ownrshp* 2009
Sales 161.0MM^E *EMP* 360^E
SIC 8711 Engineering services
CEO: Dickerson Wright
Ex VP: Richard Tong

D-U-N-S 18-839-8247
NVH INC
(*Suby of* NOUVEAU VERRE HOLDINGS INC) ★
3802 Robert Porcher Way, Greensboro, NC 27410-2190
Tel (336) 545-0011 *Founded/Ownrshp* 2004
Sales 252.7MM^E *EMP* 864^E
SIC 2221 3624 2241 2295 Glass broadwoven fabrics; Fibers, carbon & graphite; Glass narrow fabrics; Mats, varnished glass
CEO: Philippe Porcher
**CFO:* Philippe R Dorier

D-U-N-S 80-672-4555 IMP/EXP
▲ NVIDIA CORP
2701 San Tomas Expy, Santa Clara, CA 95050-2519
Tel (408) 486-2000 *Founded/Ownrshp* 1993
Sales 5.0MMM *EMP* 9,228
Accts Pricewaterhousecoopers Llp Sa
Tkr Sym NVDA *Exch* NGS
SIC 3674 Semiconductors & related devices
Pr: Jen-Hsun Huang
V Ch: Gerald Luiz
Pr: Kenneth Macdonald
CFO: Colette M Kress
Treas: Jay Landre
Bd of Dir: Eric Anderson
Bd of Dir: Darrell Boggs
Bd of Dir: Matthew Bolitho
Bd of Dir: Keegan Brown
Bd of Dir: Gautam Chakrabarti
Bd of Dir: Luke Durant
Bd of Dir: Venerando Ilagan
Bd of Dir: Guru Nutheti
Bd of Dir: Hyungon Ryu
Bd of Dir: Nancy Smith
Ofcr: David M Shannon
Ex VP: Ajay K Puri
Ex VP: Debora Shoquist
Ex VP: Debora C Shoquist
Sr VP: Bill Dally
Sr VP: Brian Kelleher
Board of Directors: Mark A Stevens, Robert Burgess, Persis S Drell, James C Gaither, Dawn Hudson, Harvey C Jones, Michael G McCaffery, William J Miller, Mark L Perry, A Brooke Seawell

D-U-N-S 80-839-4621
▲ NVR INC
11700 Plaza America Dr # 500, Reston, VA 20190-4751
Tel (703) 956-4000 *Founded/Ownrshp* 1980
Sales 5.0MMM *EMP* 4,300
Accts Kpmg Llp Mclean Virginia
Tkr Sym NVR *Exch* NYS
SIC 1531 6162 Operative builders; Speculative builder, single-family houses; Townhouse developers; Condominium developers; Mortgage bankers
Pr: Paul C Saville
**Ch Bd:* Dwight C Schar
Pr: Robert W Henley
Pr: Jeffrey D Martchek
CFO: Daniel D Malzahn
Ofcr: Eugene J Bredow
Board of Directors: W Grady Rosier, C E Andrews, Susan Williamson Ross, Timothy M Donahue, Paul W Whetsell, Thomas D Eckert, Alfred E Festa, Ed Grier, Manuel H Johnson, Mel Martinez, William A Moran, David A Preiser

D-U-N-S 00-905-0934
NW CENTER INDUSTRIES 5307
7272 W Marginal Way S, Seattle, WA 98108-4140
Tel (206) 285-9140 *Founded/Ownrshp* 2009
Sales 50.5MM^E *EMP* 1,500
SIC 3999 Manufacturing industries

NW NATURAL
See NORTHWEST NATURAL GAS CO

D-U-N-S 78-513-5757
NW PIPELINE INC
3535 Briarpark Dr Ste 135, Houston, TX 77042-5233
Tel (713) 789-4311 *Founded/Ownrshp* 1983
Sales 158.5MM^E *EMP* 502
Accts Grant Thorton Llp Houston T
SIC 1623 Pipeline construction
Pr: Paul Somerville
**Sec:* Clyde Fowler

NWAS
See NATIONWIDE ARGOSY SOLUTIONS LLC

NWEA
See NORTHWEST EVALUATION ASSOCIATION

D-U-N-S 00-740-8102 IMP/EXP
NWL HOLDINGS INC
NATIONAL WHOLESALE LIQUIDATORS
111 Hempstead Tpke, West Hempstead, NY 11552-2155
Tel (516) 489-3300 *Founded/Ownrshp* 1998
Sales NA *EMP* 1,006
SIC 6712 Bank holding companies
Pr: Eva Rosen
Treas: Scott Rosen
VP: Carrie Rosen

D-U-N-S 78-507-4829
NWN CORP
271 Waverley Oaks Rd # 302, Waltham, MA 02452-8470
Tel (781) 472-3400 *Founded/Ownrshp* 2000
Sales 224.2MM^E *EMP* 486
SIC 7373 Computer integrated systems design
CEO: Mont Phelps
**COO:* Skip Tappen
**CFO:* Kevin Bullock
VP: Pierre Abdel-Malak
VP: Tim Joyce
Netwrk Eng: Michael Louis
Sales Asso: Lee Guillory
Sales Asso: Carolyn Hunter

D-U-N-S 06-866-2415 IMP
NWS MICHIGAN INC
NATIONAL WINE & SPIRITS MICH
17550 Allen Rd, Brownstown, MI 48193-8488
Tel (734) 324-3000 *Founded/Ownrshp* 1996
Sales 246.4MM^E *EMP* 540
SIC 5182 Liquor
CEO: James E Lacrosse
**COO:* John J Baker
**Treas:* Patrick Trefun
**VP:* Dwight Deming
Mktg Mgr: Cliff Parr

D-U-N-S 94-972-0465 IMP
NWT WORLD ARTS INC
NEW WORLD TRADING
36660 Bankside Dr Ste A, Cathedral City, CA 92234-7833
Tel (760) 321-8780 *Founded/Ownrshp* 2002
Sales 1.0MMM *EMP* 3
SIC 5021 Furniture
Pr: Elizabeth Cervantes
**Treas:* Fernando Cervantes

NWTC
See NORTHEAST WISCONSIN TECHNICAL COLLEGE DISTRICT

D-U-N-S 80-000-8286 IMP
NXP SEMICONDUCTORS USA INC
411 E Plumeria Dr, San Jose, CA 95134-1924
Tel (408) 518-5500 *Founded/Ownrshp* 2006
Sales 4.8MMM *EMP* 5,000
SIC 3674

D-U-N-S 14-141-7928 IMP
NXP USA INC
SWELL SOFTWARE
(*Suby of* FREESCALE SEMICONDUCTOR HOLDINGS V INC) ★
6501 W William Cannon Dr, Austin, TX 78735-8523
Tel (512) 933-8214 *Founded/Ownrshp* 2003
Sales 4.5MMM^E *EMP* 16,500
SIC 3674 Semiconductors & related devices; Semiconductor diodes & rectifiers; Semiconductor circuit networks
CEO: Rich Beyer
**Ch Bd:* J Daniel McCranie
**Pr:* Alan Campbell
**CEO:* Gregg Lowe
COO: Monica Davis
**Treas:* Dave Stasse
Top Exec: Judith Watkins
**Sr VP:* James Bates
**Sr VP:* Dan Durn
**Sr VP:* Paul Hart
Sr VP: Reza Kazerounian
**Sr VP:* Brandon Tolany
VP: Kim Cooke
**VP:* Ken Hansen
**VP:* Randy A Hyzak
VP: Barbara King
VP: Steve Wainwright

D-U-N-S 08-801-3219
▲ NXSTAGE MEDICAL INC
350 Merrimack St, Lawrence, MA 01843-1748
Tel (978) 687-4700 *Founded/Ownrshp* 1998
Sales 336.1MM *EMP* 3,600^E
Tkr Sym NXTM *Exch* NGS
SIC 3845 Electromedical equipment; Dialyzers, electromedical
CEO: Jeffrey H Burbank
**Ch Bd:* Robert G Funari
Pr: Joseph E Turk Jr
CFO: Matthew W Towse
Sr VP: Winifred L Swan
VP: Schrader Mike
VP: Michael O'Connell
VP: Matt Pearman
VP: Curt Scovel
VP: Todd M Snell
Area Mgr: Kimberly Davis
Board of Directors: Daniel A Giannini, Earl R Lewis, Jean K Mixer, Craig W Moore, Reid S Perper, Barry M Straube

D-U-N-S 06-522-6057
NXTRANET CORP
1500 Mcandrews Rd W, Burnsville, MN 55337-4432
Tel (952) 808-5554 *Founded/Ownrshp* 1997
Sales 100.0MM *EMP* 8
SIC 7371 Computer software development
Pr: Fuat Kerkinni

D-U-N-S 07-270-5783
NYACK HOSPITAL FOUNDATION INC (NY)
160 N Midland Ave, Nyack, NY 10960-1998
Tel (845) 348-2000 *Founded/Ownrshp* 1984
Sales 216.2MM *EMP* 1,300
SIC 8062 8011 8082 Hospital, AMA approved residency; Medical centers; Home health care services
Pr: Mark Geller
COO: Peter Evola
**Ch:* Lisa Hayes
**Ch:* Richard L Kohlhausen
**Ch:* John Mecchella

Chf Mktg O: Marge Zemek
VP: Jeffrey Keahon
VP: Robert Mackey
Dir Risk M: Jennifer Morris
Dir Rad: Daniel Cohen
CIO: John Volanto

D-U-N-S 96-489-2298
NYC DISTRICT COUNCIL OF CARPENTERS WELFARE FUND
395 Hudson St Lbby 3, New York, NY 10014-7450
Tel (212) 366-7300 *Founded/Ownrshp* 2010
Sales NA *EMP* 3
Accts Schultheis & Panettieri Llp N
SIC 6371 Pension, health & welfare funds
Prin: David Halmers

NYC EMPOWERMENT SCHOOLS
See NEW YORK CITY DEPT OF EDUCATION

NYCM INSURANCE
See NEW YORK CENTRAL MUTUAL FIRE INSURANCE CO

D-U-N-S 09-653-5687 IMP/EXP
NYCO MINERALS INC
PARENT IS IMERYS USA
(*Suby of* S&B INDUSTRIAL MINERALS NORTH AMERICA INC) ★
803 Mountain View Dr, Willsboro, NY 12996-3659
Tel (518) 963-4262 *Founded/Ownrshp* 1979
Sales 505.3MM^E *EMP* 100
SIC 1499 5052 3295 3291

NYISO
See NEW YORK INDEPENDENT SYSTEM OPERATOR INC

NYIT
See NEW YORK INSTITUTE OF TECHNOLOGY INC

D-U-N-S 93-774-5404
NYK GROUP AMERICAS INC
(*Suby of* NIPPON YUSEN KABUSHIKI KAISHA)
300 Lighting Way Ste 500, Secaucus, NJ 07094-3672
Tel (201) 330-3000 *Founded/Ownrshp* 1995
Sales 132.8MM^E *EMP* 400
SIC 4412 4731 4011 4491 7519 Deep sea foreign transportation of freight; Agents, shipping; Railroads, line-haul operating; Marine cargo handling; Utility trailer rental
CEO: Masao Takebayashi
**Pr:* Tomoo Kitayama
**CFO:* Peter Keller
**Treas:* Kazuhiro Kamoi
**VP:* Jeff Baker
**VP:* Peter Hsu
**VP:* Shin Matsuda
IT Man: Tan Phoo Yong
Opers Mgr: Louis Ferrer

D-U-N-S 19-488-9648 IMP
NYK LINE (NORTH AMERICA) INC
NIPPON YUSEN KABUSHIKI
(*Suby of* NYK GROUP AMERICAS INC) ★
300 Lighting Way 4th, Secaucus, NJ 07094-3647
Tel (201) 330-3000 *Founded/Ownrshp* 1995
Sales 95.5MM^E *EMP* 400
SIC 4412 4731 4213 4011 7519 4491

D-U-N-S 85-848-2508
NYLIFE LLC
(*Suby of* NEW YORK LIFE INSURANCE CO) ★
51 Madison Ave, New York, NY 10010-1603
Tel (212) 576-7000 *Founded/Ownrshp* 1984
Sales 124.1MM^E *EMP* 562
Accts Pricewaterhousecoopers Llp N
SIC 6282 6211 6733 6153 Investment advisory service; Brokers, security; Personal investment trust management; Direct working capital financing
Ch Bd: Fredrick J Sievert
Mng Pt: Scott Norris
**Treas:* Edward T Pilner
Ex VP: Brian A Murdock
**Sr VP:* Thomas English
VP: Elizabeth A Bryson
VP: Robert Gardner
**VP:* Katherine Marrion
VP: Richard E McGee
VP: Mark Meirowitz
**VP:* Anjilo Scialabba
VP: Richard Topp
**VP:* Richard W Xuccaro
VP: Richard Zuccarro
Dir Soc: Kathy Gallant

D-U-N-S 08-783-4714 IMP
NYLONCRAFT INC
616 W Mckinley Ave, Mishawaka, IN 46545-5597
Tel (574) 256-1521 *Founded/Ownrshp* 2001
Sales 211.9MM^E *EMP* 679
SIC 3089 Injection molding of plastics
COO: Bob Krzozowski
Pr: Mark Hagan
**CFO:* Don Dames
**VP:* Roland Erb
VP: Dennis Wasikowski
Ql Cn Mgr: Thomas Hyde

D-U-N-S 10-105-8282
NYLONCRAFT OF MICHIGAN INC
(*Suby of* NYLONCRAFT INC) ★
1640 E Chicago Rd, Jonesville, MI 49250-9110
Tel (517) 849-9911 *Founded/Ownrshp* 2002
Sales 91.4MM^E *EMP* 260
SIC 3089 Plastic processing
Ch: Glenn Scolnik
**Pr:* James Krzyzewski
**CFO:* Lee Powers
**VP:* Roland Erb
**VP:* Terry Rensberger

D-U-N-S 82-973-4750
NYLSI INC
SUNRISE TOYOTA SCION
3984 Sunrise Hwy, Oakdale, NY 11769-1003
Tel (631) 589-9000 *Founded/Ownrshp* 2008
Sales 110.0MM *EMP* 135
SIC 5511 Automobiles, new & used
Ch Bd: James Berg

NYMEX
See NEW YORK MERCANTILE EXCHANGE INC

D-U-N-S 36-154-6299
■ **NYMEX HOLDINGS INC**
(*Suby of* CME GROUP INC) ★
1 N End Ave Rm 1215, New York, NY 10282-1102
Tel (212) 299-2000 *Founded/Ownrshp* 2008
Sales 97.5MM^E *EMP* 635
SIC 6231 Futures exchanges, contract; Commodity contract exchanges; Stock option exchanges
Pr: James Newsome
**V Ch:* Thomas Gordon
V Ch: Robert Halper
COO: Jerome H Bailey
CFO: Kenneth D Shifrin
**Ch:* Richard Schaeffer
**Treas:* Frank Siciliano
Sr Cor Off: Joyce Flake
Bd of Dir: Bulkeley E Griswold
Bd of Dir: Harley Lippman
Bd of Dir: John L McNamara
Sr VP: Richard D Kerschner
Sr VP: Lewis A Ribley
VP: Charles Bebel
VP: Bob Biolsi
VP: Madeline Boyd
VP: Michael Campanelli
VP: Patrick Conti
VP: George Henderson

D-U-N-S 14-468-9288
■ **NYNEX INFORMATION SOLUTIONS GROUP INC**
VERIZON
(*Suby of* VERIZON COMMUNICATIONS INC) ★
1095 Ave Of The Amer Fl 7, New York, NY 10036-6797
Tel (212) 395-1000 *Founded/Ownrshp* 1999
Sales 98.4MM^E *EMP* 3,800
SIC 8732 7371 7379 Business research service; Market analysis or research; Custom computer programming services; Computer related consulting services
Pr: Richard Blackburn
Ex Dir: Edward Diaz
Ex Dir: Anne Hogan

D-U-N-S 83-100-0583 IMP
■ **NYP HOLDINGS INC**
NEW YORK POST
(*Suby of* NEWS PREFERRED HOLDINGS INC.)
1211 Avenue Of The Amer, New York, NY 10036-8790
Tel (212) 997-9272 *Founded/Ownrshp* 2013
Sales 175.5MM^E *EMP* 725
SIC 2711 Commercial printing & newspaper publishing combined
Pr: K Rupert Murdoch
Ex VP: Joe Vincent
VP: John Ancona
VP: Michael Carvalhido
VP: Michelle Dalmeida
Creative D: Tory Shobe
Netwrk Mgr: Dimitri Finkler
Opers Mgr: Greg Gallo
Ql Cn Mgr: Gideon Sober
Sls Mgr: Liz Clyman
Snr Mgr: Mario Rogowicz

D-U-N-S 80-881-0543 IMP
■ **NYPRO HEALTHCARE BAJA INC**
NYPRO PRECISION ASSEMBLIES
(*Suby of* NYPRO INC) ★
2195 Britannia Blvd # 107, San Diego, CA 92154-6290
Tel (619) 498-9250 *Founded/Ownrshp* 2002
Sales 178.1MM^E *EMP* 600
SIC 3841 3679 Surgical & medical instruments; Electronic circuits
Ch: Joe Borden
**Pr:* Courtney Ryan
**Treas:* Thomas J Flannery

D-U-N-S 04-613-1678 IMP/EXP
■ **NYPRO INC**
(*Suby of* JABIL CIRCUIT INC) ★
101 Union St, Clinton, MA 01510-2935
Tel (978) 365-8100 *Founded/Ownrshp* 2013
Sales 5.4MMM^E *EMP* 16,900
SIC 3089 3559 7389 8711 Injection molding of plastics; Robots, molding & forming plastics; Design, commercial & industrial; Engineering services
Pr: Courtney Ryan
**Pr:* Gregory G Adams
**Treas:* Sergio Cadavid
Ofcr: Tara Shirley
VP: Jack McCabe
VP: S Patrick
VP: Eric Pettes
VP: Thomas Taylor
Prgrm Mgr: William Boston
Prgrm Mgr: Jason Durkin
Prgrm Mgr: Frank Foley

NYPRO PRECISION ASSEMBLIES
See NYPRO HEALTHCARE BAJA INC

D-U-N-S 09-041-4988 IMP/EXP
■ **NYPRO PUERTO RICO INC**
(*Suby of* NYPRO INC) ★
15 Ave Luis Mnoz Rivera S, Cayey, PR 00736-4701
Tel (787) 738-4211 *Founded/Ownrshp* 1973
Sales 98.4MM^E *EMP* 500
SIC 3089 Injection molded finished plastic products
Pr: Courtney Ryan
**Treas:* Nicholas D Aznoian
**Treas:* Sergio Cadavid
**VP:* Reynaldo Encarnacion

D-U-N-S 00-170-7371 IMP/EXP
NYRA INC
BELMONT PARK
11000 Rockaway Blvd Ste 1, Jamaica, NY 11420-1010
Tel (718) 641-4700 *Founded/Ownrshp* 1955
Sales 93.7MM^E *EMP* 1,300
SIC 7948 Horse race track operation
Ch: David Skorton
**Pr:* Anthony J Bonomo
**COO:* Steven Duncker
**COO:* Peter Karches
**CFO:* Alexander W Ingle
Ofcr: John Ryan
**VP:* Rick Cotton
VP: John Giombarrese
Ex Dir: Donna Chenkin
Info Man: Daniel Felix
Info Man: Tom Oakley
Board of Directors: John W Meriwether, Daniel P Tully, H Douglas Barclay, Paul F Oreffice, Peggy Vandervoort, Allan R Dragone, John H Peace, Charles V Wait, Robert S Evans, Ogden Mills Phipps, Jobruces-llewellyn, Richard L Gelb, Dolph Rotfeld, Richard Gi-ancola, Lewis Rudin, Charles E Hayward, Peter G Schiff, John A Hettinger, Barry K Schwartz, Earle I Mack, Joseph V Shields Jr, Timothy M McGinn, Delbert Staley

NYRT
See NEW YORK REIT INC

NYS DEPARTMENT TRANSPORTATION
See NEW YORK DEPARTMENT OF TRANSPORTATION

NYS DPRTMENT CORRECTIONAL SVCS
See NEW YORK DEPARTMENT OF CORRECTIONS AND COMMUNITY SUPERVISION

D-U-N-S 83-685-7404
NYS POLICE INVESTIGATORS ASSOCIATION EMERGENCY ASSISTANCE FUND INC
11 N Pearl St Ste 1202, Albany, NY 12207-2818
Tel (518) 436-0120 *Founded/Ownrshp* 2007
Sales 116.3M *EMP* 1,000
Accts Staff Ciampino & Company Pc
SIC 8631 Labor unions & similar labor organizations
Pr: Jeffrey J Keyser
**Sec:* Brian Meier

D-U-N-S 10-193-0621
NYSARC
AHRC NEW YORK CITY
252 W 29th St Rm 700, New York, NY 10001-5271
Tel (212) 780-2500 *Founded/Ownrshp* 1981
Sales 227.3MM *EMP* 2
SIC 8322 Association for the handicapped
Prin: Steve Towler

D-U-N-S 07-525-9507
NYSARC INC
29 British American Blvd # 2, Latham, NY 12110-1437
Tel (518) 439-8311 *Founded/Ownrshp* 1949
Sales 8.8MM *EMP* 28,000
Accts Bonadio & Co Llp Pittsford N
SIC 8361 8322 8093 8331 Rehabilitation center, residential: health care incidental; Association for the handicapped; Rehabilitation center, outpatient treatment; Job training & vocational rehabilitation services
Pr: John A Schuppenhauer
V Ch: Susan Limongello
**CFO:* John J Sherman Jr
**Ex Dir:* Marc N Brandt
MIS Dir: Robert Goodman

D-U-N-S 13-672-6564
NYSARC INC
ASSOC FOR HELP
(*Suby of* NYSARC INC) ★
83 Maiden Ln, New York, NY 10038-4812
Tel (212) 780-2635 *Founded/Ownrshp* 1949
Sales 188.2MM^E *EMP* 2,000
SIC 8099 Blood related health services
CFO: Amy West
**Pr:* Laura J Kennedy
Trst Ofcr: Joseph Livote
**VP:* Raymond Ferrigno
**VP:* Gail Fishkind
**VP:* Marilyn Jaffe Ruiz
**VP:* Sharyn Vanreepinghen
Rgnl Mgr: Juan Guzman

D-U-N-S 96-723-9893
NYSARC INC FULTON COUNTY CHAPTER
465 N Perry St, Johnstown, NY 12095-1014
Tel (518) 773-7931 *Founded/Ownrshp* 2011
Sales 84.0MM *EMP* 7^E
Accts Loeb & Troper Llp New York N
SIC 8641 Social associations
Prin: Matthew Johnston

D-U-N-S 79-475-9840
■ **NYSE EURONEXT HOLDINGS LLC**
(*Suby of* ICE) ★
11 Wall St, New York, NY 10005-1905
Tel (212) 656-3000 *Founded/Ownrshp* 2013
Sales 1.8MMM^E *EMP* 3,079^E
SIC 6231 Security exchanges; Stock exchanges
CEO: Duncan L Niederauer
Pr: Thomas W Farley
COO: Stacey Cunningham
COO: Lawrence E Leibowitz
COO: Michael Urkonis
CFO: Michael S Geltzeiler
CFO: Frank Nairne
Chf Cred: Janice Neill
Bd of Dir: Andre Bergen
Ex VP: Gabriella Bell
Ex VP: Bruce Bourque
Ex VP: Dennis Carangelo
Ex VP: Daniel Douglas
Ex VP: Richard A Edgar
Ex VP: David Fainer
Ex VP: Dana Ferguson
Ex VP: Byron Friedman
Ex VP: Dawn Furner
Ex VP: Jennie Halbert
Ex VP: John K Halvey
Ex VP: Brian Helms

D-U-N-S 61-961-7728
■ **NYSE GROUP INC**
(*Suby of* NYSE EURONEXT HOLDINGS LLC) ★
11 Wall St, New York, NY 10005-1905
Tel (212) 656-3000 *Founded/Ownrshp* 2006
Sales 649.9MM^E *EMP* 1,975
SIC 6231 6289 Security & commodity exchanges; Security exchanges; Stock exchanges; Stock option exchanges; Exchange clearinghouses, security; Stock transfer agents
Ch Bd: Marshall N Carter
**Pr:* Gerald D Putnam
**CEO:* Duncan L Niederauer
**CFO:* Nelson Chai
Ex VP: Dale B Bernstein
Ex VP: Albert Bocchetti
**Ex VP:* Kevin J P Ohara
**Ex VP:* Rachel F Robbins
**Sr VP:* William Freeman
VP: David W Bartges
VP: Michael Ferraro
VP: Vincent Lanzillo
VP: Paul Mayerowitz
VP: Warren Rosenbaum
VP: Anand Rufino
Exec: Faith A Peyser

NYSID
See NEW YORK STATE INDUSTRIES FOR DISABLED INC

NYSIF
See INSURANCE FUND NEW YORK STATE

NYSUT
See NEW YORK STATE UNITED TEACHERS

D-U-N-S 05-017-8515
NYU
120 Sullivan St Apt 1b, New York, NY 10012-3655
Tel (212) 998-1212 *Founded/Ownrshp* 2010
Sales 146.1MM^E *EMP* 2,345^E
SIC 8221 Colleges universities & professional schools
Prin: Rimalovski Frank
Assoc Dir: Cassandre Stump

NYU COLLEGE OF NURSING
See NEW YORK UNIVERSITY

D-U-N-S 07-103-6685
NYU HOSPITAL FOR JOINT DISEASES
(*Suby of* NY U) ★
301 E 17th St Fl 14, New York, NY 10003-3804
Tel (212) 598-6000 *Founded/Ownrshp* 1905
Sales 62.9MM^E *EMP* 1,343
Accts Ernst & Young Llp New York N
SIC 8069 Orthopedic hospital
Pr: David Dibner
**Pr:* Robert Grossman
**Sr VP:* David A Dibner
Exec: Robert Glickman
**Dir Surg:* Alex Malarchuk
Off Admin: Leslie Haber
MIS Dir: Paul Scotto
Dir IT: Harry Defendini
Surgeon: Sanjit R Konda
Surgeon: Patrick A Meere
Ansthlgy: Arthur Atchabahian

D-U-N-S 82-854-3236 IMP
NYU HOSPITALS CENTER
NY U
(*Suby of* NY U) ★
550 1st Ave, New York, NY 10016-6402
Tel (212) 263-7300 *Founded/Ownrshp* 1997
Sales 2.1MMM *EMP* 20,424^E
SIC 8062 General medical & surgical hospitals
CEO: Robert I Grossman
Ofcr: Andrew Brotman
Ofcr: Gary Cohn
Ofcr: Richard Crater
Ofcr: Elizabeth Dater
Ex VP: Darla Moore
**Sr VP:* Michael T Burke
VP: Debra Berger
VP: Thomas Feuerstein
Assoc Dir: Hilda Pineda-Lopez
Mktg Mgr: Lourdes L Torres

NYU LANGONE MEDICAL CENTER
See NEW YORK UNIVERSITY MEDICAL CENTER

NYU LUTHERAN FAMILY HEALTH CEN
See SUNSET PARK HEALTH COUNCIL INC

D-U-N-S 06-829-2572
NYU LUTHERAN MEDICAL CENTER
150 55th St, Brooklyn, NY 11220-2508
Tel (718) 630-7000 *Founded/Ownrshp* 1883
Sales 540.5MM *EMP* 3,000
SIC 8062 8621 General medical & surgical hospitals; Professional membership organizations
Pr: Wendy Goldstein
Pt: Mary Qui Ones
Pr: Amy Mugavero
CFO: Richard Langfelger
Treas: Alan Schechter
Ofcr: Toni Cesta
**Ex VP:* Richard Langfelder
Ex VP: Jeanne Lee
Ex VP: Larry McReynolds
Sr VP: Sandra Conti
Sr VP: George Martin
**Sr VP:* Michael Parks
Sr VP: Donald Stiger
**VP:* Claudia Caine
VP: William Dionne
VP: Barry Kohn
VP: Patricia Lavely
VP: Deb McCarthy
VP: Beth Moore
VP: Hector Perez
VP: Mary Tirolo

NYU-POLY
See POLYTECHNIC INSTITUTE OF NEW YORK UNIVERSITY

D-U-N-S 03-860-5341 IMP
NYX LLC
NYX TECHNOLOGIES
36111 Schoolcraft Rd, Livonia, MI 48150-1216
Tel (734) 462-2385 *Founded/Ownrshp* 1989
Sales 687.1MM^E *EMP* 1,800

Section I
Businesses Alphabetically

SIC 3089 3714 3565 2671 Injection molding of plastics; Motor vehicle parts & accessories; Packaging machinery; Packaging paper & plastics film, coated & laminated
CEO: Chain S Sandhu
**Pr:* Jatinder-Bir S Sandhu
CFO: Mark Greer
Plnt Mgr: Dennis Dunlop
Plnt Mgr: Steve Huchkins
Sls Mgr: Mike Brook

NYXTECHNOLOGIES
See NYX LLC

D-U-N-S 80-753-2184
NZR RETAIL OF TOLEDO INC
4820 Monroe St, Toledo, OH 43623-4310
Tel (419) 724-0005 *Founded/Ownrshp* 2004
Sales 110.0MM *EMP* 85
SIC 5172 Gasoline
CEO: Nick Hasan
**Prin:* Yazeed Qaimari

O

D-U-N-S 01-883-8136 IMP/EXP
O & G INDUSTRIES INC
112 Wall St, Torrington, CT 06790-5464
Tel (860) 489-9261 *Founded/Ownrshp* 1923
Sales 698.0MM^E^ *EMP* 1,000
SIC 1542 1541 1611 1623 5032 2951

D-U-N-S 18-508-8598 IMP
O & S CALIFORNIA INC
OSCA-ARCOSA
(*Suby of* ONAMBA CO., LTD.)
9731 Siempre Viva Rd E, San Diego, CA 92154-7200
Tel (619) 661-1800 *Founded/Ownrshp* 1986
Sales 183.5MM^E^ *EMP* 400
SIC 3699 Electrical equipment & supplies
Pr: Kazuo Murata
**VP:* Jos Luis Furlong
Sls Mgr: Hiro Kawamata
Sls Mgr: Eddy Liano
Sls Mgr: Tsuji Moto

O C C
See OFFICE OF THE COMPTROLLER OF THE CURRENCY

O C I
See ORASCOM E&C USA INC

D-U-N-S 00-966-7965
O C JONES & SONS INC (CA)
1520 4th St, Berkeley, CA 94710-1748
Tel (510) 526-3424 *Founded/Ownrshp* 1924
Sales 114.3MM^E^ *EMP* 250
SIC 1611 Grading; Highway & street paving contractor
Pr: Kelly Kolander
**Ch Bd:* Robert Pelascini
**CEO:* Rob Layne
**CFO:* Beth Yoshida

D-U-N-S 00-194-7686 IMP/EXP
O C TANNER CO (UT)
THANKS
1930 S State St, Salt Lake City, UT 84115-2383
Tel (801) 486-2430 *Founded/Ownrshp* 1927
Sales 344.1MM *EMP* 1,700
SIC 3911 2759 2741 Pins (jewelry), precious metal; Commercial printing; Invitation & stationery printing & engraving; Announcements: engraved; Yearbooks: publishing & printing
Ch Bd: Carolyn Tanner Irish
Pr: David Petersen
COO: Scott Sperry
CFO: Scott Archibald
Treas: Richard Clegg
Ex VP: John McVeigh
Sr VP: Steve Kimball
Sr VP: Niel Nickolaisen
VP: Mike Cullins
VP: Doug Duckworth
VP: Paul Terry
VP: Spencer Toomey
VP: Charlie Wall
VP: Julie Walters
VP Bus Dev: Michelle Smith
Creative D: Chris Drysdale

D-U-N-S 00-907-3149 IMP
O C TANNER MANUFACTURING (UT)
(*Suby of* THANKS) ★
1930 S State St, Salt Lake City, UT 84115-2311
Tel (801) 486-2430 *Founded/Ownrshp* 1927, 1951
Sales 232.2MM *EMP* 1,100
SIC 3911 Jewelry, precious metal
Pr: Dave Petersen
**Ch Bd:* Carolyn Tanner Irish
**COO:* Scott Sperry
**Treas:* Robert K Anger
**Ex VP:* David Sturt
**Sr VP:* Scott Archibald
**VP:* John McVeigh
Software D: Catherine Sylvester

D-U-N-S 79-118-8139
O C TANNER RECOGNITION CO
THANKS
(*Suby of* THANKS) ★
1930 S State St, Salt Lake City, UT 84115-2311
Tel (801) 486-2430 *Founded/Ownrshp* 1986
Sales 401.1MM *EMP* 1,700
SIC 5094 Precious stones & metals
Pr: David Petersen
**CFO:* Scott Sperry
VP: David Berg
VP: Chester Elton
Dir IT: David Eghert
Dir IT: Nihar Nanda
Software D: Masoud Abbasi
Mfg Mgr: Drew Butler
Mktg Dir: Leona Fox

O D L
See ODL INC

O D W
See ODW LOGISTICS INC

O E I
See OMRON ELECTRONICS LLC

O F R
See FLORIDA DEPARTMENT OF FINANCIAL SERVICES

O F S
See OFS FITEL LLC

O H B
See ORLEANS HOMEBUILDERS INC

O I ANALYTICAL
See OI CORP

D-U-N-S 03-549-9086 IMP/EXP
O K FOODS INC
4601 N 6th St, Fort Smith, AR 72904-2208
Tel (479) 783-4186 *Founded/Ownrshp* 1959, 2015
Sales 868.6MM^E^ *EMP* 3,600
SIC 2015 Poultry, processed; Poultry, processed: fresh; Poultry, slaughtered & dressed
CEO: Trent Goins
VP: Scott Hunter
Opers Mgr: Billy Douglas

O K I
See OKI DATA AMERICAS INC

O N R
See ORTHOPAEDIC & NEUROLOGICAL REHABILITATION SPEECH PATHOLOGY INC

O P D
See OPTIMIZED PROCESS DESIGNS LLC

D-U-N-S 10-306-2204 IMP/EXP
■ **O P I PRODUCTS INC**
(*Suby of* COTY INC) ★
13034 Saticoy St, North Hollywood, CA 91605-3510
Tel (818) 759-8688 *Founded/Ownrshp* 2010
Sales 352.0MM^E^ *EMP* 535
SIC 5087 2844 Beauty parlor equipment & supplies; Toilet preparations
CEO: Jules Kaufman
**Pr:* John Heffner
**COO:* Eric Schwartz
**Ex VP:* William Halfacre
**Ex VP:* Susan Weiss-Fischmann
VP: Jason Lumsden
Sls Mgr: Scott Smith

O P M
See U S OFFICE OF PERSONNEL MANAGEMENT

O R I
See OFFICE RESOURCES INC

O R MANAGER
See ACCESS INTELLIGENCE LLC

O S H
See ORCHARD SUPPLY CO LLC

O S T
See OPEN SYSTEMS TECHNOLOGIES DE LLC

O T S
See OFFICE OF THRIFT SUPERVISION

O X Y
See OCCIDENTAL CHEMICAL CORP

D-U-N-S 00-210-2069 IMP/EXP
O-AT-KA MILK PRODUCTS COOPERATIVE INC (NY)
700 Ellicott St, Batavia, NY 14020-3744
Tel (585) 343-0536 *Founded/Ownrshp* 1956, 1959
Sales 295.5MM *EMP* 302^E^
Accts Dopkins & Company Buffalo Ne
SIC 2023 2021 2026 Concentrated skim milk; Evaporated milk; Dried nonfat milk; Creamery butter; Fluid milk
CEO: Robert Hall
**Ch Bd:* Herbert Nobles
**COO:* Dan Wolf
**CFO:* Michael Patterson
**Treas:* Dudley Chaffee
**VP:* Clyde Rutherford

O-I
See OWENS-BROCKWAY GLASS CONTAINER INC

D-U-N-S 07-866-0642
O-N MINERALS CO (OHIO)
CARMEUSE LIME & STONE
(*Suby of* CARMEUSE LIME & STONE INC) ★
11 Stanwix St Fl 21, Pittsburgh, PA 15222-1327
Tel (412) 995-5500 *Founded/Ownrshp* 2012
Sales 72.7MM^E^ *EMP* 1,438^E^
SIC 1422 Crushed & broken limestone
Pr: Thomas A Buck
CFO: Bruce Inglis
Treas: Mary D Colin
VP: Jack Fahler
VP: Paul Tunnicliffe
VP: Kevin White
S&M/VP: Bruce Routhieaux

D-U-N-S 80-830-6034
O-TEX PUMPING LLC
7045 N Highway 81, Duncan, OK 73533-4001
Tel (580) 255-3111 *Founded/Ownrshp* 2008
Sales 429.5MM^E^ *EMP* 400
SIC 1389 Cementing oil & gas well casings
Dist Mgr: Doug Caldwell
Dist Mgr: Brian Martin
Dist Mgr: Craig Pankratz
Dir IT: Davin Fryer
Opers Mgr: Jesse Ulate
Sls Mgr: James Hattenbach

O/B LEASING COMPANY
See BUDCO GROUP INC

D-U-N-S 79-959-3640
OAHU PUBLICATIONS INC
HONOLULU STAR ADVERTISER
(*Suby of* SOUND PUBLISHING HOLDING INC) ★
500 Ala Moana Blvd, Honolulu, HI 96813-4920
Tel (808) 529-4700 *Founded/Ownrshp* 2001
Sales 92.2MM^E^ *EMP* 551^E^
SIC 2711 Newspapers, publishing & printing
Pr: Dennis Francis
Treas: Nadine Kam
**Sec:* Tc Gray
Ofcr: Christine Donnelly
**VP:* David Black
Exec: Rich Frank
Off Mgr: Lorenzo Trinidad
Pr Dir: Erika Engle
Manager: Jeffrey Williams
Sls Mgr: Brandon Yamashita
Sales Asso: Mark Christiansen

D-U-N-S 78-533-2370
OAHU TRANSIT SERVICES INC
BUS, THE
811 Middle St Rm 225, Honolulu, HI 96819-2343
Tel (808) 848-4400 *Founded/Ownrshp* 1991
Sales 70.1MM^E^ *EMP* 1,700
SIC 4111 Bus line operations
Pr: J Roger Morton
**Ch:* Anthony R Guerrero Jr
**Sr VP:* Robert Yu
Genl Mgr: James E Cowan
Genl Mgr: Melvin Higa
Genl Mgr: Georgia Shinagawa
Dir IT: Guy Moriwaki
IT Man: Nick Awana
Netwrk Mgr: Peter Ridore
Sftwr Eng: Viviana Zheng
Sls Dir: Tom Enomoto

D-U-N-S 03-714-3427 IMP
OAK BEVERAGES INC
1 Flower Ln, Blauvelt, NY 10913-1139
Tel (718) 652-8555 *Founded/Ownrshp* 1980
Sales 125.5MM^E^ *EMP* 125
SIC 5181 Beer & other fermented malt liquors
Pr: Debra Boening
**Treas:* James Tozar
Snr Mgr: Harold Boening

D-U-N-S 87-840-5117
OAK CREST VILLAGE INC
VILLAGE SQUARE
8800 Walther Blvd Ste 1, Baltimore, MD 21234-9023
Tel (410) 665-2222 *Founded/Ownrshp* 1994
Sales 91.0MM *EMP* 1,100
Accts Pricewaterhousecoopers Llp Ba
SIC 8051 8052 8059 Skilled nursing care facilities; Intermediate care facilities; Nursing home, except skilled & intermediate care facility
Ex Dir: Mark Erickson
**Ex Dir:* Eric Gross

OAK DISTRIBUTION
See OAK PAPER PRODUCTS CO INC

D-U-N-S 00-278-8347
OAK HARBOR FREIGHT LINES INC (WA)
1339 W Valley Hwy N, Auburn, WA 98001-4123
Tel (206) 246-2600 *Founded/Ownrshp* 1936
Sales 221.1MM^E^ *EMP* 1,000
SIC 4213 4214 Trucking, except local; Local trucking with storage
Pr: Edward Vanderpol
**Treas:* Karen Miller
**VP:* David Vanderpol
Off Mgr: Diane Gonzales
Off Mgr: Shelly Rigsby
DP Exec: Sam Choi

D-U-N-S 03-918-6809
OAK HEALTH AND REHABILITATION CENTERS INC
5 Morgan Hwy, Scranton, PA 18508-2641
Tel (215) 346-6454 *Founded/Ownrshp* 2014
Sales 36.3MM^E^ *EMP* 1,266^E^
SIC 8361 Home for the aged
Pr: Howard Jaffe

D-U-N-S 96-874-2127
OAK HILL CAPITAL PARTNERS III LP
65 E 55th St Fl 32, New York, NY 10022-3228
Tel (212) 527-8400 *Founded/Ownrshp* 2007
Sales 73.7MM^E^ *EMP* 7,939^E^
SIC 5812 5813 7999 7993 Eating places; Bar (drinking places); Billiard parlor; Coin-operated amusement devices
Prin: Andrea W Joseph

D-U-N-S 06-451-2762
OAK HILL CAPITAL PARTNERS LP
65 E 55th St Fl 32, New York, NY 10022-3228
Tel (212) 527-8400 *Founded/Ownrshp* 1998
Sales 173.7MM^E^ *EMP* 2,311^E^
SIC 7379
Genl Pt: Robert M Bass
Mng Pt: Scott A Baker
Mng Pt: J Taylor Crandall
Mng Pt: Steven B Gruber
Mng Pt: Denis J Nayden
COO: John Malfettone
VP: John Rachwalski
VP: Jessica Reed
VP: Chris Williams
VP: Christopher M Williams
Mng Dir: Steven Wayne

OAK HILL HOSPITAL
See HCA HEALTH SERVICES OF FLORIDA INC

D-U-N-S 03-831-6274
■ **OAK HILL HOSPITAL MEDICAL STAFF INC**
(*Suby of* HOSPITAL COPORATION OF AMERICA) ★
11375 Cortez Blvd, Brooksville, FL 34613-5409
Tel (352) 596-6632 *Founded/Ownrshp* 1984
Sales 148.3MM^E^ *EMP* 930
SIC 8062 General medical & surgical hospitals
CEO: Mickey Smith
**Pr:* Garnesh M Chari

CFO: David Deam
**CFO:* Chance Phillips
Treas: Christine Piaquaddio
Chf Mktg O: Mallik Piduru
Dir OR: Randall Weeks
Dir Inf Cn: Christine Piacquaddio
Dir Rad: Lanny Chuang
Dir Rad: Tyler Crickette
Dir Rad: Robert Dubion
Dir Rad: Ruth Holliday
Dir Rad: Linda Petrovich

OAK HILL SCHOOL
See CONNECTICUT INSTITUTE FOR BLIND INC

D-U-N-S 06-981-8680
OAK LANE GOLF COURSE INC
800 N Main St, Webberville, MI 48892-9533
Tel (517) 521-3900 *Founded/Ownrshp* 1966
Sales 1.5MM *EMP* 3,035
SIC 7992 5812 Public golf courses; Eating places
Pr: Bernard Simons
**Sec:* Lisa Lane
**Ex VP:* James Simons
**VP:* Richard Simons

D-U-N-S 02-856-8152 IMP
OAK PAPER PRODUCTS CO INC
OAK DISTRIBUTION
3686 E Olympic Blvd, Los Angeles, CA 90023-3146
Tel (323) 268-0507 *Founded/Ownrshp* 1976
Sales 143.4MM^E^ *EMP* 200
SIC 5113 5199 5087 2653 Shipping supplies; Packaging materials; Janitors' supplies; Corrugated & solid fiber boxes
Pr: Max Weissberg
**Ch Bd:* Richard Seff
**CEO:* David Weissberg
**COO:* David Karr
CFO: Bernie Singer
**Ch:* Dick Seff
Treas: Chris Jordan
Div Mgr: John Gilligan
Sls Mgr: Ramiro Manzano
Sales Asso: Adela Barajas
Sales Asso: Raquel Green

D-U-N-S 08-292-9472
OAK PARK & RIVER FOREST HIGH SCHOOL DIST 200
OAK PARK RVER FOREST HIGH SCHL
201 N Scoville Ave, Oak Park, IL 60302-2264
Tel (708) 383-0700 *Founded/Ownrshp* 1873
Sales 86.3MM *EMP* 438^E^
Accts Baker Tilly Virchow Krause Ll
SIC 8211 Public senior high school
**Pr:* Terry Finnegan
COO: Doug Brown
CFO: Cherie Witham
Div/Sub He: Julie Frey
Comm Dir: Karin Sullivan
CIO: Michael Carioscio
HC Dir: Mary E Sjostrom

OAK PARK RVER FOREST HIGH SCHL
See OAK PARK & RIVER FOREST HIGH SCHOOL DIST 200

D-U-N-S 04-115-2224
OAK RIDGE ASSOCIATED UNIVERSITIES INC
ORAU
100 Orau Way, Oak Ridge, TN 37830-6209
Tel (865) 576-3000 *Founded/Ownrshp* 1946
Sales 83.7MM *EMP* 600
Accts Lattimore Black Morgan & Cain
SIC 8733 Scientific research agency
Pr: Andy Page
**CFO:* Phil Andrews
**Ex VP:* Eric Abelquist
**VP:* Ivan Boatner
VP: Arlene A Garrison
VP: Dick Toohey
VP: Marcus Weseman
Assoc Dir: Brian Cook
Comm Dir: Pam Bonee
Dir Bus: Tony Lester
Prgrm Mgr: Lois Chrisman

OAK RIDGE NATIONAL LABORATORY
See UT-BATTELLE LLC

D-U-N-S 00-518-0971
OAK STATE PRODUCTS INC (IL)
775 State Route 251, Wenona, IL 61377-7587
Tel (815) 853-4348 *Founded/Ownrshp* 1956
Sales 118.9MM^E^ *EMP* 350
SIC 2051

D-U-N-S 07-799-3665
OAK WHITE MANOR INC
WHITE OAK MANAGEMENT
130 E Main St, Spartanburg, SC 29306-5113
Tel (864) 582-7503 *Founded/Ownrshp* 1968
Sales 146.7MM *EMP* 2,300
Accts Cliftonlarsonallen Llp Charlo
SIC 8051 Skilled nursing care facilities
CEO: Oliver K Cecil Jr
**Pr:* Doug Cecil
**CFO:* John P Barber
Nrsg Dir: Sherry Chrisp

D-U-N-S 07-391-4723
OAKBEND MEDICAL CENTER
MONTEBELLO WELLNESS CENTER
1705 Jackson St, Richmond, TX 77469-3246
Tel (713) 453-0446 *Founded/Ownrshp* 2004
Sales 167.8MM *EMP* 600
SIC 8062 8051 General medical & surgical hospitals; Skilled nursing care facilities
CEO: Joe Freudenberger
**COO:* Donna Ferguson
CFO: Jim Simone
**CFO:* Robert Smelser
**Ch:* Jeff Council
**Treas:* Jack Moore
**V Ch Bd:* Walter Ansel
**VP:* Sue McCarty
Dir Lab: Reginal Felder

Dir Rx: Nancy Helfrick
Chf Nrs Of: Sue Carty

OAKDALE COMM HOSPITAL
See RAPIDES HEALTHCARE SYSTEM LLC

D-U-N-S 60-406-6548
OAKHURST INDUSTRIES INC
FREUND BAKING
2050 S Tubeway Ave, Commerce, CA 90040-1624
Tel (323) 724-3000 *Founded/Ownrshp* 1981
Sales 148.0MM[E] *EMP* 400
SIC 2051 5149 Buns, bread type: fresh or frozen; Rolls, bread type: fresh or frozen; Groceries & related products
Pr: James Freund
* *VP:* Jonathan Freund
* *VP:* Ronald Martin
Sfty Mgr: Will Gallardo

D-U-N-S 07-421-7100
OAKLAND COMMUNITY COLLEGE FOUNDATION
2480 Opdyke Rd, Bloomfield Hills, MI 48304-2223
Tel (248) 341-2000 *Founded/Ownrshp* 1964
Sales 50.5MM[E] *EMP* 1,200
Accts Plante & Moran Pllc Auburn H
SIC 8222 Community college
Ex Dir: David Dunshee
Ex Dir: Janet Roberts
Prgrm Mgr: Bonnie George
Prgrm Mgr: Robert Ginther
Prgrm Mgr: Matt Majestic
Prgrm Mgr: Joe Marchetti
DP Dir: Henry Austin
DP Dir: Robin Boeling
DP Dir: David Boudreau
DP Dir: Daisy Johnson
DP Dir: James Miteff

D-U-N-S 00-663-7995 EXP
OAKLAND FOODS LLC
OSI
(*Suby of* OTTO & SONS DIV) ★
21876 Highway 59, Oakland, IA 51560-4508
Tel (712) 482-6640 *Founded/Ownrshp* 1997
Sales 152.5MM[E] *EMP* 700
SIC 2013 Sausages & other prepared meats
COO: Esmeralda Garcia
Sr VP: Dan Milovanovic
QA Dir: Tyler Brix
QA Dir: Tom Miller
Ql Cn Mgr: Duane Carlile
Trfc Mgr: Evan Jones

D-U-N-S 79-880-4761
OAKLAND HOSPITAL
ST JOHN OAKLAND HOSPITAL
27351 Dequindre Rd, Madison Heights, MI 48071-3487
Tel (248) 967-7000 *Founded/Ownrshp* 1986
Sales 102.5MM[E] *EMP* 800
SIC 8062 Hospital, medical school affiliation
Pr: Joseph Tasse
VP: Tomasine Marx
Exec: Lucy Vail
IT Man: Jerry Baker
HC Dir: Christine Foster
Board of Directors: Thomas De Gregorio, Arthur J Miller Jr

OAKLAND INTERMEDIATE SCHL DIST
See OAKLAND SCHOOLS INC

OAKLAND LOGISTICS SERVICE
See LOGISTICS INSIGHT CORP

OAKLAND PACKAGING AND SUPPLY
See OAKLAND PAPER & SUPPLY INC

D-U-N-S 05-878-0362 IMP
OAKLAND PAPER & SUPPLY INC
OAKLAND PACKAGING AND SUPPLY
3200 Regatta Blvd Ste F, Richmond, CA 94804-6418
Tel (510) 307-4242 *Founded/Ownrshp* 1988
Sales 111.3MM[E] *EMP* 120
SIC 5113 5087

D-U-N-S 82-894-6470
OAKLAND PHYSICIANS MEDICAL CENTER LLC
DOCTORS' HOSPITAL OF MICHIGAN
461 W Huron St, Pontiac, MI 48341-1601
Tel (248) 857-7200 *Founded/Ownrshp* 2008
Sales 109.2MM[E] *EMP* 700
SIC 8062 General medical & surgical hospitals
CEO: Robert H Barrow
Chf Rad: Vikram RAO
* *Ch Bd:* Yatinder Singhal
CFO: John Cookingham
Exec: Laura Gibbard
Dir OR: Marisel Estrada
Comm Dir: Kathi Mcinally
Chf Nrs Of: Sherrie Berg
* *Prin:* John Ponczocha
Off Mgr: James Schulte
CIO: Chuck Lawsley

D-U-N-S 07-841-8456
OAKLAND SCHOOLS INC
OAKLAND INTERMEDIATE SCHL DIST
2111 Pontiac Lake Rd, Waterford, MI 48328-2736
Tel (248) 209-2000 *Founded/Ownrshp* 2003
Sales 254.4MM *EMP* 450
Accts Plante & Moran Pllc Clinton
SIC 8211 Public elementary & secondary schools; Public special education school
Pr: Theresa Rich
CFO: Janice Gray
* *Treas:* Connie Williams
* *Trst:* Mrs Barb Demarco
Trst: Susan Loveland
Trst: Mitchell Moses
Trst: Joan Sutherland
Exec: Sherry McMillan
* *Prin:* George Ehlert
Genl Mgr: Heather Odinga
Off Admin: Kim Mason

D-U-N-S 07-655-4500
OAKLAND UNIFIED SCHOOL DISTRICT
1000 Broadway Fl 4, Oakland, CA 94607-4099
Tel (510) 434-7790 *Founded/Ownrshp* 1952
Sales 496.5MM[E] *EMP* 7,200
SIC 8211 Public elementary & secondary schools
Dir Vol: Brittany Love
Pr: Alina Chow
CFO: Vernon Hal
Bd of Dir: Noel Gallo
Dir Sec: Jeff Godown
Prgrm Mgr: Rachelle Ard
Prgrm Mgr: Chen Kong
Off Mgr: Thuy Nguyen
Off Mgr: Mildred Otis
Nurse Mgr: Belinda Campbell
MIS Dir: Janice Chin

D-U-N-S 04-180-8262
OAKLAND UNIVERSITY
2200 N Squirrel Rd, Rochester, MI 48309-4401
Tel (248) 370-2100 *Founded/Ownrshp* 1958
Sales 253.9MM *EMP* 2,650
Accts Andrews Hooper Pavlik Plc Au
SIC 8221 University
Pr: George W Hynd
Pr: Nicole Stallworth
Ofcr: Shona Jocollins
Ofcr: Jennifer A Lumpkin
Ofcr: Marvella R Ramsey
Assoc VP: Terry Stollsteimer
VP: Rochelle Black
VP: James Lentini
VP: Betty J Youngblood
VP: Victor Zambardi
Assoc Dir: Pamela Mitzelfeld
Assoc Dir: Kimberly L Zelinski

OAKLAWN HOSPITAL
See ELLA E M BROWN CHARITABLE CIRCLE

D-U-N-S 94-518-0529
■ **OAKLEAF WASTE MANAGEMENT LLC**
(*Suby of* WM) ★
415 Day Hill Rd, Windsor, CT 06095-7100
Tel (860) 290-1250 *Founded/Ownrshp* 1995
Sales 89.1MM[E] *EMP* 285[E]
SIC 8741 4953 Management services; Refuse systems
Pr: Paul J Foody
CFO: Tom Nelson
Sr VP: Gregory A Pstore
VP: Paul Davi
VP: Bob Duff
* *VP:* Mark A Lockett
Mktg Mgr: Susan Stansfield

D-U-N-S 08-538-6522 IMP/EXP
OAKLEY INC
(*Suby of* LUXOTTICA GROUP SPA)
1 Icon, Foothill Ranch, CA 92610-3000
Tel (949) 951-0991 *Founded/Ownrshp* 1994
Sales 1.3MMM[E] *EMP* 3,400
SIC 3851 2331 2339 3021 3873 3143 Ophthalmic goods; Glasses, sun or glare; Goggles: sun, safety, industrial, underwater, etc.; Women's & misses' blouses & shirts; Women's & misses' outerwear; Rubber & plastics footwear; Watches, clocks, watchcases & parts; Men's footwear, except athletic
Pr: Colin Baden
* *Ch Bd:* Jim Jannard
* *Ch Bd:* D Scott Olivet
Pr: Don Krause
CFO: Gianluca Pagliabue
CFO: Richard J Shields
* *CFO:* Gianluca Tagliabue
Sr VP: Scott Bowers
* *Sr VP:* Jon Krause
* *VP:* Derek Baker
* *VP:* Michael Boxer
VP: Chris Donnelly
VP: Devon Ferreira
* *VP:* Vito Giannola
VP: Erik Johnson
VP: Robert Maher
VP: Raphael J Peck
* *VP:* Carlos Reyes

D-U-N-S 11-523-0088
OAKLEY INDUSTRIES SUB ASSEMBLY DIVISION INC
4333 Matthew, Flint, MI 48507-3160
Tel (810) 720-4444 *Founded/Ownrshp* 1984
Sales 148.5MM[E] *EMP* 300
SIC 3714 Motor vehicle wheels & parts; Motor vehicle body components & frame
Pr: Ronald Oakley
* *COO:* Moshe Kraus
* *Sec:* Michael Oakley
* *VP:* Robert O Trygstad
Exec: James Cooke
* *Prin:* Arthur Meisels

D-U-N-S 07-884-6449
OAKLEY INTERNATIONAL LLC (AR)
(*Suby of* BRUCE OAKLEY INC) ★
3700 Lincoln Ave, North Little Rock, AR 72114-6448
Tel (501) 945-0875 *Founded/Ownrshp* 2013
Sales 300.0MM *EMP* 3
SIC 5191 Fertilizer & fertilizer materials
CFO: Tim Cummings
VP: Edward S Bubba Vance

D-U-N-S 15-171-5851
OAKLEY TRANSPORT INC
(*Suby of* OAKLEY GROVES, INC.)
101 Abc Rd, Lake Wales, FL 33859-6844
Tel (863) 638-1435 *Founded/Ownrshp* 1961
Sales 98.4MM *EMP* 70
SIC 4213 6531 Trucking, except local; Real estate agents & managers
Pr: Thomas E Oakley
* *CFO:* Ty Sherman
* *Ex VP:* Ronald E Oakley
* *VP:* Wade Walker

D-U-N-S 09-684-9401
OAKS INTEGRATED CARE INC
770 Woodlane Rd Ste 23, Westampton, NJ 08060-3803
Tel (609) 267-5928 *Founded/Ownrshp* 1962
Sales 81.9MM *EMP* 1,000
Accts Bowman & Company Llp Voorhees
SIC 8322 Family service agency
CEO: Bob Pekar
* *CFO:* Qindi Shi
VP: Edith McRae
VP: Laxmi Parmeswar
* *Ex Dir:* Mary Wells

D-U-N-S 07-441-3766
OAKTON COMMUNITY COLLEGE
1600 E Golf Rd Rm 1505, Des Plaines, IL 60016-1256
Tel (847) 635-1600 *Founded/Ownrshp* 1977
Sales 24.1MM *EMP* 2,000
Accts Sikich Naperville Illinois
SIC 8221 8222 Colleges universities & professional schools; Community college
Pr: Margaret B Lee
Bd of Dir: Susan Maltese
VP: Michele Brown
VP: Susan Humm
VP: Bonnie Lucas
Snr Mgr: Janet Bishop

D-U-N-S 96-887-8756
OAKTREE CAPITAL GROUP HOLDINGS LP
333 S Grand Ave Fl 28, Los Angeles, CA 90071-1504
Tel (213) 830-6300 *Founded/Ownrshp* 2007
Sales 712.7MM[E] *EMP* 4,100[E]
SIC 6282 Investment advice
Ch: Howard S Marks
Genl Pt: Oaktree Capital Group Holdings
Pr: Bruce Allen Karsh

D-U-N-S 83-003-8415
▲ **OAKTREE CAPITAL GROUP LLC**
333 S Grand Ave Ste 2800, Los Angeles, CA 90071-1530
Tel (213) 830-6300 *Founded/Ownrshp* 1995
Sales 201.9MM *EMP* 7,551[E]
Tkr Sym OAK *Exch* NYS
SIC 6282 Investment advice
CEO: Jay S Wintrob
Pr: Bruce A Karsh
CFO: David M Kirchheimer
Ofcr: Todd E Molz
CIO: Bob Frank

D-U-N-S 87-994-4569
■ **OAKTREE CAPITAL MANAGEMENT LP**
(*Suby of* OAKTREE CAPITAL GROUP LLC) ★
333 S Grand Ave Ste 2800, Los Angeles, CA 90071-1530
Tel (213) 830-6300 *Founded/Ownrshp* 2010
Sales 1.5MMM[E] *EMP* 6,627
SIC 6282 6722 6211 Investment advisory service; Management investment, open-end; Security brokers & dealers
Pr: Bruce Karsh
Pt: J B Forth
Pt: Larry Gilson
Pt: Larry W Keele
Pt: D R Masson
Pt: Sheldon M Stone
Pr: Jay Ghiya
Pr: Shahram Haghighi
Pr: Dominic Keenan
CFO: David Kirchheimer
CFO: David Kirchheiner
Sr Cor Off: Andrew Fastow
Ex VP: Eugenia Tsang
Sr VP: Aaron A Bendikson
Sr VP: Erin Boasberg
Sr VP: Lisa Kenyon
Sr VP: Jared Lazarus
Sr VP: Andrew Salter
Sr VP: Bill Santangelo
Sr VP: Nebil Senman
Sr VP: David Tanner

D-U-N-S 07-937-6118
OAKTREE HOLDINGS INC
(*Suby of* OAKTREE CAPITAL GROUP HOLDINGS LP) ★
333 S Grand Ave Ste 2800, Los Angeles, CA 90071-1530
Tel (213) 830-6300 *Founded/Ownrshp* 2014
Sales 138.9M[E] *EMP* 1,258[E]
SIC 6799 Investors

D-U-N-S 07-964-2685
OAKTREE REAL ESTATE OPPORTUNITIES FUND V GP LP
(*Suby of* OAKTREE CAPITAL GROUP HOLDINGS LP) ★
333 S Grand Ave Fl 28, Los Angeles, CA 90071-1504
Tel (213) 830-6300 *Founded/Ownrshp* 2014
Sales 183.2M[E] *EMP* 1,258[E]
SIC 6531 Real estate agents & managers

D-U-N-S 08-211-9025
OAKVILLE PRODUCE PARTNERS LLC
GREENLEAF
453 Valley Dr, Brisbane, CA 94005-1209
Tel (415) 647-2991 *Founded/Ownrshp* 1974
Sales 110.5MM[E] *EMP* 150
SIC 5148 5451 Fruits, fresh; Vegetables, fresh; Dairy products stores
* *Pr:* Frank Ballentine
COO: Peter Napolitano
Sls Mgr: Ted Cavagnaro

OAKWOOD GROUP, THE
See OAKWOOD METAL FABRICATING CO

OAKWOOD HEALTH LINE
See OAKWOOD HEALTHCARE INC

D-U-N-S 07-841-0842
OAKWOOD HEALTHCARE INC
OAKWOOD HEALTH LINE
(*Suby of* BEAUMONT BOTSFORD OAKWOOD HLTH) ★
18101 Oakwood Blvd, Dearborn, MI 48124-4089
Tel (313) 593-7000 *Founded/Ownrshp* 2014
Sales 1.1MMM[E] *EMP* 9,200
SIC 8062 General medical & surgical hospitals
Pr: Brain Connolly
COO: Gregory Bock
COO: Kathleen Cronin
CFO: Greg Messer
Chf Mktg O: Amy Middleton
Ofcr: Jennifer Doumanian
Ofcr: Laura Wolan
Sr VP: Mark Hannis
Sr VP: Seth Lloyd
VP: Tim Turner
Exec: Christine Hartfield
Dir Rad: Tim Vargus

OAKWOOD HOMES
See CLAYTON HOMES INC

D-U-N-S 78-778-8405
OAKWOOD HOMES LLC
4908 Tower Rd, Denver, CO 80249-6684
Tel (303) 486-8500 *Founded/Ownrshp* 1991
Sales 120.2MM[E] *EMP* 150
SIC 1521 New construction, single-family houses
CEO: Patrick Hamill
* *COO:* Scott Thorson
* *CFO:* Chad Bakken
VP: Jay Small
Genl Mgr: Charlie Burkett
VP Opers: Frank Walker
S&M/VP: Kristen White
Manager: Vanise Fuqua
Sls Mgr: Sam Litzau
Sales Asso: Kristofer Ceretto

D-U-N-S 00-539-0778 IMP
OAKWOOD METAL FABRICATING CO
OAKWOOD GROUP, THE
1100 Oakwood Blvd, Dearborn, MI 48124-2820
Tel (313) 561-7740 *Founded/Ownrshp* 1945
Sales 132.7MM[E] *EMP* 390
SIC 5199 3714 3469 Art goods & supplies; Motor vehicle engines & parts; Household cooking & kitchen utensils, metal
Pr: Richard Audi
Pr: Don Smith
VP: R Szkody
Prgrm Mgr: Hilding Holcombe

OAKWOOD WORLDWIDE
See R & B REALTY GROUP A CALIFORNIA LIMITED PARTNERSHIP

OAKWOOD WORLDWIDE
See R & B REALTY GROUP LP

D-U-N-S 07-483-0209
■ **OAO CORP**
(*Suby of* LEIDOS HOLDINGS INC) ★
700 N Frederick Ave, Gaithersburg, MD 20879-3328
Tel (301) 240-7000 *Founded/Ownrshp* 2016
Sales 48.1MM[E] *EMP* 2,100
SIC 7371 8711 3823 3559 Computer software development; Aviation &/or aeronautical engineering; Thermal conductivity instruments, industrial process type; Robots, molding & forming plastics
CEO: Cecile D Barker
CFO: Hubert M Reid
Sr VP: Robert L Lohfeld
Sr VP: Edwin S Warrell
VP: Jay Jones

D-U-N-S 96-737-5833
OAO TECHNOLOGY SOLUTIONS INC
(*Suby of* PLATINUM EQUITY LLC) ★
7500 Greenway Center Dr # 150, Greenbelt, MD 20770-3502
Tel (301) 486-0400 *Founded/Ownrshp* 2010
Sales 36.6MM[E] *EMP* 1,600
SIC 7379 Computer related consulting services
Pr: Sidney E Fuchs
Pr: Duke Dickson
Pr: Sherry Robertson
VP: Stephen Brinch
VP: Joanne Connelly
VP: Robert Ohfed
VP: Emmett Paige
VP: Tony Rignola
VP: Mary Sigler
VP: John Weisman
IT Man: Mark Hamrol

OASAM
See OFFICE OF ASSISTANT SECRETARY FOR ADMINISTRATION AND MANAGEMENT

D-U-N-S 96-267-9358 IMP
OASIS BRANDS INC
6700 Artesia Blvd, Buena Park, CA 90620-1014
Tel (540) 658-2830 *Founded/Ownrshp* 2009
Sales 156.0MM *EMP* 75
SIC 5113 Napkins, paper

D-U-N-S 17-196-3598
OASIS OUTSOURCING INC
KING EMPLOYER SERVICES
(*Suby of* NAUTIC PARTNERS LLC) ★
2054 Vista Pkwy Ste 300, West Palm Beach, FL 33411-6742
Tel (561) 227-6500 *Founded/Ownrshp* 1996
Sales 118.8MM[E] *EMP* 600
SIC 8721 8742 7363 Accounting, auditing & bookkeeping; Human resource consulting services; Employee leasing service; Temporary help service
CEO: Mark Perlberg
* *Ex VP:* Terry Mayotte
* *Ex VP:* Mike Viola
* *Sr VP:* Ruth Trezevant Cyrus
Sr VP: Kathleen A Rainey
VP: Kerrin Giraldo
VP: Mark Reinisch
Exec: Amy Mohr
Dist Mgr: Bill Leahy

Dist Mgr: Scott Ward
Sales Exec: Todd Puig

D-U-N-S 96-404-3199
▲ OASIS PETROLEUM INC
1001 Fannin St Ste 1500, Houston, TX 77002-6739
Tel (281) 404-9500 *Founded/Ownrshp* 2007
Sales 789.7MM *EMP* 558E
Accts Pricewaterhousecoopers Llp H
Tkr Sym OAS *Exch* NYS
SIC 1311 Crude petroleum production; Natural gas production
Ch Bd: Thomas B Nusz
*Pr: Taylor L Reid
CFO: Michael H Lou
Ofcr: Jose Lantigua
Ex VP: Nickolas J Lorentzatos
Counsel: Natara Williams
Board of Directors: William J Cassidy, Ted Collins Jr, John E Hagale, Michael McShane, Bobby S Shackouls, Douglas E Swanson Jr

D-U-N-S 07-929-0871
OASIS REPOWER LLC
15445 Innovation Dr, San Diego, CA 92128-3432
Tel (888) 903-6926 *Founded/Ownrshp* 2013
Sales 283.6MME *EMP* 826
SIC 4911 Electric services
Pr: Tristan Grimbert
Sec: Robert Miller
VP: Ryan Pfaff

OASYS
See OMGEO LLC

OATEY COMPANY
See OATEY SUPPLY CHAIN SERVICES INC

D-U-N-S 00-419-8388 IMP
OATEY CO (OH)
4700 W 160th St, Cleveland, OH 44135-2632
Tel (216) 267-7100 *Founded/Ownrshp* 1916
Sales 187.6MME *EMP* 800
SIC 3444

D-U-N-S 10-165-4916 IMP/EXP
OATEY SUPPLY CHAIN SERVICES INC
OATEY COMPANY
20600 Emerald Pkwy, Cleveland, OH 44135-6022
Tel (216) 267-7100 *Founded/Ownrshp* 2001
Sales 83.0MM *EMP* 300
SIC 5074 Plumbing & hydronic heating supplies
CEO: John H McMillan
Ch Bd: Gary Oatey
CFO: Neal Restivo

OATI
See OPEN ACCESS TECHNOLOGY INTERNATIONAL INC

D-U-N-S 13-447-5768
OBAYASHI USA LLC
(*Suby of* OBAYASHI CORPORATION)
577 Airport Blvd Ste 600, Burlingame, CA 94010-2057
Tel (650) 952-4910 *Founded/Ownrshp* 2002
Sales 175.5MME *EMP* 1,302E
SIC 6531 Real estate agents & managers
Mtls Mgr: Allen Myers

D-U-N-S 00-434-4644 IMP/EXP
OBERG INDUSTRIES INC (PA)
OBERG MEDICAL
2301 Silverville Rd, Freeport, PA 16229-1630
Tel (724) 295-2121 *Founded/Ownrshp* 1948
Sales 223.8MME *EMP* 760
SIC 3469 3545 Metal stampings; Precision tools, machinists'
Pr: David L Bonvenuto
*COO: Richard Bartek
COO: Mark P Paolillo
*CFO: Jeffrey M Mattiuz
*Ch: D Eric Oberg II
*Ex VP: David Rugaber
VP: Ron Norris
VP: Brian Roofner
IT Man: Scott Adams
IT Man: Susan Britton
Mfg Mgr: Marlin Boltz

OBERG MEDICAL
See OBERG INDUSTRIES INC

D-U-N-S 06-891-1908
OBERLIN COLLEGE
173 W Lorain St, Oberlin, OH 44074-1073
Tel (440) 775-8121 *Founded/Ownrshp* 1833
Sales 184.5MM *EMP* 1,140
Accts Maloney & Novotny Llc Clevela
SIC 8221 College, except junior
Pr: Marvin Krislov
Top Exec: Jason Hudson
Top Exec: Blake New
Top Exec: Deb Ranieri
Assoc VP: Jane Mathison
VP: Mike Frandsen
VP: Ben Jones
*VP: Ronald R Watts
Exec: Heidi Pycraft
Assoc Dir: Michele N Gross
Adm Dir: James Howsmon

D-U-N-S 03-174-2971
OBERON ASSOCIATES INC
(*Suby of* C G I) ★
9700 Capital Ct Ste 301, Manassas, VA 20110-2048
Tel (703) 365-8801 *Founded/Ownrshp* 2004
Sales 94.0MM *EMP* 777
SIC 7379 Computer related consulting services
Pr: Philip O Nolan
*Treas: James H Brabston
VP: Michael Daconta
Comm Dir: Susan Balding
Dir Bus: John McGlone
Prgrm Mgr: David L Dutton
Brnch Mgr: William Weigeshoff
Prd Mgr: Patti Rusher

D-U-N-S 13-125-6377 IMP
OBERTHUR TECHNOLOGIES OF AMERICA CORP
(*Suby of* OBERTHUR TECHNOLOGIES)
4250 Pleasant Valley Rd, Chantilly, VA 20151-1278
Tel (703) 263-0100 *Founded/Ownrshp* 1999
Sales 274.7MME *EMP* 1,000
SIC 3089 7382 3953 3578 3499 Identification cards, plastic; Security systems services; Embossing seals, corporate & official; Banking machines; Safes & vaults, metal; Safe deposit boxes or chests, metal
Pr: Martin Ferenczi
VP: Mehdi Elhaoussine
Dir Bus: Marc Bertin
Genl Mgr: Tiffany Le
Genl Mgr: Rick Patrick
IT Man: Sandra Sammer
IT Man: Yuriy Yunusov
Software D: Ashwin Dsousa
Sftwr Eng: Thomas McKinney
QC Dir: Joe Blossic
QC Dir: Faisal Haque

D-U-N-S 00-924-7172 IMP/EXP
OBERTO SAUSAGE CO
OH BOY OBERTO
7060 S 238th St, Kent, WA 98032-2914
Tel (253) 437-6100 *Founded/Ownrshp* 1918
Sales 181.5MME *EMP* 500
SIC 2013 Sausages from purchased meat; Snack sticks, including jerky: from purchased meat
Ch Bd: John Clearman
Pr: Thomas C Ennis
Treas: Dorothy J Oberto
V Ch Bd: Laura Oberto
VP: Gregory S Christemson
VP: Nancy Reagan
Exec: Jeff Kent
Exec: Losan Saetern
Exec: Kim Uppal
Dir IT: Tom Kingsley
Sfty Mgr: Nick Bissen

D-U-N-S 05-108-2980
OBERWEIS DAIRY INC
951 Ice Cream Dr, North Aurora, IL 60542-1475
Tel (630) 801-6100 *Founded/Ownrshp* 1927
Sales 202.6MME *EMP* 1,000
SIC 5963 5451

OBI SUSHI
See THOMPSON HOSPITALITY CORP

OBICI HEALTH SYSTEMS
See LOUISE OBICI MEMORIAL HOSPITAL INC

D-U-N-S 14-461-4203
OBRIEN & GERE LIMITED
333 W Washington St # 400, Syracuse, NY 13202-5253
Tel (315) 437-6100 *Founded/Ownrshp* 1985
Sales 219.4MM *EMP* 800
Accts Dannible & Mckee Llp Syracuse
SIC 8711 8741 Civil engineering; Management services
CEO: James A Fox
COO: R Leland Davis
CFO: Joseph M McNulty
VP: Robert R Bowers
VP: Ron Harting
VP: William A Lester
VP: Stephen C Palin
VP: George Rest
VP: Edward J Zawadzki
Div Mgr: Steve Anagnost
Off Mgr: Anita Trecartin
Board of Directors: Tim J Barry, Thomas Nowlan, George Rest

D-U-N-S 80-915-2585
OBRIEN & GERE/ CROWDER JOINT VENTURE
6425 Brookshire Blvd, Charlotte, NC 28216-0301
Tel (704) 372-3541 *Founded/Ownrshp* 2007
Sales 30.8MME *EMP* 1,000
SIC 1542 Commercial & office building contractors
Pt: Otis A Crowder
Pt: Crowder Construction
Pt: O'Brien Gere

D-U-N-S 07-921-1309
OBRIEN AUTOMOTIVE OF FLORIDA LLC
2850 Colonial Blvd, Fort Myers, FL 33966-1030
Tel (239) 277-1222 *Founded/Ownrshp* 2012
Sales 109.0MM *EMP* 110
SIC 5511 Automobiles, new & used
Genl Mgr: Gary Matern

D-U-N-S 07-934-1668
■ OC ACQUISITION LLC
(*Suby of* ORACLE CORP) ★
500 Oracle Pkwy, Redwood City, CA 94065-1677
Tel (650) 506-7000 *Founded/Ownrshp* 2011
Sales 1.8MMME *EMP* 5,202E
SIC 7371 7372 Computer software development; Business oriented computer software
Pr: Dorian Daley
Pr: Greg McAllister
Treas: Eric Ball
VP: Eric Domski
Snr Sftwr: Frank Carlesimo
Snr Sftwr: Lee Damico
Snr Sftwr: Praveen Muthuswamy
Snr Sftwr: Tim Penick
Software D: Tushar Shah
Sftwr Eng: Wenjie Hu
Sftwr Eng: John Qiang

D-U-N-S 94-107-9717
OC COMMUNICATIONS INC
2204 Kausen Dr Ste 100, Elk Grove, CA 95758-7176
Tel (916) 686-3700 *Founded/Ownrshp* 1995
Sales 104.5MME *EMP* 650
Accts Moss Adams Llp Stockton Cal
SIC 4841 Cable & other pay television services
*CFO: Peter Tataryn

D-U-N-S 06-656-2703
OCADIAN CARE CENTERS LLC
104 Main St, Belvedere Tiburon, CA 94920-2510
Tel (415) 789-5427 *Founded/Ownrshp* 1994
Sales 4.8MM *EMP* 3,785
SIC 8051 Skilled nursing care facilities
Pr: Robert G Peirce
CFO: Elaine Vonblohn

OCALA REGIONAL MEDICAL CENTER
See MARION WEST COMMUNITY HOSPITAL

D-U-N-S 83-053-4777 EXP
OCAMPOS INC
480 Tam Oshanter Dr Se, Marietta, GA 30067-4831
Tel (770) 509-2595 *Founded/Ownrshp* 2007
Sales 300.0MM *EMP* 5
SIC 5084 Printing trades machinery, equipment & supplies
Pr: Jorge A Ocampo
*CFO: Ashley Ocampo

D-U-N-S 02-000-8736
OCAT INC (CA)
TACO BELL
4306 Sisk Rd, Modesto, CA 95356-9760
Tel (209) 529-6802 *Founded/Ownrshp* 1967
Sales 48.5MME *EMP* 1,204
SIC 5812 Fast-food restaurant, chain
Pr: J Allen Beebe

D-U-N-S 61-169-9059 IMP
OCB RESTAURANT CO LLC
OLD COUNTRY BUFFET
(*Suby of* OLD COUNTRY BUFFET RESTAURANTS) ★
120 Chula Vis, San Antonio, TX 78232-2234
Tel (210) 403-3725 *Founded/Ownrshp* 1990
Sales 208.9MME *EMP* 10,239E
SIC 5812 Buffet (eating places)
*CEO: Richard Michael Andrews
*COO: David Goronkin
CFO: Keith Wall

D-U-N-S 01-524-9022
OCC NATIONAL BANK EXAMINERS
CONTROLLERS OF THE CURRENCY
111 Wall St Bsmt 1, New York, NY 10005-3544
Tel (212) 527-1020 *Founded/Ownrshp* 1863
Sales 2.0MM *EMP* 2,800
SIC 7389 Personal service agents, brokers & bureaus

D-U-N-S 62-716-4887
OCCASIONS GROUP INC
(*Suby of* TAYLOR CORP) ★
1725 Roe Crest Dr, North Mankato, MN 56003-1807
Tel (208) 359-1000 *Founded/Ownrshp* 2006
Sales 489.3MME *EMP* 3,200E
SIC 2759 Commercial printing
CEO: Ron Hoffmeyer
*Pr: Keith Herwig
*CEO: Bill Rose
*VP: Jean Andersen
*VP: Stephanie Schmid
*VP: Nancy Thompson
*VP: John Zellmer
MIS Dir: Stacy Svir
Natl Sales: Linda Hiniker
VP Mktg: Lane Nordquist
Sls Dir: Lisa Haman

D-U-N-S 06-727-1981 IMP/EXP
■ OCCIDENTAL CHEMICAL CORP
O XY
(*Suby of* OCCIDENTAL PETROLEUM CORP) ★
5005 Lyndon B Johnson Fwy # 2200, Dallas, TX 75244-6100
Tel (972) 404-3800 *Founded/Ownrshp* 1968
Sales 427.1MME *EMP* 750
SIC 2812 Alkalies & chlorine; Chlorine, compressed or liquefied; Caustic soda, sodium hydroxide; Potassium carbonate
VP: Dennis Blake
Treas: D C Yen
Sr VP: James Usher
IT Man: Larry Garza
IT Man: Mark Lockmyer
VP Opers: Nigel Hopkinson
Board of Directors: Keith C McDole

D-U-N-S 04-643-6051
OCCIDENTAL COLLEGE (CA)
1600 Campus Rd, Los Angeles, CA 90041-3314
Tel (323) 259-2500 *Founded/Ownrshp* 1887
Sales 188.6MM *EMP* 610
Accts Moss Adams Llp Stockton Ca
SIC 8221 College, except junior
Pr: Theodore R Mitchell
Pr: Barbara Valiente
*Pr: Jonathan Veitch
CFO: Michael Groener
Bd of Dir: John Power
Trst: Ronald Arnault
Trst: Harry W Colmery Jr
Trst: David Roberts
Ofcr: Pamela Wick
VP: Barbara Avery
VP: Hannah Barnes
VP: Michele Cole
VP: Sandra Cooper
VP: Michael P Groener
VP: Amos Himmelstein
VP: Andrew Larkin
VP: Pamela McQuesten
VP: Amy Mua Oz
VP: Rich Stephens
VP: William Tingley
VP: Tom Tomlinson

D-U-N-S 05-229-8721 IMP
■ OCCIDENTAL ENERGY MARKETING INC
(*Suby of* OCCIDENTAL PETROLEUM CORP) ★
5 Greenway Plz Ste 110, Houston, TX 77046-0521
Tel (713) 215-7000 *Founded/Ownrshp* 1987
Sales 636.4MME *EMP* 132
SIC 5172 1382 4924 Crude oil; Oil & gas exploration services; Natural gas distribution
Pr: Ronald K Takeuchi
*Ex VP: Michael R Soland
*Sr VP: Marc Waugh
*VP: Shayne Buchanan
*VP: Gordon E Goodman
Plnt Mgr: David Crawford

D-U-N-S 00-691-5904
OCCIDENTAL FIRE & CASUALTY CO OF NORTH CAROLINA
(*Suby of* MCM CORP) ★
702 Oberlin Rd Ste 300, Raleigh, NC 27605-1357
Tel (919) 833-1600 *Founded/Ownrshp* 1961, 1986
Sales NA *EMP* 175E
SIC 6331 Fire, marine & casualty insurance & carriers
Ch Bd: George E King
*Pr: Stephen L Stephano
*Sr VP: Michael D Blinson
*Sr VP: Deborah Rinkle
Netwrk Eng: Ryan Smith

D-U-N-S 61-484-9375 IMP/EXP
■ OCCIDENTAL OIL AND GAS CORP
OXY
(*Suby of* OCCIDENTAL PETROLEUM CORP) ★
5 Greenway Plz Ste 110, Houston, TX 77046-0521
Tel (713) 215-7000 *Founded/Ownrshp* 1977
Sales 1.4MMME *EMP* 1,800E
SIC 1311 Crude petroleum production; Natural gas production
*Treas: Christopher G Stavros
VP: Nathan Fagre
VP: Michael Keough
Dir Bus: Edward Barrows
*Prin: Steve Jason
*Ex Dir: William E Albrecht
Dir IT: John Hogenson
Corp Couns: Robert Gray
Corp Couns: Brenton Moore

D-U-N-S 79-595-6205 IMP/EXP
■ OCCIDENTAL PERMIAN LTD
(*Suby of* OCCIDENTAL PETROLEUM CORP) ★
5 Greenway Plz Ste 110, Houston, TX 77046-0521
Tel (713) 215-7000 *Founded/Ownrshp* 1997
Sales 1.0MMME *EMP* 900
SIC 1382 1311 Oil & gas exploration services; Crude petroleum production
Pr: Tom Menges

D-U-N-S 00-690-8354
▲ OCCIDENTAL PETROLEUM CORP
5 Greenway Plz Ste 110, Houston, TX 77046-0521
Tel (713) 215-7000 *Founded/Ownrshp* 1920
Sales 12.7MMM *EMP* 11,100
Tkr Sym OXY *Exch* NYS
SIC 1382 1311 Oil & gas exploration services; Crude petroleum & natural gas
Pr: Vicki A Hollub
*Ch Bd: Eugene L Batchelder
Pr: Edward A Lowe
CFO: Christopher G Stavros
Chf Cred: Marcia E Backus
Sr VP: Cynthia L Walker
VP: Jennifer M Kirk
Dir Bus: Lettie Pavlovsky
Genl Mgr: Abdulla Seliem
Board of Directors: Spencer Abraham, Howard I Atkins, Stephen I Chazen, John E Feick, Margaret M Foran, Carlos M Gutierrez, William R Klesse, Jack B Moore, Jack B Moore

D-U-N-S 07-531-2041
OCCIDENTAL PETROLEUM INVESTMENT CO INC
10889 Wilshire Blvd Fl 10, Los Angeles, CA 90024-4213
Tel (310) 208-8800 *Founded/Ownrshp* 1969
Sales 1.3MMME *EMP* 4,000
SIC 1382 8744

D-U-N-S 02-064-5128
OCCUPATIONAL HEALTH SERVICE
WCA HOSPITAL
207 Foote Ave, Jamestown, NY 14701-7077
Tel (716) 664-8165 *Founded/Ownrshp* 2001
Sales 98.3MM *EMP* 9
SIC 8011 8062 Offices & clinics of medical doctors; General medical & surgical hospitals
CEO: Betsy Wright

OCCUPATIONAL MEDICINE
See NATIVIDAD HOSPITAL INC

D-U-N-S 87-824-9515
■ OCCUPATIONAL SAFETY AND HEALTH ADMINISTRATION
(*Suby of* UNITED STATES DEPARTMENT OF LABOR) ★
200 Constitution Ave Nw N3626, Washington, DC 20210-0001
Tel (202) 693-2000 *Founded/Ownrshp* 1981
Sales NA *EMP* 2,384
SIC 9651 Labor regulatory agency; Inspection for labor standards & safety, government;
Dir IT: Cheryle A Greenaugh

OCCUPATIONAL THERAPY
See SAINT LUKES METHODIST HOSPITAL INC

D-U-N-S 18-571-1918 IMP/EXP
OCE-USA HOLDING INC
(*Suby of* OCE HOLDING B.V.)
100 Oakview Dr, Trumbull, CT 06611-4724
Tel (773) 714-8500 *Founded/Ownrshp* 1987
Sales 319.9MME *EMP* 11,000
SIC 3861 5044

D-U-N-S 07-174-3603 IMP
OCEAN BANK
(*Suby of* OCEAN BANKSHARES INC) ★
780 Nw 42nd Ave Ste 300, Miami, FL 33126-5536
Tel (305) 448-2265 *Founded/Ownrshp* 1982
Sales NA *EMP* 639
SIC 6022 State commercial banks
CEO: A Alfonso Macedo
*Ch Bd: Agostino De Sousa Macedo
*COO: Terry J Curry
*CFO: Stan Rubin
*CFO: Alberto Vega

Bd of Dir: Antonio Fern Ndez
Ofcr: John Borum
**Ofcr:* Mariano Fernandez
Ofcr: Rolando Lopez
Ofcr: Guillermo J Molina
Ofcr: Ileana Carrera Portal
Ofcr: Carlos Sandino
Ofcr: Maria Sandino
Ofcr: Frank Sequeira
Assoc VP: Vivian Hernandez
Ex VP: Rolando Bichara
Ex VP: Manuel M Del Canal
Ex VP: Candy Fitzek
**Ex VP:* Sam Monti
**Sr VP:* Benigno Aguirre
Sr VP: Manuel Cabanas
Board of Directors: Juan Del Busto

D-U-N-S 03-254-2800
OCEAN BANKSHARES INC
780 Nw 42nd Ave Ste 626, Miami, FL 33126-5538
Tel (305) 442-2660 *Founded/Ownrshp* 1985
Sales NA *EMP* 896
SIC 6712 Bank holding companies
Pr: Alfonso Macedo
V Ch: Jos A Concepci N
Pr: Rafael Arteaga
COO: Terry J Curry
COO: Vito Nardelli
CFO: Pamela Frank
Bd of Dir: Benigno Concepcion
Bd of Dir: Luis Consuegra
Ofcr: Alina Anzardo
Ofcr: Mayra Nua EZ
Ofcr: Mariano H Fern Ndez
Assoc VP: Michelle Martin
Assoc VP: Joanna Martinez
Ex VP: Ricardo Bajandas
Ex VP: Orlando Baro
Ex VP: Jack Cussen
Ex VP: Walter De Villiers
Ex VP: Lorraine Dellert
Ex VP: Andrew Finkle
Ex VP: Neyda Hermosa
Ex VP: Marta A Hicks

D-U-N-S 00-924-8071 IMP/EXP
OCEAN BEAUTY SEAFOODS LLC
1100 W Ewing St, Seattle, WA 98119-1321
Tel (206) 285-6800 *Founded/Ownrshp* 1996
Sales 437.8MM *EMP* 18,000
Accts Rsm Us Llp Seattle Washingto
SIC 2092 2091 Fresh or frozen packaged fish; Canned & cured fish & seafoods
**Pr:* Mark Palmer
**CFO:* Tony Ross
Ql Cn Mgr: Duane McIntire
Mktg Dir: Todd Sunderland

OCEAN DESIGN
See TELEDYNE ODI INC

OCEAN HOUSE BUILDERS
See NAN INC

D-U-N-S 14-427-0295 IMP
OCEAN INVESTMENTS CORP
700 Maine Ave, Bangor, ME 04401-3021
Tel (207) 942-7000 *Founded/Ownrshp* 1986
Sales 872.8MM^E *EMP* 900
SIC 5541 5411 Filling stations, gasoline; Convenience stores, independent
Pr: Arthur L Irving

OCEAN PINES FAMILY MEDICINE
See PENNINSULA REGIONAL MEDICAL CENTER

OCEAN PRIME
See CAMERON MITCHELL RESTAURANTS LLC

D-U-N-S 05-985-9504
OCEAN PROPERTIES LTD
1001 E Atl Ave Ste 202, Delray Beach, FL 33483
Tel (603) 559-2100 *Founded/Ownrshp* 1973
Sales 464.3MM^E *EMP* 5,800^E
SIC 7011 6552 1522 5719 5812 5813 Hotels & motels; Land subdividers & developers, commercial; Hotel/motel, new construction; Linens; Eating places; Bars & lounges
Pr: Michael Walsh
CFO: Richard Aid
**Treas:* Mark Walsh
VP: John Ogrady
**VP:* William Walsh
Genl Mgr: Christopher Torrey

D-U-N-S 00-105-0897 IMP/EXP
OCEAN SPRAY CRANBERRIES INC
1 Ocean Spray Dr, Middleboro, MA 02349-0001
Tel (508) 946-1000 *Founded/Ownrshp* 1930
Sales 1.7MMM *EMP* 2,000
Accts Pricewaterhousecoopers Llp Bo
SIC 2033 2034 2037 Fruits & fruit products in cans, jars, etc.; Fruit juices: packaged in cans, jars, etc.; Fruits: packaged in cans, jars, etc.; Fruit juices: concentrated, hot pack; Fruits, dried or dehydrated, except freeze-dried; Fruit juice concentrates, frozen
Pr: Randy C Papadellis
**Treas:* Richard A Lees
VP: Woody Chittick
VP: Marguerite Copel
VP: Dan Crocker
VP: Kevin M Kavanaugh
VP: Mike Stamatokos
VP: David Williams
VP: Geoffrey Woolford
Exec: Paul Ganvin
Exec: Chris Kinder
Dir Risk M: Pricilla Hill
Board of Directors: Stephen Lee III, Michael G Bartling, Ralph May, Herbert M Baum, Paul Morse, Gary Dempze, Alfred Piergallini, Peter Dhillon, Francis J Podvin, W Cody Estes, Martin Potter, Guy M Glenn, Richard Poznysz, Guy A Gottschalk, Daryl C Robison, Thomas Hurley, Robert Rosbe Jr, Jerome J Jenko

D-U-N-S 07-926-7184 IMP/EXP
OCEAN SPRAY INTERNATIONAL INC
(*Suby of* OCEAN SPRAY CRANBERRIES INC) ★
1 Ocean Spray Dr, Middleboro, MA 02349-0001
Tel (508) 946-1000 *Founded/Ownrshp* 1996
Sales 102.7MM^E *EMP* 400^E
SIC 2037 2034 2033 Fruit juice concentrates, frozen; Fruits, dried or dehydrated, except freeze-dried; Fruits & fruit products in cans, jars, etc.; Fruit juices: packaged in cans, jars, etc.; Fruits: packaged in cans, jars, etc.; Fruit juices: concentrated, hot pack
Pr: Kenneth Romanzi
**Treas:* Richard A Lees
VP: Laura Tobin
Mng Dir: John Kaczynski
Dir IT: Gail Ledoux
Dir IT: Paula Savini
IT Man: Ginny Owens
VP Mfg: Erich Fritz
Opers Supe: Ryan Porter
Opers Mgr: Mark Rauenzahn
Opers Mgr: Suzanne Salka

D-U-N-S 94-970-8556
OCEAN SPRAY INTERNATIONAL SALES INC
(*Suby of* OCEAN SPRAY CRANBERRIES INC) ★
1 Ocean Spray Dr, Lakeville, MA 02347-1339
Tel (508) 946-1000 *Founded/Ownrshp* 1995
Sales 118.4MM^E *EMP* 500
SIC 5149 Juices
Pr: Randy Tapadoulis

OCEAN STATE JOB LOT
See OCEAN STATE JOBBERS INC

OCEAN STATE JOBBERS
See A & M SPECIAL PURCHASING INC

D-U-N-S 08-480-9417 IMP/EXP
OCEAN STATE JOBBERS INC
OCEAN STATE JOB LOT
375 Commerce Park Rd, North Kingstown, RI 02852-8420
Tel (401) 295-2672 *Founded/Ownrshp* 1977
Sales 996.3MM^E *EMP* 4,000
SIC 5331 5199 Variety stores; Variety store merchandise
CEO: Marc Perlman
Pr: Karina Barchus
Pr: Marka Croce
**Sec:* Alan Perlman
Chf Mktg O: Paul Conforti
**VP:* John Conforti
Off Mgr: Laura Hind
Store Mgr: Marc Pasquazzi
Dir IT: Jasona Duclos
Dir IT: Catherinea Gilchrist
Dir IT: Arthura Nelson

D-U-N-S 07-953-6801
OCEAN VIEW SCHOOL DISTRICT (INC)
OVSD
17200 Pinehurst Ln, Huntington Beach, CA 92647-5569
Tel (714) 847-2551 *Founded/Ownrshp* 1874
Sales 107.7MM *EMP* 1,050
Accts Vavrinek Trine Day & Co Ll
SIC 8211 Public elementary & secondary schools; Public junior high school; Kindergarten; School board
Trst: Debbie Cotton
Pr Dir: Julie Jennings
Schl Brd P: John Ortiz

D-U-N-S 05-514-7490 IMP/EXP
▲ OCEANEERING INTERNATIONAL INC
11911 Fm 529 Rd, Houston, TX 77041-3000
Tel (713) 329-4500 *Founded/Ownrshp* 1964
Sales 3.0MMM *EMP* 11,000^E
Accts Ernst & Young Llp Houston Te
Tkr Sym OII *Exch* NYS
SIC 1389 3731 8711 Oil field services; Submersible marine robots, manned or unmanned; Engineering services
CEO: M Kevin McEvoy
Ch Bd: John R Huff
Pr: Roderick A Larson
COO: Clyde W Hewlett
CFO: Alan R Curtis
Sr VP: Stephen P Barrett
Sr VP: William J Boyle
Sr VP: W Cardon Gerner
Sr VP: David K Lawrence
Sr VP: Eric A Silva
VP: Greg Arris
VP: Steve Barrett
VP: Martin McDonald
VP: Nicholas K Miller
VP: Robert Mingoia
Board of Directors: William B Berry, T Jay Collins, D Michael Hughes, Paul B Murphy Jr, Harris J Pappas, Steven A Webster

D-U-N-S 07-514-3131
■ OCEANFIRST BANK (NJ)
(*Suby of* OCEANFIRST FINANCIAL CORP) ★
975 Hooper Ave, Toms River, NJ 08753-8320
Tel (732) 240-4500 *Founded/Ownrshp* 1902
Sales NA *EMP* 486
SIC 6035 Federal savings & loan associations
Ch: John R Garbarino
Pr: Vito Nardelli
Treas: Robert Laskowski
Trst Ofcr: Brandon Kaletkowski
Trst Ofcr: Craig Spengeman
Ex VP: Michael Fitzpatrick
VP: Gary A Casperson
VP: Michael Dellabarca
VP: Ed Fitzpatrick
VP: Philip Gogarty
VP: Christina Paccione
VP: Patricia Siciliano
VP: Beth Stefanelli
Board of Directors: Christopher D Maher, Mark G Solow

D-U-N-S 96-117-8761
▲ OCEANFIRST FINANCIAL CORP
975 Hooper Ave, Toms River, NJ 08753-8320
Tel (732) 240-4500 *Founded/Ownrshp* 1996
Sales NA *EMP* 700^E
Tkr Sym OCFC *Exch* NGS
SIC 6035 Federal savings & loan associations
Pr: Christopher D Maher
Ch Bd: John R Garbarino
CFO: Michael J Fitzpatrick
Ofcr: Joseph R Iantosca
Ofcr: Joseph J Lebel III
Ex VP: Craig C Spengeman
Ex VP: Steven J Tsimbinos
VP: Barbara Baldwin
VP: Dave Howard

D-U-N-S 12-667-8254 IMP/EXP
■ OCEANIA CRUISES INC
(*Suby of* PRESTIGE CRUISE HOLDINGS INC) ★
7665 Nw 19th St, Miami, FL 33126-1201
Tel (305) 514-2300 *Founded/Ownrshp* 2008
Sales 573.7MM^E *EMP* 100
Accts Pricewaterhousecoopers Llp Mi
SIC 4481 Deep sea passenger transportation, except ferry
Pr: Bob Binder
**Pr:* Kunal S Kamlani
**CFO:* Jason Montague
**Treas:* Lisa Wilson
Ex VP: Robin Lindsay
Sr VP: James Rodriguez
Sr VP: Howard Sherman
**Sr VP:* Harry Sommer
VP: Katina Athanasiou
VP: Scott Kluesner
**VP:* James Peterson
VP: Tricia Wolf
Exec: Kathryn Kelly

D-U-N-S 07-749-0269
OCEANS HEALTH CARE
5850 Granite Pkwy Ste 300, Plano, TX 75024-6760
Tel (972) 464-0022 *Founded/Ownrshp* 2015
Sales 52.2MM^E *EMP* 2,000
SIC 8063 Hospital for the mentally ill
CEO: Stuart Archer
**COO:* Nick Guillory
**CFO:* Patrick Corbett
**Ex VP:* Daryl Doise
Board of Directors: Stuart Archer, Nick Guillory, Michael Jellinek, Gabe Ling, Brian Shortsleeve, Paul Verrochi

D-U-N-S 07-873-2062
OCEANSIDE UNIFIED SCHOOL DISTRICT
2111 Mission Ave, Oceanside, CA 92058-2395
Tel (760) 966-4000 *Founded/Ownrshp* 1970
Sales 90.9MM^E *EMP* 2,200
Accts Christywhite Accountancy Corpo
SIC 8211 Public elementary & secondary schools
Ofcr: Joe Sepulveda
Comm Dir: Lisa Contreras
Comm Dir: Terry Loftus
Dir IT: Matt Evans

D-U-N-S 92-781-7262
OCH-ZIFF CAPITAL MANAGEMENT GROUP LLC
9 W 57th St, New York, NY 10019-2701
Tel (212) 790-0000 *Founded/Ownrshp* 1994
Sales 1.3MMM *EMP* 659
Accts Ernst & Young Llp New York N
Tkr Sym OZM *Exch* NYS
SIC 6282 Manager of mutual funds, contract or fee basis
Ch Bd: Daniel S Och
COO: Wayne Cohen
**CFO:* Joel M Frank
Ofcr: David Becker
Ofcr: Anna Song
VP: Hap Pollard
VP: Andres Schumann
Mng Dir: Adam Broder
Mng Dir: Sameer Dalamal
Mng Dir: Mike Thompson
Snr Sftwr: Abraham Heidebrecht
Board of Directors: William P Barr, Allan S Bufferd, J Barry Griswell, Jerome P Kenney, Georganne C Proctor, David Windreich

O'CHARLEYS
See COVELLI ENTERPRISES INC

D-U-N-S 10-176-5436
OCHARLEYS LLC
O'CHARLEY'S RESTAURANTS
(*Suby of* VILLAGE INN RESTAURANT) ★
3038 Sidco Dr, Nashville, TN 37204-4516
Tel (615) 256-8500 *Founded/Ownrshp* 2013
Sales 498.5MM^E *EMP* 24,079^E
Accts Kpmg Llp Nashville Tennessee
SIC 5812 Restaurant, family: chain
CFO: R Jeffrey Williams
Pr: George T Agarelis
Pr: Marc A Buehler
Pr: Wilson Craft
Pr: Charles F DOE Jr
Pr: John R Grady
Pr: Anthony J Halligan III
Ofcr: Lawrence Hyatt
VP: J Harold Allen
VP: Tim Kaliher
VP: Jim Kiley
VP: James K Quackenbush

O'CHARLEY'S RESTAURANTS
See OCHARLEYS LLC

D-U-N-S 01-438-4213
OCHOA AG UNLIMITED FOODS INC
OCHOA FOODS
910 W Main St Ste 248, Boise, ID 83702-5732
Tel (208) 343-6882 *Founded/Ownrshp* 2001
Sales 100.0MM *EMP* 300
SIC 5142 Packaged frozen goods
Pr: Thoma Martinez
**CFO:* Howard Bafford

OCHOA FOODS
See OCHOA AG UNLIMITED FOODS INC

D-U-N-S 07-790-0207 IMP
OCHSNER CLINIC FOUNDATION
1514 Jefferson Hwy, New Orleans, LA 70121-2483
Tel (504) 842-3000 *Founded/Ownrshp* 1944
Sales 2.2MMM *EMP* 10,500
Accts Ernst & Young Us Llp Austin
SIC 8062 5947 General medical & surgical hospitals; Gift, novelty & souvenir shop
Pr: Patrick J Quinlan MD
Chf Path: Greg Sossaman
COO: Eric McMillen
Ex VP: B C Brannon
Sr VP: Lawrence Van Hoose
VP: Mark Beckstrom
Dir Rx: Arlene Workmen
Ex Dir: Ethel U Madden
MIS Dir: Glenn Doherty
MIS Dir: Stacie Falati
Mktg Mgr: Lisa Fine

D-U-N-S 15-748-7471
OCHSNER CLINIC HEALTH SERVICES CORP
1514 Jefferson Hwy, New Orleans, LA 70121-2483
Tel (504) 842-4000 *Founded/Ownrshp* 1978
Sales 164.6MM *EMP* 132^E
SIC 8011 General & family practice, physician/surgeon
Ch Bd: Dr Gary Goldstein
**Treas:* Scott J Posecai
**Acting Pr:* Shannon Cooper MD
Bd of Dir: Jonathan McCall
Bd of Dir: William A Norton
Bd of Dir: A Jusin Ourso III
VP: Edward D Frohlich
VP: Laura Wilt
Dir Rx: Reggie Labat
Orthpdst: Peter Bleey
Orthpdst: Stephen A Gick

D-U-N-S 96-835-0731
OCHSNER COMMUNITY HOSPITALS
1514 Jefferson Hwy, New Orleans, LA 70121-2429
Tel (504) 842-3400 *Founded/Ownrshp* 2011
Sales 517.1MM *EMP* 99
Accts Ernst & Young Us Llp Austin
SIC 8062 General medical & surgical hospitals
Treas: Bobby C Brannon
Nurse Mgr: Lara Tedesco
Doctor: Patrick Breaux
Snr Mgr: Forrest Whichard

D-U-N-S 94-901-4393
OCHSNER FOUNDATION HOSPITAL
OCHSNER MEDICAL CENTER
1514 Jefferson Hwy, New Orleans, LA 70121-2429
Tel (504) 842-4000 *Founded/Ownrshp* 1942
Sales 206.1MM^E *EMP* 9,000
SIC 8062 General medical & surgical hospitals
CEO: Patrick Quinlan
VP: Timothy Maier
Dir Rad: Oussama Nachar
CIO: Jonathan McCall
CIO: Bill Saussaye
CIO: Cindy Stowe
QA Dir: Mark Milner
IT Man: Kathryn Watson
Orthpdst: Roger Racz
Pathlgst: Elise A Occhipinti
Pathlgst: Leo Pei

D-U-N-S 08-007-5941
OCHSNER HEALTH SYSTEM
1516 Jefferson Hwy, New Orleans, LA 70121-2429
Tel (504) 842-3483 *Founded/Ownrshp* 2006
Sales 141.5MM^E *EMP* 238^E
SIC 8099 Childbirth preparation clinic
Sr VP: Mark Muller
VP: Shelly Monks
Exec: Terri Virga
Nurse Mgr: Donna Jones
Nurse Mgr: Traci Termine
Surgeon: Pamela Petrocy
Doctor: Sapna Desai
Doctor: Stephen Morris

OCHSNER KENNER MEDICAL CTR
See OCHSNER MEDICAL CENTER - KENNER LLC

OCHSNER MEDICAL CENTER
See OCHSNER FOUNDATION HOSPITAL

OCHSNER MEDICAL CENTER - BATON
See EAST BATON ROUGE MEDICAL CENTER LLC

D-U-N-S 78-671-6915
OCHSNER MEDICAL CENTER - KENNER LLC
OCHSNER KENNER MEDICAL CTR
(*Suby of* OCHSNER HEALTH SYSTEM) ★
180 W Esplanade Ave, Kenner, LA 70065-2467
Tel (504) 468-8600 *Founded/Ownrshp* 2006
Sales 141.5MM *EMP* 2
SIC 8062 8099 General medical & surgical hospitals; Childbirth preparation clinic
CEO: Scott Posecai
Dir Rad: Kendy Martinez
Dir Rx: Arlene Workmon
Off Mgr: Donna Blandy
Off Mgr: Miguel Bran
Nurse Mgr: Simon Cantrelle
Dir QC: Erin Ray
Dir QC: Erin Wray
Mktg Dir: Nancy St Germain
Nutrtnst: Corie Gardner
Nutrtnst: Nick Romagnano

D-U-N-S 07-887-6977
■ OCI PARTNERS LP
(*Suby of* OCIP HOLDING LLC) ★
5470 N Twin City Hwy, Nederland, TX 77627
Tel (409) 723-1900 *Founded/Ownrshp* 2013
Sales 309.4MM *EMP* 128^E
Tkr Sym OCIP *Exch* NYS
SIC 2861 2873 Methanol, natural (wood alcohol); Ammonium nitrate, ammonium sulfate; Anhydrous ammonia

Pr: Frank Bakker
Genl Pt: Oci GP LLC
CFO: Fady Kiama

D-U-N-S 03-915-1506
OCIMUM BIOSOLUTIONS INC
50 W Watkins Mill Rd, Gaithersburg, MD 20878-4023
Tel (317) 228-0600 *Founded/Ownrshp* 2000
Sales 23.0MM *EMP* 5,260
SIC 8731 Agricultural research; Biological research
Pr: Anuradha Acharya
Genl Mgr: Sridhar Kolanu
Mktg Dir: Ashwin Sivakumar

D-U-N-S 08-030-6613
▲ OCIP HOLDING LLC
660 Madison Ave Fl 19, New York, NY 10065-8415
Tel (646) 589-6180 *Founded/Ownrshp* 2014
Sales 309.4MM[E] *EMP* 128[E]
SIC 2861 2873 Methanol, natural (wood alcohol); Ammonium nitrate, ammonium sulfate

D-U-N-S 61-486-0646
▲ OCLARO INC
225 Charcot Ave, San Jose, CA 95131-1107
Tel (408) 383-1400 *Founded/Ownrshp* 2004
Sales 407.9MM *EMP* 1,233[E]
Tkr Sym OCLR *Exch* NGS
SIC 3674 3826 3827 Light emitting diodes; Laser scientific & engineering instruments; Optical instruments & apparatus
CEO: Greg Dougherty
**Ch Bd:* Marissa Peterson
Pr: Richard Craig
Pr: Yves Lemaitre
COO: Jim Haynes
CFO: Pete Mangan
Ofcr: Adam Carter
Ex VP: Previn Brito
Ex VP: Adrian Meldrum
Ex VP: Lisa Paul
Ex VP: David Teichmann
Ex VP: David L Teichmann
VP: Scott Parker
Board of Directors: Edward Collins, Kendall Cowan, Denise Haylor, Lori Holland, Joel A Smith III, William L Smith

D-U-N-S 06-358-7745
OCLC ONLINE COMPUTER LIBRARY CENTER INCORPORATE
6565 Kilgour Pl, Dublin, OH 43017-3395
Tel (614) 764-6000 *Founded/Ownrshp* 1967
Sales 202.7MM *EMP* 1,227
Accts Deloitte & Touche Llp Columbu
SIC 7375 On-line data base information retrieval
Pr: David A Prichard
Pr: Susan Walker
Trst: Tony Ferguson
Ofcr: Nancy Lensenmayer
VP: Dena K Bovee
VP: Ronald Edelsteis
**VP:* William J Rozek
VP: Michael Teets
Prin: Pat Ring
Ex Dir: Irene Hoffman
Mng Dir: Norbert Weinberger

OCLI
See OPTICAL COATING LABORATORY LLC

D-U-N-S 03-794-3742
OCM LLC
OHIO COMMUNITY MEDIA
(*Suby of* CIVITAS MEDIA LLC) ★
4500 Lyons Rd, Miamisburg, OH 45342-6447
Tel (937) 247-2700 *Founded/Ownrshp* 2016
Sales 137.0MM[E] *EMP* 839[E]
SIC 2711 Newspapers
CEO: Roy Brown

D-U-N-S 07-965-8947
OCM PE HOLDINGS LP
333 S Grand Ave Fl 28, Los Angeles, CA 90071-1504
Tel (213) 830-6213 *Founded/Ownrshp* 2012
Sales 626.6MM[E] *EMP* 10,000[E]
SIC 3679 3612 3663 Electronic circuits; Transformers, except electric; Antennas, transmitting & communications
CEO: Mark C J Twaalfhoven

D-U-N-S 07-965-3801
OCM REAL ESTATE OPPORTUNITIES FUND II LP
(*Suby of* OAKTREE CAPITAL GROUP HOLDINGS LP) ★
333 S Grand Ave Fl 28, Los Angeles, CA 90071-1504
Tel (213) 830-6300 *Founded/Ownrshp* 2014
Sales 224.4M[E] *EMP* 1,258[E]
SIC 6799 Investors

D-U-N-S 06-933-3789
OCONEE MEDICAL CENTER (SC)
LILA DOYLE NURSING CARE FCILTY
298 Memorial Dr, Seneca, SC 29672-9443
Tel (864) 482-3100 *Founded/Ownrshp* 1937
Sales 137.6MM *EMP* 1,345[E]
Accts Dixon Hughes Goodman Llp Gree
SIC 8062 8051 General medical & surgical hospitals; Skilled nursing care facilities
Ch: William Howiler
**Pr:* Jeanne L Ward
**Treas:* Bob M Toggweiler
Opthamlgy: Scott Massios
Doctor: Carmine Fiorentino MD
Pharmcst: Jay Rabalais

D-U-N-S 09-744-5399
OCONNELL COMPANIES INC
480 Hampden St, Holyoke, MA 01040-3309
Tel (413) 534-0246 *Founded/Ownrshp* 1879
Sales 191.5MM[E] *EMP* 730
SIC 1541 Industrial buildings, new construction; Renovation, remodeling & repairs: industrial buildings
Pr: Dennis A Fitzpatrick
**Treas:* James N Sullivan
**VP:* Nathan C Clinard
**VP:* Martin F Schoenemann

D-U-N-S 00-379-2322
OCONNELL ELECTRIC CO INC (NY)
7001 Performance Dr, Syracuse, NY 13212-3403
Tel (585) 924-2176 *Founded/Ownrshp* 1911, 1968
Sales 153.3MM[E] *EMP* 550
SIC 1731 General electrical contractor
CEO: Victor E Salerno
**Ch Bd:* Walter T Parkes
**COO:* Thomas W Parkes
**CFO:* Jeffrey T Gould
CFO: Jeffrey Gould
Ofcr: Richard Oconnell
**VP:* Susan Parkes McNally
Dir IT: Jon Weiss
IT Man: Dave Adam
IT Man: David Adams
Sfty Dirs: Paul Driscoll

D-U-N-S 07-357-6951 IMP
OCONNELL LANDSCAPE MAINTENANCE INC (CA)
23091 Arroyo Vis, Rcho STA Marg, CA 92688-2605
Tel (949) 589-2007 *Founded/Ownrshp* 1977
Sales 145.8MM[E] *EMP* 1,000
SIC 0782 Landscape contractors
CEO: George O'Connell
**Pr:* Jim Vienneau
**VP:* Brady O'Connell
VP: Brady Oconnell
**VP:* Darren Payne
Brnch Mgr: Mike Clark
Brnch Mgr: Tony Hartvigsen
Sls Dir: Kevin O'Connell

D-U-N-S 07-290-6944
OCONNOR CO
4909 N Lewis Ave, Sioux Falls, SD 57104-7113
Tel (605) 336-0333 *Founded/Ownrshp* 1970
Sales 88.4MM[E] *EMP* 120
SIC 5075 Warm air heating & air conditioning
Pr: Mike O'Connor

D-U-N-S 00-724-7430
OCONNOR CO INC
16910 W 116th St, Lenexa, KS 66219-9604
Tel (913) 894-8788 *Founded/Ownrshp* 1920
Sales 90.0MM *EMP* 120
SIC 5075 Warm air heating & air conditioning
Pr: Lynn J Piller
VP: Stephanie Atkinson
Off Mgr: Cathy Griffith
Mktg Mgr: Melissa McDonald
Sls Mgr: Mike Cunningham
Sls Mgr: Craig Sayre

D-U-N-S 07-630-0169
OCONNOR HOSPITAL
O'CONNOR WOUND CARE CLINIC
2105 Forest Ave, San Jose, CA 95128-1471
Tel (408) 947-2500 *Founded/Ownrshp* 1954
Sales 283.1MM *EMP* 1,300
Accts Grant Thornton Llp San Franci
SIC 8062 General medical & surgical hospitals
CEO: James F Dover
COO: Ron Galonsky
**Sr VP:* David W Carroll
Sr VP: David Carroll
**VP:* Craig Rucker
Genl Mgr: Mike Manansala
Sfty Dirs: John Hryndej
HC Dir: Pam Woods

O'CONNOR MOTRO COMPANY
See HUTCHINS MOTORS INC

O'CONNOR WOUND CARE CLINIC
See OCONNOR HOSPITAL

OCONOMOWOC DEVELOPMENTAL TRAIN
See OCONOMOWOC RESIDENTIAL PROGRAMS INC

D-U-N-S 82-585-6834
OCONOMOWOC RESIDENTIAL PROGRAMS INC
OCONOMOWOC DEVELOPMENTAL TRAIN
1746 Executive Dr, Oconomowoc, WI 53066-4830
Tel (262) 569-5515 *Founded/Ownrshp* 1984
Sales 113.6MM *EMP* 1,500
Accts Bdo Usa Llp Milwaukee Wi
SIC 8052 8361 Intermediate care facilities; Home for the mentally handicapped; Home for the emotionally disturbed
Pr: James Balestrieri
COO: Terrence Leahy
**COO:* Richard Macnally
**CFO:* David Nagy
CFO: Adam Whitehill
VP: Debbie Frisk
**VP:* Michael Warczyglowa
Ex Dir: Michael Flores
Dist Mgr: Kevin Silkey
Dir IT: Tim Hornak
IT Man: Angi Rieker

OCSD5
See ORANGEBURG CONSOLIDATED SCHOOL DISTRICT 5

D-U-N-S 02-732-3557
OCTAPHARMA PLASMA INC
(*Suby of* OCTAPHARMA AG)
10644 Westlake Dr, Charlotte, NC 28273-3930
Tel (704) 654-4600 *Founded/Ownrshp* 2008
Sales 237.1MM[E] *EMP* 300[E]
SIC 2836 Plasmas
Pr: Dennis D Curtin
**COO:* Judy Smith
**VP:* Barry Pomeroy
Exec: Heather Devereux
Genl Mgr: Tobias Marguerre
QA Dir: Rita Bryant
QA Dir: Jenny Dannen
QA Dir: John Fulcher
QA Dir: Donna Raymond
QA Dir: Tanita Weathers
Netwrk Eng: Jeff Nobles

D-U-N-S 60-164-1319 IMP
OCULAR LCD INC
12700 Park Central Dr # 750, Dallas, TX 75251-1553
Tel (972) 437-3888 *Founded/Ownrshp* 2005
Sales NA *EMP* 2,000
SIC 3679

OCULAR SCIENCES A COOPERVISION
See COOPERVISION INC

OCULAR SCIENCES CARRIBEAN
See OCULAR SCIENCES PUERTO RICO INC

D-U-N-S 10-581-3414 IMP
■ OCULAR SCIENCES PUERTO RICO INC
OCULAR SCIENCES CARRIBEAN
(*Suby of* COOPER COMPANIES INC) ★
500 Carr 584, Juana Diaz, PR 00795-2870
Tel (787) 260-0555 *Founded/Ownrshp* 2007
Sales 54.3MM *EMP* 1,193
SIC 3851 Contact lenses
CFO: Sidney Landman
**Genl Mgr:* Fernando Torre
Snr Mgr: Vannessa Alvaravo

D-U-N-S 18-695-7114
▲ OCWEN FINANCIAL CORP
1661 Worthington Rd # 100, West Palm Beach, FL 33409-6488
Tel (561) 682-8000 *Founded/Ownrshp* 1988
Sales NA *EMP* 10,500[E]
Tkr Sym OCN *Exch* NYS
SIC 6162 Mortgage bankers & correspondents; Mortgage bankers
Pr: Ronald M Faris
**Ch Bd:* Phyllis R Caldwell
CFO: Michael R Bourque Jr
Ofcr: Marcelo G Cruz
Ex VP: Scott W Anderson
Ex VP: John V Britti
Ex VP: Timothy M Hayes
Ex VP: Otto J Kumbar
Sr VP: Catherine M Dondzila
Sr VP: Arthur C Walker Jr
Dir IT: Joanne Perez
Board of Directors: Alan J Bowers, Jacques J Busquet, Carol J Galante, Ronald J Korn, Robert A Salcetti, Deforest B Soaries Jr

D-U-N-S 06-901-7515
■ OCWEN LOAN SERVICING LLC
(*Suby of* OCWEN FINANCIAL CORP) ★
1661 Worthington Rd # 100, West Palm Beach, FL 33409-6493
Tel (561) 682-8000 *Founded/Ownrshp* 2002
Sales NA *EMP* 1,981
Accts Pricewaterhousecoopers Llp Fo
SIC 6162 Mortgage bankers & correspondents
CEO: Ronald M Faris
**CFO:* John V Britti
CFO: David J Hunter
**Ex VP:* Scott W Anderson
**Sr VP:* Sp Ravi
VP: Stewart Fink
VP: Michael Murphy
**VP:* Kenneth D Najour
Dir IT: Tricia Brabs
IT Man: Kelly McClain
IT Man: Rajeev Nair

OCZ ENTERPRISE
See ZCO LIQUIDATING CORP

D-U-N-S 01-746-1380
ODANIEL AUTOMOTIVE INC
5611 Illinois Rd, Fort Wayne, IN 46804-1183
Tel (260) 435-5300 *Founded/Ownrshp* 1987
Sales 94.4MM[E] *EMP* 100
SIC 5511 New & used car dealers
Pr: Randy O'Daniel
**Sec:* Germaine O'Daniel
**VP:* Jeffrey O'Daniel
Telecom Ex: Dave Gutting

D-U-N-S 06-345-0412 IMP
ODC CONSTRUCTION LLC (FL)
5701 Carder Rd, Orlando, FL 32810-4742
Tel (407) 447-5999 *Founded/Ownrshp* 2011
Sales 133.0MM *EMP* 102
SIC 1521 Single-family housing construction
CEO: Isaac Lidsky
**Pr:* Tony Hartsgrove
**CFO:* Zac Merriman

D-U-N-S 02-267-8634 IMP
ODDELLO INDUSTRIES LLC
425 Jones Franklin Rd, Morristown, TN 37813-1121
Tel (423) 307-1240 *Founded/Ownrshp* 2008
Sales 115.1MM[E] *EMP* 375
Accts Melissa F Hill Cpa Tennesse
SIC 2511 Wood household furniture
Sfty Mgr: Ryan Carpenter

D-U-N-S 62-076-6626 EXP
ODEBRECHT CONSTRUCTION INC
(*Suby of* BELGRAVIA EMPREENDIMENTOS IMOBILIARIOS S/A.)
201 Alhambra Cir Ste 1000, Coral Gables, FL 33134-5103
Tel (305) 341-8800 *Founded/Ownrshp* 1993
Sales 154.3MM[E] *EMP* 250
SIC 1622 1522 Highway construction, elevated; Bridge construction; Residential construction
CEO: Jairo Flor
**VP:* James Storey Jr
Brnch Mgr: Robert Baer
CIO: Ricardo Gajordoni
CTO: Omar Postigo
Sales Exec: Eric Appel
Mktg Dir: Renata Pinheiro

D-U-N-S 03-903-9441
■ ODESSA PUMPS AND EQUIPMENT INC
(*Suby of* NOW INC) ★
8161 Dorado Dr, Odessa, TX 79765-8533
Tel (432) 333-2817 *Founded/Ownrshp* 1980, 2015
Sales 180.6MM[E] *EMP* 300
SIC 5084 Petroleum industry machinery; Oil well machinery, equipment & supplies; Pumps & pumping equipment; Water pumps (industrial)
CEO: Sondra Eoff
**Pr:* Joey Lewallen
**COO:* Clayton Kenworthy
**Ofcr:* Toby Eoff
**VP:* Jackie Swanson
**CIO:* Jana Lewallen

D-U-N-S 12-110-7718
ODESSA REGIONAL HOSPITAL LP
(*Suby of* IASIS HEALTHCARE CORP) ★
520 E 6th St, Odessa, TX 79761-4527
Tel (432) 582-8000 *Founded/Ownrshp* 1975
Sales 178.2MM *EMP* 570
SIC 8062 General medical & surgical hospitals
CEO: Bill Porter
**COO:* Stacey Gerig
Dir: Betty Harrold

ODFW
See OREGON DEPARTMENT OF FISH AND WILDLIFE

ODH
See DEPARTMENT OF HEALTH OHIO

ODJFS
See OHIO DEPARTMENT OF JOB AND FAMILY SERVICES

D-U-N-S 00-641-0781 IMP
ODL INC (MI)
O D L
215 E Roosevelt Ave, Zeeland, MI 49464-1239
Tel (616) 772-9111 *Founded/Ownrshp* 1951
Sales 180.7MM[E] *EMP* 425
SIC 2431 Doors & door parts & trim, wood
Ch Bd: Dave Killoran
**CEO:* Jeffrey Mulder
**CFO:* Michael Burke
Dir IT: Donald Taylor
IT Man: Keith Juhola
Plnt Mgr: Mark Zitricki
Prd Mgr: Jeff Johnson
Mktg Dir: Keith Early
Mktg Dir: Angelo Marasco
Sls Mgr: George Barber
Sales Asso: Gloria Secord

D-U-N-S 06-955-1018 IMP/EXP
ODOM CORP
COCA-COLA
11400 Se 8th St Ste 300, Bellevue, WA 98004-6409
Tel (425) 456-3535 *Founded/Ownrshp* 1933
Sales 583.2MM[E] *EMP* 1,500
Accts Grant Thornton Llp Seattle W
SIC 5149 Soft drinks
Ch Bd: John P Odom
**Pr:* Dick Barkett
**CFO:* Randy Halter
**V Ch Bd:* William L Odom
Bd of Dir: Gene Odom
**VP:* Jerry Dexter
VP: Adam Ferns
VP: Bill Odom
**VP:* Jim Odom
Exec: Dave Newton
Admn Mgr: Carolyn Searles

D-U-N-S 04-615-8424
ODONNELL FOUNDATION
100 Crescent Ct Ste 1660, Dallas, TX 75201-1824
Tel (214) 871-5800 *Founded/Ownrshp* 1957
Sales 87.9MM *EMP* 8
SIC 8699 Charitable organization
Pr: Peter O'Donnell Jr
**COO:* Tom Luce
**Sec:* Edith J O'Donnell
VP: Rita Clements
**Prin:* Leslie Brosi

D-U-N-S 82-525-1390
ODONNELL/SNIDER CONSTRUCTION LLC
1900 West Loop S Ste 350, Houston, TX 77027-3236
Tel (713) 782-7660 *Founded/Ownrshp* 1991
Sales 122.8MM *EMP* 48
SIC 1542 Commercial & office building contractors
Genl Pt: Duncan O'Donnell
**Pt:* Walter H Snider III
**Prin:* Randy O'Donnell
**Prin:* Trey Snider
**VP Opers:* Terry Atmar

ODS COMPANIES
See OREGON DENTAL SERVICE

ODS COMPANIES
See MODA HEALTH PLAN INC

D-U-N-S 05-780-1268
ODW LOGISTICS INC
O D W
1580 Williams Rd, Columbus, OH 43207-5183
Tel (614) 497-1660 *Founded/Ownrshp* 1971
Sales 178.2MM[E] *EMP* 600
SIC 4225 4226 General warehousing; Special warehousing & storage
Ch: Robert E Ness
**COO:* Ted Nikolai
CFO: Dave Hill
**CFO:* David L Hill
**Sec:* Lynn Ness
**VP:* Macy A Bergoon
VP: Carl Neverman
Ex Dir: Denise Bauer
Genl Mgr: Chris Copsey
Genl Mgr: Noel Johnson
Genl Mgr: Scott Leonard

ODWALLA FRESH SQZED FRT VGTBLE
See ODWALLA INC

D-U-N-S 10-276-2234 IMP
■ ODWALLA INC
ODWALLA FRESH SQZED FRT VGTBLE
(*Suby of* COCA-COLA CO) ★
1 Coca Cola Plz Nw, Atlanta, GA 30313-2420
Tel (479) 721-6260 *Founded/Ownrshp* 1980
Sales 222.0MM[E] *EMP* 900

SIC 2033 Fruit juices: packaged in cans, jars, etc.; Vegetable juices: packaged in cans, jars, etc.
CEO: D Stephen Williamson
**Pr:* Alison Lewis
**CFO:* James R Steichen
Sr Cor Off: Gary Fayard
Sr VP: Bill Hopkins
**VP:* Susan M Kirmayer
VP: Laura Lopez
VP: Elizabeth McDonough
Exec: Todd Daniels
Dir IT: Gary Hensley
S&M/VP: Tom Philp

D-U-N-S 78-767-2174
ODYSSEA MARINE HOLDINGS INC
11864 Highway 308, Larose, LA 70373-5877
Tel (985) 385-0189 *Founded/Ownrshp* 1997
Sales 1.4MMM^E *EMP* 17,000^E
SIC 1381 Drilling oil & gas wells
Ch Bd: Charles A Denning
**Pr:* David W Sharp
Mktg Mgr: Chad Johnson

D-U-N-S 05-567-8361 IMP
ODYSSEY ENTERPRISES INC (WA)
2729 6th Ave S, Seattle, WA 98134-2101
Tel (206) 285-7445 *Founded/Ownrshp* 1981, 2012
Sales 162.7MM *EMP* 250
Accts Rhodes & Associates Pllc Fede
SIC 5146 Fish & seafoods
Pr: Phil Crean
CFO: Paul Adams
Sales Exec: Dennis Offner
Board of Directors: Phil Crean, Cora Edmonds

ODYSSEY GROUP - INFO SVCS
See ODYSSEY GROUP OF COMPANIES

D-U-N-S 36-225-5234
ODYSSEY GROUP OF COMPANIES
ODYSSEY GROUP - INFO SVCS
11 Overlook Way, Setauket, NY 11733-1344
Tel (631) 751-8400 *Founded/Ownrshp* 1985
Sales 93.0MM *EMP* 146
SIC 7373 3577 7371 1731 Computer systems analysis & design; Systems engineering, computer related; Computer peripheral equipment; Computer software development; Electrical work
Ch Bd: Adam Grill
**Pr:* George Kaplan
**CFO:* Alexander Marshall
**VP:* Alan Grant
**VP:* Viswanathan Hariharan
**Ex Dir:* Robert Goldman

D-U-N-S 94-571-5217
■ **ODYSSEY HEALTHCARE INC**
(*Suby of* GENTIVA HEALTH SERVICES INC) ★
7801 Mesquite Bend Dr # 105, Irving, TX 75063-6043
Tel (888) 600-2411 *Founded/Ownrshp* 1995
Sales 113.2MM^E *EMP* 6,207
SIC 8051 Skilled nursing care facilities
CEO: Tony Strange
COO: David C Gasmire
**COO:* Craig P Goguen
COO: Deborah A Hoffpuir
**CFO:* R Dirk Allison
**CFO:* Eric R Slusser
Ex VP: Holly Franko
**Sr VP:* Brenda A Belger
**Sr VP:* W Bradley Bickham
VP: Bruce Kemper
Exec: Nicole Miller

D-U-N-S 05-528-4520
ODYSSEY INVESTMENT PARTNERS LLC
590 Madison Ave Fl 39, New York, NY 10022-8526
Tel (212) 351-7900 *Founded/Ownrshp* 1997
Sales 1.5MMM^E *EMP* 5,494
SIC 6211 Investment firm, general brokerage
Ch: Stephen Berger
VP: Robert Aikman
VP: Dennis Moore
VP: Matthew Satnick
VP: Thomas Zanios
VP: Brian Zaumeyer
**Exec:* Doug Hitchner
**Admn Mgr:* Doug Rotatori
Web Prj Mg: Lisa Carnes
Info Man: John McNamara

D-U-N-S 13-019-8588
ODYSSEY LOGISTICS & TECHNOLOGY CORP
39 Old Ridgebury Rd Ste 7, Danbury, CT 06810-5100
Tel (203) 448-3900 *Founded/Ownrshp* 2002
Sales 520.5MM *EMP* 1,213
SIC 4731 Customs clearance of freight
Ch Bd: Edward M Straw
**Pr:* Robert H Shellman
**CFO:* Cosmo J Alberico
Ofcr: Raymond G Maier
Sr VP: Lori Davlos
Sr VP: Lawrence Hu
**Sr VP:* Raymond Maier
**Sr VP:* Russell Marky
Sr VP: Charles H Midkiff
Sr VP: Glenn E Riggs
VP: Nelson Baltazar
VP: Mark Casiano
VP: Leonid Podoshev
VP: Deborah Pritchard
VP: Bob Shellman
Exec: Mark Gallucci
Dir Bus: Paul Palmieri

D-U-N-S 01-818-0419
ODYSSEY RE HOLDINGS CORP
(*Suby of* FAIRFAX FINANCIAL HOLDINGS LIMITED)
300 Stamford Pl, Stamford, CT 06902-6765
Tel (203) 977-8000 *Founded/Ownrshp* 2009
Sales NA *EMP* 721^E
SIC 6411 Insurance agents, brokers & service; Insurance agents & brokers; Fire insurance underwriters' laboratories
Pr: Andrew A Barnard
Pr: James Mortensen
CEO: Isabelle Dubots-Lafitte
CEO: Chris Gallagher
**CEO:* Brian D Young
**CFO:* Jan Christiansen
**CFO:* R Scott Donovan
CFO: Hervt Leduc
Bd of Dir: Francis D James
**Ofcr:* Michael G Wacek
**Ex VP:* Alane R Carey
Ex VP: Brian Quin
Ex VP: Michael Wacek
**Sr VP:* Peter H Lovell
Sr VP: Gary Maile
Sr VP: Anthony J Narciso
Sr VP: Elizabeth Sander
Sr VP: Mark Welshons
VP: Tom Bredahl
VP: Richard Coerver
VP: James J Danbrowney
Board of Directors: James F Dowd, Anthony F Griffiths, Alan D Horn, Brandon W Sweitzer, V Prem Watsa

D-U-N-S 17-814-6536
ODYSSEY REINSURANCE CO
(*Suby of* ODYSSEY RE HOLDINGS CORP) ★
300 Stamford Pl Ste 700, Stamford, CT 06902-6735
Tel (203) 965-0004 *Founded/Ownrshp* 2001
Sales NA *EMP* 340
SIC 6411 6361 6331 6324 6311 Insurance agents, brokers & service; Title insurance; Fire, marine & casualty insurance; Hospital & medical service plans; Life insurance
CEO: Brian D Young
Ex VP: Brian D Quinn
**Ex VP:* Michael G Wacek
**Sr VP:* James B Salvesen
VP: Tom Bredahl
VP: Francis Cerasoli
**VP:* Greg Horkachuck
VP: Roy Toppel
S&M/VP: John Ceci
Board of Directors: Greg Horkachuck, James B Salvesen, Michael G Wacek, Brian D Young

OE FILTERS
See MANN+HUMMEL PUROLATOR FILTERS LLC

OEC BUSINESS INTERIORS
See FORWARD SPACE LLC

D-U-N-S 08-530-5274 IMP/EXP
■ **OEC MEDICAL SYSTEMS INC**
(*Suby of* GENERAL ELECTRIC CO) ★
384 N Wright Brothers Dr, Salt Lake City, UT 84116-2862
Tel (801) 328-9300 *Founded/Ownrshp* 1999
Sales 196.3MM^E *EMP* 850
SIC 3844 7699 Radiographic X-ray apparatus & tubes; Fluoroscopic X-ray apparatus & tubes; X-ray equipment repair
Pr: Carrie Englintonmanner
**Pr:* Patrick McNamee
**Pr:* Joseph W Pepper
**Ex VP:* Larry E Harrawood
**VP:* Ann-Marie McElligott
Genl Mgr: Dick Call
Snr Mgr: Rick Cleveland

D-U-N-S 07-881-5579
OECO HOLDINGS LLC
(*Suby of* MEGGITT PLC)
4607 Se International Way, Milwaukie, OR 97222-4693
Tel (503) 659-5999 *Founded/Ownrshp* 1961
Sales 132.0MM^E *EMP* 425^E
SIC 3679 5065 Cores, magnetic; Electronic parts & equipment

D-U-N-S 00-902-4233 IMP
OECO LLC
(*Suby of* OECO HOLDINGS LLC) ★
4607 Se International Way, Milwaukie, OR 97222-4693
Tel (503) 659-5999 *Founded/Ownrshp* 1961, 2000
Sales 132.0MM^E *EMP* 425
SIC 3679 5065 4911 3621 3694 Cores, magnetic; Electronic parts & equipment; Generation, electric power; Frequency converters (electric generators); Battery charging generators, automobile & aircraft; Generators, automotive & aircraft
Pr: Jeramy Davis
**VP:* Eric Lardiere
**VP:* James Salita
Genl Mgr: Rich Dagostino
Genl Mgr: Teresa Knecht
Ql Cn Mgr: Fred Fleener
Sls Dir: Gary Turner

D-U-N-S 18-508-5149
OEM FABRICATORS INC
OEM MICRO
300 Mcmillan Rd, Woodville, WI 54028-9578
Tel (715) 698-2111 *Founded/Ownrshp* 1986
Sales 93.9MM^E *EMP* 485
SIC 3599

OEM MICRO
See OEM FABRICATORS INC

D-U-N-S 07-969-5964
OEP CAPITAL ADVISORS LP
ONE EQUITY PARTNERS
510 Madison Ave Fl 19, New York, NY 10022-5730
Tel (212) 277-1552 *Founded/Ownrshp* 2014
Sales 965.2MM^E *EMP* 2,901^E
SIC 6726 Management investment funds, closed-end
Sr VP: Torsten Strauch
VP: Brad Coppens
VP: Charles Gedge

D-U-N-S 11-832-5158 IMP/EXP
OERLIKON BALZERS COATING USA INC
(*Suby of* OERLIKON BALZERS COATING AG)
1475 E Wdfield Rd Ste 201, Schaumburg, IL 60173
Tel (847) 619-5541 *Founded/Ownrshp* 1984
Sales 113.1MM^E *EMP* 400
SIC 3479 3471 Coating of metals & formed products; Finishing, metals or formed products
CEO: Christian Kunz
**Pr:* Kent Connell
VP: Mario Vitale
Dir IT: Joaquin Hernandez
IT Man: Josh Abbitt
Tech Mgr: Juan Orozco
Plnt Mgr: Tom Vaeth
Mktg Dir: Thomas Schmalberger
Sales Asso: Joshua Miller

OERLIKON FAIRFIELD
See FAIRFIELD MANUFACTURING CO INC

D-U-N-S 00-533-2366 IMP/EXP
OERLIKON METCO (US) INC
(*Suby of* OERLIKON SURFACE SOLUTIONS AG, PFAFFIKON)
1101 Prospect Ave, Westbury, NY 11590-2724
Tel (516) 334-1300 *Founded/Ownrshp* 1950, 2014
Sales 131.4MM^E *EMP* 400
SIC 3399 5084 3479

D-U-N-S 06-000-2243
OERLIKON USA HOLDING INC
5700 Mellon Rd, Export, PA 15632-8900
Tel (303) 273-9700 *Founded/Ownrshp* 2000
Sales NA *EMP* 2,842
SIC 3563 3823 3699 3479 3599 5084

D-U-N-S 80-534-6462
OFC MANAGEMENT INC
ONTERIE FITNESS CENTER
(*Suby of* LAKESHORE MANAGEMENT GROUP INC) ★
446 E Ontario St 10-100, Chicago, IL 60611-4418
Tel (312) 642-0031 *Founded/Ownrshp* 2007
Sales 3.2MM^E *EMP* 1,464^E
SIC 7991 Health club
Prin: Michael N Kochevar

D-U-N-S 00-941-6934 IMP/EXP
OFD FOODS INC
OREGON FREEZE DRY
525 25th Ave Sw, Albany, OR 97322-4371
Tel (541) 926-6001 *Founded/Ownrshp* 2012
Sales 90.0MM^E *EMP* 400
SIC 2013 2015 2091 2032 2023 Sausages & other prepared meats; Poultry, processed; Fish, dried; Soups, except seafood: packaged in cans, jars, etc.; Dried milk preparations
CEO: James S Merryman
**Ch Bd:* Philip Unverzagt
CFO: Dale Bookwalter
Ofcr: James Desai
Ofcr: John Fitzgerald
Ofcr: John Ostrin
Sr VP: Jeni Billups
VP: Walter Pebley
VP: Fred Vetter
CIO: Dan Johnson
Sfty Mgr: Doug Richards

D-U-N-S 95-741-0475
OFFDUTYOFFICERS.COM
2365 La Mirada Dr, Vista, CA 92081-7863
Tel (888) 408-5900 *Founded/Ownrshp* 1993
Sales 31.5MM^E *EMP* 1,300
SIC 7381 8742 Security guard service; Management consulting services
Pr: Aram Minasian
**Mng Pt:* Terry Degelder
**CFO:* Kevin Hansen

D-U-N-S 03-200-8682
OFFEN PETROLEUM INC
5100 E 78th Ave, Commerce City, CO 80022-1458
Tel (303) 297-3835 *Founded/Ownrshp* 1997
Sales 621.1MM *EMP* 38
SIC 5172 5541

D-U-N-S 18-356-0952 IMP
OFFICE BASICS INC
22 Creek Cir, Boothwyn, PA 19061-3156
Tel (610) 471-1000 *Founded/Ownrshp* 1987
Sales 158.0MM^E *EMP* 175^E
SIC 5112 Stationery & office supplies
Pr: John Leighton
**Treas:* Richard Leighton

D-U-N-S 15-083-1758
■ **OFFICE CLUB INC**
OFFICE DEPOT
(*Suby of* OFFICE DEPOT INC) ★
2200 Germantown Rd, Delray Beach, FL 33445-8223
Tel (561) 438-4800 *Founded/Ownrshp* 1991
Sales 71.8MM^E *EMP* 2,200
SIC 5943 5112 Stationery stores; Office supplies
CEO: Juan Guerrero
Pr: Mark D Begelman
CFO: Barry J Goldstein
Ex VP: Elisa Garcia
Ex VP: Mike Newman
Sr VP: Michele Henderson
VP: Brian Turcotte
Comm Man: Rebecca Rakitin
Dist Mgr: Cary Marsh
Dist Mgr: Diane Miller
IT Man: Brett Bailey

OFFICE COASTAL ZONE MANAGEMENT
See MASSACHUSETTS EXECUTIVE OFFICE OF ENERGY & ENVIRONMENTAL AFFAIRS

OFFICE DEPOT
See OFFICE CLUB INC

D-U-N-S 15-353-1108 IMP
▲ **OFFICE DEPOT INC**
6600 N Military Trl, Boca Raton, FL 33496-2434
Tel (561) 438-4800 *Founded/Ownrshp* 1986
Sales 14.4MMM *EMP* 49,000
Tkr Sym ODP *Exch* NGS
SIC 5943 5044 5734 5045 Stationery stores; Office equipment; Computer & software stores; Personal computers; Computers, peripherals & software; Computers
Ch Bd: Roland C Smith
Pr: Mark Cosby
COO: Troy Rice
CFO: Stephen E Hare
Ofcr: Michael Allison
Ofcr: Steve Calkins
Ex VP: Juliet Johansson
Ex VP: Thomas Kroeger
Ex VP: Ronald Lalla
Ex VP: Barry Litwin
Ex VP: Monica Luchtefeld
Ex VP: Kim Maguire
Ex VP: Tim REA
Ex VP: Frank P Scruggs Jr
Sr VP: Tim Beauchamp
Sr VP: Teddy Chung
Sr VP: Todd Hale
Sr VP: Tom Markert
Sr VP: Kim Moehler
VP: Frank Betancourt
VP: Carl Brisco
Board of Directors: Warren F Bryant, Kristin A Campbell, Francesca Ruiz De Luzuriag, Cynthia T Jamison, V James Marino, Michael J Massey, David M Szymanski, Nigel Travis, Joseph Vassalluzzo

D-U-N-S 02-138-6255
OFFICE ENVIRONMENTS INC (NC)
11407 Granite St Ste B, Charlotte, NC 28273-6698
Tel (704) 714-7200 *Founded/Ownrshp* 1961
Sales 91.2MM^E *EMP* 73
SIC 5021 7641 7389 Office furniture; Office furniture repair & maintenance; Interior designer
CEO: Robert Maczka
**Pr:* Cynthia R Cox
Sales Exec: Barry Bale

OFFICE FISCAL ADMINISTRATION
See STATE OF OHIO OFFICE OF BUDGET AND MANAGEMENT STATE ACCOUNTING

OFFICE GRAPHIC DESIGN
See GRAPHIC CENTER GROUP CORP

D-U-N-S 94-399-2107
■ **OFFICE OF ASSISTANT SECRETARY FOR ADMINISTRATION AND MANAGEMENT**
OASAM
(*Suby of* UNITED STATES DEPARTMENT OF LABOR) ★
200 Constitution Ave Nw S-2203, Washington, DC 20210-0001
Tel (202) 693-4040 *Founded/Ownrshp* 1997
Sales NA *EMP* 6,000^E
SIC 9651 Labor regulatory agency;
Prin: Michael Kerr
CFO: Kim Veney
**Ofcr:* Chris Yerxa
CIO: Gwellnar Bank
IT Man: Evelyn Kelb
IT Man: Steven Van Arsdel

OFFICE OF THE ATTORNEY GENERAL
See NEW JERSEY DEPT OF LAW & PUBLIC SAFETY

OFFICE OF CAMPUS COUNSEL
See UNIVERSITY OF CALIFORNIA IRVINE

OFFICE OF CONTRACTING AND PROC
See GOVERNMENT OF DISTRICT OF COLUMBIA

OFFICE OF THE CONTROLLER
See BUCKS COUNTY OF

OFFICE OF COUNTY ADMINISTRATOR
See COUNTY OF HAMILTON

OFFICE OF THE DIRECTOR
See UNITED STATES DEPT OF GEOLOGICAL SURVEY

OFFICE OF ECONOMIC STIMULUS
See EXECUTIVE OFFICE OF STATE OF NEW HAMPSHIRE

OFFICE OF THE GOVERNOR
See EXECUTIVE OFFICE OF VIRGINIA

OFFICE OF THE GOVERNOR
See EXECUTIVE OFFICE OF STATE OF ALASKA

OFFICE OF INSPECTOR GENERAL
See US DEPARTMENT OF COMMERCE

D-U-N-S 80-747-7963
OFFICE OF LEGISLATIVE COUNSEL
(*Suby of* STATE OF CALIFORNIA) ★
State Cpitol Bldg Rm 3021, Sacramento, CA 95814
Tel (916) 341-8000 *Founded/Ownrshp* 1913
Sales NA *EMP* 1,600
SIC 9121 Legislative bodies, state & local;
Prin: Diane Boyer-Vine

OFFICE OF MAYOR
See CITY OF MILWAUKEE

OFFICE OF NATIONAL RESPONSE
See EMPLOYMENT AND TRAINING ADMINISTRATION

D-U-N-S 16-004-2354
■ **OFFICE OF OCEANIC AND ATMOSPHERIC RESEARCH**
(*Suby of* NATIONAL OCEANIC AND ATMOSPHERIC ADMINISTRATION) ★
1315 E West Hwy Fl 11, Silver Spring, MD 20910-6233
Tel (301) 713-2458 *Founded/Ownrshp* 1970
Sales NA *EMP* 1,805^E
SIC 9511 Air, water & solid waste management;
Prin: Richard Spinrad
Prgrm Mgr: John Cortinas

OFFICE OF THE PRESIDENT
See SUNY UNIVERSITY AT BUFFALO

OFFICE OF THE PRESIDENT
See UNIVERSITY OF NORTH CAROLINA

D-U-N-S 96-479-4353
■ **OFFICE OF REGULATORY AFFAIRS**
(*Suby of* FDA- OFM) ★
10903 Nh Ave Wo31 Rm 3528, Silver Spring, MD 20993-0001
Tel (301) 796-8800 *Founded/Ownrshp* 2010
Sales NA *EMP* 3,044^E
SIC 9431 Administration of public health programs;

OFFICE OF THE SECRETARY
See LOUISIANA DEPARTMENT OF ENVIRONMENTAL QUALITY

OFFICE OF THE SECRETARY STATE
See EXECUTIVE OFFICE OF STATE OF ALABAMA

OFFICE OF SPONSORED PROGRAMS
See GEORGIA TECH RESEARCH CORP

OFFICE OF SPONSORED PROGRAMS
See GEORGIA TECH APPLIED RESEARCH CORP

OFFICE OF THE SUPERINTENDENT
See HAWAII STATE DEPARTMENT OF EDUCATION

D-U-N-S 87-982-6139
■ OFFICE OF THE COMPTROLLER OF THE CURRENCY
O C C
(*Suby of* UNITED STATES DEPT OF TREASURY) ★
400 7th St Sw Ste 3e218, Washington, DC 20219-0006
Tel (202) 649-6800 *Founded/Ownrshp* 1863
Sales NA *EMP* 4,000
Accts Gka Pc Washington Dc
SIC 9651 Banking regulatory agency, government;
Ofcr: Paul Ginger
Adm Dir: Karen Smith
**CIO:* Edward J Dorris
IT Man: Bernard Colebrook
Info Man: Wesley Wilbur

D-U-N-S 78-485-9167
■ OFFICE OF THE INSPECTOR GENERAL
DCIS
(*Suby of* OFFICE OF THE SECRETARY OF DEFENSE) ★
4800 Mark Center Dr, Alexandria, VA 22350-0002
Tel (703) 604-8669 *Founded/Ownrshp* 1982
Sales NA *EMP* 1,538
SIC 9711 National security;
Prin: Gordon Heddell
Snr Mgr: Brett Mansfield

D-U-N-S 02-883-7123
■ OFFICE OF THE SECRETARY OF DEFENSE
(*Suby of* UNITED STATES DEPARTMENT OF DEFENSE) ★
1400 Defense Pentagon, Washington, DC 20301-1400
Tel (703) 545-6700 *Founded/Ownrshp* 1947
Sales NA *EMP* 1,346,022
SIC 9711 National security;
Genl Couns: Paul Black

OFFICE OF THE TREASURER
See CITY OF CHELSEA

D-U-N-S 16-158-0469
■ OFFICE OF THRIFT SUPERVISION
O T S
(*Suby of* UNITED STATES DEPT OF TREASURY) ★
1700 G St Nw, Washington, DC 20552-0003
Tel (202) 906-6900 *Founded/Ownrshp* 1989
Sales NA *EMP* 1,269
Accts Deva & Associates Pc
SIC 9651 Financial regulatory agency;

D-U-N-S 17-815-7699
OFFICE RESOURCES INC
O R I
263 Summer St, Boston, MA 02210-1506
Tel (617) 423-9100 *Founded/Ownrshp* 1991
Sales 87.3MM^E *EMP* 236
SIC 5021 Office furniture
VP: Mike Dignard
**Pr:* Paul J Fraser
**Treas:* Kevin Barbary
Sr VP: Rob Tenaglia
VP: Steve Chiocco
VP: Nadim Jamal
VP: Ray Theberge
Mktg Dir: Kelsey Simonds

OFFICE SCIENCE CHICAGO OFFICE
See US DEPT OF ENERGY CHICAGO OFFICE

OFFICE WKRS CMPNSTION PROGRAMS
See EMPLOYMENT STANDARDS ADMINISTRATION

D-U-N-S 17-892-3231 IMP/EXP
■ OFFICEMAX CONTRACT INC
(*Suby of* OFFICEMAX INC) ★
263 Shuman Blvd, Naperville, IL 60563-1255
Tel (630) 438-7800 *Founded/Ownrshp* 1995
Sales 254.4MM^E *EMP* 1,411
SIC 5021 5112 5044 5111 5943 5712

D-U-N-S 00-907-3099 IMP/EXP
■ OFFICEMAX INC
(*Suby of* OFFICE DEPOT INC) ★
6600 N Military Trl, Boca Raton, FL 33496-2434
Tel (630) 438-7800 *Founded/Ownrshp* 2013
Sales 3.6MMM^E *EMP* 29,000^E
SIC 5943 5021 Stationery stores; Office forms & supplies; School supplies; Writing supplies; Office furniture
Pr: Ravichandra K Saligram
Pr: John Kenning
Pr: Michael Lewis
CEO: Steve Miller
COO: Samuel M Martin
Treas: Tony Giuliano
Bd of Dir: Rachel Deane
Ofcr: James Barr IV
Ofcr: Bruce H Besanko
Ofcr: Stephen B Parsons
Ofcr: Steve Parsons
Ex VP: Matthew R Broad
Ex VP: Kim Feil
Ex VP: Ann Hewitt
Ex VP: Ronald Lalla
Ex VP: Deborah Oconnor
Sr VP: David Armstrong
Sr VP: Larry Hartley
Sr VP: Deb O'Connor
Sr VP: Bob Thacker
Sr VP: Scott Williams

OFFICESCAPES
See JUPITER I LLC

D-U-N-S 05-844-6022
OFFSET PAPERBACK MFRS INC
STUDIO PRINT GROUP
(*Suby of* BERRYVILLE GRAPHICS INC) ★
2211 Memorial Hwy, Dallas, PA 18612-9244
Tel (570) 675-5261 *Founded/Ownrshp* 1980
Sales 143.8MM^E *EMP* 750
SIC 2731 2752 Book publishing; Commercial printing, offset
Pr: David Liess
**CFO:* Richard R Pincofski
VP: Jack O'Donnell
**VP:* Jack Odonnell
**VP:* William L Rogers
Off Mgr: Tressa Schwartz
Netwrk Eng: Brian Bedosky
Plnt Mgr: Bob Scheifflee
Prd Mgr: Dave Thomas

D-U-N-S 83-755-7974 IMP
OFFSHORE DRILLING CO
TODCO
(*Suby of* TRANSOCEAN INC) ★
24 Concord Rd, Houma, LA 70360-7561
Tel (985) 876-6987 *Founded/Ownrshp* 2001
Sales 45.2MM^E *EMP* 1,300
SIC 1381 Drilling oil & gas wells
Pr: Steven A Webster
VP: Don Rodney

D-U-N-S 07-261-4845 IMP
OFFSHORE ENERGY SERVICES (LA)
5900 Highway 90 E, Broussard, LA 70518-5701
Tel (337) 837-1024 *Founded/Ownrshp* 1974
Sales 372.4MM^E *EMP* 490
SIC 1389 Oil field services
Pr: Charles M Garber
VP: Samuel Broussard
**VP:* Roy Garber
Prd Mgr: Rudy Roy
Ql Cn Mgr: Kirk Pepper

D-U-N-S 83-032-2173 IMP
OFFSHORE INLAND MARINE & OILFIELD SERVICES INC
(*Suby of* OIMO HOLDINGS INC) ★
700 S Barracks St, Pensacola, FL 32502-6049
Tel (251) 443-5550 *Founded/Ownrshp* 2001
Sales 96.6MM^E *EMP* 125^E
SIC 1389 Oil field services; Oil consultants; Gas field services
CEO: Robin D Roberts
**VP:* Crystal Yasurek

D-U-N-S 87-432-5822
OFFSHORE MARINE CONTRACTORS INC
OMC
133 W 113th St, Cut Off, LA 70345-3639
Tel (985) 632-7927 *Founded/Ownrshp* 1994
Sales 120.8MM^E *EMP* 200
SIC 1389 Servicing oil & gas wells
CEO: Michael M Eymard
**Pr:* Louis Eymard II
**Sec:* Raimy D Eymard
Bd of Dir: Brad Wildey
**Sr VP:* Avis J Bourg Jr
Genl Mgr: Jordan Orgeron

D-U-N-S 05-458-9176 IMP/EXP
OFFSHORE RENTAL LTD
TIGER TANKS OFFSHORE RENTAL
1655 Louisiana St, Beaumont, TX 77701-1120
Tel (409) 833-2665 *Founded/Ownrshp* 1998
Sales 230.4MM^E *EMP* 1,500^E
SIC 2911 Oils, fuel
CEO: Will Crenshaw
**CFO:* Brian Bomer
**Prin:* Casey Crenshaw

D-U-N-S 06-467-6281
OFFSHORE SERVICE VESSELS LLC
EDISON CHOUEST OFFSHORE
16201 E Main St, Cut Off, LA 70345-3804
Tel (985) 601-4444 *Founded/Ownrshp* 2010
Sales 294.1MM^E *EMP* 1,000
SIC 4491 Marine cargo handling
CFO: Charles Comeaux
Sr VP: Rick Fox
Exec: Lindsay Guidry
Genl Mgr: Lee Bouziga
CTO: Rogerio Lacourt
Sfty Dirs: Louis Richmond
Opers Mgr: Emile Parra
Opers Mgr: Roddy Pitre
Counsel: Renata Palagi

D-U-N-S 01-475-0843
▲ OFG BANCORP
254 Ave Munoz Rivera Fl 8, San Juan, PR 00918-1900
Tel (787) 771-6800 *Founded/Ownrshp* 1996
Sales NA *EMP* 1,466^E
Tkr Sym OFG *Exch* NYS
SIC 6022 State commercial banks
Pr: Jose R Fernandez
**Ch Bd:* Julian S Inclan
CFO: Ganesh Kumar
Treas: Ramon Rosado
Sr VP: Maritza Arizmendi
Sr VP: Cesar Ortiz

D-U-N-S 00-636-4434 IMP/EXP
OFS BRANDS HOLDINGS INC
1204 E 6th St, Huntingburg, IN 47542-9375
Tel (800) 521-5381 *Founded/Ownrshp* 1937
Sales 202.7MM^E *EMP* 2,000
SIC 2521 2522 2511 2599 Wood office furniture; Office furniture, except wood; Wood household furniture; Hospital furniture, except beds
Pr: Robert H Menke Jr
**Ch Bd:* Joseph Bellino
**CFO:* Jim Huebner
**Sr VP:* Jeff Eckert
**Sr VP:* Ryan Menke
**Sr VP:* Michael Wagner
Dist Mgr: Loretta Shamsey
Genl Mgr: Steve Robinson
DP Exec: Michael Bell
IT Man: Kim Schwindel
Software D: John Hulsman
Board of Directors: Karen Middendorf, Arthur Nordhoff, Jeff Weir, Dr William Williams

D-U-N-S 08-449-3506 IMP
OFS BRIGHTWAVE LLC
(*Suby of* FURUKAWA ELECTRIC CO.,LTD.)
2000 Northeast Expy, Norcross, GA 30071-2932
Tel (770) 798-3000 *Founded/Ownrshp* 2005
Sales 331.2MM^E *EMP* 2,300^E
SIC 3357 3229 Fiber optic cable (insulated); Pressed & blown glass
Ofcr: Toshiya Hirose

D-U-N-S 08-374-8611 IMP/EXP
OFS FITEL LLC
O F S
(*Suby of* FURUKAWA ELECTRIC CO.,LTD.)
2000 Northeast Expy, Norcross, GA 30071-2932
Tel (770) 798-2000 *Founded/Ownrshp* 2001
Sales 470.9MM^E *EMP* 1,400
SIC 3229 3357 Pressed & blown glass; Fiber optic cable (insulated)
Ch Bd: Timothy F Murray
**Ex VP:* Patrice Dubois
**Sr VP:* Gudmund Knudsen
**Sr VP:* Robert Lake
VP: Stephanie Street
Mktg Dir: Fernando Costantino
Mktg Mgr: Stephen Cardone
Manager: Tim Swink

D-U-N-S 00-624-5658
OFTEDAL CONSTRUCTION INC
434 Highway 59 N 59n, Miles City, MT 59301-6318
Tel (406) 232-5911 *Founded/Ownrshp* 1970
Sales 100.8MM^E *EMP* 250
SIC 1629 3273 1611 Earthmoving contractor; Dam construction; Land reclamation; Ready-mixed concrete; General contractor, highway & street construction
Pr: Jeff McDonald
**Pr:* James Halvor Fuglevand
**CFO:* Roy Thorneycroft
**Ch:* William Oftedal
**VP:* Greg Jackson
**VP:* Cameron G Lundby
IT Man: Jacie Smith
Sfty Dirs: Payton Zierolf
Mtls Mgr: John Lampert

OGDEN
See CHROMALOX INC

D-U-N-S 19-925-0119
OGDEN ARNOT MEDICAL CENTER
(*Suby of* ARNOT HEALTH INC) ★
600 Roe Ave, Elmira, NY 14905-1676
Tel (607) 737-4100 *Founded/Ownrshp* 1972
Sales 212.3MM *EMP* 2,400
SIC 8011 Medical centers
CEO: Robert Lambert
**CFO:* Ronald Kintz
Dir Lab: Barbara Lawrence
Dir Lab: Barry Winters
Dir Rx: William Bacon
Dir Rx: Hazel Boyd
Comm Man: Nancy Kujawski
Off Mgr: Lisa Donegan
Off Mgr: Laurie Randolph
CTO: Kathy Wilkens
Info Man: Scott Perry

D-U-N-S 18-435-3480
OGDEN CITY SCHOOL DISTRICT
1950 Monroe Blvd, Ogden, UT 84401-0619
Tel (801) 737-8000 *Founded/Ownrshp* 1955
Sales 126.8MM *EMP* 115
SIC 8211 Elementary & secondary schools; Public elementary school
Bd of Dir: Shane Story
Pr Dir: Zac Williams

D-U-N-S 00-431-9703
OGDEN NEWSPAPERS INC (WV)
INTELLIGENCER, THE
1500 Main St, Wheeling, WV 26003-2826
Tel (304) 233-0100 *Founded/Ownrshp* 1890
Sales 561.0MM^E *EMP* 3,520
SIC 2711 2754 2741 2791 2752 Newspapers: publishing only, not printed on site; Job printing, gravure; Directories: publishing & printing; Typesetting; Commercial printing, lithographic
Pr: Robert M Nutting
**Ch:* G Ogden Nutting
Treas: Duane Wittman
VP: Bart Leath
**VP:* William C Nutting
Genl Mgr: Perry Nardo
Genl Mgr: Don Smith
CTO: Wojciechowski Katherine
MIS Dir: Dave Frisch
IT Man: Cindy Gross
Software D: Michael Smith

OGDEN REGIONAL MEDICAL CENTER
See COLUMBIA OGDEN MEDICAL CENTER INC

OGE ENERGY
See ENABLE OKLAHOMA INTRASTATE TRANSMISSION LLC

D-U-N-S 96-386-0044
▲ OGE ENERGY CORP
321 N Harvey Ave, Oklahoma City, OK 73102-3405
Tel (405) 553-3000 *Founded/Ownrshp* 1995
Sales 2.2MMM *EMP* 2,586^E
Tkr Sym OGE *Exch* NYS
SIC 4911 4922 4925 Distribution, electric power; Generation, electric power; Transmission, electric power; ; Natural gas transmission; Storage, natural gas; Gas production and/or distribution
Ch Bd: Sean Trauschke
CFO: Stephen E Merrill
Treas: Charles B Walworth
VP: Patricia D Horn
VP: Jean C Leger Jr
VP: Cristina F McQuistion
VP: Paul L Renfrow
VP: Fred Schmidt
Ex Dir: Joey Garza
CTO: Stephanie Abrahamson
Software D: James Ryan
Board of Directors: Frank A Bozich, James H Brandi, Luke R Corbett, John D Groendyke, David L Hauser, Kirk Humphreys, Robert O Lorenz, Judy R McReynolds, Sheila G Talton

OGIHARA AMERICA COR
See THAI SUMMIT AMERICA CORP

OGILVY & MATHER WORLDWIDE
See OGILVY GROUP LLC

D-U-N-S 15-277-2315
OGILVY & MATHER WORLDWIDE INC
(*Suby of* WPP 2005 LIMITED)
636 11th Ave, New York, NY 10036-2005
Tel (212) 237-4000 *Founded/Ownrshp* 1989
Sales 828.6MM^E *EMP* 15,000
SIC 7311 7812 7375 8742 Advertising agencies; Motion picture & video production; Information retrieval services; Marketing consulting services
CEO: John Seifert
Sr Pt: Steve Bender
Sr Pt: Alvaro Cabrera
Sr Pt: Colin Drummond
Sr Pt: Kurt Lundberg
Sr Pt: Sean Remler
Sr Pt: Rafael Reyes
Sr Pt: Gerri Stone
V Ch: Steve Hayden
Pr: Lee Newman
Pr: Jacco Ter Schegget
Pr: Gunther Schumacher
CEO: Lou Aversano
CEO: Steve Harding
CEO: Carla Hendra
COO: Laird Stiefvater
CFO: Steve Goldstein
Ch: Christopher Graves
Ch: John Seifert
Ch: Miles Young
Sr Cor Off: Bob Donovan
Board of Directors: Angel Chen, Sean Muzzy, Sam Williams-Thomas

D-U-N-S 00-892-0233
OGILVY GROUP LLC
OGILVY & MATHER WORLDWIDE
(*Suby of* W P P) ★
636 11th Ave, New York, NY 10036-2005
Tel (212) 237-4000 *Founded/Ownrshp* 2008
Sales 998.5MM^E *EMP* 18,000
SIC 7311 8743 8748 7336 7361 8732 Advertising agencies; Public relations & publicity; Communications consulting; Graphic arts & related design; Employment agencies; Market analysis or research
CEO: Miles Young
Sr Pt: Kimberly Duffy
Sr Pt: Debra Fried
Sr Pt: Chris Halsall
Sr Pt: Jennifer Peterson
Pt: Lauren Crampsie
Pt: Sue Funkhouser
Pt: Hilary Love
Pt: Jessica Pezzullo
**Ch Bd:* Rochelle Lazarus
**CFO:* Steven Goldstein
**Ofcr:* Corinna Falusi
Ex VP: Angela Johnson
Ex VP: Jennifer Wayman
Sr VP: Alda Abbracciamento
Sr VP: Gemma Craven
VP: Nicholas Ludlum
VP: Melissa Ng
Exec: Martin Lange
Assoc Dir: Sarah Howell
Assoc Dir: Gregory Lefave

D-U-N-S 09-296-8502 EXP
OGILVY PUBLIC RELATIONS WORLDWIDE INC
(*Suby of* WPP 2005 LIMITED)
636 11th Ave, New York, NY 10036-2005
Tel (212) 880-5200 *Founded/Ownrshp* 1989
Sales 132.4MM^E *EMP* 1,500
SIC 8743 8999 Public relations & publicity; Communication services
CEO: Christopher Graves
Ch Bd: Marcia Silverman
Pr: Mitch Markson
CEO: Paul Hicks
CFO: Andrew Kochar
Ex VP: Rachel Caggiano
Ex VP: Monique Da Silva
Ex VP: Chris Fillip
Ex VP: Suzanne O'Leary Lopez
Ex VP: Michelle Rios
Ex VP: Kerry Sette
Ex VP: Tony Silva
Ex VP: Andrew Silver
Ex VP: Melissa Smith
Sr VP: Emily Bader
Sr VP: Geoffrey Colon
Sr VP: Beth Haiken
Sr VP: Richard Lukstat
Sr VP: Stephen Marino
Sr VP: Mark O'Connor
Sr VP: Cindy Oertel

D-U-N-S 10-333-6835
OGLEBAY RESORT CONFERENCE CENTER
Rr 88 Box N, Wheeling, WV 26003
Tel (304) 243-4063 *Founded/Ownrshp* 1925
Sales 1.8MM *EMP* 1,700
SIC 7011 7992 5812 Resort hotel, franchised; Public golf courses; Eating places
CEO: Doug Dalby
VP: Kenneth Morgan

OGLETHORPE POWER
See CENTRAL GEORGIA ELECTRIC MEMBERSHIP CORP

D-U-N-S 07-346-0305 IMP
OGLETHORPE POWER CORP
2100 E Exch Pl Ste 203, Tucker, GA 30084
Tel (770) 270-7600 Founded/Ownrshp 1974
Sales 1.3MMM EMP 265E
Accts Ernst & Young Llp Atlanta Ge
SIC 4911 Generation, electric power
Pr: Michael L Smith
*Ch Bd: Bobby C Smith Jr
COO: Michael W Price
COO: William F Ussery
CFO: Elizabeth B Higgins
Bd of Dir: Ken Rosanski
Sr VP: Annalisa M Bloodworth
Sr VP: Lori K Holt
Sr VP: W Clayton Robbins
Sr VP: Keith D Russell
Sr VP: Charles W Whitney
VP: Thomas Brendiar
VP: Jim Messersmith
VP: Toni M Presnell
VP: Keith Russell
Board of Directors: George L Weaver, C Hill Bentley, James I White, Ronald Duffey, M Anthony Ham, Ernest A Jakins III, Fred A McWhorter, Marshall S Millwood, Jeffrey W Murphy, Danny L Nichols, Sammy G Simonton

D-U-N-S 08-019-4946
OGLETREE DEAKINS NASH SMOAK & STEWART PC
1243 N 10th St Ste 210, Milwaukee, WI 53205-2566
Tel (414) 239-6400 Founded/Ownrshp 2016
Sales 12.2MME EMP 1,500
SIC 8111 General practice attorney, lawyer
Prin: Timothy G Costello

D-U-N-S 08-342-1131
OGLETREE DEAKINS NASH SMOAK & STEWART PC
300 N Main St Ste 500, Greenville, SC 29601-2195
Tel (864) 271-1300 Founded/Ownrshp 1977
Sales 401.3MME EMP 1,308
SIC 8111

OH BOY OBERTO
See OBERTO SAUSAGE CO

O.H. KRUSE GRAIN AND MILLING
See WESTERN MILLING LLC

D-U-N-S 18-005-0387 IMP
OHASHITECHNICA USA INC
(Suby of OHASHITECHNICA INC.)
111 Burrer Dr, Sunbury, OH 43074-9323
Tel (740) 965-5115 Founded/Ownrshp 1953
Sales 90.0MM EMP 70
SIC 5013 5072 3452 Automotive supplies & parts; Automotive supplies; Hardware; Bolts, nuts, rivets & washers
*Pr: Hikaru Tateiwa
Treas: Trish Burnside

D-U-N-S 07-997-5091
OHI PARENT INC
(Suby of KOHLBERG & CO) ★
111 Radio Circle Dr, Mount Kisco, NY 10549-2609
Tel (914) 241-7430 Founded/Ownrshp 2012
Sales 3.3MME EMP 4,237E
SIC 8641 Booster club
Pr: Ron Childress
*CFO: Gary Edwards

OHIO ADJUTANT GENERAL
See OHIO NATIONAL GUARD

D-U-N-S 00-790-1093
■ OHIO BELL TELEPHONE CO
AT&T OHIO
(Suby of AT&T MIDWEST) ★
45 Erieview Plz, Cleveland, OH 44114-1801
Tel (216) 822-3439 Founded/Ownrshp 1984
Sales 804.8MME EMP 7,971
SIC 4813 8721 Local & long distance telephone communications; Local telephone communications; Voice telephone communications; Data telephone communications; Billing & bookkeeping service

D-U-N-S 62-708-2209
OHIO BUREAU OF WORKERS COMPENSATION
(Suby of EXECUTIVE OFFICE STATE OF OHIO) ★
30 W Spring St Fl 2-29, Columbus, OH 43215-2216
Tel (614) 644-6292 Founded/Ownrshp 1911
Sales NA EMP 3,000
Accts Schneider Downs & Co Inc C
SIC 6331 9199 Workers' compensation insurance; General government administration
Ofcr: Sarah Morrison
Ex Dir: Bernard Susko
IT Man: King Hill
IT Man: Keith Reiley
Counsel: Thomas Sico

D-U-N-S 00-806-9534
OHIO BUSINESS DEVELOPMENT COALITION
41 S High St Ste 3625, Columbus, OH 43215-6112
Tel (614) 469-1044 Founded/Ownrshp 2007
Sales 390.3MM EMP 2E
Accts Rea & Associates Inc Cpa S Du
SIC 8611 Business associations
Prin: Richard Stoff

D-U-N-S 78-657-0494
OHIO CARPENTERS PENSION FUND
3611 Chester Ave, Cleveland, OH 44114-4622
Tel (330) 652-3475 Founded/Ownrshp 2006
Sales 111.5MM EMP 8E
Accts Ciuni & Panichi Inc Beachwood
SIC 6722 Management investment, open-end
Prin: Roger Newman

D-U-N-S 05-444-0920
OHIO CASUALTY CORP (OH)
(Suby of LIBERTY MUTUAL INSURANCE CO) ★
9450 Seward Rd, Fairfield, OH 45014-5412
Tel (513) 603-2400 Founded/Ownrshp 1969, 2007
Sales NA EMP 2,114
SIC 6331 Fire, marine & casualty insurance: stock; Property damage insurance; Automobile insurance; Workers' compensation insurance
Pr: Mike Winner
Treas: Kelly Hicks
Ex VP: John S Buby
Sr VP: Elizabeth M Riczko
Sr VP: Derrick D Shannon
VP: Dennis McDaniel
VP: Cassy Morgan
VP: Howard Sloneker
Sftwr Eng: Brian Cornell
Sftwr Eng: Alicia Grout
Sftwr Eng: Dennis Huntington

OHIO CASUALTY INSURANCE
See OHIO NATIONAL LIFE INSURANCE CO

D-U-N-S 00-790-3040
OHIO CASUALTY INSURANCE CO
(Suby of OHIO CASUALTY CORP) ★
9450 Seward Rd, Fairfield, OH 45014-5412
Tel (800) 843-6446 Founded/Ownrshp 1919
Sales NA EMP 2,114
SIC 6331 6311 Fire, marine & casualty insurance; Workers' compensation insurance; Fire, marine & casualty insurance: stock; Life insurance carriers
CEO: Dan R Carmichael
COO: Cindy Cox
*Sr VP: Debra K Crane
*Sr VP: Ralph G Goode
*Sr VP: John S Kellington
*Sr VP: Thomas E Schadler
*Sr VP: Howard Sloneker
*Sr VP: Howard L Sloneker III
*Sr VP: Michael E Sullivan

OHIO COMMUNITY MEDIA
See OCM LLC

D-U-N-S 02-276-2331
■ OHIO CVS STORES LLC
(Suby of CVS HEALTH CORP) ★
641 Graham Rd, Cuyahoga Falls, OH 44221-1048
Tel (330) 922-1298 Founded/Ownrshp 2009
Sales 29.6MME EMP 2,882E
SIC 5912 Proprietary (non-prescription medicine) stores

D-U-N-S 00-503-6264 IMP/EXP
OHIO DECORATIVE PRODUCTS LLC (OH)
220 S Elizabeth St, Spencerville, OH 45887-1315
Tel (419) 647-9033 Founded/Ownrshp 1970
Sales 166.7MME EMP 1,200
SIC 3086 3369 3471 3363 Plastics foam products; Zinc & zinc-base alloy castings, except die-castings; Plating & polishing; Aluminum die-castings
Pr: Charles D Moeller
*Pr: Candace Moeller
*Sec: Donald L Jerwers
*VP: Rick Moeller
*Prin: George J Bowers
*Prin: Charles E Neuman
Plnt Mgr: Sonny Degan

D-U-N-S 80-884-7578
OHIO DEPARTMENT OF ADMINISTRATIVE SERVICES
(Suby of EXECUTIVE OFFICE STATE OF OHIO) ★
30 E Broad St Fl 39, Columbus, OH 43215-3414
Tel (614) 466-6511 Founded/Ownrshp 1973
Sales NA EMP 5,731
SIC 9199 General government administration;
IT Man: Jim Arens
IT Man: Scott Feilhamer

D-U-N-S 80-955-0163
OHIO DEPARTMENT OF DEVELOPMENTAL DISABILITIES
DODD
(Suby of EXECUTIVE OFFICE STATE OF OHIO) ★
30 E Broad St Fl 13, Columbus, OH 43215-3414
Tel (614) 728-5544 Founded/Ownrshp 1838
Sales NA EMP 5,000
SIC 9441 Administration of social & manpower programs;
Genl Mgr: Jessica Levy

D-U-N-S 80-937-6072
OHIO DEPARTMENT OF JOB AND FAMILY SERVICES
ODJFS
(Suby of EXECUTIVE OFFICE STATE OF OHIO) ★
30 E Broad St Fl 32, Columbus, OH 43215-3414
Tel (614) 466-6282 Founded/Ownrshp 1937
Sales NA EMP 3,600
SIC 9441 Administration of social & human resources;
IT Man: Marvene Mitchell

D-U-N-S 80-955-0106
OHIO DEPARTMENT OF MENTAL HEALTH
MHAS
30 E Broad St Fl 8, Columbus, OH 43215-3414
Tel (614) 466-2337 Founded/Ownrshp 1838
Sales 81.5MME EMP 2,500
SIC 8052

D-U-N-S 80-884-7669
OHIO DEPARTMENT OF MENTAL HEALTH AND ADDICTION SERVICES
(Suby of EXECUTIVE OFFICE STATE OF OHIO) ★
30 E Broad St Fl 11, Columbus, OH 43215-3414
Tel (614) 466-2337 Founded/Ownrshp 1989
Sales NA EMP 3,000
SIC 9431 Administration of public health programs;
*CFO: Rosaland Tye
Off Mgr: Michele Sherman

D-U-N-S 80-917-2638
OHIO DEPARTMENT OF NATURAL RESOURCES
(Suby of EXECUTIVE OFFICE STATE OF OHIO) ★
2045 Morse Rd Bldg D-3, Columbus, OH 43229-6605
Tel (614) 265-6875 Founded/Ownrshp 1949
Sales NA EMP 2,000
SIC 9512 Land, mineral & wildlife conservation;
Genl Mgr: Michael Eberhardt
IT Man: Paula Jones
IT Man: Stacy Xenakis

D-U-N-S 80-884-7842
OHIO DEPARTMENT OF PUBLIC SAFETY
(Suby of EXECUTIVE OFFICE STATE OF OHIO) ★
1970 W Broad St Fl 5, Columbus, OH 43223-1102
Tel (614) 466-3383 Founded/Ownrshp 1925
Sales NA EMP 4,000
SIC 9229 Public order & safety statistics centers;
Ofcr: Rich Nagel
CIO: John Conomy
CIO: Ken Kreitel
Telecom Mg: Lori Click
Telecom Mg: Lydia Wagner
Netwrk Mgr: Kathy Bryan

D-U-N-S 80-917-4501
OHIO DEPARTMENT OF REHABILITATION AND CORRECTION
(Suby of EXECUTIVE OFFICE STATE OF OHIO) ★
770 W Broad St, Columbus, OH 43222-1419
Tel (614) 752-1233 Founded/Ownrshp 1972
Sales NA EMP 13,600
SIC 9223 Prison, government;
IT Man: Ollie Chandler

D-U-N-S 80-917-2356
OHIO DEPARTMENT OF TAXATION
(Suby of EXECUTIVE OFFICE STATE OF OHIO) ★
30 E Broad St Fl 22, Columbus, OH 43215-3414
Tel (614) 466-3020 Founded/Ownrshp 1939
Sales NA EMP 1,300
SIC 9311 Taxation;

D-U-N-S 80-917-4402
OHIO DEPARTMENT OF TRANSPORTATION
(Suby of EXECUTIVE OFFICE STATE OF OHIO) ★
1980 W Broad St, Columbus, OH 43223-1102
Tel (614) 466-7170 Founded/Ownrshp 1975
Sales NA EMP 6,500
SIC 9621 Regulation, administration of transportation;
Ex Dir: Matthew Dietrich
CIO: Chris Chapman
Dir IT: Spencer Woods
IT Man: Marvin Harris
Opers Mgr: Michael T Gramza II

OHIO DEPARTMENT YOUTH SERVICES
See STATE OF OHIO

D-U-N-S 00-699-8371
■ OHIO EDISON CO (OH)
(Suby of FIRSTENERGY CORP) ★
76 S Main St Bsmt, Akron, OH 44308-1817
Tel (800) 736-3402 Founded/Ownrshp 1930
Sales 719.6MME EMP 1,190E
Accts Pricewaterhousecoopes Lp Clev
SIC 4911 Electric services; Generation, electric power; Transmission, electric power; Distribution, electric power
Pr: Charles E Jones Jr
CFO: R H Marsh
*CFO: James F Pearson
Ex VP: Leila Vespoli
*VP: Harvey L Wagner
Board of Directors: Anthony J Alexander, Mark T Clark

OHIO ELECTRIC MOTORS
See PEERLESS-WINSMITH INC

D-U-N-S 05-223-3042
OHIO ENVIRONMENTAL PROTECTION AGENCY
50 W Town St Ste 700, Columbus, OH 43215-4173
Tel (614) 644-3020 Founded/Ownrshp 1972
Sales NA EMP 1,100E
SIC 9511 Environmental protection agency, government
IT Man: Antionette Antion

OHIO ENVMTL PROTECTION AGCY
See STATE OF OHIO OFFICE OF BUDGET AND MANAGEMENT STATE ACCOUNTING

D-U-N-S 00-790-3263
OHIO FARMERS INSURANCE CO
WEST FIELD GROUP
1 Park Cir, Westfield Center, OH 44251-9700
Tel (800) 243-0210 Founded/Ownrshp 1848
Sales NA EMP 2,319
SIC 6411 6331 Property & casualty insurance agent; Fire, marine & casualty insurance
Pr: Robert Joyce
Pr: Jim Clay
COO: Roger McManus
Treas: Robert Krisowaty
Ofcr: Ed Largent
Trst Ofcr: Jerome Grant
Prin: Robert J Joyce
Div Mgr: Connie Frey
Genl Mgr: Alex Mosyjowski
CTO: Stuart Rosenberg
DP Dir: Lorene Clemens

D-U-N-S 11-851-4835 IMP
OHIO FRESH EGGS LLC
11212 Croton Rd, Croton, OH 43013-9725
Tel (740) 893-7200 Founded/Ownrshp 1984
Sales 123.5MME EMP 250
SIC 5144 2015 Eggs; Egg processing
Genl Mgr: Donald Hersey

D-U-N-S 05-293-1938 EXP
OHIO GRATINGS INC (OH)
5299 Southway St Sw, Canton, OH 44706-1992
Tel (330) 477-6707 Founded/Ownrshp 1970
Sales 98.7MME EMP 323
SIC 3446 3444 3441 3312 Gratings, open steel flooring; Open flooring & grating for construction; Sheet metalwork; Fabricated structural metal; Blast furnaces & steel mills
Pr: John Bartley
*Ch Bd: David Bartley
*VP: Ronald Lenney
Sales Exec: Kevin Collins
Mktg Dir: Carl Griffin

D-U-N-S 00-790-1101 IMP/EXP
OHIO MACHINERY CO
CATERPILLAR AUTHORIZED DEALER
3993 E Royalton Rd, Broadview Heights, OH 44147-2898
Tel (440) 526-6200 Founded/Ownrshp 1961
Sales 233.3MME EMP 1,050
SIC 7513 6159 7699 5082 7353 Truck rental, without drivers; Machinery & equipment finance leasing; Aircraft & heavy equipment repair services; Construction equipment repair; General construction machinery & equipment; Mining machinery & equipment, except petroleum; Heavy construction equipment rental
Pr: Ken Taylor
*CFO: David J Blocksom
*VP: Eric W Emch
*VP: Paul Liesem
*VP: Kelly Love
Brnch Mgr: Tim Wagner
Div Mgr: Janie Hovan
DP Exec: Mike Uher
Dir IT: Kevin O'Callaghan
Tech Mgr: Terry Comer
Web Dev: William Smith

D-U-N-S 00-543-8262 IMP/EXP
■ OHIO MATTRESS CO LICENSING AND COMPONENTS GROUP
(Suby of TEMPUR SEALY INTERNATIONAL INC) ★
1 Office Parkway Rd, Trinity, NC 27370-9449
Tel (336) 861-3500 Founded/Ownrshp 1933, 2016
Sales 333.2MME EMP 1,550
SIC 2515 6794 Box springs, assembled; Franchises, selling or licensing
Pr: Lawrence Rogers
*VP: Kenneth L Walker
VP Sls: Gary Fazio

D-U-N-S 04-635-9444
OHIO MUTUAL INSURANCE CO (OH)
1725 Hopley Ave, Bucyrus, OH 44820-3596
Tel (419) 562-3011 Founded/Ownrshp 1901
Sales NA EMP 186
SIC 6411 6331 Insurance brokers; Fire, marine & casualty insurance: mutual; Fire, marine & casualty insurance: stock
Pr: Jim Kennedy
Pr: Brad McCormack
*CFO: David Hendrix
*VP: Todd Albert
*VP: Michael Brogan
VP: Marsha Clady
VP: Kathy Guinther
*VP: Thomas Holtshouse
*VP: Mike Horvath
*VP: Randy O'Conner
VP: Randu Oconner

D-U-N-S 00-699-9718
OHIO NATIONAL FINANCIAL SERVICES INC
(Suby of OHIO NATIONAL MUTUAL HOLDINGS INC) ★
1 Financial Way Ste 100, Montgomery, OH 45242-5852
Tel (513) 794-6100 Founded/Ownrshp 1959
Sales NA EMP 800
SIC 6311 Mutual association life insurance
Pr: Gary T Huffman
V Ch: Christopher A Carlson
*V Ch: Ronald Dolan
Pr: Leigh A Morgan
Pr: Traci Nelson
*Pr: Arthur J Roberts
CFO: Adam J Hicks
Treas: Patrick Demmer
Ex VP: Thomas Barefield
Ex VP: Barbara A Turner
*Sr VP: Larry J Adams
Sr VP: David A Azzarito
Sr VP: Richard J Bodner
Sr VP: Allen R Bowen
Sr VP: Michael J Deweirdt
Sr VP: Paul J Gerard
Sr VP: George B Pearson
VP: Wayne Baca
VP: Michael Begley
VP: Robin Benoit
VP: Todd Brockman
Board of Directors: Gary Wendlandt

D-U-N-S 80-884-7560
OHIO NATIONAL GUARD
OHIO ADJUTANT GENERAL
(Suby of EXECUTIVE OFFICE STATE OF OHIO) ★
2825 W Dblin Granville Rd, Columbus, OH 43235-2712
Tel (614) 336-7000 Founded/Ownrshp 1803
Sales NA EMP 2,800
SIC 9711 National security;
Ex Dir: Gregory L Wayt
*CFO: Mark Ostler
Ofcr: Richard Willinger
*VP: Candice Barnhardt

D-U-N-S 00-230-5069
OHIO NATIONAL LIFE ASSURANCE CORP
(Suby of OHIO CASUALTY INSURANCE) ★
1 Financial Way Ste 100, Montgomery, OH 45242-5852
Tel (513) 794-6100 Founded/Ownrshp 1979
Sales NA EMP 730E
SIC 6411 Insurance agents, brokers & service
CEO: David B Omaley
CFO: Ronald J Dolan
Sec: Michael F Haverkamp
Sec: Therese S McDonough
Ofcr: Cletus L Davis
*Ex VP: Gates Smith
Sr VP: Robert Bowen
VP: Terry L Garrard

D-U-N-S 78-734-4758
OHIO NATIONAL LIFE INSURANCE CO
OHIO CASUALTY INSURANCE
(*Suby of* OHIO NATIONAL FINANCIAL SERVICES INC) ★
1 Financial Way Ste 100, Montgomery, OH 45242-5852
Tel (513) 794-6100 *Founded/Ownrshp* 1979
Sales NA *EMP* 799ᴱ
SIC 6331 Fire, marine & casualty insurance
CEO: David B Omaley
Sr VP: Ronald Heibert
VP: Michael Vogel

D-U-N-S 00-230-4397
OHIO NATIONAL MUTUAL HOLDINGS INC (OH)
1 Financial Way Ste 100, Montgomery, OH 45242-5852
Tel (513) 794-6100 *Founded/Ownrshp* 1993
Sales NA *EMP* 800
SIC 6311 Mutual association life insurance
Ch Bd: David O'Maley
**Treas:* Roylene Broadwell
Chf Cred: Dennis R Taney
**Sr VP:* Ronald Dolan
**VP:* Michael S Haberkamp
VP: Jed R Martin
DP Dir: William Martin
Mktg Mgr: Terry Garrett
Board of Directors: David R Jones

D-U-N-S 05-162-5564
OHIO NORTHERN UNIVERSITY
ONU
525 S Main St Unit 1, Ada, OH 45810-1599
Tel (419) 772-2000 *Founded/Ownrshp* 1899
Sales 87.6MM *EMP* 700
Accts Bkd Llp Fort Wayne Indiana
SIC 8221 University
Pr: Dr Daniel A Dibiasio
Treas: Jennifer Schleicher
**VP:* William Ballard
VP: David Crago
VP: Gary North
Exec: Jane Williams
Assoc Dir: Mary Wilkin
Ex Dir: Kenneth Block
Dir IT: Jeff Rieman
Corp Couns: Howard Fenton
Pgrm Dir: Kelly Swearingen

D-U-N-S 07-501-4977
OHIO OPERATING ENGINEERS HEALTH & WELFARE FUND
1180 Dublin Rd, Columbus, OH 43215-1008
Tel (614) 488-0708 *Founded/Ownrshp* 1959
Sales NA *EMP* 8
SIC 6371 Union welfare, benefit & health funds
Ex Dir: Ray Orrand
Netwrk Mgr: Tim Tolley

D-U-N-S 01-797-3025
OHIO PIZZA PRODUCTS INC
PRESTO AMERICAS FAVORITE FOODS
201 Lawton Ave, Monroe, OH 45050-1213
Tel (937) 294-6969 *Founded/Ownrshp* 1981
Sales 167.9MMᴱ *EMP* 150
SIC 5149 Pizza supplies; Specialty food items; Baking supplies
Ch: Phil Weeda Sr
**Ch Bd:* Vito P Weeda
**Pr:* Jeff Schrand
**CFO:* Dale Lipa
VP: Roberta Schrater
VP: Weeda Vito
**VP:* Dewey Weeda
Opers Mgr: Eugene Douglass
VP Mktg: Anderson Erickson
Mktg Mgr: Rick Deitering
Sales Asso: Scott Putnam

D-U-N-S 00-289-9953
■ **OHIO POWER CO**
AEP
(*Suby of* AEP) ★
1 Riverside Plz, Columbus, OH 43215-2355
Tel (614) 716-1000 *Founded/Ownrshp* 1907
Sales 3.1MMM *EMP* 1,516ᴱ
SIC 4911 Electric services; Distribution, electric power; Generation, electric power; Transmission, electric power
Ch Bd: Nicholas K Akins
**CFO:* Brian X Tierney
Board of Directors: Lisa M Barton, David M Feinberg, Lana L Hillebrand, Mark C McCullough, Robert P Powers, Dennis E Welch

D-U-N-S 80-884-0748
OHIO PRESBYTERIAN RETIREMENT SERVICES (INC)
1001 Kingsmill Pkwy, Columbus, OH 43229-1129
Tel (614) 888-7800 *Founded/Ownrshp* 1992
Sales 5.2MM *EMP* 3,100
Accts Plante & Moran Pllc Columbus
SIC 8361 Rest home, with health care incidental
CEO: Laurence Gumina
**CFO:* Robert Stillman
VP: Chris McKenzie
CIO: Joyce Randhawa
Dir IT: Leslie K Belfance
IT Man: David Sloan

D-U-N-S 10-568-2090
OHIO PUBLIC EMPLOYEES RETIREMENT SYSTEM
(*Suby of* EXECUTIVE OFFICE STATE OF OHIO) ★
277 E Town St, Columbus, OH 43215-4627
Tel (614) 228-8471 *Founded/Ownrshp* 1935
Sales NA *EMP* 468
SIC 6371 9441 Pension funds; Administration of social & manpower programs
Ch: Cinthia Sledz
**COO:* Blake W Sherry
**CFO:* Jenny Starr
**Prin:* Sharon Downs

OHIO RURAL ELECTRIC COOPS
See BUCKEYE POWER INC

D-U-N-S 00-196-4634 IMP
OHIO STATE UNIVERSITY
Student Acade Servi Bldg, Columbus, OH 43210
Tel (614) 292-6446 *Founded/Ownrshp* 1870
Sales 2.9MMMᴱ *EMP* 39,120
SIC 8221 5812

D-U-N-S 96-956-5469
OHIO STATE UNIVERSITY FOUNDATION
364 W Lane Ave Ste B, Columbus, OH 43201-4350
Tel (614) 292-6261 *Founded/Ownrshp* 2011
Sales 129.8MM *EMP* 3ᴱ
SIC 8641

D-U-N-S 03-125-1873
OHIO STATE UNIVERSITY WEXNER MEDICAL CENTER
UNIVERSITY HOSPITAL EAST
1492 E Broad St, Columbus, OH 43205-1546
Tel (614) 293-8000 *Founded/Ownrshp* 2010, 1910
Sales 397.9MMᴱ *EMP* 20,000
SIC 8741 Hospital management
Pr: Michael V Drake
Ofcr: Curt Brown
**Ex VP:* Sheldon M Retchin

D-U-N-S 00-786-2378 IMP/EXP
OHIO TRANSMISSION CORP (OH)
OTP INDUSTRIAL SOLUTIONS
1900 Jetway Blvd, Columbus, OH 43219-1681
Tel (614) 342-6247 *Founded/Ownrshp* 1963, 2015
Sales 358.8MMᴱ *EMP* 379
SIC 5084 5085 Industrial machinery & equipment; Materials handling machinery; Compressors, except air conditioning; Pumps & pumping equipment; Power transmission equipment & apparatus; Bearings
CEO: Philip Derrow
**CFO:* Matt Piatt
**Ch:* David D Derrow
**Ex VP:* Kurt Lang
VP: Jim Golinski
**VP:* Kevin Kammer
VP: Steven Strain
Area Mgr: Dan Benjamin
Sftwr Eng: Chuck Bohon
Sftwr Eng: Rustin Thomas
Opers Mgr: Cathy Kler

D-U-N-S 02-063-9340
OHIO TURNPIKE AND INFRASTRUCTURE COMMISSION
(*Suby of* EXECUTIVE OFFICE STATE OF OHIO) ★
682 Prospect St, Berea, OH 44017-2711
Tel (440) 234-2081 *Founded/Ownrshp* 1949
Sales 275.6MM *EMP* 953
Accts C&P Advisors Llc Cleveland
SIC 4785 Toll road operation
CEO: Randy Cole
COO: Lauren Hakis
**CFO:* Martin S Seekely
CFO: James Steiner
**Ch:* Jerry N Hruby
**Sec:* Sandy Barber
MIS Dir: Dick Morgan

D-U-N-S 04-107-7983 IMP
OHIO UNIVERSITY
1 Ohio University, Athens, OH 45701-2979
Tel (740) 593-1000 *Founded/Ownrshp* 1804
Sales 493.8MM *EMP* 6,162
SIC 8221

D-U-N-S 17-831-6949
OHIO UNIVERSITY FOUNDATION
Hdl Center Ste 218 Rm 168, Athens, OH 45701
Tel (740) 593-1901 *Founded/Ownrshp* 1945
Sales 88.8MM *EMP* 72
Accts Crowe Horwath Llp Louisville
SIC 7389 Fund raising organizations
Prin: Candice Casto
**Ch Bd:* James Daley
**Ch:* Charlotte Eufinger
**Treas:* Larry Corrigan
**VP:* Frand Krasovec
**Ex Dir:* Leonard Raley
Genl Mgr: Julie Cashin

D-U-N-S 00-636-4558 IMP
OHIO VALLEY ALUMINUM CO II LLC (KY)
ALTEC
(*Suby of* INTERLOCK INDUSTRIES INC) ★
1100 Brooks Industrial Rd, Shelbyville, KY 40065-9197
Tel (502) 633-2783 *Founded/Ownrshp* 1955
Sales 225.0MMᴱ *EMP* 125ᴱ
SIC 3341 Aluminum smelting & refining (secondary)
Pr: Mike Mackin

OHIO VALLEY COAL
See OHIO VALLEY RESOURCES INC

D-U-N-S 18-860-6438
OHIO VALLEY COAL CO
(*Suby of* OHIO VALLEY COAL) ★
46226 National Rd W, Saint Clairsville, OH 43950-8742
Tel (740) 926-1351 *Founded/Ownrshp* 1988
Sales 333.4MMᴱ *EMP* 400
SIC 1241 Bituminous coal mining services, contract basis
CEO: Robert E Murray
**Pr:* Ryan M Murray
**Sr VP:* John R Forrelli
**Sr VP:* Michael O McKown
**VP:* Robert D Moore
CTO: Joe Templin
VP Mktg: B Cornelius
Board of Directors: Richard Homko, Paul Piccolini

D-U-N-S 00-790-3925
OHIO VALLEY ELECTRIC CORP
OVEC
3932 Us Rte 23, Piketon, OH 45661
Tel (740) 289-7200 *Founded/Ownrshp* 1952
Sales 265.3MM *EMP* 428
SIC 4911 Generation, electric power; Transmission, electric power; Distribution, electric power
Pr: Nicholas Akins
CFO: Kassandra Martin
**Sec:* John Brodt
**VP:* Mark Piefer
IT Man: George Brady
VP Opers: David E Jons
Plnt Mgr: Jeff Bolen
Secur Mgr: William Squibb
Board of Directors: Steve Nelson, Anthony Ahern, Patrick O'loughlin, Nicholas Akins, Robert Powers, Eric Baker, Paul Thompson, Wayne Games, John Verderame, James Haney, John Voyles, Philip Herrington, Lana Hillebrand, Charles Lasky, Mark McCullough

D-U-N-S 09-281-5109 IMP
OHIO VALLEY FLOORING INC
5555 Murray Ave, Cincinnati, OH 45227-2707
Tel (513) 271-3434 *Founded/Ownrshp* 1978
Sales 119.8MM *EMP* 162
Accts Clark Schaefer Hackett & Co C
SIC 5023 Floor coverings; Carpets; Resilient floor coverings: tile or sheet; Wood flooring
Pr: Al Hurt
**CFO:* Mark Roflow
Chf Mktg O: Jeffery J Garber

OHIO VALLEY GENERAL HOSPITAL
See OHIO VALLEY MEDICAL CENTER INC

D-U-N-S 05-604-2831
OHIO VALLEY HEALTH SERVICES AND EDUCATION CORP
2000 Eoff St, Wheeling, WV 26003-3823
Tel (304) 234-8174 *Founded/Ownrshp* 1914
Sales 174.7MM *EMP* 3,650
Accts Arnett Carbis Toothman Llp Ch
SIC 8741 8062 8011 Hospital management; General medical & surgical hospitals; Offices & clinics of medical doctors
Ch Bd: James Squibb
**Pr:* Michael Caruso
**CEO:* Jan Jennings
**CFO:* Lisa Simon
**Treas:* Kristine Molnar
**VP:* Matt Thomasgerald Narcisi
QA Dir: Staci Trudo

D-U-N-S 07-216-3892
OHIO VALLEY MEDICAL CENTER INC
OHIO VALLEY GENERAL HOSPITAL
2000 Eoff St, Wheeling, WV 26003-3823
Tel (304) 234-0123 *Founded/Ownrshp* 1981
Sales 103.2MM *EMP* 1,275
SIC 8062 8011 General medical & surgical hospitals; Offices & clinics of medical doctors
Pr: Michael J Caruso
VP: Charles J Kaiser Jr
Dir OR: Francine Broadwater
Dir Soc: Mary Ann Carter
Dir Pat Ac: Dave Lucy
Dir Pat Ac: Chad Wyckoff
Genl Mgr: Gene Townsend
IT Man: Wendy Mirandy
Mktg Dir: Cathy West
Pathlgst: Souheil Nassar
Ansthlgy: Shishir Shah

D-U-N-S 05-552-1686
OHIO VALLEY RESOURCES INC
OHIO VALLEY COAL
(*Suby of* MURRAY ENERGY CORP) ★
29325 Chagrin Blvd # 300, Beachwood, OH 44122-4600
Tel (216) 765-1240 *Founded/Ownrshp* 1988
Sales 752.3MMᴱ *EMP* 3,000
SIC 1241

D-U-N-S 12-949-5755
OHIO VALLEY TRANSLOADING CO INC
(*Suby of* OHIO VALLEY COAL) ★
46226 National Rd W, Saint Clairsville, OH 43950-8742
Tel (740) 795-4967 *Founded/Ownrshp* 1989
Sales 57.6MMᴱ *EMP* 2,566ᴱ
SIC 1241 Bituminous coal mining services, contract basis
CEO: Robert Murray

D-U-N-S 13-112-8402
OHIO VIRTUAL ACADEMY
1690 Woodlands Dr Ste 200, Maumee, OH 43537-4045
Tel (419) 482-0948 *Founded/Ownrshp* 2002
Sales 94.1MM *EMP* 65
SIC 8211
Prin: Jeff Shaw
Exec: Melissa A Shoemaker
Snr Mgr: Heidi Ragar

D-U-N-S 05-535-2140
OHIO WESLEYAN UNIVERSITY
61 S Sandusky St, Delaware, OH 43015-2398
Tel (800) 922-8953 *Founded/Ownrshp* 1842
Sales 118.8MM *EMP* 630
SIC 8221

D-U-N-S 01-623-8990
OHIOGUIDESTONE
434 Eastland Rd, Berea, OH 44017-1217
Tel (440) 234-2006 *Founded/Ownrshp* 1864
Sales 54.2MM *EMP* 1,237
Accts Mcgladrey Llp Cleveland Oh
SIC 8322 8361 8351 8051 Child related social services; Home for the emotionally disturbed; Child day care services; Skilled nursing care facilities
CEO: Richard Frank
**VP:* Donna Keegan
Exec: Judy Hlavna
IT Man: John Lavelle
Sls&Mrk Ex: Alyssa Evanoff

D-U-N-S 07-164-3589
OHIOHEALTH CORP
180 E Broad St, Columbus, OH 43215-3707
Tel (614) 788-8860 *Founded/Ownrshp* 1984
Sales 2.1MMM *EMP* 15,000
Accts Deloitte Tax Llp Cincinnati
SIC 8049 8062 8082 8051 Occupational therapist; General medical & surgical hospitals; Home health care services; Convalescent home with continuous nursing care; Extended care facility
Pr: David Blom
Dir Vol: Carol Conner
**COO:* Michael W Louge
**COO:* Robert P Millen
CFO: Vinson M Yates
**Sr VP:* Michael S Bernstein
**Sr VP:* Steve Garlock
**Sr VP:* Donna Hanly
Sr VP: Michael Krouse
VP: Arash Arshi
VP: Michael Bernstein
VP: Tanya Blackmon
VP: Bob Boswell
VP: Thomas Chickerella
VP: Suzanne Dewoody
VP: Troy Hammett
VP: Allen Heilman
VP: Cheryl Herbert
VP: Joe Hooper
VP: Sue Jablonski
VP: Frank Pandora

OHIOHEALTH MANSFIELD HOSPITAL
See MEDCENTRAL HEALTH SYSTEM

OHIOHEALTH O'BLENESS HOSPITAL
See SHELTERING ARMS HOSPITAL FOUNDATION INC

OHL
See GEODIS LOGISTICS LLC

D-U-N-S 02-559-8670
OHL GLOBAL FREIGHT MANAGEMENT
(*Suby of* OZBURN-HESSEY HOLDING CO LLC) ★
223 E Cy Hall Ave Ste 208, Norfolk, VA 23510
Tel (757) 314-4300 *Founded/Ownrshp* 2009
Sales 44.8MMᴱ *EMP* 1,269ᴱ
SIC 8741 Management services
Prin: Brenda Bailey

D-U-N-S 83-293-8364
OHL USA INC
(*Suby of* OBRASCON HUARTE LAIN SA)
2615 Ulmer St, Flushing, NY 11354-1144
Tel (718) 554-2320 *Founded/Ownrshp* 2005
Sales 527.0MMᴱ *EMP* 145
SIC 8711 Construction & civil engineering; Civil engineering
COO: Ashok Patel
**CFO:* Manuel Mateos

OHMART VEGA
See VEGA AMERICAS INC

D-U-N-S 06-247-8268 IMP
OHMITE HOLDING LLC
OHMITE MANUFACTURING
(*Suby of* HEICO COMPANIES L L C) ★
27501 Bella Vista Pkwy, Warrenville, IL 60555-1609
Tel (847) 258-0300 *Founded/Ownrshp* 1988
Sales 89.6MMᴱ *EMP* 423
SIC 3625 5065 Resistors & resistor units; Rheostats; Industrial electrical relays & switches; Resistors, electronic; Electronic parts
Pr: Greg Pace

OHMITE MANUFACTURING
See OHMITE HOLDING LLC

D-U-N-S 10-219-7899 IMP/EXP
■ **OHMSTEDE LTD**
(*Suby of* EMCOR GROUP INC) ★
895 N Main St, Beaumont, TX 77701-1813
Tel (409) 833-6375 *Founded/Ownrshp* 2007
Sales 415.8MMᴱ *EMP* 1,000
SIC 5075 3443 Heat exchangers; Heat exchangers: coolers (after, inter), condensers, etc.
CEO: William Reid
**Pt:* Glenda Barnwell
**Pt:* Douglas Harrington
**Pt:* John Marcotte
COO: Bill Reid
IT Man: James Nicklebur
Snr Mgr: Daniel Gallion

OHSU
See OREGON HEALTH & SCIENCE UNIVERSITY

D-U-N-S 04-890-4361
■ **OI CORP**
O I ANALYTICAL
(*Suby of* XYLEM INC) ★
151 Graham Rd, College Station, TX 77845-9654
Tel (979) 690-1711 *Founded/Ownrshp* 1963
Sales 224.2MMᴱ *EMP* 1,077ᴱ
SIC 3826 Analytical instruments; Gas chromatographic instruments
CEO: J Bruce Lancaster
**Pr:* Donald P Segers
COO: Richard W Chapman
**Treas:* Peter K Anderson
Genl Mgr: Karl Brinkmann
Genl Mgr: Laura Cummings
Genl Mgr: Hank Hahn
S&M/VP: Craig Marvin
Manager: Scott Hazard

OI PLASTIC PRODUCTS FTS INC
See BPREX PLASTIC PACKAGING INC

OIA GLOBAL LOGISTICS
See OREGON INTERNATIONAL AIR FREIGHT CO INC

D-U-N-S 61-238-8715
OIA GLOBAL LOGISTICS-SCM INC
(*Suby of* LDI LOGISTICS INC) ★
2100 Sw Rver Pkwy Ste 800, Portland, OR 97201
Tel (503) 736-5900 *Founded/Ownrshp* 2003
Sales 253.8MMᴱ *EMP* 559
Accts Ernst & Young Llp Indianapoli
SIC 4731 Freight consolidation; Agents, shipping
Pr: Charles F Hornecker
**Pr:* Harles F Hornecker

*CFO: Tim Sether
*Ex VP: Steve Akre
*Ex VP: Dante Fornari
*Ex VP: Eric Okimoto
*VP: Daniel McMorris
Opers Mgr: Angel Thomas

D-U-N-S 80-702-9764
OIL & GAS ASSET CLEARINGHOUSE LP
(Suby of PETROLEUM PL ENRGY SOLUTIONS) ★
1235 North Loop W Ste 500, Houston, TX 77008-4704
Tel (281) 873-4600 Founded/Ownrshp 1992
Sales 450.5MM EMP 54
SIC 6531 Auction, real estate
Pt: Kenneth Olive Jr
Sr VP: Ron Barnes
Sr VP: Mark K Roach

D-U-N-S 11-088-1562
OIL MOP LLC
OMI ENVIRONMENTAL SOLUTIONS
131 Keating Dr, Belle Chasse, LA 70037-1629
Tel (504) 394-6110 Founded/Ownrshp 2003
Sales 91.9MM[E] EMP 130
SIC 4959 Environmental cleanup services
Pr: Shaw Thompson
*VP: Joe Christiana
Dir IT: Jesse White

OIL PATCH DOWNHOLE SERVICES
See OIL PATCH GROUP INC

D-U-N-S 07-935-8013
OIL PATCH GROUP INC
OIL PATCH DOWNHOLE SERVICES
(Suby of SCF PARTNERS) ★
11767 Katy Fwy Ste 510a, Houston, TX 77079-1768
Tel (832) 300-0000 Founded/Ownrshp 2013
Sales 143.1MM[E] EMP 250
SIC 1389 7353 Grading oil & gas well foundations; Oil field equipment, rental or leasing
Pr: Jim Elzner
*CFO: Gabe Urban

D-U-N-S 07-832-1409 IMP
■ OIL STATES ENERGY SERVICES LLC
(Suby of OIL STATES INTERNATIONAL INC) ★
333 Clay St Ste 2100, Houston, TX 77002-2570
Tel (713) 425-2400 Founded/Ownrshp 2012
Sales 613.4MM[E] EMP 2,000
SIC 3533 5082 Oil field machinery & equipment; Oil field equipment
CEO: Cindy B Taylor
*VP: Christopher E Cragg

D-U-N-S 93-250-7288 IMP/EXP
■ OIL STATES INDUSTRIES INC
(Suby of OIL STATES INTERNATIONAL INC) ★
7701 S Cooper St, Arlington, TX 76001-7015
Tel (817) 548-4200 Founded/Ownrshp 1995
Sales 325.7MM[E] EMP 1,062
SIC 1389 3061 3561 3533 Oil & gas wells: building, repairing & dismantling; Oil field services; Oil & gas field machinery rubber goods (mechanical); Pumps & pumping equipment; Drilling tools for gas, oil or water wells
Pr: Charles J Moses
CFO: Bradley Dodson
*CFO: Tama D Lucas
CFO: Cindy Taylor
*Sr VP: Scott Moses
*VP: Timothy Diadiun
*VP: Ricky Simic
Exec: Matt Moody
Ql Cn Mgr: Steven Kreitzberg
Sales Exec: Simick Ricky
Sls Mgr: David Gian

D-U-N-S 16-002-7850
▲ OIL STATES INTERNATIONAL INC
333 Clay St Ste 4620, Houston, TX 77002-4101
Tel (713) 652-0582 Founded/Ownrshp 1995
Sales 1.1MMM EMP 3,586
Tkr Sym OIS Exch NYS
SIC 3353 3061 3053 3561 3491 Aluminum sheet, plate & foil; Oil & gas field machinery rubber goods (mechanical); Gaskets, packing & sealing devices; Pumps & pumping equipment; Industrial valves
Pr: Cindy B Taylor
*Ch Bd: Mark G Papa
CFO: Lloyd A Hajdik
Sr VP: Christopher E Cragg
Sr VP: Philip S Moses
Sr VP: Lias J Steen
VP: Mike Hogan
VP: Scott Moses
VP: Sarah A Munson
Genl Mgr: Stephen Guinn
Opers Mgr: Randy Minton
Board of Directors: Lawrence R Dickerson, S James Nelson Jr, Gary L Rosenthal, Christopher T Seaver, William T Van Kleef, Stephen A Wells

D-U-N-S 02-842-5338
OIL WELL SERVICE CO
10840 Norwalk Blvd, Santa Fe Springs, CA 90670-3826
Tel (562) 612-0600 Founded/Ownrshp 2007
Sales 94.0MM[E] EMP 225
SIC 1389 Oil field services
Pr: Jack Frost
*Treas: Connie Laws
*VP: Richard Laws

D-U-N-S 00-521-3954
▲ OIL-DRI CORP OF AMERICA
410 N Michigan Ave # 400, Chicago, IL 60611-4293
Tel (312) 321-1515 Founded/Ownrshp 1941
Sales 262.3MM EMP 797
Tkr Sym ODC Exch NYS
SIC 2842 3295 Sweeping compounds, oil or water absorbent, clay or sawdust; Earths, ground or otherwise treated; Cat box litter; Filtering clays, treated
Pr: Daniel S Jaffee
*Ch Bd: Richard M Jaffee
COO: Mark E Lewry
CFO: Daniel T Smith
*V Ch Bd: Joseph C Miller
VP: Douglas A Graham
Tech Mgr: L'Tanya King
VP Mfg: Thomas F Cofsky
Plnt Mgr: Tracy Smithey
Manager: Steven Powell
Board of Directors: J Steven Cole, Michael A Nemeroff, George C Roeth, Allan H Selig, Paul E Suckow, Lawrence Washow

D-U-N-S 07-685-8547 IMP
■ OIL-DRI CORP OF GEORGIA
(Suby of OIL-DRI CORP OF AMERICA) ★
28990 Hwy 3, Ochlocknee, GA 31773-2399
Tel (229) 574-5131 Founded/Ownrshp 1991
Sales 103.1MM[E] EMP 275
SIC 3295 3564 2842 Fuller's earth, ground or otherwise treated; Blowers & fans; Specialty cleaning, polishes & sanitation goods
Pr: Daniel S Jaffee
*CFO: Daniel T Smith
*Prin: Richard M Jaffee
Plnt Mgr: Craig Paisley

D-U-N-S 00-609-5038 IMP
OILGEAR CO
(Suby of MASON WELLS BUYOUT FUND II LIMITED PARTNERSHIP) ★
1424 International Dr, Traverse City, MI 49686-8751
Tel (231) 929-1660 Founded/Ownrshp 1921
Sales 139.9MM[E] EMP 499
SIC 3594 3492 3593 Fluid power pumps; Motors: hydraulic, fluid power or air; Control valves, fluid power: hydraulic & pneumatic; Fluid power cylinders, hydraulic or pneumatic
COO: Craig Lafave

D-U-N-S 83-241-9886
OIMO HOLDINGS INC
2735 Middle Rd, Mobile, AL 36605-9515
Tel (251) 443-5550 Founded/Ownrshp 2009
Sales 96.6MM[E] EMP 130[E]
SIC 1389 Oil field services; Oil consultants; Gas field services
Pr: Robin D Roberts
VP: Crystal Yasurek

OK BRAND
See OKLAHOMA STEEL & WIRE CO INC

D-U-N-S 00-633-8057
OK INDUSTRIES INC
(Suby of INDUSTRIAS BACHOCO, S.A.B. DE C.V.)
4601 N 6th St, Fort Smith, AR 72904-2208
Tel (479) 783-4186 Founded/Ownrshp 1933, 2011
Sales 3.2MM[E] EMP 4,000
SIC 2048 2015 0251 Poultry feeds; Poultry, slaughtered & dressed; Poultry, processed: fresh; Poultry, processed; Broiling chickens, raising of
Pr: Randall W Goins
CFO: Ron Brown
*CFO: Ronald E Brown

OK PRODUCE
See CHARLIES ENTERPRISES

D-U-N-S 06-953-0947
OKALOOSA COUNTY SCHOOL DISTRICT (FL)
120 Lowery Pl Se, Fort Walton Beach, FL 32548-5547
Tel (850) 689-7300 Founded/Ownrshp 1900
Sales 274.1M EMP 3,400
SIC 8211 Public elementary & secondary schools
Dir Sec: Andy Johnson
IT Man: Diane Holman
Opers Mgr: Donna Pease
Schl Brd P: Cathy Thigpen
Pgrm Dir: Ryan Gore

OKCPS
See OKLAHOMA CITY PUBLIC SCHOOLS

D-U-N-S 01-340-5167 IMP
OKI DATA AMERICAS INC
O K I
(Suby of OKI DATA CORPORATION)
2000 Bishops Gate Blvd, Mount Laurel, NJ 08054-4603
Tel (856) 235-2600 Founded/Ownrshp 1999
Sales 173.7MM[E] EMP 400
SIC 5045 Computer peripheral equipment
Pr: Masahiko Morioka
CFO: Akio Samata
Treas: Michael Bozek
Treas: Hidetoshi Inoue
Ofcr: Susan De Mars
Ex VP: Kazutaka Onodera
Sr VP: Dan Murphy
Sr VP: Jiro Tanuma
VP: Steve Boyd
VP: Jim Butterworth
VP: Paula Ford
VP: Harold Garrison
VP: Kris Hackney
VP: Clifford Mingle
VP: Mitsuaki Takahara
VP: Vito Torregi
VP: Vito Torregiano
VP: Greg Van Acker

D-U-N-S 03-026-5342
OKIN-WALLACK CORP
GREEN ART ENTERPRISE
65 S Columbus Ave, Freeport, NY 11520-3940
Tel (516) 379-0449 Founded/Ownrshp 1946
Sales 83.6MM[E] EMP 85[E]
SIC 5074 Plumbing & hydronic heating supplies; Heating equipment (hydronic)
Pr: Lewis Okin
*CFO: Herb Rosenberg
*VP: Alex Okin

D-U-N-S 82-968-9363
OKLAHOMA CITY ENVIRONMENTAL ASSISTANCE TRUST
(Suby of CITY OF OKLAHOMA CITY) ★
200 N Walker Ave Ste 302, Oklahoma City, OK 73102-2232
Tel (405) 297-2424 Founded/Ownrshp 1904
Sales 13.8MM[E] EMP 4,000
SIC 8611 Business associations

D-U-N-S 61-741-5211
OKLAHOMA CITY PUBLIC SCHOOLS
OKCPS
900 N Klein Ave, Oklahoma City, OK 73106-7036
Tel (405) 587-0000 Founded/Ownrshp 1910
Sales 171.0MM[E] EMP 7,000
SIC 8211 Public elementary & secondary schools
Bd of Dir: Justin Ellis
Ex Dir: Eric Hileman

D-U-N-S 06-544-1842
OKLAHOMA CITY UNIVERSITY
2501 N Blackwelder Ave, Oklahoma City, OK 73106-1402
Tel (405) 208-5000 Founded/Ownrshp 1904
Sales 107.0MM EMP 503
Accts Mcgladrey Llp Oklahoma City
SIC 8221 University
Pr: Robert Henry
*Pr: Thomas Mc Daniel
COO: Farida Shams
*CFO: Brian Holland
Top Exec: Benjamin Chang
Ex VP: Bernie Patterson
VP: Susan Barber
*VP: Mary Coffey
Exec: Danne Johnson
Assoc Dir: Dennis Arrow
Assoc Dir: Mark Clouse
Assoc Dir: Jennifer Prilliman
Comm Dir: Melissa Cory

D-U-N-S 82-470-0058
OKLAHOMA DEPARTMENT OF COMMERCE
(Suby of EXECUTIVE OFFICE OF STATE OF OKLAHOMA) ★
900 N Stiles Ave, Oklahoma City, OK 73104-3234
Tel (405) 815-6552 Founded/Ownrshp 1987
Sales NA EMP 1,007
Accts Finnely & Cook
SIC 9611 Administration of general economic programs;
Ex Dir: Kathy Taylor
Ofcr: Amy Polonchek
Dir Bus: Christie Myers
Sls&Mrk Ex: John Ogders
S&M/Dir: John Reid

D-U-N-S 93-366-2934
OKLAHOMA DEPARTMENT OF MENTAL HEALTH AND SUBSTANCE ABUSE SERVICES
(Suby of EXECUTIVE OFFICE OF STATE OF OKLAHOMA) ★
1200 Ne 13th St, Oklahoma City, OK 73117-1022
Tel (405) 522-3878 Founded/Ownrshp 2011
Sales 103.2MM[E] EMP 1,856[E]
SIC 8399 9431 Health & welfare council; Administration of public health programs
*COO: Dave Statton
Ofcr: Brenda Boyle
Prgrm Mgr: Thomas Thomson
Genl Mgr: Gretchen Geis
CTO: David Faupell
MIS Dir: Leo Fortelney

D-U-N-S 82-470-0074
OKLAHOMA DEPARTMENT OF TRANSPORTATION
(Suby of EXECUTIVE OFFICE OF STATE OF OKLAHOMA) ★
200 Ne 21st St, Oklahoma City, OK 73105-3204
Tel (405) 521-2631 Founded/Ownrshp 1986
Sales NA EMP 2,600
SIC 9621 Regulation, administration of transportation;
Area Mgr: Dan Harris
Brnch Mgr: Richard Buchanan
Brnch Mgr: Christa Sawyer

D-U-N-S 80-992-9904
OKLAHOMA DEPT OF HUMAN SERVICES
(Suby of EXECUTIVE OFFICE OF STATE OF OKLAHOMA) ★
2400 N Lincoln Blvd, Oklahoma City, OK 73105-4601
Tel (405) 521-3646 Founded/Ownrshp 1936
Sales NA EMP 8,000
SIC 9431 9441 Administration of public health programs; ;
*COO: Marq Youngblood
*CFO: Phil Motley
Comm Man: Casey White
Genl Mgr: Kimerly Sanders
MIS Dir: Bryan Moore
IT Man: John Guin
Mktg Mgr: Deena Brown
Counsel: Richard Freeman

D-U-N-S 88-489-3264
OKLAHOMA DEPT OF MILITARY
ADJUTANT GENERALS OFFICE
(Suby of EXECUTIVE OFFICE OF STATE OF OKLAHOMA) ★
3501 Ne Military Cir, Oklahoma City, OK 73111-4305
Tel (405) 228-5000 Founded/Ownrshp 1951
Sales NA EMP 9,979
SIC 9111 Governors' offices;
Prin: Maj Gen Harry M Wyatt III
Brnch Mgr: Jack Self

D-U-N-S 82-470-0017
OKLAHOMA DEPT OF PUBLIC SAFETY
HIGHWAY PATROL
(Suby of EXECUTIVE OFFICE OF STATE OF OKLAHOMA) ★
3600 N Martin Luther Knl, Oklahoma City, OK 73111-4223
Tel (405) 425-2424 Founded/Ownrshp 1937
Sales NA EMP 1,400
SIC 9229 Public order & safety statistics centers;
Ofcr: C Addinton
Exec: Ward Kevin
Counsel: Joseph Claro

D-U-N-S 82-470-0033
OKLAHOMA DEPT OF TOURISM AND RECREATION
EXECUTIVE OFFC OF THE ST OF OK
(Suby of EXECUTIVE OFFICE OF STATE OF OKLAHOMA) ★
120 N Robinson Ave # 600, Oklahoma City, OK 73102-7509
Tel (405) 230-8300 Founded/Ownrshp 1972
Sales NA EMP 1,500
SIC 9611 Administration of general economic programs;
Ex Dir: Deby Snobgrass
CFO: Lindsey Flowers
*CFO: Lisa McKim
Mktg Dir: Dick Dutton

D-U-N-S 00-790-6027
OKLAHOMA ELECTRIC CO-OPERATIVE INC
OKLAHOMA ELECTRIC COOPERATIVE
242 24th Ave Nw, Norman, OK 73069-6371
Tel (405) 321-2024 Founded/Ownrshp 1937
Sales 130.3MM EMP 103
SIC 4911 2721 Distribution, electric power; Periodicals
Genl Mgr: Max Meek
Pr: Patrick Grace
CFO: Edith Ratcliff
Dept Mgr: John Spencer
IT Man: Derek Looper
VP Opers: Randy Simmons
Snr Mgr: Pat Brown

OKLAHOMA ELECTRIC COOPERATIVE
See OKLAHOMA ELECTRIC CO-OPERATIVE INC

D-U-N-S 00-790-6654
OKLAHOMA FARM BUREAU MUTUAL INSURANCE CO (OK)
FARM BUREAU INSURANCE
2501 N Stiles Ave, Oklahoma City, OK 73105-3119
Tel (405) 523-2300 Founded/Ownrshp 1946
Sales NA EMP 300
SIC 6331 6351 Fire, marine & casualty insurance & carriers; Fire, marine & casualty insurance: mutual; Automobile insurance; Property damage insurance; Liability insurance
Pr: Tom Buchanan
Ex VP: Richard Newberry
Ex VP: Darrayl Sinclair
VP: Thad Doye
VP: Bob Sheehan
Dir IT: Marla Peek
Netwrk Mgr: Philip Miller
Sls Mgr: Gale Heard
Corp Couns: Steve Lawson

D-U-N-S 00-790-6662
■ OKLAHOMA GAS AND ELECTRIC CO
(Suby of OGE ENERGY CORP) ★
321 N Harvey Ave, Oklahoma City, OK 73102-3405
Tel (405) 553-3000 Founded/Ownrshp 1902
Sales 2.2MMM EMP 1,884
SIC 4911 Distribution, electric power; Generation, electric power; Transmission, electric power
Ch Bd: Peter B Delaney
Pr: Sean Trauschke
COO: E Keith Mitchell
CFO: Stephen E Merrill
VP: R Trauschke
Genl Couns: William J Bullard
Board of Directors: James H Brandi, Wayne H Brunetti, Luke R Corbett, John D Groendyke, Kirk Humphreys, Robert Kelly, Robert O Lorenz, Judy R McReynolds, Sheila G Talton

D-U-N-S 10-067-9096
OKLAHOMA HEART HOSPITAL LLC
4050 W Memorial Rd, Oklahoma City, OK 73120-8358
Tel (405) 608-3200 Founded/Ownrshp 1999
Sales 241.2MM EMP 440
SIC 8069 Specialty hospitals, except psychiatric
Doctor: John Harvey
CFO: Carol Walker
VP: Jeffrey Taylor
Chf Nrs Of: Janet Fundaro
CIO: Michelle Mullins
IT Man: Jennifer Wiggins
Netwrk Eng: Brian Goff
Plnt Mgr: Justin Price
Secur Mgr: Sheridan Spencer
Mktg Dir: Wendi Wilson
Orthpdst: Michael Haslam

D-U-N-S 83-323-4219
OKLAHOMA HEART HOSPITAL SOUTH LLC
5200 E I 240 Service Rd, Oklahoma City, OK 73135-2610
Tel (405) 628-6000 Founded/Ownrshp 2007
Sales 105.2MM EMP 550
SIC 8062 General medical & surgical hospitals
CEO: John Harvey MD
COO: John Austin
CIO: Deanna Armitage

OKLAHOMA METAL PROCESSSING CO.
See DERICHEBOURG RECYCLING USA INC

D-U-N-S 14-826-8782
OKLAHOMA MUNICIPAL POWER AUTHORITY
OMPA
2701 W I 35 Frontage Rd, Edmond, OK 73013-8543
Tel (405) 340-5047 Founded/Ownrshp 1983
Sales 186.6MM EMP 50
Accts Baker Tilly Virchow Krause Ll
SIC 4911 Distribution, electric power
Genl Mgr: Cindy Holman
Bd of Dir: William Martin
Genl Couns: Max Speegle

D-U-N-S 09-341-6329
OKLAHOMA NURSING HOMES LTD
210 E Choctaw Ave, Sallisaw, OK 74955-4604
Tel (918) 775-4439 Founded/Ownrshp 1963
Sales 35.7MM[E] EMP 1,000
SIC 8051 Convalescent home with continuous nursing care

Pt: Lloyd Haskins

D-U-N-S 80-992-9821
OKLAHOMA OFFICE OF MANAGEMENT AND ENTERPRISE SERVICES
(*Suby of* EXECUTIVE OFFICE OF STATE OF OKLAHOMA) ★
2300 N Lincoln Blvd # 122, Oklahoma City, OK 73105-4805
Tel (405) 521-2141 *Founded/Ownrshp* 1947
Sales NA *EMP* 1,600
SIC 9311 Finance, taxation & monetary policy;
Ofcr: Riley Shaull
Comm Man: Doug DOE
Genl Mgr: Lynne Bajema

D-U-N-S 55-604-7918
OKLAHOMA PUBLISHING CO OF OKLAHOMA
DAILY OKLAHOMAN, THE
9000 N Brdwy, Oklahoma City, OK 73114
Tel (405) 475-3311 *Founded/Ownrshp* 1903
Sales 290.4MM^E *EMP* 2,800
SIC 2711 1311 6512 7375 2752

D-U-N-S 06-911-4093
OKLAHOMA ROOF MASTERS INC
OKLAHOMA ROOF SUPPLY
601 Evergreen Dr, Guthrie, OK 73044-7531
Tel (405) 814-6440 *Founded/Ownrshp* 1979
Sales 2.5MMM *EMP* 5,000
SIC 1761 1541 4731 4212 4213 Roofing contractor; Industrial buildings, new construction; Freight transportation arrangement; Domestic freight forwarding; Local trucking, without storage; Heavy hauling
CEO: John Shilpey

OKLAHOMA ROOF SUPPLY
See OKLAHOMA ROOF MASTERS INC

D-U-N-S 80-992-9789
OKLAHOMA SECRETARY OF ENERGY & ENVIRONMENT
(*Suby of* EXECUTIVE OFFICE OF STATE OF OKLAHOMA) ★
204 N Robinson Ave # 1010, Oklahoma City, OK 73102-7001
Tel (405) 522-7099 *Founded/Ownrshp* 1990
Sales NA *EMP* 1,102
SIC 9511 Air, water & solid waste management;

OKLAHOMA STATE UNIV MED CTR
See OKLAHOMA STATE UNIVERSITY MEDICAL TRUST

D-U-N-S 04-998-7720
OKLAHOMA STATE UNIVERSITY
401 Whitehurst Hall, Stillwater, OK 74078-1030
Tel (405) 744-5892 *Founded/Ownrshp* 2013
Sales 747.4MM *EMP* 8,882
Accts Grant Thornton Llp Oklahoma C
SIC 8221 University
Pr: Burns Hargis
Pr: Debbie Lane
VP: Gail Gates
VP: Linda Goodwin
Exec: Joyce Hise
Exec: Jan Pratt
Exec: Grant Rezabek
Assoc Dir: Sharon Nivens
Dir Soc: Jeremy Brown
VP Admn: David Bosserman
Ex Dir: Jerry Gill

D-U-N-S 04-488-0214
OKLAHOMA STATE UNIVERSITY FOUNDATION
400 S Monroe St, Stillwater, OK 74074-3322
Tel (405) 385-5100 *Founded/Ownrshp* 1968
Sales 150.0MM *EMP* 47
Accts Kpmg Llp Oklahoma City Ok
SIC 8611 Business associations
Pr: Kirk Jewell
**Pr:* Ron Area
Pr: David Loyless
Pr: Brandon Meyer
Assoc VP: Dee Niles
VP: David Mays
VP: Kenneth E Sigmon
Assoc Dir: Jacob Astley
Assoc Dir: John Strah
Ex Dir: Phyllis Hudecki
Counsel: Robyn Baker

D-U-N-S 83-048-0427
OKLAHOMA STATE UNIVERSITY MEDICAL TRUST
OKLAHOMA STATE UNIV MED CTR
744 W 9th St, Tulsa, OK 74127-9020
Tel (918) 599-1000 *Founded/Ownrshp* 2004
Sales 113.9MM *EMP* 1,200
SIC 8062 General medical & surgical hospitals
Ch: Jerry Hudson
CFO: Craig McKnight
Off Mgr: Barbara Mapp

D-U-N-S 09-971-4354 IMP/EXP
OKLAHOMA STEEL & WIRE CO INC
OK BRAND
Hwy 70 S, Madill, OK 73446
Tel (580) 795-7311 *Founded/Ownrshp* 1978
Sales 83.8MM^E *EMP* 400^E
SIC 3496 Fencing, made from purchased wire; Concrete reinforcing mesh & wire
Ch Bd: Craig Moore
**CFO:* Kathleen Moore
**Sec:* Colleen Moore
Admn Mgr: Cliff Donahue
Plnt Mgr: Jay Combs
Prd Mgr: Danny Awalt
S&M/VP: Johnny Raper

OKLAHOMA SURETY COMPANY
See MID-CONTINENT CASUALTY CO

D-U-N-S 01-302-6765
OKLAHOMA SURGICAL HOSPITAL LLC (OK)
2408 E 81st St Ste 900, Tulsa, OK 74137-4283
Tel (918) 477-5000 *Founded/Ownrshp* 1999
Sales 108.8MM *EMP* 400
SIC 8062 General medical & surgical hospitals
CEO: Rick Ferguson
**CFO:* Dub Cleland
CFO: Melinda Johnson
Off Mgr: Madonna Burton
IT Man: Richard Alge
IT Man: Richard Flewellen
HC Dir: Patty Hawkins

D-U-N-S 02-073-4265
OKLAHOMA TURNPIKE AUTHORITY
3500 N Martin Luther, Oklahoma City, OK 73111-4221
Tel (405) 425-3600 *Founded/Ownrshp* 1982
Sales 257.8MM *EMP* 528
Accts Grant Thornton Llp Oklahoma C
SIC 4785 Toll road operation
Ch: Mr Albert C Kelly Jr
Ch Bd: Robert Rayner
**Ch:* Mr David A Burrage
**Sec:* Mr G Carl Gibson
Ofcr: Eric Strong
CTO: Julie Wells
Dir IT: Tim Kraft
IT Man: Ronny Blankenship
Sfty Mgr: Bob Rayner

D-U-N-S 05-609-0319 IMP
OKLAND CONSTRUCTION CO INC
1978 S West Temple, Salt Lake City, UT 84115-7103
Tel (801) 486-0144 *Founded/Ownrshp* 1967
Sales 343.5MM^E *EMP* 600
SIC 1542 1541 Commercial & office building, new construction; Industrial buildings, new construction
Pr: Randy Okland
**Sec:* John McEntire
**VP:* Brett Okland
Dir IT: Lee Holland
Mktg Dir: Michele Kawahara

D-U-N-S 04-834-1655 IMP/EXP
OKONITE CO
102 Hilltop Rd, Ramsey, NJ 07446-1171
Tel (201) 825-0300 *Founded/Ownrshp* 1878
Sales 428.3MM^E *EMP* 1,100
SIC 3357 3315 3355 Nonferrous wiredrawing & insulating; Cable, steel: insulated or armored; Aluminum wire & cable
Ch Bd: Victor A Viggiano
Pr: A C Coppola
Treas: David Mitchell
Treas: Bob Morrow
Treas: D J Sokira
Ofcr: Veronica Malkowski
VP: James Fitzgerald
VP: Tm Scanlon
VP: Jf Silver
VP: WD Turner
VP: Willam Turner
Exec: Kelly Evans

D-U-N-S 13-920-8172 IMP/EXP
OLAM AMERICAS INC
(*Suby of* OLAM US HOLDINGS INC) ★
25 Union Pl Ste 3, Fresno, CA 93720
Tel (559) 447-1390 *Founded/Ownrshp* 2010
Sales 782.3MM^E *EMP* 3,500
Accts Ernst And Young Llp Singapore
SIC 0723 Crop preparation services for market
CEO: Gregory C Estep
VP: Siva Subramanian

D-U-N-S 96-863-8697
OLAM HOLDINGS PARTNERSHIP
(*Suby of* OLAM INTERNATIONAL LIMITED)
25 Union Pl Fl 2, Summit, NJ 07901-3603
Tel (908) 988-1960 *Founded/Ownrshp* 2006
Sales 802.0MM *EMP* 3,500
SIC 8741 Management services
Sr VP: Ray Steitz
Mktg Mgr: Kevin Long

OLAM SPCES VGTABLE INGREDIENTS
See OLAM WEST COAST INC

D-U-N-S 07-840-8822 IMP/EXP
OLAM US HOLDINGS INC
(*Suby of* OLAM HOLDINGS PARTNERSHIP) ★
2077 Convention Ctr 150, College Park, GA 30337-4204
Tel (404) 209-2676 *Founded/Ownrshp* 2012
Sales 813.4MM^E *EMP* 1,650^E
SIC 0723 Crop preparation services for market
Sls Mgr: Martha Barnette

D-U-N-S 00-230-1929 IMP/EXP
OLAM WEST COAST INC
OLAM SPCES VGTABLE INGREDIENTS
(*Suby of* OLAM HOLDINGS PARTNERSHIP) ★
205 E Rver Pk Cir Ste 310, Fresno, CA 93720
Tel (559) 447-1390 *Founded/Ownrshp* 2008
Sales 291.9MM^E *EMP* 1,274^E
SIC 2034 Dried & dehydrated vegetables
Pr: John Gibbons

D-U-N-S 02-318-8757
OLAMETER CORP
(*Suby of* OLAMETER INC)
2261 Brookhollow Plaza Dr # 111, Arlington, TX 76006-7420
Tel (817) 385-0053 *Founded/Ownrshp* 2008
Sales 61.7MM^E *EMP* 1,522
SIC 7389 Meter readers, remote
Pr: Jan Peeters
**VP:* Jean-Pierre Carette
**VP:* John Feltis

D-U-N-S 04-272-4395
OLAMETER CORP
4325 Concourse Dr, Ann Arbor, MI 48108-9688
Tel (734) 769-2600 *Founded/Ownrshp* 1985
Sales 127.8MM *EMP* 17^E
Accts Ernst & Young Llp Montreal
SIC 7389 Business services
CEO: Jan Peeters
CFO: Jean-Pierre Carette
Ex VP: Patrick Burk
VP: Rachel Fuller
VP: Russell McCloud
VP: Mae Reliszko

D-U-N-S 03-458-0779 IMP
OLAN MILLS INC
OLAN MILLS STUDIOS
735 Broad St Ste 218, Chattanooga, TN 37402-1855
Tel (423) 622-5141 *Founded/Ownrshp* 2011
Sales NA *EMP* 4,000
SIC 7221 2752

OLAN MILLS STUDIOS
See OLAN MILLS INC

OLATHE FORD LINCOLN
See FORD OLATHE SALES INC

D-U-N-S 18-273-4996
OLATHE HEALTH SYSTEM INC
OLATHE MEDICAL CENTER
20333 W 151st St, Olathe, KS 66061-5350
Tel (913) 791-4200 *Founded/Ownrshp* 1953
Sales 217.1MM *EMP* 130
Accts Bkd Llp Kansas City Mo
SIC 5912 Drug stores
Pr: Frank H Devocelle
Sec: Dennis C Meyer
Chf Mktg O: Michael Jensen
Sr VP: Dorothy Carey
Sr VP: John Staton
VP: David Klimek
Prin: Richard Johnson
CIO: Peggy Donovan
VP Mktg: Karen Wray
Diag Rad: Brian A Fletcher

OLATHE MEDICAL CENTER
See OLATHE HEALTH SYSTEM INC

D-U-N-S 07-624-9945
OLATHE MEDICAL CENTER INC
HOSPICE HM HLTH OLATHE MED CTR
20333 W 151st St, Olathe, KS 66061-7211
Tel (913) 791-4200 *Founded/Ownrshp* 1948
Sales 232.7MM *EMP* 2,500
SIC 8082 8062 Home health care services; General medical & surgical hospitals
Pr: Frank H Devocelle
**CFO:* Tierney Grasser
**Sr VP:* Dorothy Carey
**Sr VP:* John Staton
**VP:* Mike Jensen
Doctor: Kristine G Herron MD

OLATHE PUBLIC SCHOOLS
See OLATHE UNIFIED SCHOOL DISTRICT 233

D-U-N-S 01-516-4064
OLATHE UNIFIED SCHOOL DISTRICT 233
OLATHE PUBLIC SCHOOLS
14160 S Blackbob Rd, Olathe, KS 66062-2024
Tel (913) 780-7000 *Founded/Ownrshp* 1965
Sales 361.6MM *EMP* 4,000
Accts Mize Houser & Company Pa La
SIC 8211 Public elementary & secondary schools
VP: Rita Ashley
Ex Dir: Jim Payne
Dir Sec: Rick Castillo
DP Exec: Mike Preuss
MIS Dir: Josh Anderson
Dir IT: Kathi Tully
Teacher Pr: Catherine Donovan
Teacher Pr: Mark O'Dell
Psych: Laurinda Culpepper

D-U-N-S 09-047-5799 IMP
OLAY CO INC
Km 2 Hm 3 Rr 735, Cayey, PR 00736
Tel (787) 738-2191 *Founded/Ownrshp* 1995
Sales 84.5MM^E *EMP* 300
SIC 2844

D-U-N-S 07-825-9389
OLD BRIDGE TOWNSHIP BOARD OF EDUCATION
4207 Hwy 516, Matawan, NJ 07747-7026
Tel (732) 566-1000 *Founded/Ownrshp* 1900
Sales 67.7MM^E *EMP* 1,200
SIC 8211 School board
Pr: Donna Andriani
**VP:* Sal Diprima

D-U-N-S 18-066-0078 IMP/EXP
OLD CARCO INTERNATIONAL CORP
DODGE DAKOTA
(*Suby of* FCA US LLC) ★
1000 Chrysler Dr, Auburn Hills, MI 48326-2766
Tel (248) 576-5741 *Founded/Ownrshp* 2011
Sales 221.8MM^E *EMP* 425
SIC 5012 Automobiles & other motor vehicles
Ch Bd: R J Eaton
VP: Thomas Capo
**VP:* Harry Lewis
VP: Laurie Macaddino
VP: Hao Ren
Prgrm Mgr: Chris Micha
Genl Mgr: Adam Voss
CIO: Scott Sandschafer
IT Man: Martin Taylor
Netwrk Eng: Julie Selby
Plnt Mgr: Tyree Minner

D-U-N-S 61-538-1969
OLD COLONY Y
OLD COLONY YMCA
320 Main St, Brockton, MA 02301-5340
Tel (508) 583-2155 *Founded/Ownrshp* 1940
Sales 52.3MM *EMP* 1,400^E
Accts Alexander Aronson Finning &
SIC 8641 7991 8351 7032 8322 Youth organizations; Physical fitness facilities; Child day care services; Youth camps; Individual & family services
Pr: Vincent Marturano
**CFO:* Keenyn McFarlane
**Treas:* William Daisy
Exec: Kim Moran
CTO: Colby Linkletter
Psych: Almon White
Pgrm Dir: Allison Daley
Pgrm Dir: Heather Greene

OLD COLONY YMCA
See OLD COLONY Y

OLD COUNTRY BUFFET
See BUFFETS HOLDINGS LLC

OLD COUNTRY BUFFET
See HOMETOWN BUFFET INC

OLD COUNTRY BUFFET
See OCB RESTAURANT CO LLC

OLD COUNTRY BUFFET RESTAURANTS
See BUFFETS LLC

D-U-N-S 07-043-1218
OLD DOMINION ELECTRIC CO-OPERATIVE
4201 Dominion Blvd # 300, Glen Allen, VA 23060-6721
Tel (804) 747-0592 *Founded/Ownrshp* 1948
Sales 1.0MMM *EMP* 111
SIC 4911

D-U-N-S 00-687-0877
▲ OLD DOMINION FREIGHT LINE INC
500 Old Dominion Way, Thomasville, NC 27360-8923
Tel (336) 889-5000 *Founded/Ownrshp* 1934
Sales 2.9MMM *EMP* 17,931
Tkr Sym ODFL *Exch* NGS
SIC 4213 4212 4731 Trucking, except local; Less-than-truckload (LTL) transport; Local trucking, without storage; Freight transportation arrangement
CEO: David S Congdon
**Ch Bd:* Earl E Congdon
Pr: Greg C Gantt
CFO: Adam N Satterfield
Sr VP: David J Bates
Sr VP: Kevin M Freeman
Sr VP: Cecel E Overbey Jr
Sr VP: Cecil E Overbey
Sr VP: Ross H Parr
VP: John P Booker III
VP: Richard F Keeler
VP: Chris Young
Board of Directors: John R Congdon Jr, Robert G Culp III, John D Kasarda, Leo H Suggs, D Michael Wray

D-U-N-S 00-794-0786
OLD DOMINION TOBACCO CO INC (VA)
ATLANTIC DOMINION DISTRIBUTORS
5400 Virginia Beach Blvd, Virginia Beach, VA 23462-1724
Tel (757) 497-1001 *Founded/Ownrshp* 1874, 1982
Sales 300.0MM *EMP* 200
Accts Kpmg
SIC 5194 5145 Tobacco & tobacco products; Cigarettes; Confectionery; Candy; Chewing gum; Snack foods
Pr: Robin D Ray
**Treas:* Andrea Tanner
**Ex VP:* Kevin Barney
Dir Bus: Kathy Hines
DP Dir: David Baglione

D-U-N-S 04-144-8465 EXP
OLD DOMINION UNIVERSITY
(*Suby of* STATE COUNCIL OF HIGHER EDUCATION FOR VIRGINIA) ★
5115 Hampton Blvd, Norfolk, VA 23529-0001
Tel (757) 683-3000 *Founded/Ownrshp* 1930
Sales 402.2MM^E *EMP* 4,390
SIC 8221 9411 University;
Pr: John Broderick
**Pr:* John Browerick
Ofcr: Jacqueline Alexander
Ofcr: Nathan Fronczek
Ofcr: Bill Smith
Assoc VP: Jim Duffy
VP: Brittany Hollis
VP: Ellen Neufeldt
VP: September Sanderlin
Exec: Jennifer Mullen
Assoc Dir: Aaron Hodnett
Assoc Dir: Alex Parr

D-U-N-S 00-625-9261
OLD DUTCH FOODS INC (MN)
2375 Terminal Rd, Saint Paul, MN 55113-2577
Tel (651) 633-8810 *Founded/Ownrshp* 1934, 1951
Sales 88.4MM^E *EMP* 500
SIC 2096

D-U-N-S 00-732-6879 IMP/EXP
OLD FRITO-LAY INC
7701 Legacy Dr, Plano, TX 75024-4002
Tel (972) 334-7000 *Founded/Ownrshp* 1965
Sales 5.4MMM^E *EMP* 39,870
SIC 2096 2052 2013 5812 6794 2086

D-U-N-S 00-287-6571
OLD GES INC (TX)
GREENE'S ENERGY GROUP
11757 Katy Fwy Ste 700, Houston, TX 77079-0011
Tel (281) 598-6830 *Founded/Ownrshp* 1978, 2004
Sales 658.6MM^E *EMP* 500
SIC 1389 7353 3599 7359 1382 Oil field services; Oil field equipment, rental or leasing; Machine shop, jobbing & repair; Equipment rental & leasing; Oil & gas exploration services
**CFO:* Brad Farnsworth
Treas: Anders Jensen
**Sr VP:* Gene Garber
**VP:* Tom Sawyer
Sfty Mgr: Cherry Patterson

D-U-N-S 18-761-5534
OLD HARBOR NATIVE CORP
2702 Denali St Ste 100, Anchorage, AK 99503-2747
Tel (907) 278-6100 *Founded/Ownrshp* 1973
Sales 121.1MM^E *EMP* 402
SIC 8748 Business consulting
Pr: Emil Christiansen Sr
CFO: Dave L Jarrett
**Treas:* Jeff Peterson
**VP:* Al Cratti

VP: Carl Gatter
IT Man: Cynthia Berns

D-U-N-S 18-628-3768 IMP/EXP
OLD HB INC
HOSTESS BRANDS
3101 Mercier St Ste 422, Kansas City, MO 64111-3647
Tel (816) 502-4000 *Founded/Ownrshp* 1987
Sales 228.8MM[E] *EMP* 21,962
SIC 2051 5461

D-U-N-S 02-515-1341 IMP
OLD HF LLC
ROOM PLACE, THE
(*Suby of* ROOM PLACE) ★
1000 N Rohlwing Rd Ste 46, Lombard, IL 60148-1187
Tel (630) 261-3900 *Founded/Ownrshp* 2012
Sales 157.8MM[E] *EMP* 580
SIC 5712 Furniture stores; Bedding & bedsprings; Mattresses
Pr: Bruce Berman
* *CFO:* Joe Connolly

D-U-N-S 19-503-7783 EXP
OLD LADDER CO
WERNER EXTRUDED PRODUCTS
93 Werner Rd, Greenville, PA 16125-9434
Tel (888) 523-3371 *Founded/Ownrshp* 1994
Sales 185.2MM[E] *EMP* 2,100
SIC 3446 3089 3334 3444 3499 Scaffolds, mobile or stationary: metal; Synthetic resin finished products; Primary aluminum; Sheet metalwork; Ladders, portable: metal
Pr: Steven P Richman
Ch Bd: Donald M Werner
Pr: Edward Gericke
CEO: James J Loughlin Jr
CFO: Larry V Friend
Treas: Eric I Werner
Sr VP: John J Fiumefreddo
Sr VP: Edward W Gericke
Sr VP: Peter R O'Coin
Sr VP: John M Remmers
VP: Steven R Bentson
VP: Eric J Werner

D-U-N-S 01-734-7592
OLD MUTUAL (US) HOLDINGS INC
OMAN INC
(*Suby of* OLD MUTUAL PUBLIC LIMITED COMPANY)
200 Clarendon St Fl 53, Boston, MA 02116-5055
Tel (617) 369-7300 *Founded/Ownrshp* 2011
Sales 421.0MM[E] *EMP* 1,283
SIC 6726 Investment offices; Management investment funds, closed-end
Pr: Peter Bain
CEO: Julian Ide
CEO: Karen Rowe
* *COO:* Linda Tilton Gibson
* *CFO:* Matthew E Berger
Ex VP: Kevin Hunt
Sr VP: Matt Berger
VP: Matthew J Appelstein
VP: Thomas McLain
VP: Molly Mugler
VP: Clarke Stephen
Exec: Lynda Cooper

OLD MUTUAL FINANCIAL NETWORK
See FIDELITY & GUARANTY LIFE INSURANCE CO

D-U-N-S 06-833-1164
▲ **OLD NATIONAL BANCORP**
1 Main St, Evansville, IN 47708-1464
Tel (812) 464-1294 *Founded/Ownrshp* 1982
Sales NA *EMP* 2,652[E]
Tkr Sym ONB *Exch* NGS
SIC 6021 National commercial banks
Ch Bd: Robert G Jones
Pr: James A Sandgren
Pr: James Schmidt
CFO: James C Ryan
Treas: Brendon Falconer
Treas: Mike Loyd
Chf Cred: Daryl D Moore
Ofcr: Julie Williams Daugherty
Ofcr: Ryan Doughty
Ofcr: Candice J Rickard
Ex VP: Caroline J Ellspermann
Ex VP: John R Kamin
Ex VP: Kendra L Vanzo
Sr VP: Mark Gorski
Sr VP: Jennifer Guzman
VP: Steve Brown
VP: Jamie Guise
VP: Tammy Hall
VP: Janet Heldt
VP: George Lance
VP: John Myrland
Board of Directors: Kelly N Stanley, Alan W Braun, Derrick Stewart, Niel C Ellerbrook, Katherine White, Andrew E Goebel, Linda White, Jerome Henry Jr, Phelps L Lambert, Arthur H McElwee Jr, James T Morris, Randall T Shepard, Rebecca S Skillman

D-U-N-S 00-693-6959
■ **OLD NATIONAL BANK**
(*Suby of* OLD NATIONAL BANCORP) ★
1 Main St, Evansville, IN 47708-1464
Tel (800) 731-2265 *Founded/Ownrshp* 1834
Sales NA *EMP* 1,938
SIC 6021 6022 National commercial banks; State commercial banks
Ch Bd: Barbara Murphy
* *Ch Bd:* James A Risinger
* *Pr:* Steve Bennett
Pr: Amy Casavant
Pr: Chris Fleck
* *Pr:* Janet Heldt
* *CFO:* Gene Smith
* *Treas:* Danyelle Granger
Ex VP: Richard Dube
* *Ex VP:* Wayne Henning
Ex VP: Jeffrey Knight
Ex VP: Daryl Moore
Ex VP: Allen R Mounts
Ex VP: Jim Ryan
Ex VP: Kathy Schoettlin
Ex VP: Gina Stuart
Ex VP: Kendra Vanzo

Ex VP: Stephanie White
Sr VP: Gary Case
* *Sr VP:* Steve Deputy
Sr VP: Dave Keller

OLD NATIONAL INSURANCE
See ONI RISK PARTNERS INC

D-U-N-S 17-082-3376 IMP
■ **OLD NAVY INC**
(*Suby of* GAP INC) ★
2 Folsom St, San Francisco, CA 94105-1205
Tel (650) 952-4400 *Founded/Ownrshp* 1997
Sales 556.3MM[E] *EMP* 5,000
SIC 5651 Family clothing stores
Pr: John Thomson Wyatt
Pr: Stefan Larsson
CFO: John J Lenk
Sr VP: Stacey Lavalle Fraser

D-U-N-S 08-512-4196 IMP/EXP
OLD RAZOR CO LLC
AMERICAN SAFETY RAZOR COMPANY
240 Cedar Knolls Rd, Cedar Knolls, NJ 07927-1621
Tel (973) 753-3000 *Founded/Ownrshp* 2010
Sales 614.1MM[E] *EMP* 1,522
SIC 3421

D-U-N-S 02-284-1340
■ **OLD REPUBLIC HOME PROTECTION CO INC**
(*Suby of* OLD REPUBLIC INTERNATIONAL CORP) ★
2 Annabel Ln Ste 112, San Ramon, CA 94583-1377
Tel (925) 866-1500 *Founded/Ownrshp* 1981
Sales NA *EMP* 305
SIC 6411 Insurance agents, brokers & service
Pr: Gwen M Gallagher
VP: Pj Cochran
VP: Cathy Hall
* *VP:* Lorna Mello
VP: Jim Mullery
Web Dev: Corey Klass

D-U-N-S 00-791-1035
■ **OLD REPUBLIC INSURANCE CO** (PA)
(*Suby of* OLD REPUBLIC INTERNATIONAL CORP) ★
133 Oakland Ave, Greensburg, PA 15601-2247
Tel (724) 838-5400 *Founded/Ownrshp* 1935, 2001
Sales NA *EMP* 200
SIC 6411 6321 6311 Insurance agents, brokers & service; Health insurance carriers; Life insurance carriers
Pr: Aldo C Zucaro
Pr: Deb Matthews
CFO: Karl Mueller
* *Sr VP:* Spencer Leroy III
VP: Christine Mundell
* *VP:* Albert M Slotter Jr
VP: Albert Slotter

D-U-N-S 06-948-8849
▲ **OLD REPUBLIC INTERNATIONAL CORP**
307 N Michigan Ave, Chicago, IL 60601-5311
Tel (312) 346-8100 *Founded/Ownrshp* 1969
Sales NA *EMP* 8,000[E]
Tkr Sym ORI *Exch* NYS
SIC 6351 Surety insurance; Liability insurance
Ch Bd: Aldo C Zucaro
Pr: R Scott Rager
CFO: Karl W Mueller
Treas: Charles S Boone
Ex VP: Charles Gregory
Sr VP: John R Heitkamp Jr
VP: Spencer Leroy
VP: Stephanie Richards
MIS Dir: Jim Arends
Dir IT: Don Ebert
Dir IT: Ken Nelson
Board of Directors: Jimmy A Dew, John M Dixon, James C Hellauer, Spencer Leroy III, Arnold L Steiner, Charles F Titterton, Dennis P Van Mieghem, Steven R Walker

D-U-N-S 17-540-5901
■ **OLD REPUBLIC MORTGAGE GUARANTEE GROUP INC**
(*Suby of* OLD REPUBLIC INTERNATIONAL CORP) ★
307 N Michigan Ave # 1400, Chicago, IL 60601-5311
Tel (312) 346-8100 *Founded/Ownrshp* 1973
Sales NA *EMP* 578
SIC 6361 Title insurance
Pr: William Simpson
* *VP:* Paul Davenport

D-U-N-S 07-176-7412
■ **OLD REPUBLIC NATIONAL TITLE HOLDING CO**
(*Suby of* OLD REPUBLIC TITLE INSURANCE GROUP INC (DEL)) ★
400 2nd Ave S, Minneapolis, MN 55401-2406
Tel (612) 371-1111 *Founded/Ownrshp* 1981
Sales NA *EMP* 2,300
SIC 6361 Title insurance
Treas: Shannon Ade
Ex VP: Stephen C Wilson
Sr VP: William Torpey
VP: Jeff Bluhm
VP: Stephanie Cournoyer
VP: Robert Kennedy
VP: Spencer Leroy III
VP: Barry Martin
VP: Stephen Nazian
VP: Stephen Oberst
VP: Kim Silva
Exec: Alan Hall
Comm Man: Lori Turpin

D-U-N-S 00-696-2716
■ **OLD REPUBLIC NATIONAL TITLE INSURANCE CO**
(*Suby of* OLD REPUBLIC NATIONAL TITLE HOLDING CO) ★
400 2nd Ave S, Minneapolis, MN 55401-2406
Tel (612) 371-1111 *Founded/Ownrshp* 1907
Sales NA *EMP* 2,300
SIC 6361 Real estate title insurance
Pr: Rande K Yeager
Pr: William Patsos

Pr: Steven Vcard
* *Pr:* Stephen C Wilson
Pr: Pamela Zimmerman
* *CFO:* Gary J Horn
Ofcr: Drucilla Asa-Awuku
* *Ex VP:* Mark M Budzinski
Sr VP: Martha Love
VP: Julie Bergh
VP: Barb Brennan
VP: Hoyum Chuck
VP: Patricia Clement
VP: John Hall
VP: Carla Hawkins
VP: Joseph A Johnson
VP: Charles Jordan
VP: Tom Leavitt
VP: Gayle Lynch
VP: Chad Novak
VP Bus Dev: Trisha Ewert

D-U-N-S 80-738-3286
■ **OLD REPUBLIC SECURITY HOLDINGS INC**
(*Suby of* OLD REPUBLIC INTERNATIONAL CORP) ★
307 N Michigan Ave # 1400, Chicago, IL 60601-5311
Tel (312) 346-8100 *Founded/Ownrshp* 2001
Sales NA *EMP* 160
SIC 6411 6361 Insurance agents, brokers & service; Title insurance
Pr: Aldo C Zucaro
* *Ofcr:* Paul Adams

D-U-N-S 80-738-3229
■ **OLD REPUBLIC SURETY GROUP INC**
(*Suby of* OLD REPUBLIC INTERNATIONAL CORP) ★
307 N Michigan Ave # 1400, Chicago, IL 60601-5311
Tel (312) 346-8100 *Founded/Ownrshp* 2001
Sales NA *EMP* 170
SIC 6411 6361 Insurance agents, brokers & service; Title insurance
Pr: Aldo Zucaro

D-U-N-S 07-655-2850
■ **OLD REPUBLIC TITLE CO**
(*Suby of* OLD REPUBLIC TITLE INSURANCE GROUP INC (DEL)) ★
275 Battery St Ste 1500, San Francisco, CA 94111-3334
Tel (415) 421-3500 *Founded/Ownrshp* 1972
Sales NA *EMP* 1,076
Accts Pricewaterhousecoopers Llp Sa
SIC 6361 6531 Real estate title insurance; Escrow agent, real estate
Ch Bd: Rande K Yeager
* *Pr:* Wayne Shupe
COO: Sam Carlisi
* *Treas:* Dick Neves
Sr Cor Off: Patrick Connor
Sr Cor Off: Cliff Johnson
Ex VP: Kathy Brolin
Ex VP: David Hartman
Sr VP: Rob J Chapman
* *Sr VP:* Carleton R Lago
Sr VP: Margaret Serrano-Foster
* *VP:* Jim Beaty
VP: Carolyn Broadwater
VP: Rob Kernutt

D-U-N-S 09-335-7721
■ **OLD REPUBLIC TITLE CO** (CA)
(*Suby of* OLD REPUBLIC TITLE HOLDING CO INC) ★
101 N Brand Blvd Ste 1400, Glendale, CA 91203-2691
Tel (818) 240-1936 *Founded/Ownrshp* 1967, 1989
Sales NA *EMP* 657[E]
SIC 6361 Title insurance
Pr: Merv Morris
Ofcr: Devon H Beesley
Ofcr: Rudy Cortez
Ofcr: Michael Demers
Ofcr: Laurel Leftwich
Ofcr: Julia Lockrem
Ofcr: Chris Ritter
Ofcr: Ward Taylor
Sr VP: Jeffrey Bernatz
Sr VP: Elaine Layton
Sr VP: John Snelgrove
VP: Judith Braun
VP: Jeff Dasse
VP: Mike Demers
VP: Jamie Gavello
VP: Wendy McLaughlin
VP: Richard Neves
VP: Kelly Quam
VP: Bill Rossi
VP: Robert Sylvester
Exec: Lou Collier

D-U-N-S 02-635-5700
■ **OLD REPUBLIC TITLE CO OF NORTHERN OHIO LLC**
(*Suby of* OLD REPUBLIC NATIONAL TITLE INSURANCE CO) ★
6480 Rockside Woods Blvd S, Independence, OH 44131-2233
Tel (216) 524-5700 *Founded/Ownrshp* 2002
Sales NA *EMP* 935[E]
SIC 6411 6162 6211 Insurance agents, brokers & service; Mortgage bankers; Underwriters, security
VP: John R Monacelli

D-U-N-S 06-613-2911
■ **OLD REPUBLIC TITLE HOLDING CO INC**
(*Suby of* OLD REPUBLIC NATIONAL TITLE HOLDING CO) ★
275 Battery St Ste 1500, San Francisco, CA 94111-3334
Tel (415) 421-3500 *Founded/Ownrshp* 1979
Sales NA *EMP* 1,076
SIC 6361 6531 5045 Real estate title insurance; Escrow agent, real estate; Computers, peripherals & software
CEO: Rande K Yeager
* *Treas:* Dick Neves
Ofcr: Cheri Williams
Sr VP: Lauren Gray
Off Admin: Vickie Kube

D-U-N-S 05-231-5116
■ **OLD REPUBLIC TITLE INSURANCE GROUP INC (DEL)**
(*Suby of* OLD REPUBLIC INTERNATIONAL CORP) ★
307 N Michigan Ave # 1400, Chicago, IL 60601-5311
Tel (312) 346-8100 *Founded/Ownrshp* 1979
Sales NA *EMP* 2,300
SIC 6361 6531 Real estate title insurance; Escrow agent, real estate
Pr: Aldo C Zucaro
V Ch: James Kellogg
COO: Craig Smiddy
Ex VP: Leonard Milazzo
Sr VP: Charles Boone
* *Sr VP:* Spencer Leroy
Sr VP: Rande K Yeager
VP: Jim Arends
VP: Larry Davis
VP: John Heitkamp
VP: Dana Loncar
VP: Zandra Morris
VP: Christine Mundell
VP: Roger Strickland
VP: Kirk Wilson

OLD SALT SEAFOOD
See SEA WATCH INTERNATIONAL LTD

D-U-N-S 10-382-9156
▲ **OLD SECOND BANCORP INC**
37 S River St, Aurora, IL 60506-4173
Tel (630) 892-0202 *Founded/Ownrshp* 1981
Sales NA *EMP* 492[E]
Accts Plante & Moran Pllc Chicago
Tkr Sym OSBC *Exch* NGS
SIC 6022 State commercial banks
Pr: James Eccher
* *Ch Bd:* William B Skoglund
Pr: Kyle Ray
COO: Jackie Allison
* *CFO:* J Douglas Cheatham
Chf Cred: John Juffre
Trst Ofcr: Steven Coates
VP: Michelle Almond
VP: Chris Barry
VP: Brian Cota
VP: Robert Duplessis
VP: Stan Faries
VP: Robert Ferrigan
VP: Keith Gottschalk
VP: Linda Mendoza
VP: Laurie Rogman
VP: Sue Turner
VP: Kristin Zell
VP Bus Dev: Jacqueline Runnberg

D-U-N-S 00-692-7818
■ **OLD SECOND NATIONAL BANK OF AURORA**
(*Suby of* OLD SECOND BANCORP INC) ★
37 S River St, Aurora, IL 60506-4172
Tel (630) 844-3555 *Founded/Ownrshp* 1871, 1982
Sales NA *EMP* 300
SIC 6021 National commercial banks
Pr: William Skoglund
Ch Bd: James Echert
Pr: Sally Kerby
CFO: Doug Cheatham
Ofcr: David Bach
Ofcr: Mary Randel
Ex VP: June Courtney
Ex VP: Mary Wilson
Sr VP: Charles A Barber
Sr VP: Robert A Ferrigan Jr
Sr VP: Keith Gottschalk
VP: Layne Burns
VP: Kathy Diedrick
VP: Greg Kuda
VP: Steve Marchio
VP: Karen Nelson
VP: Kenneth Spaeth
VP: Tim Vaughan
Exec: Robert Dicosola

OLD SPAGHETTI FACTORY
See OSF INTERNATIONAL INC

D-U-N-S 15-201-5848 IMP
OLD TIME POTTERY LLC
480 River Rock Blvd, Murfreesboro, TN 37128-4804
Tel (615) 890-6060 *Founded/Ownrshp* 2014
Sales 848.9MM[E] *EMP* 3,000
SIC 5999 5023 Art, picture frames & decorations; Home furnishings
Pr: Scott Peterson
* *CFO:* Robert Sharp
* *VP:* Sallie S Peterson

OLD WORLD INDUSTRIES AUTO
See OLD WORLD INDUSTRIES LLC

D-U-N-S 19-516-6624 IMP/EXP
OLD WORLD INDUSTRIES LLC
OLD WORLD INDUSTRIES AUTO
4065 Commercial Ave, Northbrook, IL 60062-1828
Tel (847) 559-2000 *Founded/Ownrshp* 1973
Sales 563.9MM[E] *EMP* 300
SIC 5013 5169 Automotive supplies; Anti-freeze compounds
Pr: Khalid Mahmood
CFO: Anthony Ciesceri
* *CFO:* Mark Rocco
* *Treas:* Anthony J Clesceri
* *Sr VP:* Daniel M Leep
VP: Spaeth Jim
VP: Kelley O'Donnell
* *Genl Mgr:* Charles Culverhouse
CIO: Steve Thallmer
CTO: Alan Walters
Dir IT: Don Johenan

D-U-N-S 16-989-8736
OLDCASTLE ARCHITECTURAL INC
(*Suby of* OLDCASTLE INC) ★
900 Ashwood Pkwy Ste 600, Atlanta, GA 30338-7501
Tel (770) 804-3363 *Founded/Ownrshp* 1987
Sales 170.6MM[E] *EMP* 367
SIC 3251 Brick & structural clay tile
CEO: Keith Haas
* *Pr:* Rick Mergens

*CFO: Michael Schaeffer
Off Mgr: Rose Hughes
Dir IT: Lou McNeil
VP Sls: Kathy Rudolph
Mktg Mgr: Donald Foster
Sls Mgr: Aaron Faubli

D-U-N-S 82-771-9506
OLDCASTLE BUILDING PRODUCTS INC
(Suby of OLDCASTLE INC) ★
900 Ashwood Pkwy Ste 600, Atlanta, GA 30338-7501
Tel (770) 804-3363 Founded/Ownrshp 2000
Sales 141.5MM^E EMP 160
SIC 5031 Building materials, exterior
Pr: Liam O'Mahony

D-U-N-S 18-114-0815 IMP/EXP
OLDCASTLE BUILDINGENVELOPE INC
(Suby of OLDCASTLE INC) ★
5005 Lndn B Jnsn Fwy 10 Ste 1050, Dallas, TX 75244
Tel (214) 273-3400 Founded/Ownrshp 2016
Sales 959.5MM^E EMP 4,010
SIC 3231 5231 Tempered glass: made from purchased glass; Insulating glass: made from purchased glass; Glass
CEO: Edwin B Hathaway
*Ch Bd: Liam O'Nahony
*Pr: Doug Black
CFO: Cassandra Harris
*CFO: Dominic Maggiano
*Sec: Michael O'Driscoll
VP: J Quick

D-U-N-S 13-241-3167
OLDCASTLE DISTRIBUTION INC
ALLIED BUILDING PRODUCTS CO
(Suby of OLDCASTLE INC) ★
15 E Union Ave, East Rutherford, NJ 07073-2127
Tel (201) 507-8400 Founded/Ownrshp 2002
Sales 1.7MMM^E EMP 3,300^E
SIC 5031 5032 Building materials, exterior; Building materials, interior; Brick, stone & related material
Pr: Don Toth
VP: Gregory Bloom
Brnch Mgr: Sarah Aiken
Dist Mgr: Adam Carscadden
Trfc Dir: Donald Whalen
Sls Mgr: Natalie Colon
Sls Mgr: Stewart Staples
Sales Asso: Dawn Cintron
Sales Asso: Sheri Johnson
Sales Asso: John Kiefat
Sales Asso: Heath Meyer

D-U-N-S 03-717-6591 IMP/EXP
OLDCASTLE INC
(Suby of CRH PUBLIC LIMITED COMPANY)
900 Ashwood Pkwy Ste 600, Atlanta, GA 30338-7501
Tel (770) 804-3363 Founded/Ownrshp 1978
Sales 21.3MMM^E EMP 35,000
SIC 3273 3272 3271 3255 Ready-mixed concrete; Pipe, concrete or lined with concrete; Concrete block & brick; Clay refractories
CEO: Mark S Towe
COO: Jim Avanzini
CFO: Stephen Colman
*CFO: Michael G O'Driscoll
CFO: Michael Odreiscoll
CFO: Michael G Odriscoll
Sr Cor Off: Jeff Schaffer
VP: Jerry Cottelberg
VP: Chris Garrie
VP: Mjichael Lynch
VP: David Majher
VP: John Martin
VP: Ken O'Neill

OLDCASTLE MATERIALS GROUP
See OLDCASTLE MATERIALS INC

D-U-N-S 80-670-9812
OLDCASTLE MATERIALS INC
OLDCASTLE MATERIALS GROUP
(Suby of OLDCASTLE INC) ★
900 Ashwood Pkwy Ste 700, Atlanta, GA 30338-4780
Tel (770) 522-5600 Founded/Ownrshp 1985
Sales 4.3MMM^E EMP 2,405
SIC 3272 1622 1611 2951 5032 Concrete products, precast; Prestressed concrete products; Bridge construction; General contractor, highway & street construction; Asphalt paving mixtures & blocks; Stone, crushed or broken
CEO: Randy Lake
*Pr: Mark Towe
*CFO: Glenn Culpepper
VP: John Rice
VP: Steven N Ross
Dir IT: Chris Picerno
IT Man: Richard Chan

OLDCASTLE PRECAST ENCLO
See OLDCASTLE PRECAST INC

D-U-N-S 00-948-4866 IMP/EXP
OLDCASTLE PRECAST INC
DRAINAGE PROTECTION SYSTEMS
(Suby of CRH AMERICA INC) ★
1002 15th St Sw Ste 110, Auburn, WA 98001-6502
Tel (253) 833-2777 Founded/Ownrshp 1981
Sales 401.9MM^E EMP 3,336
SIC 3272 3446

D-U-N-S 05-226-2235 IMP
OLDCASTLE PRECAST INC
OLDCASTLE PRECAST ENCLO
(Suby of DRAINAGE PROTECTION SYSTEMS) ★
2434 Rubidoux Blvd, Riverside, CA 92509-2144
Tel (951) 788-9720 Founded/Ownrshp 2008
Sales 245.7MM^E EMP 3,000^E
SIC 3089 Boxes, plastic
CEO: David Steevens
*Treas: Eric Farinha

OLDCASTLE SURFACES
See CREATIVE SURFACES INC

D-U-N-S 03-208-0996
OLDCASTLE SW GROUP INC
UNITED PAVING
(Suby of CRH PUBLIC LIMITED COMPANY)
2273 River Rd, Grand Junction, CO 81505-7179
Tel (970) 243-4900 Founded/Ownrshp 1954
Sales 139.8MM^E EMP 392
SIC 1611 3273 5032 General contractor, highway & street construction; Ready-mixed concrete; Sand, construction; Gravel
Pr: Rich Umbel
*CFO: Phill Raimer
Genl Mgr: Janel Tanner
Off Mgr: Julie Brown

D-U-N-S 00-610-1968 IMP/EXP
OLDENBURG GROUP INC
VISA LIGHTING
1717 W Civic Dr, Milwaukee, WI 53209-4433
Tel (414) 354-6600 Founded/Ownrshp 1982
Sales 187.5MM^E EMP 610
SIC 3537 3532 3646 Industrial trucks & tractors; Dollies (hand or power trucks), industrial except mining; Mining machinery; Commercial indusl & institutional electric lighting fixtures
CEO: Wayne C Oldenburg
Pr: Tim Nerenz
VP: Joseph Wouters
Dir Sec: Tom Fischer
QA Dir: Brian Lenten
Dir IT: Jim Stalewski
Info Man: Kate Carberry
Info Man: Kate Dorsey
Sfty Mgr: Chad Mays
Prd Mgr: Jake Bishop
VP Sls: Mary Champagne

D-U-N-S 08-101-5232
OLDHAM COUNTY SCHOOL DISTRICT
6165 W Highway 146, Crestwood, KY 40014-9531
Tel (502) 241-3500 Founded/Ownrshp 1875
Sales 111.7MM EMP 1,300
Accts Stiles Carter & Associates
SIC 8211 Public elementary & secondary schools
Pr Dir: Lori McDowell
Teacher Pr: Richard Graviss

D-U-N-S 01-348-3438
OLE HBO PARTNERS
HBO LATIN AMERICA GROUP
396 Alhambra Cir Ste 400, Coral Gables, FL 33134-5087
Tel (305) 648-8100 Founded/Ownrshp 1996
Sales 206.9MM^E EMP 700
SIC 4841 Cable television services
Pr: Gaston Comas
Pt: Thomas Short
Pt: David Torkington
VP: Edgar Villapando

D-U-N-S 62-099-2081 EXP
OLE MEXICAN FOODS INC
6585 Crescent Dr, Norcross, GA 30071-2901
Tel (770) 582-9200 Founded/Ownrshp 1988
Sales 269.1MM EMP 920
Accts Windham Brannon Pc Atlanta
SIC 2099 2032 Tortillas, fresh or refrigerated; Mexican foods: packaged in cans, jars, etc.
CEO: Veronica Moreno
*VP: Eduardo Moreno
Sls Mgr: Charles Marvin

D-U-N-S 03-022-3192
OLEAN GENERAL HOSPITAL
(Suby of UPPER ALLEGHENY HEALTH SYSTEM INC) ★
515 Main St, Olean, NY 14760-1598
Tel (716) 373-2600 Founded/Ownrshp 1898
Sales 104.7MM EMP 983
Accts Lumsden & Mccormick Llp Buff
SIC 8062 General medical & surgical hospitals
CEO: Tim Finan
Chf Rad: Alexandra Wesley
*Pr: Timothy Finan
COO: Zahid Chohan
*CFO: Richard Braun
Sr VP: Rebecca Bruso
*VP: Karen Fohl
VP: Jeff Zewe
Nurse Mgr: Mary Beyth
Nurse Mgr: Jamie Glover
Nurse Mgr: Katherine Watkins

D-U-N-S 00-448-7633
OLEN CORP (OH)
4755 S High St, Columbus, OH 43207-4080
Tel (614) 491-1515 Founded/Ownrshp 1951
Sales 289.1MM^E EMP 86
SIC 1442

D-U-N-S 02-915-6189
OLENTANGY LOCAL SCHOOL DISTRICT
814 Shanahan Rd Ste 100, Lewis Center, OH 43035-9192
Tel (740) 657-4050 Founded/Ownrshp 1920
Sales 216.5MM EMP 1,500
Accts Robert Hinkle Cpa Cgfm Colu
SIC 8211 Public elementary school; Public junior high school; Public senior high school
*Prin: Linda Martin
Teacher Pr: Todd Meyer

D-U-N-S 06-982-3714
OLGAS KITCHEN INC
(Suby of ROBERT B SOLOMON HOLDING COMPANY)
2125 Butterfield Dr # 301, Troy, MI 48084-3441
Tel (248) 362-0001 Founded/Ownrshp 1977
Sales 4.5MM^E EMP 1,107^E
SIC 5812 Greek restaurant
Pr: Robert B Solomon
COO: William M Carpenter
Brnch Mgr: Susan Taylor

OLIN BRASS
See GBC METALS LLC

D-U-N-S 08-016-2119
■ **OLIN CHLOR ALKALI LOGISTICS INC**
(Suby of OLIN SUNBELT II INC) ★
490 Stuart Rd Ne, Cleveland, TN 37312-4918
Tel (423) 336-4850 Founded/Ownrshp 2016
Sales 98.6MM^E EMP 941^E
SIC 2812 Alkalies & chlorine; Caustic soda, sodium hydroxide; Chlorine, compressed or liquefied

D-U-N-S 00-133-8086
▲ **OLIN CORP**
190 Carondelet Plz # 1530, Saint Louis, MO 63105-3467
Tel (314) 480-1400 Founded/Ownrshp 1892
Sales 2.8MMM EMP 6,200
Accts Kpmg Llp St Louis Missouri
Tkr Sym OLN Exch NYS
SIC 2812 2819 2821 2842 2869 2891 Alkalies & chlorine; Caustic soda, sodium hydroxide; Chlorine, compressed or liquefied; Hydrochloric acid; Sulfuric acid, oleum; Potasssium chloride & cyanide; Calcium chloride & hypochlorite; Polyurethane resins; Cleaning or polishing preparations; Glycol ethers; Adhesives & sealants
Ch Bd: Joseph D Rupp
Pr: Pat D Dawson
Pr: John E Fischer
Pr: Clive A Grannum
Pr: James A Varilek
CFO: Todd A Slater
Ex VP: Michael E Campbell
Sr VP: George H Pain
VP: Roger Jones
VP: John McIntosh
VP: Frank Obrien
VP: John M Sampson
VP: Robert Steel
VP: Randee N Sumner
Board of Directors: Carol A Williams, Gray G Benoist, Donald W Bogus, C Robert Bunch, Randall W Larrimore, John M B O'connor, Richard M Rompala, Philip J Schulz, Vincent J Smith, William H Weideman

D-U-N-S 96-768-4593
■ **OLIN SUNBELT II INC**
(Suby of OLIN CORP) ★
190 Carondelet Plz # 1530, Saint Louis, MO 63105-3443
Tel (314) 480-1400 Founded/Ownrshp 2011
Sales 107.4MM^E EMP 1,245^E
SIC 2812 Caustic soda, sodium hydroxide
Prin: David Dye

OLINGER DISTRIBUTING COMPANY
See GLAZERS DISTRIBUTORS OF INDIANA LLC

OLIVE GARDEN
See GMRI INC

OLIVE GARDEN
See RARE HOSPITALITY INTERNATIONAL INC

D-U-N-S 03-738-5759
OLIVE VIEW-UCLA MEDICAL CENTER
VALLEY CARE OLIVE VIEW MEDICAL
14445 Olive View Dr, Sylmar, CA 91342-1438
Tel (818) 364-1555 Founded/Ownrshp 2001
Sales 357.8MM EMP 2,000^E
SIC 8011 Medical centers
CEO: Carolyn Rhee
Exec: Cynthia O'Donnell
Obsttrcn: Barbara Fletcher
HC Dir: Jeffrey Guterman
HC Dir: Sharon Ryun

D-U-N-S 00-945-7672
OLIVER DE SILVA INC
GALLAGHER & BURK
11555 Dublin Blvd, Dublin, CA 94568-2854
Tel (925) 829-9220 Founded/Ownrshp 1931
Sales 106.0MM^E EMP 200
SIC 1429 Igneous rock, crushed & broken-quarrying
Ch: Edwin O De Silva
*Pr: Richard B Gates
*Ex VP: David De Silva
*VP: J Scott Archibald
*VP: Ernest Lampkin

D-U-N-S 07-829-8780
OLIVER PRODUCTS CO
OLIVER-TOLAS HEALTHCARE PACKG
(Suby of BERWIND CORP) ★
445 6th St Nw, Grand Rapids, MI 49504-5298
Tel (616) 456-7711 Founded/Ownrshp 1890
Sales 253.0MM^E EMP 225^E
SIC 5084 5199 3053 Processing & packaging equipment; Packaging materials; Packing materials
Pr: Jerry Bennish
CFO: Ted Heininger
Rgnl Mgr: Julian Benavides
IT Man: Richard Brady
Mtls Mgr: Penny Lakanen
Mtls Mgr: Lisa McCool
Ql Cn Mgr: Zach Bazzi
Ql Cn Mgr: Steve Morgan
Natl Sales: David Haines
Advt Mgr: Jon Andreasen
Snr Mgr: Jennifer Buchin

D-U-N-S 17-905-9522 IMP
OLIVER-TOLAS HEALTHCARE PACKAGING INC
(Suby of OLIVER-TOLAS HEALTHCARE PACKG) ★
905 Pennsylvania Blvd, Feasterville Trevose, PA 19053-7815
Tel (215) 322-7900 Founded/Ownrshp 2013
Sales 124.4MM^E EMP 162
SIC 2671 Packaging paper & plastics film, coated & laminated
Pr: Scott Dickman
Mktg Mgr: Karen Barr
Snr Mgr: Denise Dilissio

D-U-N-S 02-545-1170 IMP/EXP
OLIVER-TOLAS HEALTHCARE PACKAGING LLC
445 6th St Nw, Grand Rapids, MI 49504-5253
Tel (616) 456-7711 Founded/Ownrshp 2007
Sales 133.2MM^E EMP 356^E
SIC 2672

OLIVER-TOLAS HEALTHCARE PACKG
See OLIVER PRODUCTS CO

D-U-N-S 05-610-8244
OLIVERMCMILLAN LLC
733 8th Ave, San Diego, CA 92101-6407
Tel (619) 321-1111 Founded/Ownrshp 1978
Sales 85.9MM^E EMP 60^E
SIC 6552 Land subdividers & developers, commercial; Land subdividers & developers, residential
CEO: Morgan Dene Oliver
*Pr: Paul Buss
*Pr: Dan Nishikawa
*CFO: Bill Persky
*Ch: Jim McMillan
Mng Dir: Darrell Thibodeaux
Mng Dir: Jack Webster
Rgnl Mgr: Alan Ong
Off Mgr: Ellen Ostler
Mktg Dir: Rick Burritt
Mktg Dir: Colin Moussa

D-U-N-S 15-690-0078 IMP
OLIVET INTERNATIONAL INC
11015 Hopkins St, Mira Loma, CA 91752-3248
Tel (951) 681-8888 Founded/Ownrshp 1984
Sales 145.3MM^E EMP 200
SIC 5099 Luggage
CEO: David Yu
Pr: Lydia Hsu
Dir IT: Chan Banh
VP Opers: Neal Weinstein

D-U-N-S 07-143-3668
OLIVET NAZARENE UNIVERSITY (IL)
1 University Ave, Bourbonnais, IL 60914-1996
Tel (815) 939-5247 Founded/Ownrshp 1907
Sales 130.1MM EMP 754
SIC 8221 University
Pr: John C Bowling
*Ch Bd: David Rowland
COO: Scott Dombrowski
*CFO: Dr Douglas Perry
Assoc Dir: Adam Banter
Assoc Dir: Stacey Hutton
Assoc Dir: Poppy Miller
Assoc Dir: Erinn Proehl
Dir Soc: Dana Carrigan
Store Mgr: Rachel Piazza
*CIO: Dennis Seymour

D-U-N-S 19-664-4053 IMP
▲ **OLLIES BARGAIN OUTLET HOLDINGS INC**
6295 Allentown Blvd Ste 1, Harrisburg, PA 17112-2694
Tel (717) 657-2300 Founded/Ownrshp 1982
Sales 762.3MM EMP 5,000
Tkr Sym OLLI Exch NGM
SIC 5399 5311 Surplus & salvage goods; Department stores, non-discount
Ch Bd: Mark Butler
CFO: John Swygert
Sr VP: Kevin McLain
Sr VP: Omar Segura
Sr VP: Jay Stasz
VP: Robert Bertram
VP Merchng: Howard Freedman
Board of Directors: Douglas Cahill, Robert Fisch, Stanley Fleishman, Thomas Hendrickson, Joseph Scharfenberger, Stephen W White, Richard Zannino

D-U-N-S 03-152-4424
■ **OLLIES BARGAIN OUTLET INC** (PA)
(Suby of OLLIES HOLDINGS INC) ★
6295 Allentown Blvd Ste 1, Harrisburg, PA 17112-2694
Tel (717) 657-8243 Founded/Ownrshp 1982, 2003
Sales 2.1MMM^E EMP 1,800
Accts Ernst & Young Llp
SIC 6799 Investors
Pr: Mark L Butler
*Pr: Howard Freedman
COO: Dave Campbell
COO: Kevin Phillips
*CFO: John Swygert
Sr VP: Kevin McLain
Sr VP: Omar Segura
*VP: Jerry Altland
*VP: Andre Dickemann
*VP: Dan Haines
VP: Daniel Haines
*VP: Doug Wisehaupt

D-U-N-S 08-005-4615
■ **OLLIES HOLDINGS INC**
(Suby of OLLIES BARGAIN OUTLET HOLDINGS INC) ★
6295 Allentown Blvd Ste 1, Harrisburg, PA 17112-2694
Tel (717) 657-2300 Founded/Ownrshp 2015
Sales 2.1MMM^E EMP 1,800^E
SIC 6799 Investors
Ch Bd: Mark Butler
Ex VP: John Swygert
Sr VP: Omar Segura
VP: Jeffrey Anderson

OLLINTECHNOLOGY
See ENRIQUE MENDOZA

D-U-N-S 78-255-0966
OLMOS CONSTRUCTION INC
440 Pinn Rd, San Antonio, TX 78227-1232
Tel (210) 675-4990 Founded/Ownrshp 1991
Sales 84.0MM^E EMP 300
SIC 1611 1794 1795 Surfacing & paving; Excavation work; Wrecking & demolition work
Pr: Hugh E Long
*CEO: Richard F Romane
CFO: Tracy Janicke
Ch: Carolyn Chamberlain
VP: Mark E Linneman
VP: Mark Linneman
*VP: Larry Struthoff
*VP: Jim Weynand

OLMSTED COUNTY HEALTH DEPT
See COUNTY OF OLMSTED

D-U-N-S 07-074-4388
OLMSTED MEDICAL CENTER
210 9th St Se Ste 1, Rochester, MN 55904-6400
Tel (507) 288-3443 *Founded/Ownrshp* 1949
Sales 189.2MM *EMP* 950
Accts Mcgladrey Llp Des Moines Ia
SIC 8062 General medical & surgical hospitals
Pr: Roy Yawn
CFO: Kevin Higgins
**Ofcr:* Kevin Pitzer
Exec: Geri Steele
Exec: Lois Till-Tarara
Dir Teleco: Shirley Claffy
IT Man: Richard Skagerberg
Netwrk Mgr: Dave Heller
Obsttrcn: Patricia Agudelo
Obsttrcn: Kimberly McKeon
Opthamlgy: T L Edwards

OLMSTED-KIRK EQUIPMENT & SUP
See OLMSTED-KIRK PAPER CO

D-U-N-S 00-894-7186 IMP
OLMSTED-KIRK PAPER CO
OLMSTED-KIRK EQUIPMENT & SUP
1601 Valley View Ln # 101, Dallas, TX 75234-9042
Tel (214) 637-2220 *Founded/Ownrshp* 1905
Sales 143.0MM^E *EMP* 300
SIC 5111

D-U-N-S 19-716-7802
OLS HOTELS & RESORTS LP
16000 Ventura Blvd # 1010, Encino, CA 91436-2744
Tel (818) 905-8280 *Founded/Ownrshp* 1989
Sales 84.8MM^E *EMP* 2,045
SIC 7011 Hotels & motels
CFO: Martti Mannaoja
Ex VP: Martti Mannoja
**Ex VP:* Roger Vasey
VP: Alan Bear
Genl Mgr: Stephen Bohjalian
Genl Mgr: Skip Sikora
Genl Mgr: Chad Thompson
Genl Mgr: Mark Vinsko
VP Mktg: Claudia Jackson

D-U-N-S 07-290-0368
OLSSON ASSOCIATES INC
601 P St, Lincoln, NE 68508-2305
Tel (402) 474-6311 *Founded/Ownrshp* 1956
Sales 194.2MM^E *EMP* 692
SIC 8711 Consulting engineer
CEO: Roger K Severin
**Pr:* Brad Strittmatter
**CFO:* Jeff Jenkins
Sr VP: Ryan Beckman
**Sr VP:* John S Olsson
**VP:* James L Condon
**VP:* Chip Corcoran
**VP:* Sterling Cramer
**VP:* Charles L Doane
**VP:* Kenneth Fairchild
**VP:* Stephen Ingracia
**VP:* Jerry L Kamtz
**VP:* Randall Kaster
**VP:* Bradley Korell
**VP:* Jeffrey R Kratzke
**VP:* Todd Lorenz
**VP:* Melissa Newton
**VP:* Kevin L Prior
**VP:* Daryoush Razavian
**VP:* Michael J Yost

OLSTEN
See ADO STAFFING INC

D-U-N-S 00-959-0399 EXP
OLTMANS CONSTRUCTION CO
10005 Mission Mill Rd, Whittier, CA 90601-1739
Tel (562) 948-4242 *Founded/Ownrshp* 1932
Sales 293.6MM^E *EMP* 535
SIC 1541 1542 Industrial buildings, new construction; Renovation, remodeling & repairs: industrial buildings; Commercial & office building, new construction; Commercial & office buildings, renovation & repair
Ch Bd: Joseph O Oltmans II
**Pr:* John Gormly
CFO: Greg Grupp
**CFO:* Dan Schlothan
**VP:* Tom Augustine
**VP:* Robert Larson
**VP:* Charles Roy
**VP:* Gerald Singh
**VP:* Jim Woodside
Sfty Dirs: Al Garcia
Sfty Dirs: Rebecca Wade

D-U-N-S 80-882-5657
■ OLYMPIA BALLYS LIMITED PARTNERSHIP
(*Suby of* HILTON) ★
1450 Ballys Blvd, Robinsonville, MS 38664-9721
Tel (662) 357-1500 *Founded/Ownrshp* 1996
Sales 4.9MM^E *EMP* 1,077
SIC 7999 7011 5813 5812 Gambling establishment; Hotels & motels; Drinking places; Eating places
Pr: Arthur Goldberg
**Genl Pt:* D J Brata
**Genl Pt:* Bally's Operator

D-U-N-S 07-557-6314
OLYMPIA ENTERTAINMENT INC
FOX THEATRE
(*Suby of* LITTLE CAESARS) ★
2211 Woodward Ave, Detroit, MI 48201-3467
Tel (313) 471-3200 *Founded/Ownrshp* 1982
Sales 80.6MM^E *EMP* 1,000
SIC 7832 Motion picture theaters, except drive-in
Ch Bd: Michael Ilitch
**Pr:* Dana Warg
**CFO:* Scott Fisher
**Sec:* Marian Ilitch
**VP:* Richard Fenton
**VP:* Bill Lee
Dir IT: Jenna Altobelli
Dir IT: Rob Chambers
Dir IT: Jason Flowers
Dir IT: Caroline Syran

D-U-N-S 84-731-8755
OLYMPIA FOOD INDUSTRIES INC
9501 Nevada Ave, Franklin Park, IL 60131-3331
Tel (847) 349-9358 *Founded/Ownrshp* 1989
Sales 126.3MM^E *EMP* 65^E
SIC 5149 Groceries & related products
Pr: Andre Papantoniou
Off Mgr: Joanne Barrera

D-U-N-S 02-182-0352
OLYMPIA SCHOOL DISTRICT
1113 Legion Way Se, Olympia, WA 98501-1697
Tel (360) 596-6100 *Founded/Ownrshp* 1852
Sales 51.6MM^E *EMP* 1,200
SIC 8211 Public elementary & secondary schools
Genl Mgr: Justin Lanting
Pr Dir: Susan Gifford
Schl Brd P: Frank Wilson
Teacher Pr: Scott Neman
Psych: Jennifer Boelts
Psych: Craig Costello
Psych: John Forrester
Psych: Eileen Haydu

D-U-N-S 82-853-5877 IMP
OLYMPIA SPORT CENTER INC
OLYMPIA SPORTS
5 Bradley Dr, Westbrook, ME 04092-2013
Tel (207) 854-2794 *Founded/Ownrshp* 2008
Sales 194.3MM^E *EMP* 2,500^E
Accts Baker Newman Noyes Llc Portl
SIC 5941 Sporting goods & bicycle shops
CEO: Ed Manganello
**CFO:* John Lesniak

OLYMPIA SPORTS
See OSC SPORTS INC

OLYMPIA SPORTS
See OLYMPIA SPORT CENTER INC

OLYMPIAN
See FLYERS ENERGY LLC

OLYMPIC COLLEGE
See WA STATE COMMUNITY COLLEGE DIST 3

OLYMPIC MEDICAL CENTER
See CLALLAM COUNTY PUBLIC HOSPITAL DISTRICT 2

OLYMPIC MILL SERVICES DIVISION
See TMS INTERNATIONAL LLC

D-U-N-S 00-886-1627 IMP/EXP
▲ OLYMPIC STEEL INC
22901 Millcreek Blvd # 650, Cleveland, OH 44122-5732
Tel (216) 292-3800 *Founded/Ownrshp* 1954
Sales 1.1MMM *EMP* 1,740
Tkr Sym ZEUS *Exch* NGS
SIC 5051 Metals service centers & offices; Pipe & tubing, steel; Iron or steel flat products
Ch Bd: Michael D Siegal
**Pr:* David A Wolfort
COO: Andrew Greiff
COO: Andrew S Greiff
CFO: Richard T Marabito
Treas: Richard A Manson
VP: John W Brieck
VP: John J Mooney
VP: Stephen Reyes
VP: Steve Reyes
Sales Asso: Ray Joyner
Board of Directors: Arthur F Anton, Howard L Goldstein, Dirk A Kempthorne, Donald R McNeeley, Ralph M Della Ratta Jr, Michael G Rippey

D-U-N-S 02-615-8563 IMP
■ OLYMPIC STEEL IOWA INC
(*Suby of* OLYMPIC STEEL INC) ★
6425 State St, Bettendorf, IA 52722-5548
Tel (563) 332-7785 *Founded/Ownrshp* 1997
Sales 85.1MM^E *EMP* 75
SIC 5051 3444 Metals service centers & offices; Sheet metalwork
CEO: Michael D Siegal
**Pr:* David A Wolfort
**CFO:* Richard Marabito
Sfty Dirs: Richard Shook
Sales Asso: Blake Hughes

D-U-N-S 01-776-3731
■ OLYMPIC STEEL LAFAYETTE INC (OH)
LAFAYETTE STEEL PROCESSING
(*Suby of* OLYMPIC STEEL INC) ★
3600 Military St, Detroit, MI 48210-2964
Tel (313) 894-4552 *Founded/Ownrshp* 1946, 1995
Sales 111.1MM^E *EMP* 220
SIC 5051 Metals service centers & offices
Ch Bd: Michael D Siegal
**COO:* David A Wolfort
VP: David Frink
VP: Ron Gore
VP: Steve Mallory
VP: Clay Treska
MIS Dir: Chris Garrett

D-U-N-S 06-032-1254 IMP
OLYMPUS AMERICA INC
(*Suby of* OLYMPUS CORP OF AMERICAS) ★
3500 Corporate Pkwy, Center Valley, PA 18034-8229
Tel (484) 896-5000 *Founded/Ownrshp* 1968
Sales 663.1MM^E *EMP* 2,009
SIC 5047 5043 5064 3827 3695 3572

D-U-N-S 60-993-6195
OLYMPUS CORP OF AMERICAS
(*Suby of* OLYMPUS CORPORATION)
3500 Corp Pkwy, Center Valley, PA 18034
Tel (484) 896-5000 *Founded/Ownrshp* 1990
Sales 1.2MMM^E *EMP* 2,500

SIC 5047 5043 5064 3827 3695 3572 Medical equipment & supplies; Diagnostic equipment, medical; Cameras & photographic equipment; Photographic cameras, projectors, equipment & supplies; Electrical entertainment equipment; Tape players & recorders; Video cassette recorders & accessories; Optical instruments & lenses; Magnetic & optical recording media; Computer storage devices
Pr: Masaharu Okubo
COO: Nadine Clark
Treas: Hironobu Kawamata
**Treas:* Kazuhiro Watanabe
Ofcr: Kevin Dill
VP: Rob Cermak
VP: Carol Eckert
VP: Robert Guida
VP: Adrian Marsh
VP: Tim Ovington
VP: Robert Tobin
Exec: Robert Heiler
Exec: John Temple

D-U-N-S 82-850-6282
OLYMPUS HOLDINGS LLC
67 E Park Pl Ste 475, Morristown, NJ 07960-7138
Tel (973) 889-9100 *Founded/Ownrshp* 2006
Sales 124.8MM^E *EMP* 482^E
SIC 4911 Generation, electric power
CEO: Dean N Vanech

D-U-N-S 61-474-6998
OLYMPUS PARTNERS LP
1 Station Pl Ste 4, Stamford, CT 06902-6893
Tel (203) 353-5900 *Founded/Ownrshp* 1998
Sales 5.7MMM^E *EMP* 34,653^E
SIC 6799 Investors
Mng Pt: Jim Conroy
Pt: Manu Bettegowda
Pt: David Cardenas
Pt: Evan Eason
Pt: David Haddad
Pt: Mike Horgan
Pt: Jason Miller
Pt: Lou Mischianti
Pt: Rob Morris
Pt: Paul Rubin
CFO: Jim Villa
VP: Matt Boyd
VP: Robby Polakoff

D-U-N-S 06-897-3119
OLYMPUS POWER LLC
(*Suby of* OLYMPUS HOLDINGS LLC) ★
67 E Park Pl Ste 4, Morristown, NJ 07960-7105
Tel (973) 889-9100 *Founded/Ownrshp* 2006
Sales 124.5MM^E *EMP* 224
SIC 4911 Generation, electric power
CEO: Dean N Vanech
Treas: Joanne Piasecki
**VP:* Dennis T Odonnell
Dir IT: Robert Dixon

D-U-N-S 88-341-1845
OLYMPUS REAL ESTATE CORP
5080 Spectrum Dr, Addison, TX 75001-4648
Tel (972) 980-2200 *Founded/Ownrshp* 1994
Sales 33.7MM^E *EMP* 2,000
SIC 7011 6512 Hotels; Nonresidential building operators
Pr: David Deniger
**Pt:* Greg Adair
**Pt:* Bob Briggs
**Pt:* Hal Hall
**Pt:* Clark Hanrattie
**Pt:* Rob Landin
**Pt:* Tim Smith
Mng Dir: Laurie Cameron

D-U-N-S 96-787-9912
OLYMPUS SCIENTIFIC SOLUTIONS AMERICAS CORP
OSSA
(*Suby of* OLYMPUS CORP OF AMERICAS) ★
48 Woerd Ave Ste 105, Waltham, MA 02453-3824
Tel (781) 419-3900 *Founded/Ownrshp* 2005
Sales 183.0MM^E *EMP* 950^E
SIC 5013 Testing equipment, electrical: automotive; Testing equipment, engine
CEO: Toshihiko Okubo
**Pr:* Kenji Kowata
**COO:* Fabrice Cancre
**CFO:* Etienne Marcoux
**Treas:* Kaoru Suzuki
Snr Sftwr: Jayesh Patel
Sftwr Eng: Ehab Ghabour
Board of Directors: Fabrice Cancre

D-U-N-S 60-621-7128 IMP/EXP
OLYMPUS SCIENTIFIC SOLUTIONS AMERICAS INC
(*Suby of* OLYMPUS CORP OF AMERICAS) ★
48 Woerd Ave, Waltham, MA 02453-3824
Tel (781) 419-3900 *Founded/Ownrshp* 1997
Sales 89.6MM^E *EMP* 300
SIC 5084 Instruments & control equipment
CEO: Fabrice Cancre
Treas: Hiroshi Shiina
Genl Mgr: Heather Addley
QA Dir: Sebastien McKenny
Prd Mgr: Richard Cassineri
S&M/VP: Jeffrey Walker

D-U-N-S 84-208-2638
OLYMPUS SCIENTIFIC SOLUTIONS TECHNOLOGIES INC
(*Suby of* OLYMPUS CORPORATION)
48 Woerd Ave, Waltham, MA 02453-3824
Tel (781) 419-3900 *Founded/Ownrshp* 2003
Sales 148.1MM^E *EMP* 300
SIC 5047 Medical equipment & supplies
Pr: Fabrice Cancre
Sr VP: David Park
Manager: Tom Metzinger

D-U-N-S 79-576-1188
OMAHA COMMUNITY FOUNDATION
302 S 36th St Ste 100, Omaha, NE 68131-3845
Tel (402) 342-3458 *Founded/Ownrshp* 1982
Sales 166.8MM *EMP* 13

SIC 8399 8733 Community development groups; Noncommercial research organizations
CEO: Sara Boyd
Treas: John L Maginn
Counsel: Thomas R Pansing Jr

D-U-N-S 08-027-0875
OMAHA HOLDINGS LLC
(*Suby of* OMAHA INTERMEDIATE HOLDING LLC) ★
1551 Wewatta St, Denver, CO 80202-6173
Tel (303) 744-1911 *Founded/Ownrshp* 2014
Sales 652.1MM^E *EMP* 13,433^E
SIC 3052 3089 3568 5084 4789 Rubber belting; Plastic belting; Automobile hose, rubber; V-belts, rubber; Fiber, vulcanized; Pulleys, power transmission; Water pumps (industrial); Cargo loading & unloading services
CEO: Ivo Jurek

D-U-N-S 08-026-9949
OMAHA INTERMEDIATE HOLDING LLC
(*Suby of* OMAHA TOPCO LTD)
1551 Wewatta St, Denver, CO 80202-6173
Tel (303) 744-1911 *Founded/Ownrshp* 2014
Sales 652.1MM^E *EMP* 13,434^E
SIC 3052 3089 3568 5084 4789 Rubber belting; Plastic belting; Automobile hose, rubber; V-belts, rubber; Fiber, vulcanized; Pulleys, power transmission; Water pumps (industrial); Cargo loading & unloading services
CEO: Ivo Jurek

D-U-N-S 00-697-0453 IMP
OMAHA PUBLIC POWER DISTRICT (NE)
OPPD
444 S 16th St, Omaha, NE 68102-2247
Tel (402) 636-2000 *Founded/Ownrshp* 1945
Sales 1.1MMM *EMP* 2,300
SIC 4911 ; Distribution, electric power; Generation, electric power; Transmission, electric power
Ch Bd: Anne McGuire
**Pr:* Gary Gates
COO: Timothy J Burke
CFO: Edward E Easterlin
CFO: Charles N Eldred
**Treas:* Michael J Cavanaugh
Treas: John Thurber
**Treas:* Frederick J Ulrich
Ofcr: Ron Miller
VP: Lou Cortopassi
VP: Mohamad Doghman
VP: Anne Farrar
VP: Leland Jacobson
VP: Kevin McCormick
VP: Tim Nissen
VP: Dayton Wittke
Creative D: Joe Comstock
Board of Directors: N P Dodge Jr, Michael J Cavanaugh,geoffr, John K Green, Frederick J Ulrich

D-U-N-S 08-956-2375
OMAHA PUBLIC SCHOOLS
3215 Cuming St, Omaha, NE 68131-2024
Tel (402) 557-2120 *Founded/Ownrshp* 1890
Sales 626.0MM *EMP* 8,000^E
Accts Seim Johnson Llp Omaha Nebr
SIC 8211 Public elementary & secondary schools; Secondary school
Exec: Anita Harkins
Exec: David Lavender
Off Admin: Gary Aquino
Dir IT: Georgiann Benish
Dir IT: Diana Casey
Dir IT: Lisa Dugan
Dir IT: James Mayberger
Dir IT: Gary Rech
Dir IT: Jean Ullrich
IT Man: Cindy Heidelberg
Psych: Josette Taylor

D-U-N-S 00-726-2074 IMP
OMAHA STANDARD LLC
(*Suby of* PALFINGER INC)
3501 S 11th St Ste 1, Council Bluffs, IA 51501-8243
Tel (712) 328-7444 *Founded/Ownrshp* 1932, 2013
Sales 103.3MM^E *EMP* 350
SIC 3713 3536 3537 Truck bodies (motor vehicles); Hoists; Lift trucks, industrial: fork, platform, straddle, etc.
Pr: Michael Berger
COO: Allan Mauseth
CFO: Eric Kluver
**Prin:* Mark Wahley
Dir IT: Gordon McKinsey
Manager: Jim Brown

D-U-N-S 00-749-9692 EXP
OMAHA STEAKS INTERNATIONAL INC
11030 O St, Omaha, NE 68137-2346
Tel (402) 597-3000 *Founded/Ownrshp* 1917
Sales 414.6MM^E *EMP* 600
SIC 5142 8741 Meat, frozen: packaged; Administrative management
Ch Bd: Alan Simon
**Pr:* Bruce A Simon
**CFO:* Dave L Hershiser
CFO: David Hershiser
**Ex VP:* Fred Simon
**VP:* Todd Simon

D-U-N-S 07-011-7346
OMAHA TRUCK CENTER INC (NE)
EXPRESS TRUCK CENTER
10550 I St, Omaha, NE 68127-1012
Tel (402) 592-2440 *Founded/Ownrshp* 1975
Sales 231.8MM *EMP* 398
Accts Seim Johnson Llp Omaha Nebr
SIC 5511 Trucks, tractors & trailers: new & used
Pr: Trey Mytty
**Treas:* Kathy Williams
**VP:* Bruce Fox
Brnch Mgr: John Schroeder

OMAHA WORLD TIMES
See OMAHA WORLD-HERALD CO

D-U-N-S 00-726-9616 IMP
■ **OMAHA WORLD-HERALD CO**
OMAHA WORLD TIMES
(*Suby of* BERKSHIRE HATHAWAY INC) ★
1314 Douglas St Ste 700, Omaha, NE 68102-1811
Tel (402) 444-1000 *Founded/Ownrshp* 2011
Sales 433.7MM[E] *EMP* 2,323
SIC 2711 7331 Newspapers; Mailing list brokers
CEO: Bailey Lauerman
**Ch Bd:* John Gottschalk
**Pr:* Terry Kroeger
**Treas:* Brenda Draheim
**Prin:* Mike Reilly
Sales Exec: Liz Breci
Advt Dir: Dave Storey
Sls Dir: Sharon Lucas
Mktg Mgr: Rhonda Gray
Mktg Mgr: David Sanders
Snr Mgr: Dan Golden

OMAN INC
See OLD MUTUAL (US) HOLDINGS INC

OMATION
See OPEX CORP

D-U-N-S 84-918-0518 IMP/EXP
OMAX CORP
21409 72nd Ave S, Kent, WA 98032-1944
Tel (253) 872-2300 *Founded/Ownrshp* 1993
Sales 139.4MM[E] *EMP* 250
SIC 3545 3561 Cutting tools for machine tools; Pumps & pumping equipment
Pr: John Bosco Cheung
**VP:* John Henry Olsen
IT Man: Anthony Davis
IT Man: Carl Olsen
Web Dev: Chris Lee
Software D: Jerry Thomas
Ql Cn Mgr: Rick Zeine
VP Sls: Michael Ruppenthal
Mktg Dir: Sandra McLain
Manager: Miguel Cervantes
Manager: David Kvasnicka

OMC
See OFFSHORE MARINE CONTRACTORS INC

OMCA
See OMRON MANAGEMENT CENTER OF AMERICA INC

D-U-N-S 12-808-3354
■ **OMD USA LLC**
(*Suby of* ANNALLECT GROUP) ★
195 Broadway, New York, NY 10007-3100
Tel (212) 590-7100 *Founded/Ownrshp* 2007
Sales 152.2MM[E] *EMP* 1,420[E]
SIC 7311 Advertising agencies
CEO: Mainardo De Nardis
Pr: Chris Pyne
**Pr:* Daryl Simm
Chf Mktg O: Monica Karo
Ofcr: David Desocio
Assoc Dir: Allison Klein
Assoc Dir: Maureen Kuehhas
Assoc Dir: Matthew Mansour
Mng Dir: Vas Banschikov
Mng Dir: Tom Benelli
Mng Dir: Leroy Whitaker

OMEGA CABINETRY
See OMEGA CABINETS LTD

D-U-N-S 03-995-0845 IMP/EXP
■ **OMEGA CABINETS LTD**
OMEGA CABINETRY
(*Suby of* FORTUNE BRANDS HOME & SECURITY INC) ★
1205 Peters Dr, Waterloo, IA 50703-9691
Tel (319) 235-5700 *Founded/Ownrshp* 2011
Sales 300.7MM[E] *EMP* 2,400
SIC 2434 5211 Wood kitchen cabinets; Vanities, bathroom: wood; Lumber & other building materials
Pr: Greg Stoner
VP: Clay Shimo
VP: Chase Thornbird
Dir IT: Ignacio Martin
Dir IT: Chris Schmitz
Mfg Mgr: Keith Westemeier
Board of Directors: Phil Carroll, Terry Goerdt, Tom Nelson

OMEGA DALLAS
See ESSILOR OF AMERICA INC

D-U-N-S 00-145-5856 IMP/EXP
OMEGA ENGINEERING INC (DE)
OMEGADYNE
(*Suby of* SPECTRIS PLC)
800 Connecticut Ave 5n01, Norwalk, CT 06854-1631
Tel (203) 359-1660 *Founded/Ownrshp* 1962, 2011
Sales 143.1MM[E] *EMP* 479
SIC 3823 3575 3577 3433 3826 2759 Temperature measurement instruments, industrial; PH instruments, industrial process type; Flow instruments, industrial process type; Computer interface equipment for industrial process control; Computer terminals; Printers, computer; Plotters, computer; Heating equipment, except electric; Environmental testing equipment; Periodicals: printing
Pr: James R Dale
**CFO:* Carol Donnelly
VP: John Coschigano
VP: Jim Ferguson
Exec: Chris Herrick
Genl Mgr: Bill Keating
Genl Mgr: Michael Lopez
CIO: Tom Sullivan
Web Dev: Hans Swanson
Trfc Mgr: Gary Collins
Sls Mgr: Martie Dow

OMEGA ENVIRONMENTAL TECH
See AUTO AIR EXPORT INC

D-U-N-S 07-551-8944
▲ **OMEGA FLEX INC**
451 Creamery Way, Exton, PA 19341-2509
Tel (610) 524-7272 *Founded/Ownrshp* 1975
Sales 93.2MM *EMP* 132[E]
Tkr Sym OFLX *Exch* NGM
SIC 3599 3429 Hose, flexible metallic; Clamps, couplings, nozzles & other metal hose fittings
Pr: Kevin R Hoben
**Ch Bd:* Stewart B Reed
**COO:* Mark F Albino
CFO: Paul J Kane
Sr VP: Steven A Treichel
Board of Directors: David Evans, J Nicholas Filler, Bruce C Klink

D-U-N-S 79-294-8531
▲ **OMEGA HEALTHCARE INVESTORS INC**
200 International Cir # 3500, Hunt Valley, MD 21030-1394
Tel (410) 427-1700 *Founded/Ownrshp* 1992
Sales 504.7MM *EMP* 53[E]
Tkr Sym OHI *Exch* NYS
SIC 6798 Real estate investment trusts
CEO: C Taylor Pickett
Ch Bd: Bernard J Korman
COO: Daniel J Booth
CFO: Robert O Stephenson
Ofcr: Michael D Ritz
Sr VP: R Lee Crabill Jr
VP: Laurence D Rich
Board of Directors: Craig R Callen, Thomas F Franke, Barbara B Hill, Harold J Kloosterman, Edward Lowenthal, Stephen D Plavin

OMEGA MORGAN MACHINERY MOVING
See MORGAN INDUSTRIAL INC

D-U-N-S 87-765-4574
OMEGA PLASTIC CORP
OMEGA PLASTICS OF KY
(*Suby of* SIGMA PLASTICS GROUP) ★
901 Commerce Cir, Shelbyville, KY 40065-9131
Tel (502) 633-0168 *Founded/Ownrshp* 1980
Sales 221.8MM[E] *EMP* 1,800
SIC 2673 Plastic & pliofilm bags
CEO: Alfred Teo
**Pr:* Fred Mancuso
**CFO:* John Reier
VP: Bill Lenchinsky
Off Mgr: Maria Diaz
Off Mgr: Hector Gocman

OMEGA PLASTICS
See AMERICA PLASTICS LLC

D-U-N-S 11-278-7973 IMP
OMEGA PLASTICS CORP
SIGMA PLASTICS GROUP
(*Suby of* SIGMA PLASTICS GROUP) ★
Page & Schuyler Ave Ste 5, Lyndhurst, NJ 07071
Tel (201) 933-1270 *Founded/Ownrshp* 1982
Sales 90.6MM[E] *EMP* 220
SIC 2673 Plastic bags: made from purchased materials
Pr: Alfred Teo
**CFO:* John Reier
**Ex VP:* Stanley Band

OMEGA PLASTICS OF KY
See OMEGA PLASTIC CORP

D-U-N-S 05-902-4163
OMEGA PROBE INC
308 Southwest Dr, Cheyenne, WY 82007-1917
Tel (877) 323-2201 *Founded/Ownrshp* 2011
Sales 80.7MM[E] *EMP* 2,200
SIC 7371 6552 Computer software systems analysis & design, custom; Subdividers & developers
Pr: Gus Williams

D-U-N-S 00-926-8124
▲ **OMEGA PROTEIN CORP**
2105 Citywest Blvd # 500, Houston, TX 77042-2838
Tel (713) 623-0060 *Founded/Ownrshp* 1913
Sales 359.3MM *EMP* 627
Tkr Sym OME *Exch* NYS
SIC 2077 5199 Fish meal, except as animal feed; Fish oil; Oils, animal or vegetable
Pr: Bret D Scholtes
**Ch Bd:* Gary R Goodwin
Pr: Mark E Griffin
Pr: Joseph R Vidal
CFO: Andrew C Johannesen
Ex VP: John D Held
VP: Montgomery C Deihl
VP: Mark A Livingston
Genl Mgr: Scott Springwer
Genl Mgr: Jennifer Vega
Genl Mgr: Al Vidrine
Board of Directors: Gary L Allee, Stephen Bryan, David H Clarke, Gary Ermes, David A Owen, David W Wehlmann

D-U-N-S 06-304-8953 IMP
OMEGA WIRE INC
BARE WIRE DIV
(*Suby of* BARE WIRE DIVISION) ★
12 Masonic Ave, Camden, NY 13316-1202
Tel (315) 245-3800 *Founded/Ownrshp* 1997
Sales 106.6MM[E] *EMP* 1,200
SIC 3351 Wire, copper & copper alloy
Pr: Rodney D Kent
**VP:* Peter Ernenwein
Board of Directors: Adam Kleinman

D-U-N-S 06-236-3593
OMEGA WORLD TRAVEL INC
3102 Omega Office Park # 1, Fairfax, VA 22031-2408
Tel (703) 359-0200 *Founded/Ownrshp* 1972
Sales 243.3MM[E] *EMP* 920[E]
SIC 4724 Travel agencies
Pr: Gloria Bohan
**VP:* Daniel P Bohan
VP: Diane Bozicevich
**VP:* Goran Gligorovic
VP Bus Dev: Stan Brown
Exec: Regina Davies
Dir Soc: Judy Weitz
Rgnl Mgr: Laura Gantt
Brnch Mgr: Teresa Organ
Brnch Mgr: Denise Skiba
Brnch Mgr: Donna Watkins
Board of Directors:

OMEGADYNE
See OMEGA ENGINEERING INC

D-U-N-S 00-959-2379
OMELVENY & MYERS LLP
400 S Hope St Fl 19, Los Angeles, CA 90071-2831
Tel (213) 430-6000 *Founded/Ownrshp* 1950
Sales 365.1MM[E] *EMP* 2,100
SIC 8111 General practice law office
Mng Pt: Kurt J Berney
**Mng Pt:* Riccardo Celli
Mng Pt: Elizabeth L McKeen
COO: Bruce Bouwere
COO: George C Demos
CFO: David Page
Bd of Dir: Cathy Hagen
Snr Ntwrk: David Doran
Dir IT: Steve Devine
Dir IT: Steve Divine
IT Man: Charles Bender

D-U-N-S 00-696-1213
OMG MID WEST INC
HALLETT MATERIALS
(*Suby of* OLDCASTLE MATERIALS GROUP) ★
2401 Se Tones Dr Ste 13, Ankeny, IA 50021-8886
Tel (515) 266-9928 *Founded/Ownrshp* 2001
Sales 122.6MM[E] *EMP* 101
SIC 1442 1422 Construction sand mining; Gravel mining; Limestones, ground
Pr: Eric Leverson
**Treas:* Charles Brown

D-U-N-S 07-989-2655
OMGANICS INC
1821 Waterston Ave Unit B, Austin, TX 78703-3938
Tel (512) 560-3262 *Founded/Ownrshp* 2014
Sales 61.1MM[E] *EMP* 2,014
SIC 2676 Infant & baby paper products
CEO: Carissa Hoop

D-U-N-S 02-831-8454
■ **OMGEO LLC**
OASYS
(*Suby of* CEDE AND CO) ★
55 Thomson Pl, Boston, MA 02210-1219
Tel (877) 664-3625 *Founded/Ownrshp* 2013
Sales 192.6MM[E] *EMP* 600
SIC 6211 Security brokers & dealers
Pr: Paula Sausville Arthus
**CFO:* Antonio Nunes
Exec: Tony Remedios
Ex Dir: Andy Hughes
Ex Dir: Doris Jurisson
Ex Dir: Timothy Keady
Snr Ntwrk: Jayesh Mankodi

OMH
See ONEMAIN HOLDINGS INC

OMI ENVIRONMENTAL SOLUTIONS
See OIL MOP LLC

D-U-N-S 07-854-5028
OMICS GROUP INC (NV)
OMICS PUBLISHING GROUP
2360 Corp Cir Ste 400, Henderson, NV 89074
Tel (888) 843-8169 *Founded/Ownrshp* 2012
Sales 72.7MM[E] *EMP* 1,000
SIC 2721 Trade journals: publishing & printing
Pr: Srinu B Gedela

OMICS PUBLISHING GROUP
See OMICS GROUP INC

D-U-N-S 14-810-5344
OMIDYAR NETWORK SERVICES LLC
1991 Broadway St Ste 200, Redwood City, CA 94063-1958
Tel (650) 482-2500 *Founded/Ownrshp* 2004
Sales 85.4MM *EMP* 20
Accts Comprehensive Financial Mgt
SIC 8742 Administrative services consultant
Mng Pt: Kelsey King
VP: Christopher Keefe
VP: Mike Kubzansky
VP: Susan Phillips
Exec: Lisa Kolenda
Exec: Chez Murphy
Dir Soc: Jeff Kumataka
Dir IT: Larry Ho
Corp Couns: Emiliano Martinez
Snr Mgr: Allen Babaran
Snr Mgr: Claudia A Parazzoli

D-U-N-S 17-411-2102
OMNI AIR INTERNATIONAL LLC
3303 N Sheridan Rd Hngar19, Tulsa, OK 74115-2219
Tel (918) 836-5393 *Founded/Ownrshp* 2004
Sales 167.9MM[E] *EMP* 1,083
SIC 4522 Flying charter service
Pr: Jeffrey C Crippen
Ch Bd: Robert Coretz
Dir Bus: Pablo Aguirre
Tech Mgr: Dan Ross
Trfc Dir: Pete McGuirk
Sls Dir: Sean Ralson

OMNI AUTO PARTS
See OMNISOURCE CORP

D-U-N-S 10-134-9165
OMNI BAKING CO LLC
2621 Freddy Ln Bldg 7, Vineland, NJ 08360-1559
Tel (856) 205-1485 *Founded/Ownrshp* 1996
Sales 142.8MM[E] *EMP* 500
SIC 2051 Bread, cake & related products
Pt: Lanny Amoroso Jr
Pt: Daniel Amoroso Jr
Pt: John V Mulloy Sr
CFO: Daniel Mulloy
Exec: Eleanore Mesiano
Genl Mgr: Danny Maloy

D-U-N-S 10-144-2903 IMP
OMNI CABLE CORP
2 Hagerty Blvd, West Chester, PA 19382-7594
Tel (610) 701-0100 *Founded/Ownrshp* 1978
Sales 234.7MM *EMP* 216
SIC 5063 Wire & cable
Pr: William J Siegfried
**COO:* Greg Donato
**CFO:* Steve Glinski
CFO: Mike Schafer
Ex VP: Jason Obetz
VP: John Russ
VP: Dan Trotta
Rgnl Mgr: Steve Letourneau
Rgnl Mgr: Rob Orio
Rgnl Mgr: Jim Saffery
Rgnl Mgr: Dave Santoro

D-U-N-S 18-179-4538
OMNI ENERGY SERVICES CORP
OMNI GIBSON
(*Suby of* GIBSON ENERGY INC)
4500 Ne Evangeline Trwy, Carencro, LA 70520-5253
Tel (337) 896-6664 *Founded/Ownrshp* 2012
Sales 480.5MM[E] *EMP* 950[E]
SIC 1382 1389 7349 Seismograph surveys; Lease tanks, oil field: erecting, cleaning & repairing; Cleaning service, industrial or commercial
Pr: Brian J Recatto
**CFO:* Geoff A Jones
**VP:* Donald Fowlis
VP: John Harris
**VP:* Gregory B Milton
**VP:* Mark E Stipe
VP: Nolan C Vice Jr
Dir IT: Darren Crader

OMNI GIBSON
See OMNI ENERGY SERVICES CORP

D-U-N-S 07-917-3305
OMNI GROVE PARK LLC
GROVE PARK INN, THE
(*Suby of* OMNI HOTELS CORP) ★
290 Macon Ave, Asheville, NC 28804-3711
Tel (828) 252-2711 *Founded/Ownrshp* 2013
Sales 99.7MM[E] *EMP* 950
SIC 7299 5812 7011 5813 7992 7991 Banquet hall facilities; Eating places; Hotels & motels; Drinking places; Public golf courses; Health club
Sales Asso: Yanna Davis

OMNI HOME CARE
See OMNI HOME HEALTH SERVICES LLC

D-U-N-S 14-075-3638
■ **OMNI HOME HEALTH SERVICES LLC**
OMNI HOME CARE
(*Suby of* SUNCREST HEALTHCARE INC) ★
9510 Ormsby Station Rd # 300, Louisville, KY 40223-5016
Tel (615) 712-2248 *Founded/Ownrshp* 2011
Sales 38.5MM[E] *EMP* 1,340
SIC 8082 Home health care services
CEO: Fred Portnoy
**CFO:* Steve Marble
Ex VP: Mark Dermott
VP: John Kiehl

OMNI HOTELS
See TRT HOLDINGS INC

D-U-N-S 19-395-1381 IMP
OMNI HOTELS CORP
(*Suby of* OMNI HOTELS) ★
4001 Maple Ave Ste 500, Dallas, TX 75219-3241
Tel (972) 730-6664 *Founded/Ownrshp* 1988
Sales 971.0MM[E] *EMP* 8,000
SIC 7011 Hotels & motels
Pr: James D Caldwell
**Pr:* Michael J Deitemeyer
**CFO:* Mike Garcia
CFO: Mike Gracia
CFO: Kate Hoenicke
Sr Cor Off: Margaret David
Bd of Dir: Melody Rhodan
**Chf Mktg O:* Peter Strebel
**Ex VP:* Stephen Rosenstock
VP: Michael Garcia
VP: Elizabeth Keliiholokai
VP: Kerry Kennedy
VP: Charlie Muller
VP: David Perkins
VP: Joy Rothschild
VP: Jeff Smith
VP: Mark Wykes
Dir Soc: Beverly Garlington
Dir Soc: Sarah Hanshaw

D-U-N-S 04-023-0161
OMNI HOTELS MANAGEMENT CORP
(*Suby of* TRT DEVELOPMENT CO - CCB) ★
4001 Maple Ave Ste 500, Dallas, TX 75219-3241
Tel (972) 871-5600 *Founded/Ownrshp* 1975
Sales 246.0MM[E] *EMP* 2,200
SIC 7011 Hotels & motels
Pr: James D Caldwell
**COO:* Michael Dietemeyer
**Treas:* Laurie Talarico
**Chf Mktg O:* Tom Santora
**Sr VP:* Michael Garcia
**Sr VP:* Stephen Rosenstock
**VP:* Caryn Kabudi

D-U-N-S 83-776-7540
OMNI INSURANCE CO
(*Suby of* OMNI INSURANCE GROUP INC) ★
2018 Powers Ferry Rd Se # 100, Atlanta, GA 30339-7200
Tel (770) 952-4500 *Founded/Ownrshp* 1980
Sales NA *EMP* 240
SIC 6331 Fire, marine & casualty insurance
Ch Bd: Dudley L Moore
**Pr:* James Paul Kennedy
CFO: Sue Sacalf
**Treas:* Susan Hamlett Scalf
**Sr VP:* Lawrence J Korth
**Sr VP:* Carl J Leo
**Sr VP:* David Peters
**Sr VP:* Lowell E Sims
**Sr VP:* Mary E Skeeles
**Sr VP:* Kathy Renee Weese
Mktg Dir: John Haney

D-U-N-S 15-337-3584
OMNI INSURANCE GROUP INC
(*Suby of* INDEPENDENT INSURANCE INVESTMENTS INC) ★
20018 Powers Ferry Rd, Atlanta, GA 30339
Tel (770) 952-4500 *Founded/Ownrshp* 2006
Sales NA *EMP* 250
SIC 6331 Property damage insurance; Fire, marine & casualty insurance & carriers
Pr: J Paul Kennedy
**VP:* Lawrence J Korth
**VP:* Carl J Leo
**VP:* David S Peters
**VP:* Susan H Scalf
**VP:* Lowell Sims
**VP:* Mary Skeeles
**VP:* K Renee Weese

D-U-N-S 03-894-8139
OMNI MANOR INC
101 W Liberty St, Girard, OH 44420-2844
Tel (330) 545-1550 *Founded/Ownrshp* 1980
Sales 57.8M *EMP* 1,200
SIC 8051 Convalescent home with continuous nursing care
Pr: John Masternick
CFO: Kenneth James
**Treas:* Dorothy Masternick
**VP:* Leo Grimes

D-U-N-S 83-036-6212
OMNI UNITED (USA) INC
(*Suby of* OMNI UNITED (S) PTE. LTD.)
5350 Birch Point Dr, Interlochen, MI 49643-9579
Tel (231) 943-9804 *Founded/Ownrshp* 2009
Sales 200.0MM *EMP* 12^E^
SIC 3011 Tires & inner tubes
VP: Scott Rhodes

D-U-N-S 83-235-9384
OMNI VISION INC
301 S Perimeter Park Dr # 210, Nashville, TN 37211-4143
Tel (615) 726-3603 *Founded/Ownrshp* 2011
Sales 34.5MM^E^ *EMP* 1,209
SIC 8361 Home for the aged
Pr: Eric Strickland
Bd of Dir: Gary Dowdy
Off Mgr: Kourtney Hedden
Off Mgr: Kim Moore
Dir IT: Shane Frazier
Snr Mgr: Jessica Brock

D-U-N-S 83-487-3473
OMNI WORKSPACE CO LLC
A & M BUSINESS INTERIOR SVCS
1300 Washington Ave N # 200, Minneapolis, MN 55411-3435
Tel (612) 627-1600 *Founded/Ownrshp* 1980
Sales 162.0MM^E^ *EMP* 400
SIC 7641 4212 4226 Office furniture repair & maintenance; Furniture moving, local: without storage; Furniture storage, without local trucking
**Pr:* Karston Anderson
IT Man: Jerry Crisman

D-U-N-S 05-643-3907
■ OMNICARE INC
(*Suby of* CVS PHARMACY INC) ★
900 Omnicare Ctr, Cincinnati, OH 45202-2520
Tel (513) 719-2600 *Founded/Ownrshp* 2015
Sales 7.6MMM^E^ *EMP* 12,451
SIC 5122 5047 8082 8741 Pharmaceuticals; Medical & hospital equipment; Home health care services; Nursing & personal care facility management
Pr: Nitin Sahney
CFO: Robert O Kraft
Chf Cred: Steve Skware
Sr VP: David Hileman
Sr VP: Amit Jain
Sr VP: Alexander M Kayne
Sr VP: Patrick Lee
Sr VP: Kirsten Marriner
Sr VP: Kirsten M Marriner
Sr VP: Ashok Singh
VP: Jonathan Borman
VP: Robert Dunlap

D-U-N-S 85-880-2002
■ OMNICARE MANAGEMENT CO
(*Suby of* OMNICARE HOLDING COMPANY)
201 E 4th St Ste 900, Cincinnati, OH 45202-1513
Tel (513) 719-1535 *Founded/Ownrshp* 1981
Sales 86.8MM^E^ *EMP* 3,000
SIC 8741 Management services
Pr: David Hileman
**Treas:* Amkur Bhandari
**VP:* Cheryl Hodges

D-U-N-S 80-541-2665 IMP
▲ OMNICELL INC
590 E Middlefield Rd, Mountain View, CA 94043-4008
Tel (650) 251-6100 *Founded/Ownrshp* 1992
Sales 484.5MM *EMP* 1,551
Tkr Sym OMCL *Exch* NGS
SIC 3571 Electronic computers
Ch Bd: Randall A Lipps
CFO: Peter J Kuipers
Ex VP: J Christopher Drew
Ex VP: Dan S Johnston
Ex VP: Nhat H Ngo
Ex VP: Robin G Seim
Ex VP: Jorge R Taborga
VP: Pat Diresta
VP: William Wingfield
Sftwr Eng: Phil Chan
Board of Directors: Joanne B Bauer, James T Judson, Vance B Moore, Mark W Parrish, Gary S Petersmeyer, Bruce D Smith, Sara J White

D-U-N-S 14-785-7429
▲ OMNICOM GROUP INC
437 Madison Ave, New York, NY 10022-7001
Tel (212) 415-3600 *Founded/Ownrshp* 1944
Sales 15.1MMM *EMP* 74,900
Tkr Sym OMC *Exch* NYS
SIC 7311 Advertising agencies
Pr: John D Wren
Ch Bd: Bruce Crawford
CEO: Dale A Adams
CEO: Jez Frampton
CFO: Philip J Angelastro
Treas: Shelly Laskin
Ex VP: Janet Riccio
Ex VP: Rita Rodriguez
Ex VP: Peter Sherman
Sr VP: Andrew L Castellaneta
Sr VP: Michael J O'Brien
Sr VP: Peter L Swieciciki
VP: Fred Canoro
VP: Min Chang
VP: Kenneth Corriveau
VP: Robert Miller
VP: Peter Swiecicki
VP: Tiffany R Warren
Assoc Dir: Anupama Hume
Dir Rx: Jonathan Hill
Board of Directors: John R Purcell, Alan R Batkin, Linda Johnson Rice, Mary C Choksi, Gary L Roubos, Robert Charles Clark, Leonard S Coleman Jr, Errol M Cook, Susan S Denison, Michael A Henning, Deborah Kissire, John R Murphy

D-U-N-S 00-570-3710
■ OMNICOM MEDIA GROUP
ANNALLECT GROUP
(*Suby of* OMNICOM GROUP INC) ★
195 Broadway Fl 12, New York, NY 10007-3126
Tel (212) 590-7100 *Founded/Ownrshp* 2000
Sales 196.6MM^E^ *EMP* 1,420
SIC 7311 Advertising agencies
CEO: Daryl Simm
Pr: Shari Vera
**Pr:* John Wren
**CEO:* Barry Cupples
**CEO:* Mainardo De Nardis
**CEO:* Colin Gottlieb
CFO: Ken McNaughton
**CFO:* Brad Nodiff
**Chf Mktg O:* Erin Matts
VP: Elisa Chua
VP: David Levy
VP: Filippo Padovan
Exec: Mark Bullingham
Exec: Sara Captan
Assoc Dir: Priscilla Aydin
Assoc Dir: Joel P Balcita
Assoc Dir: Amy Lee
Assoc Dir: Ashleigh Pembroke
Assoc Dir: Shelina Taki
Assoc Dir: Oscar Taylor
Assoc Dir: Jian Yang

D-U-N-S 61-971-2672
OMNIPLEX WORLD SERVICES CORP
OMNISEC INTL INVESTIGATIONS
14151 Park Meadow Dr # 300, Chantilly, VA 20151-4230
Tel (703) 652-3100 *Founded/Ownrshp* 1990
Sales 184.1MM^E^ *EMP* 3,420
SIC 7381 Guard services; Detective services
Pr: Michael S Santelli
**Ch Bd:* Philip T Sweeney
**Pr:* Mike Wines
CFO: David Mathews
**CFO:* John Peterson
**Treas:* Julien Patterson
Ofcr: Pat Jeffers
Ofcr: Alanna Slocum
Ex VP: Steven Banner
**Sr VP:* Kelly Grems
**VP:* Scott Meyier
**VP:* James Moore
VP: Mark Poirier
**VP:* William Turk
Exec: Maureen Sullivan
Dir Bus: Jamin Rogovoy

OMNISEC INTL INVESTIGATIONS
See OMNIPLEX WORLD SERVICES CORP

D-U-N-S 01-631-9345 IMP/EXP
■ OMNISOURCE CORP
OMNI AUTO PARTS
(*Suby of* SDI) ★
7575 W Jefferson Blvd, Fort Wayne, IN 46804-4131
Tel (260) 422-5541 *Founded/Ownrshp* 2007
Sales 1.1MMM^E^ *EMP* 2,500
SIC 5093 3462 3399 Ferrous metal scrap & waste; Nonferrous metals scrap; Iron & steel forgings; Metal powders, pastes & flakes
Pr: Russell Rinn
Ex VP: Rich Brady
**VP:* Mike Hausfeld
**VP:* Denny Luma
**VP:* Jason Redden
Genl Mgr: Pat Sitcler
IT Man: Ali Zadeh
Plnt Mgr: Andrew Niezer
Mktg Mgr: Christy Coons
Board of Directors: Danny Rifkin

D-U-N-S 80-857-3781 EXP
■ OMNISOURCE SOUTHEAST LLC
ATLANTIC SCRAP & PROCESS
(*Suby of* OMNI AUTO PARTS) ★
2061 Nazareth Church Rd, Spartanburg, SC 29301-5943
Tel (864) 439-7039 *Founded/Ownrshp* 1920
Sales 119.3MM^E^ *EMP* 180^E^
SIC 4953 Refuse systems
Ex VP: Bob Brewer
Rgnl Mgr: Bennett Graham
Sfty Dirs: David Campbell

D-U-N-S 07-880-1627
OMNITRACS LLC (CA)
(*Suby of* OMNITRACS MIDCO LLC) ★
717 N Harwood St Ste 1300, Dallas, TX 75201-6533
Tel (888) 627-2716 *Founded/Ownrshp* 2012, 2013
Sales 96.9MM^E^ *EMP* 475^E^
SIC 8741 4214 Industrial management; Local trucking with storage
CEO: John Graham
**Ch Bd:* Robert F Smith
**Pr:* David Post
**CFO:* Jordan Copland
Ofcr: David Vice
VP: Mansoor Bajowala
VP: Sathish Gaddipati
VP: Tom Neppl
**VP:* Marc V Teillon
**CTO:* Dan Speicher
Genl Couns: David Arnold

D-U-N-S 07-939-6942
OMNITRACS MIDCO LLC
10182 Telesis Ct Ste 100, San Diego, CA 92121-4777
Tel (858) 651-5812 *Founded/Ownrshp* 2013
Sales 96.9MM^E^ *EMP* 519^E^
SIC 7372 Business oriented computer software; Utility computer software

D-U-N-S 87-944-7183
OMNITRAX INC
252 Clayton St Fl 4, Denver, CO 80206-4814
Tel (303) 398-4500 *Founded/Ownrshp* 1993
Sales 86.1MM^E^ *EMP* 172^E^
SIC 4013 Switching & terminal services
CEO: Kevin Shuba
**Ch Bd:* Edmond Harris
**Pr:* Darcy Brede
**CFO:* Hubert Gassner
**Sec:* Thomas Mandula
Ofcr: Peter Touesnard
**Ex VP:* Alex Yeros
Dir Bus: Trent Weber

D-U-N-S 08-338-1728
■ OMNITURE LLC
(*Suby of* ADOBE SYSTEMS INC) ★
550 E Tmpngos Cle Bldng G, Orem, UT 84097
Tel (801) 722-7000 *Founded/Ownrshp* 1996
Sales 94.6MM^E^ *EMP* 1,092
SIC 7371 Custom computer programming services
Pr: Mark Garrett
**CFO:* Michael S Herring
**VP:* Brett M Error
VP: Alan Gurock
**VP:* Christopher Harrington
VP: John Mellor
VP: Brad Rencher
Software D: David Adams
VP Sls: Robbie Traube
Mktg Dir: Kevin Lindsay
Mktg Mgr: Mike Stiles

D-U-N-S 92-848-5176
OMNIVISION TECHNOLOGIES INC
4275 Burton Dr, Santa Clara, CA 95054-1512
Tel (408) 567-3000 *Founded/Ownrshp* 1995
Sales 1.3MMM *EMP* 2,176^E^
SIC 3674 Semiconductors & related devices
CEO: Shaw Hong
Pr: Raymond Wu
COO: Glenn He
CFO: Anson Chan
CFO: Anson H Chan
Ofcr: Howard E Rhodes
**Ofcr:* Henry Yang
Sr VP: Y Vicky Chou
VP: John Yue
Exec: Simon Wong
Prgrm Mgr: Jim McIntyre

D-U-N-S 08-849-8618 IMP/EXP
▲ OMNOVA SOLUTIONS INC (OH)
25435 Harvard Rd, Beachwood, OH 44122-6201
Tel (216) 682-7000 *Founded/Ownrshp* 1952
Sales 838.0MM *EMP* 2,235
Accts Ernst & Young Llp Akron Ohio
Tkr Sym OMN *Exch* NYS
SIC 2819 2211 3069 3081 Industrial inorganic chemicals; Decorative trim & specialty fabrics, including twist weave; Roofing, membrane rubber; Unsupported plastics film & sheet; Plastic film & sheet; Vinyl film & sheet
Ch Bd: Kevin M McMullen
Pr: David H Maynard
Pr: Anne P Noonan
CFO: Paul F Desantis
Ofcr: Mike Curran
Ofcr: Michael A Quinn
Sr VP: James C Lemay
Sr VP: Douglas E Wenger
VP: Jay T Austin
QA Dir: Michael Moseley
Dir IT: Steve Lopez
Board of Directors: Robert A Stefanko, David J D'antoni, Janet Plaut Giesselman, Joseph M Gingo, Michael J Merriman, James A Mitarotonda, Steven W Percy, Larry B Porcellato, Allan R Rothwell, William R Seelbach

OMP FOODS
See OZARK MOUNTAIN POULTRY INC

OMPA
See OKLAHOMA MUNICIPAL POWER AUTHORITY

D-U-N-S 80-441-9273 IMP
OMRON AUTOMOTIVE ELECTRONICS INC
OMRON GLOBAL
(*Suby of* OMCA) ★
3709 Ohio Ave, Saint Charles, IL 60174-5437
Tel (630) 443-6800 *Founded/Ownrshp* 1992
Sales 502.7MM^E^ *EMP* 600
SIC 5065 3625 3714 8742 Electronic parts; Relays & industrial controls; Motor vehicle parts & accessories; Real estate consultant
CEO: Yoshihito Yamada
**Ch Bd:* Fumio Tateishi
**Pr:* Yoshinobu Morishita
**Pr:* Katsuhiro Wada
**Ch:* Yoshinori Suzuki
**Treas:* Dale Morrison
Prgrm Mgr: Graham McFarlane
Prgrm Mgr: Guy Wojtanek
**Genl Mgr:* Randy Wara
Dir IT: Fred Burmeister
Netwrk Mgr: Dave Decho
Board of Directors: Randy Wara

D-U-N-S 11-537-2062
OMRON ELECTRONICS LLC
O E I
(*Suby of* OMCA) ★
2895 Greenspt Pkwy 200, Hoffman Estates, IL 60169
Tel (847) 843-7900 *Founded/Ownrshp* 2001
Sales 95.8MM^E^ *EMP* 275^E^
SIC 5065 3699 Electronic parts; Electrical equipment & supplies
CEO: Nigel Blakeway
COO: Thomas F Mabrey
Ofcr: Dheeraj Menon
Genl Mgr: Robb Black
Genl Mgr: Hajime Fujii
Mfg Mgr: Mark McLean
Mktg Mgr: Marina Welk

OMRON GLOBAL
See OMRON AUTOMOTIVE ELECTRONICS INC

D-U-N-S 61-470-6620 IMP
OMRON MANAGEMENT CENTER OF AMERICA INC
OMCA
(*Suby of* OMRON CORPORATION)
2895 Greenspoint Pkwy # 100, Hoffman Estates, IL 60169-7261
Tel (224) 520-7650 *Founded/Ownrshp* 1989
Sales 717.7MM^E^ *EMP* 1,885
SIC 5044 5046 5065 5047 5045 8732 Cash registers; Store machines; Electronic parts; Hospital equipment & supplies; Surgical equipment & supplies; Computer peripheral equipment; Commercial nonphysical research
CEO: Nigel Blakeway
**Ch Bd:* Fumio Tateishi
**Treas:* Thaski Kasi
**Ex VP:* Yoshinobu Morishita
**Ex VP:* Akio Sakumiya
**Ex VP:* Yoshinori Suzuki
VP: Jack Lee
**VP:* Blake Thatcher
**Prin:* Yoshihito Yamada
Prgrm Mgr: Bob Anderson
Prgrm Mgr: Ted Konopacki

D-U-N-S 96-747-2965 EXP
OMTRON USA LLC
TOWNSENDS
22855 Dupont Blvd, Georgetown, DE 19947-8801
Tel (302) 855-7131 *Founded/Ownrshp* 2011
Sales NA *EMP* 1,200^E^
SIC 2015

OMU
See OWENSBORO MUNICIPAL UTILITIES ELECTRIC LIGHT & POWER SYSTEM

D-U-N-S 03-822-2063
OMX (US) INC
NASDAQ OMX
140 Broadway Fl 25, New York, NY 10005-1142
Tel (646) 428-2800 *Founded/Ownrshp* 1999
Sales 55.9MM^E^ *EMP* 1,500
SIC 7372 Application computer software
Pr: Roland Tibell

D-U-N-S 00-206-9136 IMP/EXP
OMYA INC
CALLAHAN AMS MACHINE COMPANY
(*Suby of* OMYA INDUSTRIES INC) ★
9987 Carver Rd Ste 300, Blue Ash, OH 45242-5563
Tel (513) 387-4600 *Founded/Ownrshp* 1978
Sales 180.1MM^E^ *EMP* 564
SIC 2819

D-U-N-S 08-695-3312 IMP/EXP
OMYA INDUSTRIES INC (VT)
(*Suby of* OMYA AG)
9987 Carver Rd Ste 300, Blue Ash, OH 45242-5563
Tel (513) 387-4600 *Founded/Ownrshp* 1977
Sales 227.0MM^E^ *EMP* 564
SIC 1422 Crushed & broken limestone
Pr: Anthony Colak
**CFO:* Michael Phillips
CFO: Thomas G Turner
**VP:* John Suddarth

D-U-N-S 15-767-4896
▲ ON ASSIGNMENT INC
26745 Malibu Hills Rd, Calabasas, CA 91301-5355
Tel (818) 878-7900 *Founded/Ownrshp* 1985
Sales 2.0MMM *EMP* 3,320^E^
Tkr Sym ASGN *Exch* NYS
SIC 7363 7361 Help supply services; Temporary help service; Employment agencies
Pr: Peter T Dameris
**Ch Bd:* Jeremy M Jones
Pr: Randolph C Blazer
COO: Michael J McGowan
CFO: Edward L Pierce
Ex VP: Theodore S Hanson
VP Bus Dev: Garrett Hunt
Board of Directors: William E Brock, Brian J Callaghan, Jonathan S Holman, Marty R Kittrell, Edwin A Sheridan IV

ON THE BORDER
See OTB ACQUISITION LLC

D-U-N-S 88-464-6647 IMP
ON BORDER CORP
ON THE BORDER MEXICAN
(*Suby of* ON BORDER) ★
2201 W Royal Ln Ste 240, Irving, TX 75063-3208
Tel (972) 499-3000 *Founded/Ownrshp* 2010
Sales 220.6MM^E^ *EMP* 6,029
SIC 5812 5813 Mexican restaurant; Bar (drinking places)
CEO: Stephen Clark
Mng Pt: James Snyder
**Pr:* Ward Whitworth
**COO:* Monte Batson
**CFO:* Christopher Morris
Sr VP: Kevin Carroll
Sr VP: Becky Johnson
Sr VP: William Simon
VP: G Centioli
VP: Cedric L Harre

VP: Michael Moser
VP: Mark Payne
Dir Surg: Jerry Brennan
Dir Surg: Shawn Jenkins
Dir Surg: Diane Sanford

ON THE BORDER MEXICAN
See ON BORDER CORP

ON THE BORDER PRODUCTS
See TRUCO ENTERPRISES LP

D-U-N-S 00-387-7073 IMP
■ ON ELECTRIC GROUP INC
OREGON ELECTRIC GROUP
(*Suby of* MDU CONSTRUCTION SERVICES GROUP INC) ★
1709 Se 3rd Ave, Portland, OR 97214-4547
Tel (503) 234-9900 *Founded/Ownrshp* 1947
Sales 221.3MM^E *EMP* 800
SIC 1731 3613 General electrical contractor; Telephone & telephone equipment installation; Panel & distribution boards & other related apparatus
CEO: Jeffrey Thiede
**Pr:* Bart Dickson
**Treas:* Jon Hunke
Div Pres: Curtis Dickerson
Sr VP: Michael Martin
VP: James Fortkamp
VP: Thomas Nosbusch
VP: Clint Valiton
Div Mgr: Ken Dunn
Genl Mgr: Aimee Casper
CIO: Jason Behring

ON LOK LIFEWAYS
See ON LOK SENIOR HEALTH SERVICES

D-U-N-S 07-018-2910
ON LOK SENIOR HEALTH SERVICES
ON LOK LIFEWAYS
1333 Bush St, San Francisco, CA 94109-5691
Tel (415) 292-8888 *Founded/Ownrshp* 1971
Sales NA *EMP* 600
Accts Armanino Llp San Ramon Ca
SIC 6324 8082 Health maintenance organization (HMO), insurance only; Home health care services
CEO: Robert Edmondson
**COO:* Grace Li
**CFO:* Sue Wong
Ofcr: Kelvin Quan

ON MEDIA ADVERTISING SALES
See ONMEDIA COMMUNICATIONS CO INC

D-U-N-S 18-378-4409
ON Q FINANCIAL INC
4800 N Scottsdale Rd, Scottsdale, AZ 85251-7630
Tel (480) 444-7100 *Founded/Ownrshp* 2004
Sales 133.8MM^E *EMP* 350^E
SIC 6282 6162 Investment advice; Mortgage bankers & correspondents
Pr: John Bergman
CFO: Frank Adronjna
**CFO:* Michael Jones
**Sr VP:* Shirley Boynton
VP: Lisa Sleeper
Rgnl Mgr: Andrew Looker
Brnch Mgr: Andy Enloe
Brnch Mgr: John Macandrew
Opers Mgr: Moira Aranas
Mktg Mgr: Mitch Beyer
Mktg Mgr: Patti Passow
Board of Directors: Michelle

ON SEMICONDUCTOR
See SEMICONDUCTOR COMPONENTS INDUSTRIES LLC

ON SEMICONDUCTOR
See AMI SEMICONDUCTOR INC

D-U-N-S 07-621-6865
▲ ON SEMICONDUCTOR CORP
5005 E Mcdowell Rd, Phoenix, AZ 85008-4229
Tel (602) 244-6600 *Founded/Ownrshp* 1999
Sales 3.5MMM *EMP* 30,879^E
Tkr Sym ON *Exch* NAS
SIC 3674 3825 3651 Semiconductors & related devices; Transistors; Diode & transistor testers; Amplifiers: radio, public address or musical instrument
Pr: Keith D Jackson
Ch Bd: J Daniel McCranie
COO: William A Schromm
CFO: Bernard Gutmann
Ex VP: George H Cave
Ex VP: Donald Colvin
Ex VP: William M Hall
Ex VP: Robert A Klosterboer
Ex VP: Paul E Rolls
Sr VP: Taner Ozcelik
Sr VP: Mamoon Rashid
VP: Debbie Brogan
VP: David Wagner
Board of Directors: Alan Campbell, Curtis J Crawford, Gilles S Delfassy, Emmanuel T Hernandez, Paul Mascarenas, Daryl A Ostrander, Teresa M Ressel

D-U-N-S 62-085-0045
ON TIME STAFFING LLC
535 Route 38 Ste 412, Cherry Hill, NJ 08002-2961
Tel (866) 333-3007 *Founded/Ownrshp* 1999
Sales 98.4MM^E *EMP* 10,000
Accts Bbd Llp
SIC 7361 Employment agencies
CEO: Brian Kares
CFO: Donald Sullivan
VP: Brian Sams
MIS Dir: Brian Smith
VP Sls: Donte Vaughn

D-U-N-S 04-210-8233
ON TOP OF WORLD COMMUNITIES INC (FL)
8445 Sw 80th St, Ocala, FL 34481-9440
Tel (352) 854-3600 *Founded/Ownrshp* 1947
Sales 102.8MM^E *EMP* 150
SIC 6552 1522 Land subdividers & developers, residential; Condominium construction
**Treas:* C Guy D Woolbright
**VP:* Leslee R Colen
**VP:* Philip Faranda

Dir IT: Jorge Santiago
Sls Dir: Jason Taflinger

ONTRACK ADVERTISING
See SLEEP TRAIN INC

ON YOUR WAY
See WESCO INC

D-U-N-S 10-177-8004
ON-SITE E DISCOVERY INC
806 N Henry St, Alexandria, VA 22314-1619
Tel (703) 683-9710 *Founded/Ownrshp* 1993
Sales 60.0MM *EMP* 2,100
SIC 2759 Commercial printing
Pr: Mark Hawn
VP: Christopher Schrumm

D-U-N-S 04-892-4026
ON-SITE FUEL SERVICE INC
1089 Old Fannin Rd Ste A, Brandon, MS 39047-9201
Tel (601) 353-4142 *Founded/Ownrshp* 1996
Sales 238.0MM *EMP* 120
Accts Elliott Davis Llc Greenville
SIC 5983 Fuel oil dealers
CEO: Kevin T French
**CFO:* Margaret Wong
VP Opers: Larry Rice
Opers Mgr: Al Kendall

D-U-N-S 06-952-7013
ON24 INC
201 3rd St Fl 3, San Francisco, CA 94103-3165
Tel (877) 202-9599 *Founded/Ownrshp* 1998
Sales 119.5MM^E *EMP* 300^E
SIC 4813
Pr: Sharat Sharan
CFO: Drew Hamer
Chf Mktg O: Joe Hyland
Chf Mktg O: Ken Robinson
VP: Gary Gilchrist
VP: Mahesh Kheny
VP: Thomas Masotto
VP: Michael Nelson
VP: Ben Sullivan
Snr Sftwr: Alberto Perez
Dir IT: Brian Scott
Board of Directors: Mark Hoffman

D-U-N-S 06-815-7101 IMP
ONCOR ELECTRIC DELIVERY CO LLC
(*Suby of* ONCOR ELECTRIC DELIVERY HOLDINGS CO LLC) ★
1616 Woodall Rodgers Fwy, Dallas, TX 75202-1234
Tel (214) 486-2000 *Founded/Ownrshp* 2001
Sales 3.8MMM *EMP* 3,450^E
SIC 4911 Distribution, electric power; Transmission, electric power
CEO: Robert S Shapard
COO: James A Greer
CFO: David M Davis
Sr VP: Deborah L Dennis
Sr VP: E Allen Nye Jr
VP: Debbie Dennis
VP: Debra Elmer
VP: James Greer
VP: Stephen Guy
VP: Walt Jordan
Exec: John Hardesty
Board of Directors: James R Adams, Thomas M Dunning, Robert A Estrada, Rhys Evenden, Thomas D Ferguson, William T Hill Jr, Timothy A Mack, Richard W Wortham III, Steven J Zucchet

D-U-N-S 82-700-2622
ONCOR ELECTRIC DELIVERY HOLDINGS CO LLC
(*Suby of* ENERGY FUTURE HOLDINGS CORP) ★
1616 Woodall Rodgers Fwy, Dallas, TX 75202-1234
Tel (214) 486-2000 *Founded/Ownrshp* 2007
Sales 3.8MMM^E *EMP* 3,810^E
SIC 4911 Distribution, electric power; Transmission, electric power
CEO: Robert S Shapard
**COO:* James A Greer
**CFO:* David Davis
Sr VP: Allen Nye
VP: John Casey
VP: Don Clevenger
VP: Mike Guyton
Prgrm Mgr: Kenneth Blackburn
Prgrm Mgr: Garry Jones
Area Mgr: Ken Harriss
IT Man: Gary Hendley

D-U-N-S 07-830-5998
ONCOR ELECTRIC DELIVERY TRANSITION BOND CO LLC
1616 Woodall Rodgers Fwy, Dallas, TX 75202-1234
Tel (214) 486-2000 *Founded/Ownrshp* 2011
Sales 119.6MM *EMP* 6^E
Accts Deloitte & Touche Llp Dallas
SIC 4911 Electric services
COO: James Greer

D-U-N-S 78-272-8430 IMP
ONCORE MANUFACTURING LLC
NEO TECH
(*Suby of* NEOTECH) ★
9340 Owensmouth Ave, Chatsworth, CA 91311-6915
Tel (818) 734-6500 *Founded/Ownrshp* 2015
Sales 443.7MM^E *EMP* 950
SIC 3672 8711 Printed circuit boards; Electrical or electronic engineering
Pr: Sudesh Arora
COO: Kunal Sharma
CFO: Laura Siegal
Ex VP: Sajjad Malik
VP: Steve Heinzen
VP: Magdy Henry
VP: Zareen Mohta
VP: Victor Yamauchi
CIO: Abbas Arsiwala
CTO: David Lane

D-U-N-S 11-329-6784 IMP
ONCORE MANUFACTURING SERVICES INC
NEO TECH NATEL EPIC ONCORE
(*Suby of* NEOTECH) ★
9340 Owensmouth Ave, Chatsworth, CA 91311-6915
Tel (510) 360-2222 *Founded/Ownrshp* 2007
Sales 118.8MM^E *EMP* 230
SIC 3672 Printed circuit boards
CEO: Sudesh Arora
**COO:* Walt Hussey
**Ex VP:* Sajjad Malik
**Sr VP:* David Brakenwagen
**VP:* Magdy Henry
**VP:* Zareen Mohta
VP: David Yu
VP Opers: Jae Chang

ONE CALL CARE MANAGEMENT
See ONE CALL MEDICAL INC

D-U-N-S 93-785-7340
ONE CALL LOCATORS LTD
ELM LOCATING & UTILITY SERVICE
(*Suby of* ELM CONSULTING) ★
60 State St Ste 201, Peoria, IL 61602-5154
Tel (309) 673-2851 *Founded/Ownrshp* 2003
Sales 77.4MM^E *EMP* 1,125
Accts Heinold-Banwart Ltd East Peo
SIC 7389 Inspection & testing services
Pr: Matt Quinn
**Pr:* James Bourazak
**CFO:* Marlys Gillon
**VP:* Josh Hinrichs
**VP:* Don Malerk

D-U-N-S 80-719-8064
ONE CALL MEDICAL INC
ONE CALL CARE MANAGEMENT
841 Prudential Dr Ste 900, Jacksonville, FL 32207-8371
Tel (904) 646-0199 *Founded/Ownrshp* 2013
Sales 900.0MM^E *EMP* 1,956
SIC 8742 7389 Compensation & benefits planning consultant; Financial services
Pr: Jim Phifer
COO: Will Smith
COO: Chris Watson
CFO: Andrew Behrends
CFO: Rick McCook
Chf Mktg O: Robert Zeccardi
Ex VP: John Stanzi
Sr VP: Jeff Flanegin
VP: Don Barber
VP: Audrey Fischer
VP: Wayne Lombardo
VP: Ron McNatt
VP: Chris Toepke

D-U-N-S 02-280-9193
ONE COMMUNICATIONS CORP
EARTHLINK BUSINESS
5 Wall St Fl 5, Burlington, MA 01803-4771
Tel (781) 362-5700 *Founded/Ownrshp* 2011
Sales NA *EMP* 1,068
SIC 4813

D-U-N-S 14-414-5443
ONE DIVERSIFIED LLC
DIVERSIFIED MEDIA GROUP
37 Market St, Kenilworth, NJ 07033-1761
Tel (908) 245-4833 *Founded/Ownrshp* 2004
Sales 239.5MM^E *EMP* 976
SIC 5099 7373 4899 8711 Video & audio equipment; Systems integration services; Data communication services; Acoustical engineering
CEO: Alfred D' Allesandro
**Pr:* Kevin Collins
**CFO:* Bruce Herman
Exec: Robert Cameron
Exec: Mitch Rabil
Mng Dir: Russell Townshend
Admn Mgr: Kevin Powers
Opers Mgr: Stephen Zalucki
Sls Mgr: Stephen Dickinson

ONE EQUITY PARTNERS
See OEP CAPITAL ADVISORS LP

D-U-N-S 78-323-2734
ONE EQUITY PARTNERS LLC
320 Park Ave Fl 18, New York, NY 10022-6815
Tel (212) 794-3434 *Founded/Ownrshp* 2001
Sales NA *EMP* 2,901^E
SIC 6726 8748

ONE FULLER WAY
See FULLER BRUSH CO INC

D-U-N-S 07-925-4828
▲ ONE GAS INC
15 E 5th St, Tulsa, OK 74103-4346
Tel (918) 947-7000 *Founded/Ownrshp* 1906
Sales 1.5MMM *EMP* 3,400^E
Tkr Sym OGS *Exch* NYS
SIC 1311 4924 Natural gas production; Natural gas distribution
Pr: Pierce H Norton II
CFO: Curtis L Dinan
Sr VP: Mark A Bender
Sr VP: Caron A Lawhorn
Sr VP: Robert S McAnnally
Sr VP: Joseph L McCormick
VP: Joe McCormick
Board of Directors: Robert B Evans, John W Gibson, Michael G Hutchinson, Pattye L Moore, Eduardo A Rodriguez, Douglas H Yaeger

D-U-N-S 96-249-0194
▲ ONE GROUP HOSPITALITY INC
411 W 14th St Fl 3, New York, NY 10014-1082
Tel (212) 277-5301 *Founded/Ownrshp* 2013
Sales 60.5MM *EMP* 1,300^E
Accts Grant Thornton Llp New York
Tkr Sym STKS *Exch* NAS
SIC 5812 Eating places
Pr: Jonathan Segal
**Ch Bd:* Michael Serruya
COO: Alejandro Munoz-Suarez

CFO: Samuel Goldfinger
Sr VP: Celeste Fierro
Board of Directors: Eugene M Bullis, Nicholas L Giannuzzi, Richard E Perlman

ONE INTERNATIONAL CENTER
See ULTRAMAR DIAMOND SHAMROCK INC

ONE JEANSWEAR
See NINE WEST HOLDINGS INC

D-U-N-S 83-176-7186 IMP/EXP
■ ONE KINGS LANE INC
(*Suby of* BED BATH & BEYOND INC) ★
633 Folsom St Fl 2, San Francisco, CA 94107-3620
Tel (415) 489-9918 *Founded/Ownrshp* 2016
Sales 94.6MM^E *EMP* 270^E
SIC 5719 Housewares; Wicker, rattan or reed home furnishings; Window furnishings
CEO: Dinesh Lathi
Ofcr: Susan Feldman
VP: Richard Hansen
VP: Josh Liberson
VP: Andrea Stanford
VP: Susan Stick
VP: Ethan Trask
Co-Founder: Ali Pincus
Prin: Alison Picus
CTO: Arun Rajan
IT Man: Leepatrick McIntire

ONE LIBERTY PLAZA
See CLEARY GOTTLIEB STEEN & HAMILTON LLP

D-U-N-S 07-834-9773
▲ ONE MAIN FINANCIAL SERVICES
601 Nw 2nd St, Evansville, IN 47708-1013
Tel (800) 961-5577 *Founded/Ownrshp* 1926
Sales NA *EMP* 11,400
SIC 6141 6351 6331 Consumer finance companies; Credit & other financial responsibility insurance; Property damage insurance
Pr: Frederick W Geissinger
**Pr:* Jay Levine

D-U-N-S 83-051-9463
ONE ROCK CAPITAL PARTNERS LLC
30 Rockefeller Plz # 5400, New York, NY 10112-5403
Tel (212) 605-6000 *Founded/Ownrshp* 2009
Sales 847.0MM^E *EMP* 1,350
SIC 6282 Investment advice
Mng Pt: Tony Lee
VP: Joshua Goldman
VP: Deepa Patil

D-U-N-S 00-584-7897
ONE ROTARY CENTER
1560 Sherman Ave Ste Ll1, Evanston, IL 60201-4802
Tel (847) 869-5417 *Founded/Ownrshp* 2001
Sales 284.1MM *EMP* 2
SIC 8621 Professional membership organizations
Pr: Frank Dedlyn
Trst: Kazuhiko Ozawa
Genl Mgr: Lori O Carlson

ONE SECURITIES CENTER
See QUIKRETE COMPANIES LLC

D-U-N-S 82-959-6746
ONE SOURCE VIRTUAL HR INC
ONESOURCE VIRTUAL
5601 N Macarthur Blvd, Irving, TX 75038-2616
Tel (972) 916-9847 *Founded/Ownrshp* 2008
Sales 106.9MM^E *EMP* 650^E
SIC 8742 Human resource consulting services
CEO: Brian D Williams
**Pr:* John Wesley Bryant
**Pr:* Trey Campbell
**CFO:* John D Bax
**Sec:* Mark Turner
**Ex VP:* Michael Simpson
**Sr VP:* Britt Wirt
Ex Dir: Jim Adams

ONE TOWER SQUARE 8MS
See TRAVELERS CASUALTY CO OF CONNECTICUT

ONE TOWER SQUARE 8MS
See TRAVELERS PROPERTY CASUALTY CORP

D-U-N-S 09-950-5943 IMP/EXP
ONE UP ENTERPRISES INC
7777 Lsburg Pike Ste 302s, Falls Church, VA 22043
Tel (703) 448-7333 *Founded/Ownrshp* 1977
Sales 500.8MM^E *EMP* 1,461
SIC 2731 2711 2092 6531 Books: publishing only; Newspapers: publishing only, not printed on site; Fresh or frozen packaged fish; Real estate managers
Pr: Michael Runyon
**Pr:* Victor Walters
**Treas:* Victor E Walters

D-U-N-S 15-861-9655 IMP
ONE WATER SOURCE LLC
WATER SOURCE ONE
1114 Lost Creek Blvd # 100, Austin, TX 78746-6370
Tel (512) 347-9280 *Founded/Ownrshp* 1998
Sales 150.0MM *EMP* 11
SIC 2086 Mineral water, carbonated: packaged in cans, bottles, etc.
Pr: Dave Evans
**CFO:* Stephen Brazier
**VP:* Sid Maxwell
**VP:* Ben Mottesheard

D-U-N-S 02-929-5375 IMP
ONE WORKPLACE L FERRARI LLC
2500 De La Cruz Blvd, Santa Clara, CA 95050-2617
Tel (669) 800-2500 *Founded/Ownrshp* 1925
Sales 186.4MM^E *EMP* 550
SIC 5021 8744

D-U-N-S 82-807-5528 IMP/EXP
ONE WORLD TECHNOLOGIES INC
TECHTRONIC INDUSTRIES PWR EQP
(*Suby of* TTI) ★
1428 Pearman Dairy Rd, Anderson, SC 29625-2000
Tel (864) 226-6511 *Founded/Ownrshp* 2000
Sales 973.0MM *EMP* 750
SIC 5251 Tools, power

CEO: Horst J Pudwill
**Treas:* Bette Ann Braeutigam

D-U-N-S 03-389-1180 IMP
ONEAL CONSTRUCTORS LLC
(*Suby of* ONEAL INC) ★
10 Falcon Crest Dr # 300, Greenville, SC 29607-1583
Tel (864) 298-6510 *Founded/Ownrshp* 1997
Sales 191.7MM *EMP* 110
Accts Elliott Davis Greenville Sc
SIC 8742 Construction project management consultant
Pr: Kevin Bean
**CFO:* Judy Castleberry
**VP:* Shane Bolding
**VP:* Craig Crowther
**VP:* Jeff Hall

D-U-N-S 15-466-5913 IMP
ONEAL FLAT ROLLED METALS LLC
(*Suby of* ONEAL INDUSTRIES INC) ★
1229 Fulton St, Brighton, CO 80601-6743
Tel (303) 654-0300 *Founded/Ownrshp* 1997
Sales 227.4MM^E *EMP* 350
SIC 5051 Metals service centers & offices
CEO: Jeff Simons
**Pr:* Ronald Sardaro
**Sr VP:* Bruce Pole
Software D: Huan Nguyen
Sls Mgr: Dustin Garza
Sales Asso: Cortny Hutchison
Sales Asso: Jacy Marrs
Sales Asso: Natasha Mosier
Sales Asso: Rick Williams

D-U-N-S 08-223-3057
ONEAL INC
10 Falcon Crest Dr, Greenville, SC 29607-1583
Tel (864) 298-2000 *Founded/Ownrshp* 1975
Sales 217.2MM *EMP* 400
SIC 8711 8712 Consulting engineer; Architectural services
Pr: Kevin C Bean
CFO: Judy Castleberry
Off Mgr: Lolita Spencer
Dir IT: David Larocque
Mktg Mgr: Liza Dibden
Sls Mgr: Kathleen A Riordan
Sls Mgr: Lavisse Smith

D-U-N-S 07-940-5982
ONEAL INDUSTRIES INC
2311 Highland Ave S # 200, Birmingham, AL 35205-2972
Tel (205) 721-2880 *Founded/Ownrshp* 2013
Sales 2.4MM *EMP* 3,100
SIC 5051 Metals service centers & offices
Pr: Holman Head
**Ch Bd:* Craft O'Neal
**CFO:* Stephen Armstrong
**VP:* Mitchell Harrison
**VP:* Jodi Parnell
VP: Ron Travis
Comm Dir: Shirley Fagan
Opers Mgr: John Elrod
Mktg Mgr: Henley Smith

D-U-N-S 00-339-6959 IMP/EXP
ONEAL STEEL INC
IOWA LASER TECHNOLOGY
(*Suby of* ONEAL INDUSTRIES INC) ★
744 41st St N, Birmingham, AL 35222-1124
Tel (205) 599-8000 *Founded/Ownrshp* 1987
Sales 1.1MMM^E *EMP* 1,500
SIC 5051 Metals service centers & offices
Pr: Stephen Armstrong
V Ch: Bill Jones
CFO: Suzanne Lane
CFO: Kirk Moore
VP: Michael Gooldrup
VP: Gary Gray Sr
VP: Mitchell Harrison
VP: Holman Head
VP: Jodi Parnell
VP: Jeff Robertson
VP: Jay Satterfield
VP: Jeff Stephen
Exec: Shea Kennedy

D-U-N-S 06-523-3749
ONEAMERICA FINANCIAL PARTNERS INC
(*Suby of* AMERICAN UNITED MUTUAL INSURANCE HOLDING CO) ★
1 American Sq, Indianapolis, IN 46282-0020
Tel (317) 285-1877 *Founded/Ownrshp* 2000
Sales NA *EMP* 9,875
SIC 6371 6311 6321 Pension funds; Life insurance carriers; Health insurance carriers
Ch Bd: Dayton H Molendorp
Pr: Stewart Buskirk
Pr: Patrick M Foley
COO: Robert McCourt
**CFO:* J Scott Davison
Treas: Mark Wutt
Bd of Dir: Hardeep S Rekhi
Ex VP: Douglas Collins
Ex VP: Jeff Garrison
Ex VP: Dennis Martin
Sr VP: David Brentlinger
VP: Pam Becker
VP: Dan Bleck
VP: Mike Bullock
VP: Doug Collins
VP: Enoch Edusei
VP: Jerry Eichhorst
VP: Michael Grimme
VP: Kevin Kidwell
VP: Hoyt Klingaman
VP: Lynette Miller

D-U-N-S 07-955-5382
ONEAMERICA RETIREMENT SERVICES LLC
(*Suby of* ONEAMERICA FINANCIAL PARTNERS INC) ★
1 American Sq, Indianapolis, IN 46282-0020
Tel (317) 285-1877 *Founded/Ownrshp* 2014
Sales NA *EMP* 2,269^E
SIC 6411 Pension & retirement plan consultants
Pr: Dayton H Molendorp

ONEBEACON
See BEDIVERE INSURANCE CO

D-U-N-S 61-528-4531
ONEBEACON INSURANCE CO
(*Suby of* WHITE MOUNTAINS CAPITAL INC) ★
11 Norfolk St, Mansfield, MA 02048-1833
Tel (781) 332-7000 *Founded/Ownrshp* 2008
Sales NA *EMP* 5,045^E
SIC 6411 Insurance agents, brokers & service
Prin: Pat Dalton

D-U-N-S 06-935-8885
ONEBEACON INSURANCE GROUP LLC
COMMERCIAL UNION/ ONEBEACON
(*Suby of* WHITE MOUNTAINS INSURANCE GROUP, LTD.)
150 Royall St, Canton, MA 02021-1031
Tel (781) 332-7000 *Founded/Ownrshp* 2001
Sales NA *EMP* 1,500
SIC 6331 Fire, marine & casualty insurance & carriers; Property damage insurance
Pr: Darlene Bailey
Pr: Sue Bauer
Pr: Craig Collins
Pr: Dennis Crosby
Pr: Steve Schaeberle
Pr: Bradley York
COO: Timothy Shaw
Sr VP: Alexander Archimedes
Sr VP: Clyde Jones
Sr VP: Michael Seff
VP: Linda Clarke
VP: John Ferrari
VP: Laura Kenney
VP: James Lassen
VP: Dennis Molenaar
VP: Virginia E Murray
VP: Stephen Seeber
VP: George S Skells
VP: Suzanne Uva
Dir Risk M: Paul Brehm

D-U-N-S 78-875-2579
▲ **ONEBEACON INSURANCE GROUP LTD**
605 Highway 169 N Ste 800, Plymouth, MN 55441-6533
Tel (952) 852-2431 *Founded/Ownrshp* 1831
Sales NA *EMP* 1,150^E
Accts Pricewaterhousecoopers Llp Mi
Tkr Sym OB *Exch* NYS
SIC 6331 Fire, marine & casualty insurance
Pr: T Michael Miller
**Ch Bd:* Lowndes A Smith
Pr: David Bearl
Pr: Eric Chambers
Pr: Duncan Morrison
CFO: Paul H McDonough
Treas: John C Treacy
Ex VP: Paul J Brehm
Ex VP: Dennis A Crosby
Sr VP: Marc Garganigo
Sr VP: Maureen A Phillips
VP: Carmen Duarte
Exec: Mike Foley

D-U-N-S 01-200-2278
ONEBLOOD FOUNDATION INC
FLORIDA'S BLOOD CENTER
8669 Commodity Cir, Orlando, FL 32819-9003
Tel (407) 248-5480 *Founded/Ownrshp* 1980
Sales 230.7M *EMP* 2,700^E
Accts Mcgladrey Llp Melbourne Fl
SIC 8099 Blood bank
Pr: Don Doddridge
**CFO:* John E Murphy Jr
**Treas:* Christopher S Stiles
VP: Tom Kurella
**VP:* Pam Sawh
Mktg Mgr: Julie Watkinson

D-U-N-S 07-920-8542
ONEBLOOD INC
COMMUNITY BLOOD CENTERS FLA
8669 Commodity Cir, Orlando, FL 32819-9003
Tel (407) 455-7551 *Founded/Ownrshp* 1992
Sales 134.1MM^E *EMP* 2,100
Accts Mcgladrey Llp Orlando Florid
SIC 8099 Blood bank
CEO: Donald D Doddridge
**Pr:* German F Leparc
**CFO:* John E Murphy Jr
**Treas:* Harold L Harkins Jr
**Sr VP:* Susan Forbes
**Sr VP:* Andrea Levenson
**Sr VP:* Judy Smith
**VP:* JD Gaskins
**VP:* Pam Sawh
VP: Ernst A Upmeyer III
Dir Lab: Ivette Rosado

ONECARE COMPANY, THE
See EVERCARE CO

D-U-N-S 78-450-7233
ONECIS INSURANCE CO
BUREAU VERITAS
(*Suby of* US LABORATORIES INC) ★
1601 Sawgrs Corp Pkwy, Sunrise, FL 33323-2883
Tel (954) 236-8100 *Founded/Ownrshp* 2005
Sales 248.0MM *EMP* 130
Accts Pricewaterhousecoopers Llp
SIC 7389 6331 Inspection & testing services; Industrial & commercial equipment inspection service; Boiler insurance
Pr: Pedro Guimaraes
CFO: Luis Damasceno
CFO: Carlos Esnard
VP: Janice Mondello

ONEEXCHANGE
See EXTEND HEALTH INC

ONEIDA BINGO & CASINO
See ONEIDA TRIBE OF INDIANS OF WISCONSIN

D-U-N-S 93-269-3377
ONEIDA HEALTH CARE CENTER
321 Genesee St, Oneida, NY 13421-2699
Tel (315) 361-2342 *Founded/Ownrshp* 1996
Sales 93.0MM *EMP* 800
Accts First Charles Chambers Llp Sy
SIC 8062 General medical & surgical hospitals
CEO: Gene F Morreale
Dir Vol: Terri Welcher
**CFO:* Vincent Maneen
**CFO:* John Milligan
Ofcr: Kevin Prosser
VP: Mike Fifield
Dir Rx: Brian Dodge
CIO: Mary N Fox
Sfty Mgr: Renee Stone
Obsttrcn: Hazem Qalla
Ansthlgy: Chowdary Chirumamilla

D-U-N-S 07-581-6801
ONEIDA HEALTH SYSTEMS INC
ONEIDA MEDICALCARE
321 Genesee St, Oneida, NY 13421-2611
Tel (315) 363-6000 *Founded/Ownrshp* 1996
Sales 105.6MM^E *EMP* 900
Accts Fust Charles Chambers Llp Syr
SIC 8062 8051 General medical & surgical hospitals; Extended care facility
CEO: Gene Morreale
**CFO:* John Milligan
VP: Greg Muscato
**VP:* Mary Parry
**VP:* Dewey Rowlands
Dir Rx: Laurie Cronin
Telecom Ex: Joann Clarey
Orthpdst: James White
Ansthlgy: Chowdary Chirumamilla
Ansthlgy: Jong-Hwa Hsieh
Ansthlgy: Mark Moosikasuwan

D-U-N-S 15-416-1335
ONEIDA INDIAN NATION
TURNING STONE CASINO
2037 Dream Catcher Plz, Oneida, NY 13421-2710
Tel (315) 829-8900 *Founded/Ownrshp* 1601
Sales 225.6MM^E *EMP* 5,000
SIC 5812 Ice cream stands or dairy bars; Luncheonette
Pr: Ray Halbritter
Pr Mgr: Kelly Abdo

D-U-N-S 78-790-3462 IMP/EXP
ONEIDA LTD
(*Suby of* EVERYWARE GLOBAL INC) ★
163 Kenwood Ave, Oneida, NY 13421-2829
Tel (315) 361-3000 *Founded/Ownrshp* 2012
Sales 126.4MM^E *EMP* 244
Accts Bdo Seidman Llp Melville Ny
SIC 5046 5719 5023 5094 Commercial cooking & food service equipment; Kitchenware; Cutlery; Glassware; Kitchenware; Glassware; Kitchen tools & utensils; Stainless steel flatware; Silverware or plated ware
Ch Bd: James E Joseph
Pr: Timothy J Shine
**COO:* Andrew G Church
Treas: Brian Suba
**Sr VP:* Paul E Gebhardt
**Sr VP:* Bill Grannis
**Sr VP:* Catherine H Suttmeier
VP: Vincent Delcid
VP: Bob Delekta
VP: Glenn Geoffroy
VP: David Keenan
Exec: Ben Gambitta

ONEIDA MEDICALCARE
See ONEIDA HEALTH SYSTEMS INC

ONEIDA TRIBE OF INDIANS OF WISCONSIN
ONEIDA BINGO & CASINO
N7210 Seminary Rd, Oneida, WI 54155-9501
Tel (920) 869-2214 *Founded/Ownrshp* 1934
Sales NA *EMP* 3,000
SIC 9131

D-U-N-S 01-087-1333
ONEIL INDUSTRIES INC
1245 W Washington Blvd, Chicago, IL 60607-1929
Tel (773) 244-6003 *Founded/Ownrshp* 1981
Sales 605.3MM *EMP* 400
Accts Crowe Horwath Llp Oak Brook
SIC 1542 1541 Commercial & office building, new construction; Institutional building construction; Industrial buildings, new construction; Renovation, remodeling & repairs: industrial buildings
Ch Bd: William E O'Neil
Pr: Richard J Erickson
CFO: Robert R Dukes
Ex VP: Oleh Karawan
VP: Tim Addis
VP: Dean J Arnold
VP: Patrick J McGowan
VP: Paul V Roundy IV
Dir IT: Brian Konie
IT Man: Michael Macellaio
Board of Directors: Tracey L Cantarutti, Michael J Faron, John T Hickey Jr, John S Hobbs, Dennis L Kessler, Mary B O'neil

D-U-N-S 00-778-2597
ONEILL PROPERTIES GROUP LP (PA)
2701 Renaissance Blvd # 4, King of Prussia, PA 19406-2781
Tel (610) 337-5560 *Founded/Ownrshp* 1996
Sales 95.2MM^E *EMP* 100
SIC 6552 Subdividers & developers
Ch: Jay Brian O'Neill
Ex VP: Richard Heany
Sr VP: Bruce Auerbach
Sr VP: James Savard
VP: Bob Follet
VP: Kevin Kyle
VP: Georgann McKenna
VP: Dale Stesko
VP: Jamie M Watson
Counsel: Joseph Rocco

D-U-N-S 06-467-2519
■ **ONEMAIN FINANCIAL GROUP LLC**
ONEMAIN FINANCIAL, INC.
(*Suby of* ONEMAIN FINANCIAL HOLDINGS LLC) ★
100 Intl Dr 15000, Baltimore, MD 21202
Tel (855) 663-6246 *Founded/Ownrshp* 2010
Sales NA *EMP* 1,411^E
SIC 6141 Consumer finance companies; Installment sales finance, other than banks
Pr: James W Schneider
**Treas:* Lechner Gregory
Sr VP: April Park
VP: Russell Canady
**VP:* Davis Linda

D-U-N-S 07-957-6940
■ **ONEMAIN FINANCIAL HOLDINGS LLC**
(*Suby of* INDEPENDENCE HOLDINGS, LLC)
100 Intl Dr Ste 15000, Baltimore, MD 21202
Tel (410) 332-3000 *Founded/Ownrshp* 2015
Sales NA *EMP* 1,415^E
SIC 6162 6163 Loan correspondents; Loan brokers
CFO: Scott T Parker

ONEMAIN FINANCIAL, INC.
See ONEMAIN FINANCIAL GROUP LLC

D-U-N-S 07-916-3928
■ **ONEMAIN HOLDINGS INC**
OMH
(*Suby of* ONE MAIN FINANCIAL SERVICES) ★
601 Nw 2nd St, Evansville, IN 47708-1013
Tel (812) 424-8031 *Founded/Ownrshp* 1920
Sales NA *EMP* 11,400^E
Tkr Sym OMF *Exch* NYS
SIC 6141 Personal credit institutions; Personal finance licensed loan companies, small
Pr: Jay N Levine
**Ch Bd:* Wesley R Edens
COO: Robert A Hurzeler
CFO: Scott T Parker
Ofcr: Lawrence N Skeats
Ex VP: John C Anderson
Ex VP: Bradford D Borchers
Ex VP: Angela Celestin
Ex VP: Timothy S Ho
Ex VP: David Hogan
Sr VP: Michael A Hedlund
Board of Directors: Roy A Guthrie, Douglas L Jacobs, Ronald M Lott

D-U-N-S 80-755-8072
■ **ONEOK FIELD SERVICES CO LLC**
(*Suby of* ONEOK PARTNERS LP) ★
100 W 5th St Ste Ll, Tulsa, OK 74103-4298
Tel (918) 588-7000 *Founded/Ownrshp* 2006
Sales 299.7MM^E *EMP* 600
SIC 1321 Natural gas liquids
CEO: John W Gibson
Pr: Terry K Spencer
Treas: Mark Smith
Ex VP: Robert F Martinovich
Ex VP: Pierce H Norton
Sr VP: Stephen W Lake
Sr VP: Robert S Mareburger
VP: Curtis Dinan
VP: John Sommers

D-U-N-S 00-790-7827
▲ **ONEOK INC**
100 W 5th St Ste Ll, Tulsa, OK 74103-4298
Tel (918) 588-7000 *Founded/Ownrshp* 1906
Sales 7.7MMM *EMP* 2,364
Tkr Sym OKE *Exch* NYS
SIC 4922 4924 1311 1321 5172 Natural gas transmission; Pipelines, natural gas; Storage, natural gas; Natural gas distribution; Crude petroleum & natural gas; Crude petroleum production; Natural gas production; Natural gas liquids; Gases
Pr: Terry K Spencer
Ch Bd: John W Gibson
CFO: Derek S Reiners
Bd of Dir: Michael Ryan
Ofcr: Robert F Martinovich
Ex VP: Walter S Hulse III
Sr VP: Kevin L Burdick
Sr VP: Wesley J Christensen
Sr VP: Stephen W Lake
Sr VP: Sheridan C Swords
VP: Stephen B Allen
VP: Walter Allen
VP: Charles Andrews
VP: John R Barker
VP: Ronald Bridgewater
VP: Michael Crisman
VP: George Drake
VP: Wesley Dunbar
VP: James Fallan
VP: Jim Falon
VP: Craig A Forsander
Board of Directors: Eduardo A Rodriguez, James C Day, Brian L Derksen, Julie H Edwards, Randall J Larson, Steven J Malcolm, Kevin S McCarthy, Jim W Mogg, Pattye L Moore, Gary D Parker

D-U-N-S 80-897-3234
▲ **ONEOK PARTNERS LP**
100 W 5th St Ste Ll, Tulsa, OK 74103-4298
Tel (918) 588-7000 *Founded/Ownrshp* 1993
Sales 7.7MMM *EMP* 2,364^E
Tkr Sym OKS *Exch* NYS
SIC 4922 1321 1381 4925 Natural gas transmission; Natural gas liquids; Drilling oil & gas wells; Gas production and/or distribution
Pr: Terry K Spencer
Genl Pt: Oneok P GP
CFO: Derek S Reiners

D-U-N-S 93-384-5604
■ **ONEOK ROCKIES MIDSTREAM LLC**
(*Suby of* ONEOK PARTNERS LP) ★
100 W 5th St Ste Ll, Tulsa, OK 74103-4298
Tel (918) 588-7000 *Founded/Ownrshp* 2001
Sales 1.2MMM^E *EMP* 130
SIC 1311

ONEONTA STARR RANCH GROWERS
See ONEONTA TRADING CORP

D-U-N-S 02-757-7782 IMP/EXP
ONEONTA TRADING CORP
ONEONTA STARR RANCH GROWERS
1 Oneonta Dr, Wenatchee, WA 98801-1500
Tel (509) 663-2631 *Founded/Ownrshp* 1965
Sales 341.0MM *EMP* 56
SIC 5148 Fruits, fresh; Vegetables, fresh
Pr: Dalton Thomas
**VP:* Bradley Thomas
Genl Mgr: Brian Focht
Prd Mgr: Sam Moss
Genl Couns: Jim Brown

D-U-N-S 62-445-4810
ONEPATH SYSTEMS LLC
(*Suby of* ONEPATH HOLDING CORPORATION)
2053 Franklin Way Se, Marietta, GA 30067-8712
Tel (678) 695-5500 *Founded/Ownrshp* 2006
Sales 109.1MM *EMP* 901
Accts Cherry Bekaert Llp Atlanta G
SIC 7389 8744 7378 7376 7382 Design services; Facilities support services; Computer peripheral equipment repair & maintenance; Computer facilities management; Security systems services; Fire alarm maintenance & monitoring
CEO: Ben Balsley
CFO: Brian Lane
CFO: Jeff Spranger
VP: Chad Merrell
VP: Kevin Simmons
Off Mgr: Melania Ricard
Snr Ntwrk: Steve Moser
QA Dir: Rcdd Thorne
Netwrk Eng: Mark Warren
VP Opers: Bob Catanach
VP Opers: Chris Lewis

D-U-N-S 02-854-7479 IMP
ONESOURCE DISTRIBUTORS LLC
SAN DIEGO WHOLESALE ELECTRIC
(*Suby of* SONEPAR USA) ★
3951 Oceanic Dr, Oceanside, CA 92056-5846
Tel (760) 966-4500 *Founded/Ownrshp* 2011
Sales 488.5MM^E *EMP* 400
SIC 5063 3699 Electrical apparatus & equipment; Electrical equipment & supplies
Pr: Mike Smith
CFO: Tim Walsh
Genl Mgr: Leslie McCoy
IT Man: Tim Logan
Opers Mgr: Debbie Marshall
Sls Mgr: Wendy Cano

ONESOURCE VIRTUAL
See ONE SOURCE VIRTUAL HR INC

D-U-N-S 06-820-8129 IMP
ONESUBSEA LLC
(*Suby of* CAMERON INTERNATIONAL CORP) ★
4646 W Sam Houston Pkwy N, Houston, TX 77041-8214
Tel (713) 939-2211 *Founded/Ownrshp* 2013
Sales 228.8MM^E *EMP* 6,500
SIC 3533 3563 3491 Oil & gas field machinery; Oil field machinery & equipment; Gas field machinery & equipment; Air & gas compressors; Automatic regulating & control valves
Pr: Henning Berg
Ofcr: Meredith Canada
VP: Justin Rounce
VP: Jon Arve Svaeren
VP Sls: Hal Goldie

D-U-N-S 82-689-8178
ONETOUCHPOINT CORP
TOUCHPOINT PRINT SOLUTIONS
1225 Walnut Ridge Dr, Hartland, WI 53029-8300
Tel (630) 586-9002 *Founded/Ownrshp* 2014
Sales 228.5MM^E *EMP* 487^E
SIC 2759 Commercial printing
CEO: Tom Simunek
**CFO:* Kevin Kotche
Dir Bus: Brad Bush
Snr Mgr: Rebecca Gibbs

D-U-N-S 06-203-9078 IMP
ONETOUCHPOINT MIDWEST CORP
CCI/COAKLEYTECH
(*Suby of* TOUCHPOINT PRINT SOLUTIONS) ★
1225 Walnut Ridge Dr, Hartland, WI 53029-8300
Tel (262) 369-6000 *Founded/Ownrshp* 1982
Sales 111.7MM^E *EMP* 280
SIC 2752 Offset & photolithographic printing
Pr: Chris Illman
COO: Norm Keene
Genl Mgr: James Parker
CIO: Phil Bartelme
CIO: Phil Bartleme
Opers Mgr: Rob Tynan
Plnt Mgr: Carey Howard
S&M/VP: Joni Diderrich

D-U-N-S 83-000-0068
ONEWEST BANK GROUP LLC
888 E Walnut St, Pasadena, CA 91101-1895
Tel (626) 535-4870 *Founded/Ownrshp* 2009
Sales NA *EMP* 850^E
SIC 6035

D-U-N-S 60-607-9168
ONEX INVESTMENT CORP
(*Suby of* ONEX CORPORATION)
712 5th Ave Fl 40, New York, NY 10019-4108
Tel (212) 582-2211 *Founded/Ownrshp* 1987
Sales 1.6MMM^E *EMP* 20,000
SIC 6799 6282 Venture capital companies; Investment advisory service

D-U-N-S 08-517-1973
ONGWEOWEH CORP
767 Warren Rd, Ithaca, NY 14850-1255
Tel (607) 266-7070 *Founded/Ownrshp* 1980
Sales 180.0MM *EMP* 102
SIC 8741 4953 Management services; Recycling, waste materials
Ch Bd: Frank C Bonamie
**Pr:* Justin M Bennett
Treas: Kristi Pierce
Dir IT: Jim Davies
Natl Sales: Kevin Benckendorf
Sls Mgr: Erica Belonosoff
Snr Mgr: Doreen Gebhard

D-U-N-S 08-704-5845
ONI RISK PARTNERS INC
OLD NATIONAL INSURANCE
(*Suby of* PRIME RISK PARTNERS INC) ★
600 E 96th St Ste 400, Indianapolis, IN 46240-3842
Tel (317) 706-9500 *Founded/Ownrshp* 2016
Sales NA *EMP* 190
SIC 6411 Insurance agents
Pr: Tom Flynn
Pr: Mark Bienz
Pr: Steve Danielson
Pr: John Flynn
Pr: Frank Krisanits
Pr: Jack Matthews
COO: Jim Hynes
Assoc VP: Marie Comparet
Assoc VP: Linda Kalber
Assoc VP: Martha Williamson
Ex VP: Mike Gilbert
Sr VP: Tom Dickman
VP: Patrick Carney
VP: Deb Eovaldi
VP: Denny Wright

D-U-N-S 82-845-9664
ONIN STAFFING LLC
1 Perimeter Park S 450n, Birmingham, AL 35243-3201
Tel (205) 298-7233 *Founded/Ownrshp* 1996
Sales 144.2MM^E *EMP* 6,500^E
SIC 7361 Labor contractors (employment agency)
Brnch Mgr: Barbara Thomas
Sls Dir: John Calero

D-U-N-S 06-432-5327 EXP
■ **ONITY INC**
(*Suby of* CHUBB LIMITED)
4001 Fairview Indus Dr Se, Salem, OR 97302-1142
Tel (503) 581-9101 *Founded/Ownrshp* 1993
Sales 1.7MM^E *EMP* 22,000
SIC 5072 Security devices, locks
Pr: Ronald Virden
**CFO:* Jay Weaver
IT Man: Debbie Saunders

D-U-N-S 93-849-7302
ONLIFE HEALTH INC
(*Suby of* BLUECARE) ★
9020 Overlook Blvd # 300, Brentwood, TN 37027-3259
Tel (615) 844-2100 *Founded/Ownrshp* 1995
Sales NA *EMP* 200^E
SIC 6324 Hospital & medical service plans
Pr: J Mark McConnell
Pr: Steven Davidson
**Pr:* Jed Dodd
Rgnl VP: Seth R Hart
Sr VP: Philip H Hadden
Sr VP: William Seibels
VP: Lori Close
VP: Lori Huss
VP: Kevin Jett
VP: Victor Mattingly
VP: Joann Russell

D-U-N-S 17-762-0122
ONLINE TRANSPORT INC
6311 W Stoner Dr, Greenfield, IN 46140-7413
Tel (317) 894-6860 *Founded/Ownrshp* 1999
Sales 101.4MM *EMP* 480^E
SIC 4213 Heavy hauling
Pr: Dan Cook
**CFO:* James Henry

D-U-N-S 83-497-8475
ONMEDIA COMMUNICATIONS CO INC
ON MEDIA ADVERTISING SALES
115 N Industrial Park Rd, Excelsior Springs, MO 64024-1734
Tel (913) 491-4030 *Founded/Ownrshp* 2008
Sales 95.8MM^E *EMP* 500^E
SIC 4841 Cable & other pay television services
Pr: Rocco Commisso
**VP:* Kay Evans
**VP:* Bob Montgomery
**Genl Mgr:* Michele Cropp
**Genl Mgr:* John Pauley
Manager: Ron Snyder

D-U-N-S 05-372-3334
ONONDAGA COMMUNITY COLLEGE
(*Suby of* SUNY ADMINISTRATION) ★
4585 W Seneca Tpke, Syracuse, NY 13215-4585
Tel (315) 498-2622 *Founded/Ownrshp* 1962
Sales 1.7MM *EMP* 1,021
Accts Bonadio & Co Llp Syracuse Ny
SIC 8222 9411 Community college; Administration of educational programs;
CEO: Debbie L Sydow
Pr: Kevin M Moore
Pr: Larry Page
Ofcr: Nicole T Schlater
Assoc VP: John Paddock
Sr VP: Linda Kelley
VP: Agatha Awuah
**VP:* Ralph Feola
VP: Sarah Gaffney
VP: Anastasia Urtz
VP: Julie White
VP: Steve Wiley

ONONDAGA CRTLAND MADISON BOCES
See ONONDAGA-CORTLAND-MADISON BOCES

D-U-N-S 01-077-0964
ONONDAGA-CORTLAND-MADISON BOCES
ONONDAGA CRTLAND MADISON BOCES
6820 Thompson Rd, Syracuse, NY 13211-1321
Tel (315) 433-8300 *Founded/Ownrshp* 1968
Sales 109.0MM^E *EMP* 1,457
SIC 8211 Public elementary & secondary schools
Teacher Pr: Mark Pettit

D-U-N-S 08-745-8311
ONPOINT COMMUNITY CREDIT UNION (OR)
2701 Nw Vaughn St Ste 800, Portland, OR 97210-5387
Tel (503) 228-8255 *Founded/Ownrshp* 1932
Sales NA *EMP* 426
SIC 6062 State credit unions, not federally chartered
CEO: Robert A Stuart
**Pr:* Steve Gray
Ofcr: Karen Carter
Ofcr: Constance Wilhelm
**Sr VP:* Jim Armstrong
**Sr VP:* Jim Hunt
**Sr VP:* Tory McVay
Sr VP: Tony Mendezona
**Sr VP:* Kelly Schrader
VP: Michele Debuhr
**VP:* Wayne Pederson

D-U-N-S 01-409-1420
ONPROCESS TECHNOLOGY INC
200 Homer Ave, Ashland, MA 01721-1717
Tel (508) 520-2711 *Founded/Ownrshp* 1998
Sales 93.0MM^E *EMP* 450^E
SIC 7379 Computer related consulting services
CEO: Michael Wooden
Pr: Joseph Hamilton
Ex VP: Michele Donaldson
**Ex VP:* Robert Kenney
Ex VP: Michael Stann
Sr VP: Gustavo Estrella
**Sr VP:* Subhratanu Paul
VP: Jim Flinton
VP: Dan Gettens
VP: Ted Moriarty
VP: Candyce Plante
Dir Bus: Adam Barry

D-U-N-S 06-228-7253
ONRAMP TRANSPORTATION SERVICES LLC
5416 W Amelia Earhart Dr # 201, Salt Lake City, UT 84116-3723
Tel (801) 736-9420 *Founded/Ownrshp* 2011
Sales 100.0MM *EMP* 130
SIC 4789 Freight car loading & unloading
Pr: Spencer Angerbauer
**Sr VP:* Randy Olsen

D-U-N-S 02-446-9944
ONSITE DENTAL LLC
(*Suby of* ONSITE HEALTH INC) ★
85 Argonaut Ste 220, Aliso Viejo, CA 92656-4105
Tel (888) 411-2290 *Founded/Ownrshp* 2008
Sales 400.0MM *EMP* 20
SIC 8021 Offices & clinics of dentists
CEO: Ernest Blackwelder
Rgnl Mgr: Camie Worley
VP Opers: Ryan Principi

D-U-N-S 83-025-0051
ONSITE HEALTH INC
1308 Devils Reach Rd # 302, Woodbridge, VA 22192-2806
Tel (949) 441-9530 *Founded/Ownrshp* 2009
Sales 400.0MM^E *EMP* 120^E
SIC 8099 Medical services organization
CEO: Ernest Blackwelder
**CFO:* David Joe
Sr VP: Paige Beville
Dir Soc: Frances Pickering

ONSLOW COUNTY BOARD EDUCATION
See ONSLOW COUNTY SCHOOLS INC

D-U-N-S 03-410-4067
ONSLOW COUNTY HOSPITAL AUTHORITY
ONSLOW MEMORIAL HOSPITAL
317 Western Blvd, Jacksonville, NC 28546-6338
Tel (910) 577-2345 *Founded/Ownrshp* 1972
Sales 141.3MM *EMP* 1,200^E
SIC 8062 General medical & surgical hospitals
CEO: Ed Piper PHD
CFO: William Bass
**CFO:* Roy Smith
Sr VP: Dottie Sigman
Sr VP: Daniel Waller
VP: Erin Tallman
Dir Risk M: Richard Thompson
Telecom Ex: Pat Banks
HC Dir: John Stewart

D-U-N-S 08-236-3573
ONSLOW COUNTY SCHOOLS INC
ONSLOW COUNTY BOARD EDUCATION
200 Broadhurst Rd, Jacksonville, NC 28540-3551
Tel (910) 455-2211 *Founded/Ownrshp* 1900
Sales 121.3MM^E *EMP* 2,800
SIC 8211 Public elementary & secondary schools
**CFO:* Jeff Hollamon
Dir Sec: Dusty Rhodes
Pr Dir: Beth Folger
Teacher Pr: C J Koreneck

ONSLOW MEMORIAL HOSPITAL
See ONSLOW COUNTY HOSPITAL AUTHORITY

D-U-N-S 07-556-0672
ONSLOW MEMORIAL HOSPITAL INC
(*Suby of* ONSLOW MEMORIAL HOSPITAL) ★
241 New River Dr, Jacksonville, NC 28540-5928
Tel (910) 577-4703 *Founded/Ownrshp* 1946
Sales 141.3MM *EMP* 864
SIC 8062 General medical & surgical hospitals
CEO: Ed Piper

D-U-N-S 07-607-0192 IMP
ONTARIO-MONTCLAIR SCHOOL DISTRICT
950 W D St, Ontario, CA 91762-3026
Tel (909) 459-2500 *Founded/Ownrshp* 1884
Sales 114.8MM^E *EMP* 2,114
Accts Vavrinek Trine Day & Co Ll
SIC 8211 Public elementary & secondary schools
MIS Dir: Bill Ameeri
Netwrk Eng: Jon Lewis
Psych: Delia Mariscal

ONTERIE FITNESS CENTER
See OFC MANAGEMENT INC

D-U-N-S 15-538-9224
ONTIC ENGINEERING AND MANUFACTURING INC
(*Suby of* BBA AVIATION PLC)
20400 Plummer St, Chatsworth, CA 91311-5372
Tel (818) 678-6555 *Founded/Ownrshp* 1987
Sales 165.0MM^E *EMP* 170
SIC 5088 3728 3812 Aircraft equipment & supplies; Aircraft parts & equipment; Search & navigation equipment
Pr: Peg Billson

ONTRAC
See EXPRESS MESSENGER SYSTEMS INC

ONU
See OHIO NORTHERN UNIVERSITY

D-U-N-S 62-110-1823
ONVOY LLC
10300 6th Ave N, Plymouth, MN 55441-6371
Tel (763) 230-2036 *Founded/Ownrshp* 2016
Sales 156.5MM^E *EMP* 290
SIC 4813 Telephone communication, except radio
COO: Fritz Hendricks
**Pr:* Teri Asiala
**Pr:* John Hanna
**Pr:* Surenda Saboo
**CFO:* Michael Donahue
VP: Gary Tabachnik
Exec: Allan Flinn
Admn Mgr: Sandy McWilliams
Genl Mgr: Steven Miske
**CIO:* Justin Nelson
**CTO:* Kelly Murphy

D-U-N-S 09-568-9290
■ **ONWARD HEALTHCARE INC**
(*Suby of* AMN HEALTHCARE INC) ★
64 Danbury Rd Ste 100, Wilton, CT 06897-4438
Tel (203) 834-3000 *Founded/Ownrshp* 2015
Sales 98.9MM^E *EMP* 1,400
SIC 7361 Employment agencies
CEO: Kevin Clark
**Pr:* John Martins
VP: John Paterson

D-U-N-S 07-864-4755
ONX ACQUISITION LLC
ONX ENTERPRISE SOLUTIONS
5910 Landerbrook Dr # 250, Mayfield Heights, OH 44124-6508
Tel (440) 569-2300 *Founded/Ownrshp* 2011
Sales 255.0MM *EMP* 300^E
SIC 7372 7379

ONX ENTERPRISE SOLUTIONS
See ONX ACQUISITION LLC

ONYX
See GINO MORENA ENTERPRISES LLC

D-U-N-S 08-218-4156 IMP/EXP
ONYX ENVIRONMENTAL SERVICES LLC
(*Suby of* VEOLIA ENVIRONMENTAL SERVICES NORTH AMERICA CORP) ★
700 E Bttrfeld Rd Ste 201, Lombard, IL 60148
Tel (630) 218-1500 *Founded/Ownrshp* 1999
Sales 290.1MM^E *EMP* 1,210
SIC 8711 4953 2869 1799 1629 Engineering services; Hazardous waste collection & disposal; Solvents, organic; Asbestos removal & encapsulation; Power plant construction
CEO: Jim Bell
VP: Mark Dennis
VP: Greig Siedor
Genl Mgr: Melanie Free
VP Opers: Robert Cappadona
Mktg Dir: Jim Dykhuis

D-U-N-S 78-959-1724
■ **ONYX PHARMACEUTICALS INC**
(*Suby of* AMGEN INC) ★
1 Amgen Center Dr, Newbury Park, CA 91320-1730
Tel (650) 266-0000 *Founded/Ownrshp* 2013
Sales 228.8MM^E *EMP* 741
SIC 2834 8049 Drugs affecting parasitic & infective diseases; Occupational therapist
Pr: Pablo Cagnoni
COO: Helen Torley
CFO: Matthew K Fust
Ex VP: Juergen Lasowski PHD
Ex VP: Matthew Fust
Ex VP: Suzanne M Shema Jdl
Ex VP: J Rgen Lasowski
Ex VP: Ted W Love
Sr VP: John E Osborn
VP: Judy Batlin
VP: Rosh Dias
VP: Scott Geyer
VP: Rekha Hemrajani
VP: Sujay Kango
VP: Meghan Leader
VP: Mark McClung
VP: Mary Ann Rafferty
VP: Wendell Wieronga
VP: Marilyn E Wortzman
Assoc Dir: Philip Chou
Assoc Dir: Shibao Feng
Board of Directors: Paul Goddard, Antonio J Grillo-Lopez, Magnus Lundberg, Corinne H Nevinny, William R Ringo, Wendell Wierenga, Thomas G Wiggans

D-U-N-S 00-618-8438
ONYX SERVICES LLC (TX)
22971 Keith Dr, New Caney, TX 77357-8337
Tel (281) 577-5131 *Founded/Ownrshp* 2012, 2013
Sales 500.0MM *EMP* 40
SIC 6531 Real estate agents & managers

D-U-N-S 03-946-3997
OOCL (USA) INC
(*Suby of* ORIENT OVERSEAS (INTERNATIONAL) LIMITED)
10913 S River Front Pkwy # 200, South Jordan, UT 84095-3507
Tel (801) 302-6625 *Founded/Ownrshp* 1981
Sales 148.7MM^E *EMP* 690

SIC 4731 Agents, shipping; Transportation agents & brokers
Pr: Peter Leng
**Pr:* Paul Devine
**Sr VP:* T F Hau
**Sr VP:* Stephen Ng
VP: M Bjerre
VP: B Laverdin
Mng Dir: Bernard Soh
Snr Sftwr: Orlando Palis
Snr Sftwr: Steven Wart
Sftwr Eng: Jose Bacoy
Sftwr Eng: Jon Paynter

D-U-N-S 60-682-8726 IMP
OOMA INC
1880 Embarcadero Rd, Palo Alto, CA 94303-3308
Tel (650) 566-6600 *Founded/Ownrshp* 2003
Sales 88.7MM *EMP* 139
Tkr Sym OOMA *Exch* NYS
SIC 4813
Ch Bd: Eric B Stang
CFO: Ravi Narula
Treas: John Summers
Treas: Anita Yang
VP: Tami Bhaumik
VP: Jamie Buckley
VP: Aaron Duran
VP: James Im
VP: Spencer D Jackson
VP: Tim Sullivan
Exec: Minika Esposo
Board of Directors: Susan Butenhoff, Alison Davis, Andrew H Galligan, Peter J Goettner, Russell Mann, William D Pearce, James Wei

D-U-N-S 08-030-7238
OOYALA HOLDINGS INC
(*Suby of* TELSTRA CORPORATION LIMITED)
4750 Patrick Henry Dr, Santa Clara, CA 95054-1851
Tel (650) 961-3400 *Founded/Ownrshp* 2014
Sales 124.4MM[E] *EMP* 551
SIC 7812 6719 Video production; Investment holding companies, except banks
Ex Dir: Jay Fulcher
**CFO:* David Wilson
**Ex Dir:* Charlotte Yarkoni

D-U-N-S 82-535-2896
OOYALA INC
(*Suby of* OOYALA HOLDINGS INC) ★
4750 Patrick Henry Dr, Santa Clara, CA 95054-1851
Tel (650) 961-3400 *Founded/Ownrshp* 2014
Sales 124.4MM[E] *EMP* 550[E]
SIC 7371 Software programming applications
CEO: Ramesh Srinivasan
**Pr:* Jay Fulcher
**CFO:* David Wilson
Sr VP: Dave Hare
Sr VP: Scott Smith
Sr VP: Sorosh Tavakoli
Sr VP: Issac Vaughn
VP: Keith Budge
VP: Jonathan Knight
VP: Jonathan Wilner
**Co-Founder:* Belsasar Lepe

D-U-N-S 01-694-3136
OPAA FOOD MANAGEMENT INC
100 Chesterfield Business, Chesterfield, MO 63005-1271
Tel (636) 812-0777 *Founded/Ownrshp* 1976
Sales 45.9MM[E] *EMP* 1,250
SIC 5812 Contract food services
Pr: Kevin Short
COO: Scott Hoffmann
VP: Craig Cohen
VP: Sheila Frost
Exec: Linda Jones

D-U-N-S 07-941-0696
OPAL FOODS LLC
1100 Blair Ave, Neosho, MO 64850-9117
Tel (417) 455-5000 *Founded/Ownrshp* 2014
Sales 276.2MM *EMP* 310
Accts Frost Pllc Little Rock Arkan
SIC 0252 Chicken eggs
CEO: Jerry Welch
CFO: Craig Bonet

D-U-N-S 07-843-3214
OPAL HOLDINGS LLC
(*Suby of* SOUTHEASTERN GROCERS LLC) ★
208 Bi Lo Blvd, Greenville, SC 29607-5346
Tel (864) 213-2500 *Founded/Ownrshp* 2011
Sales 71.8MM[E] *EMP* 47,005
SIC 5411 5541 5912 Supermarkets, chain; Gasoline service stations; Drug stores

OPA'S
See GREEKTOWN CASINO LLC

D-U-N-S 07-508-0069
OPELOUSAS GENERAL HEALTH SYSTEM
OPELOUSAS GENERAL HOSP AUTH
539 E Prudhomme St, Opelousas, LA 70570-6499
Tel (337) 948-3011 *Founded/Ownrshp* 1972
Sales 129.4MM[E] *EMP* 1,000
Accts Broussard Poche Lewis & Brea
SIC 8062 General medical & surgical hospitals
Pr: Bob Hardy
**Ch Bd:* Gina Tuttle
**CFO:* Jim Juneau
**Sec:* Morris Weinstein
Dir Lab: A C Thiboudeaux
Mktg Mgr: Judy Thell

OPELOUSAS GENERAL HOSP AUTH
See OPELOUSAS GENERAL HEALTH SYSTEM

D-U-N-S 94-503-1771
OPEN ACCESS TECHNOLOGY INTERNATIONAL INC
OATI
3660 Technology Dr, Minneapolis, MN 55418-1006
Tel (763) 201-2000 *Founded/Ownrshp* 1995
Sales 105.7MM[E] *EMP* 300[E]
SIC 7371 8711 Computer software development; Electrical or electronic engineering
Pr: Sasan Mohktari
Ex VP: Nelson Muller
Ex VP: Kash Nodehi
Sr VP: Manuel Santos
VP: Farrokh Albuyeh
VP: Jerry Dempsey
VP: Ali Ipakchi
VP: Farrokh Rahimi
VP: Jagjit Singh
VP: Paul Sorenson
CTO: Erik Amundson

OPEN LINK
See OPENLINK FINANCIAL LLC

OPEN ROAD AUTO GROUP
See RYAN AUTOMOTIVE LLC

D-U-N-S 11-207-6989
OPEN SOCIETY INSTITUTE
224 W 57th St Frnt 1, New York, NY 10019-3212
Tel (212) 548-0600 *Founded/Ownrshp* 1993
Sales 155.6MM *EMP* 445
Accts Kpmg Llp Mclean Va
SIC 8399 Social change association
Pr: Aryeh Neier
**CFO:* Maija Arbolino
Ofcr: Jason T Garrett
Ofcr: Emma Oppenheim
VP: Gara Lamarch
Ex Dir: Farda Asadov
Ex Dir: Diana Morris
Prgrm Mgr: Melissa Hagemann
Genl Mgr: Bonnie Blocker
Netwrk Mgr: Oleg Kolokoltsev
Software D: Jason Lantz

D-U-N-S 80-267-8524
■ **OPEN SOLUTIONS LLC**
(*Suby of* FISERV INC) ★
455 Winding Brook Dr # 101, Glastonbury, CT 06033-4351
Tel (860) 815-5000 *Founded/Ownrshp* 2013
Sales 234.7MM[E] *EMP* 1,700
SIC 7372 7373 Business oriented computer software; Systems integration services
Pr: Stephen J Cameron
Pr: Mike Cardell
Pr: Mike Reiskis
Chf Mktg O: David Mitchell
Ex VP: Sam Boggs
Ex VP: Ross M Curtis
Ex VP: Roswell M Curtis
Sr VP: Wayne Ginn
Sr VP: Jonathan Lee
VP: Tom Black
VP: Neale Brown
VP: Jan Frymyer
VP: Kelly Gardner
VP: Jim Glancy
VP: John McDonald
VP: Brian Molloy
VP: David Vanpelt

D-U-N-S 80-137-1758
OPEN SYSTEMS INTERNATIONAL INC
4101 Arrowhead Dr, Medina, MN 55340-9457
Tel (763) 551-0559 *Founded/Ownrshp* 1992
Sales 90.3MM[E] *EMP* 265[E]
Accts Mcgladrey & Pullen Llp Minne
SIC 7371 5734 Computer software development; Computer & software stores
Pr: Bahman Hoveida
VP: Margaret Boiano
VP: Hormoz Kazemzadeh
VP: Karen Peterson

OPEN SYSTEMS TECHNOLOGIES
See BAHA INDUSTRIES CORP

D-U-N-S 02-066-1509
OPEN SYSTEMS TECHNOLOGIES DE LLC
O S T
(*Suby of* K D C) ★
605 Seward Ave Nw Ste 101, Grand Rapids, MI 49504-5693
Tel (616) 574-3500 *Founded/Ownrshp* 2012
Sales 148.2MM *EMP* 106[E]
Accts Kpmg Llp Anchorage Ak
SIC 7379 Computer related maintenance services
Pr: Daniel Behm
**COO:* Meredith Bronk
**CIO:* James Vandermey
IT Man: Brad Bailie
Software D: Andrea Houg
Mktg Mgr: Michael Lomonaco
Sales Asso: Lori Grinwis
Board of Directors: David Gerrity, John Thayer, John Vancil

D-U-N-S 05-423-4390
OPEN SYSTEMS TECHNOLOGIES INC
1818 Market St Ste 2510, Philadelphia, PA 19103-3650
Tel (215) 399-5800 *Founded/Ownrshp* 1997
Sales 105.6MM *EMP* 650
Accts Rosenblatt Radezky Schiff & Te
SIC 7379 Computer related consulting services
Exec: Rick West
Dir Bus: Randy Potter
Ex Dir: Robert Rose
IT Man: John Buth

D-U-N-S 06-459-6158
OPEN TEXT INC
(*Suby of* OPEN TEXT CORPORATION)
951 Mariners Island Blvd # 7, San Mateo, CA 94404-1561
Tel (650) 645-3000 *Founded/Ownrshp* 2004
Sales 125.0MM[E] *EMP* 475
SIC 7379 Computer related consulting services
CEO: Mark J Barrenechea
Pr: John Shackleton
CFO: John Doolittle
CFO: Daniel Gaudreau
Sr VP: James McGourlay
VP: Allen Bonde
VP: Wenfeng Li
VP: Tom McKeever
Genl Mgr: Steve Jones
Genl Mgr: Paul Walker
IT Man: Bryon Darner

D-U-N-S 60-248-4227
OPENGATE CAPITAL LLC
10250 Constellation Blvd, Los Angeles, CA 90067-6200
Tel (310) 432-7000 *Founded/Ownrshp* 2005
Sales 915.6MM[E] *EMP* 2,400
SIC 2721 6799 8621 Magazines: publishing & printing; Investors; Professional membership organizations
CEO: Lisa J Bahash
CFO: Michelle Lindquist
CFO: James Neelley
CFO: Jay Yook
Sr VP: Daniel Abrams
Sr VP: Joshua Adams
Sr VP: Alanna Chaffin
Prin: Matthias Gundlach

D-U-N-S 83-110-6430
OPENLINK FINANCIAL LLC
OPEN LINK
1502 Rxr Plz Fl 15w, Uniondale, NY 11556-3810
Tel (516) 227-6600 *Founded/Ownrshp* 1992
Sales 230.5MM[E] *EMP* 1,300[E]
Accts Ernst & Young Llp New York N
SIC 7371 7372 8742 Computer software development; Prepackaged software; Financial consultant
Ch Bd: Coleman Fung
**CEO:* Kevin J Hesselbirg
**CEO:* John O'Malley
CFO: Joe Dwyer
**CFO:* David M Obstler
**Ex VP:* Roger Burkhardt
**Ex VP:* Andrew Goodman
**Ex VP:* Rich Grossi
**Ex VP:* Robert Kalish
Ex VP: Ken Knowles
Sr VP: Diane W Montaruli
VP: David Barish
VP: Tom Hannon
VP: Mark Otoole
VP: Phil Wang

OPENSQUARE
See WORKSPACE DEVELOPMENT LLC

D-U-N-S 05-530-5523
■ **OPENTABLE INC**
(*Suby of* PRICELINE GROUP) ★
1 Montgomery St Ste 700, San Francisco, CA 94104-4536
Tel (415) 344-4200 *Founded/Ownrshp* 2014
Sales 190.0MM *EMP* 625[E]
SIC 7389 Restaurant reservation service
CEO: Christa Quarles
**Ch Bd:* Matthew Roberts
**CFO:* Jeff McCombs
**CFO:* I Duncan Robertson
Sr VP: Prasad Gune
Sr VP: Charles McCullough
**CTO:* Joseph Essas

OPENTEXT
See EASYLINK SERVICES INTERNATIONAL CORP

D-U-N-S 82-852-3287 IMP
OPENX TECHNOLOGIES INC
(*Suby of* OPENX LIMITED)
888 E Walnut St Fl 2, Pasadena, CA 91101-1897
Tel (855) 673-6948 *Founded/Ownrshp* 2008
Sales 95.4MM[E] *EMP* 359[E]
SIC 7311 Advertising agencies
CEO: Tim Cadogan
Pr: John Gentry
Pr: Dan Sheehy
CFO: Tom Fuelling
CFO: Eric W Muhlheim
Chf Cred: Deborah Roth
Chf Cred: Tish Whitcraft
Ofcr: Laura Revenko
Sr VP: Nicholas Cumins
Sr VP: Manoj Goyal
Sr VP: Qasim Saifee
VP: Laura Buchman
VP: Jeff Faxon
VP: John Murphy
VP: Andy Negrin
VP: Todd Rosenberg
VP: Trevor Thomas
VP: Jin Yu
Board of Directors: Pascal Gauthier

D-U-N-S 36-111-4437
OPERA SOLUTIONS LLC
10 Exchange Pl Fl 11, Jersey City, NJ 07302 4934
Tel (646) 520-4320 *Founded/Ownrshp* 2003
Sales 95.0MM[E] *EMP* 360
SIC 7371 Computer software development
CEO: Arnab Gupta
CFO: Sridhar Ramasubbu
Ex VP: Shawn Blevins
Sr VP: Craig Peterson
VP: Jack Cain
VP: Jonathan Di Giambattista
VP: Herb Kelsey
VP: Phuong Nguyen
VP: Julian Romeu
Genl Mgr: Eric Michlowitz
Off Mgr: Elvis Antigua

D-U-N-S 96-487-1961
OPERATING ENGINEERS HEALTH & WELFARE FUND
100 Corson St, Pasadena, CA 91103-3840
Tel (626) 356-1000 *Founded/Ownrshp* 2014
Sales 228.0MM *EMP* 2[E]
Accts Bernard Kotkin And Company Llp
SIC 6733 Trusts, except educational, religious, charity: management
CFO: Chuck Killian

D-U-N-S 04-899-7162
OPERATING ENGINEERS LOCAL 49
INTERNATIONAL UNN OF OPRTNG EN
308 Lundin Blvd, Mankato, MN 56001-2706
Tel (507) 625-3670 *Founded/Ownrshp* 2001
Sales 96.0MM *EMP* 3
SIC 8631 Labor unions & similar labor organizations

D-U-N-S 96-959-1572
OPERATING ENGINEERS LOCAL NO 825 WELFARE FUND
65 Springfield Ave Ste 2, Springfield, NJ 07081-1308
Tel (973) 921-1661 *Founded/Ownrshp* 2011
Sales 116.7MM *EMP* 2[E]
Accts Calibre Cpa Group Pllc Washin
SIC 8711 Engineering services
Prin: Randy Fork

D-U-N-S 62-295-8445
OPERATION BLESSING INTERNATIONAL RELIEF AND DEVELOPMENT CORP
977 Centerville Tpke, Virginia Beach, VA 23463-1001
Tel (757) 226-3401 *Founded/Ownrshp* 1986
Sales 267.1MM[E] *EMP* 50[E]
Accts Kpmg Llp Mclean Va
SIC 8699 Charitable organization
Pr: William F Horan
**COO:* Robert W Fanning
VP: Steve O'Grady
Ex Dir: Ronda Sherman
Genl Mgr: Kara Waddell
Snr Ntwrk: Dan Moore
Opers Mgr: Manny Gonzalez
Mktg Mgr: Lauren Cory

D-U-N-S 00-270-1715
OPERATION COMPASSION
114 Stuart Rd Ne Ste 370, Cleveland, TN 37312-4803
Tel (423) 479-3770 *Founded/Ownrshp* 1997
Sales 127.2MM *EMP* 25
Accts Arnettkirkseykimseysullivanlay
SIC 8399 Social service information exchange
Pr: David Lorency
VP: Casey Smith

OPERATIONS CENTER
See CENTURY BANK AND TRUST CO

D-U-N-S 05-014-7297
OPERATIONS MANAGEMENT INTERNATIONAL INC
(*Suby of* CH2M HILL COMPANIES LTD) ★
9193 S Jamaica St Ste 400, Englewood, CO 80112-5946
Tel (303) 740-0019 *Founded/Ownrshp* 1980
Sales 508.2MM[E] *EMP* 1,300
SIC 4952 4941

OPERATIONS/RISK GROUP
See PARSONS CONSTRUCTORS INC

D-U-N-S 06-738-0386 IMP/EXP
OPEX CORP
OMATION
305 Commerce Dr, Moorestown, NJ 08057-4234
Tel (856) 727-1100 *Founded/Ownrshp* 1973
Sales 124.8MM[E] *EMP* 650
SIC 3579 Mailing, letter handling & addressing machines
CEO: David Stevens
**Ch Bd:* Albert Stevens
CEO: Mark Stevens
Treas: David Kammeyer
VP: James M Liebler
Dir IT: Glenn Buchanan
IT Man: Jamey Anthony
Web Dev: Tim Parent
Software D: Joe Garcia
Sftwr Eng: Ryan Corcoran
Sftwr Eng: Doug Perham

OPICIWINES
See B D AMERICAN CO

D-U-N-S 18-912-5602
OPINIONOLOGY LLC
SURVEY SAMPLING INTERNATIONAL
701 Timpanogos Pkwy Ste M, Orem, UT 84097-6213
Tel (801) 373-7735 *Founded/Ownrshp* 1991
Sales 115.2MM[E] *EMP* 2,000[E]
SIC 7389 8732 Telephone services; Commercial nonphysical research
Pr: David Haynes
COO: Greg Graul
VP: John Thompson

D-U-N-S 78-398-0345
▲ **OPKO HEALTH INC**
4400 Biscayne Blvd, Miami, FL 33137-3212
Tel (305) 575-4100 *Founded/Ownrshp* 2007
Sales 491.7MM *EMP* 5,936[E]
Tkr Sym OPK *Exch* NGS
SIC 2834 2835 8731 Pharmaceutical preparations; In vitro & in vivo diagnostic substances; Biotechnical research, commercial
Ch Bd: Phillip Frost
Pr: David Okrongly
CEO: Charles W Bishop
CFO: Adam Logal
V Ch Bd: Jane H Hsiao
Ex VP: Steven D Rubin
Ex VP: Steven Rubin
Sls Dir: Brandon Gross

D-U-N-S 92-878-1459 IMP
OPLINK COMMUNICATIONS LLC
(*Suby of* MOLEX LLC) ★
46335 Landing Pkwy, Fremont, CA 94538-6407
Tel (510) 933-7200 *Founded/Ownrshp* 2014
Sales 735.0MM[E] *EMP* 3,716[E]
SIC 3661 4899 Telephone & telegraph apparatus; Fiber optics communications equipment; Autotransformers for telephone switchboards; Carrier equipment, telephone or telegraph; Communication signal enhancement network system; Data communication services
CEO: Joseph Y Liu
**Pr:* Peter Lee
**CFO:* Shirley Yin
Ofcr: Erica Abrams
**Ex VP:* River Gong
Sr VP: Jim Li
Sr VP: Stephen M Welles
Genl Mgr: Qin Yuan
VP Mfg: Haiguang Lu

VP Mktg: Shawn Lin
Genl Couns: Jeff Friedman

D-U-N-S 80-564-8982
■ OPOWER INC
(*Suby of* OC ACQUISITION LLC) ★
1515 N Courthouse Rd Fl 8, Arlington, VA 22201-2909
Tel (703) 778-4544 *Founded/Ownrshp* 2007
Sales 148.6MM *EMP* 599^E
SIC 7372

OPPD
See OMAHA PUBLIC POWER DISTRICT

D-U-N-S 07-423-5730
■ OPPENHEIMER & CO INC
(*Suby of* FREEDOM INVESTMENTS) ★
3310 W Big Beaver Rd # 205, Troy, MI 48084-2807
Tel (248) 637-8300 *Founded/Ownrshp* 2003
Sales 211.5MM^E *EMP* 3,000
SIC 6211 Security brokers & dealers
Pr: Albert Lowenthel

D-U-N-S 14-464-3400
■ OPPENHEIMER & CO INC
FREEDOM INVESTMENTS
(*Suby of* OPPENHEIMER HOLDINGS INC) ★
85 Broad St Bldg 85, New York, NY 10004-2434
Tel (212) 668-8000 *Founded/Ownrshp* 1954
Sales 940.8MM^E *EMP* 3,334
SIC 6211 Brokers, security; Dealers, security
CEO: Albert G Lowenthal
Pr: Steve Libertucci
Pr: Ted Mattas
**CFO:* Jeffery Alfano
**Chf Cred:* Doug Siegel
**Chf Mktg O:* Joan Khoury
Ofcr: Violet Rozkowski
Assoc VP: Jenny Chan
Assoc VP: Ashish Khandelwal
Ex VP: Dan Kohn
**Ex VP:* Lawrence Spaulding
Sr VP: Terence Duggan
Sr VP: Ronald Gershon
Sr VP: Rafi Krikorian
Sr VP: Robert Sablowsky
Sr VP: Bernard Taradash
Sr VP: John Woods
VP: Joni Ballas
VP: Nina Dante
VP: Francis Dewolf
VP: Albert Fedorov

D-U-N-S 62-794-2436
OPPENHEIMER FUNDS
(*Suby of* MASSMUTUAL MORTGAGE FINANCE LLC) ★
2 Wrld Fncl Ctr Ste 1100, New York, NY 10281-1008
Tel (212) 323-0200 *Founded/Ownrshp* 1990
Sales 707.7MM^E *EMP* 2,000
SIC 6289 6282 Stock transfer agents; Investment advisory service
Pr: Art Steinnetz
**VP:* Tim Abbuhl

OPPENHEIMER GROUP
See DAVID OPPENHEIMER & CO I LLC

D-U-N-S 96-746-1406
▲ OPPENHEIMER HOLDINGS INC
85 Broad St, New York, NY 10004-2434
Tel (212) 668-8000 *Founded/Ownrshp* 1881
Sales 928.3MM *EMP* 3,434
Tkr Sym OPY *Exch* NYS
SIC 6211 6712 6722 Security brokers & dealers; Bank holding companies; Management investment, open-end
Ch Bd: Albert G Lowenthal
CFO: Jeffrey J Alfano
Mng Dir: Jane Ross

D-U-N-S 04-616-2319
OPPENHEIMERFUNDS INC
(*Suby of* OPPENHEIMER FUNDS) ★
2 Wrld Fncl Ctr Fl 14, New York, NY 10281-1020
Tel (303) 768-3200 *Founded/Ownrshp* 1990
Sales 691.2MM *EMP* 1,923
SIC 6282 6289 Investment advisory service; Stock transfer agents
CEO: William Glavin Jr
Pr: Donal Bishnoi
Pr: Amanda Dampier
Pr: Matthew Farkas
Pr: Eric Hall
Pr: Greg Mehok
Pr: Kevin Neznek
Pr: Tan Nguyen
Pr: Tricia O'Connor
Pr: Andrea Pash
**Pr:* Art Steinmetz
Pr: Kelly Wellesley
**Chf Inves:* George Evans
Chf Inves: George R Evans
Chf Inves: Mark Hamilton
Ofcr: Geoffrey J Craddock
Ofcr: Mitchell Lindauer
Ofcr: Jerry A Webman
Assoc VP: Rene Vecka
Ex VP: Kirti Srikant
**Sr VP:* John Damian
Board of Directors: Joanne Pace

D-U-N-S 12-230-3316
OPPORTUNITY INTERNATIONAL INC
OPPORTUNITY INTERNATIONAL-US
550 W Van Buren St # 200, Chicago, IL 60607-3827
Tel (630) 242-4100 *Founded/Ownrshp* 1971
Sales 132.6MM *EMP* 85
Accts Cliftonlarsonallen Llp Oak Br
SIC 8399 Social change association
CEO: Atul Tandon
Pt: Richard Hoefs
**Pr:* Christophe Crane
COO: Frank Gamble
**CFO:* Richard John
CFO: Steve Lavey
VP: April Dubois
VP: Simona Haiduc
VP: Christina Koliopoulos
VP: Andrew Stearns
Exec: Mary Barry
Exec: Jamie Hubick
Exec: Connie Stryjak
Board of Directors: Alana Aldag Ackerson, John R Hart

OPPORTUNITY INTERNATIONAL-US
See OPPORTUNITY INTERNATIONAL INC

D-U-N-S 09-971-0451 IMP/EXP
OPTEK TECHNOLOGY INC
(*Suby of* TT ELECTRONICS PLC)
1645 Wallace Dr, Carrollton, TX 75006-6696
Tel (972) 323-2200 *Founded/Ownrshp* 2003
Sales 91.2MM^E *EMP* 650
SIC 3674 3825 3812 3661 3643 Semiconductors & related devices; Light sensitive devices; Infrared sensors, solid state; Hall effect devices; Instruments to measure electricity; Search & navigation equipment; Telephone & telegraph apparatus; Current-carrying wiring devices
Ch: Geraint Anderson
**Pr:* Billal Hammoud
**Pr:* Robert Taber
**CFO:* Daniel M Bankus
Ex VP: Rodney Bailey
Genl Mgr: Frank Echevarria

D-U-N-S 07-741-7256
■ OPTEUM FINANCIAL SERVICES LLC
(*Suby of* BIMINI CAPITAL MANAGEMENT, INC.)
3305 Flamingo Dr, Vero Beach, FL 32963-1731
Tel (772) 231-1245 *Founded/Ownrshp* 2005
Sales NA *EMP* 900
Accts Deloitte
SIC 6162 Mortgage bankers
Ch Bd: Peter R Norden
V Ch: Robert E Cauley
**COO:* Martin Levine
Treas: Mark R Gruber
**Co-COO:* Robert Filiberto
**Co-COO:* G Hunter Haas IV
Ex VP: Rick E Floyd
VP: Chuck Johnson
VP: Shannon Kilborn
VP: Alex J Koutouzis
VP: Amber K Luedke
VP: Jerry Sintes

D-U-N-S 00-911-0768
■ OPTICAL COATING LABORATORY LLC
OCLI
(*Suby of* VIAVI SOLUTIONS INC) ★
2789 Northpoint Pkwy, Santa Rosa, CA 95407-7397
Tel (707) 545-6440 *Founded/Ownrshp* 2009
Sales 121.1MM^E *EMP* 700
SIC 3479 3577 3827 Coating of metals & formed products; Computer peripheral equipment; Optical instruments & lenses
Pr: Fred Van Milligen
VP: Pat Higgins
Plng Mgr: Joyce Orecchia
Snr Mgr: Tim Walker

D-U-N-S 06-181-2996
OPTICAL FOR EYES CO
INSIGHT OPTICAL MANUFACTURING
1630 Walnut St, Philadelphia, PA 19103-5403
Tel (800) 367-3937 *Founded/Ownrshp* 1972
Sales 207.9MM^E *EMP* 1,200
SIC 5995 Optical goods stores
Pr: Philip Wolman
CFO: David H Dunbar
**VP:* Robert Messa
Doctor: Sara Oliver

OPTICAL GAGING PRODUCTS DIV
See QUALITY VISION INTERNATIONAL INC

D-U-N-S 11-851-7445 IMP
OPTICSPLANET INC
ECENTRIA
3150 Commercial Ave, Northbrook, IL 60062-1906
Tel (847) 513-6190 *Founded/Ownrshp* 2000
Sales 112.8MM^E *EMP* 231
Accts Allan J Brachman Cpa Ltd
SIC 5995 5049 Optical goods stores; Optical goods
CEO: Mark Levitin
**Pr:* Pavel Shvartsman
**VP:* Kelly Swaine

D-U-N-S 62-279-6873
■ OPTIM ENERGY TWIN OAKS LP
ALTURA POWER
(*Suby of* PNMR SERVICES CO) ★
Alvarado Sq Ms-Z110, Albuquerque, NM 87158-0001
Tel (505) 241-2821 *Founded/Ownrshp* 2006
Sales 278.1MM^E *EMP* 584
SIC 4911 Electric services
Pr: Nick Rahn
Pt: John Myers

D-U-N-S 79-497-3388
OPTIMA HEALTH PLAN
SENTARA CANCER NETWORK (NORFOL
(*Suby of* SENTARA CNCER NTWRK NORFOLK CI) ★
4417 Corp Ln Ste 150, Virginia Beach, VA 23462
Tel (757) 552-7401 *Founded/Ownrshp* 1984
Sales NA *EMP* 50^E
SIC 6324 Health maintenance organization (HMO), insurance only
Pr: Ted Wille Jr
CFO: Ronald Bennion
VP: Karen Bray
Sales Exec: Robin Mitchell

D-U-N-S 07-846-0646
OPTIMA SPECIALTY STEEL INC
200 S Biscayne Blvd # 5500, Miami, FL 33131-2333
Tel (877) 289-2277 *Founded/Ownrshp* 2008
Sales 610.1MM^E *EMP* 1,010^E
SIC 3317 Tubes, seamless steel
CEO: Mordechai Korf
**COO:* Michael Salamon
**CFO:* Anthony Verkruyse
**Ofcr:* Ted Fairley

D-U-N-S 07-979-3020
OPTIMAS OE SOLUTIONS HOLDING LLC
(*Suby of* OPTIMAS OE SOLUTIONS INTERMED LLC) ★
2651 Compass Rd, Glenview, IL 60026-8004
Tel (224) 521-8000 *Founded/Ownrshp* 2015
Sales 112.4MM^E *EMP* 519^E
SIC 5063 Electrical apparatus & equipment; Wire & cable; Control & signal wire & cable, including coaxial; Hanging & fastening devices, electrical
Pr: Paul Bamatter
**VP:* Richard Hoffman

D-U-N-S 07-979-3017
OPTIMAS OE SOLUTIONS INTERMED LLC
2651 Compass Rd, Glenview, IL 60026-8004
Tel (224) 521-8000 *Founded/Ownrshp* 2015
Sales 112.4MM^E *EMP* 522^E
SIC 5063 Electrical apparatus & equipment; Wire & cable; Control & signal wire & cable, including coaxial; Hanging & fastening devices, electrical
Pr: Paul Bamatter
**VP:* Richard Hoffman

D-U-N-S 18-391-1999
OPTIMATION TECHNOLOGY INC
50 High Tech Dr, Rush, NY 14543-9772
Tel (585) 321-2300 *Founded/Ownrshp* 2012
Sales 122.8MM^E *EMP* 384
Accts Mengel Metzger Barr & Co L
SIC 8711 Engineering services
Pr: William K Pollock
**Pr:* Wendy Smith
**CFO:* Kelly Burns
Prgrm Mgr: Mark Haboian
Genl Mgr: Craig Eidson
Snr Sftwr: James Farnham
IT Man: Diane Trentini
Sftwr Eng: Jojo Cash

D-U-N-S 03-817-2599 IMP
OPTIMIZED PROCESS DESIGNS LLC
O P D
(*Suby of* KOCH-GLITSCH LP) ★
25610 Clay Rd, Katy, TX 77493-7898
Tel (281) 371-7500 *Founded/Ownrshp* 2000
Sales 94.2MM^E *EMP* 200
SIC 1629 Industrial plant construction
Pr: James Kuehler
**Treas:* Jeanne R Hernandez
**VP:* Matthew Flamini
**VP:* Gary Thompson

OPTIMUM NUTRITION
See GLANBIA PERFORMANCE NUTRITION INC

OPTIMUM PLASTICS
See BLOOMER HOLDINGS INC

D-U-N-S 01-124-6407 IMP/EXP
■ OPTIMUM QUALITY GRAINS LLC (IA)
PIONEER
(*Suby of* PIONEER HI-BRED INTERNATIONAL INC) ★
7100 Nw 62nd Ave, Johnston, IA 50131-2937
Tel (515) 270-3200 *Founded/Ownrshp* 1998
Sales 111.2MM^E *EMP* 68
SIC 5153 Grain elevators
Pr: Dean Oestreich
CFO: Frank Ross
VP: Diane Bridgewater
VP: Paul Shickler
VP: John Soper
Prgrm Mgr: Rod Bergren
Netwrk Mgr: Steve Huber
Sfty Mgr: Kay Hannasch
Doctor: Dilbag Multani
Snr Mgr: Dwight Lager
Snr Mgr: Mairi Winslow

OPTIMUM WEST
See BRESNAN BROADBAND HOLDINGS LLC

D-U-N-S 83-309-4779
OPTION 1 NUTRITION SOLUTIONS LLC
(*Suby of* OPTION 1 NUTRITION HOLDINGS, LLC)
2460 E Germann Rd Ste 18, Chandler, AZ 85286-1573
Tel (480) 883-1188 *Founded/Ownrshp* 2002
Sales 105.3MM^E *EMP* 130^E
SIC 5047 Medical & hospital equipment
Netwrk Mgr: Don Wyatt
Nutrtnst: Mallory Knight

OPTION CARE
See WALGREENS INFUSION SERVICES INC

D-U-N-S 92-740-3915 IMP
OPTION CARE ENTERPRISES INC
(*Suby of* OPTION CARE) ★
3000 Lakeside Dr Ste 300n, Bannockburn, IL 60015-5405
Tel (847) 964-4950 *Founded/Ownrshp* 1979
Sales 63.6MM^E *EMP* 1,400^E
SIC 8082 5122 6794 5912 8049 Home health care services; Medicinals & botanicals; Patent owners & lessors; Drug stores; Nutritionist
Pr: Paul Mastrapa
**Treas:* Rich Hugel

D-U-N-S 82-825-9759
OPTION ENERGY LLC
5481 N Whitetail Ln, Ludington, MI 49431-9672
Tel (269) 329-4317 *Founded/Ownrshp* 2008
Sales 275.0MM *EMP* 15
SIC 4924 1311 4931 1711 Natural gas distribution; Natural gas production; ; Solar energy contractor

D-U-N-S 07-440-9020
OPTIONS CLEARING CORP
OPTIONS INDUSTRY COUNCIL
1 N Wacker Dr Fl 5, Chicago, IL 60606-2818
Tel (312) 322-6200 *Founded/Ownrshp* 1972
Sales 250.1MM *EMP* 338
Accts Deloitte & Touche Llp Chicag
SIC 6289 Security & commodity clearinghouses
Ch Bd: Wayne P Luthringshausen
Pr: James E Brown
Pr: Michael E Cahill
CFO: Frank J Larocca
CFO: Kimberly McGarry
**V Ch Bd:* Paul Brody
**V Ch Bd:* Richard R Lindsey
Chf Cred: Jean Cawley
Ofcr: Michael Walinskas
Ex VP: Michael McClain
Ex VP: Gina McFadden
VP: Larry P Brown
VP: John Dodson
VP: William Eineke
VP: Amy Farnstrom
VP: Chris Hudon
VP: Geri Love
VP: Douglas Mackay
Board of Directors: Thomas A Wittman, Thomas Callahan, William T Yates, George S Fischer, Thomas A Frank, Andrew D Kolinsky, Susan E Lester, Eric W Noll, Philip A Pendergraft, Tom Stern, John S Willian

OPTIONS FOR INDEPENDENT
See CEREBRAL PALSY OF MASSACHUSETTS INC

OPTIONS INDUSTRY COUNCIL
See OPTIONS CLEARING CORP

D-U-N-S 07-976-4996
OPTIV INC
1125 17th St Ste 1700, Denver, CO 80202-2032
Tel (303) 298-0600 *Founded/Ownrshp* 1995
Sales 1.8MMM^E *EMP* 1,550
SIC 5045 5065 6719 7381 Accounting machines using machine readable programs; Diskettes, computer; Investment holding companies, except banks; Detective & armored car services
CEO: Daniel Burns
VP: Joe Felz
Genl Mgr: Joanne Morrow

D-U-N-S 01-946-6684
OPTIV SECURITY INC
(*Suby of* OPTIV INC) ★
1125 17th St Ste 1700, Denver, CO 80202-2032
Tel (888) 732-9406 *Founded/Ownrshp* 2016
Sales 1.8MMM *EMP* 1,550
Accts Bkd Llp Kansas City Missour
SIC 5045 7379 7382 5065 Accounting machines using machine readable programs; ; Burglar alarm maintenance & monitoring; Diskettes, computer
CEO: Dan Burns
Pt: Dan Wilson
**CFO:* David Roshak
**Chf Mktg O:* Steve Perkins
**Ex VP:* Tim Hoffman
VP: Wendee Boeding
VP: Larry Whiteside Jr
Rgnl Mgr: Bryan Barkhaus
**CIO:* Paul Lehman
Sales Exec: Doug Hebert
VP Sls: Troy Richards

OPTUM HEALTH
See OPTUMHEALTH HOLDINGS LLC

D-U-N-S 07-967-4279
■ OPTUM INC
(*Suby of* UNITED HEALTHCARE SERVICES INC) ★
11000 Optum Cir, Eden Prairie, MN 55344-2503
Tel (952) 936-1300 *Founded/Ownrshp* 2009
Sales NA *EMP* 1,000^E
SIC 6324 Health maintenance organization (HMO), insurance only
CEO: Larry Renfro
CFO: John F Rex
Treas: Robert Worth Oberrender
Ofcr: Brian Wenger
Ex VP: Steve Larsen
VP: Francisca Azocar
VP: Kristin Landry
Sls Mgr: Janet Charpilloz
Sls Mgr: Michael Leary
Sls Mgr: Tara Mittleman
Board of Directors: Amy Lynn Shaw

OPTUM RX
See CATAMARAN CORP

D-U-N-S 18-417-0082
■ OPTUMHEALTH CARE SOLUTIONS INC
(*Suby of* UNITED HEALTHCARE SERVICES INC) ★
6300 Olson Memorial Hwy, Golden Valley, MN 55427-4946
Tel (877) 801-3507 *Founded/Ownrshp* 1987
Sales NA *EMP* 4,000
SIC 6324 7374 8999 Hospital & medical service plans; Data processing & preparation; Personal services
Ch Bd: William McGuire
Pr: Stephen Hemsley
CEO: Jeanine Rivet
CFO: Patrick Erlandson
VP Opers: David Cole
Mktg Mgr: Bridget Jo
Board of Directors: Gail Wilensky, William C Ballard Jr, Richard T Burke, James A Johnson, Thomas H Kean, Douglas W Leatherdale, Mary O Mundinger, Robert L Ryan, Donna E Shalala, William G Spears

D-U-N-S 79-113-6612
■ OPTUMHEALTH HOLDINGS LLC
OPTUM HEALTH
(*Suby of* UNITEDHEALTH GROUP INC) ★
13625 Technology Dr, Eden Prairie, MN 55344-2252
Tel (763) 595-3200 *Founded/Ownrshp* 2000
Sales NA *EMP* 24,000
SIC 6324 8741 6411 Hospital & medical service plans; Management services; Insurance agents, brokers & service
Pr: Dawn Owens
Pr: Mike Bradley
Pr: Roslyn Farmer
Pr: Don Yee
COO: Jason Vanden Akker
**CFO:* Paul Emerson
Ex VP: John M Prince
Sr VP: Deborah Adler
Sr VP: Gregory Pederson
VP: Ken Anderson
VP: Francisca Azocar
VP: James E Conlin
VP: Joel Costa
VP: Mary Dondelinger

VP: Robert Dufek
VP: Michael Fogarty
VP: Jolene Gardner
VP: Elizabeth Hevenstone
VP: Richard Lahrman
VP: Jess Lewis
VP: Edward Loftus

D-U-N-S 10-564-8369
■ OPTUMINSIGHT INC
(*Suby of* UNITED HEALTHCARE SERVICES INC) ★
11000 Optum Cir, Eden Prairie, MN 55344-2503
Tel (952) 833-7100 *Founded/Ownrshp* 1996
Sales 559.0MM^E *EMP* 2,703
SIC 7371 7375 8742 8741 Computer software development; Data base information retrieval; Management consulting services; Business management
CEO: Bill Miller
Pt: Patrice Matejka
Pr: Jeff Bergen
**Pr:* William H Crown
Pr: Ron Jones
**Pr:* Eric D Murphy
**Pr:* Lee Valenta
Pr: Tim Wicks
**Pr:* Timothy A Wicks
**CFO:* Gerald Knutson
CFO: John Rex
Ofcr: Brian Wenger
Ex VP: Tami Reller
Sr VP: James Franke
**Sr VP:* Lynn Myhran
VP: Dorothea Allen
VP: Ruth Baulch
VP: Paul Bihm
VP: Lou Brooks
VP: Larry Cohen
VP: Katie Doll

D-U-N-S 86-866-7106
■ OPTUMRX INC
PRESCRIPTION SOLUTIONS
(*Suby of* UNITED HEALTHCARE SERVICES INC) ★
2300 Main St, Irvine, CA 92614-6223
Tel (714) 825-3600 *Founded/Ownrshp* 1990
Sales NA *EMP* 5,080
SIC 6324 6321 Hospital & medical service plans; Accident & health insurance
CEO: Mark Thierer
**Pr:* Timothy Wicks
**COO:* Jeff Park
**CFO:* Jeffrey Grosklags
Sr VP: David Spivack
VP: Todd Ebersole
VP: Mark Knutson
VP: Robert Lahman
VP: Scott Neururer
VP: Pedram Pahlavan
Exec: Rosanna Narvaez
Comm Dir: Jerry O"brien
Dir Rx: Heidi C Lew

D-U-N-S 15-558-1291
■ OPTUMRX PBM OF ILLINOIS INC
(*Suby of* INFORMEDRX INC) ★
1600 Mcconnor Pkwy, Schaumburg, IL 60173-6801
Tel (224) 231-1743 *Founded/Ownrshp* 2008
Sales NA *EMP* 465
SIC 6371 Pension, health & welfare funds; Union welfare, benefit & health funds
Pr: Mark Thierer
CFO: Stuart Fleischer
Ch: Steven Klinsky
Treas: Barry Denaro
Treas: Robert Oberrender
Ofcr: Jonathan I Friedman
Sr VP: Martin A Magill
Sr VP: Sandra S Russell
Sr VP: James R Thompson
CIO: Bill Masters

OPUS AND W CONTRACTORS
See OPUS NORTHWEST LLC

D-U-N-S 80-778-8245
▲ OPUS BANK
19900 Macarthur Blvd # 1200, Irvine, CA 92612-8427
Tel (949) 250-9800 *Founded/Ownrshp* 2010
Sales NA *EMP* 607
Tkr Sym OPB *Exch* NGS
SIC 6029 Commercial banks
CEO: Stephen H Gordon
Pr: Dino J D'Auria
Pr: Debi Hill
Pr: Mary Killian
Pr: Ngoc Trieu
COO: Jennifer Simmons
CFO: Thea Stuedli
Treas: Terrin Enssle
Treas: Erin Pryor
Chf Mktg O: Brad Davis
Ofcr: Balaji Krishna
Ex VP: Geoff Anfuso
Ex VP: Dan Borland
Ex VP: Bob Granfelt
Ex VP: Ed Padilla
Ex VP: Kelly Rodriques
Sr VP: Jason Raefski
Sr VP: Volkan Salar
Sr VP: Michael Trivich
Sr VP: Brett Villaume
Sr VP: Grant Word

D-U-N-S 07-972-4101
OPUS DESIGN BUILD LLC
(*Suby of* OPUS HOLDING LLC) ★
10350 Bren Rd W, Minnetonka, MN 55343-9014
Tel (952) 656-4444 *Founded/Ownrshp* 2009
Sales 352.0MM *EMP* 28^E
SIC 1522 1541 Hotel/motel & multi-family home construction; Dry cleaning plant construction
Pr: David F Bangasser
**VP:* James R Caesar
**VP:* James J Erwin
**VP:* Manish Gandhi
**VP:* Michael K Healy
**VP:* Craig Larson
VP: Dean Newins
VP: Doug Swain
**VP:* John Williams
Snr Ntwrk: Ken Stieers

D-U-N-S 07-023-5752
OPUS HOLDING LLC
10350 Bren Rd W, Minnetonka, MN 55343-9014
Tel (952) 656-4444 *Founded/Ownrshp* 2011
Sales 377.2MM^E *EMP* 245
SIC 6531 Real estate managers
Pr: Tim W Murnane
Pr: David J Menke
Pr: Timothy W Murnane
CFO: Dennis Power
Sr VP: Lawrence Bobuda
Sr VP: Peter Coakley
VP: Margaret A Bozesky
VP: Davis L Everson
VP: Linda A Gonzales
VP: Sean P Spellman
VP: Douglas J Swain
VP: Michael P Youngerman

D-U-N-S 96-458-9134
OPUS INSPECTION INC
ENVIRONMENTAL SYSTEMS PRODUCTS
7 Kripes Rd, East Granby, CT 06026-9720
Tel (860) 392-2100 *Founded/Ownrshp* 2008
Sales 111.1MM^E *EMP* 240^E
SIC 7371 Computer software development
Pr: Lothar Geilen
**Treas:* Jeff Bagley
Prgrm Mgr: David Lewis
Dist Mgr: Michael Neisser
Snr Ntwrk: Mark Dufault
VP Sls: John Bradley

D-U-N-S 16-526-9395
■ OPUS INVESTMENT MANAGEMENT INC
(*Suby of* HANOVER INSURANCE GROUP INC) ★
440 Lincoln St, Worcester, MA 01653-0002
Tel (508) 855-1000 *Founded/Ownrshp* 1985
Sales NA *EMP* 3,000
SIC 6311 6321 6324 6351 6722 Life insurance carriers; Health insurance carriers; Hospital & medical service plans; Liability insurance; Mutual fund sales, on own account
Pr: Frederick Effinger
Genl Pt: Robert Henderson
V Ch: John Towers
**Pr:* John F O'Brien
COO: Kristen Park
CFO: Edward J Parry III
VP: Bruce Anderson
VP: Richard J Baker
VP: John Chandler
VP: Daniel Desmarais
VP: Brian Duke
VP: David Firstenberg
VP: John Jack
VP: John Kavanaugh
VP: John F Kelly
VP: Bruce Letizia
VP: Joseph Rovito
VP: Donald Wayman

D-U-N-S 82-508-0492
OPUS NORTHWEST LLC
OPUS AND W CONTRACTORS
2025 1st Ave Ph B, Seattle, WA 98121-2100
Tel (425) 467-2701 *Founded/Ownrshp* 1994
Sales 98.8MM^E *EMP* 1,200
SIC 6552 1542 Subdividers & developers; Commercial & office building contractors
Pr: John Solberg
**VP:* Jim Heller
**VP:* Tom Parsons
**VP:* Mike Ruhl

OPWDD
See PEOPLE WITH DEVELOPMENTAL DISABILITIES NEW YORK STATE OFFICE FOR

D-U-N-S 01-304-4532 IMP
■ ORACLE AMERICA INC
SUN MICROSYSTEMS
(*Suby of* ORACLE CORP) ★
500 Oracle Pkwy, Redwood City, CA 94065-1677
Tel (650) 506-7000 *Founded/Ownrshp* 2010
Sales 11.4MMM^E *EMP* 29,000
SIC 3571 7379 7373 7372 3674 Minicomputers; Computer related consulting services; Systems integration services; Operating systems computer software; Microprocessors
Ch: Jeffrey O Henley
Pr: Safra A Catz
Pr: Mark V Hurd
CFO: Kevin Melia
Bd of Dir: William Crowell
Ex VP: Michael A Dillon
Ex VP: Michael E Lehman
Ex VP: William N Macgowan
Ex VP: Gregory M Papadopoulos
Sr VP: Dorian Daley
Sr VP: Cindy Reese
VP: Steve Au Yeung
Exec: Keith Bigsby
Exec: Kathleen Dawson
Exec: Kim Dombrowsky
Exec: Kathy Randall
Dir Bus: Debbie Brown
Dir Bus: Thanachart Numnonda

D-U-N-S 14-470-9193
▲ ORACLE CORP
500 Oracle Pkwy, Redwood City, CA 94065-1675
Tel (650) 506-7000 *Founded/Ownrshp* 1977
Sales 37.0MMM *EMP* 136,034
Accts Ernst & Young Llp San Jose C
Tkr Sym ORCL *Exch* NYS
SIC 7372 7379 8243 3571 3674 Prepackaged software; Business oriented computer software; Application computer software; Computer related consulting services; Software training, computer; Minicomputers; Microprocessors
CEO: Safra A Catz
Ch Bd: Lawrence J Ellison
V Ch: Jeffrey O Henley
Pr: Peter Hill
Pr: Thomas Kurian
CEO: Mark V Hurd
Ex VP: Dorian E Daley
Ex VP: John Fowler
Ex VP: Douglas Kehring
Ex VP: Steve Miranda
Ex VP: Inderjeet Singh
Ex VP: Mike Splain
Ex VP: Rex Wang
Ex VP: William Corey West
Sr VP: Karl Braitberg
Sr VP: Shawn Price
Sr VP: Sonny Singh
Sr VP: Joyce Westerdahl
VP: Gretchen Alarcon
VP: Richard Allison
VP: Eric Ball
Board of Directors: Jeffrey S Berg, H Raymond Bingham, Michael J Boskin, Bruce R Chizen, George H Conrades, Renee James, Hector Garcia-Molina, Leon E Panetta, Naomi O Seligman

D-U-N-S 11-204-3448 IMP
■ ORACLE FINANCIAL SERVICES SOFTWARE INC
(*Suby of* ORACLE CORP) ★
399 Thornall St Ste 6, Edison, NJ 08837-2238
Tel (732) 623-0399 *Founded/Ownrshp* 2001
Sales 106.4MM^E *EMP* 693
SIC 5045 Computer software
Ch: Rajesh Hukku
**COO:* Cafo Boga
Manager: Naren Mathavan

D-U-N-S 36-286-3768 IMP/EXP
ORACLE FLEXIBLE PACKAGING INC
ORACLE PACKAGING
220 Polo Rd, Winston Salem, NC 27105-3441
Tel (336) 777-4695 *Founded/Ownrshp* 2012
Sales 109.8MM^E *EMP* 285
SIC 2672 Coated & laminated paper
CEO: James Squatrito
COO: Kevin Hughes
CFO: Jon Heard
VP: Chris Payne
VP: Andy Starr

ORACLE PACKAGING
See ORACLE FLEXIBLE PACKAGING INC

D-U-N-S 61-910-0691
■ ORACLE SYSTEMS CORP
(*Suby of* ORACLE CORP) ★
500 Oracle Pkwy, Redwood City, CA 94065-1677
Tel (650) 506-7000 *Founded/Ownrshp* 2005
Sales 4.2MMM^E *EMP* 56,134
SIC 7372 7379 8243 Prepackaged software; Business oriented computer software; Application computer software; Data processing consultant; Software training, computer
CEO: Safra A Catz
Ch Bd: Lawrence J Ellison
Ch Bd: Jeffrey O Henley
Pr: Mark V Hurd
CEO: Mark Hurd
COO: Andy Kuo
COO: Rich Polehber
COO: Larry Rall
COO: Nancy Zhang
Ex VP: Nicholas Aneshansley
Ex VP: John Fowler
Ex VP: Thomas Kurian
Ex VP: Charles Rozwat
Ex VP: Mike Splain
Sr VP: Dorian Daley
VP: Gail Coury
VP: Tyler Prince
VP: Robert Shimp
VP: Jill Suarez
Exec: Jim Barr
Exec: Charles Briggs

D-U-N-S 00-553-6698
■ ORACLE USA INC
(*Suby of* ORACLE SYSTEMS CORP) ★
500 Oracle Pkwy, Redwood City, CA 94065-1677
Tel (650) 506-7000 *Founded/Ownrshp* 1987, 2005
Sales 85.2MM^E *EMP* 526
SIC 7372 Prepackaged software
Pr: Safra A Catz
**Pr:* Mark Hurd
**Pr:* Charles Phillips
**Sr VP:* Judson Althoff
**Sr VP:* Matthew Mills
VP: Susan Charley

D-U-N-S 05-983-1180 IMP
ORAFOL AMERICAS INC
REFLECTIVE SOLUTIONS AMERICAS
(*Suby of* ORAFOL EUROPE GMBH)
120 Darling Dr, Avon, CT 06001-4217
Tel (860) 223-9297 *Founded/Ownrshp* 2011
Sales 102.1MM^E *EMP* 500
SIC 3082 Unsupported plastics profile shapes
Pr: Michael Foley
Pr: Bob Nielson
**COO:* Andrew McNeill
CFO: Phil Ferrari
Treas: Loretta Thompson
VP: Robert Nilson
VP: Tim Pedrotty
**VP:* Steve Scott
Exec: Rich McNeeley
Genl Mgr: Rebecca Cavazuti
Genl Mgr: Joseph Lupone

D-U-N-S 96-880-1118 IMP
■ ORAL COLGATE PHARMACEUTICALS INC
(*Suby of* COLGATE-PALMOLIVE CO) ★
300 Park Ave Fl 3, New York, NY 10022-7412
Tel (212) 310-2000 *Founded/Ownrshp* 1993
Sales 117.1MM^E *EMP* 300
SIC 5122 2834 Drugs, proprietaries & sundries; Pharmaceutical preparations
Ch Bd: Julie Dillon
VP: Maria E Carvajal
VP: Andreas Somers
Genl Mgr: Massimo Poli

D-U-N-S 05-808-0060
ORAL ROBERTS UNIVERSITY
7777 S Lewis Ave, Tulsa, OK 74171-0001
Tel (918) 495-6161 *Founded/Ownrshp* 1963
Sales 120.9MM *EMP* 2,100^E
Accts Capin Crouse Llp Colorado Spr
SIC 8221 University
Pr: Dr William Wilson
COO: Nick R Garza
COO: John Suan
**CFO:* Michelle Finley
**Treas:* F Rick Anderson
Ex VP: Tessie Devore
Ex VP: John Laffitte
VP: Suzanne Behr
**VP:* D Michael Bernard
VP: Daniel Delgado
**VP:* Ralph Fagin
**VP:* George Fisher
VP: Terry Fisher
VP: Bob Fouch
**VP:* Jeff Ogle

ORANG-LSTER BD COOP EDCTL SVCS
See ORANGE-ULSTER BOCES INC

D-U-N-S 00-699-3406 IMP
■ ORANGE AND ROCKLAND UTILITIES INC
(*Suby of* CONSOLIDATED EDISON INC) ★
1 Blue Hill Plz Ste 20, Pearl River, NY 10965-3100
Tel (845) 352-6000 *Founded/Ownrshp* 1899
Sales 832.9MM^E *EMP* 1,060
SIC 4924 4911 1311 6552 Natural gas distribution; Generation, electric power; Transmission, electric power; Distribution, electric power; Crude petroleum & natural gas; Subdividers & developers
Pr: John McAvoy
**Pr:* William G Longhi
CFO: Robert Hoglund
VP: Edwin Ortiz
**VP:* Francis Peverly
Prgrm Mgr: Robert Melvin
Genl Mgr: Meyers Glenn
Pr Mgr: Trish Austin
Pr Mgr: Michelle Damiani
Pr Mgr: Sophia Salis
Pr Mgr: Katherine Wysokowski

ORANGE BLOSSOM HILLS G&C CLUB
See VILLAGES OF LAKE-SUMTER INC

D-U-N-S 17-593-6426
ORANGE BUSINESS SERVICES HOLDINGS US INC
(*Suby of* ORANGE)
13775 Mclearen Rd, Herndon, VA 20171-3212
Tel (703) 471-2300 *Founded/Ownrshp* 2001
Sales 673.9MM^E *EMP* 2,000^E
SIC 4813 Data telephone communications
Pr: Bruce Berenson
**Ex VP:* Howard Ford
**VP:* Bruce McWhirter

D-U-N-S 78-579-9362 IMP
ORANGE BUSINESS SERVICES US INC
(*Suby of* ORANGE BUSINESS SERVICES HOLDINGS US INC) ★
13775 Mclearen Rd, Herndon, VA 20171-3212
Tel (866) 849-4185 *Founded/Ownrshp* 1992
Sales 666.8MM^E *EMP* 1,411
SIC 4813 8748 Data telephone communications; Telecommunications consultant
Pr: Diana Einterz
CFO: Yves Guillaumot
Ch: Louis-Pierre Wenes
**Treas:* Julie Maniez
**VP:* Norman Wentworth
IT Man: Steven C Belling
Snr Mgr: Manvinder Singh

ORANGE CNTY SPRNTNDENT SCHOOLS
See ORANGE COUNTY SUPERINTENDENT OF SCHOOLS

D-U-N-S 08-359-4929
ORANGE COAST COLLEGE
ORANGE COAST COLLEGE SNACK BAR
2701 Fairview Rd, Costa Mesa, CA 92626-5561
Tel (714) 432-5772 *Founded/Ownrshp* 1948
Sales 133.2MM^E *EMP* 1,900
SIC 8221 8299 Colleges universities & professional schools; Educational services
VP: Richard T Pagel
Treas: Andrea Valencia
VP: Hiba Ajmal
VP: Benjamin Hobbs
VP: Candice Nguyen
VP: Candace Sundine
Exec: Maxwell Pedroza
Genl Mgr: Kristen Clark
Off Mgr: Mary Roda
Psych: Robert Zhe

ORANGE COAST COLLEGE SNACK BAR
See ORANGE COAST COLLEGE

D-U-N-S 93-266-9658
ORANGE COAST MEMORIAL MEDICAL CENTER
(*Suby of* MEMORIAL CARE MEDICAL CENTERS) ★
9920 Talbert Ave, Fountain Valley, CA 92708-5153
Tel (714) 378-7000 *Founded/Ownrshp* 1961
Sales 242.6MM *EMP* 1,000^E
SIC 8062 General medical & surgical hospitals
Pr: Marcia Manker
Chf Rad: Richard Wasley
**CFO:* Aaron Coley
**CFO:* Steve McNamara
VP: Brennan James
Ex Dir: Emily Randle
Brnch Mgr: Don Cato
CTO: Nagdi Sidhom
CTO: Karen Testman
MIS Dir: Debbie Marino
Pathlgst: Emanuel Fero

D-U-N-S 80-738-3708
ORANGE COAST TITLE CO OF SOUTHERN CALIFORNIA
640 N Tustin Ave Ste 106, Santa Ana, CA 92705-3731
Tel (714) 558-2836 *Founded/Ownrshp* 1967
Sales 160.8MM^E^ *EMP* 650
SIC 7389 6361 6541 Personal service agents, brokers & bureaus; Title insurance; Title & trust companies
CEO: John L Marconi
Pr: William Fajardo
**Pr:* Rich Mac Aluso
Pr: Fred Nilsen
Bd of Dir: Gloria Kessell
Bd of Dir: Macaluso Rich
Ofcr: Luis Cerda
Ofcr: John Fernando
Ofcr: Steve Fernando
Ofcr: Brandy Kelly
Ofcr: Erin Lincke
Ofcr: Audrey Lopez
Ofcr: Roger Reinhard
Ofcr: Eric Tafolla
Ex VP: William Burding
Sr VP: Diana Martinez
VP: Teresa Harrah
**VP:* Mike Marconi
VP: John Wiley
Exec: Kelli Lowe

D-U-N-S 83-881-7815
ORANGE COUNTY COMMUNITY FOUNDATION
4041 Macarthur Blvd # 510, Newport Beach, CA 92660-2512
Tel (949) 553-4202 *Founded/Ownrshp* 1989
Sales 98.8MM *EMP* 13
Accts Moss Adams Llp San Diego Ca
SIC 6732 Charitable trust management
Pr: Shelley Hoss
**Treas:* Jeffrey A Dankberg
**VP:* Tracy Branson
**VP:* Todd Hanson
**VP:* Richard Lombardi
**VP:* Frank Quevedo
VP: Cynthia Ragland
Opers Mgr: Joanne Udell

D-U-N-S 80-736-1472
ORANGE COUNTY EMERGENCY SERVICES DISTRICT
2351 Highway 12, Vidor, TX 77662-3404
Tel (409) 769-6241 *Founded/Ownrshp* 1973
Sales NA *EMP* 5,060
Accts Edgar Kiker & Cross Pc Beau
SIC 9224 Fire department, volunteer
**Pr:* Terry Woodward
**VP:* Wyatt Boyett

D-U-N-S 07-861-2387
ORANGE COUNTY FIRE & RESCUE
(*Suby of* ORANGE COUNTY GOVERNMENT) ★
6590 Amory Ct, Winter Park, FL 32792-7426
Tel (407) 836-9112 *Founded/Ownrshp* 2012
Sales NA *EMP* 1,200
SIC 9224 Fire department, not including volunteer

D-U-N-S 62-237-5124
ORANGE COUNTY FIRE AUTHORITY
1 Fire Authority Rd, Irvine, CA 92602-0125
Tel (714) 573-6000 *Founded/Ownrshp* 2006
Sales NA *EMP* 1,160^E^
Accts Mayer Hoffman Mccann Pc Irv
SIC 9224 Fire department, not including volunteer;
**Treas:* Patricia Jakubiak
Dir Soc: Eric Elmer
Comm Dir: Sandy Cooney
Mng Dir: Bob George
IT Man: McVey Dave
Snr Mgr: Joe Brock
Snr Mgr: Dave Lopez
Snr Mgr: Kelly Zimmerman

D-U-N-S 08-002-0707
ORANGE COUNTY GOVERNMENT
21 S Roseland Ave, Orlando, FL 32801
Tel (407) 836-7370 *Founded/Ownrshp* 2015
Sales NA *EMP* 1,257^E^
SIC 9199 Civil rights commission, government
Prin: Vernon Pierce

D-U-N-S 84-931-7391
ORANGE COUNTY HEALTH AUTHORITY A PUBLIC AGENCY
505 City Pkwy W, Orange, CA 92868-2924
Tel (714) 246-8500 *Founded/Ownrshp* 1994
Sales 113.8MM^E^ *EMP* 422
SIC 8621 8011 Professional membership organizations; Offices & clinics of medical doctors
CEO: Richard Chambers
**CEO:* Michael Schrader
**COO:* William Jones
**CFO:* Chet Uma
Ofcr: Kim Cunningham
**Ofcr:* Richard Helmer
Ex Dir: Gary Crockett
Ex Dir: Kurt Hubler
Ex Dir: Eileen Moscaritolo
Ex Dir: Javier Sanchez
Ex Dir: Margaret Tatar
Board of Directors: Arthur B Birtcher, Mary Anne Foo, Edward B Kacic, Jim McAleer, Janet Nguyen, Margarita Pereyda MD, David L Riley, Michel D Stephens, John M W Moorlach CPA Cfp

D-U-N-S 07-979-8850
ORANGE COUNTY PUBLIC SCHOOLS
445 W Amelia St, Orlando, FL 32801-1128
Tel (407) 317-3200 *Founded/Ownrshp* 2015
Sales 2.2MMM *EMP* 25,000^E^
SIC 8211 Public elementary & secondary schools
Psych: Farideh Sabeth
Snr Mgr: Pamela Carson

D-U-N-S 14-447-8682 IMP
ORANGE COUNTY SANITATION DISTRICT FINANCING CORP
10844 Ellis Ave, Fountain Valley, CA 92708-7018
Tel (714) 962-2411 *Founded/Ownrshp* 1954
Sales 304.5MM *EMP* 626
Accts Mcgladrey Llp Irvine Ca
SIC 4953 Waste materials, disposal at sea
Genl Mgr: James Herberg
V Ch: Cathy Green
VP: Clarice Marcin
Dir Risk M: Randall Mason
Ex Dir: Nancy Dooley
**Genl Mgr:* James Ruth

D-U-N-S 07-979-8783
ORANGE COUNTY SCHOOLS
200 E King St, Hillsborough, NC 27278-2623
Tel (919) 732-8126 *Founded/Ownrshp* 2015
Sales 12.6MM^E^ *EMP* 1,054^E^
SIC 8211 Public elementary & secondary schools
COO: Patrick Abele
Exec: Maurice Boswell
Dir Sec: Sarah Pitts
Pr Dir: Seth Stephens
Teacher Pr: Teresa Cunningham-Bro
Psych: Elise Kechele
HC Dir: Sherita Cobb

D-U-N-S 12-114-7912
ORANGE COUNTY SUPERINTENDENT OF SCHOOLS
ORANGE CNTY SPRNTNDENT SCHOOLS
200 Kalmus Dr, Costa Mesa, CA 92626-5922
Tel (714) 966-4000 *Founded/Ownrshp* 1960
Sales 130.9MM^E^ *EMP* 1,500
SIC 8211 Public elementary & secondary schools
CEO: Elizabeth Parker
Pr: Trisha Martinez
Ofcr: Ian Hanigan
Ofcr: Marc Lerner
Ofcr: Joanne Olimberio
Ex Dir: Claire Braeburn
Prgrm Mgr: Nancy Melgares
Prgrm Mgr: Elke Petras
Prgrm Mgr: Wendy Rogan
CTO: Judy Murley
Teacher Pr: Gina Lance

D-U-N-S 15-394-7940
ORANGE COUNTY TRANSPORTATION AUTHORITY
ORANGE COUNTY TRNSP AUTH
550 S Main St, Orange, CA 92868-4506
Tel (714) 636-7433 *Founded/Ownrshp* 1972
Sales 607.7MM *EMP* 1,050
Accts Vavrinek Trine Day & Co Ll
SIC 4111 8711 Bus line operations; Construction & civil engineering
CEO: Darrell Johnson
COO: Jaime Hernandez
CFO: Ly Tran
Bd of Dir: Michael Hennessey
Bd of Dir: Chris Norby
Ofcr: Chris Boucly
Ex Dir: Jim Kenan
Ex Dir: Lance Larson
Plng Mgr: Dave Elbaum
CIO: Satish Ajmani
Site Mgr: Ron Wolf

ORANGE COUNTY TRNSP AUTH
See ORANGE COUNTY TRANSPORTATION AUTHORITY

D-U-N-S 05-304-8468
ORANGE LAKE COUNTRY CLUB INC
8505 W Irlo Bronson Hwy, Kissimmee, FL 34747-8201
Tel (407) 239-0000 *Founded/Ownrshp* 1981
Sales 405.6MM *EMP* 800
Accts Grant Thornton Llp Orlando F
SIC 7011 6552 7997 5812 5813 Tourist camps, cabins, cottages & courts; Resort hotel; Land subdividers & developers, residential; Country club, membership; Golf club, membership; Ethnic food restaurants; Bars & lounges
CEO: Charles K Swan III
**Ch Bd:* Spence Wilson
CFO: Thomas Nelson
Ofcr: Carl Mugnolo
VP: Jerry Butcher
VP: Brian T Lower
VP: Bill Sell
VP: Stacey Sutherland
Exec: Lonny Huot
**Prin:* Don Harrill
CIO: Ann Chandler

D-U-N-S 11-279-8488 EXP
ORANGE PARK MEDICAL CENTER
FLEMING ISLAND IMAGING CENTER
2001 Kingsley Ave, Orange Park, FL 32073-5156
Tel (904) 276-8500 *Founded/Ownrshp* 1974
Sales 228.4MM *EMP* 903
Accts Harrington & Associates Cpas
SIC 8069 Specialty hospitals, except psychiatric
CEO: Chad Patrick
Trst: Deevid Miller
Dir Inf Cn: Melody Miller
Dir Rad: Larry Smith
Chf Nrs Of: Kayth Hester
Prin: Rajesh Vishen
Plnt Mgr: Bill Westbay
Mktg Dir: David Goldberg
Doctor: Jack Cohen
Doctor: Maria Ramirez
Doctor: Arjav Shah

D-U-N-S 07-668-0404
ORANGE REGIONAL MEDICAL CENTER
ARDEN HILL HOSPITAL
707 E Main St, Middletown, NY 10940-2667
Tel (845) 343-2424 *Founded/Ownrshp* 1908
Sales 408.6MM *EMP* 2,000
SIC 8062 General medical & surgical hospitals
CEO: Scott Batulis
Chf Rad: J Yacovone
**Ch:* Rolland Peacock III
**VP:* Mitchell Amado
**VP:* Joe Anesi
**VP:* Rosemary Baczewski
VP: Sandra Iberger
Exec: Joanne Sturans
Dir Rx: Maria Russo
CIO: Brian Tew
Cmptr Lab: Catherine Ganz

D-U-N-S 07-953-6439
ORANGE UNIFIED SCHOOL DISTRICT
1401 N Handy St, Orange, CA 92867-4434
Tel (714) 628-4000 *Founded/Ownrshp* 1953
Sales 185.5MM^E^ *EMP* 3,100
Accts Vavrinek Trine Day & Co Ll
SIC 8211 Public elementary & secondary schools
Pr: Cathie Hunsberger
CFO: Barbara Stephen
VP: Gunn Hansen
VP: Robin Nelson
Adm Dir: Linda Stoterau
Genl Mgr: Denise M Allister
Off Mgr: Angela Cutts
Off Mgr: Olga Parker
Off Mgr: Theresa Shortreed
IT Man: Patty Smith
VP Opers: Jaime Beidler

D-U-N-S 08-417-0380
ORANGE WATER AND SEWER AUTHORITY
OWASA
400 Jones Ferry Rd, Carrboro, NC 27510-2001
Tel (919) 960-6142 *Founded/Ownrshp* 1975
Sales 94.1MM^E^ *EMP* 130^E^
Accts Martin Starnes & Associates C
SIC 4941 4952 Water supply; Sewerage systems
Ex Dir: Ed Kerwin
**CFO:* Stephen Winters
Exec: Bob Morgan
**Genl Mgr:* John Greene
Dir IT: Richard Wyatt

D-U-N-S 12-052-4277
ORANGE-ULSTER BOCES INC
ORANG-LSTER BD COOP EDCTL SVCS
53 Gibson Rd, Goshen, NY 10924-6709
Tel (845) 291-0100 *Founded/Ownrshp* 1948
Sales 61.0MM^E^ *EMP* 1,200
SIC 8211 Public elementary & secondary schools
**COO:* Terry Olivo
Exec: Marguerite Flood
Genl Mgr: Kathleen Roberts
Occ Thrpy: Pam Bavx
Occ Thrpy: Kim Williams
Occ Thrpy: Vicky Zouzias

D-U-N-S 10-050-0248
ORANGEBURG CONSOLIDATED SCHOOL DISTRICT 5
OCSD5
578 Ellis Ave, Orangeburg, SC 29115-5022
Tel (803) 534-5454 *Founded/Ownrshp* 1954
Sales 58.6MM^E^ *EMP* 1,200
SIC 8211 Public elementary & secondary schools
**Ch:* Mary Berry Ulmer
Ex Dir: Shasity Harley
Pr Dir: Bill Clark
Teacher Pr: Shawna Williams
HC Dir: Janice Westbury

D-U-N-S 07-957-5658
ORASCOM E&C USA INC
O C I
(*Suby of* ORASCOM CONSTRUCTION S.A.E.)
6862 Elm St Ste 400, Mc Lean, VA 22101-3886
Tel (703) 358-8800 *Founded/Ownrshp* 2012
Sales 729.0MM^E^ *EMP* 500
SIC 1521 1522 1542 Single-family housing construction; Residential construction; Nonresidential construction
CEO: Nassef Sawiris
**CEO:* Maged Abadir
**CFO:* Salman Butt
**Treas:* Dalia Khorshid

D-U-N-S 11-415-2184
▲ ORASURE TECHNOLOGIES INC
220 E 1st St, Bethlehem, PA 18015-1360
Tel (610) 882-1820 *Founded/Ownrshp* 2000
Sales 119.7MM *EMP* 326^E^
Tkr Sym OSUR *Exch* NGS
SIC 2835 In vitro diagnostics
Pr: Douglas A Michels
**Ch Bd:* Stephen S Tang
**COO:* Ronald H Spair
Ex VP: Anthony Zezzo II
Sr VP: Jack E Jerrett
Sr VP: Mark L Kuna
Mktg Dir: Jackie Pirone
Board of Directors: Michael Celano, Ronny B Lancaster, Charles W Patrick, Stephen S Tang

ORAU
See OAK RIDGE ASSOCIATED UNIVERSITIES INC

D-U-N-S 14-611-8901
▲ ORBCOMM INC
395 W Passaic St Ste 3, Rochelle Park, NJ 07662-3016
Tel (703) 433-6361 *Founded/Ownrshp* 2003
Sales 178.2MM *EMP* 462
Tkr Sym ORBC *Exch* NGM
SIC 4899 8748 Satellite earth stations; Telecommunications consultant
Pr: Marc J Eisenberg
**Ch Bd:* Jerome B Eisenberg
CFO: Robert G Costantini
Ex VP: Christian G Le Brun
Ex VP: Craig Malone
Ex VP: John J Stolte Jr
Sr VP: Tom Robinson
CTO: Chris Ryan

D-U-N-S 12-716-5319 IMP/EXP
ORBIS CORP
LEWISBINS
(*Suby of* MENASHA CORP) ★
1055 Corporate Center Dr, Oconomowoc, WI 53066-4829
Tel (262) 560-5000 *Founded/Ownrshp* 1999
Sales 541.4MM^E^ *EMP* 850
SIC 3089 Synthetic resin finished products
Pr: Bill Ash
Treas: William F Ash
VP: Kevin Geason
VP: Mike Hyjek
VP: Andy McDonald
VP: Dennis A Rooney
Dir Bus: Scott Buss
Dir Bus: Stephan Tobias
**Prin:* Dave Schopp
Rgnl Mgr: Kenneth J Rivard
VP Opers: Anne Norris

ORBIT IRRIGATION
See PRO-MARK INC

D-U-N-S 94-985-3766 IMP/EXP
ORBIT IRRIGATION PRODUCTS INC
(*Suby of* ORBIT IRRIGATION) ★
845 Overland St, North Salt Lake, UT 84054-2123
Tel (801) 299-5555 *Founded/Ownrshp* 1996
Sales 179.4MM^E^ *EMP* 500
SIC 3523 Irrigation equipment, self-propelled
**VP:* Mike Ericksen
Dept Mgr: Jake Hall
CIO: Steve Slater

ORBITAL ATK
See ORBITAL SCIENCES CORP

D-U-N-S 61-870-5925 IMP/EXP
▲ ORBITAL ATK INC
45101 Warp Dr, Dulles, VA 20166-6874
Tel (703) 406-5000 *Founded/Ownrshp* 1990
Sales 6.8MMM^E^ *EMP* 12,300
Tkr Sym OA *Exch* NYS
SIC 3764 3812 3483 3482 3489 Propulsion units for guided missiles & space vehicles; Search & navigation equipment; Warfare counter-measure equipment; Detection apparatus: electronic/magnetic field, light/heat; Ammunition, except for small arms; Mortar shells, over 30 mm.; Rockets (ammunition); Bombs & parts; Small arms ammunition; Guns, howitzers, mortars & related equipment
Pr: David W Thompson
**Ch Bd:* Ronald R Fogleman
COO: Blake E Larson
CFO: Garrett E Pierce
Ofcr: Denice Clark
Ofcr: Natalie Losik
Ex VP: Antonio L Elias
Sr VP: Thomas E McCabe
Sr VP: Christine A Wolf
VP: Paul Barcomb
VP: Kristin Boetticher
VP: David Dorman
VP: Alan Jones
Dir Bus: Peter Beyerle
Board of Directors: Harrison H Schmitt, Kevin P Chilton, Scott L Webster, Roxanne J Decyk, Martin C Faga, Lennard A Fisk, Robert M Hanisee, Roman Martinez IV Janice I, Ronald T Kadish, Douglas L Maine, James G Roche

D-U-N-S 10-191-6062 IMP/EXP
■ ORBITAL SCIENCES CORP
ORBITAL ATK
(*Suby of* ORBITAL ATK INC) ★
45101 Warp Dr, Dulles, VA 20166-6874
Tel (703) 406-5000 *Founded/Ownrshp* 2015
Sales 1.2MMM^E^ *EMP* 12,000
SIC 3812 4899 7372 Defense systems & equipment; Aircraft control systems, electronic; Navigational systems & instruments; Satellite earth stations; Data communication services; Prepackaged software
Ch Bd: David W Thompson
Pr: Ted McFarland
CFO: Garrett E Pierce
Ex VP: Antonio L Elias
Ex VP: Ronald J Grabe
Ex VP: Carl A Marchetto
Ex VP: Marty Titland
Sr VP: Frank L Culbertson
Sr VP: Michael A Hamel
Sr VP: G David Low
Sr VP: Pamela J Lupien
Sr VP: Tom E McCabe
Sr VP: Leslie C Seeman
VP: Daniel Robert
VP: John Scott
VP: Ferguson Bruce W

D-U-N-S 80-031-8441
■ ORBITZ INC
(*Suby of* ORBITZ.COM) ★
200 S Wacker Dr, Chicago, IL 60606-5829
Tel (312) 894-5000 *Founded/Ownrshp* 2006
Sales 91.1MM^E^ *EMP* 1,200
SIC 4724 Travel agencies
Pr: Steven Barnhart
Pt: Kit Simon
**CFO:* Marsha C Williams
Chf Mktg O: Randy Wagner
Sr VP: Bahman Koohestani
VP: Peggy Bianco
VP: Richard Buchband
VP: Barbara Buckridge
VP: Aaron Cooper
VP: Keith Dale
VP: Gary Doernhoefer
VP: Brian Hoyt
VP: Richard Lee
VP: Michael Mooradian
VP: Anne Razza
VP: Ian Ross

D-U-N-S 80-212-1587 IMP
■ ORBITZ LLC
ORBITZ PARTNER NETWORK
(*Suby of* ORBITZ.COM) ★
500 W Madison St Ste 1000, Chicago, IL 60661-2559
Tel (312) 894-5000 *Founded/Ownrshp* 1999
Sales 77.9MM^E^ *EMP* 1,200^E^
SIC 4724 Travel agencies
CEO: Barney Harford
**Pr:* Ronnie Gurion
**COO:* Mike Nelson
Chf Mktg O: Mike Sands
Sr VP: Frank Petito
**Sr VP:* Jim Shaughnessy

VP: Jane Denman
VP: Carol Jouzaitis
VP: Michael Sites
Sftwr Eng: Siou Lin
Sls Mgr: Phil Hammer

ORBITZ PARTNER NETWORK
See ORBITZ LLC

D-U-N-S 80-701-6568
■ ORBITZ WORLDWIDE INC
ORBITZ.COM
(*Suby of* EXPEDIA INC) ★
500 W Madison St Ste 1000, Chicago, IL 60661-2559
Tel (312) 894-5000 *Founded/Ownrshp* 2015
Sales 932.0MM *EMP* 1,530ᴱ
SIC 4724 Travel agencies; Tourist agency arranging transport, lodging & car rental
CEO: Barney Harford
CFO: Mitch Marcus
CFO: Michael Randolfi
Sr VP: Ronnie Gurion
Sr VP: Roger Liew
Sr VP: Frank Petito
Sr VP: Nigel Pocklington
VP: Greg Ball
VP: Tom Underwood
Exec: Christie Crawford
Exec: Joe Ward
Board of Directors: Gavin Baiera, Martin J Brand, Mark S Britton, Kenneth S Esterow, Scott Forbes, Robert L Friedman, Bradley T Gerstner, Kristina M Leslie

ORBITZ.COM
See ORBITZ WORLDWIDE INC

D-U-N-S 10-141-0801 IMP
ORBOTECH INC
(*Suby of* ORBOTECH LTD.)
44 Manning Rd, Billerica, MA 01821-3990
Tel (978) 667-6037 *Founded/Ownrshp* 1983
Sales 222.2MMᴱ *EMP* 1,700
SIC 5065 3823 3674 Electronic parts & equipment; Industrial instrmnts msrmnt display/control process variable; Solid state electronic devices
Pr: Raanan Cohen
Pr: Ken Maylor
COO: Amichai Steinberg
VP: Margaret Duncan
VP: Sriram Krishnaswami
VP: Reuven Losh
VP: Errol Moore
VP: Gil Oron
VP: Yovav Sameah
Genl Mgr: Alan Yip
IT Man: Ll Davidi
Board of Directors: Dani Falk, Shimon Ullman, Arie Weisberg

ORBUS EXHIBIT & DISPLAY GROUP
See ORBUS LLC

D-U-N-S 00-717-1449 IMP/EXP
ORBUS LLC (IL)
ORBUS EXHIBIT & DISPLAY GROUP
9033 Murphy Rd, Woodridge, IL 60517-1100
Tel (630) 226-1155 *Founded/Ownrshp* 2005
Sales 85.0MMᴱ *EMP* 320
SIC 3999 Advertising display products
Pr: Giles Douglas
CFO: Aurelia Sirbu
VP: Aaron Kozar
Rgnl Mgr: Kate Kincaid
Off Mgr: Nicole Berry
Off Admin: Claudia Simental
Web Dev: Patrick Lee
Manager: Doug Davidson
Sales Asso: Melissa Tenerelli

D-U-N-S 00-254-3239
ORC INTERNATIONAL INC
(*Suby of* LAKE CAPITAL MANAGEMENT LLC) ★
902 Carnegie Ctr Ste 220, Princeton, NJ 08540-6530
Tel (609) 452-5400 *Founded/Ownrshp* 1938, 2011
Sales 130.0MM *EMP* 1,800
SIC 8732 Market analysis or research; Opinion research
CEO: Simon Kooyman
CFO: Jim Karr
**CFO:* Stace Lee
CFO: Stacy S Lee
Ex VP: Richard Catrone
**Ex VP:* Walter Dempsey
Ex VP: Rory Macneill
**Sr VP:* Brian Cruikshank
Sr VP: Judith Lescher
Sr VP: Mia Wong
VP: Laurie Gelb
VP: Philip Gorski
VP: Rick Hedrick
VP: Laura Kleckner
VP: Kris Klein
VP: Eve Oster
VP: Bob Reitter
VP: Adrianne Tipton

D-U-N-S 05-573-0062
■ ORCHARD - POST ACUTE CARE CENTER
(*Suby of* ENDURA HEALTHCARE) ★
12385 Washington Blvd, Whittier, CA 90606-2502
Tel (562) 693-7701 *Founded/Ownrshp* 2015
Sales 15.6MM *EMP* 1,640ᴱ
SIC 8051 Convalescent home with continuous nursing care
Prin: Rich Jorgensen

D-U-N-S 78-814-6640
ORCHARD BRANDS CORP
BEDFORD FAIR APPAREL
(*Suby of* FINGERHUT) ★
138 Conant St Ste 3, Beverly, MA 01915-1666
Tel (978) 998-3800 *Founded/Ownrshp* 2015
Sales 768.9MMᴱ *EMP* 1,200ᴱ
SIC 5621 5611 5719 Women's clothing stores; Clothing, men's & boys': everyday, except suits & sportswear; Housewares; Towels; Beddings & linens; Kitchenware
CEO: James P Fogarty
**Pr:* Marc Fieger

**CFO:* Brain Gowen
VP: Nuku Aggor
**CIO:* Bill Nixon
VP Mktg: Kevin McGrain
Mktg Mgr: Patty Hamme
Mktg Mgr: Robyn Mohr
Snr Mgr: Rich Hanson

ORCHARD FOOD DIV
See ROHTSTEIN CORP

D-U-N-S 55-542-3177 IMP
■ ORCHARD SUPPLY CO LLC
O S H
(*Suby of* LOWES COMPANIES INC) ★
6450 Via Del Oro, San Jose, CA 95119-1208
Tel (408) 281-3500 *Founded/Ownrshp* 2013
Sales 1.5MMMᴱ *EMP* 5,329
SIC 5251 5261 Hardware; Nurseries & garden centers
Pr: Bob Tellier
Pr: Joe Kamleiter
Pr: Richard Marano
Ex VP: Steve Olsen
Sr VP: Mark A Bussard
Sr VP: David I Bogage
Sr VP: Mark Kauffman
VP: Woody Gray
**VP:* David R Green
**VP:* Bruce J Levitin
VP: Bruce Levitin

ORCHID ORTHOPEDIC SOLUTIONS
See TULIP US HOLDINGS INC

D-U-N-S 06-312-1057 IMP
ORCHIDS PAPER PRODUCTS CO
4826 Hunt St, Pryor, OK 74361-4512
Tel (918) 825-0616 *Founded/Ownrshp* 1998
Sales 168.4MM *EMP* 352
Tkr Sym TIS *Exch* ASE
SIC 2676 Sanitary paper products; Facial tissues: made from purchased paper; Napkins, paper: made from purchased paper; Towels, paper: made from purchased paper
Pr: Jeffrey S Schoen
**Ch Bd:* Steven R Berlin
CFO: Rodney D Gloss
Board of Directors: Mario Armando Garcia, John C Gutilla, Douglas E Hailey, Elaine Macdonald, Mark H Ravich

D-U-N-S 04-137-7474
ORDERS CONSTRUCTION CO INC
501 6th Ave, Saint Albans, WV 25177-2842
Tel (304) 722-4237 *Founded/Ownrshp* 1952
Sales 83.9MMᴱ *EMP* 125
SIC 1622 1611 Bridge construction; Highway & street construction
Pr: Nate R Orders
**VP:* John H Person

D-U-N-S 15-285-7090
ORDNER CONSTRUCTION CO INC
1600 Executive Dr Ste 100, Duluth, GA 30096-4942
Tel (678) 380-7400 *Founded/Ownrshp* 1987
Sales 83.7MM *EMP* 30
Accts Westbrook Mcgrath Bridges O
SIC 1542 Commercial & office building, new construction; Commercial & office buildings, renovation & repair
Pr: Dave A Ordner
**COO:* David Stoller
**Sec:* Lisa Ordner
VP: Dicky Piland

D-U-N-S 00-590-5906 EXP
ORECK CORP
1400 Salem Rd, Cookeville, TN 38506-6221
Tel (800) 219-2044 *Founded/Ownrshp* 1963
Sales 347.6MMᴱ *EMP* 1,000
SIC 3589 3564 5064 5087 Vacuum cleaners & sweepers, electric: industrial; Floor washing & polishing machines, commercial; Air purification equipment; Vacuum cleaners, household; Vacuum cleaners; Floor machinery, maintenance
CEO: Doug Cahill
Ch Bd: William Fry
CFO: Rethann Cox
CFO: Stanley W Eilers
CFO: Jeffrey T Gray
VP: John Arena
VP: Jeff Collins
VP: Anthony Conversa
Prin: David Oreck
CIO: Don Chrobot
Board of Directors: James Amos Jr, Peter Frank, Mary George, David Horing

D-U-N-S 03-240-3800
OREGON CITY SCHOOL DISTRICT 62
1417 12th St, Oregon City, OR 97045-2128
Tel (503) 785-8000 *Founded/Ownrshp* 1850
Sales 86.9MM *EMP* 850
SIC 8211 Public elementary & secondary schools
COO: Betty Draper
IT Man: Mike Hyder
HC Dir: Cynthia Panko

D-U-N-S 04-683-5039
OREGON COMMUNITY FOUNDATION
1221 Sw Ymhill St Ste 100, Portland, OR 97205
Tel (503) 227-6846 *Founded/Ownrshp* 1974
Sales 161.4MM *EMP* 40ᴱ
SIC 8399 2741 Social change association; Newsletter publishing
Pr: Gregory A Chaille
Bd of Dir: Sandi Vincent
Ofcr: Art Frank
Exec: Linda Weisel
Comm Dir: Joan Vallejo
VP Opers: Sheila Murty
Sales Exec: Cynthia Hayes

D-U-N-S 08-096-9355
OREGON DENTAL SERVICE
ODS COMPANIES
601 Sw 2nd Ave Ste 900, Portland, OR 97204-3195
Tel (503) 228-6554 *Founded/Ownrshp* 1961
Sales NA *EMP* 1,200
Accts Pricewaterhousecoopers Llp Sa
SIC 6324 Dental insurance
CEO: Robert Gootee
**Pr:* William S Ten Pas
CFO: Jon Jurevic
**Treas:* David Adams
Ofcr: Debra Florence
**Sr VP:* Robin Richardson
VP: Jonathan Nicholas
VP: Christopher Verbiest
IT Man: Rod Hart
Sftwr Eng: Rolf Schilasky
Natl Sales: David Novitsky

D-U-N-S 80-957-9485
OREGON DEPARTMENT OF ADMINISTRATIVE SERVICES
STATE CONTROLLER DIVISION
(*Suby of* EXECUTIVE OFFICE OF STATE OF OREGON) ★
155 Cottage St Ne Ste U50, Salem, OR 97301-3969
Tel (503) 378-8344 *Founded/Ownrshp* 1863
Sales NA *EMP* 1,000
SIC 9199 General government administration;
Ex Dir: John Radford
**COO:* Katy Coba

D-U-N-S 80-957-9451
OREGON DEPARTMENT OF CONSUMER AND BUSINESS SERVICES
(*Suby of* EXECUTIVE OFFICE OF STATE OF OREGON) ★
350 Winter St Ne, Salem, OR 97301-3875
Tel (503) 378-4100 *Founded/Ownrshp* 1993
Sales NA *EMP* 1,100
SIC 9651 9311 Insurance commission, government; ;
Pr: Tricia Wheeler

D-U-N-S 80-957-9535
OREGON DEPARTMENT OF CORRECTIONS
(*Suby of* EXECUTIVE OFFICE OF STATE OF OREGON) ★
2575 Center St Ne, Salem, OR 97301-6854
Tel (503) 945-9090 *Founded/Ownrshp* 1987
Sales NA *EMP* 4,500
SIC 9223 Prison, government;
Ex Dir: Coolette Peters
V Ch: Glen Ltc
Bd of Dir: Pamela Weatherspoon
Exec: Madilyn Zike
Assoc Dir: Michael Gower
**Ex Dir:* Max Williams
Prgrm Mgr: Wally Rogers
Dist Mgr: Pat Cimmiyotti
Dist Mgr: Mike Stinson
Off Admin: Michelle Van Schaick
IT Man: Scott Sanetel

D-U-N-S 80-957-9774
OREGON DEPARTMENT OF FISH AND WILDLIFE
ODFW
(*Suby of* EXECUTIVE OFFICE OF STATE OF OREGON) ★
4034 Fairview Indus Dr Se, Salem, OR 97302-1142
Tel (503) 947-6000 *Founded/Ownrshp* 1975
Sales NA *EMP* 1,100
SIC 9512 Wildlife conservation agencies;
Snr Mgr: Gregory Krutzikowsky

D-U-N-S 80-958-0319
OREGON DEPARTMENT OF HUMAN SERVICES
ADMINISTRATION OFFICE
(*Suby of* EXECUTIVE OFFICE OF STATE OF OREGON) ★
500 Summer St Ne Dept 4, Salem, OR 97301-1073
Tel (503) 945-5944 *Founded/Ownrshp* 1971
Sales NA *EMP* 9,500
SIC 9431 9441 Administration of public health programs; ;
Genl Mgr: Robert Johnson
Mktg Dir: Gary B Roth

D-U-N-S 80-979-0223
OREGON DEPARTMENT OF JUSTICE
ATTORNEY GENERAL
(*Suby of* EXECUTIVE OFFICE OF STATE OF OREGON) ★
1162 Court St Ne, Salem, OR 97301-4095
Tel (503) 378-4320 *Founded/Ownrshp* 1891
Sales NA *EMP* 1,000
SIC 9222 Attorney General's office;
IT Man: Lyn Johnson
Counsel: Beth Stratton
Snr Mgr: Sheila H Potter

D-U-N-S 80-958-0673
OREGON DEPARTMENT OF STATE POLICE
(*Suby of* EXECUTIVE OFFICE OF STATE OF OREGON) ★
255 Capitol St Ne Fl 4, Salem, OR 97310-1308
Tel (503) 378-3720 *Founded/Ownrshp* 1931
Sales NA *EMP* 1,400
SIC 9221 State police;
VP: Michael Hormann
CIO: Albert Gauthier
CIO: Jane Malecky-Scott
Snr Mgr: Dominique Rossi

D-U-N-S 80-958-0681
OREGON DEPARTMENT OF TRANSPORTATION
(*Suby of* EXECUTIVE OFFICE OF STATE OF OREGON) ★
355 Capitol St Ne Ms21, Salem, OR 97301-3871
Tel (503) 378-5849 *Founded/Ownrshp* 1969
Sales NA *EMP* 4,800
SIC 9621 Regulation, administration of transportation;
Genl Mgr: Shari Boedigheimer

D-U-N-S 93-295-6618
OREGON DIVISION OF ADULT & FAMILY SERVICES
CHILDREN ADULT AND FAMILY
(*Suby of* ADMINISTRATION OFFICE) ★
500 Summer St Ne, Salem, OR 97301-1063
Tel (503) 945-5601 *Founded/Ownrshp* 1971
Sales NA *EMP* 1,975
SIC 9441

OREGON ELECTRIC GROUP
See ON ELECTRIC GROUP INC

OREGON FREEZE DRY
See OFD FOODS INC

D-U-N-S 09-699-7515
OREGON HEALTH & SCIENCE UNIVERSITY
OHSU
3181 Sw Sam Jackson Pk Rd, Portland, OR 97239-3011
Tel (503) 494-8311 *Founded/Ownrshp* 1887
Sales 2.2MMM *EMP* 14,000
Accts Kpmg Llp Portland Or
SIC 8221 8069 University; Specialty hospitals, except psychiatric
Pr: Joseph Robertson Jr
**CFO:* Lawrence J Furnstahl
CFO: Lawrence Furnstahl
CFO: Diana Gernhart
CFO: James Walker
Treas: Thomas Hilton
VP: Sigrid Button
VP: Mary Turina
Assoc Dir: Sally Bowman
Assoc Dir: Ashok Reddy
Prin: Nancy L Haigwood

D-U-N-S 80-265-8286
OREGON HEALTH & SCIENCE UNIVERSITY FOUNDATION INC
MEDICAL RES FOUNDATION ORE
1121 Sw Salmon St Ste 100, Portland, OR 97205-2020
Tel (503) 228-1730 *Founded/Ownrshp* 1999
Sales 133.5MM *EMP* 115
Accts Kpmg Llp Seattle Wa
SIC 8399 6091 8733 6732 Fund raising organization, non-fee basis; Nondeposit trust facilities; Medical research; Trusts: educational, religious, etc.
Pr: Keith Todd
CFO: Mary Turina
Dir IT: Heather Wilberger

D-U-N-S 18-790-2689
OREGON INTERNATIONAL AIR FREIGHT CO INC
OIA GLOBAL LOGISTICS
(*Suby of* LDI LTD LLC) ★
2100 Sw Rver Pkwy Ste 800, Portland, OR 97201
Tel (503) 736-5900 *Founded/Ownrshp* 2010
Sales 996.0MMᴱ *EMP* 1,000
Accts Ernst & Young Llp Indianapoli
SIC 4731 Freight forwarding
Pr: Charles F Hornecker
**Pr:* Steve Akre
**CFO:* Timothy Sether
**Sr VP:* Dante Fornari
CIO: Jay Hemmady

D-U-N-S 00-902-1221
OREGON METAL SLITTERS INC (OR)
7227 N Leadbetter Rd, Portland, OR 97203-6490
Tel (503) 286-0300 *Founded/Ownrshp* 1956, 1999
Sales 119.5MMᴱ *EMP* 65ᴱ
SIC 5051 7389 Steel; Metal slitting & shearing
Pr: Steve Elorriaga
**Ex VP:* Kurt Roseler
**Ex VP:* Stanley Walker
Opers Mgr: Hans Polte
Plnt Mgr: Chuck Sanders
Ql Cn Mgr: Kyler Bruno
Sales Exec: Chris Holzgang
Sales Asso: Nick Call
Sales Asso: Karson Kobelin

D-U-N-S 00-790-8411
OREGON MUTUAL INSURANCE CO INC
WESTERN PROTECTORS INSURANCE
400 Ne Baker St, McMinnville, OR 97128-4906
Tel (503) 472-2141 *Founded/Ownrshp* 1894
Sales NA *EMP* 295
SIC 6331 Property damage insurance
Ch Bd: Michael Keyes
**Pr:* Brian Steffel
Pr: Wes Thomas
**Treas:* Steven Patterson
VP: Lori Burton
**VP:* Bryan Fowler
**VP:* Lisa Hargis
**VP:* Charles Katter
VP: Steve Patterson
Genl Mgr: Roy Duitman
QA Dir: Cindy Becker

OREGON OVERLAYS
See SIMPSON TIMBER CO

D-U-N-S 06-524-3834 IMP
OREGON PACIFIC BUILDING PRODUCTS (CALIF) INC
OREPAC BUILDING PRODUCTS
(*Suby of* OREPAC HOLDING CO) ★
30170 Sw Ore Pac Ave, Wilsonville, OR 97070-9794
Tel (503) 685-5499 *Founded/Ownrshp* 1980
Sales 156.5MMᴱ *EMP* 750
SIC 5031 Building materials, exterior; Building materials, interior; Lumber: rough, dressed & finished; Millwork
Pr: Bradley Hart
COO: Bryce Muir
**Sec:* Lee Daggett
**VP:* Alan Kirk
Genl Mgr: Gene Gillett
Genl Mgr: Bill Nabozny
Snr Mgr: Glenn Hart

D-U-N-S 79-992-6444 EXP
OREGON POTATO CO
WASHINGTON POTATO COMPANY
6610 W Court St Ste B, Pasco, WA 99301-2010
Tel (509) 349-8803 *Founded/Ownrshp* 2000
Sales 254.2MM^E *EMP* 220
SIC 2034 Potato products, dried & dehydrated
Pr: Frank S Tiegs
CFO: Karen Taylor
**VP:* Tim M Tippett

OREGON PRODUCTS
See BLOUNT INTERNATIONAL INC

OREGON R&H CONSTRUCTION
See R&H CONSTRUCTION CO

D-U-N-S 05-359-9908 IMP
OREGON STATE UNIVERSITY
308 Kerr Adm Bldg, Corvallis, OR 97331
Tel (541) 737-1000 *Founded/Ownrshp* 1858
Sales 587.3MM *EMP* 8,188^E
Accts Cliftonlarsonallen Llp Greenw
SIC 8221 University
Pr: Edward J Ray
Treas: Jae Park
VP: Steve Clark
**VP:* Glenn Ford
VP: Rich Holdren
Exec: Suzanne Grey
Assoc Dir: Rosemary Garagnani
Assoc Dir: Karen Steele
Assoc Dir: Blake Vawter
Dir Soc: Kate Sanders
Off Mgr: Penny Montgomery

D-U-N-S 07-072-8431
OREGON STATE UNIVERSITY FOUNDATION INC
850 Sw 35th St, Corvallis, OR 97333-4046
Tel (541) 737-4218 *Founded/Ownrshp* 1947
Sales 113.8MM *EMP* 115
SIC 6732 Educational trust management
Pr: J Michael Goodwin
VP: Ronald Adams
Assoc Dir: Travis Smith

D-U-N-S 04-126-8673
OREGON UNIVERSITY SYSTEM
BOARD OF HIGHER EDUCATION
P.O. Box 488, Corvallis (97339-0488)
Tel (541) 737-0827 *Founded/Ownrshp* 2003
Sales 1.7MMM *EMP* 26,000
SIC 8221

OREGONIAN, THE
See OREGONIAN PUBLISHING CO LLC

D-U-N-S 00-903-2517 IMP
OREGONIAN PUBLISHING CO LLC
OREGONIAN, THE
(*Suby of* ADVANCE PUBLICATIONS, INC.)
1500 Sw 1st Ave Ste 500, Portland, OR 97201-5870
Tel (503) 221-8327 *Founded/Ownrshp* 1873
Sales 184.9MM^E *EMP* 1,200
SIC 2711 Newspapers, publishing & printing
CFO: Motoko Komatsubara
Dir IT: Mike Melick
IT Man: Paul Lindstrom
Netwrk Mgr: Thad Macmillan
VP Opers: John Karafottas
VP Sls: Barbara Swanson
Advt Dir: Elizabeth Y Sell
Snr Mgr: Jake Arnold
Assoc Ed: Rick Attig

D-U-N-S 07-941-5585
■ **OREILLY AUTO ENTERPRISES LLC**
(*Suby of* OREILLY AUTOMOTIVE INC) ★
233 S Patterson Ave, Springfield, MO 65802-2210
Tel (417) 862-6708 *Founded/Ownrshp* 2013
Sales 5.5MMM^E *EMP* 50,000^E
SIC 5531 Automotive parts
CEO: Gregory Henslee

O'REILLY AUTO PARTS
See OREILLY AUTOMOTIVE STORES INC

D-U-N-S 96-878-3162
▲ **OREILLY AUTOMOTIVE INC**
233 S Patterson Ave, Springfield, MO 65802-2298
Tel (417) 862-6708 *Founded/Ownrshp* 1957
Sales 7.9MMM *EMP* 71,943
Tkr Sym ORLY *Exch* NGS
SIC 5531 5013 Automotive & home supply stores; Automotive parts; Automotive accessories; Motor vehicle supplies & new parts; Automotive supplies & parts
Pr: Greg Henslee
**Ch Bd:* David O'Reilly
**V Ch:* Charles H O'Reilly Jr
V Ch: Lawrence P O'Reilly
Pr: Greg L Henslee
CFO: Thomas McFall
**V Ch Bd:* Larry O'Reilly
Ex VP: Gregory D Johnson
Ex VP: Jeff Shaw
Sr VP: Tony Bartholomew
Sr VP: Brad W Beckham
Sr VP: Keith Childers
Sr VP: Jeffrey L Groves
Sr VP: Scott Kraus
Sr VP: Jeffrey A Lauro
VP: Michael Swearengin
Board of Directors: Jay D Burchfield, Thomas T Hendrickson, Paul R Lederer, John R Murphy, Ronald Rashkow, Rosalie O'reilly Wooten

D-U-N-S 03-114-1534 IMP
■ **OREILLY AUTOMOTIVE STORES INC**
O'REILLY AUTO PARTS
(*Suby of* OREILLY AUTOMOTIVE INC) ★
233 S Patterson Ave, Springfield, MO 65802-2298
Tel (417) 862-6708 *Founded/Ownrshp* 1957
Sales 5.2MMM^E *EMP* 47,142
SIC 5013 5531 Automotive supplies & parts; Automotive parts
CEO: Greg Henslee
V Ch: Larry P O'Reilly
CFO: Jim Batton
**Ch:* David O Reilly
**Ex VP:* Tom McFall
**Ex VP:* Jeff Shaw
**Sr VP:* Michael D Swearengin
VP: Linda Keeth
**VP:* Ted Wise
Genl Mgr: Jackie Centers
Genl Mgr: Ken Gower
Board of Directors: Jay D Burchfield, Thomas T Hendrickson, Paul R Lederer, John Murphy, Charles H O'reilly Jr, David E O'reilly, Lawrence P O'reilly, Ronald Rashkow, Rosalie O'reilly-Wooten

D-U-N-S 13-084-0077 IMP
OREILLY MEDIA INC
1005 Gravenstein Hwy N, Sebastopol, CA 95472-2811
Tel (707) 827-7000 *Founded/Ownrshp* 1978
Sales 107.9MM^E *EMP* 400
SIC 2731 2741 Books: publishing only; Technical manuals: publishing & printing
Pr: Timothy F O'Reilly
Mng Pt: Mark Jacobsen
Dir Soc: Catharine Lipton
**Prin:* Christina F O'Reilly
Genl Mgr: Kathy Lanterman
CTO: Andrew Odewahn
Sftwr Eng: Zachary Ogren
Sftwr Eng: Aaron Sumner
Natl Sales: John Holdcroft
Sls Mgr: Katie Kunde
Sales Asso: Ashley Newby

OREPAC BUILDING PRODUCTS
See OREGON PACIFIC BUILDING PRODUCTS (CALIF) INC

D-U-N-S 08-364-5069 IMP
OREPAC HOLDING CO
30170 Sw Orepac Ave, Wilsonville, OR 97070
Tel (503) 682-5050 *Founded/Ownrshp* 1976
Sales 558.1MM^E *EMP* 800
SIC 5031 Windows
Pr: Bradley Hart
VP: Gary Hart
**Prin:* Alan Kirk
VP Opers: Glenn Dutton
Opers Mgr: Tom Clark
Opers Mgr: Tom Reddy
Sls Mgr: Adam McCartie
Sls Mgr: David Searle

ORGANIC VALLEY
See COOPERATIVE REGIONS OF ORGANIC PRODUCER POOLS

D-U-N-S 10-405-6973 IMP
ORGANICALLY GROWN CO
1800 Prairie Rd Ste B, Eugene, OR 97402-9722
Tel (541) 689-5320 *Founded/Ownrshp* 1978
Sales 176.3MM *EMP* 189
SIC 5148 Fresh fruits & vegetables
Pr: David Amorose
**CEO:* Josh Hinerfeld
**CFO:* Robbie Vasilinda
Mktg Dir: David Lively

D-U-N-S 03-118-6894
ORGANICLIFE LLC
445 W Erie St Ste 110, Chicago, IL 60654-6924
Tel (312) 929-2005 *Founded/Ownrshp* 2006
Sales 26.2MM^E *EMP* 1,000
SIC 5812 Eating places
CEO: Jonas S Falk

D-U-N-S 15-216-5817 IMP
ORGANOGENESIS INC
150 Dan Rd Ste 3, Canton, MA 02021-2820
Tel (781) 575-0198 *Founded/Ownrshp* 1985
Sales 179.0MM^E *EMP* 525^E
SIC 2836 Biological products, except diagnostic
CEO: Gary S Gillheeney Sr
**CEO:* Geoff Mackay
**CFO:* Tim Cunningham
**VP:* Milka Bedikian
**VP:* Patrick Bilbo
**VP:* Dario Eklund
**VP:* Phillip Nolan
**VP:* Zorina Pitkin
Exec: Joe Bennett
Exec: Amy Fontenot
Exec: Andrae Johnson
Assoc Dir: Nathan Parsons

D-U-N-S 00-792-2123 IMP/EXP
ORGILL INC (TN)
3742 Tyndale Dr, Memphis, TN 38125-8500
Tel (901) 754-8850 *Founded/Ownrshp* 1847
Sales 2.3MMM^E *EMP* 2,006
SIC 5072 Hardware; Builders' hardware; Shelf or light hardware; Hand tools
Pr: Ron Beal
**Ch Bd:* Joseph Orgill III
**CFO:* Byrne Whitehead
**Sr VP:* Ken Post
VP: Bryce Abbott
VP: Jeannine Akin
VP: Myron Boswell
VP: Everett Clark
VP: John Dillon
VP: Steve East
VP: Vic Price

D-U-N-S 02-576-2725
ORIANA HOUSE INC
885 E Buchtel Ave, Akron, OH 44305-2338
Tel (330) 535-8116 *Founded/Ownrshp* 1981
Sales 48.4MM *EMP* 1,513
Accts Lb Bruner Cox Llp Akron Oh
SIC 8322 9111 Substance abuse counseling; Rehabilitation services; County supervisors' & executives' offices
Pr: James Lawrence
**Ex VP:* Anne Connell-Freund
**Ex VP:* Bernard Rochford
**VP:* Joyce Allen
VP: George De Bord
**VP:* George Debord
VP: Illya McGee
Prin: Gina D'Aurelio
VP Admn: Mary Jones
Mng Dir: William Scheub
Prgrm Mgr: Deana Brutto

D-U-N-S 61-348-2306
ORIANNA HEALTH SYSTEMS
2723 Summer Oaks Dr, Bartlett, TN 38134-2858
Tel (901) 937-7994 *Founded/Ownrshp* 1986
Sales 222.7MM^E *EMP* 300^E
SIC 6282 8051 Investment advisory service; Skilled nursing care facilities
CEO: Christopher Murphy
Pr: Chuck Dunn
Pr: Curtis Moore
Pr: James Palculict
**CFO:* Helen Sain
VP: Mark Bixler
**VP:* Jason Calvasina
VP: David Duffield
VP: Dan Estes
VP: Monica Pappas
VP: Dell Workman
Exec: Diane Ellis

ORIBE
See JAY GROUP INC

ORICA
See NELSON BROTHERS LLC

D-U-N-S 05-837-0685 IMP/EXP
ORICA GROUND SUPPORT INC
MINOVA AMERICAS
(*Suby of* MINOVA HOLDING INC) ★
150 Summer Ct, Georgetown, KY 40324-9369
Tel (502) 863-6800 *Founded/Ownrshp* 2003
Sales 175.2MM^E *EMP* 531
SIC 5082 3564 2439 7699

D-U-N-S 04-686-0750 IMP
ORICA US SERVICES INC
(*Suby of* ORICA LIMITED)
33101 E Quincy Ave, Watkins, CO 80137-9406
Tel (303) 268-5000 *Founded/Ownrshp* 1998
Sales 175.2MM^E *EMP* 700
SIC 2892 5169 Explosives; Explosives
Pr: Craig Elkington
CFO: Richard Best
Exec: Gavin Jackman
VP Sls: Laura Babaeva

D-U-N-S 94-929-9622 IMP
ORICA USA INC
(*Suby of* ORICA LIMITED)
33101 E Quincy Ave, Watkins, CO 80137-9406
Tel (720) 870-1809 *Founded/Ownrshp* 1998
Sales 221.2MM^E *EMP* 700
SIC 2892 5169 Explosives; Explosives
CEO: Ian K Smith
COO: Sherree Woodroffe
**CFO:* Craig Elkington
CFO: Stuart Hutton
VP: Steven Burchell
VP: Christopher Curtis
VP: Richard Omeara
VP: Cluny Randell
Dir Risk M: Oliver Ramirez
Mng Dir: Knut Reed
Mng Dir: Alan Smith

ORIENT EX HTELS TRAINS CRUISES
See ORIENT EXPRESS HOTELS INC

D-U-N-S 04-835-3460
ORIENT EXPRESS HOTELS INC
ORIENT EX HTELS TRAINS CRUISES
(*Suby of* BELMOND LTD.)
441 Lexington Ave Rm 504, New York, NY 10017-3938
Tel (212) 302-5055 *Founded/Ownrshp* 2000
Sales 102.2MM^E *EMP* 5,000
SIC 7011 3743 5947 6552 Hotels; Train cars & equipment, freight or passenger; Gift shop; Subdividers & developers
Pr: Paul White
Sls Mgr: Nicola Price

D-U-N-S 09-117-1199
■ **ORIENTAL BANK**
ORIENTAL GROUP
(*Suby of* OFG BANCORP) ★
254 Ave Munoz Rivera, San Juan, PR 00918-1900
Tel (787) 771-6800 *Founded/Ownrshp* 1997
Sales NA *EMP* 350
SIC 6035 7359 7515 6733 Federal savings banks; Equipment rental & leasing; Passenger car leasing; Trusts
Pr: Jose Rafael Fernadez
**Ch Bd:* Jose Gil Delamadrid
**Treas:* Julio Micheo
VP: Maureen Cilano
Brnch Mgr: Mary Hosler
Mktg Mgr: Michael Laskoe
Assoc Ed: Corina Rivera

ORIENTAL GROUP
See ORIENTAL BANK

ORIENTAL TRADING COMPANY
See OTC DIRECT INC

D-U-N-S 00-952-4152 IMP/EXP
■ **ORIENTAL TRADING CO INC**
(*Suby of* OTC WORLDWIDE HOLDINGS INC) ★
5455 S 90th St, Omaha, NE 68127-3501
Tel (402) 596-1200 *Founded/Ownrshp* 2011, 2012
Sales 923.5MM^E *EMP* 1,005^E
SIC 5199 4813 Gifts & novelties;
CEO: Sam Taylor
**Treas:* Steve Mendlik
VP: Nachiket Desai
VP: Chris Merritt
IT Man: Erich Ross
Sys Mgr: Debra Corsbie
Software D: Marvin Konwinski
Opers Mgr: Michele Bruun
Secur Mgr: James Nelson
Natl Sales: Kari Onken
VP Mktg: Robert Goldsmith

D-U-N-S 05-853-2169
ORIGIN BANK
(*Suby of* COMMUNITY TRUST FINANCIAL CORP) ★
3921 Elm St, Choudrant, LA 71227-3082
Tel (318) 255-2222 *Founded/Ownrshp* 1987
Sales NA *EMP* 261
SIC 6022 State commercial banks
Pr: Drake D Mills
**Ch Bd:* Ronnie Myrick
COO: Debbie Barrett
**CFO:* James K Kendrick
Ex VP: Linda Tuten
VP: Robert Brewer
VP: Alicia Bullock
VP: Wayne Darnell
VP: Skip Portman
VP: Jeremy Rigney

D-U-N-S 00-120-1045 IMP/EXP
ORIGINAL BRADFORD SOAP WORKS INC (RI)
(*Suby of* BRADFORD SOAP INTERNATIONAL INC) ★
200 Providence St, West Warwick, RI 02893-2508
Tel (401) 821-2141 *Founded/Ownrshp* 1876
Sales 111.2MM^E *EMP* 400
SIC 2841 Soap: granulated, liquid, cake, flaked or chip
CEO: John H Howland
**CFO:* Stuart Benton
**Ex VP:* Chris Buckley
**Ex VP:* Jimmy Curran
Sr VP: William F Schmiedeknecht Jr
VP: Rick Dowling
VP: Ed George
VP: Skip Watson
Ql Cn Mgr: Sonny Russell
Sls Dir: Deb Duquette

ORIGINAL ISLAND SPORT
See VIEWPOINT INTERNATIONAL INC

ORIGINAL PENNYSAVER, THE
See PENNYSAVER USA PUBLISHING LLC

D-U-N-S 61-171-6283 IMP
■ **ORIGINS NATURAL RESOURCES INC**
ESTEE LAUDER
(*Suby of* ESTEE LAUDER INC) ★
767 5th Ave Fl 38, New York, NY 10153-0023
Tel (212) 572-4200 *Founded/Ownrshp* 1991
Sales 117.3MM^E *EMP* 127
SIC 5122 Drugs, proprietaries & sundries
CEO: Lynne Greene
VP: Jenny Belknap
VP: Beth Spruance
Assoc Dir: Mary Campbell
**Prin:* William P Lauder
Ex Dir: Mark Ferdman
Ex Dir: Helen Jones
Dir IT: Anne Basile
Sls Dir: Alicia Cummins
Mktg Mgr: Daria Myers
Counsel: Gregg Marrazzo

ORIGLIO BEVERAGE
See ANTONIO ORIGLIO INC

D-U-N-S 82-766-5688 IMP/EXP
■ **ORION CONSTRUCTION LP**
(*Suby of* ORION GROUP HOLDINGS INC) ★
4440 Highway 225 Ste 180, Deer Park, TX 77536-2443
Tel (713) 852-6500 *Founded/Ownrshp* 1994
Sales 98.7MM *EMP* 700
SIC 1629

D-U-N-S 13-038-2208 IMP/EXP
ORION ENGINEERED CARBONS LLC
(*Suby of* ROOSEN MARIO)
4501 Magnolia Cove Dr, Kingwood, TX 77345-2252
Tel (832) 445-3300 *Founded/Ownrshp* 2000
Sales 524.6MM *EMP* 200
SIC 2895 Carbon black
CEO: Jack Clem
**CFO:* Charles Herlinger
**Sr VP:* Jorg Kruger
**Sr VP:* Mark Leigh
**Sr VP:* Jeff Malenky
**Sr VP:* Lixing Min
**Sr VP:* Claudine Mollenkopf
**Sr VP:* Erik Thiry
VP: Johnny Covey
**VP:* Michael Reers
**Genl Couns:* Christian Eggert

D-U-N-S 87-770-0518
ORION FOOD SYSTEMS LLC
HOT STUFF FOODS
(*Suby of* ONE ROCK CAPITAL PARTNERS LLC) ★
2930 W Maple St, Sioux Falls, SD 57107-0745
Tel (605) 336-6961 *Founded/Ownrshp* 1982
Sales 90.0MM *EMP* 300
SIC 5149 2033 2026 2041 Pizza supplies; Pizza sauce: packaged in cans, jars, etc.; Bakers' cheese; Pizza dough, prepared
CEO: Steve K Watkins
VP: Rich Carlson
VP: Devon Clark
VP: John Cooper
VP: Rick Ochs
VP: Linda Roemen
Dir Bus: Jeff Mozingo
Opers Mgr: Tom Bale
Mktg Mgr: Rachel Quintanilla

D-U-N-S 80-767-6908
▲ **ORION GROUP HOLDINGS INC**
12000 Aerospace Ave # 300, Houston, TX 77034-5587
Tel (713) 852-6500 *Founded/Ownrshp* 1994
Sales 466.5MM *EMP* 2,300^E
Tkr Sym ORN *Exch* NYS
SIC 1629 Marine construction
Pr: Mark R Stauffer
**Ch Bd:* Richard L Daerr Jr
COO: L Dwayne Breaux
CFO: Christopher J Dealmeida
Ofcr: Peter R Buchler
IT Man: Robert Spencer
Board of Directors: Thomas N Amonett, J Michael Pearson, Austin J Shanfelter, Gene G Stoever

D-U-N-S 06-798-5403 IMP/EXP
ORION INSTRUMENTS LLC
(*Suby of* MAGNETROL INTERNATIONAL INC) ★
2105 Oak Villa Blvd, Baton Rouge, LA 70815-8518
Tel (225) 906-2343 *Founded/Ownrshp* 2001
Sales 90.2MM[E] *EMP* 364
SIC 3823 Liquid level instruments, industrial process type
Prd Mgr: Henry Mosses
Mktg Mgr: Craig Carroll
Sales Asso: Reid Hughes

D-U-N-S 04-149-7165 IMP/EXP
■ **ORION MARINE CONSTRUCTION INC**
MISENER MARINE CONSTRUCTION
(*Suby of* ORION CONSTRUCTION LP) ★
5440 W Tyson Ave, Tampa, FL 33611-3228
Tel (813) 839-8441 *Founded/Ownrshp* 2001
Sales 214.7MM *EMP* 305
SIC 1629 Marine construction
Pr: Mark R Stauffer
**CFO:* Mark Stauffer
Ex VP: Jim Rose
**Sr VP:* David Thornton
**VP:* John Whalen

ORIONTECH
See COMPUCASE CORP

D-U-N-S 07-669-2698
■ **ORITANI BANK**
(*Suby of* ORITANI FINANCIAL CORP) ★
370 Pascack Rd, Twp Washinton, NJ 07676-4835
Tel (201) 664-5400 *Founded/Ownrshp* 1911
Sales NA *EMP* 150
Accts Kpmg Llp
SIC 6036 Savings & loan associations, not federally chartered
Pr: Kevin J Lynch
CFO: John M Fields Jr
Ofcr: Diane Fenton
Ofcr: Thomas Guinan
Sr VP: Philip M Wyks
VP: Robert J Barbarino
VP: Rosanne Buscemi
VP: Neil Minardi
VP: Robert Pierson
VP: Michael Sandberg
VP: Daniel Schapira
Board of Directors: Nicholas Antonaccio, Dominic F Cundari, Michael A Debernardi, Joseph Deferrari Jr, Robert F Gerrie, William E Gott, Kevin J Lynch, David T Peterson Jr, Phillip D Wyks

D-U-N-S 79-076-9850
▲ **ORITANI FINANCIAL CORP**
370 Pascack Rd, Twp Washinton, NJ 07676-4835
Tel (201) 664-5400 *Founded/Ownrshp* 1998
Sales NA *EMP* 235[E]
Tkr Sym ORIT *Exch* NGS
SIC 6022 State commercial banks
Ch Bd: Kevin J Lynch
CFO: John M Fields Jr
Chf Cred: Louis A Manderino
Ofcr: Thomas Guinan
Ofcr: Thomas G Guinan
Ex VP: Michael Debernardi
Sr VP: Rosanne Buscemi
Sr VP: Philip M Wyks
VP: Jack Anastasi
VP: Paul Cordero
VP: Noah Littell
VP: Bing Luh
VP: John Pagano
VP: Paul C Skinner
VP: Philip Wyks

D-U-N-S 07-421-4490
ORIUS CORP
1000 Hart Rd Ste 140, Barrington, IL 60010-2668
Tel (847) 277-8444 *Founded/Ownrshp* 2003
Sales 85.9MM[E] *EMP* 1,200
SIC 4813 Telephone communication, except radio
Pr: Willaim Shuttleworth
CFO: Gary F Berger
Ex VP: Robert Waerman
Sr VP: Thomas W Hartmann
VP: John W Starr

D-U-N-S 02-865-8306
ORIX USA CORP
676 W Prospect Rd, Oakland Park, FL 33309-3949
Tel (214) 237-2000 *Founded/Ownrshp* 2010
Sales 22.0MM[E] *EMP* 1,400
SIC 8741 Business management
Pr: James Thompson
**Ch Bd:* Yuki Oshima

D-U-N-S 02-885-8306 IMP
ORIX USA CORP
(*Suby of* ORIX CORPORATION)
1717 Main St Ste 1100, Dallas, TX 75201-4612
Tel (214) 237-2000 *Founded/Ownrshp* 1981
Sales 272.3MM[E] *EMP* 720
SIC 6211 6282

D-U-N-S 36-441-1496
ORIZON INDUSTRIES INC
(*Suby of* SPITZER INDUSTRIES INC) ★
7007 Fm 362 Rd, Brookshire, TX 77423-9418
Tel (281) 375-7700 *Founded/Ownrshp* 1996
Sales 146.5MM[E] *EMP* 250
SIC 3441 Fabricated structural metal
Ch: Cullen R Spitzer
**Pr:* Curtis F Jones
**CFO:* Marcy Brigman
CFO: Marcy Prigman
**Sec:* Ted Johnson
**VP:* Charles O'Hara

ORKIN
See ROLLINS SUPPLY INC

D-U-N-S 00-250-9420
■ **ORKIN LLC** (GA)
ORKIN PEST CONTROL
(*Suby of* ROLLINS INC) ★
2170 Piedmont Rd Ne, Atlanta, GA 30324-4135
Tel (404) 888-2000 *Founded/Ownrshp* 1901
Sales 929.2MM[E] *EMP* 4,005
SIC 7342 Pest control in structures; Termite control
CEO: Gary W Rollins
**VP:* Clyde Cobb
VP: Lee Krump
VP: Robert Price
Exec: Freeman Elliott
Brnch Mgr: Darryl Murdock
Brnch Mgr: David Peraza
Opers Mgr: Dave Schwieger
Manager: Paul Strickland
Sls Mgr: Rhonda McAulay
Sls Mgr: Doug Robinson

ORKIN PEST CONTROL
See ORKIN LLC

D-U-N-S 00-417-4355 IMP
ORLANDO BAKING CO
7777 Grand Ave, Cleveland, OH 44104-3061
Tel (216) 361-1872 *Founded/Ownrshp* 1872
Sales 100.4MM[E] *EMP* 350[E]
SIC 2051 Bread, all types (white, wheat, rye, etc): fresh or frozen; Rolls, bread type: fresh or frozen
Pr: Chester Orlando
**CFO:* Christine Brindle
Treas: John A Peca Jr
**VP:* Joseph Orlando
**Prin:* Glenn W Eckert
**Prin:* Edna Rosenblum
**Prin:* Hattie Wagner
QA Dir: Craig Lovato
QA Dir: Ronald Zendarski
Dir IT: Brett Ferlin
QI Cn Mgr: Paul Storsin

ORLANDO HARLEY DAVIDSON
See HD AMERICAN ROAD LLC

D-U-N-S 07-867-9697
ORLANDO HEALTH CENTRAL INC
(*Suby of* ORLANDO HEALTH INC) ★
10000 W Colonial Dr, Ocoee, FL 34761-3400
Tel (407) 296-1820 *Founded/Ownrshp* 2011
Sales 208.0MM *EMP* 1,500[E]
SIC 8062 General medical & surgical hospitals
Pr: Greg Ohe
Dir Risk M: Haresh Ramjas
Dir Lab: Margie Weissgerber
Chf Nrs Of: Christina McGuirk
QA Dir: Emily Garcia
Mtls Mgr: Marc Lillis
Mktg Dir: Brenda Labattaglia
Obsttrcn: Carlos Dieguez
HC Dir: Cassie Deel

D-U-N-S 08-240-6638 IMP
ORLANDO HEALTH INC
52 W Underwood St, Orlando, FL 32806-1110
Tel (321) 843-7000 *Founded/Ownrshp* 1977
Sales 2.3MMM *EMP* 10,000
Accts Grant Thornton Llp Orlando F
SIC 8062 8741 8069 General medical & surgical hospitals; Hospital management; Specialty hospitals, except psychiatric
CEO: David Strong
COO: Jamal Hakim
CFO: Bernadette Spong
Sr VP: Mildred Beam
VP: Jimenez Kelsy
IT Man: Chuck Hana
Info Man: Jean-Marc Francis
Doctor: Deepak Vivek

ORLANDO INTERNATIONAL AIRPORT
See GREATER ORLANDO AVIATION AUTHORITY

ORLANDO SENTINNEL MEDIA GROUP
See SENTINEL COMMUNICATIONS NEWS VENTURES INC

D-U-N-S 00-407-6071 IMP
ORLANDO UTILITIES COMMISSION
OUC
100 W Anderson St, Orlando, FL 32801-4408
Tel (407) 246-2121 *Founded/Ownrshp* 1923
Sales 825.3MM *EMP* 1,000
Accts Ernst & Young Llp
SIC 4941 4931 4939 4911 Water supply; Electric & other services combined; Combination utilities; Electric services
CEO: Kenneth P Ksionek
VP: Tim Amilibia
VP: Clint Bullock
**VP:* Linda Ferrone
VP: Frederick F Haddad
VP: Kelly Peek
**VP:* David Repollet
VP: Greg Rodeghier
**VP:* Darlene Scott
VP: Rob Teegarden
VP: Christi Valdes

D-U-N-S 04-860-2817
ORLEANS HOMEBUILDERS INC
O H B
3333 Street Rd Ste 101, Bensalem, PA 19020-2022
Tel (215) 245-7500 *Founded/Ownrshp* 1969
Sales 330.6MM[E] *EMP* 480[E]
SIC 1531 1521 Operative builders; Single-family housing construction; Townhouse construction
CEO: Alan E Laing
Pr: Jeffrey P Orelans
Pr: Mitch Sanner
CEO: George Casey
COO: C Dean Amann II
CFO: Marek Bakun
Chf Mktg O: Lee Darnold
Ex VP: Linda Kelly
Sr VP: Michael Karmatz
VP: Lawrence J Dugan
VP: Ward Harris
VP: Garry Herdler
VP: Jack Raymond

ORLEANS HOTEL AND CASINO, THE
See COAST HOTELS AND CASINOS INC

D-U-N-S 01-694-2302 IMP/EXP
ORLEANS INTERNATIONAL INC (MI)
CENTURY TRADING
30600 Northwestern Hwy # 300, Farmington Hills, MI 48334-3172
Tel (248) 855-5556 *Founded/Ownrshp* 1935
Sales 856.1MM *EMP* 37
Accts Freedman & Goldberg Farmingto
SIC 5142 Meat, frozen: packaged
CEO: Earl Tushman
CFO: Jerry Castellano
**CFO:* Lori Wigler
**Sec:* Lawrence Tushman
**VP:* Steve Sanger
**VP:* Larry Tushman
Comm Man: Elmer Rodrigez
Sales Exec: Larry Berger

ORLEANS PARISH SCHOOL BOARD
See ORLEANS PARISH SCHOOL DISTRICT

D-U-N-S 07-946-0093
ORLEANS PARISH SCHOOL DISTRICT
ORLEANS PARISH SCHOOL BOARD
3520 Gen Degaulle Dr # 5055, New Orleans, LA 70114-4000
Tel (504) 304-3520 *Founded/Ownrshp* 1841
Sales 299.7MM[E] *EMP* 7,062
Accts La Porte Metairie La
SIC 8211 Public elementary & secondary schools
**CEO:* Alphonse G Davis
**COO:* Roger Reese
Prin: Victor Gordon
Ex Dir: Jan Kasofsky
Ex Dir: Debbie Schum
Ex Dir: Michael Teague
Telecom Mg: Cynthia Miller
Teacher Pr: Armand Devezin

D-U-N-S 78-443-0238 IMP
■ **ORMAT NEVADA INC**
(*Suby of* ORMAT TECHNOLOGIES INC) ★
6225 Neil Rd, Reno, NV 89511-1151
Tel (775) 356-9029 *Founded/Ownrshp* 1991
Sales 251.9MM[E] *EMP* 400[E]
SIC 4939 Combination utilities
CEO: Isaac Angel
CFO: Doron Blachar
Ex VP: Zvi Krieger
Prin: Yehudit Bronicki
Prin: Yoram Bronicki
Prin: Connie Stechman

D-U-N-S 92-931-5661 IMP/EXP
▲ **ORMAT TECHNOLOGIES INC**
6225 Neil Rd, Reno, NV 89511-1151
Tel (775) 356-9029 *Founded/Ownrshp* 1965
Sales 594.6MM *EMP* 1,060[E]
Tkr Sym ORA *Exch* NYS
SIC 4911 3511 Generation, electric power; Turbines & turbine generator sets; Turbines & turbine generator set units, complete; Turbo-generators
CEO: Isaac Angel
**Ch Bd:* Gillon Beck
CFO: Doron Blachar
Treas: Anat L Ben-Schlomo
Ex VP: Shlomi Argas
Ex VP: Shimon Hatzir
Ex VP: Erez Klein
Ex VP: Zvi Krieger
Ex VP: Bob Sullivan
Ex VP: Nir Wolf
Sr VP: Etty Rosner
VP: Barbara Allen
VP: Aaron Lewis
Dir Risk M: Chen Cohen
Dir Bus: Ram Orenstein
Board of Directors: Ami Boehm, Robert F Clarke, Dan Falk, David Granot, Robert E Joyal, Stanley B Stern

D-U-N-S 15-461-4119 IMP/EXP
■ **ORMCO CORP**
SYBRON ENDO
(*Suby of* ANALYTIC ENDODONTICS) ★
1717 W Collins Ave, Orange, CA 92867-5422
Tel (714) 516-7400 *Founded/Ownrshp* 2013
Sales 149.6MM[E] *EMP* 599
SIC 3843 Orthodontic appliances
CEO: Patrik Eriksson
Pr: Vicente Reynal
VP: Mike Beaudoin
VP: Jason R Davis
Ex VP: Ed Wong
Sftwr Eng: Hua Zhang
Mktg Mgr: Brandy Lewis
Mktg Mgr: Alex Miroshnichenko
Mktg Mgr: Jennifer Riad
Sls Mgr: Amy Cyman
Sls Mgr: Bridger Hodsden

D-U-N-S 60-935-5383 IMP
ORMET CORP
43840 State Rte 7, Hannibal, OH 43931
Tel (740) 483-1381 *Founded/Ownrshp* 1990
Sales 175.6MM[E] *EMP* 1,250
SIC 3334 Primary aluminum
Pr: Mike Tanchuk
**Ch Bd:* Jeffrey Marshall
**CFO:* James Burns Riley
VP: Matt Powell
Plnt Mgr: Gary Mallett

D-U-N-S 00-437-9970 IMP
ORMET PRIMARY ALUMINUM CORP
VELVETFLOW
43840 State Rt 7, Hannibal, OH 43931
Tel (740) 483-1381 *Founded/Ownrshp* 1956
Sales 144.6MM[E] *EMP* 1,100
SIC 3334 3297

D-U-N-S 18-251-8485
ORO VALLEY HOSPITAL LLC
NMCOV
1551 E Tangerine Rd, Oro Valley, AZ 85755-6213
Tel (520) 901-3500 *Founded/Ownrshp* 2009
Sales 91.9MM[E] *EMP* 500
SIC 8062 General medical & surgical hospitals
**CFO:* Jeff Daneff
Dir Case M: Kimberly Browning
Chf Nrs Of: Donna Zubay
Surgeon: Alex Westerband
Doctor: Lynne Gossett
Doctor: Mark Ramirez
Pharmcst: Meridee Febus
Pharmcst: Rebecca Malone
Counsel: Jeffrey N Danis
Art Dir: Jason King
Snr Mgr: Wendy Lheron

D-U-N-S 00-207-8244
OROGRAIN BAKERIES MANUFACTURING INC
255 Business Center Dr, Horsham, PA 19044-3424
Tel (518) 463-2221 *Founded/Ownrshp* 1994
Sales 136.2MM[E] *EMP* 1,300
SIC 2051

D-U-N-S 15-340-4397
OROHEALTH CORP
2767 Olive Hwy, Oroville, CA 95966-6118
Tel (530) 533-8500 *Founded/Ownrshp* 1985
Sales 3.3MM *EMP* 1,167
SIC 8741 Hospital management
Pr: Robert J Wentz
CFO: Jo Dilbeck
Ofcr: Debra Jones

D-U-N-S 00-886-0678 IMP/EXP
ORORA PACKAGING SOLUTIONS (CA)
LANDSBERG ORORA
(*Suby of* ORORA LIMITED)
6600 Valley View St, Buena Park, CA 90620-1145
Tel (714) 562-6000 *Founded/Ownrshp* 1951
Sales 2.2MMM[E] *EMP* 2,397
SIC 5113 2653 Paper & products, wrapping or coarse; Sanitary food containers; Boxes, corrugated: made from purchased materials
Pr: Bernardino Salvatore
Pr: Preston Geeting
**Pr:* Bernardino Salvatorre
**CFO:* David Conley
VP: Michael Hodges
VP: Ray Huelskamp
VP: Gary Noonan
Div Mgr: Neil Tennant
CIO: Kathy Linares
Opers Mgr: David Hingco
Natl Sales: Jeff Goldstein

D-U-N-S 02-663-3289 EXP
OROURKE DISTRIBUTING CO INC
O'ROURKE PETROLEUM PRODUCTS
223 Mccarty St, Houston, TX 77029-1137
Tel (713) 672-4500 *Founded/Ownrshp* 1932
Sales 102.8MM[E] *EMP* 136
SIC 5171 5172

O'ROURKE PETROLEUM PRODUCTS
See OROURKE DISTRIBUTING CO INC

D-U-N-S 07-609-9282
OROVILLE HOSPITAL
2767 Olive Hwy, Oroville, CA 95966-6118
Tel (530) 533-8500 *Founded/Ownrshp* 1966
Sales 236.9MM *EMP* 1,400
Accts Kcoe Isom Llp Chico Califo
SIC 8062 General medical & surgical hospitals
CEO: Robert J Wentz
**COO:* Scott Chapple
**CFO:* Ashok Khanchandani
Chf Mktg O: Matthew Fine
Ofcr: David Bryning
Ofcr: Gil Zarate
VP: Carol S Smith
Dir Lab: Larry Kean
Dir Lab: Kim Taylor
Nurse Mgr: Robyn North
QA Dir: Debbie Jones

D-U-N-S 02-407-7364
ORR CORP
11601 Interchange Dr, Louisville, KY 40229-2159
Tel (502) 774-5791 *Founded/Ownrshp* 1947, 1973
Sales 195.0MM *EMP* 450
SIC 5084

D-U-N-S 55-572-4652 IMP/EXP
ORR SAFETY CORP
(*Suby of* ORR CORP) ★
11601 Interchange Dr, Louisville, KY 40229-2159
Tel (502) 774-5791 *Founded/Ownrshp* 1952
Sales 138.9MM *EMP* 300
SIC 5099 Safety equipment & supplies
CEO: Raymond Aldridge
**CFO:* Angela Druin
**Treas:* Clark Orr Jr
VP: Ted Buck
VP: Butch Haskins
VP: Paul Nelson
IT Man: Bob Neville
IT Man: Jonathan Nichter
S&M/VP: Jeff Sweedler
Manager: Jim Healy
Sls Mgr: Fred Bonn

D-U-N-S 07-187-0661
ORRICK HERRINGTON & SUTCLIFFE LLP
405 Howard St, San Francisco, CA 94105-2625
Tel (415) 773-5700 *Founded/Ownrshp* 2009
Sales 391.1MM[E] *EMP* 2,500[E]
SIC 8111 General practice law office
CEO: Ralph H Baxter Jr
Pt: Martin Bartlam
Pt: Neel Chatterjee
Pt: Luigi Colombo
Pt: Cameron L Cowan
Pt: Arno Frings
Pt: Norman C Hile
Pt: Karen G Johnson-Mckewan
Pt: J RG Ritter
Pt: Kai Tseng
Pt: Mark Weeks
Pt: Christoph Wetzler
Mng Pt: Christopher Stephens
CFO: Linda Havard
Top Exec: Deb Moore
VP: Angela Padilla

D-U-N-S 00-722-4256 IMP/EXP
■ ORS NASCO INC
(*Suby of* MICROUNITED DIVISION) ★
907 S Detroit Ave Ste 500, Tulsa, OK 74120-4283
Tel (918) 781-5300 *Founded/Ownrshp* 2007
Sales 332.4MM[E] *EMP* 440
SIC 5085 5084 Industrial supplies; Fasteners & fastening equipment; Industrial machinery & equipment; Petroleum industry machinery
Pr: Ric Phillips
**Ex VP:* Craig Loos
**VP:* Mike Denning
Area Mgr: Ben Brumfield
Area Mgr: Jason Hartman
Area Mgr: Ron Linsten
Brnch Mgr: Dean Fink
Brnch Mgr: Brian Grigor
Brnch Mgr: Mitch Sterling
QA Dir: Kendra Riley
VP Opers: Ors Nasco

D-U-N-S 02-991-8281 IMP
ORSCHELN FARM AND HOME LLC (MO)
ORSCHELN INDUSTRIES
1800 Overcenter Dr, Moberly, MO 65270-9466
Tel (800) 577-2580 *Founded/Ownrshp* 1960, 1963
Sales 642.3MM[E] *EMP* 2,475
SIC 5251 5999 5945 5731 Hardware; Farm equipment & supplies; Toys & games; Consumer electronic equipment
CEO: Barry L Orscheln
**Pr:* Stephen Chick
**VP:* James L O'Loughlin
**VP:* Barbara Westhues
Dir Bus: Kristee Ornburn
Genl Mgr: Carol Craig
Store Mgr: Terry Eighmy
IT Man: Kerry Gettemeier
IT Man: Michael Tilton
Sls Mgr: Rick Trowman

ORSCHELN INDUSTRIES
See ORSCHELN FARM AND HOME LLC

D-U-N-S 06-871-5424 IMP
ORTHO-CLINICAL DIAGNOSTICS INC
1001 Us Highway 202, Raritan, NJ 08869-1424
Tel (908) 218-8000 *Founded/Ownrshp* 2014
Sales 1.0MMM[E] *EMP* 1,650
SIC 2835 2834 Blood derivative diagnostic agents; Pharmaceutical preparations
Ch Bd: Dr Martin D Madaus
COO: Robert Yates
CFO: Joseph Bondi
Ofcr: Judith Fernandez
VP: Michael Davidson
VP: Jim Haney
VP: Charles Hartwig
VP: Holly Hillberg
VP: Tony Zazo
Genl Mgr: John Rich
Mtls Mgr: Dave Orchard

D-U-N-S 92-708-3808 IMP
ORTHOFIX INC
3451 Plano Pkwy, Lewisville, TX 75056-9453
Tel (214) 937-2000 *Founded/Ownrshp* 1996
Sales 167.2MM[E] *EMP* 525[E]
SIC 3841 Surgical & medical instruments; Medical instruments & equipment, blood & bone work
Prin: Alan Milinazzo
**CFO:* Emily Buxton
Ofcr: Jill Mason
Ofcr: Denise Pedulla
Ex VP: Vicente Trelles
Sr VP: Steve Martin
VP: Brent Alldredge
VP: Cory Brenner
Dist Mgr: Christopher Schaffer
Web Dev: Jason Allen
Mktg Dir: Terrence Wright

D-U-N-S 36-301-7070
ORTHOPAEDIC & NEUROLOGICAL REHABILITATION SPEECH PATHOLOGY INC
O N R
1101 S Cpitl Of Texas Hwy, West Lake Hills, TX 78746-6445
Tel (512) 327-4444 *Founded/Ownrshp* 1988
Sales 47.9MM[E] *EMP* 1,400
Accts Crawford Pimentel & Co Inc
SIC 8049 Occupational therapist; Physical therapist; Speech specialist; Audiologist
CEO: Jill Capela
**CFO:* Janis Jones
CFO: Michael Moulton
Ofcr: Julie Rettberg
Exec: Mary Mikhail
Ex Dir: Krista Cardenas
Area Mgr: Jenn Groen
Netwrk Mgr: Adam Johnson
Mktg Dir: Michael Raffee
Mktg Dir: Venus Vidaurri
Phys Thrpy: Rama Bowen

ORTHOPEDIC DEPARTMENT
See TULANE UNIVERSITY HOSPITAL AND CLINIC

D-U-N-S 84-900-4726
■ ORTHOPEDIC HOSPITAL LTD
TEXAS ORTHOPEDIC HOSPITAL
(*Suby of* HOSPITAL COPORATION OF AMERICA) ★
7401 Main St, Houston, TX 77030-4509
Tel (713) 799-8600 *Founded/Ownrshp* 1995
Sales 142.3MM *EMP* 230
SIC 8069 Orthopedic hospital
CEO: R Trent Lind
Genl Pt: Alice Adams
Pr: G William Woods M D
Bd of Dir: Santana Dotson
Dir Teleco: Mark Schlichter
Dir Lab: Barbara Powell
Prin: David P Loncarich
Prin: Gary McGuire
Dir Sec: Michael Chadwick
Telecom Ex: Cherri Perry
CTO: Mark Schlicher

D-U-N-S 61-094-9195
ORTHOPEDIC SURGERY CENTER L P
SOUTH EASTERN ORTHAPEDIC CTR
210 E Derenne Ave, Savannah, GA 31405-6736
Tel (912) 644-5300 *Founded/Ownrshp* 1999
Sales 87.5MM[E] *EMP* 1,000
SIC 8011 Clinic, operated by physicians
CEO: Michael Kleinpeter
CFO: Mike Hester
Off Mgr: Reagan Owens
Off Mgr: Tricia Stephen
Off Admin: Jessica Green
Doctor: Jay A Chmpion
Doctor: Bradley A Heiges
Doctor: Sidney Morgan
Doctor: Benjamin D Sutker

D-U-N-S 00-207-5539 IMP/EXP
ORVIS CO INC (VT)
ORVIS SPORTING TRADITIONS
178 Conservation Way, Sunderland, VT 05250-4465
Tel (802) 362-3622 *Founded/Ownrshp* 1856, 1964
Sales 197.0MM *EMP* 960
SIC 5961 5941 3949

ORVIS SPORTING TRADITIONS
See ORVIS CO INC

D-U-N-S 11-345-5823
■ OS PRIME INC
ROY'S
(*Suby of* OUTBACK STEAKHOUSE) ★
2202 N West Shore Blvd # 50, Tampa, FL 33607-5747
Tel (813) 282-1225 *Founded/Ownrshp* 2000
Sales 24.2MM[E] *EMP* 1,125
SIC 5812 Eating places
Ch Bd: Chris Sullivan
**Pr:* Paul Avery
**VP:* Tim Gannon

OSAGE CASINOS
See OSAGE NATION GAMING ENTERPRISE

D-U-N-S 07-949-0235
OSAGE NATION GAMING ENTERPRISE
OSAGE CASINOS
1121 W 36th St, Tulsa, OK 74127
Tel (918) 699-7710 *Founded/Ownrshp* 2014
Sales 29.7MM[E] *EMP* 1,171
SIC 7999 Gambling establishment
CEO: Neal Cornelius
**COO:* Joe Olujic
**CFO:* Richard Lobdell

D-U-N-S 78-812-3552
OSBURN CONTRACTORS INC
2747 Oakland Ave Ste A, Garland, TX 75041-3926
Tel (972) 205-9086 *Founded/Ownrshp* 1992
Sales 158.5MM[E] *EMP* 900
SIC 1771 Concrete work
CEO: Dave Osburn
Pr: Victor Marshal
CFO: Eric Cooley

D-U-N-S 06-835-3908 IMP
OSC SPORTS INC
OLYMPIA SPORTS
5 Bradley Dr, Westbrook, ME 04092-2013
Tel (207) 854-2794 *Founded/Ownrshp* 1975
Sales 200.0MM *EMP* 2,000
Accts Baker Newman Noyes Portland
SIC 5699 5661 5941 Sports apparel; Footwear, athletic; Sporting goods & bicycle shops
Ch Bd: Edward Manganello
**Pr:* Richard Coffey
**CFO:* John Lesniak

OSCA-ARCOSA
See O & S CALIFORNIA INC

D-U-N-S 07-100-7918 IMP
OSCAR DE LA RENTA LLC
11 W 42nd St Fl 24, New York, NY 10036-8002
Tel (212) 282-0500 *Founded/Ownrshp* 1974
Sales 120.9MM *EMP* 250
Accts Mayer Hoffman Mccann Cpas New
SIC 5137 Women's & children's accessories
CEO: Alexander L Bolen
**CFO:* Giuseppe Celio
Ex VP: Erica Bearman
Ex VP: Eliza Bolen
VP: Michele Bourbon
VP: Melissa L Cobb
VP: Claudine Jorgensen
VP: Robert Kogan
VP: Daniel Lawler
VP: Rosanna Miniaci
VP: Lisa Treiber
Creative D: Peter Copping

D-U-N-S 06-014-9218
OSCAR RENDA CONTRACTING INC
608 Henrietta Creek Rd, Roanoke, TX 76262-6339
Tel (817) 491-2703 *Founded/Ownrshp* 1974
Sales 122.0MM[E] *EMP* 248[E]
Accts Milbern Ray And Company Grap
SIC 1623 1799 1622 Water main construction; Sewer line construction; Pumping station construction; Exterior cleaning, including sandblasting; Tunnel construction
Pr: Oscar Renda
**CFO:* Corey Wells
**VP:* Frank Renda

D-U-N-S 01-648-2911 IMP/EXP
OSCAR WINSKI CO INC
LAFAYETTE STEEL AND ALUM SLS
2407 N 9th Street Rd, Lafayette, IN 47904-1047
Tel (765) 742-1102 *Founded/Ownrshp* 1985
Sales 127.5MM[E] *EMP* 200
SIC 5051 5093 Steel; Metal scrap & waste materials
CEO: Michael J Bluestein
**Ex VP:* Roger Carnes
**Sr VP:* Steve Bluestein
VP Admn: Jim Bronchik
Genl Mgr: Ron Addaman
Genl Mgr: Oscar Winski
Sfty Dirs: Daniel Fay
Sls Mgr: Alex Bluestein

D-U-N-S 01-831-2114
OSCEOLA COUNTY SCHOOL BOARD (FL)
817 Bill Beck Blvd, Kissimmee, FL 34744-4495
Tel (407) 870-4600 *Founded/Ownrshp* 2010
Sales 527.0MM *EMP* 6[E]
Accts Moore Stephens Lovelace Pa C
SIC 8211 School board
Ch: Tim Weisheyer

D-U-N-S 00-412-3121 IMP
OSCEOLA FARMS CO (FL)
(*Suby of* FANJUL CORP) ★
340 Royal Poinciana Way # 315, Palm Beach, FL 33480-4048
Tel (561) 655-6303 *Founded/Ownrshp* 1960
Sales 192.3MM[E] *EMP* 1,631
SIC 2099 Sugar grinding
Ch Bd: Alfonso Fanjul Jr
**Pr:* Jose Fanjul
**VP:* Donald W Carson

D-U-N-S 03-278-1837
OSCEOLAK12FL
SCHOOL DST OF OSCEOLA CNTY FLA
817 Bill Beck Blvd, Kissimmee, FL 34744-4492
Tel (407) 870-4630 *Founded/Ownrshp* 2011
Sales 159.7MM[E] *EMP* 4,749[E]
SIC 8211 Elementary school
Prin: Mark Munas

OSCO DRUG
See AMERICAN DRUG STORES LLC

D-U-N-S 02-525-2263
OSCO INC (IL)
OSCO OIL
13351 Main St, Lemont, IL 60439-9374
Tel (630) 257-8000 *Founded/Ownrshp* 1920, 1953
Sales 112.6MM[E] *EMP* 50
SIC 5172 Petroleum products; Diesel fuel; Gasoline; Service station supplies, petroleum
Pr: Maureen B McGovern
**Pr:* John P Mc Govern
Genl Mgr: Mark Domeier

D-U-N-S 00-428-0947 EXP
OSCO INDUSTRIES INC (OH)
PORTSMOUTH DIVISION
734 11th St, Portsmouth, OH 45662-3407
Tel (740) 354-3183 *Founded/Ownrshp* 1872, 1942
Sales 97.3MM[E] *EMP* 440
Accts Kelley Galloway Smith Goolsby
SIC 3321 Gray & ductile iron foundries; Gray iron castings
Ch Bd: William J Burke
**Pr:* John M Burke
**Sr VP:* Jeffrey A Burke
**VP:* Keith Denny
**VP:* Philip L Vetter

OSCO OIL
See OSCO INC

D-U-N-S 06-741-4946
OSF HEALTHCARE SYSTEM
(*Suby of* SISTERS OF THIRD ORDER OF ST FRANCIS) ★
800 Ne Glen Oak Ave, Peoria, IL 61603-3200
Tel (309) 655-2850 *Founded/Ownrshp* 2001
Sales 86.1MM *EMP* 4,000
Accts Kpmg Llp Columbus Oh
SIC 8062 8051 Hospital, medical school affiliated with nursing & residency; Extended care facility
CEO: Kevin Schoeplein
Dir Vol: Victoria Hennenfent
COO: Suzanne Hinderliter
CFO: Emiel Michelet
Exec: Mary Boudreau
Exec: Joseph Piccione
Exec: Bill Swearinger
Ex Dir: Jim Brace
Ex Dir: Gordon Wesner
CIO: Rich Johnson
MIS Dir: Jeff Martin
Board of Directors: Sister Judith Ann Duvall, R N

D-U-N-S 06-525-2405
OSF INTERNATIONAL INC
OLD SPAGHETTI FACTORY
0715 Sw Bancroft St, Portland, OR 97239-4273
Tel (503) 222-5375 *Founded/Ownrshp* 1969
Sales 142.1MM[E] *EMP* 3,700
SIC 5812 6794 Italian restaurant; Franchises, selling or licensing
Pr: Chris Dussin
COO: Mark Roark
CFO: Theresa Stempel
Ex VP: Dean Griffith
**VP:* Sally Dussin
Genl Mgr: Tom Cantor
Genl Mgr: Jason Davis
Genl Mgr: Patrick Evans
Genl Mgr: Brett Lindquist
Genl Mgr: John Maurice
Dir IT: Fred Anderson

D-U-N-S 05-377-3255
OSF SAINT FRANCIS MEDICAL CENTER
530 Ne Glen Oak Ave, Peoria, IL 61637-0001
Tel (309) 655-2000 *Founded/Ownrshp* 1880
Sales 836.1MM[E] *EMP* 14,000
SIC 8011 Medical centers
Pr: Michael Cruz
**CFO:* Ken Harbaugh

D-U-N-S 61-032-1221
OSF ST JOSEPH MEDICAL CENTER BLOOMINGTON
2200 E Washington St, Bloomington, IL 61701-4364
Tel (309) 662-3311 *Founded/Ownrshp* 1880
Sales 72.3MM[E] *EMP* 1,000[E]
SIC 8011 Medical centers
CEO: James Moore
**Pr:* Sister Diane Mureen
**Pr:* Kenneth Natzke
**COO:* Larry E Wills
Dir Rx: Michael Novario

D-U-N-S 61-276-0959
OSH 1 LIQUIDATING CORP
6450 Via Del Oro, San Jose, CA 95119-1208
Tel (408) 281-3500 *Founded/Ownrshp* 2013
Sales NA *EMP* 5,329
SIC 5251

D-U-N-S 08-047-8782
OSHAUGHNESSY REALTY CO INC
PRUDENTIAL
4024 Salt Pointe Pkwy, Charleston, SC 29405-8419
Tel (843) 202-2016 *Founded/Ownrshp* 1976
Sales 90.0MM *EMP* 30
SIC 6531 Real estate agent, residential
CEO: Patricia Scarafile
**Ch Bd:* Michael Oshaughnessy
**V Ch:* Grange Cuthbert
CFO: Walton Orvin
VP: Ross Rhudy
Ex Dir: Tom Daniel
Dir IT: Les Sease

D-U-N-S 02-111-4251
OSHKOSH AREA SCHOOL DISTRICT
215 S Eagle St, Oshkosh, WI 54902-5624
Tel (920) 424-0160 *Founded/Ownrshp* 1890
Sales 78.1MM[E] *EMP* 1,279
SIC 8211 Public elementary & secondary schools
**Pr:* Matthew Wiedenhoeft
**Treas:* Allison Garner
Treas: Kelly Olmsted
**VP:* Steve Dedow
Dir Sec: Tim Fox
Software D: Craig Schlieve
Pr Dir: Lori Miron

D-U-N-S 00-607-0445
▲ OSHKOSH CORP (WI)
2307 Oregon St, Oshkosh, WI 54902-7062
Tel (920) 235-9151 *Founded/Ownrshp* 1917
Sales 6.2MMM *EMP* 13,800
Accts Deloitte & Touche Llp Milwauk
Tkr Sym OSK *Exch* NYS
SIC 3711 3531 3715 Motor vehicles & car bodies; Military motor vehicle assembly; Fire department vehicles (motor vehicles), assembly of; Snow plows (motor vehicles), assembly of; Mixers, concrete; Truck trailers
Pr: Wilson R Jones
**Ch Bd:* Richard M Donnelly
Pr: James W Johnson
Pr: Bradley M Nelson
Pr: Frank R Nerenhausen
CFO: David M Sagehorn
Ofcr: Robert H Sims
Ex VP: Ignacio A Cortina
Ex VP: Joseph H Kimmitt
Ex VP: Mark M Radue
Sr VP: John J Bryant
Sr VP: Marek W May
Sr VP: Robert S Messina
Sr VP: Colleen R Moynihan
Board of Directors: Keith J Allman, Peter B Hamilton, Leslie F Kenne, Steven C Mizell, Stephen D Newlin, Craig P Omtvedt, Duncan J Palmer, John S Shiely, William S Wallace

D-U-N-S 07-946-7211
■ OSHKOSH DEFENSE LLC
(*Suby of* OSHKOSH CORP) ★
2307 Oregon St, Oshkosh, WI 54902-7062
Tel (920) 235-9151 *Founded/Ownrshp* 2014
Sales 650.9MM[E] *EMP* 2,100[E]
SIC 3711 3531 3715 Motor vehicles & car bodies; Military motor vehicle assembly; Fire department vehicles (motor vehicles), assembly of; Snow plows (motor vehicles), assembly of; Mixers, concrete; Truck trailers
CEO: Charles L Szews
**Pr:* Wilson R Jones
**CFO:* David M Sagehorn
**Ex VP:* Bryan J Blankfield
VP: Bill Mooney

OSI
See OAKLAND FOODS LLC

D-U-N-S 78-884-7148 IMP/EXP
OSI GROUP LLC
1225 Corp Blvd Ste 300, Aurora, IL 60505
Tel (630) 851-6600 *Founded/Ownrshp* 2001
Sales 2.6MMM[E] *EMP* 9,200[E]
SIC 2099 Food preparations
CEO: Sheldon Lavin
**Pr:* David G McDonald
**CFO:* Bill Weimer
CFO: William J Weimer Jr
VP: Paul Carlstrom
VP: Sherry Demeulenaerer
VP: Thomas Kotsovos
VP: Phil Pierchala
VP: Kevin Scott
Div Mgr: Jim Svajgl
Off Mgr: Pat Turner

D-U-N-S 02-562-6342 IMP/EXP
OSI INDUSTRIES LLC
OTTO & SONS DIV
(*Suby of* OSI GROUP LLC) ★
1225 Corp Blvd Ste 105, Aurora, IL 60505
Tel (630) 851-6600 *Founded/Ownrshp* 1918, 2004
Sales 1.5MMM[E] *EMP* 9,200
SIC 2099 Ready-to-eat meals, salads & sandwiches
CEO: Sheldon Lavin
VP: Michael Boccio
VP: Gerald Kolschowsky
QI Cn Mgr: Laurel Stoltzner

D-U-N-S 61-277-0974 IMP
■ OSI OPTOELECTRONICS INC
UNITED DETECTOR TECHNOLOGY
(*Suby of* OSI SYSTEMS INC) ★
12525 Chadron Ave, Hawthorne, CA 90250-4807
Tel (310) 978-0516 *Founded/Ownrshp* 1967
Sales 96.5MM[E] *EMP* 1,205[E]
SIC 3674 3827 3812 3672

D-U-N-S 62-810-7245 IMP/EXP
■ OSI RESTAURANT PARTNERS LLC
OUTBACK STEAKHOUSE
(*Suby of* OUTBACK STEAKHOUSE) ★
2202 N West Shore Blvd # 5, Tampa, FL 33607-5754
Tel (813) 282-1225 *Founded/Ownrshp* 2007
Sales 2.5MMM^E *EMP* 85,000^E
SIC 5812 5813 Steak restaurant; Grills (eating places); Seafood restaurants; Wine bar
Pr: Jeff Smith
CFO: David J Deno
CFO: James Tipps
Ofcr: Jody L Bilney
Ofcr: Tanita Brooks
Ofcr: Dirk A Montgomery
Ex VP: Joseph J Kadow
Ex VP: Richard L Renninger
Sr VP: Richard Renninger
Sr VP: Kaelyn Tomaszewski
VP: Trudy Cooper
VP: Chris Olson
VP: Jayne Portnoy
Board of Directors: Andrew B Balson, Robert D Basham, J Michael Chu, Philip H Loughlin, Mark E Nunnelly, Chris T Sullivan, Mark A Verdi

OSI SOFTWARE
See OSISOFT LLC

D-U-N-S 17-829-5812
▲ OSI SYSTEMS INC
12525 Chadron Ave, Hawthorne, CA 90250-4807
Tel (310) 978-0516 *Founded/Ownrshp* 1987
Sales 829.6MM *EMP* 5,810
Tkr Sym OSIS *Exch* NGS
SIC 3674 3845 Semiconductors & related devices; Photoconductive cells; Photoelectric cells, solid state (electronic eye); Electromedical equipment; Ultrasonic scanning devices, medical
Ch Bd: Deepak Chopra
Pr: Pak Chin
Pr: Manoocher Mansouri
CFO: Alan Edrick
Ofcr: Rick Merritt
**Ex VP:* Ajay Mehra
Ex VP: Victor Sze
Ex VP: Victor S Sze
VP: Ghazi Kashmolah
VP: Mark Loman
CTO: Andreas Kotowski
Board of Directors: William F Ballhaus Jr, David T Feinberg, Steven C Good, James B Hawkins, Meyer Luskin

D-U-N-S 04-494-6382 IMP
OSISOFT LLC
OSI SOFTWARE
1600 Alvarado St, San Leandro, CA 94577-2600
Tel (510) 297-5800 *Founded/Ownrshp* 1980
Sales 297.8MM^E *EMP* 900
SIC 7372 7371 7373 Application computer software; Custom computer programming services; Computer integrated systems design
Ch Bd: Dr J Patrick Kennedy
**Pr:* Jenny Linton
**COO:* Susanna Kass
**CFO:* Bob Guilbault
Ofcr: Gary Zies S
**Sr VP:* Martin Otterson
VP: Maureen Coveney
**VP:* Mike Kennedy
VP: John Oshea
VP: Don Smith
Exec: Osvaldo Basur
Exec: Mike Ellis
Exec: Marc Gallant
**Co-Founder:* Richard A Sara
Board of Directors: Ben Kortland, Jake Reynolds, Eric Streed

D-U-N-S 04-725-0444 IMP
OSMONICS INC
OSMONICS MINNETONKA OPERATIONS
5951 Clearwater Dr, Hopkins, MN 55343-8995
Tel (952) 933-2277 *Founded/Ownrshp* 1969
Sales 207.4MM *EMP* 1,318
SIC 3569 3589 3561 3824 3823 3089 Filters; Sewage & water treatment equipment; Water treatment equipment, industrial; Pumps & pumping equipment; Integrating & totalizing meters for gas & liquids; Industrial flow & liquid measuring instruments; Flow instruments, industrial process type; Fluidic devices, circuits & systems for process control; Plastic hardware & building products
Ch Bd: D Dean Spatz
Pr: Edward J Fierko
CFO: Keith B Robinson
Bd of Dir: Ralph Crump
Bd of Dir: William Eykamp
Bd of Dir: Wil Pergande
Bd of Dir: Verity Smith
Bd of Dir: Michael Snow
Sr VP: Roger S Miller
VP: Emanuel Amato
VP: Lee Comb
VP: Howard Dicke
VP: Bjarne Nicholaisen
VP: Bjarne N Nicolaisen
Div/Sub He: Michael Fabich
Div/Sub He: Clifford Frith
Div/Sub He: Patrick Kelly
Div/Sub He: Kurt Weintauer
Div/Sub He: Kurt Weitnauer
Board of Directors: Charles M Brennan, Ralph E Crump, William Eykamp, Charles W Palmer, Verity C Smith

OSMONICS MINNETONKA OPERATIONS
See OSMONICS INC

D-U-N-S 12-850-9804 IMP/EXP
■ OSMOSE HOLDINGS INC
(*Suby of* OAKTREE CAPITAL MANAGEMENT LP) ★
2475 George Urban Blvd # 160, Depew, NY 14043-2022
Tel (716) 882-5905 *Founded/Ownrshp* 2012
Sales 228.8MM^E *EMP* 1,335
SIC 2491 Preserving (creosoting) of wood
Pr: James R Spengler Jr
**CFO:* Michael R Leach
**VP:* David L Bradley
VP: Jim McGiffert
Dist Mgr: Joe Dobyns
CTO: Joseph Jeffries
IT Man: Walter Jaworski
Opers Mgr: Christopher Macauley

D-U-N-S 12-851-0141
OSMOSE UTILITIES SERVICES INC
635 Highway 74 S, Peachtree City, GA 30269-3003
Tel (770) 632-6700 *Founded/Ownrshp* 1934
Sales 270.0MM *EMP* 1,000^E
SIC 8741 8711 1623 Industrial management; Engineering services; Communication line & transmission tower construction
Pr: Ron Childress
**CFO:* Gary Edwards
VP: Joe Zamborsky
VP: Rich Ziobro
Opers Mgr: Toby Spelling
Mktg Mgr: Lauren Glass

D-U-N-S 82-697-7121 IMP
■ OSO BIOPHARMACEUTICAL MANUFACTURING LLC
(*Suby of* ALO ACQUISITION LLC) ★
4401 Alexander Blvd Ne, Albuquerque, NM 87107-6804
Tel (505) 923-1500 *Founded/Ownrshp* 1984
Sales 116.4MM^E *EMP* 335^E
SIC 2834 Pharmaceutical preparations
Pr: Milton Boyer
**CFO:* Julie Miner
Ex VP: Rick Lapointe

D-U-N-S 92-655-2688
OSPREY RIDGE HEALTHCARE CENTER INC
PHOENIX HEALTHCARE GROUP
45 N Scott St, Carbondale, PA 18407-1833
Tel (570) 282-1099 *Founded/Ownrshp* 1996
Sales 631.1MM *EMP* 105
SIC 8051 8052 Skilled nursing care facilities; Intermediate care facilities
Pr: Gregory J Salko MD

D-U-N-S 03-174-6456 IMP/EXP
OSRAM SYLVANIA INC
(*Suby of* OSRAM LICHT AG)
200 Ballardvale St # 305, Wilmington, MA 01887-1075
Tel (978) 570-3000 *Founded/Ownrshp* 1958, 2013
Sales 2.6MMM^E *EMP* 7,400
SIC 3646 3641 3647 3643 3297 Commercial indusl & institutional electric lighting fixtures; Electric lamps; Headlights (fixtures), vehicular; Current-carrying wiring devices; Crucibles: graphite, magnesite, chrome, silica, etc.
Pr: Richard Leaman
COO: William Moore
COO: Nick Papathanasiou
CFO: Martin Goetzler
Bd of Dir: Charlie Jerabek
Ex VP: Ashel Parmelee
Sr VP: Joerg Ayrle
Sr VP: Jeff Hunt
VP: Scott Butler
VP: Mark Corcoran
VP: James Gass
VP: Christoph Kreutner
VP: Jane Running
VP: William Schwidder
VP: James Scott
VP Bus Dev: Debra Powers
Assoc Dir: Chuck McMahon
Assoc Dir: Don Varley

OSSA
See OLYMPUS SCIENTIFIC SOLUTIONS AMERICAS CORP

OSSEO AREA PUBLIC SCHOOLS
See INDEPENDENT SCHOOL DISTRICT 279

D-U-N-S 09-384-0403
OSSINING UNION FREE SCHOOL DISTRICT
400 Executive Blvd, Ossining, NY 10562-2559
Tel (914) 941-7700 *Founded/Ownrshp* 1900
Sales 124.8MM *EMP* 750
SIC 8211 Public senior high school; Public junior high school; Public elementary school; Kindergarten
Bd of Dir: Nicole Reis
Schl Brd P: Bill Kress
Teacher Pr: Joan Garone

D-U-N-S 13-928-0028 IMP/EXP
OSSUR AMERICAS INC
(*Suby of* OSSUR HF.)
27051 Towne Centre Dr, Foothill Ranch, CA 92610-2819
Tel (949) 362-3883 *Founded/Ownrshp* 1984
Sales 115.6MM^E *EMP* 500^E
SIC 3842 Orthopedic appliances
CEO: Mahesh Mansukhani
**CFO:* Avanindra Chaturvedi
VP: Egill Jonsson
VP: David McGill
VP: Lou Ruggiero
IT Man: Diane Choi
Sls Mgr: Chris Watson

D-U-N-S 60-641-7780
OSTEOMED LLC
(*Suby of* COLSON ASSOCIATES INC) ★
3885 Arapaho Rd, Addison, TX 75001-4314
Tel (972) 677-4600 *Founded/Ownrshp* 2002
Sales 86.2MM^E *EMP* 250
SIC 3841 Surgical instruments & apparatus
Pr: Walter J Humann
VP: David Kelly
Exec: Katie Hancock
Genl Mgr: Harla Hawkins
Dir IT: Robert Astone
IT Man: Vickie Thompson
VP Mktg: Toby Miles
Sls Mgr: David Maberry
Sls Mgr: Andy Schmitt

D-U-N-S 06-035-6540 IMP/EXP
OSTERMAN & CO INC
OSTERMAN TRADING DIV
726 S Main St, Cheshire, CT 06410-3472
Tel (203) 272-2233 *Founded/Ownrshp* 1976
Sales 342.9MM^E *EMP* 98
SIC 5162 Plastics materials
Ch Bd: James O Dwyer
**Pr:* John Dwyer
**Treas:* Jennifer Vestergaard
**Ex VP:* Jeff Elsen
**Ex VP:* Glenn Fredericks
**VP:* Mike Sentelik

OSTERMAN TRADING DIV
See OSTERMAN & CO INC

D-U-N-S 55-582-9725 IMP/EXP
OSULLIVAN FILMS INC
(*Suby of* KONRAD HORNSCHUCH INTERNATIONAL GMBH)
1944 Valley Ave, Winchester, VA 22601-6306
Tel (540) 667-6666 *Founded/Ownrshp* 2006
Sales 107.7MM *EMP* 521
SIC 3081 Vinyl film & sheet
CEO: Denis Belzile
**Pr:* Ewen Campbell
**CFO:* Ronald G Shade
VP: Paul Nicolai
**VP:* Dennis Ruen
Dir Lab: John Duncan
Genl Mgr: Eric Buchanan
DP Exec: Bartley Drew
QA Dir: Martha Jenkins
QA Dir: Rick Lineberg
Dir IT: Dennis Painter

OSWALD COMPANIES, THE
See JAMES B OSWALD CO

D-U-N-S 01-077-2630
OSWEGO HOSPITAL INC
110 W 6th St, Oswego, NY 13126-2598
Tel (315) 349-5511 *Founded/Ownrshp* 1881
Sales 102.8MM *EMP* 1,200
Accts Fust Charles Chambers Llp Syr
SIC 8062 8063 General medical & surgical hospitals; Hospital for the mentally ill
CEO: Charles Gijanto
Dir Vol: Sara Weigelt
Pr: Margaret Glass
**CFO:* Eric Campbell
VP: Allison Duggan
Off Admin: Debra Littlefield
CIO: David Frasier
Software D: Mary Bucher
Software D: Jane Nalle
Software D: Katie Pagliaroli
Doctor: Jeffery Bogart

D-U-N-S 03-182-8783
OTAK INC
808 Sw 3rd Ave Ste 220, Portland, OR 97204-2439
Tel (503) 274-5445 *Founded/Ownrshp* 1981
Sales 101.0MM^E *EMP* 269
SIC 0781 8712 8711 8713 8742 8999 Landscape services; Architectural services; Civil engineering; Surveying services; Management consulting services; Earth science services
CEO: James Hamann
**CFO:* Dave Johnson
**Prin:* Don Hanson
**Prin:* Mike Peebles
**Prin:* Nico Vanderhorst

D-U-N-S 07-872-6031
OTAY WATER DISTRICT (INC) (CA)
2554 Swetwater Sprng Blvd, Spring Valley, CA 91978-2096
Tel (619) 670-2222 *Founded/Ownrshp* 1956
Sales 83.8MM *EMP* 170
Accts Teaman Ramirez & Smith Inc
SIC 4941 1623 Water supply; Water, sewer & utility lines
Pr: Gary Croucher
**Pr:* Jose Lopez
**CFO:* Joseph R Beachem
Exec: Armando Buelna
**Genl Mgr:* Mark Watton
CIO: Oscar Ramirez
CIO: Geoff Stevens

D-U-N-S 96-343-0850
OTB ACQUISITION LLC
ON THE BORDER
2201 W Royal Ln Ste 240, Irving, TX 75063-3208
Tel (972) 499-3000 *Founded/Ownrshp* 2010
Sales 346.0MM^E *EMP* 8,000^E
SIC 5812 Mexican restaurant
CFO: Gary Harper

D-U-N-S 79-989-3370 IMP/EXP
■ OTC DIRECT INC
ORIENTAL TRADING COMPANY
(*Suby of* ORIENTAL TRADING CO INC) ★
4206 S 108th St, Omaha, NE 68137-1215
Tel (402) 331-5511 *Founded/Ownrshp* 2011
Sales 117.1MM^E *EMP* 1,000
SIC 5961 Catalog & mail-order houses
Pr: Sam S Taylor
**Pr:* Stephen R Frary
**Treas:* Steve Mendlik
VP: Chris Merritt
IT Man: Kim Lamb
Secur Mgr: Thomas E Jones

OTC INTERNATIONAL
See ANAYA GEMS INC

D-U-N-S 07-843-4220
■ OTC WORLDWIDE HOLDINGS INC
(*Suby of* BERKSHIRE HATHAWAY INC) ★
4206 S 108th St, Omaha, NE 68137-1215
Tel (800) 348-6483 *Founded/Ownrshp* 2011
Sales 923.5MM^E *EMP* 1,010^E
SIC 4813
CEO: Sam Taylor

D-U-N-S 07-761-8023
OTERO COUNTY HOSPITAL ASSOCIATION INC
GERALD CHMPN REGIONAL MED CTR
2669 Scenic Dr, Alamogordo, NM 88310-8700
Tel (575) 439-6100 *Founded/Ownrshp* 1948
Sales 122.3MM *EMP* 600^E
SIC 8062 General medical & surgical hospitals
CEO: Jim Heckert
Ofcr: Becky Roberts
VP: Martha Gorman
VP: Mary Harding
VP: Karen O'Brien
Dir Inf Cn: Bonnie Clements
Dir Lab: Vicki Leonard
Dir Lab: Rosemary Orr
Nurse Mgr: Lorena Stovell
CTO: Paul Martin
Sfty Dirs: Lori Haden

D-U-N-S 08-014-2618
OTG EXP INC
352 Park Ave S Fl 10, New York, NY 10010-1726
Tel (212) 776-1478 *Founded/Ownrshp* 1996
Sales 20.8MM^E *EMP* 4,400
SIC 5812 Eating places
Ch Bd: Eric J Blatstein
Pr: Brian Britton
CFO: Joseph G Ozalas
Ex VP: Christopher Redd

OTHER STYLES-SEE OPERATION
See P KAUFMANN INC

OTHER STYLES-SEE OPERATION
See COBORNS INC

D-U-N-S 05-181-3921
OTIS EASTERN SERVICE LLC
2971 Andover Rd, Wellsville, NY 14895-9536
Tel (585) 593-4760 *Founded/Ownrshp* 1936
Sales 225.1MM *EMP* 15
Accts Brock Schechter & Polakoff L
SIC 1623 1389 Oil & gas pipeline construction; Oil field services
Pr: Charles P Joyce
CFO: Steve Cummings
**VP:* Tony Deusenbery
**VP:* Richard Joyce

D-U-N-S 00-153-4676 IMP/EXP
■ OTIS ELEVATOR CO
COASTAL ELEVATOR SERVICE
(*Suby of* UNITED TECHNOLOGIES CORP) ★
10 Farm Springs Rd, Farmington, CT 06032-2577
Tel (860) 676-6000 *Founded/Ownrshp* 1976
Sales 11.3MMM^E *EMP* 63,000^E
SIC 3534 1796 7699 Elevators & equipment; Escalators, passenger & freight; Walkways, moving; Installing building equipment; Elevator installation & conversion; Miscellaneous building item repair services; Elevators: inspection, service & repair
Pr: Pedro S D BY Riva
**Pr:* Mario Abajo
**Pr:* Todd M Bluedorn
**Pr:* Bruno Grob
**Pr:* Angelo J Messina
CFO: Jeff Nelson
**Treas:* Christopher Witzky
**Sr VP:* Raymond J Moncini
VP: Ron Beaver
**VP:* Johan Bill
VP: Patrick Blethon
VP: Sandy Diehl
VP: Ted Fetterman
VP: Edward Fitch
VP: Vern Stait
Exec: John Arle
Exec: Jim Cherry
Exec: Tammi Girard
Exec: Jack Sede
Exec: Dave Tremaglio
Exec: Tom Wiafe

D-U-N-S 02-923-7179 IMP/EXP
OTIS MCALLISTER INC
300 Frank H Ogawa Plz # 400, Oakland, CA 94612-2037
Tel (415) 421-6010 *Founded/Ownrshp* 1892
Sales 84.5MM^E *EMP* 60
SIC 5149 5141 Canned goods: fruit, vegetables, seafood, meats, etc.; Groceries, general line
Ch Bd: Royce A Nicolaisen
**Pr:* Everett C Golden III
**CFO:* Robert Westerlund
**Ex Dir:* James Bailey
Dir IT: R Harris

OTIWTI
See QUALITROL CO LLC

OTP INDUSTRIAL SOLUTIONS
See OHIO TRANSMISSION CORP

D-U-N-S 07-929-4179
OTSEGO MEMORIAL HOSPITAL ASSOCIATION
825 N Center Ave, Gaylord, MI 49735-1592
Tel (989) 731-2100 *Founded/Ownrshp* 1946
Sales 87.4MM *EMP* 550
SIC 8062

D-U-N-S 60-711-1846 IMP/EXP
OTSUKA AMERICA INC
(*Suby of* OTSUKA PHARMACEUTICAL CO., LTD.)
1 Embarcadero Ctr # 2020, San Francisco, CA 94111-3750
Tel (415) 986-5300 *Founded/Ownrshp* 1989
Sales 586.7MM^E *EMP* 2,065
SIC 3829 3499 5122 2833 2084 2086 Spectrometers, liquid scintillation & nuclear; Magnets, permanent: metallic; Pharmaceuticals; Vitamins, natural or synthetic: bulk, uncompounded; Wines; Mineral water, carbonated: packaged in cans, bottles, etc.
Ch Bd: Hiromi Yoshikawa
**Pr:* Shun Uchida
Ofcr: Sheila Cleary
**VP:* William Mc Hale
VP: Robert Sedor

CTO: Ray Mullins
IT Man: Lori Holter

D-U-N-S 00-831-4390 IMP
OTSUKA AMERICA PHARMACEUTICAL INC
(*Suby of* OTSUKA AMERICA INC) ★
2440 Res Blvd Ste 500, Rockville, MD 20850
Tel (301) 990-0030 *Founded/Ownrshp* 1989
Sales 133.0MM^E^ *EMP* 631^E^
SIC 8733 8011 8731 Medical research; Offices & clinics of medical doctors; Commercial physical research
CEO: Hiromi Yoshikawa
**Treas:* Steve Cobourn
Ofcr: Hideji Nonomura
**VP:* Richard Obrig
**VP:* Terry Prime
VP: Raymond Tripp
Dir Surg: Frank Gray
Software D: Sherri Palumbo

D-U-N-S 07-834-7187
■ **OTTAWA ACQUISITION LLC**
(*Suby of* SOUTHERN CO GAS) ★
1844 W Ferry Rd, Naperville, IL 60563-9662
Tel (888) 642-6748 *Founded/Ownrshp* 2011
Sales 2.8MMM^E^ *EMP* 3,750^E^
SIC 4924 Natural gas distribution
Prin: Andrew W Evans

D-U-N-S 00-745-4929
OTTAWA COOPERATIVE ASSOCIATION INC
302 N Main St, Ottawa, KS 66067-1920
Tel (785) 242-5170 *Founded/Ownrshp* 1950
Sales 139.7MM *EMP* 42
SIC 5191 5171 5153 Feed; Seeds: field, garden & flower; Fertilizer & fertilizer materials; Petroleum bulk stations; Grain elevators
Genl Mgr: Adrian Derousseau
IT Man: Clark Wenger

OTTER BOX
See OTTER PRODUCTS LLC

D-U-N-S 04-813-4238 IMP
OTTER PRODUCTS LLC
OTTER BOX
209 S Meldrum St, Fort Collins, CO 80521-2603
Tel (970) 493-8446 *Founded/Ownrshp* 1998
Sales 347.5MM^E^ *EMP* 320^E^
SIC 3089 Plastic kitchenware, tableware & houseware
CEO: Jim Parke
**Ch Bd:* Curtis Richardson
**Pr:* Steve Nisbet
**Pr:* Brian Thomas
VP: Danyel Day
VP: Meghan Ledington
VP: Tary Mauk
VP: Athena Woods
Exec: Kati Jacobson
Dir Bus: Kyle Seaser
Snr Sftwr: Eric Blake

D-U-N-S 61-485-3609
OTTERTAIL AG ENTERPRISES LLC
24096 170th Ave, Fergus Falls, MN 56537-7518
Tel (218) 998-4301 *Founded/Ownrshp* 2008
Sales 95.9MM *EMP* 33
SIC 2869 Ethanolamines
CEO: Anthony Hicks
**Treas:* Hans Ronnevik
Prd Mgr: Keith Wetzel
Board of Directors: John Anderson, Philip Deal, Jonathan Piekarski, Hans Ronnevik, Gary Thompson, Ronald Tobkin

D-U-N-S 83-143-0322 IMP/EXP
▲ **OTTER TAIL CORP**
215 S Cascade St, Fergus Falls, MN 56537-2801
Tel (218) 739-8200 *Founded/Ownrshp* 1907
Sales 779.8MM *EMP* 651^E^
Tkr Sym OTTR *Exch* NGS
SIC 4911 3084 5047 2099 1731 Electric services; Plastics pipe; Medical & hospital equipment; Potatoes, dried: packaged with other ingredients; General electrical contractor
CEO: Charles S Macfarlane
**Ch Bd:* Nathan Partain
**Pr:* John Abbott
**CFO:* Kevin G Moug
**Sr VP:* George A Koeck
**Sr VP:* Timothy J Rogelstad
Sr VP: Shane Waslaski
VP Admn: Tom Brause
Board of Directors: Karen M Bohn, John Erickson, Steven L Fritze, Kathryn O Johnson, Timothy J O'-keefe, Joyce N Schuette, James B Stake

D-U-N-S 00-952-1043
■ **OTTER TAIL ENERGY SERVICES CO INC** (MN)
(*Suby of* OTTER TAIL CORP) ★
224 E Washington Ave, Fergus Falls, MN 56537-2812
Tel (218) 739-8888 *Founded/Ownrshp* 1997
Sales 1.0MMM^E^ *EMP* 900
SIC 4932 Gas & other services combined
Pr: Charles Macfarlane
**Treas:* Kevin G Mong

D-U-N-S 00-696-1353 IMP/EXP
■ **OTTER TAIL POWER CO** (MN)
(*Suby of* OTTER TAIL CORP) ★
215 S Cascade St, Fergus Falls, MN 56537-2897
Tel (218) 739-8200 *Founded/Ownrshp* 1907
Sales 779.7MM^E^ *EMP* 651^E^
SIC 4911 Electric services; Distribution, electric power; Generation, electric power; Transmission, electric power
CEO: Chuck Macfarlane
**Pr:* Timothy J Rogelstad
**CFO:* George D Bell
Sr VP: Ward L Uggerud
**VP:* Mark H Helland
VP: Marlowe Johnson
VP: Michael J Olsen
**VP Admn:* Thomas R Brause
Mng Dir: Brian Carlson
Netwrk Eng: Shane Wevley
VP Sls: Mike Olsen

D-U-N-S 11-621-4982
■ **OTTER TAIL POWER CO**
(*Suby of* OTTER TAIL CORP) ★
215 S Cascade St, Fergus Falls, MN 56537-2897
Tel (218) 739-8200 *Founded/Ownrshp* 1907
Sales 406.0MM^E^ *EMP* 339^E^
SIC 3699 4953 6531 Electrical welding equipment; Incinerator operation; Real estate agent, residential
CEO: Chuck Macfarland
**CEO:* Chuck Mac Farland
CFO: Kevin Moug
Bd of Dir: Nathan Partain
Bd of Dir: Robert Spolum
VP: Ron S Salisbury
Pr Dir: Kandace Olsen

OTTO & SONS DIV
See OSI INDUSTRIES LLC

D-U-N-S 01-033-2831 IMP
OTTO BOCK HEALTHCARE LP (MN)
(*Suby of* OTTO BOCK HEALTHCARE GMBH)
11501 Alterra Pkwy # 600, Austin, TX 78758-3597
Tel (800) 328-4058 *Founded/Ownrshp* 1958
Sales 116.7MM^E^ *EMP* 430
SIC 5047 Artificial limbs
CEO: Brad Ruhl
CFO: Rick Schmidt
**CFO:* Andreas Schultz
VP Mfg: John Hendrickson
Mktg Dir: Rod McCrimmon
Manager: Angi Danner

D-U-N-S 08-023-0550
OTTO BREMER FOUNDATION (MN)
30 7th St E Ste 2900, Saint Paul, MN 55101-2988
Tel (651) 227-8036 *Founded/Ownrshp* 1944
Sales 52.8MM *EMP* 1,800
Accts Deloitte Tax Llp Minneapolis
SIC 6732 6022 Trusts: educational, religious, etc.; State commercial banks
Trst: Charlotte Johnson
Ofcr: Diane Benjamin
Ofcr: Rose Carr
Ofcr: Kristine Kosek
Comm Dir: Christine Fuglestad
**Ex Dir:* Randi Ilyse Roth

OTTO CONSTRUCTION
See JOHN F OTTO INC

OTTO CONTROLS
See OTTO ENGINEERING INC

D-U-N-S 00-543-4170 IMP
OTTO ENGINEERING INC (IL)
OTTO CONTROLS
2 E Main St, Carpentersville, IL 60110-2624
Tel (847) 428-7171 *Founded/Ownrshp* 1961, 1964
Sales 100.0MM *EMP* 500
SIC 3643

D-U-N-S 07-934-7052
OTTO ENVIRONMENTAL SYSTEMS (NC) LLC
(*Suby of* OTTO INDUSTRIES NORTH AMERICA INC) ★
12700 General Dr, Charlotte, NC 28273-6415
Tel (704) 588-9191 *Founded/Ownrshp* 2003
Sales 158.6MM^E^ *EMP* 300
SIC 3537 Industrial trucks & tractors
CEO: Robert Engle
CFO: Anthony Todaro
Dir IT: Brandon Wright

D-U-N-S 10-834-3013 IMP/EXP
OTTO INDUSTRIES NORTH AMERICA INC
(*Suby of* INDUSTRIAL PARTICIPATIONS HOLDING B.V.)
12700 General Dr, Charlotte, NC 28273-6415
Tel (704) 588-9191 *Founded/Ownrshp* 1992
Sales 220.8MM^E^ *EMP* 350
SIC 3537 Industrial trucks & tractors
CEO: Robert Engle
**Pr:* Luc Mueller

OU MEDICAL CENTER
See HCA HEALTH SERVICES OF OKLAHOMA INC

OU MEDICAL CENTER
See EVERETT HOSPITAL

OUACHITA FERTILIZER CO DIV
See ABELL CORP

D-U-N-S 61-819-6026
OUACHITA PARISH SCHOOL SYSTEM
100 Bry St, Monroe, LA 71201-8406
Tel (318) 432-5000 *Founded/Ownrshp* 1896
Sales 225.2MM *EMP* 2,804
Accts Huffman & Soignier Monroe Lo
SIC 8211 Public elementary & secondary schools
Teacher Pr: Todd Guice
HC Dir: Kenneth Slusher

OUC
See ORLANDO UTILITIES COMMISSION

D-U-N-S 14-934-5840
OUR KIDS OF MIAMI-DADE/MONROE INC
401 Nw 2nd Ave Ste S212, Miami, FL 33128-1721
Tel (305) 455-6000 *Founded/Ownrshp* 2002
Sales 105.9MM *EMP* 60
Accts Verdeja De Armas & Trujillo Ll
SIC 8322 Child related social services
CEO: Fran Allegra
IT Man: Patrick Travers
Ql Cn Mgr: Andrea Mendez

OUR LADY BELLEFONTE HOSPITAL
See OUR LADY OF BELLEFONTE HOSPITAL INC

OUR LADY LAKE REGIONAL MED CTR
See OUR LADY OF LAKE HOSPITAL INC

D-U-N-S 09-977-0968
OUR LADY OF BELLEFONTE HOSPITAL INC
OUR LADY BELLEFONTE HOSPITAL
(*Suby of* BON SECOURS HEALTH SYSTEM INC) ★
1000 Saint Christopher Dr, Ashland, KY 41101-7071
Tel (606) 833-3333 *Founded/Ownrshp* 1988
Sales 156.3MM *EMP* 1,100
SIC 8062 8082 8011 5999 General medical & surgical hospitals; Home health care services; Medical centers; Medical apparatus & supplies
Pr: Thom Morris
**Treas:* Joe Buchheit
**Prin:* John Wallenhorst
VP Mktg: Wills Coburan
Ansthlgy: Virgio Hoback

D-U-N-S 96-593-1434
OUR LADY OF LAKE ASCENSION COMMUNITY HOSPITAL
ST ELIZABETH HOSPITAL
1125 W Highway 30, Gonzales, LA 70737-5004
Tel (225) 647-5000 *Founded/Ownrshp* 2010
Sales 87.9MM *EMP* 25^E^
Accts Kpmg Llp Baton Rouge La
SIC 8062 General medical & surgical hospitals
Prin: Dolores Lejeune

D-U-N-S 06-548-0121
OUR LADY OF LAKE HOSPITAL INC
OUR LADY LAKE REGIONAL MED CTR
(*Suby of* FMOL HEALTH SYSTEM) ★
5000 Hennessy Blvd, Baton Rouge, LA 70808-4367
Tel (225) 765-7709 *Founded/Ownrshp* 1923
Sales 984.6MM *EMP* 1,800^E^
SIC 8062 General medical & surgical hospitals
Pr: K Scott Wester
**Ch Bd:* Charles Valluzzo
CFO: Robert Ramsey
Ofcr: Scott Wester
Dir Rx: Jerry Langlos
Ex Dir: Karen Allen
Dir Sec: James Lewis
MIS Dir: Shannon Simpson
Doctor: Henry Eiserloh
Doctor: Thomas Mego
Pharmcst: Victoria Ngo

D-U-N-S 03-726-0775
OUR LADY OF LORDES REGIONAL MEDICAL CENTER INC
(*Suby of* FMOL HEALTH SYSTEM) ★
4801 Ambssdor Cffery Pkwy, Lafayette, LA 70508-6917
Tel (337) 289-2000 *Founded/Ownrshp* 1949
Sales 204.8MM *EMP* 1,800^E^
SIC 8011 8021 Gynecologist; Obstetrician; Offices & clinics of dentists
CEO: William F Barrow
**Ch:* Bryan Hanks
**Treas:* Mike Moncla
Dir Lab: Tim Touchet
**Prin:* Robert Peebles

D-U-N-S 80-789-4944
OUR LADY OF LOURDES HEALTH CARE SERVICES INC
CATHOLIC HEALTH EAST
(*Suby of* CATHOLIC HEALTH EAST) ★
1600 Haddon Ave, Camden, NJ 08103-3101
Tel (856) 757-3500 *Founded/Ownrshp* 1993
Sales 35.1MM *EMP* 3,500^E^
SIC 8741 Hospital management
Pr: Alexander J Hatala
**CFO:* Michael Hammond
**CFO:* Thomas J Regner

D-U-N-S 07-185-3519
OUR LADY OF LOURDES HOSPITAL AT PASCO
LOURDES HEALTH NETWORK
520 N 4th Ave, Pasco, WA 99301-5248
Tel (509) 547-7704 *Founded/Ownrshp* 1916
Sales 90.5MM *EMP* 633
Accts Deloitte Tax Llp Cincinnati
SIC 8062 8063 General medical & surgical hospitals; Psychiatric hospitals
CEO: John Serle
Bd of Dir: Ron Davis
Dir Lab: Jean Lewis
Ex Dir: Sam Crawford
Ex Dir: Esther Polacci
QA Dir: Anita Kongslie
IT Man: Tabitha Liebrecht
Mktg Dir: Melanie Johnston
Doctor: Laurie Zimmerman

D-U-N-S 07-145-7295
OUR LADY OF LOURDES MEDICAL CENTER INC
NEW JERSEY HEART INSTITUTE
(*Suby of* CATHOLIC HEALTH EAST) ★
1600 Haddon Ave, Camden, NJ 08103-3101
Tel (856) 757-3500 *Founded/Ownrshp* 1965
Sales 298.1MM *EMP* 3,000
SIC 8062 General medical & surgical hospitals
CEO: Alex Hatala
Dir Recs: Octavia Gaston
**COO:* Mark Nessel
**CFO:* Michael Hammond
VP: Kim Barnes
**VP:* Andrew Guarni
VP: Barbara Holfelner
VP: Alan Pope
VP: Maureen Shaughnessy
Exec: Tony Dicarlo
Dir Lab: Theresa Santoferrano

D-U-N-S 07-159-9021
OUR LADY OF LOURDES MEMORIAL HOSPITAL INC
LOURDES HOSPITAL
169 Riverside Dr, Binghamton, NY 13905-4198
Tel (607) 798-5111 *Founded/Ownrshp* 1969
Sales 160.7MM *EMP* 1,500
Accts P Deloitte Tax Llp Cincinnat
SIC 8062 General medical & surgical hospitals
Pr: David Patak
**Ch Bd:* Thomas J Oven
**CFO:* Michael Hammond
Sr VP: Linda Miller
Dir Inf Cn: Jill Patak
Chf Nrs Of: Audrey Jadczak
Prac Mgr: Felecia Wagstaff
Admn Mgr: Diane Brooks
Opers Mgr: Eric Skorupa
Opers Mgr: Jeffery Walburger
Orthpdst: Daniel P Federowicz

D-U-N-S 07-260-5439
OUR LADY OF LOURDES REGIONAL MEDICAL CENTER INC
FMOL HEALTH SYSTEM
(*Suby of* FMOL HEALTH SYSTEM) ★
4801 Ambssdor Cffery Pkwy, Lafayette, LA 70508-6917
Tel (337) 470-2000 *Founded/Ownrshp* 1949
Sales 197.1MM *EMP* 1,700
Accts Kpmg Llc Baton Rouge La
SIC 8062 General medical & surgical hospitals
Pr: William F Barrow
VP: Michelle Crain
Exec: Jennifer Trahan
Dir Risk M: Paula Jenkins
Dir QC: Monica Chiasson
Mtls Mgr: Kevin Bowen
Sfty Mgr: Donald Simon
Ansthlgy: Timothy D Faul

D-U-N-S 80-810-0130 IMP/EXP
OURAY SPORTSWEAR LLC
1201 W Mansfield Ave, Englewood, CO 80110-3453
Tel (303) 798-4035 *Founded/Ownrshp* 2007
Sales 98.0MM^E^ *EMP* 200
SIC 5091 Sporting & recreation goods; Skiing equipment
VP: Jon Boris
VP: Roger Landry
Sls Mgr: Jim Rogers

OUTAGAMIE COUNTY
See COUNTY OF OUTAGAMIE

OUTBACK STEAKHOUSE
See OSI RESTAURANT PARTNERS LLC

OUTBACK STEAKHOUSE
See BLOOMIN BRANDS INC

D-U-N-S 18-583-8968 IMP/EXP
■ **OUTBACK STEAKHOUSE OF FLORIDA LLC**
(*Suby of* OUTBACK STEAKHOUSE) ★
2202 N West Shore Blvd # 500, Tampa, FL 33607-5747
Tel (813) 282-1225 *Founded/Ownrshp* 1991
Sales 1.3MMM^E^ *EMP* 50,000
Accts Pricewater House Coopers Llp
SIC 5812 Steak restaurant
CEO: A William I Allen
**Pr:* Paul E Avery
**COO:* Robert Basham
**CFO:* Dirk A Montgomery
**Ex VP:* Joseph J Kadow
**Sr VP:* J T Gannon
Sr VP: Timothy Gannon
Sr VP: Nancy Scheid
VP: Pablo Brizi
**VP:* Stephen C Erickson

OUTDOOR CAP COMPANY
See OUTDOOR CAP CO INC

D-U-N-S 08-493-2573 IMP/EXP
OUTDOOR CAP CO INC
OUTDOOR CAP COMPANY
1200 Melissa Dr, Bentonville, AR 72712-6654
Tel (479) 273-3732 *Founded/Ownrshp* 1976
Sales 112.0MM^E^ *EMP* 224
SIC 5136 Caps, men's & boys'
Pr: Paul Mahan
**CFO:* Jerry House
**Treas:* Michael Hill
Ex VP: Thomas Frank
**Ex VP:* Jeremy Laney
**Ex VP:* Chris McConnell
**Ex VP:* Nicole Tillman
VP: Douglas Keiser
Dir Soc: Amanda Bernhagen
VP Opers: Peel Chronister
Prd Mgr: Jerry Chamberlain

D-U-N-S 60-821-2163
OUTDOOR CHANNEL HOLDINGS INC
(*Suby of* KROENKE SPORTS & ENTERTAINMENT) ★
1000 Chopper Cir, Denver, CO 80204-5805
Tel (951) 699-6991 *Founded/Ownrshp* 2013
Sales 127.8MM^E^ *EMP* 402
SIC 4841 4833 Direct broadcast satellite services (DBS); Television broadcasting stations
Pr: Jim Liberatore
V Ch: Thomas Massie
CFO: Thomas D Allen
Sr VP: Jason F Brist
Sr VP: Douglas J Langston
Ex Dir: Chris Cox
Board of Directors: Thomas Hornish

D-U-N-S 00-691-4253 IMP/EXP
■ **OUTDOOR SPORTS GEAR INC**
(*Suby of* NEWELL BRANDS) ★
2320 Cousteau Ct Ste 100, Vista, CA 92081-8363
Tel (914) 967-9400 *Founded/Ownrshp* 1946
Sales 2.5MMM^E^ *EMP* 5,000
SIC 3949 3069 2339 2329 Winter sports equipment; Snow skiing equipment & supplies, except skis; Fishing equipment; Life jackets, inflatable: rubberized fabric; Women's & misses' athletic clothing & sportswear; Jogging & warmup suits: women's, misses' & juniors'; Ski jackets & pants: women's, misses' & juniors'; Uniforms, athletic: women's, misses' & juniors'; Men's & boys' athletic uniforms; Men's & boys' sportswear & athletic clothing
CEO: Richard Sansone
Pt: Sandy Chavez
Pr: Timothy C Cronin
Pr: Jeff Larsen
Pr: Gary Remensnyder

CFO: Dudley Mendenhall
Treas: Kary Betro
Bd of Dir: Jerry E Goldress
Bd of Dir: Alfred Osborn
VP: D Herzberg
VP: David Herzberg
VP: Ian Kashton
VP: Sandy McElfresh
VP: Robert Totte

D-U-N-S 05-957-0937
OUTDOOR VENTURE CORP
30 Venture Dr, Stearns, KY 42647
Tel (606) 376-5021 *Founded/Ownrshp* 1972
Sales 140.0MM[E] *EMP* 1,439
SIC 2394 Tents: made from purchased materials
Pr: James Egnew
**VP:* Joe Fields
**VP:* Patty Kidd
**VP:* Lori Miller

OUTDOORSMAN, THE
See JEAN NELL ENTERPRISES INC

OUTERWALL
See COINSTAR LLC

D-U-N-S 07-888-0385
▲ **OUTFRONT MEDIA INC** (MD)
405 Lexington Ave Fl 17, New York, NY 10174-1801
Tel (212) 297-6400 *Founded/Ownrshp* 2013
Sales 1.5MMM *EMP* 2,581[E]
Tkr Sym OUT *Exch* NYS
SIC 7312 7319 6798 Outdoor advertising services; Billboard advertising; Poster advertising, outdoor; Display advertising service; Real estate investment trusts
Ch Bd: Jeremy J Male
CFO: Donald R Shassian
Treas: Jonathan Karabas
Chf Mktg O: Jodi Senese
Ofcr: Clive Punter
Ofcr: Nancy Tostanoski
Ex VP: Richard H Sauer
Ex VP: Richard Sauer
Ex VP: Andrew Sriubas
VP: Victor Gomez
VP: Peter Raulli
Board of Directors: William Apfelbaum, Nicolas Brien, Manuel A Diaz, Peter Mathes, Susan M Tolson, Joseph H Wender

D-U-N-S 04-681-2905 IMP
■ **OUTFRONT MEDIA LLC**
CBS OUTDOOR LLC
(*Suby of* OUTFRONT MEDIA INC) ★
405 Lexington Ave, New York, NY 10174-0002
Tel (212) 297-6400 *Founded/Ownrshp* 1999
Sales 78.0MM[E] *EMP* 2,100
SIC 7312 Outdoor advertising services; Billboard advertising
CEO: Jeremy J Male
**CFO:* Donald R Shassian
**Chf Mktg O:* Jodi Senese
**Ex VP:* Steve Hillwig
**Ex VP:* Clive Punter
**Ex VP:* Richard Sauer
**Ex VP:* Andrew R Sriubas
**Ex VP:* Nancy Tostanoski
VP: Michael Costello
Prd Mgr: Debbie Policastro

D-U-N-S 11-886-3604 IMP
OUTOKUMPU STAINLESS INC
(*Suby of* OUTOKUMPU STAINLESS AB)
2275 Half Day Rd Ste 300, Deerfield, IL 60015-1232
Tel (847) 317-1400 *Founded/Ownrshp* 2004
Sales 226.0MM[E] *EMP* 550
SIC 5051 Metals service centers & offices; Plates, metal; Sheets, metal; Strip, metal
Pr: Mats Norden
CFO: Kevin Keeley
Ex VP: Jarmo Tonteri
VP: Andy Personett
VP: Kari Tuutti
Genl Mgr: Tapani Eerikkila
Genl Mgr: Simon Jacobsen
Genl Mgr: Gunnar Meller
Dir IT: Peter Stromberg
VP Mktg: Mika Toikka
Mktg Dir: Doug Zimmerman

D-U-N-S 80-841-0349 IMP
OUTOKUMPU STAINLESS USA LLC
(*Suby of* OUTOKUMPU OYJ)
1 Steel Dr, Calvert, AL 36513
Tel (251) 829-3600 *Founded/Ownrshp* 2013
Sales 656.8MM[E] *EMP* 2,200
SIC 3312 3399 Stainless steel; Iron ore recovery from open hearth slag
CEO: Michael Wallis
**CFO:* Reinhard Florey
**VP:* Jose Ramon Salas
**VP Sls:* Stephan Lacor
S&M/VP: Mick Carnevale
Counsel: Robert Feldman

OUTPATENT CHEM DPNDNCY PROGRAM
See FAIRVIEW HEALTH SERVICES

OUTPATIENT CHEMICAL DEPENDENCY
See EBENEZER SOCIETY

OUTPATIENT PROGRAM
See ST MARYS MEDICAL CENTER

D-U-N-S 78-662-1391
OUTREACH HEALTH CARE INC
OUTREACH HEALTH SERVICES
(*Suby of* INTEGRACARE HOLDINGS INC) ★
269 W Renner Rd, Richardson, TX 75080-1300
Tel (972) 840-7360 *Founded/Ownrshp* 2011
Sales 124.9MM[E] *EMP* 5,600
SIC 8093 8049 8082 Specialty outpatient clinics; Physical therapist; Home health care services
Pr: William Ball
Off Mgr: Betty Ned
Netwrk Mgr: Victor Delephimne

OUTREACH HEALTH SERVICES
See VERNON HOME HEALTH CARE AGENCY INC

OUTREACH HEALTH SERVICES
See OUTREACH HEALTH CARE INC

OUTRIGGER HOTELS AND RESORTS
See OUTRIGGER HOTELS HAWAII

D-U-N-S 11-322-8522
OUTRIGGER HOTELS HAWAII
OUTRIGGER HOTELS AND RESORTS
2375 Kuhio Ave Fl 4, Honolulu, HI 96815-2939
Tel (808) 921-6510 *Founded/Ownrshp* 1953
Sales 108.6MM[E] *EMP* 2,500
SIC 7011 Resort hotel
Pt: Richard Kelley
Pt: W David P Carey III
Pt: Mel Wilinsky
Ex VP: Mel Kaneshige
Ex VP: Barry Wallace
Sr VP: Stephanie Nojima

D-U-N-S 06-734-8131
■ **OUTSOURCE GROUP INC**
(*Suby of* PARALLON WORKFORCE SOLUTIONS) ★
3 Cityplace Dr Ste 690, Saint Louis, MO 63141-7089
Tel (314) 692-6500 *Founded/Ownrshp* 2013
Sales 53.4MM[E] *EMP* 1,420[E]
SIC 7322 Collection agency, except real estate
CEO: Michael A Dimarco
COO: Mike Treash
**CFO:* Mark Rowland
**Ofcr:* Brigitte Burks
**Ofcr:* Lisa Phillips
**Ex VP:* Daniel A Schulte
**Sr VP:* Alan Aleia
**Sr VP:* Jeff Ellerbrock
**Sr VP:* Donald W Rappp
**Sr VP:* Don D Wright
**CIO:* Mike Aufdembrink

D-U-N-S 01-070-0297
■ **OUTSOURCE PARTNERS INTERNATIONAL INC**
(*Suby of* EXLSERVICE HOLDINGS INC) ★
280 Park Ave Rm 3801w, New York, NY 10017-1284
Tel (212) 752-2439 *Founded/Ownrshp* 2011
Sales 94.1MM[E] *EMP* 3,700
SIC 8721 8748 Accounting, auditing & bookkeeping; Business consulting
CEO: Clarence T Schmitz
**Pr:* Kishore Mirchandani
**CFO:* James D Floyd
Mng Dir: Peter J Mares
IT Man: Sanjay Kumar

D-U-N-S 17-547-9765
OUZINKIE NATIVE CORP
500 Main St, Ouzinkie, AK 99644
Tel (907) 680-2208 *Founded/Ownrshp* 1973
Sales 85.3MM *EMP* 815
SIC 6799 Investors
Ch: Jackie Muller
Bd of Dir: Crystal Boskofsky
Bd of Dir: Nicholas Pestrikoff
**VP:* Laura Muller

D-U-N-S 02-719-5317
■ **OVATIONS FOOD SERVICES LP**
(*Suby of* COMCAST SPECTACOR INC) ★
18228 N Us Highway 41, Lutz, FL 33549-4400
Tel (813) 948-6900 *Founded/Ownrshp* 2000
Sales 256.9MM[E] *EMP* 1,500
SIC 8742 7922 Restaurant & food services consultants; Ticket agency, theatrical
Pr: Ken Young
Pt: Lawrence Hoffman
Pt: Sandy Lipstein
Pr: Glen Brandeburg
Ex VP: Doug Drewes
Sr VP: Charlie Neary
Sr VP: Todd Wickner
VP: Mike Frost
VP: Steve Gregosky
VP: Tony Hendryx
VP: Lachance John
VP: John Lachance
VP: Kareen Muros
VP: Linda Recke
VP: Jay Satenspiel
VP: Mark Stone
VP: Pam Svec
VP: Martin Thorson
VP: Karen Wittig
VP Bus Dev: Nick Nicora
Exec: Bob St Lawrence

D-U-N-S 13-986-7282
■ **OVATIONS FOOD SERVICES LP**
(*Suby of* COMCAST HOLDINGS CORP) ★
21 Stadium Dr, Frederick, MD 21703-6553
Tel (301) 815-9935 *Founded/Ownrshp* 2003
Sales 22.9MM[E] *EMP* 1,893[E]
SIC 5812 Eating places
Pt: Gary Horvbath

D-U-N-S 12-889-3208
■ **OVATIONS INC**
(*Suby of* UNITEDHEALTH GROUP INC) ★
9900 Bren Rd E Ste 300w, Hopkins, MN 55343-9693
Tel (952) 936-1300 *Founded/Ownrshp* 1998
Sales NA *EMP* 3,500
SIC 6324 Hospital & medical service plans
CEO: Larry C Renfro
**CFO:* Jerry Knutson
**VP:* Lisa Johnson

OVEC
See OHIO VALLEY ELECTRIC CORP

OVERAA CONSTRUCTION
See C OVERAA & CO

D-U-N-S 00-750-3592 IMP
OVERHEAD DOOR CORP
(*Suby of* SANWA USA INC) ★
2501 S State Hwy 121 Ste, Lewisville, TX 75067
Tel (469) 549-7100 *Founded/Ownrshp* 2009
Sales 639.3MM[E] *EMP* 2,500
SIC 3442 2431 3699 3537 3589 Garage doors, overhead: metal; Rolling doors for industrial buildings or warehouses, metal; Metal doors; Doors, wood; Door opening & closing devices, electrical; Industrial trucks & tractors; Loading docks: portable, adjustable & hydraulic; Vacuum cleaners & sweepers, electric: industrial
Pr: Dennis Stone
Pr: Mike Kridel
Pr: Howard Simons
**CFO:* Paul A Lehmann
**Ch:* Toshitaka Takayama
**Treas:* Martha Ross
Founder: Cg Johnson
Ex VP: Nelson Newcomer
VP: David Knight
**VP:* Gregory J Kunsman
VP: Rhonda McAndrew
VP: Brett Sailors
**VP:* William A Schochet
VP: Craig Smith

D-U-N-S 04-742-6663
OVERHILL FARMS INC
CHICAGO BROTHERS
(*Suby of* YU SING) ★
2727 E Vernon Ave, Vernon, CA 90058-1822
Tel (323) 582-9977 *Founded/Ownrshp* 2013
Sales 130.8MM[E] *EMP* 400
SIC 2038 Frozen specialties
Pr: James Rudis
**Pr:* Rick Alvarez
**CFO:* Robert C Bruning
CFO: Robert Bruning
Genl Mgr: Francisco Andrade
Dir IT: Neil Bellinger

D-U-N-S 96-939-1312
OVERLAKE HOSPITAL ASSOCIATION
1035 116th Ave Ne, Bellevue, WA 98004-4604
Tel (425) 688-5000 *Founded/Ownrshp* 2011
Sales 511.8MM *EMP* 271[E]
Accts Kpmg Llp Seattle Wa
SIC 8621 Professional membership organizations
Prin: Diane Sperry
Nurse Mgr: Jody Burnell
Nurse Mgr: Mariam Gould
Software D: David CPC

D-U-N-S 07-663-1704
OVERLAKE HOSPITAL MEDICAL CENTER
1035 116th Ave Ne, Bellevue, WA 98004-4687
Tel (425) 688-5000 *Founded/Ownrshp* 1952
Sales 485.7MM *EMP* 2,450
Accts Kpmg Llp Seattle Wa
SIC 8062 General medical & surgical hospitals
Treas: Lynnette Anderson
Ofcr: Katherine Pliska
Ofcr: Cathy Whitaker
VP: Caitlin Hillary
Prgrm Mgr: Kathy Hellum
Dir IT: Kevin Keeffe
Netwrk Mgr: Charles Jackson
Netwrk Eng: Shawn Shiroma
Opers Supe: Alice Cabe
Opers Mgr: Mike Wade
Orthpdst: Mark Silver

OVERLAND LIMOUSINE SERVICE
See WHEATLAND ENTERPRISES INC

D-U-N-S 03-453-3904
OVERLAND PARK REGIONAL MEDICAL CENTER INC
10500 Quivira Rd, Overland Park, KS 66215-2306
Tel (913) 541-0000 *Founded/Ownrshp* 2014
Sales 39.3MM[E] *EMP* 1,125
SIC 8062 General medical & surgical hospitals
Pr: Kevin Hicks
VP: Kristen Feiger
Dir Rx: Cheryl Hurst

OVERLAND PETROLEUM
See DATS TRUCKING INC

D-U-N-S 12-835-0142
■ **OVERLAND SOLUTIONS INC**
(*Suby of* EXLSERVICE HOLDINGS INC) ★
10975 Grandview Dr # 400, Overland Park, KS 66210-1523
Tel (913) 451-3222 *Founded/Ownrshp* 2014
Sales NA *EMP* 1,180
SIC 6411 Loss prevention services, insurance
Pr: Mike Ferguson
**CFO:* Bryan Griffin
**Sr VP:* Gilbert Bourk
**Sr VP:* David Greene
Exec: Dorothy Doyle
Genl Mgr: Pat O Glesby
**CIO:* Chayan Dasgupta

D-U-N-S 06-980-9770
OVERLAND WEST INC
HERTZ
2805 Washington Blvd, Ogden, UT 84401-4212
Tel (801) 621-5663 *Founded/Ownrshp* 1941
Sales 138.6MM[E] *EMP* 425
SIC 7514

D-U-N-S 03-023-9297
OVERLOOK HOSPITAL ASSOCIATION (NJ)
(*Suby of* MORRISTOWN MEMORIAL HOSPITAL) ★
99 Beauvoir Ave, Summit, NJ 07901-3595
Tel (908) 522-2000 *Founded/Ownrshp* 1906, 1984
Sales 188.1MM[E] *EMP* 3,198
SIC 8621 Professional membership organizations
COO: Alan Lieber
CFO: Karen Lump
Bd of Dir: Steven J Sheris
VP: Robert Oberhand
Dir Rad: Al Kerestes
Dir IT: Robin J Hill
VP Sls: Judy Kastango
Surgeon: Charbel Salamon
Doctor: Mark Krell MD
Pharmcst: Rachna Kapoor
Pharmcst: Thomas Vogt

D-U-N-S 10-117-4472
OVERSEAS ADVENTURE TRAVEL
347 Congress St Ste 2, Boston, MA 02210-1222
Tel (800) 955-1925 *Founded/Ownrshp* 1994
Sales 79.2MM[E] *EMP* 2,000
SIC 4725 Arrangement of travel tour packages, wholesale
Sr VP: Mary Marks
**Owner:* Allan Lewis
Sr VP: Heather Gordon
VP: Dave Krijger
Mktg Dir: Erin Leigh

D-U-N-S 16-162-3152 EXP
OVERSEAS MILITARY SALES CORP - OMSC LTD
175 Crossways Park Dr W, Woodbury, NY 11797-2002
Tel (516) 921-2800 *Founded/Ownrshp* 1961
Sales 94.5MM[E] *EMP* 225
SIC 5511 New & used car dealers
CEO: David J Goldring
**CFO:* Edward A Smith
**VP:* Tim Daniels
**VP:* Stephen Frisch

D-U-N-S 05-049-6140
▲ **OVERSEAS SHIPHOLDING GROUP INC**
600 3rd Ave, New York, NY 10016-1901
Tel (212) 953-4100 *Founded/Ownrshp* 1969
Sales 964.5MM *EMP* 890[E]
Tkr Sym OSG *Exch* NYS
SIC 4412 4424 Deep sea foreign transportation of freight; Deep sea domestic transportation of freight
Pr: Ian T Blackley
**Ch Bd:* Douglas D Wheat
CFO: Rick F Oricchio
Treas: Geoffrey L Carpenter
Sr VP: James D Small III
VP: Adewale O Oshodi
VP: Eric Smith
Netwrk Eng: Rachel Cornelius
Sls&Mrk Ex: Vanessa Costanza
Board of Directors: Timothy J Bernlohr, Ronald Stegeronerg, Gary Eugene Taylor, Chad L Valerio, Ty E Wallach, Gregory A Wright

D-U-N-S 01-126-6280
▲ **OVERSTOCK.COM INC**
799 W Coliseum Way, Midvale, UT 84047-4867
Tel (801) 947-3100 *Founded/Ownrshp* 1997
Sales 1.6MMM *EMP* 1,900
Tkr Sym OSTK *Exch* NGM
SIC 5961 Catalog & mail-order houses; General merchandise, mail order
CEO: Patrick M Byrne
**Ch Bd:* Jonathan E Johnson III
**Pr:* Stormy D Simon
Sr VP: Mitch L Edwards
Sr VP: Robert P Hughes
Sr VP: Vidya Jwala
Sr VP: Carter Lee
Sr VP: Natalie Malaszenko
Sr VP: Brian L Popelka
Sr VP: Alec S Wilkins
VP: Seth Moore
VP: Carroll Morale
VP: Michael Skirucha
Board of Directors: Allison H Abraham, Barclay F Corbus, Samuel A Mitchell, Joseph J Tabacco Jr

OVERTON BROOKS VA MEDICAL CTR
See VA HOSPITAL

OVERTON HOTEL & CONFERENCE CTR
See 1859-HISTORIC HOTELS LTD

OVSD
See OCEAN VIEW SCHOOL DISTRICT (INC)

OWASA
See ORANGE WATER AND SEWER AUTHORITY

D-U-N-S 00-694-6065
OWEN ELECTRIC COOPERATIVE INC (KY)
8205 Highway 127 S, Owenton, KY 40359-9378
Tel (502) 484-3471 *Founded/Ownrshp* 1937
Sales 192.7MM *EMP* 134
SIC 4911 Distribution, electric power
CEO: Mark Stallons
**Ch Bd:* J Sam Penn
COO: Charles Gill
**Sec:* Stanley Gosney
**V Ch Bd:* Frank E Jackson
Sfty Mgr: Tony Dempsey

OWEN HEALTH CARE
See CARDINAL HEALTH 109 INC

D-U-N-S 10-759-8963 IMP
OWEN INDUSTRIES INC
PVS METALS
501 Avenue H, Carter Lake, IA 51510-1513
Tel (800) 831-9252 *Founded/Ownrshp* 1979
Sales 155.4MM[E] *EMP* 375
SIC 5051 3441 Sheets, metal; Steel; Bars, metal; Pipe & tubing, steel; Fabricated structural metal; Bridge sections, prefabricated highway; Bridge sections, prefabricated railway; Joists, open web steel: long-span series
Ch Bd: Robert E Owen
**CFO:* Ed Korbel
**Sr VP:* Keith Siebels
**VP:* Chad Bortherms
**VP:* Ron Debord
**VP:* Mark Radtke

D-U-N-S 10-705-1823 IMP/EXP
OWEN OIL TOOLS INC
(*Suby of* CORE LABORATORIES LP) ★
12001 County Road 1000, Godley, TX 76044-3141
Tel (817) 396-4570 *Founded/Ownrshp* 1978
Sales 86.1MM[E] *EMP* 540
SIC 2892 3533 Well shooting torpedoes (explosive); Drilling tools for gas, oil or water wells
CEO: David M Demshur
**CFO:* R L Bergmark
VP: Jerry Kier
**VP:* Dan W Pratt
VP: Les Weisner
Exec: Martha Holland

Genl Mgr: Ernie Ramirez
IT Man: Irene Kjornes
Sfty Mgr: Yvie Ellison
Mfg Mgr: Brett Schaffer
Plnt Mgr: David Oneal

D-U-N-S 10-718-5923 EXP
OWEN STEEL CO INC
727 Mauney Dr, Columbia, SC 29201-5177
Tel (803) 251-7680 *Founded/Ownrshp* 2001
Sales 110.0MM^{E} *EMP* 350
SIC 3441 Fabricated structural metal
CEO: Anny Zalesne
Pr: Chris Krueger
**Pr:* David Zalesne
VP: Mike Cooke
Assoc Dir: Thaer Faraj
IT Man: Mark Sury

D-U-N-S 06-157-2882
OWEN STEPHENS PRODUCTIONS LLC
1304 Sw 176th Ter, Beaverton, OR 97003-7562
Tel (503) 810-0812 *Founded/Ownrshp* 2011
Sales 85.0MM *EMP* 1
SIC 3861 Motion picture film

D-U-N-S 00-794-1230 IMP
■ **OWENS & MINOR DISTRIBUTION INC** (VA)
(*Suby of* OWENS & MINOR INC) ★
9120 Lockwood Blvd, Mechanicsville, VA 23116-2015
Tel (804) 723-7000 *Founded/Ownrshp* 1882, 1994
Sales 9.0MMM *EMP* 4,500
SIC 5047 Medical equipment & supplies; Surgical equipment & supplies
Pr: Craig R Smith
**Ch Bd:* G Gilmer Minor III
**Pr:* James L Bierman
**COO:* Charles Coopel
**CFO:* Richard Andrew Meier
**Sr VP:* Grace Denharttog
**Sr VP:* David Guzman
VP: Erika Davis
**VP:* Drew Edwards
**VP:* Wargo Natalie K
**VP:* Mike Lowry
VP: Mark Van Sumeren

D-U-N-S 84-741-2269 IMP
▲ **OWENS & MINOR INC**
9120 Lockwood Blvd, Mechanicsville, VA 23116-2015
Tel (804) 723-7000 *Founded/Ownrshp* 1882
Sales 9.7MMM *EMP* 5,700
Accts Kpmg Llp Richmond Virginia
Tkr Sym OMI *Exch* NYS
SIC 5047 Medical & hospital equipment; Hospital equipment & furniture; Surgical equipment & supplies; Medical equipment & supplies
Pr: P Cody Phipps
**Ch Bd:* Craig R Smith
Pr: Dan Hess
COO: James L Bierman
CFO: Richard A Meier
Ex VP: William Fife
Ex VP: Rony C Kordahi
Ex VP: Nancy Schneid
Sr VP: Charles C Colpo
Sr VP: Erika T Davis
Sr VP: Grace R Den Hartog
Sr VP: Grace R Hartog
Sr VP: Richard W Mears
Sr VP: Thomas J Sherry
VP: Charles Eismamn
VP: Carla Fox
VP: Hugh F Gouldthorpe Jr
VP: Martha Huston
VP: Gavin Jeffs
VP: Mike La Croix
VP: Wayne B Luck

D-U-N-S 17-186-5459
■ **OWENS & MINOR MEDICAL INC**
(*Suby of* OWENS & MINOR INC) ★
9120 Lockwood Blvd, Mechanicsville, VA 23116-2015
Tel (804) 723-7000 *Founded/Ownrshp* 1994
Sales 112.0MM^{E} *EMP* 400
SIC 5047 Medical equipment & supplies
Pr: Craig Smith
**CFO:* Jeff Kaczka
**Treas:* Richard Bozard
Bd of Dir: James Redding
Sr VP: Jack Clark
Sr VP: Erika T Davis
Sr VP: Grace R Den Hartog

D-U-N-S 06-371-1873
OWENS COMMUNITY COLLEGE
30335 Oregon Rd, Perrysburg, OH 43551-4593
Tel (567) 661-7000 *Founded/Ownrshp* 1966
Sales 46.9MM^{E} *EMP* 1,200
SIC 8222 Technical institute
Ch Bd: Rich Rowe
**Pr:* Mike Bower
Pr: Larry Cser
**CFO:* J D John Satkowski
Ofcr: John Eggleston
Assoc VP: Thomas Perin
VP: Mike Bankey
VP: Pamela Beck
**VP:* Renay Scott
Ex Dir: Marc Levy

D-U-N-S 79-651-4466 IMP/EXP
▲ **OWENS CORNING**
1 Owens Corning Pkwy, Toledo, OH 43659-0001
Tel (419) 248-8000 *Founded/Ownrshp* 1938
Sales 5.3MMM *EMP* 15,000
Tkr Sym OC *Exch* NYS
SIC 3296 2952 3229 3089 Fiberglass insulation; Insulation: rock wool, slag & silica minerals; Acoustical board & tile, mineral wool; Roofing mats, mineral wool; Asphalt felts & coatings; Glass fibers, textile; Yarn, fiberglass; Windows, plastic
Ch Bd: Michael H Thaman
Ch Bd: Rickey Bridges
Pr: Brian D Chambers
Pr: Julian Francis
Pr: Arnaud Genis
COO: Jose Mancia
CFO: Michael C McMurray
Sr VP: Ava Harter
Sr VP: Daniel T Smith
VP: Joe Chuba
VP: Teresa May
VP: Gary Nieman
VP: Doug Pontsler
VP: Kelly J Schmidt
Board of Directors: Suzanne P Nimocks, Cesar Conde, John D Williams, J Brian Ferguson, Ralph F Hake, F Philip Handy, Ann Iverson, Edward F Lonergan, Maryann T Mannen, James J McMonagle, W Howard Morris

D-U-N-S 00-131-7452 IMP
■ **OWENS CORNING SALES LLC**
(*Suby of* OWENS CORNING) ★
1 Owens Corning Pkwy, Toledo, OH 43659-0001
Tel (419) 248-8000 *Founded/Ownrshp* 2006
Sales 3.1MMM^{E} *EMP* 9,000
SIC 3296 2952 3229 3089 1761 Fiberglass insulation; Insulation: rock wool, slag & silica minerals; Acoustical board & tile, mineral wool; Roofing mats, mineral wool; Asphalt felts & coatings; Glass fibers, textile; Yarn, fiberglass; Windows, plastic; Roofing, siding & sheet metal work
Ch Bd: Michael H Thaman
Pr: Rhonda L Brooks
Pr: Carl B Hedlund
Pr: George E Kiemle
Pr: William E Lebaron
Pr: Chuck Stein
Pr: Jerry L Weinstein
VP: Jeff Craney
VP: Scott A Deitz
VP: Bob Doyle
VP: Jim Drew
VP: Frank O'Brien-Bernini
VP: John Pagano

OWENS TRANSPORT SERVICE
See A MICHAEL OWENS INC

D-U-N-S 61-616-8472 IMP/EXP
■ **OWENS-BROCKWAY GLASS CONTAINER INC**
O-I
(*Suby of* OWENS-ILLINOIS INC) ★
1 Michael Owens Way, Perrysburg, OH 43551-2999
Tel (567) 336-8449 *Founded/Ownrshp* 2004
Sales 6.1MMM *EMP* 6,800
Accts Ernst & Young Llp Toledo Oh
SIC 3221 Glass containers
Ch: Mr Albert P L Stroucken
Pr: Mathew Longthorne
CEO: Steve McCracken
Sr VP: Jim Baehren
Sr VP: Steve Bramlage
Sr VP: Paul Jarrell
VP: Giancarlo Currarino
VP: Andres Lopez
CTO: Gregory Burns
Sls Mgr: Dana Palmer
Board of Directors: R Lanigan

D-U-N-S 78-205-1239 IMP/EXP
■ **OWENS-BROCKWAY PACKAGING INC**
(*Suby of* OWENS-ILLINOIS INC) ★
1 Michael Owens Way, Perrysburg, OH 43551-2999
Tel (567) 336-5000 *Founded/Ownrshp* 1987
Sales 6.1MMM *EMP* 7,000
Accts Ernst & Young Llp Toledo Oh
SIC 3221 Glass containers
CEO: Al Stroucken
CFO: Ed White

D-U-N-S 78-423-8433 IMP/EXP
■ **OWENS-ILLINOIS GROUP INC**
(*Suby of* OWENS-ILLINOIS INC) ★
1 Michael Owens Way, Perrysburg, OH 43551-2999
Tel (567) 336-5000 *Founded/Ownrshp* 1903
Sales 6.1MMM *EMP* 21,100
Accts Ernst & Young Llp Toledo Oh
SIC 3221 Glass containers
Ch Bd: Albert P L Stroucken
**Pr:* Stephen P Bramlage Jr
**VP:* James W Baehren
**VP:* Paul A Jarrell

D-U-N-S 00-503-4566
▲ **OWENS-ILLINOIS INC**
1 Michael Owens Way, Perrysburg, OH 43551-2999
Tel (567) 336-5000 *Founded/Ownrshp* 1903
Sales 6.1MMM *EMP* 27,000^{E}
Tkr Sym OI *Exch* NYS
SIC 3221 Glass containers; Food containers, glass; Bottles for packing, bottling & canning: glass; Medicine bottles, glass
CEO: Andres A Lopez
CFO: Jan A Bertsch
Ofcr: Paul A Jarrell
Sr VP: James W Baehren
Sr VP: John A Haudrich
Board of Directors: Dennis K Williams, Gary F Colter, Joseph J Deangelo, Gordon J Hardie, Peter S Hellman, Anastasia D Kelly, John J McMackin Jr, Alan J Murray, Hugh H Roberts, Carol A Williams

OWENSBORO DIALYSIS CENTER
See RENAL TREATMENT CENTERS-ILLINOIS INC

D-U-N-S 13-097-2115
OWENSBORO GRAIN EDIBLE OILS LLC
OWENSBORO GRAINS EDIBLE OIL
822 E 2nd St, Owensboro, KY 42303-3302
Tel (270) 926-2032 *Founded/Ownrshp* 2001
Sales 100.0MM *EMP* 26
SIC 2079 Edible fats & oils

OWENSBORO GRAINS EDIBLE OIL
See OWENSBORO GRAIN EDIBLE OILS LLC

D-U-N-S 83-754-7074
OWENSBORO HEALTH INC
1201 Pleasant Valley Rd, Owensboro, KY 42303-9811
Tel (270) 688-2000 *Founded/Ownrshp* 1995
Sales 450.3MM *EMP* 3,200
Accts Ernst & Young Us Llp Indianap
SIC 8062 General medical & surgical hospitals
Pr: Philip A Patterson
Chf Rad: Charles Bea
Chf Rad: David Graham
V Ch: G Smith
Pr: Ed Heath
COO: Debbie Bostic
**CFO:* John Hackbarth Jr
Sr VP: Don Martin
**Sr VP:* Vicki Stogsdill
VP: Liz Belt
**VP:* Lisa Jones
**VP:* Greg Strahan
Dir Rx: Jim Besier

D-U-N-S 01-345-0632
OWENSBORO MUNICIPAL UTILITIES
2070 Tamarack Rd, Owensboro, KY 42301-6876
Tel (270) 926-3200 *Founded/Ownrshp* 1940
Sales 150.0MM *EMP* 240
SIC 4911 Electric services
Genl Mgr: Terry Naulty
VP: David Poe
Exec: Jan Howard
Dir Lab: Kim Hook
Dir Lab: Cathy Vesells
Genl Mgr: Robert Huntzinger
Off Mgr: Marilyn Smeathers
DP Dir: David Boreman
Dir IT: Terry Horne
IT Man: Mike Reel
Mfg Dir: Louise Keach

D-U-N-S 17-477-5544
OWENSBORO MUNICIPAL UTILITIES ELECTRIC LIGHT & POWER SYSTEM
OMU
2070 Tamarack Rd, Owensboro, KY 42301-6876
Tel (270) 926-3200 *Founded/Ownrshp* 1901
Sales 140.8MM *EMP* 235
Accts Riney Hancock Cpas Psc Owensb
SIC 4911 4941 Distribution, electric power; Generation, electric power; Transmission, electric power; Water supply
Prin: Terrance Naulty

OWENSBORO PAVING CO
See YAGER MATERIALS LLC

D-U-N-S 04-443-7796
OWL COMPANIES (CA)
4695 Macarthur Ct Ste 950, Newport Beach, CA 92660-1841
Tel (949) 797-2000 *Founded/Ownrshp* 1942, 1984
Sales 108.5MM^{E} *EMP* 1,389
SIC 8331 6519 4911 Job training & vocational rehabilitation services; Real property lessors; Generation, electric power
CEO: Gregory J Burden
VP: Eric Perea
VP: Jeff Stinson
Sls Mgr: Theresa Kholoma

D-U-N-S 60-257-1403
OWL EDUCATION AND TRAINING INC
(*Suby of* OWL COMPANIES) ★
2465 Campus Dr, Irvine, CA 92612-1502
Tel (949) 797-2000 *Founded/Ownrshp* 2005
Sales 5.3MM^{E} *EMP* 1,380
SIC 8331 Job training & vocational rehabilitation services
Pr: Gregory J Burden
Treas: Stephen E Sastrom
**Sec:* Stephen Seastrom

D-U-N-S 78-771-5721
OWNERS INSURANCE CO
(*Suby of* AUTO-OWNERS INSURANCE CO) ★
6101 Anacapri Blvd, Lansing, MI 48917-3968
Tel (517) 323-1200 *Founded/Ownrshp* 1975
Sales NA *EMP* 10
SIC 6411 6331 Property & casualty insurance agent; Property damage insurance
CEO: Jeffray F Harrold
**Pr:* Jeffrey S Tagsold
**CFO:* Eileen K Fhaner
**Sec:* William F Woodbury
**Ex VP:* Katherine M Noirot
Sr VP: R L Ooyenga

OWNERS OF UNITED CHARITIES BUI
See UNITED CHARITIES

D-U-N-S 19-059-0760 IMP/EXP
OXBOW CARBON & MINERALS HOLDINGS INC
1601 Forum Pl Ste 1400, West Palm Beach, FL 33401-8104
Tel (561) 907-5400 *Founded/Ownrshp* 1983
Sales 1.7MMM^{E} *EMP* 1,220^{E}
SIC 5052 1222 Coal; Coke; Bituminous coal-underground mining
CEO: William Bil Koch
**Pr:* David Nestler
**COO:* Steven E Fried
**CFO:* William D Parmelee
CFO: William Parmelee
**CFO:* Zachary Shipley
**Ex VP:* James R Freney
**Ex VP:* Eric Johnson
**VP:* Richard P Callahan
IT Man: Bill Wade

D-U-N-S 80-811-1228
OXBOW CARBON LLC
(*Suby of* OXBOW GROUP) ★
1601 Forum Pl Ste 1400, West Palm Beach, FL 33401-8104
Tel (561) 907-5400 *Founded/Ownrshp* 2016
Sales 452.2MM^{E} *EMP* 230^{E}
SIC 1241 2999 5052 Coal mining services; Coke, calcined petroleum: made from purchased materials; Coal
Pr: William I Koch
COO: Steven E Fried
CFO: William Parmalee
CFO: William D Parmelee
Treas: Ben Klein
Ex VP: James R Freney
Ex VP: Eric Johnson
Dir Risk M: Donna Gulbransen
Counsel: James Laws

D-U-N-S 11-423-3158
OXBOW CORP
OXBOW GROUP
(*Suby of* OXBOW CARBON & MINERALS HOLDINGS INC) ★
1601 Forum Pl Ste 1400, West Palm Beach, FL 33401-8104
Tel (561) 907-5422 *Founded/Ownrshp* 1983
Sales 598.3MM^{E} *EMP* 230
SIC 8731 Natural resource research
Pr: William I Koch
**COO:* Steven E Fried
CFO: Bill Parmelee
**CFO:* William D Parmelee
**Treas:* Benjamin L Klein
Ofcr: Jim Douglas
Ex VP: Richard Callahan
**Ex VP:* James R Freney
Ex VP: James Freney
Ex VP: Mark Whittemore
VP: Brian Bilnoski
VP: Dennis Courtney
VP: Craig Cynor
VP: Clayton Headley
VP: Maggie Inniss
VP: Thomas Itty
VP: Ben Kline
VP: Steve Lassonde
VP: Randy Litwiller
VP: Mark McCormick
VP: Charles Middleton

D-U-N-S 14-588-0055 IMP/EXP
OXBOW ENERGY SOLUTIONS LLC
(*Suby of* OXBOW CARBON LLC) ★
1601 Forum Pl Ste 1400, West Palm Beach, FL 33401-8104
Tel (561) 907-4300 *Founded/Ownrshp* 2003
Sales 266.9MM^{E} *EMP* 800
SIC 5052 Coal
COO: Eric Johnson
Genl Mgr: Tom Brandlin

OXBOW GROUP
See OXBOW CORP

D-U-N-S 05-667-4310 IMP
OXBOW SULPHUR INC
ICEC
(*Suby of* OXBOW GROUP) ★
1450 Lake Robbins Dr # 500, The Woodlands, TX 77380-3258
Tel (281) 907-9500 *Founded/Ownrshp* 1986
Sales 146.0MM^{E} *EMP* 60^{E}
Accts Grant Thornton Llp Houston T
SIC 5191 5169 Fertilizer & fertilizer materials; Phosphate rock, ground; Industrial chemicals
Pr: William Zisson
CFO: Peter Engelking
CFO: William D Parmelee
Treas: Benjamin L Klein
Sr VP: Vincent Leone
Sr VP: Jeremy Sheppe
VP: Mark Whittemore
Sfty Dirs: Dean Fournier
Mktg Mgr: Yu Chen
Mktg Mgr: Peter Goemans
Mktg Mgr: Michael Ward

D-U-N-S 79-228-3405 IMP/EXP
OXEA CORP
(*Suby of* OXEA HOLDING CORP) ★
1505 L B Johnson Fwy # 400, Dallas, TX 75234-6082
Tel (972) 481-2700 *Founded/Ownrshp* 2006
Sales 125.6MM^{E} *EMP* 205
SIC 2869 Industrial organic chemicals
Pr: Robert Gengelbach
Sr VP: Stefan Schmidt
VP: Cristobal Ascencio
VP: Steve Friedewald
**VP:* Wolfgang Hackenberg
VP: Bernhard Herzog
VP: Purnendu Rai
**Prin:* Martina Flel
**Prin:* Miguel Mantas
**Prin:* Cornelius Robertson
Mng Dir: Salim A Huthaili

D-U-N-S 96-642-2045
OXEA HOLDING CORP
(*Suby of* OXEA GMBH)
1505 Lyndon B Johnson Fwy, Dallas, TX 75234-6069
Tel (972) 481-2700 *Founded/Ownrshp* 2010
Sales 125.6MM^{E} *EMP* 205^{E}
SIC 2899 Chemical preparations
Pr: Wolfgang Hackenberc
**Prin:* Robert Gengelbach

D-U-N-S 07-662-1713
OXFAM AMERICA INC
226 Causeway St Fl 5, Boston, MA 02114-2206
Tel (617) 482-1211 *Founded/Ownrshp* 1970
Sales 92.3MM *EMP* 180^{E}
Accts Lb Cbiz Tofias Boston Ma
SIC 8399 Antipoverty board
Pr: Raymond C Offenheiser
**COO:* Jim Daniell
COO: Jane Skelton
**CFO:* Mark F Kripp
Trst: Matthew Martin
Ofcr: Mary Babic
Ofcr: Sarah Livingston
Ofcr: Telley Madina
Ofcr: Vanessa Parra
Ofcr: Sue Rooks
Ofcr: Laura Rusu
Ofcr: Josh Silva
**VP:* John Ambler
VP: Barbara Durr
**VP:* Stephanie Kurzina
**VP:* Paul O'Brien
Assoc Dir: Gregory Adams
Creative D: Jane Huber

OXFORD AMHERST LLC
See PHARMACYCLICS LLC

OXFORD CAPITAL GROUP
See OXFORD CAPITAL PARTNERS INC

D-U-N-S 82-542-6559
OXFORD CAPITAL GROUP LLC
350 W Hubbard St Ste 440, Chicago, IL 60654-6900
Tel (312) 755-9500 *Founded/Ownrshp* 2006
Sales 1.0MMM *EMP* 500
SIC 6719 Investment holding companies, except banks

D-U-N-S 94-379-1707
OXFORD CAPITAL PARTNERS INC
OXFORD CAPITAL GROUP
350 W Hubbard St Ste 440, Chicago, IL 60654-6900
Tel (312) 755-9500 *Founded/Ownrshp* 1994
Sales 199.6MM^E *EMP* 2,000
SIC 6719 Investment holding companies, except banks
Pr: John W Rutledge
CFO: Chris Hill
**Mng Dir:* Vann A Avedisian
Mng Dir: Vann A Vedisin
Sls Dir: Adam Schomaker

D-U-N-S 00-580-8282
OXFORD CONSTRUCTION CO (GA)
3200 Palmyra Rd, Albany, GA 31707-1221
Tel (229) 883-3232 *Founded/Ownrshp* 1948
Sales 91.2MM^E *EMP* 250
Accts Draffin & Tucker Llp Albany
SIC 1611 1629 Highway & street paving contractor; Earthmoving contractor
Pr: J Bruce Melton
**CFO:* Keith Miller
**VP:* J Melvin Edwards
Genl Mgr: Melvin Edwards
Genl Mgr: Bill Gahring
Genl Mgr: Kalin Peavy
Sfty Mgr: Steve Burton

D-U-N-S 07-217-4964
OXFORD DEVELOPMENT CO INC
301 Grant St Ste 4500, Pittsburgh, PA 15219-1489
Tel (412) 261-1500 *Founded/Ownrshp* 1960
Sales 161.2MM^E *EMP* 2,200
SIC 7011 Hotels & motels; Ski lodge
Pr: Steven J Guy
**COO:* Louis G Dinardo
Treas: Mark Mason
**VP:* Brian M Albert
**VP:* Scott Bergstein
**VP:* Laurence R Castonguay
VP: Shawn Fox
**VP:* Grant B Mason
**VP:* Frank Molinero
**VP:* Stephen J Nicotra
VP: Stephen Nicotra
**VP:* Joseph G Piccini
**VP:* R Scott Pollock
Exec: Christopher Koch
Exec: Kathy Lamarca
Comm Dir: Mark Grasso

D-U-N-S 14-412-3791
■ **OXFORD GLOBAL RESOURCES LLC**
OXFORD INTERNATIONAL
(*Suby of* ON ASSIGNMENT INC) ★
100 Cummings Ctr Ste 206c, Beverly, MA 01915-6104
Tel (978) 236-1182 *Founded/Ownrshp* 1994
Sales 500.0MM^E *EMP* 400
SIC 7363 8748 Help supply services; Business consulting
Pr: Michael J McGowan
Mng Pt: Cornell Johnson
COO: Susan Varano
**CFO:* Jim Brill
**Treas:* Dean Burdett
Treas: Edward P Kelly
Ex VP: Stephen Mahle
Ex VP: David Scott
VP: Chris Freeman
Prin: Nick Penny
Brnch Mgr: Matt Griffin

D-U-N-S 87-893-0015
■ **OXFORD HEALTH PLANS (CT) INC**
(*Suby of* OXFORD HEALTH PLANS INC) ★
48 Monroe Tpke, Trumbull, CT 06611-1341
Tel (203) 459-9100 *Founded/Ownrshp* 1993
Sales NA *EMP* 800
SIC 6324 Health maintenance organization (HMO), insurance only
CEO: Chuck Berg
**CFO:* Kurt Thompson

D-U-N-S 11-118-8814
■ **OXFORD HEALTH PLANS (NY) INC**
(*Suby of* OXFORD HEALTH PLANS INC) ★
48 Monroe Tpke, Trumbull, CT 06611-1341
Tel (203) 459-9100 *Founded/Ownrshp* 1996
Sales NA *EMP* 1,690
SIC 6324 Health maintenance organization (HMO), insurance only
Prin: Charles Burg
VP: Robert Murphy
MIS Dir: Thomas Beauchamp

D-U-N-S 13-175-8153
■ **OXFORD HEALTH PLANS INC**
(*Suby of* UNITEDHEALTH GROUP INC) ★
48 Monroe Tpke, Trumbull, CT 06611-1341
Tel (203) 459-9100 *Founded/Ownrshp* 2004
Sales NA *EMP* 3,200
SIC 6324 Health maintenance organization (HMO), insurance only; Dental insurance
Pr: Charles G Berg
**Ch Bd:* Kent J Thiry
**CFO:* Kurt B Thompson
Bd of Dir: Robin Fiore
Ofcr: John Marcus
Ofcr: Alan M Muney MD Mha
**Ex VP:* Steve Black
**Ex VP:* Steven H Black
Ex VP: Rita Bourgeois
**Ex VP:* Daniel N Gregoire
Ex VP: Robert Natt

OXFORD HEALTHCARE
See HEALTHCARE SERVICES OF OZARKS INC

OXFORD HEALTHCARE
See HELP AT HOME LLC

D-U-N-S 00-326-4041 IMP
▲ **OXFORD INDUSTRIES INC**
999 Peachtree St Ne # 688, Atlanta, GA 30309-3915
Tel (404) 659-2424 *Founded/Ownrshp* 1942
Sales 969.2MM *EMP* 5,500
Accts Ernst & Young Llp Atlanta G
Tkr Sym OXM *Exch* NYS
SIC 2321 2325 2311 Men's & boys' dress shirts; Men's & boys' sports & polo shirts; Men's & boys' trousers & slacks; Men's & boys' jeans & dungarees; Shorts (outerwear): men's, youths' & boys'; Men's & boys' suits & coats
Ch Bd: Thomas C Chubb III
Pr: J Wesley Howard Jr
CEO: Scott A Beaumont
CEO: Terry R Pillow
**CFO:* K Scott Grassmyer
**Ex VP:* Thomas E Campbell
VP: Chris Collier
VP: Scott Grassmyer
VP: Cindy McDonald
VP: Robert P Peak
Genl Couns: Raj Palakshappa

OXFORD INTERNATIONAL
See OXFORD GLOBAL RESOURCES LLC

D-U-N-S 02-069-5029
■ **OXFORD LIFE INSURANCE CO INC**
(*Suby of* AMERCO) ★
2721 N Central Ave Fl 5, Phoenix, AZ 85004-1137
Tel (602) 263-6666 *Founded/Ownrshp* 1996
Sales NA *EMP* 150
SIC 6311 6321 Life reinsurance; Disability health insurance
Pr: Mark A Haydukovich
**CFO:* Jason A Berg
CFO: Steve Taylor
VP: Amanda Chester
VP: Jin Y Kim
VP: Mae Kirk
Exec: Anthony Gertos
IT Man: Joshua Poso
Mktg Dir: Mike Baker
Mktg Dir: Alison Benson
Mktg Dir: Alex Gomez

D-U-N-S 15-549-1517
■ **OXFORD MINING CO INC**
(*Suby of* WESTMORELAND RESOURCE PARTNERS LP) ★
544 Chestnut St, Coshocton, OH 43812-1209
Tel (740) 622-6302 *Founded/Ownrshp* 1985
Sales 263.0MM^E *EMP* 450
SIC 1221 Strip mining, bituminous
Pr: Charles C Ungurean
**CFO:* Jeffrey M Gutman
Treas: Michael Ungurean
**Sr VP:* Gregory J Honish
**Sr VP:* Daniel M Maher
**VP:* Thomas T Ungurean
**Dir Surg:* Denise M Maksimoski
IT Man: Joel Ramshaw

D-U-N-S 96-519-3548
■ **OXFORD MINING CO-KENTUCKY LLC**
(*Suby of* WESTMORELAND RESOURCE PARTNERS LP) ★
544 Chestnut St, Coshocton, OH 43812-1209
Tel (740) 622-6302 *Founded/Ownrshp* 2010
Sales 106.9MM^E *EMP* 183^E
SIC 1221 Strip mining, bituminous

D-U-N-S 00-146-8149 IMP/EXP
OXFORD UNIVERSITY PRESS LLC
OXFORD UNIVERSITY PRESS USA
(*Suby of* UNIVERSITY OF OXFORD)
198 Madison Ave Fl 8, New York, NY 10016-4308
Tel (212) 726-6000 *Founded/Ownrshp* 1973
Sales 116.5MM^E *EMP* 530
Accts Deloitte Tax Llp Raleigh Nc
SIC 2731 5961 Book publishing; Book & record clubs
Pr: Niko Pfund
Ofcr: Dan Carter
VP: John Challice
Exec: Nancy Toff
Assoc Dir: Rose Pintaudi-Jones
Mng Dir: Ameena Saiyid
Genl Mgr: Laura Pearson
IT Man: Michael Cai
Web Dev: Ben Freund
Opers Mgr: Hannah Ryu
Prd Mgr: Diem Bloom

OXFORD UNIVERSITY PRESS USA
See OXFORD UNIVERSITY PRESS LLC

D-U-N-S 01-310-7176
OXFORD-COLUMBIA ASSOCIATES A MARYLAND LIMITED PARTNERSHIP
CHIMNEYS CRDLE ROCK APARTMENTS
6531 Quiet Hours, Columbia, MD 21045-4903
Tel (410) 381-1906 *Founded/Ownrshp* 2009
Sales 33.4MM^E *EMP* 3,900
SIC 6513 Apartment building operators
Sr VP: Leeann Morein

D-U-N-S 96-232-0797 IMP
OXITENO USA LLC
(*Suby of* OXITENO MEXICO, S.A. DE C.V.)
9801 Bay Area Blvd, Pasadena, TX 77507-1863
Tel (281) 909-7600 *Founded/Ownrshp* 2009
Sales 110.0MM^E *EMP* 62
SIC 5172 Gases, liquefied petroleum (propane)
Pr: Joao Benjamin Parolin
Sls Dir: Carlos Tooge

OXNARD CITY HALL
See CITY OF OXNARD

D-U-N-S 07-064-5957
OXNARD SCHOOL DISTRICT
1051 S A St, Oxnard, CA 93030-7442
Tel (805) 487-3918 *Founded/Ownrshp* 1873
Sales 189.1MM *EMP* 2,100
Accts Nigro & Nigro Pc Murrieta Ca
SIC 8211 Public elementary & secondary schools; Secondary school; Specialty education; Vocational high school
Prin: Anthony Zubia
CTO: Rachel McClanahan
Dir IT: Tracy Haddenham
Pr Dir: Terri Giern
Psych: Cynthia Angel
Psych: Shanell Semien
Psych: Steve Tobey
HC Dir: Carmen Rosenberg

D-U-N-S 09-445-2117
OXNARD UNION HIGH SCHOOL DIST
309 S K St, Oxnard, CA 93030-5212
Tel (805) 385-2500 *Founded/Ownrshp* 1901
Sales 130.5MM^E *EMP* 1,700
Accts Vavrinek Trine Day & Co Ll
SIC 8211 Public elementary & secondary schools
CEO: Cynthia L Herrera
**Pr:* Wayne Edmonds
**Pr:* Dick Jaquez
**CFO:* Kathy Thomas
**VP:* John Alamillo
Opers Supe: Henry Williams

OXY
See OCCIDENTAL OIL AND GAS CORP

D-U-N-S 14-766-7240
OXY CHEMICAL CORP
5005 L B Johnson Fwy 2200, Dallas, TX 75244
Tel (972) 404-3800 *Founded/Ownrshp* 1972
Sales 191.7MM^E *EMP* 2,500^E
SIC 2869 2873 2874 2899 3089

D-U-N-S 11-510-2402 IMP
■ **OXY INC**
(*Suby of* OCCIDENTAL PETROLEUM CORP) ★
5 Greenway Plz Ste 2400, Houston, TX 77046-0532
Tel (713) 215-7000 *Founded/Ownrshp* 1988
Sales 2.2MMM^E *EMP* 1,300
SIC 1311 1382 Crude petroleum production; Natural gas production; Oil & gas exploration services
Pr: Vicki A Hollub
Pr: Donald L Moore
Treas: J R Havert
VP: Shayne Buchanan
VP: Z Melissa Hunt
VP: Paul A Parsons
VP: Linda S Peterson
VP: Michael S Stutts

D-U-N-S 00-673-3514
■ **OXY USA INC**
(*Suby of* OCCIDENTAL PETROLEUM CORP) ★
1001 S County Rd W, Odessa, TX 79763-5003
Tel (432) 335-0995 *Founded/Ownrshp* 1982
Sales 234.4MM^E *EMP* 126
SIC 1311 Crude petroleum production; Natural gas production
Pr: John W Morgan
**Ex VP:* R Casey Olson
**Ex VP:* Stephen I Chazen
**VP:* Jo Ellen Drisko
**VP:* J R Havert
**VP:* Harry F Hufft
**VP:* Donald G Jackson
**VP:* Thomas A Janiczewski
**VP:* Thomas A Menges
**VP:* Marzi J Mistry
**VP:* Linda S Peterson
**VP:* Michael L Preston
**VP:* Todd Stevens

D-U-N-S 06-180-5003 IMP/EXP
■ **OXY VINYLS LP**
(*Suby of* OCCIDENTAL PETROLEUM CORP) ★
5005 Lbj Fwy Ste 2200, Dallas, TX 75244-6152
Tel (972) 720-7000 *Founded/Ownrshp* 1999
Sales 643.8MM^E *EMP* 1,583
SIC 2821 2899 2819 1382 Vinyl resins; Chemical preparations; Industrial inorganic chemicals; Oil & gas exploration services
Ch: Ray R Irani
IT Man: Everett Hamby

D-U-N-S 03-114-1625 IMP
■ **OZARK AUTOMOTIVE DISTRIBUTORS INC**
(*Suby of* OREILLY AUTOMOTIVE INC) ★
233 S Patterson Ave, Springfield, MO 65802-2210
Tel (417) 862-6708 *Founded/Ownrshp* 1960
Sales 232.5MM^E *EMP* 2,100
SIC 5013 Automotive supplies & parts
Ch: David E O'Reilly
**Pr:* Greg Hansely
**Pr:* Ted Wise
CFO: James R Batten
**CFO:* Tom McFall

D-U-N-S 07-304-7631
OZARK KENWORTH INC
MIDWEST KENWORTH
(*Suby of* MURPHY-HOFFMAN CO) ★
1524 N Corrington Ave, Kansas City, MO 64120-1944
Tel (816) 483-7035 *Founded/Ownrshp* 1975
Sales 124.1MM^E *EMP* 540
SIC 5012 Truck tractors
**CFO:* Jeffrey Johnson
VP: Todd Rice
CIO: Jeff Murphy
Natl Sales: Andy Douglas

D-U-N-S 00-686-8590
OZARK MOTOR LINES INC
3934 Homewood Rd, Memphis, TN 38118-6132
Tel (901) 251-9711 *Founded/Ownrshp* 1979
Sales 146.2MM *EMP* 875
Accts Dixon Hughes Goodman Memphis
SIC 4213 Trucking, except local
Pr: Steven F Higginbotham
**CEO:* Thomas Higginbotham
**COO:* Donnie Caldwell
**CFO:* Michael Hopper
Sr VP: Ron Hamby
VP: Michael Gilmore
VP Opers: Mark Laine
Natl Sales: Mark Baker
Natl Sales: Sheryll Steele
VP Sls: Bobby Hartley
Manager: J Coke
Board of Directors: Steven F Higginbotham, Thomas M Higginbotham, Michael E Hopper

D-U-N-S 79-991-0448 EXP
OZARK MOUNTAIN POULTRY INC
OMP FOODS
750 W E St, Rogers, AR 72756
Tel (479) 633-8700 *Founded/Ownrshp* 2000
Sales 171.3MM^E *EMP* 650^E
SIC 2015 5144 Poultry slaughtering & processing; Poultry & poultry products
CEO: Ed Fryar Jr
**CFO:* Terry King
CIO: Larry Dillier
Dir IT: Kerry Crawford
Plnt Mgr: Scott Southerly
Mktg Dir: Melinda Acoach
Sales Asso: Justin Young

D-U-N-S 06-795-2846
OZARK NATIONAL LIFE INSURANCE CO
(*Suby of* CNS CORP) ★
500 E 9th St, Kansas City, MO 64106-2627
Tel (314) 664-4389 *Founded/Ownrshp* 1964, 1982
Sales NA *EMP* 80^E
SIC 6311 6321 Life insurance; Disability health insurance
Ch Bd: Charles N Sharpe Jr
**Treas:* Tim Emerson

D-U-N-S 10-914-4126
■ **OZARK PURCHASING LLC**
(*Suby of* OREILLY AUTO PARTS) ★
233 S Patterson Ave, Springfield, MO 65802-2210
Tel (417) 862-6708 *Founded/Ownrshp* 2001
Sales NA *EMP* 1,200
SIC 7389 Purchasing service
COO: Lawrence P O'Reilly

OZARKS CMNTY HOSP - SPRNGFIELD
See OZARKS COMMUNITY HOSPITAL INC

D-U-N-S 00-713-3754
OZARKS COCA-COLA/DR PEPPER BOTTLING CO (MO)
1777 N Packer Rd, Springfield, MO 65803-5274
Tel (417) 865-9900 *Founded/Ownrshp* 1921, 1954
Sales 100.2MM^E *EMP* 330
SIC 2086 5149 Carbonated beverages, nonalcoholic: bottled & canned; Soft drinks
Ch: Edwin C Rice
**Pr:* John Schaefer
**Treas:* Virginia R Heer
**VP:* Harriet H Brown
**VP:* Marty Meyers
IT Man: Chrissy Stillings
Opers Mgr: Randy Henkle
Sls Mgr: Bruce Long
Board of Directors: Joe Greene, Suzy Heer, Peggy Rice, Sally Hargis Are Stockhold

D-U-N-S 82-739-7949
OZARKS COMMUNITY HOSPITAL INC
OZARKS CMNTY HOSP - SPRNGFIELD
2828 N National Ave, Springfield, MO 65803-4306
Tel (417) 837-4000 *Founded/Ownrshp* 2007
Sales 45.2MM *EMP* 2,535^E
SIC 8062 General medical & surgical hospitals
CEO: Paul Taylor
Exec: Jay Baker

D-U-N-S 00-385-2019
OZARKS ELECTRIC COOPERATIVE CORP (AR)
3641 W Wedington Dr, Fayetteville, AR 72704-5742
Tel (479) 521-2900 *Founded/Ownrshp* 1938
Sales 123.2MM *EMP* 190
SIC 4911 Distribution, electric power
Pr: Mitchell Johnson
VP: Kay Wilkerson
VP: Phyllis Young
Genl Mgr: Patrick Oehlschlager
IT Man: Carl Thomas

D-U-N-S 07-696-5391
OZARKS MEDICAL CENTER
1100 N Kentucky Ave, West Plains, MO 65775-2029
Tel (417) 256-9111 *Founded/Ownrshp* 1955
Sales 134.7MM *EMP* 1,000
SIC 8062 Hospital, affiliated with AMA residency
CEO: David Zechman
**COO:* Pamela Lee
**CFO:* Kim Thompson
Treas: Roger Hunt
VP: Jeffery Jones
Dir Inf Cn: Torrance Hughes
Dir Rad: John McKinzie
Dir Rx: Jeremiah McWilliams
Genl Mgr: Tammy Barstow
CIO: John Wilcox
CTO: Valarie Williams

OZARKS TECHNICAL CMNTY COLLEGE
See COMMUNITY COLLEGE DISTRICT OF CENTRAL SW MO

D-U-N-S 13-245-1134
OZBURN-HESSEY HOLDING CO LLC
(*Suby of* GEODIS WILSON USA INC) ★
7101 Executive Center Dr # 333, Brentwood, TN 37027-3283
Tel (615) 401-6400 *Founded/Ownrshp* 2015
Sales 1.2MMM^E *EMP* 6,000^E
SIC 4225 8742 General warehousing & storage; Management consulting services
COO: Mike Honious
CFO: Matt Hoogerland
Ofcr: Frank M Eichler
Ex VP: Fred Loeffel

Sr VP: Al Benki
CIO: Eric Douglas
Sfty Mgr: Tim Whittle

D-U-N-S 00-787-0256
OZINGA BROS INC (IL)
19001 Old Lagrange Rd # 30, Mokena, IL 60448-8012
Tel (708) 326-4200 *Founded/Ownrshp* 1928
Sales 200.0MM^E *EMP* 350
SIC 3273 5032 Ready-mixed concrete; Brick, stone & related material
Ch Bd: Martin Ozinga III
Treas: Brent Dyk
**VP:* James A Ozinga

OZZ PROPERTIES
See JET INDUSTRIES INC

D-U-N-S 17-592-1311 IMP
P & C GROUP I INC
CHEMICAL
37000 W 12 Mile Rd, Farmington Hills, MI 48331-3032
Tel (248) 442-6800 *Founded/Ownrshp* 1996
Sales 581.8MM^E *EMP* 2,000
SIC 3499 3465 Automobile seat frames, metal; Automotive stampings
Pr: Arvind Pradhan
CTO: Dave Smith

D-U-N-S 13-100-4033
P & J FUEL INC
2456 Saint Georges Ave, Rahway, NJ 07065-2123
Tel (732) 382-5100 *Founded/Ownrshp* 2002
Sales 662.7MM *EMP* 3
SIC 5172 Gasoline
Pr: Jasbir S Chandi

D-U-N-S 80-001-4821
P & L DEVELOPMENT LLC
PL DEVELOPMENTS
200 Hicks St, Westbury, NY 11590-3323
Tel (516) 986-1700 *Founded/Ownrshp* 1992
Sales 275.9MM^E *EMP* 600
SIC 2834 Pharmaceutical preparations
Ch Bd: Mitchell Singer
**Pr:* Evan Singer
**CFO:* Richard Martorella
**Sr VP:* John Francis
**Sr VP:* Dana S Toops
VP: Brad Larson
**VP:* Linda Singer
**VP:* Sophia Sutphen
Creative D: Anthony Bartolomeo
Opers Mgr: Patrick Heelan
Sls Dir: Earl Cassell

P & N BIG 8 SUPERMARKET
See BIG 8 FOODS LTD

D-U-N-S 04-604-5423
P & R ENTERPRISES INC
5681 Columbia Pike # 101, Falls Church, VA 22041-2886
Tel (703) 379-2018 *Founded/Ownrshp* 1969
Sales 45.1MM^E *EMP* 1,500
SIC 7349 Janitorial service, contract basis
Ch Bd: Charles H Solem
**Pr:* Carlos Sanchez
CFO: Marshall Gross
**Sec:* Santos Medina
**Ex VP:* Richard Thompson

D-U-N-S 02-866-8770 EXP
P & R PAPER SUPPLY CO INC
1898 E Colton Ave, Redlands, CA 92374-9798
Tel (909) 389-1811 *Founded/Ownrshp* 1991
Sales 122.4MM^E *EMP* 103^E
SIC 5113 5169 5149 5072 5046 Industrial & personal service paper; Chemicals & allied products; Groceries & related products; Hardware; Commercial equipment
CEO: Mark S Maiberger
**CFO:* Joe Maiberger
**VP:* Luke Maiberger

P A E
See PAE GOVERNMENT SERVICES INC

D-U-N-S 09-744-3311
P A LANDERS INC
351 Winter St, Hanover, MA 02339-2509
Tel (781) 826-8818 *Founded/Ownrshp* 1978
Sales 111.3MM^E *EMP* 280^E
SIC 1611 1442 Highway & street construction; Construction sand & gravel
Pr: David R Prosper
**Pr:* Joseph R Timmons
**Treas:* Louise M Landers
CTO: Joe Durant
Sfty Dirs: Steve Casey
Site Mgr: John Fontes
Sfty Mgr: Bob Haggerty

P A M L
See PATHOLOGY ASSOCIATES MEDICAL LABORATORIES LLC

P A T H
See PORT AUTHORITY TRANS-HUDSON CORP

P B
See PARSONS BRINCKERHOFF INC

P B A
See PALM BEACH ATLANTIC UNIVERSITY ALUMNI ASSOCIATION

P B ELECTRICAL SUPPLY
See CAPE ELECTRICAL SUPPLY LLC

D-U-N-S 16-165-9735
P C BOHLER ENGINEERING
35 Technology Dr Ste 5, Warren, NJ 07059-5172
Tel (908) 222-0023 *Founded/Ownrshp* 1985
Sales 90.6MM^E *EMP* 225
SIC 8711 Consulting engineer
Pr: Ludwig H Bohler

**COO:* Brian Zappala
**CFO:* Lewis Sidorsky
Trst: Jim P AIA
**VP:* Eric L Steinfeldt
Dir Bus: Dan Duggan
**Prin:* Joseph A Deal
**Prin:* William D Goebel
Mktg Dir: Jessica Spina

P C C
See POLYNESIAN CULTURAL CENTER INC

P C C
See PRECISION CUSTOM COATINGS LLC

D-U-N-S 18-445-5975
P C CORTLAND PATHOLOGY
CORTLAND REGIONAL MEDICAL CENT
134 Homer Ave, Cortland, NY 13045-1206
Tel (607) 756-3500 *Founded/Ownrshp* 1997
Sales 96.8MM *EMP* 4
SIC 8071 Pathological laboratory
Ch Bd: Paul D Digiovanni MD
Dir IT: Robin Puzo

P C M
See PMC GLOBAL INC

P C M
See PROFESSIONAL COMMUNITY MANAGEMENT OF CALIFORNIA

D-U-N-S 10-006-1329
P C NORTHWEST PERMANENTE
KAISER PERMANENTE
500 Ne Multnomah St # 100, Portland, OR 97232-2031
Tel (877) 313-3424 *Founded/Ownrshp* 1977
Sales 117.3MM^E *EMP* 3,000
SIC 8082 Home health care services
CEO: Andrew McCulloch
**Pr:* Jeffrey A Weisz
Ofcr: Charles Stearns
VP: Karen Schartman
Exec: Patricia A Peters
Ex Dir: Kay Marshall
Ex Dir: Sabrina Tsymbalenko
CIO: Robin Riversong
Dir IT: Belinda Green
IT Man: Alec Lee
IT Man: Gale Moore

D-U-N-S 01-355-0645 IMP
P C RICHARD & SON LONG ISLAND CORP (NY)
(*Suby of* PC RICHARD & SON) ★
150 Price Pkwy, Farmingdale, NY 11735-1315
Tel (631) 843-4300 *Founded/Ownrshp* 1909, 1993
Sales 147.2MM^E *EMP* 1,445^E
SIC 5722 5731 5064 Household appliance stores; Radio, television & electronic stores; Electrical appliances, television & radio
CEO: Gregg Richard
**Pr:* Alfred J Richard
**Treas:* Kevin Hughey
**VP:* Thomas Pohmer
**VP:* Peter C Richard

P C S
See PROJECT CONSULTING SERVICES INC

D-U-N-S 18-347-0074
P C YOUNGWILLIAMS
141 Township Ave Ste 200, Ridgeland, MS 39157-8699
Tel (601) 990-3100 *Founded/Ownrshp* 1994
Sales 65.9MM *EMP* 1,156
Accts Haddox Reid Eubank Betts Pllc
SIC 8111 Specialized legal services
Pr: Robert L Wells
**Pr:* Robert Johnson
**Ofcr:* Arthur Dale Currie
VP: Lori Bengston
VP: Darrin Greene
**CTO:* John Tidwell
**VP Mktg:* Mary Ann Wellbank
Board of Directors: Wes Ellis, James Neeld IV

P D A
See PRODUCTION DESIGN ASSOCIATES INC

P D C
See PERORIA DISPOSAL CO

P D C
See PDNC LLC

P D C
See PREMIER DISTRIBUTING CO

P D I
See PERISHABLE DISTRIBUTORS OF IOWA LTD

P D I
See PLUMBING DISTRIBUTORS INC

D-U-N-S 04-262-5590
P D M CO INC
BURGER KING
185 Ferguson Ave, Shavertown, PA 18708-1114
Tel (570) 675-3636 *Founded/Ownrshp* 1967
Sales 37.3MM^E *EMP* 1,000
SIC 5812 Fast-food restaurant, chain
Pr: Stephen I Morris
**Treas:* Kimetha D Morris
**VP:* John McCafferty

P D S
See PARAGON DEVELOPMENT SYSTEMS INC

P. F. D. LEBANON
See P F D SUPPLY CORP

D-U-N-S 04-772-6534
P F D SUPPLY CORP
P. F. D. LEBANON
(*Suby of* PRAIRIE FARMS DAIRY INC) ★
1100 Broadway, Carlinville, IL 62626-1183
Tel (217) 854-2547 *Founded/Ownrshp* 1968
Sales 131.5MM^E *EMP* 209
SIC 5143 Milk & cream, fluid; Butter; Cheese; Ice cream & ices
Pr: Paul Mills

P F G
See PERFORMANCE FOOD GROUP INC

P F S C M
See PARTNERSHIP FOR SUPPLY CHAIN MANAGEMENT INC

D-U-N-S 00-342-4082 IMP
P FLANIGAN AND SONS INC
2444 Loch Raven Rd, Baltimore, MD 21218-5491
Tel (410) 467-5900 *Founded/Ownrshp* 1885
Sales 84.0MM *EMP* 275
Accts Mcgladrey Llp Baltimore Mar
SIC 1611 Highway & street paving contractor
Pr: Pierce Flanigan IV
**VP:* Kevin Mullen
**VP:* Glenn Schultz
**VP:* Steve Whitecotton
VP Sls: Rod Barnes
Board of Directors: Pierce Flanigan IV, Glenn Schultz

P G E
See PENNSYLVANIA GENERAL ENERGY CORP

D-U-N-S 00-300-3407 IMP/EXP
▲ P H GLATFELTER CO
96 S Gorge St Ste 500, York, PA 17401
Tel (717) 225-4711 *Founded/Ownrshp* 1864
Sales 1.6MMM *EMP* 4,375
Tkr Sym GLT *Exch* NYS
SIC 2621 Book paper; Copy paper; Envelope paper; Filter paper
Ch Bd: Dante C Parrini
Pr: Christopher W Astley
Pr: John Jacunski
CFO: John P Jacunski
Treas: J R Anke
Treas: Donald Gross
VP: Timothy R Hess
VP: Brian E Janki
VP: Kent K Matsumoto
VP: John Stachowiak
VP: Calvin Staudt Jr
VP: Mark A Sullivan
VP: Joseph Zakutney
Board of Directors: Bruce Brown, Kathleen A Dahlberg, Nicholas Debenedictis, Kevin M Fogarty, J Robert Hall, Richard C III, Ronald J Naples, Richard L Smoot, Lee C Stewart

P H I
See PILKINGTON HOLDINGS INC

P H R
See PROFESSIONAL HOSPITALITY RESOURCES INC

P I I
See PHARMACEUTICS INTERNATIONAL INC

D-U-N-S 00-780-3224
P J HOERR INC
107 N Commerce Pl, Peoria, IL 61604-5285
Tel (309) 688-9567 *Founded/Ownrshp* 1914
Sales 98.8MM^E *EMP* 260
SIC 1542 Commercial & office building, new construction; Commercial & office buildings, renovation & repair
CEO: Robert A Hoerr
**Pr:* Joseph R Hart
Ofcr: Gene Fandel
**VP:* Kirk Anderson
**VP:* Paul Bright
**VP:* Kurt Davis
**VP:* Mike Eskridge
**VP:* John Moses
Exec: Alesia Conover
Exec: Jerry Schoenholtz
IT Man: Jesse Hoerr

D-U-N-S 05-518-9856
P J K FOOD SERVICE CORP
KEANY PRODUCE COMPANY
3310 75th Ave, Landover, MD 20785-1501
Tel (301) 772-3333 *Founded/Ownrshp* 1970
Sales 221.8MM^E *EMP* 350
SIC 5148 Fresh fruits & vegetables
Pr: Kevin Keany
CFO: Michael Timberlake
**VP:* Christopher Keany
VP: Dana Rolander
Ex Dir: Roy Cargiulo
QA Dir: Hassan Sesay
IT Man: Dave Zuchelli
Opers Mgr: Norman Keany

D-U-N-S 87-750-9398
P J UNITED INC
PAPA JOHN'S
2300 Resource Dr, Birmingham, AL 35242-2996
Tel (205) 981-7173 *Founded/Ownrshp* 2014
Sales 45.1MM^E *EMP* 1,500
SIC 5812 Pizzeria, chain
Pr: Doug Stephens

P J'S CONSTRUCTION SUPPLIES
See PJS LUMBER INC

P K F CONSTRUCTION
See PKF-MARK III INC

D-U-N-S 00-194-9007 IMP/EXP
P KAUFMANN INC (NY)
OTHER STYLES-SEE OPERATION
3 Park Ave, New York, NY 10016-5902
Tel (212) 292-2200 *Founded/Ownrshp* 1950, 1957
Sales 207.7MM^E *EMP* 400
SIC 5131 5714 5712 2262 Cotton goods; Drapery material, woven; Upholstery fabrics, woven; Curtains; Draperies; Furniture stores; Finishing plants, manmade fiber & silk fabrics
Ch Bd: Ronald Kaufmann
**CFO:* Laurence Seigel
**VP:* Robert Appelbaum
**VP:* Curtis Breedlove
**VP:* Lance Garcy
**VP:* Neil Paladino
**VP:* Howard Tooter
Prin: Patrick Finnen

P M A
See PACIFIC MARITIME ASSOCIATION INC

P M C
See PIKEVILLE MEDICAL CENTER INC

D-U-N-S 08-614-7246
P M GROUP INC
1050 Corporate Office Dr, Milford, MI 48381-5009
Tel (248) 529-2000 *Founded/Ownrshp* 1973
Sales 11.0MM^E *EMP* 1,200
Accts Plante/Moran
SIC 6531 1522 6552 Cooperative apartment manager; Residential construction; Subdividers & developers
Ch Bd: Daniel Armstead
Pr: John J Hayes

P M I
See PMI MORTGAGE INSURANCE CO

P M I
See PROJECT MANAGEMENT INSTITUTE INC

P M I
See PERFORMANCE MECHANICAL INC

P M T
See ANTARCTIC MECHANICAL SERVICES INC

P N I
See PROFESSIONAL NURSING INC

D-U-N-S 14-341-3529
P O I ACQUISITION I INC
(*Suby of* POI ACQUISITION, LLC)
375 Park Ave Ste 1202, New York, NY 10152-0002
Tel (212) 418-1700 *Founded/Ownrshp* 2004
Sales 52.9MM^E *EMP* 3,025^E
SIC 6799 Venture capital companies
Genl Mgr: Andrew Jackson

P O S
See PROFESSIONAL OFFICE SERVICES INC

P R I
See PHYSICIANS RECIPROCAL INSURERS

P R MEDICAL CENTER
See ADMINISTRACION DE SERVICIOS MEDICOS DE PR

D-U-N-S 96-354-0542
P R PATHEON LLC
(*Suby of* PATHEON INC)
2 Calle Aquamarina Villa, Caguas, PR 00725-1944
Tel (787) 746-8500 *Founded/Ownrshp* 2007
Sales 338.1MM^E *EMP* 1,064^E
SIC 2834 Pharmaceutical preparations
CEO: Wes Wheeler

P S
See PEERLESS STEEL CO

P S
See PRIMESOURCE BUILDING PRODUCTS INC

P S C
See PSC INDUSTRIES INC

P S E & G
See PUBLIC SERVICE ELECTRIC AND GAS CO INC

P S I
See PLANNED SYSTEMS INTERNATIONAL INC

P S P
See PUGET SOUND PIPE AND SUPPLY CO

P U D
See MASON COUNTY PUBLIC UTILITY DISTRICT NO 3

P U P
See PHYSICIANS UNITED PLAN INC

P V A
See PARALYZED VETERANS OF AMERICA

P W C
See PUBLIC WORKS COMMISSION OF CITY OF FAYETTEVILLE

P X P
See VIRTUS PARTNERS INC

P&G
See PROCTER & GAMBLE CO

D-U-N-S 78-001-4226
P&MCS HOLDING LLC
(*Suby of* CASTLE HARLAN PARTNERS IV LP) ★
150 E 58th St, New York, NY 10155-0002
Tel (212) 644-8600 *Founded/Ownrshp* 2005
Sales 36.8MM^E *EMP* 5,011^E
SIC 5812 Restaurant, family: chain
Pr: Joseph Trungale

D-U-N-S 16-546-2842
P&S TRANSPORTATION LLC
(*Suby of* PS LOGISTICS LLC) ★
1810 Avenue C, Birmingham, AL 35218-1552
Tel (205) 788-4000 *Founded/Ownrshp* 2004
Sales 122.1MM^E *EMP* 350
SIC 4213 4789 Trucking, except local; Cargo loading & unloading services
CEO: Robbie Pike
CFO: Brian Barze
CFO: Steve Majewski
Ex VP: Scott Smith
VP: Kevin Atenhan
VP: Joe Thornton

P-NETIX
See EVERCOM SYSTEMS INC

D-U-N-S 07-872-9057
P-WAVE HOLDINGS LLC
10877 Wilshire Blvd, Los Angeles, CA 90024-4341
Tel (310) 209-3010 *Founded/Ownrshp* 2012
Sales 38.1MM^E *EMP* 2,179
SIC 6799 Investors

D-U-N-S 02-975-4418
P1 GROUP INC
13605 W 96th Ter, Lenexa, KS 66215-1253
Tel (913) 529-5000 *Founded/Ownrshp* 1997
Sales 203.5MM *EMP* 825
Accts Mayer Hoffman Mccann Pc Tope
SIC 1711 1731 Mechanical contractor; Electrical work
CEO: Smitty Belcher
VP: Dave Beebe
VP: Rick Cline
VP: Steve Cole
VP: Phil Nehring
VP: Stuart Sherrow
VP: Paul Smith
Opers Mgr: Casey Walsh
Snr PM: Rick Ellis
Snr PM: Carey Minihan
Snr PM: David Sall

D-U-N-S 82-855-6048
P2 ACQUISITION LLC
216 16th St Ste 1700, Denver, CO 80202-5142
Tel (303) 390-9400 *Founded/Ownrshp* 2008
Sales 488.6MM[E] *EMP* 350[E]
SIC 7389 Auction, appraisal & exchange services
VP: Gerry Conroy
VP: Chris Kelly
VP: George Telford

D-U-N-S 83-178-2300
P2 ENERGY SOLUTIONS INC
1670 Broadway Ste 2800, Denver, CO 80202-4800
Tel (303) 292-0990 *Founded/Ownrshp* 2013
Sales 804.6MM[E] *EMP* 755[E]
SIC 1382 Oil & gas exploration services
CEO: Amy Zupon
Ch Bd: Harry Debes
Pr: Andy Bane
CEO: Bret Bolin
COO: Chad Martin
COO: David Muse
Sr VP: Peter Huggard
Sr VP: Richard Pang
Sr VP: Audrey Rogers
Sr VP: Jerry Rugg
VP: Gerry Conroy
Board of Directors: Mike McCrory

D-U-N-S 82-820-3633
P2 NEWCO INC
(*Suby of* P2 ACQUISITION LLC) ★
216 16th St Ste 1700, Denver, CO 80202-5142
Tel (303) 390-9400 *Founded/Ownrshp* 2008
Sales 488.6MM[E] *EMP* 353[E]
SIC 7389 Auction, appraisal & exchange services
Prin: Gary R Vickers
VP: Chris Kelly

D-U-N-S 11-109-8252
P2P STAFFING CORP
TEKPARTNERS
5810 Coral Ridge Dr # 250, Coral Springs, FL 33076-3381
Tel (954) 656-8600 *Founded/Ownrshp* 2002
Sales 179.9MM *EMP* 950
SIC 7361 Employment agencies
Pr: Vito Scutero
Mng Pt: Alfred Mazzo Sr
**Pr:* Harris Katz
**CFO:* Gregg Straus
**Ex VP:* Jay Bevilacqua
Ex VP: Jerald Sowell
Natl Sales: Cindy Adler
Natl Sales: Jennifer G Reed
Mktg Dir: Milgrim Bello
Mktg Dir: Michelle Blanford

D-U-N-S 06-260-1338
P3 INFRASTRUCTURE INC
3105 Preakness Dr, Stow, OH 44224-6243
Tel (330) 686-1129 *Founded/Ownrshp* 2012
Sales 33.5MM[E] *EMP* 2,012
SIC 7389
Prin: Puneet Singh

D-U-N-S 02-423-0302
P4 CORP
DAYCON PRODUCTS COMPANY
16001 Trade Zone Ave, Upper Marlboro, MD 20774-8795
Tel (301) 218-7039 *Founded/Ownrshp* 1966
Sales 102.1MM[E] *EMP* 157
Accts Reznick Group
SIC 5087 5072 Janitors' supplies; Hardware
CEO: Robert N Cohen
**Pr:* John Poole
**Ex VP:* Harry Feldman
CIO: Don Mackellar
MIS Dir: Kerry Gao
VP Sls: Robert Baldwin
Sls Mgr: Fred Page
Sales Asso: Casey Payne

D-U-N-S 00-832-5230 IMP
■ **PA ACQUISITION CORP**
PARTY AMERICA
(*Suby of* PARTY CITY HOLDINGS INC) ★
25 Green Pond Rd Ste 1, Rockaway, NJ 07866-2047
Tel (973) 453-8600 *Founded/Ownrshp* 1990
Sales 155.7MM[E] *EMP* 1,764
SIC 5947 7389 Party favors; Balloons, novelty & toy
Pr: Marty Allen
**CFO:* Robert Dillon
**VP:* Alice Tang

D-U-N-S 79-656-7683
PA DEPARTMENT OF MILITARY AND VETERANS AFFAIRS
(*Suby of* GOVERNORS OFFICE) ★
47 Bldg S-O, Annville, PA 17003
Tel (717) 861-8500 *Founded/Ownrshp* 1793
Sales NA *EMP* 6,628
SIC 9711 9451 National security; ; Administration of veterans' affairs;

D-U-N-S 60-597-2512
PA EMPLOYEES BENEFIT TRUST FUND (INC)
PEBTF
150 S 43rd St Ste 1, Harrisburg, PA 17111-5708
Tel (717) 561-4750 *Founded/Ownrshp* 1988
Sales NA *EMP* 175
SIC 6411 Pension & retirement plan consultants
Bd of Dir: Jerry Anastasio
Ex Dir: Kathryn M Farley
CIO: Bruce Shearer
Telecom Mg: John-Marc Blanch
Sales Exec: Virginia McGarvey
Sls&Mrk Ex: Christy Leo

D-U-N-S 80-838-4767
PA MEADOWS LLC
9107 W Russell Rd, Las Vegas, NV 89148-1233
Tel (702) 856-5158 *Founded/Ownrshp* 2005
Sales 249.5MM *EMP* 2
Accts Piercy Bowler Taylor & Kern
SIC 7999 Gambling & lottery services

D-U-N-S 87-621-2861
■ **PAACO AUTOMOTIVE GROUP LP**
PAACO CARS & TRUCKS
(*Suby of* AMERICAS CAR-MART INC) ★
3200 E Randol Mill Rd, Arlington, TX 76011-6838
Tel (817) 635-2000 *Founded/Ownrshp* 1998
Sales 110.9MM[E] *EMP* 400
SIC 5521 Used car dealers

PAACO CARS & TRUCKS
See PAACO AUTOMOTIVE GROUP LP

PAAS EASTER EGG
See SIGNATURE BRANDS LLC

D-U-N-S 12-907-1838 IMP
PABCO BUILDING PRODUCTS LLC
(*Suby of* PACIFIC COAST BUILDING PRODUCTS INC) ★
10600 White Rock Rd # 100, Rancho Cordova, CA 95670-6293
Tel (510) 792-1577 *Founded/Ownrshp* 1976
Sales 193.5MM[E] *EMP* 803
Accts Boden Klein & Sneesby Rosevil
SIC 3275 3251 3259 Gypsum products; Brick clay: common face, glazed, vitrified or hollow; Architectural terra cotta
Pr: Ryan Lucchetti
**CFO:* Brian Hobdy
**Bd of Dir:* Jack Haarlander
**Bd of Dir:* Alfred Mueller
**Bd of Dir:* Larry Solari
**VP:* John Corbett
**VP:* Michael Willoughby
**VP Mfg:* Emil Kopilovich

D-U-N-S 78-940-4675
PABST BREWING CO LLC
10635 Santa Monica Blvd, Los Angeles, CA 90025-8300
Tel (310) 470-0962 *Founded/Ownrshp* 2014
Sales 218.2MM[E] *EMP* 280
SIC 2082 Malt beverages
CEO: Simon Thorpe
**Ch Bd:* Eugene Kashper
**CFO:* Cordell Sweeney
VP: Mark S Beatty
VP: Tim McGettigan
**VP:* Ed Prike
VP: Lyssa Reynolds
VP: Doug Walker
VP Bus Dev: Richard Pascucci
Area Mgr: Alex Merrick
Area Mgr: Jay Toxey

D-U-N-S 02-025-5360 IMP
PAC WORLDWIDE CORP
(*Suby of* PAC WORLDWIDE HOLDING CO) ★
15435 Ne 92nd St, Redmond, WA 98052-3516
Tel (425) 202-4015 *Founded/Ownrshp* 1996
Sales 178.1MM[E] *EMP* 250
SIC 5199 Packaging materials
Pr: James Boshaw
VP: Murray Fullerton
IT Man: Debbie Flowers

D-U-N-S 96-885-4240 IMP/EXP
PAC WORLDWIDE HOLDING CO
15435 Ne 92nd St, Redmond, WA 98052-3516
Tel (800) 535-0039 *Founded/Ownrshp* 1996
Sales 188.8MM[E] *EMP* 250
SIC 5199 Packaging materials
Pr: James Boshaw
**CFO:* Jeff Snow
**Ch:* Phillip Boshaw
CTO: Linda Hansen
CTO: Jeff Rogers

PAC/GRO AND ASSOCIATES
See NATIONAL FROZEN FOODS CORP

PACBELL
See PACIFIC BELL TELEPHONE CO

D-U-N-S 00-794-2469
■ **PACCAR FINANCIAL CORP** (WA)
(*Suby of* PACCAR INC) ★
777 106th Ave Ne, Bellevue, WA 98004-5027
Tel (425) 468-7100 *Founded/Ownrshp* 1961
Sales NA *EMP* 402[E]
SIC 6153 Financing of dealers by motor vehicle manufacturers organ.
Ch Bd: Ronald E Armstrong
**Pr:* Todd R Hubbard
**CFO:* Robert A Bengston
Treas: Beth Kent
Sr VP: Nicholas P Panza
Dir IT: Steve Bach
Dir IT: John Holtman
Dir IT: Charles Lreamy
Dir IT: Phat Ourn
Dir IT: Eric Skinner
Dir IT: Arron Vanwormer

D-U-N-S 04-834-1267
▲ **PACCAR INC**
777 106th Ave Ne, Bellevue, WA 98004-5027
Tel (425) 468-7400 *Founded/Ownrshp* 1905
Sales 19.1MMM *EMP* 23,000[E]
Tkr Sym PCAR *Exch* NGS
SIC 3711 3714 3713 3537 5013 6153 Truck & tractor truck assembly; Truck tractors for highway use, assembly of; Motor vehicle parts & accessories; Truck & bus bodies; Industrial trucks & tractors; Motor vehicle supplies & new parts; Financing of dealers by motor vehicle manufacturers organ.
CEO: Ronald E Armstrong
**Ch Bd:* Mark C Pigott
Pr: Robert J Christensen
Ex VP: Dan Sobic
Sr VP: Michael T Barkley
Sr VP: Robert A Bengston
VP: David C Anderson
VP: David Anderson
VP: Michael Barkley
VP: James Cardillo
VP: Art Clemencia
VP: Michele Conrad
VP: Peter Danes
VP: Val O Leary
VP: Jay Van Leeuwen
Exec: Bob Southern
Dir Risk M: Rebecca McQuade
Board of Directors: Dame Alison J Carnwath, Beth E Ford, Kirk S Hachigian, Luiz Kaufmann, Roderick C McGeary, John M Pigott, Mark A Schulz, Gregory M E Spierkel, Charles R Williamson

D-U-N-S 80-668-1446
PACE AMERICAS LLC
ARRIS
(*Suby of* PACE AMERICAS HOLDINGS, INC.)
3701 Fau Blvd Ste 200, Boca Raton, FL 33431-6491
Tel (561) 995-6000 *Founded/Ownrshp* 2007
Sales 124.8MM[E] *EMP* 310
SIC 7371 5065 Custom computer programming services; Television parts & accessories
VP: Marty Novak
Snr Sftwr: Adam Sternberg
Sls Dir: Mark R Besocke

PACE ANALYTICAL SERVICES, INC.
See PACE ANALYTICAL SERVICES LLC

D-U-N-S 83-733-2196
PACE ANALYTICAL SERVICES LLC
PACE ANALYTICAL SERVICES, INC.
(*Suby of* LAB HOLDINGS INC) ★
1800 Elm St Se, Minneapolis, MN 55414-2500
Tel (612) 607-6369 *Founded/Ownrshp* 1995
Sales 336.0MM[E] *EMP* 1,350
SIC 8734 8748 8731 Hazardous waste testing; Soil analysis; Water testing laboratory; Business consulting; Commercial physical research
Pr: Steve A Vanderboom
**Ch Bd:* Rodney Burwell
**COO:* Jack Dullaghan
**COO:* Gregory D Kupp
**COO:* Gabe Lebrun
**CFO:* Michael R Prasch
CFO: Mike Prasch
Ofcr: Sarah Cherney
VP: Jack P Dullaghan
Dir Lab: Ben Messay
Prgrm Mgr: Nathan Eklund

PACE BUS
See PACE SUBURBAN BUS DIVISION OF REGIONAL TRANSPORTATION AUTHORITY

D-U-N-S 05-196-4583 IMP
PACE INDUSTRIES LLC
(*Suby of* KPI INTERMEDIATE HOLDINGS INC) ★
481 S Shiloh Dr, Fayetteville, AR 72704-7552
Tel (479) 443-1455 *Founded/Ownrshp* 2007
Sales 719.4MM[E] *EMP* 2,800
SIC 3363 Aluminum die-castings
CEO: Scott J Bull
CFO: Jim Hurley
VP: Kenny Sandlin
Brnch Mgr: Bruce Kreutzer

D-U-N-S 05-562-8788
PACE RESOURCES INC
140 E Market St Fl 2, York, PA 17401-1219
Tel (717) 852-1300 *Founded/Ownrshp* 1970
Sales 101.9MM[E] *EMP* 500
SIC 2752 5049 7334 2789 Commercial printing, offset; Photolithographic printing; Drafting supplies; Engineers' equipment & supplies; Photocopying & duplicating services; Bookbinding & related work
Pr: William Dannehl
**Pr:* Russell E Horn Jr
CFO: Hal G McClure
Treas: Fae Byers
Founder: Russell E Horn Sr
VP: Brian Funkhouser
IT Man: Mark Valenti

D-U-N-S 13-120-5833
PACE SUBURBAN BUS DIVISION OF REGIONAL TRANSPORTATION AUTHORITY
PACE BUS
550 W Algonquin Rd, Arlington Heights, IL 60005-4412
Tel (847) 364-7223 *Founded/Ownrshp* 1984
Sales 72.0MM *EMP* 1,480
SIC 4111

D-U-N-S 86-761-6906
PACE SUPPLY CORP
6000 State Farm Dr # 200, Rohnert Park, CA 94928-2226
Tel (707) 303-0320 *Founded/Ownrshp* 1994
Sales 206.7MM[E] *EMP* 150
SIC 5074 Plumbing & hydronic heating supplies
Pr: Ted M Green
VP: Kelly Hubley
Dir IT: Gene Gorman
VP Sls: Jim Bresnahan
Sales Asso: Brittany Castillo
Sales Asso: Ray Solomon

D-U-N-S 06-496-1022
PACE UNIVERSITY
1 Pace Plz, New York, NY 10038-1598
Tel (212) 346-1956 *Founded/Ownrshp* 1948
Sales 492.9MM *EMP* 1,862
Accts Pricewaterhousecoopers Llp Ne
SIC 8221 University
Pr: Stephen J Friedman
Mng Pt: Jack J Ribeiro
Pr: Angelica Ferreira
**CFO:* Robert C Almon
**CFO:* Toby Weiner
Trst: Mark M Besca
Trst: Philip F Bleser
Trst: Donald L Boudreau
Trst: Christopher A Edwards
Trst: John A Gerson
Trst: Cynthia G Goldstein
Trst: Barry M Gosin
Trst: Bridget-Anne Hampden
Trst: James E Healey
Trst: Charles N Jordan Jr
Trst: Harold O Levy
Trst: Suresh Munshani
Trst: Edward F Murphy
Trst: John T O'Connor
Trst: Michael O'Reilly
Trst: Barbara Ann Porceddu
Board of Directors: Matthew B Poli

D-U-N-S 78-239-4964
PACEC LLC
333 Baldwin Rd, Pittsburgh, PA 15205-1751
Tel (412) 429-2324 *Founded/Ownrshp* 1998
Sales 105.1MM *EMP* 2
SIC 8748 Business consulting
Pr: Gregory C Black

D-U-N-S 07-939-4187
PACEM SOLUTION INTERNATIONAL LLC
2941 Frview Pk Dr Ste 550, Falls Church, VA 22042
Tel (703) 309-1891 *Founded/Ownrshp* 2014
Sales 227.0MM *EMP* 40
SIC 8748 Business consulting

D-U-N-S 60-900-4536
PACER ENERGY MARKETING LLC
823 S Detroit Ave Ste 300, Tulsa, OK 74120-4281
Tel (918) 398-2713 *Founded/Ownrshp* 1986
Sales 180.8MM[E] *EMP* 150
SIC 5172 Crude oil
VP: Orville Nichols
**Pr:* Larry Durham
**Treas:* Phil Burch

D-U-N-S 05-251-7369
■ **PACER TRANSPORTATION SOLUTIONS INC**
(*Suby of* XPO INTERMODAL INC) ★
5165 Emerald Pkwy, Dublin, OH 43017-1063
Tel (614) 923-1400 *Founded/Ownrshp* 1984
Sales 121.3MM[E] *EMP* 908
SIC 4731 Agents, shipping
Pr: Daniel W Avramovich
Pr: Charles Hoffman
CFO: John J Hafferty
Chf Cred: Michael A Burns
Ex VP: Michael F Killea
Ex VP: James E Ward
VP: Michael D Gordon
Netwrk Eng: Cullen REA

D-U-N-S 79-944-0698
PACESETTER CLAIMS SERVICE INC
2871 N Highway 167, Catoosa, OK 74015-2709
Tel (918) 665-8887 *Founded/Ownrshp* 1998
Sales NA *EMP* 325
SIC 6411 Insurance claim adjusters, not employed by insurance company
CEO: William Brassfield
**Pr:* Dale Brassfield
**CFO:* Amit Nihalani
**VP:* Stan Brown
**VP:* Barry Coleman
**VP:* Kelly Smoot
Dir IT: John Ray

D-U-N-S 88-499-4641 IMP
■ **PACESETTER INC**
VENTRITEX
(*Suby of* ST JUDE MEDICAL INC) ★
15900 Valley View Ct, Sylmar, CA 91342-3585
Tel (818) 362-6822 *Founded/Ownrshp* 1994
Sales 304.6MM[E] *EMP* 2,100
SIC 3845 Electromedical equipment; Defibrillator
CEO: Eric Fain
**Pr:* Ronald A Matricaria
Ofcr: Diane Frazier
VP: Gene Bornzin
VP: Paul A Levine
VP: Euljoon Park
VP: Ron Thompson
Snr Sftwr: Jean Harber
Snr Sftwr: Madhu Karnani
Snr Sftwr: Dan Starks
CTO: Fred Colen

D-U-N-S 08-491-3961 IMP
PACESETTER STEEL SERVICE INC
1045 Big Shanty Rd Nw, Kennesaw, GA 30144-3642
Tel (770) 919-8000 *Founded/Ownrshp* 1977
Sales 143.1MM[E] *EMP* 150
SIC 5051 Steel
CEO: Aviva Leebow
Pr: Steve Leebow
Ex VP: Jonathan C Rapaport

PACFIC PLUG LINER
See SMITH GARDENS INC

D-U-N-S 61-851-4413
■ **PACIFIC AG PRODUCTS LLC**
(*Suby of* PACIFIC ETHANOL INC) ★
400 Capitol Mall Ste 2060, Sacramento, CA 95814-4436
Tel (916) 403-2123 *Founded/Ownrshp* 2003
Sales 1.0MMM *EMP* 1[E]
SIC 2869 Ethanolamines
CEO: Neil Koehler

D-U-N-S 03-687-8999
PACIFIC ALLIANCE MEDICAL CENTER INC
PORTERCARE ADVENTIST HOSPITAL
(*Suby of* PORTERCARE ADVENTIST HOSPITAL) ★
2525 S Downing St, Denver, CO 80210-5817
Tel (303) 778-1955 *Founded/Ownrshp* 2002
Sales 315.4MM *EMP* 2,400
Accts Ernst & Young Llp
SIC 8062 General medical & surgical hospitals
CEO: Randy Haffner
Dir Vol: Geri Hopkins
**Pr:* Joe Swedish
**COO:* Dave Dookeeram
CFO: Terry Forde
**CFO:* Andrew Gaasch
Ofcr: Ryan Roux
**Sr VP:* Jim Boyle
VP: Carol Dozier
Dir Lab: Michael Ortt
**Prin:* Thomas Drake

D-U-N-S 08-541-0736 IMP/EXP
PACIFIC AMERICAN FISH CO INC
PAFCO
5525 S Santa Fe Ave, Vernon, CA 90058-3523
Tel (323) 319-1551 *Founded/Ownrshp* 1980
Sales 225.0MM^E *EMP* 300
SIC 5146 2091 Fish, fresh; Fish, frozen, unpackaged; Seafoods; Fish, filleted (boneless)
CEO: Peter Huh
**Ex VP:* Paul Huh

D-U-N-S 04-443-5766
PACIFIC ARCHITECTS AND ENGINEERS INC
PAE
(*Suby of* PAE APPLIED TECHNOLOGIES) ★
1320 N Courthouse Rd # 800, Arlington, VA 22201-2598
Tel (888) 526-5416 *Founded/Ownrshp* 2011
Sales 964.4MM^E *EMP* 5,000
SIC 8711 8712 Building construction consultant; Architectural services
Pr: John Heller
CFO: Clint Bickett
CFO: Dan Corbett
**Treas:* Brian Gorka
**Treas:* Robert Volpi
VP: Tom Callahan
VP: Mehdi Cherqaoui
**VP:* Tina Dolph
VP: Rich Greene
VP: Larry Helfand
VP: Randall Hose
Exec: Regina Fleming
Board of Directors: Robert Lindsay

D-U-N-S 14-709-4668 IMP
PACIFIC BELL DIRECTORY
SBC
101 Spear St Fl 5, San Francisco, CA 94105-1554
Tel (800) 303-3000 *Founded/Ownrshp* 1985
Sales NA *EMP* 2,400
SIC 2741

D-U-N-S 10-340-1618 IMP
■ **PACIFIC BELL TELEPHONE CO**
PACBELL
(*Suby of* AT&T INC) ★
430 Bush St Fl 3, San Francisco, CA 94108-3735
Tel (415) 542-9000 *Founded/Ownrshp* 1997
Sales 10.2MMM^E *EMP* 46,440
SIC 4813 2741 4822 Local & long distance telephone communications; Local telephone communications; Voice telephone communications; Data telephone communications; Directories, telephone: publishing only, not printed on site; Telegraph & other communications; Electronic mail
CEO: Kenneth P McNeely
**Pr:* Ray Wilkins Jr
VP: Paul Suchecki
Area Mgr: Howard Duff

D-U-N-S 86-116-7591
PACIFIC BELLS LLC
TACO BELL
111 W 39th St Ste A, Vancouver, WA 98660-1974
Tel (360) 694-7855 *Founded/Ownrshp* 1987
Sales 83.7MM^E *EMP* 1,500
SIC 5812 Fast-food restaurant, chain
Pr: Tom Cook
CFO: Mary Duhart-Bottoms

D-U-N-S 14-913-0325
▲ **PACIFIC BIOSCIENCES OF CALIFORNIA INC**
1380 Willow Rd, Menlo Park, CA 94025-1516
Tel (650) 521-8000 *Founded/Ownrshp* 2000
Sales 92.7MM *EMP* 394^E
Tkr Sym PACB *Exch* NGS
SIC 3826 Analytical instruments
CEO: Michael Hunkapiller
Pr: Denis Zaccarin
CFO: Susan K Barnes
Bd of Dir: Bill Ericson
Sr VP: Kevin Corcoran
Sr VP: Michael Phillips
VP: Lloyd Kunimoto
VP: Glenn Powell
Software D: Phillip Vallejo
Sales Exec: Steven Chow
Mktg Mgr: Mozhgan Novbakhtian
Board of Directors: David Botstein, Brook Byers, William Ericson, Randy Livingston, John F Milligan, Marshall Mohr, Kathy Ordonez, Lucy Shapiro

D-U-N-S 06-612-0825 IMP/EXP
PACIFIC CHEESE CO INC
21090 Cabot Blvd, Hayward, CA 94545-1110
Tel (510) 784-8800 *Founded/Ownrshp* 1970
Sales 800.0MM *EMP* 288^E
SIC 5143 Cheese
Pr: Stephen B Gaddis
COO: Tony Ricker
CFO: Dale Tate
**Sec:* June M Gaddis
VP: Jeff Richmond

D-U-N-S 02-550-0125 IMP
PACIFIC CLINICS (CA)
800 S Santa Anita Ave, Arcadia, CA 91006-3536
Tel (626) 254-5000 *Founded/Ownrshp* 1926
Sales 97.4MM *EMP* 800
SIC 8093 Mental health clinic, outpatient
Pr: Susan Mandel PHD
Chf Mktg O: George Drucker
**Ex VP:* James Balla
Genl Mgr: Joseph Wong
Dir IT: Michael Guition
IT Man: Yasmin Navarro

D-U-N-S 02-904-3056 IMP/EXP
PACIFIC COAST BUILDING PRODUCTS INC
10600 White Rock Rd # 100, Rancho Cordova, CA 95670-6294
Tel (916) 631-6500 *Founded/Ownrshp* 1953
Sales 926.8MM^E *EMP* 3,800
SIC 3275 3271 5031 1761 2952 2426

PACIFIC COAST CHEMICALS CO.
See HART CHEMICALS INC

D-U-N-S 19-449-8473
PACIFIC COAST CONTAINER INC
PCC NORTHWEST
432 Estudillo Ave Ste 1, San Leandro, CA 94577-4908
Tel (510) 346-6100 *Founded/Ownrshp* 1988
Sales 84.7MM^E *EMP* 280^E
Accts Armanino Mckenna Llp Cpa
SIC 4789 4225 4222 Cargo loading & unloading services; General warehousing; Warehousing, cold storage or refrigerated
CEO: Michael Mc Donnell
**CFO:* Abdel Zaharan

D-U-N-S 00-926-1280 IMP/EXP
PACIFIC COAST FEATHER CO
NATIONAL SLEEP PRODUCTS
1964 4th Ave S, Seattle, WA 98134-1504
Tel (206) 624-1057 *Founded/Ownrshp* 1939
Sales 434.3MM^E *EMP* 1,200
SIC 2392 Cushions & pillows; Comforters & quilts: made from purchased materials
Ch: Nick Hanauer
**Pr:* Joseph T Crawford
**VP:* Gwen Babcock
VP: Stew Bayuk
VP: Alex Blanco
**VP:* Allan Bundrick
**VP:* Lenore Hanauer
VP: Fritz Kruger
VP: Bud Pedersen
IT Man: Bob Rein
VP Mfg: Rafal Nakonieczny
Board of Directors: Adrian Hanauer, John Sinsheimer

D-U-N-S 05-744-2758 IMP/EXP
PACIFIC COAST PRODUCERS
631 N Cluff Ave, Lodi, CA 95240-0756
Tel (209) 367-8800 *Founded/Ownrshp* 1971
Sales 630.7MM *EMP* 1,000
Accts Kpmg Llp Sacramento Califor
SIC 2033 Fruits: packaged in cans, jars, etc.; Vegetables: packaged in cans, jars, etc.
CEO: Daniel L Vincent
V Ch: Ronald Vella
**CFO:* Matthew Strong
**Treas:* Zeb Rocha
VP: Ehrler Richard
**VP:* Andrew K Russick
**VP:* Mona Shulman
**VP:* Matt Strong
**VP:* Peter C Wtulich
CIO: Peter Woulich
VP Opers: Daniel Sroufe

D-U-N-S 12-907-3461
PACIFIC COAST SUPPLY LLC
(*Suby of* PACIFIC COAST BUILDING PRODUCTS INC) ★
4290 Roseville Rd, North Highlands, CA 95660-5710
Tel (916) 971-2301 *Founded/Ownrshp* 2001
Sales 451.2MM^E *EMP* 1,100^E
SIC 5031 Lumber, plywood & millwork
Pr: Curt Gomes
COO: Robert Ramos
**CFO:* Lisa Goeppner
**Bd of Dir:* Walter Payne
**VP:* Joe Gower
Dir IT: Ed Lawson
Opers Mgr: David Swallow

D-U-N-S 79-060-4511
■ **PACIFIC COMPENSATION CORP**
(*Suby of* ALLEGHANY CORP) ★
30301 Agoura Rd Ste 100, Agoura Hills, CA 91301-2096
Tel (818) 575-8500 *Founded/Ownrshp* 2007
Sales NA *EMP* 211^E
SIC 6411 Insurance agents, brokers & service
Ch Bd: Janet D Frank

D-U-N-S 12-136-2474
■ **PACIFIC COMPENSATION INSURANCE CO**
(*Suby of* PACIFIC COMPENSATION CORP) ★
1 Baxter Way Ste 170, Westlake Village, CA 91362-3819
Tel (818) 575-8500 *Founded/Ownrshp* 2002
Sales NA *EMP* 150
SIC 6331 Workers' compensation insurance
Ch Bd: Janet D Frank
Sr VP: Kris Mathis
VP: Joe Cardenas
VP: Chris Closser
VP: Mark Webb
Software D: Yanina Blyumina
Software D: Allan Kenworthy

D-U-N-S 83-245-3018
PACIFIC CONVENIENCE & FUELS LLC
7180 Koll Center Pkwy, Pleasanton, CA 94566-3184
Tel (925) 884-0800 *Founded/Ownrshp* 2008
Sales 107.0MM^E *EMP* 639^E
SIC 5411 5541 Convenience stores, chain; Filling stations, gasoline
CEO: Sam Hirbod
CFO: Dawn Croft
**Genl Mgr:* Chris Wilson

D-U-N-S 08-362-1032 IMP
PACIFIC CYCLE INC (DE)
(*Suby of* DOREL INDUSTRIES INC)
4902 Hammersley Rd, Madison, WI 53711-2614
Tel (608) 268-2468 *Founded/Ownrshp* 1998, 2004
Sales 129.0MM^E *EMP* 350
SIC 5091 5941 Bicycles; Sporting goods & bicycle shops
Pr: Bob Kmoch
**Treas:* Doug Eklund
VP: Rob Tecco
Creative D: Shanley Jue
CTO: Ed Matthews
Netwrk Eng: Michael Garrison
VP Sls: Bob Habersaat

D-U-N-S 96-376-7389
PACIFIC DENTAL SERVICES INC
PDS
17000 Red Hill Ave, Irvine, CA 92614-5626
Tel (714) 845-8500 *Founded/Ownrshp* 1995
Sales 327.2MM^E *EMP* 4,500
SIC 8021 6794 Offices & clinics of dentists; Franchises, selling or licensing
CEO: Stephen E Thorne IV
**CFO:* Brady Ace
**Sr VP:* Dan Burke
**Sr VP:* Joe Feldsien
**Sr VP:* Jon Thorne
VP: Ken Davis
VP: Emilios Mariolis
VP: Thomas Sydow
VP: Don Webb
Rgnl Mgr: Crystal Aguilar
Rgnl Mgr: Jacquelyn Janzen

D-U-N-S 82-778-1501
PACIFIC DUNLOP HOLDINGS (USA) LLC
(*Suby of* PACIFIC DUNLOP INVESTMENTS (USA) INC) ★
200 Schulz Dr, Red Bank, NJ 07701-6776
Tel (732) 345-5400 *Founded/Ownrshp* 1992
Sales 171.9MM^E *EMP* 2,126^E
SIC 3069 3691 Balloons, advertising & toy: rubber; Birth control devices, rubber; Finger cots, rubber; Storage batteries
CEO: Doug Tough
**Treas:* Rustom Jilla
**Sr VP:* Phil Corke
**Sr VP:* William Reed
Dir IT: Eric Thompson

D-U-N-S 11-973-7364 IMP/EXP
PACIFIC DUNLOP INVESTMENTS (USA) INC
(*Suby of* ANSELL LIMITED)
200 Schulz Dr, Red Bank, NJ 07701-6776
Tel (732) 345-5400 *Founded/Ownrshp* 1992
Sales 241.5MM^E *EMP* 3,030^E
SIC 3069 3842 Rubber coated fabrics & clothing; Gloves, safety
Pr: Doug Tough
**Treas:* Rustom Jilla
VP: Craig Cameron
VP: David Graham
**VP:* William Reed
IT Man: John Rossi

D-U-N-S 04-645-3635 EXP
■ **PACIFIC ENTERPRISES**
(*Suby of* SEMPRA ENERGY) ★
101 Ash St, San Diego, CA 92101-3017
Tel (619) 696-2020 *Founded/Ownrshp* 1886
Sales 3.4MMM^E *EMP* 8,196^E
SIC 4924 Natural gas distribution
Ch Bd: Michael W Allman
COO: Anne S Smith
CFO: Robert M Schlax

D-U-N-S 13-088-4695
▲ **PACIFIC ETHANOL INC**
400 Capitol Mall Ste 2060, Sacramento, CA 95814-4436
Tel (916) 403-2123 *Founded/Ownrshp* 2003
Sales 1.1MMM *EMP* 465
Tkr Sym PEIX *Exch* NAS
SIC 2869 Ethanolamines
Pr: Neil M Koehler
**Ch Bd:* William L Jones
**COO:* Michael D Kandris
COO: Mike Kandris
CFO: Bryon T McGregor
VP: Paul P Koehler
VP: James R Sneed
VP: Christopher W Wright

D-U-N-S 92-992-2839
■ **PACIFIC ETHANOL PEKIN INC**
AVENTINE RNWBLE ENRGY HOLDINGS
(*Suby of* AVENTINE RENEWABLE ENERGY HOLDINGS LLC) ★
1300 S 2nd St, Pekin, IL 61554-5402
Tel (309) 347-9200 *Founded/Ownrshp* 1999
Sales 92.5MM^E *EMP* 200
SIC 2869 Alcohols, industrial: denatured (non-beverage); Ethyl alcohol, ethanol
Pr: John Castle
**Pr:* Mark Beemer
**Pr:* Ronald H Miller
**COO:* Daniel R Trunfio Jr
**VP:* Brian Steenhard
VP Opers: John Valenti

PACIFIC FIRE SAFETY
See FERGUSON FIRE & FABRICATION INC

D-U-N-S 19-848-2374 IMP/EXP
PACIFIC FOODS OF OREGON INC
19480 Sw 97th Ave, Tualatin, OR 97062-8505
Tel (503) 692-9666 *Founded/Ownrshp* 1987
Sales 99.1MM^E *EMP* 200
SIC 2033 2099 2086 Vegetable juices: packaged in cans, jars, etc.; Food preparations; Bottled & canned soft drinks
Pr: Charles W Eggert
**Sr VP:* Jonathan C Gehrs
**VP:* Edward Lynch
VP: Ted Ottmar
**VP:* Carolyn Rayback
Dir IT: David Pimentel
VP Opers: Erik Gottschalk
Sfty Dirs: Frank Ramirez
Plnt Mgr: Bob Dickson
Ql Cn Mgr: Justina Alvarado
Mktg Mgr: Ben Hummel

D-U-N-S 00-691-2877 IMP
■ **PACIFIC GAS AND ELECTRIC CO**
PG&E
(*Suby of* PG&E CORP) ★
77 Beale St, San Francisco, CA 94105-1814
Tel (415) 973-7000 *Founded/Ownrshp* 1905
Sales 16.8MMM *EMP* 22,581
SIC 4911 4924 Generation, electric power; Transmission, electric power; Distribution, electric power; Natural gas distribution
Pr: Christopher P Johns
CFO: Dinyar B Mistry
Ex VP: Nickolas Stavropoulos
Ex VP: Bryant Tong
Ex VP: Geisha J Williams
Sr VP: Karen A Austin
Sr VP: Desmond A Bell
Sr VP: Jack Keenan
Sr VP: R Peters
VP: Helen Burt
VP: Kevin J Dasso
VP: John C Higgins
VP: Aaron J Johnson
VP: Mary K King
VP: Travis Kiyota
VP: Rand Rosenberg
Board of Directors: Barbara L Rambo, Lewis Chew, Anne Shen Smith, Anthony F Earley Jr, Barry Lawson Williams, Fred J Fowler, Maryellen C Herringer, Richard C Kelly, Roger H Kimmel, Richard A Meserve, Forrest E Miller, Rosendo G Parra

PACIFIC GLOBAL PACKAGING SOUTH
See PACIFIC PACKAGING PRODUCTS INC

D-U-N-S 06-649-8346 IMP
PACIFIC GROSERVICE INC
PITCO FOODS
567 Cinnabar St, San Jose, CA 95110-2306
Tel (408) 727-4826 *Founded/Ownrshp* 1982
Sales 215.8MM^E *EMP* 360
SIC 5194 5145 5141 5113 5087 Tobacco & tobacco products; Candy; Groceries, general line; Industrial & personal service paper; Service establishment equipment
Ch Bd: Pericles Navab
**Pr:* David Luttway
**COO:* Vince Bertolacci

D-U-N-S 08-008-4693
PACIFIC GROUP RESORTS INC
1389 Center Dr Ste 200, Park City, UT 84098-7660
Tel (435) 241-7000 *Founded/Ownrshp* 2013
Sales 18.0MM *EMP* 1,400
SIC 7011 Resort hotel
Pr: Bern Greco

D-U-N-S 05-389-8367
PACIFIC GUARDIAN LIFE INSURANCE CO LIMITED
(*Suby of* MEIJIYASUDA LIFE INSURANCE COMPANY)
1440 Kalani St Ste 1700, Honolulu, HI 96817
Tel (808) 942-6541 *Founded/Ownrshp* 1965
Sales NA *EMP* 155
SIC 6311 6321 Life insurance; Accident & health insurance
Ch Bd: Alan Goda
Pr: Hideaki Hattori
**Pr:* Yoji Nakamura
**Treas:* Margolee Lee
**Ex VP:* Douglas Goto
Sr VP: Paul Carmody
**Sr VP:* Kenneth Nishibun
Dir Risk M: Monique Pascual

D-U-N-S 09-824-3173 IMP
■ **PACIFIC GYPSUM SUPPLY INC**
J & B MATERIALS
(*Suby of* G M S) ★
1165 N Johnson Ave, El Cajon, CA 92020-1906
Tel (619) 447-2413 *Founded/Ownrshp* 2015
Sales 108.4MM^E *EMP* 70
SIC 5032 5211 Drywall materials; Lumber & other building materials
CEO: Michael Callahan
**Pr:* Robert J Young

D-U-N-S 11-540-0368
PACIFIC HEALTH CORP
(*Suby of* HEALTH INVESTMENT CORP) ★
14642 Newport Ave, Tustin, CA 92780-6057
Tel (714) 838-9600 *Founded/Ownrshp* 1984
Sales 136.2MM^E *EMP* 1,700
SIC 8062 General medical & surgical hospitals
CEO: Michael Choo
**Pr:* James Young
CFO: Gary Lewis

D-U-N-S 00-890-9681
PACIFIC HIDE & FUR DEPOT (MT)
PACIFIC STEEL & RECYCLING
5 River Dr S, Great Falls, MT 59405-1872
Tel (406) 771-7222 *Founded/Ownrshp* 1885, 1985
Sales 486.8MM^E *EMP* 780
SIC 5051 5093 Steel; Iron or steel semifinished products; Scrap & waste materials
Pr: Jeff Millhollin
CFO: Tim Culliton
VP: Stuart Boylan
VP: Ken Halko
**VP:* Ed Joyce
**VP:* Patrick Kons
VP: Laura Mangan
Rgnl Mgr: Michael Cataldo
CIO: Dave Richards
Board of Directors: Steve Ball, Lyle Knight, Marcus

Lampros, Daniel Larson, Ivan Rice, Rob Vanausdol

D-U-N-S 09-192-5925
PACIFIC INVESTMENT MANAGEMENT CO LLC
PIMCO
(*Suby of* FOREIGN PRNT IS ALANZ AG MNCHN) ★
650 Nwport Ctr Dr Ste 100, Newport Beach, CA 92660
Tel (949) 720-6000 *Founded/Ownrshp* 1994
Sales 400.9MM^E *EMP* 284
SIC 6282 Investment advice
CEO: Douglas M Hodge
Pr: Jay Jacobs
CEO: Douglas Hodge
CFO: Bob Fitzgerald
CFO: John Lane
Ofcr: Andrew T Balls
Ofcr: Steven Ludwig
Ex VP: Yacov Anropolin
Ex VP: Brian Baker
Ex VP: Jeremie Banet
Ex VP: Andreas Berndt
Ex VP: Philippe Bodereau
Ex VP: Bruce Brittain
Ex VP: Rick Chan
Ex VP: Devin Chen
Ex VP: Marcia Clark
Ex VP: Anthony Crescenzi
Ex VP: Joe Deane
Ex VP: Bill Deleon
Ex VP: SAI S Devabhaktuni
Ex VP: Sandra Durn

D-U-N-S 13-445-6789
PACIFIC LIFE & ANNUITY CO
(*Suby of* PACIFIC LIFE INSURANCE CO) ★
700 Newport Center Dr, Newport Beach, CA 92660-6307
Tel (949) 219-3011 *Founded/Ownrshp* 1996
Sales NA *EMP* 650
SIC 6311 6411 Life insurance; Insurance agents, brokers & service
Pr: James Morris
Pr: Mary Hawkins
**CFO:* Khanh T Tran
**VP:* Audrey L Milfs

D-U-N-S 82-920-6932
PACIFIC LIFE FUND ADVISORS LLC
(*Suby of* PACIFIC LIFE INSURANCE CO) ★
700 Newport Center Dr, Newport Beach, CA 92660-6307
Tel (800) 800-7646 *Founded/Ownrshp* 2007
Sales 212.3MM^E *EMP* 2,268^E
SIC 6282 Investment advisory service
Pr: Doug Kalmey
Pr: Gail McIntosh
Sr VP: Sharon Cheever
Sr VP: Joseph Krum
Sr VP: Brian Woolfolk
VP: Michael Adams
VP: Howard Hirakawa
VP: Jane Hsu
VP: Mark Pellicano
VP: Thomas Ronce
Dir IT: Wayne Lee

D-U-N-S 00-690-8495
PACIFIC LIFE INSURANCE CO
(*Suby of* PACIFIC LIFECORP) ★
700 Newport Center Dr, Newport Beach, CA 92660-6307
Tel (949) 219-3011 *Founded/Ownrshp* 1868 1936
Sales NA *EMP* 3,760
SIC 6311 6371 6321 7359 Life insurance carriers; Pension funds; Accident insurance carriers; Aircraft rental
Ch Bd: James T Morris
Pr: Stephanie Babkow
Pr: Denny Bahlmann
Pr: Karen Brown
Pr: Kathleen A Clune
Pr: Pierre Delisle
Pr: Jeffrey Dey
Pr: Michael K Difley
Pr: Ann Farley
Pr: Hany Gobreial
Pr: Dale Hawley
Pr: Shelly Higgins
Pr: Jeff Johnson
Pr: Greg Larson
Pr: Liam Monaghan
Pr: Joyce Pead
Pr: Anna Popov
Pr: Joseph Pum
Pr: Douglas L Robbins
Pr: Steve Turi
Pr: John Waldeck

D-U-N-S 17-596-6530 IMP
PACIFIC LIFECORP
(*Suby of* PACIFIC MUTUAL HOLDING CO) ★
700 Newport Center Dr, Newport Beach, CA 92660-6307
Tel (949) 219-3011 *Founded/Ownrshp* 1997
Sales NA *EMP* 3,782
SIC 6371 6311 6321 6035 8111 Pension, health & welfare funds; Life insurance; Accident & health insurance; Federal savings banks; Legal services
Ch Bd: James T Morris
COO: Frank Boynton
VP: Richard Banno
CTO: Jill Walsh
Mktg Dir: Hana Nishioka

D-U-N-S 09-189-4787
PACIFIC LOGISTICS CORP
PACLO
7255 Rosemead Blvd, Pico Rivera, CA 90660-4047
Tel (562) 478-4700 *Founded/Ownrshp* 1999
Sales 115.4MM^E *EMP* 350
SIC 4731 Freight transportation arrangement
Pr: Douglas E Hockersmith
**COO:* Timothy K Hewey
Dir IT: Bob Bullock
Opers Mgr: Fernando Bautista
Opers Mgr: Carol Seladones

D-U-N-S 92-949-0548 EXP
PACIFIC LTD CORP
825 Brickell Bay Dr, Miami, FL 33131-2936
Tel (305) 358-1900 *Founded/Ownrshp* 1982
Sales 83.4MM *EMP* 7
Accts Crowe Horwath Llp Fort Laude
SIC 5162 Resins, synthetic
Pr: Jose Massuh
**VP:* Jose M Buraye

D-U-N-S 07-183-6019
PACIFIC LUTHERAN UNIVERSITY INC
12180 Park Ave S, Tacoma, WA 98447-0014
Tel (253) 531-6900 *Founded/Ownrshp* 1890
Sales 98.3MM *EMP* 979
Accts Baker Tilly Virchow Krause Ll
SIC 8221 University
Pr: Thomas W Krise
V Ch: David P Robbins
Ofcr: Charlene F Gingrich
VP: Laura Polcyn
VP: Sheri Tonn
Assoc Dir: Melannie Cunningham
Assoc Dir: Katie Hoover
Assoc Dir: Paula Meiers
**Prin:* Loren Anderson
VP Admn: Tommy Flanagan
Store Mgr: Amanda Hawkins

D-U-N-S 12-824-2331 IMP
PACIFIC MANUFACTURING OHIO INC
(*Suby of* PACIFIC INDUSTRIAL CO., LTD.)
8955 Seward Rd, Fairfield, OH 45011-9109
Tel (513) 860-3900 *Founded/Ownrshp* 1999
Sales 204.3MM^E *EMP* 450
SIC 3714 3469 Motor vehicle parts & accessories; Metal stampings
Pr: Toshiteru Ando
Ex VP: Kazuya Hayashi
Snr Mgr: Norma North

D-U-N-S 07-878-6001
PACIFIC MARITIME ASSOCIATION INC
P M A
555 Market St Fl 3, San Francisco, CA 94105-5801
Tel (415) 576-3200 *Founded/Ownrshp* 1949
Sales 120.2MM *EMP* 172
Accts Pricewaterhousecoopers Llp Wa
SIC 8631 Collective bargaining unit
Ex VP: Michael Lueskow
VP: Bill Alverson
Snr Ntwrk: Julia Guzman
Netwrk Eng: Guillermo Aquino
Sales Exec: Scott Munger

PACIFIC MEDICAL CENTERS
See PACMED CLINICS

D-U-N-S 17-596-4881
PACIFIC MUTUAL HOLDING CO
700 Newport Center Dr, Newport Beach, CA 92660-6307
Tel (949) 219-3011 *Founded/Ownrshp* 1997
Sales NA *EMP* 4,000
SIC 6371 6311 6321 Pension funds; Life insurance; Accident insurance carriers
Ch Bd: James T Morris
**Pr:* Glenn S Schafer
**Pr:* Khanh T Tran
**CEO:* Thomas C Sutton
**CFO:* Adrian S Griggs
CFO: Khanh Tran
**Ex VP:* Mary Ann Brown
Sr VP: Anthony J Bonno
**Sr VP:* Edward R Byrd

D-U-N-S 00-685-3626
PACIFIC NATIONAL GROUP (CA)
2392 Bateman Ave, Irwindale, CA 91010-3312
Tel (626) 357-4400 *Founded/Ownrshp* 1950
Sales 113.0MM *EMP* 25^E
Accts Hart & Vandenberg Inc Whitt
SIC 1542 Commercial & office building contractors
Pr: Steven Mathison
**Pr:* Arden L Boren
**VP:* Ciaran Barry
**VP:* Joseph Cheatham

D-U-N-S 05-861-5360
PACIFIC NORTHWEST FARMERS COOPERATIVE INC
117 W Chestnut, Genesee, ID 83832
Tel (208) 285-1141 *Founded/Ownrshp* 1909
Sales 118.8MM *EMP* 80
Accts Jurgens & Co Pa Lewiston I
SIC 5153 2099 Grains; Food preparations
CEO: Bill Newbry

D-U-N-S 17-194-7500
PACIFIC NORTHWEST GENERATING COOPERATIVE
PNGC POWER
711 Ne Halsey St, Portland, OR 97232-1268
Tel (503) 288-1234 *Founded/Ownrshp* 1996
Sales 163.0MM *EMP* 36
Accts Moss-Adams Llp Portland Oreg
SIC 4911 Electric services; Distribution, electric power; Generation, electric power; Transmission, electric power
Pr: John Prescott
**Ch Bd:* Rick Crinklaw
**CEO:* Joseph W Nadal Jr
CFO: Jon R Wissle
**CFO:* Jon R Wissler
**Treas:* Jon Shelby
**V Ch Bd:* Steve Eldrige
**VP:* R Scott Corwin
VP: Aleka Scott
**VP:* Kevin M Watkins
Snr Ntwrk: Dragan Dokic

D-U-N-S 86-939-3470
PACIFIC NUTRITIONAL INC
6317 Ne 131st Ave Buildb, Vancouver, WA 98682-5879
Tel (360) 253-3197 *Founded/Ownrshp* 1979
Sales 121.2MM^E *EMP* 180
SIC 5122 2099 Vitamins & minerals; Food preparations

Pr: Michael Schaeffer
**CEO:* Chris Taylor
**Treas:* Ron Golden
**VP:* Pamela Nielson
Mktg Mgr: Tim Patrick

PACIFIC NW NATIONAL
See BATTELLE MEMORIAL INSTITUTE

D-U-N-S 06-060-0996
PACIFIC OFFICE AUTOMATION INC
14747 Nw Greenbrier Pkwy, Beaverton, OR 97006-5601
Tel (503) 641-2000 *Founded/Ownrshp* 1976
Sales 190.7MM^E *EMP* 600
SIC 5044 Office equipment
Pr: Douglas Pitassi
**Sec:* Gerry N Romjue
**VP:* Connie Holt
**VP:* Karen Newsom
Brnch Mgr: Dino Andereggen
Brnch Mgr: Phil Burns
Brnch Mgr: James Pierson
CIO: Todd Rosenow
Tech Mgr: Rich Frunk
Tech Mgr: Chuck Hampsten
Tech Mgr: Joe Pesetsky

D-U-N-S 00-142-6667 IMP/EXP
PACIFIC PACKAGING PRODUCTS INC
PACIFIC GLOBAL PACKAGING SOUTH
24 Industrial Way, Wilmington, MA 01887-3434
Tel (978) 657-9100 *Founded/Ownrshp* 1952
Sales 97.1MM *EMP* 165
Accts Mcgladrey Llp Wilmington Ma
SIC 5113 5199 5084 5162 2671 2653 Industrial & personal service paper; Shipping supplies; Packaging materials; Packaging machinery & equipment; Printing trades machinery, equipment & supplies; Plastics materials & basic shapes; Packaging paper & plastics film, coated & laminated; Corrugated & solid fiber boxes
CEO: Frank D Goldstein
**Pr:* Robert H Goldstein
CFO: John Leydon
**Treas:* David A Varsano
Sls Mgr: Lou Faragher

D-U-N-S 87-764-5267
PACIFIC PHARMA INC
(*Suby of* ALLERGAN INC) ★
18600 Von Karman Ave, Irvine, CA 92612-1513
Tel (714) 246-4600 *Founded/Ownrshp* 1997
Sales 108.7MM^E *EMP* 2,000
SIC 5122

PACIFIC POWER EQUIPMENT CO
See FRANK EDWARDS CO INC

D-U-N-S 05-940-3154 IMP
PACIFIC POWER GROUP LLC
PACIFIC POWER PRODUCTS
805 Broadway St Ste 700, Vancouver, WA 98660-3301
Tel (360) 887-7400 *Founded/Ownrshp* 1984
Sales 113.3MM^E *EMP* 277
SIC 5088 3621 5063 3519 5084 Marine propulsion machinery & equipment; Motor generator sets; Generators; Diesel engine rebuilding; Engines & parts, diesel
Pr: Timothy Price
Opers Mgr: David Ehlinger
Sales Exec: Ted Ostrye

PACIFIC POWER PRODUCTS
See PACIFIC POWER GROUP LLC

D-U-N-S 96-998-7114
▲ PACIFIC PREMIER BANCORP INC
17901 Von Karman Ave, Irvine, CA 92614-6297
Tel (949) 864-8000 *Founded/Ownrshp* 1996
Sales NA *EMP* 285^E
Accts Vavrinek Trine Day & Co Llp
Tkr Sym PPBI *Exch* NGM
SIC 6022 State commercial banks
Pr: Steven R Gardner
**Ch Bd:* Jeff C Jones
Pr: Londa Fee
Pr: Scott Muir
Pr: Chandra Olivas
Pr: Rudy Quintana
Pr: Lauren Tedford
COO: Thomas Rice
COO: Tom Rice
CFO: E Allen Nicholson
CFO: Ronald J Nicolas
Chf Cred: Mike Karr
Ofcr: Edward Wilcox
VP: Christian Buell
VP: Kathrine Duncan
VP: Jon A Hagan
VP: Chris Hilliard
VP: Michael A Kowalski
VP: Shane Pierson
VP: Chris Porcelli
VP: John Quibodeaux

D-U-N-S 06-815-7262
■ PACIFIC PREMIER BANK
(*Suby of* PACIFIC PREMIER BANCORP INC) ★
17901 Von Karman Ave, Irvine, CA 92614-6297
Tel (714) 431-4000 *Founded/Ownrshp* 1997
Sales 93.0MM *EMP* 104^E
SIC 6531 Real estate listing services
Pr: Steven R Gardner
**Ch Bd:* Jeff C Jones
**CFO:* Ronald J Nicolas Jr
CFO: John Shindler
**CFO:* Kent Smith
Ex VP: Michael Karr
VP: Michelle Coberly
VP: Lorraine Cochran
VP: Kathi Hallock
VP: Diane Heyden
VP: Shane Pierson
VP: Chris Porcelli
VP: Trisha Romero
VP: Diana Treadway
VP: Josh Young

D-U-N-S 92-747-0724 EXP
PACIFIC PROCESS SYSTEMS INC
7401 Rosedale Hwy, Bakersfield, CA 93308-5736
Tel (661) 321-9681 *Founded/Ownrshp* 1995
Sales 252.7MM^E *EMP* 300
SIC 1389 7353 5082 Testing, measuring, surveying & analysis services; Oil field equipment, rental or leasing; Oil field equipment
CEO: Jerry Wise
**CFO:* Robert Peterson
**Sec:* Alan George
Sfty Mgr: Darrell Miller

PACIFIC PUBLISHING
See FISHER INVESTMENTS INC

PACIFIC PULMONARY SERVICES CO
See BRADEN PARTNERS LP A CALIFORNIA LIMITED PARTNERSHIP

D-U-N-S 18-718-7166
PACIFIC RAIL SERVICES LLC
1131 Sw Klickitat Way, Seattle, WA 98134-1108
Tel (206) 382-4462 *Founded/Ownrshp* 1985
Sales 106.6MM^E *EMP* 800
SIC 4789 Railroad maintenance & repair services
Mng Pt: John Gray

D-U-N-S 84-748-5562
PACIFIC RETIREMENT SERVICES INC
1 W Main St Ste 303, Medford, OR 97501-2796
Tel (541) 857-7777 *Founded/Ownrshp* 1990
Sales 15.9MM *EMP* 3,000
Accts Moss Adams Llp Stockton Ca
SIC 8741 8051 Management services; Skilled nursing care facilities
Pr: Brian McLemore
**COO:* Mike Morris
**CFO:* Mary Schoeggl
Bd of Dir: Lyn Hennion
**Sr VP:* Paul Riepma
VP: Sheri Dressler
**VP:* Torsten Hirche
VP: Jennifer Jacobs
VP: Marc Johnson
**VP:* Mary Naylor
**VP:* Debbie Rayburn
VP: Marc Whitlock
Exec: Sandy Martin
Exec: James Munn
Exec: Lee Patterson
Dir Risk M: Kristi Scales

D-U-N-S 13-060-6713
PACIFIC RIM MECHANICAL CONTRACTORS INC
7655 Convoy Ct, San Diego, CA 92111-1103
Tel (858) 974-6500 *Founded/Ownrshp* 2002
Sales 112.2MM *EMP* 650
Accts Akt Llp San Diego California
SIC 1711 Plumbing, heating, air-conditioning contractors
CEO: Joseph Mucher
**CFO:* Eric Bader
**VP:* Colin Cook
VP: Randy Foco
**VP:* John Heusner
**VP:* Theodore J Keenan
**VP:* Brent Koch
VP: James O Mahney
VP: Jim O'Mahoney
VP: Jim Omahoney
**VP:* Michael Schatz
**VP:* Brian Turner

D-U-N-S 00-837-0470 IMP
PACIFIC SCIENTIFIC CO INC
ELECTRO KINETICS DIVISION
(*Suby of* MEGGITT POLYMERS & COMPOSITES) ★
1785 Voyager Ave Ste 101, Simi Valley, CA 93063-3370
Tel (805) 526-5700 *Founded/Ownrshp* 2011
Sales 97.4MM^E *EMP* 500
SIC 3812 3669 3621 3694 3823 3625 Aircraft control systems, electronic; Fire detection systems, electric; Generators & sets, electric; Motors, electric; Servomotors, electric; Alternators, automotive; Water quality monitoring & control systems; Control equipment, electric
**Genl Mgr:* James Healey

D-U-N-S 07-997-5806
■ PACIFIC SCIENTIFIC ENERGETIC MATERIALS CO (CALIFORNIA)
(*Suby of* FORTIVE CORP) ★
3601 Union Rd, Hollister, CA 95023-9635
Tel (831) 637-3731 *Founded/Ownrshp* 1998
Sales 200.0MM *EMP* 705
SIC 2892 2899 3489 3483 3699 3728 Explosives; Fuses, safety; Igniter grains, boron potassium nitrate; Projectors: depth charge, grenade, rocket, etc.; Arming & fusing devices for missiles; High-energy particle physics equipment; Aircraft armament, except guns
Pr: Gregory Scaven
Pr: Amy Merkley
CFO: John Collins
Treas: Bill Sanborn
VP: John Davis
VP: Kenneth Hadley
VP: Mike Herzog
Dir Bus: Neal Kerr
Prgrm Mgr: Will Hunter
Prgrm Mgr: Dustin Rowland
Prgrm Mgr: Frederick Sanchez

D-U-N-S 06-292-8119 IMP
PACIFIC SCIENTIFIC ENERGETIC MATERIALS CO (CALIFORNIA) LLC
PACIFIC SCNTFIC ENERGETIC MTLS
7073 W Willis Rd Ste 5002, Chandler, AZ 85226-5166
Tel (480) 763-3000 *Founded/Ownrshp* 1975
Sales 200.0MM *EMP* 705
SIC 2892 2899 3483 3489 3699 3728

PACIFIC SCNTFIC ENERGETIC MTLS
See PACIFIC SCIENTIFIC ENERGETIC MATERIALS CO (CALIFORNIA) LLC

D-U-N-S 02-774-5876 IMP
PACIFIC SEA FOOD CO INC (OR)
JAKES CRAWFISH & SEAFOOD
(*Suby of* PACIFIC SEAFOOD GROUP) ★
16797 Se 130th Ave, Clackamas, OR 97015-8966
Tel (503) 905-4500 *Founded/Ownrshp* 1941, 1986
Sales 211.9MME *EMP* 300
SIC 5146 5142 Fish & seafoods; Fish, frozen, unpackaged; Seafoods; Fish, fresh; Fish, frozen: packaged; Meat, frozen: packaged; Poultry, frozen: packaged
Pr: Frank Dominic Dulcich
COO: Timothy Horgan
**CFO:* Paul Minter
Chf Mktg O: Rajiv Kaul
**VP:* Mark Bowen
**VP:* Dominic Dulcich
VP: Dan Obradovich
**VP:* Steve Spencer
Exec: Tracie Coberly
Exec: Maria Ferry
Dist Mgr: Chris Hamilton

PACIFIC SEAFOOD GROUP
See DULCICH INC

D-U-N-S 03-858-3050
PACIFIC SHELLFISH INC
FISHERY, THE
5040 Cass St, San Diego, CA 92109-1801
Tel (858) 272-9940 *Founded/Ownrshp* 1990
Sales 85.1MME *EMP* 307E
SIC 5146 5421 5812 Fish & seafoods; Seafood markets; Seafood restaurants
Pr: Judd Brown
**Sec:* Mary Ann Brown
Dir Bus: Vicki Cornett
Sls Mgr: Steve Wright

D-U-N-S 06-301-9442 IMP
PACIFIC SOUTHWEST CONTAINER LLC
4530 Leckron Rd, Modesto, CA 95357-0517
Tel (209) 526-0444 *Founded/Ownrshp* 1973
Sales 121.3MME *EMP* 500
SIC 2671 2657 3086 2653 2752 Packaging paper & plastics film, coated & laminated; Folding paperboard boxes; Packaging & shipping materials, foamed plastic; Boxes, corrugated: made from purchased materials; Commercial printing, lithographic
**Pr:* Bryan Smith
**CFO:* Lester H Mangold
Ex VP: Darin Jones
Sr VP: Mac McCullough
Sr VP: Robert Nagle
VP: Kevin Allen
Exec: Ron Everson
Mtls Mgr: Sherren Bartlett
VP Sls: Joseph Donahue
VP Sls: Jim Heller
VP Sls: Jerry Hill

PACIFIC STAR SEAFOODS
See E & E FOODS INC

D-U-N-S 09-852-9456 IMP
PACIFIC STATES INDUSTRIES INC
REDWOOD EMPIRE WHL LBR PDTS
10 Madrone Ave, Morgan Hill, CA 95037-9227
Tel (408) 779-7354 *Founded/Ownrshp* 1979
Sales 211.3MME *EMP* 575
SIC 5031 2421 1751 Lumber: rough, dressed & finished; Sawmills & planing mills, general; Carpentry work
Pr: Roger Roger Burch
Ex VP: Austin Vander
**Ex VP:* Austin Vanderhoof
VP: Austin Nanderhoof
IT Man: Rena Gooding
Opers Mgr: Tim Semons
Mktg Dir: John Reger
Sls Mgr: Dennis Tyrrell

PACIFIC STEEL & RECYCLING
See PACIFIC HIDE & FUR DEPOT

D-U-N-S 03-977-0959
PACIFIC STRUCTURES INC
953 Mission St Ste 200, San Francisco, CA 94103-2987
Tel (415) 367-9399 *Founded/Ownrshp* 2008
Sales 137.7MM *EMP* 250
Accts Dzh Phillips Llp San Francisc
SIC 1771 Concrete work
Ch Bd: Ross Edwards
**Pr:* David E Williams
**CFO:* Stephen Nerhein
**Treas:* Eric Horn
Genl Mgr: Jason Berry

D-U-N-S 05-056-0002 IMP
PACIFIC SUNWEAR OF CALIFORNIA LLC
(*Suby of* GGC ACQUISITION HOLDINGS CORP) ★
3450 E Miraloma Ave, Anaheim, CA 92806-2101
Tel (714) 414-4000 *Founded/Ownrshp* 2016
Sales 826.7MM *EMP* 8,777
SIC 5611 5621 5699 Clothing, sportswear, men's & boys'; Women's sportswear; Bathing suits
Pr: Gary H Schoenfeld
CFO: Ernie Sibal
Sr VP: Brieane Breuer
Sr VP: Alfred Chang
Sr VP: Craig E Gosselin
VP: Kelly C Bladow
VP: Jonathan Brewer
VP: Amber Fredman-Tarshis
VP: Mark Kibler
VP: Thomas Larry
VP: Coleen McNally
VP: Tony Pfeiffer
VP: Rebecca Reeder
VP: MAI Zazueta

D-U-N-S 03-159-2269 IMP
PACIFIC SUNWEAR STORES CORP
(*Suby of* PACIFIC SUNWEAR OF CALIFORNIA LLC) ★
3450 E Miraloma Ave, Anaheim, CA 92806-2101
Tel (714) 414-4000 *Founded/Ownrshp* 1998
Sales 809.9MME *EMP* 8,200
SIC 5611 5699 5661 5621 5999 Men's & boys' clothing stores; Clothing, men's & boys': everyday, except suits & sportswear; Clothing accessories: men's & boys'; Hats, men's & boys'; Sports apparel; Bathing suits; Shoe stores; Teenage apparel; Sales barn
CEO: Gary Schoenfeld
CFO: Michael Henry
Sr VP: Thomas Larry
VP: Gar Jackson

PACIFIC TERMINAL SERVICES
See HARLEY MARINE SERVICES INC

D-U-N-S 05-555-7128 EXP
PACIFIC TOMATO GROWERS LTD (FL)
503 10th St W, Palmetto, FL 34221-3801
Tel (941) 729-8410 *Founded/Ownrshp* 1982
Sales 105.6MME *EMP* 300
SIC 0161 0174 0723 Tomato farm; Melon farms; Rooted vegetable farms; Citrus fruits; Vegetable packing services; Fruit crops market preparation services
Pt: Joseph Esformes
Pr: Robert Spence
CFO: Dave Bacek
CFO: Mac Carraway
CFO: Jean-Pierre Gorgue
VP: Harvey Heller
VP: Mabel Naranjo
Plnt Mgr: John Dupee
Sls Mgr: Joseph Poklemba

D-U-N-S 11-447-1878 IMP
PACIFIC TRELLIS FRUIT LLC
DULCINEA FARMS
5108 E Clinton Way # 108, Fresno, CA 93727-2043
Tel (559) 255-5437 *Founded/Ownrshp* 1999
Sales 202.2MME *EMP* 170
SIC 5148 Fruits
Genl Mgr: Josh Leichter

D-U-N-S 09-148-1937
PACIFIC TRUST BANK
18500 Von Karman Ave # 1100, Irvine, CA 92612-0546
Tel (949) 236-5211 *Founded/Ownrshp* 1941
Sales NA *EMP* 107
SIC 6035

D-U-N-S 00-825-5994
PACIFIC UNION ASSOCIATION OF SEVENTH-DAY ADVENTISTS (CA)
2686 Townsgate Rd, Thousand Oaks, CA 91361-2701
Tel (805) 497-9457 *Founded/Ownrshp* 1933
Sales 150.4MME *EMP* 2,200
SIC 8661 Seventh Day Adventist Church
Pr: Ricardo Graham
**Sec:* Frank Cornwell
**VP:* Theodore Benson
Assoc Dir: Thambi Thomas

D-U-N-S 07-017-4982
PACIFIC UNION CO
1 Letterman Dr Ste 300, San Francisco, CA 94129-1495
Tel (415) 929-7100 *Founded/Ownrshp* 1975
Sales 99.1MME *EMP* 360
SIC 6552 6512 6531 Land subdividers & developers, residential; Land subdividers & developers, commercial; Nonresidential building operators; Real estate managers; Real estate brokers & agents
Pr: John G Montgomery
**CFO:* Charles H Pratt
VP: Felicia Chan
**VP:* H William Harlan

D-U-N-S 07-091-5403
PACIFIC UNION FINANCIAL LLC
8900 Freeport Pkwy Ste 150, Irving, TX 75063
Tel (800) 809-0421 *Founded/Ownrshp* 2004
Sales 278.1MME *EMP* 545
SIC 6282 Investment advice
Pr: Rick Skog
**Pr:* Evan Stone
Ofcr: Shevon Valantine
**Ex VP:* Bill Berg
Ex VP: John Hummel
Ex VP: Dwayne Smith
Ex VP: James Wyble
Sr VP: Paul Gorske
Sr VP: Jim McDiarmid
Sr VP: Tim Owens
VP: John Brumund
VP: Mason Caldwell
VP: Chuck Dimiceli
VP: Gerry Fernandez
VP: Katherine Gardner
VP: Casey Jones
VP: Steve S Nam
VP: Scott Smith
VP: Brandon Unruh

D-U-N-S 05-597-8035
PACIFIC UNIVERSITY
2043 College Way, Forest Grove, OR 97116-1797
Tel (503) 357-6151 *Founded/Ownrshp* 1849
Sales 148.7MM *EMP* 600
SIC 8221

D-U-N-S 13-275-7621 IMP
PACIFIC VIAL MFG INC
2738 Supply Ave, Commerce, CA 90040-2704
Tel (323) 721-7004 *Founded/Ownrshp* 2001
Sales 100.0MM *EMP* 40
SIC 3221 Vials, glass
VP Mfg: David Cobb

D-U-N-S 00-108-3500 IMP
■ **PACIFIC WESTERN BANK** (CA)
(*Suby of* PACWEST BANCORP) ★
456 Santa Monica Blvd, Santa Monica, CA 90401-2307
Tel (310) 458-1521 *Founded/Ownrshp* 1980, 2002
Sales NA *EMP* 920
SIC 6021 National commercial banks
CEO: Matthew P Wagner
Pr: Lynda Nahra
Pr: Michael J Perdue
COO: Christopher D Blake
COO: Kathleen McIntire
CFO: Peggy Hansen
CFO: Lynn M Hopkins
Chf Cred: Bob Llorens
Ofcr: Robert G Dyck
Ex VP: Robert M Borgman
Ex VP: Suzanne Brennan
Sr VP: Ed Cuff
Sr VP: Peter Fan
Sr VP: Holly Hayes
Sr VP: Larry Lee
VP: Soledad Escobedo
VP: Irene Higinio
VP: Gregory Matthews
VP: Jon Meeks
VP: Gloria Taracena
VP: Sali Tice

D-U-N-S 61-046-2728
PACIFICA COMPANIES LLC
1775 Hancock St Ste 200, San Diego, CA 92110-2036
Tel (619) 296-9000 *Founded/Ownrshp* 2004
Sales 496.5MME *EMP* 2,000E
SIC 6798 6512 Real estate investment trusts; Nonresidential building operators
Pr: Deepak Israni
**Ch:* Ashok Israni

PACIFICA CONSULTING SERVICES
See SERVICON SYSTEMS INC

PACIFICA ENTERPRISES
See PACIFICA HOSTS INC

D-U-N-S 17-510-6350
PACIFICA HOSTS INC
PACIFICA ENTERPRISES
1775 Hancock St Ste 200, San Diego, CA 92110-2036
Tel (619) 296-9000 *Founded/Ownrshp* 1994
Sales 147.9MME *EMP* 1,500
SIC 7011 Hotels & motels
Pr: Ashok Israni
Genl Mgr: Lee Barnes
Genl Mgr: Jason Duemmel
IT Man: Hilton Sher

PACIFICARE
See UNITEDHEALTHCARE OF WASHINGTON INC

D-U-N-S 09-171-2414
■ **PACIFICARE HEALTH PLAN ADMINISTRATORS INC**
(*Suby of* PACIFICARE HEALTH SYSTEMS LLC) ★
3120 W Lake Center Dr, Santa Ana, CA 92704-6917
Tel (714) 825-5200 *Founded/Ownrshp* 1975, 1999
Sales NA *EMP* 4,900
SIC 6324 Group hospitalization plans
Ch Bd: David Reed
CFO: Kenneth L Watkins
Treas: Coy F Baugh
Sr VP: James A Frey
Sr VP: John KAO
Sr VP: David Taaffe
Sr VP: William Young
IT Man: Kristine Noble
Mktg Dir: Michael Eaton
Mktg Mgr: Steven Peskin
Board of Directors: David R Carpenter, Gary L Leary, Warren E Pinckert II, David A Reed, Lloyd E Ross, Jean Bixby Smith

D-U-N-S 96-385-8378
■ **PACIFICARE HEALTH SYSTEMS LLC**
(*Suby of* UNITEDHEALTH GROUP INC) ★
5995 Plaza Dr, Cypress, CA 90630-5028
Tel (714) 952-1121 *Founded/Ownrshp* 2005
Sales NA *EMP* 7,500
SIC 6324 Hospital & medical service plans
CEO: Howard Phanstiel
Bd of Dir: C W Wood
Ex VP: Coy Baugh
Ex VP: Sue Berkel
Ex VP: David Burch
Ex VP: Maria Connelly
Ex VP: Chuck Czerny
Ex VP: Katherine Feeny
Ex VP: Sharon Garrett
Ex VP: Warren Kane
Ex VP: Jacqueline Kosecoff
Ex VP: Wanda Lee
Ex VP: Alice Reuter
Ex VP: Bob Royer
Sr VP: Mary Langsdorf
VP: Diwakar Raman
VP: Tim Rhatigan

PACIFICARE OF CALIFORNIA
See UHC OF CALIFORNIA

D-U-N-S 00-790-9013 IMP/EXP
■ **PACIFICORP** (OR)
ROCKY MOUNTAIN POWER
(*Suby of* PPW HOLDINGS LLC) ★
825 Ne Multnomah St # 300, Portland, OR 97232-2157
Tel (503) 813-5645 *Founded/Ownrshp* 1910, 2006
Sales 5.2MMM *EMP* 5,700E
SIC 4911 Electric services; Distribution, electric power; Generation, electric power; Transmission, electric power
Ch Bd: Gregory E Abel
CFO: Nikki L Kobliha
CFO: Douglas K Stuver
Bd of Dir: Brent Gale
Sr VP: Donald N Furman
Sr VP: Natalie L Hocken
Sr VP: Robert A Klein
Sr VP: Robert Moir
VP: Paula Broussard
VP: Matt Feist
VP: Esther Giezendanner
VP: Ann Johnson
VP: Robert Klein
VP: Chris Moore
VP: Chris Turner
VP: Cathy Woollums
Dir Teleco: Bob Ward
Dir Risk M: John Fritz
Board of Directors: Douglas L Anderson, Stefan A Bird, Cindy A Crane, Patrick J Goodman, Natalie L Hocken, Andrea L Kelly

D-U-N-S 08-525-2971
PACIFICSOURCE HEALTH PLANS
110 International Way, Springfield, OR 97477-1034
Tel (541) 686-1242 *Founded/Ownrshp* 1933
Sales NA *EMP* 590
SIC 6321 Accident & health insurance carriers
Pr: Kenneth P Provencher
**COO:* Sujata Sanghvi
**CFO:* Peter Davidson
**Sec:* Clark Compton
Ofcr: Triet Tran
Sr VP: Troy M Kirk
Sr VP: Steven D Marks
VP: Martin Martinez
**VP:* Drew Mashaw
VP: Paul Wynkoop
IT Man: Anthony Nguyen

D-U-N-S 80-949-7592
▲ **PACIRA PHARMACEUTICALS INC**
5 Sylvan Way Ste 300, Parsippany, NJ 07054-3813
Tel (973) 254-3560 *Founded/Ownrshp* 2007
Sales 249.0MM *EMP* 487E
Accts Cohnreznick Llp Roseland New
Tkr Sym PCRX *Exch* NGS
SIC 2834 Pharmaceutical preparations
Ch Bd: David Stack
Pr: James S Scibetta
CFO: Charles A Reinhart III
Chf Cred: Robert Weiland
Ofcr: Kristen Williams
Sr VP: James B Jones
VP: Timothy M Ciaccio
VP: Vladimir Kharitonov
Mng Ofcr: Joyce Davis
QA Dir: Lulu Ronquillo
VP Mktg: Matthew Lehmann
Board of Directors: Laura Brege, Yvonne Greenstreet, Paul Hastings, Mark A Kronenfeld, John Longenecker, Gary Pace, Andreas Wicki, Dennis L Winger

D-U-N-S 06-685-8192 IMP/EXP
PACKAGING CONCEPTS INC
PCI
9832 Evergreen Indus Dr, Saint Louis, MO 63123-7249
Tel (314) 329-9700 *Founded/Ownrshp* 1972
Sales 176.1MME *EMP* 250
SIC 5113 2674 2671 Bags, paper & disposable plastic; Paper & products, wrapping or coarse; Bags: uncoated paper & multiwall; Packaging paper & plastics film, coated & laminated
Pr: John J Irace
**COO:* Anthony W Irace
QC Dir: Michael Bush
VP Sls: Terry Maffitt
Board of Directors: Richard Agostinelli, Abraham Mendenhall, Jack Wurtz

D-U-N-S 07-852-5133
PACKAGING COORDINATORS LLC
(*Suby of* FRAZIER & CO) ★
3001 Red Lion Rd, Philadelphia, PA 19114-1123
Tel (215) 613-3600 *Founded/Ownrshp* 2012
Sales 212.0MME *EMP* 1,010
SIC 7389 Packaging & labeling services
CEO: Bill Mitchell
**COO:* Bill Bolding
**CFO:* Mitchell Blumenfeld

D-U-N-S 06-004-7151 IMP/EXP
▲ **PACKAGING CORP OF AMERICA**
1955 W Field Ct, Lake Forest, IL 60045-4824
Tel (847) 482-3000 *Founded/Ownrshp* 1999
Sales 5.7MMM *EMP* 13,300
Tkr Sym PKG *Exch* NYS
SIC 2631 2653 Container board; Container, packaging & boxboard; Corrugated & solid fiber boxes
Ch Bd: Mark W Kowlzan
**CFO:* Robert P Mundy
Treas: Pamela Larson
**Ex VP:* Thomas A Hassfurther
Sr VP: Charles J Carter
**Sr VP:* Kent A Pflederer
**Sr VP:* Thomas W H Walton
VP: Tracy Ewing
VP: Bob Garstack
VP: Catherine Givens
VP: Bernadette Madarieta
VP: Jason Malone
VP: Lance Miller
VP: Ryan Morgan
VP: Cheryl Sheffield
VP: Tom Watson
VP: Richard West
Comm Man: Barbara Sessions

PACKAGING DYNAMICS
See BAGCRAFTPAPERCON I LLC

D-U-N-S 55-639-4026 IMP
PACKAGING DYNAMICS CORP
BAGCRAFT
(*Suby of* NOVOLEX) ★
3900 W 43rd St, Chicago, IL 60632-3421
Tel (773) 254-8000 *Founded/Ownrshp* 2014
Sales 482.5MME *EMP* 1,200
SIC 2671 Packaging paper & plastics film, coated & laminated
Ex VP: Patrick T Chamblis
**CFO:* Michael F Arduino
**CFO:* Henry Newell
Ex VP: Mary Hayes
**VP:* Dan Vice
VP: Russ Wanke
VP: Mark Wilcox
VP: Tom Wolf
Exec: Mike Arduiono
Genl Mgr: Richard Goulet
Netwrk Mgr: Patti Poquette

PACKAGING FILMS CO.
See PROFESSIONAL PLASTICS INC

D-U-N-S 04-000-6728 IMP
PACKAGING INNOVATORS CORP
6650 National Dr, Livermore, CA 94550-8802
Tel (925) 371-2000 *Founded/Ownrshp* 1975
Sales 90.3MME *EMP* 90

SIC 5113 2653 3993 Shipping supplies; Corrugated & solid fiber boxes; Display items, solid fiber: made from purchased materials; Signs & advertising specialties
CEO: William E Mazzocco
**Sec:* Beverly J Flynt
**VP:* John Hart
**VP:* Mark Andrew Mazzocco
**Genl Mgr:* Michael Anthony Mazzocco

D-U-N-S 00-843-5950
PACKAGING SERVICE CO INC
1904 Mykawa Rd, Pearland, TX 77581-3210
Tel (281) 485-1458 *Founded/Ownrshp* 1964
Sales 85.9MM[E] *EMP* 250
SIC 3563 Spraying outfits: metals, paints & chemicals (compressor)
Pr: Jean Pierre Baizan
**CFO:* Carl Caldwell
CFO: Andy Plagens
Sfty Mgr: Stephen Craig
Opers Mgr: Michael Brantley
Plnt Mgr: Hector Arreola
Plnt Mgr: Luis Delacruz
VP Mktg: Lynn Place
VP Sls: Andrew Tomlinson
Mktg Mgr: Amber Livesey
Manager: Chris Matherne

PACKAGING SPECTRUM
See ADVANCE PAPER BOX CO

D-U-N-S 07-965-1105 IMP/EXP
PACKAGING UNLIMITED LLC
KIT PAK
1729 Mccloskey Ave, Louisville, KY 40210-1755
Tel (502) 515-3900 *Founded/Ownrshp* 1975
Sales 115.8MM[E] *EMP* 350
SIC 2653 Boxes, corrugated: made from purchased materials
CEO: Pete Hanekamp
MIS Dir: Pat Creed
Sfty Mgr: Gary Holland
Plnt Mgr: Ed Gun
Prd Mgr: Wayne Bland
Sales Exec: Jim Schmitt
Sls Mgr: Ron Stapleton

PACKERLAND BROADBAND
See CCI SYSTEMS INC

D-U-N-S 94-676-3638
PACKERLAND HOLDINGS INC
(*Suby of* JBS S/A)
1770 Promontory Cir, Greeley, CO 80634-9039
Tel (970) 506-8000 *Founded/Ownrshp* 2008
Sales 214.2MM[E] *EMP* 1,500
SIC 2011 4213 Boxed beef from meat slaughtered on site; Trucking, except local
Pr: Richard V Vesta
**CFO:* Craig A Liegel
CFO: Fabio Sandri
Bd of Dir: Don Jackson
Ex VP: Jeff Johnson
VP: Jerry Shelton
VP: Scott Walker
DP Exec: Curt Vancalster
Sls Dir: Dave Maslanka

D-U-N-S 02-793-8706
PACKERS HOLDINGS LLC
(*Suby of* HARVEST PARTNERS LP) ★
1010 E Washington St # 202, Mount Pleasant, IA 52641-1887
Tel (800) 881-9558 *Founded/Ownrshp* 2011
Sales 82.0MM[E] *EMP* 9,000[E]
SIC 7342 7349 Washroom sanitation service (industrial locations); Cleaning service, industrial or commercial
CEO: Jeff Kaiser

PACKERS PROVISION
See TRAFON GROUP INC

D-U-N-S 04-825-7448 IMP
■ **PACKERWARE LLC**
(*Suby of* BERRY PLASTICS CORP) ★
2330 Packer Rd, Lawrence, KS 66049-8900
Tel (785) 331-4236 *Founded/Ownrshp* 2008
Sales 140.0MM[E] *EMP* 700
SIC 3089 Injection molding of plastics
Pr: Roberto Buaron
**Pr:* Martin Imbler
**CFO:* Jon Rich
Sr Cor Off: John Landgrebe
**Ex VP:* James Kratochvil
Ex VP: Mark Miles

D-U-N-S 07-828-2437
PACKSIZE LLC
6440 S Wasatch Blvd # 305, Salt Lake City, UT 84121-6310
Tel (801) 944-4814 *Founded/Ownrshp* 2007
Sales 120.0MM *EMP* 137
SIC 7389 Packaging & labeling services
CEO: Hanko Kiessner
Pr: Niklas Pettersson
Area Mgr: Luke Anderson
Area Mgr: Mike Conlan
Area Mgr: James Cundiff
Area Mgr: Scott Jones
Area Mgr: Jill Lau
Area Mgr: Ted Phifer
Area Mgr: Eric Shepard
Genl Mgr: Horst Reinkensmeyer
Opers Mgr: Alex Rossato

PACLEASE
See PALMER TRUCKS INC

PACLO
See PACIFIC LOGISTICS CORP

D-U-N-S 01-920-2050
PACMED CLINICS
PACIFIC MEDICAL CENTERS
1200 12th Ave S, Seattle, WA 98144-2712
Tel (206) 326-2400 *Founded/Ownrshp* 1981
Sales 184.8MM *EMP* 1,000
Accts Clark Nuber Ps Bellevue Wa
SIC 8011 General & family practice, physician/surgeon
CEO: William Reilly
**Pr:* Harvey Smith
**COO:* Linda Marzano
Ofcr: Pamela Shepard
**VP:* Scott Combs
**VP:* Gina Marble
**VP:* Allen Salmieri
IT Man: Moung Finh
Surgeon: Chad Marion
Surgeon: Daniel Nadig
Doctor: Akiko Hall

PACOA
See PAINT APPLICATOR CORP OF AMERICA

D-U-N-S 00-612-6031 IMP/EXP
PACON CORP (WI)
BEMIS JASON
(*Suby of* MASON WELLS INC) ★
2525 N Casaloma Dr, Appleton, WI 54913-8865
Tel (920) 830-5050 *Founded/Ownrshp* 1951, 2011
Sales 145.8MM[E] *EMP* 400
SIC 2679 Paper products, converted
CEO: James J Schmitz
**CFO:* Thomas O Hurley
Ex VP: John Carlberg
**VP:* Brian Higgins
VP: Corey Perry
VP: Steven Spangenberg
**VP:* Steve Spaninberg
Plnt Mgr: Terry Szczepaniak
Mktg Dir: Tom Harper
Manager: Mark Dahl
Manager: Paul Libassi

D-U-N-S 15-969-6285
PACPIZZA LLC
PIZZA HUT
220 Porter Dr Ste 100, San Ramon, CA 94583-9206
Tel (925) 838-8567 *Founded/Ownrshp* 1997
Sales 71.4MM[E] *EMP* 2,000
SIC 5812 Pizzeria, chain
CEO: James Gressett
CFO: Brad Brooks
Opers Mgr: Bruce McKinnon

D-U-N-S 07-770-5911
PACT INC
1828 L St Nw Ste 300, Washington, DC 20036-5104
Tel (202) 466-5666 *Founded/Ownrshp* 1973
Sales 109.0MM *EMP* 230
Accts Mcgladrey Llp Mc Lean Va
SIC 8399 8699 Social change association; Personal interest organization
CEO: Mark Viso
**COO:* Will Warshauer
CFO: Rick Garza
**CFO:* Leonard F Williams
CFO: Ken Wojcik
Ofcr: Latin America
Ofcr: Meg McDermott
**VP:* Graham Wood
**Dir Surg:* Mark Miebach
Comm Man: May Y Pyae
Mng Dir: Nancy Zucker Boswell

D-U-N-S 08-452-6354
PACTERA TECHNOLOGIES NA INC
(*Suby of* PACTERA TECHNOLOGY INTERNATIONAL LTD)
14980 Ne 31st Way Ste 120, Redmond, WA 98052-5349
Tel (425) 233-8578 *Founded/Ownrshp* 2007
Sales 106.1MM *EMP* 500
Accts Archibald M Sam & Company Cpa
SIC 7371 8742 Software programming applications; Management consulting services
CEO: Tiak Koon Loh
Pr: Peter Korsos
CFO: Sidney Chan
Chf Mktg O: George Wu
**Ofcr:* Xiangguang Zou
VP: Shi LI
VP: Wutai Shi

D-U-N-S 00-521-1768 IMP/EXP
PACTIV LLC
(*Suby of* REYNOLDS GROUP HOLDINGS LIMITED)
1900 W Field Ct, Lake Forest, IL 60045-4828
Tel (847) 482-2000 *Founded/Ownrshp* 1965, 2010
Sales 10.6MMM[E] *EMP* 12,000
SIC 5113 3089 2673 Containers, paper & disposable plastic; Food casings, plastic; Food storage & frozen food bags, plastic
CEO: Richard L Wambold
Genl Pt: Jay Gruskowski
Genl Pt: Scott Schneider
**CEO:* Jacquelyne Huerta
Ex Ofcr: Jason Dennis
Trst Ofcr: Helen E Blask
**Ex VP:* Peter J Lazaredes
**Sr VP:* John N Schwab
VP: William Antonace
VP: Barbara Border
**VP:* Joseph E Doyle
VP: Jeff Eggert
VP: Christine Hanneman
VP: John McGrath
**VP:* Edward T Walters
Dir Risk M: Walt Danko
Dir Risk M: Ritchie Wionziek

D-U-N-S 17-892-1420
▲ **PACWEST BANCORP**
9701 Wilshire Blvd # 700, Beverly Hills, CA 90212-2007
Tel (310) 887-8500 *Founded/Ownrshp* 1999
Sales NA *EMP* 1,670[E]
Tkr Sym PACW *Exch* NGS
SIC 6021 National commercial banks
Pr: Matthew P Wagner
**Ch Bd:* John Eggemeyer
**CFO:* Patrick J Rusnak
**Ex VP:* Lynn M Hopkins
**Ex VP:* Kori L Ogrosky
**Ex VP:* James J Pieczynski
Board of Directors: Paul R Burke, Craig A Carlson, Barry C Fitzpatrick, Andrew B Fremder, C William Hosler, Susan E Lester, Roger H Molvar, Daniel B Platt, Robert A Stine

D-U-N-S 96-769-4121
PADDOCK LABORATORIES LLC
(*Suby of* PERRIGO CO) ★
3940 Quebec Ave N, Minneapolis, MN 55427-1244
Tel (763) 546-4676 *Founded/Ownrshp* 2011
Sales 122.4MM[E] *EMP* 350
SIC 2834 Pharmaceutical preparations
Opers Mgr: Angie Zroker

D-U-N-S 00-510-0680
PADDOCK PUBLICATIONS INC
DAILY HERALD
155 E Algonquin Rd, Arlington Heights, IL 60005-4617
Tel (847) 427-4300 *Founded/Ownrshp* 1872
Sales 104.8MM[E] *EMP* 600
SIC 2711 Newspapers, publishing & printing
Pr: Doug Ray
**CFO:* Kent Johnson
**Ch:* Daniel E Baumann
VP: Bob Finch
VP: John Lampinen
CIO: Mike Schoepke
IT Man: Gary Morrill

D-U-N-S 14-645-4285
PADFIELD INC
QUALITY TIRE SLC
1335 W 2100 S, Salt Lake City, UT 84119-1403
Tel (801) 972-1944 *Founded/Ownrshp* 1986
Sales 91.3MM[E] *EMP* 123
SIC 5014 5531 3711 Tires & tubes; Automotive tires; Truck & tractor truck assembly
Pr: Alden Padfield
**Treas:* Dana Robinson
**VP:* Bonnie L Padfield
Exec: Jennifer Demil
**Prin:* Greg Robinson

D-U-N-S 07-336-7203
PADRES LP
SAN DIEGO PADRES
100 Pk Blvd Petco Park Petco Pk, San Diego, CA 92101
Tel (619) 795-5000 *Founded/Ownrshp* 2009
Sales 247.5M[E] *EMP* 1,100
SIC 7941 Baseball club, professional & semi-professional
Sr VP: Wayne Partello
VP: Scott Marshall
Ex Dir: Jim Kiersnowski
Genl Mgr: Kevin Towers

PADUCAH SUN, THE
See PAXTON MEDIA GROUP LLC

PAE
See PACIFIC ARCHITECTS AND ENGINEERS INC

PAE
See A-T SOLUTIONS INC

PAE APPLIED TECHNOLOGIES
See PAE HOLDING CORP

D-U-N-S 12-713-6252
PAE APPLIED TECHNOLOGIES LLC
6500 West Fwy Ste 600, Fort Worth, TX 76116-2118
Tel (817) 737-1500 *Founded/Ownrshp* 2016
Sales 965.7MM[E] *EMP* 12,000
SIC 8741 8711 8744 4581 7381 Management services; Engineering services; Facilities support services; Airports, flying fields & services; Aircraft maintenance & repair services; Guard services
Pr: Michael A Dignam
**CFO:* Clinton D Bickett
**VP:* Paul W Cobb
VP: Harold Watson

D-U-N-S 13-984-7276
PAE AVIATION AND TECHNICAL SERVICES LLC
(*Suby of* PAE) ★
1320 N Courthouse Rd # 800, Arlington, VA 22201-2501
Tel (856) 866-2200 *Founded/Ownrshp* 2004
Sales 542.9MM[E] *EMP* 5,000
SIC 4581 3728 8742 Airports, flying fields & services; Aircraft parts & equipment; Materials mgmt. (purchasing, handling, inventory) consultant
CEO: John Heller
**Sr VP:* Micheal Kaut
Dir Surg: Donal W Smith

D-U-N-S 80-979-0017
PAE GOVERNMENT SERVICES INC
P A E
1320 N Courthouse Rd # 800, Arlington, VA 22201-2598
Tel (703) 717-6000 *Founded/Ownrshp* 2016
Sales 157.2MM[E] *EMP* 899
SIC 8748 Safety training service
CEO: John Heller
**Pr:* Michael Dignam
**Pr:* Mick Fox
**Pr:* Kenneth Myers
**CFO:* Clint Bickett
Ch: Paul Cofoni
Sr VP: Whit Cobb
Prin: Edgardo Perez
**CIO:* John Lambeth

D-U-N-S 96-807-1493
PAE HOLDING CORP
PAE APPLIED TECHNOLOGIES
1320 N Courthouse Rd # 800, Arlington, VA 22201-2501
Tel (703) 717-6000 *Founded/Ownrshp* 2016
Sales 1.4MMM[E] *EMP* 5,003[E]
SIC 6719 8742 8711 Personal holding companies, except banks; Personnel management consultant; Building construction consultant
CEO: John Heller
**COO:* Karl Williams
**CFO:* Charles Peiffer
**Ex VP:* Mick Fox
Sr VP: Whit Cobb
**Sr VP:* Patricia Munchel
VP: Tom Callahan
**CIO:* John Lambeth

PAETEC BUSINESS SERVICES
See US LEC COMMUNICATIONS LLC

D-U-N-S 02-071-2241
■ **PAETEC COMMUNICATIONS INC**
(*Suby of* PAETEC HOLDING CORP) ★
600 Willowbrook Office Pa, Fairport, NY 14450-4233
Tel (585) 340-2500 *Founded/Ownrshp* 1998
Sales 377.3MM[E] *EMP* 1,072
SIC 4813 7375 7372 Telephone communication, except radio; Data telephone communications; Local telephone communications; Long distance telephone communications; Information retrieval services; Prepackaged software
Ch Bd: Arunas A Chesonis
**Pr:* Joseph D Ambersley
**Pr:* Christopher Bantoft
**Pr:* Jack Baron
**COO:* Bradford M Bono
**COO:* Edward J Butler Jr
**CFO:* Keith Wilson
**Ex VP:* Timothy Bancroft
**Ex VP:* Jeffrey L Burke
**Ex VP:* Richard Padulo
**Ex VP:* Daniel Venuti
**Sr VP:* Al Chesonis
**Sr VP:* Karen Dupke
**Sr VP:* Bob Moore
**Sr VP:* Reginald Scales
**Sr VP:* Donna Wenk
VP: Patricia C Lynott

D-U-N-S 79-544-9920
■ **PAETEC HOLDING CORP**
(*Suby of* WINDSTREAM SERVICES LLC) ★
1 Paetec Plz, Fairport, NY 14450
Tel (585) 340-2500 *Founded/Ownrshp* 2011
Sales 1.1MMM[E] *EMP* 4,546
SIC 4813 Telephone communication, except radio
COO: Brent Whittington
Pr: Mario Deriggi
Pr: Kevin Errity
Pr: Dan Reinbold
Pr: Stan Rich
Pr: Jeff Rowe
**CFO:* Anthony W Thomas
Sr Cor Off: Faith Mavretich
Ex VP: John P Baron
Ex VP: Andy Drotleff
Ex VP: James M Hvisdas
Ex VP: Sharon Lamantia
Ex VP: Robert D Moore Jr
Ex VP: Richard E Ottalagana
Ex VP: Matt Pinto
Ex VP: J Ryan
Ex VP: Keith Wilson
Sr VP: Sean Pflaging
VP: Richard Cunningham
VP: Jim Falvey
VP: Richard Fruchterman
Board of Directors: Richard T Aab, Shelley Diamond, H Russell Frisby Jr, Michael C Mac Donald, William R McDermott, Alex Stadler, Mark Zupan

PAFCO
See PACIFIC AMERICAN FISH CO INC

D-U-N-S 06-813-6980
■ **PAG WEST LLC**
ROLLS-ROYCE N SCOTTSDALE
(*Suby of* PENSKE AUTOMOTIVE GROUP INC) ★
7015 E Chauncey Ln, Phoenix, AZ 85054-6143
Tel (480) 538-6677 *Founded/Ownrshp* 2000
Sales 152.8MM[E] *EMP* 700
SIC 5511 Automobiles, new & used
Exec: Annmarie Ryan

D-U-N-S 07-929-3287
PAGE SOUTHERLAND PAGE INC
1615 M St Nw Ste 700, Washington, DC 20036-3220
Tel (202) 909-4900 *Founded/Ownrshp* 2013
Sales 116.7MM *EMP* 500
SIC 8712 8711 Architectural services; Consulting engineer
CEO: James Wright
**Pr:* Mattia Flabiano
**Sec:* Catherine Britt
**Ex VP:* Robert Burke
**Ex VP:* Arturo Chavez
**Ex VP:* Michael Mace
**Ex VP:* Thomas McCarthy
**Ex VP:* Lawrence Speck

PAGE/NTRNTIONAL COMMUNICATIONS
See BEACON PRINTING & GRAPHICS INC

D-U-N-S 06-049-7674
PAGNOTTI ENTERPRISES INC
46 Public Sq Ste 600, Wilkes Barre, PA 18701-2609
Tel (570) 825-8700 *Founded/Ownrshp* 1974
Sales NA *EMP* 540
SIC 6411 1231 4841 Insurance agents, brokers & service; Strip mining, anthracite; Cable television services
CEO: Charles E Parente
**Pr:* Michalene Kennedy
**VP:* Mary Ann Eggleston
**VP:* David Swisher

PAGNY
See PHYSICIAN AFFILIATE GROUP OF NEW YORK PC

PAHO
See PAN AMERICAN HEALTH ORGANIZATION INC

D-U-N-S 06-458-3263 IMP/EXP
PAI INDUSTRIES INC
950 Northbrook Pkwy, Suwanee, GA 30024-2928
Tel (770) 822-1000 *Founded/Ownrshp* 1973
Sales 154.6MM[E] *EMP* 4[E]
SIC 3714 5013 Motor vehicle parts & accessories; Truck parts & accessories
CEO: Habib Yavari
CFO: Thomas R Huff
VP: G Parsai
Exec: Francisco Ramirez

Manager: Theresa Myers
Manager: John Dodero
Manager: Jerry Holton

D-U-N-S 01-151-9113 IMP/EXP
PAIGE ELECTRIC CO LP
1160 Springfield Rd, Union, NJ 07083-8121
Tel (908) 687-7810 *Founded/Ownrshp* 1992
Sales 134.9MM *EMP* 116
SIC 5063 3699 Electronic wire & cable; Electrical equipment & supplies
CEO: Louis Grotta
Pt: Henry Coffey
Pt: William Watkins
CFO: Ramon Santiago
Ex VP: Vince Nolletti
IT Man: Wendy Davis
IT Man: Joe Dolbies
IT Man: Dan Pritchard
IT Man: John Vargas
VP Opers: Frank Conaty
Sls Mgr: Joseph Rienzo

D-U-N-S 07-273-3694 IMP
PAINT APPLICATOR CORP OF AMERICA
PACOA
7 Harbor Park Dr, Port Washington, NY 11050-4655
Tel (516) 284-3000 *Founded/Ownrshp* 1974
Sales 116.7MME *EMP* 104
SIC 5072 5198 Hardware; Paint brushes, rollers, sprayers
Ch Bd: Steven Geismar
**Ch Bd:* Herbert Geismar
Sr Cor Off: Theodore Obermeit
Manager: Frank Barravecchio

D-U-N-S 62-094-2495 IMP
PAINT SUNDRIES SOLUTIONS INC
930 7th Ave, Kirkland, WA 98033-5748
Tel (425) 827-9200 *Founded/Ownrshp* 2003
Sales 165.3MME *EMP* 140
SIC 5198 Paints, varnishes & supplies
CEO: Don Walker
**Pr:* Andrew Walsh
CFO: Bradley Mansker
**Treas:* Philip Greger
**Sr VP:* John Mittenthal
**Sr VP:* John Ure
**VP:* Shawn Fernandez

D-U-N-S 00-281-1201
PAINTED POST PARTNERS
3131 Elliott Ave Ste 500, Seattle, WA 98121-1032
Tel (206) 298-2909 *Founded/Ownrshp* 1995
Sales 27.9MME *EMP* 6,500
SIC 8059 Personal care home, with health care
Pt: Daniel R Baty
Pt: Raymond R Brandstrom

D-U-N-S 01-720-9321 IMP/EXP
PAINTERS SUPPLY AND EQUIPMENT CO
PAINTERS SUPPLY COMPANY
25195 Brest, Taylor, MI 48180-6849
Tel (734) 946-8119 *Founded/Ownrshp* 1953
Sales 133.6MME *EMP* 192
SIC 5198 5231 Paints, varnishes & supplies; Paint & painting supplies
Pr: Patrick Mayette

PAINTERS SUPPLY COMPANY
See PAINTERS SUPPLY AND EQUIPMENT CO

D-U-N-S 02-038-7650
PAINTING INDUSTRY INSURANCE FUND
45 W 14th St Fl 5, New York, NY 10011-7419
Tel (212) 255-2950 *Founded/Ownrshp* 1946
Sales NA *EMP* 15
Accts Novak Francella Llc Bala Cynw
SIC 6411 Insurance agents

D-U-N-S 03-796-0606 IMP
PAJ INC
PRIME ART & JEWEL
18325 Waterview Pkwy Frnt, Dallas, TX 75252-8001
Tel (214) 575-6080 *Founded/Ownrshp* 1976
Sales 93.9MME *EMP* 110
SIC 5094 Jewelry
CEO: Felix Chen
**VP:* Candice Chen
IT Man: Tesha Nash
IT Man: Nash Tesha
Software D: Peter Liang
VP Sls: Patricia Price
Sls Dir: Penny Berg
Mktg Mgr: Jared Leshin

D-U-N-S 01-094-3181
PAJARO VALLEY UNIFIED SCHOOL DISTRICT
PAJARO VALLEY USD
294 Green Valley Rd Fl 1, Watsonville, CA 95076-1382
Tel (831) 786-2100 *Founded/Ownrshp* 1965
Sales 133.0MME *EMP* 2,139
Accts Vavrinek Trine Day & Co Ll
SIC 8211 Public elementary & secondary schools

PAJARO VALLEY USD
See PAJARO VALLEY UNIFIED SCHOOL DISTRICT

PAK WEST PAPER & PACKAGING
See BLOWER-DEMPSAY CORP

PAK-A-SAK
See JAY PETROLEUM INC

PAKLAB
See UNIVERSAL PACKAGING SYSTEMS INC

D-U-N-S 00-799-5983
PALA CASINO SPA & RESORT
35008 Pala Temecula Rd, Pala, CA 92059-2419
Tel (760) 510-5100 *Founded/Ownrshp* 2000
Sales 89.9MME *EMP* 1,800
SIC 7991 Spas
Ch Bd: Robert Smith
Pr: Garlon Banks
**CEO:* Bill Bembenek
**CFO:* Shauna Anton
VP: Michael Crenshaw
VP: Sue Welp
Exec: Marc Green
Exec: Linda Jackson
Exec: Kathy Sharp
Genl Mgr: Alonzo Dicarlo
Dir IT: Steve Woodward

D-U-N-S 00-986-0537
PALA GROUP INC
16347 Old Hammond Hwy, Baton Rouge, LA 70816-1730
Tel (225) 272-5194 *Founded/Ownrshp* 2000
Sales 100.9MM *EMP* 650E
Accts Hannis T Bourgeois Llp Bato
SIC 1629 1541 Chemical plant & refinery construction; Prefabricated building erection, industrial
CEO: Jorge L Tarajano
**CFO:* Gay Young
CIO: Tracy Blair

D-U-N-S 15-524-9923 IMP
PALA INTERSTATE LLC
(*Suby of* PALA GROUP INC) ★
16347 Old Hammond Hwy, Baton Rouge, LA 70816-1730
Tel (225) 272-5194 *Founded/Ownrshp* 2000
Sales 99.2MM *EMP* 420E
Accts Hannis T Bourgeois Llp Bato
SIC 1541 8711 Industrial buildings, new construction; Engineering services
Off Mgr: Lynette Watson
IT Man: Tracy Ezernack
Sfty Dirs: Barry Abshire
Site Mgr: Justin Shotwell

PALACE ENTERTAINMENT
See FESTIVAL FUN PARKS LLC

D-U-N-S 14-669-9272
PALACE ENTERTAINMENT INC
(*Suby of* PARQUE DE ATRACCIONES MADRID SA)
4590 Macarthur Blvd # 400, Newport Beach, CA 92660-2027
Tel (949) 261-0404 *Founded/Ownrshp* 1998
Sales 111.9MME *EMP* 2,229
SIC 7999 7993 Miniature golf course operation; Arcades
CEO: Alexander Weber Jr
**Pr:* John Cora
VP: Bill Lentz
VP: A Scherpenzeel
Exec: Diana Tran
Ex Dir: Dan Vogt
Genl Mgr: Ismet Dakaj
Genl Mgr: Marc Glissman
Genl Mgr: Jeff Moody
Genl Mgr: Justin White
IT Man: Steve Martinez

THE PALACE OF AUBURN HILLS
See PALACE SPORTS & ENTERTAINMENT LLC

D-U-N-S 18-510-7042
PALACE SPORTS & ENTERTAINMENT LLC
THE PALACE OF AUBURN HILLS
6 Championship Dr, Auburn Hills, MI 48326-1753
Tel (248) 377-0165 *Founded/Ownrshp* 2011
Sales 177.1MME *EMP* 3,000
SIC 7941 7922 Stadium event operator services; Summer theater
COO: Alan Otsfield

D-U-N-S 82-541-6852
PALACE STATION HOTEL & CASINO INC
(*Suby of* STATION CASINOS LLC) ★
2411 W Sahara Ave, Las Vegas, NV 89102-4377
Tel (702) 367-2411 *Founded/Ownrshp* 1977
Sales 109.8MME *EMP* 1,500
SIC 7011 Casino hotel
Pr: Frank J Fertitta III
**Pr:* Kevin L Kelley
**CFO:* Thomas Friel

PALADIN ATTACHMENTS
See PALADIN BRANDS GROUP INC

D-U-N-S 16-910-1107 IMP/EXP
PALADIN BRANDS GROUP INC
PALADIN ATTACHMENTS
(*Suby of* IES) ★
2800 Zeeb Rd, Dexter, MI 48130-2204
Tel (319) 378-3696 *Founded/Ownrshp* 1996
Sales 380.2MME *EMP* 1,300
SIC 3531 Finishers & spreaders (construction equipment); Subgraders (construction equipment); Drags, road (construction & road maintenance equipment)
CEO: Steve Andrews
**Pr:* Matt Roney
CFO: John Gelp
VP: Timothy Allen
VP: David Crummy
VP: Bob Ferguson
VP: Paul Lam
VP: Andrew Macdonald
VP: Wendell Moss
VP: Joe Preuth
Exec: Tim Adkisson

PALAGRAVE MACMILLAN
See MACMILLAN PUBLISHING GROUP LLC

D-U-N-S 36-213-0952
PALANTIR TECHNOLOGIES INC
100 Hamilton Ave Ste 300, Palo Alto, CA 94301-1651
Tel (650) 815-0200 *Founded/Ownrshp* 2004
Sales 555.9MME *EMP* 1,500E
SIC 7371 Computer software development
Pr: Alex Karp
Dir Bus: Eric Poirier
Prgrm Mgr: Sofia Aldape
Snr Sftwr: Dan Cervelli
Snr Sftwr: ARI Gesher
Snr Sftwr: Eric Porter
CTO: Nathan Gettings
IT Man: Chris Bond
IT Man: Alex Marcal
Software D: Alex Chaphiv
Software D: Justin Lan

PALATINE SCHOOL DISTRICT 15
See COMMUNITY CONSOLIDATED SCHOOL DISTRICT 15 COOK COUNTY

D-U-N-S 14-474-3408 IMP
PALERMO VILLA INC
PALERMO'S PIZZA
3301 W Canal St, Milwaukee, WI 53208-4137
Tel (414) 342-8898 *Founded/Ownrshp* 1964
Sales 300.3MME *EMP* 400
SIC 5149 Groceries & related products
Pr: Giacomo Fallucca
**COO:* Angelo Fallucca
Ql Cn Mgr: Jon Falk
Sls Mgr: Chris Johnson

PALERMO'S PIZZA
See PALERMO VILLA INC

PALIG
See PAN-AMERICAN LIFE INSURANCE GROUP INC

D-U-N-S 61-095-8998
PALISADE BUILDERS INC
1875 S Bascom Ave # 2400, Campbell, CA 95008-2356
Tel (408) 429-7700 *Founded/Ownrshp* 2004
Sales 143.2MM *EMP* 30
Accts Gallina Llp San Jose Califor
SIC 1522 Multi-family dwellings, new construction
CEO: J Douglas Ross
**CFO:* Joyce E Converse
**VP:* Jeffrey Jelniker

D-U-N-S 19-575-7823
PALISADES ASSOCIATES HOLDING INC
9140 Vendome Dr, Bethesda, MD 20817-4021
Tel (301) 469-7564 *Founded/Ownrshp* 2005
Sales NA *EMP* 1,000
SIC 6719 Investment holding companies, except banks
Pr: Greg Rosenbaum
CFO: Richard Berger

D-U-N-S 87-851-7556
PALISADES GENERAL HOSPITAL GIFT SHOP
(*Suby of* PMC) ★
7600 River Rd, North Bergen, NJ 07047-6217
Tel (201) 854-5123 *Founded/Ownrshp* 1978
Sales 153.6MM *EMP* 2
SIC 5947 Gift, novelty & souvenir shop
Surgeon: Shubha Varma

D-U-N-S 04-574-4513 IMP/EXP
PALISADES HOLDINGS INC
2266 Groom Rd, Baker, LA 70714-2124
Tel (225) 236-1440 *Founded/Ownrshp* 2006
Sales 118.8MME *EMP* 49E
SIC 5051 Ferroalloys
CEO: Kurt Friedmann
VP: Brian Dees

D-U-N-S 06-751-8811
PALISADES MEDICAL CENTER INC
PMC
7600 River Rd, North Bergen, NJ 07047-6217
Tel (201) 854-5000 *Founded/Ownrshp* 1978
Sales 158.9MM *EMP* 1,200E
SIC 8062 General medical & surgical hospitals
Pr: Bruce J Markowitz
Chf Rad: Bob Greenwald
**COO:* David J Berkowitz
COO: David Berkowitz
CFO: John Calandrillo
Ofcr: Rose Lee
**VP:* Donna Cahill
**VP:* Elisse E Glennon
VP: Suresh Raina
Dir Inf Cn: Miriam Stablein
Dir Lab: Maria Garcia

PALISADES NUCLEAR PLANT
See ENTERGY NUCLEAR PALISADES LLC

D-U-N-S 79-617-1015
PALISADES SAFETY INSURANCE AGENCY INC
200 Connell Dr, Berkeley Heights, NJ 07922-2805
Tel (908) 790-7800 *Founded/Ownrshp* 1992
Sales NA *EMP* 600E
SIC 6321 Reciprocal interinsurance exchanges
Pr: Ed Fernandes
**Treas:* Loren Mattingly
Ofcr: Carl Peterson
**VP:* Willam Emmons
**VP:* Michael Luciani
**VP:* Karen Murdock
Dir IT: Ross Brooks
Dir IT: John Chepulis
Dir IT: Mark Pfenning
Snr PM: Tricia Kranz

D-U-N-S 80-744-5499 IMP/EXP
■ PALL AEROPOWER CORP
(*Suby of* PALL CORP) ★
10540 Ridge Rd Ste 100, New Port Richey, FL 34654-5111
Tel (727) 849-9999 *Founded/Ownrshp* 1981
Sales 178.4MME *EMP* 958
SIC 3569 Filters, general line: industrial
Pr: Lawrence Mr Kingsley
Pr: Mark Morris
**Treas:* John Adamovich
Dir Lab: Mitch Eick
Netwrk Mgr: Colleen Kenny
Opers Mgr: Jill Costanzo
Sls Mgr: Laura Casale

D-U-N-S 00-205-4419 IMP
■ PALL CORP (NY)
(*Suby of* DANAHER CORP) ★
25 Harbor Park Dr, Port Washington, NY 11050-4664
Tel (516) 484-5400 *Founded/Ownrshp* 2015
Sales 2.7MMM *EMP* 10,400
SIC 3569 3599 3714 2834 3841 Filters; Filters, general line: industrial; Filter elements, fluid, hydraulic line; Separators for steam, gas, vapor or air (machinery); Air intake filters, internal combustion engine, except auto; Gasoline filters, internal combustion engine, except auto; Oil filters, internal combustion engine, except automotive; Filters: oil, fuel & air, motor vehicle; Solutions, pharmaceutical; Surgical & medical instruments; IV transfusion apparatus
Pr: Rainer Blair
Pr: Yves Baratelli
Pr: Michael Egholm
Pr: Naresh Narasimhan
**Sr VP:* Brian Burnett
Sr VP: Jeff Wooten
VP: Moira Bilich
VP: Keitha Buckingham
VP: Mike Caspall
VP: Robert Cooper
VP: Ken Del Giudice
VP: Mark Demmink
VP: Dan Dhanraj
**VP:* Rob Fener
VP: Tom Gsell
VP: Holly Haughney
VP: Steve Kim
VP: Mani Krishnan
VP: Victor A Maurtua
VP: Michael Mesawich
VP: Jeff Molin

D-U-N-S 06-976-3225 IMP
■ PALL FILTER SPECIALISTS INC
F S I
(*Suby of* PALL CORP) ★
100 Anchor Rd, Michigan City, IN 46360-2802
Tel (219) 879-3307 *Founded/Ownrshp* 2014
Sales 169.9MME *EMP* 593
SIC 3569 Filters, general line: industrial
Pr: H W Morgan Jr
**COO:* Bernard C Faulkner
Tech Mgr: Robert Weimer
Ql Cn Mgr: Amy Chlebowski
Sls Mgr: Brandon Peterson

D-U-N-S 14-752-7535 IMP
■ PALL FILTRATION AND SEPARATIONS GROUP INC
FLUID DYNAMICS
(*Suby of* PALL CORP) ★
2118 Greenspring Dr, Lutherville Timonium, MD 21093-3112
Tel (410) 252-0800 *Founded/Ownrshp* 1986
Sales 191.4MME *EMP* 715
SIC 3569 Filters
Genl Mgr: Ted Foreman
CFO: John Adamovich Jr
Treas: James W Dierker
VP: Patrick J Crotty

PALL LIFE SCIENCES
See GELMAN SCIENCES INC

D-U-N-S 04-940-2969 IMP
■ PALL LIFE SCIENCES PUERTO RICO LLC
(*Suby of* PALL CORP) ★
Carr 194 Pall Blvd 98, Fajardo, PR 00738
Tel (787) 863-1124 *Founded/Ownrshp* 2006
Sales 116.1MME *EMP* 850
SIC 3842 Surgical appliances & supplies
Ch: Eric Krasnoff
**CFO:* Lisa McDermott
**Sr VP:* Felix Megron

D-U-N-S 09-051-4365 IMP
■ PALL PUERTO RICO INC
(*Suby of* PALL CORP) ★
Km 0 Hm 4 Rr 194, Fajardo, PR 00738
Tel (787) 863-1124 *Founded/Ownrshp* 1974
Sales 97.0MME *EMP* 458
SIC 3569 Filters, general line: industrial
Ch Bd: Larry Kingsley

D-U-N-S 00-204-3396 IMP
■ PALL TRINITY MICRO CORP
PALL WELL TECHNOLOGY DIV
(*Suby of* PALL CORP) ★
3643 State Route 281, Cortland, NY 13045-3591
Tel (607) 753-6041 *Founded/Ownrshp* 1961
Sales 150.5MME *EMP* 600
SIC 3677 Filtration devices, electronic
Sr VP: Glen Petaja

PALL WELL TECHNOLOGY DIV
See PALL TRINITY MICRO CORP

D-U-N-S 17-601-0783
PALLADIUM EQUITY PARTNERS III LP
1270 Ave Of The, New York, NY 10020
Tel (212) 218-5150 *Founded/Ownrshp* 1997
Sales 2.2MMME *EMP* 16,075
SIC 6211 6799 Investment firm, general brokerage; Investors
Genl Pt: Marcos A Rodriguez
Pt: Pierson M Grieve
Pt: Robert J Lanigan
CFO: Kevin Raymond
CFO: Kevin Reymon
CFO: Kevin Reynold
Ofcr: Eugenie Cesar
VP: Maria D Avila
VP: Caleb Clark
VP: Daniel Ilundain
Exec: Susan Lyons

D-U-N-S 03-296-4531
PALLADIUM EQUITY PARTNERS IV LP
1270 Ave Of The Americas, New York, NY 10020-1700
Tel (212) 218-5150 *Founded/Ownrshp* 2012
Sales NA *EMP* 148E
SIC 6411 Insurance claim processing, except medical

D-U-N-S 07-347-7890 IMP
PALLETONE INC
1470 Us Highway 17 S, Bartow, FL 33830-6627
Tel (863) 533-1147 *Founded/Ownrshp* 2001
Sales 361.1MME *EMP* 1,135
SIC 2448 Pallets, wood

CEO: Howe Q Wallace
COO: Jeffery Johnson
**CFO:* Casey A Fletcher
CFO: Steve Jones
**VP:* Bridget Kennedy Hull
**VP:* Donnie Isaacson

D-U-N-S 03-453-7303
PALM BAY HOSPITAL INC (FL)
1425 Malabar Rd Ne, Palm Bay, FL 32907-2506
Tel (321) 434-8000 *Founded/Ownrshp* 1992
Sales 84.2MM *EMP* 350
SIC 8062 General medical & surgical hospitals
Pr: Christopher Rehak
**CEO:* Gail Schuneman
CFO: Bob C Galloway
**VP:* Jennifer McCarthy
VP: Suzanne Woods
Dir Lab: Darlene Beasley
Snr Ntwrk: Mark Davidson
Snr Ntwrk: Dan Tesenair
CIO: Rich Rogers
Netwrk Eng: Bracken Watts
Ansthlgy: Patrick Murtha

PALM BEACH AT MOODY GARDENS
See MOODY GARDENS INC

D-U-N-S 07-222-1302
PALM BEACH ATLANTIC UNIVERSITY ALUMNI ASSOCIATION
P B A
901 S Flagler Dr, West Palm Beach, FL 33401-6505
Tel (561) 803-2000 *Founded/Ownrshp* 1968
Sales 84.8MM *EMP* 504
SIC 8641 Alumni association
Pr: Lu Hardin
**VP:* William Fleming
VP: William M Fleming
**Prin:* Joe Kloba

D-U-N-S 03-844-6303
PALM BEACH ATLANTIC UNIVERSITY INC
901 S Flagler Dr, West Palm Beach, FL 33401-6505
Tel (561) 803-2000 *Founded/Ownrshp* 1968
Sales 102.8MM *EMP* 551^E
Accts Templeton & Company Llp West
SIC 8221 Colleges universities & professional schools
Pr: William Fleming Jr
CFO: Sue Varella
Assoc VP: Gary Parker
Sr VP: John Kautz
VP: William M Fleming Jr
VP: Philip Major
VP: Becky Peeling
Comm Dir: Stephanie Bennett
CTO: Linda Ellington
Web Dev: Mitchell Adams
Mktg Mgr: Bill Rork

PALM BEACH BEAUTE
See GREAT AMERICAN BEAUTY INC

D-U-N-S 03-052-2390
PALM BEACH CAPITAL FUND I LP (FL)
525 S Flagler Dr Ste 208, West Palm Beach, FL 33401-5932
Tel (561) 659-9022 *Founded/Ownrshp* 2001
Sales 254.8MM^E *EMP* 2,303^E
SIC 6211 Investment firm, general brokerage
Sr Pt: James W Harpel
**Pt:* Shaun L McGruder
**Pt:* Richard M Schlanger
**Pt:* Michael L Schmickle
**Pt:* Nathan S Ward
CFO: Adam P Klien
Chf Mktg O: Christopher Havlicek
Sr VP: Michael J Chalhub
VP: Scott M Long
Off Mgr: Szilvia Gagyi

D-U-N-S 79-055-0136
PALM BEACH CAPITAL FUND II LP
(*Suby of* PALM BEACH CAPITAL FUND I LP) ★
180 Royal Palm Way, Palm Beach, FL 33480-4215
Tel (561) 659-9022 *Founded/Ownrshp* 2005
Sales 40.0MM^E *EMP* 1,731
SIC 6799 2621 Venture capital companies; Toilet tissue stock; Absorbent paper
Sr Pt: James W Harpel

PALM BEACH COUNTY PUBLIC SCHL
See SCHOOL DISTRICT OF WEST PALM BEACH COUNTY

PALM BEACH MOTOR CARS
See MYERS AUTO GROUP LLC

D-U-N-S 05-043-4893 IMP
PALM BEACH NEWSPAPERS INC
PALM BEACH POST, THE
(*Suby of* COX ENTERPRISES INC) ★
2751 S Dixie Hwy, West Palm Beach, FL 33405-1298
Tel (561) 820-4100 *Founded/Ownrshp* 1969
Sales 127.9MM^E *EMP* 1,200
SIC 2711 2721 Newspapers; Periodicals
Pr: Tom Giuffrida
**Treas:* Lawrence E Siedlik
**VP:* Maria Friedman
**VP:* Charles Gerardi
**VP:* Neil O Johnston
VP: Teal Pontarelli
VP Opers: Chris Caneles
Snr Mgr: Mark Josaitis
Snr Mgr: Maria Velez

PALM BEACH POST, THE
See PALM BEACH NEWSPAPERS INC

D-U-N-S 05-134-3119 IMP/EXP
PALM BEACH STATE COLLEGE
4200 S Congress Ave, Lake Worth, FL 33461-4705
Tel (561) 868-3350 *Founded/Ownrshp* 1933
Sales 58.2MM *EMP* 2,300^E
SIC 8222 8351 8221 Technical institute; Montessori child development center; Colleges universities & professional schools
Pr: Dennis P Gallon
**VP:* Richard A Becker
VP: Freddie Bennett
VP: Patricia Hoyle
**VP:* Sharon Sass
VP: Geri Spain
Ex Dir: Donald Taylor
Off Admin: Nerva Edwards

D-U-N-S 96-811-8039
■ **PALM HARBOR HOMES INC**
(*Suby of* CAVCO INDUSTRIES INC) ★
1001 N Central Ave # 800, Phoenix, AZ 85004-1935
Tel (602) 256-6263 *Founded/Ownrshp* 2011
Sales 85.9MM^E *EMP* 275^E
SIC 2452 5211 6141 Modular homes, prefabricated, wood; Modular homes; Installment sales finance, other than banks
CEO: Joseph H Stegmayer
**Pr:* Larry H Keener
**Treas:* Daniel L Urness
**VP:* Kelly Tacke

D-U-N-S 79-015-8661 IMP
PALM INC
(*Suby of* TCL COMMUNICATIONS TECHNOLOGY CO., LTD.)
950 W Maude Ave, Sunnyvale, CA 94085-2801
Tel (408) 617-7000 *Founded/Ownrshp* 2015
Sales 151.4MM^E *EMP* 939
SIC 3663 Mobile communication equipment
Pr: Jonathan J Rubinstein
**Sr VP:* Michael A Bell
Sr VP: Michael R Farese
Sr VP: Brodie C Keast
Sr VP: Ronald Rhodes
VP: Guy Mascioli
VP: Rick Mathieson
VP: Page Murray
VP: Tim Roper
Exec: Tom Krum
Dir Bus: Ibrahim Ifsasse
Comm Man: Kimberly McCloud
Board of Directors: Fred D Anderson, Gordon A Campbell, William T Coleman, Robert C Hagerty, Roger B McNamee, D Scott Mercer

D-U-N-S 07-601-1154 IMP
PALM SPRINGS GENERAL HOSPITAL INC
1475 W 49th St, Hialeah, FL 33012-3222
Tel (305) 558-2500 *Founded/Ownrshp* 1964
Sales 84.3MM *EMP* 600
SIC 8062
Pr: Oakley G Smith
**Treas:* Manny Fernandez
**VP:* Carlos Milanes
Dir Risk M: Sharon Rodriguez
Dir Rx: Laidys Roque

D-U-N-S 08-116-3545
PALM SPRINGS UNIFIED SCHOOL DIST
PSUSD
980 E Tahquitz Canyon Way, Palm Springs, CA 92262-6708
Tel (760) 416-6177 *Founded/Ownrshp* 1948
Sales 281.7MM *EMP* 2,370
SIC 8211 Public elementary & secondary schools
Bd of Dir: John Gerardi
Bd of Dir: James Williamson
Dir Risk M: Renee Brunelle
Comm Man: Joan Boiko
Ex Dir: Ellen Goodman
Dir Sec: Rudy Villarreal
IT Man: Peter Smit
Trfc Dir: Debby Lenburg
Schl Brd P: Elaine Robertson
Psych: James Christopoulos
Board of Directors: Don Aiken, Leslie Demersseman, Rev Andrew Greene, Michael McCabe, Meredith Schoenberger

PALMDALE ELEMENTARY SCHOOL DST
See PALMDALE SCHOOL DISTRICT

D-U-N-S 08-180-0427 IMP/EXP
PALMDALE OIL CO INC
911 N 2nd St, Fort Pierce, FL 34950-9121
Tel (772) 461-2300 *Founded/Ownrshp* 1984
Sales 138.8MM^E *EMP* 85
SIC 5172 Engine fuels & oils; Gasoline; Diesel fuel; Lubricating oils & greases
Pr: Lachlan Cheatham
**Treas:* Robert A Reskin
**VP:* Kendall Cheatham

D-U-N-S 03-063-7770
■ **PALMDALE REGIONAL MEDICAL CENTER**
(*Suby of* UNIVERSAL HEALTH SERVICES INC) ★
38600 Medical Center Dr, Palmdale, CA 93551-4483
Tel (661) 382-5000 *Founded/Ownrshp* 2001
Sales 159.2MM *EMP* 800
SIC 8011 Medical centers
CEO: Richard Allen
Dir OR: Yolanda Douglas
**Prin:* Ed Callahan
QA Dir: Suzette Creighton
Dir QC: Nawanna Chaidez

D-U-N-S 03-084-3429
PALMDALE SCHOOL DISTRICT
PALMDALE ELEMENTARY SCHOOL DST
39139 10th St E, Palmdale, CA 93550-3419
Tel (661) 947-7191 *Founded/Ownrshp* 1880
Sales 109.3MM^E *EMP* 1,800
Accts Nigro Nigro & White Pc San D
SIC 8211 Public elementary school
Pr: Juan Carrillo
V Ch: Kathleen Duren
Bd of Dir: Joyce Ricks
**Bd of Dir:* Nancy Smith
Bd of Dir: Dennis Trujillo
Ex Dir: Julie Ferebee

D-U-N-S 07-939-7940
PALMER FAMILY OF COMPANIES INC
900 Jefferson Rd Ste 1000, Rochester, NY 14623-3218
Tel (585) 424-3210 *Founded/Ownrshp* 2008
Sales 675.0MM *EMP* 0^E
SIC 6719 Personal holding companies, except banks
Ch Bd: Dwight M Palmer
CFO: Jack Whittier

D-U-N-S 01-312-7279
PALMER FISH CO INC
PALMER FOOD SERVICES
900 Jefferson Rd Ste 1000, Rochester, NY 14623-3218
Tel (585) 424-3210 *Founded/Ownrshp* 1992
Sales 90.0MM *EMP* 180
SIC 5146 5147 5142 2013 Fish & seafoods; Meats & meat products; Packaged frozen goods; Bacon, side & sliced: from purchased meat
Pr: Dwight M Palmer
Pr: Gene Siesto
**CFO:* John M Whittier
VP: Chuck Bianchi
Dir IT: Frank Smith
Dir IT: Steve Strasser
Opers Mgr: Joseph Costello
VP Sls: Ron Andreano

PALMER FOOD SERVICES
See PALMER FISH CO INC

D-U-N-S 01-781-3635 IMP
PALMER HOLLAND INC (OH)
25000 Country Club Blvd # 444, North Olmsted, OH 44070-5331
Tel (440) 686-2300 *Founded/Ownrshp* 1925
Sales 117.4MM^E *EMP* 95
SIC 5169 Industrial chemicals
Pr: Bryn Irvine
**Prin:* Bert D Bradley
**Prin:* Fred H Palmer III
**Prin:* Dorothy Waldern
Mktg Mgr: Christine Steedman

PALMER HOUSE HILTON
See THOR PALMER HOUSE HOTEL LLC

D-U-N-S 00-612-8698
PALMER JOHNSON ENTERPRISES INC (WI)
128 Kentucky St, Sturgeon Bay, WI 54235-2510
Tel (920) 746-6342 *Founded/Ownrshp* 1918, 1956
Sales 226.9MM^E *EMP* 500
SIC 5085 4493 3732 Power transmission equipment & apparatus; Boat yards, storage & incidental repair; Yachts, building & repairing
CEO: Andrew J McKelvey
**Pr:* Martin C Kelsey Jr
**Pr:* William C Parsons
**VP:* Thomas Kuffel

D-U-N-S 16-047-1707 IMP
PALMER JOHNSON YACHTS LLC
128 Kentucky St, Sturgeon Bay, WI 54235-2510
Tel (920) 743-4412 *Founded/Ownrshp* 2004
Sales 90.3MM^E *EMP* 190
SIC 3732 Yachts, building & repairing

D-U-N-S 04-113-0519
PALMER TRUCKS INC
PACLEASE
2929 S Holt Rd, Indianapolis, IN 46241-6021
Tel (317) 243-1668 *Founded/Ownrshp* 1965
Sales 196.8MM^E *EMP* 475
SIC 5511 5531 7538 7513 5012 Trucks, tractors & trailers: new & used; Truck equipment & parts; Truck engine repair, except industrial; Truck leasing, without drivers; Automobiles & other motor vehicles
Pr: John A Nichols
**Pr:* Tom Kapitan
**CFO:* Jeffrey L Curry
**Ch:* Eldon D Palmer
**VP:* James A Roemer
Brnch Mgr: Bill Evans
Brnch Mgr: Tracy Walters
**CIO:* Jeremy Beck
CTO: John Nicholos
IT Man: Craig Bernard

D-U-N-S 00-892-8871 IMP
PALMER-DONAVIN MANUFACTURING CO
3210 Centerpoint Dr, Columbus, OH 43212
Tel (614) 486-0975 *Founded/Ownrshp* 1967
Sales 200.0MM^E *EMP* 400^E
SIC 5033 Roofing & siding materials
Ch Bd: Robert J Woodward Jr
**Pr:* Ronald Calhoun
**CFO:* Robyn Polline
**Bd of Dir:* Glenn Corlett
**Bd of Dir:* James Wiles
**VP:* Eric Belke
**VP:* Robert J McCollow
**VP:* David Zimmerman
Off Mgr: Paula Gledhill
CIO: Peri Hass

PALMER'S COCOA BUTTER FORMULA
See ET BROWNE DRUG CO INC

D-U-N-S 18-551-5541
PALMETTO CORP OF CONWAY
PALMETTO SEALING
3873 Highway 701 N, Conway, SC 29526-5737
Tel (843) 365-2156 *Founded/Ownrshp* 1987
Sales 85.3MM^E *EMP* 200
SIC 2951 Asphalt & asphaltic paving mixtures (not from refineries)
Owner: Shawn Godwin
**Pr:* G Marshall Godwin
**COO:* Rusty Faulk
**CFO:* Craig Berkey
**VP:* Kenneth A Atkinson
Mktg Dir: Sarah Jeffcoat

D-U-N-S 00-379-3379
PALMETTO ELECTRIC COOPERATIVE INC (SC)
4063 Grays Hwy, Ridgeland, SC 29936-4360
Tel (843) 726-5551 *Founded/Ownrshp* 1940
Sales 176.8MM *EMP* 142
Accts K Eve Mccoy Cpa Llc Columbia
SIC 8611 4911 Business associations; Distribution, electric power
Pr: A Berl Davis Jr
Sr VP: Gary E Jeger
VP: Lewis F Davis
VP: Trey Hunter
VP: Wilson Saleeby
Board of Directors: Eunice Spilliards, Dr Earl Bostick Sr, C Alex Ulmer, Henry Driessen Jr, Jeremiah E Vaigneur, James O Freeman, Carolyn Grant, Jimmie D McMillan, William J Nimmer, Jimmy L Rowe, Terrell Smith, David Solaro

D-U-N-S 00-681-1389
PALMETTO GBA LLC
(*Suby of* BLUE CROSS BLUE SHIELD OF SOUTH CAROLINA) ★
17 Technology Cir, Columbia, SC 29203-9591
Tel (803) 735-1034 *Founded/Ownrshp* 1997
Sales NA *EMP* 2,452
SIC 6324 Hospital & medical service plans
Pr: Bruce Hughes
Pt: Margaret Wonning
Pr: Jean Catalano
Pr: Sharon Cook
Pr: Joe Johnson
Pr: Walter J Johnson
CFO: Joseph D Wright
Ofcr: Paige Easley
VP: Richard Butler
VP: Richard P Butler
CIO: Steve Wiggins
Board of Directors: Robert E Shields

PALMETTO GENERAL HOSPITAL
See LIFEMARK HOSPITALS OF FLORIDA INC

D-U-N-S 00-903-5853
PALMETTO HEALTH
1301 Taylor St Ste 8a, Columbia, SC 29201-2955
Tel (803) 296-2100 *Founded/Ownrshp* 1996
Sales 1.1MMM^E *EMP* 10,200
Accts Grant Thornton Llp Columbia
SIC 8062 General medical & surgical hospitals
CEO: Charles D Beaman Jr
V Ch: William L Freeman III
**Pr:* John J Singerling III
COO: Ellie Lucitti
**CFO:* Paul Duane
Bd of Dir: Sarah Pregnall
VP: Willis Gregory
Exec: Diane Talbot
Prgrm Mgr: Angela Peterson
Dir IT: Stephanie Davis
IT Man: Dave Garrette

D-U-N-S 14-768-9702
PALMETTO HEALTH ALLIANCE INC
(*Suby of* PALMETTO HEALTH) ★
293 Greystone Blvd, Columbia, SC 29210-8004
Tel (803) 296-5220 *Founded/Ownrshp* 1996
Sales 206.1MM^E *EMP* 7,000
SIC 8062 General medical & surgical hospitals
CEO: Kester Freeman
**Pr:* Charles Beaman
Genl Mgr: Clay Drummond

D-U-N-S 07-799-0505
PALMETTO HEALTH TUOMEY
TUOMEY HEALTHCARE SYSTEM
129 N Washington St, Sumter, SC 29150-4949
Tel (803) 774-9000 *Founded/Ownrshp* 1914
Sales 176.7MM^E *EMP* 1,800
SIC 8062 General medical & surgical hospitals
CEO: Charles D Beaman Jr
**COO:* Michelle Logan-Owen
VP: Usah Lilavivat
Exec: Joey Boyce
Adm Dir: Charlene Brogdon
Adm Dir: Michelle Logan-Owens
Off Mgr: Curt Ackerman
Off Mgr: David A Burchett
Off Admin: Michelle Breaux-Smith
Plnt Mgr: Gray Maklary
VP Mktg: William Renwick

D-U-N-S 78-232-0568
PALMETTO INDUSTRIAL CONSTRUCTION CO INC
831 Old Wire Rd, Gaston, SC 29053-9025
Tel (803) 739-0381 *Founded/Ownrshp* 1990
Sales 400.0MM^E *EMP* 40
SIC 1541

PALMETTO SEALING
See PALMETTO CORP OF CONWAY

D-U-N-S 07-805-1778
PALMETTO-RICHLAND MEMORIAL HOSPITAL
(*Suby of* PALMETTO HEALTH) ★
5 Richland Medical Pk Dr, Columbia, SC 29203-6897
Tel (803) 434-3460 *Founded/Ownrshp* 2000
Sales 685.2MM *EMP* 3,900
SIC 8062 Hospital, medical school affiliated with nursing & residency
Pr: Kester S Freeman Jr
COO: Jim Lathren
Chf Nrs Of: Cheryl Hunter
Dir IT: Chuck Beaman
Doctor: John Egbert
Occ Thrpy: Iris Smith

PALMS HOTEL & RESORT, THE
See FP HOLDINGS LP

D-U-N-S 80-620-1992
■ **PALMS WEST HOSPITAL LIMITED PARTNERSHIP**
(*Suby of* HOSPITAL COPORATION OF AMERICA) ★
13001 Southern Blvd, Loxahatchee, FL 33470-9203
Tel (561) 798-3300 *Founded/Ownrshp* 1995
Sales 84.0MM^E *EMP* 850
SIC 8062 General medical & surgical hospitals
CEO: Eric Goldsman
COO: Patrick Connor
Dir Lab: Carol Sheets
Dir Env Sv: Doris Elms
Dir Pat Ac: Jeremy Redden
CIO: Kevin Marinus
Dir IT: Vincent Arecibia
Dir IT: Martha Steinson
IT Man: Robert Rubin
Mfg Mgr: Michael Jordan
Obsttrcn: Steven Pliskow

PALO ALTO CLINIC
See PALO ALTO MEDICAL FOUNDATION FOR HEALTH CARE RESEARCH AND EDUCATION (INC)

D-U-N-S 07-631-3832
PALO ALTO MEDICAL FOUNDATION FOR HEALTH CARE RESEARCH AND EDUCATION (INC) (CA)
PALO ALTO CLINIC
(*Suby of* SUTTER C H S) ★
795 El Camino Real, Palo Alto, CA 94301-2302
Tel (650) 321-4121 *Founded/Ownrshp* 1948
Sales 159.3MM[E] *EMP* 1,168
Accts Ernst & Young Llp Roseville
SIC 8011 Clinic, operated by physicians
CEO: Jeff Gerard
**Pr:* David Drucker
COO: James Hereford
Treas: Christine Kontgas
Treas: Mark McLaughlin
Treas: Jane A Risser
Trst: Richard J Elkus
Ofcr: Null M Null Akhtar
Ofcr: Kathleen Boice
Ofcr: Kathryen Engle
Ofcr: Madeleine Viden
VP: Anne B Jigger
VP: Kathy Korbholz
VP: Janet Lederer
VP: Harold S Luft
VP: Cecilia Montalvo
VP: Michael Reandeau
VP: Paul C Tang
Dir Rx: Steve Carlson

D-U-N-S 03-505-6337
PALO ALTO MEDICAL FOUNDATION STA CRUZ
2025 Soquel Ave, Santa Cruz, CA 95062-1323
Tel (831) 458-5670 *Founded/Ownrshp* 2004
Sales 76.8MM[E] *EMP* 2,000
SIC 8011 Physical medicine, physician/surgeon
Pr: Larry Beghttaldi
CFO: Glenn Groves

D-U-N-S 19-814-4771
▲ PALO ALTO NETWORKS INC
4401 Great America Pkwy, Santa Clara, CA 95054-1211
Tel (408) 753-4000 *Founded/Ownrshp* 2005
Sales 1.3MMM *EMP* 2,637
Tkr Sym PANW *Exch* NYS
SIC 3577 7371 Computer peripheral equipment; Computer software development & applications
Ch Bd: Mark D McLaughlin
Pr: Mark F Anderson
CFO: Steffan C Tomlinson
Chf Mktg O: Ren Bonvanie
Ex VP: Jeff Geller
Ex VP: Lee Klarich
Ex VP: Dave Peranich
Ex VP: Wilson Xu
Sr VP: Wendy N Barnes
Sr VP: Brett Eldridge
Sr VP: Jeff True
VP: Joshua Hoffman
VP: Tony McIlvenna
VP: Punit Minocha
VP: Tang Song
Board of Directors: Frank Calderoni, John M Donovan, Carl Eschenbach, James J Goetz, Mary Pat McCarthy, Stanley J Meresman, Daniel J Warmenhoven

D-U-N-S 96-092-1948
PALO ALTO UNIFIED SCHOOL DISTRICT
25 Churchill Ave, Palo Alto, CA 94306-1099
Tel (650) 329-3804 *Founded/Ownrshp* 1998
Sales 211.9MM *EMP* 100
SIC 8211 Public elementary & secondary schools

D-U-N-S 07-875-0478
PALOMAR COMMUNITY COLLEGE DISTRICT FINANCING CORP
1140 W Mission Rd, San Marcos, CA 92069-1415
Tel (760) 744-1150 *Founded/Ownrshp* 1947
Sales 106.2MM[E] *EMP* 3,323
SIC 8222 Community college
Pr: Robert P Deegan
Trst: Neill Kovrig
Trst: Darrell L McMullen
**Trst:* Paul P McNamara
**Trst:* John J Halc N
VP: Elaine Armstrong
VP: Bonnie Dowd
Comm Dir: Mea Daum
Genl Mgr: Meg Banta
Psych: Rebecca Barr

D-U-N-S 07-337-9026
PALOMAR HEALTH
PALOMAR MEDICAL CENTER
456 E Grand Ave, Escondido, CA 92025-3319
Tel (442) 281-5000 *Founded/Ownrshp* 1950
Sales 614.2MM *EMP* 3,000
Accts Deloitte & Touche Llp San Die
SIC 8062 8059 General medical & surgical hospitals; Convalescent home
Ex VP: Diane Hansen
Dir Recs: Kimberly Jackson
**CEO:* Robert A Hemker
Ofcr: Robert Trifunovic MD
Ex VP: Frank Beirne
VP: Prudence August
Exec: Brenda Turner
Dir Lab: Gloria Austria
Chf Nrs Of: Joy Gorzeman
**Prin:* Linda Greer
Brnch Mgr: Kamen N Zakov
Board of Directors: Dara Czerwonka, Linda Greer, Jeff Griffith, Jerry Kaufman, Ray McCune, Hans Sison

PALOMAR MEDICAL CENTER
See PALOMAR HEALTH

PALOMAR MOUNTAIN OUTDOOR SCHL
See PALOMAR MOUNTAIN OUTDOOR SCHOOL CAMP

D-U-N-S 95-694-5026
PALOMAR MOUNTAIN OUTDOOR SCHOOL CAMP
PALOMAR MOUNTAIN OUTDOOR SCHL
(*Suby of* SAN DIEGO COUNTY OFF EDUCATN) ★
19452 State Park Rd, Palomar Mountain, CA 92060
Tel (760) 742-2128 *Founded/Ownrshp* 1996
Sales 8.6MM[E] *EMP* 1,100
SIC 8211 Elementary school
Dir IT: Greg Vanidsinga

D-U-N-S 07-913-2693
PALOMAR POMERADO HOSPITAL DISTRICT
(*Suby of* PALOMAR MEDICAL CENTER) ★
15615 Pomerado Rd, Poway, CA 92064-2405
Tel (858) 613-4000 *Founded/Ownrshp* 2013
Sales 156.6MM *EMP* 1[E]
SIC 8062 General medical & surgical hospitals
CEO: Robert Hemker
Pathlgst: Pamela Danque
Nrsg Dir: Alivia Munson

D-U-N-S 06-858-6106
PALOS COMMMUNITY HOSPITAL
12251 S 80th Ave, Palos Heights, IL 60463-1256
Tel (708) 923-4000 *Founded/Ownrshp* 1938
Sales 352.2MM *EMP* 2,300
SIC 8062

PALOS PARK DIALYSIS
See TOTAL RENAL CARE INC

D-U-N-S 94-837-3071 IMP
PALPILOT INTERNATIONAL CORP
500 Yosemite Dr, Milpitas, CA 95035-5444
Tel (408) 855-8866 *Founded/Ownrshp* 1992
Sales 87.1MM *EMP* 100
SIC 3672 3089 Printed circuit boards; Injection molding of plastics
Pr: Eddy C Niu
**VP:* Yichien Hwang
**VP:* Bruce Lee
VP: Hank Ly
VP Opers: Christy Qian
Opers Mgr: Cindy Ho

PALRAM 2000
See PALRAM AMERICAS INC

D-U-N-S 80-908-2126 IMP/EXP
PALRAM AMERICAS INC
PALRAM 2000
(*Suby of* PALRAM ISRAEL LTD.)
9735 Commerce Cir, Kutztown, PA 19530-8579
Tel (610) 285-9918 *Founded/Ownrshp* 2004
Sales 112.6MM[E] *EMP* 71
SIC 5162 Plastics materials & basic shapes
Pr: Yuval Hen
**CFO:* Mitch Still
**VP:* John Seiffert
Admn Mgr: Johana Gonzalez
Admn Mgr: David Kirk
CTO: Reuven Hugi
Mfg Dir: Hagit Gavish
Opers Mgr: Tracy Barker
Sls Mgr: Jolene Van Rooyen

PAM DEDICATED SERVICES
See PAM TRANSPORT INC

D-U-N-S 09-857-1433
■ PAM TRANSPORT INC (AR)
PAM DEDICATED SERVICES
(*Suby of* PAM TRANSPORTATION SERVICES INC) ★
297 W Henri De Tonti Blvd, Tontitown, AR 72770
Tel (479) 361-9111 *Founded/Ownrshp* 1980, 1986
Sales 142.5MM[E] *EMP* 800
SIC 4213 Trucking, except local
Pr: Daniel Cushman
Pr: Boyd Thomas
CFO: Allen West
Ofcr: Linda Scott
VP: Clark Gray
VP: Cookie Mingin
VP: David Toothaker
Dir Risk M: Anthony Longinatti
Store Mgr: Jerry Martin
Telecom Mg: Christine Fairchild
Counsel: Kenneth Hixson

D-U-N-S 13-974-6275
▲ PAM TRANSPORTATION SERVICES INC
297 W Henri De Tonti Blvd, Tontitown, AR 72770
Tel (479) 361-9111 *Founded/Ownrshp* 1986
Sales 417.0MM *EMP* 3,049[E]
Tkr Sym PTSI *Exch* NGM
SIC 4213 4731 Trucking, except local; Freight transportation arrangement
Pr: Daniel H Cushman
**Ch Bd:* Matthew T Moroun
Pr: Joshua Cushman
CFO: Allen W West
VP: Garth Hill
Opers Mgr: Jim Debartolo
Opers Mgr: Jason Erb
Board of Directors: Frederick P Calderone, W Scott Davis, Norman E Harned, Franklin H McLarty, Manuel J Moroun, Daniel C Sullivan

D-U-N-S 96-552-3004
PAMAL BROADCASTING LTD
WHUD
6 Johnson Rd, Latham, NY 12110-5641
Tel (518) 786-6600 *Founded/Ownrshp* 1996
Sales 86.0MM[E] *EMP* 330
SIC 4832 Radio broadcasting stations
Pr: James J Morrell
Treas: Mike Dufort
**Treas:* John Vandenburgh
Opers Mgr: Jon Reilly
Sls Mgr: Donnna Brownson
Pgrm Dir: Chris Herrmann
Pgrm Dir: Jay Pugliese

D-U-N-S 86-788-6863 IMP
PAMARCO TECHNOLOGIES LLC
235 E 11th Ave, Roselle, NJ 07203-2090
Tel (908) 241-1200 *Founded/Ownrshp* 1994
Sales 126.8MM[E] *EMP* 1,050[E]
SIC 3555 Printing trades machinery
CEO: Terrence W Ford
**CFO:* Doug Johnson
Exec: John Burgess
IT Man: Tony Tagiaferro
S&M/VP: John Rastetter
Sls Mgr: David Parr

D-U-N-S 15-206-1099
PAMIDA BRANDS HOLDING LLC
8800 F St, Omaha, NE 68127-1507
Tel (402) 493-4765 *Founded/Ownrshp* 2007
Sales NA *EMP* 1,000[E]
SIC 5331 5912

D-U-N-S 11-028-0810
PAMLICO CAPITAL MANAGEMENT LP
150 N College St Ste 2400, Charlotte, NC 28202-2397
Tel (704) 374-6100 *Founded/Ownrshp* 2008
Sales 107.7MM[E] *EMP* 915
SIC 6799 Venture capital companies
CEO: Art Zeile
Mng Pt: Scott Perper

D-U-N-S 79-387-4793
PAMONA VALLEY MEDICAL GROUP INC
PRO MED HLTH NETWRK POMONA VLY
9302 Pttsbrgh Ave Ste 220, Rancho Cucamonga, CA 91730
Tel (909) 932-1045 *Founded/Ownrshp* 1988
Sales 90.0MM *EMP* 82[E]
SIC 8011 8741 Offices & clinics of medical doctors; Administrative management
CEO: Kishon Thapar
CFO: Baram Bahremand
**Treas:* Victor Pappoe MD

D-U-N-S 00-158-8099
PAMPA REGIONAL MEDICAL CENTER AUXILIARY
GOLDEN PHOENIX CENTER
1 Medical Plz, Pampa, TX 79065
Tel (806) 665-3721 *Founded/Ownrshp* 2008
Sales 100.0MM *EMP* 275
SIC 8011 Offices & clinics of medical doctors
CEO: Brad Morse
**Ch:* Doug Ware

D-U-N-S 05-355-7468 IMP
■ PAMPERED CHEF LTD
(*Suby of* BERKSHIRE HATHAWAY INC) ★
140 N Swift Rd, Addison, IL 60101-1498
Tel (630) 261-8900 *Founded/Ownrshp* 1980
Sales 195.6MM[E] *EMP* 825
SIC 5963 Home related products, direct sales
CEO: Tracy Britt Cool
**Ch Bd:* Doris Christopher
Ex VP: Rick Geu
Sr VP: Susan Gustasson
VP: Jane Edwards
VP: Richard Hlava
Dir Bus: Ralf Vandike
CIO: Rich Chubkegel
QA Dir: Pat Gavin
IT Man: Judy Sherbagill
Mtls Mgr: Barb Bennett

D-U-N-S 95-721-6146
PAMPLIN COMMUNICATIONS CORP
PAMPLIN INTRANET
6605 Se Lake Rd, Portland, OR 97222-2161
Tel (503) 546-5100 *Founded/Ownrshp* 1995
Sales 100.6MM[E] *EMP* 500
SIC 4899 Data communication services
Pr: Andrea J Marek
**Pr:* Andrea Marek
**CFO:* Chuck Nadrow
VP: Donna Munsey
Web Dev: Bart Betz

PAMPLIN INTRANET
See PAMPLIN COMMUNICATIONS CORP

D-U-N-S 03-962-2543
PAN AM RAILWAYS INC
1700 Iron Horse Park, North Billerica, MA 01862-1641
Tel (978) 663-1129 *Founded/Ownrshp* 1981
Sales 215.7MM[E] *EMP* 1,000
SIC 4011 Railroads, line-haul operating
Ch Bd: Timothy Mellon
**Pr:* David A Fink
Ex VP: Sydney Culliford
VP: Eric Lawler
VP: Jim Patterson
VP: Cynthia Scarano
Genl Mgr: Theodore Carves
Dir IT: Kevin Blaisdell
S&M/VP: Phillip D Kingman
Pr Dir: Tony Lomanto
Mktg Mgr: Joseph Kania

D-U-N-S 07-781-1172
PAN AMERICAN DEVELOPMENT FOUNDATION INC
1889 F St Nw Fl 2, Washington, DC 20006-4401
Tel (202) 458-3969 *Founded/Ownrshp* 1962
Sales 91.4MM *EMP* 300
Accts Rsm Mcgladrey Inc Vienna Va
SIC 8399 Council for social agency
CEO: Judith Hermanson
Prgrm Mgr: Camila Payan
**Pgrm Dir:* Magalie Brunet
**Pgrm Dir:* Luisa Villegas
Pgrm Dir: Marc Wachtenheim

D-U-N-S 09-107-4203 IMP/EXP
PAN AMERICAN GRAIN CO INC
Calle Claudia 9 Esqu, Guaynabo, PR 00968
Tel (787) 792-3355 *Founded/Ownrshp* 1980
Sales 108.3MM[E] *EMP* 300
Accts Aquino De Cordova Alfaro & C
SIC 2048 Prepared feeds
Pr: Jose Gonzalez
**Treas:* Eduardo Fernandez
**VP:* Rene A Gonzalez

D-U-N-S 15-692-9895 IMP/EXP
PAN AMERICAN GRAIN MANUFACTURING CO INC
PAN AMERICAN GRAIN MFG
Calle Caludia 9cnr, Guaynabo, PR 00968
Tel (787) 273-6100 *Founded/Ownrshp* 1984
Sales 128.0MM *EMP* 200
Accts Aquino De Cordova Alfaro & C
SIC 2099 Rice, uncooked: packaged with other ingredients
Pr: Jose Gonzalez
**Treas:* Eduardo Fernandez
**VP:* Milton R Gonzalez
**VP:* Rene A Gonzalez

PAN AMERICAN GRAIN MFG
See PAN AMERICAN GRAIN MANUFACTURING CO INC

D-U-N-S 06-676-9738 IMP
PAN AMERICAN HEALTH ORGANIZATION INC
PAHO
(*Suby of* UNITED NATIONS SECRETARIAT) ★
525 23rd St Nw, Washington, DC 20037-2825
Tel (202) 974-3000 *Founded/Ownrshp* 1902
Sales 114.7MM[E] *EMP* 1,500
SIC 8399 Health & welfare council
**Pr:* Mirta R Periago
**CFO:* Esteban Alzamora
CFO: William Golden
Ofcr: Daniela Cracel
Ofcr: James Hill
Ofcr: Nicolas Lagomarsino
Ofcr: Jose M Parisi
Ofcr: Roberto Samayoa
Ofcr: Sandy Summers
Area Mgr: Jean Poncelet
Dept Mgr: Giubella Zavaleta

D-U-N-S 07-846-2496
PAN AMERICAN HOSPITAL CORP
5959 Nw 7th St, Miami, FL 33126-3198
Tel (305) 261-2273 *Founded/Ownrshp* 1963
Sales 37.7MM[E] *EMP* 1,172
SIC 8062 General medical & surgical hospitals
CEO: Roberto Tejidor
Chf Rad: Carlos Sanchez
CFO: Jim Geogatos
Dir Lab: Natacha Vega
Off Mgr: Marian Schonburg
CIO: Frank Carnavaca
QA Dir: Daisy Baez
Sales Exec: Marianne Williams
Pathlgst: Raul I Villa
Doctor: Raul Villa
Pharmcst: Albena Dokova

PAN AMERICAN SCREW DIV
See MARMON GROUP LLC

PAN AMERICAN SEED COMPANY
See BALL HORTICULTURAL CO

D-U-N-S 09-013-9122 IMP/EXP
PAN PEPIN INC
Plaza Laurel, Bayamon, PR 00956-3273
Tel (787) 787-1717 *Founded/Ownrshp* 1974, 1998
Sales 143.2MM[E] *EMP* 500
Accts Fpv & Galindez Cpas Psc
SIC 2051 Bread, cake & related products
Ch Bd: Jose Texidor
**Pr:* Mario Somoza
**Treas:* Juan A Texidor
**VP:* Carolina Rodriguez
MIS Dir: Anibal Rivera
IT Man: Yolanda Torres

D-U-N-S 00-694-7865
PAN-AMERICAN LIFE INSURANCE GROUP INC
PALIG
(*Suby of* PAN-AMERICAN LIFE MUTUAL HOLDING CO) ★
601 Poydras St Ste 1000, New Orleans, LA 70130-6060
Tel (504) 566-1300 *Founded/Ownrshp* 1911
Sales NA *EMP* 1,134
SIC 6311 7389 Life insurance carriers; Financial services
Ch Bd: Jose S Suquet
CFO: Myriam De Gracia
Treas: Lory Anne Dupuy
Ofcr: Barbara Rosa-Viera
Sr VP: Michael Carricarte
Sr VP: Robert Dicianni
VP: Floriano Alencar
VP: Jorge Endevica
VP: Paul Engeriser
VP: John Foley
VP: Patrick C Fraizer
VP: Carmen Gomez
VP: Gavin Langston
**VP:* Carlos F Mickan
VP: Enrique Monzon
VP: Valerie Moscona
VP: Carlo Mulvenna
VP: Josephine Pagnozzi
VP: Bruce Parker
VP: Frank Recio
VP: Marta Reeves
Board of Directors: Carlos F Mickan

D-U-N-S 07-888-9210
PAN-AMERICAN LIFE MUTUAL HOLDING CO (LA)
601 Poydras St Ste 1000, New Orleans, LA 70130-6060
Tel (877) 939-4550 *Founded/Ownrshp* 2013
Sales 322.3MM[E] *EMP* 1,136[E]
SIC 6799 Investors
Prin: Jose Suquet

D-U-N-S 00-615-8133 IMP
PAN-O-GOLD BAKING CO (MN)
COUNTRY HEARTH
444 E Saint Germain St, Saint Cloud, MN 56304-0749
Tel (320) 251-9361 *Founded/Ownrshp* 1911, 1940
Sales 1.5MMM[E] *EMP* 1,400

SIC 5149 2051 Bakery products; Bread, all types (white, wheat, rye, etc): fresh or frozen
Pr: Howard R Alton III
**CFO:* Dennis Leisten
**Treas:* Camilla Alton
**Treas:* Howard R Alton Jr
**VP:* James K Akervik
**VP:* Daniel P Cotton

D-U-N-S 00-584-8957 IMP
PAN-PACIFIC MECHANICAL LLC
18250 Euclid St, Fountain Valley, CA 92708-6112
Tel (949) 474-9170 *Founded/Ownrshp* 1947
Sales 257.7MM *EMP* 1,000
Accts Sutor Krystad & Rosenfeld In
SIC 1711 Plumbing contractors
CEO: Cindy Lanette McMackin
**CFO:* Steve Sylvester
**VP:* Ryan Cavanaugh
**VP:* Pat George
**VP:* Jon Houchin
**VP:* Joe Koh
**VP:* Reed McMackin
**Prin:* Ronald G McMackin
CIO: Erik Roth
Board of Directors: Rebecca Campbell, Joseph Koh, Cindy McMackin, Reed McMackin

PANA-PACIFIC
See BRIX GROUP INC

D-U-N-S 00-179-3009 IMP/EXP
PANALPINA INC (NY)
(*Suby of* PANALPINA WELTTRANSPORT (HOLDING) AG)
1776 On The Green 67, Morristown, NJ 07960
Tel (973) 683-9000 *Founded/Ownrshp* 1923
Sales 657.4MM[E] *EMP* 2,000
SIC 4731 Foreign freight forwarding; Customhouse brokers; Agents, shipping; Brokers, shipping
Ch Bd: Ralph Riehl
V Ch: Beat Walti
**CEO:* Lucas Kuehner
COO: Andy Weber
CFO: Robert J Erni
**CFO:* Hans Moller
**Sr VP:* Armin Heinlein
VP: Frederik Ebert
VP: Christoph Ritt
Mng Dir: Andreas Behnke
Mng Dir: Luis De Freitas

PANAM RAILWAYS
See BOSTON AND MAINE CORP

D-U-N-S 10-000-7939
PANAMA-BUENA VISTA UNION SCHOOL DISTRICT
4200 Ashe Rd, Bakersfield, CA 93313-2029
Tel (661) 831-8331 *Founded/Ownrshp* 1875
Sales 152.3MM *EMP* 2,000
Accts Daniells Phillips Vaughan & Bo
SIC 8211 Public elementary & secondary schools
MIS Dir: Brook McKnight
Teacher Pr: Darryl Johnson
HC Dir: Rita Pierucci

D-U-N-S 16-666-9742
PANAMERICA COMPUTERS INC
PCITEC
1386 Big Oak Rd, Luray, VA 22835-5233
Tel (540) 635-4402 *Founded/Ownrshp* 1993
Sales 115.4MM *EMP* 14
Accts Yount Hyde & Barbour Pc W
SIC 5045 Computers, peripherals & software
Pr: Rosina Kling
CFO: Diana Little
VP: John Bruton
Prgrm Mgr: Nina Long

D-U-N-S 80-947-1238 IMP
PANASONIC AVIONICS CORP
(*Suby of* PANASONIC SOLUTIONS CO) ★
3303 Monte Villa Pkwy, Bothell, WA 98021-8969
Tel (425) 415-9000 *Founded/Ownrshp* 1990
Sales 722.9MM[E] *EMP* 2,725
SIC 8711 Aviation &/or aeronautical engineering
CEO: Paul Margis
**Pr:* Yasu Enokido
Sr VP: Priscilla Germain
Prgrm Mgr: Kim Cai
Prgrm Mgr: Jana McFadden
Prgrm Mgr: Mike Moeller
Prgrm Mgr: Brett Revoir
Prgrm Mgr: Randy Tyler
Snr Sftwr: Chris Vandenberg
IT Man: Bill Reilly
Pr Mgr: Theresa Yeoh
Board of Directors: Bill Edgar

D-U-N-S 00-891-9813 IMP/EXP
PANASONIC CORP OF NORTH AMERICA
PANASONIC SOLUTIONS COMPANY
(*Suby of* PANASONIC CORPORATION)
2 Riverfront Plz Ste 200, Newark, NJ 07102-5490
Tel (201) 348-7000 *Founded/Ownrshp* 1974
Sales 7.6MMM[E] *EMP* 13,000
SIC 5064 5045 5065 5044 5084 5063

D-U-N-S 79-089-4679 IMP/EXP
PANASONIC ENERGY CORP OF AMERICA
(*Suby of* PANASONIC SOLUTIONS CO) ★
1 Panasonic Dr, Columbus, GA 31907-3051
Tel (706) 561-7730 *Founded/Ownrshp* 2008
Sales 135.0MM *EMP* 240[E]
SIC 3691 5531 Lead acid batteries (storage batteries); Batteries, automotive & truck
Pr: Sakae Sadakuni
**Pr:* Scotty Scott
**Treas:* Yusuke Onoe
**VP:* John Rowe
**MIS Dir:* Toru Tagakaki

D-U-N-S 78-290-8446 IMP/EXP
PANASONIC INDUSTRIAL DEVICES CORP OF AMERICA
PANASONIC/ACOM
4900 George Mcvay Dr Ste C, Mcallen, TX 78503
Tel (956) 984-3700 *Founded/Ownrshp* 1985
Sales 0.0 *EMP* 2,800
SIC 3651 3675 3471

D-U-N-S 02-979-6984
PANASONIC PROCUREMENT CORP OF AMERICA
(*Suby of* PANASONIC SOLUTIONS CO) ★
20000 Mariner Ave Ste 200, Torrance, CA 90503-1670
Tel (310) 783-4100 *Founded/Ownrshp* 1981
Sales 258.0MM *EMP* 10
Accts Kpmg Llp Los Angeles Ca
SIC 6221 Commodity contracts brokers, dealers

PANASONIC SOLUTIONS COMPANY
See PANASONIC CORP OF NORTH AMERICA

PANASONIC/ACOM
See PANASONIC INDUSTRIAL DEVICES CORP OF AMERICA

PANAVISION GROUP
See PANAVISION INC

D-U-N-S 96-752-4232
PANAVISION INC
PANAVISION GROUP
6101 Variel Ave, Woodland Hills, CA 91367-3722
Tel (818) 316-1000 *Founded/Ownrshp* 2010
Sales 202.1MM[E] *EMP* 1,211
SIC 7359 3861 3648 5063 Equipment rental & leasing; Cameras & related equipment; Stage lighting equipment; Lighting fixtures
Ch Bd: Ronald O Perelman
Pr: William C Bevins
CEO: Kimberly Snyder
COO: Ross Landsbaum
COO: Will Paice
CFO: Scott Siebold
CFO: John Suh
V Ch Bd: Howard Gittis
Bd of Dir: Bob Beitcher
Ex VP: Eric W Golden
Ex VP: Phillip Radin
VP: Larry Hezzelwood
VP: Marvin Schaffer
VP: Damien Sullivan
Exec: David Demont
Board of Directors: Edward Grebow, Ed Gregory Hookstratten, James R Maher, Martin D Payson, John A Scarcella, Robert S Wiesenthal, Kenneth Ziffrenm

D-U-N-S 78-523-1119 IMP
PANAVISION INTERNATIONAL LP
(*Suby of* PANAVISION GROUP) ★
6101 Variel Ave, Woodland Hills, CA 91367-3722
Tel (818) 316-1000 *Founded/Ownrshp* 1996
Sales 134.6MM[E] *EMP* 576
SIC 3861 Cameras & related equipment
Pr: Robert Beitcher
**CFO:* Ross Landfbuam
CTO: Albertl Mayer
Dir IT: John Galt

PANDA EXPRESS
See PANDA RESTAURANT GROUP INC

D-U-N-S 85-873-2290 IMP
PANDA EXPRESS INC
(*Suby of* PANDA EXPRESS) ★
1683 Walnut Grove Ave, Rosemead, CA 91770-3711
Tel (626) 799-9898 *Founded/Ownrshp* 1990
Sales 205.9MM[E] *EMP* 7,000
SIC 5812 Fast-food restaurant, chain; Chinese restaurant
Co-Ch Bd: Andrew Cherng
**Pr:* Peggy T Cherng
COO: Alan Huang
Genl Mgr: Kevin Herren

PANDA POWER FUND
See PANDA POWER GENERATION INFRASTRUCTURE FUND GP LP

D-U-N-S 96-802-9053
PANDA POWER GENERATION INFRASTRUCTURE FUND GP LP
PANDA POWER FUND
5001 Spring Valley Rd 1150w, Dallas, TX 75244-3946
Tel (972) 361-2000 *Founded/Ownrshp* 2010
Sales 173.7MM[E] *EMP* 193[E]
SIC 1382 Oil & gas exploration services
Pt: R W Carter
Pt: Robert W Carter
Sr VP: Richard Evans
Sr VP: Edward E Graham
Sr VP: Ralph Killian
Sr VP: Derek Porter
VP: Rick Blandford
VP: Yang Chen
VP: Bill Pentak
VP: Nicole Wolf
Mng Dir: Eddy Daniels

D-U-N-S 17-582-3673 IMP/EXP
PANDA RESTAURANT GROUP INC
PANDA EXPRESS
1683 Walnut Grove Ave, Rosemead, CA 91770-3711
Tel (626) 799-9898 *Founded/Ownrshp* 1986
Sales 543.4MM[E] *EMP* 13,000
SIC 5812 Chinese restaurant; Fast food restaurants & stands
CEO: Andrew Cherng
**CFO:* David Landsberg
**Sr VP:* Monte Baier
**Sr VP:* Al Chaib
Sr VP: John R Mitchell
VP: John Fu
VP: Robert Lustig
VP: Donna Wanser
VP: Rif Wiguna
VP: Leonard Yip
Dir Risk M: Steven Lin

D-U-N-S 14-687-2432 IMP/EXP
PANDORA JEWELRY LLC
(*Suby of* PANDORA A/S)
250 W Pratt St, Baltimore, MD 21201-2423
Tel (410) 309-0200 *Founded/Ownrshp* 2003
Sales 251.4MM[E] *EMP* 400[E]
SIC 5094 Jewelry
Genl Couns: Matt Scott

D-U-N-S 13-163-7105
▲ **PANDORA MEDIA INC**
2101 Webster St Ste 1650, Oakland, CA 94612-3015
Tel (510) 451-4100 *Founded/Ownrshp* 2000
Sales 1.1MMM *EMP* 2,219[E]
Tkr Sym P *Exch* NYS
SIC 4832 Radio broadcasting stations
CEO: Tim Westergren
**Ch Bd:* James M P Feuille
Pr: Michael Herring
COO: Sara Clemens
COO: Etienne Handman
Ofcr: Christopher Phillips
Ofcr: Kristen Robinson
Ofcr: John Trimble
Ex VP: David Gerbitz
VP: Jordan Bick
VP: Heidi Browning
VP: John Donaldson
VP: Steven Kritzman
VP: Chris Long
VP: George Lynch
VP: Heidi B Pearson
VP: Chris Record
VP: Sarah Wagener
VP: Scott Walker

D-U-N-S 00-517-8363 IMP/EXP
PANDUIT CORP (DE)
18900 Panduit Dr, Tinley Park, IL 60487-3600
Tel (708) 532-1800 *Founded/Ownrshp* 1953
Sales 924.5MM *EMP* 5,050
SIC 3699 3644 5063 Electrical equipment & supplies; Electric conduits & fittings; Electrical apparatus & equipment
Pr: Thomas C Donovan
CFO: Patricia Brow
Treas: Scott Fraser
VP: Mark Acklin
**VP:* Andrew M Caveney
VP: Timothy Dee
VP: Glenn Henning
**VP:* Michael G Kenny
VP: Cheryl Lewis
VP: Barry Page
VP: Ron Partridge
VP: Ronald K Partridge
VP: Dennis Renaud
VP: Hank Smith
VP: James Wator
Exec: John Durante
Dir Lab: Greg Skaper
Board of Directors: Andrew M Caveney

D-U-N-S 04-562-2602
■ **PANENERGY CORP**
(*Suby of* DUKE ENERGY REGISTRATION SERVICES INC) ★
526 S Church St, Charlotte, NC 28202-1802
Tel (704) 594-6200 *Founded/Ownrshp* 1998
Sales 263.7MM[E] *EMP* 5,000
SIC 4922 1321 2813 5172 4911 4613 Pipelines, natural gas; Storage, natural gas; Natural gas liquids production; Helium; Gases; Generation, electric power; Refined petroleum pipelines
CEO: James E Rogers

PANERA BREAD
See PR RESTAURANTS LLC

PANERA BREAD
See LEMEK LLC

PANERA BREAD
See BREADS OF WORLD LLC

D-U-N-S 09-384-4462 IMP
▲ **PANERA BREAD CO**
3630 S Geyer Rd Ste 100, Saint Louis, MO 63127-1234
Tel (314) 984-1000 *Founded/Ownrshp* 1981
Sales 2.6MMM *EMP* 47,200
Tkr Sym PNRA *Exch* NGS
SIC 5812 5461 6794 Cafe; Bakeries; Franchises, selling or licensing
Ch Bd: Ronald M Shaich
Pr: Andrew H Madsen
COO: Charles J Chapman III
CFO: Michael J Bufano
Ofcr: Elizabeth A Dunlap
Ofcr: William H Simpson
Ex VP: Blaine E Hurst
Ex VP: Ken Koziol
Ex VP: Kenneth Koziol
Sr VP: Scott G Blair
Sr VP: John M Meister
VP: Mike Bufano
VP: Mike Nettles
Board of Directors: Domenic Colasacco, Fred K Foulkes, Larry J Franklin, Diane Hessan, Thomas E Lynch, Mark Stoever, James D White

PANEX
See ZOLTEK COMPANIES INC

D-U-N-S 07-957-6002
PANGAEA LOGISTICS SOLUTIONS LTD
109 Long Wharf, Newport, RI 02840-2406
Tel (401) 846-7790 *Founded/Ownrshp* 1996
Sales 287.3MM *EMP* 72
Tkr Sym PANL *Exch* NAS
SIC 4412 Deep sea foreign transportation of freight
Ch Bd: Edward Coll
**Pr:* Carl Claus Boggild
**CFO:* Anthony Laura
Board of Directors: Richard T Du Moulin, Mark L Filanowski, Paul Hong, Eric S Rosenfeld, David S Sgro, Peter M Yu

D-U-N-S 00-891-0846
PANHANDLE COOPERATIVE ASSOCIATION
FLOWER BASKET
401 S Beltline Hwy W, Scottsbluff, NE 69361-1335
Tel (308) 632-5301 *Founded/Ownrshp* 1942
Sales 131.8MM[E] *EMP* 357
SIC 5541 0721 Gasoline service stations; Crop planting & protection
Ch Bd: Jim Lapaseates
V Ch: Thomas Flaherty
**Pr:* Robert Pile
**COO:* Mike Hofer
**CFO:* Kimberli Anderson
VP: Daryl Arneson
**VP:* Clay Peterson
**VP:* Norman Strong

D-U-N-S 04-525-6641
■ **PANHANDLE EASTERN PIPE LINE CO LP**
SOUTHERN UNION GAS
(*Suby of* SOUTHERN UNION GAS) ★
8111 Westchester Dr # 600, Dallas, TX 75225-6142
Tel (214) 981-0700 *Founded/Ownrshp* 2014
Sales 548.0MM *EMP* 562
Accts Grant Thornton Llp Houston T
SIC 4922 Natural gas transmission; Pipelines, natural gas
CEO: Kelcy L Warren
Genl Pt: Southern Union Panhandle LLC
CFO: Martin Salinas Jr

PANHANDLE ENERGY
See FLORIDA GAS TRANSMISSION CO LLC

D-U-N-S 61-109-2776
PANHANDLE OILFIELD SERVICE COMPANIES INC
PANHANDLE PIPE SUPPLY
14000 Quail Springs Pkwy # 300, Oklahoma City, OK 73134-2600
Tel (405) 608-5330 *Founded/Ownrshp* 2013
Sales 121.9MM[E] *EMP* 130[E]
SIC 1389 7389 3498 4212 5082 1794
CEO: Tim Long
Dist Mgr: Steve Archibeque
Off Admin: Stephanie Ramsey
Opers Mgr: Dave McHenry
Opers Mgr: Kevin Savely

PANHANDLE PIPE SUPPLY
See PANHANDLE OILFIELD SERVICE COMPANIES INC

D-U-N-S 02-368-8588 IMP
PANOLAM INDUSTRIES INC
(*Suby of* PANOLAM SURFACE SYSTEMS) ★
20 Progress Dr, Shelton, CT 06484-6216
Tel (203) 925-1556 *Founded/Ownrshp* 1998
Sales 199.0MM[E] *EMP* 1,000
SIC 3089 3083 Panels, building: plastic; Laminated plastics plate & sheet
Pr: Robert Muller
**Pr:* Alan S Kabus
**CFO:* Vincent Miceli
**Ex VP:* Lawrence Grossman
VP Mktg: Joel Reynolds

D-U-N-S 94-732-4158 IMP/EXP
PANOLAM INDUSTRIES INTERNATIONAL INC
PANOLAM SURFACE SYSTEMS
20 Progress Dr, Shelton, CT 06484-6216
Tel (203) 925-1556 *Founded/Ownrshp* 2016
Sales 500.5MM[E] *EMP* 1,042
SIC 2493 3089 Particleboard products; Panels, building: plastic
Pr: Alan Kabus
**CFO:* James Stiff
Exec: Sharon E Metz
Genl Mgr: John Fulkerson
Netwrk Mgr: Peter Zacharias
Ql Cn Mgr: Marc Riviere
Natl Sales: Scott Beverage
Sls Mgr: Kevin Ball
Sls Mgr: Bruce Irons

PANOLAM SURFACE SYSTEMS
See PANOLAM INDUSTRIES INTERNATIONAL INC

D-U-N-S 62-419-1867
■ **PANTHER PREMIUM LOGISTICS INC**
(*Suby of* ARCBEST CORP) ★
84 Medina Rd, Medina, OH 44256-9616
Tel (800) 685-0657 *Founded/Ownrshp* 2012
Sales 300.0MM[E] *EMP* 400
SIC 4213 4212 Trucking, except local; Local trucking, without storage
Pr: R Louis Schneeberger
**COO:* Edward Wadel
**CFO:* Bob Businger
**VP:* David Buss
**VP:* Frank Ilacqua
VP: Mark Pare
Sls Dir: Fred Patterson
Sls Mgr: John Blahut
Sls Mgr: Travis Eick
Sls Mgr: Pat Walsh
Board of Directors: John Anderson, Raymond Greer, Michael P Haley, Marc Kramer, Peter Lamm, Timothy Mayhew, Edward M Straw

D-U-N-S 12-226-5960
PANTHER SUMMIT INDUSTRIES INC
4807 Beryl Rd, Raleigh, NC 27606-1406
Tel (919) 828-0641 *Founded/Ownrshp* 1957
Sales 473.6MM[E] *EMP* 901
SIC 5082 5084 4931 Road construction & maintenance machinery; General construction machinery & equipment; Lift trucks & parts; Materials handling machinery; Electric & other services combined
Ch Bd: J Gregory Poole III
Sales Exec: Richard F Donnelly

PANTHER TRANSPORTATION SVCS
See CELADON TRUCKING SERVICES INC

D-U-N-S 15-274-6244 IMP
■ **PANTHERS BRHC LLC**
BOCA RATON HOTEL
(*Suby of* BOCA RESORTS INC) ★
501 E Camino Real, Boca Raton, FL 33432-6127
Tel (888) 543-1277 *Founded/Ownrshp* 2004
Sales 97.8MM[E] *EMP* 1,585[E]
SIC 7011 5812 7997 Resort hotel; Eating places; Country club, membership; Golf club, membership; Tennis club, membership
CFO: Steve Shaver
Top Exec: Laurent Bortoluzzi
Ex VP: Mark Komine

VP: Mary Finacchiaro
Comm Man: Anne Hersley
Ex Dir: Mary Frederick
IT Man: John Carres
Sales Exec: Stephen Catena
Sales Exec: Phillis Hoynacky
VP Mktg: Craig Colton
Advt Dir: Ann Henkins

D-U-N-S 17-761-0961 IMP
PANTROPIC POWER INC
CATERPILLAR AUTHORIZED DEALER
8205 Nw 58th St, Doral, FL 33166-3406
Tel (305) 477-3329 *Founded/Ownrshp* 1986
Sales 89.7MM^E *EMP* 230
SIC 5084 5085 5063 7353 Industrial machinery & equipment; Industrial supplies; Generators; Heavy construction equipment rental
Pr: Luis Botas
CFO: Fernando Cabrera

PANTRY EXPRESS
See WINNSBORO PETROLEUM CO INC

D-U-N-S 18-145-8357
PANTRY INC
KANGAROO EXPRESS
(*Suby of* COUCHE-TARD US INC) ★
305 Gregson Dr, Cary, NC 27511-6496
Tel (919) 774-6700 *Founded/Ownrshp* 2015
Sales 4.6MMM^E *EMP* 15,140
SIC 5541 5411 Gasoline service stations; Convenience stores, chain
Pr: Darrell Davis
VP: Kathy Cunnington

D-U-N-S 00-636-4764 IMP/EXP
■ **PAOLI LLC** (IA)
(*Suby of* HNI CORP) ★
201 E Martin St, Orleans, IN 47452-9013
Tel (800) 457-7415 *Founded/Ownrshp* 2004
Sales 101.0MM *EMP* 625
SIC 2521 Wood office furniture
Pr: Brandon Sieben
VP: John Cahill
VP: Dean Marotta
**VP:* Kurt A Tjaden
Genl Mgr: Amanda Keithley
IT Man: Gregory Bauer
Site Mgr: James Saliba
Opers Mgr: Mark Davis
Plnt Mgr: Bob Parsley
VP Mktg: Sandra Horton

D-U-N-S 78-765-0902
PAPA GINOS HOLDINGS CORP
D' ANGELO'S SANDWICH SHOP
600 Providence Hwy, Dedham, MA 02026-6848
Tel (781) 461-1200 *Founded/Ownrshp* 1992
Sales 203.1MM^E *EMP* 5,000
SIC 5812 6794 Italian restaurant; Sandwiches & submarines shop; Franchises, selling or licensing
Pr: Rick Wools
**Ch Bd:* Thomas Galligan
**CFO:* Andrew Almquist
VP: Tim Lamson
VP: Paul Valle
Dist Mgr: Bruce Belenger
Genl Mgr: Tom Dusker
Mktg Mgr: John Bayley

D-U-N-S 04-276-2997 IMP
PAPA GINOS INC
(*Suby of* D ANGELOS SANDWICH SHOP) ★
600 Providence Hwy, Dedham, MA 02026-6848
Tel (781) 461-1200 *Founded/Ownrshp* 1991
Sales 156.6MM^E *EMP* 3,750
SIC 5812 Pizzeria, chain
Pr: Rick Wolf
Sr VP: Michael McManama
VP: Bruce Archambault
VP: Bob Lanehan
Genl Mgr: Ron Walker
MIS Dir: Orlando Jagonda
MIS Dir: Martha Lieber
Info Man: Debra Kulka

PAPA JOHN'S
See RO HO HO INC

PAPA JOHN'S
See P J UNITED INC

D-U-N-S 14-779-4812
▲ **PAPA JOHNS INTERNATIONAL INC**
2002 Papa Johns Blvd # 100, Louisville, KY 40299-2333
Tel (502) 261-7272 *Founded/Ownrshp* 1985
Sales 1.6MMM *EMP* 22,350
Tkr Sym PZZA *Exch* NGS
SIC 5812 6794 2099 Pizzeria, chain; Franchises, selling or licensing; Food preparations
Ch Bd: John H Schnatter
Pr: Steve M Ritchie
CFO: Lance Tucker
Sr VP: Timothy C O'Hern
VP: Tim O'Hern
VP Opers: Steve McNeil
Mktg Mgr: Amy Nicholson
Snr Mgr: Sean Stapleton
Board of Directors: Christopher L Coleman, Olivia F Kirtley, Laurette T Koellner, Sonya E Medina, Mark S Shapiro, W Kent Taylor

D-U-N-S 82-706-2550
■ **PAPA JOHNS INTERNATIONAL INC**
(*Suby of* PAPA JOHNS INTERNATIONAL INC) ★
2002 Papa Johns Blvd # 100, Louisville, KY 40299-2333
Tel (502) 261-7272 *Founded/Ownrshp* 1993
Sales 14.3MM^E *EMP* 1,000
SIC 5812 Pizzeria, chain
CEO: John Schnatter
**VP:* Sean Muldon

D-U-N-S 80-099-0814
PAPA JOHNS SALADS & PRODUCE INC
859 S 86th Ave, Tolleson, AZ 85353-9221
Tel (480) 894-6885 *Founded/Ownrshp* 1995
Sales 134.9MM^E *EMP* 150
SIC 5148 Fresh fruits & vegetables
CEO: Kevin Jones

D-U-N-S 07-924-1586
▲ **PAPA MURPHYS HOLDINGS INC**
8000 Ne Parkway Dr # 350, Vancouver, WA 98662-6744
Tel (360) 260-7272 *Founded/Ownrshp* 1981
Sales 97.4MM *EMP* 1,718^E
Tkr Sym FRSH *Exch* NGS
SIC 5812 Pizzeria, chain
Pr: Ken Calwell
**Ch Bd:* John Barr
CFO: Mark Hutchens
Chf Mktg O: Brandon Solano

PAPA RAZZI
See TAVISTOCK RESTAURANT GROUP

PAPAYA CLOTHING
See CORNERSTONE APPAREL INC

D-U-N-S 05-098-7460 EXP
■ **PAPCO INC**
(*Suby of* WORLD FUEL SERVICES CORP) ★
4920 Southern Blvd, Virginia Beach, VA 23462-5314
Tel (757) 499-5977 *Founded/Ownrshp* 2016
Sales 150.3MM^E *EMP* 150
SIC 4923 Gas transmission & distribution
CEO: John F Malbon
**Pr:* Gary Gilmore
VP: Beth W Johnson
VP Sls: Eric Rosenfeldt

D-U-N-S 61-829-6420 IMP
PAPE GROUP INC
355 Goodpasture Island Rd # 300, Eugene, OR 97401-2119
Tel (541) 334-3400 *Founded/Ownrshp* 1990
Sales 598.1MM^E *EMP* 1,525
SIC 5084 5082 7699 6141 5599 4581 Industrial machinery & equipment; Hydraulic systems equipment & supplies; Materials handling machinery; Construction & mining machinery; General construction machinery & equipment; Mining machinery & equipment, except petroleum; Industrial equipment services; Financing: automobiles, furniture, etc., not a deposit bank; Aircraft, self-propelled; Aircraft cleaning & janitorial service
Pr: Randall J Pape
**Pr:* Danny W Hollingshead
**CEO:* Jordan Pape
**CFO:* Thomas Saylor
**Prin:* Kate Anderson
**Prin:* Jerry Lightner
Dir IT: Shaun Swift
Sls Dir: Hal Hansen
Sls Mgr: Grant Salisbury

PAPE' KENWORTH
See PAPE TRUCKS INC

D-U-N-S 10-655-4491 IMP
PAPE MACHINERY INC
JOHN DEERE AUTHORIZED DEALER
(*Suby of* PAPE GROUP INC) ★
355 Goodpasture Island Rd, Eugene, OR 97401-2119
Tel (541) 683-5073 *Founded/Ownrshp* 2006
Sales 97.6MM^E *EMP* 250
SIC 5082 General construction machinery & equipment
CEO: Jordan Pape
Pr: Ken Newell
**Pr:* Rodger Spears
**CFO:* Randall Jordan Pape
Sls Mgr: Bob Adams

D-U-N-S 62-002-3259 IMP
PAPE MATERIAL HANDLING INC
BOBCAT WEST
(*Suby of* PAPE GROUP INC) ★
355 Goodpasture Island Rd, Eugene, OR 97401-2119
Tel (541) 683-5073 *Founded/Ownrshp* 1990
Sales 211.8MM^E *EMP* 600
SIC 5084 Industrial machinery & equipment; Materials handling machinery
Pr: Christopher T Wetle
Trfc Dir: Brenda Jenkins
Mtls Mgr: Michelle Vervaeke
Manager: Ana M Lemley
Sls Mgr: Jack Anderson
Sls Mgr: Jim Bakkensen
Sls Mgr: Joel Buysse
Sls Mgr: Nicholas Hagen
Sls Mgr: Jeremy Jubrey
Sls Mgr: Tyler Larson

D-U-N-S 78-136-4278
PAPE TRUCKS INC
PAPE' KENWORTH
(*Suby of* PAPE GROUP INC) ★
2892 E Jensen Ave, Fresno, CA 93706-5111
Tel (559) 268-4344 *Founded/Ownrshp* 2007
Sales 103.4MM^E *EMP* 225
SIC 5511 Trucks, tractors & trailers: new & used
Pr: David B Laird
Exec: Jim Marron
Genl Mgr: Tena Dimond
Store Mgr: Marin Field-Dodgson
Mtls Mgr: Tom Wall
Sls Mgr: Tom Beam
Sls Mgr: Bob Branch
Sls Mgr: Ben Harrison
Sls Mgr: Scott Sauer
Sls Mgr: Chad Thompson

D-U-N-S 00-612-7823 IMP
PAPER CONVERTING MACHINE CO
PCMC
(*Suby of* BARRY-WEHMILLER COMPANIES INC) ★
2300 S Ashland Ave, Green Bay, WI 54304-5213
Tel (920) 494-5601 *Founded/Ownrshp* 1919
Sales 246.2MM^E *EMP* 1,304
Accts Ernst & Young Llp St Louis M
SIC 3554 Paper industries machinery
Pr: Steve Kemp
Ofcr: Kenneth Dawson
VP: Mary Edmondson
Dir IT: Keith Decramer
Dir IT: Matt Gidley
IT Man: David Parish
Snr Mgr: Joe Blume
Snr Mgr: Ernesto Cuellar
Snr Mgr: John Heier
Snr Mgr: Kurt Schlichting
Snr Mgr: Ed Schneider

D-U-N-S 07-878-2937 IMP
PAPER CUT CLOTHING LLC
PINK ROSE DIVISION
499 7th Ave Frnt 2, New York, NY 10018-6803
Tel (917) 475-9356 *Founded/Ownrshp* 2006
Sales 130.0MM *EMP* 65
SIC 5137 Women's & children's dresses, suits, skirts & blouses

D-U-N-S 01-241-3928 IMP
PAPER ENTERPRISES INC (NY)
CONSOLIDATED PAPER COMPANY
770 E 132nd St, Bronx, NY 10454-3429
Tel (718) 402-1200 *Founded/Ownrshp* 1961
Sales 108.7MM^E *EMP* 105
SIC 5113 5087 Cups, disposable plastic & paper; Dishes, disposable plastic & paper; Bags, paper & disposable plastic; Janitors' supplies
Ch Bd: Herb Sedler
**CFO:* Murray Pottruck
**VP:* Don Sabia

D-U-N-S 01-151-9410 IMP/EXP
PAPER MART INC
WALKIN PAPERS
151 Ridgedale Ave, East Hanover, NJ 07936-1296
Tel (973) 884-2505 *Founded/Ownrshp* 1998
Sales 95.6MM^E *EMP* 110
SIC 5111 Printing paper
VP: Jerold Levey
**Treas:* Howard Levey
**VP:* Jonathan Block
Exec: Michele Perillo

D-U-N-S 05-253-8279 IMP/EXP
PAPER PRODUCTS MARKETING (USA) INC
PPM
(*Suby of* PAPER AUSTRALIA PTY LTD)
4380 Sw Mcdam Ave Ste 370, Portland, OR 97239
Tel (503) 227-6615 *Founded/Ownrshp* 1981
Sales 250.0MM *EMP* 25
SIC 5111 5113 Fine paper; Industrial & personal service paper
Pr: James R Peters
**CFO:* Alice O Knight

PAPER STOCK
See SONOCO RECYCLING LLC

D-U-N-S 61-648-6080
PAPER TRANSPORT INC
2701 Executive Dr, Green Bay, WI 54304-5497
Tel (920) 497-6222 *Founded/Ownrshp* 1990
Sales 96.6MM^E *EMP* 500^E
SIC 4213 Contract haulers
CEO: Craig S Dickman
Pr: Joe Shefchik
**Pr:* Jeff Shefthik
**CFO:* Leonard J Shefchik
Sfty Mgr: Connie Vandenplas

D-U-N-S 02-922-9994 IMP
PAPERCONE CORP
3200 Fern Valley Rd, Louisville, KY 40213-3526
Tel (502) 961-9493 *Founded/Ownrshp* 1964
Sales 87.4MM^E *EMP* 150
SIC 2677 Envelopes
CEO: Brooks H Bower
**Pr:* James Beard
**VP:* Susan Huetteman
Mfg Dir: Skip Dewispelaere
VP Sls: Hunter Wilson
Manager: Jim Day

PAPERS UNLIMITED
See MIDLAND PAPER CO

D-U-N-S 10-950-4121 IMP/EXP
PAPERWEIGHT DEVELOPMENT CORP
825 E Wisconsin Ave, Appleton, WI 54911-3873
Tel (920) 734-9841 *Founded/Ownrshp* 2000
Sales 700.0MM *EMP* 1,565^E
Accts Rsm Us Llp Milwaukee Wiscons
SIC 2671 Packaging paper & plastics film, coated & laminated; Plastic film, coated or laminated for packaging
Ch Bd: Mark R Richards
Pr: Ted E Goodwin
CFO: Thomas J Ferree
VP: Jeffrey J Fletcher
VP: Tami L Van Straten
Board of Directors: Stephen P Carter, Terry M Murphy, Andrew F Reardon, Kathi P Seifert, Mark A Suwyn, George W Wurtz

D-U-N-S 82-866-3471 IMP/EXP
PAPERWORKS INDUSTRIES INC
(*Suby of* SUN CAPITAL PARTNERS INC) ★
40 Monument Rd Ste 200, Bala Cynwyd, PA 19004-1735
Tel (215) 984-7000 *Founded/Ownrshp* 2008
Sales 677.5MM^E *EMP* 1,800
Accts Pricewaterhousecoopers Llp Ph
SIC 2653 Corrugated & solid fiber boxes
CEO: Richard Leblanc
**CEO:* Tom Garland
CFO: Robert J Nobile
**CFO:* Mark Schlei
Ex VP: Mark P Roy
Plnt Mgr: Robert Black
Ql Cn Mgr: Derek Dickens
Sls Dir: Nirav Shah

D-U-N-S 05-244-4601 IMP/EXP
■ **PAPETTIS HYGRADE EGG PRODUCTS INC**
MICHAEL FOODS
(*Suby of* MG WALDBAUM CO) ★
1 Papetti Plz, Elizabethport, NJ 07206-1421
Tel (908) 282-7900 *Founded/Ownrshp* 2007
Sales 135.8MM^E *EMP* 1,060
SIC 2015 Egg processing; Eggs, processed: desiccated (dried); Eggs, processed: frozen; Eggs, processed: dehydrated
Pr: Arthur Papetti
CFO: Mark Westphal
**Ex VP:* Stephen Papetti
VP: Jack Novak
**VP:* Alfred Papetti
Exec: Larry Cooper
Exec: John Gill
IT Man: Mike Dlenchfield
Opers Mgr: Jose Murillo

D-U-N-S 07-289-2466
PAPILLION-LAVISTA PUBLIC SCHOOLS
420 S Washington St, Papillion, NE 68046-2667
Tel (402) 537-6244 *Founded/Ownrshp* 1915
Sales 114.7MM *EMP* 1,326
Accts O Donnell Ficenec Wills & Fe
SIC 8211 Public elementary & secondary schools; School board
MIS Dir: Bill Pulte
Pr Dir: Annette Eyman
Teacher Pr: Kati Settles

D-U-N-S 82-959-4139
PAPPAS GROUP LLC
(*Suby of* DMI) ★
4100 Fairfax Dr Ste 400, Arlington, VA 22203-1676
Tel (703) 349-7221 *Founded/Ownrshp* 2014
Sales 98.4MM^E *EMP* 1,192^E
SIC 7311 Advertising agencies
Pr: Anthony Pappas
**Creative D:* Stefan Poulos
Creative D: Sean Wallace
Off Mgr: Tina Dodge
Web Dev: Jeff Nyveen
Art Dir: Erin Krieger

D-U-N-S 08-016-4829
PAPPAS LASSONDE HOLDINGS INC
(*Suby of* INDUSTRIES LASSONDE INC)
1 Collins Dr Ste 200, Carneys Point, NJ 08069-3640
Tel (856) 455-1000 *Founded/Ownrshp* 2011
Sales 450.0MM^E *EMP* 600^E
SIC 2033 6719 Fruit juices: packaged in cans, jars, etc.; Fruits: packaged in cans, jars, etc.; Investment holding companies, except banks
Ch: Jean Pattuso
**CEO:* Mark A McNeil

D-U-N-S 03-235-7688
PAPPAS PARTNERS LP
PAPPAS SEAFOOD RESTAURANT
(*Suby of* PAPPASITOS CANTINA) ★
6894 Southwest Fwy 1, Houston, TX 77074-2104
Tel (713) 869-7151 *Founded/Ownrshp* 1997
Sales 147.9MM^E *EMP* 9,000
SIC 5812 Seafood restaurants; Mexican restaurant; Cajun restaurant; Steak restaurant
Pt: Harris Pappas

D-U-N-S 11-822-4963 IMP
PAPPAS RESTAURANTS INC
PAPPASITO'S CANTINA
13939 Nw Fwy, Houston, TX 77040-5115
Tel (713) 869-0151 *Founded/Ownrshp* 1983
Sales 474.6MM^E *EMP* 10,000
SIC 5812 5813 Seafood restaurants; Mexican restaurant; Cajun restaurant; Steak restaurant; Bar (drinking places)
Ch Bd: Pete H Pappas
**Pr:* Harris J Pappas
**VP:* Christopher J Pappas
Dir Soc: Sandy Blossom
Off Admin: Deannah Stjohn
Dir IT: Emily Bullard

PAPPAS SEAFOOD RESTAURANT
See PAPPAS PARTNERS LP

PAPPASITO'S CANTINA
See PAPPAS RESTAURANTS INC

PAPYRUS
See SCHURMAN FINE PAPERS

D-U-N-S 92-946-5375
■ **PAQ INC**
FOOD 4 LESS
(*Suby of* FOOD 4 LESS HOLDINGS INC) ★
8014 Lower Sacramento Rd I, Stockton, CA 95210-3747
Tel (209) 957-4917 *Founded/Ownrshp* 1995
Sales 312.2MM^E *EMP* 1,300
SIC 5411 Grocery stores
Pr: John Quinn
**Treas:* Patricia Quinn
**VP:* Glenn Evans
Ex Dir: Mary Armstrong
Genl Mgr: Rusty Peake
CIO: Rick Dickson

D-U-N-S 00-785-7451
■ **PAR ELECTRICAL CONTRACTORS INC** (MO)
(*Suby of* QUANTA SERVICES INC) ★
4770 N Belleview Ave # 300, Kansas City, MO 64116-2104
Tel (816) 474-9340 *Founded/Ownrshp* 1954
Sales 309.0MM^E *EMP* 1,000
SIC 1623 Electric power line construction
Pr: Stephen Adams
**Sr VP:* Richard Holbeck
**Sr VP:* Jim Stapp
**Sr VP:* Tim Warlen
VP: Michael Murray
Sfty Dirs: Philip Petrozzi

PAR GROUP
See PAR PLUMBING CO INC

PAR HAWAII
See MID PAC PETROLEUM LLC

D-U-N-S 04-740-2961 IMP
■ PAR HAWAII REFINING LLC
(Suby of PAR PACIFIC HOLDINGS INC) ★
800 Gessner Rd Ste 875, Houston, TX 77024-4498
Tel (281) 899-4800 Founded/Ownrshp 2013
Sales 246.5MM^E EMP 420
SIC 5541 2911 Gasoline service stations; Petroleum refining
Pr: Jim Yates
*VP: Chet Greene
*VP: John Kaiser
*VP: Eric Lee
VP: Andrew Nomura
VP: Scott Rammell
VP: Milton Tengan
*VP: Thomas Weber
*VP: Russell Whang

D-U-N-S 04-251-1766
PAR MAR OIL CO
PAR MAR STORES
(Suby of CROTON HOLDING COMPANY)
114 Westview Ave Unit A, Marietta, OH 45750-9404
Tel (740) 373-7406 Founded/Ownrshp 2016
Sales 87.5MM^E EMP 560
SIC 5411 Convenience stores, chain
CEO: Sandra Warner
COO: Sandra Morganstern
CFO: Van Olnhausen
Exec: Susan Bell
Genl Mgr: Lori Matheny

PAR MAR STORES
See PAR MAR OIL CO

D-U-N-S 18-650-8057 IMP/EXP
▲ PAR PACIFIC HOLDINGS INC
800 Gessner Rd Ste 875, Houston, TX 77024-4498
Tel (713) 969-3293 Founded/Ownrshp 1984
Sales 2.0MMM EMP 744^E
Tkr Sym PARR Exch ASE
SIC 1311 2911 4923 Crude petroleum & natural gas; Crude petroleum & natural gas production; Petroleum refining; Gas transmission & distribution
Ch Bd: Melvyn N Klein
*Pr: William C Pate
*CFO: Christopher Micklas
*V Ch Bd: Robert S Silberman
*Sr VP: Joseph Israel
*Sr VP: William Monteleone
*Sr VP: James Matthew Vaughn
Sr VP: Matt Vaughn
Sr VP: Jim Yates
VP: Kelly Rosser
VP: Jeff Shaffer

D-U-N-S 07-919-9838
PAR PHARMACEUTICAL COMPANIES INC
(Suby of ENDO HEALTH SOLUTIONS INC) ★
1 Ram Ridge Rd, Chestnut Ridge, NY 10977-6714
Tel (845) 573-5500 Founded/Ownrshp 2012
Sales 317.8MM^E EMP 1,450^E
SIC 2834 Pharmaceutical preparations
CEO: Paul V Campanelli
Pr: Tony Pera
COO: Terrance J Coughlin
CFO: Michael Tropiano

D-U-N-S 78-200-0269 IMP
PAR PHARMACEUTICAL COMPANIES INC
1 Ram Ridge Rd, Spring Valley, NY 10977-6714
Tel (201) 802-4000 Founded/Ownrshp 2012
Sales 1.3MMM EMP 1,450^E
SIC 2834

D-U-N-S 09-273-3690 IMP
PAR PHARMACEUTICAL INC
(Suby of PAR PHARMACEUTICAL COMPANIES INC) ★
1 Ram Ridge Rd, Spring Valley, NY 10977-6714
Tel (845) 425-7100 Founded/Ownrshp 1978
Sales 207.2MM^E EMP 400^E
SIC 2834 Pharmaceutical preparations; Druggists' preparations (pharmaceuticals); Tablets, pharmaceutical; Medicines, capsuled or ampuled
CEO: Paul V Campanelli
*Pr: Thomas J Haughey
*CFO: Dennis O'Connor
*Ex VP: Michael A Tropiano
*Sr VP: Joseph Barbarite
*Sr VP: Renee Kenney
*Sr VP: Stephen Montalto
*Sr VP: Robert Polke
*VP: Michelle Bonomi-Huvala
*VP: Robert Femia PHD
*Prin: Kenneth I Sawyer

D-U-N-S 01-261-4541
PAR PLUMBING CO INC
PAR GROUP
60 N Prospect Ave, Lynbrook, NY 11563-1395
Tel (516) 887-4000 Founded/Ownrshp 1928
Sales 90.4MM^E EMP 400
SIC 1711 Plumbing contractors
Pr: Martin Levine
*CFO: James Martone
VP: Chris Hagen
VP: Sondra Krinsky
VP: Brendan McMonagle
*VP: Steve O'Hara
*VP: Neil Skidell
Genl Mgr: Kathleen Cannata
Board of Directors: Jeffrey Levine, Jesse Levine

D-U-N-S 80-489-4611
PAR STERILE PRODUCTS LLC
(Suby of PAR PHARMACEUTICAL INC) ★
1 Ram Ridge Rd, Chestnut Ridge, NY 10977-6714
Tel (845) 573-5500 Founded/Ownrshp 2007
Sales 118.9MM^E EMP 346
SIC 2834 Pharmaceutical preparations
CEO: Paul V Campanelli
*CFO: Michael Tropiano
Sls Mgr: Valerie Luczak
Sls Mgr: Tina Maxwell
Sls Mgr: Jennifer Rojano
Board of Directors: Ernest Toth

D-U-N-S 15-610-9303 IMP/EXP
PAR SYSTEMS INC
707 County Road E W, Shoreview, MN 55126-7007
Tel (651) 484-7261 Founded/Ownrshp 2008
Sales 170.2MM^E EMP 400
SIC 8742 Automation & robotics consultant
CEO: Mark Wrightsman
*Ch Bd: Rick Shand
*Pr: Brian Behm
Pr: Eivind Stenersen
COO: Tom Donovan
*CFO: Brad Yopp
*Ch: Charles Chadwell
Bd of Dir: Daren Pietsch
VP: Carrie Koliha
*VP: Karen O'Rourke
*VP: Albert Sturm

D-U-N-S 05-527-1183
▲ PAR TECHNOLOGY CORP
8383 Seneca Tpke Ste 2, New Hartford, NY 13413-4991
Tel (315) 738-0600 Founded/Ownrshp 1968
Sales 229.0MM EMP 1,010
Tkr Sym PAR Exch NYS
SIC 7372 7832 Prepackaged software; Motion picture theaters, except drive-in
Pr: Karen E Sammon
Treas: Matthew J Trinkaus
VP: John Darby
VP: Viola A Murdock
Exec: Dan Jones
Exec: John W Sammon
Dir Sec: Dan Cain
Software D: April Hoyt
Sftwr Eng: Timothy Masters
Board of Directors: Ronald J Casciano, Paul D Eurek, Donald H Foley, Cynthia A Russo, John W Sammon

D-U-N-S 13-337-8281
PARACELSUS LOS ANGELES COMMUNITY HOSPITAL INC
4081 E Olympic Blvd, Los Angeles, CA 90023-3330
Tel (323) 267-0477 Founded/Ownrshp 2011
Sales 141.6MM EMP 250
SIC 8062 General medical & surgical hospitals
Acting CEO: Lou Rubino
COO: Omar Ramirez
CFO: Rick Monroe
Sfty Mgr: Osvaldo Montiel

D-U-N-S 07-962-8762
PARACO GAS CORP
800 Westchester Ave S604, Rye Brook, NY 10573-1397
Tel (800) 647-4427 Founded/Ownrshp 1982
Sales 326.7MM^E EMP 300^E
SIC 1321 Propane (natural) production
CEO: Joseph Armentano
*Pr: Michael Gioffre
*CFO: Charles Schwartz
*VP: John Armentano
*VP: Michael Devoe
Rgnl Mgr: Patrick Brennan
Rgnl Mgr: Bob Pearce
Rgnl Mgr: Peter Teresi
Admn Mgr: Lori Greer
Brnch Mgr: Fred Jacques
Sales Exec: Stuart Soycher

D-U-N-S 78-828-3195
PARACO GAS OF NEW YORK INC
(Suby of PARACO GAS CORP) ★
800 Westchester Ave, Rye Brook, NY 10573-1354
Tel (914) 250-3740 Founded/Ownrshp 1956
Sales 326.7MM^E EMP 268^E
SIC 4925 Gas production and/or distribution
CEO: Joseph Armentano
*Pr: Michael Gioffre
*CFO: Charles Schwartz
*Ex VP: Michael Devoe
*VP: John Armentano

PARADIES AND COMPANY
See PARADIES GIFTS INC

D-U-N-S 80-104-7119 IMP
PARADIES GIFTS INC
PARADIES AND COMPANY
2305 W Airport Blvd, Sanford, FL 32771-3004
Tel (407) 290-5288 Founded/Ownrshp 1992
Sales 84.0MM^E EMP 137
SIC 5199 General merchandise, non-durable

PARADIES LAGARDRE
See PARADIES SHOPS LLC

D-U-N-S 03-350-2493 IMP
PARADIES SHOPS LLC
PARADIES LAGARDRE
(Suby of LSTRAVEL RETAIL NORTH AMERICA) ★
2849 Paces Ferry Rd Se, Atlanta, GA 30339-6201
Tel (404) 344-7905 Founded/Ownrshp 2015
Sales 550.0MM^E EMP 4,000
Accts Habif Arogeti & Wynne Llp A
SIC 5947 5994 5621 5611 5912 5941 Gift shop; Souvenirs; Newsstand; Magazine stand; Ready-to-wear apparel, women's; Men's & boys' clothing stores; Proprietary (non-prescription medicine) stores; Golf goods & equipment
Pr: Gregg Paradies
*V Ch: James N Paradies
Pr: Bruce Seuer
*COO: Lou Bottino
*CFO: Don Marek
CFO: Kevin Smith
Ofcr: Eric Hedberg
*Ex VP: Gerry Savaria
*Sr VP: William J Casey
Sr VP: John Cugasi
Sr VP: Richard Dickson
*Sr VP: Jeff Flowers
*Sr VP: Nikki Harland
VP: Bill Casey
VP: William Casey
VP: Tony Dudek
VP: Bruce Feuer
VP: Karen Leach
VP: Rick Lillie
VP: Pat Wallace
VP: Charlene Yde

D-U-N-S 00-552-9395
PARADIGM HEALTHCARE DEVELOPMENT LLC
177 Whitewood Rd, Waterbury, CT 06708-1545
Tel (860) 748-4750 Founded/Ownrshp 2008
Sales 54.4MM^E EMP 1,200^E
SIC 8051 Skilled nursing care facilities

PARADIGM PRECISION
See MANCHESTER PARADIGM INC

PARADIGM PRECISION
See TURBOCOMBUSTOR TECHNOLOGY INC

PARADIGM SOLUTIONS
See K & R HOLDINGS INC

D-U-N-S 04-975-3630
■ PARADISE BAKERY & CAFES INC
(Suby of PANERA BREAD CO) ★
3630 S Geyer Rd Ste 400, Saint Louis, MO 63127-1234
Tel (480) 889-5347 Founded/Ownrshp 2007
Sales 36.8MM^E EMP 1,200
SIC 5812 Cafe
CEO: Bill Moreton
*Pr: David Birzon
CFO: Laura Danks
*CFO: Laurie Danks
Genl Mgr: Cindy Reyes

D-U-N-S 03-318-1512 IMP/EXP
PARADISE BEVERAGES INC
(Suby of TOPA RISK MANAGEMENT SERVICES) ★
94-1450 Moaniani St, Waipahu, HI 96797-4632
Tel (808) 678-4000 Founded/Ownrshp 1980
Sales 194.6MM^E EMP 450
SIC 5181 5182 5149 Beer & other fermented malt liquors; Wine; Liquor; Juices; Mineral or spring water bottling
Ch Bd: John Anderson
*Pr: Michael Shibuya
Genl Mgr: Eugene Yamashiro

D-U-N-S 06-763-1382
PARADISE VALLEY HOSPITAL (CA)
2400 E 4th St, National City, CA 91950-2098
Tel (619) 470-4100 Founded/Ownrshp 1904
Sales 134.1MM EMP 1,200
SIC 8062 General medical & surgical hospitals
CEO: Alan Soderblom
*Ch Bd: Robert Carmen
*Ch Bd: Prem Reddy
*CEO: Luin Leon
Ofcr: Jon May
VP: Kurt Hoekendorf
VP: Sam Itani
Ex Dir: Katie Delmore
Ex Dir: Chad Mundy
Off Mgr: Marilyn Nicholson
Cmptr Lab: Brian Dixon

D-U-N-S 05-544-9482
PARADISE VALLEY UNIFIED SCHOOL DISTRICT
15002 N 32nd St, Phoenix, AZ 85032-4441
Tel (602) 867-5100 Founded/Ownrshp 1976
Sales 145.9MM^E EMP 3,600
Accts Heinfeld Meech & Co Pc P
SIC 8211 Public elementary & secondary schools
Pr: Julie Bacon
Prin: Sarah Hartley
Off Admin: Debbie Theiss
Dir IT: Dina Brulles
IT Man: Ginny Williams
Pr Dir: Anna Lieggi-Nadler
Psych: Julie Scott
Psych: Kathleen Wade
Psych: Satinder Walia
Psych: Holly Wertz

PARAGON CASINO RESORT
See TUNICA-BILOXI TRIBAL ECONOMIC DEVELOPMENT CORP

PARAGON CASINO RESORT
See TUNICA-BILOXI GAMING AUTHORITY

D-U-N-S 17-481-1695
PARAGON DEVELOPMENT SYSTEMS INC
P D S
13400 Bishops Ln Ste 190, Brookfield, WI 53005-6237
Tel (262) 569-5300 Founded/Ownrshp 1986
Sales 180.0MM EMP 290
SIC 5734 7379 Computer peripheral equipment; Disk & diskette conversion service
Pr: Craig Schiefelbein
*COO: Michael Grall
*CFO: Todd Adams
*CFO: Thomas Mount
VP: Ray Arndt
*VP: Rich King
*VP: Kerry Marti
*VP: John Miller
*VP: Chris Thorsen
VP: Anita Wietrzny
IT Man: Dave Harrold

PARAGON FOODS
See PARAGON WHOLESALE FOODS CORP

D-U-N-S 02-817-7830 IMP
PARAGON INDUSTRIES INC
BEDROSIAN'S TILES & STONE
4285 N Golden State Blvd, Fresno, CA 93722-6316
Tel (559) 275-5000 Founded/Ownrshp 1974
Sales 178.6MM^E EMP 500
SIC 5211 5032 Lumber & other building materials; Tile, ceramic; Brick, stone & related material; Tile, clay or other ceramic, excluding refractory
CEO: Larry E Bedrosian
CFO: Gardnar O'Brien
*Treas: Linda Bedrosian
*VP: Gary Bedrosian
Genl Mgr: Richie Mills
Opers Mgr: Eric Parker
Sales Asso: Diego Brenes
Sales Asso: Beatriz Gomez
Sales Asso: Russ Zitch

D-U-N-S 05-426-2969
PARAGON INDUSTRIES INC
3378 W Highway 117, Sapulpa, OK 74066-6987
Tel (918) 291-4459 Founded/Ownrshp 1981
Sales 125.0MM EMP 300
SIC 3317 Steel pipe & tubes
CEO: Derek Wachob
VP: Derrick Wachob
VP Sls: Doug Paschal

D-U-N-S 02-169-0045 IMP
PARAGON INTERNATIONAL INC (IA)
731 W 18th St, Nevada, IA 50201-7847
Tel (515) 382-8000 Founded/Ownrshp 1991
Sales 690.0MM EMP 40
SIC 3589 3556 3431 Asbestos removal equipment; Bakery machinery; Drinking fountains, metal
Plnt Mgr: Alan Webb
S&M/VP: Bruce Ludemann

D-U-N-S 60-924-4454 IMP
PARAGON MEDICAL INC
PIERCETON CASE & TRAY
8 Matchett Dr, Pierceton, IN 46562-9075
Tel (574) 594-2140 Founded/Ownrshp 1986
Sales 162.6MM^E EMP 820^E
Accts Baden Gage & Schroeder Llc
SIC 3089 3841 7371 Plastic containers, except foam; Thermoformed finished plastic products; Surgical & medical instruments; Computer software development & applications
Pr: Tobias W Buck
*COO: Gary Mc Gill
CFO: Maureen Adams
VP: Scott Anderson
Dir Bus: Rick Stetler
Dir IT: Mark Baker
VP Opers: Gary McGill
VP Opers: Clive Scott
Sfty Mgr: Diane Latral
Ql Cn Mgr: Brady Binnion
Ql Cn Mgr: Gregg Carpenter

PARAGON OFFSHORE LIMITED
See PARAGON OFFSHORE PLC

D-U-N-S 07-962-6171
PARAGON OFFSHORE PLC
PARAGON OFFSHORE LIMITED
(Suby of PARAGON OFFSHORE PLC)
3151 Briarpark Dr Ste 700, Houston, TX 77042-3809
Tel (832) 783-4000 Founded/Ownrshp 2014
Sales 1.1MMM^E EMP 2,625^E
SIC 1382 Oil & gas exploration services
Pr: Randall D Stilley
CFO: Steven A Manz
Sr VP: Lee M Ahlstrom
Sr VP: Andrew W Tietz
Sr VP: William C Yester
VP: Todd D Strickler
VP: Alejandra Veltmann
Board of Directors: Anthony R Chase, Thomas L Kelly II, John P Reddy, Julie J Robertson, Todd D Strickler, Dean E Taylor, William L Transier, David W Wehlmann

D-U-N-S 78-391-1217 IMP/EXP
PARAGON REHABILITATION INC
(Suby of CENTENNIAL HEALTHCARE CORP) ★
3100 West End Ave Ste 400, Nashville, TN 37203-5800
Tel (615) 345-2200 Founded/Ownrshp 1996
Sales 17.7MM^E EMP 1,000
SIC 8049 Physical therapist
Pr: David R Wilson
*CFO: Danny E Carpenter
Sys/Dir: Leigh Ann Thompson

D-U-N-S 17-535-7672
PARAGON SYSTEMS INC
(Suby of SECURITAS CRITICAL INFRASTRUCTURE SERVICES INC) ★
13655 Dulles Tech Dr # 100, Herndon, VA 20171-4634
Tel (703) 263-7176 Founded/Ownrshp 1983
Sales 360.0MM^E EMP 6,000
SIC 7381 7382 7374 Detective & armored car services; Security systems services; Data processing & preparation
CEO: Kevin M Sandkuhler
*Pr: Leslie Kaciban Jr
Bd of Dir: Robert Rubin
*VP: Grady Baker
VP: Phillip M Border
*VP: Ronald Cunigan
VP: Toney Davis
*VP: Ilene Reiter
IT Man: Matthew Kaciban

D-U-N-S 00-291-0933
PARAGON WHOLESALE FOODS CORP (PA)
PARAGON FOODS
173 Thorn Hill Rd, Warrendale, PA 15086-7527
Tel (412) 621-2626 Founded/Ownrshp 1957
Sales 129.2MM^E EMP 135
SIC 5148 5141 Fruits, fresh; Vegetables, fresh; Groceries, general line
CEO: Antonio Perez
*Pr: Elaine Bellin
Sr VP: Ron Becker
VP: Gloria Boyle
*VP: Jack W Crayne
VP: John McClelland
*VP: Andy Turner
VP Opers: Rich Mosgrove
Sales Exec: Shane Hall
Sales Asso: Carol Anderson
Sales Asso: Deb Burkintas

D-U-N-S 09-250-3221
PARALLEL INVESTMENT PARTNERS LLC
3889 Maple Ave Ste 220, Dallas, TX 75219-3917
Tel (214) 740-3600 Founded/Ownrshp 1999
Sales 134.6MM^E EMP 631
SIC 6211 Investment firm, general brokerage
Pt: F Barron Fletcher III
Bd of Dir: Jared Johnson

D-U-N-S 13-666-8386
PARALLELS INC
110 110th Ave Ne Ste 410, Bellevue, WA 98004-5861
Tel (425) 728-8239 Founded/Ownrshp 1999

Sales 111.5MM[E] *EMP* 750
SIC 7379 Computer related maintenance services
CEO: Birger Steen
Pr: Dmitri Poukhovski
CFO: David Arkley
CFO: Karin Sandsjo
Ch: Serguei Beloussov
Ex VP: Jack Zubarev
Sr VP: Jim Herman
Sr VP: Ken McGraw
Sr VP: Mauro Meanti
Sr VP: Oleg Melnikov
Sr VP: Stanislav Protassov
VP: Michael Erisman
VP: Jesper Frederiksen
VP: Kellie Green
VP: Kim Johnston
VP: Nancy Norton
Board of Directors: Bertrand Serlet

D-U-N-S 05-536-9639
■ PARALLON BUSINESS SOLUTIONS LLC
PARALLON WORKFORCE SOLUTIONS
(*Suby of* HOSPITAL COPORATION OF AMERICA) ★
6640 Carothers Pkwy, Franklin, TN 37067-6323
Tel (615) 344-3000 *Founded/Ownrshp* 2011
Sales 482.9MM[E] *EMP* 21,070
SIC 8082 Home health care services
Pr: Brendan Courtney
CEO: Curtis Watkins
Ex VP: Tom Fee
Ex VP: Kirk Richardson
Ex VP: Joe Roddy
Sr VP: Gail Sims
Assoc Dir: Dominique Minor
Assoc Dir: Miles Patterson
Dir Soc: Bethany Tate
Prin: John Guevara
Prgrm Mgr: Ron Frost

PARALLON WORKFORCE SOLUTIONS
See PARALLON BUSINESS SOLUTIONS LLC

D-U-N-S 05-736-4705
PARALYZED VETERANS OF AMERICA
P V A
801 18th St Nw Frnt 1, Washington, DC 20006-3532
Tel (202) 872-1300 *Founded/Ownrshp* 1945
Sales 152.8MM *EMP* 267
Accts Gelman Rosenberg & Freedman B
SIC 8399 7389 8641 Community action agency; Fund raising organizations; Civic social & fraternal associations
Pr: Bill J Lawson
**CFO:* John D Ring
Bd of Dir: Homer S Townsend Jr
Ofcr: Raul Acosta
Ofcr: John Allen
Ofcr: Nichelle Edwards
Ofcr: Brad Friez
Ofcr: Robert Kamei
Ofcr: Demarlon Pollard
Ofcr: Terry Thomas
**Sr VP:* Al F Kovach Jr
Assoc Dir: Alan Earl
Assoc Dir: Rodney Harris
Assoc Dir: Jessica Moreland
Assoc Dir: Aimee Schimmel

D-U-N-S 06-956-9168
PARAMETRIX INC
1019 39th Ave Se Ste 100, Puyallup, WA 98374-2115
Tel (206) 394-3700 *Founded/Ownrshp* 1974
Sales 90.0MM[E] *EMP* 575
SIC 8748 8711 8742 1389 4789 Environmental consultant; Sanitary engineers; Business consultant; Construction, repair & dismantling services; Cargo loading & unloading services
Pr: Jeff Peacock
**CFO:* Darlene Brown
**Treas:* Holli Moeini
**VP:* Diane Lenius
**VP:* Robin McManus
Comm Dir: Denise Ledingham
Prgrm Mgr: Heather Catron
IT Man: Geralyn Stonack
Mktg Mgr: Nicole Mackie
Mktg Mgr: Kami Matiatos

D-U-N-S 06-625-8377 IMP
PARAMIT CORP (CA)
18735 Madrone Pkwy, Morgan Hill, CA 95037-2876
Tel (408) 782-5600 *Founded/Ownrshp* 1990
Sales 88.0MM[E] *EMP* 287[E]
SIC 3841 Tonometers, medical
Pr: Balbir Rataul
**CFO:* Tom La Rose
VP Sls: Matt Davis
Board of Directors: William Rhodes

D-U-N-S 00-628-9128 IMP
PARAMOUNT APPAREL INTERNATIONAL INC
(*Suby of* PARAMOUNT HOLDING INC) ★
1 Paramount Dr, Bourbon, MO 65441-8309
Tel (573) 732-4411 *Founded/Ownrshp* 1946
Sales 154.5MM[E] *EMP* 835
SIC 2353 Hats: cloth, straw & felt; Caps: cloth, straw & felt
Ex VP: Alex Levinson
VP: Dennis Watz
**Prin:* Bruce Levinson
Off Mgr: Diane Vaughn
IT Man: Bobby Carrico
VP Opers: Todd Johnson
QC Dir: Pamela Volner
Mtls Mgr: Toni Vance
Sfty Mgr: Wendy Ferguson
Sfty Mgr: Renee Graven
Prd Mgr: James Hamel

PARAMOUNT ASPHALT
See PARAMOUNT PETROLEUM CORP

D-U-N-S 14-735-7565
PARAMOUNT BUILDING SOLUTIONS LLC
JMS BUILDING SOLUTIONS, LLC
10235 S 51st St Ste 185, Phoenix, AZ 85044-5227
Tel (480) 348-1177 *Founded/Ownrshp* 2003
Sales 154.2MM[E] *EMP* 2,800
SIC 7349 Janitorial service, contract basis
CEO: Glen Kucera
COO: Philip R Williams
Sls Dir: Louise Smith

PARAMOUNT CITRUS PACKING CO
See WONDERFUL CITRUS PACKING LLC

D-U-N-S 61-617-1237
■ PARAMOUNT COMMUNICATIONS ACQUISITION CORP
(*Suby of* VIACOM INC) ★
1515 Broadway Lbby, New York, NY 10036-8901
Tel (212) 258-6000 *Founded/Ownrshp* 2006
Sales NA *EMP* 8,000
SIC 6719 Investment holding companies, except banks
Sr VP: Rudolph Hertlein

PARAMOUNT CONFECTION CO
See MIAMI-LUKEN INC

D-U-N-S 14-223-0544
PARAMOUNT EQUITY MORTGAGE LLC
8781 Sierra College Blvd, Roseville, CA 95661-5920
Tel (916) 290-9999 *Founded/Ownrshp* 2003
Sales NA *EMP* 487[E]
SIC 6162 Mortgage bankers & correspondents
Pr: Hayes Barnard
VP: Kelly Resendez
Sls Mgr: Mike Cavanaugh
Sls Mgr: Dusty Dunaway
Sls Mgr: Michael A Ferreira
Sls Mgr: Alex Hughes
Sls Mgr: David Thorsen

PARAMOUNT FARMING
See WONDERFUL ORCHARDS LLC

PARAMOUNT FARMS
See WONDERFUL PISTACHIOS & ALMONDS LLC

PARAMOUNT FUNDING COMPANY
See VAN DYK MORTGAGE CORP

D-U-N-S 93-211-8755
PARAMOUNT FUNDING GROUP INC
212 E Ocean Ave, Lantana, FL 33462-3207
Tel (561) 586-6290 *Founded/Ownrshp* 1995
Sales NA *EMP* 25
SIC 6163 Mortgage brokers arranging for loans, using money of others
Pr: Timothy Atteberry

D-U-N-S 09-751-0903
PARAMOUNT GROUP INC
1633 Broadway Ste 1801, New York, NY 10019-6765
Tel (212) 974-1450 *Founded/Ownrshp* 1978
Sales 662.4MM *EMP* 200
SIC 6552 6531 Subdividers & developers; Real estate managers
Ch Bd: Albert P Behler
**CFO:* Wilbur Paes
Ex VP: Ted Koltis
**Sr VP:* Jolanta K Bott
**Sr VP:* Roger S Newman
Sr VP: David Spence
VP: Peter Brindley
VP: Ralph Diruggiero
VP: Matthew Gannon
VP: Gage Johnson
VP: Daniel Lauer
VP: Douglas Neye
VP: David Zobel

D-U-N-S 02-654-8193
PARAMOUNT HOLDING INC
1 Paramount Dr, Bourbon, MO 65441-8309
Tel (573) 732-4411 *Founded/Ownrshp* 1993
Sales 154.5MM[E] *EMP* 835
SIC 2353 Hats: cloth, straw & felt; Caps: cloth, straw & felt
Ch: Mark Rubenstein
**Pr:* Bruce Levinson

D-U-N-S 07-278-4523 IMP/EXP
■ PARAMOUNT PETROLEUM CORP
PARAMOUNT ASPHALT
(*Suby of* ALON USA ENERGY INC) ★
14700 Downey Ave, Paramount, CA 90723-4526
Tel (562) 531-2060 *Founded/Ownrshp* 2006
Sales 127.5MM[E] *EMP* 300
SIC 2911 Petroleum refining
CEO: W S Lovejoy
Ofcr: Jack Dougherty
Ofcr: Gail Harder
Sr VP: Craig Studwell
Sr VP: William L Thorpe
VP: Steve Farkas
VP: Ken Palmer
VP: William Winters
Exec: Bonnie Hall
CIO: Gary Grimes
Dir IT: Fred Hakimi

PARAMOUNT PICTURES
See PARAMOUNT TELEVISION SERVICE INC

D-U-N-S 00-698-8802 IMP/EXP
■ PARAMOUNT PICTURES CORP
PARAMOUNT STUDIOS
(*Suby of* VIACOM INC) ★
5555 Melrose Ave, Los Angeles, CA 90038-3197
Tel (323) 956-5000 *Founded/Ownrshp* 1912, 1994
Sales 330.9MM[E] *EMP* 1,847
SIC 7812 5099 4833 7829 Motion picture production & distribution, television; Motion picture production & distribution; Video cassettes, accessories & supplies; Television broadcasting stations; Motion picture distribution services
Ch Bd: Brad Grey
V Ch: Rob Moore
Pr: Fred T Gallo
Pr: Adam Goodman
Pr: Shana Levin
Pr: Dennis Maguire
Pr: David Stainton
COO: Frederick Huntsberry
CFO: Mark Badagliacca
Ex VP: Bob Bacon
Ex VP: Gaspare Benso
Ex VP: Stables Leeanne
Ex VP: Ellen Martello
Ex VP: Scott Martin
Ex VP: Thomas G McGrath
Ex VP: Al Rives
Ex VP: Lee Rosenthal
Ex VP: Bruce Tobey
Sr VP: Carmen Desiderio
Sr VP: Leslie Pound
Sr VP: Steve Selover
Board of Directors: Jonathan Dolgen

PARAMOUNT STUDIOS
See PARAMOUNT PICTURES CORP

PARAMOUNT TELEVISION DIVISON
See DETROIT TELEVISION STATION WKBD INC

D-U-N-S 61-617-1369
■ PARAMOUNT TELEVISION SERVICE INC
PARAMOUNT PICTURES
(*Suby of* PARAMOUNT STUDIOS) ★
5555 Melrose Ave, Los Angeles, CA 90038-3989
Tel (323) 956-5000 *Founded/Ownrshp* 1977
Sales 14.0MM[E] *EMP* 1,800
SIC 7812 Motion picture production & distribution, television; Motion picture production & distribution
CEO: Brad Grey

D-U-N-S 08-389-8650
PARAMOUNT UNIFIED SCHOOL DISTRICT (CA)
15110 California Ave, Paramount, CA 90723-4378
Tel (562) 602-6000 *Founded/Ownrshp* 1885
Sales 64.9MM[E] *EMP* 1,500
SIC 8211 Public elementary & secondary schools
**Bd of Dir:* Linda Garcia
IT Man: Elvia Galicia

D-U-N-S 00-820-0081
PARAMUS BOARD OF EDUCATION INC
145 Spring Valley Rd, Paramus, NJ 07652-5347
Tel (201) 261-7800 *Founded/Ownrshp* 1922
Sales 88.8MM *EMP* 654
Accts Lerch Vinci & Higgins Llp F
SIC 8211 Public elementary & secondary schools
**Pr:* Gary Enrico
**VP:* Anthony Balestrieri
Board of Directors: Anthony Balestrieti, Mike Brown, Gary Enrico, Kathleen Igoe, Clare Petti, Frank Straka

D-U-N-S 06-979-5271
PARATA SYSTEMS LLC
2800 Meridian Pkwy, Durham, NC 27713-2203
Tel (919) 433-4400 *Founded/Ownrshp* 2001
Sales 149.7MM[E] *EMP* 500
SIC 3826 8733 Automatic chemical analyzers; Research institute
CEO: Dj Dougherty
**Pr:* Mark Longley
**Ex VP:* Jay Blandford
**VP:* Mindi McLendon
Genl Mgr: Scott Hollis
IT Man: Rick Harris
Tech Mgr: John Compton
Sftwr Eng: Adam Philyaw
Sftwr Eng: Tess Stamper
Ql Cn Mgr: Samantha Flood
Sls Dir: Patrick Hogan
Board of Directors: Emilie Ray

D-U-N-S 02-807-5117
■ PARBALL CORP
BALLYS LAS VEGAS
(*Suby of* HARRAHS) ★
3655 Las Vegas Blvd S, Las Vegas, NV 89109-4345
Tel (702) 967-4111 *Founded/Ownrshp* 2005
Sales 106.1MM[E] *EMP* 4,000[E]
SIC 7011 7999 6512 7521 7211 Hotels; Gambling establishment; Gambling machines, operation; Shopping center, property operation only; Parking lots; Laundry collecting & distributing outlet
Pr: Gary W Loveman
Pr: Bobbie Yee
Sr VP: David Zerfing

D-U-N-S 12-251-6305 IMP/EXP
PARBEL OF FLORIDA INC
(*Suby of* L'OREAL)
6100 Blue Lagoon Dr # 200, Miami, FL 33126-2086
Tel (305) 262-7500 *Founded/Ownrshp* 1991
Sales 105.7MM[E] *EMP* 222
Accts Pwc
SIC 5122 Perfumes; Cosmetics
Pr: Javier Lavarta
**Ch:* Yann Jaffre
**Prin:* Eric Tarral
Off Mgr: Cecila Posada

D-U-N-S 15-552-3801
PARC MANAGEMENT LLC
7892 Baymeadows Way, Jacksonville, FL 32256-7512
Tel (904) 732-7272 *Founded/Ownrshp* 2007
Sales 102.9MM[E] *EMP* 2,613[E]
SIC 7996 Kiddie park
COO: Marie Bell
VP: Krishelle Hancock
VP: Russell Melton
**Ex Dir:* Deborah D Drew

PARENT ASSISTANCE NETWORK
See GOOD SAMARITAN HOSPITAL

PARENT IS IMERYS USA
See NYCO MINERALS INC

D-U-N-S 05-479-3039 IMP
PAREX USA INC
(*Suby of* PAREXGROUP PARTICIPATIONS SAS)
4125 E La Palma Ave, Anaheim, CA 92807-1860
Tel (714) 778-2266 *Founded/Ownrshp* 1965
Sales 117.0MM[E] *EMP* 300
SIC 3299 5031 Stucco; Building materials, interior
Pr: Rodrigo Lacerda
COO: Chris Robinson
CFO: Nicolas Corcia
Dist Mgr: Kent Taylor
Genl Mgr: Bill Olsen
IT Man: Ben Bautista
IT Man: Dannie Castro
Plnt Mgr: Mario Arellano
Plnt Mgr: Wes Seis
Prd Mgr: Ron Hise
Natl Sales: Clint Anna

D-U-N-S 04-021-0627
▲ PAREXEL INTERNATIONAL CORP
195 West St, Waltham, MA 02451-1146
Tel (781) 487-9900 *Founded/Ownrshp* 1983
Sales 2.4MMM *EMP* 18,660[E]
Accts Ernst & Young Llp Boston Mas
Tkr Sym PRXL *Exch* NGS
SIC 8731 Commercial physical research; Biotechnical research, commercial
Ch Bd: Josef H Von Rickenbach
Pr: Mark A Goldberg
CFO: Ingo Bank
CFO: Emma Reeve
Ofcr: Michelle Graham
Ofcr: Sy Pretorius
Ofcr: Ulf Schneider
Sr VP: Douglas A Batt
Sr VP: Christian Dreger
Sr VP: Joshua Schultz
VP: Joseph Avellone
VP: Mary Backstrom
VP: Mary Bareilles
VP: Michael Brandt
VP: David Brown
VP: Anita Cooper
VP: Joachim Heinrich
VP: Judith Millard
VP: Terry Munson
VP: Kurt Norris
VP: Lisa Rahilly
Board of Directors: A Dana Callow Jr, Eduard E Holdener, Christopher J Lindop, Richard L Love, Ellen M Zane

D-U-N-S 83-328-4305
■ PAREXEL INTERNATIONAL LLC
(*Suby of* PAREXEL INTERNATIONAL CORP) ★
195 West St, Waltham, MA 02451-1146
Tel (781) 487-9900 *Founded/Ownrshp* 2000
Sales 34.2MM[E] *EMP* 15,000
SIC 8731 Commercial physical research
Top Exec: Hady Khoury
VP: Susan Alexander
VP: Jacque Fisher
Off Admin: Erin Gleason
IT Man: Dennis Granger
IT Man: Russell Stead
Opers Mgr: Samantha Hurley
Doctor: Radmila Kanceva
Corp Couns: Beverley Crump
Snr PM: Alexander Artyomenko

D-U-N-S 36-129-9733 IMP
PARI ROBOTICS INC
(*Suby of* PRECISION AUTOMATION AND ROBOTICS INDIA LIMITED)
2930 Technology Dr, Rochester Hills, MI 48309-3588
Tel (248) 377-4447 *Founded/Ownrshp* 2001
Sales 126.8MM[E] *EMP* 12[E]
SIC 5084 Robots, industrial
CEO: Ranjit Date
**COO:* Mangesh Kale
Top Exec: Pari World
Snr Mgr: Renee Compeau
Snr Mgr: Prasad Deshpande

D-U-N-S 14-786-0993
■ PARIBAS PROPERTIES INC
(*Suby of* BNP PARIBAS)
787 7th Ave Fl 33, New York, NY 10019-6018
Tel (212) 841-3000 *Founded/Ownrshp* 1960
Sales 446.7MM[E] *EMP* 1,700
SIC 6211 6221 6799 8742 Brokers, security; Dealers, security; Futures brokers & dealers, commodity; Real estate investors, except property operators; Industrial consultant
COO: Philippe Bordenave
**CEO:* Everet Schenk
COO: Larry Sobin
**CFO:* Donna Kiernan
VP: Thomas Marcot

D-U-N-S 09-548-4457
PARIC CORP
77 West Port Plz Ste 250, Saint Louis, MO 63146-3121
Tel (636) 561-9500 *Founded/Ownrshp* 1979
Sales 232.2MM *EMP* 291
Accts Mueller Prost St Louis Miss
SIC 1542 1541 Nonresidential construction; Commercial & office building, new construction; Specialized public building contractors; Institutional building construction; Industrial buildings & warehouses
Pr: P Joseph Mc Kee III
**Ch Bd:* Larry J Young
**Pr:* Keith Wolkoff
**CFO:* Joseph Gerwitz
**Sr VP:* Michael Rallo Sr
VP: Russ Bryant
**VP:* Todd Goodrich
VP: Joe McIlee
VP: Rebecca Wall
MIS Dir: Tim Hough
Dir IT: Pam Dotson

D-U-N-S 05-544-6348 IMP
PARIGI GROUP LTD
BABY PHAT GIRLZ
20 W 33rd St Fl 12, New York, NY 10001-3305
Tel (212) 736-0688 *Founded/Ownrshp* 1981
Sales 127.6MM[E] *EMP* 400
Accts Anchin Block & Anchin Llp Ne
SIC 5137 Sportswear, women's & children's
Ch Bd: Marco Srour
**CFO:* William Finkelstein
VP: Scott Ryan
**VP:* Morris Srour
Dir IT: Dan Keller
Sales Exec: Dina Mandelbaum

D-U-N-S 06-435-6231 IMP
PARIS CORP OF NEW JERSEY (NJ)
800 Highland Dr, Westampton, NJ 08060-5109
Tel (609) 265-9200 *Founded/Ownrshp* 1994
Sales 112.9MM^E *EMP* 90
SIC 5112 2752 5063 Computer paper; Business forms, lithographed; Commercial printing, offset; Batteries
Prin: Gerard Toscani
**CFO:* Bill Lomanno
CFO: William Lomanno
**Prin:* Sharon Hennelly
**Prin:* John Murray
**Prin:* Don Showmaker
Mktg Mgr: Brian Bell

D-U-N-S 02-079-2156
■ **PARIS LAS VEGAS**
PARIS LAS VEGAS HOTEL & CASINO
(*Suby of* HARRAHS) ★
3655 Las Vegas Blvd S, Las Vegas, NV 89109-4343
Tel (702) 946-7000 *Founded/Ownrshp* 2005
Sales 152.1MM^E *EMP* 4,000
SIC 7011 Casino hotel
Pr: David Hoenemeyer
**Pr:* Marrylin Winn
VP: Robin Riviera
Exec: Natasha Diamant
Exec: Jerry Grossman
IT Man: Jeffrey Petrick

PARIS LAS VEGAS HOTEL & CASINO
See PARIS LAS VEGAS

PARIS REGIONAL MEDICAL CENTER
See ESSENT PRMC LP

PARISH OF EAST BATON ROUGE
See CITY OF BATON ROUGE

D-U-N-S 07-263-0486
PARISH OF JEFFERSON
MAIN EXECUTIVE OFFICE
200 Derbigny St, Gretna, LA 70053-5850
Tel (504) 364-2600 *Founded/Ownrshp* 1825
Sales NA *EMP* 3,217
Accts Kushner Lagraize Llc Meta
SIC 9111 County supervisors' & executives' offices;
Pr: John Young
Ofcr: Rhonda P Collins
Ofcr: Eric Hunt
Ofcr: Tamika Smith
IT Man: Cynthia Austin
IT Man: Christopher Cox
Board of Directors: Aaron F Broussard, Nicholas P Giambelluca, Lloyd T Giardina, Donald R Jones, John Lavarine Jr, Edmond J Muniz Sr, T J Butch Ward

D-U-N-S 18-447-8936
PARIVEDA SOLUTIONS INC
2811 Mckinney Ave Ste 220, Dallas, TX 75204-8565
Tel (214) 777-4600 *Founded/Ownrshp* 2003
Sales 83.1MM^E *EMP* 300
SIC 8748 Business consulting
Pr: Bruce V Ballengee
CFO: James Kupferschmid
VP: Steve Cardwell
VP: Dbrav Dunkley
VP: Michael Evans
**VP:* Cyndi Flaugher
VP: Nathan Hanks
VP: Michael Hockridge
**VP:* John Humphrey
VP: Luther Miller
VP: Susan Paul
**VP:* Kerry Stover
VP: Liem Vu
Dir Soc: Carrie Beckner

PARK & RECREATION DEPT
See CITY OF SPOKANE

D-U-N-S 07-959-0220 IMP
PARK 100 FOODS INC
326 E Adams St, Tipton, IN 46072-2001
Tel (765) 675-3480 *Founded/Ownrshp* 1979
Sales 92.0MM^E *EMP* 300
SIC 2013 2032 2035 Frozen meats from purchased meat; Cooked meats from purchased meat; Soups, except seafood: packaged in cans, jars, etc.; Pickles, sauces & salad dressings
Ch: Jim Washburn
**Pr:* Gary Meade
**CFO:* Thom Bondus
**VP:* David Alves
Off Mgr: Crystal Harpring
Opers Mgr: Tom Sheehan
Plnt Mgr: Jorge Gonima
Plnt Mgr: Brian Lavengood
Plnt Mgr: Dan Ringlespaugh
Mktg Mgr: Robert Orr
Sls Mgr: Michael Taft

D-U-N-S 07-925-7150
PARK CLOVER SCHOOL DISTRICT
10903 Gravelly Lake Dr Sw, Lakewood, WA 98499-1341
Tel (253) 583-5494 *Founded/Ownrshp* 1940
Sales 58.2MM^E *EMP* 1,050
SIC 8211 Public elementary school; Public junior high school; Public senior high school; Kindergarten
Bd of Dir: Mary Carlisle
VP: Holly Shaffer
Dir Sec: Jay Cash
Cmptr Lab: Rob Collins
Pr Dir: Kim Prentice
Pr Mgr: Gary Sabol
Psych: America Fulmer

D-U-N-S 00-644-8369
PARK CONSTRUCTION CO
1481 81st Ave Ne, Minneapolis, MN 55432-1795
Tel (763) 786-9800 *Founded/Ownrshp* 1916
Sales 89.2MM *EMP* 200
Accts Cliftonlarsonallen Llp Minnea
SIC 1611 1622 1629 Highway & street construction; Grading; Highway & street paving contractor; Bridge construction; Land preparation construction; Dams, waterways, docks & other marine construction; Dam construction; Power plant construction
Ch Bd: Richard N Carlson
**Pr:* Jeff Carlson
**CFO:* John Hedquist
**VP:* Bruce Carlson
**VP:* Michael Christianson
**VP:* Michael Nottestad

D-U-N-S 06-346-1115 IMP/EXP
PARK CORP
6200 Riverside Dr, Cleveland, OH 44135-3132
Tel (216) 267-4870 *Founded/Ownrshp* 1948
Sales 565.6MM^E *EMP* 1,800
Accts Meaden & Moore Ltd Clevelan
SIC 3547 1711 3443 5084 6512 7999 Rolling mill machinery; Boiler maintenance contractor; Mechanical contractor; Boilers: industrial, power, or marine; Industrial machinery & equipment; Commercial & industrial building operation; Exposition operation
Ch Bd: Raymond P Park
**Pr:* Daniel K Park
**CFO:* Joseph J Adams
**VP:* Ricky L Bertrem
**VP:* Shelva J Davis
**VP:* Kelly C Park
Plnt Mgr: Tim Herbert

D-U-N-S 08-032-9783
PARK COVEY GAS LLC
(*Suby of* COVEY PARK II LLC) ★
8401 N Central Expy # 700, Dallas, TX 75225-4402
Tel (214) 548-6000 *Founded/Ownrshp* 2016
Sales 130.0MM *EMP* 28
SIC 4924 Natural gas distribution
Co-CEO: Alan Levande
Co-CEO: John D Jacobi

D-U-N-S 04-447-6224 IMP
▲ **PARK ELECTROCHEMICAL CORP**
48 S Service Rd Ste 300, Melville, NY 11747-2335
Tel (631) 465-3600 *Founded/Ownrshp* 1954
Sales 145.8MM *EMP* 451^E
Tkr Sym PKE *Exch* NYS
SIC 3672 3674 Printed circuit boards; Microcircuits, integrated (semiconductor)
Ch Bd: Brian E Shore
Pr: Christopher T Mastrogiacomo
CFO: P Matthew Farabaugh
Ex VP: Stephen E Gilhuley
VP: Mark A Esquivel
VP: Constantine Petropoulos
Board of Directors: Dale E Blanchfield, Emily J Groehl, Carl W Smith, Steven T Warshaw

D-U-N-S 09-661-4839
PARK GALENA INDEPENDENT SCHOOL DISTRICT
14705 Woodforest Blvd A, Houston, TX 77015-3259
Tel (832) 386-1000 *Founded/Ownrshp* 1920
Sales 237.6MM *EMP* 3,000
Accts Whitley Penn Llp Houston Tex
SIC 8211 Public elementary & secondary schools; Public junior high school; Public elementary school
Dir Sec: Bryan Clements
MIS Dir: Darlene Lovinggood
Pr Dir: Jonathan Frey
HC Dir: Michelle Epps
**Pgrm Dir:* Janis Gaul
**Pgrm Dir:* Carol Kent

D-U-N-S 06-997-6645
PARK GLENVIEW DISTRICT
1930 Prairie St, Glenview, IL 60025-2800
Tel (847) 657-3215 *Founded/Ownrshp* 1927
Sales 27.6MM *EMP* 1,000
Accts Lauterbach & Amen Llp
SIC 7997 7992 Membership sports & recreation clubs; Public golf courses
Ex Dir: Charles T Balling
Treas: William Moore

PARK HIGHLAND NURSING CENTER
See SSC ATHENS OPERATING CO LLC

D-U-N-S 09-674-1269
PARK HILL SCHOOL DISTRICT
7703 Nw Barry Rd, Kansas City, MO 64153-1792
Tel (816) 359-4040 *Founded/Ownrshp* 1954
Sales 152.4MM^E *EMP* 2,181
Accts Marr And Company Pc Kansas
SIC 8211 Public elementary school; Public junior high school; Public senior high school
Genl Mgr: Mary Carrier
CIO: Mike Reeb
Site Mgr: Stephanie Amaya

D-U-N-S 00-693-0531 IMP/EXP
■ **PARK HOTELS & RESORTS INC**
HILTON
(*Suby of* HILTON WORLDWIDE HOLDINGS INC) ★
7930 Jones Branch Dr # 700, Mc Lean, VA 22102-3388
Tel (703) 883-1000 *Founded/Ownrshp* 1946
Sales 1.9MMM^E *EMP* 7,640
SIC 7011 6794 Hotels & motels; Franchises, selling or licensing
Pr: Christopher J Nassetta
Pr: Martin Rinck
CFO: Phillip Gaye
**CFO:* Thomas C Kennedy
CFO: William Samenos
Ch: Edmond Ip
**Treas:* Sean Dell'orto
Bd of Dir: Tiffany Floyd
Bd of Dir: Susan Heinis
Bd of Dir: Pierre Middleton-Baez
Bd of Dir: Brenda Morgan-Davis
**Chf Inves:* Matthew Sparks
Ex VP: Kathryn Beiser
**Ex VP:* Madeleine A Kleiner
Ex VP: Richard Lucas
**Ex VP:* Matthew W Schuyler
Sr VP: J David Greydanus
**Sr VP:* Kevin Jacobs
Sr VP: Tom Potter
VP: Andrew Flack
VP: Robert G Harper

D-U-N-S 96-719-7703
■ **PARK HOTELS & RESORTS INC**
HILTON WORLDWIDE, INC.
(*Suby of* HILTON WORLDWIDE HOLDINGS INC) ★
755 Crossover Ln, Memphis, TN 38117-4906
Tel (901) 374-5000 *Founded/Ownrshp* 1988
Sales 206.1MM^E *EMP* 5,208^E
SIC 7011

PARK HYATT AVIARA RESORT
See AVIARA RESORT ASSOCIATES LIMITED PARTNERSHIP A CALIFORNIA LIMITED PARTNERSHIP

D-U-N-S 78-658-4131 IMP
PARK MANAGEMENT GROUP LLC
JAMESON INN
(*Suby of* LH INVESTMENTS LLC)
1825 Gillespie Way Ste 101, North Hollywood, CA 91601
Tel (404) 350-9990 *Founded/Ownrshp* 2012
Sales 119.3MM^E *EMP* 3,500
SIC 7011 Hotels & motels
CEO: Dan E Burdakin

D-U-N-S 17-728-7836
■ **PARK MOUNTAINEER INC**
MOUNTAINEER RACE TRACK RESORT
(*Suby of* MTR GAMING GROUP INC) ★
Hc 2, Chester, WV 26034
Tel (304) 387-8300 *Founded/Ownrshp* 1992
Sales 53.5MM^E *EMP* 1,700
SIC 7999 7011 7389 6512 Gambling establishment; Golf services & professionals; Resort hotel; Convention & show services; Theater building, ownership & operation
Pr: Edson R Arneault
**Treas:* John W Bittner Jr
Bd of Dir: Robert Bedner
**VP:* Chris Kern
VP: Alan Selp
Ex Dir: Maria A Catignani

D-U-N-S 04-088-7044
PARK NAPERVILLE DISTRICT
SPRINGBROOK GOLF COURSE
320 Jackson Ave, Naperville, IL 60540-5275
Tel (630) 848-5000 *Founded/Ownrshp* 1967
Sales 602.9M *EMP* 1,200
Accts Susan S Lewis Ltd Napervil
SIC 7992 7999 8322 8741 Public golf courses; Recreation services; Community center; Management services
Ex Dir: Barbara Heller
Treas: Bill Eagan
**Treas:* Mindy Munn
Ofcr: Fred Malayter
Ofcr: David White
**VP:* Steve Born
VP: Scott McKibbin
Exec: Nancy Thompson
**Ex Dir:* Ray McGury
Prgrm Mgr: Brock Atwell
Prgrm Mgr: Sara Cass

D-U-N-S 00-790-3818
■ **PARK NATIONAL BANK**
(*Suby of* PARK NATIONAL CORP) ★
50 N 3rd St, Newark, OH 43055-5548
Tel (740) 349-8451 *Founded/Ownrshp* 1909
Sales NA *EMP* 200
SIC 6021 National commercial banks
Ch: Dan Delawder
**Pr:* David Trautman
**CFO:* John W Kozak
Trst Ofcr: Lawrence E Green
**Sr VP:* Thomas J Button
**Sr VP:* Cheryl Snyder

D-U-N-S 16-125-0998
▲ **PARK NATIONAL CORP**
50 N 3rd St, Newark, OH 43055-5523
Tel (740) 349-8451 *Founded/Ownrshp* 1992
Sales NA *EMP* 1,793
Tkr Sym PRK *Exch* ASE
SIC 6021 National commercial banks
Pr: David L Trautman
**Ch Bd:* C Daniel Delawder
CFO: Brady T Burt

D-U-N-S 07-176-7966
PARK NICOLLET CLINIC
(*Suby of* HEALTH SYSTEMS MINNESOTA) ★
3800 Park Nicollet Blvd, Minneapolis, MN 55416-2527
Tel (952) 993-3123 *Founded/Ownrshp* 1892
Sales 85.4MM^E *EMP* 1,300
Accts Deloitte Tax Llp Minneapolis
SIC 8011 5912 5999 Clinic, operated by physicians; Drug stores; Medical apparatus & supplies
Ex VP: David K Wessner
**CEO:* David Abelson
CFO: Sheila Mc Millan
**CFO:* William F Telleen
**VP:* Rodney R Dueck MD
VP: Mark Skubic
Sfty Mgr: Teresa Tice
Doctor: William D Borkon
Doctor: Marcia A Cron MD
Doctor: Daniel Freking MD
Doctor: Rachel Hub

PARK NICOLLET HEALTH SERVICES
See PARK NICOLLET METHODIST HOSPITAL

D-U-N-S 80-680-7780
PARK NICOLLET HEALTH SERVICES
HEALTH SYSTEMS MINNESOTA
3800 Park Nicollet Blvd, St Louis Park, MN 55416-2527
Tel (952) 993-3123 *Founded/Ownrshp* 1987
Sales 504.6MM^E *EMP* 4,500
SIC 8011 Offices & clinics of medical doctors
CEO: David K Wessner
Chf Rad: Kurt Simpson
**COO:* John W Herman
COO: Mary Johnson
COO: Michael B Kaupa
COO: Ted Wegleitner
**CFO:* David J Cooke
CFO: Sheila McMillan
Treas: Lori Ross
**Ex VP:* Michael Kaupa
**Sr VP:* Richard Migliori MD
**VP:* Julie Flaschenriem
**VP:* Laura Frazier
**VP:* Roxanna Gapstur
VP: Kathy Kallism
VP: Mark Skubic
Dir Rx: Erika Milne

D-U-N-S 04-178-7482
PARK NICOLLET METHODIST HOSPITAL
PARK NICOLLET HEALTH SERVICES
6500 Excelsior Blvd, Saint Louis Park, MN 55426-4702
Tel (952) 993-5000 *Founded/Ownrshp* 1892
Sales 489.9MM *EMP* 2,503
SIC 8062

D-U-N-S 06-310-3014
PARK NORTH LINCOLN-MERCURY INC
NORTH PARK
9207 San Pedro Ave, San Antonio, TX 78216-4499
Tel (210) 341-8841 *Founded/Ownrshp* 1982
Sales 104.6MM^E *EMP* 235
SIC 5511 Automobiles, new & used
Pr: Clarence Kahlig
**VP:* Billy Vaughn
CIO: Mike McNeilike

D-U-N-S 06-997-2958
PARK PALATINE DISTRICT
250 E Wood St, Palatine, IL 60067-5358
Tel (847) 991-0333 *Founded/Ownrshp* 1945
Sales 32.1MM^E *EMP* 1,100
SIC 7999

D-U-N-S 18-052-1932
PARK PLACE MOTORCARS LTD
6113 Lemmon Ave, Dallas, TX 75209-5715
Tel (214) 526-8701 *Founded/Ownrshp* 1987
Sales 153.6MM^E *EMP* 317
SIC 5511 Automobiles, new & used
CEO: Ken Schnitzer
Pt: Neil Grossman
Pt: Paul Morgan
Board of Directors: Park Place Motorcars of Te, Gen Partner

D-U-N-S 78-065-6492
PARK PLACE TECHNOLOGIES LLC
5910 Landerbrook Dr # 300, Mayfield Heights, OH 44124-6500
Tel (877) 778-8707 *Founded/Ownrshp* 1991
Sales 99.2MM^E *EMP* 390
SIC 7378 Computer maintenance & repair
CEO: Ed Kenty
Pr: Tony Susi
**COO:* Chris Adams
**Ex VP:* Mike Knightly
**Ex VP:* Hal Malstrom
**VP:* Judy Collister
VP: Scott Crosby
VP: Mark Middleton
**VP:* Ted Rieple
Genl Mgr: Christine Pesicka
**CTO:* Leo Vigeant

D-U-N-S 05-857-7946
PARK PLAZA HOSPITAL
5209 Chenevert St, Houston, TX 77004-5916
Tel (713) 527-5000 *Founded/Ownrshp* 1993
Sales 93.8MM *EMP* 2
SIC 6719 Investment holding companies, except banks
Pt: Russell C Moench

D-U-N-S 07-139-9062
■ **PARK PLAZA HOSPITAL INC**
RESPIRATORY CARE DEPARTMENT
(*Suby of* TENET HEALTHCARE CORP) ★
1313 Hermann Dr, Houston, TX 77004-7092
Tel (713) 527-5128 *Founded/Ownrshp* 1984
Sales 86.5MM *EMP* 20
SIC 8071 Medical laboratories
CEO: John Tressa
Dir Rad: David Blackburn
Dir Rad: Dennis Carlyle
Dir Rad: Susan Hightower
Dir Rad: Frank Pavlick
Dir Rad: Justin Quocly
Dir Rad: Edwin Rodriguez-Reyes
Sls&Mrk Ex: Donna Smith
Pharmcst: Tricia Teweleit

D-U-N-S 13-226-9197
PARK RDG APOTHECARIES
89 Genesee St, Rochester, NY 14611-3201
Tel (585) 368-3928 *Founded/Ownrshp* 2003
Sales 395.4MM *EMP* 4^E
SIC 5912 Drug stores & proprietary stores
Prin: Warren Hern
Dir Rad: Tad Dambrosio

PARK RIDGE HOSPITAL
See FLETCHER HOSPITAL INC

PARK RIDGE LIVING CENTER
See PARK RIDGE NURSING HOME INC

D-U-N-S 07-368-6933
PARK RIDGE NURSING HOME INC
PARK RIDGE LIVING CENTER
1555 Long Pond Rd, Rochester, NY 14626-4182
Tel (585) 723-7205 *Founded/Ownrshp* 1972
Sales 26.0MM *EMP* 1,000
SIC 8051 Skilled nursing care facilities
Pr: Tim McCormick
**Pr:* Sandra Mac Williams
**VP:* Joyce A Zimowski
Sfty Dirs: Debbie Laino
Mtls Mgr: Robert Donahue

PARK ST REFRIGERATED SERVICES
See G & C FOOD DISTRIBUTORS & BROKERS INC

D-U-N-S 78-788-0470
■ **PARK STERLING BANK**
(*Suby of* PARK STERLING CORP) ★
1043 E Morehead St # 201, Charlotte, NC 28204-2898
Tel (704) 370-2444 *Founded/Ownrshp* 2006
Sales NA *EMP* 86E
SIC 6036 State savings banks, not federally chartered
Pr: Bryan F Kennedy III
Pr: Emory Ware
Bd of Dir: Larry W Carroll
Ofcr: Joann Kirk
Ofcr: Stacy Wideman
Ex VP: Stephen A Arnall
Ex VP: Anne Hanson
Sr VP: Robert Faulkner
Sr VP: Tracey K Hill
Sr VP: Tim Howell
Sr VP: Barbara H Jacks
Sr VP: Jeffrey Kane
Sr VP: Cindy Pruitt
Sr VP: Michael Williams
VP: Judy Buchanan
VP: Tracey Fraley
VP: Barbara Jacks
VP: Daryle M Marr
VP: E McAdams
VP: Brian McDonnell
VP: Tracy S Porterfield
Board of Directors: Jean E Davis

D-U-N-S 96-560-6788
▲ **PARK STERLING CORP**
1043 E Morehead St # 111, Charlotte, NC 28204-2866
Tel (704) 716-2134 *Founded/Ownrshp* 2011
Sales NA *EMP* 584
Accts Dixon Hughes Goodman Llp Cha
Tkr Sym PSTB *Exch* NGS
SIC 6022 State commercial banks
CEO: James C Cherry
**Ch Bd:* Leslie M Baker Jr
**V Ch:* Kim S Price
Pr: John Channell
Pr: Robert Cowgill
Pr: Bryan F Kennedy III
CFO: David L Gaines
CFO: Donald K Truslow
Chf Cred: Robert Faulkner
Chf Mktg O: Angela Ross
Ex VP: Nancy J Foster
Sr VP: Mark S Ladnier
VP: Mandy R Arrowood
VP: Judy Buchanan
VP: Tracey Hill
VP: Richard York

D-U-N-S 07-302-7021
PARK UNIVERSITY
8700 Nw River Park Dr, Parkville, MO 64152-3795
Tel (816) 741-2000 *Founded/Ownrshp* 2001
Sales 81.1MM *EMP* 2,500
SIC 8221 College, except junior
Ch: Eugene Ruiz
**Pr:* Beverley Byers Pevitts
**CFO:* Dorla Watkins
**Treas:* Benny Lee
VP: Roger W Hershey
**VP:* Robert Martin
VP: Laurie McCormack

D-U-N-S 00-833-6393
PARK VIEW HOSPITAL
400 W 16th St, Pueblo, CO 81003-2745
Tel (719) 584-4556 *Founded/Ownrshp* 2001
Sales 313.1MM *EMP* 2
SIC 8741 Hospital management
Pr: C W Smith

D-U-N-S 01-948-3432
PARK WEST COMPANIES INC (NV)
TRACY & RYDER
22421 Gilberto Ste A, Rcho STA Marg, CA 92688-2104
Tel (949) 546-8300 *Founded/Ownrshp* 1997
Sales 86.2MME *EMP* 500E
SIC 0782 1629 6719 Landscape contractors; Golf course construction; Personal holding companies, except banks
**CEO:* Tom Tracy
**COO:* Jack Lantry
**Sec:* Jim Tracy
**VP:* Bart Ryder
S&M/VP: Paul Kapsch
Mktg Mgr: Chad Sivcovich

D-U-N-S 04-974-6014 IMP/EXP
▲ **PARK-OHIO HOLDINGS CORP**
6065 Parkland Blvd Ste 1, Cleveland, OH 44124-6145
Tel (440) 947-2000 *Founded/Ownrshp* 1998
Sales 1.4MMM *EMP* 5,000
Accts Ernst & Young Llp Cleveland
Tkr Sym PKOH *Exch* NGS
SIC 3462 3069 3567 3363 3631 3524 Iron & steel forgings; Internal combustion engine forgings, ferrous; Aircraft forgings, ferrous; Ordnance forgings, ferrous; Molded rubber products; Roll coverings, rubber; Rubber hardware; Rubber automotive products; Induction heating equipment; Aluminum die-castings; Barbecues, grills & braziers (outdoor cooking); Lawn & garden tractors & equipment
Ch Bd: Edward F Crawford
V Ch: James W Wert
**Pr:* Matthew V Crawford
CFO: W Scott Emerick
CFO: Patrick W Fogarty
CFO: Jeffrey L Rutherford
VP: Chad Cannan
VP: Don P Conkle
VP: Sean Elliott
VP: Scott Emerick
VP: Brian Murkey
VP: Jeffrey Rutherford
Exec: Sean Jackson

D-U-N-S 04-106-7752 IMP/EXP
■ **PARK-OHIO INDUSTRIES INC**
(*Suby of* PARK-OHIO HOLDINGS CORP) ★
6065 Parkland Blvd Ste 1, Cleveland, OH 44124-6145
Tel (440) 947-2000 *Founded/Ownrshp* 1984
Sales 1.4MMM *EMP* 5,000E
SIC 3462 3069 3567 3363 3524 Iron & steel forgings; Internal combustion engine forgings, ferrous; Aircraft forgings, ferrous; Ordnance forgings, ferrous; Molded rubber products; Roll coverings, rubber; Rubber hardware; Rubber automotive products; Induction heating equipment; Aluminum die-castings; Lawn & garden tractors & equipment
Ch Bd: Edward F Crawford
**Pr:* Matthew V Crawford
CFO: W Scott Emerick
Board of Directors: Patrick V Auletta, Kevin R Greene, A Malachi Mixon III, Dan T Moore, Ronna Romney, Steven H Rosen, James W Wert

D-U-N-S 15-289-4119 IMP/EXP
PARKDALE AMERICA LLC
PARKDALE1
531 Cotton Blossom Cir, Gastonia, NC 28054-5245
Tel (704) 864-8761 *Founded/Ownrshp* 1997
Sales 550.7MME *EMP* 2,128
SIC 2281 Polyester yarn, spun: made from purchased staple; Cotton yarn, spun; Carded yarn, spun
CEO: Anderson D Warlick
Ex VP: Charles Heilg
VP: Lee Thomas
**Prin:* W Duke Kimbrell
**Prin:* Anderson W Warlick
Plnt Mgr: George Cole
Plnt Mgr: Chris Sprinkle

D-U-N-S 00-315-6023 IMP/EXP
PARKDALE MILLS INC (NC)
531 Cotton Blossom Cir, Gastonia, NC 28054-5245
Tel (704) 864-8761 *Founded/Ownrshp* 1916
Sales 1.0MMME *EMP* 3,000
SIC 2281 2844 2241 Cotton yarn, spun; Polyester yarn, spun: made from purchased staple; Carded yarn, spun; Toilet preparations; Cotton narrow fabrics
Pr: Anderson W Warlick
**Ch Bd:* W Duke Kimbrell
**CFO:* Cecelia Meade
VP: John Nims
CIO: Troy Bush
Opers Mgr: Billy Lemmons
Plnt Mgr: Bill Tyler
Plnt Mgr: Charles Wilson
Genl Couns: Julia Singh
Board of Directors: J Carlton Fleming, George F Henry Jr

PARKDALE1
See PARKDALE AMERICA LLC

D-U-N-S 13-300-3348
PARKER ADVENTIST HOSPITAL
PORTERCARE ADVENTIST HOSPITAL
(*Suby of* PORTERCARE ADVENTIST HOSPITAL) ★
9395 Crown Crest Blvd, Parker, CO 80138-8573
Tel (303) 269-4000 *Founded/Ownrshp* 2004
Sales 241.1MM *EMP* 250
SIC 8062 General medical & surgical hospitals
Pr: Morre Dean
**Chf Mktg O:* Elizabeth Kincannon
Off Mgr: Pauline Robitaille
Doctor: Lowell J Greenwall

D-U-N-S 00-790-7850 IMP/EXP
▲ **PARKER DRILLING CO**
5 Greenway Plz Ste 100, Houston, TX 77046-0506
Tel (281) 406-2000 *Founded/Ownrshp* 1934
Sales 712.1MM *EMP* 2,567
Accts Kpmg Llp Houston Texas
Tkr Sym PKD *Exch* NYS
SIC 1381 7353 Drilling oil & gas wells; Oil equipment rental services; Oil field equipment, rental or leasing; Oil well drilling equipment, rental or leasing
Ch Bd: Gary G Rich
CFO: Christopher T Weber
Treas: David W Tucker
Ofcr: Jon-Al Duplantier
Sr VP: Philip L Agnew
Sr VP: David R Farmer
VP: Philip A Schlom
VP Bus Dev: John Gass
DP Dir: Anthony Gleason
IT Man: Parker Drilling
IT Man: Rigo Reyes
Board of Directors: Jonathan M Clarkson, George J Donnelly, Peter T Fontana, Gary R King, Robert L Parker Jr, Richard D Paterson, Roger B Plank, R Rudolph Reinfrank, Zaki Selim

D-U-N-S 13-139-7457
PARKER HOLDING CO INC
1428 W Danville St, South Hill, VA 23970-3904
Tel (434) 447-3146 *Founded/Ownrshp* 1979
Sales 136.6MME *EMP* 175
SIC 5171 5541 5983 Petroleum bulk stations; Filling stations, gasoline; Truck stops; Fuel oil dealers
Pr: Charles F Parker

PARKER HUNTER
See JANNEY MONTGOMERY SCOTT LLC

D-U-N-S 06-597-2069
PARKER JEWISH INSTITUTE FOR HEALTH CARE AND REHABILITATION FOUNDATION
27111 76th Ave, New Hyde Park, NY 11040-1423
Tel (516) 247-6500 *Founded/Ownrshp* 1968
Sales 97.9MM *EMP* 1,130
Accts Oconnor Davies Llp Harrison
SIC 8051 8082 8069 Skilled nursing care facilities; Home health care services; Alcoholism rehabilitation hospital
Pr: Michael N Rosenblut
VP: Ginger Portnoy
VP: Sylvia Williams
Prgrm Mgr: Andrea Gowie
Sls Dir: Leslee Mavrovic
Sls Mgr: Richard Gage
Sls Mgr: Jessie Hummel
Sls Mgr: Dan Pekny
Pharmcst: Setta Bijimenian
Pgrm Dir: Tara Buonocore-Rut

D-U-N-S 02-396-1055
PARKER OIL CO INC
SIMMONS TRUCK TERMINAL
(*Suby of* PARKER HOLDING CO INC) ★
1428 W Danville St, South Hill, VA 23970-3904
Tel (434) 447-3146 *Founded/Ownrshp* 1935
Sales 136.6MME *EMP* 175
SIC 5171 5541 5983 Petroleum bulk stations; Petroleum terminals; Gasoline service stations; Truck stops; Fuel oil dealers
Ch: Charles F Parker
**Pr:* Charles F Parker Jr
VP: Allen Lofton
Dist Mgr: Mike Tatum
Genl Mgr: Bill Hudson
Sfty Dirs: C Roberts

D-U-N-S 00-807-3009 IMP
PARKER SCHOOL UNIFORMS LLC
6300 W By Northwest Blvd # 100, Houston, TX 77040-4968
Tel (713) 957-1511 *Founded/Ownrshp* 2015
Sales 99.0MME *EMP* 375
SIC 2389

D-U-N-S 07-664-4087
PARKER SMITH & FEEK INC
INSURANCE BROKER
2233 112th Ave Ne, Bellevue, WA 98004-2936
Tel (425) 709-3600 *Founded/Ownrshp* 1937
Sales NA *EMP* 185
SIC 6411 6351 8748 Insurance agents & brokers; Surety insurance bonding; Employee programs administration
Pr: Greg Collins
**CFO:* Jaan Lumi
VP: Sally Borte
VP: Steven Brown
VP: John Claeys
VP: Gary Grosenick
VP: Gregor Hodgson
VP: Ron Lange
VP: Susan Larson
VP: Scott McGilvray
VP: Todd Miller
VP: Jeff Murphy
VP: Terry Reilly
VP: Ryan Roberts
VP: John Schmidt
VP: Mary E Stin
VP: James Waskom
VP: Todd Wheeler
VP: Walter Winter

D-U-N-S 00-417-5550 IMP/EXP
▲ **PARKER-HANNIFIN CORP**
6035 Parkland Blvd, Cleveland, OH 44124-4186
Tel (216) 896-3000 *Founded/Ownrshp* 1918
Sales 11.3MMM *EMP* 48,950
Tkr Sym PH *Exch* NYS
SIC 3594 3593 3492 3569 3053 3829 Fluid power pumps & motors; Fluid power pumps; Fluid power motors; Fluid power cylinders & actuators; Fluid power actuators, hydraulic or pneumatic; Fluid power cylinders, hydraulic or pneumatic; Control valves, fluid power: hydraulic & pneumatic; Hose & tube fittings & assemblies, hydraulic/pneumatic; Control valves, aircraft: hydraulic & pneumatic; Valves, hydraulic, aircraft; Filter elements, fluid, hydraulic line; Gaskets & sealing devices; Aircraft & motor vehicle measurement equipment
Ch Bd: Thomas L Williams
**Pr:* Lee C Banks
Pr: Yoon Chung
Pr: John R Greco
Pr: Kurt A Keller
Pr: Robert W Malone
Pr: Jennifer A Parmentier
Pr: Andrew D Ross
Pr: Roger S Sherrard
Pr: Andrew M Weeks
CFO: Jon P Marten
Ofcr: M Craig Maxwell
Ex VP: Mark J Hart
VP: Robert W Bond
VP: John G Dedinsky Jr
VP: William G Eline
VP: Joseph R Leonti
VP: Catherine A Suever
Board of Directors: James L Wainscott, Robert G Bohn, Linda S Harty, Robert J Kohlhepp, Kevin A Lobo, Candy M Obourn, Joseph M Scaminace, Wolfgang R Schmitt, Ake Svensson, James R Verrier

D-U-N-S 02-496-6892
PARKERJEWISH GERIATRIC INSTITUTE
27111 76th Ave, New Hyde Park, NY 11040-1436
Tel (718) 289-2100 *Founded/Ownrshp* 1998
Sales 109.9MM *EMP* 1
SIC 7389 Personal service agents, brokers & bureaus
Pr: David Glaser
CFO: James Langrock
VP: Sylvia Willia
IT Man: Rise Krome
VP Mktg: Richard Beitlich
VP Mktg: Judith Beizer
Sls Mgr: Jeffrey Turner
Sls Mgr: Greg Verdino

D-U-N-S 08-388-7307 IMP/EXP
PARKHOUSE TIRE SERVICE INC
5960 Shull St, Bell Gardens, CA 90201-6235
Tel (562) 928-0421 *Founded/Ownrshp* 1971
Sales 136.7MME *EMP* 375
SIC 5531

PARKHURST DINING SERVICES
See EATN PARK HOSPITALITY GROUP INC

D-U-N-S 07-248-0361
PARKING CO OF AMERICA INC
AIRPORT FAST PARK
250 W Court St Ste 200e, Cincinnati, OH 45202-1078
Tel (513) 241-0415 *Founded/Ownrshp* 1974
Sales 83.2MME *EMP* 1,000
SIC 7521

D-U-N-S 07-617-7203
PARKING CONCEPTS INC
TRANSPORTATION CONCEPTS
12 Mauchly Ste I, Irvine, CA 92618-6302
Tel (949) 753-7525 *Founded/Ownrshp* 1974
Sales 53.2MME *EMP* 1,500
SIC 6531

D-U-N-S 88-448-7331
PARKING SERVICE INC
180 N La Salle St # 1700, Chicago, IL 60601-2603
Tel (312) 819-5050 *Founded/Ownrshp* 1994
Sales 44.1MME *EMP* 1,700
SIC 7521 Parking garage; Parking lots
Pr: Thomas P Phillips
**Sec:* John Phillips

PARKING SLTIONS FOR HEALTHCARE
See PARKING SOLUTIONS INC

D-U-N-S 83-698-6919
PARKING SOLUTIONS INC
PARKING SLTIONS FOR HEALTHCARE
(*Suby of* TOWNE PARK LLC) ★
353 W Nationwide Blvd, Columbus, OH 43215-2311
Tel (614) 469-7000 *Founded/Ownrshp* 2016
Sales 30.0MME *EMP* 1,100
SIC 7299 Valet parking
Pr: Aaron D Shocket
Genl Mgr: Gwynn Haven
Genl Mgr: Rudy Touvell

PARKING SPOT, THE
See TPS PARKING MANAGEMENT LLC

PARKLAND ADMINISTRATIVE CENTER
See PARKLAND SCHOOL DISTRICT AUTHORITY

D-U-N-S 14-913-8658
PARKLAND COMMUNITY HEALTH PLAN
2777 N Stemmons Fwy, Dallas, TX 75207-2277
Tel (214) 266-2100 *Founded/Ownrshp* 1995
Sales 519.7MM *EMP* 2
Accts Bruce E Bernstein & Assoc Pc
SIC 8099 Medical services organization
CEO: Rob Smith
Assoc Dir: Paula Keblar

PARKLAND HEALTH & HOSPITAL SYS
See DALLAS COUNTY HOSPITAL DISTRICT

D-U-N-S 82-775-6110
PARKLAND HEALTH AND HOSPITAL SYSTEM AUXILIARY
(*Suby of* PARKLAND HEALTH & HOSPITAL SYS) ★
5200 Harry Hines Blvd, Dallas, TX 75235-7709
Tel (214) 590-4123 *Founded/Ownrshp* 2011
Sales NA *EMP* 9,500
Accts Bruce E Bernstien & Assoc Pc
SIC 9431 Administration of public health programs
Pr: Mary Ann Blome
**Treas:* Joe Meyer

D-U-N-S 62-398-6853
■ **PARKLAND MEDICAL CENTER**
(*Suby of* COLUMBIA HCA) ★
1 Parkland Dr, Derry, NH 03038-2746
Tel (603) 432-1500 *Founded/Ownrshp* 2006
Sales 108.5MM *EMP* 600
SIC 8062 General medical & surgical hospitals
CEO: Jeff Scionti
Chf Path: John Bissionette
Chf Rad: Daniel G Miner
COO: Angie Machi
**COO:* John Skevington
**CFO:* Jacob Wiesmann
Trst: Albert Northcutt
Ofcr: Thea Lacorte
Dir Lab: Catherine Ayres
Dir Rad: Brendon Meattey
Dir Rx: Marc Dupuis

D-U-N-S 09-536-6456
PARKLAND SCHOOL DISTRICT AUTHORITY
PARKLAND ADMINISTRATIVE CENTER
1210 Springhouse Rd, Allentown, PA 18104-2119
Tel (610) 351-5503 *Founded/Ownrshp* 1952
Sales 101.7MME *EMP* 1,500
SIC 8211 Public elementary & secondary schools
Treas: David Frederick
VP: Lisa Roth
Prin: Deborah Donnelly
Prin: Joan B Failla
Prin: David A Grim
Prin: Richard A Houck
Prin: Charles A Klein Jr
Prin: Carl G Tershak
Prin: Rodney R Troutman
Dir IT: Tracy Smith
Pr Dir: Nicole M McGalla

D-U-N-S 92-641-7809
■ **PARKRIDGE MEDICAL CENTER INC**
(*Suby of* HOSPITAL COPORATION OF AMERICA) ★
2333 Mccallie Ave, Chattanooga, TN 37404-3258
Tel (423) 698-6061 *Founded/Ownrshp* 1970
Sales 117.6MME *EMP* 1,364
SIC 8062 General medical & surgical hospitals
CEO: Darrie Moore
CFO: Jay St Pierre
VP: Mike Goins
Mtls Dir: Scott Sebring
Surgeon: John Johnston
Doctor: Adam Royer

PARKS PETROLEUM PRODUCTS
See R M PARKS INC

D-U-N-S 06-994-9931
PARKS XANTERRA & RESORTS INC
(*Suby of* XANTERRA INC) ★
6312 S Fiddlers Green Cir 600n, Greenwood Village, CO 80111-4943
Tel (303) 600-3400 *Founded/Ownrshp* 1996
Sales 350.7MM *EMP* 3,500
SIC 7011 5947 5812 Hotels; Gift shop; Restaurant, family: independent
Pr: Andrew N Todd

Pr: Robert Yow
VP: Hans Desai
VP: Chris Lane
VP: Kate A Longenecker
**VP:* Michael F Welch
Dir Risk M: Gretchen R Langston
Brnch Mgr: Laura Weirick
Genl Mgr: Daisy Hobbs
Genl Mgr: Alan Kerner
Genl Mgr: Charles Willis

PARKSAFE SYSTEMS
See METRO PARKING CORP

D-U-N-S 78-336-1483
PARKSIDE LENDING LLC
1130 Howard St, San Francisco, CA 94103-3914
Tel (415) 771-3700 *Founded/Ownrshp* 2005
Sales 94.0MM[E] *EMP* 60
SIC 6211 Mortgages, buying & selling
CFO: Hanford Chiu
Ex VP: Patty Gong
Ex VP: Chuck Wong
Sr VP: Linda Jacopetti
Rgnl Mgr: Fred Freeman
Off Mgr: Nancy Jo Brooks
Opers Mgr: Ronya Rjaile
Mktg Mgr: Robert Heggestad

PARKSITE GROUP
See PARKSITE INC

D-U-N-S 05-541-4296 IMP/EXP
PARKSITE INC
PARKSITE GROUP
1563 Hubbard Ave, Batavia, IL 60510-1419
Tel (630) 761-9490 *Founded/Ownrshp* 1971
Sales 127.2MM[E] *EMP* 300
SIC 5031 5162

PARKVIEW CENTER FOR REHABILITA
See PARKVIEW MEDICAL CENTER INC

D-U-N-S 07-359-7940
PARKVIEW COMMUNITY HOSPITAL MEDICAL CENTER
3865 Jackson St, Riverside, CA 92503-3919
Tel (951) 354-7404 *Founded/Ownrshp* 1980
Sales 159.7MM *EMP* 1,149
Accts Marcum Llp San Francisco Ca
SIC 8062 8011 General medical & surgical hospitals; Offices & clinics of medical doctors
Pr: Norm Martin
**CEO:* Doug Drumwright
Ofcr: Cheryl Daniels
Dir Rad: Carol Parker
Dir Rx: Ken Culver
Chf Nrs Of: Tom Santos
**Prin:* Alberta Glenn
**Prin:* J D Lansing
CIO: Brent Ciccarelli
Telecom Mg: John Day
Mktg Dir: Debbie Novellino

D-U-N-S 17-135-7606
PARKVIEW FOUNDATION INC
PARKVIEW HOSPITAL
2200 Randallia Dr, Fort Wayne, IN 46805-4638
Tel (260) 373-4000 *Founded/Ownrshp* 1987
Sales 830.5MM *EMP* 8[E]
Accts Crowe Horwath Llp South Bend
SIC 8062 General medical & surgical hospitals
CEO: Mike Packnett
Exec: Roland Hamilton
**Prin:* Mike Browning
CTO: Charles Mason
Tech Mgr: Anita Surfus
Opthamlgy: Donald A Bollheimer
Doctor: Gerry Easterday
Doctor: Lynda Otto
Doctor: Abhijit Shukla
Pharmcst: Ally Gaylor
Pharmcst: Andrew Hayes

D-U-N-S 01-329-2305
PARKVIEW HEALTH SERVICES OF NEW YORK LLC
(*Suby of* ANDERSON GROUP LLC) ★
1770 Colvin Blvd, Buffalo, NY 14223-1166
Tel (716) 876-2323 *Founded/Ownrshp* 2014
Sales 193.8MM[E] *EMP* 182[E]
SIC 5912 Drug stores & proprietary stores
CFO: Peter Rice
Genl Mgr: Paul O Leary
IT Man: Sean Rautenstrauch
Pharmcst: Lisa French
Pharmcst: Adam Huard

D-U-N-S 05-683-0037
PARKVIEW HEALTH SYSTEM INC
400 W 16th St, Pueblo, CO 81003-2745
Tel (719) 584-4000 *Founded/Ownrshp* 1923
Sales 49.2M *EMP* 1,900[E]
Accts Stockman Kast Ryan & Co Llp C
SIC 8062 7389 General medical & surgical hospitals; Fund raising organizations
Pr: Mike Baxter
**Pr:* C W Smith
**CFO:* William Patterson
**VP:* Bill Patterson

D-U-N-S 94-676-4958
PARKVIEW HEALTH SYSTEM INC
10501 Corporate Dr, Fort Wayne, IN 46845-1700
Tel (260) 484-6636 *Founded/Ownrshp* 1996
Sales 1.0MMM[E] *EMP* 7,107
Accts Crowe Horwath Llp South Bend
SIC 8741 8062 Hospital management; Nursing & personal care facility management; General medical & surgical hospitals
CEO: Mike Packnett
COO: Sue Ehinger
**COO:* Rick Henvey
COO: Matt Kien
**CFO:* Mike Browning
Sr VP: Christopher Stroud
VP: Philip Smith
VP: Donna Vanvlerah
Prac Mgr: Jim Dougal

Off Mgr: Terri Bell
Off Mgr: Donna Hawk

PARKVIEW HOSPITAL
See PARKVIEW FOUNDATION INC

D-U-N-S 06-470-3861
PARKVIEW HOSPITAL INC
PARKVIEW RESEARCH CENTER
(*Suby of* PARKVIEW HEALTH SYSTEM INC) ★
10501 Corporate Dr, Fort Wayne, IN 46845-1700
Tel (260) 373-4000 *Founded/Ownrshp* 1998
Sales 629.1MM *EMP* 4,500
SIC 8062 General medical & surgical hospitals
Pr: Mike Packnett
VP: Mike Browning

D-U-N-S 78-707-5407
PARKVIEW MEDICAL CENTER INC
PARKVIEW CENTER FOR REHABILITA
400 W 16th St, Pueblo, CO 81003-2781
Tel (719) 584-4000 *Founded/Ownrshp* 1924
Sales 285.7MM *EMP* 2,400
SIC 8062 8063

PARKVIEW RESEARCH CENTER
See PARKVIEW HOSPITAL INC

D-U-N-S 01-677-6531
PARKWAY AG CENTER INC (NC)
2801 Industrial Pkwy, Tarboro, NC 27886-1998
Tel (252) 823-5778 *Founded/Ownrshp* 1997
Sales 100.0MM *EMP* 22
SIC 5191 Farm supplies
VP: Jeff Webb
**Treas:* Bill Carstarphen
**VP:* Don Anderson

D-U-N-S 08-025-3331
PARKWAY C&A LP
1000 Civic Cir, Lewisville, TX 75067-3493
Tel (972) 221-1979 *Founded/Ownrshp* 2015
Sales 100.0MM *EMP* 150
SIC 1542 Commercial & office building contractors
Pt: John Elmer
Pt: Vaughn Hancock
Pt: Rick Wojciechowski
CFO: Melvin Chadwick

D-U-N-S 02-715-0895
PARKWAY CHEVROLET INC
25500 State Highway 249, Tomball, TX 77375-7730
Tel (281) 351-8211 *Founded/Ownrshp* 1979
Sales 142.6MM *EMP* 140
SIC 5511 7549 5531 Automobiles, new & used; Pickups, new & used; Vans, new & used; Automotive maintenance services; Automotive parts
Ch Bd: Jean W Durdin
**Treas:* Sharilyn Durdin
**VP:* Granger Durdin
Exec: Patty Werner
Genl Mgr: Chris Hughes
IT Man: Chrissy Lett
Sls Mgr: Todd Dickson
Sls Mgr: Michael Richey

D-U-N-S 07-976-6910
PARKWAY CONSTRUCTION & ARCHITECTURE LP
1000 Civic Cir, Lewisville, TX 75067-3493
Tel (972) 221-1979 *Founded/Ownrshp* 2015
Sales 100.0MM *EMP* 3[E]
SIC 1542 Commercial & office building contractors

D-U-N-S 05-788-6921
PARKWAY CONSTRUCTION & ASSOCIATES LP
1000 Civic Cir, Lewisville, TX 75067-3493
Tel (972) 221-1979 *Founded/Ownrshp* 1981
Sales 100.0MM[E] *EMP* 150
SIC 1542 Restaurant construction; Commercial & office building, new construction; Religious building construction; Commercial & office buildings, renovation & repair
Pt: Joe Elmer
CEO: Rick Wojciechowski
VP: Sean Broadbent
Dir Bus: Ryan Elmer
Snr PM: David Dotter
Snr PM: Ryan Fry

D-U-N-S 03-908-7978
PARKWAY PROPERTIES INC
390 N Orange Ave Ste 2400, Orlando, FL 32801-1679
Tel (407) 650-0593 *Founded/Ownrshp* 1996
Sales 473.9MM *EMP* 245[E]
SIC 6798

D-U-N-S 07-997-4769
PARKWAY SCHOOL DISTRICT
455 N Woods Mill Rd, Chesterfield, MO 63017-3385
Tel (314) 415-8100 *Founded/Ownrshp* 1954
Sales 19.0MM[E] *EMP* 2,300
SIC 8211 Public elementary & secondary schools
COO: Donna Volk
Ex Dir: Jan Misuraca
Dir Sec: Fred Crawford
Pr Dir: Paul Tandy

D-U-N-S 06-854-0350
PARKWAY SCHOOL DISTRICT PARENT-TEACHERS ORGANIZATION COUNCIL (MO)
455 N Woods Mill Rd, Chesterfield, MO 63017-3385
Tel (314) 415-8100 *Founded/Ownrshp* 1954
Sales 229.8MM *EMP* 2,300
Accts Kerber Eck & Braeckel Llp St
SIC 8641 Parent-teachers' association
Pr: Sandy Lohss

D-U-N-S 86-109-8499
PARKWEST MEDICAL CENTER
(*Suby of* COVENANT HEALTH) ★
9352 Park West Blvd, Knoxville, TN 37923-4387
Tel (865) 373-1000 *Founded/Ownrshp* 1999
Sales 337.2MM *EMP* 1,300
SIC 8062 General medical & surgical hospitals
Pr: Rick Laffiter
COO: Barbara Blevins

**COO:* Janice McKinley
**CFO:* Scott Hamilton
VP: Rhonda Crabtree
**Dir Sec:* Em Cobble
Nurse Mgr: Amanda Underwood
Mktg Mgr: Shelby Bowers

D-U-N-S 93-350-6599
PARKWEST MEDICAL CENTER
1420 Centerpoint Blvd, Knoxville, TN 37932-1960
Tel (865) 374-6872 *Founded/Ownrshp* 2008
Sales 346.4MM *EMP* 12[E]
SIC 8011 Medical centers
Prin: Stephen Sherlin

D-U-N-S 07-777-5435
PARMA CITY SCHOOL DISTRICT
5311 Longwood Ave, Parma, OH 44134-3800
Tel (440) 842-5300 *Founded/Ownrshp* 1931
Sales 117.2MM[E] *EMP* 1,575
Accts Mary Taylor Cpa
SIC 8211 Public elementary & secondary schools; High school, junior or senior
Genl Mgr: Tom Brahler
Teacher Pr: Edward Rashong

D-U-N-S 07-777-5278
PARMA COMMUNITY GENERAL HOSPITAL
7007 Powers Blvd, Parma, OH 44129-5437
Tel (440) 743-3000 *Founded/Ownrshp* 1956
Sales 180.9MM *EMP* 2,000
SIC 8062 General medical & surgical hospitals
Pr: Patricia A Ruflin
Chf Rad: Robert Jacobson
**CFO:* Barry Franklin
Ofcr: Donna Cortwright
VP: Richard Jacobs
VP: Mike Mainwaring
VP: Sharon Thomas
Dir Risk M: Lou Skolegsky
Dir Lab: Jim Economou
Ex Dir: Louana Peters
Dir Pat Ac: Anthony Granito

D-U-N-S 79-035-0248
PARMAN CAPITAL GROUP LLC
1000 La St Ste 5900, Houston, TX 77002
Tel (713) 751-2700 *Founded/Ownrshp* 2004
Sales 22.7MM[E] *EMP* 2,301
SIC 1389 7353 Testing, measuring, surveying & analysis services; Oil equipment rental services
Ch Bd: Hushang Ansary

D-U-N-S 78-131-6054
PARMAN ENERGY CORP
PARMAN LUBRICANTS COMPANY
7101 Cockrill Bend Blvd, Nashville, TN 37209-1005
Tel (615) 350-7447 *Founded/Ownrshp* 1989
Sales 160.7MM *EMP* 87
Accts Lattimore Black Morgan & Cain
SIC 5172 Petroleum products
Pr: Steve Moore
**Ch Bd:* Andrew D Crichton
**CFO:* David A Thomas
Treas: Rachel Mitchell
**VP:* Charles W Crichton
**VP:* John B Jewell III
**VP:* Lisa Kimbrough
Genl Mgr: Keith Pemberton
IT Man: Adam Covington
Opers Mgr: Robert Giffin
Opers Mgr: Colin Hockenberger

PARMAN LUBRICANTS COMPANY
See PARMAN ENERGY CORP

D-U-N-S 09-213-7459
PAROLE DIVISION TEXAS
PAROLE OFFICE
(*Suby of* TEXAS DEPARTMENT OF CRIMINAL JUSTICE) ★
209 W 14th St Ste 500, Austin, TX 78701-1614
Tel (512) 926-7570 *Founded/Ownrshp* 2004
Sales NA *EMP* 2,079
SIC 9223 Prison, government;

PAROLE OFFICE
See PAROLE DIVISION TEXAS

D-U-N-S 02-774-6619 IMP
PARR LUMBER CO
5630 Nw Century Blvd, Hillsboro, OR 97124-8620
Tel (503) 614-2500 *Founded/Ownrshp* 1930
Sales 319.7MM[E] *EMP* 558
SIC 5031 5211 5072 5251 Lumber, plywood & millwork; Building materials, exterior; Building materials, interior; Lumber & other building materials; Builders' hardware; Builders' hardware
Pr: James Boyer
**CEO:* David C Hamill
COO: Scott Coffey
**CFO:* Patrick Brophy
CFO: Steve Johnson
Exec: Mary Brophy
Genl Mgr: Marc Larry
Store Mgr: Brian Busey
Dir IT: Ken Munson
IT Man: Mike Jansen
Mktg Mgr: Renee Coffman

D-U-N-S 92-794-6566
PARRISH CONSTRUCTION GROUP INC
221 Industrial Park Dr, Perry, GA 31069-2428
Tel (478) 987-5544 *Founded/Ownrshp* 2001
Sales 111.9MM *EMP* 28
SIC 1542 Commercial & office building contractors
Pr: David Cyr
CFO: Jimmy Faircloth
Genl Mgr: Lucas Molina
Snr PM: Jim Fallon

PARRISH MEDICAL CENTER
See BREVARD NORTH COUNTY HOSPITAL

D-U-N-S 00-352-4204 IMP
PARRISH TIRE CO (NC)
PTC
5130 Indiana Ave, Winston Salem, NC 27106-2822
Tel (336) 767-0202 *Founded/Ownrshp* 1946, 1978
Sales 397.6MM[E] *EMP* 240

Accts Butler & Burke Llp Winston-Sa
SIC 5014 5531 7534 Tires & tubes; Automotive tires; Tire recapping
Pr: William L Jackson Jr
**CFO:* Charles M Everhart
**Treas:* Michael Everhart
**VP:* Bill Jackson
Store Mgr: Tony Dinkins
Sls Mgr: Jonathan Hoppes

D-U-N-S 06-668-7906
PARRISH-HARE ELECTRICAL SUPPLY LP
PH
1211 Regal Row, Dallas, TX 75247-3613
Tel (214) 905-1001 *Founded/Ownrshp* 1983
Sales 191.3MM[E] *EMP* 100
SIC 5063 Electrical fittings & construction materials; Cable conduit
Pr: Pat Hare
CFO: Randy Maxey
IT Man: Cheri Kemper
Opers Mgr: Becky Maberry
Sales Exec: Wes Butler

D-U-N-S 02-391-3908
PARSEC INC
PARSEC INTERMODAL CANNADA
1100 Gest St, Cincinnati, OH 45203-1114
Tel (513) 621-6111 *Founded/Ownrshp* 1982
Sales 197.0MM[E] *EMP* 1,506
SIC 4789 Cargo loading & unloading services
Pr: Otto Budig Jr
**VP:* George J Budig
Dir Risk M: Anne Tooley
Off Mgr: Barbara Seeman
Sfty Mgr: Lloyd Shadley
Opers Mgr: Jamie Hribar

PARSEC INTERMODAL CANNADA
See PARSEC INC

D-U-N-S 08-060-9639
PARSIPPANY-TROY HILLS TOWNSHIP SCHOOL DISTRICT
292 Parsippany Rd, Parsippany, NJ 07054-5104
Tel (973) 263-7200 *Founded/Ownrshp* 1928
Sales 111.7MM[E] *EMP* 1,600[E]
SIC 8211 9111 Public elementary school; Public junior high school; Public senior high school; Mayors' offices
**CFO:* Ronald Smith
Ex Dir: Anthony Giordano

D-U-N-S 07-935-7977
▲ PARSLEY ENERGY INC
303 Colorado St Ste 3000, Austin, TX 78701-4654
Tel (737) 704-2300 *Founded/Ownrshp* 2008
Sales 266.0MM *EMP* 212[E]
Tkr Sym PE *Exch* NYS
SIC 1311 Crude petroleum & natural gas
Ch Bd: Bryan Sheffield
COO: Matthew Gallagher
CFO: Ryan Dalton
VP: Mike Hinson
VP: Thomas B Layman
VP: Colin Roberts
VP: Brad Smith
VP: Paul Treadwell
Sfty Mgr: Retha Scott

D-U-N-S 07-911-1801
■ PARSLEY ENERGY LLC
(*Suby of* PARSLEY ENERGY INC) ★
500 W Texas Ave Ste 200, Midland, TX 79701-4216
Tel (432) 818-2100 *Founded/Ownrshp* 2013
Sales 125.0MM *EMP* 65[E]
SIC 1311 Crude petroleum & natural gas
**CFO:* Ryan Dalton
Exec: Katie Ball
Genl Couns: Colin Roberts

D-U-N-S 14-464-1321
PARSONS & WHITTEMORE ENTERPRISES CORP
4 International Dr # 300, Port Chester, NY 10573-1064
Tel (914) 937-9009 *Founded/Ownrshp* 1947
Sales 85.6MM[E] *EMP* 727
SIC 2611 Pulp mills
Ch Bd: George F Landegger
**CFO:* Steven Sweeney
**Treas:* Frank Grasso
**V Ch Bd:* Carl C Landegger

D-U-N-S 11-263-5537
PARSONS BRINCKERHOFF CONSTRUCTION SERVICES INC
(*Suby of* PARSONS BRINCKERHOFF GROUP LLC) ★
13530 Dulles Tech Dr # 100, Herndon, VA 20171-4641
Tel (703) 742-5700 *Founded/Ownrshp* 1979
Sales 158.3MM *EMP* 60
SIC 8741 Construction management
Pr: C Herndon
**Treas:* B N Peone
VP: Thomas Farrell III

D-U-N-S 02-789-9087
PARSONS BRINCKERHOFF GROUP LLC
(*Suby of* GROUPE WSP GLOBAL INC)
1 Penn Plz 2nd, New York, NY 10119-0002
Tel (212) 465-5000 *Founded/Ownrshp* 2014
Sales 491.6MM[E] *EMP* 9,039
SIC 8742 8711 8741 Management consulting services; Consulting engineer; Construction management
Ch Bd: Christopher Cole
CIO: Keith Zecchini
IT Man: Chad Brown
Ql Cn Mgr: Raymond Crawford

D-U-N-S 05-666-8700
PARSONS BRINCKERHOFF INC
P B
(*Suby of* GROUPE WSP GLOBAL INC)
1 Penn Plz Ste 200, New York, NY 10119-0002
Tel (212) 465-5000 *Founded/Ownrshp* 2014
Sales 1.4MMM[E] *EMP* 4,400
SIC 8711 8748 Consulting engineer; Environmental consultant
Pr: George Pierson

*Pr: Gregory A Kelly
*COO: Nick Flew
CFO: John Murphy
*CFO: Richard Shredder
*Treas: Stephanie Brickey
Sr VP: Patrick Drennon
Sr VP: Richard Earl
Sr VP: Neil Lucey
Sr VP: Richard Madenburg
Sr VP: Jim Rozek
VP: James Byrnes
VP: Michelle Ennis
VP: David R Gehr
VP: John Isley
VP: Michael J Kane
VP: Paul Mosier
VP: Mark Thompson
Dir Bus: Peter Button

D-U-N-S 18-810-8435
PARSONS BRINCKERHOFF INTERNATIONAL INC
(Suby of PARSONS BRINCKERHOFF GROUP LLC) ★
1401 K St Nw Ste 701, Washington, DC 20005-3430
Tel (202) 783-0241 Founded/Ownrshp 1975
Sales 183.4MM EMP 8,500
SIC 8711 Consulting engineer
CEO: Stuart C Glenn
*Treas: Matthew Bray
*Sec: Lisa M Palumbo

D-U-N-S 09-748-2863
PARSONS CONSTRUCTORS INC
OPERATIONS/RISK GROUP
(Suby of PARSONS CORP) ★
100 W Walnut St, Pasadena, CA 91124-0001
Tel (626) 440-2000 Founded/Ownrshp 1978
Sales 98.4MM[E] EMP 10,000
SIC 8741 8711 Management services; Engineering services
CEO: Chuck Harrington

D-U-N-S 03-086-6545 IMP/EXP
PARSONS CORP
100 W Walnut St, Pasadena, CA 91124-0001
Tel (626) 440-2000 Founded/Ownrshp 1985
Sales 846.7MM EMP 15,000
Accts Pricewaterhousecoopers Llp Lo
SIC 1629 1611 8711 8741 Chemical plant & refinery construction; Highway & street construction; Industrial engineers; Chemical engineering; Management services
Ch Bd: Charles L Harrington
V Ch: James R Shappell
*Pr: John A Scott
Pr: Carey A Smith
*CFO: George L Ball
Treas: Shelley Green
*V Ch Bd: Curtis A Bower
Ex VP: Thomas E Barron
*Sr VP: Maureen C Hayes
Sr VP: Bob Pearson
*Sr VP: Gary L Stone
Sr VP: James E Thrash
*VP: C Michael Armstrong
*VP: Molly C Broad
VP: David A Brown
VP: Jon Carder
VP: Frank Destadio
*VP: Leonard D Dorr
VP: Darrell Fernandez
VP: Ray Fulcher
VP: Paul Gallagher

D-U-N-S 03-115-1595
PARSONS ELECTRIC LLC
5960 Main St Ne, Minneapolis, MN 55432-5480
Tel (763) 571-8000 Founded/Ownrshp 2001
Sales 240.0MM EMP 690
SIC 1731 7382 8711 Electrical work; Security systems services; Electrical or electronic engineering
Pr: Joel Moryn
*CFO: Michael Northquest
*VP: Wendy Boosalis
VP: Steve Jandro
*VP: Dave Nielsen
*VP: Bill Olson
VP: William Olson
*VP: Steve Stone
Div Mgr: Monty Talbert
Div Mgr: Brian Wellens
Opers Mgr: Ryan Halvorson

D-U-N-S 04-308-8707
PARSONS ENGINEERING SCIENCE INC
(Suby of PARSONS GOVERNMENT SERVICES INC) ★
100 W Walnut St, Pasadena, CA 91124-0001
Tel (626) 440-2000 Founded/Ownrshp 1981
Sales 157.8MM[E] EMP 4,000
SIC 8711 Consulting engineer
CEO: Charles Harrington
*Pr: Mary Ann Hopkins
*Ex VP: Curtis A Bower
Sr VP: Brian Curin
*Sr VP: Nicholas L Presecan
*Sr VP: Gary L Stone
VP: Robert W Jones Jr
VP: Ken Miller
VP: Steve Shrive
Prin: Guy Thomas
VP Opers: David Datz

D-U-N-S 03-992-6154 IMP
PARSONS ENVIRONMENT & INFRASTRUCTURE GROUP INC
(Suby of PARSONS CORP) ★
4701 Hedgemore Dr, Charlotte, NC 28209-3281
Tel (704) 529-6246 Founded/Ownrshp 2000
Sales 861.3MM EMP 1,205
SIC 8711 Engineering services
Pr: Virginia L Grebbien
*CFO: Leslie Bradley
Bd of Dir: Zap Zlatoper
*Ex VP: Brent Harvey
VP: Phil Sciabarrasi
VP Admn: James Kyles
Sfty Mgr: Brad Barber

D-U-N-S 00-690-8511
PARSONS GOVERNMENT SERVICES INC
(Suby of PARSONS CORP) ★
100 W Walnut St, Pasadena, CA 91124-0001
Tel (626) 440-2000 Founded/Ownrshp 1978
Sales 319.5MM[E] EMP 4,000
SIC 8711 Engineering services; Designing: ship, boat, machine & product; Petroleum engineering; Chemical engineering
Ch Bd: Charles L Harrington
*Pr: Mary Ann Hopkins
Sr VP: Anthony F Leketa
*VP: Gary L Stone
*VP: Joseph M Zika
Exec: James Brookhouser
*Ex Dir: Thomas L Roell

D-U-N-S 03-826-7076
PARSONS GOVERNMENT SERVICES INC
(Suby of PARSONS CORP) ★
25531 Commercentre Dr, Lake Forest, CA 92630-8873
Tel (949) 768-8161 Founded/Ownrshp 2011
Sales 127.3MM[E] EMP 1,200
SIC 8731 Commercial physical research
CEO: Charles L Harrington
COO: Melissa Burnett
VP: Garth Bloxham
VP: Joe Hidalgo
VP: Sophie B O'Donnell
*VP: Sophie Odonnell
Exec: Frances Ely
Brnch Mgr: Benny Sharp
Div Mgr: David Eissler
Div Mgr: Steve Painter
CTO: John Dyer

D-U-N-S 00-102-6447
PARSONS GOVERNMENT SERVICES INTERNATIONAL INC
(Suby of PARSONS CORP) ★
100 W Walnut St, Pasadena, CA 91124-0001
Tel (626) 440-6000 Founded/Ownrshp 1969
Sales 408.1MM EMP 268
Accts Pricewaterhousecoopers
SIC 1542 Commercial & office building, new construction
Pr: Thomas L Roell
*Ex VP: Curtis A Bower
*Sr VP: Gary L Stone
VP: J Zlatoper

D-U-N-S 02-165-9412
PARSONS GOVERNMENT SUPPORT SERVICES INC
(Suby of PARSONS CORP) ★
1301 W President George B, Richardson, TX 75080-1140
Tel (972) 991-0800 Founded/Ownrshp 2013
Sales 35.6MM[E] EMP 3,000
SIC 8744 Base maintenance (providing personnel on continuing basis)
CEO: Chuck Harrington
*Pr: Mary Ann Hopkins
*Ex VP: George L Ball
*Sr VP: Clyde E Ellis Jr
*Sr VP: Michael K Loose
*Sr VP: Randy Morgan
*VP: David Larsen
IT Man: Justin Flowers

D-U-N-S 00-797-9396
PARSONS TRANSPORTATION GROUP INC (IL)
(Suby of PARSONS CORP) ★
100 M St Se Ste 1200, Washington, DC 20003-3520
Tel (202) 775-3300 Founded/Ownrshp 1919
Sales 142.0MM[E] EMP 2,500
SIC 8711 Engineering services
CEO: Charles L Harrington
*Pr: James Shappell
*CFO: Curtis A Bower
VP: George Ball
VP: Thomas E Barron
*VP: Gary L Stone
VP: Paul Thompson
Dir: R Desanto
Board of Directors: Curtis A Bower

D-U-N-S 06-186-2798
PARSONS TRANSPORTATION GROUP INC OF VIRGINIA
(Suby of PARSONS CORP) ★
1133 15th St Nw Ste 800, Washington, DC 20005-2716
Tel (202) 775-3300 Founded/Ownrshp 1929
Sales 948.1M[E] EMP 1,825
SIC 8711 Engineering services
Pr: Robert S O'Neil
*Ex VP: Curtis A Bower
*Ex VP: Clifford C EBY
VP: Michael R Christensen
VP: William H George
MIS Dir: John Carter
Snr PM: Gary Petersen

D-U-N-S 61-705-1813
PARSONS WATER & INFRASTRUCTURE INC
(Suby of PARSONS CORP) ★
100 W Walnut St, Pasadena, CA 91124-0001
Tel (626) 440-7000 Founded/Ownrshp 2003
Sales 71.6MM[E] EMP 1,522
SIC 8711 Engineering services
CEO: Virginia Grebbien
*Pr: Anthony F Leketa

PART OF SPECIAL METALS
See HUNTINGTON ALLOYS CORP

D-U-N-S 09-557-6989
■ **PARTECH INC**
(Suby of PARTECHNOLOGY CORP) ★
8383 Seneca Tpke Ste 2, New Hartford, NY 13413-4991
Tel (315) 738-0600 Founded/Ownrshp 1977
Sales 83.1MM[E] EMP 520
SIC 7373 Computer integrated systems design
CEO: Ronald J Casciano
Pr: Karen E Sammon
Ofcr: Bob Mooney
Sr VP: Christopher Haley
Sr VP: Karen Sammon
Sr VP: Tim Votaw
VP: Rick Franklin
Exec: Sam Hua
Software D: Yilin Yin

D-U-N-S 04-056-1511
PARTHENON CAPITAL PARTNERS
1 Federal St Fl 21, Boston, MA 02110-2003
Tel (617) 960-4000 Founded/Ownrshp 2011
Sales 227.8MM[E] EMP 1,386
SIC 6211 Investment firm, general brokerage
Co-Ownr: John C Rutherford
CFO: Victor Ditommaso
*CFO: Gerri H Grossmann
VP: Anthony Orazio
VP: Don Pannier
VP: Zachary F Sadek
VP: Bradley Sloan
Off Mgr: Molly Fazio

D-U-N-S 07-858-0899
PARTHENON DCS HOLDINGS LLC
4 Embarcadero Ctr, San Francisco, CA 94111-4106
Tel (925) 960-4800 Founded/Ownrshp 2003
Sales 25.5MM[E] EMP 1,400
SIC 8741 Management services

D-U-N-S 62-639-6444
PARTNER REINSURANCE CO OF US
(Suby of PARTNERRE LTD.)
1 Greenwich Plz Fl 3, Greenwich, CT 06830-6387
Tel (203) 622-1279 Founded/Ownrshp 1991
Sales NA EMP 177
SIC 6331 Property damage insurance
Pr: Costas Miranthis
*Pr: Scott Moore
*CFO: Bill Babcock
CFO: Thomas Smith
Top Exec: Stephen Smigel
*Ex VP: Thomas L Forsyth
*Sr VP: Maria V Amelio
VP: William Camperlengo
VP: Michael Covney
*VP: Laurie Desmet
*VP: Lisa A Fidelibus
VP: Yerger Morehead
VP: Michael Penney
VP: Joe Saydlowski
Assoc Dir: William Cadigan

D-U-N-S 96-596-0714
PARTNERRE US CORP
1 Greenwich Plz, Greenwich, CT 06830-6352
Tel (203) 485-4200 Founded/Ownrshp 2010
Sales NA EMP 201[E]
SIC 6411 Insurance agents, brokers & service
Prin: Robin Williams
V Ch: Francois Vilnet
Ex VP: John Hickey
Sr VP: Jorge Linero
Sr VP: Giuseppe Ruggieri
VP: Louis Benevento
VP: Robert Brian
VP: Andrew Cavazzini
VP: Michael D Covney
VP: Christina Cronin
VP: John Ferris
VP: Nick Giuntini
VP: Jorge Gonzalez
VP: Kenneth Graham
VP: John Klages
VP: Jim Konstanty
VP: Joseph Marcianti
VP: Michael J McDonald
VP: Richard Meyerholz
VP: David Molyneux
VP: Lewis Paul

D-U-N-S 14-446-3197 IMP
PARTNERS BOOK DISTRIBUTING INC
2325 Jarco Dr, Holt, MI 48842-1209
Tel (517) 694-3205 Founded/Ownrshp 1984
Sales 152.1MM[E] EMP 90
SIC 5192 Books
Pr: Vicky Lynn Eaves
*CFO: Tim Spalding
*VP: Samuel Speigel
Mktg Mgr: Gloria Genee

D-U-N-S 82-563-6988
PARTNERS HEALTHCARE SYSTEM INC
800 Boylston St Ste 1150, Boston, MA 02199-8123
Tel (617) 278-1000 Founded/Ownrshp 1994
Sales 11.6MMM EMP 67,000
SIC 8741 Hospital management
Pr: David Torchiana
Ch Bd: John M Conners Jr
CFO: Peter K Markell
VP: Leonard Debenedictis
VP: Lynne J Eickholt
VP: Brent L Henry
VP: David McGuire
VP: Rosemary Sheehan
Exec: Elena Muench
Dir Risk M: Timothy Murray
Comm Dir: Richard Copp
Dir Rad: Tina Maloney
Board of Directors: Katherine K Treadway MD, William E Caplan MD, Blenda J Wilson Phd, James I Cash Jr Phd, Steven D Fischman, Michael A Gimbrone MD, Arthur L Goldstein, Edward P Lawrence Esq, G Marshall Moriarty Esq, Terrence Murray, Gary Spiess

PARTNERS IN CARE
See NEW PARTNERS INC

D-U-N-S 07-963-7668
PARTNERS MEDICAL INTERNATIONAL INC
(Suby of PARTNERS HEALTHCARE SYSTEM INC) ★
100 Cambridge St Fl 20, Boston, MA 02114-2509
Tel (617) 535-6400 Founded/Ownrshp 1993
Sales 99.9M[E] EMP 1,014[E]
SIC 8741 Hospital management
Pr: Gilbert H Mudge Jr
*Treas: Peter K Markell

D-U-N-S 17-706-6792
PARTNERS NATIONAL HEALTH PLANS OF NORTH CAROLINA INC
(Suby of BLUE CROSS AND BLUE SHIELD NORTH CAROLINA) ★
5660 University Pkwy, Winston Salem, NC 27105-1312
Tel (336) 760-4822 Founded/Ownrshp 2002
Sales NA EMP 3,432
Accts Mcgladrey & Pullen Llp Ralei
SIC 6324 Dental insurance
Pr: James Broderick
*Treas: William S White

D-U-N-S 80-034-1237
PARTNERS PHARMACY LLC
(Suby of CARE ONE LLC) ★
50 Lawrence Rd, Springfield, NJ 07081-3121
Tel (908) 931-9111 Founded/Ownrshp 1998
Sales 279.2MM[E] EMP 650
SIC 5122 Pharmaceuticals
CEO: Patrick Downing
*Pr: Mindy Ferris
*VP: Marc Altholz

D-U-N-S 11-829-6628
PARTNERS SPECIALTY GROUP LLC
PARTNERS SPECIALTY INSUR SVCS
100 Tournament Dr Ste 214, Horsham, PA 19044-3602
Tel (484) 322-0400 Founded/Ownrshp 1999
Sales NA EMP 161
SIC 6411 Insurance agents, brokers & service
Ex VP: William Trumbower
VP: Joe De Francesco
VP: Layla Greytok
VP: Rick Lunney

PARTNERS SPECIALTY INSUR SVCS
See PARTNERS SPECIALTY GROUP LLC

D-U-N-S 62-377-6940
PARTNERSHIP FOR SUPPLY CHAIN MANAGEMENT INC
P F S C M
1616 Fort Myer Dr Fl 12, Arlington, VA 22209-3110
Tel (571) 227-8600 Founded/Ownrshp 2005
Sales 1.0MMM EMP 140
SIC 8399 Health systems agency
Ch Bd: Joel Lamstein
*Treas: Jonathan Quick
Ofcr: Ross Douthard
Ofcr: Andrew Schmidt
Ofcr: Mirela Smole
*Mng Dir: Richard C Owens
Rgnl Mgr: Juan Valladares

D-U-N-S 80-778-8344
PARTNERSHIP HEALTH PLAN OF CALIFORNIA
4665 Business Center Dr, Fairfield, CA 94534-1675
Tel (707) 863-4100 Founded/Ownrshp 1994
Sales NA EMP 290
Accts Moss Adams Llp San Francisco
SIC 6324 Hospital & medical service plans
CEO: Jack Horn
*COO: Liz Gibboney
*CFO: Gary Erickson
IT Man: Ben Jones

D-U-N-S 03-362-3740 IMP/EXP
PARTS AUTHORITY INC
CLEARWAY AUTO PARTS
495 Merrick Rd, Rockville Centre, NY 11570-5436
Tel (516) 678-3900 Founded/Ownrshp 1997
Sales 396.6MM[E] EMP 460
SIC 5013 5015 5531 Automotive supplies & parts; Automotive supplies; Motor vehicle parts, used; Automotive parts; Automotive accessories
CEO: Yaron Rosenthal
*Pr: Randy Buller
*CFO: David Wotman
VP: David Morris
*VP: Steven Yanofsky
CTO: Robert Pesiri
Software D: Reshedial Billar
Software D: Michael Morris
Netwrk Eng: Steve Spritzer
Site Mgr: Robert White
Natl Sales: Jeff Beiser

D-U-N-S 60-678-3561 IMP
PARTS DEPOT INC
401 Albemarle Ave Se, Roanoke, VA 24013-2323
Tel (540) 345-1001 Founded/Ownrshp 1998
Sales 119.5MM[E] EMP 1,450
SIC 5013 5531 Automotive supplies & parts; Automotive parts
Pr: Richard A Clark
*Pr: William Alexander
*CEO: Rollance E Olson
*VP: Bob Budzinski
*VP: Mark Noble
*VP: J Richard
Brnch Mgr: Tracy Brenson
Off Admin: Gabriella Shelden

THE PARTS DIVISION
See MID STATE AUTOMOTIVE DISTRIBUTORS INC

PARTS HOUSE, THE
See TPH ACQUISITION LLLP

PARTS PRO AUTOMOTIVE WAREHOUSE
See GTM SERVICE INC

D-U-N-S 16-229-2994 IMP/EXP
PARTS TOWN LLC
(Suby of PT HOLDINGS LLC) ★
1150 N Swift Rd Ste A, Addison, IL 60101-1453
Tel (708) 865-7278 Founded/Ownrshp 2004
Sales 99.3MM[E] EMP 220[E]
SIC 5084 Industrial machinery & equipment
Pr: Steve Snower
*CFO: Lori Sherwood
Sr VP: David Wenger
VP: Jeff Musur
Creative D: Maureen McKenzie
Dir Bus: Derek Knapp
Mktg Dir: Emanuela Franzone

PARTSCHANNEL DALLAS
See PARTSCHANNEL INC

D-U-N-S 13-032-7302 IMP
■ PARTSCHANNEL INC
PARTSCHANNEL DALLAS
(*Suby of* LKQ CORP) ★
4003 Grand Lakes Way # 200, Grand Prairie, TX 75050-0002
Tel (214) 688-0018 *Founded/Ownrshp* 2015
Sales 84.6MM[E] *EMP* 409
SIC 5013 Body repair or paint shop supplies, automotive
CEO: John M Palumbo
**Pr:* Ray Chen

D-U-N-S 83-363-8047 IMP
PARTSMASTER INC
(*Suby of* CHEMSEARCH DIVISION) ★
1400 E Northgate Dr, Irving, TX 75062-4716
Tel (972) 438-0711 *Founded/Ownrshp* 1973
Sales 221.8MM[E] *EMP* 1,800
SIC 5085 Industrial supplies
CEO: Matt Oldroyd
VP: Barry Williams
Sls Dir: Roy Levin

D-U-N-S 09-997-5109
PARTSSOURCE INC
777 Lena Dr, Aurora, OH 44202-8025
Tel (330) 562-9900 *Founded/Ownrshp* 2001
Sales 202.8MM[E] *EMP* 210
SIC 5047 Medical equipment & supplies
Pr: A Ray Dalton
COO: Rick Hopkins
CFO: Charlie Koch
Sr VP: Don Hubbard
VP: Dan Betting
Mng Dir: Allie Baylock

PARTY AMERICA
See PA ACQUISITION CORP

D-U-N-S 79-847-2221
■ PARTY CITY CORP
(*Suby of* AMSCAN HOLDINGS INC) ★
25 Green Pond Rd Ste 1, Rockaway, NJ 07866-2099
Tel (973) 453-8600 *Founded/Ownrshp* 2005
Sales 2.5MMM[E] *EMP* 4,100
SIC 6794 5947 7299 Franchises, selling or licensing; Gifts & novelties; Party planning service
Pr: Lisa Laube
**COO:* George Granoff
**COO:* Richard H Griner
**CFO:* Gregg A Melnick
VP: Bill Bub
VP: Jules Cohn
VP: Jeff Fink
VP: Billy Fowler
VP: Joseph Savini
**VP:* Steven Skiba
VP: Valerie Szymaniak
VP: Richard Yockelson

D-U-N-S 07-923-5575
▲ PARTY CITY HOLDCO INC
80 Grasslands Rd, Elmsford, NY 10523-1100
Tel (914) 345-2020 *Founded/Ownrshp* 1947
Sales 2.2MMM *EMP* 18,231[E]
Tkr Sym PRTY *Exch* NYS
SIC 5947 5963 5199 6794 Party favors; Party-plan merchandising; Party favors, balloons, hats, etc.; Franchises, selling or licensing
CEO: James M Harrison
**Ch Bd:* Gerald C Rittenberg
Pr: Gregg A Melnick
Pr: Ryan Vero
CFO: Michael Correale

D-U-N-S 15-079-6212
■ PARTY CITY HOLDINGS INC
(*Suby of* PC TOPCOL HOLDING) ★
80 Grasslands Rd, Elmsford, NY 10523-1100
Tel (973) 453-8600 *Founded/Ownrshp* 2004
Sales 3.9MMM[E] *EMP* 15,097
SIC 5947 6794 Gifts & novelties; Franchises, selling or licensing
Ch Bd: Robert J Small
**Pr:* Gregg A Melnick
**CFO:* Michael A Correale

D-U-N-S 07-542-9241 IMP
PARTY RENTAL LTD
275 North St, Teterboro, NJ 07608-1201
Tel (201) 727-4700 *Founded/Ownrshp* 1972
Sales 85.7MM[E] *EMP* 550
SIC 7359 Party supplies rental services
CEO: Michael Halperin
**Pr:* Gary Halperin
**CFO:* Alan Gottlich
**VP:* Barney Drew
**VP:* Neal Moran
Ex Dir: Jim McManus
MIS Dir: Amy Wisenbaker
Software D: Elie Hirschman
Software D: Jonathan Nunez
Trfc Dir: Carmen Perez
Opers Supe: Ivan Duran
Board of Directors: Michael Halperin

D-U-N-S 09-680-0578 IMP/EXP
■ PARTYLITE INC
(*Suby of* CARLYLE GROUP L P) ★
59 Armstrong Rd, Plymouth, MA 02360-4840
Tel (203) 661-1926 *Founded/Ownrshp* 1977, 2015
Sales 490.0MM *EMP* 1,600[E]
SIC 2023 3999 3641 5199 5023 Dietary supplements, dairy & non-dairy based; Candles; Potpourri; Electric lamps; Candles; Decorative home furnishings & supplies
CEO: Harry Slatkin
COO: Dan Chad
VP: Martin Cuddy
VP: Martin Hler
VP: Tammie King
VP: James Mannion
VP: Deb Tatlock
Mng Dir: Jennifer Messenger
CIO: Dennis Haltinner
Snr Mgr: Debbie Benham
Snr Mgr: Erica Wingard

D-U-N-S 10-797-5679 EXP
■ PARTYLITE WORLDWIDE LLC
(*Suby of* PARTYLITE INC) ★
600 Cordwainer Dr Ste 202, Norwell, MA 02061-1644
Tel (508) 830-3100 *Founded/Ownrshp* 2015
Sales 490.0MM[E] *EMP* 1,600
SIC 5199 Candles
CEO: Harry Slatkin
**Pr:* Robert B Goergen Jr
**Pr:* Kathleen Luce
Pr: Lisa Parketny
**COO:* Dan Chad
**CFO:* William Looney
Ofcr: Dennis Sera
Dir Soc: Alexandra Auer
Genl Mgr: Martin K Hler
VP Opers: Linda Ragle

D-U-N-S 78-244-9107 IMP/EXP
PAS TECHNOLOGIES INC
(*Suby of* KRG CAPITAL PARTNERS LLC) ★
1234 Atlantic Ave, North Kansas City, MO 64116-4142
Tel (816) 556-5113 *Founded/Ownrshp* 2006
Sales 101.7MM[E] *EMP* 500
SIC 7699 1389 Aviation propeller & blade repair; Lease tanks, oil field: erecting, cleaning & repairing
CEO: Thomas C Hutton
Pr: Daniel Adamski
**COO:* Dennis Orzel
**CFO:* Tim Puglielli
VP: Nancy Hitchins
Prgrm Mgr: Barry Minbiole
Genl Mgr: Luis Coreano
DP Exec: Wendall Waller
Tech Mgr: Kent Clay
Manager: Ray Bowen
Sls Mgr: Ian Macmillan

D-U-N-S 08-219-6171
PASADENA AREA COMMUNITY COLLEGE DISTRICT
PASADENA CITY COLLEGE
1570 E Colorado Blvd, Pasadena, CA 91106-2003
Tel (626) 585-7123 *Founded/Ownrshp* 1924
Sales 68.0MM[E] *EMP* 1,607
Accts Vavrinek Trine Day & Co Ll
SIC 8222 Community college
Pr: Paulette J Perfumo
Genl Pt: George Cynthia
**Pr:* Robert B Miller
Trst: Beth Wells-Miller
Ofcr: Jose L Arechiga
Ofcr: Alan Chan
Ofcr: Michael De Spain
Ofcr: Tyler Robins
Ofcr: Mary Walker
VP: Debra Cantarero
VP: Jacqueline W Jacobs
VP: Kindred Murillo
VP: Lisa Sugimoto

D-U-N-S 02-692-7608
■ PASADENA BAYSHORE HOSPITAL INC
BAYSHORE MEDICAL CENTER
(*Suby of* HOSPITAL COPORATION OF AMERICA) ★
4000 Spencer Hwy, Pasadena, TX 77504-1202
Tel (713) 359-2000 *Founded/Ownrshp* 1968
Sales 284.6MM *EMP* 1,200
SIC 8062 General medical & surgical hospitals
Netwrk Mgr: Eddie Garcia
Mktg Dir: Shebib Zaher
Pathlgst: Robin Brunnemann

PASADENA CITY COLLEGE
See PASADENA AREA COMMUNITY COLLEGE DISTRICT

D-U-N-S 06-668-3962
PASADENA HOSPITAL ASSOCIATION LTD
HUNTINGTON MEMORIAL HOSPITAL
100 W California Blvd, Pasadena, CA 91105-3010
Tel (626) 397-5000 *Founded/Ownrshp* 1932
Sales 569.3MM *EMP* 2,800
Accts Ernst & Young Us Llp Irvine
SIC 8062 8051 8063 General medical & surgical hospitals; Skilled nursing care facilities; Psychiatric hospitals
Ch: Lois Matthews
**Ch Bd:* Paul Ouyang
**Pr:* Stephen A Ralph
Ch: Christian Rutland
**Treas:* Leonard M Marangi
Treas: James Shankwiler
**Ex VP:* Jim Noble
**Sr VP:* Jane Haderlein
**Sr VP:* Bonnie Kass
**Sr VP:* Paula Verrette
VP: Nancy Greengold
VP: Debra Tafoya
VP: Raj Takhar
VP: Christopher Williams
Dir Lab: George Noujaim
Dir Lab: Paul Spivey
Dir Lab: Karen Watkins
Dir Rx: Jean Pallares

D-U-N-S 07-219-2925
PASADENA INDEPENDENT SCHOOL DISTRICT
PASADENA ISD
1515 Cherrybrook Ln, Pasadena, TX 77502-4099
Tel (713) 740-0000 *Founded/Ownrshp* 1895
Sales 522.1MM *EMP* 5,000
Accts Whitley Penn Llp Texas City
SIC 8211 Public elementary & secondary schools
Pr: Mariselle Quijano-Lerma
**VP:* Vickie Morgan
Adm Dir: Steve Devillier
Dir Sec: Stewart Russell
MIS Dir: Steven Wentz
Tech Mgr: Joe Hart
Instr Medi: Christine Van Hammersvel

PASADENA ISD
See PASADENA INDEPENDENT SCHOOL DISTRICT

D-U-N-S 18-416-6325 IMP/EXP
PASADENA REFINING SYSTEM INC
(*Suby of* PETROBRAS TRANSPORTE S/A - TRANSPETRO)
111 Red Bluff Rd, Pasadena, TX 77506-1530
Tel (713) 920-1874 *Founded/Ownrshp* 2006
Sales 223.3MM[E] *EMP* 384
SIC 2911 Petroleum refining
Prin: Fernando Oliveira
**Pr:* Francisco Neto
**CEO:* Fernando Feitosa De Oliveira
Treas: John Colling
Ofcr: Michael Tudorache
VP: Ron Chapman
Dir Lab: Pj Wille
Cmptr Lab: Gloria Gatlin
QA Dir: James Vinson
IT Man: Bill Domescik
Opers Mgr: Al Graves

D-U-N-S 06-383-8437
PASADENA TOURNAMENT OF ROSES ASSOCIATION
391 S Orange Grove Blvd, Pasadena, CA 91184-0001
Tel (626) 449-4100 *Founded/Ownrshp* 1890
Sales 102.0MM *EMP* 25
Accts Martin Werbelow Llp Pasadena
SIC 8641 Civic associations
Pr: Richard L Chinen
**COO:* Jeff Allen
**Ofcr:* Kevin R Ash
**Ex VP:* Ira Mike Matthiessen
**VP:* Laura V Farber
**VP:* Gerald K Freeny
**VP:* Robert B Miller
Dir Bus: Jane Smith
**Prin:* Sally M Bixby
**Ex Dir:* William B Flinn
**Ex Dir:* Scott McKibben

D-U-N-S 03-818-5682
PASADENA UNIFIED SCHOOL DISTRICT
PUSD
351 S Hudson Ave, Pasadena, CA 91101-3599
Tel (626) 396-3600 *Founded/Ownrshp* 1874
Sales 129.5MM[E] *EMP* 2,840
SIC 8211 Public elementary & secondary schools; Public elementary school; Public junior high school; Public senior high school
Dir Vol: Julia Marshall
**Pr:* Scott Phelps
Ofcr: Shelly James
VP: Amar Jha
**Prin:* Kim Kenne
Ex Dir: Fal Asrani
Off Admin: Marleni Martinez
IT Man: Bennett Kayser
Mktg Dir: Monica Lopez
Teacher Pr: Cy Chukwumezie
Teacher Pr: Kathleen Sanchez

D-U-N-S 19-170-6738
PASCAGOULA SCHOOL DISTRICT
1006 Communy Ave, Pascagoula, MS 39567-5664
Tel (228) 938-6491 *Founded/Ownrshp* 1909
Sales 57.5MM[E] *EMP* 1,180
SIC 8211 Public vocational/technical school
Pr Dir: Debbie Anglin
Teacher Pr: Cindy Brister
HC Dir: Polly Sumrow

PASCHAL HARPER
See ROBERT MADDEN INDUSTRIES LTD

PASCHALL TRUCK LINES
See INTERSTATE PERSONNEL SERVICES INC

D-U-N-S 06-297-5578
PASCHALL TRUCK LINES INC
(*Suby of* PASCHALL TRUCK LINES) ★
3443 Us Highway 641 S, Murray, KY 42071-7139
Tel (270) 753-1717 *Founded/Ownrshp* 1973
Sales 178.6MM[E] *EMP* 1,150
SIC 4213 Trucking, except local
Pr: Randall A Waller
CFO: John Hayman
CFO: Charles Wilson
Treas: Judy Ingersoll
Ex VP: Tom Stephens
VP: Tom Adams
VP: Barry Crutcher
VP: Dean Davis
VP: Greg Davis
VP: Greg Hester
VP: Bob Ingle
VP: Jeff Kramer
VP: Danny McElya
VP: Bobby Molnar
VP: Chip Norford
VP: Dan Rebosky
VP: Dan Smock
VP: Luther Waller
Comm Dir: Lynne Ochoa

D-U-N-S 07-979-8983
PASCO COUNTY SCHOOLS
7227 Land O Lakes Blvd, Land O Lakes, FL 34638-2826
Tel (813) 794-2651 *Founded/Ownrshp* 2015
Sales 150.0MM[E] *EMP* 19,687[E]
SIC 8211 Public elementary & secondary schools
Comm Man: Sue Zanatta
Dir IT: Barbara Trippiedi
Psych: Amelia Maseda
HC Dir: Lisa Kern

D-U-N-S 13-940-1376
PASCO SCHOOL DISTRICT 1
1215 W Lewis St, Pasco, WA 99301-5472
Tel (509) 546-2691 *Founded/Ownrshp* 1885
Sales 181.5MM *EMP* 2,400
SIC 8211 Public elementary school; Public junior high school; Public senior high school
Dir IT: Denny Dalafield
Dir IT: Jaime Morales
Schl Brd P: Sherry Lancon

D-U-N-S 04-957-7344
PASCO SHERIFFS OFFICE
(*Suby of* COUNTY OF PASCO) ★
8700 Citizens Dr, New Port Richey, FL 34654-5501
Tel (727) 847-5878 *Founded/Ownrshp* 1887
Sales NA *EMP* 1,100
SIC 9221 Sheriffs' offices
Exec: Eddie Daniels
Pr Dir: Kevin Doll

PASHA FREIGHT
See PASHA GROUP

D-U-N-S 01-139-1158 IMP/EXP
PASHA GROUP (CA)
PASHA FREIGHT
4040 Civic Center Dr # 350, San Rafael, CA 94903-4187
Tel (415) 927-6400 *Founded/Ownrshp* 1973, 1977
Sales 303.6MM[E] *EMP* 600
SIC 4731 Freight transportation arrangement
Ch Bd: George W Pasha III
**CFO:* James Britton
CFO: Glenn Yamaguchi
**Treas:* Steve Hunter
Sr VP: David Beckerman
**Sr VP:* Jeff Burgin
Sr VP: Missy Donnelly
Genl Mgr: Margaret Groth
Off Mgr: Mandy Garcia
Dir IT: Lisa Stewart
Mktg Dir: Michel Bechirian

D-U-N-S 05-060-2093
PASLIN CO (MI)
(*Suby of* ZHEJIANG WANFENG TECHNOLOGY DEVELOPMENT CO., LTD. ENGINEERING CENTER)
25303 Ryan Rd, Warren, MI 48091-3778
Tel (586) 758-0200 *Founded/Ownrshp* 1937, 2016
Sales 204.7MM[E] *EMP* 750
SIC 3548 3544 3545 Electric welding equipment; Jigs & fixtures; Machine tool accessories
CEO: Kirk Goins
VP: Ronald Pasque
Board of Directors: Chuck Pasque

D-U-N-S 00-222-8799 IMP/EXP
PASS & SEYMOUR INC (NY)
(*Suby of* LEGRAND HOLDING INC) ★
50 Boyd Ave, Syracuse, NY 13209-2313
Tel (315) 468-6211 *Founded/Ownrshp* 1901
Sales 333.8MM[E] *EMP* 1,328
SIC 3643 5731 Current-carrying wiring devices; Consumer electronic equipment
CEO: Halsey Cook
**CFO:* Steve Schneider
**Treas:* James Laperriere
Ex VP: Robert P Smith
**Sr VP:* Phil Leroux
VP: Patrick Davin
**VP:* Robert Julian
VP: Frederick Kandel
VP: Jack Wells
**Prin:* Steve Schoffstall
Natl Sales: Jamie Militi

D-U-N-S 07-980-6912
PASSAIC CITY PUBLIC SCHOOLS
101 Passaic Ave, Passaic, NJ 07055-4828
Tel (973) 470-5500 *Founded/Ownrshp* 2015
Sales 639.8M[E] *EMP* 1,512[E]
SIC 8211 Public elementary & secondary schools
MIS Dir: Amanuel Teklu
Teacher Pr: Zaida Polanco

D-U-N-S 06-427-9243
PASSAIC COUNTY COMMUNITY COLLEGE (INC)
PCCC
1 College Blvd, Paterson, NJ 07505-1102
Tel (973) 684-6868 *Founded/Ownrshp* 1971
Sales 40.1MM[E] *EMP* 1,400[E]
SIC 8222 8221 Community college; Colleges universities & professional schools
Pr: Steven M Rose
Ofcr: Maretta Hodges
Ofcr: Shirley McFarlane
Ofcr: Patricia Medieros
Ex VP: Margo Hollingsworth
**Sr VP:* Jacqueline Kineavy
**VP:* Maurice Feigenbaum
VP: Josephine Figueras
VP: Josephine Hernandez
VP: Jacquelyn Kanieady
Assoc Dir: Andrew Maceczek
Comm Man: Randall Lassiter

D-U-N-S 05-244-5210
PASSAIC METAL & BUILDING SUPPLIES CO
SIDING DEPOT
5 Central Ave Ste 1, Clifton, NJ 07011-2399
Tel (973) 546-9000 *Founded/Ownrshp* 1913
Sales 216.8MM[E] *EMP* 100[E]
SIC 5033 5031 5051 5075 3444 3296 Roofing & siding materials; Doors & windows; Doors; Windows; Sheets, metal; Air conditioning & ventilation equipment & supplies; Sheet metalwork; Mineral wool
Pr: Franklin S Gurtman
CFO: Steven Blankrot
**VP:* Michael Gurtman
Genl Mgr: Rick Hahn
Sales Asso: Barry Fishbane

D-U-N-S 06-581-6969 IMP
PASSAIC VALLEY SEWERAGE COMMISSION
PVSC
600 Wilson Ave, Newark, NJ 07105-4885
Tel (973) 344-1800 *Founded/Ownrshp* 1927
Sales 177.0MM[E] *EMP* 500
SIC 4952 Sewerage systems
Ex Dir: Michael Defrancisci
V Ch: Carl S Czaplicki Jr
COO: Bridget McKenna
CFO: Joseph Kelly
CFO: George F McGehrin
VP: Maher Demian

Ex Dir: Brian Christenson
Ex Dir: J Christiansen
Opers Supe: Jack Spoto
Genl Couns: Gregory A Tramontozzi

PASSAVANT AREA HOSPITAL
See PASSAVANT MEMORIAL AREA HOSPITAL ASSOCIATION

D-U-N-S 07-143-8667
PASSAVANT MEMORIAL AREA HOSPITAL ASSOCIATION
PASSAVANT AREA HOSPITAL
1600 W Walnut St, Jacksonville, IL 62650-1136
Tel (217) 245-4640 *Founded/Ownrshp* 1906
Sales 90.8MM *EMP* 1,800
Accts Ernst & Young Llp St Louis
SIC 8062 General medical & surgical hospitals
Pr: Doug Rahn
Chf Path: Mark Dolz
**CFO:* David Bolen
CFO: Terri Briggs
Dir Rx: Lori Smith
Ex Dir: Pam Martin
Mng Dir: Peter Russotto
Surgeon: Charles M Sheaff
Obsttrcn: Alexander M Hrynewych
Occ Thrpy: Todd Thorsen
HC Dir: Christine Evans

D-U-N-S 09-374-4360 IMP
PASSION GROWERS LLC
7499 Nw 31st St, Miami, FL 33122-1221
Tel (305) 935-6657 *Founded/Ownrshp* 2001
Sales 140.0MM^E *EMP* 130^E
SIC 5193 Flowers, fresh
**VP:* Samuel Ferrara

PASSPORT AUTOMOTIVE GROUP
See INTERNATIONAL MOTOR CARS INC

PASSPORT COLLECTION'S
See TWOS CO INC

PASSPORT HEALTH PLAN
See UNIVERSITY HEALTH CARE INC

PASSPORT HEATH PLAN
See UNIVERSITY HEALTHCARE INC

PASSPORT HLTH CMMNICATIONS INC
See EXPERIAN HEALTH INC

PASTA & CO
See SUGAR MOUNTAIN CAPITAL LLC

D-U-N-S 07-696-3578
PASTA HOUSE CO
700 N New Ballas Rd, Saint Louis, MO 63141-6716
Tel (314) 535-6644 *Founded/Ownrshp* 1974
Sales 71.0MM^E *EMP* 2,500
SIC 5812 5813 Restaurant, family: chain; Cocktail lounge
Pr: Kim Tucci
**VP:* Joseph Fresta
Off Mgr: Debbie Saxon

D-U-N-S 00-340-4832
PASTA POMODORO INC
1550 Bryant St Ste 100, San Francisco, CA 94103-4852
Tel (415) 431-2681 *Founded/Ownrshp* 2009
Sales 40.4MM^E *EMP* 1,000
SIC 5812 Italian restaurant
CEO: Matthew Janopaul
**CFO:* Girish Satya
Genl Mgr: James Richardson

PASTORAL CENTER
See ROMAN CATHOLIC DIOCESE OF CHARLOTTE

PAT CATAN'S CRAFT CENTERS
See DARICE INC

D-U-N-S 07-954-0875
PAT LAFRIEDA MEAT PURVEYORS INC
3701 Tonnelle Ave, North Bergen, NJ 07047-2421
Tel (201) 537-8210 *Founded/Ownrshp* 1970
Sales 120.0MM *EMP* 140
SIC 5147 Meats & meat products
CEO: Patrick Lafrieda Jr
Off Mgr: Jane Minati

D-U-N-S 00-656-2961
PAT SALMON & SONS INC (AR)
3809 Roundtop Dr, North Little Rock, AR 72117-2628
Tel (501) 945-0778 *Founded/Ownrshp* 1946
Sales 201.1MM^E *EMP* 1,800
SIC 4213

D-U-N-S 14-768-7727 IMP/EXP
PATAGONIA INC
GREAT PACIFIC PATAGONIA
(*Suby of* PATAGONIA WORKS) ★
259 W Santa Clara St, Ventura, CA 93001-2545
Tel (805) 643-8616 *Founded/Ownrshp* 1979
Sales 172.8MM^E *EMP* 1,000
SIC 2329 2339

D-U-N-S 07-034-6982
PATAGONIA SEAFARMS INC (FL)
7205 Corp Cntr Dr Ste 402, Miami, FL 33126
Tel (786) 693-8711 *Founded/Ownrshp* 2012
Sales 102.0MM^E *EMP* 7
SIC 5146 Fish & seafoods
Pr: Edgard Beyer
**CFO:* Hernan Arancibia
Sls Mgr: Alejandro Cabanellas

D-U-N-S 00-958-6835 IMP/EXP
PATAGONIA WORKS
259 W Santa Clara St, Ventura, CA 93001-2545
Tel (805) 643-8616 *Founded/Ownrshp* 1966
Sales 193.3MM^E *EMP* 1,000
SIC 5699 2339 2329 5961

D-U-N-S 07-464-8197
PATELCO CREDIT UNION
5050 Hopyard Rd, Pleasanton, CA 94588-3353
Tel (800) 358-8228 *Founded/Ownrshp* 1936
Sales NA *EMP* 650
SIC 6061 Federal credit unions
CEO: Erin Mendez
**CFO:* Sue Gruber
Chf Cred: Kenn D Darling
Sr VP: Jose Jimenez
**Sr VP:* Alison Jones
VP: Martin Doyle
VP: Mike Poirier
Adv Bd Mbr: Momina Foss
Rgnl Mgr: Deborah Regalia
Brnch Mgr: Theresa Bermudez
Brnch Mgr: Bernie Martinez
Board of Directors: Jeffrey Parks, Vickie Rath, Jesse Rivera, Tracey Scott, Gerald Upson

D-U-N-S 04-075-6769
PATERSON CITY OF (INC)
155 Market St Fl 2, Paterson, NJ 07505-1414
Tel (973) 321-1350 *Founded/Ownrshp* 1951
Sales NA *EMP* 1,701^E
Accts Donohue Gironda & Doria Bayo
SIC 9111 Executive offices
Counsel: Susan Champion

PATERSON DIOCESE CENTER
See ROMAN CATHOLIC DIOCESE OF PATERSON (INC)

D-U-N-S 07-930-5892
PATERSON PUBLIC SCHOOL DISTRICT
90 Delaware Ave, Paterson, NJ 07503-1804
Tel (973) 321-0980 *Founded/Ownrshp* 1902
Sales 584.2MM *EMP* 3,055
Accts Lerch Vinci & Higgins Llp F
SIC 8211 Public elementary & secondary schools
Teacher Pr: Jacqueline Jones
Dir Sec: James Smith
CTO: Abada Yacine
Teacher Pr: Marnie McKoy
HC Dir: Anna T Adams

D-U-N-S 93-035-4639
PATEWOOD MEMORIAL HOSPITAL
(*Suby of* GREENVILLE HEALTH SYSTEM) ★
175 Patewood Dr, Greenville, SC 29615-3570
Tel (864) 797-1000 *Founded/Ownrshp* 2007
Sales 118.1MM *EMP* 74^E
SIC 8062 General medical & surgical hospitals
Prin: Ken Skrzesz

D-U-N-S 10-371-3624
PATH
2201 Westlake Ave Ste 200, Seattle, WA 98121-2767
Tel (206) 285-3500 *Founded/Ownrshp* 1980
Sales 289.2MM *EMP* 12,000^E
Accts Gelman Rosenberg & Freedman B
SIC 8399 Health systems agency
CEO: Steve Davis
**Ch Bd:* George Gotsadze
**V Ch:* Dean Allen
COO: Jeffrey Brown
**COO:* Michael Kollins
**CFO:* Olivia Polius
Bd of Dir: Awa M Coll-Seck
Ofcr: Anton Luchitsky
Ofcr: Fay Venegas
VP: Erick Rabins
IT Man: Joe Vennarucci

D-U-N-S 04-001-2689
PATH FINDER SCHOOLS INC
JOHNSON APARTMENTS
425 E Trickey Ln, Jacksonville, AR 72076-5380
Tel (501) 982-0528 *Founded/Ownrshp* 2001
Sales 17.4MM^E *EMP* 1,400
SIC 6513 Apartment building operators

D-U-N-S 96-360-8372
PATHEON INC
(*Suby of* PATHEON HOLDINGS I B.V.)
4815 Emperor Blvd Ste 300, Durham, NC 27703-8470
Tel (919) 226-3200 *Founded/Ownrshp* 2014
Sales 922.2MM^E *EMP* 4,897^E
SIC 2834 Pharmaceutical preparations
CEO: James C Mullen
Pr: Gilles Cottier
**Pr:* Michael Lehmann
Ofcr: Pete McCullough
**Ex VP:* Aqeel Fatmi
**Ex VP:* Paul M Garofolo
Sr VP: Patrick Glaser
Sr VP: Steve Lam
**Sr VP:* Andrew G Long
Sr VP: Christopher Tama
VP: Harry Gill
VP: Linda Gottschalk
VP: Wendy McLawhorn

D-U-N-S 17-405-0377 IMP
PATHEON PUERTO RICO INC
(*Suby of* P R PATHEON LLC) ★
State Rd 670 Km 2/7 # 27, Manati, PR 00674
Tel (787) 746-8500 *Founded/Ownrshp* 2004
Sales 338.1MM^E *EMP* 1,798
SIC 2834 Pharmaceutical preparations
CEO: James C Mullen
Pr: Peter Bigelow
Treas: Brad Mitchell
Treas: Richard Stockmans
VP Mfg: Robert Salcedo

D-U-N-S 00-219-3829 IMP/EXP
PATHEON SOFTGELS INC
(*Suby of* PATHEON U.S. HOLDINGS INC.)
4125 Premier Dr, High Point, NC 27265-8144
Tel (336) 812-8700 *Founded/Ownrshp* 2012
Sales 143.4MM^E *EMP* 500^E
SIC 2834 Pharmaceutical preparations; Vitamin preparations
Ofcr: Karen McCollun
VP: Sal Fondaco
Telecom Mg: Kim Hillebrand
Prd Mgr: Carlos Herrera

D-U-N-S 05-470-3793 IMP
PATHFINDER ENERGY SERVICES LLC (LA)
(*Suby of* W-H ENERGY SERVICES LLC) ★
23500 Colonial Pkwy, Katy, TX 77493-3592
Tel (281) 769-4501 *Founded/Ownrshp* 1999
Sales 174.8MM^E *EMP* 800
SIC 1389 Oil field services

D-U-N-S 08-258-5514
PATHFINDER INC (AR)
2520 W Main St, Jacksonville, AR 72076-4214
Tel (501) 982-0528 *Founded/Ownrshp* 1971
Sales 44.8MM *EMP* 1,200
Accts Bkd Llp Little Rock Ar
SIC 8211 School for physically handicapped
Ch: Joan R Zumwalt

D-U-N-S 06-215-7045
PATHFINDER INTERNATIONAL
9 Galen St Ste 217, Watertown, MA 02472-4523
Tel (617) 924-7200 *Founded/Ownrshp* 1957
Sales 107.8MM *EMP* 628
Accts Cbiz Tofias Boston Ma
SIC 8322 Family counseling services
Pr: Purnima Mane
**CFO:* Mike Zeitouny
Treas: Susan Swift
Ofcr: Meggin Blanch
Ofcr: Jodi Diprofio
Ofcr: Colleen Fazio
Ofcr: Mahua Heath
Ofcr: Sarah Lance
Ofcr: Leila Percy
**Sr VP:* Caroline Crosbie
VP: Lee Gelb
**VP:* Demet Gral
VP: Demet Gural
VP: Anne Hale-Johnson
VP: Demet G Ral
**VP:* Scott Schroeder

D-U-N-S 00-697-4950
PATHMARK STORES INC
(*Suby of* A & P) ★
2 Paragon Dr, Montvale, NJ 07645-1718
Tel (866) 443-7374 *Founded/Ownrshp* 1966
Sales 2.3MMM^E *EMP* 22,400
SIC 5411 Supermarkets, chain
CEO: Eric Claus
Pr: Kenneth A Martindale
Pr: Frank Vitrano
Ex VP: Mark C Kramer
Sr VP: Joseph W Adelhart
Sr VP: Marc A Strassler
VP: Joseph W Adelhardt

D-U-N-S 17-382-3642
PATHOLOGY ASSOCIATES MEDICAL LABORATORIES LLC
P A M L
(*Suby of* PROVIDENCE HEALTH & SERVICES) ★
110 W Cliff Dr, Spokane, WA 99204-3614
Tel (800) 541-7891 *Founded/Ownrshp* 2010
Sales 100.3MM^E *EMP* 1,400
SIC 8071 Pathological laboratory
CEO: Francisco R Velzquez
**Ch Bd:* John Fletcher
**Ofcr:* Marguerite Busch
**Sr VP:* Rosalee Allan
**Sr VP:* Patty A Sipes
IT Man: Stephanie Filice
Sftwr Eng: Carol Walker
Netwrk Eng: Del Murphy
Sfty Mgr: Jolette M Barber
Opers Mgr: Larry Foss
Ql Cn Mgr: Craig Brown

PATHWAYS CMNTY BHVRAL HLTHCARE
See COMPASS HEALTH INC

D-U-N-S 08-856-1930
■ PATHWAYS HEALTH AND COMMUNITY SUPPORT LLC
PATHWAYS SM
(*Suby of* MOLINA PATHWAYS LLC) ★
10304 Spotsylvania Ave, Fredericksburg, VA 22408-8602
Tel (540) 710-6085 *Founded/Ownrshp* 2015
Sales 80.2MM^E *EMP* 3,573^E
SIC 8093 Mental health clinic, outpatient
CEO: Michael C Fidgeon

PATHWAYS SM
See PATHWAYS HEALTH AND COMMUNITY SUPPORT LLC

D-U-N-S 07-932-9678
■ PATIENT CARE INC
(*Suby of* AFAM ACQUISITION LLC) ★
300 Executive Dr Ste 175, West Orange, NJ 07052-3383
Tel (973) 243-6299 *Founded/Ownrshp* 2008
Sales 39.7MM^E *EMP* 2,013
SIC 8082 Home health care services
Pr: Bob Nixon
**CFO:* Ira Bergstein
VP: Larry Ball
VP: Gene Carbona
VP: Brad Goodman
VP: James Kincaide
VP: Brent Linkin
VP: Linda Novotny
VP: Dave Sanders
VP: Tony Wells
VP: Nicky Wilson

D-U-N-S 78-923-1495
PATIENT FIRST CORP
5000 Cox Rd Ste 100, Glen Allen, VA 23060-9263
Tel (804) 968-5700 *Founded/Ownrshp* 1981
Sales 267.3MM^E *EMP* 1,000
SIC 8741 Management services
**Pr:* Morison George H
**Sr VP:* Haug Charles C
**VP:* Dennis Hitchcock
VP: Austin Matthews
VP: Theresa Noe
**VP:* Eleanor N Robertson
Dir Rx: Michelle Niejadlik
Surgeon: Richard L Schroff Jr
Doctor: Michele Jones
Doctor: Scott Seaton
Doctor: Randy Sendow
Board of Directors: Jane Powell

D-U-N-S 02-122-2067
PATIENT SERVICES INC (VA)
PSI
3104 E Boundary Ct, Midlothian, VA 23112-3932
Tel (804) 744-3813 *Founded/Ownrshp* 1991
Sales 93.5MM *EMP* 95
Accts Keiterstephenshurstgary & Shre
SIC 8699 Charitable organization
Pr: Dana Kuhn
**Treas:* Christy Jones
Treas: Russell Phillips Jr
VP: James A Wood III
Mktg Dir: Josh Byrd

D-U-N-S 96-554-9350
PATIENT-CENTERED OUTCOMES RESEARCH INSTITUTE
1828 L St Nw Ste 900, Washington, DC 20036-5114
Tel (202) 827-7700 *Founded/Ownrshp* 2010
Sales 425.8MM *EMP* 220
SIC 8322 Individual & family services
Pr: Joe Selby
Ofcr: Emily Evans
Ofcr: Andrea Heckert
Ofcr: Rachel Hemphill
Ofcr: Julie McCormack
Ofcr: Sarita Wahba
Prin: Anne C Beal
Ex Dir: Joe V Selby
Dir IT: Mazen Atta-Allah
Genl Couns: Nadine Peters

PATINA RESTAURANT GROUP
See DNC LANDMARK HOLDINGS LLC

D-U-N-S 01-527-9982
PATRIARCH PARTNERS LLC
1 Broadway Fl 5, New York, NY 10004-1079
Tel (212) 825-0550 *Founded/Ownrshp* 2000
Sales 4.5MMM^E *EMP* 18,112
SIC 8741 Financial management for business
CEO: Lynn Tilton
Ofcr: Maggy Girgis
Ofcr: Miriam Reznik
Ofcr: Peter Ruffini
VP: Renee Dudley
VP: John Shkolnik
Dir IT: Carly Tilton
Snr Mgr: Kevin Berube

PATRICK CADILLAC/SAAB
See PATRICK SCHAUMBURG AUTOMOBILES INC

D-U-N-S 05-472-2210 IMP/EXP
PATRICK CUDAHY LLC (DE)
(*Suby of* MORRELL JOHN & CO) ★
1 Sweet Applewood Ln, Cudahy, WI 53110-1635
Tel (414) 744-2000 *Founded/Ownrshp* 1888, 1984
Sales 41.9MM^E *EMP* 1,900
SIC 2013 Sausages from purchased meat; Bacon, side & sliced: from purchased meat; Ham, boiled: from purchased meat; Lard from purchased meat products
Pr: Daniel Kapella
**Treas:* Steve Rodey
**Sr VP:* James Matthews
CTO: Joseph W Luter
Sfty Mgr: Mike Costella
Pr Mgr: Lori Adkins

D-U-N-S 06-600-6198
PATRICK HENRY HOSPITAL INC
WEST POINT CONVALSCENT
1000 Old Denbigh Blvd, Newport News, VA 23602-2017
Tel (757) 875-2000 *Founded/Ownrshp* 1983
Sales 27.0MM *EMP* 1,000
SIC 8052 8059 8051 Intermediate care facilities; Nursing home, except skilled & intermediate care facility; Convalescent home with continuous nursing care
Pr: Richard J Pearce
**Sr VP:* David Kete

D-U-N-S 01-627-2908
▲ PATRICK INDUSTRIES INC
CANA
107 W Franklin St, Elkhart, IN 46516-3214
Tel (574) 294-7511 *Founded/Ownrshp* 1959
Sales 920.3MM *EMP* 3,542
Tkr Sym PATK *Exch* NGM
SIC 3275 2493 2435 5031 5033 2891 Gypsum products; Reconstituted wood products; Fiberboard, other vegetable pulp; Plywood, hardwood or hardwood faced; Building materials, exterior; Building materials, interior; Doors & windows; Composite board products, woodboard; Roofing & siding materials; Insulation materials; Adhesives
Ch Bd: Paul E Hassler
Pr: Andy L Nemeth
CEO: Todd M Cleveland
COO: Kip B Ellis
CFO: Joshua A Boone
Ex VP: Jeffrey M Rodino
Board of Directors: Joseph M Cerulli, John A Forbes, Michael A Kitson, M Scott Welch, Walter E Wells

D-U-N-S 03-933-8876
PATRICK SCHAUMBURG AUTOMOBILES INC
PATRICK CADILLAC/SAAB
526 Mall Dr, Schaumburg, IL 60173-5104
Tel (847) 605-4000 *Founded/Ownrshp* 1979
Sales 124.5MM^E *EMP* 350
SIC 5511 7539 7538 7532 5531 5013

D-U-N-S 07-887-8820
PATRIOT INTERMEDIATE HOLDINGS B CORP
340 Madison Ave, New York, NY 10173-0002
Tel (212) 301-4000 *Founded/Ownrshp* 2013
Sales 376.7MM *EMP* 2,837^E
SIC 6719 Investment holding companies, except banks

D-U-N-S 07-954-1765
▲ PATRIOT NATIONAL INC
401 E Las Olas Blvd # 1650, Fort Lauderdale, FL 33301-4252
Tel (954) 670-2900 *Founded/Ownrshp* 2003
Sales NA *EMP* 1,145[E]
Accts Bdo Usa Llp Miami Florida
Tkr Sym PN *Exch* NYS
SIC 6411 Insurance agents, brokers & service
Ch Bd: Steven M Mariano
Pr: Michael R McFadden
COO: Robert J Peters
CFO: Thomas Shields
Ofcr: Lisa J Balmer
Ex VP: Timothy J Ermatinger
Ex VP: Armand Fernandez
Ex VP: Michael W Grandstaff
Ex VP: Judith L Haddad
Ex VP: Paul V Halter
Ex VP: Christopher A Pesch
Ex VP: Christopher L Pizzo
Board of Directors: Sean Bidic, James O'brien, Michael Purcell, Jeffrey Rohr, Austin J Shanfelter, Quentin P Smith, Charles H Walsh, Michael J Corey John R Del

D-U-N-S 07-994-5972
▲ PATRIOT TRANSPORTATION HOLDING INC
200 W Forsyth St Fl 7, Jacksonville, FL 32202-4349
Tel (904) 858-9100 *Founded/Ownrshp* 2015
Sales 120.1MM *EMP* 979[E]
Tkr Sym PATI *Exch* NGS
SIC 4212 Live poultry haulage
CFO: John D Milton Jr
VP: James N Anderson IV
VP: Robert E Sandlin
Board of Directors: John E Anderson, Edward L Baker, Luke E Fichthorn III, Charles D Hyman

D-U-N-S 19-961-5469
■ PATRIOT TRANSPORTATION INC
(*Suby of* PATRIOT TRANSPORTATION INC. OF FLORIDA)
200 W Forsyth St Ste 700, Jacksonville, FL 32202-4321
Tel (904) 356-6110 *Founded/Ownrshp* 1988
Sales 166.7MM[E] *EMP* 886
SIC 4213 6531 6519

D-U-N-S 00-692-7925 IMP
PATTEN INDUSTRIES INC
CATERPILLAR AUTHORIZED DEALER
635 W Lake St, Elmhurst, IL 60126-1465
Tel (630) 279-4400 *Founded/Ownrshp* 1933
Sales 347.3MM[E] *EMP* 575
SIC 5084 5082 7353 Engines & parts, diesel; Tractors, industrial; General construction machinery & equipment; Tractors, construction; Heavy construction equipment rental
Co-Ownr: Byron C Patten Jr
**Pr:* B Crane Patten Jr
**Pr:* Garrett G Patten
**CFO:* George Kapitzky
VP: John Loftus
Off Mgr: Thomas Synowski
IT Man: Tim Cooper
IT Man: Donnell Jorgensen
Sls&Mrk Ex: John Nurton
Mktg Mgr: Allison Loehman
Sls Mgr: Ryan Little

D-U-N-S 07-912-2087
▲ PATTERN ENERGY GROUP INC
Bay 3 Pier 1, San Francisco, CA 94111
Tel (415) 283-4000 *Founded/Ownrshp* 2009
Sales 329.8MM *EMP* 116
Tkr Sym PEGI *Exch* NGM
SIC 4911 Electric services
Pr: Michael M Garland
**Ch Bd:* Alan R Batkin
CFO: Michael J Lyon
Chf Cred: Daniel M Elkort
Sr VP: Eric S Lillybeck
Sr VP: Dean S Russell
Sr VP: Christopher M Shugart
VP: Dyann S Blaine
CIO: Esben W Pedersen
Board of Directors: Patricia S Bellinger, John Browne, Douglas G Hall, Michael B Hoffman, Patricia M Newson

D-U-N-S 83-116-8518
PATTERN ENERGY GROUP LP
Bay 3 Pier 1, San Francisco, CA 94111
Tel (415) 283-4000 *Founded/Ownrshp* 2009
Sales 99.2MM[E] *EMP* 120[E]
SIC 4911 Transmission, electric power
Pr: Michael Garland
**Ch:* Alan Batkin
Sr VP: Christopher Shugart
Genl Mgr: Collie Powell
CIO: Ali Eghtessadi

D-U-N-S 02-722-9103
PATTERSON AUTO CENTER INC
PATTERSON DODGE
315 Central Fwy E, Wichita Falls, TX 76301-6400
Tel (940) 766-0293 *Founded/Ownrshp* 1979
Sales 180.0MM *EMP* 248
SIC 5511 Automobiles, new & used; Pickups, new & used
Pr: Harry Patterson Jr
**Sec:* Brenda J Patterson
VP: Paul Pigrett
Exec: Dianna McWhirter
Genl Mgr: Paul Tigrett
Sls Mgr: Lamont Myles
Sls Mgr: Jon Oeltjen
Sls Mgr: Elizabeth Speer

D-U-N-S 00-696-2500
▲ PATTERSON COMPANIES INC (MN)
1031 Mendota Heights Rd, Saint Paul, MN 55120-1419
Tel (651) 686-1600 *Founded/Ownrshp* 1877
Sales 5.3MMM *EMP* 7,000
Tkr Sym PDCO *Exch* NGS
SIC 5047 5112 7372 7699 2834 Dental equipment & supplies; Dentists' professional supplies; Veterinarians' equipment & supplies; X-ray machines & tubes; Stationery & office supplies; Business oriented computer software; Dental instrument repair; Veterinary pharmaceutical preparations
Ch Bd: Scott P Anderson
Pr: Doug Jones
Pr: Dave Misiak
CFO: Stephen Armstrong
CFO: Ann B Gugino
Ofcr: Paul A Guggenheim
VP: Mark Aldridge
VP: Ranell J Hamm
VP: Les B Korsh
VP: Sean M Muniz
VP: Jerome Thygesen
VP: Jerry Thygestn
VP: John Wright
Board of Directors: John D Buck, Jody H Feragen, Ellen A Rudnick, Neil A Schrimsher, Les C Vinney, James W Wiltz

D-U-N-S 17-184-3584 IMP
■ PATTERSON DENTAL SUPPLY INC
(*Suby of* PATTERSON COMPANIES INC) ★
1031 Mendota Heights Rd, Saint Paul, MN 55120-1401
Tel (651) 686-1600 *Founded/Ownrshp* 1985
Sales 830.1MM[E] *EMP* 2,909
SIC 5047 Dental equipment & supplies
CEO: Paul Guggenheim
**Pr:* Scott P Anderson
**CEO:* Scott Anderson
Sr Cor Off: James Wiltz
Bd of Dir: Scott Kabbes
Ex VP: Steve Armstrong
**VP:* Richard A Cochmann
**VP:* Grant Gerke
VP: Bill Hill
**VP:* Jim Zeller
Creative D: Daniel Patrick

PATTERSON DODGE
See PATTERSON AUTO CENTER INC

D-U-N-S 00-864-6580
■ PATTERSON DRILLING CO INC
(*Suby of* PATTERSON-UTI ENERGY INC) ★
4105 S Chadbourne St, San Angelo, TX 76904-9152
Tel (325) 651-6603 *Founded/Ownrshp* 1996
Sales 39.6MM[E] *EMP* 1,400
SIC 1381 Directional drilling oil & gas wells
Pr: Glenn Patterson
**Ch Bd:* Cloyce Talbott

D-U-N-S 00-918-2270 IMP
■ PATTERSON MEDICAL PRODUCTS INC
SAMMONS PRESTON
(*Suby of* PATTERSON COMPANIES INC) ★
28100 Torch Pkwy, Warrenville, IL 60555-3938
Tel (630) 393-6671 *Founded/Ownrshp* 1978
Sales 168.7MM[E] *EMP* 800
SIC 3841 Medical instruments & equipment, blood & bone work
Pr: Edward Donnelly
Exec: Sandra Warren
Genl Mgr: Jamie Roelke
Natl Sales: Jason Williams
Sls Dir: Melvin Lewis

D-U-N-S 08-861-0316 IMP/EXP
■ PATTERSON PUMP CO
SLOPAK
(*Suby of* GORMAN-RUPP CO) ★
2129 Ayersville Rd, Toccoa, GA 30577-3554
Tel (706) 886-2101 *Founded/Ownrshp* 1988
Sales 103.4MM[E] *EMP* 365[E]
SIC 3561 3511 3559 Pumps & pumping equipment; Turbines & turbine generator sets; Chemical machinery & equipment
Pr: Albert F Huber
CFO: Susan Harbin
VP: E Jackson Claxton
VP: Jeffrey S Gorman
VP: Bobby R Rickman
VP: Darrell Snyder
Prin: Jack Claxton
Prin: Jeff Williams
VP Mfg: Terry Fritz

D-U-N-S 10-248-4180 IMP/EXP
■ PATTERSON VETERINARY SUPPLY INC
WEBSTER MANAGEMENT
(*Suby of* PATTERSON COMPANIES INC) ★
137 Barnum Rd, Devens, MA 01434-3509
Tel (978) 353-6000 *Founded/Ownrshp* 2001
Sales 649.5MM[E] *EMP* 468
SIC 5047 Veterinarians' equipment & supplies
Pr: George Henriques
**Treas:* Stephen Armstrong

D-U-N-S 04-576-5146
PATTERSON-ERIE CORP
FAST FOOD ENTERPRISES 2 & 3
1250 Tower Ln Ste 1, Erie, PA 16505-2533
Tel (814) 455-8031 *Founded/Ownrshp* 1967
Sales 45.3MM[E] *EMP* 1,332
SIC 5812 6531 4522 Fast-food restaurant, chain; Real estate managers; Flying charter service
Pr: William L Patterson Jr
**CFO:* Cameron E Mc Cormick
**VP:* George T Abowd

D-U-N-S 16-162-6338
■ PATTERSON-UTI DRILLING SERVICES LP LLLP
NORTON DRILLING
(*Suby of* PATTERSON-UTI ENERGY INC) ★
4500 Lamesa Hwy, Snyder, TX 79549
Tel (325) 573-1104 *Founded/Ownrshp* 1999
Sales 145.3MM[E] *EMP* 100[E]
SIC 1381 Drilling oil & gas wells
CEO: Sherman H Norton
Pt: S H Norton
Pt: David Ridley
Pr: Douglas J Wall

D-U-N-S 08-888-9498
▲ PATTERSON-UTI ENERGY INC
10713 W Sam Huston Pkwy N, Houston, TX 77064-3577
Tel (281) 765-7100 *Founded/Ownrshp* 1978
Sales 1.8MMM *EMP* 3,400
Accts Pricewaterhousecoopers Llp Ho
Tkr Sym PTEN *Exch* NGS
SIC 1381 1389 1311 Drilling oil & gas wells; Oil & gas wells: building, repairing & dismantling; Cementing oil & gas well casings; Crude petroleum & natural gas; Crude petroleum production; Natural gas production
Pr: William Andrew Hendricks Jr
**Ch Bd:* Mark S Siegel
**Sr VP:* Kenneth N Berns
Sr VP: John E Vollmer III
VP: Diana L Dotolo
Prin: Keith Allen
Rgnl Mgr: Rhonda Engh
Area Mgr: Mike Unrein
IT Man: Michael Jones
Opers Mgr: Scott Lane
VP Mktg: Cory Heinecke
Board of Directors: Charles O Buckner, Michael W Conlon, Curtis W Huff, Terry H Hunt, Tiffany J Thom

D-U-N-S 07-480-4642 IMP
PATTON BOGGS LLP
2550 M St Nw Ste 200, Washington, DC 20037-1302
Tel (202) 457-6000 *Founded/Ownrshp* 1962
Sales 326.9MM *EMP* 1,023
SIC 8111

D-U-N-S 19-170-4220
PATTONAIR USA INC
(*Suby of* PATTONAIR GROUP LIMITED)
1900 Robotics Pl, Fort Worth, TX 76118-7128
Tel (817) 284-4449 *Founded/Ownrshp* 2011
Sales 140.2MM[E] *EMP* 167
SIC 5088 Aeronautical equipment & supplies
Pr: John Schneider
Treas: Tim Sale
Genl Mgr: Rachel Albizo
IT Man: Brian Davis
Ql Cn Mgr: Kian H Yeo
Sales Exec: Danny Jones
Sls&Mrk Ex: Bryan McLean
Sls Mgr: Wesley Wood

D-U-N-S 94-637-7202
PATTONVILLE SCHOOL DISTRICT
11097 St Charles Rock Rd, Saint Ann, MO 63074-1509
Tel (314) 213-8500 *Founded/Ownrshp* 2007
Sales 47.5MM[E] *EMP* 1,000
SIC 8211 Public elementary & secondary schools
CTO: Andrew Smith
Pr Dir: Mickey Schoonover
HC Dir: Teisha Ashford
Snr Mgr: Beth Kathriner

D-U-N-S 96-712-6876
PAUL G ALLEN FAMILY FOUNDATION
505 5th Ave S Ste 900, Seattle, WA 98104-3821
Tel (206) 342-2000 *Founded/Ownrshp* 1988
Sales 337.7MM *EMP* 10[E]
SIC 8699 Charitable organization
Pr: Jo Lynn Allen
**VP:* Susan M Coliton
**VP:* Susan Drake
**VP:* Paul Ghaffari

D-U-N-S 07-723-8624
PAUL HASTINGS LLP
515 S Flower St Fl 25, Los Angeles, CA 90071-2228
Tel (213) 683-6000 *Founded/Ownrshp* 1996
Sales 464.6MM[E] *EMP* 2,700[E]
SIC 8111 General practice law office
Mng Pt: Greg Nitzkowski
Pt: George W Abele
Pt: Jesse H Austin
**Pt:* Elena R Baca
Pt: Dino T Barajas
Pt: Tollie Besson
Pt: Rob R Carlson
Pt: Steven T Catlett
Pt: Eve M Coddon
Pt: Erika Collins
Pt: Roberto Cornetta
Pt: Bruno Cova
Pt: Bruce Depaola
Pt: Luc Despins
Pt: Dennis S Ellis
Pt: Jason M Frank
Pt: Norman A Futami
Pt: Terry D Garnett
Pt: Dan Goldman
Pt: Robert Grados
Pt: Stephen Harris

D-U-N-S 00-713-3887 IMP/EXP
▲ PAUL MUELLER CO
1600 W Phelps St, Springfield, MO 65802-4273
Tel (417) 831-3000 *Founded/Ownrshp* 1940
Sales 181.2MM *EMP* 948
Tkr Sym MUEL *Exch* OTO
SIC 3443 3556 3523 Tanks, standard or custom fabricated: metal plate; Food products machinery; Milk processing machinery; Meat processing machinery; Poultry processing machinery; Dairy equipment (farm)
Pr: David T Moore
CFO: Kenneth E Jeffries
Exec: James Hall
Exec: John Henning
Exec: Mike Veatch
Genl Mgr: Michael Angstadt
Genl Mgr: Russ Copeland
Genl Mgr: Cary Kapper
Genl Mgr: Mike Mills
Sfty Mgr: Bill Hewett
Prd Mgr: Jeff Forbes
Board of Directors: Curtis Dinan, Paul Mueller Chb Emeritus, William L Fuerst, W Curtis Graff, James D Hlavacek, Jean L Morris, William R Patterson, Jack Stack

D-U-N-S 04-116-0672 IMP
PAUL R BRILES INC
PB FASTENERS
1700 W 132nd St, Gardena, CA 90249-2008
Tel (310) 323-6222 *Founded/Ownrshp* 2011
Sales NA *EMP* 1,262
SIC 3452

D-U-N-S 00-695-6817
■ PAUL REVERE LIFE INSURANCE CO
(*Suby of* UNUM GROUP) ★
1 Mercantile St, Worcester, MA 01608-3102
Tel (508) 366-8707 *Founded/Ownrshp* 2000
Sales NA *EMP* 3,000
SIC 6311 6321 Life insurance; Accident insurance carriers; Health insurance carriers
Ch Bd: James Harold Chandler
CFO: Robert C Greving
**CFO:* Thomas Ros Watjen
**Treas:* John Lang
VP: E L Bishop
VP: Vicki W Corbett
VP: Gerald Michael Gates
VP: George Kane
VP: Dennis Parslow
VP: Ralph Arnold Rogers
VP: Regina Y Rose
**VP:* Susan Nance Roth
Board of Directors: Burton Erhard Sorensen, William Lester Armstron, William Howard Bolinder, Charlotte Maclellan Heffne, Hugh Benford Jacks, Hugh Owen Maclellan Jr, Albert Slocomb Macmillan, Charles William Pollard, Scott Livingston Probasco, Steven S Reinemund

PAUL RVERE VRBLE ANNUITY INSUR
See UNUM INSURANCE CO

D-U-N-S 07-103-0704
PAUL WEISS RIFKIND WHARTON & GARRISON LLP
1285 Ave Of The Americas, New York, NY 10019-6031
Tel (212) 373-3000 *Founded/Ownrshp* 1946
Sales 221.0MM[E] *EMP* 1,200
SIC 8111 8748 General practice law office; Antitrust & trade regulation law; Bankruptcy law; Real estate law; Employee programs administration
Ex Dir: Eric J Sekler
Mng Pt: Kenneth A Gallo
CFO: Sean McNamara
Ofcr: Jill D Berkowitz
VP: Martin London
VP: Joyce Willis
Adm Dir: James Smith
CIO: Andreas M Antoniou
CIO: Andreas Mantoniou
Telecom Mg: Catherine Brennan
Counsel: Diane Meyers

D-U-N-S 09-858-7926
PAULDING COUNTY BOARD OF EDUCATION
3236 Atlanta Hwy, Dallas, GA 30132-5725
Tel (770) 443-8000 *Founded/Ownrshp* 1900
Sales 150.2MM[E] *EMP* 4,200
SIC 8211 School board
**Ch Bd:* Kim Curl
**V Ch:* Sammy McClure

D-U-N-S 07-979-9695
PAULDING COUNTY SCHOOL DISTRICT
3236 Atlanta Hwy, Dallas, GA 30132-5725
Tel (770) 443-8000 *Founded/Ownrshp* 2015
Sales 19.0MM[E] *EMP* 2,925[E]
SIC 8211 Public elementary & secondary schools
Dir Sec: Don Breedlove
MIS Dir: Miriam Hall
MIS Dir: Julie Ragsdale
Pr Dir: Suzanne Wooley
Teacher Pr: Clark Maggart

D-U-N-S 01-303-9532
PAULDING MEDICAL CENTER INC
WELLSTAR PAULDING HOSPITAL
(*Suby of* WELLSTAR HEALTH SYSTEM INC) ★
600 W Memorial Dr, Dallas, GA 30132-4117
Tel (770) 445-4411 *Founded/Ownrshp* 1958
Sales 75.9MM *EMP* 1,432[E]
Accts Pricewaterhousecoopers Llp Ph
SIC 8062 8051 General medical & surgical hospitals; Skilled nursing care facilities
CEO: Reynold Jennings
COO: Michael Graue
**CFO:* A James Budzinski
Chf Nrs Of: Donna Mikeal
QA Dir: Donna Garner
Nrsg Dir: Joyce Hulsey

PAULEY CONSTRUCTION INC.
See PAULEY CONSTRUCTION LLC

D-U-N-S 85-855-1096
■ PAULEY CONSTRUCTION LLC
PAULEY CONSTRUCTION INC.
(*Suby of* DYCOM INDUSTRIES INC) ★
2021 W Melinda Ln, Phoenix, AZ 85027-2823
Tel (623) 581-1200 *Founded/Ownrshp* 2012
Sales 96.4MM[E] *EMP* 250
SIC 1623 Communication line & transmission tower construction
Pr: Bryan Dahl
Rgnl Mgr: Felix Dees

D-U-N-S 00-626-7769
PAULO PRODUCTS CO
5711 W Park Ave, Saint Louis, MO 63110-1890
Tel (314) 647-7500 *Founded/Ownrshp* 1943
Sales 95.9MM[E] *EMP* 500
SIC 3471 3398 8734 3567 Electroplating of metals or formed products; Metal heat treating; Brazing (hardening) of metal; Testing laboratories; Industrial furnaces & ovens
Pr: Benjamin Rassieur III
**Ex VP:* R Terry Rassieur
Ex VP: Terry R Rassieur
**VP:* Alan C Baethke
VP: Gregory F Glei
**VP:* C James Heman

*VP: Dennis J Ochs
Exec: Doug Manning
Admn Mgr: Heather Roberts
Genl Mgr: James Herman
QC Dir: David Mailes

D-U-N-S 00-581-6015
PAULS TV LLC (CA)
WAREHOUSE
900 Glenneyre St, Laguna Beach, CA 92651-2707
Tel (949) 596-8800 Founded/Ownrshp 2006
Sales 130.6MM[E] EMP 60[E]
SIC 5064 Television sets
Chf Mktg O: Steven Strickland
Genl Mgr: Kevin R Smith
Store Mgr: Damian Sotelo
Mktg Dir: Tamara Sauer
*Mktg Mgr: Alice Gonzales

PAULS VALLEY GENERAL HOSPITAL
See PAULS VALLEY HOSPITAL AUTHORITY

D-U-N-S 96-981-9817
PAULS VALLEY HOSPITAL AUTHORITY
PAULS VALLEY GENERAL HOSPITAL
100 Valley Dr, Pauls Valley, OK 73075-6699
Tel (405) 238-5501 Founded/Ownrshp 1997
Sales NA EMP 259[E]
SIC 6324 8062 Hospital & medical service plans; General medical & surgical hospitals
CEO: Nathan Staggs
*CFO: Steven Ewing

D-U-N-S 96-615-7245 IMP
■ **PAULSBORO REFINING CO LLC**
PBF ENERGY
(Suby of PBF HOLDING CO LLC) ★
800 Jenkins Blvd, Paulsboro, NJ 08066-1039
Tel (973) 455-7500 Founded/Ownrshp 2010
Sales 19.0MMM EMP 1,500
SIC 2911 Oils, partly refined: sold for rerunning
CEO: Thomas J Nimbley
*Pr: Michael D Gayda
Treas: John Luke
*Ex VP: Donald F Lucey
*Sr VP: Jeffrey Dill
*Sr VP: Todd Omalley
*Sr VP: Erik Young

PAULSEN CENTER
See DIAMOND PARKING SERVICES LLC

D-U-N-S 00-729-3848
PAULSEN INC
1116 E Highway 30, Cozad, NE 69130-2236
Tel (308) 784-3333 Founded/Ownrshp 1946
Sales 107.0MM EMP 140
Accts Frankel Zacharia Llc Omaha
SIC 1611 1542 3273 Highway & street construction; Commercial & office building contractors; Ready-mixed concrete
Pr: Larry Paulsen
*Treas: Jane German
*VP: Brain Engel

D-U-N-S 83-221-2729
PAULUS SOKOLOWSKI & SARTOR ENGINEERING A PROFESSIONAL CORP
PS&S ENGINEERING
67b Mountain Blvd Ext, Warren, NJ 07059-2642
Tel (732) 560-9700 Founded/Ownrshp 1993
Sales 15.0MM EMP 2,120
SIC 8711 8748 8712 Engineering services; Environmental consultant; Architectural services
Pr: Joseph Lifrieri

PAVARINI CONSTRUCTION COMPANY
See PAVARINI NORTH EAST CONSTRUCTION CO INC

D-U-N-S 00-391-6632
PAVARINI NORTH EAST CONSTRUCTION CO INC
PAVARINI CONSTRUCTION COMPANY
30 Oak St Fl 3, Stamford, CT 06905-5313
Tel (203) 327-0100 Founded/Ownrshp 1896
Sales 110.0MM EMP 60
SIC 1542 8741 Commercial & office building, new construction; Construction management
Pr: Jim Hurley
*COO: Mike Melanophy
CFO: Rudy Nance
*Treas: Ray Froimowitz
VP: Brian Lynch
Opers Mgr: Frank Pelliccione
Counsel: Joel Sciascia
Snr PM: James J Dunn

D-U-N-S 60-400-6619 IMP
PAVEMENT RECYCLING SYSTEMS INC
PRSI
10240 San Sevaine Way, Jurupa Valley, CA 91752-1100
Tel (951) 682-1091 Founded/Ownrshp 1996
Sales 129.7MM[E] EMP 185
SIC 5093 1611 Scrap & waste materials; Surfacing & paving; Concrete construction: roads, highways, sidewalks, etc.; Resurfacing contractor
Pr: Richard W Gove
*Ch Bd: Charles T Harmon
*Pr: Stephen Concannon
CFO: Nathan Beyler
*Treas: Bernard Hale
Dir Bus: Marco Estrada
Genl Mgr: Carrie Buttigieg
Sftwr Eng: Mitchell Sante
Sfty Dirs: Jim Halvorson
Sls Dir: Jim Oakane
Sls Dir: Don Sante

PAVERS SUPPLY COMPANY
See DMG EQUIPMENT CO LTD

D-U-N-S 03-094-2342
PAVESCAPES
1340 E Pomona St, Santa Ana, CA 92705-4811
Tel (714) 581-5931 Founded/Ownrshp 2013
Sales 125.0MM EMP 30[E]
SIC 1799 Fence construction
CEO: Eddie Guerrero

D-U-N-S 07-839-9627
PAVESTONE LLC (GA)
PAVESTONE PAVERS
(Suby of QUIKRETE HOLDINGS INC) ★
3490 Piedmont Rd Ne # 1300, Atlanta, GA 30305-4811
Tel (404) 926-3167 Founded/Ownrshp 2010, 1980
Sales 426.5MM[E] EMP 1,374[E]
SIC 3251 3241 3255 3272 Brick & structural clay tile; Cement, hydraulic; Masonry cement; Tile, clay refractory; Concrete products

PAVESTONE PAVERS
See PAVESTONE LLC

D-U-N-S 10-188-2132
PAVILION HEALTH SERVICES INC
(Suby of BAPTIST HEALTH SYSTEM INC) ★
3563 Phillips Hwy Ste 106, Jacksonville, FL 32207-5684
Tel (904) 202-5887 Founded/Ownrshp 2008
Sales 196.9MM EMP 785
SIC 5912 Drug stores
Ch: A Hugh Green
*Pr: Michael Lukaszewski
*VP: Christopher Durkin
Sls Mgr: Kenneth C Perry

PAVILIONS
See VONS COMPANIES INC

PAVING DIVISION
See HIGHWAYS INC

D-U-N-S 19-345-4196
PAWTUCKET SCHOOL DEPARTMENT
286 Main St, Pawtucket, RI 02860-2908
Tel (401) 729-6300 Founded/Ownrshp 1998
Sales 47.3MM[E] EMP 1,200
SIC 8211 9411 Public elementary & secondary schools; Administration of educational programs
Teacher Pr: Terry Parrera

D-U-N-S 09-429-4501 IMP
PAX HOLDINGS LLC
758 N Broadway Ste 910, Milwaukee, WI 53202-3654
Tel (414) 803-9983 Founded/Ownrshp 2007
Sales 246.8MM[E] EMP 224
SIC 5199 2759 2672 2671 2657 2752 Packaging materials; Flexographic printing; Business forms: printing; Bank notes: engraved; Bags, plastic: printing; Coated & laminated paper; Packaging paper & plastics film, coated & laminated; Folding paperboard boxes; Lithographing on metal; Business forms, lithographed
Pr: James Kornfeld
Sls Mgr: Shirin Malik

D-U-N-S 00-636-6207
PAXTON MEDIA GROUP LLC
PADUCAH SUN, THE
100 Television Ln, Paducah, KY 42003-7905
Tel (270) 575-8630 Founded/Ownrshp 2001
Sales 360.0MM[E] EMP 2,000
Accts Williams Williams & Lentz Cp
SIC 2711 4833 Newspapers, publishing & printing; Television broadcasting stations
Ch Bd: David M Paxton
*CFO: Richard Paxton
*Treas: Frank R Paxton
*VP: Jay Frizzo
*VP: David R Mathis
Genl Mgr: Karen Turner
Board of Directors: W James Brockenborough, Mrs Louise Paxton Gallaghe, Joseph G Mitchell, Martha Sinquefield

D-U-N-S 00-696-6162
PAXTON WOOD SOURCE INC (DE)
6311 Saint John Ave, Kansas City, MO 64123-1926
Tel (816) 483-7000 Founded/Ownrshp 1995
Sales 180.0MM EMP 6
SIC 5031 2431 5211 5072

D-U-N-S 04-315-6983
PAY AND SAVE INC (TX)
LOWE'S MARKET
1804 Hall Ave, Littlefield, TX 79339-5439
Tel (806) 385-3366 Founded/Ownrshp 1965
Sales 983.8MM EMP 2,000
SIC 5411

D-U-N-S 93-357-2182
PAY STAFF
HR CAPITAL MANAGEMENT
700 King Farm Blvd # 300, Rockville, MD 20850-5736
Tel (301) 527-0655 Founded/Ownrshp 1995
Sales 64.7MM[E] EMP 6,200
SIC 7363 8721 Help supply services; Accounting, auditing & bookkeeping
Pr: Bala Ramamoorthy
*CFO: Chuck Ehrig
*Treas: Becky Ramamoorthy

D-U-N-S 06-251-7511
PAY-O-MATIC CORP
(Suby of FOUNDERS MANAGEMENT SERVICES) ★
160 Oak Dr, Syosset, NY 11791-4694
Tel (516) 496-4900 Founded/Ownrshp 2008
Sales NA EMP 860
SIC 6099 7381 7999 Check cashing agencies; Armored car services; Lottery tickets, sale of
Ch Bd: Robin Miles
*CFO: Paul Norman
VP: Mitchell Wolf
Genl Couns: Alan Handler

D-U-N-S 09-439-9359
▲ **PAYCHEX INC**
911 Panorama Trl S, Rochester, NY 14625-2396
Tel (585) 385-6666 Founded/Ownrshp 1979
Sales 2.9MMM EMP 13,000
Tkr Sym PAYX Exch NGS
SIC 8721 7363 Payroll accounting service; Employee leasing service
Pr: Martin Mucci
*Ch Bd: B Thomas Golisano
Pr: Janelle M Detweiler
CFO: Efrain Rivera
Ex VP: Judy M Wu
Sr VP: Mark A Bottini
Sr VP: Michael E Gioja
VP: Maria Fornuto
VP: Sanjay Hiranandani
VP: Laurie A Maffett
VP: Michael A McCarthy
VP: Angela M Mockbee
VP: Stephanie Schaffer
VP: Jennifer Vossler
VP: Maggie Yamonaco
Board of Directors: Joseph G Doody, David J S Flaschen, Phillip Horsley, Grant M Inman, Pamela A Joseph, Joseph M Tucci, Joseph M Velli

D-U-N-S 07-934-8204
▲ **PAYCOM SOFTWARE INC**
7501 W Memorial Rd, Oklahoma City, OK 73142-1404
Tel (405) 722-6900 Founded/Ownrshp 1998
Sales 224.6MM EMP 1,461[E]
Tkr Sym PAYC Exch NYS
SIC 8721 7371 7372 Accounting, auditing & bookkeeping; Payroll accounting service; Custom computer programming services; Computer software development & applications; Prepackaged software
Pr: Chad Richison
*Ch Bd: Robert Minicucci
COO: Stacey M Pezold
CFO: Craig E Boelte
Dir Sec: Jeffrey D York
CIO: William X Kerber III

D-U-N-S 61-542-1385
PAYCOR INC
4811 Montgomery Rd, Cincinnati, OH 45212-2163
Tel (513) 381-0505 Founded/Ownrshp 2001
Sales 98.0MM[E] EMP 260
SIC 8721 Payroll accounting service
Ch: Robert J Coughlin
*Pr: Stacey Browning
CFO: Heather Kammer
*CFO: Chris Power
*Treas: Steven G Haussler
*Chf Mktg O: Glenn Cross
Ofcr: Scott Rudy
*Sr VP: Rick Chouteau
Sr VP: Jennifer Langer
VP: Don Chun
VP: Tom Fitzsimmons
VP: Jamie Griffiths
VP: Brian Vass
Exec: Karen Crone

D-U-N-S 07-939-5248
■ **PAYFLEX HOLDINGS INC**
(Suby of AETNA FINANCIAL HOLDINGS LLC) ★
10802 Farnam Dr Ste 100, Omaha, NE 68154-3200
Tel (800) 284-4885 Founded/Ownrshp 2006, 2011
Sales NA EMP 221[E]
SIC 6411 Medical insurance claim processing, contract or fee basis
COO: Brandon Wood
Dir Bus: Eric Farr

D-U-N-S 86-938-5583
■ **PAYFLEX SYSTEMS USA INC**
(Suby of PAYFLEX HOLDINGS INC) ★
10802 Farnam Dr Ste 100, Omaha, NE 68154-3200
Tel (402) 345-0666 Founded/Ownrshp 2011
Sales NA EMP 221[E]
SIC 6411 Medical insurance claim processing, contract or fee basis
Prin: Edward Steven Doyle
*COO: Brandon Wood
*Ex VP: Bob Camenzind
*VP: John Fahrer
VP: Kevin Hitzemann
VP: Teri Lind
Snr Sftwr: Jeff Meadows
CTO: Tony Dillon
Sls Dir: Jane Levin

PAYLESS CASH & CARRY CLUB
See COLONIAL GROCERS INC

PAYLESS FOODS
See KOSHAN INC

D-U-N-S 01-952-8947 IMP/EXP
PAYLESS INC
PAYLESS SHOESOURCE
(Suby of WBG-PSS HOLDINGS LLC) ★
3231 Se 6th Ave, Topeka, KS 66607-2260
Tel (785) 233-5171 Founded/Ownrshp 1956, 2012
Sales 3.4MMM[E] EMP 30,000
SIC 5661 5632 Shoe stores; Women's accessory & specialty stores; Apparel accessories; Handbags
CEO: Paul W Jones
COO: Mike Vitelli
CFO: Michael Schwindle
Ex VP: Steve Gish
Ex VP: Douglas Treff
Sr VP: Robert Bruening
Sr VP: Betty J Click
Sr VP: Randall Decker
Sr VP: Robert Donohoo
Sr VP: Lorraine Hitch
Sr VP: John D Smith
VP: Paul Fenaroli

PAYLESS SHOESOURCE
See PAYLESS INC

D-U-N-S 00-694-3872 IMP/EXP
PAYLESS SHOESOURCE INC (MO)
(Suby of PAYLESS SHOESOURCE) ★
3231 Se 6th Ave, Topeka, KS 66607-2260
Tel (785) 233-5171 Founded/Ownrshp 1961, 1998
Sales 207.2MM[E] EMP 750[E]
SIC 5661

D-U-N-S 07-927-6586
▲ **PAYLOCITY HOLDING CORP**
3850 N Wilke Rd, Arlington Heights, IL 60004-1269
Tel (847) 463-3200 Founded/Ownrshp 1997
Sales 230.7MM EMP 1,800[E]
Accts Kpmg Llp Chicago Illinois
Tkr Sym PCTY Exch NGS
SIC 7372 Prepackaged software; Business oriented computer software
Pr: Steven R Beauchamp
*Ch Bd: Steven I Sarowitz
CFO: Peter J McGrail
Bd of Dir: Jarell McGrew
Sr VP: Edward W Gaty
Sr VP: Michael R Haske
Sr VP: Mark S Kinsey
VP: Jay Schedler
Rgnl Mgr: Linda Bujnowski
Dist Mgr: Jennifer Blair
Dist Mgr: Brian Krejci

D-U-N-S 78-504-8807
PAYMENT ALLIANCE INTERNATIONAL INC
ATM SERVICES GROUP
(Suby of PAYMENT ALLIANCE PROCESSING CORP) ★
1 Paragon Ctr 6060 Dutchm, Louisville, KY 40205
Tel (502) 212-4000 Founded/Ownrshp 2006
Sales NA EMP 272
SIC 6099 Check cashing agencies
Pr: John J Leehy III
*Pr: Greg Mercer
*COO: Greg Sahrmann
*CFO: David Kozal
*Sr VP: Don Apgar
*Sr VP: Neil Clark
Sr VP: Kopp Michael
Sr VP: Keith L Myers
*Sr VP: Conrad De Lone Wilson
VP: Chris Bell
*VP: Larry Burke
VP: Lloyd Chatham
VP: Vonda Czapor
*VP: Steve Demaree
*VP: Donna Embry
*VP: Manuel Ferreira
*VP: Michael W Hammer
VP: Brian Haynes
*VP: John Jackson
*VP: Michael Kopp
*VP: Krista Lowery

D-U-N-S 80-964-4722
PAYMENT ALLIANCE PROCESSING CORP
6060 Dutchmans Ln Ste 320, Louisville, KY 40205-3380
Tel (502) 212-4000 Founded/Ownrshp 2006
Sales 101.5MM[E] EMP 350[E]
SIC 8742 Business consultant

D-U-N-S 79-761-4760
PAYMENT SERVICE NETWORK INC
2901 International Ln # 100, Madison, WI 53704-3177
Tel (608) 442-5100 Founded/Ownrshp 1999
Sales 879.7MM EMP 30
SIC 7389 6531 8721 Financial services; Real estate agents & managers; Billing & bookkeeping service
CEO: Greg Rice
*CFO: Marll Thiede
VP: Brent Hoffman
*Ex Dir: Ron Brent
*CTO: Norman Ehiorobo

PAYNECREST ELC COMMUNICATIONS
See PAYNECREST ELECTRIC INC

D-U-N-S 19-467-7225 IMP
PAYNECREST ELECTRIC INC
PAYNECREST ELC COMMUNICATIONS
10411 Baur Blvd, Saint Louis, MO 63132-1904
Tel (314) 996-0400 Founded/Ownrshp 1958
Sales 173.6MM EMP 300
Accts Cliftonlarsonallen Llp St Lo
SIC 1731 General electrical contractor
Pr: David Payne
*Pr: Bob Senf
CFO: Doug Adrian
*CFO: Kenneth Mains
VP: John Eyermann
*VP: Patrick McSalley
VP: Allan Schroer
*VP: Robert Senf
Dir IT: Scott Higgins
Dir IT: Mark Karasek
IT Man: Charlie Sciuto

D-U-N-S 02-459-5576
PAYNEWEST INSURANCE INC (MT)
3289 Gabel Rd, Billings, MT 59102-7371
Tel (406) 238-1900 Founded/Ownrshp 1992
Sales NA EMP 600
SIC 6411 Insurance agents; Insurance brokers
Ch Bd: Terry Payne
*Pr: Brian T Donahue
*COO: Sarah Walsh
*CFO: Ken Laddusaw
Ex VP: John Roberts
Sr VP: Chris Hoiness
Sr VP: Mark Theriault
VP: Mark Chelini
VP: Michael Cunningham
VP: Shannon Jensen
Sales Exec: Jennifer Buchanan

D-U-N-S 83-096-6714
PAYONEER INC
5300 Katrine Ave, Downers Grove, IL 60515-4049
Tel (331) 777-2622 Founded/Ownrshp 2012
Sales NA EMP 1,200
SIC 6153 Mercantile financing
Pr: Dean Warner

D-U-N-S 78-583-2747
■ **PAYPAL GLOBAL HOLDINGS INC**
(Suby of PAYPAL HOLDINGS INC) ★
303 Bryant St, Mountain View, CA 94041-1552
Tel (408) 967-1000 Founded/Ownrshp 2003
Sales 195.9MM[E] EMP 5,575[E]
SIC 7374 4813 Data processing & preparation; Telephone communication, except radio
Pr: Chen Christopher
Snr Sftwr: Michael Clay
CIO: James E Templeton
IT Man: Ryan Lawrence
Sftwr Eng: James Chiu
Sftwr Eng: Igor Yefimov
Sftwr Eng: Eric Yu
Mktg Mgr: Hester Seth
Counsel: Erica Dibella

D-U-N-S 07-980-9888
▲ PAYPAL HOLDINGS INC
2211 N 1st St, San Jose, CA 95131-2021
Tel (408) 967-1000 *Founded/Ownrshp* 2015
Sales 4.3MMM[E] *EMP* 16,800[E]
Tkr Sym PYPL *Exch* NGS
SIC 4813 7374 ; Data processing & preparation; Data processing service
Pr: Daniel H Schulman
**Ch Bd:* John J Donahoe
CFO: Patrick Dupuis
CFO: John D Rainey
Ofcr: Jonathan Auerbach
Ofcr: Marcia Morales-Jaffe
Sr VP: Tomer Barel
Sr VP: James Barrese
Sr VP: Hill Ferguson
Sr VP: Rupert G Keeley
Sr VP: Rohan Mahadevan
Sr VP: Gary Marino
Sr VP: John P McCabe
Sr VP: Bill Ready
Sr VP: William J Ready
Sr VP: Sripada Shivananda
Comm Man: Aarion Nielsen

D-U-N-S 18-364-1583
■ PAYPAL INC
(*Suby of* PAYPAL HOLDINGS INC) ★
2211 N 1st St, San Jose, CA 95131-2021
Tel (877) 981-2163 *Founded/Ownrshp* 2015
Sales 4.1MMM[E] *EMP* 10,001[E]
SIC 4813 7374 ; Data processing & preparation; Data processing service
Pr: Daniel H Schulman
Sr VP: Jonathan Auerbach
Sr VP: John McCabe
Sr VP: Louise Pentland
VP: Peggy Abkemeier
VP: Sachin Dhawan
VP: Patrick Dupuis
VP: Rupert Keeley
VP: Amy E Rowe
VP: Todd Shaw
Rgnl Mgr: Sheau H Chong

PAYROLL DEPT
See BOARD OF EDUCATION OF CITY OF PASSAIC INC

D-U-N-S 02-244-7169
PAYROLL MADE EASY INC
CONTINUUMHR
11691 Gateway Blvd # 104, Fort Myers, FL 33913-7922
Tel (239) 592-9700 *Founded/Ownrshp* 2012
Sales 103.0MM *EMP* 34
Accts Stroemer & Company Llc Fort
SIC 8721 Payroll accounting service
Pr: Helen Smith
COO: Robert L Sarver
VP: David C Smith

D-U-N-S 62-458-9792
PAYROLL MANAGEMENT INC
PMI EMPLOYEE LEASING
348 Miracle Strip Pkwy Sw # 39, Fort Walton Beach, FL 32548-5264
Tel (850) 243-5604 *Founded/Ownrshp* 1988
Sales 152.4MM[E] *EMP* 8,500
SIC 7363 Employee leasing service
CEO: DC Mickle-Bee
**Sr VP:* Janice Foster Brooks
Exec: Ginger Meyer
**Prin:* Gene Brooks

D-U-N-S 09-604-3930
PB ENERGY STORAGE SERVICES INC (TX)
PBESS
(*Suby of* PARSONS BRINCKERHOFF GROUP LLC) ★
16200 Park Row Ste 200, Houston, TX 77084-7347
Tel (281) 496-5590 *Founded/Ownrshp* 1978
Sales 115.6MM *EMP* 70
SIC 8711

PB FASTENERS
See PAUL R BRILES INC

D-U-N-S 09-610-3353 IMP
PBE WAREHOUSE INC (CA)
12171 Pangborn Ave, Downey, CA 90241-5624
Tel (562) 803-4691 *Founded/Ownrshp* 1979
Sales 88.7MM[E] *EMP* 105
SIC 5013 Automotive supplies; Automotive servicing equipment; Tools & equipment, automotive
Pr: Stephen Potter
CFO: Christy Jaskzewicz

PBESS
See PB ENERGY STORAGE SERVICES INC

PBF ENERGY
See PBF LOGISTICS LP

PBF ENERGY
See PAULSBORO REFINING CO LLC

D-U-N-S 82-641-4067 IMP/EXP
■ PBF ENERGY CO LLC
PBFTDO
(*Suby of* PBF ENERGY INC) ★
1 Sylvan Way Ste 2, Parsippany, NJ 07054-3879
Tel (973) 455-7500 *Founded/Ownrshp* 2010
Sales 13.1MMM[E] *EMP* 1,735
SIC 2911 Petroleum refining
CEO: Thomas J Nimbley
**Ch Bd:* Thomas O'Malley
**Pr:* Michael Gayda
**CFO:* Matthew Lucey
**Treas:* John Luke
**Chf Cred:* Donald Lucey
**Sr VP:* Jeffrey Dill
Snr PM: Joel Kriener
Board of Directors: Spencer Abraham, Jefferson Allen, Martin Brand, Timothy H Day, David I Foley, Dennis Houston, Neil Wizel

D-U-N-S 07-846-3170 IMP/EXP
▲ PBF ENERGY INC
1 Sylvan Way Ste 2, Parsippany, NJ 07054-3879
Tel (973) 455-7500 *Founded/Ownrshp* 2008
Sales 13.1MMM *EMP* 2,270
Accts Deloitte & Touche Llp Parsipp
Tkr Sym PBF *Exch* NYS
SIC 2911 Petroleum refining
CEO: Thomas J Nimbley
Ch Bd: Thomas D O'Malley
Pr: Matthew C Lucey
CFO: Erik Young
Sr VP: Jeffrey Dill
Sr VP: Thomas L O'Connor
Sr VP: Todd O'Malley
Sr VP: Herman Seedorf
Dir Risk M: Maxwell Foster
Board of Directors: Spencer Abraham, Jefferson F Allen, Wayne A Budd, S Eugene Edwards, William Hantke, Dennis M Houston, Edward F Kosnik, Robert J Lavinia

D-U-N-S 96-261-9206 IMP/EXP
■ PBF HOLDING CO LLC
(*Suby of* PBFTDO) ★
1 Sylvan Way Ste 2, Parsippany, NJ 07054-3879
Tel (888) 661-8949 *Founded/Ownrshp* 2010
Sales 13.1MMM *EMP* 1,735[E]
SIC 2911 2992 Petroleum refining; Lubricating oils
CEO: Thomas J Nimbley
**Pr:* Michael Gayda
**CFO:* Erik Young
**Sr VP:* Jeffrey Dill
**VP:* Matthew Lucey

D-U-N-S 07-939-1008
■ PBF LOGISTICS LP
PBF ENERGY
(*Suby of* PBF ENERGY INC) ★
1 Sylvan Way Ste 2, Parsippany, NJ 07054-3879
Tel (973) 455-7500 *Founded/Ownrshp* 2013
Sales 142.1MM *EMP* 5
Tkr Sym PBFX *Exch* NYS
SIC 4612 Crude petroleum pipelines
CEO: Thomas J Nimbley
Genl Pt: Pbf Logistics GP LLC
CFO: C Erik Young

PBFTDO
See PBF ENERGY CO LLC

D-U-N-S 10-588-0942 IMP
■ PBM GRAPHICS INC
(*Suby of* CONSOLIDATED GRAPHICS INC) ★
3700 S Miami Blvd, Durham, NC 27703-9130
Tel (919) 544-6222 *Founded/Ownrshp* 2008
Sales 204.3MM[E] *EMP* 800
SIC 2752 Commercial printing, offset
CEO: Rick Jones
**Pr:* Adam Geerts
**VP:* Dave Mattingly
**VP:* Johnny Mendoza
**VP:* Greg Simpson
VP: Steve Valente Sr
MIS Mgr: Jim Slocum
S&M/VP: Steve Post
Snr PM: Mike Balsamello
Snr Mgr: Jennifer Owenby
Snr Mgr: Benjamin Stover

D-U-N-S 02-346-8866 IMP
PBM HOLDINGS INC
(*Suby of* PERRIGO CO) ★
652 Peter Jefferson Pkwy # 300, Charlottesville, VA 22911-8849
Tel (540) 832-3282 *Founded/Ownrshp* 2010
Sales 91.3MM[E] *EMP* 500
SIC 5149 Dried or canned foods
Pr: Joseph C Papa
**COO:* Adam Burke
**CFO:* James C Reebals
**Ex VP:* Scott F Jamison
**Ex VP:* James W McGrath
**Ex VP:* Chris Reebals
Ex VP: Sean Stalfort
**Sr VP:* Nicholas W Danforth
**VP:* Raymond J Maggio
**VP:* Tom Ryan
VP Sls: Mark Walin

D-U-N-S 96-358-1848 IMP/EXP
PBR INC
SKAPS INDUSTRIES
335 Athena Dr, Athens, GA 30601-1616
Tel (706) 354-3700 *Founded/Ownrshp* 1995
Sales 101.3MM[E] *EMP* 235
SIC 2297 2221 3089 Nonwoven fabrics; Broadwoven fabric mills, manmade; Netting, plastic
Pr: Paresh Vyas
**CFO:* Rajendra Joshi
**Treas:* Naymish Patel
**VP:* Balu P Patel
Ex Dir: Nishant Amin
CTO: Robert Hale

D-U-N-S 01-608-9138 EXP
PBS COALS INC
(*Suby of* CORSA COAL CORP)
1576 Stoystown Rd, Friedens, PA 15541-7402
Tel (814) 443-4668 *Founded/Ownrshp* 2014
Sales 261.5MM[E] *EMP* 150
SIC 1221 Strip mining, bituminous
Pr: Lynn Shanks
COO: Keith Dyke
**CFO:* Dmitry Goryachev
**Ex VP:* Peter J Vuljanic
VP: Joseph Gallo
VP: Raymond J McElhaney

PBS KIDS
See PUBLIC BROADCASTING SERVICE

D-U-N-S 16-696-4986
▲ PC CONNECTION INC
730 Milford Rd, Merrimack, NH 03054-4612
Tel (603) 683-2000 *Founded/Ownrshp* 1982
Sales 2.5MMM *EMP* 2,205
Tkr Sym CNXN *Exch* NGS
SIC 5961 Computer equipment & electronics, mail order; Computer software, mail order; Computers & peripheral equipment, mail order
Pr: Timothy McGrath
CFO: Joseph Driscoll
V Ch Bd: Joseph Baute
VP: Sylvia Diamant
VP: Eric Keating
VP: Lila Nelms

D-U-N-S 10-887-8828 EXP
■ PC CONNECTION SALES CORP
(*Suby of* PC CONNECTION INC) ★
730 Milford Rd, Merrimack, NH 03054-4612
Tel (603) 423-2000 *Founded/Ownrshp* 2000
Sales 120.5MM[E] *EMP* 600
SIC 5961 5045 Computers & peripheral equipment, mail order; Computer software, mail order; Computers, peripherals & software; Computers; Computer peripheral equipment; Computer software
Ch Bd: Patricia Gallup
**CEO:* Timothy J McGrathl
**Treas:* Gary Anderson
**Sr VP:* Joseph S Driscoll

D-U-N-S 00-209-2773 IMP
PC CONSTRUCTION CO
193 Tilley Dr, South Burlington, VT 05403-4440
Tel (802) 658-4100 *Founded/Ownrshp* 1958
Sales 705.4MM[E] *EMP* 900
SIC 1629 1542

D-U-N-S 02-941-8768
■ PC INTERMEDIATE HOLDINGS INC
PC TOPCOL HOLDING
(*Suby of* PARTY CITY HOLDCO INC) ★
80 Grasslands Rd, Elmsford, NY 10523-1100
Tel (914) 345-2020 *Founded/Ownrshp* 2011
Sales 3.9MMM[E] *EMP* 15,097[E]
SIC 7389 Design services

D-U-N-S 00-803-3235 IMP
PC INTERNATIONAL SALES INC (TX)
SOUTHWEST SOUVENIRS
730 S Jupiter Rd Ste B, Garland, TX 75042-7701
Tel (972) 487-0580 *Founded/Ownrshp* 1993
Sales 101.0MM[E] *EMP* 3[E]
SIC 5199 Novelties, paper; Gifts & novelties
Pr: Charles W Hudson
**Sec:* Susan Grimland
**VP:* Tim Hudson
VP Sls: Dan B Grimland

P.C. RICHARD & SON
See PC RICHARD & SON INC

D-U-N-S 84-207-9873 IMP
PC RICHARD & SON INC
P.C. RICHARD & SON
(*Suby of* A J RICHARD & SONS INC) ★
150 Price Pkwy, Farmingdale, NY 11735-1315
Tel (631) 843-4300 *Founded/Ownrshp* 1993
Sales 489.9MM[E] *EMP* 2,600
SIC 5722 5064 7629 7623 Household appliance stores; Electrical appliances, television & radio; Electrical repair shops; Refrigeration service & repair
Pr: Gregg Richard
**CFO:* Thomas Pohmer
**Treas:* Kevin Hughey
**VP:* Peter Richard
VP Sls: Jack Halperin

D-U-N-S 07-839-7246
PC RICHARD & SON LLC
(*Suby of* PC RICHARD & SON) ★
150 Price Pkwy, Farmingdale, NY 11735-1315
Tel (631) 843-4300 *Founded/Ownrshp* 1999
Sales 66.0MM[E] *EMP* 2,600
SIC 5999 Alarm signal systems
Pr: Dan Cathy
**CEO:* Greg Richard

D-U-N-S 10-626-7958
PC SPECIALISTS INC
TECHNOLOGY INTEGRATION GROUP
10240 Flanders Ct, San Diego, CA 92121-2901
Tel (858) 566-1900 *Founded/Ownrshp* 1983
Sales 337.2MM *EMP* 430
SIC 5045 5734 7371

PC TOPCOL HOLDING
See PC INTERMEDIATE HOLDINGS INC

PC WHOLESALE
See INSIGHT NORTH AMERICA INC

D-U-N-S 87-909-6659
▲ PC-TEL INC
471 Brighton Ct, Bloomingdale, IL 60108-3102
Tel (630) 372-6800 *Founded/Ownrshp* 1994
Sales 106.6MM *EMP* 491[E]
Tkr Sym PCTI *Exch* NGM
SIC 5731 4812 7372 Antennas; Radio telephone communication; Prepackaged software
Ch Bd: Martin H Singer
CFO: John W Schoen
Sr VP: Rishi Bharadwaj
Sr VP: Jeffrey A Miller
Sr VP: David A Neumann
VP: David Rofola
VP: John Thakkar
VP: James Zik
Exec: Les Sgnilek
Dir Bus: Phil Duff
Opers Mgr: Aditya Shah
Board of Directors: Cindy K Andreotti, Gina Haspilaire, Brian J Jackman, Steven D Levy, Giacomo Marini, M Jay Sinder

PCA
See PHILADELPHIA CORP FOR AGING INC

D-U-N-S 00-301-1731 IMP/EXP
■ PCA CORRUGATED AND DISPLAY LLC
(*Suby of* PACKAGING CORP OF AMERICA) ★
148 Penn St, Hanover, PA 17331-1952
Tel (717) 632-4727 *Founded/Ownrshp* 2016
Sales 331.0MM *EMP* 890
SIC 2653 5113 Boxes, corrugated: made from purchased materials; Corrugated & solid fiber boxes
CEO: Thomas A Hassfurther
VP: Matthew J Heleva
Plnt Mgr: Tom Staub
Sls Mgr: Cameron Becker
Sls Mgr: Richard Segrave-Daly
Snr Mgr: Joseph Carbaugh
Snr Mgr: Scott Soderberg

PCA PHARMACY
See PCA-CORRECTIONS LLC

D-U-N-S 92-728-9785
PCA-CORRECTIONS LLC
PCA PHARMACY
2701 Chestnut Station Ct, Louisville, KY 40299-6395
Tel (502) 526-0375 *Founded/Ownrshp* 1994
Sales 142.5MM[E] *EMP* 528
SIC 5122 Pharmaceuticals
Dir Bus: Matt Young
Opers Mgr: John Murphy
Sales Exec: Belinda Cunningham
Snr Mgr: Connie O'Connell

D-U-N-S 36-414-7124
■ PCB GROUP INC
ICP
(*Suby of* MTS SYSTEMS CORP) ★
3425 Walden Ave, Depew, NY 14043-2417
Tel (716) 684-0001 *Founded/Ownrshp* 2016
Sales 224.9MM[E] *EMP* 915
SIC 3679 3823 Transducers, electrical; Industrial instrmnts msrmnt display/control process variable
CEO: Mike Lally
**Ch Bd:* James F Lally
Mng Dir: Graham Turgoose
IT Man: Wolfgang Buechler
Opers Mgr: John Betzig
Opers Mgr: Larry Dick
Mktg Mgr: Trish Steding
Sls Mgr: Terry McCarville

D-U-N-S 04-256-8774
■ PCB PIEZOTRONICS INC
IMI SENSORS
(*Suby of* ICP) ★
3425 Walden Ave, Depew, NY 14043-2495
Tel (716) 684-0001 *Founded/Ownrshp* 1967
Sales 180.0MM *EMP* 858
SIC 3829 3679

PCC
See PRECISION CASTPARTS CORP

PCC AEROSTRUCTURES
See PRIMUS INTERNATIONAL INC

D-U-N-S 14-748-9488 IMP/EXP
■ PCC AIRFOILS LLC
(*Suby of* PCC) ★
3401 Entp Pkwy Ste 200, Beachwood, OH 44122
Tel (216) 831-3590 *Founded/Ownrshp* 2002
Sales 637.0MM[E] *EMP* 3,000
SIC 3369 Nonferrous foundries
VP: Salim Sitabkhan
Genl Mgr: Michael O'Brien
Sfty Dirs: Jeff Thomas
Opers Mgr: Scott Moody
Ql Cn Mgr: Cheryl Stroup

PCC NATURAL MARKETS
See PUGET CONSUMERS CO-OP

PCC NORTHWEST
See PACIFIC COAST CONTAINER INC

PCC SCHLOSSER
See PCC STRUCTURALS INC

PCC SPS FASTENER DIVISION
See SPS TECHNOLOGIES LLC

D-U-N-S 00-121-1796 IMP
■ PCC STRUCTURALS GROTON
(*Suby of* WYMAN-GORDON CO) ★
839 Poquonnock Rd, Groton, CT 06340-4537
Tel (860) 405-3700 *Founded/Ownrshp* 1990
Sales 272.4MM[E] *EMP* 2,200
SIC 3364 Nonferrous die-castings except aluminum
Pr: Joseph B Cox
**Ch Bd:* William C McCormick
Genl Mgr: Jim Wilbur
IT Man: Steve Jesse

D-U-N-S 01-209-0945 IMP
■ PCC STRUCTURALS INC
PCC SCHLOSSER
(*Suby of* PCC) ★
4600 Se Harney Dr, Portland, OR 97206-0825
Tel (503) 777-3881 *Founded/Ownrshp* 1996
Sales 773.1MM[E] *EMP* 3,000
SIC 3728 3842 3511 3824 Aircraft parts & equipment; Limbs, artificial; Gas turbine generator set units, complete; Impeller & counter driven flow meters
Pr: Kevin M Stein
**CFO:* William Larsson
VP: Michael Kuiawa
IT Man: Bret Clayton
Tech Mgr: Larry Fishman
Ql Cn Mgr: Robert Dixon
Sls Mgr: Sean Athey
Sls Mgr: James Haman

PCCA
See PROFESSIONAL COMPOUNDING CENTERS OF AMERICA INC

PCCC
See PASSAIC COUNTY COMMUNITY COLLEGE (INC)

D-U-N-S 12-101-9462 IMP
PCCW GLOBAL INC
(*Suby of* PCCW LIMITED)
450 Springpark Pl Ste 100, Herndon, VA 20170-5269
Tel (703) 621-1600 *Founded/Ownrshp* 2002
Sales 2.4MMM[E] *EMP* 16,200
SIC 4813
CEO: Marc Halbfinger
Pr: Richard Brolly
Pr: Scott Butterworth
Pr: Carlos Dasilva
CFO: Steve Kozlowicki
CFO: Teresa Young
Sr VP: Frederick Chui
Sr VP: Jordick Wong

Sr VP: Sunny Yeung
VP: Ron Bajor
VP: Benney Cheng
VP: Sam Cheng
VP: Ronnie Klingner
VP: Olivier Lepretre
VP: Ying Liang
VP: Angela Lui
VP: Frantisek Samla
VP: Rex Stover
VP: Neil Templeton
VP: John Wat

D-U-N-S 87-803-5351
PCCW TELESERVICES (US) INC
INFLUENT
5200 Rings Rd, Dublin, OH 43017-3557
Tel (614) 652-6300 *Founded/Ownrshp* 1995
Sales 132.3MM^E *EMP* 1,300
SIC 7389 7299 Telemarketing services; Personal financial services
Ch Bd: Andrew C Jacobs
Pr: Mark K Attinger
CFO: Roger Jacobs
Sec: Scott P Lee
VP: Jim Garwood
Creative D: Miranda Kelton
Telecom Mg: Michael Barnett
VP Sls: Melanie Jones
Mktg Mgr: Dawn Foster
Board of Directors: Fred Simon

D-U-N-S 60-426-2147
PCE CONSTRUCTORS INC
13544 Eads Rd, Prairieville, LA 70769-4433
Tel (225) 677-9100 *Founded/Ownrshp* 2002
Sales 100.6MM^E *EMP* 500
SIC 1629 Industrial plant construction
Pr: Bob N Robards
**Sec:* Rhonda Gibson
**VP:* Mark H Allen
**VP:* Mark N Robards
Genl Mgr: Mark Robards
IT Man: Jared Moss

D-U-N-S 87-637-5916 IMP/EXP
PCE INC
LINCOLN PLASTICS
1711 Yolande Ave, Lincoln, NE 68521-1833
Tel (402) 474-4690 *Founded/Ownrshp* 2012
Sales 100.2MM^E *EMP* 250
SIC 3089 3644 3088 Plastic processing; Insulators & insulation materials, electrical; Plastics plumbing fixtures
Pr: Sam Featherston
Sales Exec: Ranelle Rundquist
VP Sls: John Durkin
Mktg Mgr: John EBY
Mktg Mgr: Ranelle Rundqist
Sls Mgr: Alan Kalish

PCG
See PERFORMANCE CONTRACTING GROUP INC

D-U-N-S 13-437-1207 IMP
■ **PCG PARENT CORP**
CONVERGE
(*Suby of* ARROW ELECTRONICS INC) ★
4 Technology Dr, Peabody, MA 01960-7907
Tel (978) 538-8000 *Founded/Ownrshp* 2010
Sales 85.2MM^E *EMP* 350
SIC 5045 5065 4953 5093 7378 Computers; Computer peripheral equipment; Electronic parts; Semiconductor devices; Refuse collection & disposal services; Non-hazardous waste disposal sites; Acid waste, collection & disposal; Scrap & waste materials; Computer maintenance & repair
Pr: Peter Brown
CFO: Derrick Barker
Treas: Michael Taunton

D-U-N-S 07-587-6347 IMP
■ **PCG TRADING LLC**
CONVERGE
(*Suby of* ARROW ELECTRONICS INC) ★
4 Technology Dr, Peabody, MA 01960-7907
Tel (978) 538-8000 *Founded/Ownrshp* 2015
Sales 237.1MM^E *EMP* 350
SIC 5045 5065 4953 5093 7378 Computers; Computer peripheral equipment; Electronic parts; Semiconductor devices; Refuse collection & disposal services; Non-hazardous waste disposal sites; Acid waste, collection & disposal; Hazardous waste collection & disposal; Scrap & waste materials; Computer maintenance & repair
Pr: Jerry Sheveland
Sr Pt: Slim Bargaoui
COO: George Devlin
**CFO:* Kevin J Harney
**Sr VP:* Doug Fagerstrom
**VP:* Eric Checkoway
QA Dir: Mark Maximo
IT Man: Ron Bergeron
IT Man: Dorothy McClung
IT Man: Kent Tan
Web Dev: Vinaya Tiri

D-U-N-S 00-456-3610
PCH HOTELS AND RESORTS INC
11 N Water St Ste 8290, Mobile, AL 36602-5008
Tel (251) 338-5600 *Founded/Ownrshp* 2000
Sales 100.3MM^E *EMP* 1,900
SIC 7011 Hotels & motels
CEO: Tony Davis
VP: David Brown
Genl Mgr: Bruce Smith

PCI
See PYRAMID CONSULTING INC

PCI
See PACKAGING CONCEPTS INC

PCI
See PRECISION COMPONENTS INTERNATIONAL INC

PCI SERVICES OF ILLINOIS
See ANDERSONBRECON INC

PCITEC
See PANAMERICA COMPUTERS INC

D-U-N-S 11-597-8496 IMP
PCL CIVIL CONSTRUCTORS INC
(*Suby of* PCL CONSTRUCTION ENTERPRISES INC) ★
2000 S Colo Blvd Ste 2-50, Denver, CO 80222
Tel (303) 365-6500 *Founded/Ownrshp* 1984
Sales 310.9MM^E *EMP* 800
Accts Kpmg Llp Edmonton Canada
SIC 1611 1622 1623 1629 General contractor, highway & street construction; Bridge construction; Tunnel construction; Aqueduct construction; Dam construction
Prin: Luis Ventoza
Ch Bd: Peter E Beaupre
Pr: Jason Idler
Pr: Roger Martin
Pr: John Moreno
Pr: Luis S Ventoza
Pr: Shaun Yancey
Ex VP: Gord Maron
VP: Glen Anderson
VP: Roger Keglowitsch
VP: Graham Knight
VP: Blaine Maciborsky
VP: Roger C Martin
VP: Thomas R O'Donnel
VP: Allen Ross
VP: Gary Trigg

D-U-N-S 11-883-2153
PCL CONSTRUCTION ENTERPRISES INC
(*Suby of* PCL US HOLDINGS INC) ★
2000 S Colorado Blvd 2-500, Denver, CO 80222-7908
Tel (303) 365-6500 *Founded/Ownrshp* 1984
Sales 2.4MMM^E *EMP* 3,300^E
Accts Kpmg Llp Edmonton Canada
SIC 1542 Specialized public building contractors; Hospital construction; Commercial & office building, new construction
Sr VP: Shaun P Yancey
**Treas:* Michael J Kehoe
**Rgnl VP:* Luis S Ventoza
**Ex VP:* Al E Troppmann
VP: Dave Yount

D-U-N-S 13-085-6909 IMP
PCL CONSTRUCTION SERVICES INC
(*Suby of* PCL CONSTRUCTION ENTERPRISES INC) ★
2000 S Colorado Blvd 2-500, Denver, CO 80222-7908
Tel (303) 365-6500 *Founded/Ownrshp* 1906
Sales 624.3MM^E *EMP* 1,200
SIC 1542 1541 Commercial & office building, new construction; Specialized public building contractors; Hospital construction; School building construction; Warehouse construction
Prin: Frank Terrasi
**Ch Bd:* Peter E Beaupre
**Pr:* Al E Troppmenn
**CEO:* Paul Douglas
**COO:* Rob Holmberg
**CFO:* Gordon Panas
**Treas:* Gena M Hannaway
**VP:* Deron L Brown
**VP:* Thomas R Doig
**VP:* Don B Fromme
**VP:* Dale R Kain
**VP:* Wayne W Melnyk
**VP:* James H Nobles
**VP:* Colin M Terras
**VP:* Jeff D Westphal
**VP:* David M Yount

D-U-N-S 16-063-1573
PCL INDUSTRIAL CONSTRUCTION CO
(*Suby of* PCL CONSTRUCTION ENTERPRISES INC) ★
6445 Shiloh Rd Ste E, Alpharetta, GA 30005-8407
Tel (678) 965-3100 *Founded/Ownrshp* 2003
Sales 352.5MM^E *EMP* 800^E
Accts Kpmg Llp Edmonton Canada
SIC 1629 1541 Industrial plant construction; Industrial buildings & warehouses
Pr: John Moreno
**CFO:* Donald J Knicely

D-U-N-S 10-233-3986
PCL US HOLDINGS INC
(*Suby of* PCL CONSTRUCTION GROUP INC)
2000 S Colorado Blvd 2-500, Denver, CO 80222-7900
Tel (303) 365-6591 *Founded/Ownrshp* 1983
Sales 2.4MMM^E *EMP* 4,300^E
SIC 1542 1611 Commercial & office building, new construction; Institutional building construction; Highway & street construction
Prin: Shaun Yancey
Pr: Peter E Beaupre
Ex VP: Peter A Stalenhoef
VP: Dave Filipchuk
VP: Michael Kehoe

D-U-N-S 18-108-7842
▲ **PCM INC**
1940 E Mariposa Ave, El Segundo, CA 90245-3457
Tel (310) 354-5600 *Founded/Ownrshp* 1987
Sales 1.6MMM *EMP* 3,739^E
Tkr Sym PCMI *Exch* NGM
SIC 5734 5961 5731 5045 Computer & software stores; Personal computers; Computer peripheral equipment; Computer software & accessories; Computer equipment & electronics, mail order; Computers & peripheral equipment, mail order; Computer software, mail order; Radio, television & electronic stores; Computers, peripherals & software; Computers; Computer peripheral equipment; Computer software
Ch Bd: Frank F Khulusi
Pr: Robert J Miley
CFO: Brandon H Laverne
CFO: Elizabeth Murray
Ex VP: Simon M Abuyounes
Ex VP: Daniel Devries
VP: Judith Abuyones
VP: Kristin Bolte
VP: Charles Deerinck
VP: Robert Kite
VP: Phil Mogavero
VP: Gertrud Pillay
Board of Directors: Paul C Heeschen, Thomas A Maloof, Ronald B Reck

D-U-N-S 60-837-5056 EXP
■ **PCM SALES INC**
MICRO P TECHNOLOGIES
(*Suby of* PCM INC) ★
1940 E Mariposa Ave, El Segundo, CA 90245-3457
Tel (310) 354-5600 *Founded/Ownrshp* 1985
Sales 176.6MM^E *EMP* 800^E
SIC 5734 Computer peripheral equipment
CEO: Joseph Hayek
Pr: Kristin Rogers
**CEO:* Peter Freix
**CEO:* Greg Richey
**CFO:* Brandon H Laverne
Ex VP: Simon Abuyounes
**Ex VP:* Robert I Newton
VP: Scott Sova
Exec: Rory Zaks
VP Mktg: Mathew Clarke
Sls Mgr: Adam Benedict

PCMA
See PROFESSIONAL CONVENTION MANAGEMENT ASSOCIATION

PCMC
See PAPER CONVERTING MACHINE CO

PCOM
See PHILADELPHIA COLLEGE OF OSTEOPATHIC MEDICINE

D-U-N-S 62-128-7635
PCPC DIRECT LTD
10690 Shadow Wood Dr # 132, Houston, TX 77043-2840
Tel (713) 984-8808 *Founded/Ownrshp* 2005
Sales 119.7MM^E *EMP* 68
SIC 5045 7378 7379 Computers, peripherals & software; Computer maintenance & repair; Computer related consulting services
VP: Joe Vaught
CFO: Sam Moulton

D-U-N-S 02-815-9163
PCPC INC
10690 Shadow Wood Dr # 132, Houston, TX 77043-2840
Tel (713) 984-8808 *Founded/Ownrshp* 1894
Sales 146.9MM^E *EMP* 62
SIC 5045 7378 7379 Computers, peripherals & software; Computer maintenance & repair; Computer related consulting services
VP: Joe Vaught
**CFO:* Joseph R Vaught
**VP:* Cornelia Vaught

D-U-N-S 02-761-4426 IMP
■ **PCS FERGUSON INC**
PRODUCTION CONTROL SERVICES
(*Suby of* NORRIS PRODUCTION SOLUTIONS) ★
3771 Eureka Way, Frederick, CO 80516-9446
Tel (720) 407-3550 *Founded/Ownrshp* 2012
Sales 90.5MM^E *EMP* 300
SIC 3533 5084 Oil & gas field machinery; Industrial machinery & equipment
Pr: Robert A Livingston
**CFO:* Jason Taylor
**VP:* Andrew Drew Boldt
**VP:* Darryl Polasek
Sfty Mgr: Carl Richards

D-U-N-S 85-840-4015 IMP
PCS NITROGEN FERTILIZER OPERATIONS INC
(*Suby of* PCS NITROGEN INC) ★
1101 Skokie Blvd Ste 400, Northbrook, IL 60062-4123
Tel (847) 849-4200 *Founded/Ownrshp* 1997
Sales 104.0MM^E *EMP* 324
SIC 2873 Nitrogenous fertilizers
COO: David Delaney
**Pr:* Brett Heimann
**Treas:* Wayne R Brownlee
**Sec:* Bryan E Johnson
**VP:* Fritz Bertz

D-U-N-S 60-500-2864 IMP/EXP
PCS NITROGEN INC
(*Suby of* POTASH CORPORATION OF SASKATCHEWAN INC)
1101 Skokie Blvd Ste 400, Northbrook, IL 60062-4123
Tel (847) 849-4200 *Founded/Ownrshp* 1997
Sales 376.9MM^E *EMP* 1,350
SIC 2873 2874 Nitrogenous fertilizers; Ammonia & ammonium salts; Urea; Ammonium nitrate, ammonium sulfate; Phosphatic fertilizers
Pr: Tom Regan
VP: Lee Gooch
Snr Mgr: Sam Roberts

D-U-N-S 00-131-6884 IMP/EXP
PCS PHOSPHATE CO INC
PCS SALES
(*Suby of* POTASH CORPORATION OF SASKATCHEWAN INC)
1101 Skokie Blvd Ste 400, Northbrook, IL 60062-4123
Tel (847) 849-4200 *Founded/Ownrshp* 1981
Sales 12.5MM^E *EMP* 1,600
SIC 1475 1474 2874 2819 Phosphate rock; Potash mining; Phosphatic fertilizers; Phosphates, except fertilizers: defluorinated & ammoniated
Pr: Brent Heimann
**Pr:* Thomas J Regan Jr
Genl Mgr: Richard C Atwood

PCS SALES
See PCS PHOSPHATE CO INC

D-U-N-S 11-559-4541 EXP
PCS SALES (USA) INC
(*Suby of* POTASH CORPORATION OF SASKATCHEWAN INC)
1101 Skokie Blvd Ste 400, Northbrook, IL 60062-4123
Tel (847) 849-4200 *Founded/Ownrshp* 1976
Sales 306.5MM^E *EMP* 150
SIC 5191 Fertilizer & fertilizer materials
CEO: William J Doyle
**Pr:* Bill Doyle
**CFO:* Wayne R Brown
**Ex VP:* Dave G Delaney
**VP:* Denis Sirois
Dir Surg: Annette Pilipiak

D-U-N-S 00-814-1843 IMP
PCS WIRELESS LLC
11 Vreeland Rd, Florham Park, NJ 07932-1511
Tel (973) 805-7400 *Founded/Ownrshp* 1997
Sales 221.8MM^E *EMP* 300
SIC 5065 5999 Mobile telephone equipment; Communication equipment; Mobile telephones & equipment; Communication equipment
Exec: Morris Bukai
Dir Bus: Alexandra Amrami
Dir Bus: Ronald Hans
CIO: Jason Grenard
Pr Mgr: Victor Bukai

PCS-CTS
See CSAT SOLUTIONS LP

PCSI
See PROFESSIONAL CONTRACT SERVICES INC

D-U-N-S 94-203-8196 IMP
PCT INTERNATIONAL INC
(*Suby of* ANDES INDUSTRIES INC) ★
2260 W Broadway Rd # 101, Mesa, AZ 85202-1899
Tel (480) 813-0925 *Founded/Ownrshp* 2000
Sales 154.2MM^E *EMP* 1,400
SIC 3663 Antennas, transmitting & communications
Pr: Steven Youtsey
COO: Craig Youtsey
**Sec:* Angie Rodrigue
Ex VP: Mike Sparkman
**Ex VP:* Brandon Wilson
VP: Clay Henley
VP: Rob Privett
VP: Leonard Visser
Dir IT: Jose Mariscal
Plnt Mgr: Darren Youtsey

D-U-N-S 14-625-4474 IMP
PCX AEROSTRUCTURES LLC
300 Fenn Rd, Newington, CT 06111-2277
Tel (860) 666-2471 *Founded/Ownrshp* 2009
Sales 100.0MM *EMP* 300
SIC 3728 Aircraft parts & equipment
CEO: Alan Haase
**CFO:* Tim Fagan
Genl Mgr: Trevor Hartman
Board of Directors: Jeff Frisby, Gregory L Steiner

PD TEMPO
See PROCESS DISPLAYS LLC

PDC
See PRECISION DYNAMICS CORP

D-U-N-S 05-570-0389
▲ **PDC ENERGY INC**
1775 N Sherman St # 3000, Denver, CO 80203-1100
Tel (303) 860-5800 *Founded/Ownrshp* 1969
Sales 595.3MM *EMP* 362^E
Tkr Sym PDCE *Exch* NGS
SIC 1311 1381 Crude petroleum & natural gas; Crude petroleum production; Natural gas production; Drilling oil & gas wells
Pr: Barton R Brookman Jr
**Ch Bd:* Jeffrey C Swoveland
CFO: R Scott Meyers
Ex VP: Lance A Lauck
Sr VP: Daniel W Amidon
Sr VP: Scott J Reasoner
VP: George B Courcier
VP: Jim Gaulke
Sls Dir: Arthur Seligman
Board of Directors: Joseph E Casabona, Anthony J Crisafio, Larry F Mazza, David C Parke, Kimberly Luff Wakim

D-U-N-S 78-419-7766
▲ **PDF SOLUTIONS INC**
333 W San Carlos St # 700, San Jose, CA 95110-2711
Tel (408) 280-7900 *Founded/Ownrshp* 1992
Sales 97.9MM *EMP* 390^E
Tkr Sym PDFS *Exch* NGM
SIC 7371 Computer software development
Pr: John K Kibarian
**Ch Bd:* Lucio L Lanza
CFO: Gregory Walker
VP: Thomas F Cobourn PHD
VP: Cees Hartgring
VP: Zia Malik
VP: P S Melman
**VP:* Kimon Michaels
VP: Kimon W Michaels
VP: Richard Mousti S
Genl Mgr: P K Mozumder

D-U-N-S 15-508-4460
▲ **PDL BIOPHARMA INC**
932 Southwood Blvd, Incline Village, NV 89451-7413
Tel (775) 832-8500 *Founded/Ownrshp* 1986
Sales 590.4MM *EMP* 10
Tkr Sym PDLI *Exch* NGS
SIC 2836 Biological products, except diagnostic
Pr: John P McLaughlin
CFO: Peter Garcia
VP: Danny Hart
VP: Christopher Stone

D-U-N-S 03-130-1232 IMP
■ **PDM STEEL SERVICE CENTERS INC** (CA)
SPECIALTY STEEL SERVICE
(*Suby of* RELIANCE STEEL & ALUMINUM CO) ★
3535 E Myrtle St, Stockton, CA 95205-4721
Tel (209) 943-0555 *Founded/Ownrshp* 1954
Sales 257.6MM^E *EMP* 450
SIC 5051 Steel
Pr: Derick Halecky
**VP:* Joseph Anderson
**VP:* Brad Blickle
**VP:* Randy H Kearns
**VP:* William Nixon
Genl Mgr: Mike Hill
VP Opers: Randy Kearns

D-U-N-S 02-457-7546 EXP
PDNC LLC (FL)
P D C
(*Suby of* CHENEY BROTHERS) ★
402 Commerce Ct, Goldsboro, NC 27534-7048
Tel (919) 778-3000 *Founded/Ownrshp* 1885, 2016
Sales 208.3MM^E *EMP* 425
SIC 5142 5141 5147 5148 5431

D-U-N-S 07-745-4577
PDP GROUP INC
PDP TECHNOLOGIES
10909 Mccormick Rd, Hunt Valley, MD 21031-1401
Tel (410) 584-2000 *Founded/Ownrshp* 1974
Sales NA *EMP* 350
SIC 6411 Insurance brokers; Information bureaus, insurance
Pr: William M Pitcher
**CFO:* Charles Feihe
**Ex VP:* James Pitcher
Sr VP: Beverly Devine
Dir IT: Jim Grant
IT Man: Kenneth Frey
Sls Dir: Chuck Verschoore

PDP TECHNOLOGIES
See PDP GROUP INC

PDS
See PACIFIC DENTAL SERVICES INC

D-U-N-S 09-903-5891
PDS TECH INC
300 E John Carpenter Fwy # 700, Irving, TX 75062-2383
Tel (214) 647-9600 *Founded/Ownrshp* 1977
Sales 321.4MM *EMP* 10,000
Accts Bkm Sowan Horan Llp Addison
SIC 7361 Employment agencies
CEO: Arthur R Janes
**Pr:* Cash Nickerson
CFO: Steven C Nickerson
VP Bus: Rick Vogel
Dir Bus: Jeff Castellanos
Brnch Mgr: Mary Gillham
IT Man: Steven McNeill
Counsel: Michael J Foley

D-U-N-S 08-029-1068
PDV HOLDING INC
(*Suby of* PETROLEOS DE VENEZUELA SA)
6100 S Yale Ave, Tulsa, OK 74136-1923
Tel (918) 495-4000 *Founded/Ownrshp* 1988
Sales 2.7MMM^E *EMP* 5,002^E
SIC 2911 2992 5171 4213 Petroleum refining; Gasoline; Diesel fuels; Jet fuels; Lubricating oils & greases; Petroleum bulk stations & terminals; Trucking, except local
Ch Bd: Claus Graff
**Ch Bd:* Claus Graf

D-U-N-S 15-994-1293
PDV MIDWEST REFINING LLC
CITGO REFINERY
(*Suby of* CITGO HOLDING INC) ★
135th St New Ave, Lemont, IL 60439
Tel (630) 257-7761 *Founded/Ownrshp* 1997
Sales 138.4MM^E *EMP* 540
Accts Deloitte & Touche Llp Tulsa
SIC 2992 2911 5171 4213 Lubricating oils & greases; Petroleum refining; Petroleum bulk stations & terminals; Trucking, except local
Pr: Jenny Allums

D-U-N-S 36-289-9452
PDX INC
NATIONAL HEALTH INFO NETWRK
101 S Jim Wright Fwy # 100, White Settlement, TX 76108-2212
Tel (817) 246-6760 *Founded/Ownrshp* 1986
Sales 141.9MM^E *EMP* 440
SIC 7371 Computer software development
Ch: Kenneth A Hill Sr
**Pr:* Brad Crosslin
**CEO:* Jeffrey L Farris
**CFO:* Mike Ingram
**Sr VP:* Ben Loy
Sr VP: Mark Stalzer
VP: Jason Adama
VP: Brent Barber
**VP:* Jim Cummins
VP: Steve Friedman
**VP:* Michael Ingram
VP: Benjamin Loy
VP: Stephanie McBroom
VP: Dewitt McClaran
VP: Gerald Ray
VP: Mark A Stalzer

D-U-N-S 01-805-8833
PEABODY BEAR RUN MINING LLC
(*Suby of* PEABODY ENERGY CORP) ★
7100 Eagle Crest Blvd, Evansville, IN 47715-8152
Tel (812) 659-7126 *Founded/Ownrshp* 2009
Sales 423.6MM^E *EMP* 574
SIC 1221 Bituminous coal & lignite-surface mining
Pr: Keith R Haley
**Treas:* James A Tichenor
**Sr VP:* Walter L Hawkins Jr
**Sr VP:* Bradley E Phillips
**VP:* Darral G Heaton
**VP:* Kentland D Holcomb
**VP:* John F Quinn Jr
**VP:* Brandon Risner
**VP:* Kenneth L Wagner

D-U-N-S 00-696-8234
PEABODY COAL CO
PEABODY ENERGY
(*Suby of* PEABODY HOLDING CO LLC) ★
701 Market St, Saint Louis, MO 63101-1830
Tel (314) 342-3400 *Founded/Ownrshp* 1883, 1990
Sales 5.1MMM^E *EMP* 1,900
SIC 1222 1221

D-U-N-S 80-978-3517
PEABODY COALSALES LLC
(*Suby of* PEABODY ENERGY CORP) ★
701 Market St Fl 9, Saint Louis, MO 63101-1830
Tel (314) 342-3400 *Founded/Ownrshp* 2015
Sales 110.7MM^E *EMP* 150
SIC 5052 Coal
Pr: Richard M Whiting
Treas: Walter L Hawkins Jr
VP Sls: James C Campbell

PEABODY ENERGY
See PEABODY COAL CO

PEABODY ENERGY
See PEABODY INVESTMENTS CORP

D-U-N-S 02-519-1797
PEABODY ENERGY CORP
701 Market St, Saint Louis, MO 63101-1830
Tel (314) 342-3400 *Founded/Ownrshp* 1883
Sales 5.6MMM *EMP* 7,600^E
Accts Ernst & Young Llp St Louis
SIC 1221 1222 Surface mining, bituminous; Bituminous coal-underground mining
Pr: Glenn Kellow
**Ch Bd:* Robert A Malone
Pr: Rick A Bowen
Pr: Allen T Capdeboscq
Pr: Erik L Ludtke
Pr: Mark N Schroeder
CFO: Amy B Schwetz
CFO: Gregg P Wickstra
Ex VP: Andrew P Slentz
Grp VP: Jiri Nemec
Sr VP: Allen Capdeboscq
Sr VP: Marc Hathhorn
Sr VP: Scott P Lawson
Sr VP: Delbert Lee Lobb
Sr VP: Bradley E Phillips
Sr VP: Robert L Reilly
VP: Michael Bailey
VP: Summer Belden
VP: Walter L Hawkins
VP: Jeffrey Maher
VP: James Martin
Board of Directors: William A Coley, William E James, Robert B Karn III, Henry E Lentz, William C Rusnack, Michael W Sutherlin, John F Turner, Sandra A Van Trease, Heather A Wilson

D-U-N-S 09-266-1230
PEABODY HOLDING CO LLC
(*Suby of* PEABODY ENERGY CORP) ★
701 Market St Ste 700, Saint Louis, MO 63101-1895
Tel (314) 342-3400 *Founded/Ownrshp* 1993
Sales 5.1MMM^E *EMP* 5,079^E
SIC 1221 1222 5052 2873 6719 Surface mining, bituminous; Bituminous coal-underground mining; Coal; Ammonium nitrate, ammonium sulfate; Investment holding companies, except banks
**Pr:* Glenn Kellow
**CFO:* Mike Cruz
**Treas:* Walter Hawkins
**Ex VP:* Michael C Crews
**Ex VP:* Sharon D Fiehler
**Ex VP:* Jeane L Hull

PEABODY HOTEL GROUP
See BELZ HOTEL GROUP LLC

D-U-N-S 83-251-9222
PEABODY INVESTMENTS CORP
PEABODY ENERGY
(*Suby of* PEABODY ENERGY CORP) ★
701 Market St, Saint Louis, MO 63101-1830
Tel (314) 342-3400 *Founded/Ownrshp* 2001
Sales 2.3MMM^E *EMP* 3,181^E
SIC 6211 Investment bankers
Pr: Glenn Kellow
**Ex VP:* Michael C Crews

D-U-N-S 79-664-0969
PEABODY MIDWEST MINING LLC
BLACK BEAUTY MINING DIV
(*Suby of* PEABODY ENERGY CORP) ★
566 Dickeyville Rd, Lynnville, IN 47619-8257
Tel (812) 434-8500 *Founded/Ownrshp* 2006
Sales 738.0MM^E *EMP* 1,000
SIC 1221 1222 1241 Bituminous coal surface mining; Bituminous coal-underground mining; Coal mining services
**Pr:* C A Burggraf
**Treas:* W L Hawkins Jr
VP: Eugene Aimone
**VP:* J F Quinn

D-U-N-S 04-401-5092 IMP
PEABODY NATURAL RESOURCES CO
LEE RANCH COAL
701 Market St Ste 700, Saint Louis, MO 63101-1826
Tel (314) 342-3400 *Founded/Ownrshp* 1991
Sales 88.4MM^E *EMP* 201
SIC 1221 Bituminous coal & lignite-surface mining
VP: Kennedy Collon
MIS Mgr: Gary Wendt

PEABODY ORLANDO, THE
See BELV PARTNERS LP

D-U-N-S 14-685-9285
■ PEACE CORPS
(*Suby of* EXECUTIVE OFFICE OF UNITED STATES GOVERNMENT) ★
1111 20th St Nw, Washington, DC 20526-0002
Tel (202) 692-2000 *Founded/Ownrshp* 1961
Sales NA *EMP* 1,112
Accts Clifton Gunderson Llp Arlingt
SIC 9721 Peace Corps;
CFO: George A Schutter
Ofcr: Elizabeth A Brooks
Ofcr: Kristine L Hoffer
Ofcr: Joseph Maruti
Ofcr: Brendan Scanlon
Off Admin: Laurent Clerc
Off Admin: Timothy Savoy
CIO: Judy Van Rest
IT Man: Gaddi H Vasquez

Opers Mgr: Marie Wheat
Plnt Mgr: Lloyd Pierson

D-U-N-S 05-096-7926
PEACE HEALTH SOUTHWEST MEDICAL CENTER
MEDICAL CENTER CAMPUS
(*Suby of* PEACEHEALTH SOUTHWEST MED CTR) ★
602 Ne 92nd Ave Ste 120, Vancouver, WA 98664-3265
Tel (360) 514-2250 *Founded/Ownrshp* 1966
Sales 3.9MM *EMP* 3,000
SIC 8062 7389 General medical & surgical hospitals; Fund raising organizations
Pr: Joseph M Kortum
**CFO:* David Willie
**Treas:* Laurie Kusch
Adm Dir: Christine C Rosanski
Off Mgr: Carrie Prigge
CIO: Petra Knolwles

D-U-N-S 07-970-5893
PEACE OF CHRIST ROMAN CATHOLIC PARISH
25 Empire Blvd, Rochester, NY 14609-4335
Tel (585) 288-5000 *Founded/Ownrshp* 1887
Sales 57.5MM^E *EMP* 4,300
SIC 8661 Catholic Church
Pr: Matthew Clark
Bd of Dir: Maribeth Mancini
Bd of Dir: Marilyn Trelly

D-U-N-S 18-917-5193
PEACE OFFICERS ANNUITY & BENEFITS FUND OF GEORGIA INC
1208 Greenbelt Dr, Griffin, GA 30224-4507
Tel (770) 228-8461 *Founded/Ownrshp* 1950
Sales 112.0MM *EMP* 7
Accts Russell W Hinton Cpa Cgfm
SIC 8399 Fund raising organization, non-fee basis
Pr: Roger Garrison
**Treas:* Robert Carter

D-U-N-S 00-479-5449
PEACE RIVER ELECTRIC COOPERATIVE INC (FL)
210 Metheny Rd, Wauchula, FL 33873-8721
Tel (800) 282-3824 *Founded/Ownrshp* 1940
Sales 93.4MM *EMP* 111^E
SIC 4911 Distribution, electric power
CEO: Randall Shaw
**Pr:* Bruce Vickers
**CFO:* Carol Braxton
VP: Gary Bartlett
VP: Louise Blackman
VP: Paul Roberts
Genl Mgr: William T Mulcay

D-U-N-S 10-161-3870
■ PEACE RIVER REGIONAL MEDICAL CENTER
HMA
(*Suby of* HMA) ★
2500 Harvard Blvd, Port Charlotte, FL 33952
Tel (941) 766-4122 *Founded/Ownrshp* 2004
Sales 141.8MM *EMP* 2
SIC 8062 General medical & surgical hospitals
CEO: David M Cormack
**COO:* Joane Jeannette
**CFO:* Cheryl Tibett
Ofcr: Richard Satcher
Adm Dir: Jon Rowzie
**Ex Dir:* Ted Keeley
QA Dir: Debra David
IT Man: Terri Spence

D-U-N-S 07-663-3189 IMP
PEACEHEALTH
1115 Se 164th Ave, Vancouver, WA 98683-9324
Tel (360) 788-6841 *Founded/Ownrshp* 1976
Sales 2.5MMM *EMP* 6,690
SIC 8062 8011 General medical & surgical hospitals; Medical centers
Pr: Liz Dunne
Pr: James Farley
COO: Julie Halic
**COO:* Beth O'Brien
CFO: Peggy Allen
CFO: Tom Haywood
Treas: Roshan Parikh
**Treas:* Prill Ron
Treas: Peter Rowe
Bd of Dir: James Nakashima
Ofcr: Jim Barnhart
Ofcr: Victoria King
Sr VP: Dan Hein
Sr VP: Michael Murphy
Sr VP: Nancy Steiger
VP: Carol Aaron
VP: Michele Budd
**VP:* Andrea Nenzel
VP: Greg Orr
Dir Rx: Steve Arendt
Comm Man: Jim Godbold
Board of Directors: Alan Yordy

PEACEHEALTH SOUTHWEST MED CTR
See SOUTHWEST WASHINGTON HEALTH SYSTEM

D-U-N-S 10-174-5136
PEACEHEALTH SOUTHWEST MEDICAL CENTER
(*Suby of* PEACEHEALTH SOUTHWEST MED CTR) ★
400 Ne Mother Joseph Pl, Vancouver, WA 98664-3200
Tel (360) 514-2097 *Founded/Ownrshp* 2004
Sales 573.7MM *EMP* 2,470
Accts Kpmg Llp Portland Or
SIC 8099 Medical services organization
Pr: Joseph Kortum
Psych: Rebecca Hill

D-U-N-S 04-751-7952
PEACH BOTTOM TRANSPORT LLC
2663 Robert Fulton Hwy, Peach Bottom, PA 17563-9750
Tel (717) 278-8055 *Founded/Ownrshp* 2012
Sales 175.0MM *EMP* 2
SIC 2873 Fertilizers: natural (organic), except compost

Owner: Jordan A Skipper

D-U-N-S 17-016-4003 IMP/EXP
PEACH COUNTY HOLDINGS INC
402 Bluebird Blvd, Fort Valley, GA 31030-5088
Tel (478) 825-2021 *Founded/Ownrshp* 2004
Sales 101.5MM^E *EMP* 2,194
SIC 3713 3711 Truck & bus bodies; Chassis, motor vehicle; Motor homes, self-contained, assembly of
Pr: Keith Ramundo

D-U-N-S 96-863-7665
■ PEACH STATE HEALTH PLAN INC
(*Suby of* CENTENE CORP) ★
1100 Circle 75 Pkwy Se # 1100, Atlanta, GA 30339-3176
Tel (678) 556-2300 *Founded/Ownrshp* 2005
Sales NA *EMP* 185^E
SIC 6324 Hospital & medical service plans
CEO: Patrick Healy
**CFO:* William Scheffel
Off Mgr: Barbara Perry

D-U-N-S 62-659-6902
PEACH STATE ROOFING INC
1655 Spectrum Dr Ste A, Lawrenceville, GA 30043-7875
Tel (770) 962-7885 *Founded/Ownrshp* 1990
Sales 109.8MM^E *EMP* 400
SIC 1761 Roofing contractor
Pr: Marty Kelly
**CFO:* Mary Jane Kelly
**VP:* David Schmitt
Off Admin: Carol Bishop
Natl Sales: Neil Krock
Natl Sales: Brian Lauderdale
Sls Mgr: Bo Holloway

PEACHTREE HOME
See D&S RESIDENTIAL SERVICES LP

PEACH VALLEY RESTAURANT GROUP
See STONEWOOD HOLDINGS LLC

D-U-N-S 04-802-8463
PEACHTREE COMPANIES INC
1 Weathershield Plz, Medford, WI 54451-2206
Tel (715) 748-6555 *Founded/Ownrshp* 2001
Sales 101.3MM^E *EMP* 2,000
SIC 3442 2431 Window & door frames; Windows, wood
Pr: Kevin Schield
**Sec:* Starla A Reusch
**VP:* Mark A Schield

D-U-N-S 09-264-7197
PEACHTREE SOFTWARE INC
BEST SOFTWARE SMALL BUS DIV
1715 N Brown Rd, Lawrenceville, GA 30043-8119
Tel (770) 682-1542 *Founded/Ownrshp* 1994
Sales 98.4MM^E *EMP* 525
SIC 7372 7371

PEACOCK ENGINEERING CO LLC
See PEACOCK FOODS LLC

D-U-N-S 05-944-4042
PEACOCK FOODS LLC
PEACOCK ENGINEERING CO LLC
(*Suby of* CHARLESBANK CAPITAL PARTNERS LLC) ★
1800 Averill Rd, Geneva, IL 60134-1684
Tel (630) 845-9400 *Founded/Ownrshp* 2011
Sales 825.0MM *EMP* 900
SIC 4783 7389 Packing goods for shipping; Packaging & labeling services
CEO: Tom Sampson
Pr: Larry Aubry
**COO:* Charles Metzger
**CFO:* Martin Kroll
VP: Sandy Bury
Genl Mgr: Justin Musial
Plnt Mgr: Roger Bos
Plnt Mgr: David Byrne
VP Sls: Steve Russell
Sls Dir: Don Edgerton
Snr PM: Rich Bielik

D-U-N-S 87-913-8936 IMP
PEAK 10 INC
8910 Lenox Pointe Dr G, Charlotte, NC 28273-3431
Tel (704) 264-1010 *Founded/Ownrshp* 2014
Sales 174.0MM^E *EMP* 400
SIC 4813
CEO: Chris Downie
**Pr:* David Jones
**COO:* Jeff Spalding
**CFO:* Brian Noonan
VP: Michael Belote
VP: Monty Blight
VP: Keith Greene
VP: Jim Parks
Dir Bus: Tim Bonnet
Dir Bus: Mike Hickman
Dir Bus: Marco Onorato
Dir Bus: Bill Riker

PEAK 7 DEVELOPMENT CO
See PEAK 7 LLC

D-U-N-S 61-267-8099
PEAK 7 LLC
PEAK 7 DEVELOPMENT CO
100 S Main St, Breckenridge, CO 80424
Tel (888) 783-8883 *Founded/Ownrshp* 2005
Sales 96.3MM *EMP* 282
Accts Brockman Coats Gedelian & Co
SIC 6552 Subdividers & developers
Pr: Michael C Millisor
**VP:* Michael A Dudick
**VP:* Robert A Millisor

D-U-N-S 07-838-0426
PEAK EXPLORATION & PRODUCTION LLC
PEAK POWDER RIVER RESOURCES
1910 Main Ave, Durango, CO 81301-5038
Tel (970) 247-1500 *Founded/Ownrshp* 2010
Sales 100.0MM *EMP* 20
SIC 1382 Oil & gas exploration services
CEO: Jack Vaughn
Pr: Glen Christiansen

CFO: Justin Vaughn
VP: Matthew Gray

D-U-N-S 80-837-5500
■ PEAK FINANCE HOLDINGS LLC
(*Suby of* PINNACLE FOODS INC) ★
121 Woodcrest Rd, Cherry Hill, NJ 08003-3620
Tel (856) 969-7100 *Founded/Ownrshp* 2007
Sales 2.4MMM^E *EMP* 3,700
SIC 2038 2092 2099 2045 Frozen specialties; Breakfasts, frozen & packaged; Pizza, frozen; Waffles, frozen; Prepared fish or other seafood cakes & sticks; Pancake syrup, blended & mixed; Cake flour: from purchased flour; Bread & bread type roll mixes: from purchased flour; Pancake mixes, prepared: from purchased flour

D-U-N-S 80-836-0437
PEAK HOLDINGS LLC
345 Park Ave Fl 30, New York, NY 10154-0004
Tel (212) 583-5000 *Founded/Ownrshp* 2007
Sales 228.8MM^E *EMP* 5,262
SIC 2038 2092 2099 2045 Frozen specialties; Prepared fish or other seafood cakes & sticks; Pancake syrup, blended & mixed; Cake flour: from purchased flour
Prin: Brian Jones

D-U-N-S 07-996-1118
■ PEAK MEDICAL FARMINGTON LLC
SAN JUAN CENTER
(*Suby of* GENESIS HEALTHCARE LLC) ★
806 W Maple St, Farmington, NM 87401-5631
Tel (505) 325-2910 *Founded/Ownrshp* 2003
Sales 397.6M^E *EMP* 2,743^E
SIC 8051 Skilled nursing care facilities
CEO: George V Hagaer

D-U-N-S 07-996-1048
■ PEAK MEDICAL LAS CRUCES LLC
CASA DEL SOL CENTER
(*Suby of* GENESIS HEALTHCARE LLC) ★
2905 Missouri Ave, Las Cruces, NM 88011-4813
Tel (575) 522-0404 *Founded/Ownrshp* 2013
Sales 474.7M^E *EMP* 3,236^E
SIC 8051 Skilled nursing care facilities
CEO: George V Hagaer Jr

D-U-N-S 07-996-1096
■ PEAK MEDICAL ROSWELL LLC
MISSION ARCH CENTER
(*Suby of* GENESIS HEALTHCARE LLC) ★
3200 Mission Arch Dr, Roswell, NM 88201-8307
Tel (575) 624-2583 *Founded/Ownrshp* 2013
Sales 1.3MM^E *EMP* 3,236^E
SIC 8051 Skilled nursing care facilities
CEO: George V Hagaer Jr

D-U-N-S 14-723-3472
PEAK OILFIELD SERVICE CO LLC
5015 Business Park Blvd # 4000, Anchorage, AK 99503-7177
Tel (907) 263-7000 *Founded/Ownrshp* 2011
Sales 107.1MM^E *EMP* 950^E
SIC 7699 1389 Aircraft & heavy equipment repair services; Construction equipment repair; Oil field services
CEO: Michael O'Connor
CFO: Bill Allen
Treas: Mark Lindsey
VP: Richard Beck
VP: Dennis Brandon
VP: Craig Floerchinger
VP: Kathy Johnson
VP: Greg Razo
VP: Patrick Walsh
Exec: Belinda Wilson
Genl Mgr: Brian Wakefield

D-U-N-S 07-948-4766
PEAK OILFIELD SERVICES LLC
1502 10th St Ste A, Bridgeport, TX 76426-2340
Tel (940) 683-1627 *Founded/Ownrshp* 2013
Sales 111.1MM^E *EMP* 239^E
SIC 1389 Oil field services
CEO: John Schmitz
Pr: Pat Anderle
COO: Cody Ortowski
CFO: Eric Mattson

PEAK POWDER RIVER RESOURCES
See PEAK EXPLORATION & PRODUCTION LLC

D-U-N-S 02-599-8761
▲ PEAK RESORTS INC (MO)
17409 Hidden Valley Dr, Wildwood, MO 63025-2213
Tel (636) 938-7474 *Founded/Ownrshp* 1997
Sales 95.7MM *EMP* 630^E
Tkr Sym SKIS *Exch* NGM
SIC 7992 7999 7011 Public golf courses; Ski rental concession; Resort hotel; Hotels
Ch Bd: Timothy D Boyd
**CFO:* Stephen J Mueller
VP: Christopher J Bub
**VP:* Richard K Deutsch
Board of Directors: David W Braswell, Stanley W Hansen, Carl E Kraus, Christopher S O'connor

PEAK SEASON FOODS
See WYCKOFF FARMS INC

D-U-N-S 04-733-0402 IMP
PEAK-RYZEX INC
(*Suby of* SUMMIT HOLDING ONE CORP) ★
10330 Old Columbia Rd # 102, Columbia, MD 21046-2359
Tel (410) 312-6000 *Founded/Ownrshp* 2012
Sales 345.6MM^E *EMP* 777
SIC 7378 5045 7372 Computer peripheral equipment repair & maintenance; Computers, peripherals & software; Computer peripheral equipment; Prepackaged software
Pr: Ross Young
CFO: Michelle Adams
**VP:* Chris Glennon
VP: Dave Howard
VP: Matt Kramer
VP: Janet Pelzel
VP: Steven Sheridan
Exec: Craig Fleischmann
Dir Surg: Jan Tabeling
Dir Bus: Dave Brown
Dir Bus: Elizabeth Sandall
Dir Bus: Michael Stevens

D-U-N-S 01-762-4722
PEAK6 INVESTMENTS LP
141 W Jackson Blvd # 500, Chicago, IL 60604-2980
Tel (312) 362-2401 *Founded/Ownrshp* 1997
Sales 126.8MM^E *EMP* 285
SIC 6211 Security brokers & dealers
Pt: Matthew Hulsizer
Pt: Phil Grigus
Pt: Jennifer Just
Ofcr: Michael Rothkopf
CIO: Danny P Rosenthal
Dir IT: Mike Leone
Dir IT: Eric Levin
IT Man: Matt Dillon
IT Man: Ryan Pratt
Web Dev: Seth Pychewicz
Sftwr Eng: Dave Boutcher

D-U-N-S 13-675-8781
■ PEAPACK-GLADSTONE BANK
(*Suby of* PEAPACK-GLADSTONE FINANCIAL CORP) ★
500 Hills Dr Ste 300, Bedminster, NJ 07921-1590
Tel (908) 234-0700 *Founded/Ownrshp* 2003
Sales NA *EMP* 292^E
SIC 6022 State commercial banks
Pr: Douglas L Kennedy
COO: Finn M W Caspersen Jr
CFO: Jeffrey Carfora
CFO: Margaret Volk
Chf Cred: Lisa Chalkan
Bd of Dir: Maria Goncalves
Ofcr: Timothy E Doyle
Ofcr: Michele Ravo
Ofcr: Francesco S Rossi
Ofcr: Vincent A Spero
Ex VP: Anthony V Bilotta
Ex VP: Thomas Ross
Sr VP: John Babcock
Sr VP: Martin J Brady
Sr VP: Patrick R Brocker
Sr VP: Maureen Hemhauser
Sr VP: Laurie Liebers
Sr VP: Marc Magliaro
Sr VP: Lori A Moylan
Sr VP: Raciel V Perez
Sr VP: Karen A Rockoff
Board of Directors: Susan A Cole, Richard Daingerfield, Edward A Gramigna Jr, Beth Welsh

D-U-N-S 00-891-2263
▲ PEAPACK-GLADSTONE FINANCIAL CORP
500 Hills Dr Ste 300, Bedminster, NJ 07921-1538
Tel (908) 234-0700 *Founded/Ownrshp* 1997
Sales NA *EMP* 316^E
Tkr Sym PGC *Exch* NGS
SIC 6029 Commercial banks
Pr: Douglas L Kennedy
**Ch Bd:* F Duffield Meyercord
Pr: John P Babcock
**COO:* Finn M W Caspersen Jr
CFO: Jeffrey J Carfora
Sr VP: Finn M Casperson Jr
Sr VP: Francesco Rossi
Dir Risk M: Karen A Rockoff
Board of Directors: Susan A Cole, Anthony J Consi II, Richard Daingerfield, Edward A Gramigna, John D Kissel, James R Lamb, Philip W Smith III, Beth Welsh

D-U-N-S 60-836-5441
PEAPOD LLC
(*Suby of* AFS) ★
9933 Woods Dr, Skokie, IL 60077-1049
Tel (847) 583-9400 *Founded/Ownrshp* 1989
Sales 226.2MM^E *EMP* 1,300
SIC 5411

D-U-N-S 08-268-0455 IMP/EXP
PEARCE INDUSTRIES INC
12320 Main St, Houston, TX 77035-6206
Tel (713) 723-1050 *Founded/Ownrshp* 1976
Sales 611.7MM *EMP* 750
SIC 5084 3533 5082 Industrial machinery & equipment; Oil field machinery & equipment; General construction machinery & equipment
Ch Bd: Louis M Pearce Jr
**Pr:* Gary M Pearce
**CFO:* Richard E Bean
**Treas:* Stephen R Pearce
VP: Rick Hutches
**VP:* Robert J Jesse
**VP:* Louis Pearce III
Dir Bus: Jeff Cox

D-U-N-S 03-054-8044
PEARL & ASSOCIATES LTD
PEARL INSURANCE GROUP
1200 E Glen Ave, Peoria, IL 61616-5325
Tel (309) 688-9000 *Founded/Ownrshp* 1954
Sales NA *EMP* 175
SIC 6411 Insurance agents, brokers & service
CEO: Gary P Pearl
**Ch Bd:* John P Pearl
**Pr:* Dennis Dietrich
**Ch:* Jack Pearl
**Ex VP:* Scott Whitaker
**Ex VP:* David Willett
Sr VP: George Bode
VP: Kevin Arduini
VP: Dorene Burkhalter
VP: Sharon Harman
CTO: Phil Arnold

PEARL ART & CRAFT SUPPLY
See PEARL PAINT CO INC

D-U-N-S 62-319-9809 IMP/EXP
PEARL ARTIST & CRAFT SUPPLY CORP
DESIGN IMAGES
185 Merrick Rd, Lynbrook, NY 11563-2700
Tel (954) 564-5700 *Founded/Ownrshp* 1990
Sales 78.3MM^E *EMP* 1,000
Accts Grossman Ugell & Sommers Llp
SIC 5999 5199 Art & architectural supplies; Art goods
Pr: Rosalind Perlmutter
VP: Kirk Hovenga
MIS Mgr: Ralph Niebles

PEARL INSURANCE GROUP
See PEARL & ASSOCIATES LTD

D-U-N-S 00-202-5658 IMP/EXP
PEARL PAINT CO INC (NY)
PEARL ART & CRAFT SUPPLY
1033 E Oakland Park Blvd, Oakland Park, FL 33334-2727
Tel (954) 564-5700 *Founded/Ownrshp* 1933
Sales 120.8MM^E *EMP* 900
SIC 5999 5199 7699 5112 5947 7311 Art & architectural supplies; Artists' supplies & materials; Art goods & supplies; Art goods; Picture framing, custom; Office supplies; Gift shop; Advertising agencies
Pr: Rosalind Perlmutter

D-U-N-S 08-006-4746
PEARL RIVER RESORT
SILVER STAR HOTEL & CASINO
13541 Highway 16 W, Philadelphia, MS 39350-6510
Tel (601) 663-4438 *Founded/Ownrshp* 2015
Sales 10.0MM^E *EMP* 2,700
SIC 5812 8641 Family restaurants; Bars & restaurants, members only
Pr: Sonny Johnson

D-U-N-S 62-314-0063
PEARL SENIOR CARE LLC
GOLDEN LIVING
(*Suby of* F C P) ★
4 Embarcadero Ctr Ste 710, San Francisco, CA 94111-4172
Tel (415) 834-1477 *Founded/Ownrshp* 2005
Sales 643.5MM^E *EMP* 35,100
SIC 8082 Home health care services

D-U-N-S 09-575-4974
PEARLAND INDEPENDENT SCHOOL DISTRICT
1928 N Main St, Pearland, TX 77581-3306
Tel (281) 485-3203 *Founded/Ownrshp* 1932
Sales 205.4MM *EMP* 2,450
Accts Kennemer Masters & Lunsford
SIC 8211 Public elementary & secondary schools
**CFO:* Don Marshall
Comm Dir: Kim Hocott
Adm Dir: Mark McKinney
Genl Mgr: Donna Tate
Dir IT: Lisa Williams
Telecom Mg: Gary McLeod
IT Man: Janet Fake
Trfc Dir: Roland Lira
Teacher Pr: David Moody

PEARSALL PACKING SAGE
See SAN ANTONIO FOOD BANK

D-U-N-S 13-140-2042 EXP
PEARSON COMPANIES INC
RICHMOND HONDA
9530 Midlothian Pike, Richmond, VA 23225
Tel (804) 745-0300 *Founded/Ownrshp* 1984
Sales 300.0MM *EMP* 600
SIC 5511

D-U-N-S 05-454-1771 IMP/EXP
PEARSON EDUCATION HOLDINGS INC
(*Suby of* PEARSON PLC)
330 Hudson St Fl 9, New York, NY 10013-1048
Tel (201) 236-6716 *Founded/Ownrshp* 1998, 2005
Sales 2.5MMM^E *EMP* 14,045
SIC 2731 Textbooks: publishing & printing
Pr: Will Ethridge
Ex VP: Ed Bilinski
**VP:* Michael Benjamin
VP: Seth Reichlin
Dir Bus: Tina Montoya
Mng Dir: Jim Tognolini
Dist Mgr: John Contos
Dist Mgr: Sharon K Young
CTO: Douglas G Kubach
Dir IT: Laura Bohde
Dir IT: Joseph Consiglio

D-U-N-S 05-360-1050
PEARSON EDUCATION INC
(*Suby of* PEARSON EDUCATION HOLDINGS INC) ★
1 Lake St, Upper Saddle River, NJ 07458-1813
Tel (201) 236-7000 *Founded/Ownrshp* 1997
Sales 1.7MMM^E *EMP* 7,742
SIC 7371 Computer software development
CEO: Will Ethridge
Pr: John Fallon
Pr: Andy Hall
COO: Glenn Lauder
Ex VP: Pat Duffy
Ex VP: Santos Shih
VP: Bob Arthur
VP: Stuart Cohn
VP: Robert Dancy
VP: Doug Derringer
VP: Chris Doran
VP: Lauren Fogel
VP: Stephanie Foster
VP: Judy Goldstein
VP: Tom Hoffa
VP: Dan Lennon
VP: James Pecci
VP: Angela Schwers
VP: Steve Wenz
VP: Andy Yoo
Exec: James Degrassi

D-U-N-S 14-462-6306 EXP
PEARSON INC
(*Suby of* PEARSON PLC)
1330 Hudson St, New York, NY 10013
Tel (212) 641-2400 *Founded/Ownrshp* 1844
Sales 2.5MMM^E *EMP* 10,600
SIC 2711 2731 Newspapers; Books: publishing & printing; Textbooks: publishing & printing
CEO: John Fallon
**CFO:* Robin Freestone
**Ch:* Glen Moreno
Ofcr: Ron Rheinheimer
Assoc VP: Rick Budd
**VP:* Michael Fortini
**VP:* Richard Koplitz
**VP:* Ken Lockhart
**VP:* Joe Murphy
Prin: Boone Novy
Ex Dir: David Arculus

D-U-N-S 10-264-0752
PEARSON LONGMAN LLC
(*Suby of* PEARSON INC) ★
10 Bank St Ste 1030, White Plains, NY 10606-1952
Tel (212) 641-2400 *Founded/Ownrshp* 1978
Sales 151.4MM^E *EMP* 2,800
SIC 2731 2711 Books: publishing & printing; Newspapers, publishing & printing
Pr: Jeff Taylor
**Treas:* Herbert Yeates
**VP:* Roger A Brown
**VP:* John Stallon
VP: Thomas Wharton
IT Man: Cliff Dsouza

D-U-N-S 03-339-4602 IMP/EXP
PEAVEY ELECTRONICS CORP
5022 Hartley Peavey Dr, Meridian, MS 39305-8733
Tel (601) 486-1383 *Founded/Ownrshp* 1980
Sales 175.7MM^E *EMP* 1,000^E
SIC 3931 Musical instruments
Ch Bd: Hartley D Peavey
**Pr:* Mary Peavey
**COO:* Courtland Gray
COO: Walter Lutz
Genl Mgr: Kevin Ivey
Genl Mgr: Tony Moscal
Dir IT: Scott Ferguson
Sftwr Eng: Scott Dickey
Plnt Mgr: Lamar McKenzie
Mktg Dir: Ashley Neeli
Manager: Rich Dumstorff

PEBBLE BEACH COMPANY
See I CYPRESS CO

D-U-N-S 00-691-0624
PEBBLE BEACH RESORT CO DBA LONE CYPRESS SHOP
PEBBLE BEACH RESORTS
2700 17 Mile Dr, Pebble Beach, CA 93953-2668
Tel (831) 647-7500 *Founded/Ownrshp* 1999
Sales 119.8MM^E *EMP* 1,700^E
SIC 7011 7992 5941 7991 Resort hotel; Public golf courses; Golf goods & equipment; Tennis goods & equipment; Physical fitness facilities
CEO: Bill Perocchi
**Pr:* Cody Plott
**CFO:* Dave Heuck
**Ex VP:* Paul Spengler
**Ex VP:* Mark Stilwell
VP: Dominic Vannes
Off Mgr: Sarah Jones

PEBBLE BEACH RESORTS
See PEBBLE BEACH RESORT CO DBA LONE CYPRESS SHOP

D-U-N-S 83-251-1286
PEBBLEBROOK HOTEL TRUST
7315 Wisconsin Ave 1100w, Bethesda, MD 20814-3238
Tel (240) 507-1300 *Founded/Ownrshp* 2009
Sales 770.8MM *EMP* 328
Accts Kpmg Llp Mclean Virginia
SIC 6798 Real estate investment trusts
Ch Bd: Jon E Bortz
CFO: Raymond D Martz
Ex VP: Thomas C Fisher
VP: Steve Coe
VP: Wendy Heineke
VP: Robin Kennedy
Board of Directors: Ron E Jackson, Phillip M Miller, Michael J Schall, Earl E Webb, Laura H Wright

PEBTF
See PA EMPLOYEES BENEFIT TRUST FUND (INC)

D-U-N-S 93-364-2084
PECHANGA DEVELOPMENT CORP
PECHANGA RESORT & CASINO
45000 Pechanga Pkwy, Temecula, CA 92592-5810
Tel (951) 695-4655 *Founded/Ownrshp* 1995
Sales 206.1MM^E *EMP* 4,000
SIC 7011 7929 7999 Hotels & motels; Entertainment service; Gambling establishment
**CFO:* Jerry Konchar
**Treas:* Christina McMenamin
Ex VP: Gilbert Mendoza
**VP:* Edith Atwood
**VP:* Randall Bardwell
VP: Tina Cramar
VP: Buddy Frank
VP: Howard Herman
VP: Anthony Miranda
Exec: Marylou Bean
Dir: Jeff Durler

PECHANGA RESORT & CASINO
See PECHANGA DEVELOPMENT CORP

D-U-N-S 00-699-5567 IMP
PECKHAM INDUSTRIES INC
20 Haarlem Ave Ste 200, White Plains, NY 10603-2223
Tel (914) 949-2000 *Founded/Ownrshp* 1924
Sales 192.0MM^E *EMP* 400
SIC 2951 Concrete, asphaltic (not from refineries)
Pr: John R Peckham
VP: Gary W Metcalf
VP: Joseph Wildermuth
Exec: Matt June
IT Man: Seth Fenster
Sfty Mgr: Lou Merkle

D-U-N-S 00-823-6200
PECKHAM VOCATIONAL INDUSTRIES INC (MI)
3510 Capitol City Blvd, Lansing, MI 48906-2102
Tel (517) 316-4000 *Founded/Ownrshp* 1976, 1979
Sales 165.3MM *EMP* 1,540

Accts Lb Maner Costerisan Pc Lansin
SIC 8331 2396 2311 2331 2339 2326 Vocational rehabilitation agency; Automotive trimmings, fabric; Men's & boys' suits & coats; Women's & misses' blouses & shirts; Women's & misses' outerwear; Men's & boys' work clothing
CEO: Mitchell Tomlinson
Pr: Scott Derthick
Pr: Karen Jury
Pr: Stuart Muladore
*Pr: Curt Munson
Pr: Greta Wu
*Sec: J Sue Kelly
Bd of Dir: Chris Bergstrom
Bd of Dir: Stainley Koget
Bd of Dir: Heather Shawa-Becook
*Ex VP: Jo Sinha
*VP: Heather Shawa-Decook

D-U-N-S 00-791-4468 IMP
■ PECO ENERGY CO (PA)
EXELON
(Suby of EXELON ENERGY DELIVERY CO LLC) ★
2301 Market St, Philadelphia, PA 19103-1380
Tel (215) 841-4000 Founded/Ownrshp 1929, 2012
Sales 3.0MMM EMP 2,418E
Accts Pricewaterhousecoopers Llp Ph
SIC 4911 4924 4923 Distribution, electric power; Natural gas distribution; Gas transmission & distribution
Pr: Craig L Adams
*Ch Bd: Christopher M Crane
COO: Michael A Innocenzo
CFO: Phillip S Barnett
CFO: John Young
*V Ch Bd: Denis P O'Brien
Ex VP: Craig Adams
Ex VP: Oliver D Kingsley Jr
VP: Scott A Bailey
VP: Doyle Beneby
VP: Ellen M Cavanaugh
VP: Romulo L Diaz Jr
VP: Eric Helt
Board of Directors: M Walter D'alessio, Nicholas Debenedictis, Ronald Rubin

D-U-N-S 03-413-0328 EXP
PECO FOODS INC
1020 Lurleen B Wallace, Tuscaloosa, AL 35401-2225
Tel (205) 345-4711 Founded/Ownrshp 1929
Sales 810.7MME EMP 3,800
SIC 0254 0251 2015 2048 Chicken hatchery; Broiling chickens, raising of; Frying chickens, raising of; Roasting chickens, raising of; Poultry, processed; Livestock feeds; Poultry feeds
Ch Bd: George Hickman
*Pr: Mark Hickman
*Sr VP: Jerome Hickman

D-U-N-S 09-884-6116
PECO FOODS INC
(Suby of PECO FOODS INC) ★
145 2nd Ave Nw, Gordo, AL 35466-2245
Tel (205) 364-7121 Founded/Ownrshp 1969
Sales 155.8MME EMP 609
SIC 0251 Broiling chickens, raising of
*Pr: Mark Hickman
*Sec: Jerome Hickman
Dir IT: Mark Fouscher

D-U-N-S 04-126-8210 IMP
■ PECO INC
PECO MANUFACTURING
(Suby of ASTRONICS CORP) ★
11241 Se Highway 212, Clackamas, OR 97015-9160
Tel (503) 233-6401 Founded/Ownrshp 2013
Sales 99.2MME EMP 220
SIC 3089 3822 3364 3363 Injection molded finished plastic products; Temperature controls, automatic; Zinc & zinc-base alloy die-castings; Aluminum die-castings
CEO: Stephen M Scheidler
*VP: Dave Freund
VP: Michael Innocenzo
*VP: Merrick Smith
QA Dir: Tony Gioia
Mfg Mgr: Tom Moss
Prd Mgr: Brad Gray
Ql Cn Mgr: Mark Heisler
Ql Cn Mgr: Vicki Watson
Ql Cn Mgr: Tony Woods
Sls Mgr: Becky Calvert

PECO MANUFACTURING
See PECO INC

D-U-N-S 00-802-2725 IMP/EXP
■ PECOFACET (US) INC
PECOFACET US
(Suby of CLARCOR INC) ★
118 Washington Ave, Mineral Wells, TX 76067-9502
Tel (940) 325-2575 Founded/Ownrshp 1936, 2007
Sales 107.8MME EMP 447
SIC 3823 5082 Flow instruments, industrial process type; Oil field equipment
Ch Bd: M Dunman Perry Jr
*Pr: Scott Thompson
*Treas: David Fallon
Sr Ex VP: Clyde Copeland
*Sr VP: John Krogue
VP: Brian Czajkowski
VP: Doyle Gould
*VP: Richard D Harcourt
*VP: Lawrence Hyman
*VP: Bruce Klein
Area Mgr: Kyle Kelley
Board of Directors: David Fallon, Richard Wolfaon

PECOFACET US
See PECOFACET (US) INC

PECONIC BAY MEDICAL CENTER
See CENTRAL SUFFOLK HOSPITAL

D-U-N-S 02-958-0672
PECONIC BAY PRIMARY MEDICAL CARE PC
1300 Roanoke Ave, Riverhead, NY 11901-2031
Tel (631) 288-6622 Founded/Ownrshp 2000
Sales 151.0MM EMP 8
SIC 8011 Offices & clinics of medical doctors
Pr: Richard Kubiak
V Ch: Jesse R Goodale

D-U-N-S 01-229-9744 IMP
PECOS INC
SC FUELS
(Suby of SC FUELS) ★
19501 S Santa Fe Ave, Compton, CA 90221-5913
Tel (310) 356-2300 Founded/Ownrshp 2006
Sales 144.3MME EMP 225
SIC 5172 Crude oil; Engine fuels & oils; Diesel fuel; Gasoline
Pr: Michael Ruehring
CFO: Tracy Mausser
*VP: Sean Kha

PECUE CONTRACTORS
See PERFORMANCE CONTRACTORS INC

D-U-N-S 00-509-2903 IMP/EXP
PEDDINGHAUS CORP
300 N Washington Ave, Bradley, IL 60915-1600
Tel (815) 937-3800 Founded/Ownrshp 1977
Sales 128.7MME EMP 300
SIC 3541 Numerically controlled metal cutting machine tools
Pr: Carl G Peddinghaus
Pr: Kenneth Coulter
*Sec: Greg Kubick
VP: Terry Chinn
VP: Bob Meltzer
Rgnl Mgr: Ted Trybek
CTO: Brian Lundmark
Sftwr Eng: Mark McDermott
Sls Mgr: Todd Cordes
Genl Couns: David Zeglis

D-U-N-S 00-792-4111
PEDERNALES ELECTRIC COOPERATIVE INC (TX)
201 S Avenue F, Johnson City, TX 78636-4827
Tel (830) 868-7155 Founded/Ownrshp 1938
Sales 569.0MM EMP 741
Accts Bkd Llp Houston Tx
SIC 4911 Distribution, electric power
CEO: John Hewa
CFO: Tracy Golden
CFO: Diann Hamilton
CFO: Frank Skube
VP: Steven Baca
VP: Emily Pataki
VP: Ingmar Sterzing
Prgrm Mgr: Philip Hons
Dist Mgr: Archie Lopez
IT Man: Brett Holley
IT Man: Zelenny Martinez
Board of Directors: William D Boggs, Dr Patrick Cox, Larry Landaker, James Oakley, Chris Perry, Kathryn Scanlon

PEDIATRIA HEALTHCARE FOR KIDS
See PEDIATRIA HEALTHCARE LLC

D-U-N-S 80-403-1578
PEDIATRIA HEALTHCARE LLC
PEDIATRIA HEALTHCARE FOR KIDS
(Suby of EPIC HEALTH SERVICES INC) ★
5185 Peachtree Pkwy # 350, Norcross, GA 30092-6545
Tel (770) 840-1966 Founded/Ownrshp 2016
Sales 55.6MME EMP 1,500
SIC 8082 8741 Home health care services; Nursing & personal care facility management
CEO: Joe Sansone
*Pr: Joseph M Harrelson
Dist Mgr: Joanne Accardi

D-U-N-S 96-463-5044
PEDIATRIC ACADEMIC ASSOCIATION
700 Childrens Dr, Columbus, OH 43205-2664
Tel (614) 722-2459 Founded/Ownrshp 2010
Sales 108.5MM EMP 3
Accts Bdo Usa Llp Columbus Oh
SIC 8621 Professional membership organizations
COO: Amyjo Hernandez

PEDIATRIC ASSOCIATES
See RMC JACKSONVILLE

PEDIATRIC HOME NURSING SVCS NY
See PEDIATRIC SERVICES OF AMERICA INC

PEDIATRIC PHYSICIANS OF NEWARK
See AMERICAN HEALTH NETWORK INC

D-U-N-S 87-850-6302
PEDIATRIC RHEUMATOLOGY
GILLETTE CHLDRN SPCLTY HLTH
200 University Ave E, Saint Paul, MN 55101-2507
Tel (651) 229-3892 Founded/Ownrshp 1994
Sales 213.4MM EMP 54
SIC 8011 8062 Pediatrician; General medical & surgical hospitals

D-U-N-S 80-820-1102
PEDIATRIC SERVICES HOLDING CORP
PSA HEALTHCARE
(Suby of J H WHITNEY CAPITAL PARTNERS LLC) ★
3720 Da Vinci Ct, Norcross, GA 30092
Tel (770) 441-1580 Founded/Ownrshp 2015
Sales 136.5MME EMP 4,500E
SIC 8082 6719 Home health care services; Personal holding companies, except banks
Pr: Eric Minkove
Assoc VP: Jim Kanelos
CIO: Cigdem Delano
Software D: Michael Gurliaccio
VP Opers: Darien Zimmerman
Nrsg Dir: Katie Stark
Counsel: Carmen Butler

D-U-N-S 12-094-1042
PEDIATRIC SERVICES OF AMERICA INC
PEDIATRIC HOME NURSING SVCS NY
(Suby of PEDIATRIC SERVICES OF AMERICA INC (DE)) ★
3720 Davinci Ct Ste 200, Norcross, GA 30092-7625
Tel (770) 441-1580 Founded/Ownrshp 1989
Sales 61.1MME EMP 1,680
SIC 8082 Home health care services
CEO: James McCurry

D-U-N-S 78-689-5136 IMP
PEDIATRIC SERVICES OF AMERICA INC (DE)
(Suby of PSA HEALTHCARE) ★
3720 Davinci Ct Ste 200, Norcross, GA 30092-7625
Tel (770) 441-1580 Founded/Ownrshp 1989
Sales 127.5MME EMP 3,911E
SIC 8082 Home health care services
Pr: Daniel J Kohl
CFO: Opal Ferraro
*CFO: James M McNeill
VP: Angela Bullins
VP: Joseph M Harrelson
VP: Mary Hartman
VP: Keith Jones
VP: Kristy Maddox
VP: Kim Singleton
Off Mgr: Juanita Ashley
Genl Couns: John R Hamilton
Board of Directors: Michael E Axelrod, David Crane, Michael J Finn, Robert P Pinkas

PEDIATRIC SPECIALTY CLINIC
See GENESYS REGIONAL MEDICAL CENTER

PEDIATRIC SPECIALTY CLINIC
See GENESYS HEALTH SYSTEM

PEEBLES
See SPECIALTY RETAILERS INC

PEEK'N PEAK RESORT AND SPA
See SCOTTS PEEK N PEAK LLC

D-U-N-S 01-181-0231 IMP
PEERLESS BEVERAGE CO
1000 Floral Ave, Union, NJ 07083-7759
Tel (908) 351-0101 Founded/Ownrshp 1933
Sales 112.0MME EMP 220
SIC 5181 Beer & other fermented malt liquors
Ch: Richard Salzman
*Pr: Scott Beim
*VP: Norman H Beim
*VP: Charles Salzman
IT Man: Bruno Vadale
Sales Exec: Tom Brucker
Sls Mgr: David Caneschi

D-U-N-S 00-891-6801 IMP/EXP
PEERLESS IMPORTERS INC
(Suby of QUAKER EQUITIES LTD) ★
16 Bridgewater St, Brooklyn, NY 11222-3891
Tel (718) 383-5500 Founded/Ownrshp 1943, 1987
Sales 586.5ME EMP 1,149
SIC 5182 Wine; Liquor
Pr: Antonio Magliocco Jr
*Ch Bd: John T Magliocco
COO: Tony Magliocco
*VP: Joseph J Magliocco
Genl Mgr: Fedele Miranda
Off Mgr: Peter Berend
Dir IT: Ed Lederer
Sys Eng: Gregory Jones

D-U-N-S 11-088-7056 IMP
PEERLESS INDUSTRIAL GROUP INC
1416 E Sanborn St, Winona, MN 55987-4948
Tel (507) 457-9100 Founded/Ownrshp 1997
Sales 87.0MME EMP 375
SIC 3496 Tire chains
Ch: Clark F Davis
Ex VP: George Kosidowski
*VP: Gilman King
Exec: Curt Mihm
Dir IT: Gary Lind
Natl Sales: Ben McKinney
Natl Sales: Jed Ranzenberger
VP Sls: Andrew Grimm
Mktg Mgr: Troy Baumgartner
Sls Mgr: Charles Joachim
Sls Mgr: Rich Klabnik

D-U-N-S 00-697-1188
PEERLESS INSURANCE CO (NH)
(Suby of LIBERTY MUTUAL GROUP INC) ★
62 Maple Ave, Keene, NH 03431-1600
Tel (603) 352-3221 Founded/Ownrshp 1901, 1984
Sales NA EMP 1,400
SIC 6331 Property damage insurance; Fire, marine & casualty insurance & carriers
Ch Bd: Roger L Jean
*Treas: Stephen Powell
VP: Carl Canales
VP: Thomas McDonough
Sls Mgr: Laura Gauthier
Sls Mgr: Amy Lacroix
Snr Mgr: Steven Alward

PEERLESS PUMP COMPANY
See STERLING FLUID SYSTEMS (USA) LLC

D-U-N-S 00-285-4792 IMP
PEERLESS STEEL CO (MI)
P S
2450 Austin Dr, Troy, MI 48083-2098
Tel (248) 528-3200 Founded/Ownrshp 1957
Sales 91.0MME EMP 150
SIC 5051 Steel
Pr: Randy Remdenok
*CFO: Jeff Zydeck
*Ch: Stuart E Wood
VP: Carl Bartells
*VP: Gary W Bradley
*VP: Robert Wesling
*VP: Dave Wolff
*VP: Douglas Wood
Sfty Mgr: David Wolf
Mktg Dir: Bernie Davis
Sales Asso: Tom McDermott

D-U-N-S 04-379-5244 IMP
PEERLESS TYRE CO
U-PUMP-IT
5000 Kingston St, Denver, CO 80239-2522
Tel (303) 371-4300 Founded/Ownrshp 1967
Sales 129.8MME EMP 260
SIC 5541 5531

D-U-N-S 13-045-7336 IMP
PEERLESS-WINSMITH INC
OHIO ELECTRIC MOTORS
(Suby of HBD INDUSTRIES INC) ★
5200 Upper Metro Pl # 110, Dublin, OH 43017-5378
Tel (614) 526-7000 Founded/Ownrshp 1985
Sales 152.4MME EMP 1,016
SIC 3621 3566 3634 3812 3559 Motors & generators; Speed changers (power transmission equipment), except auto; Electric household cooking utensils; Magnetic field detection apparatus; Separation equipment, magnetic
Ch Bd: R L Greely
*CFO: Mike Feschak
*Treas: R0bert A Sirak

D-U-N-S 00-201-9375 IMP
PEETS COFFEE & TEA LLC (WA)
(Suby of JAB BEECH INC) ★
1400 Park Ave, Emeryville, CA 94608-3520
Tel (510) 594-2100 Founded/Ownrshp 1971, 2012
Sales 1.5MMME EMP 3,642E
SIC 2095 5149 Roasted coffee; Coffee, green or roasted
CEO: David Burwick
Pr: Paul Clayton
Ofcr: Shawn Conway
VP: Jim Grimes
VP: Peter B Mehrberg
VP: Bruce Schroder
VP: Joel Sjostrom
Exec: Paul Yee
Dist Mgr: Gregory Borunda

D-U-N-S 80-140-5510
■ PEETZ TABLE WIND ENERGY LLC
(Suby of NEXTERA ENERGY RESOURCES LLC) ★
9500 County Road 78, Peetz, CO 80747-9718
Tel (970) 334-2230 Founded/Ownrshp 2006
Sales 130.3MME EMP 18E
SIC 4911 Electric services

D-U-N-S 88-399-0181
PEGASUS BUILDERS INC
3340 Frlane Frms Rd Ste 8, Wellington, FL 33414
Tel (561) 791-7037 Founded/Ownrshp 2008
Sales 180.0MM EMP 36
SIC 1521 1542 New construction, single-family houses; Commercial & office building contractors
Pr: David C Forkey
*Prin: Charisse Sorena

PEGASUS COMM & COOPERATION
See PEGASUS TOWERS INC

D-U-N-S 95-911-4182
PEGASUS COMMUNICATIONS HOLDINGS INC
1055 Westlakes Dr Ste 300, Berwyn, PA 19312-2410
Tel (302) 651-8300 Founded/Ownrshp 1993
Sales 862.8MME EMP 1,012
SIC 4833 4841 Television broadcasting stations; Cable television services; Direct broadcast satellite services (DBS); Subscription television services
Ch Bd: Marshall W Pagon

D-U-N-S 84-791-4660
PEGASUS MEDIA & COMMUNICATIONS INC
225 E City Ave Ste 200, Bala Cynwyd, PA 19004-1724
Tel (610) 934-7000 Founded/Ownrshp 1994
Sales 109.4MME EMP 800
SIC 4833 4841 Television broadcasting stations; Cable television services; Direct broadcast satellite services (DBS)
Pr: Marshall W Pagon
*CFO: Robert N Verdecchio
Sr VP: Scott Blank
*Sr VP: Ted S Lodge
*VP: Howard E Verlin

PEGASUS SOLUTIONS COMPANIES
See PEGASUS SOLUTIONS INC

D-U-N-S 00-876-3917
PEGASUS SOLUTIONS INC
PEGASUS SOLUTIONS COMPANIES
(Suby of PERSEUS HOLDING CORP) ★
14000 N Pima Rd Ste 200, Scottsdale, AZ 85260-3977
Tel (480) 624-6000 Founded/Ownrshp 1989, 2006
Sales 309.1MME EMP 1,200
SIC 7374 Data processing & preparation
CEO: David Millili
COO: Mark Wells
Bd of Dir: Pamela H Patsley
Ex VP: Supreet Singh
Sr VP: Chris Klimko
VP: Craig Miller
Software D: Lee Buzalek
Mktg Dir: Karen Plumb
Sls Mgr: Gregory Jones
Snr PM: Ward Bierle
Snr PM: David Kvitka

D-U-N-S 17-601-6160
PEGASUS TOWERS INC
PEGASUS COMM & COOPERATION
225 E City Ave Ste 200, Bala Cynwyd, PA 19004-1724
Tel (610) 934-7000 Founded/Ownrshp 1994
Sales 15.4MME EMP 1,000
SIC 4833 Television broadcasting stations
CEO: Marshall Pagan
*CFO: Jeff Pooler

D-U-N-S 11-422-3183
▲ PEGASYSTEMS INC
1 Rogers St, Cambridge, MA 02142-1209
Tel (617) 374-9600 Founded/Ownrshp 1983
Sales 682.7MM EMP 3,333E
Tkr Sym PEGA Exch NGS
SIC 7379 7371 7372 Computer related consulting services; Computer software development; Computer software development & applications; Business oriented computer software
Ch Bd: Alan Trefler
CFO: Ken Stillwell
Treas: Efstathios Kouninis
Sr VP: Douglas Kra

Sr VP: Michael Pyle
Sr VP: Michael R Pyle
Sr VP: Leon Trefler
Snr Sftwr: David Picariello
VP Mktg: Dave Donelan
Sls Dir: Nishan Khoshafian
Snr Mgr: Dana Basilone
Board of Directors: Peter Gyenes, Richard Jones, Steven Kaplan, Dianne Ledingham, James O'halloran, Sharon Rowlands, Larry Weber, William Wyman

D-U-N-S 13-108-8056 IMP
PEI/GENESIS INC
RELIANCE MERCHANDISING CO DIV
2180 Hornig Rd Ste 2, Philadelphia, PA 19116-4204
Tel (215) 464-1410 *Founded/Ownrshp* 1945
Sales 329.6MM^E *EMP* 660
SIC 3678 3677 Electronic connectors; Transformers power supply, electronic type
CEO: Steven Fisher
Pr: Russell A Dorwart
* *Treas:* Carol Rosenthal
VP: Peter Austin
VP: Russ Dorwart
VP: John Gilligan
VP: Dennis Liu
Brnch Mgr: Heather Williams
Genl Mgr: Jane Fischetti
Genl Mgr: John Hufnagle
Genl Mgr: Mary Stuart
Board of Directors: David Bernbaum

D-U-N-S 00-791-4260 IMP
PEIRCE-PHELPS INC
516 Township Line Rd, Blue Bell, PA 19422-2197
Tel (215) 879-7000 *Founded/Ownrshp* 1926
Sales 160.8MM^E *EMP* 250
Accts Kreischer Miller Horsham Pen
SIC 5075 Air conditioning & ventilation equipment & supplies; Warm air heating equipment & supplies
Pr: Brian G Peirce
* *CFO:* Robert Subranni
* *VP:* Dennis Egan
* *VP:* Bruce McConnell
* *VP:* Dana Peirce
CIO: Jeff Marinucci
IT Man: Bob Fox
Mktg Dir: Mike Peirce
Sls Mgr: Diane Camburn
Sls Mgr: Steve Cohen
Sls Mgr: Lisa Garman

D-U-N-S 06-742-0448
■ **PEKIN INSURANCE**
FARMERS INSURANCE
(*Suby of* FARMERS AUTOMOBILE INSURANCE ASSOCIATION (INC)) ★
2505 Court St, Pekin, IL 61558-0002
Tel (888) 735-4611 *Founded/Ownrshp* 1921
Sales NA *EMP* 730
SIC 6411 Insurance agents, brokers & service
Ch Bd: Gordon Walker
Treas: Daniel Connell
VP: Joseph C Ricigliano
* *VP:* Mike Zabinski
Exec: Jim Tillhof
IT Man: Steve Weibering
IT Man: Greg Wheeler
Software D: Bill Quigley

D-U-N-S 06-742-0380
■ **PEKIN LIFE INSURANCE CO**
(*Suby of* FARMERS AUTOMOBILE INSURANCE ASSOCIATION (INC)) ★
2505 Court St, Pekin, IL 61554-5308
Tel (309) 346-1161 *Founded/Ownrshp* 1961
Sales NA *EMP* 156
Tkr Sym PKIN *Exch* OTO
SIC 6311 6321 Life insurance carriers; Health insurance carriers
Pr: Paul A Tornatore
* *COO:* Scott A Martin
* *Treas:* Daniel V Connell
VP: Brian K Lee

D-U-N-S 00-826-0234 IMP/EXP
PELCO INC
PELCO WORLDWIDE
(*Suby of* SCHNEIDER ELECTRIC SE)
3500 Pelco Way, Clovis, CA 93612-5621
Tel (559) 292-1981 *Founded/Ownrshp* 2007
Sales 377.1MM^E *EMP* 2,250
SIC 3663 7382

PELCO WORLDWIDE
See PELCO INC

PELICAN LIFE SCIENCES
See BIOTIX HOLDINGS INC

D-U-N-S 08-219-3277 IMP/EXP
PELICAN PRODUCTS INC
23215 Early Ave, Torrance, CA 90505-4002
Tel (310) 326-4700 *Founded/Ownrshp* 2007
Sales 260.9MM^E *EMP* 603^E
SIC 3648 3161 3089 Flashlights; Luggage; Plastic containers, except foam
CEO: Lyndon J Faulkner
* *Ch Bd:* Peter Pace
* *Pr:* Phil Gyori
Pr: Dave Williams
COO: Diana Otto
* *COO:* John Padian
CFO: Connie Abela
* *CFO:* Don Jordan
* *CFO:* Richard D Kern
* *V Ch Bd:* David Parker
* *Sr VP:* Joe Baltronis
* *Sr VP:* Scott Ermeti
VP: Jeff Cushing
VP: Joe Eckerle
* *VP:* John P Hoven
VP: Rolfes Mark
* *VP:* Jamie Mearns
VP: Nick Newman
VP: David Silver
Exec: Kenny Silver

D-U-N-S 00-527-8502 IMP/EXP
PELLA CORP (IA)
102 Main St, Pella, IA 50219-2198
Tel (641) 621-1000 *Founded/Ownrshp* 1925
Sales 2.0MMM^E *EMP* 8,726
SIC 2431 Windows, wood; Doors, wood
Pr: Pat Meyer
Pr: Rob Jablonski
Pr: Tim Yaggi
CFO: David Smart
VP: Rick Hassman
VP: Jerry Lockridge
VP: Elaine Sagers
VP: Dan Sorenson
Dir Rx: Scott R Keplinge
Genl Mgr: Joel Haveman
Dir IT: Peter Hutchinson

PELLA WINDOW & DOOR
See GUNTON CORP

PELTON & CRANE
See KAVO DENTAL TECHNOLOGIES LLC

D-U-N-S 11-559-7960
PEM HOLDING CO INC
(*Suby of* TINICUM CAPITAL PARTNERS II LP) ★
800 3rd Ave Fl 40, New York, NY 10022-7604
Tel (212) 446-9300 *Founded/Ownrshp* 2005
Sales 446.0MM^E *EMP* 1,700
SIC 6211 3429 3621 Security brokers & dealers; Metal fasteners; Motors, electric
Prin: Eric Ruttenberg

D-U-N-S 00-233-9885 IMP/EXP
PEMBERTON FABRICATORS INC (NJ)
PEMFAB
(*Suby of* INDEL INC) ★
30 Indel Ave, Rancocas, NJ 08073
Tel (609) 267-0922 *Founded/Ownrshp* 1962, 1967
Sales 11.3MM *EMP* 2,124^E
SIC 3444 3824 Sheet metal specialties, not stamped; Fluid meters & counting devices
Pr: Robert Murnane
Off Mgr: Sheryl Parker

D-U-N-S 02-692-4001
PEMBERTON TOWNSHIP SCHOOL DISTRICT
1 Egbert St, Pemberton, NJ 08068-1211
Tel (609) 893-8141 *Founded/Ownrshp* 1906
Sales 192.4M *EMP* 1,044
Accts Holman & Frenia P C Toms R
SIC 8211 Public elementary & secondary schools
Admn Mgr: Pamela Kelly
Admn Mgr: Frank Miller
IT Man: Karen Chappel
Pr Dir: Michael Pinto
Teacher Pr: Jodi Flaherty

PEMCO
See POWELL ELECTRICAL SYSTEMS INC

PEMCO INSURANCE
See PEMCO MUTUAL INSURANCE CO

D-U-N-S 07-926-5054
PEMCO MUTUAL INSURANCE CO
PEMCO INSURANCE
1300 Dexter Ave N, Seattle, WA 98109-3571
Tel (425) 712-7700 *Founded/Ownrshp* 1948
Sales NA *EMP* 1,150
SIC 6331 Fire, marine & casualty insurance & carriers; Property damage insurance; Automobile insurance
* *Treas:* Steven A Ricco
* *VP:* Stephen H Miller
IT Man: Chris Browne
IT Man: John Burgess

D-U-N-S 01-729-5000
PEMCO WORLD AIR SERVICES INC
4102 N West Shore Blvd, Tampa, FL 33614-7763
Tel (813) 322-9600 *Founded/Ownrshp* 2012
Sales 91.1MM^E *EMP* 400
SIC 4581 3728 Aircraft maintenance & repair services; Aircraft servicing & repairing; Aircraft parts & equipment
* *CFO:* Ben Ward
* *Treas:* Jane Marlow

PEMFAB
See PEMBERTON FABRICATORS INC

PEN AIR
See PENINSULA AIRWAYS INC

PEN BAY HEALTHCARE
See PEN BAY MEDICAL CENTER

D-U-N-S 10-818-4615
PEN BAY MEDICAL CENTER
PEN BAY HEALTHCARE
6 Glen Cove Dr, Rockport, ME 04856-4240
Tel (207) 921-8000 *Founded/Ownrshp* 1983
Sales 147.8MM^E *EMP* 1,200
Accts Baker Newman Noyes
SIC 8062 8082 General medical & surgical hospitals; Home health care services
Ch Bd: Frank Mudle
* *Pr:* Roy Hitchings Jr
* *Treas:* Peter Van Alstine
* *V Ch Bd:* Susan Sulzer
VP: Tom Girard
* *VP:* Barry Hurtt
Dir Rx: Jeff Kubel
Dir Rx: Amy Warrington
* *Prin:* Frank L Muddle
CIO: Brooks Betts
QA Dir: Beth Dodge

D-U-N-S 80-867-9773 IMP
PENCO PRODUCTS INC
(*Suby of* INDUSTRIAL MANUFACTURING CO LLC) ★
1820 Stonehenge Dr, Greenville, NC 27858-5965
Tel (252) 917-5287 *Founded/Ownrshp* 1979
Sales 139.8MM^E *EMP* 550
SIC 2599 2542 Factory furniture & fixtures; Lockers (not refrigerated): except wood; Shelving, office & store: except wood; Cabinets: show, display or storage: except wood
Pr: Thomas Kulikawski
* *Pr:* Greg Grogan
* *CFO:* Alan Kolody
Sr Cor Off: Wayne Howell
* *VP:* Charlie McBride
VP: Harry Popolow
Sls Mgr: Tony Taylor

PENCOM
See PENINSULA COMPONENTS INC

D-U-N-S 01-490-7182
PENCOR SERVICES INC
TIMES NEWS, THE
613 3rd Street Palmerton, Palmerton, PA 18071
Tel (610) 826-2115 *Founded/Ownrshp* 1955
Sales 110.6MM^E *EMP* 397
SIC 2711 7371 4813 4841 Newspapers: publishing only, not printed on site; Custom computer programming services; Local & long distance telephone communications; Cable television services
Pr: David Masenheimer
* *Pr:* Avii Masenheimer
CFO: Jeff Langdon
* *Treas:* Jeff Gehman
* *VP:* Styles S Butz
* *VP:* Fred Masenheimer
VP: Johnathan Slanina
Dir IT: William Schwab
Sls Dir: Joseph Lorah

D-U-N-S 82-639-5477 IMP/EXP
PENDA CORP
PENDA LINER
(*Suby of* PENDAFORM CO) ★
2344 W Wisconsin St, Portage, WI 53901-1008
Tel (608) 742-5301 *Founded/Ownrshp* 2000
Sales 422.1MM^E *EMP* 800
SIC 5013 3714 3792 3713 2273 Automotive supplies & parts; Automotive trim; Truck parts & accessories; Motor vehicle parts & accessories; Motor vehicle body components & frame; Pickup covers, canopies or caps; Truck & bus bodies; Carpets & rugs
CEO: Jack Slinger
* *CFO:* Jim Smith
Netwrk Mgr: Janice Hartwig
MIS Mgr: Pam Barreau
QC Dir: Mike Johnson
Mtls Mgr: Joel H Leeland
Ql Cn Mgr: Dennis Sutton
Mktg Dir: Mike Freye
Sls Dir: Buddy Triplett
Sls Mgr: Debbie Sweet

PENDA LINER
See PENDA CORP

D-U-N-S 07-921-4357
PENDAFORM CO
200 S Friendship Dr, New Concord, OH 43762-9641
Tel (740) 826-5000 *Founded/Ownrshp* 2013
Sales 408.0MM^E *EMP* 1,260
SIC 3089 Thermoformed finished plastic products
Pr: Jack Linger
Pr: Jason Zajicek
CEO: Jack Slinger
Sls Mgr: Debbie Sweet

D-U-N-S 19-301-6854
PENDER COUNTY SCHOOLS
925 Penderlea Hwy, Burgaw, NC 28425-4546
Tel (910) 259-2187 *Founded/Ownrshp* 1890
Sales 62.2MM^E *EMP* 1,200
SIC 8211 Public elementary & secondary schools
Dir Sec: Rick Dutka
Pr Dir: Miranda Roberts

D-U-N-S 18-268-7756
PENDERGAST ELEMENTARY SCHOOL DISTRICT 92
3802 N 91st Ave, Phoenix, AZ 85037-2368
Tel (623) 772-2200 *Founded/Ownrshp* 1897
Sales 61.4MM^E *EMP* 1,214
SIC 8211 Public junior high school; Public elementary school
Exec: Susan Torrejos
Ex Dir: Maria Rodriguez
Ex Dir: Dianne Smith
Off Admin: Cathe Goff
Sfty Dirs: Amy Perhamus
Psych: Kira Billow
Snr Mgr: Alma Pacheco

PENDLETON FLOUR MILLS
See KERR PACIFIC CORP

D-U-N-S 07-193-7171
■ **PENDLETON MEMORIAL METHODIST HOSPITAL**
(*Suby of* UNIVERSAL HEALTH SERVICES INC) ★
5620 Read Blvd, New Orleans, LA 70127-3106
Tel (504) 244-5100 *Founded/Ownrshp* 2004
Sales 27.1MM^E *EMP* 1,210
SIC 8062 General medical & surgical hospitals
Pr: Allen Miller
* *Pr:* Frederick C Young Jr
* *COO:* Cameron Barr
* *VP:* Paul R Page Jr

D-U-N-S 00-903-2459 IMP
PENDLETON WOOLEN MILLS INC
COLUMBIA WOOL SCOURING MILLS
220 Nw Broadway, Portland, OR 97209-3509
Tel (503) 226-4801 *Founded/Ownrshp* 1909
Sales 351.1MM^E *EMP* 1,000^E
SIC 2337 Women's & misses' suits & coats
Ch Bd: J P Bishop
* *Pr:* C M Bishop III
* *CEO:* Mark Korros
* *CFO:* D M Simmonds
* *Chf Cred:* Mary Richter
* *VP:* C B Bishop
* *VP:* P V Bishop
Software D: Lori Hajarizadeh
Software D: Kristin Shearer

Opers Mgr: Dorothy Monte
Sales Exec: Laurie Livingstone

D-U-N-S 80-902-1699
PENDUM LLC
(*Suby of* BURROUGHS INC) ★
558 W Lamont Rd, Elmhurst, IL 60126-1022
Tel (800) 422-6835 *Founded/Ownrshp* 2015
Sales NA *EMP* 2,400
SIC 6099 7381 Automated teller machine (ATM) network; Armored car services
Pr: Brad Browder
VP: Katherine Moberg
VP: Joan Sherlock

D-U-N-S 06-791-5959
PENFIELD CENTRAL SCHOOL DISTRICT INC
2590 Atlantic Ave, Rochester, NY 14625-1543
Tel (585) 249-5700 *Founded/Ownrshp* 1887
Sales 86.7MM *EMP* 900
Accts Raymond F Wager Cpa Pc H
SIC 8211 Public elementary school; Public junior high school; Public senior high school
Ex Dir: John Carlevatti
Treas: William Maloney
Treas: Lily Shur
* *Treas:* Andrew Whitmore
Schl Brd P: Carole Nasra
HC Dir: Gwenda Buckman

D-U-N-S 11-302-2586 IMP
■ **PENFORD CORP**
(*Suby of* INGREDION INC) ★
345 Inverness Dr S # 200, Englewood, CO 80112-5890
Tel (303) 649-1900 *Founded/Ownrshp* 2015
Sales 190.2MM^E *EMP* 443^E
SIC 2046 2869 Industrial starch; Edible starch; Corn starch; Ethyl alcohol, ethanol
Pr: Thomas D Malkoski
CFO: Steven O Cordier
Treas: Andy Linajs
VP: Randy Burns
VP: Andy Dratt
VP: Allen Freed
VP: Greg Keenan
VP: Christopher L Lawlor
VP: Nik Nikolic
VP: Paul Stephens
VP: Dan Walter

D-U-N-S 05-558-5582 EXP
■ **PENFORD PRODUCTS CO**
(*Suby of* PENFORD CORP) ★
1001 1st St Sw, Cedar Rapids, IA 52404-2175
Tel (319) 398-3700 *Founded/Ownrshp* 1968, 1984
Sales 92.7MM^E *EMP* 300^E
SIC 2046 Corn starch; Potato starch; Corn sugar
Ch Bd: Jeffrey T Cook
* *Pr:* Greg Keeley
VP: Nick Nikolip
Exec: Lisa Wade
DP Exec: Trent Buenzow
Sfty Mgr: Lori Garin
Prd Mgr: Phil Kluetz
Ql Cn Mgr: Timothy Garms
VP Mktg: Kurt Moberg
Manager: Keith Hays
Snr Mgr: Scott Crawford

D-U-N-S 03-065-1579
PENGUIN COMPUTING INC
45800 Northport Loop W, Fremont, CA 94538-6413
Tel (415) 954-2800 *Founded/Ownrshp* 1999
Sales 95.0MM *EMP* 100
Accts Shea Labagh Dobberstein San F
SIC 5045 7379 Computers, peripherals & software; Computer related maintenance services
Pr: Tom Coull
* *CFO:* Lisa Cummins
* *Sr VP:* Matt Jacobs
* *Sr VP:* Andreas Junge
Sr VP: Sidney Mair
Sr VP: Charles Wuischpard
VP: Dan Stuart
VP: Garth Thompson
Snr Sftwr: Gary V Yee
* *CTO:* Phil Pokorny
CTO: Phillip Pokorny

D-U-N-S 00-161-3678 IMP
PENGUIN GROUP (USA) LLC
375 Hudson St Bsmt 1, New York, NY 10014-7464
Tel (212) 367-0200 *Founded/Ownrshp* 2013
Sales NA *EMP* 2,000^E
SIC 2731

D-U-N-S 07-888-8404
PENGUIN RANDOM HOUSE LLC
(*Suby of* BERTELSMANN SE & CO. KGAA)
1745 Broadway, New York, NY 10019-4640
Tel (212) 782-9000 *Founded/Ownrshp* 2013
Sales 1.5MMM^E *EMP* 4,000^E
SIC 2731 Books: publishing only
CEO: Markus Dohle
* *Pr:* Madeline McIntosh
* *CFO:* Coram Williams
Sr VP: Lauren Shakely
VP: Susan Driskill-Donney
VP: Carolyn Foley
VP: Beth Koehler
VP: Christine McNamara
VP: Paolo Pepe
VP: Kate Tyler
Assoc Dir: Joelle Dieu
Assoc Dir: Lilly Kim
Assoc Dir: Carmelin Lopez

D-U-N-S 80-444-1558
PENHALL CO
(*Suby of* CONCRETE DEMOLITION) ★
2121 W Crescent Ave Ste A, Anaheim, CA 92801-3810
Tel (714) 772-6450 *Founded/Ownrshp* 1999
Sales 358.8MM^E *EMP* 1,500
Accts Ernst & Young Llp Los Angeles
SIC 1741 1795 Foundation & retaining wall construction; Demolition, buildings & other structures
CEO: Jeff Long
* *Pr:* C George Bush

Pr: Luke Hovde
**CFO:* Lynn Behler
Ofcr: John Smith
VP: George Bush
VP: Sean Butler
VP: Billy Miller
**VP:* Bruce Varney
Exec: Elizabeth Wilson
Area Mgr: Cathy Roof

D-U-N-S 07-446-7648
PENHALL INTERNATIONAL CORP
CONCRETE DEMOLITION
(*Suby of* CENTERBRIDGE PARTNERS LP) ★
320 N Crescent Way, Anaheim, CA 92801-6752
Tel (714) 772-6450 *Founded/Ownrshp* 1957, 2010
Sales 358.8MM^E *EMP* 1,600
SIC 1795 1771 Wrecking & demolition work; Concrete work
Prin: Jeff Long
**CEO:* C George Bush
**CFO:* Bruce Lux
Admn Mgr: Erika L Maniace
Off Mgr: Ruby Belew
Telecom Ex: Linda Lindsey
Sls Dir: Steve Cross

D-U-N-S 00-684-7412
PENINSULA AIRWAYS INC
PEN AIR
6200 Boeing Ave Ste 300, Anchorage, AK 99502-0909
Tel (907) 771-2500 *Founded/Ownrshp* 1956
Sales 96.5MM^E *EMP* 400
SIC 4512 Air passenger carrier, scheduled
CEO: Danny Seybert
**Pr:* Scott Bloomquist
Pr: Coleen Donald
**COO:* Dave Hall
**CFO:* Annette Anzelini
Bd of Dir: Orin D Seybert
Chf Mktg O: Linda Bustamante
Ofcr: Sam Adams
Ofcr: Mike Lawson
Ofcr: Winslow Whitten
Ofcr: Mik Wojcik
**VP:* Mike Bradley
**VP:* Bryan Carricabara
VP: Murphy Forner
**VP:* Melissa Roberts

PENINSULA CENTER FOR EXTENDED
See PENINSULA GENERAL NURSING HOME CORP

D-U-N-S 03-099-2184
PENINSULA COMMUNITY FOUNDATION
CENTER FOR VENTR PHILANTHROPY
1700 S El Camino Real # 300, San Mateo, CA 94402-3047
Tel (650) 358-9369 *Founded/Ownrshp* 1993
Sales 200.0MM *EMP* 55
SIC 6732 Charitable trust management
Pr: Sterling K Speirn
IT Man: Kathy Lee

D-U-N-S 60-613-7065 IMP
PENINSULA COMPONENTS INC
PENCOM
1300 Industrial Rd Ste 21, San Carlos, CA 94070-4141
Tel (650) 593-3288 *Founded/Ownrshp* 1982
Sales 146.8MM^E *EMP* 481
SIC 5085 5065

D-U-N-S 19-650-7896
PENINSULA CORRIDOR JOINT POWERS BOARD
CALTRAIN
1250 San Carlos Ave, San Carlos, CA 94070-2468
Tel (650) 508-6200 *Founded/Ownrshp* 2005
Sales 90.7MM *EMP* 105
Accts Maze & Associates Pleasant Hi
SIC 4111 Local railway passenger operation
Ex Dir: Michael J Scanlon
**CEO:* Virginia Harrington
**CEO:* Chuck Harvey
COO: David Olmeda
Bd of Dir: Don Gage
**Prin:* Jose Cisneros
**Prin:* Malia Cohen
**Prin:* Jeff Gee
**Prin:* Rose Guilbault
**Prin:* Tom Nolan
Genl Mgr: Peter Skinner
Board of Directors: Jose Cisneros, Sean Elsbernd, Nathaniel Ford, Don Gage, Jim Hartnett, Jerry Hill, Arthur L Lloyd, Forrest Williams, Ken Yeager

D-U-N-S 09-983-2805
■ **PENINSULA GAMING LLC**
(*Suby of* BOYD GAMING CORP) ★
301 Bell St, Dubuque, IA 52001-7004
Tel (563) 690-4975 *Founded/Ownrshp* 2012
Sales 43.9MM^E *EMP* 1,945^E
SIC 7999 7011 Gambling establishment; Casino hotel
CEO: M Brent Stevens
**Pr:* Michael S Luzich
**COO:* Jonathan C Swain
**CFO:* Natalie A Schramm
Genl Mgr: George T Papanier

D-U-N-S 82-882-7779
PENINSULA GAMING PARTNERS LLC
600 Star Brewery Dr # 110, Dubuque, IA 52001-7006
Tel (563) 690-4975 *Founded/Ownrshp* 1998
Sales 20.5MM^E *EMP* 3,445
SIC 7999 7011 Gambling establishment; Casino hotel
VP: James Adams

D-U-N-S 07-744-3042
PENINSULA GENERAL NURSING HOME CORP
PENINSULA CENTER FOR EXTENDED
5015 Beach Channel Dr, Far Rockaway, NY 11691-1110
Tel (718) 734-2000 *Founded/Ownrshp* 1969
Sales 1.6MM *EMP* 1,000
Accts Jh Cohn Llp New York Ny
SIC 8051 Skilled nursing care facilities
Pr: Robert Levine

PENINSULA OUTPATIENT CENTER
See COVENANT HEALTHCARE INC

D-U-N-S 06-940-1875
PENINSULA REGIONAL MEDICAL CENTER (MD)
100 E Carroll St, Salisbury, MD 21801-5493
Tel (410) 546-6400 *Founded/Ownrshp* 1897
Sales 397.9MM *EMP* 2,500
SIC 8062

D-U-N-S 08-993-4822
PENINSULA SCHOOL DISTRICT
14015 62nd Ave Nw, Gig Harbor, WA 98332-8607
Tel (253) 530-1000 *Founded/Ownrshp* 1941
Sales 42.7MM^E *EMP* 1,200
SIC 8299 Educational services
Psych: Colleen Blauvelt
Psych: Todd Dempewolf

D-U-N-S 06-989-4780
PENINSULA UNITED METHODIST HOMES INC
PUMH
726 Loveville Rd Ste 3000, Hockessin, DE 19707-1536
Tel (302) 235-6800 *Founded/Ownrshp* 1954
Sales 20.8MM^E *EMP* 1,000
SIC 8361 Home for the aged; Rest home, with health care incidental
VP: Robert Supper
Pr: Charles W Coxson III
Ex VP: Ray Boyle
VP: Howard C Braxton II
VP: Mary L Fera

D-U-N-S 00-296-8527 EXP
PENINSULAR ELECTRIC DISTRIBUTORS INC (FL)
1301 Okeechobee Rd, West Palm Beach, FL 33401-6820
Tel (561) 832-1626 *Founded/Ownrshp* 1946
Sales 97.7MM^E *EMP* 80
SIC 5063 Electrical construction materials; Wire & cable
Pr: John M Larmoyeux
**Sec:* Margaret J Larmoyeux
**VP:* Pierre A Larmoyeux Jr
Genl Mgr: Larry Carron
Board of Directors: Margaret Larmoyeux

PENN COLLEGE
See PENNSYLVANIA COLLEGE OF TECHNOLOGY

D-U-N-S 05-471-1163 IMP/EXP
PENN COLOR INC (PA)
400 Old Dublin Pike, Doylestown, PA 18901-2399
Tel (215) 345-6364 *Founded/Ownrshp* 1977, 1971
Sales 196.6MM^E *EMP* 600
SIC 2865 2816 Color pigments, organic; Color pigments
Pr: Kevin Putman
CFO: David B Hill III
VP: James P Garton
VP: David Mc Garrity
VP: Charles Rybny
Dir Lab: Bob Rudick
Board of Directors: Stanley Hallman

D-U-N-S 00-232-3228 IMP
PENN DETROIT DIESEL ALLISON LLC (PA)
PENN POWER GROUP
8330 State Rd, Philadelphia, PA 19136-2915
Tel (215) 335-5010 *Founded/Ownrshp* 1942
Sales 90.5MM^E *EMP* 480
SIC 7699 7538 Engine repair & replacement, non-automotive; Diesel engine repair: automotive
VP: Joe Paliotta
Brnch Mgr: Norm Weltmer
IT Man: Roberta Goldstein
Sls Dir: Al Clark

D-U-N-S 00-237-1987 IMP
PENN ENGINEERING & MANUFACTURING CORP
(*Suby of* PEM HOLDING CO INC) ★
5190 Old Easton Rd, Danboro, PA 18916
Tel (215) 766-8853 *Founded/Ownrshp* 1942
Sales 446.0MM^E *EMP* 1,700
SIC 3429 3549 8711 Metal fasteners; Metalworking machinery; Industrial engineers
Pr: Mark Petty
CFO: Joseph Coluzzi
Treas: Elliott Israel

PENN HIGHLANDS DUBOIS
See DUBOIS REGIONAL MEDICAL CENTER INC

D-U-N-S 01-478-2304 IMP/EXP
PENN JERSEY PAPER CO
PJP
9355 Blue Grass Rd, Philadelphia, PA 19114-2311
Tel (215) 671-9800 *Founded/Ownrshp* 1963
Sales 298.4MM^E *EMP* 225^E
SIC 5113 5087 Industrial & personal service paper; Janitors' supplies
Prin: Thomas R Furia Sr
**Pr:* Thomas R Furia Jr
CTO: Robert Loeble
Mktg Dir: Glenn Harbison
Sls Mgr: Bill Hill
Sls Mgr: Paul Lang

D-U-N-S 00-893-9258
PENN LINE SERVICE INC
300 Scottdale Ave, Scottdale, PA 15683-1299
Tel (724) 887-9110 *Founded/Ownrshp* 1953
Sales 314.0MM^E *EMP* 900
SIC 1629 1623 1611 0782 Land clearing contractor; Subway construction; Electric power line construction; Guardrail construction, highways; Seeding services, lawn
Pr: Paul Mongell
**Treas:* James Wishart
Ofcr: June Copenhaver
**VP:* Mike Mongell
Sfty Mgr: Chad Showalter
Opers Mgr: Mandy Brown

D-U-N-S 00-791-4294
PENN MUTUAL LIFE INSURANCE CO (PA)
600 Dresher Rd, Horsham, PA 19044-2204
Tel (215) 956-8000 *Founded/Ownrshp* 1847
Sales NA *EMP* 3,000
SIC 6311 Mutual association life insurance
Ch: Eileen C McDonnell
**Ch Bd:* Robert E Chappel
Pr: Ray Caucci
Pr: Nicola Charlton
Pr: Greg Engler
Pr: Eric Johnson
Pr: Bob Lauer
Pr: Mark Smith
**COO:* David M O'Malley
**CFO:* Susan T Deakins
CFO: David O'Malley
**Ch:* Paul C Jeffers
**Ch:* Een C McDonnell
Trst: Julia C Bloch
Trst: Edward G Boehne
Trst: William R Cook
Trst: Allan B Miller
Trst: Edmond F Notebaert
Trst: Robert H Rock
Trst: Anthony M Santomero
Chf Mktg O: Eileen Mc Donnell

D-U-N-S 14-731-8356
▲ **PENN NATIONAL GAMING INC**
825 Berkshire Blvd # 200, Wyomissing, PA 19610-1247
Tel (610) 373-2400 *Founded/Ownrshp* 1972
Sales 2.8MMM *EMP* 18,204
Tkr Sym PENN *Exch* NGS
SIC 7011 7948 Casino hotel; Horse race track operation; Motor vehicle racing & drivers
Pr: Timothy J Wilmott
Ch Bd: Peter M Carlino
COO: Jay Snowden
CFO: Saul V Reibstein
Bd of Dir: Harold Cramer
Ex VP: William J Fair
Ex VP: Phillip Ohara
Ex VP: Carl Sottosanti
Sr VP: Richard Primus
Sr VP: Eric Schippers
VP: James Baum
VP: Tom Beaunchamp
VP: Albert T Britton Sr
VP: Desiree Burke
VP: Gene Clark
VP: Frank Donaghue
VP: Johnathan Finamore
VP: John V Finnamore
VP: Gregg Hart
VP: Robert Ippolito
VP: Jon Johnson
Board of Directors: Harold Cramer, David A Handler, John M Jacquemin, Barbara Shattuck Kohn, Ronald J Naples, Jane Scaccetti

D-U-N-S 17-935-7066
PENN NATIONAL HOLDING CORP
(*Suby of* PENN NATIONAL INSURANCE) ★
2 N 2nd St Ste 2, Harrisburg, PA 17101-1619
Tel (717) 234-4941 *Founded/Ownrshp* 1995
Sales NA *EMP* 750
Accts Pricewaterhousecoopers Llp Ph
SIC 6712 Bank holding companies
Pr: Dennis C Rowe
**CFO:* Christine Sears
**Ex VP:* Kenneth Shutts
IT Man: Kathy Mader
S&M/VP: Christopher Markley

PENN NATIONAL INSURANCE
See PENNSYLVANIA NATIONAL MUTUAL CASUALTY INSURANCE CO

D-U-N-S 07-551-0529
PENN NORTH SCHOOL DISTRICT
401 E Hancock St, Lansdale, PA 19446-3960
Tel (215) 368-0400 *Founded/Ownrshp* 1955
Sales 171.5MM^E *EMP* 1,700
Accts Maillie Falconiero & Company
SIC 8211 Public elementary & secondary schools
**Prin:* Frank R Bartle
Off Mgr: Robert Haler
Teacher Pr: Cheryl McCue

PENN POWER
See PENNSYLVANIA POWER CO INC

PENN POWER GROUP
See PENN DETROIT DIESEL ALLISON LLC

D-U-N-S 00-238-0632 EXP
PENN STAINLESS PRODUCTS INC
PSP
190 Kelly Rd, Quakertown, PA 18951-4208
Tel (215) 536-3053 *Founded/Ownrshp* 1979
Sales 91.4MM^E *EMP* 155
SIC 5051 3443 3471

PENN STATE
See PENNSYLVANIA STATE UNIVERSITY

PENN STATE HERSHEY MEDICAL CTR
See MILTON S HERSHEY MEDICAL CENTER

D-U-N-S 60-300-6318
PENN STATE MILTON S HERSHEY MEDICAL CENTER
500 University Dr, Hershey, PA 17033-2360
Tel (717) 531-5337 *Founded/Ownrshp* 1970
Sales 1.5MM^E *EMP* 10,000
SIC 8062 8733 8211

D-U-N-S 14-841-2570
PENN TANK LINES INC
300 Lionville Station Rd, Chester Springs, PA 19425-9601
Tel (484) 713-1500 *Founded/Ownrshp* 1996
Sales 84.3MM^E *EMP* 400
Accts Preston And Company Chadds Fo
SIC 4213 Liquid petroleum transport, non-local
Pr: John A Mc Sherry Jr
**CEO:* Jack McSherry
**CFO:* Stephen McSherry
**Treas:* Charles Wilson
**Treas:* Sherry Wisdo
**VP:* Jack Willams
Exec: Matt Hamersky
Dist Mgr: Dan Hensley

PENN TOOL
See PENNSYLVANIA TOOL SALES & SERVICE INC

D-U-N-S 07-916-9900
PENN TREATY AMERICAN CORP (PA)
2500 Legacy Dr Ste 130, Frisco, TX 75034-5984
Tel (469) 287-7044 *Founded/Ownrshp* 1965
Sales NA *EMP* 362^E
SIC 6311 Life insurance
CEO: Eugene Woznicki
**CFO:* Mark D Cloutier
**Ex VP:* Cameron B Waite

D-U-N-S 07-365-9062
PENN TREATY NETWORK AMERICA INSURANCE CO
(*Suby of* PENN TREATY AMERICAN CORP) ★
3440 Lehigh St Ste 4, Allentown, PA 18103-7001
Tel (800) 362-0700 *Founded/Ownrshp* 1999
Sales NA *EMP* 200^E
SIC 6321 Health insurance carriers; Accident insurance carriers
VP: Jose Vinas
CFO: Cameron Waite
**Treas:* Michael F Grill
**VP:* Aldysius J Carden

D-U-N-S 05-686-6536 EXP
PENN UNITED TECHNOLOGIES INC
AMERICAN CARBIDE TOOLING DIV
799 N Pike Rd, Cabot, PA 16023-2297
Tel (724) 352-1507 *Founded/Ownrshp* 1971
Sales 117.6MM^E *EMP* 600
Accts Carbis Walker Llp New Castle
SIC 3544 2819 Special dies & tools; Industrial inorganic chemicals
Pr: William A Jones
**Ex VP:* Barry C Barton
**Ex VP:* Jerry R Purcell
**VP:* John Lee
**VP:* Jim Mahan
Dir IT: Al Carr
IT Man: Thomas Bridge
IT Man: Ron Hilliard
IT Man: Dan Olean
Mfg Mgr: Tom Flick
Opers Mgr: Karen Craig

D-U-N-S 00-791-5093
▲ **PENN VIRGINIA CORP** (VA)
100 Matsonford Rd Ste 200, Radnor, PA 19087-4558
Tel (610) 687-8900 *Founded/Ownrshp* 1882
Sales 305.3MM *EMP* 112^E
Accts Kpmg Llp Houston Texas
Tkr Sym PVAH *Exch* OTC
SIC 1311 Crude petroleum & natural gas; Coal gasification; Coal liquefaction
Ch Bd: Edward B Cloues II
COO: John A Brooks
CFO: Steven A Hartman
Ofcr: Nancy M Snyder
Rgnl Mgr: Randy Adrian

D-U-N-S 86-142-5262
■ **PENN VIRGINIA OIL & GAS CORP**
(*Suby of* PENN VIRGINIA CORP) ★
4 Radnor Corp Ctr Ste 200, Radnor, PA 19087-4564
Tel (610) 687-8900 *Founded/Ownrshp* 1994
Sales 90.0MM^E *EMP* 110
SIC 1382 Oil & gas exploration services
VP: John Brooks
**Pr:* H Baird Whitehead
**CFO:* Frank Pici
Bd of Dir: Joe Averett
Bd of Dir: Alexander R Boyle
Bd of Dir: Edward Cloues
Bd of Dir: Philippe De Lummen
Bd of Dir: Steve Krablin
Bd of Dir: Merrill Miller
Bd of Dir: Ronald Page
Bd of Dir: Marsha Perelman
**VP:* Steven A Hartman
**VP:* Ann Horton
**VP:* Keith Horton
**VP:* Jim McKinney
**VP:* Mike Mooney
**VP:* Nancy M Snyder

D-U-N-S 07-162-5313
PENN WILLIAM SCHOOL DISTRICT
100 Green Ave, Lansdowne, PA 19050-1449
Tel (610) 284-8080 *Founded/Ownrshp* 1972
Sales 86.3MM *EMP* 495
Accts Barbacane Thornton & Company
SIC 8211 Public elementary & secondary schools; Public elementary school; Public combined elementary & secondary school; Public senior high school
Pr Dir: Pamela Bookman
Teacher Pr: Joseph Conley

D-U-N-S 62-522-6998
PENNANT FOODS LLC
WENDY'S
(*Suby of* BROCKWAY MORAN & PARTNERS INC) ★
310 Corporate Dr Ste 103, Knoxville, TN 37923-4639
Tel (865) 691-1393 *Founded/Ownrshp* 1991
Sales 110.0MM *EMP* 500
SIC 5812 Fast-food restaurant, chain
Pr: Michael Cardinal

D-U-N-S 80-142-0402
PENNANTPARK INVESTMENT CORP
590 Madison Ave Fl 15, New York, NY 10022-2524
Tel (212) 905-1000 *Founded/Ownrshp* 2007
Sales 161.6MM *EMP* 3
Accts Rsm Us Llp New York New York
Tkr Sym PNNT *Exch* NGS
SIC 6726 Management investment funds, closed-end
Ch Bd: Arthur H Penn
CFO: Aviv Efrat
Chf Cred: Guy F Talarico
Bd of Dir: Adam K Bernstein

PENNEX ALUMINUM COMPANY
See METAL EXCHANGE CORP

D-U-N-S 83-118-4358 IMP
PENNEX ALUMINUM CO LLC
(*Suby of* PENNEX ALUMINUM CO) ★
50 Community St, Wellsville, PA 17365-9661
Tel (717) 432-9647 *Founded/Ownrshp* 1960
Sales 141.8MM[E] *EMP* 305[E]
SIC 5051 Metals service centers & offices
Manager: Janet Wilson

PENNINGTON SEED - GEORGIA DIV
See PENNINGTON SEED INC

D-U-N-S 02-350-0465 IMP/EXP
■ **PENNINGTON SEED INC**
PENNINGTON SEED - GEORGIA DIV
(*Suby of* CENTRAL GARDEN & PET CO) ★
1280 Atlanta Hwy, Madison, GA 30650-2065
Tel (706) 342-1234 *Founded/Ownrshp* 1998
Sales 254.5MM[E] *EMP* 1,000
SIC 5261 2873 5191 6799 0723

D-U-N-S 94-675-5998
PENNINSULA REGIONAL MEDICAL CENTER
OCEAN PINES FAMILY MEDICINE
10514 Racetrack Rd Ste C, Berlin, MD 21811-3241
Tel (410) 641-8585 *Founded/Ownrshp* 1999
Sales 362.0MM *EMP* 8
Accts Ernst & Young Llp
SIC 8011

D-U-N-S 06-435-5282
PENNONI ASSOCIATES INC
3001 Market St Ste 200, Philadelphia, PA 19104-2847
Tel (215) 222-3000 *Founded/Ownrshp* 1967
Sales 146.1MM *EMP* 900
Accts Merves Amon Barsz Llc Media
SIC 8711 Consulting engineer
Ch: C R Pennoni
**Pr:* Anthony Bartolomeo
**COO:* David Delizza
**CFO:* Stacey M McPeak
Assoc VP: Mark Davidson
Assoc VP: Hugh Dougherty
Assoc VP: Ronald Moore
Assoc VP: Jeffrey Purdy
**Ex VP:* Nelson Shaffer
VP: Dennis Cannon
VP: Bruce Frederick
VP: Joe Viscuso

D-U-N-S 07-374-3387
PENNRIDGE SCHOOL DISTRICT
1200 N 5th St, Perkasie, PA 18944-1898
Tel (215) 257-5011 *Founded/Ownrshp* 1964
Sales 62.0M *EMP* 1,100
SIC 8211 Public elementary & secondary schools; High school, junior or senior
CFO: Dennis M Call
**VP:* Joan Kulesza
Adm Dir: Denise McCue
MIS Dir: Chris Chamuris
Teacher Pr: Jacquelin McHale

D-U-N-S 07-708-2071
PENNSBURY SCHOOL DISTRICT
FALLSINGTON
19058-0338 Yardley Ave, Levittown, PA 19058
Tel (215) 428-4100 *Founded/Ownrshp* 1949
Sales 174.4MM *EMP* 1,609
Accts Maillie Llp Oaks Pennsylvani
SIC 8211 Public elementary & secondary schools; Public elementary school; Public junior high school; Public senior high school
**Treas:* Joann Godzieba
**Prin:* Donna M Dunar
**Prin:* Elliott H Lewis
Pr Dir: Ann Langtry
Teacher Pr: Bettie Ann Rarrick
HC Dir: Kathleen McGinnis

PENNSY PAVING
See PENNSY SUPPLY INC

D-U-N-S 00-302-0575
PENNSY SUPPLY INC (PA)
PENNSY PAVING
(*Suby of* OLDCASTLE INC) ★
1001 Paxton St, Harrisburg, PA 17104-1697
Tel (717) 233-4511 *Founded/Ownrshp* 1921, 1993
Sales 9.2MMM[E] *EMP* 1,000
SIC 1422 2951 3273 4212 5032

D-U-N-S 00-791-6380
■ **PENNSYLVANIA - AMERICAN WATER CO** (PA)
(*Suby of* AMERICAN WATER WORKS CO INC) ★
800 W Hershey Park Dr, Hershey, PA 17033-2400
Tel (717) 533-5000 *Founded/Ownrshp* 1904
Sales 589.8MM *EMP* 1,007
SIC 4941 Water supply
Pr: Kathy Pape
CFO: Ellen C Wolf
**Treas:* Stephen F Analdo
VP: Emily A Ashworth
**VP:* William C Kelvinton
VP: Craig Levinsky
MIS Dir: David Jerpe
Dir IT: Bill Cox
Opers Supe: Alan Sechman
Genl Couns: Eric Westfall
Counsel: Susan Simms
Board of Directors: Jon Delano

D-U-N-S 00-691-9039
■ **PENNSYLVANIA CO INC**
(*Suby of* AMERICAN FINANCIAL GROUP INC) ★
1 E 4th St, Cincinnati, OH 45202-3717
Tel (513) 579-2121 *Founded/Ownrshp* 2003
Sales NA *EMP* 1,150
SIC 6321 Disability health insurance
**Pr:* Carl H Lindner III
**VP:* Robert Amory
**VP:* James E Evans
**VP:* Robert E Gill
**VP:* James C Kennedy
**VP:* Fred J Runk

D-U-N-S 06-958-9638
PENNSYLVANIA COLLEGE OF TECHNOLOGY (PA)
PENN COLLEGE
(*Suby of* PENN STATE) ★
1 College Ave, Williamsport, PA 17701-5778
Tel (570) 320-2400 *Founded/Ownrshp* 1966
Sales 148.5MM[E] *EMP* 1,650
Accts Larson Kellett & Associates
SIC 8221 Colleges universities & professional schools
Pr: Davie Jane Gilmour
**CFO:* Suzanne Stopper
VP: Robert Fisher
VP: Charles Kern
CIO: Michael Cunningham
CIO: Mike M Cunningham
Pgrm Dir: Sheryl Goss

PENNSYLVANIA CRUSHER
See K-TRON INTERNATIONAL INC

D-U-N-S 06-978-1128
PENNSYLVANIA DENTAL SERVICE CORP (PA)
DELTA DENTAL OF PENNSYLVANIA
1 Delta Dr, Mechanicsburg, PA 17055-6999
Tel (717) 766-8500 *Founded/Ownrshp* 1964
Sales NA *EMP* 600
SIC 6324 8021

D-U-N-S 08-178-2927
PENNSYLVANIA DEPARTMENT OF CONSERVATION & NATURAL RESOURCES
(*Suby of* GOVERNORS OFFICE) ★
400 Market St Fl 7, Harrisburg, PA 17101-2301
Tel (717) 787-2869 *Founded/Ownrshp* 1995
Sales NA *EMP* 3,273
SIC 9512 Land, mineral & wildlife conservation;

D-U-N-S 79-656-7790
PENNSYLVANIA DEPARTMENT OF HUMAN SERVICES
(*Suby of* GOVERNORS OFFICE) ★
625 Forster St, Harrisburg, PA 17120-0701
Tel (717) 787-2600 *Founded/Ownrshp* 1921
Sales NA *EMP* 20,000
SIC 9441 Administration of social & manpower programs;
Snr Mgr: Jim Weaver

D-U-N-S 55-654-9160
PENNSYLVANIA DEPARTMENT OF LABOR & INDUSTRY
(*Suby of* GOVERNORS OFFICE) ★
Labor/Industry Bldg Fl 17, Harrisburg, PA 17120-0001
Tel (717) 787-5279 *Founded/Ownrshp* 1889
Sales NA *EMP* 6,000
SIC 9651 Labor regulatory agency
CFO: Connie Huber

D-U-N-S 79-609-7806
PENNSYLVANIA DEPARTMENT OF REVENUE
(*Suby of* GOVERNORS OFFICE) ★
1147 Strawberry Sq, Harrisburg, PA 17128-0001
Tel (717) 787-6300 *Founded/Ownrshp* 1927
Sales NA *EMP* 2,577
SIC 9311 Finance, taxation & monetary policy;
Mng Ofcr: Chris Stoklos
Counsel: Maryellen Martin

D-U-N-S 13-566-8887
PENNSYLVANIA DEPT OF ENVIRONMENTAL PROTECTION
(*Suby of* GOVERNORS OFFICE) ★
400 Market St, Harrisburg, PA 17101-2301
Tel (717) 787-1319 *Founded/Ownrshp* 1970
Sales NA *EMP* 3,000
SIC 9511 Air, water & solid waste management;
Prgrm Mgr: Marc Neville
Genl Mgr: Jennifer Brandt
IT Man: Robert Rottet
IT Man: Kurt Smith

D-U-N-S 36-070-0769
PENNSYLVANIA DEPT OF STATE POLICE
(*Suby of* GOVERNORS OFFICE) ★
1800 Elmerton Ave, Harrisburg, PA 17110-9718
Tel (717) 783-5599 *Founded/Ownrshp* 1905
Sales NA *EMP* 5,270
SIC 9221 State police;
Genl Mgr: William Box
CIO: Wesley Waugh

D-U-N-S 19-230-0564
PENNSYLVANIA DEPT OF TRANSPORTATION
(*Suby of* GOVERNORS OFFICE) ★
400 North St Fl 8, Harrisburg, PA 17120-0208
Tel (717) 787-6875 *Founded/Ownrshp* 1970
Sales NA *EMP* 12,400
SIC 9621 Regulation, administration of transportation;
Snr Mgr: Chris De

D-U-N-S 00-896-7614
■ **PENNSYLVANIA ELECTRIC CO**
(*Suby of* FIRSTENERGY CORP) ★
76 S Main St Bsmt, Akron, OH 44308-1817
Tel (800) 545-7741 *Founded/Ownrshp* 1919
Sales 541.8MM[E] *EMP* 896[E]
Accts Pricewaterhousecoopers Llp Cl
SIC 4911 Electric services
Pr: Charles E Jones
**CFO:* Mark T Clark
Treas: James F Pearson
Ex VP: Leila L Vespoli
VP: Harvey L Wagner
Board of Directors: Anthony J Alexander

D-U-N-S 06-396-7921
PENNSYLVANIA GENERAL ENERGY CORP
P G E
120 Market St, Warren, PA 16365-2510
Tel (814) 723-3230 *Founded/Ownrshp* 1980
Sales 153.6MM[E] *EMP* 105
SIC 1311 Crude petroleum production; Natural gas production
CEO: Douglas E Kuntz
**Pr:* Thomas H Henry
**Treas:* Frank J Reidy
VP: Edward Gens
**VP:* Charles W Kirkwood
Netwrk Mgr: Joe Levis

D-U-N-S 00-736-8103
PENNSYLVANIA HIGHER EDUCATION ASSISTANCE AGENCY (PA)
FEDLOAN SERVICING
(*Suby of* GOVERNORS OFFICE) ★
1200 N 7th St, Harrisburg, PA 17102-1419
Tel (717) 720-2700 *Founded/Ownrshp* 1963
Sales NA *EMP* 2,700
Accts Ernst & Young Llp Mclean Va
SIC 9411 Administration of educational programs;
Ch Bd: William F Adolph Jr
Pr: Donna Orris
**CEO:* James L Preston
CFO: Timothy A Guenther
Sr VP: Mary Miller
VP: Lori Fehr
**VP:* Stephanie Foltz
**VP:* Nathan Hench
**VP:* Todd E Mosko
VP: Pamela Roda-Kline
VP: James Roush
VP: Matt Sessa
**VP:* Matthew D Sessa
VP: John Wozniak
VP: Christine Zuzack
Board of Directors: Vincent J Hughes, Sandra J Major, Roy Reinard, James R Roebuck, Robert M Tomlinson

D-U-N-S 07-161-3954 IMP
PENNSYLVANIA HOSPITAL OF UNIVERSITY OF PENNSYLVANIA HEALTH SYSTEM
800 Spruce St, Philadelphia, PA 19107-6130
Tel (215) 829-3000 *Founded/Ownrshp* 1997
Sales 534.3MM *EMP* 2,200
SIC 8062 8063 Hospital, affiliated with AMA residency; Psychiatric hospitals
Chf Rad: Bruce Kneeland
Dir Recs: Scott Gilyard
CFO: George Haddad
Chf Mktg O: Dennis Policastro
VP: Arthur Bartolozzi
VP: Kevin Guynn
VP: Stephen Wanta
Exec: Salvatore Dipalma
Dir Risk M: Janet Creeley
Chf Nrs Of: Mary Delguidice
Mng Dir: Jennifer Debellis

D-U-N-S 00-791-4344
PENNSYLVANIA LUMBERMENS MUTUAL INSURANCE CO (PA)
2005 Market St Ste 1200, Philadelphia, PA 19103-7008
Tel (800) 752-1895 *Founded/Ownrshp* 1895
Sales NA *EMP* 170
SIC 6331 Fire, marine & casualty insurance & carriers
Ch Bd: William J Lee
**Pr:* Harold Jamison
**Pr:* John K Smith
**Treas:* Michael O' Malley
**Sr VP:* Joseph W McCrea
**VP:* Stephan D Firko

D-U-N-S 00-791-4351
■ **PENNSYLVANIA MANUFACTURERS ASSOCIATION INSURANCE CO** (PA)
PMA INSURANCE GROUP, THE
(*Suby of* PMA CAPITAL) ★
380 Sentry Pkwy, Blue Bell, PA 19422-2357
Tel (610) 397-5000 *Founded/Ownrshp* 1915, 2010
Sales NA *EMP* 1,000
SIC 6331 Workers' compensation insurance; Property damage insurance; Fire, marine & casualty insurance: mutual
Pr: Vincent T Donnelly
Ofcr: Joe Greco
Assoc VP: Kay Stepler
Ex VP: Anthony J Ciofani Jr
Ex VP: John M Cochrane
Ex VP: John Santulli III
Sr VP: Kevin M Brady
Sr VP: Jennifer J Johnston
Sr VP: Kurt L Schuhl
Sr VP: Stephen D Warfel
VP: Donald F Borrell
VP: John Burke
VP: William G Carney
VP: Vincent Donnelly
VP: Glenn R Giveans
VP: Jennifer Johnston
VP: Andrew J McGill
VP: Jon Miles
VP: Raymond Rocchio
VP: Edward W Scannell III
VP: Tony Steinauer

D-U-N-S 78-792-4869
■ **PENNSYLVANIA MANUFACTURERS INDEMNITY CO**
(*Suby of* PMA CAPITAL INSURANCE CO) ★
380 Sentry Pkwy, Blue Bell, PA 19422-2357
Tel (610) 397-5000 *Founded/Ownrshp* 1982
Sales NA *EMP* 400
SIC 6331 Workers' compensation insurance
Pr: Vincent Thomas Donnelly
**Treas:* William Edward Hitselberger
IT Man: John Gentile

D-U-N-S 07-121-8176
PENNSYLVANIA NATIONAL MUTUAL CASUALTY INSURANCE CO (PA)
PENN NATIONAL INSURANCE
2 N 2nd St Ste 2, Harrisburg, PA 17101-1619
Tel (717) 230-8200 *Founded/Ownrshp* 1920
Sales NA *EMP* 750
Accts Pricewaterhousecoopers Llp Ph
SIC 6331 Fire, marine & casualty insurance
Ch Bd: Dennis C Rowe
**Pr:* Kenneth R Shutts
**COO:* Christine Sears
**CFO:* Jacquelyn Anderson
**CFO:* Gregory Stine
Ofcr: Kelly McClory
**Sr VP:* Karen C Yarrish
VP: Frank J Benedek
VP: Monica Jacobs
Genl Mgr: Susanna Smith
CIO: Bill Jekins

D-U-N-S 00-791-2736
■ **PENNSYLVANIA POWER CO INC** (PA)
PENN POWER
(*Suby of* OHIO EDISON CO) ★
76 S Main St Bsmt, Akron, OH 44308-1817
Tel (800) 720-3600 *Founded/Ownrshp* 1930
Sales 338.9MM[E] *EMP* 610
Accts Pricewaterhousecoopers Llp Cl
SIC 4911 Distribution, electric power; Generation, electric power; Transmission, electric power
Pr: Anthony J Alexander
**Sr VP:* T M Welsh
VP: W Reeher
**VP:* Robert Wuschinske
**Genl Couns:* Leila Vespoli

D-U-N-S 05-716-1028
PENNSYLVANIA REAL ESTATE INVESTMENT TRUST
PREIT
200 S Broad St, Philadelphia, PA 19102-3803
Tel (215) 875-0700 *Founded/Ownrshp* 1960
Sales 425.4MM *EMP* 397[E]
SIC 6798 6531 Real estate investment trusts; Real estate leasing & rentals
CEO: Joseph F Coradino
**Ch Bd:* Ronald Rubin
CFO: Robert F McCadden
Ex VP: Bruce Goldman
Ex VP: Andrew M Ioannou
Ex VP: Mario C Ventresca Jr
Sr VP: Jonathen Bell
Board of Directors: M Walter D'allessio, Michael J Demarco, Rosemarie B Greco, Leonard I Korman, Mark E Pasquerilla, Charles P Pizzi, John J Roberts

D-U-N-S 03-943-9435
PENNSYLVANIA STATE EMPLOYEES CREDIT UNION
PSECU
1500 Elmerton Ave, Harrisburg, PA 17110-9214
Tel (800) 237-7328 *Founded/Ownrshp* 1933
Sales NA *EMP* 400
Accts Rsm Us Llp New York New York
SIC 6062 9199 State credit unions; General government administration;
Pr: Gregory A Smith
Pr: Tammy L Heimbaugh
VP: Toni Carey
VP: Richard Long
Dir IT: Eric Garber
Mktg Dir: Karen Roland

D-U-N-S 00-340-3953 IMP/EXP
PENNSYLVANIA STATE UNIVERSITY
PENN STATE
201 Old Main, University Park, PA 16802-1503
Tel (814) 865-4700 *Founded/Ownrshp* 1855
Sales 5.7MMM *EMP* 44,000
Accts Deloitte & Touche Llp Philade
SIC 8221 University
Pr: Eric J Barron
**Pr:* Rodney A Erickson
**Ch:* Keith Masser
**Ch:* Karen Peetz
Treas: Connie Manchester
Trst: Charles C Brosius
Trst: Eugene B Chaiken
Trst: George R Henning Jr
Trst: Barron L Hetherington
Trst: Edward R Hintz
Trst: Rodney P Hughes
Trst: David R Jones
Trst: David M Joyner
Trst: Edward P Junker
Trst: Keith E Masser
Trst: Joel N Meyers
Trst: Anne Riley
Trst: Carl T Schaffer
Chf Inves: John Pomeroy II
Assoc VP: Karen Helsley
Assoc VP: Dave Lieb

D-U-N-S 07-045-5175 IMP
PENNSYLVANIA TOOL SALES & SERVICE INC
PENN TOOL
625 Bev Rd, Youngstown, OH 44512-6421
Tel (330) 758-0845 *Founded/Ownrshp* 1976
Sales 110.0MM *EMP* 196
SIC 7699 5085 5084 Tool repair services; Industrial tools; Hoists
Pr: Robert Baxter
Board of Directors: Shawn Baxter, John Frank, Pat Lydon

D-U-N-S 10-915-2462 IMP
PENNSYLVANIA TRANSFORMER TECHNOLOGY INC
30 Curry Ave Ste 2, Canonsburg, PA 15317-1786
Tel (724) 873-2100 *Founded/Ownrshp* 1988
Sales 87.6MM[E] *EMP* 390
SIC 3612 5063 3677 Distribution transformers, electric; Power transformers, electric; Electrical apparatus & equipment; Electronic coils, transformers & other inductors

Pr: Ravi Rahangdale
VP: Dennis Blake
**VP:* Shashi Rahangdale

D-U-N-S 00-722-2078
PENNWELL CORP (OK)
PENNWELL PUBLISHING COMPANY
1421 S Sheridan Rd, Tulsa, OK 74112-6619
Tel (918) 835-3161 *Founded/Ownrshp* 1910
Sales 246.7MM^E *EMP* 1,000
SIC 2721 2731 2741 7389 Periodicals: publishing only; Magazines: publishing only, not printed on site; Books: publishing only; Telephone & other directory publishing; Convention & show services; Promoters of shows & exhibitions; Trade show arrangement
Pr: Mark C Wilmoth
**Sr VP:* Jayne Gilsinger
VP: Paul Andrews
**VP:* Jeff Berend
VP: Peter Christensen
VP: Patti Glaza
VP: Roy Markum
VP: James Pfister
Genl Mgr: Scott Tevis
Genl Mgr: Tim Wise
Off Mgr: Shelly Haire

PENNWELL PUBLISHING COMPANY
See PENNWELL CORP

D-U-N-S 00-921-5377 IMP/EXP
PENNY NEWMAN GRAIN CO
2691 S Cedar Ave, Fresno, CA 93725-2032
Tel (559) 499-0691 *Founded/Ownrshp* 1987
Sales 192.3MM^E *EMP* 90
SIC 5153 Grains; Wheat; Barley; Corn
CEO: Mike Nicoletti
VP: James Netto
Genl Mgr: Bill Slivkoff

D-U-N-S 00-234-1592 IMP
PENNY PLATE LLC
14000 Horizon Way Ste 300, Mount Laurel, NJ 08054-4342
Tel (856) 429-7583 *Founded/Ownrshp* 1949, 1948
Sales 97.9MM^E *EMP* 272
SIC 3411 3556 Metal cans; Aluminum cans; Food products machinery
Pr: Helen Buff
**CFO:* John J Dillenschneider
**Ex VP:* George Buff III
**VP:* John Charles Buff

PENNYMAC
See PRIVATE NATIONAL MORTGAGE ACCEPTANCE CO LLC

D-U-N-S 96-802-3601
PENNYMAC CORP
(*Suby of* PENNYMAC MORTGAGE INVESTMENT TRUST) ★
27001 Agoura Rd, Agoura Hills, CA 91301-5339
Tel (818) 878-8416 *Founded/Ownrshp* 2012
Sales NA *EMP* 1,797^E
SIC 6163 Loan brokers
Pr: Stanford L Kurland

D-U-N-S 07-874-8445
PENNYMAC FINANCIAL SERVICES INC
3043 Townsgate Rd, Westlake Village, CA 91361-3027
Tel (818) 224-7442 *Founded/Ownrshp* 2008
Sales NA *EMP* 2,509
Tkr Sym PFSI *Exch* NYS
SIC 6162 6282 Mortgage bankers & correspondents; Investment advice
Ch Bd: Stanford L Kurland
**Pr:* David A Spector
CFO: Anne D McCallion
Ofcr: Andrew S Chang
Ofcr: Jeffrey P Grogin
Ofcr: David M Walker
Board of Directors: Matthew Botein, James K Hunt, Patrick Kinsella, Joseph Mazzella, Mark Wiedman, Emily Youssouf

D-U-N-S 83-129-5923
PENNYMAC MORTGAGE INVESTMENT TRUST
6101 Condor Dr, Moorpark, CA 93021-2602
Tel (818) 224-7442 *Founded/Ownrshp* 2009
Sales 373.4MM *EMP* 1,816^E
Accts Deloitte & Touche Llp Los An
SIC 6798 Real estate investment trusts; Mortgage investment trusts
Ch Bd: Stanford L Kurland
**Pr:* David A Spector
COO: Steve Bailey
CFO: Anne D McCallion
Chf Cred: David M Walker
Chf Inves: Vandad Fartaj
Ofcr: Andrew S Chang
Ofcr: Jeffrey P Grogin

D-U-N-S 00-694-4821
PENNYRILE RURAL ELECTRIC COOPERATIVE CORP
2000 Harrison St, Hopkinsville, KY 42240-6000
Tel (270) 886-2555 *Founded/Ownrshp* 1937
Sales 128.7MM *EMP* 127
SIC 4911 Distribution, electric power
Ex Dir: Eston Glover
VP: Alan Gates
**VP:* Sandra Grogan
Dist Mgr: Ricky Turner
IT Man: Francis Henderson
Sfty Dirs: Robyn Bybee

PENNYSAVER
See TRIBTOTAL MEDIA INC

D-U-N-S 06-310-9318
PENNYSAVER USA PUBLISHING LLC
ORIGINAL PENNYSAVER, THE
2830 Orbiter St, Brea, CA 92821-6224
Tel (866) 640-3900 *Founded/Ownrshp* 2013
Sales NA *EMP* 1,000
SIC 2741

D-U-N-S 16-180-9744 EXP
PENNZOIL-QUAKER STATE CO
SOPUS PRODUCTS
(*Suby of* SHELL OIL CO) ★
700 Milam St Ste 125, Houston, TX 77002-2815
Tel (713) 546-4000 *Founded/Ownrshp* 1998
Sales 726.5MM^E *EMP* 1,400
SIC 2992 Lubricating oils & greases; Oils & greases, blending & compounding
Pr: Istvan Kapitany
**Pr:* Lynn Elsenhans
**CFO:* Duncan Palmer
**Treas:* David P Davis
Sr VP: Richard L Edmonson
Sr VP: Robert A Flivene
**VP:* Annette Craig
**VP:* Stuart Crum
VP: Marc C Graham
**VP:* Brian J Huisman
**VP:* Brett L Marks
**VP:* Todd S Miner
**VP:* Richard M Oblath
VP: William M Robb
VP: John E Roueche
**VP:* Viet Van

D-U-N-S 93-110-4178 IMP
PENNZOIL-QUAKER STATE NOMINEE CO
(*Suby of* ROYAL DUTCH SHELL PLC)
700 Milam St Ste 400, Houston, TX 77002-2815
Tel (713) 546-4000 *Founded/Ownrshp* 1999
Sales 129.3MM^E *EMP* 850
SIC 5172 Petroleum products
Ch: James Pate

D-U-N-S 07-174-4759
PENOBSCOT BAY MEDICAL CENTER (ME)
(*Suby of* PEN BAY HEALTHCARE) ★
6 Glen Cove Dr, Rockport, ME 04856-4240
Tel (207) 230-6380 *Founded/Ownrshp* 1975
Sales 111.9MM *EMP* 800
SIC 8062 8059 General medical & surgical hospitals; Nursing home, except skilled & intermediate care facility
CEO: Wade C Johnson
COO: Thomas Schuhley
**COO:* Eric Waters
**CFO:* Elmer Doucette
CFO: Mer Doucette
**CFO:* Maura Kelly
CFO: Theresa Nizio
Treas: Diane Haskell
Ofcr: Daniel Breen
VP: Chris Baldwin
VP: Dana Goldsmith
Exec: John Roy

D-U-N-S 15-448-1519 EXP
PENROD CO
272 Bendix Rd Ste 550, Virginia Beach, VA 23452-1393
Tel (757) 498-0186 *Founded/Ownrshp* 1986
Sales 87.6MM^E *EMP* 500
SIC 3429 5039 2821 Door locks, bolts & checks; Structural assemblies, prefabricated: non-wood; Polyvinyl chloride resins (PVC)
CEO: Edward Heidt Jr
**Pr:* Timothy G Heidt
**Pr:* Karsten Nielsen
CFO: Stewart P Mitchell
VP: Robert M McCarthy

PENROSE - ST FRANCES HLTH SVCS
See CATHOLIC HEALTH INITIATIVES COLORADO

D-U-N-S 61-277-3981
PENROSE HOSPITAL
(*Suby of* ST ANTHONY CENTRAL HOSPITAL) ★
2222 N Nevada Ave Ste 1, Colorado Springs, CO 80907-6794
Tel (719) 776-5000 *Founded/Ownrshp* 1997
Sales 1.0MM^E *EMP* 1,750
SIC 8062 General medical & surgical hospitals
Pr: Margaret Sabin
**COO:* Jameson Smith
**CFO:* Danny Reeves
**VP:* Peter Walsh MD

PENROSE ST FRANCIS HEALTH SVCS
See CENTURA HEALTH CORP

PENSACOLA CHRISTIAN COLLEGE
See W P C S FM

D-U-N-S 07-263-1336
PENSACOLA CHRISTIAN COLLEGE INC
ABEKA BOOK PUBLICATIONS
250 Brent Ln, Pensacola, FL 32503-2267
Tel (850) 478-8496 *Founded/Ownrshp* 1960
Sales 92.2MM *EMP* 1,204
Accts Habif Arogeti & Wynne Llp Atl
SIC 8221 Colleges & universities; Service academy
Ch: Charles Buettner
**Pr:* Troy A Shoemaker
Ofcr: Gregg Bryant
VP: Paul Ohman
Exec: Amy Glenn
Dir Sec: Shawn Ross
Brnch Mgr: Eric Fears
IT Man: Thomas Mahoney
IT Man: Philip Musgrave
Web Dev: Laura Pribyl
Psych: Nino Mendez

D-U-N-S 05-022-5416
PENSE BROTHERS DRILLING CO INC
800 Newberry St, Fredericktown, MO 63645-1526
Tel (573) 783-3011 *Founded/Ownrshp* 1962
Sales 89.4MM^E *EMP* 225
SIC 1081 1381 Test boring, metal mining; Drilling oil & gas wells
Pr: Clifford L Pense
**Pr:* Ronald Pense
VP: David Pense
Off Mgr: Annie Elders

D-U-N-S 79-649-1330 IMP
▲ **PENSKE AUTOMOTIVE GROUP INC**
2555 S Telegraph Rd, Bloomfield Hills, MI 48302-0974
Tel (248) 648-2500 *Founded/Ownrshp* 1992
Sales 19.2MMM *EMP* 22,000
Tkr Sym PAG *Exch* NYS
SIC 5511 New & used car dealers; Automobiles, new & used
Ch Bd: Roger S Penske
**Pr:* Robert H Kurnick Jr
CFO: John D Carlson Jr
Treas: Johnnie Reed
Ex VP: Bud Denker
Ex VP: David Jones
Ex VP: Terri Mulcahey
Ex VP: Rwhitfield Ramonat
Ex VP: Randall Seymore
Ex VP: Shane M Spradlin
VP: Yoshimi Namba
VP: Robert Wilshaw

D-U-N-S 04-069-7273 IMP
PENSKE CO LLC
(*Suby of* PENSKE CORP) ★
2555 S Telegraph Rd, Bloomfield Hills, MI 48302-0974
Tel (248) 648-2000 *Founded/Ownrshp* 2000
Sales 227.7MM^E *EMP* 1,301
SIC 3647 Vehicular lighting equipment
Chf Mktg O: Bud Denker
VP: Lawrence Bluth
VP: Richard Harris
Dir Bus: Mike Hintenach
Genl Mgr: Amy Ilyes
Telecom Ex: Peter Lubin
CTO: Leonso Garcia
Dir IT: Stephanie Frink
Site Mgr: Mike Smith
Mktg Mgr: Suzanne Claypoole
Sales Asso: Brandon Davis

D-U-N-S 06-978-3694 IMP/EXP
PENSKE CORP
2555 S Telegraph Rd, Bloomfield Hills, MI 48302-0974
Tel (248) 648-2000 *Founded/Ownrshp* 1969
Sales 12.3MMM^E *EMP* 36,000
SIC 5511 7538 7948

D-U-N-S 08-363-7215
PENSKE DEDICATED LOGISTICS CORP
Green Hls Rr 10, Reading, PA 19607
Tel (610) 775-6000 *Founded/Ownrshp* 1983
Sales NA *EMP* 1,500
SIC 7513

D-U-N-S 12-694-9747 IMP/EXP
PENSKE LOGISTICS LLC
(*Suby of* PENSKE TRUCK LEASING CO LP) ★
Green Hls Rr 10, Reading, PA 19603
Tel (800) 529-6531 *Founded/Ownrshp* 2002
Sales 1.0MMM *EMP* 9,033
SIC 7513 4213 Truck leasing, without drivers; Truck rental, without drivers; Contract haulers
Pr: Marc Althen
Treas: Wayne Angelbeck
**Sr VP:* Dennis Abruzzi
Sr VP: Jeffery A Bullard
Sr VP: Joe Carlier
**Sr VP:* Dave Cumbo
Sr VP: Jim Erdman
Sr VP: Amy Ilyes
Sr VP: Andy Moses
**Sr VP:* Paul Ott
**Sr VP:* Bill Scroggie
**VP:* Terry Miller

D-U-N-S 62-114-3791
PENSKE MOTOR GROUP LLC
(*Suby of* PENSKE CORP) ★
3534 Peck Rd, El Monte, CA 91731-3526
Tel (626) 580-6000 *Founded/Ownrshp* 2011
Sales 284.9MM^E *EMP* 950
SIC 5511 Automobiles, new & used
Pr: Greg Penske
**CFO:* Gregory J Houfley
**CFO:* David K Jones
Ofcr: Renee Lawson
**Ex VP:* George Brochick
**Ex VP:* Calvin C Sharp
VP: J D Carlson
**VP:* Robert H Kurnick Jr
**VP:* Dave Summers
VP: Ryan Ward
Exec: Mike Bronowicki
Exec: Ken Rankin

D-U-N-S 01-057-8508
PENSKE REALTY INC
(*Suby of* PENSKE CORP) ★
Green Hls Rr 10, Reading, PA 19607
Tel (610) 775-6000 *Founded/Ownrshp* 1974
Sales 26.2MM^E *EMP* 1,000
SIC 6531 Real estate agents & managers
Pr: Brian Hard

D-U-N-S 19-455-1644
PENSKE TRANSPORTATION HOLDINGS CORP
(*Suby of* PENSKE CORP) ★
13400 W Outer Dr, Detroit, MI 48239-1309
Tel (313) 592-7311 *Founded/Ownrshp* 1987
Sales 399.2MM^E *EMP* 23,000
SIC 6799 Investors
Ch Bd: Roger S Penske
**V Ch Bd:* Brian D Hard
**Ex VP:* Walter P Czarnecki
Board of Directors: Roger E Birk, A Gordon Clark, John F Devaney, Donald J Hofmann, Gregory Penske, Richard J Peters

D-U-N-S 36-270-2664 IMP/EXP
PENSKE TRUCK LEASING CO LP
(*Suby of* PENSKE CORP) ★
2675 Morgantown Rd, Reading, PA 19607-9676
Tel (610) 775-6000 *Founded/Ownrshp* 1988
Sales 1.4MMM^E *EMP* 23,000
SIC 7513 Truck leasing, without drivers; Truck rental, without drivers
Pr: Marc Althen
Pr: Roger S Penske
Pr: Brian Hard
CFO: Frank Cocuzza
Treas: Wayne Angelbeck
Ex VP: Terry Miller
Ex VP: Art Vallely
Sr VP: Joe Carlier
Sr VP: Kenneth Coots
Sr VP: Dave Cumbo
Sr VP: Michael Duff
Sr VP: Sherry Sanger
Sr VP: William L Stobbart
VP: Thomas Janowicz
VP: Mike Krut
VP: Dan Luginbuhl
VP: Paul Maglionico
VP: Karen Shchuka

D-U-N-S 04-395-7885
PENSKE TRUCK LEASING CORP
(*Suby of* PENSKE CORP) ★
2675 Morgantown Rd, Reading, PA 19607-9676
Tel (610) 775-6000 *Founded/Ownrshp* 1982
Sales 1.3MMM^E *EMP* 23,000
SIC 7513 Truck rental & leasing, no drivers
Pr: Brian Hard
**Ch Bd:* Roger S Penske
Pr: Lisa Swanson
**Sr VP:* Frank Cocuzza
**Sr VP:* Frank Mileto
Sr VP: Sherry Sanger
VP: Emily Day
VP: Joe Moleski
Genl Mgr: Art Narmi
Genl Mgr: Kurt Seymour
Snr Ntwrk: Daniel Morton

D-U-N-S 93-122-1738
PENSON WORLDWIDE INC
1700 Pacific Ave Ste 1400, Dallas, TX 75201-4607
Tel (214) 765-1100 *Founded/Ownrshp* 1995
Sales 149.4MM^E *EMP* 815^E
SIC 6289 Exchange clearinghouses, security
CEO: Daniel P Son
Pr: Bryce Engel
COO: Liam Cheung
CFO: Bart McCain
Bd of Dir: John Drew
Ofcr: Mark Bell
Ofcr: Ken Belter
Ex VP: Andrew B Koslow
Sr VP: Barry Shamas
Sr VP: Peter Wind
VP: Charles B Piroli

PENSPEN
See GREYSTAR CORP

D-U-N-S 01-007-8975
PENTA BUILDING GROUP INC
181 E Warm Springs Rd, Las Vegas, NV 89119-4101
Tel (702) 614-1678 *Founded/Ownrshp* 2000
Sales 161.0MM^E *EMP* 250
SIC 1542 Commercial & office building, new construction
Pr: Jeffrey H Ehret
**Sr VP:* Ken Alber
**Sr VP:* Blake Anderson
VP: Steve Jones
VP: Glen Maxwell
Exec: Joseph A Miller
IT Man: Ian Jones
Mktg Mgr: Tim Putnam

D-U-N-S 07-265-5137
PENTAGON FEDERAL CREDIT UNION
2930 Eisenhower Ave, Alexandria, VA 22314-4557
Tel (800) 247-5626 *Founded/Ownrshp* 1934
Sales NA *EMP* 2,479
SIC 6061 Federal credit unions
CEO: Christopher J Flynn
Pr: James Schenck
COO: Kate Kohler
COO: Joseph Thomas
CFO: Denise McGlone
Ofcr: Sandy Crowley
Ofcr: Jeannell Graham
Ex VP: Tamara Darvish
Ex VP: Betsy Henkel
Ex VP: Shashi Vohra
VP: Larry Blake
VP: Dorothy Emig
VP: Thomas Johnson
VP: David S Jonas
VP: Angela Patel
VP: Fred Rubin

D-U-N-S 14-332-7489
■ **PENTAGON FORCE PROTECTION AGENCY**
PFPA
(*Suby of* OFFICE OF THE SECRETARY OF DEFENSE) ★
The Pentagon 2e165b, Washington, DC 20301-0001
Tel (703) 697-1001 *Founded/Ownrshp* 2004
Sales NA *EMP* 5,014^E
SIC 9711 National security;

D-U-N-S 03-802-8759 IMP/EXP
PENTAIR AQUATIC ECO-SYSTEMS INC
PENTAIR AQUATIC HABITATS
2395 Apopka Blvd, Apopka, FL 32703-7772
Tel (407) 886-7575 *Founded/Ownrshp* 1993
Sales 139.1MM^E *EMP* 140^E
SIC 5074 5999 Plumbing & hydronic heating supplies; Water purification equipment
Pr: Karl R Frykman
**Ch:* Martin Hoffinger
**Treas:* Michael G Meyer
**VP:* Robert D Miller
Manager: Eric Moore

PENTAIR AQUATIC HABITATS
See PENTAIR AQUATIC ECO-SYSTEMS INC

D-U-N-S 00-819-3216 IMP/EXP
PENTAIR FILTRATION INC
EVER PURE
(*Suby of* PENTAIR INC) ★
5730 N Glen Park Rd, Milwaukee, WI 53209-4403
Tel (800) 645-0267 *Founded/Ownrshp* 1958
Sales 145.8MM^E *EMP* 370
SIC 3561 Pumps & pumping equipment
CEO: Randy Hogan
Genl Mgr: Neil Desmond
Sls Mgr: Lori Laseke

D-U-N-S 03-960-1471 IMP/EXP
PENTAIR FLOW TECHNOLOGIES LLC
PENTAIR WATER
(*Suby of* FLOW CONTROL US HOLDING CORP) ★
1101 Myers Pkwy, Ashland, OH 44805-1969
Tel (419) 289-1144 *Founded/Ownrshp* 1980
Sales 359.7MM[E] *EMP* 1,031[E]
SIC 3561 Pumps, oil well & field
CEO: Randall J Hogan
**Ex VP:* John L Stauch
**Sr VP:* Todd R Gleason
**Sr VP:* Frederick S Koury
**Sr VP:* Angela D Lageson
VP: Kamala Puram
Genl Mgr: Linda Thompson
Sfty Mgr: David Christine
Advt Mgr: Norma Gassway

D-U-N-S 00-645-1249 IMP/EXP
PENTAIR INC (MN)
(*Suby of* PENTAIR PUBLIC LIMITED COMPANY)
5500 Wayzata Blvd Ste 600, Minneapolis, MN 55416-3576
Tel (763) 545-1730 *Founded/Ownrshp* 1966, 2014
Sales 4.5MMM[E] *EMP* 15,300
SIC 3491 3559 4971 3589 Industrial valves; Desalination equipment; Water distribution or supply systems for irrigation; Swimming pool filter & water conditioning systems
CEO: Randall J Hogan
**CFO:* John L Stauch
CFO: John Stauch
**Treas:* Mark C Borin
Ex VP: Pete Dyke
**Sr VP:* Angela D Jilek
VP: Todd R Gleason
VP: Todd Gleason
VP: Jim Lucas
VP: Robert Miller
VP: Rolchigo Philip
VP: John Righini
VP: Tony Stolp
Dir Risk M: Tom Gratz
Dir Bus: Tim Reckinger

PENTAIR POOL PRODUCTS
See PENTAIR WATER POOL AND SPA INC

PENTAIR TECHNICAL PRODUCTS
See HOFFMAN ENCLOSURES INC

D-U-N-S 02-049-1833 IMP
PENTAIR TECHNICAL PRODUCTS
MCLEAN THERMAL
(*Suby of* FLOW CONTROL US HOLDING CORP) ★
2100 Hoffman Way, Anoka, MN 55303-1738
Tel (763) 323-8200 *Founded/Ownrshp* 2009
Sales 228.8MM[E] *EMP* 3,000
SIC 3585 3443 Air conditioning units, complete: domestic or industrial; Fabricated plate work (boiler shop)
CEO: Randall J Hogan
**CFO:* Richard Carroll
**Treas:* Michael Meyer
**VP:* Phill Pejovich
Board of Directors: Steve Chlupsa

D-U-N-S 01-746-3451 IMP
PENTAIR THERMAL MANAGEMENT LLC
(*Suby of* FLOW CONTROL US HOLDING CORP) ★
899 Broadway St, Redwood City, CA 94063-3104
Tel (650) 474-7414 *Founded/Ownrshp* 2000
Sales 300.0MM *EMP* 2,500
SIC 1711 3822 Heating & air conditioning contractors; Auto controls regulating residntl & coml environment & applncs
Pr: Alok Maskara
CFO: Judy Carley
Genl Mgr: Kevin Friel
CIO: Dick Kashnow
Sftwr Eng: Cheaulong Ng
Ql Cn Mgr: Dave Roecks
Sales Exec: Jerald Sauter

PENTAIR VALVES & CONTROLS INC
See PENTAIR VALVES & CONTROLS LLC

D-U-N-S 13-932-3224 IMP
PENTAIR VALVES & CONTROLS LLC
PENTAIR VALVES & CONTROLS INC
(*Suby of* PENTAIR PUBLIC LIMITED COMPANY)
10707 Clay Rd Ste 200, Houston, TX 77041-6190
Tel (713) 986-4665 *Founded/Ownrshp* 2013
Sales 351.2MM[E] *EMP* 1,500
SIC 3491 Pressure valves & regulators, industrial; Process control regulator valves
Pr: Patrick Decker
Pr: David Alan Dunbar
Treas: Michael G Meyer
VP: Angela D Lageson
VP: Rashmi Raj

D-U-N-S 79-757-8288 IMP
PENTAIR VALVES & CONTROLS US LP
(*Suby of* FLOW CONTROL US HOLDING CORP) ★
10707 Clay Rd Ste 200, Houston, TX 77041-6190
Tel (713) 986-4665 *Founded/Ownrshp* 1999
Sales 452.4MM[E] *EMP* 1,500
SIC 3491 3625 3494 Industrial valves; Relays & industrial controls; Valves & pipe fittings
CEO: Randall J Hogan
CFO: John L Stauch
Sr VP: Frederick S Koury
Sr VP: Angela D Lageson
VP: Kevin Teague

PENTAIR WATER
See PENTAIR FLOW TECHNOLOGIES LLC

D-U-N-S 05-923-5838 IMP/EXP
PENTAIR WATER POOL AND SPA INC
PENTAIR POOL PRODUCTS
(*Suby of* FLOW CONTROL US HOLDING CORP) ★
1620 Hawkins Ave, Sanford, NC 27330-9501
Tel (919) 774-4151 *Founded/Ownrshp* 1971
Sales 586.3MM[E] *EMP* 1,500
SIC 3589 3561 3569 3648 Swimming pool filter & water conditioning systems; Pumps, domestic: water or sump; Heaters, swimming pool: electric; Underwater lighting fixtures
Pr: Mike Fowler
Pr: Karl Frykman
CFO: Robert D Miller
VP: Dave Murray
Dir IT: Michael Tebrinke

D-U-N-S 03-699-9621
PENTALON CONSTRUCTION INC
PENTOWER
132 E 13065 S Ste 175, Draper, UT 84020-8643
Tel (801) 619-1900 *Founded/Ownrshp* 1993
Sales 93.5MM *EMP* 50
Accts Karren Hendrix Stagg Allen
SIC 1522 1542 Multi-family dwellings, new construction; Nonresidential construction
Pr: Carl Tippets
**Sec:* Michele Tippets
**VP:* Shay Johansen
**VP:* Richard Workman
Div Mgr: Dennis Smith

D-U-N-S 08-321-1284 IMP
PENTAX OF AMERICA INC
(*Suby of* HOYA CORPORATION)
3 Paragon Dr, Montvale, NJ 07645-1782
Tel (201) 391-4229 *Founded/Ownrshp* 2006
Sales 122.7MM[E] *EMP* 412
SIC 5047 Medical & hospital equipment
Pr: Hiroshi Suzuki
IT Man: Luis Collado
Sftwr Eng: Matthew Alverson
VP Sls: Robert Gerol
Mktg Dir: Ann Connolly-Garcia
Mktg Mgr: Frank Canonica

D-U-N-S 14-732-7340
PENTEC HEALTH INC
4 Creek Pkwy Ste A, Upper Chichester, PA 19061-3132
Tel (610) 494-8700 *Founded/Ownrshp* 1983
Sales 124.7MM[E] *EMP* 470
SIC 2834 8082 Druggists' preparations (pharmaceuticals); Home health care services
Pr: Joseph Cosgrove
**CFO:* Art REA
**Ex VP:* Michael Abens
**Ex VP:* Robert Provonche
Ex VP: David Pulham
**VP:* Barbara Knightly
**VP:* Karen McHenry
VP: Joey Ryan
**VP:* Charlie Wilson
Dir Bus: Barbara Knightley
Off Mgr: Michelle Perez

PENTEGRA RETIREMENT SERVICES
See PENTEGRA SERVICES INC

D-U-N-S 82-683-1344
PENTEGRA SERVICES INC
PENTEGRA RETIREMENT SERVICES
701 Westchester Ave 320e, White Plains, NY 10604-3002
Tel (800) 872-3473 *Founded/Ownrshp* 1940
Sales NA *EMP* 208[E]
SIC 6371 Pension, health & welfare funds
Ch Bd: John E Pinto
Pr: Jill Williams
COO: Tony Whitaker
Chf Inves: Scott Stone
Sr VP: Michael Palmiere
Sr VP: Pete Swisher
**VP:* Robert Alin
VP: Chuck Coldwell
VP: Kevin Killian
**VP:* Jeffrey A Kissel
VP: William Pieper
VP: Rick Rausser
VP: Charles Sorrentino

D-U-N-S 08-030-5374
PENTHOL LLC
333 Clay St Ste 3300, Houston, TX 77002-4104
Tel (832) 548-5832 *Founded/Ownrshp* 2016
Sales 100.0MM *EMP* 3
SIC 5172 Lubricating oils & greases
Pr: Saruk Erkoc
VP: Hakan Erkoc

D-U-N-S 00-714-5873
PENTON BUSINESS MEDIA INC
(*Suby of* U S EQUITY PARTNERS) ★
9800 Metcalf Ave, Shawnee Mission, KS 66212-2286
Tel (913) 341-1300 *Founded/Ownrshp* 2005
Sales 277.8MM[E] *EMP* 881[E]
SIC 2721 Periodicals
CEO: Sharon T Rowlands
**CFO:* Nicola Allais

D-U-N-S 08-018-7962
PENTON BUSINESS MEDIA INC
1100 Superior Ave E Fl 8, Cleveland, OH 44114-2530
Tel (216) 696-7000 *Founded/Ownrshp* 2007
Sales 310.0MM *EMP* 1,100
SIC 2741 7379 Miscellaneous publishing;
CEO: David Kieselstein
**CFO:* Nicola Allais
Ex Dir: Willie Vogt
Genl Mgr: Margaret McCartney
Sales Asso: Lynne McLaughlin
Assoc Ed: Ginger Christ

PENTON MEDIA - AVIATION WEEK
See PENTON MEDIA INC

D-U-N-S 08-015-3844 IMP
PENTON MEDIA INC
PENTON MEDIA - AVIATION WEEK
(*Suby of* PENTON BUSINESS MEDIA INC) ★
1166 Avenue Of The Americ, New York, NY 10036-2743
Tel (212) 204-4200 *Founded/Ownrshp* 1976, 2007
Sales 232.7MM[E] *EMP* 711
SIC 2721 7389 7313 7375 Periodicals; Periodicals: publishing & printing; Magazines: publishing & printing; Advertising, promotional & trade show services; Printed media advertising representatives; On-line data base information retrieval
Ch Bd: David Kieselstein
**Pr:* Paul Miller
**CFO:* Nicola Allais
CFO: Preston Keeling
Ex VP: Jean Clifton
Ex VP: Michael Lang
Ex VP: Matthew Mrowczynski
Sr VP: Kim Paulsen
VP: George Assimakopoulos
VP: Bill Baumann
VP: Sue Boehlke
VP: Barbara Couchois
VP: Curtis Davies
VP: John Ecke
VP: Mark Flinn
VP: Amruta Gadre
VP: Gregg Herring
VP: Chris Keating
VP: Dave Kingsbury
VP: Neil Mackay
VP: Wayne Madden

PENTOWER
See PENTALON CONSTRUCTION INC

D-U-N-S 19-107-7671
PENUMBRA INC
1351 Harbor Bay Pkwy, Alameda, CA 94502-6541
Tel (510) 748-3200 *Founded/Ownrshp* 2004
Sales 186.1MM *EMP* 1,100
Tkr Sym PEN *Exch* NYS
SIC 3841 Surgical & medical instruments
Ch Bd: Adam Elsesser
Pr: Daniel Davis
Pr: James Pray
CFO: SRI Kosaraju
Ex VP: Robert Evans
Ex VP: Lynn Rothman
VP: Sean Donahue
Creative D: Cheong Yong
Rgnl Mgr: Brian Norton
Rgnl Mgr: Mitzi Welk
Off Mgr: Elizabeth Zaldivar
Board of Directors: Don Kassing, Walter Wang

D-U-N-S 14-586-5635
PEOPLE CARE HOLDINGS INC
116 W 32nd St Fl 15, New York, NY 10001-3207
Tel (212) 631-7300 *Founded/Ownrshp* 1994
Sales 74.4MM[E] *EMP* 2,500
SIC 8082 Home health care services
CEO: Bruce Jacobson
**Pr:* Jerry Lewkowitz
**COO:* Susan Brett

D-U-N-S 08-259-7063
PEOPLE CARE INC (NY)
(*Suby of* PEOPLE CARE HOLDINGS INC) ★
116 W 32nd St Fl 15, New York, NY 10001-3207
Tel (212) 631-7300 *Founded/Ownrshp* 1976
Sales 68.4MM[E] *EMP* 2,500
SIC 8082 Home health care services
CEO: Bruce Jacobson
**Pr:* Jerry Lewkowitz
Dir IT: Edward Wilson

D-U-N-S 03-020-5488
PEOPLE INC
1219 N Forest Rd, Williamsville, NY 14221-3292
Tel (716) 817-7400 *Founded/Ownrshp* 1970
Sales 148.8MM *EMP* 2,000
Accts Bryans & Gramuglia Cpas Llc
SIC 8361 Residential care for the handicapped; Home for the mentally handicapped
CEO: Rhonda Frederick
CFO: Anne Stone
Treas: Marlene Pinzka
Ex VP: Francisco M Vasquez
Sr VP: Anna Korus
VP: Nancy Palumbo
Snr Ntwrk: Ronald Wechter
Doctor: Tracy Harrienger
Doctor: Denise Paszkiewicz
Pgrm Dir: Denise Litz
Pgrm Dir: Margaret M Moffat

D-U-N-S 85-943-7910
PEOPLETECH GROUP INC
601108 Ave Ne Ste 310, Bellevue, WA 98004
Tel (425) 880-7981 *Founded/Ownrshp* 2008
Sales 160.0MM *EMP* 90
SIC 7361 Employment agencies
CEO: Vishwa Prasad

D-U-N-S 04-441-5979
PEOPLE WITH DEVELOPMENTAL DISABILITIES NEW YORK STATE OFFICE FOR
OPWDD
(*Suby of* EXECUTIVE OFFICE OF STATE OF NEW YORK) ★
44 Holland Ave, Albany, NY 12208-3411
Tel (518) 473-1997 *Founded/Ownrshp* 1978
Sales NA *EMP* 2,200
SIC 9431 Administration of public health programs;

D-U-N-S 13-368-8023
PEOPLELINK LLC
PEOPLELINK STAFFING SOLUTIONS
(*Suby of* GROUPE CRIT)
431 E Colfax Ave Ste 200, South Bend, IN 46617-2790
Tel (574) 232-5400 *Founded/Ownrshp* 1987
Sales 468.9MM[E] *EMP* 12,008
SIC 7361

PEOPLELINK STAFFING SOLUTIONS
See PEOPLELINK LLC

D-U-N-S 93-365-1374 IMP
■ PEOPLENET COMMUNICATIONS CORP
(*Suby of* TRIMBLE INC) ★
4400 Baker Rd, Minnetonka, MN 55343-8668
Tel (952) 908-6200 *Founded/Ownrshp* 1994
Sales 92.2MM[E] *EMP* 230[E]
SIC 7373 3663 4812 Systems engineering, computer related; Radio & TV communications equipment; Radio telephone communication
CEO: Ron Konezny
**COO:* Brian McLaughlin
**COO:* Steve Taylor
**CFO:* Mike Goergen
VP: Trent Lezer
VP: Kelly Nehowig
VP: Eric Witty
**Dir Risk M:* Andy Zarkadas
Snr Sftwr: Alok Gupta
Snr Sftwr: John Macdonald
Snr Sftwr: Kevin Pichelman

D-U-N-S 05-715-4007
▲ PEOPLES BANCORP INC
138 Putnam St, Marietta, OH 45750-2923
Tel (740) 373-3155 *Founded/Ownrshp* 1980
Sales NA *EMP* 817[E]
Tkr Sym PEBO *Exch* NGS
SIC 6021 National commercial banks
Pr: Charles W Sulerzyski
Ch Bd: David L Mead
CFO: John C Rogers
V Ch Bd: George W Broughton
Chf Cred: Robyn A Stevens
Ofcr: Carol A Schneeberger
Ex VP: Daniel K McGill
Board of Directors: Tara M Abraham, Carl L Baker Jr, S Craig Beam, David F Dierker, Brooke W James, Brenda F Jones, Susan D Rector, Thomas J Wolf

D-U-N-S 07-268-9607
■ PEOPLES BANK (KY)
PEOPLES BANK F S B
(*Suby of* PEOPLES BANCORP INC) ★
138 Putnam St, Marietta, OH 45750-2923
Tel (740) 373-3155 *Founded/Ownrshp* 1914, 1997
Sales NA *EMP* 200[E]
SIC 6035 Federal savings banks
Treas: Ronald L Fraley
CFO: Lynn Van Beek
Sr VP: Tom Essig
Sr VP: Staci Matheney
Sr VP: Rich Vaughan
VP: Bill Barnett
VP: Dennis Boe
VP: Matt Edgell
VP: Ann Helmick
VP: Ladd Hoef
VP: Melanie McCoy
**VP:* Shirley Menshouse
VP: Karma Meuret
VP: Andy Pohlman
Dir Bus: Pat Sauber

D-U-N-S 94-513-8253
PEOPLES BANK
(*Suby of* PEOPLES NATIONAL BANK)
4831 W 6th St, Lawrence, KS 66049-5201
Tel (785) 842-4004 *Founded/Ownrshp* 1987
Sales NA *EMP* 40[E]
SIC 6712 Bank holding companies
CEO: Winton Winters Jr
**CFO:* Stephanie Nauert
**Ch:* Winton A Winter
**Ex VP:* Dale Dietrich
Ex VP: Ron Megli
**VP:* Kathy Richards
**VP:* Malaina Walker
Store Mgr: Devynn Carter
Store Mgr: Megan Lutes

PEOPLES BANK F S B
See PEOPLES BANK

D-U-N-S 00-450-4627
■ PEOPLES BANKING AND TRUST CO
(*Suby of* PEOPLES BANCORP INC) ★
138 Putnam St, Marietta, OH 45750-2923
Tel (740) 373-3155 *Founded/Ownrshp* 1902
Sales NA *EMP* 513
SIC 6022 State commercial banks
Ch Bd: Paul T Theisen
Pr: Mark Bradley
Pr: Larry E Holdren
CFO: Carroll Schneeberger
V Ch Bd: Wilford D Dimit
Board of Directors: Tara Abraham, James S Huggins, Susan D Rector

D-U-N-S 05-899-9921
PEOPLES BENEFIT LIFE INSURANCE CO
(*Suby of* AEGON USA, INC.)
300 Eagleview Blvd, Exton, PA 19341-1155
Tel (610) 648-5000 *Founded/Ownrshp* 1981
Sales NA *EMP* 500
SIC 6311 6321 Life insurance; Accident & health insurance
Pr: Bart Herbert Jr
**CFO:* Brenda Kramer
**Treas:* Martha Ann McConnell

D-U-N-S 04-361-4189
■ PEOPLES ENERGY LLC
(*Suby of* WEC ENERGY GROUP INC) ★
200 E Randolph St Fl 22, Chicago, IL 60601-6433
Tel (312) 240-4000 *Founded/Ownrshp* 2015
Sales 925.9MM[E] *EMP* 2,223
SIC 4924 4925 4911 Natural gas distribution; Gas production and/or distribution;
Pr: Willard S Evans
COO: Lawrence A Borgard
CFO: Thomas Nardi
CFO: Joseph P O'Leary
Ex VP: William E Morrow
Sr VP: Katherine A Donofrio
VP: Joan Gagen

D-U-N-S 78-205-7673
PEOPLES FIRST PROPERTIES INC
1002 W 23rd St Ste 400, Panama City, FL 32405-3648
Tel (850) 769-8981 *Founded/Ownrshp* 1990
Sales 170.3MM[E] *EMP* 1,500
SIC 1522 6552 Apartment building construction; Land subdividers & developers, commercial
Ch Bd: Joseph F Chapman III
**VP:* Joseph F Chapman IV

VP: Renee Johns
VP: Denise Ost

D-U-N-S 78-562-9820
PEOPLES GAS
TECO PEOPLES GAS SYSTEM
(*Suby of* TECO ENERGY INC) ★
702 N Franklin St Ste 516, Tampa, FL 33602-4454
Tel (727) 824-0990 *Founded/Ownrshp* 2006
Sales 147.3MM^E *EMP* 2,000
Accts Pricewaterhousecoopers Llp Ta
SIC 4923 Gas transmission & distribution
Pr: Gordon Gillette
**Prin:* Sherrill W Hudson

D-U-N-S 00-693-2115
■ PEOPLES GAS LIGHT AND COKE CO
(*Suby of* PEOPLES ENERGY LLC) ★
200 E Randolph St # 2200, Chicago, IL 60601-6302
Tel (312) 744-7000 *Founded/Ownrshp* 1855
Sales 756.3MM^E *EMP* 1,520
SIC 4925 Gas production and/or distribution
V Ch Bd: William E Morrow
**Pr:* Willard Evans Jr
**CEO:* Charles Schrock
COO: Donald M Field
**CFO:* Thomas A Nardi
**Treas:* Douglas M Ruschau
Sr VP: Katherine A Donofrio
Sr VP: James Hinchliff
Sr VP: Joseph P O'Leary
VP: Linda M Kallas
VP: Joseph Phillips
VP: Judith Pokorny
VP: Binney Williamson
Board of Directors: Keith E Bailey, James R Boris, William J Brodsky, Diana S Ferguson, John W Higgins, Michael E Lavin, Homer J Livingston Jr, Richard P Toft

D-U-N-S 00-791-6208
PEOPLES NATURAL GAS CO (PA)
(*Suby of* STEELRIVER INFRASTRUCTURE FUND NORTH AMERICA LP) ★
225 N Shore Dr Fl 2, Pittsburgh, PA 15212-5861
Tel (412) 208-6810 *Founded/Ownrshp* 1949, 2010
Sales 786.7MM^E *EMP* 1,300
SIC 4924 Natural gas distribution
CEO: Morgan O'Brien
VP: Martin L Bowling Jr
VP: Ruth Delost
VP: Robert D Fratangelo
VP: Beverly E Jons
VP: Anton Witte
MIS Dir: Sam Stotler

D-U-N-S 01-482-1502
PEOPLES TRUST INSURANCE CO
18 Peoples Trust Way, Deerfield Beach, FL 33441-6270
Tel (561) 988-9170 *Founded/Ownrshp* 2008
Sales NA *EMP* 550
SIC 6411 6021 Insurance agents, brokers & service; National commercial banks
Prin: Jennifer Kuntz

D-U-N-S 07-749-3252
PEOPLES TWP LLC
(*Suby of* STEELRIVER INFRASTRUCTURE FUND NORTH AMERICA LP) ★
205 N Main St, Butler, PA 16001-4904
Tel (724) 287-2751 *Founded/Ownrshp* 2011
Sales 130.7MM^E *EMP* 208
SIC 4924

D-U-N-S 07-214-7077
■ PEOPLES UNITED BANK NATIONAL ASSOCIATION
(*Suby of* PEOPLES UNITED FINANCIAL INC) ★
850 Main St Fl 6, Bridgeport, CT 06604-4917
Tel (203) 338-7171 *Founded/Ownrshp* 1988
Sales NA *EMP* 2,970
SIC 6022 State commercial banks
Pr: John P Barnes
Pr: Patrick J Sullivan
CFO: Paul Burner
CFO: David Rosato
Bd of Dir: Samuel Ladd
Ofcr: Mark Herron
Ofcr: David Norton
Ofcr: Jeffrey Zajac
Ex VP: Robert Amore
Ex VP: Jacinta A Coleman
Ex VP: John P Costa
Ex VP: Robert R D'Amore
Ex VP: Dexter Freeman
Ex VP: William T Kosturko
Ex VP: Michael J Leone
Ex VP: Michael J Maiorino
Ex VP: Hank Mandel
Ex VP: Mark Melchione
Ex VP: Chantal Simon
Ex VP: Scott Skorobohaty
Sr VP: Vincent J Calabrese
Board of Directors: Kirk W Walters

D-U-N-S 80-040-7673
▲ PEOPLES UNITED FINANCIAL INC
850 Main St, Bridgeport, CT 06604-4917
Tel (203) 338-7171 *Founded/Ownrshp* 2006
Sales NA *EMP* 5,139
Tkr Sym PBCT *Exch* NGS
SIC 6411 National commercial banks
Pr: John P Barnes
**Ch Bd:* George P Carter
Pr: Linda Wyman
CFO: R David Rosato
Ofcr: Kelly McDermott
Ofcr: Tracey Sanangelo
Trst Ofcr: Michael Gauding
Ex VP: Robert R D'Amore
Ex VP: Candace C Fitzek
Ex VP: Dexter Freeman
VP: Roberta Anderson
VP: John Bundschuh
VP: David Canestri
VP: Valerie C Carlson
VP: Frank Cory
VP: Jill Desousa
VP: Marilyn Hardacre
VP: Keith Higgins
VP: Lisa Hook
VP: James Kilcommons
VP: Peter Lange

PEOPLESCOUT
See STAFF MANAGEMENT SOLUTIONS LLC

D-U-N-S 78-952-3388
■ PEOPLESCOUT INC
(*Suby of* PEOPLESCOUT) ★
860 W Evergreen Ave, Chicago, IL 60642-2634
Tel (312) 915-0505 *Founded/Ownrshp* 1991
Sales 40.3MM^E *EMP* 1,200
SIC 7361 Executive placement
CEO: A Patrick Beharelle
**CFO:* Chris Averill

D-U-N-S 07-560-3126
PEORIA BOARD OF EDUCATION (INC)
3202 N Wisconsin Ave, Peoria, IL 61603-1299
Tel (309) 672-6512 *Founded/Ownrshp* 1855
Sales 72.9MM^E *EMP* 2,000
SIC 8211

D-U-N-S 07-444-7673
PEORIA UNIFIED SCHOOL DISTRICT NO11
6330 W Thunderbird Rd, Glendale, AZ 85306-4002
Tel (623) 486-6000 *Founded/Ownrshp* 1890
Sales 152.1MM^E *EMP* 3,889
Accts Heinfeld Meech & Co Pc P
SIC 8211 Public elementary school; Public senior high school
Ex Dir: Michelle R Myers
Off Admin: Connie Churchill
CIO: Ryan Logan
Netwrk Eng: Mike Treguboff
Pr Dir: Danielle Airey
Schl Brd P: Matt Bullock
Teacher Pr: Tahlya Visintainer
Psych: Kahlil Day

PEP
See PRECISION ENGINEERED PRODUCTS LLC

D-U-N-S 00-791-4401 IMP/EXP
■ PEP BOYS - MANNY MOE & JACK (PA)
(*Suby of* ICAHN ENTERPRISES LP) ★
3111 W Allegheny Ave, Philadelphia, PA 19132-1116
Tel (215) 430-9000 *Founded/Ownrshp* 1921, 1925
Sales 2.0MMM *EMP* 18,914
SIC 5531 7539 7533 Automotive & home supply stores; Automotive parts; Automotive accessories; Batteries, automotive & truck; Automotive repair shops; Wheel alignment, automotive; Shock absorber replacement; Brake services; Auto exhaust system repair shops
Pr: Brent Windom
**CEO:* Michael R Odell
**CEO:* Scott P Sider
CFO: Mike Englert
CFO: Jon Moeller
**CFO:* David R Stern
CFO: Harry F Yanowitz
**Ofcr:* James F Flanagan
Assoc VP: Daniel Condrasky
Assoc VP: Greg Wiedor
Ex VP: Mark Bacon
Ex VP: William E Shull III
Ex VP: Scott A Webb
Sr VP: Chris Adams
Sr VP: Christopher J Adams
Sr VP: Pete Bednarzyk
Sr VP: Sunghwan Cho
**Sr VP:* Gary Desai
Sr VP: Matt Flannery
Sr VP: John Holt
**Sr VP:* John J Kelly

D-U-N-S 95-681-9684 IMP
■ PEP BOYS - MANNY MOE & JACK OF DELAWARE INC
PEP BOYS - MANNY MOE JACK DEL
(*Suby of* PEP BOYS - MANNY MOE & JACK) ★
3111 W Allegheny Ave, Philadelphia, PA 19132-1116
Tel (215) 229-7555 *Founded/Ownrshp* 1995
Sales 2.8MMM *EMP* 17,718
SIC 5531 Automotive & home supply stores
VP: Raymond Aurthur
Ex VP: George Babich
Sr VP: Don L Casey
**Prin:* Tracy Hasson

PEP BOYS - MANNY MOE JACK DEL
See PEP BOYS - MANNY MOE & JACK OF DELAWARE INC

D-U-N-S 00-690-8560 IMP/EXP
■ PEP BOYS MANNY MOE & JACK OF CALIFORNIA
(*Suby of* PEP BOYS - MANNY MOE & JACK) ★
3111 W Allegheny Ave, Philadelphia, PA 19132-1116
Tel (215) 430-9095 *Founded/Ownrshp* 1932
Sales 3.5MMM^E *EMP* 8,700
SIC 5531 7533 7539 Automobile & truck equipment & parts; Automotive parts; Automotive accessories; Batteries, automotive & truck; Auto exhaust system repair shops; Automotive repair shops
Sr VP: Frederick A Stampone
**Ex VP:* Michael J Holden
Ex VP: Mark Stubbs
Sr VP: Troy E Fee
Sr VP: James Flanagan
VP: Bryan B Hoppe
Genl Mgr: Hugo Lecaro
IT Man: Michael G Elmore
VP Mktg: Ronald J Stoupa
Board of Directors: Paul Davis, Bill Donkin, Mark Thomas

D-U-N-S 95-682-0377
■ PEP BOYS-MANNY MOE & JACK OF PUERTO RICO INC
(*Suby of* PEP BOYS - MANNY MOE & JACK) ★
3111 W Allegheny Ave, Philadelphia, PA 19132-1116
Tel (215) 229-9000 *Founded/Ownrshp* 1994
Sales 123.7MM^E *EMP* 700
SIC 5531 Automotive parts
CEO: M G Leibovitz
Pr: Michael J Holden
CFO: Flor Ortiz
Treas: George Babbage
Treas: Scott Webb
Sr VP: Tom Carey
VP: Michael McSorley
VP: Stuart Rosenfeld
VP: Brian Zuckerman
Genl Mgr: Edwin Cruz
Genl Mgr: Frank Gortarez

D-U-N-S 07-829-8609
PEP INDUSTRIES LLC
110 Frank Mossberg Dr, Attleboro, MA 02703-4632
Tel (508) 226-5600 *Founded/Ownrshp* 2010
Sales 304.3MM^E *EMP* 1,053^E
SIC 3089 3351 3469 3471 3643 3841 Plastic containers, except foam; Copper rolling & drawing; Stamping metal for the trade; Plating & polishing; Contacts, electrical; Surgical & medical instruments
CEO: Alan Huffenus
**Prin:* John Manci

PEPCO
See POTOMAC ELECTRIC POWER CO

D-U-N-S 10-617-3672
■ PEPCO ENERGY SERVICES INC
(*Suby of* EXELON) ★
701 9th St Nw Ste 2100, Washington, DC 20001-4572
Tel (703) 253-1800 *Founded/Ownrshp* 1995
Sales 140.5MM^E *EMP* 140
SIC 1711 1731 1623 4961 Boiler & furnace contractors; Mechanical contractor; Ventilation & duct work contractor; Energy management controls; Lighting contractor; Underground utilities contractor; Steam & air-conditioning supply
Pr: John Huffman
Pr: Mark Kumm
Pr: David Zabetakis
Ex VP: Peter Meier
VP: Ed Borroni
VP: Stephen J Fabiani
VP: Carla Haggler
VP: Dennis Haines
VP: Bob Hollis
VP: Shailesh Negi
VP: Diane Rehe
VP: Paul Salfi
VP: Scott S Snyder
VP: Patrick Towbin

D-U-N-S 10-589-5010
■ PEPCO HOLDINGS LLC
EXELON
(*Suby of* EXELON CORP) ★
701 9th St Nw Ste 3, Washington, DC 20001-4572
Tel (202) 872-2000 *Founded/Ownrshp* 2016
Sales 5.3MMM^E *EMP* 5,184^E
SIC 4931 Electric & other services combined
Pr: David M Velazquez
**Ch Bd:* Christopher M Crane
CFO: Donna J Kinzel
**V Ch Bd:* Denis P O'Brien
Ex VP: Kevin C Fitzgerald
VP: David Velazquez

D-U-N-S 04-305-0269 IMP
PEPIN DISTRIBUTING CO (FL)
4121 N 50th St, Tampa, FL 33610-8002
Tel (813) 626-6176 *Founded/Ownrshp* 1960, 1986
Sales 190.7MM^E *EMP* 250
SIC 5181 Beer & other fermented malt liquors
Pr: Thomas Pepin
**CFO:* Robert J Ammon

D-U-N-S 12-147-4902
PEPPER COMPANIES INC
643 N Orleans St, Chicago, IL 60654-3608
Tel (312) 266-4703 *Founded/Ownrshp* 1983
Sales 1.1MMM^E *EMP* 1,100
Accts Deloitte & Touche Llp Chicago
SIC 1542 1541 Commercial & office building, new construction; Commercial & office buildings, renovation & repair; Shopping center construction; Specialized public building contractors; Industrial buildings, new construction; Renovation, remodeling & repairs: industrial buildings
Pr: J David Pepper
Ex VP: Christopher R Averill
Ex VP: Thomas M O'Leary
Board of Directors: Bruce W Ficken, Thomas Z Hayward, Thomas M O'leary, Glenn Reed

D-U-N-S 00-798-0576
PEPPER CONSTRUCTION CO
(*Suby of* PEPPER CONSTRUCTION GROUP LLC) ★
643 N Orleans St, Chicago, IL 60654-3690
Tel (312) 266-4700 *Founded/Ownrshp* 1927, 2000
Sales 709.8MM *EMP* 900^E
Accts Deloitte & Touche Llp Chicag
SIC 1542 1541 Commercial & office building contractors; Industrial buildings & warehouses
CEO: J David Pepper
Pr: Kenneth Egidi
CFO: Chris Averill
Chf Mktg O: Jacqueline Lavigne
Sr VP: Richard Schuster
Sr VP: Michael Stensland
VP: Bill Bennett
VP: Bob Eckl
VP: Steve Green
VP: Michelle Lieb
VP: Ronald A Monroe
VP: Ron Nelson
VP: Tim Sullivan
Exec: James Belange
Exec: Fred Berglund
Exec: Brian Forsythe
Exec: Brian Peter
Exec: Kenneth Russell
Comm Dir: Shannan Ghera
Comm Man: Cassie Kelleher

D-U-N-S 87-827-3481
PEPPER CONSTRUCTION CO OF INDIANA LLC
(*Suby of* PEPPER CONSTRUCTION GROUP LLC) ★
1850 W 15th St, Indianapolis, IN 46202-2027
Tel (317) 681-1000 *Founded/Ownrshp* 2000
Sales 130.7MM *EMP* 120
Accts Deloitte & Touche Llp Chicag
SIC 1542 1541 Nonresidential construction; Industrial buildings & warehouses
Pr: William J McCarthy
COO: Mike McCann
Mktg Mgr: Meg King
Board of Directors: J David Pepper

D-U-N-S 00-948-6163
PEPPER CONSTRUCTION GROUP LLC
(*Suby of* PEPPER COMPANIES INC) ★
643 N Orleans St, Chicago, IL 60654-3690
Tel (312) 266-4700 *Founded/Ownrshp* 2000
Sales 1.1MMM *EMP* 1,100
Accts Deloitte & Touche Llp Chicag
SIC 1542 Commercial & office building, new construction
Ch: Dave Pepper
**CFO:* Chris Averill
**VP:* Michelle Lieb
**VP:* Tom O'Leary
Off Mgr: Debbie Connolly

D-U-N-S 03-930-9571
■ PEPPER DINING HOLDING CORP
CHILI'S
(*Suby of* BRINKER INTERNATIONAL INC) ★
6820 Lyndon B Johnson Fwy, Dallas, TX 75240-6511
Tel (704) 943-5276 *Founded/Ownrshp* 2015
Sales 165.1MM^E *EMP* 20^E
SIC 5812 Restaurant, family: chain
CEO: John McGlone
**CFO:* Gary Sachs

D-U-N-S 84-769-6130
■ PEPPER DINING INC
CHILI'S
(*Suby of* CHILIS) ★
6820 Lyndon B Johnson Fwy, Dallas, TX 75240-6511
Tel (704) 943-5276 *Founded/Ownrshp* 2006
Sales 165.1MM *EMP* 6,000
SIC 5812 Restaurant, family: chain
Pr: John McGlone
**CFO:* Gary Sachx

D-U-N-S 07-549-6034
PEPPER HAMILTON LLP
3000 Two Logan Sq, Philadelphia, PA 19103
Tel (215) 981-4000 *Founded/Ownrshp* 1959
Sales 191.8MM^E *EMP* 1,044
SIC 8111 General practice law office; Specialized legal services
CEO: Scott Green
Genl Pt: Barry M Abelson
Pt: Bennett L Aaron
Pt: Matthew H Adler
Pt: Jon A Baughman
Pt: James M Beck
Pt: Harold R Berk
Pt: Norman B Berlin
Pt: J Bradley Boericke
Pt: George W Braun
Pt: Charles R Bruton
Pt: Mitchell E Burack
Pt: John J Burke
Pt: Vincent V Carissimi
Pt: Peter O Clauss
Pt: Lawrence S Coburn
Pt: Deborah Fuchs Cohen
Pt: Thomas J Cole
Pt: Hope Comisky
Pt: Julia D Correlli
Pt: Kenneth M Cushman

D-U-N-S 15-748-3793
PEPPER-LAWSON CONSTRUCTION LP
(*Suby of* WEBBER LLC) ★
4555 Katy Hockley Rd, Katy, TX 77493-4832
Tel (281) 371-3100 *Founded/Ownrshp* 1975
Sales 190.5MM *EMP* 132
Accts Deloitte & Touche Llp Chicag
SIC 1542 Commercial & office building, new construction; Commercial & office buildings, renovation & repair
Pr: Atul Raj
Exec: Mark Akers
Exec: William Davidson
Store Mgr: Steve Graber
IT Man: Mike Richardson
Opers Mgr: Bennier Fretwell
Snr PM: Tom McManus

D-U-N-S 07-228-0175
PEPPERDINE UNIVERSITY
24255 Pacific Coast Hwy # 5000, Malibu, CA 90263-5000
Tel (310) 506-4000 *Founded/Ownrshp* 1937
Sales 302.4MM *EMP* 1,300
SIC 8221 University
Pr: Andrew K Benton JD
COO: Gary A Hanson
**CFO:* Paul Lasiter
CFO: Paul B Lasiter
Ofcr: Curt Portzel
**Sr VP:* Charles Pippin
Sr VP: Jeff Pippin
VP: Jessica Barnes
VP: Arabo Beiki
VP: Daniel Chang
VP: Joel Denning
VP: Sara Jackson
VP: Liesl Kim
VP: Christopher Marks
VP: David Nguyen
VP: Brenda Pena
VP: Brian Thomason
VP Bus Dev: Scott Carlyle
Assoc Dir: Margaret E Barfield
Assoc Dir: Andrea R Barrett
Assoc Dir: Taylor Becket

D-U-N-S 00-118-4472 IMP/EXP
■ PEPPERIDGE FARM INC (CT)
(*Suby of* CAMPBELL SOUP CO) ★
595 Westport Ave, Norwalk, CT 06851-4413
Tel (203) 846-7000 *Founded/Ownrshp* 1937
Sales 686.7MM^E *EMP* 2,399
SIC 5963 2052 2099 2053 5961 Snacks, direct sales; Cookies; Bread crumbs, not made in bakeries; Frozen bakery products, except bread; Pastries (danish): frozen; Cakes, bakery: frozen; Doughnuts, frozen; Food, mail order
Pr: Irene Chang Britt
CFO: William J Shea
**Treas:* Ashok Madhavan
**Sr VP:* Tom Smith
**VP:* Richard J Landers
VP: Mark Schreiber
Dir IT: John Dustar
IT Man: Krystyna Yoo
Sfty Mgr: Janice Pridemoore
Ql Cn Mgr: Holly Thompson
Sls Dir: Bradley Troup

D-U-N-S 10-151-6110 IMP
PEPPERL + FUCHS INC
(*Suby of* PEPPERL + FUCHS GMBH)
1600 Enterprise Pkwy, Twinsburg, OH 44087-2245
Tel (330) 425-3555 *Founded/Ownrshp* 1999
Sales 94.5MM^E *EMP* 271
SIC 5065 3625 3822 3674 Electronic parts & equipment; Relays & industrial controls; Auto controls regulating residntl & coml environmt & applncs; Semiconductors & related devices
Pr: Wolfgang Mueller
COO: James Bolin
Bd of Dir: Gunther Kegel
Ofcr: Webster Sandra
Exec: Kevin Catalfamo
Mng Dir: Hermann Best
Mng Dir: Claus Michael
Area Mgr: Yeo H Guan
Area Mgr: Bhushan Lilhare
Dept Mgr: David Hohenstein
Genl Mgr: Kishore K Kumble

D-U-N-S 87-926-3192
PEPPERMILL CASINOS INC
PEPPERMILL HOTEL CASINO
90 W Grove St Ste 600, Reno, NV 89509-4001
Tel (775) 689-8900 *Founded/Ownrshp* 1993
Sales 243.1MM^E *EMP* 2,500
SIC 7011 7999 Casino hotel; Gambling establishment
Pr: William A Paganetti
**CFO:* Scott Loder
Dir Soc: Preston Davis
Ex Dir: Aaron Robyns
DP Exec: Kerti Clark
DP Exec: Ken Roesler

PEPPERMILL HOTEL CASINO
See PEPPERMILL CASINOS INC

D-U-N-S 09-539-9747
PEPRO ENTERPRISES INC
GEMINI PLASTICS
(*Suby of* GEMINI GROUP INC) ★
2147 Leppek Rd, Ubly, MI 48475-9790
Tel (989) 658-3200 *Founded/Ownrshp* 1977
Sales 146.2MM^E *EMP* 480
SIC 3089 Extruded finished plastic products
Pr: Lyn Drake
Plnt Mgr: Dan Rothe

D-U-N-S 00-523-5015 IMP/EXP
■ PEPSI AMERICAS INC
PEPSICO
(*Suby of* PEPSICO) ★
60 S 6th St, Minneapolis, MN 55402-4400
Tel (612) 661-4000 *Founded/Ownrshp* 2010
Sales 1.9MMM^E *EMP* 20,800
SIC 2086 Carbonated soft drinks, bottled & canned
CEO: Robert C Pohlad
**Pr:* Kenneth E Keiser
**CFO:* Alexander H Ware
**Treas:* Andrew R Stark
Ex VP: G M Durkin Jr
**Sr VP:* Kenneth L Johnsen
VP: Allan Church
Exec: Aaron Adams
Prgrm Mgr: Matt Herman
Prgrm Mgr: James W Tigert
Genl Mgr: Gregory M Owens

PEPSI BEVERAGES COMPANY
See BOTTLING GROUP LLC

PEPSI BEVERAGES COMPANY
See BOTTLING GROUP LLC

D-U-N-S 02-338-4860
■ PEPSI BEVERAGES CO
(*Suby of* PEPSICO INC) ★
110 S Byhalia Rd, Collierville, TN 38017-9322
Tel (901) 853-5736 *Founded/Ownrshp* 1979, 2011
Sales 280.3MM^E *EMP* 1,770
SIC 2086 5181 Soft drinks: packaged in cans, bottles, etc.; Beer & other fermented malt liquors
Pr: Eric Hanson
Pr: Delmer Bussell
**Pr:* Indra Nyooi
VP: Brad Braun
VP: Jay Hulbert
VP: Ray Stitle
Exec: Kimberly Gillam
Off Mgr: Kelly Slemons
MIS Mgr: Danny McGowan

PEPSI BOTTLE AND GROUP
See GENERAL CINEMA BEVERAGES OF OHIO INC

D-U-N-S 00-206-1687
PEPSI BOTTLING VENTURES LLC
(*Suby of* SUNTORY INTERNATIONAL CORP) ★
4141 Parklake Ave Ste 600, Raleigh, NC 27612-2380
Tel (919) 865-2300 *Founded/Ownrshp* 1980, 1999
Sales 146.8MM^E *EMP* 2,185
SIC 5149 2086 Soft drinks; Carbonated beverages, nonalcoholic: bottled & canned
Pr: Paul Finney
**CFO:* Derek Hill
**Sr VP:* Shinichi Leo Adachi
**Sr VP:* Matthew Bucherati
**Sr VP:* Chris McCool
VP: Leo Adachi
VP: Doug Helman
**VP:* Katsuyasu Kato
Exec: Ruben Rodriguez
Mktg Dir: Mike Spanos
Mktg Dir: Sandy Williams

D-U-N-S 00-412-8369 IMP/EXP
■ PEPSI COLA BOTTLING FORT LAUNDERDALE
PEPSICO
(*Suby of* PEPSICO) ★
7305 Garden Rd, Riviera Beach, FL 33404-3490
Tel (561) 848-1000 *Founded/Ownrshp* 1920, 2007
Sales 141.3MM^E *EMP* 1,000
SIC 2086 Carbonated soft drinks, bottled & canned
CEO: Indra Nooyi
Ch: John Koons
**VP:* Paula Hopkins
VP: Joe Newman
Opers Mgr: Mark Neisen

D-U-N-S 00-626-8858
PEPSI MIDAMERICA CO (MO)
2605 W Main St, Marion, IL 62959-4932
Tel (618) 997-1377 *Founded/Ownrshp* 1936
Sales 271.7MM^E *EMP* 1,390
SIC 2086 Carbonated soft drinks, bottled & canned
Ch: Harry L Crisp II
**Pr:* Harry L Crisp III
Software D: Sarah Ayling
Opers Mgr: Jeff McGee
Sls Dir: Thomas Hastings

D-U-N-S 00-237-1359
PEPSI-COLA & NATIONAL BRAND BEVERAGES LTD (INC) (NJ)
8275 N Crescent Blvd, Pennsauken, NJ 08110-1435
Tel (856) 665-6200 *Founded/Ownrshp* 1956
Sales 178.8MM^E *EMP* 425
SIC 2086 Soft drinks: packaged in cans, bottles, etc.
CEO: Jeff Honickman
**Ch Bd:* Harold Honickman
Pr: Charles Ciraulo
Pr: Gwen Dolceamore
**CFO:* Walter Wilkinson
**V Ch Bd:* Marvin Goldstein
IT Man: Angel Ciruulo

D-U-N-S 00-312-5267
PEPSI-COLA BOTTLING CO OF CENTRAL VIRGINIA (VA)
1150 Pepsi Pl, Charlottesville, VA 22901-2865
Tel (434) 978-2140 *Founded/Ownrshp* 1908, 1983
Sales 111.1MM *EMP* 370
SIC 2086 Soft drinks: packaged in cans, bottles, etc.
Pr: James L Jessup Jr
**Ex VP:* Suzanne J Brooks
**VP:* Mary H Jessup
**VP:* Robert Pflugfelder

D-U-N-S 00-322-7865
PEPSI-COLA BOTTLING CO OF HICKORY NC INC (NC)
2401 14th Avenue Cir Nw, Hickory, NC 28601-7336
Tel (828) 322-8090 *Founded/Ownrshp* 1926
Sales 155.7MM^E *EMP* 370
SIC 5149 2086 Soft drinks; Bottled & canned soft drinks
Pr: James Lee Teeter
**CFO:* Michael Wingler
**Treas:* Margaret Brady
**Ex VP:* Katherine Frans
**VP:* John Teeter
IT Man: Albert Kaylor

D-U-N-S 08-972-8869
PEPSI-COLA BOTTLING CO OF NEW YORK INC
11402 15th Ave Ste 5, College Point, NY 11356-1402
Tel (718) 392-1000 *Founded/Ownrshp* 1987
Sales 234.2MM^E *EMP* 1,100
SIC 2086 Soft drinks: packaged in cans, bottles, etc.
Ch Bd: William Wilson
Ex VP: Richard Goodman
Ex VP: Jim Wilkinson
VP: Umran Beba
VP: Santo Bonanno
VP: Peter A Bridgman
VP: Jim McDowell
VP: Tim Minges
Exec: Pat Recio
Dir Sec: Jim Kavanagh

D-U-N-S 06-480-4081 EXP
■ PEPSI-COLA BOTTLING CO OF TAMPA
(*Suby of* PEPSICO) ★
11315 N 30th St, Tampa, FL 33612-6495
Tel (813) 971-2550 *Founded/Ownrshp* 1936
Sales 190.8MM^E *EMP* 2,000
SIC 2086 Soft drinks: packaged in cans, bottles, etc.
Pr: Brenda C Barnes
**Treas:* Peter Bridgman
Genl Mgr: Brian Spearman
Tech Mgr: Dan Stone
Plnt Mgr: Tonya Ward

D-U-N-S 62-052-6426 IMP/EXP
■ PEPSI-COLA BOTTLING GROUP
PEPSICO
(*Suby of* PEPSICO) ★
1111 Westchester Ave, White Plains, NY 10604-4000
Tel (914) 767-6000 *Founded/Ownrshp* 2010
Sales 240.9MM^E *EMP* 434
SIC 2086 Carbonated soft drinks, bottled & canned
VP: Micheal Matney
Pr: Sean Bishop
Sr VP: Dick W Boyce
Sr VP: Jeff Campbell
VP: Paulette Alviti
Admn Mgr: Douglas W Swigert
Dist Mgr: Mike Satterfield
Genl Mgr: Jenny Nelson
Plnt Mgr: Gary K Wandschneider
Prd Mgr: Gary Harris
Natl Sales: Michael Dwyer

D-U-N-S 00-514-6295 EXP
■ PEPSI-COLA GENERAL BOTTLERS INC
PEPSICO
(*Suby of* PEPSICO) ★
1475 E Wdfeld Rd Ste 1300, Schaumburg, IL 60173
Tel (847) 598-3000 *Founded/Ownrshp* 1939, 2000
Sales 1.7MMM^E *EMP* 12,000
SIC 2086 5149 Soft drinks: packaged in cans, bottles, etc.; Carbonated beverages, nonalcoholic: bottled & canned; Soft drinks
Pr: Kenneth E Keiser
**CFO:* Alex Ware
VP: Jay Hulbert
IT Man: Leo Marchevsky
Opers Supe: Lisa Schmitte
Sfty Mgr: Tim McHale

D-U-N-S 00-129-4131 IMP/EXP
■ PEPSI-COLA METROPOLITAN BOTTLING CO INC
PEPSICO
(*Suby of* PEPSICO INC) ★
1111 Westchester Ave, White Plains, NY 10604-4000
Tel (914) 767-6000 *Founded/Ownrshp* 1949
Sales 26.6MMM^E *EMP* 112,050
SIC 2086 2087 Carbonated soft drinks, bottled & canned; Syrups, drink
Pr: Philip A Marineau
**Ch:* Robert Carl Biggart
**Sr VP:* Dick W Boyce
Sr VP: Todd Eveland
**Sr VP:* Brian Swette
VP: Alex Baxter
VP: Renee Garbus
VP: Robert C King
**VP:* Mark L Wheless
Dir IT: Anthony Navarra
Dir IT: Paul Vaghi

D-U-N-S 00-706-9446
■ PEPSI-COLA METROPOLITAN BOTTLING CO INC (NJ)
(*Suby of* PEPSICO INC) ★
3801 Brighton Blvd, Denver, CO 80216-3693
Tel (303) 292-9220 *Founded/Ownrshp* 1936, 1988
Sales 86.2MM^E *EMP* 500
SIC 2086 Carbonated beverages, nonalcoholic: bottled & canned; Tea, iced: packaged in cans, bottles, etc.; Pasteurized & mineral waters, bottled & canned
VP: Eric Reinhard
**CFO:* Jerry Urbanski
Dir Bus: Lyndon Knowles
Genl Mgr: Chris Harr
Dir IT: Kent Brown
IT Man: Andra Hernandez

D-U-N-S 07-870-0912 IMP/EXP
PEPSI-COLA PUERTO RICO DISTRIBUTING LLC
Carr 865 Km 0 4 Barrio Ca St Ca, TOA Baja, PR 00949
Tel (787) 251-2000 *Founded/Ownrshp* 1993
Sales 116.0MM^E *EMP* 550
SIC 2086 Carbonated soft drinks, bottled & canned; Mineral water, carbonated: packaged in cans, bottles, etc.
IT Man: Lucy C Carrasquillo

PEPSICO
See PEPSI-COLA METROPOLITAN BOTTLING CO INC

PEPSICO
See BUFFALO ROCK CO

PEPSICO
See PEPSI COLA BOTTLING FORT LAUNDERDALE

PEPSICO
See PEPSI-COLA GENERAL BOTTLERS INC

PEPSICO
See PEPSI AMERICAS INC

PEPSICO
See NOEL CORP

PEPSICO
See BROWN BOTTLING GROUP INC

PEPSICO
See REFRESHMENT SERVICES INC

PEPSICO
See PEPSI-COLA BOTTLING GROUP

PEPSICO AMERICAS FOODS
See FRITO-LAY NORTH AMERICA INC

D-U-N-S 82-860-6496 IMP
■ PEPSICO CARIBBEAN INC
(*Suby of* PEPSICO INC) ★
668 Calle Cubitas, Guaynabo, PR 00969-2801
Tel (787) 720-6825 *Founded/Ownrshp* 2006
Sales 129.7MM^E *EMP* 600
SIC 2013 Snack sticks, including jerky: from purchased meat
Prin: Jose J Aulet Robles
IT Man: Syvelle Miranda

D-U-N-S 00-128-7762 IMP/EXP
▲ PEPSICO INC (NC)
700 Anderson Hill Rd, Purchase, NY 10577-1444
Tel (914) 253-2000 *Founded/Ownrshp* 1919
Sales 63.0MMM *EMP* 263,000
Accts Kpmg Llp New York New York
Tkr Sym PEP *Exch* NYS
SIC 2096 2087 2086 2037 2052 2043 Potato chips & similar snacks; Corn chips & other corn-based snacks; Potato chips & other potato-based snacks; Cheese curls & puffs; Flavoring extracts & syrups; Syrups, drink; Fruit juices: concentrated for fountain use; Concentrates, drink; Bottled & canned soft drinks; Iced tea & fruit drinks, bottled & canned; Soft drinks: packaged in cans, bottles, etc.; Carbonated beverages, nonalcoholic: bottled & canned; Fruit juices; Cookies & crackers; Cereal breakfast foods; Oatmeal: prepared as cereal breakfast food
Ch Bd: Indra K Nooyi
V Ch: Hugh F Johnston
V Ch: Mehmood Khan
Pr: John Shumate
Pr: Kirk Tanner
CEO: Sanjeev Chadha
CEO: Ramon Laguarta
CEO: Laxman Narasimhan
CEO: Vivek Sankaran
COO: Anne Fink
CFO: John Adams
Treas: Lori Demny
Bd of Dir: Gustavo Salas
Ofcr: Grace Puma Whiteford
Ex VP: David C Rader
Ex VP: Cynthia M Trudell
Ex VP: Tony West
Ex VP: Eugene Willemsen
Sr VP: Rich Beck
Sr VP: Andrea Ferrara
Sr VP: Marie T Gallagher
Board of Directors: David C Page, Shona L Brown, Robert C Pohlad, George W Buckley, Lloyd G Trotter, Cesar Conde, Daniel Vasella, Ian M Cook, Alberto Weisser, Dina Dublon, Rona A Fairhead, Richard W Fisher, Alberto Ibarguen, William R Johnson

D-U-N-S 04-537-2521
PER MAR SECURITY AND RESEARCH CORP
1910 E Kimberly Rd, Davenport, IA 52807-2033
Tel (563) 359-3200 *Founded/Ownrshp* 1953
Sales 271.1MM^E *EMP* 2,500
SIC 8732 7381 5099 7389 7382

D-U-N-S 07-656-7718
PERALTA COMMUNITY COLLEGE DISTRICT
333 E 8th St, Oakland, CA 94606-2889
Tel (510) 466-7200 *Founded/Ownrshp* 1963
Sales 94.6MM^E *EMP* 2,100
SIC 8222 Community college
Pr: Abel Guillen
Exec: Bruce Goddard
Dir Risk M: Gregory Valentine
CIO: Calvin B Madlock
IT Man: Deborah Budd
IT Man: Ron Gerhard
Psych: Lilia Chavez

D-U-N-S 13-489-4547
■ PERCEPTA LLC
PERCEPTA ULC
(*Suby of* TELETECH HOLDINGS INC) ★
290 Town Center Dr # 610, Dearborn, MI 48126-2765
Tel (866) 737-2378 *Founded/Ownrshp* 1999
Sales 104.8MM^E *EMP* 4,450^E
SIC 7389 Telemarketing services
CEO: Ron Chamara
COO: Angela Gulley
VP: Tim O'Brien
Prin: Bill Schotanus
Opers Mgr: Suzan Tew
Mktg Dir: Alan Meldrum

PERCEPTA ULC
See PERCEPTA LLC

PERCHERON ENERGY
See PERCHERON SERVICES

D-U-N-S 85-951-7844
PERCHERON SERVICES
PERCHERON ENERGY
1904 W Grand Pkwy N, Katy, TX 77449-1697
Tel (832) 300-6400 *Founded/Ownrshp* 2007
Sales 131.5MM^E *EMP* 300^E
SIC 6552 Subdividers & developers
CEO: Asa M Bowers
**Pr:* Trent Oglesby
**CFO:* Nathan McBrayer
VP: Curtis Horne

D-U-N-S 80-558-3239 EXP
PERDUE AGRIBUSINESS LLC
PERDUE GRAIN AND OILSEED
(*Suby of* PERDUE FARMS INC) ★
6906 Zion Church Rd, Salisbury, MD 21804-1860
Tel (410) 543-3000 *Founded/Ownrshp* 2006
Sales 869.9MM^E *EMP* 1,000
SIC 5159 3556 Oil nuts, kernels, seeds; Oilseed crushing & extracting machinery
Pr: Richard Willey
**Sr VP:* John Ade

D-U-N-S 02-266-6820 IMP/EXP
PERDUE FARMS INC
31149 Old Ocean City Rd, Salisbury, MD 21804-1806
Tel (410) 543-3000 *Founded/Ownrshp* 1969
Sales 6.3MMM^E *EMP* 21,050
SIC 2015 2075 4213 Chicken, processed: fresh; Turkey, processed: fresh; Poultry, processed: fresh; Soybean oil, cake or meal; Refrigerated products transport
Ch Bd: Jim Perdue
**CFO:* Eileen Burza
**CFO:* Mark Garth
Ex VP: Mark McKay
VP: Kelly Berrie
VP: Charlie Carrigan
VP: John Cassidy
VP: Lisa Chasak
VP: Sharon Clark
VP: Michelle Paschal
VP: Chas Schaffernoth
VP: Craig Shreeves
VP: Randy Todd
VP: Andrew Urban
Exec: Valerie Haldeman

PERDUE GRAIN AND OILSEED
See PERDUE AGRIBUSINESS LLC

D-U-N-S 78-412-4620 IMP
PEREGRINE SEMICONDUCTOR CORP
(*Suby of* MURATA ELECTRONICS NORTH AMERICA INC) ★
9380 Carroll Park Dr, San Diego, CA 92121-2256
Tel (858) 731-9400 *Founded/Ownrshp* 2014
Sales 182.0MM^E *EMP* 423
SIC 3674 Silicon wafers, chemically doped

Ch Bd: James S Cable
CFO: Jay C Biskupski
*CFO: Takaki Muratajay C Biskupski
Ex VP: John Horsley
VP: Colin Hunt
VP: Dylan J Kelly
*VP: Takaki Murata
VP: Ian Warbrick
Comm Dir: Mark Schrepferman
Prgrm Mgr: Sung Im
Dir IT: Cary Etcheverry

D-U-N-S 78-099-7388
PERELLA WEINBERG PARTNERS GROUP LP
767 5th Ave Fl 3, New York, NY 10153-0029
Tel (212) 287-3200 Founded/Ownrshp 2005
Sales 218.3MM[E] EMP 400
SIC 6282 Investment advisory service
Mng Pt: Tarek Abdel-Meguid
Pt: Steven Asciutto
Pt: Chip Baird
Pt: David Baker
Pt: Gary Barancik
Pt: Andrew Bednar
Pt: Michael J Dickman
Pt: Michael McGrath
Pt: Ryan Moss
Pt: Brian Silver
Pt: Jeffrey Silverman

D-U-N-S 11-675-3711
PEREZ CONCRETE INC
5502 Gregg St, Dallas, TX 75235-7316
Tel (214) 522-9480 Founded/Ownrshp 1996
Sales 158.5MM[E] EMP 6,570
SIC 1771 Foundation & footing contractor
Pr: Luis Perez
*VP: Araceli Perez

D-U-N-S 00-168-6120 IMP/EXP
PEREZ TRADING CO INC (FL)
3490 Nw 125th St, Miami, FL 33167-2412
Tel (305) 769-0761 Founded/Ownrshp 1947, 1969
Sales 514.3MM EMP 148
Accts Berkowitz Pollack Brant Adviso
SIC 5199 Packaging materials
Pr: John D Perez
*Treas: Carl A Perez
*Sr VP: Roberta Perez
VP: Jose Arenas
Rgnl Mgr: Joseph Velasquez
Area Mgr: Domingo Cappuccio
Div Mgr: Erick Bonilla
Opers Mgr: Rudy Higa
Sls Mgr: Ivan Benitez
Sls Mgr: Eduardo Julio
Sls Mgr: Stephen Lannan

PERFECT 10 SATELLITE DISTRG CO
See PERFECTVISION MANUFACTURING INC

D-U-N-S 00-510-5168 EXP
PERFECTION BAKERIES INC
AUNT MILLIE'S BAKERIES
350 Pearl St, Fort Wayne, IN 46802-1508
Tel (260) 424-8245 Founded/Ownrshp 1901, 1953
Sales 561.5MM[E] EMP 1,600
SIC 2051 Bread, all types (white, wheat, rye, etc): fresh or frozen; Rolls, bread type: fresh or frozen
Pr: John F Popp
*CFO: Jay E Miller
CFO: Jay Miller

PERFECTION OIL
See MULGREW OIL CO

D-U-N-S 62-292-7820 IMP/EXP
PERFECTVISION MANUFACTURING INC
PERFECT 10 SATELLITE DISTRG CO
16101 La Grande Dr, Little Rock, AR 72223-9140
Tel (501) 955-0033 Founded/Ownrshp 1990
Sales 87.4MM[E] EMP 267
SIC 3679 Antennas, satellite: household use
VP: David Lord
*Pr: Terry Fleming
COO: Daryl Miller
*Sec: David Shaw
Ofcr: Chris Abshire
VP: Eddy Duke
*VP: Park Fleming
Exec: Jan Ramirez
Store Mgr: Gaylynn Taylor
IT Man: Britt Davidson
IT Man: Bob Goostree

D-U-N-S 05-889-5418 IMP/EXP
PERFETTI VAN MELLE USA INC
(Suby of PERFETTI VAN MELLE SPA)
3645 Turfway Rd, Erlanger, KY 41018-1165
Tel (859) 283-1234 Founded/Ownrshp 2009
Sales 221.8MM[E] EMP 200
SIC 5145 2064 Candy; Lollipops & other hard candy; Chewing candy, not chewing gum
Pr: Mehmet Yuksek
*Treas: Fred King
Bd of Dir: Travis Eilers
VP: Sylvia Buxton
*VP: Ralph Chauvin
VP: Michael Wodke
CIO: Basant K Chaturvedi
IT Man: Kevin Banke
Sfty Dirs: Brandon Reilman
Opers Mgr: Stacy Garrett
Opers Mgr: G W Wilson

D-U-N-S 01-126-0838
▲ PERFICIENT INC
555 Maryville Univ Dr 6, Saint Louis, MO 63141-5805
Tel (314) 529-3600 Founded/Ownrshp 1997
Sales 473.6MM EMP 2,738
Tkr Sym PRFT Exch NGS
SIC 7371 Computer software development
Pr: Jeffrey S Davis
Ch Bd: James R Kackley
COO: Kathryn J Henely
CFO: Paul Martin
VP: Emil Fernandez
VP: Mike Gersten
VP: Chris Gianattasio
VP: Kathy Henely
VP: Ed Hoffman
VP: Ganesh Rangarajan
VP: Kevin Sheen
Exec: Clint Couse
Creative D: Tor Gundersen
Dir Bus: James Farquharson
Dir Bus: Alicia Heaton
Dir Bus: Lauri Nicolaus
Dir Bus: Cully Templeton
Dir Bus: Brent Velde
Dir Bus: Lester Wakinaka
Board of Directors: Ralph C Derrickson, John S Hamlin, David S Lundeen

PERFOREX FREST SVCS LTD PARTNR
See PERFOREX LLC

D-U-N-S 07-839-7302
PERFOREX LLC
PERFOREX FREST SVCS LTD PARTNR
(Suby of MARTIN COMPANIES LLC ROM) ★
2663 E Coulee Crossing Rd, Woodworth, LA 71485-9736
Tel (318) 445-6799 Founded/Ownrshp 2012
Sales 161.2M[E] EMP 1,010[E]
SIC 0851 Forestry services
Prin: Pete Celone

PERFORMANCE BICYCLE
See PERFORMANCE DIRECT INC

D-U-N-S 17-355-2423
PERFORMANCE CONTRACTING GROUP INC
PCG
11145 Thompson Ave, Lenexa, KS 66219-2302
Tel (913) 888-8600 Founded/Ownrshp 1985
Sales 1.1MMM EMP 4,000
SIC 1799 1742

D-U-N-S 13-947-0587 IMP
PERFORMANCE CONTRACTING INC
ISSD
(Suby of PCG) ★
11145 Thompson Ave, Lenexa, KS 66219-2302
Tel (913) 888-8600 Founded/Ownrshp 1984
Sales 317.2MM[E] EMP 3,000
Accts Bkd Llp Kansas City Mo
SIC 1742 8711 Plastering, drywall & insulation; Building construction consultant
CEO: Craig D Davis
*Pr: William P Massey
*CFO: Dan Hefferon
*Treas: Daniel Hefferon
*Sr VP: Darrel Bailey
*Sr VP: Charles F Williams
VP: Darrel E Bailey
*VP: Stephen Barnes
*VP: Robert Dean
*VP: J Walter Eskeberg
*VP: Vaughn Grubaugh
*VP: Chris Mumford
VP: Paul E Settles
*VP: David W Watkins
Exec: Ed Stagg

D-U-N-S 09-859-9582 IMP/EXP
PERFORMANCE CONTRACTORS INC
PECUE CONTRACTORS
9901 Pecue Ln, Baton Rouge, LA 70810-3502
Tel (225) 490-2000 Founded/Ownrshp 1979
Sales 1.1MMM[E] EMP 1,500
SIC 1541 3498 Industrial buildings, new construction; Renovation, remodeling & repairs: industrial buildings; Fabricated pipe & fittings
Pr: Arthur E Favre
Rgnl Mgr: Jeremy Cooper
Area Mgr: Garnet Walker
Genl Mgr: Brandon Ardrey
Genl Mgr: Daniel Breaux
Off Mgr: Sue Broussard
Off Mgr: Judy Clark
Off Mgr: Evalyn Gurr
Dir IT: Rusty Pierce
Sfty Dirs: Victor Alanis
Sfty Dirs: Laine Lalonde

D-U-N-S 61-722-5347 IMP/EXP
PERFORMANCE DESIGNED PRODUCTS LLC
(Suby of PATRIARCH PARTNERS LLC) ★
2300 W Empire Ave # 600, Burbank, CA 91504-3341
Tel (323) 234-9911 Founded/Ownrshp 1990
Sales 182.5MM[E] EMP 190
SIC 5092 Toys & games; Video games
Pr: Kathryn Browne
Pr: Storm Orion
CFO: Kevin Johnson
CFO: Dave Muscatel
VP: Todd Koniares
Mktg Mgr: Jean Mitchell

D-U-N-S 00-288-4724 IMP/EXP
PERFORMANCE DIRECT INC
PERFORMANCE BICYCLE
(Suby of ADVANCED SPORTS ENTERPRISES INC) ★
1 Performance Way, Chapel Hill, NC 27517-9502
Tel (919) 933-9113 Founded/Ownrshp 1981
Sales 231.9MM[E] EMP 1,019
SIC 5961 5941 Fitness & sporting goods, mail order; Sporting goods & bicycle shops
Ch Bd: Garry A Snook
Pr: Robert Martin
CEO: David Pruitt
Prin: Jim Thompson

D-U-N-S 15-152-4910
PERFORMANCE ENERGY SERVICES LLC
PES
132 Valhi Lagoon Xing, Houma, LA 70360-3208
Tel (985) 868-4895 Founded/Ownrshp 2000
Sales 159.3MM[E] EMP 600[E]
SIC 1623 1389 7363 Oil & gas pipeline construction; Oil field services; Help supply services
CEO: Scott Lagrange

D-U-N-S 07-952-5714
▲ PERFORMANCE FOOD GROUP CO
12500 West Creek Pkwy, Richmond, VA 23238-1110
Tel (804) 484-7700 Founded/Ownrshp 2002
Sales 16.1MMM EMP 12,000[E]
Tkr Sym PFGC Exch NYS
SIC 5141 Groceries, general line
Pr: George L Holm
*Ch Bd: Douglas M Steenland
Pr: Patrick T Hagerty
Pr: Craig H Hoskins
CFO: Robert D Evans
Bd of Dir: Susan McManus
Ofcr: Carol A O'Connell
Ex VP: David Flitman
Ex VP: James Hope
Sr VP: A Brent King
VP: Selene Amberson
VP: Scott Barnewolt
VP: Mark Francis
VP: J Jackson
VP: David McCarthy
VP: Michael Miller
VP: Fred Sanelli
VP: Curtis Zachary
Board of Directors: William F Dawson Jr, Bruce McEvoy, Jeffrey Overly, Arthur B Winkleblack, John J Zillmer

D-U-N-S 01-743-1466 IMP/EXP
■ PERFORMANCE FOOD GROUP INC
P F G
(Suby of PFGC INC) ★
12500 West Creek Pkwy, Richmond, VA 23238-1110
Tel (804) 484-7700 Founded/Ownrshp 2001
Sales 11.3MMM[E] EMP 11,000
SIC 5149 Canned goods: fruit, vegetables, seafood, meats, etc.; Dried or canned foods
Pr: Dave Flitman
*Pr: Danny Berry
*Pr: Glenn Blayney
*Pr: Steve Broad
*Pr: Joe Copeland
*CEO: George Holm
*CFO: Bob Evans
*Ex VP: Jim Hope
*Sr VP: Kent Berke
*Sr VP: Ernie Gilchrist
*Sr VP: Brent King
*Sr VP: Michael L Miller
*Sr VP: Carol Oconnell
*Sr VP: Carol Price
*Sr VP: Terry West
Sr VP: Jeff Williamson

D-U-N-S 03-372-4360
PERFORMANCE FOOD GROUP OF GEORGIA LLC
PFG-MILTON
3501 Old Oakwood Rd, Oakwood, GA 30566-2802
Tel (770) 532-7779 Founded/Ownrshp 1995
Sales NA EMP 1,000
SIC 5141

D-U-N-S 02-210-0705
PERFORMANCE FOOD SERVICE TPC
PFG - THOMS PROESTLER COMPANY
8001 51st St W, Rock Island, IL 61201-7315
Tel (309) 787-1234 Founded/Ownrshp 2006
Sales 133.5MM[E] EMP 410
SIC 5149 Groceries & related products

PERFORMANCE FOODSERVICE-AFI
See AFI FOOD SERVICE DISTRIBUTORS INC

PERFORMANCE GROUP
See NORTHERN CALIFORNIA TPG INC

D-U-N-S 14-709-0435
■ PERFORMANCE MECHANICAL INC
P M I
(Suby of EMCOR GROUP INC) ★
701 Willow Pass Rd Ste 2, Pittsburg, CA 94565-1803
Tel (925) 432-4080 Founded/Ownrshp 1985
Sales 165.6MM[E] EMP 600
SIC 1541 1711 8711

D-U-N-S 96-695-0201 IMP
PERFORMANCE SPORTS GROUP LTD
100 Domain Dr, Exeter, NH 03833-4801
Tel (603) 610-5802 Founded/Ownrshp 2010
Sales 654.6MM EMP 872[E]
SIC 3949 Sporting & athletic goods; Baseball equipment & supplies, general; Hockey equipment & supplies, general; Lacrosse equipment & supplies, general
CEO: Harlan Kent
*Ch Bd: Bernard McDonell
CFO: Mark Vendetti
Ofcr: Angela Bass
Ex VP: Paul Gibson
Ex VP: Dan Sills
Ex VP: Mike Thorne
Sr VP: Jennifer Hughey
VP: Michael Wall
Board of Directors: Karyn Barsa, Joan Dea, C Michael Jacobi, Matthew Mannelly, Bob Nicholson

D-U-N-S 14-460-1148
PERFORMANCE SYSTEMS INC
PSI
2204 E Lanark St, Meridian, ID 83642-5916
Tel (208) 287-0800 Founded/Ownrshp 2003
Sales 100.6MM[E] EMP 140
SIC 1542 Nonresidential construction
Pr: Kaleo Nawahine
Brnch Mgr: Travis Conger
Genl Mgr: Hank Nawahine
Off Mgr: Candy Siemens
Ql Cn Mgr: Erik Westberg

D-U-N-S 18-178-5163
PERFORMANCE TEAM FREIGHT SYS INC
2240 E Maple Ave, El Segundo, CA 90245-6507
Tel (562) 345-2200 Founded/Ownrshp 1987
Sales 470.2MM[E] EMP 1,500
SIC 4731 4225 4213 Freight transportation arrangement; General warehousing & storage; Trucking, except local
CEO: Craig Kaplan
*Pr: Cliff Katab
*CFO: Thierno Amath Fall
CFO: Michael Kaplan
CFO: Mark Norris
CFO: Amath Sall
Sr VP: Marc Koenig
VP: Joe Corniuk
VP: Fred Gilbert
*VP: Robert Kaplan
*VP: Tracy Kaplan
VP: Terry Vera
VP: Tom Wilkinson
Dir Bus: David Casey
Dir Bus: Mac Forehand
Dir Bus: Maria Gonzalez

PERFORMANCE TRUCK
See MACK CLEVELAND SALES INC

D-U-N-S 09-289-5085 IMP
PERFORMANCE WAREHOUSE CO (OR)
9440 N Whitaker Rd, Portland, OR 97217-7794
Tel (503) 417-5302 Founded/Ownrshp 1969
Sales 86.2MM[E] EMP 150
SIC 5013 Automotive supplies & parts
Pr: Lyle D Moore
*CFO: Ken Moore
*Treas: Ray Baxter Jr
Dir IT: Ray Howard
Opers Mgr: Brian Lusby

D-U-N-S 78-442-4728
▲ PERFORMANT FINANCIAL CORP
333 N Canyons Pkwy # 100, Livermore, CA 94551-9478
Tel (925) 960-4800 Founded/Ownrshp 1976
Sales 159.3MM EMP 1,218[E]
Tkr Sym PFMT Exch NGS
SIC 7375 Information retrieval services
Ch Bd: Lisa C Im
COO: Jeffrey R Haughton
CFO: Hakan L Orvell
Chf Cred: Harold T Leach Jr
Snr Mgr: Lara Simmons
Board of Directors: Bradley M Fluegel, Todd R Ford, Brian P Golson, Bruce E Hansen, William D Hansen

D-U-N-S 08-184-0787
■ PERFORMANT RECOVERY INC
D C S
(Suby of PERFORMANT FINANCIAL CORP) ★
333 N Canyons Pkwy # 100, Livermore, CA 94551-9478
Tel (209) 858-3994 Founded/Ownrshp 1976
Sales 52.2MM[E] EMP 1,350
SIC 7322 8742 7371 Adjustment & collection services; Financial consultant; Custom computer programming services
CEO: Lisa Im
*CFO: Hakan Orvell
Genl Mgr: Lara Crapo

PERFORMNCE FDSERVICE-FOX RIVER
See FOX RIVER FOODS INC

PERFORMNCE FDSRVCE- LTTLE ROCK
See PFG BROADLINE HOLDINGS LLC

PERFORMNCE FOODSERVICE-HICKORY
See INSTITUTION FOOD HOUSE INC

PERFUMANIA
See MAGNIFIQUE PARFUMES AND COSMETICS INC

D-U-N-S 18-638-8500
▲ PERFUMANIA HOLDINGS INC
35 Sawgrass Dr Ste 2, Bellport, NY 11713-1577
Tel (631) 866-4100 Founded/Ownrshp 1997
Sales 541.9MM EMP 2,044[E]
Tkr Sym PERF Exch NAS
SIC 5122 5999 Perfumes; Perfumes & colognes
Pr: Michael W Katz
*Ch Bd: Stephen Nussdorf
COO: Neal Montany
CFO: Donna L Dellomo
Board of Directors: Joseph Bouhadana, Paul Garfinkle, Glenn H Gopman

D-U-N-S 96-695-7409 IMP
■ PERFUMANIA INC
(Suby of PERFUMANIA HOLDINGS INC) ★
5900 N Andrews Ave # 500, Fort Lauderdale, FL 33309-2370
Tel (866) 600-3600 Founded/Ownrshp 1997
Sales 397.7MM[E] EMP 1,500
SIC 5122 5999 Perfumes; Toiletries, cosmetics & perfumes
Pr: Michael W Katz
CFO: Donna Dellomo
Ex VP: Donald J Loftus
VP: Terry Head
Software D: Aditi Jain
Site Mgr: Tracey Rivera
Site Mgr: Sheila Sanders
VP Mktg: Mireya Puett
Mktg Dir: Debra Milano
Mktg Dir: Bonnie Nelson

D-U-N-S 88-359-9789 IMP/EXP
PERFUME CENTER OF AMERICA INC
2020 Ocean Ave, Ronkonkoma, NY 11779-6536
Tel (516) 348-1127 Founded/Ownrshp 1993
Sales 271.6MM EMP 70
Accts Raich Ende Malter & Co Llp
SIC 5122 Perfumes
Ch: Kanak R Golia
*VP: Prebha Golia

D-U-N-S 14-607-0524 IMP
PERFUME WORLDWIDE INC
2020 Ocean Ave Unit A, Ronkonkoma, NY 11779-6536
Tel (516) 575-2499 Founded/Ownrshp 2002
Sales 107.4MM EMP 200
Accts Raich Ende Malter & Co Llp
SIC 5122 5999 Perfumes; Perfumes & colognes
Pr: Piyush Golia
*VP: Prabha Golia

D-U-N-S 62-607-8794 IMP
■ **PERICOM SEMICONDUCTOR CORP**
(*Suby of* DIODES INC) ★
1545 Barber Ln, Milpitas, CA 95035-7409
Tel (408) 232-9100 *Founded/Ownrshp* 2015
Sales 128.8MM *EMP* 913E
SIC 3674 3825 Semiconductors & related devices; Integrated circuits, semiconductor networks, etc.; Instruments to measure electricity; Frequency synthesizers
Pr: Alex Chiming Hui
CFO: Kevin S Bauer
Sr VP: Angela Chen
Sr VP: CHI-Hung Hui
VP: George KAO
Exec: Tonya Wilson
Snr Mgr: Johann Wu

PERIMETER GLOBAL LOGISTICS
See PERIMETER INTERNATIONAL

D-U-N-S 78-532-3440
PERIMETER INTERNATIONAL
PERIMETER GLOBAL LOGISTICS
2700 Story Rd W Ste 150, Irving, TX 75038-7391
Tel (877) 701-1919 *Founded/Ownrshp* 2006
Sales 115.9MME *EMP* 125E
SIC 7389 4412 4731 4581 4449 Personal service agents, brokers & bureaus; Deep sea foreign transportation of freight; Foreign freight forwarding; Airfreight loading & unloading services; Intracoastal (freight) transportation
CEO: Merry L Lamothe
**Pr:* Raj Sobhani
**CFO:* Dustin Eash
**Treas:* Beau Lamothe

D-U-N-S 13-085-4128 IMP/EXP
■ **PERINI MANAGEMENT SERVICES INC**
(*Suby of* TUTOR PERINI CORP) ★
73 Mount Wayte Ave, Framingham, MA 01702-5803
Tel (508) 628-2000 *Founded/Ownrshp* 1975
Sales 85.4MM *EMP* 100E
Accts Deloitte & Touche Llp Los Ang
SIC 1541 1542 1611 1629 Industrial buildings, new construction; Nonresidential construction; Highway & street construction; Airport runway construction; Waste water & sewage treatment plant construction
Pr: Robert Band
Sec: William B Sparks
Sr VP: J Gerstenlauter
Sr VP: P Lloyd
Sr VP: William G O'Brien
Sr VP: C Olsen
Sfty Dirs: Roger Bruce
Sls Mgr: Sandrah Yuen
Board of Directors: James A Frost, Ronald W Tutor

D-U-N-S 05-650-5795 IMP/EXP
PERISHABLE DISTRIBUTORS OF IOWA LTD
P D I
(*Suby of* HY-VEE INC) ★
2741 Se Pdi Pl, Ankeny, IA 50021-3958
Tel (515) 965-6300 *Founded/Ownrshp* 1982
Sales 1.2MMM *EMP* 570
SIC 5146 5144 5147 Fish & seafoods; Eggs; Poultry products; Meats & meat products
Pr: Randy Kruse
**Ex VP:* Linda Sharp
Sr VP: Kevin Gass
Exec: Janel Jones
Sfty Dirs: Kyle Oberender

D-U-N-S 01-218-6557 IMP/EXP
PERK-UP INC
KARI OUT COMPANY
399 Knollwood Rd Ste 309, White Plains, NY 10603-1938
Tel (914) 580-3200 *Founded/Ownrshp* 1965
Sales 111.8MME *EMP* 200
SIC 5113 5149 2673 3411 2674 2035

D-U-N-S 03-948-5537 IMP
■ **PERKINELMER HEALTH SCIENCES INC**
(*Suby of* PERKINELMER HOLDINGS INC) ★
940 Winter St, Waltham, MA 02451-1457
Tel (617) 482-9595 *Founded/Ownrshp* 1997
Sales 173.6MME *EMP* 719E
SIC 3821 Laboratory apparatus & furniture
Pr: Robert F Friel
Treas: Scott P Kennedy
VP: Steven J Delahunt
VP: Paul Leblanc
VP: David E Pantazi
VP: Edward R Schleper
Genl Mgr: Jesse Baumgold
CIO: Gone Datillo
Mtls Mgr: Jenny Zaremba
Pgrm Dir: Linda Lacy
Snr Mgr: John Comley

D-U-N-S 80-834-0921
■ **PERKINELMER HOLDINGS INC**
(*Suby of* PERKINELMER INC) ★
940 Winter St, Wellesley, MA 02481
Tel (781) 663-6900 *Founded/Ownrshp* 1970
Sales 318.6MME *EMP* 450
SIC 3053 Gaskets, packing & sealing devices
CEO: Gregory Summe
Prgrm Mgr: Gail Fons

D-U-N-S 00-105-3610 IMP
▲ **PERKINELMER INC** (MA)
940 Winter St, Waltham, MA 02451-1457
Tel (781) 663-6900 *Founded/Ownrshp* 1947
Sales 2.2MMM *EMP* 8,000
Tkr Sym PKI *Exch* NYS
SIC 3826 3845 Analytical instruments; Environmental testing equipment; Electromedical equipment
Ch Bd: Robert F Friel
Pr: James Corbett
Pr: Jon Divincenzo
**CFO:* Frank A Wilson
**Sr VP:* Joel S Goldberg
**Sr VP:* Daniel R Tereau
VP: Fran Bates
VP: Mike Close
VP: Leeann Dennewitz
VP: Nicolas Encina
VP: Alan Fletcher
VP: JP Fournier
VP: Joel Goldberg
VP: Jessica Killmon
VP: Brian McGrattan
**VP:* Andrew Okun
VP: Adam Ortiz
VP: Nitin Sood
VP: Gintas Vildzius
Board of Directors: Samuel R Chapin

D-U-N-S 12-043-4209
PERKINS & MARIE CALLENDERS HOLDING INC
(*Suby of* PERKINS & MARIE CALLENDER'S HOLDING, LLC)
6075 Poplar Ave Ste 800, Memphis, TN 38119-4717
Tel (901) 766-6400 *Founded/Ownrshp* 1999
Sales 613.9MME *EMP* 16,300
SIC 5812 Restaurant, family: chain
CEO: Joseph F Trungale
VP: Jim Frank
VP: Danny Weaver
Rgnl Mgr: Bill Backmann
Rgnl Mgr: Marie Pippio
Genl Mgr: Pat Doyle
Dir IT: Jim Lewis
Sales Exec: Bob Winters
Sls Dir: Karen Craig
Mktg Mgr: Sheryl Butler
Mktg Mgr: Erin Vanveen

D-U-N-S 14-824-4593
PERKINS & MARIE CALLENDERS LLC
PERKINS FAMILY RESTAURANT
(*Suby of* PERKINS & MARIE CALLENDERS HOLDING INC) ★
6075 Poplar Ave Ste 800, Memphis, TN 38119-4717
Tel (901) 766-6400 *Founded/Ownrshp* 1985
Sales 613.9MME *EMP* 13,700
SIC 5812 6794 Restaurant, family: chain; Franchises, selling or licensing
CEO: Joseph F Trungale
**CFO:* Fred T Grant Jr
Treas: Karen L Young
**Ex VP:* Cheryl S Ahlbrandt
Sr VP: Cheryl Ahlbrandt
**Sr VP:* Robert J Winters
VP: Jim Vickers

D-U-N-S 06-620-8489
PERKINS & WILL GROUP LTD
410 N Michigan Ave # 1600, Chicago, IL 60611-3757
Tel (312) 755-0770 *Founded/Ownrshp* 1935, 1986
Sales 256.0MME *EMP* 1,500
SIC 8712 7389 Architectural services; Interior designer
CEO: Phil Harrison
Pr: Robert Peterson
CEO: Phila Harrison
CFO: Joseph Dailey

D-U-N-S 06-003-0707 IMP
PERKINS COIE LLP
1201 3rd Ave Ste 4900, Seattle, WA 98101-3099
Tel (206) 359-8000 *Founded/Ownrshp* 1997
Sales 313.0MME *EMP* 1,454
SIC 8111 General practice law office
Mng Pt: Robert E Giles
Genl Pt: Perkins Coie II
Pt: Elizabeth A Alaniz
Pt: R Michael Ananian
Pt: Robert F Bauer
Pt: Stephen C Bishop
Pt: David J Burman
Pt: David C Clarke
Pt: Brian Coleman
Pt: David Dort
Pt: James P Dugan
Pt: Orna A Edgar
Pt: Scott M Edwards
Pt: Susan D Fahringer
Pt: David Frazee
Pt: Craig Gilbert
Pt: Paul L Hickman
Pt: Riaz Karamali
Pt: David J Katz
Pt: Allison Kendrick
Pt: Tamiz Khan

D-U-N-S 09-834-4708 IMP
PERKINS EASTMAN ARCHITECTS DPC
115 5th Ave Fl 3, New York, NY 10003-1004
Tel (212) 353-7200 *Founded/Ownrshp* 1980
Sales 143.3MME *EMP* 700
SIC 8712 8742 7389 Architectural services; Management consulting services; Interior designer
Ch: Lawrence Bradford Perkins
**Pr:* J David Hoglund
Exec: Doreen E Carbone
Ex Dir: Doug Helman
Admn Mgr: Elisabeth Marner
Opers Mgr: Anne Ludwig
Opers Mgr: Munter Martin
Sls&Mrk Ex: Minuette Le
Mktg Mgr: Nancy Cheung

PERKINS FAMILY RESTAURANT
See K INVESTMENTS LIMITED PARTNERSHIP

PERKINS FAMILY RESTAURANT
See PERKINS & MARIE CALLENDERS LLC

PERKINS FAMILY RESTAURANT
See NORTHCOTT HOSPITALITY INTERNATIONAL LLC

D-U-N-S 01-927-7144 IMP
PERKINS PAPER INC (MA)
(*Suby of* GORDON FOOD SERVICE INC) ★
630 John Hancock Rd, Taunton, MA 02780-7380
Tel (508) 824-2800 *Founded/Ownrshp* 1915
Sales 482.4MME *EMP* 613
SIC 5113 5149 5087 5046 Industrial & personal service paper; Bakery products; Janitors' supplies; Restaurant equipment & supplies
**Pr:* Larry Perkins
CFO: Ray Lebanc
**Treas:* Laurence Perkins
VP: Pam Furey
Exec: Jim Dwyer
Dist Mgr: John Desisto
Plng Mgr: James Voyer
Store Mgr: Jon Conroy
MIS Dir: Ed Matthews
IT Man: Chris Andrews
Sls Mgr: George Clark
Board of Directors: Jean Z Perkins

PERKINSTON CAMPUS
See MISSISSIPPI GULF COAST COMMUNITY COLLEGE

D-U-N-S 00-411-7677 IMP
PERKO INC
16490 Nw 13th Ave, Miami, FL 33169-5707
Tel (305) 621-7525 *Founded/Ownrshp* 1961
Sales 142.7MME *EMP* 525
SIC 3429 Marine hardware
Ch Bd: Marvin S Perkins
**Pr:* Frederick M Perkins
**Sec:* Jeni M Bedran

D-U-N-S 93-796-3903
PERLITE INSTITUTE INC
2207 Forest Hills Dr, Harrisburg, PA 17112-1005
Tel (717) 238-9723 *Founded/Ownrshp* 2008
Sales 505.3MME *EMP* 50E
Accts Lisa Acri Cpa And Associates I
SIC 5045 Computer software

D-U-N-S 08-403-3646
PERLMART INC
SHOP-RITE
954 Route 166 Ste 1, Toms River, NJ 08753-6679
Tel (732) 341-0700 *Founded/Ownrshp* 1976
Sales 117.2MME *EMP* 1,052
SIC 5411 5912 Supermarkets, chain; Drug stores
Pr: Joel Perlmutter
**Sec:* Michael Perlmutter
VP: Jim Haslett

PERMA-BOUND
See HERTZBERG-NEW METHOD INC

D-U-N-S 87-296-4358 IMP/EXP
■ **PERMA-PIPE INC**
PERMALERT E S P
(*Suby of* MFRI INC) ★
7720 N Lehigh Ave, Niles, IL 60714-3416
Tel (847) 966-2190 *Founded/Ownrshp* 1909
Sales 158.0MM *EMP* 250
SIC 3498 Fabricated pipe & fittings
Pr: Fati Elgendy
Ex VP: Robert Maffei
**VP:* Michael D Bennett
VP: Mike Bennett
**VP:* Billy E Ervin
Exec: Robert Marasco
Ex Dir: Stephen Harbough
Genl Mgr: Tom Railsback

PERMABOND AMERICAS
See ICI AMERICAN HOLDINGS LLC

PERMACEL-AUTOMOTIVE
See NITTO AMERICAS INC

PERMALERT E S P
See PERMA-PIPE INC

D-U-N-S 15-442-9877
PERMANENT GENERAL ASSURANCE CORP
(*Suby of* GENERAL INSURANCE) ★
2636 Elm Hill Pike # 510, Nashville, TN 37214-3169
Tel (615) 744-1351 *Founded/Ownrshp* 1994
Sales NA *EMP* 195
SIC 6331 6411 6141 Automobile insurance; Insurance agents, brokers & service; Financing: automobiles, furniture, etc., not a deposit bank
Pr: Randy Parker
Sftwr Eng: Terry Frymire
Mktg Dir: Barry Dice

D-U-N-S 08-351-3705
PERMANENT GENERAL COMPANIES INC
GENERAL INSURANCE, THE
(*Suby of* AMERICAN FAMILY INSURANCE) ★
2636 Elm Hill Pike # 510, Nashville, TN 37214-3169
Tel (615) 242-1961 *Founded/Ownrshp* 2012
Sales NA *EMP* 195
SIC 6411 Insurance agents, brokers & service
Pr: Randy Parker
**Sr VP:* David L Hettinger
VP: Barry Dice
**VP:* Brian M Donovan
CIO: Kent Fourman

D-U-N-S 07-393-2931
PERMANENTE MEDICAL GROUP INC
(*Suby of* KAISER PERMANENTE) ★
1950 Franklin St Fl 18th, Oakland, CA 94612-5118
Tel (866) 858-2226 *Founded/Ownrshp* 1945
Sales 692.8MME *EMP* 26,000
SIC 8099 Medical services organization
CEO: Robert M Pearl
**CFO:* Gerard C Bajada
Ch: Christopher J Palkowski
Treas: Judy D Lively
**Ex Dir:* Pat Conolly
Surgeon: David Fisher
Doctor: Richard Blohm
Doctor: Letha Jayakrishnan
Doctor: Rhoda Wynn

D-U-N-S 61-179-3936 IMP/EXP
PERMASTEELISA NORTH AMERICA CORP
(*Suby of* PERMASTEELISA SPA)
123 Day Hill Rd, Windsor, CT 06095-1709
Tel (860) 298-2000 *Founded/Ownrshp* 2000
Sales 344.1MME *EMP* 1,000
SIC 1793 1799 Glass & glazing work; Office furniture installation
CEO: Alberto De Gobbi
**COO:* Claudio Daniele
VP: Alan Elder
VP: Mike Kneeland
Genl Mgr: Paul Lailey
Genl Mgr: Laura Rankin
Genl Mgr: Otto Rieder
MIS Dir: Martin Novotny
Tech Mgr: Ron Koenig
Sys/Mgr: Nury Plumley
Software D: Robert Strickland

PERMASWAGE USA
See DESIGNED METAL CONNECTIONS INC

PERMIAN BASIN DIVISION
See REF-CHEM LP

PERMIAN BASIN RAILWAYS
See IOWA PACIFIC HOLDINGS LLC

D-U-N-S 00-793-5257 IMP/EXP
PERMIAN MUD SERVICE INC
3200 Southwest Fwy # 2700, Houston, TX 77027-7528
Tel (713) 627-1101 *Founded/Ownrshp* 1946
Sales NA *EMP* 3,000
SIC 2819

D-U-N-S 02-032-3333
PERMIAN TANK & MANUFACTURING INC (TX)
2701 W Interstate 20, Odessa, TX 79766-9102
Tel (432) 580-1050 *Founded/Ownrshp* 1976
Sales 116.4MME *EMP* 264
SIC 3443 Tanks, standard or custom fabricated: metal plate; Vessels, process or storage (from boiler shops): metal plate
Exec: Jerry Golden
Exec: Dianne Smith
Sfty Dirs: Javier Salazar

D-U-N-S 13-057-1966
PERMIRA ADVISERS LLC
(*Suby of* PERMIRA ADVISERS LLP)
320 Park Ave Fl 33, New York, NY 10022-6815
Tel (212) 386-7480 *Founded/Ownrshp* 2002
Sales 99.6MME *EMP* 400E
SIC 6282 Investment advisory service
CFO: Wynne Chan

D-U-N-S 60-689-6405 IMP
PERMOBIL INC
(*Suby of* PERMOBIL AB)
300 Duke Dr, Lebanon, TN 37090-8115
Tel (615) 547-1889 *Founded/Ownrshp* 1985
Sales 123.2MME *EMP* 375
SIC 5047 Medical & hospital equipment
Pr: Larry Jackson
COO: Darin Lowery
Sr VP: Johan Ulleryd
**VP:* Todd Walling
IT Man: Steve Hill
Manager: Joshua Foerster
Manager: Erik Tillman
Sls Mgr: Stephen Burke
Sls Mgr: Tony Campanella
Sls Mgr: Mike Duda
Sls Mgr: Scott Ingraham

D-U-N-S 08-036-9331
■ **PERNIX BUILDING GROUP LLC**
(*Suby of* PERNIX GROUP INC) ★
151 E 22nd St Ste 101e, Lombard, IL 60148-6227
Tel (630) 620-4787 *Founded/Ownrshp* 2015
Sales 284.6MME *EMP* 410E
SIC 1521 Single-family housing construction

D-U-N-S 93-965-7847
▲ **PERNIX GROUP INC**
151 E 22nd St Ste 101e, Lombard, IL 60148-6227
Tel (630) 620-4787 *Founded/Ownrshp* 1994
Sales 195.4MM *EMP* 475E
Tkr Sym PRXG *Exch* OTO
SIC 1542 4911 Nonresidential construction; Commercial & office building, new construction; Generation, electric power
Ch Bd: Nidal Zayed
CFO: Marco A Martinez
Ex VP: Grant G McCullagh
Snr PM: Micah Conrad
Board of Directors: C Robert Campbell, Trudy Clark, Max Engler, Don Gunther, Ibrahim M Ibrahim, Carl Smith

D-U-N-S 01-599-7570 IMP
▲ **PERNIX THERAPEUTICS HOLDINGS INC** (MD)
10 N Park Pl Ste 201, Morristown, NJ 07960-7101
Tel (800) 793-2145 *Founded/Ownrshp* 1996
Sales 175.8MM *EMP* 274E
Tkr Sym PTX *Exch* NGM
SIC 2834 Pharmaceutical preparations
Ch Bd: John Sedor
Pr: Graham G Miao
VP: Raegan A McClain
Board of Directors: Steven A Elms, Tasos G Konidaris, Gabriel Leung

D-U-N-S 06-974-4783 IMP/EXP
PERNOD RICARD AMERICAS TRAVEL RETAIL INC
(*Suby of* PERNOD RICARD USA LLC) ★
200 E Las Olas Blvd, Fort Lauderdale, FL 33301-2299
Tel (954) 940-9000 *Founded/Ownrshp* 2011
Sales 168.4MME *EMP* 939E
SIC 5182 Wine
Pr: Franck Lapeyre
**VP:* Audrey Yayon-Dauvet
**Prin:* Sharon Mayers
**Prin:* Guillaume Des Sagets
Netwrk Eng: David Dutt

D-U-N-S 09-823-2619 IMP/EXP
PERNOD RICARD USA LLC
(*Suby of* PERNOD RICARD NORTH AMERICA)
250 Park Ave Ste 17a, New York, NY 10177-1702
Tel (914) 848-4800 *Founded/Ownrshp* 2009
Sales 472.9MME *EMP* 1,985
SIC 2085 Distilled & blended liquors
Pr: Bryan Fry
Pr: Mathieu Lambotte
CFO: John Nicodemo
Ex VP: Gopi Nambiar
Sr VP: Matt Aeppli

Sr VP: Pierre Berard
Sr VP: Marty Crane
Sr VP: Dan Denisoff
Sr VP: Stephen O'Neill
Sr VP: Amandine Robin
VP: Jeff Agdern
VP: Stephen Ballas
VP: Ron Brown
VP: Terry Collins
VP: Mauve Croizat
VP: Mike Fuller
VP: Jim Green
VP: Shawn Higgins
VP: Deborah Joseph
VP: Clare Kanter
VP: Kate Pomeroy

D-U-N-S 60-651-1020 EXP
PERO FAMILY FARMS FOOD CO LLC
14095 Us Highway 441, Delray Beach, FL 33446-9600
Tel (561) 498-4533 *Founded/Ownrshp* 1986
Sales 97.7MM^E *EMP* 100
SIC 5148 Fresh fruits & vegetables
CEO: Peter Pero IV
**Pr:* Angela Pero
**VP:* Charles Pero

D-U-N-S 96-831-9413 IMP/EXP
PERO FAMILY FARMS LLC
14095 Us Highway 441, Delray Beach, FL 33446-9600
Tel (561) 498-4533 *Founded/Ownrshp* 1986
Sales 85.6MM^E *EMP* 100
SIC 5148 Fresh fruits & vegetables
CEO: Peter Pero
Chf Mktg O: Ed Sullivan
VP: Charles Pero
VP Sls: Nick Bergstrom
Sls Mgr: Evrard Van Malderen

D-U-N-S 00-984-8193
PERORIA DISPOSAL CO (NV)
P D C
(*Suby of* COULTER COMPANIES INC) ★
4700 N Sterling Ave Ste 2, Peoria, IL 61615-3665
Tel (309) 686-8033 *Founded/Ownrshp* 1929, 1985
Sales 98.0MM^E *EMP* 180
SIC 4953 Hazardous waste collection & disposal; Liquid waste, collection & disposal; Garbage: collecting, destroying & processing
Pr: Royal Coulter
**Sec:* Steve Davison
Exec: Steven Petersen
Off Mgr: Kara Sedgwick
Dir IT: Robert Gordon
Dir IT: Glenn Knott
Sales Exec: Chris Coulter
Sales Exec: Matt Coulter

D-U-N-S 19-169-2813 IMP
■ **PEROT SYSTEMS CORP**
(*Suby of* DELL COMPUTER) ★
2300 W Plano Pkwy, Plano, TX 75075-8427
Tel (972) 577-0000 *Founded/Ownrshp* 2009
Sales 1.2MMM^E *EMP* 23,100
SIC 7376 7379 Computer facilities management; Computer related consulting services
Pr: Peter A Altabef
**COO:* Russell Freeman
COO: Ruell Reeman
COO: Peggy Rodebusch
**CFO:* John E Harper
**Ofcr:* Darcy Anderson
Ex VP: Darrell Montgomery
VP: Joseph G Bedner
VP: Sheri Groom
VP: Eric Hutto
VP: Robert Mattana
VP: Jill Mullen
VP: W David Sanders
VP: Niraj Singhal
**VP:* Thomas D Williams
Assoc Dir: Vinay K Gupta
Dir Soc: Anne Clarke
Board of Directors: Cecil H Moore, Patricia Snodgrass

D-U-N-S 07-929-3524 IMP/EXP
■ **PEROXYCHEM LLC**
(*Suby of* PEROXYCHEM HOLDINGS LP)
1 Commerce Sq, Philadelphia, PA 19103-1415
Tel (267) 422-2400 *Founded/Ownrshp* 2014
Sales 340.0MM^E *EMP* 500
SIC 5169 2819 Chemicals & allied products; Peroxides, hydrogen peroxide
Pr: Bruce Lerner
CFO: Pete Zograsakis
Treas: Michael Donnelly
VP: Alberto Garibi
Tech Mgr: Barbara Pilmore

D-U-N-S 78-826-8147
■ **PERPETUAL CAPITAL PARTNERS LLC**
(*Suby of* SINCLAIR TELEVISION GROUP INC) ★
1000 Wilson Blvd Ste 2700, Arlington, VA 22209-3921
Tel (703) 647-8709 *Founded/Ownrshp* 2014
Sales 274.1MM^E *EMP* 815^E
SIC 6726 Investment offices
CEO: Robert Allbritton
**CEO:* Robert Albritton

PERRIER WATER
See NESTLE WATERS NORTH AMERICA INC

PERRIGO ANIMAL HEALTH
See SERGEANTS PET CARE PRODUCTS INC

D-U-N-S 03-861-6769 IMP/EXP
PERRIGO CO
(*Suby of* PERRIGO COMPANY PUBLIC LIMITED COMPANY)
515 Eastern Ave, Allegan, MI 49010-9070
Tel (269) 673-8451 *Founded/Ownrshp* 1987
Sales 4.0MMM *EMP* 14,000
Accts Ernst & Young Llp Grand Rapi
SIC 2834 Pharmaceutical preparations; Analgesics; Cold remedies; Vitamin preparations
Ch Bd: Joseph C Papa
Pr: Douglas S Boothe
**Pr:* John T Hendrickson
CFO: Judy L Brown
Treas: Lou Cherico
Bd of Dir: Mark Taylor
**Ex VP:* Marc Coucke
Ex VP: Thomas M Farrington
**Ex VP:* Tom Farrington
**Ex VP:* Todd W Kingma
Ex VP: Sharon Kochan
Ex VP: Jeffrey R Needham
Ex VP: Mike Smith
VP: Rajesh Bhaye
VP: Gretel Eubanks
VP: Anne Guy
VP: Ron Janish
**VP:* Bradley Joseph
VP: Andy Kjellberg
VP: Gregory Kurdys
VP: Herbert Luther

D-U-N-S 07-884-6912 IMP
PERRIGO NEW YORK INC
SUPPOSITORIA LABORATORY
(*Suby of* PERRIGO CO) ★
1700 Bathgate Ave, Bronx, NY 10457-7512
Tel (718) 960-9900 *Founded/Ownrshp* 2005
Sales 108.3MM^E *EMP* 720
SIC 2834 Pharmaceutical preparations; Ointments; Dermatologicals
Pr: Giora Carni
**Ch Bd:* Joseph C Papa
COO: Juan Guzman
**CFO:* John Kratochwil
CFO: Bill Miller
VP: Ofir Sova
Genl Mgr: Raj Thota
Sfty Mgr: Judy Riley
Ql Cn Mgr: Altin Leka
Mktg Mgr: James Booydegraaff

D-U-N-S 08-650-6987
PERRIN BERNARD SUPOWITZ INC
FERGADIS ENTERPRISES
5496 Lindbergh Ln, Bell, CA 90201-6409
Tel (323) 981-2800 *Founded/Ownrshp* 2009
Sales 108.0MM^E *EMP* 50
SIC 5141 Groceries, general line
Pr: Steve Supowitz
Genl Mgr: Chris Oyama
VP Sls: Steven Arroyo

D-U-N-S 96-867-6069
PERRY CHARLES PARTNERS INC
8200 Nw 15th Pl, Gainesville, FL 32606-5203
Tel (352) 333-9292 *Founded/Ownrshp* 2011
Sales 97.8MM *EMP* 112
Accts James Moore Daytona Beach Fl
SIC 1542 1541 Nonresidential construction; Industrial buildings & warehouses
Ch: Breck A Weingart
**CEO:* John V Carlson
**VP:* Brian K Leslie

D-U-N-S 04-402-9452 IMP
▲ **PERRY ELLIS INTERNATIONAL INC**
3000 Nw 107th Ave, Doral, FL 33172-2133
Tel (305) 592-2830 *Founded/Ownrshp* 1967
Sales 899.5MM *EMP* 2,700
Tkr Sym PERY *Exch* NGS
SIC 2321 2325 2339 2337 5611 5621 Men's & boys' furnishings; Men's & boys' dress shirts; Men's & boys' sports & polo shirts; Men's & boys' trousers & slacks; Men's & boys' dress slacks & shorts; Women's & misses' outerwear; Women's & misses' suits & coats; Men's & boys' clothing stores; Women's clothing stores
Pr: Oscar Feldenkreis
**Ch Bd:* George Feldenkreis
Pr: Denise Miller
COO: David Enright
COO: Bill Johnsen
CFO: Anita Britt
Treas: Fanny Hanono
Ofcr: Doug Jakubowski
Ex VP: Cory Shade
Sr VP: Joel Blumenthal
Sr VP: Rick Gatian
VP: Derek Carroll
VP: Claudia Cordic
VP: Sean Coyle
VP: Matthew Cronin
VP: Tom D'Ambrosio
VP: Jeannie Davila
VP: Douglas Jamieson
VP: May Martinez
VP: Randy Miller
VP: Neil Novellas
Board of Directors: Joe Arriola, Jane Deflorio, Bruce Klatsky, Michael W Rayden, J David Scheiner, Alexandra Wilson

D-U-N-S 18-712-9309
PERRY GREEN VALLEY NURSING HOME INC
1103 Birch St, Perry, OK 73077-6269
Tel (580) 336-2285 *Founded/Ownrshp* 1977
Sales 336.2MM *EMP* 74
SIC 8051 Skilled nursing care facilities
Pr: Gerald Dendeuh

D-U-N-S 61-319-4138
PERRY JOHNSON & ASSOCIATES INC
1489 W Warm Springs Rd, Henderson, NV 89014-7635
Tel (800) 803-6330 *Founded/Ownrshp* 1980
Sales 39.2MM^E *EMP* 5,000^E
SIC 7338 Secretarial & court reporting
CEO: Perry Johnson
**CEO:* Jeffrey R Hubbard

D-U-N-S 07-958-9008
PERRY TOWNSHIP SCHOOLS
6548 Orinoco Ave, Indianapolis, IN 46227-4820
Tel (317) 789-3700 *Founded/Ownrshp* 1959
Sales 101.3MM^E *EMP* 1,800
SIC 8211 Public elementary & secondary schools; Public junior high school; Public senior high school
**CFO:* Mike Bagley
Genl Mgr: John Bagley
MIS Dir: Matthew Willey
Teacher Pr: Rhonda Jones-Jointer

D-U-N-S 00-737-7898
PERRYTON EQUITY EXCHANGE (TX)
4219 S Main St, Perryton, TX 79070-9706
Tel (806) 435-4016 *Founded/Ownrshp* 1919
Sales 149.3MM *EMP* 110
Accts Campbell Shaffer & Company P
SIC 5153 5191 5541 Wheat; Corn; Barley; Farm supplies; Fertilizer & fertilizer materials; Filling stations, gasoline
Pr: Doug Mitchell
VP: Wade Alexander
VP: Neil Hays
**VP:* J D Latham
Brnch Mgr: Darren Patton
Genl Mgr: Shawn Hughes
Sls&Mrk Ex: Wes Beal

PERSECO COMPANY DIV
See HAVI GROUP LIMITED PARTNERSHIP

PERSEUS BOOKS GROUP
See CLP PB LLC

D-U-N-S 06-217-7543 IMP/EXP
PERSEUS DISTRIBUTION INC
(*Suby of* PERSEUS BOOKS GROUP) ★
210 American Dr, Jackson, TN 38301-5037
Tel (731) 988-4440 *Founded/Ownrshp* 2006
Sales 115.4MM^E *EMP* 250
SIC 5192 Books, periodicals & newspapers
CEO: David Steinberger
**Pr:* Chris Wagner
**VP:* Jo Ann Neergaard
Sfty Mgr: David Garland

D-U-N-S 78-041-3246
PERSEUS HOLDING CORP
8350 N Central Expy, Dallas, TX 75206-1600
Tel (214) 234-4000 *Founded/Ownrshp* 2006
Sales 309.1MM^E *EMP* 1,200
SIC 7374 Data processing & preparation
Pr: John F Davis III

D-U-N-S 08-115-7021
PERSEUS LLC
4350 East West Hwy # 202, Bethesda, MD 20814-4426
Tel (301) 652-3200 *Founded/Ownrshp* 1995
Sales 1.0MMM^E *EMP* 215
SIC 6799 Venture capital companies
Ch: Kenneth M Socha
CFO: Christopher Davis

D-U-N-S 11-645-6000
■ **PERSHING LLC**
(*Suby of* BNY MELLON) ★
95 Chrstopher Columbus Dr, Jersey City, NJ 07302-2995
Tel (201) 413-2078 *Founded/Ownrshp* 2003
Sales 11.0MM *EMP* 3,700
SIC 6211 Security brokers & dealers
CEO: Ronald Decicco
Pr: Gregory Allen
Pr: Lolita Delgado
Pr: Maureen Kunzler
Pr: Joseph Mattiello
Pr: Sabina Phillips
Pr: Jerry Santiago
Pr: Patrick Troy
Pr: Suzanne Turner
Pr: Edward Valentine
**COO:* Lisa Dolly
COO: Pat Mahon
Chf Inves: Don Robinson
Ofcr: James T Crowley
**Ofcr:* David Hopkins
Ofcr: Ramaswamy Nagappan
Ofcr: Caroline O'Connell
Ofcr: Caroline Oconnell
Ofcr: Claire Santaniello
Assoc VP: Anna Shuster
Ex VP: Prakash Jayaram

PERSONAL CARE APPLIANCES DIV
See CONAIR CORP

D-U-N-S 05-884-3277
PERSONAL SERVICE INSURANCE CO
2760 Airport Dr Ste 130, Columbus, OH 43219-2294
Tel (800) 282-9416 *Founded/Ownrshp* 2005
Sales NA *EMP* 380
SIC 6331 Property damage insurance; Fire, marine & casualty insurance & carriers; Automobile insurance
Pr: William Lockhorn

D-U-N-S 07-851-8347
PERSONAL TOUCH HOME CARE (NY)
PT HOME CARE
22215 Northern Blvd Fl 3, Bayside, NY 11361-3603
Tel (718) 468-4747 *Founded/Ownrshp* 1974
Sales 322.6MM^E *EMP* 15,000
SIC 8082 Home health care services
CEO: David N Slifkin
**Pr:* Felix Glaubach
CFO: Yitzy Hollander
**Treas:* Robert Marx
**VP:* Dr Trudy Balk
Off Mgr: Erika Ramirez
Off Mgr: Annette Rivera
Off Mgr: Joanne Zukerman
Dir IT: Jay Chatterpaul

D-U-N-S 86-902-6203
PERSONNEL SERVICES INC
2260 Palm Bch Lks 210, West Palm Beach, FL 33409-3411
Tel (561) 965-7070 *Founded/Ownrshp* 1994
Sales 17.7MM^E *EMP* 2,000^E
SIC 7363 Temporary help service
Pr: Jeffery Dowling
**VP:* Chris Dowling

PERTH AMBOY DIVISION
See RARITAN BAY MEDICAL CENTER A NEW JERSEY NONPROFIT CORP

D-U-N-S 07-979-9178
PERTH AMBOY PUBLIC SCHOOLS
178 Barracks St, Perth Amboy, NJ 08861-3402
Tel (732) 376-6200 *Founded/Ownrshp* 2015
Sales 18.6MM^E *EMP* 1,400^E
SIC 8211 Public elementary & secondary schools
Bd of Dir: Anthony Bermudez
Bd of Dir: Maria Garcia
Bd of Dir: William Ortiz
Pr Dir: Judy Rodriguez
Schl Brd P: Samuel Lebreault
HC Dir: Nephtaly Cardona

PES
See PERFORMANCE ENERGY SERVICES LLC

D-U-N-S 01-920-6908 IMP
PESCANOVA INC
PESCANOVA LADEX
(*Suby of* PESCANOVA SA)
1430 S Dixie Hwy Ste 303, Coral Gables, FL 33146-3159
Tel (305) 663-4380 *Founded/Ownrshp* 1997
Sales 90.0MM *EMP* 28
SIC 5142 Fish, frozen: packaged
Pr: Carlos Casals
Genl Couns: Lisa Landy
Board of Directors: Ignacio Pesquera, Rafael Prieto

PESCANOVA LADEX
See PESCANOVA INC

PESCO
See PROCESS EQUIPMENT & SERVICE CO INC

PET DAIRY
See LAND-O-SUN DAIRIES LLC

D-U-N-S 60-144-2106 IMP
PET FOOD EXPERTS INC
175 Main St, Pawtucket, RI 02860-4132
Tel (401) 721-5593 *Founded/Ownrshp* 1989
Sales 134.4MM^E *EMP* 200^E
SIC 5199 2047 General merchandise, non-durable; Dog & cat food
Pr: Michael G Baker
**CFO:* James Alden
CFO: Mikelle Gross
VP: Buddy Baker
Sls Mgr: Sarah Daniels

D-U-N-S 96-496-0553 IMP
PET PARTNERS INC
NORTH AMERICAN PET PRODUCTS
450 N Sheridan St, Corona, CA 92880-2020
Tel (951) 279-9888 *Founded/Ownrshp* 1995
Sales 188.5MM^E *EMP* 515
SIC 5199 Pet supplies
CEO: Keith Bonner
**Pr:* Ronald Bonner
**Treas:* Yvonne Thulemeyer

D-U-N-S 87-888-8866 IMP
PET SUPERMARKET INC
1100 International Pkwy # 200, Sunrise, FL 33323-2886
Tel (866) 434-1990 *Founded/Ownrshp* 1976
Sales 453.0MM^E *EMP* 2,000
SIC 5999 3999 5199 Pets; Pet supplies; Pets & pet supplies; Pet supplies; Pets & pet supplies
CEO: Charles E West Jr
**CEO:* Diane Holtz
Sr VP: Steve Feinberg
VP: Tania Artiles
VP: Christopher Stone
Rgnl Mgr: Stacy Annone
Dist Mgr: Christopher M Lunardi
Dist Mgr: Ryan Steiner
Dist Mgr: Mike Stuart
Store Mgr: Mitch Hughes
Opers Mgr: John Archangel

PET SUPPLIES PLUS
See USA SELLER CO LLC

PET SUPPLIES PLUS
See PSP STORES LLC

D-U-N-S 02-836-4727 IMP/EXP
PETCO ANIMAL SUPPLIES INC
(*Suby of* PETCO HOLDINGS INC LLC) ★
10850 Via Frontera, San Diego, CA 92127-1705
Tel (858) 453-7845 *Founded/Ownrshp* 2006
Sales 7.9MMM^E *EMP* 21,350
SIC 0752 5199 5999 Grooming services, pet & animal specialties; Pet supplies; Pet supplies
Ch Bd: James M Myers
**Pr:* Brad Weston
CEO: James Lampassi
COO: Bruce Hall
**CFO:* Michael M Nuzzo
Treas: David Carr
**Ofcr:* Charlie Piscitello
Sr VP: Bob Brann
Sr VP: Robert E Brann
Sr VP: Kelly Breitenbecher
Sr VP: John Carcasi
Sr VP: William Engen
Sr VP: Steve Lossing
Sr VP: Janet D Mitchell
Sr VP: Jodi Watson
**Sr VP:* John Zavada
**Sr VP:* Michael W Zuna
VP: Marc Brown
VP: Michael S Brown
VP: David A Carr
VP: Marc Corless

D-U-N-S 82-992-4625
PETCO ANIMAL SUPPLIES STORES INC
(*Suby of* PETCO ANIMAL SUPPLIES INC) ★
9125 Rehco Rd, San Diego, CA 92121-2270
Tel (858) 453-7845 *Founded/Ownrshp* 1991
Sales 3.1MMM^E *EMP* 17,900
SIC 5999 0752 5199 Pets & pet supplies; Pet food; Pet supplies; Tropical fish; Grooming services, pet & animal specialties; Pet supplies
CEO: James M Myers
**Pr:* Bruce C Hall
VP: Rebecca Frechette
VP: Kelly Gorman
VP: Neil Juliano
VP: Danielleporto Mohn
VP: Razia Richter
VP: Jeffrey Urry
VP: Kevin Whalen

Dir Risk M: Jerry Ferris
Dir Soc: Alex Deering

D-U-N-S 08-001-8280
PETCO HOLDINGS INC LLC
(*Suby of* CVC CAPITAL PARTNERS LIMITED)
10850 Via Frontera, San Diego, CA 92127-1705
Tel (858) 453-7845 *Founded/Ownrshp* 2012
Sales 7.9MMM[E] *EMP* 21,350[E]
SIC 5999 Pet food

D-U-N-S 79-608-1909
PETCO PETROLEUM CORP
108 E Ogden Ave Ste 100, Hinsdale, IL 60521-3874
Tel (630) 654-1740 *Founded/Ownrshp* 1988
Sales 135.9MM[E] *EMP* 235
SIC 1389 Oil field services
Pr: Jay D Bergman

D-U-N-S 00-386-0210
PETE LIEN & SONS INC
DAKOTA BLOCK CO
3401 Universal Dr, Rapid City, SD 57702-9360
Tel (605) 342-7224 *Founded/Ownrshp* 1944
Sales 142.7MM[E] *EMP* 400
Accts Mcgladrey & Pullen Llp Rapid
SIC 3273 3441 1422 3274 Ready-mixed concrete; Fabricated structural metal; Crushed & broken limestone; Hydrated lime; Quicklime
Ch Bd: Bruce H Lien
**Pr:* Peter C Lien
**CFO:* Suzanne Lien Gabrielson
**Treas:* Charles H Lien
**VP:* Pete Birrenkott
**VP:* Joel D De Vries
VP: Lynne Gish
VP: Scott Landguth
VP Admn: Mike Vidal
Off Mgr: Sam Brannan
Opers Mgr: Mike Greear

PETE STORE, THE
See PETERBILT OF KNOXVILLE INC

PETEDGE ADMINISTRATIVE SVCS
See PETEDGE MASSACHUSETTS BUSINESS TRUST

D-U-N-S 62-811-8353
PETEDGE INC
(*Suby of* PETEDGE ADMINISTRATIVE SVCS) ★
100 Cummings Ctr Ste 307b, Beverly, MA 01915-6107
Tel (978) 998-8100 *Founded/Ownrshp* 1973
Sales 118.0MM[E] *EMP* 199
SIC 5199 Pets & pet supplies
Pr: Andy Katz
**CFO:* Greg Drisco
**Sec:* Loeb Katz
Sls Mgr: Deborah Reddeck

D-U-N-S 01-966-7526 IMP
PETEDGE MASSACHUSETTS BUSINESS TRUST
PETEDGE ADMINISTRATIVE SVCS
100 Cummings Ctr Ste 307b, Beverly, MA 01915-6107
Tel (978) 998-8100 *Founded/Ownrshp* 2000
Sales 212.4MM[E] *EMP* 393
SIC 5199 Pet supplies
Creative D: John McGlynn

D-U-N-S 08-208-0136
PETER BRASSELER HOLDINGS LLC
BRASSELER USA DENTAL
1 Brasseler Blvd, Savannah, GA 31419-9576
Tel (912) 925-8525 *Founded/Ownrshp* 1989
Sales 93.6MM[E] *EMP* 420
SIC 5047 3841 3843 Dental equipment & supplies; Medical equipment & supplies; Surgical & medical instruments; Dental equipment
Dist Mgr: Jim Still
Genl Mgr: Bill Miller

D-U-N-S 07-072-9517 IMP/EXP
PETER KIEWIT SONS INC
3555 Farnam St Ste 1000, Omaha, NE 68131-3374
Tel (402) 342-2052 *Founded/Ownrshp* 1997
Sales 19.9MMM[E] *EMP* 14,700
Accts Kpmg Llp Omaha Nebraska
SIC 1611 1622 1711 1542 1629 1221 Highway & street construction; Bridge, tunnel & elevated highway; Plumbing, heating, air-conditioning contractors; Nonresidential construction; Dams, waterways, docks & other marine construction; Power plant construction; Waste water & sewage treatment plant construction; Railroad & subway construction; Surface mining, lignite
Pr: Bruce E Grewcock
**CFO:* Michael J Piechoski
Treas: Kevin Anderson
Bd of Dir: Arlan Darrington
Bd of Dir: George B Toll
**Ex VP:* Richard W Colf
Ex VP: Allan K Irwood
**Ex VP:* Douglas E Patterson
Sr VP: Robert Mattuci
**Sr VP:* Tobin A Schropp
VP: Don Baratta
VP: Larry Cantwell
VP: Lawrence J Cochran
VP: Jason Dedrickson
VP: Daniel Dubois
VP: Michael Geary
VP: Richard Lanoha
VP: Jake Macholtz
VP: Gerald Pfeffer
VP: Bob Taylor
Exec: Michele Duffy
Board of Directors: Thomas S Shelby, Scott L Cassels, Kenneth E Stinson, Richard Geary, Steven Hansen, Allan K Kirkwood, Michael R McCarthy, Christopher J Murphy, R Michael Phelps, Kirk R Samuelson, Walter Scott Jr

D-U-N-S 00-279-1374
PETER PAN BUS LINES INC (MA)
1776 Main St Ste 1, Springfield, MA 01103-1025
Tel (413) 781-2900 *Founded/Ownrshp* 1933
Sales 103.9MM[E] *EMP* 750
SIC 4131 Interstate bus line
CEO: Peter A Picknelly
**Treas:* Brian R Stefano
**VP:* Thomas Picknelly
Comm Man: Robert Schwartz

D-U-N-S 00-924-9533 IMP/EXP
PETER PAN SEAFOODS INC
(*Suby of* MARUHA CAPITAL INVESTMENT INC) ★
The Tenth Fl 2200 6th Ave, Seattle, WA 98121
Tel (206) 728-6000 *Founded/Ownrshp* 1979
Sales 200.0MM *EMP* 204[E]
SIC 2092 2091 Seafoods, fresh: prepared; Seafoods, frozen: prepared; Fish, fresh: prepared; Fish, frozen: prepared; Seafood products: packaged in cans, jars, etc.; Fish: packaged in cans, jars, etc.
Pr: Barry D Collier
**Treas:* Adrian Yonke
**VP:* Steven N Chartier
VP: Curt Koch
**VP:* Kirk J Koch
Off Mgr: Edward Schneider
Off Mgr: Char Stanley
**VP Prd:* Dale Schwarz Miller
Plnt Mgr: Tom Whiniham
Manager: John Daly
Sls Mgr: Dean Pugh

D-U-N-S 09-452-3669
PETER PIPER INC
PETER PIPER PIZZA
(*Suby of* CEC ENTERTAINMENT INC) ★
4745 N 7th St Ste 350, Phoenix, AZ 85014-3671
Tel (480) 609-6400 *Founded/Ownrshp* 2014
Sales 71.0MM[E] *EMP* 1,400
SIC 5812 7993 6794 Pizzeria, chain; Game machines; Franchises, selling or licensing
Pr: Charles Bruce
**Sr VP:* Richard Kerley
**VP:* Jason Greenwood
**VP:* Bill Toole

PETER PIPER PIZZA
See PETER PIPER INC

PETER PIPER PIZZA
See PIZZA PROPERTIES LTD

D-U-N-S 04-735-7918
PETERBILT OF KNOXVILLE INC
PETE STORE, THE
5218 Rutledge Pike, Knoxville, TN 37924-2753
Tel (800) 552-7779 *Founded/Ownrshp* 2001
Sales 327.2MM[E] *EMP* 2,000
SIC 5012 7538 Truck tractors; Trailers for trucks, new & used; Truck engine repair, except industrial
Pr: John C Arscott
**Genl Mgr:* Nate Frederick
Store Mgr: Al Monroe

PETERBILT OF SIOUX CITY
See SIOUX CITY TRUCK SALES INC

D-U-N-S 06-531-2787
PETERBILT OF SPRINGFIELD INC
3026 N Mulroy Rd, Strafford, MO 65757-7213
Tel (417) 865-5355 *Founded/Ownrshp* 1988
Sales 243.1MM[E] *EMP* 450
SIC 5511 5012 Trucks, tractors & trailers: new & used; Automobiles & other motor vehicles
Ch: Claire Larson
**Pr:* Glenn Larson
CFO: Mike Headley
**Treas:* Margaret Larson
Exec: Rodney Street
Genl Mgr: Evan Barnard
Genl Mgr: Skip Wendt
IT Man: Ismael Hernandez

D-U-N-S 07-475-3526
■ **PETERSBURG HOSPITAL CO LLC**
SOUTHSIDE REGIONAL MEDICAL CTR
(*Suby of* COMMUNITY HEALTH SYSTEMS INC) ★
200 Medical Park Blvd, Petersburg, VA 23805-9274
Tel (804) 765-5000 *Founded/Ownrshp* 2003
Sales 217.5MM *EMP* 1,400
SIC 8062 General medical & surgical hospitals
CEO: David Fikse
**CFO:* Steve Embree
Dir Risk M: Kimberly Overton

D-U-N-S 02-386-9936
PETERSBURG MOTOR CO INC
CARTER MYERS AUTOMOTIVE
100 Myers Dr, Charlottesville, VA 22901-1166
Tel (434) 951-1000 *Founded/Ownrshp* 1971
Sales 335.1MM *EMP* 388
Accts Mitchell Wiggins & Company L
SIC 5511 7515 Automobiles, new & used; Passenger car leasing
Pr: Elizabeth M Borches
**VP:* Peter Borches

D-U-N-S 03-055-3465
PETERSEN HEALTH CARE INC
830 W Trailcreek Dr, Peoria, IL 61614-1862
Tel (309) 691-8113 *Founded/Ownrshp* 2002
Sales 161.3MM[E] *EMP* 4,500
Accts Ginoli & Company Ltd Peoria
SIC 8059 Rest home, with health care
Pr: Mark B Petersen
CFO: Larry Templin
Off Mgr: Patty Goetten
Off Mgr: Sharon Vitacco
MIS Dir: Tim Workheiser
Mktg Dir: Lindsey Bright
Nrsg Dir: Karlie Hasselbring

D-U-N-S 09-931-3462 IMP/EXP
PETERSEN INC
1527 N 2000 W, Ogden, UT 84404-9687
Tel (801) 731-1366 *Founded/Ownrshp* 1961
Sales 296.6MM[E] *EMP* 452
Accts Steve Johnstun & Associates Cp
SIC 5084 3441 7692 3444 Robots, industrial; Fabricated structural metal; Welding repair; Sheet metalwork
CEO: Mark Jenkins
CFO: Ted Jhonstun
**CFO:* Casey Jones
**VP:* Rob Despain
**VP:* Stephen Grange
Exec: Bob Despain
IT Man: Jake Schumers
Opers Mgr: Kyle Ross
Ql Cn Mgr: Kirk Douglass
Ql Cn Mgr: Jeff Hodgson
Ql Cn Mgr: Blaine Maez

D-U-N-S 60-995-7162
PETERSEN-DEAN INC
PETERSENDEAN
39300 Civic Center Dr # 300, Fremont, CA 94538-2337
Tel (707) 469-7470 *Founded/Ownrshp* 1984
Sales 376.9MM[E] *EMP* 1,100
SIC 1761 Roofing contractor
CEO: James P Petersen
**CFO:* Richard W Lange
**CFO:* David Van Beek
**VP:* Joseph Dean
Div Mgr: Chad Pricolo

PETERSENDEAN
See PETERSEN-DEAN INC

D-U-N-S 05-467-4361 IMP
PETERSON AMERICAN CORP (MI)
PETERSON SPRNG-TECHNICAL PRODS
21200 Telegraph Rd, Southfield, MI 48033-4243
Tel (248) 799-5400 *Founded/Ownrshp* 1932
Sales 198.4MM[E] *EMP* 800
SIC 3495 Wire springs
**Ch Bd:* Alfred H Peterson III
**CFO:* Tim Masserant
Sr VP: Lowe Done
**Sr VP:* Don Lowe
**VP:* Ron Check
**VP:* Craig Gray
**VP:* Mike Kohout
**VP:* Les Smith
Mng Dir: Todd Peterson
Plnt Mgr: Jack Sims
Ql Cn Mgr: Tammy Hoehn

PETERSON CAT
See PETERSON MACHINERY CO

PETERSON CAT
See PETERSON HOLDING CO

PETERSON CHEESE COMPANY
See FLOYD PETERSON CO

D-U-N-S 88-423-5326
PETERSON COMPANIES L C
PETERSON MANAGEMENT
12500 Fair Lakes Cir # 400, Fairfax, VA 22033-3804
Tel (703) 631-7570 *Founded/Ownrshp* 1970
Sales 118.9MM[E] *EMP* 165[E]
SIC 6552 Subdividers & developers
Pr: Taylor Chess
**Ch Bd:* Milton V Peterson
COO: William E Ptrson
**COO:* James J Vecchiarelli
**CFO:* Claudia Sensi
VP: Alan Gault
VP: Jason Gruber
VP: Howard Jensen
VP: Jim Mertz
VP: William Peterson
Exec: Vivinia Villavicencio
Dir Risk M: Van Gloss

PETERSON CONCRETE
See JAMES PETERSON SONS INC

D-U-N-S 00-480-6998
PETERSON CONSTRUCTION CO
18817 State Route 501, Wapakoneta, OH 45895-9392
Tel (419) 941-2233 *Founded/Ownrshp* 2000
Sales 83.9MM[E] *EMP* 150
SIC 1542 1629 Commercial & office building, new construction; Institutional building construction; School building construction; Waste water & sewage treatment plant construction
Pr: Donald J Bergfeld
**VP:* Douglas J Crusey

D-U-N-S 04-110-1809 IMP
PETERSON CONTRACTORS INC
104 Blackhawk St, Reinbeck, IA 50669-1012
Tel (319) 345-2713 *Founded/Ownrshp* 1963
Sales 190.2MM *EMP* 400
Accts Amling & Pruisner Cpas Cedar
SIC 1611 General contractor, highway & street construction
Pr: Cordell Q Peterson

D-U-N-S 16-130-3086 IMP/EXP
PETERSON FARMS INC
3104 W Baseline Rd, Shelby, MI 49455-9633
Tel (231) 861-6333 *Founded/Ownrshp* 1984
Sales 152.6MM[E] *EMP* 400
SIC 2037 0723 Fruits, quick frozen & cold pack (frozen); Fruit (fresh) packing services
CEO: Aaron L Peterson
**Ch Bd:* Earl L Peterson
Pr: Lorraine Odle Dp
COO: Todd Simmons
**Sec:* Linda A Peterson
Ex VP: Kerry Kinyon
**VP:* Sarah M Peterson-Schlkebir
Off Mgr: Kyle Benkert
Dir IT: Clark Williams
IT Man: Brian Glerum
VP Opers: Richard Raffaelli

D-U-N-S 83-298-0960
PETERSON HOLDING CO
PETERSON CAT
955 Marina Blvd, San Leandro, CA 94577-3440
Tel (510) 357-6200 *Founded/Ownrshp* 1977
Sales 391.9MM[E] *EMP* 11[E]
SIC 5082 Construction & mining machinery
CEO: Duane S Doyle
CFO: Mark Macguidwin
Exec: Rich Hasper
Dir IT: Bill Nicholson

D-U-N-S 62-485-9232
PETERSON MACHINERY CO
PETERSON CAT
955 Marina Blvd, San Leandro, CA 94577-3440
Tel (541) 302-9199 *Founded/Ownrshp* 2006
Sales 74.5MM[E] *EMP* 1,200
SIC 7629 Electrical repair shops
CEO: Duane S Doyle
CFO: Keith Davidge
VP: Ernie Fierro
Genl Mgr: Bill Bean
Dir IT: Bill Nicholson
VP Mktg: Tom Bagwell

PETERSON MANAGEMENT
See PETERSON COMPANIES L C

D-U-N-S 00-714-6095 IMP/EXP
PETERSON MANUFACTURING CO (MO)
4200 E 135th St, Grandview, MO 64030-2896
Tel (816) 765-2000 *Founded/Ownrshp* 1955
Sales 449.7MM[E] *EMP* 3,100
SIC 3647 4111 3089 3714

PETERSON MILANEY INSUR ASSOC
See HUB INTERNATIONAL INSURANCE SERVICES INC

D-U-N-S 10-295-3700
PETERSON POWER SYSTEMS INC
(*Suby of* PETERSON CAT) ★
2828 Teagarden St, San Leandro, CA 94577-5717
Tel (510) 618-2921 *Founded/Ownrshp* 1983
Sales 195.5MM[E] *EMP* 250
SIC 5084 7353 Engines, gasoline; Heavy construction equipment rental
CEO: Duane Doyle Sr
Pr: Jeff Goggin
CFO: Mark Macguidwin
VP: Rick Ferguson
VP: John Krumman
VP: Randy Richter
Exec: Hal Sommers
Genl Mgr: Robert Klapperich
Telecom Ex: Monica Simsek
Trfc Dir: Nancy Elkins
Mktg Mgr: Thomas Bagwell

PETERSON REGIONAL MEDICAL CTR
See PETERSON SID MEMORIAL HOSPITAL

D-U-N-S 07-460-8977
PETERSON SID MEMORIAL HOSPITAL
PETERSON REGIONAL MEDICAL CTR
551 Hill Country Dr, Kerrville, TX 78028-6085
Tel (830) 896-4200 *Founded/Ownrshp* 1949
Sales 118.5MM *EMP* 796
SIC 8051 8062 Skilled nursing care facilities; General medical & surgical hospitals
CEO: Patrick Murray
Chf Path: Michael Jackson
**Pr:* Thomas H Murray Jr
CFO: Julie Johnson
**CFO:* Robert H Walther
VP: V E Merritt Jr
Dir Lab: Deborah Zink
Dir Rx: Sonny Baker
Dir Sec: Paul Gonzales
Off Mgr: Rhonda Dieringer
Nurse Mgr: Joellen Klohn

PETERSON SPRNG-TECHNICAL PRODS
See PETERSON AMERICAN CORP

D-U-N-S 08-013-8480 IMP
PETERSON TRACTOR CO (CA)
(*Suby of* PETERSON CAT) ★
955 Marina Blvd, San Leandro, CA 94577-3400
Tel (530) 343-1911 *Founded/Ownrshp* 1936, 1977
Sales 121.7MM[E] *EMP* 11[E]
SIC 5082 5084 5083 Tractors, construction; Logging equipment & supplies; Industrial machinery & equipment; Engines & parts, diesel; Tractors, agricultural
CEO: Duane S Doyle
Pr: Mark Ehni
**Pr:* Jerry Lopus
CFO: Walter Perry
Ex VP: Buster Peterson
VP: John Krummen
Exec: Joyce McCaffery
Comm Man: Eileen Grafton
IT Man: Julie Cunha
Mktg Dir: Shannon Thomas
Sls Mgr: Jim Lanphear

PETES FRESH MARKET
See PETES FRESH MARKET 4700 CORP

D-U-N-S 06-995-1432
PETES FRESH MARKET 4700 CORP
PETES FRESH MARKET
4333 S Pulaski Rd, Chicago, IL 60632-4008
Tel (773) 927-4300 *Founded/Ownrshp* 1970
Sales 104.1MM[E] *EMP* 130[E]
SIC 5148 5431 Fresh fruits & vegetables; Fruit & vegetable markets
Pr: James Dremonas
Exec: Charles Poulakis
Off Mgr: James Sakelaris

D-U-N-S 01-241-6368
PETLAND DISCOUNTS INC
355 Crooked Hill Rd, Brentwood, NY 11717-1034
Tel (631) 273-6363 *Founded/Ownrshp* 1965
Sales 139.6MM[E] *EMP* 850
SIC 5999 Pets & pet supplies
Ch Bd: Neil Padron
**Ex VP:* Rose Consigilio
**VP:* Patricia Rose

PETMAR BUILDERS DIVISION
See YONKERS CONTRACTING CO INC

PETMATE
See DOSKOCIL MANUFACTURING CO INC

D-U-N-S 07-877-2099
PETMATE HOLDINGS CO
2300 E Randol Mill Rd, Arlington, TX 76011-6333
Tel (817) 467-5116 *Founded/Ownrshp* 2010
Sales 149.2MM[E] *EMP* 667[E]

SIC 3999 5999 Pet supplies; Pet supplies
CEO: Larry Rembold

D-U-N-S 94-653-9525 EXP
▲ PETMED EXPRESS INC
1-800-PETMEDS
1441 Sw 29th Ave, Pompano Beach, FL 33069-4820
Tel (954) 979-5995 Founded/Ownrshp 1996
Sales 234.6MM EMP 178
Tkr Sym PETS Exch NGS
SIC 5999 5122 Pet food; Pet supplies; Animal medicines
Pr: Menderes Akdag
*Ch Bd: Robert C Schweitzer
CFO: Bruce S Rosenbloom
Board of Directors: Frank J Formica, Gian M Fulgoni, Ronald J Korn

D-U-N-S 09-990-2728
PETR-ALL PETROLEUM CONSULTING CORP
EXPRESS MART
7401 Round Pond Rd, Syracuse, NY 13212-2515
Tel (315) 446-0125 Founded/Ownrshp 1975
Sales 390.2MM EMP 600
Accts Dermody Burke Brown Syracuse
SIC 5172 5411 Gasoline; Convenience stores, independent
CEO: Francis E Borer
*CFO: Daniel Twombly
VP: Mark Maher
Dir IT: Timothy Gorman
IT Man: Tim Garman

D-U-N-S 14-826-5713 IMP
PETRA INDUSTRIES LLC
2101 S Kelly Ave, Edmond, OK 73013-3665
Tel (405) 216-2100 Founded/Ownrshp 1985
Sales 162.3MM^E EMP 310
SIC 5065

PETRA SOLAR
See PETRA SYSTEMS INC

D-U-N-S 94-399-3225
PETRA SYSTEMS INC
PETRA SOLAR
1 Cragwood Rd Ste 303, South Plainfield, NJ 07080-2416
Tel (908) 462-5200 Founded/Ownrshp 2007
Sales 109.0MM^E EMP 116
SIC 5074 3671 Heating equipment & panels, solar; Light sensing & emitting tubes
CEO: Shihab Kuran
Pr: Imran A Bhutta
*COO: Dan Brdar
Sr VP: Dan Davis
*VP: Imran Bhutta
*VP: Mary Grikas
VP: Hisham Othman
VP: Tony Pawelec
*VP: John E Warren III
Sls Dir: Joe Polaski
Snr Mgr: Phil Ryser

PETRALEX
See PETRALEX USA INC

D-U-N-S 09-126-3876 IMP/EXP
PETRALEX USA INC
PETRALEX
(Suby of PETRALEX S DE RL)
4740 Coml Pk Ct Ste 2, Clemmons, NC 27012
Tel (336) 778-1049 Founded/Ownrshp 1999
Sales 145.0MM^E EMP 750
SIC 2396 Apparel & other linings, except millinery
Pr: C J Sadosky

PETREY W L WHOLESALE CO
See W L PETREY WHOLESALE CO INC

D-U-N-S 06-682-0242
PETRICCA INDUSTRIES INC
UNISTRESS
550 Cheshire Rd, Pittsfield, MA 01201-1823
Tel (413) 499-1441 Founded/Ownrshp 1973
Sales 146.0MM^E EMP 491
SIC 1611 1623 3273 3272 1442 General contractor, highway & street construction; Sewer line construction; Pipeline construction; Ready-mixed concrete; Prestressed concrete products; Construction sand & gravel
Ch Bd: Basil A Petricca
CFO: Thomas A Groff
Ex VP: Perri C Petricca
Ex VP: Robert Petricca
VP: Michael Macdondald
Exec: Pete Libardi
Sls Mgr: Terry Seymour
Snr PM: Bruce Miller
Snr Mgr: Darryl Lamoureaux

D-U-N-S 07-506-7918
PETRIN CORP
1405 Commercial Dr, Port Allen, LA 70767-3229
Tel (225) 343-0471 Founded/Ownrshp 1995
Sales 108.5MM^E EMP 670^E
SIC 1799 2952 Insulation of pipes & boilers; Asbestos removal & encapsulation; Asphalt felts & coatings
VP: John K Freeman
Pr: Roger Greer
*Pr: James N Hall
Treas: Robert Rosenthal
Exec: Patrick Wasiloski
Div Mgr: Chad Ronkartz
*Genl Mgr: J Kenneth Freeman

D-U-N-S 00-691-8353
■ PETRO INC (DE)
STAR GAS
(Suby of STAR GAS PARTNERS LP) ★
9 W Broad St Ste 3, Stamford, CT 06902-3734
Tel (203) 325-5400 Founded/Ownrshp 1900, 1983
Sales 112.9MM^E EMP 600
SIC 5983 7699 Fuel oil dealers; Boiler & heating repair services
Pr: Daniel P Donovan
*CFO: Richard F Ambury
Treas: George Leibowitz
Sr VP: Richard Zaweski
*VP: Richard G Oakley
Exec: Joseph Cavanaugh
CTO: Gael Doar
Dir IT: Dave Harwood
Dir IT: Rafay Seyal
IT Man: Brian Boschert
Sls Dir: Chris Stavac

PETRO STOPPING CENTER
See TA OPERATING LLC

D-U-N-S 16-234-3391
PETRO VM INC
2188 Kirby Ln, Syosset, NY 11791-9614
Tel (516) 921-7190 Founded/Ownrshp 2004
Sales 185.4MM EMP 2
Accts Kamlesh Shah Cpa Hicksville
SIC 5172 Gasoline
CEO: Manoj Narang

D-U-N-S 10-311-3684 EXP
PETRO-DIAMOND INC
1100 Main St Fl 2, Irvine, CA 92614-6714
Tel (949) 553-0112 Founded/Ownrshp 1983
Sales 92.4MM^E EMP 30^E
SIC 5172 Petroleum products; Crude oil
Pr: Andrew Hausing
*CFO: Robert A Semm
*Treas: Kathy Heaton
MIS Mgr: Reed Wilson
Mktg Mgr: C M McMonigle
Mktg Mgr: Chelsea Pascu

D-U-N-S 07-445-0664
PETRO-HUNT LLC
(Suby of WILLIAM HERBERT HUNT TRUST ESTATE) ★
2101 Cedar Springs Rd, Dallas, TX 75201-2104
Tel (214) 880-8400 Founded/Ownrshp 1998
Sales 5.0MMM^E EMP 202
SIC 1311 Crude petroleum production; Natural gas production
Pr: Bruce W Hunt
*VP: Alan Bain
VP: Bobby Donohue
*VP: Robert M Donohue Jr
*VP: Thomas E Nelson
VP: Thomas Nelson
*VP: Charles Rigdon
Dir Bus: Bryant Winn
Opers Mgr: Steve Chisler
Genl Couns: Fred Hosey

D-U-N-S 36-370-2457 IMP/EXP
PETROBRAS AMERICA INC
(Suby of PETROLEO BRASILEIRO S/A. - PETROBRAS.)
10350 Richmond Ave, Houston, TX 77042-4129
Tel (713) 808-2000 Founded/Ownrshp 1987
Sales 3.8MMM^E EMP 450
SIC 5172 1382 2911

D-U-N-S 15-463-1865
PETROCARD INC
(Suby of BBNC) ★
730 Central Ave S, Kent, WA 98032-6109
Tel (253) 852-7801 Founded/Ownrshp 1987
Sales 1.1MMM EMP 190
SIC 5172 Service station supplies, petroleum
CEO: David Harris
COO: Patrick Emerick
*COO: Scott Walters
*Ch: Joseph Chythlook
*Treas: Andrew Rewolinski
*VP: Lanny Michael
CIO: Roger Hall

D-U-N-S 07-395-3119
PETROCHEM INSULATION INC
(Suby of ASRC ENERGY SERVICES LLC) ★
110 Corporate Pl, Vallejo, CA 94590-6968
Tel (707) 644-7455 Founded/Ownrshp 1974
Sales 144.2MM^E EMP 1,100
SIC 1742 1799

D-U-N-S 06-199-4122
PETROCHOICE HOLDINGS INC
(Suby of GREENBRIAR EQUITY GROUP LLC) ★
1300 Virginia Dr Ste 405, Fort Washington, PA 19034-3221
Tel (267) 705-2015 Founded/Ownrshp 2007
Sales 147.0MM^E EMP 548^E
SIC 5172 Lubricating oils & greases
CEO: Shane O'Kelly
VP: Scot Milroy
Manager: Cindy Spence

D-U-N-S 03-799-3394
PETROCHOICE LLC
18385 Route 287, Tioga, PA 16946-8511
Tel (570) 835-5858 Founded/Ownrshp 1969
Sales 377.0MM^E EMP 305
SIC 5172 Petroleum products
Pr: Robert Black
VP: Scot Milroy

D-U-N-S 14-123-5148
PETROENERGY LLC
920 10th Ave N, Onalaska, WI 54650-2166
Tel (608) 783-6411 Founded/Ownrshp 2006
Sales 176.2MM^E EMP 100^E
SIC 5171 4925 5172 Petroleum bulk stations & terminals; Mixed natural & manufactured gas, distribution; Diesel fuel

D-U-N-S 04-527-1561
PETROHAWK ENERGY CORP
(Suby of BHP BLLITON PETRO AMERICAS INC) ★
1360 Post Oak Blvd # 150, Houston, TX 77056-3030
Tel (713) 961-8500 Founded/Ownrshp 2011
Sales 862.2MM^E EMP 598
SIC 1311 Crude petroleum & natural gas
Pr: Timothy Cutt
*VP: David Powell
*VP: Jeffrey Lee Sahlberg
*VP: John Allen Simmons
*VP: Rodney Mark Skaufel

PETROL-MART
See WESTERN OIL INC

D-U-N-S 15-170-5522 IMP
PETROLEUM GEO-SERVICES INC
PGS AMERICAS
(Suby of PETROLEUM GEO-SERVICES ASA)
15375 Memorial Dr Ste 100, Houston, TX 77079-4138
Tel (281) 509-8000 Founded/Ownrshp 1995
Sales 879.7MM^E EMP 5,000
SIC 3827 8713 1382 Optical instruments & lenses; Surveying services; Oil & gas exploration services; Geophysical exploration, oil & gas field
Pr: Jon Erik Reinhardsen
Pr: Rune Eng
*CFO: Gottfred Langseth
*Ex VP: Guillaume Cambois
*Ex VP: Per Arild Reksnes
Ex VP: Aker Kva Rner
*Ex VP: Sverre Strandenes
Sr VP: Dick Mackewn
IT Man: Bud Moline
Board of Directors: Jens Ulltveit-Moe Chmn, Gerhard Heiberg, Marianne Johnsen, Reidar Michaelsen, Rolf Erik Rolfsen, Endre Ording Sund

D-U-N-S 11-837-7951
■ PETROLEUM HEAT AND POWER CO INC
(Suby of STAR GAS PARTNERS LP) ★
9 W Broad St Ste 3, Stamford, CT 06902-3734
Tel (800) 645-4328 Founded/Ownrshp 1999
Sales 624.4M^E EMP 2,226
SIC 5983 5172 5722 Fuel oil dealers; Petroleum products; Fuel oil; Kerosene; Gasoline; Gas household appliances
Pr: Daniel P Donovan
*Pr: Steve Goldman
*CFO: Richard F Ambury
CFO: Richard Ambury
*VP: Richard G Oakley
Genl Mgr: Eva Gladson
VP Sls: Joseph McDonald
Snr Mgr: Jennifer Scott

D-U-N-S 00-313-9144
■ PETROLEUM MARKETERS INC (VA)
FUEL OILS
(Suby of PINEHURST PETROLEUM, LLC)
645 Hamilton St Ste 500, Allentown, PA 18101-2193
Tel (540) 772-4900 Founded/Ownrshp 1950
Sales 252.1MM^E EMP 1,500
SIC 5983 5411 Fuel oil dealers; Convenience stores
Pr: Ronald R Hare
*CFO: Annette Willis
*Treas: Kathy Draper
VP: John Newton
IT Man: Nathan Sutrell
MIS Mgr: Kim Lorden

PETROLEUM PL ENRGY SOLUTIONS
See PETROLEUM PLACE INC

D-U-N-S 11-347-9047
PETROLEUM PLACE INC
PETROLEUM PL ENRGY SOLUTIONS
(Suby of P2 NEWCO INC) ★
1670 Broadway Ste 2800, Denver, CO 80202-4800
Tel (303) 515-5400 Founded/Ownrshp 2007
Sales 488.6MM^E EMP 350
SIC 4813 7371 ; Computer software development
CEO: Charles Goodman
Sr VP: Dan Sodersten
*VP: Kenneth R Olive Jr
Mktg Dir: Mark Levonyak

PETROLEUM PRODUCTS INC.
See PETROLEUM PRODUCTS LLC

D-U-N-S 01-600-7023
PETROLEUM PRODUCTS LLC (WV)
PETROLEUM PRODUCTS INC.
(Suby of PILOT FOODMART) ★
500 River East Dr Ste 1, Belle, WV 25015-1081
Tel (304) 204-1720 Founded/Ownrshp 1938
Sales 108.0MM^E EMP 75
SIC 5171 Petroleum bulk stations
Pr: Patrick C Graney III
VP: Gouverneur Graney
CTO: Shawna Whanger

D-U-N-S 02-164-0487
PETROLEUM TRADERS CORP
7120 Pointe Inverness Way, Fort Wayne, IN 46804-7928
Tel (260) 432-6622 Founded/Ownrshp 1979
Sales 1.6MMM EMP 150
Accts Baden Gage & Schroeder Llc F
SIC 5172 Petroleum brokers
Pr: Michael Himes
*CFO: Linda Stephens
Ofcr: Ryan Macabasco
VP: Vicky Himes
Netwrk Mgr: Dan Espich
Trfc Dir: Jeff Fearnow
Opers Mgr: Joe Jurczak

D-U-N-S 05-907-1084
PETROLEUM WHOLESALE LP
SUNMART TRAVEL CENTERS & CONV
8550 Technology Forest Pl, The Woodlands, TX 77381-1174
Tel (281) 681-7500 Founded/Ownrshp 1971
Sales 568.5MM^E EMP 1,000
SIC 5172 5541 Petroleum products; Gasoline service stations
Pr: John William Cook
CFO: Ryan Edone
VP: Richard Osburn
Dir IT: Brent Gordon
Mktg Dir: Dan Miller
Sls Mgr: Martin Christensen
Sls Mgr: Denise Thompson

D-U-N-S 78-471-6933
PETROLIANCE LLC
(Suby of PETROCHOICE LLC) ★
1009 Schieffelin Rd, Apex, NC 27502-1777
Tel (919) 387-9810 Founded/Ownrshp 2014
Sales 275.2MM^E EMP 206
SIC 5171 Petroleum bulk stations
CEO: Kevin McCarter
Pr: Ken Johnson
CFO: Jeff Krizic
Manager: Dana Griffith
Manager: Mark Isgette

D-U-N-S 00-628-7163
■ PETROLITE CORP (DE)
(Suby of BAKER HUGHES INC) ★
369 Marshall Ave, Saint Louis, MO 63119-1831
Tel (314) 961-3500 Founded/Ownrshp 1997
Sales 108.1MM^E EMP 1,748^E
SIC 3559 2999 2899 2821 2911 Desalination equipment; Separation equipment, magnetic; Waxes, petroleum: not produced in petroleum refineries; Corrosion preventive lubricant; Antiscaling compounds, boiler; Oil treating compounds; Water treating compounds; Plasticizer/additive based plastic materials; Fuel additives
Pr: Paul Hatfield

D-U-N-S 18-682-2540
PETROMARK INC
WHITE OAK STATION
308 W Industrial Park Rd, Harrison, AR 72601-6803
Tel (870) 741-3560 Founded/Ownrshp 1972
Sales 370.0MM EMP 320
SIC 5541 Filling stations, gasoline
Pr: Steven Lair
*CFO: Gale Davis

D-U-N-S 03-732-5946 IMP/EXP
▲ PETROQUEST ENERGY INC
400 E Kaliste Saloom Rd # 6000, Lafayette, LA 70508-8523
Tel (337) 232-7028 Founded/Ownrshp 1983
Sales 115.9MM EMP 119^E
Tkr Sym PQ Exch NYS
SIC 1311 Crude petroleum & natural gas production
Ch Bd: Charles T Goodson
CFO: J Bond Clement
Ex VP: Edward E Abels Jr
Ex VP: Arthur M Mixon III
Ex VP: Tracy Price
VP: Edgar Anderson
VP: Art Mixon
Opers Mgr: Jonathan Sprague
Board of Directors: W J Gordon III, Charles F Mitchell II, E Wayne Nordberg, William W Rucks IV

D-U-N-S 79-608-2923
PETROSANTANDER (COLOMBIA) INC
(Suby of PETROSANTANDER COLOMBIA) ★
6363 Woodway Dr Ste 350, Houston, TX 77057-1798
Tel (713) 784-8700 Founded/Ownrshp 1995
Sales 132.0MM EMP 190
SIC 1311 1382 Crude petroleum production; Natural gas production; Oil & gas exploration services
Pr: Christopher Whyte
*CFO: Victor Low
*Ex VP: Ian Gollop
Board of Directors: Trevor Carmichael, Victor Low, Christopher Whyte

PETROSANTANDER COLOMBIA
See PETROSANTANDER INC

D-U-N-S 83-588-7977 IMP
PETROSANTANDER INC
PETROSANTANDER COLOMBIA
6363 Woodway Dr Ste 350, Houston, TX 77057-1798
Tel (713) 784-8700 Founded/Ownrshp 1995
Sales 171.9MM EMP 750
Accts Pricewaterhousecoopers Llp Ho
SIC 1311 Crude petroleum production
CEO: Christopher Whyte
Treas: Oliver Alvaro
*Ex VP: Ian Gollop
*VP: Troy Finney
*VP: Jeremy Mathalone

D-U-N-S 10-820-9586
PETROSMITH EQUIPMENT LP
SMITH PIPE OF ABILENE
7435 Us Highway 277 S, Abilene, TX 79606-6103
Tel (325) 691-1085 Founded/Ownrshp 1983
Sales 181.6MM^E EMP 400
SIC 5084 7353 Oil well machinery, equipment & supplies; Oil well drilling equipment, rental or leasing
Pr: Cliff Smith
CFO: Robert Cockrell
CFO: George Persival
Ex VP: Matt Smith
Exec: Jim Mayfield
Sls Mgr: Lee Harris

PETSAFE
See RADIO SYSTEMS CORP

D-U-N-S 17-380-8684 IMP/EXP
PETSMART INC
(Suby of ARGOS HOLDINGS INC) ★
19601 N 27th Ave, Phoenix, AZ 85027-4010
Tel (623) 580-6100 Founded/Ownrshp 2015
Sales 12.7MMM^E EMP 53,000
SIC 5999 0742 0752 Pet supplies; Pets; Tropical fish; Veterinarian, animal specialties; Animal specialty services
Pr: Michael J Massey
CFO: Rob Anderson
CFO: Carrie W Teffner
CFO: Noel Watanabe
Chf Mktg O: Eran Cohen
Ex VP: Matt McAdam
Ex VP: Bruce K Thorn
Sr VP: John Alpaugh
Sr VP: Donald E Beaver
Sr VP: Paulette R Dodson
Sr VP: Michael Goodwin
Sr VP: Michael W Goodwin
Sr VP: Donald J Lyons
VP: Brian Amkraut
VP: Pete Jorgenson
VP: Jim Morris
VP: Brian Murphy
Exec: Marco Furforo
Exec: Glenn Smith

Board of Directors: Paulette R Dodson, Michael J Massey

D-U-N-S 01-336-4991
PETTERS AVIATION LLC
431 S 7th St Ste 2530, Minneapolis, MN 55415-1855
Tel (612) 238-7780 *Founded/Ownrshp* 2006
Sales 43.1MM^E *EMP* 3,000^E
SIC 4581 Aircraft maintenance & repair services
Pr: Jay Salmen
VP: Susan Geitzenauer

D-U-N-S 17-625-7558 IMP/EXP
PETTIBONE LLC
AN AFFLIATE OF HEICO COMPANIES
(*Suby of* HEICO HOLDING INC) ★
27501 Bella Vista Pkwy, Warrenville, IL 60555-1609
Tel (630) 353-5000 *Founded/Ownrshp* 1979
Sales 317.4MM^E *EMP* 2,300
SIC 6719 Investment holding companies, except banks
Ch Bd: Michael E Heisley Sr
**Pr:* El Roskovensky
CFO: Kevin Shudy
**VP:* Douglas J Johnson

D-U-N-S 16-034-4599
PEW CHARITABLE TRUSTS
2005 Market St Fl 28, Philadelphia, PA 19103-7019
Tel (215) 575-9050 *Founded/Ownrshp* 2002
Sales 874.7MM *EMP* 500^E
Accts Grant Thornton Llp Philadelph
SIC 8732 6732 Commercial nonphysical research; Charitable trust management
Pr: Rebecca W Rimel
CFO: Gina Burkett
Sr Cor Off: Renee Arnold
Sr Cor Off: Cindy L Jobbins
Sr Cor Off: Elizabeth Kromm
Sr Cor Off: Morgan Shaw
Sr Cor Off: Peter Whinn
Bd of Dir: Patricia Bonney
Ofcr: Stephanie Bosh
Ofcr: Joan Casper
Ofcr: Jessica Hallstrom
Ofcr: REA Holmes
Ofcr: Jen Knutzen
Ofcr: Sarah Leiseca
Ofcr: Elizabeth Lowe
Ofcr: Jessica Lubetsky
Ofcr: Seemin Pasha
Ofcr: Anne Sorensen
Ex VP: Usha Chaudhary
VP: Diana Deane
VP: Andrew Fulton

D-U-N-S 02-219-2566 IMP
PEXCO LLC
(*Suby of* ODYSSEY INVESTMENT PARTNERS LLC) ★
2500 Northwinds Pkwy # 472, Alpharetta, GA 30009-2249
Tel (404) 564-8560 *Founded/Ownrshp* 2012
Sales 391.2MM^E *EMP* 920
SIC 3089 Plastic hardware & building products
CEO: Neil Shillingford
**COO:* Sam Patel
Div Pres: Mauricio Arellano
VP: Dan Bardgett
IT Man: Kevin Forsyth
Sls Mgr: Cheryl Trojanowski

PEXCO PRODUCE SALES
See PRODUCE EXCHANGE CO INC

D-U-N-S 00-556-9728 IMP
PEZ CANDY INC (NY)
(*Suby of* PEZ AG)
35 Prindle Hill Rd, Orange, CT 06477-3616
Tel (203) 795-0531 *Founded/Ownrshp* 1953
Sales 91.0MM^E *EMP* 152
SIC 5145 Candy
CEO: Joseph Vittoria
**CFO:* Brian Fry
IT Man: Brandon Maciag
VP Opers: Pat Early
Plnt Mgr: Steve Rowe

D-U-N-S 03-564-6538
PEZOLD MANAGEMENT ASSOCIATES INC
MCDONALD'S
600 Brookstone Centre Pkwy, Columbus, GA 31904-3097
Tel (706) 576-6400 *Founded/Ownrshp* 1974
Sales 69.9MM^E *EMP* 2,000
SIC 5812 Fast-food restaurant, chain
Pr: John D Pezold
**COO:* Tracy Sayers
**CFO:* David B Lewis
**VP:* Jorhee Pezold

D-U-N-S 87-788-6416
PF CHANGS CHINA BISTRO INC
(*Suby of* WOK PARENT LLC) ★
7676 E Pinnacle Peak Rd, Scottsdale, AZ 85255-3404
Tel (480) 888-3000 *Founded/Ownrshp* 2012
Sales 1.0MMM^E *EMP* 26,000
SIC 5812 Chinese restaurant
CEO: Michael Osanloo
Pr: F Lane Cardwell Jr
Pr: R Michael Welborn
COO: Larry Ryback
CFO: Mark D Mumford
Co-CEO: Robert T Vivian
VP: Heidi Berger
VP: Nevielle Panthaky
VP: Jim Umberger
Creative D: Jereme Clymer
CIO: Gerald Gluscic

D-U-N-S 15-214-5611 IMP
■ PFALTZGRAFF FACTORY STORES INC
(*Suby of* LIFETIME BRANDS INC) ★
140 E Market St, York, PA 17401-1219
Tel (717) 848-5500 *Founded/Ownrshp* 2005
Sales 89.5MM^E *EMP* 1,000
SIC 3269 5719 Stoneware pottery products; Kitchenware
Pr: Marsha M Everton
Pr: Clair Bange
**VP:* Peter P Brubaker
**VP:* John L Finlayson

D-U-N-S 17-576-5692 IMP/EXP
■ PFAUDLER INC
GLASSTEEL PARTS AND SERVICES
(*Suby of* NOV) ★
1000 West Ave, Rochester, NY 14611-2442
Tel (585) 464-5663 *Founded/Ownrshp* 1994
Sales 117.0MM^E *EMP* 400
SIC 3559 Refinery, chemical processing & similar machinery; Pharmaceutical machinery
Prin: Micheal F Powers
Board of Directors: Daniel W Duval

D-U-N-S 07-972-7999
PFCCB EDGEWATER LLC
(*Suby of* PF CHANGS CHINA BISTRO INC) ★
7676 E Pinnacle Peak Rd, Scottsdale, AZ 85255-3404
Tel (480) 888-3000 *Founded/Ownrshp* 2015
Sales 8.0MM^E *EMP* 1,152^E
SIC 5812 Chinese restaurant

D-U-N-S 94-817-7142 IMP
PFEIFFER VACUUM INC
(*Suby of* PFEIFFER VACUUM TECHNOLOGY AG)
24 Trafalgar Sq, Nashua, NH 03063-1988
Tel (603) 578-6500 *Founded/Ownrshp* 1995
Sales 526.5MM^E *EMP* 132
SIC 3561 Pumps & pumping equipment; Industrial pumps & parts
Pr: Robert Campbell
CFO: Michael Morin
IT Man: Ron Cieslikowski
Manager: Tom Ziemba

D-U-N-S 94-325-7840
PFF BANCORP INC
2058 N Mills Ave Ste 139, Claremont, CA 91711-2812
Tel (213) 683-6393 *Founded/Ownrshp* 1995
Sales NA *EMP* 885^E
SIC 6035 Federal savings & loan associations
Pr: Kevin McCarthy
**Ch Bd:* Robert W Burwell
COO: Gregory C Talbott
Treas: Larry Hueth
Assoc VP: Liz Perez
Sr VP: Robert Golish
VP: Carole Olson

PFFCU
See POLICE AND FIRE FEDERAL CREDIT UNION (INC)

PFG - THOMS PROESTLER COMPANY
See PERFORMANCE FOOD SERVICE TPC

D-U-N-S 03-555-9962
■ PFG BROADLINE HOLDINGS LLC
PERFORMNCE FDSRVCE- LTTLE ROCK
(*Suby of* P F G) ★
4901 Asher Ave, Little Rock, AR 72204-7968
Tel (501) 568-3141 *Founded/Ownrshp* 2002
Sales 86.9MM^E *EMP* 950
SIC 5149 5148 5147 5141

PFG CUSTOMIZED DISTRIBUTION
See KENNETH O LESTER CO INC

D-U-N-S 15-448-3457 IMP/EXP
PFG HOLDINGS LLC
12500 West Creek Pkwy, Richmond, VA 23238-1110
Tel (804) 484-7700 *Founded/Ownrshp* 2008
Sales NA *EMP* 11,000
SIC 5141 5144 5147 5146 5142 5148

PFG VIRGINIA FOODSERVICE
See VIRGINIA FOODSERVICE GROUP LLC

PFG-MILTON
See PERFORMANCE FOOD GROUP OF GEORGIA LLC

D-U-N-S 82-880-0404
■ PFGC INC
(*Suby of* PERFORMANCE FOOD GROUP CO) ★
12500 West Creek Pkwy, Richmond, VA 23238-1110
Tel (804) 484-7700 *Founded/Ownrshp* 2008
Sales 14.7MMM^E *EMP* 11,000^E
SIC 5141 5142 Groceries, general line; Packaged frozen goods
Pr: George Holm
Dir IT: Chris Bush

D-U-N-S 60-478-5451 IMP/EXP
PFINGSTEN PARTNERS LLC
300 N Lasalle St 5400, Chicago, IL 60654
Tel (312) 222-8707 *Founded/Ownrshp* 2016
Sales 138.2MM^E *EMP* 797
SIC 5065 6211 3679 3578 Video equipment, electronic; Investment firm, general brokerage; Electronic switches; Coin counters

PFISD
See PFLUGERVILLE INDEPENDENT SCHOOL DISTRICT

PFIZER
See WYETH PHARMACEUTICALS INC

PFIZER
See KING PHARMACEUTICALS LLC

D-U-N-S 00-132-6495 IMP/EXP
▲ PFIZER INC
235 E 42nd St, New York, NY 10017-5703
Tel (212) 733-2323 *Founded/Ownrshp* 1942
Sales 48.8MMM *EMP* 97,900
Tkr Sym PFE *Exch* NYS
SIC 2834 2833 Pharmaceutical preparations; Drugs acting on the cardiovascular system, except diagnostic; Drugs affecting parasitic & infective diseases; Veterinary pharmaceutical preparations; Antibiotics
Ch Bd: Ian C Read
CFO: Frank A D'Amelio
Chf Mktg O: Freda C Lewis-Hall
Ex VP: Rady A Johnson
Ex VP: Douglas M Lankler
Board of Directors: Dennis A Ausiello, W Don Cornwell, Joseph J Echevarria, Frances D Fergusson, Helen H Hobbs, Suzanne Nora Johnson, James M Kilts, Stephen W Sanger, James C Smith

D-U-N-S 09-034-6909 IMP
■ PFIZER PHARMACEUTICALS INC (DE)
(*Suby of* PFIZER INC) ★
Km 58 Hm 2 Rr 2, Barceloneta, PR 00617
Tel (787) 846-4300 *Founded/Ownrshp* 1971
Sales 106.5MM^E *EMP* 640
SIC 2834 Medicines, capsuled or ampuled; Tablets, pharmaceutical
Pr: Henry Mc Kinnell
**Treas:* Alan Levin
**VP:* John W Mitchell

D-U-N-S 06-945-7893
PFLUGERVILLE INDEPENDENT SCHOOL DISTRICT
PFISD
1401 W Pecan St, Pflugerville, TX 78660-2518
Tel (512) 594-0000 *Founded/Ownrshp* 1902
Sales 119.8MM^E *EMP* 2,631
Accts Null-Lairson Pc Houston T
SIC 8211 Public senior high school; Secondary school; Public elementary school
Pr: Vernagene Mott
**CFO:* Kenneth Adix
CFO: Gerrell Moore
Bd of Dir: James Hamann
**VP:* Larry D Bradley
Dir Sec: Mike Barrow
Pr Dir: Steve Scheffler
Teacher Pr: Rhonda McWilliams

PFPA
See PENTAGON FORCE PROTECTION AGENCY

PFS - PNT FNAL ASSMBLY SYSTEMS
See DURR SYSTEMS INC

PFS WEB
See PRIORITY FULFILLMENT SERVICES INC

D-U-N-S 09-380-0428
▲ PFSWEB INC
505 Millenium Dr, Allen, TX 75013-2774
Tel (972) 881-2900 *Founded/Ownrshp* 1999
Sales 288.2MM *EMP* 2,100
Tkr Sym PFSW *Exch* NAS
SIC 8741 7389 8742 Management services; Business management; Merchandise liquidators; Manufacturing management consultant
Pr: Michael C Willoughby
**Ch Bd:* James F Reilly
CFO: Thomas J Madden
Chf Cred: Cynthia D Almond
Ex VP: C Travis Hess
Sr VP: Mark Fuentes
Sr VP: Elizabeth E Johnson
Sr VP: Steven J Stephan
Sr VP: Zach Thomann
VP: Gibson T Dawson
QA Dir: Neetu Tripathi
Board of Directors: David I Beatson, Monica Luechtefeld, Benjamin Rosenzweig, Peter J Stein

PG&E
See PACIFIC GAS AND ELECTRIC CO

D-U-N-S 96-489-9132 IMP
▲ PG&E CORP
77 Beale St, San Francisco, CA 94105-1814
Tel (415) 973-1000 *Founded/Ownrshp* 1905
Sales 16.8MMM *EMP* 23,000^E
Tkr Sym PCG *Exch* NYS
SIC 4931 4923 Electric & other services combined; Gas transmission & distribution
Ch Bd: Anthony F Earley Jr
Pr: Nickolas Stavropoulos
Pr: Geisha J Williams
CFO: Jason P Wells
Ofcr: Loraine M Giammona
Ex VP: John R Simon
Sr VP: Karen A Austin
Sr VP: Desmond A Bell
Sr VP: Helen A Burt
Sr VP: Edward D Halpin
Sr VP: Kent M Harvey
Sr VP: Julie M Kane
Sr VP: Gregory K Kiraly
Sr VP: Steven E Malnight
Sr VP: Dinyar B Mistry
Sr VP: Hyun Park
Sr VP: Jesus Soto Jr
Sr VP: Fong Wan
VP: David S Thomason
Board of Directors: Barbara L Rambo, Lewis Chew, Anne Shen Smith, Fred J Fowler, Barry Lawson Williams, Maryellen C Herringer, Richard C Kelly, Roger H Kimmel, Richard A Meserve, Forrest E Miller, Eric Mullins, Rosendo G Parra

PGA GOLF SHOP
See PROFESSIONAL GOLFERS ASSOCIATION OF AMERICA INC

D-U-N-S 03-076-0458
PGA RESORT & SPA
ECCLESTONE ORGANIZATION
1555 Palm Beach Lks, West Palm Beach, FL 33401-2323
Tel (561) 686-2000 *Founded/Ownrshp* 1968
Sales 25.0MM^E *EMP* 1,000
SIC 8741 7377 7513 7515 Management services; Computer rental & leasing; Truck rental & leasing, no drivers; Passenger car leasing
Ch Bd: E L Ecclestone
**VP:* Ron Ferschke

D-U-N-S 80-267-1321
PGA TOUR HOLDINGS INC
(*Suby of* PGA TOUR INC) ★
112 Pga Tour Blvd, Ponte Vedra Beach, FL 32082-3077
Tel (904) 285-3700 *Founded/Ownrshp* 1992
Sales 77.6MM^E *EMP* 2,999
SIC 7992 7997 Public golf courses; Golf club, membership
Chf Mktg O: Tom Wade
VP: Ty Votaw
Genl Mgr: Steve Winsor

D-U-N-S 02-030-4754
PGA TOUR INC (FL)
112 Pga Tour Blvd, Ponte Vedra Beach, FL 32082-3077
Tel (904) 285-3700 *Founded/Ownrshp* 1968
Sales 1.0MMM *EMP* 3,563
Accts Pricewaterhousecoopers Llp Ja
SIC 7997 Golf club, membership
COO: Edward L Moorhouse
**Pr:* Richard J Ferris
**COO:* W William Calfee
**COO:* Henry Hughes
**COO:* Jeff Monday
COO: Rick Shoemaker
CFO: Alan Kessock
**CFO:* Charles L Zink
**Treas:* John Cook
Bd of Dir: Lou Guzzi
Top Exec: Sean Lingi
Ex VP: Andy Pazder
VP: Tom Alter
VP: Donna Fiedorowicz
VP: Luis Goicouria
VP: Chris Gray
VP: Scott Gutterman
VP: Paul Hardwick
VP: Paul Johnson
VP: Peter Kent
VP: Curtis Leeper

D-U-N-S 61-905-1287
PGAC CORP
9630 Ridgehaven Ct Ste B, San Diego, CA 92123-5605
Tel (858) 560-8213 *Founded/Ownrshp* 1988
Sales 78.9MM^E *EMP* 1,500
SIC 2671 Paper coated or laminated for packaging
Pr: Mark Grantham
**VP:* Florentina Shields

D-U-N-S 11-923-6318
PGBA LLC
(*Suby of* BLUE CROSS BLUE SHIELD OF SOUTH CAROLINA) ★
I-20 Alpine Rd, Columbia, SC 29219-0001
Tel (803) 788-3860 *Founded/Ownrshp* 2002
Sales 270.0MM *EMP* 2,161
SIC 8322 Individual & family services
Pr: Mike Skarupa
VP: Myriam G Alonso
VP: Kay Andrews
VP: Cynthia E Connelly
VP: Jordan D Evans
VP: Michael J Gurrera
VP: Allen R Jones
VP: T Jeff Littlefield
VP: Mark Macdougal
VP: Katherine H Norton
VP: Dedee Rowe
VP: Ron Rushton
VP: Jamie Watson

PGCPS
See PRINCE GEORGES COUNTY PUBLIC SCHOOLS

D-U-N-S 83-640-9359 IMP/EXP
■ PGI NONWOVEN/CHICOPEE INC
(*Suby of* AVINTIV SPECIALTY MATERIALS INC) ★
9335 Harris Corners Pkwy, Charlotte, NC 28269-3818
Tel (704) 697-5100 *Founded/Ownrshp* 1995
Sales 125.2MM^E *EMP* 560
SIC 2297 2392 Spunbonded fabrics; Slip covers & pads
**CEO:* Veronica M Hagen
**COO:* Michael W Hale
**CFO:* Robert Kocourek

PGI NONWOVENS
See CHICOPEE INC

D-U-N-S 18-783-4502
■ PGIM INC
(*Suby of* PRUDENTIAL FINANCIAL INC) ★
655 Broad St, Newark, NJ 07102-4410
Tel (973) 802-6791 *Founded/Ownrshp* 1984
Sales NA *EMP* 665
Accts Price Waterhousecoopers
SIC 6411 6799 6282 Insurance agents, brokers & service; Investors; Real estate investors, except property operators; Manager of mutual funds, contract or fee basis
Ch: John R Strangfeld
**CEO:* David Hunt
**CEO:* Jurgen Muhlhauser
**COO:* Betsy Friedman
**Sr VP:* Michael Lillard
Sr VP: James Lyday
VP: Steven Labold
Mng Dir: Youguo Liang
IT Man: C Andrew Pu

PGS AMERICAS
See PETROLEUM GEO-SERVICES INC

D-U-N-S 12-995-4579 EXP
▲ PGT INC
1070 Technology Dr, North Venice, FL 34275-3617
Tel (941) 480-1600 *Founded/Ownrshp* 1980
Sales 389.8MM *EMP* 2,300^E
Tkr Sym PGTI *Exch* NGM
SIC 3442 2431 3211 Window & door frames; Windows & window parts & trim, wood; Doors & door parts & trim, wood; Laminated glass
Ch Bd: Rodney Hershberger
**Pr:* Jeffrey T Jackson
CFO: Bradley West
Board of Directors: Alexander R Castaldi, Richard D Feintuch, M Joseph McHugh, Brett N Milgrim, William J Morgan, Floyd F Sherman

D-U-N-S 62-520-8798 EXP
■ PGT INDUSTRIES INC
(*Suby of* PGT INC) ★
1070 Technology Dr, North Venice, FL 34275-3617
Tel (352) 335-5556 *Founded/Ownrshp* 1980
Sales 209.6MM^E *EMP* 1,105

SIC 3442 2431 3231 Window & door frames; Windows & window parts & trim, wood; Doors & door parts & trim, wood; Products of purchased glass
Pr: Rodney Hershberger
**CFO:* Jeffrey Jackson
VP: Todd Antonelli
**VP:* Brad West
Dir IT: Nathan Hall
VP Opers: Ken Hilliard
Board of Directors: Floyd F Sherman, Daniel Agroskin, Randy L White, Alexander R Castaldi, Richard D Feintuch, Ramsey A Frank, Rodney Hershberger, Paul S Levy, M Joseph McHugh, Brett N Milgrim, William J Morgan

D-U-N-S 06-875-2856
PGT TRUCKING INC
1 Pgt Way, Monaca, PA 15061-2255
Tel (724) 728-3500 *Founded/Ownrshp* 1981
Sales 176.0MM^E *EMP* 330
SIC 4213 4731 Trucking, except local; Freight transportation arrangement
Pr: Patrick Gallagher
COO: Joeseph Vargo
**VP:* Catherine Gallagher
VP: John Terrill
Dir Bus: Bill Hershey
Ex Dir: Darren Coast
IT Man: Michelle Burd
Trfc Dir: Roman Grigorashenko
Sls Dir: Thomas Tomasko
Snr Mgr: Paul Vargo

PGW
See PITTSBURGH GLASS WORKS LLC

D-U-N-S 11-247-0765 IMP/EXP
■ **PGW AUTO GLASS LLC**
(*Suby of* PGW) ★
1 Ppg Pl Fl 6, Pittsburgh, PA 15272-0001
Tel (412) 434-4058 *Founded/Ownrshp* 2008
Sales 84.2MM^E *EMP* 900
SIC 7536 Automotive glass replacement shops

PH
See PARRISH-HARE ELECTRICAL SUPPLY LP

D-U-N-S 05-488-5111
PHACIL INC
800 N Glebe Rd Ste 700, Arlington, VA 22203-2151
Tel (703) 526-1800 *Founded/Ownrshp* 2001
Sales 109.5MM^E *EMP* 650
Accts Moss-Adams Cpa S
SIC 7379 7371 Computer related consulting services; Computer software development & applications
CEO: Tom Shoemaker
**Co-Ownr:* Rafael Collado
**Co-Ownr:* Sascha Mornell
Sr VP: Mehdi Cherqaoui
Sr VP: William Grabner
VP: Robert Cottingham
Prgrm Mgr: Richard Berry
Snr Sftwr: Christian Watt
QA Dir: Annette Gorham
Web Dev: Jeff Pascoe
Netwrk Eng: Russ Gaer

D-U-N-S 01-193-1822
PHALCON LTD (CT)
505 Main St, Farmington, CT 06032-2912
Tel (860) 677-9797 *Founded/Ownrshp* 2006
Sales 352.4MM *EMP* 1,000
Accts Blum Shapiro & Company Pc
SIC 1731 General electrical contractor
Pr: Michael E McPhee
**CFO:* John D Conroy
**VP:* Marcus W McPhee
Exec: Steve Dauphinais
Opers Mgr: Doug Barker

PHANTOM FIREWORKS
See BJ ALAN CO

PHARMA CHEM
See PHARMACHEM LABORATORIES INC

D-U-N-S 04-788-9642
PHARMA CORR LLC
(*Suby of* CORIZON LLC) ★
6705 Camille Ave, Oklahoma City, OK 73149-5202
Tel (405) 670-1400 *Founded/Ownrshp* 1996
Sales 151.2MM^E *EMP* 645^E
SIC 5122 Proprietary (patent) medicines
Prin: Gaylan Williams
Pharmcst: John Carter
Pharmcst: Adam Curling
Pharmcst: Billy Wilson

PHARMA TECH INDUSTRIES
See PTI UNION LLC

D-U-N-S 03-190-3446 IMP
PHARMACA INTEGRATIVE PHARMACY INC
4940 Pearl East Cir # 301, Boulder, CO 80301-2442
Tel (303) 442-2304 *Founded/Ownrshp* 2000
Sales 95.5MM^E *EMP* 400
SIC 5912 Drug stores
Pr: Richard S Willis
VP: Allison Janda
Creative D: Pam Simach

D-U-N-S 80-849-1737
■ **PHARMACARE HOLDING CORP**
(*Suby of* CVS HEALTH CORP) ★
1 Cvs Dr, Woonsocket, RI 02895-6146
Tel (401) 765-1500 *Founded/Ownrshp* 2007
Sales 45.4MM^E *EMP* 1,801^E
SIC 5912 Drug stores & proprietary stores

PHARMACARE MANAGEMENT SVCS LLC
See CAREMARK PHC LLC

D-U-N-S 07-883-5682
PHARMACEUTICAL PRODUCT DEVELOPMENT LLC
929 N Front St, Wilmington, NC 28401-3331
Tel (910) 251-0081 *Founded/Ownrshp* 2012
Sales 1.7MMM^E *EMP* 15,000
SIC 8731 Commercial physical research; Biotechnical research, commercial
CEO: David Simmons
CFO: Robert Hureau
Ex VP: David Johnston
Ex VP: Henry Levy
VP: Jon Denissen
Snr PM: Patricia Keegan

D-U-N-S 00-325-2038
PHARMACEUTICAL RESEARCH AND MANUFACTURERS OF AMERICA
PHRMA
950 F St Nw Ste 300, Washington, DC 20004-1440
Tel (202) 835-3400 *Founded/Ownrshp* 1958
Sales 204.7MM *EMP* 170
Accts Tate And Tryon Washington Dc
SIC 8611 Business associations
Ch Bd: Kenneth C Frazier
Pr: John Castellani
Pr: Mark Grayson
CEO: Stephen Ubl
CFO: Kimberly Sidhu
Sr VP: Matthew D Bennett
Sr VP: Robert Zirkelbach
VP: Salvatore Alesci
VP: Jan Faiks
VP: Shannon Graham
VP: Pamela Smith
VP: Tina Stow
Exec: Michelle Bundy
Board of Directors: Ian Read, Werner Baumann, George A Scangos, Giovanni Caforio, Ramona Sequeira, Joaquin Duato, Daniel Tasse, Joaquin Duato, Timothy P Walbert, Peter Greenleaf, William Heiden, Mark Iwicki, Joseph Jimenez, Michael Narachi

D-U-N-S 06-339-7731
PHARMACEUTICAL RESEARCH ASSOCIATES INC
(*Suby of* PRA HOLDINGS INC) ★
1 Stamford Forum, Stamford, CT 06901-3516
Tel (203) 588-8000 *Founded/Ownrshp* 2001
Sales 105.8MM^E *EMP* 675
SIC 2834 5122 Pharmaceutical preparations; Pharmaceuticals; Proprietary (patent) medicines
VP: Stuart Baker
**VP:* Howard Udell

D-U-N-S 87-826-5586 IMP/EXP
PHARMACEUTICS INTERNATIONAL INC
P I I
10819 Gilroy Rd Ste 100, Hunt Valley, MD 21031-8214
Tel (410) 584-0001 *Founded/Ownrshp* 1994
Sales 111.5MM^E *EMP* 475
SIC 2834 5122

D-U-N-S 02-492-2619 IMP/EXP
PHARMACHEM LABORATORIES INC
PHARMA CHEM
265 Harrison Tpke, Kearny, NJ 07032-4315
Tel (201) 246-1000 *Founded/Ownrshp* 1980
Sales 122.5MM^E *EMP* 235
SIC 2099 2834 Food preparations; Pharmaceutical preparations
Pr: David Holmes
CFO: Brian Bunch
**Treas:* Andrea Bauer
VP: Lynn Dahle
VP: Colin Intyre
VP: George Joseph
**VP:* Colin Macintyre
Prd Mgr: Jeremy Berger
Prd Mgr: Doug Hall
Pharmcst: Mahesh Pharmachem

D-U-N-S 92-949-7972 IMP
■ **PHARMACIA & UPJOHN INC**
(*Suby of* PFIZER INC) ★
100 Route 206 N, Peapack, NJ 07977
Tel (908) 901-8000 *Founded/Ownrshp* 2003
Sales 836.3MM^E *EMP* 16,000
SIC 2834 2833 Pharmaceutical preparations; Medicinal chemicals
Ex VP: Goran A Ando
CFO: Christopher J Coughlin
Board of Directors: Frank C Carlucci, Gustaf A S Douglas, M Kathryn Eickhoff, R L Berthold Lindqvist, Olof G Lund, C Steven McMillan, William U Parfet, Ulla B Reinius, Bengt I Samuelsson

D-U-N-S 00-530-2518
PHARMACISTS MUTUAL INSURANCE CO (IA)
808 Highway 18 W, Algona, IA 50511-7234
Tel (515) 295-2461 *Founded/Ownrshp* 1909
Sales NA *EMP* 300
SIC 6331 Fire, marine & casualty insurance: mutual
Pr: Edward J Yorty
Pr: Matthew Even
**Pr:* Edward Yorty
COO: Jon Grether
**Ch:* Kirk Hayes
Ofcr: Michael Warren
VP: Kenneth Baker
VP: Steven Hoskins
VP: Mark Knutson
VP: Julie Murphy
VP: Shirley Pierson

PHARMACY DEPARTMENT
See TRIUMPH HOSPITAL BAYTOWN

D-U-N-S 79-117-9526
PHARMACYCLICS INC
995 E Arques Ave, Sunnyvale, CA 94085-4521
Tel (408) 774-0330 *Founded/Ownrshp* 1992
Sales 729.7MM *EMP* 607^E
SIC 2834

D-U-N-S 07-985-7498
■ **PHARMACYCLICS LLC**
OXFORD AMHERST LLC
(*Suby of* ABBVIE INC) ★
999 E Arques Ave, Sunnyvale, CA 94085-4521
Tel (408) 774-0330 *Founded/Ownrshp* 2015
Sales 172.3MM^E *EMP* 900^E
SIC 2834 Pharmaceutical preparations
Pr: Wulff-Erik Von Borcke
COO: Maky Zanganeh
Ofcr: Sumita Ray
Ex VP: Ramses Erdtmann
Ex VP: Heow Tan
Sr VP: Urte Gayko
VP: Betty Chang
VP: Fong Clow
VP: Elizabeth Faust PHD
VP: Thorsten Graef MD
VP: Gregory Hemmi
VP: Dana Lee
Assoc Dir: Amoni Green
Assoc Dir: Jay Li
Assoc Dir: Ravi Monangi
Assoc Dir: Davina Moussa
Assoc Dir: Hanh Nguyen
Assoc Dir: Samuel Suzuki
Assoc Dir: Patrick Vonlanthen

PHARMADERM
See FOUGERA PHARMACEUTICALS INC

PHARMANEX DIVISION
See NU SKIN INTERNATIONAL INC

D-U-N-S 05-389-0000 IMP
PHARMAVITE LLC
(*Suby of* OTSUKA AMERICA INC) ★
8510 Balboa Blvd Ste 300, Northridge, CA 91325-3582
Tel (818) 221-6200 *Founded/Ownrshp* 2002
Sales 354.5MM^E *EMP* 850
SIC 2833 2834 Vitamins, natural or synthetic: bulk, uncompounded; Pharmaceutical preparations
Pr: Bob McQuillan
**COO:* Mark Walsh
**CFO:* Nitin Deshpande
Bd of Dir: Carolyn Sabatini
**Chf Mktg O:* Etienne Patout
**Ofcr:* Timothy Toll
Ex VP: Skip Aldridge
Ex VP: Bill Tullis
VP: Erin Bunkley
VP: John Vickers
Cmptr Lab: Hector Cervantez

D-U-N-S 80-040-6709
▲ **PHARMERICA CORP**
1901 Campus Pl, Louisville, KY 40299-2308
Tel (502) 627-7000 *Founded/Ownrshp* 2006
Sales 2.0MMM *EMP* 5,800
Tkr Sym PMC *Exch* NYS
SIC 5912 5122 Drug stores & proprietary stores; Pharmaceuticals
CEO: Gregory S Weishar
**Ch Bd:* Geoffrey G Meyers
CFO: David W Froesel Jr
Ex VP: Suresh Vishnubhatla
Sr VP: Thomas A Caneris
Sr VP: Mark R Lindemoen
Sr VP: Robert A McKay
Sr VP: Berard E Tomassetti
VP: Joshua Bucy
VP: Bob McKay
VP: Kerry Richardson
Exec: Terry Sanders

D-U-N-S 13-050-5985 IMP
■ **PHARMERICA LONG-TERM CARE LLC**
(*Suby of* PHARMERICA CORP) ★
3625 Queen Palm Dr, Tampa, FL 33619-1309
Tel (877) 975-2273 *Founded/Ownrshp* 1997
Sales 427.2MM^E *EMP* 2,758
SIC 5912 5961 8082 5122 Drug stores; Pharmaceuticals, mail order; Home health care services; Oxygen tent service; Pharmaceuticals
Pr: William G Shields
**Pr:* David Weidner
**COO:* Thomas A Caneris
**Treas:* Michael Culotta
**Sr VP:* Janice Rutkowski
**VP:* John Lanier
VP: Richard Momberger
**VP:* James Snyder
**Prin:* Gregory S Weishar

D-U-N-S 83-000-0134
PHARMSCRIPT LLC
150 Pierce St, Somerset, NJ 08873-4185
Tel (908) 389-1818 *Founded/Ownrshp* 2009
Sales 100.0MM *EMP* 150
SIC 5122 Pharmaceuticals
CEO: Michael Segal
COO: Michael Rosenblum
CFO: Marcos Monheit
VP: Janine Fiore
VP: Allyson Taylor
Dir Rx: Michael Gerdes
Dir IT: Carol S Chen
Pharmcst: Ankit Patel
Cert Phar: Misty Radford

D-U-N-S 02-388-4067
PHARR SAN JUAN-ALAMO INDEPENDENT SCHOOL DISTRICT
PSJA
601 E Kelly Ave, Pharr, TX 78577-4905
Tel (956) 354-2000 *Founded/Ownrshp* 1919
Sales 270.3MM^E *EMP* 3,500
Accts Osar R Gonzalez Cpa & Associ
SIC 8211 Public elementary & secondary schools
**Pr:* Ronaldo Cantu
**VP:* Jesus Vela Jr
IT Man: Anna Pena

D-U-N-S 00-314-7584 IMP/EXP
PHARR YARNS LLC (NC)
100 Main St, Mc Adenville, NC 28101
Tel (704) 824-3551 *Founded/Ownrshp* 1939
Sales 714.0MM^E *EMP* 1,800
SIC 2281 2282 2824 Manmade & synthetic fiber yarns, spun; Manmade & synthetic fiber yarns: twisting, winding, etc.; Acrylic fibers
COO: Frederick Erickson
Plnt Mgr: Woody Gosney

D-U-N-S 79-610-1871
PHARR-PALOMAR INC
(*Suby of* PHARR YARNS LLC) ★
6781 8th St, Buena Park, CA 90620-1097
Tel (714) 522-4811 *Founded/Ownrshp* 1982
Sales 102.2MM^E *EMP* 1,600
SIC 2282 2281 Throwing & winding mills; Carpet yarn: twisting, winding or spooling; Yarn spinning mills
Prin: H W Gosney
**Sec:* Jim Howard
**VP:* Walt Davenport

D-U-N-S 82-841-7472
PHAZE CONCRETE INC
JACK DANIELS CONSTRUCTION
1280 W Utah Ave, Hildale, UT 84784
Tel (435) 656-9500 *Founded/Ownrshp* 2004
Sales 120.3MM^E *EMP* 190
SIC 1542 Nonresidential construction
Pr: Paul Beagley
**Treas:* Esther Neilsen
**Sec:* Rob Allred

D-U-N-S 12-416-1931
■ **PHC-LAKE HAVASU INC**
HAVASU REGIONAL MEDICAL CENTER
(*Suby of* LIFEPOINT HEALTH INC) ★
101 Civic Center Ln, Lake Havasu City, AZ 86403-5607
Tel (928) 855-8185 *Founded/Ownrshp* 2006
Sales 180.5MM *EMP* 650
SIC 8062 General medical & surgical hospitals
CEO: Michael Patterson
**Treas:* Michael S Coggin
Chf Mktg O: Colleen Savage
**VP:* Christopher J Monte
Pathlgst: Edward P Fuller

D-U-N-S 55-658-8080
■ **PHC-LAS CRUCES INC**
MEMORIAL MEDICAL CENTER
(*Suby of* LIFEPOINT HEALTH INC) ★
2450 S Telshor Blvd, Las Cruces, NM 88011-5141
Tel (575) 522-8641 *Founded/Ownrshp* 2004
Sales 199.1MM *EMP* 1,000
SIC 8062 General medical & surgical hospitals
CEO: John Harris
**COO:* Steve Ruwoldt
**CFO:* Jim McGonnell
Dir Inf Cn: Twyla Anderson
Tech Mgr: Carrie Spratford

PHEC DUCOM
See PHILADELPHIA HEALTH EDUCATION CORP

PHELON COMPANY
See FENIX MANUFACTURING SOLUTIONS LLC

D-U-N-S 11-420-7053 IMP
PHELPS COUNTY REGIONAL MEDICAL CENTER
1000 W 10th St, Rolla, MO 65401-2905
Tel (573) 364-8899 *Founded/Ownrshp* 1946
Sales 190.8MM *EMP* 1,600
SIC 8062 General medical & surgical hospitals
CEO: John Denbo
Chf OB: Timothy Isakson
**CFO:* Ed Clayton
**Sr VP:* Ellis Hawkins
**Sr VP:* Don James
**VP:* Keri Brookshire Heavin
Dir Risk M: Pam Karr
Dir Rx: Craig Moore
Off Mgr: Linda Moore
Off Mgr: Tina Pridgeon
Nurse Mgr: Regina Shaffer

PHELPS DODGE
See FREEPORT-MCMORAN SIERRITA INC

D-U-N-S 09-494-3321
■ **PHELPS DODGE INTERNATIONAL CORP**
(*Suby of* GENERAL CABLE CORP) ★
9850 Nw 41st St Ste 200, Doral, FL 33178-2987
Tel (305) 648-7888 *Founded/Ownrshp* 2008
Sales 139.9MM^E *EMP* 3,031
SIC 8742 3357 3315 Management consulting services; Industrial consultant; Nonferrous wiredrawing & insulating; Steel wire & related products
Pr: Mathias Sandoval
Sr VP: Keith Macintosh
VP: Chris Kesl
VP: Jose Sierra
VP: Karl Zimmer
Snr Ntwrk: Guillermo Cuadra
IT Man: Anthony Garcia
IT Man: Shaleen Pinero

D-U-N-S 08-892-5185
PHELPS DUNBAR LLP
365 Canal St Ste 2000, New Orleans, LA 70130-6534
Tel (504) 566-1311 *Founded/Ownrshp* 1853
Sales 89.9MM^E *EMP* 611
SIC 8111 General practice attorney, lawyer
Pt: Jeffrey M Baudier
Sr Pt: Reuben Anderson
Pt: Brent B Barriere
Pt: Richard N Dicharry
Pt: George M Gilly
Pt: John Phillips
Pt: James Wily
Mng Pt: Ross F Bass
Mng Pt: David Crawford
Mng Pt: Michael D Hunt
Mng Pt: Lawrence P Ingram
Mng Pt: Alston H Jonson
Mng Pt: James O Mara
Mng Pt: Greg D Pirkle
Mng Pt: Patrick R Richard
Mng Pt: Cooper C Thurber
Mng Pt: James G Wyly III

D-U-N-S 07-271-0031
PHELPS MEMORIAL HOSPITAL ASSOCIATION
PHELPS MEMORIAL HOSPITAL CENTE
701 N Broadway, Sleepy Hollow, NY 10591-1096
Tel (914) 366-3000 *Founded/Ownrshp* 1956
Sales 229.9MM *EMP* 1,200

Accts Cohnreznick Llp New York Ny
SIC 8062 General medical & surgical hospitals
Pr: Keith F Safian
Pr: William Reifer
**COO:* Bruce Davidow
COO: Bruce B Davidow
**CFO:* Vincent Desantis
**Chf Mktg O:* Lawrance Faulks
VP: Barbara S Allar
VP: Lucy Cioffiro
VP: Leonard Fogel
VP: Robert Lane
VP: Saleem M Mir
VP: Kerry Pisano
Dir Lab: Michelle Tanzillo
Dir Soc: Marissa Coratti
Dir Rad: Silvia Alves

PHELPS MEMORIAL HOSPITAL CENTE
See PHELPS MEMORIAL HOSPITAL ASSOCIATION

D-U-N-S 10-297-6396 IMP
PHENOMENEX INC
411 Madrid Ave, Torrance, CA 90501-1430

Tel (310) 212-0555 *Founded/Ownrshp* 1982
Sales 98.0MM^E *EMP* 400
SIC 3826 Analytical instruments
Pr: Farshad Mahjoor
CFO: Edi Kunz
Dir Bus: Lars Torstensson
Ex Dir: Alex Gharagozlow
Dist Mgr: Luke Steece
IT Man: George Hanson
Info Man: Kevin Richie
Sfty Mgr: Rick Leonard
Natl Sales: Ryan Asplund
Natl Sales: Sam Lodge
Mktg Dir: Lance Foshe

PHFE
See PUBLIC HEALTH FOUNDATION ENTERPRISES INC

D-U-N-S 92-678-4948
PHFE
12801 Crossrds Pkwy S 2 200 S, City of Industry, CA 91746
Tel (562) 699-7320 *Founded/Ownrshp* 2012
Sales 98.1MM *EMP* 21^E
SIC 8082 Home health care services
Prin: Mark Bertler

PHH ARVAL
See ELEMENT VEHICLE MANAGEMENT SERVICES GROUP LLC

PHH ARVAL
See ELEMENT VEHICLE MANAGEMENT SERVICES LLC

D-U-N-S 00-695-0349
▲ PHH CORP (MD)
1 Mortgage Way, Mount Laurel, NJ 08054-4624
Tel (856) 917-1744 *Founded/Ownrshp* 1953
Sales 790.0MM *EMP* 3,800
Accts Deloitte & Touche Llp Philade
Tkr Sym PHH *Exch* NYS
SIC 6531 8741 Real estate agent, residential; Fiduciary, real estate; Management services
Pr: Glen A Messina
CFO: Robert B Crowl
Ofcr: Kathryn M Ruggieri
Sr VP: William F Brown
Sr VP: Leith W Kaplan
Sr VP: Bruce Van Fleet
VP: Ed Robinson
VP: David Trone
VP: Peter Yang
QA Dir: Joann Festoff
Counsel: Christine Bonavita

D-U-N-S 09-286-9924
■ PHH MORTGAGE CORP
(*Suby of* PHH CORP) ★
1 Mortgage Way, Mount Laurel, NJ 08054-4624
Tel (866) 946-0081 *Founded/Ownrshp* 1997
Sales NA *EMP* 2,000
Accts Deloitte & Touche Llp Philade
SIC 6162 Mortgage bankers
**Pr:* David E Tucker
**Sr VP:* William F Brown
Sr VP: Jonathan McGrain
Sr VP: William J Steinmetz
Sr VP: Bruce Van Fleet
Sr VP: Kate Williamson
VP: Wheeler Andrea
VP: David Bricker
VP: Kevin Johnson
VP: Kim Walliser
VP: Sandra Warren
VP: Jason Watson
VP: Adam Werner
VP: Thomas Wesley
VP: Kim Wetten
Board of Directors: Terence W Edwards, James J Madewell

D-U-N-S 06-490-1739
■ PHH VEHICLE SALES INC
(*Suby of* PHH CORP) ★
940 Ridgebrook Rd, Sparks, MD 21152-9390
Tel (800) 665-9744 *Founded/Ownrshp* 1950, 2005
Sales 36.9MM^E *EMP* 1,200^E
SIC 7513

D-U-N-S 01-101-4235
■ PHI AIR MEDICAL LLC
AIR EVAC SERVICES
(*Suby of* PHI INC) ★
2800 N 44th St Ste 800, Phoenix, AZ 85008-1584
Tel (602) 224-3500 *Founded/Ownrshp* 1997
Sales 300.0MM *EMP* 1,200
SIC 4522 Ambulance services, air

D-U-N-S 00-694-7873
▲ PHI INC (LA)
2001 Se Evangeline Trwy, Lafayette, LA 70508-2156
Tel (337) 235-2452 *Founded/Ownrshp* 1949
Sales 804.2MM *EMP* 2,694
Tkr Sym PHII *Exch* NGM
SIC 4512 4522 4581 Helicopter carrier, scheduled; Helicopter carriers, nonscheduled; Aircraft maintenance & repair services
Ch Bd: Al A Gonsoulin
**Pr:* Lance F Bospflug
CFO: Trudy P McConnaughhay
Ofcr: Richard A Rovinelli
CTO: Schwaiger Gregory

D-U-N-S 18-330-8043
■ PHI SERVICE CO
(*Suby of* EXELON) ★
701 9th St Nw, Washington, DC 20001-4572
Tel (202) 872-2000 *Founded/Ownrshp* 1998
Sales 87.6MM^E *EMP* 1,700
SIC 7389 Legal & tax services
CEO: Joseph M Rigby

D-U-N-S 00-698-9008 IMP/EXP
■ PHIBRO ANIMAL HEALTH CORP
(*Suby of* BFI CO LLC) ★
300 Frank W Burr Blvd, Teaneck, NJ 07666-6704
Tel (201) 329-7300 *Founded/Ownrshp* 1946
Sales 751.5MM *EMP* 1,200
Accts Pricewaterhousecoopers Llp Fl
Tkr Sym PAHC *Exch* NGM
SIC 2819 5169 2899 2834 Industrial inorganic chemicals; Chemicals & allied products; Chemical preparations; Pharmaceutical preparations
Ch Bd: Jack C Bendheim
Pr: Dean J Warras
COO: Larry L Miller
CFO: Richard G Johnson
Treas: David C Storbeck
**Ex VP:* Daniel M Bendheim
Sr VP: Thomas G Dagger
Sr VP: Daniel A Welch
VP: Jonathan Bendheim
VP: Richard Coulter
VP: Frederick Iversen
VP: Mike Murphy
Board of Directors: E Thomas Corcoran, Sam Gejdenson, George Gunn, Mary Lou Malanoski, Carol A Wrenn

D-U-N-S 00-400-2853 IMP/EXP
PHIFER INC (AL)
4400 Kauloosa Ave, Tuscaloosa, AL 35401-7042
Tel (205) 345-2120 *Founded/Ownrshp* 1952
Sales 290.8MM^E *EMP* 950
SIC 3496 2221 3357 2295 3442 3354 Screening, woven wire: made from purchased wire; Fiberglass fabrics; Polyester broadwoven fabrics; Aluminum wire & cable; Yarns, plastic coated: made from purchased yarns; Metal doors, sash & trim; Aluminum extruded products
Pr: Beverly Phifer
Treas: Karen Phifer Brooks
Sr VP: John G Hogue
VP: Susan Phifer Cork
VP: Sherrill Harper
VP: W Larry Suttles
Exec: Ben T Barnett
Exec: James Brooks
Exec: Brad Cork

D-U-N-S 60-916-5022 IMP
PHIHONG USA CORP
(*Suby of* PHIHONG TECHNOLOGY CO., LTD.)
47800 Fremont Blvd, Fremont, CA 94538-6551
Tel (510) 445-0100 *Founded/Ownrshp* 1990
Sales 132.0MM *EMP* 75
Accts Vincent Chong & Co San Jose
SIC 5045 3572 Computer peripheral equipment; Computer disk & drum drives & components
Pr: Fei Hung Alex Lin
VP: Keith Hapwood
VP: Jane Zheng
Sls Dir: Bill Morrison
Manager: Paul Brady
Manager: Richard Huang

D-U-N-S 01-314-9567
PHIL LONG DEALERSHIPS INC
PHIL LONG FORD
1114 Motor City Dr, Colorado Springs, CO 80905-7313
Tel (719) 575-7555 *Founded/Ownrshp* 1997
Sales 395.2MM^E *EMP* 1,300
SIC 5511 7514 7515 Automobiles, new & used; Passenger car rental; Passenger car leasing
Pr: Gerald Cimino
**CFO:* Tony Basile
**Ex VP:* Marvin A Boyd
**Ex VP:* Robert J Fenton
**Ex VP:* Jim Fynes
Genl Mgr: Mark Barton
Genl Mgr: John Chavez
Off Mgr: Krista Sedilo
Store Mgr: Rafael Castro
Dir IT: Shawn Flynn
Sls Mgr: Jon Amos

PHIL LONG FORD
See PHIL LONG DEALERSHIPS INC

D-U-N-S 03-192-8013
PHIL LONG FORD LLC
(*Suby of* PHIL LONG FORD) ★
1212 Motor City Dr, Colorado Springs, CO 80905-7392
Tel (719) 575-7100 *Founded/Ownrshp* 2000
Sales 130.5MM^E *EMP* 300^E
SIC 5511 7515 7538 5531 Automobiles, new & used; Passenger car leasing; General automotive repair shops; Automotive & home supply stores
COO: Marvin Boyd
**COO:* Trevor Mack
Bd of Dir: Angela Cesario
Genl Mgr: Ron Cassetta
Genl Mgr: Brent Hall
Genl Mgr: Todd Hilleboe
Sls Mgr: Michael Kujawa
Sls Mgr: Jamie Passarelli
Sales Asso: Douglas Adkins

D-U-N-S 03-816-3226 IMP/EXP
PHILADELPHIA AGUSTAWESTLAND CORP
(*Suby of* AGUSTAWESTLAND SPA)
3050 Red Lion Rd, Philadelphia, PA 19114-1128
Tel (215) 281-1400 *Founded/Ownrshp* 1980
Sales 115.4MM^E *EMP* 375
SIC 3721 5088 Helicopters; Aeronautical equipment & supplies
CEO: William Hunt
**Pr:* Robert J Budica
Sr VP: Bob Caldwell
VP: Lou Bartolotta
**VP:* Vincent Genovese
VP: Craig Zysk
IT Man: Reeda Sheuchuk
Manager: Eric Crawford
Manager: Robert Fontello
Manager: Bill Kirk
Manager: Luis Rivera

D-U-N-S 00-227-6301 IMP
PHILADELPHIA BUNZL
(*Suby of* BUNZL USA INC) ★
10814 Northeast Ave, Philadelphia, PA 19116-3447
Tel (215) 969-0600 *Founded/Ownrshp* 1946, 2006
Sales 139.7MM^E *EMP* 300
SIC 5087 5023 5113 7213 Janitors' supplies; China; Glassware; Kitchen tools & utensils; Industrial & personal service paper; Linen supply
Pr: Richard Maier
Exec: Wollman Donna
Genl Mgr: Rick Maier
Genl Mgr: Michael Pavlicka
Genl Mgr: Mike Pazlicka
Opers Mgr: Dave Miller
Sls Mgr: Paul Feldman

D-U-N-S 01-440-8197
PHILADELPHIA CARPENTERS BENEFIT FUNDS
1811 Spring Garden St, Philadelphia, PA 19130-3916
Tel (215) 568-0430 *Founded/Ownrshp* 2002
Sales 112.4MM *EMP* 27
SIC 1751 Carpentry work

D-U-N-S 00-229-8271 IMP
■ PHILADELPHIA COCA-COLA BOTTLING CO
(*Suby of* COCA-COLA CO) ★
725 E Erie Ave, Philadelphia, PA 19134-1210
Tel (215) 427-4500 *Founded/Ownrshp* 1919, 2008
Sales 81.7MM^E *EMP* 1,000
SIC 2086

D-U-N-S 07-549-0854
PHILADELPHIA COLLEGE OF OSTEOPATHIC MEDICINE (PA)
PCOM
4190 City Ave, Philadelphia, PA 19131-1626
Tel (215) 871-6100 *Founded/Ownrshp* 1896
Sales 116.4MM *EMP* 551
Accts Deloitte & Touche Llp Philad
SIC 8221 Professional schools
Pr: Jay Feldstein Do
Pr: Joan McGettigan
CFO: Peter Doulis
**Ch:* Paul W McGloin
Sr VP: Kenneth Veit
VP: Robert Cuzzolino
Assoc Dir: Kari Shotwell
Telecom Mg: Robert Battle
Mktg Dir: Wendy Romano
Psych: Desiree Carriker
Psych: Carly Iannone

D-U-N-S 17-551-0916
PHILADELPHIA CONSOLIDATED HOLDING CORP
(*Suby of* TOKIO MARINE HOLDINGS, INC.)
1 Bala Plz Ste 100, Bala Cynwyd, PA 19004-1401
Tel (610) 617-7900 *Founded/Ownrshp* 1981
Sales NA *EMP* 1,374^E
SIC 6331 Fire, marine & casualty insurance & carriers; Property damage insurance
Ch: James J Maguire
Pr: Richard Kukosky
Pr: Fay Maffei
Pr: Robert Oleary
**CEO:* Robert D O'Leary
**Ex VP:* William J Benecke
**Ex VP:* Karen A Gilmer-Pauciello
**Ex VP:* Ms Karen A Gilmer-Pauciello
**Ex VP:* Brian O'Reilly
VP: Michael Freeman
VP: Samuel Garro
VP: Frank Giardina
VP: Michael Kelly

D-U-N-S 06-902-3695
PHILADELPHIA CONTRIBUTIONSHIP FOR INSURANCE OF HOUSES FROM LOSS BY FIRE
CONTRIBUTIONSHIP COMPANIES
212 S 4th St, Philadelphia, PA 19106-3704
Tel (215) 627-1752 *Founded/Ownrshp* 1752
Sales NA *EMP* 1,500^E
SIC 6331 6311 7382 6321 Fire, marine & casualty insurance; Life insurance carriers; Protective devices, security; Accident & health insurance
Ch: Shaun F O'Malley
Pr: Christina T Webber
Ex VP: Robert J Riffert
VP: John Summits
Dir IT: Mark Montagna
Mktg Dir: Joe Morris
Snr Mgr: Brian Kaiser

D-U-N-S 07-028-1225
PHILADELPHIA CORP FOR AGING INC
PCA
642 N Broad St Fl 5, Philadelphia, PA 19130-3424
Tel (215) 765-9040 *Founded/Ownrshp* 1973
Sales 94.4MM *EMP* 650
Accts Citrin Cooperman & Company Llp
SIC 8322 Senior citizens' center or association
Pr: Holly Lange
VP: Louis Colbert
VP: Benjamin Ellis
Prgrm Mgr: Kimberley Johnson
MIS Dir: Kimberly Upchurch
Corp Couns: Lisa Alexander

D-U-N-S 96-312-2911
PHILADELPHIA ENERGY SOLUTIONS LLC
JOINT VENTURE BETWEEN
1735 Market St Fl 10, Philadelphia, PA 19103-7505
Tel (267) 238-4300 *Founded/Ownrshp* 2012
Sales 228.8MM^E *EMP* 1,195
SIC 2911 Petroleum refining
CEO: Philip Rinaldi
**COO:* Gregory Gatta
**CFO:* James Rens
**Ex VP:* Thomas Scargle
Comm Man: Cherice Corley
Dir IT: Mark Quarles
**Genl Couns:* John McShane

D-U-N-S 07-862-5328
PHILADELPHIA ENERGY SOLUTIONS REFINING AND MARKETING LLC
JOINT VENTURE BETWEEN THE CARL
1735 Market St Fl 11, Philadelphia, PA 19103-7535
Tel (267) 238-4300 *Founded/Ownrshp* 2012
Sales 355.5MM^E *EMP* 1,195
SIC 2911 Petroleum refining
CEO: Phillip Rinaldi
COO: Gregory Gatta
CFO: James Rens
Chf Cred: Thomas Scargle

D-U-N-S 07-161-3897
PHILADELPHIA FACILITIES MANAGEMENT CORP
PHILADELPHIA GAS WORKS
800 W Montgomery Ave, Philadelphia, PA 19122-2806
Tel (215) 684-3000 *Founded/Ownrshp* 1972
Sales 115.3MM^E *EMP* 365^E
Accts Kpmg Llp Philadelphia Pennsy
SIC 8744 Facilities support services
CEO: Craig E White
Ex VP: Joseph F Golden Jr
Ex VP: Douglas A Moser
Sr VP: Douglas I Oliver
Sr VP: Daniel P Murray
VP: Alfred M Degen
VP: Les Fyock
VP: Paul Mondimore
VP: Jo A Muniz
VP: Joseph Smith
Exec: Maryanne Campbell
Dir Risk M: Jane Lamb
Board of Directors: Allan J Davis, Chris Vandeveld

PHILADELPHIA GAS WORKS
See PHILADELPHIA FACILITIES MANAGEMENT CORP

D-U-N-S 06-119-7161
PHILADELPHIA HEALTH AND EDUCATION CORP
MCP HAHNEMANN UNIVERSITY
245 N 15th St, Philadelphia, PA 19102-1101
Tel (215) 762-8288 *Founded/Ownrshp* 1998
Sales 92.7MM^E *EMP* 1,600
SIC 8221

D-U-N-S 79-393-8965
PHILADELPHIA HEALTH EDUCATION CORP
PHEC DUCOM
1601 Cherry St Ste 11511, Philadelphia, PA 19102-1310
Tel (215) 255-7755 *Founded/Ownrshp* 2006
Sales 20.7MM^E *EMP* 3,000
SIC 8011

PHILADELPHIA HEALTH MANAGEMENT
See PUBLIC HEALTH MANAGEMENT CORP

D-U-N-S 00-259-7821
PHILADELPHIA HOUSING AUTHORITY
12 S 23rd St, Philadelphia, PA 19103-3014
Tel (215) 684-4000 *Founded/Ownrshp* 1937
Sales NA *EMP* 2,000
SIC 9531 Housing authority, non-operating: government
Pr: Kelvin A Jeremiah
Comm Dir: Maurice Browne
**Prin:* Estelle Richman
Rgnl Mgr: Carl Childs
Genl Couns: Morris Hershman

D-U-N-S 80-124-0995
PHILADELPHIA INDEMNITY INSURANCE CO
(*Suby of* PHILADELPHIA CONSOLIDATED HOLDING CORP) ★
1 Bala Plz Ste 100, Bala Cynwyd, PA 19004-1401
Tel (610) 642-8400 *Founded/Ownrshp* 1987
Sales NA *EMP* 350^E
SIC 6411 Property & casualty insurance agent
Pr: James Maguire Jr
Sr VP: Robert Morgan
Sr VP: Andrew Peel
**VP:* William J Benecke
**VP:* Philip D Eldridge
VP: Chris Hartley
**VP:* Craig P Keller
**VP:* Robert D O'Leary Jr
**VP:* Charles K Pedone
**VP:* Douglas S Platt
**VP:* Michael G Russell
**VP:* Sean S Sweeney
**VP:* Philip W Tweitmeyer

PHILADELPHIA INQUIRER
See PHILDELPHIA-NEWSPAPERS-LLC

PHILADELPHIA INQUIRER
See PHILADELPHIA MEDIA NETWORK PBC

PHILADELPHIA INSUR COMPANIES
See PHILADELPHIA INSURANCE CO

D-U-N-S 19-045-1005
PHILADELPHIA INSURANCE CO
PHILADELPHIA INSUR COMPANIES
(*Suby of* PHILADELPHIA CONSOLIDATED HOLDING CORP) ★
231 Sint Asphs Rd Ste 100, Bala Cynwyd, PA 19004
Tel (877) 438-7459 *Founded/Ownrshp* 1986
Sales NA *EMP* 500
SIC 6331 6411 Fire, marine & casualty insurance; Insurance agents, brokers & service
CEO: Bob O'Leary
**Ch Bd:* James J Maguire
**CFO:* Craig P Keller
**Co-Pr:* Christopher J Maguire
**Co-Pr:* Sean S Sweeney
**Chf Mktg O:* Brian J O'Reilly
Sr VP: Seth Hall
Sr VP: Timothy Maguire
Sr VP: Bob Morgan
Sr VP: Robert Oleary
VP: Susan Doering
VP: Jeffrey E Frick
VP: Brian Kilroy
VP: Bryan Luci
VP: Robert Morgan
VP: Charles K Pedone
VP: Stuart Sadwin
VP: Neal Schmidt
VP: Steve Stefanic
Board of Directors: Michael J Cascio, Margaret M Mattix

D-U-N-S 96-586-6804
PHILADELPHIA MEDIA NETWORK PBC
PHILADELPHIA INQUIRER
801 Market St Ste 300, Philadelphia, PA 19107-3183
Tel (215) 854-2000 *Founded/Ownrshp* 2009
Sales 327.9MM[E] *EMP* 2,000[E]
SIC 2711 Newspapers, publishing & printing
CEO: Terry Egger
**CFO:* Andy Harrison
**Ch:* H F Gerry Lenfest
Mktg Mgr: Rob Roper

D-U-N-S 07-161-0851 IMP
PHILADELPHIA MUSEUM OF ART INC
2600 Bnjmin Franklin Pkwy, Philadelphia, PA 19130-2302
Tel (215) 763-8100 *Founded/Ownrshp* 1875
Sales 105.1MM *EMP* 430
Accts Kpmg Llp Mc Lean Va
SIC 8412 Museums & art galleries
Ch: Constance H Williams
Pt: Kiki Gaffney
Pt: Allison Riepe
**Ch Bd:* Jerry H F Lemfest
V Ch: Julian Brodsky
Pr: Rachel Dye
**CEO:* Timothy Rub
**COO:* Gail M Harrity
COO: Sandy Russow
CFO: Marty Mbzern
Ofcr: Mary Assini
Ofcr: Robin Barnes
Ofcr: Elisabeth Flynn
Ofcr: Eileen Matchett
Ofcr: Paul Pincus

D-U-N-S 62-659-7249
PHILADELPHIA NORTH HEALTH SYSTEM
GIRARD MEDICAL CENTER
801 W Girard Ave, Philadelphia, PA 19122-4212
Tel (215) 787-9001 *Founded/Ownrshp* 1990
Sales 103.9MM *EMP* 900
Accts Smart Devine Philadelphia Pa
SIC 8062 8069 8063 General medical & surgical hospitals; Specialty hospitals, except psychiatric; Substance abuse hospitals; Psychiatric hospitals
Pr: George Walmsley III
**CEO:* Catherine Kutzler
**CEO:* Marlene Walse
CFO: Margaret Boemmel
CFO: Peggy Boemmeo
Ofcr: Jason Hauser
Sr VP: Alvan S Mc Neal
VP: Cathy Kutzler
Opers Supe: Ana Vazquez

D-U-N-S 07-551-2582 IMP
PHILADELPHIA PARKING AUTHORITY
701 Market St Ste 5400, Philadelphia, PA 19106-2895
Tel (215) 222-0224 *Founded/Ownrshp* 1950
Sales 68.6MM[E] *EMP* 1,100
SIC 7521 Parking lots
CEO: Vincent J Fenerty Jr
**Ch Bd:* Joseph Ashdale
**CFO:* Barry Kavtsty

D-U-N-S 07-145-7568
PHILADELPHIA PHILLIES
1 Citizens Bank Way Ofc, Philadelphia, PA 19148-5249
Tel (215) 463-5000 *Founded/Ownrshp* 1981
Sales 123.0MM[E] *EMP* 1,800
SIC 7941 Baseball club, professional & semi-professional
Ch: David P Montgomery
Genl Pt: Mary Gettis
**COO:* Michael Stiles
**CFO:* John N Nickolas
VP: Michael R Stiles
VP: William Webb
Dir Bus: Joe Giles
IT Man: John Stranix
Sls Dir: John Weber
**Genl Couns:* Richard L Strouse

D-U-N-S 07-547-8776
PHILADELPHIA PRESBYTERY HOMES INC
ROSEMONT PRESBYTERIAN VILLAGE
2000 Joshua Rd, Lafayette Hill, PA 19444-2430
Tel (610) 834-1001 *Founded/Ownrshp* 1955
Sales 67.9MM *EMP* 1,100
Accts Baker Tilly Virchow Krause Llp
SIC 8361 8052 8051 Residential care; Intermediate care facilities; Skilled nursing care facilities
Pr: Judee M Bavaria
**CFO:* Cindy Hoffman
**VP:* Michelle T Bryk
**VP:* Jennifer Kappen
VP: Lynn Porter

D-U-N-S 07-871-5710
PHILADELPHIA GAS WORKS
1800 N 9th St, Philadelphia, PA 19122-2099
Tel (215) 684-6710 *Founded/Ownrshp* 2012
Sales 697.2MM *EMP* 2
SIC 4923 Gas transmission & distribution
CEO: Craig E White
COO: John Murray
**Ex VP:* Joseph F Golden
**Ex VP:* Douglas A Moser
VP: Randy Gyory
VP: Steven Hershey
VP: Joseph Smith
Exec: Anne Breyer
Exec: Thomas Kolodij
Exec: Joe Stengel
CTO: Carolyn Harding

D-U-N-S 06-143-7604 IMP/EXP
PHILCOR TV & ELECTRONIC LEASING INC (NV)
NEDCO SUPPLY
4200 Spring Mountain Rd, Las Vegas, NV 89102-8748
Tel (702) 367-0400 *Founded/Ownrshp* 1982
Sales 147.5MM[E] *EMP* 84
SIC 5063 5065 Electrical fittings & construction materials; Lighting fixtures; Video equipment, electronic
Pr: Marshall E Hunt
**Sec:* Marc Winard
Exec: Peter Giallanza
Sales Exec: Juston Shearer
S&M/VP: Rod Gowen
Sales Asso: Jeff Comeaux
Sales Asso: Joe Cordova
Sales Asso: Dan Davia
Sales Asso: Matt Guild
Sales Asso: Eddie Moggia

D-U-N-S 05-139-3296 IMP
PHILDELPHIA-NEWSPAPERS-LLC
PHILADELPHIA INQUIRER
801 Market St Ste 300, Philadelphia, PA 19107-3183
Tel (215) 854-2000 *Founded/Ownrshp* 2012
Sales 317.5MM[E] *EMP* 3,066
SIC 2711 Newspapers, publishing & printing
Ch Bd: Gerry Lenfest
**Pr:* Frederick B Mott
**CEO:* Brian Tierney
**COO:* Robert J Hall
CFO: Andrew Harrison
**Chf Mktg O:* Ed Mahlman
**Ex VP:* William Marimow
**Ex VP:* Mark Srisby
**Ex VP:* Richard Thayer
Ex VP: Butch Ward
Netwrk Mgr: Paul Rowlings

PHILHAVEN BEHAVIORAL HLTH SVCS
See PHILHAVEN HOSPITAL

D-U-N-S 07-119-6364
PHILHAVEN HOSPITAL
PHILHAVEN BEHAVIORAL HLTH SVCS
283 Butler Rd, Lebanon, PA 17042-8999
Tel (717) 270-2414 *Founded/Ownrshp* 1949
Sales 60.6MM *EMP* 1,000
Accts Parentebeard Llc Philadelphia
SIC 8011 8063 Psychiatric clinic; Psychiatric hospitals
CEO: Philip D Hess
Dir Recs: Sonia Kiehl
**Pr:* David Hernley
**Pr:* George Stolzfus
CFO: Matt Rogers
**CFO:* Matthew Rogers
**Treas:* Ken Moore
Bd of Dir: Ann Marie Heilman
Bd of Dir: E A Sosa Vazquez
Dir Case M: Joyce Simmers
Dir Rx: Linda Schneiter

D-U-N-S 07-782-1312
■ **PHILIP MORRIS CAPITAL CORP**
(*Suby of* ALTRIA GROUP INC) ★
225 High Ridge Rd Ste 300, Stamford, CT 06905-3034
Tel (203) 348-1350 *Founded/Ownrshp* 1986
Sales NA *EMP* 56
SIC 6159 Machinery & equipment finance leasing
Pr: John J Mulligan
**VP:* Douglas B Levene
**VP:* George Lewis

D-U-N-S 19-707-4024 IMP/EXP
▲ **PHILIP MORRIS INTERNATIONAL INC**
120 Park Ave Fl 6, New York, NY 10017-5592
Tel (917) 663-2000 *Founded/Ownrshp* 1987
Sales 73.9MMM *EMP* 80,200[E]
Tkr Sym PM *Exch* NYS
SIC 2111 Cigarettes
CEO: Andre Calantzopoulos
**Ch Bd:* Louis C Camilleri
Pr: Drago Azinovic
Pr: Frederic De Wilde
Pr: Martin King
Pr: Jeanne Polls
Pr: Miroslaw Zielinski
CFO: Ashwin Nair
CFO: Jacek Olczak
Sr VP: Werner Barth
Sr VP: Patrick Brunel
Sr VP: Marc S Firestone
Sr VP: Marco Mariotti
Sr VP: Antonio Marques
Sr VP: James R Mortensen
VP: Hafed Belhadj
VP: Andreas Kurali
VP: Randy T Lawrence
VP: Peter J Luongo
Board of Directors: Stephen M Wolf, Harold Brown, Massimo Ferragamo, Werner Geissler, Jennifer Li, Jun Makihara, Sergio Marchionne, Lucio A Noto, Frederik Paulsen, Robert B Polet

D-U-N-S 00-130-6497 IMP/EXP
■ **PHILIP MORRIS USA INC** (VA)
(*Suby of* ALTRIA GROUP INC) ★
6601 W Brd St, Richmond, VA 23230
Tel (804) 274-2000 *Founded/Ownrshp* 1919, 1985
Sales 2.3MMM[E] *EMP* 7,300
SIC 2111 2141 5194 Cigarettes; Tobacco stemming & redrying; Cigarettes
**Pr:* John R Nelson
**CFO:* William F Gifford Jr
**Ex VP:* David R Beran
Sr VP: Kevin P Bennar
Sr VP: Roy C Harris
**Sr VP:* Craig G Schwartz
**Sr VP:* Harry G Steele
VP: Dede T Bartlett
**VP:* Cliff B Fleet
**VP:* Denise F Keane
VP: Francisca Rahardja
VP: Linda Warren

PHILIPS
See RESPIRONICS INC

D-U-N-S 60-389-4002 IMP
PHILIPS CONSUMER ELECTRONIC CO
PHILLIPS CONSUMER ELECTRONICS
12430 Mercantile Ave, El Paso, TX 79928-5235
Tel (915) 298-4111 *Founded/Ownrshp* 1996
Sales 108.1MM[E] *EMP* 1,000
SIC 3663 Cameras, television
CEO: Roger De Moor
Prin: Philips Juarez

PHILIPS CONSUMER LIFESTYLE
See PHILIPS HOLDING USA INC

D-U-N-S 00-129-1111 IMP
PHILIPS ELECTRONICS NORTH AMERICA CORP
(*Suby of* PHILIPS CONSUMER LIFESTYLE) ★
3000 Minuteman Rd Ms1203, Andover, MA 01810-1032
Tel (978) 687-1501 *Founded/Ownrshp* 1933
Sales 10.1MMM[E] *EMP* 24,000
SIC 5064 3651 3674 3641 3645 5047 Electrical appliances, television & radio; Electrical entertainment equipment; Television sets; Video cassette recorders & accessories; Household audio & video equipment; Semiconductors & related devices; Integrated circuits, semiconductor networks, etc.; Electric lamps; Electric lamps & parts for generalized applications; Lamps, incandescent filament, electric; Lamps, fluorescent, electric; Residential lighting fixtures; Electromedical equipment
CEO: Brent Shafer
Sr VP: David A Dripchak
Sr VP: Joseph E Innamorati
VP: Paul Cavanaugh
VP: Nitin Chhabra
VP: Michel Claassens
VP: James Cyrier
VP: Raymond C Fleming
VP: Andrew Hatt
VP: Martin King
VP: Scott Schwartz
Dir Surg: Leverda Wallace
Dir Bus: Jose Downes

PHILIPS ENTERTAINMENT LIGHTING
See GENLYTE THOMAS GROUP LLC

PHILIPS HEALTHCARE
See PHILIPS MEDICAL SYSTEMS MR INC

D-U-N-S 94-310-2368 IMP/EXP
PHILIPS HOLDING USA INC
PHILIPS CONSUMER LIFESTYLE
(*Suby of* KONINKLIJKE PHILIPS N.V.)
3000 Minuteman Rd Ste 109, Andover, MA 01810-1032
Tel (978) 687-1501 *Founded/Ownrshp* 1995
Sales 12.8MMM[E] *EMP* 25,000
SIC 5064 3674 5045 5047 3641 Electrical appliances, television & radio; Electrical entertainment equipment; Television sets; Video cassette recorders & accessories; Semiconductors & related devices; Computers, peripherals & software; Medical & hospital equipment; Electric lamps; Electric lamps & parts for generalized applications; Lamps, incandescent filament, electric; Lamps, fluorescent, electric
CEO: Brent Shafer
**Sr VP:* Joseph E Innamorati
VP: Deborah Mikell
Dir Surg: Leverda Wallace
Snr Sftwr: Paul Mancini
Sftwr Eng: Kevin Quan
Mktg Mgr: Ashley Cappel

PHILIPS LIFELINE
See LIFELINE SYSTEMS CO

D-U-N-S 01-270-2812 IMP
PHILIPS LIGHTING NORTH AMERICA CORP
COLOR KINETICS
(*Suby of* KONINKLIJKE PHILIPS N.V.)
3 Burlington Woods Dr # 4, Burlington, MA 01803-4532
Tel (617) 423-9999 *Founded/Ownrshp* 1997
Sales 27.0MMM *EMP* 4,480
SIC 3646 Commercial indusl & institutional electric lighting fixtures
CEO: Brent Shafer
**CEO:* Brent Shaper
CFO: Eugene De Lannoy
**CFO:* Raoul Gatzen
CFO: David K Johnson
Dir Surg: Leverda Wallace
Dir IT: John Warwick
VP Mfg: Paul Kennedy
Mktg Mgr: Jim Casella
Sls Mgr: John Sollenberger

PHILIPS LUMILEDS LIGHTING CO
See LUMILEDS LLC

PHILIPS MEDICAL SYSTEMS
See PHILIPS ULTRASOUND INC

D-U-N-S 00-122-4989 IMP/EXP
PHILIPS MEDICAL SYSTEMS (CLEVELAND) INC
MEDICAL IMAGING EQUIPMENT
(*Suby of* PHILIPS CONSUMER LIFESTYLE) ★
595 Miner Rd, Cleveland, OH 44143-2131
Tel (440) 247-2652 *Founded/Ownrshp* 1970
Sales 385.8MM[E] *EMP* 2,716
SIC 3844 5047 5137 3842 3821 3699 X-ray apparatus & tubes; X-ray film & supplies; Instruments, surgical & medical; Hospital gowns, women's & children's; Surgical appliances & supplies; Laboratory apparatus & furniture; Electrical equipment & supplies
CEO: David A Dripchak
**CFO:* Robert Blankenship
**Ex VP:* Jerry C Cirino
**VP:* William J Cull Sr
VP: Hillary Sullivan
VP: Eliezer Tokman
VP: Karl Wolcott
Exec: Tom Andriola
Dir Surg: Leverda Wallace
Genl Mgr: Arlene Burnside
Snr Sftwr: Subodh Vaidya

D-U-N-S 79-060-5856 IMP/EXP
PHILIPS MEDICAL SYSTEMS HSG
3000 Minuteman Rd, Andover, MA 01810-1032
Tel (978) 687-1501 *Founded/Ownrshp* 2007
Sales 201.2MM[E] *EMP* 2,500[E]
SIC 3675 3676 Electronic capacitors; Electronic resistors
Pr: Jorod Klesterkei
**CFO:* Ron Wirahadiraksa
Software D: Dick Corrigan
Sftwr Eng: Greg Millett
Ql Cn Mgr: Kristen Lessard
Mktg Dir: Krystyna Niklarz
Mktg Mgr: Maria Gerea
Snr Mgr: Kim Hanna

D-U-N-S 05-572-9800 IMP/EXP
PHILIPS MEDICAL SYSTEMS MR INC
PHILIPS HEALTHCARE
(*Suby of* PHILIPS CONSUMER LIFESTYLE) ★
450 Old Niskayuna Rd, Latham, NY 12110-1569
Tel (518) 782-1122 *Founded/Ownrshp* 2006
Sales 152.5MM[E] *EMP* 1,150
SIC 3845 3674 3679 Electromedical equipment; Magnetic resonance imaging device, nuclear; Integrated circuits, semiconductor networks, etc.; Cryogenic cooling devices for infrared detectors, masers; Cores, magnetic
CEO: Stephen H Rusckowski
Pr: Leo Blecher
Pr: Richard Stevens
CFO: Gerard Van Spaenbonck
Ex VP: Thomas J O'Brien
Ex VP: Thomas J Obrien
VP: Robert Sokolowski
Dir Surg: Leverda Wallace

D-U-N-S 60-872-9869 EXP
PHILIPS ORAL HEALTHCARE LLC
SONICCARE
(*Suby of* PHILIPS ELECTRONICS NORTH AMERICA CORP) ★
22100 Bothell Everett Hwy, Bothell, WA 98021-8431
Tel (425) 487-7000 *Founded/Ownrshp* 1988
Sales 209.7MM[E] *EMP* 1,800
SIC 3843 Dental equipment & supplies
Pr: Sinead Kwant
**Pr:* Jack Gallagher
**Pr:* Frank McGillin
**Pr:* Steffen Michael Mueller
**Treas:* David Dripchak
Act CFO: Meindert Exoo
**VP:* Paul Cavanaugh
**VP:* Joseph Innamorati
Dir Surg: Leverda Wallace
Prgrm Mgr: Craig Wood
Board of Directors: Vincent F Coviello Jr, L David Engel, Louis G Yaseen

D-U-N-S 06-337-7717 IMP
PHILIPS ULTRASOUND INC (WA)
PHILIPS MEDICAL SYSTEMS
(*Suby of* PHILIPS ELECTRONICS NORTH AMERICA CORP) ★
22100 Bothell Everett Hwy, Bothell, WA 98021-8431
Tel (800) 982-2011 *Founded/Ownrshp* 1969, 1998
Sales 276.3MM[E] *EMP* 1,000
SIC 3845 Electromedical equipment; Electromedical apparatus; Electrotherapeutic apparatus
CEO: Conrad Smits
**Pr:* David A Dripchak
**Pr:* James Mark Mattern II
**CFO:* Pamela L Dunlap
CFO: Scott M Weisenhoff
Treas: Nick Jarus
**Treas:* Dana Lance-Petri
Chf Mktg O: Ronald De Jong
Ofcr: Judy Bennett
Ofcr: Raj Rajeswari
Ofcr: Clement Revetti
**Sr VP:* Donald D Blem
**Sr VP:* Victor H Reddick
**Sr VP:* Jacquet Souquet
VP: Anne Bugge
**VP:* Paul Cavanaugh
VP: Jim Haisler
**VP:* Andrew T Hatt
**VP:* Joseph Innamorati
VP: Robert N Smith
VP: Terrence J Sweeney

D-U-N-S 06-652-5213 IMP
PHILLIPS & TEMRO INDUSTRIES INC
TRUFLO
(*Suby of* HARBOUR GROUP LTD) ★
9700 W 74th St, Eden Prairie, MN 55344-3515
Tel (952) 941-9700 *Founded/Ownrshp* 2015
Sales 198.3MM[E] *EMP* 720
SIC 3714 Heaters, motor vehicle
CEO: Harry Sumpter
Pr: Tom Meline
**CFO:* Dave Hawkins

**CFO:* Michael Ramsay
VP: Tom Splinter
CIO: Butch Sumpter
IT Man: Scott Anderson
Sfty Mgr: Peter Tollefson
Opers Mgr: Pat Gilson
Opers Mgr: Jennifer Gouette
Plnt Mgr: Roy Smith

PHILLIPS 66
See CONRAD & BISCHOFF INC

D-U-N-S 07-842-3447 IMP/EXP
▲ PHILLIPS 66
2331 City West Blvd, Houston, TX 77042
Tel (832) 765-3300 *Founded/Ownrshp* 2012
Sales 100.9MMM *EMP* 14,000^E
Tkr Sym PSX *Exch* NYS
SIC 1311 2911 2869 Crude petroleum & natural gas; Petroleum refining; Olefins
Ch Bd: Greg C Garland
Pr: Tim G Taylor
COO: Kevin Miller
CFO: Kevin J Mitchell
Ex VP: Paula A Johnson
Ex VP: Lawrence M Ziemba
VP: Ann Oglesby
VP: Chukwuemeka A Oyolu
Board of Directors: Gary K Adams, J Brian Ferguson, William R Loomis Jr, John E Lowe, Harold W McGraw III, Denise L Ramos, Glenn F Tilton, Victoria J Tschinkel, Marna C Whittington

D-U-N-S 07-837-8508 IMP/EXP
■ PHILLIPS 66 CO
(*Suby of* PHILLIPS 66) ★
1075 W Sam Houston Pkwy N # 200, Houston, TX 77043-5018
Tel (281) 293-6600 *Founded/Ownrshp* 2012
Sales 118.7MMM *EMP* 130^E
SIC 2911 Petroleum refining; Acid oil; Alkylates; Aromatic chemical products
CEO: Greg C Garland
Sr VP: Phillip D Brady
Board of Directors: Carin S Knickel, Jeff W Sheets

D-U-N-S 07-879-4614
■ PHILLIPS 66 PARTNERS LP
(*Suby of* PHILLIPS 66) ★
3010 Briarpark Dr, Houston, TX 77042-3706
Tel (855) 283-9237 *Founded/Ownrshp* 2013
Sales 348.1MM *EMP* 180^E
Tkr Sym PSXP *Exch* NYS
SIC 4612 1311 5541 Crude petroleum pipelines; Crude petroleum & natural gas; Gasoline service stations
Ch Bd: Greg C Garland
Genl Pt: Phillips 6 LLC
Pr: Tim G Taylor
CFO: Greg Maxwell
Ex VP: Lawrence Ziemba
Sr VP: Sonya Reed
VP: Ben Hur
Pr Mgr: Nancy Sadlon

D-U-N-S 00-384-5336 IMP
PHILLIPS AND JORDAN INC (NC)
10201 Parkside Dr Ste 300, Knoxville, TN 37922-1983
Tel (865) 688-8342 *Founded/Ownrshp* 1953
Sales 340.3MM *EMP* 650
Accts Rodgers Moss & Co Pllc Knox
SIC 1611 1629 Highway & street construction; Land clearing contractor
CEO: William T Phillips Jr
**Pr:* J Patrick McMullen
**Ch:* William T Phillips Sr
**Sr VP:* Connie H Nichols
VP: Eric Hedrick
VP: Randy Jorda
VP: Randy Jordan
**VP:* John D Lawrence
VP: Patrick McMullen
VP: Max G Morton
VP: Steve Thompson

PHILLIPS CONSUMER ELECTRONICS
See PHILIPS CONSUMER ELECTRONIC CO

D-U-N-S 00-325-8043
PHILLIPS CORP (MD)
FEDERAL DIVISION
(*Suby of* CNC SERVICING & SOLUTIONS (INDIA) PRIVATE LIMITED)
7390 Coca Cola Dr Ste 200, Hanover, MD 21076-1937
Tel (800) 878-4747 *Founded/Ownrshp* 1961
Sales 204.7MM^E *EMP* 400
SIC 5084 7373 3542 Metalworking machinery; Computer integrated systems design; Presses: forming, stamping, punching, sizing (machine tools)
Pr: Alan M Phillips
Pr: Bill Withers
**CFO:* Matthew Phillips
Treas: Sherri Tempchin
Exec: Neil Stephenson
Exec: Amy Yasneski
Sales Exec: Ronald Schultz
VP Sls: Tim McClanahan

D-U-N-S 96-264-1119
PHILLIPS EDISON - ARC SHOPPING CENTER REIT INC
11501 Northlake Dr Fl 1, Cincinnati, OH 45249-1667
Tel (513) 554-1110 *Founded/Ownrshp* 1991
Sales 188.2MM *EMP* 18^E
Accts Deloitte & Touche Llp Cincinn
SIC 6512 Shopping center, property operation only
Ch Bd: Jeffrey S Edison
**Pr:* John Bessey
**COO:* R Mark Addy
**CFO:* Devin I Murphy
**CFO:* Richard J Smith
**Co-Ch Bd:* Michael C Phillips
**CIO:* Hal Scudder

D-U-N-S 07-926-1904
PHILLIPS EDISON-ARC GROCERY CENTER REIT II INC (MD)
11501 Northlake Dr, Cincinnati, OH 45249-1669
Tel (513) 554-1110 *Founded/Ownrshp* 2013
Sales 188.2MM *EMP* 1^E
Accts Deloitte & Touche Llp Cincinn
SIC 6798 Real estate investment trusts
Ch Bd: Jeffrey S Edison

D-U-N-S 07-397-8348 IMP
PHILLIPS EXETER ACADEMY
20 Main St, Exeter, NH 03833-2460
Tel (603) 772-4311 *Founded/Ownrshp* 1781
Sales 135.3MM *EMP* 520
Accts Pricewaterhousecoopers Llp Bo
SIC 8211 Preparatory school
Prin: Thomas Sheppard
**Pr:* G Thompson
**CFO:* Christopher Wejchert
Treas: Joseph E Fllows
Ofcr: Mark Blackman
Exec: Kate Anatone
Assoc Dir: Randy Armstrong
Assoc Dir: Gretchen B Bergill
Assoc Dir: Karen Ingraham
Comm Dir: Robin Giampa
**Prin:* Thomas Hassan

PHILLIPS FEED & PET SUPPLY
See PHILLIPS FEED SERVICE INC

D-U-N-S 01-413-7988 IMP
PHILLIPS FEED SERVICE INC (CA)
PHILLIPS FEED & PET SUPPLY
3747 Hecktown Rd, Easton, PA 18045-2350
Tel (610) 250-2099 *Founded/Ownrshp* 1959, 1941
Sales 657.3MM^E *EMP* 700
SIC 5199 Pets & pet supplies
Pr: Blaine Phillips
**Treas:* Lavern Phillips
VP: John Lawton
Sls Dir: Lon Zeigler
Manager: Joe Semonich
Manager: Brian Smith
Manager: Shannon Taylor

D-U-N-S 87-793-6922
PHILLIPS JANE HEALTH CARE FOUNDATION INC
3500 E Frank Philips Blvd, Bartlesville, OK 74006-2411
Tel (918) 333-7200 *Founded/Ownrshp* 1985
Sales 607.7M *EMP* 1,000
SIC 8062 General medical & surgical hospitals
CEO: David Stire

D-U-N-S 96-260-2806
PHILLIPS PET FOOD AND SUPPLIES
3885 Seaport Blvd Ste 10, West Sacramento, CA 95691-3527
Tel (916) 373-7300 *Founded/Ownrshp* 2005
Sales 200.0MM *EMP* 200
SIC 5149 Pet foods
Treas: Rusty Haley
Opers Supe: David Pacheco
**Mktg Mgr:* Kelli Wall
Sls Mgr: Sean Zyer

D-U-N-S 00-136-8265 IMP/EXP
■ PHILLIPS PETROLEUM CO
(*Suby of* CONOCOPHILLIPS) ★
600 N Dairy Ashford Rd, Houston, TX 77079-1100
Tel (281) 293-1000 *Founded/Ownrshp* 1917
Sales 19.5MMM^E *EMP* 16,900
SIC 1382 2911 5171 5541 Oil & gas exploration services; Gasoline; Petroleum bulk stations; Filling stations, gasoline
CEO: Ryan M Lance
**Ch Bd:* J J Mulva
**CFO:* John A Carrig
Ex VP: Ellen R Desanctis
Ex VP: Al J Hirshberg
Sr VP: Dodd W Decamp
Sr VP: Ryan Lance
Sr VP: John E Lowe
Sr VP: Luc Messier
Sr VP: J C Mihm
VP: E L Batchelder
VP: Michael Carr
**VP:* Matt Fox
VP: E K Grigsby
VP: Rocco Iannapollo
VP: Robert A Ridge
Exec: Lisa Befort
Dir Bus: Scott Mason
Board of Directors: John Faraci

D-U-N-S 80-759-8313
■ PHILLIPS PETROLEUM INTERNATIONAL INVESTMENT CO LLC
(*Suby of* PHILLIPS PETROLEUM CO) ★
2711 Centerville Rd # 400, Wilmington, DE 19808-1660
Tel (918) 661-6600 *Founded/Ownrshp* 2000
Sales 25.6MM^E *EMP* 3,500
SIC 8742 Management consulting services
Pr: Glen D Moore
**Treas:* Scott F Hussey
**Treas:* Caryl A Mc Bride
**VP:* Jim Bowles
**VP:* E W Heaton

D-U-N-S 12-151-6686
PHILLIPS SERVICE INDUSTRIES INC
PSI
11878 Hubbard St, Livonia, MI 48150-1733
Tel (734) 853-5000 *Founded/Ownrshp* 1984
Sales 112.0MM^E *EMP* 489
SIC 7699 7694 7629 Pumps & pumping equipment repair; Valve repair, industrial; Electric motor repair; Circuit board repair
Ch: William T Phillips
**Pr:* W Scott Phillips
**CFO:* Lawrence Perlin
Treas: Michael D Fitzpatrick
VP: Ralph C Staelgraeve

D-U-N-S 00-643-1191 IMP
PHILLIPS-MEDISIZE CORP
(*Suby of* MOLEX LLC) ★
1201 Hanley Rd, Hudson, WI 54016-9372
Tel (715) 386-4320 *Founded/Ownrshp* 1964, 2016
Sales 691.0MM^E *EMP* 1,600
SIC 3089 3444 3544 Injection molded finished plastic products; Plastic hardware & building products; Hardware, plastic; Sheet metalwork; Special dies, tools, jigs & fixtures
Pr: Matthew J Jennings
VP: Winston Brown
VP: Zach Hayman
VP: Tim Lipp
**VP:* Bill Welch
VP: Rob Werge
Exec: Dave Kolbeck
Dir Bus: Tom Rothgery
Mng Dir: Nick Schumer
Prgrm Mgr: Larry Krznarich
Prgrm Mgr: Anthony Rensch

D-U-N-S 94-810-2256 IMP
■ PHILOSOPHY INC
BIOTECH RESEARCH LABORATORIES
(*Suby of* COTY INC) ★
1400 Broadway Rd, Sanford, NC 27332-7713
Tel (602) 794-8500 *Founded/Ownrshp* 2010
Sales 174.9MM^E *EMP* 75
SIC 5122 2844 Cosmetics; Toilet preparations
VP: Michele Carlino
**VP:* Mark Harshbarger

D-U-N-S 78-588-6177
PHINEAS CORP
SUNRISE GROUP, THE
9040 Sw 72nd St, Miami, FL 33173-3432
Tel (305) 596-9040 *Founded/Ownrshp* 1990
Sales 137.7MM *EMP* 2,000
Accts Moore Stephens Lovelace Pa
SIC 8361 8399 6531 Home for the mentally retarded; Fund raising organization, non-fee basis; Real estate managers
Pr: Stephen T Rice

D-U-N-S 11-600-7386
PHL VARIABLE INSURANCE CO
(*Suby of* PM HOLDINGS INC) ★
1 American Row, Hartford, CT 06115-2521
Tel (860) 253-1000 *Founded/Ownrshp* 1994
Sales NA *EMP* 2
SIC 6411 Insurance agents & brokers
Pr: Donna Young
**CFO:* Mike Callian

D-U-N-S 15-807-6712
PHMH HOLDING CO
(*Suby of* MMH AMERICAS INC) ★
315 W Forest Hill Ave, Oak Creek, WI 53154-2905
Tel (414) 764-6200 *Founded/Ownrshp* 1998
Sales 135.0MM^E *EMP* 350^E
SIC 3625 6719 Crane & hoist controls, including metal mill; Investment holding companies, except banks
Pr: Tom Sothard
**Treas:* Steve Mayes

D-U-N-S 02-151-7956
PHOEBE PUTNEY MEMORIAL HOSPITAL INC
GIFTS FROM THE HEART
(*Suby of* GIFTS FROM THE HEART) ★
2000 Palmyra Rd, Albany, GA 31701-1528
Tel (229) 434-2000 *Founded/Ownrshp* 1990, 2011
Sales 490.6MM *EMP* 1^E
SIC 8062 General medical & surgical hospitals
Pathlgst: Tibor Gyorfi
HC Dir: Patsy Ivey

D-U-N-S 06-922-5209
PHOEBE PUTNEY MEMORIAL HOSPITAL INC (GA)
GIFTS FROM THE HEART
417 W 3rd Ave, Albany, GA 31701-1943
Tel (229) 312-1000 *Founded/Ownrshp* 1990
Sales 490.6MM *EMP* 3,000
Accts Draffin & Tucker Llp Albany
SIC 8062 General medical & surgical hospitals
Pr: Joel Wernick
V Ch: John Cochran
V Ch: John Culbreath
V Ch: Mary Helen Dykes
Treas: James Reynolds
**Ex VP:* Joe Austin
**Sr VP:* Richard Bowe
**Sr VP:* Tommy Chambless
Sr VP: John Fischer
**Sr VP:* Bob Lagesse
VP: Gail Carter
VP: Pam Deeter
VP: Bob Farr
VP: Cynthia George
VP: Brad Hallford
VP: Maureen Jackson
VP: Frances Marthone
VP: Linda Van Der Merwe
VP: Audrey Pike
VP: Tom Sullivan
VP: Debra Williamson

D-U-N-S 02-209-3932
PHOENICIAN RESORT
6000 E Camelback Rd, Scottsdale, AZ 85251-1949
Tel (480) 941-8200 *Founded/Ownrshp* 2009
Sales 44.3MM^E *EMP* 1,000
SIC 7011 Hotels
CEO: Denise Seomin
Genl Mgr: John Gomersall
Merch Mgr: Jessica Magusin

D-U-N-S 84-702-5236 IMP
PHOENIX AROMAS HOLDINGS LLC
355 Chestnut St, Norwood, NJ 07648-2001
Tel (201) 784-6100 *Founded/Ownrshp* 1994
Sales 92.0MM *EMP* 37
SIC 5169 Aromatic chemicals; Essential oils
CEO: Jean P Berveriste
CFO: Sam Au

D-U-N-S 14-413-1976 IMP
PHOENIX BEVERAGES INC
LOBO DISTRIBUTING
2 Atlantic Ave Pier 7, Brooklyn, NY 11201-5572
Tel (718) 609-7200 *Founded/Ownrshp* 1982
Sales 357.0MM^E *EMP* 600
SIC 5181

PHOENIX CARE SYSTEMS
See WILLOWGLEN ACADEMY-WISCONSIN INC

D-U-N-S 92-990-7749
PHOENIX CARE SYSTEMS INC
1744 N Farwell Ave, Milwaukee, WI 53202-1806
Tel (414) 225-4460 *Founded/Ownrshp* 1999
Sales 35.9MM^E *EMP* 1,400
SIC 8361 Residential care
Pr: Donald Fritz
COO: Henry R Kunath
**VP:* Leonard Dziubla
**VP:* David Perhach
HC Dir: Scott Wilcox

D-U-N-S 11-044-3595
PHOENIX CHILDRENS HOSPITAL INC
1919 E Thomas Rd, Phoenix, AZ 85016-7710
Tel (602) 546-1000 *Founded/Ownrshp* 2006
Sales 661.6MM *EMP* 3,000
SIC 8069 Children's hospital
Pr: Robert Meyer
Chf Rad: Richard B Tobin
Genl Pt: Ken Kendrick
COO: Betsy Kuzas
CFO: Shane Brophy
CFO: Pat Lash
**CFO:* Craig McKnight
CFO: Craig L McKnight
Bd of Dir: Greg Kruzel
Ofcr: David Higginson
Ex VP: Dennis N Lund
Sr VP: Pamela J Carlson
VP: Pamela Carlson
VP: Michael Dee
VP: Thomas J Diederich
VP: Linda Flink
VP: Kyle Green
VP: Douglas Henson
VP: Ethel Hoffman
VP: Brian Meyer
VP: Robert Sarnecki

D-U-N-S 09-647-7864 IMP
■ PHOENIX COLOR CORP
LEHIGH PHOENIX
(*Suby of* ALJ REGIONAL HOLDINGS INC) ★
18249 Phoenix Rd, Hagerstown, MD 21742-1351
Tel (301) 733-0018 *Founded/Ownrshp* 1979, 2015
Sales 159.9MM^E *EMP* 555
SIC 2732 3469 2796

D-U-N-S 01-074-0046
PHOENIX COMPANIES INC
(*Suby of* NASSAU REINSURANCE GROUP HOLDINGS, L.P.)
1 American Row, Hartford, CT 06103-2801
Tel (860) 403-5000 *Founded/Ownrshp* 2016
Sales NA *EMP* 620^E
SIC 6411 Insurance agents, brokers & service; Fire loss appraisal; Medical insurance claim processing, contract or fee basis
CEO: Phillip J Gass
Pt: Daniel Lampe
Pr: Doreen Bonner
COO: Thomas M Buckingham
CFO: Ernest McNeill Jr
Ex VP: Jody A Beresin
Sr VP: Edward W Cassidy
Sr VP: Amy Fisher
Sr VP: Mary E Genet
Sr VP: Robert Lombardi
Sr VP: Gina Collopy O'Connell
VP: Justin Banulski
VP: Terry Davis
VP: Alice S Ericson
VP: Naomi Kleinman
VP: Craig Michaud
VP: Thomas Sardinha
VP: Mark Sinopoli
VP: Joleen Speight
VP: Nancy Turner

D-U-N-S 01-748-6234 IMP
PHOENIX CONTACT SERVICES INC
(*Suby of* PHOENIX CONTACT GMBH & CO. KG)
586 Fulling Mill Rd, Middletown, PA 17057-2966
Tel (717) 944-1300 *Founded/Ownrshp* 1980
Sales 209.5MM^E *EMP* 410
SIC 5063 3678 3643 Electrical apparatus & equipment; Electronic connectors; Current-carrying wiring devices
Pr: Jack L Nehlig
Pr: Spencer Bolgard
VP: Russell Moser
VP: Doug Peterson
Genl Mgr: Kevin McKenna
Snr Sftwr: Jesse Bajwa
CIO: Clinton Myers
IT Man: Nathan Raupach
Netwrk Eng: Rich Hornberger
Sfty Mgr: Doug Ferguson
Opers Mgr: Bill Sheaffer

D-U-N-S 06-144-7587 EXP
■ PHOENIX CORP (GA)
PHOENIX METALS
(*Suby of* RELIANCE STEEL & ALUMINUM CO) ★
4685 Buford Hwy, Peachtree Corners, GA 30071-2810
Tel (770) 447-4211 *Founded/Ownrshp* 1979
Sales 416.8MM^E *EMP* 620
SIC 5051 Metals service centers & offices
CEO: Stephen E Almond
**Pr:* Barry Epps
**COO:* Mark Haynes
**CFO:* Bill Hellstein
**VP:* Wayne Grant
VP: Scott Schultz
Sls Mgr: Dan Roberts
Sls Mgr: Jug Twitty
Sales Asso: Brian Barnes
Sales Asso: Donny Burleson
Board of Directors: Kay Coggins, Kay Fowler

D-U-N-S 02-229-1226
PHOENIX ELEMENTARY SCHOOL DISTRICT 1
1817 N 7th St, Phoenix, AZ 85006-2100
Tel (602) 257-3755 Founded/Ownrshp 2009
Sales 11.6MM^E EMP 1,108^E
SIC 8211 Public elementary & secondary schools
Bd of Dir: Daniil Gunitskiy
CIO: Ruthann Marston
MIS Dir: Paul Chase
Dir IT: Jill Andrews
IT Man: Andrea Shores
HC Dir: Diane Wray

D-U-N-S 05-204-7490
PHOENIX FORGE GROUP LLC (PA)
CAPITOL MANUFACTURING DIVISION
1020 Macarthur Rd, Reading, PA 19605-9404
Tel (800) 234-8665 Founded/Ownrshp 1997, 1882
Sales 167.2MM^E EMP 650
SIC 3089 Plastic hardware & building products
CTO: Fred Hammers
IT Man: Lorraine Kressley

PHOENIX FUEL
See WESTERN REFINING WHOLESALE INC

PHOENIX GLOBAL DISTRIBUTION
See THERMO KING CORP

D-U-N-S 86-841-6095
PHOENIX GROUP INC
164 S Park Blvd, Greenwood, IN 46143-8837
Tel (317) 884-3600 Founded/Ownrshp 1991
Sales 107.4MM^E EMP 91
SIC 8742 6719 Management consulting services; Personal holding companies, except banks
CEO: Harry Sherman
*Pr: Gary Sherman
CFO: Larry Snyder
*Sec: Patrick Sherman
VP: Bryce Durham

PHOENIX HEALTHCARE GROUP
See OSPREY RIDGE HEALTHCARE CENTER INC

D-U-N-S 06-120-2511
PHOENIX HOUSE FOUNDATION INC
50 Jay St, Brooklyn, NY 11201-1144
Tel (646) 505-2000 Founded/Ownrshp 1967
Sales 117.4MM^E EMP 1,600
Accts Grant Thorton Llp New York N
SIC 8361 Rehabilitation center, residential: health care incidental
Pr: Howard Meitiner
*COO: Michael E Moreland
*CFO: Robert Wilson
*Ch: Jeffrey A McDermott
Sr VP: Michael Berkowitz
Sr VP: Deborah Taylor
VP: Mary Aquino
*VP: Stephen Donowitz
VP: Fred Trapassi
VP: Richard Turner
VP Mktg: Karen Palmiero

D-U-N-S 00-691-7306
■ **PHOENIX INSURANCE CO**
TRAVELERS INSURANCE
(Suby of TRAVELERS INSURANCE) ★
1 Tower Sq, Hartford, CT 06183-0001
Tel (860) 277-0111 Founded/Ownrshp 1850, 1966
Sales NA EMP 35
SIC 6351 6331 Liability insurance; Fire, marine & casualty insurance
Ch Bd: Charles Clark
*Pr: Douglas Elliot
*CFO: Jay Benet
*Ex VP: Joseph Kiernan

D-U-N-S 07-946-4014
PHOENIX INTERNATIONAL PUBLICATIONS INC
PIKIDS
(Suby of JIANGSU PHOENIX PUBLISHING AND MEDIA CORPORATION LIMITED)
8501 W Higgins Rd Ste 300, Chicago, IL 60631-2812
Tel (312) 739-4400 Founded/Ownrshp 2014
Sales 100.0MM EMP 300
SIC 5942 2731 Children's books; Books: publishing & printing
CEO: Vincent Douglas
*CFO: Alen Qin
Sr VP: Liam Qian
*Sr VP: Liang Qian

D-U-N-S 00-691-7314
PHOENIX LIFE INSURANCE CO
(Suby of PHOENIX COMPANIES INC) ★
1 American Row, Hartford, CT 06103-2899
Tel (860) 403-5000 Founded/Ownrshp 1851
Sales NA EMP 600
SIC 6311 Life insurance carriers
Pr: James D Wehr
*Pr: James D Wahr
*Ex VP: Edward W Cassidy
*Ex VP: Thomas M Buckingham FSA
*Ex VP: Michael E Haylon
VP: Judi Fitol
VP: Giang Le
VP: Chad Rege
*VP: Brian H Simmons
VP: Michael Socola
MIS Dir: Patricia Theorkauf

PHOENIX METALS
See PHOENIX CORP

D-U-N-S 00-839-8539
■ **PHOENIX NEWSPAPERS INC**
ARIZONA REPUBLIC
(Suby of GANNETT CO INC) ★
200 E Van Buren St, Phoenix, AZ 85004-2238
Tel (602) 444-8000 Founded/Ownrshp 2015
Sales 387.6MM^E EMP 2,480
SIC 2711 Newspapers, publishing & printing
CEO: John M Zidich
*CFO: Jon Held
*Treas: Michael A Hart
*VP: Gracia C Martore
Mktg Mgr: Michael Gorman

D-U-N-S 96-681-0843 IMP/EXP
PHOENIX PACKAGING OPERATIONS LLC
GRUPO PHOENIX
(Suby of GRUPO PHOENIX CORPORATE SERVICES LLC) ★
4800 Lina Ln, Dublin, VA 24084
Tel (540) 307-4084 Founded/Ownrshp 2010
Sales 159.1MM EMP 443
Accts Deloitte & Touche Ltda Bogota
SIC 2631 Container, packaging & boxboard
CEO: Alberto Peisach

PHOENIX RANCH MARKET
See PROS MARKET INC

D-U-N-S 00-417-5979
PHOENIX RANCH MARKET III
(Suby of PHOENIX RANCH MARKET) ★
1602 E Roosevelt St, Phoenix, AZ 85006-3678
Tel (602) 254-6676 Founded/Ownrshp 2007
Sales 16.8MM^E EMP 1,505^E
SIC 0291 General farms, primarily animals
Prin: Micahel Provenzano Jr

D-U-N-S 02-785-2081
PHOENIX TECHNOLOGY SERVICES USA INC
(Suby of PHOENIX TECHNOLOGY SERVICES INC)
12329 Cutten Rd, Houston, TX 77066-1807
Tel (713) 337-0600 Founded/Ownrshp 1999
Sales 182.0MM^E EMP 130
SIC 1381 Directional drilling oil & gas wells
Pr: Edward Chiaramonte
IT Man: Kevin Thompson
VP Opers: Brent Clark

D-U-N-S 07-448-8990
PHOENIX UNION HIGH SCHOOL DISTRICT NO 210
4502 N Central Ave, Phoenix, AZ 85012-1817
Tel (602) 271-3302 Founded/Ownrshp 1895
Sales 301.5MM EMP 2,704
Accts Heinfeld Meech & Co Pc P
SIC 8211 Public senior high school
Exec: Jeff Allemang
Psych: Ilene Thelen
Snr Mgr: Cassie Sawyer

D-U-N-S 10-147-1600 IMP/EXP
PHOENIX V LLC
BEI HAWAII
311 Pacific St, Honolulu, HI 96817-5089
Tel (808) 532-7400 Founded/Ownrshp 2001
Sales 143.2MM^E EMP 147
SIC 5169 8748 Chemicals & allied products; Environmental consultant
Pr: Marc C Tilker
Bd of Dir: Richard Ing
Sr VP: Jim Mistysyn
Exec: John Dirienzo
Exec: Richard Hill
Genl Mgr: James Saulez
Sls&Mrk Ex: Carolyn Ambrose

D-U-N-S 96-338-8769
■ **PHOENIXVILLE HOSPITAL CO LLC**
(Suby of COMMUNITY HEALTH SYSTEMS INC) ★
140 Nutt Rd, Phoenixville, PA 19460-3900
Tel (610) 983-1000 Founded/Ownrshp 2004
Sales 15.0MM EMP 1,000
SIC 8062 General medical & surgical hospitals
CEO: Steve Tullman

D-U-N-S 07-695-7943
■ **PHOENIXVILLE HOSPITAL OF UNIVERSITY OF PENNSYLVANIA HEALTH SYSTEM**
(Suby of COMMUNITY HEALTH SYSTEMS INC) ★
140 Nutt Rd, Phoenixville, PA 19460-3906
Tel (610) 983-1000 Founded/Ownrshp 2004
Sales 136.4MM^E EMP 789^E
SIC 8062 8011 General medical & surgical hospitals; Offices & clinics of medical doctors
CEO: Steve Tullman
COO: B Mahoney
Dir OR: Nancy Hall
Dir Risk M: Jadwiga Bobowska
Dir Case M: Elizabeth Rowan
Dir Lab: Mary Zielinski
Pathlgst: Wendy Coull

D-U-N-S 60-270-5550 IMP
PHONAK LLC
(Suby of SONOVA AG)
4520 Weaver Pkwy Ste 1, Warrenville, IL 60555-4027
Tel (630) 821-5000 Founded/Ownrshp 1989
Sales 184.2MM^E EMP 700
SIC 3842 5999 Hearing aids; Hearing aids
Pr: Mark A Sanger
*CFO: Peter Knapp
Ex VP: Paul Thompson
VP: William Dickinson
VP: Cindy Strohm
*VP: Eric Timm
*VP: Heath A Wilson
Mng Dir: Claude Diversi
Mng Dir: Vincent Lefevre
Mng Dir: Mike Sharp
Area Mgr: Ernst Petras

D-U-N-S 15-525-6233
■ **PHOSPHATE RESOURCE PARTNERS LIMITED PARTNERSHIP**
(Suby of MOSAIC GLOBAL HOLDINGS INC) ★
100 Saunders Rd Ste 300, Lake Forest, IL 60045-2508
Tel (847) 739-1200 Founded/Ownrshp 1997
Sales 154.2MM^E EMP 2,972
SIC 2874 1311 1475 2819 1094 Phosphatic fertilizers; Phosphoric acid; Superphosphates, ammoniated or not ammoniated; Crude petroleum production; Phosphate rock; Sulfuric acid, oleum; Uranium ore mining
CEO: J Reid Porter

D-U-N-S 08-479-7745
▲ **PHOTRONICS INC**
15 Secor Rd, Brookfield, CT 06804-3937
Tel (203) 775-9000 Founded/Ownrshp 1969
Sales 524.2MM EMP 1,550^E
Tkr Sym PLAB Exch NGS
SIC 3674 Semiconductors & related devices; Light sensitive devices; Light sensitive devices, solid state
Pr: Peter S Kirlin
Ch Bd: Constantine S Macricostas
CFO: Sean T Smith
Sr VP: Jack P Moneta
Sr VP: John G Smith
VP: Richelle E Burr
VP: Christopher J Progler
CIO: James Jang
Sftwr Eng: Darrin Jacques
VP Opers: Jim Kellogg
QI Cn Mgr: Dan Pullen
Board of Directors: Walter M Fiederowicz, Joseph A Fiorita Jr, George Macricostas, Mitchell G Tyson

PHPNI
See PHYSICIANS HEALTH PLAN OF NORTHERN INDIANA INC

PHRMA
See PHARMACEUTICAL RESEARCH AND MANUFACTURERS OF AMERICA

D-U-N-S 80-858-1078 IMP
PHT INTERNATIONAL INC
8133 Ardrey Kell Rd # 204, Charlotte, NC 28277-5722
Tel (704) 246-3480 Founded/Ownrshp 1993
Sales 87.0MM EMP 55
SIC 5169

PHYLE INVNTORY CTRL SPCIALISTS
See PICO ENTERPRISES INC

D-U-N-S 01-410-7831
■ **PHYSASSIST SCRIBES INC** (TX)
(Suby of TEAMHEALTH) ★
6451 Brentwood Stair Rd # 100, Fort Worth, TX 76112-3200
Tel (817) 496-1009 Founded/Ownrshp 1995, 2014
Sales 127.7MM^E EMP 2,770^E
SIC 8011 Physicians' office, including specialists
Pr: J Alexander Geesbreght
VP: Raegan Baskin
VP: Amanda Buffington
VP: Chelsey Spurgin
Rgnl Mgr: Laura Bustamante
Dir IT: Phillip De Verges
VP Mktg: Scott Hagood
VP Sls: Ben Stolz
Corp Couns: Amber Altemose

PHYSERVE PHYSICIAN SERVICES
See MEDSYNERGIES NORTH TEXAS INC

PHYSICAL MEDICINE
See JEWISH HOSPITAL CINCINNATI INC

D-U-N-S 05-436-7844
PHYSICANS AT SUGAR CREEK
(Suby of MEMORIAL HERMANN HEALTHCARE SYSTEM) ★
14023 Southwest Fwy, Sugar Land, TX 77478-3550
Tel (281) 325-4100 Founded/Ownrshp 2013
Sales 168.0MM^E EMP 16,505
SIC 8011 General & family practice, physician/surgeon
Psych: Gordon A Bush

D-U-N-S 08-283-9848
PHYSICIAN AFFILIATE GROUP OF NEW YORK PC
PAGNY
55 W 125th St Rm 1002, New York, NY 10027-4533
Tel (646) 672-3651 Founded/Ownrshp 2010
Sales 524.5MM EMP 75
SIC 8011 Physical medicine, physician/surgeon; Medical centers
Pr: Bijan Safai
CEO: Luis R Marcos
COO: Michael J Chambers
CFO: Anthony Mirdita

D-U-N-S 96-948-1634
PHYSICIAN ENTERPRISE LLC
2001 Medical Pkwy, Annapolis, MD 21401-3773
Tel (443) 481-6554 Founded/Ownrshp 2011
Sales 109.7MM EMP 4
Accts Sc&H Tax & Advisory Services L
SIC 8011 General & family practice, physician/surgeon

D-U-N-S 10-946-2390
PHYSICIAN GROUP
6801 Dixie Hwy Ste 133, Louisville, KY 40258-3952
Tel (502) 937-3864 Founded/Ownrshp 1999
Sales 140.2MM EMP 3
SIC 8011 Physicians' office, including specialists; General & family practice, physician/surgeon
Prin: Michael Becker MD

D-U-N-S 14-864-6602
PHYSICIAN MATCH
LITTLE CO OF MARYS HOSPITAL
2800 W 95th St, Evergreen Park, IL 60805-2701
Tel (708) 423-3070 Founded/Ownrshp 2004
Sales 44.0MM^E EMP 2,000
SIC 8062 General medical & surgical hospitals
Pr: Dennis Riley
*VP: Dennis Day
Opers Mgr: Mary Gallik
Doctor: Michael J Mc Grail MD
Doctor: Tenkasi V Subramanian MD

D-U-N-S 83-702-3530
PHYSICIAN NETWORK
2000 Q St Fl 5th, Lincoln, NE 68503-3610
Tel (402) 421-0896 Founded/Ownrshp 1994
Sales 154.5MM EMP 225
SIC 8011 Offices & clinics of medical doctors
Pr: Robert J Lanik
*VP: Kent Reckewey

PHYSICIAN OFFICE SUPPORT SERVI
See TORRANCE MEMORIAL MEDICAL CENTER

PHYSICIAN OFFICE SUPPORT SVCS
See TORRANCE HEALTH ASSOCIATION INC

D-U-N-S 82-567-2769
■ **PHYSICIAN RELIANCE NETWORK INC**
U S ONCOLOGY
(Suby of US ONCOLOGY INC) ★
10101 Woodloch Forest Dr, Spring, TX 77380-1975
Tel (281) 863-1000 Founded/Ownrshp 1993
Sales 58.0MM^E EMP 1,192
SIC 8741 Administrative management
Pr: R Dale Ross
*Treas: Bruce Broussard
*VP: Phillip Watts

PHYSICIAN SALES & SERVICE
See PSS WORLD MEDICAL INC

D-U-N-S 11-514-8207
■ **PHYSICIAN SUPPORT SYSTEMS INC**
(Suby of N D C) ★
15 Eby Chiques Rd, Mount Joy, PA 17552-9317
Tel (717) 653-5340 Founded/Ownrshp 1991
Sales 45.2MM^E EMP 1,100
SIC 8011 General & family practice, physician/surgeon
Pr: Douglas Estock

D-U-N-S 17-442-0653
PHYSICIANS CLINIC INC
8601 W Dodge Rd Ste 216, Omaha, NE 68114-3495
Tel (402) 354-1700 Founded/Ownrshp 1982
Sales 140.3MM EMP 675
Accts Kpmg Llp Omaha Ne
SIC 8011 8031 Physicians' office, including specialists; Offices & clinics of osteopathic physicians
Pr: Todd Grages
Ofcr: Janelle Deitloff
Doctor: Rebecca McCrery MD

D-U-N-S 05-402-1743
PHYSICIANS FOR HEALTHY HOSPITALS INC
HEMET VALLEY MEDICAL CENTER
1117 E Devonshire Ave, Hemet, CA 92543-3083
Tel (951) 652-2811 Founded/Ownrshp 2009
Sales 150.8MM EMP 633^E
SIC 8062 General medical & surgical hospitals
CEO: Chaudhuri
*VP: Ashok Agarwal
*VP: Kali Priyo Chaudhuri
*VP: Neelam Gupta

D-U-N-S 11-927-7820 IMP
PHYSICIANS HEALTH PLAN OF MID-MICHIGAN INC
(Suby of SPARROW HEALTH SYSTEM) ★
1400 E Michigan Ave, Lansing, MI 48912-2107
Tel (517) 364-8400 Founded/Ownrshp 1981
Sales 161.8MM EMP 120^E
Accts Andrews Hooper Pavlik Plc Oke
SIC 8011 6321 Health maintenance organization; Accident & health insurance
Pr: Scott Wilkerson
Dir Rx: Ann Hunt-Fugate
Off Mgr: Tracy Davis
Dir IT: Mary A Sesti

D-U-N-S 15-341-4586
PHYSICIANS HEALTH PLAN OF NORTHERN INDIANA INC
PHPNI
8101 W Jefferson Blvd, Fort Wayne, IN 46804-4163
Tel (260) 432-6690 Founded/Ownrshp 1983
Sales NA EMP 96
Accts Bkd Llp Fort Wayne In
SIC 6321 8011 6411 Accident & health insurance; Health maintenance organization; Insurance agents, brokers & service
Pr: Rick Cochran
COO: Gail Doran
*Treas: Michael R Dewald
Ex Dir: Carrie Marion
Dir IT: Suzanne Fisk

D-U-N-S 10-531-4439
PHYSICIANS INSURANCE A MUTUAL CO
NORDIC
1301 2nd Ave Ste 2700, Seattle, WA 98101-3803
Tel (206) 343-7300 Founded/Ownrshp 1981
Sales NA EMP 95^E
SIC 6411 Property & casualty insurance agent
Pr: Mary Lou Misahry
V Ch: James Pritchett
Pr: Perry Evans
Pr: David Kinard
CFO: Rod Pierson
Sr VP: Leslie Mallonee
Sr VP: Alison Talbot
VP: James Corgan
VP: Terry Evans
VP: John Karlen
VP: Kristin Kenny
VP: Thomas Kirchmeier
VP: Judith Mix
VP: Bob Nickles
VP: Vince Rota
VP: Bruce Schafer
VP: Pamela Tinsley

D-U-N-S 07-291-8634
PHYSICIANS LIFE INSURANCE CO
(Suby of PHYSICIANS MUTUAL INSURANCE CO) ★
2600 Dodge St, Omaha, NE 68131-2672
Tel (402) 633-1000 Founded/Ownrshp 1970
Sales NA EMP 1,250
SIC 6311 Life reinsurance
Pr: R A Reed
COO: E W Graycar
Ex VP: G E Theel

D-U-N-S 07-291-8402
PHYSICIANS MUTUAL INSURANCE CO
2600 Dodge St, Omaha, NE 68131-2671
Tel (402) 633-1000 Founded/Ownrshp 1902

Sales NA *EMP* 1,410
SIC 6321 6311 Mutual accident & health associations; Life insurance
Pr: Robert A Reed Jr
**Ch Bd:* William Hamsa MD
Pr: Grant Christensen
**COO:* E W Graycar
COO: Ed Mullen
**CFO:* Roger J Hermsen
VP: Margaret R Balkus
VP: Michael Carstens
VP: John Hogan
VP: James B Juhler
VP: Rick Kingsland
VP: Frederick T Rahn
VP: Thomas A Sick
**VP:* G E Theel

D-U-N-S 93-284-0523
PHYSICIANS OF OHIO STATE UNIVERSITY
700 Ackerman Rd Ste 360, Columbus, OH 43202-2328
Tel (614) 263-2450 *Founded/Ownrshp* 1995
Sales 335.8MM *EMP* 14E
Accts Blue & Co Llc Columbus Oh
SIC 8621 Professional membership organizations

D-U-N-S 01-317-4562
PHYSICIANS PARTNERS PLUS LLC
1131 Nw 74th Ter, Hollywood, FL 33024-5301
Tel (352) 622-7000 *Founded/Ownrshp* 2007
Sales 200.0MM *EMP* 80E
SIC 8748 Business consulting
CEO: Deviah Pagidipati

D-U-N-S 06-583-9784
PHYSICIANS PRACTICE GROUP
1499 Walton Way Ste 1400, Augusta, GA 30901-2660
Tel (706) 724-6100 *Founded/Ownrshp* 1999
Sales 154.2MM *EMP* 250
Accts Bdo Usa Llp Bethesda Md
SIC 8011 General & family practice, physician/surgeon
CEO: Michael Herbert

D-U-N-S 07-884-5993
PHYSICIANS REALTY TRUST
309 N Water St Ste 500, Milwaukee, WI 53202-5772
Tel (414) 367-5600 *Founded/Ownrshp* 2013
Sales 129.4MM *EMP* 25
SIC 6798 Real estate investment trusts
Pr: John T Thomas
CFO: Jeffrey Theiler
Ex VP: John W Sweet Jr
Sr VP: John W Lucey
Sr VP: Mark D Theine

D-U-N-S 05-590-9410
PHYSICIANS RECIPROCAL INSURERS
P R I
1800 Northern Blvd, Roslyn, NY 11576-1140
Tel (516) 365-6690 *Founded/Ownrshp* 1982
Sales NA *EMP* 260
SIC 6321 Reciprocal interinsurance exchanges
Ch Bd: Herman Robbins MD
**Pr:* Gerald Dolman
**CEO:* Anthony Bonomo
**COO:* Bernard McArthur
**Sec:* Mehmet Cetin MD
**V Ch Bd:* Bruce Goldberg MD
Chf Mktg O: Chris Curcio
**Sr VP:* Clifton Stepp
VP: Laura Archer
VP: John Bedford
VP: Walter Buck
VP: Kurt Driscoll
**VP:* Walter Long
VP: Angie Nykamp
VP: Samuel Pippin
VP: Cliff Rapp
VP: Lou Sicilian

D-U-N-S 80-076-5567
■ PHYSICIANS REGIONAL MEDICAL CENTER
HMA
(*Suby of* HMA) ★
6101 Pine Ridge Rd, Naples, FL 34119-3900
Tel (239) 348-4400 *Founded/Ownrshp* 2007
Sales 223.5MM *EMP* 1E
SIC 8011 8062 Offices & clinics of medical doctors; General medical & surgical hospitals
CEO: C Scott Campbell
Chf Nrs Of: Carol M Conn

D-U-N-S 82-706-6932
PHYSICIANS UNITED PLAN INC
P U P
2020 Capital Cir Se 310, Tallahassee, FL 32301-5138
Tel (888) 827-5787 *Founded/Ownrshp* 2005
Sales NA *EMP* 110
SIC 6321 Health insurance carriers
Pr: Imtiaz Sattaur
**COO:* Kevin P Enterlein
**CFO:* Bob Trinh
**Sr VP:* James D Kollefrath

D-U-N-S 09-533-8703
PHYSICIANS WEIGHT LOSS CENTERS OF AMERICA INC
395 Springside Dr, Akron, OH 44333-2434
Tel (330) 666-7952 *Founded/Ownrshp* 1979
Sales 124.0MME *EMP* 398
SIC 5141 5122 6794 Groceries, general line; Vitamins & minerals; Franchises, selling or licensing
Pr: Charles E Sekeres

PHYSIO CONTROL
See PHYSIO-CONTROL INC

D-U-N-S 00-925-1992 IMP
PHYSIO-CONTROL INC
PHYSIO CONTROL
11811 Willows Rd Ne, Redmond, WA 98052-2015
Tel (425) 867-4000 *Founded/Ownrshp* 2012
Sales 411.0MME *EMP* 1,000
SIC 3841 3845 7699 7372

D-U-N-S 08-015-3168
■ PHYSIO-CONTROL INTERNATIONAL INC
(*Suby of* STRYKER CORP) ★
11811 Willows Rd Ne, Redmond, WA 98052-2015
Tel (425) 867-4000 *Founded/Ownrshp* 2016
Sales 306.0ME *EMP* 1,800
SIC 3845 Defibrillator; Pacemaker, cardiac
Pr: Brian D Webster
CEO: Mitch Parrish
CFO: David Stafford
Chf Mktg O: CAM Pollock
Chf Mktg O: Traci Umberger
Genl Mgr: Mathieu Badard
Genl Mgr: Dale Pearson
Genl Mgr: Erik Von Schenck

PHYSIOTHERAPY ASSOCIATES
See PHYSIOTHERAPY CORP

D-U-N-S 18-681-7961
PHYSIOTHERAPY ASSOCIATES INC
LIVING HOPE PHYSIOTHERAPY
(*Suby of* PHYSIOTHERAPY ASSOCIATES) ★
855 Springdale Dr Ste 200, Exton, PA 19341-2852
Tel (610) 644-7824 *Founded/Ownrshp* 2012
Sales 178.3MME *EMP* 3,050
SIC 8049 8093 Nutrition specialist; Physical therapist; Specialty outpatient clinics; Respiratory therapy clinic; Rehabilitation center, outpatient treatment
CEO: Hank Balavender
**Pr:* Peter Limeri
**COO:* Pete Grabaskas
**CFO:* Edwin Bode
Ex VP: Dan Dourney
VP: Susan Hoeflich
VP: Laura Porter
VP: Michael Roy
Dir IT: Jovin Olikara
Phys Thrpy: Lauren Lederer

D-U-N-S 80-703-0486
PHYSIOTHERAPY CORP
PHYSIOTHERAPY ASSOCIATES
855 Springdale Dr Ste 200, Exton, PA 19341-2852
Tel (610) 644-7824 *Founded/Ownrshp* 2012
Sales 216.7MME *EMP* 4,500
SIC 8049 Physical therapist
CEO: Hank Balavender
**COO:* Dan Dourney
**CFO:* Paul Solomon
**Chf Cred:* Cindy Goldberg

D-U-N-S 96-632-6345
PHYSIOTHERAPY-BMI INC
(*Suby of* PHYSIOTHERAPY ASSOCIATES) ★
855 Springdale Dr Ste 200, Exton, PA 19341-2852
Tel (610) 644-7824 *Founded/Ownrshp* 1999
Sales 25.3MME *EMP* 2,108E
Accts Kpmg Llp Philadelphia Pa
SIC 8049 Physical therapist
CEO: William Floyd
**Pr:* Eric Williams
**CFO:* Dennis Fitzpatrick
**Ex VP:* Richard S Binstein

D-U-N-S 00-333-2210 IMP
PI INC (TN)
HYDRA POOLS
213 Dennis St, Athens, TN 37303-2995
Tel (423) 745-6213 *Founded/Ownrshp* 1952
Sales 90.3MME *EMP* 250
SIC 2519 3949 3089 2499 3086 3081 Furniture, household: glass, fiberglass & plastic; Swimming pools, plastic; Trays, plastic; Saddle trees, wood; Plastics foam products; Unsupported plastics film & sheet
Pr: James Beene
**CFO:* Todd Harris

D-U-N-S 88-344-0406 IMP
PIATTI RESTAURANT CO LP
625 Rdwood Hwy Frntage Rd, Mill Valley, CA 94941-3008
Tel (415) 380-2511 *Founded/Ownrshp* 1991
Sales 38.1MME *EMP* 1,200
SIC 5812 Italian restaurant
Pt: Claude Rouas
Pt: Robert Harmon
Exec: Felix Acosta

D-U-N-S 01-643-5653
PIAZZA PRODUCE INC
(*Suby of* INDIANAPOLIS FRUIT CO) ★
5941 W 82nd St, Indianapolis, IN 46278-1339
Tel (317) 872-0101 *Founded/Ownrshp* 1997
Sales 103.9MME *EMP* 225
SIC 5148 Fruits; Vegetables
Pr: Pete Piazza
**Pr:* Michael Mascari
**Sec:* Greg Corsaro
**Ex VP:* Joe Corsaro
**Sr VP:* Dan Corsaro
**VP:* Christopher Mascari
IT Man: Charles Elsener
Sales Exec: Marcus Agresta
Sales Exec: Shane Ledford
Sales Asso: Mark A Carpenter
Sales Asso: Jill Naiser

D-U-N-S 00-710-4466
PIAZZA PRODUCE LLC
5941 W 82nd St, Indianapolis, IN 46278-1339
Tel (317) 872-0101 *Founded/Ownrshp* 1970
Sales 132.3MME *EMP* 250
SIC 5148

PIC-N-PAC
See WUESTS INC

PICCADILLY CAFETERIA
See PICCADILLY RESTAURANTS LLC

D-U-N-S 14-753-8636
PICCADILLY RESTAURANTS LLC
PICCADILLY CAFETERIA
(*Suby of* YUCAIPA COMPANIES LLC) ★
4150 S Shrwood Frest Blvd, Baton Rouge, LA 70816
Tel (225) 293-9440 *Founded/Ownrshp* 2004
Sales 227.2MME *EMP* 5,000
SIC 5812 Cafeteria; Restaurant, family: independent
CEO: Azam Malik
**CEO:* David Green
CFO: M L Mestayer
CFO: Mark Mestayer
VP: Brian Dixon
VP: Joseph Polito
VP: Patrick Prudhomme
Ex Dir: Robert Guyton
Ex Dir: Dale Redman
Brnch Mgr: Ed Walker
Genl Mgr: Dorothy Johnson

D-U-N-S 93-365-6274
PICERNE DEVELOPMENT CORP OF FLORIDA
(*Suby of* PICERNE PROPERTIES) ★
247 N Westmonte Dr, Altamonte Springs, FL 32714-3398
Tel (407) 772-0200 *Founded/Ownrshp* 1983
Sales 97.3MME *EMP* 350
SIC 1522 Multi-family dwelling construction
CEO: David Picerne
**Pr:* Robert M Picerne
**Treas:* Jan C Heflinger
**VP:* Ray Uritescu
MIS Dir: Keith Vincent

D-U-N-S 07-569-7706
PICERNE INVESTMENT CORP (RI)
PICERNE PROPERTIES
75 Lambert Lind Hwy # 300, Warwick, RI 02886-1163
Tel (401) 732-3700 *Founded/Ownrshp* 1925
Sales 211.2MME *EMP* 900
SIC 6552 6531 1521 1522 1542 Subdividers & developers; Real estate managers; New construction, single-family houses; Multi-family dwellings, new construction; Commercial & office building, new construction
Pr: Ronald R S Picerne
CFO: Ken Richard
**Treas:* Raymond M Uritescu
**Ex VP:* Robert M Picerne
Comm Man: Brandon Masters

PICERNE PROPERTIES
See PICERNE INVESTMENT CORP

D-U-N-S 18-574-2442
■ PICK AND PULL AUTO DISMANTLING INC
AUTO PARTS GROUP
(*Suby of* SCHNITZER STEEL INDUSTRIES INC) ★
10850 Gold Center Dr # 325, Rancho Cordova, CA 95670-6177
Tel (916) 689-2000 *Founded/Ownrshp* 2003
Sales 366.5MME *EMP* 1,400
SIC 5093 Automotive wrecking for scrap
Pr: Thomas Klauer
CFO: Maun Tom
Site Mgr: Chris Kulvicki
Genl Couns: Michael Marino
Genl Couns: Juanita Rodriguez
Genl Couns: Keith Solar
Snr Mgr: Tom Maun

PICK 'N SAVE
See ROUNDYS SUPERMARKETS INC

D-U-N-S 03-868-5913
■ PICK-YOUR-PART AUTO WRECKING
(*Suby of* LKQ CORP) ★
1235 S Beach Blvd, Anaheim, CA 92804-4804
Tel (714) 385-1200 *Founded/Ownrshp* 1979
Sales 106.1MME *EMP* 308
SIC 5531 5093 Automotive parts; Metal scrap & waste materials
Pr: Joseph M Holsten
**Pr:* Glenn C Mc Elroy
Ex VP: Cindi Galfin

PICKERINGTON BOARD EDUCATION
See PICKERINGTON LOCAL SCHOOL DISTRICT

D-U-N-S 08-274-5530
PICKERINGTON LOCAL SCHOOL DISTRICT
PICKERINGTON BOARD EDUCATION
90 N East St, Pickerington, OH 43147-1170
Tel (614) 833-2110 *Founded/Ownrshp* 1960, 1986
Sales 65.5MME *EMP* 1,025
Accts Julian & Grube Inc Westervill
SIC 8211 Public elementary & secondary schools
Pr Dir: David Ball

PICKETT SYSTEMS
See STRIKE LLC

D-U-N-S 80-179-5027
PICO ENTERPRISES INC
PHYLE INVNTORY CTRL SPCIALISTS
4150 Grange Hall Rd, Holly, MI 48442-1112
Tel (248) 328-5000 *Founded/Ownrshp* 2006
Sales 67.0MME *EMP* 2,000
SIC 8742 Materials mgmt. (purchasing, handling, inventory) consultant
Pr: Charles E Phyle Sr
**CFO:* Tim Mahler
VP: David Cox
**Prin:* John Phyle

D-U-N-S 12-136-8203
▲ PICO HOLDINGS INC
7979 Ivanhoe Ave Ste 300, La Jolla, CA 92037-4506
Tel (888) 389-3222 *Founded/Ownrshp* 1981
Sales 266.6MM *EMP* 220E
Tkr Sym PICO *Exch* NGS
SIC 6531 Real estate agents & managers
Pr: Maxim C W Webb
**Ch Bd:* Raymond V Marino II
**CFO:* John T Perri

D-U-N-S 00-793-3104 IMP
PICTSWEET CO
10 Pictsweet Dr, Bells, TN 38006-4274
Tel (731) 663-7600 *Founded/Ownrshp* 1956, 1999
Sales 357.2MME *EMP* 1,200
SIC 2037 4213 Vegetables, quick frozen & cold pack, excl. potato products; Trucking, except local
CEO: James I Tankersley
**Pr:* Wesley F Eubanks
**CFO:* Brad Strange
VP: Wesley Eubanks
VP: David Everson
VP: Kevin Janiga
VP: Lissa Mullins
VP: Mark Northern
VP: Bill Shipman
VP: Chris Wilkerson
Genl Mgr: Maurice Batson

D-U-N-S 09-283-0863
PICTSWEET LLC
10 Pictsweet Dr, Bells, TN 38006-4274
Tel (731) 422-7600 *Founded/Ownrshp* 1998
Sales 318.5MME *EMP* 1,250E
SIC 4213 2037

PICTURE PEOPLE, THE
See TPP ACQUISITION INC

D-U-N-S 00-280-6693
■ PIEDMONT AIRLINES INC (MD)
AMERICAN EAGLE
(*Suby of* AMERICAN AIRLINES GROUP INC) ★
5443 Airport Terminal Rd, Salisbury, MD 21804-1545
Tel (410) 742-2996 *Founded/Ownrshp* 1931, 2013
Sales 195.0MME *EMP* 5,500
SIC 4512 Air passenger carrier, scheduled
Pr: Stephen R Farrow
Ofcr: Brad Guthrie
**VP:* William W Arndt
VP: Lyle Hogg
**VP:* Stephen Keefer
**VP:* Eric H Morgan
VP: Eric Morgan
Genl Mgr: John Melendez
MIS Dir: Jack Moscony
Tech Mgr: Paul Douglas
Corp Couns: Marija Kuren

D-U-N-S 60-083-1650
■ PIEDMONT AIRLINES INC
US AIRWAYS EXPRESS
(*Suby of* AMERICAN AIRLINES INC) ★
1000 Rosedale Ave, Middletown, PA 17057-4834
Tel (410) 742-2996 *Founded/Ownrshp* 1987
Sales 91.1MME *EMP* 6,000
SIC 4512 Air transportation, scheduled
CEO: Stephen R Farrow
**VP:* William W Arndt
**VP:* Eric H Morgan
**VP:* Terry Petrun
**VP:* Michael J Scrobola
MIS Dir: Jack Moscony
Sfty Dirs: Steve Keefer

D-U-N-S 07-593-8811
PIEDMONT ATHENS REGIONAL MEDICAL CENTER INC
ATHENS REGIONAL HEALTH SYSTEM
1510 Prince Ave, Athens, GA 30606-6006
Tel (706) 475-7000 *Founded/Ownrshp* 1994
Sales 392.8MM *EMP* 3,000
SIC 8062 General medical & surgical hospitals
CEO: James G Thaw
Chf OB: John Elder
Dir Recs: Pam Carey
COO: Gary Thelts
**CFO:* G Grant Tribble
CFO: William Webb
VP: Diane Todd
VP: Grant Tribble
Exec: Tiffany Griggs
Dir Risk M: Kim Colfer
Dir Lab: Sue Ensley
Dir Lab: Patricia Maypole
Assoc Dir: Pamela Booker
Dir Rad: Steven G Bramlet
Dir Rad: Brigid M Gerety
Dir Rx: Lori Giles
Dir Rx: Don Tyson

D-U-N-S 00-321-5779 IMP/EXP
PIEDMONT CHEMICAL INDUSTRIES INC (NC)
331 Burton Ave, High Point, NC 27262-8071
Tel (336) 885-5131 *Founded/Ownrshp* 1958
Sales 106.9MME *EMP* 275
SIC 2841 2843 Textile soap; Surface active agents
Pr: Fred Wilson Jr
Ch Bd: Michael Chestnut
**Treas:* Ray Soyars
**VP:* Bill Goodman
**VP:* Fred Wilson III
Dir IT: Felix Yang
Opers Mgr: Tonya Eddinger
Plnt Mgr: Bob Burges
Mktg Dir: Gary Reynolds

D-U-N-S 14-297-8670
■ PIEDMONT COCA-COLA BOTTLING PARTNERSHIP
(*Suby of* COCA-COLA BOTTLING CO CONSOLIDATED) ★
4115 Coca Cola Plz, Charlotte, NC 28211-3400
Tel (704) 551-4400 *Founded/Ownrshp* 2004
Sales 68.3MME *EMP* 1,300
SIC 2086 Bottled & canned soft drinks
CEO: Frank Harrison
CFO: David V Singer
Sr VP: Michael Strong

D-U-N-S 96-571-4244
PIEDMONT COMMUNITY HEALTH PLAN INC
(*Suby of* VIRGINIA BAPTIST HOSPITAL) ★
2316 Atherholt Rd, Lynchburg, VA 24501-2100
Tel (434) 947-4463 *Founded/Ownrshp* 1994
Sales NA *EMP* 1,174E
SIC 6321 Health insurance carriers
Pr: Alan J Wood
CFO: Jacquelyn Mosby
**Treas:* David Donald Adams
Ofcr: Brenda Grant
Exec: Jim Blevins
Exec: Cheryl Midkiff

D-U-N-S 78-938-1006
PIEDMONT COMMUNITY HEALTHCARE INC
(*Suby of* PIEDMONT COMMUNITY HEALTH PLAN INC) ★
2316 Atherholt Rd, Lynchburg, VA 24501-2100
Tel (434) 947-4463 *Founded/Ownrshp* 2006
Sales 331.0M^E *EMP* 1,156^E
SIC 8011 Offices & clinics of medical doctors
Pr: Alan J Wood

PIEDMONT EXPRESS AIRWAYS
See PIEDMONT EXPRESS INC

D-U-N-S 16-811-9191
PIEDMONT EXPRESS INC
PIEDMONT EXPRESS AIRWAYS
7343 W Friendly Ave, Greensboro, NC 27410-6371
Tel (336) 855-7300 *Founded/Ownrshp* 1988
Sales 300.0MM *EMP* 1,900
SIC 4729 4731 Airline ticket offices; Freight transportation arrangement
CEO: Jack Freeman
**Pr:* Ronald Elliot
**Pr:* Dwight Hall

PIEDMONT FAYETTE HOSPITAL
See FAYETTE COMMUNITY HOSPITAL INC

D-U-N-S 18-855-6971
PIEDMONT HAWTHORNE AVIATION LLC
LANDMARK AVIATION
(*Suby of* SIGNATURE FLIGHT SUPPORT) ★
1500 City W Blvd Ste 600, Houston, TX 77042
Tel (713) 895-9243 *Founded/Ownrshp* 2003
Sales 244.3MM^E *EMP* 898
SIC 5599 4581 4522 5172

D-U-N-S 87-879-9303
PIEDMONT HEALTH CARE AUTHORITY
PIEDMONT HEALTH CARE CENTER
30 Roundtree Dr, Piedmont, AL 36272-5892
Tel (256) 447-8258 *Founded/Ownrshp* 1955
Sales 579.4MM *EMP* 135
SIC 8051 Skilled nursing care facilities
Off Mgr: Freda Fagan

PIEDMONT HEALTH CARE CENTER
See PIEDMONT HEALTH CARE AUTHORITY

PIEDMONT HEALTHCARE
See PIEDMONT HOSPITAL INC

PIEDMONT HEALTHCARE
See PIEDMONT NEWNAN HOSPITAL INC

D-U-N-S 83-235-0982
PIEDMONT HEALTHCARE INC
(*Suby of* PIEDMONT HEALTHCARE) ★
1800 Hwll Mll Rd Nw 850, Atlanta, GA 30318
Tel (770) 801-2550 *Founded/Ownrshp* 1983
Sales 92.5MM *EMP* 600
Accts Ernst & Young Us Llp Atlanta
SIC 8059 Personal care home, with health care
CEO: R Timothy Stack
Pr: Harold Moore
**CFO:* Charlie Hall
Dir Lab: Gwendolyn Tyson
Ex Dir: Jackie Bauer
Ex Dir: Jill Morrisey
Ex Dir: Jim Rooy
Software D: Carla Lofton
Opers Mgr: Catherine Hoffman
Snr PM: Linda Jubinsky

D-U-N-S 09-579-4707
PIEDMONT HENRY HOSPITAL INC
(*Suby of* PIEDMONT HEALTHCARE INC) ★
1133 Eagles Landing Pkwy, Stockbridge, GA 30281-5085
Tel (678) 604-1001 *Founded/Ownrshp* 2012
Sales 219.4MM *EMP* 600^E
Accts Kpmg Llp Greensboro Nc
SIC 8062 General medical & surgical hospitals
Pr: Charles F Scott
Chf Rad: William Land
**CFO:* Claude Carruth
**VP:* Jeffrey A Cooper

D-U-N-S 06-532-5466 IMP
PIEDMONT HOSPITAL INC
PIEDMONT HEALTHCARE
1968 Peachtree Rd Nw, Atlanta, GA 30309-1285
Tel (404) 605-5000 *Founded/Ownrshp* 1940
Sales 857.5MM *EMP* 6,419
SIC 8062 General medical & surgical hospitals
CEO: Leslie Les A Donahue
V Ch: Harry M McFarling III
COO: Jeff A Cooper
COO: Gregory A Hurst
**COO:* William D Knopf
CFO: Thomas Arnold
**CFO:* Charlie Hall
CFO: Michael McAnder
Ofcr: Matt Gove
**VP:* Mark Cohen
VP: Rob Simmons
Exec: Pauline Harris
Exec: Toni Kraft
Exec: Denise Ray
Exec: Darryl Start
Dir Lab: Dawn Moore
Dir Bus: Randy Greene

D-U-N-S 78-470-1596
PIEDMONT LIVING CENTER LLC
401 Chandler Rd, Greer, SC 29651-1243
Tel (864) 879-1370 *Founded/Ownrshp* 2005
Sales 821.2MM *EMP* 14^E
SIC 8051 Skilled nursing care facilities

D-U-N-S 14-776-2921
PIEDMONT MEDICAL CENTER INC
(*Suby of* PIEDMONT HEALTHCARE) ★
1968 Peachtree Rd Nw, Atlanta, GA 30309-1281
Tel (404) 605-5000 *Founded/Ownrshp* 1983
Sales 756.0MM *EMP* 4
SIC 8011 Medical centers
CEO: R Timothy Stack

D-U-N-S 13-078-2907
PIEDMONT MUNICIPAL POWER AGENCY
121 Village Dr, Greer, SC 29651-1291
Tel (864) 877-9632 *Founded/Ownrshp* 1979
Sales 250.6MM *EMP* 11
Accts Cherry Bekaert Llp Greenville
SIC 4911 Distribution, electric power
**Ch Bd:* Comer Randall
**CFO:* Steven Ruark
Bd of Dir: David McCuen
Bd of Dir: Jimmy Powell
Bd of Dir: Marc Regier
Bd of Dir: Dale Satterfield
Bd of Dir: Andy Sevic
**Bd of Dir:* Frank Stovall
Bd of Dir: David Vehaun
**Genl Mgr:* Colman Smoak

D-U-N-S 00-331-4549 IMP
PIEDMONT NATIONAL CORP (GA)
1561 Southland Cir Nw, Atlanta, GA 30318-3630
Tel (404) 351-6130 *Founded/Ownrshp* 1950
Sales 145.5MM *EMP* 192
SIC 5199 5113 Packaging materials; Industrial & personal service paper
CEO: Albert Marx
**Pr:* Gary Marx
**VP:* Jack Deleon
**VP:* Eric Feldman
VP: Jack Leon
VP: Jerry Milner
VP: Lamar Rains
Genl Mgr: Ken Draffin
CIO: Tim Grigsby

D-U-N-S 00-699-6219
■ **PIEDMONT NATURAL GAS CO INC**
(*Suby of* DUKE ENERGY CORP) ★
4720 Piedmont Row Dr # 100, Charlotte, NC 28210-4294
Tel (704) 364-3120 *Founded/Ownrshp* 2016
Sales 1.3MMM *EMP* 1,943
SIC 4924 4923 4925 Natural gas distribution; Gas transmission & distribution; Gas production and/or distribution
CEO: Thomas E Skains

D-U-N-S 07-812-2066
PIEDMONT NEWNAN HOSPITAL INC (GA)
PIEDMONT HEALTHCARE
(*Suby of* PIEDMONT HEALTHCARE) ★
745 Poplar Rd, Newnan, GA 30265-1618
Tel (770) 253-2330 *Founded/Ownrshp* 1925, 2007
Sales 205.9MM *EMP* 1,000
Accts Ernst & Young Us Llp Atlanta
SIC 8062 General medical & surgical hospitals
Pr: Michael Bass
**COO:* Nathan Nipper
**CFO:* John G Miles
**CFO:* Courtney Reece
Dir IT: Henry Scott
Doctor: Barbara Phillips

D-U-N-S 11-154-9015
▲ **PIEDMONT OFFICE REALTY TRUST INC**
11695 Johns Creek Pkwy, Johns Creek, GA 30097-1825
Tel (770) 418-8800 *Founded/Ownrshp* 1998
Sales 584.7MM *EMP* 143
Tkr Sym PDM *Exch* NYS
SIC 6798 Real estate investment trusts
Pr: Donald A Miller
**Ch Bd:* Michael R Buchanan
CFO: Robert E Bowers
**V Ch Bd:* Frank C McDowell
Ex VP: Raymond L Owens
Ex VP: Joseph H Pangburn
Ex VP: Thomas R Prescott
Ex VP: Carroll A Reddic IV
Ex VP: C Brent Smith
Ex VP: George M Wells
Ex VP: Robert K Wiberg
Sr VP: Laura P Moon
VP: Kevin Fossum
Board of Directors: Kelly H Barrett, Wesley E Cantrell, Barbara B Lang, Raymond G Milnes Jr, Jeffrey L Swope, Dale H Taysom

D-U-N-S 04-443-9941 IMP
PIEDMONT PLASTICS INC
5010 W Wt Harris Blvd, Charlotte, NC 28269
Tel (704) 597-8200 *Founded/Ownrshp* 1985
Sales 164.1MM^E *EMP* 429
SIC 3081 3082 5162 Plastic film & sheet; Rods, unsupported plastic; Tubes, unsupported plastic; Plastics sheets & rods; Plastics products
Pr: Owen H Whitfield Jr
COO: Boyce Gault
**CFO:* Greg Young
**Ofcr:* William Barth
**VP:* Tyler Booth
Brnch Mgr: Carlos Bennett
Brnch Mgr: Elek Lukes
Brnch Mgr: Gregg Metropulos
Brnch Mgr: Daniel Walsh
Dist Mgr: Mark Zaba
**CIO:* Marc Klinger

PIEHLER-VISION BUICK GMC
See VISION BUICK GMC LLC

D-U-N-S 36-440-7262 IMP/EXP
■ **PIER 1 IMPORTS (US) INC**
(*Suby of* PIER 1 LICENSING INC) ★
100 Pier 1 Pl, Fort Worth, TX 76102-2600
Tel (817) 252-8000 *Founded/Ownrshp* 1979
Sales 1.9MMM^E *EMP* 12,571
SIC 5713 5719 Rugs; Bedding (sheets, blankets, spreads & pillows)
Pr: Alexander W Smith
**CFO:* Charles H Turner
**Ex VP:* Michael R Benkel
**Ex VP:* Laura A Coffey
**Ex VP:* Catherine David
**Ex VP:* Gregory S Humenesky
**Ex VP:* Eric W Hunter
**Ex VP:* Jay R Jacobs
**Ex VP:* Sharon M Leite

D-U-N-S 09-584-9360
▲ **PIER 1 IMPORTS INC**
100 Pier 1 Pl, Fort Worth, TX 76102-2600
Tel (817) 252-8000 *Founded/Ownrshp* 1962
Sales 1.8MMM *EMP* 22,000^E
Accts Ernst & Young Llp Fort Worth
Tkr Sym PIR *Exch* NYS
SIC 5719 6794 5712 Wicker, rattan or reed home furnishings; Lamps & lamp shades; Bedding (sheets, blankets, spreads & pillows); Housewares; Franchises, selling or licensing; Furniture stores
Pr: Alexander W Smith
**Ch Bd:* Terry E London
CFO: Jeffrey N Boyer
Ex VP: Michael R Benkel
Ex VP: Michael A Carter
Ex VP: Laura A Coffey
Ex VP: Catherine David
Ex VP: Gregory S Humenesky
Ex VP: Eric W Hunter
Sr VP: Andrew Laudato
VP: Jim B Prucha
Exec: Rosie Ericson
Dir: Todd L Barnett
Board of Directors: Claire H Babrowski, Cheryl A Bachelder, Hamish A Dodds, Brendan L Hoffman, Cynthia P McCague, Michael A Peel, Ann M Sardini

D-U-N-S 82-619-6446 IMP/EXP
■ **PIER 1 LICENSING INC**
(*Suby of* PIER 1 IMPORTS INC) ★
100 Pier 1 Pl, Fort Worth, TX 76102-2600
Tel (817) 878-8000 *Founded/Ownrshp* 1993
Sales 1.9MMM^E *EMP* 13,500
SIC 5719 5712 5621 5632 Bedding (sheets, blankets, spreads & pillows); Cookware, except aluminum; Housewares; Wicker, rattan or reed home furnishings; Custom made furniture, except cabinets; Ready-to-wear apparel, women's; Apparel accessories; Costume jewelry
Ch Bd: Marvin Girouard
VP: Beck Hudson
**VP:* J Rodney Lawrence

D-U-N-S 04-169-4431 IMP/EXP
PIERCE ALUMINUM CO INC
34 Forge Pkwy, Franklin, MA 02038-3134
Tel (508) 541-7007 *Founded/Ownrshp* 1967
Sales 103.8MM^E *EMP* 200
SIC 5051 Aluminum bars, rods, ingots, sheets, pipes, plates, etc.
Pr: Jeffrey Pierce
VP: Jim Pringle
Brnch Mgr: Michael Drew
Brnch Mgr: Scott Stewart
Dist Mgr: Frank J Domingue
Software D: Josh Klein
Sales Asso: Joe Ayube
Sales Asso: William Donahue
Sales Asso: V Ericksen
Sales Asso: Bo Howard
Sales Asso: Justin R Lafleur

D-U-N-S 00-981-9624 IMP
PIERCE ASSOCIATES INC
4216 Wheeler Ave, Alexandria, VA 22304-6400
Tel (703) 751-2400 *Founded/Ownrshp* 1961
Sales 90.4MM^E *EMP* 430
SIC 1711 Warm air heating & air conditioning contractor; Plumbing contractors
Pr: Stephen C Pierce
**Pr:* John J Dunleavy
**Treas:* Robert A Pierce

D-U-N-S 12-517-2130 IMP
PIERCE CO INC
(*Suby of* AVIS INDUSTRIAL CORP) ★
35 N 8th St, Upland, IN 46989
Tel (765) 998-8100 *Founded/Ownrshp* 1985
Sales 77.8MM^E *EMP* 1,123^E
SIC 3714 Motor vehicle parts & accessories; Fuel pipes, motor vehicle; Water pump, motor vehicle; Governors, motor vehicle
Pr: Leland E Boren
**Treas:* Tracee L Pennington
Genl Mgr: Bob Magasi
IT Man: Lisa Weaver

D-U-N-S 00-612-6999 IMP/EXP
■ **PIERCE MANUFACTURING INC**
(*Suby of* OSHKOSH CORP) ★
2600 American Dr, Appleton, WI 54914-9010
Tel (920) 832-3000 *Founded/Ownrshp* 1996
Sales 2.3MMM^E *EMP* 11,900
SIC 3711 Fire department vehicles (motor vehicles), assembly of
CEO: Wilson Jone
**Pr:* John Randjelovic
**COO:* Charles L Szews
**CFO:* David Sagehorn
**VP:* Patrick N Davidson
VP: Mike Moore
**VP:* Matthew J Zolnowski
Prgrm Mgr: Tim Hawkinson
Mktg Dir: Don Daemmrich
Snr Mgr: Doug Morley

PIERCETON CASE & TRAY
See PARAGON MEDICAL INC

PIERCING PAGODA
See ZALE CORP

PIERCING PAGODA
See ZALE DELAWARE INC

D-U-N-S 36-128-9023
PIERPASS INC
444 W Ocean Blvd Ste 700, Long Beach, CA 90802-4581
Tel (562) 437-9112 *Founded/Ownrshp* 2005
Sales 117.0MM^E *EMP* 6
Accts Windes & Mcclaughry Acct Corp
SIC 8399 7322 Fund raising organization, non-fee basis; Adjustment & collection services
Pr: John Cushing
**CFO:* Kevin Recker

D-U-N-S 80-576-4847
PIERRE HOLDING CORP
(*Suby of* MADISON DEARBORN PARTNERS IV LP) ★
9990 Prnceton Glendale Rd, West Chester, OH 45246-1116
Tel (513) 874-8741 *Founded/Ownrshp* 2004
Sales 224.5MM^E *EMP* 2,800
SIC 2013 2015 2051 Prepared beef products from purchased beef; Prepared pork products from purchased pork; Chicken slaughtering & processing; Bread, cake & related products
Pr: Norbert E Wooadhams
CFO: Joseph W Meyers
Sr VP: Robert C Naylor

PIGGLY WIGGLY
See SOUTHERN FAMILY MARKETS LLC

D-U-N-S 00-791-9277 IMP
PIGGLY WIGGLY CAROLINA CO INC (SC)
176 Croghan Spur Ste 400, Charleston, SC 29407-7557
Tel (843) 554-9880 *Founded/Ownrshp* 1947
Sales 322.4MM^E *EMP* 3,429
Accts Websterrogers Llp Florence S
SIC 7311 5411 5148 5141 2752 1542 Advertising agencies; Supermarkets, chain; Fresh fruits & vegetables; Groceries, general line; Commercial printing, offset; Commercial & office building, new construction
Ch Bd: Joseph T Buzzy Newton III
Pr: John Owens
**Pr:* David R Schools
**CFO:* William A Edenfield Jr
Dist Mgr: Louis Sherman

D-U-N-S 03-627-4942
PIGGLY WIGGLY CENTRAL INC
SUP-RX-PHARMACY
415 N Salem Ave, Sumter, SC 29150-4115
Tel (803) 775-3020 *Founded/Ownrshp* 1954
Sales 138.3MM^E *EMP* 900^E
SIC 5411 Supermarkets, chain
Pr: William McLeod Jr

D-U-N-S 02-710-3485
PIGGLY WIGGLY MIDWEST LLC
2215 Union Ave, Sheboygan, WI 53081-5561
Tel (920) 457-4433 *Founded/Ownrshp* 2007
Sales 2.4MMM^E *EMP* 2,400
SIC 5141 5411 Groceries, general line; Grocery stores, independent
Owner: Paul Butera
CFO: Elwood F Winn
Opers Mgr: Judy Gagnon
Opers Mgr: Rob Kober
Opers Mgr: Brent Mattox

PIH HEALTH
See INTERHEALTH CORP

PIH HOME HEALTH SERVICES
See DOWNEY REGIONAL MEDICAL CENTER-HOSPITAL INC

PIH HOME HEALTH SERVICES
See PRESBYTERIAN INTERCOMMUNITY HOSPITAL INC

D-U-N-S 07-992-2039
PII HOLDINGS INC
(*Suby of* BERWIND CONSOLIDATED HOLDINGS INC) ★
2150 Elmwood Ave, Buffalo, NY 14207-1910
Tel (716) 876-9951 *Founded/Ownrshp* 2015
Sales 220.0MM^E *EMP* 1,200
SIC 3089 3822 6719 Molding primary plastic; Temperature controls, automatic; Investment holding companies, except banks
CEO: Mike McLelland
Treas: Ray Baran

D-U-N-S 06-851-8315
PII INC
17 Research Park Dr # 100, Weldon Spring, MO 63304-5620
Tel (636) 685-1047 *Founded/Ownrshp* 1974
Sales 304.0MM^E *EMP* 1,700
SIC 2311 2326 Military uniforms, men's & youths': purchased materials; Work uniforms
Pr: Amy Coyne
**Pr:* Tom Kellim
**COO:* John Minard
**Ch:* Earl Weinman

D-U-N-S 17-501-7573
PIKE CO INC
1 Circle St, Rochester, NY 14607-1007
Tel (585) 271-5256 *Founded/Ownrshp* 1985
Sales 312.1MM^E *EMP* 385
SIC 1542 Commercial & office building, new construction; Commercial & office buildings, renovation & repair
CEO: Thomas F Judson Jr
**Pr:* Rufus Judson
**COO:* William Tehan CPA
COO: William P Tehan
CFO: Bill Tehan
CFO: Richard Tyler
**Ex VP:* Leonard E Bower
**Ex VP:* William J Ketchen
**Ex VP:* Paul J Moyer
**Ex VP:* Ted H Orr
Ex VP: Mauricio Riveros
Ex VP: Patrick Rogers
VP: Raymond Freeman
VP: Ann Hutchinson
VP: Bill Ketchen

D-U-N-S 06-742-4788
PIKE CORP
(*Suby of* PIONEER PARENT INC) ★
100 Pike Way, Mount Airy, NC 27030-8147
Tel (336) 789-2171 *Founded/Ownrshp* 2014
Sales 1.0MMM^E *EMP* 5,800
SIC 1731 8711 Electrical work; Electric power systems contractors; Engineering services
Pr: J Eric Pike
CFO: Rita Francis

CFO: Richard Wimmer
Sr VP: Jim Hicks
VP: Donald Anderson
VP: Stanley J Marion
VP: Robert B Ratliff Jr
VP: Don Robertson
VP: Michael Seymour
VP: Audie G Simmons
VP: Matt Simmons

D-U-N-S 10-000-0819
PIKE COUNTY BOARD OF EDUCATION
101 W Love St, Troy, AL 36081-1918
Tel (334) 566-1850 *Founded/Ownrshp* 1895
Sales 88.3MM *EMP* 400
SIC 8211 School board
Pr: Chris Wilkes
IT Man: Derrick Stinson

PIKE COUNTY SCHOOL SYSTEM
See PIKE COUNTY SCHOOLS

D-U-N-S 10-002-7796
PIKE COUNTY SCHOOLS
PIKE COUNTY SCHOOL SYSTEM
316 S Mayo Trl, Pikeville, KY 41501-1522
Tel (606) 432-7700 *Founded/Ownrshp* 1800
Sales 90.0MM *EMP* 1,400
Accts John B Tackett Psc Pikev
SIC 8211 Public elementary & secondary schools; Public elementary school; Public junior high school; Public senior high school
Pr Dir: Rosalind Stanley
HC Dir: Leandra Johnson

D-U-N-S 00-388-5514
PIKE ELECTRIC LLC (NC)
(*Suby of* PIKE CORP) ★
100 Pike Way, Mount Airy, NC 27030-8147
Tel (336) 789-2171 *Founded/Ownrshp* 1945, 2010
Sales 776.8MM[E] *EMP* 4,143
Accts Ernst & Young Llp Greensboro
SIC 1731 8711 General electrical contractor; Electrical or electronic engineering
VP: James T Benfield
VP: Ken Flechler
**VP:* Stan Marion
**VP:* Matt Simmons
Board of Directors: J Eric Pike, Rick Wimmer

D-U-N-S 96-665-3714
PIKE ENTERPRISES LLC
(*Suby of* PIKE CORP) ★
100 Pike Way, Mount Airy, NC 27030-8147
Tel (336) 789-2171 *Founded/Ownrshp* 2015
Sales 100.5MM[E] *EMP* 4,145
SIC 8741 Administrative management
Pr: J Eric Pike

PIKE FAMILY NURSERIES
See PIKE NURSERY HOLDING LLC

D-U-N-S 01-897-0517 IMP
PIKE INDUSTRIES INC
(*Suby of* OLDCASTLE INC) ★
3 Eastgate Park Dr, Belmont, NH 03220-3603
Tel (603) 527-5100 *Founded/Ownrshp* 1993
Sales 207.3MM[E] *EMP* 300
SIC 1611 2951 3295 General contractor, highway & street construction; Highway & street paving contractor; Asphalt & asphaltic paving mixtures (not from refineries); Minerals, ground or treated
Pr: Christian E Zimmermann
**Treas:* Charles Brown
**VP:* Christopher J Madden
CTO: Christian Zimmermann
VP Mktg: Jay Perkins

D-U-N-S 03-355-1573 IMP
PIKE NURSERY HOLDING LLC
PIKE FAMILY NURSERIES
(*Suby of* ARMSTRONG GROWERS) ★
3555 Koger Blvd Ste 360, Duluth, GA 30096-8903
Tel (770) 921-1022 *Founded/Ownrshp* 2008
Sales 95.2MM[E] *EMP* 500
SIC 5261 Nursery stock, seeds & bulbs
Ex VP: Dana P Vanvlake
Comm Man: Kathy Pipcorn
Store Mgr: John Blackstock
Store Mgr: Patricia Starnes
Site Mgr: Ryan Tobin
Opers Mgr: Matt Gross
VP Merchng: Michael Chapman
Mktg Dir: Desiree Heimann
Mktg Mgr: Brittany Harper

PIKES PEAK LODGE 38
See INDEPENDENT ORDER OF ODD FELLOWS

D-U-N-S 05-556-9057
PIKEVILLE MEDICAL CENTER INC
P M C
911 Bypass Rd, Pikeville, KY 41501-1689
Tel (606) 218-3500 *Founded/Ownrshp* 1923
Sales 381.5MM *EMP* 2,527[E]
SIC 8062 Hospital, affiliated with AMA residency
Pr: Walter E May
Pr: Sheila Belcher
**COO:* Juanita Deskins
**COO:* Debbie Puckett
**CFO:* Michelle Hagey
**Sec:* Joe Dean Anderson
VP: Brett Akers
**VP:* Ronald Burchett
VP: Kermit Gibson
**VP:* Michelle Hagy
**VP:* Peggy Rasnick Justice
VP: Patty Thompson
Dir Teleco: Oliver Mead
Dir Risk M: Jerry Krevinghaus

PIKIDS
See PHOENIX INTERNATIONAL PUBLICATIONS INC

D-U-N-S 01-074-8197 IMP
PIKSEL INC
2100 Powers Ferry Rd Se # 400, Atlanta, GA 30339-5014
Tel (646) 553-4845 *Founded/Ownrshp* 2003
Sales 321.8MM[E] *EMP* 15[E]
SIC 4813
Ch Bd: Peter Heilord
Pt: Don Terry
**COO:* Allan Dunn
**CFO:* Fabrice Hamaide
Ofcr: Kirk Feathers
Ex VP: Neil Berry
Ex VP: Trish Iboshi
Sr VP: Brian Kisslak
Sr VP: Michel Meyer
VP: Brian Auckland
VP: Anders Berglund
VP: Jonathan Dyson
VP: Ian Kennedy
VP: Robert Lauer
VP: Chance Mason
VP: Brendan O'Shaughnessy
VP: Joseph Oliver
VP: Alan Riley
Creative D: Chris Gannon

PILGRIM DRILLING CO
See KAISER-FRANCIS OIL CO

D-U-N-S 00-733-4170 IMP/EXP
▲ PILGRIMS PRIDE CORP
1770 Promontory Cir, Greeley, CO 80634-9039
Tel (970) 506-8000 *Founded/Ownrshp* 2009
Sales 8.1MMM *EMP* 38,850
Tkr Sym PPC *Exch* NGS
SIC 2015 0254 0252 2048 5999 Chicken, slaughtered & dressed; Chicken, processed: fresh; Chicken hatchery; Chicken eggs; Poultry feeds; Livestock feeds; Feed & farm supply
Pr: William W Lovette
**Ch Bd:* Gilberto Tomazoni
CFO: Fabio Sandri
Ex VP: Walt Shafer
VP: Roger Austin
VP: Cynthia Cinatl
VP: Stacy Fiedler
VP: Mark Glover
VP: Matthew Herman
VP: Phil Hurwitz
VP: Alexander Ivannikov
VP: Heath Loyd
VP: Rick Stevens
VP: Aaron Wiegand
Board of Directors: Wesley Mendonca Batista, David E Bell, Michael L Cooper, Andre Nogueira De Souza, Charles Macaluso

D-U-N-S 06-702-7052 EXP
PILGRIMS PRIDE CORP
1965 Evergreen Blvd # 100, Duluth, GA 30096-1208
Tel (770) 232-4200 *Founded/Ownrshp* 2003
Sales NA *EMP* 11,000
SIC 2015 5144 5141

D-U-N-S 00-327-3554 IMP/EXP
■ PILGRIMS PRIDE CORP OF GEORGIA INC (DE)
(*Suby of* PILGRIMS PRIDE CORP) ★
244 Perimeter Ctr Pkwy Ne, Atlanta, GA 30346-1402
Tel (770) 393-5000 *Founded/Ownrshp* 1933, 2007
Sales 1.9MMM[E] *EMP* 16,800
SIC 2015 0254 Chicken, slaughtered & dressed; Chicken, processed: fresh; Chicken, processed: frozen; Game, small: slaughtered & dressed; Chicken hatchery
CEO: Ob Goolsby
CFO: Richard A Cogdill

D-U-N-S 15-136-6283 IMP/EXP
PILKINGTON HOLDINGS INC
P H I
(*Suby of* PILKINGTON GROUP LIMITED)
811 Madison Ave Fl 1, Toledo, OH 43604-5688
Tel (419) 247-3731 *Founded/Ownrshp* 1982
Sales 688.0MM[E] *EMP* 5,200
SIC 3211 Flat glass
CEO: Warren D Knowlton
**Pr:* A R Graham
**Treas:* Jeffrey Bowman
VP: Rick Frampton
**VP:* G M Gray
**VP:* S P Harris
**VP:* J Mc Kenna
VP: William N McCreary
**VP:* Dan Vermilya
Dir Sec: Adam Barton
CIO: Philip Wilkinson
Board of Directors: Ian Lough

D-U-N-S 15-126-6129 IMP/EXP
PILKINGTON NORTH AMERICA INC
(*Suby of* P H I) ★
811 Madison Ave Fl 1, Toledo, OH 43604-5688
Tel (419) 247-4955 *Founded/Ownrshp* 1986
Sales 20.0MM *EMP* 3,747[E]
SIC 3211 Flat glass; Construction glass
Pr: Richard Altman
Genl Mgr: Kevin Malpass
Plnt Mgr: Gordon Labrech
Mktg Dir: Bill George

D-U-N-S 07-877-0302 IMP
PILLSBURY WINTHROP SHAW PITTMAN LLP
1540 Broadway Fl 9, New York, NY 10036-4083
Tel (212) 858-1000 *Founded/Ownrshp* 2000
Sales 365.7MM[E] *EMP* 1,800
SIC 8111 General practice law office
COO: Richard Donaldson
Pt: David Stanton
Mng Pt: Bruce A Ericson
Mng Pt: William R Huss
Mng Pt: John E Jensen
Mng Pt: Woon-Wah Siu
Mng Pt: Sheryl E Stein
Mng Pt: Samuel E Stubbs
Mng Pt: Tim Wright
Mng Pt: Stephen M Wurzburg
CFO: Sean Whelan
VP: Gwen Davis
Exec: Deborah L Johnson

D-U-N-S 79-473-4228
PILOT CATASTROPHE SERVICES INC
1055 Hillcrest Rd, Mobile, AL 36695-4046
Tel (251) 607-7700 *Founded/Ownrshp* 1989
Sales NA *EMP* 1,200
SIC 6411 Insurance claim adjusters, not employed by insurance company
CEO: W Davis Pilot Jr
**Sec:* Elma G Pilot
**VP:* Daphne Pilot Fonde
**VP:* Curtis Pilot
Genl Mgr: Terry Aucoin
IT Man: Tray Sparks
Software D: Tim Giertz

D-U-N-S 04-997-6186
PILOT CORP
PILOT FOODMART
5508 Lonas Dr, Knoxville, TN 37909-3221
Tel (865) 588-7488 *Founded/Ownrshp* 1958
Sales 785.3MM[E] *EMP* 24,337
Accts Kpmg Llp Knoxville Tn
SIC 5411 5541 Convenience stores, chain; Filling stations, gasoline
CEO: John Compton
CFO: James P Pardue
Ch: Jimmy Haslam
VP: Spencer Ferrier
VP: Mark A Hazelwood
Dir Risk M: Joseph Butler
Snr Ntwrk: Richard Proffitt
Snr Ntwrk: Jeremy Todd
Dir IT: Robert Massengill
IT Man: Robert Byington
Sys Mgr: Chris Drouin
Board of Directors: James A Haslam II, James A Haslam III

D-U-N-S 06-472-1194 IMP
PILOT CORP OF AMERICA
PILOT PEN
(*Suby of* PILOT CORPORATION)
3855 Regent Blvd, Jacksonville, FL 32224-6505
Tel (904) 645-9999 *Founded/Ownrshp* 1972
Sales 132.5MM[E] *EMP* 250
SIC 5112 3951 Writing instruments & supplies; Pens & mechanical pencils
Pr: Dennis Burleigh
Treas: Joji Ota
**VP:* Kim Cooper
VP: Jim Matese
VP: Tom Restivo
Dept Mgr: Mary Holmes
Prd Mgr: Anthony Kalil
Mktg Mgr: Ariann Langsam
Manager: Eric Holland

PILOT FLYING J
See PILOT TRAVEL CENTERS LLC

PILOT FOODMART
See PILOT CORP

D-U-N-S 13-602-1735
PILOT GROUP LP
1270 Ave Of The Americas, New York, NY 10020-1700
Tel (212) 486-4446 *Founded/Ownrshp* 2003
Sales 177.6MM[E] *EMP* 755
SIC 4833 Television broadcasting stations
Pt: Paul McNicol
Pt: Robert W Pittman
Pt: Andrew Russell
Pt: Robert Sherman
Pt: Mayo S Stuntz
Mng Pt: Paul M McNicol
Mktg Mgr: Katherine Chen

PILOT LOGISTIC SERVICES
See PILOT THOMAS LOGISTICS LLC

PILOT LOGISTICS SERVICES
See SIMONS PETROLEUM

PILOT PEN
See PILOT CORP OF AMERICA

PILOT THOMAS LOGISTICS
See MAXUM ENTERPRISES LLC

D-U-N-S 04-130-8008
PILOT THOMAS LOGISTICS LLC
PILOT LOGISTIC SERVICES
(*Suby of* PILOT FLYING J) ★
201 N Rupert St Ste 101, Fort Worth, TX 76107-1460
Tel (435) 789-1832 *Founded/Ownrshp* 2012
Sales 209.2MM[E] *EMP* 235[E]
SIC 5172 Petroleum products
**CFO:* Janis Kline

D-U-N-S 02-133-9648 IMP
PILOT TRAVEL CENTERS LLC
PILOT FLYING J
(*Suby of* PILOT FOODMART) ★
5508 Lonas Dr, Knoxville, TN 37909-3221
Tel (865) 588-7488 *Founded/Ownrshp* 2001
Sales 628.9MM[E] *EMP* 400[E]
SIC 5411 5541 Convenience stores; Truck stops
CEO: John Compton
Genl Mgr: Donna Brough
Sls Mgr: Jay Stinnett
Genl Couns: Kyle A Baisley
Snr Mgr: Robert Byington

D-U-N-S 78-451-2985
PILOT TRAVEL CENTERS LLC
(*Suby of* PILOT FOODMART) ★
1340 Piggott Ave, East Saint Louis, IL 62201-2701
Tel (618) 875-5800 *Founded/Ownrshp* 2006
Sales 101.2M[E] *EMP* 5,007[E]
SIC 5541 Gasoline service stations

D-U-N-S 96-810-2454
■ PIM HIGHLAND HOLDING LLC
(*Suby of* ASHFORD HOSPITALITY LIMITED PARTNERSHIP) ★
14185 Dallas Pkwy # 1100, Dallas, TX 75254-1319
Tel (972) 778-9452 *Founded/Ownrshp* 2011
Sales 132.9MM[E] *EMP* 2,366[E]
SIC 6719 Investment holding companies, except banks

PIMA COMMUNITY COLLEGE
See PIMA COUNTY COMMUNITY COLLEGE DISTRICT INC

D-U-N-S 07-447-7969
PIMA COUNTY
REGIONAL FLOOD CONTROL DST
97 E Congress St Fl 3, Tucson, AZ 85701-1794
Tel (520) 243-1800 *Founded/Ownrshp* 1864
Sales 789.1MM *EMP* 7,500
Accts Debbie Davenport Phoenix Ari
SIC 9111 1623 County supervisors' & executives' offices; Water, sewer & utility lines
Sr Cor Off: Richard Elias
Ofcr: Gabriel Aguilera
Ofcr: Karen Couture
Admn Mgr: Ellen Cuddeback
Genl Mgr: Marilyn Hutzler
QA Dir: Michael Draper
Netwrk Mgr: Kevin Wallace

D-U-N-S 07-447-0964
PIMA COUNTY AMPHITHEATER SCHOOLS
AMPHITHEATER PUBLIC SCHOOLS
701 W Wetmore Rd, Tucson, AZ 85705-1547
Tel (520) 696-5000 *Founded/Ownrshp* 1893
Sales 124.3MM *EMP* 2,000
Accts Heinfeld Meech & Co Pc T
SIC 8211 Public elementary & secondary schools
**CFO:* Scott Little
Treas: Natalie Walker
Prin: Charles Bermudez
Prin: Harold Doran
Prin: Cathy Eiting
Prin: Alice Farley
Prin: Gail Gault
Prin: Micheal Gemma
Prin: Adrian Hannah
Prin: Anita Howard
Prin: Donna Kelley

D-U-N-S 06-841-4630
PIMA COUNTY COMMUNITY COLLEGE DISTRICT INC
PIMA COMMUNITY COLLEGE
4905 E Broadway Blvd, Tucson, AZ 85709-1010
Tel (520) 206-4500 *Founded/Ownrshp* 1970
Sales 124.5MM[E] *EMP* 3,800
SIC 8222 Community college
Ofcr: Matt Szady
Ex VP: David Bea
VP: Victoria Cook
VP: Caroline Lee
Int Pr: Sheila Ortego
Ex Dir: Peter Becskehazy
Ex Dir: Nicola Richmond
Prgrm Mgr: Moore Helin
Dir IT: Keith McIntosh
IT Man: Donald Shaffer
Netwrk Mgr: Brad Mathis

PIMCO
See PACIFIC INVESTMENT MANAGEMENT CO LLC

D-U-N-S 01-009-2336
PIMLICO RACING ASSOCIATION INC (MD)
MARYLAND JOCKEY CLUB
(*Suby of* THE STRONACH GROUP INC)
5201 Park Heights Ave, Baltimore, MD 21215-5116
Tel (410) 542-9400 *Founded/Ownrshp* 1743, 2002
Sales 11.2MM[E] *EMP* 1,500
Accts Ernst & Young Llp Baltimore
SIC 7948 Horse race track operation
Ch Bd: Frank Stronach
CFO: Douglas Illig
**Ex VP:* Karin Defrancis

D-U-N-S 00-599-1195 IMP
PINDLER & PINDLER INC (CA)
WHOLESALE FABRICS
11910 Poindexter Ave, Moorpark, CA 93021-1748
Tel (805) 531-9090 *Founded/Ownrshp* 1939, 1986
Sales 118.4MM[E] *EMP* 165
SIC 5131 Drapery material, woven; Upholstery fabrics, woven
Pr: Curt R Pindler
**Ex VP:* S L Crawford Jr
IT Man: Bill Crawford

PINE BELT CHEVORLET
See PINE BELT ENTERPRISES INC

D-U-N-S 01-138-2785
PINE BELT ENTERPRISES INC
PINE BELT CHEVORLET
1088 Route 88, Lakewood, NJ 08701-4512
Tel (732) 363-2900 *Founded/Ownrshp* 1937
Sales 83.1MM[E] *EMP* 240
SIC 5511 7537 5531 Automobiles, new & used; Automotive transmission repair shops; Automotive parts
Owner: David Sickel
**VP:* Kenneth Martin
VP: Rob Sickel
Genl Mgr: Dan Ariel
Dir IT: Steve Sabo
Sales Asso: Eugene Pascucci
Sales Asso: Bob Penny
Sales Asso: Jim Pfister

D-U-N-S 05-822-6457
PINE BELT OIL CO INC
RAMCO
343 Highway 589, Purvis, MS 39475-3035
Tel (601) 794-5900 *Founded/Ownrshp* 2000
Sales 179.1MM[E] *EMP* 200
SIC 5172 Petroleum products
Pr: Allen Morgan
IT Man: Kayla Norris

PINE BLUFF FOUNDATION FUND
See UNVRSTY OF AR FONDTIN INC

D-U-N-S 00-634-1861
PINE BLUFF SAND AND GRAVEL CO (AR)
RIVER MOUNTAIN QUARRIES
1501 Heartwood St, White Hall, AR 71602-4705
Tel (870) 534-7120 *Founded/Ownrshp* 1913
Sales 99.3MM[E] *EMP* 250

SIC 2951 3273 1442 5032 1629 Asphalt & asphaltic paving mixtures (not from refineries); Ready-mixed concrete; Construction sand & gravel; Sand, construction; Dams, waterways, docks & other marine construction
Pr: W Scott Mc George
COO: Brian McGeorge
*Treas: Drew Atkinson
*VP: Gerald W Majors
VP: Wallace P McGeorge III
VP: Wallace McGeorge
IT Man: Alan Perry
Snr PM: Tony Cinkovich

PINE GROVE RECOVERY
See FORREST GENERAL HEALTH SERVICES INC

D-U-N-S 04-141-4541 IMP
PINE HALL BRICK CO INC
RIVERSIDE BRICK & SUPPLY
2701 Shorefair Dr, Winston Salem, NC 27105-4235
Tel (336) 721-7500 Founded/Ownrshp 1967
Sales 90.7MM^E EMP 365
SIC 3251 5032 Brick & structural clay tile; Brick, except refractory
Pr: Fletcher Steele
Pr: Flake F Steele Jr
CFO: Ed Harrell
Treas: Scott E Richardson
VP: John Dowdle
DP Dir: Tom Voigner
VP Mfg: Hugh Dowdle Jr
VP Sls: C R Griffin

D-U-N-S 01-635-0035 IMP
PINE MANOR INC
(Suby of MILLER MEAT POULTRY) ★
9622 W 350 N, Orland, IN 46776-5468
Tel (800) 532-4186 Founded/Ownrshp 1959
Sales 88.1MM^E EMP 500
SIC 2048 2015 0254 Poultry feeds; Livestock feeds; Poultry slaughtering & processing; Chicken hatchery
Pr: Galen Miller
*VP: Ursula Miller
*VP: John Sauder
*Prin: Kevin Diehl
Sfty Mgr: Bob Heff

D-U-N-S 05-585-7478
PINE REST CHRISTIAN MENTAL HEALTH SERVICES
300 68th St Se, Grand Rapids, MI 49548-6927
Tel (616) 455-5000 Founded/Ownrshp 1913
Sales 108.8MM EMP 1,600
SIC 8063 Psychiatric hospitals
CEO: Mark Eastburg
COO: Bob Nykamp
CFO: Paul Karsten
*CFO: Paul Kersten
Dir Risk M: Dolores Sears-Ewald
Comm Man: Colleen Cullison
Ex Dir: Teresa Newmarch
Prgrm Mgr: Tiffany Idziak
Sfty Dirs: Joan Hibma
Ql Cn Mgr: Dawn Poeller
Psych: Jon Weeldreyer

D-U-N-S 11-137-4901
PINE RIVER CAPITAL MANAGEMENT LP
601 Carlson Pkwy Ste 330, Minnetonka, MN 55305-7703
Tel (612) 238-3300 Founded/Ownrshp 2002
Sales 109.2MM^E EMP 340^E
SIC 6722 Management investment, open-end
*CFO: Jeff Stolt
Ofcr: Annette Krassner
Top Exec: Colin Teichholtz
VP: Boris Alyurov
Dir Risk M: Paul Richardson
Mng Dir: Jack Cahill
CTO: David Kelly
Genl Couns: Tim Obrien
Corp Couns: Cassie Myhro
Snr Mgr: James Clark

PINE RIVER GROUP
See BIEWER LUMBER LLC

PINE STATE BEVERAGE CO
See PINE STATE TRADING CO

D-U-N-S 01-898-0342 IMP
PINE STATE TRADING CO
PINE STATE BEVERAGE CO
47 Market St, Gardiner, ME 04345-6285
Tel (207) 622-2345 Founded/Ownrshp 1941
Sales 622.4MM^E EMP 550
SIC 5181 5194 5145 Beer & other fermented malt liquors; Tobacco & tobacco products; Confectionery
Ch Bd: Charles F Canning Jr
Pr: Paul Cottrell
CEO: Nick Alberding
CFO: Gary Pelletier
VP: Nick Alberdang
VP: Paul N Alberding
VP: Geraldine R Canning
Exec: D Wiliams
Genl Mgr: Mark Bubier
CIO: Scott Rollins
Dir IT: Chris Leavitt
Board of Directors: Keith M Canning, Sue Reed

D-U-N-S 83-297-4047
PINEBRIDGE INVESTMENTS LLC
(Suby of PACIFIC CENTURY GROUP HOLDINGS (HK) LIMITED)
399 Park Ave Fl 4, New York, NY 10022-4417
Tel (646) 857-8000 Founded/Ownrshp 2009
Sales 332.5MM^E EMP 5,750^E
SIC 8741 Management services
CEO: David T Jiang
V Ch: Win J Neuger
Pr: Pierre Mellinger
CEO: Talal Al Zain
COO: George R Hornig
CFO: David Kolker
Sr VP: Michael Luft
Sr VP: Justin Pollack
Sr VP: James J Smith
VP: Carleen Chuang
VP: Jennifer Daw
VP: Elliot Hayes
VP: Ash Jogi
VP: Janine Miller
VP: Jay Quenville
VP: Stacia Rogers
VP: Alissa Ruiz
VP: Gunter Seeger
VP: Omar Slim
VP: W Michael Verge
VP: Catherine Wade
Board of Directors: C Kim Goodwin, Don M Wilson

D-U-N-S 11-598-8586
PINEHURST LLC
PINEHURST RESORT & COUNTRY CLB
80 Carolina Vista Dr, Pinehurst, NC 28374-9251
Tel (910) 295-6811 Founded/Ownrshp 1984
Sales 106.0MM^E EMP 1,300^E
SIC 7011 7997 7992 5813 5812 Resort hotel; Golf club, membership; Public golf courses; Drinking places; Eating places
Pr: Don Padgett II
CFO: Kenneth W Baer
VP: Mollie Case
VP: Beth A Kocher
Off Mgr: Ronnie Meltzer

PINEHURST PARK TERRACE
See EAGLE HEALTHCARE INC

PINEHURST RESORT & COUNTRY CLB
See PINEHURST LLC

D-U-N-S 96-352-7549
PINELAKE HEALTH & REHAB
801 Pinehurst Ave, Carthage, NC 28327-9338
Tel (910) 947-5155 Founded/Ownrshp 2010
Sales 642.9MM EMP 25^E
SIC 8051 Skilled nursing care facilities
Ex Dir: Dawn Cookan

D-U-N-S 07-846-8164
PINELLAS COUNTY PUBLIC SCHOOLS
301 4th St Sw, Largo, FL 33770-3536
Tel (727) 588-6000 Founded/Ownrshp 1926
Sales 12.3MM^E EMP 18,000
SIC 8211 Public elementary & secondary schools
Pr Dir: Melanie Marquez Parra
Pr Dir: Lisa Wolf
Instr Medi: Laura Woods
Psych: Nandelyne Metellus
HC Dir: Sara O'Toole

D-U-N-S 01-050-8844
PINELLAS COUNTY SCHOOL BOARD
301 4th St Sw, Largo, FL 33770-3536
Tel (727) 588-6000 Founded/Ownrshp 1926
Sales 206.1MM^E EMP 13,122^E
SIC 8211 4832 School board; Educational
Ch: Linda S Lerner
Exec: Clinton Herbic
Exec: Thomas Scott
QA Dir: Natalye Seay
Schl Brd P: Janet Clark
HC Dir: Cheryl Guldenschuhc

D-U-N-S 12-510-9111
PINELOCH FAMILY CARE
2898 S Osceola Ave, Orlando, FL 32806-5469
Tel (407) 812-8110 Founded/Ownrshp 1999
Sales 375.1MM EMP 5
SIC 8011 Offices & clinics of medical doctors
Prin: Robert Gaynor

D-U-N-S 13-143-3294
PINEWOOD PLACE APARTMENTS
1210 Collingwood Blvd, Toledo, OH 43604-8112
Tel (419) 243-1413 Founded/Ownrshp 1978
Sales 43.4MM^E EMP 3,900
SIC 6513 Apartment building operators
Pt: Leean Morein

D-U-N-S 02-876-2748
■ **PINEY WOODS HEALTHCARE SYSTEM LP**
WOODLAND HEIGHTS MEDICAL CTR
(Suby of COMMUNITY HEALTH SYSTEMS INC) ★
505 S John Redditt Dr, Lufkin, TX 75904-3120
Tel (936) 634-8311 Founded/Ownrshp 1998
Sales 122.5MM EMP 600^E
SIC 8062 8071 8099 8051 General medical & surgical hospitals; Testing laboratories; Medical services organization; Skilled nursing care facilities
CEO: Casey Robertson
Genl Pt: William Weldon
COO: Brad Holland
CFO: Sam Minkowitz
CIO: Virginia De Leonardis
Sls&Mrk Ex: Tara Watson

PING
See KARSTEN MANUFACTURING CORP

PINK ROSE DIVISION
See PAPER CUT CLOTHING LLC

PINNACLE
See AMERICAN MANAGEMENT SERVICES WEST LLC

PINNACLE
See AMERICAN MANAGEMENT SERVICES LLC

D-U-N-S 10-339-6821
PINNACLE AIRLINES CORP
7500 Airline Dr, Minneapolis, MN 55450-1101
Tel (800) 603-4594 Founded/Ownrshp 2002
Sales 522.1MM^E EMP 7,797^E
SIC 4512

D-U-N-S 05-810-3342
PINNACLE BANCORP INC
COLORADO BANK, THE
1801 Burt St, Elkhorn, NE 68022
Tel (402) 697-8666 Founded/Ownrshp 1977
Sales NA EMP 1,300
Accts Bkd Llp
SIC 6022 6712 State commercial banks; Bank holding companies
Pr: J Sid Dinsdale
V Ch: J A Dinsdle
*COO: Justin Horst
*CFO: Greg Dushan
*Sec: Lynn Barclay
*V Ch Bd: J A Dinsdale
VP: Amber Barton
VP: Andy Elder
VP: Marc J Hock
VP: Brett Michael
VP: Perry Severson
VP: Becky Snider
Exec: Matt Dinsdale
Exec: Christine Wendlandt

D-U-N-S 88-394-2760
■ **PINNACLE BANK**
(Suby of PINNACLE FINANCIAL PARTNERS INC) ★
150 3rd Ave S Ste 900, Nashville, TN 37201-2034
Tel (615) 744-3700 Founded/Ownrshp 2000
Sales NA EMP 250
SIC 6021 National commercial banks
Pr: M Terry Turner
Ex VP: Edward White
Sr VP: Mike Hammontree
Sr VP: Tim Huestis
Sr VP: Michael G Lindseth
VP: Scott Ractliffe

D-U-N-S 55-684-0556
PINNACLE BUSINESS SOLUTIONS INC
ARKANSAS BLUE CROSS & BLU
(Suby of ARKANSAS BLUE CROSS & BLUE) ★
515 W Pershing Blvd, North Little Rock, AR 72114-2147
Tel (501) 210-9000 Founded/Ownrshp 2004
Sales NA EMP 919
SIC 6411 7371 Medical insurance claim processing, contract or fee basis; Software programming applications
VP: Charles G Clem
*CEO: Dan Bloodworth
*CFO: Amy Green
*Treas: Janie W Fenton
Treas: Patricia Jenkins

D-U-N-S 02-417-0928
PINNACLE COMPANIES INC (TX)
PINNACLE FABRICATION COMPANY
903 Interstate Hwy 30 E, Sulphur Springs, TX 75482-6115
Tel (903) 885-6772 Founded/Ownrshp 2008
Sales 155.5MM^E EMP 300
SIC 5082 General construction machinery & equipment
Prin: Matthew Hannah
*CFO: Heath Halbert
*VP: J Miles Arnold
Dir IT: William Kirby
Sls Mgr: Tim Harry
Sls Mgr: Bert Middleton

PINNACLE DISTRIBUTING COMPANY
See BEVERAGE DISTRIBUTORS CO LLC

D-U-N-S 96-381-5423
PINNACLE ENERGY MARKETING LLC
90 S 400 W Ste 320, Salt Lake City, UT 84101-1380
Tel (435) 940-9001 Founded/Ownrshp 2010
Sales 90.0MM EMP 5
SIC 5172 Crude oil; Gases
CEO: Curtis Chisholm

D-U-N-S 08-024-9441
PINNACLE ENTERTAINMENT INC
3980 Howard Hughes Pkwy, Las Vegas, NV 89169-0992
Tel (702) 541-7777 Founded/Ownrshp 2015
Sales 86.2MM^E EMP 14,726
Tkr Sym PNK Exch NGS
SIC 7999 7011 Gambling establishment; Gambling machines, operation; Hotels & motels; Casino hotel
Ch Bd: James L Martineau
Pr: Carlos A Ruisanchez
CEO: Anthony M Sanfilippo
Bd of Dir: Jaynie Studenmund
Ofcr: Charlotte McGarr
Ofcr: Virginia E Shanks
Ex VP: Ginny Shanks
Ex VP: Troy A Stremming
Ex VP: Troy Stremming
Ex VP: Neil E Walkoff
Ex VP: Neil Walkoff
VP: Susan Ascanio
VP: David Begonis
VP: David Blitch
VP: Matthew Block
VP: Maria Cohen
VP: Chris Corrado
VP: Jeff Danis
VP: George Donelson
VP: Geoffrey Goodman
VP: Elliot Hoops

PINNACLE FABRICATION COMPANY
See PINNACLE COMPANIES INC

D-U-N-S 18-863-0565
▲ **PINNACLE FINANCIAL PARTNERS INC**
150 3rd Ave S Ste 900, Nashville, TN 37201-2034
Tel (615) 744-3700 Founded/Ownrshp 2000
Sales NA EMP 1,065^E
Tkr Sym PNFP Exch NGS
SIC 6021 National commercial banks
Pr: M Terry Turner
Ch Bd: Robert A McCabe Jr
CFO: Harold R Carpenter Jr
Chf Cred: J Harvey White
Ofcr: Hugh M Queener
Top Exec: Amy Charles
VP: Jeff Anderson
VP: Kirk Garrett
VP: Mary Isham
VP: Rex Jones
VP: Lynn Kendrick
VP: Steve King
VP: Wanda Mahan
VP: Doug Nall
VP: Kendria Northcutt
VP: Cynthia Oliva
VP: Rhonda Smith
Board of Directors: David Ingram, Harold Gordon Bone, Ed C Loughry Jr, Charles E Brock, Ronald L Samuels, Gregory L Burns, Gary L Scott, Marty Dickens, Reese L Smith III, Thomas C Farnsworth III, Colleen Conway-Welch, Joe Galante, Glenda Baskin Glover, William F Hagerty IV, William H Huddleston IV

D-U-N-S 80-837-7878 IMP
■ **PINNACLE FOODS FINANCE LLC**
(Suby of PEAK FINANCE HOLDINGS LLC) ★
399 Jefferson Rd, Parsippany, NJ 07054-3707
Tel (973) 541-6620 Founded/Ownrshp 2007
Sales 2.4MMM EMP 3,700^E
Accts Deloitte & Touche Llp Parsipp
SIC 2038 2092 2099 2045 Frozen specialties; Breakfasts, frozen & packaged; Pizza, frozen; Waffles, frozen; Prepared fish or other seafood cakes & sticks; Pancake syrup, blended & mixed; Cake flour: from purchased flour; Pancake mixes, prepared: from purchased flour
CEO: Robert J Gamgort
CFO: Peter Menikofs
*CFO: Craig Steeneck
*Treas: Lynne M Misericordia
Ex VP: John Butler
Ex VP: Mary B Denooyer
Ex VP: Evan Metropoulos
Ex VP: Jon Roberts
*Sr VP: M Kelley Maggs
VP: Gregory Bostick
VP: Kurt Buckman
VP: Pablo Cusatti
VP: Rick Klauser
*VP: John F Kroeger
VP: Anthony Lobue
VP: Thomas Meyers
VP: Dan Parker
Exec: Kit Nolan
Board of Directors: Roger Deromedi, Ann Fandozzi, Jason Giordano, Jeff Overly, Raymond P Silcock

D-U-N-S 96-595-3359 IMP
■ **PINNACLE FOODS GROUP LLC**
(Suby of PINNACLE FOODS FINANCE LLC) ★
399 Jefferson Rd, Parsippany, NJ 07054-3707
Tel (856) 969-7100 Founded/Ownrshp 2007
Sales 588.9MM^E EMP 1,585
SIC 2038 2092 2099 2045 Frozen specialties; Breakfasts, frozen & packaged; Pizza, frozen; Waffles, frozen; Prepared fish or other seafood cakes & sticks; Pancake syrup, blended & mixed; Cake flour: from purchased flour; Bread & bread type roll mixes: from purchased flour; Pancake mixes, prepared: from purchased flour
CEO: Robert J Gamgort
*Ch Bd: Roger Deromedi
*Pr: Mark L Schiller
*CFO: Craig Steeneck
Treas: Lynne Misericordia
*Ofcr: Christopher J Boever
*Ofcr: Mary Beth Denooyer
Ex VP: John Butler
*Ex VP: Antonio F Fernandez
Ex VP: Craig S Kussman
Sr VP: Paul A Grven
*Sr VP: M Kelley Maggs
Sr VP: Ron Trine
VP: John Currie
VP: Seijidoe Davidson
VP: Tom Little
VP: Andrew Rosen
VP: John Wampler
VP: Kim Whitler
Board of Directors: Ann Fandozzi, Robert J Gamgort, Jason Giordano, Jane Nielson, Raymond P Silcock

D-U-N-S 14-507-8395
▲ **PINNACLE FOODS INC**
399 Jefferson Rd, Parsippany, NJ 07054-3707
Tel (973) 541-6620 Founded/Ownrshp 2001
Sales 2.5MMM EMP 4,000^E
Tkr Sym PF Exch NYS
SIC 2038 2035 Frozen specialties; Pickles, sauces & salad dressings
CEO: Robert J Gamgort
Pr: Mark L Schiller
CFO: Craig Steeneck
Chf Cred: Christopher J Boever
Ofcr: Mary Beth Denooyer
Ex VP: Michael J Barkley
Ex VP: Antonio F Fernandez
Ex VP: Tony Fernandez
Ex VP: Kelley Maggs
Ex VP: M Kelley Maggs
Ex VP: Mike Wittman
VP: Phillip Barone
VP: Steve Gunther
VP: Greg Watkins
Board of Directors: Roger K Deromedi, Ann Fandozzi, Mark Jung, Jane Nielsen, Raymond P Silcock

D-U-N-S 84-467-7992 EXP
■ **PINNACLE FOODS LLC**
(Suby of PINNACLE FOODS GROUP LLC) ★
2467 Henry Ladyn Dr, Fort Madison, IA 52627
Tel (319) 463-7111 Founded/Ownrshp 2012
Sales 228.8MM^E EMP 1,585
SIC 2011 Cured meats from meat slaughtered on site; Luncheon meat from meat slaughtered on site; Variety meats, fresh edible organs
CEO: Bob Gamgort
*CFO: Craig Steeneck
*Ex VP: Chris Boever
*Ex VP: Sally Genster Robling
*Ex VP: Mark Schiller
Dir Lab: Thomas Getz
Plnt Mgr: Bryan Langerud

PINNACLE FRAMES & ACCENTS
See NIELSEN & BAINBRIDGE LLC

D-U-N-S 07-121-4142
PINNACLE HEALTH HOSPITAL
PINNACLE HEALTH SYSTEM
(Suby of PINNACLE HLTH HARRISBURG HOSP) ★
4300 Londonderry Rd, Harrisburg, PA 17109-5317
Tel (717) 782-3131 Founded/Ownrshp 1945
Sales 759.0MM EMP 4,800
Accts Baker Tilly Virchow Krause Llp

SIC 8062 General medical & surgical hospitals
CEO: Roger Longenderfer
CFO: Fred Fetters
**CFO:* William Pugh
Ofcr: Ray Herbert
VP: Steven Roth
Dir Lab: Judy Darr
Nurse Mgr: Connie Lauffer
Netwrk Mgr: Terry Freed
Tech Mgr: Joe Morrison
Info Man: Karen Mikita
Netwrk Eng: Daniel Tischendorf

D-U-N-S 96-718-8160
PINNACLE HEALTH HOSPITALS
409 S 2nd St Ste 1c, Harrisburg, PA 17104-1612
Tel (717) 782-5678 *Founded/Ownrshp* 1995
Sales 191.5MM[E] *EMP* 4,500
Accts Parentebeard Llc York Pa
SIC 8062 General medical & surgical hospitals
Pr: Michael Young
Sr VP: George Beauregard
Sr VP: Susan Edwards
**Sr VP:* Dana Kellis
Sr VP: Christopher P Markley
**VP:* Louise K Rich
VP: Steven Roth
VP: William Wilkison
Off Mgr: Pam Kohr
Nurse Mgr: Barbara Woods
Surgeon: Brynn Wolff

D-U-N-S 96-718-3484
PINNACLE HEALTH MEDICAL SERVICES
409 S 2nd St Ste 2b, Harrisburg, PA 17104-1612
Tel (717) 231-8341 *Founded/Ownrshp* 1995
Sales 86.5MM *EMP* 61
Accts Baker Tilly Virchow Krause Llp
SIC 8011 8063 Offices & clinics of medical doctors; Psychiatric hospitals
CEO: Roger Longenderfer

PINNACLE HEALTH SYSTEM
See PINNACLE HEALTH HOSPITAL

D-U-N-S 96-662-1930
PINNACLE HEALTH SYSTEM
PINNACLE HLTH HARRISBURG HOSP
409 S 2nd St Ste 2b, Harrisburg, PA 17104-1612
Tel (717) 231-8010 *Founded/Ownrshp* 1873
Sales 28.7MM *EMP* 4,837[E]
Accts Parentebeard Llc Philadelphia
SIC 8741 8062 Hospital management; General medical & surgical hospitals
CEO: Michael A Young
COO: Lori Wagner
VP: William Pugh
VP: Barbara Terry
Off Mgr: Debra Fleagle
Doctor: Hayden Boyce MD
Doctor: Roberto Hodara
Doctor: Russell S Owens MD
Doctor: Richard Prensner
Pharmcst: Joseph Pramik

PINNACLE HLTH HARRISBURG HOSP
See PINNACLE HEALTH SYSTEM

D-U-N-S 03-346-8213
PINNACLE HOTEL MANAGEMENT CO LLC
1480 Royal Palm Bch Blvd, Royal Palm Beach, FL 33411-1608
Tel (561) 242-9066 *Founded/Ownrshp* 1998
Sales 66.2MM[E] *EMP* 1,000
SIC 8741 Management services
Pr: Ron Franklin
CFO: Dick Vilardo

D-U-N-S 07-835-4972
PINNACLE LIGHT INDUSTRIAL LLC
5501 Lyndon B Johnson Fwy Fw600, Dallas, TX 75240-6225
Tel (214) 740-2443 *Founded/Ownrshp* 2009
Sales 23.5MM[E] *EMP* 1,000
SIC 7361 Employment agencies

D-U-N-S 96-474-8318
PINNACLE OIL HOLDINGS LLC
5009 W 81st St, Indianapolis, IN 46268-1639
Tel (317) 875-9465 *Founded/Ownrshp* 2008
Sales 127.0MM *EMP* 41
SIC 2992 5172 8742 Lubricating oils & greases; Lubricating oils & greases; Marketing consulting services
Pr: Kenton L Morris
Ex VP: Gregory Morris
VP: Don Swan

D-U-N-S 06-454-2280
PINNACLE ONE PARTNERS LP
300 Decker Dr, Irving, TX 75062-8177
Tel (214) 812-4600 *Founded/Ownrshp* 2001
Sales 52.1MM[E] *EMP* 1,500
SIC 4813 Telephone communication, except radio
Pt: Erle Nye

D-U-N-S 03-411-9722
PINNACLE PACKAGING CO INC
ORACLE PACKAGING COMPANY
1203 E 33rd St Ste 200, Tulsa, OK 74105-2015
Tel (918) 744-5400 *Founded/Ownrshp* 2000
Sales 37.2MM[E] *EMP* 1,000[E]
SIC 7389 Packaging & labeling services
Pr: J Scott Dickman
**COO:* Jeff Gibbs
**CFO:* Randall J Schmitz

D-U-N-S 96-463-5101
PINNACLE PROPANE LLC
600 Las Colinas Blvd E # 2000, Irving, TX 75039-5616
Tel (972) 444-0300 *Founded/Ownrshp* 2010
Sales 114.3MM[E] *EMP* 120[E]
SIC 1321 Propane (natural) production
CEO: Patrick Barley
CFO: Jeffrey W Allen
**CFO:* Pat Welch
VP Cor Dev: David R Stroupe

D-U-N-S 87-843-3218
PINNACLE REALTY MANAGEMENT CO
(*Suby of* PINNACLE) ★
2801 Alaskan Way Ste 200, Seattle, WA 98121-1136
Tel (206) 215-9700 *Founded/Ownrshp* 1994
Sales 30.8MM[E] *EMP* 2,400
SIC 6531 8741 6513 6512 1522 Real estate managers; Real estate brokers & agents; Construction management; Apartment building operators; Commercial & industrial building operation; Residential construction
Ch Bd: John A Goodman
**Pr:* Stan Harrelson
CFO: Donald J Markley
VP: Deanne Davis
VP: Kathryn Mansfield
Prin: Gregory Beckel
MIS Dir: John Glasman
IT Man: Richard Davenhauer

D-U-N-S 96-592-1109
PINNACLE STAFFING INC
127 Tanner Rd, Greenville, SC 29607-5918
Tel (864) 297-4212 *Founded/Ownrshp* 1996
Sales 25.9MM[E] *EMP* 1,200
SIC 7363 Help supply services; Temporary help service
CEO: Ryan Hendley
**Pr:* David Ballinger
Site Mgr: Daniel Jones

D-U-N-S 05-281-9989
PINNACLE SUMMER INVESTMENTS INC
(*Suby of* LEE SUMMER HOLDINGS LLC) ★
600 Travis St Ste 5800, Houston, TX 77002-3008
Tel (781) 749-7409 *Founded/Ownrshp* 1998, 2012
Sales 146.5MM[E] *EMP* 498[E]
SIC 6282 8741 Investment advice; Management services
Ch Bd: George Ball
**Pr:* Ric Edelman
**COO:* Edward Moore
**VP:* Joseph Bottazzi
VP: John Watras
IT Man: Constantine Keller
Board of Directors: George L Ball, Richard E Bean, Diana F Cantor, Charles W Duncan III, Scott W McClelland, Ben T Morris, Albert W Niemi Jr, Don A Sanders

D-U-N-S 13-115-5400
▲ PINNACLE WEST CAPITAL CORP
400 N 5th St, Phoenix, AZ 85004-3903
Tel (602) 250-1000 *Founded/Ownrshp* 1985
Sales 3.5MMM *EMP* 6,407[E]
Tkr Sym PNW *Exch* NYS
SIC 4911 6552 Generation, electric power; Transmission, electric power; Distribution, electric power; Subdividers & developers
Ch Bd: Donald E Brandt
CFO: James R Hatfield
Treas: Lee R Nickloy
Ex VP: David P Falck
Ex VP: Mark A Schiavoni
VP: Denise R Danner
VP: Bryan A Kearney
VP: Jessica Pacheco
IT Man: Jim Connor
IT Man: Jamie Moore
Genl Couns: Jennifer Spina
Board of Directors: David P Wagener, Denis A Cortese, Richard P Fox, Michael L Gallagher, Roy A Herberger Jr, Dale E Klein, Humberto S Lopez, Kathryn L Munro, Bruce J Nordstrom, Paula Sims

D-U-N-S 87-804-1102
PINNACOL ASSURANCE
7501 E Lowry Blvd, Denver, CO 80230-7006
Tel (303) 361-4000 *Founded/Ownrshp* 1915
Sales NA *EMP* 540
SIC 6331 Workers' compensation insurance
CEO: Phil Kalin
CFO: Kathy Kranz
**VP:* Lori Fox
**VP:* Mark Isakson
**VP:* Terrence Leve
**VP:* Debra Magures
VP: Robert Norris
VP: Jon Scott
VP: Edie Sonn
**VP:* Carole B Sumption
Comm Dir: Corrine Mahoney
Comm Dir: Kim Singer
Dir Rx: Sarah Bensman
Dir Rx: Matt Liebgott
Dir Rx: Amy Newtown

D-U-N-S 02-888-7388 IMP
PINNER CONSTRUCTION CO INC
1255 S Lewis St, Anaheim, CA 92805-6424
Tel (714) 490-4000 *Founded/Ownrshp* 1961
Sales 112.5MM *EMP* 75[E]
Accts Mcgladrey Llp Irvine Ca
SIC 1542 Commercial & office building, new construction; Hospital construction; Stadium construction
Pr: John Pinner
**CFO:* Dirk Griffin
Treas: R Pinner
**VP:* Johnny R Pinner
IT Man: Michael Gilbert
IT Man: Ron Rasmussen
Mktg Dir: Gary Riehle

D-U-N-S 78-532-6919
PINNERGY LTD
111 Congress Ave Ste 2020, Austin, TX 78701-4080
Tel (512) 343-8880 *Founded/Ownrshp* 2003
Sales 870.9MM[E] *EMP* 750[E]
SIC 1389 Oil field services
Pr: Randy Taylor
**Pr:* Tommy Mouser
**Pr:* Steve Nations
**COO:* Wade Webster
Sr VP: Barbara Mayfield
VP: Lonnie Applegate
**VP:* Brandon Taylor
IT Man: Michael McMahand
IT Man: Charles Smith

Sfty Dirs: Josh Rich
Sls Mgr: Lance Cauthen

D-U-N-S 96-640-7913 EXP
PINOVA HOLDINGS INC
(*Suby of* SYMRISE AG)
2801 Cook St, Brunswick, GA 31520-6160
Tel (888) 807-2958 *Founded/Ownrshp* 2016
Sales 102.7MM[E] *EMP* 450[E]
SIC 2869 Industrial organic chemicals
Pr: Theodore H Butz
Ch Bd: David Bookbinder
**CFO:* Bill Collier

D-U-N-S 96-206-3561 IMP/EXP
PINOVA INC
(*Suby of* PINOVA HOLDINGS INC) ★
2801 Cook St, Brunswick, GA 31520-6160
Tel (888) 807-2958 *Founded/Ownrshp* 2010
Sales 102.7MM[E] *EMP* 236
SIC 2861 Naval stores, wood & gum
Pr: Jodie Morgan
**Ch Bd:* David Bookbinder
**CFO:* Bill Collier
**Sr VP:* Ken Kennedy
VP: Dale Becker
**VP:* Pat Grozier
VP: Mario Villamarzo
Manager: Bryan Croft

D-U-N-S 07-852-1935
PINTEREST INC
808 Brannan St, San Francisco, CA 94103-4904
Tel (650) 561-5407 *Founded/Ownrshp* 2008
Sales 108.6MM[E] *EMP* 400[E]
SIC 7375 On-line data base information retrieval
Pr: Tim Kendall
**CEO:* Benjamin Silbermann
**Co-Founder:* Evan Sharp
Ex Dir: Jeannie Rollo
Dir IT: Matt Thorne
Sftwr Eng: Xiaofang Chen
Sftwr Eng: Pavan Chitumalla
Sftwr Eng: Daniel Chu
Sftwr Eng: Stephanie Dewet
Sftwr Eng: Andrew Erickson
Sftwr Eng: Wangfan Fu

PIONEER
See OPTIMUM QUALITY GRAINS LLC

D-U-N-S 95-642-1432 IMP
PIONEER AUTOMOTIVE TECHNOLOGIES INC
(*Suby of* PIONEER NORTH AMERICA INC) ★
100 S Pioneer Blvd, Springboro, OH 45066-1177
Tel (937) 746-2293 *Founded/Ownrshp* 1981
Sales 95.8MM[E] *EMP* 360
SIC 5013 3714 3651 Motor vehicle supplies & new parts; Motor vehicle parts & accessories; Household audio & video equipment
Pr: Steven Moerner
**Treas:* Mike Honda
Treas: Shigeyoshi Okubo
Sr VP: Gary Jordahl
Brnch Mgr: Yoshio Natsume
Software D: Robin Fleenor
Ql Cn Mgr: Jason Rowlands

PIONEER BALLOON CO
See CONTINENTAL AMERICAN CORP

D-U-N-S 07-151-6637
PIONEER CREDIT CO
1870 Executive Park Nw, Cleveland, TN 37312-2700
Tel (423) 476-6511 *Founded/Ownrshp* 1974
Sales NA *EMP* 400
SIC 6141 Consumer finance companies; Installment sales finance, other than banks
Pr: John W Holden Jr
Pr: Ross Howe
**CFO:* Todd Copic
**Treas:* Robert Abrahams
VP: John R Hentz
VP: Kellye Mull
Mktg Dir: Emily Beaty

D-U-N-S 13-693-6114
■ PIONEER CREDIT RECOVERY INC
(*Suby of* NAVIENT CORP) ★
26 Edward St, Arcade, NY 14009-1012
Tel (585) 492-1234 *Founded/Ownrshp* 2001
Sales 86.1MM[E] *EMP* 1,100
SIC 7322 Adjustment & collection services
CEO: John Kane
**Pr:* Jeffery Mersmann
**Treas:* John Terry
**VP:* Chad Wilson
**Mng Dir:* Michael Amstadt

D-U-N-S 01-606-0142 EXP
■ PIONEER DRILLING SERVICES LTD
(*Suby of* PIONEER ENERGY SERVICES CORP) ★
1250 Ne Loop 410 Ste 1000, San Antonio, TX 78209-1560
Tel (210) 828-7689 *Founded/Ownrshp* 1968
Sales 540.7MM[E] *EMP* 1,700
SIC 1381 Drilling oil & gas wells
CEO: Wm Stacy Locke
**CFO:* Lorne E Phillips
**Ex VP:* Franklin C West
**Sr VP:* William Hibbetts
**Sr VP:* Carlos R Pena

D-U-N-S 00-638-0141 IMP/EXP
PIONEER ELECTRONICS (USA) INC (DE)
(*Suby of* PIONEER NORTH AMERICA INC) ★
1925 E Dominguez St, Long Beach, CA 90810-1089
Tel (310) 952-2000 *Founded/Ownrshp* 1982
Sales 185.4MM[E] *EMP* 500
SIC 5064 High fidelity equipment
CEO: Satoshi Ohdate
**Pr:* Kiyokazu Igarahi
**Treas:* Naoki Horie
Sr VP: Russ Johnston
VP: Louis Brugman
VP: Augusto Cardoso
VP: Matt Dever
VP: Gary Jordahl
**VP:* Febien Lijiam

VP: Jay Meibers
VP: Hideki Ono
VP: Dennis Stepien

D-U-N-S 04-477-3091 EXP
▲ PIONEER ENERGY SERVICES CORP
1250 Ne Loop 410 Ste 1000, San Antonio, TX 78209-1560
Tel (855) 884-0575 *Founded/Ownrshp* 1968
Sales 540.7MM *EMP* 1,700[E]
Tkr Sym PES *Exch* NYS
SIC 1381 7353 Drilling oil & gas wells; Oil well drilling equipment, rental or leasing
Pr: Wm Stacy Locke
**Ch Bd:* Dean A Burkhardt
CFO: Lorne E Phillips
Ex VP: Carlos R Pea
Ex VP: Brian L Tucker
Sr VP: Bill W Bouziden
Sr VP: Joe P Freeman
VP: Rich Plageman
Opers Mgr: Juan Lopez
Board of Directors: J Michael Rauh, C John Thompson, Scott D Urban

D-U-N-S 11-326-7702
PIONEER EXPLORATION CO
15603 Kuykendahl Rd, Houston, TX 77090-3654
Tel (281) 893-9400 *Founded/Ownrshp* 1991
Sales 103.7MM[E] *EMP* 110
SIC 1311 1321 Crude petroleum production; Natural gas liquids
Pr: Younas Chaudhary
Pt: John Gilbert

D-U-N-S 88-385-4499 IMP
PIONEER FARM EQUIPMENT CO
2589 N A Fresno Drste 109, Fresno, CA 93727
Tel (559) 253-0526 *Founded/Ownrshp* 1999
Sales 85.0MM[E] *EMP* 200
SIC 5083 Farm equipment parts & supplies
CEO: Ht Wilson Jr
**CFO:* John Daugherty

D-U-N-S 06-213-5249 IMP
PIONEER FASTENERS & TOOL INC
202 S Ector Dr, Euless, TX 76040-4425
Tel (817) 545-0121 *Founded/Ownrshp* 1982
Sales 91.0MM[E] *EMP* 27
SIC 5085 Fasteners, industrial: nuts, bolts, screws, etc.
Pr: Mary Van Tol
**Sec:* Tom Broadbent
Opers Mgr: Robert Summers
Sales Asso: Jon Elliott

D-U-N-S 05-087-1888
PIONEER FEEDYARD LLC
1021 County Road Cc, Oakley, KS 67748-6093
Tel (785) 672-3257 *Founded/Ownrshp* 1960
Sales 350.0MM *EMP* 35
SIC 0111 0211 0115 0212 Wheat; Beef cattle feedlots; Corn; Beef cattle except feedlots
Pr: James L Keller

PIONEER FLOUR MILLS
See C H GUENTHER & SON INC

D-U-N-S 05-111-4817 IMP
PIONEER FROZEN FOODS INC (TX)
(*Suby of* PIONEER FLOUR MILLS) ★
627 Big Stone Gap Rd, Duncanville, TX 75137-2223
Tel (972) 298-4281 *Founded/Ownrshp* 1982, 1987
Sales 99.0MM[E] *EMP* 750
SIC 2051 Rolls, bread type: fresh or frozen; Biscuits, baked: baking powder & raised
CEO: Dale W Tremblay
**Ch Bd:* Forrest R Word
**Pr:* J Steven Stroud
**CFO:* Chip Moede
**CFO:* Janelle M Sykes
CFO: Janelle Sykes
**VP:* Dennis Daniels
**VP:* Charles V Hanson
**VP:* Chris Redkey

D-U-N-S 00-694-1363 IMP/EXP
■ PIONEER HI-BRED INTERNATIONAL INC
(*Suby of* E I DU PONT DE NEMOURS AND CO) ★
7100 Nw 62nd Ave, Johnston, IA 50131-2937
Tel (515) 535-3200 *Founded/Ownrshp* 1999
Sales 8.3MMM[E] *EMP* 5,200
SIC 5191 Seeds: field, garden & flower; Hay
Pr: Paul E Schickler
VP: Tony Cavalieri
VP: Laurie Conslato
VP: Nancy Koethe
VP: Alejandro S Munoz
VP: Paul Shickler
VP: Tom West
Exec: G W Fuhr
Comm Dir: Tim Martin
Area Mgr: Rick Radliff
CIO: Barney Debnam

PIONEER HOMES
See MCGUYER HOMEBUILDERS INC

D-U-N-S 79-830-6858
PIONEER INVESTMENT MANAGEMENT INC
(*Suby of* PIONEER INVESTMENT MANAGEMENT USA INC) ★
60 State St, Boston, MA 02109-1800
Tel (617) 742-7825 *Founded/Ownrshp* 1962
Sales 197.4MM[E] *EMP* 530[E]
SIC 6282 Investment advisory service
CEO: Lisa Jones
**Pr:* Osbert Hood
Treas: Steven Forss
**Chf Cred:* Martin J Wolin
Ex VP: Alicja K Maleca
Sr VP: Barbara Bucher
Sr VP: Tom Coffey
Sr VP: John Jul
MIS Dir: Edmund Sefton
Dir IT: Steve Carnet

D-U-N-S 07-662-1184
PIONEER INVESTMENT MANAGEMENT USA INC
(Suby of PIONEER GLOBAL ASSET MANAGEMENT SPA)
60 State St Ste 700, Boston, MA 02109-1894
Tel (617) 742-7825 Founded/Ownrshp 2004
Sales 286.3MM^E EMP 2,000
SIC 6722 6282 Management investment, open-end; Investment advice
Ch Bd: John F Cogan Jr
*Pr: Daniel K Kingsbury
*COO: Mark Goodwin
*CFO: Tony Koenig
*Treas: Eric W Reckard
*V Ch Bd: Allan Strassman
Ex VP: John A Crey
*Ex VP: Stephen G Kasnet
Ex VP: Joseph D Kringdon
*Ex VP: Alicja K Malecka
*Ex VP: William H Smith Jr
Ex VP: Mark Spina
*Ex VP: David D Tripple
Sr VP: Michael Dirstine
Sr VP: Erik Gosule
Sr VP: Dwight D Jacobsen
*Sr VP: Robert P Nault
*Sr VP: Peter Noll
*Sr VP: Adriana Stadecker
*VP: Roy Rossi

PIONEER MANAGEMENT SYSTEMS
See PIONEER SPEAKERS INC

D-U-N-S 17-856-9380 IMP
PIONEER METAL FINISHING LLC
480 Pilgrim Way Ste 1400, Green Bay, WI 54304-5279
Tel (920) 499-6996 Founded/Ownrshp 1997
Sales 106.4MM^E EMP 500
SIC 3471 Plating & polishing
CEO: Bob Pyle
*Pr: Robert Pyle
*CFO: Steve King
Ex VP: Paul Michaels
VP: Carl Heilman
*VP: Scott Turner
Exec: Richard Dudkiewicz
Natl Sales: Brian Isola

D-U-N-S 16-003-2199
▲ PIONEER NATURAL RESOURCES CO
5205 N Oconnor Connor, Irving, TX 75039
Tel (972) 444-9001 Founded/Ownrshp 1997
Sales 4.8MMM EMP 3,732
Tkr Sym PXD Exch NYS
SIC 1311 1321 Crude petroleum & natural gas; Crude petroleum production; Natural gas production; Natural gas liquids
Ch Bd: Scott D Sheffield
*Pr: Timothy L Dove
CFO: Richard P Dealy
Bd of Dir: Frank Risch
Ex VP: Mark S Berg
Ex VP: J D Hall
Ex VP: Kenneth H Sheffield Jr
Sr VP: Mark H Kleinman
VP: Todd Abbott
VP: James Cunningham
VP: Margaret M Montemayor
VP: Glen Paris
VP: Mike Siragusa
Exec: Royce Mitchell
Board of Directors: Phoebe A Wood, Edison C Buchanan, Michael D Wortley, Andrew F Cates, Phillip A Gobe, Larry R Grillot, Stacy P Methvin, Royce W Mitchell, Frank A Risch, Mona K Sutphen, J Kenneth Thompson

D-U-N-S 96-907-5394
■ PIONEER NATURAL RESOURCES PUMPING SERVICES LLC
(Suby of PIONEER NATURAL RESOURCES CO) ★
5205 N O Connor Blvd # 200, Irving, TX 75039-4412
Tel (972) 444-9001 Founded/Ownrshp 2011
Sales 118.4MM^E EMP 100
SIC 1389 Pumping of oil & gas wells
Treas: Keith Pickett

D-U-N-S 15-467-9435 IMP/EXP
■ PIONEER NATURAL RESOURCES USA INC
(Suby of PIONEER NATURAL RESOURCES CO) ★
5205 N Oconnor Blvd Ste, Irving, TX 75039
Tel (972) 444-9001 Founded/Ownrshp 1997
Sales 4.7MMM^E EMP 3,667
SIC 1311 1321

D-U-N-S 03-947-1552
PIONEER NORTH AMERICA INC
(Suby of PIONEER CORPORATION)
2265 E 220th St, Long Beach, CA 90810-1639
Tel (213) 746-6337 Founded/Ownrshp 1978
Sales 314.3MM^E EMP 2,000
SIC 5064 3651 High fidelity equipment; Video cassette recorders & accessories; Household audio & video equipment; Phonograph & radio combinations; Video cassette recorders/players & accessories; Phonograph turntables
CEO: Masao Kawabata
Pr: Augusto Cardoso
*Pr: Kazunori Yamamoto
Sr VP: Ross Johnston
Sr VP: Kerry McCammon
Sr VP: Kevan Morris
Sr VP: Michael Townsen
VP: Febien Lijiam
Prgrm Mgr: Jason Johnson
Snr Sftwr: Swetha Toshniwal
QA Dir: Vincent Celli

D-U-N-S 02-666-1801 IMP/EXP
■ PIONEER OVERSEAS CORP
(Suby of PIONEER HI-BRED INTERNATIONAL INC) ★
7100 Nw 62nd Ave, Johnston, IA 50131-2937
Tel (515) 535-3200 Founded/Ownrshp 1919
Sales 257.8MM^E EMP 1,909
SIC 5191 Seeds: field, garden & flower
Pr: Rick McConnell
Dir Risk M: Jim O'Hare
Genl Mgr: Serge Gauthier
Opers Mgr: Andrew Long
Mktg Mgr: Brad Burnett
Mktg Mgr: Bob Weisenberger

D-U-N-S 01-069-0238 IMP
PIONEER PACKING INC (CA)
2430 S Grand Ave, Santa Ana, CA 92705-5211
Tel (714) 540-9751 Founded/Ownrshp 1976
Sales 175.8MM^E EMP 210^E
SIC 5113 2653 Shipping supplies; Boxes, corrugated: made from purchased materials; Pads, corrugated: made from purchased materials
Pr: Michael S Blower
*VP: Ronald Scagliotti
Off Mgr: Karen Beery

D-U-N-S 07-968-8626
PIONEER PARENT INC
100 Pike Way, Mount Airy, NC 27030-8147
Tel (336) 789-2171 Founded/Ownrshp 2014
Sales 1.0MMM^E EMP 5,800
SIC 1731 8711 Electrical work; Engineering services
Pr: J Pike
*CFO: Anthony K Slater
*Ex VP: Audie G Simmons
*Sr VP: Timothy G Harshbarger

PIONEER PIPE FABRICATING
See PIONEER PIPE INC

D-U-N-S 04-823-9172 IMP
PIONEER PIPE INC
PIONEER PIPE FABRICATING
2021 Hanna Rd, Marietta, OH 45750-8255
Tel (740) 376-2400 Founded/Ownrshp 1981
Sales 170.9MM^E EMP 275
SIC 3498 1711 3443 3441 3312 Pipe sections fabricated from purchased pipe; Pipe fittings, fabricated from purchased pipe; Plumbing contractors; Warm air heating & air conditioning contractor; Mechanical contractor; Fabricated plate work (boiler shop); Fabricated structural metal; Blast furnaces & steel mills
Pr: David M Archer
Sec: Matthew Hilverding
*VP: Arlene M Archer
VP: Karl Robinson
IT Man: Carol Gaughan
Plnt Mgr: Mike Archer

D-U-N-S 19-447-5992 IMP/EXP
PIONEER PLASTICS CORP
PIONITE DECORATIVE SURFACES
(Suby of PANOLAM SURFACE SYSTEMS) ★
20 Progress Dr, Shelton, CT 06484-6216
Tel (203) 925-1556 Founded/Ownrshp 1999
Sales 174.7MM^E EMP 800^E
SIC 3083 3087 Laminated plastics plate & sheet; Custom compound purchased resins
Pr: Alan S Kabus
*Pr: Robert Muller
*COO: Jeffrey Muller
*CFO: Larry Grossman
*CFO: Vincent Miceli
VP: Patrick Peyton

D-U-N-S 04-179-0569
PIONEER POWER INC
2500 Ventura Dr, Woodbury, MN 55125-3927
Tel (651) 488-5561 Founded/Ownrshp 1988
Sales 116.4MM EMP 90
Accts Rsm Us Llp Minneapolis Minne
SIC 1711 Mechanical contractor
Pr: Randall S Olson
*Sr VP: Scott A Wenzel
*VP: Daniel R Goetzke

D-U-N-S 83-310-7712
▲ PIONEER POWER SOLUTIONS INC
400 Kelby St Ste 12, Fort Lee, NJ 07024-2938
Tel (212) 867-0700 Founded/Ownrshp 2008
Sales 106.5MM EMP 449^E
Tkr Sym PPSI Exch NAS
SIC 3612 Transformers, except electric; Control transformers
Ch Bd: Nathan J Mazurek
*CFO: Thomas Klink
Board of Directors: David J Landes, Ian Ross, David Tesler, Jonathan Tulkoff

D-U-N-S 07-986-6937
PIONEER RESTAURANTS LLC
7490 Clubhouse Rd Fl 2, Boulder, CO 80301-3720
Tel (720) 485-6841 Founded/Ownrshp 2015
Sales 12.4MM^E EMP 1,300
SIC 5812 Fast-food restaurant, chain
Pr: Buddy Brown
*CFO: Todd M Paul

D-U-N-S 05-683-7883
PIONEER SAND CO INC
5000 Northpark Dr, Colorado Springs, CO 80918-3894
Tel (719) 599-8100 Founded/Ownrshp 1973
Sales 118.6MM^E EMP 400
SIC 5211 5031 1794 Sand & gravel; Building materials, exterior; Excavation work
CEO: Michael McGrady
Div Mgr: Greg Rinedollar
Genl Mgr: Julie Sevier
Sfty Mgr: Jeff Fettig
Sls Mgr: Joe Johnson

D-U-N-S 80-861-0195
PIONEER SOUTHWEST ENERGY PARTNERS LP
5205 N Oconner Blvd 200 Connor, Irving, TX 75039
Tel (972) 444-9001 Founded/Ownrshp 2007
Sales 208.2MM EMP 3,667^E
SIC 1311

D-U-N-S 60-997-5925 IMP
PIONEER SPEAKERS INC
PIONEER MANAGEMENT SYSTEMS
(Suby of TOHOKU PIONEER CORPORATION)
2427 Transportation Ave, National City, CA 91950-6664
Tel (619) 477-0850 Founded/Ownrshp 1988
Sales 82.8MM^E EMP 1,250
SIC 3679 Commutators, electronic
CEO: Hiroyuki Mineta
*CFO: Kazuo Goto
*Prin: Makoto Takano
*Prin: Nobuhiko Yamaguchi

D-U-N-S 07-279-1478
PIONEER STATE MUTUAL INSURANCE CO
1510 N Elms Rd, Flint, MI 48532-2033
Tel (810) 733-2300 Founded/Ownrshp 1908
Sales NA EMP 155^E
SIC 6411

D-U-N-S 00-720-9976 IMP
PIONEER TELEPHONE COOPERATIVE INC
108 E Robberts Ave, Kingfisher, OK 73750-2742
Tel (405) 375-4111 Founded/Ownrshp 1953
Sales 113.5MM^E EMP 550
SIC 5999 Mobile telephones & equipment
Genl Mgr: Richard Ruhl
*Pr: Dave Krittenbrink
*Treas: Gail Parker
*Treas: Mary Petty
*VP: Jim Eaton
*VP: Jerry Kadavy
*VP: David Shepard
Dist Mgr: Johnny McAlexander
Genl Mgr: Mike Baustert
Genl Mgr: Kent Kadavy
IT Man: Carly Franks

D-U-N-S 14-909-9194
PIONEER TITLE AGENCY INC
580 E Wilcox Dr, Sierra Vista, AZ 85635-2532
Tel (520) 459-4100 Founded/Ownrshp 1985
Sales NA EMP 200
SIC 6361 6163 Real estate title insurance; Loan agents
Ch Bd: Robert H Newlon
*Pr: R Keith Newlon
*Treas: Cynthia Newlon
Ofcr: Joanne Bowen
Ofcr: Barb Hynd
Ofcr: Shirley Parker
Ofcr: Cabrina Weems
Ofcr: Brenda Wehrle
Area Mgr: Edwin Lamoreaux
Brnch Mgr: Denice Goodmiller
Brnch Mgr: Shelley Moore

D-U-N-S 82-889-8721
■ PIONEER WELL SERVICES LLC
(Suby of PIONEER ENERGY SERVICES CORP) ★
1250 Ne Loop 410 Ste 1000, San Antonio, TX 78209-1560
Tel (210) 828-7689 Founded/Ownrshp 1968
Sales 254.4MM^E EMP 800
SIC 1389 Oil field services
Pr: JB Eustace
*Pr: Wm Stacy Locke
*Pr: Lorne E Phillips
*Sr VP: William D Hibbetis
*Sr VP: Carlos R Pena
*VP: Joseph E Eustace
*VP: Joe Freeman

D-U-N-S 83-178-9479
■ PIONEER WIRELINE SERVICES LLC
(Suby of PIONEER ENERGY SERVICES CORP) ★
1250 Ne Loop 410 Ste 1000, San Antonio, TX 78209-1560
Tel (210) 828-7689 Founded/Ownrshp 2005
Sales 111.3MM^E EMP 700^E
SIC 1389 Oil field services
Pr: Joe Eustace
*VP: Martin O'Neil

PIONEER-LINCOLN-MERCURY
See JIM BURNS AUTOMOTIVE GROUP INC

D-U-N-S 07-334-2057
PIONEERS MEMORIAL HEALTHCARE DISTRICT
PIONEERS MEMORIAL HOSPITAL
207 W Legion Rd, Brawley, CA 92227-7780
Tel (760) 351-3333 Founded/Ownrshp 1947
Sales 91.0MM^E EMP 576
SIC 8062 General medical & surgical hospitals
CEO: Richard L Mendoza
Chf OB: David F Hagen
CFO: Roger Armstrong
*CFO: Daniel Heckathorne
*VP: Justina Aguirre
Dir Inf Cn: Diedra McKinley
Dir Case M: Clara Miranda
Dir Lab: Bill Railsback
Dir Lab: Margo Sanchez
Dir Rx: Santo Milosevich
Telecom Ex: Jo Lane

PIONEERS MEMORIAL HOSPITAL
See PIONEERS MEMORIAL HEALTHCARE DISTRICT

PIONITE DECORATIVE SURFACES
See PIONEER PLASTICS CORP

PIPE & SUPPLY
See MACK ENERGY CORP

D-U-N-S 01-060-7307
PIPE FITTERS RETIREMENT FUND LOCAL 597
45 N Ogden Ave Fl 1, Chicago, IL 60607-1813
Tel (312) 829-4191 Founded/Ownrshp 1955
Sales NA EMP 25
SIC 6371 Pensions
Pr: Greg Watson
*Pr: Kenneth Lee
*Trst: Donald Enright
*Trst: Lee E Getschow
*Trst: Robert F Lawinger
*Trst: Patrick Murray
*Trst: Edward Usher
*Trst: George Wyatt

D-U-N-S 80-377-6079 IMP
PIPELINE PACKAGING CORP
(Suby of CLEVELAND STEEL CONTAINER CORP) ★
30310 Emerald Valley Pkwy, Solon, OH 44139-4394
Tel (440) 349-3200 Founded/Ownrshp 1986
Sales 156.8MM^E EMP 85
SIC 5099 Containers: glass, metal or plastic
Ch Bd: Christopher I Page
*Pr: Christopher Nelson
*CFO: Daniel Herbert

D-U-N-S 17-759-0593
PIPELINE SUPPLY & SERVICE LLC
PORTA LATHE
1010 Lamar St Ste 710, Houston, TX 77002-6312
Tel (713) 741-8127 Founded/Ownrshp 1990
Sales 122.2MM^E EMP 108^E
SIC 4922 5085 1623

D-U-N-S 07-949-4682
PIPELINE SUPPLY INC (NY)
100 Middlesex Ave Ste 1, Carteret, NJ 07008-3499
Tel (908) 436-1100 Founded/Ownrshp 2003
Sales 90.0MM^E EMP 3^E
SIC 5074 Plumbing fittings & supplies
Ch Bd: David Templer

D-U-N-S 92-720-1061
PIPER AIRCRAFT INC
2926 Piper Dr, Vero Beach, FL 32960-1964
Tel (772) 567-4361 Founded/Ownrshp 1937
Sales 177.0MM^E EMP 825
SIC 3721 3728 Airplanes, fixed or rotary wing; Aircraft parts & equipment
VP Opers: Simon Caldecott
CFO: John Calcagno
QA Dir: Stuart McSorley
QA Dir: Greg Osborne
IT Man: Ed Benzio
Software D: Jeffrey Bonham
VP Opers: Jim Funk
Ql Cn Mgr: Bruce Hawkins
Mktg Dir: Jacqueline Carlon
Sls Dir: Drew McEwen
Counsel: Margaret Napolitan

D-U-N-S 00-622-4729
▲ PIPER JAFFRAY COMPANIES
800 Nicollet Mall Ste 800, Minneapolis, MN 55402-5679
Tel (612) 303-6000 Founded/Ownrshp 1895
Sales 696.3MM EMP 1,192^E
Accts Ernst & Young Llp Minneapolis
Tkr Sym PJC Exch NYS
SIC 6211 Security brokers & dealers; Brokers, security; Dealers, security; Investment bankers
Ch Bd: Andrew S Duff
Pr: Rex Hale
Pr: Stuart C Harvey Jr
Pr: Kevin Pomerenke
CFO: Debbra L Schoneman
Ofcr: Christine N Esckilsen
Ofcr: Sandra Jones
VP: Landon Boehm
VP: Matthew M Breese
VP: William Davis
VP: Jimmer Dorweiler
VP: Christopher Flannery
VP: James Folsom
VP: Adam Forman
VP: Ogieva E Guobadia
VP: Kevin Jakuc
VP: Craig Johnson
VP: Michael Keith
VP: Jin Kim
VP: Nancy Koski
VP: Kevin P Krouse
Board of Directors: William R Fitzgerald, Michael E Frazier, B Kristine Johnson, Addison L Piper, Lisa K Polsky, Sherry M Smith, Philip E Soran, Scott C Taylor, Michele Volpi

D-U-N-S 96-823-9611
PIPING AND EQUIPMENT
1001 Consol Energy Dr, Canonsburg, PA 15317-6506
Tel (724) 514-3990 Founded/Ownrshp 2007
Sales 320.0MM EMP 100
SIC 3317

D-U-N-S 09-397-7817 IMP/EXP
PIPING TECHNOLOGY & PRODUCTS INC
3701 Holmes Rd, Houston, TX 77051-1545
Tel (800) 787-5914 Founded/Ownrshp 1975
Sales 153.9MM^E EMP 750
SIC 3494 8711 3441 Expansion joints pipe; Engineering services; Fabricated structural metal
Pr: Durga D Agrawal
COO: George Dadiani
*CFO: Ray E Walker
*VP: R K Agrawal
*VP: Randy Bailey
QA Dir: Alan Cooper
Dir IT: Tu Ngo
Plnt Mgr: Steve Hernanadez
Prd Mgr: Jerry Pratt

D-U-N-S 61-149-3276 IMP
PIRAMAL GLASS - USA INC
(Suby of PIRAMAL GLASS LIMITED)
329 Herrod Blvd, Dayton, NJ 08810-1564
Tel (856) 293-6400 Founded/Ownrshp 2005
Sales 197.4MM^E EMP 880
SIC 3221 Glass containers
CEO: Niraj Tipre
VP: William Reed
Sales Exec: Pinakin Shah

D-U-N-S 04-834-1366 IMP/EXP
PIRELLI TIRE LLC (GA)
(Suby of PIRELLI & C. SPA)
100 Pirelli Dr Se, Rome, GA 30161-3538
Tel (706) 368-5800 Founded/Ownrshp 1912, 1997
Sales 179.6MM^E EMP 450
SIC 3011 Automobile tires, pneumatic; Truck or bus tires, pneumatic; Automobile inner tubes; Truck or bus inner tubes
Mktg Dir: Jason Fort

D-U-N-S 92-721-1763
PISCES FOODS LP
WENDY'S
5407 Parkcrest Dr Ste 200, Austin, TX 78731-4992
Tel (512) 452-5454 *Founded/Ownrshp* 1995
Sales 27.2MM[E] *EMP* 1,000
SIC 5812 Fast-food restaurant, chain
Ltd Pt: David Near
**Genl Pt:* Near Group
**Ltd Pt:* Jason Near
VP Opers: Philip Stanton

PISGAH MANOR HEALTH CARE CTR
See CAROLINA ADVENTIST RETIREMENT SYSTEMS INC

D-U-N-S 00-432-8675 IMP/EXP
PISTON AUTOMOTIVE LLC
PISTON GROUP
12723 Telegraph Rd Ste 1, Redford, MI 48239-1489
Tel (313) 541-8674 *Founded/Ownrshp* 1997
Sales 308.9MM[E] *EMP* 720
Accts Baker Tilly Virchow Krause L
SIC 3714 Motor vehicle parts & accessories
Ch: Vinnie Johnson
**Pr:* Steven L Hayworth
Dir Bus: Ronald Gesquiere
Genl Mgr: Robert Holloway
CIO: Jim Curry
CTO: Jim Feeley
IT Man: Robert Filiau

PISTON GROUP
See PISTON AUTOMOTIVE LLC

PIT STOP FOOD MART
See MIDTEX OIL LP

PITCO FOODS
See PACIFIC GROSERVICE INC

D-U-N-S 96-006-6322 EXP
PITCO FOODS
567 Cinnabar St, San Jose, CA 95110-2306
Tel (916) 372-7772 *Founded/Ownrshp* 1954
Sales 305.3MM[E] *EMP* 190
SIC 5141 Groceries, general line
CEO: Peri Navab
**Pr:* David Luttway
Genl Mgr: Terry Villegas

D-U-N-S 00-108-5299 IMP
■ **PITCO FRIALATOR INC** (NH)
MAGIC KITCH'N
(*Suby of* MIDDLEBY CORP) ★
553 Route 3a, Bow, NH 03304-3215
Tel (603) 225-6684 *Founded/Ownrshp* 1918, 1981
Sales 155.0MM *EMP* 380
SIC 3589 Cooking equipment, commercial
Pr: Roger McGhee
VP: Robert Granger
IT Man: Debra Green
IT Man: Bob Phaneuf
Plnt Mgr: Steve Reale

D-U-N-S 02-121-2332
■ **PITNEY BOWES BANK INC**
(*Suby of* PITNEY BOWES INC) ★
1245 E Brickyard Rd # 250, Salt Lake City, UT 84106-4094
Tel (801) 832-4440 *Founded/Ownrshp* 1996
Sales NA *EMP* 16[E]
SIC 6141 Industrial loan banks & companies, not a deposit bank
Pr: Sheldon Woods

D-U-N-S 00-116-1793 IMP/EXP
▲ **PITNEY BOWES INC**
3001 Summer St Ste 3, Stamford, CT 06905-4321
Tel (203) 356-5000 *Founded/Ownrshp* 1920
Sales 3.5MMM *EMP* 14,800
Accts Pricewaterhousecoopers Llp St
Tkr Sym PBI *Exch* NYS
SIC 3579 7359 3661 8744 7372 Mailing machines; Postage meters; Forms handling equipment; Business machine & electronic equipment rental services; Facsimile equipment; Facilities support services; Prepackaged software
Pr: Marc B Lautenbach
**Ch Bd:* Michael I Roth
Pr: Robert Guidotti
Pr: Mark L Shearer
Pr: Lila Snyder
Pr: Christoph Stehmann
COO: Michael Monahan
Chf Mktg O: Abby F Kohnstamm
Ofcr: Roger J Pilc
Ofcr: Johnna G Torsone
Ex VP: Mark F Wright
VP: Tim Bates
VP: Amy Corn
VP: Anthony Defrancesco
VP: Chris Johnson
VP: Ramdas Sunder
VP: Shirley Tou
Dir Bus: Vic Walker
Board of Directors: Linda G Alvarado, Anne M Busquet, Roger Fradin, Anne Sutherland Fuchs, S Douglas Hutcheson, Eduardo R Menasce, Linda S Sanford, David L Shedlarz, David B Snow Jr

D-U-N-S 92-829-3513
■ **PITNEY BOWES INTERNATIONAL HOLDINGS INC**
(*Suby of* B WILLIAMS HOLDING CORP) ★
801 N West St Fl 2, Wilmington, DE 19801-1525
Tel (302) 656-8595 *Founded/Ownrshp* 1987
Sales 1.3MMM *EMP* 12
SIC 6719 Investment holding companies, except banks
Pr: Bruce Nolop
**VP:* Kennith Kubacki

D-U-N-S 78-696-8677
■ **PITNEY BOWES PRESORT SERVICES INC**
(*Suby of* PITNEY BOWES INC) ★
10110 I St, Omaha, NE 68127-1129
Tel (402) 339-6500 *Founded/Ownrshp* 2002
Sales 118.5MM[E] *EMP* 869
SIC 7389 Presorted mail service
Pr: Marc B Lautenbach
Pr: Greg Kneifl
**Pr:* Jay Oxton
**CEO:* Deborah Pfeiffer
**Treas:* Debbie Salce
**Treas:* Helen Shan
**Ex VP:* Daniel J Goldstein
**VP:* Patrick Brand
**VP:* Larry Morlan
Genl Mgr: Jim Andrews
Off Admin: Cori Martin

D-U-N-S 07-555-6399
PITT COMMUNITY COLLEGE (NC)
BOARD OF TRUSTEES
(*Suby of* NORTH CAROLINA COMMUNITY COLLEGE SYSTEM) ★
1986 Pitt Tech Dr, Winterville, NC 28590-7822
Tel (252) 321-4200 *Founded/Ownrshp* 1961
Sales 80.0MM *EMP* 1,000
SIC 8222 Community college
CFO: Ricky Brown
Ofcr: Sonji Rowsom
VP: Jermaine McNair
Dir IT: William B Lewis
Dir IT: April Moore
Mktg Dir: Ashley Smith
Psych: Olivia Sutton

D-U-N-S 05-640-3462 IMP
PITT COUNTY MEMORIAL HOSPITAL INC
VIDANT MEDICAL CENTER
(*Suby of* VIDANT HEALTH) ★
2100 Stantonsburg Rd, Greenville, NC 27834-2832
Tel (252) 847-4100 *Founded/Ownrshp* 1953
Sales 1.0MMM *EMP* 8,373
Accts Rsm Us Llp Minneapolis Minne
SIC 8062 Hospital, medical school affiliated with residency
Pr: Brian Floyd
Chf Rad: Julian R Vainight
Dir Vol: Jennifer Congleton
**CEO:* Dave McRae
CFO: Jack Holsten
VP: Martha M Dixon
VP: William Floyd
VP: Offord Kp
QA Dir: Lynn Dale
Dir IT: Been Aycock
Dir IT: Phillip Bowen

D-U-N-S 96-871-1015
PITT COUNTY SCHOOLS
1717 W 5th St, Greenville, NC 27834-1603
Tel (252) 830-4200 *Founded/Ownrshp* 2012
Sales 21.7MM *EMP* 3,440
SIC 8211 Public elementary & secondary schools
Dir IT: Carol Rankin
Pr Dir: Travis Lewis

PITT OHIO
See PITT-OHIO EXPRESS LLC

PITT STOP
See BRANDI BOB STATIONS INC

D-U-N-S 09-712-4739
PITT-OHIO EXPRESS LLC (PA)
PITT OHIO
15 27th St, Pittsburgh, PA 15222-4729
Tel (412) 232-3015 *Founded/Ownrshp* 1999
Sales 431.8MM[E] *EMP* 3,000
SIC 4213 Less-than-truckload (LTL) transport
**COO:* James Fields
**CFO:* Scott Sullivan
CFO: Scott R Sullivan
Ex VP: Geoffrey Muessig
Off Admin: Janet Sapet
Netwrk Eng: Hector Leger
Opers Mgr: Cory Diethorn
Mktg Mgr: Tiffany Schneider
Mktg Mgr: Jacquie Ward
Sls Mgr: Jennifer Best
Sls Mgr: Robert Rupert

PITTS ENERGY GROUP
See DALLAS PRODUCTION INC

D-U-N-S 07-014-6345
PITTSBURG UNIFIED SCHOOL DISTRICT FINANCING CORP
2000 Railroad Ave, Pittsburg, CA 94565-3830
Tel (925) 473-2300 *Founded/Ownrshp* 1937
Sales 2.7MM *EMP* 1,000
Accts Christy White Associates San
SIC 8211 Public elementary & secondary schools
CEO: Linda Rondeau
Teacher Pr: Tracy Catalde

D-U-N-S 01-564-3287
PITTSBURGH
200 Lothrop St, Pittsburgh, PA 15213-2536
Tel (412) 648-8454 *Founded/Ownrshp* 2009
Sales 816.1MM *EMP* 4[E]
SIC 8011 Offices & clinics of medical doctors
Prin: Louis D Falo Jr

D-U-N-S 00-433-7325 IMP/EXP
PITTSBURGH CORNING CORP
800 Presque Isle Dr, Pittsburgh, PA 15239-2799
Tel (724) 327-6100 *Founded/Ownrshp* 1937
Sales 126.3MM[E] *EMP* 490[E]
SIC 3296 Mineral wool
CEO: James R Kane
CFO: Joseph A Kirby
VP: John C Caverno
VP: Jean Piere Collet
VP: Tom Pirosko
VP: Don Tanner
VP: Alberto Vazquez
VP: Harry Walkoff
VP: Andrew P Williams
IT Man: Tim Bovard
IT Man: Carol McDowell
Board of Directors: Ed Bond, Robert Ecklin, Roger Frankel, Mark Gleason, Harry Huge, Charles Koppelman

D-U-N-S 07-216-7141
PITTSBURGH FOUNDATION
5 Ppg Pl Ste 250, Pittsburgh, PA 15222-5414
Tel (412) 391-5122 *Founded/Ownrshp* 1946
Sales 128.5MM *EMP* 40
Accts Schneider Downs & Co Inc Pitt
SIC 6732 Charitable trust management; Educational trust management
Pr: Grant Oliphant
Board of Directors: Phyllis Moorman Goode, Byron R Brown, Mary Lou McLaughlin, Estelle F Comay, Samuel Y Stoh, Daniel D Danforth, Aaron A Walton, George A Davidson Jr, Dorothy R Williams, Robert Dickey III, Robert D Duncan, Arthur J Edmonds, Herbert Elish, Benjamin R Fisher Jr

D-U-N-S 82-851-3080 EXP
■ **PITTSBURGH GLASS WORKS LLC**
PGW
(*Suby of* LKQ CORP) ★
30 Isabella St Ste 500, Pittsburgh, PA 15212-5864
Tel (412) 995-6500 *Founded/Ownrshp* 2016
Sales 2.1MMM[E] *EMP* 5,000
SIC 3211 5013 Flat glass; Automobile glass
CEO: Joe Stas
CFO: Jeff Gronbeck
VP: David Slaman
Brnch Mgr: John Traversone
CTO: Anthony Buccilli
QA Dir: Kevin Cook
IT Man: Jignesh Modi
IT Man: Thomas Schwarz
VP Opers: Glen Hartman
Sls Mgr: Michael Martini

D-U-N-S 96-894-9748
PITTSBURGH HOLDINGS LLC
301 Commerce St Ste 3300, Fort Worth, TX 76102-4133
Tel (817) 871-4000 *Founded/Ownrshp* 2011
Sales 253.0MM[E] *EMP* 1,133
SIC 2721 Magazines: publishing & printing
CEO: Chris Cartwright

D-U-N-S 78-950-7209
PITTSBURGH LOGISTICS SYSTEMS INC
PLS LOGISTICS SERVICES
3120 Unionville Rd Ste 110, Cranberry Township, PA 16066
Tel (724) 814-5100 *Founded/Ownrshp* 1987
Sales 750.0MM *EMP* 500
SIC 4731 Freight transportation arrangement
Pr: Gregory Burns
**CFO:* Chris Ristau
**CIO:* Jon Herberger
IT Man: Russell Rand

PITTSBURGH SAVINGS BANK
See FIRST COMMONWEALTH BANK

D-U-N-S 07-979-9120
PITTSBURGH SCHOOL DISTRICT
341 S Bellefield Ave, Pittsburgh, PA 15213-3552
Tel (412) 622-3500 *Founded/Ownrshp* 2015
Sales 639.1MM *EMP* 5,562[E]
Accts Maher Duessel Pittsburgh Pen
SIC 8211 Public elementary & secondary schools

D-U-N-S 17-782-2780
PITTSBURGH WATER & SEWER AUTHORITY
PWSA
1200 Penn Ave Ste 100, Pittsburgh, PA 15222-4216
Tel (412) 255-8935 *Founded/Ownrshp* 1984
Sales 174.1MM *EMP* 250
Accts Maher Duessel Pittsburgh Pen
SIC 4941 7389 Water supply; Sewer inspection service
Ex Dir: Gregory F Tutsock
**Ch:* Dan Deasy
**Treas:* Scott Kunka
VP: Kevin Donahue
Dir Risk M: Tracy Smith
**Prin:* Patrick Bigley
**Prin:* Robert P Jablonowski

D-U-N-S 08-694-9997
PITTSFIELD PUBLIC SCHOOLS
269 1st St, Pittsfield, MA 01201-4727
Tel (413) 395-0101 *Founded/Ownrshp* 1900
Sales 14.0MM *EMP* 1,000
SIC 8211 Public combined elementary & secondary school
Off Mgr: Kathie Barrett
Teacher Pr: Harry Hayes
Psych: Bethany Nichols

D-U-N-S 02-174-5658
PITTSFORD CENTRAL SCHOOL DISTRICT (NY)
75 Barker Rd, Pittsford, NY 14534-2929
Tel (585) 267-1800 *Founded/Ownrshp* 1894, 2001
Sales 123.6MM *EMP* 900
Accts Raymond F Wager Cpa Pc Hen
SIC 8211 Public elementary & secondary schools; Public junior high school; Public senior high school
Netwrk Mgr: Linda Traynor
Pr Dir: Nancy Wayman
Schl Brd P: Peter Sullivan

D-U-N-S 10-007-9862
PITTSYLVANIA COUNTY SCHOOL BOARD
39 Bank St, Chatham, VA 24531
Tel (434) 432-2761 *Founded/Ownrshp* 1890
Sales 64.0MM *EMP* 1,500
Accts Robinson Farmers Cox Associa
SIC 8211 Public elementary & secondary schools
Ch: Neal W Oakes
**CFO:* Don Johnson
**Ch:* Calvin D Doss
IT Man: Jennifer Houck
Psych: Jim Dooley

D-U-N-S 06-354-7277 IMP
PIVOT INTERIORS INC
SPACE DESIGNS
3355 Scott Blvd Ste 110, Santa Clara, CA 95054-3138
Tel (408) 432-5600 *Founded/Ownrshp* 1973
Sales 171.0MM *EMP* 250
SIC 5712 7389 7299 Furniture stores; Interior design services; Home improvement & renovation contractor agency
Pr: Kenneth B Baugh
**Ch:* Boyd Baugh
**Ex VP:* Harvey Vander Baan
**Ex VP:* Barbara Carlyle
Sales Exec: Kirsten Beaulieu
Snr PM: Sal Beltran

PIVOT TECHNOLOGY SOLUTIONS
See PROSYS INFORMATION SYSTEMS INC

D-U-N-S 05-671-1344
■ **PIVOTAL UTILITY HOLDINGS INC**
(*Suby of* SOUTHERN CO GAS) ★
1085 Morris Ave Ste 1, Union, NJ 07083-7136
Tel (908) 289-5000 *Founded/Ownrshp* 2006
Sales 712.0MM[E] *EMP* 940
SIC 4924 Natural gas distribution
Pr: John Kean Jr
COO: Mark Abramovic
VP: Richard L Gruber
VP: Jay Sutton

D-U-N-S 15-151-6259 IMP
■ **PIXAR**
PIXAR ANIMATION STUDIOS
(*Suby of* WALT DISNEY CO) ★
1200 Park Ave, Emeryville, CA 94608-3677
Tel (510) 922-3000 *Founded/Ownrshp* 2006
Sales 184.1MM[E] *EMP* 850
SIC 7812 7372 7371 Cartoon motion picture production; Commercials, television: tape or film; Prepackaged software; Computer software development
CEO: James W Morris
Bd of Dir: Liz Gazzano
**Ex VP:* John Lasseter
Ex VP: Ann Mather
VP: Michael Agulnek
VP: Robin Chandler
VP: Rob Cook
VP: Marc Greenberg
VP: Adam Woodbury
Admn Mgr: Elizabeth Sullivan
Dept Mgr: Courtney Casper

PIXAR ANIMATION STUDIOS
See PIXAR

PIZZA HUT
See RESTAURANTS RESOURCES INC

PIZZA HUT
See ECPH MANAGEMENT INC

PIZZA HUT
See HIGH PLAINS PIZZA INC

PIZZA HUT
See HOSPITALITY WEST LLC

PIZZA HUT
See RAGE ADMINISTRATIVE AND MARKETING SERVICES INC

PIZZA HUT
See V & J NATIONAL ENTERPRISES LLC

PIZZA HUT
See S & W MANAGEMENT INC

PIZZA HUT
See NPC INTERNATIONAL INC

PIZZA HUT
See PACPIZZA LLC

PIZZA HUT
See AMERICAN RESTAURANT PARTNERS LP

PIZZA HUT
See AMERICAN PIZZA PARTNERS LP

PIZZA HUT
See V & J NATIONAL AND UNITED ENTERPRISES LLC

PIZZA HUT
See KONING RESTAURANTS INTERNATIONAL LC

PIZZA HUT
See KURANI PIZZA INC

D-U-N-S 09-770-4928 IMP
■ **PIZZA HUT INC**
(*Suby of* YUM BRANDS INC) ★
7100 Corporate Dr, Plano, TX 75024-4100
Tel (972) 338-7700 *Founded/Ownrshp* 1997
Sales 6.7MMM[E] *EMP* 300,000
SIC 5812 Pizzeria, chain
CEO: Scott Bergren
Pr: Peter Hearl
COO: Joe Kim
CFO: David Gibbs
CFO: Artie Starrs
Ofcr: Helen Vaid
VP: Robert Millen
Exec: Wiley Bates
Prin: Teresa J Roll
Area Mgr: Ward Setmayer
QA Dir: John Thornton

D-U-N-S 03-597-2926
PIZZA HUT OF ARIZONA INC
5902 E Pima St, Tucson, AZ 85712-4322
Tel (520) 838-5171 *Founded/Ownrshp* 1965
Sales 45.5MM[E] *EMP* 1,100
Accts Clifton Gunderson Llc
SIC 5812 Pizzeria, chain
Pr: Pat McConaughey

D-U-N-S 04-512-5218
PIZZA HUT OF SOUTHERN WISCONSIN INC
434 S Yellowstone Dr D, Madison, WI 53719-1086
Tel (608) 833-2113 *Founded/Ownrshp* 1968
Sales 40.5M *EMP* 1,200

SIC 5812 Pizzeria, chain
Pr: Richard Divelbiss
VP: Gayla L Divebiss
*VP: Gayla L Divelbiss

D-U-N-S 04-957-2621
■ PIZZA HUT OF TITUSVILLE INC
(Suby of PIZZA HUT INC) ★
7100 Corporate Dr, Plano, TX 75024-4100
Tel (972) 338-7700 Founded/Ownrshp 1989
Sales 18.9MM^E EMP 2,169^E
SIC 5812 Pizzeria, chain
Pr: David Novak

D-U-N-S 95-997-8586
■ PIZZA HUT OF UTAH INC
(Suby of PIZZA HUT INC) ★
76 N 100 E Ste 3, American Fork, UT 84003-1794
Tel (801) 756-9696 Founded/Ownrshp 2001
Sales 21.5MM^E EMP 1,000
SIC 5812 Pizzeria, chain
Prin: Shelly Stephens

D-U-N-S 05-167-2673
■ PIZZA HUT WEST INC
(Suby of PIZZA HUT INC) ★
14841 Dallas Pkwy Frnt, Dallas, TX 75254-7558
Tel (972) 338-7700 Founded/Ownrshp 1987
Sales 22.3MM^E EMP 1,500
SIC 5812 Pizzeria, chain
Pr: Peter Hearl

D-U-N-S 11-334-9385
PIZZA PROPERTIES LTD
PETER PIPER PIZZA
4445 N Mesa St Ste 100, El Paso, TX 79902-1109
Tel (915) 544-8565 Founded/Ownrshp 1982
Sales 90.3MM^E EMP 1,900
SIC 5812 Pizzeria, chain
Ch Bd: J Kirk Robison
*Pr: John T Hjalmquist
*CFO: Polly H Vaughn
*Ex VP: Hal Davis
*VP: Judith L Robinson
*VP: Sharon Voelz
Dir IT: Elaine Morton

D-U-N-S 10-229-9542
PIZZA RANCH INC
204 19th St Se, Orange City, IA 51041-4400
Tel (712) 707-8800 Founded/Ownrshp 1984
Sales 125.5MM^E EMP 3,800
Accts Deloitte & Touche Llp
SIC 5812 6794 Pizzeria, chain; Franchises, selling or licensing
Pr: Adrie Groeneweg
*VP: Ted King

PIZZERIA UNO
See URC LLC

D-U-N-S 09-633-8223 EXP
PJ DICK INC
225 N Shore Dr, Pittsburgh, PA 15212-5860
Tel (412) 462-9300 Founded/Ownrshp 1979
Sales 226.6MM^E EMP 400
SIC 1542 8741 Commercial & office building, new construction; Hospital construction; School building construction; Institutional building construction; Construction management
CEO: Clifford R Rowe Jr
*Pr: Jeffrey D Turconi
*Ex VP: Stephen M Clark
Ex VP: John P Maffeo
Ex VP: Jeffrey Turconi
*VP: Joseph J Franceschini
VP: Dale Lostetter
VP: Michael Roarty
VP: William Woodford
Area Mgr: Robert Park
Off Mgr: John Davis

D-U-N-S 78-783-1122 EXP
■ PJ FOOD SERVICE INC
(Suby of PAPA JOHNS INTERNATIONAL INC) ★
2002 Papa Johns Blvd, Louisville, KY 40299-3393
Tel (502) 261-7272 Founded/Ownrshp 1991
Sales 488.8MM^E EMP 750
SIC 5149 5087 2045 Pizza supplies; Restaurant supplies; Prepared flour mixes & doughs
Pr: Anthony N Thompson
*Treas: Lance F Tucker
*VP: R Shane Hutchins
*VP: Sean A Muldoon

D-U-N-S 86-741-2686
PJ HOUSING PRESERVATION LP
MACHACKEMACH APARTMENTS
230 Jersey Ave, Port Jervis, NY 12771-2252
Tel (845) 856-7677 Founded/Ownrshp 1995
Sales 27.0MM^E EMP 1,828
SIC 6513 Apartment building operators
*Prin: Larry Lipton

PJ TRAILER MANUFACTURING
See PJ TRAILERS MANUFACTURING INC

D-U-N-S 82-588-9103 IMP
PJ TRAILERS INC
(Suby of AMERICAN TRAILER WORKS INC) ★
1807 Farm Road 2352, Sumner, TX 75486-4808
Tel (903) 785-6879 Founded/Ownrshp 2008
Sales 124.8MM^E EMP 342^E
SIC 3715 Truck trailers
Pr: Doug Clark
VP: Tom Keene
VP: Todd Robichaux
VP: Doug Wheat
Dir IT: Travis Peters

D-U-N-S 62-246-8528 IMP
PJ TRAILERS MANUFACTURING INC
PJ TRAILER MANUFACTURING
(Suby of PJ TRAILERS INC) ★
1807 Farm Road 2352, Sumner, TX 75486-4808
Tel (903) 785-6879 Founded/Ownrshp 2008
Sales 124.5MM^E EMP 342
SIC 3799 Trailers & trailer equipment
VP: Doug Wheat
*VP: Tom Keene

PJAX TRANSPORT
See VITRAN EXPRESS INC

D-U-N-S 07-987-5099
PJD CONSTRUCTION INC
447 London St, San Francisco, CA 94112-2727
Tel (415) 218-3031 Founded/Ownrshp 2015
Sales 98.0MM EMP 4
SIC 1542 1522 Commercial & office building, new construction; Residential construction
Pr: Paul Joseph Doherty

D-U-N-S 07-364-7877
PJM INTERCONNECTION LLC
2750 Monroe Blvd, Norristown, PA 19403-2429
Tel (610) 666-8980 Founded/Ownrshp 1993
Sales 521.1MM^E EMP 600
Accts Pricewaterhousecoopers Llp P
SIC 4911 Electric services
CEO: Terry Boston
COO: Michael J Kormos
CFO: Suzanne Daugherty
Chf Cred: Ian McLeod
Ofcr: Susan Buehler
VP: Frederick Bresler
VP: Thomas F O'Brien
Ex Dir: Michael Bryson
Prgrm Mgr: Jeff Schmitt
Genl Mgr: Frank L Osen
Genl Mgr: Jim Snow

PJP
See PENN JERSEY PAPER CO

D-U-N-S 14-708-9072
PJS LUMBER INC
P J'S CONSTRUCTION SUPPLIES
45055 Fremont Blvd, Fremont, CA 94538-6318
Tel (510) 743-5300 Founded/Ownrshp 1984
Sales 112.6MM^E EMP 145
SIC 5031 5051 Lumber: rough, dressed & finished; Steel
CEO: Shane McMillan
*Pr: Carlton J McMillan
*CEO: Terry W Protto
*VP: Jeff Veilleux
Opers Supe: John Hayes

D-U-N-S 07-996-0503
■ PJT PARTNERS HOLDINGS LP
(Suby of PJT PARTNERS INC) ★
280 Park Ave Fl 15w, New York, NY 10017-1206
Tel (212) 364-7800 Founded/Ownrshp 2014, 2016
Sales 400.0MM EMP 250
SIC 6282 Investment advisory service

D-U-N-S 07-995-5461
▲ PJT PARTNERS INC
280 Park Ave Fl 16, New York, NY 10017-1206
Tel (212) 364-7800 Founded/Ownrshp 2015
Sales 416.0MM^E EMP 353^E
Tkr Sym PJT Exch NYS
SIC 6282 6153 Investment advisory service; Working capital financing
Ch Bd: Paul J Taubman
Mng Pt: Ji-Yeun Lee
CFO: Helen T Meates
Genl Couns: James W Cuminale

D-U-N-S 19-433-1435 IMP
PK USA INC
(Suby of PRESS KOGYO CO., LTD.)
600 Northridge Dr, Shelbyville, IN 46176-8929
Tel (317) 395-5500 Founded/Ownrshp 1988
Sales 94.9MM^E EMP 405
SIC 3465 3089 3714 3429 Body parts, automobile: stamped metal; Injection molding of plastics; Motor vehicle engines & parts; Furniture builders' & other household hardware
*Pr: Kazuhiko Onami
*VP: Mori Toki
DP Dir: Jill Johnson
Sys/Mgr: Soichi Namiki

PKC GROUP
See AEES INC

D-U-N-S 04-962-6740
PKF-MARK III INC
P K F CONSTRUCTION
17 Blacksmith Rd Ste 101, Newtown, PA 18940-3405
Tel (215) 968-5031 Founded/Ownrshp 1969
Sales 91.4MM^E EMP 200^E
SIC 1611 1629 1711 1731 1771 8711 General contractor, highway & street construction; Pile driving contractor; Mechanical contractor; General electrical contractor; Foundation & footing contractor; Construction & civil engineering
Pr: Glenn Ely
*Ex VP: Craig Kolbman
*VP: Larry Keough
*VP: Mark Reisinger
Genl Mgr: Don Michell

PL DEVELOPMENTS
See P & L DEVELOPMENT LLC

D-U-N-S 04-782-3666
PLACE PROPERTIES LP
3445 Peachtree Rd Ne # 1400, Atlanta, GA 30326-3253
Tel (404) 495-7500 Founded/Ownrshp 1999
Sales 152.5MM^E EMP 400
SIC 6552 Land subdividers & developers, residential
CEO: Cecil M Phillips
Pr: Brent Little
*Pr: Jim Rosenberg
*COO: John M Crocker
CFO: Bob Clark
*Chf Cred: Dan Fitzpatrick
VP: Tresa Harting
Rgnl Mgr: Roger Dickson
Brnch Mgr: Sierra Stephens
*CIO: Cynthia Pfeifer

D-U-N-S 04-052-7558
PLACENTIA-YORBA LINDA UNIFIED SCHOOL DISTRICT
1301 E Orangethorpe Ave, Placentia, CA 92870-5302
Tel (714) 986-7000 Founded/Ownrshp 1936
Sales 99.6MM^E EMP 1,500
Accts Vavrinek Trine Day & Co Ll
SIC 8211 Public elementary & secondary schools
*VP: Carrie Buck
MIS Dir: Jeremy Powell
Trfc Dir: Allyson Holt
Pr Dir: Douglas Schultz
Psych: Cathleen Lopez

D-U-N-S 01-097-3832
PLACER TITLE CO (CA)
(Suby of MOTHER LODE HOLDING CO) ★
189 Fulweiler Ave, Auburn, CA 95603-4507
Tel (530) 887-2410 Founded/Ownrshp 1973, 1989
Sales NA EMP 479
SIC 6361 Title insurance
CEO: Marsha Emmett
*Pr: Jim Johnston
*CFO: David Philipp
Ofcr: Tami Baker
Ofcr: Kelly Guglielmo
Ofcr: Sherry Gumm
Ex VP: Darrick Blatnick
Ex VP: Randy Bradley
Ex VP: Pat Laffin
VP: Cindy Andersen
Brnch Mgr: Elena Velarde

D-U-N-S 07-672-7528
PLACID HOLDING CO
1601 Elm St Ste 3900, Dallas, TX 75201-4708
Tel (214) 880-8479 Founded/Ownrshp 1994
Sales 4.9MMM EMP 2
Accts Hein & Associates Llp Dallas
SIC 2911 Petroleum refining
Pr: Dan Robinson
VP: Larry Doty
VP: Ron Hurst

D-U-N-S 02-774-7997
PLAID PANTRIES INC
PLAID PANTRY
10025 Sw Allen Blvd, Beaverton, OR 97005-4124
Tel (503) 646-4246 Founded/Ownrshp 1988
Sales 136.1MM^E EMP 750
SIC 5411

PLAID PANTRY
See PLAID PANTRIES INC

PLAIN DEALER, THE
See PLAIN DEALER PUBLISHING CO

D-U-N-S 00-416-1675
PLAIN DEALER PUBLISHING CO
PLAIN DEALER, THE
(Suby of ADVANCE PUBLICATIONS, INC.)
4800 Tiedeman Rd, Cleveland, OH 44144-2336
Tel (216) 999-5000 Founded/Ownrshp 1932
Sales 257.5MM^E EMP 1,520
SIC 2711 Newspapers
Pr: Terrance C Z Egger
*Sr VP: Joseph J Bowman
*Sr VP: William V Mickey
*Sr VP: Robert A Perona
*VP: Robert M Long
VP: William Mickey
*VP: Rob Ritterbusch
*VP: Virginia Wang
Exec: William Calaiacovo Jr
IT Man: Matthew H Franduto
Info Man: Terry Kozak

D-U-N-S 02-095-8336
PLAINFIELD COMMUNITY CONSOLIDATED SCHOOL DISTRICT 202
15732 S Howard St, Plainfield, IL 60544-2399
Tel (815) 439-5482 Founded/Ownrshp 1920
Sales 298.8MM EMP 3,100
Accts Klein Hall Cpas Aurora Illin
SIC 8211 Public elementary & secondary schools; Public junior high school; Public senior high school
VP: Michael Kelly
MIS Dir: Margie Bonuchi
IT Man: Madonna Marks
Pr Dir: Thomas Hernandez
Psych: Joe Lindsey

D-U-N-S 08-565-1016
PLAINFIELD PUBLIC SCHOOL DISTRICT
1200 Myrtle Ave, Plainfield, NJ 07063-1139
Tel (908) 731-4200 Founded/Ownrshp 1900
Sales 45.3MM^E EMP 1,000
SIC 8211 Elementary & secondary schools
VP: Wilma Campbell
VP: Keisha Edwards
Dir Sec: Troy Edwards
Genl Mgr: Kiesha Mack
Teacher Pr: E J Brown-Johnson
Teacher Pr: Michele Gill
Teacher Pr: Carletta Jones

PLAINFIELD RENAL CENTER
See ISD PLAINFIELD LLC

D-U-N-S 04-241-3856 IMP
PLAINFIELD TOBACCO AND CANDY CO INC
RESNICK DISTRIBUTORS
25 Van Dyke Ave, New Brunswick, NJ 08901-3495
Tel (732) 296-8900 Founded/Ownrshp 1967
Sales 129.3MM^E EMP 130^E
SIC 5194 5145 Smoking tobacco; Candy
Pr: Lawrence Resnick
*VP: Eileen Resnick

PLAINS ALL AMERICAN PIPELINE
See PLAINS MARKETING LP

D-U-N-S 03-617-0624
■ PLAINS ALL AMERICAN PIPELINE LP
(Suby of PLAINS GP HOLDINGS LP) ★
333 Clay St Ste 1600, Houston, TX 77002-4101
Tel (713) 646-4100 Founded/Ownrshp 1998
Sales 23.1MMM EMP 5,400^E
Tkr Sym PAA Exch NYS
SIC 4612 5172 Crude petroleum pipelines; Crude oil
Ch Bd: Greg L Armstrong
Genl Pt: PAA GP LLC
Pr: Harry N Pefanis
COO: Willie Chiang
CFO: Al Swanson
Ex VP: John V Berg
Ex VP: Mark Gorman
Ex VP: Mark J Gorman
Ex VP: Richard K McGee
Sr VP: John R Keffer
Sr VP: Alfred A Lindseth
Sr VP: Dan Nerbonne
VP: Patrick Diamond
VP: Stephen Falgoust
VP: Dean Gore
VP: Barry Holtzman
VP: Rebecca McConnell
VP: Megan Prout
VP: James Roberts
VP: Robert M Sanford
VP: Jim Tillis

PLAINS CAPITAL BANK
See PLAINSCAPITAL CORP

PLAINS COTTON COOPERATIVE ASSN
See PLAINS COTTON COOPERATIVE ASSOCIATION

D-U-N-S 00-793-4144 IMP/EXP
PLAINS COTTON COOPERATIVE ASSOCIATION (TX)
PLAINS COTTON COOPERATIVE ASSN
3301 E 50th St, Lubbock, TX 79404-4331
Tel (806) 763-8011 Founded/Ownrshp 1953
Sales 892.0MM EMP 170
Accts Crowe Horwath Llp Dallas Tex
SIC 5159 4221 Cotton merchants; Cotton compresses & warehouses
CEO: Kevin Brinkley
*Pr: Marco Cotton
COO: Jan Owens
CFO: Billy Morton
*Ch: Eddie Smith
*VP: Greg Bell
*VP: Jay Cowart
*VP: Bryan Gregory
*VP: Sam Hill
*VP: Joe Tubb
VP: Jeff Turner
Exec: John Duncan
Dir Bus: Dick Cooper

D-U-N-S 02-597-9279 IMP
PLAINS DAIRY LLC (TX)
(Suby of A F) ★
300 N Taylor St, Amarillo, TX 79107-5238
Tel (806) 374-0385 Founded/Ownrshp 1934, 1996
Sales 173.2MM^E EMP 1,010
SIC 2026 2086 2033 Milk processing (pasteurizing, homogenizing, bottling); Cottage cheese; Cream, sour; Buttermilk, cultured; Water, pasteurized: packaged in cans, bottles, etc.; Fruit juices: packaged in cans, jars, etc.
Treas: Shirley Cooper
*VP: George Lankford
Board of Directors: Lonnie Allsup, Dale Carter, William Glen Holt, Roger Lowe, Dennis Denny Porter Jr

D-U-N-S 80-857-2916
▲ PLAINS GP HOLDINGS LP
333 Clay St Ste 1600, Houston, TX 77002-4101
Tel (713) 646-4100 Founded/Ownrshp 2013
Sales 23.1MMM EMP 5,400^E
Tkr Sym PAGP Exch NYS
SIC 4612 1321 Crude petroleum pipelines; Natural gas liquids; Fractionating natural gas liquids
Ch Bd: Greg L Armstrong
Genl Pt: PAA GP Holdings LLC
Pr: Harry N Pefanis

D-U-N-S 03-181-5384
PLAINS GRAIN & AGRONOMY LLC (ND)
109 3rd Ave, Enderlin, ND 58027-1369
Tel (701) 437-2565 Founded/Ownrshp 1901, 2002
Sales 221.0MM EMP 34
Accts Erickson And Associates Ltd
SIC 5153 5191 5171 Grain elevators; Farm supplies; Fertilizer & fertilizer materials; Feed; Seeds: field, garden & flower; Petroleum bulk stations
Plnt Mgr: Kent Baertsch

D-U-N-S 12-725-2153 IMP
■ PLAINS MARKETING LP
PLAINS ALL AMERICAN PIPELINE
(Suby of PLAINS ALL AMERICAN PIPELINE LP) ★
333 Clay St Ste 1600, Houston, TX 77002-4101
Tel (713) 646-4100 Founded/Ownrshp 1998
Sales 869.2MM^E EMP 321
SIC 5172 4213 Crude oil; Liquid petroleum transport, non-local
Pr: Harry N Pefanis
CFO: Al Swanson
Ex VP: Mark J Gorman
Ex VP: Phil D Kramer

D-U-N-S 00-793-4151
■ PLAINSCAPITAL BANK
(Suby of PLAINS CAPITAL BANK) ★
2323 Victory Ave Ste 1400, Dallas, TX 75219-7695
Tel (214) 252-4100 Founded/Ownrshp 1965, 1988
Sales NA EMP 1,306
SIC 6022 State commercial banks
Ch Bd: Alan B White
Pr: Jerry Schaffner
COO: Brian Heflin
Ch: Robert C Norman
Ofcr: Vera Gutierrez
Ofcr: Robert Veach
Ex VP: Deric Barnett
Sr VP: Nancy Thomas
VP: Stacey Ferris
VP: Ian Fleming
VP: Brenda Gallagher
VP: Delma Garcia

D-U-N-S 14-962-6624
■ PLAINSCAPITAL CORP
PLAINS CAPITAL BANK
(*Suby of* HILLTOP HOLDINGS INC) ★
2323 Victory Ave Ste 1400, Dallas, TX 75219-7695
Tel (214) 252-4100 *Founded/Ownrshp* 2012
Sales 996.8MM *EMP* 3,400^E
SIC 7389 Financial services
Ch Bd: Alan B White
Pr: Andy Friederichs
Pr: Amy Graham
**Pr:* James R Huffines
**CFO:* John A Martin
Ofcr: Mike Brown
Ofcr: Barbara Buckel
Ofcr: Rosie Castillo
Ofcr: Michael Lowe
Ex VP: Allen Custard
Ex VP: George H McCleskey
Ex VP: Roseanna McGill
Ex VP: Alan Nirenberg
Ex VP: Rich Wyatt
Sr VP: Suzie Coghlan
VP: Tye Barton
VP: Clint Chavarria
VP: Adam Chong
VP: Megahn Collins
VP: Corbin Cook
VP: Chris Defrancisco
Board of Directors: Charlotte J Anderson, Tracy A Bolt, Lee Lewis, Andrew J Littlefair, Michael T McGuire, A Haag Sherman, Robert Taylor Jr

D-U-N-S 07-963-4009
PLAINVIEW HOSPITAL (NY)
(*Suby of* NSLIJ) ★
888 Old Country Rd, Plainview, NY 11803-4914
Tel (516) 719-2200 *Founded/Ownrshp* 1994
Sales 156.7MM *EMP* 1,200
SIC 8062 General medical & surgical hospitals
CEO: Michael Dowling
Ex Dir: Michael Fener

D-U-N-S 00-615-1930
PLAINVIEW MILK PRODUCTS COOPERATIVE (MN)
130 2nd St Sw, Plainview, MN 55964-1394
Tel (507) 534-3872 *Founded/Ownrshp* 1905
Sales 116.3MM *EMP* 62
SIC 2023 2021

D-U-N-S 09-236-3993
PLAINVIEW-OLD BETHPAGE CENTRAL SCHOOL DISTRICT
106 Washington Ave, Plainview, NY 11803-4047
Tel (516) 937-6300 *Founded/Ownrshp* 1950
Sales 143.9MM *EMP* 900
Accts Rs Abrams & Co Llp Island
SIC 8211 Public elementary & secondary schools; Public elementary school; Public junior high school; Public senior high school
Assoc Dir: Tara Zahtila
Genl Mgr: Jennifer Segui
Pr Dir: Bob Zimmerman

D-U-N-S 03-776-1228
PLAMONDON ENTERPRISES INC
ROY ROGERS
4991 New Design Rd # 109, Frederick, MD 21703-7342
Tel (301) 695-5051 *Founded/Ownrshp* 1979
Sales 51.4MM^E *EMP* 1,000
SIC 5812 7011

D-U-N-S 12-314-1942
PLAN INTERNATIONAL INC
155 Plan Way Ste A, Warwick, RI 02886-1099
Tel (401) 294-3693 *Founded/Ownrshp* 1982
Sales 684.3MM *EMP* 7
Accts Dyl & Perillo Inc Providence
SIC 8399 Community development groups
Ex Dir: Thomas Miller

D-U-N-S 06-390-2761
PLAN INTERNATIONAL USA INC
CHILDREACH
(*Suby of* FOSTER PARENTS PLAN INTERNATIONAL (UK) LTD.)
155 Plan Way Ste A, Warwick, RI 02886-1099
Tel (401) 562-8400 *Founded/Ownrshp* 2012
Sales 84.7MM *EMP* 140
Accts Pricewaterhousecoopers Llp B
SIC 8322 Child guidance agency; Family service agency
CEO: Tessie Martin
Sr Cor Off: James Emerson
Ofcr: Roman Assefa
Ofcr: Ashraf Khan
Comm Dir: Robin Costello
Adm Dir: Carlos Barros
Mng Dir: Ed James
Prgrm Mgr: Katie Appel
Prgrm Mgr: Holly Christofferson
Dir IT: Yvonne Norman
Web Dev: Lori Burlingham

D-U-N-S 10-301-7166 IMP
PLANAR SYSTEMS INC
(*Suby of* LEYARD AMERICAN CORPORATION)
1195 Nw Compton Way, Beaverton, OR 97006-6959
Tel (503) 748-1100 *Founded/Ownrshp* 2015
Sales 179.0MM *EMP* 355
SIC 3679 Antennas, receiving
CFO: Ryan Gray
**Pr:* Zach Zhang
**VP:* Rob Baumgartner
**VP:* Jennifer Davis
VP: Bill Hanrahan
**VP:* Jeff Maurer
**VP:* Samantha Phenix
VP Bus Dev: Sal Digiacomo
Genl Mgr: Nancy Kirkpatrick
Snr Sftwr: Dez Moleski
IT Man: Brad Becker

D-U-N-S 13-921-3060
■ PLANCO FINANCIAL SERVICES INC
(*Suby of* HARTFORD LIFE AND ACCIDENT INSURANCE CO INC) ★
1500 Liberty Ridge Dr # 100, Chesterbrook, PA 19087-5564
Tel (610) 695-9500 *Founded/Ownrshp* 1998
Sales 102.3MM^E *EMP* 900
SIC 6211 6311 Security brokers & dealers; Life insurance
Mng Dir: Kevin O'Connor
Pr: Nancy Felice
**CFO:* Julie Croow
**VP:* Edwin Gold
VP: Jane K Sagendorph
**Mng Dir:* Kevin M Connor

D-U-N-S 00-446-0809 EXP
PLANET AUTOMOTIVE GROUP INC (FL)
POTAMKIN AUTOMOTIVE
6200 Nw 167th St B, Miami Lakes, FL 33014-6145
Tel (305) 728-5000 *Founded/Ownrshp* 1998
Sales 353.5MM^E *EMP* 1,500
SIC 5511 New & used car dealers
CEO: Alan H Potamkim
**Pr:* Barry Frieder
CFO: Dave Yusko
**Co-CEO:* Robert Potamkim
**Ex VP:* David Winton
**VP:* David Frieder
**VP:* Ralph Perkins
**VP:* Andrew Pfeifer
Opers Mgr: Andy Pheifer

D-U-N-S 92-918-2640
▲ PLANET FITNESS INC
26 Fox Run Rd, Newington, NH 03801-2810
Tel (603) 750-0001 *Founded/Ownrshp* 1992
Sales 330.5MM *EMP* 756
Tkr Sym PLNT *Exch* NYS
SIC 7991 Physical fitness facilities
CEO: Chris Rondeau
CFO: Dorvin Lively
Ofcr: Richard Moore
Sr VP: Jim Esposito
VP: Josh Beyer
Mktg Dir: Jamie Medeiros
Board of Directors: David P Berg, Charles Esserman, Marc Grondahl, Michael Layman, Pierre Lecomte, Frances Gregg Rathke, Stephen Spinelli Jr, Edward Wong

PLANET FORD
See WORLD CLASS AUTOMOTIVE GROUP LP

D-U-N-S 78-598-8619
PLANET HOLLYWOOD INTERNATIONAL INC
4700 Millenia Blvd # 400, Orlando, FL 32839-6020
Tel (407) 903-5500 *Founded/Ownrshp* 1993
Sales 233.4MM^E *EMP* 8,000
SIC 5812 6794 5699 Restaurant, family: chain; Franchises, selling or licensing; Customized clothing & apparel; Shirts, custom made; T-shirts, custom printed
CEO: Robert I Earl
**Pr:* David Crabtree
**CFO:* Bruce Hawkins
**Treas:* Thomas Avallone
**VP:* Martha H McIntosh
VP: Martha McIntosh
Exec: Freddy Espinoza
Exec: Luis Monge
Exec: Barbara Tabor
Genl Mgr: Peter Cording
Genl Mgr: Scott Wade

PLANET HONDA
See TIMCO INC

PLANET ORGANIC MARKET
See NATURAL MARKETS FOOD GROUP

D-U-N-S 18-043-7329
■ PLANETECHS LLC
(*Suby of* TRUEBLUE INC) ★
1520 Kensington Rd # 311, Oak Brook, IL 60523-2128
Tel (630) 468-1766 *Founded/Ownrshp* 2007
Sales 41.2MM^E *EMP* 1,100
SIC 7363 Labor resource services
Sr VP: Stephen Fisher

PLANETMAGPIE
See MAGPIE INTERNET COMMUNICATIONS CORP

D-U-N-S 15-255-3046
PLANNED ADMINISTRATORS INC
(*Suby of* BLUE CROSS BLUE SHIELD OF SOUTH CAROLINA) ★
17 Technology Cir E2ag, Columbia, SC 29203-9591
Tel (803) 462-0151 *Founded/Ownrshp* 1986
Sales NA *EMP* 300
Accts Derrick Stubbs & Stith Llp
SIC 6411 Insurance brokers
CEO: M Edward Sellers
**Pr:* David J Huntington
**CFO:* Robert A Leichtle
Exec: Ty Bedenbaugh
Dir IT: Scot Dawkins
Opers Supe: Melanie P Gainey
Opers Mgr: Amoy C Huggins

D-U-N-S 07-520-3943 IMP
PLANNED PARENTHOOD FEDERATION OF AMERICA INC
PLANNED PRNTHD-WRLD POPULATION
123 William St Fl 10, New York, NY 10038-3844
Tel (212) 541-7800 *Founded/Ownrshp* 1922
Sales 196.8MM *EMP* 530
Accts Kpmg Llp New York Ny
SIC 8093 Family planning & birth control clinics
Pr: Cecile Richards
**COO:* Melvin Galloway
**CFO:* Wallace D'Sousa
CFO: Wallace D'Souza
CFO: Jonathan S Fache
CFO: Howard Lorch
Ofcr: Elizabeth Clark
Ofcr: Alencia Johnson
VP: Cassandra Austin
VP: Barbara Bushnell
VP: Nancy Clack
VP: Keith Corso
VP: Molly Eagan
VP: Caroline Green
VP: Alicia Kenaley
VP: David Nova
VP: Dana Singiser
Assoc Dir: Emily Kokernak
Assoc Dir: Chakshu Patel
Assoc Dir: Paul Vogel
Dir Soc: Lucy Eilbacher

D-U-N-S 07-717-0694
PLANNED PARENTHOOD MAR MONTE INC
1691 The Alameda, San Jose, CA 95126-2203
Tel (408) 287-7532 *Founded/Ownrshp* 1989
Sales 95.9MM *EMP* 800
Accts Harrington Group San Francisc
SIC 8093 Family planning clinic
Pr: Linda T Williams
COO: Adelina Garcia
**CFO:* John Giambruno
**VP:* Jeanne Ewy
**VP:* Alison Gaulden
**VP:* Rosemary Kamei
**VP:* Elena Love
Genl Mgr: Julie Smith-Reid

PLANNED PRNTHD-WRLD POPULATION
See PLANNED PARENTHOOD FEDERATION OF AMERICA INC

D-U-N-S 60-357-1613
PLANNED SYSTEMS INTERNATIONAL INC
P S I
10632 Little Patuxent Pkw, Columbia, MD 21044-6250
Tel (410) 964-8000 *Founded/Ownrshp* 1988
Sales 110.0MM *EMP* 425
SIC 8742 Management consulting services
CEO: Terry Lin
Pr: Ted Rogers
**COO:* Michael Snyder
**CFO:* Steve Crespy
**Ofcr:* Jerry Ambrosh
Sr VP: Joseph Knoblock
Sr VP: Robert J Matz
VP: Zane Jones
VP: Sandy Kelley
VP: Michael McCormick
VP: Kinga Niecko
VP: Kristin Pennypacker
Creative D: Christina Santo

D-U-N-S 01-049-1686
PLANO INDEPENDENT SCHOOL DISTRICT
2700 W 15th St, Plano, TX 75075-7524
Tel (469) 752-8100 *Founded/Ownrshp* 1899
Sales 669.8MM *EMP* 5,610^E
Accts Weaver And Tidwell Llp Dalla
SIC 8211 Public elementary & secondary schools
Ex Dir: Mark Allen
Admn Mgr: Emelia Ahmed
Off Mgr: Odelia Yocum
Off Mgr: Sandi Youngblood
Teacher Pr: Tamara Griffin
Teacher Pr: Jun Melvin
Instr Medi: Mary L Skinner

D-U-N-S 01-223-5644 IMP
PLANSEE USA LLC
(*Suby of* SCHWARZKOPF HOLDING CORP) ★
115 Constitution Blvd, Franklin, MA 02038-2584
Tel (508) 553-3800 *Founded/Ownrshp* 1996
Sales 99.5MM^E *EMP* 126^E
SIC 3499 Fire- or burglary-resistive products
**Pr:* Mark Wilbur
**CFO:* Mary Poniktera
**CFO:* Andreas Schwenninger
Dir IT: Frank Libertine
Plnt Mgr: Mike Lepage

PLANT 1
See VALEO LIGHTING SYSTEMS NORTH AMERICA LLC

PLANT 5
See TENNSCO CORP

D-U-N-S 61-530-7097 IMP
PLANT CONSTRUCTION CO LP
300 Newhall St, San Francisco, CA 94124-1498
Tel (415) 285-0500 *Founded/Ownrshp* 1990
Sales 350.0MM *EMP* 300
SIC 1542

D-U-N-S 02-581-2389
PLANT EQUIPMENT CO
2515 5th Ave, Rock Island, IL 61201-9016
Tel (309) 786-3369 *Founded/Ownrshp* 1949
Sales 116.5MM *EMP* 7
SIC 5084 Materials handling machinery
Pr: Lee A Macdonald
**Pr:* Elizabeth Hoenshell
**Pr:* Alinda Littrel
**VP:* Bernard C Sommer

D-U-N-S 13-704-3803 IMP/EXP
■ PLANT PERFORMANCE SERVICES LLC
(*Suby of* FLUOR DANIEL INTERCONTINENTAL) ★
4800 Sugar Grove Blvd # 450, Stafford, TX 77477-2630
Tel (832) 532-5600 *Founded/Ownrshp* 2003
Sales 295.9MM^E *EMP* 5,000
SIC 1731 1799 7699

D-U-N-S 15-510-3799 IMP
PLANT SCIENCES INC
342 Green Valley Rd, Watsonville, CA 95076-1305
Tel (831) 728-3323 *Founded/Ownrshp* 1985
Sales 143.7MM^E *EMP* 375
Accts Hutchinson And Bloodgood Llp
SIC 5122 8748 8731 Biologicals & allied products; Agricultural consultant; Agricultural research
CEO: Steven D Nelson
**Pr:* Richard Nelson
**VP:* Michael D Nelson
Off Mgr: Gloria Gonzalez
IT Man: Jeffrey Nelson
Sfty Mgr: Luis Macario
Opers Mgr: John Giaimo

PLANTATION ESTATES
See KAPALUA LAND CO LTD

D-U-N-S 07-386-8853
■ PLANTATION GENERAL HOSPITAL LP
(*Suby of* HOSPITAL COPORATION OF AMERICA) ★
401 Nw 42nd Ave, Plantation, FL 33317-2882
Tel (954) 587-5010 *Founded/Ownrshp* 1995
Sales 159.0MM^E *EMP* 3,258^E
SIC 8062 General medical & surgical hospitals
CEO: Randy Gross
Chf Path: Simon Cohen
Pr: Michael G Joseph
COO: Barbara Simmons
Ch: Joel M Jancko
Ofcr: David Hughes
VP: Anthony M Degina Jr
Dir Lab: Cynthia B Gold
Dir Sec: Jesus Muriel
IT Man: Iris Drelich
IT Man: Laurie Meyer

PLANTATION HOMES
See MHI PARTNERSHIP LTD

D-U-N-S 17-417-3815
PLANTATION MANAGEMENT CO LLC
HERITAGE MANOR NURSING HOME
301 Veterans Blvd, Denham Springs, LA 70726-4722
Tel (225) 664-6697 *Founded/Ownrshp* 1997
Sales 69.5MM^E *EMP* 4,500
SIC 8051

D-U-N-S 02-020-2892
PLANTATION PATTERNS LLC
(*Suby of* EMARICO INC) ★
146 Resource Center Pkwy, Birmingham, AL 35242-8095
Tel (205) 545-9229 *Founded/Ownrshp* 2011
Sales 102.7MM^E *EMP* 350^E
SIC 2392 Cushions & pillows
CEO: E J Marino Jr

PLANTE & MORAN
See PLANTE MORAN PC

D-U-N-S 00-491-3299
PLANTE & MORAN PLLC
(*Suby of* PLANTE & MORAN) ★
27400 Northwestern Hwy # 300, Southfield, MI 48034-4798
Tel (248) 223-3247 *Founded/Ownrshp* 2002
Sales 154.7MM^E *EMP* 1,500
SIC 8721 8742 Certified public accountant; Business consultant
Pt: Michelle Carey
**Pt:* Jerry Smith
Mng Pt: Ron Eckstein
Chf Mktg O: Jeff Antaya
Off Admin: Arlene Veltri
CIO: Paul Blowers
QA Dir: Tom Degregorio
Sftwr Eng: Michael Obrycki
Snr Mgr: Lisa Vargo

D-U-N-S 14-326-3254
PLANTE MORAN PC
PLANTE & MORAN
27400 Northwestern Hwy # 300, Southfield, MI 48034-4798
Tel (248) 352-2500 *Founded/Ownrshp* 2002
Sales 160.9MM^E *EMP* 1,600
SIC 8721 Accounting, auditing & bookkeeping
Mng Pt: Gordon Krater
**Mng Pt:* Sue Novak
**CFO:* Jerry Smith
VP: Peter Bitter
VP: Eamon Moran
Off Mgr: Mark Sharf
Doctor: Kim Greenspan
Snr Mgr: Carol Dooley
Snr Mgr: Mary Wade

D-U-N-S 00-918-0902 IMP
▲ PLANTRONICS INC
345 Encinal St, Santa Cruz, CA 95060-2146
Tel (831) 426-5858 *Founded/Ownrshp* 1961
Sales 856.9MM *EMP* 3,398^E
Tkr Sym PLT *Exch* NYS
SIC 3661 3679 Telephones & telephone apparatus; Headsets, telephone; Telephone sets, all types except cellular radio; Headphones, radio
Pr: Joe Burton
**Ch Bd:* Marv Tseu
Pr: Jamie Van Den Bergh
CFO: Pamela Strayer
Ofcr: Inamarie Johnson
Ofcr: Marilyn Mersereau
Sr VP: Alejandro Bustamante
Sr VP: Don Houston
VP: Vedat Bilgutay
VP: Kris Diamond
VP: Michael Gjerstad
Board of Directors: Brian Dexheimer, Robert Hagerty, Gregg Hammann, John Hart, Maria Martinez, Marshall Mohr

D-U-N-S 61-530-6438
PLANVIEW INC
12301 Research Blvd 5-100, Austin, TX 78759-2483
Tel (512) 346-8600 *Founded/Ownrshp* 2013
Sales 145.0MM *EMP* 600
SIC 7371 8748 8742 Computer software development & applications; Business consulting; New products & services consultants
CEO: Gregory Gilmore
COO: Tobias Andersson
**CFO:* Vic Chynoweth
**CFO:* Randy Jonkers
CFO: Rikard Olsson
Ex VP: Scott Hardey
Sr VP: Kevin Dolan
VP: Louise K Allen
VP: Eric S Hurley
VP: Eric Hurley
VP: Mike McPhilliamy

VP: Rob Reesor
Exec: Gino Marroso
Board of Directors: Larry Singer

PLASKOLITE CONTINENTAL
See PLASKOLITE LLC

D-U-N-S 00-428-1093 IMP
PLASKOLITE LLC
PLASKOLITE CONTINENTAL
1770 Joyce Ave, Columbus, OH 43219-1026
Tel (614) 294-3281 *Founded/Ownrshp* 1950
Sales 166.8MM[E] *EMP* 528
SIC 2821 Plastics materials & resins
Pr: Mitchell P Grindley
CTO: Richard J Larkin

D-U-N-S 00-511-3188 IMP
PLASSER AMERICAN CORP
(*Suby of* PLASSER & THEURER, EXPORT VON BAHN-BAUMASCHINEN, GESELLSCHAFT M.B.H.)
2001 Myers Rd, Chesapeake, VA 23324-3231
Tel (757) 543-3526 *Founded/Ownrshp* 1970
Sales 86.6MM[E] *EMP* 220
SIC 3531 Railway track equipment
Pr: Joseph W Neuhofer
**Sec:* Robin R Laskowski
**VP:* Dr Gunther W Oblechner
Plnt Mgr: Garhard Reikersdorfer
Ql Cn Mgr: Jim Rusho
Manager: Piffl Siegfried

PLASTEK GROUP, THE
See PLASTEK INDUSTRIES INC

D-U-N-S 05-482-2986 IMP/EXP
PLASTEK INDUSTRIES INC (PA)
PLASTEK GROUP, THE
2425 W 23rd St, Erie, PA 16506-2920
Tel (814) 878-4400 *Founded/Ownrshp* 1971
Sales 477.5MM[E] *EMP* 1,100
SIC 3089 Injection molding of plastics
Pr: Joseph J Prischak
**Sec:* Daniel J Prischak
**VP:* Narendra Handa
Dir IT: Alan A Holeman

PLASTI-FORM
See BRAIFORM ENTERPRISES INC

D-U-N-S 05-874-2875 IMP
PLASTIC INGENUITY INC
1017 Park St, Cross Plains, WI 53528-9631
Tel (608) 798-3071 *Founded/Ownrshp* 1972
Sales 112.1MM[E] *EMP* 450
Accts Sva & Associates Llc
SIC 3089 Plastic containers, except foam
Pr: Thomas Kuehn
Manager: Craig Lowell

D-U-N-S 80-986-2907 IMP
PLASTIC OMNIUM AUTO EXTERIORS LLC
(*Suby of* PLASTIC OMNIUM AUTO EXTERIORS)
2710 Bellingham Dr # 400, Troy, MI 48083-2045
Tel (248) 458-0700 *Founded/Ownrshp* 1996
Sales 257.4MM[E] *EMP* 591
SIC 3089 Automotive parts, plastic
Pr: Marc Cornet
**CFO:* Bruno Courtet

PLASTIC OMNIUM AUTOMOTIVE
See PLASTIC OMNIUM INDUSTRIES INC

D-U-N-S 62-085-4070 IMP
PLASTIC OMNIUM INDUSTRIES INC
PLASTIC OMNIUM AUTOMOTIVE
(*Suby of* COMPAGNIE PLASTIC OMNIUM)
5100 Old Pearman Dairy Rd, Anderson, SC 29625-1314
Tel (864) 260-0000 *Founded/Ownrshp* 1993
Sales 152.9MM[E] *EMP* 350
SIC 3089 Injection molding of plastics
CEO: Laurent Burelle
COO: Paul-Henry Lemarie
Ofcr: Sheila Holcombe
Ex VP: Philippe Hugon
VP: Bruno Asselin
VP: Olivier Pouteau

D-U-N-S 00-616-8470 IMP/EXP
PLASTIC PRODUCTS CO INC (MN)
SMITH METAL PRODUCTS
30355 Akerson St, Lindstrom, MN 55045-9456
Tel (651) 257-5980 *Founded/Ownrshp* 1962
Sales 170.0MM *EMP* 900
SIC 3089 Plastic processing; Injection molded finished plastic products
Pr: Rick Carlson
VP: Ben Holder
QC Dir: Susie Robey
Plnt Mgr: Randy Kincaid
Board of Directors: David Diehl, Jeanne Kramer, Kim Maguire, Ward Simon

D-U-N-S 07-619-1519 IMP/EXP
PLASTIC SERVICES AND PRODUCTS
GENERAL PLASTICS
(*Suby of* P C M) ★
12243 Branford St, Sun Valley, CA 91352-1010
Tel (818) 896-1101 *Founded/Ownrshp* 1971
Sales 429.9MM[E] *EMP* 3,000
SIC 3086 3674 2865 2816 3296 2819 Plastics foam products; Semiconductors & related devices; Food dyes or colors, synthetic; Color pigments; Fiberglass insulation; Industrial inorganic chemicals
Pr: Philip E Kamins
**CEO:* Steven G Cohen
**CFO:* T C Cheong
**VP:* Gary Kamins

D-U-N-S 01-110-8024 IMP/EXP
PLASTIC SUPPLIERS INC
2450 Marilyn Ln, Columbus, OH 43219-1721
Tel (614) 471-9100 *Founded/Ownrshp* 1949
Sales 92.5MM[E] *EMP* 252
SIC 3081 Unsupported plastics film & sheet
Pr: George L Thomas
**Ch Bd:* Peter Driscoll
COO: Theodore Riegert

**CFO:* Steve H Dudley
CFO: Steve Dudly
VP: Dave Dittman
**VP:* Erich Emhuff
VP Opers: Robert Scholz
Plnt Mgr: Brad McDaniel

D-U-N-S 03-049-3543
PLASTIC SYSTEMS LLC
15055 32 Mile Rd, Bruce Twp, MI 48065-4901
Tel (586) 336-9696 *Founded/Ownrshp* 2001
Sales 83.1MM[E] *EMP* 350
SIC 3089

PLASTIC TECHNOLOGY DIVISION
See HUB FOLDING BOX CO INC

D-U-N-S 13-270-7766 IMP
PLASTIC TRIM INTERNATIONAL INC
(*Suby of* MINTH GROUP LIMITED)
935 Aulerich Rd, East Tawas, MI 48730-9565
Tel (248) 259-7468 *Founded/Ownrshp* 2007
Sales 150.0MM[E] *EMP* 459[E]
SIC 3465 Body parts, automobile: stamped metal
CEO: Howard Boyer
**VP:* Kathleen Burgess

D-U-N-S 94-431-6249 IMP
PLASTICOS PROMEX USA INC
(*Suby of* QUANTUM PLASTICS LLC) ★
1220 Barranca Dr Ste 4c, El Paso, TX 79935-4606
Tel (915) 592-5447 *Founded/Ownrshp* 2016
Sales 115.4MM[E] *EMP* 800
SIC 3089 Injection molding of plastics
Pr: Don Labbruzzo
**Sec:* Carlos Camarillo

D-U-N-S 17-959-3769
PLASTICS COLOR CORP
(*Suby of* GENERAL PLASTICS) ★
14201 Paxton Ave, Calumet City, IL 60409-3235
Tel (708) 868-3800 *Founded/Ownrshp* 1997
Sales 86.4MM[E] *EMP* 130
SIC 3559 Plastics working machinery
CEO: Doug Borgsdorf
**Ch Bd:* Timothy Workman
**Pr:* Joe Byrne
**CFO:* T C Cheong
Netwrk Eng: Jerry Kucsera

D-U-N-S 00-514-3722 IMP
PLASTICS GROUP INC
7409 S Quincy St, Willowbrook, IL 60527-5521
Tel (630) 325-1210 *Founded/Ownrshp* 1963, 1997
Sales 104.7MM[E] *EMP* 500
SIC 3089

D-U-N-S 01-091-5619 IMP
PLASTIKON INDUSTRIES INC
688 Sandoval Way, Hayward, CA 94544-7129
Tel (510) 400-1010 *Founded/Ownrshp* 2010
Sales 124.0MM[E] *EMP* 252[E]
SIC 3544 3089 Special dies, tools, jigs & fixtures; Injection molded finished plastic products
Pr: Fred Soofer
**CEO:* Fereydoon Soofer
CFO: Paul Gutwald
**VP:* Peter F Petri
Exec: Calr Oronfki
Prgrm Mgr: Herry Sukimin
Prgrm Mgr: Kevin Welp
Prd Mgr: Angelica Lopez
Ql Cn Mgr: Chris Carmine
Ql Cn Mgr: Talal Talhouk
Ql Cn Mgr: Tony Trapolino

D-U-N-S 11-917-4162 IMP/EXP
PLASTIPAK HOLDINGS INC
41605 Ann Arbor Rd E, Plymouth, MI 48170-4304
Tel (734) 455-3600 *Founded/Ownrshp* 1998
Sales 36.3MM *EMP* 3,300
Accts Doeren Mayhew Troy Mi
SIC 3089 Blow molded finished plastic products
Pr: William C Young
Pr: Sharon Hedgecock
**CFO:* Michael Plotzke
Treas: Chris Zimmer
VP: Greg Dean
**VP:* Pradeep Modi
**VP:* Frank Pollock
**VP:* William Slat
CTO: Joe Reane
S&M/VP: Gene Mueller

D-U-N-S 05-248-6016 IMP
PLASTIPAK PACKAGING INC (DE)
MULTI-FINANCIAL
(*Suby of* PLASTIPAK HOLDINGS INC) ★
41605 Ann Arbor Rd E, Plymouth, MI 48170-4304
Tel (734) 455-3600 *Founded/Ownrshp* 1908, 1998
Sales 28.6MM[E] *EMP* 2,600
SIC 3089 Blow molded finished plastic products
Pr: William C Young
Pr: Frank Pollack
COO: Jim Kulp
CFO: Michael Plotzke
Ofcr: Bob O'Donnell
VP: Jerry Cornell
VP: Greg Dean
VP: Renee Naud
Exec: Ron Ratliff
Plng Mgr: Harry Melton
CIO: David Doherty

D-U-N-S 11-853-1490
PLATEAU EXCAVATION INC
375 Lee Industrial Blvd, Austell, GA 30168-7427
Tel (770) 944-0205 *Founded/Ownrshp* 1984
Sales 147.2MM *EMP* 300
Accts Cooper Travis & Company Pllc
SIC 1794 Excavation & grading, building construction
COO: Brad Carroll
VP: Christopher Duke
**VP:* Ryan Duke
VP: William Hancock
VP: David Shewchuk
Genl Mgr: Lisa Carroll
Mtls Mgr: Greg Farr

Snr PM: John Osterland
Snr PM: Colby Rutledge

D-U-N-S 07-927-0103
▲ **PLATFORM SPECIALTY PRODUCTS CORP**
1450 Centrepark Blvd, West Palm Beach, FL 33401-7429
Tel (561) 207-9600 *Founded/Ownrshp* 2013
Sales 843.2MM *EMP* 8,200[E]
Accts Securities And Exchange Commis
Tkr Sym PAH *Exch* NYS
SIC 2869 2899 Industrial organic chemicals; Hydraulic fluids, synthetic base; Chemical preparations
CEO: Rakesh Sachdev
Ch Bd: Martin E Franklin
CFO: Sanjiv Khattri
Ex VP: Benjamin Gliklich
Board of Directors: Ian G H Ashken, Nicolas Berggruen, Michael F Goss, Ryan Israel, E Stanley O'neal

D-U-N-S 12-471-5827
PLATINUM CORRAL LLC
GOLDEN CORRAL
521 New Bridge St, Jacksonville, NC 28540-5430
Tel (910) 347-3971 *Founded/Ownrshp* 1996
Sales 61.5MM[E] *EMP* 1,500[E]
SIC 5812 Restaurant, family: chain
Pt: Billy Sewell
**Pt:* Kirby Mitchels

PLATINUM EQUITY
See FINN HOLDING CORP

D-U-N-S 83-760-1723 IMP/EXP
PLATINUM EQUITY LLC
360 N Crescent Dr Bldg S, Beverly Hills, CA 90210-2529
Tel (310) 712-1850 *Founded/Ownrshp* 1997
Sales 12.4MMM[E] *EMP* 50,038
SIC 6726 Investment offices
Pt: Louis Samson
Pt: Mary Ann Sigler
Ofcr: David Anglin
VP: David Glatt
VP: Angelo Perez
Off Admin: Jacqueline Desmond
Snr Mgr: Jon Hall

D-U-N-S 08-047-7553
PLATINUM EQUITY PARTNERS LLC
360 N Crescent Dr, Beverly Hills, CA 90210-2529
Tel (310) 712-1850 *Founded/Ownrshp* 2003
Sales 1.7MMM[E] *EMP* 6,481[E]
SIC 6726 Investment offices
Ch Bd: Tom Gores
**CFO:* Mary Ann Sigler

D-U-N-S 12-584-2570
PLATINUM PARTNERS VALUE ARBITRAGE FUND LP
250 W 55th St Fl 14, New York, NY 10019-7599
Tel (212) 581-0500 *Founded/Ownrshp* 2002
Sales 100.0MM *EMP* 15
SIC 6726 Management investment funds, closed-end
Pt: Mark Nordlicht
COO: Joan Janczewski

PLATO LEARNING
See EDMENTUM INC

D-U-N-S 00-941-8740 IMP
PLATT ELECTRIC SUPPLY INC
(*Suby of* REXEL ENERGY SOLUTIONS) ★
10605 Sw Allen Blvd, Beaverton, OR 97005-4896
Tel (503) 641-6121 *Founded/Ownrshp* 1953, 2014
Sales 268.0MM[E] *EMP* 714
SIC 5063

D-U-N-S 04-780-3051 IMP/EXP
PLATTE CHEMICAL CO
(*Suby of* CROP PRODUCTION SERVICES INC) ★
3005 Rocky Mountain Ave, Loveland, CO 80538-9001
Tel (970) 685-3300 *Founded/Ownrshp* 1970
Sales 225.6MM[E] *EMP* 340
SIC 2879 Agricultural chemicals
Pr: Thomas E Warner
VP: Warren Hammerbeck

D-U-N-S 07-575-7948
PLATTE RIVER POWER AUTHORITY (INC)
2000 E Horsetooth Rd, Fort Collins, CO 80525-5721
Tel (970) 229-5332 *Founded/Ownrshp* 1975
Sales 199.8MM *EMP* 172
Accts Bkd Llp Denver Colorado
SIC 4911 Distribution, electric power; Generation, electric power
CFO: David D Smalley
Comm Dir: Pete Hoelscher
Prgrm Mgr: Joel Danforth
Div Mgr: Jason Frisbie
Genl Mgr: Brian Moeck
IT Man: Dan North
IT Man: Kirby Pilcher
Secur Mgr: Carol Ballantine
Genl Couns: Ryan Donovan
Genl Couns: Caroline Schmiedt

D-U-N-S 78-430-5380
PLATTE RIVER VENTURES LLC
200 Fillmore St Ste 200, Denver, CO 80206-5024
Tel (303) 292-7300 *Founded/Ownrshp* 1999
Sales 155.9MM[E] *EMP* 445
SIC 6799 Venture capital companies
VP: Michelle Eidson

PLATTE VALLEY MEDICAL CENTER
See BRIGHTON COMMUNITY HOSPITAL ASSOCIATION

D-U-N-S 07-647-8270
PLATTE VALLEY MEDICAL CENTER FOUNDATION
1600 Prairie Center Pkwy, Brighton, CO 80601-4006
Tel (303) 498-1600 *Founded/Ownrshp* 1958
Sales 94.8MM *EMP* 475
SIC 8062 General medical & surgical hospitals
CEO: John Hicks

**CFO:* Harold Dupper
**VP:* Cheryl Bentley
Doctor: Jeremiah Bartley
Doctor: Camela Billick
Doctor: Stephen Cardos
Doctor: Keith Cook
Doctor: Anthony Euser
Doctor: Dane Floberg
Doctor: Felix Gaido
Doctor: John James

D-U-N-S 03-526-8809
PLAYCORE HOLDINGS INC
(*Suby of* PLAYCORE HOLDINGS LLC) ★
401 Chestnut St Ste 410, Chattanooga, TN 37402-4935
Tel (423) 756-0015 *Founded/Ownrshp* 2000
Sales 212.3MM[E] *EMP* 576
SIC 3949 Playground equipment
CEO: Robert Farnsworth
Pr: Chris Allen
COO: John L Conely
COO: Conely John
**CFO:* Richard E Ruegger
VP: Spencer Cheak
VP: Jesse Taylor
VP: Tom Whittier

D-U-N-S 00-273-8545 IMP/EXP
PLAYCORE HOLDINGS LLC
401 Chestnut St Ste 410, Chattanooga, TN 37402-4935
Tel (877) 762-7563 *Founded/Ownrshp* 2000
Sales 251.1MM[E] *EMP* 700
SIC 2452 3949 3448 Prefabricated wood buildings; Playground equipment; Prefabricated metal buildings
Pr: Robert A Farnsworth
**CFO:* Richard E Ruegger

D-U-N-S 01-486-9887 IMP/EXP
PLAYCORE WISCONSIN INC
(*Suby of* PLAYCORE HOLDINGS INC) ★
401 Chestnut St Ste 410, Chattanooga, TN 37402-4935
Tel (423) 265-7529 *Founded/Ownrshp* 2000
Sales 101.6MM[E] *EMP* 475
SIC 3949 Playground equipment
CEO: Robert Farnsworth
**COO:* John Conely
**CFO:* Richard E Ruegger
**Sr VP:* Lisa Moore
**Sr VP:* Jim Underwood
VP: Bob Barron
**VP:* Joni Manley

D-U-N-S 19-379-9918 IMP/EXP
PLAYPOWER INC
11515 Vanstory Dr Ste 100, Huntersville, NC 28078-6300
Tel (704) 875-6550 *Founded/Ownrshp* 2005
Sales 263.4MM[E] *EMP* 821
SIC 3949 Playground equipment
CEO: Joseph Copeland
CFO: Michael Pruss
Treas: Karla Cooper-Wright
Chf Mktg O: Lynne Vandeveer
Ex VP: Mark Hardy
VP: Ken Schober
Genl Mgr: Kevin Walker
CTO: David York
Prd Mgr: Nick Witt

D-U-N-S 04-939-6471
■ **PLAYTEX MANUFACTURING INC**
(*Suby of* PLAYTEX PRODUCTS LLC) ★
50 N Dupont Hwy, Dover, DE 19901-4261
Tel (302) 678-6000 *Founded/Ownrshp* 1995
Sales 87.3MM[E] *EMP* 200[E]
SIC 2676 2844 2842 Sanitary paper products; Toilet preparations; Specialty cleaning, polishes & sanitation goods
CEO: Michael R Gallagher
VP: Chris Crowell
VP: Russ Reece

D-U-N-S 19-855-4354 EXP
■ **PLAYTEX PRODUCTS LLC**
(*Suby of* EDGEWELL PERSONAL CARE CO) ★
6 Research Dr Ste 400, Shelton, CT 06484-6228
Tel (203) 944-5500 *Founded/Ownrshp* 2007
Sales 492.0MM[E] *EMP* 1,250
SIC 2676 3069 2844 3842 Tampons, sanitary: made from purchased paper; Diapers, paper (disposable): made from purchased paper; Nipples, rubber; Baby pacifiers, rubber; Bibs, vulcanized rubber or rubberized fabric; Water bottles, rubber; Suntan lotions & oils; Hair preparations, including shampoos; Towelettes, premoistened; Gloves, safety
Sr VP: Andrew Abraham
Sr VP: Irwin Butensky
VP: Perry Beadon
VP: Parker Gilbert
DP Exec: Tammy Stephens
Dir IT: Philip Lawlor
Sfty Mgr: Peter Maclachlan
Snr PM: Pete Lease

PLAZA CELLARS
See PLAZA PROVISION CO (PUERTO RICO)

PLAZA CHMOTHERAPY INFUSION CTR
See COLUMBIA PLAZA MEDICAL CENTER OF FORT WORTH SUBSIDIARY LP

D-U-N-S 61-178-6468 IMP
PLAZA CONSTRUCTION LLC
1065 Avenue Of The Americ, New York, NY 10018-0828
Tel (212) 849-4800 *Founded/Ownrshp* 1986
Sales 457.2MM[E] *EMP* 271
SIC 1542 8741 Nonresidential construction; Construction management
CEO: Richard Wood
**Pr:* Michael Gabbay
**CFO:* Joseph Parrone
**Sr VP:* Lester Rivelis
VP: Peter Hulbert
VP: Alan Kensek
**VP:* Christopher Mills
VP: Michael Moore
Exec: Paul Fleckenstein

Exec: Allen Kasden
Exec: Christian Lipke
Exec: Chris Mills
Exec: Alan Sparn
Exec: Robert Thompson

D-U-N-S 92-821-9682 IMP
PLAZA GROUP INC
10375 Richmond Ave # 1620, Houston, TX 77042-4292
Tel (713) 266-0707 *Founded/Ownrshp* 1994
Sales 288.7MM *EMP* 18^E
Accts Uhy Llp Houston Tx
SIC 8742 Marketing consulting services
Pr: Randy E Velarde
CFO: Bob Imm
Genl Mgr: Laura Sanchez
Sls Dir: Venere Vitiello
Sls Dir: Steve Willett
Sls Mgr: Garrett Velarde

D-U-N-S 01-099-4114
PLAZA HOME MORTGAGE INC
4820 Eastgate Mall # 100, San Diego, CA 92121-1993
Tel (858) 346-1200 *Founded/Ownrshp* 2000
Sales NA *EMP* 700
SIC 6162 Mortgage bankers & correspondents
Pr: Kevin Parra
**Ex VP:* James Cutri
**Ex VP:* Michael Fontaine
Sr VP: Julie Manson
**Sr VP:* Michael Modell
**Sr VP:* Karin Neidhart
IT Man: Bob Gerardi

PLAZA HOTEL
See CPS 1 REALTY LP

D-U-N-S 05-732-4246
PLAZA HOTEL & CASINO LLC
1 S Main St, Las Vegas, NV 89101-6370
Tel (702) 386-2110 *Founded/Ownrshp* 2004
Sales 73.5MM^E *EMP* 1,300
SIC 7011 Casino hotel
CEO: John D Gaughan
V Ch: J K Houssels
CFO: Travis Anderson
**CFO:* Alan J Woody
VP: Kenny Epstein

D-U-N-S 83-221-2075
PLAZA MANOR PRESERVATION LP
SUMMER CREST APARTMENTS
2615 E Plaza Blvd, National City, CA 91950-4017
Tel (619) 475-2125 *Founded/Ownrshp* 2000
Sales 34.4MM^E *EMP* 1,828
SIC 6531 Real estate agents & managers
Prin: Larry Lipton
Pt: Las Palmas Foundation
Pt: Michael Herrington

D-U-N-S 09-004-6996 IMP/EXP
PLAZA PROVISION CO (PUERTO RICO)
PLAZA CELLARS
Carretera 165 Esq, Guaynabo, PR 00965
Tel (787) 781-2070 *Founded/Ownrshp* 1960
Sales 221.8MM^E *EMP* 320
Accts Deloitte & Touche Llp San Jua
SIC 5182 4222 2841 Liquor; Storage, frozen or refrigerated goods; Dishwashing compounds
Ch Bd: James N Cimino
**Pr:* Angel Torres
**CFO:* Jos A Vlez
Dist Mgr: Maribel Renta
Sls Mgr: Luis Marrero

D-U-N-S 02-971-5133 IMP
PLAZA TIRE SERVICE INC
2075 Corporate Cir, Cape Girardeau, MO 63703-7671
Tel (573) 334-5036 *Founded/Ownrshp* 1963
Sales 229.0MM^E *EMP* 300
SIC 5014 5531 7538 Automobile tires & tubes; Automotive tires; General automotive repair shops
Pr: Mark E Rhodes
**Treas:* Scott Rhodes

D-U-N-S 00-632-4669 IMP/EXP
PLAZE INC
PLZ AEROSCIENCE
(*Suby of* PLZ AEROSCIENCE CORP) ★
105 Bolte Ln, Saint Clair, MO 63077-3219
Tel (630) 543-7600 *Founded/Ownrshp* 1940
Sales 252.3MM^E *EMP* 150
SIC 5169 2819 Aerosols; Charcoal (carbon), activated
Ch Bd: John Ferring IV
**CFO:* Ben Lacroffe

PLC CENTER
See RADWELL INTERNATIONAL INC

PLCB
See LIQUOR CONTROL BOARD PENNSYLVANIA

D-U-N-S 93-205-2801
PLEASANT HILL PRESERVATION LP
2501 Anken Dr Ofc, Austin, TX 78741-4561
Tel (512) 447-7244 *Founded/Ownrshp* 2009
Sales 22.3MM^E *EMP* 3,900
SIC 6513 Apartment building operators
Prin: Don Wilson
Sr VP: Leeann Morein

D-U-N-S 10-000-8119
PLEASANT VALLEY SCHOOL DISTRICT
EL DESCANSO
600 Temple Ave, Camarillo, CA 93010-4835
Tel (805) 445-8637 *Founded/Ownrshp* 1993
Sales 58.4MM^E *EMP* 1,051
Accts Vicenti Lloyd & Stutzman Llp
SIC 8211 Public elementary & secondary schools
CEO: Suzanne Kitchens
**Pr:* Bob Rust
MIS Dir: Rob James
Schl Brd P: Kelly Long
HC Dir: Carol Bjordaho

D-U-N-S 08-202-5511
PLEASANT VALLEY SCHOOL DISTRICT
2233 Route 115 Ste 100, Brodheadsville, PA 18322-7103
Tel (570) 402-1000 *Founded/Ownrshp* 1956
Sales 76.0MM *EMP* 1,100
SIC 8211 Public elementary & secondary schools
VP: Thomas Murphy
Prin: John Gress
HC Dir: Thomasine Falcone

D-U-N-S 08-071-5139
PLEASANTON UNIFIED SCHOOL DISTRICT
4665 Bernal Ave, Pleasanton, CA 94566-7449
Tel (925) 462-5500 *Founded/Ownrshp* 1867
Sales 88.9MM^E *EMP* 1,700
SIC 8211 Public senior high school; Elementary school; Secondary school
DP Dir: Andrew Di Di Girolamo
Pr Dir: Patrick Gannon
Teacher Pr: Aileen Parsons
Psych: Rebecca Jordan

D-U-N-S 05-337-8626
PLEASANTS CONSTRUCTION INC
24024 Frederick Rd, Clarksburg, MD 20871-9718
Tel (301) 428-0800 *Founded/Ownrshp* 1970
Sales 94.9MM^E *EMP* 400
SIC 1794 1623 1611 Excavation & grading, building construction; Water & sewer line construction; Underground utilities contractor; Highway & street paving contractor
Pr: William D Pleasants Jr
COO: Ginger Nance
CFO: Paul Minkin
Sr VP: Mark B Singleton
**VP:* Eric Newquist
VP: Tom Rudesill
Sales Exec: Tim Cook

D-U-N-S 01-430-7867
PLETHORA BUSINESSES
2117 W Orangewood Ave A, Orange, CA 92868-1958
Tel (714) 255-8862 *Founded/Ownrshp* 2002
Sales 120.0MM *EMP* 3
SIC 6211 Security brokers & dealers
Prin: Dora Lanza
**VP:* Michael Jeub
**VP:* Nickolas Lanza

D-U-N-S 92-910-9452
PLEX SYSTEMS INC
900 Tower Dr Ste 1400, Troy, MI 48098-2832
Tel (248) 391-8001 *Founded/Ownrshp* 2006
Sales 161.0MM^E *EMP* 385^E
SIC 7374 Data processing & preparation
CEO: Jason Blessing
Pt: Tina Holm
**CFO:* Don Clarke
**Sec:* Michael Twarozynski
**Chf Mktg O:* Heidi Melin
Ex VP: Thomas Mackey
VP: Raj Amin
VP: Patrick Fetterman
VP: Todd Weeks
Snr Sftwr: Jonathan Demski
Snr Sftwr: Mark Meier
Board of Directors: Edwin J Gillis, Mike Hilton, Kevin Parker

D-U-N-S 09-854-4398 IMP/EXP
▲ PLEXUS CORP
1 Plexus Way, Neenah, WI 54956-3045
Tel (920) 969-6000 *Founded/Ownrshp* 1979
Sales 2.5MMM *EMP* 14,000
Tkr Sym PLXS *Exch* NGS
SIC 3672 3825 Printed circuit boards; Test equipment for electronic & electric measurement; Meters: electric, pocket, portable, panelboard, etc.
Ch Bd: Dean A Foate
**Pr:* Todd P Kelsey
COO: Steven J Frisch
CFO: Patrick J Jermain
Ofcr: Angelo M Ninivaggi
Sr VP: Ronald Darroch
VP: Joseph E Mauthe
VP: Scott Theune
Board of Directors: Ralf R Boer, Stephen P Cortinovis, David J Drury, Joann M Eisenhart, Rainer Jueckstock, Peter Kelly, Phil R Martens, Michael V Schrock

D-U-N-S 61-243-0012
PLEXUS HOLDINGS INC
PLEXUS LEARNING CENTER
9145 E Pima Center Pkwy, Scottsdale, AZ 85258-4627
Tel (480) 998-3490 *Founded/Ownrshp* 2005
Sales 121.5MM^E *EMP* 184
SIC 5149 Health foods
CEO: Tarl Robinson
Sls Dir: James Elliott

PLEXUS LEARNING CENTER
See PLEXUS HOLDINGS INC

D-U-N-S 02-408-6029
PLG HOLDINGS INC
1 Greenway Plz Ste 400, Houston, TX 77046-0102
Tel (713) 439-1010 *Founded/Ownrshp* 2009
Sales 28.5MM^E *EMP* 1,000
SIC 4214 Local trucking with storage
Pr: Robert Stull
Pr: Ike Nixon
COO: James Armstrong
CFO: Marty Brogden
VP: Lou Riccitelli
CTO: James Stephens
IT Man: James Vincent
Opers Mgr: Elvis Rodriguez
Opers Mgr: Gary Storey
Mktg Mgr: Christine Prior

D-U-N-S 07-875-8292
PLH GROUP INC
400 Las Colinas Blvd E, Irving, TX 75039-5579
Tel (214) 272-0500 *Founded/Ownrshp* 2012
Sales 668.4MM^E *EMP* 1,302^E
SIC 1623 Pipeline construction
Pr: Mark Alan Crowson
**CFO:* Ken M Dodgen
**Ofcr:* Daniel S Terrell
Sr VP: Matthew C Compher
Sr VP: Lacy Kiser
Sr VP: Thomas P McShane
Sr VP: Dan A Reyero
Sr VP: Russelll Smith
VP: Jeffrey Armbruster
Ex Dir: Perry Cole

D-U-N-S 80-108-6570 EXP
■ PLIANT LLC
ROLL-O-SHEETS
(*Suby of* BERRY PLASTICS CORP) ★
1701 Golf Rd Ste 2-900, Rolling Meadows, IL 60008-4255
Tel (812) 424-2904 *Founded/Ownrshp* 2009
Sales 224.1MM^E *EMP* 2,800
SIC 3081 2673 3089 Plastic film & sheet; Bags: plastic, laminated & coated; Food storage & frozen food bags, plastic; Air mattresses, plastic
Pr: Harold Davis
Pr: Len Azzaro
**COO:* R David Corey
**CFO:* Thomas C Spielberger
Treas: Chris M Nielsen
Sr VP: Paul Franz
Sr VP: Greg E Gard
**Sr VP:* Joseph J Kwederis
**VP:* Stephen Auburn
VP: Steve Auburn
VP: Keith Brechtelsbauer
VP: Thomas E McShane

D-U-N-S 00-797-1419 IMP
PLIMPTON & HILLS CORP (CT)
2 Brainard Rd, Hartford, CT 06114-1604
Tel (860) 522-4233 *Founded/Ownrshp* 1902
Sales 150.2MM^E *EMP* 150
SIC 5074 5085 Plumbing fittings & supplies; Heating equipment (hydronic); Mill supplies
Pr: Calvin Tripp Hills

D-U-N-S 14-456-0448 EXP
PLM HOLDING CO LLC
(*Suby of* CAMBRIAN COAL CORP) ★
200 Allison Blvd, Corbin, KY 40701-7964
Tel (606) 523-4444 *Founded/Ownrshp* 2015
Sales 158.5MM^E *EMP* 900
SIC 1222 Bituminous coal-underground mining
CEO: James Booth
**CFO:* Mark Teague
VP: Scott Blackburn
VP: Deirdre Brown
VP: Charles Hinson
VP: Clark Taylor
Dir IT: Jeff Sharpe
Sfty Mgr: Dave Blankenship

D-U-N-S 80-897-2913
PLOCHER CONSTRUCTION CO INC
2808 Thole Plocher Rd, Highland, IL 62249-4716
Tel (618) 654-9408 *Founded/Ownrshp* 1991
Sales 99.5MM *EMP* 50
Accts Gateway Business Services Inc
SIC 1542 Commercial & office building, new construction
Pr: Scott Plocher
**Ex VP:* Gene Plocher
**VP:* Chad Plocher
**VP:* Chuck Wagner

D-U-N-S 96-230-6218 IMP/EXP
PLOW & HEARTH LLC
HEARTHSONG
(*Suby of* ASHFORD COURT RICHMOND CI) ★
7021 Wolftown Hood Rd, Madison, VA 22727-2200
Tel (540) 948-2272 *Founded/Ownrshp* 2009
Sales 85.3MM^E *EMP* 199
SIC 5961 5251 Mail order house; Hardware
CFO: Dana Pappas
Area Mgr: Heather Bogdanowicz
Store Mgr: Margaret Layne
Store Mgr: Michelle Schaefer
Manager: Susan Couch
Mktg Mgr: Brianne Forst
Sales Asso: Tiffany Jenkins
Art Dir: Pat Cornwall
Snr Mgr: Karen Weaver

PLS CHECK CASHIERS
See PLS FINANCIAL SERVICES INC

D-U-N-S 13-505-1519
PLS FINANCIAL SERVICES INC
PLS CHECK CASHIERS
1 S Wacker Dr Fl 36, Chicago, IL 60606-4603
Tel (312) 491-7300 *Founded/Ownrshp* 1997
Sales 510.4MM^E *EMP* 3,800^E
SIC 7389 6798 Financial services; Real estate investment trusts
Pr: Dan Wolfberg
**CFO:* Larry Roach
Chf Mktg O: Aaron Caid
Sr VP: Mary J Downes
VP: Michael Petrovich
VP: Michael Williams
Dir IT: Ed Pieklo
Dir IT: Zabdi Rosero
IT Man: Daniela Nunez
Netwrk Eng: Roman Mazurok
Mktg Dir: Kristin Dunn

D-U-N-S 07-879-1257
PLS GROUP INC
1 S Wacker Dr Fl 36, Chicago, IL 60606-4603
Tel (312) 491-7300 *Founded/Ownrshp* 2011
Sales 255.6MM *EMP* 3,800
SIC 6719 Investment holding companies, except banks
Pr: Daniel Wolfberg

PLS LOGISTICS SERVICES
See PITTSBURGH LOGISTICS SYSTEMS INC

D-U-N-S 08-690-8444 IMP
▲ PLUG POWER INC
968 Albany Shaker Rd, Latham, NY 12110-1428
Tel (518) 782-7700 *Founded/Ownrshp* 1997
Sales 103.2MM *EMP* 439^E
Accts Kpmg Llp Albany New York
Tkr Sym PLUG *Exch* NAS
SIC 2679 Fuel cell forms, cardboard: made from purchased material
Pr: Andrew J Marsh
**Ch Bd:* George C McNamee
COO: Keith C Schmid
CFO: Paul B Middleton
Sr VP: Gerard L Conway Jr
VP: Jose Luis Crespo
Snr Mgr: Eric Smith
Board of Directors: Larry G Garberding, Maureen O Helmer, Douglas T Hickey, Gregory L Kenausis, Xavier Pontone, Johannes M Roth, Gary K Willis

D-U-N-S 62-755-5626
■ PLUM CREEK MANUFACTURING LP
(*Suby of* PLUM CREEK TIMBERLANDS LP) ★
999 3rd Ave Ste 4300, Seattle, WA 98104-4096
Tel (206) 467-3600 *Founded/Ownrshp* 1989
Sales 243.6MM^E *EMP* 1,600
SIC 2421 2436 2493 5031 Lumber: rough, sawed or planed; Plywood, softwood; Fiberboard, other vegetable pulp; Lumber, plywood & millwork
CEO: Rick R Holley
Pt: James A Kraft
VP: Elwood Coley Jr
VP: David Lambert Sr

D-U-N-S 00-696-5235
PLUM CREEK TIMBER CO INC
601 Union St Ste 3100, Seattle, WA 98101-1374
Tel (206) 467-3600 *Founded/Ownrshp* 1989
Sales 1.4MMM *EMP* 1,325^E
SIC 6798 1311

D-U-N-S 60-438-2754
■ PLUM CREEK TIMBERLANDS LP
(*Suby of* WEYERHAEUSER CO) ★
601 Union St Ste 3100, Seattle, WA 98101-1374
Tel (206) 467-3600 *Founded/Ownrshp* 2016
Sales 282.8MM^E *EMP* 10^E
SIC 2421 2436 2493 5031 Lumber: rough, sawed or planed; Plywood, softwood; Fiberboard, other vegetable pulp; Lumber, plywood & millwork; Plywood; Medium density fiberboard
CEO: Rick Holley
CFO: William R Brown
Ex VP: Tom Lindquist
Sr VP: Michael Covey
Sr VP: Russell Hagen
Sr VP: James Kilberg
Sr VP: David Lambert
Sr VP: Timothy Punke
VP: David Brown
VP: James A Kraft
VP: Mark Miller
VP: Thomas Reed
Exec: Christine Wiltz
Comm Dir: Kate Tate
Mng Ofcr: Mark Waterman

PLUMB PAK MEDICAL
See KEENEY MANUFACTURING CO

D-U-N-S 00-798-8397
PLUMB SUPPLY CO LLC
(*Suby of* GLAS-COL DIV) ★
1622 Ne 51st Ave, Des Moines, IA 50313-2194
Tel (515) 262-9511 *Founded/Ownrshp* 1946
Sales 124.4MM^E *EMP* 255
Accts Bkd Llp Indianapolis Indian
SIC 5074 5075 Plumbing & hydronic heating supplies; Pipes & fittings, plastic; Heating equipment (hydronic); Warm air heating equipment & supplies
Ch Bd: Curt Brighton
Pr: Scott Anshutz
Treas: Alan Darnielle
VP: John Templeton
VP Mktg: Robert Phillips
Board of Directors: John A Templeton III, John A Templeton

D-U-N-S 00-694-5620
PLUMBERS SUPPLY CO
PLUMBERS SUPPLY CO BOWL GREEN
1000 E Main St, Louisville, KY 40206-1841
Tel (502) 582-2261 *Founded/Ownrshp* 1926
Sales 127.6MM^E *EMP* 225
SIC 5074 5085 Plumbing & hydronic heating supplies; Plumbing fittings & supplies; Industrial supplies
Pr: Jay B Johnson
**Ch:* John J Werst
**Treas:* James Wilson
**VP:* Douglas Madison
Opers Mgr: John Franklin
Opers Mgr: John Skees
Manager: David McIntosh

D-U-N-S 01-951-7093 IMP
PLUMBERS SUPPLY CO
CENTRAL SUPPLY
429 Church St, New Bedford, MA 02745-5101
Tel (508) 985-4966 *Founded/Ownrshp* 1977
Sales 101.6MM^E *EMP* 160
Accts Rsm Mcgladrey
SIC 5074 5084 5082 Plumbing & hydronic heating supplies; Industrial machinery & equipment; Construction & mining machinery
Pr: James T Jones
**Treas:* Kevin J Jones
VP: Scott Ritchey
VP Sls: Lenny Dipasqua

PLUMBERS SUPPLY CO BOWL GREEN
See PLUMBERS SUPPLY CO

PLUMBEST
See JONES STEPHENS CORP

D-U-N-S 06-533-3338
PLUMBING DISTRIBUTORS INC
P D I
1025 Old Norcross Rd, Lawrenceville, GA 30046-4323
Tel (770) 963-9231 *Founded/Ownrshp* 1973
Sales 105.7MM *EMP* 108
SIC 5074 Plumbing fittings & supplies
CEO: Lyn Wright

Pr: Coley Herrin
Sls Mgr: Kenny Rogers

PLUMBING WAREHOUSE, THE
See LCR-M LIMITED PARTNERSHIP

PLUMBROOK FAMILY MEDICINE
See MOUNT CLEMENS REGIONAL MEDICAL CENTER

D-U-N-S 10-597-6836
PLUMCHOICE INC
PLUMCHOICE ONLINE PC SERVICES
900 Chelmsford St Ofc 1, Lowell, MA 01851-8100
Tel (866) 811-3321 *Founded/Ownrshp* 2004
Sales 113.8MM^E *EMP* 760^E
SIC 7378 Computer maintenance & repair
Pr: David Shimoni
* *Ch Bd:* Theodore Werth
* *COO:* Fred King
* *CFO:* James E Carr
Ex VP: James S Williams III
VP: Dave Hauser
Dir Bus: Al Koch
* *CIO:* Charles Welti
* *CTO:* Chanchal Samanta
QA Dir: Bill Yerkes
Software D: Joaquin Agramonte

PLUMCHOICE ONLINE PC SERVICES
See PLUMCHOICE INC

PLUMMERS FURNITURE
See SCANDINAVIAN DESIGNS INC

D-U-N-S 80-580-2485 IMP
PLUMROSE USA INC
(*Suby of* DANISH CROWN A/S)
1901 Butterfield Rd # 305, Downers Grove, IL 60515-7915
Tel (732) 257-6600 *Founded/Ownrshp* 1992
Sales 580.0MM *EMP* 1,160
SIC 2011 5147 2013 5149 Hams & picnics from meat slaughtered on site; Bacon, slab & sliced from meat slaughtered on site; Meats & meat products; Sausages & other prepared meats; Specialty food items
CEO: Dave Schanzer
Sr VP: Freddy Mortsenen
* *VP:* Freddy Mortensen
Dir IT: Jackues Hodges

D-U-N-S 04-400-5160
PLURALSIGHT LLC
182 N Union Ave, Farmington, UT 84025-2907
Tel (801) 784-9007 *Founded/Ownrshp* 2011
Sales 130.0MM *EMP* 500
SIC 8742 Training & development consultant
Chf Mktg O: Brett Barlow
* *Ofcr:* Heather Zynczak
VP: Jeff Adams
VP: Jody Bailey
VP: Dana Gagnon
VP: Geoffrey Grosenbach
VP: Gilbert Lee
VP: Andy Rahden
VP: Chad Sollis
VP: Chad Utley
* *Dir Risk M:* Joe Dibartolomeo
Creative D: Phil Hunter
Board of Directors: Gary Crittenden, Tim Maudlin, Brad Rencher

D-U-N-S 79-335-9456
PLUS GROUP INC
JOBS PLUS
7425 Janes Ave Ste 201, Woodridge, IL 60517-2332
Tel (630) 515-0500 *Founded/Ownrshp* 1992
Sales 12.0MM *EMP* 1,500
SIC 7361 7363 Employment agencies; Temporary help service
CEO: John M Seelander
* *Pr:* Suzanne Seelander
* *Ch:* Marilyn Seelander

PLUS ONE CLINICS
See PLUS ONE HOLDINGS INC

D-U-N-S 80-317-4093
PLUS ONE HOLDINGS INC
PLUS ONE CLINICS
77 Water St Fl 15, New York, NY 10005-4406
Tel (212) 269-2896 *Founded/Ownrshp* 1991
Sales 99.1MM^E *EMP* 915
SIC 6719 Investment holding companies, except banks
CEO: Chris Ciatto
CFO: David Todhunter
* *Sr VP:* John Holding
* *VP:* Veronica Hyatt
* *Ex Dir:* Mike Motta
Netwrk Eng: Elazar Broad

D-U-N-S 07-883-7407
▲ PLY GEM HOLDINGS INC
5020 Weston Pkwy Ste 400, Cary, NC 27513-2322
Tel (919) 677-3900 *Founded/Ownrshp* 2004
Sales 1.8MMM *EMP* 8,669^E
Tkr Sym PGEM *Exch* NYS
SIC 2431 2952 Millwork; Siding materials
Ch Bd: Gary E Robinette
COO: John C Wayne
CFO: Shawn K Poe
Sr VP: Timothy D Johnson
Sr VP: David N Schmoll
VP: Brian Boyle
VP: Ralph Bruno
VP: Mark Montgomery
VP: David Schmoll
VP: Jennifer Ward
VP: Thomas Winters
Board of Directors: Jeffrey T Barber, John Forbes, Michael Haley, Timothy T Hall, Frederick J Iseman, Mary K Rhinehart Janice E

D-U-N-S 01-572-4996
■ PLY GEM INDUSTRIES INC
(*Suby of* PLY GEM HOLDINGS INC) ★
5020 Weston Pkwy Ste 400, Cary, NC 27513-2322
Tel (919) 677-3900 *Founded/Ownrshp* 1987, 2010
Sales 1.5MMM^E *EMP* 4,300
SIC 2431 Windows, wood; Doors, wood
Pr: Gary E Robinette
* *CFO:* Shawn K Poe
Dir IT: Dan Church
VP Sls: Kevin Riedy
Mktg Mgr: Andrew Thompson
Manager: Brad Fisher
Sls Mgr: Keelan Jones
Sls Mgr: Richard Turner
Genl Couns: Timothy Johnson
Board of Directors: Jeffrey T Barber

D-U-N-S 80-835-5510
PLY GEM PACIFIC WINDOWS CORP
5001 D St Nw, Auburn, WA 98001-2415
Tel (253) 850-9000 *Founded/Ownrshp* 2006
Sales 88.2MM^E *EMP* 1,000
SIC 1751 Window & door (prefabricated) installation
Pr: Lynn J Morstad
* *Pr:* Art Steinhafel
* *Ch:* Gary Robinette
* *VP:* Brian Boyle
* *VP:* Shawn Poe
Manager: Dirk R Myers

D-U-N-S 96-363-5748
PLY GEM PRIME HOLDINGS INC
2600 Grand Blvd Ste 900, Kansas City, MO 64108-4626
Tel (888) 975-9436 *Founded/Ownrshp* 2006
Sales 1.1MMM^E *EMP* 4,300
SIC 2431 Millwork

D-U-N-S 96-342-4994
PLY GEM SIDING GROUP
(*Suby of* PLY GEM PRIME HOLDINGS INC) ★
2600 Grand Blvd, Kansas City, MO 64108-4630
Tel (816) 426-8200 *Founded/Ownrshp* 2010
Sales 1.1MMM *EMP* 1,500
SIC 3272 Building materials, except block or brick: concrete
Pr: John Buckley
* *VP:* Rick Veach
* *VP Sls:* Chris Brown

D-U-N-S 87-886-0535
PLYMOUTH PUBLIC SCHOOLS
253 S Meadow Rd, Plymouth, MA 02360-9200
Tel (508) 830-4348 *Founded/Ownrshp* 1995
Sales 74.9MM^E *EMP* 1,630
SIC 8211 Public elementary & secondary schools
Dir IT: Chris Baker
Dir IT: Ann Ross

D-U-N-S 10-946-9580
PLYMOUTH ROCK ASSURANCE CORP
(*Suby of* PLYMOUTH ROCK CO INC) ★
695 Atlantic Ave Fl 7, Boston, MA 02111-2605
Tel (866) 353-6292 *Founded/Ownrshp* 1983
Sales NA *EMP* 550^E
SIC 6331 Property damage insurance
Prin: Hal Belodoff
* *Sec:* James Nathan Bailey
* *Chf Mktg O:* Keith Jensen
VP: Jim Flynn
VP: Paula Gold
VP: Bob Hallinan
VP: Eric Kramer
VP: Frank Palmer
Mng Dir: Andrew Brown
Mng Dir: Jennifer Gregor
Mng Dir: Patti West

D-U-N-S 10-118-8449
PLYMOUTH ROCK CO INC
695 Atlantic Ave, Boston, MA 02111-2605
Tel (617) 720-1620 *Founded/Ownrshp* 1982
Sales NA *EMP* 1,000^E
SIC 6331 Property damage insurance; Fire, marine & casualty insurance & carriers
Pr: Hal Belodoff
* *CEO:* James M Stone
* *Treas:* James Nathan Bailey
VP: Brendan Kirby
VP: Paul Luongo
S&M/VP: Mark A Sweeney
Mktg Mgr: Tim Quinn
Corp Couns: Kenneth Willis

D-U-N-S 04-981-3314 IMP/EXP
PLYMOUTH TUBE CO (MI)
NONE
29w 150 Warrenville Rd, Warrenville, IL 60555
Tel (630) 393-3550 *Founded/Ownrshp* 1924, 1974
Sales 282.3MM^E *EMP* 800
SIC 3317 3354 Tubes, seamless steel; Tubes, wrought: welded or lock joint; Shapes, extruded aluminum; Tube, extruded or drawn, aluminum
Pr: Donald C Van Pelt Jr
* *Ch Bd:* Donald C Van Pelt Sr
CFO: David Barnes
Ex VP: Frank Daleo
VP: Tom Centa
VP: John Tassone
VP Bus Dev: Scott Morling
Genl Mgr: David Crouch
Genl Mgr: Marvin Dunham
Genl Mgr: Gavin Ford
Opers Mgr: Mike Kennerson
Board of Directors: Lance Foust, Dennis Gudgel, David Kleinman, Deb Lang, Gary Neal, Art Simmons, Tom Weiss

D-U-N-S 07-420-9388
PLYMOUTH-CANTON COMMUNITY SCHOOLS
454 S Harvey St, Plymouth, MI 48170-1717
Tel (734) 416-2700 *Founded/Ownrshp* 1897
Sales 87.9MM^E *EMP* 1,849
SIC 8211 Public elementary & secondary schools
Pr: Kimberley Crouch
Teacher Pr: Elizabeth Bartanian-Gibb

PLZ AEROSCIENCE
See PLAZE INC

D-U-N-S 03-818-2928
PLZ AEROSCIENCE CORP
1005 S Westgate St, Addison, IL 60101-5021
Tel (636) 334-9100 *Founded/Ownrshp* 2015
Sales 254.8MM *EMP* 350
SIC 2813 Aerosols
Pr: Ed Byczynski
* *CFO:* Ben Lacrosse
VP: Michael Magner

D-U-N-S 04-738-2911
PM BEEF HOLDINGS LLC
PM SPECIALTY FOODS
810 7th Ave Fl 29, New York, NY 10019-5871
Tel (507) 831-2761 *Founded/Ownrshp* 1993
Sales 215.3MM^E *EMP* 800
SIC 5144 5147 2011 Poultry & poultry products; Meats & meat products; Meat packing plants
* *Pr:* Greg Miller
* *VP:* John Hagerla

PM COMPANY
See PMCO LLC

D-U-N-S 10-395-5514
PM HOLDINGS INC
(*Suby of* PHOENIX LIFE INSURANCE CO) ★
1 American Row, Hartford, CT 06103-2801
Tel (860) 403-5000 *Founded/Ownrshp* 1981
Sales NA *EMP* 32^E
SIC 6411 6162 6722 6282 6211 6552 Insurance agents; Bond & mortgage companies; Mutual fund sales, on own account; Manager of mutual funds, contract or fee basis; Underwriters, security; Subdividers & developers
Pr: Dona Young
CEO: Robert Fiondella
Treas: David Searfoss
VP: Phillip Mc Loughlin

D-U-N-S 96-861-1280
PM MANAGEMENT - KILLEEN II NC LLC
INDIAN OAKS LIVING CENTER
415 Indian Oaks Dr, Harker Heights, TX 76548-6202
Tel (254) 699-5051 *Founded/Ownrshp* 2011
Sales 201.5MM *EMP* 0^E
SIC 8051 Convalescent home with continuous nursing care

D-U-N-S 03-150-8141 IMP
PM REALTY GROUP LP
1000 Main St Ste 2400, Houston, TX 77002-6359
Tel (713) 209-5800 *Founded/Ownrshp* 1954, 1988
Sales 80.7MM^E *EMP* 1,100
SIC 6531 Real estate agent, commercial
Ch: Rick Kirk
Pr: Jimmy Gunn
CFO: Roger Gregory
CFO: Tom Kennedy
Ex VP: Wade Bowlin
Ex VP: Bruce Edwards
Ex VP: Ernest J Ohnson
Ex VP: Jim Proehl
Sr VP: Matthew G Bittick
Sr VP: Scott Kuklish
Sr VP: Steven Smith
Sr VP: Chris Strickfaden
VP: Shea Byers
VP: Beth Devries
VP: Shane Flanigan
VP: Dan Jones
VP: Geoff Kieffer
VP: Bridget Lancaster
VP: Stacy Langston
VP: Charlotte Liberda
VP: Joe Lugiano

PM SPECIALTY FOODS
See PM BEEF HOLDINGS LLC

PMA CAPITAL
See PMA COMPANIES INC

PMA CAPITAL INSURANCE COMPANY
See EXCALIBUR REINSURANCE CORP

D-U-N-S 11-846-4031
■ PMA COMPANIES INC
PMA CAPITAL
(*Suby of* OLD REPUBLIC INTERNATIONAL CORP) ★
380 Sentry Pkwy Ste 200, Blue Bell, PA 19422-2328
Tel (610) 397-5298 *Founded/Ownrshp* 2010
Sales NA *EMP* 1,362^E
SIC 6331 Workers' compensation insurance; Fire, marine & casualty insurance & carriers; Property damage insurance
Pr: Vincent T Donnelly
Pr: Jack Aspen
* *CFO:* John M Cochrane
* *Ex VP:* Anthony J Ciofani
* *Ex VP:* Stephen L Kibblehouse
* *Ex VP:* John Santulli III
* *Sr VP:* Jennifer J Johnston
* *Sr VP:* Andrew J McGill
VP: Mario Spina
Off Mgr: Sheila Ehret
Off Mgr: Patrice Moody

PMA INSURANCE GROUP, THE
See PENNSYLVANIA MANUFACTURERS ASSOCIATION INSURANCE CO

PMC
See PALISADES MEDICAL CENTER INC

PMC
See POCONO MEDICAL CENTER

D-U-N-S 80-980-4979 IMP/EXP
PMC BIOGENIX INC
(*Suby of* PMC GROUP INC) ★
1231 Pope St, Memphis, TN 38108-2535
Tel (901) 320-5800 *Founded/Ownrshp* 2008
Sales 175.2MM^E *EMP* 500
SIC 2899 Chemical preparations
Ch Bd: Chakra Barti
VP: Bob Jones

D-U-N-S 00-531-8584 IMP/EXP
PMC GLOBAL INC
P C M
12243 Branford St, Sun Valley, CA 91352-1010
Tel (818) 896-1101 *Founded/Ownrshp* 1996
Sales 1.3MMM^E *EMP* 3,600
SIC 3086 3674 2865 2816 3296 2819 Plastics foam products; Semiconductors & related devices; Food dyes or colors, synthetic; Color pigments; Fiberglass insulation; Industrial inorganic chemicals
CEO: Philip E Kamins
* *Pr:* Gary E Kamins
* *CFO:* Thian C Cheong
VP: Doug Borgsdorf
Sls&Mrk Ex: Glen Adams

D-U-N-S 96-812-6888 IMP/EXP
PMC GROUP INC
1288 Route 73 Ste 401, Mount Laurel, NJ 08054-2237
Tel (856) 533-1866 *Founded/Ownrshp* 1997
Sales 322.9MM^E *EMP* 760
SIC 3089 2812 Injection molding of plastics; Plastic hardware & building products; Alkalies & chlorine
CEO: Paritosh M Chakrabarti
COO: Christian Reuland
Exec: John Kohler
Genl Mgr: Risa Shiber
Dir IT: Joseph Mathew

PMC SERVICE COMPANY
See POLK MECHANICAL CO LLC

D-U-N-S 00-228-0683 IMP
PMCO LLC
PM COMPANY
9220 Glades Dr, West Chester, OH 45011-8821
Tel (513) 825-7626 *Founded/Ownrshp* 1905
Sales 96.1MM^E *EMP* 140
SIC 2679 Paper products, converted
Pr: Mike Webster
* *CFO:* Stuart Blair

D-U-N-S 18-937-6119
PMD RESTAURANTS LLC
WENDY'S
2117 Elkhorn Dr, Eugene, OR 97408-1204
Tel (541) 684-7655 *Founded/Ownrshp* 1999
Sales 85.0MM *EMP* 200
SIC 5812 Fast-food restaurant, chain

D-U-N-S 82-831-9488
PMFG INC
14651 Dallas Pkwy Ste 500, Dallas, TX 75254-8809
Tel (214) 357-6181 *Founded/Ownrshp* 2008
Sales 158.6MM *EMP* 500^E
SIC 3569

D-U-N-S 05-747-0361 IMP
PMG INTERNATIONAL LTD
1011 N Frio St, San Antonio, TX 78207-1811
Tel (210) 226-6820 *Founded/Ownrshp* 1997
Sales 195.2MM^E *EMP* 250^E
SIC 5192 Magazines; Books
Pt: Brian L Weiner
* *Pt:* John Hundley
* *Pt:* Bill Salomon

PMI
See PRODUCTION MANAGEMENT INDUSTRIES LLC

PMI EMPLOYEE LEASING
See PAYROLL MANAGEMENT INC

D-U-N-S 83-553-4066
PMI GROUP INC
350 5th Ave, New York, NY 10118-0110
Tel (925) 658-7878 *Founded/Ownrshp* 1993
Sales NA *EMP* 712^E
SIC 6351 6211 Surety insurance; Mortgage guarantee insurance; Warranty insurance, home; Underwriters, security
CEO: L Stephen Smith
* *COO:* Thomas J Clancy
Ex VP: Arthur P Slepian
Sr VP: David W Berson
Sr VP: Charles F Broom
Sr VP: Bonita Z Dorland
Sr VP: Pete Pannes
VP: Jon M Ballard
VP: Jon Ballard
VP: Jonathan CM Chan
VP: Robert H Fore III
VP: John Jelavich
VP: Harrison J Thomas
Board of Directors: Timothy R Eller, Carmine Guerro, Louis G Lower II, Raymond L Ocampo Jr, Charles R Rinehart, John D Roach, Jose H Villarreal, Mary Lee Widener, Ronald H Zech

D-U-N-S 08-918-1424
PMI MORTGAGE INSURANCE CO
P M I
(*Suby of* PMI GROUP INC) ★
350 5th Ave, New York, NY 10118-0110
Tel (925) 658-7878 *Founded/Ownrshp* 1994
Sales NA *EMP* 20^E
SIC 6351 6331 Mortgage guarantee insurance; Fire, marine & casualty insurance
Pr: L Stephen Smith
* *CFO:* Donald Lofe
* *Ex VP:* John Fulford
* *Ex VP:* David Katkov
* *Sr VP:* Victor Bacigalupi
* *Sr VP:* Mark F Milner
* *Sr VP:* Tony Porter

PMMA
See PRESBYTERIAN MANORS INC

PMR
See PRIME MATERIALS RECOVERY INC

D-U-N-S 78-433-0727
PMSI LLC
(*Suby of* HIG CAPITAL LLC) ★
175 Kelsey Ln, Tampa, FL 33619-4336
Tel (813) 626-7788 *Founded/Ownrshp* 2008
Sales NA *EMP* 460

SIC 6331 Workers' compensation insurance
CEO: Emry Sisson
Pr: Paul Difrancesco
Treas: David Farmer
VP: John Bencvivenga
VP: Jeffrey Gurtcheff
VP: Luanne Stark
Ex Dir: Ashley Cabrera
Ex Dir: Rey Quinones
Ex Dir: Teresa Stephenson
CIO: David Lozano
QA Dir: Vinitha Cheruku

D-U-N-S 61-295-8512
PMX AGENCY INC
5 Hanover Sq Fl 6, New York, NY 10004-2706
Tel (212) 387-0300 *Founded/Ownrshp* 1990
Sales 88.9MM^E *EMP* 298
SIC 8742 Marketing consulting services
Co-CEO: Chris Paradysz
Pr: John Ernst
Pr: Rob Stagno
**Co-CEO:* Mike Cousineau
Chf Mktg O: Mary B Keelty
VP: Walter Chistoni
VP: John Iozzia
VP: Valeria Maltoni
VP: Paul Masse
VP: Joe Reid
VP: Bill Sheldon
VP: Nancy Small
Assoc Dir: Diane Martins

D-U-N-S 60-662-8410 IMP
PMX INDUSTRIES INC
(*Suby of* POONGSAN CORPORATION)
5300 Willow Creek Dr Sw, Cedar Rapids, IA 52404-4303
Tel (319) 368-7700 *Founded/Ownrshp* 1989
Sales 430.0MM *EMP* 450
SIC 3366 5051 3444 3364 3351 3331 Copper foundries; Brass foundry; Metals service centers & offices; Sheet metalwork; Nonferrous die-castings except aluminum; Copper rolling & drawing; Primary copper
Pr: S G Kim
Pr: Karen Brown
VP: Tom Bobish
Area Mgr: Jerry Johnson
IT Man: Rouja Daskalova
QI Cn Mgr: Joseph Wells
Mktg Dir: Chol Hwang
Manager: Robert J Carlson
Sls Mgr: Rob Carlson
Sls Mgr: John Kellbach
Sls Mgr: Greg Lombardi

D-U-N-S 08-047-9715 IMP/EXP
PNA HOLDINGS LLC
3150 Pleasant View Rd, Madison, WI 53713
Tel (608) 203-1500 *Founded/Ownrshp* 1999
Sales 77.9MM^E *EMP* 1,280
SIC 5044 5045 5112 7699 Office equipment; Computers, peripherals & software; Stationery & office supplies; Industrial equipment services
Pr: Brook Douglas
VP: Mary Cutshall
Exec: Joe Lalley
Genl Mgr: Patrick Beaudin

D-U-N-S 83-829-1946
■ PNC BANCORP INC
(*Suby of* PNC FINANCIAL SERVICES GROUP INC) ★
300 Delaware Ave, Wilmington, DE 19801-1607
Tel (302) 427-5896 *Founded/Ownrshp* 1995
Sales NA *EMP* 15,585^E
SIC 6021 National trust companies with deposits, commercial
Ch Bd: James E Rohr
Sr Cor Off: Calvert Morgan
**Ex VP:* Maria Schaffer

D-U-N-S 00-691-8767
■ PNC BANK DELAWARE
(*Suby of* PNC BANCORP INC) ★
222 Delaware Ave Lbby, Wilmington, DE 19801-1637
Tel (302) 655-7221 *Founded/Ownrshp* 1885
Sales NA *EMP* 826
SIC 6022 State trust companies accepting deposits, commercial
Pr: William S Demchak
Ch Bd: Calvert A Morgan Jr
Ex VP: George W Forbes III
VP: Maria C Schaffer

D-U-N-S 00-697-3747 IMP
■ PNC BANK NATIONAL ASSOCIATION
(*Suby of* PNC BANCORP INC) ★
249 5th Ave Ste 1200, Pittsburgh, PA 15222-2707
Tel (412) 762-2000 *Founded/Ownrshp* 1983
Sales NA *EMP* 14,485
Accts Sr Snodgrass Pc Wexford
SIC 6021 National trust companies with deposits, commercial
Ch: William S Demchak
V Ch: Joseph Whiteside
**Pr:* Joseph C Guyaux
**CFO:* Robert Q Reilly
Chf Cred: Michael J Hannon
Ofcr: Adam Hamill
**Ex VP:* Richard Johnson
Ex VP: Bill Rosner
Ex VP: Alan Silberstein
Ex VP: Ellen Van Derrst
Sr VP: John Alden
Sr VP: Bob Bardusch
Sr VP: Neal Heiss
Sr VP: Patrick Martin
Sr VP: William McAndrew
Sr VP: Terrence Mech
Sr VP: Samuel Patterson
Sr VP: Noel Ross Safford
Sr VP: Donald Smith
VP: Patty Bojarski
VP: Mark Bortfeld

D-U-N-S 00-790-1010
■ PNC BANK NATIONAL ASSOCIATION
NATIONAL CITY BANK
(*Suby of* PNC FINANCIAL SERVICES GROUP INC) ★
1900 E 9th St Lowr Ll1, Cleveland, OH 44114-3484
Tel (877) 762-2000 *Founded/Ownrshp* 1845, 2008
Sales NA *EMP* 30,770^E
SIC 6021 National commercial banks
Prin: Peter Raskind
V Ch: William McDonald
CFO: Bill Heavilin
Ch: William Demchak
Trst Ofcr: Vincent A Elhilow
Ex VP: Joseph Barbieri
Ex VP: James R Bell
Ex VP: Robert Housel
Ex VP: Michael J Stewart
Sr VP: Jon Beck
VP: Heather Anderson
VP: Brian Elder
VP: Nancy Monterusso
VP: Gregg Orenstein
VP: Robert Scarmuzzi
VP: Mark Stricklin

PNC BUSINESS CREDIT
See PNC INVESTMENTS LLC

D-U-N-S 05-798-0500
▲ PNC FINANCIAL SERVICES GROUP INC
300 5th Ave, Pittsburgh, PA 15222-2401
Tel (412) 762-2000 *Founded/Ownrshp* 1983
Sales NA *EMP* 52,513^E
Tkr Sym PNC *Exch* NYS
SIC 6021 6162 7389 6282 6211 National commercial banks; Mortgage bankers; Credit card service; Investment advisory service; Security brokers & dealers
Ch Bd: William S Demchak
Pr: James Andzelik
Pr: Carol Hoburg
Pr: Azalea Mackey
Pr: David Wood
COO: Mike Harkins
CFO: Robert Q Reilly
Treas: Lynn Aleksov
Treas: E William Parsley III
Chf Mktg O: Brian Gray
Ofcr: Michael J Hannon
Ofcr: Joseph E Rockey
Ex VP: Gordon Cameron
Ex VP: Orlando C Esposito
Ex VP: Frederick Frank
Ex VP: Vicki C Henn
Ex VP: Gregory B Jordan
Ex VP: Carolyn King
Ex VP: Harry Klein
Ex VP: Steve Kunk
Ex VP: Debra Lakatosh
Board of Directors: Dennis F Strigl, Charles E Bunch, Michael J Ward, Marjorie Rodgers Cheshire, Gregory D Wasson, Andrew T Feldstein, Daniel R Hesse, Kay Coles James, Richard B Kelson, Jane G Pepper, Donald J Shepard, Lorene K Steffes

D-U-N-S 82-863-3466
■ PNC INVESTMENTS LLC
PNC BUSINESS CREDIT
(*Suby of* PNC BANK NATIONAL ASSOCIATION) ★
620 Liberty Ave Bsmt, Pittsburgh, PA 15222-2723
Tel (800) 762-6111 *Founded/Ownrshp* 2003
Sales 120.3MM^E *EMP* 600^E
SIC 6799 Investors
Sr VP: Sean B Grindall

PNC MULTIFAMILY CAPITAL
See COLUMBIA HOUSING/PNC INSTITUTIONAL FUND XX LIMITED PARTNERSHIP

D-U-N-S 96-857-6355
■ PNC NATIONAL BANK OF DELAWARE
(*Suby of* PNC BANK NATIONAL ASSOCIATION) ★
300 Bellevue Pkwy Ste 200, Wilmington, DE 19809-3704
Tel (302) 479-4529 *Founded/Ownrshp* 1996
Sales NA *EMP* 450
SIC 6022 State commercial banks
Pr: James Gorman
**CFO:* Mike Sheanen
**Sr VP:* Karen Blair
**Sr VP:* Chaonei Chan
**Sr VP:* David Tomlinson
**VP:* Don Catsadimas
**VP:* Ed Seaver
Mktg Mgr: Daniel A Dalton

PNCT
See PORT NEWARK CONTAINER TERMINAL LLC

PNEUMATIC SCALE ANGELUS
See PNEUMATIC SCALE CORP

D-U-N-S 00-103-7985 IMP
PNEUMATIC SCALE CORP (MA)
PNEUMATIC SCALE ANGELUS
(*Suby of* BARRY-WEHMILLER COMPANIES INC) ★
10 Ascot Pkwy, Cuyahoga Falls, OH 44223-3325
Tel (330) 923-0491 *Founded/Ownrshp* 1895, 1989
Sales 84.5MM^E *EMP* 300
Accts Ernst & Young Llp St Louis
SIC 3565 3569 3535 Packaging machinery; Bottling machinery: filling, capping, labeling; Centrifuges, industrial; Conveyors & conveying equipment
CEO: Timothy J Sullivan
Pr: William J Morgan
Ch: Robert H Chapman
Treas: Michael D Zaccarello
Ex VP: Paul Kearney
VP: David Belletg
VP: David M Gianini
VP: Paul Kelly
VP: Bill Morgan
VP: Greg Myer
Dir IT: Mike McLaughlin

PNGC POWER
See PACIFIC NORTHWEST GENERATING COOPERATIVE

D-U-N-S 80-030-8608
■ PNK (LAKE CHARLES) LLC
L'AUBERGE DU LAC CASINO RESORT
(*Suby of* GOLD MERGER SUB LLC) ★
777 Ave Lauberge, Lake Charles, LA 70601-8483
Tel (337) 395-7777 *Founded/Ownrshp* 2005
Sales 65.4MM^E *EMP* 2,000
SIC 7011 Hotels; Casino hotel
VP: Larry Lepinski
Ofcr: Glenn Akins
**Dir Surg:* Joe Farruggio
**Dir Surg:* Dennis Gentry
**Dir Surg:* Kirk Houser
**Dir Surg:* Paul Hutchens
**Dir Surg:* Lucien Marioneaux
**Dir Surg:* Julie Ragusa
**Dir Surg:* Harold Rowland
**Dir Surg:* Paul Sherlock
**Dir Surg:* Jacqueline St Romain

D-U-N-S 00-697-5395
▲ PNM RESOURCES INC (NM)
414 Silver Ave Sw Fl 4, Albuquerque, NM 87102-3239
Tel (505) 241-2700 *Founded/Ownrshp* 1917
Sales 1.4MMM *EMP* 1,868
Tkr Sym PNM *Exch* NYS
SIC 4911 4922 4924 Electric services; Generation, electric power; Transmission, electric power; Distribution, electric power; Natural gas transmission; Natural gas distribution
Ch Bd: Patricia K Collawn
COO: Ron E Talbot
CFO: Charles N Eldred
Sr VP: Patrick V Apodaca
VP: Joseph D Tarry
Board of Directors: Norman P Becker, E Renae Conley, Alan J Fohrer, Sidney M Gutierrez, Maureen T Mullarkey, Donald K Schwanz, Bruce W Wilkinson

D-U-N-S 17-222-4201
■ PNMR SERVICES CO
(*Suby of* PNM RESOURCES INC) ★
414 Silver Ave Sw Fl 4, Albuquerque, NM 87102-3239
Tel (505) 241-2700 *Founded/Ownrshp* 2004
Sales 278.1MM^E *EMP* 186^E
SIC 7539 Electrical services
**Treas:* Terry R Horn
**VP:* Charles N Eldred

PNTN
See PROFESSIONAL NATIONAL TITLE NETWORK

D-U-N-S 19-988-3968 IMP
PNY TECHNOLOGIES INC
100 Jefferson Rd, Parsippany, NJ 07054-3708
Tel (973) 515-9700 *Founded/Ownrshp* 1985
Sales 264.8MM^E *EMP* 450
Accts Kpmg Llp
SIC 3572 Computer storage devices
Ch Bd: Gadi Cohen
Sr VP: John Hughes
Sr VP: Robert Stone
Off Admin: Kathleen Diaz
IT Man: Bob Dutch
VP Sls: Anthony Gomez
Mktg Mgr: Dario Avalos
Mktg Mgr: Cori Bundenthal

PO-FOLKS
See FOLKS RESTAURANTS LTD

D-U-N-S 08-654-3469
POARCH BAND OF CREEK INDIANS
303 Poarch Rd, Atmore, AL 36502-6312
Tel (251) 368-9136 *Founded/Ownrshp* 1950
Sales NA *EMP* 1,500
SIC 9131 Indian reservation
Ch: Stephanie Bryan
Dir IT: Greg McCarthy
IT Man: Ed Henderickson
Netwrk Mgr: Jon Vaneville

D-U-N-S 01-775-4408
POCATELLO HEALTH SYSTEM LLC
PORTNEUF MEDICAL CENTER
(*Suby of* LEGACY HOSPITAL PARTNERS (HOLDINGS))
777 Hospital Way, Pocatello, ID 83201-5175
Tel (208) 239-1000 *Founded/Ownrshp* 2008
Sales 251.1MM *EMP* 54^E
SIC 8062 General medical & surgical hospitals
Prin: John Abreu
Chf Rad: Steven Larson
Pr: Bill Mitchell
COO: Daniel Ordyna
Exec: Amy Kramer
Exec: Neomi Perez
Dir Inf Cn: Joyce Olson
Dir Risk M: Richelle Heldwine
Dir Lab: Robert Smith
Ex Dir: Dani Jones
Off Mgr: Cynthia Barron

D-U-N-S 02-961-4922
POCATELLO/CHUBBUCK SCHOOL DISTRICT 25
EDUCATION CENTER
3115 Pole Line Rd, Pocatello, ID 83201-6119
Tel (208) 235-3295 *Founded/Ownrshp* 1900
Sales 79.8MM *EMP* 1,645
Accts Deaton & Company Pocatello I
SIC 8211 Public elementary & secondary schools; School board
MIS Dir: Joel Burklin
Pr Dir: Shelley Allen
Teacher Pr: Susan Pettit
HC Dir: C B Giles

D-U-N-S 83-005-2606
POCH STAFFING INC
TRILLIUM ENVIRONMENTAL SVCS
5555 Gull Rd Ste 300, Kalamazoo, MI 49048-7640
Tel (810) 229-2033 *Founded/Ownrshp* 1996
Sales 45.4MM^E *EMP* 1,700^E
SIC 7363 Help supply services
CEO: Oskar Rene Poch
**Pr:* Kate Spiegel

POCKET COMMUNICATIONS
See YOUGHIOGHENY COMMUNICATIONS-TEXAS LLC

POCKETS CONVENIENCE STORE
See KENTUCKY LAKE OIL CO INC

D-U-N-S 61-475-6047 IMP
POCLAIN HYDRAULICS INC
POCLAIN USA
(*Suby of* POCLAIN HYDRAULICS)
1300 Grandview Pkwy, Sturtevant, WI 53177-1273
Tel (262) 321-0676 *Founded/Ownrshp* 1986
Sales 204.2MM^E *EMP* 225
SIC 5084 Hydraulic systems equipment & supplies
Ch Bd: Laurent Bataille
**Sec:* Olivier Jacqueau
Dist Mgr: Mark Debruine
Telecom Ex: Tim Nissila
IT Man: Meghan Dorn
QI Cn Mgr: Dan Marohl
QI Cn Mgr: Ray Mirzaei
VP Sls: Scott Betzen

POCLAIN USA
See POCLAIN HYDRAULICS INC

D-U-N-S 01-561-7400
POCOLA NURSING CENTER
200 Home St, Pocola, OK 74902-1994
Tel (918) 436-2228 *Founded/Ownrshp* 1996
Sales 311.3MM *EMP* 75
SIC 8052

D-U-N-S 55-643-6319
POCONO HEALTH SYSTEM
206 E Brown St, East Stroudsburg, PA 18301-3006
Tel (570) 421-4000 *Founded/Ownrshp* 1988
Sales 480.8M *EMP* 1,204
Accts Baker Tilly Virchow Krause Llp
SIC 8062 General medical & surgical hospitals
CEO: Charles Garris
**CEO:* Eugene A Leblond
COO: Susan B Labus
**Treas:* Joseph B Conahan
Bd of Dir: Christopher Pomrink
Bd of Dir: Paul Schuchman
VP: Howard Davis
VP: Michael Wilk
Dir Rad: Charles Kempf
Dir Rad: Richard Kennedy
Dir Rad: Javed Malik

D-U-N-S 06-857-2460
POCONO MEDICAL CENTER
PMC
206 E Brown St, East Stroudsburg, PA 18301-3094
Tel (570) 421-4000 *Founded/Ownrshp* 1915
Sales 258.1MM *EMP* 1,057
Accts Baker Tilly Virchow Krause Llp
SIC 8062 General medical & surgical hospitals
CEO: Jeffrey E Snyder
**V Ch:* Darell T Covington
**CEO:* Eugene A Leblond
COO: Joseph Bonanno
**COO:* Kathleen Kuck
**COO:* Jeff Snyder
**CFO:* Michael A Wilk
Ofcr: Gerri Noyes
Ofcr: Nancy Schaefer
**Sr VP:* Stephen J Cunningham
**VP:* Joseph B Fisne
VP: Marian Moran
Dir Rx: Sajal Roy

D-U-N-S 07-366-2355
POCONO MOUNTAIN SCHOOL DISTRICT
134 Pocono Mtn Schl Rd, Swiftwater, PA 18370
Tel (570) 839-7121 *Founded/Ownrshp* 1956
Sales 91.0MM^E *EMP* 1,476
SIC 8211 Public senior high school; Public junior high school; Public elementary school
CFO: Ann Barber
**Treas:* Joseph P Colozza
Bd of Dir: Annabella Lastowski
Bd of Dir: Dawn Wood
Snr Ntwrk: Andrew Lilly
Sls Mgr: Ashley Wagner
Psych: Nick Lopuhovsky
Psych: Kristin Stanavitch
Psych: Carolyn Walsh

D-U-N-S 01-460-7105
POCONO PRODUCE CO INC
POCONO PROFOODS
Chipperfield Dr Rr 191, Stroudsburg, PA 18360
Tel (570) 421-1533 *Founded/Ownrshp* 1944
Sales 137.0MM^E *EMP* 177
SIC 5149 5142 5148 Canned goods: fruit, vegetables, seafood, meats, etc.; Packaged frozen goods; Fruits, fresh; Vegetables, fresh
Pr: Terrence Snyder
CFO: Neil Cooper
**Ch:* Rosemary Driebe Olofsson
**VP:* Rosemary Olofsson
CIO: Kevin Ahnert
Mktg Dir: Doug Petruzzi
Manager: Louis Cala

POCONO PROFOODS
See POCONO PRODUCE CO INC

D-U-N-S 96-995-8446
PODS ENTERPRISES LLC
(*Suby of* ONTARIO TEACHERS' PENSION PLAN BOARD)
5585 Rio Vista Dr, Clearwater, FL 33760-3114
Tel (727) 538-6300 *Founded/Ownrshp* 2015
Sales 312.5MM^E *EMP* 650
SIC 4225 6794 General warehousing & storage; Franchises, selling or licensing
Pr: John B Koch
CFO: Simon Gregorich
Sr VP: Anne Lehman
VP: George Easley
VP: Jeff Hacker
VP: Mike Hamilton
Exec: Ted Cobb
Exec: Scott Scalzo
Genl Mgr: Jason Felty

Snr Sftwr: Lance Coffman
Snr Sftwr: David Williams

D-U-N-S 82-649-1834
PODS HOLDINGS INC
5585 Rio Vista Dr, Clearwater, FL 33760-3114
Tel (727) 538-6300 *Founded/Ownrshp* 2007
Sales 115.3MME *EMP* 700
SIC 6719 Investment holding companies, except banks
Pr: John Koch
**Prin:* Tom Ryan

POET ETHANOL PRODUCTS
See ETHANOL PRODUCTS LLC

D-U-N-S 82-714-3533
POET LLC
BROIN COMPANIES
4615 N Lewis Ave, Sioux Falls, SD 57104-7116
Tel (605) 965-2200 *Founded/Ownrshp* 2007
Sales 4.8MMME *EMP* 47E
SIC 2869 Ethyl alcohol, ethanol
Tech Mgr: Chad Poppe
Snr Mgr: James Moe

D-U-N-S 03-889-9936
POETTKER CONSTRUCTION CO
380 S Germantown Rd, Breese, IL 62230-2088
Tel (314) 994-0004 *Founded/Ownrshp* 1980
Sales 108.0MM *EMP* 50
Accts Scheffel Boyle Highland Il
SIC 1542 Commercial & office building, new construction
Pr: Charles V Poettker
**VP:* Thomas C Albers
**VP:* Kimberly Luitohan
**VP:* Keith Poettker
Genl Mgr: Floyd Hollenkamp
Snr PM: Jonathan Carroll

POGO MINES
See SUMITOMO METAL MINING POGO LLC

D-U-N-S 09-829-4465
POGUE CONSTRUCTION CO LP
1512 Bray Central Dr # 300, McKinney, TX 75069-8267
Tel (972) 529-9401 *Founded/Ownrshp* 1979
Sales 244.5MM *EMP* 110
Accts Rsm Us Llp Dallas Texas
SIC 1542 Commercial & office building, new construction; Commercial & office buildings, renovation & repair
Pr: Benjamin P Pogue
COO: Bob Paulk
CFO: Mark Wheelis
VP: Zach Walker
VP Opers: Benjamin Pogue
Snr PM: Brian Rose

POH MEDICAL CENTER
See MCLAREN OAKLAND

D-U-N-S 09-301-2847
POHANKA OF SALISBURY INC
2015 N Salisbury Blvd, Salisbury, MD 21801-3336
Tel (410) 749-2301 *Founded/Ownrshp* 1999
Sales 85.9MME *EMP* 270E
SIC 5511 7513 7514 7538 7515 New & used car dealers; Truck leasing, without drivers; Rent-a-car service; General automotive repair shops; Passenger car leasing
Pr: Scott Crabtree
VP: Sandy Angello
**VP:* Sandy Fitzgerald
Genl Mgr: Paul Eaton
Genl Mgr: Bob Johns
Opers Mgr: Daniel Fitzgerald
Pr Dir: Nina Dicarlo
Sls Mgr: George Angello
Sls Mgr: Chuck Campbell
Sls Mgr: Brad Kleinburd
Sls Mgr: Mike Morgan
Board of Directors: Wayne Bowen, Wayne Smith

D-U-N-S 06-282-4198
POHLAD COMPANIES
STARQUEST SECURITIES
60 S 6th St Ste 3700, Minneapolis, MN 55402-4437
Tel (612) 661-3700 *Founded/Ownrshp* 1969
Sales 96.1MME *EMP* 746
SIC 8742 7929 6531 5013 7549 7379 Banking & finance consultant; Entertainment service; Real estate agent, commercial; Automotive supplies & parts; Automotive maintenance services;
CEO: Michael Reinarts
**Pr:* Robert C Pohlad
**VP:* John Bierbaum
VP: Pamela Omann
**VP:* James O Pohlad
**VP:* Raymond Zehr Jr
Board of Directors: William M Pohlad

D-U-N-S 06-198-9235
POINT 180 LLC
(*Suby of* 20/20 COMPANIES) ★
3575 Lone Star Cir, Fort Worth, TX 76177-8904
Tel (817) 490-0100 *Founded/Ownrshp* 2009
Sales 61.1MME *EMP* 1,400
SIC 8742 Marketing consulting services

POINT BEACH NUCLEAR PLANT
See NEXTERA ENERGY POINT BEACH LLC

D-U-N-S 07-885-5857 IMP/EXP
POINT BLANK ENTERPRISES INC
PROTECTIVE GROUP A POINT BLANK
2102 Sw 2nd St, Pompano Beach, FL 33069-3116
Tel (954) 630-0900 *Founded/Ownrshp* 2011, 2015
Sales 428.3MME *EMP* 1,474
SIC 3842 3462 3728 8711 Bulletproof vests; Armor plate, forged iron or steel; Aircraft parts & equipment; Engineering services
CEO: Daniel Gaston
Ex VP: Mark Edwards
Sr VP: Brian Kopan
VP: John Butz
Prd Mgr: Shelby Carpenter

D-U-N-S 80-131-6613 IMP/EXP
POINT BLANK SOLUTIONS INC
SS BODY ARMOR I, INC.
2101 Sw 2nd St, Pompano Beach, FL 33069-3100
Tel (800) 413-5155 *Founded/Ownrshp* 1994
Sales 212.3MME *EMP* 1,398
SIC 3842 Bulletproof vests
Ch Bd: James R Henderson
COO: John C Siemer
CFO: James F Anderson
CFO: Michelle Doery
CFO: Tom Steffen
CFO: Lawrence Young
Ex VP: Ishmon F Burks
VP: David Bell
VP: Deniese Miranda
VP: Dale Wise
CTO: Lawrence C Perkins

D-U-N-S 94-879-2098
POINT GROUP HEALTH CARE GROUP & SENIOR LIVING CENTER INC
3 Allied Dr Ste 106, Dedham, MA 02026-6148
Tel (781) 251-9001 *Founded/Ownrshp* 1994
Sales 70.0MM *EMP* 1,000
SIC 8051 8741 Extended care facility; Management services
Pr: Mark Tobin
**COO:* Barry Fried
**Treas:* Gerald Fried

D-U-N-S 07-872-6247
POINT LOMA NAZARENE UNIVERSITY (CA)
3900 Lomaland Dr, San Diego, CA 92106-2899
Tel (619) 221-2200 *Founded/Ownrshp* 1918
Sales 95.5MM *EMP* 688
Accts Capin Crouse Llp San Diego C
SIC 8221 University
CEO: Robert Brower
**Pr:* Myra Fisher
Ofcr: Garrett Blevins
Ofcr: Brad Soriano
Ofcr: Eva Wilson
VP: Cindy Chappell
VP: Joyce Falk
VP: Jeff Herman
VP: George R Latte
VP: George R Latter
VP: George Latter
VP: Austin McKinley
VP: Scott Shoemaker
VP: Caye B Smith
VP: Caye Smith
VP: Joe Watkins
VP: Joseph E Watkins
Assoc Dir: Myrna May

POINT OF SERVICES DIV
See TRANSACTION NETWORK SERVICES INC

D-U-N-S 06-873-2718
POINT PARK UNIVERSITY
201 Wood St, Pittsburgh, PA 15222-1912
Tel (412) 391-4100 *Founded/Ownrshp* 1960
Sales 105.4MM *EMP* 252
Accts Schneider Downs & Co Inc Pitt
SIC 8221 College, except junior
Pr: Paul Hennigan
Pr: Sharon Navoney
Pr: Pam Palmer
VP: Mariann K Geyer
VP: Tom McMillan
Mng Dir: David Vinski
Tech Mgr: Bryan Sheffar
VP Opers: Bill Cameron
Sls&Mrk Ex: Bridget Mancosh
Mktg Dir: Chris A Hays
Pr Dir: Ginny Frizzi

D-U-N-S 07-983-2006
■ **POINTE HILTON SQUAW PEAK RESORT**
(*Suby of* HILTON WORLDWIDE HOLDINGS INC) ★
7677 N 16th St, Phoenix, AZ 85020-4434
Tel (602) 997-2626 *Founded/Ownrshp* 2013
Sales 350.1ME *EMP* 5,008E
SIC 7011 Hotels

POINTE HLTON TPTIO CLFFS RSORT
See 11111 NORTH 7TH STREET PROPERTY LLC

POINTSECURE
See IDERA INC

POIPU BAY RESORT
See KAWAILOA DEVELOPMENT LLP

POKOLY, THOS B
See UMASS MEMORIAL COMMUNITY MEDICAL GROUP INC

POL-TEX INTERNATIONAL DIVISION
See POLY-AMERICA LP

POLAR BEVERAGES
See POLAR CORP

D-U-N-S 00-112-5988 EXP
POLAR CORP
POLAR BEVERAGES
1001 Southbridge St, Worcester, MA 01610-2218
Tel (508) 753-6383 *Founded/Ownrshp* 1882
Sales 361.3MME *EMP* 1,000
SIC 2086 5149 Soft drinks: packaged in cans, bottles, etc.; Pasteurized & mineral waters, bottled & canned; Soft drinks; Water, distilled
Pr: Ralph D Crowley Jr
**CFO:* Michael J Mulrain
**Treas:* Christopher Crowley
Genl Mgr: Bill Wall
Off Mgr: Bob Lord
Off Mgr: Lisa Sarcia
Dir IT: Michael Petursson
Netwrk Mgr: Edwick Quiles
Mtls Mgr: Andy Richardson
Opers Mgr: Jim Robert
Mktg Dir: Elizabeth Crowley

D-U-N-S 10-399-4240 IMP/EXP
POLAR CORP
(*Suby of* QUESTOR PARTNERS FUND II LP) ★
1015 W St Germain St 42 Ste 420, Hopkins, MN 55305
Tel (612) 430-6401 *Founded/Ownrshp* 1997
Sales 571.0MME *EMP* 1,500
SIC 3443 5012 7699 Tanks for tank trucks, metal plate; Trailers for trucks, new & used; Tank repair
Pr: Robert D Denious
VP: Rick Connelly
VP: Mike McCall
Genl Mgr: Jason Courville
Off Mgr: Anja Waaga
IT Man: Mike Noe
Ql Cn Mgr: Tyson Szewczyk
VP Sls: Mark Hunsley
Sls Dir: John Koll
Manager: Dave Adolphson
Manager: Rick Ralph

POLAR CUSTOM TRAILERS
See POLAR TANK TRAILERS

D-U-N-S 62-194-8884 IMP/EXP
POLAR SEMICONDUCTOR LLC
(*Suby of* SANKEN ELECTRIC CO., LTD.)
2800 E Old Shakopee Rd, Bloomington, MN 55425-1350
Tel (952) 876-3000 *Founded/Ownrshp* 2005
Sales 139.1MME *EMP* 450
SIC 3674 Semiconductors & related devices; Integrated circuits, semiconductor networks, etc.
CEO: Yoshihiro Suzuki
**COO:* Hamid Berenjian
**VP:* Steve Kosier
Prd Mgr: Greg Gonet

POLAR SERVICE CENTERS
See PSC CUSTOM LP

D-U-N-S 00-712-3243
POLAR TANK TRAILERS
POLAR CUSTOM TRAILERS
(*Suby of* POLAR CORP) ★
12810 County Road 17, Holdingford, MN 56340-9773
Tel (417) 862-5526 *Founded/Ownrshp* 2002
Sales 228.8MME *EMP* 1,100
SIC 3443 3715 Tanks for tank trucks, metal plate; Truck trailers
Pr: Jim Painter
**Pr:* Mike Evans
**VP:* Scott Fike

D-U-N-S 94-111-4084
■ **POLARIS CONSULTING & SERVICES LTD**
POLARIS SOFTWARE LAB
(*Suby of* VIRTUSA CONSULTING SERVICES PRIVATE LIMITED)
20 Corporate Pl S, Piscataway, NJ 08854-6144
Tel (732) 590-8100 *Founded/Ownrshp* 2011
Sales 92.2MM *EMP* 750
Accts Pandya Kapadia & Associates
SIC 7371 Computer software systems analysis & design, custom
CEO: Jitin Goyal
Pr: Vikram Aligh
**CFO:* Subramaniam Swaminathan
Chf Mktg O: George Ravich
**Ex VP:* Sanjeev Gulati
IT Man: Mohammed Jahoor

D-U-N-S 08-999-2205
■ **POLARIS CONTRACT MANUFACTURING INC** (MA)
(*Suby of* LOCKHEED MARTIN SIPPICAN INC) ★
15 Barnabas Rd, Marion, MA 02738-1421
Tel (508) 748-3399 *Founded/Ownrshp* 2000
Sales 102.9MME *EMP* 400
SIC 3812 Warfare counter-measure equipment
Pr: Lisa B Callahan

D-U-N-S 05-169-1673
▲ **POLARIS INDUSTRIES INC**
2100 Highway 55, Medina, MN 55340-9100
Tel (763) 542-0500 *Founded/Ownrshp* 1954
Sales 4.7MMM *EMP* 8,102E
Tkr Sym PII *Exch* NYS
SIC 3799 3751 3714 5699 All terrain vehicles (ATV); Snowmobiles; Motorcycles & related parts; Motor vehicle parts & accessories; Sports apparel
Ch Bd: Scott W Wine
Pr: Stephen L Eastman
CFO: Michael T Speetzen
Chf Mktg O: Craig Scanlon
Ofcr: Matthew J Homan
Ofcr: James P Williams
Ex VP: Kenneth J Pucel
Sr VP: Stacy L Bogart
Sr VP: David C Longren
VP: Joel Houlton
VP: John M Olson
Dir Soc: Wanda Campbell
Board of Directors: Annette K Clayton, Kevin M Farr, Gary E Hendrickson, Gwenne A Henricks, Bernd F Kessler, Lawrence D Kingsley, John P Wiehoff

POLARIS SOFTWARE LAB
See POLARIS CONSULTING & SERVICES LTD

POLARIS TECHNOLOGIES
See MODERN BUILDERS SUPPLY INC

D-U-N-S 12-023-4161 IMP
POLAROID CONSUMER ELECTRONICS INTERNATIONAL LLC
4400 Baker Rd Ste 900, Minnetonka, MN 55343-8668
Tel (952) 936-5000 *Founded/Ownrshp* 2009
Sales 191.3MME *EMP* 2,700
SIC 5199 General merchandise, non-durable
Pr: Scott W Hardy
Ofcr: McGaunn Jon

D-U-N-S 79-561-3418 IMP/EXP
POLARTEC LLC
46 Stafford St, Lawrence, MA 01841-2422
Tel (978) 685-6341 *Founded/Ownrshp* 2007
Sales 240.1MME *EMP* 700
SIC 2299 Broadwoven fabrics: linen, jute, hemp & ramie; Coir yarns & roving; Fabrics: linen, jute, hemp, ramie; Grease, wool
CEO: Gary Smith
CFO: William Hollyer
VP: William Baggeroer
Genl Mgr: Walter Tkach
Plng Mgr: Kevin J Byron
Dir IT: Ruthann Brown
VP Opers: Phillip Murrell
Prd Mgr: Larry Paulo
VP Sls: Jon Adelman
Manager: David Adair
Counsel: Kathleen A Potter
Board of Directors: Michael Spillane

D-U-N-S 15-163-1496
POLICE AND FIRE FEDERAL CREDIT UNION (INC)
PFFCU
901 Arch St, Philadelphia, PA 19107-2404
Tel (215) 931-0300 *Founded/Ownrshp* 1938
Sales NA *EMP* 400
SIC 6061 6163 Federal credit unions; Loan brokers
CEO: John Larosa
**Ch:* Anthony Larosa
Sr VP: Geoff Garlow
Sr VP: Michael Valiante
VP: Chris McGann
VP: Anthony Orlando
VP: Ken Wolstenholme
Genl Couns: Joseph Loverdi

POLICE DEPARTMENT
See COUNTY OF STARK

D-U-N-S 14-941-0573
■ **POLICY STUDIES INC**
PSI
(*Suby of* PSHI) ★
1515 Wynkoop St Ste 400, Denver, CO 80202-5558
Tel (303) 863-0900 *Founded/Ownrshp* 2006
Sales 96.7MME *EMP* 1,313
SIC 8741 8742 7371 Administrative management; Management consulting services; Custom computer programming services
CEO: Richard Montoni
**Pr:* Bruce Caswell
**Pr:* Eric Rubin
**CEO:* Margaret Laub
**CFO:* Rick Nadeau
**CFO:* Carroll Wallace
Ofcr: Gary Rum
Ofcr: Susan K Williams
Ex VP: Cameron Horan
Sr VP: John F Walz
VP: Dawn Baxter
VP: Karl Erickson
VP: James Hennessey
VP: Kim Jaudon
VP: Mary Miller
VP: Bev Schulman
VP: Christie Van Cleave
VP: Jeff Wilkins
VP Bus Dev: Jeff Susich

POLISHER RESEARCH INSTITUTE
See MADLYN AND LEONARD ABRAMSON CENTER FOR JEWISH LIFE

D-U-N-S 07-831-5959
POLK COUNTY FLORIDA (FL)
330 W Church St, Bartow, FL 33830-3760
Tel (863) 534-6000 *Founded/Ownrshp* 1861
Sales NA *EMP* 3,600
SIC 9111 Executive offices;
Ch: Todd Dantdler
V Ch: Melony Bell
Ofcr: Stacey Spivey
Prgrm Mgr: Shaneal Allen
Off Mgr: Rose Boatwright
Off Mgr: Cherie Simmons
Dir IT: Edward Wolfe
Tech Mgr: Richard Petrelli
Netwrk Eng: Chad Johnson
Opers Mgr: Eric Hoog
Snr Mgr: Tony Crouse

D-U-N-S 78-699-3852
POLK COUNTY SCHOOL DISTRICT
1915 S Floral Ave, Bartow, FL 33830-7124
Tel (863) 534-0500 *Founded/Ownrshp* 1886
Sales 871.8MM *EMP* 3,021E
Accts Cherry Bekaert Llp Orlando F
SIC 8211 Public elementary & secondary schools
Dir Sec: Rick Wright
Admn Mgr: Linda Clark
IT Man: Robert M Laubach
Netwrk Mgr: Miranda Collins
Netwrk Mgr: Brad Fales
Netwrk Mgr: Brian Voisard
Netwrk Mgr: Todd Webb
Pr Dir: Leah Lauderdale
Teacher Pr: Brian Warren
Instr Medi: Jacqueline Rose
Snr Mgr: Lisa Martin

D-U-N-S 12-795-0595
POLK MECHANICAL CO LLC
PMC SERVICE COMPANY
2425 Dillard St, Grand Prairie, TX 75051-1004
Tel (972) 339-1200 *Founded/Ownrshp* 2003
Sales 110.2MME *EMP* 370
SIC 1711 3444 3498 3599 3999 Mechanical contractor; Pipe, sheet metal; Fabricated pipe & fittings; Hose, flexible metallic; Cleaners, pipe & cigarette holder
Pr: Fran McCann
**Ch Bd:* Ken Polk
**VP:* Barry Duncan
VP: Yancey Jones
VP: Timothy Sidwell

D-U-N-S 07-979-8967
POLK SCHOOL DISTRICT
612 S College St, Cedartown, GA 30125-3522
Tel (770) 748-3821 *Founded/Ownrshp* 2015
Sales 11.5MME *EMP* 1,000E
SIC 8211 Public elementary & secondary schools

Teacher Pr: David Robinson
HC Dir: Greg Teems

D-U-N-S 02-281-3786
POLKA DOT DAIRY INC (MN)
110 17th St E, Hastings, MN 55033-3198
Tel (651) 438-2793 *Founded/Ownrshp* 1956
Sales 195.3MM[E] *EMP* 1,000
SIC 5143 Dairy products, except dried or canned
Pr: Wallace Pettit
**VP:* Marlene Pettit
VP: Patrick Pettit

D-U-N-S 55-639-7313 IMP
POLLO OPERATIONS INC
POLLO TROPICAL
(*Suby of* FIESTA RESTAURANT GROUP INC) ★
7300 N Kendall Dr Fl 8, Miami, FL 33156-7840
Tel (305) 671-1225 *Founded/Ownrshp* 1998
Sales 80.7MM[E] *EMP* 1,700
SIC 5812 Chicken restaurant
Pr: Alan Vituli
Pr: Timothy Taft
COO: James Tunnessen
CFO: Lynn Schweinfurth
VP: Glenn Rozansky
VP: Joseph Zirkman
VP Opers: Bob Moore
VP Opers: Vicky Timmer

POLLO TROPICAL
See POLLO OPERATIONS INC

D-U-N-S 00-736-6958 IMP
POLLOCK INVESTMENTS INC
POLLOCK PAPER DISTRIBUTORS
1 Pollock Pl, Grand Prairie, TX 75050-7939
Tel (972) 263-8448 *Founded/Ownrshp* 1918
Sales 507.7MM[E] *EMP* 455
SIC 5113 5087 Paper & products, wrapping or coarse; Boxes, paperboard & disposable plastic; Janitors' supplies
Pr: Lawrence S Pollock III
**COO:* Tracy Evatt
**CFO:* Paul A Garcia
**Sec:* Richard Robert Pollock
Chf Mktg O: Harry Page
VP: Eric Harris
**VP:* Robert G Pollock
Exec: Angela Tucker
Genl Mgr: Katie Hochstetler
Off Mgr: Karen Baker
Telecom Ex: Patti Robertson

POLLOCK PAPER DISTRIBUTORS
See POLLOCK INVESTMENTS INC

POLLOK ELECTRONICS
See POLLOK INC

D-U-N-S 11-079-6583 IMP
■ POLLOK INC
POLLOK ELECTRONICS
(*Suby of* STONERIDGE INC) ★
6 Butterfield Trail Blvd, El Paso, TX 79906-4902
Tel (915) 592-5700 *Founded/Ownrshp* 1992
Sales 101.1MM[E] *EMP* 600
SIC 5065 3823 3714 3545 Electronic parts & equipment; Industrial instrmnts msrmnt display/control process variable; Motor vehicle parts & accessories; Machine tool accessories
Ch Bd: David M Draime
**Pr:* Cloyd J Abruzzo
**CFO:* Kevin Bagby
VP: Glennon Roth
Plnt Mgr: Laura Lujan
Ql Cn Mgr: Peter Trainer
Sales Exec: Linda Palingo

POLLYS COUNTRY MARKET
See POLLYS FOOD SERVICE INC

D-U-N-S 01-716-3056
POLLYS FOOD SERVICE INC
POLLYS COUNTRY MARKET
1821 Spring Arbor Rd, Jackson, MI 49203-2703
Tel (517) 787-5228 *Founded/Ownrshp* 1963
Sales 123.2MM[E] *EMP* 1,100
SIC 5411 5921 Supermarkets, chain; Beer (packaged); Wine
Pr: Kim Kennedy
**VP:* Sean Kennedy

D-U-N-S 11-828-5782
POLLYS INC
KFC
(*Suby of* E D D INVESTMENT CO) ★
14325 Iseli Rd, Santa Fe Springs, CA 90670-5203
Tel (714) 773-9588 *Founded/Ownrshp* 1982
Sales 32.4MM[E] *EMP* 1,100
SIC 5812 Fast-food restaurant, chain
Pr: Harvey Sheldrake
COO: James Sheldrake
**VP:* Donald Sheldrake

D-U-N-S 78-077-0918
POLLYS INC
173 E Freedom Ave, Anaheim, CA 92801-1006
Tel (714) 459-0041 *Founded/Ownrshp* 1982
Sales 250.0M *EMP* 1,060
Accts Martin Werbelow Llp Pasadena
SIC 8748 Business consulting
CEO: Eddie Sheldrake

POLO RALPH LAUREN
See RALPH LAUREN RETAIL INC

D-U-N-S 03-712-8824
POLSINELLI PC
900 W 48th Pl Ste 900, Kansas City, MO 64112-1899
Tel (816) 753-1000 *Founded/Ownrshp* 1972
Sales 328.5MM[E] *EMP* 1,250
SIC 8111

D-U-N-S 03-002-2321 IMP/EXP
POLY-AMERICA LP (TX)
POL-TEX INTERNATIONAL DIVISION
2000 W Marshall Dr, Grand Prairie, TX 75051-2795
Tel (972) 337-7100 *Founded/Ownrshp* 1976, 2001
Sales 590.7MM[E] *EMP* 1,750
SIC 3081 2673 Polyethylene film; Trash bags (plastic film): made from purchased materials
Mng Pt: Michael A Ross
**COO:* George Hall

D-U-N-S 05-049-2594 IMP/EXP
POLY-PAK INDUSTRIES INC
COLORPAK
125 Spagnoli Rd, Melville, NY 11747-3518
Tel (631) 293-6767 *Founded/Ownrshp* 1958
Sales 91.0MM[E] *EMP* 350
SIC 2673 2677 Plastic bags: made from purchased materials; Envelopes
Ch Bd: Peter Levy
**CFO:* Michael Losak
**Ch:* Leonard Levy
Sr VP: Rose Matty
VP: Mitchell Cohen
**VP:* Doug Kiesel
VP: Adam Kugler
VP Mktg: Ken Trottere

D-U-N-S 00-308-9661 IMP
■ POLY-SEAL LLC
(*Suby of* BERRY PLASTICS GROUP INC) ★
101 Oakley St, Evansville, IN 47710-1237
Tel (812) 306-2573 *Founded/Ownrshp* 1969, 2000
Sales 118.5MM[E] *EMP* 525
SIC 3089 Closures, plastic; Caps, plastic
Pr: Jonathan Rich

D-U-N-S 07-454-3638 IMP
POLYCHEM CORP
6277 Heisley Rd, Mentor, OH 44060-1899
Tel (440) 357-1500 *Founded/Ownrshp* 1978
Sales 153.7MM[E] *EMP* 400
SIC 2671 Plastic film, coated or laminated for packaging
CEO: Brian Jeckering
VP: Jim Cantelmi
VP: Mihai Cojocaru
IT Man: Ed Bret
Plnt Mgr: Dan Quick
Natl Sales: Marybeth Quick
Sls Dir: Scott Jeckering
Manager: Michael Dowdall
Manager: Warren Garnier
Manager: Mel Littrell
Manager: Ozzie Oswald

D-U-N-S 62-344-8073 IMP
POLYCOM INC
6001 America Center Dr, San Jose, CA 95002-2562
Tel (408) 586-6000 *Founded/Ownrshp* 2016
Sales 1.2MMM *EMP* 3,451[E]
SIC 8741 Management services
CEO: Mary T McDowell
**Pr:* Christopher M Jones
**Pr:* Marco Landi
**Pr:* Geoff Thomas
**CFO:* Laura J Durr
**Chf Mktg O:* Jim Kruger
**Ex VP:* Michael Frendo
**Sr VP:* Laura Owen
Sr VP: Ashan Willy
VP: Robert B Steele
**CIO:* Scott McCool

D-U-N-S 80-959-6765
POLYCONCEPT NORTH AMERICA INC
(*Suby of* POLYCONCEPT HOLDING B.V.)
400 Hunt Valley Rd, New Kensington, PA 15068-7059
Tel (724) 334-9000 *Founded/Ownrshp* 2000
Sales 674.3MM[E] *EMP* 1,100[E]
SIC 5199 5111 5112 3172 3161 2394 Advertising specialties; Writing paper; Stationery & office supplies; Personal leather goods; Luggage; Canvas & related products
CEO: Micahel Bernstein
**Pr:* David Nicholson
**CFO:* Marty Vuono
CIO: Marc Brown

POLYGON SERVICES
See POLYGON US CORP

D-U-N-S 96-500-4935
POLYGON US CORP
POLYGON SERVICES
(*Suby of* POLYGON AB)
15 Sharpners Pond Rd F, North Andover, MA 01845-5716
Tel (800) 422-6379 *Founded/Ownrshp* 2010
Sales 88.5MM[E] *EMP* 130[E]
SIC 1521 Repairing fire damage, single-family houses; General remodeling, single-family houses
Pr: John Campanelli
**Ch:* A Christopher Young
**VP:* Mats Johansson
Sls Mgr: Doug Haas

D-U-N-S 07-979-5537
POLYMER ADDITIVES HOLDINGS INC
7500 E Pleasant Valley Rd, Independence, OH 44131-5536
Tel (216) 875-7200 *Founded/Ownrshp* 2014
Sales 210.0MM[E] *EMP* 224[E]
SIC 5169 2899 Chemicals & allied products; Chemical preparations; Fire retardant chemicals

D-U-N-S 07-967-5279
POLYMER ADDITIVES INC
VALTRIS SPECIALTY CHEMICALS
(*Suby of* POLYMER ADDITIVES HOLDINGS INC) ★
7500 E Pleasant Valley Rd, Independence, OH 44131-5536
Tel (216) 875-7200 *Founded/Ownrshp* 2014
Sales 210.0MM *EMP* 317
SIC 5169 2899 Chemicals & allied products; Chemical preparations; Fire retardant chemicals
CEO: Paul Angus
Pr: Kaval Patel
CFO: Craig Fitzpatrick
VP: Gaurav Golechna
VP: Matthew Gullen
VP: Jim Mason
Genl Mgr: Bob Knighton

D-U-N-S 00-432-1576 IMP/EXP
POLYMER ENTERPRISES INC (PA)
4731 State Route 30 # 401, Greensburg, PA 15601-7260
Tel (724) 838-2340 *Founded/Ownrshp* 1915
Sales 96.0MM[E] *EMP* 700
SIC 3069 3011 Rolls, solid or covered rubber; Tires & inner tubes; Airplane tires, pneumatic; Industrial tires, pneumatic; Truck or bus tires, pneumatic
CEO: Donald D Mateer III
**Treas:* William E Moreau

POLYMERLINE
See RAVAGO AMERICAS LLC

D-U-N-S 03-704-0805 IMP/EXP
POLYMET ALLOYS INC
1701 Providence Park # 100, Birmingham, AL 35242-4688
Tel (205) 981-2200 *Founded/Ownrshp* 1995
Sales 88.0MM[E] *EMP* 7
SIC 5051 Ferroalloys
Pr: Braulio Lage
**Treas:* Sandy Vinson

D-U-N-S 04-399-6768 IMP
POLYNESIAN CULTURAL CENTER INC
P C C
55-370 Kamehameha Hwy, Laie, HI 96762-2113
Tel (808) 293-3000 *Founded/Ownrshp* 1963
Sales 44.6MM *EMP* 1,100
Accts Eide Bailly Llp Salt Lake Cit
SIC 7999 5812 5947 Tourist attraction, commercial; Eating places; Gift shop; Souvenirs
Pr: Von D Orgill
**Ch:* Richard E Marriott
Ofcr: Brian R Carrington
Ofcr: Ira A Fulton
**VP:* Logo Apelu
**VP:* Greg Gollaher
**VP:* John Muaina
QA Dir: Ll Wong
Netwrk Mgr: Shaun Niu
Tech Mgr: Sak Yalimaiwai
Sls Mgr: Pane Meatoga III

D-U-N-S 96-825-9981 IMP
POLYNT COMPOSITES USA INC
(*Suby of* INVESTINDUSTRIAL HOLDINGS SA)
99 E Cottage Ave, Carpentersville, IL 60110-1803
Tel (847) 428-2657 *Founded/Ownrshp* 2011
Sales 318.6MM[E] *EMP* 450
SIC 2821 Polyurethane resins; Polyethylene resins
CEO: Rosario Valido
**CFO:* David Betti
**Treas:* Don Pittman
**Treas:* Donny Edward Pittman Jr
**Ex VP:* Sergio Conni
Genl Mgr: Kevin Brolsma
Genl Mgr: Scott Kaphingst
Tech Mgr: Eric Swartz
Plnt Mgr: Chuck Doebler
Sls Dir: Alessandro Verde

D-U-N-S 84-508-2861 IMP/EXP
▲ POLYONE CORP
33587 Walker Rd, Avon Lake, OH 44012-1145
Tel (440) 930-1000 *Founded/Ownrshp* 2000
Sales 3.3MMM *EMP* 6,900
Tkr Sym POL *Exch* NYS
SIC 2821 3087 5162 3081 Thermoplastic materials; Polyvinyl chloride resins (PVC); Vinyl resins; Custom compound purchased resins; Resins; Plastics basic shapes; Unsupported plastics film & sheet
Pr: Robert M Patterson
Pr: Richard N Altice
Pr: Mark D Crist
Pr: Michael A Garratt
Pr: Craig M Nikrant
Pr: John V Van Hulle
Pr: Donald K Wiseman
CFO: Bradley C Richardson
Treas: James N Sloan
Chf Cred: Michael A Garrat
Ofcr: Ana G Rodriguez
Sr VP: Lisa K Kunkle
Sr VP: M John Midea Jr
Sr VP: Joel R Rathbun
VP: Tom Kedrowski
VP: Joseph Kelley
VP: Holger Kronimus
VP: Joel Rathbun
VP: Kurt Schuering
VP: Frank Vari
Exec: Rafael Ramirez
Board of Directors: Richard H Fearon, Gregory J Goff, William R Jellison, Sandra Beach Lin, Richard A Lorraine, William H Powell, Kerry J Preete, William A Wulfsohn

D-U-N-S 07-880-4673
■ POLYONE DESIGNED STRUCTURES AND SOLUTIONS LLC
SPARTECH TECHNOLOGY CENTER.
(*Suby of* POLYONE CORP) ★
11650 Lkeside Crossing Ct, Saint Louis, MO 63105
Tel (888) 721-4242 *Founded/Ownrshp* 2013
Sales 120.9MM[E] *EMP* 79[E]
SIC 5199 Packaging materials
Pr: Julie A McAlindon

POLYPORE INTERNATIONAL, INC.
See POLYPORE INTERNATIONAL LP

D-U-N-S 15-212-8042
POLYPORE INTERNATIONAL LP
POLYPORE INTERNATIONAL, INC.
(*Suby of* ASAHI KASEI CORPORATION)
11430 N Community House R, Charlotte, NC 28277-0454
Tel (704) 587-8409 *Founded/Ownrshp* 2015
Sales 592.5MM[E] *EMP* 2,400[E]
SIC 3691 Lead acid batteries (storage batteries)
Pr: Shgeki Takayama
CFO: Lynn Amos
CFO: Rob Whitsett
VP: Jay Wilson
Genl Couns: Ginger Daly
Genl Couns: Christopher J McKee
Board of Directors: Michael Chesser, Charles L Cooney, William Dries, Frederick C Flynn Jr, Michael Graff, Christopher J Kearney, David A Roberts

D-U-N-S 06-607-6225 IMP
POLYTECHNIC INSTITUTE OF NEW YORK UNIVERSITY
NYU-POLY
6 Metrotech Ctr, Brooklyn, NY 11201-3840
Tel (718) 260-3600 *Founded/Ownrshp* 1854
Sales 183.9MM *EMP* 552
SIC 8221

D-U-N-S 61-867-3073 IMP
■ POLYVISION CORP
POLYVISION NORTH AMERICA
(*Suby of* STEELCASE INC) ★
10700 Abbotts Bridge Rd # 100, Johns Creek, GA 30097-8459
Tel (678) 542-3100 *Founded/Ownrshp* 1954
Sales 199.7MM[E] *EMP* 1,100
SIC 3281 3993 Blackboards, slate; Signs & advertising specialties; Signs, not made in custom sign painting shops; Displays & cutouts, window & lobby
CEO: Robert L Crain
**CEO:* Michael Dunn
**CFO:* Peter Lewchanin
**Treas:* Gary L Fetterman
VP: Scott Campbell
VP: Joe Josephson
Prin: Sandra Lemken
Dir IT: Tom Hunnewell
IT Man: Perry Dougherty
Manager: Matthew Clarke
Manager: Vipin Makkar

POLYVISION NORTH AMERICA
See POLYVISION CORP

D-U-N-S 07-862-5706
POM WONDERFUL HOLDINGS LLC
(*Suby of* TELEFLORA) ★
11444 W Olympic Blvd # 210, Los Angeles, CA 90064-1559
Tel (310) 966-5800 *Founded/Ownrshp* 2011
Sales 762.7MM[E] *EMP* 300
SIC 5149 5148 5085 Beverage concentrates; Juices; Tea; Fruits, fresh; Plastic bottles

D-U-N-S 00-921-8454 IMP
POMARE LTD
HILO HATTIE
670 Auahi St Ste I03, Honolulu, HI 96813-5166
Tel (808) 524-3966 *Founded/Ownrshp* 2008
Sales 96.6MM[E] *EMP* 700
SIC 5651

POMCO GROUP
See POMCO INC

D-U-N-S 09-558-5345
POMCO INC
POMCO GROUP
2425 James St, Syracuse, NY 13206-2821
Tel (315) 432-9171 *Founded/Ownrshp* 2003
Sales NA *EMP* 380
SIC 6411 Insurance agents, brokers & service
Pr: Robert W Pomfrey
Pr: Lawrence Thompson
COO: Jeff Winchell
**CFO:* Terry Dowd
**Sr VP:* Donald Napier
**VP:* Loretta Zolkowski
Dir Bus: Stacey Hotaling
Snr Sftwr: Dennis Powers
Snr Sftwr: Matthew Vicki
QA Dir: Kristen Sotherden
IT Man: Mark Rowan

D-U-N-S 08-026-7333
POMEGRANATE HOLDINGS INC
628 Green Valley Rd # 500, Greensboro, NC 27408-7730
Tel (336) 272-1338 *Founded/Ownrshp* 2016
Sales 1.8MMM[E] *EMP* 21,574[E]
SIC 5411 Grocery stores, chain
Pr: Richard A Anicetti

D-U-N-S 08-014-1214
POMEROY GROUP HOLDINGS INC
1020 Petersburg Rd, Hebron, KY 41048-8222
Tel (859) 586-6000 *Founded/Ownrshp* 2015
Sales 284.0MM[E] *EMP* 2,748[E]
SIC 7373 7374 7361 6719 Systems engineering, computer related; Office computer automation systems integration; Data processing service; Executive placement; Investment holding companies, except banks
Pr: Chris Froman
VP: Anne O'Neill

D-U-N-S 04-315-2388
POMEROY IT SOLUTIONS INC
POMEROY IT SOLUTIONS SALES CO
1020 Petersburg Rd, Hebron, KY 41048-8222
Tel (859) 586-0600 *Founded/Ownrshp* 1981
Sales 523.4MM[E] *EMP* 2,013[E]
SIC 7373 5045 7378

POMEROY IT SOLUTIONS SALES CO
See POMEROY IT SOLUTIONS INC

D-U-N-S 96-847-4309
POMEROY IT SOLUTIONS SALES CO INC
(*Suby of* POMEROY GROUP HOLDINGS INC) ★
1020 Petersburg Rd, Hebron, KY 41048-8222
Tel (859) 586-0600 *Founded/Ownrshp* 2015
Sales 41.8MM[E] *EMP* 2,013[E]
SIC 7373 7374 7361 Systems engineering, computer related; Office computer automation systems integration; Data processing service; Executive placement
Pr: Christopher C Froman
Pr: Chris Morgan
**CFO:* Craig Propst
Ex VP: Byron Walters
VP: Christopher Etter
VP: Marcia Pfiester

Dir Bus: Jim Boughey
CTO: Terry Smith
Dir IT: Hugh Mohan
Dir IT: Jay Sanborn
Dir IT: Peter Teneyck

D-U-N-S 07-529-3357
POMONA COLLEGE (CA)
550 N College Ave, Claremont, CA 91711-4434
Tel (909) 621-8135 *Founded/Ownrshp* 1887
Sales 281.0MM *EMP* 500
Accts Kpmg Llp Los Angeles Ca
SIC 8221 College, except junior
CEO: David Oxtoby
COO: Gary Kates
**Treas:* Karen Sisson
Ofcr: Michelle Gonzalez
VP: Seth Allen
**VP:* Pamela Besnard
**VP:* Christopher Ponce
Assoc Dir: Ellie Ash-Bala
Assoc Dir: Hilary Laconte
Assoc Dir: Linda Mazur
Genl Mgr: Victoria Roberts

D-U-N-S 07-533-4318
POMONA UNIFIED SCHOOL DISTRICT
800 S Garey Ave, Pomona, CA 91766-3325
Tel (909) 397-4700 *Founded/Ownrshp* 1954
Sales 132.4MM[E] *EMP* 2,764
Accts Roger Pearce-Pearce & Associat
SIC 8211 Public elementary & secondary schools
Adm Dir: Nathaniel Holt
Dir Sec: Al Dominguez
Dir Sec: Amy McElwain
Prgrm Mgr: David Jaramillo
Prgrm Mgr: Christine Seitsinger
Off Mgr: Ercilia Gomez
IT Man: Ann Harrington
Opers Mgr: Jody Lopez
Schl Brd P: Frank Guzman
HC Dir: Mark Maine

D-U-N-S 07-724-6197
POMONA VALLEY HOSPITAL MEDICAL CENTER
PVHMC
1798 N Garey Ave, Pomona, CA 91767-2918
Tel (909) 865-9500 *Founded/Ownrshp* 1903
Sales 553.9MM *EMP* 2,209
SIC 8062 Hospital, medical school affiliated with residency
CEO: Richard E Yochum
**COO:* Kurt Weinmeister
**CFO:* Michael Nelson
**Ch:* Alan Smith
VP: Jim Dale
Dir Lab: Beverley Roberts
Off Mgr: Tamara Warner
Nurse Mgr: Susan Miller
CTO: Kent Hoyas
MIS Dir: Ken Hoyos
QA Dir: Karen Hughes

D-U-N-S 02-325-1499 IMP
POMPS TIRE SERVICE INC
1122 Cedar St, Green Bay, WI 54301-4704
Tel (920) 435-8301 *Founded/Ownrshp* 1965
Sales 625.9MM[E] *EMP* 1,200
Accts Schenck Sc Green Bay Wiscons
SIC 5531 5014 7534 Automotive tires; Automobile tires & tubes; Truck tires & tubes; Tire recapping
Pr: James R Wochinske
**Treas:* Thomas Snyder
**Ex VP:* Paul Wochinske
VP: Theresa Chapman
**VP:* Garry Glime
Brnch Mgr: Tom Bober
Software D: Jack Broskovetz
Mfg Dir: Bill Waerzeggers
Opers Mgr: Adam Hoover
Opers Mgr: Chris Nikiel
Plnt Mgr: Tom Bauknecht

POMPTONIAN FOOD SERVICE
See POMPTONIAN INC

D-U-N-S 05-812-6723
POMPTONIAN INC
POMPTONIAN FOOD SERVICE
3 Edison Pl Ste 5, Fairfield, NJ 07004-3511
Tel (973) 882-8070 *Founded/Ownrshp* 1959
Sales 55.6MM[E] *EMP* 1,500
SIC 5812 Contract food services
Pr: Mark Vidovich
**VP:* Candy Vidovich

D-U-N-S 03-807-0236 IMP/EXP
POMWONDERFUL LLC
(*Suby of* POM WONDERFUL HOLDINGS LLC) ★
4805 Centennial Ste 100, Bakersfield, CA 93301
Tel (310) 966-5800 *Founded/Ownrshp* 2000
Sales 762.7MM[E] *EMP* 296[E]
SIC 5149 5148 5085 Beverage concentrates; Juices; Tea; Fruits, fresh; Plastic bottles
CEO: Richard Cottrell
**Pr:* Matt Tupper
CFO: Mark Norris
Chf Mktg O: Paul Coletta
CFO: Malcolm Knight
**VP:* Kurt Vetter
Mktg Dir: Molly Flynn
Mktg Mgr: Jason Osborn
Mktg Mgr: Alisa Pospekhova

D-U-N-S 07-833-0796
PON MATERIAL HANDLING NA INC
(*Suby of* PON HOLDINGS B.V.)
840 Gessner Rd Ste 950, Houston, TX 77024-4593
Tel (713) 365-2547 *Founded/Ownrshp* 2011
Sales 191.0MM[E] *EMP* 350[E]
SIC 5084 Materials handling machinery
CEO: Wilhelmus J Claes
**COO:* Robert Schermer
**CFO:* Karl J Scott
VP: Adrienne Soule

D-U-N-S 05-926-9972 IMP/EXP
PON NORTH AMERICA INC
(*Suby of* PON HOLDINGS B.V.)
840 Gessner Rd Ste 950, Houston, TX 77024-4593
Tel (713) 365-2547 *Founded/Ownrshp* 1996
Sales 905.0MM *EMP* 3,000
SIC 5942 5082 Comic books; General construction machinery & equipment
CEO: Adrianus B Smalbraak
**CFO:* Everett Grant

PONDEROSA STEAKHOUSE
See B M J FOODS PR INC

PONDEROSA STEAKHOUSE
See BELLEHOFF CORP

PONTIAC IN GLENVIEW
See LOREN BUICK & PONTIAC INC

PONTIAC SCHOOL DISTRICT
See SCHOOL DISTRICT OF CITY OF PONTIAC

D-U-N-S 09-011-7508
PONTIFICAL CATHOLIC UNIVERSITY OF PUERTO RICO (NY)
2250 Blvd Luis Ferre, Ponce, PR 00717-0655
Tel (787) 841-2000 *Founded/Ownrshp* 1948
Sales 71.3MM *EMP* 1,000
Accts Deloitte & Touche Llp San Jua
SIC 8221 University
Pr: Jorge Ivan
Pr: Carolyn Costas
**Treas:* Juan Roman
**VP:* Leandro Colon
HC Dir: Ana Bonilla

D-U-N-S 96-181-0145 EXP
PONTOON BOAT LLC
BENNINGTON
2805 Decio Dr, Elkhart, IN 46514-7666
Tel (574) 264-6336 *Founded/Ownrshp* 2009
Sales 86.4MM[E] *EMP* 158[E]
SIC 3069 Pontoons, rubber
CEO: Steven H Vogel
CFO: John P Hoyer
**VP:* Diana J Engle
VP Sls: Todd Meier
Sls Dir: Tom Cooper
Art Dir: Amanda Jean

D-U-N-S 78-808-9100
POOL & ELECTRICAL PRODUCTS INC
1250 E Francis St, Ontario, CA 91761-5712
Tel (909) 673-1160 *Founded/Ownrshp* 1994
Sales 425.9MM[E] *EMP* 175
SIC 5091 Swimming pools, equipment & supplies
Pr: Andres Becerra
**CFO:* Sandy Becerra
Brnch Mgr: David Acosta
Brnch Mgr: Carlos Becerra
Brnch Mgr: Isidro Cardoso
Brnch Mgr: Jose Fernandez
Brnch Mgr: Kevin Fogarty
Brnch Mgr: Juan Gasca
Brnch Mgr: Bobbi Linderman
Brnch Mgr: Antonio Lopez
Brnch Mgr: Frank Maldonado

D-U-N-S 07-106-4000 IMP
POOL BUILDERS SUPPLY OF CAROLINAS INC
1124 Central Ave, Charlotte, NC 28204-2104
Tel (704) 375-7573 *Founded/Ownrshp* 1974
Sales 103.8MM[E] *EMP* 125[E]
SIC 5091 5999 Swimming pools, equipment & supplies; Swimming pool chemicals, equipment & supplies
CEO: Olen E Morgan
**Pr:* Matt Morgan
**VP:* Taryn Springsteed
Off Mgr: Tiffany Albright

D-U-N-S 87-296-5363 IMP/EXP
▲ POOL CORP
109 Northpark Blvd # 400, Covington, LA 70433-5096
Tel (985) 892-5521 *Founded/Ownrshp* 1993
Sales 2.3MMM *EMP* 3,800
Tkr Sym POOL *Exch* NGS
SIC 5091 Swimming pools, equipment & supplies
Pr: Manuel J Perez De La Mesa
**Ch Bd:* Wilson B Sexton
COO: Randy Higgins
CFO: Mark W Joslin
VP: A David Cook
VP: Kenneth G St Romain
Brnch Mgr: Todd Maxwell
Genl Mgr: Todd Mecke
CIO: Timothy M Babco
Board of Directors: Andrew W Code, Timothy M Graven, Harlan F Seymour, Robert C Sledd, John E Stokely, David G Whalen

D-U-N-S 02-823-5398 IMP
POOL WATER PRODUCTS
17872 Mitchell N Ste 250, Irvine, CA 92614-6034
Tel (949) 756-1666 *Founded/Ownrshp* 1964
Sales 188.0MM[E] *EMP* 290
SIC 5091 2899 2812 Swimming pools, equipment & supplies; Chemical preparations; Alkalies & chlorine
Pr: Dean C Allred
**Ch Bd:* Zelma Mabel Allred

D-U-N-S 83-159-3533
■ POOLE & KENT CO OF FLORIDA
(*Suby of* EMCOR GROUP INC) ★
1781 Nw North River Dr, Miami, FL 33125-2311
Tel (305) 325-1930 *Founded/Ownrshp* 2004
Sales 119.1MM[E] *EMP* 300
SIC 1611 General contractor, highway & street construction
CEO: Patrick Carr
**Pr:* Steven C Jordan
**CFO:* Richard Harrington
**Sr VP:* David Strickland
**VP:* Stephen Polk

POOLINE PRODUCTS
See TIANJIN POOL & SPA CORP

POP CHIPS
See SONORA MILLS FOODS INC

D-U-N-S 07-275-9632 IMP/EXP
POP DISPLAYS USA LLC
(*Suby of* SUN CAPITAL PARTNERS INC) ★
555 Tuckahoe Rd, Yonkers, NY 10710-5709
Tel (914) 771-4200 *Founded/Ownrshp* 2006
Sales 221.8MM[E] *EMP* 650
SIC 5046 Store fixtures & display equipment
CEO: Mark Champagne
Mng Pt: Jon Watson
Pr: Andrew Abatemarco
COO: Tony Orisini
**Chf Mktg O:* Joe Berzok
**Sr VP:* Scott Katcher
VP: Roseanne Alletto
VP: Larry Alper
VP: Deanna Barrett
VP: Greg Guyette
VP: Dan Harrington
VP: Wendell McGill
Dir: Carrie Keane
Creative D: Josh Chen

POPEYES CHICKEN & BISCUITS
See SAILORMEN INC

POPEYES CHICKEN & BISCUITS
See MIRABILE INVESTMENT CORP

POPEYES CHICKEN & BISCUITS
See COPELANDS OF NEW ORLEANS INC

D-U-N-S 80-273-4558
▲ POPEYES LOUISIANA KITCHEN INC
400 Perimeter Ctr Ter, Atlanta, GA 30346-1227
Tel (404) 459-4450 *Founded/Ownrshp* 1972
Sales 259.0MM *EMP* 1,784
Tkr Sym PLKI *Exch* NGS
SIC 5812 6794 Chicken restaurant; Franchises, selling or licensing
CEO: Cheryl A Bachelder
**Ch Bd:* John M Cranor III
COO: John K Merkin
COO: Andrew Skehan
CFO: William P Matt
Sr VP: Harold M Cohen
VP: Harold Cohen
Area Mgr: Sean Rahman
Genl Mgr: Franco Dantes-Lewis
Genl Mgr: Billy Flannigan
Genl Mgr: Nanette James
Board of Directors: Carolyn Hogan Byrd, S Kirk Kinsell, Joel K Manby, Candace S Matthews

D-U-N-S 01-008-8057
■ POPLAR BLUFF REGIONAL MEDICAL CENTER
HMA
(*Suby of* HMA) ★
3100 Oak Grove Rd, Poplar Bluff, MO 63901-1573
Tel (573) 686-4111 *Founded/Ownrshp* 1991
Sales 216.6MM *EMP* 30
SIC 8093 Specialty outpatient clinics
COO: Levah Lowe
Dir Env Sv: Chad Lester
Dir QC: Yelena Korenberg
Pharmcst: Dave Lourwood

D-U-N-S 82-833-9007
POPLAR BLUFF REGIONAL MEDICAL CENTER INC
(*Suby of* MEDICAL PROPERTIES TRUST INC) ★
3100 Oak Grove Rd, Poplar Bluff, MO 63901-1573
Tel (573) 785-7721 *Founded/Ownrshp* 1981
Sales 215.1MM *EMP* 19[E]
SIC 8062 General medical & surgical hospitals
CEO: Kenneth James
Chf OB: Carrie L Carda
Chf OB: John Patty
**Pr:* Bruce Eady
**COO:* Lavah Lowe
**CFO:* Kevin Fowler
**CFO:* Mark Johnson
Ofcr: Kevin Billoman
Exec: Denise Rushin
Dir OR: Marilyn Eason
Dir Risk M: Yelena Korenberg

D-U-N-S 09-049-8130
■ POPULAR FINANCE INC
(*Suby of* BANCO POPULAR DE PUERTO RICO (INC)) ★
326 Salud St El El Senorial Cond, Ponce, PR 00716
Tel (787) 844-2760 *Founded/Ownrshp* 1990
Sales NA *EMP* 1,188
Accts Price Waterhouse Llp
SIC 6141 Personal finance licensed loan companies, small
Pr: Rafael G Negron
**Treas:* Victor Morales
VP: Juan Bigas
**VP:* Carlos Zaragosa
**Prin:* Edgardo Negron

D-U-N-S 14-865-8529
▲ POPULAR INC
209 Munoz Rivera, San Juan, PR 00918-1000
Tel (787) 765-9800 *Founded/Ownrshp* 1984
Sales NA *EMP* 7,810[E]
Tkr Sym BPOP *Exch* NGS
SIC 6022 State commercial banks
Ch Bd: Richard L Carrion
Pr: Ignacio Alvarez
CFO: Carlos J Vazquez
Ofcr: Lidio V Soriano
Ex VP: Camille Burckhart
Ex VP: Manuel Chinea
Ex VP: Ileana Gonzalez
Ex VP: Eli S Sep Lveda
Ex VP: Gilberto Monzon
Ex VP: Gilberto Monz N
Ex VP: Eduardo J Negron
Ex VP: N Stor O Rivera
Ex VP: Nestor Obie Rivera
Ex VP: Eli S Sepulveda
Sr VP: Michael Macdonald
VP: Martin Klauber
VP: Jorge Roig
VP: Teruca Rullan
Board of Directors: Joaquin E Bacardi III, Alejandro M Ballester, John W Diercksen, Maria Luisa Ferre, David E Goel, C Kim Goodwin, William J Teuber Jr, Carlos A Unanue

D-U-N-S 04-005-4827
POPULATION SERVICES INTERNATIONAL
PSI
1120 19th St Nw Ste 600, Washington, DC 20036-3605
Tel (202) 785-0072 *Founded/Ownrshp* 1970
Sales 650.0MM[E] *EMP* 417
SIC 8733 8732 Noncommercial research organizations; Commercial nonphysical research
Pr: Karl Hofmann
Ofcr: Brabble Hoffman
Ofcr: Zaneta Kific
Ofcr: Priti Patel
Ofcr: Peter Schwarz
**Ex VP:* Michelle Cato
**Ex VP:* Peter Clancy
**Ex VP:* Dana Hovig
**Sr VP:* Steven Chapman
**Sr VP:* Kate Roberts
**Sr VP:* Kim Schwartz
**VP:* Douglas Call
**VP:* Krishna Jafa

D-U-N-S 01-961-8562
POPULOUS HOLDINGS INC
4800 Main St Ste 300, Kansas City, MO 64112-2520
Tel (816) 221-1500 *Founded/Ownrshp* 1983
Sales 184.0MM[E] *EMP* 493[E]
SIC 1542

D-U-N-S 12-271-7007
POPULUS GROUP LLC
850 Stephenson Hwy, Troy, MI 48083-1174
Tel (248) 581-1100 *Founded/Ownrshp* 2002
Sales 250.0MM *EMP* 140
SIC 7363 Help supply services
CEO: Tom Mehl

D-U-N-S 18-697-2733 IMP
POREX CORP
POREX TECHNOLOGY
(*Suby of* FILTRATION GROUP CORP) ★
500 Bohannon Rd, Fairburn, GA 30213-2828
Tel (800) 241-0195 *Founded/Ownrshp* 2013
Sales 169.9MM[E] *EMP* 609
SIC 3082 3842 3841 Unsupported plastics profile shapes; Implants, surgical; Surgical & medical instruments
CEO: William G Midgette
**COO:* Gary Kessinger
**CFO:* Victor Marrero
**Sr VP:* William Foughty
**Sr VP:* Nils Gustavsson
**Sr VP:* James P Wingo
**VP:* Jeff Williams
Sales Exec: Jim Malore

POREX TECHNOLOGY
See POREX CORP

D-U-N-S 01-262-1488 IMP
PORKY PRODUCTS INC
PROTIMEX
400 Port Carteret Dr, Carteret, NJ 07008-3526
Tel (732) 541-0200 *Founded/Ownrshp* 1961
Sales 355.7MM[E] *EMP* 259
SIC 5147 5146 5144 5143 Meats & meat products; Seafoods; Poultry: live, dressed or frozen (unpackaged); Cheese
Pr: Jonathan Ewig
**Co-Pr:* Elliot Schnier
**Sr VP:* Robert Hughes
**VP:* Anthony Giaconelli
**VP:* William Melloy

D-U-N-S 04-783-9220
PORPOISE POOL & PATIO INC
14480 62nd St N, Clearwater, FL 33760-2721
Tel (727) 531-8913 *Founded/Ownrshp* 1979
Sales 269.1MM[E] *EMP* 280
SIC 6794 5999 5712 5091 Franchises, selling or licensing; Swimming pool chemicals, equipment & supplies; Outdoor & garden furniture; Swimming pools, equipment & supplies
CEO: John C Thomas
**COO:* Jim Eisch
**CFO:* Robert Milner
**Ch:* Frederich A Thomas
**VP:* James P Eisch
Off Mgr: Dan Rueb
Dir IT: Cyndi Schmitt
IT Man: Bonnie Barthelemy
Tech Mgr: John Doty

D-U-N-S 11-519-6479 IMP/EXP
PORSCHE CARS NORTH AMERICA INC
(*Suby of* VOLKSWAGEN AG)
1 Porsche Dr, Atlanta, GA 30354-1654
Tel (770) 290-3500 *Founded/Ownrshp* 1984
Sales 160.6MM[E] *EMP* 225
SIC 5511 5013 Automobiles, new & used; Automotive supplies & parts
Pr: Detlev Von Platen
Pr: Ross A Dupper
Pr: Larry Holbert
**COO:* Michael Bartsch
**CFO:* Thierry Kartochian
Ex VP: Konrad Riedl
Sr VP: Richard S Ford
VP: Ross Dupper
VP: Andre Oosthuizen
VP: Mick Pallardy
Rgnl Mgr: Michael Schwind

D-U-N-S 02-646-8850
PORT AGGREGATES INC
314 N Main St, Jennings, LA 70546-5342
Tel (337) 656-3224 *Founded/Ownrshp* 1979
Sales 111.1MM *EMP* 40
SIC 5032 3273 Concrete building products; Aggregate; Ready-mixed concrete
Pr: Andrew L Guinn

**Treas:* James Maddox
VP: Stuart Guinn
Off Mgr: Holley Durkes
IT Man: Timothy Guinn
Sfty Mgr: Christopher Guinn
Opers Mgr: Kirk Jourel

D-U-N-S 08-085-3088
PORT ARTHUR INDEPENDENT SCHOOL DISTRICT
4801 9th Ave, Port Arthur, TX 77642-5802
Tel (409) 989-6100 *Founded/Ownrshp* 1899
Sales 115.7MM *EMP* 1,400
Accts Whitley Penn Llp Houston Tex
SIC 8211 Public elementary & secondary schools
Treas: Danielle Vu
VP: Theodore Victor
Dir Bus: Stella Phillis Jeans
Dir Sec: Mark Rouly
Genl Mgr: Denise Dixon-Davis
IT Man: Rhonda Hall
IT Man: Harold Hankins
Pr Dir: Kristyn Hunt
Teacher Pr: Jimmy Wyble
Instr Medi: Tuyen Tran

D-U-N-S 07-215-8041
PORT AUTHORITY OF ALLEGHENY COUNTY
345 6th Ave Fl 3, Pittsburgh, PA 15222-2541
Tel (412) 566-5500 *Founded/Ownrshp* 1956
Sales 195.2MM[E] *EMP* 1,428
Accts Maher Duessel Pittsburgh Pen
SIC 4119 Local passenger transportation
CEO: Ellen McLean
Ofcr: Dan Debone
IT Man: Padu Byrappa

D-U-N-S 82-982-2159
PORT AUTHORITY OF ALLEGHENY COUNTY
345 6th Ave Fl 3, Pittsburgh, PA 15222-2541
Tel (412) 566-5500 *Founded/Ownrshp* 2009
Sales 107.4MM *EMP* 63
Accts Maher Duessel Pittsburgh Pa
SIC 4131 Intercity bus line
CFO: Ellen McLean
Ofcr: Cameil D Williams
Ofcr: Erich Wilson
Creative D: Tim Frank
Ex Dir: Paul Skoutelas
Counsel: Dana Bacsi

D-U-N-S 00-179-4205
PORT AUTHORITY OF NEW YORK & NEW JERSEY (NY)
4 World Trade Ctr 150, New York, NY 10007-2366
Tel (212) 435-7000 *Founded/Ownrshp* 1921
Sales 4.8MMM *EMP* 7,128
SIC 4581 4785 6512 4491 4111 Airport; Highway bridge operation; Tunnel operation, vehicular; Commercial & industrial building operation; Waterfront terminal operation; Commuter rail passenger operation
Ex Dir: Patrick J Foye
**CFO:* Elizabeth McCarthy
Ofcr: Scott Calandra
Ofcr: Joe Defelice
Ofcr: Suzanne Diaz
Ofcr: Christopher Johnson
VP: Robert Edgell
Exec: Bill Young
Prin: Siu Moy
**Ex Dir:* Ernesto L Butcher
Ex Dir: Kenneth Ringler

D-U-N-S 00-486-2082
PORT AUTHORITY TRANS-HUDSON CORP (NY)
PATH
(*Suby of* PORT AUTHORITY OF NEW YORK & NEW JERSEY) ★
1 Path Plz, Jersey City, NJ 07306-2905
Tel (201) 239-3500 *Founded/Ownrshp* 1962
Sales 73.3MM[E] *EMP* 1,075
SIC 4111 Commuter rail passenger operation
Ch: Lewis M Eisenberg
Pr: Robert E Boyle
Sr Cor Off: Daniel Reynolds
VP: Ernesto Butcher

PORT BARRE HIGH SCHOOL
See ST LANDRY PARISH SCHOOLS

PORT CHESTER PUBLIC SCHOOLS
See PORT CHESTER-RYE UNION FREE SCHOOL DISTRICT

D-U-N-S 04-566-2269
PORT CHESTER-RYE UNION FREE SCHOOL DISTRICT
PORT CHESTER PUBLIC SCHOOLS
113 Bowman Ave, Rye Brook, NY 10573-2808
Tel (914) 934-7900 *Founded/Ownrshp* 1900
Sales 95.3MM *EMP* 500
Accts Cullen & Danowski Llp Port J
SIC 8211 Public elementary & secondary schools
Treas: Coleen Kotzur
Bd of Dir: Chris Wolff
VP: Marlon Lopez
Off Admin: Stacey Losito
Schl Brd P: Carol Brakewood
Schl Brd P: Richard Johnson
Teacher Pr: Joseph Durney
HC Dir: Robert Barrett

D-U-N-S 07-881-7532
PORT CITY GROUP INC
(*Suby of* PACE INDUSTRIES LLC) ★
1985 E Laketon Ave, Muskegon, MI 49442-6127
Tel (231) 777-3941 *Founded/Ownrshp* 2012, 2015
Sales 167.6MM[E] *EMP* 600[E]
SIC 3542 3089 Die casting & extruding machines; Casting of plastic
Pr: B John Essex Jr
COO: Mark Pickett
CFO: Jim Hurley
Prgrm Mgr: Tom Farage
Prgrm Mgr: Kory Shaw
Ql Cn Mgr: Michael Cole
Ql Cn Mgr: Lee Dake
Ql Cn Mgr: Justin Lanore
Ql Cn Mgr: Heather Reed

D-U-N-S 96-141-2426
PORT CITY JAVA INC
101 Portwatch Way, Wilmington, NC 28412-7010
Tel (910) 796-6646 *Founded/Ownrshp* 1995
Sales 106.0MM[E] *EMP* 900
SIC 6719 Investment holding companies, except banks
Pr: Don Reynolds Jr
VP: Mike Brandson

PORT COLUMBUS INTERNATIONAL AI
See COLUMBUS REGIONAL AIRPORT AUTHORITY

D-U-N-S 04-677-7751 IMP/EXP
PORT CONSOLIDATED INC
3141 Se 14th Ave, Fort Lauderdale, FL 33316-4222
Tel (954) 522-1182 *Founded/Ownrshp* 1967
Sales 444.9MM[E] *EMP* 150
SIC 5172 Lubricating oils & greases; Engine fuels & oils
Pr: Donald Carlton
**COO:* Michael Simmons
**Sec:* Joseph R Siska
**Prin:* Donald R Carlton Jr
**Prin:* Noel M Griffith Jr

D-U-N-S 07-277-5331
PORT HURON AREA SCHOOL DISTRICT
2720 Riverside Dr, Port Huron, MI 48060-2653
Tel (810) 984-3101 *Founded/Ownrshp* 1857
Sales 94.0MM *EMP* 1,000
Accts Plante & Moran Pllc Clinton
SIC 8211 Public elementary school; Public junior high school; Public senior high school
Trst: Ann Murphy
Trst: Brian Winters
Psych: Tammy Beebe

PORT HURON HOSPITAL MEDICAL EQ
See WILLOW ENTERPRISES INC

D-U-N-S 82-913-4001
PORT LOGISTICS GROUP INC
288 S Mayo Ave, Walnut, CA 91789-3091
Tel (713) 439-1010 *Founded/Ownrshp* 2014
Sales 227.0MM[E] *EMP* 1,000
SIC 4214 Local trucking with storage
CEO: Robert Stull
**COO:* James Armstrong
**CFO:* Marty Brogden
**CFO:* Tim Smith
**Chf Cred:* Jeffrey Wolpov
**Chf Mktg O:* Greg Morello
VP: Michael Heilman
VP: Lou Riccitelli
**CIO:* James Stephens

D-U-N-S 10-288-5600
■ PORT NEWARK CONTAINER TERMINAL LLC
PNCT
(*Suby of* PORTS AMERICA.COM) ★
241 Calcutta St, Newark, NJ 07114-3324
Tel (973) 522-2200 *Founded/Ownrshp* 2000
Sales 91.1MM[E] *EMP* 400
SIC 4491 Stevedoring
Pr: Michael Hassing
**COO:* Scott Schoenfeld
**CFO:* Markus Braun
CFO: Pedro Motta
**VP:* Chris Garbarino
Opers Mgr: Mike Sullivan
Secur Mgr: Frank Chinmento

D-U-N-S 00-810-7914 IMP/EXP
PORT OF HOUSTON AUTHORITY
111 East Loop N, Houston, TX 77029-4326
Tel (713) 670-2662 *Founded/Ownrshp* 1911
Sales 293.7MM *EMP* 595
Accts Grant Thornton Llp Houston T
SIC 4491 Marine cargo handling
Prin: Janiece M Longoria
Exec: Kelli Green
Exec: Stan Swigart
Mng Dir: Phyllis Saathoff
Mng Dir: Rd Tanner
IT Man: Kelli Gallagher
IT Man: Albert Lyne

D-U-N-S 00-941-9300
PORT OF PORTLAND
7200 Ne Airport Way, Portland, OR 97218-1016
Tel (503) 944-7000 *Founded/Ownrshp* 1891
Sales 295.0MM *EMP* 785
Accts Pricewaterhousecoopers Llp P
SIC 4491 4512 Marine cargo handling; Air transportation, scheduled
Ex Dir: Bill Wyatt
**Pr:* Jim Carter
COO: Rhonnda Edmiston
CFO: E B Galligan
**CFO:* Cynthia Nichol
Treas: Paul Rosenbaum
Ex Dir: Robin White
IT Man: Michael Croston
IT Man: Chenai Nziramasanga
Tech Mgr: Terry Cross
Web Dev: Jesse Milan

PORT OF SAN DIEGO
See SAN DIEGO UNIFIED PORT DISTRICT

D-U-N-S 00-948-3694
PORT OF SEATTLE
2711 Alaskan Way Pier 69, Seattle, WA 98121-1107
Tel (206) 728-3000 *Founded/Ownrshp* 1911
Sales 558.9MM *EMP* 1,515
Accts Moss Adams Llp Seattle Washi
SIC 4491 Docks, incl. buildings & facilities: operation & maintenance
CEO: Ted J Fick
V Ch: Sally Fierro
**CEO:* Kurt Beckett
CFO: Tom Tierney
VP: Debbie Browning
VP: Karen Buchholz
Dir Bus: Kim Albert
Ex Dir: Mic Dinsmore
Prgrm Mgr: Lynnette Consego
Genl Mgr: David Dean
Software D: Dwayne Forehand
Board of Directors: Tom Albro, Bill Bryant, John Creighton, Rob Holland, Gael Tarleton

D-U-N-S 06-334-1911 IMP/EXP
PORT OF TACOMA
1 Sitcum Way, Tacoma, WA 98421-3000
Tel (253) 383-5841 *Founded/Ownrshp* 1918
Sales 143.9MM *EMP* 250
Accts Rsm Us Llp Tacoma Washington
SIC 4491 Marine cargo handling
CEO: John Wolfe
COO: Louis P Cooper Jr
CFO: Erin Galeno
Treas: David Morrison
**Treas:* Thomas Mulledy
Ofcr: Terry Carter
Ofcr: Adrian Cruz
Ofcr: Gilbert Fussell
Ofcr: Ken Harris
Ofcr: Bill Jarmon
Ex Dir: Annika Dean

D-U-N-S 02-870-2470 IMP
PORT PLASTICS INC
BOLCOF PLASTIC MATERIALS
5800 Campus Circle Dr E 150a, Irving, TX 75063-2776
Tel (469) 299-7000 *Founded/Ownrshp* 1961
Sales 173.3MM[E] *EMP* 200
SIC 5162

D-U-N-S 13-088-6500 IMP
PORT ROYAL SALES LTD
95 Froehlich Farm Blvd # 200, Woodbury, NY 11797-2930
Tel (516) 921-8383 *Founded/Ownrshp* 1989
Sales 110.0MM *EMP* 15
SIC 5149 Canned goods: fruit, vegetables, seafood, meats, etc.
Ch Bd: Steven Zwecker
**CFO:* Wayne Wellner
Natl Sales: Nyles Fruchter

D-U-N-S 01-239-3869
PORT TOWNSEND HOLDINGS CO INC
(*Suby of* CROWN PAPER GROUP INC) ★
100 Mill Rd, Port Townsend, WA 98368-2246
Tel (360) 385-3170 *Founded/Ownrshp* 2015
Sales 329.0MM[E] *EMP* 1,270
SIC 2611 2653 Pulp mills; Corrugated & solid fiber boxes
Ch: Steven Klinger
**CFO:* Matthew Denton
**Treas:* Brad Madison

D-U-N-S 10-336-1754 IMP/EXP
PORT TOWNSEND PAPER CORP
(*Suby of* PORT TOWNSEND HOLDINGS CO INC) ★
100 Mill Rd, Port Townsend, WA 98368-2246
Tel (360) 385-3170 *Founded/Ownrshp* 2007
Sales 326.5MM *EMP* 585
SIC 2631 Paperboard mills
CEO: Steven Klinger
**CFO:* Matthew Denton
**Treas:* Brad Madison
Sls Mgr: Kevin Wright

PORTA LATHE
See PIPELINE SUPPLY & SERVICE LLC

D-U-N-S 05-290-5734
PORTAGE PUBLIC SCHOOLS
8107 Mustang Dr, Portage, MI 49002-5577
Tel (269) 323-6800 *Founded/Ownrshp* 1922
Sales 103.3MM *EMP* 1,200
Accts Rehmann Robson Grand Rapids
SIC 8211 Public elementary & secondary schools
Pr: Randy Vanantwerp
**Trst:* Kurt Droppers
**Trst:* Terri Novaria
**VP:* Randy Van Antwerp
Brnch Mgr: Donald Eastman
IT Man: Lou Cramer
Pr Dir: Michelle Kardinski
Teacher Pr: Brad Galin
Teacher Pr: Jennifer Tuyls

D-U-N-S 19-322-1645
PORTAGE TOWNSHIP SCHOOLS
PTS
6240 Us Highway 6, Portage, IN 46368-5057
Tel (219) 762-6511 *Founded/Ownrshp* 1958
Sales 57.5MM[E] *EMP* 1,200
SIC 8211 Public elementary school; Public junior high school; Public senior high school
Pr: Cheryl Opriskco
**Pr:* William Fekete
**VP:* Debra Ekdahl
Netwrk Eng: Ron Glos
Pr Dir: Shelley Campbell
HC Dir: Pat Olson
Pgrm Dir: Amber Morris

PORTAL INSURANCE AGENCY INC
See ASCENSION INSURANCE INC

D-U-N-S 03-813-8313
PORTAL INSURANCE AGENCY INC
ASCENSION BNFITS INSUR SLTIONS
1277 Treat Blvd Ste 650, Walnut Creek, CA 94597-7983
Tel (925) 937-8787 *Founded/Ownrshp* 2007
Sales NA *EMP* 450
SIC 6411 Insurance agents, brokers & service
Pr: Joe Tatum

PORTER CABLE/DELTA MACHINERY
See PORTER-CABLE CORP

PORTER CHEVROLET/HYUNDAI
See WILLIAM H PORTER INC

D-U-N-S 18-143-5892
■ PORTER FOUNDATION INC
PORTER MEMORIAL HOSPITAL
(*Suby of* COMMUNITY HEALTH SYSTEMS INC) ★
802 Laporte Ave, Valparaiso, IN 46383-5860
Tel (219) 465-4600 *Founded/Ownrshp* 2007
Sales 319.5MM[E] *EMP* 2,200
SIC 8062 General medical & surgical hospitals
Pr: Ronald C Winger
Pr: Terri Cummins
Bd of Dir: Susan Bauman
Trst: David A Butterfield
Dir Lab: Betty Fritts
Dir Rad: Brenda Shaw
Mtls Mgr: Pat Klancer
Mtls Mgr: Susan Sadler
Opers Mgr: Mark Huffman
Ansthlgy: Ahmad Khan
Ansthlgy: Richard Krizmanich

PORTER HEALTH CARE SYSTEM
See PORTER REGIONAL HOSPITAL

D-U-N-S 01-694-1051
■ PORTER HEALTH SERVICES INC
(*Suby of* PORTER MEMORIAL HOSPITAL) ★
814 Laporte Ave, Valparaiso, IN 46383-5860
Tel (219) 477-1013 *Founded/Ownrshp* 1994
Sales NA *EMP* 643[E]
SIC 6324 Hospital & medical service plans
Pr: Jonathan Nalli
**CFO:* Cheryl Sharmon
Sr VP: Jeff Waite
Dir Case M: Mirko Bebekoski
**Prin:* Passy Arias
Off Mgr: Talia Healy
Off Admin: Sue Erickson
MIS Dir: Paul Braun
QA Dir: Rayanna Henderson
QA Dir: Sandy Horst

PORTER MEMORIAL HOSPITAL
See PORTER FOUNDATION INC

PORTER NISSAN INFINITI
See RCP III LLC

D-U-N-S 07-051-8918
PORTER REGIONAL HOSPITAL
PORTER HEALTH CARE SYSTEM
85 E Us 6 Frontage Rd, Valparaiso, IN 46383
Tel (219) 263-4600 *Founded/Ownrshp* 2007
Sales 247.2MM[E] *EMP* 2,217[E]
SIC 8062 General medical & surgical hospitals
CEO: Stephen Lunn
Pr: Mary Brewer
CFO: Cheryl Harmon
Bd of Dir: Joseph Venditti
IT Man: Mark Wellons
Mtls Mgr: Susan Sadler
Pathlgst: Jun Hu
Pathlgst: Philip McGuire
Pathlgst: Timothy Prahlow
Doctor: Jyoti Patel

D-U-N-S 00-724-7679 IMP
■ PORTER-CABLE CORP
PORTER CABLE/DELTA MACHINERY
(*Suby of* BLACK & DECKER CORP) ★
4825 Highway 45 N Ste 880, Jackson, TN 38305-7900
Tel (731) 660-5986 *Founded/Ownrshp* 1981
Sales 128.4MM[E] *EMP* 1,000
SIC 3546 Power-driven handtools; Drills, portable, except rock: electric or pneumatic; Grinders, portable: electric or pneumatic; Sanders, hand: electric
Pr: Charles M Brown
**CEO:* Randall J Hohan
**Sr VP:* Tom Dewitt
VP: Marikay Jung
VP: Mike Strickland
Dir IT: Rocco Pizza
IT Man: Dave Tillman

D-U-N-S 13-373-0291
PORTERCARE ADVENTIST HEALTH SYSTEM
PORTERCARE ADVENTIST HOSPITAL
2525 S Downing St, Denver, CO 80210-5817
Tel (303) 778-5736 *Founded/Ownrshp* 1990
Sales 559.7MM[E] *EMP* 3,000
SIC 8062 Hospital, medical school affiliated with residency
CEO: Moore L Dean
**COO:* Dave Dookeram
**CFO:* Andrew Gaasch
**Chf Mktg O:* Thomas Drake

PORTERCARE ADVENTIST HOSPITAL
See PACIFIC ALLIANCE MEDICAL CENTER INC

PORTERCARE ADVENTIST HOSPITAL
See PARKER ADVENTIST HOSPITAL

PORTERCARE ADVENTIST HOSPITAL
See PORTERCARE ADVENTIST HEALTH SYSTEM

PORTERVILLE DEVELOPMENTAL CTR
See CALIFORNIA DEPARTMENT OF DEVELOPMENTAL SERVICES

D-U-N-S 82-837-0960
PORTFOLIO HOTELS & RESORTS LLC
601 Oakmont Ln Ste 420, Westmont, IL 60559-5557
Tel (630) 366-2018 *Founded/Ownrshp* 2005
Sales 3.1MM *EMP* 1,500
SIC 7011 Hotels & motels
Pr: Helmut Horn
**COO:* Graham Hershman
VP: Linda Leahy
**VP:* Michael Payne
Opers Mgr: Dennis Igoe
Opers Mgr: Alec Rummler
Sls Dir: Todd Wessing
Sls Mgr: Linda Eliopoulos

D-U-N-S 60-419-4204
PORTFOLIO LOGIC LLC
600 New Hampshire Ave Nw 9f, Washington, DC 20037-2403
Tel (202) 266-6519 *Founded/Ownrshp* 2003
Sales 182.3MM^E *EMP* 3,922
SIC 6726 8741 Investment offices; Management services

PORTICO BENEFIT SERVICES
See BOARD OF PENSIONS OF EVANGELICAL LUTHERAN CHURCH IN AMERICA

PORTILLO RESTAURANT GROUP, THE
See PORTILLOS HOT DOGS INC

D-U-N-S 06-848-9350
PORTILLOS HOT DOGS INC
PORTILLO RESTAURANT GROUP, THE
2001 Spring Rd Ste 400, Oak Brook, IL 60523-1903
Tel (630) 954-3773 *Founded/Ownrshp* 1963
Sales 131.1MM^E *EMP* 2,500
SIC 5812 5813 Fast-food restaurant, chain; Drinking places
Pr: Richard J Portillo
**VP:* Sharon Portillo
Exec: John Meyer
IT Man: Mike Dudzik
IT Man: Matt Harrison
Mktg Dir: John Keen

D-U-N-S 06-399-3000 EXP
■ **PORTION PAC INC**
(*Suby of* HEINZ KRAFT FOODS CO) ★
7325 Snider Rd, Mason, OH 45040-9193
Tel (513) 398-0400 *Founded/Ownrshp* 1989
Sales 185.3MM^E *EMP* 1,700
SIC 2033 2035 Catsup: packaged in cans, jars, etc.; Jams, including imitation: packaged in cans, jars, etc.; Jellies, edible, including imitation: in cans, jars, etc.; Marmalade: packaged in cans, jars, etc.; Seasonings & sauces, except tomato & dry; Mustard, prepared (wet); Horseradish, prepared; Dressings, salad: raw & cooked (except dry mixes)
Prin: Timothy E Hoberg
**Pr:* Jeffrey Berger
**Pr:* Pete Jack
Treas: Jill Aultman
**VP:* Leslie Boettcher
Mng Dir: Arthur C Jack
Genl Mgr: Susan Al

D-U-N-S 04-980-1640
PORTLAND ADVENTIST MEDICAL CENTER
ADVENTIST HEALTH
10123 Se Market St, Portland, OR 97216-2599
Tel (503) 257-2500 *Founded/Ownrshp* 1980
Sales 351.2MM *EMP* 12,000
SIC 8062 General medical & surgical hospitals
Ch Bd: Larry Dodds
**Pr:* Scott Reiner
CFO: Mark Perry
**Ex VP:* Bill Wing
**VP:* Mark Ashlock
**VP:* John Beaman
VP: Carol Kunau
Telecom Ex: Mike Bickford
CIO: Dave Eastman
CIO: Bill McQuaid
Dir IT: John Ruell

D-U-N-S 05-597-0453
PORTLAND CLINIC LLP
800 Sw 13th Ave, Portland, OR 97205-1999
Tel (503) 221-0161 *Founded/Ownrshp* 1943
Sales 89.6MM^E *EMP* 600
SIC 8011 Clinic, operated by physicians
CEO: J Michael Schwab
Pt: John M Barnes DPM
Pt: Laura E Bledsoe MD
Pt: Jeffrey C Cleven MD
Pt: Stewart D Cole Do
Pt: Clifford Cooper MD
Pt: Christina Duran MD
Pt: Zusman Ehud I
Pt: Michael Ericksen MD
Pt: Marni Foley MD
Pt: Suzanne Gwilliam MD
Pt: Thomas F Hirsh MD
Pt: Mary B Horrall MD
Pt: Nancy K Johnson MD
Pt: Kara M Kassay MD
Pt: Andrea M Kielich MD
Pt: Burton Lazar MD
Pt: Michael J Lee MD
Pt: Roger B Leverette MD
Pt: Jon C Malachowski MD
Pt: Andrew C McIvor MD

D-U-N-S 05-097-2025
PORTLAND COMMUNITY COLLEGE FOUNDATION INC
12000 Sw 49th Ave, Portland, OR 97219-7198
Tel (971) 722-6111 *Founded/Ownrshp* 1961
Sales 99.7MM *EMP* 3,000
Accts Kenneth Kuhns & Co Salem Or
SIC 8222 Community college
Pr: Dick Stenson
CFO: Wing-Kit Chung
**Sec:* Cheryl Burgermeister
**Prin:* Preston Pulliams
Ex Dir: Rick Zurow
Off Admin: Alycia Patterson
DP Exec: Katherine Fan
DP Exec: Eva Trujillo
MIS Dir: Wayne Chase
Dir IT: Tammy Billick
Sys/Dir: Ray Grant

PORTLAND FASTENERS
See ACME CONSTRUCTION SUPPLY CO INC

D-U-N-S 00-790-9054 IMP
▲ **PORTLAND GENERAL ELECTRIC CO** (OR)
121 Sw Salmon St, Portland, OR 97204-2977
Tel (503) 464-8000 *Founded/Ownrshp* 1930
Sales 1.9MMM *EMP* 2,646
Tkr Sym POR *Exch* NYS
SIC 4911 4922 Electric services; Distribution, electric power; Generation, electric power; Transmission, electric power; Natural gas transmission
Pr: James J Piro
**Ch Bd:* Jack E Davis
CFO: James F Lobdell
Ex VP: Jim Piro
Sr VP: William O Nicholson
Sr VP: Maria M Pope
VP: Larry N Bekkedahl
VP: Carol A Dillin
VP: J Jeffrey Dudley
VP: Campbell A Henderson
VP: Bradley Y Jenkins
VP: Dave Robertson
VP: W David Robertson
VP: Steve Sprague
VP: Kristin A Stathis
Exec: Gwen Willia
Board of Directors: John W Ballantine, Rodney L Brown Jr, David A Dietzler, Kirby A Dyess, Mark B Ganz, Kathryn J Jackson, Neil J Nelson, M Lee Pelton, Charles W Shivery

D-U-N-S 02-397-3816
PORTLAND GROUP INC
TPG
74 Salem Rd, Billerica, MA 01821
Tel (978) 262-1444 *Founded/Ownrshp* 1937
Sales 190.3MM^E *EMP* 250
SIC 5074 Plumbing & hydronic heating supplies
Pr: Howard E Rose
**Treas:* Richard E Fox

D-U-N-S 06-821-6716
PORTLAND HOTEL GARDEN INN
(*Suby of* NEW CASTLE HOTELS LLC) ★
145 Jetport Blvd, Portland, ME 04102-1990
Tel (207) 828-1117 *Founded/Ownrshp* 2012
Sales 5.8MM^E *EMP* 1,837^E
SIC 7011 Hotels
Prin: James Hackett

PORTLAND MACK TRUCKS
See TEC EQUIPMENT INC

PORTLAND PLASTICS
See ELKHART PLASTICS

D-U-N-S 10-721-5282
PORTLAND PUBLIC SCHOOL DISTRICT
353 Cumberland Ave, Portland, ME 04101-2957
Tel (207) 874-8100 *Founded/Ownrshp* 1850
Sales 77.3MM *EMP* 1,500
SIC 8211 Public elementary & secondary schools
V Ch: Laurie Davis
COO: Craig Worth
Bd of Dir: Elizabeth Holton
Ex Dir: Kate Snyder
Genl Mgr: Michelle Cravinho
Genl Mgr: Ray O'Donnell
Off Mgr: Lila Conley
Software D: Nicole Barnes
Pr Dir: Tess Nacelewicz
Pr Dir: Barbra Stobbard
Teacher Pr: Christine Racine

D-U-N-S 05-497-1650
PORTLAND PUBLIC SCHOOLS
501 N Dixon St, Portland, OR 97227-1876
Tel (503) 916-2000 *Founded/Ownrshp* 1856
Sales 691.8MM *EMP* 5,244
Accts Talbot Korvola & Warwick Llp
SIC 8211 Public elementary & secondary schools
VP: Scott Robinson
MIS Dir: Shawn Helm
Dir IT: Sarah Mongue
IT Man: Steve Fulmer
Software D: David Kaplan
Pr Dir: Jon Isaacs

D-U-N-S 05-222-6800
PORTLAND STATE UNIVERSITY
1600 Sw 4th Ave Ste 730, Portland, OR 97201-5519
Tel (503) 725-4444 *Founded/Ownrshp* 1946, 2014
Sales 351.7MM *EMP* 4,000
Accts Cliftonlarsonallen Llp Greenw
SIC 8221 University
Pr: Wim Weiwel
COO: Lisa Gray
CFO: Rebecca Hein
Ofcr: Paul Thomas
VP: Lindsay A Desrochers
VP: Mary C King
VP: Richard Knight
**VP:* Kevin Reynolds
Assoc Dir: Jeff Millard
Assoc Dir: Judy Van Dyck
Ex Dir: Jan Kurtz
Board of Directors: Dawn Boatman, Alan Finn

PORTLAND THORACIC SURGERY
See MERCY HOSPITAL

D-U-N-S 06-100-2440
PORTLAND WATER DISTRICT
225 Douglass St, Portland, ME 04102-2567
Tel (207) 761-8310 *Founded/Ownrshp* 1907
Sales 123.0MM^E *EMP* 200
Accts Macpage Llc South Portland
SIC 4941 4952 8741 Water supply; Sewerage systems; Management services
Treas: David Kane
Dir Lab: Mike Koza
Dir Lab: Roger Paradis
**Ex Dir:* James West
Genl Mgr: Ronald Miller
Dir IT: Chad Davis
VP Opers: Nate Whalen
**Snr Mgr:* Christopher Crovo

PORTNEUF MEDICAL CENTER
See POCATELLO HEALTH SYSTEM LLC

D-U-N-S 07-297-5253
PORTNEUF MEDICAL CENTER INC
651 Memorial Dr, Pocatello, ID 83201-4071
Tel (208) 239-1000 *Founded/Ownrshp* 2009
Sales 239.7MM *EMP* 1,200
SIC 8062

D-U-N-S 04-525-5726 IMP/EXP
■ **PORTS AMERICA INC**
PORTS AMERICA.COM
(*Suby of* AIG HIGHSTAR CAPITAL LP) ★
525 Washington Blvd, Jersey City, NJ 07310-1606
Tel (732) 635-3899 *Founded/Ownrshp* 2007
Sales 227.6MM^E *EMP* 400
SIC 4491 Stevedoring; Marine terminals
Pr: Michael F Hassing
**CFO:* Kevin Brown
Sr VP: Tom Wellman
VP: Tim Smith
Genl Mgr: Luke Doremus
Off Mgr: Yvonne Causby
Snr Sftwr: Mark Delcambre
Snr Sftwr: Geeta Desai
CIO: Nathan Johnson
IT Man: Martha Pasznik
Site Mgr: Chris Noble

PORTS AMERICA.COM
See PORTS AMERICA INC

D-U-N-S 04-271-0376
PORTS PETROLEUM CO INC
FUEL MART
1337 Blachleyville Rd, Wooster, OH 44691-9705
Tel (330) 264-1885 *Founded/Ownrshp* 1967
Sales 131.1MM^E *EMP* 250
SIC 5172 5983 5541

D-U-N-S 01-516-3483 EXP
PORTSMOUTH CHEVROLET INC
549 Us Highway 1 Byp, Portsmouth, NH 03801-4131
Tel (603) 436-5010 *Founded/Ownrshp* 1997
Sales 95.1MM^E *EMP* 300
SIC 5511 Automobiles, new & used
Pr: Anthony Dilorenzo

PORTSMOUTH CITY PUBLIC SCHOOLS
See PORTSMOUTH CITY SCHOOL BOARD

D-U-N-S 07-979-8847
PORTSMOUTH CITY PUBLIC SCHOOLS
801 Crawford St, Portsmouth, VA 23704-3822
Tel (757) 393-8751 *Founded/Ownrshp* 2015
Sales 55.1MM^E *EMP* 3,000^E
SIC 8211 Public elementary & secondary schools
IT Man: Karen S Streeter
Teacher Pr: Scott Ziegler
HC Dir: Frances L Gray
HC Dir: Herbert Robinson

D-U-N-S 87-755-2505
PORTSMOUTH CITY SCHOOL BOARD
PORTSMOUTH CITY PUBLIC SCHOOLS
801 Crawford St Fl 3, Portsmouth, VA 23704-3822
Tel (757) 393-8751 *Founded/Ownrshp* 1847
Sales 165.1MM *EMP* 3,000
Accts Cherry Bekaert & Holland Llp
SIC 8211 School board
Ch Bd: James Bridgeford
**Ch Bd:* Elizabeth N Hudgins

PORTSMOUTH DIVISION
See OSCO INDUSTRIES INC

D-U-N-S 07-874-1858
PORTSMOUTH HOSPITAL CORP
KING'S DAUGHTERS' MEDICAL CENT
(*Suby of* KINGS DAUGHTERS MEDICAL CTR) ★
1901 Argonne Rd, Portsmouth, OH 45662-2827
Tel (740) 991-4000 *Founded/Ownrshp* 2010
Sales 20.8MM *EMP* 2,082^E
SIC 8011 Medical centers
Ch: David Jones

D-U-N-S 36-106-8422
POSADOS CAFE INC
204 W Main St, Tyler, TX 75701
Tel (903) 534-1076 *Founded/Ownrshp* 1990
Sales 61.1MM^E *EMP* 1,800
SIC 5812 Mexican restaurant
Pr: Andrew Gugar
**COO:* Scott Nordon

D-U-N-S 07-886-3503 IMP
POSCO DAEWOO AMERICA CORP
(*Suby of* POSCO DAEWOO CORPORATION)
300 Frank W Burr Blvd, Teaneck, NJ 07666-6704
Tel (201) 591-8000 *Founded/Ownrshp* 1973
Sales 955.6MM^E *EMP* 31
Accts Kpmg Llp New York Ny
SIC 5131 5051 5169 5015 Textiles, woven; Pipe & tubing, steel; Chemicals, industrial & heavy; Tires, used
**CFO:* Sang C Shin

D-U-N-S 00-693-9367
POSEY COUNTY FARM BUREAU COOPERATIVE ASSOCIATION INC
817 W 4th St, Mount Vernon, IN 47620-1689
Tel (812) 838-4468 *Founded/Ownrshp* 1927
Sales 101.7MM^E *EMP* 65
Accts Blue & Co Llc Seymour In
SIC 5191 5172 5153 Farm supplies; Gases, liquefied petroleum (propane); Gasoline; Lubricating oils & greases; Grains
Pr: Thomas Weilbrenner
**Treas:* Christopher Cash
Genl Mgr: Jim Swinney

D-U-N-S 83-328-7506
POSEY COUNTY LLC
(*Suby of* POSEY COUNTY FARM BUREAU COOPERATIVE ASSOCIATION INC) ★
817 W 4th St, Mount Vernon, IN 47620-1621
Tel (812) 838-4468 *Founded/Ownrshp* 2001
Sales 101.2MM^E *EMP* 64
SIC 5191 Farm supplies
Ofcr: Jon Fifer

D-U-N-S 01-356-4216 IMP
POSILLICO CIVIL INC
1750 New Hwy, Farmingdale, NY 11735-1562
Tel (631) 249-1872 *Founded/Ownrshp* 1946
Sales 158.5MM^E *EMP* 350
Accts Grassi & Co Cpas Pc Jerich
SIC 1611 1542 General contractor, highway & street construction; Commercial & office building contractors
Ch Bd: Joseph K Posillico
CFO: Stephen C Bongiorno
**Ch:* Mario Posillico
**Ex VP:* Michael J Posillico
**Sr VP:* Joseph D Posillico III
**Sr VP:* Paul F Posillico
Sr VP: Joseph Sheehan
VP: Mike Trotta
Area Mgr: Peter Brindley
Snr PM: Adam Sobotka

D-U-N-S 10-605-4245 IMP/EXP
POSITEC TOOL CORP
(*Suby of* POSITEC POWER TOOLS (SUZHOU) CO., LTD.)
10130 Perimeter Pkwy # 300, Charlotte, NC 28216-2447
Tel (704) 599-3711 *Founded/Ownrshp* 2005
Sales 126.5MM^E *EMP* 114
SIC 5072 6719 Power tools & accessories; Personal holding companies, except banks
CEO: Yan Ko
**Pr:* Thomas E Duncan
**COO:* Paul Tellefsen
**Sr VP:* David Johnson
VP Mktg: Craig Taylor

D-U-N-S 96-795-0101 IMP
POSITEC USA INC
(*Suby of* POSITEC TOOL CORP) ★
10130 Perimeter Pkwy # 300, Charlotte, NC 28216-2447
Tel (704) 599-3711 *Founded/Ownrshp* 2011
Sales 121.0MM *EMP* 114
SIC 5072 Power tools & accessories
Pr: Tom Duncan
**COO:* Paul Tellefsen
Sr VP: David Johnson

D-U-N-S 00-744-7196 IMP
POSITRONIC INDUSTRIES INC (MO)
423 N Campbell Ave, Springfield, MO 65806-1007
Tel (417) 866-2322 *Founded/Ownrshp* 1966
Sales 75.0MM *EMP* 1,147
SIC 3678

POST & COURIER, THE
See EPI GROUP LLC

POST AND CAREER, THE
See CORDILLERA COMMUNICATIONS LLC

D-U-N-S 80-719-9112
POST APARTMENT HOMES LP
(*Suby of* POST PROPERTIES INC) ★
4401 Northsde Pkwy 800, Atlanta, GA 30327
Tel (404) 846-5000 *Founded/Ownrshp* 1993
Sales 384.0MM *EMP* 594
Accts Deloitte & Touche Llp Atlanta
SIC 6798 6513 Real estate investment trusts; Apartment building operators
Pr: David P Stockert
Pr: James Barnard
CFO: Christopher J Papa
Chf Inves: Tom Senkbeil
Ofcr: Arthur Quirk
Ex VP: Sherry Cohen
VP: Janet Appling
VP: Carla Barrie
VP: Holly Berney
VP: Carl Bonner
VP: Tricia Carlson
VP: Christi Clark
VP: Elizabeth Long
VP: Kathleen Mason
VP: Jamie Teabo
VP: David Wagner

D-U-N-S 04-475-9942
POST COMMUNITY MEDIA LLC
POST-NEWSWEEK MEDIA
(*Suby of* NASH HOLDINGS LLC) ★
1301 K St Nw, Washington, DC 20071-0004
Tel (301) 670-2565 *Founded/Ownrshp* 2013
Sales 92.9MM^E *EMP* 500
SIC 2711 2732 2721 Newspapers, publishing & printing; Newspapers: publishing only, not printed on site; Books: printing only; Magazines: publishing & printing
Pr: Chuck Lyons

POST CONSUMER BRANDS
See MOM BRANDS CO LLC

D-U-N-S 83-062-4628
■ **POST FOODS LLC**
(*Suby of* POST HOLDINGS INC) ★
275 Cliff St, Battle Creek, MI 49014-6354
Tel (269) 966-1000 *Founded/Ownrshp* 2011
Sales 92.6MM^E *EMP* 249^E
SIC 2043 Cereal breakfast foods
CEO: Kevin Hunt
Netwrk Eng: Bernice Klein
Sfty Mgr: Ted Krenkel
Plnt Mgr: Don Holtan

D-U-N-S 92-654-7287
■ **POST FOODS LLC**
(*Suby of* POST HOLDINGS INC) ★
20802 Kensington Blvd, Lakeville, MN 55044-8052
Tel (973) 658-2457 *Founded/Ownrshp* 2012
Sales 190.7MM^E *EMP* 1,600
SIC 2041 Grain cereals, cracked
Pr: Stephen Van Tassel
VP: Richared Cachion
VP: Bob Olson
Sls Mgr: David Hallman

D-U-N-S 80-573-0178
▲ **POST HOLDINGS INC**
2503 S Hanley Rd, Saint Louis, MO 63144-2503
Tel (314) 644-7600 *Founded/Ownrshp* 1897
Sales 5.0MMM *EMP* 7,950
Tkr Sym POST *Exch* NYS

SIC 2015 2034 2038 2041 2099 Egg processing; Potato products, dried & dehydrated; Frozen specialties; Flour mills, cereal (except rice); Packaged combination products: pasta, rice & potato; Peanut butter
Pr: Robert V Vitale
Ch Bd: William P Stiritz
Pr: Robert Vitale
CFO: Jeff A Zadoks
Ex VP: James L Holbrook
Sr VP: Diedre J Gray
VP: Brad Harper
Sls Dir: Duane Meade
Board of Directors: Jay W Brown, Edwin H Callison, Gregory H Curl, Robert E Grote, David W Kemper, David P Skarie

D-U-N-S 05-103-7513
POST PROPERTIES INC
4401 Northside Pkwy Nw # 800, Atlanta, GA 30327-5282
Tel (404) 846-5000 *Founded/Ownrshp* 1971
Sales 384.0MM *EMP* 619E
SIC 6798 6531 Real estate investment trusts; Real estate agents & managers; Rental agent, real estate
Pr: David P Stockert
**Ch Bd:* Robert C Goddard III
Ex VP: Sherry W Cohen
Ex VP: Charles A Konas
Ex VP: Thomas Senkbeil
Ex VP: S Jamie Teabo
Ex VP: David C Ward
Sr VP: Arthur J Quirk
VP: Linda Ricklef
VP: Shannon Sear
Exec: Lynn Allmond
Board of Directors: Ronald De Waal, Walter M Deriso Jr, Russell R French, Toni Jennings, John F Morgan Sr, Donald C Wood

D-U-N-S 80-738-0266
■ **POST SERVICES LLC**
(*Suby of* MAA) ★
4401 Northside Pkwy Nw # 800, Atlanta, GA 30327-3093
Tel (404) 846-5000 *Founded/Ownrshp* 2016
Sales 33.8MME *EMP* 1,108
SIC 6531 Real estate agents & managers
CEO: David Stockert
CFO: Christopher Papa

POST-NEWSWEEK MEDIA
See POST COMMUNITY MEDIA LLC

D-U-N-S 14-316-8610
POSTAL FLEET SERVICES INC
2808 N 5th St Ste 501, Saint Augustine, FL 32084-1907
Tel (904) 824-2007 *Founded/Ownrshp* 2002
Sales 29.1MM *EMP* 1,000
SIC 4214 Local trucking with storage
Pr: Don Dorris
**CFO:* Craig Gregory
**VP:* Brenda Dorris

POSTAL PRODUCTS UNLIMITED
See INTERNATIONAL COMMERCE & MARKETING CORP

D-U-N-S 83-247-0467
POSTROCK ENERGY CORP
210 Park Ave Ste 2750, Oklahoma City, OK 73102-5641
Tel (405) 600-7704 *Founded/Ownrshp* 2009
Sales 83.5MM *EMP* 143
SIC 1311 Crude petroleum & natural gas
CEO: Clark Edwards
Board of Directors: William H Damon III, Thomas J Edelman, Duke R Ligon, Alexander P Lynch, J Philip McCormick

POSTSECONDARY EDUCATN ALA DEPT
See ALABAMA COMMUNITY COLLEGE SYSTEM

POTAMKIN AUTOMOTIVE
See PLANET AUTOMOTIVE GROUP INC

D-U-N-S 83-570-4040
POTANDON PRODUCE LLC
1210 Pier View Dr, Idaho Falls, ID 83402-4966
Tel (208) 419-4200 *Founded/Ownrshp* 1994
Sales 370.6MM *EMP* 100E
Accts Rudd & Company Idaho Falls I
SIC 5148 0161 0722 Potatoes, fresh; Onion farm; Potatoes, machine harvesting services
COO: Steve Ottum
**Sr VP:* Mel Davenport
**VP:* Steve Elfering
**VP:* Lisa Swenson
**VP:* Dick Thomas
CIO: Travis Kearney
IT Man: Larry Sieg
Sales Asso: April Barnes
Sales Asso: Justin Hart
Sales Asso: Andrea Siepert
Sales Asso: Maureen Webster

POTAWATOMI BINGO CASINO
See BINGO POTAWATOMI

D-U-N-S 07-911-5651 IMP
▲ **POTBELLY CORP**
111 N Canal St Ste 850, Chicago, IL 60606-7204
Tel (312) 951-0600 *Founded/Ownrshp* 1977
Sales 372.8MM *EMP* 7,000
Tkr Sym PBPB *Exch* NGS
SIC 5812 Sandwiches & submarines shop
Ch Bd: Aylwin Lewis
COO: John Morlock
CFO: Michael Coyne
Sr VP: Anne Ewing
Sr VP: Sherry Ostrowski
Sr VP: Julie Younglove-Webb
Dist Mgr: James Waldner
Genl Mgr: Duane Acha
Genl Mgr: Anna Paine
Genl Mgr: Jessica Scheffel
Sls Mgr: Karen Holden
Board of Directors: Peter Bassi, Dan Ginsberg, Marla Gottschalk, Susan Chapman-Hughes, Harvey Kanter, Carl Warschausky

D-U-N-S 02-754-8767 IMP
■ **POTELCO INC**
(*Suby of* QUANTA SERVICES INC) ★
14103 Stewart Rd, Sumner, WA 98390-9641
Tel (253) 826-7300 *Founded/Ownrshp* 1965
Sales 247.2MME *EMP* 800
SIC 1623 Telephone & communication line construction; Electric power line construction
CEO: Gary A Tucci
**Pr:* Stephen C Wetherford
**Treas:* Rick Beloit
VP Bus Dev: Steve Wetherford
VP Opers: Craig Davis

D-U-N-S 07-961-8716 IMP/EXP
POTENTIAL INDUSTRIES INC
922 E E St, Wilmington, CA 90744-6145
Tel (310) 807-4466 *Founded/Ownrshp* 1975
Sales 166.0MME *EMP* 150
SIC 4953 5093 Recycling, waste materials; Scrap & waste materials
Pr: Anthony J Fan
**Pr:* Tony Fan
**CEO:* Henry J Chen
**Sec:* Jessie Chen
VP: Dan Domonoske
**VP:* Daniel J Domonoske
VP: Dan Domonosky
Dir Bus: Ken Wong
Off Mgr: Teresa Huang

D-U-N-S 00-944-8200 IMP/EXP
▲ **POTLATCH CORP**
601 W 1st Ave Ste 1600, Spokane, WA 99201-3807
Tel (509) 835-1500 *Founded/Ownrshp* 1903
Sales 575.3MM *EMP* 927
Tkr Sym PCH *Exch* NGS
SIC 0831 6798 Gathering of forest products; Real estate investment trusts
Ch Bd: Michael J Covey
**Pr:* Eric J Cremers
CFO: Jerald W Richards
VP: William R Dereu
VP: William Dereu
VP: Lorrie D Scott
VP: Thomas J Temple
VP: Tom Temple
CTO: Shane Hamby
Sfty Dirs: Randy Lipscy
Board of Directors: Linda M Breard, William L Driscoll, Charles P Grenier, John S Moody, Lawrence S Peiros, Gregory L Quesnel

D-U-N-S 02-920-2330
■ **POTLATCH TELEPHONE CO**
TDS
(*Suby of* TDS TELECOMMUNICATIONS CORP) ★
702 E Main, Kendrick, ID 83537
Tel (208) 289-5701 *Founded/Ownrshp* 1988
Sales 853.0MM *EMP* 99
SIC 4813 Local telephone communications; Long distance telephone communications
Pr: David Wittwer
**VP:* David Folsom
**Prin:* Daniel Schuelke

D-U-N-S 04-338-1565
■ **POTOMAC EDISON CO** (VA)
FIRSTENERGY
(*Suby of* ALLEGHENY ENERGY INC) ★
10802 Bower Ave, Williamsport, MD 21795-3016
Tel (800) 686-0011 *Founded/Ownrshp* 1947, 1922
Sales 418.9MME *EMP* 1,150
SIC 4911 Transmission, electric power; Distribution, electric power
CEO: Anthony J Alexander
**Pr:* Charles E Jones Jr
**Pr:* Joseph H Richardson
**Ex VP:* Mark T Clark
**Ex VP:* Leila L Vespoli
**Sr VP:* Lynn M Cavalier
**Sr VP:* Michael J Dowling
Genl Mgr: Donald Beatty
Genl Mgr: Daniel Tompkins

D-U-N-S 00-692-0284
■ **POTOMAC ELECTRIC POWER CO** (VA)
PEPCO
(*Suby of* EXELON) ★
701 9th St Nw Ste 3, Washington, DC 20001-4572
Tel (202) 872-2000 *Founded/Ownrshp* 1896
Sales 2.1MMM *EMP* 1,471E
SIC 4911 Distribution, electric power; Transmission, electric power
Pr: David M Velazquez
**Ch Bd:* Joseph M Rigby
CFO: Frederick J Boyle
Chf Mktg O: Charlie Driggs
Sr VP: Leslie Zimberg
VP: Ronald K Clark
VP: Peter E Meier
Prin: Charles R Dickerson
Prin: Kevin C Fitzgerald
Prin: William M Gausman
Prin: Michael J Sullivan
Board of Directors: Charles R Dickerson, Kevin C Fitzgerald, William M Gausman, Michael J Sullivan

D-U-N-S 01-547-8465
■ **POTOMAC HOLDING LLC**
(*Suby of* NETSCOUT SYSTEMS INC) ★
2200 Penn Ave Nw Ste 800w, Washington, DC 20037-1731
Tel (202) 828-0850 *Founded/Ownrshp* 2014
Sales 114.5MME *EMP* 483
SIC 3823 Industrial instrmnts msrmnt display/control process variable
Pr: James A Lico
CFO: Daniel L Comas

D-U-N-S 01-010-0196
POTOMAC HOSPITAL CORP OF PRINCE WILLIAM
SENTARA NORTHERN VA MED CTR
(*Suby of* SENTARA CNCER NTWRK NORFOLK CI) ★
2300 Opitz Blvd, Woodbridge, VA 22191-3399
Tel (703) 523-1000 *Founded/Ownrshp* 1968
Sales 214.3MM *EMP* 1,300
Accts Kpmg Llp Norfolk Va
SIC 8062 General medical & surgical hospitals
Pr: David L Bernd
Board of Directors: James M Cooper, Kenneth S Rholl

D-U-N-S 14-621-4242
POTTER CONCRETE OF HOUSTON INC
POTTER SUPPLY
2400 E Pioneer Dr, Irving, TX 75061-8900
Tel (214) 630-2191 *Founded/Ownrshp* 1999
Sales 152.6MME *EMP* 1,200
SIC 1771 Concrete work
Pr: Dennis Lewis
VP: Noel Nalls
Sfty Dirs: Randy Ridgdill

POTTER SUPPLY
See POTTER CONCRETE OF HOUSTON INC

D-U-N-S 00-201-0858 IMP/EXP
POTTERS INDUSTRIES LLC
(*Suby of* PQ CORP) ★
300 Lindenwood Dr, Malvern, PA 19355-1740
Tel (610) 651-4700 *Founded/Ownrshp* 1914, 2005
Sales 183.8MME *EMP* 635
SIC 3231 Reflector glass beads, for highway signs or reflectors
Pr: Robert Mulhall
CFO: William Levy
Treas: Amy Ard
Treas: Mike Feehan
VP: Hector Martinez-Rossier
VP: Robert Muhlhall
VP: Timothy J Palmer
VP: Maxwell James Singleton
Off Admin: Janet Mizdol
QA Dir: Alexander Williams
Opers Mgr: Milt Ginsiorsky

POTTERY BARN
See WILLIAMS-SONOMA STORES INC

D-U-N-S 17-823-3490 EXP
■ **POTTERY BARN INC**
(*Suby of* WILLIAMS-SONOMA INC) ★
3250 Van Ness Ave, San Francisco, CA 94109-1012
Tel (415) 421-7900 *Founded/Ownrshp* 1986
Sales 516.5MME *EMP* 5,300
SIC 5719 Kitchenware; Lighting, lamps & accessories; Window furnishings; Beddings & linens
Pr: W Howard Lester
**VP:* Patrick J Connolly
Genl Mgr: Amanda Hemsley
Opers Mgr: Kim Stahley
Sls&Mrk Ex: Alison Bagley
Sls&Mrk Ex: Nancy Bull
Sls Mgr: Allison Lepage

D-U-N-S 12-155-3494
■ **POTTERY BARN KIDS INC**
(*Suby of* WILLIAMS-SONOMA INC) ★
3250 Van Ness Ave, San Francisco, CA 94109-1012
Tel (415) 421-7900 *Founded/Ownrshp* 1998
Sales 155.9MME *EMP* 1,300
SIC 5999 Children's furniture
CEO: Dale W Hilpert
**CEO:* Patrick J Connolly

D-U-N-S 62-079-3778
POTTSTOWN AREA HEALTH & WELLNESS FOUNDATION
152 E High St Ste 500, Pottstown, PA 19464-5400
Tel (610) 323-2006 *Founded/Ownrshp* 2003
Sales NA *EMP* 1,050
SIC 6324 Hospital & medical service plans
Pr: Steve Maclauchlan
**CFO:* Micahel Zwetschkenbaum
Treas: Neal Fegely
Ofcr: Laurie Betts
Ofcr: Ashley Pultorak
Ex Dir: Rob Henry

D-U-N-S 07-987-9619
POTTSTOWN HOSPITAL CO LLC
1600 E High St, Pottstown, PA 19464-5093
Tel (610) 327-7000 *Founded/Ownrshp* 2015
Sales 641.8ME *EMP* 1,000
SIC 8062 General medical & surgical hospitals
CEO: Rich Newell

D-U-N-S 07-550-7442
■ **POTTSTOWN MEMORIAL MEDICAL CENTER**
(*Suby of* COMMUNITY HEALTH SYSTEMS INC) ★
1600 E High St, Pottstown, PA 19464-5093
Tel (610) 327-7000 *Founded/Ownrshp* 1965, 2003
Sales 180.1MM *EMP* 1,100
SIC 8062 General medical & surgical hospitals
CEO: Rich Newell
**CEO:* John Kirby
CFO: Mike Zwetchkenbaum
Dir Lab: Dante Dimarzio
Dir Rx: Diana Gordon
Dir QC: Joan Garzarelli
Mktg Mgr: Helen Guardiani
Dir Health: Alice Colosimo
HC Dir: Lindsay Prendergrast
Board of Directors: Alan Mitchell

D-U-N-S 07-834-2219
POUDRE SCHOOL DISTRICT
2407 Laporte Ave, Fort Collins, CO 80521-2211
Tel (970) 482-7420 *Founded/Ownrshp* 1960
Sales 300.2MM *EMP* 907
Accts Cliftonlarsonallen Llp Broom
SIC 8211 Public elementary school; Public junior high school; Public senior high school
Pr: Cathy Kipp
V Ch: Marcene Sonneborn
Bd of Dir: Vicki Brackens
Ofcr: Barb Ozee
**VP:* David Trask
Ex Dir: Robert Hix
Ex Dir: Vicki Thompson
Teacher Pr: Victoria Thompson

D-U-N-S 07-996-2759
POUDRE VALLEY HEALTH CARE INC
POUDRE VALLEY HEALTH SYSTEM
(*Suby of* UNIVERSITY COLORADO HOSPITAL) ★
2315 E Harmony Rd Ste 200, Fort Collins, CO 80528-8620
Tel (970) 495-7000 *Founded/Ownrshp* 1962
Sales 480.4MM *EMP* 2,800
SIC 8062 Hospital, affiliated with AMA residency
CEO: Rulon Stacey
**Pr:* Keving Unger
Ofcr: Rich Cohan
Ofcr: Steve Eberle
VP: William A Neff
VP: Fernando Pedroza
Dir Lab: Karen Getzy
Dir Rad: Christopher M Fleener
Genl Mgr: Christy Evans
Sls Dir: Bob Formicola
Mktg Mgr: Armi Hall

POUDRE VALLEY HEALTH SYSTEM
See POUDRE VALLEY HEALTH CARE INC

D-U-N-S 18-558-3986
POULSBO RV INC
19705 Viking Ave Nw, Poulsbo, WA 98370-8351
Tel (360) 697-4445 *Founded/Ownrshp* 1992
Sales 92.4MME *EMP* 275
SIC 5561 Recreational vehicle dealers
Pr: Ken Wakazuru
Exec: Scott Foreman
Genl Mgr: Ondine Bonser
IT Man: Malcolm Clark
Sls Mgr: Jim Renzo

D-U-N-S 01-891-9274
POULTRY PRODUCTS CO INC
(*Suby of* POULTRY PRODUCTS CO OF NEW ENGLAND INC) ★
11 Bemis Rd, Hooksett, NH 03106-2620
Tel (603) 668-7414 *Founded/Ownrshp* 1978
Sales 160.8MME *EMP* 180
SIC 5144 Poultry products
Pr: Julian S Stogniew

D-U-N-S 13-335-8544
POULTRY PRODUCTS CO OF NEW ENGLAND INC
11 Bemis Rd, Hooksett, NH 03106-2620
Tel (603) 263-1600 *Founded/Ownrshp* 1999
Sales 160.8MME *EMP* 250
SIC 5147 5149 Meats, fresh; Canned goods: fruit, vegetables, seafood, meats, etc.
Pr: Julian S Stogniew
Genl Mgr: Mike Chasse
Sales Asso: MEI Jiang

D-U-N-S 07-872-7336 IMP
POWAY UNIFIED SCHOOL DISTRICT
15250 Ave Of Science, San Diego, CA 92128-3406
Tel (858) 748-0010 *Founded/Ownrshp* 1962
Sales 370.3MM *EMP* 2,800
Accts Wilkinson Hadley King & Co L
SIC 8211 Public elementary school; Public junior high school; Public senior high school
VP: Jennifer Boles
Dir Sec: Steve Salvati
Off Admin: Debbie Sweezey
Pr Dir: Christine Paik
Schl Brd P: Kimberley Beatty
Teacher Pr: Sandra Huezo
HC Dir: Kathy Purcell

D-U-N-S 79-140-8388
POWCO OF LOUISIANA LLC
POWER WELL SERVICE
208 Gunther Ln, Belle Chasse, LA 70037-3156
Tel (504) 394-6005 *Founded/Ownrshp* 2002
Sales 137.7MME *EMP* 502
SIC 3593 Fluid power cylinders & actuators

D-U-N-S 00-783-6273
POWDER RIVER ENERGY CORP
221 Main St, Sundance, WY 82729
Tel (307) 283-3531 *Founded/Ownrshp* 1945
Sales 200.6MM *EMP* 269
SIC 4911 Distribution, electric power
CEO: Michael E Easley
**Pr:* Tom L Davis
Pr: Doug Fink
Pr: Dave Werner
**CFO:* Floyd Kanode
Treas: Philip Habeck
**Sec:* Pam Kinchen
Sr Cor Off: Ray Destefano
**VP:* Walt Christensen
VP: Todd Dughman
VP: Doug Wilson

D-U-N-S 00-787-5164
POWDR CORP
1790 Bonanza Dr Ste W201, Park City, UT 84060-7529
Tel (435) 647-5490 *Founded/Ownrshp* 1984
Sales 96.7MME *EMP* 1,839
SIC 7011 Ski lodge
Pr: John Cumming
Sr VP: Herwig Demschar
Sr VP: Krista Parry
**VP:* David Cumming
Dir IT: Anthony Flores

D-U-N-S 02-732-2346
POWELL - CHRISTENSEN INC
R E POWELL DISTRIBUTING
501 E Wine Country Rd, Grandview, WA 98930-1091
Tel (509) 882-2115 *Founded/Ownrshp* 1980
Sales 115.8MME *EMP* 290
SIC 5171 4212 Petroleum bulk stations; Petroleum haulage, local
Pr: Gary B Christensen
**COO:* Tony Christensen
**CFO:* Bill Betterton
**CFO:* Annette H Christensen
CFO: Annette H Cristensen
**VP:* Brandon Z Christensen
Genl Mgr: Rudy Oldbrich

POWELL COMPANIES
See POWELL CONSTRUCTION CO INC

D-U-N-S 04-735-8775 IMP
POWELL CONSTRUCTION CO INC
POWELL COMPANIES
3622 Bristol Hwy Ste 1, Johnson City, TN 37601-1390
Tel (423) 282-0111 *Founded/Ownrshp* 1969
Sales 156.0MM^E *EMP* 400
SIC 1542 1221 1541 Nonresidential construction; Commercial & office building contractors; Institutional building construction; Coal preparation plant, bituminous or lignite; Steel building construction
Ch: James J Powell
Treas: Richard Powell
VP: George Bajko
VP: David Horton
VP: Danny King

D-U-N-S 00-807-4387 IMP/EXP
■ **POWELL ELECTRICAL SYSTEMS INC**
PEMCO
(*Suby of* POWELL INDUSTRIES INC) ★
8550 Mosley Rd, Houston, TX 77075-1180
Tel (708) 409-1200 *Founded/Ownrshp* 1977
Sales 495.0MM^E *EMP* 2,200
SIC 3625 Control equipment, electric
Ch Bd: Thomas W Powell
**Pr:* M Lucas
**Pr:* Michael Lucas
**CFO:* Don R Madison
Sales Asso: Thomas Hegemeyer

D-U-N-S 00-281-1768
POWELL ELECTRONICS INC
200 Commodore Dr, Swedesboro, NJ 08085-1270
Tel (856) 241-8000 *Founded/Ownrshp* 1946
Sales 108.4MM^E *EMP* 205
Accts Kelly Welde & Co Llp Brooma
SIC 3678 Electronic connectors
CEO: Ernest Schilling Jr
**CFO:* Schawn E Beatty
VP: T Roy McGain
Opers Mgr: Bobbi Martin
Sls&Mrk Ex: Pete Holcombe
Manager: James McGuinness
Sales Asso: Dawn Bray
Sales Asso: Barb Gaulin
Sales Asso: Pat Moore
Sales Asso: Teresa Tavalone
Board of Directors: Charles P Connolly Jr, Edward Kicak, Stuart Newman, Merle Wolfson

D-U-N-S 08-835-6563 IMP/EXP
▲ **POWELL INDUSTRIES INC**
8550 Mosley Rd, Houston, TX 77075-1180
Tel (713) 944-6900 *Founded/Ownrshp* 1947
Sales 565.2MM *EMP* 2,940
Tkr Sym POWL *Exch* NGS
SIC 3612 3613 3625 3643 3823 Power & distribution transformers; Switchgear & switchgear accessories; Motor controls & accessories; Bus bars (electrical conductors); Industrial process control instruments
Pr: Brett A Cope
Ofcr: Don R Madison
VP: Milburn E Honeycutt
VP: Jimmy Pendley
CIO: Rob Duncan
Dir IT: Toby Derry
IT Man: Ram Kurelli
Netwrk Mgr: Theresa Brummett
Web Dev: Julie Spears
Plnt Mgr: Joe Eapen
Sales Exec: Matthew Richards
Board of Directors: Joseph L Becherer, Eugene L Butler, Christopher E Cragg, Bonnie V Hancock, Scott E Rozell, Stephen W Seale Jr, John D White

D-U-N-S 03-478-8521 IMP/EXP
POWER & TELEPHONE SUPPLY CO
PT SUPPLY
2673 Yale Ave, Memphis, TN 38112-3396
Tel (901) 324-6116 *Founded/Ownrshp* 1963
Sales 263.7MM^E *EMP* 347
SIC 5063 5999 Power wire & cable; Telephone & telegraph wire & cable; Power transmission equipment, electric; Telephone equipment & systems
CEO: Jennifer Pentecost Sims
**Ch Bd:* Jim Pentecost
COO: Dale Stevenson
COO: Judy Wakefield
Treas: Varnell Henry
Sr Cor Off: Mark Kaman
VP: Jim Drain
VP: William Meadley
**VP:* Don Pentecost
VP: Jim Qualkenbush
VP: Carol Tosh

POWER AUTH OF THE STATE NY
See NEW YORK POWER AUTHORITY

POWER AUTOMATION SYSTEMS
See CALIFORNIA NATURAL PRODUCTS

D-U-N-S 02-537-9575
■ **POWER CO USA LLC**
(*Suby of* PREMIER HOLDING CORPORATION)
1165 N Clark St Ste 400, Chicago, IL 60610-7919
Tel (312) 496-3729 *Founded/Ownrshp* 2010
Sales 348.3MM^E *EMP* 67
SIC 8748 Energy conservation consultant
**Mng Pt:* Patrick Farah
VP Sls: Mark Link

D-U-N-S 17-123-8095
POWER CONSTRUCTION CO LLC
8750 W Bryn Mawr Ave, Chicago, IL 60631-3655
Tel (312) 596-6960 *Founded/Ownrshp* 1999
Sales 185.9MM^E *EMP* 185
SIC 1541 1542 Industrial buildings & warehouses; Commercial & office building, new construction
Pr: Terry Graber
**Ex VP:* Jeff Geier
**VP:* Bob Gallo
VP: Jonathan Gorman
VP: Gary Schreiber
Exec: Carl Brown
Exec: Bob Deven
Exec: Chris Goray
Ex Dir: Jamie Hendricks
CTO: Mike McLaughlin
Dir IT: Pat Kenny

D-U-N-S 07-988-7942
■ **POWER CORP OF AMERICA**
(*Suby of* GOLDFIELD CORP DEL) ★
4647 Clyde Morris Blvd, Port Orange, FL 32129-3000
Tel (386) 333-6441 *Founded/Ownrshp* 2013
Sales 114.0MM^E *EMP* 128^E
SIC 1731 1623 Electric power systems contractors; General electrical contractor; Electric power line construction; Communication line & transmission tower construction
Pr: Robert Jones

D-U-N-S 62-282-1494
POWER DESIGN INC
11600 9th St N, Saint Petersburg, FL 33716-2320
Tel (727) 210-0492 *Founded/Ownrshp* 1989
Sales 101.7MM^E *EMP* 275^E
Accts Cherry Bekaert Llp Tampa Flo
SIC 1731 Electrical work
CEO: Mitch Permuy
Pr: Rob McMillian
Pr: Joe Micallef
Pr: Lauren Permuy
Pr: Mikhail Zeltser
COO: Meredith Zdon
**CFO:* Dana Permuy
VP: Jack Brock
VP: Ken Norton
**VP:* Dana F Permuy
Exec: Colette Meyer
Dir Soc: Jayme White

D-U-N-S 07-871-7370 IMP
POWER DISTRIBUTORS LLC
CENTRAL POWER SYSTEMS
3700 Paragon Dr, Columbus, OH 43228-9750
Tel (614) 876-3533 *Founded/Ownrshp* 2012
Sales 204.3MM^E *EMP* 230^E
SIC 5084 Engines & parts, air-cooled
Pr: Matthew Finn
VP: Rob Smith
Rgnl Mgr: Richard Baer
IT Man: Ryan McAlister
Sales Asso: Clarice Haney

D-U-N-S 08-932-0642
POWER ENGINEERS INC
3940 Glenbrook Dr, Hailey, ID 83333-8446
Tel (208) 788-3456 *Founded/Ownrshp* 1976
Sales 395.1MM *EMP* 503
Accts Deloitte & Touche Llp Boise
SIC 8711 Electrical or electronic engineering; Industrial engineers
Pr: Jack Hand
**Ch Bd:* Randy Pollock
CFO: Leslie Carter
**Treas:* Jan James
**Ex VP:* John Cavanaugh
Ex VP: Bill Eisinger
**Ex VP:* Gerry Murray
VP: Ron Beazer
VP: Mark Conroy
VP: Connie Conway
**VP:* William Eisinger
**VP:* Frank Halverson
**VP:* William Hansen
**VP:* John Henning
**VP:* Brent Lackey
**VP:* Timothy Ostermeier
Board of Directors: Randy Pollock, John Cavanaugh, Bruce Truxal, Bill Eisinger, Randy Grass, Frank Halverson, Jack Hand, Bill Hansen, Jan James, Christopher Kensel, Brent Lackey

D-U-N-S 00-792-1455 IMP/EXP
POWER EQUIPMENT CO (TN)
(*Suby of* BRAMCO INC) ★
3300 Alcoa Hwy, Knoxville, TN 37920-5591
Tel (865) 577-5563 *Founded/Ownrshp* 1946
Sales 83.8MM^E *EMP* 200
SIC 5082 3531 7353 Road construction equipment; Road construction & maintenance machinery; Construction machinery; Heavy construction equipment rental; Earth moving equipment, rental or leasing
Pr: Chris Gaylor
CFO: Michael Brennan
Sr VP: Bob Tucker
VP: Priscilla W Galgan
VP Mktg: Bill Kurtz
Mktg Dir: Jennifer Hagemeyer
Mktg Dir: Rob Hatcher
Mktg Dir: Karl Kaukins
Mktg Dir: David Klein
Mktg Dir: Bob McClure
Mktg Dir: Simon Robins

D-U-N-S 87-303-0142
POWER HOME REMODELING GROUP LLC
2501 Seaport Dr Lbby 1, Chester, PA 19013-2249
Tel (610) 874-5000 *Founded/Ownrshp* 2012
Sales 16.3MM^E *EMP* 1,650^E
SIC 1751 1761 Window & door (prefabricated) installation; Roofing contractor; Siding contractor
CEO: Corey Schiller
Pr: Seth Brombacher
Pr: Jeff Gordun
Pr: Michael McGoldrick
Pr: Tat Nsindu
**CEO:* Jeff Kaliner
**COO:* Rob Borislow
**CFO:* Alfred Ferraioli
**CFO:* Adam Kaliner
Ofcr: JD Diskin
VP: Aj Arrese
Exec: Jacquelyn Smith

D-U-N-S 18-891-9468
▲ **POWER INTEGRATIONS INC**
5245 Hellyer Ave, San Jose, CA 95138-1002
Tel (408) 414-9200 *Founded/Ownrshp* 1988
Sales 343.9MM *EMP* 595^E
Accts Deloitte & Touche Llp San Jos
Tkr Sym POWI *Exch* NGS
SIC 3674 Integrated circuits, semiconductor networks, etc.
Pr: Balu Balakrishnan
CFO: Sandeep Nayyar
VP: Wolfgang Ademmer
VP: Radu Barsan
VP: Derek Bell
VP: Mike Matthews
VP: Raja Petrakian
VP: Thomas Simonis
VP: Ben Sutherland
VP: Clifford J Walker
VP Mktg: Douglas Bailey
Board of Directors: Alan D Bickell, Nicholas E Brathwaite, William George, E Floyd Kvamme, Steven J Sharp

D-U-N-S 00-312-6971 IMP
POWER LINE INFRASTRUCTURE SERVICES INC (TX)
TESSCO
(*Suby of* POWER LINE SERVICES INC) ★
1031 Andrews Hwy, Midland, TX 79701-3805
Tel (432) 682-1991 *Founded/Ownrshp* 1998
Sales 119.4MM^E *EMP* 470
Accts Johnson Miller & Co Cpa S Pc
SIC 1623 Water, sewer & utility lines
CEO: Mark Crowson
**CFO:* Ken Dodgen
**CFO:* Bobby Page
**CFO:* Bradley P Romanchuk
**CFO:* Gena Steelman
**Sr VP:* Michael Cutrone
**Sr VP:* Mike Lawson
**Sr VP:* Ronald L Moose
**VP:* John Dolan
**VP:* Dennis Grubb
VP: Billy King
**VP:* Kendall C Shirley
Exec: Barry Woods
Board of Directors: Don Bishop, Mike Black, Ted Collins, Jerry L Hudgeons, Mike Lawson, Ricky L Smith, Jim Whitney

D-U-N-S 83-233-2493
POWER LINE SERVICES INC
(*Suby of* PLH GROUP INC) ★
400 Las Colinas Blvd E, Irving, TX 75039-5579
Tel (214) 272-0500 *Founded/Ownrshp* 2009
Sales 407.7MM^E *EMP* 1,000
SIC 1623 Electric power line construction
Pr: Mark Crowson

D-U-N-S 01-733-4285
POWER LINE SUPPLY CO
(*Suby of* UTILITY SUPPLY AND CONSTRUCTION CO) ★
420 S Roth St Ste A, Reed City, MI 49677-9115
Tel (231) 832-2297 *Founded/Ownrshp* 1963
Sales 127.4MM^E *EMP* 350
SIC 5063

D-U-N-S 08-011-1104
POWER PACKAGING INC
(*Suby of* EXEL LOGISTICS) ★
525 Dunham Rd Ste 3, Saint Charles, IL 60174-1493
Tel (630) 377-3838 *Founded/Ownrshp* 2007
Sales 50.2MM^E *EMP* 1,200
SIC 7389 Packaging & labeling services
Pr: Gordon Gruszka
**VP:* Ernest Shepard
**Ex Dir:* Chuck Woods
QA Dir: Ashley Schmitting
Natl Sales: Sharon Widauf

D-U-N-S 60-892-6952 EXP
■ **POWER PARAGON INC**
POWER SYSTEMS GROUP
(*Suby of* L-3 COMMUNICATIONS HOLDINGS INC) ★
901 E Ball Rd, Anaheim, CA 92805-5916
Tel (714) 956-9200 *Founded/Ownrshp* 1994
Sales 131.3MM^E *EMP* 619
SIC 3612 3613 3621 3643 Transformers, except electric; Switchgear & switchboard apparatus; Motors & generators; Current-carrying wiring devices
Pr: David R Riley
Pr: Bruce Moore
VP: Michael R Allen
VP: Michael Benthale
VP: Klaus Kahrs
VP: Richard Meyer
VP: Monte Wilcox

D-U-N-S 13-178-0202 IMP/EXP
POWER PARTNERS INC
(*Suby of* OPENGATE CAPITAL LLC) ★
200 Newton Bridge Rd, Athens, GA 30607-1144
Tel (706) 548-3121 *Founded/Ownrshp* 2016
Sales 228.8MM^E *EMP* 500
SIC 3612 Transformers, except electric
Pr: Jack Roberts
**CFO:* James Murray
VP: Stonecipher Mike
**CTO:* Joe Lishok
IT Man: Cammi Bell-Garrison
VP Mktg: Tom Lopp
VP Sls: Scott Childs
Snr Mgr: Wesley Farris

POWER PLUS
See SR BRAY LLC

D-U-N-S 07-923-5793 IMP
POWER PRODUCTS LLC
GARDNER BENDER
N85w12545 Westbrook Xing, Menomonee Falls, WI 53051-3330
Tel (262) 293-0600 *Founded/Ownrshp* 2009
Sales 378.6MM^E *EMP* 971^E
SIC 3679 3699 3691 Power supplies, all types: static; Electrical equipment & supplies; Nickel cadmium storage batteries

D-U-N-S 06-577-2584 IMP
POWER SALES AND ADVERTISING
9909 Lakeview Ave, Lenexa, KS 66219-2503
Tel (913) 324-4900 *Founded/Ownrshp* 1975
Sales 90.7MM^E *EMP* 55
SIC 5199 Advertising specialties
Pr: David Roberts
**VP:* Trent Bernard
Mktg Dir: Courtney Ryan
Manager: Zach Fletcher
Sls Mgr: Nathan Quance

D-U-N-S 01-052-6643 IMP/EXP
■ **POWER SOLUTIONS INC**
COMMANDER GREAT LAKES
(*Suby of* POWER SOLUTIONS INTERNATIONAL INC) ★
201 Mittel Dr, Wood Dale, IL 60191-1116
Tel (630) 350-9400 *Founded/Ownrshp* 1988
Sales 101.5MM^E *EMP* 149^E
SIC 5084 Engines & parts, diesel
Pr: Gary S Winemaster
**COO:* Eric Cohen
**CFO:* Daniel Gorey
Treas: Ken Winemaster
VP: Jeff Ehlers
VP: Ryan King
Prgrm Mgr: Ryan Smith
Genl Mgr: Jim Needham
Snr Ntwrk: Tab Browning
Opers Mgr: Michael Laut
Prd Mgr: John Ehlen

D-U-N-S 96-974-2498
▲ **POWER SOLUTIONS INTERNATIONAL INC**
201 Mittel Dr, Wood Dale, IL 60191-1116
Tel (630) 350-9400 *Founded/Ownrshp* 2011
Sales 348.0MM *EMP* 819^E
Tkr Sym PSIX *Exch* NGM
SIC 5084 Oil refining machinery, equipment & supplies
Ch Bd: Gary Winemaster
CFO: Michael Lewis
Sr VP: Kenneth Winemaster
Board of Directors: Jay Hansen, Ellen Hoffing, Kenneth Landini, Mary Vogt

D-U-N-S 12-245-1573
POWER SOLUTIONS LLC
17201 Melford Blvd Ste C, Bowie, MD 20715-4414
Tel (301) 794-0330 *Founded/Ownrshp* 1998
Sales 238.7MM *EMP* 350
Accts Regan Schickner Shah Harper Ll
SIC 1731 Electrical work
Genl Mgr: Ron Council
Sfty Mgr: Adam Geller

D-U-N-S 61-344-1737 IMP
POWER STOP LLC
6112 W 73rd St Unit C, Bedford Park, IL 60638-6115
Tel (708) 575-9745 *Founded/Ownrshp* 2005
Sales 129.9MM^E *EMP* 134
SIC 5013 Automotive brakes
CEO: Arvin Scott
**COO:* Joe Stephan
VP: Mark Pritt
Off Mgr: Kathryn Acosta
Art Dir: Rodion R Galperin

POWER SYSTEMS GROUP
See POWER PARAGON INC

D-U-N-S 13-303-3931 IMP
POWER SYSTEMS MFG LLC
(*Suby of* ANSALDO ENERGIA SPA)
1440 W Indiantown Rd # 200, Jupiter, FL 33458-7925
Tel (561) 354-1100 *Founded/Ownrshp* 2016
Sales 134.9MM^E *EMP* 330
SIC 3463 Engine or turbine forgings, nonferrous
CEO: Alexander Hoffs
Treas: Michael J Tolpa
VP: Jeff Benoit
VP: Charles M Biondo
VP: Mark Bissonnette
VP: Pierre Gauthier
VP: Bob Kraft
Prgrm Mgr: John Henriquez
CTO: Eric Rosenlieb
Ql Cn Mgr: Matt Merlin
Ql Cn Mgr: Jesus Ozuna

POWER TRAX
See ZIMMERMAN ADVERTISING LLC

POWER WELL SERVICE
See POWCO OF LOUISIANA LLC

D-U-N-S 06-458-5565 IMP
POWER-ONE INC
(*Suby of* ABB LTD)
2626 S 7th St, Phoenix, AZ 85034-6504
Tel (805) 987-8741 *Founded/Ownrshp* 2013
Sales 695.9MM^E *EMP* 3,231^E
SIC 3679 Power supplies, all types: static; Static power supply converters for electronic applications
Pr: Richard J Thompson
COO: Bill Yeates
CFO: Marcel Filipek
CFO: Jeffery Kyle
**CFO:* Gary R Larsen
Ex VP: Raul Valerino
**Sr VP:* Tina D McKnight
Sr VP: Martin Schnider
VP: John Andrus
VP: Mike Ballerini
VP: Sharon Reisinger
VP: Mahesh Thaker
VP: Anita Winsnes
VP: Dave Wojciechowski

POWER-TEL ELECTRICAL
See HALL CONTRACTING OF KENTUCKY INC

D-U-N-S 02-288-5859
POWER/MATION DIVISION INC
1310 Energy Ln, Saint Paul, MN 55108-3500
Tel (651) 605-3300 *Founded/Ownrshp* 1990
Sales 115.3MM^E *EMP* 150
SIC 5085 5065 5084 5045 8742 7549 Industrial supplies; Telephone & telegraphic equipment; Food industry machinery; Computer peripheral equipment; Automation & robotics consultant; Automotive maintenance services
CEO: Jim Landes

Pr: Mark Felts
VP: Doug Dagenais
VP: Scott Hurkes
Dir IT: Jason Goudy
Sls Mgr: Jesse Dummer
Sls Mgr: Sharon Wagner
Sales Asso: John Bragg
Sales Asso: Meredith Edlhuber
Sales Asso: Mark Feilen
Sales Asso: Kris Grinstead

D-U-N-S 13-574-5540
POWERCARE AND SERVICE SOLUTIONS INC
INTERSTATE POWERCARE
(*Suby of* INTERSTATE BATTERY SYSTEM INTERNATIONAL INC) ★
12770 Merit Dr Ste 400, Dallas, TX 75251-1296
Tel (972) 991-1444 *Founded/Ownrshp* 2002
Sales 34.5MM^E *EMP* 1,200
SIC 5063 Batteries
Pr: Wendell Samuel
**VP:* Walter C Holmes III
**VP:* Lisa Huntsberry
**VP:* Christopher S Willis

POWERCORDS
See VOLEX INC

D-U-N-S 18-486-2113
POWERHOUSE RETAIL SERVICES LLC
812 S Crowley Rd Ste A, Crowley, TX 76036-3714
Tel (817) 297-8575 *Founded/Ownrshp* 2004
Sales 190.5MM^E *EMP* 350
Accts Tp Anderson & Company
SIC 1542 1799 Commercial & office building contractors; Home/office interiors finishing, furnishing & remodeling
Pr: Matt Shelton
VP: Amber Johnson
VP: James Steinman
Dir IT: Robin Garrison
IT Man: David Hargrave
Snr PM: Garry Smith

D-U-N-S 96-345-8745
POWERPLUS GROUP INC USA
(*Suby of* POWERPLUS GROUP PTE. LTD.)
1521 E Grand Ave, Pomona, CA 91766-3808
Tel (909) 622-5888 *Founded/Ownrshp* 2008
Sales 580.0MM^E *EMP* 5
SIC 3531 Cranes, locomotive
Ch: Derek Hong
Genl Mgr: Tent Taylor

D-U-N-S 01-731-7306 IMP
POWERS DISTRIBUTING CO INC (MI)
3700 Giddings Rd, Orion, MI 48359-1306
Tel (248) 393-3700 *Founded/Ownrshp* 1931, 1955
Sales 168.9MM^E *EMP* 225
SIC 5181 Beer & other fermented malt liquors
Pr: Gerald Powers
**Treas:* Gary L Thompson
VP: William Brazier
Exec: Ann Smith
Dir IT: Zandra Lemons

D-U-N-S 01-621-8385
■ **POWERSECURE INC**
(*Suby of* POWERSECURE INTERNATIONAL INC) ★
1609 Heritage Commerce Ct, Wake Forest, NC 27587-4245
Tel (919) 556-3056 *Founded/Ownrshp* 2000
Sales 358.9MM^E *EMP* 753
SIC 7373 Turnkey vendors, computer systems
Pr: Sidney Hinton
Opers Mgr: Danny Dotson
Mktg Dir: Michael Breit
Board of Directors: Chris Hulter

D-U-N-S 78-108-2938
■ **POWERSECURE INTERNATIONAL INC**
(*Suby of* SOUTHERN CO) ★
1609 Heritage Commerce Ct, Wake Forest, NC 27587-4245
Tel (919) 556-3056 *Founded/Ownrshp* 2016
Sales 331.5MM^E *EMP* 1,035^E
SIC 3629 4931 Electronic generation equipment;
Pr: Sidney Hinton
**Ch Bd:* W Kent Geer
COO: Christopher T Hutter
CFO: Eric Dupont
**V Ch Bd:* Thomas J Madden III
Sr VP: John Bluth
VP: David Condon
VP: Ken Hurd
VP: Earl Shaddix
VP: Gary J Zuiderveen
Sls&Mrk Ex: Shannon King
Board of Directors: Kevin P Collins, A Dale Jenkins

D-U-N-S 00-690-0005
POWERSOUTH ENERGY COOPERATIVE (AL)
SUNSOUTH ADVERTISING
2027 E Three Notch St, Andalusia, AL 36421-2427
Tel (334) 427-3000 *Founded/Ownrshp* 1941
Sales 622.9MM *EMP* 640
Accts Deloitte & Touche Llp Atlanta
SIC 4911 Generation, electric power; Transmission, electric power; Distribution, electric power
CEO: Gary Smith
**COO:* Damon Morgan
**CFO:* Rick Kyle
Trst: Ben Floyd
Trst: William Rimes
VP: Larry Auery
VP: Seth Hammett
VP: Lewis Jeffers
VP: Herman Williams
VP: Beth Woodard
VP: Elizabeth Woodard
VP: Beth Woodward
Exec: Jim Byrd
Exec: Kyle Tharpe

D-U-N-S 03-446-3517
POWERTEAM SERVICES LLC
477 S Main St, Plymouth, MI 48170-1708
Tel (919) 372-8614 *Founded/Ownrshp* 2012
Sales 179.1MM^E *EMP* 1,360^E
SIC 1623 1629 Gas main construction; Electric power line construction; Oil & gas pipeline construction; Power plant construction
CEO: James Wigginton
**COO:* Jeffrey Wigginton

D-U-N-S 83-268-8423 IMP
POWERTECH AMERICA INC
(*Suby of* HYUNDAI POWERTECH CO., LTD.)
6801 Kia Pkwy, West Point, GA 31833-4937
Tel (706) 902-6800 *Founded/Ownrshp* 2008
Sales 1.2MMM *EMP* 500
Accts Pk Llp Opelika Alabama
SIC 5012 3714 Automobiles; Power transmission equipment, motor vehicle
CEO: Sam Ho Cha
**CFO:* Sang Ik Kim

D-U-N-S 06-234-7700
POWERTECH AMERICA SALES LLC
(*Suby of* HYUNDAI POWERTECH CO., LTD.)
6801 Kia Pkwy, West Point, GA 31833-4937
Tel (706) 902-6800 *Founded/Ownrshp* 2012
Sales 401.8MM *EMP* 20^E
Accts Pk Llp Opelika Alabama
SIC 5013 Automotive supplies & parts

D-U-N-S 14-882-5107
PP HOLDING CORP
(*Suby of* POLYPORE INTERNATIONAL INC) ★
13800 S Lakes Dr, Charlotte, NC 28273-6738
Tel (704) 587-8409 *Founded/Ownrshp* 2004
Sales 56.1MM^E *EMP* 1,000
SIC 3081 3089 Plastic film & sheet; Monofilaments, nontextile
Pr: Robert B Toth
**CFO:* Lynn Amos
**V Ch Bd:* Frank Nasisi

D-U-N-S 07-976-7347
PP&A-GA CORP (GA)
5425 Peachtree Pkwy, Norcross, GA 30092-6536
Tel (678) 906-2806 *Founded/Ownrshp* 2014
Sales 100.0MM *EMP* 8
SIC 7361 Executive placement
CEO: Richard Cannady
**COO:* Matthew Oppriecht

D-U-N-S 00-296-8246 IMP/EXP
■ **PPC BROADBAND INC**
(*Suby of* BELDEN INC) ★
6176 E Molloy Rd, East Syracuse, NY 13057-4010
Tel (315) 431-7200 *Founded/Ownrshp* 2002
Sales 224.9MM^E *EMP* 800
SIC 8748 Business consulting
CEO: John D Mezzalingua
CFO: John Young
VP: Brian Kelly
VP: Michael Reed
Area Mgr: Milos Dvorak
Genl Mgr: Jose Rosa
Opers Mgr: Kristin Ballard
Opers Mgr: Donald Dakoske
Manager: Ryan Hagan
Sls Mgr: Hector Gonzalez
Sls Mgr: Lars Jensen

D-U-N-S 02-172-1762
PPC LUBRICANTS INC
305 Micro Dr, Jonestown, PA 17038-8744
Tel (717) 865-9993 *Founded/Ownrshp* 2000
Sales 113.6MM^E *EMP* 120^E
SIC 5172 Gasoline
Ch: John Arnold
**Pr:* David Klinger
VP: John Warrington
Ex Dir: Geoff Bohlender
Genl Mgr: Malinda Rivera
Sales Exec: Eric May

D-U-N-S 04-737-5204
PPC PARTNERS INC
5464 N Port Washington Rd E, Milwaukee, WI 53217-4925
Tel (414) 831-1251 *Founded/Ownrshp* 1998
Sales 141.8MM^E *EMP* 1,117^E
SIC 1731 Electrical work
CEO: Jim Ditter
**Ch:* Richard R Pieper Sr

D-U-N-S 10-935-9435
PPD DEVELOPMENT LP
929 N Front St, Wilmington, NC 28401-3331
Tel (910) 251-0081 *Founded/Ownrshp* 1997
Sales 958.6M^E *EMP* 2,240
SIC 8731
Pt: David Simmons
Sr VP: William Richardson

D-U-N-S 36-257-4527
PPD DEVELOPMENT LP
(*Suby of* PHARMACEUTICAL PRODUCT DEVELOPMENT LLC) ★
929 N Front St, Wilmington, NC 28401-3331
Tel (910) 251-0081 *Founded/Ownrshp* 2012
Sales 1.6MMM^E *EMP* 15,000
SIC 8731 Commercial physical research; Biotechnical research, commercial
Pr: David Simmons
Pr: Susan Atkinson
COO: William J Sharbaugh
CFO: Robert Hureau
Ch: Lee E Babiss
Ex VP: Paul D Colvin
Ex VP: David Johnston
Ex VP: William W Richardson
Ex VP: Charles Rozwat
Ex VP: Michael O Wilkinson PHD
Sr VP: Elena Logan
Sr VP: Ed Murray
Sr VP: Henrietta Ukwu
VP: Edward Ian
VP: Loren Miller
VP: Agostino Pede
VP: Louis Renzetti
VP: Peter Wilkinson
Assoc Dir: Vellalore Kakkanaiah

D-U-N-S 82-875-2829
PPD INTERNATIONAL HOLDINGS INC
929 N Front St, Wilmington, NC 28401-3331
Tel (910) 251-0081 *Founded/Ownrshp* 1990
Sales 108.5MM^E *EMP* 1,122^E
SIC 2834 Pharmaceutical preparations
CEO: Frederick Frank
Assoc Dir: Richard Covington
Ex Dir: Lynne Boone
Snr PM: Paul Brandt

PPG AEROSPACE
See PRC - DESOTO INTERNATIONAL INC

PPG AEROSPACE
See SIERRACIN/SYLMAR CORP

PPG ARCHITECTURAL COATINGS
See PPG ARCHITECTURAL FINISHES INC

D-U-N-S 02-662-7919 EXP
■ **PPG ARCHITECTURAL FINISHES INC**
PPG ARCHITECTURAL COATINGS
(*Suby of* PPG INDUSTRIES INC) ★
1 Ppg Pl, Pittsburgh, PA 15272-0001
Tel (412) 434-3131 *Founded/Ownrshp* 1989
Sales 204.8MM^E *EMP* 1,010
SIC 2851 2891

D-U-N-S 04-870-5235
■ **PPG INDUSTRIES FIBER GLASS PRODUCTS INC**
(*Suby of* PPG INDUSTRIES INC) ★
940 Washburn Switch Rd, Shelby, NC 28150-9400
Tel (704) 434-2261 *Founded/Ownrshp* 1998
Sales 180.8MM^E *EMP* 3,150
SIC 3229 Pressed & blown glass
Pr: Charles Bunch

D-U-N-S 00-134-4803
▲ **PPG INDUSTRIES INC** (PA)
1 Ppg Pl, Pittsburgh, PA 15272-0001
Tel (412) 434-3131 *Founded/Ownrshp* 1883
Sales 15.3MMM *EMP* 46,400
Tkr Sym PPG *Exch* NYS
SIC 2851 3211 3231 3229 2812 2821 Paints & allied products; Paints & paint additives; Coating, air curing; Lacquers, varnishes, enamels & other coatings; Flat glass; Strengthened or reinforced glass; Windshields, glass: made from purchased glass; Glass fiber products; Fiber optics strands; Alkalies & chlorine; Chlorine, compressed or liquefied; Caustic soda, sodium hydroxide; Plastics materials & resins
Pr: Michael H McGarry
Ch Bd: Charles E Bunch
CFO: Frank S Sklarsky
Ex VP: Viktoras R Sekmakas
Sr VP: Glenn E Bost II
Board of Directors: Stephen F Angel, James G Berges, John V Faraci, Hugh Grant, Victoria F Haynes, Michele J Hooper, Michael W Lamach, Michael H McGarry, Martin H Richenhagen

D-U-N-S 05-422-2760 IMP/EXP
■ **PPG INDUSTRIES OHIO INC**
PPG KANSAI AUTOMOTIVE FINISHES
(*Suby of* PPG INDUSTRIES INC) ★
3800 W 143rd St, Cleveland, OH 44111-4997
Tel (216) 671-0050 *Founded/Ownrshp* 1999
Sales 363.5MM^E *EMP* 1,472
SIC 2851 Paints & allied products
CEO: Charles E Bunch
**Pr:* Bill Silvestri
**VP:* J Rich Alexander
Dir IT: Douglas Tittle

PPG KANSAI AUTOMOTIVE FINISHES
See PPG INDUSTRIES OHIO INC

PPG-METOKOTE
See METOKOTE CORP

D-U-N-S 83-543-3830 IMP/EXP
▲ **PPL CORP**
2 N 9th St, Allentown, PA 18101-1170
Tel (610) 774-5151 *Founded/Ownrshp* 1920
Sales 7.6MMM *EMP* 12,799
Tkr Sym PPL *Exch* NYS
SIC 4911 4924 Electric services; Generation, electric power; Distribution, electric power; Transmission, electric power; Natural gas distribution
Ch Bd: William H Spence
Genl Pt: Jeffrey R Shurr
Ch Bd: Victor A Staffieri
Pr: Gregory N Dudkin
Pr: Mary Kelly-Merenda
CEO: Robert A Symons
CFO: Rvincent Sorgi
Treas: Mark Wilten
VP: Stephen K Breininger
VP: Robert Grey
VP: Linda Miller
VP: Matt L Symons
Board of Directors: Rodney C Adkins, John W Conway, Armando Zagalo De Lima, Steven G Elliott, Craig A Rogerson, Keith H Williamson

D-U-N-S 00-790-9427 IMP/EXP
■ **PPL ELECTRIC UTILITIES CORP** (PA)
(*Suby of* PPL CORP) ★
2 N 9th St, Allentown, PA 18101-1170
Tel (610) 774-5151 *Founded/Ownrshp* 1919
Sales 2.1MMM *EMP* 2,311^E
SIC 4911 Electric services; Distribution, electric power; Transmission, electric power
Pr: Gregory N Dudkin
IT Man: Kristin Branning
IT Man: Maria Dibilio
Counsel: Michael Marino
Board of Directors: Robert J Grey, Vincent Sorgi, William H Spence

PPL ENERGY SERVICES NORTHEAST
See TALEN ENERGY SERVICES NORTHEAST INC

D-U-N-S 19-008-2888
■ **PPL SERVICES CORP**
(*Suby of* PPL CORP) ★
2 N 9th St, Allentown, PA 18101-1170
Tel (610) 774-5151 *Founded/Ownrshp* 2000
Sales 399.2MM^E *EMP* 13,500
SIC 6289 4911 Financial reporting; Electric services
CEO: William H Spence

PPM
See PAPER PRODUCTS MARKETING (USA) INC

D-U-N-S 83-812-0087
PPM AMERICA INC
(*Suby of* PPM HOLDINGS, INC.)
225 W Wacker Dr Ste 1200, Chicago, IL 60606-1348
Tel (312) 634-2500 *Founded/Ownrshp* 2001
Sales 136.3MM *EMP* 195
SIC 6282 Investment advisory service
Pr: Leandra R Knes
Genl Pt: Matthew J Napoli
**COO:* Mark B Mandich
Ofcr: Tom Barrus
Ex VP: Craig Close
**Sr VP:* Grant Davidson
Sr VP: Kenneth Schelmmel
VP: Tom Barnicle
VP: Brian Booker
VP: Joel Brown
VP: Patrick Condon
VP: James Cox
VP: Catherine Drake
VP: Kliton Duri
VP: Sam Fusco
VP: Laura Galiano
VP: John Heshelman
VP: Nicole Kidder
VP: Lisa Lynch
VP: Sundeep Mullangi
VP: Susan Perrino

D-U-N-S 16-191-2212
PPS HOLDINGS INC
6409 N Quail Hollow Rd, Memphis, TN 38120-1414
Tel (901) 748-0470 *Founded/Ownrshp* 2000
Sales 92.1MM^E *EMP* 1,900^E
SIC 8741 Management services
Pr: Don Nickleson
**Ex VP:* Glenn Etow Pharmd
**Ex VP:* Walker Upshaw
Sr VP: Jill Schaffner

D-U-N-S 07-973-0265
■ **PPW HOLDINGS LLC**
(*Suby of* BERKSHIRE HATHAWAY ENERGY CO) ★
666 Grand Ave Ste 500, Des Moines, IA 50309-2511
Tel (515) 242-4300 *Founded/Ownrshp* 2005
Sales 5.2MMM^E *EMP* 19,700^E
SIC 4911 4924 6531 Electric services; Transmission, electric power; Distribution, electric power; Natural gas distribution; Real estate agents & managers
Ch Bd: Gregory E Abel

D-U-N-S 00-228-4933 IMP/EXP
PQ CORP (PA)
(*Suby of* PQ HOLDING INC) ★
300 Lindenwood Dr, Malvern, PA 19355-1740
Tel (610) 651-4429 *Founded/Ownrshp* 1904
Sales 715.8MM^E *EMP* 2,300
SIC 2819 3231 Industrial inorganic chemicals; Sodium silicate, water glass; Potassium compounds or salts, except hydroxide or carbonate; Silica, amorphous; Products of purchased glass
Pr: George J Blitz
**Pr:* Michael R Boyce
**Pr:* Michael R Imbriani
Ch: R Wood
**Treas:* Alan Mcllroy
Treas: Mark Valentino
VP: Scott Barger
VP: Erwin Goede
VP: Walt Grainger
VP: Hector Martinez
VP: Robert Mulhall
VP: Jeanne Pool
**VP:* Scott Randolph
VP: William Sichko
VP: Elaine Simpson
Exec: Pam Klipstein

D-U-N-S 07-929-1269
PQ HOLDING INC
(*Suby of* CCMP CAPITAL ADVISORS LP) ★
300 Lindenwood Dr, Malvern, PA 19355-1740
Tel (610) 651-4400 *Founded/Ownrshp* 1977
Sales 1.0MMM^E *EMP* 2,418^E
Accts Pricewaterhousecoopers Llp
SIC 2819 Industrial inorganic chemicals; Sodium silicate, water glass; Catalysts, chemical
Ch Bd: Michael Boyce
Pr: John M Steitz
CFO: Alan Mcllroy
Ofcr: William Sichko Jr

D-U-N-S 03-640-8396 IMP
PQ NEWYORK INC
LE PAIN QUOTIDIEN
(*Suby of* PQ LICENSING SA)
50 Broad St Fl 12, New York, NY 10004-2790
Tel (212) 359-9000 *Founded/Ownrshp* 1995
Sales 87.4MM^E *EMP* 1,325
SIC 5812 Cafe
Pr: Jay Wainwright
**CEO:* Vincent Herbert
**CFO:* Thomas Hallen
Genl Mgr: Ryan Arnold
Genl Mgr: Andrew Gordon
Prd Mgr: Zayd Augustus
Board of Directors: Thomas Hallen, Vincent Herbert

D-U-N-S 07-851-5161
PR EDUCATION LLC
111 Speen St, Framingham, MA 01701-2000
Tel (508) 663-5050 *Founded/Ownrshp* 2011
Sales 15.7MM^E *EMP* 1,500
SIC 8748 8299 Business consulting; Educational services
CFO: Edward Spies

D-U-N-S 06-497-6343 IMP
PR NEWSWIRE ASSOCIATION LLC
(*Suby of* CISION US INC) ★
350 Hudson St Fl 3, New York, NY 10014-5827
Tel (800) 776-8090 *Founded/Ownrshp* 2016
Sales 132.0MM^E *EMP* 845
SIC 7383 Press service
CEO: Peter Granat
Sr VP: Whitney Benner
VP: Joaquin Burgos
VP: Marco Franca
VP: Jennifer Howard
VP: Andrew Meranus
VP: Sreedhar Pentyala
VP: Jeff Shulman
VP: Lauren Sloane
VP: David Wertheimer
VP: Kevin West

D-U-N-S 01-744-0277
PR RESTAURANTS LLC
PANERA BREAD
2150 Washington St # 125, Newton, MA 02462-1469
Tel (617) 581-6160 *Founded/Ownrshp* 1997
Sales 118.2MM^E *EMP* 1,500
SIC 5461 5812 Bakeries; Cafe

D-U-N-S 09-115-2678 IMP/EXP
PR RETAIL STORES INC
ALMACENES PITUSA
Edif Kodak Ave Campo, San Juan, PR 00924
Tel (787) 641-8200 *Founded/Ownrshp* 2002
Sales 222.6MM^E *EMP* 4,000
Accts Goas Psc San Juan Pr
SIC 5311 5712 5722 5331 Department stores, discount; Furniture stores; Electric household appliances; Variety stores
Pr: Israel Kopel
**VP:* Mercedes Ballester
Genl Mgr: Enrique Torano

D-U-N-S 07-931-0075
PR SITE DEVELOPMENT LLC
2000 Corporate Dr, Canonsburg, PA 15317-8564
Tel (724) 416-2000 *Founded/Ownrshp* 2010
Sales 15.1MM^E *EMP* 1,000
SIC 4899 Data communication services; Communication signal enhancement network system
VP: Blake Hawek

PR2 BLUEPRINT
See T & T REPROGRAPHICS INC

D-U-N-S 07-834-1876
■ **PRA GOVERNMENT SERVICES LLC**
(*Suby of* PRA GROUP INC) ★
120 Corporate Blvd # 100, Norfolk, VA 23502-4952
Tel (757) 519-9300 *Founded/Ownrshp* 2011
Sales 1.2MM^E *EMP* 1,443^E
SIC 7322 Adjustment & collection services

D-U-N-S 11-895-9001
▲ **PRA GROUP INC**
120 Corporate Blvd # 100, Norfolk, VA 23502-4952
Tel (888) 772-7326 *Founded/Ownrshp* 1996
Sales 942.0MM *EMP* 3,799^E
Tkr Sym PRAA *Exch* NGS
SIC 7322 Adjustment & collection services; Collection agency, except real estate
Ch Bd: Steven D Fredrickson
Pr: James Dickson
Pr: Dave Mellott
Pr: Michael Petit
Pr: Bill Sheehan
Pr: Daniel Viar
CEO: Tiku Patel
CFO: Peter M Graham
Ofcr: Michelle Link
**Ofcr:* Kevin P Stevenson
Ofcr: Laura White
Ex VP: Chris Graves
Ex VP: Craig Grube
Ex VP: Peter K McCammon
Ex VP: Neal Stern
Sr VP: Deborah Cassidy
Sr VP: Neil Chakravarty
Sr VP: Chris Lagow
VP: Gary Ochs
VP: Neal Petrovich
Board of Directors: Vikram A Atal, John H Fain, Penelope W Kyle, James A Nussle, David N Roberts, Scott M Tabakin, James M Voss, Lance L Weaver

D-U-N-S 07-957-1062
■ **PRA HEALTH SCIENCES INC**
(*Suby of* KKR PRA INVESTORS LP) ★
4130 Parklake Ave Ste 400, Raleigh, NC 27612-4462
Tel (919) 786-8200 *Founded/Ownrshp* 2013
Sales 1.6MMM *EMP* 12,000^E
Tkr Sym PRAH *Exch* NGS
SIC 8731 Commercial physical research
Ch Bd: Colin Shannon
**CFO:* Linda Baddour
**Chf Cred:* David W Dockhorn
VP: Brant Nicks
QA Dir: Sean Kotrady

D-U-N-S 18-840-0337
PRA HOLDINGS INC
1 Stamford Forum, Stamford, CT 06901-3516
Tel (203) 853-0123 *Founded/Ownrshp* 1987
Sales 105.8MM^E *EMP* 675
SIC 2834 5122 8742 Pharmaceutical preparations; Pharmaceuticals; Industry specialist consultants
Pr: Stuart Baker
**VP:* Howard Udell
Dir IT: Aidan Doyle

D-U-N-S 19-248-1620
■ **PRA INTERNATIONAL OPERATIONS INC**
(*Suby of* PRA HEALTH SCIENCES INC) ★
4130 Parklake Ave Ste 400, Raleigh, NC 27612-4462
Tel (919) 786-8200 *Founded/Ownrshp* 2013
Sales 1.1MMM^E *EMP* 11,200^E
SIC 8731 Commercial physical research; Biotechnical research, commercial
Pr: Colin Shannon
Pr: Sara Davis
**Pr:* Tami Klerr
**Pr:* Harris Koffer
CEO: Emily Weisberg
COO: Samir Shah
**CFO:* Linda Baddour
**Ofcr:* David W Dockhorn
Ofcr: Jana Kapustikova
**Ex VP:* Paul Bunch
**Ex VP:* Willem Jan Drijfhout
Ex VP: Tami Klerr-Naivar
Ex VP: Sean Leech
Ex VP: David Marks
**Ex VP:* Tami Klerr Naivar
Ex VP: Monika Pietrek
Ex VP: Susan C Stansfield
**Sr VP:* Steve Powell
**Sr VP:* Andrew Strayer
**Sr VP:* Kent Thoelke
Sr VP: William Walsh

D-U-N-S 86-936-9439 IMP/EXP
PRADA USA CORP
MIU MIU
(*Suby of* PRADA SPA)
609 W 51st St, New York, NY 10019-5008
Tel (212) 307-9300 *Founded/Ownrshp* 1994
Sales 406.5MM^E *EMP* 475
SIC 5136 5137 5139 5661 5632 8741 Leather & sheep lined clothing, men's & boys'; Handbags; Women's & children's accessories; Shoes; Men's shoes; Women's shoes; Apparel accessories; Management services
CEO: Patrizio Bertelli
**CEO:* Ruggero Caterini
**COO:* Rogero Petrini
CFO: Donatello Galli
Sr VP: Claudia Cividino
VP: Adam Garza
VP: Matteo Vitali
Rgnl Mgr: Anthony Koo
Genl Mgr: Cortney Guebara
Genl Mgr: Mery McFadden
Genl Mgr: Maya Piascik

D-U-N-S 15-387-4623
PRAGMATICS INC
1761 Business Center Dr # 110, Reston, VA 20190-5333
Tel (703) 890-8500 *Founded/Ownrshp* 1980
Sales 147.0MM^E *EMP* 500^E
SIC 7379 Computer related consulting services
CEO: Long Nguyen
V Ch: Paul Cohen
COO: Joe B Broc Jr
**COO:* Joe B Brock Jr
COO: Paul Strasser
**CFO:* Kimmy Duong
CFO: Michael A Zaramba
Ofcr: Patricia Ford
Ofcr: Kim Nguyen
Ofcr: Carl B Rosenblatt
**Ofcr:* Rich Silver
Ofcr: Rick Wilmoth
**Sr VP:* Michael Yocom
**VP:* Brian Brennan
VP: Michelle Geddes
VP: Ronald Gornto
VP: Christopher Hegedus
VP: Kerri Moreh
VP: Dan Navarro
VP: Thomas Thoma

D-U-N-S 04-708-3266
PRAIRIE BAND POTAWATOMI NATION
16281 Q Rd, Mayetta, KS 66509-8970
Tel (785) 966-2255 *Founded/Ownrshp* 1976
Sales NA *EMP* 1,193
SIC 9131 Indian reservation;
Ch Bd: Stephen Ortiz
V Ch: Calvin Evans
**Treas:* Ryan Dyer
**VP:* Rey Kitchkumme
Genl Mgr: William Mitchell
Off Mgr: Rebekah Jones
Dir IT: Ben Joslin
IT Man: Gordon Lamme
Sls&Mrk Ex: Darrel Kammeyer

D-U-N-S 00-631-2995
PRAIRIE FARMS DAIRY INC (IL)
1100 Broadway, Carlinville, IL 62626-1183
Tel (217) 854-2547 *Founded/Ownrshp* 1971
Sales 1.8MMM *EMP* 1,965
Accts Bkd Llp St Louis Mo
SIC 2026 Milk processing (pasteurizing, homogenizing, bottling)
CEO: Ed Mullins
**Pr:* Fred Kuenstler
**CFO:* Jason Geminn
**CFO:* Tom Weber
VP: Ronnie G McMillan
Dir Risk M: John Hiller
Genl Mgr: Harry Carter
Genl Mgr: Dominic Fontana
Genl Mgr: David Phaup
Off Mgr: Mary C Robosan
QA Dir: Ashly Matthews

D-U-N-S 79-957-3071
PRAIRIE ISLAND INDIAN COMMUNITY
5636 Sturgeon Lake Rd, Welch, MN 55089-9635
Tel (800) 554-5473 *Founded/Ownrshp* 1934
Sales 57.0MM^E *EMP* 1,665
SIC 7999 5812 7011 Bingo hall; Eating places; Casino hotel
Pr: Audrey Kohnen
**Treas:* Allen Childs Sr
**VP:* Mason Pacini
Counsel: Jessie Seim

D-U-N-S 15-159-0668
PRAIRIE LAKES HEALTH CARE SYSTEM INC
401 9th Ave Nw, Watertown, SD 57201-1548
Tel (605) 882-7000 *Founded/Ownrshp* 1986
Sales 91.7MM *EMP* 530
Accts Cliftonlarsonallen Llp Minnea
SIC 8062 General medical & surgical hospitals
Ch: Mark Roby
Chf Rad: William Bishop
CFO: David Hinderaker
**Treas:* Dustin Flatten
Pharmcst: Debbie Meadows

D-U-N-S 15-345-7031
PRAIRIE MEADOWS RACETRACK AND CASINO INC
1 Prairie Meadows Dr, Altoona, IA 50009-2115
Tel (515) 967-1000 *Founded/Ownrshp* 1984
Sales 202.2MM *EMP* 1,250
Accts Deloitte & Touche Llp Des Moi
SIC 7948 7993 7999 5947 5812 5813 Horse race track operation; Gambling machines; Slot machines; Gambling establishment; Gambling machines, operation; Off-track betting; Gift shop; Snack bar; Family restaurants; Drinking places
Pr: Gary Palmer
Chf Mktg O: Jeff Nelson
**VP:* Ann Atkin
VP: Steve Berry
**VP:* Brian Wessels
Genl Mgr: Tresa Vedder
Dir IT: Tony Guzman
IT Man: Melissa Caster
IT Man: Antonio Guzman
Mktg Dir: Clay Willey
Pr Dir: Julie Stewart

D-U-N-S 00-708-5624
PRAIRIE MOUNTAIN PUBLISHING CO LLC
DAILY CAMERA
(*Suby of* DIGITAL FIRST MEDIA) ★
2500 55th St Ste 210, Boulder, CO 80301-5740
Tel (303) 442-1202 *Founded/Ownrshp* 1891, 2009
Sales 89.2MM^E *EMP* 1,124^E
SIC 2711 Newspapers, publishing & printing
Dir Opers: Garth Hospers

D-U-N-S 16-104-6438 EXP
PRAIRIE PACKAGING INC
(*Suby of* PACTIV LLC) ★
7200 S Mason Ave, Bedford Park, IL 60638-6226
Tel (708) 496-1172 *Founded/Ownrshp* 2007
Sales 107.5MM^E *EMP* 900
SIC 3089 3421 Kitchenware, plastic; Plates, plastic; Table & food cutlery, including butchers'
Pr: John McGrath
Pr: Earl W Shapiro
VP: Scott Mansholt
VP: Sandra Musachia
VP: Steve Patyk
VP: Benjamin Shapiro
Prd Mgr: Gary Herbert

D-U-N-S 09-258-4614
PRAIRIE POWER INC
3130 Pleasant Run, Springfield, IL 62711-6347
Tel (217) 245-6161 *Founded/Ownrshp* 1963
Sales 148.6MM *EMP* 45
Accts Bkd Llp Decatur Il
SIC 4911 Generation, electric power
CEO: Jay Bartlett
VP: Dan Breden
VP: Lyndon Gabbert

D-U-N-S 80-944-3869 IMP
PRAIRIE STATE GENERATING CO LLC
3872 County Highway 12, Marissa, IL 62257-3434
Tel (618) 824-7600 *Founded/Ownrshp* 2001
Sales 132.9MM^E *EMP* 105^E
SIC 4911 Generation, electric power
**COO:* Randy Short

D-U-N-S 13-817-0220
PRAIRIE VIEW A&M UNIVERSITY
100 University Dr, Prairie View, TX 77445-6964
Tel (936) 261-3311 *Founded/Ownrshp* 1876
Sales 88.0MM *EMP* 965^E
SIC 8221 Colleges universities & professional schools
Pr: George C Wright
Ofcr: Craig Nunn
Exec: Camille Gibson
Pr Dir: Sheleah Hughes

D-U-N-S 82-709-1674 IMP
■ **PRANA LIVING LLC**
(*Suby of* COLUMBIA SPORTSWEAR CO) ★
3209 Lionshead Ave, Carlsbad, CA 92010-4710
Tel (866) 915-6457 *Founded/Ownrshp* 2008
Sales 105.1MM^E *EMP* 90
SIC 5136 5137 Men's & boys' clothing; Women's & children's clothing
CEO: Scott Kerslake
**CFO:* Larry Callette
VP: Jessica Mahoney

PRASCO LABORATORIES
See PRASCO LLC

D-U-N-S 06-596-9375 IMP
PRASCO LLC
PRASCO LABORATORIES
6125 Commerce Ct, Mason, OH 45040-6723
Tel (513) 204-1100 *Founded/Ownrshp* 2002
Sales 142.5MM^E *EMP* 130
SIC 5122 Pharmaceuticals
CEO: Christopher H Arington
Mng Pt: Jeff Arington
Pr: Michael Rohlfs
Pr: Herman Snyder
Pr: David Vucurevich
CFO: David Furniss
VP: Patrick Christensen
VP: David Lewis
VP: Christopher Young
Ex Dir: Bill Locke
CTO: Dan Neal

D-U-N-S 03-824-3176 IMP
■ **PRATT & WHITNEY COMPONENT SOLUTIONS INC**
(*Suby of* UNITED TECHNOLOGIES CORP) ★
4905 Stariha Dr, Norton Shores, MI 49441-5559
Tel (231) 798-8464 *Founded/Ownrshp* 1999
Sales 300.0MM *EMP* 100
SIC 5088 Aircraft & parts
Pr: Benoit Brossoit
**Treas:* John Dibert
Genl Mgr: Pete Gibson

D-U-N-S 05-553-0604 IMP
■ **PRATT & WHITNEY ENGINE SERVICES INC**
(*Suby of* UNITED TECHNOLOGIES CORP) ★
1525 Midway Park Rd, Bridgeport, WV 26330-9688
Tel (860) 565-4321 *Founded/Ownrshp* 1926, 2002
Sales 2.3MMM^E *EMP* 38,577
SIC 7699 3724 4581 Aircraft & heavy equipment repair services; Aircraft engines & engine parts; Airports, flying fields & services
Pr: Maria Valerio
**Treas:* Richard Coulombe
**VP:* Lisa Cronin
Counsel: Michael Funk

D-U-N-S 15-405-8309 IMP/EXP
PRATT (JET CORR) INC
PRATT INDUSTRIES
(*Suby of* CORRUGATING DIVISION) ★
1800 Sarasot Bus Pkwy Ne B, Conyers, GA 30013-5775
Tel (770) 929-1300 *Founded/Ownrshp* 1988
Sales 541.4MM^E *EMP* 3,500
SIC 2653 Boxes, corrugated: made from purchased materials; Sheets, solid fiber: made from purchased materials
Ch Bd: Richard Pratt
Pr: Anthony Pratt
Pr: Jeff Turner
CEO: Gary B Byrd
COO: Phillip Bulger
COO: Brian McKeely
COO: Brian McPheely
CFO: David Wiser
Genl Mgr: Marty Pate
Genl Mgr: Doug Thiesse
CTO: Tim Price

D-U-N-S 00-724-0740 EXP
PRATT (LOVE BOX) LLC
LOVE BOX COMPANY, LLC
(*Suby of* PRATT INDUSTRIES (USA) INC) ★
700 E 37th St N, Wichita, KS 67219-3510
Tel (316) 838-0851 *Founded/Ownrshp* 2005
Sales 15.3MM^E *EMP* 1,400
SIC 2653 2448 4213

PRATT INDUSTRIES
See PRATT (JET CORR) INC

D-U-N-S 61-945-3509 IMP
PRATT INDUSTRIES (USA) INC
1800-A Sarasota Pkwy, Conyers, GA 30013
Tel (770) 918-5678 *Founded/Ownrshp* 1985
Sales 1.6MMM^E *EMP* 4,244
SIC 2621 Paper mills; Packaging paper
CEO: Brian McPheely
**COO:* David Dennis
**CFO:* David Wiser
**VP:* Gary Byrd
**VP:* David J Kyles
Netwrk Mgr: Juan Merelo
Sfty Mgr: Randy Clark
Sales Exec: Brad Varnado

D-U-N-S 00-195-8503
PRATT INSTITUTE (NY)
200 Willoughby Ave, Brooklyn, NY 11205-3899
Tel (718) 636-3600 *Founded/Ownrshp* 1887
Sales 225.5MM *EMP* 900
Accts Kpmg Llp New York Ny
SIC 8221 University
Pr: Thomas F Schutte
Ch Bd: Hans Lischewski
VP: Judy Aaron
VP: Julie Karns
VP: Kathleen Rice
**VP:* Edmund Rutkowski
Ex Dir: Adam Friedman
Dir Sec: William Schmitz
Dept Mgr: Rachel Dove

D-U-N-S 83-954-8898 IMP
PRATT PAPER (NY) INC
(*Suby of* PRATT INDUSTRIES (USA) INC) ★
1800 Sarasota Business, Conyers, GA 30013-5775
Tel (770) 918-5678 *Founded/Ownrshp* 1994
Sales 137.0MM *EMP* 74
SIC 2611 Pulp manufactured from waste or recycled paper
Ch Bd: Anthony Pratt
**CEO:* Brian McPheely
**CFO:* David Wiser
**VP:* Gary Byrd
**VP:* Lewis Henao

D-U-N-S 04-284-5636 IMP/EXP
■ **PRAXAIR DISTRIBUTION INC**
(*Suby of* PRAXAIR INC) ★
39 Old Ridgebury Rd, Danbury, CT 06810-5103
Tel (203) 837-2000 *Founded/Ownrshp* 2007
Sales 597.1MM^E *EMP* 1,767
SIC 2813 5084 5999 Industrial gases; Carbon dioxide; Dry ice, carbon dioxide (solid); Oxygen, compressed or liquefied; Welding machinery & equipment; Welding supplies
Pr: Scott Kaltrider
**Treas:* Lisa Hurley
Ex VP: James Sawyer
VP: Rick Fitzgerald
IT Man: Jonna Eder
S&M/VP: Lisa Taylor
Sls Mgr: John Ward

D-U-N-S 80-846-1896 IMP
■ **PRAXAIR DISTRIBUTION MID-ATLANTIC LLC**
GTS-WELCO
(*Suby of* WELCO-CGI GAS TECHNOLOGIES LLC) ★
5275 Tilghman St, Allentown, PA 18104-9378
Tel (610) 398-2211 *Founded/Ownrshp* 2007
Sales 113.1MM^E *EMP* 600
SIC 4925 3548 Gas production and/or distribution; Welding apparatus

D-U-N-S 19-715-4586 IMP/EXP
▲ PRAXAIR INC
10 Riverview Dr, Danbury, CT 06810-6268
Tel (203) 837-2000 *Founded/Ownrshp* 1907
Sales 10.7MMM *EMP* 26,657
Tkr Sym PX *Exch* NYS
SIC 2813 3569 3471 3479 Industrial gases; Oxygen, compressed or liquefied; Nitrogen; Argon; Gas producers (machinery); Plating of metals or formed products; Coating of metals & formed products
Ch Bd: Stephen F Angel
CFO: Matthew J White
Ofcr: Karen L Keegans
Ex VP: Eduardo F Menezes
Ex VP: Eduardo Menezes
Ex VP: Scott E Telesz
Sr VP: Anne K Roby
VP: Guillermo Bichara
VP: Elizabeth T Hirsch
VP: Earl Newsome
Exec: William Couch
Board of Directors: Oscar Bernardes, Edward G Galante, Ira D Hall, Raymond W Leboeuf, Larry D McVay, Denise L Ramos, Martin H Richenhagen, Wayne T Smith, Robert L Wood

D-U-N-S 13-523-6594 IMP/EXP
■ PRAXAIR SURFACE TECHNOLOGIES INC
(*Suby of* PRAXAIR INC) ★
1500 Polco St, Indianapolis, IN 46222-3285
Tel (317) 240-2500 *Founded/Ownrshp* 1989
Sales 958.0MM^E *EMP* 2,636
SIC 3479 3548 3563 Painting, coating & hot dipping; Coating, rust preventive; Hot dip coating of metals or formed products; Electric welding equipment; Spraying outfits: metals, paints & chemicals (compressor)
Pr: Pierre Luthi
Bd of Dir: Wayne T Smith
**VP:* Randy Brittingham
VP: Zena Galloway
**VP:* Dean Hackett
**VP:* Thomas Lewis
**VP:* Bruce Phillips
VP: Jeffrey P Standish
MIS Dir: Mark Eberly
QC Dir: Fred Mundt
Sales Exec: Leo Buchakjian

D-U-N-S 94-514-8989 EXP
■ PRAXAIR TECHNOLOGY INC
(*Suby of* PRAXAIR INC) ★
39 Old Ridgebury Rd, Danbury, CT 06810-5103
Tel (203) 837-2000 *Founded/Ownrshp* 1994
Sales 151.1MM^E *EMP* 250
SIC 5172 5084 5169 5085 Gases; Metalworking machinery; Chemicals & allied products; Industrial supplies
Pr: Wayne Yakich
Pr: Sean Durbin
**Pr:* Raymond P Roberge
**Treas:* Michael Allan
**Treas:* Timothy S Heenan
**VP:* Patrick Heffernan
**VP:* Carl Koch
**VP:* Stewart K Mehlman

D-U-N-S 01-823-8829
PRAXIS COMPANIES LLC
435 Industrial Rd, Savannah, TN 38372-5996
Tel (731) 925-7656 *Founded/Ownrshp* 2003
Sales 116.7MM^E *EMP* 375
SIC 3088 Shower stalls, fiberglass & plastic; Tubs (bath, shower & laundry), plastic
CEO: Rick Stonecipher
VP Opers: Scott Stonecipher
Mktg Dir: Jim Davidson
Manager: Tim McKey

D-U-N-S 08-781-2512
PRAXIS ENGINEERING TECHNOLOGIES INC (MD)
135 Natl Bus Pkwy, Annapolis Junction, MD 20701-1013
Tel (301) 490-4299 *Founded/Ownrshp* 2001
Sales 121.3MM *EMP* 290
SIC 7371 Software programming applications
Pr: William S Dunahoo
**Pr:* Bill Dunahoo
**Treas:* Harry J Schepers
**Ex VP:* Mark Klein
**VP:* Jeremy L Kaufman
**VP:* Jerry Schepers
Prgrm Mgr: Lisa Auld
Prgrm Mgr: Jen Diffenderfer
Prgrm Mgr: Sherry McDonald
Snr Sftwr: Lisa Chang
Snr Sftwr: Thomas Denn

D-U-N-S 00-823-7539 IMP
■ PRC - DESOTO INTERNATIONAL INC (CA)
PPG AEROSPACE
(*Suby of* PPG INDUSTRIES INC) ★
24811 Ave Rockefeller, Valencia, CA 91355-3468
Tel (661) 678-4209 *Founded/Ownrshp* 1945, 1999
Sales 169.0MM^E *EMP* 540
SIC 2891 3089 Sealing compounds, synthetic rubber or plastic; Adhesives; Plastic containers, except foam
Pr: Michael H McGarry
**CEO:* Barry Gillespie
**CFO:* Ralph Dyba
Ex VP: Rich Alexander
**Ex VP:* Frank S Sklarsky
**Sr VP:* Glenn E Bost II
VP: Glenn Bost
VP: Richard Elias
**VP:* John Machin
VP: Michael McGarry
**VP:* David P Morris
VP: Cynthia Niekamp
**VP:* Viktoras R Sekmakas
VP: Viktoras Sekmakas
**VP:* Donna Lee Walker
Board of Directors: Bob Hawrylo

D-U-N-S 11-862-4618
PRC LLC
(*Suby of* PRIORITY ONE SUPPORT) ★
8151 Peters Rd Ste 4000, Plantation, FL 33324-4012
Tel (954) 693-3700 *Founded/Ownrshp* 2010
Sales 134.9MM^E *EMP* 6,000
SIC 8741 Management services
CEO: Andy Lee
**COO:* Art Dibari
**COO:* Sean Minter
**CFO:* Thomas L Garrett
**Treas:* Michael Wilson
**Sr VP:* Gregory M Carr
**Sr VP:* William Porpiglia
**Sr VP:* Mabel M Rodriguez
**Sr VP:* Robert Wren
VP: Gregory Carr
VP: Andy Mitchell
Exec: Tonya Goforth

PRE-MIX
See CPM DEVELOPMENT CORP

D-U-N-S 11-948-4165 IMP/EXP
PRECEPT BRANDS LLC
PRECEPT WINE
1910 Frview Ave E Ste 400, Seattle, WA 98102
Tel (206) 267-5252 *Founded/Ownrshp* 2002
Sales 203.1MM^E *EMP* 300
SIC 5182 Wine
CEO: Andrew Browne
**Pr:* Mike Williamson
Sr VP: Mark Harmann
VP: Lisa Clarkson
**VP:* Phil Kazanjian
VP: Shane Owens
VP Prd: Mark Castaldi
Mktg Mgr: Nicole Button
Manager: Pat McClaskey

PRECEPT WINE
See PRECEPT BRANDS LLC

D-U-N-S 05-385-9500 IMP
▲ PRECIOUS A-MARK METALS INC
429 Santa Monica Blvd # 230, Santa Monica, CA 90401-3409
Tel (310) 587-1477 *Founded/Ownrshp* 1965
Sales 6.7MMM *EMP* 83^E
Accts Grant Thornton Llp
Tkr Sym AMRK *Exch* NGS
SIC 5094 Jewelry & precious stones; Precious metals
CEO: Gregory N Roberts
**Ch Bd:* Jeffrey D Benjamin
Pr: Thor G Gjerdrum
CFO: Cary Dickson
Ex VP: Carol Meltzer
Board of Directors: Joel R Anderson, Ellis Landau, William Montgomery, John U Moorhead, Jess M Ravich

PRECISE HARD CHROME
See TEXAS HYDRAULICS INC

D-U-N-S 06-454-4224
PRECISE MACHINING & MANUFACTURING LLC
(*Suby of* ACCURUS AEROSPACE CORP) ★
12716 E Pine St, Tulsa, OK 74116-2033
Tel (918) 438-3121 *Founded/Ownrshp* 2013
Sales 83.8MM^E *EMP* 210
SIC 3728 Aircraft parts & equipment
CFO: Dennis Gilbert
Genl Mgr: Larry Johnson
Genl Mgr: Phil Miller
Plnt Mgr: Joe McWethy
Prd Mgr: Robert Schlomann

D-U-N-S 00-902-7970 IMP/EXP
■ PRECISION CASTPARTS CORP
PCC
(*Suby of* BERKSHIRE HATHAWAY INC) ★
4650 Sw Mcdam Ave Ste 300, Portland, OR 97239
Tel (503) 946-4800 *Founded/Ownrshp* 2016
Sales 10.0MMM *EMP* 30,100
SIC 3324 3369 3724 3511 3519 Aerospace investment castings, ferrous; Commercial investment castings, ferrous; Nonferrous foundries; Aerospace castings, nonferrous: except aluminum; Titanium castings, except die-casting; Aircraft engines & engine parts; Airfoils, aircraft engine; Turbines & turbine generator sets & parts; Parts & accessories, internal combustion engines
Pr: Mark Donegan
CFO: Shawn R Hagel
Chf Cred: EMI Donis
Ex VP: Steven G Hackett
Ex VP: Steven Hackett
Sr VP: Ruth A Beyer
VP: Roger P Becker
VP: Mark Ellis
VP: Byron J Gaddis
VP: Jay Khetani
VP: Kirk G Pulley
Dir Risk M: Sarah Craft
Dir Risk M: Kenneth Wood

D-U-N-S 87-812-5715 IMP
PRECISION COMPONENTS INTERNATIONAL INC
PCI
(*Suby of* BLADES TECHNOLOGY INTERNATIONAL INC) ★
8801 Macon Rd, Midland, GA 31820-4117
Tel (706) 568-5900 *Founded/Ownrshp* 1985
Sales 122.1MM^E *EMP* 400
SIC 3728 5088 3724 Blades, aircraft propeller: metal or wood; Aircraft & parts; Aircraft engines & engine parts
CEO: George Hudgins
**CFO:* Ricky B Gibson
IT Man: Shari Lewack

D-U-N-S 17-712-1373
PRECISION CONCRETE CONSTRUCTION INC
2075 Brandon Trl, Alpharetta, GA 30004-8499
Tel (770) 751-9158 *Founded/Ownrshp* 1986
Sales 102.2MM^E *EMP* 450
SIC 1771 Concrete work
CEO: Lenny Moniz Jr
**CEO:* Daniel Dolan
**CFO:* Tracy Pierce
**VP:* Dave Bradbury
Genl Mgr: Karl Yurek
Opers Mgr: Brian McCormick

D-U-N-S 17-420-0634 IMP/EXP
PRECISION CUSTOM COATINGS LLC
P C C
200 Maltese Dr, Totowa, NJ 07512-1404
Tel (973) 785-4390 *Founded/Ownrshp* 1997
Sales 152.0MM^E *EMP* 430^E
SIC 2295 Coated fabrics, not rubberized
Ch: Peter Longo
**Pr:* Scott Tesser
**CFO:* Richard Noble
VP: Jay Waxer
Mng Dir: Mario Longo
Genl Mgr: Moe Kovangji
MIS Dir: Leon Lenc
Dir IT: John Borjeson
Opers Mgr: Rino Baldecci
Opers Mgr: Gail Salvetti
Sls Dir: Carl Cimno

D-U-N-S 10-620-9307 IMP
PRECISION CUSTOM COMPONENTS LLC
500 Lincoln St, York, PA 17401-3367
Tel (717) 848-1126 *Founded/Ownrshp* 1983
Sales 116.7MM^E *EMP* 280
SIC 3443 3699 Fabricated plate work (boiler shop); High-energy particle physics equipment
CEO: Gary C Butler
VP: Art Hendrix
Dir Bus: Robert Jacobs
Prgrm Mgr: Brett Butler
Genl Mgr: Robert Bingman
Genl Mgr: Mandie Funk
IT Man: John Meerbach
Ql Cn Mgr: Lewis Detter
Snr Mgr: Nevin Speicher

D-U-N-S 80-010-6726 IMP
PRECISION DRILLING CO LP
PRECISION DRILLING US
(*Suby of* PRECISION DRILLING CORP) ★
10350 Richmond Ave # 700, Houston, TX 77042-4129
Tel (713) 435-6100 *Founded/Ownrshp* 1980
Sales 1.4MMM^E *EMP* 3,200
SIC 1381 Drilling oil & gas wells
Pt: Thomas P Richards
**Pt:* Forrest Conley
**Pt:* Donald Guedry Jr
**Pt:* Gary D Lee
**Pt:* David Wehlmann
VP: Ron Hale
VP: James Tolsma
IT Man: Merrie Costley
IT Man: Charles Hodges

D-U-N-S 06-356-9313 IMP/EXP
PRECISION DRILLING CORP
(*Suby of* PRECISION DRILLING CORPORATION)
10350 Richmond Ave # 700, Houston, TX 77042-4129
Tel (713) 435-6100 *Founded/Ownrshp* 2008
Sales 2.2MMM^E *EMP* 6,000
SIC 1381 Drilling oil & gas wells
CEO: Kevin Neveu
**Ch Bd:* Thomas P Richards
**COO:* David J Crowley
**CFO:* Carey Ford
**CFO:* David W Wehlmann
**Treas:* Donald J Guedry Jr
**V Ch Bd:* William R Ziegler
Sr VP: Edward S Jacob III
Sr VP: Gary D Lee
**VP:* Kent D Cauley
VP: Edward H Stammel Jr
VP: Kyle Swingle
VP: James Tolsma
VP: Jim G Winters

PRECISION DRILLING US
See PRECISION DRILLING CO LP

D-U-N-S 00-848-6367 IMP/EXP
■ PRECISION DYNAMICS CORP (CA)
PDC
(*Suby of* BRADY CORP) ★
27770 N Entrmt Dr Ste 200, Valencia, CA 91355
Tel (818) 897-1111 *Founded/Ownrshp* 1956, 2012
Sales 96.9MM^E *EMP* 200^E
SIC 2672 2754 5047 3069 Adhesive papers, labels or tapes: from purchased material; Labels (unprinted), gummed: made from purchased materials; Labels: gravure printing; Instruments, surgical & medical; Tape, pressure sensitive: rubber
Pr: Robert Case
CFO: Mohammed Shentenawy
**VP:* Robin Barber
**VP:* John Park
VP: Shane Tagali
Creative D: Cristina Telebrico
Mktg Mgr: Jonathan Trachtman
Sales Asso: Darshon Ware

D-U-N-S 78-968-0873 IMP/EXP
PRECISION ENERGY SERVICES INC
(*Suby of* WEATHERFORD INTERNATIONAL LLC) ★
2000 Saint James Pl, Houston, TX 77056-4123
Tel (713) 693-4000 *Founded/Ownrshp* 2005
Sales 179.3MM^E *EMP* 740
SIC 3533 1389 Oil field machinery & equipment; Oil field services
CEO: B Duroc-Danner

D-U-N-S 12-929-8126
PRECISION ENGINEERED PRODUCTS LLC
PEP
(*Suby of* PEP INDUSTRIES LLC) ★
110 Frank Mossberg Dr, Attleboro, MA 02703-4632
Tel (508) 226-5600 *Founded/Ownrshp* 1926
Sales 304.3MM^E *EMP* 1,053
SIC 3643 3469 3841 3471 3089 3351 Contacts, electrical; Stamping metal for the trade; Surgical & medical instruments; Plating & polishing; Plastic containers, except foam; Copper rolling & drawing
Pr: John Manzi
**CFO:* Tom Murray
Genl Mgr: Don William
Sls Mgr: Scot Macgillivray

D-U-N-S 18-507-1727 IMP/EXP
PRECISION FABRICS GROUP INC
301 N Elm St Ste 600, Greensboro, NC 27401-2185
Tel (336) 510-8000 *Founded/Ownrshp* 1988
Sales 261.1MM^E *EMP* 800
SIC 2262 2221 Decorative finishing of manmade broadwoven fabrics; Manmade & synthetic broadwoven fabrics
Ch: Lanty Smith
**CEO:* Pat Burns
VP: Terry Montgomery
Exec: Bary Blackard
Dir Rx: Doug Small
Tech Mgr: David Stalls
Mfg Dir: Jeff Robson
QC Dir: Carol Lowe
Manager: Jeff Carr
Ql Cn Mgr: Kathryn Hudson
Mktg Mgr: Mike Shaltry

PRECISION GLOBAL
See PRECISION VALVE CORP

D-U-N-S 08-727-3744 IMP/EXP
PRECISION INC (IA)
PRECISION PULLEY & IDLER
300 Se 14th St, Pella, IA 50219-2232
Tel (641) 628-3115 *Founded/Ownrshp* 1977
Sales 160.0MM^E *EMP* 500^E
SIC 2499 3429 Spools, reels & pulleys: wood; Pulleys metal
Pr: Stan Poortinga
**Pr:* Roger Brown
**CFO:* Sam Iogha
**VP:* Richard Brown

D-U-N-S 04-704-4110 IMP/EXP
■ PRECISION INDUSTRIES INC
(*Suby of* DXP ENTERPRISES INC) ★
7272 Pinemont Dr, Houston, TX 77040-6606
Tel (713) 996-4700 *Founded/Ownrshp* 2007
Sales 156.7MM^E *EMP* 650
SIC 5211 5085 Lumber & other building materials; Industrial supplies
Pr: David R Little
**Sec:* Mac McConnell
Sales Exec: J B Church

D-U-N-S 80-917-4738 IMP
PRECISION INTERCONNECT LLC
TYCO ELECTONIC
(*Suby of* TE CONNECTIVITY) ★
10025 Sw Freeman Dr, Wilsonville, OR 97070-9289
Tel (503) 620-9400 *Founded/Ownrshp* 2008
Sales 144.5MM^E *EMP* 566
SIC 3679 Harness assemblies for electronic use: wire or cable
CEO: Thomas J Lynch

D-U-N-S 12-890-2454
PRECISION PARTS HOLDINGS INC
(*Suby of* FIRST ATLANTIC CAPITAL LTD) ★
2129 Austin Ave, Rochester Hills, MI 48309-3668
Tel (248) 853-9010 *Founded/Ownrshp* 2006
Sales 4.8MM^E *EMP* 1,163
SIC 3465 3469 3544 Automotive stampings; Metal stampings; Die sets for metal stamping (presses)
Ch Bd: John Lutsi
**Pr:* Michael Bryant
**Treas:* Michael Niemic
Prd Mgr: Greg Gasper

D-U-N-S 14-363-1807
■ PRECISION PIPELINE LLC
(*Suby of* MASTEC INC) ★
3314 56th St, Eau Claire, WI 54703-6332
Tel (715) 874-4510 *Founded/Ownrshp* 2009
Sales 569.0MM *EMP* 1,800
SIC 1623 Oil & gas pipeline construction
Pr: Daniel Murphy
CFO: Glen Elias
VP: Kara Linderholm
VP: Ryan McKone
**VP:* Steven R Rooney
Dir IT: Eric Nordquist
VP Opers: Bobby Poteete
Sfty Dirs: Mark Gonzales

D-U-N-S 00-397-8413 IMP
PRECISION PRESS INC
(*Suby of* COMMERCIAL PRINT GROUP INC) ★
2020 Lookout Dr, North Mankato, MN 56003-1713
Tel (507) 625-7155 *Founded/Ownrshp* 1983
Sales 94.1MM^E *EMP* 300
SIC 2678 2752 Tablets & pads; Commercial printing, offset
CEO: Lee Timmerman
Pr: Al Hughes
CFO: Kevin Christian
**VP:* Tom Johnson
VP Opers: Lane Gravley

PRECISION PULLEY & IDLER
See PRECISION INC

D-U-N-S 04-959-3734 IMP
PRECISION RESOURCE INC (CT)
25 Forest Pkwy, Shelton, CT 06484-6122
Tel (203) 925-0012 *Founded/Ownrshp* 1953
Sales 216.2MM^E *EMP* 700
SIC 3469 Stamping metal for the trade
CEO: Peter Wolcott
**VP:* Charles Polatsek
Div Mgr: Chris Cartwright
Div Mgr: Robert Domogala
Div Mgr: Robert Fitzgerald
Div Mgr: Horst Griesbaum
Div Mgr: Ron Hunt
Div Mgr: Curt Krueger

D-U-N-S 09-988-1856 IMP
PRECISION SOUTHEAST INC
PRECISION SOUTHEAST-MYRTLE BCH
4900 Highway 501, Myrtle Beach, SC 29579-9447
Tel (843) 347-4218 *Founded/Ownrshp* 1991
Sales 103.6MM^E *EMP* 315
SIC 3089 8731 3083 Injection molding of plastics; Commercial physical research; Laminated plastics plate & sheet
Pr: Harry Ussery
Exec: Sarah Skipper
Exec: Peggy Smith
Mtls Mgr: Gary Bullard
Sfty Mgr: Dale Smith
Plnt Mgr: Brett Byers
Sales Asso: Erica Sparks

PRECISION SOUTHEAST-MYRTLE BCH
See PRECISION SOUTHEAST INC

D-U-N-S 05-183-3903 EXP
PRECISION SOYA LLC
6501 Constitution Dr, Fort Wayne, IN 46804-1551
Tel (260) 459-9353 *Founded/Ownrshp* 1978
Sales 485.3MM^E *EMP* 190
SIC 0723

D-U-N-S 08-121-2326
■ **PRECISION STRIP INC** (OH)
(*Suby of* RELIANCE STEEL & ALUMINUM CO) ★
86 S Ohio St, Minster, OH 45865-1246
Tel (419) 501-1347 *Founded/Ownrshp* 1977
Sales 199.1MM^E *EMP* 1,000
SIC 7389 Metal slitting & shearing
Pr: Joe Wolf
**Ch Bd:* Thomas A Compton
Prd Mgr: John Kennison

D-U-N-S 00-147-9567 IMP/EXP
PRECISION VALVE CORP (NY)
PRECISION GLOBAL
800 Westchester Ave, Rye Brook, NY 10573-1354
Tel (914) 969-6500 *Founded/Ownrshp* 1949
Sales 443.9MM^E *EMP* 2,000
SIC 3499 0273 5085

D-U-N-S 08-416-9101
PRECISION WALLS INC (NC)
1230 Ne Maynard Rd, Cary, NC 27513-4174
Tel (919) 832-0380 *Founded/Ownrshp* 1977
Sales 211.8MM^E *EMP* 1,000
SIC 1743 1742 1799 Tile installation, ceramic; Drywall; Plastering, plain or ornamental; Stucco work, interior; Demountable partition installation
CEO: Elizabeth Allen
**Ch Bd:* Loy C Allen
**Pr:* Brian Allen
**Sr VP:* Gary W Roth
VP: John Fuldner

D-U-N-S 18-695-6314
PRECISION-AIRE INC
2100 Artic Ave Unit 9, Bohemia, NY 11716-2430
Tel (631) 563-8280 *Founded/Ownrshp* 2014
Sales 90.0MM *EMP* 20
SIC 1711 Heating & air conditioning contractors; Warm air heating & air conditioning contractor
Pr: Richard Troy

D-U-N-S 05-519-7545 IMP
PRECISIONAIRE INC
PRECISIONAIRE OF SMITHFIELD
(*Suby of* FLANDERS CORP) ★
531 Flanders Filter Rd, Washington, NC 27889-7805
Tel (252) 946-8081 *Founded/Ownrshp* 1996
Sales 248.0MM^E *EMP* 2,400^E
SIC 3564 Filters, air: furnaces, air conditioning equipment, etc.
Ch: Ted Beneski
**CEO:* Harry Smith
**Ex VP:* Warren Bonham
**Ex VP:* Brad Buser
**Ex VP:* Eliot Kerlin
VP: David Keating
**VP:* Mark Sokolowski

PRECISIONAIRE OF SMITHFIELD
See PRECISIONAIRE INC

PRECIX
See ACUSHNET RUBBER CO INC

D-U-N-S 83-468-7365
PRECOA LLC
13221 Sw 68th Pkwy # 100, Portland, OR 97223-8685
Tel (503) 244-7755 *Founded/Ownrshp* 2003
Sales NA *EMP* 120
SIC 6311 Funeral insurance
VP: Ben Nagel
Rgnl Mgr: Dylan Morrison
VP Mktg: Tyler Hornibrook
Mktg Dir: Jonathan Lefrandt

D-U-N-S 61-476-5472 IMP
■ **PRECOAT METALS**
(*Suby of* KOLLSMAN INSTRUMENT DIVISION) ★
1310 Papin St Ste 300, Saint Louis, MO 63103-3132
Tel (314) 436-7010 *Founded/Ownrshp* 1961
Sales 489.7MM^E *EMP* 750
SIC 3479 Painting of metal products
CEO: Gerard Dombek
Pr: Greg Conroy
**Pr:* Kurt Russell
**CFO:* Jason Crawford
VP: Michael Blickensderfer
VP: John Messbarger
VP: Rick Miller
VP: Steven Schaus
VP: Jeff Vellines
VP: Jeff Widenor
Exec: Michele Miles

D-U-N-S 00-642-0087
■ **PRECOAT METALS CORP**
(*Suby of* PRECOAT METALS) ★
1950 E Main St, Greenfield, IN 46140-8128
Tel (317) 462-7761 *Founded/Ownrshp* 2014
Sales 233.7MM^E *EMP* 750
SIC 3479 Painting of metal products; Painting, coating & hot dipping
Pr: Gerard Dombek
Exec: Larry Harper
IT Man: Dave Prince
Opers Mgr: Ron Fuqua
Plnt Mgr: Gary Hollo
Sls&Mrk Ex: Joe Morgan
Sls Dir: Chuck Parks
Manager: Brian Baker
Manager: Marty Ferreby
Manager: Brian Quick
Manager: Marty Scott

D-U-N-S 02-736-6947 IMP
PRECOR INC
PRECOR USA
(*Suby of* AMER SPORTS OYJ)
20031 142nd Ave Ne, Woodinville, WA 98072-8473
Tel (425) 486-9292 *Founded/Ownrshp* 2002
Sales 191.9MM^E *EMP* 590
SIC 3949 Exercise equipment; Exercising cycles; Treadmills
Pr: Rob Barker
COO: Kirk Hahn
CFO: Mark Gooding
VP: Micheal Feeney
VP: Greg May
VP: Elisa Mogelever
VP: Tom Nnapa
VP: Ken Reaves
Ex Dir: Armando Covarrubias
Snr Sftwr: Philip Lee
DP Exec: Randy Sacha
Board of Directors: Greg Girton

PRECOR USA
See PRECOR INC

D-U-N-S 07-854-6037
PRECYSE ADVANCED TECHNOLOGIES LLC
(*Suby of* NTHRIVE SOLUTIONS INC) ★
1275 Drummers Ln Ste 200, Wayne, PA 19087-1571
Tel (800) 555-2311 *Founded/Ownrshp* 2010
Sales 112.8M^E *EMP* 1,170^E
SIC 8748 Business consulting
Pr: Ken Lacy

D-U-N-S 07-854-4990
PRECYSE HOLDINGS LLC
1275 Drummers Ln Ste 200, Wayne, PA 19087-1571
Tel (800) 555-2311 *Founded/Ownrshp* 2008
Sales 39.4MM^E *EMP* 1,200
SIC 8748 Business consulting
VP: Kevin Sleeper

D-U-N-S 07-005-7624
PREDICTIF SOLUTIONS
8588 Katy Fwy Ste 435, Houston, TX 77024-1820
Tel (713) 457-7471 *Founded/Ownrshp* 2011
Sales 98.4MM^E *EMP* 6,000
SIC 7379 Computer related consulting services
CEO: Jeff Huang
VP Sls: Karl Harrocks

D-U-N-S 96-734-9098
▲ **PREFERRED APARTMENT COMMUNITIES INC**
3284 Northside Pkwy Nw # 150, Atlanta, GA 30327-2282
Tel (770) 818-4100 *Founded/Ownrshp* 2009
Sales 109.3MM *EMP* 5^E
Accts Pricewaterhousecoopers Llp A
Tkr Sym APTS *Exch* NYS
SIC 6798 Real estate investment trusts
Ch Bd: John A Williams
V Ch: Dan Dupree
Pr: Leonard A Silverstein
Treas: Michael J Cronin
V Ch Bd: Daniel M Dupree
Ex VP: William Randolph Forth
Ex VP: Albert Haworth
Ex VP: William F Leseman

D-U-N-S 78-806-8575
▲ **PREFERRED BANK**
601 S Figueroa St # 2900, Los Angeles, CA 90017-5734
Tel (213) 891-1188 *Founded/Ownrshp* 1991
Sales NA *EMP* 110
Tkr Sym PFBC *Exch* NGS
SIC 6022 State commercial banks
Ch Bd: Li Yu
V Ch: Clark Hsu
**Pr:* Wellington Chen
**CFO:* Edward J Czajka
**Chf Cred:* Lucilio M Couto
**Chf Cred:* Walter Duchanin
**Chf Cred:* Robert J Kosof
**Chf Cred:* Nick Pi
Ofcr: Rita Luu
Ex VP: Frederick B Denitz
Ex VP: Thomas Lo
Sr VP: Anna Bagdasarian
**Sr VP:* Chris Chan
**Sr VP:* Eddie Lam
VP: Jim Belanic
VP: Sally Chang
VP: Elsa Chen
VP: Ann Cheung
VP: Wayne Chow
VP: Louie Couto
VP: Brandon George

D-U-N-S 79-610-4347
PREFERRED CARE PARTNERS MANAGEMENT GROUP LP
5420 W Plano Pkwy, Plano, TX 75093-4823
Tel (972) 931-3800 *Founded/Ownrshp* 1992
Sales 91.3MM^E *EMP* 4,500
SIC 8051 8052 Skilled nursing care facilities; Home for the mentally retarded, with health care
Pr: Thomas D Scott
VP: Gary D Anderson
VP: Cheryl B Levy

D-U-N-S 61-033-6000 IMP
PREFERRED COMPOUNDING CORP
1020 Lambert St, Barberton, OH 44203-1612
Tel (330) 798-4790 *Founded/Ownrshp* 1973
Sales 83.7MM^E *EMP* 237
SIC 3069 Custom compounding of rubber materials
Pr: Ken Bloom
COO: Michael Magno
**VP:* Andrew Chan
**VP:* Joe Hudson
**VP:* Scott Lieberman
VP: Scott Liverman
VP: Don Myhan
**VP:* Randy Niedermier
VP: Jodi Rogers

D-U-N-S 00-253-0400 IMP
PREFERRED FOODS MARTIN L P (TX)
MARTIN PREFERRED LOGISTICS
2011 Silver St, Houston, TX 77007-2801
Tel (713) 869-6191 *Founded/Ownrshp* 1944, 1998
Sales 212.4MM^E *EMP* 340
SIC 5142 2015 2011 5141 5144 Packaged frozen goods; Poultry slaughtering & processing; Meat packing plants; Groceries, general line; Poultry: live, dressed or frozen (unpackaged); Poultry products; Eggs
CEO: Mike Tapick
Pr: Jeffrey Tapick
Ex VP: Steve Potaniek
VP: Art Morton
Dir IT: Roland Galvan
IT Man: Robert Neff
Opers Mgr: Kammie Shay
Prd Mgr: Doug Pettit
Sls Dir: Steve Potaniec

D-U-N-S 61-193-4159
PREFERRED FREEZER SERVICES INC
1 Main St Fl 3, Chatham, NJ 07928-2426
Tel (973) 820-4040 *Founded/Ownrshp* 1999
Sales 394.4MM^E *EMP* 800
SIC 4222 Warehousing, cold storage or refrigerated
CEO: John J Galiher
**Pr:* Brian Beattie
**CFO:* Samuel Hensley
**Ex VP:* Kevin Daly
**Ex VP:* Dan Didonato
VP: James Gladis
VP Sls: Jerry Gonzalez
Sls Mgr: Rod Armesto

D-U-N-S 94-789-8953
■ **PREFERRED HEALTH SYSTEMS INC**
(*Suby of* COVENTRY HEALTH CARE INC) ★
8535 E 21st St N, Wichita, KS 67206-2911
Tel (316) 609-2345 *Founded/Ownrshp* 2010
Sales NA *EMP* 230
SIC 6324 Hospital & medical service plans
Pr: Marlon Dauner
COO: Brad Clochier
**COO:* Brad Clothier
**CFO:* Todd Kasitz
Assoc Dir: Jill Lee
Dir Rx: James H Utley

D-U-N-S 03-321-2351
PREFERRED HOME CARE INC
PREFFERED HOME CARE OF NY
1267 57th St Ste 1p, Brooklyn, NY 11219-4572
Tel (718) 841-8000 *Founded/Ownrshp* 1998
Sales 2.6MM^E *EMP* 2,000^E
SIC 8059 Personal care home, with health care
Pr: Berey Weiss
CFO: Shmuel Chesir

PREFERRED HOME HEALTH CARE OF
See E WALSH MANAGEMENT CORP

PREFERRED HOMECARE
See FOUNDERS HEALTHCARE LLC

D-U-N-S 01-458-2324 EXP
PREFERRED MATERIALS INC
APAC
(*Suby of* APAC HOLDINGS INC) ★
500 Rvrhills Bus Park, Birmingham, AL 35242-5039
Tel (205) 995-5900 *Founded/Ownrshp* 1980
Sales 163.8MM^E *EMP* 450
SIC 1611 1771 3531 5032 Concrete construction: roads, highways, sidewalks, etc.; Airport runway construction; Parking lot construction; Asphalt plant, including gravel-mix type; Sand, construction; Gravel
CEO: Robert F Duke
Pr: Sean O'Sullivan
CFO: Charles Brown
Sec: Michael R Halpin
VP: Joe V Burrows
VP: W E Merritt Jr
VP: W S Watkins
Area Mgr: Jeff Janeway
Genl Mgr: Anita Billingsley
IT Man: Charlotte Garvin

D-U-N-S 04-895-2527 IMP
PREFERRED MEAL SYSTEMS INC
5240 Saint Charles Rd, Berkeley, IL 60163-1341
Tel (309) 697-4550 *Founded/Ownrshp* 1991
Sales 118.8MM^E *EMP* 1,000
SIC 5963 Food services, direct sales
Pr: George Chivari
**CFO:* Linda Janczkowski
**Sr VP:* Mark Goodman
**VP:* Art Bell
**VP:* Patrice Tillman
Mng Dir: Shane Krukowski
CTO: Jennifer Grigsby
MIS Dir: Al Crowe

D-U-N-S 93-072-8571
PREFERRED MEDICAL PLAN INC
4950 Sw 8th St Fl 4, Coral Gables, FL 33134-2400
Tel (305) 324-5585 *Founded/Ownrshp* 1972
Sales NA *EMP* 120
SIC 6324 Health maintenance organization (HMO), insurance only
CEO: Tamara P Meyerson
COO: Nancy Garcia
**CFO:* Albert Arca
Ofcr: Debbie Bishamber
Genl Mgr: Eva Rico
CIO: Ernie Prytz
Dir QC: Kamal Hamdan
Pr Mgr: Jose Cordero
Mktg Mgr: Lizette Maranon-Cancela

D-U-N-S 00-225-3425
PREFERRED MUTUAL INSURANCE CO (NY)
1 Preferred Way, New Berlin, NY 13411-1896
Tel (607) 847-6161 *Founded/Ownrshp* 1896
Sales NA *EMP* 260
SIC 6331 Property damage insurance
CEO: Christopher P Taft
**CFO:* Aaron Valentine
**Ch:* Robert A Wadsworth
VP: Greg Clancy
**VP:* James Crandall
VP: Fred Schneider
**VP:* Gary Strong
IT Man: Brent Walworth
Mktg Mgr: Paul Quinn
Board of Directors: Paul O Stillman, Matthew T Cooney Jr, William C Westbrook, William C Craine, Peter De Cordova, David B Emerson, Everett A Gilmour, James W Honeywell, Irad Ingraham, John C Mitchell, Geoffrey A Smith

PREFERRED PERSONNEL CALIFORNIA
See CORPORATE PERSONNEL NETWORK INC

D-U-N-S 79-713-2123
■ **PREFERRED PLUS OF KANSAS INC**
(*Suby of* PREFERRED HEALTH SYSTEMS INC) ★
8535 E 21st St N, Wichita, KS 67206-2911
Tel (316) 609-2345 *Founded/Ownrshp* 1992
Sales 285.9MM *EMP* 200
SIC 8011 Health maintenance organization
Pr: Marlon Dauner
**Sr VP:* Brad Clothier

D-U-N-S 07-119-6062 IMP
PREFERRED PUMP & EQUIPMENT LP
2201 Scott Ave Ste 100, Fort Worth, TX 76103-2238
Tel (817) 536-9800 *Founded/Ownrshp* 1982
Sales 432.7MM^E *EMP* 400
SIC 5084 5083 5074 3533 5082 Water pumps (industrial); Irrigation equipment; Plumbing & hydronic heating supplies; Drilling tools for gas, oil or water wells; Construction & mining machinery
Pt: Randy Lyne
Brnch Mgr: Kevin Audette
Brnch Mgr: Randy N Carnes
Brnch Mgr: Timmy Chormicle
Brnch Mgr: Scott Dobry
Brnch Mgr: Judy Durning
Brnch Mgr: Tommy N Ford
Brnch Mgr: Nina Forehand
Brnch Mgr: Craig Janzen
Brnch Mgr: Craig Kelly
Brnch Mgr: Marv Meininger

D-U-N-S 07-973-5750
PREFERRED RISK INSURANCE SERVICES INC
6640 S Cicero Ave Ste 400, Bedford Park, IL 60638-5846
Tel (708) 552-2424 *Founded/Ownrshp* 1998
Sales 100.0MM *EMP* 200
SIC 7389 Financial services
CEO: James P Hallberg
VP: Gary Randant

D-U-N-S 03-285-6538
PREFERRED SANDS LLC
1 Radnor Corp Ctr 1-101, Radnor, PA 19087-4515
Tel (610) 834-1969 *Founded/Ownrshp* 2007
Sales 280.5MM^E *EMP* 513^E
SIC 6719 Investment holding companies, except banks
CEO: Michael O Neill
**Pr:* Christian Rheault
**CFO:* Chris Close
**Ex VP:* Mike Balitsaris
**Ex VP:* Tj Doyle
**Ex VP:* Kevin Traynor
**VP:* Brian McTear
**VP:* Miguel Pena

D-U-N-S 78-885-4248
PREFERRED SYSTEMS SOLUTIONS INC
PSS FEDERAL
7925 Jones Branch Dr # 6200, Mc Lean, VA 22102-3376
Tel (703) 663-2777 *Founded/Ownrshp* 1991
Sales 97.1MM^E *EMP* 375^E
SIC 7379 Computer related consulting services
CEO: Scott Goss
Ofcr: Keith Landry
Sr VP: Fred Funk
Sr VP: Dean McKendrick
Sr VP: Joseph Rexrode
Sr VP: Joseph A Rexrode Jr
VP: William Raters
VP: Ryan Rohr
VP: John Ross
VP: Steven Russell
VP: Gary Welch
Exec: Ashley Carter
Dir Bus: Nicole Johnson

PREFFERED HOME CARE OF NY
See PREFERRED HOME CARE INC

D-U-N-S 00-420-2420
▲ **PREFORMED LINE PRODUCTS CO**
660 Beta Dr, Mayfield Village, OH 44143-2398
Tel (440) 461-5200 *Founded/Ownrshp* 1947
Sales 354.6MM *EMP* 2,645^E
Tkr Sym PLPC *Exch* NGS
SIC 3644 3661 Pole line hardware; Fiber optics communications equipment
Ch Bd: Robert G Ruhlman
Pr: Bob Hazenfield
COO: Jean Reilly
CFO: Eric R Graef
Ex VP: Dennis F McKenna
VP: William H Haag
Opers Mgr: John Bentley

VP Mktg: J Ryan Ruhlman
Manager: Kurt Nelson
Board of Directors: Glenn E Corlett, Richard R Gascoigne, Michael E Gibbons, R Steven Kestner, Barbara P Ruhlman

D-U-N-S 96-333-5596
PREGIS HOLDING I CORP
1650 Lake Cook Rd Ste 400, Deerfield, IL 60015-4747
Tel (847) 597-2200 *Founded/Ownrshp* 2005
Sales 207.9MM[E] *EMP* 4,001[E]
SIC 2671 5199 7336 Packaging paper & plastics film, coated & laminated; Packaging materials; Package design
Pr: Glenn M Fischer
**Pr:* Michael T McDonnell

D-U-N-S 60-969-2012 IMP/EXP
PREGIS LLC
(*Suby of* OLYMPUS PARTNERS LP) ★
1650 Lake Cook Rd Ste 400, Deerfield, IL 60015-4747
Tel (847) 597-9330 *Founded/Ownrshp* 2014
Sales 309.3MM[E] *EMP* 786
SIC 3086 Packaging & shipping materials, foamed plastic
Pr: Kevin Baudhuin
Pr: Tom Pienkowski
**CFO:* Keith Lavanway
Rgnl Mgr: Ivan Brewington
IT Man: Gary Kempster
VP Opers: Dan Donofrio
Plnt Mgr: Don Crites
Natl Sales: Matthew Heil
VP Sls: Mike Pichotta
Mktg Dir: Sean Condon
Sales Asso: Margaret Hammer

D-U-N-S 79-651-5240
PREGIS LLC
(*Suby of* PREGIS HOLDING I CORP) ★
1650 Lake Cook Rd Ste 400, Deerfield, IL 60015-4747
Tel (847) 597-2200 *Founded/Ownrshp* 2005
Sales 207.9MM[E] *EMP* 4,000
SIC 2671 2673 3086 Packaging paper & plastics film, coated & laminated; Bags: plastic, laminated & coated; Insulation or cushioning material, foamed plastic; Packaging & shipping materials, foamed plastic
Pr: Kevin J Baudhuin
**CFO:* D Keith Lavanway
Board of Directors: Glenn M Fischer, Brian R Hoesterey, James W Leng, James D Morris, John P O'leary Jr, Thomas J Pryma, James E Rogers

D-U-N-S 14-965-2211 IMP
PREH INC
(*Suby of* PREH GMBH)
28850 Cabot Dr Ste 1300, Novi, MI 48377-2961
Tel (248) 381-3800 *Founded/Ownrshp* 2005
Sales 186.1MM[E] *EMP* 50
SIC 5013 Automotive supplies & parts
Pr: Nick Lontscharitsch
**CFO:* Kimberly Goodes
IT Man: Rafael Garcia
Sftwr Eng: Ulises Hernandez
Sftwr Eng: Michael Pearson

PREIT
See PENNSYLVANIA REAL ESTATE INVESTMENT TRUST

D-U-N-S 07-574-7816
PREMERA BLUE CROSS
7001 220th St Sw Bldg 1, Mountlake Terrace, WA 98043-2160
Tel (425) 670-4000 *Founded/Ownrshp* 1945
Sales NA *EMP* 3,000
Accts Kpmg Llp Seattle Wa
SIC 6321 Accident & health insurance
Pr: Jeff Roe
Pr: Scott Forslund
COO: Ryan Duffy
**CFO:* Kent S Marquardt
**Bd of Dir:* Jaja Okigwe
**Ex VP:* Yoram Milo
**Sr VP:* David Braza
**Sr VP:* Barbara Magusin
Sr VP: Jack McRae
**Sr VP:* John Pierce
VP: Lonnie Crone
VP: Richard L Grover
VP: Curtis Kopf
VP: Robert M Mill
VP: Darryl Prace
VP: Peter Rowe
VP: Ed Wong
VP: Dave Young
Exec: Daron Brown
Exec: Rick Devenuti
Dir Rx: John Watkins

PREMERIAN
See US GOLD INC

PREMIER
See KGP PRODUCTS INC

D-U-N-S 78-414-1384 EXP
PREMIER & COMPANIES INC
460 W 34th St Fl 5, New York, NY 10001-2320
Tel (212) 947-1365 *Founded/Ownrshp* 1991
Sales 118.2MM[E] *EMP* 75
SIC 5112 Office supplies
Pr: Sheldon Lehman
**VP:* Mitchell Wergiles
Genl Mgr: Stuart Fein
IT Man: Josmil Olio
Prd Mgr: Steven Scott
Mktg Dir: Michael Kanik

D-U-N-S 00-798-5245
PREMIER AG CO-OP INC
785 S Marr Rd, Columbus, IN 47201-7490
Tel (812) 379-9501 *Founded/Ownrshp* 1923
Sales 121.6MM *EMP* 100
SIC 5153 5191 5172 5411 2429 Grain elevators; Farm supplies; Petroleum brokers; Convenience stores; Cooperage stock products: staves, headings, hoops, etc.
CEO: Harold Cooper
**Pr:* James Geis
**VP:* Dennis Stewart
Genl Mgr: Cooper Harold

D-U-N-S 96-370-5061
■ **PREMIER BANK & TRUST NATIONAL ASSOCIATION**
(*Suby of* OHIO LEGACY CORP)
600 S Main St, North Canton, OH 44720-3031
Tel (330) 499-1900 *Founded/Ownrshp* 2010
Sales 224.0MM *EMP* 77[E]
SIC 6733 6029 Trusts; Commercial banks
Pr: Rick Hull
Trst Ofcr: John Prelac
Sr VP: John Falatok
Sr VP: Jeff Snyder
VP: Danielle Bailey
VP: Scott Beck
VP: Doug Featheringham
VP: David Hall
VP: Brian Hartong
VP: Amy Holbrook
VP: Pam McKim
VP: Ken Meyer
VP: Marc Ohler
VP: Cindy Pfaus
VP: Pam Shields
VP: Jason Smith
VP: Mike Taylor

D-U-N-S 83-180-8998
PREMIER BANKCARD HOLDINGS LLC
(*Suby of* UNITED NATIONAL CORP) ★
3820 N Louise Ave, Sioux Falls, SD 57107-0145
Tel (605) 357-3440 *Founded/Ownrshp* 2010
Sales NA *EMP* 2,890[E]
SIC 6022 State commercial banks
CFO: Jim Harrenga
VP: Lisa Irvine
VP: Bob Van Liere
Software D: Nick Holzemer
Software D: Alison Jones
Software D: Jason Zeisler
Prd Mgr: Sharon Crawford
Prd Mgr: William Dale
Snr Mgr: Dana Dykhouse

D-U-N-S 12-478-6422
PREMIER BANKCARD LLC
(*Suby of* PREMIER BANKCARD HOLDINGS LLC) ★
3820 N Louise Ave, Sioux Falls, SD 57107-0145
Tel (605) 335-4000 *Founded/Ownrshp* 1997
Sales 98.4MM[E] *EMP* 1,700
SIC 7389 Credit card service
CEO: Dana Dykhouse
**Pr:* Dave Rozenboom
CFO: Jim Harrenga
VP: Lisa Irvine
VP: Dave Reznicek
VP: Dave Shaw
VP: Dan Zerfas
Dir Teleco: Kathy Hess-Williams
Mng Ofcr: Chuck Heatley
Dir IT: Chris Point
Dir IT: Chris Slaba

D-U-N-S 13-647-9602 IMP
PREMIER BEVERAGE CO LLC
CHARMERS SUNBELT
(*Suby of* BREAKTHRU BEVERAGE GROUP) ★
9801 Premier Pkwy, Miramar, FL 33025-3200
Tel (954) 436-9200 *Founded/Ownrshp* 1997
Sales 536.8MM[E] *EMP* 1,400
SIC 5181 5182 Beer & ale; Wine & distilled beverages
**CFO:* Eric Roth
VP: Mike Schick
Area Mgr: Brian Berube
Area Mgr: Bobby Emanuel
Area Mgr: Stacy Macmichael
Genl Mgr: David Anderson
Genl Mgr: Courtney Halperin
Opers Mgr: Harold Crespo
Sls Mgr: Tim Columbus
Sls Mgr: Carlos Pulido
Sls Mgr: Mark Schaffer

D-U-N-S 82-957-3190
PREMIER BUILDERS LLC
PREMIER BUILDING GROUP
3191 E 44th St, Tucson, AZ 85713-5244
Tel (520) 293-0300 *Founded/Ownrshp* 2009
Sales 32.5MM *EMP* 1,100
SIC 1521 Single-family housing construction

PREMIER BUILDING GROUP
See PREMIER BUILDERS LLC

D-U-N-S 93-291-8600
PREMIER COLLECTION
299 Kisco Ave, Mount Kisco, NY 10549-1005
Tel (877) 360-9162 *Founded/Ownrshp* 1995
Sales 107.5MM[E] *EMP* 400
SIC 5511 Automobiles, new & used
**CFO:* Dale Leake
Genl Mgr: John Deangelis
Genl Mgr: Mark Edens
Genl Mgr: Chris Lynch
Off Mgr: Sandra Stark
Sales Exec: Anthony Sergi

D-U-N-S 94-841-2101
PREMIER CONCEPTS SC
2701 Se J St, Bentonville, AR 72712-4266
Tel (479) 271-6000 *Founded/Ownrshp* 1996
Sales 84.3MM[E] *EMP* 350
SIC 5141 Food brokers
CEO: Darren Horton
CFO: Jennifer Clark
Ex VP: Steve Freeman
Ex VP: Allan Main
Ex VP: Josh Wilson
VP: Mark Brittain
VP: Jeff Green
Rgnl Mgr: Sonja Skrocki
Snr Sftwr: Brandon Ledbetter
Dir IT: Lance Spanke
Sls&Mrk Ex: Dan Krohn

D-U-N-S 02-346-0116
PREMIER COOPERATIVE
DO IT BEST
501 W Main St, Mount Horeb, WI 53572-1903
Tel (608) 251-0199 *Founded/Ownrshp* 1893
Sales 208.3MM *EMP* 55
SIC 5211 5171 5191 5541 Lumber & other building materials; Petroleum bulk stations; Feed; Seeds: field, garden & flower; Fertilizer & fertilizer materials; Filling stations, gasoline
CEO: Andy Fiene
Off Mgr: Ray Billman

D-U-N-S 95-834-0841
PREMIER COOPERATIVE INC
2104 W Park Ct, Champaign, IL 61821-2986
Tel (217) 355-1983 *Founded/Ownrshp* 2009
Sales 394.3MM *EMP* 160
SIC 5153 5191 Grain elevators; Farm supplies
CEO: Roger Miller
**Ch Bd:* John G Murray

D-U-N-S 15-053-7827
PREMIER DESIGNS INC
1551 Corporate Dr Ste 150, Irving, TX 75038-2498
Tel (972) 550-0955 *Founded/Ownrshp* 1985
Sales 200.9MM[E] *EMP* 260
SIC 5094 Jewelry
CEO: Andrew J Horner
**Pr:* Timothy A Horner
**Sr VP:* James A Johnson
VP: Bob Bolander
**VP:* Robert Bolander
VP: Don Cook
**VP:* James Johnson
VP: Kevin Moses
**Exec:* Joan Horner
Dir IT: Eric Wilson
Mktg Dir: Mandy Eaton

D-U-N-S 05-819-0620 IMP
PREMIER DISTRIBUTING CO
P D C
4321 Yale Blvd Ne, Albuquerque, NM 87107-4141
Tel (575) 524-1661 *Founded/Ownrshp* 1982
Sales 180.0MM *EMP* 371
SIC 5181 5149 Beer & other fermented malt liquors; Soft drinks
Pr: Edward J Dobbs
**CFO:* Alan A Markey
**VP:* Reggie Hardway
Genl Mgr: Jody Cole
Genl Mgr: Howard Moss
Dir IT: Robert Suttles
Manager: Mike Ortiz

D-U-N-S 80-790-8249
PREMIER EDUCATION GROUP LIMITED PARTNERSHIP
BRANFORD HALL CAREER INSTITUTE
545 Long Wharf Dr Fl 5, New Haven, CT 06511-5960
Tel (203) 672-2300 *Founded/Ownrshp* 1993
Sales 62.2MM[E] *EMP* 1,000
SIC 8249 Vocational schools; Medical & dental assistant school
CEO: Gary Camp
COO: Nick Hastain
CFO: Bill Anjos
Sr VP: Michele Sinusas
VP: Michelle Sinunas
Board of Directors: W Roderick Gagne

PREMIER FACILITY SERVICES ILL
See LACOSTA INC

D-U-N-S 00-417-7325 IMP/EXP
■ **PREMIER FARNELL CORP**
(*Suby of* PREMIER FARNELL HOLDING INC) ★
4180 Highlander Pkwy, Richfield, OH 44286-9352
Tel (216) 525-4300 *Founded/Ownrshp* 1940, 1996
Sales 598.0MM *EMP* 1,042
SIC 3451

D-U-N-S 13-100-6111 IMP/EXP
■ **PREMIER FARNELL HOLDING INC**
(*Suby of* ELEMENT14 US HOLDINGS INC) ★
4180 Highlander Pkwy, Richfield, OH 44286-9352
Tel (330) 523-4273 *Founded/Ownrshp* 1998
Sales 598.0MM *EMP* 1,043
SIC 5065 3429 Electronic parts & equipment; Nozzles, fire fighting
Pr: Dan Hill
**Treas:* Paul M Barlak
Sr VP: Kenneth Jochum
Sr VP: Marco Ryan
VP: George Arteaga
VP: Darrell Cooper
**VP:* Joseph R Daprile
VP: Jerry Delezen
VP: Mason Rotelli
**VP:* Steven Webb
Exec: Gale Randall

D-U-N-S 01-641-3820
PREMIER GRAPHICS HOLDINGS INC
2500 West Loop S Ste 500, Houston, TX 77027-4521
Tel (713) 961-4700 *Founded/Ownrshp* 2001
Sales 90.5MM[E] *EMP* 700
SIC 2752 Commercial printing, lithographic
Pr: Donald Gilbert Jr
VP Bus Dev: Robert Muralles

D-U-N-S 02-269-4454
PREMIER HEALTH PARTNERS
MIAMI VALLEY
110 N Main St, Dayton, OH 45402-1795
Tel (937) 499-9596 *Founded/Ownrshp* 1991
Sales 340.1MM *EMP* 36[E]
SIC 8082 Home health care services
Pr: James R Pancoast
COO: Mikki Clancy
**CFO:* Thomas M Duncan
Ofcr: Dale E Creech
**Sr VP:* Mark Shaker
**VP:* Mary H Boosalis
VP: Renee George
**VP:* William E Linesch
**Prin:* Sharon Rector

PREMIER HEALTH PLANS
See MERCY HEALTH PLANS INC

PREMIER HEALTHCARE ALLIANCE
See PREMIER HEALTHCARE SOLUTIONS INC

D-U-N-S 78-136-9707
PREMIER HEALTHCARE ALLIANCE LP
13034 Balntyn Corp Pl, Charlotte, NC 28277-1498
Tel (704) 357-0022 *Founded/Ownrshp* 1990
Sales 663.7MM[E] *EMP* 199[E]
SIC 8741 Hospital management
CEO: Susan Devore
**Ch Bd:* Glenn Steel Jr
**CEO:* Richard A Norling
**COO:* Michael Alkire
**CFO:* Craig McKasson
**V Ch Bd:* Dennis Vonderfecht
**Sr VP:* Ann D Rhoads
CIO: Joe Pleasant
VP Inf Sys: Larry D Grandia
Dir IT: Michael Francischiello
Web Dev: Jake Leblanc

D-U-N-S 14-119-7702
PREMIER HEALTHCARE EXCHANGE CORP
2 Crossroads Dr Ste 101b, Bedminster, NJ 07921-1564
Tel (908) 658-3535 *Founded/Ownrshp* 2016
Sales 96.4MM[E] *EMP* 415[E]
SIC 7372 Prepackaged software
CEO: Douglas Klinger
Pr: Tina Ellex
Pr: Jay Ver Hulst
Pr: Lori Sempervive
CFO: Charles Garner
Chf Mktg O: Leo Garneau
Chf Mktg O: Steven Wolinsky
Ex VP: Terry Harris
Ex VP: Meridith Herdes
Ex VP: Matt Hintz
VP: Matthew Albright
VP: Stephen Bradshaw
VP: Kim Elliott
VP: Jim Jeffers
VP: Molly Lenz
VP: Mark Savaryn
VP: William G Schneider
VP: Willliam Schneider

D-U-N-S 02-784-9561
■ **PREMIER HEALTHCARE SOLUTIONS INC**
PREMIER HEALTHCARE ALLIANCE
(*Suby of* PREMIER INC) ★
13034 Balntyn Corp Pl, Charlotte, NC 28277-1498
Tel (704) 357-0022 *Founded/Ownrshp* 1996
Sales 768.2MM *EMP* 1,380
SIC 8741 Hospital management
CEO: Susan D Devore
Pr: Durral Gilbert
**COO:* Mike Alkire
COO: Leigh Anderson
**CFO:* Craig McKasson
**V Ch Bd:* Dennis Vonderfecht
**Sr VP:* Jennifer Arcudi
**Sr VP:* Andy Brailo
**Sr VP:* Blair Childs
Sr VP: David Vorhoff
VP: Robert Horst

D-U-N-S 15-767-2098 IMP
PREMIER IMAGE CORP
G B N
635 Trade Center Dr, Las Vegas, NV 89119-3712
Tel (702) 263-3500 *Founded/Ownrshp* 1981
Sales 86.5MM *EMP* 30[E]
Accts Houlsworth Russo & Company L
SIC 5399 Catalog showrooms
Pr: Brian E Brown
CFO: Robert Myers
IT Man: Will Harris

D-U-N-S 07-917-4944
▲ **PREMIER INC**
13034 Balntyn Corp Pl, Charlotte, NC 28277-1498
Tel (704) 357-0022 *Founded/Ownrshp* 2013
Sales 1.1MMM *EMP* 1,800
Tkr Sym PINC *Exch* NGS
SIC 8742 7375 Hospital & health services consultant; Information retrieval services
Pr: Susan D Devore
Pr: R Wesley Champion
**Ch Bd:* Richard J Statuto
Pr: Durral R Gilbert
COO: Michael J Alkire
CFO: Craig S McKasson
**V Ch Bd:* Terry D Shaw
Sr VP: Leigh Anderson
Sr VP: David Klatsky
Sr VP: Kelli L Price
Sr VP: Andrew Ziskind
Board of Directors: Marc D Miller, Barclay E Berdan, Marvin R O'quinn, Eric J Bieber, Keith B Pitts, Stephen R D'arcy, Scott Reiner, Jody R Davids, Ellen C Wolf, William B Downey, Peter S Fine, Philip A Incarnati, Robert Issai, William E Mayer

PREMIER MORTGAGE COMPANY
See CHERRY CREEK MORTGAGE CO INC

D-U-N-S 62-224-7708 IMP
PREMIER PACKAGING LLC
3900 Produce Rd, Louisville, KY 40218-3006
Tel (502) 935-8786 *Founded/Ownrshp* 2003
Sales 150.0MM[E] *EMP* 350
SIC 5085 5113 3086 Packaging & shipping materials, foamed plastic; Packing, industrial; Corrugated & solid fiber boxes
**CFO:* Andy Hennessy
Div Mgr: Erik Moe
Trfc Dir: Glenn Scott
Opers Supe: Ken Hess
Mfg Mgr: Bobby Osbourne
Prd Mgr: Jason Stinnett
Sls Mgr: Mike Maci

D-U-N-S 05-048-7110 IMP
PREMIER PERFORMANCE LLC
PREMIER PERFORMANCE PRODUCTS
278 Dividend Dr, Rexburg, ID 83440-3559
Tel (208) 356-0106 *Founded/Ownrshp* 2000

Sales 88.1MM[E] *EMP* 130[E]
SIC 4923 Gas transmission & distribution
CEO: Rus Michaelson
**Pr:* Mark Nye
**CFO:* Kim Hatch
**VP:* Parley Pallra
VP: Parley Valora
Rgnl Mgr: Phil Rasmussen
Info Man: Seth Long
Web Dev: Seth Green
Manager: Kirk Abegglen

PREMIER PERFORMANCE PRODUCTS
See PREMIER PERFORMANCE LLC

D-U-N-S 07-845-4143
■ PREMIER SILICA LLC
(*Suby of* PIONEER NATURAL RESOURCES CO) ★
5205 N O Connor Blvd # 200, Irving, TX 75039-3712
Tel (972) 444-9001 *Founded/Ownrshp* 2012
Sales 258.5MM[E] *EMP* 200[E]
SIC 1446 Silica sand mining
**Pr:* Denny Bullard
**CFO:* Rich Dealy
**VP:* Michael Siragusa
VP Sls: Michael Miclette

PREMIER TURBINES
See DALLAS AIRMOTIVE INC

D-U-N-S 14-230-0032
PREMIER UTILITY SERVICES LLC
(*Suby of* S M & P UTILITY RESOURCES) ★
100 Marcus Blvd Ste 1, Hauppauge, NY 11788-3749
Tel (631) 758-7038 *Founded/Ownrshp* 2001
Sales 92.2MM[E] *EMP* 350
SIC 1623 Water, sewer & utility lines
Pr: Marc Makely
VP: Vincent Marchese III
VP: Rick Reed
VP: Craig See
Opers Mgr: Ed Heaney

D-U-N-S 79-282-7669
PREMIERE GLOBAL SERVICES INC
(*Suby of* SIRIS CAPITAL GROUP LLC) ★
3280 Peachtree Rd Ne # 1000, Atlanta, GA 30305-2451
Tel (404) 262-8400 *Founded/Ownrshp* 2015
Sales 567.0MM *EMP* 2,250
SIC 7372 7389 Prepackaged software; Teleconferencing services
Ch Bd: Boland T Jones
Pr: Theodore P Schrafft
CFO: Kevin McAdams
CFO: David E Trine
Chf Mktg O: John Templeton
Ofcr: Erik Petrik
Ex VP: Scott Askins
Ex VP: Michael Dickerson
Ex VP: Frank Naylor
Ex VP: Warren Neuburger
Ex VP: John D Stone
Sr VP: Angelina Beitia
Sr VP: Paul Crighton
Sr VP: Tammy Hammond
Sr VP: Joel J Hughey
Sr VP: Marc Lambert
Sr VP: Colin Pople
VP: Robert Bush
VP: Don Doggett
VP: Craig Kirksey
VP: Todd McCormick
Board of Directors: John F Cassidy, K Robert Draughon, John R Harris, W Steven Jones, Raymond H Pirtle Jr, J Walker Smith Jr

D-U-N-S 60-667-0065 EXP
PREMIERE INC
615 N Landry Dr, New Iberia, LA 70563-1610
Tel (337) 369-1000 *Founded/Ownrshp* 1980
Sales 88.2MM[E] *EMP* 350
SIC 5961 Catalog & mail-order houses
Pr: Kyle Mowbray
**Pr:* Lee Matherne Jr
**VP:* Joseph Hawkins
**VP:* James Williams
VP Sls: Chris Meche

D-U-N-S 07-974-9620
PREMISE HEALTH HOLDING CORP
(*Suby of* ONSITE HOLDING LLC)
5500 Maryland Way Ste 200, Brentwood, TN 37027-4973
Tel (615) 468-6295 *Founded/Ownrshp* 2014
Sales 581.1MM *EMP* 4,100
SIC 8099 Medical services organization
CEO: Edward Stuart Clark
**COO:* Trent Riley
**CFO:* Shannon Farrington
**Ofcr:* Mark Farrington
**Ofcr:* Dana Field
**Ofcr:* Elizebeth Reimer
**CIO:* Haden Mc Whorter

PREMIUM BEVERAGE CO
See HORIZON BEVERAGE CO INC

D-U-N-S 18-616-9710
PREMIUM RETAIL SERVICES INC
618 Spirit Dr Ste 200, Chesterfield, MO 63005-1258
Tel (636) 728-0592 *Founded/Ownrshp* 1986
Sales 10.0M *EMP* 4,000
Accts Brown Wmith Wallace Llc St L
SIC 8742 Merchandising consultant
CEO: Ronald Travers
Pr: Luke Macken
**Pr:* Brian Travers
**Pr:* Kevin Travers
VP: Beth Klaser
VP: Dan Meehan
CTO: Dolores Wilson
Opers Mgr: Genevieve Cavataio-Cosens
Mktg Mgr: Sue Kohlberg
Sls Mgr: Hector Mora

D-U-N-S 95-605-4472
PREMIUM TRANSPORTATION STAFFING INC
190 Highland Dr, Medina, OH 44256-3199
Tel (330) 722-7974 *Founded/Ownrshp* 1996
Sales 142.7MM[E] *EMP* 5,561
SIC 7291 7363 Tax return preparation services; Employee leasing service
Pr: Todd Packard
CFO: Bill Thomas
**VP:* John Willett
Admn Mgr: Claire Bolek
Dist Mgr: Connie Duncan

D-U-N-S 02-318-2983 IMP
PREMIUM WATERS INC
(*Suby of* COCA-COLA) ★
2100 Summer St Ne Ste 200, Minneapolis, MN 55413-3068
Tel (612) 379-4141 *Founded/Ownrshp* 1994
Sales 152.8MM[E] *EMP* 500
SIC 2086 Water, pasteurized: packaged in cans, bottles, etc.
Pr: Greg Nemec
**Ch Bd:* Cy W Chesterman
Pr: Scott Moore
CFO: Gary Meyer
**Sr VP:* Bill Scott
VP: Bill Hicks
Exec: Douglas E Grant
IT Man: Mike Hesse
Ql Cn Mgr: Teddy Fillers
Manager: Jamie Jackson

D-U-N-S 00-420-0044 IMP/EXP
■ PREMIX INC (OH)
MOLDED PARTS DIVISION
(*Suby of* COMPOSITE GROUP) ★
3365 E Center St, North Kingsville, OH 44068
Tel (440) 224-2181 *Founded/Ownrshp* 1959, 2011
Sales 116.6MM[E] *EMP* 320[E]
SIC 3089 2821 Thermoformed finished plastic products; Injection molding of plastics; Plastic kitchenware, tableware & houseware; Plastics materials & resins
Pr: Thomas J Meola
**CFO:* Dane Zoul
Chf Mktg O: Ed Galda
VP: Scott Fleming
Genl Mgr: David Marple
Genl Mgr: Mike Morehouse
Dir IT: Linda Nemitz
Dir IT: Mike Seibert
IT Man: Sonny Kuehner
Sls Mgr: Richard B Sjogren

D-U-N-S 04-201-2724 IMP/EXP
PRENT CORP (WI)
2225 Kennedy Rd, Janesville, WI 53545-0885
Tel (608) 754-0276 *Founded/Ownrshp* 1967
Sales 177.2MM[E] *EMP* 2,000
SIC 3081 Plastic film & sheet
**CFO:* Sara Lemke
**Ch:* Jack E Pregont
VP Mfg: Mark Rothlisberger
Sls&Mrk Ex: Cee Philipps
Mktg Mgr: Mark Talabac

PREPA
See PUERTO RICO ELECTRIC POWER AUTHORITY

D-U-N-S 00-819-5830
PREPAY NATION LLC
(*Suby of* MINUTE TRANSFER INC) ★
1055 Westlakes Dr Ste 300, Berwyn, PA 19312-2410
Tel (215) 987-3711 *Founded/Ownrshp* 2010
Sales 135.0MM *EMP* 20[E]
SIC 7389
CEO: Anurag Jain
Pr: Carlos Rodriguez
COO: Ajay Goyal
VP: Herve Perrin
Snr Sftwr: Supreet Jain
Sls Mgr: Roger Kean

D-U-N-S 06-251-1175
PRESBYTERIAN CHURCH (USA) A CORP
MISSION SUPPORT SERVICES
100 Witherspoon St, Louisville, KY 40202-6300
Tel (800) 728-7228 *Founded/Ownrshp* 1799
Sales 120.9MM[E] *EMP* 1,794
SIC 8661 Presbyterian Church
Prin: John J Detterick
COO: Mike Hooper
**CFO:* Joey B Bailey
**Ex VP:* Curtis Kearns
Assoc Dir: Toni Carver-Smith
Assoc Dir: Marcia Myers
Ex Dir: Frank Diaz
Ex Dir: Linda Valentine
Off Mgr: Annette Greer
IT Man: Angela Lucear
IT Man: Jimmy Meyers

D-U-N-S 17-355-9345
PRESBYTERIAN HEALTH SERVICES CORP
PRESBYTERIAN LAB SERVICES
200 Hawthorne Ln, Charlotte, NC 28204-2515
Tel (704) 384-4000 *Founded/Ownrshp* 1983
Sales 376.5MM *EMP* 8
Accts Coopers & Lybrand Llp Cpa
SIC 8062 Hospital, medical school affiliated with nursing & residency
Ch Bd: H Perrin Anderson
**Pr:* Paul F Betzold
**COO:* Richard T Howerton
**CFO:* Philip R Manz
**Treas:* James H Hance Jr
VP: Leeanne Smith
Doctor: Robin Filippi

D-U-N-S 00-711-4655
PRESBYTERIAN HEALTHCARE SERVICES (NM)
9521 San Mateo Blvd Ne, Albuquerque, NM 87113-2237
Tel (505) 923-5700 *Founded/Ownrshp* 1908
Sales 1.7MMM *EMP* 10,000
SIC 8062 General medical & surgical hospitals
Pr: James H Hinton
**COO:* Paul Briggs
COO: Pete Clarkson
**CFO:* Dale Maxwell
CFO: Tete McCanna
CFO: Billie Peterman
Treas: Bob Davis
**Treas:* Chris Spencer
Bd of Dir: John Landis
Ofcr: Betsy Thompson
Sr VP: Joseph Calvaruso
Sr VP: Lee Marley
VP: Margherita Aikman
VP: Michelle Campbell
VP: Cesar Martinez
VP: Giuseppe Rizza
VP: Peter Snow
Exec: Bridget Alcala
Dir Risk M: Nancy Cope
Dir Rad: Scott Sees
Dir Rx: Mauro Florentine

D-U-N-S 06-746-3950
PRESBYTERIAN HOMES
WESTMINSTER PLACE
3200 Grant St, Evanston, IL 60201-1999
Tel (847) 492-4800 *Founded/Ownrshp* 1904
Sales 114.5MM *EMP* 1,300
Accts Cliftonlarsonallen Llp Oak Br
SIC 8361 Home for the aged
Pr: Peter Mulvey
CFO: Mark Havrilka
Chf Mktg O: Bob Werdan
VP: Nadim ABI-Antoun
VP: Peter Jaggard
Mktg Dir: Mary K Bochenek
Mktg Dir: Sylvia Jones

PRESBYTERIAN HOMES & SERVICES
See SENIOR PHS LIVING INC

PRESBYTERIAN HOMES & SERVICES
See SENIOR SPRINGPOINT LIVING INC

D-U-N-S 03-000-3065
PRESBYTERIAN HOMES AND SERVICES (MN)
2845 Hamline Ave N # 200, Roseville, MN 55113-7116
Tel (651) 631-6100 *Founded/Ownrshp* 1953, 1995
Sales 363.6MM *EMP* 4,750
Accts Cliftonlarsonallen Llp Minnea
SIC 8361 Home for the aged
CEO: Daniel A Lindh
Dir Vol: Marilyn Bumsted
**Pr:* Daniel Lindh
**CFO:* Mark T Meyer
**Ch:* Kenneth S Larson
Bd of Dir: Nancy Schwartz
Ex Dir: David Benni
Ex Dir: Dan Erickson
Ex Dir: Karen McKenna
CTO: Laura Lenertz
IT Man: Jim Armstrong

D-U-N-S 06-977-9148
PRESBYTERIAN HOMES INC
EASTON HOME, THE
1 Trinity Dr E Ste 201, Dillsburg, PA 17019-8522
Tel (717) 697-2255 *Founded/Ownrshp* 1927
Sales 163.4MM[E] *EMP* 4,000
SIC 8361 Home for the aged
CEO: Stephen Proctor
CFO: Jeffrey Davis
Ex VP: James Bernardo
Sr VP: Maryanne Adamczyk
VP: Nicholas Wentz
Exec: Laurel Spagnolo
Genl Mgr: Diane Shaffer
VP Opers: Louise Sobke
Sls&Mrk Ex: Melissa Wagner
Mktg Dir: Amy Carr
Sls Dir: Jane Erikson

D-U-N-S 06-529-1960
PRESBYTERIAN HOSPITAL
NOVANT HEALTH PRESBT MED CTR
200 Hawthorne Ln, Charlotte, NC 28204-2528
Tel (704) 384-4000 *Founded/Ownrshp* 1993
Sales 1.1MMM *EMP* 3,100
SIC 8062 General medical & surgical hospitals
CEO: Carl Armato
**Pr:* Lynn Bodgs
Dir Rx: Elizabeth Conforti
Brnch Mgr: Paul Betzold
Doctor: Lisa D Rohde MD
Pharmcst: Tammy Loayza

PRESBYTERIAN HOSPITAL DALLAS
See GENERAL HEALTH SERVICES CORP

D-U-N-S 00-478-8926
PRESBYTERIAN HOSPITAL OF ROCKWALL
3150 Horizon Rd, Rockwall, TX 75032-7805
Tel (469) 698-1000 *Founded/Ownrshp* 2007
Sales 130.0MM *EMP* 48[E]
SIC 8062 General medical & surgical hospitals
Prin: Sharon S Hughes
CFO: Jason Linscott
VP: Joanna Hailey
Chf Nrs Of: Tami Hawkins
Mtls Mgr: Kay Talley
Mktg Dir: Nikki Mutschler

D-U-N-S 05-922-7538
PRESBYTERIAN INTERCOMMUNITY HOSPITAL INC
PIH HOME HEALTH SERVICES
12401 Washington Blvd, Whittier, CA 90602-1006
Tel (562) 698-0811 *Founded/Ownrshp* 1954
Sales 555.9MM *EMP* 3,150
SIC 8062 General medical & surgical hospitals
CEO: James R West
**CFO:* Mitchell Thomas
Sr VP: Rosalio J Lopez
VP: Patricia Bray
VP: Carol Lugo
VP: Terry Sepulveda
Ex Dir: Amy Fitzgerald
Brnch Mgr: Priscilla Jahangiri
CIO: Kevin Ritter
CTO: Dan Adams
CTO: Jim Pelgrin

PRESBYTERIAN LAB SERVICES
See PRESBYTERIAN HEALTH SERVICES CORP

D-U-N-S 01-066-0579
PRESBYTERIAN MANORS INC (KS)
PMMA
(*Suby of* PRESBYTERIAN MANORS OF MID-AMERICA INC)
2414 N Woodlawn Blvd, Wichita, KS 67220-3958
Tel (316) 685-1100 *Founded/Ownrshp* 1948
Sales 105.0MM *EMP* 345
SIC 8051

D-U-N-S 87-717-9465
PRESBYTERIAN MEDICAL CARE CORP
LAKESIDE FAMILY PHYSICIANS
(*Suby of* LAKESIDE FAMILY PHYSICIANS) ★
1500 Matthews Twnship Pkwy, Matthews, NC 28105-4656
Tel (704) 384-6500 *Founded/Ownrshp* 1997
Sales 216.6MM *EMP* 437
SIC 8062 Hospital, medical school affiliated with nursing & residency
Pr: Harry L Smith Jr
**Ex VP:* Lynn Boggs
VP: Tom Zweng
IT Man: Kenneth Alexander
IT Man: Michelle Johnson
Pharmcst: Elena Marsh

D-U-N-S 06-904-7694
PRESBYTERIAN MEDICAL CENTER OF UNIVERSITY OF PENNSYLVANIA HEALTH SYSTEM
51 N 39th St, Philadelphia, PA 19104-2692
Tel (215) 662-8000 *Founded/Ownrshp* 1871
Sales 546.8MM *EMP* 1,370
Accts Pricewaterhousecoopers Llp Ph
SIC 8062 General medical & surgical hospitals
Ex Dir: Michele Volpe
VP: Ana McKee
Adm Dir: John Donuhue
Doctor: Christine Gasperetti MD
Nrsg Dir: Denise Gilanelli

D-U-N-S 07-339-3761
PRESBYTERIAN MEDICAL SERVICES INC
1422 Paseo De Peralta # 1, Santa Fe, NM 87501-4304
Tel (505) 982-5565 *Founded/Ownrshp* 1969
Sales 94.3MM[E] *EMP* 1,067
Accts Pulakos Cpas Pc Albuquerque
SIC 8011 Medical centers
Pr: Steven C Hansen
**CFO:* Roberta Lee
**Ex VP:* Doug Smith
**VP:* Don Daniel
**VP:* Diane Martinez
Info Man: Bonnie Webster

D-U-N-S 06-965-9480
PRESBYTERIAN RETIREMENT COMMUNITIES INC
WINTER PARK TOWERS
80 W Lucerne Cir, Orlando, FL 32801-3779
Tel (407) 839-5050 *Founded/Ownrshp* 1959
Sales 97.3MM[E] *EMP* 1,700
Accts Hoskins Quiros Osborne Labeaum
SIC 8361 8052 8051 Home for the aged; Intermediate care facilities; Skilled nursing care facilities
Ch: John Milton
**Ch Bd:* William Gay
**Pr:* Dick Strum
**CEO:* James F Emerson
**CFO:* Henry Keith
**Prin:* Roger Stevens

D-U-N-S 08-396-6002
PRESBYTERIAN SENIORCARE
1215 Hulton Rd, Oakmont, PA 15139-1135
Tel (412) 828-5600 *Founded/Ownrshp* 1928
Sales 132.0MM *EMP* 2,075
Accts Presbyterian Seniorcare Oakmo
SIC 8051 8052 6513 8741 Skilled nursing care facilities; Personal care facility; Retirement hotel operation; Nursing & personal care facility management
Ch Bd: Paul Winkler
Ch Bd: Peter Mcilroy II
Ex VP: James Pieffer
Sr VP: Andrew E Mangene
Prin: David Lowe

PRESBYTERIAN ST LUKES MED CTR
See HCA-HEALTHONE LLC

D-U-N-S 18-792-1903
PRESBYTERIAN-ORTHOPEDIC HOSPITAL
(*Suby of* LAKESIDE FAMILY PHYSICIANS) ★
1901 Randolph Rd, Charlotte, NC 28207-1195
Tel (704) 316-2000 *Founded/Ownrshp* 1997
Sales 84.3MM *EMP* 482
SIC 8069 Orthopedic hospital
Dir Inf Cn: Jenny Morgan
Dir Rx: Diane Walter
Nurse Mgr: Shana Sebold
Ansthlgy: Joseph Ducey

PRESCHOOL
See MORONGO UNIFIED SCHOOL DISTRICT

PRESCOTT CAMPUS
See YAVAPAI COUNTY COMMUNITY COLLEGE DISTRICT

PRESCRIPTION SOLUTIONS
See OPTUMRX INC

D-U-N-S 79-790-1662
PRESCRIPTION SOLUTIONS
2858 Loker Ave E Ste 100, Carlsbad, CA 92010-6673
Tel (760) 804-2370 *Founded/Ownrshp* 2006
Sales 81.5MM[E] *EMP* 1,000
SIC 8742 Hospital & health services consultant
Pr: Bobby Robert Bliatout
IT Man: Phil Haworth
Snr Mgr: Shaun Davis

D-U-N-S 01-837-6095
PRESCRIPTION SUPPLY INC
2233 Tracy Rd, Northwood, OH 43619-1302
Tel (419) 661-6600 *Founded/Ownrshp* 1955
Sales 83.5MM *EMP* 54
Accts Bock Korsnack & Hinds Inc

SIC 5122 Pharmaceuticals
Pr: Thomas Schoen
**Sec:* Jacquelyn J Harbauer
VP Mktg: Christopher Schoen
Sls Mgr: Fred Mengerink

D-U-N-S 02-238-7521
PRESENCE CENTRAL AND SUBURBAN HOSPITALS NETWORK
(*Suby of* PRESENCE PRV HEALTH) ★
9223 W Saint Francis Rd, Frankfort, IL 60423-8330
Tel (312) 308-3200 *Founded/Ownrshp* 1997
Sales 67.3MM^E *EMP* 4,334
SIC 8062 General medical & surgical hospitals
Pr: Michael Englehart
**CFO:* Anthony Filer
**Treas:* Patrick Quinn

D-U-N-S 00-386-8182
PRESENCE CHICAGO HOSPITALS NETWORK
PRESENCE RESURRECTION MED CTR
(*Suby of* RESURRECTION MEDICAL CENTER) ★
7435 W Talcott Ave, Chicago, IL 60631-3707
Tel (773) 737-4636 *Founded/Ownrshp* 2013
Sales 238.8MM *EMP* 99
SIC 8062 General medical & surgical hospitals
CEO: Robert Dahl
**Prin:* Paul Brydon
QA Dir: Pat Monnelly

D-U-N-S 06-747-6903
PRESENCE CHICAGO HOSPITALS NETWORK
RESURRECTION MEDICAL CENTER
(*Suby of* PRESENCE HEALTH NETWORK) ★
7435 W Talcott Ave, Chicago, IL 60631-3707
Tel (773) 774-8000 *Founded/Ownrshp* 1949
Sales 618.4MM^E *EMP* 8,295
SIC 8062 8059 Hospital, medical school affiliated with nursing & residency; Nursing home, except skilled & intermediate care facility
**Pr:* Sandra B Bruce
**CFO:* John Orsini
Chf Mktg O: Madison Sample
Ex VP: Tom Capobianco
Ex VP: David A Diloreto
Ex VP: James Hill
Sr VP: Frank Madel
VP: Rick Salzer
**VP:* Jim Sykes
VP: Julie Ward
Dir Surg: Brian Crawford
Dir Lab: Loretta Grubb

D-U-N-S 07-853-1593
PRESENCE HEALTH NETWORK
200 S Wacker Dr Fl 12, Chicago, IL 60606-5863
Tel (773) 774-8000 *Founded/Ownrshp* 1939
Sales 1.9MMM^E *EMP* 18,500
SIC 8082 8062 8011 8051 Home health care services; General medical & surgical hospitals; Offices & clinics of medical doctors; Skilled nursing care facilities
Pr: Sandra Bruce
COO: Susan Enright
Ofcr: Janice Nemri
Ofcr: Kathleen L Rhine
Exec: Susan Parker
Dir Lab: Keena Holland
Prac Mgr: Deena Gibson
Sys Mgr: Brian Byrnes
Cert Phar: Raluca Birza
Genl Couns: Brandy Canady
Snr PM: Tom Blackburn

PRESENCE HOLY FAMILY MED CTR
See PRESENCE HOLY FAMILY MEDICAL CENTER

D-U-N-S 07-443-2808
PRESENCE HOLY FAMILY MEDICAL CENTER
PRESENCE HOLY FAMILY MED CTR
(*Suby of* RESURRECTION MEDICAL CENTER) ★
100 N River Rd, Des Plaines, IL 60016-1209
Tel (847) 297-1800 *Founded/Ownrshp* 2013
Sales 76.5MM *EMP* 1,100
Accts Ernst & Young Us Llp Chicago
SIC 8062 Hospital, affiliated with AMA residency
CEO: Joseph Hugar
**CFO:* Rich Franco
Ofcr: Arlene Arellano-Brown
VP: Don Franke
VP: Guy T Kochvar
Dir Sec: Anthony Marsh
CIO: George Chessum
Dir QC: Claudia Teich
Pathlgst: Catherine T Britton-Kuzel

D-U-N-S 08-015-9822
PRESENCE HOSPITALS PRV
(*Suby of* PRESENCE HEALTH NETWORK) ★
1000 Remington Blvd # 100, Bolingbrook, IL 60440-5114
Tel (877) 737-4636 *Founded/Ownrshp* 2016
Sales 1.0MMM *EMP* 1^E
SIC 8062 General medical & surgical hospitals
Prin: Sue Ellen Schumacher

D-U-N-S 01-764-6154
PRESENCE LIFE CONNECTIONS
18927 Hickory Creek Dr # 300, Mokena, IL 60448-8652
Tel (708) 478-7900 *Founded/Ownrshp* 1982
Sales 111.5MM *EMP* 1,300
SIC 8052 Intermediate care facilities
CEO: Joseph Hugar
**CFO:* Michael Gordon
Treas: Jeffrey Port
VP: Leonard Schmidt

D-U-N-S 00-345-8903
PRESENCE PRV HEALTH
(*Suby of* PRESENCE HEALTH NETWORK) ★
19827 Hickory Crk Dr 30 Ste 300, Mokena, IL 60448
Tel (815) 741-7137 *Founded/Ownrshp* 1985, 2011
Sales 155.2MM *EMP* 10,000^E
Accts Kpmg Llp Columbus Oh
SIC 8051 8062 Convalescent home with continuous nursing care; Hospital, professional nursing school with AMA residency
CEO: Guy Wiebking
**Pr:* Michael Englehart
Pr: John Lynch
COO: Michael Arno
CFO: Judy Browne
CFO: Anthony Filer
CFO: Michael Gordon
CFO: Maureen Panattoni
**Treas:* Patrick Quinn
Chf Mktg O: Cheryl Balhouse
Ofcr: David Schultz
Ex VP: Nancy K McKenna
VP: Craig Culver
VP: Tony Filer
VP: Susan S Morelli
VP: Janet Payne
Exec: Lindsey Charley
Exec: Connie-March Curtis
Exec: Mike Gordon
Dir Risk M: Jenise Lowe
Dir Risk M: Julie Lyons

PRESENCE RESURRECTION MED CTR
See PRESENCE CHICAGO HOSPITALS NETWORK

D-U-N-S 10-399-7755
PRESENCE SAINT FRANCIS HOSPITAL
355 Ridge Ave, Evanston, IL 60202-3328
Tel (847) 316-4000 *Founded/Ownrshp* 2013
Sales 145.9MM *EMP* 1,400^E
SIC 8062 8059

D-U-N-S 06-950-9016
PRESENCE SAINT JOSEPH HOSPITAL - CHICAGO
(*Suby of* RESURRECTION MEDICAL CENTER) ★
2900 N Lake Shore Dr, Chicago, IL 60657-5640
Tel (773) 665-3000 *Founded/Ownrshp* 2013
Sales 203.3MM *EMP* 1,600
SIC 8062 Hospital, AMA approved residency
Pr: Roberta Luskin Hawk
**Prin:* Victor Butler
Sls&Mrk Ex: Russell Milligan
HC Dir: Denise Ladolce

D-U-N-S 07-443-9035
PRESENCE SAINTS MARY AND ELIZABETH MEDICAL CENTER
SMEMC
2233 W Division St, Chicago, IL 60622-8151
Tel (312) 770-2000 *Founded/Ownrshp* 2013
Sales 289.6MM *EMP* 2,100
SIC 8062

D-U-N-S 05-895-1401 IMP
PRESIDENT & TRUSTEES OF BATES COLLEGE
2 Andrews Rd, Lewiston, ME 04240-6020
Tel (207) 786-6255 *Founded/Ownrshp* 1855
Sales 109.9MM *EMP* 720
Accts Pricewaterhousecoopers Llp B
SIC 8221 College, except junior
Pr: A Clayton Spencer
Pr: Margaret Kimmel
Treas: Rob Spellman
Ofcr: Rick Miller
Ex VP: Bonnie Shulman
VP: Francis Cheng
VP: Sarah Pearson
Assoc Dir: Catherine Griffiths
**Prin:* Natalie Williamson
Off Mgr: Donna Polhamus
Off Mgr: Courtney A Sparks

D-U-N-S 02-066-5972
PRESIDENT & TRUSTEES OF WILLIAMS COLLEGE
880 Main St Fl 1, Williamstown, MA 01267-2600
Tel (413) 597-4412 *Founded/Ownrshp* 1793
Sales 101.3MM^E *EMP* 950
Accts Pricewaterhousecoopers Llp Ha
SIC 8221 College, except junior
Pr: Adam Falk
**Ch Bd:* Gregory M Avis
**Treas:* Frederick W Puddester
Trst: C Sar J Alvarez
Trst: Sar C Alvarez
Trst: Delos M Cosgrove
Trst: William E Simon
VP: Shelby Lacoffe-Sect
VP: John Malcolm

D-U-N-S 05-480-0214 IMP
PRESIDENT AND BOARD OF TRUSTEES OF SANTA CLARA COLLEGE
S C U
500 El Camino Real, Santa Clara, CA 95050-4345
Tel (408) 554-4000 *Founded/Ownrshp* 1851
Sales 457.9MM *EMP* 1,431
Accts Moss Adams Llp Stockton Ca
SIC 8221 University
Prin: Robert J Finocchio Jr
Pr: Chris Shay
Pr: Gregory R Bonfiglio Sj
Ch: Jon R Aboitiz
Trst: John Lewis
Trst: Dennis Parnell
Trst: Francis Smith
Ofcr: Marguerite Moses
Top Exec: Deborah Whiteman
Assoc VP: Caroline Chang
Ex VP: Lisa Koen
VP: Lucia Gilbert
VP: Robert Gunsalus
VP: Michael Hindery
VP: James Lyons
VP: Megumi Mori
VP: Jeremy Pool
Dir Lab: Daryn Baker
Assoc Dir: Maureen Muscat
Comm Dir: Michael Nuttall

D-U-N-S 00-196-3263 IMP/EXP
PRESIDENT AND FELLOWS OF HARVARD COLLEGE
HARVARD UNIVERSITY
1350 Massachusetts Ave, Cambridge, MA 02138-3846
Tel (617) 496-4873 *Founded/Ownrshp* 1636
Sales 1.0MMM^E *EMP* 13,500
SIC 8221 8732 2721

D-U-N-S 02-065-1675
PRESIDENT AND FELLOWS OF MIDDLEBURY COLLEGE
38 College St, Middlebury, VT 05753
Tel (802) 443-5000 *Founded/Ownrshp* 1800
Sales 260.7MM *EMP* 1,000
Accts Pricewaterhousecoopers Llp Al
SIC 8221 College, except junior
Pr: Ken Pierce
Pr: Jami Black
Treas: Robert Huth
Treas: Courtney Taylor
Trst: Donald M Elliman
Trst: Richard S Fuld
Trst: Robert C Graham
Trst: William H Kieffer
Trst: John Spencer
Trst: Kendrick R Wilson
Ofcr: Kathy Foley
Sr VP: Michael D Schoenfeld
**VP:* Brook Escobedo
VP: Heidi Grasswick
VP: Drew Macan
VP: Michael Schoenfeld

D-U-N-S 96-939-4738
PRESIDENT AND TRUSTEES OF COLBY COLLEGE
4120 Mayflower Hl, Waterville, ME 04901-8841
Tel (207) 859-4127 *Founded/Ownrshp* 2011
Sales 214.1MM *EMP* 4^E
SIC 6733 Trusts
Prin: Bruce McDougal

D-U-N-S 79-820-4640
PRESIDENT CASINOS INC
1000 N Lnor K Sllvan Blvd, Saint Louis, MO 63102-2568
Tel (314) 622-3000 *Founded/Ownrshp* 1992
Sales 75.5MM^E *EMP* 1,025
SIC 6799 Investors
Pr: John S Aylsworth
**CFO:* Ralph J Vaclavik
VP: Rob Long
CTO: Geno Polumbo

D-U-N-S 00-132-1371 IMP
PRESIDENT CONTAINER INC
200 W Commercial Ave, Moonachie, NJ 07074-1684
Tel (201) 933-7500 *Founded/Ownrshp* 1955
Sales 98.9MM^E *EMP* 375
SIC 2653

D-U-N-S 10-679-5875
PRESIDENTIAL LIFE CORP
ATHENE ANNUITY & LF ASRN CO NY
(*Suby of* ATHENE ANNUITY & LIFE ASSURANCE CO) ★
69 Lydecker St, Nyack, NY 10960-2103
Tel (845) 358-2300 *Founded/Ownrshp* 2012
Sales NA *EMP* 99^E
SIC 6311 Life insurance; Life insurance carriers
Pr: Donald L Barnes
**CFO:* Paul B Pheffer
VP: Gary Mettler
VP: Dominic Minieri

PRESIDENTIAL LIFE INSURANCE CO
See ATHENE ANNUITY & LIFE ASSURANCE CO OF NEW YORK

D-U-N-S 17-126-4075
PRESIDIAN DESTINATIONS LTD
9000 Tesoro Dr Ste 300, San Antonio, TX 78217-6132
Tel (210) 646-8811 *Founded/Ownrshp* 2000
Sales 1.3MMM *EMP* 10
SIC 6512 Property operation, retail establishment
Pt: H Drake Leddy
CFO: Jeanette Mosley

D-U-N-S 79-906-4451
PRESIDIO INC
1 Penn Plz Ste 2832, New York, NY 10119-2832
Tel (212) 324-4398 *Founded/Ownrshp* 1980
Sales 1.1MMM^E *EMP* 2,375^E
SIC 7373 Computer system selling services; Computer systems analysis & design; Computer-aided engineering (CAE) systems service; Computer-aided manufacturing (CAM) systems service
CEO: Bob Cagnazzi
COO: Dave Hart
CFO: Paul Fletcher
CFO: Paul D Fletcher
Treas: Michael Malesardi
Ex VP: Kevin Mulloy
Sr VP: John Desarbo
VP: Bill Ferrato
VP: Stacy Hutchings
VP: Misha Kenin
VP: Kip Poindexter
VP: George Santa
VP: Eric Schondorf
Exec: Sue Quackenbush

D-U-N-S 87-699-7495 IMP/EXP
PRESIDIO INTERNATIONAL INC
ARMANI EXCHANGE
(*Suby of* GIORGIO ARMANI SPA)
450 W 15th St 4, New York, NY 10011-7097
Tel (212) 462-1100 *Founded/Ownrshp* 1984
Sales 71.8MM^E *EMP* 1,600
SIC 5651 7379 Family clothing stores;
CEO: Harlan Bratcher
**Ch Bd:* Steven Grapstein
Pr: John Kreuz
CFO: Edward O'Connor
**Ch:* Susan Quackenbush
**Ex VP:* Lee Buird
**VP:* Victor Wong
Dist Mgr: Abby Fernandez
Dist Mgr: Brian Wood
Pr Dir: Patrick Poddy
Mktg Mgr: Diana Koo

D-U-N-S 11-436-9671 IMP
PRESIDIO NETWORKED SOLUTIONS GROUP LLC
(*Suby of* PRESIDIO NETWORKED SOLUTIONS LLC) ★
1955 Lakeway Dr Ste 220, Lewisville, TX 75057-6448
Tel (469) 549-3800 *Founded/Ownrshp* 2011
Sales 211.1MM^E *EMP* 470
SIC 5045 7372 7373 Computers, peripherals & software; Prepackaged software; Computer integrated systems design
CEO: Robert Cagnazzi
Pr: Andy Cadwell
COO: Dave Hart
CFO: Paul Fletcher
CFO: George Lezaun
VP: Eric Schondorf
Off Mgr: Sue Roy
Netwrk Eng: Charles Galler
VP Sls: Andrew Cadwell
Mktg Dir: Lauren D Decker
Sls Mgr: Mike Grady

D-U-N-S 15-405-0959
PRESIDIO NETWORKED SOLUTIONS LLC
(*Suby of* PRESIDIO INC) ★
8161 Maple Lawn Blvd # 150, Fulton, MD 20759-2538
Tel (301) 313-2000 *Founded/Ownrshp* 2001
Sales 1.1MMM^E *EMP* 2,100^E
SIC 7373 Computer system selling services; Computer systems analysis & design; Computer-aided engineering (CAE) systems service; Computer-aided manufacturing (CAM) systems service
Ch: Kevin Penn
Pr: Raphael Meyerowitz
Pr: Robert Murphy
**CEO:* Robert Cagnazzi
**COO:* David Hart
**CFO:* JD Larsen
CFO: Teresa McMahon
CFO: Terry McMahon
**Treas:* Paul Fletcher
**Div Pres:* Rudy Casasola
Ex VP: Kevin Mulloy
Ex VP: Dale Shilling
VP: David Ferrie
VP: Kip Poindexter
**VP:* Jay T Staples
VP: George Troy
Dir Rx: Dave Garr

D-U-N-S 79-155-6652
■ **PRESQUE ISLE DOWNS INC**
(*Suby of* MTR GAMING GROUP INC) ★
8199 Perry Hwy, Erie, PA 16509-6640
Tel (814) 860-8999 *Founded/Ownrshp* 2001
Sales 46.5MM^E *EMP* 1,000
SIC 7011 Casino hotel
Pr: Jeff Favre
Exec: Daniel Arnold
MIS Dir: John Blakeslee
Info Man: Paul Light

D-U-N-S 05-905-2431
PRESRITE CORP
3665 E 78th St, Cleveland, OH 44105-2048
Tel (216) 441-5990 *Founded/Ownrshp* 1969
Sales 105.9MM^E *EMP* 425
SIC 3462 Iron & steel forgings; Automotive & internal combustion engine forgings
Ch Bd: Donald J Diemer
**Pr:* Chris Carman
**Ex VP:* William Berglund
**VP:* George Longhour
Plnt Mgr: Roy Stainfield

PRESS ENTERPRISE, THE
See FREEDOM COMMUNICATIONS HOLDINGS INC

D-U-N-S 17-829-9905
PRESS GANEY ASSOCIATES INC
(*Suby of* PRESS GANEY HOLDINGS INC) ★
404 Columbia St, South Bend, IN 46601-2355
Tel (574) 232-3387 *Founded/Ownrshp* 1985
Sales 203.0MM^E *EMP* 945
SIC 8742 Hospital & health services consultant
Pr: Patrick T Ryan
**COO:* Jonathan Black
**CFO:* Matt Hallgren
**CFO:* Eileen Kamerick
Chf Mktg O: James Merlino
**Sr VP:* Greg Ericson
Sr VP: Balaji Gandhi
VP: Mike Dipirro
VP: Dennis Kaldenberg
VP: Ken Kimmel
VP: Daniel Merz
VP: Brad Morton
VP: Deirdre Mylod
VP: Anne M Stern
VP: Nell Wood-Buhlman
Board of Directors: Edward M Kennedy Jr, Leslie Norwalk, Ralph Snyderman

D-U-N-S 07-983-9340
PRESS GANEY HOLDINGS INC
(*Suby of* EMERALD TOPCO, INC.)
401 Edgewater Pl Ste 500, Wakefield, MA 01880-6204
Tel (781) 295-5000 *Founded/Ownrshp* 2016
Sales 318.6MM *EMP* 1,941^E
SIC 8731 Medical research, commercial; Biological research
CEO: Patrick T Ryan
Pr: Joseph Greskoviak
Ofcr: Thomas H Lee
VP: Debbie O'Brien

D-U-N-S 00-850-1553 IMP
PRESS-ENTERPRISE CO
3450 14th St, Riverside, CA 92501-3878
Tel (951) 684-1200 *Founded/Ownrshp* 2011
Sales 203.2MM^E *EMP* 1,200
SIC 2711 Newspapers, publishing & printing

Pr: Ronald Redfern
**CFO:* Ed Lasak
**VP:* Sue Barry
VP: Ginger Neal
VP: Ken Nelson
**VP:* Kathy Weiermiller

D-U-N-S 80-482-4050
PRESSLEY RIDGE FOUNDATION
5500 Corporate Dr Ste 400, Pittsburgh, PA 15237-5848
Tel (412) 872-9400 *Founded/Ownrshp* 1992
Sales 4.3MM *EMP* 1,000
Accts Maher Duessel Cpas Pittsburgh
SIC 8399 Fund raising organization, non-fee basis
CEO: Susanne L Cole
**COO:* Laurah Currey
**CFO:* Douglas A Mullins
**Prin:* Scott Finnell
Off Mgr: Jaime Belcastro
Off Mgr: Jennifer Clarke
Off Mgr: Vicki Jones
Off Mgr: Jacqueline Terry
Opers Supe: Christina Zimmerman
Psych: Erin Davis
Psych: Kevin Depew

D-U-N-S 18-361-5426 IMP/EXP
PRESSTEK LLC
(*Suby of* MAI HOLDINGS, INC.)
55 Executive Dr, Hudson, NH 03051-4903
Tel (603) 595-7000 *Founded/Ownrshp* 2012
Sales 93.4MM^E *EMP* 338
SIC 3555 3577 3861 Printing trades machinery; Printing plates; Magnetic ink & optical scanning devices; Graphic arts plates, sensitized
Pr: Jeffrey Beck
Pr: Tom Leibrandt
Pr: Mark J Levin
Pr: Mark McElhinney
Pr: Guy Sasson
Pr: Tim Turner
Pr: Victor J Wiley
Pr: Joshua C Wotsch
**COO:* Geoff Loftus
**CFO:* Sean Downey
Ofcr: David Ventola
Sr VP: William C Keller
VP: Robert Barry
VP: Eugene L Langlais
VP: James W Larue
VP: Susan McLaughlin

D-U-N-S 00-653-0273 IMP/EXP
PRESSURE VESSEL SERVICE INC
PVS CHEMICALS
10900 Harper Ave, Detroit, MI 48213-3364
Tel (313) 921-1200 *Founded/Ownrshp* 1946
Sales 494.3MM^E *EMP* 800
SIC 5169 2819 2899 4953 3535 Acids; Industrial chemicals; Sulfuric acid, oleum; Water treating compounds; Acid waste, collection & disposal; Conveyors & conveying equipment
Pr: James B Nicholson
Pr: Mark P Dixon
**CFO:* Candee M Saferian
Ex VP: Lauren Kovaleski
VP: Rick Billings
VP: Dean Larson
**VP:* David A Nicholson
**VP:* Allan Schlumberger
**VP:* Jonathan S Taub
VP: Tracy Temple
Dir Bus: Jeff Stein

D-U-N-S 10-174-1403
PRESTAGE FARMS INC
4651 Taylors Bridge Hwy, Clinton, NC 28328-8064
Tel (910) 596-5700 *Founded/Ownrshp* 1983
Sales 402.8MM^E *EMP* 1,000
SIC 0213 0253 Hogs; Turkey farm
Pr: William H Prestage
**CFO:* Clark Peterson
Sr Cor Off: Dennis Carter
Ofcr: Von Johnson
**Sr VP:* John L Prestage
**VP:* Zack McCullen III
**VP:* Scottj Prestage
Exec: Terry Emerson
**Exec:* Ron Prestage
Dir Lab: Fran Cornatzer
Genl Mgr: Greg Stephens
Board of Directors: John L Prestage

D-U-N-S 83-625-5901
PRESTAGE FARMS OF SOUTH CAROLINA LIMITED LIABILITY CO
1889 Highway 1 N, Cassatt, SC 29032-9213
Tel (803) 432-6396 *Founded/Ownrshp* 1994
Sales 102.1MM^E *EMP* 160
SIC 5144 0253 Poultry & poultry products; Turkeys & turkey eggs
Pr: Ronald W Prestage

D-U-N-S 18-541-4377 EXP
PRESTAGE FOODS INC
4470 Hwy 20 E, Saint Pauls, NC 28384
Tel (910) 865-6611 *Founded/Ownrshp* 2000
Sales 89.8MM^E *EMP* 350
SIC 2015 Turkey, processed
Pr: John Prestage
**CEO:* Kevin Kniefel
**VP:* Ron Prestage
Genl Mgr: Robby Mills
Off Mgr: Janet Smith
Sls Mgr: Kent Puffenbarger

D-U-N-S 15-965-5021
▲ PRESTIGE BRANDS HOLDINGS INC
660 White Plains Rd, Tarrytown, NY 10591-5139
Tel (914) 524-6800 *Founded/Ownrshp* 1996
Sales 806.2MM *EMP* 259^E
Tkr Sym PBH *Exch* NYS
SIC 2834 2841 Pharmaceutical preparations; Soap & other detergents; Detergents, synthetic organic or inorganic alkaline
Pr: Ronald M Lombardi
CFO: Christine Sacco
Ex VP: Timothy J Connors
Sr VP: Jean A Boyko
Sr VP: Christopher Heye
Sr VP: John F Parkinson
VP: Thomas Hochuli
Board of Directors: John E Byom, Gary E Costley, Sheila A Hopkins, James M Jenness, Carl J Johnson, Natale S Ricciardi

D-U-N-S 10-683-9421 IMP/EXP
■ PRESTIGE BRANDS INC
(*Suby of* PRESTIGE BRANDS HOLDINGS INC) ★
660 White Plains Rd, Tarrytown, NY 10591-5139
Tel (914) 524-6810 *Founded/Ownrshp* 1947
Sales 128.1MM^E *EMP* 43
SIC 5149 5087 Health foods; Cleaning & maintenance equipment & supplies
Ch Bd: Robert S Martin
Pr: Joe Bilello
Pr: Carlton Blackburn
Pr: Steve Hewes
Pr: Scott Prud'homme
**CFO:* Peter Anderson
Sr VP: John Parkinson
VP: Jeff Burnett
VP: Matt Flood
VP: Albert Hwang
VP: Paul Migaki
VP: Jayne Reiss

PRESTIGE CARE INC
See COAST FORK NURSING CENTER INC

D-U-N-S 14-769-4335
PRESTIGE CARE INC
7700 Ne Parkway Dr # 300, Vancouver, WA 98662-6654
Tel (360) 735-7155 *Founded/Ownrshp* 1985
Sales 128.4MM *EMP* 3,000
SIC 8051 Skilled nursing care facilities
Pr: Harold Delamarter
**Ch Bd:* Dr Rick Delamater
**Ex VP:* Gregory Vislocky
Ex Dir: Susan Sundell
Ex Dir: Marcia Turner
Dir IT: Cody M Causland

D-U-N-S 80-943-3381
■ PRESTIGE CRUISE HOLDINGS INC
(*Suby of* PRESTIGE CRUISES INTERNATIONAL INC) ★
7665 Nw 19th St, Miami, FL 33126-1201
Tel (305) 514-2300 *Founded/Ownrshp* 2010
Sales 1.1MMM^E *EMP* 415
SIC 4481 Deep sea passenger transportation, except ferry
CEO: Frank J Del Rio
**Pr:* Jason Montague
Ex VP: Howard Sherman
Ex VP: Randall Soy
**Sr VP:* Harry Sommer
VP: Katina Athanasiou
VP: Camilla Bock
VP: Michael Moore
**VP:* James Peterson
VP: Luigi Razeto
VP: Lisa Wilson

D-U-N-S 07-987-5335
■ PRESTIGE CRUISES INTERNATIONAL INC
(*Suby of* NORWEGIAN CRUISE LINE HOLDINGS LTD) ★
8300 Nw 33rd St Ste 100, Doral, FL 33122-1940
Tel (305) 514-2300 *Founded/Ownrshp* 2014
Sales 1.1MMM^E *EMP* 415^E
SIC 4449 Transportation (freight) on bays & sounds of the ocean
CEO: Frank J Del Rio
VP: Camilla Bock

D-U-N-S 15-675-1567
PRESTIGE FABRICATORS INC
(*Suby of* KLAUSSNER HOME FURNISHINGS) ★
905 Nc Highway 49 S, Asheboro, NC 27205-9566
Tel (336) 626-4595 *Founded/Ownrshp* 2005
Sales 117.5MM^E *EMP* 270
SIC 3069 Foam rubber
Pr: Joseph R Wingfield
**Ch:* Hans Klaussner
**VP:* David O Bryant
**VP:* J B Davis
IT Man: Jim Trogdon
Plnt Mgr: Darrell Kennedy
Plnt Mgr: Eddie Latham

D-U-N-S 04-367-7707
PRESTIGE FARMS INC
7120 Orr Rd, Charlotte, NC 28213-6447
Tel (704) 596-2824 *Founded/Ownrshp* 1965
Sales 105.6MM^E *EMP* 200
SIC 5144 Poultry products
Pr: Edward Thompson
**CFO:* George S Thompson
**Sec:* Randall Thompson
IT Man: James Bennitt

D-U-N-S 61-052-9372
PRESTIGE MAINTENANCE USA LTD
1808 10th St Ste 300, Plano, TX 75074-8013
Tel (800) 321-4773 *Founded/Ownrshp* 1996
Sales 108.2MM^E *EMP* 2,500^E
SIC 7349 Building maintenance services
CEO: Rachel Sanchez
Pt: Alex Dinverno
Pr: Jason Dinverno
Pr: Marie Dinverno
CFO: Tamara Jones
VP: Patrick Harrison
Rgnl Mgr: Frank Kubec

D-U-N-S 01-501-6905
PRESTIGE OF BERGEN INC
PRESTIGE TOYOTA
50 Williams Dr, Ramsey, NJ 07446-1218
Tel (201) 825-2700 *Founded/Ownrshp* 1997
Sales 89.0MM *EMP* 60
Accts Mironov Goldman Wortzel Slo
SIC 5511 5521 5012 Automobiles, new & used; Used car dealers; Automobiles & other motor vehicles
CEO: Joseph T Dockery
**Pr:* Peter Callaghan
**Treas:* Suzanne Turner
**VP:* Isaac Ashwal
Genl Mgr: Steven Reedy
Sales Asso: Anthony Amelio
Sales Asso: Rob Kant
Sales Asso: Erik Laberge
Sales Asso: Osiel Mancha
Sales Asso: Oscar Morejon
Sales Asso: Ken Shattuck

PRESTIGE TOYOTA
See PRESTIGE OF BERGEN INC

PRESTO AMERICAS FAVORITE FOODS
See OHIO PIZZA PRODUCTS INC

PRESTO PRODUCTS COMPANY
See REYNOLDS PRESTO PRODUCTS INC

D-U-N-S 55-646-4592
PRESTOLITE ELECTRIC HOLDING INC
PRESTOLITE INTERNATIONAL HOLDG
(*Suby of* PRESTOLITE ELECTRIC LLC) ★
30120 Hudson Dr, Novi, MI 48377-4115
Tel (248) 313-3807 *Founded/Ownrshp* 1991
Sales 178.3MM^E *EMP* 2,500
SIC 3621 3694 Motors, electric; Motors, starting: automotive & aircraft; Ignition apparatus, internal combustion engines; Alternators, automotive
Ch Bd: Charles Lu
Pr: Tom Hogan
CEO: Michael Shen
CFO: Kerry Zhang
Board of Directors: Dennis Chelminski, Beverley Hounslow, Charles Lu, Michael Shen, Tony Wong, Kerry Zhang, Terry Zhang

D-U-N-S 55-687-5185 IMP
PRESTOLITE ELECTRIC INC
(*Suby of* PRESTOLITE INTERNATIONAL HOLDG) ★
30120 Hudson Dr, Novi, MI 48377-4115
Tel (585) 492-1700 *Founded/Ownrshp* 1991
Sales 110.0MM *EMP* 500
SIC 3621 3694 Starters, for motors; Alternators, automotive; Motors, starting: automotive & aircraft
Ofcr: Tony Wong
VP: Marion Jett
IT Man: Tim Pearson

D-U-N-S 15-096-1717 IMP
PRESTOLITE ELECTRIC LLC
30120 Hudson Dr, Novi, MI 48377-4115
Tel (248) 313-3807 *Founded/Ownrshp* 2004
Sales 273.2MM^E *EMP* 2,500
SIC 3643 3824 3621 3625 3694 Electric switches; Electromechanical counters; Motors, electric; Electric controls & control accessories, industrial; Motors, starting: automotive & aircraft
**COO:* Peter J Corrigan
**CFO:* Kenneth C Cornelius
Div Pres: Michael Lea
VP: John Jenkins
VP: Kenneth C Wilson

PRESTOLITE INTERNATIONAL HOLDG
See PRESTOLITE ELECTRIC HOLDING INC

D-U-N-S 15-136-2019 IMP
■ PRESTOLITE WIRE LLC
(*Suby of* GENERAL CABLE CORP) ★
200 Galleria Officentre, Southfield, MI 48034-4708
Tel (248) 355-4422 *Founded/Ownrshp* 2012
Sales 274.5MM^E *EMP* 900
SIC 3694 Engine electrical equipment; Battery cable wiring sets for internal combustion engines; Harness wiring sets, internal combustion engines; Ignition apparatus, internal combustion engines
Pr: Gregory Ulewicz
**VP Bus Dev:* Michael Murphy
VP Opers: Lanny Million
Opers Mgr: Phillip Holloway
Sls Dir: Oliver Theiss

D-U-N-S 09-220-3371
PRESTON PIPELINES INC
133 Bothelo Ave, Milpitas, CA 95035-5325
Tel (408) 262-1418 *Founded/Ownrshp* 1978
Sales 139.5MM^E *EMP* 250
SIC 1623 Pipeline construction
Pr: Michael D Preston
**COO:* Ron Bianchini
**CFO:* Bob Chance
**CFO:* John Soares
**VP:* Dave Heslop
**VP:* Rich Lewis
**VP:* Gary Menges
**VP:* Rick Seifert
IT Man: Robert Denes

D-U-N-S 84-915-9744 EXP
PRESTONE PRODUCTS CORP
(*Suby of* KIK DANVILLE) ★
1900 W Field Ct, Lake Forest, IL 60045-4828
Tel (847) 482-2045 *Founded/Ownrshp* 1994
Sales 101.6MM^E *EMP* 220
SIC 2899 Antifreeze compounds
Pr: Steven Clancy
**COO:* David Lundstedt
**CFO:* Ricardo F Alvergue
**Ex VP:* Leonard A Dececchis

D-U-N-S 36-259-9909
PRESTRESS SERVICES INDUSTRIES LLC
250 N Hartford Ave, Columbus, OH 43222-1100
Tel (859) 299-0461 *Founded/Ownrshp* 2003
Sales 100.4MM^E *EMP* 360
SIC 3272 Concrete products
VP: Conn Abnee

D-U-N-S 02-169-5205 IMP
PRET A MANGER (USA) LIMITED
(*Suby of* PRET A MANGER LIMITED)
853 Broadway Ste 700, New York, NY 10003-4733
Tel (646) 728-0505 *Founded/Ownrshp* 1999
Sales 47.9MM^E *EMP* 1,200
SIC 5812 Eating places
CEO: Martin Bates
**Pr:* Robert Naylor

D-U-N-S 03-630-1603
PRETIUM HOLDING LLC
15450 South Outer 40 Rd, Chesterfield, MO 63017-2066
Tel (314) 727-8200 *Founded/Ownrshp* 2011
Sales NA *EMP* 1,250
SIC 6719 Personal holding companies, except banks

D-U-N-S 04-506-5141 IMP
PRETIUM PACKAGING LLC
15450 S Outer Forty Dr St Ste 120, Chesterfield, MO 63017
Tel (314) 727-8200 *Founded/Ownrshp* 2014
Sales 827.1MM^E *EMP* 1,100^E
SIC 3089 Blow molded finished plastic products
Pr: George Abd
**CFO:* Robert A Robison
Treas: Pat Lyons
VP Bus Dev: Barry Sak
Plnt Mgr: Dojai Hill
Plnt Mgr: Jeff Oathout
Plnt Mgr: Mike Rajecki
Prd Mgr: Josh Black
Prd Mgr: Tom Matechik
Ql Cn Mgr: Rhonda Barker
Sales Exec: Paul Noble

PRETTL GROUP
See PRETTL INTERNATIONAL INC

D-U-N-S 13-427-4328
PRETTL INTERNATIONAL INC
PRETTL GROUP
(*Suby of* PRETTL KABELKONFEKTION GMBH)
1721 White Horse Rd, Greenville, SC 29605-4825
Tel (864) 220-1010 *Founded/Ownrshp* 1996
Sales 106.8MM^E *EMP* 900
SIC 3357 Nonferrous wiredrawing & insulating
Pr: Carlos Barroso
**Treas:* Donald Pfeiffer

PRETZEL TIME
See GLOBAL FRANCHISE GROUP LLC

D-U-N-S 09-455-8251 EXP
PRETZELS INC
123 W Harvest Rd, Bluffton, IN 46714-9007
Tel (260) 824-4838 *Founded/Ownrshp* 1978
Sales 83.5MM^E *EMP* 325
SIC 2052 2099 Pretzels; Food preparations
CEO: Steven R Huggins
**Pr:* William Huggins
**Pr:* William A Mann II
CFO: Craig Anderson
**Treas:* Lu Ann Garton
Exec: Marla Morrison
Off Mgr: Miriam Mitchell
Opers Mgr: Tony Mann
Sls Mgr: Katherine Grover

D-U-N-S 07-478-9082
PREVEA CLINIC INC
PREVEA HEALTH SERVICES
2710 Executive Dr, Green Bay, WI 54304-5496
Tel (920) 272-1100 *Founded/Ownrshp* 1996
Sales 116.1MM^E *EMP* 1,300
SIC 8011 Clinic, operated by physicians
CEO: Ashok Rai
Pr: Karla Roth
Ofcr: Samantha J Tonn
**Sr VP:* Brian Charlier
**Sr VP:* Lorrie Jacobetti
**Sr VP:* Deb Mauthe
VP: Kathy Fett
Exec: Joseph Cullen
Dir Lab: Cheryl Giguere
Assoc Dir: Marlene Miller
Off Mgr: Rose Turba

PREVEA HEALTH SERVICES
See PREVEA CLINIC INC

D-U-N-S 83-102-4323
PREVOST CAR US INC
NOVA BUS LFS, A DIVISION OF PR
260 Banker Rd, Plattsburgh, NY 12901-7310
Tel (518) 957-2052 *Founded/Ownrshp* 1993
Sales 104.2MM^E *EMP* 202
SIC 3711 Buses, all types, assembly of
Sls Mgr: Mathew Nadal

PRG INTEGRATED SOLUTIONS
See PRODUCTION RESOURCE GROUP LLC

D-U-N-S 78-376-5860
▲ PRGX GLOBAL INC
600 Galleria Pkwy Se # 100, Atlanta, GA 30339-5991
Tel (770) 779-3900 *Founded/Ownrshp* 1990
Sales 138.3MM *EMP* 1,460
Tkr Sym PRGX *Exch* NGM
SIC 8721 Auditing services
Pr: Ronald E Stewart
Ch Bd: Joseph E Whitters
CFO: Peter Limeri
Sr VP: Victor A Allums
Sr VP: Michael Cochrane
Sr VP: Tushar K Sachdev
Sr VP: Louise P Winstone
VP: Amy Andrade
Board of Directors: David A Cole, Patrick G Dills, William F Kimble, Gregory J Owens

D-U-N-S 08-029-8849
PRH PRO INC
13089 Peyton Dr Ste C362, Chino Hills, CA 91709-6018
Tel (714) 510-7226 *Founded/Ownrshp* 2016
Sales 100.0MM *EMP* 161
SIC 5085 Cooperage stock
Pr: Wayman Bill Peng

D-U-N-S 06-471-2409
PRI MAR PETROLEUM INC
1207 Broad St, Saint Joseph, MI 49085-1258
Tel (269) 983-7314 *Founded/Ownrshp* 1972
Sales 100.0MM *EMP* 135
SIC 5411 5172 Convenience stores; Gasoline
CEO: L Richard Marzke
**Pr:* Guy Arrans
**CFO:* Thomas Kuhar

**Treas:* Nancy Marzke
**VP:* Kurt Marzke
Exec: Carol Christy
MIS Dir: Susan Woodrick

D-U-N-S 02-695-5336
PRICE & CO
PRICE CIGAR & CANDY
3530 W Cardinal Dr, Beaumont, TX 77705-2937
Tel (409) 842-0677 *Founded/Ownrshp* 1953
Sales 94.6MM *EMP* 48
Accts Kershaw K Khumbatta Pllc Su
SIC 5194 5145 5122 5141 Tobacco & tobacco products; Candy; Drugs & drug proprietaries; Groceries, general line
CEO: M Israr Ahmad
**Pr:* Lionel J Arsement Jr

PRICE CHOPPER
See MARKET OF CHOICE INC

PRICE CHOPPER
See MCKEEVER ENTERPRISES INC

PRICE CHOPPER GROCERY STORE
See COSENTINO ENTERPRISES INC

D-U-N-S 00-699-4289 IMP
PRICE CHOPPER OPERATING CO INC
PRICE CHOPPER SUPERMARKETS
(*Suby of* PRICE CHOPPER SUPERMARKETS) ★
501 Duanesburg Rd, Schenectady, NY 12306-1058
Tel (518) 379-1600 *Founded/Ownrshp* 1937
Sales 958.3MM^E *EMP* 9,000
SIC 5411 Supermarkets, chain
CEO: Neil Golub
**Pr:* Jerel Golub
COO: Lawrence Zettle
**CFO:* John Endres
Sr VP: Blaine Bringhurst
**Sr VP:* William Kenneally
IT Man: Mark Memoli
VP Opers: David Golub
Opers Mgr: Jon Strom

D-U-N-S 82-903-9390
PRICE CHOPPER OPERATING CO OF CONNECTICUT INC
PRICE CHOPPER SUPERMARKETS
(*Suby of* PRICE CHOPPER SUPERMARKETS) ★
501 Duanesburg Rd, Schenectady, NY 12306-1058
Tel (518) 861-5099 *Founded/Ownrshp* 2008
Sales 74.1MM^E *EMP* 1,251
SIC 5411 Grocery stores
CEO: Neil Golub
Pr: Jerel Golub

D-U-N-S 18-784-0681
PRICE CHOPPER OPERATING CO OF VERMONT INC
PRICE CHOPPER SUPERMARKETS
(*Suby of* PRICE CHOPPER SUPERMARKETS) ★
501 Duanesburg Rd, Schenectady, NY 12306-1058
Tel (518) 355-5000 *Founded/Ownrshp* 1975
Sales 74.3MM^E *EMP* 1,251
SIC 5411 Grocery stores
CEO: Neil Golub
**Pr:* John Endres
**Pr:* Jerel Golub
**Pr:* Wililam Kenneally

PRICE CHOPPER SUPERMARKETS
See PRICE CHOPPER OPERATING CO INC

PRICE CHOPPER SUPERMARKETS
See GOLUB CORP

PRICE CHOPPER SUPERMARKETS
See PRICE CHOPPER OPERATING CO OF VERMONT INC

PRICE CHOPPER SUPERMARKETS
See PRICE CHOPPER OPERATING CO OF CONNECTICUT INC

PRICE CIGAR & CANDY
See PRICE & CO

D-U-N-S 07-874-3424 IMP
■ PRICE CO
COSTCO WHOLESALE
(*Suby of* COSTCO WHOLESALE CORP) ★
999 Lake Dr Ste 200, Issaquah, WA 98027-8982
Tel (425) 313-8100 *Founded/Ownrshp* 1976, 1993
Sales 71.8MM^E *EMP* 25,000
SIC 5399 Warehouse club stores
Pr: James D Sinegal
**Ch Bd:* Jeffrey H Brotman
COO: Dennis R Zook
Sr VP: Charles Burnett

D-U-N-S 18-654-7204
PRICE COMPANIES INC
218 Midway Rte, Monticello, AR 71655-8606
Tel (870) 367-9751 *Founded/Ownrshp* 1988
Sales 86.7MM^E *EMP* 300
SIC 2421 2426 Chipper mill; Lumber, hardwood dimension
Pr: Dick Carmical
**VP:* Claude Yearwood

D-U-N-S 00-608-5450
PRICE ENGINEERING CO INC (WI)
1175 Cottonwood Ave, Hartland, WI 53029-8349
Tel (262) 369-2147 *Founded/Ownrshp* 1953
Sales 83.6MM^E *EMP* 120
SIC 5084 Instruments & control equipment
Pr: Thomas Price Jr
**CFO:* Joseph E Konyn
Mng Dir: Jason Biwer
Opers Mgr: Rod Vannatta
Sales Asso: Brian Chapin
Sales Asso: Micah Taylor

D-U-N-S 96-561-5854
PRICE FAMILY CHARITABLE FUND
7979 Ivanhoe Ave Ste 520, La Jolla, CA 92037-4513
Tel (858) 551-2327 *Founded/Ownrshp* 2010
Sales 280.7MM *EMP* 2
Accts Lindsay & Brownell Llp La Jo
SIC 8699 Charitable organization
Prin: Sherry Bahrambeygui

PRICE GREGORY
See GREGORY PRICE INTERNATIONAL INC

D-U-N-S 15-170-4277 IMP/EXP
PRICE INDUSTRIES INC
(*Suby of* PRICE INDUSTRIES LIMITED)
2975 Shawnee Ridge Ct, Suwanee, GA 30024-3638
Tel (770) 623-8050 *Founded/Ownrshp* 1995
Sales 206.8MM^E *EMP* 650
SIC 3444 Ducts, sheet metal
CEO: Gerry V Price
**Pr:* Marv Dehart
Pr: Jerry Sipes
**VP:* John Evans
Area Mgr: Paul Schimnowski
CIO: Mark Warner
Dir IT: James Schmidt
Dir IT: Jeff Walker
Sfty Mgr: Ed Floyd
VP Sls: Chuck Fraley
Snr Mgr: Julian Rimmer

PRICE PFISTER BRASS MFG
See PRICE PFISTER INC

D-U-N-S 10-888-1335 IMP
■ PRICE PFISTER INC
PRICE PFISTER BRASS MFG
(*Suby of* RAYOVAC) ★
19701 Da Vinci, Foothill Ranch, CA 92610-2622
Tel (949) 672-4000 *Founded/Ownrshp* 2012
Sales 95.2MM^E *EMP* 2,300
SIC 3432 Faucets & spigots, metal & plastic; Plumbers' brass goods: drain cocks, faucets, spigots, etc.
CEO: Gregory John Gluchowski

PRICELINE GROUP, THE
See PRICELINE GROUP INC

D-U-N-S 11-125-5238
▲ PRICELINE GROUP INC
PRICELINE GROUP, THE
800 Connecticut Ave 3w01, Norwalk, CT 06854-1625
Tel (203) 299-8000 *Founded/Ownrshp* 1997
Sales 9.2MMM *EMP* 15,500^E
Tkr Sym PCLN *Exch* NGS
SIC 4724 7375 Travel agencies; Tourist agency arranging transport, lodging & car rental; Information retrieval services; On-line data base information retrieval
CEO: Brett Keller
**Ch Bd:* Jeffery H Boyd
COO: Andrew Loewen
CFO: Daniel J Finnegan
Ex VP: Glenn D Fogel
Ex VP: Maelle Gavet
Ex VP: Peter J Millones
VP: Schickler Craig
VP: Vinny Degennaro
VP: Matthew Dewald
VP: William Jose
VP: Linda Pittore
VP: Steve Sonne
Board of Directors: Timothy M Armstrong, Jan L Docter, Jeffrey E Epstein, James M Guyette, Charles H Noski, Nancy B Peretsman, Thomas E Rothman, Craig W Rydin, Lynn M Vojvodich

D-U-N-S 17-676-6905
▲ PRICESMART INC
9740 Scranton Rd Ste 125, San Diego, CA 92121-1776
Tel (858) 404-8800 *Founded/Ownrshp* 1994
Sales 2.9MMM *EMP* 7,592
Tkr Sym PSMT *Exch* NGS
SIC 5331 Variety stores
Pr: Jose Luis Laparte
**Ch Bd:* Robert E Price
COO: William J Naylon
CFO: John M Heffner
Chf Mktg O: Thomas D Martin
Ex VP: Rodrigo Calvo
Ex VP: Brud E Drachman
Ex VP: Robert M Gans
Ex VP: John D Hildebrandt
Ex VP: John D Hilderbrandt
VP: Atul Patel
Exec: Rosa Bedolla
Exec: Roberto Ruano
Board of Directors: Sherry S Bahrambeygui, Gonzalo Barrutieta, Gordon B Hanson, Katherine L Hensley, Leon C Janks, Mitchell Lynn, Gary M Malino, Pierre Mignault, Edgar Zurcher

D-U-N-S 00-186-3794 IMP
PRICEWATERHOUSECOOPERS LLP
300 Madison Ave Fl 24, New York, NY 10017-6232
Tel (646) 471-4000 *Founded/Ownrshp* 1898
Sales 7.7MMM^E *EMP* 38,935
SIC 8721 8742 Certified public accountant; Management consulting services
Pt: Robert E Moritz
Sr Pt: Tim Ryan
Sr Pt: Norbert Winkeljohann
Pt: Jeffrey R Boyle
Pt: Michael Braunstein
Pt: Mike Cooke
Pt: Joseph J Cousin
Pt: Cyrus Daftary
Pt: Timothy P Golden
Pt: Thomas J Guaraldo
Pt: Michael A Guelker
Pt: Alicemarie Hand
Pt: Andrew Hill
Pt: Mark E Johnson
Pt: Mark Kibby
Pt: Jennifer L Kreischer
Pt: Stephen C Lis
Pt: Matthew Littlewood
Pt: Robert K McDonald
Pt: Edward Muhl
Pt: Ai Lyn Ng

D-U-N-S 08-124-3800
PRIDE AIR CONDITIONING & APPLIANCE INC
2150 Nw 18th St, Pompano Beach, FL 33069-1534
Tel (954) 977-7433 *Founded/Ownrshp* 1974
Sales NA *EMP* 136
SIC 6399 7623 Warranty insurance, product; except automobile; Air conditioning repair
Pr: Barry Pearl
**Sec:* Bill Barcheski
Dir IT: Thomas Defelice

D-U-N-S 79-560-4672
PRIDE CAPITAL PARTNERS LLC
PRIDE TECHNOLOGIES
420 Lexington Ave Rm 2903, New York, NY 10170-2904
Tel (212) 235-5300 *Founded/Ownrshp* 2004
Sales 97.0MM^E *EMP* 851^E
SIC 7373 Computer systems analysis & design

D-U-N-S 07-609-4218 IMP
PRIDE INDUSTRIES
10030 Foothills Blvd, Roseville, CA 95747-7102
Tel (916) 788-2100 *Founded/Ownrshp* 1966
Sales 290.6MM *EMP* 5,003
Accts Moss Adams Llp Sacramento Ca
SIC 4226 7349 3679 Special warehousing & storage; Building maintenance services; Electronic circuits
CEO: Michael Ziegler
Pr: Mary Flores
Pr: Steve Twitchell
**COO:* Peter Berghuis
**CFO:* Jeff Dern
**Sr VP:* Tina Oliveira
Sr VP: Sam Seaton
VP: Mauro Lara Jr
VP: Tony Lopez
VP: Don Nelson
VP: Samuel Seaton
VP: David Wickersham
**VP:* Tim Yamauchi
Board of Directors: Jim Barone, Rob Lynch, Claire Pomeroy

D-U-N-S 96-586-4031
PRIDE INDUSTRIES ONE INC
(*Suby of* PRIDE INDUSTRIES) ★
10030 Foothills Blvd, Roseville, CA 95747-7102
Tel (916) 788-2100 *Founded/Ownrshp* 1997
Sales 228.8MM^E *EMP* 4,300
Accts Moss Adams Llp Stockton Ca
SIC 3999 Barber & beauty shop equipment
CEO: Michael Ziegler
**COO:* Pete Berghuis
**CFO:* Jeff Dern

D-U-N-S 04-891-0947 IMP/EXP
PRIDE INTERNATIONAL INC
(*Suby of* ENSCO PLC)
5847 San Felipe St # 3400, Houston, TX 77057-3291
Tel (713) 789-1400 *Founded/Ownrshp* 2011
Sales 557.0MM^E *EMP* 3,900
SIC 1381 1389 8711 Drilling oil & gas wells; Servicing oil & gas wells; Petroleum, mining & chemical engineers
Pr: David A Armour
COO: Carlos Etchevery
CFO: Dennis Fairchild
CFO: Brian C Voegele
Treas: Leroy S Guidry
Ex VP: Steve Richards
Sr VP: Gregory Looser
VP: Bobby E Bnton
VP: Robert Bolton
VP: David Bourgeois
VP: Tommy E Darby
VP: Carlos Etcheverry
VP: Douglas E Hancock
VP: Jenny Rub
VP: Imran Toufeeqsenior
VP: Leonard E Travis
Exec: Alex Barker
Exec: Sandra Calhoun
Exec: Steven Manz

D-U-N-S 00-411-4864 IMP
PRIDE MANUFACTURING CO LLC
PRIDE SPORTS
10 N Main St, Burnham, ME 04922-3300
Tel (207) 487-3322 *Founded/Ownrshp* 2001
Sales 114.9MM^E *EMP* 500
SIC 2411 3949 Handle bolts, wood: hewn; Bags, golf
Pr: Joe Zeller
**CFO:* Richard Dupont
Sales Exec: Derek Maroon

D-U-N-S 04-147-7449 IMP/EXP
PRIDE MOBILITY PRODUCTS CORP
182 Susquehanna Ave, Exeter, PA 18643-2653
Tel (570) 655-5574 *Founded/Ownrshp* 1998
Sales 205.2MM^E *EMP* 1,000
SIC 3842 3799 3751

D-U-N-S 10-902-0099 IMP/EXP
PRIDE PRODUCTS CORP
4333 Veterans Mem Hwy, Ronkonkoma, NY 11779-7631
Tel (631) 737-4444 *Founded/Ownrshp* 1983
Sales 85.7MM^E *EMP* 100
SIC 5113 5122 5023 5072 5199 Disposable plates, cups, napkins & eating utensils; Cosmetics, perfumes & hair products; Toiletries; Home furnishings; Kitchenware; Decorative home furnishings & supplies; Hardware; Hand tools; Miscellaneous fasteners; General merchandise, non-durable
Ch Bd: David Emrani
**Sec:* Roya Emrani
Exec: Mickey Hodzik

D-U-N-S 04-408-1354 IMP/EXP
PRIDE SOLVENTS & CHEMICAL CO OF NEW JERSEY INC
211 Randolph Ave, Avenel, NJ 07001-2402
Tel (732) 499-0123 *Founded/Ownrshp* 1986
Sales 92.4MM^E *EMP* 66
SIC 5169 Chemicals & allied products
CEO: Arthur W Dhom Sr
**Pr:* Arthur Dhom Jr
**VP:* Robert Dhom

PRIDE SPORTS
See PRIDE MANUFACTURING CO LLC

PRIDE TECHNOLOGIES
See PRIDE CAPITAL PARTNERS LLC

D-U-N-S 03-778-6399
PRIDE TRANSPORT INC (UT)
5499 W 2455 S, Salt Lake City, UT 84120-1273
Tel (801) 972-8890 *Founded/Ownrshp* 1975
Sales 118.2MM *EMP* 420
SIC 4213 Trucking, except local; Refrigerated products transport
CEO: Jay England
**Treas:* Greg Low
**VP:* Howard Reynolds
Exec: Nikki Johnson
Exec: Tressa Pack
Off Mgr: Karla Thomas
Sfty Dirs: Ian Peterson
Opers Mgr: Flynn Wallace
Opers Mgr: Kevin Williams
Sales Exec: Gary Bogers
Sales Exec: Denise Smith

PRIDECRAFT ENTERPRISES
See STANDARD TEXTILE CO INC

D-U-N-S 00-601-2330 IMP
PRIDGEON & CLAY INC
50 Cottage Grove St Sw, Grand Rapids, MI 49507-1685
Tel (616) 241-5675 *Founded/Ownrshp* 1976
Sales 287.6MM^E *EMP* 600
Accts Plante & Moran Pllc Grand Ra
SIC 3714 3465 Motor vehicle parts & accessories; Automotive stampings
Ch Bd: Robert Edwin Clay
VP: Bill McKibben
**VP:* D Bruce Penno
Exec: Donald Clay
Exec: Bryan Holcomb
Exec: Stephen Koets
Exec: Angella Nadeau
**Prin:* Donald C Clay
Prgrm Mgr: Tracy Obrien
Cmptr Lab: Mary Kasper
Dir IT: Doug Slopsema

PRIEFERT COMPLEX DESIGNS
See PRIEFERT MFG CO INC

D-U-N-S 00-750-7957 IMP/EXP
PRIEFERT MFG CO INC
PRIEFERT COMPLEX DESIGNS
2630 S Jefferson Ave, Mount Pleasant, TX 75455-5961
Tel (903) 572-1741 *Founded/Ownrshp* 1964
Sales 228.8MM^E *EMP* 800
Accts Mcclanahan And Holmes Llp Pa
SIC 3523 3446 3444 3317 3449 Cattle feeding, handling & watering equipment; Haying machines: mowers, rakes, stackers, etc.; Poultry brooders, feeders & waterers; Turf & grounds equipment; Architectural metalwork; Sheet metalwork; Welded pipe & tubes; Custom roll formed products
Ch: William Priefert
**Pr:* Eddie Priefert
**VP:* Virginia Priefert

D-U-N-S 00-420-2516
PRIMA MARKETING LLC
7-ELEVEN
21 Inverness Way E, Englewood, CO 80112-5710
Tel (303) 436-9510 *Founded/Ownrshp* 1996
Sales 95.9MM^E *EMP* 800
SIC 5411 5541 Convenience stores, chain;
CEO: Jeff Kramer

D-U-N-S 80-941-8171
PRIMADONNA CO LLC
PRIMM VALLEY RESORTS
(*Suby of* AFFINITY GAMING FINANCE CORP) ★
31900 Las Vegas Blvd S, Jean, NV 89019-7002
Tel (702) 386-7867 *Founded/Ownrshp* 2010
Sales 106.1MM^E *EMP* 3,000^E
SIC 7011 Casino hotel; Resort hotel
COO: Michael Villamor

D-U-N-S 04-655-3447
PRIMARY RESIDENTIAL MORTGAGE INC
1480 N 2200 W, Salt Lake City, UT 84116-4127
Tel (801) 596-8707 *Founded/Ownrshp* 1998
Sales NA *EMP* 1,050
SIC 6163 Mortgage brokers arranging for loans, using money of others
Pr: David Zitting
Pr: Charlie Brown
**Chf Cred:* Burton Embry
Sr VP: Ruth Green
Sr VP: Chris Jones
VP: Greg Frost
**VP:* Tom M George
VP: Leo Mclsaac
VP: Aj Swope
**VP:* Jeffrey Zitting
Brnch Mgr: Jeff Daniels

D-U-N-S 55-749-8172
PRIME ADMINISTRATION LLC
PRIME GROUP
357 S Curson Ave, Los Angeles, CA 90036-5201
Tel (323) 549-7155 *Founded/Ownrshp* 2004
Sales 89.0MM^E *EMP* 522
SIC 6798 Real estate investment trusts
Ch: Daniel H James
CEO: John C Atwater
Sr VP: Christopher Anderson

PRIME ART & JEWEL
See PAJ INC

D-U-N-S 07-862-9636
PRIME COMMUNICATIONS LP (TX)
AT&T AUTHORIZED RETAILER
12550 Reed Rd Ste 100, Sugar Land, TX 77478-2867
Tel (281) 240-7800 *Founded/Ownrshp* 1999

Sales 280.0MM *EMP* 1,800
SIC 4812 Cellular telephone services
Pt: Farid Virani
Pt: Akbar Mohamed
Treas: Aslam Jiwani
Ex VP: Gary Fritzhand
VP: Shaheen Kayani
VP: Naushad Kermally
Sls Mgr: Rana Kutob

D-U-N-S 04-655-2316
PRIME CONTROLS LP
1725 Lakepointe Dr, Lewisville, TX 75057-6409
Tel (972) 221-4849 *Founded/Ownrshp* 1988
Sales 90.2MM *EMP* 260
Accts Milbern Ray And Company Grape
SIC 5065 1731 Electronic parts; Electrical work; Electronic controls installation; Computerized controls installation
Mng Pt: Jason McNeil
Sr VP: Gary McNiel
Brnch Mgr: Dustin Crawford
Off Mgr: Mendy Archer
Off Admin: Vanessa Ornelas
VP Sls: Bill Bivens

PRIME GROUP
See PRIME ADMINISTRATION LLC

D-U-N-S 01-067-5726
PRIME HEALTHCARE ANAHEIM LLC
WEST ANAHEIM MEDICAL CENTER
(*Suby of* PRIME HEALTHCARE SERVICES INC) ★
3033 W Orange Ave, Anaheim, CA 92804-3156
Tel (714) 827-3000 *Founded/Ownrshp* 1963, 2006
Sales 120.0MM^E *EMP* 800
SIC 8062 Hospital, affiliated with AMA residency
CEO: Virg Narbutas
**CFO:* Kora Guoyavatin
Dir Lab: Elbert Tiangco
Pharmcst: Vivian Cheng
Board of Directors: Rod Natale, Karen Andreassen, Emily Patterson, Lora Bailey, Roger Smith, George Baskevitch, Jonathan Birnbaum, Jonathan Birnbaum, Connie Del Fonzo, Darlene Fishman, Minerva Garcia, Ching Lee

D-U-N-S 04-310-3563
PRIME HEALTHCARE CENTINELA LLC (CA)
CENTINELA HOSPITAL MEDICAL CTR
(*Suby of* PRIME HEALTHCARE SERVICES INC) ★
555 E Hardy St, Inglewood, CA 90301-4011
Tel (310) 673-4660 *Founded/Ownrshp* 1952, 2007
Sales 260.0MM *EMP* 1,500
SIC 8062 General medical & surgical hospitals
CEO: Linda Bradley
Dir Lab: Richard Just
Chf Nrs Of: Mohammad Abdelnaser
Mng Dir: Firooz Pak
Mtls Mgr: Guillermo Cervantes
Nrsg Dir: Lakesha Dixon

D-U-N-S 08-015-5848
PRIME HEALTHCARE FOUNDATION - SOUTHERN REGIONAL LLC
SOUTHERN REGIONAL MEDICAL CENTER
(*Suby of* PRIME HEALTHCARE SERVICES INC) ★
11 Upper Riverdale Rd Sw, Riverdale, GA 30274-2615
Tel (770) 991-8000 *Founded/Ownrshp* 2016
Sales 157.9MM *EMP* 1,550^E
SIC 8062 General medical & surgical hospitals
CEO: Charlotte W Dupre
Dir Risk M: Sue Nemchik
Software D: Laura Fisher
Pathlgst: Ann Early

D-U-N-S 07-963-3626
PRIME HEALTHCARE FOUNDATION INC
3300 E Guasti Rd Fl 3, Ontario, CA 91761-8655
Tel (909) 235-4400 *Founded/Ownrshp* 2006
Sales 11.9MM^E *EMP* 1,550
SIC 8011 Health maintenance organization
CEO: Prem Reddy

D-U-N-S 19-237-0781
PRIME HEALTHCARE LLC
LAFAYETTE EXTENDED CARE
314 W Columbus St, Dadeville, AL 36853-1337
Tel (256) 825-9273 *Founded/Ownrshp* 1987
Sales 238.0MM *EMP* 350
SIC 8059 Nursing home, except skilled & intermediate care facility
**VP:* Molly Chapman
VP: Ryan Murray

D-U-N-S 14-754-0926
PRIME HEALTHCARE SERVICES - RENO LLC
SAINT MARYS REGIONAL MED CTR
(*Suby of* PRIME HEALTHCARE SERVICES INC) ★
235 W 6th St, Reno, NV 89503-4548
Tel (775) 770-3000 *Founded/Ownrshp* 2012
Sales 287.6MM^E *EMP* 1,800
SIC 8062 General medical & surgical hospitals
CEO: Helen Lidholm
CFO: Dan Galles
Doctor: Dave Challis

D-U-N-S 08-020-1414
PRIME HEALTHCARE SERVICES - SAINT CLARES LLC
(*Suby of* PRIME HEALTHCARE SERVICES INC) ★
25 Pocono Rd, Denville, NJ 07834-2954
Tel (973) 625-6000 *Founded/Ownrshp* 2013
Sales 2.9MM^E *EMP* 2,400
SIC 8062 General medical & surgical hospitals
CEO: Prem Reddy

D-U-N-S 15-612-3866
PRIME HEALTHCARE SERVICES - SHASTA LLC
SHASTA REGIONAL MEDICAL CENTER (SRMC)
(*Suby of* PRIME HEALTHCARE SERVICES INC) ★
1100 Butte St, Redding, CA 96001-0852
Tel (530) 244-5400 *Founded/Ownrshp* 2008
Sales 152.3MM *EMP* 1,500
SIC 8062 8011 General medical & surgical hospitals; Offices & clinics of medical doctors
CEO: Cyndy Gordon
**Ch Bd:* Marcia McCampbell
**CEO:* Randall Hempling
COO: Linda Leaell
**CFO:* Sandie Bowen
**CFO:* Becky Levy
**CFO:* Richard Phillips
Bd of Dir: Mary L Stegall
Chf Nrs Of: Edward Price
Sfty Dirs: Tom Salerno
Mktg Dir: Suzie Wood

D-U-N-S 06-751-9827
PRIME HEALTHCARE SERVICES - ST MARYS PASSAIC LLC
ST. MARY'S HOSPITAL
(*Suby of* PRIME HEALTHCARE SERVICES INC) ★
350 Boulevard, Passaic, NJ 07055-2840
Tel (973) 365-4300 *Founded/Ownrshp* 2014
Sales 125.9MM *EMP* 1,000^E
Accts Baker Tilly Virchow Krause Llp
SIC 8062 General medical & surgical hospitals
Pr: Edward Condit
Chf Rad: Charles Herbstman
**CFO:* Nicholas Lanza
Ansthlgy: Varalakshmi Annadanam
Ansthlgy: Carlos Frias
Ansthlgy: Margaret J Wu
HC Dir: Louann Visotcky

D-U-N-S 07-991-1291
PRIME HEALTHCARE SERVICES - ST MICHAELS LLC
SAINT MICHAEL'S MEDICAL CENTER
(*Suby of* PRIME HEALTHCARE SERVICES INC) ★
111 Central Ave, Newark, NJ 07102-1909
Tel (973) 877-5000 *Founded/Ownrshp* 2016
Sales 180.4MM *EMP* 1,357
SIC 8062 General medical & surgical hospitals
CEO: Robert Iannaccone
Trst: Roosevelt Nesmith
Dir Rx: Kathleen Ryan
Adm Dir: Lois Greene
Software D: Melody Hasty
Doctor: Elie Chakhtoura
Doctor: Jonathan Goldstein
Nrsg Dir: Johanna Magner
Pharmcst: Joe Hessell

D-U-N-S 79-075-3722
PRIME HEALTHCARE SERVICES INC
3300 E Guasti Rd Ste 300, Ontario, CA 91761-8657
Tel (909) 235-4400 *Founded/Ownrshp* 2000
Sales 3.1MMM^E *EMP* 10,617
SIC 8062 General medical & surgical hospitals
Pr: Prem Reddy
**CFO:* Roger Krissman
Ofcr: Suzanne Richards
VP: Michael Sarrao
Dir Rad: Seetha Reddy
Dir Rx: Christopher Casella
CTO: Curtis Thompson
Dir IT: Vikram Mahan
Mktg Dir: Manny Chacon

D-U-N-S 03-768-0299
PRIME HEALTHCARE SERVICES-LANDMARK LLC
LANDMARK MEDICAL CENTER
(*Suby of* PRIME HEALTHCARE SERVICES INC) ★
115 Cass Ave, Woonsocket, RI 02895-4705
Tel (401) 769-4100 *Founded/Ownrshp* 2012
Sales 117.2MM *EMP* 76^E
SIC 8062 General medical & surgical hospitals
CEO: Richard Charest
Exec: Ken D'Amico
Exec: Mona Willis
Nurse Mgr: William Dias
Diag Rad: Dennis L Priolo

D-U-N-S 00-274-4981
PRIME HEALTHCARE SERVICESFOUNDATION
16716 Bear Valley Rd, Victorville, CA 92395-5797
Tel (760) 241-1200 *Founded/Ownrshp* 2010
Sales 302.4MM *EMP* 2^E
SIC 8099 Health & allied services
Prin: Bonnie Nitz

D-U-N-S 61-101-7158 EXP
PRIME INTERNATIONAL LLC
1047 S 100 W Ste 240, Logan, UT 84321-6790
Tel (435) 753-6533 *Founded/Ownrshp* 2005
Sales 100.0MM *EMP* 7
SIC 5147 Meats & meat products
Opers Mgr: Don Darrington
Opers Mgr: Weston Ross

PRIME LINE
See PRIME RESOURCES CORP

D-U-N-S 01-888-4924 IMP/EXP
PRIME MATERIALS RECOVERY INC
PMR
99 E River Dr, East Hartford, CT 06108-3288
Tel (860) 622-7626 *Founded/Ownrshp* 2002
Sales 181.4MM^E *EMP* 134
SIC 5093 Ferrous metal scrap & waste
CEO: Bernard C Schilberg
**Pr:* Nathan B Schilberg
VP Opers: Thomas Dewhirst

D-U-N-S 83-570-3810
PRIME NATURAL RESOURCES LLC
2500 Citywest Blvd # 1750, Houston, TX 77042-3030
Tel (713) 953-3200 *Founded/Ownrshp* 1998
Sales 100.4MM^E *EMP* 30^E
SIC 1311 Crude petroleum & natural gas
Ex VP: Michael Welch

D-U-N-S 09-976-1066 IMP/EXP
PRIME RESOURCES CORP
PRIME LINE
1100 Boston Ave Bldg 1, Bridgeport, CT 06610-2658
Tel (203) 331-9100 *Founded/Ownrshp* 1980
Sales 96.0MM^E *EMP* 500
SIC 3993 2759 Signs & advertising specialties; Promotional printing
Ch Bd: Robert Lederer
**Pr:* Robert Brenner
**CEO:* Jeff Lederer
**VP:* Jerry Russo
Dir IT: Crystal Poole
Sls&Mrk Ex: Darrell Marriott
Manager: Joe Haddox

D-U-N-S 07-979-7988
PRIME RISK PARTNERS INC
2475 Northwinds Pkwy, Alpharetta, GA 30009-4807
Tel (770) 856-9332 *Founded/Ownrshp* 2014
Sales NA *EMP* 321^E
SIC 6411 Insurance agents
CEO: Bret Quigley
CFO: Robert Schneider
Ex VP: Scot Kees
Ex VP: Adam Meyerowitz
Sr VP: Steve Germundson

D-U-N-S 08-023-9058
PRIME SECURITY SERVICES BORROWER LLC
9 W 57th St Fl 43, New York, NY 10019-2700
Tel (212) 515-3200 *Founded/Ownrshp* 2015
Sales 3.5MMM^E *EMP* 17,100^E
SIC 6799 7382 3699 7381 Investors; Security systems services; Security devices; Detective & armored car services
CEO: Leon Black

D-U-N-S 06-294-5683
PRIME THERAPEUTICS LLC
1305 Corporate Center Dr, Eagan, MN 55121-1204
Tel (612) 777-4000 *Founded/Ownrshp* 1998
Sales 559.3MM^E *EMP* 2,457
SIC 8741 6411 2834 Management services; Insurance agents, brokers & service; Adrenal pharmaceutical preparations
Pr: Ellen Hosch
**COO:* Glen Laschober
**CFO:* Jim Ducharme
Ch: Mark Banks
**Chf Mktg O:* Michael Showalter
Chf Mktg O: Cathy Starner
Ofcr: Sara Ratner
Ofcr: Ann Tobin
VP: Donald E Amorosi
VP: Scott Fries
VP: Jim Graham
VP: Tom Hoffman
VP: Damon Smith
VP: Kent Wangsness
Exec: Bessy Erickson
Creative D: Molly Sullivan
Comm Man: Meredith Wolf

PRIME TIME INTERNATIONAL
See SUN AND SANDS ENTERPRISES LLC

D-U-N-S 19-472-5032 IMP/EXP
PRIME WHEEL CORP
17705 S Main St, Gardena, CA 90248-3516
Tel (310) 516-9126 *Founded/Ownrshp* 1989
Sales 421.7MM^E *EMP* 650
SIC 3714 Wheels, motor vehicle
CEO: Henry Chen
Pr: Philip Chen
**Pr:* Mitchell M Tung
VP: Jojo Gokim
**VP:* Albert Huang
MIS Dir: Arman Maldonado
QA Dir: Jun Estiva
Opers Mgr: Carolyn Pao
Opers Mgr: Julio Pong
Plnt Mgr: Peter Liang
Plnt Mgr: Ismael Perez

D-U-N-S 09-470-8617 IMP/EXP
PRIME-LINE PRODUCTS CO
SLIDE GO
26950 San Bernardino Ave, Redlands, CA 92374-5022
Tel (909) 887-8118 *Founded/Ownrshp* 1978
Sales 110.8MM^E *EMP* 375
SIC 5072 Hardware
Pr: Ronald F Turk
CFO: Rick Papworth
CFO: David Richards
**VP:* Bryan Aernan
**VP:* Paul Entwisele
**VP:* Jeff Grande
**VP:* Howard Kauffman
VP: Jerome Kelleher
Dist Mgr: Reiichi Emerson
Dir IT: Laj Abraham
VP Mktg: Les Burns

PRIMEDIA
See CONSUMER SOURCE INC

PRIMEDIA
See RENTPATH INC

D-U-N-S 00-810-7824
PRIMERATURF INC
2065 Lamberton Rd, Cleveland Heights, OH 44118-2714
Tel (216) 397-9716 *Founded/Ownrshp* 2000
Sales 327.0MM *EMP* 4^E
Accts Dixon Hughes Goodman Llp Roan
SIC 5191 Fertilizers & agricultural chemicals
CEO: John M Gertz Jr
**Ch:* Randy Tischer
**Treas:* Kevin Connelly
**Prin:* Brian K Dixon

D-U-N-S 05-339-5752
■ **PRIMERICA FINANCIAL SERVICES INC**
(*Suby of* PRIMERICA INC) ★
3120 Breckinridge Blvd, Duluth, GA 30099-4900
Tel (800) 544-5445 *Founded/Ownrshp* 1991
Sales NA *EMP* 600
SIC 6411 Insurance agents & brokers
Co-CEO: John A Addison
**Pr:* Glenn J Williams
CFO: Alison Rand
**Co-CEO:* D Richard Williams
**Ex VP:* Mark L Supic
Ex VP: Danny Woodard
Sr VP: Jan Dunham
Sr VP: Michael Miller
VP: Dennise Bamberry
Off Mgr: Kasey Linhart
CIO: Mike Ziegenbein
Board of Directors: P George Benson, Ellyn A McColgan

D-U-N-S 94-116-7298
▲ **PRIMERICA INC**
1 Primerica Pkwy, Duluth, GA 30099-4000
Tel (770) 381-1000 *Founded/Ownrshp* 1977
Sales NA *EMP* 1,953^E
Tkr Sym PRI *Exch* NYS
SIC 6411 Insurance agents & brokers
CEO: Glenn J Williams
Pt: Julian Villalpando
Pr: Norman Mitchell
Pr: Susan Riff
Pr: Peter W Schneider
COO: Jay Mandelbaum
COO: Gregory C Pitts
CFO: William Hofmann
CFO: Alison S Rand
Ofcr: Garry Louis
Ofcr: Mark Vale
Assoc VP: Kathy Newlin
Ex VP: Michael Adams
Ex VP: Chess E Britt
Ex VP: Chess Britt
Ex VP: Shirley Cate
Ex VP: Daniel Settle
Ex VP: Jan Trantham
Sr VP: Joseph Gill
Sr VP: Debbie M Miller
Sr VP: Michael Miller
Board of Directors: Joel M Babbit, P George Benson, Gary C Crittenden, Cynthia N Day, Mark Mason, Robert M McCollough, Beatriz R Perez, D Richard Williams, Barbara A Yastine

D-U-N-S 08-470-2729
PRIMERICA LIFE INSURANCE CO
1 Primerica Pkwy, Duluth, GA 30099-4000
Tel (770) 381-1000 *Founded/Ownrshp* 2010
Sales NA *EMP* 1,469
SIC 6311 Life insurance
Ch Bd: Rick Williams
**Ch Bd:* John Addison
**Pr:* David T Chadwick
**COO:* Douglas G Elliott
**CFO:* Allison Rand
Sr Cor Off: Tim Foster
Sr VP: Gregg Scroggs
VP: Joe Alessi
VP: Howard Glassman
VP: Cynthia Mitchell
VP: Bill Raser

PRIMERRO FROZEN FOODS
See LADY LITTLE FOODS INC

D-U-N-S 16-158-9254 IMP/EXP
PRIMESOURCE BUILDING PRODUCTS INC
P S
1321 Greenway Dr, Irving, TX 75038-2504
Tel (972) 999-8500 *Founded/Ownrshp* 1998
Sales 824.1MM^E *EMP* 1,200
SIC 5033 5031 Roofing, siding & insulation; Building materials, exterior; Building materials, interior
CEO: David Fishbein
CFO: Jerry Kegley
Co-CEO: Bob Furio
VP: Bruce Staggs
VP: James Stratton
Off Mgr: Kim Perez
Opers Mgr: Mike Davis
Opers Mgr: Lance Ponder
Sales Exec: Jeff Leach
Manager: Ralph Magdaleno
Sls Mgr: Lonnie Burrus

D-U-N-S 15-223-2398 IMP
PRIMETALS TECHNOLOGIES USA HOLDINGS INC
MITSUBISHI HEAVY INDS AMER
(*Suby of* PRIMETALS TECHNOLOGIES, LIMITED)
501 Technology Dr, Canonsburg, PA 15317-7535
Tel (724) 514-8500 *Founded/Ownrshp* 2015
Sales 364.5MM^E *EMP* 130
SIC 5084 6719 Industrial machinery & equipment; Petroleum industry machinery; Machine tools & metalworking machinery; Engines & transportation equipment; Investment holding companies, except banks
Pr: Shunichi Miyanaga

D-U-N-S 07-956-7534
PRIMETALS TECHNOLOGIES USA LLC (GA)
SIEMENS VAI METALS TECH
(*Suby of* MITSUBISHI HEAVY INDS AMER) ★
5895 Windward Pkwy Fl 2, Alpharetta, GA 30005-5203
Tel (770) 740-3800 *Founded/Ownrshp* 2014, 2015
Sales 364.5MM^E *EMP* 130
SIC 3312 Coated or plated products
Pr: Satoru Iijima
Treas: Kevin O'Steen
Ex VP: Jack Mueller
Sr VP: Ralf Hanneken
VP: Darryl Peake

D-U-N-S 08-783-7261 IMP
PRIMETIME INTERNATIONAL INC
(*Suby of* PRIME TIME INTERNATIONAL) ★
86705 Avenue 54 Ste A, Coachella, CA 92236-3814
Tel (760) 399-4166 *Founded/Ownrshp* 2001
Sales 200.0MM *EMP* 95
SIC 5148 4783 Vegetables, fresh; Packing goods for shipping
CEO: Carl Sam Maggio
Mktg Dir: Mike Aiton

D-U-N-S 06-653-7630 IMP
■ **PRIMEWOOD INC**
(*Suby of* WOODCRAFT INDUSTRIES INC) ★
2217 9th St N, Wahpeton, ND 58075-3014
Tel (701) 642-2727 *Founded/Ownrshp* 1998
Sales 100.9MM^E *EMP* 525

SIC 2434 2431 Wood kitchen cabinets; Millwork
CEO: John Fitzpatrick
**Pr:* Dale Herbst
**CFO:* Dan Miller
Chf Mktg O: Ken Terfehr
**VP:* Joel Beyer

D-U-N-S 11-202-5775
PRIMEX FARMS LLC
16070 Wildwood Rd, Wasco, CA 93280-9210
Tel (661) 758-7790 *Founded/Ownrshp* 2002
Sales 116.5MM *EMP* 135
SIC 2068 Nuts: dried, dehydrated, salted or roasted
Pr: Ali Amin
Plnt Mgr: Luis Fabian

D-U-N-S 09-697-6345 IMP/EXP
PRIMEX PLASTICS CORP
(*Suby of* ICC INDUSTRIES INC) ★
1235 N F St, Richmond, IN 47374-2448
Tel (765) 966-7774 *Founded/Ownrshp* 1965
Sales 470.2MM^E *EMP* 1,100
SIC 3081 2821 Plastic film & sheet; Polyethylene film; Thermoplastic materials
Pr: Mike Cramer
**VP:* Gus Finet
VP: Linda Miller
**VP:* Tim Schultz
Genl Mgr: Steve Cramer
Genl Mgr: Jeff Longsworth
Genl Mgr: Blake Pace
Genl Mgr: Mark Preston
Genl Mgr: Ray Van Walleghem
IT Man: Nadeem Rasheed
**QC Dir:* Rob Wells
Board of Directors: Dr John J Farber

D-U-N-S 00-641-7468
PRIMM VALLEY RESORT AND CASINO
31900 Las Vegas Blvd S, Jean, NV 89019-7002
Tel (702) 679-5160 *Founded/Ownrshp* 1999
Sales 53.4MM^E *EMP* 3,000
SIC 7011 Casino hotel; Resort hotel
Pr: Rene West
Sls&Mrk Ex: David Cross
Sls Mgr: Mark Foley
Sls Mgr: Robin Johnson

PRIMM VALLEY RESORTS
See PRIMADONNA CO LLC

D-U-N-S 79-074-8891
PRIMO NO 1 IN PRODUCE INC
PRIMO NUMBER ONE IN PRODUCE
2100 Hoover Ave, Allentown, PA 18109-9319
Tel (610) 264-5000 *Founded/Ownrshp* 1991
Sales 103.4MM^E *EMP* 130
SIC 5148 Fresh fruits & vegetables
Pr: David R Ickes
**Pr:* George D Paxos
**VP:* Dennis D Michael
IT Man: Robin Kroschwitz

PRIMO NUMBER ONE IN PRODUCE
See PRIMO NO 1 IN PRODUCE INC

D-U-N-S 19-802-1508 IMP
▲ PRIMO WATER CORP
101 N Cherry St Ste 501, Winston Salem, NC 27101-4080
Tel (336) 331-4000 *Founded/Ownrshp* 2004
Sales 126.9MM *EMP* 135^E
Tkr Sym PRMW *Exch* NGM
SIC 5149 3585 5141 Mineral or spring water bottling; Cold drink dispensing equipment (not coin-operated); Groceries, general line
Ch Bd: Billy D Prim
Pr: Matthew T Sheehan
CFO: Mark Castaneda
VP: Brent Boydston
VP: Jamila Granger
Dir Bus: Betty Kinney
Board of Directors: Richard A Brenner, Susan E Cates, Jack C Kilgore, Malcolm McQuilkin, David L Warnock

D-U-N-S 07-976-2821
■ PRIMORIS AV ENERGY & ELECTRICAL CONSTRUCTION CORP (TX)
(*Suby of* PRIMORIS SERVICES CORP) ★
3030 24th Ave S, Moorhead, MN 56560-5933
Tel (218) 284-9500 *Founded/Ownrshp* 2015
Sales 147.7MM^E *EMP* 537^E
SIC 1731 1623 Electrical work; Electric power systems contractors; Electric power line construction
Pr: Mike Hanson

D-U-N-S 07-851-2922
■ PRIMORIS ENERGY SERVICES CORP (TX)
SPRINT PIPELINE SERVICES
(*Suby of* PRIMORIS SERVICES CORP) ★
1109 W 13th St, Deer Park, TX 77536-3159
Tel (281) 478-5100 *Founded/Ownrshp* 2004
Sales 96.3MM^E *EMP* 350^E
SIC 1623 Water, sewer & utility lines
CEO: Robert Grimes
**Pr:* James Henry
Area Mgr: Mark Graham
Area Mgr: Ernie Langley

D-U-N-S 07-990-4321
■ PRIMORIS PIPELINE SERVICES CORP
(*Suby of* PRIMORIS SERVICES CORP) ★
1010 County Road 59, Rosharon, TX 77583-2566
Tel (281) 431-5900 *Founded/Ownrshp* 2013
Sales 147.7MM^E *EMP* 537^E
SIC 1623 Pipeline construction
Pr: Frank Patterson

D-U-N-S 60-688-6054
▲ PRIMORIS SERVICES CORP
2100 Mckinney Ave # 1500, Dallas, TX 75201-6928
Tel (214) 740-5600 *Founded/Ownrshp* 1946
Sales 1.9MMM *EMP* 7,011
Tkr Sym PRIM *Exch* NGS
SIC 1623 8711 Water, sewer & utility lines; Heating & ventilation engineering
Pr: David L King
**Ch Bd:* Brian Pratt
COO: Thomas E McCormick
**CFO:* Peter J Moerbeek
Ex VP: John M Perisich
Sr VP: R Steve Lewis
Sr VP: Alfons Threeuwes
Board of Directors: Peter C Brown, Stephen C Cook, John P Schauerman, Robert A Tinstman, Thomas E Tucker

D-U-N-S 80-559-1000 IMP
PRIMROSE ALLOYS INC
CHANNEL ALLOLY
330 Primrose Rd Ste 205, Burlingame, CA 94010-4026
Tel (650) 678-5781 *Founded/Ownrshp* 2007
Sales 1.7MMM *EMP* 25
SIC 3317 Steel pipe & tubes
CEO: Craig Yarde
**Pr:* Robert Wren
**CFO:* David Kim
**CFO:* Perry Reyes

D-U-N-S 11-879-6515
■ PRIMUS AUTOMOTIVE FINANCIAL SERVICES INC
JAGUAR CREDIT
(*Suby of* FORD MOTOR CREDIT CO LLC) ★
9009 Carothers Pkwy, Franklin, TN 37067-1704
Tel (800) 374-7000 *Founded/Ownrshp* 1983
Sales NA *EMP* 2,400
SIC 6141 Automobile loans, including insurance
Pr: Andy Menzyk
Board of Directors: Edsel B Ford II, William E Odom

D-U-N-S 16-331-6750
PRIMUS BUILDERS INC
8294 Highway 92 Ste 210, Woodstock, GA 30189-3672
Tel (770) 928-7120 *Founded/Ownrshp* 2000
Sales 175.0MM *EMP* 88
SIC 1542 Commercial & office building, new construction
Pr: Richard A O'Connell
**COO:* John Navarro
**VP:* Erik Gunderson
VP Bus Dev: Tony Pitrone
**VP Sls:* Paul Grenier

D-U-N-S 00-490-5295 IMP/EXP
■ PRIMUS INTERNATIONAL INC
PCC AEROSTRUCTURES
(*Suby of* PCC) ★
610 Bllvue Way Ne Ste 200, Auburn, WA 98001
Tel (425) 688-0444 *Founded/Ownrshp* 1966
Sales 134.9MM^E *EMP* 415
SIC 3728 Aircraft body & wing assemblies & parts
Ch: Shawn Hagel
**Pr:* Jim Hoover
**Pr:* Joseph Snowden
**CFO:* Douglas P Fletcher
**Treas:* Steven Blackmore
**VP:* Roger Becker
Dir IT: Athena Koeppel
Dir IT: Howard Murray
IT Man: Tim Smith
QC Dir: Mark Schuller

D-U-N-S 08-297-1578
PRIMUS SOLUTIONS LLC (MD)
(*Suby of* ASRC FEDERAL HOLDING CO LLC) ★
7000 Muirkirk Meadows Dr # 100, Beltsville, MD 20705-6351
Tel (301) 345-5500 *Founded/Ownrshp* 1998
Sales 173.5MM^E *EMP* 1,724^E
SIC 7379 Computer related consulting services
Pr: Matt Allard
Prgrm Mgr: Alina Dmitriev
Snr Sftwr: Kevin Robair

D-U-N-S 80-838-5363 IMP
PRIMUS TECHNOLOGIES CORP
2333 Reach Rd, Williamsport, PA 17701-5579
Tel (570) 326-6591 *Founded/Ownrshp* 1993
Sales 128.0MM *EMP* 470
SIC 3672 Printed circuit boards
Ch: Jeremiah W Sullivan
**Pr:* Stephen Stone
**CEO:* Christopher Sullivan
VP: Larry Veiga
VP Opers: Paul Cary

D-U-N-S 83-567-7295 IMP/EXP
■ PRIMUS TELECOMMUNICATIONS INC
(*Suby of* HC2 HOLDINGS INC) ★
3903 Northdale Blvd 220e, Tampa, FL 33624-1864
Tel (703) 902-2800 *Founded/Ownrshp* 1994
Sales 236.7MM^E *EMP* 834
SIC 4813 Telephone communication, except radio
Pr: Dg Gulati
**COO:* Neil Hazzard
CFO: Tom Kloster
**Co-Pr:* John Melick
**Co-Pr:* Jay Rosenblatt
**Ex VP:* John F Depodesta
CTO: William Love
DP Exec: Jeff Robbins
IT Man: Rajiv Dalal
IT Man: Patty Marotta
Netwrk Eng: Travis Pugh

D-U-N-S 01-782-0986 IMP
PRINCE & IZANT CO
NUTEC METAL JOINING PRODUCTS
12999 Plaza Dr, Cleveland, OH 44130-1093
Tel (216) 362-7000 *Founded/Ownrshp* 1927
Sales 120.0MM^E *EMP* 90
SIC 5051 3398 3351 3341 3339 2899

PRINCE CASTLE, INC.
See PRINCE CASTLE LLC

D-U-N-S 04-561-6679 IMP/EXP
■ PRINCE CASTLE LLC
PRINCE CASTLE, INC.
(*Suby of* MARMON INDUSTRIAL LLC) ★
355 Kehoe Blvd, Carol Stream, IL 60188-1833
Tel (630) 462-8800 *Founded/Ownrshp* 1988
Sales 88.6MM^E *EMP* 345
SIC 3589 Commercial cooking & foodwarming equipment

**Pr:* Randy Garvin
**Pr:* N L Terry
**CFO:* Lance Cermainn
Ex Dir: Carol Imperato
IT Man: Maria Roman
Sfty Dirs: Glenn Deyoung
Opers Mgr: Renee Huffnus
Ql Cn Mgr: Kirk Miller
Board of Directors: Kim Riehman, John Ulrich

D-U-N-S 10-895-0395
PRINCE CONTRACTING LLC
(*Suby of* DRAGADOS USA INC) ★
10210 Highland Manor Dr # 110, Tampa, FL 33610-9146
Tel (813) 699-5900 *Founded/Ownrshp* 2014
Sales 193.5MM^E *EMP* 337
SIC 1611 General contractor, highway & street construction
CEO: John D Watson
**CFO:* Luis M Faustino
VP: Robert V Burr Sr
VP: Doug Delaney Pe

D-U-N-S 00-614-5403 IMP
PRINCE CORP
8351 County Road H, Marshfield, WI 54449-8502
Tel (800) 777-2486 *Founded/Ownrshp* 1997
Sales 107.2MM^E *EMP* 110
SIC 5031 5191 2048 5083 5072 Lumber, plywood & millwork; Animal feeds; Seeds: field, garden & flower; Fertilizer & fertilizer materials; Prepared feeds; Feeds from meat & from meat & vegetable meals; Lawn & garden machinery & equipment; Hardware; Builders' hardware
Pr: Jay Emling
**VP:* Dennis Wessel
IT Man: Brent Hurlburt

D-U-N-S 07-838-5131
PRINCE ENERGY LLC
GRINDING SZING LLC FORMER NAME
(*Suby of* PRINCE MINERAL HOLDING CORP) ★
7707 Wallisville Rd, Houston, TX 77020-3607
Tel (713) 673-5176 *Founded/Ownrshp* 2012
Sales 84.7MM^E *EMP* 700
SIC 7389 Grinding, precision: commercial or industrial
CEO: Ronald A Rose Sr
**Pr:* Harvey Oyler
Plnt Mgr: Bryan Conlin
Ql Cn Mgr: Marvin Hoffman
Ql Cn Mgr: Jackie McDermott

PRINCE FOUNDRY
See PRINCE MINERALS LLC

D-U-N-S 80-753-7766
PRINCE GEORGE COUNTY SCHOOL BOARD
6410 Courts Dr, Prince George, VA 23875-2562
Tel (804) 733-2700 *Founded/Ownrshp* 1900
Sales 70.5MM^E *EMP* 1,000
SIC 8211 School board
Ch: Robert E Cox Jr
**Prin:* Lewis E Stevenson
Sys/Dir: Dorothea Shannon

D-U-N-S 07-481-9046
PRINCE GEORGES COMMUNITY COLLEGE
301 Largo Rd, Upper Marlboro, MD 20774-2199
Tel (301) 336-6000 *Founded/Ownrshp* 1958
Sales 61.0MM *EMP* 1,700^E
Accts Bond Beebe Pc Bethesda Md
SIC 8221 8222 Colleges universities & professional schools; Community college
Pr: Charlene M Dukes
**CFO:* Thomas E Knapp
**VP:* Sandra F Dunnington
**Ex Dir:* Brenda Mitchell
IT Man: Bridgett Watson
Mktg Dir: Deidra Hill
Pgrm Dir: Nancy Meman

PRINCE GEORGE'S COUNTY GOV
See COUNTY OF PRINCE GEORGES

D-U-N-S 07-484-5256
PRINCE GEORGES COUNTY PUBLIC SCHOOLS
PGCPS
14201 School Ln, Upper Marlboro, MD 20772-2866
Tel (301) 952-6000 *Founded/Ownrshp* 1694
Sales 1.9MMM *EMP* 18,000
Accts Cliftonlarsonallen Llp Baltim
SIC 8211 Public elementary & secondary schools
CEO: Kevin Maxwell
COO: Darlene Bond
Bd of Dir: Jose Morales
Ofcr: Donald Mitchell
Ofcr: Max Pugh
VP: Eileen Cave
Exec: Tanzi West
IT Man: Michael Langford
Genl Couns: Shauna Battle
Board of Directors: Dianne Daniels

D-U-N-S 01-819-3032 IMP
PRINCE GROUP LLC
(*Suby of* PRINCE GROUP OF VIRGINIA LLC) ★
3227 Sunset Blvd Ste E101, West Columbia, SC 29169-3201
Tel (803) 708-4789 *Founded/Ownrshp* 1997
Sales 144.3MM^E *EMP* 500
SIC 2759 3479 Commercial printing; Coating of metals & formed products
Sr VP: Kent Thompson

D-U-N-S 04-518-1836
PRINCE GROUP OF VIRGINIA LLC
901 N Glebe Rd Ste 901, Arlington, VA 22203-1854
Tel (703) 953-0577 *Founded/Ownrshp* 2007
Sales 144.3MM^E *EMP* 520^E
SIC 3479 Coating of metals & formed products

D-U-N-S 00-725-7397 IMP
PRINCE MANUFACTURING CORP
612 N Derby Ln, North Sioux City, SD 57049-5170
Tel (605) 235-1220 *Founded/Ownrshp* 1950
Sales 93.4MM^E *EMP* 350
SIC 3593 3492 3594 Fluid power cylinders, hydraulic or pneumatic; Hose & tube couplings, hydraulic/pneumatic; Fluid power pumps; Fluid power motors
CEO: Geoge Sully
**Pr:* Roland Junck
**Treas:* Pete Mullen
Sr Cor Off: Pete Mulen
**Ex VP:* Dan D Vaneldik
**Sr VP:* Joel Nelson
VP: Lance Penfield
Dir IT: Thomas Widner
Opers Mgr: Dennis Knudsen
VP Mktg: Richard Young

D-U-N-S 80-934-2244
PRINCE MANUFACTURING CORP
36 W 8th St Ste 250, Holland, MI 49423-2708
Tel (616) 494-5374 *Founded/Ownrshp* 1998
Sales 40.1MM^E *EMP* 1,000
SIC 1611 3613 5013 Highway & street paving contractor; Power circuit breakers; Automobile service station equipment
Pr: Barnard Talwin
**VP:* Dean Marsman

D-U-N-S 07-868-7826
PRINCE MINERAL HOLDING CORP
21 W 46th St Fl 14th, New York, NY 10036-4119
Tel (646) 747-4222 *Founded/Ownrshp* 2003
Sales 84.7MM^E *EMP* 758^E
SIC 2819 Industrial inorganic chemicals
CEO: Willson Ropp

D-U-N-S 04-513-6884 EXP
PRINCE MINERALS LLC
PRINCE FOUNDRY
(*Suby of* PALLADIUM EQUITY PARTNERS III LP) ★
21 W 46th St Fl 14, New York, NY 10036-4119
Tel (646) 747-4222 *Founded/Ownrshp* 2003
Sales 291.6MM^E *EMP* 271
SIC 3295 3356 Minerals, ground or treated; Silicon, ultra high purity: treated; Zirconium
Pr: John Ropp
CFO: J F Alewijnse
VP: Alan Petefish

D-U-N-S 08-521-6930
■ PRINCE TELECOM LLC
LEADING COMMUNICATION CONTRS
(*Suby of* DYCOM INDUSTRIES INC) ★
551 Mews Dr Ste A, New Castle, DE 19720-2798
Tel (302) 324-1800 *Founded/Ownrshp* 2008
Sales 223.0MM^E *EMP* 1,300
SIC 1731 Cable television installation
CFO: Kelly Roux
Treas: Richard L Dunn
Treas: William Kaufman
Sr VP: Barry L Fischer
VP: Hoss Olson
VP: Anitha Verghese
DP Exec: David Sullivan
VP Mktg: Scott Gruff

D-U-N-S 06-488-0511
PRINCE WILLIAM COUNTY SCHOOL BOARD
14800 Joplin Rd, Manassas, VA 20112-3909
Tel (703) 791-8308 *Founded/Ownrshp* 1920
Sales 1.0MMM *EMP* 8,000
Accts Cherry Bekaert Llp Tysons Cor
SIC 8211 School board
V Ch: Lisa Bell
Bd of Dir: Megan Link
Ofcr: Mark Chmelko
Ofcr: Roseann Cole
Ofcr: Tamra Koca
Comm Dir: Phil Kavits
Ex Dir: Alma Robinson
Dir Sec: Ronald Crowe
Genl Mgr: Lisa Thorne
Dir IT: Vincent Bess
Pr Dir: Jason Grant

D-U-N-S 07-829-3446
PRINCE WILLIAM COUNTY SERVICE AUTHORITY INC (VA)
PWCSA
4 County Complex Ct, Woodbridge, VA 22192-9201
Tel (703) 335-7900 *Founded/Ownrshp* 1950
Sales 104.4MM *EMP* 254
Accts Pbmares Llp Harrisonburg Vi
SIC 4941 4952 4953 Water supply; Sewerage systems; Refuse systems
Ch: Alex Vanegas
COO: Frank Pesce
**CFO:* Leslie A Griffith
**Sec:* William Becker
VP: Lyle Beefelt
VP: Christina Campbell
VP: Diana Cox
Exec: Sherry Boyce
Exec: Rosalind Jeffries
Comm Dir: Keenan Howell
Genl Mgr: John W Sloper

PRINCE WILLIAM COUNTY, VIRGINI
See COUNTY OF PRINCE WILLIAM

D-U-N-S 07-228-6024 IMP/EXP
PRINCESS CRUISE LINES LTD
PRINCESS CRUISES
(*Suby of* CARNIVAL PLC)
24305 Town Center Dr, Santa Clarita, CA 91355-1307
Tel (661) 753-0000 *Founded/Ownrshp* 1965
Sales 2.6MMM^E *EMP* 25,000
SIC 4481 4725 7011 Deep sea passenger transportation, except ferry; Tour operators; Hotels
CEO: Jan Swartz
Pr: Nina Kass
Ex VP: Dean Brown
Ex VP: Mary Horwath
VP: Deanna Austin

VP: David De Merlier
VP: Mark Dundore
VP: Wolfgang Ebenbichler
VP: David Franco
VP: Anthony Kaufman
Creative D: Pat Mannion

PRINCESS CRUISES
See PRINCESS CRUISE LINES LTD

D-U-N-S 80-098-9860
■ PRINCESS CRUISES AND TOURS INC
(*Suby of* CARNIVAL CORP) ★
24305 Town Center Dr # 200, Valencia, CA 91355-4999
Tel (206) 336-6000 *Founded/Ownrshp* 1987
Sales 4.0MM[E] *EMP* 5,048[E]
SIC 7999 Tour & guide services
Prin: Will Wenholz

PRINCETON BOARD OF EDUCATION
See PRINCETON CITY SCHOOL DISTRICT

D-U-N-S 06-894-4065
PRINCETON CITY SCHOOL DISTRICT
PRINCETON BOARD OF EDUCATION
3900 Cottingham Dr, Cincinnati, OH 45241-1616
Tel (513) 864-1000 *Founded/Ownrshp* 1955
Sales 101.9MM *EMP* 800
Accts Clark Schaefer Hackett Cincin
SIC 8211 Public adult education school; Public elementary school; Public junior high school; Public senior high school
Bd of Dir: Susan Wyder
Dir Sec: Steven Castator
Dir Sec: James Freland
MIS Dir: Athie Zavokas
MIS Dir: Athena Zazakos
Dir IT: Steve Meece
IT Man: Brian Lien
Psych: Markie Falotico

D-U-N-S 07-266-7132
PRINCETON COMMUNITY HOSPITAL ASSOCIATION INC (WV)
122 12th St, Princeton, WV 24740-2312
Tel (304) 487-7000 *Founded/Ownrshp* 1965
Sales 129.0MM *EMP* 1,000
SIC 8062 General medical & surgical hospitals
CEO: Wayne Griffith
**CFO:* Frank Sinicrope
Ofcr: Rosa Moody
Ofcr: Danny Posey
Dir Case M: Rick Puckett
Dir Lab: Deby Templeton
Dir Lab: Anita Wells
Dir Sec: Nick Poe
Mktg Dir: Richard Hypes
Doctor: Brenda Stratton
Occ Thrpy: Karen Goad

PRINCETON HEALTH INTERNATIONAL
See PRINCETON HEALTHCARE SYSTEM HOLDING INC

D-U-N-S 14-753-0336
PRINCETON HEALTHCARE SYSTEM A NEW JERSEY NONPROFIT CORP
1 Plainsboro Rd, Plainsboro, NJ 08536-1913
Tel (609) 497-4000 *Founded/Ownrshp* 2004
Sales 366.4MM *EMP* 12
Accts Withumsmithbrown Pc Morristow
SIC 8741 Hospital management
Pr: Barry Rabner
Sr VP: Melissa Schori
Sr VP: Linda Sieglen
VP: Lucille Mason
Off Mgr: Sharon Wilson
Mktg Dir: Amy Rodriguez

D-U-N-S 83-125-8921
PRINCETON HEALTHCARE SYSTEM HOLDING INC
PRINCETON HEALTH INTERNATIONAL
1 Plainsboro Rd, Plainsboro, NJ 08536-1913
Tel (609) 497-4190 *Founded/Ownrshp* 1996
Sales 611.1MM[E] *EMP* 2,000[E]
Accts Withumsmith Brown Pc Morristo
SIC 6733 Trusts
Pr: Barry S Rabner
Ofcr: Shari Woogen
Exec: Theresia McGuire
Dir Rad: Gerard Compito
Dir Rad: Matthew Difazio
Off Mgr: Denise Hudson
Nurse Mgr: Jean Anderson
Nurse Mgr: Janice Love
Nurse Mgr: Connie Oldham
Nurse Mgr: Kelly Peate
Nurse Mgr: Donna Post

D-U-N-S 13-137-5685
PRINCETON INFORMATION LTD
100 Plaza Ten Ste 1101h, Jersey City, NJ 07311-4022
Tel (201) 604-9900 *Founded/Ownrshp* 1985
Sales 115.0MM[E] *EMP* 1,100
SIC 7374 7379 Data processing & preparation; Computer related consulting services
Ch Bd: Noel Marcus
**COO:* Justin Marcus
**VP:* Natalie Marcus
Dir Bus: Jeff Barone
Opers Mgr: Melissa Forbes
Sales Exec: Jocelyn Michaelson
Natl Sales: Kevin Dooley

D-U-N-S 07-058-0840
PRINCETON PUBLIC SCHOOLS INC
25 Valley Rd, Princeton, NJ 08540-3450
Tel (609) 806-4204 *Founded/Ownrshp* 1966
Sales 89.1MM *EMP* 611
Accts Wiss & Company Llp Iselin N
SIC 8211 Public elementary & secondary schools
MIS Dir: John Hannigan

D-U-N-S 78-068-9170
PRINCETON REVIEW INC
24 Prime Park Way Ste 201, Natick, MA 01760-1528
Tel (800) 273-8439 *Founded/Ownrshp* 2000
Sales 159.2MM[E] *EMP* 1,038[E]
SIC 8748 8299 Educational consultant; Educational services
Pr: John M Connolly
**Pr:* Frank Britt
**Pr:* Scott Kirkpatrick
CFO: Judy David
Ofcr: Christian G Kasper
Ex VP: Neal S Winneg
VP: Michelle Bergland
VP: Frank Treu
Opers Mgr: Lauren W Walsh
S&M/VP: Jung Shin
Sls Dir: Jayson Cooper

D-U-N-S 79-131-2069
▲ PRINCIPAL FINANCIAL GROUP INC
711 High St, Des Moines, IA 50392-0001
Tel (515) 247-5111 *Founded/Ownrshp* 1879
Sales NA *EMP* 14,895[E]
Accts Ernst & Young Llp Des Moines
Tkr Sym PFG *Exch* NYS
SIC 6321 6799 6722 6311 Accident & health insurance; Investors; Management investment, open-end; Life insurance
Pr: Daniel J Houston
Pr: Roberto Walker
COO: Ned A Burmeister
COO: Renee Schaaf
CFO: Terrance J Lillis
Chf Mktg O: Carol Burns
Ofcr: Jeff Farmer
Ofcr: Nancy Ford
Ofcr: Mary O'Keefe
Ofcr: Carl Chanson Williams
Ex VP: Timothy M Dunbar
Ex VP: Gary P Scholten
Ex VP: Karen E Shaff
Ex VP: Deanna D Strable-Soethout
Sr VP: Gregory J Burrows
Sr VP: Gregory B Elming
Sr VP: Ellen Z Lamale
Sr VP: Jerry Patterson
Sr VP: Angela Sanders
Sr VP: Deanna Strable
VP: Steven Becker
Board of Directors: Blair C Pickerell, Betsy J Bernard, Karen E Shaff, Gary E Costley, Elizabeth E Tallett, Michael T Dan, Larry D Zimpleman, Dennis H Ferro, C Daniel Gelatt Jr, Sandra L Helton, Roger C Hochschild, Jocelyn Carter-Miller, Scott M Mills

D-U-N-S 02-405-4749
■ PRINCIPAL FINANCIAL SERVICES INC
(*Suby of* PRINCIPAL FINANCIAL GROUP INC) ★
711 High St, Des Moines, IA 50392-0001
Tel (515) 247-5111 *Founded/Ownrshp* 1998
Sales NA *EMP* 1,600
SIC 6311 Life insurance carriers
Ch Bd: David J Drury
**Ch:* J Barry Griswell
VP: Arthur Filean
Exec: Linda Brock
Mng Dir: William Hayen
Off Mgr: Ester Brinjin
DP Dir: Kay Kelly
IT Man: Pinki Rudra

D-U-N-S 18-121-8124
■ PRINCIPAL GLOBAL INVESTORS LLC
(*Suby of* PRINCIPAL FINANCIAL GROUP INC) ★
801 Grand Ave, Des Moines, IA 50309-8000
Tel (515) 247-6582 *Founded/Ownrshp* 1984
Sales NA *EMP* 130
SIC 6311 Life insurance
CEO: James P McCaughan
**CEO:* James Mc Caughan
**CFO:* Gerald Hipner
Chf Inves: Mustafa Sagun
Ofcr: Amy M Anderson
Ofcr: Tim Dunbar
Exec: Patrick J Mc Nelis
Ex Dir: Craig Barnes
Ex Dir: David Blake
Ex Dir: Paul A Dow
Ex Dir: George Jamgochian

D-U-N-S 78-371-6129
■ PRINCIPAL INTERNATIONAL INC
(*Suby of* PRINCIPAL FINANCIAL SERVICES INC) ★
711 High St, Des Moines, IA 50392-0001
Tel (515) 247-5013 *Founded/Ownrshp* 1990
Sales 107.6MM *EMP* 693
SIC 6282 6311 6321 6331 Investment advice; Life insurance; Accident & health insurance; Fire, marine & casualty insurance
Pr: Luis Valdes
Pr: Roberto Walker
COO: Ned A Burmeister
Ch: Norman R Sorensen
MIS Dir: Atul Gupta

D-U-N-S 00-694-9069
■ PRINCIPAL LIFE INSURANCE CO (IA)
(*Suby of* PRINCIPAL FINANCIAL SERVICES INC) ★
711 High St, Des Moines, IA 50392-0001
Tel (515) 247-5111 *Founded/Ownrshp* 1879, 1998
Sales NA *EMP* 900[E]
SIC 6311 6211 6162 6321 6411 Life insurance; Investment bankers; Mortgage bankers; Accident insurance carriers; Pension & retirement plan consultants
Ch Bd: J Barry Griswell
CEO: Larry Donald Zimpleman
Sr VP: Julia M Lawler

D-U-N-S 00-547-5694 IMP
PRINCIPAL MANUFACTURING CORP (IL)
2800 S 19th Ave, Broadview, IL 60155-4754
Tel (708) 865-7500 *Founded/Ownrshp* 1957
Sales 112.9MM[E] *EMP* 350
SIC 3469 Stamping metal for the trade
Pr: Paul A Barnett
**VP:* Benjamin Barnett
Dir IT: Wallace Paprocki
VP Mfg: Rick Barnett
Sls Mgr: Kevin Fox
Board of Directors: Kevin Fox

D-U-N-S 00-633-0674
PRINCIPIA CORP
PRINCIPIA SCHOOL & COLLEGE
13201 Clayton Rd, Saint Louis, MO 63131-1002
Tel (314) 434-2100 *Founded/Ownrshp* 1898
Sales 266.3MM *EMP* 600
Accts Kpmg Llp St Louis Missouri
SIC 8211 8221 Private combined elementary & secondary school; College, except junior
Treas: Linda Robbins
Bd of Dir: Leslie Thompson
Exec: Becky Oates
Assoc Dir: Steve Babcock
CTO: Keith Preston
Dir IT: Holly Webster
IT Man: Sidney Williams

PRINCIPIA SCHOOL & COLLEGE
See PRINCIPIA CORP

D-U-N-S 00-503-8856 IMP
PRINCIPLE BUSINESS ENTERPRISES INC
20189 Pine Lake Rd, Bowling Green, OH 43402-4091
Tel (419) 352-1551 *Founded/Ownrshp* 1961
Sales 99.1MM[E] *EMP* 200
SIC 2676 3142 Diapers, paper (disposable): made from purchased paper; House slippers
CEO: Carol Stocking
**Pr:* Charles A Stocking
**CFO:* Michael Kirby
VP: Alan Clifford
IT Man: Tim Brant
Plnt Mgr: Darrell Smith
Sls Dir: Richard Lavoie

D-U-N-S 62-444-6741
PRINCIPLE SOLUTIONS GROUP LLC
5 Concourse Pkwy Ste 2700, Atlanta, GA 30328-7104
Tel (770) 399-4500 *Founded/Ownrshp* 2006
Sales 99.4MM *EMP* 450
Accts Warren Averett Llc Atlanta
SIC 7363 Labor resource services
**Admn Mgr:* Josh Nazarian
Off Mgr: Addy Schilling

D-U-N-S 79-318-9817 IMP
PRINOVA HOLDINGS LLC
285 Fullerton Ave, Carol Stream, IL 60188-1886
Tel (630) 868-0300 *Founded/Ownrshp* 1991
Sales 159.0MM[E] *EMP* 200
SIC 8049 Nutrition specialist
Pr: Ron Juergens
Genl Mgr: Stephens Watts
Off Mgr: Shelly Bigler
Opers Mgr: Tom Neputy
VP Sls: Rich Calabrese
Sls Dir: Robert Pecsi

D-U-N-S 80-740-1872 IMP/EXP
PRINOVA US LLC
PRINOVA USA
(*Suby of* PRINOVA HOLDINGS LLC) ★
285 Fullerton Ave, Carol Stream, IL 60188-1886
Tel (630) 868-0300 *Founded/Ownrshp* 1992
Sales 152.3MM[E] *EMP* 110
SIC 5141 Food brokers
Pr: Donald K Thorp
Treas: Damon Dabels
**VP:* Daniel T Thorp
Dir IT: Donna Matz
Plnt Mgr: Eloy Diaz

PRINOVA USA
See PRINOVA US LLC

D-U-N-S 02-299-5880 IMP
PRINSBURG FARMERS CO-OP
CLARA CITY FARMERS ELEVATOR
404 Railroad Ave, Prinsburg, MN 56281-3709
Tel (320) 978-8100 *Founded/Ownrshp* 1927
Sales 90.5MM *EMP* 50
Accts Widmer Roel Pc Fargo North D
SIC 5153 5191 0253 Grains; Fertilizer & fertilizer materials; Animal feeds; Seeds: field, garden & flower; Turkey farm
Pr: Donald Grussing
**CEO:* Harvey Van Eps
**Sec:* Arvin Brouwer
**VP:* Ronald Post
Genl Mgr: Harvey V Eps

D-U-N-S 07-652-3836 IMP/EXP
PRINSCO INC
1717 16th St Ne Fl 3, Willmar, MN 56201-4592
Tel (320) 978-4116 *Founded/Ownrshp* 1974
Sales 91.2MM[E] *EMP* 350
SIC 3084 Plastics pipe
CEO: Trevor Duininck
**Pr:* Willis Duininck
**VP:* Curtis Duininck
VP: Jamie Duininck
Rgnl Mgr: Judd Efinger
Genl Mgr: Jennifer Breems
Dir IT: Joe Hawkins
IT Man: Leann Nord
Plnt Mgr: Byron Brouwer
Plnt Mgr: John Hoff
Plnt Mgr: Mark McClain

D-U-N-S 06-448-9677
■ PRINTEGRA CORP
(*Suby of* CRABAR/GBF INC) ★
5040 Highlands Pkwy Se, Smyrna, GA 30082-5135
Tel (770) 487-5151 *Founded/Ownrshp* 2012
Sales 127.4MM[E] *EMP* 1,001
SIC 2761 2782 2677 2678 2679 Continuous forms, office & business; Blankbooks & looseleaf binders; Envelopes; Stationery: made from purchased materials; Memorandum books, except printed: purchased materials; Labels, paper: made from purchased material
Pr: Joe Cortez
VP: Tom Yearwood
Genl Mgr: Monty Ferguson
Genl Mgr: Monty Ferugson
Prd Mgr: Matt Turner

D-U-N-S 04-179-8328 IMP/EXP
PRINTPACK ENTERPRISES INC
(*Suby of* PRINTPACK HOLDINGS INC) ★
River Rd & Grantham Ln, New Castle, DE 19720
Tel (302) 323-0900 *Founded/Ownrshp* 1998
Sales 1.3MMM *EMP* 3,800
SIC 2673 Bags: plastic, laminated & coated
Ch Bd: Gay M Love
**Pr:* Dennis M Love
**VP:* James E Love III

D-U-N-S 04-179-6553 IMP/EXP
PRINTPACK HOLDINGS INC
2800 Overlook Pkwy Ne, Atlanta, GA 30339-6240
Tel (404) 460-7000 *Founded/Ownrshp* 1996
Sales 1.3MMM[E] *EMP* 3,850
SIC 2673 Bags: plastic, laminated & coated
Pr: Dennis M Love
**CFO:* R Michael Hembree
**Treas:* David Kenny
**VP:* James E Love III
Dir Soc: Terri Moss

D-U-N-S 00-327-4545 IMP/EXP
PRINTPACK INC
(*Suby of* PRINTPACK ENTERPRISES INC) ★
2800 Overlook Pkwy Ne, Atlanta, GA 30339-6240
Tel (404) 460-7000 *Founded/Ownrshp* 1956
Sales 26.5MM[E] *EMP* 3,500
Accts Moore Colson & Company P C
SIC 2673 3081 Bags: plastic, laminated & coated; Plastic film & sheet
CEO: Dennis M Love
Mng Pt: John Pizzano
CFO: Cindy Fain
CFO: Michael R Hembree
**CFO:* Dellmer B Seitter
Treas: Dave Kenny
Bd of Dir: Jim Anderson
**VP:* James J Greco
**VP:* Terrence P Harper
**VP:* R Michael Hembree
**VP:* James E Love III
VP: R Pamplin
VP: Jack Peugh
**VP:* Nicklas D Stucky
Exec: Gina Derrick
Exec: Jim Hopkins
Exec: Rhonda Turner
Comm Man: Lisa Preston
Board of Directors: Hugh M Chapman, Daniel K Frierson, C Keith Love, Gay M Love, William J Love, Roy Richards Jr, Timothy C Tuff, Neil Williams

D-U-N-S 06-617-7007 IMP
PRINTRONIX LLC
15345 Barranca Pkwy, Irvine, CA 92618-2216
Tel (714) 368-2300 *Founded/Ownrshp* 2012
Sales 100.8MM[E] *EMP* 108[E]
SIC 3577 Computer peripheral equipment; Printers, computer
CEO: Werner Heid
Sr VP: Mark Edwards
**VP:* Sean Irby
VP: Bill Mathewes
**VP:* Bill Matthewes
VP: Sreenath Pendyala
VP: Rosemarie Zito
Genl Mgr: Ramon Ramirez
Snr Sftwr: Raul Velasquez
CIO: Jeff Reid
Sftwr Eng: Don Elflein

PRIOR CHEMICAL
See ICC CHEMICAL CORP

D-U-N-S 96-399-9651
■ PRIORITY FULFILLMENT SERVICES INC
PFS WEB
(*Suby of* PFSWEB INC) ★
505 Millenium Dr, Allen, TX 75013-2774
Tel (972) 881-2900 *Founded/Ownrshp* 2000
Sales 106.5MM[E] *EMP* 1,100
SIC 7389 Telemarketing services
CEO: Michael Willoughby
CFO: Thomas J Madden
Ofcr: Steven Graham
VP: Harvey Achatz
VP: Cindy Almond
VP: David Reese
VP: Scott R Talley
VP Sls: Bruce McClung

D-U-N-S 79-805-8095
PRIORITY HEALTH MANAGED BENEFITS INC
(*Suby of* SPECTRUM HEALTH SYSTEM) ★
1231 E Beltline Ave Ne, Grand Rapids, MI 49525-4501
Tel (616) 942-0954 *Founded/Ownrshp* 1992
Sales NA *EMP* 640
Accts Crowe Horwath Lp Louisville
SIC 6324 Hospital & medical service plans
Chf Mktg O: Joan Budden
COO: Guy S Gauthier
COO: Michael Koziara
CFO: Greg Hawkins
CFO: Mary Anne Jones
Sr VP: James D Forshee
VP: Scott Norman
VP: Wayne Wilson
VP: Krischa Winright
Ex Dir: Jeffrey Hoerle
Software D: Dave Doorlag

D-U-N-S 87-940-2170
■ PRIORITY HEALTHCARE DISTRIBUTION INC
CURASCRIPT SPECIALTY DIST
(*Suby of* EXPRESS SCRIPTS INC) ★
255 Technology Park, Lake Mary, FL 32746-6216
Tel (407) 833-7000 *Founded/Ownrshp* 2001
Sales 264.3MM[E] *EMP* 1,300
SIC 5122 5047 Drugs & drug proprietaries; Biotherapeutics; Patent medicines; Medical equipment & supplies; Therapy equipment
Pr: Gayle Johnston
**VP:* Linda O Neal

PRIORITY ONE SUPPORT
See ALORICA INC

PRIORITY SYSTEMS FOR EMPLOYEES
See BAYLOR MEDICAL CENTER AT GARLAND

D-U-N-S 80-465-5744 IMP/EXP
PRIORITY WIRE & CABLE INC
PWC
1800 E Roosevelt Rd, Little Rock, AR 72206-2516
Tel (501) 372-5444 *Founded/Ownrshp* 1993
Sales 280.3MM^E *EMP* 90
SIC 5063 Electrical apparatus & equipment
Pr: James Newman
**CFO:* Candice Hill

D-U-N-S 80-778-4830
PRISM COMPANIES INC
PRISM MERCHANDISING GROUP
248 Spring Lake Dr, Itasca, IL 60143-3202
Tel (630) 216-5788 *Founded/Ownrshp* 1990
Sales 34.0MM *EMP* 3,000
SIC 8742 Marketing consulting services; Merchandising consultant
Ch Bd: Robert H Shallenberg
**Pr:* Tom Dennis
CFO: Eric Radke
VP: Tom McNulty

D-U-N-S 92-777-0586
PRISM ELECTRIC INC
2985 Market St, Garland, TX 75041-2429
Tel (972) 926-2000 *Founded/Ownrshp* 1994
Sales 150.6MM^E *EMP* 480
SIC 1731 Electrical work
**CFO:* Eddie Corbitt
**Sec:* Kim Combs
**Ex VP:* Luis J Hernandez
**Ex VP:* Dale Payne
**Ex VP:* Paul Roberts
Ex VP: Dwain Smith
Ex VP: Wayne Vardell
Sr VP: Gary May
VP: Glenn Burns
Dir Bus: Clinton Fiddes
Genl Mgr: Jose Alfaro

PRISM MERCHANDISING GROUP
See PRISM COMPANIES INC

D-U-N-S 60-856-8036
PRITCHARD INDUSTRIES (NEW ENGLAND) INC
(*Suby of* PRITCHARD INDUSTRIES INC) ★
111 Court St, New Haven, CT 06511-6926
Tel (203) 624-3200 *Founded/Ownrshp* 1990
Sales 14.1MM^E *EMP* 1,200
SIC 7349 Janitorial service, contract basis
Pr: Peter Pritchard
**VP:* Steve Sadler

D-U-N-S 14-786-0159
PRITCHARD INDUSTRIES INC
1120 Ave Of The Amrcs 17r, New York, NY 10036-6700
Tel (212) 382-2295 *Founded/Ownrshp* 1986
Sales 250.0MM *EMP* 4,062
SIC 7349 Janitorial service, contract basis; Building maintenance, except repairs
Pr: Peter D Pritchard
Pr: Mark Calvert
**CFO:* David K Strupinsky
Treas: Debra Lans
Treas: Louisa Lee
VP: Ed Higgins
VP: Steve Sadler
Brnch Mgr: Bill Hudson
Genl Mgr: Dean Lanza
CTO: Rob Wilson
Dir IT: David Lindenauer

D-U-N-S 15-747-9791
PRITCHARD INDUSTRIES SOUTHWEST INC
(*Suby of* PRITCHARD INDUSTRIES INC) ★
4040 Directors Row, Houston, TX 77092-8702
Tel (713) 957-1387 *Founded/Ownrshp* 1994
Sales 31.5MM^E *EMP* 1,400
SIC 7349 Janitorial service, contract basis
VP: Peter Pritchard
**Pr:* Donald Rankin
**Treas:* Frank Squeri
VP: Steve Alberts
VP: Peter Sperduti

D-U-N-S 80-785-0743
PRITZKER GROUP- CHICAGO LLC
111 S Wacker Dr Ste 4000, Chicago, IL 60606-4309
Tel (312) 447-6000 *Founded/Ownrshp* 2005
Sales 249.0MM^E *EMP* 257
SIC 8111 General practice law office
Mng Pt: J B Pritzker
Pt: Adam Koopersmith
Pt: Matthew McCall
Mng Pt: Chris Girgenti
Mng Pt: Tony Pritzker
VP: Matt Bowman

D-U-N-S 05-408-9110
PRITZKER ORGANIZATION LLC
71 S Wacker Dr Fl 47, Chicago, IL 60606-4637
Tel (312) 873-4900 *Founded/Ownrshp* 1881
Sales NA *EMP* 447
SIC 6159 Intermediate investment banks
Pr: Kenneth HM Leet
**Prin:* Hayek Andrew

D-U-N-S 14-411-6381
PRIVATE HEALTHCARE SYSTEMS INC
(*Suby of* MULTIPLAN INC) ★
1100 Winter St Ste 2300, Waltham, MA 02451-1440
Tel (781) 895-7500 *Founded/Ownrshp* 2006
Sales NA *EMP* 954
SIC 6324 Hospital & medical service plans
Pr: Joseph R Driscoll
**CFO:* Barbara Dailey
Ofcr: Beth Scanzani
**VP:* Leeann Solomon Christ
**VP:* Jason Dunn
VP: Marcy E Feller
**VP:* Kevin O'Reilly
Exec: Lindsay Deyoung
Snr PM: Jennifer Sartor

D-U-N-S 01-895-4779
PRIVATE NATIONAL MORTGAGE ACCEPTANCE CO LLC
PENNYMAC
6101 Condor Dr, Agoura Hills, CA 91301
Tel (818) 224-7401 *Founded/Ownrshp* 2008
Sales NA *EMP* 875
SIC 6162 Mortgage bankers & correspondents
Prin: Jeff Grogin
Dir Sec: Steve Bailey

PRIVATE PORTFOLIO
See COTY US LLC

D-U-N-S 61-731-2871
▲ PRIVATEBANCORP INC
120 S Lasalle St Ste 400, Chicago, IL 60603
Tel (312) 564-2000 *Founded/Ownrshp* 1989
Sales NA *EMP* 1,219^E
Accts Ernst & Young Llp Chicago Il
Tkr Sym PVTB *Exch* NGS
SIC 6022 State commercial banks
Pr: Larry D Richman
**Ch Bd:* James M Guyette
CFO: Kevin M Killips
Ofcr: Vicki Znavor
Ex VP: Jennifer R Evans
Ex VP: Kevin J Van Solkema
Mng Dir: Mark Kosiek
Sls Dir: Kay Baker

D-U-N-S 61-731-3085
■ PRIVATEBANK AND TRUST CO
(*Suby of* PRIVATEBANCORP INC) ★
120 S La Salle St, Chicago, IL 60603-3403
Tel (312) 564-2000 *Founded/Ownrshp* 1991
Sales NA *EMP* 200
SIC 6022 State commercial banks
Ch Bd: Ralph B Mandell
Pr: Andy Dawson
Chf Invest: William Norris
Ofcr: Christopher Bagnall
Ofcr: Torri Bivins
Ofcr: Harry Hoff
Ofcr: Tina Morris
Ofcr: John O'Connell
Ofcr: Joan Schellhorn
Ofcr: Bryan Scherer
Ofcr: Kenny Shogren
Ofcr: Julie Suminski
Trst Ofcr: Jason Danz
VP: Elizabeth Gerhardt
VP: Matthew Gibbons
VP: Lisa Miller
Exec: Heather Pratt

D-U-N-S 83-894-2647
PRN HEALTH SERVICES INC
740 Ford St Ste A, Kimberly, WI 54136-2216
Tel (920) 830-8811 *Founded/Ownrshp* 1995
Sales 40.8MM^E *EMP* 1,000
SIC 7361 7363 Placement agencies; Medical help service
Pr: Pete Hietpas
**CFO:* Angie Berghuis
CIO: Ralph Taylor

PRO CAL
See HC COMPANIES INC

PRO CASE MANAGEMENT
See ACT FOR HEALTH INC

PRO CO OP BUSINESS OFFICE
See PRO COOPERATIVE

PRO CON
See PROGRESSIVE CONVERTING INC

PRO CON CONSTRUCTION
See STEBBINS ENTERPRISES INC

PRO CON CONSTRUCTION
See PRO CON INC

D-U-N-S 06-442-4401
PRO CON INC
PRO CON CONSTRUCTION
(*Suby of* PRO CON CONSTRUCTION) ★
1359 Hooksett Rd Ste 16, Hooksett, NH 03106-1809
Tel (603) 623-8811 *Founded/Ownrshp* 1973
Sales 83.4MM^E *EMP* 132
SIC 1542 1541 Commercial & office building, new construction; Industrial buildings, new construction
Pr: John Samenfeld
**CFO:* Bruce Desmarais
**Treas:* Mark Stebbins
VP: Matthew Labonte
Snr PM: Charles Landsman
Snr PM: Larry Osmer

D-U-N-S 04-705-8185
PRO COOPERATIVE
PRO CO OP BUSINESS OFFICE
17 3rd Ave Ne, Pocahontas, IA 50574-1614
Tel (712) 335-3060 *Founded/Ownrshp* 1922
Sales 240.3MM^E *EMP* 110
Accts Gardiner Thomsen Pc Lincol
SIC 5153 5191 5172 Grains; Feed; Chemicals, agricultural; Fertilizer & fertilizer materials; Diesel fuel; Gasoline
Prin: Kyle Kuepker
**Pr:* Norman Zaugg

D-U-N-S 00-507-1220
PRO CORP
(*Suby of* PRO UNLIMITED GLOBAL SOLUTIONS INC) ★
999 Stewart Ave Ste 100, Bethpage, NY 11714-3632
Tel (516) 437-3300 *Founded/Ownrshp* 1980, 2010
Sales 199.6MM^E *EMP* 3,247^E
SIC 7363 7361 Labor resource services; Employment agencies
CEO: Andrew Schultz
**CFO:* Harry V Maccarrone
**Ex VP:* Terrie Weinand
**Sr VP:* Ben Barstow
**Sr VP:* Allie Ben-Shlomo
**Sr VP:* Robert F Ende
**Sr VP:* Ted Sergott
Info Man: Scott Nyer
Sls Dir: Linda Steele

PRO DIRECTIONAL
See PROFESSIONAL DIRECTIONAL ENTERPRISES INC

D-U-N-S 04-862-4121 IMP/EXP
PRO MACH INC
50 E Rivercntr Blvd 180 Ste 1800, Covington, KY 41011
Tel (513) 831-8778 *Founded/Ownrshp* 2014
Sales 378.8MM^E *EMP* 1,200
SIC 3565 Packaging machinery
Pr: Mark W Anderson
Pr: Don Cotney
Pr: Barry Heiser
Pr: Bud Lane
Pr: Alan Shipman
Pr: Robert Zuilhof
**CFO:* William M Schult
VP: Otis Cobb
VP: Breton Ranc
VP: Thomas Scheper
VP: Brad Wegner

D-U-N-S 17-703-5466
PRO MARKETING INC
1350 Bluegrass Lakes Pkwy, Alpharetta, GA 30004-3395
Tel (770) 521-1421 *Founded/Ownrshp* 1984
Sales 140.4MM^E *EMP* 1,000
SIC 5072 5085 Hardware; Industrial supplies
Pr: Jack Harvey Hall Jr
CFO: Jan Chambers
**Sec:* Beatrice Hall
**VP:* Richard H Hall

PRO MED HLTH NETWRK POMONA VLY
See PAMONA VALLEY MEDICAL GROUP INC

PRO MUTUAL
See MEDICAL PROFESSIONAL MUTUAL INSURANCE CO

D-U-N-S 04-179-5331
PRO OILFIELD SERVICES LLC
3 Riverway Ste 1110, Houston, TX 77056-1954
Tel (281) 496-5810 *Founded/Ownrshp* 2014
Sales 216.4MM^E *EMP* 300
SIC 1381 Drilling oil & gas wells
CEO: J Darrell Brewer
**CFO:* Scott McMahon

D-U-N-S 60-884-8727
PRO PETROLEUM INC
4710 4th St, Lubbock, TX 79416-4900
Tel (806) 795-8785 *Founded/Ownrshp* 1989
Sales 1.0MMM *EMP* 150
Accts Garrett And Swann Llp Lubbock
SIC 5172 Gases; Diesel fuel; Gasoline
Pr: Marcus Griffin
**CFO:* Don Hayden

D-U-N-S 08-463-7586 IMP/EXP
PRO TAPES & SPECIALTIES INC
621 Us Highway 1 Unit A, North Brunswick, NJ 08902-6302
Tel (732) 346-0900 *Founded/Ownrshp* 1977
Sales 92.1MM^E *EMP* 115
SIC 5113 2675 Pressure sensitive tape; Die-cut paper & board
CEO: Arnold S Silver
**Pr:* Ed Miller
**COO:* Barry Hart
**VP:* Barney Silver

D-U-N-S 96-726-0659
PRO UNLIMITED GLOBAL SOLUTIONS INC
999 Stewart Ave Ste 100, Bethpage, NY 11714-3632
Tel (516) 437-3300 *Founded/Ownrshp* 2010
Sales 614.2MM^E *EMP* 18,000
SIC 7363 7361 Labor resource services; Employment agencies; Labor contractors (employment agency)
CEO: Andrew Schultz
**CFO:* Bob Andy
**Sr VP:* Ben Barstow
**Sr VP:* Ted Sergott
**Sr VP:* Allie Ben Shlomo
**VP:* Terrie Weinand

D-U-N-S 07-837-5080
PRO UNLIMITED INC
(*Suby of* PRO CORP) ★
7777 Glades Rd Ste 208, Boca Raton, FL 33434-4150
Tel (800) 291-1099 *Founded/Ownrshp* 1992
Sales 126.1MM^E *EMP* 850^E
SIC 8741 Management services
CEO: Andrew Schultz
Pr: Andrew Popler
Opers Mgr: Elizabeth Johnson
Ql Cn Mgr: Vadim Sheynkman

D-U-N-S 94-310-7417
PRO UNLIMITED INC
(*Suby of* INVESTCORP SERVICES INC) ★
7777 Glades Rd Ste 208, Boca Raton, FL 33434-4150
Tel (561) 994-9500 *Founded/Ownrshp* 1991
Sales 83.8MM^E *EMP* 400^E
SIC 8741 7372 Personnel management; Application computer software; Business oriented computer software
CEO: Andrew Schultz
**COO:* Terrie Weinand
Ex VP: Brad Turkin
Sr VP: Ben Barstow
Sr VP: Allie Ben-Shlomo
Sr VP: Teresa Golio
Sr VP: Andrew Popler
VP: David Kiner
VP: Bahram Mahbod
VP: Martin Schultz
VP: Ted Sergott
Exec: Elyssa Match

PRO VIEW FOODS
See JOHN SOULES ACQUISITIONS LLC

D-U-N-S 07-714-9029
PRO-AM INC
CEDARGATE, THE
2350 Kanell Blvd, Poplar Bluff, MO 63901-4036
Tel (573) 785-0858 *Founded/Ownrshp* 1970
Sales 381.9MM *EMP* 80
SIC 8051 8741 Skilled nursing care facilities; Management services
Pr: D James Markel
**Treas:* W A Hoja MD
**Genl Mgr:* Shirley Davenport

D-U-N-S 06-333-2563 IMP/EXP
PRO-MARK INC
ORBIT IRRIGATION
845 Overland St, North Salt Lake, UT 84054-2123
Tel (801) 299-5500 *Founded/Ownrshp* 1971
Sales 181.5MM^E *EMP* 500^E
SIC 7311 7336 Advertising agencies; Commercial art & graphic design
**VP:* Mike Ericksen

D-U-N-S 02-438-8513
PRO-TECH ENERGY SOLUTIONS LLC
215 Executive Dr, Moorestown, NJ 08057-4221
Tel (856) 437-6220 *Founded/Ownrshp* 2012
Sales 90.0MM *EMP* 43^E
Accts Topche & Company Llc Cranford
SIC 1711 Solar energy contractor
CEO: Richard Cooper
COO: Guy Winters
CFO: Paul Shust

D-U-N-S 08-491-5540
■ PRO-TELLIGENT LLC
PRO-TELLIGENT LLC A TETRA TECH
(*Suby of* TETRATECH INC) ★
1320 N Courthouse Rd # 600, Arlington, VA 22201-2501
Tel (703) 387-2100 *Founded/Ownrshp* 2011
Sales 91.0MM *EMP* 570^E
SIC 7371 7379 Custom computer programming services; Computer related consulting services
CFO: Ashesh Langhnoja
Sr VP: Bobbie G Boykin Jr

PRO-TELLIGENT LLC A TETRA TECH
See PRO-TELLIGENT LLC

PRO2 RESPIRATORY SERVICES
See PROMPTCARE COMPANIES INC

PROACTIV
See GUTHY-RENKER LLC

PROACTIVE
See MADONNA REHABILITATION HOSPITAL

PROAMPAC
See AMPAC HOLDINGS LLC

D-U-N-S 08-013-9606
PROAMPAC HOLDINGS INC
(*Suby of* PROAMPAC LLC) ★
12025 Tricon Rd, Cincinnati, OH 45246-1719
Tel (513) 671-1777 *Founded/Ownrshp* 2015
Sales 1.2MMM^E *EMP* 1,279^E
SIC 6722 Management investment, open-end

D-U-N-S 08-013-9614
PROAMPAC INTERMEDIATE INC
(*Suby of* PROAMPAC HOLDINGS INC) ★
12025 Tricon Rd, Cincinnati, OH 45246-1719
Tel (513) 671-1777 *Founded/Ownrshp* 2015
Sales 1.2MMM^E *EMP* 1,275^E
SIC 6722 Management investment, open-end
CEO: John Q Baumann

D-U-N-S 08-013-9596
PROAMPAC LLC
12025 Tricon Rd, Cincinnati, OH 45246-1719
Tel (513) 671-1777 *Founded/Ownrshp* 2016
Sales 1.2MMM^E *EMP* 2,400^E
SIC 2671 Paper coated or laminated for packaging
CEO: Greg Tucker
CFO: Eric Bradford

D-U-N-S 02-880-0329
▲ PROASSURANCE CORP
100 Brookwood Pl Ste 500, Birmingham, AL 35209-6832
Tel (205) 877-4400 *Founded/Ownrshp* 2000
Sales NA *EMP* 938^E
Tkr Sym PRA *Exch* NYS
SIC 6351 6321 Liability insurance; Indemnity plans health insurance, except medical service
Ch Bd: W Stancil Starnes
CFO: Edward L Rand Jr
Chf Cred: Frank B O'Neil
Ex VP: Jeffrey P Lisenby
Board of Directors: Bruce D Angiolillo, Robert E Flowers, M James Gorrie, John J McMahon Jr, Ann F Putallaz, Frank A Spinosa, Thomas A S Wilson Jr, Samuel A Di Piazza Jr

D-U-N-S 05-018-1599
PROBIDDER LLC
945 E Kenilworth Ave, Palatine, IL 60074-6466
Tel (847) 962-3140 *Founded/Ownrshp* 2014
Sales 1.5MMM *EMP* 10
SIC 8742 7371 Real estate consultant; Computer software development & applications

D-U-N-S 78-391-9348
PROBST ELECTRIC INC
875 S 600 W, Heber City, UT 84032-2257
Tel (435) 657-1955 *Founded/Ownrshp* 2004
Sales 135.0MM *EMP* 200
SIC 1623 1731 Water, sewer & utility lines; General electrical contractor
Pr: Redgie Probst
**CFO:* Riley Probst
**VP:* Karl Stucer
Off Mgr: Mary Arwyle

D-U-N-S 00-893-2295 IMP
■ PROBUILD CO LLC
BUILDERS FIRSTSOURCE
(*Suby of* PROBUILD HOLDINGS LLC) ★
7595 E Technology Way # 500, Denver, CO 80237-3007
Tel (303) 262-8500 *Founded/Ownrshp* 2006
Sales 753.1MM^E *EMP* 1,745
SIC 5211 5031 Lumber & other building materials; Lumber products; Planing mill products & lumber; Door & window products; Lumber, plywood & millwork; Lumber: rough, dressed & finished
CEO: Robert Marchbank
Pr: Rick Johnson
Pr: Kevin Remsen
Treas: Larry Hamershock
Treas: Larry Smith
**Ex VP:* Don Riley
**Ex VP:* Tim Trenary
Exec: Michael Carman
Area Mgr: Paul Mills
Admn Mgr: Doris Hurt
Brnch Mgr: Craig Perseo

D-U-N-S 61-921-1522 IMP
■ PROBUILD HOLDINGS LLC
(*Suby of* BUILDERS FIRSTSOURCE INC) ★
7595 Tech Way Ste 500, Denver, CO 80237
Tel (303) 262-8500 *Founded/Ownrshp* 2015
Sales 1.3MMM^E *EMP* 1,745
SIC 5031 5211 Lumber, plywood & millwork; Building materials, exterior; Building materials, interior; Lumber & other building materials
CEO: Robert Marchbank
Pr: Joseph Lawrence
CFO: Jeff Pinkerman
Sr VP: Lonnie Bernardoni
Sr VP: Michael D Mahre
Sr VP: John O' Loughlin
VP: Timothy Drouillard
VP: Lisa Peterson
CIO: Karin Catton
IT Man: Tony Hays
Software D: Greg Akers

D-U-N-S 00-227-1021 IMP/EXP
PROCACCI BROS SALES CORP (PA)
GARDEN STATE FARMS
3333 S Front St, Philadelphia, PA 19148-5605
Tel (215) 463-8000 *Founded/Ownrshp* 1948
Sales 361.3MM^E *EMP* 525
SIC 5148 Fresh fruits & vegetables
Pr: Joseph M Procacci
**Pr:* Micheal R Maxwell
**VP:* George Binck
Comm Dir: Lou Struble
Opers Mgr: Todd Huber
Sls Dir: Michael Barber
Sls Dir: Ken White

D-U-N-S 00-625-4601 IMP
PROCESS DISPLAYS LLC (MN)
PD TEMPO
7108 31st Ave N, Minneapolis, MN 55427-2848
Tel (763) 541-1245 *Founded/Ownrshp* 1949, 2002
Sales 128.0MM *EMP* 310
Accts Mcgladrey Llp Minneapolis M
SIC 2541 2542 2599 2675 2752 2759 Display fixtures, wood; Fixtures: display, office or store: except wood; Restaurant furniture, wood or metal; Hotel furniture; Die-cut paper & board; Posters, lithographed; Screen printing
CEO: Peter Strommen
CFO: Dean Friedrichs
**Treas:* Jay Strommen
Ex VP: Scott Ingram
**VP:* Rick Anderson
**VP:* Michael Strommen
IT Man: Todd Dubord

D-U-N-S 06-491-4542
PROCESS EQUIPMENT & SERVICE CO INC
PESCO
5680 Us 64, Farmington, NM 87401-1563
Tel (505) 327-2222 *Founded/Ownrshp* 1970
Sales 100.2MM^E *EMP* 280
SIC 3443 5084 7699 3533 Fabricated plate work (boiler shop); Oil well machinery, equipment & supplies; Industrial equipment services; Industrial machinery & equipment repair; Oil & gas field machinery
Pr: Kyle Rhodes
**Ch Bd:* James E Rhodes
**CFO:* Charley Tyler
VP: Blake Wallace
Ql Cn Mgr: Shane Galloway

D-U-N-S 03-338-0627 IMP/EXP
PROCESS EQUIPMENT INC (AL)
PROCESSBARRON
2770 Welborn St, Pelham, AL 35124-1760
Tel (205) 663-5330 *Founded/Ownrshp* 1981, 2015
Sales 125.0MM *EMP* 200
SIC 3564 3535 3441 3443 Blowing fans: industrial or commercial; Dust or fume collecting equipment, industrial; Conveyors & conveying equipment; Expansion joints (structural shapes), iron or steel; Breechings, metal plate
Pr: Kenneth C Nolan Jr
**CFO:* James A Woods
VP: Andy Woodbury
Dir IT: Paul Heller
Dir IT: Russel Hunter
Mktg Dir: Brian Butts

PROCESSBARRON
See PROCESS EQUIPMENT INC

PROCESSING DIVISION
See MAR-JAC POULTRY INC

D-U-N-S 00-131-6827 IMP/EXP
▲ PROCTER & GAMBLE CO (OH)
P&G
1 Procter And Gamble Plz, Cincinnati, OH 45202-3393
Tel (513) 983-1100 *Founded/Ownrshp* 1837
Sales 65.3MMM *EMP* 105,000^E
Accts Deloitte & Touche Llp Cincinn
Tkr Sym PG *Exch* NYS
SIC 2844 2676 3421 2842 2841 Toilet preparations; Hair preparations, including shampoos; Oral preparations; Deodorants, personal; Towels, napkins & tissue paper products; Diapers, paper (disposable): made from purchased paper; Feminine hygiene paper products; Razor blades & razors; Specialty cleaning preparations; Fabric softeners; Soap: granulated, liquid, cake, flaked or chip; Detergents, synthetic organic or inorganic alkaline
Ch Bd: David S Taylor
Pr: Steven D Bishop
Pr: Giovanni Ciserani
Pr: Gary A Coombe
Pr: Mary Lynn Ferguson-Mchugh
Pr: Patrice Louvet
Pr: Charles E Pierce
Pr: Juan Fernando Posada
Pr: Matthew Price
Pr: Mohamed Samir
Pr: Magesvaran Suranjan
Pr: Carolyn M Tastad
CFO: Jon R Moeller
Treas: Valarie L Sheppard
Bd of Dir: Lou Cedrone
Bd of Dir: Janusz Dziurzynski
Ofcr: Mark F Biegger
Ofcr: Marc S Pritchard
Ofcr: Yannis Skoufalos
VP: Pramod Agarwal
VP: Doreen Bayliff
Board of Directors: Francis S Blake, Angela F Braly, Kenneth I Chenault, Scott D Cook, Terry J Lundgren, W James McNerney Jr, Margaret C Whitman, Patricia A Woertz, Ernesto Zedillo

PROCTER & GAMBLE COSMETICS
See NOXELL CORP

D-U-N-S 00-190-2212 IMP/EXP
■ PROCTER & GAMBLE DISTRIBUTING LLC
(*Suby of* P&G) ★
1 Procter And Gamble Plz, Cincinnati, OH 45202-3393
Tel (513) 983-1100 *Founded/Ownrshp* 1902
Sales 3.1MMM^E *EMP* 5,142
SIC 5169 5122 5149 5113 5137 Detergents; Laundry soap chips & powder; Drugs, proprietaries & sundries; Groceries & related products; Coffee, green or roasted; Napkins, paper; Towels, paper; Dishes, disposable plastic & paper; Diapers
CEO: Robert A McDonald
**CFO:* C C Daley Jr
Treas: G W Price
VP: Andrew Knapschaefer
VP: Donna Rumfelt
**VP:* D R Walker
Assoc Dir: Jay Nadel
Sls Mgr: Dena Hawkins
Snr Mgr: Ken Milar

D-U-N-S 10-857-6372
■ PROCTER & GAMBLE FAR EAST INC
(*Suby of* P&G) ★
1 Procter And Gamble Plz, Cincinnati, OH 45202-3393
Tel (513) 983-1100 *Founded/Ownrshp* 1837
Sales 100.7MM^E *EMP* 2,824
SIC 2841 2844 2676 Laundry cleaning preparations; Fabric softeners; Toilet preparations; Hair preparations, including shampoos; Shampoos, rinses, conditioners: hair; Napkins, sanitary: made from purchased paper
Prin: C Daley
Pr: A G Lafley
Treas: JP Hernandez
VP: RI Antoine
VP: F Benvegnu
VP: RG Pease
Board of Directors: M Kamachi, A Kayamoto, R Shin-I, Y Shiozawa, H Wada

D-U-N-S 00-423-8200 IMP
■ PROCTER & GAMBLE MANUFACTURING CO
(*Suby of* P&G) ★
1 Procter And Gamble Plz, Cincinnati, OH 45202-3393
Tel (513) 983-1100 *Founded/Ownrshp* 1910
Sales 1.1MMM^E *EMP* 4,212
SIC 2841 2079 2099 2844 2045 Soap: granulated, liquid, cake, flaked or chip; Detergents, synthetic organic or inorganic alkaline; Shortening & other solid edible fats; Peanut butter; Toilet preparations; Cake mixes, prepared: from purchased flour
Pr: Bob McDonald
**Pr:* Keith Harrison
**Treas:* John Goodwin
**VP:* John Jensen
IT Man: Frank Bernhardt

D-U-N-S 00-613-9711 IMP/EXP
■ PROCTER & GAMBLE PAPER PRODUCTS CO
(*Suby of* P&G) ★
1 Procter And Gamble Plz, Cincinnati, OH 45202-3393
Tel (513) 983-1100 *Founded/Ownrshp* 1893
Sales 1.2MMM^E *EMP* 8,626
SIC 2676 Sanitary paper products; Towels, napkins & tissue paper products; Toilet paper: made from purchased paper; Towels, paper: made from purchased paper
Pr: David Taylor
**Treas:* C C Daley
**VP:* E G Nelson
**VP:* D R Walker
**Prin:* Samuel Benedict
**Prin:* Richard R Deupree Jr
**Prin:* KY Siddall

D-U-N-S 96-962-9307
PROCTER AND GAMBLE RETIREE BENEFIT TRUST
2 Procter And Gamble Plz, Cincinnati, OH 45202-3315
Tel (513) 698-4501 *Founded/Ownrshp* 2011
Sales 153.5MM *EMP* 2^E
Accts Deloitte Tax Llp Chicago Il
SIC 6733 Trusts

PROCTER HOSPITAL
See PROCTOR HEALTH CARE INC

D-U-N-S 00-653-9852
■ PROCTOR FINANCIAL INC
(*Suby of* BROWN & BROWN INC) ★
5225 Crooks Rd, Troy, MI 48098-2823
Tel (248) 269-5700 *Founded/Ownrshp* 1934
Sales NA *EMP* 300
SIC 6411 Insurance agents, brokers & service
Pr: Paul A Glantz
Pr: Gretchan P Francis
Ch: Thomas W Proctor
Sr VP: Mike Cox
Sr VP: Valentine M Dickerson
Sr VP: Diane N Whipple
VP: Valentine Dickerson
VP: Maureen Johnston
VP: Karen I Schickel
VP: Cory T Walker
VP: Sue Wardzinski

D-U-N-S 10-929-2045
PROCTOR HEALTH CARE INC
PROCTER HOSPITAL
12529 N Fillyside Dr, Dunlap, IL 61525-9393
Tel (309) 691-1000 *Founded/Ownrshp* 1983
Sales 53.7MM^E *EMP* 1,100
Accts Mcgladrey & Pullen Llp Sprin
SIC 8741 Hospital management
Pr: Norman La Conte
Pr: Janelle Hamilton
COO: Karen Kyle
CFO: Kevin Robert
**CFO:* David Underwood
Ex VP: Ralph McGowan
Sr VP: Donald B McElroy
Exec: Joy Ledbetter
Dir: Patricia Odell
Genl Mgr: Todd Baker
IT Man: Michelle Aller

D-U-N-S 06-741-4284 IMP
PROCTOR HOSPITAL
UNITYPINT HLTH METHDST PROCTOR
5409 N Knoxville Ave # 1, Peoria, IL 61614-5076
Tel (309) 691-1000 *Founded/Ownrshp* 1983
Sales 83.2MM *EMP* 1,100
SIC 8062 Hospital, medical school affiliation
CEO: Paul E Macek
**Ch Bd:* James F Vergon
**V Ch:* Donald B McElroy MD
Pr: Janelle Hamilton
**Pr:* Norman La Conte
CFO: John Bell
CFO: Calvin Kay
CFO: Can Mackay
**Treas:* Jayne Mueller
Chf Mktg O: Sami Zabaneh
Ofcr: Mary Groter
VP: Kathy Abbott
VP: Mary J Davis
VP: Dave Underwood
Dir Rad: Mike Korenchuk

PROCUREMENT SYSTEMS SERVICES
See TRIPLE A SUPPLIES INC

D-U-N-S 79-468-3896
PROCURIAN LLC
(*Suby of* ACCENTURE SUB INC) ★
211 S Gulph Rd Ste 500, King of Prussia, PA 19406-3101
Tel (484) 690-5000 *Founded/Ownrshp* 2013
Sales 92.4MM^E *EMP* 704
SIC 7389 8748 Purchasing service; Business consulting
CEO: Carl Guarino
CFO: Joseph Waterman
Treas: Eric S Berry
Sr VP: David Clary
Sr VP: Jason Gilroy
Sr VP: Keith Hausmann
Sr VP: Kristen Knouft
Sr VP: Bob Kothari
VP: Chris Banschbach
Dir Bus: Bob Moran
CIO: Rick Bunker

D-U-N-S 14-254-9166 EXP
PRODUCE ALLIANCE LLC
100 Lexington Dr Ste 201, Buffalo Grove, IL 60089-6937
Tel (847) 808-3030 *Founded/Ownrshp* 1996
Sales 326.1MM *EMP* 75
Accts Miller Cooper & Co Ltd Deer
SIC 5148 Fruits, fresh; Vegetables, fresh
Bd of Dir: George Melshenker
**CFO:* Rob Feldgreber
**VP:* Melissa Melshenker Ackerman
**VP:* Joe Collier
**VP:* Mike Williams
MIS Dir: Michael McColllum
Software D: Joey Cochran

D-U-N-S 03-279-6443
PRODUCE EXCHANGE CO INC
PEXCO PRODUCE SALES
2801 E Hillsborough Ave, Tampa, FL 33610-4410
Tel (813) 237-3374 *Founded/Ownrshp* 1947
Sales 84.3MM *EMP* 60
Accts Andrew A Wunderlin St Peter
SIC 5148 Vegetables, fresh
Pr: Charles P Grizzaffe
**CFO:* Ray Flemming
**Sec:* Virginia Flemming
**VP:* John T Grizzaffe
**VP:* James T Guida

D-U-N-S 02-119-4097 IMP
PRODUCE EXCHANGE INC
(*Suby of* LIPMAN PRODUCE) ★
7407 Southfront Rd, Livermore, CA 94551-8224
Tel (925) 454-8700 *Founded/Ownrshp* 1980
Sales 116.5MM^E *EMP* 251
SIC 5148 Fruits; Vegetables
**Pr:* Samuel E Jones Jr
CFO: Kyle Hickey

D-U-N-S 00-886-0371 IMP
PRODUCERS DAIRY FOODS INC
250 E Belmont Ave, Fresno, CA 93701-1405
Tel (559) 264-6583 *Founded/Ownrshp* 1948
Sales 282.8MM^E *EMP* 330
SIC 5142 5143 Fruit juices, frozen; Dairy products, except dried or canned
Ch Bd: Lawrence A Shehadey
**CEO:* Richard Shehadey
VP: Scott Shehadey
Plnt Mgr: Ken Gauer
Sls Mgr: Randy Chavira

D-U-N-S 00-634-7157 IMP/EXP
PRODUCERS RICE MILL INC
518 E Harrison St, Stuttgart, AR 72160-3700
Tel (870) 673-4444 *Founded/Ownrshp* 1943
Sales 415.0MM *EMP* 600
Accts Erwin & Company Little Rock
SIC 2044 5153 2099 Milled rice; Polished rice; Soybeans; Wheat; Grains; Food preparations
Pr: Keith A Glover
**Ch Bd:* Gary Sebree
**V Ch Bd:* Jerry Hoskyn
**VP:* Marvin B Baden
VP: Steven Caver
**VP:* Ken Dryden
**VP:* Kent Lockwood
Off Mgr: Becky Meier
Sfty Dirs: David Hodges
Opers Mgr: Raymond Ponder
Sls&Mrk Ex: Mike Fisher
Board of Directors: John Stephens, Jerry Brown, Gilbert E Thomas Jr, Jay Coker, Ray Vester, Brooks Davis, Dan Eldridge, Greg Kerksieck, Donald Lee Martin, Roy O Mc Collum III, Travis Satterfield, Jimmy Ray Sherman

D-U-N-S 08-012-3820
PRODUCT CENTRE - SW INC
SOUTHWEST SOUVENIRS
(*Suby of* SOUTHWEST SOUVENIRS) ★
730 S Jupiter Rd Ste B, Garland, TX 75042-7701
Tel (972) 487-0580 *Founded/Ownrshp* 1982
Sales 101.0MM *EMP* 3^E
SIC 5099 Souvenirs
Pr: Dan Grimland
**Treas:* Tim Hudson
**VP:* Susan Grimland

D-U-N-S 04-934-4021
PRODUCT DEVELOPMENT CORP
20 Ragsdale Dr Ste 100, Monterey, CA 93940-7812
Tel (831) 333-1100 *Founded/Ownrshp* 1949
Sales 106.7MM^E *EMP* 895^E
SIC 7389 Telephone directory distribution, contract or fee basis
Pr: Tim Dinovo
**CFO:* David Forey
Sr VP: Ed King
CIO: David Hersey

PRODUCT PARTNERS
See BEACHBODY LLC

D-U-N-S 92-776-8135 IMP
PRODUCT QUEST MANUFACTURING LLC
330 Carswell Ave, Daytona Beach, FL 32117-4416
Tel (386) 239-8787 *Founded/Ownrshp* 1995
Sales 135.1MM *EMP* 425
SIC 2844 Face creams or lotions
CEO: John Regan
**Pr:* Todd Kwait
**CFO:* Bill Jennings
**Ex VP:* Rick Webb

PRODUCTION CHEMICALS
See IMPACT CHEMICAL TECHNOLOGIES INC

PRODUCTION CONTROL SERVICES
See PCS FERGUSON INC

D-U-N-S 80-671-1529
PRODUCTION DESIGN ASSOCIATES INC
PDA
2799 Three Lakes Rd, North Charleston, SC 29418-5900
Tel (843) 554-3466 *Founded/Ownrshp* 1991
Sales 250.0MM *EMP* 17
SIC 7812 1731 Video production; Electronic controls installation
Pr: Jeff Nickles
Prd Mgr: Tommy Brown

D-U-N-S 11-276-8981 IMP
■ PRODUCTION MANAGEMENT INDUSTRIES LLC
PMI
(*Suby of* SESI LLC) ★
1204 Youngs Rd, Morgan City, LA 70380-2937
Tel (985) 631-3837 *Founded/Ownrshp* 1971
Sales 145.8MM^E *EMP* 600
SIC 1389 8731 4789 Oil & gas wells: building, repairing & dismantling; Environmental research; Pipeline terminal facilities, independently operated
CEO: Mark Langley

D-U-N-S 96-425-6077 IMP/EXP
PRODUCTION RESOURCE GROUP LLC
PRG INTEGRATED SOLUTIONS
200 Business Park Dr # 109, Armonk, NY 10504-1751
Tel (212) 589-5400 *Founded/Ownrshp* 1995
Sales 429.9MM^E *EMP* 1,057
SIC 3999 7922 Theatrical scenery; Equipment rental, theatrical; Lighting, theatrical
CEO: Jeremiah Harris
**Pr:* Stephan Paridaen
**COO:* John Hovis
**CFO:* Joseph T Cirillo
**CFO:* Ryan Schroeter
Bd of Dir: Anthony J Bolland
Ex VP: Steven Greenberg
**Ex VP:* Robert Manners
Ex VP: John Prg
**Ex VP:* Nicole Scano Schwiebert
VP: James Jim
VP: Barry Rackover
Exec: Michael Orlando

D-U-N-S 17-108-1479
PRODUCTION SERVICES MANAGEMENT INC
PSMI
1255 Beach Ct, Saline, MI 48176-9185
Tel (734) 677-0454 *Founded/Ownrshp* 2004
Sales 187.5MM^E *EMP* 275^E
SIC 5085 Industrial tools
Pr: Dilip K Mullick
**COO:* Scott Burk
**CFO:* Manoj Ksachdeva
**Ex Dir:* Jay Mullick

D-U-N-S 78-012-4595
PRODUCTION SERVICES NETWORK US INC
(*Suby of* WOOD GROUP PSN LIMITED)
9821 Katy Fwy Ste 400, Houston, TX 77024-1212
Tel (713) 984-1000 *Founded/Ownrshp* 2006
Sales 29.1MM^E *EMP* 1,032
SIC 8742 General management consultant
Pr: John Z Lucas III
CFO: Duncan Skinner
Dir Bus: Ali Green
Genl Mgr: Pat Fogarty
IT Man: Damien Gillis
VP Opers: Joseph Versnel
Opers Mgr: Kurt Boudreaux
Opers Mgr: Danny Lejeune
Opers Mgr: Randy Lepretre
Opers Mgr: Todd Wind

D-U-N-S 61-704-4474
PRODUCTION SPECIALTY SERVICES LLC
511 W Missouri Ave, Midland, TX 79701-5016
Tel (432) 620-0059 *Founded/Ownrshp* 1990
Sales 120.0MM *EMP* 160
SIC 5082 7699

D-U-N-S 00-653-8052 IMP/EXP
PRODUCTION TOOL SUPPLY CO LLC
PTS
8655 E 8 Mile Rd, Warren, MI 48089-4030
Tel (586) 755-2200 *Founded/Ownrshp* 1953
Sales 280.8MM *EMP* 357
Accts Baker Tilly Virchow Krause Llp
SIC 5085 5084 Industrial supplies; Industrial machinery & equipment
Pr: Lawrence A Wolfe
CFO: Michael D Brenner
**Treas:* Andrea Wolfe
VP: Richard Caliandro
Store Mgr: Ed North
Dir IT: Patty Sommerville
VP Sls: Kim Zrepskey
Sales Asso: Dick Shotwell

D-U-N-S 07-149-8273
PRODUCTIVITY INC
REDLINE
15150 25th Ave N, Minneapolis, MN 55447-2169
Tel (763) 476-8600 *Founded/Ownrshp* 1968
Sales 96.7MM^E *EMP* 220
SIC 5085 5084 Industrial tools; Machine tools & accessories
Pr: Greg Buck
**COO:* Kevin Timm
Sls Mgr: Andy Archer
Sls Mgr: Michael O'Connor
Sls Mgr: Kip Shefveland
Sales Asso: Robert North
Sales Asso: Lisa Schramm
Sales Asso: Craig Wilcox

PRODUCTOS CHATA
See CULINARY HISPANIC FOODS INC

PROENERGY INTERNATIONAL
See PROENERGY SERVICES LLC

D-U-N-S 13-197-6875 IMP/EXP
PROENERGY SERVICES LLC
PROENERGY INTERNATIONAL
2001 Proenergy Blvd, Sedalia, MO 65301-2470
Tel (660) 829-5100 *Founded/Ownrshp* 2002
Sales 145.9MM^E *EMP* 154
SIC 1629 Power plant construction
**CFO:* Scott Pollard
VP: Bob Bosse
VP: Keith Kubicek
Plnt Mgr: Stevens John
Ql Cn Mgr: Donald Buehrig
Sales Asso: Chris Mayfield

D-U-N-S 06-613-9924
PROFESSIONAL COMMUNITY MANAGEMENT OF CALIFORNIA
P C M
27051 Towne Centre Dr # 200, Foothill Ranch, CA 92610-2819
Tel (800) 369-7260 *Founded/Ownrshp* 1994
Sales 41.3MM^E *EMP* 1,300
SIC 6531 Real estate managers
CEO: Donny Disbro
**Sr VP:* Russ Disbro
VP: Susan Finley
VP: Sherri McGillivary
IT Man: Ed Thira
Site Mgr: Juan Morales

D-U-N-S 04-791-9147 IMP
PROFESSIONAL COMPOUNDING CENTERS OF AMERICA INC
PCCA
9901 S Wilcrest Dr, Houston, TX 77099-5132
Tel (281) 933-6948 *Founded/Ownrshp* 1981
Sales 338.3MM^E *EMP* 166^E
SIC 5047 5122 Medical equipment & supplies; Pharmaceuticals
Pr: L David Sparks
**Ch Bd:* Lewson Kloesel
Pr: Ernie Rapp
**Pr:* Jim Smith
**COO:* Fabian Zaccardo
VP: Bill Letendre
**VP:* William Letendre
QA Dir: Carlos Townsend
Manager: Richard Harwood
Manager: Erin Michael

D-U-N-S 95-847-3357
PROFESSIONAL CONTRACT SERVICES INC
PCSI
718 W Fm 1626 Bldg 100, Austin, TX 78748-3820
Tel (512) 358-8887 *Founded/Ownrshp* 1999
Sales 106.7MM *EMP* 1,300
Accts Holtzman Partners Llp Austin
SIC 7349 Building maintenance services
Pr: Carroll Schubert
**CFO:* Trina Baumgarten
**VP:* Eric Barbosa
**VP:* Kevin Cloud
**VP:* Keith Walker
Sfty Dirs: Barbara Curd

D-U-N-S 04-918-1563
PROFESSIONAL CONVENTION MANAGEMENT ASSOCIATION
PCMA
35 E Wacker Dr Ste 500, Chicago, IL 60601-2105
Tel (312) 423-7262 *Founded/Ownrshp* 1958
Sales 10.2MM^E *EMP* 2,000
SIC 8611 Trade associations
Pr: Deborah Sexton
Pt: Jennifer Saliba
COO: Sherrif Karamat
Treas: Remy Perrot
Bd of Dir: James S Goodman
Bd of Dir: Joseph V Popolo Jr
Trst: Susan Euritt
VP: Mona Cotton
VP: Kelly Peacy
**VP:* Paulette Phillips
VP: Mary Lou Sarmiento

D-U-N-S 05-742-4249
PROFESSIONAL DIRECTIONAL ENTERPRISES INC
PRO DIRECTIONAL
850 Conroe Park West Dr, Conroe, TX 77303-1966
Tel (936) 441-7266 *Founded/Ownrshp* 2001
Sales 224.6MM^E *EMP* 400^E
SIC 1389 1381 Oil field services; Drilling oil & gas wells
Pr: Karen O'Neil
**Pr:* Lee Wright
**CFO:* Vince Ekleberry
**CFO:* Jeff Martini

D-U-N-S 80-077-7117 IMP/EXP
PROFESSIONAL DISPOSABLES INC
2 Nice Pak Park, Orangeburg, NY 10962-1317
Tel (845) 365-1700 *Founded/Ownrshp* 1975
Sales 181.0MM^E *EMP* 1,000^E
SIC 2676 7389 2621 Sanitary paper products; Packaging & labeling services; Towels, tissues & napkins: paper & stock; Sanitary tissue paper
Pr: Robert P Julius
**Sr VP:* William E Dwan
Software D: Peter Giallorenzo
Natl Sales: Ron Kraus

D-U-N-S 07-130-6625
PROFESSIONAL GOLFERS ASSOCIATION OF AMERICA INC
PGA GOLF SHOP
100 Avenue Of Champions, Palm Beach Gardens, FL 33418-3653
Tel (561) 624-8400 *Founded/Ownrshp* 1962
Sales 108.2MM *EMP* 270
Accts Thomas & Clough Co Pa West Pa
SIC 7941 5961 Sports clubs, managers & promoters; Gift items, mail order
CEO: Jim L Awtrey
**Pr:* Ken Lindsay
**Pr:* Allen Wronowski
**CEO:* Peter Bevacqua
**CEO:* Joe Steranka
**COO:* Paul M Bogin
COO: Randy Joyner
CFO: Chip Essig
**VP:* Ted Bishop
VP: Steve Brewer
**VP:* William C Mann
VP: Ed Marzec
VP: Jason Taylor
VP: Michael Thomas

D-U-N-S 05-615-0964 IMP
PROFESSIONAL HOSPITAL SUPPLY INC
(*Suby of* MEDLINE INDUSTRIES INC) ★
42500 Winchester Rd, Temecula, CA 92590-2570
Tel (951) 699-5000 *Founded/Ownrshp* 2014
Sales 1.1MMM^E *EMP* 1,600
SIC 5047 Medical & hospital equipment
CEO: Jenise Luttgens
**CFO:* John Augustine
**Ex VP:* Doug Hoffee
QA Dir: Shawn Huber
QA Dir: Linda Langhans
Dir IT: Cory Dacio
IT Man: John Gatti
MIS Mgr: David House
Sales Exec: Chuck Kunin
VP Mktg: John Luyben
VP Sls: John Abele

D-U-N-S 60-662-3684
PROFESSIONAL HOSPITALITY RESOURCES INC
P H R
932 Laskin Rd, Virginia Beach, VA 23451-3990
Tel (757) 491-3000 *Founded/Ownrshp* 1986
Sales 82.8MM^E *EMP* 1,200
SIC 7011 7389 5812

D-U-N-S 16-104-4284
PROFESSIONAL NATIONAL TITLE NETWORK
PNTN
70 W Madison St Ste 1600, Chicago, IL 60602-4262
Tel (312) 621-1105 *Founded/Ownrshp* 1985
Sales NA *EMP* 215
SIC 6361 Title insurance
Pr: Kevin Cooney
QA Dir: Konstantin Byvaltcev
**VP Opers:* Joseph Burke

D-U-N-S 78-825-4050
PROFESSIONAL NURSING INC
P N I
325 N Wells St Ste 900, Chicago, IL 60654-7024
Tel (312) 527-1839 *Founded/Ownrshp* 1988
Sales 38.3MM^E *EMP* 1,000
SIC 7361 7363 Nurses' registry; Help supply services
Pr: Choon CHI
**VP:* Vincent B Royal
Dir IT: Jed Sullivan

D-U-N-S 06-277-3585
PROFESSIONAL OFFICE SERVICES INC
P O S
2757 Burton Ave, Waterloo, IA 50703-9729
Tel (319) 235-6777 *Founded/Ownrshp* 1970
Sales 111.6MM^E *EMP* 375
SIC 2761 Manifold business forms; Computer forms, manifold or continuous
Pr: Herbert E Williams
COO: Steve Gilloley
**Sec:* Mark E Weak
**VP:* J Robert Thomas
Assoc Dir: Patrick Moran
Rgnl Mgr: Rick Woods
Plnt Mgr: Paul Buchanan
Mktg Dir: Stacey Christensen
Manager: David Coppock

D-U-N-S 04-964-4461
PROFESSIONAL PACKAGING SYSTEMS LLC
QUALITY PACKAGING
2010 S Great Sw Pkwy, Grand Prairie, TX 75051-3507
Tel (972) 988-0777 *Founded/Ownrshp* 1981
Sales 106.5MM^E *EMP* 160
SIC 5199

D-U-N-S 01-520-1908
PROFESSIONAL PERSONNEL SERVICE INC
ATWORK PERSONNEL SERVICE
3815 Highway 66 S Ste 4, Rogersville, TN 37857-5197
Tel (423) 764-1334 *Founded/Ownrshp* 1993
Sales 68.4MM^E *EMP* 2,000
SIC 7363 Temporary help service
Pr: David Luttrell
**VP:* Marty Luttrell

D-U-N-S 11-838-1227 IMP/EXP
PROFESSIONAL PLASTICS INC
PACKAGING FILMS CO.
1810 E Valencia Dr, Fullerton, CA 92831-4847
Tel (714) 446-6500 *Founded/Ownrshp* 1984
Sales 193.9MM^E *EMP* 295
SIC 5162

D-U-N-S 02-749-6441
PROFESSIONAL PLUMBING GROUP INC
(*Suby of* DUNES POINT CAPITAL LLC) ★
2951 E Highway 501, Conway, SC 29526-9514
Tel (415) 124-5678 *Founded/Ownrshp* 2013
Sales 99.4MM^E *EMP* 250^E
SIC 3432 Plumbing fixture fittings & trim; Plastic plumbing fixture fittings, assembly; Plumbers' brass goods: drain cocks, faucets, spigots, etc.
CEO: Lloyd Coppedge

PROFESSIONAL PROGRAM
See ELMHURST MEMORIAL HEALTHCARE

D-U-N-S 55-648-7445
PROFESSIONAL SECURITY CONSULTANTS
11454 San Vicente Blvd # 2, Los Angeles, CA 90049-6208
Tel (310) 207-7729 *Founded/Ownrshp* 1985
Sales 77.7MM^E *EMP* 2,300^E
SIC 7381 7382 Security guard service; Security systems services
Pr: Moshe Alon
**VP:* Ilene Alon
Dir Bus: Sam Adlerstein
Ex Dir: Grant Erickson
Dir Sec: Glen Blaylock
Dir Sec: Oscar Diaz
Dir Sec: Jason Fishman
Dir Sec: Jacob Maenner
Dir Sec: Carlos Quintanilla
Dir Sec: George Rawson
Dir Sec: Brooks Rollins

D-U-N-S 19-935-7542
PROFESSIONAL SERVICE INDUSTRIES HOLDING INC
PSI HOLDING
(*Suby of* PSI ACQUISITION INC) ★
1901 S Meyers Rd Ste 400, Oakbrook Terrace, IL 60181-5208
Tel (630) 691-1490 *Founded/Ownrshp* 2005
Sales 130.4MM^E *EMP* 1,800
SIC 8711 8734 Building construction consultant; Testing laboratories; Hazardous waste testing; Soil analysis
CEO: Murray R Savage
Dept Mgr: James Inman
Dept Mgr: Sherri Jones
Brnch Mgr: Samuel Filisko
CTO: Debbie Delestowicz

D-U-N-S 06-524-1176 IMP
PROFESSIONAL SERVICE INDUSTRIES INC
PSI CORPORATE HEADQUARTERS
(*Suby of* INTERTEK) ★
1901 S Meyers Rd Ste 400, Oakbrook Terrace, IL 60181-5260
Tel (630) 691-1490 *Founded/Ownrshp* 2015
Sales 563.4MM^E *EMP* 2,400
SIC 8711 8734

D-U-N-S 82-952-4060
PROFESSIONAL SYSTEMS LLC
6055 Lakeside Ste 440, Macon, GA 31210
Tel (478) 752-7000 *Founded/Ownrshp* 2007
Sales 79.7MM^E *EMP* 3,200
SIC 7349 7361 Janitorial service, contract basis; Employment agencies
CEO: Mark Horn
CFO: James Fritze
Comm Man: Denise Fritze
Rgnl Mgr: Roberto Soto

D-U-N-S 85-919-4946
PROFESSIONAL TRANSPORTATION INC
3700 E Morgan Ave, Evansville, IN 47715-2240
Tel (812) 471-2440 *Founded/Ownrshp* 1980
Sales 196.9MM^E *EMP* 1,400
SIC 4011

D-U-N-S 02-976-2390
PROFFER WHOLESALE PRODUCE INC
920 5th St, Park Hills, MO 63601-2403
Tel (573) 431-0625 *Founded/Ownrshp* 1964
Sales 85.1MM^E *EMP* 200
SIC 5148 4213 Fruits, fresh; Vegetables, fresh; Trucking, except local
Pr: Benjy Proffer
Genl Mgr: Tiffany Huskey
Off Mgr: Shelly Proffer
IT Man: Tammy King
Natl Sales: Chad Keown

D-U-N-S 80-909-7517
PROFICIO MORTGAGE VENTURES LLC
2225 Village Walk Dr # 200, Henderson, NV 89052-7809
Tel (407) 476-2400 *Founded/Ownrshp* 2005
Sales NA *EMP* 70
SIC 6162 Mortgage bankers & correspondents
Pr: John Miller
Ofcr: Margaret Allen

D-U-N-S 13-329-1612 IMP
PROFILL HOLDINGS LLC
255 W Crescentville Rd, Cincinnati, OH 45246-1713
Tel (513) 742-4000 *Founded/Ownrshp* 2002
Sales 260.6MM^E *EMP* 665
SIC 5199 5136 5137 6798 Advertising specialties; Men's & boys' clothing; Women's & children's clothing; Real estate investment trusts
Mng Dir: Richard C Mouty
**Mng Dir:* Joseph L Rippe
**Mng Dir:* J Philip Vollmer
Off Mgr: Rhonda Dunn
VP Sls: Michael White

PROFITSTARS
See GOLDLEAF FINANCIAL SOLUTIONS INC

D-U-N-S 01-347-3271
PROG FINANCE LLC (UT)
11629 S 700 E Ste 200, Draper, UT 84020-8377
Tel (877) 898-1970 *Founded/Ownrshp* 1999
Sales NA *EMP* 135
SIC 6141 Personal credit institutions
Pr: Brent L Wilson
Off Mgr: Naeet Roe
Snr Sftwr: Kevin McCallum
Snr Sftwr: Lee Wiltbank
Software D: Brian Mitchell
Software D: Troy Sampson
Sls Dir: Eric Carlson

D-U-N-S 94-583-7219
PROGENY SYSTEMS CORP
9500 Innovation Dr, Manassas, VA 20110-2210
Tel (703) 368-6107 *Founded/Ownrshp* 1995
Sales 91.7MM^E *EMP* 200
SIC 7373 Computer integrated systems design; Systems software development services
Pr: Walter Paul Kitonis
Ofcr: Ted Edwards
**VP:* Michael Mackay
Dir Bus: Tom Barns
Dir Bus: David Beers
Prgrm Mgr: Tim Hench
Prgrm Mgr: Glenn Snyder
Snr Sftwr: Frank Crow
Snr Sftwr: David Raines
Dir IT: Rod Murphy
IT Man: Dave Garner

PROGRESS ENERGY FLORIDA
See DUKE ENERGY FLORIDA LLC

PROGRESS ENERGY FLORIDA
See FLORIDA PROGRESS CORP

D-U-N-S 18-748-0087
■ **PROGRESS ENERGY INC**
(*Suby of* DUKE ENERGY CORP) ★
410 S Wilmington St, Raleigh, NC 27601-1849
Tel (704) 382-3853 *Founded/Ownrshp* 2012
Sales 10.2MMM *EMP* 28,344^E
Accts Deloitte & Touche Llp Charlot
SIC 4911 Electric services; Distribution, electric power; Generation, electric power; Transmission, electric power
CEO: Lynn J Good
CFO: Steven K Young
Bd of Dir: William Cavanaugh
Ex VP: Geoffrey S Chatas
VP: Cari Boyce
VP: Vincent M Dolan
VP: Jon Franke
VP: Tucker Mann
VP: John Smith
VP: Danny Stancil
Prgrm Mgr: Christie Hill
Board of Directors: Julia S Janson

D-U-N-S 10-210-4846
■ **PROGRESS ENERGY SERVICE CO LLC**
(*Suby of* PROGRESS ENERGY INC) ★
602 Raleigh Rd, Henderson, NC 27536-5368
Tel (919) 508-5400 *Founded/Ownrshp* 2000
Sales 252.6MM^E *EMP* 1,436
SIC 4911 Electric services
Ch: James E Rogers
**Ex VP:* Jeffrey J Lyash
**Ex VP:* B Keith Trent
**Ex VP:* Lloyd M Yates
**Sr VP:* Lee T Mazzocchi
VP: Martha Bamwell
VP: Bob Duncan
VP: Robert Duncan
VP: Jim Massengill

VP: David Rumbarger
Genl Mgr: Raymond Davis

D-U-N-S 78-948-2473
PROGRESS ENERGY SERVICE CO LLC
299 1st Ave N, Saint Petersburg, FL 33701-3308
Tel (727) 820-5151
Sales NA *EMP* 3,117[E]
SIC 4911

D-U-N-S 08-137-1635 IMP
■ PROGRESS FUELS CORP
(*Suby of* PROGRESS ENERGY INC) ★
1 Progress Plz Fl 11, Saint Petersburg, FL 33701-4322
Tel (727) 824-6600 *Founded/Ownrshp* 1988
Sales 712.5MM[E] *EMP* 4,050
SIC 1221 Bituminous coal & lignite loading & preparation
Pr: Richard D Keller
**Sr VP:* W D Carter
**VP:* A W Pitcher
VP: E A Upmeyer III
Board of Directors: Dr Jack B Critchfield, J R Heinicka, Richard Korpan

D-U-N-S 18-816-8124 IMP
■ PROGRESS LIGHTING INC
(*Suby of* HUBBELL INC) ★
701 Millennium Blvd, Greenville, SC 29607-5251
Tel (864) 678-1000 *Founded/Ownrshp* 1987
Sales 140.6MM[E] *EMP* 899
SIC 3645 3646 Residential lighting fixtures; Commercial indusl & institutional electric lighting fixtures
Pr: Charles Harris
VP: James Decker
**VP:* Walter Gragg
CIO: Ronald Davidson
VP Opers: Richard Kyle
VP Sls: Robert Sale
Manager: Jim Serpliss
Manager: Jared Souza

D-U-N-S 19-575-1750 IMP/EXP
■ PROGRESS RAIL LOCOMOTIVE INC
EMD
(*Suby of* PROGRESS RAIL SERVICES CORP) ★
9301 W 55th St, Mc Cook, IL 60525-3214
Tel (800) 255-5355 *Founded/Ownrshp* 2004
Sales 1.1MMM[E] *EMP* 2,000
SIC 3621 3519 3647 Motors & generators; Internal combustion engines; Locomotive & railroad car lights
CEO: William P Ainsworth
COO: Keri Harkne
CFO: Randall Gonzalez
Sr VP: Tim Heilig
VP: Ronald Cloyd
VP: Doug Creech
VP: Marty Haycraft
Exec: Tim Milewski
Genl Mgr: Andy Anderson
Genl Mgr: Craig McKeen
Snr Sftwr: Ashish Kachrani

D-U-N-S 17-490-1504
■ PROGRESS RAIL SERVICES CORP
(*Suby of* CATERPILLAR INC) ★
1600 Progress Dr, Albertville, AL 35950-8545
Tel (256) 593-1260 *Founded/Ownrshp* 2006
Sales 2.8MMM[E] *EMP* 5,000
SIC 4789 7389 Railroad maintenance & repair services; Railroad car repair; Metal cutting services
Pr: William P Ainsworth
**CFO:* Randall Gonzales
**Sr VP:* Marc Buncher
**Sr VP:* Jean Francois Cloutier
**Sr VP:* Bruno Couteille
Sr VP: Dan Hanback
Sr VP: Marty Haycraft
VP: Ken Hofacker
VP: James Lawley
VP: Bud Lawlor
VP: Jackie A Nesmith
VP: Edward O'Neal
VP: Dave Roeder
VP: Jean Savage
VP: Jim Shrivinski
VP: Beth Smith
VP: Elizabeth Smith
Exec: Robert Powell

D-U-N-S 10-885-4894
▲ PROGRESS SOFTWARE CORP
14 Oak Park Dr, Bedford, MA 01730-1485
Tel (781) 280-4000 *Founded/Ownrshp* 1981
Sales 377.5MM *EMP* 1,766
Tkr Sym PRGS *Exch* NGS
SIC 7372 7371 Prepackaged software; Computer software development
CEO: Yogesh Gupta
**COO:* Jerry Rulli
**CFO:* Kurt J Abkemeier
Chf Mktg O: Melissa Puls
Ofcr: Michael Benedict
**Ofcr:* Mitch Breen
Ofcr: Sean Doherty
Ofcr: Robert Steward
**Ofcr:* Faris Sweis
Ofcr: Dimitre Taslakov
Ofcr: Vassil Terziev
Sr VP: Svetozar Georgiev
Board of Directors: Barry N Bycoff, John R Egan, Ram Gupta, Charles F Kane, David A Krall, Michael L Mark

D-U-N-S 78-696-9266
PROGRESS WEST HEALTHCARE CENTER
BJC HEALTHCARE
(*Suby of* BJC HEALTHCARE) ★
2 Progress Point Ct, O Fallon, MO 63368-2208
Tel (636) 344-1000 *Founded/Ownrshp* 2004
Sales 61.7MM *EMP* 27,000
SIC 8062 General medical & surgical hospitals
Pr: John Antes

D-U-N-S 83-550-2881
■ PROGRESSIVE AGENCY INC
PROGRESSIVE INSURANCE
(*Suby of* PROGRESSIVE INSURANCE) ★
6300 Wilson Mills Rd, Cleveland, OH 44143-2109
Tel (440) 461-5000 *Founded/Ownrshp* 2007
Sales NA *EMP* 250
SIC 6331 Fire, marine & casualty insurance
Ch: Peter B Lewis
Genl Mgr: James Haas
Dir IT: Joe Blanchard
Dir IT: Elaine Hersman
Dir IT: Debbie Kraska
IT Man: Kevin Brandich
IT Man: Chris Gallagher
IT Man: Bob Gottschick
IT Man: Srikanth Krishnaswami
IT Man: Lynn Schreffler
IT Man: Mike Ziccardi

D-U-N-S 05-440-2201
■ PROGRESSIVE AMERICAN INSURANCE CO
PROGRESSIVE INSURANCE
(*Suby of* PROGRESSIVE INSURANCE) ★
6300 Wilson Mills Rd, Cleveland, OH 44143-2109
Tel (440) 461-5000 *Founded/Ownrshp* 1946, 1991
Sales NA *EMP* 6
SIC 6331 Fire, marine & casualty insurance
CEO: Glenn Renwick
CFO: Brian Domeck
Treas: David Krew
VP: David Pratt
IT Man: Anthony Alesci

PROGRESSIVE BALLOONS & GIFTS
See PROGRESSIVE BALLOONS INC

D-U-N-S 15-042-2798 IMP/EXP
PROGRESSIVE BALLOONS INC
PROGRESSIVE BALLOONS & GIFTS
3100 Industrial Park Pl W, Saint Peters, MO 63376-1198
Tel (636) 240-0444 *Founded/Ownrshp* 1985
Sales 186.0MM *EMP* 200
SIC 5092 Balloons, novelty
Pr: Judy Burns
**VP:* Clark Burns

D-U-N-S 07-908-8896
■ PROGRESSIVE BAYSIDE INSURANCE CO
PROGRESSIVE INSURANCE
(*Suby of* PROGRESSIVE INSURANCE) ★
6300 Wilson Mills Rd, Cleveland, OH 44143-2109
Tel (440) 395-4460 *Founded/Ownrshp* 2013
Sales NA *EMP* 251[E]
SIC 6311 Life insurance

D-U-N-S 80-581-7616
■ PROGRESSIVE BAYSIDE INSURANCE CO
(*Suby of* PROGRESSIVE INSURANCE) ★
4030 Crescent Park Dr B, Riverview, FL 33578-3569
Tel (813) 487-1000 *Founded/Ownrshp* 1986
Sales NA *EMP* 793
SIC 6331 Fire, marine & casualty insurance
Pr: Robert J Mc Millan

PROGRESSIVE BUS PUBLICATIONS
See AMERICAN FUTURE SYSTEMS INC

D-U-N-S 07-674-3699 EXP
■ PROGRESSIVE CASUALTY INSURANCE CO
PROGRESSIVE INSURANCE
(*Suby of* PROGRESSIVE INSURANCE) ★
6300 Wilson Mills Rd, Mayfield Village, OH 44143-2109
Tel (440) 461-5000 *Founded/Ownrshp* 1965
Sales NA *EMP* 11,724
SIC 6331 6351 6411 6321 Fire, marine & casualty insurance; Fire, marine & casualty insurance & carriers; Automobile insurance; Property damage insurance; Surety insurance; Credit & other financial responsibility insurance; Insurance agents, brokers & service; Insurance claim adjusters, not employed by insurance company; Insurance agents & brokers; Insurance agents; Accident & health insurance; Accident insurance carriers
Ch Bd: Glenn M Renwick
COO: Jim Mauck
**CFO:* Brian Domeck
Bd of Dir: Bernadine P Healy
Bd of Dir: Norman S Matthews
Bd of Dir: Bradley T Sheares
Chf Inves: William M Cody
Sr VP: Jonathan Klein
VP: Mary B Andreano
VP: Jeffrey W Basch
Dir Risk M: Joe Platko

D-U-N-S 83-012-4967
■ PROGRESSIVE CHOICE INSURANCE CO
(*Suby of* PROGRESSIVE DIRECT HOLDINGS, INC.)
6300 Wilson Mills Rd, Cleveland, OH 44143-2109
Tel (440) 461-5000 *Founded/Ownrshp* 2009
Sales NA *EMP* 1,254[E]
SIC 6331 Fire, marine & casualty insurance
Pr: Steven A Broz
Tech Mgr: Paul Wilson

D-U-N-S 62-339-3634 IMP
PROGRESSIVE CONVERTING INC
PRO CON
2430 E Glendale Ave, Appleton, WI 54911-8683
Tel (800) 637-7310 *Founded/Ownrshp* 1991
Sales 91.8MM[E] *EMP* 200
SIC 2679 Paper products, converted
Pr: Dan Curtin
Sales Exec: David Vanhoof

D-U-N-S 04-841-5509
▲ PROGRESSIVE CORP
PROGRESSIVE INSURANCE
6300 Wilson Mills Rd, Mayfield Village, OH 44143-2109
Tel (440) 461-5000 *Founded/Ownrshp* 1937
Sales NA *EMP* 28,580
Tkr Sym PGR *Exch* NYS
SIC 6331 6351 Automobile insurance; Property damage insurance; Fire, marine & casualty insurance: stock; Credit & other financial responsibility insurance
Ch Bd: Glenn M Renwick
Pr: Michael D Sieger
CFO: John P Sauerland
Treas: Thomas A King
Chf Mktg O: M Jeffrey Charney
Chf Inves: William M Cody
Ofcr: Valerie Krasowski
VP: Jeffrey W Basch
VP: Kathy Cramer
VP: Susan Patricia Griffith
CIO: Steven A Broz

D-U-N-S 80-581-8176
■ PROGRESSIVE DIRECT INSURANCE CO
(*Suby of* PROGRESSIVE DIRECT HOLDINGS, INC.)
6300 Wilson Mills Rd, Cleveland, OH 44143-2109
Tel (440) 461-5000 *Founded/Ownrshp* 2003
Sales NA *EMP* 10
SIC 6331 Fire, marine & casualty insurance
Pr: Christine A Johnson

D-U-N-S 01-908-5612
PROGRESSIVE DISTRIBUTORS INC
(*Suby of* HANNAFORD SUPERMARKET & PHRM) ★
145 Pleasant Hill Rd, Scarborough, ME 04074-9309
Tel (207) 883-2911 *Founded/Ownrshp* 1967
Sales 159.1MM[E] *EMP* 250
SIC 5122 5149 5199 Druggists' sundries; Pharmaceuticals; Specialty food items; General merchandise, non-durable
Pr: Brad Wise
**Treas:* Garrett D Bowne IV

D-U-N-S 07-955-6675
PROGRESSIVE ENTERPRISES HOLDINGS INC
250 N Sunny Slope Rd # 110, Brookfield, WI 53005-4809
Tel (262) 207-2101 *Founded/Ownrshp* 2010
Sales 135.5MM[E] *EMP* 2,200[E]
SIC 7371 Computer software development
CEO: Kenneth Dowd

D-U-N-S 96-681-4589
PROGRESSIVE ENTERPRISES HOLDINGS INC
250 Progressive Way, Westerville, OH 43082-9615
Tel (614) 794-3300 *Founded/Ownrshp* 2010
Sales 289.7MM[E] *EMP* 531[E]
SIC 8742 Compensation & benefits planning consultant

D-U-N-S 82-969-5530
PROGRESSIVE ENVIRONMENTAL SERVICES INC
SWS ENVIRONMENTAL SERVICES
1619 Moylan Rd, Panama City Beach, FL 32407-4073
Tel (850) 234-8428 *Founded/Ownrshp* 2008
Sales 581.9MM[E] *EMP* 544
SIC 4959 Oil spill cleanup
Pr: Eugene A Cookson Jr
Prin: Jeffrey Sweren

D-U-N-S 79-698-0311
■ PROGRESSIVE HAWAII INSURANCE CORP
PROGRESSIVE INSURANCE
(*Suby of* PROGRESSIVE INSURANCE) ★
6300 Wilson Mills Rd, Cleveland, OH 44143-2109
Tel (440) 461-5000 *Founded/Ownrshp* 2007
Sales NA *EMP* 501[E]
SIC 6411 Insurance agents, brokers & service
Pr: Glenn M Renwick

D-U-N-S 15-479-1545
PROGRESSIVE HOME HEALTH SERVICES INC
225 W 34th St Fl 9, New York, NY 10122-0901
Tel (212) 273-5500 *Founded/Ownrshp* 1985
Sales 52.8MM[E] *EMP* 2,000
SIC 8059 Personal care home, with health care
Pr: Elliot Green
CFO: Paul Belitsis
CFO: Cliff McClinton
**CFO:* Robin Richards
**VP:* Kenneth Kilroy
Ex Dir: Sobeida Valdez

PROGRESSIVE INSURANCE
See PROGRESSIVE MAX INSURANCE CO

PROGRESSIVE INSURANCE
See PROGRESSIVE CORP

PROGRESSIVE INSURANCE
See PROGRESSIVE AMERICAN INSURANCE CO

PROGRESSIVE INSURANCE
See PROGRESSIVE CASUALTY INSURANCE CO

PROGRESSIVE INSURANCE
See PROGRESSIVE BAYSIDE INSURANCE CO

PROGRESSIVE INSURANCE
See PROGRESSIVE MARATHON INSURANCE CO INC

PROGRESSIVE INSURANCE
See PROGRESSIVE PREFERRED INSURANCE CO

PROGRESSIVE INSURANCE
See PROGRESSIVE SPECIALTY INSURANCE CO

PROGRESSIVE INSURANCE
See PROGRESSIVE NORTHERN INSURANCE CO

PROGRESSIVE INSURANCE
See PROGRESSIVE SOUTHEASTERN INSURANCE CO INC

PROGRESSIVE INSURANCE
See PROGRESSIVE NORTHWESTERN INSURANCE CO

PROGRESSIVE INSURANCE
See PROGRESSIVE HAWAII INSURANCE CORP

PROGRESSIVE INSURANCE
See PROGRESSIVE AGENCY INC

D-U-N-S 07-673-4482 IMP
PROGRESSIVE LABORATORIES INC
KORDIAL NTRNTS PROF SPPLEMENTS
3131 Story Rd W, Irving, TX 75038-3514
Tel (972) 518-9660 *Founded/Ownrshp* 1972
Sales 198.0MM *EMP* 78
SIC 2834 Vitamin, nutrient & hematinic preparations for human use
CEO: Joseph C O'Neal
**Pr:* Larry Thompson
**CFO:* Maurice Carter
**CFO:* Damon Wolfe
**VP:* Carol Thompson
Genl Mgr: Laura Koellman
IT Man: David Graves
Sls Mgr: Nancy Craig

D-U-N-S 04-997-4954
PROGRESSIVE LOGISTICS SERVICES LLC (GA)
6 Piedmont Ctr Ne Ste 606, Atlanta, GA 30305-1542
Tel (404) 495-5300 *Founded/Ownrshp* 1999
Sales 35.6MM[E] *EMP* 1,000
SIC 4213 Trucking, except local

D-U-N-S 12-352-1283
PROGRESSIVE LOGISTICS SERVICES LLC
6525 The Corners Pkwy # 520, Norcross, GA 30092-3344
Tel (404) 564-1222 *Founded/Ownrshp* 1999
Sales 71.3MM[E] *EMP* 3,000
SIC 8631 Labor unions & similar labor organizations
CEO: Thomas Caudell
COO: Michael Adams
CFO: Chad Kapfhamer
Dir Bus: Bob Johnson

D-U-N-S 13-854-3462
■ PROGRESSIVE MARATHON INSURANCE CO INC
PROGRESSIVE INSURANCE
(*Suby of* PROGRESSIVE INSURANCE) ★
6300 Wilson Mills Rd, Cleveland, OH 44143-2109
Tel (888) 223-3558 *Founded/Ownrshp* 2000
Sales NA *EMP* 20
SIC 6331 Fire, marine & casualty insurance
Pr: Mark D Niehaus

D-U-N-S 00-790-1192
■ PROGRESSIVE MAX INSURANCE CO
PROGRESSIVE INSURANCE
(*Suby of* PROGRESSIVE INSURANCE) ★
6300 Wilson Mills Rd, Cleveland, OH 44143-2109
Tel (440) 461-5000 *Founded/Ownrshp* 1991
Sales NA *EMP* 80
SIC 6331 6411 Fire, marine & casualty insurance; Insurance agents, brokers & service
Pr: Glenn M Renwick
**Pr:* Peter B Lewis
**CFO:* Brian Domeck
Treas: David Krew
Treas: Stephen Peterson
Ofcr: Moira A Lardakis
Ofcr: Tiona M Thompson
VP: Jeffrey W Basch
VP: Lisa Dems
VP: Craig Edmonds
VP: Michael J Moroney

D-U-N-S 09-098-9224
■ PROGRESSIVE MICHIGAN INSURANCE CO
(*Suby of* DRIVE INSURANCE HOLDINGS INC) ★
46333 Five Mile Rd 100, Plymouth, MI 48170-2421
Tel (734) 456-5742 *Founded/Ownrshp* 2001
Sales NA *EMP* 1,971[E]
SIC 6411 Insurance agents, brokers & service

D-U-N-S 17-558-6056
■ PROGRESSIVE NORTHERN INSURANCE CO
PROGRESSIVE INSURANCE
(*Suby of* PROGRESSIVE INSURANCE) ★
44 E Mifflin St, Madison, WI 53703-4205
Tel (440) 461-5000 *Founded/Ownrshp* 1980
Sales NA *EMP* 10
SIC 6331 Fire, marine & casualty insurance; Fire, marine & casualty insurance & carriers
Ch Bd: Peter B Lewis
**Pr:* Glenn Renwick

D-U-N-S 78-739-0541
■ PROGRESSIVE NORTHWESTERN INSURANCE CO
PROGRESSIVE INSURANCE
(*Suby of* PROGRESSIVE INSURANCE) ★
6300 Wilson Mills Rd, Cleveland, OH 44143-2109
Tel (440) 461-5000 *Founded/Ownrshp* 1982
Sales NA *EMP* 25
SIC 6331 Fire, marine & casualty insurance
CEO: Glenn Renwick
**Pr:* Robert Williams
**Treas:* Stephen Peterson

D-U-N-S 19-814-0683
PROGRESSIVE NURSING STAFFERS OF VIRGINIA INC
5531 Hempstead Way Ste B, Springfield, VA 22151-4019
Tel (703) 750-3991 *Founded/Ownrshp* 1987
Sales 88.8MM[E] *EMP* 4,500
SIC 7363 Temporary help service
Pr: Gary Hughes
**VP:* Jim Narron
Exec: John Hughes
Genl Mgr: Patti Jones
Mktg Dir: Sharon Hogan

D-U-N-S 02-369-8874
PROGRESSIVE PIPELINE CONSTRUCTION LLC
12340 Qitman Meridian Hwy, Meridian, MS 39301-7778
Tel (601) 693-8777 *Founded/Ownrshp* 2008
Sales 141.6MM *EMP* 1,000
Accts Warren Averett Birmingham Al
SIC 1623 Oil & gas pipeline construction
CEO: Mike Castle Sr
Pr: Michael Castle Jr
CFO: Roger Booker

D-U-N-S 07-921-8056
PROGRESSIVE PIPELINE HOLDINGS LLC
12340 Qitman Meridian Hwy, Meridian, MS 39301-7778
Tel (601) 693-8777 *Founded/Ownrshp* 2008
Sales 141.6MM *EMP* 2
Accts Warren Averett Llc Cpas And
SIC 6719 1623 Investment holding companies, except banks; Water, sewer & utility lines
VP: Miles Hester

D-U-N-S 17-558-5934
■ **PROGRESSIVE PREFERRED INSURANCE CO**
PROGRESSIVE INSURANCE
(*Suby of* PROGRESSIVE INSURANCE) ★
6300 Wilson Mills Rd, Cleveland, OH 44143-2109
Tel (216) 464-8000 *Founded/Ownrshp* 1979
Sales NA *EMP* 5
SIC 6331 Fire, marine & casualty insurance
CEO: Glenn Renwick
CIO: Raymond Voelker

D-U-N-S 80-814-1118
■ **PROGRESSIVE PREMIER INSURANCE CO OF ILLINOIS**
(*Suby of* PROGRESSIVE INSURANCE) ★
6300 Wilson Mills Rd W33, Cleveland, OH 44143-2109
Tel (440) 461-5000 *Founded/Ownrshp* 2007
Sales NA *EMP* 251^E
SIC 6411 Insurance agents, brokers & service
CEO: Toby K Alfred

D-U-N-S 13-007-9143
PROGRESSIVE QUALITY CARE INC
5553 Broadview Rd, Parma, OH 44134-1604
Tel (216) 661-6800 *Founded/Ownrshp* 2001
Sales 59.1MM^E *EMP* 1,000^E
SIC 7389 Personal service agents, brokers & bureaus
Pr: Mike Flank
CFO: Eitan Flank
Ex Dir: Evan Hamilton
Snr Mgr: Carl Holbrook

PROGRESSIVE ROOFING
See PROGRESSIVE SERVICES INC

D-U-N-S 83-012-4090
■ **PROGRESSIVE SELECT INSURANCE CO**
(*Suby of* PROGRESSIVE DIRECT HOLDINGS, INC.)
6300 Wilson Mills Rd, Cleveland, OH 44143-2109
Tel (440) 461-5000 *Founded/Ownrshp* 2009
Sales NA *EMP* 418^E
SIC 6331 Fire, marine & casualty insurance
Prin: James R Haas

D-U-N-S 09-123-5275
PROGRESSIVE SERVICES INC
PROGRESSIVE ROOFING
23 N 35th Ave, Phoenix, AZ 85009-4728
Tel (602) 278-4900 *Founded/Ownrshp* 1997
Sales 95.5MM *EMP* 800
Accts Brock Schechter & Polakoff L
SIC 1761 Roofing, siding & sheet metal work; Roofing contractor
Pr: John Farrell
**Treas:* Scott Manning
**Sec:* Lauren Farrell
**VP:* Mark E Farrell
Genl Mgr: Sophia Galan
Genl Mgr: Bob Gardner
Genl Mgr: Greg Skinner
Genl Mgr: Chris Sonnenberg
Genl Mgr: Dan Straight
Genl Mgr: Ted Thornburg
Genl Mgr: Juan Vega

D-U-N-S 18-758-8017
■ **PROGRESSIVE SOUTHEASTERN INSURANCE CO INC**
PROGRESSIVE INSURANCE
(*Suby of* PROGRESSIVE INSURANCE) ★
4030 Crescent Park Dr B, Riverview, FL 33578-3569
Tel (813) 487-1000 *Founded/Ownrshp* 1980
Sales NA *EMP* 1,588^E
SIC 6331 Fire, marine & casualty insurance
Pr: Robert J Mc Millian
**Ch Bd:* Peter B Lewis
Board of Directors: Charles B Chokel, Glen E Combs, Gary Feuerstein, William T Forrester III, William H Graves

D-U-N-S 17-558-5991
■ **PROGRESSIVE SPECIALTY INSURANCE CO**
PROGRESSIVE INSURANCE
(*Suby of* PROGRESSIVE INSURANCE) ★
6300 Wilson Mills Rd, Cleveland, OH 44143-2109
Tel (440) 461-5000 *Founded/Ownrshp* 1975
Sales NA *EMP* 16^E
SIC 6331 Fire, marine & casualty insurance
CEO: Peter B Lewis

PROGRESSIVE WASTE SOLUTIONS
See IESI MD CORP

D-U-N-S 02-650-6746
PROGRESSIVE WASTE SOLUTIONS LTD
(*Suby of* IESI-BFC HOLDINGS INC)
2301 Eagle Pkwy Ste 200, Fort Worth, TX 76177-2326
Tel (817) 632-4000 *Founded/Ownrshp* 2010
Sales 1.8MMM^E *EMP* 1,990
SIC 4953 Refuse systems
CFO: Thomas J Cowee
**Pr:* Charles Flood
**COO:* Thomas L Brown
**Sr VP:* P Lawrence McGee
Sr VP: Jeff Peckham
**VP:* Edward Apuzzi
**VP:* Thomas J Fowler
VP: Lori Joyce
VP: Shawn McCash
VP: Larry McGee
**VP:* Stephen Moody
**VP:* Ron Neese
**VP:* Gordon D Peckham

D-U-N-S 88-360-1676
PROGRESSIVE WASTE SOLUTIONS LTD
SC REGION OFFICE
(*Suby of* PROGRESSIVE WASTE SOLUTIONS LTD) ★
2138 Country Ln, McKinney, TX 75069-1240
Tel (469) 452-8000 *Founded/Ownrshp* 1994
Sales 301.8MM^E *EMP* 500
SIC 4953 Refuse systems
Pr: William P Hulligan
**Pr:* Charles Flood
**COO:* Thomas L Brown
**CFO:* Thomas J Cowee
VP: John C Gustafson
VP: Geoff Rathbone
Exec: Sandra Anderson
Dist Mgr: Shawn Eiras

D-U-N-S 14-743-6799
PROGRESSIVE WASTE SOLUTIONS OF FL INC
SE REGION OFFICE
(*Suby of* WASTE SERVICES INC) ★
2860 W State Road 84, Fort Lauderdale, FL 33312-4808
Tel (954) 888-4300 *Founded/Ownrshp* 2003
Sales 121.3MM^E *EMP* 175
SIC 4953 Recycling, waste materials
Pr: Thomas Brown
**Pr:* Larry D Henk
**Treas:* Kevin May
**VP:* Kirk Muter
Sls Mgr: Stephen Ramsay

PROHEALTH CARE
See PROHEALTHCARE FOUNDATION

D-U-N-S 79-964-0961
PROHEALTH CARE ASSOCIATES LLP
1 Dakota Dr, New Hyde Park, NY 11042-1119
Tel (516) 622-6000 *Founded/Ownrshp* 1996
Sales 99.2MM^E *EMP* 600
SIC 8011 Offices & clinics of medical doctors
CFO: Nancy Nelson
Bd of Dir: Nancy Crispi
Chf Nrs Of: Cathy Rapp
Off Mgr: Danielle Beltran
Snr Ntwrk: Harold Cramer
CTO: Dashmir Dalipi
QC Dir: Kris Kelm
Sfty Mgr: Kathryn Stolz
Surgeon: Elliot Hershman
Surgeon: Michael C Schwartz
Ansthlgy: Karl C Coloma

D-U-N-S 80-441-2914
PROHEALTH CARE INC
PROHEALTH CARE MORELAND SURGER
725 American Ave, Waukesha, WI 53188-5031
Tel (262) 544-2011 *Founded/Ownrshp* 1983
Sales 747.1MM *EMP* 3,000
SIC 8011 8062 Clinic, operated by physicians; General medical & surgical hospitals
CEO: Donald W Fundingsland
**Pr:* Daniel P Blask
COO: Lynn Wojnowski
Bd of Dir: Kathy Ricco
VP: Melissa Anderson
VP: Cathy Rapp
Dir Risk M: Karen Bewer
Snr Ntwrk: Adam Granatella
Snr Ntwrk: Mike Heileman
CTO: Bill Miller
IT Man: Denise Vollbrecht

D-U-N-S 07-385-1529
PROHEALTH CARE MEDICAL ASSOCIATES INC
MEDICAL ASSOCIATES HEALTH CTRS
W180n8000 Town Hall Rd, Menomonee Falls, WI 53051-4002
Tel (262) 255-2500 *Founded/Ownrshp* 1965
Sales 109.6MM *EMP* 900
SIC 8011 Clinic, operated by physicians
Ch: Mark Timm
**Pr:* Clyde M Chumbley
**Treas:* Randall R Newman
Dir IT: Kelly Lillegard

PROHEALTH CARE MORELAND SURGER
See PROHEALTH CARE INC

D-U-N-S 94-836-0656
PROHEALTH PHYSICIANS INC
3 Farm Glen Blvd Ste 202, Farmington, CT 06032-1981
Tel (860) 409-7700 *Founded/Ownrshp* 1996
Sales 89.7MM^E *EMP* 350
SIC 8741 Nursing & personal care facility management
Ch: Charles Staub MD
CFO: Libbie Barrows
**CFO:* Philip Pin
**Chf Mktg O:* James Cox-Chapman MD
**Ex VP:* Jack Reed
Rgnl Mgr: Mark Bugos
IT Man: Michelle Kelly
Doctor: Douglas H Mac Gilpin

D-U-N-S 07-383-0994
PROHEALTHCARE FOUNDATION
PROHEALTH CARE
791 Summit Ave, Oconomowoc, WI 53066-3844
Tel (262) 569-9400 *Founded/Ownrshp* 1998
Sales 101.7MM *EMP* 611
Accts Plante & Moran Pllc Grand Ra
SIC 8062 8011 General medical & surgical hospitals; Offices & clinics of medical doctors
Pr: Douglas Guy
**Ex Dir:* Nora Saile
CTO: John Schmidt
Sfty Dirs: Jennifer Carroll
Mktg Dir: Sara Estell

D-U-N-S 83-323-8772
PROJECT BOAT HOLDINGS LLC
(*Suby of* PLATINUM EQUITY LLC) ★
360 N Crescent Dr Bldg S, Beverly Hills, CA 90210-2529
Tel (310) 712-1850 *Founded/Ownrshp* 2009
Sales NA *EMP* 3,174
SIC 6719 Investment holding companies, except banks

D-U-N-S 85-992-4680
PROJECT CONSULTING SERVICES INC
P C S
3300 W Esplanade Ave S, Metairie, LA 70002-7406
Tel (504) 219-3426 *Founded/Ownrshp* 1992
Sales 1.0MMM^E *EMP* 160
SIC 1389

D-U-N-S 09-866-1135 EXP
PROJECT HOPE-PEOPLE-TO-PEOPLE HEALTH FOUNDATION INC
255 Carter Hall Ln, Millwood, VA 22646-0255
Tel (540) 837-2100 *Founded/Ownrshp* 1958
Sales 296.7MM *EMP* 174
SIC 8399 Health systems agency
Ch: Richard T Clark
CFO: Laura Cramutola
**Ex VP:* Linda N Heitzman
Ex VP: Michael D Maves
**VP:* Donald M Hill IV
**VP:* Richard Rumsey
**VP:* M Miriam Wardak
Prgrm Mgr: Katie Kowalski
DP Exec: Tina Larrick
Netwrk Eng: Rick Parra

D-U-N-S 08-569-7787
PROJECT MANAGEMENT INSTITUTE INC
P M I
14 Campus Blvd, Newtown Square, PA 19073-3299
Tel (610) 356-4600 *Founded/Ownrshp* 1969
Sales 180.5MM *EMP* 200^E
Accts Elko & Associates Ltd Media
SIC 8699 Charitable organization
Ch: Deanna Landers
Ch Bd: E Frasier
Pr: Frank Schettini
CEO: Greg Balestrero
Treas: Philip Diab
Treas: Zbigniew J Traczyk
Bd of Dir: James Snyder
Bd of Dir: Jennifer Tharp
VP: Warren Allen
VP: Andrea Buell
VP: Richard Hancock
VP: John Hudson
VP: Michael Katagiri III
VP: Dick McCandless
VP: Dick Sharad
Board of Directors: Peter Monkhouse, Frederick A Arnold, William Moylan, Eugene C Bounds, Frank Parth, Eugene Bounds, Beth Partleton, Shirley Edwards, Bruce Rodrigues, Jane Farley, Kathleen Romero, Deanna Landers, Ricardo Triana, Mark Owen Mathieson, Ricardo Triana, Louis Mercken, Ricardo Viana Vargas, Jon Milhalic, Linda Vella

D-U-N-S 78-086-4617
PROJECT OHR INC
80 Maiden Ln Fl 10, New York, NY 10038-4811
Tel (718) 853-2700 *Founded/Ownrshp* 1979
Sales 51.9MM *EMP* 1,550
Accts Raich Ende Malter & Co Llp Ne
SIC 8322 8742 Homemakers' service; Industry specialist consultants
Ex Dir: D'Vorah Kohn
**Ch Bd:* Merryl Tisch
**Pr:* Menachem Lubinsky

D-U-N-S 09-938-9637
PROJECT ORBIS INTERNATIONAL INC
520 8th Ave Rm 1101, New York, NY 10018-4186
Tel (646) 674-5500 *Founded/Ownrshp* 1973
Sales 151.5MM *EMP* 158
Accts Bdo Usa Llp New York Ny
SIC 8699 Charitable organization
CEO: Jenny Hourihan
CFO: Tom Hill
**Ch:* Ted Hartley
**Treas:* John Howitt
**Treas:* James T Ueltschi
**VP:* A L Ueltschi
Assoc Dir: Jennifer Berman
Assoc Dir: Inge Ceunen
**Prin:* James R Parker
**Ex Dir:* John J McHale
Dir IT: Ming Chang
Board of Directors: Ted Hartley

D-U-N-S 83-271-2041
PROJECT SKYLINE INTERMEDIATE HOLDING CORP
360 N Crescent Dr Bldg S, Beverly Hills, CA 90210-2529
Tel (310) 712-1850 *Founded/Ownrshp* 2009
Sales NA *EMP* 2,020
SIC 6719 Investment holding companies, except banks
Pr: Tom Gores

PROJECT TRADE SOLUTIONS
See CLP RESOURCES INC

D-U-N-S 16-047-2531
PROJECT VIKING LLC
(*Suby of* GRANITE FALLS ENERGY LLC) ★
501 Highway 212 W, Granite Falls, MN 56241-1308
Tel (320) 564-3324 *Founded/Ownrshp* 2004
Sales 115.6MM^E *EMP* 48^E
SIC 1321 Ethane (natural) production
Prin: Roland J Fagen

D-U-N-S 05-491-1964
PROJECT WORLDWIDE INC (MI)
3600 Giddings Rd, Auburn Hills, MI 48326-1515
Tel (248) 475-8863 *Founded/Ownrshp* 1938, 2014
Sales 269.4MM^E *EMP* 1,700^E
SIC 7311 Advertising agencies
CEO: Robert G Vallee Jr
**Pr:* Laurence S Vallee
**CEO:* Joost Dop
**CFO:* David Drews
Sr VP: Brian Bartkowiak
Sr VP: Peter Lambousis
**Prin:* Ben Taylor
Mng Dir: Achim Reinhuber
Snr Mgr: Dave Yonkos

PROJECT X
See TRUE TEMPER SPORTS INC

PROJECTOR POINT.COM
See TIERNEY BROTHERS INC

PROJISTICS
See NAGARRO INC

D-U-N-S 19-073-0742
PROKARMA INC
222 S 15th St Ste 505n, Omaha, NE 68102-1693
Tel (877) 527-6226 *Founded/Ownrshp* 2004
Sales 102.8MM^E *EMP* 594
SIC 7379 Computer related consulting services
COO: Manish Mehta
**Pr:* Vivek Kumar
**CFO:* Craig Stack
**Chf Mktg O:* Jeff Miller
Ex VP: Jim Vanettinger
VP: Tom Mitchell
Snr Sftwr: Kishore Thotakuri
**CTO:* Vijay Ijju
IT Man: Suresh Kumar
Sftwr Eng: Areef Ali
Sftwr Eng: Jozeph Bautista

PROLAMINA
See JEN-COAT INC

D-U-N-S 96-881-2557 IMP
PROLAMINA CORP
(*Suby of* PROAMPAC INTERMEDIATE INC) ★
132 N Elm St, Westfield, MA 01085-1604
Tel (413) 562-2315 *Founded/Ownrshp* 2015
Sales 412.6MM^E *EMP* 750
SIC 2671 5199 Paper coated or laminated for packaging; Packaging materials
CEO: Gregory R Tucker
COO: Tim French
CFO: Eric Bradford
VP: Matt Conlin
VP: Paul Schabow
Exec: Greg Davidson
Tech Mgr: Corey Peterson

D-U-N-S 80-971-7085
PROLER SOUTHWEST INC
METAL MANAGEMENT SOUTHWEST
(*Suby of* SIMS METAL MANAGEMENT) ★
90 Hirsch Rd, Houston, TX 77020-6332
Tel (713) 671-2900 *Founded/Ownrshp* 1997
Sales 141.3MM^E *EMP* 190
SIC 5051 Metals service centers & offices; Iron & steel (ferrous) products; Miscellaneous nonferrous products
Pr: Rafael Carrasco
**Ch Bd:* Ronnie Proler
**Pr:* Bill Proler
**Pr:* Steve Skurnac
**CEO:* Galdino Claro
**Treas:* Robert C Larry
**VP:* Joel Helton
**VP:* Amit N Patel
**VP:* Tom Whitman

D-U-N-S 07-923-3393
PROLIFICS APPLICATION SERVICES INC
(*Suby of* PROLIFICS CORPORATION LIMITED)
24025 Park Sorrento # 405, Calabasas, CA 91302-4018
Tel (646) 201-4967 *Founded/Ownrshp* 2008
Sales 97.2MM^E *EMP* 335
SIC 7379
CEO: Satya Bolli
**Pr:* Sam Ourfalian
Sr VP: Mark McNamara
VP: Alan Shemelya

D-U-N-S 02-128-8089
PROLIFICS INC
(*Suby of* PROLIFICS APPLICATION SERVICES INC) ★
24025 Park Sorrento # 450, Calabasas, CA 91302-4018
Tel (212) 267-7722 *Founded/Ownrshp* 2008
Sales 90.0MM^E *EMP* 295
SIC 7379 7371 Computer related consulting services; Computer software development
CEO: Satya Bolli
**Pr:* Sam Ourfalian
VP: K Ewanyk
VP Mktg: Jason Harvey

D-U-N-S 78-711-3310
PROLOGIC DISTRIBUTION SERVICES (EAST) LLC
6016 Brookvale Ln 110b, Knoxville, TN 37919-4003
Tel (865) 584-9765 *Founded/Ownrshp* 2005
Sales 43.9MM^E *EMP* 2,093
SIC 4212 4213 Local trucking, without storage; Trucking, except local

D-U-N-S 01-966-1125
PROLOGIC REDEMPTION SOLUTIONS INC
2121 Rosecrans Ave, El Segundo, CA 90245-4743
Tel (310) 322-7774 *Founded/Ownrshp* 2008
Sales 39.5MM^E *EMP* 2,200
SIC 7389 Coupon redemption service
CEO: William Atkinson
Pr: Paul Cooley
CFO: Robb Warwick
Chf Cred: Kelly Fuller
Chf Mktg O: Ross Ely
Ex VP: John McCurry

D-U-N-S 87-806-4807 IMP
■ PROLOGIS
(*Suby of* PROLOGIS LP) ★
4545 Airport Way, Denver, CO 80239-9801
Tel (303) 375-9292 *Founded/Ownrshp* 2011
Sales 907.5MM^E *EMP* 1,100
SIC 6798 6552 Real estate investment trusts; Land subdividers & developers, commercial
CEO: Hamid R Moghadam
Genl Pt: Stuart Phillips
Pr: Margan Mitchell
**CEO:* Gary E Anderson
CEO: Eugene F Reilly
**CFO:* Thomas S Olinger
**CFO:* William E Sullivan
Ofcr: Eduardo Gonzalez
Ofcr: Darin Manning
**Ofcr:* Edward S Nekritz
Ex VP: Mike Del Santo
Sr VP: Michele Hromish
Sr VP: Douglas A Kiersey Jr
Sr VP: W Scott Lamson
Sr VP: Michael Mercier
Sr VP: Neville D E Teagarden
VP: Tim Arndt
VP: John Aviles
VP: Wayne Barrett
VP: Gregory Bauer
VP: Steven Callaway

D-U-N-S 11-293-7446
▲ PROLOGIS INC
Bay 1 Pier 1, San Francisco, CA 94111
Tel (415) 394-9000 *Founded/Ownrshp* 1997
Sales 2.2MMM *EMP* 1,555
Tkr Sym PLD *Exch* NYS
SIC 6798 Real estate investment trusts
Ch Bd: Hamid R Moghadam
CEO: Gary E Anderson
CEO: Eugene F Reilly
CFO: Thomas S Olinger
Sr VP: Jeremy Giles
VP: Tim Arndt
VP: Irene Duran
VP: Christina Jackson
VP: Grace Leung
VP: Richard Malloy
VP: Richard Shleymovich
Board of Directors: George L Fotiades, Christine N Garvey, Lydia H Kennard, J Michael Losh, Irving F Lyons III, David P O'connor, Jeffrey L Skelton, Carl B Webb, William D Zollars

D-U-N-S 14-073-7490
■ PROLOGIS LP
(*Suby of* PROLOGIS INC) ★
Bay 1 Pier 1, San Francisco, CA 94111
Tel (415) 394-9000 *Founded/Ownrshp* 1997
Sales 2.2MMM *EMP* 1,505
Accts Kpmg Llp Denver Colorado
SIC 6798 6799 Real estate investment trusts; Real estate investors, except property operators
Ch Bd: Hamid R Moghadam
CFO: Thomas S Olinger
Board of Directors: William D Zollars, George L Fotiades, Christine N Garvey, Lydia H Kennard, J Michael Losh, Irving F Lyons III, David P O'connor, Jeffrey L Skelton, D Michael Steuert, Carl B Webb

PROLOGISTIX
See STAFFING SOLUTIONS SOUTHWEST INC

PROLOGISTIX
See STAFFING SOLUTIONS OF CENTRAL TEXAS INC

D-U-N-S 78-694-5019
PROLOGIX DISTRIBUTION SERVICES (WEST) LLC
3995 70th Ave E Ste B, Fife, WA 98424-3616
Tel (253) 952-7150 *Founded/Ownrshp* 2006
Sales 221.8MM^E *EMP* 2,200
SIC 5199 General merchandise, non-durable
Exec: Michal Weisinger
Opers Mgr: Hank Miller

PROMEDICA
See ST LUKES HOSPITAL

D-U-N-S 19-707-3398
PROMEDICA HEALTH SYSTEMS INC
1801 Richards Rd, Toledo, OH 43607-1037
Tel (419) 469-3800 *Founded/Ownrshp* 1986
Sales 525.2MM *EMP* 8,970
Accts Deloitte Tax Llp Indianapolis
SIC 8062 6324 8351 8741 General medical & surgical hospitals; Health maintenance organization (HMO), insurance only; Child day care services; Management services
CEO: Alan W Brass
Pr: Jeremy Zeisloft
CFO: Allen Fatler
Ex VP: Tom Dellaflora
Ex VP: Terri McLain
VP: Tom Borer
VP: Mike Ruhlen
VP: Jered Wilson
Adm Dir: Vicki Boes
Adm Dir: Paula Grieb
Ex Dir: Matthew Gilroy

D-U-N-S 05-428-2053
PROMEDICA NORTH REGION INC
(*Suby of* PROMEDICA HEALTH SYSTEMS INC) ★
818 Riverside Ave, Adrian, MI 49221-1446
Tel (517) 265-0390 *Founded/Ownrshp* 1996
Sales 110.2MM^E *EMP* 807
Accts Deloitte Tax Llp Indianapolis
SIC 8011 Orthopedic physician
Pr: Greg Corbett
VP: James Wheeler

PROMEDICA TOLEDO HOSPITAL
See TOLEDO HOSPITAL

D-U-N-S 08-985-5696 IMP
PROMEGA CORP (WI)
2800 Woods Hollow Rd, Fitchburg, WI 53711-5399
Tel (608) 274-4330 *Founded/Ownrshp* 1980
Sales 356.4MM^E *EMP* 782
SIC 2836 Biological products, except diagnostic
Ch Bd: William A Linton
**Sr VP:* Martin Rosenberg
**VP:* Andrew Bertera
**VP:* Randall Dimond
**VP:* Tom Evans
**VP:* Laura Francis
**VP:* Brenda Furlow
VP: Herly Karlen
VP: Thomas Livelli
**VP:* Ruth Lundy
**VP:* Edward Pahuski
**VP:* W Gary Tarpley
**VP:* Lisa Witte
Exec: Sharon Ferderer
Board of Directors: Donald Duncan, Richard Pauls, Peter Tong

D-U-N-S 14-930-0381 IMP/EXP
PROMETHEAN INC
PROMETHEAN WORLD
(*Suby of* PROMETHEAN (HOLDINGS) LIMITED)
1165 Sanctuary Pkwy # 400, Alpharetta, GA 30009-4838
Tel (678) 762-1500 *Founded/Ownrshp* 2002
Sales 121.0MM^E *EMP* 227
SIC 5049 5045 School supplies; Computers, peripherals & software
Ch Bd: Graham Howe
**Pr:* Mark Elliott
**CEO:* Jean-Yves Charlier
**CEO:* Jim Marshall
**CFO:* Ian Baxter
**CFO:* Neil Johnson
**Ch:* Philip Rowley
Chf Mktg O: Iwan Streichenberger
Sr VP: Ken Uhlig
VP: Vincent Jungels
Exec: Julia Landon
Board of Directors: Judy Verses, Jackie Yeaney

PROMETHEAN WORLD
See PROMETHEAN INC

D-U-N-S 96-700-0860
PROMETHEUS LABORATORIES INC
(*Suby of* NESTLE HEALTH SCIENCE SA)
9410 Carroll Park Dr, San Diego, CA 92121-5201
Tel (858) 824-0895 *Founded/Ownrshp* 2011
Sales 178.5MM^E *EMP* 405
SIC 2834 8011 Pharmaceutical preparations; Offices & clinics of medical doctors
CEO: Lisa A Miller
**Pr:* Joseph Limber
**CFO:* Mark Spring
**CFO:* Peter Westlake
**Ofcr:* Anthony J Yost
**Sr VP:* Peter Heseltine
**VP:* Frederick Fletcher
**VP:* William Franzblau
VP: David Furlano
**VP:* Beth Kriegel
VP: Tharak RAO
**VP:* Sharat Singh
**VP:* Bruce M Wagman
**VP:* Toni L Wayne
**VP:* David Williams
Assoc Dir: Subra Mallampalli

D-U-N-S 09-238-9399
PROMETRIC INC
PROMETRIC TESTING CENTER
(*Suby of* E T S) ★
1501 S Clinton St # 1200, Baltimore, MD 21224-5732
Tel (443) 455-8000 *Founded/Ownrshp* 2007
Sales 380.6MM^E *EMP* 2,077
SIC 8748 8741 Testing service, educational or personnel; Management services
Pr: Michael Brannick
**CFO:* Chris Derr
**Sr VP:* Paul Forrester
VP: Erika Bloss
VP: Jean Pierron
Dir IT: Eric Rokke
Dir IT: Takao Yamaguchi
Sys Mgr: Steven Walk
Snr Mgr: Kevin P Kane

PROMETRIC TESTING CENTER
See PROMETRIC INC

D-U-N-S 93-377-1545
PROMINA HEALTH SYSTEM INC
2727 Paces Ferry Rd Se, Atlanta, GA 30339-4053
Tel (404) 541-1111 *Founded/Ownrshp* 1994
Sales 34.9MM^E *EMP* 1,700
SIC 8741 8062 Hospital management; General medical & surgical hospitals
Ch Bd: Duane Blair
**Pr:* Gordon L Church
**CFO:* Jim Eyerman
VP: Mark Mixer
VP: Debra Peterson-Smith
Dir Rx: Rex Parker
Advt Dir: Pamela Frazier

D-U-N-S 13-579-8580
PROMISE HEALTHCARE INC
999 Yamato Rd Ste 300, Boca Raton, FL 33431-4476
Tel (561) 869-3100 *Founded/Ownrshp* 2014
Sales 722.6MM^E *EMP* 4,000
SIC 8741 Hospital management
CEO: Peter R Baronoff
**Pr:* Richard A Gold
**CFO:* James Hopwood
Ofcr: Janet Thigpen
Ex VP: David Armstrong
**Ex VP:* Bryan Day
**Ex VP:* Brian Dunn
Sr VP: Trevor Klein
Sr VP: Nancy F Spivack
Sr VP: Mary Topper
VP: Mike Hibbard
VP: Nish Patel
Dir Bus: Kenny Peterson

PROMISE REGIONAL MEDICAL CENTE
See HEALTH CARE INC

D-U-N-S 01-997-3769
PROMMIS SOLUTIONS LLC
400 Northridge Rd, Atlanta, GA 30350-3312
Tel (800) 275-7171 *Founded/Ownrshp* 2006
Sales NA *EMP* 1,350^E
SIC 6111 Federal Home Loan Mortgage Corporation
CEO: Charles T Piper
CFO: George Dunaway
CFO: Daniel Weinblatt
Trst: Ed Hill
Sr VP: Thomas A Gillis
VP: Dan Hoover
VP Opers: Monica Mora
Sls Dir: Steven Collier

D-U-N-S 10-797-9093
■ PROMONTORY FINANCIAL GROUP LLC
(*Suby of* IBM) ★
801 17th St Nw Ste 1100, Washington, DC 20006-3922
Tel (202) 384-1200 *Founded/Ownrshp* 2016
Sales 259.0MM *EMP* 500
SIC 8742 Financial consultant
CEO: Eugene A Ludwig
**CFO:* Charles McDonough
VP: Christopher Riti
Creative D: Robb Stout
**CTO:* David Countryman
QA Dir: Beverley Legg
Mktg Mgr: Sophie Hanrahan
Snr Mgr: Christine Link
Snr Mgr: Julie Williams

D-U-N-S 12-744-7717
PROMONTORY INTERFINANCIAL NETWORK LLC
1300 17th St N Ste 1800, Arlington, VA 22209-3810
Tel (703) 292-3400 *Founded/Ownrshp* 2002
Sales 135.0MM *EMP* 184
Accts Kpmg Llp Mclean Va
SIC 7389 Financial services
**CFO:* John Couric
Ofcr: Susan Gayle
Ofcr: Arun Shastri
Sr VP: Phil Battey
VP: Brian Christie
Dir Risk M: Beth Pile
Creative D: Amy Manship
Mng Dir: Robert Hartheimer
Mng Dir: Carolyn Tobin
Mng Dir: Richard Walter
Mng Dir: Rusty Wright

PROMOTING SPCIALIZED CARE HLTH
See PSCH INC

PROMOTION IN MOTION COMPANIES
See PROMOTION IN MOTION INC

D-U-N-S 04-931-4511 IMP/EXP
PROMOTION IN MOTION INC
PROMOTION IN MOTION COMPANIES
25 Commerce Dr, Allendale, NJ 07401-1617
Tel (201) 962-8530 *Founded/Ownrshp* 1986
Sales 181.7MM^E *EMP* 425
SIC 2064 5441 5145 2066 Candy & other confectionery products; Candy, nut & confectionery stores; Confectionery; Chocolate & cocoa products
Pr: Michael G Rosenberg
**CFO:* Robert Purcell
Ex VP: Joseph Vittoria
VP: Ellen Dale
VP: Jim Finelli
VP: David Fleischer
VP: Larue Rick
VP: Keith Von Zup
Dir IT: Robert Lascar
Ql Cn Mgr: Margarita Rugeles
Natl Sales: Jody King

D-U-N-S 86-878-8972
PROMPTCARE COMPANIES INC
PRO2 RESPIRATORY SERVICES
741 3rd Ave, King of Prussia, PA 19406-1409
Tel (610) 278-1623 *Founded/Ownrshp* 2008
Sales 373.6M^E *EMP* 2,800
SIC 8093 Respiratory health clinic
Prin: Mary Rose Simon
Genl Mgr: Lynn Allen
Genl Mgr: Scott Lea

D-U-N-S 00-234-4971
PROMUS HOTEL CORP (DE)
755 Crossover Ln, Memphis, TN 38117-4900
Tel (901) 374-5000 *Founded/Ownrshp* 1997
Sales 1.1MMM *EMP* 1,200
Accts Arthur Andersen Llp Memphis
SIC 7011 8741 6794 Hotels & motels; Hotel or motel management; Franchises, selling or licensing
Ch Bd: Norman P Blake Jr
Treas: William S Harrison
Ex VP: Daniel L Hale
Ex VP: J Kendall Huber
Ex VP: Thomas L Keltner
Ex VP: Peter Leddy
Ex VP: Steven D Porter
Ex VP: M Ann Rhoades
Ex VP: Thomas W Storey
VP: James T Harvey
VP: Si Sloman
VP: Greg Swearingen
Board of Directors: Jay Stein, John H Dasburg, Ronald Terry, Priscilla Florence, Peter V Ueberroth, Dale F Frey, Robert E Gregory Jr, Christopher W Hart, Michael W Michelson, John H Myers, C Warren Neel, Michael I Roth

D-U-N-S 94-860-5480
■ PROMUS HOTELS LLC
HOMEWOOD SUITES
(*Suby of* PROMUS OPERATING CO INC) ★
755 Crossover Ln, Memphis, TN 38117-4900
Tel (719) 265-6600 *Founded/Ownrshp* 1999
Sales 110.3MM^E *EMP* 7,140
SIC 7011 8741 6794 Hotels & motels; Hotel or motel management; Franchises, selling or licensing
Pr: Thomas Keltner
CFO: Dan Hale
VP: Steve Armitage
Genl Mgr: Charles Friend
Genl Mgr: Katie Henry
Genl Mgr: John Melstrom
CTO: John Flack
S&M/VP: Frank Passanante

D-U-N-S 88-442-7196 IMP
■ PROMUS OPERATING CO INC
(*Suby of* HILTON) ★
755 Crossover Ln, Memphis, TN 38117-4906
Tel (901) 374-5000 *Founded/Ownrshp* 1999
Sales 118.4MM^E *EMP* 7,140
SIC 7011 8741 6794 Hotels & motels; Hotel or motel management; Franchises, selling or licensing
Pr: Thomas L Keltner
Genl Mgr: Smith Branstad
Genl Mgr: Shannon Deraad
Genl Mgr: Rick Lutchman
Genl Mgr: Cassandra Macveagh
Genl Mgr: Matt Sease
Genl Mgr: Trevor Taggart
Genl Mgr: Tanya Yurko
IT Man: Douglas Sampson
Snr Mgr: Rochelle Raven

D-U-N-S 96-525-5334
PROMUTUAL GROUP INC
COVERYS
1 Financial Ctr Fl 13, Boston, MA 02111-2688
Tel (617) 330-1755 *Founded/Ownrshp* 1995
Sales NA *EMP* 405
Accts Pricewaterhousecoopers Llp
SIC 6321 8742 Health insurance carriers; Hospital & health services consultant
Pr: Gregg L Hanson Sr
CFO: John J Donehue
Sr VP: Ted Kelly
Sr VP: Mary Ursul
VP: Geri Amori
VP: Erin Bagley
VP: Tara Gibson
VP: Robert Hanscom
VP: Barry Manuel
VP: Veronica Matejko
VP: Barbara Staples
VP: Paul Traynor
VP: Joe Zorola
Dir Risk M: Annemarie Provencher

D-U-N-S 02-403-1118
PRONTO GENERAL AGENCY LTD (TX)
PRONTO INSURANCE
(*Suby of* PALLADIUM EQUITY PARTNERS IV LP) ★
805 Media Luna St Ste 100, Brownsville, TX 78520-4058
Tel (956) 574-9787 *Founded/Ownrshp* 2006, 2014
Sales NA *EMP* 300
SIC 6331 6361 7291 Automobile insurance; Title insurance; Tax return preparation services
Pr: Jorge Barzena
Mng Pt: Rafael Varela
VP: John Rappazco
VP Sls: Sasha Krauss

PRONTO INSURANCE
See PRONTO GENERAL AGENCY LTD

D-U-N-S 13-572-0063
▲ PROOFPOINT INC
892 Ross Dr, Sunnyvale, CA 94089-1443
Tel (408) 517-4710 *Founded/Ownrshp* 2002
Sales 265.4MM *EMP* 1,203^E
Tkr Sym PFPT *Exch* NGM
SIC 7371 Custom computer programming services; Computer software systems analysis & design, custom; Computer software development & applications
CEO: Gary Steele
Ch Bd: Eric Hahn
CFO: Paul Auvil
CFO: Sydney Carey
Ex VP: David Knight
Ex VP: Tracey Newell
Sr VP: Darren Lee
CTO: Gregory Shapiro
Board of Directors: Anthony Bettencourt, Dana Evan, Jonathan Feiber, Douglas Garn, Kevin Harvey, R Scott Herren

D-U-N-S 06-642-4106
PROOVE MEDICAL LABORATORIES INC
15326 Elton Pkwy, Irvine, CA 92618
Tel (949) 427-5303 *Founded/Ownrshp* 2012
Sales 201.0MM *EMP* 175
SIC 8071 Biological laboratory
CEO: Brian Meshkin
**COO:* Sean Roddi
**CFO:* Russell Skibsted

D-U-N-S 83-449-6361
PROPAK LOGISTICS INC
1100 Garrison Ave, Fort Smith, AR 72901-2617
Tel (479) 478-7800 *Founded/Ownrshp* 2003
Sales 115.7MM *EMP* 1,400
Accts Bell Barclay & Company Plc F
SIC 7699 4731 Pallet repair; Freight forwarding
Pr: Steven W Clark
**CFO:* John Cooley
**Ex VP:* Justin Marshall
**Ex VP:* John Shaw
**VP:* Jim Jordan
VP: Kent Watson
Software D: Samuel Shores
Plnt Mgr: Kirk Chapman

D-U-N-S 82-784-9865
PROPEMAR INC
19101 Mystic Pointe Dr # 1709, Aventura, FL 33180-4518
Tel (954) 775-7002 *Founded/Ownrshp* 2006
Sales 118.0MM *EMP* 300
SIC 5146 Seafoods
Pr: Jorge Diaz
**VP Mktg:* Vivi Bonilla

D-U-N-S 82-940-9015
PROPER GROUP INTERNATIONAL INC
PROPER TOOLING
13870 E 11 Mile Rd, Warren, MI 48089-1471
Tel (586) 779-8787 *Founded/Ownrshp* 1971
Sales 108.8MM^E *EMP* 306

SIC 3089 Automotive parts, plastic
Pr: Geoff O'Brien
**CFO:* Mark Rusch
Dir IT: Mark Obrien

PROPER TOOLING
See PROPER GROUP INTERNATIONAL INC

PROPERTY AND CASUALTY INSUR CO
See TENNESSEE FARMERS MUTUAL INSURANCE CO

D-U-N-S 19-519-6154 IMP
PROPETRO SERVICES INC
(*Suby of* PROPETRO HOLDING CORP)
1706 S Midkiff Rd Ste B, Midland, TX 79701-8844
Tel (432) 688-0012 *Founded/Ownrshp* 2013
Sales 349.6MM[E] *EMP* 300[E]
SIC 1381 Service well drilling
VP: Dale Redman
**Treas:* John Lavoi

D-U-N-S 83-053-0767
PROPEX HOLDING LLC
(*Suby of* WAYZATA INVESTMENT PARTNERS LLC) ★
1110 Market St Ste 300, Chattanooga, TN 37402-2253
Tel (800) 621-1273 *Founded/Ownrshp* 2009
Sales 215.3MM[E] *EMP* 2,500[E]
SIC 6719 2221 2297 2262 2211 Investment holding companies, except banks; Polypropylene broadwoven fabrics; Nonwoven fabrics; Finishing plants, manmade fiber & silk fabrics; Broadwoven fabric mills, cotton
CFO: Martin T Tim De Vries
**CFO:* Mark J Thomas
CFO: Dan Zimmerely
**Treas:* Steve Carr
**Ex VP:* Ralph Bruno
**Ex VP:* Randal D Powell
VP: Rick Hodges
VP: Steve Paul
Plnt Mgr: Stan Brant
Plnt Mgr: Noah Nichols
Sls Mgr: Dave Orzel

D-U-N-S 83-054-3505 IMP/EXP
PROPEX OPERATING CO LLC
(*Suby of* PROPEX HOLDING LLC) ★
1110 Market St Ste 300, Chattanooga, TN 37402-2253
Tel (423) 855-1466 *Founded/Ownrshp* 2009
Sales 652.5MM[E] *EMP* 1,539
SIC 2221 Broadwoven fabric mills, manmade
Pr: Michael Gorey
**CFO:* Mark Thomas
Ex VP: Randal D Powell
VP: John W Goers
VP: Craig Martin
Off Mgr: Carol Keith
Plnt Mgr: Charlie Stiner
VP Sls: Robert F Dahl
Manager: Patrick Greer
Manager: David Hale
Snr Mgr: Jeff Adams

D-U-N-S 82-520-7863
PROPHET BRAND STRATEGY
1 Bush St Fl 7, San Francisco, CA 94104-4413
Tel (415) 677-0909 *Founded/Ownrshp* 1992
Sales 100.0MM *EMP* 360
Accts Pricewaterhousecoopers San Fr
SIC 8742 Marketing consulting services
Pr: Michael Dunn
V Ch: David A Ker
Pr: Rune Gustafson
**COO:* Simon Marlow
CTO: Paul Wang
Opers Mgr: Laurie Santos
Mktg Mgr: Amanda Nizzere

D-U-N-S 01-216-8448
PROPHET EQUITY LP
1460 Main St Ste 200, Southlake, TX 76092-7651
Tel (817) 898-1500 *Founded/Ownrshp* 2008
Sales 984.4MM[E] *EMP* 2,215
SIC 6282 Investment advisory service
CEO: Ross Gatlin
VP: Michael Sullivan
Genl Couns: David Rex

PROPN RAIL
See D & I SILICA LLC

D-U-N-S 01-231-7528 EXP
PROPORTION FOODS LLC
4020 Compton Ave, Los Angeles, CA 90011-2228
Tel (323) 231-7777 *Founded/Ownrshp* 2009
Sales 108.1MM[E] *EMP* 278[E]
Accts Meloni Hribal Tratner Llp Woo
SIC 2099 Food preparations
Genl Mgr: Brian Levy

D-U-N-S 09-013-5989 IMP/EXP
PROPPER INTERNATIONAL INC
(*Suby of* PII INC) ★
308 Km 0 6 375 Clljon Fas, Cabo Rojo, PR 00623
Tel (787) 254-8020 *Founded/Ownrshp* 1967
Sales 254.0MM *EMP* 1,700[E]
SIC 2311 2326 Military uniforms, men's & youths': purchased materials; Work uniforms
Owner: Earl Weinman
**Pr:* Tom Kellim
**COO:* John Minard
VP: Derick Deliv
Genl Mgr: Jose Mahia

D-U-N-S 11-871-7529
PROQUEST LLC
(*Suby of* C I G) ★
789 E Eisenhower Pkwy, Ann Arbor, MI 48108-3218
Tel (734) 761-4700 *Founded/Ownrshp* 2007
Sales 430.5MM[E] *EMP* 1,502
SIC 7375 Information retrieval services; On-line data base information retrieval
Ch: Andy Snyder
**CEO:* Kurt Sanford
**CFO:* Jonathan Collins
**Sr VP:* John Chirapurath
Sr VP: James Holmes
Sr VP: Kristi Marchbanks
Sr VP: Kevin Sayar
**Sr VP:* Kellie Teal-Guess
VP: Simon Beale
VP: Susan Brock
VP: Chris Cowan
VP: Michael Hirsch
VP: Lynda James-Gilboe
VP: John Law
VP: Vaughn Parsons
VP: Roger Retke
VP: Tony Rummans
VP: Kevin Stehr
VP: Tiffany Williamson

D-U-N-S 01-544-1970 IMP
PROS CHOICE BEAUTY CARE INC
35 Sawgrass Dr Ste 4, Bellport, NY 11713-1579
Tel (631) 803-3200 *Founded/Ownrshp* 2000, 1996
Sales 220.0MM *EMP* 900
SIC 5122 Cosmetics, perfumes & hair products
Ch Bd: Ruth Nussdorf
**Pr:* Michael Ross
**CFO:* Joseph Gewolb
**VP:* May Chormey
Assoc Dir: Javier Morales

D-U-N-S 80-193-6746
▲ PROS HOLDINGS INC
3100 Main St Ste 900, Houston, TX 77002-9320
Tel (713) 335-5151 *Founded/Ownrshp* 1985
Sales 168.2MM *EMP* 1,033[E]
Accts Pricewaterhousecoopers Llp Sa
Tkr Sym PRO *Exch* NYS
SIC 7371 7372 Custom computer programming services; Prepackaged software
Pr: Andres D Reiner
**Ch Bd:* William Russell
CFO: Stefan B Schulz
Ofcr: Wagner Williams
Ofcr: Craig Zawada
Sr VP: Ajay Damani
Sr VP: Mike Jahoda
Sr VP: Chris Jones
Sr VP: Jeff Robinson
Sr VP: Benson Yuen
Dir Sec: Tim Girgenti
Board of Directors: Ellen Keszler, Greg B Petersen, Leslie J Rechan, Timothy V Williams, Mariette M Woestemeyer, Ronald F Woestemeyer

D-U-N-S 07-854-6284
■ PROS INC
(*Suby of* PROS HOLDINGS INC) ★
3100 Main St Ste 900, Houston, TX 77002-9320
Tel (713) 335-5151 *Founded/Ownrshp* 2001
Sales 162.8MM[E] *EMP* 1,000
SIC 7372 Prepackaged software
Pr: Andres D Reiner
**COO:* Blair Crump
**CFO:* Stefon Schultz
Chf Mktg O: Patrick Schneidau
Ex VP: Stefan Schulz
**Ex VP:* Ron Woestemeyer
Sr VP: John Billings
Sr VP: Rob Christenson
Sr VP: Kevin Wholey
Sr VP: Wagner Williams
VP: Brent Burns
VP: Ajay Damani
VP: Chris Mills
VP: Jorge Quinones
VP: John Salch
Exec: Kim Ferrarie
Board of Directors: Leslie J Rechan

D-U-N-S 02-883-1824
PROS MARKET INC
PHOENIX RANCH MARKET
1700 S De Soto Pl Ste A, Ontario, CA 91761-8060
Tel (909) 930-9552 *Founded/Ownrshp* 1976
Sales 172.0MM[E] *EMP* 1,575
SIC 5411 Grocery stores, independent
CEO: Michael A Provenzano Jr
Sales Asso: Helen Barnes

PROSAFE
See WOOD GROUP PSN INC

PROSAFE
See ELKHORN CONSTRUCTION INC

D-U-N-S 62-264-0969
PROSERV OPERATIONS INC
13105 Nw Fwy Ste 250, Houston, TX 77040-6313
Tel (281) 407-2405 *Founded/Ownrshp* 2013
Sales 8.1MMM[E] *EMP* 1,700
SIC 1389

D-U-N-S 61-030-8074
PROSIGHT SPECIALTY INSURANCE GROUP INC
412 Mount Kemble Ave 300c, Morristown, NJ 07960-6666
Tel (973) 532-1900 *Founded/Ownrshp* 2010
Sales NA *EMP* 159
SIC 6351 6331 Surety insurance; Fire, marine & casualty insurance
Pr: George R Trumbull
Pr: Andreas Graham
**CFO:* Thomas J Iacopelli
CFO: Anthony Piszel
**Chf Cred:* George Sutcliffe
Ofcr: Bob Bailey
Ofcr: Frank Bosse
Ofcr: Larry Hannon
Ofcr: Paul Kush
Ofcr: Frank Papalia
**Ex VP:* Michael P Gabriele
**Ex VP:* Paul J Hart
**Ex VP:* Timothy B McAndrew
**Ex VP:* Edwin A Skoch
**Ex VP:* Glenn R Yanoff
**Sr VP:* Diane Votinelli
VP: Bob Hamburger
Dir Risk M: Vivek Syal

D-U-N-S 00-169-7747 IMP
PROSKAUER ROSE LLP
11 Times Sq Fl 17, New York, NY 10036-8299
Tel (212) 969-3000 *Founded/Ownrshp* 1878
Sales 226.9MM[E] *EMP* 1,400
SIC 8111 General practice attorney, lawyer
Ch Bd: Allen I Fagin
Pt: Alicia J Batts
Pt: Caroline Chabrerie
Pt: Jim Chapman
Pt: Martin J Oppenheimer
Pt: Jonathan H Oram
Pt: Anthony Pacheco
Pt: Monica Shilling
Pt: Janice Smith
Pt: Ivan Taback
Pt: Yuval Tal
Mng Pt: Bruce L Lieb
Trst: Robert Campbell

D-U-N-S 03-089-1626
PROSPECT AIRPORT SERVICES INC
2130 S Wolf Rd Fl 2, Des Plaines, IL 60018-1932
Tel (847) 299-3636 *Founded/Ownrshp* 1966
Sales 328.0MM[E] *EMP* 5,300
SIC 4581 7349 Aircraft maintenance & repair services; Aircraft servicing & repairing; Janitorial service, contract basis
Pr: Vicki Strobel
Pr: Michael Durocher
**COO:* James Wajda
Sr VP: Ron Claypool
**Sr VP:* Michael Strobel
**VP:* Mary Strobel
Dir Risk M: Jo Storie
Mng Dir: Terry Hoffman
Genl Mgr: Tim Fisher
Genl Mgr: Tariq Mohamed
Genl Mgr: Paul Verdi

D-U-N-S 19-943-1896
▲ PROSPECT CAPITAL CORP
10 E 40th St Fl 42, New York, NY 10016-0301
Tel (212) 448-0702 *Founded/Ownrshp* 2004
Sales 791.9MM *EMP* 61
Accts Bdo Usa Llp New York New Yo
Tkr Sym PSEC *Exch* NGS
SIC 6726 Investment offices
Ch Bd: John F Barry III
**Pr:* M Grier Eliasek
CFO: Brian H Oswald

D-U-N-S 03-411-9225
PROSPECT CHARTERCARE LLC (RI)
CHARTERCARE HEALTH PARTNERS
825 Chalkstone Ave, Providence, RI 02908-4728
Tel (401) 456-2001 *Founded/Ownrshp* 2013
Sales 21.8MM *EMP* 1,206[E]
Accts Kpmg Llp Boston Ma
SIC 8082 Home health care services
CEO: Kenneth H Belcher
**CFO:* Michael E Conklin
Ofcr: Jason Marsden
**Sr VP:* Kimberly A Oconnell
VP: R Otis Brown
VP: Brandon M Klar
VP: Darleen L Souza
**CIO:* Susan Cerrone Abely
HC Dir: Sandra Yarumian

D-U-N-S 07-568-1429
PROSPECT CHARTERCARE SJHSRI LLC
ST JOSEPH HOSP FOR SPCLTY CARE
(*Suby of* CHARTERCARE HEALTH PARTNERS) ★
200 High Service Ave, North Providence, RI 02904-5113
Tel (401) 456-3000 *Founded/Ownrshp* 2014
Sales 33.8MM[E] *EMP* 1,865
SIC 8062 General medical & surgical hospitals
Pr: Thomas Hughes
CFO: Michael Conklin Jr
IT Man: Dick Sepe
Doctor: Steven Weisblatt

D-U-N-S 15-729-3614
PROSPECT CROZER LLC
CROZER-KEYSTONE HEALTH SYSTEM
(*Suby of* PROSPECT MEDICAL HOLDINGS INC) ★
100 W Sproul Rd, Springfield, PA 19064-2033
Tel (610) 338-8200 *Founded/Ownrshp* 2016
Sales 97.5MM[E] *EMP* 7,100
Accts Withumsmithbrown Pc Morristow
SIC 8741 Hospital management; Nursing & personal care facility management
Pr: Joan K Richards
Pr: Donna M McGinnis
**COO:* Patrick J Gavin
CFO: Richard Bennet
**CFO:* Philip J Ryan
Ofcr: Paul McLaughlin
Ofcr: Dale Schumacher
Chf Nrs Of: Robert Haffey
Nurse Mgr: Mary T Kopp
QA Dir: John Harper
Doctor: Christine Donohue-Henry

D-U-N-S 00-955-5137 IMP
PROSPECT ENTERPRISES INC
AMERICAN FISH AND SEAFOOD
625 Kohler St, Los Angeles, CA 90021-1023
Tel (213) 599-5700 *Founded/Ownrshp* 1971
Sales 296.1MM[E] *EMP* 350
SIC 5146 2092 Fish, fresh; Fish, frozen, unpackaged; Seafoods; Fresh or frozen packaged fish
Ch Bd: Ernest Y Doizaki
**Pr:* Jack King
**CFO:* Paula Eberhardt
IT Man: Shawn Sisler

D-U-N-S 01-281-0201
PROSPECT MEDICAL HOLDINGS INC
3415 S Sepulveda Blvd # 9, Los Angeles, CA 90034-6060
Tel (310) 943-4500 *Founded/Ownrshp* 2010
Sales 648.7MM[E] *EMP* 9,269[E]
SIC 8011 Health maintenance organization
Ch Bd: Samuel S Lee
**CFO:* Mike Heather
**Ex VP:* Linda Hodges
VP: Rosa Catalano
VP: Cheryl Hurst
VP: Mark Marten
Prgrm Mgr: Norma Tirado
Snr Ntwrk: Mauricio Faya
Dir IT: Yenvi Tran
Mktg Dir: Jeanette Cruz

D-U-N-S 00-416-3481 IMP
PROSPECT MOLD & DIE CO (OH)
1100 Main St, Cuyahoga Falls, OH 44221-4922
Tel (330) 929-3311 *Founded/Ownrshp* 1945
Sales 94.7MM[E] *EMP* 100
SIC 5084 3544 Industrial machinery & equipment; Forms (molds), for foundry & plastics working machinery
CEO: Bruce W Wright
**Pr:* Brandon Wenzlik
COO: Jane Deaton
**CFO:* Thomas M Orr
VP: John Bolam
**VP:* Jeff Glick
Sls Mgr: Dave Glavic

D-U-N-S 00-291-5887
PROSPECT MORTGAGE LLC
15301 Ventura Blvd D300, Sherman Oaks, CA 91403-3102
Tel (818) 981-0606 *Founded/Ownrshp* 1999
Sales NA *EMP* 1,700
SIC 6163 Mortgage brokers arranging for loans, using money of others
Ch Bd: Michael J Williams
Mng Pt: Ron Bergum
Pr: Richard D Powers
COO: Amy Brandt
CFO: Sandra E Bell
CFO: Mark Szczpaniak
Ex VP: Joseph J Grassi III
Ex VP: Gary Meek
Sr VP: Cindy Hampton
Sr VP: Virginia Martinez
VP: Robert B Pothier
VP: Steven E Wells

D-U-N-S 62-344-1883
PROSPER MARKETPLACE INC
221 Main St Fl 3, San Francisco, CA 94105-1911
Tel (415) 593-5400 *Founded/Ownrshp* 2005
Sales NA *EMP* 231[E]
Accts Deloitte & Touche Llp San Fra
SIC 6163 Loan brokers
CEO: Aaron Vermut
Pr: Ronald Suber
COO: Joshua M Tonderys
CFO: David Kimball
CFO: Xiaopei Lee
**Ch:* Stephen P Vermut
Chf Mktg O: Cheryl Law
Ofcr: Alexandra Crocco
Ex VP: Kunal Kaul
Dir Soc: Matt Seely
Snr Sftwr: Scott Erickson
Board of Directors: Christopher Bishiko, David R Golob, Patrick W Grady, Nigel Morris

D-U-N-S 01-288-2481
▲ PROSPERITY BANCSHARES INC
4295 San Felipe St, Houston, TX 77027-2942
Tel (281) 269-7199 *Founded/Ownrshp* 1983
Sales NA *EMP* 3,037[E]
Tkr Sym PB *Exch* NYS
SIC 6022 State commercial banks
Ch Bd: David Zalman
Pr: Edward Z Safady
CFO: David Hollaway
**V Ch Bd:* H E Timanus Jr
Ofcr: Bridgette Jones
Ex VP: Michael Epps
Ex VP: Mike Harris
Ex VP: Randy Hester
Ex VP: Charlotte M Rasche
VP: Rhonda Hamm
VP: Scott Voland
Board of Directors: James A Bouligny, W R Collier, Leah Henderson, Ned S Holmes, Jack Lord, William T Luedke IV, Perry Mueller Jr, Harrison Stafford II, Robert Steelhammer

D-U-N-S 00-493-0079
■ PROSPERITY BANK
FIRST VICTORIA NATIONAL BANK
(*Suby of* PROSPERITY BANCSHARES INC) ★
1301 N Mechanic St, El Campo, TX 77437-2633
Tel (979) 543-1426 *Founded/Ownrshp* 1997
Sales NA *EMP* 1,133
SIC 6022 State commercial banks
Ch Bd: David Zalman
**Ch Bd:* Tim Timanus
**Pr:* Bob Benter
COO: Patricia Moreno
**V Ch Bd:* Edward Z Safady
**Ofcr:* Theresa Hollaway
Ex VP: Robert Benter
**Ex VP:* Robert Dowdell
**Ex VP:* Charlie Norris
Ex VP: Charlotte Rasche
**Ex VP:* Downy Vickery
Sr VP: Sally Aman-Barnes
Sr VP: Ross Bishop
Sr VP: Heidi Carney
Sr VP: John Harrell
Sr VP: Steve Hilton
Sr VP: Julie Mikeska
Sr VP: Marilyn Morris
Sr VP: Randy Price
Sr VP: Dale Rahlfs
Sr VP: Katy C Ranch

D-U-N-S 01-371-4706
PROSPERITY FUNDING INC (NC)
200 S Andrews Ave 201c, Fort Lauderdale, FL 33301-1864
Tel (919) 954-0232 *Founded/Ownrshp* 2007
Sales NA *EMP* 11
SIC 6153 Working capital financing
Pr: Eric Feinstein
Chf Cred: William Elliott

D-U-N-S 03-457-5129
PROSPERITY LIFE INSURANCE GROUP
650 Madison Ave Fl 26, New York, NY 10022-1034
Tel (212) 223-5627 *Founded/Ownrshp* 2010
Sales NA *EMP* 101

SIC 6311 Life insurance
CEO: Anurag Chandra
Ex VP: Richard Soja
Sr VP: Martin Brauner
Sr VP: Jude Dibattista
Sr VP: Ray Hannan
Sr VP: Kevin Igoe
Sr VP: Sean Upton
VP: Erin Brown
VP: Janet Guerrini
VP: Mark Jones
VP: Barbara Kenyon
VP: Gary Schmidt

D-U-N-S 79-234-0189
PROSYS INC
(*Suby of* ACS ACQUISITION CORP) ★
6575 The Corners Pkwy # 300, Norcross, GA 30092-3312
Tel (678) 268-1300 *Founded/Ownrshp* 2011
Sales 972.8MM^E *EMP* 360
SIC 5045 7374 Computers, peripherals & software; Computers; Computer software; Data processing & preparation
CEO: John Paget
**CFO:* Warren Barnes
Snr Ntwrk: Erick Pedersen

D-U-N-S 11-165-1469
PROSYS INFORMATION SYSTEMS INC
PIVOT TECHNOLOGY SOLUTIONS
(*Suby of* PROSYS INC) ★
6575 The Corners Pkwy # 300, Norcross, GA 30092-3312
Tel (678) 268-1300 *Founded/Ownrshp* 1997
Sales 710.2MM^E *EMP* 300
SIC 5045 7373 Computer peripheral equipment; Computer system selling services
CEO: Michelle Clery
**CEO:* Ted Glahn
CFO: Holly Anderson
**CFO:* Kerri Brass
Treas: David Caldwell
**Sec:* David Gittelman
**VP:* Donnie Clemmons
VP: Jill Littrell
VP: Matt Merriman
VP: Bob Roddewig
VP: John Slone

PROTEC LABORATORY
See SSB HOLDINGS INC

PROTECT CELL
See DIGITAL LEASH LLC

D-U-N-S 78-715-3113
PROTECTION ONE ALARM MONITORING INC
(*Suby of* PROTECTION ONE INC) ★
1035 N 3rd St Ste 101, Lawrence, KS 66044-1491
Tel (785) 856-5500 *Founded/Ownrshp* 1991
Sales 450.0MM *EMP* 2,870
SIC 7382 Security systems services; Burglar alarm maintenance & monitoring; Fire alarm maintenance & monitoring
Pr: Tim Whall
COO: Peter Pefanis
CFO: Darius G Nevin
Treas: Eric Andrew Devin
VP: Rex Gillette
VP: Eric Griffin
VP: Michael Keen
VP: Ryan Klompus
VP: Kimberly Lessner
VP: Tom Raftery
VP: Tim Roberts
VP: Joseph R Sanchez
Board of Directors: Alex Hocherman, Raymond C Kubacki, Robert J McGuire, Jeffrey S Nordhaus, Thomas J Russo, Edward F Sippel, Michael Weinstock, Arlene M Yocum

D-U-N-S 78-709-1222
PROTECTION ONE INC
1267 Windham Pkwy, Romeoville, IL 60446-1763
Tel (877) 938-2214 *Founded/Ownrshp* 2015
Sales 513.8MM^E *EMP* 845
SIC 7382 Security systems services
Pr: Timothy J Whall
**COO:* Donald Young
**CFO:* Dan Bresingham
**Chf Mktg O:* Jamie Rosand Haenggi
Sr VP: Stephen Hopkins
**Sr VP:* Joseph R Sanchez
VP: Joe Colon
VP: Michael Keen
VP: Joe Longfield
VP: Joe Mac McConnell
VP: Keith Moreman
VP: Patrick J Mulhern
VP: Tim Roberts
VP: Ken Rosen

PROTECTIVE GROUP A POINT BLANK
See POINT BLANK ENTERPRISES INC

D-U-N-S 13-163-9874 IMP/EXP
PROTECTIVE INDUSTRIAL PRODUCTS INC
968 Albany Shaker Rd, Latham, NY 12110-1401
Tel (518) 861-0133 *Founded/Ownrshp* 1984
Sales 84.8MM^E *EMP* 110
SIC 5085 Industrial supplies
Pr: Joseph A Milot Jr
**Pt:* Wellson Tao
**CFO:* Sean Weil
**VP:* Bridget Amicone
VP: Bridget Milot
Genl Mgr: Joe Ditoro
Natl Sales: Robert Clark
VP Sls: Mike Brooks
Mktg Mgr: Don Wilkinson
Manager: James Cuellar
Manager: Paul Wright

D-U-N-S 02-231-3717 IMP/EXP
PROTECTIVE INDUSTRIES INC
CAPLUGS
(*Suby of* PII HOLDINGS INC) ★
2150 Elmwood Ave, Buffalo, NY 14207-1910
Tel (716) 876-9951 *Founded/Ownrshp* 2015
Sales 220.0MM *EMP* 1,200
SIC 3089 3822 Molding primary plastic; Temperature controls, automatic
Pr: Gregory J Tucholski
**CFO:* Jeffrey Smith
Sr VP: Steven Smith
VP: Ron Livecchi
VP: Susan McElligott
VP: Kennery Rob
Dir IT: Anthony Vakos
IT Man: Deborah Kipler
Info Man: Carl Ruby
Software D: Jacob Oetinger
VP Opers: Jim Ray

D-U-N-S 04-103-7219
PROTECTIVE LIFE CORP
(*Suby of* DAI-ICHI LIFE HOLDINGS, INC.)
2801 Highway 280 S Ofc, Birmingham, AL 35223-2490
Tel (205) 268-1000 *Founded/Ownrshp* 2015
Sales NA *EMP* 2,415
SIC 6311 6321 6351 6411 Life insurance; Accident & health insurance; Liability insurance; Property & casualty insurance agent
Ch Bd: John D Johns
**Pr:* Richard J Bielen
Pr: Kristin Blake
Pr: Don Farber
Pr: Steve Grondin
Pr: Dina Hawkins
Pr: Stephen Pardue
Pr: Richard Samuels
Pr: Kevin Speed
Pr: Anne Wallace
Pr: Pamela White
CFO: Steven G Walker
Treas: Lance Black
Ofcr: D Scott Adams
Ofcr: Deborah J Long
Ofcr: Michelle Moloney
Div VP: Mike Gliori
Ex VP: Michael G Temple
Ex VP: Carl S Thigpen
Sr VP: Mark J Cyphert
Sr VP: Frank R Sottosanti
Board of Directors: Vanessa Leonard, John J McMahon Jr, Jesse J Spikes, William A Terry, Shigeo Tsuyuki, W Michael Warren Jr

D-U-N-S 00-690-0476
PROTECTIVE LIFE INSURANCE CO
(*Suby of* PROTECTIVE LIFE CORP) ★
2801 Highway 280 S, Birmingham, AL 35223-2488
Tel (205) 268-1000 *Founded/Ownrshp* 1907
Sales NA *EMP* 2,415
SIC 6311 6411 7389 Life insurance; Insurance agents, brokers & service; Financial services
Ch Bd: John D Johns
**CFO:* Richard J Bielen
CFO: Steven G Walker
Ofcr: Deborah J Long
Ex VP: Michael G Temple
**Ex VP:* Carl S Thigpen
Sr VP: Mark J Cyphert
VP: Teri Schultz
Sys/Mgr: Phil Ferguson

D-U-N-S 07-996-3290
PROTEIN BAR INC
200 N Lasalle Ste 1880, Chicago, IL 60601
Tel (312) 300-2566 *Founded/Ownrshp* 2013
Sales 200.0MM *EMP* 500^E
SIC 5812 Fast food restaurants & stands; Food bars
**CEO:* Samir Wagle

D-U-N-S 00-705-6799 IMP/EXP
PROTEIN PROVIDERS INC
JBS SWIFT & CO.
(*Suby of* JBS USA HOLDINGS LLC) ★
1770 Promontory Cir, Greeley, CO 80634-9039
Tel (970) 506-7678 *Founded/Ownrshp* 1935
Sales 235.5MM^E *EMP* 180
SIC 5147 5146 Meats, fresh; Seafoods; Fish, fresh
Pr: John Simons
Sr VP: Brad Lorenger
VP: John Ruby
VP: Doug Schult
Genl Mgr: Judd Butler
Genl Mgr: Jerry Peterson
CIO: Rogerio Peres
IT Man: James Bliss
IT Man: Amanda Earle
IT Man: Jeff McBride
IT Man: Bruce Roehrkasse

D-U-N-S 07-988-6479
PROTESTANT MEMORIAL MEDICAL CENTER INC
MEMORIAL HOSPITAL
4500 Memorial Dr, Belleville, IL 62226-5360
Tel (618) 233-7750 *Founded/Ownrshp* 1947
Sales 281.8MM *EMP* 2,344
SIC 8062 8051 General medical & surgical hospitals; Convalescent home with continuous nursing care
CEO: Mark J Turner
**Ch Bd:* Lary Eckert
CFO: Brent Smith
**Treas:* Roland Phouvenot
VP: Mario Gioia
VP: Ruth Holmes
VP: Joe Lanius
Dir Lab: Jan Greenwood
Dir Rx: Lori Adams
Dir Rx: Hiral Patel
Dir Sec: Donald Schneider

PROTIMEX
See PORKY PRODUCTS INC

D-U-N-S 11-270-6572
■ **PROTIVITI INC**
(*Suby of* ROBERT HALF INTERNATIONAL INC) ★
2884 Sand Hill Rd Ste 200, Menlo Park, CA 94025-7072
Tel (650) 234-6000 *Founded/Ownrshp* 2002
Sales 333.1MM^E *EMP* 2,103
SIC 8742 8721 Industry specialist consultants; Auditing services
Mng Dir: Joseph A Tarantino
Ex VP: Carol M Beaumier
**Ex VP:* Brian Christensen
Ex VP: Bob Hirth
Ex VP: James Pajakowski
Assoc Dir: Ashley Cuevas
Assoc Dir: John Diduro
Assoc Dir: Michael Mask
Assoc Dir: Barry Rieger
Assoc Dir: Jason Roberts
Mng Dir: Erick Christensen

D-U-N-S 13-212-9250 IMP
▲ **PROTO LABS INC**
5540 Pioneer Creek Dr, Maple Plain, MN 55359-9003
Tel (763) 479-3680 *Founded/Ownrshp* 1999
Sales 264.1MM *EMP* 1,549
Tkr Sym PRLB *Exch* NYS
SIC 3089 Molding primary plastic; Plastic processing
Pr: Victoria M Holt
**Ch Bd:* Lawrence J Lukis
CFO: John A Way
Ex VP: Donald G Krantz
Ex VP: William Langton
VP: Robert Bodor
VP: Renee Conklin
VP: Shelia Snook
VP: John B Tumelty
Dir Risk M: David Fein
CTO: Rich Baker
Board of Directors: Archie C Black, Rainer Gawlick, John B Goodman, Brian K Smith, Sven A Wehrwein

PROTRANS DE
See PROTRANS INTERNATIONAL INC

D-U-N-S 80-864-5188
PROTRANS INTERNATIONAL INC
PROTRANS DE
8311 N Perimeter Rd, Indianapolis, IN 46241-3628
Tel (317) 240-4100 *Founded/Ownrshp* 1993
Sales 292.6MM^E *EMP* 500
Accts Bgbc Partners Llp Indianapoli
SIC 4731 Truck transportation brokers
Pr: Craig Roeder
CFO: Lisa Doerner
VP: Lisa Doener
VP: Hubert Jones
**VP:* Michael Kattawar
VP: Gerardo Perez
VP: Dennis Smith
VP: Harald Walther
VP: John Wood
Dir Bus: Randy Ofiara
Mng Dir: Timr Gartner

PROVALI
See TECHNISOURCE INC

D-U-N-S 12-180-1120 EXP
PROVANTAGE LLC
7576 Freedom Ave Nw, North Canton, OH 44720-6902
Tel (330) 494-3781 *Founded/Ownrshp* 2011
Sales 225.0MM *EMP* 60
SIC 5961 5719 5734 5045 Computer software, mail order; Computers & peripheral equipment, mail order; Housewares; Computer software & accessories; Computers, peripherals & software
CEO: Arno Zirngibl
**COO:* Scott Dibattista
Genl Mgr: Alison Carey
Sls Dir: Joanne Newman
Mktg Mgr: Debbie Venuto

D-U-N-S 13-257-8340
PROVEN BUSINESS SYSTEMS LLC
18450 Crossing Dr Ste D, Tinley Park, IL 60487-9370
Tel (708) 614-1770 *Founded/Ownrshp* 2003
Sales 89.9MM^E *EMP* 239^E
SIC 5044 5999 Office equipment; Photocopy machines

PROVIA - HERITAGE STONE
See PROVIA DOOR INC

D-U-N-S 09-162-8602
PROVIA DOOR INC
PROVIA - HERITAGE STONE
2150 State Route 39, Sugarcreek, OH 44681-9201
Tel (330) 852-4711 *Founded/Ownrshp* 1983
Sales 120.3MM *EMP* 420
SIC 3442 5031 Metal doors; Door frames, all materials
**Pr:* Brian Miller
Pr: Willis Schlabach
VP: Patti Margo
VP: Freddie Miller
VP: Steve Tybor
Genl Mgr: Jeff Yoder
QA Dir: Tom Brewer
QA Dir: Ryan Rowe
QA Dir: Rick Schmiedl
QA Dir: Chad Wells
IT Man: Brent Mullet

D-U-N-S 07-562-4978
PROVIDEA CONFERENCING LLC
(*Suby of* STRATEGIC PRODUCTS AND SVCS) ★
1297 Flynn Rd Ste 100, Camarillo, CA 93012-8015
Tel (805) 384-9995 *Founded/Ownrshp* 1999, 2012
Sales 94.9MM^E *EMP* 165
SIC 4813
Pr: Mary E Williams
VP: Paul Kang
VP: Gregory Scott
VP: Tom Volk
Genl Mgr: John Swoyer

PROVIDENCE & ST PETER HOSPITAL
See PROVIDENCE HEALTH AND SERVICES

D-U-N-S 07-570-4601
PROVIDENCE COLLEGE
1 Cunningham Sq, Providence, RI 02918-7001
Tel (401) 865-1000 *Founded/Ownrshp* 1917
Sales 254.0MM *EMP* 800
Accts Kpmg Llp Boston Ma
SIC 8221 College, except junior
Pr: Brian J Shanley
Pr: Gail Dyer
**Ch:* Michael A Ruane
Ofcr: Joseph Hulbig
Ofcr: Gregory Myers
Ofcr: David Petit
Ofcr: Harold Starks
Assoc VP: Rafael Zapata
Ex VP: Hugh Frazier
VP: Robert Driscoll
VP: Kristine Goodwin
VP: Warren Gray
VP: Steven Maurano
VP: Kevin Robb
VP: John Sweeney
VP: Jacqueline White

D-U-N-S 93-886-0012
PROVIDENCE CORP
500 W Broadway St, Missoula, MT 59802-4008
Tel (406) 543-7271 *Founded/Ownrshp* 1987
Sales NA *EMP* 1,100
SIC 6719 Personal holding companies, except banks
Pr: Lawrence L White Jr

D-U-N-S 96-488-7632
PROVIDENCE EQUITY PARTNERS INC
100 Westminster St # 1800, Providence, RI 02903-2306
Tel (401) 751-1700 *Founded/Ownrshp* 1995
Sales 352.0MM^E *EMP* 2,280
SIC 6211

D-U-N-S 06-844-0564
PROVIDENCE EVERETT MEDICAL CENTER
FAMILY RESOURCE CENTER
900 Pacific Ave Ste 501, Everett, WA 98201-4189
Tel (425) 258-7311 *Founded/Ownrshp* 2000
Sales 677.9MM *EMP* 3
SIC 8099 Medical services organization
Prin: Lynn Chapman
Exec: Susan Moses

PROVIDENCE GOOD HEALTH PLAN
See PROVIDENCE HEALTH PLAN

PROVIDENCE HEALTH & SERVICES
See PROVIDENCE MEDFORD MEDICAL CENTER

D-U-N-S 88-472-7413
PROVIDENCE HEALTH & SERVICES
1801 Lind Ave Sw, Renton, WA 98057-3368
Tel (425) 525-3355 *Founded/Ownrshp* 1992
Sales 10.2MMM^E *EMP* 57,722
Accts Clark Nuber Ps Bellevue Wa
SIC 8062 General medical & surgical hospitals
Pr: John Koster
CFO: Todd Hofheins
Chf Mktg O: Gil Rodriguez
Ofcr: Deborah Burton
Ex VP: Debra A Canales
Sr VP: Orest Holubec
Sr VP: Janice Newell
Sr VP: Cindy Strauss
VP: Dave Hunter
Exec: Ron Chavira
Dir Risk M: William H Tately
Comm Man: Katie Pope

D-U-N-S 06-148-2048
PROVIDENCE HEALTH & SERVICES - OREGON
PROVIDENCE HEALTH SYSTEM
(*Suby of* PROVIDENCE HEALTH & SERVICES) ★
1801 Lind Ave Sw, Renton, WA 98057-3368
Tel (425) 525-3355 *Founded/Ownrshp* 1876
Sales 2.7MMM *EMP* 8,511
Accts Clark Nuber Ps Bellevue Wa
SIC 8062 General medical & surgical hospitals
Pr: John Koster
Pr: Rodney Hochman
CFO: Mike Butler
CFO: Sean Douglas
Treas: Todd Hofheins
Dir Rad: Kevin Nimeric
Ex Dir: Tom Fritz
CIO: Molly Swain
Mktg Mgr: John Cogan
Doctor: Geoffrey Baum
Doctor: Helen Chen
Board of Directors: John Collins Jr MD, Edward E Doejsi, Fredric Herskowitz MD, Phyllis Gutierrez Kenney, Sister Celestia Kobel, Sister Yvonne Leblanc, Sister Betsy Mickel, Al Parrish, Susanne Hartung Sp

D-U-N-S 07-850-9988
PROVIDENCE HEALTH & SERVICES AND SWEDISH HEALTH SERVICES
(*Suby of* PROVIDENCE HEALTH & SERVICES) ★
1801 Lind Ave Sw, Renton, WA 98057-3368
Tel (425) 525-3355 *Founded/Ownrshp* 2013
Sales 4.4MMM *EMP* 715^E
Accts Clark Nuber Ps Bellevue Wa
SIC 8062 General medical & surgical hospitals
Prin: Ian Pina

D-U-N-S 36-211-1150
PROVIDENCE HEALTH & SERVICES FOUNDATION/SAN FERNANDO AND SANTA
PROVIDENCE HOLY CROSS FOUNDATI
501 S Buena Vista St, Burbank, CA 91505-4809
Tel (818) 843-5111 *Founded/Ownrshp* 1980
Sales 21.4MM *EMP* 2,000
Accts Clark Nuber Ps Bellevue Wa
SIC 8399 Fund raising organization, non-fee basis
CEO: Patricia Modrzejewski
COO: Julie Sprengel
**Ch:* Lee Kanon Alpert
Nurse Mgr: Nancy Loporchio
Dir IT: Tom Kohler

IT Man: Charles Fink
IT Man: Linda Harris
IT Man: Doug Jones
Pharmcst: Eric Beesmeyer
Pharmcst: Laura Condra
Pharmcst: Maria Conty

D-U-N-S 05-730-6581
PROVIDENCE HEALTH & SERVICES-WASHINGTON
(*Suby of* PROVIDENCE HEALTH & SERVICES) ★
1801 Lind Ave Sw 9016, Renton, WA 98057-3368
Tel (425) 525-3355 *Founded/Ownrshp* 1995
Sales 1.1MMM^E *EMP* 9,700
Accts Clark Nuber Ps Bellevue Wa
SIC 8062 8051 8052 6513 8069 General medical & surgical hospitals; Skilled nursing care facilities; Intermediate care facilities; Retirement hotel operation; Substance abuse hospitals
Pr: Rodney Hochman
**Pr:* John Koster
**CFO:* Mike Butler
**Treas:* Todd Hofheins
VP: Sue Byington
Board of Directors: Sister Patricia Vartanian, John Collins Jr MD, Edward E Doejsi, Sister Karin Dufault, Fredric Herskowitz MD, Phyllis Gutierrez Kenney, Sister Celestia Kobel, Sister Yvonne Leblanc, Sister Betsy Mickel, Al Parrish

D-U-N-S 08-000-9554
PROVIDENCE HEALTH & SERVICES-WASHINGTON
PROVIDENCE HOLY FAMILY HOSP
5633 N Lidgerwood St, Spokane, WA 99208-1224
Tel (509) 482-0111 *Founded/Ownrshp* 2006
Sales 12.5MM^E *EMP* 1,300
SIC 8062 General medical & surgical hospitals
CEO: Alexander M Jackson
CIO: Cheryl Wheeler
Mktg Dir: Cathy Simchuk
Pharmcst: Joy Anyan

PROVIDENCE HEALTH AND SERVICES
See SACRED HEART MEDICAL CENTER

D-U-N-S 01-007-1764
PROVIDENCE HEALTH AND SERVICES
PROVIDENCE & ST PETER HOSPITAL
413 Lilly Rd Ne, Olympia, WA 98506-5133
Tel (360) 491-9480 *Founded/Ownrshp* 1895, 1992
Sales 277.0MM^E *EMP* 2,400
SIC 8062 Hospital, AMA approved residency
Pr: Rodney Hochman
**CEO:* Jim Leonard
CFO: Thomas Raffe
**CFO:* Thomas Risse
**Treas:* Todd Hofheins
Brnch Mgr: Deborah Monteralo
Off Mgr: Irvina Crepeau
CTO: David Schrodel
Doctor: Michael Bell

PROVIDENCE HEALTH CENTER
See PROVIDENCE HEALTH SERVICES OF WACO

D-U-N-S 15-152-8478
PROVIDENCE HEALTH PLAN
PROVIDENCE GOOD HEALTH PLAN
10126 Sw Park Way, Portland, OR 97225-5008
Tel (503) 574-5000 *Founded/Ownrshp* 1995
Sales NA *EMP* 870
SIC 6324 Health maintenance organization (HMO), insurance only
CEO: Jack A Friedman
**COO:* Michael White
**CFO:* Jeff Butcher
**Ofcr:* Robert Gluckman
**Ofcr:* Alison Schrupp
**Ofcr:* Carrie Smith

D-U-N-S 07-761-7843 IMP
PROVIDENCE HEALTH SERVICES OF WACO
PROVIDENCE HEALTH CENTER
6901 Medical Pkwy, Waco, TX 76712-7910
Tel (254) 751-4000 *Founded/Ownrshp* 1969
Sales 277.8MM *EMP* 2,000
Accts Deloitte Tax Llp Indianapolis
SIC 8062 General medical & surgical hospitals
CEO: Brett Esrock
Chf Rad: James Olmsted
**Treas:* Hal Whitaker
**Sr VP:* Philip E Halford
CIO: Jay Scherelr
Dir IT: Alan Carlson
VP Mktg: Jonathan D Ford
VP Mktg: Jana Whitaker
Doctor: Debbie Kucera
Doctor: Richard Uptergrove
HC Dir: Vicki Beckner

PROVIDENCE HEALTH SYSTEM
See PROVIDENCE HEALTH & SERVICES - OREGON

D-U-N-S 09-914-2093
PROVIDENCE HEALTH SYSTEM-OREGON
PROVIDENCE MEDICAL CENTER
(*Suby of* PROVIDENCE HEALTH & SERVICES) ★
4805 Ne Glisan St, Portland, OR 97213-2933
Tel (503) 215-6111 *Founded/Ownrshp* 2009
Sales 155.9MM^E *EMP* 3,600
SIC 8062 General medical & surgical hospitals
CEO: Larry Bowe
Off Mgr: Nicki Scholes

D-U-N-S 07-190-6283
PROVIDENCE HEALTH SYSTEM-SOUTHERN CALIFORNIA
(*Suby of* PROVIDENCE HEALTH & SERVICES) ★
1801 Lind Ave Sw, Renton, WA 98057-3368
Tel (425) 525-3355 *Founded/Ownrshp* 1903
Sales 287.3MM^E *EMP* 2,946
SIC 8062 General medical & surgical hospitals
Pr: Rodney F Hochman
COO: Jim Leonard
Treas: Lynn Chappell
Chf Mktg O: Martha Barstow
**Ex VP:* Randy Axelrod
**VP:* Deborah Burton
**VP:* Claudia L Haglund
VP: Greg Vanpelt
Dir Lab: Paul Fitzpatrick
Ex Dir: Susan Green
CTO: Sue Samet

PROVIDENCE HOLY CROSS FOUNDATI
See PROVIDENCE HEALTH & SERVICES FOUNDATION/SAN FERNANDO AND SANTA

D-U-N-S 04-800-7525 IMP
PROVIDENCE HOLY CROSS MEDICAL CENTER GUILD
15031 Rinaldi St, Mission Hills, CA 91345-1207
Tel (818) 365-8051 *Founded/Ownrshp* 1960
Sales 257.9MM^E *EMP* 3,000^E
SIC 8062 General medical & surgical hospitals
Ch: Lee Kanon Alpert
**CEO:* June E Drake
COO: Michael White
Prac Mgr: Valerie Sullivan
CIO: Patty Mayberry
Dir QC: Margy Brown
Opers Mgr: Ray Brink
Mktg Dir: Tiffany Devall
Obsttrcn: Farid Yasharpour
Ansthlgy: Victoria Bendebel
Opthamlgy: Robert Feinfield

PROVIDENCE HOLY FAMILY HOSP
See PROVIDENCE HEALTH & SERVICES-WASHINGTON

D-U-N-S 06-883-5206
PROVIDENCE HOSPITAL
PROVIDENCE HOSPITAL AND MEDICA
16001 W 9 Mile Rd, Southfield, MI 48075-4803
Tel (248) 849-3000 *Founded/Ownrshp* 1923
Sales 654.0MM *EMP* 4,700
Accts Deloitte Tax Lp Cincinnati O
SIC 8062 General medical & surgical hospitals
COO: Vijay Mittal
CFO: Dave Mast
Exec: Carole Gilbert
**Prin:* Diane Radloff
Dir Sec: Harold Jones
Dir IT: Ronald Smith
Sftwr Eng: Rose Aisanich
Surgeon: Laurence Y Cheung
Surgeon: Sunu J Philip
Obsttrcn: Urva Naik
Nrsg Dir: Kathy Ryan

D-U-N-S 06-894-0329
PROVIDENCE HOSPITAL
2446 Kipling Ave, Cincinnati, OH 45239-6650
Tel (513) 853-5000 *Founded/Ownrshp* 1999
Sales 23.1MM^E *EMP* 1,178
SIC 8062 General medical & surgical hospitals
VP: Edward Roeber
**Pr:* Paul Hiltz
Mktg Mgr: Brandie Schroeder

D-U-N-S 07-780-3757
PROVIDENCE HOSPITAL
1150 Varnum St Ne, Washington, DC 20017-2104
Tel (202) 269-7000 *Founded/Ownrshp* 1861
Sales 212.3MM *EMP* 2,517
Accts Deloitte Tax Llp Cincinnati
SIC 8062 General medical & surgical hospitals
CEO: Amy Freeman
Dir Vol: Roxanne Crooks
V Ch: Mary Bader
**Pr:* Julius D Spears Jr
CFO: Rick Talento
**Ch:* William J Cox
**Ch:* Steve Strazzella
Treas: Paul Grenaldo
Ex VP: Robert A Hutson
**Sr VP:* Patricia Evans
VP: Anastasia Gyptopolis
**VP:* Matt Lukasiak
VP: Paul Y Smith
Exec: Christina Schreiber

D-U-N-S 07-790-0066
PROVIDENCE HOSPITAL
6801 Airport Blvd, Mobile, AL 36608-3785
Tel (251) 633-1000 *Founded/Ownrshp* 1854
Sales 227.1MM *EMP* 2,000
Accts Deloitte Tax Lp Cincinnati O
SIC 8062 8011 General medical & surgical hospitals; Offices & clinics of medical doctors
Pr: Clark Christianson
Chf Rad: Michael Pennington
COO: Todd S Kennedy
**CFO:* Vince Formica
**Ch:* SIS Loftin
Sr VP: Rick V Talento
**VP:* David Powell
Dir Lab: Mark Deakle
Chf Nrs Of: Suzanne Felder
Adm Dir: Daniel Scarcliff
Ex Dir: Christopher Southwick

PROVIDENCE HOSPITAL AND MEDICA
See PROVIDENCE HOSPITAL

D-U-N-S 80-480-2742
PROVIDENCE HOSPITAL FOUNDATION
2601 Laurel St, Columbia, SC 29204-2033
Tel (803) 256-5300 *Founded/Ownrshp* 1993
Sales 338.8MM *EMP* 2^E
SIC 7389 Fund raising organizations

D-U-N-S 07-799-0877
■ PROVIDENCE HOSPITAL LLC
(*Suby of* LIFEPOINT HEALTH INC) ★
2435 Forest Dr, Columbia, SC 29204-2098
Tel (803) 256-5300 *Founded/Ownrshp* 2016
Sales 228.5MM^E *EMP* 1,900
SIC 8062

D-U-N-S 87-829-8876
PROVIDENCE LITTLE CO OF MARY MEDICAL CENTER-TORRANCE
LITTLE COMPANY MARY SVC AREA
(*Suby of* PROVIDENCE HEALTH SYSTEM-SOUTHERN CALIFORNIA) ★
4101 Torrance Blvd, Torrance, CA 90503-4607
Tel (310) 540-7676 *Founded/Ownrshp* 1992
Sales 151.0MM^E *EMP* 2,946
SIC 8741 Hospital management
CEO: Blair Contratto
Bd of Dir: Karl Carrier
Chf Mktg O: Louise Pilati
Ex Dir: Joseph M Zanetta
QA Dir: Patti Hamaguchi
Mktg Mgr: Jane Sakurai
Doctor: Howard Abrams
Doctor: Peter Borden
Doctor: David Eppard
Doctor: Nicholas Halikis
Doctor: Glen Huber

D-U-N-S 12-480-2179
PROVIDENCE MEDFORD MEDICAL CENTER
PROVIDENCE HEALTH & SERVICES
1111 Crater Lake Ave, Medford, OR 97504-6241
Tel (541) 732-5000 *Founded/Ownrshp* 1988
Sales 177.0MM *EMP* 2
SIC 8322 Senior citizens' center or association
CEO: Cindy Mayo
**Pr:* Tom Hall
**COO:* Chris Pizzi
**VP:* Gloria Schell
**VP:* Don Skundrick
Dir Inf Cn: Yvonne Chilcoht
**Ex Dir:* Jodi Barnard
Prgrm Mgr: Barbara Sexton
Dir QC: Eugene Ogrod

PROVIDENCE MEDICAL CENTER
See PROVIDENCE HEALTH SYSTEM-OREGON

PROVIDENCE MEDICAL CENTER
See PROVIDENCE/SAINT JOHN FOUNDATION INC

D-U-N-S 15-422-3747
PROVIDENCE MEDICAL CENTER
PROVIDENCE-MEDICAL CENTER GIFT SHOP
(*Suby of* PRIME HEALTHCARE SERVICES INC) ★
8929 Parallel Pkwy, Kansas City, KS 66112-3607
Tel (913) 596-4870 *Founded/Ownrshp* 1977
Sales 153.5MM *EMP* 10
SIC 8062 General medical & surgical hospitals
CEO: Randy Nyp
CFO: Joe Jeans
VP: Steve Marcus
Adm Dir: Maria Johar
Counsel: Heather L Allred

D-U-N-S 05-708-0087
PROVIDENCE MILWAUKIE HOSPITAL INC
10150 Se 32nd Ave, Milwaukie, OR 97222-6516
Tel (503) 513-8300 *Founded/Ownrshp* 2009
Sales 86.6MM *EMP* 276
SIC 8062 General medical & surgical hospitals
COO: Theron Park

D-U-N-S 79-995-8819
PROVIDENCE PUBLIC SCHOOLS
797 Westminster St, Providence, RI 02903-4018
Tel (401) 456-9100 *Founded/Ownrshp* 1900
Sales 126.6MM^E *EMP* 2,600
SIC 8211 8742 Public elementary & secondary schools; Management consulting services
Treas: Frances Rotella
Bd of Dir: Yamil Baez
Bd of Dir: Diagneris Garcia
Bd of Dir: Muyideen Ibiyemi
Bd of Dir: Lorraine Lalli
Bd of Dir: Mark Santow
Dir Sec: Andre Thibeault
Genl Mgr: Mark Jeffrey
Pr Dir: Christina O'Reilly
Pr Dir: Robert Taboada
Teacher Pr: Craig Bickley

D-U-N-S 15-983-2542
▲ PROVIDENCE SERVICE CORP
700 Canal St Ste 3, Stamford, CT 06902-5937
Tel (203) 307-2800 *Founded/Ownrshp* 1996
Sales 1.7MMM *EMP* 9,072^E
Tkr Sym PRSC *Exch* NGS
SIC 8322 8742 7389 General counseling services; Transportation consultant; Telephone services
Pr: James Lindstrom
**Ch Bd:* Christopher S Shackelton
CFO: David Shackelton
Chf Cred: Sophia Tawil
Board of Directors: Todd J Carter, David A Coulter, Richard A Kerley, Kristi L Meints, Leslie V Norwalk, Frank J Wright

D-U-N-S 15-147-3840
PROVIDENCE ST MARY MEDICAL CENTER
ST MARY PHYSICIAN GROUP
401 W Poplar St, Walla Walla, WA 99362-2846
Tel (509) 525-3320 *Founded/Ownrshp* 1880
Sales 155.9MM *EMP* 683^E
SIC 8062 General medical & surgical hospitals
**CEO:* Steve Burdick
**COO:* Susan Blackburn
**CFO:* Michael Parenteau

PROVIDENCE ST VINCENT MEDICAL
See ST VINCENT MEDICAL CENTER EAST PAVILION LOBBY GIFT SHOP

D-U-N-S 82-886-4467
PROVIDENCE TARZANA MEDICAL CENTER
18321 Clark St, Tarzana, CA 91356-3501
Tel (818) 881-0800 *Founded/Ownrshp* 2008
Sales 221.2MM *EMP* 1,300
SIC 8011 Offices & clinics of medical doctors
CEO: Jerry Clute
**COO:* Phyllis Bushart
**CFO:* Nick Lymberopoulos

PROVIDENCE-MEDICAL CENTER GIFT SHOP
See PROVIDENCE MEDICAL CENTER

D-U-N-S 13-948-6617
PROVIDENCE/SAINT JOHN FOUNDATION INC
PROVIDENCE MEDICAL CENTER
8929 Parallel Pkwy, Kansas City, KS 66112-1689
Tel (913) 596-4000 *Founded/Ownrshp* 1981
Sales 130.1MM *EMP* 140
SIC 8062 8741 8011 General medical & surgical hospitals; Hospital management; Medical centers
CEO: Randall Nyp
Chf Rad: Rick Moritz
Dir Risk M: Nancy May
Dir Rad: Janet Seeman
Dir Rx: Dennis Brown
Dir Rx: Erin Kirkland
Chf Nrs Of: Karen Orr
Adm Dir: Jean Clark
Ex Dir: Karla Kimerer
Prac Mgr: Robert Cole
Cmptr Lab: Karen Culey

PROVIDENT BANK
See STERLING NATIONAL BANK

D-U-N-S 00-697-2913
■ PROVIDENT BANK
(*Suby of* PROVIDENT FINANCIAL SERVICES INC) ★
100 Wood Ave S Ste 119, Iselin, NJ 08830-2716
Tel (800) 448-7768 *Founded/Ownrshp* 1839
Sales NA *EMP* 825
SIC 6036 6029 Savings institutions, not federally chartered; Commercial banks
Ch Bd: Paul M Pantozzi
Pr: Tim Buffo
Pr: George Celetano
CFO: Linda A Niro
CFO: Giacomo Novielli
Treas: Ed Reilly
Ofcr: Pat Grazioso
Ofcr: Alan D Segars
Ex VP: Don Blum
Ex VP: C Gabriel Haagensen
Ex VP: Kevin J Ward
Sr VP: Bruce Dansbury
Sr VP: David Frye
Sr VP: Leonard G Gleason
Sr VP: Micheal Revesz
Sr VP: Kenneth J Wagner
VP: Jennifer Adamec
VP: Richard Burzynski
VP: Joseph Covell
VP: Angel Denis
VP: Gregory Haines
Board of Directors: Terence Gallagher, Matthew K Harding, Thomas B Hogan Jr

D-U-N-S 11-834-9070
▲ PROVIDENT FINANCIAL SERVICES INC
239 Washington St, Jersey City, NJ 07302-3828
Tel (732) 590-9200 *Founded/Ownrshp* 2003
Sales NA *EMP* 1,064^E
Tkr Sym PFS *Exch* NYS
SIC 6035 Savings institutions, federally chartered
Ch Bd: Christopher Martin
CFO: Thomas M Lyons
Ex VP: John Kuntz

D-U-N-S 13-078-5041
PROVIDENT HEALTH SERVICES INC
(*Suby of* MEMORIAL HEALTH UNIVERSITY MEDICAL CENTER INC) ★
4700 Waters Ave, Savannah, GA 31404-6220
Tel (912) 350-8000 *Founded/Ownrshp* 1990
Sales 36.4MM^E *EMP* 3,000
SIC 8082 4119 Home health care services; Ambulance service
Pr: Robert A Colvin

D-U-N-S 00-792-0853
■ PROVIDENT LIFE & ACCIDENT INSURANCE CO (TN)
(*Suby of* UNUM GROUP) ★
1 Fountain Sq Ste 1, Chattanooga, TN 37402-1303
Tel (423) 755-1011 *Founded/Ownrshp* 1887, 1995
Sales NA *EMP* 2,000
SIC 6311 6321 Life insurance; Accident & health insurance; Disability health insurance
Ex VP: Thomas B Heys Jr
Ofcr: Dean F Copeland
Dir Sec: Linda French
CIO: Robert O Best

D-U-N-S 96-343-9026
PROVIDENT RESOURCES GROUP INC
5565 Bankers Ave, Baton Rouge, LA 70808-2608
Tel (225) 766-3977 *Founded/Ownrshp* 1999
Sales 100.0MM *EMP* 100
Accts Crowe Horwath Llp Oak Brook
SIC 8051 Skilled nursing care facilities
CEO: Steve E Hicks
**Pr:* Debra W Lockwood
Nrsg Dir: William Garrett

D-U-N-S 06-399-1434 IMP/EXP
PROVIMI NORTH AMERICA INC
NUTRITION TRANSPORTATION SVCS
(*Suby of* CARGILL THE NETHERLANDS HOLDING B.V.)
10 Collective Way, Brookville, OH 45309-8878
Tel (937) 770-2400 *Founded/Ownrshp* 2000
Sales 211.0MM^E *EMP* 500
SIC 2048 5191 Prepared feeds; Animal feeds
Pr: Charles Shininger
**CFO:* Brett A Hartman
**VP:* Ken Bryant
VP: Kenneth Bryant
CTO: Gary Cannady
IT Man: Alek Culbreath
Sfty Mgr: Mark Hemrick
Opers Mgr: John Peck
Plnt Mgr: Kyle Hunter
Plnt Mgr: Scott Swenson

D-U-N-S 95-992-9308
■ PROVINCE HEALTHCARE CO
(*Suby of* LIFEPOINT HEALTH INC) ★
103 Powell Ct Ste 200, Brentwood, TN 37027-5079
Tel (205) 487-7900 *Founded/Ownrshp* 2005
Sales 85.7MM^E *EMP* 7,298
Accts Ernst & Young Llp Nashville
SIC 8741 Hospital management
CEO: Martin S Rash
**Pr:* Daniel S Slipkovich
**CFO:* Christopher T Hannon
**Sr VP:* James Thomas Anderson
**Sr VP:* Samuel H Moody
**Sr VP:* Howard T Wall III
VP: Troy Napier
VP: Roberto F Pantoja
VP: Charles Thornburg
Pdt Mgr: John Rutledge

D-U-N-S 61-474-7322
PROVISION LIVING LLC
1630 Des Peres Rd Ste 310, Saint Louis, MO 63131-1800
Tel (314) 238-3800 *Founded/Ownrshp* 2005
Sales 3.0MM *EMP* 1,000
SIC 6531 Housing authority operator
CEO: Todd Spittal
Ex Dir: Tracy Parker
Off Mgr: Joyce Younts
Sls Dir: Beth Huck

D-U-N-S 02-334-0524
PROVISION PARTNERS COOPERATIVE
2327 W Veterans Pkwy, Marshfield, WI 54449-8829
Tel (715) 687-4443 *Founded/Ownrshp* 1996
Sales 96.3MM *EMP* 160
Accts Clifton Larson Allen Llp Mars
SIC 5191 5984 5541 Feed; Seeds: field, garden & flower; Fertilizer & fertilizer materials; Liquefied petroleum gas, delivered to customers' premises; Filling stations, gasoline
Ch Bd: Joseph Fuchs
**CFO:* Robert C Bauer
Sec: Tom Bauer
**Sec:* Ben Daul

D-U-N-S 01-833-9705
PROVO CITY SCHOOL DISTRICT
280 W 940 N, Provo, UT 84604-3326
Tel (801) 374-4800 *Founded/Ownrshp* 1890
Sales 86.9MM^E *EMP* 1,670
SIC 8211 Public elementary & secondary schools
Ofcr: Roy Edwards
Ofcr: ARI Lecheminant
VP: Julie Austin
VP: McKay Jensen
Off Mgr: Deena Sackey
MIS Dir: Chad Duncan
IT Man: Brooke Robinson
Schl Brd P: Michelle Kaufusi
Instr Medi: Christine Durst
Psych: Lori Rich
Pgrm Dir: Jared Ferguson

D-U-N-S 03-534-1122 IMP
PROVO CRAFT & NOVELTY INC
PROVOCRAFT
10855 S Rvr Frnt Pkwy # 400, South Jordan, UT 84095-5763
Tel (800) 937-7686 *Founded/Ownrshp* 1985
Sales 211.9MM^E *EMP* 600
SIC 5092 5199 5945 5947 Arts & crafts equipment & supplies; Gifts & novelties; Arts & crafts supplies; Novelties
CEO: Ashish Arora
Pr: James Thornton
CFO: David Chase
Treas: Lance Evenson
Chf Mktg O: Matt Wilburn
VP: Jeff Cooper
VP: Don Olsen
VP: Robert Workman
Exec: Becky Tully
Exec: Jenna Waite
Creative D: Dan Larsen

PROVOCRAFT
See PROVO CRAFT & NOVELTY INC

D-U-N-S 80-998-8996 IMP
PROXIMO SPIRITS INC
333 Washington St Ste 401, Jersey City, NJ 07302-3095
Tel (201) 204-1720 *Founded/Ownrshp* 2007
Sales 152.5MM^E *EMP* 100^E
SIC 5182 Wine & distilled beverages
Pr: Mark Teasdale
Pr: Landon Wells
Pr: Garrett Yee
**CFO:* Martin Halmi
Sr VP: Edward Manning
Sr VP: Michael Peterson
Rgnl Mgr: Emmett King
Area Mgr: Joe Barbieri
Area Mgr: Christopher Mastores
Area Mgr: Matan Steinfeld
Area Mgr: Kristi Taylor

PRSI
See PAVEMENT RECYCLING SYSTEMS INC

P.R.U. BUILDING SYSTEMS
See RUBLOFF CONSTRUCTION INC

D-U-N-S 13-444-1658
■ PRUCO LIFE INSURANCE CO
PRUDENTIAL
(*Suby of* PRUDENTIAL INSURANCE CO OF AMERICA) ★
213 Washington St, Newark, NJ 07102-2917
Tel (973) 802-6000 *Founded/Ownrshp* 1971
Sales NA *EMP* 209
Accts Pricewaterhousecoopers Llp Ne
SIC 6311 6411 Mutual association life insurance; Insurance agents, brokers & service
Pr: Esther Hook Milnes
**Sr VP:* Shirley Hwei-Chung Shao
**VP:* Dave Jungk

D-U-N-S 15-002-8660
■ PRUCO LIFE INSURANCE CO OF NEW JERSEY
(*Suby of* PRUDENTIAL) ★
213 Washington St, Newark, NJ 07102-2917
Tel (973) 802-6000 *Founded/Ownrshp* 1982
Sales NA *EMP* 209
Accts Pricewaterhousecoopers Llp Ne
SIC 6311 Life insurance
Pr: Robert F O'Donnell
**CFO:* Yanela C Frias
VP: Barbara G Koster
VP: Barbara Koster
Sls&Mrk Ex: Mark Hug
Board of Directors: John Chieffo, Robert M Falzon, Bernard J Jacob, Richard F Lambert, Kent D Sluyter

D-U-N-S 06-748-8718
■ PRUCO SECURITIES LLC
(*Suby of* PRUDENTIAL INSURANCE CO OF AMERICA) ★
751 Broad St, Newark, NJ 07102-3714
Tel (800) 235-7637 *Founded/Ownrshp* 1970
Sales NA *EMP* 18,000
SIC 6321 6331 6211 6282 8071 Accident & health insurance; Reinsurance carriers, accident & health; Fire, marine & casualty insurance; Brokers, security; Investment advice; Medical laboratories

PRUDENTIAL
See OSHAUGHNESSY REALTY CO INC

PRUDENTIAL
See PRUCO LIFE INSURANCE CO

PRUDENTIAL
See BRER AFFILIATES INC

PRUDENTIAL
See BROOKFIELD RELOCATION INC

D-U-N-S 36-195-5602
■ PRUDENTIAL ANNUITIES DISTRIBUTORS INC
(*Suby of* PRUDENTIAL ANNUITIES INC) ★
1 Corporate Dr, Shelton, CT 06484-6208
Tel (203) 926-1888 *Founded/Ownrshp* 1987
Sales NA *EMP* 356
Accts Ernst & Young Llp Hartford C
SIC 6411 Insurance agents, brokers & service
Ch Bd: Jan R Carendi
**Pr:* Gordon Boronow
**CEO:* Wade A Dokken
**CFO:* Thomas M Mazzaferro
**Treas:* M Patricia Paez
Treas: Patricia M Paez
Sr VP: Nicholas J Campanella
Sr VP: Marc Levine
**VP:* Amanda C Sutyak
VP: Laurita Warner
MIS Dir: Nick Campanela

D-U-N-S 17-435-2377
■ PRUDENTIAL ANNUITIES INC
(*Suby of* PRUDENTIAL FINANCIAL INC) ★
1 Corporate Dr Ste 800, Shelton, CT 06484-6243
Tel (203) 926-1888 *Founded/Ownrshp* 2003
Sales NA *EMP* 800
Accts Ernst & Young Hartford Ct
SIC 6411 8741 Insurance agents, brokers & service; Professional standards services, insurance; Business management
Pr: Wade Dokken
**COO:* Gordon Boronow
**COO:* Lincoln Collins
COO: William Marsh
**CFO:* Thomas M Mazzaferro
**Treas:* Claes Svensson
**Chf Mktg O:* Patricia J Abram
Ex VP: Timothy Cronin
Ex VP: Zafar Rashid
**Ex VP:* Anderes Soderstrom
Sr VP: Richard Jimenez
VP: Patricia Abram
VP: Ching M Lee Chang
VP: Jerry Cooperman
VP: Jan Hoffmeister
VP: Christpher Luise
**VP:* M Patricia Paez
VP: Gary Palmer
VP: Yvonne Rocco

D-U-N-S 79-650-4710
■ PRUDENTIAL ANNUITIES LIFE ASSURANCE CORP
(*Suby of* PRUDENTIAL ANNUITIES INC) ★
1 Corporate Dr Ste 800, Shelton, CT 06484-6243
Tel (203) 926-1888 *Founded/Ownrshp* 1988
Sales NA *EMP* 2
SIC 6411 Insurance agents, brokers & service
Pr: Robert F O'Donnell
COO: Pelle Wahlstrom
**CFO:* Yanela C Frias
Chf Inves: Michael Long
Sr VP: Robert M Arena
VP: Jan Hoffmeister
VP: Gary Palmer
Exec: Scott Hawkins
CIO: Ulf Tingstrom
Software D: Dave Gianetti
Sales Exec: Lynn Erikson

D-U-N-S 01-830-0884
▲ PRUDENTIAL FINANCIAL INC
751 Broad St, Newark, NJ 07102-3714
Tel (973) 802-6000 *Founded/Ownrshp* 1875
Sales NA *EMP* 49,384
Tkr Sym PRU *Exch* NYS
SIC 6311 6321 6331 6211 6552 Life insurance; Life insurance carriers; Life reinsurance; Accident insurance carriers; Health insurance carriers; Disability health insurance; Reinsurance carriers, accident & health; Property damage insurance; Fire, marine & casualty insurance: mutual; Security brokers & dealers; Investment bankers; Brokers, security; Dealers, security; Subdividers & developers
Ch Bd: John R Strangfeld Jr
COO: Charles F Lowrey
CFO: Robert M Falzon
V Ch Bd: Mark B Grier
Chf Mktg O: David Bessey
Chf Inves: Scott G Sleyster
Ofcr: Nicholas C Silitch
Ex VP: Edward P Baird
Ex VP: Michael Caulfield
Ex VP: Timothy P Harris
Sr VP: Barbara G Koster
Sr VP: Richard F Lambert
Sr VP: Marc Pester
Sr VP: Sharon C Taylor
VP: Nina Antony
VP: Scott B Barnett
VP: Joseph Billy
VP: Angel Bowens
VP: Thomas Brennan
VP: Sharon S Brody
VP: John L Bronson
Board of Directors: Douglas A Scovanner, Thomas J Baltimore Jr, Michael A Todman, Gilbert F Casellas, James G Cullen, Karl J Krapek, Peter Rupert Lighte, Martina Hund-Mejean, George Paz, Sandra Pianalto, Christine A Poon

D-U-N-S 79-065-5109
■ PRUDENTIAL HOLDINGS LLC
(*Suby of* PRUDENTIAL FINANCIAL INC) ★
751 Broad St, Newark, NJ 07102-3714
Tel (973) 802-6000 *Founded/Ownrshp* 2001
Sales 16.2MMM^E *EMP* 30,000
SIC 6282 6321 6324 Investment advice; Accident insurance carriers; Health insurance carriers; Reinsurance carriers, accident & health; Disability health insurance; Group hospitalization plans
Ch Bd: Arthur Ryan

D-U-N-S 00-697-3804 IMP/EXP
■ PRUDENTIAL INSURANCE CO OF AMERICA
(*Suby of* PRUDENTIAL HOLDINGS LLC) ★
751 Broad St, Newark, NJ 07102-3714
Tel (973) 802-6000 *Founded/Ownrshp* 1875
Sales NA *EMP* 30,000
SIC 6311 6371 6282 6722 Life insurance; Welfare pensions; Manager of mutual funds, contract or fee basis; Management investment, open-end
CEO: John Strangfeld
Pr: C E Chaplin
**Pr:* Arthur F Ryan
COO: Charles F Crane
**CFO:* Richard J Carbone
Ex VP: Paul Chong
**Ex VP:* Robert Charles Golden
Ex VP: Jean Hamilton
Sr VP: Vivian Banta
Sr VP: Sharon A Mueller
VP: Susan L Blount
VP: Sandy Fox
VP: Dawn Kelly
VP: John Kinghorn
VP: Rob Lowther
VP: Anthony Piszel
VP: Louise M Talijan
VP: Richard Tavis

D-U-N-S 02-857-9803
PRUDENTIAL OVERALL SUPPLY
1661 Alton Pkwy, Irvine, CA 92606-4877
Tel (949) 250-4855 *Founded/Ownrshp* 2004
Sales 158.2MM *EMP* 1,457
Accts Squar Milner Peterson Miran
SIC 7218 Industrial launderers; Wiping towel supply; Clean room apparel supply; Industrial uniform supply
CEO: Dan Clark
**Pr:* Thomas C Watts
COO: Dean Killion
CFO: John Thompson
**V Ch Bd:* Donald C Lahn
Exec: Stefan Schurter
Rgnl Mgr: Jeff Nelson
Rgnl Mgr: Chris Welch
Genl Mgr: Mark Elberson
Off Mgr: Erikha Phan
Natl Sales: Myles Reukema

D-U-N-S 07-279-6477
■ PRUDENTIAL SECURITIES GROUP INC
(*Suby of* PRUDENTIAL CAPITAL AND INVESTMENT SERVICES, LLC)
199 Water St, New York, NY 10038-3526
Tel (212) 778-1000 *Founded/Ownrshp* 1982
Sales 628.5MM^E *EMP* 17,100
SIC 6722 Management investment, open-end
Pr: Hardwick Simmons
**Ex VP:* Robert C Golden
**Ex VP:* Alan D Hogan
**VP:* Victor Ramos
**VP:* Leslie Ryan
MIS Dir: Ralph Duerr

D-U-N-S 07-926-9521
PRUDENTIAL SECURITY INC
20600 Eureka Rd Ste 900, Taylor, MI 48180-5376
Tel (734) 286-6000 *Founded/Ownrshp* 2012
Sales 23.4MM^E *EMP* 1,200^E
SIC 7381 Protective services, guard
Prin: Greg Wier

D-U-N-S 79-513-4600
■ PRUDENTIAL TRUST CO
(*Suby of* PRUCO SECURITIES LLC) ★
30 Ed Preate Dr, Scranton, PA 18507-1755
Tel (570) 341-6000 *Founded/Ownrshp* 1981
Sales 153.5MM^E *EMP* 803
SIC 6282 6722 6211 Investment advice; Management investment, open-end; Security brokers & dealers
VP: Mike Williamson
VP: Lakshmi Aiyar
VP: Joseph Poremba
IT Man: Jerry Crinella
IT Man: Marlene Zaic
Mktg Dir: Edward Gowarty

D-U-N-S 96-632-3763
PRUDENTIAL WELFARE BENEFITS TRUST
751 Broad St Fl 18, Newark, NJ 07102-3714
Tel (973) 802-7490 *Founded/Ownrshp* 2011
Sales 240.5MM *EMP* 2^E
SIC 6733 Trusts
Prin: Paul Boxer

D-U-N-S 02-507-1860
PRUITT CORP
UHS-PRUITT
1626 Jeurgens Ct, Norcross, GA 30093-2219
Tel (706) 552-1699 *Founded/Ownrshp* 1977
Sales 586.5MM^E *EMP* 16,000^E
SIC 8621 Health association
CEO: Neil L Pruitt Jr
**CFO:* Philip W Small
VP: Annette Salisbury
Exec: George Hunt
Netwrk Eng: Theodore Smith
Counsel: Erin Kendall

D-U-N-S 08-481-7188
PRUITTHEALTH CORP
209 E Doyle St, Toccoa, GA 30577-2960
Tel (706) 886-8493 *Founded/Ownrshp* 1977
Sales 228.6MM^E *EMP* 1,610
SIC 8741 Management services
CEO: Neil L Pruitt
COO: Chris Bryson
IT Man: Sheila Boyd
IT Man: Rick Elmore

D-U-N-S 60-272-2258
PRWT SERVICES INC
1835 Market St Ste 800, Philadelphia, PA 19103-2919
Tel (215) 563-7698 *Founded/Ownrshp* 2010
Sales 165.9MM^E *EMP* 1,312
Accts Mitchell & Titus Llp Philade
SIC 7374 Data processing service
Ch Bd: Willie F Johnson
**CEO:* Harold Epps
**CFO:* Don Peloso
Ex VP: Peter Rockett
Ex VP: Ray Saulino
Comm Man: Yolanda Sample
Genl Mgr: Shirlene White
QA Dir: Brandon Colvard
Dir IT: Sheldon Myers
**Genl Couns:* Malik Majeed

D-U-N-S 07-937-5809
■ PRYOR CHEMICAL CO (OK)
(*Suby of* LSB INDUSTRIES INC) ★
4463 Hunt St, Pryor, OK 74361-4511
Tel (918) 825-3383 *Founded/Ownrshp* 1980
Sales 100.0MM *EMP* 150
SIC 2873 Ammonium nitrate, ammonium sulfate; Anhydrous ammonia; Fertilizers: natural (organic), except compost; Urea
CEO: Jack Golsen
**VP:* Phil Gough
**VP:* Ann Rendon
**Prin:* Barry Golsen

PRYSMIAN CABLES & SYSTEMS USA
See DRAKA HOLDINGS USA INC

D-U-N-S 08-895-2171 IMP
PRYSMIAN CABLES AND SYSTEMS USA LLC
PRYSMIAN POWER CABLE & SYS
(*Suby of* PRYSMIAN SPA)
700 Industrial Dr, Lexington, SC 29072-3755
Tel (803) 951-4800 *Founded/Ownrshp* 1900
Sales 91.8MM^E *EMP* 250^E
SIC 3357 Nonferrous wiredrawing & insulating; Communication wire; Fiber optic cable (insulated); Building wire & cable, nonferrous
Prgrm Mgr: Giovanni Cauteruccio
Plnt Mgr: Terry Cummings
Mktg Mgr: Jonathan Fitz

PRYSMIAN POWER CABLE & SYS
See PRYSMIAN CABLES AND SYSTEMS USA LLC

D-U-N-S 00-288-2434 IMP/EXP
▲ PS BUSINESS PARKS INC
701 Western Ave, Glendale, CA 91201-2349
Tel (818) 244-8080 *Founded/Ownrshp* 1990
Sales 373.6MM *EMP* 142^E
Tkr Sym PSB *Exch* NYS
SIC 6798 Real estate investment trusts
CEO: Joseph D Russell Jr
**Ch Bd:* Ronald L Havner Jr
Pr: Maria R Hawthorne
COO: John W Petersen
CFO: Edward A Stokx
VP: Candace Krol
VP: Viola Sanchez
VP: Eugene Uhlman
VP: Gene Uhlman
Exec: Claire Kelvin
Rgnl Mgr: Dennis Fay
Board of Directors: Jennifer Holden Dunbar, James H Kropp, Sara Grootwassink Lewis, Michael V McGee, Gary E Pruitt, Robert S Rollo, Peter Schultz

D-U-N-S 15-101-5831
PS ENERGY GROUP INC
4480 N Shallowford Rd # 100, Dunwoody, GA 30338-6470
Tel (770) 350-3000 *Founded/Ownrshp* 1986
Sales 150.0MM *EMP* 34
SIC 8742 5172 4924 Management consulting services; Transportation consultant; Materials mgmt. (purchasing, handling, inventory) consultant; Site location consultant; Petroleum products; Gases, liquefied petroleum (propane); Gasoline; Natural gas distribution
CEO: Livia Whisenhunt
**COO:* Roger Murray
Bd of Dir: Rachel Jensen
CIO: Jack Whisenhunt
Dir IT: Dan Hamilton

D-U-N-S 07-913-1527
PS LOGISTICS LLC
1810 Avenue C, Birmingham, AL 35218-1552
Tel (205) 788-4000 *Founded/Ownrshp* 2011
Sales 214.7MM^E *EMP* 350^E
SIC 4214 3537 Local trucking with storage; Industrial trucks & tractors

PS&S ENGINEERING
See PAULUS SOKOLOWSKI & SARTOR ENGINEERING A PROFESSIONAL CORP

D-U-N-S 07-459-0183
■ PSA AIRLINES INC
US AIRWAYS EXPRESS
(*Suby of* AMERICAN AIRLINES GROUP INC) ★
3400 Terminal Rd, Vandalia, OH 45377-1041
Tel (937) 454-1116 *Founded/Ownrshp* 2005
Sales 104.2MM^E *EMP* 1,000
SIC 4512 Air passenger carrier, scheduled
Pr: Keith D Houk
Ofcr: Kevin Lauck
VP: Randy Fusi
**VP:* James Schear
QA Dir: Gregory Scoumis
Dir IT: Bobby Jones
**VP Opers:* Timothy Keuscher
VP Opers: Mark Zweidinger

PSA HEALTHCARE
See PEDIATRIC SERVICES HOLDING CORP

D-U-N-S 05-251-5502
PSA HEALTHCARE
(*Suby of* PORTFOLIO LOGIC LLC) ★
760 North Dr Ste D, Melbourne, FL 32934-9247
Tel (321) 254-4254 *Founded/Ownrshp* 2010
Sales 5.9MM^E *EMP* 2,409^E
SIC 8099 Health & allied services

D-U-N-S 07-945-0689
PSAV HOLDINGS LLC
111 W Ocean Blvd Ste 1110, Long Beach, CA 90802-4688
Tel (562) 366-0138 *Founded/Ownrshp* 2013
Sales 98.4MM^E *EMP* 8,200
SIC 7359 Equipment rental & leasing
Ex Dir: J Michael McIlwain

D-U-N-S 08-024-1729
PSAV INC
5100 River Rd Ste 300, Schiller Park, IL 60176-1058
Tel (847) 222-9800 *Founded/Ownrshp* 2015
Sales 81.2MM^E *EMP* 8,350^E
SIC 7371 7359 Software programming applications; Equipment rental & leasing
Pr: J Michael McIlwain
COO: Skylar Cunningham
CFO: Benjamin E Erwin
Sr VP: Arthur A Clyne Jr
Sr VP: Catherine E Kozik
Sr VP: Stephen Lipa
Sr VP: John Rissi
Sr VP: Ken Russell
Sr VP: Mike Stengel
Sr VP: Ali Vafa
Sr VP: Jeff Winkler
Board of Directors: Louis J D'ambrosio, Evan Eason, John J Gavin, Bradley J Gross, Larry B Porcellato, Leonard Seevers

PSAV PRESENTATION SERVICES
See AUDIO VISUAL SERVICES GROUP INC

D-U-N-S 02-345-0345
PSC CUSTOM LP
POLAR SERVICE CENTERS
(*Suby of* POLAR CORP) ★
1015 W Saint Germain St # 420, Saint Cloud, MN 56301-5426
Tel (320) 746-2255 *Founded/Ownrshp* 2006
Sales 88.2MM^E *EMP* 500
SIC 7539 5012 Trailer repair; Trailers for trucks, new & used
Pt: Micael Evans

D-U-N-S 13-202-0020 IMP/EXP
■ PSC ENVIRONMENTAL SERVICES LLC
(*Suby of* STERICYCLE INC) ★
5151 San Felipe St # 1100, Houston, TX 77056-3607
Tel (713) 623-8777 *Founded/Ownrshp* 2014
Sales 431.2MM^E *EMP* 950^E
SIC 4953 4959 5093 Hazardous waste collection & disposal; Environmental cleanup services; Ferrous metal scrap & waste
CEO: Bruce Roberson
**Sr VP:* Jeffery Stocks

D-U-N-S 82-757-2541
PSC HOLDINGS I LP
5151 San Felipe St # 1600, Houston, TX 77056-3607
Tel (713) 623-8777 *Founded/Ownrshp* 2011
Sales 2.1MMM^E *EMP* 3,404
SIC 4212 Garbage collection & transport, no disposal
Pt: Bruce E Roberson
CFO: Michael W Ramirez
Sr VP: Jeffrey Stocks
VP: Josh McMorrow

D-U-N-S 96-850-5235
PSC HOLDINGS II LP
(*Suby of* PSC HOLDINGS I LP) ★
5151 San Felipe St # 1600, Houston, TX 77056-3607
Tel (713) 623-8777 *Founded/Ownrshp* 2010
Sales 2.1MMM *EMP* 3,350
SIC 4953 8748 Sanitary landfill operation; Business consulting
Pt: Bruce Roberson
Pr: Brad Clark
CFO: Michael W Ramirez
VP: MO Azose
VP: Carl Britsch
VP: Jeff Stocks

D-U-N-S 82-932-2937
PSC HOLDINGS INC
(*Suby of* PSC HOLDINGS II LP) ★
5151 San Felipe St # 1100, Houston, TX 77056-3607
Tel (713) 623-8777 *Founded/Ownrshp* 2010
Sales 2.3MMM^E *EMP* 1,138^E
SIC 4953 4959 Hazardous waste collection & disposal; Environmental cleanup services
Ch Bd: Victor J Huebner
**Pr:* Brad Clark
**Pr:* Bruce E Roberson
**Sec:* C D Landherr
**VP:* Carole A Clause
**VP:* Josh McMorrow
**VP:* P S Spielman
**VP:* Jeffrey Stocks
**Prin:* Jim Burns

D-U-N-S 96-192-3500
PSC HOLDINGS INC
109 Graham St, Zanesville, OH 43701-3103
Tel (740) 454-6253 *Founded/Ownrshp* 2008
Sales 83.5MM *EMP* 98^E
SIC 1389 Hydraulic fracturing wells
Prin: Dan Pottmeyer
**Prin:* Kelly Hartman
**Prin:* Jim Rose
Sls Mgr: Chris Berns

D-U-N-S 00-192-0636 IMP
PSC INDUSTRIES INC
P S C
(*Suby of* GENERAL PLASTICS) ★
1100 W Market St, Louisville, KY 40203-1438
Tel (502) 625-7700 *Founded/Ownrshp* 1987
Sales 192.4MM^E *EMP* 600
SIC 3411 Metal cans
**CEO:* Philip E Kamins
CFO: Chris Hart
Mktg Dir: Heather Deitchman

D-U-N-S 62-254-0037 IMP/EXP
PSC LLC
(*Suby of* PSC HOLDINGS INC) ★
5151 San Felipe St Ste 11, Houston, TX 77056-3607
Tel (713) 623-8777 *Founded/Ownrshp* 2010
Sales 2.3MMM^E *EMP* 5,321
SIC 4953 4959 Hazardous waste collection & disposal; Environmental cleanup services
Pr: Brad Clark
**CFO:* Jeff Stocks
Rgnl VP: David Johnson
VP: David V Andrews
VP: Carl Britsch
VP: Bradford Clark
**VP:* Liz Crow
**VP:* Joe Davis
VP: Brent Mason
VP: Mary Monell
**VP:* Jeff Nyberg
**VP:* Rick Pitman
VP: Jeffrey Stocks
VP: Dan Sturmon

D-U-N-S 05-700-0994
PSCH INC (NY)
PROMOTING SPCIALIZED CARE HLTH
14202 20th Ave Rm 301, Flushing, NY 11351-3000
Tel (718) 559-0516 *Founded/Ownrshp* 1980
Sales 90.6MM *EMP* 900
SIC 8361 8331 8093 Rehabilitation center, residential: health care incidental; Job training & vocational rehabilitation services; Mental health clinic, outpatient
Pr: Alan Weinstock
CTO: Nadia Hrvatin
IT Man: Sandra Hinds

D-U-N-S 15-476-6539
PSCU INC
560 Carillon Pkwy, Saint Petersburg, FL 33716-1294
Tel (727) 572-8822 *Founded/Ownrshp* 1981
Sales 388.0MM^E *EMP* 1,400
Accts Pricewaterhousecoopers Llp Ta
SIC 7389 Credit card service; Financial services
CEO: Chuck Fagan
Pr: Sheila Fenton
**Pr:* Mike Kelly
**COO:* Tom Gandre
CFO: Betsy Bennett
Ch: Brian Caldarelli
**Ch:* Craig Esrael
Bd of Dir: Darren Williams
Ex VP: Fredda McDonald
Ex VP: Steve Salzer
VP: Tom Chandler
VP: Dan Csont
VP: Glynn Frechette
VP: David Hall
VP: Mario Jiron
VP: Jack Lynch
VP: Norma Martinez
VP: Steven Mathias
VP: Brenden McGinness
VP: John McPherson
VP: Ron Metsker

PSE
See PUGET HOLDING CO LLC

D-U-N-S 01-673-1946
PSE HOLDING CORP
SCHWARZKOPF HOLDING CORP
(*Suby of* PLANSEE SE)
115 Constitution Blvd, Franklin, MA 02038-2584
Tel (508) 553-3800 *Founded/Ownrshp* 2009
Sales 89.5MM^E *EMP* 130^E
SIC 8742 Management consulting services
Prin: Paul Schwarzkopf
Ql Cn Mgr: Mike Lapage
Ql Cn Mgr: David Lopez

PSECU
See PENNSYLVANIA STATE EMPLOYEES CREDIT UNION

D-U-N-S 05-984-8452
PSECU SERVICES INC
1 Credit Union Pl Ste 1, Harrisburg, PA 17110-2912
Tel (800) 237-7238 *Founded/Ownrshp* 1995
Sales 195.1MM *EMP* 5
SIC 8742 Financial consultant
Pr: Gregory A Smith
Pr Mgr: Melissa Etshied

PSEG ENERGY HOLDINGS, LLC
See PSEG ENERGY HOLDINGS LLC

D-U-N-S 61-310-1385 IMP
■ PSEG ENERGY HOLDINGS LLC
PSEG ENERGY HOLDINGS, LLC
(*Suby of* PUBLIC SERVICE ENTERPRISE GROUP INC) ★
80 Park Plz Ste 3, Newark, NJ 07102-4194
Tel (973) 430-7000 *Founded/Ownrshp* 1989
Sales NA *EMP* 2,756
SIC 6153 6512 Short-term business credit; Nonresidential building operators
CEO: Robert J Dougherty

D-U-N-S 12-466-6269 IMP
■ PSEG FOSSIL LLC
(*Suby of* PSEG POWER LLC) ★
80 Park Plz Ste 3, Newark, NJ 07102-4194
Tel (973) 430-7000 *Founded/Ownrshp* 1903
Sales 122.9MM^E *EMP* 169^E
SIC 4911 Electric services
**Pr:* Richard P Lopriore
**CFO:* Thomas M O'Flynn

D-U-N-S 61-598-0351
■ PSEG NUCLEAR LLC
(*Suby of* PSEG POWER LLC) ★
80 Park Plz, Hancocks Bridge, NJ 08038
Tel (856) 339-1002 *Founded/Ownrshp* 1903
Sales 228.8MM^E *EMP* 2,387^E
SIC 3462 Nuclear power plant forgings, ferrous
CEO: Ralph Izzo
**Pr:* William Levis

D-U-N-S 84-879-3910 IMP
■ PSEG POWER LLC
(*Suby of* PUBLIC SERVICE ENTERPRISE GROUP INC) ★
80 Park Plz T-9, Newark, NJ 07102-4109
Tel (973) 430-7000 *Founded/Ownrshp* 1999
Sales 4.9MMM *EMP* 2,939^E
SIC 4911 Generation, electric power
Ch Bd: Ralph Izzo
**Pr:* William Levis
CFO: Daniel J Cregg
**Ex VP:* Tamara L Linde
VP: Stuart Black
Board of Directors: Derek M Dirisio, Margaret M Pego

D-U-N-S 16-969-4606
■ PSEG SERVICES CORP
(*Suby of* PUBLIC SERVICE ENTERPRISE GROUP INC) ★
80 Park Plz Ste 3, Newark, NJ 07102-4194
Tel (973) 430-7000 *Founded/Ownrshp* 1999
Sales 98.7MM^E *EMP* 1,029
SIC 8611 Public utility association
Ch Bd: Ralph Izzl
**Pr:* Elbert Simpson
VP: John E Anderson
VP: J Brian Smith
VP: Eric B Svenson

PSEGLI AS AGENT FOR LIPA
See LONG ISLAND POWER AUTHORITY

PSERS
See PUBLIC SCHOOL EMPLOYEES RETIREMENT SYSTEM

D-U-N-S 78-321-3606
PSF MECHANICAL INC
11621 E Marginal Way S, Tukwila, WA 98168-1965
Tel (206) 764-9663 *Founded/Ownrshp* 1991
Sales 100.7MM^E *EMP* 225
Accts Berntson Porter & Co Pllc B
SIC 1711 8711 Plumbing, heating, air-conditioning contractors; Mechanical contractor; Engineering services
Ch Bd: Warren Beardsley
**Pr:* James Reynolds
**CEO:* Andrew Read
**COO:* Chris Lawson
**CFO:* Doug Long
Exec: Derek Benson
**Exec:* John King
Exec: Carrie Rulison
Off Mgr: Traci Staffen
Dir IT: Jim Critchlow
Sys Mgr: Tricia Reed

PSHI
See PSI SERVICES HOLDING INC

PSI
See PATIENT SERVICES INC

PSI
See POPULATION SERVICES INTERNATIONAL

PSI
See PHILLIPS SERVICE INDUSTRIES INC

PSI
See PERFORMANCE SYSTEMS INC

PSI
See POLICY STUDIES INC

D-U-N-S 83-080-8361
PSI ACQUISITION INC
(*Suby of* PSI CORPORATE HEADQUARTERS) ★
1901 S Meyers Rd Ste 400, Oakbrook Terrace, IL 60181-5260
Tel (630) 691-1490 *Founded/Ownrshp* 2005
Sales 10.0MM *EMP* 2,340^E
SIC 6719 Investment holding companies, except banks
**Prin:* Murray R Savage

PSI CORPORATE HEADQUARTERS
See PROFESSIONAL SERVICE INDUSTRIES INC

PSI HOLDING
See PROFESSIONAL SERVICE INDUSTRIES HOLDING INC

D-U-N-S 13-371-5198
■ PSI SERVICES HOLDING INC
PSHI
(*Suby of* MAXIMUS INC) ★
1515 Wynkoop St Ste 400, Denver, CO 80202-5558
Tel (303) 863-0900 *Founded/Ownrshp* 2012
Sales 96.7MM^E *EMP* 1,315
SIC 8741 8742 7371 8748 Administrative management; Management consulting services; Custom computer programming services; Business consulting
CEO: Margaret M Laub
Ch Bd: Alec Machiels
Pr: Eric Rubin
Treas: Carroll Wallace

D-U-N-S 04-309-1602
PSI SERVICES LLC (WV)
2950 N Hollywood Way # 200, Burbank, CA 91505-1072
Tel (818) 847-6180 *Founded/Ownrshp* 2001
Sales 150.2MM^E *EMP* 1,020
SIC 8748

D-U-N-S 05-882-7069
PSILOS GROUP MANAGERS LLC
1 Liberty Plz Ste 2301, New York, NY 10006-1404
Tel (212) 242-8844 *Founded/Ownrshp* 1998
Sales 83.2MM^E *EMP* 200
SIC 6799 8059 Venture capital companies; Nursing home, except skilled & intermediate care facility

PSJA
See PHARR SAN JUAN-ALAMO INDEPENDENT SCHOOL DISTRICT

D-U-N-S 80-138-6660 IMP
PSL-NORTH AMERICA LLC
13092 Sea Plane Road Bay, Bay St Louis, MS 39520
Tel (228) 533-7779 *Founded/Ownrshp* 2007
Sales 110.5MM^E *EMP* 350
SIC 3312 Pipes & tubes
**CFO:* John Heinemann
IT Man: Craig Evans
S&M/VP: Steve Oyler

PSMI
See PRODUCTION SERVICES MANAGEMENT INC

PSNC ENERGY
See PUBLIC SERVICE CO OF NORTH CAROLINA INC

D-U-N-S 05-081-3773
PSOMAS
555 S Flower St Ste 4300, Los Angeles, CA 90071-2405
Tel (310) 954-3700 *Founded/Ownrshp* 2003
Sales 114.4MM^E *EMP* 575
SIC 8713 8711 Surveying services; Engineering services
CEO: Blake Murillo
**Pr:* Jacob Lipa
**Treas:* Loren Sokolow
VP: Joel Miller
VP: Sean P Vargas
CTO: Terry Fuller
Sys Mgr: Glenn Pfleiderer
Tech Mgr: Dennis Phinney
Software D: Daniel Mejia
Mktg Dir: Tanya Gross
Snr PM: Edward G McCarthy

PSP
See PENN STAINLESS PRODUCTS INC

PSP ENGINEERING
See PSP INDUSTRIES INC

D-U-N-S 00-914-5103
PSP INDUSTRIES INC
PSP ENGINEERING
(*Suby of* STOCKTON STEEL DIVISION) ★
9885 Doerr Ln, Schertz, TX 78154-9408
Tel (210) 651-9595 *Founded/Ownrshp* 1990
Sales 165.9MM^E *EMP* 500
SIC 3533 3531 3564 3532 3559 Oil & gas field machinery; Construction machinery; Air purification equipment; Mining machinery; Refinery, chemical processing & similar machinery
Pr: Michael Senneway
**Pr:* Bennie Ray Hooper
**VP:* Dennis Stirm
**VP:* Roy Stokes
Plnt Mgr: Larry Koether

D-U-N-S 88-435-6932 IMP
PSP STORES LLC
PET SUPPLIES PLUS
(*Suby of* PET SUPPLIES PLUS) ★
17197 N Laurel Park Dr, Livonia, MI 48152-2680
Tel (734) 793-6600 *Founded/Ownrshp* 1994
Sales 769.9MM^E *EMP* 4,000
SIC 5999 Pets & pet supplies
CEO: Christopher Rowland
**Pt:* Alvin Weisberg
Pr: Tom Slater
**Ex VP:* Dominic Buccellato
**Sr VP:* DerekT Panfil
**Sr VP:* Kenneth Miles Tedder Jr
VP: Jim Jelinek
VP: Nick Russo
VP: Reina Vandelft-
Snr Mgr: Pat Partridge

PSS FEDERAL
See PREFERRED SYSTEMS SOLUTIONS INC

D-U-N-S 10-182-2682 IMP/EXP
■ PSS WORLD MEDICAL INC
PHYSICIAN SALES & SERVICE
(*Suby of* MCKESSON CORP) ★
4345 Southpoint Blvd # 110, Jacksonville, FL 32216-6106
Tel (904) 332-3000 *Founded/Ownrshp* 2013
Sales 1.9MMM^E *EMP* 4,100
SIC 5122 5047 Pharmaceuticals; Medical & hospital equipment; Medical equipment & supplies
Pr: Gary A Corless

*CFO: David M Bronson
*Treas: David D Klarner
*Chf Mktg O: John F Sasen Sr
Sr VP: Kevin P English
Sr VP: Bradley J Hilton
VP: Andrew E Behrends
VP: Bob Bluford
VP: Randy Chittum
*VP: Joshua H Derienzis
VP: Thomas Dinnocenzi
VP: Carl A Duhnoski
VP: Patrick Dunigan
VP: Robert Filer
VP: Robbie Forste
VP: Brad Hilton
VP: Ted Hirsch
VP: Pat Holmes
VP: John G Kammlade
VP: Jenny R Kobin
VP: Anthony Record

PSUSD
See PALM SPRINGS UNIFIED SCHOOL DIST

D-U-N-S 36-452-5360
■ PSYCHIATRIC SOLUTIONS INC
(Suby of UNIVERSAL HEALTH SERVICES INC) ★
6640 Carothers Pkwy # 500, Franklin, TN 37067-6324
Tel (615) 312-5700 Founded/Ownrshp 1988
Sales 784.2MM[E] EMP 23,000
SIC 8011 8063 Psychiatric clinic; Psychiatric hospitals
Pr: Joey A Jacobs
COO: Lisa Cocca
*COO: Ronald M Fincher
CFO: Chris Statz
*Ex VP: Christopher L Howard
*Ex VP: Jack E Polson
Exec: Brent Turner
Chf Nrs Of: Larry Skinner
CIO: Kaaren Harger
QA Dir: Darcie Johnson
Doctor: David Fulton

D-U-N-S 07-993-6554
PT HOLDINGS LLC
1150 N Swift Rd Ste A, Addison, IL 60101-1453
Tel (800) 438-8898 Founded/Ownrshp 2013
Sales 105.9MM[E] EMP 280
SIC 5084 5046 7699 6719 Industrial machinery & equipment; Commercial cooking & food service equipment; Restaurant equipment repair; Investment holding companies, except banks
CEO: Steve Snower
CFO: Lori Sherwood

PT HOME CARE
See PERSONAL TOUCH HOME CARE

PT SUPPLY
See POWER & TELEPHONE SUPPLY CO

D-U-N-S 08-016-0006
PT-1 HOLDINGS LLC
720 Portal St, Cotati, CA 94931-3060
Tel (707) 665-4295 Founded/Ownrshp 2012
Sales 52.6MM[E] EMP 1,600
SIC 6719 Personal holding companies, except banks
Ex Dir: Michael Sechrist

PTC
See TURNPIKE COMMISSION PA

PTC
See PARRISH TIRE CO

D-U-N-S 96-451-6137 IMP/EXP
PTC GROUP HOLDINGS CORP
6051 Wallace Road Ext # 2, Wexford, PA 15090-7386
Tel (412) 299-7900 Founded/Ownrshp 2009
Sales 300.1MM[E] EMP 800
SIC 3317 Tubing, mechanical or hypodermic sizes: cold drawn stainless
Pr: Peter Whiting
*Treas: Patty Coleman
*VP: Thomas W Crowley

D-U-N-S 17-574-9431
▲ PTC INC
140 Kendrick St, Needham, MA 02494-2739
Tel (781) 370-5000 Founded/Ownrshp 1985
Sales 1.1MMM EMP 5,800
Accts Pricewaterhousecoopers Llp Bo
Tkr Sym PTC Exch NGS
SIC 7372 7373 7371 Prepackaged software; Application computer software; Computer-aided system services; Computer-aided design (CAD) systems service; Computer-aided engineering (CAE) systems service; Computer-aided manufacturing (CAM) systems service; Computer software development & applications; Computer software development
Pr: James E Heppelmann
*Ch Bd: Robert P Schechter
Pr: Robert Gremley
Pr: Craig Hayman
CFO: Andrew Miller
Ex VP: Barry Cohen
Ex VP: Matthew Cohen
Ex VP: Anthony Dibona
VP: Aaron C Von Staats
Board of Directors: Janice D Chaffin, Phillip Fernandez, Donald K Grierson, Klaus Hoehn, Paul A Lacy, Renato Zambonini

D-U-N-S 05-711-4966
PTERIS GLOBAL (USA) INC
208 Shoreline Pkwy, Fort Mill, SC 29708-8398
Tel (980) 253-3267 Founded/Ownrshp 2012
Sales 145.5MM EMP 10
SIC 3535 Conveyors & conveying equipment

D-U-N-S 80-730-8858
PTI UNION LLC
PHARMA TECH INDUSTRIES
1310 Stylemaster Dr, Union, MO 63084-1155
Tel (636) 583-8664 Founded/Ownrshp 2008
Sales 110.0MM[E] EMP 85
SIC 5122 Pharmaceuticals

D-U-N-S 10-860-5213
PTMW INC
5040 Nw Us Highway 24, Topeka, KS 66618-3815
Tel (785) 232-7792 Founded/Ownrshp 1983
Sales 103.3MM[E] EMP 200
SIC 3441 Building components, structural steel
Pr: Patti Jon Goff
COO: John Butterfield
VP: Bryan Christensen
VP: Fred Gantz
VP: Pamala Ludlow
VP Prd: Sean Ryan
QC Dir: Clay Searles
VP Sls: Darren Lepage

PTS
See PRODUCTION TOOL SUPPLY CO LLC

PTS
See PORTAGE TOWNSHIP SCHOOLS

D-U-N-S 07-964-0064
■ PTS INTERMEDIATE HOLDINGS LLC
(Suby of CATALENT INC) ★
14 Schoolhouse Rd, Somerset, NJ 08873-1213
Tel (732) 537-6200 Founded/Ownrshp 2007
Sales 45.6MM[E] EMP 8,300
SIC 2834 Pharmaceutical preparations

PTS VAM CO
See VAM USA LLC

D-U-N-S 00-692-0292 IMP/EXP
PUBCO CORP
3830 Kelley Ave, Cleveland, OH 44114-4534
Tel (216) 881-5300 Founded/Ownrshp 1996
Sales 92.0MM[E] EMP 260
SIC 3531 6512 3955 Construction machinery; Nonresidential building operators; Carbon paper & inked ribbons
Pr: William Dillingham
*CFO: Maria Szubski
*VP: Stephen R Kalette

D-U-N-S 07-482-9417
PUBLIC BROADCASTING SERVICE
PBS KIDS
2100 Crystal Dr Ste 100, Arlington, VA 22202-3784
Tel (703) 739-5000 Founded/Ownrshp 1970
Sales 473.2MM EMP 507
Accts Bdo Usa Llp Bethesda Md
SIC 4833 Television broadcasting stations
Pr: Paula A Kerger
*Ch Bd: Donald A Baer
COO: Jonathan Barzilay
*COO: Michael Jones
*CFO: Barbara L Landes
Sr VP: Betsy Gerdeman
Sr VP: Lesli Rotenberg
Sr VP: Ira Rubenstein
VP: Matt Baird
VP: Thomas Crockett
VP: Caryn Ginsberg
*VP: Katherine Lauderdale
VP: Alicia Levi
VP: Pete Quinlivan
VP: Juan Seplveda
VP: Elizabeth Suarez
VP: William Weber
VP: Don Wilcox
Assoc Dir: Tim Bawcombe
Assoc Dir: Maria Vera
Creative D: Travis Daub

D-U-N-S 09-013-2903
PUBLIC BUILDING AUTHORITY
AUTORDAD DE EDIFICIOS PUBLICOS
Cond Centro Plz, San Juan, PR 00909-2110
Tel (787) 722-0101 Founded/Ownrshp 1958
Sales 295.8MM EMP 1,486
Accts Parissi Psc San Juan/Hato
SIC 8611 Business associations
Ex Dir: Lina Hernandez
IT Man: Jaime Belgodere

D-U-N-S 18-282-6909
PUBLIC CONSULTING GROUP INC
148 State St Fl 10, Boston, MA 02109-2589
Tel (617) 426-2026 Founded/Ownrshp 1986
Sales 341.4MM EMP 1,015
Accts Dicicco Gulman & Company Llp
SIC 8742 Business consultant
Pr: William S Mosakowski
Pr: Tim Walker
*CFO: Dan Heaney
Sr VP: Amy W Smith
*VP: Tony McLean Brown
VP: Gary Reimers
VP: Laurie Thornton
*Prin: Stephen Skinner
Mng Dir: Dennis Jackson
Prgrm Mgr: April Boehm
Prgrm Mgr: Geoffrey Dudley
Board of Directors: Marc Fenton Benjamin Bobo, T McLean Brown, William Mosakowski, Stephen Skinner

D-U-N-S 19-130-4724
PUBLIC EMPLOYEE DEFERRED COMPENSATION OHIO
EXECUTIVE OFFICE
(Suby of EXECUTIVE OFFICE STATE OF OHIO) ★
257 E Town St Ste 457, Columbus, OH 43215-4626
Tel (614) 466-7245 Founded/Ownrshp 1976
Sales 1.1MMM EMP 20
SIC 8721 9311 Payroll accounting service; Finance, taxation & monetary policy;
Ex Dir: R Keith Overly
CFO: Paul D Miller

D-U-N-S 07-918-5479
PUBLIC EMPLOYEES INDIVIDUAL RETIREMENT ACCOUNT FUND/DEFERRED COMPENSATION PLAN
(Suby of STATE OF ALABAMA) ★
201 S Union St, Montgomery, AL 36104-4369
Tel (334) 517-7000 Founded/Ownrshp 2013
Sales NA EMP 4,740[E]
SIC 9441 Workmen's compensation office, government

PUBLIC GAS PARTNERS
See MUNICIPAL GAS AUTHORITY OF GEORGIA

D-U-N-S 08-219-9324
PUBLIC HEALTH FOUNDATION ENTERPRISES INC
PHFE
12801 Crossrds Pkwy S 200, City of Industry, CA 91746
Tel (562) 692-4643 Founded/Ownrshp 1968
Sales 97.5MM EMP 1,437[E]
Accts Haskell & White Llp Irvine C
SIC 8741 Management services
Pr: Mark J Bertler
Pr: Gerald D Jensen
CEO: Michael R Gomez
CFO: Margarita Buitrago
*Ch: Michael Ascher
*Ch: Azhar K Qureshi
Treas: Karen L Angel
*Treas: Ellen Digiampaolo
*VP: Susan Vacko
Exec: Monique Black
Prin: Weston F Milliken

D-U-N-S 12-866-3390
PUBLIC HEALTH INSTITUTE
555 12th St Ste 1050, Oakland, CA 94607-3630
Tel (510) 285-5500 Founded/Ownrshp 1964
Sales 106.7MM EMP 630
Accts Gelman Rosenberg & Freedman B
SIC 8733 Scientific research agency; Medical research
Pr: Mary Pittman
*COO: Melange Matthews
*COO: Bob Wolfson
*CFO: Tamar Dorfman
*VP: Matthew Marsom
*VP: Carmen Nevarez
Assoc Dir: Douglas Jutte
Ex Dir: Jessie Gruman
Ex Dir: Joan Twiss
Ex Dir: Robert Valdez
Prgrm Mgr: Carol Alliger

D-U-N-S 06-905-3379
PUBLIC HEALTH MANAGEMENT CORP
PHILADELPHIA HEALTH MANAGEMENT
Centre Sq E 1500 Market, Philadelphia, PA 19102
Tel (215) 985-2500 Founded/Ownrshp 1972
Sales 131.7MM EMP 1,100
Accts Eisneramper Llp Jenkintown P
SIC 8741 Nursing & personal care facility management
CEO: Richard J Cohen
*CFO: Marino Pulite
*Treas: Robert W Gage
*Sr VP: John G Lobe
*VP: Tina Wolfman Baker
*VP: Michael Bedrosian
*VP: Celeste Collins
*VP: Elaine Fox
*VP: Amy Friedlander
*VP: Tine Hansen-Turton
*VP: Leslie Hurtig
*VP: Lynne Kotranski
*VP: Jacqueline Link
*VP: Michael Moore
*VP: Deborah Schlater
*VP: William Weber
*VP: Myra Woll

D-U-N-S 07-327-8368
PUBLIC HEALTH SOLUTIONS
MHRA
40 Worth St Fl 5, New York, NY 10013-2955
Tel (646) 619-6400 Founded/Ownrshp 1957
Sales 211.9MM EMP 650
Accts Lb Marks Paneth Llp New York
SIC 8733 Medical research
Pr: Ellen Rautenberg
*COO: Steven Newman
*VP: Mary Ann Chiasson
*VP: Kathryn Miller
*VP: Claire T Oliver
VP: Claire Th Roux Oliver
CIO: Joseph Difilippi
CTO: Susan Vitucci
IT Man: Chris Kovoleski
QI Cn Mgr: Ada Feng
Counsel: Bertie Nei

D-U-N-S 07-663-4252 IMP
PUBLIC HOSPITAL DISTRICT 1 OF KING COUNTY
VALLEY MEDICAL CENTER
400 S 43rd St, Renton, WA 98055-5714
Tel (425) 228-3440 Founded/Ownrshp 1948
Sales 480.4MM EMP 2,700[E]
Accts Kpmg Llp Seattle Washington
SIC 8062 General medical & surgical hospitals
CEO: Richard D Roodman
*COO: Paul Hayes
*CFO: Michael Bernstein
Treas: Jeannine Grinnell
Ofcr: Terry Block
Ofcr: Drew Hunt
Sr VP: Kathryn Beattie
Dir Risk M: Steven Haton
Dir Lab: Dorina McKnight
Dir Rx: Ron Williams
Dir Sec: Jeff Dosch

D-U-N-S 01-019-7556
PUBLIC HOSPITAL DISTRICT 1 SKAGIT COUNTY
SKAGIT VALLEY HOSPITAL
1415 E Kincaid St, Mount Vernon, WA 98274-4126
Tel (360) 424-4111 Founded/Ownrshp 1958
Sales 281.8MM EMP 2,000
Accts Moss Adams Llp Everett Washi
SIC 8062 General medical & surgical hospitals
CEO: Gregg A Davidson
*CFO: Tom Litaker
Bd of Dir: Corey Mendoza
Chf Mktg O: Kathleen Abhold
*Prin: Mike Liepman
Dir IT: Doug Reilly
Dir IT: Karl Stansbury
IT Man: Cherrayl Harrsch
Sftwr Eng: Steve Duncan
Netwrk Eng: Bob Cole
Mtls Dir: Bill Thomas

D-U-N-S 00-697-6310
PUBLIC LOAN CO INC (NY)
(Suby of P L C ENTERPRISES INC)
300 Plaza Dr, Vestal, NY 13850-3647
Tel (607) 584-5274 Founded/Ownrshp 1933
Sales NA EMP 400
SIC 6153 Short-term business credit
Pr: Burton I Koffman
Ex VP: Richard E Koffman

PUBLIC SAFETY & HOMELND SECRTY
See VIRGINIA DEPARTMENT OF CORRECTIONS

D-U-N-S 80-491-5221
PUBLIC SAFETY ARIZONA
AZ DPS
(Suby of EXECUTIVE OFFICE OF STATE OF ARIZONA) ★
2102 W Encanto Blvd, Phoenix, AZ 85009-2847
Tel (602) 223-2000 Founded/Ownrshp 1969
Sales NA EMP 2,500
SIC 9229 Public order & safety statistics centers;
*CFO: Phil Case
Ofcr: Roger Wilson
Ex VP: Donald Brandt
Genl Mgr: Christy Kramer

D-U-N-S 01-713-8116 IMP
PUBLIC SAFETY EQUIPMENT INC
(Suby of STIRLING SQUARE CAPITAL PARTNERS, LLP)
10986 N Warson Rd, Saint Louis, MO 63114-2029
Tel (314) 426-2700 Founded/Ownrshp 1971, 2007
Sales 130.3MM[E] EMP 1,406
SIC 3647 3669

D-U-N-S 17-320-3522
PUBLIC SCHOOL EMPLOYEES RETIREMENT SYSTEM
PSERS
5 N 5th St, Harrisburg, PA 17101-1905
Tel (717) 720-4734 Founded/Ownrshp 1917
Sales NA EMP 309
SIC 6371 9441 Pension funds; Administration of social & manpower programs;
Ex Dir: Jefferey Clay

D-U-N-S 07-421-6409
PUBLIC SCHOOLS OF CITY ANN ARBOR
ANN ARBOR PUBLIC SCHOOLS
2555 S State St, Ann Arbor, MI 48104-6145
Tel (734) 994-2200 Founded/Ownrshp 1904
Sales 247.1MM EMP 2,000
Accts Plante & Moran Pllc Clinton
SIC 8211 Public elementary & secondary schools; Secondary school; High school, junior or senior
*Pr: Deb Mexicotte
*Treas: Irene Patalan
*VP: Christine Stead

D-U-N-S 10-005-8999
PUBLIC SCHOOLS OF ROBESON COUNTY
410 Caton Rd, Lumberton, NC 28360-0450
Tel (910) 671-6000 Founded/Ownrshp 1890
Sales 184.2MM[E] EMP 6,000
SIC 8211 Public elementary & secondary schools
*CFO: Erica Setzer
Bd of Dir: John Campbell
Bd of Dir: Brenda Fairley
VP: James Locklear
*Prin: Rebecca Ward
Dir IT: Todd Russ
IT Man: Clark O'Neal
Info Man: Amy Davis
Info Man: Annette Jones
Info Man: Allison Strickland
Info Man: Rhonda West

D-U-N-S 00-691-5953 IMP
■ PUBLIC SERVICE CO OF COLORADO
XCEL ENERGY
(Suby of XCEL ENERGY INC) ★
1800 Larimer St Ste 1100, Denver, CO 80202-1402
Tel (303) 571-7511 Founded/Ownrshp 1924
Sales 4.1MMM EMP 2,690
Accts Deloitte & Touche Llp Minnea
SIC 4911 4922 4924 Generation, electric power; Transmission, electric power; Distribution, electric power; Natural gas transmission; Natural gas distribution
Ch Bd: Benjamin G S Fowke III
*Pr: David L Eves
*CFO: Teresa S Madden
Sr VP: Jeffrey S Savage
Genl Mgr: Mark Schwartz
Board of Directors: Marvin E McDaniel Jr

D-U-N-S 00-697-1352 IMP
■ PUBLIC SERVICE CO OF NEW HAMPSHIRE (NH)
EVERSOURCE ENERGY
(Suby of EVERSOURCE ENERGY) ★
780 North Commercial St, Manchester, NH 03101-1134
Tel (603) 669-4000 Founded/Ownrshp 1926
Sales 972.2MM EMP 1,025[E]
SIC 4911 Generation, electric power; Transmission, electric power; Distribution, electric power
CEO: Leon J Olivier
*Ch Bd: Thomas J May
*Pr: William J Quinlan
*CFO: James J Judge
*Sr VP: Gregory B Butler
VP: Joseph Purington
VP: Paul Ramsey
Prgrm Mgr: Jack Schelling
Board of Directors: Werner J Schweiger

D-U-N-S 04-001-6268
■ **PUBLIC SERVICE CO OF NEW MEXICO**
(*Suby of* PNM RESOURCES INC) ★
414 Silver Ave Sw Fl 4, Albuquerque, NM 87102-3239
Tel (505) 241-2700 *Founded/Ownrshp* 1917
Sales 1.1MMM *EMP* 1,093
SIC 4911 Electric services; Distribution, electric power; Transmission, electric power
Ch Bd: Patricia K Collawn
CFO: Charles N Eldred
Sr VP: Edward Padilla
Board of Directors: Ronald N Darnell, Ronald E Talbot

D-U-N-S 00-699-6607
■ **PUBLIC SERVICE CO OF NORTH CAROLINA INC** (NC)
PSNC ENERGY
(*Suby of* SCANA CORP) ★
800 Gaston 800 Gas, Gastonia, NC 28056
Tel (704) 864-6731 *Founded/Ownrshp* 1917, 2000
Sales 664.1MM^E *EMP* 859
SIC 4924 Natural gas distribution
Pr: Rusty Harris
**COO:* Jerry W Richardson
VP: Francis P Mood
VP: Fred L Schmidt
Exec: David Newton
Exec: Katherleen Williams
Rgnl Mgr: Tucker Bullock
Rgnl Mgr: Ken Griffin
Netwrk Eng: John Connolly
Netwrk Eng: Joe Hullender

D-U-N-S 00-790-7926
■ **PUBLIC SERVICE CO OF OKLAHOMA**
AEP
(*Suby of* AEP) ★
1 Riverside Plz, Columbus, OH 43215-2355
Tel (614) 716-1000 *Founded/Ownrshp* 1913
Sales 1.3MMM *EMP* 1,133^E
SIC 4911 Electric services; Distribution, electric power; Generation, electric power; Transmission, electric power
CEO: Nicholas K Akins
CFO: Brian X Tierney
VP: Bill McKamey
VP: Tommy Slater
Board of Directors: Lisa M Barton, David M Feinberg, Lana L Hillebrand, Mark C McCullough, Robert P Powers, Dennis E Welch

D-U-N-S 80-678-1175
PUBLIC SERVICE COMMISSION NEW YORK STATE
(*Suby of* EXECUTIVE OFFICE OF STATE OF NEW YORK) ★
3 Empire State Plz 20th, Albany, NY 12223-1000
Tel (518) 474-7080 *Founded/Ownrshp* 1907
Sales NA *EMP* 2,767
SIC 9441 Administration of social & manpower programs;
Ch: Garry Brown

D-U-N-S 00-697-3812
■ **PUBLIC SERVICE ELECTRIC AND GAS CO INC**
P S E & G
(*Suby of* PUBLIC SERVICE ENTERPRISE GROUP INC) ★
80 Park Plz Ste 3, Newark, NJ 07102-4194
Tel (973) 430-7000 *Founded/Ownrshp* 1924
Sales 6.6MMM *EMP* 6,780
SIC 4931

D-U-N-S 16-094-5242 IMP
▲ **PUBLIC SERVICE ENTERPRISE GROUP INC**
80 Park Plz, Newark, NJ 07102-4194
Tel (973) 430-7000 *Founded/Ownrshp* 1985
Sales 10.4MMM *EMP* 13,025^E
Tkr Sym PEG *Exch* NYS
SIC 4931 4911 4924 Electric & other services combined; Generation, electric power; Transmission, electric power; Distribution, electric power; Natural gas distribution
Ch Bd: Ralph Izzo
Pr: Sheila Rostiac
CFO: Daniel J Cregg
Treas: Bradford Huntington
Treas: John Povich
Bd of Dir: Michael Percarpio
Ofcr: Robert C Braun
Ofcr: Laura Langer
Ex VP: Tamara L Linde
Sr VP: Stephen C Byrd
Sr VP: Eileen Moran
Sr VP: Kevin Quinn
VP: Stuart J Black
VP: Rose Chernick
VP: David M Daly
VP: Kathleen Fitzgerald
VP: Thomas Flaherty
VP: Robert Krueger
VP: Shawn Leyden
VP: Laurent Pommier
VP: Donald Staudt
Board of Directors: Willie A Deese, Albert R Gamper Jr, William V Hickey, Shirley Ann Jackson, David Lilley, Thomas A Renyi, Richard J Swift, Susan Tomasky, Alfred W Zollar

D-U-N-S 04-339-4881 IMP/EXP
▲ **PUBLIC STORAGE** (MD)
701 Western Ave, Glendale, CA 91201-2349
Tel (818) 244-8080 *Founded/Ownrshp* 1980
Sales 2.3MMM *EMP* 5,300
Tkr Sym PSA *Exch* NYS
SIC 6798 4225 Real estate investment trusts; Mini-warehouse, warehousing
Ch Bd: Ronald L Havner Jr
Pr: Joseph D Russell
CFO: John Reyes
Ofcr: Candace N Krol
Sr VP: Mark Delcher
Sr VP: David F Doll
Board of Directors: Tamara Hughes Gustavson, Uri P Harkham, B Wayne Hughes Jr, Gary E Pruitt, Ronald P Spogli, Daniel C Staton

D-U-N-S 80-847-4100
PUBLIC TELECOMMUNICATIONS COMMISSION GEORGIA
GEORGIA PUBLIC BROADCASTING
(*Suby of* EXECUTIVE OFFICE OF STATE OF GEORGIA) ★
260 14th St Nw, Atlanta, GA 30318-5360
Tel (404) 685-4788 *Founded/Ownrshp* 1982
Sales 91.3MM^E *EMP* 200
SIC 4833 Television broadcasting stations
Ch: Michael H McDougald
COO: Anthony Padgett
CFO: Bonnie R Bean
CFO: Erin Burns
VP: Bob Brienza
VP: Bert Huffman
VP: Tanya Ott
VP: Bill Overall
Exec: Melvin Jones
Genl Mgr: Teya Ryan
Sls&Mrk Ex: Aishah Rashied-Hyman

PUBLIC TRANSPORTATION
See NEW YORK CITY TRANSIT AUTHORITY

PUBLIC TRANSPORTATION
See MANHATTAN AND BRONX SURFACE TRANSIT OPERATING AUTHORITY

D-U-N-S 60-634-7037
PUBLIC UTILITIES BOARD
BROWNSVILLE PUBLIC UTILITIES B
1425 Robinhood St, Brownsville, TX 78521-4230
Tel (956) 350-8819 *Founded/Ownrshp* 1960
Sales 202.9MM *EMP* 482
SIC 4931 Electric & other services combined
Ch: Noemi Garcia
CEO: John C Bruciak
COO: Fernando Saenz
CFO: Leandro G Garcia
Sec: Nurith Galonsky
CIO: Eddy Hernandez
Mktg Dir: Paul Chavez

PUBLIC UTILITIES, DEPARTMENT O
See COUNTY OF HENRICO

D-U-N-S 00-354-7122
PUBLIC UTILITY DISTRICT 1 OF BENTON COUNTY
ELECTRIC UTILITY
2721 W 10th Ave, Kennewick, WA 99336-4813
Tel (509) 582-2175 *Founded/Ownrshp* 1946
Sales 138.8MM *EMP* 155
SIC 4911 Distribution, electric power
Pr: Jeff Hall
Treas: Janet White
**VP:* Lori Sanders
Genl Mgr: Michelle Ochweri

D-U-N-S 04-411-1037
PUBLIC UTILITY DISTRICT 1 OF CLARK COUNTY
CLARK PUBLIC UTILITIES
1200 Fort Vancouver Way, Vancouver, WA 98663-3527
Tel (360) 992-3000 *Founded/Ownrshp* 1938
Sales 464.7MM *EMP* 325
Accts Moss Adams Llp Portland Ore
SIC 4911 Distribution, electric power
CEO: Wayne Nelson
Treas: Richard Dyer
Trst: Jane Van Dyke
VP: Nancy Barnes
VP: Byron Hanke
Genl Mgr: Erica Erland
Genl Mgr: Lena Wittler
IT Man: Lisa Cruz
IT Man: Jon Mills
Software D: Steve Dentel

D-U-N-S 04-133-4368 EXP
PUBLIC UTILITY DISTRICT 1 OF SNOHOMISH COUNTY
SNOHOMISH CNTY PUB UTILITY DST
2320 California St, Everett, WA 98201-3750
Tel (425) 257-9288 *Founded/Ownrshp* 1936
Sales 626.8MM *EMP* 879
Accts Baker Tilly Madison Wi
SIC 4911 4941 Electric services; Water supply
Pr: Kathleen Vaughn
**VP:* Toni Olson
Genl Mgr: Steve Klein
CIO: Benjamin Beberness

D-U-N-S 00-794-2246
PUBLIC UTILITY DISTRICT 2 GRANT COUNTY
ELECTRIC SYSTEM
30 C St Sw, Ephrata, WA 98823-1876
Tel (509) 754-0500 *Founded/Ownrshp* 1938
Sales 433.1MM^E *EMP* 650
SIC 4911 Distribution, electric power
Pr: Terry Brewer
**VP:* Bob Bernd
IT Man: Richard Geddes
IT Man: Jill Hensley
Sfty Dirs: Mitch Awbrey
Opers Mgr: Michael Harris
Psych: Dorinda Gardner
Surg Cl Rc: Carson Keeler
Doctor: Diane Clark
Doctor: Don James
Nrsg Dir: Becky Booth

D-U-N-S 04-158-5290 IMP
PUBLIC UTILITY DISTRICT NO 1 OF CHELAN COUNTY
CHELAN HYDRO
327 N Wenatchee Ave, Wenatchee, WA 98801-2011
Tel (509) 663-8121 *Founded/Ownrshp* 1936
Sales 542.5MM^E *EMP* 841
SIC 4911 Generation, electric power; Distribution, electric power
Genl Mgr: John Janney
Genl Couns: Carol Wardell

D-U-N-S 00-794-2337
PUBLIC UTILITY DISTRICT NO 1 OF COWLITZ COUNTY
COWLITZ COUNTY PUD
961 12th Ave, Longview, WA 98632-2507
Tel (360) 577-7507 *Founded/Ownrshp* 1936
Sales 138.8MM *EMP* 170
Accts Moss Adams Llp Portland Oreg
SIC 4911 Distribution, electric power
Pr: Jeff Hall
**CFO:* Royce Hagelstein
CFO: Donald McMaster
**Treas:* Pat Lloyd
Dir Risk M: Heather Allen
Genl Mgr: Chad Bartram
**Genl Mgr:* Brian Skeahan
IT Man: McMahon Greg
Pr Dir: Brent Arnold
Genl Couns: Paul Brachvogel
Counsel: Gary Huhta

D-U-N-S 07-185-2016
PUBLIC UTILITY DISTRICT NO 1 OF GRAYS HARBOR COUNTY
GRAYS HARBOR PUD
2720 Sumner Ave, Aberdeen, WA 98520-4321
Tel (360) 532-4220 *Founded/Ownrshp* 1938
Sales 199.1MM^E *EMP* 160
SIC 4911 Distribution, electric power
CFO: Doug Streeter
**Ex Dir:* Richard D Lovely
Genl Mgr: Katy Moore
**Genl Mgr:* Dave Ward
IT Man: Robert Hanny
IT Man: Katy Williamsen
Sls&Mrk Ex: Liz Anderson
Genl Couns: Rick Pitt

D-U-N-S 08-088-7367
PUBLIC WORKS COMMISSION OF CITY OF FAYETTEVILLE (NC)
P W C
955 Old Wilmington Rd, Fayetteville, NC 28301-6357
Tel (910) 223-4005 *Founded/Ownrshp* 1903
Sales 311.1MM *EMP* 467^E
Accts Cherry Bekaert Llp Raleigh N
SIC 4911 4941 Electric services; Water supply
CEO: Steven K Blanchard
**COO:* Marion J Noland
**COO:* Walter V Truitt
**CFO:* J Dwight Miller
Prin: Joseph Callis
Off Admin: Norma Lanthorn
MIS Dir: Barney McClure
Dir IT: Oj Dennings
Sfty Mgr: Andrew Dunlap

D-U-N-S 04-424-2337 IMP/EXP
PUBLICATIONS INTERNATIONAL LTD
CONSUMER GUIDE
8140 Lehigh Ave, Morton Grove, IL 60053-2627
Tel (847) 676-3470 *Founded/Ownrshp* 1967
Sales 84.3MM^E *EMP* 400
SIC 2731 2721 Books: publishing only; Magazines: publishing only, not printed on site
Pr: Louis Weber
Pr: Ann Taylor
CFO: Tim Light
VP: Jennifer Barney
VP: Mary Cunningham
VP: Su Oliveira
Creative D: Anne Oconnor
Dir Bus: Sandy Lau
MIS Dir: Randy Whitlock
VP Opers: Mike Murphy
Mfg Dir: James Zimmermann

D-U-N-S 18-635-8214 IMP
PUBLICIS HEALTHCARE SOLUTIONS INC
TOUCHPOINT
(*Suby of* PUBLICIS GROUPE S A)
1000 Floral Vale Blvd # 400, Morrisville, PA 19067-5569
Tel (866) 616-4777 *Founded/Ownrshp* 1987
Sales 353.2MM^E *EMP* 8,849
SIC 8742 Marketing consulting services
CEO: Rick Keefer
Pr: Larry Green
**Pr:* D R Keefer
**COO:* Michelle Keefe
VP: Tom Clark
VP: Marianne Nugent
VP: Archie Robinson
**VP:* Robert S Westphal
Ex Dir: Nicole Romano
Rgnl Mgr: Cedric Amin
Dist Mgr: Ron Lafevers

D-U-N-S 06-496-4315
PUBLICIS INC
PUBLICIS USA
(*Suby of* PUBLICIS GROUPE S A)
1675 Broadway Fl 2, New York, NY 10019-5852
Tel (212) 279-5000 *Founded/Ownrshp* 1973, 1993
Sales 174.4MM^E *EMP* 850
SIC 7311 Advertising agencies
CEO: Susan Gianinno
COO: Nathalie Fagnan
**CFO:* Doug Henderson
CFO: Kevin Sweeney
Chf Mktg O: Chris Schumaker
Ex VP: David Corr
Ex VP: Jason Sullivan
Sr VP: Erica Herman
Sr VP: Lisa Hersh
Sr VP: Joel Machak
Sr VP: Julie Reiger
VP: Jennifer Baldwin
VP: Victor Basile
VP: Dan Bollin
VP: Richard Concepcion
VP: Richard Delvecchio
VP: Liz Der
VP: Dennis Greeley
VP: Tanya Hill
VP: Barbara Ivancich
VP: Helen Jackers

PUBLICIS USA
See PUBLICIS INC

D-U-N-S 01-657-5748
PUBLISHERS CIRCULATION FULFILLMENT INC
502 Wshington Ave Ste 500, Towson, MD 21204
Tel (410) 821-8614 *Founded/Ownrshp* 1997
Sales 206.3MM^E *EMP* 1,600
SIC 5963

D-U-N-S 00-263-3592 IMP/EXP
PUBLISHERS CLEARING HOUSE LLC
382 Channel Dr, Port Washington, NY 11050-2297
Tel (516) 883-5432 *Founded/Ownrshp* 2002
Sales 163.5MM^E *EMP* 500^E
SIC 5961 8742 Magazines, mail order; Marketing consulting services
Pr: Matt Gately
CEO: Darlene Federbush
Sr VP: Todd Sloane
VP: Mark Cullinane
VP: John Klimaszewski
Creative D: Matthew Lamorte
Creative D: Maryann Lebowitz
Admn Mgr: Robert Mazzella
CIO: Kevin Prinz
DP Exec: Scott Leff
Dir IT: Bob Viscovich

PUBLISHERS COLLECTION SERVICE
See R L POLK & CO

PUBLISHERS INFORMATION BUREAU
See MAGAZINE PUBLISHERS OF AMERICA

PUBLISHERS PRESS
See PUBLISHERS PRINTING CO LLC

D-U-N-S 00-637-3138 IMP
PUBLISHERS PRINTING CO LLC (KY)
PUBLISHERS PRESS
100 Frank E Simon Ave, Shepherdsville, KY 40165-6013
Tel (502) 955-6526 *Founded/Ownrshp* 1866, 1997
Sales 430.6MM^E *EMP* 1,700
SIC 2752 2791 2789 Periodicals, lithographed; Typesetting; Bookbinding & related work
VP Prd: Kelly Reesor
**CEO:* Nicholas X Simon
**Ex VP:* Michael J Simon
VP: Steve Sahloff
VP: Clint Sawyer
Dir IT: Deborah Glasscock
Ql Cn Mgr: Larry Blanton
VP Mktg: Wendy Stratton
Mktg Dir: Amanda Bledsoe
Mktg Mgr: Tj Hume

D-U-N-S 00-692-2009
PUBLIX SUPER MARKETS INC
3300 Publix Corp Pkwy, Lakeland, FL 33811-3311
Tel (863) 688-1188 *Founded/Ownrshp* 1921
Sales 32.6MMM *EMP* 180,000
SIC 5411 Supermarkets, chain
CEO: William E Crenshaw
**Ch Bd:* Charles H Jenkins Jr
**Pr:* Randall T Jones Sr
**CFO:* David P Phillips
**V Ch Bd:* Hoyt R Barnett
Sr VP: John A Attaway Jr
Sr VP: Laurie Z Douglas
VP: Marilyn Camacho
VP: Shiloh Emery
Board of Directors: Jessica L Blume, Jane B Finley, G Thomas Hough, Howard M Jenkins, Stephen M Knopilk

D-U-N-S 06-265-5535 IMP/EXP
PUCKETT MACHINERY CO
CATERPILLAR AUTHORIZED DEALER
100 Caterpillar Dr, Flowood, MS 39232-6204
Tel (601) 969-6000 *Founded/Ownrshp* 1982
Sales 155.3MM^E *EMP* 400
SIC 5082 5084 5063 7699 General construction machinery & equipment; Logging equipment & supplies; Engines & parts, diesel; Generators; Construction equipment repair; Industrial machinery & equipment repair
Pr: Richard Puckett
**Treas:* Bill Farlow
**VP:* Ben T Puckett
Prgrm Mgr: John Lebreton
IT Man: Vince Thacker
Sales Exec: Dean Hennigan
Sls Mgr: Paul Gregory
Sales Asso: Beck Barlow

PUEBLO CITY SCHOOL
See PUEBLO SCHOOL DISTRICT NO 60

D-U-N-S 08-037-3236
PUEBLO COUNTY GOVERNMENT
215 W 10th St, Pueblo, CO 81003-2945
Tel (719) 583-6000 *Founded/Ownrshp* 1861
Sales NA *EMP* 1,017
Accts Mcpherson Breyfogle Daveline
SIC 9111 Executive offices;

PUEBLO DISPOSAL
See US WASTE INDUSTRIES INC

D-U-N-S 80-837-3612 IMP/EXP
PUEBLO INC
Calle Diana Ste 14, Guaynabo, PR 00968
Tel (787) 757-3131 *Founded/Ownrshp* 2007
Sales 166.0MM^E *EMP* 2,000^E
SIC 5411 Grocery stores
Pr: Ramon Calderon
Ex VP: Juan Rodriguez
**Prin:* Ana T Cruz

D-U-N-S 17-555-0771
PUEBLO OF ISLETA
GOVERNOR'S OFFICE
Tribal Rd 40 Bldg 117-A, Isleta, NM 87022
Tel (505) 869-3111 *Founded/Ownrshp* 1858
Sales NA *EMP* 1,649
SIC 9111 City & town managers' offices;
Ofcr: Virgil Lucero

*Prin: Robert Benavides
Dir IT: Terry Honeycut

D-U-N-S 08-037-3228
PUEBLO SCHOOL DISTRICT 70
24951 E Us Highway 50, Pueblo, CO 81006-2027
Tel (719) 542-0220 Founded/Ownrshp 1952
Sales 56.6MM[E] EMP 1,000
Accts Garren Ross & Denardo Inc
SIC 8211 Public elementary & secondary schools

D-U-N-S 07-646-5285
PUEBLO SCHOOL DISTRICT NO 60
PUEBLO CITY SCHOOL
315 W 11th St, Pueblo, CO 81003-2804
Tel (719) 549-7100 Founded/Ownrshp 1950
Sales 132.6MM EMP 2,400
Accts Hoelting & Company Inc Colo
SIC 8211 Public elementary & secondary schools
Bd of Dir: Leanne Carabelos
Bd of Dir: Monica Richards
Ex Dir: Rhonda Holcomb
Tech Mgr: William Shaffer
Teacher Pr: Paula Chostner
Teacher Pr: Donna Crawford
Psych: Michelle Alconmontoya
Psych: Michael Horton
HC Dir: Amy Winegartner

PUERTO RICO AQEDUCT SEWER AUTH
See AUTORIDAD DE ACUEDUCTOSY ALCANTARILLADOS DE PR

D-U-N-S 14-656-8746
PUERTO RICO DEPARTMENT OF LABOR AND HUMAN RESOURCES
DEPARTAMENTO DEL TRABAJO
(Suby of SECRETARY OF COMMONWEALTH) ★
505 Ave Munoz Rivera, San Juan, PR 00918-3352
Tel (787) 754-2119 Founded/Ownrshp 1931
Sales NA EMP 1,350
SIC 9199 General government administration
Ex Dir: Maria La Santa
IT Man: Ivonne Rivera

D-U-N-S 09-031-9278
PUERTO RICO DEPARTMENT OF TREASURY
DEPARTAMENTO DE HACIENDA DE PR
(Suby of SECRETARY OF COMMONWEALTH) ★
10 Paseo Covadonga, San Juan, PR 00901-2613
Tel (787) 721-2020 Founded/Ownrshp 1952, 1966
Sales NA EMP 3,100
SIC 9311 Treasurers' office, government;

D-U-N-S 09-003-4703 IMP/EXP
PUERTO RICO ELECTRIC POWER AUTHORITY
PREPA
1110 Ave Ponce De Leon, San Juan, PR 00907-3802
Tel (787) 289-3434 Founded/Ownrshp 1908
Sales 4.8MMM[E] EMP 10,586
SIC 4911 Generation, electric power; Transmission, electric power; Distribution, electric power
Ex Dir: M A Cordero Lopez
V Ch: Jos A P Rez Canabal
*Ch: Josy Del Valle
*Ofcr: Lisa J Donahue
Ex Dir: Miguel A Cordero
*Ex Dir: Hyctro R Rosario
Ex Dir: Miguel Zordero
Sys/Dir: Jorge Hernandez

D-U-N-S 10-575-1044
PUERTO RICO FIREFIGHTERS CORPS
SERVICIO DE BOMBEROS DE PR
(Suby of PR DEPARTMENT OF PUBLIC SAFETY)
2432 Calle Loiza, San Juan, PR 00913-4731
Tel (787) 725-3444 Founded/Ownrshp 1942
Sales NA EMP 1,500
SIC 9224 Fire department, not including volunteer

D-U-N-S 09-010-5610 IMP
PUERTO RICO PORTS AUTHORITY
AUTORIDAD DE PUERTOS DE PR
(Suby of SECRETARY OF COMMONWEALTH) ★
Lindbergh St 64antigu, San Juan, PR 00907
Tel (787) 723-2260 Founded/Ownrshp 1942
Sales NA EMP 1,174
Accts Pkf International Limited San
SIC 9621 Regulation, administration of transportation
Ex Dir: Alvaro Pilar

D-U-N-S 09-004-7705 IMP/EXP
PUERTO RICO SUPPLIES GROUP INC
Parkeast, Bayamon, PR 00961-8300
Tel (787) 780-4043 Founded/Ownrshp 1945, 1998
Sales 529.4MM[E] EMP 410
Accts Valdes Garcia Marin & Martin
SIC 5194 5149 5122 5143 5148 Tobacco & tobacco products; Crackers, cookies & bakery products; Cosmetics, perfumes & hair products; Dairy products, except dried or canned; Fresh fruits & vegetables
Pr: Edwin Perez
*CFO: Carmen Marrero
VP: Alicia Echevarria
Board of Directors: Ana M Perez

D-U-N-S 00-389-7626 IMP/EXP
PUFFER-SWEIVEN HOLDINGS INC
PUFFER-SWEIVEN SPECIALTIES
4230 Greenbriar Dr, Stafford, TX 77477-3917
Tel (281) 240-2000 Founded/Ownrshp 1945, 1983
Sales 509.2MM[E] EMP 350
SIC 5084 Controlling instruments & accessories
Pr: Albert Grobmyer
CFO: Jan Wolansky
VP: Bob Bonsignore
VP: Henry Dedek
VP: Robert Elson
VP: Jack Jennings
VP: Donna Jett
VP: John Mangel
VP: Steve Pearce
VP: Randy Rister
VP: Steve Shaver
VP: Jerry Siler
Exec: Pete Douglas

PUFFER-SWEIVEN SPECIALTIES
See PUFFER-SWEIVEN HOLDINGS INC

D-U-N-S 05-550-1290
PUGET CONSUMERS CO-OP
PCC NATURAL MARKETS
4201 Roosevelt Way Ne, Seattle, WA 98105-6092
Tel (206) 547-1222 Founded/Ownrshp 1959
Sales 124.4MM[E] EMP 950
SIC 5411

D-U-N-S 00-730-0051
PUGET ENERGY INC
(Suby of PUGET EQUICO LLC) ★
10885 Ne 4th St Ste 1200, Bellevue, WA 98004-5591
Tel (425) 454-6363 Founded/Ownrshp 2009
Sales 3.0MMM EMP 2,700[E]
Accts Pricewaterhousecoopers Llp S
SIC 4931 4924 Electric & other services combined; ; Natural gas distribution
Pr: Kimberly J Harris
*Ch Bd: Melanie Dressel
CFO: Daniel A Doyle
Ofcr: Gary Veach
Sr VP: Philip K Bussey
Sr VP: Marla D Mellies
Sr VP: Steve R Secrist
Sr VP: Steven R Secrist
VP: Paul Wiegand
Dir IT: Wayne Gould
IT Man: Chris Lonack
Board of Directors: Christopher Trumpy, Andrew Chapman, Daniel Fetter, Benjamin Hawkins, Steven W Hooper, Alan James, Christopher Leslie, David McMillan, Mary O McWilliams, Drew Murphy

D-U-N-S 83-170-3157
PUGET EQUICO LLC
10885 Ne 4th St Ste 1200, Bellevue, WA 98004-5591
Tel (425) 454-6363 Founded/Ownrshp 2008
Sales 3.0MMM[E] EMP 2,800[E]
SIC 4911 Electric services
Pr: Kimberly J Harris

D-U-N-S 82-955-8902
PUGET HOLDING CO LLC
PSE
10885 Ne 4th St Ste 1200, Bellevue, WA 98004-5591
Tel (425) 454-6363 Founded/Ownrshp 2004
Sales 4.3MMM[E] EMP 22,860
SIC 4911 4922 4924 Electric services; Natural gas transmission; Natural gas distribution
Ch Bd: Stephen Reynolds
Prgrm Mgr: Cuong Luu
IT Man: Eileen Figone
IT Man: Pankaj Gupta
IT Man: Alex Malesis
Plnt Mgr: Gerald Klug
Ql Cn Mgr: Dave Wharton
Mktg Mgr: Jenifer Gonzales
Mktg Mgr: Anna Mikelsen
Genl Couns: Steve Secrist

PUGET SOUND BLOOD CENTER AND P
See BLOODWORKS

D-U-N-S 00-128-8828 IMP
PUGET SOUND COMMERCE CENTER INC
(Suby of MILES MARINE INC) ★
1801 16th Ave Sw, Seattle, WA 98134-1017
Tel (206) 623-1635 Founded/Ownrshp 1916, 2011
Sales 92.4MM[E] EMP 800[E]
SIC 3731 Shipbuilding & repairing; Combat vessels, building & repairing; Military ships, building & repairing; Commercial cargo ships, building & repairing
Pr: Frank J Foti
COO: David R Whitcomb
CFO: Berger A Dodge
CFO: Lon V Leneve
Board of Directors: Brent D Baird, Steven A Clifford, Patrick W E Hodgson, Joseph D Lehrer, William L Lewis, J Paul Reason

D-U-N-S 00-794-2113
PUGET SOUND ENERGY INC (WA)
(Suby of PUGET ENERGY INC) ★
10885 Ne 4th St Ste 1200, Bellevue, WA 98004-5591
Tel (425) 454-6363 Founded/Ownrshp 1960
Sales 3.0MMM EMP 2,700[E]
SIC 4939 4911 Combination utilities; Electric services
Pr: Kimberly J Harris
*Ch Bd: Melanie J Dressel
CFO: Daniel A Doyle
Ofcr: Marla D Mellies
Sr VP: Philip K Bussey
Sr VP: Steven R Secrist
IT Man: Jerry Vancorbach
Board of Directors: Herbert B Simon, Andrew Chapman, Christopher Trumpy, Daniel Fetter, Benjamin Hawkins, Steven W Hooper, Alan W James, Christopher J Leslie, David Macmillan, Mary O McWilliams, Drew Murphy

D-U-N-S 02-746-4486 IMP
PUGET SOUND PIPE AND SUPPLY CO
PSP
7816 S 202nd St, Kent, WA 98032-1345
Tel (206) 682-9350 Founded/Ownrshp 1917
Sales 114.8MM[E] EMP 148
SIC 5074 5085 Pipes & fittings, plastic; Industrial supplies; Valves & fittings
Ch: Philip Stratiner
*Pr: Gary Stratiner
*CFO: Steven Lewis
VP: Pat Manning
Brnch Mgr: Erik Heilbrun
Brnch Mgr: Sean Nadeau
Ql Cn Mgr: Kevin McNeill
Sls Mgr: Scott English
Sls Mgr: Rich Newton
Sales Asso: Travis Bryant
Sales Asso: Alex Hess

D-U-N-S 02-441-2363 EXP
PUGH OIL CO INC (NC)
TANK & TUMMY STORES
701 Mcdowell Rd, Asheboro, NC 27205-7370
Tel (336) 629-2061 Founded/Ownrshp 1947, 1982
Sales 143.0MM[E] EMP 80
SIC 5172 5983 5541 5411 5149 Fuel oil; Kerosene; Lubricating oils & greases; Gasoline; Fuel oil dealers; Filling stations, gasoline; Convenience stores, independent; Soft drinks
Pr: Ronald K Pugh
*Treas: Michael K Pugh
*VP: Steven K Pugh
IT Man: Pete Myrick

PUGI OF CHICAGOLAND
See DOWNERS GROVE IMPORTS LTD

D-U-N-S 03-041-7182
PULASKI COUNTY
201 Broadway St Ste 440, Little Rock, AR 72201-2325
Tel (501) 340-8381 Founded/Ownrshp 1831
Sales NA EMP 2,547
SIC 9211
Sr Pt: Randy Murphy
Comm Dir: Cozetta Jones

PULASKI COUNTY BOARD EDUCATION
See PULASKI COUNTY SCHOOL DISTRICT FINANCE CORP

D-U-N-S 78-895-9591
PULASKI COUNTY SCHOOL DISTRICT FINANCE CORP
PULASKI COUNTY BOARD EDUCATION
501 E University Dr, Somerset, KY 42503-2467
Tel (606) 679-1123 Founded/Ownrshp 1798
Sales 72.6MM EMP 1,400
Accts Ross & Company Pllc Louisvil
SIC 8211 8741 Public elementary school; Public junior high school; Public senior high school; School board; Management services
Ch Bd: Brandy Daniels
Adm Dir: William Bennet
Dir Sec: Wanda Absher
Pr Dir: Roxanna Bishop
Teacher Pr: Sarah Roberts

D-U-N-S 07-989-3783
PULASKI COUNTY SCHOOLS
501 E University Dr, Somerset, KY 42503-2467
Tel (606) 679-1123 Founded/Ownrshp 2015
Sales 47.6MM[E] EMP 1,542[E]
SIC 8211 Public elementary & secondary schools
Info Man: John Haynes

D-U-N-S 07-740-0752
PULASKI COUNTY SPECIAL SCHOOL DISTRICT
925 E Dixon Rd, Little Rock, AR 72206-4115
Tel (501) 490-2000 Founded/Ownrshp 1927
Sales 110.4MM[E] EMP 2,500
Accts Roger A Norman Jd Cpa Cfe
SIC 8211 Public elementary & secondary schools
Dir Sec: Mark Warner
Genl Mgr: Deneise Palmer
Web Dev: Tevis Woods

D-U-N-S 07-245-5058
PULICE CONSTRUCTION INC
(Suby of DRAGADOS SA FCC CONSTRUCCION SA UTE BOETTICHER LEY 18-1982)
2033 W Mountain View Rd, Phoenix, AZ 85021-1999
Tel (602) 944-2241 Founded/Ownrshp 1969
Sales 172.8MM[E] EMP 350[E]
SIC 1611 8711 General contractor, highway & street construction; Engineering services
Pr: Christopher B Rogers
*COO: Victor Jimenez
*CFO: Oscar Perello Tedo
*Treas: Fernando Gonzalez Alcaniz
VP: Steven Campbell
VP: Roger J Eischen
*VP: Tom A Lawless
VP: Don Pavoggi
IT Man: Mimi Berryman

D-U-N-S 00-628-8849
PULITZER INC (DE)
ST. LOUIS POST-DISPATCH
900 N Tucker Blvd, Saint Louis, MO 63101-1069
Tel (314) 340-8000 Founded/Ownrshp 1878
Sales 425.0MM EMP 3,500
SIC 2711 4833 4832 Newspapers, publishing & printing; Television broadcasting stations; Radio broadcasting stations
Ch Bd: Michael E Pulitzer
*Pr: Robert C Woodworth
Treas: James M Vogelpohl
*Sr VP: Ken J Elkins
*Sr VP: Allen G Silverglat
VP: Marvin G Kanne
VP: Matthew Kra
VP: Thomas L Rees
Genl Mgr: Gary Grange
Off Mgr: Cheryl Laut
Dir IT: Joe Ashkar
Board of Directors: Alice B Hayes, David E Moore, Emily Rauh Pulitzer, William Bush James M Snow

D-U-N-S 07-163-8006
■ **PULITZER INC**
LP ACQUISITION
(Suby of TIMES-NEWS) ★
900 N Tucker Blvd, Saint Louis, MO 63101-1069
Tel (314) 340-8000 Founded/Ownrshp 2005
Sales 146.9MM[E] EMP 1,800
SIC 2711 Newspapers
Pr: Mary E Junck
V Ch: Robert Bagby
V Ch: John Dunham
V Ch: Michael Miller
V Ch: Anthony Torcasio
COO: Sandra Van Trease
CFO: Carl G Schmidt
Treas: Robert Kuapl
Ex VP: John Jacob
Ex VP: David Mueller
Ex VP: Graham Watson
Sr VP: Alfred Brennan
Sr VP: Robert Clausen
Sr VP: Michael Collins
Sr VP: Charles Gillman
Sr VP: Michael Newman
Sr VP: George Paz
Sr VP: Michael Rocca
VP: Ron Birdwell
Exec: Diane Vonhof
Board of Directors: William Bush, Susan T Congalton, Ken J Elkins, Alice B Hayes, Richard W Moore, Emily Rauh Pulitzer, Ronald H Ridgway, James M Snowden Jr

PULL-N-PAC
See CROWN POLY INC

D-U-N-S 10-334-3760
■ **PULLMAN CO**
(Suby of TENNECO AUTOMOTIVE OPERATING CO INC) ★
1 International Dr, Monroe, MI 48161-9345
Tel (734) 243-8000 Founded/Ownrshp 1996
Sales 90.1MM[E] EMP 2,000
SIC 3714 3715 3061 Motor vehicle parts & accessories; Trailer bodies; Automotive rubber goods (mechanical)
Pr: Thomas E Evans
*Pr: James Gray

PULLMAN WHEEL WORKS APARTMENTS
See PULLMAN WHEEL WORKS ASSOCIATES

D-U-N-S 01-102-2746
PULLMAN WHEEL WORKS ASSOCIATES
PULLMAN WHEEL WORKS APARTMENTS
901 E 104th St Ste 2, Chicago, IL 60628-3093
Tel (773) 785-1300 Founded/Ownrshp 1987
Sales 49.0MM[E] EMP 3,900
SIC 6513 Apartment building operators
Prin: Leeann Morein
*Prin: Jennifer Hardee

D-U-N-S 78-336-8314 IMP/EXP
PULMUONE FOODS USA INC
MIDWEST PRO SERV
(Suby of SOGA FOODS) ★
2315 Moore Ave, Fullerton, CA 92833-2510
Tel (714) 578-2800 Founded/Ownrshp 1998
Sales 134.2MM[E] EMP 160
SIC 5149 5141 2075 Natural & organic foods; Groceries, general line; Soybean protein concentrates & isolates
CEO: Young Chul Kang
*Pr: Patrick Lemoine
Pr: Jeff Wilkins
*Sec: Doseok Kim
Ex VP: Tom Lacina
Dir IT: Michael Marian
Ql Cn Mgr: Elysse Espiritu
Mktg Dir: Ivan Hayashi
Sls Mgr: John Sim

D-U-N-S 87-864-5050 IMP
PULMUONE USA INC
SOGA FOODS
(Suby of PULMUONE HOLDINGS CO., LTD.)
2315 Moore Ave, Fullerton, CA 92833-2510
Tel (714) 578-2800 Founded/Ownrshp 1991
Sales 250.7MM[E] EMP 461
SIC 5149 5141 2075 Natural & organic foods; Groceries, general line; Soybean protein concentrates & isolates
CEO: Young Chul Kang

PULSAR
See SEIKO CORP OF AMERICA

D-U-N-S 00-230-0556 IMP
PULSE ELECTRONICS CORP (PA)
(Suby of OCM PE HOLDINGS LP) ★
12220 World Trade Dr, San Diego, CA 92128-3765
Tel (858) 674-8100 Founded/Ownrshp 1947
Sales 343.5MM EMP 9,400[E]
Accts Grant Thornton Llp San Diego
SIC 3679 3612 3663 Electronic circuits; Transformers, except electric; Antennas, transmitting & communications
CEO: Mark C J Twaalfhoven
COO: John Kowalski
Grp VP: Michael Kirchoff
VP: Dennis Ackerman
VP: Colin Dunn
VP: Robert H Fisher
VP: Thomas J Flakoll
VP: Michael J McGrath
VP: Brian E Morrissey
VP: Ken Taquia
VP Bus Dev: Mary Lynch
Exec: Ka Au
Board of Directors: Steven G Crane, David W Heinzmann, Gary E Sutton, Robert E Switz

D-U-N-S 92-958-7046 IMP
PULSE ELECTRONICS INC
(Suby of PULSE ELECTRONICS CORP) ★
12220 World Trade Dr, San Diego, CA 92128-3765
Tel (858) 674-8100 Founded/Ownrshp 1995
Sales 343.5MM EMP 12,000
Accts Grant Thornton Llp San Diego
SIC 3612 3674 3677 Specialty transformers; Modules, solid state; Filtration devices, electronic
CEO: Alan Benjamin
*CFO: Drew A Moyer
*Sr VP: Mike Bond
*Sr VP: John R D Dickson
*Sr VP: John Houston
VP: John Carpentar
VP: Bill Fister
VP: Pat McCready
VP: Steven D Mentas
VP: Bo Rasmussen
Rgnl Mgr: Edward Burton

D-U-N-S 18-646-2677
■ PULTE DIVERSIFIED COMPANIES INC
(*Suby of* PULTEGROUP INC) ★
3350 Peachtree Rd Ne, Atlanta, GA 30326-1039
Tel (248) 647-2750 *Founded/Ownrshp* 1987
Sales 636.2M *EMP* 5,300^E
SIC 1521 New construction, single-family houses
Pr: Richard J Dugas Jr
Area Mgr: Carissa Hammel
Prd Mgr: Melissa White
Sales Asso: Michelle Adler
Sales Asso: Mark Glodowski

D-U-N-S 00-383-2557
■ PULTE HOME CORP
(*Suby of* PULTE DIVERSIFIED COMPANIES INC) ★
3350 Peachtree Rd Ne # 150, Atlanta, GA 30326-1424
Tel (248) 647-2750 *Founded/Ownrshp* 1987
Sales 637.4MM^E *EMP* 5,300
SIC 1531 6552 6162 Speculative builder, single-family houses; Townhouse developers; Condominium developers; Speculative builder, multi-family dwellings; Land subdividers & developers, residential; Mortgage bankers
Pr: Richard D Dugas
**CFO:* Roger A Cregg
**Treas:* Bruce E Robinson
**Ex VP:* James R Ellinghausen
**Ex VP:* Ryan R Marshall
**Ex VP:* Harmon D Smith
VP: Jamie Chung
**VP:* Vincent J Frees
VP: Jim Goar
VP: Daniel Harrison
VP: Michael J Schweninger
VP: Kenny Spradling
**VP:* John R Stoller
VP: Mark Williams
VP: Mike Wyatt

D-U-N-S 87-699-9582
■ PULTE HOMES OF MINNESOTA LLC
(*Suby of* PULTE HOME CORP) ★
7500 Office Ridge Cir, Eden Prairie, MN 55344-3782
Tel (952) 936-7833 *Founded/Ownrshp* 2000
Sales 250.0MM *EMP* 100^E
SIC 1521 Single-family housing construction
Pr: Keith Tomlinson
**VP:* Marty Gergen

D-U-N-S 87-711-1112
■ PULTE HOMES OF TEXAS LP
(*Suby of* PULTE HOME CORP) ★
4800 Regent Blvd Ste 100, Irving, TX 75063-2439
Tel (972) 304-2800 *Founded/Ownrshp* 1984
Sales 94.0MM^E *EMP* 387
SIC 6552 1521 Subdividers & developers; Single-family housing construction
Pt: Richard Dix
VP: Timothy Stewart

D-U-N-S 07-038-2205
■ PULTE MORTGAGE LLC
(*Suby of* PULTE HOME CORP) ★
7390 S Iola St, Englewood, CO 80112-3803
Tel (303) 740-8800 *Founded/Ownrshp* 1972
Sales NA *EMP* 399
Accts Ernst & Young Llp Denver Co
SIC 6162 Mortgage bankers
Pr: Roger C Pastore
Pr: Glenn Koutecky
Bd of Dir: Patrick Oleary
Bd of Dir: John Shea
Sr VP: Leslie Devera-Duncan
Sr VP: Scott E Harris
Sr VP: Marc Rego
Sr VP: Michael Sullivan
Sr VP: David Willmarth
VP: Don Blea
VP: Trey Hodapp
VP: Anthony Koblinski

D-U-N-S 18-620-8351
▲ PULTEGROUP INC
3350 Peachtree Rd Ne # 150, Atlanta, GA 30326-1424
Tel (404) 978-6400 *Founded/Ownrshp* 1956
Sales 5.9MMM *EMP* 4,542
Accts Ernst & Young Llp Atlanta Ge
Tkr Sym PHM *Exch* NYS
SIC 1531 6552 6162 Operative builders; Condominium developers; Townhouse developers; Land subdividers & developers, residential; Mortgage bankers
CEO: Ryan Marshall
Ch Bd: Richard J Dugas Jr
Pr: Scott Withington
COO: Harmon Smith
CFO: Robert T O'Shaughnessy
Div Pres: Kevin Meuth
Ofcr: Scottie Celestini
Ex VP: James R Ellinghausen
VP: Dan Carroll
VP: Joseph L Drouin
Mktg Mgr: Kevin Lum
Board of Directors: Patrick J O'leary, Brian P Anderson, John R Peshkin, Bryce Blair, James J Postl, Richard W Dreiling, Scott F Powers, Debra J Kelly-Ennis, William J Pulte, Thomas J Folliard, Joshua Gotbaum, Cheryl W Grise, James J Grosfeld, Andre J Hawaux

D-U-N-S 93-397-3588 IMP/EXP
PUMA NORTH AMERICA INC
(*Suby of* PUMA SE)
10 Lyberty Way, Westford, MA 01886-3616
Tel (978) 698-1000 *Founded/Ownrshp* 1995
Sales 433.1MM^E *EMP* 507
SIC 5136 5139 8741 5137 Sportswear, men's & boys'; Footwear, athletic; Management services; Sportswear, women's & children's
Pr: Jay Piccola
**CEO:* Franz Koch
**COO:* Klaus Bauer
**COO:* Stefano Caroti
COO: Eric Logan
**Treas:* Cyril Hottot
VP: Jeffrey Dunn
**VP:* Helmut Leibbrandt
VP: John Trott
VP: Jon Vacca
Exec: Regina Beausoleil

PUMH
See PENINSULA UNITED METHODIST HOMES INC

PUMP HANDLE SNACK SHOPS
See WALLIS OIL CO

D-U-N-S 03-262-6489
■ PUMP SOLUTIONS GROUP
(*Suby of* DOVER CORP) ★
1815 S Meyers Rd Ste 670, Oakbrook Terrace, IL 60181-5262
Tel (630) 487-2240 *Founded/Ownrshp* 2010
Sales 147.6MM^E *EMP* 359^E
SIC 3561 Pumps & pumping equipment
Pr: John D Allen

PUMP-N-SHOP
See ARGUINDEGUI OIL CO II LTD

D-U-N-S 05-887-1476
■ PUMPCO INC
(*Suby of* MASTEC NORTH AMERICA INC) ★
1209 S Main St, Giddings, TX 78942-4922
Tel (979) 542-9054 *Founded/Ownrshp* 1981
Sales 97.1MM^E *EMP* 175
SIC 1623 1389 Pipeline construction; Oil field services
Pr: Alan Roberts
**Sec:* Robyn Roberts

D-U-N-S 03-317-2057
PUNA PLANTATION HAWAII LIMITED (HI)
KTA SUPER STORES
50 E Puainako St, Hilo, HI 96720-5294
Tel (808) 959-9111 *Founded/Ownrshp* 1916
Sales 133.3MM^E *EMP* 750
SIC 5411 Supermarkets, chain
Pr: Barry Taniguchi
**Treas:* Andrew Chun
**Ex VP:* Toby Taniguchi
VP: Glenn Kodama
**VP:* Lon Taniguchi
Store Mgr: Merle Unoki
Mktg Dir: Tracey Yamane
Pharmcst: Kerri Okamura

PUNAHOU BOOKSTORE
See PUNAHOU SCHOOL

D-U-N-S 07-767-4612
PUNAHOU SCHOOL
PUNAHOU BOOKSTORE
1601 Punahou St, Honolulu, HI 96822-3399
Tel (808) 944-5711 *Founded/Ownrshp* 1841
Sales 110.0MM *EMP* 750
Accts Kpmg Llp Honolulu Hi
SIC 8211 Private combined elementary & secondary school
Pr: James K Scott PHD
**Ch Bd:* C F Damon Jr
**Treas:* Judith M Dawson
Ofcr: Linda Torres
**VP:* Warren Luke
VP: Kathryn Nelson
Assoc Dir: Darlee Kishimoto
Prin: Greg Foster
IT Man: Matt Awaya

D-U-N-S 10-399-8324 IMP
PURAC AMERICA INC
CORBION-PURAC
(*Suby of* CORBION N.V.)
7905 Quivira Rd, Lenexa, KS 66215-2732
Tel (847) 634-6330 *Founded/Ownrshp* 1983
Sales 268.5MM^E *EMP* 810
SIC 2869 Industrial organic chemicals
Pr: Eddy Van Rhede
**Pr:* Gerrit Vreeman
**VP:* Peter Kooijman
Mktg Mgr: Ria Zanhoef

D-U-N-S 06-680-0558
PURCELL CONSTRUCTION CORP
566 Coffeen St, Watertown, NY 13601-2685
Tel (315) 782-1050 *Founded/Ownrshp* 1972
Sales 93.0MM^E *EMP* 300
SIC 1542 1541 1522

PURCHASING DEPARTMENT
See COMMUNITY MEMORIAL HOSPITAL SAN BUENAVENTURA INC

PURCHASING DEPT
See REGIONS HOSPITAL

PURCHASING DEPT
See RUTGER STATE UNIVERSITY

D-U-N-S 17-075-2252
PURCHASING POWER LLC
EMPLOYEE CMPT PRCHASE PROGRAMS
1349 W Peachtree St Nw # 1100, Atlanta, GA 30309-2956
Tel (404) 609-5100 *Founded/Ownrshp* 2016
Sales 243.2MM *EMP* 200
SIC 5961 General merchandise, mail order
Pr: Richard Carano
COO: Scott Wheeler
CFO: Scott Rosenberg
CIO: Prakash Muthukrishnan

PURDUE FOUNDATION INC
See PURDUE RESEARCH FOUNDATION

D-U-N-S 93-232-3652 IMP
PURDUE PHARMA LP
201 Tresser Blvd Fl 1, Stamford, CT 06901-3432
Tel (203) 588-8000 *Founded/Ownrshp* 1991
Sales 324.9MM^E *EMP* 805^E
SIC 2834 5122 Pharmaceutical preparations; Pharmaceuticals
Pr: Mark Timney
CFO: Jean-Jacques Charhon
CFO: Edward B Mahony
Treas: Willy Chang
Treas: Ralph Orr
Ofcr: Saeed Motahari
Ofcr: Daniel Russo
Ex VP: Stuart D Baker
Sr VP: Alan Butcher
Sr VP: Alan W Dunton
VP: Robin Abrams
VP: Gail Cawkwell
VP: Robert Kupper
VP: Diana Lenkowsky
VP: Edward Migliarese
VP: Anthony C Santopolo
Exec: Jagadeesh Narasimhaiah
Assoc Dir: Steven Projansky
Assoc Dir: Beth Purdon

D-U-N-S 14-191-6531
PURDUE PRODUCTS LP
1 Stamford Forum, Stamford, CT 06901-3516
Tel (203) 588-8000 *Founded/Ownrshp* 2002
Sales 72.6MM^E *EMP* 1,500
SIC 2834 Pharmaceutical preparations
Pr: John Stewart
CFO: Edward Mahony

D-U-N-S 07-071-0447
PURDUE RESEARCH FOUNDATION
PURDUE FOUNDATION INC
1281 Win Hentschel Blvd, West Lafayette, IN 47906-4182
Tel (765) 588-3470 *Founded/Ownrshp* 1930
Sales 187.8MM *EMP* 85^E
Accts Crowe Horwath Llp Indianapoli
SIC 8733 Educational research agency
Pr: Mitchell E Daniels
**Treas:* Joseph B Hornett
Bd of Dir: Alok Chaturvedi
Chf Inves: Scott Seidle
VP: Chad Pittman
VP: Michelle White
IT Man: Mike Chappell

D-U-N-S 07-205-1394
PURDUE UNIVERSITY
FREEHAFER HALL ADMIN. SERVICES
401 S Grant St, West Lafayette, IN 47907-2024
Tel (765) 494-8000 *Founded/Ownrshp* 1862
Sales 1.4MMM *EMP* 18,715
Accts Paul D Joyce Cpa Indianapoli
SIC 8221 University
Pr: Mitch Daniels
V Ch: John D Hardin
CFO: William E Sullivan
**Treas:* Morgan R Olsen
**Sr VP:* Murray Blackwelder
VP: Richard O Buckius
VP: William G McCartney
Assoc Dir: Doug Gotham
IT Man: Dennis Depew
Art Dir: Kaylie Hall

D-U-N-S 00-727-2289 IMP/EXP
■ PURE FISHING INC
(*Suby of* NEWELL BRANDS INC) ★
7 Science Ct, Columbia, SC 29203-9344
Tel (803) 754-7000 *Founded/Ownrshp* 2016
Sales 3.6MMM^E *EMP* 650
SIC 3949 Fishing equipment
CEO: Michael Polk
**Pr:* Mark S Tarchetti
CFO: Karim Bouaziz
**CFO:* John K Stipancich
VP: Den Stulc
Exec: Keith Mason
**CTO:* Russ Torres
IT Man: Robert Robbins
VP Sls: Ron Berge

D-U-N-S 07-234-4542
PURE METAL RECYCLING LLC
100 Tri State Intl # 215, Lincolnshire, IL 60069-4427
Tel (773) 523-4500 *Founded/Ownrshp* 2014
Sales 482.1MM^E *EMP* 400
SIC 5093 Metal scrap & waste materials; Ferrous metal scrap & waste; Nonferrous metals scrap
CEO: Christopher Dandrow
**Pr:* Brett Baron
**COO:* Tom Bochenek
CFO: Roger Gusloff
VP: Micheal O'Malley
**VP:* Mike Omalley

D-U-N-S 08-020-5053
PURE POWER TECHNOLOGIES INC
1410 Northpoint Blvd, Blythewood, SC 29016-7300
Tel (803) 744-7020 *Founded/Ownrshp* 2015
Sales 96.0MM *EMP* 250
SIC 3363 Aluminum die-castings
Pr: Jerry Sweetland
**CFO:* Richard Marsden

D-U-N-S 92-981-4601
▲ PURE STORAGE INC
650 Castro St Ste 400, Mountain View, CA 94041-2081
Tel (800) 379-7873 *Founded/Ownrshp* 2009
Sales 440.3MM *EMP* 1,300^E
Tkr Sym PSTG *Exch* NYS
SIC 3572

D-U-N-S 83-177-6757 IMP
PURECIRCLE USA INC
(*Suby of* PURECIRCLE SDN. BHD.)
915 Harger Rd Ste 250, Oak Brook, IL 60523-1492
Tel (866) 960-8242 *Founded/Ownrshp* 2008
Sales 101.0MM *EMP* 30
SIC 2869 Sweeteners, synthetic
CEO: Magomet Malsagov
Pr: Mauricio Bacigaluppo
**Pr:* Peter Milsted
**COO:* Gordi Ferre
**CFO:* William Mitchell
**VP:* Jordi Ferre

PUREFORMANCE CABLES
See LYNN PRODUCTS INC

PUREGEAR
See SUPERIOR COMMUNICATIONS INC

D-U-N-S 00-907-1668
PUREWORKS INC
UL EHS SUSTAINABILITY
(*Suby of* UL) ★
5000 Meridian Blvd # 600, Franklin, TN 37067-6678
Tel (615) 367-4404 *Founded/Ownrshp* 2000
Sales 96.0MM^E *EMP* 250^E
SIC 4813 ;
Pr: William Grana
CFO: Salome Isbell
VP: Tom Gaudreau
VP: Dennis Hines
VP: Ron A Kirsch
VP: Ron Kirsch
VP: Mike Kroll
VP: Tom Neville
CTO: Jeff Lamb
Sls Mgr: Earl Weissert

D-U-N-S 17-705-1294
PURFOODS LLC
MOM'S MEALS
3210 Se Corp Woods Dr, Ankeny, IA 50021
Tel (515) 963-0641 *Founded/Ownrshp* 2002
Sales 132.9MM^E *EMP* 517
SIC 2099 Food preparations
Pr: Rick Anderson
CFO: Brian Hoey
**VP:* Michael Anderson
Exec: Jon Benedict
Genl Mgr: Nathan Jensen
Opers Mgr: Jon Bellis

D-U-N-S 80-657-8337 IMP
PURINA ANIMAL NUTRITION LLC
LAND OLAKES ANIMAL MILK PDTS
(*Suby of* LAND OLAKES INC) ★
1080 County Road F W, Shoreview, MN 55126-2910
Tel (651) 375-5500 *Founded/Ownrshp* 2000
Sales 2.6MMM^E *EMP* 2,310
SIC 5191 Feed
Sls Mgr: Caulder Bookout

D-U-N-S 80-885-5373
PURINA MILLS LLC
(*Suby of* LAND OLAKES ANIMAL MILK PDTS) ★
555 Maryvle Univ Dr 200, Saint Louis, MO 63141-5805
Tel (877) 454-7094 *Founded/Ownrshp* 2001
Sales 376.2MM^E *EMP* 2,300
SIC 2048 2047 Feed premixes; Dog & cat food
**CFO:* Daniel Knutson
VP: Brad Kerbs
VP: Darrell Swank

D-U-N-S 06-587-8860
PURITY CYLINDER GASES INC
(*Suby of* GRANITE HOLDINGS INC) ★
2580 28th St Sw, Wyoming, MI 49519-2190
Tel (616) 532-2375 *Founded/Ownrshp* 1938
Sales 105.1MM^E *EMP* 225
SIC 5085 7359 5999 7699 Industrial supplies; Rental store, general; Welding supplies; Welding equipment repair
Pr: Douglas Nyhuis
**VP:* Beverly Nyhuis
Sls Mgr: Dick Starck
Sales Asso: Brent Helms
Sales Asso: Kevin Kaufmann
Sales Asso: Scott King
Sales Asso: Dave Przybysz
Sales Asso: Andy Tunis
Board of Directors: Douglas Nyhuis, Gary Nyhuis

D-U-N-S 00-404-1109
PURITY DAIRIES LLC (TN)
360 Murfreesboro Pike, Nashville, TN 37210-2816
Tel (615) 760-2296 *Founded/Ownrshp* 1946
Sales 1.0MMM^E *EMP* 10,080
SIC 2026

D-U-N-S 02-146-0859
PURITY OILFIELD SERVICES LLC
(*Suby of* PETRO-HUNT LLC) ★
2101 Cedar Springs Rd, Dallas, TX 75201-2104
Tel (214) 880-8400 *Founded/Ownrshp* 2012
Sales 88.7MM^E *EMP* 175^E
SIC 1389 Oil field services
Pr: Marshall T Hunt
Treas: Tom Nelson

D-U-N-S 10-762-6012 EXP
PURITY WHOLESALE GROCERS INC
AMERICAN WHOLESALE GROCERS
5300 Broken Sound Blvd Nw # 110, Boca Raton, FL 33487-3520
Tel (561) 997-8302 *Founded/Ownrshp* 1982
Sales 186.9MM^E *EMP* 180
SIC 5141 5122 5199 Groceries, general line; Drugs, proprietaries & sundries; General merchandise, non-durable
Ch Bd: Jeffrey A Levitetz
**Pr:* Dave Groomes
**Pr:* Alan Rutner
VP: Bruce Krichmar
Prgrm Mgr: George Brown
IT Man: Steve Cirelli
Sls&Mrk Ex: Dan Davis

D-U-N-S 36-125-3511 IMP
■ PUROLATOR PRODUCTS AIR FILTRATION CO
AIR FILTERS SALES & SERVICE
(*Suby of* CLARCOR INC) ★
100 River Ridge Cir, Jeffersonville, IN 47130-8974
Tel (866) 925-2247 *Founded/Ownrshp* 1999
Sales 193.0MM^E *EMP* 800
SIC 3564 3433 Filters, air: furnaces, air conditioning equipment, etc.; Heating equipment, except electric
Pr: Bill Pappas
**Pr:* Alan H Spicer
VP: John Hanna
VP: Tom Justice
VP: Kevin Nelson
VP: Jim Snoddy
MIS Dir: Peter Richardson

D-U-N-S 04-876-3031 IMP/EXP
PUROLITE CORP
150 Monument Rd Ste 202, Bala Cynwyd, PA 19004-1725
Tel (610) 668-9090 *Founded/Ownrshp* 1981
Sales 266.9MM[E] *EMP* 810
SIC 2821 Plastics materials & resins
Pr: Stefan Brodie
**CFO:* James F Downey
**VP:* Don Brodie
MIS Mgr: James Mitchell
Sls Mgr: James Sabzali

D-U-N-S 12-371-6578 IMP
PURPLE COMMUNICATIONS INC
595 Menlo Dr, Rocklin, CA 95765-3708
Tel (888) 600-4780 *Founded/Ownrshp* 1999
Sales 222.9MM[E] *EMP* 428
Accts Withum Smith & Brown New Brun
SIC 4812 7389 Radio telephone communication; Translation services
Pr: Robert Rae
Ch Bd: John R Ferron
VP: Fran Cummings
VP: Ellen Flora
VP: Mark L Stern
Board of Directors: Steven C Chang, Aaron Dobrinsky, Steven Eskenazi, Jose E Feliciano, Christopher Gibbons, William M McDonagh, Ronald E Obray

D-U-N-S 02-719-7458 IMP
PURVIS INDUSTRIES LTD
BATES SALES COMPANY
10500 N Stemmons Fwy, Dallas, TX 75220-2425
Tel (214) 358-5500 *Founded/Ownrshp* 1945
Sales 372.3MM[E] *EMP* 500
SIC 5013 5085 3822 Automotive supplies & parts; Bearings; Electric air cleaner controls, automatic
Pr: Robert W Purvis
**CFO:* Robert Moran
**Sec:* Gail Purvis
**VP:* Joe Hardwick
VP: Jeremiah Johnson
Exec: Robyn Hollas
Brnch Mgr: David Manees
Brnch Mgr: Ward McDonough
Brnch Mgr: Scott Wynn
Opers Mgr: Richard Jezek
Opers Mgr: Scott Morin

PUSD
See PASADENA UNIFIED SCHOOL DISTRICT

D-U-N-S 04-624-8886
PUTNAM CITY SCHOOL DISTRICT I-001 OKLAHOMA COUNTY
5401 Nw 40th St, Warr Acres, OK 73122-3302
Tel (405) 495-5200 *Founded/Ownrshp* 1914
Sales 63.5MM[E] *EMP* 2,076
Accts Eide Bailly Llp Norman Okla
SIC 8211 Public elementary & secondary schools
Pr: Cindy Gibbs
Bd of Dir: Sandy Adcox
MIS Dir: Karen Literal

D-U-N-S 96-908-3372
PUTNAM CITY SCHOOLS
5401 Nw 40th St, Warr Acres, OK 73122-3302
Tel (405) 495-5200 *Founded/Ownrshp* 1914
Sales 272.9M *EMP* 2,012[E]
Accts Bell & Rhodes P C Oklahoma C
SIC 8211 Public elementary & secondary schools
Exec: Caroline Gist
Ex Dir: Jim Hooper
CTO: Georgine Westerndorf
MIS Dir: Corey Boggs
Pr Dir: Steve Lindley
Schl Brd P: Cindy Gibbs
HC Dir: Karen Body
Pgrm Dir: Jennifer Richardson

PUTNAM CNTY AMBLATORY CARE CTR
See ST RITAS MEDICAL CENTER

PUTNAM COUNTY SCHOOL DISTRICT
See SCHOOL DISTRICT OF PUTNAM COUNTY FLORIDA

D-U-N-S 07-669-6475 IMP
PUTNAM HOSPITAL CENTER FOUNDATION INC
670 Stoneleigh Ave, Carmel, NY 10512-3997
Tel (845) 279-5711 *Founded/Ownrshp* 1986
Sales 154.1MM *EMP* 1,039
SIC 8062 General medical & surgical hospitals
CEO: Donna M McGregor
Admn Mgr: Caleste Baccari
Sfty Dirs: Stepaen Fajfer

D-U-N-S 80-865-3674
PUTNAM HOSPITAL CENTER HOME HEALTH AGENCY PRIVATE DUTY CARE SERVICE INC
(*Suby of* HEALTH QUEST SYSTEMS INC) ★
670 Stoneleigh Ave, Carmel, NY 10512-3997
Tel (845) 279-5711 *Founded/Ownrshp* 1998
Sales 158.9MM *EMP* 12
Accts Pricewaterhousecoopers Llp N
SIC 8062 General medical & surgical hospitals
Pr: Donna McGregor
**CFO:* Maryann Kepple

D-U-N-S 78-627-6204
PUTNAM INTERMEDIATE GOVERNMENT INCOME TRUST
1 Post Office Sq, Boston, MA 02109-2106
Tel (617) 292-1000 *Founded/Ownrshp* 1992
Sales 99.6MM[E] *EMP* 3,000
SIC 6211 Mutual funds, selling by independent salesperson
VP: Oleg Cohen

D-U-N-S 07-662-0855
PUTNAM INVESTMENTS
(*Suby of* GREAT-WEST LIFE ASSURANCE COMPANY, THE)
1 Post Office Sq, Boston, MA 02109-2106
Tel (617) 292-1000 *Founded/Ownrshp* 2007
Sales 1.0MMM[E] *EMP* 1,827
SIC 6722 6282 6726 Mutual fund sales, on own account; Investment advisory service; Investment offices
Pr: Ryan Cottreau
Pr: Laurie Grossman
CFO: Adrian Dillon
CFO: Clare Richer
Sr Cor Off: Lawrenze Lanfer
Chf Inves: Kevin Divney
Ofcr: Jed Moore
Sr VP: Peter Curran
VP: Robert Cannata
VP: Margaret Cerilli
VP: Nicholas Chingris
VP: Paul Drury
VP: Robert Kea
VP: Steve Luken
VP: John Palmer
Creative D: Kris Rodammer
Comm Dir: Mark McKenna
Board of Directors: Walter C Donovan

D-U-N-S 09-218-6824
PUTNAM INVESTOR SERVICES INC (DE)
(*Suby of* PUTNAM INVESTMENTS) ★
1 Post Office Sq Ste 500, Boston, MA 02109-2199
Tel (617) 292-1000 *Founded/Ownrshp* 1937, 1974
Sales 108.1MM[E] *EMP* 1,400
SIC 6289 Stock transfer agents
Pr: Robert Lloyd Reynolds
**Pr:* Jonathan S Horwitz
**Pr:* Steven D Krichmar
**Pr:* Francis Joseph McNamara

D-U-N-S 08-943-9913 IMP/EXP
PUTZMEISTER AMERICA INC
(*Suby of* PUTZMEISTER CONCRETE PUMPS GMBH)
1733 90th St, Sturtevant, WI 53177-1805
Tel (262) 886-3200 *Founded/Ownrshp* 1982
Sales 109.7MM[E] *EMP* 400
SIC 3561 Pumps & pumping equipment
Pr: Dave Adams
VP: Marc Aguilar
VP: Jim Bury
VP: Stephen Crane
VP: Bill Dwyer
VP: Hinrich Maehlmann
VP: Brian Zydzik
DP Exec: Brian Poulsen
Sls Dir: Tom McKernan
Manager: Alejandro Monasterio

D-U-N-S 07-184-6646
PUYALLUP SCHOOL DISTRICT
302 2nd St Se, Puyallup, WA 98372-3220
Tel (253) 840-8971 *Founded/Ownrshp* 1900
Sales 252.1MM *EMP* 3,000
SIC 8211 School board
Ofcr: Pamela Humiston

PV POWERED
See AE SOLAR ENERGY INC

D-U-N-S 00-136-1005 IMP/EXP
▲ PVH CORP
200 Madison Ave Bsmt 1, New York, NY 10016-3913
Tel (212) 381-3500 *Founded/Ownrshp* 1881
Sales 8.0MMM *EMP* 34,200
Accts Ernst & Young Llp New York N
Tkr Sym PVH *Exch* NYS
SIC 2321 2331 2253 3143 5621 5611 Men's & boys' dress shirts; Sport shirts, men's & boys': from purchased materials; Blouses, women's & juniors': made from purchased material; Shirts, women's & juniors': made from purchased materials; Sweaters & sweater coats, knit; Shirts (outerwear), knit; Men's footwear, except athletic; Ready-to-wear apparel, women's; Men's & boys' clothing stores
Ch Bd: Emanuel Chirico
CEO: Francis K Duane
CEO: Daniel Grieder
CEO: Steven B Shiffman
COO: Michael A Shaffer
Ofcr: Dave Kozel
Ex VP: Richard Deck
Ex VP: Mark D Fischer
Ex VP: Eugene Gosselin
Ex VP: Jarratt John
Ex VP: Michael Kelly
Ex VP: David F Kozel
Sr VP: James W Holmes
VP: Douglas Christian
VP: Jin Chung
VP: Jeanne Clarke
VP: Judith Colaiacovo
VP: Todd Cook
VP: Kathryn Diaz
VP: Lenore Dunn
VP: Joel Friedman
Board of Directors: Craig Rydin, Mary Baglivo, Brent Callinicos, Juan R Figuereo, Joseph B Fuller, Judith Amanda Sourry Knox, V James Marino, Geraldine Penny McIntyre, Henry Nasella, Edward R Rosenfeld

D-U-N-S 00-220-7561 IMP
■ PVH NECKWEAR INC
(*Suby of* PVH CORP) ★
1735 S Santa Fe Ave, Los Angeles, CA 90021-2904
Tel (213) 688-7970 *Founded/Ownrshp* 2007
Sales 140.7MM[E] *EMP* 660
SIC 2323 Men's & boys' neckwear
CEO: Marc Schneider
CFO: Armando Sosa
VP: James Beckaman
VP: Jim Beckman
VP: Edward Walker
VP: Sang Yoo

PVHMC
See POMONA VALLEY HOSPITAL MEDICAL CENTER

D-U-N-S 82-776-0435
PVI HOLDINGS INC
(*Suby of* PON NORTH AMERICA INC) ★
840 Gessner Rd Ste 950, Houston, TX 77024-4593
Tel (713) 365-6805 *Founded/Ownrshp* 2010
Sales 342.4MM[E] *EMP* 459
SIC 5085 5084 7699 Industrial supplies; Valves & fittings; Instruments & control equipment; Valve repair, industrial
CEO: Jack Guidry
**Pr:* Cees A Drogendijk
**VP:* Peter R Osterman Jr

D-U-N-S 03-186-3330
PVR PARTNERS LP
3 Radnor Corp Ctr Ste 301, Radnor, PA 19087-4556
Tel (610) 975-8200 *Founded/Ownrshp* 2001
Sales 1.1MMM *EMP* 305[E]
SIC 1221 1311

D-U-N-S 80-966-6147
PVS CHEMICAL SOLUTIONS INC
(*Suby of* PVS CHEMICALS) ★
10900 Harper Ave, Detroit, MI 48213-1247
Tel (313) 921-1200 *Founded/Ownrshp* 1981
Sales 102.0MM *EMP* 118
SIC 5169 Chemicals, industrial & heavy
Pr: Dean H Larson
Ofcr: Robert C Adams
**VP:* Allan Schlumberger

PVS CHEMICALS
See PRESSURE VESSEL SERVICE INC

PVS METALS
See OWEN INDUSTRIES INC

D-U-N-S 00-491-2309 IMP/EXP
PVS-NOLWOOD CHEMICALS INC (MI)
(*Suby of* PVS CHEMICALS) ★
10900 Harper Ave, Detroit, MI 48213-3364
Tel (313) 921-1200 *Founded/Ownrshp* 1958, 1945
Sales 153.6MM *EMP* 71
SIC 5169 Chemicals & allied products; Alkalines
CEO: James B Nicholson
**Pr:* Richard Peacock
**CFO:* Candee Saferian
Opers Mgr: Jim Lawson
Sls Mgr: Jim Westerdahl

PVSC
See PASSAIC VALLEY SEWERAGE COMMISSION

D-U-N-S 15-445-9713 EXP
PW EAGLE INC
JM EAGLE
5200 W Century Blvd, Los Angeles, CA 90045-5928
Tel (800) 621-4404 *Founded/Ownrshp* 2007
Sales 119.3MM[E] *EMP* 1,087
SIC 3084

PWC
See PRIORITY WIRE & CABLE INC

D-U-N-S 82-706-8326
PWC STRATEGY& (US) LLC
(*Suby of* PRICEWATERHOUSECOOPERS LLP) ★
101 Park Ave Fl 18, New York, NY 10178-1702
Tel (212) 697-1900 *Founded/Ownrshp* 2014
Sales 217.5MM[E] *EMP* 3,460
SIC 8742 Management consulting services
CEO: Cesare R Mainardi
Sr Pt: Barry Jaruzelski
Pt: Jono Anderson
Pt: Igor Belokrinitsky
Pt: Michael Duvall
Pt: Jay Godla
Pt: Jayant Gotpagar
Pt: Albert Kent
Pt: Kelley Mavros
Pt: Jason Palmenberg
Pt: Samrat Sharma
Pt: Earl Simpkins
CFO: Douglas G Swenson
Ofcr: Mike Connolly
VP: Charley Beever
VP: Peter Bertone
VP: S Bianco
VP: Vinay Couto
VP: Donald Dawson
VP: Kenneth Favaro
VP: Tom Flaherty

D-U-N-S 96-808-2664
PWC STRATEGY& (US) LLC
300 Campus Dr Ste 100, Florham Park, NJ 07932-1039
Tel (973) 630-6791 *Founded/Ownrshp* 2008
Sales 148.3MM[E] *EMP* 3,460
SIC 8742

PWCSA
See PRINCE WILLIAM COUNTY SERVICE AUTHORITY INC

PWSA
See PITTSBURGH WATER & SEWER AUTHORITY

PX DRUG STORE
See MODERNHEALTH SPECIALTY (PX) LLC

D-U-N-S 13-201-3249
PX HOLDING CORP
(*Suby of* MACANDREWS & FORBES HOLDINGS INC) ★
35 E 62nd St, New York, NY 10065-8014
Tel (212) 688-9000 *Founded/Ownrshp* 1997
Sales 24.0MM[E] *EMP* 1,211
SIC 7359 3861 3648 Equipment rental & leasing; Cameras & related equipment; Stage lighting equipment
Pr: Ronald O Perelman

D-U-N-S 36-154-5510
PXRE CORP
(*Suby of* ARGO GROUP INTERNATIONAL HOLDINGS, LTD.)
379 Thornall St Ste 2, Edison, NJ 08837-2226
Tel (973) 321-3590 *Founded/Ownrshp* 1982
Sales NA *EMP* 105
SIC 6331 6324 6321 Fire, marine & casualty insurance; Hospital & medical service plans; Accident & health insurance
Pr: Gerald L Radke
CFO: James F Dore
Treas: Michael John
Treas: Sanford Kimmel
Ex VP: Michael J Bleisnick
Ex VP: Gordon Forsyth III
Sr VP: Peter G Butler
Sr VP: Joe Hoane
Sr VP: Eugene J Sverchek
Sr VP: Alain Tounquet
VP: Bruce J Byrnes
VP: Frank A Lo Piccolo
Board of Directors: Robert W Fiondella, Bernard Kelly, Wendy Luscombe, Edward P Lyons, Philip R McLoughlin, David W Searfoss, Donald H Trautlein, Wilson Wilde

D-U-N-S 12-250-9128
PXRE REINSURANCE CO
(*Suby of* PXRE CORP) ★
379 Thornall St Ste 2, Edison, NJ 08837-2226
Tel (732) 906-9157 *Founded/Ownrshp* 1986
Sales NA *EMP* 80[E]
SIC 6331 Property damage insurance; Reciprocal interinsurance exchanges: fire, marine, casualty
Ch Bd: Gerald L Radke
VP: Eden K Chan
VP: Kenneth J Nemlick

D-U-N-S 01-012-1551
PXU ELECTRIC DELIVERY
SOUTHWSTRN ELEC SERV COMPANY
500 N Akard St Ste 14, Dallas, TX 75201-3302
Tel (214) 486-4760 *Founded/Ownrshp* 2002
Sales 343.9MM[E] *EMP* 800
SIC 4911 Electric services
Ch: Tom Baker

D-U-N-S 00-737-3244
PYCO INDUSTRIES INC (TX)
2901 Avenue A, Lubbock, TX 79404-2231
Tel (806) 747-3434 *Founded/Ownrshp* 1936
Sales 161.0MM *EMP* 160
Accts D Williams & Co Pc Lubbo
SIC 2074 Cottonseed oil, cake or meal
Pr: Robert Lacy
**Ch:* Tommy Horsford
**Sr VP:* Ronnie Gilbert
Genl Mgr: Walt Stokes
**VP Opers:* Lewis Harvill
Board of Directors: Ty Askew, Glen Campbell, Brad Crump, Kenny Landfried

D-U-N-S 02-514-7450
PYRAMID ADVISORS LLC
PYRAMID HOTEL GROUP
1 Post Office Sq Ste 1950, Boston, MA 02109-2120
Tel (617) 202-2033 *Founded/Ownrshp* 1999
Sales 175.5MM[E] *EMP* 1,800
SIC 7011 Hotels & motels
CEO: Richard M Kellher
Pr: Daniel Dolce
Pr: Davis Sezna
COO: James Dina
CFO: Christopher Devine
Sr VP: John Green
**Sr VP:* John S Hamilton
Sr VP: Paige Koerbel
Sr VP: Jack A Levy
Sr VP: Chris Pfohl
Sr VP: Stephen D Pletcher
Sr VP: Paul Sacco
Sr VP: Gary L Sims
Sr VP: Jeff Weggeman
VP: Chuck Freije
VP: Harry Greenblatt
VP: Sarah Griffin
VP: Michael Kubick
VP: David Newhart

D-U-N-S 00-897-7373
PYRAMID CONSULTING INC
PCI
11100 Atlantis Pl, Alpharetta, GA 30022-1161
Tel (678) 514-3500 *Founded/Ownrshp* 1996
Sales 114.2MM[E] *EMP* 283[E]
SIC 7379 7371 Computer related consulting services; Custom computer programming services; Custom computer programming services; Computer software development & applications
CEO: Sanjeev Tirath
**CFO:* Ramesh Maturu
**VP:* Radha Sabhapathy
**VP:* Namita Tirath
Genl Mgr: Ashool Handoo
Software D: Amit Pyramidci

PYRAMID GROUP
See TRI-COUNTY GROUP XV INC

D-U-N-S 96-751-8325
PYRAMID HOMEMAKER SERVICES INC
(*Suby of* PYRAMID GROUP) ★
18 N Main St, Cape Girardeau, MO 63701-7307
Tel (573) 339-1864 *Founded/Ownrshp* 1994
Sales 6.8MM[E] *EMP* 1,400
SIC 7363 Help supply services
Pr: Steve Bradford
**VP:* Andrew Jones
VP: Jamie Wright

PYRAMID HOTEL GROUP
See PYRAMID ADVISORS LLC

D-U-N-S 18-500-1807
PYRAMID MANAGEMENT GROUP INC
4 Clinton Sq, Syracuse, NY 13202
Tel (315) 422-7000 *Founded/Ownrshp* 1970
Sales 159.0MM[E] *EMP* 1,200[E]
SIC 6531 6512 Real estate managers; Shopping center, property operation only
CEO: Stephen J Congel
**Pr:* Robert J Congel
**Pr:* Timothy J Kelley
**CEO:* James A Tuozzolo
**VP:* Marc A Malfitano
Assoc Dir: Robert Dusel

PYRAMID SOUND
See JAZZY ELECTRONICS CORP

D-U-N-S 36-166-2831
PYRAMID WALDEN CO LP
1 Walden Galleria, Buffalo, NY 14225-5408
Tel (315) 422-7000 Founded/Ownrshp 2003
Sales 550.0MM EMP 20
SIC 6512 Nonresidential building operators
Pt: Michael Bovalino
Pt: Pamilo Dillion
Pt: Tim Kelly
Pt: Carmen Spinosa
Genl Mgr: Jim Soos
Opers Mgr: Tom Darby

D-U-N-S 00-906-9519 IMP
PYROTEK INC
705 W 1st Ave, Spokane, WA 99201-3909
Tel (509) 926-6212 Founded/Ownrshp 1956
Sales 636.0MM[E] EMP 2,437
SIC 3365 Aluminum foundries
CEO: Allan Roy
*Pr: Don Ting
*CFO: Paul Rieckers
Div Mgr: Tom Howard
Genl Mgr: Harvey Chalker
Genl Mgr: Rejean Dault
Snr Sftwr: Alejandro Palacios
IT Man: Michael Sekedat
Sfty Mgr: David Eichenmiller
Opers Mgr: Kevin Scott
Plnt Mgr: Cheng Wang

PYXIS DATA SYSTEMS
See CARDINAL HEALTH 301 LLC

D-U-N-S 80-953-2414
▲ PZENA INVESTMENT MANAGEMENT INC
320 Park Ave Fl 8, New York, NY 10022-6815
Tel (212) 355-1600 Founded/Ownrshp 2007
Sales 116.6MM EMP 81
Accts Kpmg Llp New York New York
Tkr Sym PZN Exch NYS
SIC 6722 Management investment, open-end
Ch Bd: Richard S Pzena
*Pr: John P Goetz
*Pr: William L Lipsey
COO: Gary J Bachman
CFO: Jessica R Doran
Ex VP: Michael D Peterson
Off Mgr: Chris Markopoulos

Q

Q, THE
See CAVALIERS OPERATING CO LLC

D-U-N-S 03-496-0351
Q AND D CONSTRUCTION INC
1050 S 21st St, Sparks, NV 89431-5596
Tel (775) 353-1104 Founded/Ownrshp 1964
Sales 158.5MM[E] EMP 550
SIC 1623 Underground utilities contractor
Pr: Norman L Dianda
CFO: Chuck Cook
*Sec: Laura J Dianda
*VP: Tim Kretzschmar
*VP: Lance Semenko Sr
*Ex Dir: Mike Dianda
Off Mgr: Kathy Crutchley
CTO: Dean Whellams
Trfc Dir: Kyle Lynch
Opers Mgr: Kevin Linderman

Q B P
See QUALITY BICYCLE PRODUCTS INC

Q B S
See QUALITY BUILDING SERVICES CORP

Q BUILDING
See KIEWIT MINING GROUP INC

D-U-N-S 83-141-6198
Q C S BUILDING SERVICES INC
41619 Palermo Ct, Lancaster, CA 93536-2969
Tel (661) 267-6211 Founded/Ownrshp 2009
Sales 95.0MM EMP 42
SIC 7349 Building maintenance services
Pr: Michelle Grinstead

D-U-N-S 79-115-1744
Q CONSOLIDATED OIL WELL SERVICES LLC
1322 S Grant Ave, Chanute, KS 66720-2854
Tel (620) 431-9210 Founded/Ownrshp 2006
Sales 138.6MM EMP 140[E]
Accts Pricewaterhousecoopers Llp Tu
SIC 1389 Oil field services
CFO: John Clugh

Q F C
See QUALITY FOOD CENTERS INC

D-U-N-S 04-543-3307 IMP
Q HOLDING CO
QUALITY SYNTHETIC RUBBER
(Suby of 3I GROUP PLC)
1700 Highland Rd, Twinsburg, OH 44087-2221
Tel (330) 425-8472 Founded/Ownrshp 2014
Sales 248.7MM[E] EMP 1,340
SIC 3061 Mechanical rubber goods
CEO: Randall Ross
*CFO: Dennis J Welhouse
Genl Mgr: Joe Folach
VP Sls: John Neel

D-U-N-S 07-372-6481
Q INTERNATIONAL COURIER INC
QUICK INTERNATIONAL COURIER
17528 148th Ave, Jamaica, NY 11434-5516
Tel (718) 995-3616 Founded/Ownrshp 1981
Sales 98.6MM[E] EMP 400
SIC 7389

D-U-N-S 78-933-1881
Q K INC
101 E Hopi Dr, Holbrook, AZ 86025-2625
Tel (928) 524-3680 Founded/Ownrshp 1990
Sales 115.6MM[E] EMP 2,500
SIC 5812 Restaurant, family: chain
Pr: Robbie Qualls
*VP: Doug Koch

D-U-N-S 07-165-1467
Q N P CORP
979 High St, Worthington, OH 43085-4047
Tel (614) 846-0371 Founded/Ownrshp 1970
Sales 108.9MM[E] EMP 400
Accts Shaw & Shaw
SIC 5511 Automobiles, new & used; Pickups, new & used
Pr: Carl C Nourse
*VP: Richard Nourse

Q S T
See QST INDUSTRIES INC

Q V C
See QVC INC

D-U-N-S 94-004-2179
■ Q-COMM CORP
(Suby of WINDSTREAM SERVICES LLC) ★
3701 Communications Way, Evansville, IN 47715-8929
Tel (812) 253-7000 Founded/Ownrshp 2010
Sales 108.8MM[E] EMP 700
SIC 4813 4812 Telephone communication, except radio; Long distance telephone communications; Local telephone communications; ; Paging services
CEO: Albert E Cinelli
*Pr: John Cinelli
*Treas: Lohn H Weber
*VP: John Greenbank

Q-MART
See QUALITY STATE OIL CO INC

Q1
See QUALITY ONE WIRELESS LLC

D-U-N-S 80-810-1468
▲ Q2 HOLDINGS INC
13785 Res Blvd Ste 150, Austin, TX 78750
Tel (512) 275-0072 Founded/Ownrshp 2005
Sales 108.8MM EMP 658[E]
Tkr Sym QTWO Exch NYS
SIC 7372 Prepackaged software; Application computer software
CEO: Matthew P Flake
*Ch Bd: R H Seale III
Pr: Odus Edward Wittenburg Jr
CFO: Jennifer N Harris
Ex VP: Adam D Anderson
Sr VP: Barry G Benton
Board of Directors: Michael M Brown, Jeffrey T Diehl, Charles T Doyle, Michael J Maples Sr, James R Offerdahl, Carl James Schaper

D-U-N-S 04-815-9482
■ Q3 CONTRACTING INC
(Suby of PRIMORIS SERVICES CORP) ★
3066 Spruce St, Saint Paul, MN 55117-1061
Tel (651) 224-2424 Founded/Ownrshp 2012
Sales 110.0MM[E] EMP 400[E]
SIC 1623 7699 3669 Underground utilities contractor; Antique repair & restoration, except furniture, automobiles; Pedestrian traffic control equipment
Pr: Jay Osborn
CFO: Mark Grina
*Ex VP: Dennis Mueller
VP: Dave Odneal
Area Supr: Troy Nelson
Area Supr: Jeremiah Turner

D-U-N-S 03-956-1725
▲ QAD INC
100 Innovation Pl, Santa Barbara, CA 93108-2268
Tel (805) 566-6000 Founded/Ownrshp 1979
Sales 277.8MM EMP 1,680[E]
Tkr Sym QADA Exch NGS
SIC 7372 7371 Prepackaged software; Custom computer programming services
CEO: Karl F Lopker
*Ch Bd: Pamela M Lopker
CFO: Daniel Lender
Ex VP: Anton Chilton
Ex VP: Vincent Niedzielski
Sr VP: Kara Bellamy
VP: Steve Gardner
VP: Eric Graham
VP: Leif Peterson
VP: Tom Seadler
Assoc Dir: Alex Kemp
Board of Directors: Scott J Adelson, Lee D Roberts, Leslie J Stretch, Peter R Van Cuylenburg

QBE
See UNIGARD PACIFIC INSURANCE CO

QBE THE AMERICAS
See QBE INSURANCE CORP

D-U-N-S 00-794-6320
QBE AMERICAS INC
(Suby of WINTERTHUR U S HOLDINGS INC) ★
1 General Dr, Sun Prairie, WI 53596-0001
Tel (608) 837-4440 Founded/Ownrshp 1925, 1991
Sales NA EMP 1,636
SIC 6331 Property damage insurance; Fire, marine & casualty insurance & carriers
Pr: Paul Schulte
COO: Jim Fiore
*Sr VP: Peter McPartland
VP: Jeff Dehn
*VP: William G Fitzpatrick
VP: Art Volkman
Div Mgr: Anthony Buschur
Dir IT: Rob Rivest
IT Man: Sue Erickson
Mktg Mgr: Lyle Petersen

QBE FINANCIAL INSTITUTION
See NATIONAL GENERAL LENDER SERVICES INC

D-U-N-S 17-476-6857
■ QBE FIRST INSURANCE AGENCY INC
(Suby of QBE FINANCIAL INSTITUTION) ★
210 Interstate North Pkwy, Atlanta, GA 30339-2233
Tel (770) 690-8400 Founded/Ownrshp 1997
Sales NA EMP 1,200
SIC 6411 Insurance brokers
CEO: C D Davies
COO: John Lock
CFO: John Fitzgerald
Ex VP: Matthew Freeman
Sr VP: John Anderson
Sr VP: Arthur Castner
Sr VP: Mark Girasole
Sr VP: Barb Meredith
Sr VP: Kathy J Rasmussen
VP: Chris Browning
VP: Eric Laton
VP: Amanda Taylor
VP: Jason Thompson

D-U-N-S 11-291-9410
QBE HOLDINGS INC
(Suby of QBE EMERGING MARKETS HOLDINGS PTY LIMITED)
88 Pine St, New York, NY 10005-1801
Tel (212) 422-1212 Founded/Ownrshp 1993
Sales NA EMP 2,450
SIC 6321 6411 Reinsurance carriers, accident & health; Insurance agents
Ch Bd: John Rumpler
Pr: Mike Jacobs
COO: Sue Harnett
*CFO: Christopher C Fish
*Treas: Robert Franzino
*Ofcr: Jim Fiore
Ofcr: Dean Harring
Ofcr: Peter Maloney
Ofcr: Steven Sheinheit
Ofcr: Shaun Slynn
*Sr VP: Robert Byler
Sr VP: Shaun Flynn
Sr VP: Richard Kalina
Sr VP: Christopher Larson
Sr VP: Adam Roberts
Sr VP: Mike Scala
Sr VP: John Stovobda
Sr VP: Jennifer Vernon
Sr VP: Tom Voltz
VP: Tom Lowry
VP: Sonja Lundy

D-U-N-S 02-007-7863
QBE INSURANCE CORP
QBE THE AMERICAS
(Suby of QBE HOLDINGS INC) ★
88 Pine St Fl 16, New York, NY 10005-1819
Tel (212) 422-1212 Founded/Ownrshp 1964
Sales NA EMP 602
SIC 6311 6321 Life reinsurance; Reinsurance carriers, accident & health
Pr: John Rumpler
Pr: Joseph Kipp
Pr: John Pollock
Pr: Susan Rivera
Pr: Ed Wadhams
*COO: Jim Fiore
CFO: Chris Fish
*CFO: Christopher Fish
*Ofcr: Peter Maloney
Ofcr: Steve Rodriguez
Sr VP: Claude Chevance
Sr VP: Andy Doll
Sr VP: Robert Mezzasalma
Sr VP: Charles Valinotti
VP: Wayne Bayer
VP: Michael Connor
VP: Maureen Flint
VP: Wade Hardcastle
VP: Lori Irving
VP: Michael Loconsolo
VP: Robert Remy

D-U-N-S 61-451-0654
QBE INVESTMENTS (NORTH AMERICA) INC
(Suby of WINTERTHUR U S HOLDINGS INC) ★
1 General Dr, Sun Prairie, WI 53596-0001
Tel (608) 837-4440 Founded/Ownrshp 1972
Sales NA EMP 2,200
SIC 6331 Property damage insurance; Reciprocal interinsurance exchanges: fire, marine, casualty
CEO: David Duclos
*VP: Jenniffer Vernon

QBE THE AMERICAS
See NAU COUNTRY INSURANCE CO

D-U-N-S 11-337-6909
QC FINANCIAL SERVICES INC
QUIK CASH
(Suby of QC HOLDINGS INC) ★
9401 Indian Creek Pkwy # 1500, Shawnee Mission, KS 66210-2020
Tel (913) 439-1100 Founded/Ownrshp 1998
Sales NA EMP 1,000
SIC 6141 6099 Personal credit institutions; Consumer finance companies; Check cashing agencies
Ch Bd: Don Early
*Pr: Darrin Andersen

D-U-N-S 14-848-6868
QC HOLDINGS INC
9401 Indian Creek Pkwy # 1500, Overland Park, KS 66210-2020
Tel (866) 660-2243 Founded/Ownrshp 1984
Sales NA EMP 1,244
SIC 6141 7389 Personal credit institutions; Personal finance licensed loan companies, small; Financial services
Pr: Darrin J Andersen
*Ch Bd: Don Early
V Ch: Mary Early
CFO: Douglas E Nickerson
*V Ch Bd: Mary Lou Early
Bd of Dir: Gerald F Lamberti
VP: Matthew J Wiltanger
Board of Directors: Richard B Chalker, Gerald F Lamberti, Jack L Sutherland

D-U-N-S 02-265-7618 IMP
QCH INC
(Suby of ACCESS INTERNATIONAL CO) ★
241 Ridge St Fl 4, Reno, NV 89501-2020
Tel (510) 226-1000 Founded/Ownrshp 1989
Sales 2.3MM[E] EMP 5,012[E]
SIC 5045 Computers
Pr: Frank Lee

D-U-N-S 80-821-0665
QCH NASHVILLE LLC
QUANTA
(Suby of QCH INC) ★
1621 Heil Quaker Blvd, La Vergne, TN 37086-3655
Tel (615) 501-7500 Founded/Ownrshp 2003
Sales 773.1M[E] EMP 5,007[E]
SIC 5045 3577 Computers; Computer peripheral equipment

D-U-N-S 80-821-0546
▲ QCR HOLDINGS INC
3551 7th St Ste 204, Moline, IL 61265-6156
Tel (309) 736-3584 Founded/Ownrshp 1993
Sales NA EMP 406[E]
Tkr Sym QCRH Exch NGM
SIC 6022 State commercial banks
Pr: Douglas M Hultquist
*Ch Bd: James J Brownson
*COO: Todd A Gipple
*V Ch Bd: Patrick S Baird
Chf Cred: Dana L Nichols

D-U-N-S 02-916-0693
QCT LLC
(Suby of QUANTA COMPUTER INC.)
1010 Rincon Cir, San Jose, CA 95131-1325
Tel (510) 270-6111 Founded/Ownrshp 2011
Sales 4.8MM[E] EMP 1,000
SIC 7373 Computer integrated systems design

QDOBA MEXICAN GRILL
See QDOBA RESTAURANT CORP

D-U-N-S 15-981-9473
■ QDOBA RESTAURANT CORP
QDOBA MEXICAN GRILL
(Suby of JACK IN BOX INC) ★
7244 W Bonfils Ln, Lakewood, CO 80226-3487
Tel (720) 898-2300 Founded/Ownrshp 2003
Sales 121.2MM[E] EMP 2,500
SIC 5812 6794 Mexican restaurant; Franchises, selling or licensing
Pr: Gary Beisler
COO: Bob Kuron
*Chf Mktg O: Karen Guido
VP: Bill McMillan
VP: Bruce Vermilya
Exec: Michelle Kelsey
Dist Mgr: Greg Livingston
Genl Mgr: Herman Mitchell
Dir IT: Jerilyn Quintanilla
Site Mgr: Cindy Bartley
Site Mgr: Shawn Kromer

D-U-N-S 06-174-7432
QED INC
QED STATEWIDE ELECTRIC
1661 W 3rd Ave, Denver, CO 80223-1438
Tel (303) 825-5011 Founded/Ownrshp 2004
Sales 228.7MM[E] EMP 154
SIC 5063 Electrical supplies
Pr: Dean J Stauffer
VP: Don Higbee
Brnch Mgr: Dave Dahl
CIO: Steve Stillar
Software D: Dan Lopath
Sales Asso: Joel Ewell

QED STATEWIDE ELECTRIC
See QED INC

D-U-N-S 04-624-5411
QED SYSTEMS INC
4646 N Witchduck Rd, Virginia Beach, VA 23455-6202
Tel (757) 490-5000 Founded/Ownrshp 1990
Sales 156.1MM[E] EMP 450
SIC 8711 3731 Marine engineering; Military ships, building & repairing
Pr: Mark T Jones
*CFO: Winfred O Stant Jr
Prgrm Mgr: Lauren Troyan
Brnch Mgr: Charles Wolfe
Off Mgr: Leslie Burton
CTO: Dan Musmanno
Opers Mgr: Stuart Davidson
Ql Cn Mgr: Robert Freeburn
Sales Exec: Jimmy Jones

QEP
See QEP CO INC

D-U-N-S 03-824-2848 IMP/EXP
▲ QEP CO INC
QEP
1001 Brkn Snd Pkwy Nw A, Boca Raton, FL 33487-3532
Tel (561) 994-5550 Founded/Ownrshp 1979
Sales 309.2MM EMP 840
Tkr Sym QEPC Exch OTO
SIC 5072 5085 2891 Hand tools; Industrial tools; Adhesives
Ch Bd: Lewis Gould
Pr: Leonard Gould
CFO: Mark S Walter
Ofcr: Julie Morgan
Ex VP: Eric Demaree
Sr VP: Jamie Clingan
Sr VP: Lawrence P Levine
Sr VP: Mark Walter
VP: Terry Hirschman
VP: Jeff Johnson
VP: Stan Labanowitz
VP: Brad Miller
VP: Kenneth Mosser
VP: Joe Santinello
VP: Mike Venturelli
VP Bus Dev: Brad Blanton
Board of Directors: Martin E Cooperman, David W Kreilein, Emil Vogel

D-U-N-S 04-693-4568
■ QEP ENERGY CO
QUESTAR ENERGY
(*Suby of* QEP RESOURCES INC) ★
1050 17th St Ste 800, Denver, CO 80265-2008
Tel (303) 672-6900 *Founded/Ownrshp* 1922
Sales 420.5MM[E] *EMP* 170
SIC 1311 1382 1389 5172 Crude petroleum & natural gas production; Oil & gas exploration services; Oil field services; Petroleum products
Pr: Charles B Stanley
Treas: Martin Craven
VP: Thomas Jepperson
VP: Melvin Owen
VP: Kurt Watts

D-U-N-S 07-884-1068
■ QEP MIDSTREAM PARTNERS LP
QEPM
(*Suby of* TESORO LOGISTICS LP) ★
19100 Ridgewood Pkwy, San Antonio, TX 78259-1834
Tel (210) 626-6000 *Founded/Ownrshp* 2015
Sales 114.7MM[E] *EMP* 250[E]
SIC 4922 Natural gas transmission; Pipelines, natural gas
CEO: Gregory J Goff
Pr: Phillip M Anderson
CFO: Steven M Sterin

D-U-N-S 05-503-4086
▲ QEP RESOURCES INC
1050 17th St Ste 800, Denver, CO 80265-2008
Tel (303) 672-6900 *Founded/Ownrshp* 1988
Sales 2.0MMM *EMP* 693[E]
Tkr Sym QEP *Exch* NYS
SIC 1311 1321 1382 Natural gas production; Natural gas liquids production; Oil & gas exploration services
Ch Bd: Charles B Stanley
CFO: Richard J Doleshek
Sr VP: Austin S Murr
VP: Jeffery R Tommerup
VP: Christopher K Woosley
Exec: Rudy Nunez
Board of Directors: Julie A Dill, Robert F Heinemann, M W Scoggins, William L Thacker III, David A Trice

QEPM
See QEP MIDSTREAM PARTNERS LP

D-U-N-S 19-973-1894
QES WIRELINE LLC
ARCHER WIRELINE LLC
(*Suby of* QUINTANA ENERGY SERVICES LP) ★
801 Cherry St Ste 800, Fort Worth, TX 76102-6813
Tel (817) 546-4970 *Founded/Ownrshp* 2015
Sales 234.9MM[E] *EMP* 500
SIC 1389 Well logging
Pr: John Castetter
VP: David Chapple
VP: Neil Mills
Genl Couns: Max Bouthillette

D-U-N-S 83-266-7781 EXP
■ QG LLC
(*Suby of* WORLD COLOR (USA) HOLDING CO) ★
N61w23044 Harrys Way, Sussex, WI 53089-3995
Tel (414) 566-6000 *Founded/Ownrshp* 1971
Sales 1.0MMM[E] *EMP* 7,456
SIC 2754 Publication printing, gravure
Prin: Barbara Depass
**CEO:* Joel Quadracci

D-U-N-S 83-267-4449 EXP
■ QG PRINTING CORP
(*Suby of* QG LLC) ★
N61w23044 Harrys Way, Sussex, WI 53089-3995
Tel (414) 566-6000 *Founded/Ownrshp* 1962
Sales 247.9MM[E] *EMP* 1,810
SIC 2752 Commercial printing, offset
CEO: Joel Quadracci
**V Ch:* John Fowler
**COO:* Tom Frankowski
**Ch:* Dave Honan
**Ex VP:* Dave Blais

D-U-N-S 83-267-4316
■ QG PRINTING II CORP
QUAD/GRAPHICS
(*Suby of* QG LLC) ★
N61w23044 Harrys Way, Sussex, WI 53089-3995
Tel (414) 566-6000 *Founded/Ownrshp* 1972
Sales 337.3MM[E] *EMP* 2,681
SIC 2752 Commercial printing, offset
Pr: J Joel Quadracci
**VP:* John Fowler

D-U-N-S 11-865-5141
QGS DEVELOPMENT INC
QUALITY TURF
17502 County Road 672, Lithia, FL 33547-1201
Tel (813) 634-3326 *Founded/Ownrshp* 1982
Sales 334.7MM[E] *EMP* 103
SIC 0782 0781 1711

QHG
See GADSDEN REGIONAL MEDICAL CENTER LLC

D-U-N-S 78-290-3926
■ QHG OF SOUTH CAROLINA INC
(*Suby of* COMMUNITY HEALTH SYSTEMS INC) ★
805 Pamplico Hwy, Florence, SC 29505-6047
Tel (843) 674-5000 *Founded/Ownrshp* 2007
Sales 174.5MM[E] *EMP* 2,100
SIC 8062 General medical & surgical hospitals
CEO: Darcy Craven
COO: Jodie Beauregard
CFO: Dennis Eith
Dir Rad: Michael Cudd
Dir Rx: Richard Davis
Chf Nrs Of: Nicole Boone
Prgrm Mgr: Virginia Boyle
Off Mgr: Pamela Ham
Nurse Mgr: Pat Reeves
Nurse Mgr: Shametra Swaringer
Surgeon: Mark Harris

D-U-N-S 19-729-4564
QIAGEN INC
(*Suby of* QIAGEN NORTH AMERICAN HOLDINGS INC) ★
27220 Turnberry Ln # 200, Valencia, CA 91355-1019
Tel (661) 702-3598 *Founded/Ownrshp* 2000
Sales 101.9MM[E] *EMP* 451
SIC 3826 5047 8731 2835

D-U-N-S 00-193-8914
QIAGEN NORTH AMERICAN HOLDINGS INC
(*Suby of* QIAGEN N.V.)
27220 Turnberry Ln # 200, Valencia, CA 91355-1018
Tel (661) 702-3000 *Founded/Ownrshp* 2000
Sales 217.8MM[E] *EMP* 1,241
SIC 5122 Biologicals & allied products
Pr: Peer Schatz
Pdt Mgr: Amy Hoffer
Snr Mgr: David Dortch

D-U-N-S 07-948-4088
QINETIQ NORTH AMERICA INC
(*Suby of* QINETIQ US HOLDINGS INC) ★
350 2nd Ave Bldg 1, Waltham, MA 02451-1104
Tel (781) 684-4000 *Founded/Ownrshp* 2005
Sales 227.3MM[E] *EMP* 1,510[E]
SIC 3812 8731 Defense systems & equipment; Engineering laboratory, except testing
Pr: Dr Andrew Rogers
**Pr:* Jeff Yorsz
**Ex VP:* Dr Richard Wiesman
**VP:* Doug Ounanian
**VP:* Robert Polutchko
**VP:* Paul Sateriale

D-U-N-S 11-379-5624
QINETIQ US HOLDINGS INC
(*Suby of* QINETIQ HOLDINGS LIMITED)
5885 Trinity Pkwy Ste 130, Centreville, VA 20120-1969
Tel (202) 429-6630 *Founded/Ownrshp* 2002
Sales 348.4MM[E] *EMP* 2,350
SIC 3812 Defense systems & equipment
CEO: Robert Evers
Pr: J D Crouch II
CFO: Jeffrey R Beck
Treas: Bonnie Dennis
Sr VP: Mary Craft
Sr VP: Mark Hewitt
Sr VP: David F Toomey III
Sr VP: Austin Yamada
Board of Directors: Robert Evers, Darrell Oyer

QIVLIQ
See AKIMA LLC

D-U-N-S 08-037-9326
QLIK PARENT INC
150 N Radnor Chester Rd, Radnor, PA 19087-5252
Tel (888) 828-9768 *Founded/Ownrshp* 2016
Sales 100.3MM[E] *EMP* 2,511[E]
SIC 6719 7371 Investment holding companies, except banks; Computer software systems analysis & design, custom
CEO: Lars Bjrk

D-U-N-S 82-756-5792
QLIK TECHNOLOGIES INC
(*Suby of* QLIK PARENT INC) ★
150 N Radnor Chester Rd, Radnor, PA 19087-5252
Tel (866) 616-4960 *Founded/Ownrshp* 2016
Sales 612.7MM *EMP* 2,511[E]
Accts Ernst & Young Llp Philadelphi
SIC 7374 7371 Data processing & preparation; Computer software systems analysis & design, custom
CEO: Lars Bjork
CFO: Timothy Maccarrick
Chf Mktg O: Rick Jackson
Ofcr: Diane Adams
Ex VP: Mark Thurmond
Sr VP: Mike Potter
VP: Deborah Lofton
VP: Peter McQuade
IT Man: Heather Rossman
Mktg Mgr: Andre Keime
Sls Mgr: Jeffrey Cooper

D-U-N-S 80-855-6617 IMP
■ QLOGIC CORP
(*Suby of* CAVIUM INC) ★
26650 Aliso Viejo Pkwy, Aliso Viejo, CA 92656-2674
Tel (949) 389-6000 *Founded/Ownrshp* 2016
Sales 458.9MM *EMP* 782
SIC 3674 Semiconductors & related devices; Integrated circuits, semiconductor networks, etc.
Pr: Syed Ali
COO: M Raghib Hussain
CFO: Arthur Chadwick
Sr VP: Vincent Pangrazio
VP: Anthony E Carrozza
VP: Milt Douglass
VP: Ahmet Houssein
VP: Anil Jain
VP: Ofer Michael
VP: Perry Mulligan
VP: Nikhil Sharma

D-U-N-S 07-947-2631
QMES LLC
MONTGOMERY MEDICAL EQUIPMENT
122 Mill Rd Ste A130, Phoenixville, PA 19460-1412
Tel (610) 630-6357 *Founded/Ownrshp* 2012
Sales 200.0MM *EMP* 1,200
SIC 5047 6719 Oxygen therapy equipment; Personal holding companies, except banks

D-U-N-S 09-360-6747 IMP
■ QORVO FLORIDA INC
QORVO US
(*Suby of* QORVO US INC) ★
1818 S Orange Blossom Trl, Apopka, FL 32703-9419
Tel (407) 886-8860 *Founded/Ownrshp* 2001
Sales 89.5MM[E] *EMP* 770
SIC 3674 Semiconductors & related devices
Pr: Ralph G Quinsey
**CFO:* Steven J Buhaly
**VP:* John K Bitzer
**VP:* Steven R Grant
**VP:* Azhar Waseem
**VP Sls:* Brian P Balut

D-U-N-S 02-620-6752
▲ QORVO INC
7628 Thorndike Rd, Greensboro, NC 27409-9421
Tel (336) 664-1233 *Founded/Ownrshp* 1981
Sales 2.6MMM *EMP* 10,782[E]
Accts Kpmg Llp Greensboro North Ca
Tkr Sym QRVO *Exch* NGS
SIC 3825 3674 Oscillators, audio & radio frequency (instrument types); Semiconductors & related devices
Pr: Robert A Bruggeworth
**Ch Bd:* Ralph G Quinsey
CFO: Steve Buhaly
CFO: Mark J Murphy
Treas: Suzanne Rudy
Ex VP: William A Priddy Jr
VP: Steven E Creviston
VP: Brandi Frye
VP: Gina B Harrison
VP: James L Klein
VP: Ralph Knupp
VP: Jim Stilson
VP Bus Dev: Hans Schwarz
Exec: Lisa Beeson
Dir Soc: Kathleen Ingram
Board of Directors: Daniel A Dileo, Jeffery R Gardner, Charles Scott Gibson, John R Harding, David HY Ho, Roderick D Nelson, Walden C Rhines, Susan L Spradley, Walter H Wilkinson Jr

D-U-N-S 07-989-2693
QORVO INC
500 W Renner Rd, Richardson, TX 75080-1324
Tel (972) 994-8200 *Founded/Ownrshp* 2015
Sales 228.8MM[E] *EMP* 7,000
SIC 3663 3674 3679 Amplifiers, RF power & IF; Transistors; Oscillators
CEO: Robert Bruggeworth
**Pr:* Steven Creviston
**VP:* Brandi Frye
Sftwr Eng: Alan Davidson
Opers Mgr: John Zipko
Mktg Mgr: Richard Martin

D-U-N-S 00-386-4621 IMP
■ QORVO TEXAS LLC (TX)
QORVO US
(*Suby of* QORVO INC) ★
500 W Renner Rd, Richardson, TX 75080-1324
Tel (972) 994-8200 *Founded/Ownrshp* 1997, 2016
Sales 213.1MM[E] *EMP* 1,413
SIC 3674 Semiconductors & related devices
Ch Bd: Ralph G Quinsey
**Pr:* Robert A Bruggeworth
VP: James Klein
Dir Lab: Kim Tiv
Prgrm Mgr: Doug Cole
Prgrm Mgr: Jeff McKee
Snr Sftwr: Robert Brothers
Sftwr Eng: Alan Davidson
Opers Mgr: John Zipko
Plnt Mgr: Randy Wilson
Snr Mgr: Sita Balasubramanian

QORVO US
See QORVO TEXAS LLC

QORVO US
See QORVO FLORIDA INC

D-U-N-S 04-544-4635 IMP/EXP
■ QORVO US INC
(*Suby of* QORVO INC) ★
7628 Thorndike Rd, Greensboro, NC 27409-9421
Tel (336) 664-1233 *Founded/Ownrshp* 2015
Sales 1.6MMM[E] *EMP* 6,591
SIC 3674 Semiconductors & related devices; Microcircuits, integrated (semiconductor)
Pr: Robert Bruggeworth
**Pr:* Steven Eric Creviston
**CFO:* Steve Buhaly
**VP:* Brandi Frye
**Prin:* Jack Osborne
Prgrm Mgr: Julene Siegel
Snr Ntwrk: John Hall
Sls&Mrk Ex: George Sanders

D-U-N-S 96-337-9891
QPS HOLDINGS LLC
3 Innovation Way Ste 240, Newark, DE 19711-5456
Tel (302) 369-5601 *Founded/Ownrshp* 2007
Sales 100.7MM[E] *EMP* 450
Accts Mc Gladrey & Pullen
SIC 6719 Personal holding companies, except banks
CFO: T Ben Hsu

QPSI
See QUALITY PACKAGING SPECIALISTS INTERNATIONAL LLC

D-U-N-S 07-131-9503
QRS INC (KY)
RIVERSIDE RECYCLING
345 Marshall Ave Ste 301, Saint Louis, MO 63119-1863
Tel (314) 963-8000 *Founded/Ownrshp* 1974
Sales 93.7MM[E] *EMP* 150
SIC 4953 Recycling, waste materials
CEO: Gregory L Janson
**Ch Bd:* Timothy M Janson
Plnt Mgr: George Hurd

D-U-N-S 04-660-6976 IMP/EXP
QSC LLC (CA)
1675 Macarthur Blvd, Costa Mesa, CA 92626-1468
Tel (714) 754-6175 *Founded/Ownrshp* 2007
Sales 89.8MM[E] *EMP* 340[E]
SIC 3651 Household audio & video equipment
Pr: Joe Pham
**COO:* Jatan Shah
**Sr VP:* Barry Ferrell
**VP:* Anna Csontos
VP: Gerry Tschetter
**VP:* Ray Van Straten
**VP:* John White
CIO: Max Jen
CTO: Joseph Pham
Dir IT: John Britton
IT Man: Venu Tamirisa

D-U-N-S 03-321-1368
QSI INC (HI)
TIMES SUPER MARKET
3375 Koapaka St Ste D108, Honolulu, HI 96819-1865
Tel (808) 831-0811 *Founded/Ownrshp* 2002
Sales 149.2MM[E] *EMP* 1,000
SIC 5411 Supermarkets, chain
CEO: John Quinn
**Pr:* Roger Godfrey
**Pr:* Robert B Stout
**CFO:* Patricia Quinn
**VP:* Glenn Evans
Exec: Kimberly Nishigaya

QSR
See LEXINGTON RUBBER GROUP INC

D-U-N-S 84-001-5911
■ QSS GROUP INC
(*Suby of* DELL SVCS FDRAL GOVERNMENT INC) ★
8270 Willow Oaks Corp Dr, Fairfax, VA 22031-4516
Tel (703) 289-8000 *Founded/Ownrshp* 2007
Sales 55.3MM[E] *EMP* 1,400
SIC 8711 Engineering services
Pr: Jim Ballard
**CFO:* Arnold Cash
**CFO:* Richard Roth
Sr VP: Thomas J Connell
Mktg Mgr: Lauren Hammond
Mktg Mgr: Andrew McCann

D-U-N-S 04-900-7917 IMP/EXP
QST INDUSTRIES INC
Q S T
550 W Adams St Ste 200, Chicago, IL 60661-3665
Tel (312) 930-9400 *Founded/Ownrshp* 1969
Sales 166.7MM[E] *EMP* 500
SIC 2396 2392 2752 Automotive & apparel trimmings; Household furnishings; Commercial printing, lithographic
CFO: Jeffrey A Carlevato
CFO: Jeffrey Carlevato
CFO: Jeff Carlovato
VP: Alex Danch
VP: Sal Paterna
VP: Dick Shanhouse
VP: Richard Shanhouse
Genl Mgr: Lacramioara Curcan
Sales Exec: Berna Karacali
VP Sls: Mark Dudelson
Mktg Mgr: Alan Teo

QTS
See QUALITY TECHNOLOGY SERVICES LLC

D-U-N-S 07-915-8608
QTS REALTY TRUST INC (MD)
12851 Foster St, Overland Park, KS 66213-2705
Tel (913) 814-9988 *Founded/Ownrshp* 2013
Sales 311.0MM *EMP* 1,539[E]
Accts Ernst And Young Llp Kansas C
SIC 7375 7374 Information retrieval services; Data base information retrieval; On-line data base information retrieval; Data processing service
Ch Bd: Chad L Williams
Pr: Butch Goldi
COO: Daniel T Bennewitz
COO: James H Reinhart
CFO: Bill Schafer
CFO: William H Schafer
Ofcr: Stanley Sword
Ex VP: David McOmber
VP: Stephen Douglas
VP: Terry Land
CIO: Jeffrey H Berson

D-U-N-S 02-209-7190
QUAD CITY AUTOMOTIVE GROUP LLC
LUJACK'S NORTHPARK AUTO PLAZA
3700 N Harrison St, Davenport, IA 52806-5905
Tel (563) 386-1511 *Founded/Ownrshp* 2007
Sales 155.1MM[E] *EMP* 352
SIC 5511 5521 Automobiles, new & used; Vans, new & used; Pickups, new & used; Used car dealers
Ch Bd: Micheal Leep Sr
Genl Mgr: Rob Brock
Genl Mgr: Steve Holub
Genl Mgr: Ed Maroon
Genl Mgr: Bill Minas
Genl Mgr: Paul Penrose
Genl Mgr: Rick Vanbarg
Genl Mgr: Brad Weiss
Off Mgr: Joan Gasser
Mktg Dir: Tracy Schwind
Sls Mgr: Shane Anthony

D-U-N-S 12-163-2145 IMP
QUAD ELECTRONICS INC
CABLCON
379 Executive Dr, Troy, MI 48083-4533
Tel (800) 969-9220 *Founded/Ownrshp* 2006
Sales 94.4MM[E] *EMP* 75[E]
SIC 5063 Electronic wire & cable
Pr: Clay Pace
**Pr:* Bryan Kadrich
**VP:* Gerald Demski
Sales Asso: Sarah Lesage

D-U-N-S 07-938-4985
QUAD-C JH HOLDINGS INC
2430 Whitehall Park Dr, Charlotte, NC 28273-3422
Tel (800) 826-0270 *Founded/Ownrshp* 2009
Sales 163.0MM *EMP* 900[E]
Accts Pricewaterhousecoopers Llp Ch
SIC 5047 Hospital furniture
CEO: Mark Ludwig
**CFO:* Mark Urbania

QUAD/GRAPHICS
See QG PRINTING II CORP

D-U-N-S 05-530-2756 IMP/EXP
▲ QUAD/GRAPHICS INC
N61w23044 Harrys Way, Sussex, WI 53089-3995
Tel (414) 566-6000 *Founded/Ownrshp* 1971
Sales 4.6MMM *EMP* 22,500
Tkr Sym QUAD *Exch* NYS

SIC 2752 2754 2721 Commercial printing, lithographic; Commercial printing, gravure; Magazines: publishing & printing
Ch Bd: J Joel Quadracci
COO: Thomas J Frankowski
CFO: John C Fowler
CFO: David J Honan
Treas: Candy Funk
Treas: Mark Meylor
Ex VP: Eric Ashworth
Ex VP: Renee Badura
Ex VP: David Blais
Ex VP: Steven D Jaeger
Ex VP: Jennifer Kent
Sr VP: Carl Gauvreau
VP: James Capstick
VP: Rich Constand
VP: Bill Graushar
VP: Claudio Griguelo
VP: Arthur Hall
VP: Scott Harvey
VP: John Hubbard
VP: Jennifer J Kent
VP: Robert Kleinschmidt
Board of Directors: William J Abraham Jr, Mark A Angelson, Douglas P Buth, Kathryn Quadracci Flores, John Fowler, Steve Fuller, Christopher B Harned, Thomas O Ryder, John S Shiely

D-U-N-S 07-969-1003
QUADION HOLDINGS LLC
1100 Xenium Ln N Ste 1, Minneapolis, MN 55441-4440
Tel (952) 927-1400 *Founded/Ownrshp* 2012
Sales 150.0MM *EMP* 1,100
SIC 3069 3089 Molded rubber products; Blow molded finished plastic products
CEO: Marlin Braun
CFO: John Humbert

D-U-N-S 00-647-7244 IMP
■ QUADION LLC
MINNESOTA RUBBER & PLASTICS CO
(*Suby of* NORWEST EQUITY PARTNERS) ★
1100 Xenium Ln N Ste 1, Minneapolis, MN 55441-4440
Tel (952) 927-1400 *Founded/Ownrshp* 1945, 2012
Sales 312.9MM^E *EMP* 1,100
SIC 3069 3089 Molded rubber products; Bushings, rubber; Grommets, rubber; Blow molded finished plastic products
CEO: Marlin Braun
Pr: Ketandy Deshpande
CFO: John Humbert
Exec: Bill Pederson
Admn Mgr: Pauline Rolstad
Genl Mgr: Kurt Kiffmeyer
Mtls Mgr: Tammy Boes
Opers Mgr: Don Ritchie
Sls&Mrk Ex: Michael Iblings
Mktg Dir: Aron Yngve

D-U-N-S 04-383-5454
■ QUADION LLC
MAR-KELL SEAL
(*Suby of* NORWEST EQUITY PARTNERS) ★
17651 Armstrong Ave, Irvine, CA 92614-5727
Tel (714) 546-0994 *Founded/Ownrshp* 1945
Sales 110.7MM^E *EMP* 1,100
SIC 6282

D-U-N-S 18-706-1957
QUADRAMED CORP
(*Suby of* N. HARRIS COMPUTER CORPORATION)
12110 Sunset Hills Rd # 600, Reston, VA 20190-5916
Tel (703) 709-2300 *Founded/Ownrshp* 2013
Sales 96.3MM^E *EMP* 613
SIC 7372 Business oriented computer software
CEO: Duncan W James
**Pr:* Daniel Desaulniers
COO: Johnathan Hartzer
**COO:* David L Piazza
COO: Michael Wilstead
**Ex VP:* Jim Dowling
**Ex VP:* David L Puckett
**Ex VP:* Vicki Wheatley
**Ex VP:* Sandi Williams
Sr VP: Brook Carlon
**Sr VP:* William J Chatterton Jr
Sr VP: Thomas J Dunn
Sr VP: Thomas J Easterly
**Sr VP:* James R Klein
**Sr VP:* Steven V Russell
Sr VP: Michael J Simpson
Sr VP: Jun Zhang
VP: Linda Benson
VP: Bonnie Herron
VP: Mary McNerney
VP: Karen Mellin

D-U-N-S 06-202-1753
QUADRANGLE DEVELOPMENT CORP
(*Suby of* R G A INC) ★
1001 G St Nw Ste 700w, Washington, DC 20001-4549
Tel (202) 667-0014 *Founded/Ownrshp* 1962
Sales 108.4MM^E *EMP* 215
SIC 6552 Subdividers & developers
CEO: Robert Gladstone
Pr: Christopher D Gladstone
VP: Robert Knopff
VP: Daphne Ramsey

D-U-N-S 05-121-8115
■ QUADRANT 4 CONSULTING INC
(*Suby of* QUADRANT 4 SYSTEM CORPORATION)
1246 S River Rd Ste 102, Cranbury, NJ 08512-3699
Tel (609) 799-3762 *Founded/Ownrshp* 2010
Sales 19.5MM^E *EMP* 1,000
SIC 7379 Computer related consulting services
CEO: Nandu Thondavadi

D-U-N-S 04-804-4762 IMP
QUADRANT EPP USA INC
QUADRANT PLASTICS
(*Suby of* QUADRANT PLASTIC COMPOSITES AG)
2120 Fairmont Ave, Reading, PA 19605-3041
Tel (610) 320-6600 *Founded/Ownrshp* 2008
Sales 370.0MM^E *EMP* 966
SIC 2821 Nylon resins
Pr: Glendon T Steady
**Treas:* Daniel Michalak
**VP:* Caldwell John H
Telecom Ex: Kevin Brennan
CIO: Ed Wojciechowski
IT Man: Kevin Brennen
Info Man: Jeff Mikitka
Sfty Mgr: Michael Young
Opers Mgr: John Dutka
Plnt Mgr: Lonnie Crump
Sales Exec: Barry Riegel

QUADRANT PLASTICS
See QUADRANT EPP USA INC

D-U-N-S 00-235-0866 IMP/EXP
▲ QUAKER CHEMICAL CORP (PA)
901 E Hector St, Conshohocken, PA 19428-2380
Tel (610) 832-4000 *Founded/Ownrshp* 1918
Sales 737.5MM *EMP* 2,040
Accts Pricewaterhousecoopers Llp Ph
Tkr Sym KWR *Exch* NYS
SIC 2992 2899 2869 2891 Lubricating oils; Corrosion preventive lubricant; Hydraulic fluids, synthetic base; Sealants
Ch Bd: Michael F Barry
COO: Mark Harris
CFO: Mary Dean Hall
VP: D Jeffry Benoliel
VP: Joseph A Berquist
VP: John Dennis
VP: Michael Kelly
VP: Dieter Laininger
VP: Joseph F Matrange
VP: Jan F Nieman
VP: Wilbert Platzer
VP: Adrian Steeples
Dir Lab: Xingmin Zhao
Board of Directors: Donald R Caldwell, Robert E Chappell, William R Cook, Mark A Douglas, Jeffry D Frisby, William H Osborne, Robert H Rock, Fay West

D-U-N-S 60-341-5068 IMP
QUAKER EQUITIES LTD
257 Park Ave S Fl 7, New York, NY 10010-7304
Tel (212) 473-1510 *Founded/Ownrshp* 1987
Sales 241.8MM^E *EMP* 1,178^E
SIC 5182 Liquor; Wine
Pr: Joseph J Magliocco
**Ch Bd:* John T Magliocco

D-U-N-S 00-131-6439 IMP/EXP
■ QUAKER OATS CO (NJ)
(*Suby of* PEPSICO INC) ★
555 W Monroe St Fl 1, Chicago, IL 60661-3716
Tel (312) 821-1000 *Founded/Ownrshp* 1901
Sales 3.5MMM^E *EMP* 10,000
SIC 2086 2043 2045 2052 2064 2099 Bottled & canned soft drinks; Cereal breakfast foods; Flours & flour mixes, from purchased flour; Rice cakes; Granola & muesli, bars & clusters; Rice, uncooked: packaged with other ingredients; Pasta, uncooked: packaged with other ingredients; Maple syrup
Pr: Jose Luis Prado
Pr: Rich Schutzenhofer
**CFO:* Hugh Johnston
VP: Natalie Browne
**VP:* Mary Dillon
VP: Jim Lynch
VP: Kathy Okrzesik
VP: Karen Stallard
Exec: Alan Barney
Exec: Jill Kinney
Exec: Michael Morello

D-U-N-S 12-433-8182 IMP/EXP
■ QUAKER SALES & DISTRIBUTION INC
(*Suby of* QUAKER OATS CO) ★
555 W Monroe St, Chicago, IL 60661-3605
Tel (312) 821-1000 *Founded/Ownrshp* 1999
Sales 740.0MM *EMP* 7,000
SIC 5963 Food services, direct sales
Pr: Trish Lukasik
VP: Patricia Morrison

QUAKER STEAK & LUBE
See TRAVELCENTERS OF AMERICA LLC

D-U-N-S 06-902-2358 IMP
QUAKER VALLEY FOODS INC
2701 Red Lion Rd, Philadelphia, PA 19114-1019
Tel (215) 992-0900 *Founded/Ownrshp* 1977
Sales 239.4MM *EMP* 145^E
Accts Kreischer Miller Horsham Pa
SIC 5142 Packaged frozen goods
Pr: Wayne Hudis
**CFO:* Pat Veasey
**VP:* Kenneth Fleekop

D-U-N-S 00-630-2277
QUAKER WINDOW PRODUCTS CO (MO)
QUAKER WINDOWS AND DOORS
504 Highway 63 S, Freeburg, MO 65582-8208
Tel (800) 347-0438 *Founded/Ownrshp* 1945
Sales 96.0MM *EMP* 800
SIC 3442 Window & door frames; Metal doors
Pr: Kevin Blansett
VP: Mike Knoll
Dir IT: Curt Gruber
Natl Sales: Andre Dickneite

QUAKER WINDOWS AND DOORS
See QUAKER WINDOW PRODUCTS CO

D-U-N-S 83-238-4668 EXP
QUALAWASH HOLDINGS LLC
1302 N 19th St Ste 300, Tampa, FL 33605-5230
Tel (813) 321-6485 *Founded/Ownrshp* 2009
Sales 93.8MM^E *EMP* 570
SIC 7699 Tank truck cleaning service
CEO: Michael E Bauer
**Pr:* Terry Obrien
**COO:* Erik Leto
**CFO:* Richard Kelecy
**Sr VP:* Rudy George
VP: Jay Marcotte
**VP:* Paul Woodbury
Off Mgr: Samantha Fraidenburg
VP Opers: Daniel Langdon

D-U-N-S 07-976-0797
■ QUALCARE ALLIANCE NETWORKS INC
(*Suby of* CIGNA CORP) ★
30 Knightsbridge Rd # 530, Piscataway, NJ 08854-3948
Tel (732) 562-0833 *Founded/Ownrshp* 2000, 2015
Sales NA *EMP* 450
SIC 6324 Health maintenance organization (HMO), insurance only
CEO: Annette Catino
Opers Mgr: Shaun'tel Surratt
VP Sls: Bridget Gielis

D-U-N-S 06-296-7166 IMP
■ QUALCOMM ATHEROS INC
(*Suby of* QUALCOMM INC) ★
1700 Technology Dr, San Jose, CA 95110-1383
Tel (408) 773-5200 *Founded/Ownrshp* 2011
Sales 271.3MM^E *EMP* 1,778
SIC 3674 4899 Semiconductors & related devices; Communication signal enhancement network system
Pr: Craig H Barratt
Pr: Katrina Ganderson
CFO: George Davis
Ex VP: Cristiano Amon
Ex VP: Murthy Renduchintala
Ex VP: Donald Rosenberg
Ex VP: James Thompson
VP: Richard Bahr
VP: Sam Endy
VP: William Keitel
VP: Kenneth McKeithan
VP: Alexis Pascal

D-U-N-S 14-435-6508
▲ QUALCOMM INC
5775 Morehouse Dr, San Diego, CA 92121-1714
Tel (858) 587-1121 *Founded/Ownrshp* 1985
Sales 23.5MMM *EMP* 30,500^E
Accts Pricewaterhousecoopers Llp Sa
Tkr Sym QCOM *Exch* NGS
SIC 3674 7372 6794 Integrated circuits, semiconductor networks, etc.; Business oriented computer software; Patent buying, licensing, leasing
CEO: Steven M Mollenkopf
**Ch Bd:* Paul E Jacobs
Pr: Derek K Aberle
CFO: George S Davis
Ex VP: Donald J Rosenberg
Sr VP: Mary Gendron
Board of Directors: Barbara T Alexander, Raymond V Dittamore, Jeffrey W Henderson, Thomas W Horton, Ann M Livermore, Mark D McLaughlin, Clark T Randt Jr, Francisco Ros, Anthony J Vinciquerra

D-U-N-S 60-386-4930
■ QUALCOMM INTERNATIONAL INC
(*Suby of* QUALCOMM INC) ★
5775 Morehouse Dr, San Diego, CA 92121-1714
Tel (858) 587-1121 *Founded/Ownrshp* 1993
Sales 315.8MM^E *EMP* 7,000
SIC 6794 Patent buying, licensing, leasing
Pr: Steve Altman
**Ex VP:* Derek Aberle

D-U-N-S 07-858-1747 IMP
■ QUALCOMM TECHNOLOGIES INC
(*Suby of* QUALCOMM INC) ★
5775 Morehouse Dr, San Diego, CA 92121-1714
Tel (858) 587-1121 *Founded/Ownrshp* 2011
Sales 357.1MM^E *EMP* 1,904^E
SIC 3674 7372 6794 Integrated circuits, semiconductor networks, etc.; Business oriented computer software; Patent buying, licensing, leasing
CEO: Steve Mollenkopf
**Pr:* Derek Aberle
**Ex VP:* Cristiano Amon
**Ex VP:* James P Lederer
Ex VP: Jing Wang
Sr VP: Sanjay Mehta
Sr VP: Laurie Yoler
VP: Michael Aviotti
VP: Ji Park
Genl Mgr: Kirsten Duncan
Sftwr Eng: Ranganath Duggirala

D-U-N-S 17-921-5116
QUALEX INC
4020 Stirrup Creek Dr # 100, Durham, NC 27703-9410
Tel (919) 484-3500 *Founded/Ownrshp* 1994
Sales NA *EMP* 1,800
SIC 7384

D-U-N-S 15-879-5240
QUALIFACTS SYSTEMS INC
200 2nd Ave S, Nashville, TN 37201-2321
Tel (615) 386-6755 *Founded/Ownrshp* 2006
Sales 101.9MM^E *EMP* 900^E
SIC 7373 7371 Computer integrated systems design; Custom computer programming services
CEO: David Klements
CFO: Brad Wear
**VP:* Jason Medlin
**VP:* Rachel Vincion
QA Dir: Nicholas Jones
Software D: Jimmy Fairfax
Software D: Steven Pomatto
Sftwr Eng: Mohamed Ibrahim
Ql Cn Mgr: Kendall Joseph
Natl Sales: Jennifer Milose
Manager: Angela Lee

D-U-N-S 92-681-5226
QUALIFIED HOUSING TAX CREDITS LP V
101 Arch St Fl 16, Boston, MA 02110-1130
Tel (617) 439-3911 *Founded/Ownrshp* 1995
Sales 123.4MM^E *EMP* 1,500
SIC 6211 6531 Security brokers & dealers; Real estate agents & managers
CEO: Fred N Pratt Jr

D-U-N-S 06-285-9629 IMP/EXP
QUALIS AUTOMOTIVE LLC
(*Suby of* WDSOURCE.COM) ★
29380 John R Rd, Madison Heights, MI 48071-5404
Tel (248) 740-1668 *Founded/Ownrshp* 2014
Sales 169.0MM^E *EMP* 311
SIC 5013 7539 Automotive supplies & parts; Automotive repair shops
Ql Cn Mgr: April Robinson

D-U-N-S 17-611-9345
QUALITEL CORP
QUALITY ELECTRONIC ASSEMBLY
11831 Beverly Park Rd A, Everett, WA 98204-3526
Tel (425) 423-8388 *Founded/Ownrshp* 1988
Sales 88.8MM^E *EMP* 200
SIC 3679 Electronic switches
Pr: Tuanhai Hoang
**Sec:* Donna Sparks
Ql Cn Mgr: Martial Fougeu
Ql Cn Mgr: Jorry Lee

QUALITEST PHARMACEUTICALS
See BRENN DISTRIBUTION INC

QUALITEST PHARMACEUTICALS
See GENERICS INTERNATIONAL (US) INC

D-U-N-S 07-521-3863 IMP
QUALITOR INC
1840 Mccullough St, Lima, OH 45801-3059
Tel (248) 204-8600 *Founded/Ownrshp* 2014
Sales 189.8MM^E *EMP* 862
SIC 3714 5013 Motor vehicle engines & parts; Motor vehicle brake systems & parts; Air brakes, motor vehicle; Wipers, windshield, motor vehicle; Motor vehicle supplies & new parts
CEO: Gary Cohen
**CFO:* Scott Gibaratz

D-U-N-S 00-220-9716 IMP
■ QUALITROL CO LLC
OTIWTI
(*Suby of* FORTIVE CORP) ★
1385 Fairport Rd, Fairport, NY 14450-1399
Tel (586) 643-3717 *Founded/Ownrshp* 2016
Sales 168.0MM^E *EMP* 472
SIC 3825 Instruments for measuring electrical quantities
Pr: Ronald Meyer
Pr: John Piper
VP: Jay Cunningham
VP: Brian English

D-U-N-S 10-837-1410
QUALITY AUTO CRAFT INC
3295 Bernal Ave Ste B, Pleasanton, CA 94566-6298
Tel (925) 426-0120 *Founded/Ownrshp* 1987
Sales 30.0MM^E *EMP* 1,614
SIC 7538 7532 General automotive repair shops; Body shop, automotive
Pr: Ivo Soares

D-U-N-S 78-103-1161
QUALITY BAKERIES LLC
BURRY FOODSERVICE
1750 E Main St Ste 260, Saint Charles, IL 60174-4729
Tel (630) 553-7377 *Founded/Ownrshp* 2003
Sales 144.0MM *EMP* 17^E
SIC 2053 Frozen bakery products, except bread
Pr: Steve Spoerl
CFO: Dave Phillips
VP: John Gaches
VP: Jeanne Markus
VP: Pat Uli
**VP Sls:* Brad Guimont

D-U-N-S 03-980-0743 IMP
QUALITY BICYCLE PRODUCTS INC
Q B P
6400 W 105th St, Bloomington, MN 55438-2554
Tel (952) 941-9391 *Founded/Ownrshp* 1984
Sales 98.0MM^E *EMP* 180^E
SIC 5091

D-U-N-S 87-473-2048
QUALITY BUILDING SERVICES CORP
Q B S
801 2nd Ave Fl 8, New York, NY 10017-8642
Tel (212) 883-0009 *Founded/Ownrshp* 2000
Sales 62.0MM^E *EMP* 2,000
SIC 7349 Building maintenance services
Pr: Mirjana Mirjanic
**CFO:* David Heyman
**Ex VP:* Ljiljana Mirjanic
**Sr VP:* John L Agnello

D-U-N-S 04-981-2696
QUALITY CARRIERS INC
(*Suby of* QUALITY DISTRIBUTION LLC) ★
4041 Park Oaks Blvd # 200, Tampa, FL 33610-9524
Tel (800) 282-2031 *Founded/Ownrshp* 1913
Sales 278.6MM^E *EMP* 1,300
SIC 4213 Trucking, except local
Ch Bd: Gary R Enzor
Pr: Randall T Strutz
CFO: Dennis Farnsworth
CFO: Joseph Troy
Sr VP: John T Wilson
VP: Simon Balvin
VP: Robin Cohan
VP: Denny R Copeland
VP: Mike McDonald
VP: John Schoener
Opers Mgr: Kathy Habesch

D-U-N-S 00-563-8923
QUALITY COLLISION CENTER
42480 Ritter Cir Ste 5, Palm Desert, CA 92211-5123
Tel (760) 779-5054 *Founded/Ownrshp* 2012
Sales 100.0MM *EMP* 2
SIC 7532 Collision shops, automotive
Owner: Patricia Araujo

D-U-N-S 19-228-3414 IMP
QUALITY COMPUTER ACCESSORIES INC
BAFO TECHNOLOGIES
(*Suby of* LI KANG BIOMEDICAL CO., LTD)
70 Ethel Rd W Ste 1, Piscataway, NJ 08854-5950
Tel (732) 572-2719 *Founded/Ownrshp* 1982
Sales 84.1MM^E *EMP* 1,000

SIC 5063 5051 3315 3644 Wire & cable; Switches, except electronic; Metals service centers & offices; Steel wire & related products; Noncurrent-carrying wiring services
VP: John Smith
**CFO:* Judy Lee
**VP:* Daniel Lin

D-U-N-S 09-824-7294
QUALITY CONSTRUCTION & PRODUCTION LLC
425 Griffin Rd, Youngsville, LA 70592-5517
Tel (337) 857-6000 *Founded/Ownrshp* 2001
Sales 127.6MM^E *EMP* 400^E
SIC 1542 Commercial & office building contractors

D-U-N-S 83-953-5825
QUALITY CUSTOM DISTRIBUTION SERVICES INC
(*Suby of* GSF FOUNDATION) ★
18301 Von Karman Ave, Irvine, CA 92612-1009
Tel (949) 252-2000 *Founded/Ownrshp* 2005
Sales 131.4MM^E *EMP* 110
SIC 5087 7319 Restaurant supplies; Distribution of advertising material or sample services
Pr: Robert W Jorge
**VP:* Larry Tandoi

D-U-N-S 01-719-8789
QUALITY DAIRY CO (MI)
AUNTIE EM'S BAKERY
111 W Mount Hope Ave 3a, Lansing, MI 48910-9080
Tel (517) 319-4100 *Founded/Ownrshp* 1936
Sales 111.0MM^E *EMP* 500
SIC 5451 5411

D-U-N-S 78-485-9605
QUALITY DINING INC
BURGER KING
4220 Edison Lakes Pkwy # 300, Mishawaka, IN 46545-1440
Tel (574) 271-4600 *Founded/Ownrshp* 1981
Sales 238.6MM^E *EMP* 7,176
SIC 5812 6794 Eating places; Fast-food restaurant, chain; Grills (eating places); Italian restaurant; Franchises, selling or licensing
CEO: Daniel B Fitzpatrick
Pr: John C Firth
Sr VP: Lindley E Burns
Sr VP: James K Fitzpatric
Sr VP: Gerald O Fitzpatrick
Sr VP: James K Fitzpatrick
VP: Christopher L Collier
VP: Stephen G Marquette
VP: Jeanne M Yoder
VP Mktg: Thomas Hanson

D-U-N-S 93-112-1610
QUALITY DISTRIBUTION INC
(*Suby of* GRUDEN ACQUISITION, INC.)
4041 Park Oaks Blvd # 200, Tampa, FL 33610-9524
Tel (813) 630-5826 *Founded/Ownrshp* 2015
Sales 871.2MM^E *EMP* 4,342
SIC 4213 Trucking, except local
CEO: Gary Enzor
Pr: Chris Broussard
CFO: Joseph Troy
CFO: Joseph J Troy
Treas: Robin Cohan
Ex VP: Vergil Leslie
Sr VP: Samuel Hensley
Sr VP: David Jenkins
Sr VP: Randy Sheeler
Sr VP: John Wilson
VP: Dennis R Copeland
VP: Clifford Dixon
VP: Chris Elam
VP: Shawn Harris
VP: Joan Rodger
VP: John Thomason
VP: Joe Wilson
Dir Risk M: Mike McDonald

D-U-N-S 80-912-9054
QUALITY DISTRIBUTION LLC
(*Suby of* QUALITY DISTRIBUTION INC) ★
4041 Park Oaks Blvd # 200, Tampa, FL 33610-9524
Tel (813) 630-5826 *Founded/Ownrshp* 2003
Sales 337.9MM^E *EMP* 3,171^E
SIC 4213 7699 4212 Trucking, except local; Tank repair & cleaning services; Light haulage & cartage, local
CEO: Gary R Enzor
**VP:* Dennis R Copeland
Ql Cn Mgr: Jennifer Copeland
VP Sls: Kevin Gautreau

QUALITY ELECTRONIC ASSEMBLY
See QUALITEL CORP

D-U-N-S 06-692-0500
QUALITY ENERGY SERVICES INC
230 Menard Rd, Houma, LA 70363-7530
Tel (985) 850-0025 *Founded/Ownrshp* 2001
Sales 181.2MM^E *EMP* 206
SIC 1389 Construction, repair & dismantling services
Ch: Tommy Hebert
**Ch Bd:* Douglas Bankston
**VP:* Randy Schaff
Dist Mgr: Nelson Mitchell
VP Sls: Travis Raiford

QUALITY FABRICATION & SUPPLY
See WIGINTON CORP

QUALITY FLOORING JACKSON HOLE
See KUSSY INC

D-U-N-S 02-746-4700 IMP
■ **QUALITY FOOD CENTERS INC**
Q F C
(*Suby of* FRED MEYER INC) ★
10116 Ne 8th St, Bellevue, WA 98004-4148
Tel (425) 455-0870 *Founded/Ownrshp* 1998
Sales 594.4MM^E *EMP* 6,000
SIC 5411 Supermarkets, chain
Pr: Donna Giordano
CFO: Paul Lammert
Ofcr: Marcel Dehart

VP: Gary Debure
Exec: Jeff Brown
Exec: Marc Evanger
CTO: Jim Clendenen

QUALITY FRAGRANCE GROUP
See QUALITY KING FRAGRANCE INC

D-U-N-S 14-673-1851
QUALITY GROUP OF COMPANIES LLC
12851 Foster St Ste 205, Overland Park, KS 66213-2612
Tel (913) 814-9988 *Founded/Ownrshp* 2004
Sales 89.0MM^E *EMP* 450^E
SIC 6531 Real estate agent, commercial
CEO: Chad Williams
Dir Bus: Christina Lamb
Genl Couns: Shirley Edmonds-Goza

D-U-N-S 62-358-7313 IMP
QUALITY HOME BRANDS HOLDINGS LLC
125 Rose Feiss Blvd, Bronx, NY 10454-3624
Tel (718) 292-2024 *Founded/Ownrshp* 2004
Sales 161.3MM^E *EMP* 833
SIC 3645 5063 Residential lighting fixtures; Lighting fixtures; Lighting fixtures, residential

D-U-N-S 01-293-9393 IMP
QUALITY KING DISTRIBUTORS INC
35 Sawgrass Dr Ste 3, Bellport, NY 11713-1578
Tel (631) 439-2000 *Founded/Ownrshp* 1991
Sales 869.7MM^E *EMP* 850
SIC 5122 Drugs, proprietaries & sundries
Ch Bd: Glenn Nussdorf
**CFO:* Michael Anderson
CFO: Michael W Katz
**Ex VP:* Michael Katz
IT Man: Siobhan Conway
Info Man: Sandra Cliffered
Sls&Mrk Ex: Randy Cribbs
S&M/VP: Ron Kaufman

D-U-N-S 16-824-2746 IMP
■ **QUALITY KING FRAGRANCE INC**
QUALITY FRAGRANCE GROUP
(*Suby of* PERFUMANIA HOLDINGS INC) ★
35 Sawgrass Dr Ste 1, Bellport, NY 11713-1576
Tel (631) 866-4100 *Founded/Ownrshp* 1997
Sales 132.5MM^E *EMP* 500
SIC 5122 Perfumes
Pr: Michael Katz
**Ch Bd:* Stephen Nussdorf
**CFO:* Donna Dellomo
Sr VP: Allan Katz
Mktg Dir: Debra Milano

D-U-N-S 78-464-7625
QUALITY LIFE SERVICES
QUALITY PHARMACY
612 N Main St Ste A, Butler, PA 16001-4363
Tel (724) 431-0770 *Founded/Ownrshp* 2007
Sales 8.0MM^E *EMP* 1,300
SIC 5912 8051 Drug stores & proprietary stores; Skilled nursing care facilities
Prin: Mary Yurek

D-U-N-S 08-888-6593
QUALITY LIQUID FEEDS INC
3586 State Road 23, Dodgeville, WI 53533-8903
Tel (608) 935-2345 *Founded/Ownrshp* 1977
Sales 237.4MM^E *EMP* 200
SIC 5191 Animal feeds
Pr: Cory Berg
**VP:* Roger Larson
VP: Stuart Sliter
Rgnl Mgr: Mark Hovda
Area Mgr: Jim Lere
Off Mgr: Jenny Divall
IT Man: Jim Steil
Manager: Vance Cash
Manager: Scott Roskens
Sls Mgr: Emmett Davis
Sls Mgr: Mike Furrh

QUALITY MART
See QUALITY OIL CO LLC

D-U-N-S 00-640-5476 IMP
QUALITY METALCRAFT INC
33355 Glendale St, Livonia, MI 48150-1615
Tel (734) 261-6700 *Founded/Ownrshp* 1964, 2015
Sales 92.0MM^E *EMP* 250^E
SIC 3544 3465 3469 3444 Special dies & tools; Automotive stampings; Body parts, automobile: stamped metal; Metal stampings; Sheet metalwork
CEO: Kurt Saldana
**COO:* Ken Lerg
**CFO:* Scott Bain

D-U-N-S 09-162-5343 IMP
QUALITY MOLD INC
VERSITECH MOLD DIV
2200 Massillon Rd, Akron, OH 44312-4234
Tel (330) 645-6653 *Founded/Ownrshp* 1978
Sales 86.9MM^E *EMP* 260
SIC 3544 Industrial molds
Pr: Greg Kalikas
**VP:* Jerry Candiliotis
**VP:* Mike Politis
**Prin:* Stanley B Migdal

D-U-N-S 17-704-5960
QUALITY OIL CO LLC
QUALITY MART
1540 Silas Creek Pkwy, Winston Salem, NC 27127-3705
Tel (336) 722-3441 *Founded/Ownrshp* 1986
Sales 171.1MM^E *EMP* 1,000^E
Accts Butler & Burke Llp Winston-S
SIC 5983 5541 7011 Fuel oil dealers; Filling stations, gasoline; Hotels & motels
Pr: Graham F Bennett
**Sr VP:* Buddy Jenkins
**Sr VP:* Tim Lowman
**Sr VP:* Ernie Rhymer
**Sr VP:* Andy Sayles
VP: Tracy Harmon
VP: Carol Holt

D-U-N-S 10-235-3794
QUALITY OIL INC
55 N 400 E, Valparaiso, IN 46383-0613
Tel (219) 462-2951 *Founded/Ownrshp* 1983
Sales 91.6MM^E *EMP* 55
SIC 5171 5172

D-U-N-S 13-760-0446 IMP
QUALITY ONE WIRELESS LLC
Q1
1500 Tradeport Dr Ste B, Orlando, FL 32824-8421
Tel (407) 857-3737 *Founded/Ownrshp* 1993
Sales 440.3MM^E *EMP* 523
SIC 5065 Telephone equipment
CEO: John Chiorando
Sr Pt: Scott Turner
**Pr:* Anthony Montore
COO: Brian Moroney
**CFO:* Robert Staats
VP: Eric Bunn
VP: Thomas Cuff
CIO: Garrett Grainger
Prd Mgr: Trecia Lai
Prd Mgr: Jamie Ramos
Natl Sales: Mike Hodge

QUALITY PACKAGING
See PROFESSIONAL PACKAGING SYSTEMS LLC

D-U-N-S 82-507-8165 IMP
QUALITY PACKAGING SPECIALISTS INTERNATIONAL LLC
QPSI
5 Cooper St, Burlington, NJ 08016-2001
Tel (609) 239-0503 *Founded/Ownrshp* 1992
Sales 331.6MM^E *EMP* 1,800
SIC 7389 3565

QUALITY PHARMACY
See QUALITY LIFE SERVICES

D-U-N-S 88-492-3152 EXP
QUALITY PLUS SERVICES INC
2929 Quality Dr, Petersburg, VA 23805-9371
Tel (804) 863-0191 *Founded/Ownrshp* 1997
Sales 170.5MM^E *EMP* 650
Accts Adams Jenkins & Cheatham Ric
SIC 1711 1731 Mechanical contractor; Plumbing contractors; Electrical work
CEO: Aaron Gay
**Prin:* John T Hammen
Div Mgr: Bill Grassl
Div Mgr: Jim Moeller
Genl Mgr: Keith Adkins
Genl Mgr: Matt Peterson
Off Mgr: Diana Bradbury
CTO: Bill Bandy

D-U-N-S 10-229-6985 IMP/EXP
QUALITY PORK INTERNATIONAL INC
10404 F Plz, Omaha, NE 68127-1000
Tel (402) 339-1911 *Founded/Ownrshp* 1983
Sales 148.8MM^E *EMP* 400
SIC 2011 Hams & picnics from meat slaughtered on site; Pork products from pork slaughtered on site
COO: Laura Nelson
**VP:* Brian Maydew
Genl Mgr: Edward Miller
Dir IT: Matt Koske
Sfty Dirs: Don Birkentall

D-U-N-S 60-246-8738
QUALITY PORK PROCESSORS INC
711 Hormel Century Pkwy, Austin, MN 55912-3663
Tel (507) 434-6300 *Founded/Ownrshp* 1987
Sales 137.0MM^E *EMP* 1,100
SIC 2011 Pork products from pork slaughtered on site
Pr: Kelly Wadding
**Sr VP:* Mel Gilbertson
**VP:* Nate Jansen
**VP:* Ken Kay
Dir IT: Carlos Quirindongo
Sfty Dirs: Fred Doyle
Sfty Dirs: Didacus Guzman
Plnt Mgr: Claude Pulliam

D-U-N-S 62-336-5558
QUALITY RESTAURANT CONCEPTS LLC
APPLEBEE'S
601 Vestavia Pkwy # 1000, Vestavia, AL 35216-3764
Tel (205) 824-5060 *Founded/Ownrshp* 1988
Sales 102.6MM^E *EMP* 3,000
SIC 5812 Restaurant, family: chain
CEO: Kurt Guttshall
**Pr:* Fred W Gustin
**CFO:* Charles Galloway
**VP:* Michael Borgna
Rgnl Mgr: P J Gregory
Rgnl Mgr: Christie R Hudson

D-U-N-S 02-349-9346
QUALITY STATE OIL CO INC
Q-MART
2201 Calumet Dr, Sheboygan, WI 53083-4602
Tel (920) 459-5640 *Founded/Ownrshp* 1988
Sales 183.6MM^E *EMP* 185
SIC 5171 5541 5411 Petroleum bulk stations; Filling stations, gasoline; Convenience stores, independent
Pr: Gregory B Bultman
**CFO:* Deborah A Deblaey
**VP:* John Winter
Mktg Mgr: Scott Stangel

QUALITY SYNTHETIC RUBBER
See Q HOLDING CO

D-U-N-S 07-954-2304
▲ **QUALITY SYSTEMS INC**
18111 Von Karman Ave # 700, Irvine, CA 92612-7110
Tel (949) 255-2600 *Founded/Ownrshp* 1974
Sales 492.4MM *EMP* 2,987^E
Tkr Sym QSII *Exch* NGS
SIC 7372 7373 Prepackaged software; Computer integrated systems design
Pr: John R Frantz
**Ch Bd:* Jeffrey H Margolis
COO: Daniel J Morefield
CFO: James R Arnold

**V Ch Bd:* Craig A Barbarosh
Ex VP: Jocelyn A Leavitt
Ex VP: David A Metcalfe
Ex VP: John K Stumpf
VP: Donn E Neufeld
Exec: Kevin Clark
CIO: Zachary Sherburne
Board of Directors: George H Bristol, James C Malone, Morris Panner, D Russell Pflueger, Sheldon Razin, Lance E Rosenzweig

D-U-N-S 83-280-1174
QUALITY TECHNOLOGY SERVICES HOLDING LLC
(*Suby of* QUALITYTECH LP) ★
12851 Foster St Ste 205, Overland Park, KS 66213-2612
Tel (913) 814-9988 *Founded/Ownrshp* 2015
Sales 51.1MM^E *EMP* 1,139
SIC 6719 Investment holding companies, except banks
Ch Bd: Chad Williams
**Pr:* Mark Waddington
**COO:* Jim Reinhart
**Ex VP:* Tag Greason
**Ex VP:* Kurt Stoever
**VP:* John Storey
Genl Mgr: AGA Carpenter

D-U-N-S 60-846-6210
QUALITY TECHNOLOGY SERVICES LLC
QTS
(*Suby of* QUALITY GROUP OF COMPANIES LLC) ★
300 Satellite Blvd Nw, Suwanee, GA 30024-7123
Tel (678) 546-0064 *Founded/Ownrshp* 2005
Sales 89.0MM^E *EMP* 322
SIC 7373 4813 7378 7374 Computer integrated systems design; ; Computer maintenance & repair; Data processing & preparation
CEO: Chad Williams
Pr: Shelagh Montgomery
**Pr:* Mark Waddington
**COO:* Dan Bennewitz
**COO:* Jim Reinhart
**CFO:* William Schafer
**Ex VP:* Kurt Stoever
VP: Lee Higgins
VP: Jay Ketterling
Admn Mgr: Mike Kurtz
Genl Mgr: Brian Johnson
Board of Directors: John Barter

D-U-N-S 61-928-7589
QUALITY TECHNOLOGY SERVICES LLC
(*Suby of* QUALITY TECHNOLOGY SERVICES HOLDING LLC) ★
12851 Foster St, Overland Park, KS 66213-2705
Tel (913) 814-9988 *Founded/Ownrshp* 2005
Sales 195.9MM^E *EMP* 790
SIC 7376 8741 Computer facilities management; Management services
CEO: Chad Williams
Pr: Frank Eagle
Pr: Chris Oberkfell
**CFO:* William Schafer
**Treas:* Jay Ketterling
Ofcr: Lisa Duval
Sr VP: Joe Sardella
**VP:* Shirley Goza
VP: John Trigg
Mktg Mgr: Neelam Sachania

QUALITY TIRE
See ALDEN PADFIELD INC

QUALITY TIRE SLC
See PADFIELD INC

D-U-N-S 05-369-7256 IMP/EXP
QUALITY TRAILER PRODUCTS LP
CENTURY WHEEL & RIM
(*Suby of* POLAR CORP) ★
604 W Main St, Azle, TX 76020-2910
Tel (817) 444-4518 *Founded/Ownrshp* 1997
Sales 184.2MM^E *EMP* 500
SIC 3714 5013 Motor vehicle parts & accessories; Trailer parts & accessories
Pr: Chris Dietemann
Pt: Donald Stover
Rgnl Mgr: Robert Weekly
IT Man: Kenneth Heath
Mtls Mgr: Mark Woytalewicz
Site Mgr: Brent Pope
Site Mgr: Nathan Schauer
Manager: Kevin Davis

QUALITY TURF
See QGS DEVELOPMENT INC

D-U-N-S 00-809-9900 IMP
QUALITY VISION INTERNATIONAL INC
OPTICAL GAGING PRODUCTS DIV
850 Hudson Ave, Rochester, NY 14621-4839
Tel (585) 544-0400 *Founded/Ownrshp* 1954
Sales 90.2MM^E *EMP* 350
SIC 3827 Optical test & inspection equipment
CEO: Edward T Polidor
VP: Tom Groff
VP: David Hansen
Genl Mgr: Andrea Walker
VP Sls: Timothy Fantauzzo
Mktg Dir: Fred Mason
Sls Mgr: Alyssia Roberts

D-U-N-S 83-278-0147
QUALITYTECH LP
(*Suby of* QTS REALTY TRUST INC) ★
12851 Foster St, Overland Park, KS 66213-2705
Tel (877) 787-3282 *Founded/Ownrshp* 2009
Sales 74.6MM^E *EMP* 2,395^E
SIC 7374 Data processing & preparation
CEO: Chad Williams
Pr: Mark Waddington
CFO: William H Schafer
VP: Jay Ketterling
Genl Couns: Shirley Goza

D-U-N-S 07-886-1856
■ QUALSPEC INC
(Suby of TEAM INC) ★
5602 Ih 37, Corpus Christi, TX 78407-1334
Tel (281) 479-3300 Founded/Ownrshp 2015
Sales 68.9MM^E EMP 1,300^E
SIC 8711 Engineering services
Pr: Gary D Green
CEO: Declan Rushe
Sr VP: Isaac Lopez Sr
Sr VP: Steve McGuire
IT Man: ARA Kerestejian

D-U-N-S 07-865-6703
QUALTEK USA LLC
1150 1st Ave Ste 600, King of Prussia, PA 19406-1300
Tel (484) 804-4540 Founded/Ownrshp 2012
Sales 97.7MM EMP 1,000
SIC 8741 Construction management
Pr: C Scott Hisey
CTO: Mike Williams
QC Dir: David Morris

D-U-N-S 01-332-4464
QUALTEX LABORATORIES
(Suby of SOUTH TEXAS BLOOD & TISSUE CENTER)
6211 W Interstate 10, San Antonio, TX 78201-2023
Tel (210) 736-8952 Founded/Ownrshp 2007
Sales 145.8MM EMP 20^E
Accts Bkd Llp San Antonio Tx
SIC 2836 Biological products, except diagnostic
CEO: Linda Myers
COO: Dirk Johnson
CFO: Donna Respondek

D-U-N-S 62-393-2451
QUALTRICS LABS INC
400 W Qualtrics Dr # 100, Provo, UT 84604-7775
Tel (800) 340-9194 Founded/Ownrshp 2002
Sales 65.6MM^E EMP 1,075
SIC 8713 Surveying services
Pr: Scott M Smith
*COO: Zig Serafin
VP: Austin Bankhead
VP: John D'Agostino
Snr Sftwr: Edgar Harris
Sftwr Eng: Stephen Saunders
Sales Exec: Jeff Klakring
Corp Couns: Blake Tierney

D-U-N-S 07-866-3964
QUALTRICS LLC
(Suby of QUALTRICS LABS INC) ★
333 River Park Dr, Provo, UT 84604-5787
Tel (801) 374-6682 Founded/Ownrshp 2012
Sales 59.0MM EMP 1,075
SIC 7371 Computer software development
CEO: Ryan Smith
VP: Jared Smith
Genl Mgr: Trevor Delew
Snr Sftwr: Jeff Whiting
IT Man: Stuart Orgill
Web Dev: Brett Bloxham
Sftwr Eng: Matthew Brasfield
Sftwr Eng: Greg Burnham
Sftwr Eng: Nathan Condie
Sftwr Eng: Oliver Hall
Sftwr Eng: Owen Hancock

QUALXSERV
See WORLDWIDE TECHSERVICES LLC

QUALY INSURANCE AGENCY
See JOHN M QUALY

D-U-N-S 12-791-8394
▲ QUALYS INC
1600 Bridge Pkwy Ste 201, Redwood City, CA 94065-6127
Tel (650) 801-6100 Founded/Ownrshp 1999
Sales 164.2MM EMP 510^E
Tkr Sym QLYS Exch NGS
SIC 7371 7372 Custom computer programming services; Software programming applications; Prepackaged software
Ch Bd: Philippe F Courtot
CFO: Melissa B Fisher
Ex VP: Dan Barahona
VP: Sonu Agarwal
VP: Amer S Deeba
VP: Bruce K Posey
QA Dir: Vanessa Follys
QA Dir: Jin Wu
Software D: Chiharu Yokoyama
Sftwr Eng: Tigran Gevorgyan
Mktg Mgr: Nick Courtot
Board of Directors: Sandra E Bergeron, Donald R Dixon, Jeffrey P Hank, Todd P Headley, Peter Pace, Kristi M Rogers, Howard A Schmidt

D-U-N-S 11-852-0733
QUANDEL CONSTRUCTION GROUP INC
(Suby of QUANDEL ENTERPRISES INC) ★
3003 N Front St Ste 203, Harrisburg, PA 17110-1224
Tel (717) 657-0909 Founded/Ownrshp 1882
Sales 151.0MM^E EMP 200
SIC 1542 1541 1629 8741 Commercial & office building contractors; Institutional building construction; Industrial buildings, new construction; Waste water & sewage treatment plant construction; Construction management
Pr: Noble C Quandel
*COO: Joseph Mastrippolito
*Treas: Chris C Bushey
Ex VP: William Hauck
VP: David Beal
VP: Wayne Mace
VP: John Murphy
VP: Ted Walker
Ex Dir: Jim Thomas
Genl Mgr: Bill Hauch
IT Man: Jim Crowley

D-U-N-S 13-293-0871
QUANDEL ENTERPRISES INC
3003 N Front St Ste 203, Harrisburg, PA 17110-1224
Tel (717) 657-0909 Founded/Ownrshp 2003
Sales 198.4MM^E EMP 230
SIC 1542 1629 8741 Commercial & office building contractors; Institutional building construction; Waste water & sewage treatment plant construction; Construction management
CEO: Noble C Quandel
*COO: Stanley M Hendricks
*COO: Joseph Mastropolitto
*CFO: Chris Bushey
*VP: Ralph S Klinepeter
*VP: John M Murphy
*VP: Julia T Quandel
Plnt Mgr: Jim Benner

D-U-N-S 82-605-1265
▲ QUANEX BUILDING PRODUCTS CORP
1800 West Loop S Ste 1500, Houston, TX 77027-3246
Tel (713) 961-4600 Founded/Ownrshp 1927
Sales 928.1MM EMP 2,693
Accts Grant Thornton Llp Houston T
Tkr Sym NX Exch NYS
SIC 3272 3353 Building materials, except block or brick: concrete; Aluminum sheet & strip
CEO: William Griffiths
*Ch Bd: William C Griffiths
CFO: Brent L Korb
Treas: Jairaj Chetnani
Treas: Scott Zuehlke
Sr VP: Kevin P Delaney
VP: Kevin Connor
VP: John Gledhill
VP: Amy Noble
VP: M Dewayne Williams
Mktg Dir: Michael B Hovan

D-U-N-S 02-452-0747
■ QUANEX HOMESHIELD LLC
(Suby of QUANEX BUILDING PRODUCTS CORP) ★
311 W Coleman St, Rice Lake, WI 54868-2407
Tel (715) 234-9061 Founded/Ownrshp 2008
Sales 96.9MM^E EMP 500
SIC 3448 Prefabricated metal buildings
CEO: Bill Griffiths
Pr: Mark Hermann
CFO: Sally Bajak
CFO: Brent L Korb
VP: Martin P Ketelaar

QUANTA
See QCH NASHVILLE LLC

D-U-N-S 00-932-9582 IMP
QUANTA COMPUTER USA INC
(Suby of QUANTA COMPUTER INC.)
45630 Northport Loop E, Fremont, CA 94538-6477
Tel (510) 226-1371 Founded/Ownrshp 1991
Sales 126.3MM^E EMP 400^E
SIC 5045 Computers, peripherals & software
Ch: Barry Lam
*Pr: Alan Lam
*Pr: CC Leung
*CEO: Pak Lee Lam

D-U-N-S 14-266-9014
■ QUANTA FIBER NETWORKS INC
INFRASOURCE SERVICES, INC.
(Suby of CC SCN FIBER LLC) ★
1360 Post Oak Blvd # 2100, Houston, TX 77056-3030
Tel (713) 629-7600 Founded/Ownrshp 2015
Sales 101.2MM^E EMP 4,000
SIC 1731 8742 Electric power systems contractors; Cogeneration specialization; Standby or emergency power specialization; Construction project management consultant
Pr: David Helwig
Pr: Steve Hicks
Pr: Damir Novosel
Sr VP: Jim Urbas
Sr VP: Lee Willis
VP: Richard Brown
VP: William Schwartz

D-U-N-S 80-822-1753 IMP
QUANTA SERVICE INCORPORATION
(Suby of ACCESS INTERNATIONAL CO) ★
45630 Northport Loop E, Fremont, CA 94538-6477
Tel (510) 226-1000 Founded/Ownrshp 1998
Sales 2.4MM^E EMP 5,015^E
Accts Pricewaterhousecoopers Llp Ho
SIC 5045 Computers, peripherals & software
Prin: Alan Pak Lin Lam

D-U-N-S 80-032-7129 IMP
QUANTA SERVICE NASHVILLE LLC
(Suby of QUANTA SERVICE INCORPORATION) ★
1621 Heil Quaker Blvd, La Vergne, TN 37086-3657
Tel (615) 501-7500 Founded/Ownrshp 2003
Sales 798.0MM^E EMP 5,011^E
SIC 3577 Computer peripheral equipment
Prin: Michael Dunne

D-U-N-S 00-800-4165
▲ QUANTA SERVICES INC
2800 Post Oak Blvd # 2600, Houston, TX 77056-6175
Tel (713) 629-7600 Founded/Ownrshp 1997
Sales 7.5MMM EMP 24,500
Accts Pricewaterhousecoopers Llp Ho
Tkr Sym PWR Exch NYS
SIC 1731 Electric power systems contractors; Cogeneration specialization; Communications specialization; Cable television installation
Pr: Earl C Austin Jr
Pr: Dale L Querrey
*CFO: Derrick A Jensen
*Treas: Nicholas M Grindstaff
*Ex VP: Steven J Kemps
*Ex VP: Jesse E Morris
Ex VP: Randall C Wisenbaker
VP: Bengt Jarlsjo
VP: Peter B O'Brien
VP: Dorothy Upperman
VP: Wilson M Yancey Jr

D-U-N-S 62-362-6624
▲ QUANTENNA COMMUNICATIONS INC
3450 W Warren Ave, Fremont, CA 94538-6425
Tel (510) 743-2260 Founded/Ownrshp 2005
Sales 83.7MM EMP 303^E
Tkr Sym QTNA Exch NGS
SIC 3674 Semiconductors & related devices
Ch Bd: Sam Heidari
CFO: Sean Sobers
Sr VP: Lionel Bonnot
Sr VP: David Carroll

QUANTUM CORPORATION
See CERTANCE LLC

D-U-N-S 02-119-5540 IMP
▲ QUANTUM CORP
224 Airport Pkwy Ste 300, San Jose, CA 95110-1022
Tel (408) 944-4000 Founded/Ownrshp 1980
Sales 475.9MM EMP 1,200
Tkr Sym QTM Exch NYS
SIC 3572 8731 Computer storage devices; Tape storage units, computer; Computer (hardware) development
Pr: Jon W Gacek
Pr: Ray Robidoux
CFO: Fuad Ahmad
Treas: Jodi Tveit
Sr VP: William C Britts
Sr VP: Robert S Clark
Sr VP: Stephen P Dalton
Sr VP: Lew Frauenfelder
Sr VP: Shawn D Hall
VP: Bill Britts
VP: Brad Cohen
VP: Seth Cohen
VP: Laura Dubois
VP: Andrew Goldstein
VP: Donald Martella
VP: Yves Roumier
VP: David Wicker
VP: Brian Wilson
Board of Directors: Robert J Andersen, Paul R Auvil III, Louis Dinardo, Dale L Fuller, David A Krall, Gregg J Powers, David E Roberson, Clifford Press

D-U-N-S 62-187-4627
QUANTUM FOODS LLC
750 S Schmidt Rd, Bolingbrook, IL 60440-4813
Tel (319) 627-6000 Founded/Ownrshp 1990
Sales NA EMP 1,500^E
SIC 8742

D-U-N-S 08-019-5024
QUANTUM PLASTICS LLC
1000 Davis Rd, Elgin, IL 60123-1314
Tel (847) 695-9700 Founded/Ownrshp 2014
Sales 174.5MM^E EMP 973
SIC 7389
CEO: Morris Rowlett

D-U-N-S 05-026-4662
QUANTUM SPATIAL INC
(Suby of ARLINGTON CAPITAL PARTNERS LP) ★
10033 Mlk St N Ste 200, Saint Petersburg, FL 33716-3884
Tel (920) 457-3631 Founded/Ownrshp 2012
Sales 104.8MM^E EMP 300
SIC 2741 8713 Maps: publishing & printing; Surveying services
CEO: Rajib Roy
*CFO: Mark Abatto
CFO: Daniel R Gilbert
*VP: Robert Hickey
VP: Terrence J Keating
*VP: William McKeague
*VP: Mark Meade
*VP: Robert Vander Meer
Prin: Tom Veal
Board of Directors: Mark Abatto, G Michael Ritchie

D-U-N-S 07-893-4478
QUARLES & BRADY LLP
411 E Wisconsin Ave # 2040, Milwaukee, WI 53202-4426
Tel (414) 277-5000 Founded/Ownrshp 1974
Sales 171.7MM^E EMP 1,088
SIC 8111 General practice law office
Ch: John W Daniels Jr
Pt: Ave M Bie
Pt: Conrad G Goodkind
Pt: Kimberly L Johnson
Pt: Ann Marie Murphy
Pt: Jon E Pettibone
Pt: Patrick M Ryan
Pt: Michael J Spector
Pt: Thomas R Stiebel Jr
Pt: Paul J Tilleman
Pt: Elaine Waterhouse Wilson
Mng Pt: Craig H Kaufman
Mng Pt: Gavin J Milczarek-Desai
Ofcr: Mary K Arnberg
VP: Daniel McNally

D-U-N-S 09-958-9970 IMP/EXP
QUBICAAMF WORLDWIDE LLC
(Suby of QUBICAAMF EUROPE SPA)
8100 Amf Dr, Mechanicsville, VA 23111-3700
Tel (804) 569-1000 Founded/Ownrshp 2014
Sales 94.2MM^E EMP 415
SIC 3949 7933 Bowling equipment & supplies; Bowling balls; Bowling centers
CEO: Emanuele Govani
*Ch Bd: Patrick Ciniello
*CEO: Emanuele Govoni
*COO: Luca Drusiani
*CFO: Christopher F Caesar
Sr VP: Paul Barkley
*Sr VP: John M Buhl
*Sr VP: Mark Kilpatrick
*Sr VP: Wayne White
*VP: Terry S Manis
VP: Terry Manis
VP: John S Shearer

D-U-N-S 00-425-3886
QUEBECOR WORLD JOHNSON & HARDIN CO
3600 Red Bank Rd, Cincinnati, OH 45227-4142
Tel (614) 326-0299 Founded/Ownrshp 1997
Sales 100.0MM EMP 900
SIC 2759 2752 2732 Magazines: printing; Catalogs: printing; Commercial printing, offset; Books: printing only

Pr: Chuck Miotke
*Sr VP: James H Bossart
VP: Robert Castillo

D-U-N-S 79-747-8380
QUEEN ANNES COUNTY PUBLIC SCHOOLS
202 Chesterfield Ave, Centreville, MD 21617-1308
Tel (410) 758-2403 Founded/Ownrshp 2007
Sales 103.9MM EMP 1,200
Accts Mayer Hoffman Mccann Pc Eas
SIC 8211 Public elementary & secondary schools
VP: Beverly Kelley
Pr Dir: Jeff Straight
Teacher Pr: Daniel Lessard

D-U-N-S 06-511-7491
QUEEN OF ANGELS HOLLYWOD PRESBYTERIAN MEDICAL CENTER
1300 N Vermont Ave, Los Angeles, CA 90027-6300
Tel (213) 413-3000 Founded/Ownrshp 1978
Sales 23.7MM EMP 1,200
SIC 8062 Hospital, affiliated with AMA residency
Pr: John Fenton
Chf Nrs Of: Judith Maass
Doctor: H D Mesrobian MD

D-U-N-S 07-169-6868
QUEEN OF VALLEY MEDICAL CENTER
NAPA VALLEY MEDICAL CENTER
(Suby of ST JOSEPH HEALTH SYSTEM) ★
1000 Trancas St, NAPA, CA 94558-2906
Tel (707) 252-4411 Founded/Ownrshp 1953
Sales 243.6MM EMP 1,070
Accts Ernst & Young Us Llp San Dieg
SIC 8062 General medical & surgical hospitals
Pr: Walt Mickens
*COO: Vincent Morgese
*CFO: Bob Diehl
*CFO: Don Miller
*CFO: Mich Riccioni
Bd of Dir: Robert Hoffman
VP: Joseph Carrillo
*VP: Robert Eisen
VP: Merritt Fink
*VP: Dick Green
VP: Richard Green
VP: Marian Schubert
Dir Lab: Narayan Torke
Dir Rx: Diane Heine

D-U-N-S 05-048-4153
QUEENS BOROUGH PUBLIC LIBRARY
QUEENS LIBRARY
8911 Merrick Blvd, Jamaica, NY 11432-5242
Tel (718) 990-0700 Founded/Ownrshp 1986
Sales 142.8MM EMP 1,400^E
Accts Toski & Co Cpas Pc William
SIC 8231 Public library
Pr: Bridget Quinn-Carey
*Pr: Thomas W Galante
Ofcr: Rosanne Evans
VP: Kelvin Watson
IT Man: Stan Nenov

QUEENS HEALTH CARE CENTERS
See AMBULATORY SERVICES INC

D-U-N-S 18-592-1012 IMP
QUEENS HEALTH SYSTEMS
1301 Punchbowl St, Honolulu, HI 96813-2402
Tel (808) 691-5900 Founded/Ownrshp 1985
Sales 118.8MM EMP 4,500
Accts Ernst & Young Us Llp San Dieg
SIC 8062 General medical & surgical hospitals
CEO: Arthur A Ushijima
Pr: William G Obana
Pr: Gary A Okamoto MD
Ex VP: Tracy Woo
VP: Janice Kalanihuia
VP: Eric K Martinson
VP: Kathy Morimoto
VP: Mark Yamakawa
HC Dir: Iris Kawasaki

QUEENS LIBRARY
See QUEENS BOROUGH PUBLIC LIBRARY

D-U-N-S 05-678-3467
QUEENS MEDICAL CENTER
(Suby of QUEENS HEALTH SYSTEMS) ★
1301 Punchbowl St, Honolulu, HI 96813-2499
Tel (808) 547-4329 Founded/Ownrshp 1859
Sales 894.2MM EMP 3,014
SIC 8062 8621

D-U-N-S 06-596-0676
QUEENS-LONG ISLAND MEDICAL GROUP PC (NY)
(Suby of ADVANTAGECARE PHYSICIANS PC) ★
1000 Zeckendorf Blvd B, Garden City, NY 11530-2133
Tel (516) 542-5500 Founded/Ownrshp 1956, 2013
Sales 95.7MM^E EMP 1,700
SIC 8011 Group health association
*CFO: Peter Wolf
VP: Manuel Tressandy
Dir Rad: Karen Ross
IT Man: Neil Balson

D-U-N-S 00-834-7197 IMP
QUEMETCO INC
(Suby of RSR CORP) ★
2777 N Stemmons Fwy, Dallas, TX 75207-2277
Tel (317) 247-1303 Founded/Ownrshp 1946, 1970
Sales 86.0MM^E EMP 400
SIC 3341 4953 Lead smelting & refining (secondary); Refuse systems
Pr: Robert E Finn
CFO: Bill Haberberger
*VP: John De Paul

D-U-N-S 00-211-4853 IMP
QUENCH USA INC
(Suby of AQUA VENTURE HOLDINGS LLC) ★
780 5th Ave Ste 200, King of Prussia, PA 19406-1406
Tel (888) 554-2782 Founded/Ownrshp 2008
Sales 99.5MM^E EMP 183
SIC 5078 Drinking water coolers, mechanical
CEO: Tony Ibarguen

Pr: Mike Zavertnik
CFO: Tom Breslin
Sr VP: John B Whalen
VP: Chris Turano
Prin: Pam Kearns
Off Mgr: Joann Jacobsen
CTO: Patrick White
Sls Mgr: Zachary Serabian

QUEST ASE
See QUEST GLOBAL SERVICES-NA INC

QUEST DIAGNOSTICS
See UNILAB CORP

QUEST DIAGNOSTICS
See METWEST INC

QUEST DIAGNOSTICS
See LABONE INC

D-U-N-S 05-616-8214 IMP/EXP
■ QUEST DIAGNOSTICS CLINICAL LABORATORIES INC
(*Suby of* QUEST DIAGNOSTICS INC) ★
1201 S Collegeville Rd, Collegeville, PA 19426-2998
Tel (610) 454-6000 *Founded/Ownrshp* 1999
Sales 586.0MM[E] *EMP* 10,500
SIC 8071 Testing laboratories
Pr: Surya Mohapatra
**Treas:* Joseph Manory
**VP:* Robert Hagemann
VP: Bruce Ulmer
QA Dir: Randal Steinhoff
IT Man: David J Durante
Software D: Jennifer Bolton
**Counsel:* Robert Rossi
Snr Mgr: Tim Knight
Snr Mgr: Gregory McNutt

D-U-N-S 01-731-1374
■ QUEST DIAGNOSTICS INC
(*Suby of* QUEST DIAGNOSTICS INC) ★
1947 Technology Dr 100, Troy, MI 48083-4245
Tel (248) 364-1324 *Founded/Ownrshp* 1997
Sales 52.5MM[E] *EMP* 1,300
SIC 8071 Testing laboratories; Blood analysis laboratory; Urinalysis laboratory
VP: Gerald Scott Cartier
Dir Lab: Paul Thomas

D-U-N-S 05-635-4640 IMP
▲ QUEST DIAGNOSTICS INC
3 Giralda Farms, Madison, NJ 07940-1027
Tel (973) 520-2700 *Founded/Ownrshp* 1967
Sales 7.4MMM *EMP* 44,000
Tkr Sym DGX *Exch* NYS
SIC 8071 2835 Testing laboratories; In vitro & in vivo diagnostic substances
Pr: Stephen H Rusckowski
Ch Bd: Daniel C Stanzione
CFO: Mark J Guinan
Treas: Garrett H Hansen
Bd of Dir: Maya Patel
Sr VP: Everett V Cunningham
Sr VP: Michael E Prevoznik
Sr VP: Jay G Wohlgemuth
VP: Peter Boras
Exec: Jon R Cohen
Exec: James E Davis
Exec: Catherine T Doherty
Board of Directors: Jenne K Britell, Vicky B Gregg, Jeffrey M Leiden, Timothy L Main, Gary M Pfeiffer, Timothy M Ring, Gail R Wilensky, John B Ziegler

D-U-N-S 05-921-6655
■ QUEST DIAGNOSTICS INC
(*Suby of* QUEST DIAGNOSTICS INC) ★
4230 Burnham Ave, Las Vegas, NV 89119-5410
Tel (702) 733-7866 *Founded/Ownrshp* 1999
Sales 43.0MM[E] *EMP* 1,215
SIC 8071 8731 Medical laboratories; Commercial physical research
Pr: John P Schwartz
CFO: Barry Smith
**Treas:* Dr Henry B Soloway
**VP:* Dr Allen Anes
**VP:* Dr R R Belliveau
**VP:* Dr W H Hoffman
**VP:* Dr David Mulkey
Doctor: Diana Garcia
Doctor: Will Scamman
Doctor: Peter Scully
Doctor: Brian Strauss

D-U-N-S 17-122-2339
■ QUEST DIAGNOSTICS INC
(*Suby of* QUEST DIAGNOSTICS INC) ★
900 Business Center Dr, Horsham, PA 19044-3452
Tel (866) 697-8378 *Founded/Ownrshp* 1991
Sales 66.3MM[E] *EMP* 1,200
SIC 8071 Medical laboratories
Prin: Herman Hurwitz
**Pr:* Mark A Bristow
Pathlgst: Robert Lucas
Pathlgst: Hilary W Newman

D-U-N-S 07-881-8440
■ QUEST DIAGNOSTICS NICHOLS INSTITUTE
(*Suby of* QUEST DIAGNOSTICS INC) ★
33608 Ortega Hwy, San Juan Capistrano, CA 92675-2042
Tel (949) 728-4000 *Founded/Ownrshp* 1971
Sales 157.4MM[E] *EMP* 1,400
SIC 3826 8071 Analytical instruments; Testing laboratories
CEO: Catherine T Doherty
**VP:* Nicholas Conti
**VP:* Timothy Sharpe
Dir Lab: Maryan Sadri
**Ex Dir:* Dan Haemmerle
Brnch Mgr: Adam Abdool
Brnch Mgr: Richard L Chang
Cmptr Lab: Gira Dattani
Cmptr Lab: Avelino Diao
Cmptr Lab: Loretta Londono
Pathlgst: Alireza Bazooband

D-U-N-S 80-625-7080
■ QUEST ENERGY PARTNERS LP
(*Suby of* POSTROCK ENERGY CORP) ★
210 Park Ave Ste 2750, Oklahoma City, OK 73102-5641
Tel (405) 600-7704 *Founded/Ownrshp* 2007
Sales 147.9MM *EMP* 1[E]
SIC 1382

D-U-N-S 82-643-1744
QUEST GLOBAL SERVICES-NA INC
QUEST ASE
(*Suby of* QUEST GLOBAL ENGINEERING SERVICES PRIVATE LIMITED)
11499 Chester Rd Ste 600, Cincinnati, OH 45246-4000
Tel (513) 648-4900 *Founded/Ownrshp* 2009
Sales 47.4MM[E] *EMP* 1,150
SIC 8731 8711 Engineering laboratory, except testing; Aviation &/or aeronautical engineering; Electrical or electronic engineering; Mechanical engineering
CEO: Ajit Prabhu
Pr: Bob Harvey
**COO:* Ajay Prabhu
**CFO:* Rajendra Kumar Shreemal
Sr VP: Raman Subramanian
VP: Andrew Lewis

D-U-N-S 10-755-0055
QUEST MEDIA & SUPPLIES INC
5822 Roseville Rd, Sacramento, CA 95842-3071
Tel (916) 338-7070 *Founded/Ownrshp* 1979
Sales 168.0MM *EMP* 130
Accts Boden Klein & Sneesby Rosevil
SIC 7373 Computer integrated systems design
Pr: Cindy P Burke
**CEO:* Timothy Burke
**COO:* Kathy Campbell
**CFO:* Francine Walrath
Creative D: James Stoffel
Prac Mgr: Etienne Gadient
Snr Sftwr: Nick Johnston
CIO: Mark Aleman
Netwrk Eng: Garris Botts
Netwrk Eng: Scott McIntire
Opers Mgr: Theresa Campbell

D-U-N-S 03-378-4454
▲ QUEST RESOURCE HOLDING CORP
3481 Plano Pkwy, The Colony, TX 75056-9453
Tel (972) 464-0004 *Founded/Ownrshp* 2010
Sales 170.1MM *EMP* 112[E]
Tkr Sym QRHC *Exch* NAS
SIC 4953 Refuse collection & disposal services; Garbage: collecting, destroying & processing; Liquid waste, collection & disposal
Pr: S Ray Hatch
**Ch Bd:* Mitchell A Saltz
COO: David P Sweitzer
CFO: Laurie L Latham
Sr VP: Timothy A Semones

D-U-N-S 18-052-9000
QUEST SOFTWARE INC
(*Suby of* FRANCISCO PARTNERS MANAGEMENT LP) ★
4 Polaris Way, Aliso Viejo, CA 92656-5356
Tel (949) 754-8000 *Founded/Ownrshp* 2016
Sales 1.0MMM[E] *EMP* 3,850
SIC 7373 7372 7379 Computer integrated systems design; Business oriented computer software; Computer related consulting services
CEO: Jeff Hawn
COO: Michelle Helm
CFO: Scott J Davidson
CFO: Michael Lusis
Ofcr: Carl Eberling
VP: Eyal M Aronoff
VP: Kevin E Brooks
VP: Russell McCardle
VP: Terence J Mullin
VP: Thomas R Patterson Jr
VP: Scott H Reasoner
VP: Marshall Senk
VP: Barrie Sheers
VP: Michael Sotnick
VP: William R Stow

D-U-N-S 13-233-8364 EXP
QUEST SPECIALTY CHEMICALS INC
225 Sven Farms Dr Ste 204, Charleston, SC 29492
Tel (800) 966-7580 *Founded/Ownrshp* 2011
Sales 192.5MM[E] *EMP* 557
SIC 2851 Paints & allied products
CEO: Doug Mattscheck
**Ch Bd:* Fred Quinn
**Pr:* Gerry A Loftus
Ex VP: Dave Brunori
**Ex VP:* Wayne Byrne
Ex VP: Nick Causey
**VP:* Gary Cassata
VP: Steve Hughes
**VP:* Marcos N Mejia
**VP:* W Pete Smith
VP: Charlie Van Gelder

D-U-N-S 12-120-8789
■ QUESTAR CORP
(*Suby of* DOMINION RESOURCES INC) ★
333 S State St, Salt Lake City, UT 84111-2302
Tel (801) 324-5900 *Founded/Ownrshp* 2016
Sales 1.1MMM *EMP* 1,759
SIC 4922 1311 5172 Natural gas transmission; Storage, natural gas; Crude petroleum production; Natural gas production; Petroleum products
Pr: Craig C Wagstaff
CFO: Kevin W Hadlock
CFO: Ann Small
Treas: Anthony R Ivins
Ex VP: Micheal Dunn
Ex VP: Brady Rasmussen
VP: Colleen Larkin Bell
VP: Rey Butcher
VP: David M Curtis
Exec: Pat Teuscher
Genl Mgr: Chad K Jones

QUESTAR ENERGY
See QEP ENERGY CO

D-U-N-S 00-793-9069
■ QUESTAR GAS CO (UT)
(*Suby of* QUESTAR CORP) ★
333 S State St, Salt Lake City, UT 84111-2302
Tel (801) 324-5900 *Founded/Ownrshp* 1935
Sales 917.6MM *EMP* 917[E]
SIC 4924 4923 Natural gas distribution; Gas transmission & distribution
Ch Bd: Ronald W Jibson
**COO:* Craig C Wagstaff
**CFO:* Kevin W Hadlock
Ex VP: Ronald Jibson
VP: David M Curtis
Corp Couns: Julie A Wray

D-U-N-S 09-202-7077
■ QUESTAR PIPELINE LLC
(*Suby of* DOMINION MIDSTREAM PARTNERS LP) ★
333 S State St, Salt Lake City, UT 84111-2302
Tel (801) 324-5173 *Founded/Ownrshp* 2016
Sales 263.0MM *EMP* 100
SIC 4922 4923 Natural gas transmission; Gas transmission & distribution
Pr: Craig C Wagstaff
CFO: Kevin W Hadlock
VP: David M Curtis

D-U-N-S 83-307-7535
QUESTO INC
725 Broad St, Augusta, GA 30901-1336
Tel (706) 724-0851 *Founded/Ownrshp* 2009
Sales 785.3MM[E] *EMP* 5,578[E]
SIC 2711 Newspapers
Ch Bd: William Morris III

D-U-N-S 92-976-6301
QUESTOR MANAGEMENT CO LLC
101 Southfield Rd Fl 2, Birmingham, MI 48009-1601
Tel (248) 593-1930 *Founded/Ownrshp* 1995
Sales 26.9MM[E] *EMP* 1,097
Accts Pricewaterhousecoopers
SIC 8742 Financial consultant
Mng Pt: Jay Alix
Pt: Henry Druker
Pt: Jim Griffin
Pt: Al Koch
Pt: Wallace Rueckel
V Ch: Robert Shields
Mng Dir: Dominick J Schiano

D-U-N-S 01-464-2404 IMP/EXP
QUESTOR PARTNERS FUND II LP
101 Southfield Rd 2, Birmingham, MI 48009-1601
Tel (248) 593-1930 *Founded/Ownrshp* 1995
Sales 572.7MM[E] *EMP* 6,957
SIC 8742 2099 Management consulting services; Ready-to-eat meals, salads & sandwiches
Mng Pt: Jay Alix
Pt: Robert Shields

D-U-N-S 93-946-6009 IMP
QUETICO LLC
5521 Schaefer Ave, Chino, CA 91710-9070
Tel (909) 628-6200 *Founded/Ownrshp* 1993
Sales 143.7MM[E] *EMP* 185
SIC 5199 7389 General merchandise, non durable; Packaging & labeling services
VP: Nick Agakanian
VP: David Brudnicki
Brnch Mgr: Antonio Lopez
Mktg Mgr: Richard Voskanian

D-U-N-S 09-971-0303 IMP/EXP
QUEXCO INC
2777 N Stemmons Fwy, Dallas, TX 75207-2277
Tel (214) 688-4000 *Founded/Ownrshp* 1984
Sales 258.5MM[E] *EMP* 653[E]
SIC 3341 Lead smelting & refining (secondary)
Ch Bd: Howard M Meyers

D-U-N-S 96-831-3036
QUIBIDS HOLDINGS LLC
1601 Nw Expwy St Ste 1500, Oklahoma City, OK 73118-1442
Tel (405) 253-3883 *Founded/Ownrshp* 2009
Sales 115.2MM[E] *EMP* 130
SIC 5961

D-U-N-S 04-125-0762
QUICK CHEK CORP
3 Old Highway 28, Whitehouse Station, NJ 08889-3608
Tel (908) 534-2200 *Founded/Ownrshp* 1999
Sales 484.0MM[E] *EMP* 3,000
SIC 5411

QUICK FLASH FUEL
See JACOBUS ENERGY INC

QUICK INTERNATIONAL COURIER
See Q INTERNATIONAL COURIER INC

QUICK STOP
See GREENEVILLE OIL & PETROLEUM INC

D-U-N-S 61-515-1016
QUICK TEST INC
QUICK TEST OPINION CENTER
1061 E Indiantown Rd # 300, Jupiter, FL 33477-5143
Tel (561) 748-0931 *Founded/Ownrshp* 1995
Sales 126.3MM[E] *EMP* 1,400
SIC 7375 Information retrieval services
CEO: Morgan Van Lefferdick
**Pr:* Adam Rodgers
COO: Susan Vincent
CFO: Edward Dean

QUICK TEST OPINION CENTER
See QUICK TEST INC

D-U-N-S 08-024-1389
QUICKBASE INC
150 Cambridgepark Dr # 500, Cambridge, MA 02140-2370
Tel (855) 725-2293 *Founded/Ownrshp* 2016
Sales 88.0MM *EMP* 250
SIC 7372 Prepackaged software
Ch Bd: Rick Willett
**CFO:* Matt Hoogerland

CFO: William Markley
VP: Jeff Prus
VP: Frank Tino
VP Mktg: Karen Devine
VP Sls: Stephen Percoco
Board of Directors: Gray Hall, Robert Hughes, Allison Mnookin

QUICKEN LOANS ARENA
See CAVALIERS HOLDINGS LLC

D-U-N-S 14-423-9357
QUICKEN LOANS INC
ROCK FINANCIAL
(*Suby of* ROCK HOLDINGS INC) ★
1050 Woodward Ave, Detroit, MI 48226-1906
Tel (734) 805-5000 *Founded/Ownrshp* 2002
Sales NA *EMP* 1,700
SIC 6162 Mortgage bankers
Ch: Daniel B Gilbert
Pt: Jennifer Horvat
Pt: Chris Meerschaert
Pt: Jon Moises
**Pr:* Patrick McInnis
**CEO:* Bill Emerson
**CFO:* Julie Booth
VP: Kristin Shelton
Exec: Tom Appleton
**Prin:* William Emerson
Brnch Mgr: Linda Barrett

D-U-N-S 00-230-5191 IMP/EXP
■ QUICKIE MANUFACTURING CORP
(*Suby of* NEWELL BRANDS INC) ★
1150 Taylors Ln Ste 2, Cinnaminson, NJ 08077-2577
Tel (856) 829-7900 *Founded/Ownrshp* 1977, 2016
Sales 130.6MM[E] *EMP* 500
SIC 2392 3991 Mops, floor & dust; Brooms
Ch: Peter S Vosbikian Jr
**CEO:* Michael Magerman
Software D: Shelly Schweiger
VP Mfg: Gregory Branyon

D-U-N-S 04-186-3262
▲ QUICKSILVER RESOURCES INC
801 Cherry St Unit 19, Fort Worth, TX 76102-6883
Tel (817) 665-5000 *Founded/Ownrshp* 1997
Sales 569.4MM *EMP* 293
Accts Ernst & Young Llp Fort Worth
Tkr Sym KWKA *Exch* OTO
SIC 1311 1321 Crude petroleum & natural gas; Crude petroleum & natural gas production; Natural gas liquids
Pr: Glenn Darden
**Ch Bd:* W Yandell Rogers III
**CFO:* Vanessa Gomez Lagatta
VP: John Callanan
**VP:* Romy Massey
Counsel: Ann B House
Board of Directors: W Byron Dunn, Michael Y McGovern, Steven M Morris, Scott M Pinsonnault, Mark J Warner

D-U-N-S 02-903-2971
QUICKWAY DISTRIBUTION SERVICES INC
1116 Polk Ave, Nashville, TN 37210-4331
Tel (615) 834-9470 *Founded/Ownrshp* 1994
Sales 106.0MM *EMP* 852
SIC 4213 4212 Trucking, except local; Local trucking, without storage
CEO: Roger Blume
**Ch Bd:* H Steven George
**CEO:* Bill Prevost
**CFO:* Chris Tate
VP: Scott Herad

D-U-N-S 09-702-0739
▲ QUIDEL CORP
12544 High Bluff Dr # 200, San Diego, CA 92130-3050
Tel (858) 552-1100 *Founded/Ownrshp* 1979
Sales 196.1MM *EMP* 624[E]
Tkr Sym QDEL *Exch* NGS
SIC 2835 In vitro & in vivo diagnostic substances; Pregnancy test kits; Microbiology & virology diagnostic products
Pr: Douglas C Bryant
**Ch Bd:* Kenneth F Buechler
CFO: Randall J Steward
Sr VP: Michael D Abney Jr
Sr VP: Robert J Bujarski
Sr VP: Werner Kroll
Sr VP: Edward K Russell
Sr VP: John D Tamerius
VP Opers: Scot M McLeod
Board of Directors: Thomas D Brown, Mary Lake Polan, Jack W Schuler, Charles P Slacik, Kenneth J Widder

D-U-N-S 78-841-0475 EXP
■ QUIDSI INC
DIAPERS.COM
(*Suby of* AMAZON.COM INC) ★
10 Exchange Pl Fl 25, Jersey City, NJ 07302-4914
Tel (973) 509-5444 *Founded/Ownrshp* 2003
Sales 212.2MM[E] *EMP* 100[E]
SIC 5137 Diapers
CEO: Emilie Arel Scott
**Pr:* Marc Lore
**COO:* Vinit Bharara
**CFO:* Randy Greben
**Ex VP:* Scott Hilton
**Sr VP:* Michal Geller
**VP:* Jennifer Clarke
**VP:* Tara Lawrence
VP: Leandre Scott
VP: David Zhang
Assoc Dir: Myra Deshmukh

D-U-N-S 87-798-8105 IMP/EXP
QUIETFLEX MANUFACTURING CO LP
(*Suby of* GOODMAN MANUFACTURING CO LP) ★
4518 Brittmoore Rd, Houston, TX 77041-8006
Tel (713) 849-2163 *Founded/Ownrshp* 2008
Sales 228.3MM[E] *EMP* 400
SIC 3444 1799 3599 Ducts, sheet metal; Fiberglass work; Tubing, flexible metallic
Pr: Ardee Toppe
Off Mgr: Mark Oats

QUIK CASH
See QC FINANCIAL SERVICES INC

QUIK MART CONVENIENCE STORES
See SOUTHTENNESSEE OIL CO INC

D-U-N-S 00-430-0406 IMP/EXP
QUIKRETE COMPANIES LLC (GA)
ONE SECURITIES CENTER
(*Suby of* QUIKRETE HOLDINGS INC) ★
3490 Piedmont Rd Ne, Atlanta, GA 30305-1743
Tel (404) 634-9100 *Founded/Ownrshp* 1940
Sales 1.1MMME *EMP* 3,750
SIC 3272 3255 3251 3241 Dry mixture concrete; Clay refractories; Brick & structural clay tile; Cement, hydraulic
CEO: James E Winchester Jr
**Ch Bd:* Gene E Winchester
**COO:* William Magill
**Treas:* John D Winchester
Ex VP: Dennis Winchester
VP: Gary Bartlett
VP: Michael Cramer
VP: James Eagle
VP: Jon Tuggle
Exec: Martha Sandoval
Genl Mgr: Jay Owens
Board of Directors: Amelia O Winchester

D-U-N-S 96-958-3546
QUIKRETE HOLDINGS INC
3490 Piedmont Rd Ne # 1300, Atlanta, GA 30305-4811
Tel (404) 926-3167 *Founded/Ownrshp* 2003
Sales 2.1MMME *EMP* 3,750
SIC 3272 3241 3255 Concrete products; Cement, hydraulic; Cement, clay refractory
CEO: James E Winchester Jr
**COO:* William Magill
**CFO:* John O Winchester
**Treas:* John D Winchester
Top Exec: Brian Brown
Dist Mgr: John Zilly
Netwrk Eng: Charles Ngalle
VP Opers: James McSpadden
Opers Mgr: Richard Schwartz
Plnt Mgr: Lesley Dail
Plnt Mgr: Robert White

D-U-N-S 08-358-4029 EXP
■ **QUIKSILVER INC**
(*Suby of* OAKTREE CAPITAL MANAGEMENT LP) ★
5600 Argosy Ave Ste 100, Huntington Beach, CA 92649-1063
Tel (714) 889-2200 *Founded/Ownrshp* 2016
Sales 1.3MMM *EMP* 700
Accts Deloitte & Touche Llp Costa M
SIC 2329 2339 3949 5136 5137 Men's & boys' sportswear & athletic clothing; Women's & misses' athletic clothing & sportswear; Sporting & athletic goods; Winter sports equipment; Skateboards; Windsurfing boards (sailboards) & equipment; Sportswear, men's & boys'; Sportswear, women's & children's
CEO: Pierre Agnes
Pr: Greg Healy
Pr: Anton Nistl
CFO: Thomas Chambolle
Ex VP: Danny Kwock
Ex VP: Carol Scherman
Ex VP: Steve Tolly
VP: Tim Carey
VP: Marisa Dahlgren
VP: Christopher Dubes
VP: Steve Ellingson
VP: Patrick Finnegan
VP: Scott Fullerton
VP: Terry Gardy
VP: Pam Gobright
VP: Debi Gregg
VP: Jennifer Heslar
VP: Deanna Holloway
VP: Brian Ivanhoe
VP: Tina Kastelan
VP: Ryan Keenan
Board of Directors: William M Barnum Jr, Joseph F Berardino, Michael A Clarke, M Steven Langman, Andrew W Sweet

D-U-N-S 03-313-8157
QUIKTRIP CORP
4705 S 129th East Ave, Tulsa, OK 74134-7008
Tel (918) 615-7700 *Founded/Ownrshp* 1958
Sales 1.3MMME *EMP* 5,250
SIC 5411 5541 5172 2099 5141 6512 Grocery stores; Gasoline service stations; Petroleum products; Gasoline; Diesel fuel; Ready-to-eat meals, salads & sandwiches; Box lunches, for sale off premises; Sandwiches, assembled & packaged: for wholesale market; Groceries, general line; Commercial & industrial building operation
Pr: Chet Cadieux
**COO:* Mike Stanford
CFO: Stuart Sullivan
CFO: Sandra J Westbrook
VP: Jim Denny
VP: Ron Jeffers
VP: James Marchesano
VP: Richard Ross
Admn Mgr: David Brasfield
Div Mgr: Tim Heuback
IT Man: Dan Frost
Board of Directors: Linda Quick, Chester E Cadieux II, Stephen G Sheetz, Terry L Carter, Stephen L Cropper, Michael P Johnson, Peter W C Mather, Richard C May, Mary V McClure, Pattye L Moore, Stuart M Pearman

D-U-N-S 02-527-3202 IMP/EXP
■ **QUILL CORP**
(*Suby of* STAPLES INC) ★
100 Schelter Rd, Lincolnshire, IL 60069-3621
Tel (847) 634-6690 *Founded/Ownrshp* 1998
Sales 218.1MMME *EMP* 2,200
SIC 5943 Office forms & supplies
Pr: Ronald Sargent
**Pr:* Michael Patriarca
Sr VP: Phil Petrelli
**VP:* Cliff Howard
**VP:* Ken Wnek
Info Man: David McGreevy
VP Merchng: Kevin Wood

D-U-N-S 02-635-5597
QUILL.COM
300 Arbor Lake Dr # 1200, Columbia, SC 29223-4536
Tel (803) 333-8300 *Founded/Ownrshp* 2009
Sales 1.0MMM *EMP* 500
SIC 7363 Office help supply service
CEO: Sergio Pereira

D-U-N-S 82-856-4179
QUINCO ELECTRICAL INC
4224 Metric Dr, Winter Park, FL 32792-6890
Tel (407) 478-6005 *Founded/Ownrshp* 1993
Sales 93.9MME *EMP* 350E
SIC 1731 Electrical work
Pr: David W Deese
**CFO:* Amanda Furner
CFO: Phyllis Moscoso
**VP:* Richard Cavazos
**VP:* Vanessa Deese
**VP:* David Sanchez

QUINCY BRDCAST PRINT INTRCTIVE
See QUINCY MEDIA INC

QUINCY CITY HALL
See CITY OF QUINCY

D-U-N-S 10-322-1362 IMP/EXP
QUINCY COMPRESSOR LLC
(*Suby of* ATLAS COPCO AB)
701 N Dobson Ave, Bay Minette, AL 36507-3199
Tel (251) 937-5900 *Founded/Ownrshp* 2010
Sales 292.0MME *EMP* 806
SIC 3519 3563 3561 Engines, diesel & semi-diesel or dual-fuel; Air & gas compressors including vacuum pumps; Pumps & pumping equipment
VP: John Demers
VP: Larry Smith
VP: John West
Dir Bus: Jan Zuercher
Mfg Mgr: John Daw
Plnt Mgr: Keith Schumacher
Plnt Mgr: Michael Thompson
Natl Sales: Dave North
Sls&Mrk Ex: Jacqueline Gay
S&M/VP: Kip Robinson
Sls Mgr: Carl Stokley

D-U-N-S 00-629-6719
QUINCY MEDIA INC
QUINCY BRDCAST PRINT INTRCTIVE
130 S 5th St, Quincy, IL 62301-3916
Tel (217) 223-5100 *Founded/Ownrshp* 1926
Sales 221.7MME *EMP* 1,000
SIC 2711 4833 2752 2741 Newspapers, publishing & printing; Television broadcasting stations; Commercial printing, lithographic; Miscellaneous publishing
Pr: Ralph M Oakley
COO: Ralph Oakley
Admn Mgr: Robby Warner
Dir IT: Morey Taraska
Mktg Mgr: Annastasia Gabbert
Sales Asso: Brittany Vermeire

D-U-N-S 00-695-5678
QUINCY MUTUAL FIRE INSURANCE CO INC
57 Washington St, Quincy, MA 02169-5343
Tel (617) 770-5100 *Founded/Ownrshp* 1851
Sales NA *EMP* 200
SIC 6331 6411 Fire, marine & casualty insurance: mutual; Insurance agents, brokers & service
Ch Bd: Karl L Briggs
Pr: K Douglas Briggs
Treas: Thomas A Harris
Sr VP: Kevin M Meskell
Sr VP: James J Moran
VP: Harold E Gerbis
VP: Harold Gerbis

D-U-N-S 00-323-6572
QUINCY PUBLIC SCHOOLS
34 Coddington St, Quincy, MA 02169-4501
Tel (617) 984-8700 *Founded/Ownrshp* 2000
Sales 84.4MM *EMP* 100
SIC 8211 Public elementary & secondary schools
IT Man: Michael McGunagle
Schl Brd P: Thomas Koch
Teacher Pr: Madeline Roy

D-U-N-S 06-959-2293
■ **QUINCY SCRANTON HOSPITAL LLC**
MOSES TAYLOR HOSPITAL
(*Suby of* COMMUNITY HEALTH SYSTEMS INC) ★
700 Quincy Ave, Scranton, PA 18510-1724
Tel (570) 340-2100 *Founded/Ownrshp* 1983
Sales 143.6MM *EMP* 1,005
SIC 8062 8051 General medical & surgical hospitals; Skilled nursing care facilities
CEO: Justin Davis
**CFO:* Joseph Marino
Act CFO: James Brittain
VP: Michael Costello
Dir Rx: Michele Musheno
Chf Nrs Of: Lisa Chervanka
Dir Sec: Roy Wood
Genl Mgr: Barb Santoli
QA Dir: Cheryl Burke
Dir IT: Frank Fallo
Dir IT: Richard Pienkowski

D-U-N-S 11-272-0867 IMP/EXP
QUINN CO
CATERPILLAR AUTHORIZED DEALER
(*Suby of* QUINN USED PARTS) ★
10006 Rose Hills Rd, City of Industry, CA 90601-1702
Tel (562) 463-4000 *Founded/Ownrshp* 2003
Sales 222.8MME *EMP* 500
SIC 5082 5083 5084 7353 General construction machinery & equipment; Farm & garden machinery; Industrial machinery & equipment; Heavy construction equipment rental
CEO: Blake Quinn
Sr VP: Jay Ervine
Sr VP: Paul Lucini
VP: Robbin Camp
Genl Mgr: Eric Greene
Dir IT: Alex Tsang
IT Man: Pat Jenning
IT Man: Jon Tompkins
Sales Exec: Larry Sheldon
Sales Exec: Kevin Vivian
Advt Mgr: Susan Marshall

D-U-N-S 19-687-7203
QUINN EMANUEL URQUHART & SULLIVAN LLP
865 S Figueroa St Fl 10, Los Angeles, CA 90017-5003
Tel (213) 443-3000 *Founded/Ownrshp* 1986
Sales 175.2MME *EMP* 899
SIC 8111 General practice law office
Mng Pt: John B Quinn
Pt: Adam Abensohn
Pt: Anthony Alden
Pt: Wayne Alexander
Pt: Steven Anderson
Pt: Peter Armenio
Pt: Jim Asperger
Pt: Melissa Baily
Pt: Jennifer Barrett
Pt: Harold Barza
Pt: Robert Becher
Pt: Marc Becker
Pt: Albert Bedecarre
Pt: Fred Bennett
Pt: Andy Berdon
Pt: David Bilsker
Pt: Kristen Bird
Pt: Jeffrey Boozell
Pt: Sandra Bresnick
Pt: Todd Briggs
Pt: Daniel Brockett

D-U-N-S 02-945-1945 IMP
QUINN GROUP INC
QUINN USED PARTS
10006 Rose Hills Rd, City of Industry, CA 90601-1702
Tel (562) 463-4000 *Founded/Ownrshp* 1972
Sales 463.4MME *EMP* 1,074
SIC 5084 5082 7353 7359 Tractors, industrial; General construction machinery & equipment; Heavy construction equipment rental; Equipment rental & leasing
Pr: Blake Quinn
**VP:* Paul Lucini

D-U-N-S 04-977-4508 IMP
QUINN SHEPHERD MACHINERY
CATERPILLAR AUTHORIZED DEALER
(*Suby of* QUINN USED PARTS) ★
10006 Rose Hills Rd, City of Industry, CA 90601-1702
Tel (562) 463-6000 *Founded/Ownrshp* 2003
Sales 103.2MME *EMP* 287
SIC 5082 5084 General construction machinery & equipment; Excavating machinery & equipment; Mining machinery & equipment, except petroleum; Industrial machinery & equipment
Pr: Blake Quinn

QUINN USED PARTS
See QUINN GROUP INC

QUINN/SOUTHWEST
See HILLTOP SECURITIES INC

D-U-N-S 07-212-7368
QUINNIPIAC UNIVERSITY
275 Mount Carmel Ave, Hamden, CT 06518-1908
Tel (203) 582-8200 *Founded/Ownrshp* 1929
Sales 416.3MM *EMP* 900
SIC 8221 College, except junior
Ch: Terry W Goodwim
**Pr:* John L Lahey
Assoc VP: Sally Veira
**VP:* Lucille Marottolo
VP: Paul Tiyambe Zeleza
Mng Dir: David M Darst
Mng Dir: Frances Rowe
Genl Mgr: Grace P Levine
Sfty Dirs: Santo Manicone
Phys Thrpy: Richard Albro
Phys Thrpy: Craig Goldstein

D-U-N-S 96-662-8562
QUINNOX INC
400 N Michigan Ave # 1300, Chicago, IL 60611-4109
Tel (630) 548-4800 *Founded/Ownrshp* 2002
Sales 96.4MME *EMP* 1,250
SIC 7379 7371 Computer related consulting services; Custom computer programming services
CEO: Anil Kumar
**Pr:* Rumi Contractor
COO: Amit Nagar
**VP:* Ninan George
VP: Sanjay Singh
Exec: Juber Mujawar
Dir IT: Praveen Maramreddy
Software D: Prasham Jain
Snr Mgr: Sunil Varghese

D-U-N-S 13-351-2561
▲ **QUINSTREET INC**
950 Tower Ln Ste 600, Foster City, CA 94404-4253
Tel (650) 578-7700 *Founded/Ownrshp* 1999
Sales 297.7MM *EMP* 638
Tkr Sym QNST *Exch* NGS
SIC 7389 7372 Advertising, promotional & trade show services; Prepackaged software; Business oriented computer software
Ch Bd: Douglas Valenti
CFO: Gregory Wong
Chf Cred: Martin J Collins
Sr VP: Peter Brooks
VP: Marty Collins
VP: Edton Mock
Off Mgr: Tracy Shewchuk
Snr Sftwr: Robert Schulke
Snr Sftwr: Umang Shah
CTO: Nina Bhanap
QA Dir: Vaishali Sirsikar
Board of Directors: Stuart M Huizinga, Robin Josephs, John G McDonald, David Pauldine, Gregory Sands, Marjorie T Sennett, James Simons

D-U-N-S 07-972-2214
QUINTANA ENERGY SERVICES LP
601 Jefferson St Ste 3600, Houston, TX 77002-7906
Tel (713) 751-7500 *Founded/Ownrshp* 2014
Sales 235.7MME *EMP* 500E
SIC 1389 Oil & gas wells: building, repairing & dismantling
Pt: Corbin J Robertson Jr

D-U-N-S 83-283-1783
▲ **QUINTILES IMS HOLDINGS INC**
4820 Emperor Blvd, Durham, NC 27703-8426
Tel (919) 998-2000 *Founded/Ownrshp* 1982
Sales 5.7MMM *EMP* 36,100
Tkr Sym Q *Exch* NYS
SIC 8731 Medical research, commercial
CEO: Thomas H Pike
Pr: Richard Staub III
COO: Kevin K Gordon
CFO: Michael R McDonnell
Ex VP: James H Erlinger III
Sr VP: Charles E Williams
CIO: Alejandro Martinez

D-U-N-S 10-174-0405 IMP
■ **QUINTILES INC**
(*Suby of* QUINTILESTRANSNATIONAL CORP) ★
4820 Emperor Blvd, Durham, NC 27703-8426
Tel (919) 998-2000 *Founded/Ownrshp* 1982
Sales 289.9MME *EMP* 670
SIC 8731 Medical research, commercial
CEO: Tom Pike
Pr: Brian J Kelly
**Pr:* John Ratliff
**COO:* Kevin Gordon
**CFO:* Mike McDonnell
**Treas:* David Andrews
VP: Richard Cesarski
**VP:* James H Erlinger III
Assoc Dir: Ali Massoud
Assoc Dir: Diane Mikolay
Dir Bus: Jim Yang
Board of Directors: Richard Relyea

D-U-N-S 62-040-9029
■ **QUINTILES TRANSNATIONAL CORP**
(*Suby of* QUINTILES IMS HOLDINGS INC) ★
4820 Emperor Blvd, Durham, NC 27703-8426
Tel (919) 998-2000 *Founded/Ownrshp* 2003
Sales 2.5MMME *EMP* 22,000
SIC 8732 8731 8999 Commercial nonphysical research; Research services, except laboratory; Commercial physical research; Biological research; Medical research, commercial; Scientific consulting
Ch Bd: Dennis B Gillings
**Pr:* Richard Pilnik
**Pr:* John Ratliff
**Pr:* Paula B Stafford
Pr: Mike Zaranek
COO: Angus Bell
CFO: Kevin Gordon
**Ex VP:* John Goodacre
Ex VP: Neil Macallister
**Ex VP:* Derek Winstandly
Sr VP: Michael P Arlotto
Sr VP: John Doyle
Sr VP: Paul Knott
**Sr VP:* Jamie Macdonald
Sr VP: Tom Perkins
VP: Carol Breslauer
VP: Oren Cohen
VP: Robert Hauser
VP: Sonnie Kang
VP: Amar Kureishi
VP: Cheryl Murphy

D-U-N-S 04-546-7826 IMP/EXP
QUIRCH FOODS CO
E & G TRADING
2701 S Le Jeune Rd, Coral Gables, FL 33134-5809
Tel (305) 691-3535 *Founded/Ownrshp* 1967
Sales 600.2MME *EMP* 500
Accts Morrison Brown Argiz & Farra
SIC 5147 5142 5144 5146 Meats, fresh; Frozen fish, meat & poultry; Poultry & poultry products; Fish & seafoods
Pr: Francisco P Grande
**Treas:* Ignacio J Quirch
VP: Mauricio Quirch
Genl Mgr: Ramon Aldape
CIO: Ingrid Serrano
Telecom Mg: Eduardo Quirch
Ql Cn Mgr: George Torres
Mktg Dir: Victor Archavaleta

QUIRK MAZDA
See DANIEL J QUIRK INC

D-U-N-S 80-650-9720
QUIVUS SYSTEMS LLC
3803T St Nw, Washington, DC 20007-2122
Tel (202) 587-5756 *Founded/Ownrshp* 2007
Sales 100.0MM *EMP* 24
SIC 8742 Management consulting services
IT Man: Timothy Kurutz

D-U-N-S 13-086-4580
QUIZNOS CORP
QUIZNO'S SUBS
7595 E Tech Way Ste 200, Denver, CO 80237
Tel (720) 359-3300 *Founded/Ownrshp* 2007
Sales 415.2MME *EMP* 2,505E
SIC 6794 5812 Franchises, selling or licensing; Sandwiches & submarines shop
Pr: Susan Lintonsmith
Ch Bd: Greg Brenneman
Ch Bd: Richard E Schaden
COO: James Lyons
CFO: John Coletta
CFO: Christina Maxwell
Ex VP: Mark Rogers
Ex VP: Clyde Rucker
Genl Couns: Pat Meyers

QUIZNO'S SUBS
See QUIZNOS CORP

D-U-N-S 96-865-9565
■ QUOIN LLC
(*Suby of* NEWELL BRANDS) ★
555 Theodore Fremd Ave B302, Rye, NY 10580-1451
Tel (914) 967-9400 *Founded/Ownrshp* 1997
Sales 709.4MM^E *EMP* 1,402
SIC 3089 Plastic containers, except foam
CEO: Martin Franklin
Board of Directors: Angela K Knowlton, Monte L Miller

D-U-N-S 08-016-2853
▲ QUORUM HEALTH CORP
1573 Mallory Ln, Brentwood, TN 37027-2895
Tel (615) 465-7189 *Founded/Ownrshp* 2015
Sales 2.2MMM^E *EMP* 3,435^E
Tkr Sym QHC *Exch* NYS
SIC 8741 Hospital management
CEO: Thomas Miller
CFO: Michael Culotta
CFO: Michael J Culotta
Treas: James Doucette
Ex VP: Martin D Smith
Sr VP: Shaheed Koury

D-U-N-S 07-537-7911
■ QUORUM HEALTH RESOURCES LLC
(*Suby of* QUORUM HEALTH CORP) ★
1573 Mallory Ln 200, Brentwood, TN 37027-2895
Tel (615) 371-7979 *Founded/Ownrshp* 2016
Sales 201.6MM^E *EMP* 64^E
SIC 8742 8741 8082 8231 6324 Management consulting services; Management services; Home health care services; Medical library; Hospital & medical service plans
Pr: Ce Bilbrey
Pr: Jose Abreu
Pr: Douglas Degraaf Jr
Pr: Tom Gearhart
Pr: Ron McArthur
Pr: John Peel
Pr: Bama Wood
COO: Bob Vento
CFO: Timothy J Ryan
Assoc VP: William Carder
Assoc VP: Richard Knight
Assoc VP: Patricia Letchworth
Assoc VP: Richard Lopez
Assoc VP: Steve Smith
Sr VP: Kevin Andrews
Sr VP: David Dempsey
Sr VP: Rick Drake
Sr VP: John Maher
Sr VP: Chris Moore
Sr VP: John Siedlecki
Sr VP: Joan Signorille

D-U-N-S 96-362-9899
▲ QUOTIENT TECHNOLOGY INC
400 Logue Ave, Mountain View, CA 94043-4019
Tel (650) 605-4600 *Founded/Ownrshp* 1998
Sales 237.3MM *EMP* 618^E
Tkr Sym QUOT *Exch* NYS
SIC 7319 Coupon distribution
CEO: Steven R Boal
Pr: Mir Aamir
CFO: Ron J Fior
Ofcr: Michael Walsh
VP: Paul Sloan
Exec: Michele Murgel
Comm Man: Tessa Chen
Genl Couns: Connie Chen
Board of Directors: Andrew Jody Gessow, Steve Horowitz, Dawn Lepore, David E Siminoff

D-U-N-S 15-092-4769 IMP/EXP
■ QVC INC
QVC
(*Suby of* LIBERTY QVC HOLDING LLC) ★
1200 Wilson Dr, West Chester, PA 19380-4262
Tel (484) 701-1000 *Founded/Ownrshp* 1986
Sales 8.7MMM *EMP* 17,600
Accts Kpmg Llp Philadelphia Pennsy
SIC 5961 Catalog & mail-order houses; Cosmetics & perfumes, mail order; Television, home shopping; Women's apparel, mail order
Pr: Michael A George
CFO: Thaddeus J Jastrzebski
Ex VP: Bob Spieth
VP: Julie Batenburg
VP: Dave Caputo
VP: Kristi Hanifin
VP: Larry Hayes
VP: Bryce C Mason
VP: John J Misko
VP: Colleen Mordan
VP: Donald Mullen
VP: Lisa Norden
VP: Doug Rose
VP: Sanjay Singh
Board of Directors: Christopher W Shean

D-U-N-S 13-336-5648
■ QVC SAINT LUCIE INC
(*Suby of* COMCAST HOLDINGS CORP) ★
300 Nw Peacock Blvd, Port Saint Lucie, FL 34986-2207
Tel (772) 873-4300 *Founded/Ownrshp* 2003
Sales 64.0MM^E *EMP* 2,840^E
SIC 5963 Direct selling establishments
Genl Mgr: Diana Livingston
Area Mgr: Audrey Ward

QWEST
See DEX MEDIA HOLDINGS INC

D-U-N-S 10-908-0648
■ QWEST BUSINESS & GOVERNMENT SERVICES INC
(*Suby of* QWEST COMMUNICATIONS INTERNATIONAL INC) ★
1801 Calif St Ste 3800, Denver, CO 80202-2612
Tel (303) 391-8300 *Founded/Ownrshp* 2000
Sales 458.4MM^E *EMP* 1,002
SIC 5999 1731 7629 7373 7371 7622 Telephone equipment & systems; Telephone & telephone equipment installation; Telephone set repair; Computer systems analysis & design; Computer software development; Radio & television repair
CEO: Sol Trujillo
Pr: John Kelley
Treas: Barbara Japha
VP: James Smith
IT Man: James Mills
Board of Directors: James T Helwig

D-U-N-S 14-993-6007
■ QWEST BUSINESS RESOURCES INC
(*Suby of* QWEST CORP) ★
1005 17th St, Denver, CO 80202-2028
Tel (303) 896-5025 *Founded/Ownrshp* 2000
Sales 32.3MM^E *EMP* 1,250
SIC 7389 6512 Purchasing service; Commercial & industrial building operation
Pr: Peggy Milford
VP: D D Farrell

D-U-N-S 14-872-1178
■ QWEST COMMUNICATIONS INTERNATIONAL INC
(*Suby of* CENTURYLINK INC) ★
100 Centurylink Dr, Monroe, LA 71203-2041
Tel (318) 388-9000 *Founded/Ownrshp* 2011
Sales 11.3MMM *EMP* 24,800
SIC 4813 4822 4812 Telephone communication, except radio; Long distance telephone communications; Telephone/video communications; ; Cable, telegram & telex services; Radio telephone communication
Pr: Glen F Post III
**CFO:* R Stewart Ewing Jr
CFO: Robert S Woodruff
Ex VP: Stephanie Comfort
Ex VP: Dennis G Huber
Ex VP: Roland R Thornton
Ex VP: Bob Tregemba
Sr VP: David D Cole
VP: Richard Twilley
VP: Kevin Wall
Exec: Stan Fong
Exec: John Korkie
Exec: Brian Sanchez
Exec: Steven Williams
Board of Directors: Stacey W Goff

D-U-N-S 18-476-5444 IMP
■ QWEST CORP
(*Suby of* QWEST SERVICES CORP) ★
100 Centurylink Dr, Monroe, LA 71203-2041
Tel (318) 388-9000 *Founded/Ownrshp* 2000
Sales 8.9MMM *EMP* 22,000^E
Tkr Sym CTY *Exch* NYS
SIC 4813 Local & long distance telephone communications; ; Voice telephone communications; Data telephone communications
Pr: Glen F Post III
**CFO:* R Stewart Ewing Jr
Bd of Dir: Cheryl Daughtry
Ex VP: David D Cole
Board of Directors: Stacey W Goff

D-U-N-S 09-791-4985
■ QWEST CYBERSOLUTIONS LLC
(*Suby of* QWEST COMMUNICATIONS INTERNATIONAL INC) ★
1801 California St # 3800, Denver, CO 80202-2658
Tel (303) 296-2787 *Founded/Ownrshp* 2000
Sales 320.2MM^E *EMP* 700
SIC 7375 Information retrieval services
CEO: Richard C Notebaert
**CFO:* Scott Lindsey
**CFO:* Oren G Shaffer
**Treas:* Janet K Cooper
Ex VP: Gary Gauba
VP: Shane Matson
Dir Risk M: John Wolfe
Mng Dir: John Jones
Dir IT: Mike Frankfurth
IT Man: Frank Fernandez
Sftwr Eng: Srini Gude

D-U-N-S 36-228-6288 IMP
■ QWEST GOVERNMENT SERVICES INC
CENTURYLINK QGS
(*Suby of* QWEST SERVICES CORP) ★
931 14th St Ste 1000b, Denver, CO 80202-2994
Tel (303) 992-1400 *Founded/Ownrshp* 1998
Sales 2.7MMM^E *EMP* 24,000
SIC 4813 4812 Telephone communication, except radio; Long distance telephone communications; Radio telephone communication
CEO: Glen F Post III
**CFO:* John W Richardson
Treas: Rahn K Porter
Sr VP: Janet K Cooper
Sr VP: R S Davis
VP: Kenneth C Dunn
**VP:* Diana Gowen
VP: Oscar A Martinez
VP: Michael McElroy
Snr Mgr: Gary Hall

D-U-N-S 14-287-6221
■ QWEST SERVICES CORP
(*Suby of* QWEST COMMUNICATIONS INTERNATIONAL INC) ★
931 14th St Ste 1000b, Denver, CO 80202-2994
Tel (303) 992-1400 *Founded/Ownrshp* 1996
Sales 11.7MMM^E *EMP* 24,800^E
SIC 4813 Telephone communication, except radio
Pr: Richard C Notebaert

R

D-U-N-S 00-790-7934
R & B FALCON DRILLING INTERNATIONAL DEEPWATER INC (DE)
(*Suby of* TODCO) ★
2000 W Sam Houston Pkwy S, Houston, TX 77042-3615
Tel (713) 278-6000 *Founded/Ownrshp* 1937
Sales 128.8MM^E *EMP* 1,900
SIC 1381 8711 Drilling oil & gas wells; Engineering services
Ch Bd: Paul B Loyd Jr
Pr: Andrew Bakonyi
Ex VP: Tim W Nagle

D-U-N-S 04-554-4103 IMP
R & B REALTY GROUP A CALIFORNIA LIMITED PARTNERSHIP
OAKWOOD WORLDWIDE
2222 Corinth Ave, Los Angeles, CA 90064-1602
Tel (800) 888-0808 *Founded/Ownrshp* 1960
Sales 154.1MM^E *EMP* 1,500
SIC 7021 6531

D-U-N-S 94-836-9749
R & B REALTY GROUP LP
OAKWOOD WORLDWIDE
2222 Corinth Ave, Los Angeles, CA 90064-1602
Tel (310) 478-1021 *Founded/Ownrshp* 1976
Sales 51.7MM^E *EMP* 1,500
SIC 6531 Real estate agents & managers; Buying agent, real estate
Pt: Howard F Ruby
Sr VP: Marina Lubinsky

R & B RLTY GRP A CA LTD PRTNRS
See WORLDWIDE CORPORATE HOUSING LP

D-U-N-S 09-784-9400 IMP
R & B WHOLESALE DISTRIBUTORS INC
2350 S Milliken Ave, Ontario, CA 91761-2332
Tel (909) 230-5400 *Founded/Ownrshp* 1968
Sales 114.5MM^E *EMP* 102
Accts Bhuiyan & Associates Santa Cl
SIC 5064 Electrical appliances, major; Electrical entertainment equipment
Pr: Robert O Burggraf
**CFO:* Sam Snyder
Treas: Robert Burggraf
**VP:* Masako Burggraf
VP: Romeo Roque
Off Mgr: Connie Espina
Sls Mgr: Tim Hoffee

D-U-N-S 03-798-2410
R & D MAINTENANCE SERVICES INC
409 N Main St, Hennessey, OK 73742-1017
Tel (405) 853-7108 *Founded/Ownrshp* 1980
Sales 124.0MM^E *EMP* 380
SIC 1629 Marine construction; Pond construction
CEO: Richard D Moulson Sr

D-U-N-S 04-476-4129
R & D MARKETING LLC
4110 Westside Dr, Tupelo, MS 38801-7007
Tel (662) 620-2828 *Founded/Ownrshp* 2000
Sales 100.0MM *EMP* 9
SIC 5147 Meats & meat products
Pr: Daniel H Purnell

D-U-N-S 02-250-3635
R & H MOTOR CARS LTD
MERCEDES-BENZ
9727 Reisterstown Rd, Owings Mills, MD 21117-4149
Tel (410) 363-7793 *Founded/Ownrshp* 1966
Sales 89.3MM^E *EMP* 250
SIC 5511 7538 5531 Automobiles, new & used; General automotive repair shops; Automotive parts
Pr: Robert Russel
**Treas:* F Steven Russel
**VP:* Adella Russel
Sls Mgr: Dylan Jones

R & J TRUCKING
See AMERICAN BULK COMMODITIES INC

D-U-N-S 87-907-2908
R & L BROSAMER INC
(*Suby of* WALSH GROUP CONSTRUCTION) ★
1390 Willow Pass Rd # 950, Concord, CA 94520-7974
Tel (925) 627-1700 *Founded/Ownrshp* 2010
Sales 103.9MM^E *EMP* 400
SIC 1611 General contractor, highway & street construction
CEO: Matthew M Walsh
**Pr:* Robert Brosamer
**CFO:* Cindy Lundquist
**VP:* Linda Brosamer

D-U-N-S 92-919-6756
R & L CARRIERS INC
600 Gilliam Rd, Wilmington, OH 45177-9089
Tel (937) 382-1494 *Founded/Ownrshp* 1994
Sales 4.1MMM^E *EMP* 10,000
SIC 4213

D-U-N-S 04-457-4572
R & L TRANSFER INC
(*Suby of* R & L CARRIERS INC) ★
600 Gilliam Rd, Wilmington, OH 45177-9089
Tel (937) 382-1494 *Founded/Ownrshp* 1967
Sales 221.5MM^E *EMP* 10,000
SIC 4213

D-U-N-S 05-674-5268
R & O CONSTRUCTION CO INC
ROCON COMPANY CALIF ONLY
933 Wall Ave Ste 2, Ogden, UT 84404-4800
Tel (801) 627-1403 *Founded/Ownrshp* 1980
Sales 266.1MM *EMP* 180
SIC 1542 1521

D-U-N-S 09-731-7663
R & O SPECIALTIES INC
(*Suby of* GROUP O INC) ★
120 4th Ave E, Milan, IL 61264-2803
Tel (309) 736-8660 *Founded/Ownrshp* 1992
Sales 144.4MM^E *EMP* 280
Accts Crippen Reid & Bowen Llc
SIC 5085 5013 3479 Industrial supplies; Bearings; Automotive supplies; Painting of metal products
Pr: Robert Ontiveros
**CEO:* Gregg Ontiveros
**CFO:* Bob Marriott
**VP:* Kim Fox
VP: Bob Ontiveros
**VP:* Alfred Ramirez

D-U-N-S 11-061-1063
R & R EXPRESS INC
3 Crafton Sq, Pittsburgh, PA 15205-2831
Tel (412) 920-1336 *Founded/Ownrshp* 2002
Sales 98.0MM *EMP* 100^E
SIC 4731 Freight transportation arrangement
Pr: Richard S Francis
**VP:* Raymond J Francis
Genl Mgr: Michael McGarrey

D-U-N-S 07-938-9142
R & R EXPRESS LOGISTICS INC
3 Crafton Sq, Pittsburgh, PA 15205-2831
Tel (800) 223-8973 *Founded/Ownrshp* 2009
Sales 100.0MM *EMP* 35^E
SIC 4731 Freight transportation arrangement
Pr: Richard Francis
Opers Mgr: Frank Van Ameringen

D-U-N-S 15-342-6929
R & R GOLDMAN & ASSOCIATES INC
DISCOVERY CLOTHING COMPANY
4300 N Knox Ave, Chicago, IL 60641-1905
Tel (773) 777-4494 *Founded/Ownrshp* 1979
Sales 92.1MM *EMP* 750
Accts Mcgladrey Llp Chicago Illino
SIC 5621 Ready-to-wear apparel, women's
Dist Mgr: Mel Klarfeld

D-U-N-S 00-177-5337 IMP/EXP
R & R MARKETING LLC
BREAKTHRU BEVERAGE NEW JERSEY
(*Suby of* BREAKTHRU BEVERAGE GROUP LLC) ★
10 Patton Dr, West Caldwell, NJ 07006-6405
Tel (973) 228-5100 *Founded/Ownrshp* 2014
Sales 173.8MM^E *EMP* 300
SIC 5182 Liquor; Wine
Pr: Jon Maslin
**Treas:* Dennis Portsmore
Mktg Dir: John Oliver
Mktg Mgr: Keith Poskitt
Sls Mgr: Anthony Accardo
Sls Mgr: Dennis Resnick
Sls Mgr: Alan Rogers
Sls Mgr: Jasmeet Sawhney

D-U-N-S 10-759-4426
R & S PARTS AND SERVICE INC
STRAUSS DISCOUNT AUTO
7 Brick Plant Rd Ste C, South River, NJ 08882-1145
Tel (732) 525-5938 *Founded/Ownrshp* 2000
Sales 487.1MM^E *EMP* 2,000
SIC 5531 Automotive parts; Automotive accessories; Automotive tires; Batteries, automotive & truck
CEO: Glenn Langberg
**Pr:* Joseph Catalano
**VP:* Bill Belinowicz
Off Mgr: Debbie Farhy
Opers Mgr: Pete Birdsall

R A I
See RAY ANGELINI INC

D-U-N-S 09-897-8919
R A ZWEIG INC
2500 Ravine Way, Glenview, IL 60025-7629
Tel (847) 832-9001 *Founded/Ownrshp* 1979
Sales 88.1MM^E *EMP* 110
SIC 5013 Automotive engines & engine parts
Pr: Arie Zweig
**Prin:* Richard Schmidt
**Prin:* Michael Zebura
**Genl Mgr:* Mike Gniot

R B C
See ROLLER BEARING CO OF AMERICA INC

R B C CAPITAL MARKET
See RBC CAPITAL MARKETS CORP

D-U-N-S 04-708-1674 IMP/EXP
R B PAMPLIN CORP
805 Sw Brdwy Ste 2400, Portland, OR 97205
Tel (503) 248-1133 *Founded/Ownrshp* 1957
Sales 1.1MMM^E *EMP* 6,205
SIC 2211 2392 2361 2369 Broadwoven fabric mills, cotton; Gauze; Apparel & outerwear fabrics, cotton; Twills, drills, denims & other ribbed fabrics: cotton; Household furnishings; Blanket bags, plastic: made from purchased materials; Mattress pads; Napkins, fabric & nonwoven: made from purchased materials; Girls' & children's dresses, blouses & shirts; Girls' & children's outerwear
Ch Bd: Robert B Pamplin Jr
**Ex VP:* Marilyn Pamplin
**Sr VP:* Amy P North
**Sr VP:* Anne B Pamplin
**VP:* Marilyn Stewart
**VP:* Kathleen Tourijigian

R C B BANK
See RCB BANK SERVICE INC

R C I
See RESORT CONDOMINIUMS INTERNATIONAL LLC

R C O
See RCO ENGINEERING INC

R C WILLEY
See RC WILLEY HOME FURNISHINGS

D-U-N-S 03-881-8373
R CONSTRUCTION CO
1313 Hwy 79 S, Buffalo, TX 75831
Tel (903) 322-4639 *Founded/Ownrshp* 1977
Sales 101.2MM *EMP* 400
Accts Middleton Raines & Zapata Llp
SIC 1389 1794 Oil field services; Excavation & grading, building construction
Pr: Brody Maedgen
**CFO:* A David Williams
Exec: Joetta Price

R D C
See ROCHESTER DRUG CO-OPERATIVE INC

D-U-N-S 02-024-8001
R D MERRILL CO (WA)
1938 Frview Ave E Ste 300, Seattle, WA 98102
Tel (206) 676-5600 Founded/Ownrshp 1924, 1964
Sales 101.4MM^E EMP 2,500
SIC 6513 Retirement hotel operation
Ch Bd: Charles B Wright III
*Ch Bd: G Corydon Wagner Jr
*Pr: William D Pettit
*CFO: Doug Spear

D-U-N-S 15-724-9686
R D WING CO INC
517 6th St S, Kirkland, WA 98033-6717
Tel (425) 821-7222 Founded/Ownrshp 1995
Sales 102.4MM EMP 15
SIC 3299 Images, small: gypsum, clay or papier mache
Pr: Rick Wing
Opers Mgr: Brandon Wing

D-U-N-S 04-052-1601
R E GOODSPEED AND SONS DISTRIBUTING INC
GOODSPEED DISTRIBUTING
11211 G Ave, Hesperia, CA 92345-5134
Tel (760) 949-3356 Founded/Ownrshp 1980
Sales 83.7MM^E EMP 65
SIC 5171

R E I CO-OP
See RECREATIONAL EQUIPMENT INC

D-U-N-S 00-309-9207 IMP
R E MICHEL CO LLC (MD)
CROWN REFRIGERATION SUPPLY
1 Re Michel Dr, Glen Burnie, MD 21060-6408
Tel (410) 760-4000 Founded/Ownrshp 1935
Sales 756.4MM EMP 1,674
Accts Cliftonlarsonallen Llp Baltim
SIC 5075 5078 Warm air heating equipment & supplies; Air conditioning & ventilation equipment & supplies; Refrigeration equipment & supplies
Pr: John W H Michel
Treas: Ron Miller
*Ex VP: Ronald D Miller
Sr VP: Robert P Michel
VP: Glen Baker
VP: Mike Michel
VP: Holly Porter
VP: Gene Winters
Rgnl Mgr: Joseph Kuczynski
Rgnl Mgr: Randy Lane
Rgnl Mgr: Bryan Richardson

R E POWELL DISTRIBUTING
See POWELL - CHRISTENSEN INC

R F H
See ROBERT FAMILY HOLDINGS INC

D-U-N-S 00-920-7317
R F MACDONALD CO
25920 Eden Landing Rd, Hayward, CA 94545-3816
Tel (510) 784-0110 Founded/Ownrshp 1956
Sales 103.1MM^E EMP 160^E
SIC 5084 7699 5074 Pumps & pumping equipment; Industrial machinery & equipment repair; Boilers, power (industrial)
Co-Pr: Michael D Macdonald
*Pr: James T Macdonald
COO: Mike Ricci
VP: Don Patten
*VP: Chris Sentner
*VP: Robert Sygiel
Exec: Jim Swan
Mktg Mgr: Marcia Volpe

D-U-N-S 07-485-2765
R G A INC
1001 G St Nw Ste 700w, Washington, DC 20001-4549
Tel (202) 393-1999 Founded/Ownrshp 1962
Sales 113.3MM^E EMP 225
SIC 6552 7521 6531 Subdividers & developers; Automobile parking; Real estate agents & managers
Pr: Christopher Gladstone

D-U-N-S 12-260-5678
R G BRINKMANN CO
BRINKMAN CONSTRUCTORS
16650 Chstrfield Grove Rd, Chesterfield, MO 63005-1424
Tel (636) 537-9700 Founded/Ownrshp 1984
Sales 275.4MM EMP 84
Accts Larnear & Rapert Llc St L
SIC 1542 Commercial & office building, new construction; Commercial & office buildings, renovation & repair
CEO: Robert Brinkmann
*Pr: Brian Satterthwait
Treas: Gary Nelson
VP: Ted Hoog
*VP: Tom Oberle
Exec: Kevin Lasater

D-U-N-S 00-880-7778
R G REZIN INC
1602 Rezin Rd, Tomah, WI 54660-2678
Tel (608) 372-5956 Founded/Ownrshp 1957
Sales 83.4MM^E EMP 215
SIC 1623 3443 3613 3561 3523 3599 Sewer line construction; Water main construction; Fuel tanks (oil, gas, etc.): metal plate; Control panels, electric; Industrial pumps & parts; Harvesters, fruit, vegetable, tobacco, etc.; Machine shop, jobbing & repair
Pr: Patrick Rezin
*Treas: Michael Rezin
*VP: Margaret I Rezin

R H A
See RICHARD HEATH & ASSOCIATES INC

D-U-N-S 02-458-4310
R H BARRINGER DISTRIBUTING CO INC (NC)
AMERICAN PREMIUM BEVERAGE
1620 Fairfax Rd, Greensboro, NC 27407-4139
Tel (336) 854-0555 Founded/Ownrshp 1960, 1990
Sales 110.7MM^E EMP 209
SIC 5181 Beer & ale
CEO: Jasie Barringer
*Pr: Mark Craig
*Treas: Rick Craig
*VP: Bob Brown
*VP: Daniel Craig
*VP: Paul Powell

R H D
See RESOURCES FOR HUMAN DEVELOPMENT INC

D-U-N-S 04-023-4064
R H FOSTER ENERGY LLC
FAMILY FUEL
110 Mecaw Rd, Hampden, ME 04444-1945
Tel (207) 947-3835 Founded/Ownrshp 1999
Sales 91.2MM^E EMP 360
SIC 5172 5541 5411 5983 Gasoline; Lubricating oils & greases; Fuel oil; Diesel fuel; Filling stations, gasoline; Truck stops; Convenience stores, chain; Fuel oil dealers
*Ex VP: Robert Tracy
IT Man: Graham Morehead
Mktg Dir: Bruce Twombly

D-U-N-S 80-836-9586
R H G ACQUISITION CORP
(Suby of WILLIE'S ROADHOUSE GRILL, LLC)
4440 Pga Blvd Ste 201, Palm Beach Gardens, FL 33410-6540
Tel (561) 804-7676 Founded/Ownrshp 2007
Sales 46.1MM^E EMP 3,990^E
SIC 5812 Restaurant, family: chain; Steak restaurant

D-U-N-S 00-300-8521 IMP/EXP
R H SHEPPARD CO INC (PA)
101 Philadelphia St, Hanover, PA 17331-2038
Tel (717) 637-3751 Founded/Ownrshp 1937
Sales 183.2MM^E EMP 950
SIC 3714 3321 3594 Gears, motor vehicle; Gray iron castings; Ductile iron castings; Pumps, hydraulic power transfer
CEO: Peter H Sheppard
*Pr: Oliver Hoar
*CFO: Kevin Wegrzyn
*VP: John-Paul Lunn
CIO: Audrey Teselle
Dir IT: Michael Dutt
IT Man: Brow Mike
Sls Mgr: Andy Folmer
Board of Directors: William Heiser, Kathryn Hoar, Oliver Hoar, Terrence Hormel, Heather Lunn, Peter Sheppard, Thomas Sheppard

D-U-N-S 02-732-2403
R H SMITH DISTRIBUTING CO INC
SMITTY'S
315 E Wine Country Rd, Grandview, WA 98930-1044
Tel (509) 882-3377 Founded/Ownrshp 1947
Sales 95.1MM EMP 70
SIC 5171 5541 5411 5172 Petroleum bulk stations; Gasoline service stations; Convenience stores, chain; Petroleum products
Pr: Richard Smith
*Sec: Douglas M Smith
*VP: Rodney D Smith

D-U-N-S 80-988-3754
R H WHITE COMPANIES INC
41 Central St, Auburn, MA 01501-2304
Tel (508) 832-3295 Founded/Ownrshp 1923
Sales 191.1MM^E EMP 600^E
Accts Feeley & Driscoll Pc Bosto
SIC 1629 7359 1522 1521 Power plant construction; Equipment rental & leasing; Condominium construction; New construction, single-family houses; General remodeling, single-family houses
CEO: David H White
Ofcr: Richard Denham
*VP: Thomas H Descoteaux
*VP: Kenneth M Margossia
VP: Joseph D Marino
*VP: James E McCarthy
CIO: Dean Zuppio
Snr PM: Aaron Govoni

R I T
See ROCHESTER INSTITUTE OF TECHNOLOGY (INC)

D-U-N-S 16-136-5705
R J CORMAN RAILROAD GROUP LLC
1 Jay Station Rd, Nicholasville, KY 40356-9410
Tel (859) 881-7521 Founded/Ownrshp 1973
Sales 356.4MM^E EMP 1,200
SIC 4011 Railroads, line-haul operating
Pr: Craig King
*Pr: Richard J Corman
COO: Bruce Greinke
*Ch: Fred N Mudge
*VP: Ken Adams
*VP: Mike Hahn
*VP: Nathan Henderson
VP: Noel Rush
*VP: Tammie L Taylor
*VP: Michael Wester
Genl Mgr: Deborah Hawley

D-U-N-S 00-988-0279
R J PETERSON COMPANIES INC
32364 585th Ave, Cambridge, IA 50046-8569
Tel (515) 360-3337 Founded/Ownrshp 1995
Sales 108.0MM^E EMP 2
SIC 1521 New construction, single-family houses; General remodeling, single-family houses
Pr: Dean Peterson
*Sec: Judy Peterson

D-U-N-S 00-323-5926 IMP/EXP
■ **R J REYNOLDS TOBACCO CO** (NC)
(Suby of R J REYNOLDS TOBACCO HOLDINGS INC) ★
401 N Main St, Winston Salem, NC 27101-3804
Tel (336) 741-5000 Founded/Ownrshp 1875, 1999
Sales 67.4MM^E EMP 5,050
SIC 2131

D-U-N-S 04-834-1184 IMP/EXP
■ **R J REYNOLDS TOBACCO HOLDINGS INC** (DE)
(Suby of REYNOLDS AMERICAN INC) ★
401 N Main St, Winston Salem, NC 27101-3804
Tel (336) 741-5000 Founded/Ownrshp 1875, 1989
Sales 423.4MM EMP 5,050
SIC 2111 Cigarettes
Pr: Susan Ivey
CFO: Dianne M Neal
Treas: Daniel A Fauley
Ex VP: Ann A Johnston
Ex VP: Tommy J Payne
Sr VP: Daniel J Herko
Tech Mgr: Tim Welborn
Mktg Mgr: Talisa A Garcia
Sls Mgr: Stefani Lamb
Sls Mgr: Kyle Mirk
Sls Mgr: Juana Perez

D-U-N-S 02-584-3244 IMP/EXP
R J VAN DRUNEN & SONS INC (IL)
VAN DRUNEN FARMS
300 W 6th St, Momence, IL 60954-1136
Tel (815) 472-3100 Founded/Ownrshp 1880, 1958
Sales 101.5MM^E EMP 300
SIC 2034 2037 0161 2099 Dried & dehydrated vegetables; Frozen fruits & vegetables; Rooted vegetable farms; Seasonings & spices
Pr: Kevin Van Drunen
*Treas: Jeffrey Van Drunen

R. J. YOUNG COMPANY
See ROBERT J YOUNG CO INC

D-U-N-S 06-710-4364
R K ALLEN OIL CO INC
36002 Al Highway 21, Talladega, AL 35160-6833
Tel (256) 315-9825 Founded/Ownrshp 1972
Sales 139.6MM^E EMP 189
SIC 5172 Petroleum products; Gasoline; Lubricating oils & greases
Pr: R K Allen Sr
Treas: Peggy Allen
*VP: R K Allen Jr
*VP: William Keith Allen
Genl Mgr: Kris Johnson
Genl Mgr: Ginny Valentine

D-U-N-S 11-550-2106
■ **R K DIXON CO**
(Suby of GLOBAL IMAGING SYSTEMS INC) ★
5700 Utica Ridge Rd, Davenport, IA 52807-2943
Tel (563) 344-9100 Founded/Ownrshp 2012
Sales 103.4MM^E EMP 150
SIC 5044 7629 7359 Adding machines; Photocopy machines; Typewriters; Business machine repair, electric; Business machine & electronic equipment rental services
Pr: Bryan E Dixon
*CFO: Joel Slaby
*Sec: Jeffrey A Dixon
IT Man: Patrick Asher

D-U-N-S 19-061-0886
R K HALL CONSTRUCTION LTD
(Suby of RK HALL LLC) ★
2810 Nw Loop 286, Paris, TX 75460-1552
Tel (903) 785-8941 Founded/Ownrshp 2010
Sales 113.9MM^E EMP 400
SIC 1611 Highway & street construction
Pt: Robert K Hall
Exec: Susanne Waller

D-U-N-S 10-692-3949 EXP
R L C ENTERPRISES INC
TACO BELL
155 Revere Dr Ste 5, Northbrook, IL 60062-1558
Tel (847) 498-7888 Founded/Ownrshp 1983
Sales 38.8MM^E EMP 1,000
SIC 5812 Fast-food restaurant, chain
Pr: Iris M Cohn

D-U-N-S 05-047-7863
R L FORTNEY MANAGEMENT INC
FORTNEY & WEYGANDT
31269 Bradley Rd, North Olmsted, OH 44070-3875
Tel (440) 716-4000 Founded/Ownrshp 1978
Sales 89.1MM EMP 101
Accts Bober Markey Fedorovich & Co
SIC 1542 Nonresidential construction
Pr: Ruth Fortney
CFO: Freeh Greg

D-U-N-S 02-441-8808
R L JORDAN OIL CO OF NORTH CAROLINA INC (NC)
HOT SPOT
1451 Fernwood Glendale Rd, Spartanburg, SC 29307-3044
Tel (864) 585-2784 Founded/Ownrshp 1950, 1963
Sales 141.8MM^E EMP 900
Accts Scott Taylor White & Wingo S
SIC 5411 5172 5541 5812 Grocery stores; Petroleum products; Petroleum brokers; Gasoline service stations; Sandwiches & submarines shop
CEO: Wilton Jordan
*Ch Bd: Robert L Jordan
*Pr: Dan Durbin
*Pr: Carol Moeller
*Treas: J G Fields
*VP: Lynn Jordan

D-U-N-S 00-535-7835
R L POLK & CO
PUBLISHERS COLLECTION SERVICE
(Suby of IHS INC) ★
26933 Northwestern Hwy, Southfield, MI 48033-4703
Tel (248) 728-7000 Founded/Ownrshp 2013
Sales 143.0MM^E EMP 1,440
SIC 8742 Business consultant
Pr: Stephen Polk
COO: Joyce Miller
*Sr VP: Pat Barrett
*Sr VP: Michelle Goff
*Sr VP: Joe Lafeir
*Sr VP: Kendra Rawls
VP: Conrad N Barrett
VP: Jim Dimond
VP: Michelle Eissele
VP: Brad Korner
VP: Lori Lockhart
VP: Norman Marks
VP: Andrew Price
VP: Mark Western

D-U-N-S 01-912-9568
R L VALLEE INC
282 S Main St, Saint Albans, VT 05478-1866
Tel (802) 524-8710 Founded/Ownrshp 1992
Sales 181.9MM^E EMP 310
SIC 5172 5541 Filling stations, gasoline
Pr: Timothy L Vallee
*VP: Rodolphe M Vallee

R M F
See ROCKY MOUNTAIN FABRICATION INC

D-U-N-S 83-024-4344
R M L HUNTSVILLE CHEVROLET LLC
LANDERS MCLARTY CHEVROLET
4930 University Dr Nw, Huntsville, AL 35816-1804
Tel (256) 830-1600 Founded/Ownrshp 2009
Sales 82.0MM EMP 1,500
SIC 5511 Automobiles, new & used
Pr: Franklin McLarty
*Pr: Steve Landers
Sls Mgr: Brian Klie
Sales Asso: Thomas Ray

D-U-N-S 00-233-2666 IMP/EXP
R M PALMER CO (PA)
77 S 2nd Ave, Reading, PA 19611-1223
Tel (610) 372-8971 Founded/Ownrshp 1979
Sales 100.2MM^E EMP 550
SIC 2066 2064

D-U-N-S 05-038-2167
R M PARKS INC
PARKS PETROLEUM PRODUCTS
1061 N Main St, Porterville, CA 93257-1686
Tel (559) 784-2384 Founded/Ownrshp 1969
Sales 534.1MM EMP 4
Accts Gumbiner Savett Inc Santa Mo
SIC 5171 Petroleum bulk stations
Pr: R M Parks
*Sec: Marilyn Callison
*VP: Tim Callison
IT Man: Richard Tipton

D-U-N-S 01-609-9442 IMP
R M ROACH & SONS INC
ROCS
333 E John St, Martinsburg, WV 25401-4218
Tel (304) 263-3329 Founded/Ownrshp 1959
Sales 92.3MM^E EMP 190
SIC 5541 5172 Filling stations, gasoline; Petroleum products
Pr: D Scott Roach
*Sec: Stanley Corwin-Roach
*VP: Steven M Roach

D-U-N-S 02-586-1436
R P LUMBER CO INC (IL)
DO IT BEST
514 E Vandalia St, Edwardsville, IL 62025-1855
Tel (618) 656-1514 Founded/Ownrshp 1977
Sales 162.3MM EMP 500
Accts Rubinbrown Llp Cpas Saint Lo
SIC 5211 5251 Millwork & lumber; Builders' hardware
Pr: Robert L Plummer
*Treas: Bruce Riedle
*VP: Donna Sue Plummer
*VP: Jayson Plummer
Store Mgr: Danny Dyer
Store Mgr: Chuck Murphy
Store Mgr: Chad Watts
IT Man: Andrew Dean

R R B
See RAILROAD RETIREMENT BOARD UNITED STATES

R R DONNELLEY
See BANTA CORP

R R DONNELLEY
See RR DONNELLEY PRINTING CO LP

D-U-N-S 04-242-6874
R ROESE CONTRACTING CO INC
2674 S Huron Rd, Kawkawlin, MI 48631-9196
Tel (989) 684-5121 Founded/Ownrshp 1956
Sales 95.0MM^E EMP 150
SIC 1623 Telephone & communication line construction; Sewer line construction; Water main construction
Pr: Richard F Roese
*CFO: Edward Hare
*Treas: David Kolanec
Sfty Mgr: Jim Herber

R S D
See REFRIGERATION SUPPLIES DISTRIBUTOR

D-U-N-S 61-283-3012 IMP
R SISKIND & CO INC
1385 Broadway Fl 24, New York, NY 10018-6009
Tel (212) 840-0880 Founded/Ownrshp 1990
Sales 127.6MM^E EMP 100
SIC 5137 5136 Women's & children's clothing; Men's & boys' clothing
CEO: Richard Siskind
*Pr: Jon Siskind

D-U-N-S 78-292-9327
R SYSTEMS INC
(Suby of R SYSTEMS INTERNATIONAL LIMITED)
5000 Windplay Dr Ste 5, El Dorado Hills, CA 95762-9319
Tel (916) 939-9696 Founded/Ownrshp 1991
Sales 89.1MM^E EMP 350
Accts Crowe Horwath Llp Sacramento
SIC 7379 7373 7374 Computer related consulting services; Systems software development services; Data processing & preparation
CEO: Satinder S Rekhi

*Pr: Lt Gen Baldev Singh
*COO: Ralph Kenney
COO: Adheesh Prabhavalkar
*COO: Raj Swaminathan
Ex VP: Kamal Dwivedi
Ex VP: Sanjay Khurana
VP: Ashok Bhatia
VP: Mukesh Bindal
VP: Rajesh Rathi
*VP: Harpreet Rekhi
VP: Supriyo Sanyal
Exec: Abhijit Kharat
Exec: David Sanchez
Exec: Udayen Sharma
Exec: Abhishek Singh
Exec: Aditya Tandon

R T A
See REGIONAL TRANSPORTATION AUTHORITY

R T A
See GREATER CLEVELAND REGIONAL TRANSIT AUTHORITY

R T I INTERNATIONAL
See RESEARCH TRIANGLE INSTITUTE INC

D-U-N-S 00-699-1871 IMP/EXP
R T VANDERBILT CO INC
(Suby of RT VANDERBILT HOLDING CO INC) ★
30 Winfield St, Norwalk, CT 06855-1329
Tel (203) 853-1400 Founded/Ownrshp 1961
Sales 239.0MM[E] EMP 415
Accts Deloitte & Touche Llp Stanfo
SIC 5169 2869 2819 5052 1499 1459 Chemicals, industrial & heavy; Laboratory chemicals, organic; Industrial inorganic chemicals; Chemicals, reagent grade: refined from technical grade; Nonmetallic minerals & concentrate; Talc mining; Pyrophyllite mining; Clays (common) quarrying
Ch Bd: Hugh B Vanderbilt Jr
*Pr: Roger K Price
Pr: Douglas Webster
*Ex VP: Joseph Denaro
Ex VP: R L Vonneham
VP: Paul V Derbilt
*VP: Linda S Dvornek
VP: Linda Dvornek
*VP: A S Flores
*VP: Hugh T Gartland
VP: J Hattendorf
VP: John D Hattenorf
*VP: Randall L Johnson
*VP: Kenneth H Kelly
*VP: Paul Vanderbilt
Exec: Janet Kirwan
Dir Risk M: John Kelfe
Dir Risk M: Mark Mayes

D-U-N-S 88-371-9783
R U CORP
RESTAURANTS UNLIMITED
411 1st Ave S Ste 200n, Seattle, WA 98104-3831
Tel (206) 634-0550 Founded/Ownrshp 1979
Sales 32.5MM[E] EMP 2,500
SIC 5812 5813 5461 American restaurant; Cocktail lounge; Bakeries
Pr: Steve Stodbard
*Pr: Richard B Komen
COO: Attila Szabo
*CFO: Robert Nowlin
VP: Adrienne Gemperle
VP: Kathryn Murphy
*VP: James Welch
Genl Mgr: Kristin Irwin

R U S D
See RACINE UNIFIED SCHOOL DISTRICT

R V A
See DEPT OF REVENUE ARIZONA

D-U-N-S 03-288-5493
R V MCCLAINS INC
MCCLAIN'S RV SUPERSTORES
5601 S I 35 E, Denton, TX 76210-2319
Tel (940) 498-4398 Founded/Ownrshp 1963
Sales 85.8MM[E] EMP 401
SIC 5561 7538

R V PRODUCTS DIV
See AIRXCEL INC

D-U-N-S 00-302-8503
R W SAUDER INC (PA)
AMISH COUNTRY EGGS
570 Furnace Hills Pike, Lititz, PA 17543-7655
Tel (717) 626-2074 Founded/Ownrshp 1940, 1994
Sales 180.0MM EMP 400
SIC 5144 Eggs
Pr: Paul Sauder
*CFO: James Maurer
*VP: Mark Sauder
Opers Mgr: Jeff Zerbe

D-U-N-S 00-283-5296 IMP
R W SIDLEY INC
436 Casement Ave, Painesville, OH 44077-3817
Tel (440) 352-9343 Founded/Ownrshp 1933
Sales 151.4MM[E] EMP 600
SIC 1771 3299 Concrete work; Blocks & brick, sand lime
Ch Bd: Robert C Sidley
*Pr: Robert J Buescher
*CFO: Kevin Campany
*VP: Dan Kennedy
Exec: Brad Biro
*Prin: Iola Black
*Prin: R H Bostick
*Prin: S S Bostwick

D-U-N-S 02-913-7395 IMP
R W SMITH & CO
TRIMARK RW SMITH
(Suby of TRIMARK UNITED EAST) ★
8555 Miralani Dr, San Diego, CA 92126-4352
Tel (858) 530-1800 Founded/Ownrshp 2016
Sales 101.8MM EMP 215
SIC 5023

D-U-N-S 02-863-2677 IMP
R W ZANT CO (CA)
1470 E 4th St, Los Angeles, CA 90033-4288
Tel (323) 980-5457 Founded/Ownrshp 1950
Sales 301.0MM EMP 140
SIC 5147 5146 5144 4222 Meats & meat products; Fish & seafoods; Poultry & poultry products; Cheese warehouse
Pr: Robert W Zant
*Prin: William Zant
Dir IT: Ibrahim El-Helou

R&D SYSTEMS
See RESEARCH AND DIAGNOSTIC SYSTEMS INC

D-U-N-S 03-445-2425
R&H CONSTRUCTION CO
OREGON R&H CONSTRUCTION
1530 Sw Taylor St, Portland, OR 97205-1819
Tel (503) 228-7177 Founded/Ownrshp 1980
Sales 100.0MM EMP 170
SIC 1542 1522 Commercial & office building, new construction; Commercial & office buildings, renovation & repair; Multi-family dwelling construction
CEO: John W Bradley
*Pr: John C Ward
Top Exec: Brian Crosby
*VP: Norm Dowty
*VP: Steve Galash
*VP: Evelyn Galloni
*VP: Dave Gunsul
*VP: Gary North
Exec: Eric Hammond
Exec: Mike Kremers
Exec: Cheryl M McElroy

D-U-N-S 15-408-7977
R&L FOODS INC
TACO BELL
7550 W Interstate 10 # 508, San Antonio, TX 78229-5813
Tel (210) 433-3371 Founded/Ownrshp 1983
Sales 46.2MM[E] EMP 1,800
SIC 5812 Fast-food restaurant, chain
Pr: Richard Breakie
*VP: Lana Breakie

R&M ENERGY SYSTEMS
See ROBBIN & MEYERS ENERGY SYSTEMS LP

D-U-N-S 01-356-7606
R&R ENTERPRISES INC
1101 King St Ste 550, Alexandria, VA 22314-2955
Tel (703) 739-0084 Founded/Ownrshp 2007
Sales 97.5MM EMP 350[E]
Accts Bdo Usa Llp Mclean Virginia
SIC 8711 Aviation &/or aeronautical engineering
CEO: Darrell L Crapps
*CFO: Allan Shure
*Ch: Russell T Wright

D-U-N-S 09-641-8868 IMP
R-RANCH MARKET INC
13985 Live Oak Ave, Irwindale, CA 91706-1332
Tel (626) 814-2900 Founded/Ownrshp 1978
Sales 114.8MM[E] EMP 900
SIC 5411

D-U-N-S 62-199-3559
R/C THEATRES MANAGEMENT CORP
231 W Cherry Hill Ct, Reisterstown, MD 21136-6203
Tel (410) 526-4774 Founded/Ownrshp 1932
Sales 36.3MM[E] EMP 1,000
SIC 8741 7922 7832 Circuit management for motion picture theaters; Legitimate live theater producers; Motion picture theaters, except drive-in
Pr: Scott R Cohen
*Sec: Rich Hershel
Genl Mgr: Frankel Tejada
Off Mgr: Robin Hall

D-U-N-S 08-306-3248
■ **R/GA MEDIA GROUP INC**
INTERPUBLIC GROUP OF COMPANIES
(Suby of INTERPUBLIC GROUP OF COMPANIES INC) ★
450 W 33rd St Fl 12, New York, NY 10001-2610
Tel (212) 946-4000 Founded/Ownrshp 1995
Sales 153.9MM[E] EMP 795
SIC 7374 7336 7375 7311 Computer graphics service; Commercial art & graphic design; Information retrieval services; Advertising agencies
Pr: Robert Greenberg
*COO: Stephen Plumlee
*CFO: Michael Kaczmarski
Ofcr: John Antinori
Ofcr: Nick Law
*Ofcr: Barry Wacksman
Ex VP: Anne Benvenuto
Ex VP: Chris Colborn
Ex VP: Kris Kiger
Ex VP: Seth Solomons
Ex VP: Richard Ting
Ex VP: Joseph Tomasulo
*Ex VP: Dawn Winchester
Sr VP: Robyn Tombacher
VP: David Boehm
VP: Alex Morrison
Dir: Jessica Greenwood
Dir: Pete Talaba
Creative D: Chapin Clark
Creative D: Jonathan Lewis

D-U-N-S 00-610-6371 IMP
RA JONES & CO (GA)
(Suby of COESIA SPA)
2701 Crescent Springs Rd, Covington, KY 41017-1591
Tel (859) 341-0400 Founded/Ownrshp 1905, 2012
Sales 151.2MM[E] EMP 500
SIC 3565 3823 Bag opening, filling & closing machines; Analyzers, industrial process type
CEO: John Lee
*Sec: Thorsten Koch
IT Man: Dick Martin
Tech Mgr: Matt Lukes
QI Cn Mgr: Brian Steele

RA RESTAURANT GROUP DIV
See RESTAURANT ASSOCIATES CORP

D-U-N-S 06-829-0105
RAAM GLOBAL ENERGY CO
3838 N Causeway Blvd # 2800, Metairie, LA 70002-8319
Tel (859) 253-1300 Founded/Ownrshp 2003
Sales 143.1MM EMP 69
Accts Ernst & Young Llp Louisville
SIC 1311 Crude petroleum & natural gas
Ch Bd: Howard A Settle
COO: Kenneth Young
CFO: Jeffrey Craycraft
*Sr VP: Michael J Willis
VP: Elizabeth A Barr
*VP: Thomas M Lewry

D-U-N-S 01-018-0717 IMP/EXP
RAB FOOD GROUP
(Suby of B MANISCHEWITZ CO) ★
80 Avenue K, Newark, NJ 07105-3803
Tel (201) 553-1100 Founded/Ownrshp 1997
Sales 2.0MM[E] EMP 2,198[E]
SIC 5411 Grocery stores

D-U-N-S 06-117-4181
RABA KISTNER INC
12821 W Golden Ln, San Antonio, TX 78249-2298
Tel (210) 699-9090 Founded/Ownrshp 1968
Sales 90.1MM[E] EMP 324
SIC 8711 Consulting engineer; Building construction consultant
Ch Bd: Carl F Raba Jr
Pr: William L Raba
*COO: Robert Costigan
*V Ch Bd: Richard W Kistner
*Ex VP: Paul R Lampe
Sr VP: Bryan Helbert
Sr VP: Robert Wilson
*VP: Bryan C Helbert
VP: Koch Kenneth J
*VP: Steven E Jones
VP: Berna Olague
VP: Preston S Parker
*VP: Gary Raba
*VP: Chris L Schultz
VP: Martin Vila
VP: Mark Wells
Exec: Deborah Cusson

RABEN TIRE & AUTO SERVICE
See RABEN TIRE CO LLC

D-U-N-S 00-700-2421 IMP/EXP
RABEN TIRE CO LLC (IN)
RABEN TIRE & AUTO SERVICE
2100 N New York Ave, Evansville, IN 47711-3910
Tel (812) 465-5565 Founded/Ownrshp 1952
Sales 217.0MM[E] EMP 407
SIC 5531 5014 Automotive tires; Automotive accessories; Automobile tires & tubes; Truck tires & tubes; Motorcycle tires & tubes
Pr: Thomas M Raben
VP: Barry Harms
*VP: Larry Raben
Genl Mgr: Corey Wood
IT Man: Wayne Luigs
Site Mgr: Joe Hoffman
Site Mgr: Lee Smith
Plnt Mgr: Christopher Darby

D-U-N-S 10-383-2390
RABOBANK NATIONAL ASSOCIATION
RABOBANK NORTH AMERICA
(Suby of RABOBANK INTERNATIONAL HOLDING B.V.)
915 Highland Pointe Dr, Roseville, CA 95678-5419
Tel (760) 352-5000 Founded/Ownrshp 2013
Sales NA EMP 1,700
SIC 6022 State commercial banks
CEO: Ronald Blok
Pr: Michael Black
Pr: Donald Toussaint
Pr: Kathleen Waxman
COO: Daniel C Stevens
CFO: Charles Caswell
CFO: Tom Tolda
Co-Pr: Rick Arredondo
Co-Pr: James W Lokey
Ofcr: Aitor Ezcurra
Ofcr: Jessica Wheeler
Trst Ofcr: Kandy No L
Ex VP: Jack Brittain Jr
Ex VP: Chris Nelson
Ex VP: Martin Plourd
Sr VP: Janice Stewart
VP: Robert Galvan
VP: Pmp Groves
VP: Tonya Hamlin
VP: Jeffrey Hester
VP: Ben Mackin
Board of Directors: Carrol Pruett

RABOBANK NEDERLAND
See UTRECHT - AMERICA HOLDINGS INC

RABOBANK NORTH AMERICA
See RABOBANK NATIONAL ASSOCIATION

RAC
See RENT-A-CENTER FRANCHISING INTERNATIONAL INC

D-U-N-S 06-369-1299 IMP
RACETRAC PETROLEUM INC
3225 Cumberland Blvd Se # 100, Atlanta, GA 30339-6407
Tel (770) 850-3491 Founded/Ownrshp 1971
Sales 7.5MMM EMP 3,479
Accts Grant Thornton Llp Atlanta G
SIC 5541 5411 5172 Filling stations, gasoline; Convenience stores, chain; Petroleum products; Gasoline; Diesel fuel; Service station supplies, petroleum
Ch Bd: Carl E Bolch Jr
Pr: Shirley Eggers
*Pr: Max Lenker
COO: Billy Milam
*CFO: Robert J Dumbacher
CFO: Kimberly Turner
Treas: Karla Ahlert
VP: Will Alexander
VP: Phillip P Gura
VP: Bill Milam
VP: George Mrvos
VP: Norm Ritchie

D-U-N-S 08-050-7932
RACINE UNIFIED SCHOOL DISTRICT
R U S D
3109 Mount Pleasant St, Racine, WI 53404-1511
Tel (262) 635-5600 Founded/Ownrshp 1961
Sales 179.2MM[E] EMP 2,500[E]
SIC 8211 Elementary & secondary schools
*CFO: Dave Hazen
CFO: David Hazen
Bd of Dir: Julie McKenna
Pr Dir: Stacy Tapp
Teacher Pr: Julie Landry
Snr Mgr: Dan Thielen

D-U-N-S 61-479-4290
RACING ASSOCIATION OF CENTRAL
1 Prairie Meadows Dr, Altoona, IA 50009-2100
Tel (515) 967-1000 Founded/Ownrshp 2006
Sales 2.1MMM EMP 2
SIC 8611 Merchants' association
Prin: Jack Bishop

D-U-N-S 06-631-7058 IMP
RACK ROOM SHOES INC
(Suby of DEICHMANN SE)
8310 Technology Dr, Charlotte, NC 28262-0301
Tel (704) 547-9200 Founded/Ownrshp 1984
Sales 640.8MM[E] EMP 4,200
SIC 5661 Shoe stores
Pr: Mark Larde
*Treas: Ernie Shore
VP: Harvey Borden
*VP: Ricky Brown
VP: Dale Patterson
Dir Risk M: Adrian Munzell
Admn Mgr: Dane Mutter
Brnch Mgr: Kevin Hill
Dir IT: Bill Mullins
Mktg Mgr: Martina Corpening
Sls Mgr: Brenda Dixon

D-U-N-S 00-850-3476
RACKS INC
EXHIBIDORES UNIVERSALES
7565 Siempre Viva Rd, San Diego, CA 92154-7429
Tel (619) 661-0987 Founded/Ownrshp 1938
Sales 84.6MM[E] EMP 450
SIC 2542 3993 2541 Racks, merchandise display or storage: except wood; Signs & advertising specialties; Display fixtures, wood
CEO: Douglas E Wall
*Pr: Don D Wall
*Pr: R D Wall
IT Man: Jorge Hernandez
Natl Sales: David Whetnall

D-U-N-S 82-920-7120
RACKSPACE HOSTING INC
(Suby of INCEPTION PARENT INC) ★
1 Fanatical Pl, San Antonio, TX 78218-2179
Tel (210) 312-4000 Founded/Ownrshp 2016
Sales 2.0MMM EMP 6,189[E]
SIC 7371 7374 7382 4813 Custom computer programming services; Data processing & preparation; Security systems services;
Pr: Taylor Rhodes
COO: Mark Roenigk
CFO: Karl Pichler
Chf Mktg O: Carla Pieyro Sublett
Ex VP: Alex Pinchev
Sr VP: Scott Crenshaw
Sr VP: Mark W Roenigk
VP: Van Lindberg
VP: Wayne Roberts
VP Bus Dev: Mark Collier
Dir Sec: Brian Kelly

D-U-N-S 08-273-3192 IMP
RACKSPACE US INC
MAILTRUST
(Suby of RACKSPACE HOSTING INC) ★
1 Fanatical Pl, San Antonio, TX 78218-2179
Tel (210) 312-4000 Founded/Ownrshp 1998
Sales 777.2MM[E] EMP 1,661
SIC 4813
CEO: Taylor Rhodes
Pr: Paul Froutan
Pr: Robert Hsu
Pr: Kevin Minnick
CEO: Lanham Napier
*COO: Mark Roenigk
*CFO: Karl Pichler
*Treas: Chris Rosas
Chf Mktg O: Rick Jackson
VP: David Bryce
VP: Paul Carmody
VP: Thomas Hatton
VP: Kim Kasee
VP: Debbie Talley
Board of Directors: William Alberts, Morris A Miller, Fred Reichheld, Taylor Rhodes, Graham Weston, Richard Yoo

D-U-N-S 10-208-5032
RACON INC
700 Energy Center Blvd # 404, Northport, AL 35473-2793
Tel (205) 333-8500 Founded/Ownrshp 1981
Sales 113.3MM[E] EMP 450
SIC 1611 1522 General contractor, highway & street construction; Residential construction
CEO: Ramona M Andrews
*Pr: Keith Andrews
*CFO: Chet S Cowsar
*VP: Benton Andrews
*VP: John Hanley

D-U-N-S 08-639-1600
RAD POWER BIKES LLC
2622 Nw Market St Ste B, Seattle, WA 98107-4106
Tel (800) 939-0310 Founded/Ownrshp 2015
Sales 120.0MM EMP 5
SIC 5941 Sporting goods & bicycle shops

D-U-N-S 12-403-1332
RADFORD UNIVERSITY
(*Suby of* STATE COUNCIL OF HIGHER EDUCATION FOR VIRGINIA) ★
801 E Main St, Radford, VA 24142-0002
Tel (540) 831-5000 *Founded/Ownrshp* 1989
Sales 143.5MM[E] *EMP* 1,298
SIC 8221 Colleges universities & professional schools
Pr: Brian Stanley
CFO: Richard Alvarez
VP: Deborah Brown
VP: Katherine McCarthy
VP: Regis McKoy
VP: Norleen Pomerantz
VP: Melissa E Wohlstein
VP: Charles Wood
Exec: Elizabeth Jamison
Ex Dir: Ray Kirby
Ex Dir: Steve Lenhart

D-U-N-S 06-736-1956 IMP
RADIAC ABRASIVES INC
NATIONAL GRINDING WHEEL
(*Suby of* TYROLIT - SCHLEIFMITTELWERKE SWAROVSKI K.G.)
1015 S College St, Salem, IL 62881-2499
Tel (618) 548-4200 *Founded/Ownrshp* 1973
Sales 138.6MM[E] *EMP* 450
SIC 3291 Grindstones, artificial; Wheels, abrasive
CFO: Kerry Christofanelli
Exec: Joyce Carpenter
Sales Exec: Liz Mott
Mktg Mgr: Martin Perez
Manager: Mark Falck
Sls Mgr: Jay Miller
Sls Mgr: Bill Riska
Sls Mgr: Charlie Shue

D-U-N-S 08-339-5447 IMP
RADIAL INC
935 1st Ave, King of Prussia, PA 19406-1342
Tel (610) 491-7000 *Founded/Ownrshp* 1999
Sales 647.5MM[E] *EMP* 1,286
SIC 3149 5139 5091 5136 5137 7375 Athletic shoes, except rubber or plastic; Footwear; Athletic goods; Sportswear, men's & boys'; Sportswear, women's & children's; Information retrieval services
Pr: Tobias Hartmann
Pr: Craig Hayman
Pr: Michael Rubin
COO: Mark Reese
CFO: Seth Feldman
Sr VP: Michael Shelton
VP: Robert W Liewald
VP: Darrell Starnes
VP: Quinton Stemler
Prgrm Mgr: Sean Seraphin
CTO: Brent Peters

D-U-N-S 12-094-3535
RADIAL SOUTH LP
(*Suby of* BLUE EAGLE HOLDINGS LP) ★
6465 E Johns Xing, Johns Creek, GA 30097-1580
Tel (678) 584-4000 *Founded/Ownrshp* 2014
Sales 283.2MM[E] *EMP* 1,450[E]
SIC 7389 7374 8742 Telephone services; Telemarketing services; Data processing & preparation; Marketing consulting services
CEO: Ramesh Srinivasan
**COO:* Robert J Toner
**CFO:* Stephen G Keaveney
**Sr VP:* Larry C Hanger
**Sr VP:* Edgar L Ringer
VP: Brent Dorfman
**Dir Surg:* Christine A Herren
Dir IT: John Cummings
Opers Mgr: Edgar Garcia
Opers Mgr: Robert Guyer
Opers Mgr: Ben Holt
Board of Directors: Scott Dorfman

D-U-N-S 60-765-2393 IMP
RADIALL USA INC
(*Suby of* RADIALL)
8950 S 52nd St Ste 401, Tempe, AZ 85284-1045
Tel (480) 682-9400 *Founded/Ownrshp* 1998
Sales 128.3MM[E] *EMP* 887
SIC 3643 Connectors & terminals for electrical devices
Ch Bd: Dominique Buttin
**Pr:* Maite Tristan
Ex VP: Patrick Le Normand
Sr VP: Guy Clairet
Rgnl Mgr: Arpad Takacs
Genl Mgr: Justin Garrard
**Genl Mgr:* Patrice Rigoland
Plng Mgr: Roy Jaoude
Manager: Ed Lamacchia
Sales Asso: Travis Bonewell
Sales Asso: Cindy Gardner

D-U-N-S 17-375-6032
RADIAN ASSET ASSURANCE INC
(*Suby of* ASSURED GUARANTY CORP) ★
1601 Market St Fl 5, Philadelphia, PA 19103-2323
Tel (212) 983-3100 *Founded/Ownrshp* 2015
Sales NA *EMP* 145[E]
SIC 6351 Reciprocal interinsurance exchanges: surety, fidelity
Pr: Martin Kamarck
Ex VP: Rick Altman
Sr VP: John Deluca
Sr VP: Cathy Jackson
Sr VP: Jack Praschnik
Sr VP: Irene Vitti
VP: Joe Gage
Snr Mgr: Christine Lostracco

D-U-N-S 79-611-7851
▲ RADIAN GROUP INC
1601 Market St Fl 12, Philadelphia, PA 19103-2303
Tel (215) 231-1000 *Founded/Ownrshp* 1977
Sales NA *EMP* 1,881
Tkr Sym RDN *Exch* NYS
SIC 6351 Mortgage guarantee insurance
CEO: Sanford A Ibrahim
**Ch Bd:* Herbert Wender
Pr: Teresa Bryce Bazemore
Pr: Abigail Rodriguez
Pr: Jeff Tennyson
CFO: J Franklin Hall
Ofcr: Derek V Brummer
Ofcr: Anthony Bruschi
Ex VP: Franklin Hall
Ex VP: Edward J Hoffman
Ex VP: Richard I Altman
Sr VP: Peter Danna
Sr VP: Catherine M Jackson
VP: John A Castiello
VP: Christopher Curran
VP: Glenn Davis
VP: Zoe Devaney
VP: Lisa Dickson
VP: Michael Dziuba
VP: Catherine Jackson
VP: John Morozin
Board of Directors: David C Carney, Howard B Culang, Lisa W Hess, Stephen T Hopkins, Brian D Montgomery, Gaetano Muzio, Gregory V Serio, Noel J Spiegel

D-U-N-S 08-709-6350
■ RADIAN GUARANTY INC
(*Suby of* RADIAN GROUP INC) ★
1601 Market St Fl 5, Philadelphia, PA 19103-2494
Tel (215) 564-6600 *Founded/Ownrshp* 1992
Sales NA *EMP* 600[E]
SIC 6351 Mortgage guarantee insurance
CEO: S A Ibrahim
Pr: Teresa Bryce Bazemore
Pr: Joe Charlebois
Pr: Elizabeth Emmons
Pr: Christine Harney
COO: Jeff Cashmer
COO: Robert Griffith
CFO: C Robert Quint
CFO: Richard I Altman
Ofcr: Phillip Bracken
Ofcr: Mackenzie Jack
Ex VP: Paul F Fisher
Sr VP: Tim Hunter
Sr VP: Andrew T Rippert
Sr VP: Douglas S Robach
VP: Glenda Boan
VP: Deborah Conroy
VP: Scott Crews
VP: Kathleen T Egan
VP: Oscar Gunther
VP: Natasha I Campbell

D-U-N-S 03-199-4218
RADIANCE TECHNOLOGIES INC
350 Wynn Dr Nw, Huntsville, AL 35805-1961
Tel (256) 704-3400 *Founded/Ownrshp* 1998
Sales 116.7MM *EMP* 550
Accts Beason & Nalley Inc Huntsvi
SIC 3721 8711 3429 3812 Research & development on aircraft by the manufacturer; Engineering services; Manufactured hardware (general); Defense systems & equipment; Warfare counter-measure equipment
Pr: William Bailey
**CFO:* Scott Dublin
**Sr VP:* Victor Balch
Prgrm Mgr: Dan Jones
Prgrm Mgr: Karen White
Snr Sftwr: Robert Case
VP Opers: Bradley Beazer

D-U-N-S 04-460-0976 IMP/EXP
RADIANS INC
5305 Distriplex Farms Dr, Memphis, TN 38141-8231
Tel (901) 388-7776 *Founded/Ownrshp* 1996
Sales 121.3MM *EMP* 175
SIC 5085 Industrial supplies
CEO: Mike Tutor
**Pr:* Bill England
**CFO:* Ruth Tutor
VP: Craig Baker
VP: Art Kunkle
VP: Shannon Owens
Genl Mgr: Sebrina Sneller
Manager: Cindy Davey
Manager: Kevin Kairys
Sls Mgr: Leo Hill
Sls Mgr: Todd Menefee

RADIANT FOOD STORES
See RADIANT GROUP LLC

D-U-N-S 03-279-6906
RADIANT GROUP LLC
RADIANT FOOD STORES
1320 E 9th Ave Ste 211, Tampa, FL 33605-3602
Tel (813) 247-4731 *Founded/Ownrshp* 1999
Sales 232.7MM[E] *EMP* 250
SIC 5171 5411 Petroleum bulk stations; Convenience stores
CFO: John Nertney
Ex VP: Randy Rehovich
Board of Directors: Frank Capitano

D-U-N-S 18-467-5994
▲ RADIANT LOGISTICS INC
405 114th Ave Se Fl 3, Bellevue, WA 98004-6475
Tel (425) 943-4599 *Founded/Ownrshp* 2001
Sales 782.5MM *EMP* 760
Tkr Sym RLGT *Exch* ASE
SIC 4731 Freight transportation arrangement
Ch Bd: Bohn H Crain
COO: Tim Boyce
CFO: Todd E Macomber
Ofcr: Arnie Goldstein
Sr VP: Peter Jamieson
VP: Bryan Tierce
IT Man: John Klesch
Opers Mgr: Ruben Cantu
Sls Mgr: Manuel Mascorro
Board of Directors: Jack Edwards, Michael Gould, Stephen P Harrington, Richard P Palmieri

D-U-N-S 17-724-2435 IMP/EXP
■ RADIANT SYSTEMS INC
(*Suby of* NCR CORP) ★
3925 Brookside Pkwy, Alpharetta, GA 30022-4429
Tel (877) 794-7237 *Founded/Ownrshp* 2011
Sales 209.0MM[E] *EMP* 1,310
SIC 5734 7373 Computer & software stores; Computer peripheral equipment; Computer software & accessories; Modems, monitors, terminals & disk drives: computers; Systems integration services
CEO: John Bruno
**Pr:* Carlyle Taylor
**COO:* Andrew S Heyman
**CFO:* Robert Fishman
**CFO:* Mark E Haidet
Ex VP: Ivan Figueroa
VP: Chuck Dunn
VP: David Griffiin
VP: Lyn Ivester
Exec: Liz Daitch
Exec: Jimmy Frangis
Exec: Chad Strange
Exec: Jason Thompson
Exec: John Young
Dir Bus: Steve Paris

D-U-N-S 11-271-4337 IMP
RADIANZ AMERICAS INC
BT RADIANZ
(*Suby of* RADIANZ LIMITED)
620 8th Ave Fl 46, New York, NY 10018-1768
Tel (212) 205-1800 *Founded/Ownrshp* 2000
Sales 177.6MM[E] *EMP* 1,000[E]
SIC 4813
Ch Bd: Marc Carletti
**Pr:* P Howard Edelstein
**CFO:* Philip Emery
Genl Mgr: Kirsten English
CIO: Carley Brendan
CTO: Brennan Carley
MIS Dir: Michael Glickman
Netwrk Eng: Jason Goh
Sales Exec: Chris Hanley
Board of Directors: Howard Ford, David Grigson, Jacques Kerrest, Mike Sayers, David Ure

RADIATION ONCOLOGY ASSOC PA
See JEROME GROUP INC

D-U-N-S 78-558-8054
■ RADIATION SYSTEMS PRECISION CONTROLS INC
RSI PRECISION CONTROLS
(*Suby of* GENERAL DYNAMICS SATCOM TECHNOLOGIES INC) ★
1219 Digital Dr Ste 101, Richardson, TX 75081-1975
Tel (972) 907-9599 *Founded/Ownrshp* 1992
Sales 30.0MM *EMP* 1,500
SIC 3663

RADIATION THERAPY
See TODD HLAVATY MD

RADIATION THERAPY
See HIGH POINT REGIONAL HEALTH

RADIATION THERAPY AT QUEENS ME
See SUASIN CANCER CARE INC

RADIATION THERAPY CENTER
See UNITED HOSPITAL INC

D-U-N-S 00-314-9663 IMP
RADIATOR SPECIALTY CO INC
GUNK
600 Radiator Rd, Indian Trail, NC 28079-5225
Tel (704) 688-2302 *Founded/Ownrshp* 1923
Sales 83.2MM[E] *EMP* 257
SIC 2899 Chemical preparations
Ch: Alan Blumenthal
Pr: John Huber
Ofcr: Peggy Gartner
Ex VP: Rick Johnson
Ex VP: Mark Miller
VP: David Goodson
VP: Mike Guggenheimer
VP: Wally Jones
VP: Ronald Weiner
Opers Mgr: David Alexovich
Plnt Mgr: Jim Shor

RADIO FREE EUROPE
See RFE/RL INC

D-U-N-S 17-536-2508 IMP
RADIO FREQUENCY SYSTEMS INC
RFS
(*Suby of* ALCATEL-LUCENT HOLDINGS INC) ★
200 Pond View Dr, Meriden, CT 06450-7195
Tel (203) 630-3311 *Founded/Ownrshp* 1979
Sales 210.0MM[E] *EMP* 550
SIC 3663 3661 5045 5065 Antennas, transmitting & communications; Microwave communication equipment; Telephone & telegraph apparatus; Telephones & telephone apparatus; Computers, peripherals & software; Electronic parts & equipment; Communication equipment
Pr: Kenneth Farell
**Pr:* Raymond Terry III
Pr: Jing Wang
COO: John Gu
CFO: Chris Markelon
Ofcr: Amie Briggs
**Ex VP:* William L Perocchi
VP: Jack Lee
**VP:* Lawrence A Russell Jr
VP: J RG Springer
VP: Bob Treanor
Exec: Richard Bogue

D-U-N-S 82-980-6814
■ RADIO HOLDINGS INC
(*Suby of* ROCKWELL COLLINS INC) ★
2551 Riva Rd, Annapolis, MD 21401-7435
Tel (410) 266-4000 *Founded/Ownrshp* 2013
Sales 781.9MM[E] *EMP* 3,000[E]
SIC 8711 4899 Aviation &/or aeronautical engineering; Data communication services
CEO: Thomas Rabaut
VP: Monty Montero

D-U-N-S 03-880-1346
▲ RADIO ONE INC (DE)
1010 Wayne Ave Ste 1400, Silver Spring, MD 20910-5652
Tel (301) 429-3200 *Founded/Ownrshp* 1980
Sales 450.8MM *EMP* 1,306
Tkr Sym ROIA *Exch* NAS
SIC 4832 4841 4813 Radio broadcasting stations; Contemporary; Cable & other pay television services;
Pr: Alfred C Liggins III
**Ch Bd:* Catherine L Hughes
CFO: Peter D Thompson
Bd of Dir: Monique Hudspeth-Kbxx
Ex VP: Peter Thompson
Ex VP: Linda J Vilardo
VP: Linda Vilardo
Trfc Dir: Brenda Fleming
Sls Mgr: Mitch Galvin
Genl Couns: Kris Simpson
Board of Directors: D Geoffrey Armstrong, Ronald E Blaylock, Terry L Jones, Brian W McNeill

D-U-N-S 78-131-8910 IMP
RADIO SYSTEMS CORP
PETSAFE
10427 Petsafe Way, Knoxville, TN 37932-3428
Tel (865) 777-5404 *Founded/Ownrshp* 2006
Sales 1.8MMM[E] *EMP* 620
SIC 0752 1799 6794

RADIOLOGICAL ASSOC SACRAMENTO
See RADIOLOGICAL ASSOCIATES OF SACRAMENTO MEDICAL GROUP INC

D-U-N-S 08-210-6477
RADIOLOGICAL ASSOCIATES OF SACRAMENTO MEDICAL GROUP INC
RADIOLOGICAL ASSOC SACRAMENTO
1500 Expo Pkwy, Sacramento, CA 95815-4227
Tel (916) 646-8300 *Founded/Ownrshp* 1974
Sales NA *EMP* 1,000
SIC 8071 8011

D-U-N-S 05-316-8084
RADIOLOGICAL CONSULTANTS FAIRFAX PC
FAIRFAX RADIOLOGY
2722 Merrilee Dr Ste 230, Fairfax, VA 22031-4416
Tel (703) 698-4444 *Founded/Ownrshp* 1969
Sales 108.8MM *EMP* 525
Accts Thompson Greenspon Fairfax V
SIC 8011 Radiologist
Pr: Marshall C Mintz
**Treas:* Dana A Twible
**VP:* Lyndon Goodwin
IT Man: Terry A Herrity
Mktg Dir: Diane Guinter
Diag Rad: Jonathan E Alfert
Diag Rad: Kara M Beckner
Diag Rad: Erica Y Berg
Diag Rad: Leslie A Bord
Diag Rad: Theodore P Chambers
Diag Rad: Raymond Chang

RADIOLOGY ASSOCIATES
See MIDSTATE MEDICAL CENTER

D-U-N-S 13-063-9305
RADISSON HOTELS INTERNATIONAL INC
RADISSON INN
(*Suby of* CARLSON HOTELS LIMITED PARTNERSHIP) ★
701 Carlson Pkwy, Minnetonka, MN 55305-5240
Tel (763) 212-5000 *Founded/Ownrshp* 1983
Sales 618.1MM[E] *EMP* 17,800
SIC 7011 6794 6552 6531 8742 7389 Hotels & motels; Inns; Franchises, selling or licensing; Land subdividers & developers, commercial; Real estate managers; Marketing consulting services; Training & development consultant; Purchasing service
CEO: Thorsten Kirschke
**Pr:* Curtis C Nelson
**CFO:* Trudy Rautio
**Treas:* John M Diracles Jr
VP: Tom Polski
Dir Bus: Marek Chmatal

RADISSON INN
See CARLSON HOTELS MANAGEMENT CORP

RADISSON INN
See RADISSON HOTELS INTERNATIONAL INC

D-U-N-S 18-107-4055
▲ RADISYS CORP
5435 Ne Dawson Creek Dr, Hillsboro, OR 97124-5797
Tel (503) 615-1100 *Founded/Ownrshp* 1987
Sales 184.5MM *EMP* 710[E]
Tkr Sym RSYS *Exch* NGS
SIC 3825 7374 7372 Network analyzers; Data processing & preparation; Prepackaged software
Pr: Brian Bronson
**Ch Bd:* Ronald De Lange
CFO: Jonathan Wilson
VP: Stephen Collins
VP: Lawrence Lavier
VP: Wassim Matragi
VP: Ted Pennington
CTO: Bob Pebly
Sftwr Eng: Hans Kramer
Board of Directors: Hubert De Pesquidoux, C Scott Gibson, Michael G Hluchyj, M Niel Ransom, Vincent H Tobkin

D-U-N-S 82-507-2317
▲ RADNET INC
1510 Cotner Ave, Los Angeles, CA 90025-3303
Tel (310) 445-2800 *Founded/Ownrshp* 1985
Sales 809.6MM *EMP* 6,080
Tkr Sym RDNT *Exch* NGM
SIC 8071 Medical laboratories; Ultrasound laboratory; Neurological laboratory; X-ray laboratory, including dental
Ch Bd: Howard G Berger
COO: Stephen M Forthuber
CFO: Mark D Stolper
Ex VP: Norman R Hames
Ex VP: Jeffrey L Linden
Ex VP: Michael M Murdock
VP: Ann Brennan
VP: John V Crues III
Rgnl Mgr: Andrea Hassett
Mktg Mgr: Sambra Flanagan
Genl Couns: Deborah Saly

Board of Directors: Marvin S Cadwell, Lawrence L Levitt, Michael L Sherman, David L Swartz

D-U-N-S 03-970-0588
■ RADNET MANAGEMENT INC
(*Suby of* RADNET INC) ★
1510 Cotner Ave, Los Angeles, CA 90025-3303
Tel (310) 445-2800 *Founded/Ownrshp* 2008
Sales 144.1MM^E *EMP* 1,200
SIC 8741 Management services
Pr: Howard Berger
**COO:* Stephen M Forthuber
**CFO:* Marc Skelper
**CFO:* Mark D Stolper
**Ex VP:* Norman Hames
**Ex VP:* Jeffrey L Linden
**Sr VP:* Steven R Hirschtick
VP: Laura Foster
**VP:* Michael J Krane MD
Site Mgr: Tara Jennings
Obsttrcn: Ruth Wilson

D-U-N-S 88-365-1366
RADVISION INC
(*Suby of* RADVISION LTD)
17-17 State Rt 208 # 300, Fair Lawn, NJ 07410-2820
Tel (201) 689-6300 *Founded/Ownrshp* 1995
Sales 118.6MM^E *EMP* 400
SIC 5065 Electronic parts & equipment
CEO: Boaz Raviv
**CEO:* Gadi Tamri
**COO:* Yuval Bloch
**CFO:* Tsipi Kagan
VP: Ray Glynn
VP: Dan Hochberg
VP: Luther Jones
VP: Eric Le Guiniec
VP: Andreas Mattes
Exec: Cheryl Bulna
Genl Mgr: Bob Rickwood

D-U-N-S 95-915-2216
RADWARE INC
(*Suby of* RADWARE LTD.)
575 Corporate Dr Ste 205, Mahwah, NJ 07430-2330
Tel (201) 512-9771 *Founded/Ownrshp* 1996
Sales 200.0MM *EMP* 150
SIC 8731 Computer (hardware) development
CEO: Roy Zisapel
Pr: Sergio Gemo
**Pr:* Larry P Marino
CFO: Moshe Meir
**CFO:* Meir Moshe
Ex VP: Spencer Snedecor
Sr VP: Jim Bergamini
Sr VP: Jack Sorci
VP: Udi Abramovic
VP: David Aviv
**VP:* Patrick Geen
VP: Carl Herberger
VP: Oded Kovar
**VP:* Eran PRI-El
**VP:* Asaf Ronen
**VP:* Frank Rubio
VP: Howard Teicher
VP: Shlomo Tenenberg
VP: Sharon Trachtman
Exec: Linda Kajian

D-U-N-S 09-684-4824 IMP/EXP
RADWELL INTERNATIONAL INC
PLC CENTER
1 Millenium Dr, Willingboro, NJ 08046-1000
Tel (609) 288-9393 *Founded/Ownrshp* 1979, 1985
Sales 228.5MM^E *EMP* 400
SIC 5065 7629 Electronic parts & equipment; Electronic equipment repair
Pr: Brian Radwell
**Pr:* H G Radwell
CFO: Russ Batdorf
VP: Mike Bostenek
**VP:* Daniel Love
**VP:* Todd Radwell
**Prin:* John Radwell
Mng Dir: Gary Mitchell
Area Mgr: Matt Davis
Area Mgr: Dennis Delano
Area Mgr: Jessica Rodriguez

D-U-N-S 93-077-5580
RADY CHILDRENS HOSPITAL AND HEALTH CENTER
3020 Childrens Way, San Diego, CA 92123-4223
Tel (858) 576-1700 *Founded/Ownrshp* 1980
Sales 3.3MM *EMP* 1,720
Accts Kpmg Llp Los Angeles Ca
SIC 8069 Children's hospital
Pr: Donald B Kearns
**COO:* Nicholas Holmes
**CFO:* Roger G Roux
**Chf Mktg O:* Irvin A Kaufman
**Ex VP:* Margareta E Norton
Dir Lab: Darrell Kramer
Surgeon: Avrum Joffe

D-U-N-S 05-196-8808
RADY CHILDRENS HOSPITAL-SAN DIEGO (CA)
3020 Childrens Way, San Diego, CA 92123-4223
Tel (858) 576-1700 *Founded/Ownrshp* 1952
Sales 522.0MM *EMP* 2,313
SIC 8069 Children's hospital
CEO: Donald Kearns
Dir Recs: Dorothy O'Hagan
COO: Nicholas Holmes
Bd of Dir: Leonard Kornreich
Ex VP: Margareta E Norton
Sr VP: Herb Kimmons
VP: Chana Dean
VP: Mary Fagan
VP: Albert Oriol
Dir Rad: Bruce Bower
Ex Dir: Stephen Jennings

D-U-N-S 05-395-7965
RAE CORP
REFRIGERATION SYSTEMS DIVISION
4492 Hunt St, Pryor, OK 74361-4510
Tel (918) 825-7222 *Founded/Ownrshp* 1993
Sales 84.5MM^E *EMP* 325^E
SIC 3585 Refrigeration equipment, complete; Air conditioning units, complete: domestic or industrial
Pr: Eric Swank
Ex VP: Don Austin
Brnch Mgr: Shaun Barrett
Genl Mgr: Dan Crofford
QA Dir: Dan Malone
QA Dir: Alan Swank
Dir IT: Josh Herron
Dir IT: Jim Swank
Plnt Mgr: Jerry Salcher
Sls Mgr: Larry Hudson
Sls Mgr: Kevin Rowhill

D-U-N-S 62-612-2519 IMP
■ RAE SYSTEMS INC
(*Suby of* HONEYWELL ANALYTICS INC) ★
3775 N 1st St, San Jose, CA 95134-1708
Tel (408) 952-8200 *Founded/Ownrshp* 2013
Sales 95.3MM^E *EMP* 750^E
SIC 3829 3812 3699 Gas detectors; Search & detection systems & instruments; Security control equipment & systems
Pr: Robert Chen
**COO:* Christopher Toney
**CFO:* Michael Hansen
**Ex VP:* Ming Ting Tang PHD
VP: Thomas N Gre
**VP:* Peter C Hsi PHD
Manager: Ray Dauterive
Manager: Thom Riekel
Pgrm Dir: Jennifer Ong
Board of Directors: Vikram Verma

D-U-N-S 09-998-1169 IMP/EXP
RAF INDUSTRIES INC
165 Township Line Rd # 2100, Jenkintown, PA 19046-3587
Tel (215) 572-0738 *Founded/Ownrshp* 1979
Sales 374.6MM^E *EMP* 1,230
SIC 8742 3564 Distribution channels consultant; Filters, air: furnaces, air conditioning equipment, etc.
CEO: Robert A Fox
**Pr:* Richard M Horowitz
**CFO:* Michael F Daly
VP: John F Piree

D-U-N-S 05-337-6737
RAFFERTYS INC
1750 Scottsville Rd Ste 2, Bowling Green, KY 42104-3375
Tel (270) 781-2834 *Founded/Ownrshp* 1981
Sales 75.4MM^E *EMP* 1,800
SIC 5812 5813 Ethnic food restaurants; Bars & lounges
Pr: Dan J Davis
Mng Pt: John Renfrow
CFO: Doug Tobby
Treas: Kevin Rafferty
Chf Mktg O: George Thacker
Ex VP: Tony Fernandez
VP: Paula Cassady
Genl Mgr: Tony Bertagna
Genl Mgr: Jim Binkley
Genl Mgr: Jeff Brady
Genl Mgr: Paul Friedman

D-U-N-S 07-840-3372
RAG & BONE HOLDINGS LLC
425 W 13th St Ofc 2, New York, NY 10014-1123
Tel (212) 982-3992 *Founded/Ownrshp* 2012
Sales 275.0MM *EMP* 400
SIC 5621 Women's clothing stores
Mng Dir: Marcus Wainwright

D-U-N-S 03-993-0979
RAGE ADMINISTRATIVE AND MARKETING SERVICES INC
PIZZA HUT
1313 N Webb Rd Ste 200, Wichita, KS 67206-4077
Tel (316) 634-1888 *Founded/Ownrshp* 1980
Sales 86.7MM^E *EMP* 2,500
SIC 5812 Pizzeria, chain
Pr: Robert Geist
**Sec:* Dale Roach
**VP:* Steve Stansbury
Dir IT: David Logsden
Sls&Mrk Ex: Bill Frailey

RAGING WIRE
See RAGINGWIRE DATA CENTERS INC

D-U-N-S 79-956-9137 IMP
RAGINGWIRE DATA CENTERS INC
RAGING WIRE
(*Suby of* NTT COMMUNICATIONS CORPORATION)
1200 Striker Ave, Sacramento, CA 95834-1157
Tel (916) 286-3000 *Founded/Ownrshp* 2014
Sales 199.0MM^E *EMP* 350
SIC 7376 Computer facilities management
Pr: George Macricostas
**Pr:* Douglas S Adams
COO: Joel Stone
**COO:* Jason Weckworth
Ofcr: Doug Adams
**Sr VP:* William Dougherty
VP: Jaosn Weckworth
Mktg Dir: Bruno Berti
Sls Mgr: Heather Orr
Snr Mgr: Tom Manriquez

D-U-N-S 05-011-8855
RAHAL FOODS INC
(*Suby of* NATIONWIDE OF CHICAGO-FOOD BROKERS INC) ★
915 Harger Rd Ste 110, Oak Brook, IL 60523-1400
Tel (630) 286-1500 *Founded/Ownrshp* 1998
Sales 174.6MM^E *EMP* 12
SIC 5149 5431 Juices; Fruit & vegetable markets
Pr: Ian Rahal
CFO: Dan Etheridge
VP: Jordan Rahal
VP: Norman Rahal

RAI
See RESOURCE AMERICA INC

RAIL WORKS
See RAILWORKS CORP

D-U-N-S 79-778-9716
■ RAILAMERICA INC
(*Suby of* GENESEE & WYOMING INC) ★
20 West Ave, Darien, CT 06820-4401
Tel (203) 656-1092 *Founded/Ownrshp* 2012
Sales 193.7MM^E *EMP* 1,836
SIC 4011 Railroads, line-haul operating
Pr: John E Giles
COO: Paul Lundberg
CFO: Clyde Preslar
Treas: Joseph B Doherty
Ex VP: Gary M Spiegel
Sr VP: Georgi Kirov
Sr VP: David Novak
Sr VP: Charles M Patterson
Sr VP: Alfred M Sauer
Sr VP: Scott Williams
VP: Jack Conser
VP: Michael Emmons
VP: Jeffrey Geary
VP: Marc Jacobowitz
VP: Marc Jacobwitz
VP: Bob Jones
VP: Brad Ovitt
VP: Ray Stephens
VP: Reginald Thompson
VP: Peter Turrell
VP: James Wagner

D-U-N-S 13-572-3539
■ RAILAMERICA TRANSPORTATION CORP
(*Suby of* RAILAMERICA INC) ★
7411 Fullerton St Ste 300, Jacksonville, FL 32256-3629
Tel (904) 538-6100 *Founded/Ownrshp* 2000
Sales 56.1MM^E *EMP* 1,050
SIC 4011 Railroads, line-haul operating
CEO: Charles Swinburn
**Pr:* Donald D Redfearn
**CFO:* Michael Howe
Off Mgr: Amy Tollberg

RAILCAR TRACKING COMPANY LLC
See SAVAGE COMPANIES

D-U-N-S 61-302-6827
RAILCREW XPRESS LLC
9867 Widmer Rd, Lenexa, KS 66215-1239
Tel (913) 928-5000 *Founded/Ownrshp* 2005
Sales 91.1MM^E *EMP* 4,500
SIC 4131 Intercity & rural bus transportation
CEO: Brian Ohara
**Ch:* Andrew Blott
Genl Mgr: Paul Greene
Genl Mgr: Jim Henderson
Genl Mgr: Jason Moore

D-U-N-S 08-001-2838
RAILNET DR INC
100 School St Apt B, Glen Rock, PA 17327-1338
Tel (717) 817-1472 *Founded/Ownrshp* 2015
Sales 600.0MM *EMP* 5
SIC 4011 Electric railroads
Pr: Don Kress
**VP:* Walter O'Rourke

D-U-N-S 00-552-6959
■ RAILROAD RETIREMENT BOARD UNITED STATES
R R B
(*Suby of* EXECUTIVE OFFICE OF UNITED STATES GOVERNMENT) ★
844 N Rush St, Chicago, IL 60611-1275
Tel (877) 772-5772 *Founded/Ownrshp* 1935
Sales NA *EMP* 1,000
SIC 9441

D-U-N-S 92-833-2063
■ RAILSERVE INC
(*Suby of* UNION TANK CAR CO) ★
1691 Phoenix Blvd Ste 250, Atlanta, GA 30349-5565
Tel (770) 996-6838 *Founded/Ownrshp* 1994
Sales 1.0MM *EMP* 2,500
SIC 4013 Railroad switching; Railroad terminals
CEO: Timothy Benjamin
**Pr:* Timothy J Benjamin
**Pr:* Bobby R Ross
**CFO:* Christopher Hagge
**VP:* William R Holliday
**VP:* Raymond R Ricker Jr
Genl Mgr: John Roberts
Ql Cn Mgr: Larry Lewczyk
Mktg Dir: Jeff Yarbrough
Snr Mgr: Scott Barrett
Snr Mgr: Harold Charles

D-U-N-S 02-496-7189
RAILWORKS CORP
RAIL WORKS
(*Suby of* WIND POINT PARTNERS LP) ★
5 Penn Plz, New York, NY 10001-1810
Tel (212) 502-7900 *Founded/Ownrshp* 1998
Sales 814.7MM^E *EMP* 2,000
SIC 1629 Railroad & subway construction
Pr: Jeffrey Levy
Pr: Scott D Brace
Pr: Trisha Odonohue
**CFO:* Veronica Lubatkin
Treas: Alexander Motamed
**Ex VP:* John August
Ex VP: Scott Brace
Ex VP: Bob Rolf
Ex VP: John Young
VP: Brian Bennett
VP: Gene Cellini
VP: James Hansen
**VP:* Leo Villalobos
Board of Directors: Timothy B Buresh

D-U-N-S 05-274-3002
RAILWORKS TRACK SYSTEMS INC
(*Suby of* RAIL WORKS) ★
8485 210th St W, Lakeville, MN 55044-8502
Tel (212) 502-7900 *Founded/Ownrshp* 1985, 2009
Sales 395.6MM^E *EMP* 926^E
SIC 1629 Railroad & subway construction; Railroad & railway roadbed construction
Pr: Scott Brace
**Sec:* Gene Cellini
**VP:* William M Bush
VP: William King
VP: Michael Rothschild
IT Man: Anna Hudyma

D-U-N-S 00-848-9197 IMP
RAIN BIRD CORP (CA)
1000 W Sierra Madre Ave, Azusa, CA 91702-1700
Tel (626) 812-3400 *Founded/Ownrshp* 1946
Sales 94.6MM^E *EMP* 250
SIC 3494 3432 3523 Sprinkler systems, field; Lawn hose nozzles & sprinklers; Farm machinery & equipment
Pr: Anthony W La Fetra
VP: Mike Donoghue
Exec: Ofelia Velazquez
Area Mgr: Richard Bueno
Area Mgr: Guy Hoffensetz
CTO: Mark Ensworth
Netwrk Mgr: Francisco Gomez
Mfg Dir: Randy Hall
QC Dir: Michael McAfee
Mfg Mgr: Brian Scott
Plnt Mgr: Michael David

D-U-N-S 79-721-7523
RAIN BIRD CORP
6991 E Suthpoint Rd Ste 1, Tucson, AZ 85756
Tel (520) 806-5635 *Founded/Ownrshp* 2001
Sales 98.6MM^E *EMP* 521^E
SIC 3532 Grinders, stone: stationary
Pr: Anthony W La Fetra
COO: Maria E Ibarra
**Ch:* Arthur Ludwick
**VP:* Michael L Donoghue
Plnt Mgr: Maria Ibarra
Snr Mgr: Leslie Lenhart

R.A.IN HOME ATTENDENT SERVICES
See REGIONAL AID FOR INTERIM NEEDS INC

RAIN OR SHINE
See MALLORY CO

RAINBOW DAYCARE
See TEKAKWITHA LIVING CENTER INC

D-U-N-S 02-830-6660
■ RAINBOW DISPOSAL CO INC (CA)
RAINBOW REFUSE RECYCLING
(*Suby of* REPUBLIC SERVICES INC) ★
17121 Nichols Ln, Huntington Beach, CA 92647-5719
Tel (714) 847-3581 *Founded/Ownrshp* 1956, 2014
Sales 143.9MM^E *EMP* 165
SIC 4953 Garbage: collecting, destroying & processing; Recycling, waste materials
CEO: Jerry Moffatt
Pr: Stan Tkaczyck
VP: Jim Brownell
VP: Sue Gordon
VP: Mike Grumbo
VP: Mike Guilleaume
VP: Mindy Lutman
VP: Jeff Snow
IT Man: Don Nickels
Netwrk Mgr: Gisela Gamboa
Sfty Mgr: John Frixione

D-U-N-S 07-866-1253
RAINBOW HEALTHCARE CENTER INC (OK)
111 E Washington Ave, Bristow, OK 74010-3444
Tel (918) 367-2246 *Founded/Ownrshp* 1962
Sales 329.6MM *EMP* 76
SIC 8052 8051 Personal care facility; Skilled nursing care facilities
Pr: Diane Hambrick
Nrsg Dir: Amy Keeling

D-U-N-S 05-225-9010
RAINBOW INTERNATIONAL OF MIDDLE TENNESEE
667 Patterson Ave Ste C, Murfreesboro, TN 37129-5311
Tel (615) 898-8258 *Founded/Ownrshp* 2010
Sales 100.0MM *EMP* 5
SIC 1542 1521 Commercial & office building, new construction; Single-family housing construction
Owner: Eric Dill

RAINBOW REFUSE RECYCLING
See RAINBOW DISPOSAL CO INC

RAINBOW SHOP
See FASHION GALLERY INC

RAINBOW SHOPS
See AIJJ ENTERPRISES INC

D-U-N-S 78-389-2359 IMP
RAINBOW USA INC
(*Suby of* RAINBOW SHOPS) ★
1000 Pennsylvania Ave, Brooklyn, NY 11207-8417
Tel (718) 485-3000 *Founded/Ownrshp* 1988
Sales 408.2MM^E *EMP* 5,000
SIC 5621 Ready-to-wear apparel, women's
Ch Bd: Albert Chehebar
**CEO:* Joseph Chehebar
**COO:* Martin Stein
CFO: Alan Minker
**Treas:* Jack Chehebar
VP: Jonathan Appel
**VP:* Issac Chehebar
VP: David Cost
Genl Mgr: Mia Taylor
CTO: Christina Antoniewicz
Opers Mgr: Kevin Cohen

D-U-N-S 82-547-0086
RAINEY ROAD HOLDINGS INC
CROWN TONKA WALK IN COOLERS
15600 37th Ave N Ste 100, Minneapolis, MN 55446-3204
Tel (763) 541-1410 *Founded/Ownrshp* 2005
Sales NA *EMP* 325
SIC 6712 Bank holding companies
CEO: Herbert F Kahler
**Pr:* Chris Kahler

D-U-N-S 84-900-2191
RAINFOREST CAFE INC
(*Suby of* LANDRYS SEAFOOD HOUSE) ★
1510 West Loop S, Houston, TX 77027-9505
Tel (713) 850-1010 *Founded/Ownrshp* 2000
Sales 164.8MM[E] *EMP* 6,800
SIC 5812 Cafe
CFO: Rick Liem
VP: Tony Niece
**VP:* Paul West

RAINIER PAPER CO
See MOORIM USA INC

RAINSOFT WATER TREATMENT
See DISCOVERY MARKETING AND DISTRIBUTING INC

D-U-N-S 16-231-9458 IMP
RAINSVILLE TECHNOLOGY INC
(*Suby of* MORIROKU CHEMICALS COMPANY, LTD.)
189 Rti Dr, Rainsville, AL 35986-4471
Tel (256) 638-9760 *Founded/Ownrshp* 2000
Sales 112.0MM *EMP* 400
SIC 3089 Injection molding of plastics
Pr: Shinichi Sakaili
CFO: Allen Tucker
Exec: Kim Stubbs
CIO: Perry Belomy
IT Man: Jeremy Johnson
Sales Exec: Jacob Haynes
Sls&Mrk Ex: Jason Garrett

D-U-N-S 84-230-6032
RAINTREE RESORTS INTERNATIONAL INC
10000 Memorial Dr Ste 480, Houston, TX 77024-3409
Tel (713) 613-2800 *Founded/Ownrshp* 1997
Sales 29.0MM[E] *EMP* 1,500[E]
SIC 7011 Hotels & motels
Pr: Doug Bech
**COO:* Brian Tucker
VP: Gary Allcorn

RAISING CANE'S CHICKEN FINGERS
See RAISING CANES RESTAURANTS LLC

D-U-N-S 96-379-4870
RAISING CANES RESTAURANTS LLC
RAISING CANE'S CHICKEN FINGERS
400 Convention St Ste 550, Baton Rouge, LA 70802-5638
Tel (225) 383-7400 *Founded/Ownrshp* 1996
Sales 73.5MM[E] *EMP* 2,000
SIC 5812 Carry-out only (except pizza) restaurant
Mng Pt: Ashton Hecker
VP: Rick Fuchs
VP: Shawn Jenkins
VP: Vince Severns
Genl Mgr: Stephen James
Genl Mgr: Ryan Rasberry
Genl Mgr: Chris Stevens
Genl Mgr: Michael Stowe
Off Mgr: Allison Record
VP Opers: Kito Cody
Site Mgr: Ben Gegenheimer

D-U-N-S 08-904-4221
RAIT FINANCIAL TRUST
2 Logan Sq Fl 23, Philadelphia, PA 19103-2734
Tel (215) 243-9000 *Founded/Ownrshp* 1998
Sales 323.9MM *EMP* 794[E]
Accts Kpmg Llp Philadelphia Pennsy
SIC 6798 Real estate investment trusts
Ch Bd: Scott F Schaeffer
Pr: Scott L N Davidson
CFO: James J Sebra
Bd of Dir: S Kim
Bd of Dir: Robert F McCadden
Ex VP: Kenneth R Frappier
Sr VP: Jeffrey Conners
VP: Nicholas Harris
VP: Elaine Johnson
VP: Ethan Kopp
VP: Siu Lin
VP: Jessica Norman
Board of Directors: Andrew Batinovich, Edward S Brown, Frank A Farnesi, S Kristin Kim, Jon C Sarkisian, Andrew M Silberstein, Murray Stempel III

D-U-N-S 14-726-7496
RAKS BUILDING SUPPLY INC
DO IT BEST
108 Carson Dr Se, Los Lunas, NM 87031-9294
Tel (505) 865-1100 *Founded/Ownrshp* 1986
Sales 95.3MM[E] *EMP* 250
SIC 5031 5211 5072 Lumber: rough, dressed & finished; Lumber products; Hardware
Pr: Richie Tabet
**Treas:* Gloria Trujillo
**VP:* Kenny Trujillo

D-U-N-S 03-885-5537
RAKUTEN MARKETING LLC
LINKSHARE CORPORATION
(*Suby of* RAKUTEN,INC.)
215 Park Ave S Fl 9, New York, NY 10003-1622
Tel (646) 943-8200 *Founded/Ownrshp* 2005
Sales 108.4MM[E] *EMP* 500
SIC 8742 7375 Marketing consulting services; Information retrieval services
CEO: Yaz Iida
**CEO:* Tony Zito
**COO:* Liane Dietrich
CFO: Bodie Gagnon
**CFO:* Bodie Gavnon
Sr VP: Pamela A Codispoti
Sr VP: Jianhao Meng
VP: Chad Blodgett
CIO: Rohinee Mohindroo
Genl Couns: Abe Hsuan

RALCORP FROZEN BAKERY PRODUCTS
See LOFTHOUSE BAKERY PRODUCTS INC

D-U-N-S 00-732-0997
■ **RALCORP FROZEN BAKERY PRODUCTS INC**
REFRIGERATED DOUGH DIVISION
(*Suby of* TREEHOUSE FOODS INC) ★
3250 Lacey Rd Ste 600, Downers Grove, IL 60515-7918
Tel (630) 455-5200 *Founded/Ownrshp* 1957, 2011
Sales 380.6MM[E] *EMP* 700
SIC 2051 2053 2041 2035 2656 Breads, rolls & buns; Cakes, pies & pastries; Frozen bakery products, except bread; Doughs, frozen or refrigerated; Dressings, salad: raw & cooked (except dry mixes); Mayonnaise; Frozen food & ice cream containers; Food containers (liquid tight), including milk cartons
CEO: Kevin Hunt

D-U-N-S 04-830-0685 EXP
RALCORP FROZEN BAKERY PRODUCTS INC
BAKERY CHEF
3250 Lacey Rd Ste 600, Downers Grove, IL 60515-7918
Tel (630) 455-5200 *Founded/Ownrshp* 2013
Sales NA *EMP* 3,000
SIC 2053 2045

D-U-N-S 07-268-4715
RALEIGH COUNTY BOARD OF EDUCATION
105 Adair St, Beckley, WV 25801-3791
Tel (304) 256-4500 *Founded/Ownrshp* 1898
Sales 48.0MM[E] *EMP* 1,600
SIC 8211 9111 School board; County supervisors' & executives' offices
Pr: Richard Snuffer III
Treas: James Wright

D-U-N-S 93-300-2743
RALEIGH COUNTY SCHOOL DISTRICT
105 Adair St, Beckley, WV 25801-3733
Tel (304) 256-4500 *Founded/Ownrshp* 1994
Sales 88.7MM[E] *EMP* 2,236[E]
SIC 8211 Public elementary & secondary schools
Dir Sec: Jennifer Colvin
Teacher Pr: Anthony Jones
HC Dir: Deborah Kaplan

D-U-N-S 03-012-5934
■ **RALEIGH GENERAL HOSPITAL**
(*Suby of* LIFEPOINT HEALTH INC) ★
1710 Harper Rd, Beckley, WV 25801-3397
Tel (304) 256-4100 *Founded/Ownrshp* 2006
Sales 153.0MM *EMP* 930
SIC 8062 General medical & surgical hospitals
Pr: Karen Bowling
Chf Path: Suk Jung Koh
COO: Jim Bills
CFO: Vince Wyatt
VP: Michael Kelly
Dir Inf Cn: Nancy Ward
Dir Risk M: Shavana Lusk
Dir Lab: Janet Halstead
Chf Nrs Of: Alene Lewis
Dir Sec: Phillip Bolt
QA Dir: Elaine Harris

D-U-N-S 09-155-4907 IMP/EXP
RALEIGH MINE AND INDUSTRIAL SUPPLY INC
RMIS
1500 Mill Creek Rd, Mount Hope, WV 25880-1600
Tel (304) 877-5503 *Founded/Ownrshp* 1978
Sales 208.7MM[E] *EMP* 600
SIC 5085 1629 3532 3441 Industrial supplies; Industrial plant construction; Mining machinery; Fabricated structural metal
Pr: Stirl R Smith
**Treas:* Donna Zandlo
Exec: Jim Bartlett

D-U-N-S 00-699-7399
RALEIGH WINN-DIXIE INC (FL)
(*Suby of* MARKETPLACE) ★
5050 Edgewood Ct, Jacksonville, FL 32254-3601
Tel (904) 783-5000 *Founded/Ownrshp* 1958
Sales 724.7MM[E] *EMP* 8,000
SIC 5411 Convenience stores, chain
CEO: R Randall Onstead Jr
**Pr:* Matt Solana
**Treas:* Kelly Hardy
**VP:* Brian Carney
**VP:* R P McCook
**VP:* Charles Wing

D-U-N-S 00-787-4472 IMP
RALEYS (CA)
BEL AIR MARKETS
500 W Capitol Ave, West Sacramento, CA 95605-2696
Tel (916) 373-3333 *Founded/Ownrshp* 1935
Sales 3.0MMM *EMP* 14,000
SIC 5411 5912 Supermarkets, chain; Drug stores
CEO: Michael Teel
COO: Keith Knopf
COO: Lupe Murrietta
**CFO:* Ken Mueller
**Ch:* Joyce Raley Teel
Bd of Dir: Gerald Cook
Bd of Dir: Claudia Doerhoff
Sr VP: Kevin Curry
Sr VP: Kevin Konkel
VP: Christine McGlasson
VP: Matt Powers
VP: Carol Saltzman
VP: Jeff Szczesny
VP: Terrance Tremelling
Exec: Mike Gabbert
Exec: Rick Hoffman
Exec: Helen Singmaster

D-U-N-S 14-518-4292
■ **RALLY SOFTWARE DEVELOPMENT CORP**
(*Suby of* CA INC) ★
3333 Walnut St, Boulder, CO 80301-2515
Tel (303) 565-2800 *Founded/Ownrshp* 2001
Sales 105.8MM[E] *EMP* 458[E]
SIC 7372 Prepackaged software
CEO: Timothy Miller
**CFO:* James M Lejeal
**Ofcr:* Angela Tucci
Ex VP: Don F Hazell
Ex VP: Richard D Leavitt
**Ex VP:* Daniel A Patton
VP: Liz Andora
VP: Doug Golliher
VP: Adrian Jones
**VP:* Kenneth M Mesikapp
Rgnl Mgr: Jamie Webber

RALLY'S HAMBURGERS
See CHECKERS DRIVE-IN RESTAURANTS INC

D-U-N-S 06-315-6657
RALPH CLAYTON & SONS LLC
1355 Campus Pkwy, Wall Township, NJ 07753-6833
Tel (732) 363-1995 *Founded/Ownrshp* 1949
Sales 87.9MM[E] *EMP* 600
SIC 5032 Sand, construction; Gravel; Concrete mixtures
Pr: William R Clayton
CIO: Scott Milne
Sls Mgr: Joe Scaramuzzo

D-U-N-S 07-307-5020
■ **RALPH L WADSWORTH CONSTRUCTION CO LLC**
(*Suby of* STERLING CONSTRUCTION CO INC) ★
166 E 14000 S Ste 200, Draper, UT 84020-5455
Tel (801) 553-1661 *Founded/Ownrshp* 2009
Sales 155.9MM *EMP* 200[E]
Accts Grant Thornton Llp Houston T
SIC 1629 1611 Land leveling; Waste water & sewage treatment plant construction; Pile driving contractor; Highway & street construction
Pr: Con Wadsworth
**COO:* Brandon Squire
CFO: Kevin Blair
**VP:* Tod Wadsworth
Genl Mgr: Doug Clements
Snr PM: Marty Biljanic

D-U-N-S 04-616-9595 IMP/EXP
▲ **RALPH LAUREN CORP**
650 Madison Ave Fl C1, New York, NY 10022-1070
Tel (212) 318-7000 *Founded/Ownrshp* 1967
Sales 7.4MMM *EMP* 26,000
Accts Ernst & Young Llp New York
Tkr Sym RL *Exch* NYS
SIC 2325 2321 2253 2323 2311 2329 Men's & boys' trousers & slacks; Men's & boys' dress shirts; Men's & boys' sports & polo shirts; Shirts (outerwear), knit; Sweaters & sweater coats, knit; Ties, handsewn: made from purchased materials; Topcoats, men's & boys': made from purchased materials; Men's & boys' sportswear & athletic clothing; Sweaters & sweater jackets: men's & boys'
Pr: Stefan Larsson
**Ch Bd:* Ralph Lauren
Pr: Valerie Hermann
CFO: Robert L Madore
CFO: Jane H Nielsen
Ex VP: Nemerov Jackwyn
**Ex VP:* David Lauren
VP: John R Alchin
VP: Sandy Aronson
VP: Nancy Beck
VP: Michel Botbol
VP: Kristen Bowman
VP: Smita Butala
VP: Greg Corso
VP: Frederic Dechnik
VP: Vince Dellosa
VP: Mark Engebretson
VP: Phil Faust
VP: Larry Gordon
VP: Rebecca Handler
VP: John Heist
Board of Directors: John R Alchin, Arnold H Aronson, Frank A Bennack Jr, Joyce F Brown, Joel L Fleishman, Hubert Joly, Judith McHale, Robert C Wright

D-U-N-S 08-942-3490 EXP
■ **RALPH LAUREN RETAIL INC**
POLO RALPH LAUREN
(*Suby of* RALPH LAUREN CORP) ★
9 Polito Ave Fl 5, Lyndhurst, NJ 07071-3406
Tel (888) 475-7674 *Founded/Ownrshp* 1983
Sales 255.0MM[E] *EMP* 2,274
SIC 5651 5661 5719 Family clothing stores; Jeans stores; Shoe stores; Housewares
CEO: Roger Farah
Pr: Tongyan Wang
COO: Jeffrey Sherman
Ofcr: Scott Lancaster
Ex VP: Jerome Lauren
Ex VP: Jackwyn Nemeroy
Ex VP: Beth Tunney
Sr VP: Mary R Carter
Sr VP: Sharon French
Sr VP: Edward Galgay
Sr VP: Jenevieve Gorman
VP: Dean D Antonia
VP: Scott Ernst
Exec: Amy Vernazza

RALPH'S FOOD WAREHOUSE #1
See RALPHS FOOD WAREHOUSE INC

D-U-N-S 84-915-6997 IMP/EXP
RALPHS FOOD WAREHOUSE INC
RALPH'S FOOD WAREHOUSE #1
Carr 183 Industrial Park, Las Piedras, PR 00771
Tel (787) 733-0959 *Founded/Ownrshp* 1993
Sales 118.1MM[E] *EMP* 2,000[E]
Accts Stuart Cpa Group Psc Caguas
SIC 5411 5149 Grocery stores; Groceries & related products
Prin: Rafael A Soto

D-U-N-S 78-617-6628 IMP/EXP
■ **RALPHS GROCERY CO**
FOOD 4 LESS
(*Suby of* KROGER CO) ★
1100 W Artesia Blvd, Compton, CA 90220-5186
Tel (310) 884-9000 *Founded/Ownrshp* 2014
Sales 258.8MM[E] *EMP* 1,067
SIC 5411

D-U-N-S 00-481-7771
RAM CONSTRUCTION SERVICES OF MICHIGAN INC (MI)
13800 Eckles Rd, Livonia, MI 48150-1041
Tel (734) 464-3800 *Founded/Ownrshp* 1918
Sales 127.5MM[E] *EMP* 500
Accts Doerenmayhew Troy Michigan
SIC 1799 1541 1542 Waterproofing; Renovation, remodeling & repairs: industrial buildings; Commercial & office buildings, renovation & repair
Pr: Robert Mazur
**CFO:* Kevin M Houle
**Ex VP:* John Mazur

D-U-N-S 01-632-9141
RAM EXCAVATING INC
3349 Hannah Way E, Dunedin, FL 34698-9456
Tel (727) 463-6428 *Founded/Ownrshp* 2000
Sales 2.0MMM *EMP* 10
SIC 1794 Excavation work
Pr: Richard Slack

D-U-N-S 00-728-9866 IMP
RAM INDUSTRIAL SERVICES LLC
2850 Appleton St Ste D, Camp Hill, PA 17011-8036
Tel (717) 737-7810 *Founded/Ownrshp* 2000
Sales 269.4MM[E] *EMP* 187
SIC 5063 7629 Electrical apparatus & equipment; Electrical repair shops
Opers Mgr: Jennifer Hill
Sales Asso: Jolene Ulrich

D-U-N-S 13-060-4317
RAM INTERNATIONAL LTD
RAM RESTAURANT & BREWERY
10013 59th Ave Sw, Lakewood, WA 98499-2757
Tel (253) 588-1788 *Founded/Ownrshp* 1971
Sales 76.8MM[E] *EMP* 2,500
SIC 5812

D-U-N-S 78-200-8478
RAM PARTNERS LLC
3284 Northside Pkwy Nw # 300, Atlanta, GA 30327-2289
Tel (770) 437-5200 *Founded/Ownrshp* 2002
Sales 87.0MM[E] *EMP* 700
SIC 8741 8742 Management services; Management consulting services
Pr: Bill Leseman
Pr: Elizabeth Connor
**Sr VP:* Brenda R Lindner
**Sr VP:* Martha J Logan
**VP:* Teresa R Meuter

RAM RESTAURANT & BREWERY
See RAM INTERNATIONAL LTD

D-U-N-S 03-152-7211
RAM TOOL & SUPPLY CO INC
RAM TOOL CONSTRUCTION SUP CO
3620 8th Ave S Ste 200, Birmingham, AL 35222-3219
Tel (205) 714-3300 *Founded/Ownrshp* 1984
Sales 435.7MM[E] *EMP* 500
SIC 5085 Industrial supplies
Pr: Maryam B Head
**CFO:* Jeff Hicks
VP: Rob Belcher
VP: Page Naftel
Brnch Mgr: Ryan Hurley
Sls Mgr: Gary Raulerson
Sales Asso: John Reese
Sales Asso: Ben Spell

RAM TOOL CONSTRUCTION SUP CO
See RAM TOOL & SUPPLY CO INC

RAMADA INN
See TROPICANA EXPRESS INC

D-U-N-S 15-651-1792
RAMADA NEW JERSEY HOLDINGS CORP
(*Suby of* COLUMBIA SUSSEX CORP) ★
Brighton Ave Boardwalk, Atlantic City, NJ 08401
Tel (609) 340-4000 *Founded/Ownrshp* 2009
Sales 222.3MM[E] *EMP* 4,001[E]
SIC 7011 Casino hotel
Ch Bd: Paul Rubeli
Pr: Pam Popielarski
CFO: Deborah Marchese

D-U-N-S 07-668-7383
RAMAPO CENTRAL SCHOOL DISTRICT
45 Mountain Ave, Hillburn, NY 10931-2002
Tel (845) 357-7783 *Founded/Ownrshp* 1940
Sales 125.4MM *EMP* 800
SIC 8211 Public elementary school; Public junior high school; Public senior high school
Genl Mgr: Theresa Isoldi
Schl Brd P: Theresa Difalco

D-U-N-S 07-668-8399
RAMAPO COLLEGE OF NEW JERSEY
505 Ramapo Valley Rd, Mahwah, NJ 07430-1680
Tel (201) 684-7500 *Founded/Ownrshp* 1971
Sales 90.2MM[E] *EMP* 600[E]
Accts O Connor Davis Llp Paramus N
SIC 8221 College, except junior
Pr: Peter Philip Mercer
Ofcr: Janet Faber
Ofcr: Orlando Naveo
VP: Donna Crawley
**VP:* Cathleen Davey
Exec: Robert B Hiden Jr
Exec: Ellen Senese
Assoc Dir: Sean Craig
HC Dir: Nancy Jaeger

D-U-N-S 11-035-3112
RAMBOLL ENVIRON INC
ENVIRON INTERNATIONAL
4350 Fairfax Dr Ste 300, Arlington, VA 22203-1619
Tel (703) 516-2300 *Founded/Ownrshp* 1999
Sales 254.5MM[E] *EMP* 1,640
SIC 8748 8999 Environmental consultant; Earth science services
CEO: Stephen T Washburn
Pr: Thomas Vetrano
Treas: Michael Rosenvold
Div Pres: Frank Marrazza

Ofcr: Robert Powell
VP: Tracey Finn
VP: Andrew Gremos
VP: Thomas Kveiborg
Mng Dir: Chris Keller
Admn Mgr: Ranjit J Machado
Off Mgr: Joyce Morrow

D-U-N-S 05-311-1183
RAMBOLL ENVIRON US CORP (VA)
(*Suby of* ENVIRON INTERNATIONAL) ★
4350 Fairfax Dr Ste 300, Arlington, VA 22203-1619
Tel (703) 516-2300 *Founded/Ownrshp* 1989, 2015
Sales 139.9MM[E] *EMP* 946
SIC 8748 8999 Environmental consultant; Earth science services
CEO: Stephen T Washburn
**Pr:* Frank Marrazza
**CFO:* Guy Lewis
**Sr VP:* Thomas Kveiborg
**VP:* Russell Kemp
Genl Mgr: Aidan Turnbull Duncan
Snr Mgr: Frank Gonzalez
Board of Directors: Allan Delorme, Guy Lewis, Frank Marrazza, Stephen Washburn

D-U-N-S 62-257-4903 IMP/EXP
▲ RAMBUS INC
1050 Entp Way Ste 700, Sunnyvale, CA 94089
Tel (408) 462-8000 *Founded/Ownrshp* 1990
Sales 296.2MM *EMP* 495[E]
Accts Pricewaterhousecoopers Llp Sa
Tkr Sym RMBS *Exch* NGS
SIC 3674 6794 Semiconductors & related devices; Patent owners & lessors
Pr: Ronald Black
Ch Bd: Eric Stang
CFO: Rahul Mathur
CFO: Satish Rishi
Sr VP: Jae Kim
Sr VP: Jerome Nadel
Sr VP: Kit Rodgers
Sr VP: Martin Scott
Sr VP: Luc Seraphin
Sr VP: Laura S Stark
Sr VP: Steve Tobak
VP: Mark Grimse
VP: Ron Lee
Board of Directors: J Thomas Bentley, E Thomas Fisher, Penelope A Herscher, Charles Kissner, David Shrigley

RAMCO
See PINE BELT OIL CO INC

RAMCO EMPLOYMENT SERVICES
See RAMCO ENTERPRISES LP

D-U-N-S 19-054-6259
RAMCO ENTERPRISES LP
RAMCO EMPLOYMENT SERVICES
320 Airport Blvd, Salinas, CA 93905-3301
Tel (831) 758-5272 *Founded/Ownrshp* 1985
Sales 85.0MM *EMP* 3,000
SIC 0171 7361 0723 Strawberry farm; Labor contractors (employment agency); Vegetable crops market preparation services; Vegetable packing services
Pt: Carlos Ramirez
Ofcr: Tammy Nunez
VP: William Kohlbrenner
IT Man: Julie Avila
IT Man: Tino Guzman
Netwrk Mgr: Julio Sanchez

D-U-N-S 36-382-0770
▲ RAMCO-GERSHENSON PROPERTIES TRUST
31500 Northwestern Hwy, Farmington Hills, MI 48334-2567
Tel (248) 350-9900 *Founded/Ownrshp* 1988
Sales 251.7MM *EMP* 120[E]
Tkr Sym RPT *Exch* NYS
SIC 6798 6519 Real estate investment trusts; Real property lessors
Pr: Dennis E Gershenson
**Ch Bd:* Stephen R Blank
COO: John Hendrickson
CFO: Geoffrey Bedrosian
Ex VP: Catherine Clark
Ex VP: Frederick A Zantello
Board of Directors: Alice M Connell, Arthur Goldberg, David J Nettina, Joel M Pashcow, Mark K Rosenfeld, Laurie M Shanon, Michael A Ward

RAMEY'S SUPER MARKET 1-29
See ROSWIL INC

RAMMING PAVING COMPANY
See AUSTIN MATERIALS LLC

RAMMING PAVING COMPANY
See JD RAMMING PAVING MANAGEMENT LLC

RAMOCO FUELS
See HANUMAN BUSINESS INC

RAMON VALENCIA ESPINOZA
See LA VALENCIANA AVOCADOS CORP

D-U-N-S 04-400-3556
RAMOS OIL CO INC
1515 S River Rd, West Sacramento, CA 95691-2882
Tel (916) 371-2570 *Founded/Ownrshp* 1951
Sales 132.5MM[E] *EMP* 200
SIC 5171 5172 Petroleum bulk stations; Lubricating oils & greases
Pr: Kent Ramos
**CFO:* John Bailey
**CFO:* Jan Bard
**CFO:* Janet Bard
**Ch:* Bill Ramos

D-U-N-S 04-471-8476 IMP
RAMPART PLUMBING AND HEATING SUPPLY INC
RAMPART SUPPLY
1801 N Union Blvd, Colorado Springs, CO 80909-2228
Tel (719) 471-7200 *Founded/Ownrshp* 1968
Sales 104.6MM *EMP* 200
Accts Osborne Parsons & Rosacker L
SIC 5074 Plumbing & hydronic heating supplies
Pr: Colin J Perry
**COO:* Joseph Perry
Dir Bus: Carrie Schmidt
Brnch Mgr: Kevin Broder
Genl Mgr: Marc Robbins
Sls Mgr: Derek Bell
Sales Asso: Troy Bane

RAMPART SUPPLY
See RAMPART PLUMBING AND HEATING SUPPLY INC

D-U-N-S 80-009-0490
■ RAMPARTS INC
LUXOR HOTEL & CASINO
(*Suby of* MANDALAY BAY RESORT AND CASINO) ★
3900 Las Vegas Blvd S, Las Vegas, NV 89119-1004
Tel (702) 262-4000 *Founded/Ownrshp* 1988
Sales 111.6MM[E] *EMP* 3,100
SIC 7011 Casino hotel
Sr VP: Jean George
Sr VP: Micah Richins
Sr VP: Scott B Snow
VP: Joseph Glazier
VP: John Quinn
VP: Saul Wesley
Exec: Stefanie Ford
Exec: Tom Gorball
Exec: Stephen Harney
Exec: Doree Mosman
Exec: Lorna Palmer

D-U-N-S 07-943-8760
RAMSA ELECTROMECHANIC INC (TX)
207 W Ryan St, Laredo, TX 78041-4881
Tel (956) 568-5354 *Founded/Ownrshp* 2012
Sales 498.0MM *EMP* 4
SIC 7694 Electric motor repair
Pr: Raul Mireles Salinas

D-U-N-S 03-798-0224 IMP/EXP
RAMSEY INDUSTRIES INC
(*Suby of* GRIDIRON CAPITAL LLC) ★
4707 N Mingo Rd, Tulsa, OK 74117-5904
Tel (918) 438-2760 *Founded/Ownrshp* 1944
Sales 147.2MM[E] *EMP* 300
SIC 3531 3536 Winches; Cranes, industrial plant
Pr: John R Celoni Jr
**COO:* Michael A Barber
**CFO:* Don Helms
**Exec:* Bruce Barron
Exec: Robyn Stange
CIO: KAO Vang
Manager: Stan Hunt

D-U-N-S 16-993-9282
RANBAXY INC
RPI
(*Suby of* SUNPHARMA) ★
600 College Rd E Ste 2100, Princeton, NJ 08540-6636
Tel (609) 720-9200 *Founded/Ownrshp* 2004
Sales 109.8MM[E] *EMP* 250
SIC 8741 Management services
CEO: Omesh Sethi
**Pr:* Dipak Chattaraj
**CFO:* Lalit Ahluwalia
**VP:* Bernard Brothman
**VP:* Charles Caprariello
**VP:* Venkat Krishnan
**VP:* Lavesh Samtani
**VP:* Bill Winter
Snr Mgr: Sameer Manan

D-U-N-S 93-789-0044 IMP/EXP
RANBAXY PHARMACEUTICALS INC
SUNPHARMA
(*Suby of* SUN PHARMACEUTICAL INDUSTRIES LIMITED)
600 College Rd E Ste 2100, Princeton, NJ 08540-6636
Tel (609) 720-9200 *Founded/Ownrshp* 2015
Sales 437.4MM[E] *EMP* 1,000
SIC 2834 5122 Pharmaceutical preparations; Pharmaceuticals
CEO: Venkat Krishnan
**Treas:* Gaurav Mehrotra
**VP:* Bernard Brothman
**VP:* Charles M Caprariello
**VP:* Chuck Caprariello
**VP:* James Meehan
**VP:* Lavesh Samtani
VP: Omesh Sethi
**VP:* William Winter
Exec: Gunjan Kshetrapal
Assoc Dir: Ron Keegan

D-U-N-S 86-116-4762 IMP
RANCH AND HOME SUPPLY LLC
MURDOCH'S RANCH & HOME SUPPLY
2311 N 7th Ave, Bozeman, MT 59715-2538
Tel (406) 586-8466 *Founded/Ownrshp* 1994
Sales 224.5MM[E] *EMP* 1,230
SIC 5699 5191 5531 5251 Work clothing; Farm supplies; Automotive parts; Builders' hardware; Tools, hand; Tools, power
CEO: Jennifer Cogley
CFO: Craig Renkey
VP: Marykay Yeley
Exec: Chris Helstrom
Genl Mgr: Troy Franck
Store Mgr: Theodore Grossi
Store Mgr: Garett Piencikowski
Dir IT: Lance Tinseth
Mktg Mgr: John Murdock

D-U-N-S 00-617-5970
RANCHO FOODS INC (CA)
2528 E 37th St, Vernon, CA 90058-1725
Tel (323) 585-0503 *Founded/Ownrshp* 1972
Sales 111.5MM[E] *EMP* 100
SIC 5147 2013 Meats & meat products; Sausages & other prepared meats
Pr: Annette Mac Donald
**VP:* John Mac Donald
Genl Mgr: Frank Celano

D-U-N-S 96-232-6547
RANCHO LOS AMIGOS NATIONAL REHABILIATATION CENTER
7601 Imperial Hwy, Downey, CA 90242-3456
Tel (562) 401-7111 *Founded/Ownrshp* 1988
Sales 61.6MM[E] *EMP* 1,450[E]
SIC 8322 Rehabilitation services
CEO: Jorge R Orozco
**COO:* Benjamin Ovando Sr
**CFO:* Robin Bayus
**Prin:* Aries Limbaga
Ex Dir: Deborah Arroyo
**Ex Dir:* Greg Waskul
Phys Thrpy: Julie Kasayama

D-U-N-S 07-607-0283
RANCHO SANTIAGO COMMUNITY COLLEGE DISTRICT INC
SANTA ANA COLLEGE
2323 N Broadway Fl 4, Santa Ana, CA 92706-1606
Tel (714) 480-7300 *Founded/Ownrshp* 1915
Sales 104.1MM[E] *EMP* 3,000
SIC 8222 8221 Community college; Colleges universities & professional schools
Pr: Jose Solorio
**VP:* Lawrence R Labrado
Exec: John Didion
Exec: Josiem Rodriguez

RANCHO SPRINGS MEDICAL CENTER
See SOUTHWEST HEALTHCARE SYSTEM AUXILIARY

D-U-N-S 60-297-0196
RAND CONSTRUCTION CORP
1029 N Royal St Ste 100, Alexandria, VA 22314-1542
Tel (202) 449-9840 *Founded/Ownrshp* 1989
Sales 176.1MM[E] *EMP* 194
SIC 1542 Commercial & office building contractors; Commercial & office buildings, renovation & repair
Ch Bd: Linda D Rabbitt
**Pr:* Jon Couch
Exec: Cullen McGuire
IT Man: Jaime Bullock

D-U-N-S 00-691-4071
RAND CORP
1776 Main St, Santa Monica, CA 90401-3297
Tel (310) 393-0411 *Founded/Ownrshp* 1948
Sales 313.1MM *EMP* 1,400
SIC 8733 8742 8732

D-U-N-S 14-367-2637
RAND DIRECT INC
112 Truman Dr, Edison, NJ 08817-2425
Tel (732) 985-0800 *Founded/Ownrshp* 2003
Sales 74.9MM[E] *EMP* 1,200
SIC 7389 Packaging & labeling services
CEO: Don Garda
**Pr:* Stuart Sklovsky
**CFO:* David Kauffman
**VP:* John Wuensch

D-U-N-S 62-387-4794
▲ RAND LOGISTICS INC
333 Washington St Ste 201, Jersey City, NJ 07302-3095
Tel (212) 863-9427 *Founded/Ownrshp* 2006
Sales 148.4MM *EMP* 498[E]
Tkr Sym RLOG *Exch* NAS
SIC 4789 4492 Cargo loading & unloading services; Marine towing services
Pr: Edward Levy
**Ch Bd:* Michael D Lundin
CFO: Mark S Hiltwein

D-U-N-S 07-942-3593
RAND WHITNEY PACKAGING
(*Suby of* KRAFT GROUP LLC) ★
580 Fort Pond Rd, Lancaster, MA 01523-3224
Tel (978) 870-1188 *Founded/Ownrshp* 2014
Sales 547.8M[E] *EMP* 2,279[E]
SIC 1541 Industrial buildings & warehouses

D-U-N-S 18-208-5126
RAND WORLDWIDE INC
11201 Difeld Blvd Ste 112, Owings Mills, MD 21117
Tel (410) 581-8080 *Founded/Ownrshp* 1986
Sales 86.7MM *EMP* 345
Accts Stegman & Company Baltimore
SIC 7372 7373 Prepackaged software; Systems software development services; Computer systems analysis & design; Computer-aided design (CAD) systems service
Pr: Lawrence Rychlak
CFO: John Kuta
Board of Directors: Peter H Kamin, Philip Livingston, David Schneider

D-U-N-S 12-988-6826
RAND WORLDWIDE SUBSIDIARY INC
IMAGINIT TECHNOLOGIES
(*Suby of* RAND WORLDWIDE INC) ★
11201 Difeld Blvd Ste 112, Owings Mills, MD 21117
Tel (877) 726-3243 *Founded/Ownrshp* 2002
Sales 87.9MM[E] *EMP* 350
SIC 7379 7373 5045 5734 Computer related consulting services; Value-added resellers, computer systems; Computers, peripherals & software; Computer & software stores
CEO: Marc Dulude
**Pr:* Scott Harris
**CFO:* Lawrence Lichlack
VP: Jean Schaffer

D-U-N-S 04-612-8146
RAND-WHITNEY CONTAINER LLC
(*Suby of* RAND-WHITNEY GROUP LLC) ★
1 Agrand St, Worcester, MA 01607-1699
Tel (508) 890-7000 *Founded/Ownrshp* 1967
Sales 85.9MM[E] *EMP* 400
SIC 2653 2631 Boxes, corrugated: made from purchased materials; Paperboard mills
Pr: Robert K Kraft
Software D: Charles Sheehan-Miles
VP Mfg: Dick Dargan
Sfty Dirs: Jeanne Carlo
QC Dir: Steve Long

D-U-N-S 15-778-3358
RAND-WHITNEY GROUP LLC
(*Suby of* KRAFT GROUP LLC) ★
1 Agrand St, Worcester, MA 01607-1699
Tel (508) 791-2301 *Founded/Ownrshp* 1972
Sales 167.9MM[E] *EMP* 733
SIC 2653 2657 2631 Corrugated boxes, partitions, display items, sheets & pad; Folding paperboard boxes; Paperboard mills

D-U-N-S 01-926-5143
RAND-WHITNEY RECYCLING LLC
(*Suby of* KRAFT GROUP LLC) ★
546 Smith Rd, Port Matilda, PA 16870-7901
Tel (814) 692-8045
Sales 111.7M[E] *EMP* 1,823[E]
SIC 4953 Recycling, waste materials

RANDA ACCESSORIES
See RANDA CORP

D-U-N-S 02-817-7231 IMP/EXP
RANDA ACCESSORIES LEATHER GOODS LLC
5600 N River Rd Ste 500, Rosemont, IL 60018-5188
Tel (847) 292-8300 *Founded/Ownrshp* 1918
Sales 433.1MM[E] *EMP* 356
SIC 5136 5948 3172 Apparel belts, men's & boys'; Luggage & leather goods stores; Personal leather goods
CEO: Jeffrey O Spiegel
Ex VP: John Hastings
Sr VP: David J Katz
Sr VP: Mary Rice
Sr VP: Edward Turner
VP Sls: Judith Person

D-U-N-S 00-201-2987 IMP/EXP
RANDA CORP (NY)
RANDA ACCESSORIES
(*Suby of* RANDA ACCESSORIES LEATHER GOODS LLC) ★
417 5th Ave Fl 11, New York, NY 10016-2238
Tel (212) 768-8800 *Founded/Ownrshp* 1935
Sales 144.1MM[E] *EMP* 350
SIC 2323 2389

RANDALL FARMS
See RANDALL FOODS INC

D-U-N-S 03-706-1736
RANDALL FOODS INC
RANDALL FARMS
2905 E 50th St, Vernon, CA 90058-2919
Tel (323) 261-6565 *Founded/Ownrshp* 1952
Sales 198.1MM[E] *EMP* 545
SIC 5147 7299

RANDALL NOE CHRYSLER DDGE JEEP
See RANDALL NOE CHRYSLER DODGE LLP

D-U-N-S 11-991-3197
RANDALL NOE CHRYSLER DODGE LLP
RANDALL NOE CHRYSLER DDGE JEEP
1608 W Moore Ave, Terrell, TX 75160-2308
Tel (972) 524-3775 *Founded/Ownrshp* 1989
Sales 123.8MM[E] *EMP* 135
SIC 5511 Automobiles, new & used
Pr: Randall Noe

D-U-N-S 17-500-1775
RANDALL NOE FORD-MERCURY INC
RANDALL NOE HYUNDAI
1608 W Moore Ave, Terrell, TX 75160-2308
Tel (972) 524-3775 *Founded/Ownrshp* 1986
Sales 90.9MM[E] *EMP* 225[E]
SIC 5511 5521 Automobiles, new & used; Trucks, tractors & trailers: new & used; Vans, new & used; Used car dealers
Pr: Randall Noe
Sls Mgr: Mark Gathwright
Sls Mgr: Donny Luker
Board of Directors: Mark Gathwright, Donny Luker, Chad Sauer

RANDALL NOE HYUNDAI
See RANDALL NOE FORD-MERCURY INC

RANDALL'S
See TOM THUMB FOOD & DRUGS INC

D-U-N-S 05-757-8551
RANDALLS FOOD MARKETS INC
(*Suby of* SAFEWAY INC) ★
3663 Briarpark Dr, Houston, TX 77042-5229
Tel (713) 268-3500 *Founded/Ownrshp* 1999
Sales 1.2MMM[E] *EMP* 17,378
SIC 5411 5912 Grocery stores, chain; Drug stores
Ch Bd: Steven A Burd
VP: Ronnie Brennan
VP: Probes Susan

D-U-N-S 07-158-4361
RANDOLPH COUNTY BOARD OF EDUCATION
2222 S Fayetteville St C, Asheboro, NC 27205-7368
Tel (336) 318-6100 *Founded/Ownrshp* 1900
Sales 72.0MM[E] *EMP* 2,000
SIC 8211 School board
Ch Bd: Todd Cutler

D-U-N-S 07-201-3634 IMP
RANDOLPH HOSPITAL INC
HOME HEALTH RANDOLPH HOSPITAL
364 White Oak St, Asheboro, NC 27203-5400
Tel (336) 625-5151 *Founded/Ownrshp* 1931
Sales 126.0MM *EMP* 975[E]
Accts Lb Cliftonlarsonallen Llp Cha
SIC 8062 General medical & surgical hospitals
CEO: Robert E Morrison
Chf Path: Robert McGee
CFO: Helen Milleson
Bd of Dir: James Campbell Jr
Dir Lab: Johnnie Ingold
Dir Rad: Gary Abode
Brnch Mgr: Leigh Johnson
QA Dir: Patty Yow
Dir IT: Kevin Buchanan

Pr Dir: April Thornton
Pathlgst: Robert Hillard

D-U-N-S 05-511-4250 IMP
RANDOLPH-BROOKS FEDERAL CREDIT UNION
RBFCU
1600 E Court St, Seguin, TX 78155-5203
Tel (210) 945-3300 *Founded/Ownrshp* 1952
Sales NA *EMP* 989
SIC 6061 Federal credit unions
CEO: Randy M Smith
Pr: Elizabeth Apple
Pr: Paula Cerda
Pr: Gilbert Fraga
Pr: Eric Messinger
Pr: Linda Reynolds
COO: John Kelly
COO: Chris O'Connor
Ofcr: Novella Allen
Ofcr: John Corona
Ofcr: Donna Haecker
Ofcr: Damien Martinez
Ofcr: Ryan Panariso
Ofcr: Gerardo Ventura
Ex VP: Sonya McDonald
Ex VP: Drew Schmid
VP: Billy Scott
VP: Berenice Villarreal
Dir Bus: Cassandra Garcia

D-U-N-S 04-128-4951
RANDOLPH-MACON COLLEGE
204 Henry St, Ashland, VA 23005-1634
Tel (804) 752-7200 *Founded/Ownrshp* 1830
Sales 83.0MM *EMP* 46
Accts Brown Edwards & Company Llp B
SIC 8221 College, except junior
Pr: Robert Lindgren
**Ch:* Haywood A Payne Jr
**Ch:* Alan B Rashkind
Treas: Catherine H Best
VP: David Lesesne
VP: Diane M Lowder
Ex Dir: Susan H Donavant
Store Mgr: Barclay F Dupriest

D-U-N-S 00-150-4455 IMP/EXP
RANDOM HOUSE LLC
1745 Broadway Frnt 3, New York, NY 10019-4343
Tel (212) 782-9000 *Founded/Ownrshp* 2013
Sales NA *EMP* 3,600[E]
SIC 5942 2731

RANDSTAD FINANCE & ACCOUNTING
See RANDSTAD PROFESSIONALS US LP

D-U-N-S 09-951-4049
RANDSTAD NORTH AMERICA INC
(*Suby of* RANDSTAD HOLDING NV)
3625 Cumberland Blvd Se, Atlanta, GA 30339-3361
Tel (770) 937-7000 *Founded/Ownrshp* 1994
Sales 22.0MMM[E] *EMP* 225,700
SIC 7363 7361 Temporary help service; Employment agencies
CEO: Linda Galipeau
Pr: Rebecca Callahan
Pr: Robert M Dickey
Pr: Traci Fiatte
Pr: Wendy Su
**CFO:* Denise Dettingmeijer
**Chf Mktg O:* Kristin Kelley
Ex VP: Jill Richards
Sr VP: Greg Dyer
Sr VP: Ken Goodling
VP: Kathryn Bolt
VP: Karen Gonzales
VP: Kathy Van Pelt
Assoc Dir: Geetha Krishnan

D-U-N-S 83-577-1890 IMP
RANDSTAD PROFESSIONALS US LP
RANDSTAD FINANCE & ACCOUNTING
(*Suby of* RANDSTAD NORTH AMERICA INC) ★
150 Presidential Way Fl 4, Woburn, MA 01801-1100
Tel (781) 213-1500 *Founded/Ownrshp* 2008
Sales 518.4MM[E] *EMP* 8,032
Accts Pricewaterhousecoopers Llp
SIC 7361 Employment agencies
CEO: Linda Galipeau
Pr: Daniel J Foley
Ex VP: Teresa Creech
Ex VP: Robert M Dickey
Ex VP: James Fabiano
Ex VP: Steve McMahan
VP: Corey Berghoefer
VP: Cheryl Macmillan
VP: Joel Smith
Mng Dir: Jeffrey Black
Mng Dir: Matt Conley

D-U-N-S 13-825-8038
RANDSTAD TECHNOLOGIES LP
(*Suby of* RANDSTAD FINANCE & ACCOUNTING) ★
150 Presidential Way # 300, Woburn, MA 01801-1100
Tel (781) 938-1910 *Founded/Ownrshp* 2002
Sales 158.5MM[E] *EMP* 1,778
Accts Pricewaterhousecoopers Llp
SIC 7361 Employment agencies
Pr: Daniel J Foley
Pr: Rebecca Callahan
Pr: Bob Dickey
Pr: Traci L Fiatte
Pr: Nasrine Magaletta
CEO: Linda Galipeau
VP: Melita Balestieri
VP: Steve Crawford
VP: John Migliazza
VP: Thomas Weber
Exec: Allison Shepter

D-U-N-S 82-800-1367
RANDSTAD US LP
(*Suby of* RANDSTAD NORTH AMERICA INC) ★
3625 Cumberland Blvd Se, Atlanta, GA 30339-3361
Tel (770) 937-7000 *Founded/Ownrshp* 1999
Sales 1.6MMM[E] *EMP* 125,000
SIC 7361 7363 Employment agencies; Help supply services
Pr: Traci L Fiatte
Pr: Melissa Beuerlein-Fath
Pr: Emily Carlson
Pr: Jill Eubank
Pr: Kathleen Keliher
Pr: Dave Mayr
Pr: Aimee McCauley
Pr: Michael Murray
Pr: Michael Naccarato
Pr: Tony Rehak
Pr: Victoria Riley
Pr: Lisa Tringali
Pr: Elizabeth Williams
Pr: Christine Woo
COO: Jean Pardo
CFO: W Benjamin Elliott
CFO: Ron Fucillo
Ex VP: Teresa Creech
Sr VP: Marc Cirrone
Sr VP: Robin Pickering
Sr VP: Lynn Stoudt

D-U-N-S 06-048-4680
RANGE REGIONAL HEALTH SERVICES
CENTRAL MESABI MEDICAL CENTER
750 E 34th St, Hibbing, MN 55746-4511
Tel (218) 262-4881 *Founded/Ownrshp* 1976
Sales 99.2MM *EMP* 1,058
SIC 8062 General medical & surgical hospitals
CEO: David Murphy
**Ch Bd:* Frances Gardeski
**Ch Bd:* Kathy Sterk
**Pr:* Deborah Boardman
**Pr:* Richard Jenter
CIO: Joe Wivoda
Sls&Mrk Ex: Jessica Schuster

D-U-N-S 11-453-4337
■ **RANGE RESOURCES - APPALACHIA LLC**
(*Suby of* RANGE RESOURCES CORP) ★
3000 Town Center Blvd, Canonsburg, PA 15317-5839
Tel (724) 743-6700 *Founded/Ownrshp* 1999
Sales 174.6MM[E] *EMP* 480
SIC 1382 Oil & gas exploration services
Pr: Jeffrey L Ventura
**CFO:* Roger S Manny
**Ch:* John H Pinkerton
**Sr VP:* Alan W Farquharson

D-U-N-S 07-943-4733
■ **RANGE RESOURCES - LOUISIANA INC**
(*Suby of* RANGE RESOURCES CORP) ★
500 Dallas St Ste 1800, Houston, TX 77002-2067
Tel (713) 588-8300 *Founded/Ownrshp* 2014, 2016
Sales 732.1MM *EMP* 484[E]
SIC 1311 Crude petroleum & natural gas
Pr: Jeffrey L Ventura
COO: Ray N Walker Jr
CFO: Roger S Manny
VP: John K Applegath
VP: Kyle N Roane
Board of Directors: Scott A Gieselman, Kenneth A Hersh, Robert A Innamorati, Carol L O'neill, Pat Wood III

D-U-N-S 06-043-1467
▲ **RANGE RESOURCES CORP**
100 Throckmorton St # 1200, Fort Worth, TX 76102-2842
Tel (817) 870-2601 *Founded/Ownrshp* 1976
Sales 1.6MMM *EMP* 744
Accts Ernst & Young Llp Fort Worth
Tkr Sym RRC *Exch* NYS
SIC 1311 Crude petroleum & natural gas; Crude petroleum production; Natural gas production
Ch Bd: Jeffrey L Ventura
COO: George Fivgas
COO: Ray N Walker Jr
CFO: Roger S Manny
Ex VP: Jeff Ventura
Sr VP: John K Applegath
Sr VP: Alan W Farquharson
Sr VP: Dori A Ginn
Sr VP: Herb A Newhouse
Sr VP: David P Poole
Sr VP: Mark D Whitley
VP: Elie G Atme
VP: Carol Culpepper
VP: David Goldberg
VP: Mark Whitley
Dir Risk M: Kellye Scism
Dir Bus: Curt Tipton
Board of Directors: Kevin S McCarthy, Brenda A Cline, John H Pinkerton, Anthony V Dub, V Richard Eales, Allen Finkelson, James M Funk, Christopher A Helms, Jonathan S Linker, Mary Ralph Lowe, Greg G Maxwell

D-U-N-S 79-769-0666
■ **RANGE SYSTEMS ENGINEERING SUPPORT CO**
(*Suby of* RAYTHEON CO) ★
2 Wayside Rd, Burlington, MA 01803-4605
Tel (781) 983-1396 *Founded/Ownrshp* 1998
Sales 46.0MM[E] *EMP* 2,100
SIC 8711 Engineering services
Ch Bd: Philip T Lepore
**Pr:* Charles E Dry
**Treas:* John J Kryzsiak
**VP:* Anthony A Gargano

D-U-N-S 83-312-0202
RANGER AEROSPACE LLC
128 Millport Cir Ste 200, Greenville, SC 29607-5573
Tel (864) 329-9000 *Founded/Ownrshp* 2001
Sales 100.0MM *EMP* 3
SIC 6719 Personal holding companies, except banks

D-U-N-S 10-179-0079 IMP
RANGER AMERICAN OF PUERTO RICO INC
605 Calle Lodi, San Juan, PR 00924-3822
Tel (787) 999-6060 *Founded/Ownrshp* 1982
Sales 35.0MM *EMP* 1,800
Accts Aquino De Cordova Alfaro & C
SIC 1731 7382 7381 Fire detection & burglar alarm systems specialization; Burglar alarm maintenance & monitoring; Fire alarm maintenance & monitoring; Security guard service
Pr: Juan F Bravo Najul
**CFO:* Hector Rodriguez
IT Man: Nathaniel Roman

RANGER BOATS
See FISHING HOLDINGS LLC

D-U-N-S 00-584-0194 IMP/EXP
RANGER CONSTRUCTION INDUSTRIES INC
(*Suby of* VECELLIO GROUP INC) ★
101 Sansburys Way, West Palm Beach, FL 33411-3693
Tel (561) 793-9400 *Founded/Ownrshp* 1981
Sales 232.4MM[E] *EMP* 800
SIC 1611 General contractor, highway & street construction
Ch Bd: Leo Vecellio Jr
**Pr:* Robert Schafer
**Pr:* Michael Slade
CFO: Patrick Giuliani
**Sec:* Douglas J Browning
**VP:* Miguel G Correa
VP: Miquel Correa
**VP:* F Scott J Fowler
**VP:* Scott Frank
Dir IT: Paula Puckett

D-U-N-S 10-831-4253
■ **RANGER LANDSTAR INC**
(*Suby of* LANDSTAR SYSTEM HOLDINGS INC) ★
13410 Sutton Park Dr S, Jacksonville, FL 32224-5270
Tel (800) 872-9400 *Founded/Ownrshp* 1988
Sales 283.7MM[E] *EMP* 900[E]
SIC 4213 Trucking, except local
CEO: Henry H Gerkens
**CFO:* Ruth C Day
Treas: James B Gattoni
**Ex VP:* Jeff Pundt
**Sr VP:* John B Bowron
**VP:* Joe Beacom
**VP:* Jim B Gattoni
VP: John Higbe
**VP:* Michael Kneller
**VP:* Larry S Thomas
Exec: Wayne Thackston

D-U-N-S 06-422-6525
RANGER PLANT CONSTRUCTIONAL CO INC
5851 E Interstate 20, Abilene, TX 79601-7625
Tel (325) 677-2888 *Founded/Ownrshp* 1973
Sales 158.5MM[E] *EMP* 500
Accts Davis Kinard & Co Pc Abilen
SIC 1623 Natural gas compressor station construction
CFO: Kathrine Freier
**CFO:* Kathrine Freire
VP: Brenda Ball
Admn Mgr: Sylvia Garza

D-U-N-S 36-456-7615 IMP
RANIR LLC
4701 East Paris Ave Se, Grand Rapids, MI 49512-5353
Tel (616) 698-8880 *Founded/Ownrshp* 2005
Sales 179.5MM[E] *EMP* 490
SIC 3843 3991 Dental equipment & supplies; Toothbrushes, except electric
CEO: Christine Henisee
**CFO:* Andre Lebaron
**CFO:* Joseph Townshend
VP: Robbie Criado
VP: Stephen Thong
Off Mgr: Judy Fought
VP Sls: Rebekka Ervin
VP Sls: Nancy Koestler
VP Sls: Lisa Seeley
Mktg Dir: Carin Stefanelli
Mktg Mgr: Sarah Moeggenberg

RANK ONE SPORT
See ALLPLAYERS NETWORK INC

D-U-N-S 18-607-2179
RANKIN COUNTY SCHOOL DISTRICT ASSOCIATION OF EDUCATIONAL OFFICE PERSONNEL INC
RCSD
1220 Apple Park Pl, Brandon, MS 39042-4498
Tel (601) 825-5590 *Founded/Ownrshp* 1940
Sales 168.8MM *EMP* 2,200
Accts Fortenberry & Ballard Pc Bra
SIC 8211 Public elementary & secondary schools
**Pr:* Cecil McCrory
**CFO:* Kevin Brantley
Ofcr: Bo Hynes
**VP:* David Farmer
IT Man: Wayne Carlisle
Pr Dir: Crystal Wendell
Pr Mgr: Marissa Martin

D-U-N-S 06-410-0290 IMP
RANPAK CORP
7990 Auburn Rd, Concord Township, OH 44077-9701
Tel (440) 354-4445 *Founded/Ownrshp* 2015
Sales 89.4MM[E] *EMP* 355
SIC 2621 Packaging paper
Pr: Stephen A Kovach
CFO: Knute Klotz
VP: Joe Vitale
Genl Mgr: Frank Marino
Plnt Mgr: Keith Oress
Sls Mgr: Dan Kirk
Sls Mgr: Karsten Loosen
Sls Mgr: Thomas H Murphy
Sls Mgr: Ryan Wentz

RANSOME CAT
See GILES & RANSOME INC

RAPE SURVIVAL CENTER
See KEAN UNIVERSITY REALTY FOUNDATION INC

D-U-N-S 09-735-2181
RAPID CITY AREA SCHOOL DISTRICT 51 4
RAPID CITY HIGH SCHOOL - 45
300 6th St Ste 2, Rapid City, SD 57701-5035
Tel (605) 394-4031 *Founded/Ownrshp* 1900
Sales 107.2MM[E] *EMP* 1,900
SIC 8211 Public senior high school
Bd of Dir: Laura Schad
**VP:* Brian Blenner
**VP:* Jim Hansen
**Prin:* Sheryl Kirkeby
**Prin:* Bret Swanson
Genl Mgr: David Janak
Teacher Pr: Kristen Strissel
HC Dir: Troy Volesky

RAPID CITY HIGH SCHOOL - 45
See RAPID CITY AREA SCHOOL DISTRICT 51 4

D-U-N-S 06-867-7160 IMP
RAPID CITY REGIONAL HOSPITAL INC
(*Suby of* REGIONAL MEDICAL CLINIC) ★
353 Fairmont Blvd, Rapid City, SD 57701-7393
Tel (605) 719-1000 *Founded/Ownrshp* 1973
Sales 437.5MM *EMP* 4,200
SIC 8062 General medical & surgical hospitals
CEO: Charles Hart
**Treas:* Jim Sorensen
VP: Robert Allen Jr
VP: Allan Berreth
**VP:* Michael Keegan
Dir Rad: Leo P Flynn
Dir Rad: Joanie Hill
Genl Mgr: Nancy Sanders
Off Mgr: Jen Hanson
QA Dir: Shirley S Knodel
Dir IT: Evan Gross
Board of Directors: Elaine Fuhrmann

D-U-N-S 00-511-1216 IMP
RAPID DISPLAYS INC
CADACO DIVISION
4300 W 47th St, Chicago, IL 60632-4404
Tel (773) 927-5000 *Founded/Ownrshp* 1938
Sales 158.3MM[E] *EMP* 400
SIC 2675 3944 Die-cut paper & board; Board games, children's & adults'
CEO: David P Abramson
**Ch:* Earl Abramson
Sr Cor Off: Cadaco John
**VP:* Alan Foshay
**VP:* Brian McCormick
VP: Pierre Pype
CTO: Joe Cissell
Sls&Mrk Ex: Ryan Oakes

D-U-N-S 06-136-8080
RAPID GAS INC
17311 S Main St, Gardena, CA 90248-3131
Tel (310) 323-3992 *Founded/Ownrshp* 1977
Sales 108.3MM[E] *EMP* 500
SIC 5541 Gasoline service stations
Pr: Ronald Appel
**Sec:* Jeff Appel

D-U-N-S 07-935-0547
RAPID GLOBAL BUSINESS SOLUTIONS INC (MI)
RGBSI
1200 Stephenson Hwy, Troy, MI 48083-1115
Tel (248) 589-1135 *Founded/Ownrshp* 1997
Sales 92.5MM[E] *EMP* 710
SIC 8711 7371 7361 Industrial engineers; Consulting engineer; Electrical or electronic engineering; Professional engineer; Computer software development; Employment agencies
Pr: Nanua Singh
**Sr VP:* William F Olsen
**Sr VP:* Howard Puuri
**Sr VP:* Prakash Sathe
**VP:* Ravi Kumar
**VP:* Shweta Kumar

D-U-N-S 07-986-9214
▲ **RAPID7 INC**
100 Summer St Fl 13, Boston, MA 02110-2115
Tel (617) 247-1717 *Founded/Ownrshp* 2000
Sales 110.5MM *EMP* 756[E]
Tkr Sym RPD *Exch* NGM
SIC 7372 Prepackaged software
Pr: Corey E Thomas
COO: Andrew Burton
CFO: Steven Gatoff
Sr VP: Richard Moseley
Board of Directors: Michael Berry, Marc E Brown, Judy Bruner, Benjamin Holzman, Alan Matthews, Timothy McAdam, J Benjamin Nye, Thomas E Schodorf, John Sweeney

D-U-N-S 07-263-0254
■ **RAPIDES HEALTHCARE SYSTEM LLC**
OAKDALE COMM HOSPITAL
(*Suby of* HOSPITAL COPORATION OF AMERICA) ★
211 4th St, Alexandria, LA 71301-8421
Tel (318) 473-3150 *Founded/Ownrshp* 1994
Sales 72.5MM[E] *EMP* 1,661
SIC 8062 5047 General medical & surgical hospitals; Medical equipment & supplies
Mktg Dir: Charla Ducote

D-U-N-S 02-087-9367
RAPIDES PARISH SCHOOL DISTRICT
619 6th St, Alexandria, LA 71301-8150
Tel (318) 487-0888 *Founded/Ownrshp* 1900
Sales 242.5MM *EMP* 3,400
Accts Payne Moore & Herrington Llp
SIC 8211 Public elementary & secondary schools
MIS Dir: Luke Purdy
Dir IT: Dwayne Willis
Schl Brd P: Keith Breazeale
Board of Directors: Herbert Dixon, Kenneth Doyle, Lee Dunbar, Judy McLure, Stan Miller, Ruth O'quinn, Sylvia O Pearson

RAPIDES REGIONAL MED CTR HOSP
See RAPIDES REGIONAL MEDICAL CENTER

D-U-N-S 93-086-5084
RAPIDES REGIONAL MEDICAL CENTER
RAPIDES REGIONAL MED CTR HOSP
211 4th St, Alexandria, LA 71301-8421
Tel (318) 473-3000 *Founded/Ownrshp* 1903
Sales 213.9MM *EMP* 1,300
SIC 8062 General medical & surgical hospitals
CEO: Jason Cobb
**VP:* Dan Davis
VP: Beverly Lowentritt
**VP:* John Williams

Dir Lab: Kim Middleton
Dir Rad: Alfred A Mnsour
Dir Sec: Chuck Butterfield
VP Mktg: Charla Ducote
Doctor: Leo E Futrell III
HC Dir: Kelli Campbell
Board of Directors: Stuart C Head, William D Long, Nicholas P Manuel, Wayne Sibley

D-U-N-S 00-182-3350
RAPPAHANNOCK ELECTRIC COOPERATIVE
247 Industrial Ct, Fredericksburg, VA 22408-2443
Tel (540) 898-8500 *Founded/Ownrshp* 1980
Sales 461.8MM *EMP* 423
SIC 4911 Distribution, electric power
Pr: Kent D Farmer
**Ch:* Darlene H Gray
**Treas:* Thomas T Grady
**VP:* David F Koogler
VP: Brian Wolfe
Dir Teleco: Gary Schwartz
Comm Dir: Ann Lewis
Dist Mgr: Ricky Bywaters
Genl Mgr: Todd Jordan
IT Man: Doug King
Mtls Mgr: Frank Jerow

RAPTIM HUMANITARIAN TRAVEL
See RAPTIM INTERNATIONAL TRAVEL INC

D-U-N-S 96-800-5350
RAPTIM INTERNATIONAL TRAVEL INC
RAPTIM HUMANITARIAN TRAVEL
6420 Inducon Dr W Ste A, Sanborn, NY 14132-9025
Tel (716) 754-2946 *Founded/Ownrshp* 1983
Sales 92.7MM[E] *EMP* 8,100
SIC 4724 Travel agencies
**CFO:* Ronald Tartnt
**VP:* Tim Childs
Prgrm Mgr: Jordan Judd
Off Admin: Gina Anastasi
Opers Mgr: Leanna Chapman

D-U-N-S 83-965-1572
RAPTOR PHARMACEUTICAL CORP
7 Hamilton Landing # 100, Novato, CA 94949-8209
Tel (415) 408-6200 *Founded/Ownrshp* 1997
Sales 94.2MM *EMP* 158[E]
SIC 8733 2834 Medical research; Pharmaceutical preparations
Pr: Timothy P Walbert
COO: Barry J Moze
CFO: Paul W Hoelscher
Ofcr: Robert F Carey
VP: Monica Yost
Assoc Dir: Jeremy Boucher
Assoc Dir: Roland Gendron
Ex Dir: Katarina Ilic
Genl Mgr: Sissel Rodahl
Genl Couns: Ashley Gould

D-U-N-S 10-200-8349
■ **RARE HOSPITALITY INTERNATIONAL INC**
OLIVE GARDEN
(*Suby of* DARDEN RESTAURANTS INC) ★
7469 Brokerage Dr, Orlando, FL 32809-5623
Tel (407) 245-5042 *Founded/Ownrshp* 2007
Sales 510.1MM[E] *EMP* 19,773
SIC 5812 Grills (eating places); Steak restaurant
CEO: William R White
Pr: Eugene I Lee Jr
Pr: John Martin
CEO: Philip J Hickey Jr
CFO: Douglas W Benn
CFO: W Douglas Benn
Founder: George McKerrow Jr
VP: Cathy D Hampton
VP: Benjamin A Waites
Exec: Jim Nuetzi
Mng Dir: Anthony McCallum

D-U-N-S 06-869-7747 IMP/EXP
RARITAN BAY MEDICAL CENTER A NEW JERSEY NONPROFIT CORP
PERTH AMBOY DIVISION
(*Suby of* MERIDIAN HOSPITAL) ★
530 New Brunswick Ave, Perth Amboy, NJ 08861-3685
Tel (732) 442-3700 *Founded/Ownrshp* 2014
Sales 238.6MM *EMP* 1,970
SIC 8062 Hospital, medical school affiliation
Pr: Michael R Dagnes
**Ch Bd:* Mark Danielle
**COO:* Ronald Esser
**CFO:* Thomas Shanahan
**Chf Mktg O:* John Middleton
Dir IT: Lydia Trinidad
VP Opers: William F Di Stanislao

D-U-N-S 83-000-6016 IMP
RARITAN INC
(*Suby of* LEGRAND NORTH AMERICA LLC) ★
400 Cottontail Ln, Somerset, NJ 08873-1238
Tel (732) 764-8886 *Founded/Ownrshp* 2005
Sales 84.4MM[E] *EMP* 397[E]
SIC 3612 3577 Transformers, except electric; Computer peripheral equipment
Pr: Doug Fikse
CFO: Joe Delong
Sr VP: Rasul Damji
VP: Daniel Moran
Opers Mgr: Don Velard
Natl Sales: Todd Hinckley
Mktg Mgr: Nicole Espasa
Manager: John Morse
Manager: Dana Pruitt
Sls Mgr: Anna Kraemer
Sls Mgr: Chris Trovato

RASCAL'S CONVENIENCE STORE
See GRAVES OIL CO

D-U-N-S 36-461-1079
RASMUSSEN GROUP INC
5550 Ne 22nd St, Des Moines, IA 50313-2530
Tel (515) 266-5173 *Founded/Ownrshp* 1974
Sales 188.0MM[E] *EMP* 600
Accts Mc Gladrey & Pullen
SIC 1622 1611 3272 Bridge construction; Resurfacing contractor; Paving materials, prefabricated concrete
Pr: Kurt E Rasmussen
**CFO:* Wayne Nyberg
**VP:* Jeffry L Rasmussen

D-U-N-S 16-234-0157
RASMUSSEN INC
1415 W 22nd St Ste 400, Oak Brook, IL 60523-2023
Tel (630) 366-2800 *Founded/Ownrshp* 2004
Sales 82.0MM[E] *EMP* 2,450
SIC 8299 Educational services
Ch: Henry S Bienen
**Pr:* Thomas Slagle
**CEO:* Michael Locke
**CFO:* Patrick Branham
Sr VP: Florence Richman
**VP:* J Michael Locke
**CIO:* Marshall Lancaster

D-U-N-S 01-230-6445 IMP/EXP
RASTELLI BROTHERS INC
RASTELLI'S FOODS
300 Heron Dr, Swedesboro, NJ 08085-1707
Tel (856) 803-1100 *Founded/Ownrshp* 1980
Sales 130.0MM[E] *EMP* 125
SIC 5147 5421 2011 Meats, fresh; Meat markets, including freezer provisioners; Canned meats (except baby food), meat slaughtered on site
Pr: Ray Rastelli
**CFO:* Paul Zaun
**VP:* Anthony Rastelli
VP: Patrick Ternyila
Exec: Victor Orsini
Dir Bus: John Luce
Rgnl Mgr: John Roehm
Genl Mgr: Fabio Capone
IT Man: Edward Buehler
Mktg Dir: Lauren Rastelli
Manager: Paul Malvestuto

RASTELLI GLOBAL
See GLOBAL TRADING ENTERPRISES LLC

RASTELLI'S FOODS
See RASTELLI BROTHERS INC

D-U-N-S 96-644-5322
RATCLIFF CONSTRUCTORS LP
4200 Beltway Dr, Addison, TX 75001-3701
Tel (972) 432-9969 *Founded/Ownrshp* 1997
Sales 93.4MM *EMP* 40
SIC 1542 Commercial & office building contractors; Commercial & office buildings, renovation & repair
Pt: Max K Young
Genl Pt: R T Ratcliff Jr
Pt: Robert T Ratcliff
CFO: Joseph L Hebert

D-U-N-S 96-423-6207
■ **RATHGIBSON HOLDING CO LLC**
(*Suby of* PCC) ★
2505 Foster Ave, Janesville, WI 53545-0814
Tel (608) 754-2222 *Founded/Ownrshp* 2010
Sales 173.4MM[E] *EMP* 540
SIC 3317 5051 Tubing, mechanical or hypodermic sizes: cold drawn stainless; Metals service centers & offices
CEO: Mark Essig
**CFO:* Will Wolf
VP: William Anacker

D-U-N-S 00-607-5634 IMP
■ **RATHGIBSON LLC**
(*Suby of* PCC) ★
2505 Foster Ave, Janesville, WI 53545-0814
Tel (608) 754-2222 *Founded/Ownrshp* 1952, 2010
Sales 114.4MM[E] *EMP* 530
SIC 3317 Tubing, mechanical or hypodermic sizes: cold drawn stainless
VP: Timothy L Thomsen
VP: James W Coenen
VP: John Fortin
VP Admn: Bill Anacker
MIS Mgr: Audra Mandel
Opers Mgr: Monty Kuxhaus
VP Mktg: Frank Fenton
Mktg Dir: Jody Hamilton
Sales Asso: Jamie Gottschalk
Sales Asso: Pat Weaver

D-U-N-S 00-256-1835 IMP
■ **RATHGIBSON NORTH BRANCH LLC**
(*Suby of* RATHGIBSON HOLDING CO LLC) ★
100 Aspen Hill Rd, Branchburg, NJ 08876-3563
Tel (908) 253-3260 *Founded/Ownrshp* 2010
Sales 173.4MM[E] *EMP* 180
SIC 3317 Tubing, mechanical or hypodermic sizes: cold drawn stainless
Bd of Dir: Frank Fenton
VP: Kevin Campbell
VP: Dave Padowski
CIO: John Farr
Dir IT: Chris Hannemann
Web Prj Mg: Tad Austin
QC Dir: Anthony Graviano
Plnt Mgr: Paul Monaco
Plnt Mgr: Joseph Waldinger
Sls Mgr: Barry Jakimer

D-U-N-S 14-431-9464
RATHJE ENTERPRISES INC
BODINE ELECTRIC OF DECATUR
1845 N 22nd St, Decatur, IL 62526-5113
Tel (217) 423-2593 *Founded/Ownrshp* 1965
Sales 89.2MM[E] *EMP* 300
Accts Bkd Llp Decatur Il
SIC 1731 7694 5063 Electrical work; Armature rewinding shops; Electrical supplies
Pr: David W Rathje
**Pr:* Harry B Rakers
**Ex VP:* Jeanne Jones
Dir IT: Thad Meyers

D-U-N-S 10-192-5626
RATNER COMPANIES LC
(*Suby of* CREATIVE HAIRDRESSERS INC) ★
1577 Spring Hill Rd # 500, Vienna, VA 22182-2223
Tel (703) 269-5400 *Founded/Ownrshp* 1974
Sales 242.2MM[E] *EMP* 10,000
SIC 7231 Beauty shops
CEO: Dennis Ratner
**Pr:* Susan Gustafson
VP: Harold V Dingeles
VP: Rich Gatti
IT Man: David Cunningham

D-U-N-S 19-935-6460
RATNER STEEL SUPPLY CO
2500 County Road B W 1a, Saint Paul, MN 55113-3873
Tel (219) 787-6700 *Founded/Ownrshp* 1986
Sales 192.7MM[E] *EMP* 45[E]
SIC 5051 7389 Steel; Metal slitting & shearing
Pr: Mark Ratner
**VP:* Steve Gottlieb
Opers Mgr: Dennis Szymanski
Prd Mgr: Tony Steppat
Sls Mgr: Pat Dougherty
Sls Mgr: Kathi Matejka
Sales Asso: Amy Hines

D-U-N-S 02-024-8668
RATP DEV USA LLC
(*Suby of* REGIE AUTONOME TRANSPORTS PARISI)
295 Madison Ave Fl 29, New York, NY 10017-6350
Tel (646) 927-0201 *Founded/Ownrshp* 2010
Sales 117.2MM[E] *EMP* 409
SIC 4151 School buses
CEO: Catherine Chardon
**CFO:* Thierry Deleger
Dir Bus: Lucrecia Milla

D-U-N-S 00-510-5515 IMP
RAULAND-BORG CORP
(*Suby of* LOMAR CORPORATION)
1802 W Central Rd, Mount Prospect, IL 60056-2230
Tel (847) 590-7100 *Founded/Ownrshp* 1995
Sales 90.0MM[E] *EMP* 300[E]
SIC 3661 3663

D-U-N-S 11-850-5346
RAV INVESTIGATIVE & SECURITIES SERVICES LTD
347 W 36th St, New York, NY 10018-6406
Tel (212) 447-7777 *Founded/Ownrshp* 1980
Sales 13.3MM *EMP* 1,000
SIC 6211 Security brokers & dealers
Pr: Ron Allen

RAVAGO AMERICAS
See RAVAGO HOLDINGS AMERICA INC

D-U-N-S 07-949-7498
RAVAGO AMERICAS LLC
POLYMERLINE
(*Suby of* RAVAGO AMERICAS) ★
1900 Summit Tower Blvd, Orlando, FL 32810-5939
Tel (407) 875-9595 *Founded/Ownrshp* 2003
Sales 1.2MMM[E] *EMP* 520[E]
SIC 5162 Plastics resins
Pr: James Duffy
CFO: Jeffrey Bittenbinder
VP: John Provost

D-U-N-S 80-788-3819 IMP
RAVAGO HOLDINGS AMERICA INC
RAVAGO AMERICAS
(*Suby of* RAVAGO PLASTICS NV)
1900 Summit Tower Blvd, Orlando, FL 32810-5939
Tel (407) 875-9595 *Founded/Ownrshp* 2006
Sales 2.0MMM[E] *EMP* 855
SIC 5162 Plastics resins
Pr: James Duffy
CFO: Jeff Bittenbinder
VP: Mark Appelbaum
VP: Damian M Mullin
VP: Ronald Nardozzi
VP: John Provost

D-U-N-S 96-262-0592
RAVE CINEMAS LLC
3333 Welborn St Ste 100, Dallas, TX 75219-5153
Tel (214) 220-7600 *Founded/Ownrshp* 2009
Sales NA *EMP* 3,400
SIC 7832

D-U-N-S 00-725-7348 IMP
▲ **RAVEN INDUSTRIES INC**
205 E 6th St, Sioux Falls, SD 57104-5931
Tel (605) 336-2750 *Founded/Ownrshp* 1956
Sales 258.2MM *EMP* 910
Tkr Sym RAVN *Exch* NGS
SIC 5065 3523 3081 3823 3083 Electronic parts; Farm machinery & equipment; Unsupported plastics film & sheet; Industrial instrmnts msrmnt display/control process variable; Laminated plastics plate & sheet
Pr: Daniel A Rykhus
**Ch Bd:* Thomas S Everist
CFO: Steven E Brazones
VP: Stephanie Herseth Sandlin
VP Admn: Barbara Ohme
Prgrm Mgr: Laura Zumhofe
Genl Mgr: Brian E Meyer
Genl Mgr: Anthony D Schmidt
Sales Asso: Lori Christensen
Board of Directors: Jason M Andringa, Mark E Griffin, Kevin T Kirby, Marc E Lebaron, Heather Wilson

D-U-N-S 07-861-2047
■ **RAVEN POWER FINANCE LLC**
(*Suby of* TALEN ENERGY SUPPLY LLC) ★
2901 Via Fortuna Ste 600, Austin, TX 78746-7710
Tel (512) 314-8600 *Founded/Ownrshp* 2012, 2015
Sales 179.7MM[E] *EMP* 400
SIC 4911
Pr: Chuck Cook
**Genl Couns:* Janet Jamieson

D-U-N-S 07-861-1996
■ **RAVEN POWER GROUP LLC**
(*Suby of* TALEN ENERGY SUPPLY LLC) ★
2901 Via Fortuna Ste 600, Austin, TX 78746-7710
Tel (512) 314-8600 *Founded/Ownrshp* 2015
Sales 250.0MM[E] *EMP* 453
SIC 4911
Pr: Chuck Cook

D-U-N-S 08-763-3933
■ **RAVEN POWER OPERATING LLC**
(*Suby of* TALEN ENERGY SUPPLY LLC) ★
1000 Brandon Shores Rd, Baltimore, MD 21226-1746
Tel (410) 255-3072 *Founded/Ownrshp* 2015
Sales 126.6MM[E] *EMP* 456[E]
SIC 4911 Electric services

D-U-N-S 16-183-6598
RAVEN TRANSPORT CO INC
6800 Broadway Ave, Jacksonville, FL 32254-2762
Tel (904) 880-1515 *Founded/Ownrshp* 1985
Sales 93.0MM[E] *EMP* 585
SIC 4213 Contract haulers
Pr: Wrandolph Lee
**COO:* Stephen Silverman
CFO: Michele Baum
Genl Couns: Bill Wiese

D-U-N-S 05-889-0273
■ **RAVEN VENTURES LLC**
(*Suby of* RR DONNELLEY) ★
15 Wellman Ave, North Chelmsford, MA 01863-1334
Tel (978) 251-6000 *Founded/Ownrshp* 2015
Sales 112.5MM[E] *EMP* 1,038[E]
SIC 2731 Book publishing

RAVICTI
See HORIZON THERAPEUTICS INC

RAVN AIR GROUP
See HOTH INC

D-U-N-S 87-756-2603
RAWLINGS CO LLC
1 Eden Pkwy, La Grange, KY 40031-8100
Tel (502) 587-1279 *Founded/Ownrshp* 1994
Sales 96.9MM[E] *EMP* 950
SIC 8748 8111 Business consulting; Legal services
Pr: George Rawlings
VP: Matthew Birdwell
VP: Ileana Roman
**Prin:* Beverly Rawlings
Genl Mgr: Mark Fischer
Genl Mgr: Laura Plumley
IT Man: Bret McKinney

RAWLINGS GROUP
See RAWLINGS SPORTING GOODS CO INC

D-U-N-S 86-117-7327 IMP
■ **RAWLINGS SPORTING GOODS CO INC**
RAWLINGS GROUP
(*Suby of* NEWELL BRANDS) ★
510 Maryville University, Saint Louis, MO 63141-5821
Tel (866) 678-4327 *Founded/Ownrshp* 2003
Sales 809.6MM[E] *EMP* 1,600
SIC 3949 5091 Sporting & athletic goods; Baseball equipment & supplies, general; Basketball equipment & supplies, general; Football equipment & supplies, general; Sporting & recreation goods
Pr: Michael Zlaket
**COO:* Jeff Fiorini
VP: Greg Bialis
**VP:* Mark Malone
Creative D: Jeff France
**Prin:* Tonya Reynolds
Prd Mgr: Bill Garbe
Sls Mgr: Randy Kirby
Sls Mgr: Rich Scipione
Sls Mgr: Jim White

D-U-N-S 00-786-1842 IMP/EXP
RAWSON LP
2010 Mcallister Rd, Houston, TX 77092-8413
Tel (713) 684-1400 *Founded/Ownrshp* 1954, 2003
Sales 110.5MM[E] *EMP* 180
SIC 5085 5084

D-U-N-S 08-324-4442
RAY ANGELINI INC
R A I
105 Blckwood Barnsboro Rd, Sewell, NJ 08080-4201
Tel (856) 228-5566 *Founded/Ownrshp* 1973
Sales 97.0MM[E] *EMP* 300
Accts Mayer Hoffman Mccann Pc Ply
SIC 1731 1711 8741 General electrical contractor; Solar energy contractor; Construction management
Pr: Ray Angelini
**Sec:* Lorrie Merkins

D-U-N-S 06-266-4842
RAY BRANDT NISSAN INC (LA)
BRANDT, RAY NISSAN-DODGE
4000 Lapalco Blvd, Harvey, LA 70058-2373
Tel (504) 367-1666 *Founded/Ownrshp* 1972, 1983
Sales 99.3MM[E] *EMP* 299
SIC 5511 5521 Automobiles, new & used; Used car dealers
Pr: Raymond J Brandt

D-U-N-S 00-890-7776 EXP
RAY CARROLL COUNTY GRAIN GROWERS INC
807 W Main St, Richmond, MO 64085-1321
Tel (816) 776-2291 *Founded/Ownrshp* 1931
Sales 161.7MM[E] *EMP* 120
SIC 5171 5191 5153 Petroleum bulk stations; Farm supplies; Fertilizer & fertilizer materials; Feed; Grains
VP: Thomas White III
Genl Mgr: Michael Nordwald
Genl Mgr: Marvin Ritchason

D-U-N-S 02-694-7077
RAY LEE EQUIPMENT CO LTD (TX)
JOHN DEERE
910 N Date St, Plainview, TX 79072-7348
Tel (806) 293-2538 *Founded/Ownrshp* 1944, 2005
Sales 130.0MM *EMP* 134

SIC 5083 7699

D-U-N-S 06-680-5714 IMP
RAY MURRAY INC
50 Limestone, Lee, MA 01238-9621
Tel (413) 243-7700 *Founded/Ownrshp* 1973
Sales 95.9MM[E] *EMP* 71
SIC 5085 5091 Industrial supplies; Gas equipment, parts & supplies; Diving equipment & supplies
CEO: Raymond B Murray III
**CEO:* Micheal R Hopsicker
**Treas:* Katherine Amy Consolati
**VP:* Jonathan Gray
**VP:* James M Murray
**VP:* John E Murray
IT Man: Keith Ives
Sales Exec: Jay Sackett
Sls Dir: Casey Harvey
Manager: Walter Carroll
Manager: Marc Christian

D-U-N-S 62-436-8601
RAYBURN COUNTRY ELECTRIC COOPERATIVE INC
RAYBURN ELECTRIC COOP
980 Sids Rd, Rockwall, TX 75032-6512
Tel (972) 771-1336 *Founded/Ownrshp* 1979
Sales 301.3MM *EMP* 8
SIC 4911 Generation, electric power; Transmission, electric power; Distribution, electric power
Pr: John Kirkland
**CFO:* Loretto Martin

RAYBURN ELECTRIC COOP
See RAYBURN COUNTRY ELECTRIC COOPERATIVE INC

D-U-N-S 82-478-8434 IMP
RAYCAP INC
(*Suby of* RAYCAP (CYPRUS) LIMITED)
806 S Clearwater Loop, Post Falls, ID 83854-6937
Tel (208) 457-0895 *Founded/Ownrshp* 2008
Sales 160.0MM *EMP* 200[E]
Accts Moss Adams Llp Spokane Wa
SIC 3643 5063 Current-carrying wiring devices; Electrical apparatus & equipment
Ch Bd: Costas Apostolidis
**Pr:* Kostantinos Samaras
CFO: Lisa Duckett
**Treas:* Nikolaos Birakis
**VP:* Chad Farrar
IT Man: Mike Cousins
Sls Mgr: Allan Aitken
Sls Mgr: Mike Smith

D-U-N-S 94-869-4641
RAYCOM MEDIA INC
201 Monroe St Fl 20, Montgomery, AL 36104-3601
Tel (334) 206-1400 *Founded/Ownrshp* 1996
Sales 1.2MMM[E] *EMP* 3,650
SIC 4833 4832 Television broadcasting stations; Radio broadcasting stations
Pr: Paul McTear
**Ch Bd:* John Stein
Ex VP: Charles Daugherty
Ex VP: Susana Schuler
**Sr VP:* Pat Laplatney
VP: Sandy Breland
**VP:* Rebecca Bryan
VP: David Burke
**VP:* Wayne Daugherty
**VP:* Leon Long
**VP:* Don Richards
**VP:* Jeff Rosser
VP: Lyle Schulze
**VP:* Melissa Thurber

D-U-N-S 04-635-6358
RAYCOM SPORTS NETWORK INC (NC)
LINCOLN FINANCIAL SPORTS, INC.
(*Suby of* RAYCOM MEDIA INC) ★
1900 W Morehead St, Charlotte, NC 28208-5228
Tel (704) 378-4400 *Founded/Ownrshp* 1968, 2007
Sales NA *EMP* 3,100
SIC 6311 6321 6324 6411 4832 4833 Mutual association life insurance; Life insurance carriers; Accident insurance carriers; Health insurance carriers; Dental insurance; Group hospitalization plans; Property & casualty insurance agent; Radio broadcasting stations; Television broadcasting stations
Ch Bd: David A Stonecipher
Pr: Dennis R Glass
COO: Hunter Nickell
CFO: Theresa M Stone
Ex VP: Charles C Cornelio
Ex VP: Donald L McDonald
Sr VP: Jeff Tennant
Exec: Leon E Porter Jr

D-U-N-S 06-469-0654 IMP/EXP
RAYMOND BUILDING SUPPLY
RAYMOND BUILDING SUPPLY, LLC
(*Suby of* US LBM HOLDINGS LLC) ★
7751 Bayshore Rd, Fort Myers, FL 33917-3506
Tel (941) 429-1212 *Founded/Ownrshp* 1957
Sales 114.2MM[E] *EMP* 400
SIC 5211 2439 2431 3442 2434 3634 Millwork & lumber; Trusses, wooden roof; Doors, wood; Metal doors; Wood kitchen cabinets; Electric household cooking appliances
CEO: Duane Swanson Jr
**Pr:* Duane Swanson
Ofcr: William Laakkonen
**Ex VP:* Brian Martin
Sales Exec: Shane McComb

RAYMOND BUILDING SUPPLY, LLC
See RAYMOND BUILDING SUPPLY

D-U-N-S 61-775-6481 IMP/EXP
RAYMOND CONSOLIDATED CORP
(*Suby of* TOYOTA MATERIAL HANDLING EUROPE AB)
22 S Canal St, Greene, NY 13778-1244
Tel (800) 235-7200 *Founded/Ownrshp* 1994
Sales 890.1MM[E] *EMP* 2,260
SIC 3537 Industrial trucks & tractors
Pr: Jim Malvaso
**CFO:* Edward J Rompala
**Ex VP:* Timothy Combs
**VP:* John Everts
Prgrm Mgr: John Rosenberger
Ql Cn Mgr: Ryan Delaney

D-U-N-S 00-223-3856 IMP/EXP
RAYMOND CORP (NY)
(*Suby of* RAYMOND CONSOLIDATED CORP) ★
22 S Canal St, Greene, NY 13778-1244
Tel (607) 656-2311 *Founded/Ownrshp* 1987, 1997
Sales 890.1MM[E] *EMP* 2,260
Accts Pricewaterhousecoopers Llp
SIC 3537 3535 7359 Industrial trucks & tractors; Lift trucks, industrial: fork, platform, straddle, etc.; Forklift trucks; Straddle carriers, mobile; Conveyors & conveying equipment; Belt conveyor systems, general industrial use; Pneumatic tube conveyor systems; Equipment rental & leasing; Aircraft & industrial truck rental services
Pr: Michael G Field
**CFO:* Edward J Rompala
Ofcr: Tim Koval
**Ex VP:* Timothy Combs
VP: Richard Harrington
**VP:* Rick Harrington
**VP:* Patrick J Mc Manus
VP: James O'Brien
**VP:* Jim O'Brien
VP: John Osterhout
**VP:* Stephen E Vannostrand

D-U-N-S 11-948-4728
RAYMOND HANDLING SOLUTIONS INC
(*Suby of* RAYMOND CORP) ★
9939 Norwalk Blvd, Santa Fe Springs, CA 90670-3321
Tel (562) 944-8067 *Founded/Ownrshp* 2002
Sales 152.3MM[E] *EMP* 217[E]
SIC 5084 7699 7359 Industrial machinery & equipment; Industrial machinery & equipment repair; Industrial truck rental
CEO: James Wilcox
CFO: Dale Adams
Dir Bus: Chris Bausley
VP Sls: Scott Stowers

D-U-N-S 04-710-7032
■ **RAYMOND JAMES & ASSOCIATES INC**
(*Suby of* RAYMOND JAMES FINANCIAL INC) ★
880 Carillon Pkwy, Saint Petersburg, FL 33716-1100
Tel (727) 567-1000 *Founded/Ownrshp* 1974
Sales 2.8MMM *EMP* 10,000
Accts Kpmg Llp Tampa Florida
SIC 6211 6722 8741 Brokers, security; Dealers, security; Investment bankers; Management investment, open-end; Financial management for business
Ch Bd: Thomas A James
**CEO:* Paul Reilly
CFO: Richard Franz
**CFO:* Jeffrey P Julien
CFO: Toni S Matthews
Ofcr: Pete Bursik
Ofcr: Nancy Randazzo
Assoc VP: Cliff Cook
Assoc VP: Kerry Kinsella
Assoc VP: Gary J Stempinski
Assoc VP: Bill Waters
**Ex VP:* Bella Loykhter Allaire
**Ex VP:* Dennis W Zank
Sr VP: Lisa Detanna
Sr VP: George J Garro
VP: Richard Caccamise
VP: Rick Cargo
VP: Daniel Horgan
VP: Kevin Kilbane
Creative D: Susan Futterman

D-U-N-S 88-432-8659
■ **RAYMOND JAMES BANK NATIONAL ASSOCIATION**
(*Suby of* RAYMOND JAMES FINANCIAL INC) ★
710 Carillon Pkwy, Saint Petersburg, FL 33716-1101
Tel (727) 567-8000 *Founded/Ownrshp* 1994
Sales NA *EMP* 72
SIC 6035 Federal savings & loan associations
Pr: Steve Raney
CFO: Marty Gladysz

D-U-N-S 07-759-2889
▲ **RAYMOND JAMES FINANCIAL INC**
880 Carillon Pkwy, Saint Petersburg, FL 33716-1100
Tel (727) 567-1000 *Founded/Ownrshp* 1962
Sales 5.5MMM *EMP* 11,000
Accts Kpmg Llp Tampa Florida
Tkr Sym RJF *Exch* NYS
SIC 6211 Brokers, security; Dealers, security; Investment bankers; Traders, security
CEO: Paul C Reilly
**Ch Bd:* Thomas A James
Pr: Don Carlton
Pr: John C Carson Jr
Pr: Karen Fry
Pr: Raymond James
Pr: Jonathan Lewis
Pr: Paul Mahfouz
Pr: Alyssa Meyer
Pr: Brian Miller
Pr: Linda Neri
Pr: David Oras
COO: Dennis W Zank
CFO: Jeffrey P Julien
**V Ch Bd:* Francis S Godbold
Chf Cred: Jannu Sousa
Bd of Dir: Mike Brewi
Bd of Dir: Michael Ohlman
Bd of Dir: Lynn Pippenger
Ofcr: Robert Blenis
Assoc VP: Michael Lowe
Board of Directors: Shelley G Broader, Jeffrey N Edwards, Benjamin C Esty, Gordon L Johnson, Roderick C McGeary, Robert P Saltzman, Susan N Story, Charles Von Arentschildt

D-U-N-S 07-758-0199
■ **RAYMOND JAMES FINANCIAL SERVICES INC**
(*Suby of* RAYMOND JAMES FINANCIAL INC) ★
880 Carillon Pkwy, Saint Petersburg, FL 33716-1100
Tel (727) 567-1000 *Founded/Ownrshp* 1974
Sales 164.1MM[E] *EMP* 160
SIC 6211 6282 6712 6091 6035 Brokers, security; Investment advice; Bank holding companies; Nondeposit trust facilities; Savings institutions, federally chartered
Pr: Scott A Curtis
**Ch Bd:* Richard G Averitt III
**Treas:* Richard B Franz II
**Ex VP:* John Putnam
**Sr VP:* Richard Saunders
**VP:* Margie Blue
**VP:* Michael J Di Girolamo
**VP:* Robert Hinson
**VP:* William D McGovern
Board of Directors: Don E Foster,william Van L

D-U-N-S 09-634-1466
RAYMOND MANAGEMENT CO INC (WI)
8333 Greenway Blvd # 200, Middleton, WI 53562-3684
Tel (608) 833-4100 *Founded/Ownrshp* 1978
Sales 167.8MM[E] *EMP* 900
SIC 6552 8741 7011 Subdividers & developers; Hotel or motel management; Hotels & motels
Pr: Charles J Raymond
**VP:* Theodore C Widder
Exec: William Ray
Sls Dir: Teresa Blythe
Sls Mgr: Jacob Neubauer

D-U-N-S 00-526-8214 IMP
RAYMOND-MUSCATINE INC
BT PRIME MOVER
(*Suby of* TOYOTA INDUSTRIES CORPORATION)
3305 N Highway 38, Muscatine, IA 52761-8801
Tel (563) 262-7700 *Founded/Ownrshp* 1950
Sales 104.0MM[E] *EMP* 301
SIC 3537 Lift trucks, industrial: fork, platform, straddle, etc.; Skids, metal
Prin: Arthur Goodell
**CFO:* Edward J Rompala
Snr Mgr: Mary Irick

RAYMOUR & FLANIGAN
See RAYMOURS FURNITURE CO INC

D-U-N-S 01-327-3065 IMP/EXP
RAYMOURS FURNITURE CO INC (NY)
RAYMOUR & FLANIGAN
7248 Morgan Rd, Liverpool, NY 13090-4535
Tel (315) 453-2500 *Founded/Ownrshp* 1947
Sales 1.2MMM[E] *EMP* 4,400
Accts Green & Seifter Syracuse New
SIC 5712 Furniture stores
Ch Bd: Neil Goldberg
**CFO:* James Poole
**Ex VP:* Michael Goldberg
Sales Exec: Amir Hadjarian

RAYNOR GARAGE DOOR
See NEISEWANDER ENTERPRISES INC

RAYNOR GARAGE DOORS
See RAYNOR MFG CO

D-U-N-S 00-516-2987 IMP/EXP
RAYNOR MFG CO
RAYNOR GARAGE DOORS
(*Suby of* RAYNOR GARAGE DOOR) ★
1101 E River Rd, Dixon, IL 61021-3277
Tel (815) 288-1431 *Founded/Ownrshp* 1974
Sales 269.9MM[E] *EMP* 1,800
SIC 3442 7011 3699 2431 Garage doors, overhead: metal; Hotels; Electrical equipment & supplies; Millwork
Pr: Ray N Heisewander III
COO: Marianna Raynor
Rgnl Mgr: Craig Walden
Dir IT: Jim Foster
Dir IT: Patrick Hodapp
Sfty Mgr: Dan Coy
Opers Mgr: Gary Sneek
VP Sls: Rick Considine
Manager: Christopher Walter
Board of Directors: John Neisewander Sr, Catherine Vespa

D-U-N-S 07-935-7843
▲ **RAYONIER ADVANCED MATERIALS INC** (FL)
1301 Riverplace Blvd # 2300, Jacksonville, FL 32207-9047
Tel (904) 357-4600 *Founded/Ownrshp* 1926
Sales 941.3MM *EMP* 1,200[E]
Tkr Sym RYAM *Exch* NYS
SIC 2821 2823 Plastics materials & resins; Cellulose derivative materials; Cellulosic manmade fibers
Ch Bd: Paul G Boynton
CFO: Frank A Ruperto
Sr VP: Michael R Herman
Sr VP: Charles H Hood
Sr VP: James L Posze Jr
VP: Rick Bash
VP: John P Carr
VP: William R Manzer
Comm Dir: Russell Schweiss
Board of Directors: Charles E Adair, C David Brown II, Mark E Gaumond, James F Kirsch, Thomas I Morgan, Lisa M Palumbo, Ronald Townsend

D-U-N-S 00-126-5263 IMP/EXP
▲ **RAYONIER INC** (NC)
225 Water St Ste 1400, Jacksonville, FL 32202-5175
Tel (904) 357-9100 *Founded/Ownrshp* 1926
Sales 544.8MM *EMP* 325
Accts Ernst & Young Llp Jacksonvill
Tkr Sym RYN *Exch* NYS
SIC 6798 5099 6552 5031 Real estate investment trusts; Timber products, rough; Land subdividers & developers, commercial; Lumber, plywood & millwork
Pr: David L Nunes
**Ch Bd:* Richard D Kincaid
CFO: Mark McHugh
Sr VP: W S Bing
Sr VP: Christopher T Corr
VP: Charles Adams
VP: Parag Bhansali
VP: Mark R Bridwell
VP: Mike Burch
VP: Mark Ford
VP: H Edwin Kiker
VP: Joseph Lannotti
VP: Douglas Long
VP: Douglas M Long
VP: Kevin Obrien
VP: Daniel Sassy
VP: James M Stackpoole
VP: Alan Wilson
Board of Directors: John A Blumberg, Scott R Jones, Bernard Lanigan Jr, Blanche L Lincoln, V Larkin Martin, Andrew G Wiltshire

RAYONIER NW FOREST RESOURCES
See FOREST RAYONIER RESOURCES LP

D-U-N-S 14-219-9368 IMP/EXP
■ **RAYONIER PERFORMANCE FIBERS LLC**
(*Suby of* RAYONIER ADVANCED MATERIALS INC) ★
1301 Riverplace Blvd, Jacksonville, FL 32207-9047
Tel (912) 427-5000 *Founded/Ownrshp* 2014
Sales 172.5MM[E] *EMP* 600[E]
SIC 3081 Film base, cellulose acetate or nitrocellulose plastic

RAYOVAC
See SPECTRUM BRANDS INC

D-U-N-S 00-833-9483 IMP
RAYPAK INC
(*Suby of* RHEEM MANUFACTURING CO INC) ★
2151 Eastman Ave, Oxnard, CA 93030-5194
Tel (805) 278-5300 *Founded/Ownrshp* 1949
Sales 107.6MM[E] *EMP* 347
SIC 3433 Heating equipment, except electric; Heaters, swimming pool: oil or gas
CEO: J R Jones
CFO: Bill Patterson
CFO: Joe Scordamaglia
Act CFO: Mike Inlow
VP: Lou Falzer
**VP:* Kevin McDonald
VP: Michael Sentovich
CTO: Brian McDonald
Dir IT: Larry Ashton
IT Man: David A Coates
IT Man: Tom Nickel

RAY'S FOOD PLACE
See C & K MARKET INC

D-U-N-S 61-366-3285
RAYTECH COMPOSITES INC
(*Suby of* RAYTECH CORP) ★
1204 Darlington Ave, Crawfordsville, IN 47933-1958
Tel (765) 362-3500 *Founded/Ownrshp* 1987
Sales 69.0MM[E] *EMP* 1,138
Accts Pricewaterhousecoopers Llp
SIC 3714 Motor vehicle parts & accessories
Pr: Harold Pope
Plnt Mgr: Jeremy Link

D-U-N-S 15-118-4561
RAYTECH CORP
(*Suby of* RAYTECH CORP ASBESTOS PERSONAL INJURY SETTLEMENT TRUST) ★
97 Froehlich Farm Blvd, Woodbury, NY 11797-2903
Tel (718) 259-7388 *Founded/Ownrshp* 1986
Sales 109.1MM[E] *EMP* 1,704
SIC 3499 Friction material, made from powdered metal
Pr: Larry W Singleton
**CFO:* Howard Mandell

D-U-N-S 60-195-2521
RAYTECH CORP ASBESTOS PERSONAL INJURY SETTLEMENT TRUST
190 Willis Ave, Mineola, NY 11501-2672
Tel (516) 747-0300 *Founded/Ownrshp* 2000
Sales 123.9MM[E] *EMP* 1,710[E]
SIC 3499 Friction material, made from powdered metal
Mng Trst: Richard A Lippe
VP: Elena Karabatos
VP: Ron Poepple

D-U-N-S 13-163-3125
■ **RAYTHEON APPLIED SIGNAL TECHNOLOGY INC**
(*Suby of* RAYTHEON CO) ★
460 W California Ave, Sunnyvale, CA 94086-5148
Tel (408) 749-1888 *Founded/Ownrshp* 2011
Sales 184.6MM[E] *EMP* 794[E]
SIC 3669 Signaling apparatus, electric
CEO: John R Treichler
CEO: William B Van Vleet III
COO: Mark M Andersson
COO: Scribner Bani
COO: Bani M Scribner
CFO: James E Doyle
Ex VP: R Fred Roscher
Sr VP: Paul Richard
VP: Roger W Anderson
VP: David A Baciocco
VP: John Devine
VP: Richard Gooch
VP: Joseph Leonelli
VP: John F Pesaturo
VP: Valda Ruddy
Exec: Patty Baxter
Dir Bus: Ken Cumings

D-U-N-S 14-659-5736
■ **RAYTHEON BBN TECHNOLOGIES CORP**
(*Suby of* RAYTHEON CO) ★
10 Moulton St, Cambridge, MA 02138-1119
Tel (617) 873-3052 *Founded/Ownrshp* 2009
Sales 138.9MM[E] *EMP* 680
SIC 7371 7374 7373 Computer software development & applications; Data processing & preparation; Computer integrated systems design
Pr: Ed Campbell
**Pr:* Robert Elmer
Ofcr: Felistas Newman
**Ex VP:* Keith Carlson
**Ex VP:* David Lintz
VP: Heather Biehl
**VP:* William C Earle
VP: Patti Goldberger

*VP: Jack Marin
*VP: Prem Natarajan
*VP: Jim O'Connor
VP: Mark Sherman
VP: Robert Spina
*VP: Susan Wuellner
Dir Rx: Rich Lazarus

D-U-N-S 01-186-3680
■ RAYTHEON BLACKBIRD TECHNOLOGIES INC
(Suby of RAYTHEON CO) ★
13900 Lincoln Park Dr # 400, Herndon, VA 20171-3254
Tel (703) 796-1420 Founded/Ownrshp 2014
Sales 127.7MM^E EMP 500
SIC 7371 7382 Custom computer programming services; Security systems services; Protective devices, security
Pr: Thomas A Kennedy
*CFO: Anthony F O'Brien
VP: Kevin G Dasilva
VP: David C Wajsgras
Dir Bus: Jim Bahel

D-U-N-S 00-133-9159
▲ RAYTHEON CO
870 Winter St, Waltham, MA 02451-1449
Tel (781) 522-3000 Founded/Ownrshp 1922
Sales 23.2MMM EMP 61,000
Tkr Sym RTN Exch NYS
SIC 3812 3663 3761 Defense systems & equipment; Space satellite communications equipment; Airborne radio communications equipment; Guided missiles & space vehicles, research & development; Rockets, space & military, complete
Ch Bd: Thomas A Kennedy
Pr: Wesley D Kremer
CFO: Anthony F O'Brien
Bd of Dir: Ken Brown
Bd of Dir: Richard Joyce
Bd of Dir: Dan Liu
Bd of Dir: James M Reed
VP: James Cronin
VP: Catherine Dixon
VP: Pamela Donaldson
VP: Mark Esper
VP: Regina Genton
VP: Glenn D Henseler
VP: Frank R Jimenez
VP: Taylor W Lawrence
VP: Billy Lovelady
VP: Ellen Minderman
VP: Edward Miyashiro
VP: Cathy Murphy
VP: John Norton
VP: Rebecca Ransom
Board of Directors: Tracy A Atkinson, Robert Beauchamp, James E Cartwright, Vernon E Clark, Stephen J Hadley, Letitia A Long, George R Oliver, Michael C Ruettgers, William R Spivey

D-U-N-S 11-322-5986
■ RAYTHEON CYBER SOLUTIONS INC
(Suby of RAYTHEON CO) ★
1220 N Hwy A1a Ste 123, Indialantic, FL 32903-2858
Tel (321) 253-7841 Founded/Ownrshp 2008
Sales 8.3MM EMP 60,000
SIC 7379 Computer related consulting services
CEO: Thomas Kennedy

D-U-N-S 04-559-1104 IMP
■ RAYTHEON E-SYSTEMS INC
(Suby of RAYTHEON CO) ★
1727 Cityline Dr, Richardson, TX 75082-3208
Tel (972) 205-9374 Founded/Ownrshp 1964
Sales 236.3MM^E EMP 1,163^E
SIC 3663 3812 7373 3575 4581 3721 Airborne radio communications equipment; Detection apparatus: electronic/magnetic field, light/heat; Air traffic control systems & equipment, electronic; Antennas, radar or communications; Aircraft control instruments; Computer integrated systems design; Computer terminals; Aircraft servicing & repairing; Airplanes, fixed or rotary wing
Ch Bd: William H Swanson
VP: Barbara Johnson
VP: William Ru
Dir Soc: Sherry McCormick
Dir Sec: John Montgomery
Prgrm Mgr: Mike Clingempeel
Prgrm Mgr: Charles Martin
Snr Sftwr: John Carbone
Snr Ntwrk: Eric Powell
QA Dir: Eric Ames
QA Dir: Kevin Martens

D-U-N-S 03-932-1963
■ RAYTHEON LOGISTICS SUPPORT & TRAINING CO
(Suby of RAYTHEON CO) ★
180 Hartwell Rd, Bedford, MA 01730-2443
Tel (310) 647-9438 Founded/Ownrshp 1980
Sales 38.0MM^E EMP 1,000^E
SIC 3761 Guided missiles & space vehicles, research & development; Rockets, space & military, complete
Pr: William H Swanson

D-U-N-S 03-416-8885 IMP/EXP
■ RAYTHEON MISSILE SYSTEMS CO
(Suby of RAYTHEON CO) ★
1151 E Hermans Rd, Tucson, AZ 85756-9367
Tel (520) 794-3000 Founded/Ownrshp 1992
Sales 1.6MMM^E EMP 11,915^E
SIC 3761 Guided missiles & space vehicles
CEO: Thomas A Kennedy
*CEO: William H Swanson
*VP: Kevin G Dasilva
*VP: Lawrence J Harrington
*VP: John D Harris II
VP: Edward Miyashiro
*VP: Richard R Yuse
Prgrm Mgr: Jeff Maranich
Snr Sftwr: Corey Bishop
Snr Sftwr: Tom Crofts
Snr Sftwr: Jose Gonzalez

D-U-N-S 07-879-0246
RAYTHEON PIKEWERKS CORP
321 3rd Ave S Ste 203, Seattle, WA 98104-4602
Tel (310) 647-9438 Founded/Ownrshp 1997
Sales 98.4MM^E EMP 68,000
SIC 8711

D-U-N-S 11-282-0840 IMP
RAYTHEON TECHNICAL SERVICES CO LLC
22270 Pacific Blvd, Dulles, VA 20166-6924
Tel (571) 250-2100 Founded/Ownrshp 1983
Sales 3.2MMM EMP 12,000
SIC 8331 8711

D-U-N-S 07-942-2667
■ RAYTHEON TECHNICAL SERVICES INTERNATIONAL CO LLC
(Suby of RAYTHEON CO) ★
22265 Pacific Blvd, Sterling, VA 20166-6920
Tel (310) 647-9438 Founded/Ownrshp 2014
Sales 77.1MM^E EMP 6,800
SIC 8711 Engineering services
Prin: Thomas Kennedy
Prin: Donna Mc Cullough

RAYTOWN QUALITY SCHOOLS
See CONSOLIDATED SCHOOL DISTRICT 2 (INC)

D-U-N-S 02-407-1990
RAZORFISH LLC
(Suby of PUBLICIS GROUPE S A)
424 2nd Ave W, Seattle, WA 98119-4013
Tel (206) 816-8800 Founded/Ownrshp 2010
Sales 327.1MM EMP 1,503
SIC 7375 7319 Information retrieval services; Media buying service
Dir Sec: Darin Brown
Pt: Tom Bateman
Pt: Sean Smith
Pt: Andy Williams
Pr: Roger Gonzalez
*CEO: Clark Kokich
CFO: Ariel Marciano
Ofcr: Daniel Bonner
*Sr VP: Linda A Schoemaker
VP: Christian Barnard
VP: Renee Borkowski
VP: Ben Brewer
VP: Clare Casey
VP: John Ewen
VP: Christopher Follett
VP: Bryan Hamilton
VP: Jim Harrison
VP: Salim Hemdani
VP: Victoria Lea
VP: Jeremy Lockhorn
VP: Victoria Phillips

RAZZOO'S CAJUN CAFE
See RAZZOOS INC

D-U-N-S 62-651-5977
RAZZOOS INC
RAZZOO'S CAJUN CAFE
2950 Texas Sage Trl, Fort Worth, TX 76177-8209
Tel (972) 233-6399 Founded/Ownrshp 1991
Sales 43.9MM^E EMP 1,100
Accts Bdo Seidman Llp Dallas Texa
SIC 5812 5813 Cajun restaurant; Drinking places
CEO: Michael Leatherwood
*Pr: Jeff Powell
*CFO: Dianne Slaight
VP: John Jessup
IT Man: Richard Grey

RB
See RECKITT BENCKISER (NORTH AMERICA) INC

D-U-N-S 14-099-4174 IMP
■ RB DISTRIBUTION INC
(Suby of DORMAN PRODUCTS INC) ★
3400 E Walnut St, Colmar, PA 18915-9768
Tel (215) 997-1800 Founded/Ownrshp 1994
Sales 149.1MM^E EMP 500
SIC 3714 3231 Motor vehicle parts & accessories; Mirrors, truck & automobile: made from purchased glass
Ch Bd: Richard Berman
*CFO: Mathias J Barton
*Treas: Steven L Berman
*Sr VP: Ronald R Montgomery
Sr VP: Ronald R Montgomery
*Sr VP: Barry D Myers
*VP Mktg: Edward L Dean Sr

D-U-N-S 07-939-5941
RB MANUFACTURING LLC
(Suby of RECKITT BENCKISER LLC) ★
399 Interpace Pkwy, Parsippany, NJ 07054-1133
Tel (973) 404-2600 Founded/Ownrshp 2014
Sales 372.3MM^E EMP 800^E
SIC 2035 2842 Mustard, prepared (wet); Deodorants, nonpersonal; Specialty cleaning preparations; Laundry cleaning preparations; Disinfectants, household or industrial plant
Pr: Alexander Lacik
Treas: John Brennan
VP: Krista Davis
VP: Philippe Escoffier
VP: Kelly M Slavitt

D-U-N-S 62-049-1795
RBC BANCORPORATION (USA)
(Suby of ROYAL BANK OF CANADA)
301 Fayetteville St, Raleigh, NC 27601-1974
Tel (252) 454-4400 Founded/Ownrshp 2001
Sales NA EMP 4,527
SIC 6712 6022 Bank holding companies; State commercial banks
Ch Bd: Jim Westlake
V Ch: John H Holcomb
*Pr: Reggie Davis
*CFO: Glenn McCoy
*Ofcr: Dan Wall
*Sr VP: Joe Cooper

D-U-N-S 01-168-9150
▲ RBC BEARINGS INC
102 Willenbrock Rd Bldg B, Oxford, CT 06478-1033
Tel (203) 267-7001 Founded/Ownrshp 1919
Sales 597.4MM EMP 3,277^E
Tkr Sym ROLL Exch NGS
SIC 3562 Ball & roller bearings; Ball bearings & parts; Roller bearings & parts
Ch Bd: Michael J Hartnett
*CFO: Daniel A Bergeron
VP: Thomas C Crainer
VP: Richard J Edwards
CTO: Andrew Frisbie
Mfg Mgr: Deval Glover
Opers Mgr: Ben Bratton
Manager: David Tassi
Board of Directors: Richard R Crowell, Alan B Levine, Thomas J O'brien, Mitchell I Quain, Edward D Stewart

D-U-N-S 06-055-0266
RBC CAPITAL MARKETS CORP
R B C CAPITAL MARKET
(Suby of ROYAL BANK OF CANADA)
60 S 6th St Ste 700, Minneapolis, MN 55402-4413
Tel (612) 371-2711 Founded/Ownrshp 1929
Sales 301.8MM^E EMP 4,100^E
Accts Kpmg Llp
SIC 7374 Data processing service
Pr: Irving Weiser
Ofcr: Theresa Alewine
Ofcr: Schaun Kirks
Ofcr: Jim Wood
Assoc VP: Debra Purcell
Sr VP: Michael Fulton
VP: Tracy Johnson
VP: Scott Kirby
VP: Bob Konsig
Mng Dir: Todd Braff
Mng Dir: Carol Kuha

D-U-N-S 00-698-2961
RBC CAPITAL MARKETS LLC (MN)
(Suby of ROYAL BANK OF CANADA)
200 Vesey St Fl 6, New York, NY 10281-8098
Tel (212) 858-7000 Founded/Ownrshp 1929, 1975
Sales 244.1MM^E EMP 235
SIC 6211 Dealers, security
Ch: Doug McGregor
*Pr: Mark Standish
COO: John W Burbidge
COO: Mark Hughes
CFO: Steven Decicco
*CFO: Troy Maxwell
Ofcr: Mark Commander
Ex VP: Howard Plotkin
VP: David Attanasio
VP: Corey Banning
VP: Ted Brewer
VP: Greg Chow
VP: Dustin Craven
VP: Joshua Critchley
VP: Rahul Daniel
VP: Todd Forgione
VP: Sameer Garg
VP: Joseph Giammarella
VP: Geoff Gregoire
VP: Michael Harvey
VP: Jason Hedrick

D-U-N-S 06-817-7625
RBC CAPITAL MARKETS LLC
RBC WEALTH MANAGEMENT
(Suby of ROYAL BANK OF CANADA)
60 S 6th St Ste 700, Minneapolis, MN 55402-4413
Tel (612) 371-2711 Founded/Ownrshp 2001
Sales 1.7MMM^E EMP 5,000
SIC 6211 6512 6513 6282 Brokers, security; Dealers, security; Investment bankers; Underwriters, security; Commercial & industrial building operation; Apartment hotel operation; Manager of mutual funds, contract or fee basis
Pr: John Taft
Pr: Peter Armenio
Pr: Jim Chapman
Treas: Deborah Kermeen
Ofcr: Schaun Kirks
Ofcr: Ronald Tanchin
Assoc VP: Jeff Schlesinger
VP: Libby Arendt
VP: Lisa Baker
VP: Wanda Brackins
VP: Joel Cuperfain
VP: Don Douglas
VP: Courtney Duphorne
VP: Terry Fahr
VP: Christine Gehring
VP: Malia Haskins
VP: William Joas
VP: Kelly Johnson
VP: Paul King
VP: Christi Lutgen
VP: Jeff McFarlin

D-U-N-S 82-850-4055
RBC DAIN RAUSCHER LENDING SERVICES INC
(Suby of R B C CAPITAL MARKET) ★
60 S 6th Strreet, Minneapolis, MN 55402
Tel (612) 371-2941 Founded/Ownrshp 2008
Sales 295.8MM^E EMP 3,012^E
SIC 6282 Investment advice
Prin: Maren Obermeyer
VP: Craig Bishop
VP: Wanda Brackins
VP: Mike Dickson
VP: Ken Harris
Tech Mgr: Sue Richey

D-U-N-S 00-411-4312
RBC USA HOLDCO CORP
(Suby of ROYAL BANK OF CANADA)
3 World Financial Ctr, New York, NY 10281-1013
Tel (212) 858-7200 Founded/Ownrshp 2003
Sales NA EMP 3,000^E
SIC 6712 6021 6022 Bank holding companies; National commercial banks; State commercial banks
CEO: Russell Goldsmith

RBC WEALTH MANAGEMENT
See RBC CAPITAL MARKETS LLC

RBFCU
See RANDOLPH-BROOKS FEDERAL CREDIT UNION

D-U-N-S 82-995-3582
RBG HOLDINGS CORP
7855 Haskell Ave Ste 350, Van Nuys, CA 91406-1936
Tel (818) 782-6445 Founded/Ownrshp 2003
Sales 790.6MM^E EMP 5,171^E
SIC 3949 5091 3751 Sporting & athletic goods; Sporting & recreation goods; Motorcycles, bicycles & parts
Prin: Paul Harrington

D-U-N-S 05-121-1949
RBLS INC
ASHLEY FURNITURE HOMESTORE
502 Fountain Pkwy, Grand Prairie, TX 75050-1405
Tel (817) 633-6838 Founded/Ownrshp 1999
Sales 106.3MM^E EMP 500
SIC 5712 Furniture stores
Pr: Michael Levitz
CFO: Shelley Levitz

RBS BANK
See ROYAL BANK OF SCOTLAND PLC

D-U-N-S 55-607-7480
■ RBS GLOBAL INC
(Suby of REXNORD CORP) ★
4701 W Greenfield Ave, Milwaukee, WI 53214-5310
Tel (414) 643-3000 Founded/Ownrshp 2002
Sales 891.2MM^E EMP 6,200^E
Accts Ernst & Young Llp Milwaukee
SIC 3562 3566 3568 3272 3261 Ball & roller bearings; Ball bearings & parts; Roller bearings & parts; Speed changers (power transmission equipment), except auto; Joints & couplings; Concrete products used to facilitate drainage; Faucet handles, vitreous china & earthenware; Flush tanks, vitreous china
Pr: Todd A Adams
*CFO: Mark W Peterson
Ex VP: Thomas J Jansen
*Ex VP: Praveen R Jeyarajah
*Ex VP: George C Moore

D-U-N-S 79-777-0906
RBS HOLDINGS USA INC
(Suby of NATIONAL WESTMINSTER BANK PUBLIC LIMITED COMPANY)
600 Washington Blvd, Stamford, CT 06901-6000
Tel (203) 897-2700 Founded/Ownrshp 1992
Sales 171.3MM^E EMP 640
SIC 6211 Security brokers & dealers; Investment bankers
Pr: Edwin L Netzger III
*Treas: P Michael Florio
Sr VP: Liran Nehushtan
VP: Kim Crotty
*VP: Rick Stiegler
Mng Dir: Stefan D'Annibale
Mng Dir: Peter Dimartino
Mng Dir: David Viney

D-U-N-S 36-210-2019
■ RBS NATIONAL BANK
(Suby of CITIZENS BANK) ★
1000 Lafayette Blvd # 600, Bridgeport, CT 06604-4725
Tel (203) 551-7270 Founded/Ownrshp 2005
Sales NA EMP 1^E
SIC 6021 National commercial banks
CEO: Joseph Hoffman
Sr VP: Robert F Mihalcik
VP: Abhinav Goswami

D-U-N-S 01-416-4826
RBS SECURITIES INC
RBS STAMFORD
(Suby of RBS HOLDINGS USA INC) ★
600 Washington Blvd, Stamford, CT 06901-6000
Tel (203) 897-2700 Founded/Ownrshp 1985, 1996
Sales 162.1MM^E EMP 563^E
SIC 6282 6211 Investment advisory service; Dealers, security
V Ch: Raymond E Humiston III
*Pr: Jay Levine
*Treas: P Michael Florio
Ofcr: Suprio Chaudhuri
VP: Michael McKeever
Mng Dir: Martin Pryor
Mng Dir: Darryl Smith
Mng Dir: John Sullivan

RBS STAMFORD
See RBS SECURITIES INC

D-U-N-S 61-430-3154 IMP/EXP
RC ALUMINUM INDUSTRIES INC
2805 Nw 75th Ave, Miami, FL 33122-1435
Tel (305) 592-1515 Founded/Ownrshp 1990
Sales 116.4MM^E EMP 825
SIC 3442 1751 Window & door frames; Window & door (prefabricated) installation
Pr: Raul Casares
*VP: Eusebio Paredes
*VP: Nancy M Vias

D-U-N-S 00-117-6197 IMP/EXP
RC BIGELOW INC (CT)
BIGELOW TEA
201 Black Rock Tpke, Fairfield, CT 06825-5512
Tel (888) 244-3569 Founded/Ownrshp 1945
Sales 94.5MM^E EMP 350
SIC 2099 Tea blending
Ch Bd: David C Bigelow
*Pr: Cindi Bigelow
*Co-Ch Bd: Eunice Bigelow
*Co-Pr: Cynthia Bigelow
Bd of Dir: Linda Didomenico
*Sr VP: A Donald Janezic Jr
*VP: Marshall Adams
VP: Robert Hendrick
VP: Don Janezic
IT Man: Melanie Dower
IT Man: Claire Iannazzi

RC COLA
See ROYAL CROWN BOTTLING CORP

D-U-N-S 06-769-0755
RC HUNT ELECTRIC INC (UT)
1863 W Alexander St, Salt Lake City, UT 84119-2038
Tel (801) 975-8844 *Founded/Ownrshp* 2000
Sales 93.7MM[E] *EMP* 140
Accts Burnham & Schumm Pc Salt L
SIC 1731 Electrical work
Pr: Richard C Hunt
**Treas:* Brent Hugie
**Sec:* Omar Lee Andersen
**VP:* Mark Porter
Exec: Matthew Royall
Telecom Ex: Darrin Guevara
IT Man: Carrie Stoehr
Opers Mgr: Cody Eaton

D-U-N-S 80-286-1687
RC LONESTAR INC
BUZZI UNICEM USA
(*Suby of* BUZZI UNICEM SPA)
100 Brodhead Rd Ste 230, Bethlehem, PA 18017-8935
Tel (610) 882-5000 *Founded/Ownrshp* 2003
Sales 545.2MM[E] *EMP* 1,474[E]
SIC 6719 Investment holding companies, except banks
Pr: David Nepereny
**CFO:* Dirk Beese
**Sr VP:* Lawrence Hoffis
**Sr VP:* Daniel Nugent
**VP:* James Basgall
**VP:* Nancy Krial
**VP:* David Rifkind
**VP:* Raymond Seipp
**VP:* John White
**VP Sls:* Rick Sutter
**Counsel:* Patrick Lydon

D-U-N-S 80-844-3381
■ RC MARRIOTT II INC
(*Suby of* RC MARRIOTT, INC)
10400 Fernwood Rd, Bethesda, MD 20817-1102
Tel (301) 333-3333 *Founded/Ownrshp* 1995
Sales 30.6MM[E] *EMP* 15,739[E]
SIC 7011 Hotels & motels
Prin: Kevin M Kimball

D-U-N-S 03-531-5621 IMP
■ RC WILLEY HOME FURNISHINGS
R C WILLEY
(*Suby of* BERKSHIRE HATHAWAY INC) ★
2301 S 300 W, Salt Lake City, UT 84115-2516
Tel (801) 461-3900 *Founded/Ownrshp* 1995
Sales 772.2MM *EMP* 2,700
SIC 5712 5731 5722 Furniture stores; Radio, television & electronic stores; Electric household appliances, major
**Pr:* Jeffrey Child
CFO: Pamela Moser
Ofcr: Brook Wilson
VP: Jack De Mill
VP: Stu Peterson
Exec: Jamie Hammer
Genl Mgr: Brad Miller
Genl Mgr: Tom Willardson
Store Mgr: Teri Whittaker
Sftwr Eng: Gerald Hansen
Opers Mgr: Kelly Garfield

D-U-N-S 04-313-0525
RCB BANK SERVICE INC (OK)
R C B BANK
(*Suby of* RCB HOLDING COMPANY)
300 W Patti Page Blvd, Claremore, OK 74017-8039
Tel (918) 341-6150 *Founded/Ownrshp* 1935, 1985
Sales NA *EMP* 550
SIC 6022 State commercial banks
Ch: Joe Robson
Pr: Ron Reiser
**CEO:* Roger Mosier
**COO:* Tom Bayless
**CFO:* Craig Myers

RCCD
See RIVERSIDE COMMUNITY COLLEGE DISTRICT

D-U-N-S 01-269-5031
RCEB
500 Davis St Ste 100, San Leandro, CA 94577-2758
Tel (510) 432-7123 *Founded/Ownrshp* 2010
Sales 279.3MM *EMP* 41[E]
SIC 8699 Charitable organization
Prin: M Carmen Jimenez

RCG
See ROSENTHAL COLLINS GROUP LLC

D-U-N-S 03-940-0106
RCG GLOBAL SERVICES INC
379 Thornall St Ste 14, Edison, NJ 08837-2233
Tel (732) 744-3500 *Founded/Ownrshp* 2013
Sales 179.3MM[E] *EMP* 1,300[E]
SIC 8748 Business consulting
Pr: Robert Simplot
CFO: Michael Dawson
**CFO:* Gerard Lynch
VP: Mark Allnock
VP: Paul Belitsis
VP: Leslie J Fishkin
VP: Steve McDonough
Exec: Tom Mosley
Dir Bus: Mike Fischer
Dir Bus: Carlos Garay
Admn Mgr: Michael Bateman

D-U-N-S 96-785-6506
RCHP - WILMINGTON LLC
CLINTON MEMORIAL HOSPITAL INPA
610 W Main St, Wilmington, OH 45177-2125
Tel (937) 382-6611 *Founded/Ownrshp* 2010
Sales 80.9MM[E] *EMP* 2,198[E]
SIC 8062 8361 General medical & surgical hospitals; Rehabilitation center, residential: health care incidental
Ch: Marcy Hawley
CFO: Bradley Boggus
Ofcr: Mary A Randolph
Exec: Mary Foland
Dir Inf Cn: Robin Hinman

D-U-N-S 92-788-1383
▲ RCI HOSPITALITY HOLDINGS INC
10959 Cutten Rd, Houston, TX 77066-5003
Tel (281) 397-6730 *Founded/Ownrshp* 1983
Sales 134.8MM *EMP* 2,150[E]
Accts Whitley Penn Llp Dallas Texa
Tkr Sym RICK *Exch* NGM
SIC 5813 5812 Night clubs; Bar (drinking places); Eating places
Ch Bd: Eric S Langan
CFO: Phillip Marshall
**Ex VP:* Travis Reese
Board of Directors: Steven Jenkins, Luke Lirot, Robert L Watters

D-U-N-S 61-672-0314
RCM INDUSTRIES INC
ALLIED DIE CASTING COMPANY ILL
3021 Cullerton St, Franklin Park, IL 60131-2204
Tel (847) 455-1950 *Founded/Ownrshp* 1990
Sales 170.7MM[E] *EMP* 700
SIC 3363 Aluminum die-castings
Pr: Robert C Marconi
**CFO:* Vernon Reizman
**Ex VP:* Donald Kilburg
VP: William Herrington
IT Man: Jim Mock
IT Man: Ramone Santana

D-U-N-S 01-233-0601
■ RCM TECHNOLOGIES (USA) INC
(*Suby of* RCM TECHNOLOGIES INC) ★
2500 Mcclellan Ave # 350, Pennsauken, NJ 08109-4617
Tel (856) 356-4500 *Founded/Ownrshp* 1999
Sales 193.7MM *EMP* 1,460
SIC 8742 7379 8711 Management consulting services; Industry specialist consultants; Computer related consulting services; Engineering services
CEO: Leon Kopyt
**CFO:* Kevin Miller
Sr VP: Jim Schappart

D-U-N-S 08-477-0619
▲ RCM TECHNOLOGIES INC
2500 Mcclellan Ave # 350, Pennsauken, NJ 08109-4617
Tel (856) 356-4500 *Founded/Ownrshp* 1971
Sales 185.7MM *EMP* 2,360[E]
Tkr Sym RCMT *Exch* NGM
SIC 8711 8748 7373 8049 7363 Engineering services; Business consulting; Computer integrated systems design; Nurses & other medical assistants; Physical therapist; Help supply services
Pr: Rocco Campanelli
**Ch Bd:* Bradley S Vizi
COO: Mary Leonard
**CFO:* Kevin D Miller
**Sr VP:* Timothy Brandt
**Sr VP:* Frank Petraglia
**Sr VP:* Michael Saks
**Sr VP:* Danny A White
Exec: Mike Campanelli
Exec: Becky Dibble
CTO: Ray Haimson
Board of Directors: Roger H Ballou, Leon Koypt, Richard D Machon, S Gary Snodgrass

RCM&D
See RIGGS COUNSELMAN MICHAELS & DOWNES INC

D-U-N-S 78-934-7283 IMP/EXP
RCMA AMERICAS INC
(*Suby of* RCMA GROUP PTE. LTD.)
150 Boush St Ste 1000, Norfolk, VA 23510-1638
Tel (757) 627-4000 *Founded/Ownrshp* 2000
Sales 183.5MM *EMP* 36
Accts Cherry Bekaert Llp Virginia
SIC 5199 6221 Rubber, crude; Commodity traders, contracts
Pr: Lou Mucciolo
CFO: Pet Pierce
**Treas:* Petrene Pearce
Bd of Dir: Carlene McFarland

RCN
See SIDERA NETWORKS INC

D-U-N-S 02-182-3258
RCN TELECOM SERVICES LLC
650 College Rd E Ste 3100, Princeton, NJ 08540-6629
Tel (609) 452-8197 *Founded/Ownrshp* 2011
Sales 298.5MM[E] *EMP* 804[E]
SIC 4841 7375 4813 Subscription television services; Information retrieval services; Telephone communication, except radio
CEO: Jim Hollanda
CFO: John Feehan

D-U-N-S 14-719-7677
RCO ENGINEERING INC
R C O
29200 Calahan Rd, Roseville, MI 48066-1849
Tel (586) 774-0100 *Founded/Ownrshp* 1973
Sales 133.8MM[E] *EMP* 650
SIC 3714 3089 3365 7361 3325 2531

D-U-N-S 06-688-2361
RCP III LLC
PORTER NISSAN INFINITI
303 E Cleveland Ave, Newark, DE 19711-3712
Tel (302) 368-6300 *Founded/Ownrshp* 2000
Sales 107.5MM *EMP* 22[E]
SIC 5511 Automobiles, new & used
Prin: Richard Porter

D-U-N-S 02-036-1043 IMP
RCRV INC
ROCK REVIVAL
4715 S Alameda St, Vernon, CA 90058-2014
Tel (323) 235-8070 *Founded/Ownrshp* 2008
Sales 128.5MM *EMP* 40
Accts Moss Adams Llp Los Angeles
SIC 2673 5137 5136 Garment & wardrobe bags, (plastic film); Women's & children's clothing
Pr: Eric S Choi
CFO: SOO Han Kim
**VP:* Kheim Nguyen
**VP Sls:* Kevin J Chen
Mktg Mgr: Sarah Brown
Mktg Mgr: Elbert Pak

RCSD
See RANKIN COUNTY SCHOOL DISTRICT ASSOCIATION OF EDUCATIONAL OFFICE PERSONNEL INC

RCUH
See RESEARCH CORP OF UNIVERSITY OF HAWAII

D-U-N-S 07-076-1874 EXP
RD AMROSS LLC
3000 N Atl Ave Ste 207, Cocoa Beach, FL 32931-5038
Tel (321) 613-3902 *Founded/Ownrshp* 1997
Sales 112.9MM *EMP* 10
SIC 3761 Rockets, space & military, complete
Pr: William W Parsons
**Treas:* Thomas H Wonnell

D-U-N-S 87-818-6774
RD FOOD SERVICES LLC
RESTAURANT DEPOT
(*Suby of* JETRO CASH & CARRY) ★
1524 132nd St, College Point, NY 11356-2440
Tel (718) 961-4356 *Founded/Ownrshp* 1994
Sales 201.4MM[E] *EMP* 300
SIC 5141 5148 5142 5113 5046 5087 Groceries, general line; Fresh fruits & vegetables; Packaged frozen goods; Napkins, paper; Towels, paper; Dishes, disposable plastic & paper; Paper & products, wrapping or coarse; Restaurant equipment & supplies; Janitors' supplies
CEO: Stanley Fleishman

D-U-N-S 08-411-2663
RD OFFUTT CO
(*Suby of* RDO HOLDINGS CO) ★
700 7th St S, Fargo, ND 58103-2704
Tel (701) 526-9670 *Founded/Ownrshp* 1968
Sales 299.5MM[E] *EMP* 547
SIC 0134 2038 Irish potatoes; Frozen specialties
Pr: Ronald D Offutt
Treas: Thomas Espel
**Sec:* Allan Knoll

D-U-N-S 79-347-6495
RDA HOLDING CO
RITTLEWOOD HOLDING CO
750 3rd Ave, New York, NY 10017-2703
Tel (914) 238-1000 *Founded/Ownrshp* 2016
Sales 1.6MMM[E] *EMP* 5,100[E]
SIC 2721 2731 5961 2741 Periodicals; Book publishing; Catalog & mail-order houses; Miscellaneous publishing
Pr: Bonnie Kintzer
Ch Bd: Fredric G Reynolds
CEO: Harvey Golub
CFO: Paul Tomkins
Ch: Randall Curran
Ex VP: Albert L Perruzza
VP: Susan Fraysse Russ

D-U-N-S 14-417-6497
RDG CHICAGO INC
1840 Pickwick Ln, Glenview, IL 60026-1307
Tel (847) 510-2037 *Founded/Ownrshp* 2004
Sales 52.1MM[E] *EMP* 2,000
SIC 8741 Restaurant management
Pr: Roger Greenfield
**VP:* Ted Kasemir

D-U-N-S 11-247-3330 EXP
RDO AGRICULTURE EQUIPMENT CO
(*Suby of* RDO INTEGRATED CONTROLS) ★
700 7th St S, Fargo, ND 58103-2704
Tel (701) 239-8730 *Founded/Ownrshp* 2000
Sales 154.0MM[E] *EMP* 700
SIC 5083 Agricultural machinery & equipment
Pr: Christi Offutt
**Treas:* Thomas K Espel
Treas: Richard J Moen

D-U-N-S 11-247-7760
RDO CONSTRUCTION EQUIPMENT CO
JOHN DEERE AUTHORIZED DEALER
(*Suby of* RDO INTEGRATED CONTROLS) ★
2000 Industrial Dr, Bismarck, ND 58501-2508
Tel (701) 223-5798 *Founded/Ownrshp* 2000
Sales 251.4MM[E] *EMP* 700
SIC 5082 5084 7353 General construction machinery & equipment; Industrial machinery & equipment; Heavy construction equipment rental
Pr: Ronald D Offutt
Pr: Richard J Moen
Treas: Thomas Espel
Ex VP: Kenneth Horner
VP: Sonna Bakken
VP: Chris Cooper
VP: Al Wiley
Exec: Kathy Bergeron
Genl Mgr: Jason L Coles
Genl Mgr: Matt Dull
Genl Mgr: Adam Gilbertson

D-U-N-S 82-506-7937
RDO EQUIPMENT CO
RDO INTEGRATED CONTROLS
(*Suby of* RDO HOLDINGS CO) ★
700 7th St S, Fargo, ND 58103-2704
Tel (701) 239-8700 *Founded/Ownrshp* 2000
Sales 1.6MMM *EMP* 1,500
Accts Pricewaterhousecoopers Llp Mi
SIC 5083 5082 5084 7699 7359 7353 Agricultural machinery & equipment; Agricultural machinery; Farm equipment parts & supplies; Tractors, agricultural; Road construction equipment; General construction machinery & equipment; Front end loaders; Graders, motor; Materials handling machinery; Agricultural equipment repair services; Equipment rental & leasing; Heavy construction equipment rental
Ch Bd: Ronald D Offutt
**CEO:* Christi Offutt
COO: Chris Cooper
**CFO:* Steven Dewald
CFO: David Frear
**Treas:* Thomas K Espel
Ofcr: Barry Wakener
Ex VP: Dara Altman
Ex VP: Keith Kreps
Ex VP: Jean Zimmerman
VP: Skip Klinkhammer
VP: Ronald Offutt
VP: Edward T Schafer
VP: Larry Scott
VP: Terry Tolbert
VP: Gean Zimmerman
Exec: Kathy Bergeron

D-U-N-S 13-782-1935
RDO HOLDINGS CO
700 7th St S, Fargo, ND 58103-2704
Tel (701) 239-8700 *Founded/Ownrshp* 2003
Sales 1.9MMM[E] *EMP* 1,800
SIC 5083 5082 Agricultural machinery & equipment; Road construction equipment
Pr: Christi Offutt
**Ch Bd:* Ronald D Offutt
**CEO:* Sam Allen

RDO INTEGRATED CONTROLS
See RDO EQUIPMENT CO

D-U-N-S 96-802-1746
RE COMMUNITY HOLDINGS II INC
RECOMMUNITY
809 W Hill St, Charlotte, NC 28208-5342
Tel (704) 697-2000 *Founded/Ownrshp* 2011
Sales 562.8MM[E] *EMP* 634[E]
SIC 4953 Recycling, waste materials
CEO: Dennis McGill
**Pr:* Sean Duffy
**CEO:* James Devlin
**CFO:* David Eisner
**Treas:* Graham Stevens
**Sr VP:* Paula Calabrese
**VP:* Paul Odonnell

D-U-N-S 82-501-9094
RE GARRISON TRUCKING INC
1103 County Road 1194, Vinemont, AL 35179-8668
Tel (888) 640-8482 *Founded/Ownrshp* 1996
Sales 85.4MM[E] *EMP* 175
Accts Warren Averett Kimbrough & M
SIC 4213 Refrigerated products transport
Pr: Wyles Griffith
CFO: Jay Johnson
**CFO:* Shane McMinn
**Ex VP:* Jerry Lovell
**VP:* Donovan Lovell
DP Exec: Jon Duke

D-U-N-S 11-293-8878 IMP/EXP
RE TRANSPORTATION INC
(*Suby of* KUEHNE + NAGEL INVESTMENT INC) ★
855 Ridge Lake Blvd # 500, Memphis, TN 38120-9438
Tel (901) 271-8830 *Founded/Ownrshp* 2015
Sales 213.2MM[E] *EMP* 300
SIC 4731 Freight transportation arrangement
CEO: David Wedaman
**COO:* Jim Waggoner
VP: Raymond Scher
VP: Tammy Stone
Opers Mgr: Neill Russell
VP Sls: Cindy West
VP Sls: James Wharton
Manager: Amber Estes
Sales Asso: Mike Mauro
Snr Mgr: Elise Michaelson

D-U-N-S 78-318-3275
RE/MAX CONSULTANT GROUP
6650 Walnut St, New Albany, OH 43054-9138
Tel (614) 855-2822 *Founded/Ownrshp* 2009
Sales 300.0MM *EMP* 70
SIC 6531 Real estate agent, residential
CEO: Mara Ackermann

D-U-N-S 07-915-2306
▲ RE/MAX HOLDINGS INC
5075 S Syracuse St, Denver, CO 80237-2712
Tel (303) 770-5531 *Founded/Ownrshp* 1973
Sales 176.8MM *EMP* 311
Tkr Sym RMAX *Exch* NYS
SIC 6531 6411 Real estate brokers & agents; Insurance agents, brokers & service
Ch Bd: David L Liniger
Pr: Geoffrey D Lewis
COO: Adam M Contos
CFO: Karri R Callahan
**V Ch Bd:* Gail A Liniger
Board of Directors: Richard O Covey, Joseph A Desplinter, Roger J Dow, Ronald E Harrison, Daniel J Predovich, Christine M Riordan, Teresa S Van De Bogart

D-U-N-S 09-575-0592
■ RE/MAX LLC
(*Suby of* RE/MAX HOLDINGS INC) ★
5075 S Syracuse St, Denver, CO 80237-2712
Tel (303) 770-5531 *Founded/Ownrshp* 1974
Sales 101.5MM[E] *EMP* 340
SIC 6531 Real estate agent, residential
Ch Bd: David L Liniger
**Ch Bd:* Gail A Liniger
**Pr:* Jinn Tracy
**CEO:* Margaret Kelly
CFO: Kari Callahan
**CFO:* David M K Metzger
CFO: Craig Stull
Sr Cor Off: Kathleen Means
Ex VP: Elton Ash
Ex VP: Kevin Northrup
Sr VP: Adam Contos
Sr VP: Mike Reagan
VP: Nick Bailey
VP: Bruce Benham
VP: Terri Bohannon
VP: Josh Bolgren
VP: Elena Dean
VP: Tim Drouillard
VP: Jill Gill

VP: Susan Goiser
VP: Jeff Lagrange

REA CONSTRUCTION
See AMBLING MANAGEMENT CO LLC

D-U-N-S 00-432-0032 IMP/EXP
REA MAGNET WIRE CO INC
3600 E Pontiac St, Fort Wayne, IN 46803-3804
Tel (260) 421-7321 *Founded/Ownrshp* 1933, 1986
Sales 247.5MM^E *EMP* 950
SIC 3357

D-U-N-S 08-003-1894
REACH AMERICA ESG LTD (CA)
(*Suby of* JIANGSU HUALIN CHEMICAL CO., LTD.)
2033 Gateway Pl Ste 500, San Jose, CA 95110-3712
Tel (408) 573-6170 *Founded/Ownrshp* 2013
Sales 300.0MM *EMP* 10
SIC 5169 Chemicals & allied products
CEO: Liang Zhu Peter Zhu

D-U-N-S 14-959-1872
■ REACHLOCAL INC
(*Suby of* GANNETT CO INC) ★
21700 Oxnard St Ste 1600, Woodland Hills, CA 91367-7586
Tel (818) 274-0260 *Founded/Ownrshp* 2016
Sales 382.6MM *EMP* 1,300^E
SIC 7311 7375 Advertising agencies; On-line data base information retrieval
CEO: Sharon T Rowlands
CFO: Ross G Landsbaum
Sr VP: Becky Grosser
Dir Sec: Paras Maniar
Sales Exec: Paige Sachs
Mktg Mgr: Adam Shearer
Mktg Mgr: Adam Wergeles
Manager: Obe Gray
Manager: Tracy Oswald
Board of Directors: Robert J Dickey, John M Zidich

D-U-N-S 15-765-1618 IMP
■ READE DUANE HOLDINGS INC
(*Suby of* WALGREENS) ★
40 Wall St Fl 22, New York, NY 10005-1340
Tel (212) 273-5700 *Founded/Ownrshp* 2010
Sales 71.8MM^E *EMP* 6,800
SIC 5912 Drug stores
CEO: John A Lederer
**CFO:* John K Henry
**Sr VP:* Phillip A Bradley
**Sr VP:* Joseph C Magnacca
**Sr VP:* Charles Newsom
Sr VP: Vincent A Scarfone
Sr VP: Frank Scorpiniti
VP: Mark Bander
VP: Mike Knievel
VP: William M Knievel
VP: Robert Storch
VP: Donald L Yuhasz

D-U-N-S 07-424-0599 IMP
READERLINK DISTRIBUTION SERVICES LLC
READERLINK MARKETING SERVICES
(*Suby of* READERLINK LLC) ★
1420 Kensington Rd # 300, Oak Brook, IL 60523-2164
Tel (708) 356-3717 *Founded/Ownrshp* 2011
Sales 4.0MMM^E *EMP* 2,100
SIC 5192 Books
Pr: Dennis Abboud
VP: Paul Davidson
VP Sls: Mark Slater

D-U-N-S 07-827-3696 IMP
READERLINK LLC (IL)
1420 Kensington Rd # 300, Oak Brook, IL 60523-2164
Tel (708) 356-3600 *Founded/Ownrshp* 2011
Sales 7.7MMM^E *EMP* 3,100^E
SIC 5192 Books, periodicals & newspapers
Pr: Dennis E Abboud
VP: Peter Norton
Snr Mgr: Steve Carlson

READERLINK MARKETING SERVICES
See READERLINK DISTRIBUTION SERVICES LLC

READER'S DIGEST
See TRUSTED MEDIA BRANDS INC

D-U-N-S 00-233-3490 IMP/EXP
■ READING ALLOYS INC (PA)
(*Suby of* AMETEK SENSOR TECHNOLOGY BUS) ★
220 Old West Penn Ave, Robesonia, PA 19551-8904
Tel (610) 693-5822 *Founded/Ownrshp* 1953, 2008
Sales 100.0MM *EMP* 125
SIC 3313 3341 Ferroalloys; Alloys, additive, except copper: not made in blast furnaces; Secondary nonferrous metals
Pr: H I McGavisk
**Treas:* William I Burke
**VP:* Brian Higgins
**VP:* Graham P Walker
Sls Mgr: Steve Halpin

D-U-N-S 00-235-3431
READING EAGLE CO
READING EAGLE PRESS
345 Penn St, Reading, PA 19601-4029
Tel (610) 371-5000 *Founded/Ownrshp* 1904
Sales 87.4MM^E *EMP* 425
SIC 2711 2752 Newspapers, publishing & printing; Commercial printing, offset
Pr: Peter D Barbey
**Ch Bd:* William S Flippin
**CFO:* Michael J Mizak Jr
**VP:* James C Flippin
DP Dir: Kevin Lawrence
Prd Mgr: Terry Beilhart
Sls Mgr: Denice Schaeffer

READING EAGLE PRESS
See READING EAGLE CO

D-U-N-S 05-563-2517
READING EQUIPMENT & DISTRIBUTION LLC
(*Suby of* J B POINDEXTER & CO INC) ★
1363 Bowmansville Rd, Bowmansville, PA 17507-7206
Tel (717) 445-6746 *Founded/Ownrshp* 2005, 2015
Sales 109.2MM^E *EMP* 200
SIC 5531 7532 Truck equipment & parts; Truck painting & lettering
Pr: Mark Robinson
**CFO:* Bob Shangraw
**VP:* Scott Caldwell
Brnch Mgr: Scott Goodman
Brnch Mgr: Jim Matricardi
Brnch Mgr: Tim O'Neil
Sls Mgr: Jim Moorehead

D-U-N-S 62-009-1892 IMP
READING HEALTH SYSTEM
READING MEDICAL CENTER
6th Ave And Spruce St, Reading, PA 19611
Tel (610) 988-8000 *Founded/Ownrshp* 1982
Sales 37.7MM *EMP* 6,800
Accts Pricewaterhousecoopers Llp Ph
SIC 8062 6512 8093 8721 8011 7219 General medical & surgical hospitals; Hospital, professional nursing school; Nonresidential building operators; Mental health clinic, outpatient; Billing & bookkeeping service; Offices & clinics of medical doctors; Laundry, except power & coin-operated
Pr: Clint Matthews
CFO: Richard W Jones
**Treas:* Lawrence Cobaugh
Bd of Dir: Marlin Miller
Sr VP: Daniel Ahern
**VP:* Steven Finkel
**VP:* Therese Sucher
VP: Cheryl Terenchin
Adm Dir: Holli Brown
CIO: Jacob Johnson
CIO: Jayashree Rayman
Board of Directors: Cheryl Terenchin

D-U-N-S 07-121-4365
READING HOSPITAL
(*Suby of* READING MEDICAL CENTER) ★
6th And Spruce St, Reading, PA 19611
Tel (484) 628-8000 *Founded/Ownrshp* 1883
Sales 35.8MM^E *EMP* 5,500
Accts Pricewaterhousecoopers Llp Ph
SIC 8062 6512 Hospital, professional nursing school; Nonresidential building operators
Pr: Clint Matthews
**CEO:* David Clint Matthews
VP: Jay Ramon
**VP:* Theresa Sucher
Dir Rad: Robert C Guay
Dir Rad: Brent J Wagner
Adm Dir: Ellen Kellom
CIO: Jayashree Rayman
MIS Dir: Eric Wolfe
IT Man: John Les
IT Man: Cheryl Tarenched

D-U-N-S 11-426-1399
▲ READING INTERNATIONAL INC
6100 Center Dr Ste 900, Los Angeles, CA 90045-9207
Tel (213) 235-2240 *Founded/Ownrshp* 2000
Sales 257.3MM *EMP* 2,594^E
Tkr Sym RDI *Exch* NAS
SIC 7832 7922 6512 6531 Motion picture theaters, except drive-in; Theatrical producers & services; Nonresidential building operators; Real estate agents & managers
Ch Bd: Ellen M Cotter
Pr: Robert F Smerling
CFO: Devasis Ghose
**V Ch Bd:* Margaret Cotter
Ex VP: Steven Eyler
Ex VP: Andrzej J Matyczynski
VP: Michael Lasalla
Mng Dir: Wayne D Smith
Dir IT: John Goeddel
Board of Directors: Guy W Adams, Judy Codding, James Cotter Jr, William D Gould, Edward L Kane, Douglas J McEachern, Michael Wrotniak

READING MEDICAL CENTER
See READING HEALTH SYSTEM

D-U-N-S 07-283-9350
READING SCHOOL DISTRICT
800 Washington St, Reading, PA 19601-3691
Tel (484) 258-7000 *Founded/Ownrshp* 1835
Sales 117.9MM^E *EMP* 1,900
SIC 8211 Public elementary & secondary schools
**Pr:* Rebecca Acosta
**CFO:* David Szablowski
**VP:* Robin Costenbader-Jacobson
MIS Mgr: James Adams
MIS Mgr: Reuben Flores
HC Dir: Ann Fisher

D-U-N-S 00-233-8143 IMP/EXP
READING TRUCK BODY LLC
ABC
(*Suby of* J B POINDEXTER & CO INC) ★
201 Hancock Blvd, Reading, PA 19611
Tel (610) 775-3301 *Founded/Ownrshp* 2005, 2015
Sales 95.1MM^E *EMP* 1^E
SIC 3713 3792 3469 Utility truck bodies; Truck bodies & parts; Travel trailers & campers; Metal stampings
CEO: Mark Robinson
Pr: John Howley
Pr: Ken Spear
**CEO:* Dan Perlman
**CFO:* Bob Shangraw
**VP:* Scott Caldwell
VP: Gordon Treisbach
Exec: Gary De Marco
VP Mfg: Mark Anderson
VP Mfg: Michael Gehris
Natl Sales: Ryan Hauger

D-U-N-S 01-186-4758
READINGTON FARMS INC
(*Suby of* WAKEFERN GENERAL MERCHANDISE) ★
12 Mill Rd, Whitehouse, NJ 08888
Tel (908) 534-2121 *Founded/Ownrshp* 1888
Sales 190.0MM *EMP* 215^E
SIC 2026 Milk processing (pasteurizing, homogenizing, bottling)
Ch Bd: Dominick V Romano
**Pr:* Donald Merrigan
**VP:* Barry S Snyder
VP Prd: Larry Kurz
Sls&Mrk Ex: Michelle West

READY MIX CONCRETE
See BEALL CONCRETE ENTERPRISES LTD

D-U-N-S 96-638-4646 EXP
READY MIX USA LLC
(*Suby of* CEMEX INC) ★
2657 Ruffner Rd, Birmingham, AL 35210-3914
Tel (205) 967-5211 *Founded/Ownrshp* 2011
Sales 249.8MM^E *EMP* 1,000
SIC 5211 3241 Concrete & cinder block; Cement, hydraulic
Pr: Karl H Watson
**VP:* William Roy
IT Man: Keith Rickles
Plnt Mgr: Bryan Calhoun
Plnt Mgr: Eddy Rice
Sales Exec: Harold Butts

READY PAC FOODS
See READY PAC PRODUCE INC

D-U-N-S 05-133-1739 IMP
READY PAC FOODS INC
(*Suby of* READY PAC FOODS) ★
4401 Foxdale St, Irwindale, CA 91706-2161
Tel (626) 856-8686 *Founded/Ownrshp* 2004
Sales 989.6MM^E *EMP* 2,500
SIC 2099 5148 Salads, fresh or refrigerated; Vegetables, fresh
CEO: Phillip Theodore
CFO: Betty Quintero
VP: Stephen Bonaro
Prin: Craig Delaney
Prin: Richard Gonzalez
Prin: James Hoffman
Prin: Lawrence Kern
CIO: Robert Estes
Opers Mgr: Ron Cook
Plnt Mgr: Michael Ervin
Prd Mgr: Angel Baez

D-U-N-S 05-080-5027 IMP
READY PAC PRODUCE INC
READY PAC FOODS
4401 Foxdale St, Irwindale, CA 91706-2161
Tel (800) 800-4088 *Founded/Ownrshp* 1969
Sales 1.0MMM^E *EMP* 2,700
SIC 2099 5148 Salads, fresh or refrigerated; Cole slaw, in bulk; Vegetables, peeled for the trade; Fresh fruits & vegetables
Ch Bd: Dennis Gertmenian
Pr: Stephen Bonaro
**CEO:* Tony Sarsam
**CFO:* Craig Delaney
VP: Dave Chandler
VP: Robert Ott
Dir IT: Ryan Jacobs
IT Man: Jose Salcido
IT Man: Virginia Sandoval
VP Opers: Janet Walker
Opers Mgr: Joseph Segura

READYCARE
See MOUNTAIN VIEW HOSPITAL LLC

D-U-N-S 18-969-2973 IMP
READYONE INDUSTRIES INC
1414 Ability Dr, El Paso, TX 79936-6415
Tel (915) 858-7277 *Founded/Ownrshp* 1989
Sales 99.5MM *EMP* 1,300
Accts Lauterbach Borschow & Company
SIC 2331 2311 Women's & misses' blouses & shirts; Military uniforms, men's & youths': purchased materials
Pr: Antonio Martinez
**Pr:* Tom Ahmann
**CEO:* Jesse R Cross
**CFO:* Michael Mason
**VP:* Cynthia Deharo
**VP:* Russell Gibson
IT Man: Cidy Araujo

D-U-N-S 01-653-8485
REAGAN WIRELESS CORP (FL)
720 S Powerline Rd Ste D, Deerfield Beach, FL 33442-8156
Tel (954) 596-2355 *Founded/Ownrshp* 1997
Sales 104.0MM *EMP* 155
SIC 5065 4812

D-U-N-S 00-218-2228 IMP/EXP
REAGENT CHEMICAL & RESEARCH INC
115 Rte 202, Ringoes, NJ 08551
Tel (908) 284-2800 *Founded/Ownrshp* 1959
Sales 99.6MM^E *EMP* 400
SIC 3949 2819

D-U-N-S 07-972-9424 IMP/EXP
■ REAL ALLOY HOLDING INC
(*Suby of* REAL INDUSTRY INC) ★
3700 Park East Dr Ste 300, Beachwood, OH 44122-4399
Tel (216) 755-8800 *Founded/Ownrshp* 2014
Sales 1.3MMM *EMP* 1,600
SIC 3341 3313 3334 Secondary nonferrous metals; Ferromanganese, not made in blast furnaces; Pigs, aluminum
Pr: Terry Hogan
Treas: Cris Garisek

D-U-N-S 05-789-6847
■ REAL ALLOY RECYCLING INC
(*Suby of* REAL ALLOY HOLDING INC) ★
3700 Park East Dr Ste 300, Beachwood, OH 44122-4399
Tel (216) 755-8900 *Founded/Ownrshp* 2010
Sales 343.5MM^E *EMP* 1,000
SIC 3341 Secondary nonferrous metals
Pr: Terry Hogan
**CFO:* Michael Hobey

D-U-N-S 80-159-8699
■ REAL ALLOY SPECIALTY PRODUCTS INC
(*Suby of* REAL ALLOY HOLDING INC) ★
3700 Park East Dr Ste 300, Beachwood, OH 44122-4399
Tel (216) 755-8836 *Founded/Ownrshp* 2010
Sales 237.7MM^E *EMP* 1,000
SIC 3355 Aluminum rolling & drawing; Slugs, aluminum
Pr: Terry Hogan
**CFO:* Michael Hobey

D-U-N-S 02-934-4964
REAL ESTATE IN REAL TIME INC
100 Lakeshore Dr Ste 96, Altamonte Springs, FL 32714-5012
Tel (321) 312-0748 *Founded/Ownrshp* 2005
Sales 259.0MM *EMP* 600^E
SIC 6531 1542 1522 Real estate agents & managers; Commercial & office building contractors; Residential construction
Pr: Joel Hartfield
Doctor: Mark D Anderson
Doctor: Stephen B Davis
Doctor: Michael S Mann
Doctor: Todd A Stine
Doctor: Matthew G Stoner
Doctor: Jeffrey G Strickland

D-U-N-S 07-424-9566
REAL ESTATE ONE INC (MI)
REAL ESTATE ONE LICENSING CO
25800 Northwestern Hwy # 100, Southfield, MI 48075-6104
Tel (248) 208-2900 *Founded/Ownrshp* 1970
Sales 106.9MM *EMP* 2,000
SIC 6531 Real estate agent, residential
Pr: Dan Elsea
**CFO:* Kevin Dunivin
IT Man: Scott Gaffan
Web Dev: Michelle Jackson
Art Dir: Danette Sarah

REAL ESTATE ONE LICENSING CO
See REAL ESTATE ONE INC

D-U-N-S 01-537-4914
REAL HOSPITALITY GROUP LLC
12800 Hospitality Ln, Ocean City, MD 21842-9394
Tel (410) 213-1971 *Founded/Ownrshp* 2010
Sales 288.0MM *EMP* 2,100
SIC 8741 Hospital management
Pr: Benjamin Seidel
Pr: Sanjay Bedi
Pr: Ron Loman
COO: John Parker
CFO: Ken Berger
Chf Mktg O: Rick Day
**CIO:* Joseph Yi
VP Sls: David Chu
Sls Dir: Lourdes Lopez

D-U-N-S 07-795-8130
▲ REAL INDUSTRY INC
15301 Ventura Blvd # 400, Sherman Oaks, CA 91403-3102
Tel (805) 435-1255 *Founded/Ownrshp* 1972
Sales 1.1MMM *EMP* 1,700
Tkr Sym RELY *Exch* NGS
SIC 5063 6162 Circuit breakers; Mortgage bankers & correspondents
Pr: Kyle Ross
**Ch Bd:* William Hall
CFO: Michael Hobey
Ex VP: John Miller

D-U-N-S 03-945-5188
REAL LIVING INC
77 E Nationwide Blvd, Columbus, OH 43215-2512
Tel (614) 221-7400 *Founded/Ownrshp* 2001
Sales 57.0MM^E *EMP* 1,847
SIC 6531 Real estate brokers & agents
Prin: Harley E Rouda Jr
**Ex VP:* Brooks Burton
**Ex VP:* Robert W McAdams
**Sr VP:* Thomas Panattoni
**VP:* Jeff Gutowsky
**VP:* Susan Yannaccone
Sls Mgr: Mike Brunner
Sls Mgr: Doug Meese

D-U-N-S 10-287-4562
REAL MEX RESTAURANTS INC
EL TORITO MEXICAN RESTAURANT
5660 Katella Ave Ste 200, Cypress, CA 90630-5059
Tel (562) 346-1020 *Founded/Ownrshp* 2013
Sales 492.7MM^E *EMP* 10,843
SIC 5812 Mexican restaurant
CEO: Bryan Lockwood
**COO:* Edie Ames
**COO:* Rio Gueli
**CFO:* Blake Barnett
**CFO:* Richard P Dutkiewicz
**CFO:* Laurie Lawhorne
**Sr VP:* Roberto Lopez
**Sr VP:* Andy MAI
VP: Julie Browne
VP: Julie Koenig-Brown
VP: John Kontz
VP: Michael McKinnon
VP: Randy Sharpe
VP: Mark Turpin
Board of Directors: Jeff Campbell, Scott King, Anthony Polazzi, Donald V Roach, James Shein, R Lynn Skillen, Christopher R Thomas, Douglas Werking

D-U-N-S 03-229-9562
REAL PROPERTY SERVICES CORP
RPS MANAGEMENT
9960 W Chynne Ave Ste 110, North Las Vegas, NV 89030
Tel (702) 313-3700 *Founded/Ownrshp* 1981
Sales 24.2MM^E *EMP* 1,200
SIC 6531 6211 Real estate managers; Security brokers & dealers
Pr: Patricia M Green
**Treas:* James E Hebert

D-U-N-S 00-120-2183 IMP/EXP
■ REAL REEL CORP
NATIONAL PACKING SUPPLY
(*Suby of* ILLINOIS TOOL WORKS INC) ★
50 Taylor Dr, Rumford, RI 02916-1030
Tel (401) 438-4240 *Founded/Ownrshp* 1922, 2011
Sales 108.7MM^E *EMP* 550
SIC 2631 2655 2621 Packaging board; Reels (fiber), textile: made from purchased material; Packaging paper; Shipping sack paper
Pr: Charles Dunn
**Treas:* John Dunn Jr
**VP:* Gregory Dunn
VP: Mike Riegsecker
VP: Dale Von Behren
Counsel: Tom Bender

D-U-N-S 16-747-4076 IMP
REALD INC
(*Suby of* RHOMBUS CINEMA HOLDINGS, LP)
100 N Crescent Dr, Beverly Hills, CA 90210-5408
Tel (424) 702-4327 *Founded/Ownrshp* 2015
Sales 163.4MM *EMP* 162
SIC 7812 Motion picture & video production
CEO: Michael V Lewis
Pr: Anthony Marcoly
COO: Travis Reid
CFO: Andrew A Skarupa
CFO: Jeff Spain
Ex VP: Leo Bannon
Ex VP: Minard Hamilton
VP: Jill Cook
Mng Dir: Bob Mayson
Genl Mgr: Edman Chan
Genl Couns: Vivian Yang

D-U-N-S 83-610-1485 IMP
▲ REALNETWORKS INC
1501 1st Ave S Ste 600, Seattle, WA 98134-1470
Tel (206) 674-2700 *Founded/Ownrshp* 1994
Sales 125.3MM *EMP* 579^E
Tkr Sym RNWK *Exch* NGS
SIC 7371 7372 Software programming applications; Application computer software
Ch Bd: Robert Glaser
Pr: William J Patrizio
Pr: Massimiliano Pellegrini
CFO: Marjorie Thomas
Sr Cor Off: Wendy Maslowski
Sr VP: Michael Parham
Netwrk Eng: Lawrence Bizga
Snr Mgr: Katie Eiler
Snr Mgr: Bryan Ryu
Board of Directors: Bruce A Jaffe, Christopher R Jones, Dawn G Lepore, Janice Roberts, Michael B Slade, Dominique Trempont

D-U-N-S 78-014-8743
■ REALOGY GROUP LLC
(*Suby of* REALOGY INTERMEDIATE HOLDINGS LLC) ★
175 Park Ave, Madison, NJ 07940-1123
Tel (973) 407-2000 *Founded/Ownrshp* 2007
Sales 5.7MMM *EMP* 11,400^E
SIC 6531 6794 7389 6541 Real estate agents & managers; Franchises, selling or licensing; Relocation service; Title & trust companies
Ch Bd: Richard A Smith
CFO: Anthony E Hull
Ofcr: Sunita Holzer
Ex VP: Marilyn J Wasser
Sr VP: Daniel Barnett
Sr VP: DEA Benson
Sr VP: Timothy B Gustavson
IT Man: Steven Koch
Software D: Lynette C Gladdis
Board of Directors: Raul Alvarez, Marc E Becker, Fiona P Dias, V Ann Hailey, Duncan L Niederauer, Sherry M Smith, Chris Terrill, Michael J Williams

D-U-N-S 80-003-5417
▲ REALOGY HOLDINGS CORP
175 Park Ave, Madison, NJ 07940-1123
Tel (973) 407-2000 *Founded/Ownrshp* 2006
Sales 5.7MMM *EMP* 11,460
Tkr Sym RLGY *Exch* NYS
SIC 6531 6794 7389 6541 Real estate agents & managers; Franchises, selling or licensing; Relocation service; Title & trust companies
Ch Bd: Richard A Smith
CFO: Anthony E Hull
Ofcr: Sunita Holzer
Ex VP: Marilyn J Wasser
Sr VP: Stephen Fraser
Sr VP: Timothy B Gustavson
VP: David Goodlett
VP: Jason Silfies
Sales Asso: Richard Myers
Snr Mgr: Alice Bauml
Snr Mgr: Mark Burdzy
Board of Directors: Raul Alvarez, Marc E Becker, Fiona P Dias, Matthew J Espe, V Ann Hailey, Duncan Niederauer, Sherry M Smith, Chris Terrill, Michael J Williams

D-U-N-S 07-950-3309
■ REALOGY INTERMEDIATE HOLDINGS LLC
(*Suby of* REALOGY HOLDINGS CORP) ★
175 Park Ave, Madison, NJ 07940-1123
Tel (973) 407-0000 *Founded/Ownrshp* 2006
Sales 5.7MMM^E *EMP* 11,400^E
SIC 6531 6794 7389 6541 Real estate agents & managers; Franchises, selling or licensing; Relocation service; Title & trust companies
Pr: Richard A Smith

D-U-N-S 00-695-7420
■ REALOGY SERVICES GROUP LLC
(*Suby of* REALOGY GROUP LLC) ★
3001 Leadenhall Rd, Mount Laurel, NJ 08054-4609
Tel (856) 914-8500 *Founded/Ownrshp* 2004
Sales 1.8MMM^E *EMP* 964^E
SIC 6531 6211 Real estate brokers & agents; Investment firm, general brokerage
Pr: Richard A Smith
CFO: Anthony E Hull
Ex VP: David J Weaving

D-U-N-S 05-304-6541
▲ REALPAGE INC
2201 Lakeside Blvd, Richardson, TX 75082-4305
Tel (972) 820-3000 *Founded/Ownrshp* 1998
Sales 468.5MM *EMP* 4,100
Tkr Sym RP *Exch* NGS
SIC 7371 Computer software development & applications
Ch Bd: Stephen T Winn
CFO: W Bryan Hill
Ex VP: William P Chaney
Ex VP: Ashley Glover
VP: Taylor Harris
Software D: Saketh Bhaskarabotla
Software D: Deepanshu Kumar
Software D: Dinesh Panda
Software D: Varun Sheshabhattar
Netwrk Eng: Jack Rodriguez
Sales Exec: David Knoch
Board of Directors: Alfred R Berkeley III, Peter Gyenes, Scott S Ingraham, Charles Kane, Jeffrey T Leeds, Kathryn V Marinello, Jason A Wright

REALTOR MAGAZINE
See NATIONAL ASSOCIATION OF REALTORS

D-U-N-S 61-150-1904
REALTY FINANCE CORP
895 Dove St Ste 210, Newport Beach, CA 92660-2941
Tel (949) 296-3280 *Founded/Ownrshp* 2005
Sales NA *EMP* 16^E
Accts Ernst & Young Llp Hartford
SIC 6162 Mortgage bankers & correspondents
Pr: Kenneth J Witkin
CFO: Jonathan Harmer
Ex VP: David Haddad
Ex VP: Dennis Regan

D-U-N-S 92-923-6040
▲ REALTY INCOME CORP
11995 El Camino Real, San Diego, CA 92130-2539
Tel (858) 284-5000 *Founded/Ownrshp* 1969
Sales 1.0MMM *EMP* 132^E
Tkr Sym O *Exch* NYS
SIC 6798 Real estate investment trusts
Pr: John P Case
Pr: Sumit Roy
CFO: Paul M Meurer
Treas: Evelyn J Clark
Assoc VP: Jill Cossaboom
Assoc VP: Jenette O'Brien
Ex VP: Neil Abraham
Ex VP: Michael R Pfeiffer
Sr VP: Debra M Bonebrake
Sr VP: Robert J Israel
Sr VP: Laura S King
VP: Elizabeth Cate
VP: Shannon Kehle
Board of Directors: Kathleen R Allen, A Larry Chapman, Michael D McKee, Gregory T McLaughlin, Ronald L Merriman, Stephen E Sterrett

D-U-N-S 01-776-7435
REALTY ONE INC
(*Suby of* REAL LIVING INC) ★
800 W Saint Clair Ave, Cleveland, OH 44113-1266
Tel (216) 328-2500 *Founded/Ownrshp* 2002
Sales 19.0MM^E *EMP* 1,819
SIC 6531 Real estate brokers & agents
Ch Bd: Joseph Aveni
**Pr:* Anthony M Ciepiel
**Sr VP:* William P Pender Jr

REALTY SOUTH
See REALTYSOUTH ADMIN OFFICE

D-U-N-S 05-720-7714
■ REALTYSOUTH ADMIN OFFICE
REALTY SOUTH
(*Suby of* HOMESERVICES OF AMERICA INC) ★
2501 20th Pl S Ste 400, Birmingham, AL 35223-1753
Tel (205) 325-1397 *Founded/Ownrshp* 2002
Sales 29.5MM^E *EMP* 1,056^E
SIC 6531 Real estate brokers & agents
CEO: Py Dodge
Ofcr: Art Garcia
**VP:* Dawn Reeves
VP: Marilyn Seier
Off Mgr: Patty Bingham
Off Mgr: Kent Brenner
Off Mgr: Erle Morring
Off Mgr: Vicki Warner
Off Admin: Norma Melvin
Sls Mgr: Carl Adams
Sales Asso: Nebrazy Adams

REAMS 8
See UTAH NATIONAL SECURITY INC

D-U-N-S 03-310-4191
REASORS LLC
200 W Choctaw St, Tahlequah, OK 74464-3808
Tel (918) 456-1472 *Founded/Ownrshp* 1963
Sales 448.1MM^E *EMP* 3,000
SIC 5411 Grocery stores, independent
CEO: Jeff Reasor
**CFO:* Stephen Martin
VP: Brent Edstrom
VP: Steve Lehto
Exec: Tammy Hardbarger
Dir Rx: Andy Becker
Ex Dir: Tony Bell
Store Dir: Glen Stafford
Sales Exec: Ken Perry
S&M/VP: Ward Dunn

D-U-N-S 03-494-3878
REBEL OIL CO INC
REBELS
2200 Highland Dr, Las Vegas, NV 89102-4629
Tel (702) 382-5866 *Founded/Ownrshp* 1954
Sales 378.7MM^E *EMP* 500
Accts Piercy Bowler Taylor & Kern L
SIC 5171 5411 Petroleum bulk stations; Convenience stores, independent
Pr: Jack Cason
**Sec:* Dana Cason Teepe
Genl Mgr: Gregg Benson
Sls Mgr: Robert Santaella

REBELS
See REBEL OIL CO INC

REBOUND PHYSICAL THERAPY
See SW WASHINGTON HOSPITAL INC

D-U-N-S 61-540-7483 IMP/EXP
REC ADVANCED SILICON MATERIALS LLC
(*Suby of* REC SILICON INC) ★
119140 Rick Jones Way, Butte, MT 59750-9722
Tel (406) 496-9898 *Founded/Ownrshp* 2005
Sales 228.8MM^E *EMP* 700
SIC 3339 Silicon & chromium
Exec: Ken Gordner
CIO: Helge Mothes

D-U-N-S 96-358-7634
REC BOAT HOLDINGS LLC
(*Suby of* BENETEAU INC) ★
925 Frisbie St, Cadillac, MI 49601-9259
Tel (231) 775-1351 *Founded/Ownrshp* 2014
Sales 83.1MM *EMP* 480
SIC 3732 Boat building & repairing
VP Opers: Rick Videan
Plnt Mgr: Joe Perrin
Manager: Leon Larock
Sls Mgr: Bill Barnes

D-U-N-S 18-444-7824 IMP/EXP
REC SILICON INC
(*Suby of* REC SILICON AS)
3700 Buffalo Speedway # 620, Houston, TX 77098-3709
Tel (281) 325-3800 *Founded/Ownrshp* 2002
Sales 308.7MM^E *EMP* 718
Accts Kpmg Seattle Wa
SIC 3339 Silicon & chromium
Ch: Ole Enger
**CEO:* Goran Bye
**Treas:* Ken Gordner
**Sr VP:* Tor Hartmann
**Sr VP:* Jan Johannessen
**Prin:* Patrick Storck

D-U-N-S 07-923-5721
■ REC SOLAR COMMERCIAL CORP
(*Suby of* DUKE ENERGY CORP) ★
3450 Broad St Ste 105, San Luis Obispo, CA 93401-7214
Tel (844) 732-7652 *Founded/Ownrshp* 2013, 1997
Sales 110.6MM^E *EMP* 160
SIC 1623 Water, sewer & utility lines
CEO: Matt Walz
**CFO:* Tom Giovanni
VP: Art Villa
**VP:* Ted Walsh

D-U-N-S 09-158-2580
RECALL CORP
180 Technology Pkwy # 100, Norcross, GA 30092-2977
Tel (770) 776-1000 *Founded/Ownrshp* 1999
Sales 195.6MM^E *EMP* 325
SIC 8741

D-U-N-S 03-815-2310
RECCO HOME CARE SERVICE INC
524 Hicksville Rd, Massapequa, NY 11758-1204
Tel (516) 798-6688 *Founded/Ownrshp* 1974
Sales 32.9MM^E *EMP* 1,500
SIC 8082 Home health care services
Pr: Norma Recco
Sr VP: Claudia Hammar
**VP:* Hazel Ross
Ex Dir: Taryn Birkmire

D-U-N-S 01-914-8563
RECEIVABLE MANAGEMENT SERVICES CORP
IQORE
(*Suby of* RMS) ★
240 Emery St, Bethlehem, PA 18015-1980
Tel (484) 242-4000 *Founded/Ownrshp* 2001
Sales 102.6MM^E *EMP* 3,000
SIC 7322 Adjustment & collection services
COO: Michael Kronenfeld
**CEO:* Mike Baldwin
**Sr VP:* Gregory Hanlon
**Sr VP:* Hugh Kelly
**Sr VP:* Karl Nicosia
**Sr VP:* Donald Wickersham

D-U-N-S 19-984-0468
RECEIVABLE MANAGEMENT SERVICES INTERNATIONAL INC
RMS
(*Suby of* IQOR HOLDINGS INC) ★
240 Emery St, Bethlehem, PA 18015-1980
Tel (484) 242-4000 *Founded/Ownrshp* 2010
Sales 102.6MM^E *EMP* 3,000
SIC 7322 Adjustment & collection services
COO: Michael Kronenfeld
**Sr VP:* Gregory Hanlon
**Sr VP:* Hugh Kelly
**Sr VP:* Karl Nicosia
**Sr VP:* Donald Wickersham
Dir IT: Laurel Disilvestro
Mktg Mgr: Stanley Vidmar

RECINTO DE AGUADILLA
See UNIVERSIDAD INTERAMERICANA DE PUERTO RICO INC

D-U-N-S 12-659-5128 IMP/EXP
RECKITT BENCKISER (NORTH AMERICA) INC
RB
(*Suby of* RECKITT BENCKISER HOLDINGS (USA) LIMITED)
399 Interpace Pkwy # 101, Parsippany, NJ 07054-1133
Tel (973) 404-2600 *Founded/Ownrshp* 1999
Sales 87.1M^E *EMP* 1,600
SIC 2035 2842 Pickles, sauces & salad dressings; Specialty cleaning, polishes & sanitation goods
Pr: Alexander Lacik
Ofcr: Sheila Kealy
Ofcr: Amanda Landolt
**Ex VP:* Heather Allen
**Ex VP:* Rakesh Kapoor
**VP:* Amedeo Fasano
**VP:* Roberto Funari
VP: Miguel Gonzalez
**VP:* Mark Willson
Comm Dir: Lynn Kenney
Sfty Dirs: Joanne Martinez

D-U-N-S 09-440-5024 IMP/EXP
RECKITT BENCKISER LLC
(*Suby of* RECKITT BENCKISER GROUP PLC)
399 Interpace Pkwy # 101, Parsippany, NJ 07054-1133
Tel (973) 404-2600 *Founded/Ownrshp* 1977
Sales 733.4MM^E *EMP* 1,600
SIC 2035 2842 Mustard, prepared (wet); Deodorants, nonpersonal
CEO: Rakesh Kapoor
Pr: Alexander Lacik
CFO: Paul Ellis
Ex VP: Rob Degroot
VP: Frank Cervi
VP: Brendan Collins
VP: Mario Monteiro
VP: Adam Rodgers
Exec: Amy Dilks
Dir Bus: Tony Goodman
**Prin:* Javed Ahmed

D-U-N-S 82-748-7641
RECKSON OPERATING PARTNERSHIP LP
420 Lexington Ave, New York, NY 10170-0002
Tel (212) 594-2700 *Founded/Ownrshp* 1995
Sales 925.2MM *EMP* 279^E
Accts Ernst & Young Llp New York N
SIC 6531 Real estate agents & managers
Pr: Marc Holliday
Genl Pt: Wyoming Acquisition GP LLC
CFO: Matthew J Diliberto

RECO
See REINFORCED EARTH CO

D-U-N-S 02-117-3729
RECOLOGY INC (CA)
50 California St Fl 24, San Francisco, CA 94111-4796
Tel (415) 875-1000 *Founded/Ownrshp* 1988
Sales 1.6MMM^E *EMP* 2,000
SIC 4953 Garbage: collecting, destroying & processing; Recycling, waste materials
Pr: Michael J Sangiacomo
**COO:* George P McGrath
**CFO:* Mark R Lomele
CFO: Mark Lomele
**Ch:* Dennis Wu
Ex VP: George McGrath
VP: Chris E Choate
VP: Arthur Cimento
VP: Bruce Gondry
Comm Dir: Bill Burrage
Rgnl Mgr: Paul Yamamoto
Board of Directors: Larry A Colton, Dennis Wu

RECOMMUNITY
See RE COMMUNITY HOLDINGS II INC

D-U-N-S 12-732-6734
RECOMMUNITY CORP
(*Suby of* RECOMMUNITY) ★
809 W Hill St Ste E, Charlotte, NC 28208-5343
Tel (860) 289-8480 *Founded/Ownrshp* 2011
Sales 175.1MM^E *EMP* 400
SIC 4953 Recycling, waste materials
Pr: Scott Tenney
**CFO:* William Jennings
**VP:* Tim Flanagan
**VP:* Alan Gargano
**VP:* Will Herzog

D-U-N-S 03-480-1893
RECOMMUNITY RECYCLING
1007 Amble Dr, Charlotte, NC 28206-1301
Tel (704) 598-8595 *Founded/Ownrshp* 2011
Sales 122.5MM^E *EMP* 400^E
SIC 4953 Recycling, waste materials
CEO: James Devlin
**Pr:* Sean Duffy
**CEO:* James W Bohlig
**CFO:* Steve Klueg

D-U-N-S 04-355-1654
RECONSERVE INC (TN)
DEXT COMPANY
(*Suby of* SCOPE PRODUCTS) ★
2811 Wilshire Blvd # 410, Santa Monica, CA 90403-4803
Tel (310) 458-1574 *Founded/Ownrshp* 1966, 2011
Sales 264.6MM *EMP* 300
SIC 2048 Livestock feeds
CEO: Meyer Luskin
**COO:* David Luskin
CTO: Junaid Khan

RECORD THE
See BERGEN RECORD CORP

D-U-N-S 19-692-1993
RECORD STEEL AND CONSTRUCTION INC
RSCI
333 W Rossi St Ste 200, Boise, ID 83706-3806
Tel (208) 887-1401 *Founded/Ownrshp* 1988
Sales 151.5MM^E *EMP* 165
SIC 1542 1791 Commercial & office building, new construction; Commercial & office buildings, renovation & repair; Structural steel erection

CEO: Zeke Johnson
Ql Cn Mgr: Andrew Erquiaga
Pgrm Dir: Susan S Record

D-U-N-S 06-680-9344
■ **RECORD TOWN INC**
SUN COAST
(*Suby of* TRANS WORLD ENTERTAINMENT CORP) ★
38 Corporate Cir, Albany, NY 12203-5197
Tel (518) 452-1242 *Founded/Ownrshp* 1973
Sales 436.8MM^E *EMP* 4,000
SIC 5735 Audio tapes, prerecorded; Video tapes, prerecorded; Compact discs
Ch: Robert J Higgins
**Pr:* Mike Honneyman
**Treas:* Ed Spapienza
**VP:* Bruce Eisenberg
Genl Mgr: Neil Krin
Sales Exec: Michael Loader

D-U-N-S 14-230-2020
RECOVERCARE LLC
JOERNS RECOVERCARE
(*Suby of* AURORA CAPITAL GROUP) ★
1920 Stanley Gault Pkwy # 100, Louisville, KY 40223-4209
Tel (502) 489-9449 *Founded/Ownrshp* 2014
Sales 159.3MM^E *EMP* 495
SIC 5047 8099 Medical equipment & supplies; Childbirth preparation clinic
Pr: Mary Zappone
CEO: Mark Ludwig
CFO: Kevin S Boyle Sr
CFO: Kelly G Duncan
Ex VP: Brian Cousins
VP: John Barr
VP: Glenn Petracci
VP: Rodney Vinegar
CIO: Jeffrey Sadtler
Opers Mgr: Randy Tanner

D-U-N-S 07-865-8402
RECOVERY SCHOOL DISTRICT
RSD NEW ORLEANS
(*Suby of* LOUISIANA DEPARTMENT OF EDUCATION)
1615 Poydras St Ste 400, New Orleans, LA 70112-5404
Tel (504) 373-6200 *Founded/Ownrshp* 2012
Sales NA *EMP* 1,360^E
SIC 9411 State education department
Dir Sec: Eddie Compass
Pr Dir: Zoey Reed
Teacher Pr: Tiffany Delcour

RECREATION AND PARKS
See COUNTY OF ALAMANCE

RECREATION DEPARTMENT
See TOWN OF WALPOLE

RECREATION NATION
See DEHCO INC

D-U-N-S 10-283-4538
RECREATIONAL ENTERPRISES INC
ELDORADO HOTEL CASINO
345 N Virginia St, Reno, NV 89501-1136
Tel (775) 786-5700 *Founded/Ownrshp* 1975
Sales 104.2MM^E *EMP* 2,400^E
SIC 7011 7999 5813 5812 Casino hotel; Gambling establishment; Bar (drinking places); American restaurant
Pr: Donald L Carano
Ex Dir: Linda Seidl
Genl Mgr: Clyde Callicott
CIO: Peter Broughton
Sys Mgr: Brian Smith
Web Dev: Conrad Wong
VP Opers: Rob Mouchou
Advt Dir: Angela Kabisch
Sls Dir: Don Goodman

D-U-N-S 00-948-3355 IMP/EXP
RECREATIONAL EQUIPMENT INC
R E I CO-OP
6750 S 228th St, Kent, WA 98032-4803
Tel (253) 395-3780 *Founded/Ownrshp* 1938
Sales 2.2MMM *EMP* 6,000
SIC 2329 3949 2399 5941 5961 5699

D-U-N-S 95-709-8965 IMP
RECTICEL NORTH AMERICA INC
RECTICEL UREPP NORTH AMERICA
(*Suby of* RECTICEL U.S., INC)
1653 Atlantic Blvd, Auburn Hills, MI 48326-1503
Tel (248) 393-2100 *Founded/Ownrshp* 1995
Sales 87.6MM^E *EMP* 132
SIC 5169 Chemicals & allied products
Pr: Marc Clockaerts
**Treas:* Jean Pierre Mellen
Admn Mgr: Emma Foster
Plnt Mgr: Guilermo Marquez
Sls Mgr: Rony Briers
Sls Mgr: Sarah Metcalfe

RECTICEL UREPP NORTH AMERICA
See RECTICEL NORTH AMERICA INC

D-U-N-S 06-539-1526 IMP
RECTOR & VISITORS OF UNIVERSITY OF VIRGINIA
1001 Emmet St N, Charlottesville, VA 22903-4833
Tel (434) 924-0311 *Founded/Ownrshp* 1819
Sales 1.7MMM^E *EMP* 13,300
Accts Walter J Kutcharski Richmond
SIC 8221 University
Pr: Teresa A Sullivan
COO: Leonard W Sandridge Jr
CFO: Yoke San L Reynolds
Treas: Jim Matteo
Assoc VP: Karen Rendleman
Ex VP: David Black
Sr VP: Robert D Sweeney
VP: Ralph O Allen
VP: Gene Block
VP: James L Hilton
VP: Patricia M Lampkin
VP: Colette Sheehy
VP: Thomas C Skalak
Dir Lab: Jeff Ellena
Dir Lab: Larry Hollen
Assoc Dir: Jane Perry
Comm Man: Jon Bowen

D-U-N-S 85-859-4021 EXP
RECYCLE AMERICA ALLIANCE LLC
720 E Butterfield Rd Fl 2, Lombard, IL 60148-5686
Tel (630) 572-8800 *Founded/Ownrshp* 1995
Sales 795.7MM^E *EMP* 5,500
SIC 4953 Non-hazardous waste disposal sites
Pr: Steve Ragiel
**Pr:* Joseph Holsten

D-U-N-S 13-196-5126
RED APPLE GROUP INC
800 3rd Ave Fl 5, New York, NY 10022-7655
Tel (212) 956-5803 *Founded/Ownrshp* 1990
Sales 2.4MMM^E *EMP* 6,813
SIC 5461 5541 5411 Doughnuts; Filling stations, gasoline; Convenience stores, chain
Ch Bd: John A Catsimatidis
**Pr:* Myron L Turfitt
COO: Charles Criscuolo
CFO: James Murphy
**VP:* Robert Simpson
CIO: Henry Conwell
CIO: Chris McCrae
Opers Mgr: Kishore Lal

RED BALL GARAGE
See GARAGE MANAGEMENT CO LLC

D-U-N-S 04-921-3267 IMP
RED BALL OXYGEN CO INC
609 N Market St, Shreveport, LA 71107-6841
Tel (318) 425-6300 *Founded/Ownrshp* 1969
Sales 90.6MM^E *EMP* 160
SIC 5084 5085 5169 5099 5531 5013 Welding machinery & equipment; Welding supplies; Compressed gas; Safety equipment & supplies; Batteries, automotive & truck; Automotive batteries
CEO: Gary M Kennedy
**Pr:* Robert Awing
CFO: Dave Tunnell
Sec: Ralph Thomas
**Ex VP:* Larry Kennedy
VP: Marty Jones
Brnch Mgr: Nick Brown
Brnch Mgr: Lindsey Pope
Dir IT: John Vrana
VP Sls: Bob Ewing

D-U-N-S 78-216-5278
RED BLOSSOM SALES INC
400 W Ventura Blvd # 140, Camarillo, CA 93010-9139
Tel (805) 686-4747 *Founded/Ownrshp* 1991
Sales 141.5MM *EMP* 1,046
Accts Smeck Esparza & Co Cpas Ba
SIC 0171 Strawberry farm
CEO: Craig A Casca
**Pr:* David Lawrence

D-U-N-S 82-813-8169
RED BULL DISTRIBUTION CO INC
REDBULL DISTRIBUTION CO COLO
(*Suby of* RED BULL GMBH)
1740 Stewart St, Santa Monica, CA 90404-4022
Tel (916) 515-3501 *Founded/Ownrshp* 2008
Sales 109.9MM^E *EMP* 300^E
SIC 5149 Beverage concentrates
CEO: Selin Chidiak
Genl Mgr: Dave Meeks
Genl Mgr: Glynn Rowell

D-U-N-S 93-282-1218 IMP
RED BULL NORTH AMERICA INC
RED BULL TV
(*Suby of* RED BULL GMBH)
1740 Stewart St, Santa Monica, CA 90404-4022
Tel (310) 460-5356 *Founded/Ownrshp* 1995
Sales 128.6MM^E *EMP* 700
SIC 7929

RED BULL TV
See RED BULL NORTH AMERICA INC

D-U-N-S 07-908-7083
RED CAPITAL GROUP LLC
(*Suby of* ORIX USA CORP) ★
10 W Broad St Ste 1510, Columbus, OH 43215-3479
Tel (614) 857-1400 *Founded/Ownrshp* 2012
Sales 85.1MM^E *EMP* 240^E
SIC 6282 Investment advice
CEO: Michael J Moran
**Pr:* Mark C Beisler
Chf Cred: Todd Rodenberg
VP: Bob Cain
VP: Eben Cockley
VP: McMahon Misty
VP: Matthew Napoleon
VP: Tiffany Ranft
Dir Risk M: George Janes
Mng Dir: Ryan Duling
Mng Dir: Kevin Mainelli

D-U-N-S 06-460-6403 IMP/EXP
RED CHAMBER CO
1912 E Vernon Ave, Vernon, CA 90058-1611
Tel (323) 234-9000 *Founded/Ownrshp* 1980
Sales 278.1MM^E *EMP* 341^E
SIC 5146 4222 Seafoods; Warehousing, cold storage or refrigerated
Prin: Ming Bin Kou
**Ch Bd:* Shan Chun Kou
IT Man: Eddy Tjong
Info Man: Jimmy Chen

D-U-N-S 05-504-4187
■ **RED CLASSIC TRANSIT LLC**
(*Suby of* COCA-COLA BOTTLING CO CONSOLIDATED) ★
1800 Continental Blvd # 400, Charlotte, NC 28273-6388
Tel (980) 275-5721 *Founded/Ownrshp* 2010
Sales 91.1MM^E *EMP* 400
SIC 4731 Freight transportation arrangement
Pr: Ron Drogan
**Pr:* Ronald Drogan

D-U-N-S 10-822-0351
RED CLAY CONSOLIDATED SCHOOL DISTRICT
1502 Spruce Ave, Wilmington, DE 19805-2148
Tel (302) 552-3700 *Founded/Ownrshp* 1981
Sales NA *EMP* 2,000
SIC 9411 County supervisor of education, except school board
**CFO:* Jill Floore
CFO: Brett Taylor
Dir Sec: Brian Moore
Schl Brd P: Kenneth Rivera

D-U-N-S 02-427-3476
RED COATS INC
ADMIRAL SECURITY SERVICE
4520 East West Hwy # 200, Bethesda, MD 20814-3382
Tel (301) 654-4360 *Founded/Ownrshp* 1960
Sales 248.2MM^E *EMP* 5,252
SIC 7349 7381 Building cleaning service; Building maintenance, except repairs; Security guard service
Ch Bd: Barbara K Peel
Pr: George Vincent
CFO: Vickie Wells
**V Ch Bd:* William F Peel Jr
Ex VP: Leon Beresford
**Ex VP:* W Mack Wells
**Sr VP:* Bob Butorac
**VP:* Scott Kydd
VP: Carl Rowan
**VP:* Robert Wolak
VP Bus Dev: Ralph G Blasey

RED DIAMOND COFFEE & TEA
See RED DIAMOND INC

D-U-N-S 00-401-0633 IMP
RED DIAMOND INC
RED DIAMOND COFFEE & TEA
400 Park Ave, Moody, AL 35004-3330
Tel (205) 577-4000 *Founded/Ownrshp* 1906
Sales 171.5MM^E *EMP* 200
SIC 5141 2095 2099 Groceries, general line; Roasted coffee; Tea blending
Pr: Bowron William
**CFO:* Sherman Pitts
Ofcr: Steve Chain
Ex VP: Tom Ruszkowski
VP: John Padgett
VP: Rolf Van Rijn
Exec: Dave Carter
Dist Mgr: Dale Douglas
Genl Mgr: Jim Ramsdell
Opers Mgr: Kenny Langham
Secur Mgr: James Barr

RED DIGITAL CINEMA CAMERA CO
See RED.COM INC

D-U-N-S 01-035-8466
RED DOOR SALONS INC
8075 Leesburg Pike # 110, Vienna, VA 22182-2739
Tel (602) 760-2519 *Founded/Ownrshp* 2010
Sales 6.3MM^E *EMP* 4,000
SIC 7231 Beauty shops
CEO: Todd Walters

D-U-N-S 80-360-1863
■ **RED DOOR SALONS INC**
RED DOOR SPA HOLDINGS
(*Suby of* RED DOOR SPA) ★
222 S Mill Ave Ste 201, Tempe, AZ 85281-3738
Tel (480) 829-8191 *Founded/Ownrshp* 1992
Sales 21.4MM^E *EMP* 2,000
SIC 7231 5999 7299 Beauty shops; Cosmetics; Massage parlor
CEO: Todd Walter
COO: W Walter
**CFO:* Robert Broadhead
**Ch:* Brent Knudsen
**Chf Mktg O:* Lisa Hagen
**Prin:* Mario Tricoci

RED DOOR SPA
See ELIZABETH ARDEN SALON-HOLDINGS INC

RED DOOR SPA HOLDINGS
See RED DOOR SALONS INC

D-U-N-S 00-948-8495 IMP
RED DOT CORP
495 Andover Park E, Tukwila, WA 98188-7605
Tel (206) 151-3840 *Founded/Ownrshp* 1965
Sales 132.0MM^E *EMP* 390
SIC 3714 3585 Heaters, motor vehicle; Air conditioning, motor vehicle
Pr: Scott Ledbetter
**CFO:* Nick Janus
Mtls Mgr: Matt Kessler
Plnt Mgr: Jim Yantzer
Prd Mgr: Gary Wilson
Sls&Mrk Ex: Dave Lockner

D-U-N-S 00-603-5604 IMP/EXP
RED GOLD INC
1500 Tomato Country Way, Elwood, IN 46036-3437
Tel (765) 557-5500 *Founded/Ownrshp* 1942
Sales 431.6MM^E *EMP* 1,500
SIC 2033 2035 Tomato products: packaged in cans, jars, etc.; Tomato sauce: packaged in cans, jars, etc.; Tomato purees: packaged in cans, jars, etc.; Pickles, sauces & salad dressings
Pr: Brian Reichart
Ex VP: Lawrence Fettig
VP: Tina Anderson
VP: Scott Butler
**VP:* Selita Reichart
VP: Bob Savage
Exec: Connie Browne
Exec: Maurie Fettig
Creative D: Svetlana Kirilova
MIS Dir: Merle McGriss
Dir IT: Randy Merle

D-U-N-S 87-805-1556
▲ **RED HAT INC**

100 E Davie St, Raleigh, NC 27601-1806
Tel (919) 754-3700 *Founded/Ownrshp* 1993
Sales 2.0MMM *EMP* 7,300^E
Tkr Sym RHT *Exch* NYS
SIC 7372 Prepackaged software; Operating systems computer software
Pr: James M Whitehurst
**Ch Bd:* H Hugh Shelton
Pr: Paul J Cormier
CFO: Frank A Calderoni
Treas: Paul Argiry
Ofcr: Delisa K Alexander
Ex VP: Michael R Cunningham
Ex VP: Arun Oberoi
Ex VP: Brian Stevens
VP: Matt Androski
VP: Sukanta Biswas
VP: Kim Lynch
VP: Katrinka McCallum
VP: Scott Musson
VP: Gregory Symon
VP: Michael Tiemann
VP: Jeff Watts
Exec: Pam Watrous
Board of Directors: W Steve Albrecht, Charlene T Begley, Jeffrey J Clarke, Kimberly L Hammonds, William S Kaiser, Donald H Livingstone

RED HAWK CASINO
See SHINGLE SPRINGS TRIBAL GAMING AUTHORITY

D-U-N-S 01-730-5520
RED HAWK FIRE & SECURITY LLC
5100 Town Center Cir # 350, Boca Raton, FL 33486-1049
Tel (561) 672-3737 *Founded/Ownrshp* 2012
Sales 220.0MM^E *EMP* 1,100
SIC 3699 7382 Security control equipment & systems; Security systems services
COO: Michael McWilliams
**CFO:* Mark Foley
Treas: Lisa Kane
VP: Peter Alexander
VP: Mike Sanpietro
Admn Mgr: Jennifer Nelson
Dir IT: Scott Steffes
Opers Mgr: Shannan Carlson
VP Mktg: Alex Chermak

D-U-N-S 06-003-8056
▲ **RED LION HOTELS CORP**
RLHC
201 W North River Dr # 100, Spokane, WA 99201-2262
Tel (509) 459-6100 *Founded/Ownrshp* 1937
Sales 142.9MM *EMP* 1,783
Tkr Sym RLH *Exch* NYS
SIC 7011 Hotels
Pr: Gregory T Mount
Ch Bd: Robert G Wolfe
COO: Bernard T Moyle
CFO: David M Wright
Chf Mktg O: William J Linehan
Ex VP: Roger J Bloss
Ex VP: Thomas L McKeirnan
Ex VP: Harry G Sladich
Genl Mgr: Bruce Finn
Sls Dir: Ctp Bowe
Sls Dir: Todd Yohn
Board of Directors: Raymond R Brandstrom, James P Evans, Enrico Marini Fichera, David J Johnson, Melvin L Keating, Michael Vernon, Alexander Washburn

D-U-N-S 01-759-5112
■ **RED LION HOTELS HOLDINGS INC**
WESTCOAST HOSPITALITY
(*Suby of* RLHC) ★
201 W North River Dr # 100, Spokane, WA 99201-2262
Tel (509) 459-6100 *Founded/Ownrshp* 2008
Sales 163.4MM *EMP* 178
SIC 7011 Hotel, franchised
Pr: Art Coffey
**Sr VP:* Thomas McKeirnan
**VP:* Shannon Kapek
Sls Dir: Donya Alward
Sls Mgr: Erica Moloney

D-U-N-S 07-944-9205
RED LOBSTER HOSPITALITY LLC
(*Suby of* RED LOBSTER SEAFOOD CO LLC) ★
450 S Orange Ave Ste 800, Orlando, FL 32801-3344
Tel (407) 734-9000 *Founded/Ownrshp* 2014
Sales 1.5MMM^E *EMP* 62,000^E
SIC 5812 Seafood restaurants

D-U-N-S 00-444-5033
RED LOBSTER MANAGEMENT LLC
(*Suby of* GOLDEN GATE CAPITAL LP) ★
450 S Orange Ave Ste 800, Orlando, FL 32801-3344
Tel (407) 734-9000 *Founded/Ownrshp* 2012, 2014
Sales 348.5MM^E *EMP* 5,800
SIC 5812 Seafood restaurants
CEO: Kim Loperop
Genl Mgr: Jay Morgan
Genl Mgr: Amy Norman
Genl Mgr: Christine Vines
Snr Ntwrk: Billy Krebsbach
Site Mgr: Marco Holter
Site Mgr: Phillip McClanahan

D-U-N-S 07-959-1634
RED LOBSTER SEAFOOD CO LLC
1 Embarcadero Ctr Fl 39, San Francisco, CA 94111-3735
Tel (415) 983-2706 *Founded/Ownrshp* 2014
Sales 1.5MMM^E *EMP* 62,000^E
SIC 6726 Investment offices

D-U-N-S 02-706-2983 IMP
RED MCCOMBS HYUNDAI LTD
RED MCCOMBS SUPERIOR HYUNDAI
4800 Nw Loop 410, San Antonio, TX 78229-5310
Tel (210) 684-7440 *Founded/Ownrshp* 1999
Sales 88.3MM^E *EMP* 300
SIC 5511 5521 Automobiles, new & used; Pickups, new & used; Used car dealers
Mng Pt: Red McCombs
Pt: Gary V Woods
Exec: Lee Frankel
Genl Mgr: Kevin Browning

RED MCCOMBS SUPERIOR HYUNDAI
See RED MCCOMBS HYUNDAI LTD

D-U-N-S 05-833-4079 IMP/EXP
RED RIVER COMMODITIES INC
(Suby of AMSTERDAM COMMODITIES N.V.)
501 42nd St N, Fargo, ND 58102-3952
Tel (701) 282-2600 Founded/Ownrshp 2006
Sales 154.8MM^E EMP 250
SIC 5153 5145 5149 Grain & field beans; Beans, dry: bulk; Snack foods; Pet foods
Pr: Robert A Majkrzak
*CFO: Randall C Wigen
*VP: Roger C Jaeger
VP: Roger Jaeger
VP: Randy Wigen
Dir IT: Shane Johnson
VP Opers: Todd Mondry
Natl Sales: Scott Reinke

D-U-N-S 93-367-8708
RED RIVER COMPUTER CO INC
21 Water St Ste 500, Claremont, NH 03743-2247
Tel (603) 298-5293 Founded/Ownrshp 1995
Sales 332.0MM EMP 135
SIC 7379 Computer related maintenance services
Pr: Richard A Bolduc
*CFO: Edmund I Mangini III
VP: Jim Dunn
VP: Paul Krein
*VP: Richard K Mann
*VP: Jeff Sessions

D-U-N-S 80-003-8655
■ **RED RIVER ENTERTAINMENT OF SHREVEPORT**
SAM'S TOWN CASINO
(Suby of BOYD GAMING CORP) ★
315 Clyde Fant Pkwy, Shreveport, LA 71101-3204
Tel (318) 424-7777 Founded/Ownrshp 2004
Sales 14.1MM^E EMP 1,500
SIC 7999 Gambling establishment
Pt: Loren Gill
Pt: William S Boyd
Pt: Kim Etllend

D-U-N-S 83-993-6833
RED RIVER MOTOR FREIGHT LLC
451050 Marlena St, Bossier City, LA 71111
Tel (318) 884-9994 Founded/Ownrshp 2007
Sales 204.0MM EMP 10
SIC 4789 Cargo loading & unloading services
Pr: Stan Lucus

D-U-N-S 60-693-9148
RED RIVER SPECIALTIES INC
(Suby of ADAPCO INC) ★
1324 N Hearne Ave Ste 120, Shreveport, LA 71107-6563
Tel (318) 425-5944 Founded/Ownrshp 2009
Sales 91.0MM EMP 55
SIC 5191 Herbicides
Pr: Stephen M Burt
*VP: Mike Cage
Area Mgr: Keith Martin
Area Mgr: Larry Mauldin
IT Man: Kathy Rossitter

RED ROBIN
See ANSARA RESTAURANT GROUP INC

RED ROBIN
See LEHIGH VALLEY RESTAURANT GROUP INC

D-U-N-S 06-720-5950
▲ **RED ROBIN GOURMET BURGERS INC**
6312 S Fiddlers, Greenwood Village, CO 80111
Tel (303) 846-6000 Founded/Ownrshp 1969
Sales 1.2MMM EMP 28,933
Tkr Sym RRGB Exch NGS
SIC 5812 6794 Restaurant, family: chain; Franchises, selling or licensing
CEO: Denny Marie Post
*Ch Bd: Pattye L Moore
COO: Cariz Stutz
CFO: Guy J Constant
CFO: Terry Harryman
Chf Mktg O: Jonathan Muhtar
Sr VP: Michael Furlow
Sr VP: Les L Lehner
VP: Todd Brighton
Board of Directors: Robert B Aiken, Lloyd L Hill, Richard J Howell, Glenn B Kaufman, Steven K Lumpkin, Stuart I Oran

D-U-N-S 60-853-3993
■ **RED ROBIN INTERNATIONAL**
(Suby of RED ROBIN GOURMET BURGERS INC) ★
12271 Foothill Blvd, Rancho Cucamonga, CA 91739-9356
Tel (909) 803-2665 Founded/Ownrshp 2005
Sales 7.1MM^E EMP 2,292^E
SIC 5812 Restaurant, family: chain
Prin: Doug Barbee

D-U-N-S 04-868-0409
■ **RED ROBIN INTERNATIONAL INC**
(Suby of RED ROBIN GOURMET BURGERS INC) ★
6312 S Fiddlers Green Cir 200n, Greenwood Village, CO 80111-4916
Tel (303) 846-6000 Founded/Ownrshp 1969
Sales 449.8MM^E EMP 9,200
SIC 5812 6794 5813 5087 Restaurant, family: chain; Franchises, selling or licensing; Cocktail lounge; Restaurant supplies
Pr: Eric C Houseman
*Treas: Stuart B Brown
Bd of Dir: Robert Aiken
Bd of Dir: Lloyd Hill
Chf Mktg O: Denny Post
Ofcr: Michael Kaplan
Sr VP: Eric Houseman
Sr VP: Jeff Melnick
Sr VP: Dennis Mullen
VP: Christina Carlson
*VP: Douglas L Christman
VP: Bob Derian
*VP: John W Grant

D-U-N-S 08-002-7801
RED ROCK RESORTS INC
1505 S Pavilion Center Dr, Las Vegas, NV 89135-1403
Tel (702) 495-3000 Founded/Ownrshp 1976
Sales 80.2M^E EMP 11,800
Tkr Sym RRR Exch NGS
SIC 7011 Casino hotel
Ch Bd: Frank J Fertitta III
V Ch: Stephen L Cavallaro
Pr: Richard J Haskins
COO: Daniel J Roy
CFO: Marc J Falcone
Treas: Gavin Maloof
VP: Judy Alberti
VP: Wesley Allison
VP: Staci Alonso
VP: Nancy Baltz
VP: Van Baltz
VP: Matthew Heinhold
VP: Ipo Ochmann
VP: Lauren Westerfield
Exec: Mary Easter
Exec: Luigi Iannuario
Board of Directors: Robert A Cashell Jr, Lorenzo J Fertitta, Robert E Lewis, James W Nave

D-U-N-S 06-599-2794
RED ROOF INNS INC
(Suby of WRRH INVESTMENTS LP) ★
605 S Front St Ste 150, Columbus, OH 43215-5809
Tel (614) 744-2600 Founded/Ownrshp 2007
Sales 459.2MM^E EMP 5,800
SIC 7011 Hotels & motels
CEO: Andrew Alexander
CFO: Brendan P Foley
Chf Mktg O: Marina Macdonald
Ex VP: Robert Wallace
VP: Joe Merz
Brnch Mgr: Jeff Atkins
Brnch Mgr: Ellen Azu
Brnch Mgr: Shawn Farrell
Brnch Mgr: Al Gulati
Brnch Mgr: Pamela Newman
Brnch Mgr: Linda Scott
Board of Directors: Mohamed Thowfeek

D-U-N-S 00-636-9987 IMP
RED SPOT PAINT & VARNISH CO INC
(Suby of FUJIKURA KASEI CO., LTD.)
1107 E Louisiana St, Evansville, IN 47711-4747
Tel (812) 428-9100 Founded/Ownrshp 1903
Sales 145.9MM^E EMP 576
SIC 2851 Plastics base paints & varnishes
Pr: Akiro Takedk
Bd of Dir: Mallory Howard
*VP: Jeffrey M Scheu
*VP: David White
Dir Lab: Bruce Mitchell
Prd Mgr: Bryan Hildebrant
Ql Cn Mgr: Jerry Moore
Sales Asso: Meagan Farley
Sales Asso: Beth Kappler

RED STAR YEAST COMPANY
See LESAFFRE YEAST CORP

D-U-N-S 14-716-8749 IMP
RED STAR YEAST CO LLC
7475 W Main St Ste 150, Milwaukee, WI 53214-1552
Tel (800) 445-4746 Founded/Ownrshp 2004
Sales 735.1MM^E EMP 6,000
SIC 2099 Yeast

RED THREAD
See DGPM INVESTMENTS INC

D-U-N-S 15-726-2619 IMP
■ **RED THREAD SPACES LLC**
(Suby of STEELCASE INC) ★
101 Seaport Blvd Ste 600, Boston, MA 02210-2174
Tel (617) 439-4900 Founded/Ownrshp 1999
Sales 195.9MM^E EMP 470
SIC 5999 5021 8712 5198 Audio-visual equipment & supplies; Furniture; Architectural engineering; Wallcoverings
CEO: Jeff Keener
*Pr: Larry Levine
*Pr: Don Marshall
*COO: Orlando Corsi Jr
Treas: William J Nyhan
Ex VP: Casey Kalman
VP: Meghan Allen
VP: Lourdes Collins
VP: Trainor David
VP: Mike Faherty
VP: Pat Griffin
VP: Gale Moutrey
VP: Frank Tenaglia
VP: David Trainor
VP: Larry Velie
VP: Ray Wasson
Dir Rx: Stephanie Brock

D-U-N-S 14-488-5915
RED TRAIL ENERGY LLC
3682 Highway 8, Richardton, ND 58652-9365
Tel (701) 974-3308 Founded/Ownrshp 2003
Sales 100.8MM EMP 48
SIC 2869 2085 Ethyl alcohol, ethanol; Distillers' dried grains & solubles & alcohol
CEO: Gerald Bachmeier
*Ch Bd: Sid Mauch
CFO: Jodi Johnson
Board of Directors: Ronald Aberle, Ambrose Hoff, Frank Kirschenheiter, Anthony Mock

D-U-N-S 02-132-0374
RED VENTURES LLC
1101 Red Ventures Dr, Fort Mill, SC 29707-5005
Tel (704) 971-2300 Founded/Ownrshp 2000
Sales 178.9MM^E EMP 1,200^E
SIC 8742 Marketing consulting services
*Pr: Tim Kullick
*Pr: Joe Peterson
*Pr: Steve Sibley
*Pr: Rodney Sims
*CFO: Mark Brodsky
Sr Cor Off: Ashley Jones
VP: Jeff Ross
VP: Steven Sibley

VP: Darrell Sizemore
Off Admin: Linda Koziol
Snr Sftwr: Kyle Getson

RED WING BRANDS OF AMERICA
See RED WING SHOE CO INC

D-U-N-S 01-096-5122
RED WING REGIONAL HOME HEALTH
1407 W 4th St, Red Wing, MN 55066-2108
Tel (651) 385-3410 Founded/Ownrshp 1997
Sales 95.2MM EMP 1
SIC 8082 8011 Home health care services; Psychiatrist
Prin: Cheryl Voss

D-U-N-S 00-615-4496 IMP/EXP
RED WING SHOE CO INC (MN)
RED WING BRANDS OF AMERICA
314 Main St, Red Wing, MN 55066-2337
Tel (651) 388-8211 Founded/Ownrshp 1905, 1921
Sales 666.5MM EMP 1,800
SIC 3143 3149 3144 3111 5661 3021

RED-E-MADE
See CONCORD FOODS INC

D-U-N-S 61-928-6987 IMP
RED.COM INC
RED DIGITAL CINEMA CAMERA CO
34 Parker, Irvine, CA 92618-1604
Tel (949) 206-7900 Founded/Ownrshp 1999
Sales 130.5MM^E EMP 498^E
SIC 3861 Motion picture apparatus & equipment
CEO: James H Jannard
*CFO: Vince Hassel
*VP: Mike D Executive
Snr Mgr: Deanan Dasilva

D-U-N-S 96-746-1208
REDAPT INC
12226 134th Ct Ne Bldg D, Redmond, WA 98052-2429
Tel (425) 882-0400 Founded/Ownrshp 2010
Sales 88.7MM EMP 75
SIC 5045 Computers, peripherals & software
CEO: Rick Cantu
*COO: David Cantu
*CFO: Spencer Leu
*Ex VP: Matt Huff
*VP: Kolina Kilgore
*VP: Josh Lindenbaum
Prd Mgr: Mike McQuery
Mktg Dir: Jaimie Lang
Snr Mgr: David Harris

D-U-N-S 00-659-3222
REDAPT SYSTEMS INC
12226 134th Ct Ne Bldg D, Redmond, WA 98052-2429
Tel (206) 210-5440 Founded/Ownrshp 1996
Sales 102.5MM EMP 75^E
SIC 5045

D-U-N-S 08-316-7130
REDARHCS INC (CA)
MCDONALD'S
4502 Georgetown Pl, Stockton, CA 95207-6202
Tel (209) 478-0234 Founded/Ownrshp 1966
Sales 36.0MM^E EMP 1,000
SIC 5812 Fast-food restaurant, chain
Pr: Don Schrader
*Treas: Craig Schrader
*VP: Jean Schrader

D-U-N-S 94-639-7015 EXP
REDBARN PET PRODUCTS INC
REDBARN PREMIUM PET PRODUCTS
3229 E Spring St Ste 310, Long Beach, CA 90806-2478
Tel (562) 495-7315 Founded/Ownrshp 1994
Sales 91.4MM^E EMP 160
SIC 5199 2047 Pet supplies; Dog & cat food
CEO: Jeff Baikie
*Pr: Howard Bloxam
Prin: Joe Martinez

REDBARN PREMIUM PET PRODUCTS
See REDBARN PET PRODUCTS INC

D-U-N-S 17-564-1609 IMP
■ **REDBOX AUTOMATED RETAIL LLC**
(Suby of OUTERWALL) ★
1 Tower Ln Ste 1200, Oakbrook Terrace, IL 60181-4635
Tel (630) 756-8700 Founded/Ownrshp 2005
Sales 99.1MM^E EMP 750
SIC 7841 Video tape rental
CEO: Gregg Kaplan
Ofcr: Saul Gates
Sr VP: Jeff Allen
Sr VP: Kiera Hynninen
Sr VP: Pamela Smith
VP: Chas Hermann
VP: Eric Hoerstein
VP: Kevin May
VP: Frank Mesina
*VP: Brian Rady
VP: Mike Saksa
VP: Rich Spender

REDBULL DISTRIBUTION CO COLO
See RED BULL DISTRIBUTION CO INC

D-U-N-S 00-901-1156
REDBURN TIRE CO (AZ)
3801 W Clarendon Ave, Phoenix, AZ 85019-3783
Tel (602) 272-7601 Founded/Ownrshp 1946, 1991
Sales 324.6MM^E EMP 200
SIC 5014 7534 Truck tires & tubes; Automobile tires & tubes; Rebuilding & retreading tires; Tire repair shop
Pr: J D Chastain
*Sec: Donald Leffler
Sfty Dirs: Mark Pennington
Sls Dir: Randy Lowry

D-U-N-S 36-451-4133
REDDY ICE CORP
(Suby of REDDY ICE GROUP INC) ★
5720 Lyndon B Johnson Fwy # 200, Dallas, TX 75240-6396
Tel (214) 526-6740 Founded/Ownrshp 1998
Sales 404.1MM^E EMP 1,300

SIC 2097 Manufactured ice
CEO: Bill Corbin
*Treas: Steven J Janusek
Sr VP: Willie Wiginton
Sr VP: Steven Wilson
VP: Graham Davis
VP: Brian Himes
VP: Mahesh Sadarangani
*VP: Mark A Steffek
VP: Bobby Wehmeyer
Exec: Josh Vega
Genl Mgr: Kelvin Curry

D-U-N-S 79-177-7527 EXP
REDDY ICE GROUP INC
(Suby of REDDY ICE HOLDINGS INC) ★
5720 Lbj Fwy Ste 200, Dallas, TX 75240-6396
Tel (877) 295-0024 Founded/Ownrshp 2003
Sales 407.7MM^E EMP 1,300
SIC 5199 2097 Ice, manufactured or natural; Manufactured ice
Ex VP: Steven J Janusek
*Treas: Mark A Steffek
*Ex VP: Graham D Davis
VP: Ben Key
Off Mgr: Shelby Walker

D-U-N-S 13-838-3257
REDDY ICE HOLDINGS INC
(Suby of CENTERBRIDGE PARTNERS LP) ★
5720 Lbj Fwy Ste 200, Dallas, TX 75240-6396
Tel (214) 526-6740 Founded/Ownrshp 2003
Sales 410.8MM^E EMP 1,300^E
SIC 2097 Manufactured ice; Ice cubes; Block ice
Ch Bd: Gilbert M Cassagne
COO: Paul D Smith
CFO: Steven J Janusek
Ch: William P Brick
Treas: Marvin Evans
Chf Cred: Kenneth C Fernandez
Ofcr: Angela S Wallander
Ex VP: Raymond Booth
Ex VP: Steven Janusek
VP: Richard Bailey
VP: Travis Lumpkin
VP: William A Tolany
Exec: Dan Koah
Board of Directors: Kevin J Cameron, Theodore J Host, Michael S McGrath, Michael H Rauch, Robert N Verdecchio, William P Brick

REDDY RAW & AFFL COMPANIES
See REDDY RAW INC

D-U-N-S 01-262-6404 IMP
REDDY RAW INC
REDDY RAW & AFFL COMPANIES
1 Ethel Blvd Ste 1, Wood Ridge, NJ 07075-2400
Tel (201) 804-7633 Founded/Ownrshp 1948
Sales 119.5MM^E EMP 95
SIC 5142 5141 Packaged frozen goods; Vegetables, frozen; Groceries, general line
Ch Bd: Henry Senderowicz
*Sec: David Rothstein
*VP: Robert Paeprer
Sls Mgr: Laura Anzalone

REDEVELOPMENT AGENCY OF THE CI
See SACRAMENTO HOUSING AND REDEVELOPMENT AGENCY

D-U-N-S 80-077-5384
REDFIELD ENERGY LLC
38650 171st St, Redfield, SD 57469-6640
Tel (605) 302-0090 Founded/Ownrshp 2005
Sales 100.0MM EMP 43
SIC 0723 2869 Grain milling, custom services; Ethyl alcohol, ethanol
Ofcr: Dana Siefkes-Lewis
Prd Mgr: John Shine

D-U-N-S 11-263-6993
REDFLEX TRAFFIC SYSTEMS INC
(Suby of REDFLEX HOLDINGS LIMITED)
5651 W Talavi Blvd # 200, Glendale, AZ 85306-1893
Tel (623) 207-2000 Founded/Ownrshp 1998
Sales 87.4MM^E EMP 303
Accts Peterson Melbourne Australia
SIC 8748 Traffic consultant
Treas: Scott Huson
Treas: Scott Hudson
VP: Jack Weaver
Genl Mgr: Cristina Munoz
Dir IT: Brian Turico
Opers Supe: Scott Sortor
Manager: Kim Poulston
Genl Couns: Anne Osborn

REDI CARPET
See REDI-CARPET INC

D-U-N-S 00-699-0535
REDI GLOBAL TECHNOLOGIES LLC
(Suby of REDI HOLDINGS LLC) ★
30 Hudson St, Jersey City, NJ 07302-4600
Tel (212) 357-3840 Founded/Ownrshp 1931, 2013
Sales 145.8MM^E EMP 1,547
SIC 6211 Brokers, security; Dealers, security
Co-CEO: Gary F Goldring
*CEO: Rishi Nangalia
*CFO: Stephen Balsamo
CFO: David A Vinir
VP: Ryan Crooks
Mng Dir: Andrew Cohen
Mng Dir: Armando Diaz
*Mng Dir: Randy Frantel
*Mng Dir: Robert Luckow
*Mng Dir: Timothy Mullen
*Mng Dir: Steven Starker

D-U-N-S 01-204-4381
REDI HOLDINGS LLC
80 Pine St Fl 27, New York, NY 10005-1730
Tel (212) 419-9696 Founded/Ownrshp 2013
Sales 218.6MM^E EMP 1,687^E
SIC 6211 Brokers, security; Dealers, security

D-U-N-S 13-932-5310
REDI-CARPET INC
REDI CARPET
10225 Mula Rd Ste 120, Stafford, TX 77477-3346
Tel (832) 310-2000 *Founded/Ownrshp* 1985
Sales 101.2MM[E] *EMP* 315
SIC 5023 Floor coverings
CEO: Gregory Waleke
**COO:* Jerry Hosko
**CFO:* Erik Olsen
**Ch:* Bruce Caress
Genl Mgr: Kevin Ryan
Off Mgr: Christen White
Opers Mgr: Rene Galeas
Opers Mgr: Janey Jensen
Mktg Dir: Joshua Lensen

D-U-N-S 18-675-0485
REDI-FLOORS INC
1791 Williams Dr, Marietta, GA 30066-6223
Tel (770) 590-7334 *Founded/Ownrshp* 1987
Sales 125.0MM *EMP* 250[E]
SIC 5023 5032 Carpets; Wood flooring; Floor coverings; Ceramic wall & floor tile
CEO: Ed Shields
Pr: Adam Brookner
Pr: Valerie Durkin
CFO: Jack Weissman
Brnch Mgr: Brandon Williams
QA Dir: Kay Gilreath
VP Sls: Tom Cunningham
Sls Mgr: Jason Bourgeois
Snr PM: Mike Jarvis

REDLANDS COMMUNITY HOSPITAL
See RHS CORP

D-U-N-S 96-190-8519
REDLANDS COMMUNITY HOSPITAL
350 Terracina Blvd, Redlands, CA 92373-4897
Tel (909) 335-5500 *Founded/Ownrshp* 1927
Sales 174.1MM *EMP* 99[E]
SIC 8069 Specialty hospitals, except psychiatric
CEO: James R Holmes
Chf Rad: Bruce Meyer
Pr: Kathi Sankey-Robinson
CFO: Sabi A Dadabhai
VP: Harvey Hansen
Chf Nrs Of: Madonna Coughenour
QA Dir: Cathi Bell
Opers Mgr: Elizabeth Goldstein
Sls Mgr: Rodney Sheffo
Doctor: Malcolm Heppenstall
Doctor: Steve Mera

D-U-N-S 04-053-0008
REDLANDS UNIFIED SCHOOL DISTRICT
20 W Lugonia Ave, Redlands, CA 92374-2234
Tel (909) 307-5300 *Founded/Ownrshp* 1963
Sales 128.5MM[E] *EMP* 1,730
SIC 8211 Public elementary & secondary schools
Teacher Pr: Joe Hyde
Psych: Danielle Savona

REDLINE
See PRODUCTIVITY INC

D-U-N-S 07-810-1755
■ **REDMOND PARK HOSPITAL LLC**
REDMOND REGIONAL MEDICAL CTR
(*Suby of* HOSPITAL COPORATION OF AMERICA) ★
501 Redmond Rd Nw, Rome, GA 30165-1483
Tel (706) 291-0291 *Founded/Ownrshp* 1972
Sales 187.9MM *EMP* 1,000
SIC 8062 8011 General medical & surgical hospitals; Offices & clinics of medical doctors
CEO: John Quinlivan
**COO:* Carlton Ulmer
**CFO:* Kenneth Metteauer
**CFO:* William D Smith
Dir Rx: Dustin Smith
Chf Nrs Of: Ed Hannah
MIS Dir: Bradley Treglown
Sfty Dirs: Andrew Denmon
Doctor: Ann Golden
Doctor: Daniel Goldfaden
Doctor: Jodi Kuhlman

REDMOND REGIONAL MEDICAL CTR
See REDMOND PARK HOSPITAL LLC

D-U-N-S 09-674-0360 IMP
REDNECK INC
REDNECK TRAILER SUPPLIES
2100 N West Byp, Springfield, MO 65803-2208
Tel (417) 864-5210 *Founded/Ownrshp* 1979
Sales 165.5MM[E] *EMP* 504
SIC 5013 5561 5012 Trailer parts & accessories; Recreational vehicle dealers; Automobiles & other motor vehicles
Ch Bd: Ernest W Giddens
CFO: Ed Bradey

REDNECK TRAILER SUPPLIES
See REDNECK INC

D-U-N-S 05-166-0751
REDNERS MARKETS INC
REDNER'S WAREHOUSE MARKET
3 Quarry Rd, Reading, PA 19605-9787
Tel (610) 926-3700 *Founded/Ownrshp* 1970
Sales 884.9MM *EMP* 4,800
Accts Reinsel Kuntz Lesher Llp Wyo
SIC 5411 5541 5912 Supermarkets, chain; Convenience stores, chain; Filling stations, gasoline; Drug stores & proprietary stores
Pr: Richard E Redner
**Treas:* Gary W Redner
VP: Dan Eberhart
VP: Doug Emore
VP: Douglas Emore
**VP:* Gordon B Hoch
**VP:* Robert Mc Donough
**VP:* Michael McNaney
VP: Gary Obrien
VP: John W Sweigart
Genl Mgr: Matt Schramm
Board of Directors: Jason Hopp, Robert McDonough, Earl W Redner, Gary M Redner, Mary Redner, Ryan S Redner

REDNER'S WAREHOUSE MARKET
See REDNERS MARKETS INC

D-U-N-S 79-630-4947
REDROCK PARTNERS LLC
ROMANO'S MACARONI GRILL
(*Suby of* RIMROCK PARTNERS LLC) ★
8260 E Raintree Dr, Scottsdale, AZ 85260-2516
Tel (480) 596-5702 *Founded/Ownrshp* 2010
Sales 323.7MM[E] *EMP* 8,000[E]
SIC 5944 5932 5736 5941 5999 Jewelry stores; Antiques; Musical instrument stores; Firearms; Coins
Pt: Dean Risesen

REDSTONE COLLEGE
See ALTA COLLEGES INC

D-U-N-S 07-737-0732
REDWOOD CREDIT UNION
3033 Cleveland Ave # 100, Santa Rosa, CA 95403-2126
Tel (707) 545-4000 *Founded/Ownrshp* 1950
Sales NA *EMP* 390
Accts Cliftonlarsonallen Llp Phoeni
SIC 6141 Personal credit institutions
Pr: Brett Martinez
Pr: Mark Kunzor
Ofcr: John Pavelka
Ofcr: Luci Young
Sr VP: Christina Cook
Sr VP: Ron Felder
Sr VP: Tony Hildesheim
VP: Gary Fabian
VP: Mishel Kaufman
VP: Dina Miller
Brnch Mgr: Jose Alvarez

D-U-N-S 07-186-6636
REDWOOD ELECTRIC GROUP INC (CA)
2775 Northwestern Pkwy, Santa Clara, CA 95051-0947
Tel (707) 451-7348 *Founded/Ownrshp* 1974
Sales 182.1MM[E] *EMP* 720
SIC 1731 General electrical contractor
Pr: Victor Castello
**CFO:* Jeff Tarzwell
**VP:* Gordon Armstrong
**VP:* Bruce Kelly
Snr PM: Hans Gonzalez

REDWOOD EMPIRE WHL LBR PDTS
See PACIFIC STATES INDUSTRIES INC

D-U-N-S 07-312-3846
REDWOOD INDUSTRIES INC
2345 S Cci Way, Salt Lake City, UT 84119-1250
Tel (801) 973-9000 *Founded/Ownrshp* 1961
Sales 140.8MM[E] *EMP* 350
SIC 1711 Mechanical contractor
Pr: Davis Mullholand
**Sec:* Michael R Kladis
**VP:* Steven Kramer
Board of Directors: Steven Kramer

D-U-N-S 83-547-0691
▲ **REDWOOD TRUST INC**
1 Belvedere Pl Ste 300, Mill Valley, CA 94941-2493
Tel (415) 389-7373 *Founded/Ownrshp* 1994
Sales 284.6MM *EMP* 221[E]
Accts Grant Thornton Llp Irvine Ca
Tkr Sym RWT *Exch* NYS
SIC 6798 Real estate investment trusts; Mortgage investment trusts
CEO: Martin S Hughes
**Ch Bd:* Richard D Baum
Pr: Christopher J Abate
Pr: Dominick Barresi
**V Ch Bd:* Douglas B Hansen
Ex VP: Fred J Matera
Ex VP: Andrew P Stone
VP: Jennifer Adams
VP: Garnet Kanouse
VP: Whitney Keane
VP: Ian McConnell
VP Bus Dev: Danielle Weyant
Board of Directors: Mariann Byerwalter, Debora D Horvath, Greg H Kubicek, Karen R Pallotta, Jeffrey T Pero, Georganne C Proctor, Charles J Toeniskoetter

D-U-N-S 03-552-4146
REDZONE COIL TUBING LLC
701 N 1st St Ste 109, Lufkin, TX 75901-3057
Tel (936) 632-2645 *Founded/Ownrshp* 2011
Sales 125.0MM *EMP* 275[E]
SIC 1389 Oil field services
Pr: Benjamin Dee Winston
**CFO:* Stephen Greak
Sfty Mgr: Blaine Ducksworth

D-U-N-S 09-745-3682 IMP/EXP
REEBOK INTERNATIONAL LTD
(*Suby of* ADIDAS AG)
1895 J W Foster Blvd, Canton, MA 02021-1099
Tel (781) 401-5000 *Founded/Ownrshp* 1895
Sales 3.1MMM[E] *EMP* 9,102
SIC 3149 3143 3144 2329 2339 5661 Athletic shoes, except rubber or plastic; Dress shoes, men's; Dress shoes, women's; Athletic (warmup, sweat & jogging) suits: men's & boys'; Athletic clothing: women's, misses' & juniors'; Shoe stores
Pr: Mark King
Pt: Ulrich Becker
Pr: Suzanne Biszantz
Pt: David A Pace
Pt: Terry R Pillow
CFO: Melissa Gaudette
CFO: Tim Moran
CFO: John Warren
Treas: Michel Bekkers
Treas: Klaus Flock
Ofcr: Joseph Keane
Top Exec: Bill McInnis
Sr VP: David A Pce
VP: Angelo Anastasio
VP: Rick Bednarz
VP: Alan Chamberlin
VP: Frank A Dassler
VP: Steve Donald
VP: Kenny Gamble
VP: Steven Horton
VP: Todd Krinsky

D-U-N-S 02-616-0709
REECE GREGORY MD
UNIVERSITY OF TEXAS MD ANDERSO
1515 Holcombe Blvd, Houston, TX 77030-4000
Tel (713) 794-1247 *Founded/Ownrshp* 2010
Sales 81.5MM[E] *EMP* 1,071[E]
SIC 8011 General & family practice, physician/surgeon
Owner: Gregory Reece

D-U-N-S 00-682-6028 IMP
REED & REED INC
275 River Rd, Woolwich, ME 04579-4203
Tel (207) 443-9747 *Founded/Ownrshp* 1928
Sales 91.6MM[E] *EMP* 200
SIC 1622 1629 1541 Bridge construction; Marine construction; Industrial buildings, new construction; Renovation, remodeling & repairs: industrial buildings
CEO: Jackson A Parker
**CFO:* John C Cooney
**Treas:* Thomas Reed
VP: Bollie Bollenbach
Dir Risk M: Abigail Parker
IT Man: Craig Guerrette
QI Cn Mgr: Charlie Seavey

REED BUSINESS INFORMATION
See RELX INC

REED COLLEGE
See REED INSTITUTE

D-U-N-S 80-367-5156
REED CONTRACTING SERVICES INC
2512 Triana Blvd Sw, Huntsville, AL 35805-4048
Tel (256) 533-0505 *Founded/Ownrshp* 1987
Sales 133.1MM[E] *EMP* 586
SIC 1771 1794 1623 1629 1611 Driveway, parking lot & blacktop contractors; Excavation work; Water, sewer & utility lines; Land leveling; Surfacing & paving
Pr: Michael W Reed
Treas: Wayne Gladden
**VP:* Connie Reed
Off Mgr: Suzie Cissyestes
CTO: David Wilkinson
Sfty Mgr: Roger Miller

D-U-N-S 07-128-5837 IMP/EXP
REED ELSEVIER US HOLDINGS INC
(*Suby of* RELX GROUP PLC)
1105 N Market St Ste 501, Wilmington, DE 19801-1253
Tel (302) 427-2672 *Founded/Ownrshp* 1989
Sales 8.9MMM[E] *EMP* 20,840
SIC 2721 7999 8748 6719 Periodicals; Trade journals: publishing & printing; Exhibition operation; Business consulting; Personal holding companies, except banks
CFO: Mark Armour
**Treas:* Paul Richardson
**VP:* Henry Horbaczewski

D-U-N-S 05-497-2955
REED INSTITUTE
REED COLLEGE
3203 Se Woodstock Blvd, Portland, OR 97202-8138
Tel (503) 771-1112 *Founded/Ownrshp* 1908
Sales 89.1MM *EMP* 400
Accts Kpmg Llp Portland Or
SIC 8222 Technical institute
Pr: John R Kroger
Trst: Jerome H Debs
Trst: Martha A Drling
Trst: Donald M Engelman
Trst: Morris J Galen
Trst: Sally M McCracken
Trst: Gary E Rischl
Exec: Jay Brittonewing
Exec: Walter Englert
Exec: Patrick McDougal
Exec: Tony Moreno
Exec: Laurens Ruben
Assoc Dir: Gabe Leavitt

REED SMITH CENTRE
See REED SMITH LLP

D-U-N-S 06-874-4457
REED SMITH LLP
REED SMITH CENTRE
225 5th Ave Ste 1200, Pittsburgh, PA 15222-2716
Tel (412) 288-3131 *Founded/Ownrshp* 1877, 1941
Sales 409.9MM[E] *EMP* 2,000
SIC 8111 General practice law office
Pt: Gregory B Jordan
Pt: Steven Agnoli
Pt: Marie Albertini
Pt: Daniel E Bob
Pt: Benoit Charot
Pt: Philippe Lecler
Pt: Mathieu Rambaud
Pt: William V Roth Jr
Mng Pt: Reed Smith
Mng Pt: David A Thompson
Ofcr: Nicola Dingemans
Exec: Alexandra Poe

D-U-N-S 88-491-8947
REED TECHNOLOGY AND INFORMATION SERVICES INC
(*Suby of* REED BUSINESS INFORMATION) ★
7 Walnut Grove Dr, Horsham, PA 19044-2201
Tel (215) 441-6400 *Founded/Ownrshp* 1980
Sales 144.2MM[E] *EMP* 900
SIC 2791 Typesetting, computer controlled
Pr: Thomas S Barry
**Pr:* Sam Hardman
**Treas:* Peter H Kehew
VP: Cindy Kennedy
Snr Ntwrk: Stephen Sarachman
CTO: Amy Cochran
Sys Mgr: Para Agrawal
Software D: Terry Carnes
Software D: Niles Desphy
Prd Mgr: Xavier Faura
Prd Mgr: Craig Knup

REED TOOL
See SCHLUMBERGER INTERNATIONAL INC

D-U-N-S 00-791-2181
REEDMAN CHEVROLET INC (PA)
REEDMAN CHEVROLET OLDSMOBILE
Rr 1, Langhorne, PA 19047-9801
Tel (215) 757-4961 *Founded/Ownrshp* 1946
Sales 126.4MM *EMP* 288
SIC 5511 5531 7538 5521 Automobiles, new & used; Trucks, tractors & trailers: new & used; Automotive parts; Automotive accessories; General automotive repair shops; Used car dealers
Pr: Stanley Reedman
**Treas:* Thomas Reedman
**VP:* Herbert Reedman

REEDMAN CHEVROLET OLDSMOBILE
See REEDMAN CHEVROLET INC

D-U-N-S 10-914-8072
REEDS JEWELERS INC
MELART JEWELERS
2525 S 17th St, Wilmington, NC 28401-7705
Tel (910) 350-3100 *Founded/Ownrshp* 1984
Sales 127.2MM[E] *EMP* 800
SIC 5944 Jewelry stores; Jewelry, precious stones & precious metals; Watches
Pr: Alan M Zimmer
COO: Allan Metzner
**CFO:* William Reinger
**VP:* Allan E Metzner
VP: Kris Weyand
Store Mgr: Keith Dockens
Store Mgr: Lisa Malec
Store Mgr: Carlos Wilson
CIO: Rhonda Cobbs
IT Man: Kevin Gubala

D-U-N-S 82-720-4178
REEF SERVICES LLC
(*Suby of* ROCKWATER ENERGY SOLUTIONS INC) ★
515 Post Oak Blvd Ste 600, Houston, TX 77027-9408
Tel (432) 560-5600 *Founded/Ownrshp* 2006
Sales 94.3MM[E] *EMP* 290
SIC 3533 Oil & gas drilling rigs & equipment
CEO: Larry Odonnell
**CFO:* Wayne A Clayton
VP: Denise Stewart

D-U-N-S 07-465-0946
REES GORDON SCULLY MANSUKHANI LLP
275 Battery St Ste 2000, San Francisco, CA 94111-3361
Tel (415) 986-5900 *Founded/Ownrshp* 1974
Sales 122.8MM[E] *EMP* 350
SIC 8111 Specialized law offices, attorneys; Corporate, partnership & business law; Product liability law
Mng Pt: Dion N Cominos
Sr Pt: Jewel K Basse
Pt: Jorge J Perez
Mng Pt: David C Capell
Mng Pt: Linda M Moroney
Mng Pt: C A Mulrain
Mng Pt: William Shelley
Pr: Wendy Fletcher
Bd of Dir: Brandon R Carroll
Off Admin: Melissa L Schwab
Counsel: Stephen E Carlson

D-U-N-S 00-580-8449
REEVES CONSTRUCTION CO
SLOAN CONSTRUCTION COMPANY
(*Suby of* COLAS INC) ★
101 Sheraton Ct, Macon, GA 31210-1155
Tel (478) 474-9092 *Founded/Ownrshp* 1998
Sales 352.9MM[E] *EMP* 900
SIC 1611 General contractor, highway & street construction
Pr: Robert Ponton
**CFO:* Raphael Llobregat
**Treas:* Terry Looney
**VP:* Dan Garcia
**VP:* Stoy Marlow
**VP:* Sam Rapczak
VP: Janel Waters
Rgnl Mgr: Doug Trulock
Sfty Mgr: Jarrod Crum
Opers Mgr: Ricky Fowler

D-U-N-S 05-849-8650
REF-CHEM LP
PERMIAN BASIN DIVISION
1128 S Grandview Ave, Odessa, TX 79761-7137
Tel (432) 332-8531 *Founded/Ownrshp* 2001
Sales 121.1MM *EMP* 1,000
Accts Johnson Miller & Co Cpa S Pc
SIC 1629 Industrial plant construction; Oil refinery construction; Chemical plant & refinery construction
Mng Pt: Harvey J Page P E
**Pt:* Rodney J Page
Pr: Mickey Wilson
**CEO:* Trey Myers
COO: S C Myers III
**COO:* Jeff Rashall
**Chf Mktg O:* Jeff Havens
VP: Jerry Dunn
VP: Ben Nichols
VP: Jerry Pullen
Mtls Mgr: Dale Kenney

D-U-N-S 04-122-7562
REFAC OPTICAL GROUP
US VISION
1 Harmon Dr, Blackwood, NJ 08012-5103
Tel (856) 228-1000 *Founded/Ownrshp* 2011
Sales 345.8MM[E] *EMP* 1,966[E]
SIC 3827 Optical instruments & lenses
Ch Bd: Melvin Meskin
**Sr VP:* Robert L Tuchman

REFLECTIVE SOLUTIONS AMERICAS
See ORAFOL AMERICAS INC

D-U-N-S 06-147-0563
■ **REFRESHMENT PRODUCT SERVICES INC**
COCA-COLA
(*Suby of* COCA-COLA CO) ★
1 Coca Cola Plz Nw, Atlanta, GA 30313-2420
Tel (404) 676-2121 *Founded/Ownrshp* 1971
Sales 91.1MM[E] *EMP* 300[E]
SIC 2086 Bottled & canned soft drinks

Ch: Doug Ivester
**Pr:* John Hunter
COO: Don Knauss
**CFO:* James E Chestnut
**Treas:* David M Taggart
Chf Mktg O: Javier Benito
Sr VP: Jean M Arfs
VP: Pat Belinski
VP: Joe Burke
VP: Scott Corley
**VP:* William J Davis
VP: John M Farrell
**VP:* Gary P Fayard
**VP:* Joseph R Gladden
**VP:* Robert D Guy
VP: Angelo Lombardo
Comm Man: Leo Roberts
Board of Directors: Roberto Goizueta

D-U-N-S 11-934-8373
REFRESHMENT SERVICES INC
PEPSICO
1121 Locust St, Quincy, IL 62301-1919
Tel (217) 223-8600 *Founded/Ownrshp* 1977
Sales 95.5MME *EMP* 500
SIC 2086 Carbonated soft drinks, bottled & canned
Ch: Ronald J Vecchie
**Pr:* Mike Bartel
**CFO:* Jack Taylor
**VP:* Rodney Flowers
**VP:* Casey Hill

D-U-N-S 05-693-4193 IMP/EXP
REFRICENTER OF MIAMI INC
JOHNSON CONTRLS AUTHORIZED DLR
7101 Nw 43rd St, Miami, FL 33166-6829
Tel (305) 477-8880 *Founded/Ownrshp* 1971
Sales 85.4MME *EMP* 120
SIC 5075 5078 Air conditioning equipment, except room units; Refrigeration equipment & supplies
Pr: Jose H Hernandez
VP: Frank Calvo
VP Sls: Bazo Pedro
Sls Mgr: Leo Melero

REFRIGERATED DOUGH DIVISION
See RALCORP FROZEN BAKERY PRODUCTS INC

D-U-N-S 02-871-1661 IMP
REFRIGERATION SUPPLIES DISTRIBUTOR
R S D
26021 Atlantic Ocean Dr, Lake Forest, CA 92630-8831
Tel (949) 380-7878 *Founded/Ownrshp* 1907
Sales 166.3MME *EMP* 500
SIC 5078 5075

REFRIGERATION SYSTEMS DIVISION
See RAE CORP

REFUSE DERIVED FUEL PLANT
See WHEELABRATOR PORTSMOUTH INC

D-U-N-S 78-811-7716
■ REG BIOFUELS LLC
(*Suby of* RENEWABLE ENERGY GROUP INC) ★
416 S Bell Ave, Ames, IA 50010-7711
Tel (515) 239-8000 *Founded/Ownrshp* 2010
Sales 109.1MME *EMP* 300
SIC 2911 Diesel fuels
Pr: Daniel J OH
VP: Dave Elsenbast
IT Man: Laura Jordan
IT Man: Nathan Wykle
Board of Directors: Paul Chatterton, Scott P Chesnut, Delbert Christensen, Scott Gieselman, Eric Hakmiller, Randolph L Howard, Michael A Jackson, Jonathan Koch, Christopher D Sorrells

D-U-N-S 00-612-6213 IMP
■ REGAL BELOIT AMERICA INC
(*Suby of* REGAL BELOIT CORP) ★
200 State St, Beloit, WI 53511-6254
Tel (608) 364-8800 *Founded/Ownrshp* 1997
Sales 825.1MME *EMP* 2,808
SIC 3644 3621 Electric conduits & fittings; Electric outlet, switch & fuse boxes; Motors, electric; Generators & sets, electric
Pr: Mark J Gliebe
**COO:* Jonathan J Schlemmer
**CFO:* Chuck A Hinrichs
VP: Michael Logsdon
VP: Terry McCormick
**VP:* Peter C Underwood
Telecom Mg: Louise Ellenbecker
VP Sls: Raymond Kacvinsky

D-U-N-S 00-611-1751 IMP/EXP
▲ REGAL BELOIT CORP
200 State St, Beloit, WI 53511-6254
Tel (608) 364-8800 *Founded/Ownrshp* 1955
Sales 3.5MMM *EMP* 26,200
Accts Deloitte & Touche Llp Milwau
Tkr Sym RBC *Exch* NYS
SIC 3621 3714 3566 Motors & generators; Electric motor & generator parts; Motor vehicle parts & accessories; Speed changers, drives & gears; Drives, high speed industrial, except hydrostatic; Gears, power transmission, except automotive; Reduction gears & gear units for turbines, except automotive
Ch Bd: Mark J Gliebe
COO: Jonathan J Schlemmer
CFO: Charles A Hinrichs
VP: John M Avampato
VP: Jennifer Balderas
VP: Scott Brown
VP: Terry R Colvin
VP: Steve Donithan
VP: Paul Goldman
VP: Bob Slattery
VP: Peter C Underwood
VP: Peter Underwood
Board of Directors: Stephen M Burt, Christopher L Doerr, Thomas J Fischer, Dean A Foate, Henry W Knueppel, Curtis W Stoelting, Jane L Warner

REGAL BOATS
See REGAL MARINE INDUSTRIES INC

D-U-N-S 12-996-6060
■ REGAL CINEMAS CORP
(*Suby of* REGAL ENTERTAINMENT GROUP) ★
7132 Regal Ln, Knoxville, TN 37918-5803
Tel (865) 922-1123 *Founded/Ownrshp* 2002
Sales 748.4MME *EMP* 22,056
SIC 7832 5812 Motion picture theaters, except drive-in; Concessionaire
Pr: Michael Campbell
**COO:* Greg Dunn
**CFO:* Amy Miles
**Ex VP:* Peter Brandow
VP: John Roper
Off Mgr: Ana Mantellini

D-U-N-S 61-487-4972 IMP/EXP
■ REGAL CINEMAS INC
REGAL ENTERTAINMENT
(*Suby of* REGAL CINEMAS CORP) ★
7132 Regal Ln, Knoxville, TN 37918-5803
Tel (865) 922-1123 *Founded/Ownrshp* 2002
Sales 747.6MME *EMP* 16,659
SIC 7832 Motion picture theaters, except drive-in
Ch Bd: Michael L Campbell
**COO:* Gregory W Dunn
**CFO:* Amy E Miles
Treas: Chris Dzambo
VP: Rick Campbell
VP: Michael Kivett
VP: Curtis B Woods
Brnch Mgr: Sue Heagy
Brnch Mgr: Katherine Maxim
Brnch Mgr: Charlie Mazzi
Genl Mgr: Pam Cornelius

D-U-N-S 02-986-4527
REGAL DISTRIBUTING CO
WHOLESALE
17201 W 113th St, Lenexa, KS 66219-1337
Tel (913) 894-8787 *Founded/Ownrshp* 1955
Sales 101.7MME *EMP* 75
SIC 5112 5113 5046 Stationery & office supplies; Cups, disposable plastic & paper; Napkins, paper; Containers, paper & disposable plastic; Towels, paper; Restaurant equipment & supplies
CEO: Gregory Kopulos
**Ex VP:* Dean Kopulos
**VP:* Alex Kopulos
Sales Exec: Eric Bixby
VP Sls: Ben Ankrom

REGAL ENTERTAINMENT
See REGAL CINEMAS INC

D-U-N-S 10-418-9316
▲ REGAL ENTERTAINMENT GROUP
7132 Regal Ln, Knoxville, TN 37918-5803
Tel (865) 922-1123 *Founded/Ownrshp* 2002
Sales 3.1MMM *EMP* 25,915E
Tkr Sym RGC *Exch* NYS
SIC 7832 Motion picture theaters, except drive-in
Ch Bd: Amy E Miles
Pr: Gregory W Dunn
CFO: David H Ownby
Ex VP: Peter B Brandow
Ex VP: Ray Nutt
VP: David Doyle
VP: Todd King
VP: John Roper
VP: Randy Smith
VP: Timm Walsh
VP: Dick Westerling
Board of Directors: Thomas D Bell Jr, Charles E Brymer, Michael L Campbell, Stephen A Kaplan, David H Keyte, Lee M Thomas, Jack Tyrrell, Alejandro Yemenidjian

D-U-N-S 12-997-0153
■ REGAL ENTERTAINMENT HOLDINGS INC
(*Suby of* REGAL ENTERTAINMENT GROUP) ★
7132 Regal Ln, Knoxville, TN 37918-5803
Tel (865) 922-1123 *Founded/Ownrshp* 2002
Sales 180.6MME *EMP* 9,001
SIC 7832 Motion picture theaters, except drive-in
Pr: Greg Dunn
CTO: J E Henry

REGAL GRAPHICS
See REGAL SUPPLY CO

D-U-N-S 04-975-8725 EXP
REGAL MARINE INDUSTRIES INC
REGAL BOATS
2300 Jetport Dr, Orlando, FL 32809-7895
Tel (407) 851-4360 *Founded/Ownrshp* 1969
Sales 91.2MME *EMP* 450
SIC 3732 Boats, fiberglass: building & repairing
Pr: Duane Kuck
VP: Martin Clement
**VP:* Timothy Kuck
VP: Glen Naroth
IT Man: Ron Cravatta
Plnt Mgr: William Finney
VP Sls: Buffy Stenger
S&M/VP: Regal Boats
Sls Mgr: Jim Krueger
Art Dir: Jill Radcliffe

D-U-N-S 19-144-9149
REGAL METALS INTERNATIONAL INC
207 Sentry Dr, Mansfield, TX 76063-3609
Tel (817) 477-2568 *Founded/Ownrshp* 1988
Sales 90.0MME *EMP* 4
SIC 5051

REGAL SPRINGS TILAPIA
See REGAL SPRINGS TRADING CO

D-U-N-S 87-822-1563 IMP
REGAL SPRINGS TRADING CO
REGAL SPRINGS TILAPIA
2801 Sw 149th Ave Ste 270, Miramar, FL 33027-4196
Tel (954) 283-9035 *Founded/Ownrshp* 1992
Sales 221.8MM *EMP* 6,412
SIC 5146 Fish, frozen, unpackaged
Pr: Rudolph Lamprecht
**CEO:* Myrtle Turnquist

D-U-N-S 00-717-6811 IMP
REGAL SUPPLY CO (MO)
REGAL GRAPHICS
111 E 10th Ave, Kansas City, MO 64116-4326
Tel (816) 421-6290 *Founded/Ownrshp* 1954
Sales 101.6MME *EMP* 185
SIC 5162

D-U-N-S 00-611-5778 IMP
REGAL WARE INC
1675 Reigle Dr, Kewaskum, WI 53040-8923
Tel (262) 626-2121 *Founded/Ownrshp* 1945
Sales 118.0MME *EMP* 421
Accts Clifton Larson Allen Llp Milw
SIC 3634 3469 Electric household cooking appliances; Cooking ware, porcelain enameled
CEO: Jeffrey A Reigle
**COO:* Douglas Reigle
CFO: Tracy C Pearson
**Ch:* James D Reigle
**Treas:* Gerald Koch
Ex VP: David Anderson
**Ex VP:* Keith L Peterson
Sr VP: David N Lenz
**Sr VP:* Joseph A Swanson
VP: Dan Michael
VP: Richard Scott
Exec: Dawn Franzen
Comm Dir: Pat Seitz

D-U-N-S 96-166-7586 IMP/EXP
REGAL WORLDWIDE TRADING LLC
9500 Nw 108th Ave, Medley, FL 33178-2517
Tel (305) 714-7425 *Founded/Ownrshp* 2007
Sales 201.0MME *EMP* 47E
SIC 5064 Electric household appliances
Pr: Rodolfo Armando Siman
Treas: Fernando Novoa
VP: Mario Alberto Siman

D-U-N-S 00-645-3950
REGAN INTERNATIONAL INC
2141 Whittier Pl Nw, Atlanta, GA 30318-1954
Tel (603) 624-9615 *Founded/Ownrshp* 1998
Sales 300.0MME *EMP* 7
SIC 5153

D-U-N-S 88-494-2749
REGED INC
SECURITIES EDUCATION INSTITUTE
(*Suby of* FALFURRIAS CAPITAL PARTNERS LP) ★
2100 Gateway Centre Blvd # 200, Morrisville, NC 27560-6228
Tel (919) 653-5200 *Founded/Ownrshp* 2015
Sales NA *EMP* 87E
SIC 6411 Reporting services, insurance
CEO: John M Schobel
CFO: Allen Ramsay
Ex VP: Stephanie Buchanan
**Ex VP:* Lorraine Carver
Sr VP: Diane Anderson
Sr VP: Paul Hochman
Sr VP: John Ris
VP: Brandi Brown
VP: Matthew Burdick
VP: Melissa Hunt
CTO: Brian Lora

D-U-N-S 05-096-9237
REGENCE BLUECROSS BLUESHIELD OF OREGON
(*Suby of* CAMBIA HEALTH SOLUTIONS INC) ★
100 Sw Market St, Portland, OR 97201-5723
Tel (503) 225-5336 *Founded/Ownrshp* 1941
Sales NA *EMP* 1,200
SIC 6321 Health insurance carriers
CEO: Mark B Ganz
Pr: Don Antonucci
Pr: Donald M Antonucci
Pr: Angela Dowling
CFO: Vince Price
Bd of Dir: Kris Gorriaran
Chf Mktg O: Richard Popiel
Ofcr: Csaba Mera
Ex VP: Mohan Nair
Sr VP: John Cimral
VP: Chris Bailey
VP: Michael S Becker
VP: Joan Byrd
VP: Vivian Chee
VP: Steven Gaspar
VP: Joanne Gholston
VP: Robert Kuecker
VP: Patti Laughren
VP: Peggy Maguire
VP: Ralph Prows
VP: Gary REA

D-U-N-S 07-309-7404
REGENCE BLUECROSS BLUESHIELD OF UTAH
(*Suby of* CAMBIA HEALTH SOLUTIONS INC) ★
2890 E Cottonwood Pkwy, Salt Lake City, UT 84121-7089
Tel (801) 942-9205 *Founded/Ownrshp* 1944
Sales NA *EMP* 850
SIC 6324 Health maintenance organization (HMO), insurance only; Group hospitalization plans; Dental insurance
Ch: Scott Ideson
VP: Vivian CHI
Exec: Bruce Smith
Off Mgr: Andy Tally
CIO: John Cimral
CIO: Dennis Pessetto
IT Man: Robert Tateoka
Web Dev: Linda Noble
Snr Mgr: Jeewan Negi
Board of Directors: Lori

D-U-N-S 07-665-1199
REGENCE BLUESHIELD
REGENCECARE
(*Suby of* CAMBIA HEALTH SOLUTIONS INC) ★
1800 9th Ave Ste 200, Seattle, WA 98101-1314
Tel (206) 340-6600 *Founded/Ownrshp* 1933
Sales NA *EMP* 930
SIC 6324 Hospital & medical service plans
Pr: M Jonathan Hensley
**Pr:* Mary McWilliams
CFO: Vince Price
**Treas:* Steven Hooker
Dir IT: Bryn Beorse

D-U-N-S 07-665-0092
REGENCE BLUESHIELD OF IDAHO INC
(*Suby of* CAMBIA HEALTH SOLUTIONS INC) ★
1602 21st Ave, Lewiston, ID 83501-4061
Tel (208) 743-0320 *Founded/Ownrshp* 1946
Sales NA *EMP* 511
SIC 6324 Group hospitalization plans
Pr: John Ruch
Pr: Carolyn Loera
VP: Jeff Brudie
VP: Steven Clay
VP: Scott Ideson
VP: John Rusche
Exec: Pat Waller
Sales Exec: John Fisher

D-U-N-S 04-174-7114
REGENCE HMO OREGON INC
(*Suby of* REGENCE BLUECROSS BLUESHIELD OF OREGON) ★
201 High St Se, Salem, OR 97301-3674
Tel (503) 364-4868 *Founded/Ownrshp* 1976
Sales NA *EMP* 381E
Accts Deloitte & Touche
SIC 6321 Health insurance carriers
Pr: Roger B Lyman

REGENCECARE
See REGENCE BLUESHIELD

D-U-N-S 86-119-2102
▲ REGENCY CENTERS CORP
1 Independent Dr Ste 114, Jacksonville, FL 32202-5005
Tel (904) 598-7000 *Founded/Ownrshp* 1993
Sales 569.7MM *EMP* 371E
Tkr Sym REG *Exch* NYS
SIC 6798 Real estate investment trusts
Ch Bd: Martin E Stein Jr
Pr: Lisa Palmer
Ofcr: Patrick Krejs
Ex VP: Dan M Chandler III
Ex VP: James D Thompson
Sr VP: Barry E Argalas
Sr VP: Dale Johnston
Sr VP: Scott R Prigge
Sr VP: Doug Shaffer
VP: Jack Devilliers
VP: Patrick Johnson
VP: Paul Maxwell
VP: David A McNulty
VP: Shana Neel
VP: Celia Paulk
VP: Scott Porter
VP: Jim Reuter
VP: Scott Wilson
Exec: Jack Heinemann
Exec: Ilona Warren
Comm Man: Eric Davidson
Board of Directors: Bryce Blair, C Ronald Blankenship, A R Carpenter, J Dix Druce Jr, Mary Lou Fiala, David P O'connor, John C Schweitzer, Thomas G Wattles, Raymond L Bank

D-U-N-S 19-072-0599
■ REGENCY CENTERS LP
(*Suby of* REGENCY CENTERS CORP) ★
1 Independent Dr Ste 114, Jacksonville, FL 32202-5005
Tel (904) 598-7000 *Founded/Ownrshp* 1996
Sales 569.7MM *EMP* 363E
Accts Kpmg Llp Jacksonville Florid
SIC 6798 Real estate investment trusts
Ch Bd: Martin E Stein Jr
Genl Pt: Regency Centers Corporation
Pt: C Ronald Blankenship
Pt: A R Carpenter
Pt: J Dix Druce
Pt: Mary Lou Fiala
Pt: Douglas S Luke
Pt: David O'Connor
Pt: John C Schweitzer
Pt: Thomas G Wattles
**Pr:* Brian M Smith
CFO: Lisa Palmer
Treas: J Christian Leavitt
Board of Directors: C Ronald Blankenship, A R Carpenter, J Dix Druce, Mary Lou Fiala, Douglas S Luke, David O'connor, John C Schweitzer, Thomas G Wattles, Raymond L Bank

D-U-N-S 36-305-0563
■ REGENCY ENERGY PARTNERS LP
(*Suby of* ENERGY TRANSFER PARTNERS LP) ★
8111 Westchester Dr # 600, Dallas, TX 75225-6142
Tel (214) 750-1771 *Founded/Ownrshp* 2015
Sales 4.9MMM *EMP* 1,187E
SIC 1321 4925 5172 4922 Natural gas liquids; Liquefied petroleum gas, distribution through mains; Gases, liquefied petroleum (propane); Natural gas transmission
Pr: Michael J Bradley
CFO: Thomas E Long
Ex VP: Rich Rehm
Ex VP: Christofer Rozzell
Sr VP: Charles M Davis
Sr VP: Dennie W Dixon
Sr VP: Shannon A Ming
VP: Houston C Ross
VP: Christofer D Rozzell
VP Bus Dev: Coby Washburn
Sls&Mrk Ex: Patrick Giroir

D-U-N-S 10-306-3772
REGENCY ENTERPRISES INC
REGENCY LIGHTING
9261 Jordan Ave, Chatsworth, CA 91311-5739
Tel (818) 901-0255 *Founded/Ownrshp* 1981
Sales 150.0MM *EMP* 330
SIC 5063 Light bulbs & related supplies; Lighting fixtures
CEO: Ron Regenstreif
**Pr:* Scott Anderson
**Pr:* Isaac Regenstreif

*COO: Mike Goldstone
IT Man: George Panga
IT Man: Wendy Potratz
Snr Mgr: Brad Newbold

D-U-N-S 13-204-6413
■ REGENCY GAS SERVICES LP
(Suby of REGENCY ENERGY PARTNERS LP) ★
2001 Bryan St Ste 3700, Dallas, TX 75201-3093
Tel (214) 750-1771 Founded/Ownrshp 2003
Sales 360.2MM^E EMP 317
SIC 4932 Gas & other services combined
CEO: Michael J Bradley
Pt: Stephen L Arata
Pt: Lawrence B Connors
Pt: James W Hunt
Pr: Chad Lenamon
Pr: Thomas Long
Ex VP: Jim Holotik
VP: A Troy Sturrock

REGENCY HOSPITAL COMPANY, LLC
See REGENCY HOSPITAL CO LLC

D-U-N-S 02-681-3506
■ REGENCY HOSPITAL CO LLC
REGENCY HOSPITAL COMPANY, LLC
(Suby of SELECT MEDICAL HOLDINGS CORP) ★
4714 Gettysburg Rd, Mechanicsburg, PA 17055-4325
Tel (717) 972-1100 Founded/Ownrshp 2001, 2010
Sales 32.3MM^E EMP 1,700
SIC 8742 Hospital & health services consultant
CEO: William L Anderson
*Owner: Robert Ortenzio
Pr: Heather J Carter
CFO: Charlie McNight
Sr VP: Tony Torrente
VP: Kelly Laughlin
VP: David Webb
Dir Soc: Mike Seusy
Dir Bus: Arlisa Colbert
Mng Dir: Atul Kapoor
IT Man: Yannick Lemieux

REGENCY HOTEL MANAGEMENT
See REGENCY MIDWEST VENTURES LIMITED PARTNERSHIP

D-U-N-S 88-345-2195
REGENCY INTEGRATED HEALTH SERVICES
101 W Goodwin Ave Ste 600, Victoria, TX 77901-6530
Tel (361) 576-0694 Founded/Ownrshp 1992
Sales 89.2MM^E EMP 1,100
SIC 8051 Convalescent home with continuous nursing care
Ch Bd: Donald Kivowitz
*Pr: Heber Lacerda
*COO: Donovan Dekowski
*CFO: David Andrews
Off Mgr: Michelle Tanguma
Sales Exec: Jane Wehlmann

REGENCY LIGHTING
See REGENCY ENTERPRISES INC

D-U-N-S 83-087-5022
REGENCY MIDWEST VENTURES LIMITED PARTNERSHIP
REGENCY HOTEL MANAGEMENT
3211 W Sencore Dr, Sioux Falls, SD 57107-0728
Tel (605) 334-2371 Founded/Ownrshp 2008
Sales 113.3MM^E EMP 2,500^E
SIC 7011 Hotels
Pt: David Sweet
*Genl Pt: Mwg LLC
*Pt: Greg Schjodt
*Pt: Robert Thimjon
Sls Dir: Brandon Bolduc

D-U-N-S 93-897-6073
REGENCY MORTGAGE CORP
26 Londonderry Tpke, Hooksett, NH 03106-2011
Tel (603) 669-5626 Founded/Ownrshp 1996
Sales NA EMP 125
SIC 6162 Mortgage bankers
Pr: Quentin Keefe
Pr: Mark McCauley
Ofcr: Jim Farley
Ofcr: Darlene Sweet
VP: Sandra Gausch
VP: Scott Hanley
VP: Maureen Lemay
*VP: Maureen Lemy
*VP: Diane Morrissette
Brnch Mgr: Craig Farrington
Brnch Mgr: Kathleen Malloy

D-U-N-S 19-487-3139
▲ REGENERON PHARMACEUTICALS INC
777 Old Saw Mill River Rd # 10, Tarrytown, NY 10591-6707
Tel (914) 847-7000 Founded/Ownrshp 1988
Sales 4.1MMM EMP 4,300^E
Accts Pricewaterhousecoopers Llp Fl
Tkr Sym REGN Exch NGS
SIC 2834 Pharmaceutical preparations
Pr: Leonard S Schleifer
*Ch Bd: P Roy Vagelos
CFO: Robert E Landry
Ex VP: Neil Stahl
Ex VP: Daniel P Van Plew
Sr VP: Michael Aberman
Sr VP: Joseph J Larosa
Sr VP: Peter Powchik
VP: Douglas S McCorkle
*Dir Sec: George D Yancopoulos
Board of Directors: Charles A Baker, Bonnie L Bassler, Michael S Brown, Joseph L Goldstein, Marc Tessier-Lavigne, Christine A Poon, Arthur F Ryan, George L Sing

REGENESIS
See FURNITURE MARKETING GROUP INC

REGENT CARE CENTERS
See REGENT MANAGEMENT SERVICES LIMITED PARTNERSHIP

D-U-N-S 15-083-5721
REGENT MANAGEMENT SERVICES LIMITED PARTNERSHIP
REGENT CARE CENTERS
2302 Post Office St # 402, Galveston, TX 77550-1935
Tel (409) 763-6000 Founded/Ownrshp 1997
Sales 7.2MM^E EMP 2,500
SIC 8741 Nursing & personal care facility management
Pt: Charles Milos
*Pt: Carol Ostermayer
*Pt: Ellen Otte

D-U-N-S 60-907-3155
■ REGENT SEVEN SEAS CRUISES INC
RSSC
(Suby of PRESTIGE CRUISE HOLDINGS INC) ★
8300 Nw 33rd St Ste 100, Doral, FL 33122-1940
Tel (305) 514-4920 Founded/Ownrshp 2008
Sales 545.8MM EMP 217
Accts Pricewaterhousecoopers Llp Mi
SIC 4481 Deep sea passenger transportation, except ferry
CEO: Frank Del Rio
*Pr: Kunal S Kamlani
CFO: Luis S Migue
CFO: Luis S Miguel
*CFO: Jason Montague
*Treas: Lisa Wilson
Ex VP: Robin Lindsay
Sr VP: Rick D Armas
*Sr VP: Harry Sommer
VP: Darrel Hamann
*VP: James H Peterson
VP: Franco Semeraro
*VP: Randall Soy
VP: Shawn Tubman

D-U-N-S 96-892-0632
REGENTS OF MERCERSBURG COLLEGE
300 E Seminary St, Mercersburg, PA 17236-1550
Tel (717) 328-6110 Founded/Ownrshp 2011
Sales 93.4MM EMP 12^E
Accts Mcgladrey Llp Gaithersburg M
SIC 8299 Educational services

REGENTS OF THE UNIVERSITY NM
See UNIVERSITY OF NEW MEXICO

D-U-N-S 00-398-5512 IMP/EXP
REGENTS OF UNIVERSITY OF CALIFORNIA
(Suby of EXECUTIVE OFFICE OF STATE OF CALIFORNIA) ★
1111 Franklin St Fl 12, Oakland, CA 94607-5201
Tel (510) 987-0700 Founded/Ownrshp 1868
Sales 8.3MMM^E EMP 127,368
SIC 8221 8733

D-U-N-S 07-841-0927
REGENTS OF UNIVERSITY OF CALIFORNIA
NEVADA CANCER INSTITUTE
1111 Franklin St, Oakland, CA 94607-5201
Tel (619) 543-3713 Founded/Ownrshp 1868
Sales 11.7MM^E EMP 1,000
SIC 8062 General medical & surgical hospitals
Prin: Tom McAsee
*CEO: Margarita Baggett
*COO: Duncan Campbell
*Chf Mktg O: Angela Sciao

D-U-N-S 00-743-1505
REGENTS OF UNIVERSITY OF COLORADO
UNIVERSITY OF COLORADO DENVER
3100 Marine St Ste 48157, Boulder, CO 80303-1058
Tel (303) 735-6624 Founded/Ownrshp 1876
Sales 1.4MMM^E EMP 12,980
SIC 8221 8621 University; Professional membership organizations
Ex Dir: Bruce Benson
Ex VP: Laurence Nelson
Comm Dir: Deborah Mendez-Wilson
Ex Dir: Tamara Sumner
Pharmcst: Jamela Urban

D-U-N-S 07-574-6271
REGENTS OF UNIVERSITY OF IDAHO
875 Perimeter Dr Ms3020, Moscow, ID 83844-9803
Tel (208) 885-6174 Founded/Ownrshp 1889
Sales 214.7MM EMP 3,350
Accts Moss Adams Llp Eugene Oregon
SIC 8221 University
Pr: Duane Nellis
Bd of Dir: Sean Quinlan
Assoc VP: Jana Stotler
*VP: Debbie Eisinger
VP: Ronald Smith
Assoc Dir: Greg Cox
Assoc Dir: Tim Helmke
Assoc Dir: Michele Stefanic
Info Man: Leona Svancara
Mktg Dir: Jene Merrell
Sls Dir: Aaron Johnson

D-U-N-S 07-313-3571 IMP
REGENTS OF UNIVERSITY OF MICHIGAN
503 Thompson St, Ann Arbor, MI 48109-1340
Tel (734) 764-1817 Founded/Ownrshp 1817
Sales 5.5MMM EMP 34,624
Accts Pricewaterhousecoopers Llp De
SIC 8221 University
Pr: Mary Coleman
Pr: Tom Bray
Pr: Dondi Cupp
Assoc VP: Rowman Miranda
VP: John Billi
*VP: Sally J Churchill
VP: Chris Connelly
VP: Deborah Doyle
VP: Lee Doyle
VP: Adam Eickmeyer
VP: Marina Epelman
VP: Stephen Forrest
VP: Stephen R Forrest
VP: Rachel Goldman
VP: Royster Harper
VP: Michell Smith-Lewis
Assoc Dir: Michael Counts

D-U-N-S 00-622-0594
REGENTS OF UNIVERSITY OF MINNESOTA
600 Mcnamara Alumni # 200, Minneapolis, MN 55455
Tel (612) 625-5000 Founded/Ownrshp 1851
Sales 2.8MMM^E EMP 25,976
Accts Deloitte & Touche Llp Minneap
SIC 8221 University
Pr: Eric Kaler
*Pr: Robert H Bruininks
CFO: Curtis Coffer
CFO: Richard H Pfutzenreuter III
Chf Cred: Joayn Dana
Sr VP: Robert J Jones
VP: Nancy Barcel
VP: Meredith McQuaid
VP: Michael D Volna
Assoc Dir: Cathy Gillaspy
Assoc Dir: Ann Martin
Assoc Dir: Divah Yap

D-U-N-S 02-128-5077
REGIONAL AID FOR INTERIM NEEDS INC
R.A.IN HOME ATTENDENT SERVICES
811 Morris Park Ave, Bronx, NY 10462-3605
Tel (718) 892-5520 Founded/Ownrshp 1965
Sales 11.7MM EMP 1,200
Accts Ts Anand & Company Cpas Pc Ne
SIC 8322 Geriatric social service
Pr: Beatrice Castiglia-Catullo
*VP: Dr Arthur Wolstein
*Ex Dir: Louis M Vazquez

D-U-N-S 83-310-0253
REGIONAL CARE HOSPITAL PARTNERS INC
ESSENT HEALTHCARE
103 Continental Pl # 400, Brentwood, TN 37027-1073
Tel (615) 844-9800 Founded/Ownrshp 2009
Sales 501.0MM^E EMP 5,460
SIC 8741 Hospital management
CEO: Martin S Rash
Pr: Chris Minar
Pr: Chad Somerby
Sr VP: Christine Craft
VP: Gregory Flanagan
VP: Judy Gibson
VP: Adam Nunn
VP: Charley Thornburg
VP: Alan Wenk
VP Bus Dev: Jeff Forshee
Off Mgr: Linda Miller

D-U-N-S 07-015-6948
REGIONAL CENTER OF EAST BAY INC (CA)
7677 Oakport St Ste 300, Oakland, CA 94621-1933
Tel (510) 383-1200 Founded/Ownrshp 1975
Sales 311.1MM EMP 250
SIC 8322 Social services for the handicapped
CFO: Nancy Kubota
Exec: Maria Garcia-Puig
Doctor: Nancy Murphy

D-U-N-S 17-040-4560
REGIONAL DIVISION INC
UW HOSPITAL
600 Highland Ave, Madison, WI 53792-0001
Tel (608) 263-7923 Founded/Ownrshp 1984
Sales 701.9MM EMP 2,015
Accts Grant Thornton Llp Milwaukee
SIC 8741 Hospital management
Pr: Jane E Anderson
*Pr: Jane Barnett
VP: Tom Kienitz
Doctor: Lee Faucher

REGIONAL FLOOD CONTROL DST
See PIMA COUNTY

D-U-N-S 96-345-3647
REGIONAL HEALTH INC
REGIONAL MEDICAL CLINIC
353 Fairmont Blvd, Rapid City, SD 57701-7375
Tel (605) 755-1000 Founded/Ownrshp 2003
Sales 459.5MM^E EMP 4,258
SIC 8062 General medical & surgical hospitals
Ch: Tom Morrison
*CEO: Charles E Hart
*COO: Timothy Sughrue
*Treas: Roy Dishman
*Ex VP: Joseph Sluka
VP: Robert Allen
*Prin: Dennis Nesbit
CIO: Richard L Tuchie
Obsttrcn: Danielle Berdahl

REGIONAL HOSPITAL OF JACKSON
See JACKSON HOSPITAL CORP

REGIONAL HOSPITAL OF SCRANTON
See MERCY HOSPITAL SCRANTON PENNSYLVANIA

REGIONAL HOSPITAL OF SCRANTON
See SCRANTON HOSPITAL CO LLC

D-U-N-S 17-502-0031
REGIONAL INTERNATIONAL CORP
REGIONAL TRUCK & TRAILER
1007 Lehigh Station Rd, Henrietta, NY 14467-9311
Tel (585) 359-2011 Founded/Ownrshp 1989
Sales 86.1MM^E EMP 160
Accts Mengel Metzger Barr Henrietta
SIC 5013 5012 7539 7538 5531 Truck parts & accessories; Trucks, commercial; Trailers for trucks, new & used; Trailer repair; General truck repair; Automotive parts
CEO: James D Carello
*Treas: John L Di Marco
Opers Mgr: Walter Curtis

D-U-N-S 17-563-6323
▲ REGIONAL MANAGEMENT CORP
509 W Butler Rd, Greenville, SC 29607-4833
Tel (864) 422-8011 Founded/Ownrshp 1987
Sales 217.3MM EMP 1,443
Tkr Sym RM Exch NYS
SIC 7389 6141 Financial services; Personal credit institutions

CEO: Peter R Knitzer
*Ch Bd: Michael R Dunn
Pr: Jody L Anderson
CFO: Donald E Thomas
Sr VP: Daniel J Taggart
VP: Michael S Dymski
VP: Brian J Fisher
VP: Brian Switalski
Brnch Mgr: Eduardo Jaen
IT Man: Paul Taylor

D-U-N-S 96-803-2623
REGIONAL MEDICAL CENTER
REGIONAL PHYSICIANS CENTER OF
3000 Saint Matthews Rd, Orangeburg, SC 29118-1442
Tel (803) 395-2200 Founded/Ownrshp 1997
Sales 216.3MM EMP 1
SIC 8062 General medical & surgical hospitals
Prin: Sarah Benson

D-U-N-S 07-547-5020
REGIONAL MEDICAL CENTER BOARD
NORTHEAST ALA REGIONAL MED CTR
400 E 10th St, Anniston, AL 36207-4716
Tel (256) 235-5121 Founded/Ownrshp 1974
Sales 151.3MM EMP 1,500
SIC 8062

D-U-N-S 07-373-1432
REGIONAL MEDICAL CENTER OF ORANGEBURG & CALHOUN COUNTIES
3000 Saint Matthews Rd, Orangeburg, SC 29118-1442
Tel (803) 395-2200 Founded/Ownrshp 1919
Sales 216.5MM EMP 1,203
Accts Dixon Hughes Goodman Llp Gree
SIC 8062 General medical & surgical hospitals
Pr: Thomas Dandridge
COO: Lisa Goodlett
CFO: Cheryl S Mason
*Ofcr: Brenda Williams
VP: Julia Yawn
Exec: Gary Delaney
Dir Risk M: Glenda Schuler
Assoc Dir: Johanna Crider
Assoc Dir: Tonya Pratt
Dir Rx: Robert Phillips
Pr Dir: Kathryn Rhoad

REGIONAL MEDICAL CLINIC
See REGIONAL HEALTH INC

REGIONAL MEDICAL CTR SAN JOSE
See SAN JOSE MEDICAL SYSTEMS LP

REGIONAL OCCUPATIONAL PROGRAM
See FRESNO COUNTY SUPERINTENDENT OF SCHOOLS

REGIONAL PHYSICIANS CENTER OF
See REGIONAL MEDICAL CENTER

D-U-N-S 01-058-9141
REGIONAL TRANSPORTATION AUTHORITY (IL)
RTA
175 W Jackson Blvd # 1650, Chicago, IL 60604-2711
Tel (312) 913-3200 Founded/Ownrshp 1973
Sales 805.5MM EMP 80^E
Accts Rsm Us Llp Chicago Illinois
SIC 4111 Local & suburban transit; Subway operation
Ex Dir: Richard J Bacigalupo
Ch Bd: Thomas J McCraken Jr
CFO: Joseph G Costello
CFO: Bea Reyna-Hickey
Treas: Allan Sharkey
Exec: Joseph Voccia
Comm Dir: Susan Massel
Prin: Carole Brown
Prin: Julie Gomez
Prgrm Mgr: Eunice Escobar
Prgrm Mgr: James Hickey
Board of Directors: Carole Brown

D-U-N-S 06-972-1371
REGIONAL TRANSPORTATION DISTRICT
RTD
1600 Blake St, Denver, CO 80202-1399
Tel (303) 628-9000 Founded/Ownrshp 1969
Sales 125.8MM EMP 2,700
Accts Rubinbrown Llp Denver Co
SIC 4111 Local & suburban transit; Bus line operations
Genl Mgr: David Genova
CFO: Terry L Howerter
Bd of Dir: Gary Lasater
Bd of Dir: Angie Malpiede
Trst: Lou Ha
Ofcr: Martha Bembry
Ex VP: Amir Yazdani
Exec: Pat Pugh
Prgrm Mgr: Gary Godec
CIO: Trent Ratcliff
QA Dir: Kevin Diviness

REGIONAL TRUCK & TRAILER
See REGIONAL INTERNATIONAL CORP

D-U-N-S 18-060-9281
REGIONAL WEST HEALTH SERVICES INC
4021 Avenue B, Scottsbluff, NE 69361-4602
Tel (308) 635-3711 Founded/Ownrshp 1984
Sales 257.3MM EMP 1,500
Accts Contryman Associates Pc Cpa S
SIC 8741 Hospital management; Nursing & personal care facility management
Pr: Todd Sorensen MD
*Treas: Michael Gobel
VP: Shirley Knodel
Genl Mgr: Carol Bauer
Mktg Dir: Julie Franklin

D-U-N-S 07-800-9404
REGIONAL WEST MEDICAL CENTER
4021 Avenue B, Scottsbluff, NE 69361-4602
Tel (308) 635-3711 Founded/Ownrshp 1984
Sales 177.2MM EMP 1,100
SIC 8062 General medical & surgical hospitals
Pr: Todd S Sorensen
*CFO: David Griffiths
VP: Brenda Hall

*VP: Steve Hodges
Tech Mgr: Daryl Brisco
Sfty Dirs: Dan Howland
Doctor: James D Massey

D-U-N-S 14-786-3401 IMP/EXP
■ REGIONS BANK
AMSOUTH
(Suby of REGIONS FINANCIAL CORP) ★
1901 5th Ave N, Birmingham, AL 35203-2608
Tel (205) 326-5300 Founded/Ownrshp 2007
Sales NA EMP 6,289
SIC 6022 State commercial banks
CEO: Curren Coco
Pr: John M Turner Jr
*COO: Richard Horsley
*CFO: Brian Jordan
Chf Mktg O: Scott Peters
Ofcr: John Jones
*Ex VP: Wimberly Miree
Sr VP: Jason Epstein
Sr VP: Matt R Smith
Sr VP: Rick Swagler
Sr VP: Montise Walderp
VP: Diego Garcia
VP: Tim Hamilton
VP: Neuville Hotstream
VP: Joseph Mitchell
VP: Leana Mitchell
VP: Chad Oglesby
VP: Sandra Smith
Board of Directors: Jack Fleischauer, Wilbur Hufham, Pete Miller

D-U-N-S 08-654-2222
▲ REGIONS FINANCIAL CORP
1900 5th Ave N, Birmingham, AL 35203-2610
Tel (205) 581-7890 Founded/Ownrshp 1971
Sales NA EMP 23,916
Accts Ernst & Young Llp Birmingham
Tkr Sym RF Exch NYS
SIC 6022 6211 6282 State commercial banks; Brokers, security; Dealers, security; Investment bankers; Investment advice
CEO: Grayson Hall Jr
*Ch Bd: O B Grayson Hall Jr
Pr: Linda Barton
Pr: Jeremy Caruthers
Pr: Patrick Cayson
Pr: Penny Dinatale
Pr: Bryan Furlong
Pr: Rick Hilsabeck
Pr: Melissa James
Pr: Virgie Nicholson
Pr: Kelly Parianos
Pr: Janice Ray
Pr: Carlos Russell
Pr: Bridgette Slack
Pr: Martin Taylor
Pr: Gary White
CFO: Mary K Caldwell
CFO: David J Turner Jr
Chf Cred: Barb Godin
Ofcr: Barbara Godin
Trst Ofcr: Heather McElwee
Board of Directors: Charles D McCrary, George W Bryan, James T Prokopanko, Carolyn H Byrd, Lee J Styslinger III, David J Cooper Sr, Jose S Suquet, Don Defosset, Samuel A Di Piazza Jr, Eric C Fast, John D Johns, Ruth Ann Marshall, Susan W Matlock, John E Maupin Jr

D-U-N-S 11-241-4789
REGIONS HOSPITAL
PURCHASING DEPT
8170 33rd Ave S, Minneapolis, MN 55425-4516
Tel (952) 883-6280 Founded/Ownrshp 2002
Sales 691.6MM EMP 47E
Accts Kpmg Llp Minneapolis Mn
SIC 8062 General medical & surgical hospitals
Ex VP: Lora Hedin
VP: Tobi Tanzer
Exec: Barbara Thompson
CIO: Alan Abramson
Dir IT: Craig Taylor
Pharmcst: Mark Woessner
Counsel: Nancy Evert
Snr Mgr: Carrie McWell
Snr Mgr: Mark Schwob

D-U-N-S 96-359-1669
REGIONS HOSPITAL
640 Jackson St, Saint Paul, MN 55101-2595
Tel (651) 254-3456 Founded/Ownrshp 1986
Sales 636.2MM EMP 18E
SIC 8062 General medical & surgical hospitals
Pr: Brock Nelson
CFO: Heidi Conrad
VP: Beth Heinz
Nurse Mgr: Laurie Young
MIS Dir: Paul Engberg
IT Man: Kim La La Reau

D-U-N-S 15-697-4321
REGIONS HOSPITAL FOUNDATION
FAMILY PHYSICIAN HEALTH CENTER
640 Jackson St, Saint Paul, MN 55101-2595
Tel (651) 254-3456 Founded/Ownrshp 1872
Sales 248.4MME EMP 3,000
SIC 8062 General medical & surgical hospitals
Pr: Brock Nelson
*CFO: Greg Klugherz
Pathlgst: Amarnath Subramanian

D-U-N-S 78-370-9801
■ REGIONS INSURANCE GROUP
INSURANCE RESOURCES
(Suby of REGIONS FINANCIAL CORP) ★
1500 Riverfront Dr # 200, Little Rock, AR 72202-1745
Tel (501) 661-4800 Founded/Ownrshp 2007
Sales NA EMP 408
SIC 6411 Insurance agents, brokers & service
CEO: Rick Ulmer
*Pr: Allen J McDowell
*CFO: Johne Bennith
Ex VP: Fred B Stone
Sr VP: James Broglen
Sr VP: Mike Crow
*Sr VP: Bill Fisher
*Sr VP: John Howard
Sr VP: Dennis P Pauls
Sr VP: John Pierron
*Sr VP: Joe Stafford
*Sr VP: William R Stringfellow
VP: Irvin Carbalan
VP: William R Fisher
VP: Gibbs Gage
VP: Terry M Hayes
VP: James R Hill
VP: Jimmy Madigan
VP: Godfrey Marine
VP: Daryll Martin
VP: David A McDivitt

D-U-N-S 93-987-0523
REGIS 66 INC
4890 Lowell Blvd, Denver, CO 80221-1026
Tel (303) 455-6636 Founded/Ownrshp 1995
Sales 171.6MM EMP 2
SIC 5541 Filling stations, gasoline
Pr: Alan Thielen
*VP: John Schomer

D-U-N-S 04-670-9747 IMP/EXP
▲ REGIS CORP
7201 Metro Blvd, Edina, MN 55439-2103
Tel (952) 947-7777 Founded/Ownrshp 1922
Sales 1.7MMM EMP 47,000
Tkr Sym RGS Exch NYS
SIC 7231 7299 6794 Unisex hair salons; Hair weaving or replacement; Franchises, selling or licensing
Pr: Daniel J Hanrahan
*Ch Bd: Stephen E Watson
*Pr: Daniel Hanrahan
COO: Jim Lain
CFO: Steven Spiegel
Chf Mktg O: Annette Miller
Ofcr: Eric Bakken
Ofcr: Heather Passe
Ofcr: Carmen Thiede
Sr VP: Andrew Dulka
Sr VP: Ken Warfield
VP: Andy Dulka
Exec: Michelle Perry
Board of Directors: Daniel G Beltzman, David J Grissen, Mark S Light, Michael J Merriman, M Ann Rhoades, David P Williams

D-U-N-S 07-340-7579 IMP
REGIS UNIVERSITY
3333 Regis Blvd, Denver, CO 80221-1099
Tel (303) 458-4100 Founded/Ownrshp 1877
Sales 172.5MM EMP 957
SIC 8221 College, except junior
Pr: John P Fitzgibbons
COO: Charles Dahlman
*CFO: Joseph C Weber
Chf Mktg O: Soon B Yeap
VP: Andrew F Alexander
VP: Allan Service
Exec: Patricia Schoeninger
Assoc Dir: Susan Odonnell
Dir Bus: Bruce Bobitt
VP Admn: Webber Karen
Ex Dir: Jerry Mosier

REGISTRY FOR EXCELLENCE
See DONSCO INC

D-U-N-S 96-318-2019
REGULUS GROUP LLC
REGULUS WEST
(Suby of TRANSCENTRA INC) ★
860 Latour Ct, NAPA, CA 94558-6258
Tel (707) 259-7100 Founded/Ownrshp 2011
Sales 196.6MME EMP 1,800
SIC 7374 Data processing service
Sr Cor Off: Adrian Gonzalez
VP: Howard Mergelkamp
Exec: Scott Henry
Creative D: Darlene Devault
Mng Dir: Martin Steber
Prgrm Mgr: Bob Nix
MIS Dir: Perry Sautbein
Software D: Rodd Bullard
Site Mgr: Dick Mikus
Site Mgr: Margie Mitchell
VP Sls: Tom Galbo

D-U-N-S 09-447-7528
REGULUS INTEGRATED SOLUTIONS LLC
(Suby of REGULUS WEST) ★
9645-L Part Blvd, Charlotte, NC 28216
Tel (704) 904-8759 Founded/Ownrshp 2000
Sales 102.1MME EMP 600
SIC 2752 7389 3861 2759 Commercial printing, lithographic; Microfilm recording & developing service; Photographic equipment & supplies; Commercial printing

REGULUS WEST
See REGULUS GROUP LLC

D-U-N-S 16-712-9142
REGUS CORP
(Suby of REGUS GROUP LIMITED)
15305 Dallas Pkwy Ste 400, Addison, TX 75001-6922
Tel (972) 361-8100 Founded/Ownrshp 2008
Sales 478.0MME EMP 1,600
SIC 7363 7389 6531 Office help supply service; Telephone answering service; Mailbox rental & related service; Office facilities & secretarial service rental; Real estate leasing & rentals
Pr: Mark Dixon
*Pr: Guillermo Rotman
CFO: Joanna Cox
*CFO: Michael Osburn
*CFO: Dominique Yates
VP: Aaron Hughes
VP: Catherine Lefebvre-Feat
Area Mgr: Frisco Square
Genl Mgr: Neil Babuik
VP Mktg: Rebecca Tann
VP Sls: Amelia Calatrava

D-U-N-S 11-421-4281
■ REHABCARE GROUP INC
(Suby of KINDRED HEALTHCARE INC) ★
680 S 4th St, Louisville, KY 40202-2407
Tel (502) 596-7300 Founded/Ownrshp 2011
Sales 412.8MME EMP 18,200
SIC 8093 8099 8049 8051 Rehabilitation center, outpatient treatment; Medical services organization; Physical therapist; Skilled nursing care facilities
CEO: John H Short
Pr: Patricia M Henry
Ex VP: William Hardaway
Sr VP: Katherine Gilchrist
Sr VP: Herschell Sellers
Sr VP: Patricia S Williams
Sr VP: Jeff A Zadoks
VP: Stephen Cunanan
VP: Linda S Fache
VP: Catherine Knight
VP: Joseph L Landenwich
VP: Travis Rich
VP: Donald H Robinson
VP: Brian Samberg
VP: Talah Shraf

D-U-N-S 83-287-3496
■ REHABCARE HOSPITAL HOLDINGS LLC
(Suby of REHABCARE GROUP INC) ★
7733 Forsyth Blvd # 2300, Saint Louis, MO 63105-1817
Tel (800) 677-1238 Founded/Ownrshp 2006
Sales 323.9MME EMP 3,800
SIC 8093 Rehabilitation center, outpatient treatment

D-U-N-S 08-001-4779
■ REHABILITATION CENTER OF INDEPENDENCE LLC
REHABLITATION CTR INDEPENDENCE
(Suby of GENESIS HEALTHCARE LLC) ★
1800 S Swope Dr, Independence, MO 64057-1084
Tel (816) 257-2566 Founded/Ownrshp 2006
Sales 2.0MME EMP 3,238E
SIC 8051 Skilled nursing care facilities
CEO: George V Hagaer Jr
Prin: Dean Caldwell

D-U-N-S 06-847-7546
REHABILITATION INSTITUTE OF CHICAGO
RIC
345 E Superior St, Chicago, IL 60611-4805
Tel (312) 238-1000 Founded/Ownrshp 1951
Sales 256.1MM EMP 986
Accts Deloitte Tax Llp Chicago Il
SIC 8069 Specialty hospitals, except psychiatric
Pr: Joanne C Smith
V Ch: Wesley M Dixon Jr
*CFO: Edward B Case
*Treas: Greg Ward
Ofcr: Leyla Erkan
Ex VP: Beth Bridges
*Sr VP: Susan Hulce Cerletty
*Sr VP: Peggy Kirk
Sr VP: Richard L Lieber
*Sr VP: Nancy Paridy
VP: Tim McKula

REHABILITATION INSTITUTE W FLA
See WEST FLORIDA REGIONAL MEDICAL CENTER INC

REHABILITATION MEDICINE
See J F K JOHNSON REHABILITION INSTITUTE

REHABILITATION STATION
See CLC OF BILOXI LLC

D-U-N-S 94-019-9102
REHABILITATION THERAPIST
FAITH REGIONAL HEALTH SERVICES
1500 Koenigstein Ave, Norfolk, NE 68701-3664
Tel (402) 644-7396 Founded/Ownrshp 1996
Sales 168.9MM EMP 39
SIC 8093 Rehabilitation center, outpatient treatment
*Treas: Craig Boche
Sfty Dirs: Randy Chamberlain

REHABLITATION CTR INDEPENDENCE
See REHABILITATION CENTER OF INDEPENDENCE LLC

D-U-N-S 78-052-1084 IMP
REHAU INC
1501 Edwards Ferry Rd Ne, Leesburg, VA 20176-6680
Tel (703) 777-5255 Founded/Ownrshp 1987
Sales 278.5MME EMP 823
SIC 3089 Plastic processing
CEO: Kathleen Saylor
*CEO: Christian Fabian
*Treas: Bruce E Allder
*Treas: Peter Huddleston
Top Exec: Udo Steffl
*VP: Terry Barnaby
VP: Vince Koehler
*VP: Reiner Leishelm
VP: Dan Zainescu
Exec: Anuradha Thakur
Dept Mgr: Sue Martin
Board of Directors: Dr Veit Wagner, and Helmut

D-U-N-S 11-634-6193
REHMANN LLC
1500 W Big Beaver Rd, Macomb, MI 48044
Tel (866) 799-9580 Founded/Ownrshp 2000
Sales 103.9MM EMP 700
SIC 8748 8721 Agricultural consultant; Accounting, auditing & bookkeeping
Mng Pt: Thomas Mulvihill
Snr Mgr: Deb Beckley
Snr Mgr: Nelson Finley
Snr Mgr: Suzie Wanstreet

D-U-N-S 00-824-0988 IMP/EXP
REHRIG PACIFIC CO
4010 E 26th St, Vernon, CA 90058-4477
Tel (800) 421-6244 Founded/Ownrshp 1913
Sales 445.1MME EMP 1,100
Accts Bdo Seidman
SIC 3089 2821 Cases, plastic; Garbage containers, plastic; Molding primary plastic; Plasticizer/additive based plastic materials
CEO: William J Rehrig
*Pr: Michael J Doka
*CFO: James L Drew
CFO: Raj Luhar
Treas: Drew Jl
VP: Blair Chastain
VP: Jeff Hentges
*VP: William Widmann
Off Mgr: Jan Schau
Dir IT: Roger Hsu
Plnt Mgr: Samuel Bernal

D-U-N-S 96-469-2847
REHRIG PACIFIC HOLDINGS INC
4010 E 26th St, Vernon, CA 90058-4477
Tel (323) 262-5145 Founded/Ownrshp 1998
Sales 93.5MME EMP 1,100
SIC 3089 2821 Cases, plastic; Garbage containers, plastic; Molding primary plastic; Plasticizer/additive based plastic materials
CEO: William J Rehrig
*Pr: Michael J Doka
*CFO: James L Drew
*VP: William Widmann

D-U-N-S 80-099-2260 IMP
REHRIG PENN LOGISTICS INC
(Suby of REHRIG PACIFIC CO) ★
7800 100th St, Pleasant Prairie, WI 53158-2806
Tel (262) 947-0032 Founded/Ownrshp 2004
Sales 133.8MME EMP 645
SIC 3089 Plastic containers, except foam
Pr: William Rehrig
*Treas: James Drew
IT Man: Robert Martin
Sls Mgr: Brooks Curtis

D-U-N-S 14-119-6261
REICHEL FOODS INC
3706 Enterprise Dr Sw, Rochester, MN 55902-1257
Tel (507) 289-7264 Founded/Ownrshp 1995
Sales 113.9MME EMP 250
SIC 2011 5812 2013 0723 Meat packing plants; Eating places; Sausages & other prepared meats; Crop preparation services for market
CEO: Craig A Reichel
*CFO: Thomas J Wiechmann
Plnt Mgr: Alfonso Cerda
VP Sls: Greg Wilson

D-U-N-S 05-452-7502 IMP/EXP
REICHHOLD HOLDINGS US INC
(Suby of REICHHOLD CORPORATE HOLDINGS II B.V.)
1035 Swabia Ct, Durham, NC 27703-8462
Tel (919) 990-7500 Founded/Ownrshp 1970, 2005
Sales 96.8MME EMP 553
SIC 2821 2822 2891 3089 5169 5162

REICHHOLD, INC.
See REICHHOLD LIQUIDATION INC

D-U-N-S 79-700-5910
REICHHOLD INDUSTRIES INC
(Suby of I KESTREL ACQUISITION CORP) ★
1035 Swabia Ct, Durham, NC 27703-8462
Tel (919) 990-7500 Founded/Ownrshp 2006
Sales 85.1MME EMP 200E
SIC 2821 Plastics materials & resins
Ch Bd: John S Gaither
*CFO: Roger L Willis
*VP: Mitzi Vanleeuwen

D-U-N-S 83-621-5905 IMP/EXP
REICHHOLD LIQUIDATION INC
REICHHOLD, INC.
1035 Swabia Ct, Durham, NC 27703-8462
Tel (919) 990-7500 Founded/Ownrshp 1927
Sales 155.8MME EMP 550
SIC 2821 2822 2869 2899 2891 2851

D-U-N-S 07-980-4427
REICHHOLD LLC 2
1035 Swabia Ct, Durham, NC 27703-8462
Tel (919) 990-7500 Founded/Ownrshp 2015
Sales 232.1MME EMP 393
SIC 2821 2851 Styrene resins; Styrene-acrylonitile resins; Plastics base paints & varnishes
CEO: John Gaither
*CFO: Roger Willis

D-U-N-S 13-059-7672
REID COMPANIES INC
100 W Genesee St, Lockport, NY 14094-3612
Tel (716) 434-2885 Founded/Ownrshp 2003
Sales 84.7MME EMP 250
SIC 5541 Filling stations, gasoline
Pr: Paul Reid

D-U-N-S 06-685-5768
REID ENTERPRISES INC
BLOOMINGTON CHRYSLER JEEP
8000 Penn Ave S, Minneapolis, MN 55431-1317
Tel (952) 238-4300 Founded/Ownrshp 1979
Sales 87.7MME EMP 400
SIC 5511 Automobiles, new & used
Pr: Lawrence Reid

REID HEALTH
See REID HOSPITAL & HEALTH CARE SERVICES FOUNDATION INC

REID HEALTH
See REID HOSPITAL & HEALTH CARE SERVICES INC

REID HEALTH PHYSICIAN ASSOC
See REID PHYSICIAN ASSOCIATES INC

D-U-N-S 07-204-5032
REID HOSPITAL & HEALTH CARE SERVICES FOUNDATION INC
REID HEALTH
1100 Reid Pkwy, Richmond, IN 47374-1157
Tel (765) 983-3102 Founded/Ownrshp 1975
Sales 375.3MME EMP 3,012
Accts Brady Ware & Schoenfeld Inc R

SIC 8062 General medical & surgical hospitals
Pr: Denny Burns
**Pr:* Randall P Kirk
**Treas:* Jackie Carberry
Bd of Dir: Joe Pizzorno
**Sr VP:* Ted Sobol
**VP:* Lee Elzemeyer
**VP:* Craig Kinyon
CTO: Timothy Love
Surgeon: Frederick Bartlett
Surgeon: Frederick Matsen
Obsttrcn: Stephen Smith

D-U-N-S 07-521-0042
REID HOSPITAL & HEALTH CARE SERVICES INC
1100 Reid Pkwy, Richmond, IN 47374-1157
Tel (765) 983-3000 *Founded/Ownrshp* 1905
Sales 359.6MM *EMP* 1,800
SIC 8069 Specialty hospitals, except psychiatric
Pr: Craig C Kinyon
Chf Rad: Corey Gray
VP: Jeff Haist
Dir Rad: Frederic Vanbastelaer
Off Mgr: Sharon Miles

D-U-N-S 11-337-3075
REID HOSPITAL & HEALTH CARE SERVICES INC
REID HEALTH
(*Suby of* REID HEALTH) ★
1100 Reid Pkwy, Richmond, IN 47374-1157
Tel (765) 983-3000 *Founded/Ownrshp* 2006
Sales 375.3MM *EMP* 3
Accts Bkd Llp Cincinnati Oh
SIC 8062 General medical & surgical hospitals
Pr: Craig Kinyon
Pr: Christie Brewer
CFO: Tricia Ours
Ofcr: Randall Bierman
Ofcr: Julie Gindling
**VP:* Kay Cartwright
**VP:* Angie Dickman
**VP:* Jim Puffenberger
Dir Rx: Rich Fain
Dir Sec: Randy Kolentus
CIO: Timothy Love

D-U-N-S 01-284-1664
REID PETROLEUM CORP
(*Suby of* REID COMPANIES INC) ★
100 W Genesee St, Lockport, NY 14094-3612
Tel (716) 434-2885 *Founded/Ownrshp* 1987
Sales 84.7MM[E] *EMP* 250
SIC 5541 5172 Filling stations, gasoline; Petroleum brokers
Ch Bd: Paul D Reid
**Pr:* Paul A Quebral
**CFO:* Karen M Korthals
**VP:* Doug Galli
**VP:* Michael McCarthy

D-U-N-S 01-128-8544
REID PHYSICIAN ASSOCIATES INC
REID HEALTH PHYSICIAN ASSOC
1100 Reid Pkwy, Richmond, IN 47374-1157
Tel (765) 983-3000 *Founded/Ownrshp* 2008
Sales 40.0MM *EMP* 2,000
Accts Bkd Llp Indianapolis Indian
SIC 8011 General & family practice, physician/surgeon; Physicians' office, including specialists
Pr: Thomas Huth
CFO: Christopher Knight
Off Mgr: Toni R Moore
Board of Directors: Cathy Jarvis

D-U-N-S 00-849-3595
REID PLASTICS INC
(*Suby of* CCC) ★
10861 Mill Valley Rd, Omaha, NE 68154-3975
Tel (402) 934-2400 *Founded/Ownrshp* 2001
Sales 115.5MM[E] *EMP* 1,300
SIC 3085 2821 3089 Plastics bottles; Polycarbonate resins; Plastic containers, except foam
Pr: B Joseph Rokus
CFO: William Duncan
VP: David Blood
VP: Paul McDonnell
CIO: Ernie Lazor
MIS Dir: David Doolittle
MIS Mgr: R Callanan

D-U-N-S 09-478-4048
REIF OIL CO
FASTBREAK
801 N 3rd St, Burlington, IA 52601-5006
Tel (319) 758-1240 *Founded/Ownrshp* 1978
Sales 177.2MM *EMP* 100
Accts Cpa Associates Pc Burlington
SIC 5172 5411 Gasoline; Convenience stores
Pr: Clifford G Reif Jr

D-U-N-S 00-482-8208
REILLY CONSTRUCTION CO INC (IA)
110 E Main St, Ossian, IA 52161-7700
Tel (563) 532-9211 *Founded/Ownrshp* 1959
Sales 131.7MM[E] *EMP* 285[E]
SIC 1611 Grading
Ch Bd: Robert M Reilly
**Pr:* Christopher R Reilly
**Ex VP:* Larry Thompson
**VP:* Lance Thompson

D-U-N-S 87-319-2660 IMP
REILY FOODS CO
LUZIANNE
(*Suby of* REILY W M B & CO) ★
400 Poydras St Fl 10, New Orleans, LA 70130-3245
Tel (504) 524-6131 *Founded/Ownrshp* 1902
Sales 189.8MM[E] *EMP* 650
SIC 2099 2095 Tea blending; Coffee, ground: mixed with grain or chicory; Coffee roasting (except by wholesale grocers)
Pr: David Darragh
**CFO:* Harold Herrmann
Bd of Dir: William Boatner III
Trst: Joan Coulter
Creative D: Diane Hunt
Dir IT: Tom Caine
Dir IT: John Smith
VP Opers: Tony Doughty
Sfty Mgr: Jenny Keith
Mktg Mgr: Ashlee Dunn
Mktg Mgr: Phil White

REILY W M B & CO
See WM B REILY & CO INC

REIMERS-KAUFMAN CONCRETE PDTS
See NEBCO INC

D-U-N-S 06-187-7247 IMP/EXP
REINALT-THOMAS CORP (MI)
DISCOUNT TIRE
20225 N Scottsdale Rd, Scottsdale, AZ 85255-6456
Tel (480) 606-6000 *Founded/Ownrshp* 1960
Sales 2.9MMM[E] *EMP* 9,430
SIC 5531 Automotive tires
Ch Bd: Bruce T Halle
**CEO:* Michael S Zuieback
CFO: Christian Roe
**Treas:* Robert H Holman Jr
**Treas:* Timothy J Schafer
**V Ch Bd:* Gary Van Brunt
Ex VP: James Silhasek
**VP:* Rich Kuipers
Board of Directors: David N Fairbanks

D-U-N-S 78-714-8428
REINAUER TRANSPORTATION COMPANIES LLC
1983 Richmond Ter, Staten Island, NY 10302-1201
Tel (718) 816-8167 *Founded/Ownrshp* 2001
Sales 116.9MM[E] *EMP* 400[E]
SIC 4449 4492 Intracoastal (freight) transportation; Marine towing services
Treas: Albert Reinauer III
Treas: Albert H Reinauer
VP: F Reinauer
VP: Vincent D Tibbetts Jr
Netwrk Mgr: Dick Muscerer

D-U-N-S 00-643-9137 IMP
REINDERS INC (WI)
W227n6225 Sussex Rd, Sussex, WI 53089-3969
Tel (262) 786-3300 *Founded/Ownrshp* 1866
Sales 88.3MM *EMP* 200
SIC 5191 5169 5074 5999 5083

D-U-N-S 06-927-3142 IMP
REINFORCED EARTH CO
RECO
(*Suby of* ASHGROVE HOLDINGS LLC) ★
12001 Sunrise Valley Dr # 400, Reston, VA 20191-3455
Tel (703) 821-1175 *Founded/Ownrshp* 1971, 2000
Sales 87.9MM[E] *EMP* 220
SIC 5032

D-U-N-S 03-405-8164
REINHARDT MOTORS INC
REINHARDT TOYOTA
720 Eastern Blvd, Montgomery, AL 36117-1913
Tel (334) 272-7147 *Founded/Ownrshp* 1940
Sales 85.0MM[E] *EMP* 140
SIC 5511 7532 Automobiles, new & used; Body shop, automotive
Pr: James M Reinhardt Sr
**Sec:* Jamie R Raley
VP: Scott Arnold
**VP:* James M Reinhardt Jr
**VP:* Linda R Wilson
Sls Mgr: Larry Holley
Sls Mgr: Tony Hughen
Sls Mgr: Jason Stanford

REINHARDT TOYOTA
See REINHARDT MOTORS INC

D-U-N-S 06-144-1556 IMP/EXP
REINHART FOODSERVICE LLC
AGAR SUPPLY CO.
(*Suby of* REYES HOLDINGS LLC) ★
1500 Saint James St, La Crosse, WI 54603-2754
Tel (608) 782-2660 *Founded/Ownrshp* 1972
Sales 500.5MM[E] *EMP* 2,150
SIC 5963

D-U-N-S 96-722-3087
REINHART FOODSERVICE LOUISIANA LLC
(*Suby of* REYES HOLDINGS LLC) ★
6250 N River Rd, Rosemont, IL 60018-4247
Tel (847) 227-6500 *Founded/Ownrshp* 2011
Sales 259.4MM[E] *EMP* 500[E]
SIC 5149 Groceries & related products
CEO: John A Roussel
**Owner:* David K Reyes
**Owner:* James V Reyes
Pr: Fred Casinelli
**CFO:* Daniel P Doheny
VP: Carmel Barrie
VP: Mario Delgado
VP: Dean Hogan
Genl Mgr: Kevin Brouillette
VP Mktg: Eric Cronert
Sales Asso: Jim Brown

D-U-N-S 80-775-8511
▲ REINSURANCE GROUP OF AMERICA INC
RGA
16600 Swingley Ridge Rd, Chesterfield, MO 63017-1706
Tel (636) 736-7000 *Founded/Ownrshp* 1973
Sales NA *EMP* 2,201[E]
Tkr Sym RGA *Exch* NYS
SIC 6311 6321 6411 Life insurance; Accident & health insurance; Reinsurance carriers, accident & health; Insurance agents & brokers
CEO: A Greig Woodring
**Ch Bd:* J Cliff Eason
**Pr:* Anna Manning
Pr: Jim McElroy
COO: Donna H Kinnaird
CFO: Todd C Larson
Ofcr: Cari Childs
Ex VP: Brendan Galligan
Ex VP: William L Hutton
Ex VP: Bob Musen
Sr VP: John W Hayden
VP: Wayne Adams
VP: Rodney Brown
VP: Chris Cooper
VP: Larry Fite
VP: Amy Gibson
VP: Abraham Gootzeit
VP: Andy Jacobson
VP: Richard Leblanc
VP: Anne Riley
VP: Manuel Santos
Board of Directors: William J Bartlett, John F Danahy, Christine R Detrick, Patricia L Guinn, Alan C Henderson, Joyce A Phillips, Frederick J Sievert, Stanley B Tulin

D-U-N-S 96-855-5396
RELADYNE I LLC
(*Suby of* RELADYNE INC) ★
9395 Kenwood Rd Ste 104, Blue Ash, OH 45242-6819
Tel (513) 489-6000 *Founded/Ownrshp* 2010
Sales 86.7MM[E] *EMP* 72
SIC 5171 5172 Petroleum bulk stations & terminals; Diesel fuel
Pr: Larry J Stoddard
**CFO:* Paul Helton
**Ex VP:* Jeff Hart
**Ex VP:* Jay Hurt
**Ex VP:* Doug Oehler
**VP:* Jess Brown
**VP:* Dan Oehler
VP: Walt Rodgers
Genl Mgr: Glenn Pumpelly

D-U-N-S 94-588-8753
RELADYNE INC
9395 Kenwood Rd Ste 104, Blue Ash, OH 45242-6819
Tel (513) 489-6000 *Founded/Ownrshp* 2013
Sales 373.2MM[E] *EMP* 228[E]
SIC 2992 Lubricating oils & greases
Sls Mgr: Adam Buys

D-U-N-S 96-709-6483
RELATED CLINTON MANOR LLC
CLINTON MANOR APARTMENTS
100 Clinton St, Clinton, SC 29325
Tel (864) 833-3836 *Founded/Ownrshp* 2006
Sales 27.8MM[E] *EMP* 1,828
SIC 6531 6513 Real estate agents & managers; Apartment building operators
Prin: Larry Lipton

D-U-N-S 07-326-8286
RELATED COMPANIES INC
511 W 33rd St Rm 200, New York, NY 10001-1343
Tel (212) 801-1000 *Founded/Ownrshp* 1972
Sales 444.2MM[E] *EMP* 300
SIC 6552 6531 Subdividers & developers; Real estate agents & managers
Ch: Stephen M Ross
Genl Pt: Jorge M Pyrez
**Pr:* Bruce A Beal Jr
Pr: Joann Ferrante
**CEO:* Jeff T Blau
**COO:* Kenneth P Wong
CFO: Michael Brandt
CFO: Michael Brenner
**Ex VP:* Michael J Brenner
VP: Michael Antonik
VP: Joanne Billera
VP: Warren Dauber
VP: Nicholas Lanzillotto
VP: David Pearson
VP: Ron Peterson
VP: Joanna Rose
VP: Steve Silverstein
VP: Paul Tortorice
Exec: Richard Otoole
Dir Risk M: Daniel Zirpoli

D-U-N-S 03-632-4049
RELATED COMPANIES L P
60 Columbus Cir, New York, NY 10023-5802
Tel (212) 421-5333 *Founded/Ownrshp* 1992
Sales 10.6MMM[E] *EMP* 20,000[E]
SIC 6552 6531 Subdividers & developers; Real estate agents & managers
Ch: Stephen M Ross
Pr: Hector Pinero
**CEO:* Jeff T Blau
CFO: Michael J Brenner
Treas: Treha Demaio
Ex VP: Ronald Wackrow
Sr VP: Mark Boekenheide
Sr VP: Gregory Gushee
Sr VP: Frederick Knapp
VP: Stacey Feder
VP: Jay Reinhard
VP: Kimberly Sherman-Stamler
VP: Tyler Siegel
Exec: Carlos Perez
Dir Bus: Dipen Patel

D-U-N-S 96-471-7248
RELATED COMPANIES L P
WEYANT GREEN
40 W Point Hwy, Highland Falls, NY 10928-2317
Tel (845) 446-4966
Sales 22.6MM[E] *EMP* 1,645[E]
SIC 6531 Real estate agents & managers

D-U-N-S 08-258-9094
RELATED MANAGEMENT CORP
(*Suby of* RELATED COMPANIES L P) ★
423 W 55th St, New York, NY 10019-4460
Tel (212) 319-1200 *Founded/Ownrshp* 1975
Sales 49.2MM[E] *EMP* 1,920
SIC 6531 Real estate managers
Pr: Jeff Brodsky

D-U-N-S 96-930-5556
RELATED NEWBERRY ARMS LLC
186 Newberry Arms, Newberry, SC 29108-4627
Tel (803) 276-4053 *Founded/Ownrshp* 2002
Sales 28.7MM[E] *EMP* 1,828
SIC 6513 Apartment building operators

D-U-N-S 96-855-9018
RELATIVITY CAPITAL LLC
1655 Fort Myer Dr Fl 7, Arlington, VA 22209-3199
Tel (703) 812-3020 *Founded/Ownrshp* 2007
Sales 134.7MM[E] *EMP* 1,074
SIC 6282 4581 Investment advice; Aircraft maintenance & repair services; Aircraft servicing & repairing
Mng Dir: Leslie L Armitage
VP: David J Miller
Mng Dir: Joyce Johnson-Miller

RELDAN METALS COMPANY
See ABINGTON RELDAN METALS LLC

D-U-N-S 00-122-1043 IMP
RELIABLE AUTOMATIC SPRINKLER CO INC
103 Fairview Pk Dr Ste 1, Elmsford, NY 10523-1523
Tel (914) 829-2042 *Founded/Ownrshp* 1920
Sales 382.9MM[E] *EMP* 1,200
SIC 3569 Sprinkler systems, fire: automatic
Pr: Frank J Fee III
Treas: Frank Fee III
VP: Candida M Fee
VP: Kevin T Fee
VP: Michael R Fee
VP: Robert C Hultgren
Plng Mgr: Martin Hanna
CIO: Paul Rials
Tech Mgr: Brandon Telford
VP Mfg: William M Kirkpatrick
Opers Supe: Stephanie Burke

D-U-N-S 80-826-0744 IMP
RELIABLE CHURCHILL LLLP
BREAKTHRU BEVERAGE MARYLAND
1413 Tangier Dr, Baltimore, MD 21220-2876
Tel (410) 439-5000 *Founded/Ownrshp* 2001
Sales 161.7MM[E] *EMP* 3,089[E]
SIC 5182

RELIABLE HEALTH CARE SOLUTIONS
See JMJ CONSULTING GROUP INC

RELIABLE TIRE CO
See RELIABLE TIRE DISTRIBUTORS INC

D-U-N-S 00-250-4165 IMP
RELIABLE TIRE DISTRIBUTORS INC (NJ)
RELIABLE TIRE CO
805 N Black Horse Pike, Blackwood, NJ 08012-3936
Tel (800) 342-3426 *Founded/Ownrshp* 1956, 1985
Sales 248.2MM[E] *EMP* 147
SIC 5014 Tires & tubes
Pr: Richard K Betz
VP: Richard M Betz
VP: Shawan Betz

D-U-N-S 05-733-6760
RELIABLE WHOLESALE LUMBER INC
7600 Redondo Cir, Huntington Beach, CA 92648-1303
Tel (714) 848-8222 *Founded/Ownrshp* 1971
Sales 196.7MM[E] *EMP* 290
SIC 5031 2421 Lumber: rough, dressed & finished; Sawmills & planing mills, general
Pr: Jerome M Higman
**COO:* Will Higman
**CFO:* David Higman
IT Man: John Wenzel

RELIANCE & DODGE BRANDS
See RELIANCE ELECTRIC CO

D-U-N-S 79-658-1804
RELIANCE COMMUNICATIONS LLC
555 Wireless Blvd, Hauppauge, NY 11788-3966
Tel (631) 952-4800 *Founded/Ownrshp* 2007
Sales 175.0MM[E] *EMP* 260
SIC 5065 5999 Mobile telephone equipment; Mobile telephones & equipment
CEO: Mike Narula
**COO:* Andrea Tibke
**CFO:* Mark Feldman
**Ch:* Ashima Narula

RELIANCE DRILLING
See RELIANCE WELL SERVICE INC

D-U-N-S 60-814-5793 IMP
RELIANCE ELECTRIC CO
RELIANCE & DODGE BRANDS
(*Suby of* BALDOR MOTORS AND DRIVE) ★
6040 Ponders Ct, Greenville, SC 29615-4601
Tel (864) 297-4800 *Founded/Ownrshp* 1996
Sales 305.5MM[E] *EMP* 3,400
SIC 3714 3621 Power transmission equipment, motor vehicle; Motors, electric
Pr: Joseph D Swann
Pr: Clyde Fowler
**VP:* Brian Brehmer
VP: Randy Carson
**VP:* Michael A Cinquemani
**VP:* Thomas A Mascari
**VP:* Robert S Nemecek
**VP:* Rick J Payton
IT Man: Steven Allen
IT Man: Jim Sneed

D-U-N-S 01-613-9193
RELIANCE HEALTH CARE MANAGEMENT (AR)
824 Salem Rd Ste 210, Conway, AR 72034-4855
Tel (501) 932-0050 *Founded/Ownrshp* 1998
Sales 29.5MM[E] *EMP* 1,000
SIC 8059 Nursing home, except skilled & intermediate care facility
Pr: Brandon Adams
**COO:* Bryan Adams
COO: John Ellis
CFO: Tobey Koehler

D-U-N-S 96-230-4486
RELIANCE HOLDING USA INC
(*Suby of* RELIANCE INDUSTRIES LIMITED)
2000 W Sam Houston Pkwy S # 700, Houston, TX 77042-3621
Tel (713) 430-8700 *Founded/Ownrshp* 2010
Sales 544.6MM *EMP* 14
Accts Ernst & Young Llp Houston Tx
SIC 6719 Personal holding companies, except banks
Pr: Walter Vandedijver

**CEO:* Mukesh D Ambani
CFO: Gopal Krishnan
**CFO:* Howard Selzer
VP Mktg: Stuart E Nance
**Genl Couns:* Kelly Cope

RELIANCE MERCHANDISING CO DIV
See PEI/GENESIS INC

D-U-N-S 00-972-7017
RELIANCE STANDARD LIFE INSURANCE CO
(*Suby of* RELIANCE STANDARD LIFE INSURANCE CO OF TEXAS) ★
2001 Market St Ste 1500, Philadelphia, PA 19103-7000
Tel (267) 256-3500 *Founded/Ownrshp* 1987
Sales NA *EMP* 250
SIC 6311 6321 Life insurance carriers; Accident insurance carriers; Health insurance carriers
CEO: Lawrence E Daurelle
Pr: Marie Beasley
Pr: Paul Champi
Pr: Christopher A Fazzini
Pr: Michael Spinelli
Pr: John Staub
Ex VP: Thomas W Burghart
Sr VP: Warren M Cohen
Sr VP: Chad Coulter
Sr VP: Andrew B Davison
Sr VP: Gregory Esemplare
Sr VP: Gregory F Esemplare
Sr VP: Daniel J Falkenstein
Sr VP: Debra G Staples
Sr VP: Michael Wilbert
VP: Len Cavallaro
VP: Danny R Geen
Exec: Naveen Yadav

D-U-N-S 18-890-5673
RELIANCE STANDARD LIFE INSURANCE CO OF TEXAS
(*Suby of* DELPHI FINANCIAL GROUP INC) ★
7600 W Tidwell Rd Ste 111, Houston, TX 77040-5727
Tel (713) 468-2603 *Founded/Ownrshp* 1984
Sales NA *EMP* 350
SIC 6311 6321 Life insurance; Accident & health insurance
Ch Bd: Robert Rosenkranz
Pr: Lawrence E Daurelle
CEO: Donna Meunier
Treas: Thomas W Burghart
VP: Chad W Coulter

D-U-N-S 00-690-8636 IMP/EXP
▲ RELIANCE STEEL & ALUMINUM CO
350 S Grand Ave Ste 5100, Los Angeles, CA 90071-3421
Tel (213) 687-7700 *Founded/Ownrshp* 1939
Sales 9.3MMM *EMP* 14,000
Accts Kpmg Llp Los Angeles Califor
Tkr Sym RS *Exch* NYS
SIC 5051 Metals service centers & offices; Structural shapes, iron or steel; Steel; Sheets, metal
Pr: Gregg J Mollins
Ch Bd: David H Hannah
COO: James D Hoffman
CFO: Karla R Lewis
Ex VP: William K Sales Jr
Sr VP: William A Smith II
VP: John Inglis
VP: Donald Prebola
CIO: Susan C Borchers
Telecom Mg: Michael Martinez
IT Man: Shawn Wardle
Board of Directors: Sarah J Anderson, Thomas W Gimbel, Douglas M Hayes, Mark V Kaminski, Robert A McEvoy, Andrew G Sharkey III, Douglas W Stotlar, Leslie A Waite, Karen W Colonias John G Fi

D-U-N-S 02-805-0292
RELIANCE WELL SERVICE INC
RELIANCE DRILLING
237 Highway 79 S, Magnolia, AR 71753-9191
Tel (870) 234-2700 *Founded/Ownrshp* 1976
Sales 887.6MM[E] *EMP* 190
SIC 1389

D-U-N-S 07-828-1450
RELIANT ASSET MANAGEMENT LLC
ARIES BUILDING SYTEMS
2900 S Quincy St Ste 300a, Arlington, VA 22206-2279
Tel (703) 820-2900 *Founded/Ownrshp* 2010
Sales 85.0MM *EMP* 8
SIC 6512 Lessors of piers, docks, associated buildings & facilities
Pr: Barry A Roman
VP: Michael I Roman
Genl Mgr: Peter Eberle

D-U-N-S 02-969-1099
■ RELIANT ENERGY RETAIL HOLDINGS LLC
(*Suby of* NRG ENERGY INC) ★
1000 Main St, Houston, TX 77002-6336
Tel (713) 497-3000 *Founded/Ownrshp* 2001
Sales 676.7MM[E] *EMP* 1,800
SIC 4911

D-U-N-S 55-548-1316
RELIANT HOLDINGS LTD
10817 W County Road 60, Midland, TX 79707-9017
Tel (432) 617-4200 *Founded/Ownrshp* 1989
Sales 299.2MM[E] *EMP* 275
SIC 5169 Carbon dioxide
Pt: Fred Vanderburg Jr
Pt: Alan D Houk
Pt: Scott Vanderburg
Pt: Vance Vanderburg
CFO: Scott Smith
VP: Steve Donahue
Dir Risk M: Jay Treat
Div Mgr: Corey Prichard
Div Mgr: Ron Rice
Div Mgr: Dean Wilkerson

D-U-N-S 07-915-0274
RELIANT INVENTORY GROUP LLC
2601 S Byshr Dr Ste 725, Miami, FL 33133-5419
Tel (786) 268-4520 *Founded/Ownrshp* 2009
Sales 20.0MM *EMP* 1,000
SIC 7374 Data processing service
Sr VP: Charles Malzahn

D-U-N-S 03-081-5492
RELIANT MEDICAL GROUP INC
GRANTS & RESEARCH DEPT.
630 Plantation St, Worcester, MA 01605-2038
Tel (508) 368-5400 *Founded/Ownrshp* 1929
Sales 218.6MM[E] *EMP* 1,800[E]
SIC 8011 7352 5912 Clinic, operated by physicians; Medical equipment rental; Drug stores
CEO: Tarek Elsawy
**Treas:* Robert Yood MD
Trst: Joseph Sidari
Ofcr: Deb Gavron
Ex VP: Bruce Plummer
**Ex VP:* Alan Stoll
Ex Dir: John Gillespie Jr
Mng Dir: Robert B Swotinsky
Prac Mgr: Donna Arsenault
Prac Mgr: Donna Liseno
Genl Mgr: Mary Charpentier

D-U-N-S 19-636-9409
RELIANT SERVICE LLC
8850 Crawfordsville Rd, Indianapolis, IN 46234-1559
Tel (317) 295-6407 *Founded/Ownrshp* 2001
Sales 123.0MM *EMP* 60
SIC 1623 Cable laying construction
CEO: Doug Banning
Pr: Dan Waters
VP: Mark Hallet
VP: Kevin Miller
VP: Ralph Miller
VP Mktg: Mark Wallbom

D-U-N-S 00-696-2468
■ RELIASTAR LIFE INSURANCE CO (MN)
(*Suby of* VOYA HOLDINGS INC) ★
20 Washington Ave S, Minneapolis, MN 55401-1900
Tel (612) 372-5432 *Founded/Ownrshp* 1906, 1988
Sales NA *EMP* 198[E]
SIC 6311 6321 6324 Life insurance carriers; Life reinsurance; Health insurance carriers; Reinsurance carriers, accident & health; Group hospitalization plans
Ch: Tom McInerney
**Pr:* Donald Wayne Britton
**Treas:* David S Pendergrass
Ofcr: John Barmeyer
Ex VP: Arthur Kalita
Sr VP: Larry Erb
VP: Michael Bean
VP: Doug Benedetto
VP: Anthony Camp
VP: Gloria Carlson
VP: June Kaminski
VP: Joe McMillan
VP: James Salonia
VP: Victor Torchia

RELIGIOUS COMMUNITIES TRUST
See CHRISTIAN BROTHERS INVESTMENT SERVICES INC

RELIGIOUS INSTITUTE
See FRANCISCAN SISTER OF CHICAGO

D-U-N-S 04-663-0047
■ RELS LLC
RELS VALUATION
(*Suby of* CORELOGIC INC) ★
40 Pacifica Ste 900, Irvine, CA 92618-7487
Tel (949) 214-1000 *Founded/Ownrshp* 1998
Sales 438.9M[E] *EMP* 1,300
SIC 6531 7323 Appraiser, real estate; Commercial (mercantile) credit reporting bureau
Pr: Anand Nallathambi
**COO:* Frank D Martell

RELS VALUATION
See RELS LLC

D-U-N-S 18-214-4493 IMP/EXP
RELX INC
REED BUSINESS INFORMATION
(*Suby of* REED ELSEVIER US HOLDINGS INC) ★
230 Park Ave, New York, NY 10169-0005
Tel (212) 309-8100 *Founded/Ownrshp* 1993
Sales 7.1MMM[E] *EMP* 19,275
SIC 2721 2731 7389 7374 8748 Trade journals: publishing only, not printed on site; Books: publishing only; Trade show arrangement; Data processing & preparation; Systems analysis or design
CEO: Mark Kelsey
**Pr:* Dominic Feltham
**Pr:* Nicholas Luff
COO: Rene Olivieri
**CFO:* Duncan Palmer
**CFO:* John Poulin
**Treas:* Kenneth Fogarty
Bd of Dir: Dennis Brophy
Bd of Dir: Danis Carter
Bd of Dir: Charles Clark
Bd of Dir: Dmitrii Loukianov
Bd of Dir: Ron Mancini
Bd of Dir: Gabriel Patulea
Bd of Dir: Dave Robertson
Bd of Dir: Scott Smyers
Bd of Dir: Tom Szolyga
Bd of Dir: Jim Williams
Ex VP: Bruno Scrosati
Sr VP: Clemens Ceipek
**Sr VP:* Julie Goldweitz
**VP:* Henry Z Horbaczewski

D-U-N-S 80-443-8385
REM CENTRAL LAKES INC
(*Suby of* NATIONAL MENTOR HOLDINGS INC) ★
1802 Autumn Dr Nw, Alexandria, MN 56308-8697
Tel (320) 759-5650 *Founded/Ownrshp* 2007
Sales 5.3MM[E] *EMP* 1,139[E]
SIC 8011 Physicians' office, including specialists

REM DIE CASTING
See LACKS INDUSTRIES INC

D-U-N-S 19-427-8768 IMP/EXP
REMA FOODS INC
FOOD IMPORT GROUP
140 Sylvan Ave Ste 200, Englewood Cliffs, NJ 07632-2559
Tel (201) 947-1000 *Founded/Ownrshp* 1964
Sales 500.0MM *EMP* 55
SIC 5142 5149 5141 Packaged frozen goods; Dried or canned foods; Groceries, general line
Ch: Herbert Feuerstein
**Pr:* Robert Feuerstein
**COO:* David Rockwood
**Ex VP:* Lisa Maier
Dir IT: Joseph Laboy
Trfc Mgr: Michael Lindsay
Mktg Dir: Dave Cioffi
Manager: Karen Van Schaack
Manager: Desha Viener

D-U-N-S 00-833-3739
■ REMAN HOLDINGS LLC
(*Suby of* REMY HOLDINGS INC) ★
600 Corporation Dr, Pendleton, IN 46064-8610
Tel (800) 372-5131 *Founded/Ownrshp* 1995
Sales 106.8MM[E] *EMP* 1,500
SIC 3714 3694 Motor vehicle engines & parts; Battery charging alternators & generators
**Pr:* Thomas Snyder
**CFO:* Dave Stoll
**VP:* Susan Goldy

D-U-N-S 11-989-3001 IMP
REMBRANDT ENTERPRISES INC
REMBRANDT FOODS
(*Suby of* TAYLOR CORP) ★
1521 18th St, Spirit Lake, IA 51360-1023
Tel (712) 759-1800 *Founded/Ownrshp* 2002
Sales 239.3MM[E] *EMP* 700
SIC 2015 3556 Egg processing; Food products machinery
CEO: David Rettig
**Pr:* Glen Taylor
COO: Don Kellen
**CFO:* Brad Fullmer
**Treas:* Tom Seigfreid
VP: Janet Anderson
**VP:* Bill Kozitza

REMBRANDT FOODS
See REMBRANDT ENTERPRISES INC

D-U-N-S 01-662-3121
REMEC DEFENSE & SPACE INC
COBHAM
9404 Chesapeake Dr, San Diego, CA 92123-1388
Tel (858) 560-1301 *Founded/Ownrshp* 2005
Sales 68.8M[E] *EMP* 1,000
SIC 3812

D-U-N-S 96-188-9933
REMEDI SENIORCARE HOLDING CORP
1 Olympic Pl Ste 600, Towson, MD 21204-4110
Tel (443) 927-8400 *Founded/Ownrshp* 2003
Sales 195.5MM[E] *EMP* 515[E]
SIC 6719 Investment holding companies, except banks
CEO: Jeffrey Stamps
Ch Bd: Michael Bronsein
Pr: Michael Mahon
CFO: Thierry Amat
Ofcr: Jennifer L Hardesty
Sr VP: Alan Bronsein
Sr VP: Michael Bruno
Sr VP: Corey Gauff
Sr VP: Robert Kerr
Sr VP: Shay Roid
VP: Joseph Amy
VP: Jan Bohlmann
VP: Richard Hamel
VP: Bill Vaughan
VP: George Watson
VP: Richard Yannone

D-U-N-S 13-194-1895
REMEDI SENIORCARE OF MARYLAND LLC
WOODHAVEN HEALTH SERVICES
(*Suby of* REMEDI SENIORCARE HOLDING CORP) ★
9006 Yellow Brick Rd, Baltimore, MD 21237-2309
Tel (443) 927-8400 *Founded/Ownrshp* 2001
Sales 242.2MM[E] *EMP* 390
SIC 5122 Pharmaceuticals
CFO: Carol Coughlin
Sr VP: Kathleen Chagnon
VP: Jan Bohlmann
VP: Richard Yannone
Genl Mgr: Carol L Slas
Pharmcst: Jomarie Fields
Pharmcst: Joanne Stakias
Cert Phar: Stephanie Moga

D-U-N-S 01-826-6460
REMEDI SENIORCARE OF OHIO LLC
(*Suby of* REMEDI SENIORCARE HOLDING CORP) ★
962 S Dorset Rd, Troy, OH 45373-4705
Tel (800) 232-4239 *Founded/Ownrshp* 2008
Sales 130.4MM[E] *EMP* 190[E]
SIC 5122 Pharmaceuticals
Genl Mgr: Rene Deller

D-U-N-S 19-965-0631
REMEDIAL CONSTRUCTION SVCS LP
9977 W Sam Houston Pkwy N, Houston, TX 77064-7509
Tel (281) 955-2442 *Founded/Ownrshp* 2008
Sales 160.0MM *EMP* 376
SIC 8744 1629

D-U-N-S 06-576-9564 IMP
■ REMEL INC (WI)
THERMO FSHER SCNTFIC RMEL PDTS
(*Suby of* FISHER SCIENTIFIC INTERNATIONAL LLC) ★
12076 Santa Fe Trail Dr, Lenexa, KS 66215-3594
Tel (800) 255-6730 *Founded/Ownrshp* 1973, 1997
Sales 125.8MM[E] *EMP* 4,900
SIC 2836 Culture media
Pr: Susanne Garay
**Treas:* Anthony Hugh Smith

D-U-N-S 00-145-3216 IMP/EXP
■ REMINGTON ARMS CO LLC
(*Suby of* FGI OPERATING CO LLC) ★
870 Remington Dr, Madison, NC 27025-8331
Tel (336) 548-8700 *Founded/Ownrshp* 1816
Sales 670.4MM[E] *EMP* 2,275
SIC 3482 3484 Small arms ammunition; Small arms
CEO: Jim Marcotuli
CFO: Ron Kolka
Ofcr: Jim Davis
Ofcr: Fredric E Roth Jr
VP: Ryan Cleckner
VP: Corry Doyle
VP: Keith Enlow
VP: Jim C Gooch
VP: Kevin Graff
VP: Marlin R Jiranek
VP: Rob McCanna
VP: Greg Parker
VP: Alan Serven
VP: Darin Stafford
VP Bus Dev: Jay Stuart

REMINGTON COLLEGE
See EDUCATION AMERICA INC

D-U-N-S 80-962-3200
REMINGTON COLLEGES INC
(*Suby of* REMINGTON COLLEGE) ★
7131 Bus Pk Ln Ste 300, Lake Mary, FL 32746
Tel (407) 562-5500 *Founded/Ownrshp* 1998
Sales 155.2MM *EMP* 1,000
Accts Jpms Cox Pllc Little Rock Ar
SIC 8221 8222 Colleges & universities; Junior colleges & technical institutes
Pr: Jack Forrest

D-U-N-S 82-591-0669
REMINGTON HOSPITALITY SERVICES
14185 Dallas Pkwy # 1150, Dallas, TX 75254-1319
Tel (972) 980-2700 *Founded/Ownrshp* 2008
Sales 64.5MM[E] *EMP* 6,000[E]
SIC 7011 Hotels & motels
Ch Bd: Archie Bennett Jr
**Pr:* Mark A Sharkey
**CEO:* Monty J Bennett
**Sr VP:* Rob Haiman
**Sr VP:* Sonny Sra

D-U-N-S 80-464-3617
REMINGTON HOTEL CORP
14185 Dallas Pkwy # 1150, Dallas, TX 75254-4309
Tel (972) 980-2700 *Founded/Ownrshp* 1992
Sales 369.8MM[E] *EMP* 3,318
SIC 8741 Hotel or motel management
Pr: Monty Bennett
**Ch Bd:* Archie Bennett Jr
**COO:* Mark Sharkey
**Ex VP:* Karim Sachedina
Sr VP: Robert Haiman
Sr VP: Sherry Ramson
**Sr VP:* Cheryl Ransome
Sr VP: Brent Spaeth
VP: Jay Carley
VP: Homan Cull
VP: Chad Goodnough
VP: Stephen J Marvin
VP: Troy A Pentecost

D-U-N-S 15-065-8904
REMINGTON HYBRID SEED CO INC
4746 W Us Highway 24, Remington, IN 47977-8720
Tel (219) 261-3444 *Founded/Ownrshp* 1984
Sales 167.9MM[E] *EMP* 39
SIC 0191

D-U-N-S 82-595-0350
REMINGTON LODGING & HOSPITALITY LLC
14185 Dallas Pkwy # 1150, Dallas, TX 75254-1319
Tel (972) 980-2700 *Founded/Ownrshp* 2006
Sales 115.5MM[E] *EMP* 2,000[E]
SIC 7011 Hotels
CEO: Monty J Bennett
**Pr:* Michael Karicher
**Pr:* Mark A Sharkey
**Ch:* Archie Bennett Jr
**Ex VP:* Ladonna Gerhart

D-U-N-S 80-801-1709 EXP
■ REMINGTON OUTDOOR CO INC
(*Suby of* CERBERUS CAPITAL MANAGEMENT LP) ★
870 Remington Dr, Madison, NC 27025-8331
Tel (336) 548-8700 *Founded/Ownrshp* 1990
Sales 684.1MM[E] *EMP* 2,552
SIC 5099 3949 Firearms & ammunition, except sporting; Targets, archery & rifle shooting
CEO: George Kollitide
**Treas:* Corry Doyle
VP: Darin Stafford
VP Bus Dev: Jay Stuart
**Genl Couns:* Jonathan K Sprole

D-U-N-S 19-972-5797
REMKE MARKETS INC
1299 Cox Ave, Erlanger, KY 41018-1003
Tel (859) 594-3400 *Founded/Ownrshp* 1969
Sales 143.0MM[E] *EMP* 800
SIC 5912 Drug stores
Ch: William R Remke
**Pr:* Matthew Remke
**Treas:* Dennis J Francis
**VP:* James Schlosser
Dir Rx: Tom Litzler
VP Opers: Jim Schlosser

REMODELERS SUPPLY CENTER
See LOGAN SQUARE ALUMINUM SUPPLY INC

D-U-N-S 05-129-5186 IMP/EXP
REMY COINTREAU USA INC
(*Suby of* REMY COINTREAU)
1290 Ave Of The Americas, New York, NY 10104-0101
Tel (646) 277-2307 *Founded/Ownrshp* 1998
Sales 104.2MM[E] *EMP* 210
SIC 5182 Wine; Neutral spirits
CEO: Tom Jensen
**CEO:* Suriya Parksuwan
CFO: Denise Sloan

Ofcr: Terrell Christie
*Sr VP: Dennis Floam
VP: Maren Boot
VP: Yves De Launay
Exec: Matt Benson
Exec: Courtney Royal
Exec: Courtney Seithel
Rgnl Mgr: Jessica Fox

D-U-N-S 82-488-7400
■ REMY HOLDINGS INC
(Suby of BORGWARNER PDS (INDIANA) INC) ★
600 Corporation Dr, Pendleton, IN 46064-8610
Tel (765) 778-6499 Founded/Ownrshp 2014
Sales 2.2MMM^E EMP 6,605
SIC 3694 3714 Battery charging alternators & generators; Motor vehicle engines & parts; Motor vehicle transmissions, drive assemblies & parts; Motor vehicle electrical equipment
Pr: John J Pittas
*Ch Bd: William P Foley II
Pr: John Combes
Pr: John Mayfield
*COO: Mark R McFeely
CFO: Fred Knechtel
Bd of Dir: Lawrence Hagenbuch
Bd of Dir: Alan Stinson
*Ofcr: Shawn J Pallagi
*Sr VP: Michael L Gravelle
*VP: Barbara J Bitzer
VP: Marlen Silverii

D-U-N-S 82-489-3960 IMP/EXP
■ REMY INC
BORG WARNER
(Suby of REMY HOLDINGS INC) ★
600 Corporation Dr, Pendleton, IN 46064-8610
Tel (765) 778-6499 Founded/Ownrshp 1994
Sales 1.5MMM^E EMP 6,600
SIC 3714 3694 3625 3621 5013 Motor vehicle parts & accessories; Engine electrical equipment; Relays & industrial controls; Motors & generators; Automotive supplies & parts
Pr: David Nichols
Bd of Dir: Norman Stout
*Sr VP: Fred Knechtel
*Sr VP: Mark McFeely
*Sr VP: Jerry Mills
*Sr VP: Ed Neiheisel
*Sr VP: Shawn Pallagi
IT Man: Rhonda Stephens

D-U-N-S 80-800-7806
■ REMY INTERNATIONAL HOLDINGS INC
(Suby of REMY HOLDINGS INC) ★
600 Corporation Dr, Pendleton, IN 46064-8610
Tel (765) 778-6499 Founded/Ownrshp 1995
Sales NA EMP 3,007
SIC 6712 Bank holding companies
CEO: Jay Pittas
Ex VP: Thomas Summers
Sr VP: Gerald Mills
VP: Richard W Huibregtse
VP: Tom Ruth
Ex Dir: Mike Alma
Prgrm Mgr: Dane Carter
Plnt Mgr: Paul Newport
VP Sls: Joe Plomin
Snr Mgr: Bruce Sing

D-U-N-S 01-512-3897 IMP/EXP
■ REMY POWER PRODUCTS LLC
(Suby of REMY HOLDINGS INC) ★
3400 S Kelly Ave, Edmond, OK 73013-3803
Tel (405) 475-9800 Founded/Ownrshp 2005
Sales 83.0MM^E EMP 300
SIC 5063 Electrical apparatus & equipment
Pr: Jay Pittas
VP: Ken Bruehl
Exec: Sam Eiser
VP Opers: George Linze
Plnt Mgr: Bill Sherwood

D-U-N-S 08-044-5362
■ REMY POWER PRODUCTS LLC
(Suby of REMY INTERNATIONAL HOLDINGS INC) ★
600 Corporation Dr, Pendleton, IN 46064-8610
Tel (765) 778-6499 Founded/Ownrshp 2005
Sales 150.0MM EMP 3,000
SIC 3625 3694 3621 Motor starters & controllers, electric; Starter, electric motor; Alternators, automotive; Motors, electric
Pr: David Nichols
Treas: Michael Caruso

D-U-N-S 61-530-2163 IMP
■ REMY REMAN LLC
(Suby of REMAN HOLDINGS LLC) ★
214 Fellowship Rd, Taylorsville, MS 39168-4475
Tel (601) 785-9504 Founded/Ownrshp 1995
Sales 45.5MM^E EMP 1,166
SIC 3714 Motor vehicle electrical equipment

D-U-N-S 07-927-3828 IMP
■ REMY USA INDUSTRIES LLC
(Suby of REMY HOLDINGS INC) ★
215 Candlewood Rd, Bay Shore, NY 11706-2216
Tel (631) 969-2222 Founded/Ownrshp 2014
Sales 135.3MM^E EMP 300^E
SIC 5012 Automobiles
Pr: Vince Trapani

D-U-N-S 07-852-7372
RENAISSANCE ACQUISITION HOLDINGS LLC
272 E Deerpath Ste 206, Lake Forest, IL 60045-1935
Tel (847) 283-7772 Founded/Ownrshp 2012
Sales 744.3MM^E EMP 1,774^E
SIC 5122 Pharmaceuticals
Pr: Pierre Frchette
CFO: Leonard Kuhr
*CFO: Christine Woolgar
*Sr VP: Steve Merkin
*VP: Raymond Canole

D-U-N-S 06-769-3205
RENAISSANCE CHARITABLE FOUNDATION INC
SEI GIVING FUND
8910 Purdue Rd Ste 550, Indianapolis, IN 46268-6117
Tel (317) 843-5400 Founded/Ownrshp 2000
Sales 164.5MM EMP 3
SIC 8699 Charitable organization
Pr: Greg Baker
*Treas: Steven R Ko
VP: Margae Diamond

D-U-N-S 19-560-1823
RENAISSANCE CHARTER SCHOOL INC
6245 N Federal Hwy # 500, Fort Lauderdale, FL 33308-1998
Tel (954) 202-3500 Founded/Ownrshp 1998
Sales 101.5MM EMP 1
Accts Keefe Mccullough & Co Llp Cpas
SIC 8211 School board
Ch: Ken D Haiko

D-U-N-S 13-304-3781
■ RENAISSANCE FOOD GROUP LLC
(Suby of CALAVO GROWERS INC) ★
11020 White Rock Rd # 100, Rancho Cordova, CA 95670-6402
Tel (916) 638-8825 Founded/Ownrshp 2002
Sales 109.4MM^E EMP 350
SIC 2099 Salads, fresh or refrigerated
Pr: James S Catchot
Pr: Donald Ochoa
COO: Jim Gibson
CFO: Ken Catchot

D-U-N-S 18-645-6091
RENAISSANCE HEALTH CARE CORP
RENAISSANCE VILLAGE
6050 S 800 E-92, Fort Wayne, IN 46814-9201
Tel (260) 625-3545 Founded/Ownrshp 1988
Sales 619.1MM EMP 120
SIC 8052 8051 Intermediate care facilities; Skilled nursing care facilities
Pr: Michael Mohrman
*Sec: Kevin Kelley
Nrsg Dir: Julie White

D-U-N-S 15-134-1583 IMP
RENAISSANCE HOTEL OPERATING CO INC
10400 Fernwood Rd, Bethesda, MD 20817-1102
Tel (301) 380-3000 Founded/Ownrshp 1998
Sales 915.5MM^E EMP 32,000
SIC 7011 8741 6794 Hotels & motels; Hotel or motel management; Franchises, selling or licensing
Ex VP: Elizabeth Abdoo
VP: Jeffrey S Clark
*VP: Frank Faden
VP: Larry K Harvey
VP: Craig Mason

D-U-N-S 80-916-8219 IMP
RENAISSANCE JEWELRY NEW YORK INC
VERIGOLD JEWELRY
(Suby of RENAISSANCE JEWELLERY LIMITED)
3 E 54th St Ste 603, New York, NY 10022-3131
Tel (212) 986-7287 Founded/Ownrshp 2007
Sales 93.0MM EMP 46
Accts Prajapati Associates Llp New
SIC 5094 Jewelry & precious stones
Pr: Suhel Kothari
*CEO: Sumit Shah
*CFO: Nilesh Shah
Sr VP: Samir Sanghani
VP: Amy Rossman
*Genl Mgr: Bhavin Shah
VP Sls: AVI Levy

D-U-N-S 07-774-4035 IMP
RENAISSANCE LAKEWOOD LLC
RENAISSANCE PHARMACEUTICALS
(Suby of RENAISSANCE SSP HOLDINGS INC) ★
1200 Paco Way, Lakewood, NJ 08701-5938
Tel (732) 367-9000 Founded/Ownrshp 2012
Sales 224.5MM^E EMP 500
SIC 2834 2844 2675 Pharmaceutical preparations; Cold remedies; Lip balms; Ointments; Toilet preparations; Mouthwashes; Shampoos, rinses, conditioners: hair; Deodorants, personal; Die-cut paper & board
Pr: Paul Johnson
*COO: John W Feik
*Sr VP: Mark Fite
*VP: Rick Bentzinger
*VP: Kuljit Bhatia
*VP: Gene Ciolfi
QA Dir: Lucy Nobile
Sfty Dirs: Gene Shimek
Ql Cn Mgr: Lucy Noble

D-U-N-S 18-922-1526 IMP
RENAISSANCE LEARNING INC
2911 Peach St, Wisconsin Rapids, WI 54494-1905
Tel (715) 424-4242 Founded/Ownrshp 1986
Sales 182.1MM^E EMP 893
SIC 7372 5072 Educational computer software; Hardware
CEO: John J Lynch Jr
*CFO: Mary T Minch
*Chf Mktg O: D Andrew Myers
Sr VP: Alexa Posny
*VP: Gene M Kerns
*CTO: Mark A Angel
Board of Directors: John Katzman

D-U-N-S 07-839-7592
RENAISSANCE OFFSHORE LLC
920 Mmrial Cy Way Ste 800, Houston, TX 77024
Tel (832) 333-7700 Founded/Ownrshp 2011
Sales 150.0MM EMP 36
SIC 1389 1311 Oil field services; Natural gas production
CEO: Jeffrey Soine
*CFO: Brian Romere
*VP: Skip Ward
Snr Mgr: Matt McLeod

RENAISSANCE PHARMACEUTICALS
See RENAISSANCE LAKEWOOD LLC

D-U-N-S 07-876-1795
RENAISSANCE SSP HOLDINGS INC
(Suby of RENAISSANCE ACQUISITION HOLDINGS LLC) ★
272 E Deerpath Ste 350, Lake Forest, IL 60045-5326
Tel (210) 476-8194 Founded/Ownrshp 2012
Sales 224.5MM^E EMP 504
SIC 2834 Pharmaceutical preparations
Pr: Pierre Frechette
*Treas: Christine Woolgar
*VP: Glenn Kues

D-U-N-S 07-302-0919
RENAISSANCE TECHNOLOGIES LLC
800 3rd Ave Fl 33, New York, NY 10022-7659
Tel (212) 821-1502 Founded/Ownrshp 1982
Sales 92.2MM^E EMP 300
SIC 6722 6282 Management investment, open-end; Investment advice
Ch Bd: James H Simons
*CEO: Robert Mercer
*COO: James Rowen
Mng Dir: Jack Coan

RENAISSANCE VILLAGE
See RENAISSANCE HEALTH CARE CORP

D-U-N-S 96-533-2414
RENAISSANCE WOODWORKING CO INC
13 Walnut St Ne, Decatur, AL 35601-1745
Tel (256) 308-1231 Founded/Ownrshp 1994
Sales 144.0MM EMP 20
SIC 1542 1521 Nonresidential construction; Single-family housing construction
Pr: Scott Schoel
Off Mgr: Karen Graham

D-U-N-S 19-424-8969
RENAISSANCE WORLDWIDE INC
(Suby of AQUENT LLC) ★
711 Boylston St, Boston, MA 02116-2616
Tel (617) 535-5000 Founded/Ownrshp 1986
Sales 32.9MM^E EMP 3,000
SIC 7363 8742 7379 7361 8748 7371 Labor resource services; Management information systems consultant; Data processing consultant; Employment agencies; Business consulting; Computer software systems analysis & design, custom
CEO: G Drew Conway
COO: Cheryl Berry
*CFO: Joseph Pesce
Treas: John S Sales
VP: David Daganhardt
VP: Steve Dempsey
*VP: Christopher D T Guiffre
VP: Ed Krug
VP: Denise Lubaway
VP: Tom Reynolds
Mng Dir: Jenny Norwood

D-U-N-S 04-301-6281
RENAL CARE GROUP INC
(Suby of FRESENIUS MEDICAL CARE NORTH) ★
1 N Broadway Ste 100a, Denver, CO 80203-3973
Tel (303) 765-1699 Founded/Ownrshp 1999
Sales 86.1MM^E EMP 20
SIC 8082 Home health care services
Ex Dir: Kirsten Jensen
*Genl Mgr: Michelle Parker

D-U-N-S 93-264-7886
RENAL CARE GROUP INC
(Suby of FRESENIUS MEDICAL CARE AG & CO. KGAA)
2525 West End Ave Ste 600, Nashville, TN 37203-1774
Tel (615) 345-5500 Founded/Ownrshp 2006
Sales 149.6MM^E EMP 6,603
SIC 8092 Kidney dialysis centers
*Ch Bd: William P Johnston
COO: Mike Burney
CFO: David Dill
*Chf Mktg O: Raymond Hakim MD PHD
Ex VP: David Mdill
Ex VP: David Mmaloney
Ex VP: Timothy Pmartin
*Sr VP: Douglas B Chappell
VP: Jennifer Baldock
VP: Steve Oa'bryan
VP: Michael Cerino
VP: ARI Chompre
VP: Christi Dgriffin
VP: Kevin Dmanis
VP: William Dwoolverton
VP: Mignon Early
VP: Forrest Ggardner
VP: Christi Griffin
VP: Donna Hughes
VP: Clifford Jaebker
VP: Mark Jdonati

D-U-N-S 93-162-2732
RENAL RESEARCH INSTITUTE LLC
315 E 62nd St Fl 4, New York, NY 10065-7767
Tel (212) 360-6579 Founded/Ownrshp 1997
Sales 41.7MM^E EMP 1,500
SIC 8092 Kidney dialysis centers
Exec: Linda Donald

D-U-N-S 19-614-5221
■ RENAL TREATMENT CENTERS INC
(Suby of DAVITA INC) ★
601 Hawaii St, El Segundo, CA 90245-4814
Tel (310) 536-2400 Founded/Ownrshp 1998
Sales 18.3MM^E EMP 1,000
SIC 8733 Medical research
Ch: Kent Thiry
COO: David Barry
CFO: Richard Whitney

D-U-N-S 02-769-5732
■ RENAL TREATMENT CENTERS-ILLINOIS INC
OWENSBORO DIALYSIS CENTER
(Suby of DAVITA INC) ★
1930 E Parrish Ave, Owensboro, KY 42303-1443
Tel (270) 926-0120 Founded/Ownrshp 2003
Sales 41.3MM^E EMP 1,168^E
SIC 8092 Kidney dialysis centers
Pr: Kent J Thiry

D-U-N-S 83-254-4089
■ RENAL TREATMENT CENTERS-SOUTHEAST LP
GULF SHORES DIALYSIS CENTER
(Suby of DAVITA INC) ★
3947 Gulf Shores Pkwy, Gulf Shores, AL 36542-2735
Tel (251) 967-2205 Founded/Ownrshp 2009
Sales 57.3MM^E EMP 2,848^E
SIC 8092 Kidney dialysis centers
Mng Pt: Kent J Thiry

D-U-N-S 00-696-4886
■ RENASANT BANK
(Suby of RENASANT CORP) ★
209 Troy St, Tupelo, MS 38804-4827
Tel (662) 680-1001 Founded/Ownrshp 1904
Sales NA EMP 828
SIC 6022 6162 State commercial banks; Mortgage bankers
Ch Bd: E Robinson Mc Graw
*Ch Bd: Robert C Leake
Pr: Ken Davis
Pr: Linda Green
Pr: Jeff Hudson
*Pr: Mitchell Waycaster
*CFO: Kevin Chapman
Ofcr: Matt Gillis
Ofcr: Nathan Hardy
Ofcr: Jerri Pannell
*Ex VP: James Gray
Ex VP: Greg Hadaway
*Ex VP: Stuart R Johnson
*Ex VP: Harold Livingston
Ex VP: David Mays
*Ex VP: H L Robinson
*Ex VP: Claude H Springfield III
Sr VP: Tracey Morant Adams
Sr VP: Jim Brown
Sr VP: Terry L Bullard
Sr VP: Clay Hart

D-U-N-S 11-974-9786
▲ RENASANT CORP
209 Troy St, Tupelo, MS 38804-4827
Tel (662) 680-1001 Founded/Ownrshp 1982
Sales NA EMP 1,996^E
Tkr Sym RNST Exch NGS
SIC 6029 6411 Commercial banks; Insurance agents, brokers & service
Ch Bd: E Robinson McGraw
Pr: C Mitchell Waycaster
CFO: Kevin D Chapman
Ex VP: J Scott Cochran
Ex VP: Stephen M Corban
*Ex VP: R Rick Hart
Board of Directors: Neal A Holland Jr, George H Booth II, J Niles McNeel, Frank B Brooks, Hugh S Potts Jr, Hollis C Cheek, Fred F Sharpe, John M Creekmore, Michael D Shmerling, Albert J Dale III, Jill V Deer, Marshall H Dickerson, John T Foy, Richard L Heyer Jr

D-U-N-S 00-204-6514 IMP
RENCO ELECTRONICS INC (FL)
595 International Pl, Rockledge, FL 32955-4200
Tel (321) 637-1000 Founded/Ownrshp 1955
Sales 161.2MM^E EMP 1,110
SIC 5065 3677

D-U-N-S 14-785-4152 IMP/EXP
RENCO GROUP INC
1 Rockefeller Plz Fl 29, New York, NY 10020-2021
Tel (212) 541-6000 Founded/Ownrshp 1975
Sales 4.5MMM^E EMP 11,551
SIC 3312 3316 2514 2511 3171 3496 Sheet or strip, steel, cold-rolled: own hot-rolled; Corrugating iron & steel, cold-rolled; Metal kitchen & dining room furniture; Wood household furniture; Kitchen & dining room furniture; Handbags, women's; Cages, wire
Pr: Ira Leon Rennert
*Ch: ARI Rennert
*Ex VP: Marvin Koenig
*VP: Roger L Fay
*VP: John Siegel

D-U-N-S 09-853-0603 IMP
RENESAS ELECTRONICS AMERICA INC
(Suby of RENESAS ELECTRONICS CORPORATION)
2801 Scott Blvd, Santa Clara, CA 95050-2549
Tel (408) 588-6000 Founded/Ownrshp 2010
Sales 0.0^E EMP 1,169
SIC 5065 8731 5731 5045 8711 Semiconductor devices; Electronic research; Radio, television & electronic stores; Computers, peripherals & software; Engineering services
CEO: Ali Sebt
VP: Hideo Kameda
*VP: David Weigand
Exec: Bunka Tahara
Prin: Mohan Rajasekhar
Rgnl Mgr: Mike Stocker
Dept Mgr: Katsushi Asahina
Dept Mgr: Yen W Chen
Dept Mgr: Yuji Hatano
Dept Mgr: Sakae Ito
Dept Mgr: Tsutomu Tsuboi

D-U-N-S 00-419-8668
▲ RENEWABLE ENERGY GROUP INC
416 S Bell Ave, Ames, IA 50010-7711
Tel (515) 239-8000 Founded/Ownrshp 1996
Sales 1.3MMM EMP 368
Accts Deloitte & Touche Llp Des Moi
Tkr Sym REGI Exch NGM
SIC 2911 2869 Diesel fuels; Industrial organic chemicals
Pr: Daniel J OH
*Ch Bd: Jeffrey Stroburg
CFO: Chad Stone
Treas: Natalie Lischer
Ex VP: Harold Ahrenholtz
VP: David Elsenbast
Genl Mgr: Gary Hare
VP Mfg: Brad Albin
S&M/VP: Gary Haer
Sls Dir: Jon Scharingson

D-U-N-S 01-729-0430
RENEWABLE ENERGY SYSTEMS
(*Suby of* RENEWABLE ENERGY SYSTEMS LIMITED)
11101 W 120th Ave Ste 400, Broomfield, CO 80021-3436
Tel (303) 439-4200 *Founded/Ownrshp* 1998
Sales 183.2MM^E *EMP* 367^E
SIC 8731 Energy research
Ex VP: Brian Evans
Sfty Mgr: Marcus Johnshoy

D-U-N-S 07-370-1898 IMP
RENEWABLE WATER RESOURCES
MAULDIN ROAD WRRF
561 Mauldin Rd, Greenville, SC 29607-4208
Tel (864) 299-4000 *Founded/Ownrshp* 1925
Sales 88.3MM *EMP* 190
Accts Cherry Bekaert Llp Greenville
SIC 4952 Sewerage systems
Ch: L Gary Gilliam
**V Ch:* Daniel K Holliday
**Treas:* Ray C Overstreet
**Ex Dir:* Ray T Orvin Jr

RENEWAL PARTS MAINTENANCE
See MECHANICAL DYNAMICS & ANALYSIS LTD

RENEWBLE ENRGY SYSTEMS AMRICAS
See RES AMERICA CONSTRUCTION INC

D-U-N-S 61-663-1516
RENEX CORP
(*Suby of* RENAL CARE GROUP INC) ★
201 Alhambra Cir Ste 800, Coral Gables, FL 33134-5108
Tel (305) 448-2044 *Founded/Ownrshp* 2010
Sales 20.7MM^E *EMP* 2,269^E
SIC 8092 Kidney dialysis centers
Prin: Richard Tuller
CFO: Orestes Lugo

D-U-N-S 00-321-9318 IMP/EXP
RENFRO CORP (NC)
661 Linville Rd, Mount Airy, NC 27030-3101
Tel (336) 719-8000 *Founded/Ownrshp* 1921
Sales 1.3MMM^E *EMP* 5,500
SIC 2252 Socks; Tights & leg warmers
Pr: Andrew L Kilby Jr
CFO: Dave Dinkin
**CFO:* David H Dinkins
Ex VP: Dave Dinkins
**Sr VP:* Susan C Bevard
**Sr VP:* Charlie M Nichols
VP: Ian Beckstead
**VP:* G Michael Bowman
**VP:* Dave Green
VP: David S Green
VP: Dan Harrison
VP: Beckstead Ian
VP: Dean Parker
VP: Jay Robinson
VP: Ronnie Wheeler
VP: Peter Worcester
VP Bus Dev: Brad Ballentine
Dir: Mabel Myers
Dir Bus: Danny Smith

D-U-N-S 18-176-1974 IMP/EXP
RENKERT OIL LLC
3817 Main St, Morgantown, PA 19543-9641
Tel (610) 286-8010 *Founded/Ownrshp* 1987
Sales 166.9MM^E *EMP* 21
SIC 5172 Lubricating oils & greases
Treas: Michael Renker
Sr VP: Nick Livanos
VP Sls: Gerry Jackson

D-U-N-S 04-789-2252
RENO DISPOSAL CO
SPARKS SANITATION
100 Vassar St, Reno, NV 89502-2815
Tel (775) 329-8822 *Founded/Ownrshp* 1998
Sales 125.3MM^E *EMP* 420
SIC 4953 Refuse collection & disposal services
Pr: Douglas Soby
**Treas:* Ronald H Jones

D-U-N-S 15-083-2616 IMP
RENO JONES INC
2373 N Watney Way, Fairfield, CA 94533-6746
Tel (707) 422-4300 *Founded/Ownrshp* 1993
Sales 100.0MM *EMP* 48
SIC 5199 5085 3221

D-U-N-S 15-340-3076
RENOWN HEALTH
1155 Mill St, Reno, NV 89502-1576
Tel (775) 982-4100 *Founded/Ownrshp* 1985
Sales 80.1MM *EMP* 3,129
SIC 8062

D-U-N-S 05-446-6339
RENOWN REGIONAL MEDICAL CENTER (NV)
(*Suby of* RENOWN HEALTH) ★
1155 Mill St, Reno, NV 89502-1576
Tel (775) 982-4100 *Founded/Ownrshp* 1862, 1985
Sales 575.0MM *EMP* 2,500
SIC 8062

D-U-N-S 96-593-4073
RENOWN SOUTH MEADOWS MEDICAL CENTER
1155 Mill St, Reno, NV 89502-1576
Tel (775) 982-4404 *Founded/Ownrshp* 2010
Sales 115.6MM *EMP* 2
Accts Eide Badly Lp Minneapolis Mn
SIC 8099 Health & allied services
Prin: Dawn Ahner
CFO: Cora Downard
Exec: Diane Bates
Sls&Mrk Ex: Kimberly Cooney

D-U-N-S 08-046-9091
RENSSELAER COUNTY
1600 7th Ave Ste 3, Troy, NY 12180-3410
Tel (518) 270-2626 *Founded/Ownrshp* 1791, 1971
Sales NA *EMP* 1,600
Accts Drescher & Malecki Llp Cheekt
SIC 9111 Executive offices;
Exec: Kathy Jimino

D-U-N-S 00-243-0742 IMP
RENSSELAER POLYTECHNIC INSTITUTE (NY)
110 8th St, Troy, NY 12180-3522
Tel (518) 276-6000 *Founded/Ownrshp* 1824
Sales 499.1MM *EMP* 1,500
SIC 8221 College, except junior
Pr: Shirley Ann Jackson
Pr: Kelli Hudson
Pr: Joseph Medina
**Treas:* David Gaume
Top Exec: Frank Spear
VP: Kristin Bennett
VP: Francine Berman
VP: David Brond
VP: Graig Eastin
**VP:* Virginia C Gregg
VP: Virginia Gregg
VP: Meghan Helm
VP: Francesca Huber
VP: John Kolb
VP: Aditi Malhotra
VP: Curtis Powell
VP: Anna Thonis
VP: William Walker
Assoc Dir: Jackie Ellsworth
Assoc Dir: Ian Farrell
Assoc Dir: Kevin C Readdean

RENT A TIRE
See RENT A WHEEL

D-U-N-S 96-508-4502 IMP
RENT A WHEEL
RENT A TIRE
11726 San Vicente Blvd # 400, Los Angeles, CA 90049-5044
Tel (818) 786-7906 *Founded/Ownrshp* 1996
Sales 124.0MM *EMP* 900
Accts Banderi Beach Lim And Cleland
SIC 5531 Automotive tires
Pr: John Bowlin
**CFO:* Matt Seaburn
**Prin:* Don Sabino
Dist Mgr: Roger Gaeta

D-U-N-S 09-971-0246
■ **RENT-A-CENTER FRANCHISING INTERNATIONAL INC**
RAC
(*Suby of* RENT-A-CENTER INC) ★
5501 Headquarters Dr, Plano, TX 75024-5837
Tel (972) 403-4900 *Founded/Ownrshp* 1996
Sales 200.0MM *EMP* 22^E
SIC 5722 5531 Household appliance stores; Automotive tires
Pr: Catherine Skula
**VP:* Michael Landry

D-U-N-S 61-275-9738
▲ **RENT-A-CENTER INC**
5501 Headquarters Dr, Plano, TX 75024-5846
Tel (972) 801-1100 *Founded/Ownrshp* 1986
Sales 3.2MMM *EMP* 24,300
Tkr Sym RCII *Exch* NGS
SIC 7359 6794 Equipment rental & leasing; Appliance rental; Furniture rental; Home entertainment equipment rental; Franchises, selling or licensing
CEO: Robert D Davis
**Ch Bd:* Mark E Speese
CFO: Guy J Constant
Treas: Chad Bentley
Ofcr: Christopher A Korst
Div VP: Stephen McKinley
Ex VP: Mark E Denman
Ex VP: Bobby Pope
Ex VP: Charles J White
Ex VP: Jim York
Sr VP: John F Butler
Sr VP: Angela Yochem
VP: David G Ewbank
VP: Dan Glasky
VP: Fred E Herman
VP: Michael Muth
VP: Herman Nell
VP: Bill Nutt
VP: Christian Roman
VP: Maureen Short
VP: Ned Villemarette
Board of Directors: Michael J Gade, Jeffery M Jackson, J V Lentell, Steven L Pepper, Leonard H Roberts, Paula Stern

D-U-N-S 83-690-5927 IMP
RENT-A-TIRE LP
RENT-A-WHEEL
11726 San Vicente Blvd # 400, Los Angeles, CA 90049-5044
Tel (818) 786-7906 *Founded/Ownrshp* 2002
Sales 104.7MM^E *EMP* 280
Accts Banderi Beach Lim Cleland
SIC 5531 3312 Automotive & home supply stores; Automotive tires; Wheels
Mng Pt: Don Sabino
Pt: John Bowlin
CFO: Matt Seaburn

RENT-A-WHEEL
See RENT-A-TIRE LP

D-U-N-S 96-206-9233 IMP/EXP
RENTECH BOILER SYSTEMS INC
5025 E Business 20, Abilene, TX 79601
Tel (325) 672-3400 *Founded/Ownrshp* 1996
Sales 103.3MM^E *EMP* 98
SIC 5074 Boilers, power (industrial)
VP: Mark A Coleman
**VP:* Mark Colman
VP: John Hayes
IT Man: Mark Kiser
Sls Mgr: Lee King

D-U-N-S 14-948-8496
▲ **RENTECH INC**
10880 Wilshire Blvd # 1101, Los Angeles, CA 90024-4112
Tel (310) 571-9800 *Founded/Ownrshp* 1981
Sales 295.8MM *EMP* 939^E
Tkr Sym RTK *Exch* NAS
SIC 2999 2873 6794 Waxes, petroleum: not produced in petroleum refineries; Nitrogenous fertilizers; Patent buying, licensing, leasing
Pr: Keith Forman
**Ch Bd:* Halbert S Washburn
**Pr:* Keith B Forman
CFO: Jeffrey R Spain
Sr VP: Joseph V Herold
Sr VP: Colin M Morris
VP: Colin Morris
VP: Bill Regan
Counsel: Patrick Erickson
Board of Directors: Michael S Burke, Wesley K Clark, Kevin Rendino, Ronald M Sega, Edward M Stern, John A Williams

D-U-N-S 01-449-5014 IMP/EXP
RENTOKIL NORTH AMERICA INC
J.C. EHRLICH
(*Suby of* RENTOKIL INITIAL PLC)
1125 Berkshire Blvd # 150, Wyomissing, PA 19610-1218
Tel (610) 372-9700 *Founded/Ownrshp* 2007
Sales 895.0MM^E *EMP* 4,500
SIC 7342 0781 5191 Pest control services; Landscape counseling & planning; Horticulture services; Pesticides
Pr: John Myers
**Treas:* Hillary Wilson
**VP:* Mallon Charles
Opers Mgr: Herman Knerr
VP Mktg: Glen Smerdon
VP Sls: William Dickerson

D-U-N-S 07-573-9649
RENTON SCHOOL DISTRICT
300 Sw 7th St, Renton, WA 98057-2307
Tel (425) 204-2300 *Founded/Ownrshp* 1878
Sales 186.3MM *EMP* 1,846
Accts Trou Kelley Olympia Washingt
SIC 8211 Public elementary school; Public junior high school; Public senior high school; School for physically handicapped
Exec: Jon Stadler
CTO: Bill Hulten
Trfc Dir: Ida Deckert
Pr Dir: Randy Matheson
Teacher Pr: Debra Tito
Psych: Heather Krupp
HC Dir: Laura Widdice

D-U-N-S 78-935-7894 IMP
RENTPATH INC
PRIMEDIA
(*Suby of* PITTSBURGH HOLDINGS LLC) ★
950 E Paces Ferry Rd Ne # 2600, Atlanta, GA 30326-1386
Tel (678) 421-3000 *Founded/Ownrshp* 2011
Sales 253.0MM *EMP* 800
SIC 6531 Real estate listing services
Pr: Marc Lefar
Pr: Steven Aster
Pr: Jamie Clymer
Pr: David Ferm
Pr: Greg Goff
Pr: Arlene Mayfield
Pr: Steve Parr
Pr: H James Ritts III
Pr: Jim Ritts
CEO: Martin E Maleska
COO: Alan Glass
CFO: David P Kirchhoff
CFO: Kim R Payne
Treas: William Mayer
Chf Mktg O: Clark Wood
Ofcr: Blake Pierson
Sr VP: J Michael Barber
Sr VP: Al Crolius
Sr VP: Marlon Starr
VP: George Alleyne
VP: Scott Asher

D-U-N-S 05-002-0122
■ **RENTRAK CORP**
(*Suby of* COMSCORE INC) ★
7700 Ne Ambassador Pl # 300, Portland, OR 97220-1385
Tel (503) 284-7581 *Founded/Ownrshp* 2016
Sales 102.9MM *EMP* 400^E
SIC 7372 Prepackaged software; Business oriented computer software; Application computer software
CEO: William P Livek
Pr: David Paiko
COO: David I Chemerow
Sr VP: Evan Goldfarb
Sr VP: Carol Hinnant
VP: Dagmar Fischer
VP: Dawne Richards
Dir Bus: Cory Sher
Ex Dir: Jerry Cgeit
DP Exec: Darryl Martin
QA Dir: Rick Vandercar

RENTZ OIL
See EDEN OIL CO INC

D-U-N-S 55-707-0364
■ **RENZ NICHOLS FAMILY LIMITED PARTNERSHIP**
(*Suby of* FIS) ★
11601 Roosevelt Blvd N, Saint Petersburg, FL 33716-2202
Tel (727) 573-7848 *Founded/Ownrshp* 2001
Sales 86.2MM^E *EMP* 1,900
SIC 7389 Check validation service
Pr: Renz Nichols
VP: Larry Towe

D-U-N-S 10-710-0208
RENZENBERGER INC
(*Suby of* PETERSON MANUFACTURING CO) ★
14325 W 95th St, Lenexa, KS 66215-5210
Tel (913) 631-0450 *Founded/Ownrshp* 1991
Sales 113.8MM^E *EMP* 1,760
SIC 4131 4119 Intercity & rural bus transportation; Local passenger transportation
**Pr:* William M Smith
**VP:* Phil Simco
Dir Bus: Christine Sanders
Rgnl Mgr: Douglas Dock
Rgnl Mgr: Jack Pursley
Rgnl Mgr: Stanley Smith
Snr Mgr: Frank Homan

D-U-N-S 08-328-6617
RENZI BROS INC
RENZI FOOD SERVICE
901 Rail Dr, Watertown, NY 13601-2379
Tel (315) 755-5610 *Founded/Ownrshp* 1977
Sales 178.9MM^E *EMP* 140
SIC 5141 Food brokers
Pr: John M Renzi
CFO: Steve Zaremba
**VP:* David Renzi
VP Mktg: Angie Marra

RENZI FOOD SERVICE
See RENZI BROS INC

REO NETWORK
See CLEARCAPITAL.COM INC

D-U-N-S 01-075-7750
REOPCO INC
ROAD RANGER
4930 E State St Ste 1, Rockford, IL 61108-2289
Tel (815) 387-1700 *Founded/Ownrshp* 1997
Sales 110.6MM^E *EMP* 975
SIC 5411 5541 Convenience stores; Truck stops
Pr: Daniel J Arnold
**Treas:* Jason Brincks
Ex VP: Richard McMahon

D-U-N-S 10-708-7157 IMP
REPCON INC
7501 Up River Rd, Corpus Christi, TX 78409-2807
Tel (361) 289-6342 *Founded/Ownrshp* 1983
Sales 114.1MM^E *EMP* 200
SIC 1629 1389 Chemical plant & refinery construction; Oil field services
Pr: Robert E Parker
**CFO:* Kirby Morgan
**Treas:* John K Morgan
VP: Mike Blundell
VP: Robert Cagle
**VP:* Josh Causey
IT Man: Robert Morgan

D-U-N-S 03-723-1099 IMP
■ **REPCONSTRICKLAND INC** (TX)
ALTAIRSTRICKLAND
(*Suby of* EMCOR GROUP INC) ★
1605 S Battleground Rd, La Porte, TX 77571-9491
Tel (281) 478-6200 *Founded/Ownrshp* 1987, 2013
Sales 143.1MM *EMP* 400
SIC 1541 Renovation, remodeling & repairs: industrial buildings
Pr: Jeffrey Webber
**CFO:* Scott Creasman
**VP:* James Robinson
Dir Risk M: Steve Rothbauer
**Area Mgr:* Phillip Sain
Sfty Mgr: Terry Boer
Opers Mgr: Billy Dobbins
Ql Cn Mgr: Qc M Davani
Ql Cn Mgr: Tony Pisarz
Ql Cn Mgr: Andres Rivera
Ql Cn Mgr: Buck Tingle
Board of Directors: Ken Beckemeyer

D-U-N-S 60-279-0388
REPLACEMENT PARTS INC
CROW-BURLINGAME
1901 E Roosevelt Rd, Little Rock, AR 72206-2533
Tel (501) 375-1215 *Founded/Ownrshp* 1988
Sales 335.5MM^E *EMP* 1,200
SIC 5013 Automotive supplies & parts
CEO: Bill Schlatterer
**Ch Bd:* E Fletcher Lord Jr
**Treas:* Jennifer Rainwater
**VP:* Ginger Guinee
VP: Tom Singleton
Exec: Martha Harper
MIS Dir: Debbie Kimbrell
IT Man: Tracey Hart
Mktg Mgr: Fletcher Lord

D-U-N-S 04-436-3026 IMP/EXP
REPLACEMENTS LTD (NC)
1089 Knox Rd, Mc Leansville, NC 27301-9228
Tel (336) 697-3000 *Founded/Ownrshp* 1981
Sales 83.7MM *EMP* 1,000
Accts Smith Leonard Pllc High Point
SIC 5961 Mail order house
CEO: Robert L Page
**Pr:* Ken Walter
**Treas:* Kelly M Smith
**Ex VP:* D Scott Fleming
Ex VP: Scott Fleming
**VP:* Dale E Frederiksen
VP: Robin Long
VP: Tonya Minor
VP: Julie Schindler
**VP:* James W Whitley
Genl Mgr: Garrett Jackson

D-U-N-S 02-256-7668
REPLANET LLC
(*Suby of* TOMRA OF NORTH AMERICA (INC)) ★
800 N Haven Ave Ste 120, Ontario, CA 91764-4951
Tel (951) 520-1700 *Founded/Ownrshp* 2011
Sales 197.1MM^E *EMP* 600
SIC 5084 4953 Recycling machinery & equipment; Refuse systems
COO: Rod Rougelot
**CFO:* Janette Gorman

*VP: Matt Millhiser
Mktg Mgr: Hege Fossgard

D-U-N-S 01-330-8119
▲ REPLIGEN CORP
41 Seyon St Ste 100, Waltham, MA 02453-8358
Tel (781) 250-0111 Founded/Ownrshp 1981
Sales 83.5MM EMP 168E
Tkr Sym RGEN Exch NGM
SIC 2836 Biological products, except diagnostic
Pr: Tony J Hunt
*Ch Bd: Karen A Dawes
CFO: Jon K Snodgres
Sr VP: Ralf Kuriyel
VP: Howard Benjamin
VP: Michael Hall
Assoc Dir: Siddhi Shah
Assoc Dir: William Wilde
Board of Directors: Nicolas M Barthelemy, Glenn L Cooper, John G Cox, Glenn P Muir, Thomas F Ryan Jr

D-U-N-S 80-548-6276 IMP/EXP
REPSOL ENERGY NORTH AMERICA CORP
(Suby of REPSOL SA.)
2455 Tech Forest Blvd, The Woodlands, TX 77381-5205
Tel (832) 442-1000 Founded/Ownrshp 2005
Sales 696.5MME EMP 1,400
SIC 1321 Natural gas liquids
Pr: Phil Ribbeck
Ofcr: Tamara Saront
IT Man: Tony Katz
Opers Mgr: Vanessa Saunders
Counsel: M Perales
Snr Mgr: Ortin Anna

D-U-N-S 80-548-7290 IMP
REPSOL SERVICES CO
(Suby of REPSOL SA.)
2455 Tech Forest Blvd, The Woodlands, TX 77381-5205
Tel (832) 442-1000 Founded/Ownrshp 2005
Sales 318.0MME EMP 243E
SIC 1382 Oil & gas exploration services
CEO: Antonia Brufau
*Pr: Ramon Hernan
Dir IT: Ignacio Arnaiz
Dir IT: Bill Hardham

D-U-N-S 83-266-1263
■ REPUBLIC AIRLINE INC
REPUBLIC AIRWAYS
(Suby of REPUBLIC AIRWAYS HOLDINGS INC) ★
8909 Purdue Rd Ste 300, Indianapolis, IN 46268-3152
Tel (317) 484-6000 Founded/Ownrshp 2004
Sales 151.8MME EMP 2,000E
SIC 4512 Air transportation, scheduled
Ch Bd: Bryan K Bedford
*Pr: Wayne C Heller
Pr: Drew Skaff
COO: Heather Stone
*CFO: Robert H Cooper
*CFO: Timothy P Dooley
Ofcr: Wade Heverly
*Ofcr: Sean Menke
Ofcr: Cody Snyder
*VP: Joseph P Allman
VP: Thomas Duffy
VP: Don Osmundson

REPUBLIC AIRWAYS
See REPUBLIC AIRLINE INC

D-U-N-S 10-417-8475
▲ REPUBLIC AIRWAYS HOLDINGS INC
8909 Purdue Rd Ste 300, Indianapolis, IN 46268-3152
Tel (317) 484-6000 Founded/Ownrshp 1996
Sales 1.3MMM EMP 5,581
Tkr Sym RJETQ Exch OTC
SIC 4512 Air passenger carrier, scheduled; Air cargo carrier, scheduled
Ch Bd: Bryan K Bedford
COO: Paul K Kinstedt
CFO: Joseph P Allman
Ex VP: Robert Cooper
Sr VP: Lars-Erik Arnell
Sr VP: Paul Kinstedt
VP: Ethan J Blank
VP: Thomas Duffy
VP: Scott Durgin
VP: Brad Elstad
VP: Daniel Shurz
Comm Man: Warren Wilkinson
Board of Directors: Lawrence J Cohen, Neal S Cohen, Robert L Colin, Daniel P Garton, Douglas L Lambert, Mark L Plaumann

D-U-N-S 78-813-3023
■ REPUBLIC AUTOMOTIVE PARTS SALES INC
B & C AUTO
(Suby of CARQUEST AUTO PARTS) ★
2635 E Millbrook Rd, Raleigh, NC 27604-2988
Tel (919) 573-3000 Founded/Ownrshp 1998
Sales 80.9MME EMP 1,042
SIC 5013 5531 Automotive supplies & parts; Automotive parts
Ch Bd: O Temple Sloan Jr
*Pr: Joseph Owen
Treas: Richard Guirlinger
VP: Doug Buscher
VP: David Sharer
Sls Mgr: Jerry Neal

D-U-N-S 60-120-6998
▲ REPUBLIC BANCORP INC
601 W Market St Ste 100, Louisville, KY 40202-2745
Tel (502) 584-3600 Founded/Ownrshp 1974
Sales NA EMP 799E
Tkr Sym RBCAA Exch NGS
SIC 6022 State commercial banks
Ch Bd: Steven E Trager
*Pr: A Scott Trager
CFO: Kevin Sipes
Board of Directors: Craig A Greenberg, R Wayne Stratton, Susan Stout Tamme, Mark A Vogt, Michael T Trust

D-U-N-S 04-899-9684
REPUBLIC BANK
328 S Saginaw St Lbby, Flint, MI 48502-1926
Tel (810) 257-2506 Founded/Ownrshp 2013
Sales NA EMP 2,046
SIC 6022 6163 6029 State commercial banks; Loan brokers; Commercial banks
Pr: Dana M Cluckey
Pr: W Brian Black
Pr: Timothy D Dixon
CFO: Tom Menacher
CFO: Jeffrey D Saunders
Chf Cred: Craig C Foust
Bd of Dir: Gary Byrd
Bd of Dir: Sandy Metts
Ofcr: Barbara Boyd
Sr VP: Paul Fuller
Sr VP: Peter L Lemmer
VP: Rich Roty

D-U-N-S 02-665-7296
■ REPUBLIC BANK & TRUST CO INC
(Suby of REPUBLIC BANCORP INC) ★
601 W Market St Ste 100, Louisville, KY 40202-2700
Tel (502) 584-3600 Founded/Ownrshp 1925
Sales NA EMP 600
SIC 6022 6163 State commercial banks; Loan brokers
Ch Bd: Steve Trager
Pr: Carol James
*Pr: Scott Trager
COO: Robert Arnold
*COO: Anita Clemons
*COO: Bill Petter
CFO: Kevin Sipes
*CFO: Kevin Sykes
Ofcr: Danny Wang
Sr VP: Tom Fangman
Sr VP: Juan Montano
Sr VP: John Rippy
Sr VP: Margaret Wendeler
Sr VP: Darryl Witten
VP: Greg Bromley
VP: Deanna Johnson
VP: Keri Jones
VP: Mike Newton
VP: Steve Novak
VP: Jason Payne
VP: Shanon Reid
Board of Directors: Heather Howell

D-U-N-S 05-212-3619
■ REPUBLIC COMPANIES INC (DE)
(Suby of AMTRUST FINANCIAL SERVICES INC) ★
5525 Lyndon B Johnson Fwy, Dallas, TX 75240-6241
Tel (972) 788-6001 Founded/Ownrshp 2003, 2016
Sales NA EMP 345E
SIC 6321 6311 6331 Health insurance carriers; Life insurance carriers; Property damage insurance
Pr: Parker W Rush
*CFO: Martin Cummings
*VP: Michael E Ditto
VP: Robert Howey
Mktg Dir: Mary Hamel

D-U-N-S 07-505-7257
REPUBLIC FINANCE LLC
7031 Commerce Cir Ste 100, Baton Rouge, LA 70809-1996
Tel (225) 927-0005 Founded/Ownrshp 1959
Sales NA EMP 250
SIC 6141 Consumer finance companies
Pr: William Allen
Pr: David Courter
Pr: Ken Crider
Pr: John Lemonis
Pr: Dustin Messina
Pr: Bryon Nazelrod
Pr: Robert Olson
Pr: Kyle Walters
CFO: James Jolly
Sr VP: Bill Allen
Sr VP: Kyle Fenton
Exec: Angel N Phistry

D-U-N-S 05-561-0216
REPUBLIC FINANCIAL CORP
5251 Dtc Pkwy Ste 300, Greenwood Village, CO 80111-2732
Tel (800) 596-3608 Founded/Ownrshp 1971
Sales 241.7MME EMP 316
SIC 6726 6159 Investment offices; Equipment & vehicle finance leasing companies
Ch: James Possehl
*Pr: Robert Possehl
*CEO: Randy Dietrich
*COO: Margaret Reich
*CFO: Dennis Bikun
Ex Dir: Marc Crady
Mng Dir: Scott Lavie
Corp Couns: Victoria Aguilar
Corp Couns: Lisa Wendt

D-U-N-S 18-858-2977
■ REPUBLIC INDEMNITY CO OF AMERICA
(Suby of PENNSYLVANIA CO INC) ★
15821 Ventura Blvd # 370, Encino, CA 91436-2936
Tel (818) 990-9860 Founded/Ownrshp 1989
Sales NA EMP 420
SIC 6331 Workers' compensation insurance
CEO: Dwayne Marioni
*Sr VP: Marion Chappel
CTO: Debbie Billart
Board of Directors: Robert Amory, Gary Gruber, Karen Horrell

REPUBLIC INDUSTRIES
See REPUBLIC NATIONAL INDUSTRIES OF TEXAS LP

D-U-N-S 07-486-3325
REPUBLIC INSURANCE CO INC
5525 Lyndon B Johnson Fwy, Dallas, TX 75240-6241
Tel (972) 788-6001 Founded/Ownrshp 1975
Sales NA EMP 250
SIC 6331 Fire, marine & casualty insurance
CEO: Parker Rush
CFO: Marty Cummings
*Treas: William T Ellis

*VP: Michael Ditto
*VP: Tom Ellis

D-U-N-S 17-540-5968
■ REPUBLIC MORTGAGE INSURANCE CO INC
RIMC
(Suby of OLD REPUBLIC MORTGAGE GUARANTEE GROUP INC) ★
101 N Cherry St Ste 101, Winston Salem, NC 27101-4013
Tel (336) 661-0015 Founded/Ownrshp 1973
Sales NA EMP 425
SIC 6351 Mortgage guarantee insurance
Pr: Christopher Nard
*Ch Bd: William A Simpson
*CFO: David Cash
*Sr VP: Joel Pasternak
Dir IT: Steve Wright
Opers Mgr: Gay Huntsman
Sales Exec: Lisa Glunt

D-U-N-S 10-036-6967
REPUBLIC NATIONAL CABINET CORP
1400 Warren Dr, Marshall, TX 75672-5893
Tel (903) 935-3680 Founded/Ownrshp 2014
Sales 164.8MME EMP 12E
SIC 2434 Wood kitchen cabinets
Pr: Paul F Patek
*Treas: Marsha Durham
VP: Jeffrey Kroyer
*VP: Chris Thomas
VP: Jim Walls
Plnt Mgr: Kenny Ponder

REPUBLIC NATIONAL DISTRG CO
See RNDC TEXAS LLC

D-U-N-S 00-983-0951 IMP
REPUBLIC NATIONAL DISTRIBUTING CO LLC
8045 Northcourt Rd, Houston, TX 77040-4392
Tel (813) 885-3200 Founded/Ownrshp 1962, 1996
Sales 859.6MME EMP 1,100
SIC 5182 Liquor; Wine
Ex VP: Phil Beck
VP: Chris Byrne
VP: Daniel Fowler
VP: Pat Hurrle
VP: Bill Wickham
Exec: Pamela Dawson
Rgnl Mgr: Craig Valby
Area Mgr: Eric Cain
Area Mgr: Curtis Hilliard
Dist Mgr: Michael Bradley
Dist Mgr: Zack Means

D-U-N-S 02-318-7615 IMP
REPUBLIC NATIONAL DISTRIBUTING CO LLC
RNDC
809 Jefferson Hwy, New Orleans, LA 70121-2522
Tel (404) 696-9440 Founded/Ownrshp 2007
Sales 932.9MME EMP 5,085
SIC 5182 Wine; Liquor
Ch Bd: Vertner D Smith III
Pr: Tom Cole
COO: Charlie Andrews
Ex VP: Bob Hendrickson
Exec: Yvette McMahon
Exec: Chris G Waltz
Area Mgr: Joseph D Hofmann
Area Mgr: Michael Kennedy
Area Mgr: Roxanne Lee
Area Mgr: Joey Theriot
Area Mgr: Larry West
Board of Directors: Eddie Block, Chris Carlos, John Carlos, Jay Davis, Alan Dreeben, Diane Goldring Franco, Jeff Goldring, Jerry Rosenberg

D-U-N-S 80-665-5341 IMP
REPUBLIC NATIONAL DISTRIBUTING CO LLC
8000 Southpark Ter, Littleton, CO 80120-5605
Tel (303) 734-2400 Founded/Ownrshp 1970
Sales 100.5MME EMP 119E
SIC 5169 Alcohols
Pr: Tom Cole
*CEO: Jay M Davis
*COO: Charles Andrews
*CFO: Paul Fine
*CFO: Greg Johnson
Ofcr: Tom Allgeier
Ofcr: Leo Eidman
Ofcr: Jeff Gross
Ofcr: Ken Long
Ofcr: Chris Martin
Ofcr: Jason Secord
Ofcr: Brad Taylor
*VP: Bob Hendrickson
Exec: Rhonda Nash

D-U-N-S 19-682-0104
REPUBLIC NATIONAL INDUSTRIES OF TEXAS LP
REPUBLIC INDUSTRIES
(Suby of REPUBLIC NATIONAL CABINET CORP) ★
1400 Warren Dr, Marshall, TX 75672-5893
Tel (903) 935-3680 Founded/Ownrshp 2000
Sales 164.1MME EMP 613E
SIC 2434 5211 2541 Wood kitchen cabinets; Vanities, bathroom: wood; Cabinets, kitchen; Wood partitions & fixtures
Pt: Gary Edwards
Sr VP: Tom Royce
Sales Exec: Elizabeth Reed
Sls Mgr: Eric Utsey

D-U-N-S 04-775-0328
REPUBLIC PARKING SYSTEM LLC
(Suby of IMPARK) ★
633 Chestnut St Ste 2000, Chattanooga, TN 37450-2000
Tel (423) 756-2771 Founded/Ownrshp 2016
Sales 400.0MM EMP 2,700
SIC 8742 7521 Management consulting services; Parking lots; Parking garage
Pr: Scott Titmus
*COO: Bob Linehart

*CFO: Ben Wolfley
*Ex VP: Chris Howley
Sr VP: Alan Doherty
Sr VP: Robert Mitchell
VP: Brian Kern
VP: Jack Skelton
Rgnl Mgr: Jennifer Carroll
Genl Mgr: Michael Bandy
Off Mgr: Malinda Honkus

D-U-N-S 12-251-5781 IMP/EXP
■ REPUBLIC POWDERED METALS INC
(Suby of RPM INTERNATIONAL INC) ★
2628 Pearl Rd, Medina, OH 44256-9099
Tel (330) 225-3192 Founded/Ownrshp 1963
Sales 1.3MMME EMP 7,814
SIC 2851 2891 3069 2899 2865 2842 Paints & allied products; Adhesives & sealants; Roofing, membrane rubber; Waterproofing compounds; Dyes & pigments; Specialty cleaning preparations
Ch Bd: Thomas Sullivan
Pr: Lonny Diusso
*Pr: Frank C Sullivan
VP: Ken Armstrong
VP: Lonny Dirusso
VP: Russell Gordon
VP: Tim Jordan
VP: Janeen Kastner
VP: John Kramer
VP: Robert Matejka
VP: Randell McShepard
VP: Charles Pauli
VP: Matthew Ratajczak
VP: Barry Slifstein
VP: Keith Smiley
VP: Tony Wood
Exec: Janette Buckland
Dir: Melissa Schoger

D-U-N-S 08-033-4348
■ REPUBLIC RESOURCES CO
(Suby of AUTO HOLDING, LLC)
200 Sw 1st Ave, Fort Lauderdale, FL 33301-1875
Tel (954) 769-7000 Founded/Ownrshp 1999
Sales 108.2MME EMP 215E
SIC 5511 New & used car dealers

REPUBLIC SERVICES
See REPUBLIC SILVER STATE DISPOSAL INC

REPUBLIC SERVICES
See ALLIED WASTE NORTH AMERICA INC

D-U-N-S 02-013-8298
▲ REPUBLIC SERVICES INC (VA)
18500 N Allied Way # 100, Phoenix, AZ 85054-3101
Tel (480) 627-2700 Founded/Ownrshp 1996
Sales 9.1MMM EMP 33,000
Tkr Sym RSG Exch NYS
SIC 4953 Refuse collection & disposal services; Nonhazardous waste disposal sites; Recycling, waste materials; Sanitary landfill operation
Pr: Donald W Slager
*Ch Bd: Ramon A Rodriguez
CFO: Peter Hathaway
CFO: Charles F Serianni
Ofcr: Mindi Blair
Ofcr: Jeffrey A Hughes
Ex VP: Jon Vander Ark
Ex VP: Brian A Bales
Ex VP: Stuart Levy
Ex VP: Tom Lynch
Ex VP: Michael Rissman
Sr VP: Bill Halnon
VP: Brian Goebel
VP: Randy Goldberg
VP: Mike Guilleaume
VP: Edward A Lang III
VP: Brian May
VP: Jim Olson
VP: Bob Pickens
VP: Laura Schultz
VP: Richard Simon
Board of Directors: John M Trani, James W Crownover, Sandra M Volpe, Ann E Dunwoody, William J Flynn, Thomas W Handley, Manuel Kadre, Jennifer M Kirk, Michael Larson, W Lee Nutter, Allan C Sorensen

D-U-N-S 94-589-9511
■ REPUBLIC SERVICES OF FLORIDA LIMITED PARTNERSHIP
(Suby of REPUBLIC SERVICES INC) ★
18500 N Allied Way, Phoenix, AZ 85054-6164
Tel (480) 627-2700 Founded/Ownrshp 1999
Sales 242.6MME EMP 535E
SIC 4953 Hazardous waste collection & disposal
CEO: Donald Slager

D-U-N-S 00-737-5889
■ REPUBLIC SILVER STATE DISPOSAL INC (NV)
REPUBLIC SERVICES
(Suby of REPUBLIC SERVICES INC) ★
770 E Sahara Ave Ste 400, Las Vegas, NV 89104-2909
Tel (702) 735-5151 Founded/Ownrshp 1997
Sales 480.5MME EMP 1,128
SIC 4953 Refuse collection & disposal services
Pr: Bob Coyle
*Treas: Bob Kneesel

D-U-N-S 14-691-6510 IMP/EXP
REPUBLIC STEEL INC
(Suby of GRUPO SIMEC, S.A.B. DE C.V.)
2633 8th St Ne, Canton, OH 44704-2311
Tel (330) 438-5435 Founded/Ownrshp 2005
Sales 409.6MME EMP 500E
SIC 3312 Bars, iron: made in steel mills; Structural shapes & pilings, steel
Pr: Jaime Vigil
*CFO: Joseph A Kaczka
*VP: Noel J Huettich
VP: Michael Humphrey
VP: Thielens James
*VP: Ted Thielens
VP: Manny Viadero
*VP: John A Willoughby
Area Supr: Ray Hobson

Dept Mgr: John Bush
Dept Mgr: Jesse Janson

D-U-N-S 78-657-5139
REPUBLIC STORAGE SYSTEMS LLC
(*Suby of* VERSA CAPITAL MANAGEMENT LLC) ★
1038 Belden Ave Ne, Canton, OH 44705-1454
Tel (330) 438-5800 *Founded/Ownrshp* 2009
Sales 113.6MM[E] *EMP* 400[E]
SIC 2542 3441 Lockers (not refrigerated): except wood; Shelving, office & store: except wood; Fabricated structural metal
Off Mgr: Allison Suarez
Plnt Mgr: Clarence Jackson
VP Sls: Robert Patton
S&M/VP: Bob Patton

D-U-N-S 06-665-9871
■ **REPUBLIC TITLE OF TEXAS INC**
(*Suby of* FIRST AMERICAN TITLE INSURANCE CO) ★
2701 W Plano Pkwy Ste 100, Plano, TX 75075-8211
Tel (972) 578-8611 *Founded/Ownrshp* 1994
Sales NA *EMP* 444
SIC 6411 7372 6531 6541 Insurance agents, brokers & service; Prepackaged software; Real estate agents & managers; Title abstract offices
Ch Bd: William A Kramer
Pr: Courtney Slater
**COO:* Michael D Richards
**CFO:* Dennis Eastland
**Ch:* David A Shuttee
Ofcr: Sarah Mann
Ofcr: Mandy Moss
Ofcr: Jeff Porter
Ofcr: Tracy Smiley
Ofcr: Keisha Tolbert
Ex VP: David Kramer
Sr VP: Rose Boisse
Sr VP: Janet M Ceron
Sr VP: Joanna Cloud
Sr VP: Nancy Colaluca
Sr VP: Felicia Farnsworth
Sr VP: Vince Gurley
Sr VP: Lorri Henson
Sr VP: Kevin Higgs
Sr VP: Linda Hudspeth
Sr VP: Terri Matney

D-U-N-S 06-009-7060
■ **REPUBLIC UNDERWRITERS INSURANCE CO**
(*Suby of* REPUBLIC COMPANIES INC) ★
5525 Lbj Fwy, Dallas, TX 75240-6241
Tel (972) 788-6001 *Founded/Ownrshp* 1965, 1903
Sales NA *EMP* 345
SIC 6331

D-U-N-S 08-047-3693
REPUBLIC WIRELESS INC
900 Main Campus Dr, Raleigh, NC 27606-5177
Tel (877) 913-0894 *Founded/Ownrshp* 2015
Sales 100.0MM *EMP* 150
SIC 4812 Cellular telephone services
CEO: Chris Chang
Pr: Jim Mulcahy
Pr: Matt Newton

D-U-N-S 04-149-1382
REPUBLICAN CO
(*Suby of* SUNDAY STAR LEDGER) ★
1860 Main St, Springfield, MA 01103-1073
Tel (413) 788-1000 *Founded/Ownrshp* 1878
Sales 146.8MM[E] *EMP* 650
SIC 2711 Newspapers, publishing & printing
CEO: George Arwady
**Treas:* David B Evans
**VP:* Brian Long
**Prin:* Donald Newhouse
Dir IT: Steven Nanton
Prd Mgr: James Foley
Advt Dir: Mark A French
Mktg Dir: Maureen Sullivan

D-U-N-S 06-058-2939
■ **REPWEST INSURANCE CO**
(*Suby of* AMERCO) ★
2721 N Central Ave Fl 8, Phoenix, AZ 85004-1132
Tel (602) 263-6755 *Founded/Ownrshp* 1973
Sales NA *EMP* 271
SIC 6331 Fire, marine & casualty insurance
Ch: Edward J Shoen
**Pr:* Richard M Amoroso
CFO: Kristin N Korinek
**Treas:* Kristin N Spears
Treas: John Taylor
Treas: Rocky Wardrip
VP: Layton Baker
VP: Michael Hickson
**VP:* Edward R McMullin
VP: Bob Pirmann
VP: Katherine Zappavigna
Exec: Sandee Starks

D-U-N-S 04-160-9611
REQ/JQH HOLDINGS INC
INTERNATIONAL MERCHANTS
4243 Hunt Rd Ste 2, Blue Ash, OH 45242-6645
Tel (513) 891-1066 *Founded/Ownrshp* 1966
Sales 85.2MM[E] *EMP* 334
SIC 8741 6552 Hotel or motel management; Land subdividers & developers, commercial
Ch Bd: J Erik Kamfjord
**Pr:* Keith W Daub
**V Ch Bd:* John Q Hammons
**V Ch Bd:* Roy E Winegardner
**Sr VP:* John J Slaboch
**VP:* Debbie Atee
VP: Terry Dammeyer
VP: David Gordon
VP: Jerry Yates
Exec: Kent Burggman
Exec: Paul Pisegna
Exec: Justin Winkler

D-U-N-S 16-838-3144 IMP
RES AMERICA CONSTRUCTION INC
RENEWBLE ENRGY SYSTEMS AMRICAS
(*Suby of* RENEWABLE ENERGY SYSTEMS) ★
11101 W 120th Ave Ste 400, Broomfield, CO 80021-3436
Tel (512) 617-1960 *Founded/Ownrshp* 2000
Sales 158.9MM[E] *EMP* 250[E]
SIC 1629 Power plant construction
CEO: Glen Davis
**Pr:* Andrew Fowler
Pr: Craig Horne
VP: Victor Babbitt
VP: Ryan Evans
VP: Chris Hills
VP: Steve Reutcke
VP: Jason Zingerman
IT Man: Chad Carmichael

D-U-N-S 07-022-6105 IMP
RES-CARE INC
(*Suby of* ONEX PARTNERS III LP)
9901 Linn Station Rd, Louisville, KY 40223-3808
Tel (502) 394-2100 *Founded/Ownrshp* 2010
Sales 1.6MMM *EMP* 46,348
SIC 8052 8331 7363 Home for the mentally retarded, with health care; Vocational training agency; Medical help service
Pr: Ralph G Gronefeld Jr
**Pr:* Patrick G Kelley
COO: Chris Hoagland
**CFO:* Ronald Geary
**CFO:* David W Miles
**Treas:* D Ross Davison
**Chf Cred:* David S Waskey
Ofcr: David S Wakey
**Ex VP:* Jeffrey S Engelke
Ex VP: Christopher Freedom
Ex VP: Michael Hough
**Ex VP:* Richard L Tinsley
Sr VP: Jane L Steur
VP: Stephen Brunet
VP: Mike Cutchalw
VP: Mike Cutchshaw
VP: Sergei Davidenkoff
VP: Matt Doctrow
VP: Rachael Givens
VP: Dianna Hinton
VP: Cynthia K Mann

RESCAR CO
See RESCAR INDUSTRIES INC

D-U-N-S 02-004-1455
RESCAR INDUSTRIES INC
RESCAR CO
1101 31st St Ste 250, Downers Grove, IL 60515-5532
Tel (630) 963-1114 *Founded/Ownrshp* 2003
Sales 313.9MM[E] *EMP* 1,100
SIC 3743 Railroad car rebuilding
Pr: Joseph F Schieszler
**Treas:* Barry Anstandig
VP Mktg: Marvin B Hughes

RESCARE
See AMERICAN HABILITATION SERVICES INC

RESCO
See RURAL ELECTRIC SUPPLY COOPERATIVE

D-U-N-S 00-232-4655 IMP/EXP
RESCO PRODUCTS INC
NORTH STATE PYROPHYLLITE
1 Robinson Plz Ste 300, Pittsburgh, PA 15205-1021
Tel (412) 494-4491 *Founded/Ownrshp* 1946
Sales 191.9MM[E] *EMP* 700
SIC 3297 3255 1455 1499 5032

RESEARCH & SPONSORED PROGRAMS
See UNIVERSITY OF MONTANA

D-U-N-S 08-724-8183 IMP
■ **RESEARCH AND DIAGNOSTIC SYSTEMS INC** (MN)
R&D SYSTEMS
(*Suby of* BIO-TECHNE CORP) ★
614 Mckinley Pl Ne, Minneapolis, MN 55413-2610
Tel (612) 379-2956 *Founded/Ownrshp* 1976, 1986
Sales 125.5MM[E] *EMP* 598
SIC 8733 2833 8731 3829 3625 Research institute; Antibiotics; Commercial physical research; Measuring & controlling devices; Relays & industrial controls
CEO: Charles R Kummeth
Pr: Thomas E Oland
CFO: Greg Melsen
VP: Brandon Hanna
VP: Nancy Littler
VP: Monica Tsang
VP: Marcel Veronneau
VP: James Weatherbee
Genl Mgr: Paul Nealy
IT Man: Barb Larson
Software D: Jeff Wenker

RESEARCH CENTER
See FIELD MUSEUM OF NATURAL HISTORY

RESEARCH COLLEGE OF NURSING
See MIDWEST DIVISION RMC LLC

D-U-N-S 07-252-7344
RESEARCH CORP OF UNIVERSITY OF HAWAII
RCUH
2800 Woodlawn Dr Ste 200, Honolulu, HI 96822-1881
Tel (808) 988-8311 *Founded/Ownrshp* 1965
Sales 7.0MM *EMP* 2,500
Accts Accuity Llp Honolulu Hawaii
SIC 8733 Noncommercial research organizations
Ex Dir: Sylvia Yuen
Comm Dir: Diane Chang

D-U-N-S 07-991-9916
RESEARCH FOD FOR MTAL HY INC (NY)
RFMH
150 Broadway Ste 301, Menands, NY 12204-2726
Tel (518) 474-5661 *Founded/Ownrshp* 1952
Sales 124.1MM *EMP* 1,250
Accts Uhy Llp Albany New York
SIC 8733 Research institute
Genl Mgr: Michael Kavanaugh

RESEARCH FOUNDATION CUNY
See RESEARCH FOUNDATION OF CITY UNIVERSITY OF NEW YORK

D-U-N-S 02-065-7151
RESEARCH FOUNDATION FOR STATE UNIVERSITY OF NEW YORK (NY)
SPONSRED PRGRAMS OFF - SYS ADM
35 State St, Albany, NY 12207-2826
Tel (518) 434-7000 *Founded/Ownrshp* 1951
Sales 1.1MMM *EMP* 16,330
Accts Kpmg Llp Boston Ma
SIC 8733 Noncommercial research organizations
Pr: Alexander Cartwright
**CFO:* Paul Kutey
**Ex VP:* Garrett Sanders
Sr VP: John W Craine
**VP:* Kathleen Caggiano-Siino
VP: Paul Kelly
VP: Chris Wade
Assoc Dir: Mary Frieberg
Opers Mgr: Mary Reagan

D-U-N-S 06-493-2676 IMP
RESEARCH FOUNDATION OF CITY UNIVERSITY OF NEW YORK
RESEARCH FOUNDATION CUNY
(*Suby of* AFFIRMATIVE ACTION/EEO DEPT) ★
230 W 41st St Fl 7, New York, NY 10036-7207
Tel (212) 417-8300 *Founded/Ownrshp* 1963
Sales 383.9MM *EMP* 5,000[E]
SIC 8733

D-U-N-S 07-914-3230
RESEARCH FOUNDATION OF CITY UNIVERSITY OF NEW YORK
RFCUNY - STELLA AND CHARLES GU
50 W 40th St, New York, NY 10018-2602
Tel (212) 417-8557 *Founded/Ownrshp* 2013
Sales 29.2MM[E] *EMP* 6,000
SIC 8221 Colleges universities & professional schools
CEO: Jarnee Bramlette
CIO: John Stroud
Netwrk Eng: Dave Kopel

D-U-N-S 07-914-3237
RESEARCH FOUNDATION OF CITY UNIVERSITY OF NEW YORK
RFCUNY - CUNY SCHOOL OF LAW
2 Court Sq, Long Island City, NY 11101-4356
Tel (212) 417-8587 *Founded/Ownrshp* 1963
Sales 16.4MM[E] *EMP* 6,000
SIC 8221 Colleges universities & professional schools
Pr: Jarnee Bramlette

D-U-N-S 06-496-0495
RESEARCH INTERNATIONAL USA
(*Suby of* W P P) ★
222 Merchandise Mart Plz # 250, Chicago, IL 60654-1103
Tel (312) 787-4060 *Founded/Ownrshp* 1964, 2001
Sales 57.9MM[E] *EMP* 2,265
SIC 8732 Market analysis or research
CEO: Lorna Walters
CFO: Ron Hansen
Ex VP: Judy Greener
Sr VP: Cindy Whiteway
VP: David B Miller
VP: Waleed Saleh
VP: Kirk Ward
Prin: Aggie Vardos
Mng Dir: Alejandro Mondrag N
IT Man: Theresa Altgilbers
VP Mktg: Jackie Speckin

D-U-N-S 12-873-1473
RESEARCH NOW GROUP INC
5800 Tennyson Pkwy # 600, Plano, TX 75024-3992
Tel (214) 365-5000 *Founded/Ownrshp* 2015
Sales 290.7MM[E] *EMP* 1,300
SIC 8732 Market analysis, business & economic research; Market analysis or research
CEO: Gary Laben
**CFO:* Stephen Decosta
Ofcr: Miles Worne
**Ex VP:* Melanie Courtright
Ex VP: Greg Ellis
Ex VP: John Tan
**Sr VP:* Kathy Rowley
Sr VP: Aaron Simmons
VP: Mike Billingsley
VP: Steve Decosta
VP: Pat Goodnight
VP: Randi Lee
VP: Steve Myers
Exec: Bruce Phillips
Exec: Amanda Rawlings

D-U-N-S 87-664-5722
RESEARCH PHARMACEUTICAL SERVICES INC
520 Virginia Dr, Fort Washington, PA 19034-2707
Tel (215) 540-0700 *Founded/Ownrshp* 1994
Sales NA *EMP* 2,100[E]
SIC 8099

D-U-N-S 00-610-9714 IMP/EXP
RESEARCH PRODUCTS CORP (WI)
1015 E Washington Ave, Madison, WI 53703-2999
Tel (608) 257-8801 *Founded/Ownrshp* 1938
Sales 151.3MM[E] *EMP* 490
SIC 5075 3564 3569

D-U-N-S 00-486-8105
RESEARCH TRIANGLE INSTITUTE INC
R T I INTERNATIONAL
3040 Cornwallis Rd, Durham, NC 27709-0128
Tel (919) 541-6000 *Founded/Ownrshp* 1958
Sales 831.5MM *EMP* 2,680
Accts Deloitte & Touche Llp Charlo
SIC 8732 8731 Commercial nonphysical research; Commercial physical research; Biological research; Chemical laboratory, except testing; Environmental research
CEO: E Wayne Holden
Pr: David Myers
COO: James J Gibson
CFO: Michael H Kaelin Jr
Ofcr: J Scott Merrell
Ex VP: Tim Gabel
Ex VP: Satinder Sethi
Ex VP: Aaron S Williams
Sr VP: Lorena K Clark
Sr VP: Lon Emaggart
Sr VP: G Edward Story
VP: James Clary
VP: Karen Davis
VP: Wayne Holdn
VP: Josephine Mauskopf
VP: Dennis Naugle
VP: Mary Reiss
VP: Jerry Rench
VP: Allwyne Richards
VP: David Rosenberry
VP: Edward Story

D-U-N-S 00-902-6642 IMP
RESERS FINE FOODS INC
15570 Sw Jenkins Rd, Beaverton, OR 97006-6099
Tel (503) 643-6431 *Founded/Ownrshp* 1950
Sales 900.5MM[E] *EMP* 3,000
Accts Pricewaterhousecoopers Llp Po
SIC 2099 5141 Food preparations; Salads, fresh or refrigerated; Groceries, general line
Ch: Patricia Reser
Pr: Mark Reser
COO: Donna Plekan
Treas: Paul Leavy
VP: Frank Baker
VP: Scott Buchele
VP: Ron Leeper
VP: Jay Mayr
VP: Tim Osbom
VP: Angie Simons
Exec: Elaine Kelly
Exec: Alan Reser
Comm Man: Linda Stock

D-U-N-S 83-763-0391
RESERVE GROUP MANAGEMENT CO
3560 W Market St Ste 300, Fairlawn, OH 44333-2687
Tel (330) 665-6706 *Founded/Ownrshp* 1995
Sales 192.8MM[E] *EMP* 860
SIC 8741 Business management
Ch: Richard Hamlin
**Pr:* Mark Hamlin
Ex VP: Matt Parker
IT Man: Lisa Barnes
**VP Opers:* James Van Tiem

RESERVEAMERICA
See LANYON SOLUTIONS INC

D-U-N-S 55-692-7002
■ **RESIDENCE INN BY MARRIOTT LLC**
(*Suby of* MARRIOTT INTERNATIONAL INC) ★
10400 Fernwood Rd, Bethesda, MD 20817-1102
Tel (301) 380-3000 *Founded/Ownrshp* 1987
Sales 139.3MM[E] *EMP* 5,000[E]
SIC 7011 Hotels & motels
VP: Tim Sheldon
Ex VP: Anthony Capuano
Sr VP: Alexander Mooring

RESIDENTIAL MORTGAGE
See ACADEMY MORTGAGE CORP

D-U-N-S 62-697-9397
RESIDENTIAL MORTGAGE SERVICES INC
RMS
24 Christopher Toppi Dr, South Portland, ME 04106-6901
Tel (207) 675-3609 *Founded/Ownrshp* 2001
Sales NA *EMP* 600
SIC 6162 Mortgage bankers
Pr: James Selly
Pr: John Clemenz
**CFO:* Paul Musgrove
**CFO:* Robert Orlandi
Sr VP: Bill Saufley
VP: Debbie Bodwell
**VP:* Valerie M Desrochers
VP: Chris Foote
VP: Larry Haskell
VP: Linda Hausler
Exec: David Rose

D-U-N-S 96-683-7515
RESIDEX LLC
TURFGRASS
(*Suby of* JC EHRLICH) ★
46495 Humboldt Dr, Novi, MI 48377-2446
Tel (855) 737-4339 *Founded/Ownrshp* 2016
Sales 108.8MM[E] *EMP* 120[E]
SIC 5191 7342 0781 0782 Herbicides; Pest control services; Horticulture services; Lawn care services
Pr: Todd Ferguson
Sls&Mrk Ex: Sue Shockey

RESIDUAL MANAGEMENT TECHNOLOGY
See IEA RENEWABLE ENERGY INC

D-U-N-S 03-905-6408
RESILIENCE CAPITAL PARTNERS LLC
RESILIENCE MANAGEMENT
25101 Chagrin Blvd # 350, Cleveland, OH 44122-5643
Tel (216) 292-0200 *Founded/Ownrshp* 2001
Sales 179.2MM[E] *EMP* 1,493
SIC 7389 Financial services
**Pt:* Michael Cavanaugh
**Pt:* David Glickman
**Pt:* Ki Mixon
**COO:* Ziv Sarig
Sr VP: Robert Northrop
Sr VP: Scott Watson
VP: Doug Campbell
**VP:* Megan McPherson
**VP:* Robert Schwartz
IT Man: Robert Kay
Genl Couns: Chad Hesse

RESILIENCE MANAGEMENT
See RESILIENCE CAPITAL PARTNERS LLC

D-U-N-S 06-717-4680 EXP
RESINALL CORP (NC)
3065 High Ridge Rd, Stamford, CT 06903-1301
Tel (203) 329-7100 Founded/Ownrshp 1979
Sales 92.4MM[E] EMP 235
SIC 2821 Thermosetting materials; Thermoplastic materials
CEO: John M Godina Sr
*Pr: Elaine Godina
Sr VP: Roger Burke
*VP: Lee T Godina

D-U-N-S 80-587-4096 IMP
▲ RESMED INC
9001 Spectrum Center Blvd, San Diego, CA 92123-1438
Tel (858) 836-5000 Founded/Ownrshp 1994
Sales 1.8MMM EMP 4,340[E]
Tkr Sym RMD Exch NYS
SIC 3841 Surgical & medical instruments; Diagnostic apparatus, medical
CEO: Michael Farrell
*Ch Bd: Peter Farrell
Pr: Don Darkin
Pr: Rob Douglas
Pr: Jim Hollingshead
Pr: Anne Reiser
CFO: Brett Sandercock
Ofcr: David Pendarvis
VP: Adam Benjafield
VP: Colin Lawlor
VP: Tom Miller
VP: Shelly Selvaraj
Board of Directors: Carol Burt, Gary Pace, Chris Roberts, Rich Sulpizio, Ron Taylor, Jack Wareham

RESNICK DISTRIBUTORS
See PLAINFIELD TOBACCO AND CANDY CO INC

D-U-N-S 83-200-7400
▲ RESOLUTE ENERGY CORP
1700 N Lincoln St # 2800, Denver, CO 80203-4535
Tel (303) 534-4600 Founded/Ownrshp 2009
Sales 154.6MM EMP 226[E]
Tkr Sym REN Exch NYS
SIC 1311 Crude petroleum & natural gas
Ch Bd: Nicholas J Sutton
*Pr: James M Piccone
COO: Richard F Betz
CFO: Theodore Gazulis
Sr VP: Bob D Brady Jr
Sr VP: Michael N Stefanoudakis
Sr VP: James A Tuell
VP: Bill Alleman
VP: Kurt Johnson
Board of Directors: James E Duffy, Thomas O Hicks Jr, Gary L Hultquist, William K White

RESOLUTE FOREST PRODUCTS
See RESOLUTE FP US INC

D-U-N-S 08-031-8650
RESOLUTE FP FLORIDA INC
(Suby of RESOLUTE FOREST PRODUCTS INC)
3301 Nw 107th St, Miami, FL 33167-3714
Tel (800) 562-2860 Founded/Ownrshp 2015
Sales 138.7MM[E] EMP 289[E]
SIC 2621 Toilet tissue stock; Absorbent paper
CEO: Jim Brown

D-U-N-S 00-194-6011 IMP/EXP
RESOLUTE FP US INC
RESOLUTE FOREST PRODUCTS
(Suby of RESOLUTE FOREST PRODUCTS INC)
5300 Cureton Ferry Rd, Catawba, SC 29704-7700
Tel (803) 981-8000 Founded/Ownrshp 1964
Sales 217.9MM[E] EMP 605
SIC 2621 2672 2611 2421 Newsprint paper; Uncoated paper; Coated paper, except photographic, carbon or abrasive; Pulp mills; Lumber: rough, sawed or planed
Treas: William G Harvey
CFO: Jo-Ann Longworth
Sr VP: Yves Laflamme
VP: Joseph B Johnson
VP: Seth Kursman
VP: Rmi Lalonde
VP: Eric Ophoff
VP: Andre Piche
VP: Jeff Romeo
IT Man: Frank Pisano
Sfty Mgr: Justin Darrah
Board of Directors: Colin Keeler, Gaynor L Nash

D-U-N-S 16-989-4008
■ RESOLUTE NATURAL RESOURCES CO LLC
(Suby of RESOLUTE ENERGY CORP) ★
1700 N Lincoln St # 2800, Denver, CO 80203-4535
Tel (303) 573-4886 Founded/Ownrshp 2004
Sales 123.0MM[E] EMP 160[E]
SIC 1311 Gas & hydrocarbon liquefaction from coal
Ch Bd: Nicholas J Sutton
*Pr: James M Piccone
*Ex VP: Richard F Betz
*Sr VP: Michael N Stefanoudakis

D-U-N-S 15-272-2773 IMP/EXP
RESOLVE MARINE GROUP INC
RESOLVE TOWING & SALVAGE
1510 Se 17th St Ste 400, Fort Lauderdale, FL 33316-1729
Tel (954) 764-8700 Founded/Ownrshp 1978
Sales 135.0MM EMP 400
SIC 4499 4492 4491 4412 7389 Salvaging, distressed vessels & cargoes; Marine salvaging; Ship cleaning; Towing & tugboat service; Marine towing services; Shifting of floating equipment within harbors; Tugboat service; Marine cargo handling; Marine loading & unloading services; Deep sea foreign transportation of freight; Fire protection service other than forestry or public
CEO: Joseph E Farrell
COO: Farhat Imam
*CFO: William Crothers
Dir Bus: Damian Allan
*Prin: Larry Ragan
VP Mktg: Ryan Morrison
Board of Directors: Mike Holloway

RESOLVE TOWING & SALVAGE
See RESOLVE MARINE GROUP INC

D-U-N-S 07-208-1664
■ RESORT CONDOMINIUMS INTERNATIONAL LLC
R C I
(Suby of WYNDHAM WORLDWIDE CORP) ★
1 Sylvan Way, Parsippany, NJ 07054-3887
Tel (973) 753-6667 Founded/Ownrshp 1997
Sales 155.9MM[E] EMP 4,000
SIC 7011 Resort hotel
CFO: Tom Edwards
Sr VP: SRI Raghavan
VP: David Evans
Mng Dir: Jeff Tisdall
Genl Mgr: Robert Hughes
CIO: Tony Graddy
IT Man: David Scheckter

D-U-N-S 08-624-5636
RESORT HOSPITALITY ENTERPRISES LTD
HOWARD JOHNSON
1002 W 23rd St Ste 400, Panama City, FL 32405-3648
Tel (321) 953-7272 Founded/Ownrshp 1993
Sales 5.5MM EMP 1,500
SIC 8741 Hotel or motel management
Pt: Robert Henry
Pt: Jimmy Barr

D-U-N-S 06-099-6829
RESORT MARKETING HOLDINGS INC
2419 E Commercial Blvd, Fort Lauderdale, FL 33308-4042
Tel (954) 630-9449 Founded/Ownrshp 1998
Sales 100.0MM EMP 25
SIC 7011 6719 Resort hotel; Investment holding companies, except banks
Pr: James Verrillo
*Pr: James Verillo
*VP: Daniel Lambert

D-U-N-S 02-023-2836
■ RESORTQUEST INTERNATIONAL INC
(Suby of WYNDHAM HOLDINGS)
8955 Us Highway 98 W # 203, Destin, FL 32550-7263
Tel (850) 837-4774 Founded/Ownrshp 2010
Sales 104.2MM[E] EMP 5,000
SIC 7011 6519 Hotels & motels; Real property lessors
Pr: Edward H Seymour Jr
*Pr: Mark Fioravanti
*COO: L Park Brady
Sls Dir: Ann Baker

D-U-N-S 93-187-2774
■ RESORTQUEST REAL ESTATE OF FLORIDA INC
(Suby of RESORTQUEST INTERNATIONAL INC) ★
35000 Emerald Coast Pkwy, Destin, FL 32541-4701
Tel (850) 837-3700 Founded/Ownrshp 1995
Sales 46.4MM EMP 1,008
SIC 7011 8741 Resort hotel; Management services
Pr: Edward Seymor
Pr: James Olin
Opers Mgr: Ron Whitfield
Sales Asso: Chip Wasson

RESORTS CASINO HOTEL
See DGMB CASINO LLC

D-U-N-S 86-716-2497
RESORTS CASINO HOTEL
DGMB CASINO
(Suby of RESORTS CASINO HOTEL) ★
1133 Boardwalk, Atlantic City, NJ 08401-7395
Tel (609) 344-6000 Founded/Ownrshp 2010
Sales 52.7MM[E] EMP 1,400
SIC 7011 Casino hotel
CFO: Tim Ebling
CFO: Frank Mc Carthy

RESORTS EAST CHICAGO
See RIH ACQUISITIONS IN LLC

D-U-N-S 80-031-4655
RESORTS GROUP INC
Rr 209, Bushkill, PA 18324
Tel (570) 588-6661 Founded/Ownrshp 2006
Sales 58.6MM[E] EMP 2,698
SIC 7011 6552 Hotels; Land subdividers & developers, commercial
Pr: W Andrew Worthington
*COO: Mark Turner
*CFO: Kevin Lavelle
VP: Gina Bertucci
VP: Josh Herschlag
VP: Kurt Rawding
Genl Couns: Thomas Casale

RESORTS TUNICA CASINO
See RIH ACQUISITIONS MS I LLC

RESOUND
See GN HEARING CARE CORP

D-U-N-S 04-615-7046
RESOURCE AMERICA INC
RAI
(Suby of C-III CAPITAL PARTNERS LLC) ★
1 Crescent Dr Ste 203, Philadelphia, PA 19112-1015
Tel (215) 546-5005 Founded/Ownrshp 1966, 2016
Sales 99.8MM EMP 737
SIC 6531 6722 7359 Real estate managers; Management investment, open-end; Equipment rental & leasing
Pr: Jonathan Z Cohen
Ch Bd: Edward E Cohen
CFO: Thomas C Elliott
VP: Arthur J Miller
Mng Dir: David Desantis
Board of Directors: Michael J Bradley, Carlos C Campbell, Donald W Delson, Hersh Kozlov, Andrew M Lubin, Richard Reiss Jr, John S White

D-U-N-S 78-734-8395
▲ RESOURCE CAPITAL CORP
712 5th Ave Fl 12, New York, NY 10019-4154
Tel (212) 506-3870 Founded/Ownrshp 2005
Sales 167.6MM EMP 704[E]
Accts Grant Thornton Llp Philadelph
Tkr Sym RSO Exch NYS
SIC 6798 Real estate investment trusts
Pr: Robert C Lieber
*Ch Bd: Steven J Kessler
CFO: David J Bryant
Ex VP: Jeffrey F Brotman
Sr VP: Jeffrey D Blomstrom
Sr VP: David E Bloom
VP: Eldron C Blackwell

D-U-N-S 09-416-8135
RESOURCE CENTER
(Suby of NYSARC INC) ★
200 Dunham Ave, Jamestown, NY 14701-2528
Tel (716) 661-4829 Founded/Ownrshp 1994
Sales 86.1MM EMP 1,700
SIC 8093 6513 6512 8052 Rehabilitation center, outpatient treatment; Apartment building operators; Nonresidential building operators; Intermediate care facilities
Ex Dir: Paul Cesana
*CFO: Denise Jones
Exec: Cynthia Neu
Dir Rx: Gregory Bender
Prgrm Mgr: Beth Jermain
Nurse Mgr: Laura Seiberg
MIS Dir: Stephen Lindquist
Pr Dir: Steve Waterson
Nutrtnst: Sue Stull
HC Dir: Marcia Restivo

D-U-N-S 05-888-4834
RESOURCE CENTER FOR INDEPENDENT LIVING (INC)
401 Columbia St, Utica, NY 13502-3421
Tel (315) 797-4642 Founded/Ownrshp 1983
Sales 22.2MM EMP 1,250[E]
Accts Bonadio & Co Llp Clinton N
SIC 8399 Advocacy group
CFO: Wendy Gagliardo
Mktg Dir: Susan Gage
Mktg Dir: Diana Sorrento

D-U-N-S 13-186-8051
RESOURCE CO INC
1292 S Stratford Rd, Winston Salem, NC 27103-3016
Tel (336) 896-1000 Founded/Ownrshp 1986
Sales 50.0MM EMP 1,750
SIC 7363 7361 Temporary help service; Executive placement
Pr: Kathy T Lineberry
*Sec: Lester R Burnette
*VP: Betty Jo Burnette
Dir IT: Jessica Shouse
IT Man: Glenn Chamberlin
VP Opers: Christopher Wakefield

D-U-N-S 06-623-0202
RESOURCE COLLECTION INC
COMMAND GUARD SERVICES
3771 W 242nd St Ste 205, Torrance, CA 90505-6566
Tel (310) 219-3272 Founded/Ownrshp 1962
Sales 16.4MM[E] EMP 1,400
SIC 7349 7381 0782 3564 Air duct cleaning; Guard services; Lawn & garden services; Air cleaning systems
Ch Bd: Martin Benom
*Sec: Steven Jacobson
*VP: Paula Benom
*VP: Marilyn Jacobson

D-U-N-S 16-943-9192
RESOURCE EMPLOYMENT SOLUTIONS LLC
5900 Lake Ellenor Dr # 100, Orlando, FL 32809-4618
Tel (866) 412-6535 Founded/Ownrshp 1996
Sales 87.6MM EMP 135[E]
Accts Juan M Joaquin Hidalgo Cpa
SIC 7361 7363 Employment agencies; Help supply services
COO: Louis Lluberes
CFO: Moises Lluberes
VP: Eduardo Dominguez

RESOURCE GROUP, THE
See TRG HOLDINGS LLC

D-U-N-S 09-354-2517
RESOURCE HEALTHCARE OF AMERICA INC
1819 Peachtree Rd Ne # 520, Atlanta, GA 30309-1851
Tel (404) 364-2900 Founded/Ownrshp 1991
Sales 117.1MM EMP 10
SIC 6531 Real estate agents & managers
CEO: Bryant Coats
Off Mgr: Diane Fisher

D-U-N-S 62-323-7831
RESOURCE LABEL GROUP LLC
MIDSOUTH RFID
147 Seaboard Ln, Franklin, TN 37067-8217
Tel (615) 661-5900 Founded/Ownrshp 1991
Sales 108.6MM[E] EMP 700
SIC 2759 2752 Commercial printing; Commercial printing, lithographic
CEO: Robert Simko
*Pr: William E Burch
*CFO: Treina Blair
CFO: Clayton Smith
VP: Tim Goodwin
VP: Wayne Taber
Exec: Mark Davis
Plnt Mgr: Robert Craig
QI Cn Mgr: Annette Humphrey

D-U-N-S 79-188-4968 IMP/EXP
RESOURCE MANAGEMENT ENTERPRISES INC
9999 Anderson Ave, Chicago Ridge, IL 60415-1256
Tel (708) 425-8565 Founded/Ownrshp 1992
Sales 170.3MM[E] EMP 200
SIC 4953 Recycling, waste materials
Pr: Calvin Tigchelaar
Ex VP: Michael Zabalaoui
*Sr VP: Greg Maxwell
*VP: William R Slager
VP Opers: Daniel Westra

D-U-N-S 96-235-3020
RESOURCE REAL ESTATE OPPORTUNITY REIT INC
1 Crescent Dr Ste 203, Philadelphia, PA 19112-1015
Tel (215) 231-7050 Founded/Ownrshp 2010
Sales 118.3MM EMP 71[E]
Accts Grant Thornton Llp Philadelph
SIC 6798 Real estate investment trusts
Ch Bd: Jonathan Cohen
*CEO: Alan F Feldman
*CFO: Steven Saltzman

RESOURCE STAFFING GROUP
See NORTHWEST STAFFING RESOURCES INC

D-U-N-S 87-294-7143
▲ RESOURCES CONNECTION INC
17101 Armstrong Ave, Irvine, CA 92614-5730
Tel (714) 430-6400 Founded/Ownrshp 1996
Sales 598.5MM EMP 3,283
Accts Rsm Us Llp Irvine California
Tkr Sym RECN Exch NGS
SIC 8742 7389 8721 Management consulting services; Business planning & organizing services; Financial services; Legal & tax services; Accounting, auditing & bookkeeping; Auditing services
CEO: Kate W Duchene
*Ch Bd: Donald B Murray
COO: Tracy B Stephens
CFO: Nathan W Franke
Ex VP: Tanja Cebula
Ex VP: Nathan Franke
Sr VP: Tracey Figurelli
VP: Stephen Barker
Mng Dir: John Angelo
Mng Dir: Mahesh Krishnamurti
CIO: Brandon Johnson
Board of Directors: Susan J Crawford, Neil Dimick, Robert Kistinger, A Robert Pisano, Jolene Sykes Sarkis, Anne Shih, Michael H Wargotz

D-U-N-S 08-419-8928
RESOURCES FOR HUMAN DEVELOPMENT INC
R H D
4700 Wphickon Ave Ste 126, Philadelphia, PA 19144
Tel (215) 951-0300 Founded/Ownrshp 1970
Sales 242.1MM EMP 3,000
Accts Shechtman Marks Devor Pc Phil
SIC 8322 8093 8052 8331 8361 Individual & family services; Social service center; Self-help organization; Senior citizens' center or association; Mental health clinic, outpatient; Intermediate care facilities; Job training & vocational rehabilitation services; Residential care
Pr: Bob Fishman
VP: Don Bryant
Assoc Dir: Carol Flinn-Roberts
Assoc Dir: Mark Whiteman
Comm Man: Kevin Roberts
Pgrm Dir: Stephanie Dowd
Pgrm Dir: Jim McPhail

D-U-N-S 80-974-9880
RESOURCES MANAGEMENT INC
1931 Buffalo Rd, Rochester, NY 14624-1535
Tel (585) 426-8000 Founded/Ownrshp 1992
Sales 3.6MM EMP 1,200[E]
SIC 8741 Business management
Pr: Mark Fuller

D-U-N-S 13-526-2512
RESOURCING EDGE INC
1309 Ridge Rd Ste 200, Rockwall, TX 75087-4219
Tel (214) 771-4411 Founded/Ownrshp 2003
Sales 98.4MM[E] EMP 7,300
SIC 8721 8742 Payroll accounting service; Human resource consulting services
Pr: Ted Crawford
*CFO: Randal Dotson
VP: Richard Borg
VP: Mark Selby

RESPIRATORY CARE DEPARTMENT
See PARK PLAZA HOSPITAL INC

D-U-N-S 08-072-8314 IMP/EXP
RESPIRONICS INC
PHILIPS
(Suby of PHILIPS CONSUMER LIFESTYLE) ★
1010 Murry Ridge Ln, Murrysville, PA 15668-8525
Tel (724) 387-5200 Founded/Ownrshp 2008
Sales 1.5MMM[E] EMP 4,900
SIC 3641 3845 3841 3564 8351 Electric light bulbs, complete; Patient monitoring apparatus; Surgical & medical instruments; Blowers & fans; Child day care services
CEO: Brent Shafer
*Ch Bd: Gerald E McGinnis
*Pr: Pamela Dunlap
COO: Gene Rindels
CFO: Dan Beveino
*CFO: Han Jansen
*Treas: Daniel J Bevevino
Sr Cor Off: Jeff Beard
Ex VP: Robert Oates
Ex VP: R I Davis
*Ex VP: Craig B Reynolds
VP: Joseph Alampi
*VP: Paul Cavanaugh
*VP: Steven P Fulton
*VP: Susan A Lloyd
VP: James Vetricek
VP: Geoffrey C Waters
VP: Paul Woodring
Exec: Tim Murphy
Dir Surg: Leverda Wallace
Board of Directors: Jennifer Christiansen, William Decker, Terry J Dewberry, Pamela L Dunlap, Richard Gruber, Joseph E Innamorati, Eric Kulikowski

D-U-N-S 08-306-8036
RESPONSIVE EDUCATION SOLUTIONS
1301 Waters Ridge Dr, Lewisville, TX 75057-6022
Tel (972) 420-7050 *Founded/Ownrshp* 1998
Sales 134.9MM *EMP* 400
Accts Evans Pingleton And Howard P
SIC 8211 Public elementary & secondary schools
COO: Robert Davidson
**Pr:* Willard French
**Pr:* Lupe Gonzalez
**CEO:* Charles Cook
**VP:* Marvin Reynolds
CTO: Patrick Tanner
Pr Dir: Mike Terry
Teacher Pr: Elisa Yoder

D-U-N-S 62-613-0538
■ RESPONSYS INC
RESPONSYS.COM
(*Suby of* OC ACQUISITION LLC) ★
1100 Grundy Ln Ste 300, San Bruno, CA 94066-3066
Tel (650) 745-1700 *Founded/Ownrshp* 2013
Sales 103.0MM[E] *EMP* 866[E]
SIC 7371 7372 Computer software development; Business oriented computer software
CEO: Daniel D Springer
**CFO:* Christian A Paul
**Chf Mktg O:* Scott V Olrich
Sr VP: Joan Burke
**Sr VP:* Julian Ong
Sr VP: Michael Della Penna
Sr VP: Jason Zintak
VP: Dan Burcaw
VP: Tony Castiglioni
VP: Rich Fleck
VP: Sundeep Parsa

RESPONSYS.COM
See RESPONSYS INC

D-U-N-S 03-089-5031
REST HAVEN ILLIANA CHRISTIAN CONVALESCENT HOME
REST HAVEN VILLAGE WOODS
18601 North Creek Dr A, Tinley Park, IL 60477-6398
Tel (708) 342-8100 *Founded/Ownrshp* 1956
Sales 95.2MM *EMP* 1,079
SIC 8051 8361 Convalescent home with continuous nursing care; Home for the aged
CEO: Richard C Schutt
**CFO:* William De Young
Ex Dir: Henry Doorn

REST HAVEN VILLAGE WOODS
See REST HAVEN ILLIANA CHRISTIAN CONVALESCENT HOME

D-U-N-S 00-698-9552
RESTAURANT ASSOCIATES CORP (DE)
RA RESTAURANT GROUP DIV
(*Suby of* EUREST DINING SERVICES) ★
132 W 31st St Rm 601, New York, NY 10001-3103
Tel (212) 613-5500 *Founded/Ownrshp* 1919, 1994
Sales 251.2MM[E] *EMP* 7,500
SIC 5812 Restaurant, family: chain; Buffet (eating places); Contract food services
CEO: Richard Cattani
**Pr:* Ed Sirhal
Treas: John Forrest
Treas: Scott Magram
Dir Soc: Sharon Colabello
Dir Soc: Jennifer Macmillan
Dir Soc: Paul Richards
Genl Mgr: Tom Lambert
Dir IT: Irving Ng
VP Opers: Patricia Sharp
Sls&Mrk Ex: Tony Hill

D-U-N-S 61-399-1483
RESTAURANT ASSOCIATES LLC
(*Suby of* EUREST DINING SERVICES) ★
132 W 31st St Rm 601, New York, NY 10001-3103
Tel (212) 613-5500 *Founded/Ownrshp* 2003
Sales 19.0MM[E] *EMP* 2,004[E]
SIC 5812 Contract food services

RESTAURANT DEPOT
See RD FOOD SERVICES LLC

D-U-N-S 94-936-5662 IMP/EXP
RESTAURANT DEPOT LLC
(*Suby of* JETRO CASH & CARRY) ★
1524 132nd St, College Point, NY 11356-2440
Tel (718) 762-8700 *Founded/Ownrshp* 1996
Sales 349.8MM[E] *EMP* 190
SIC 5147 5141 5142 5181 5194 Meats, fresh; Groceries, general line; Packaged frozen goods; Beer & other fermented malt liquors; Tobacco & tobacco products
CEO: Stanley Fleishman
**VP:* Richard Kirshner
QA Dir: Scott Sromek

D-U-N-S 08-245-7425
RESTAURANT MANAGEMENT CO OF WICHITA INC
7700 E Polo Dr, Wichita, KS 67206-3001
Tel (316) 634-1190 *Founded/Ownrshp* 1974
Sales 10.0MM *EMP* 3,000
SIC 5812 Pizzeria, chain
Pr: Hal W Mc Coy II
Dir Risk M: Heather Matthews
Dir IT: Danny Wallace

D-U-N-S 07-432-0888
RESTAURANT MANAGEMENT CORP
1575 Adler Cir Ste C, Portage, IN 46368-6408
Tel (219) 764-3355 *Founded/Ownrshp* 1972
Sales 54.5MM[E] *EMP* 1,500
SIC 5812 Fast-food restaurant, chain
Pr: Rodney Lubeznik

D-U-N-S 06-713-4866
RESTAURANT MANAGEMENT GROUP
902 Murfreesboro Pike, Nashville, TN 37217-1502
Tel (423) 349-6204 *Founded/Ownrshp* 1971
Sales 21.5MM[E] *EMP* 1,000
SIC 5812 Pizzeria, chain
Pr: Mike H Martin
**CFO:* Randy Hooten

D-U-N-S 01-765-1811
RESTAURANT MANAGEMENT INC
ARBY'S
300 Main St, Cincinnati, OH 45202-4159
Tel (513) 362-8900 *Founded/Ownrshp* 1965
Sales 53.8MM[E] *EMP* 1,500
SIC 5812

D-U-N-S 18-610-4261
RESTAURANT SERVICES INC
5877 Sw 29th St, Topeka, KS 66614-2465
Tel (785) 273-1805 *Founded/Ownrshp* 1979
Sales 889.2M *EMP* 1,000
SIC 5812 Pizzeria, chain
Pr: David Curnutt
**CFO:* Sheldon Hochuli

D-U-N-S 02-174-1418 IMP
RESTAURANT SUPPLY CHAIN SOLUTIONS LLC
950 Breckenridge Ln # 300, Louisville, KY 40207-4674
Tel (502) 896-5900 *Founded/Ownrshp* 1999
Sales 238.5MM *EMP* 205
Accts Crowe Horwath Llp Elkhart In
SIC 5812 5046 5141 5149 Eating places; Restaurant equipment & supplies; Groceries, general line; Groceries & related products
Pr: Daniel E Woodside
**CEO:* Steve McCormick
**COO:* John Hans
**CFO:* William Bickley
**CFO:* Ray Khan
Sr VP: Ron Burks
Sr VP: Todd Silberg
VP: Gordon Crum
**VP:* William Holden
VP: Dickie Oliver
Prgrm Mgr: Aamina Akram

D-U-N-S 62-611-8806
RESTAURANT SYSTEMS INC
TACO BELL
3880 W Battlefield St, Springfield, MO 65807-8432
Tel (417) 887-5929 *Founded/Ownrshp* 2003
Sales 28.7MM[E] *EMP* 1,000
SIC 5812 Fast-food restaurant, chain
Ch Bd: Mike Treadwell
**VP:* Homer Hunt
S&M/VP: Melissa Hauswirth

D-U-N-S 12-384-9411
RESTAURANT TECHNOLOGIES INC
RTI
2250 Pilot Knob Rd # 100, Mendota Heights, MN 55120-1127
Tel (651) 796-1600 *Founded/Ownrshp* 2015
Sales 587.1MM[E] *EMP* 760
SIC 5149 3631 Cooking oils; Household cooking equipment
CEO: Jeffrey R Kiesel
**CFO:* Robert E Weil
VP: Jason Cocco
VP: Lisa Merryfield
VP: Wade Wiestling
Area Mgr: Kelly Davis
Area Mgr: David Fredd
Genl Mgr: Stalio Callas
Genl Mgr: Jim Herendeen
Genl Mgr: Rick Hinshaw
Genl Mgr: Justin Jagodzinski

D-U-N-S 01-027-3332
RESTAURANTS RESOURCES INC (IA)
PIZZA HUT
1805 State St Ste 201, Bettendorf, IA 52722-4985
Tel (563) 243-7571 *Founded/Ownrshp* 1983
Sales 18.3MM[E] *EMP* 1,000
SIC 5812 Pizzeria, chain
Pr: James V Golinvaux
**VP:* John Golinvaux

RESTAURANTS UNLIMITED
See R U CORP

D-U-N-S 04-867-4881
RESTAURANTS UNLIMITED INC (TX)
KINCAID'S
411 1st Ave S Ste 200, Seattle, WA 98104-3094
Tel (206) 634-0550 *Founded/Ownrshp* 1969, 2007
Sales 156.2MM[E] *EMP* 3,800
SIC 5812

D-U-N-S 92-830-9434
■ RESTON HOSPITAL CENTER LLC
COLUMBIA HCA
(*Suby of* HOSPITAL COPORATION OF AMERICA) ★
1 Park Plz, Nashville, TN 37203-6527
Tel (615) 344-9551 *Founded/Ownrshp* 1999
Sales 83.4MM[E] *EMP* 2,000
SIC 8011 8062 Offices & clinics of medical doctors; General medical & surgical hospitals
Genl Mgr: Jane Frey

D-U-N-S 07-867-2209
▲ RESTORATION HARDWARE HOLDINGS INC
15 Koch Rd Ste K, Corte Madera, CA 94925-1231
Tel (415) 924-1005 *Founded/Ownrshp* 2011
Sales 2.1MMM *EMP* 4,600[E]
Tkr Sym RH *Exch* NYS
SIC 5712 Furniture stores
Ch Bd: Gary Friedman
Pr: Eri Chaya
Pr: Demonty Price
Ofcr: Karen Boone
Board of Directors: Carlos Alberini, Keith C Belling, Mark Demilio, Hilary Krane, Katie Mitic, Ali Rowghani, Leonard Schlesinger

D-U-N-S 09-255-4427 IMP/EXP
■ RESTORATION HARDWARE INC
(*Suby of* RESTORATION HARDWARE HOLDINGS INC) ★
15 Koch Rd Ste J, Corte Madera, CA 94925-1231
Tel (415) 924-1005 *Founded/Ownrshp* 2012
Sales 1.2MMM[E] *EMP* 3,300
SIC 5712 Furniture stores; Office furniture; Outdoor & garden furniture
Ch Bd: Gary Friedman
Pr: Asad Jafari
**COO:* Ken Dunaj
**Chf Cred:* Eri Chaya
**Ofcr:* Karen Boone
Ex VP: Patty Island
Sr VP: Bob Hassen
Sr VP: Elyse Robinson
VP: Daniela Hartung
VP: Patti Low
VP: Vivian C Macdonald
VP: Stuart McKeachie
VP: Bonnie Miller
VP: Richard O'Donnell
VP: Vladimir Simovich
VP: Heather Smith
VP: Shawn Smith
VP: Jim Thomsen
Exec: Allan Billston
Exec: Lisa Versacio

D-U-N-S 62-534-0302
RESULTS COMPANIES LLC
100 Ne 3rd Ave Ste 200, Fort Lauderdale, FL 33301-1102
Tel (954) 921-2400 *Founded/Ownrshp* 2010
Sales 451.5MM[E] *EMP* 1,770
SIC 4813 Voice telephone communications
Pr: Alec Brecker
**CFO:* Angelo Gencarelli
VP: Brian Fallers
Prgrm Mgr: Amy Dowling
Opers Mgr: April Breeden
Opers Mgr: Rebecca Bustamante
Opers Mgr: Juan Campos

D-U-N-S 02-254-8650
RESURGENCE ASSET MANAGEMENT LLC
1185 Av Of The Amer Fl 18, New York, NY 10036-2603
Tel (212) 710-5001 *Founded/Ownrshp* 1997
Sales 91.9MM[E] *EMP* 1,600
SIC 6282 2865 2821 2869 2861 2819 Investment advisory service; Styrene; Ethylbenzene; Toluene; Acrylonitrile-butadiene-styrene resins (ABS resins); Plasticizer/additive based plastic materials; Industrial organic chemicals; Acetic & chloroacetic acid & metallic salts; Plasticizers, organic: cyclic & acyclic; Methanol, natural (wood alcohol); Sodium & potassium compounds, exc. bleaches, alkalies, alum.; Cyanides
CFO: William Packer

RESURRECTION MEDICAL CENTER
See PRESENCE CHICAGO HOSPITALS NETWORK

D-U-N-S 02-032-9762
RETA TRUST
A CATHOLIC HEALTHCARE TRUST
1255 Battery St Ste 450, San Francisco, CA 94111-6235
Tel (415) 546-9300 *Founded/Ownrshp* 2016
Sales 166.4MM *EMP* 1
SIC 6733 Trusts
Prin: John Stein

RETAIL 4 LESS
See SB CAPITAL GROUP LLC

D-U-N-S 03-924-5493 IMP
RETAIL CONCEPTS INC
SUN & SKI SPORTS
10560 Bissonnet St # 100, Houston, TX 77099-2269
Tel (281) 340-5000 *Founded/Ownrshp* 1980
Sales 95.0MM *EMP* 700
Accts Harper & Pearsin Company Pc
SIC 5941 Sporting goods & bicycle shops
CEO: Steven Rath
**CEO:* H Frank Stanley
**Sr VP:* Karl Salz
**VP:* Valerie Nixon

D-U-N-S 19-928-1887
RETAIL DATA LLC
RETAILDATA
11013 W Broad St Ste 300, Glen Allen, VA 23060-6017
Tel (804) 678-7500 *Founded/Ownrshp* 1989
Sales 63.1MM[E] *EMP* 2,100[E]
SIC 7299 Information services, consumer
CEO: Christine Cottrell
**Pr:* David Cottrell
COO: Chris Ferguson
Sr VP: Kim Watts
IT Man: Cliff McDonald
Software D: Daniel Folkes
Sales Exec: Brianne Porter

RETAIL DATA SYSTEM
See DATA SYSTEMS INC

RETAIL HOME IMPROVEMENT PDTS
See MARMON RETAIL PRODUCTS INC

D-U-N-S 06-209-5914
RETAIL INVESTORS OF TEXAS LTD
MARKET BASKET
2420 Nederland Ave, Nederland, TX 77627-6048
Tel (409) 727-3104 *Founded/Ownrshp* 1963
Sales 318.0MM[E] *EMP* 2,300
SIC 5411 Supermarkets
Pr: David S Thompson Sr
VP: Steve Cormier
**VP:* Steven Cormier
VP: Michael Rohrbaugh
**Prin:* Skylar Thompson
Div Mgr: Roger Herbert
Advt Mgr: Charles Barbee

D-U-N-S 80-956-6263
▲ RETAIL OPPORTUNITY INVESTMENTS CORP
8905 Towne Centre Dr # 108, San Diego, CA 92122-5608
Tel (858) 677-0900 *Founded/Ownrshp* 2009
Sales 192.7MM *EMP* 65[E]
Tkr Sym ROIC *Exch* NGS
SIC 6798 Real estate investment trusts
Pr: Stuart A Tanz
**Ch Bd:* Richard A Baker
COO: Richard K Schoebel
CFO: Michael B Haines

D-U-N-S 79-883-4227
▲ RETAIL PROPERTIES OF AMERICA INC
2021 Spring Rd Ste 200, Oak Brook, IL 60523-1845
Tel (630) 634-4200 *Founded/Ownrshp* 2003
Sales 603.9MM *EMP* 240[E]
Tkr Sym RPAI *Exch* NYS
SIC 6798 Real estate investment trusts
Pr: Steven P Grimes
**Ch Bd:* Gerald M Gorski
Pr: Karla Chase
COO: Shane C Garrison
CFO: Heath R Fear
Ex VP: Angela Aman
Ex VP: Paula C Maggio
IT Man: Suzanne Nadolny
Opers Mgr: Jason Garrison
Board of Directors: Bonnie S Biumi, Frank A Catalano Jr, Paul R Gauvreau, Robert G Gifford, Richard P Imperiale, Peter L Lynch, Thomas J Sargeant

D-U-N-S 18-965-3199
RETAIL SERVICES & SYSTEMS INC
TOTAL WINE AND MORE
6600 Rockledge Dr Ste 150, Bethesda, MD 20817-1806
Tel (301) 795-1000 *Founded/Ownrshp* 1985
Sales 448.1MM[E] *EMP* 1,800
SIC 5921 Liquor stores
Pr: David Trone
Recvr: Michael Martin
**CFO:* Scott Litten
Chf Mktg O: Kevin Lewis
**Sr VP:* John Jordan
**Sr VP:* Robert Schoening
VP: Sean Barton
VP: Sandra Clemens
VP: Mike Mulderig
VP: Rob O'Connell
**VP:* Mark Powell
**VP:* Roger Wright
Exec: Susan Zewicke

D-U-N-S 82-832-1401
■ RETAIL VENTURES SERVICES INC
(*Suby of* DSW INC) ★
4150 E 5th Ave, Columbus, OH 43219-1802
Tel (614) 238-4105 *Founded/Ownrshp* 2011
Sales 32.3M *EMP* 1,196[E]
SIC 5661 Shoe stores
Prin: Robert J Tannous
VP: Stephen Nicewicz
Dir IT: Greg Short
IT Man: Bill Lambeth

RETAILDATA
See RETAIL DATA LLC

D-U-N-S 96-237-7854
▲ RETAILMENOT INC
301 Congress Ave Ste 700, Austin, TX 78701-2930
Tel (512) 777-2970 *Founded/Ownrshp* 2007
Sales 249.1MM *EMP* 522[E]
Tkr Sym SALE *Exch* NGS
SIC 7311 Advertising agencies
Ch Bd: G Cotter Cunningham
COO: Kelli A Beougher
CFO: J Scott Di Valerio
Sr VP: Louis J Agnese III
VP: Michael Magaro
CTO: Paul M Rogers
Sftwr Eng: Chris Page
Sftwr Eng: Kyle Smith
Sftwr Eng: Justin Steigel
Sftwr Eng: Sam Tipton
Board of Directors: C Thomas Ball, Jeffrey M Crowe, Eric A Korman, Jules A Maltz, Greg J Santora, Brian H Sharples, Tamar Yehoshua

D-U-N-S 00-912-4640
■ RETALIX USA INC
(*Suby of* NCR CORP) ★
6100 Tennyson Pkwy # 150, Plano, TX 75024-6101
Tel (469) 241-8400 *Founded/Ownrshp* 1996, 2013
Sales 84.0MM[E] *EMP* 237
SIC 7371 Computer software development
CEO: Shuky Sheffer
Pr: Raymond G Carlin
**Pr:* Chanda L Kirchner
**CFO:* Moshe Geller
**Treas:* John A Boudreau
Ex VP: Ronen Levkovich
Ex VP: Gil Roth
Ex VP: Tammy Weant
VP: Ofer Nimts
VP: John Sehnert
**VP:* Eli Spirer
VP: Larry Susman
Exec: Amber Risteen

RETAMA MNOR NRSING CNTR/LRDO-W
See SSC LAREDO WEST OPERATING CO LLC

RETAMA MNOR NRSING CNTR/MCLLEN
See SSC MCALLEN RETAMA OPERATING CO LLC

D-U-N-S 03-426-8581
RETIF OIL & FUEL L L C
1840 Jutland Dr, Harvey, LA 70058-2361
Tel (504) 349-9000 *Founded/Ownrshp* 1965, 1993
Sales 163.7MM[E] *EMP* 120
SIC 5171 Petroleum bulk stations
**CFO:* David Hecker

D-U-N-S 96-724-8290
RETIREE HEALTH PLAN AND TRUST FOR CERTAIN EMPOF AIR LINE PILOTS ASSNINTL
535 Herndon Pkwy, Herndon, VA 20170-5226
Tel (703) 689-4238 *Founded/Ownrshp* 2011
Sales 134.6MM *EMP* 2[E]
SIC 6733 Trusts
Prin: Kelly Collie

D-U-N-S 96-783-7415
RETIREES OF GOODYEARTIRE AND RUBBER CO HEALTH CARETRUST
60 Blvd OfThe Allies, Pittsburgh, PA 15222-1214
Tel (866) 694-6477 *Founded/Ownrshp* 2011
Sales 178.9MM *EMP* 2
Accts Bond Beebe Bethesda Md
SIC 5531 Automotive tires

D-U-N-S 05-081-9952
RETIREMENT HOUSING FOUNDATION INC
911 N Studebaker Rd # 100, Long Beach, CA 90815-4980
Tel (562) 257-5100 *Founded/Ownrshp* 1961
Sales 29.7MM *EMP* 2,500
SIC 6531 Real estate agents & managers
Pr: Rev Laverne R Joseph
**Ch Bd:* Raymond East
**V Ch:* Christina E Potter
**V Ch:* Darryl M Sexton
**Treas:* Frank G Jahrling
Genl Mgr: Christopher Purcell
Site Mgr: Dena Maiolo
Mktg Dir: Amanda McHugh
Mktg Dir: Brittany Woeller
Pr Mgr: Diane Trask
Board of Directors: John Bauman, Norma Desaegher, David Ethington, Rev David S Moyer, Stewart M Simington

RETIREMENT LIVING COMMUNITIES
See CAPITAL SENIOR LIVING INC

RETRIEVER PAYMENTS SYSTEMS
See NATIONAL PROCESSING CO

D-U-N-S 01-605-3922
RETRIEVEX ACQUISITION CORP II
ACCESS
6818 Patterson Pass Rd, Livermore, CA 94550-4230
Tel (925) 583-0100 *Founded/Ownrshp* 2016
Sales 193.6MM *EMP* 1,500
SIC 4226 7375 Special warehousing & storage; Information retrieval services
CEO: Rob Alston
VP Opers: Amy Marantino

D-U-N-S 96-545-4502
▲ RETROPHIN INC
12255 El Camino Real # 250, San Diego, CA 92130-4087
Tel (760) 260-8600 *Founded/Ownrshp* 2008
Sales 99.8MM *EMP* 130[E]
Tkr Sym RTRX *Exch* NGM
SIC 2834 8731 Pharmaceutical preparations; Biotechnical research, commercial
Pr: Stephen Aselage
**Ch Bd:* Steve Richardson
COO: Neil McFarlane
CFO: Laura M Clague
Ex VP: Alvin Shih
VP: Laura Clague
Ex Dir: Karl Odquist
Genl Couns: Margaret Valeur-Jensen
Board of Directors: Roy D Banes, Timothy Coughlin, Cornelius E Golding, John W Kozarich, Gary Lyons, Jeffrey Meckler

D-U-N-S 06-771-3107
RETZER RESOURCES INC
MCDONALD'S
1215 S Main St, Greenville, MS 38701-6342
Tel (662) 335-7138 *Founded/Ownrshp* 1973
Sales 58.9MM[E] *EMP* 1,600
SIC 5812 Fast-food restaurant, chain
Pr: Michael Retzer

REUNITED CLOTHING
See REUNITED LLC

D-U-N-S 96-954-4746 IMP
REUNITED LLC
REUNITED CLOTHING
1385 Broadway Fl 22, New York, NY 10018-6022
Tel (646) 439-7576 *Founded/Ownrshp* 2011
Sales 120.0MM *EMP* 70
SIC 5137 5136 Women's & children's clothing; Men's & boys' clothing
Ch Bd: Donald Kesselman
**Pr:* Jerry Finestone
**Pr:* Jeff Sherman

D-U-N-S 14-783-3446 IMP
■ REUTERS AMERICA LLC
THOMSON REUTERS
(*Suby of* THOMSON REUTERS CORP) ★
3 Times Sq, New York, NY 10036-6564
Tel (646) 223-4000 *Founded/Ownrshp* 2006
Sales 321.5MM[E] *EMP* 2,500
SIC 7383 News syndicates; News reporting services for newspapers & periodicals
CEO: James C Smith
Pr: David Craig
Pr: Brian M D Vaughan
Ex VP: Stephane Bello
Sr VP: Paul Eedle
Sr VP: Howard C Naphtali
VP: Ellen Kroehler

D-U-N-S 10-695-7210 IMP/EXP
REV AMBULANCE GROUP ORLANDO INC
WHEELED COACH INDUSTRIES
(*Suby of* COLLINS INDUSTRIES INC) ★
2737 Forsyth Rd, Winter Park, FL 32792-6673
Tel (407) 677-7777 *Founded/Ownrshp* 1985
Sales 110.4MM[E] *EMP* 378
SIC 3711 Ambulances (motor vehicles), assembly of
Pr: Robert L Collins
CFO: Bob Mixner
**Sec:* Donald Lynn Collins
**VP:* Dino Cusamano
Sfty Mgr: Anna Fullen
Sls Mgr: Paul Holzapfel

REV GROUP
See GOLDSHIELD FIBER GLASS INC

D-U-N-S 96-194-1494
REV GROUP INC
ASV
(*Suby of* AMERICAN INDUSTRIAL PARTNERS) ★
111 E Kilbourn Ave # 2600, Milwaukee, WI 53202-6647
Tel (414) 290-0190 *Founded/Ownrshp* 2008
Sales 1.1MMM[E] *EMP* 765[E]
SIC 3711 Ambulances (motor vehicles), assembly of
CEO: Tim Sullivan
**Ch Bd:* Randall Swift
Pr: Matt Ford
Pr: Ryan Lamb
Pr: Joe Leggett
Pr: John Resnik
CEO: Kent Tyler
**COO:* Chris Eppel
**COO:* James R Meyer
**CFO:* Hans Heinsen
**CFO:* Dean Nolden
Chf Cred: Marcus Berto
VP: Mark Bevan
**VP:* John Dreasher
VP: Shawn Furman
VP: Ron Sorensen
VP: John Walsh
Board of Directors: Don Stebbins

D-U-N-S 80-386-8892
REV HOLDINGS INC
(*Suby of* REVLON HOLDINGS INC) ★
466 Lexington Ave Fl 21, New York, NY 10017-3153
Tel (212) 527-4000 *Founded/Ownrshp* 1997
Sales 228.8MM[E] *EMP* 8,000
SIC 2844 3421 5122 5199 5999 Toilet preparations; Cosmetic preparations; Perfumes & colognes; Hair preparations, including shampoos; Clippers, fingernail & toenail; Scissors, hand; Cosmetics, perfumes & hair products; Toilet preparations; Wigs; Toiletries, cosmetics & perfumes
Ch Bd: Ronald O Perelman
CFO: Todd J Slotkin
**Ofcr:* Howard Gittis
Ofcr: Robert K Kretzman
Ex VP: Mary Massimo
Ex VP: Barry F Schwartz
Sr VP: Martine Williamson
VP: Barretto Carlos

D-U-N-S 10-835-7633 IMP
REV-A-SHELF CO LLC
TRESCO LIGHTING
(*Suby of* JONES PLASTIC AND ENGINEERING CO LLC) ★
12400 Earl Jones Way, Louisville, KY 40299-3664
Tel (502) 499-5835 *Founded/Ownrshp* 1978
Sales 228.8MM[E] *EMP* 1,310
SIC 3823 5063 Controllers for process variables, all types; Lighting fittings & accessories
VP: Alline Goldsmith
VP: David P Noe

D-U-N-S 12-799-4676
REVAL.COM INC
420 5th Ave Fl 5, New York, NY 10018-0941
Tel (212) 393-1313 *Founded/Ownrshp* 1999
Sales 147.9MM[E] *EMP* 519
SIC 7371 Computer software development
CEO: Jiro Okochi
COO: Phil Pettinato
CFO: Dino Ewing
Chf Mktg O: Justin Brimfield
Ofcr: Patrick Trozzo
VP: Kirsten Colyer
VP: Jim Gilbert
VP: Leslie Regino
VP: Scott Samuells
VP: Winston Xie
Off Mgr: Maureen Cohen

D-U-N-S 18-956-3448
■ REVCO DISCOUNT DRUG CENTERS INC
CVS
(*Suby of* NASHUA HOLLIS CVS INC) ★
1 Cvs Dr, Woonsocket, RI 02895-6146
Tel (401) 765-1500 *Founded/Ownrshp* 2007
Sales 133.4MM[E] *EMP* 2,300
SIC 5912 Drug stores & proprietary stores
Pr: Tom Ryan
Treas: Phil Galbo

D-U-N-S 00-545-5183 IMP
REVCOR INC
251 Edwards Ave, Carpentersville, IL 60110-1941
Tel (847) 428-4411 *Founded/Ownrshp* 1946
Sales 84.5MM[E] *EMP* 450
SIC 3564 3089 Blowers & fans; Blowers & fans; Injection molded finished plastic products
CEO: John Reichwein Jr
**CFO:* Andrew K Groharing
CFO: Mark Stuttle
**VP:* Lee Frick
VP: Keith Funke
**VP:* Craig Hall
VP: Paul Vogel
Exec: Robert Knight
Dept Mgr: Dan Beebe
CIO: Stephen J Szorc
QC Dir: Dave Simmons

D-U-N-S 79-121-3809
REVEL ENTERTAINMENT GROUP LLC
ALAN REVEL ENTERTAINMENT
500 Boardwalk, Atlantic City, NJ 08401-7609
Tel (609) 340-0003 *Founded/Ownrshp* 2006
Sales NA *EMP* 5,500[E]
SIC 7011

D-U-N-S 07-981-3552
REVENUE PROCESSING SOLUTIONS INC
RPS
28293 Via Del Mar, San Juan Capistrano, CA 92675-6342
Tel (949) 481-9080 *Founded/Ownrshp* 2010
Sales 400.0MM *EMP* 7
SIC 7371 7389 Computer software development & applications;
CEO: Rick Pemberton

D-U-N-S 14-915-0000
■ REVENUEMED INC
(*Suby of* NAVIGANT CONSULTING INC) ★
3740 Davinci Ct Ste 300, Norcross, GA 30092-7613
Tel (770) 246-9797 *Founded/Ownrshp* 2015
Sales 63.3MM[E] *EMP* 1,400
SIC 8748 Business consulting
CEO: Michael Von Grey
Chf Cred: Scott Schrader
VP: Tim McPherson

REVERE BUILDING PRODUCTS
See GENTEK BUILDING PRODUCTS INC

D-U-N-S 00-693-2388
REVERE ELECTRIC SUPPLY CO (IL)
8807 187th St, Mokena, IL 60448-7706
Tel (312) 738-3636 *Founded/Ownrshp* 1919
Sales 172.2MM[E] *EMP* 220
SIC 5063

D-U-N-S 13-281-8647 IMP/EXP
REVERE INDUSTRIES LLC
REVERE PACKAGING
838 N Delsea Dr, Clayton, NJ 08312-1004
Tel (856) 881-3600 *Founded/Ownrshp* 2000
Sales 65.1MM[E] *EMP* 1,010
SIC 3497 3089 Foil containers for bakery goods & frozen foods; Food casings, plastic
Pr: David Charles
**VP:* David Korus
**VP:* Ron Lapointe
**VP:* John Wherry
Ql Cn Mgr: Drenise Henderson

D-U-N-S 78-377-0758
REVERE INDUSTRIES LLC
16855 Suthpark Dr Ste 100, Westfield, IN 46074
Tel (317) 580-2420 *Founded/Ownrshp* 2005
Sales 245.4MM *EMP* 1,200
SIC 3089 3399 3363 3497 Injection molding of plastics; Aluminum atomized powder; Aluminum die-castings; Metal foil & leaf
CEO: James R Hamelink
Pr: Sean Black
COO: Ben James
VP: James R Crews Jr
Genl Mgr: Danny Neff

REVERE PACKAGING
See REVERE INDUSTRIES LLC

D-U-N-S 78-068-1925
REVERE PLASTICS SYSTEMS GROUP LLC
(*Suby of* REVERE INDUSTRIES LLC) ★
401 Elm St, Clyde, OH 43410-2148
Tel (419) 547-6918 *Founded/Ownrshp* 2005
Sales 132.9MM[E] *EMP* 650
SIC 3089 Injection molded finished plastic products

D-U-N-S 78-707-7010 IMP
REVERE PLASTICS SYSTEMS LLC
(*Suby of* REVERE INDUSTRIES LLC) ★
401 Elm St, Clyde, OH 43410-2148
Tel (419) 547-6918 *Founded/Ownrshp* 2005
Sales 163.6MM[E] *EMP* 800[E]
SIC 3089 Injection molding of plastics
Genl Mgr: Rustin Shields
Dir IT: Mike Thornburg
Opers Mgr: Ben Fuentes
Ql Cn Mgr: Brian Clark

D-U-N-S 80-187-0478 IMP
■ REVLON CONSUMER PRODUCTS CORP
(*Suby of* REVLON INC) ★
1 New York Plz, New York, NY 10004-1901
Tel (212) 527-4000 *Founded/Ownrshp* 1992
Sales 1.9MMM *EMP* 5,700[E]
Accts Kpmg Llp New York New York
SIC 2844 3421 Toilet preparations; Cosmetic preparations; Perfumes & colognes; Hair preparations, including shampoos; Clippers, fingernail & toenail; Scissors, hand
Ch Bd: Ronald O Perelman
Treas: Larry Winoker
Ofcr: Lawrence B Alletto
Sr VP: Jessica T Graziano
VP: Deena Fishman
Board of Directors: Alan S Bernikow, Barry F Schwartz

D-U-N-S 00-126-5818 IMP
REVLON HOLDINGS INC (DE)
(*Suby of* RGI GROUP INC) ★
237 Park Ave, New York, NY 10017-3140
Tel (212) 527-4000 *Founded/Ownrshp* 1985, 1987
Sales 622.9MM[E] *EMP* 8,000
SIC 2844 3421 5122 5199 5999 Toilet preparations; Cosmetic preparations; Perfumes & colognes; Hair preparations, including shampoos; Clippers, fingernail & toenail; Scissors, hand; Cosmetics, perfumes & hair products; Toilet preparations; Wigs; Toiletries, cosmetics & perfumes
Ch Bd: Ronald O Perelman
Pr: David Kennedy
Sr VP: Ronald Blitstein
Prin: Donald G Drapkin
Prin: Howard Gittis

D-U-N-S 78-882-0165 IMP
▲ REVLON INC
1 New York Plz, New York, NY 10004-1901
Tel (212) 527-4000 *Founded/Ownrshp* 1932
Sales 1.9MMM *EMP* 5,700[E]
Tkr Sym REV *Exch* NYS
SIC 2844 Toilet preparations; Perfumes & colognes; Deodorants, personal; Hair coloring preparations
Pr: Fabian T Garcia
**Ch Bd:* Ronald O Perelman
COO: Giovanni Pieraccioni
CFO: Juan R Figuereo
Ex VP: Nelson Griggs
VP: Francisco Cornellana
VP: Lenny Hirsch
VP: Al A Martin
VP: John Martin
VP: Mark Sexton
Dir IT: Don Barnick
Board of Directors: Alan S Bernikow, Meyer Feldberg, Robert K Kretzman, Ceci Kurzman, Paul M Meister, Tamara Mellon, Debra G Perelman, Paul G Savas, Barry F Schwartz

D-U-N-S 04-416-1529
■ REVLON REAL ESTATE CORP
(*Suby of* REVLON CONSUMER PRODUCTS CORP) ★
466 Lexington Ave Fl 13, New York, NY 10017-3140
Tel (212) 527-4000 *Founded/Ownrshp* 1987
Sales 251.1MM[E] *EMP* 4,900
SIC 5122 2844 3421 5199 5999 Cosmetics, perfumes & hair products; Toilet preparations; Clippers, fingernail & toenail; Wigs; Toiletries, cosmetics & perfumes
Ch Bd: Ronald O Perelman

D-U-N-S 61-193-2856
▲ REVOLUTION LIGHTING TECHNOLOGIES INC
177 Broad St Fl 12, Stamford, CT 06901-5002
Tel (203) 504-1111 *Founded/Ownrshp* 1991
Sales 129.6MM *EMP* 238[E]
Tkr Sym RVLT *Exch* NAS
SIC 3674 3641 3993 Light emitting diodes; Electric light bulbs, complete; Signs & advertising specialties
Ch Bd: Robert V Lapenta
**CFO:* James A Depalma
Chf Mktg O: Michael Eckert
Sr VP: Brian L Daley
Board of Directors: Robert A Basil Jr, William D Ingram, Robert V Lapenta Jr, Dennis McCarthy, Stephen G Virtue

D-U-N-S 60-755-7423
REVOLUTION LLC
1717 Rhode Island Ave Nw # 1000, Washington, DC 20036-3027
Tel (202) 776-1400 *Founded/Ownrshp* 2005
Sales 160.4MM[E] *EMP* 850
SIC 6211 7514 Investment firm, general brokerage; Passenger car rental
V Ch: Philippe Bourguignon
Ex VP: Dale Jones
VP: Ronald Klain
Comm Dir: Jade Floyd
Mng Dir: Scott Hilleboe
Genl Couns: Jim Bramson

D-U-N-S 11-554-2123
REVSPRING INC
29241 Beck Rd, Wixom, MI 48393-3679
Tel (248) 567-7300 *Founded/Ownrshp* 2016
Sales 111.4MM[E] *EMP* 425[E]
SIC 7371 7375 Computer software development & applications; On-line data base information retrieval
Pr: Timothy Schriner
CFO: John Carson
CFO: Bob Flynn
Ofcr: Analiese Fusner
Ofcr: Barbara Rice
VP: Vincent Arminio
VP: Steven Crane
Genl Mgr: Martin Callahan
CIO: Michael Hennessy
CTO: Bill Needham
VP Sls: Frank Calderone

D-U-N-S 83-250-4059
REVSTONE INDUSTRIES LLC
2008 Cypress St Ste 100, Paris, KY 40361-1380
Tel (859) 294-5590 *Founded/Ownrshp* 2008
Sales 483.9MM[E] *EMP* 3,845
SIC 2821 3086 3341 Plastics materials & resins; Plastics foam products; Secondary nonferrous metals
Pr: Myra Moreland
**Ch Bd:* George Hofmeister
Pr: Donald W Dees
Pr: Yu Zhang
COO: Dennis Peterson
**CFO:* Kevin P Bagby
VP: Dan Dressler
Genl Mgr: Gus Miller
VP Sls: Bob Lacourciere
Genl Couns: Daniel Smith

REW MATERIALS
See KCG INC

D-U-N-S 11-862-2877
REWARDS NETWORK INC
(*Suby of* EGI ACQUISITION PARENT, L.L.C.)
2 N Riverside Plz # 200, Chicago, IL 60606-2677
Tel (312) 756-0021 *Founded/Ownrshp* 2010
Sales 120.8MM[E] *EMP* 401[E]
SIC 7389 Financial services; Advertising, promotional & trade show services
CEO: Dan Kazan
Pr: Tom Walsh
**Pr:* Ronald L Blake
Pr: Robert S Wasserman
**CFO:* Christopher J Locke
Chf Mktg O: Kara Walsh
Ex VP: Robert J Hughes
**Sr VP:* Roya Behnia
Sr VP: Stuart Chant
Sr VP: Tom Crowder
**Sr VP:* Megan E Flynn
VP: Jon Marzetta
VP Bus Dev: Hunt Kingsbury
Dir Bus: John Dybdal

D-U-N-S 11-288-6817
▲ REX AMERICAN RESOURCES CORP
7720 Paragon Rd, Dayton, OH 45459-4050
Tel (937) 276-3931 *Founded/Ownrshp* 1980
Sales 436.4MM *EMP* 116
Tkr Sym REX *Exch* NYS
SIC 2869 6531 Fuels; Ethyl alcohol, ethanol; Real estate leasing & rentals
Pr: Zafar Rizvi
**Ch Bd:* Stuart A Rose
CFO: Douglas L Bruggeman
Board of Directors: Mervyn L Alphonso, Charles A Elcan, Lee Fisher, David S Harris, Lawrence Tomchin

D-U-N-S 09-476-3307
REX ELECTRIC & TECHNOLOGIES LLC (IL)
200 W Monroe St Ste 1700, Chicago, IL 60606-5072
Tel (312) 251-3620 *Founded/Ownrshp* 1921, 1974
Sales 98.8MM *EMP* 300
Accts Plante & Moran Pllc Chicago
SIC 1731 Electrical work; Fire detection & burglar alarm systems specialization
Pr: Dominic M Sergi
**CFO:* Michael A Segreti
**Ex VP:* Thomas Q Smith
**VP:* Michael A Bosco
**VP:* Eric A Smith
Off Mgr: Pam Eichhorst
Snr PM: Duane Chenier

D-U-N-S 80-588-4769
▲ REX ENERGY CORP
366 Walker Dr, State College, PA 16801-7085
Tel (814) 278-7267 *Founded/Ownrshp* 1996
Sales 171.9MM *EMP* 274E
Tkr Sym REXX *Exch* NGS
SIC 1311 Crude petroleum & natural gas; Crude petroleum production; Natural gas production
Pr: Thomas C Stabley
**Ch Bd:* Lance T Shaner
COO: Robert W Ovitz
CFO: Thomas G Rajan
Ofcr: Curtis J Walker
Sr VP: F Scott Hodges
Sr VP: Jennifer L McDonough
Sr VP: David E Pratt
Board of Directors: Jack N Aydin, John A Lombardi, Eric L Mattson, John J Zak

D-U-N-S 02-419-1350
REX HEALTHCARE INC
(*Suby of* UNC HOSPITALS) ★
4420 Lake Boone Trl, Raleigh, NC 27607-7505
Tel (919) 784-3100 *Founded/Ownrshp* 1986
Sales 749.8MM *EMP* 5,500
Accts Clifton Larson Allen Llp Char
SIC 8082 8011 8062 Home health care services; Offices & clinics of medical doctors; General medical & surgical hospitals
CEO: Gary Park
**Pr:* David Strong
COO: Steve Burriss
COO: Susan Sandberg
**CFO:* Bernadette Spong
CFO: Andrew Zukowski
**Ch:* A Dale Jenkins
Treas: Susan Fennell
Treas: Carolina Scout
VP: Chad T Lefteris
VP: Joel Ray
Dir OR: Ruth Nelson-Mustard
Dir Rad: Kent Davis
Dir Rad: Gregory Hinn
Dir Rad: Mark Knelson
Dir Rx: Jane Green

D-U-N-S 05-851-8267
REX HOSPITAL INC
(*Suby of* REX HEALTHCARE INC) ★
4420 Lake Boone Trl, Raleigh, NC 27607-6599
Tel (919) 784-3100 *Founded/Ownrshp* 1986
Sales 813.6MM *EMP* 3,500
SIC 8062 General medical & surgical hospitals
Pr: David W Strong
**COO:* Steve Burriss
**CFO:* Bernadette M Spong
Ex VP: George S York Jr
VP: Bill Reese III
Dir Sec: Chris Main
Pathlgst: Preeti Sharma
Doctor: Ahmed Farag MD
Doctor: Naveen Narahari
Diag Rad: Andrew Moran
Genl Couns: Don Esposito Jr

D-U-N-S 12-466-3910
REX MOORE ELECTRICAL CONTRACTORS & ENGINEERS INC
6001 Outfall Cir, Sacramento, CA 95828-1020
Tel (916) 372-1300 *Founded/Ownrshp* 1922
Sales 84.9MME *EMP* 550
Accts Gallina Llp Sacramento Ca
SIC 1731 General electrical contractor
CEO: David R Moore
Pt: William C Hubbard
Pt: James B Littlejohn
Pt: Steven R Moore
Telecom Ex: Roberto Santos
Dir IT: Mike Sullivan
Mfg Mgr: Ken Fleming
Snr Mgr: Darby Brookman
Snr Mgr: Joel Westerman
Snr Mgr: Craig Wolf

D-U-N-S 12-466-4645
REX MOORE GROUP INC
6001 Outfall Cir, Sacramento, CA 95828-1020
Tel (916) 372-1300 *Founded/Ownrshp* 2001
Sales 130.2MME *EMP* 450
SIC 1731 8711 Electrical work; Engineering services
Pr: David Rex Moore
**Pr:* Doug Cuthbert
**CFO:* J Brock Littlejohn
**CFO:* James Brock Littlejohn
**Ex VP:* William C Hubbard
Brnch Mgr: Brent Iseman
Ql Cn Mgr: Brian Stone
Snr Mgr: Dave Rogers
Snr Mgr: Mark Shontz
Snr Mgr: Randy Silva
Snr Mgr: Dave Villegas

D-U-N-S 00-432-0180 IMP/EXP
REX-HIDE INC (DE)
705 S Lyons Ave, Tyler, TX 75702-6857
Tel (903) 593-7387 *Founded/Ownrshp* 1917
Sales 105.3MME *EMP* 250
SIC 3061 3069 2891 6799 Automotive rubber goods (mechanical); Rubber automotive products; Adhesives; Investors
Pr: Brad J Hoeffner
**Pr:* Tjkav Hoeffnek
**Treas:* Chris McCurry
**Treas:* Delores Thurston
Genl Mgr: Tim Allred
Sftwr Eng: Jonathan Leung
Sls Mgr: Marshall Sharp

D-U-N-S 60-380-7814 IMP/EXP
■ REXAIR HOLDINGS INC
(*Suby of* NEWELL BRANDS) ★
50 W Big Beavr Rd Ste 350, Troy, MI 48084-5203
Tel (248) 643-7222 *Founded/Ownrshp* 2014
Sales 140.0MME *EMP* 22
SIC 3635 Household vacuum cleaners
CEO: F Philip Handy

REXAIR, LLC
See REXAIR LLC

D-U-N-S 05-700-9797 IMP/EXP
■ REXAIR LLC
REXAIR, LLC
(*Suby of* REXAIR HOLDINGS INC) ★
50 W Big Beaver Rd # 350, Troy, MI 48084-5203
Tel (248) 643-7222 *Founded/Ownrshp* 2001
Sales 140.0MM *EMP* 20
SIC 3635 Household vacuum cleaners
CEO: Paul T Vidovich
Exec: Kathleen Karamanian
Dir IT: Jeff Gammon
Dir IT: Jane Gasparovich
Mktg Mgr: Greg Jackson

D-U-N-S 09-283-4233 EXP
■ REXALL SUNDOWN INC
SUNDOWN NATURALS
(*Suby of* ARCO PHARMACEUTICAL) ★
110 Orville Dr, Bohemia, NY 11716-2506
Tel (631) 567-9500 *Founded/Ownrshp* 2003
Sales 173.6MME *EMP* 1,065
SIC 5961 5122 2833 Catalog & mail-order houses; Catalog sales; Mail order house; Pharmaceuticals, mail order; Vitamins & minerals; Vitamins, natural or synthetic: bulk, uncompounded
Pr: Steven Cahillane
**Pr:* Michael Collins
**CFO:* Dipak Golechha
**VP:* Christopher Brennan
**Prin:* Scott Rudolph

REXAM
See BPREX HEALTHCARE PACKAGING INC

D-U-N-S 00-510-5366 IMP/EXP
REXAM BEVERAGE CAN CO
(*Suby of* REXAM INC) ★
8770 W Bryn Mawr Ave Fl 8, Chicago, IL 60631-3515
Tel (773) 399-3000 *Founded/Ownrshp* 1929
Sales 993.1MME *EMP* 3,000
SIC 3411 Food & beverage containers; Aluminum cans
CEO: William R Barker
**Pr:* Rich Grimley
**CFO:* Thomas Holz
CFO: Alan Schumacher
**VP:* Gene Pawula
Plng Mgr: Antony Walsh
QA Dir: Jeffrey Kruse
Dir IT: Karen Pritchett
Netwrk Eng: Humberto Corral
**VP Opers:* Mark Stafford
Plnt Mgr: John Chesnut

REXAM CLOSURE SYSTEMS
See BPREX HEALTHCARE BROOKVILLE INC

REXAM CONTAINERS
See SILGAN PLASTIC FOOD CONTAINERS CORP

REXAM INC.
See BALL INC

REXEL
See SOUTHERN ELECTRIC SUPPLY CO INC

REXEL
See BRANCH GROUP INC

REXEL ENERGY SOLUTIONS
See REXEL INC

D-U-N-S 78-666-7282
REXEL HOLDINGS USA CORP
(*Suby of* REXEL DEVELOPPEMENT SAS)
14951 Dallas Pkwy, Dallas, TX 75254-7892
Tel (972) 387-3600 *Founded/Ownrshp* 2006
Sales 4.7MMME *EMP* 7,200
SIC 5063 Electrical apparatus & equipment; Electrical supplies
Pr: Brian McNally
**Treas:* Elizabeth Jean Galloway
Treas: Gary Hibbs
**Sr VP:* James F Hibberd
**VP:* Benjamin Adams
**VP:* Lou-Anne F Annino
VP: Louanne Annino
**VP:* Edgar Aponte
**VP:* Jeff Baker
**VP:* Christopher Chickanosky
**VP:* Mark Daniel
**VP:* Patrick Davis
**VP:* Mark Denison
**VP:* Bradford Greene
**VP:* John C Gschwind
**VP:* Gary Haire
VP: Brian B Lizotte
**VP:* Janie Lunday
**VP:* Scott McLendon
**VP:* Brendan O'Hare
**VP:* Lisa Scinta
Board of Directors: Patrick Berard

D-U-N-S 04-151-3979 EXP
REXEL INC
14951 Dallas Pkwy # 1000, Dallas, TX 75254-6784
Tel (972) 387-3600 *Founded/Ownrshp* 1973
Sales NA *EMP* 4,012
SIC 5063

D-U-N-S 60-977-7701 IMP/EXP
REXEL INC
REXEL ENERGY SOLUTIONS
(*Suby of* REXEL HOLDINGS USA CORP) ★
14951 Dallas Pkwy # 1000, Dallas, TX 75254-6784
Tel (972) 387-3600 *Founded/Ownrshp* 1993
Sales 2.6MMME *EMP* 6,800
SIC 5063 Electrical supplies; Transformers, electric; Wire & cable
CEO: Brian McNally
VP: Renee Junell
Brnch Mgr: James King
Dist Mgr: Mark Nickells
Sales Asso: Joseph Campanella
Sales Asso: Billy Faulk
Sales Asso: Efrain Gonzalez
Sales Asso: Casey Jones
Sales Asso: Gregory Lawson
Sales Asso: Joe Vella

D-U-N-S 07-886-6663
REXFORD INDUSTRIAL REALTY INC
11620 Wilshire Blvd # 1000, Los Angeles, CA 90025-6821
Tel (310) 966-1680 *Founded/Ownrshp* 2013
Sales 93.9MM *EMP* 40E
SIC 6798 Real estate investment trusts
Co-CEO: Howard Schwimmer
**Ch Bd:* Richard Ziman
CFO: Adeel Khan
**Co-CEO:* Michael S Frankel

D-U-N-S 82-892-6555 IMP/EXP
▲ REXNORD CORP
4701 W Greenfield Ave, Milwaukee, WI 53214-5300
Tel (414) 643-3739 *Founded/Ownrshp* 2006
Sales 1.9MMM *EMP* 7,700
Accts Ernst & Young Llp Milwaukee
Tkr Sym RXN *Exch* NYS
SIC 3491 Water works valves; Process control regulator valves
Exec: Paul W Jones
Pr: Todd A Adams
Pr: Matthew Stillings
Pr: Craig G Wehr
Pr: Kevin J Zaba
CFO: Mark W Peterson
Ofcr: George J Powers
Sr VP: Rodney Jackson
VP: Graham Acree
VP: David Harrison
VP: Patricia M Whaley
Exec: Don Nelson

D-U-N-S 19-213-0763 IMP/EXP
■ REXNORD INDUSTRIES LLC
(*Suby of* REXNORD LLC) ★
247 W Freshwater Way # 200, Milwaukee, WI 53204-4117
Tel (414) 643-3000 *Founded/Ownrshp* 2002
Sales 474.0MME *EMP* 1,530
SIC 3568 3566 3625 3714 Chain, power transmission; Sprockets (power transmission equipment); Couplings, shaft: rigid, flexible, universal joint, etc.; Speed changers (power transmission equipment), except auto; Electromagnetic clutches or brakes; Motor vehicle parts & accessories
Ex VP: Patricia Murrin
VP: Venu Pai
Genl Mgr: Bernie Samuelson
QA Dir: Mary Rivera
IT Man: Gregg Fusselman
IT Man: Thomas Jefferson
IT Man: Waisun Wong
VP Opers: Mike Baka
Mfg Mgr: Rita Lewandowski
Mfg Mgr: Jarrod Luedtke
Opers Mgr: Robert Finzel

D-U-N-S 00-609-7083 IMP/EXP
■ REXNORD LLC
(*Suby of* RBS GLOBAL INC) ★
3001 W Canal St, Milwaukee, WI 53208-4222
Tel (414) 342-3131 *Founded/Ownrshp* 2005
Sales 822.0MME *EMP* 1,530
SIC 3566 3325 3599 Speed changers, drives & gears; Gears, power transmission, except automotive; Speed changers (power transmission equipment), except auto; Reduction gears & gear units for turbines, except automotive; Steel foundries; Machine & other job shop work
Exec: Wes Stone
Genl Mgr: Thomas Drobka
Genl Mgr: Joel Zar
Sfty Mgr: Anna Littig
S&M/VP: Pete Davis

D-U-N-S 55-636-7691 IMP/EXP
■ REXNORD-ZURN HOLDINGS INC
(*Suby of* REXNORD LLC) ★
4701 W Greenfield Ave, Milwaukee, WI 53214-5310
Tel (414) 643-3000 *Founded/Ownrshp* 1998
Sales 134.4MME *EMP* 1,530
SIC 3568 3566 3625 3714 Chain, power transmission; Sprockets (power transmission equipment); Couplings, shaft: rigid, flexible, universal joint, etc.; Speed changers (power transmission equipment), except auto; Electromagnetic clutches or brakes; Motor vehicle parts & accessories
Ch Bd: George M Sherman
Bd of Dir: Damian J Giangiacomo

D-U-N-S 93-995-2172 IMP/EXP
REYES HOLDINGS LLC
6250 N River Rd Ste 9000, Rosemont, IL 60018-4241
Tel (847) 227-6500 *Founded/Ownrshp* 1996
Sales 11.1MMME *EMP* 10,300
SIC 5181 5142 Beer & other fermented malt liquors; Packaged frozen goods
Owner: David Reyes
COO: Ray Guerin
CFO: Daniel P Doheny
Ofcr: Nicky Mintz
Ex VP: Dean Janke Business Developme
Ex VP: Dean H Janke
VP: Dan Cook
VP: Mark Forbes
VP: Loni Sonephet
VP: John Walker
VP Bus Dev: Al Christian

D-U-N-S 15-710-8643 IMP/EXP
▲ REYNOLDS AMERICAN INC
401 N Main St, Winston Salem, NC 27101-3804
Tel (336) 741-2000 *Founded/Ownrshp* 2004
Sales 10.6MMM *EMP* 5,700E
Accts Kpmg Llp Greensboro North Ca
Tkr Sym RAI *Exch* NYS
SIC 2111 2121 2131 Cigarettes; Cigars; Smoking tobacco
Pr: Susan M Cameron
Pr: Jeffery A Gentry
CFO: Andrew D Gilchrist
Treas: Daniel A Fawley
Ofcr: Lisa J Caldwell
Ex VP: Michael P Auger
Ex VP: Nancy H Hawley
Ex VP: Daniel J Herko
Ex VP: Martin L Holton III
Ex VP: Cressida Lozano
Sr VP: Frederick W Smothers
VP: Sharon Smith
VP: Ken Whitehurst
Board of Directors: Ricardo Oberlander, Jerome Abelman, Ronald S Rolfe, John Boehner, Thomas C Wajnert, Martin D Feinstein, John J Zillmer, Luc Jobin, Murray S Kessler, Holly Keller Koeppel, Robert Lerwill, Nana Mensah, Lionel L Nowell III

D-U-N-S 00-427-7430
REYNOLDS AND REYNOLDS CO (OH)
(*Suby of* UNIVERSAL COMPUTER SYSTEMS INC) ★
1 Reynolds Way, Kettering, OH 45430-1586
Tel (937) 485-2000 *Founded/Ownrshp* 1889, 2006
Sales 1.6MMME *EMP* 6,000
SIC 7373 6159 Computer integrated systems design; Machinery & equipment finance leasing
CEO: Bob Brockman
**Pr:* Ron Lamb
CFO: William Matteson
Ex VP: Jeffrey Almoney
Ex VP: Frank Caccamo
Ex VP: Greg Collins
Ex VP: Donald I Lamonds
Ex VP: Michael McLean
Sr VP: Scott Schafer
VP: Scott Barr
VP: Paul Guthrie
VP: Robert Guttman
VP: Donny Holender
VP: Terry Jones
VP: Rick Kerr
VP: Heisler Larry
VP: Keith Legg
VP: Cathy Orrico
VP: David Shimek
VP: Deidre Smith
Exec: Dee Falkenberg

D-U-N-S 13-755-7633
REYNOLDS AND REYNOLDS CO
(*Suby of* REYNOLDS AND REYNOLDS CO) ★
6700 Hollister St, Houston, TX 77040-5331
Tel (713) 718-1800 *Founded/Ownrshp* 1979
Sales 39.2M *EMP* 2,400
SIC 7371 Custom computer programming services; Software programming applications; Computer software development
CEO: Robert Brockman
**Pr:* Robert Nalley
VP: Eric Edwards
Dir Bus: Brian Seufert
CTO: Tommy Barras
Dir IT: Clint Cargill
IT Man: Walter Lowry
VP Opers: Carlin Cooper
Site Mgr: Scott Lorenz
Sls&Mrk Ex: Lyman Fong

REYNOLDS COMPANY, THE
See D REYNOLDS CO LLC

REYNOLDS CONSUMER PRODUCTS CO
See REYNOLDS CONSUMER PRODUCTS LLC

D-U-N-S 80-730-1101
REYNOLDS CONSUMER PRODUCTS HOLDINGS INC
(*Suby of* REYNOLDS GROUP HOLDINGS LIMITED)
1900 W Field Ct, Lake Forest, IL 60045-4828
Tel (847) 482-3050 *Founded/Ownrshp* 2008
Sales 1.0MMME *EMP* 3,314
SIC 7389 Packaging & labeling services
Pr: Thomas Degnan
**Treas:* Michael Graham
**VP:* Charles Cox
**VP:* Robert Smith

D-U-N-S 80-958-7194 EXP
REYNOLDS CONSUMER PRODUCTS LLC
REYNOLDS CONSUMER PRODUCTS CO
(*Suby of* REYNOLDS CONSUMER PRODUCTS HOLDINGS INC) ★
1900 W Field Ct, Lake Forest, IL 60045-4828
Tel (847) 482-3500 *Founded/Ownrshp* 2008
Sales 467.5MME *EMP* 1,081E
SIC 3353 Foil, aluminum
Pr: Lance Mitchell
**Pr:* Thomas J Degnan
CFO: David Taylor
**Treas:* Dan Zimmerlee
**Sr VP:* Paul Thomas
VP: Lisa Burns
VP: Ken Lane
VP: Jeff Wilkison
**Prin:* David Watson
CIO: Jeff Kintzle
VP Sls: Steve Pace
Board of Directors: Craig Stargardt

D-U-N-S 00-134-4209 IMP/EXP
■ REYNOLDS METALS CO LLC (DE)
(*Suby of* ARCONIC INC) ★
6603 W Broad St, Richmond, VA 23230-1711
Tel (804) 281-2000 *Founded/Ownrshp* 1928, 2000
Sales 1.6MMME *EMP* 18,000

SIC 3411 Aluminum cans; Beverage cans, metal: except beer; Beer cans, metal; Food containers, metal
Pr: Donna Dabney
**Pr:* Chris L Ayers
**CFO:* Donald A Kluthe
**Treas:* Peter Hong
Ex VP: Julian Taylor
**VP:* Mark J Davies
**VP:* James R Michaud
VP: Louanne Nabhan
Ex Dir: William Bourke
Opers Mgr: Kim Cecil

REYNOLDS NAILING CO
See REYNOLDS PACKING CO

D-U-N-S 80-460-4630
REYNOLDS PACKAGING GROUP LTD
6641 W Broad St Fl 5, Richmond, VA 23230-1728
Tel (804) 281-2000 *Founded/Ownrshp* 2007
Sales NA *EMP* 9,500
SIC 7389

D-U-N-S 80-730-3941
REYNOLDS PACKAGING INC
6641 W Broad St Fl 4, Richmond, VA 23230-1728
Tel (804) 281-2000 *Founded/Ownrshp* 2008
Sales NA *EMP* 2,897[E]
SIC 7389

D-U-N-S 04-741-0790 IMP/EXP
REYNOLDS PACKING CO
REYNOLDS NAILING CO
33 E Tokay St, Lodi, CA 95240-4149
Tel (209) 369-2725 *Founded/Ownrshp* 1955
Sales 167.5MM[E] *EMP* 85
SIC 0723 5148 2449

REYNOLDS PLANTATION
See LINGER LONGER DEVELOPMENT CO

D-U-N-S 00-612-6387 IMP/EXP
REYNOLDS PRESTO PRODUCTS INC
PRESTO PRODUCTS COMPANY
(*Suby of* REYNOLDS CONSUMER PRODUCTS HOLDINGS INC) ★
670 N Perkins St, Appleton, WI 54914-3133
Tel (800) 558-3525 *Founded/Ownrshp* 1961, 2008
Sales 508.9MM[E] *EMP* 1,663
SIC 2671 2673 3842 Plastic film, coated or laminated for packaging; Food storage & frozen food bags, plastic; Swabs, sanitary cotton
Pr: Degnan Thomas
**Treas:* Michael E Graham
**Treas:* Gleason Sandra J
VP: John Borree
**VP:* Cox Rita M
CIO: John F Rudin
IT Man: Barbara Gaab
IT Man: Ronda Olmsted
Mtls Mgr: Dustin Pankow
Sfty Mgr: Del Volpel
Mktg Mgr: Richard Custer

D-U-N-S 08-662-2719
REYNOLDS SCHOOL DISTRICT 7 (INC)
1204 Ne 201st Ave, Fairview, OR 97024-2499
Tel (503) 492-4921 *Founded/Ownrshp* 1954
Sales 140.5MM *EMP* 810
Accts Roy R Rogers Cpa-Pauly Roge
SIC 8211 Public elementary & secondary schools; Secondary school; Elementary school
Occ Thrpy: Rebec Loring

D-U-N-S 62-775-5010 IMP
RF MICRO DEVICES INC
RFMD
7628 Thorndike Rd, Greensboro, NC 27409-9421
Tel (336) 664-1233 *Founded/Ownrshp* 2015
Sales 843.1MM[E] *EMP* 3,482[E]
SIC 3674

D-U-N-S 08-026-1195
RF1 HOLDING CO
400 Nickerson Rd, Marlborough, MA 01752-4717
Tel (855) 294-3800 *Founded/Ownrshp* 2016
Sales 232.2MM[E] *EMP* 3,064[E]
SIC 3674 6719 Semiconductors & related devices; Investment holding companies, except banks
Pr: Robert Tavares
CFO: Eric F Seeton

RFCUNY - CUNY SCHOOL OF LAW
See RESEARCH FOUNDATION OF CITY UNIVERSITY OF NEW YORK

RFCUNY - STELLA AND CHARLES GU
See RESEARCH FOUNDATION OF CITY UNIVERSITY OF NEW YORK

D-U-N-S 07-103-4946
RFE/RL INC
RADIO FREE EUROPE
1201 Conn Ave Nw Ste 400, Washington, DC 20036-2646
Tel (202) 457-6900 *Founded/Ownrshp* 1976
Sales 93.2MM *EMP* 542
SIC 7922

RFMD
See RF MICRO DEVICES INC

RFMH
See RESEARCH FOD FOR MTAL HY INC

D-U-N-S 36-154-7263
RFPS MANAGEMENT CO II LP
2170 Piedmont Rd Ne, Atlanta, GA 30324-4135
Tel (404) 888-2000 *Founded/Ownrshp* 2003
Sales 56.3MM[E] *EMP* 5,900
SIC 1389 Oil field services
Genl Pt: Randall Rollins
VP: Chuck Lampman

RFS
See RADIO FREQUENCY SYSTEMS INC

RG
See ROBERTS-GORDON LLC

RG APPAREL GROUP
See EXCELLED SHEEPSKIN & LEATHER COAT CORP

D-U-N-S 07-990-8085
■ **RG PARENT LLC**
ROBERT GRAHAM
(*Suby of* DIFFERENTIAL BRANDS GROUP INC) ★
264 W 40th St Fl 10, New York, NY 10018-1516
Tel (212) 869-8001 *Founded/Ownrshp* 2016
Sales 212.5MM[E] *EMP* 100
SIC 5611 Men's & boys' clothing stores; Clothing accessories: men's & boys'
Area Mgr: Gerry Myler
Opers Mgr: Julie Rodriguez
VP Mktg: Naomi Holland

D-U-N-S 00-138-1409 IMP/EXP
RG STEEL WHEELING STEEL GROUP LLC (DE)
WHEELING-PITTSBURGH
(*Suby of* RENCO GROUP INC) ★
1134 Market St, Wheeling, WV 26003-2906
Tel (304) 234-2400 *Founded/Ownrshp* 1852, 2011
Sales 228.8MM[E] *EMP* 3,133
SIC 3312 3444 Sheet or strip, steel, hot-rolled; Sheet or strip, steel, cold-rolled: own hot-rolled; Coated or plated products; Tin-free steel; Roof deck, sheet metal; Siding, sheet metal; Culverts, sheet metal
CEO: John Goodwin
COO: Thomas Cera
CFO: Mark J Yost
Sr VP: Stephen Sorvold
VP: Martin Szymanski
VP: Wilbur B Winland
VP: Wilbur Winland
VP Opers: James Ledgard
VP Opers: Thomas Patrick
Genl Couns: David A Luptk

RG&E
See ROCHESTER GAS AND ELECTRIC CORP

RGA
See REINSURANCE GROUP OF AMERICA INC

D-U-N-S 11-628-6923 IMP
RGB SYSTEMS INC
EXTRON ELECTRONICS
1025 E Ball Rd, Anaheim, CA 92805-5957
Tel (714) 491-1500 *Founded/Ownrshp* 1983
Sales 90.2MM[E] *EMP* 200
SIC 3577 Computer output to microfilm units
Pr: Andrew C Edwards
Pr: Dave Pincek
VP: Casey Hall
VP: Bob Nichols
Prgrm Mgr: Peter Knapp
Snr Sftwr: Daniel Mocelo
Snr Sftwr: William Zhang
CTO: Oliver Montoya
Sys Mgr: Richard Callaway
Web Dev: Jason Mogera
Software D: Rutav Shah

RGBSI
See RAPID GLOBAL BUSINESS SOLUTIONS INC

D-U-N-S 04-938-6139 IMP
■ **RGH ENTERPRISES INC**
INDEPENDENCE MEDICAL
(*Suby of* CARDINAL HEALTH INC) ★
1810 Summit Commerce Park, Twinsburg, OH 44087-2300
Tel (330) 963-6998 *Founded/Ownrshp* 1990
Sales 208.1MM[E] *EMP* 850
SIC 5999 5047 8011

D-U-N-S 01-706-2373
RGI GROUP INC
(*Suby of* MACANDREWS & FORBES INC) ★
625 Madison Ave Frnt 4, New York, NY 10022-1801
Tel (212) 527-4000 *Founded/Ownrshp* 1987
Sales 628.7MM[E] *EMP* 8,241
SIC 2844 3421 5122 5199 5999 Toilet preparations; Cosmetic preparations; Perfumes & colognes; Hair preparations, including shampoos; Clippers, fingernail & toenail; Scissors, hand; Cosmetics, perfumes & hair products; Toilet preparations; Wigs; Toiletries, cosmetics & perfumes
Ch Bd: Ronald O Perelman
**V Ch:* Howard Gittis
Off Mgr: Carol Moral
Board of Directors: Donald Drapkin, Howard Gittis

D-U-N-S 80-034-3829
■ **RGIS HOLDINGS LLC**
(*Suby of* BLACKSTONE GROUP L P) ★
2000 Taylor Rd, Auburn Hills, MI 48326-1771
Tel (248) 651-2511 *Founded/Ownrshp* 2007
Sales 130.4MM[E] *EMP* 1,294
SIC 7389 Inventory computing service
CEO: Bruce Barkus

D-U-N-S 04-243-2542 IMP
■ **RGIS LLC**
(*Suby of* RGIS HOLDINGS LLC) ★
2000 Taylor Rd, Auburn Hills, MI 48326-1771
Tel (248) 651-2511 *Founded/Ownrshp* 2007
Sales 122.2MM[E] *EMP* 420
SIC 7389 Inventory computing service
CEO: Brian McDonald
VP: Richard Baxter
VP: Aamir Chinoy
VP: Kimberlee Gertz
VP: Erik Hayes
VP: Robert Hill
VP: Kevin Little
VP: Dan Sheffield
Mng Dir: Shari Hart
Mng Dir: Joel Melendez
Dist Mgr: David Aldrich

RGM
See ROUND GROUND METALS INC

RGRTA
See ROCHESTER-GENESEE REGIONAL TRANSPORTATION AUTHORITY

D-U-N-S 01-415-0593
RGS INC
SLOANE AUTO GROUP
527 N Easton Rd, Glenside, PA 19038-5017
Tel (215) 885-5400 *Founded/Ownrshp* 1979
Sales 145.0MM[E] *EMP* 400
SIC 5511 Automobiles, new & used
Pr: Robert G Sloane
CFO: Jim Clark
Genl Mgr: Mark Mischler

RGVSG
See RIO GRANDE VALLEY SUGAR GROWERS INC

D-U-N-S 61-346-0419
RGW CONSTRUCTION INC
550 Greenville Rd, Livermore, CA 94550-9297
Tel (925) 606-2400 *Founded/Ownrshp* 1990
Sales 93.0MM *EMP* 200
SIC 1611

D-U-N-S 06-960-2761
RH MONTGOMERY PROPERTIES INC (MO)
214 N Scott St, Sikeston, MO 63801-4146
Tel (573) 471-1113 *Founded/Ownrshp* 1981
Sales 24.0MM[E] *EMP* 2,200
SIC 6512 Commercial & industrial building operation
Pr: Clay Crossen
**Treas:* Jim Reiker

D-U-N-S 78-281-8801
RHA HEALTH SERVICES INC
17 Church St, Asheville, NC 28801-3303
Tel (828) 232-6844 *Founded/Ownrshp* 1989
Sales 126.2MM[E] *EMP* 1,500
SIC 8741 Nursing & personal care facility management
Ch Bd: Robert Coats
**CFO:* John West
**VP:* Bryant Coats
VP: Scott Little
Prgrm Mgr: Ivan Pride

D-U-N-S 19-283-6968
RHA/HOWELL CARE CENTERS INC
3738 Howell Day Care Rd, La Grange, NC 28551-6829
Tel (252) 566-9011 *Founded/Ownrshp* 1970
Sales 32.9MM[E] *EMP* 1,300[E]
SIC 8361 8052 Children's home; Intermediate care facilities
CEO: Bryant Coats
Exec: Sam Hedrick

D-U-N-S 83-261-6689
RHC HOLDING CORP
281 Lotus Dr, Jackson, MO 63755-8801
Tel (573) 204-0373 *Founded/Ownrshp* 2007
Sales 132.8MM[E] *EMP* 550[E]
SIC 6719 Personal holding companies, except banks
Pr: Dale Williams
**CFO:* Sandra Doubledee
**VP:* Scott Wachter
**VP:* Lisa Williams

D-U-N-S 14-823-5864 IMP
RHE HATCO INC
STETSON HATS
601 Marion Dr, Garland, TX 75042-7930
Tel (972) 494-0511 *Founded/Ownrshp* 2009
Sales 111.8MM[E] *EMP* 480
SIC 2353 Hats: cloth, straw & felt
Pr: Stan Redding
COO: Thomas Harris
CFO: Paul Corbett
CFO: Phillip Flamm

D-U-N-S 10-387-6512 IMP/EXP
RHEE BROS INC
7461 Coca Cola Dr, Hanover, MD 21076-1490
Tel (410) 381-9000 *Founded/Ownrshp* 1968
Sales 149.7MM[E] *EMP* 200
SIC 5141 Groceries, general line
Pr: Syng M Rhee
**Treas:* Seung K Rhee
**VP:* Sung K Lee

D-U-N-S 12-156-4579 IMP
RHEEM MANUFACTURING CO INC
(*Suby of* PI. US HOLDING, INC.)
1100 Abernathy Rd # 1700, Atlanta, GA 30328-5657
Tel (770) 351-3000 *Founded/Ownrshp* 1988
Sales 3.1MMM[E] *EMP* 5,700
SIC 3585 3433 Air conditioning units, complete: domestic or industrial; Boilers, low-pressure heating: steam or hot water; Heaters, swimming pool: oil or gas
Pr: J R Jones
**CFO:* Greg Henry
**CFO:* William S Ostan
**Treas:* Chris Peel
VP: Vincent Debo
VP: Joseph A Fristik
VP: Charles Holt
VP: Bill Lux
VP: Simon Parfitt
VP: Ken Rothgeb
Exec: Patricia Husted

D-U-N-S 07-872-8498
RHEEM SALES CO INC
1100 Abernathy Rd # 1400, Atlanta, GA 30328-5620
Tel (770) 351-3016 *Founded/Ownrshp* 2003
Sales NA *EMP* 2,000
SIC 3585 Air conditioning equipment, complete
CEO: Jr Jones
**CFO:* Greg Henry
Dir IT: Diana Flores
Mktg Mgr: Sherri Burkett
Sls Mgr: Michael Mullins

D-U-N-S 14-833-7231 IMP
RHEM LLC
EJ BARTELLS
700 Powell Ave Sw, Renton, WA 98057-2911
Tel (425) 228-4111 *Founded/Ownrshp* 2000
Sales 156.7MM[E] *EMP* 320
SIC 5033 3086 1742

D-U-N-S 04-839-0105
RHF INVESTMENTS INC
401 11th St Nw, Hickory, NC 28601-4750
Tel (828) 326-8350 *Founded/Ownrshp* 2013
Sales 140.0MM[E] *EMP* 1,445
SIC 6799 Investors
CEO: Brandon M Hucks
**Pr:* A Alex Shuford III
**Pr:* A Shuford

D-U-N-S 12-789-3167 IMP/EXP
RHI REFRACTORIES HOLDING CO
(*Suby of* VRD AMERICAS B.V.)
1105 N Market St Ste 1300, Wilmington, DE 19801-1241
Tel (302) 655-6497 *Founded/Ownrshp* 2003
Sales 206.9MM[E] *EMP* 4,500
SIC 3297 3255 1459 3546 3272 3589 Nonclay refractories; Crucibles: graphite, magnesite, chrome, silica, etc.; Graphite refractories: carbon bond or ceramic bond; Cement, magnesia; Clay refractories; Fire clay blocks, bricks, tile or special shapes; Foundry refractories, clay; Magnesite mining; Clays, except kaolin & ball; Power-driven handtools; Drills, portable, except rock: electric or pneumatic; Solid containing units, concrete; Battery wells or boxes, concrete; Shredders, industrial & commercial
Pr: Norbert Wittmann
Prin: Peggy Groover

D-U-N-S 78-416-3136
RHINO RESOURCE PARTNERS LP
424 Lewis Hargett Cir # 250, Lexington, KY 40503-3688
Tel (859) 389-6500 *Founded/Ownrshp* 2010
Sales 206.7MM *EMP* 551[E]
SIC 1221 1222 Bituminous coal surface mining; Coal preparation plant, bituminous or lignite; Bituminous coal-underground mining
CEO: Joe Funk
Genl Pt: Rhino GP LLC
Pr: Richard A Boone
CFO: Scott Morris
Sfty Dirs: Patsy Blackburn

RHINODOX
See ACCESS INFORMATION MANAGEMENT SHARED SERVICES LLC

D-U-N-S 07-996-1170
■ **RHN CLARK MEMORIAL HOSPITAL LLC**
LIFEPOINT/NORTON HEALTHCARE
(*Suby of* REGIONAL HEALTH NETWORK OF KENTUCKY AND SOUTHERN INDIANA LLC)
1220 Missouri Ave, Jeffersonville, IN 47130-3725
Tel (812) 282-6631 *Founded/Ownrshp* 2015
Sales 2.9MM[E] *EMP* 1,500
SIC 8062 8063 General medical & surgical hospitals; Psychiatric hospitals
Pr: Martin Padgett
Chf Path: Yohannes Yesus
CFO: Kirk Strack
Bd of Dir: Debbie Meyer
Bd of Dir: Jennifer Wilcox
Exec: Carol Welch
Dir Inf Cn: Cathy Fugate
Dir Rx: Mark Martin
Ex Dir: Kerri Cokeley
Dir IT: Garry Young
Info Man: Dave Hunt

RHO AMERICAS
See SCHENKER AMERICAS INC

D-U-N-S 80-849-1653
■ **RHODE CVS ISLAND INC**
(*Suby of* CVS HEALTH CORP) ★
1 Cvs Dr, Woonsocket, RI 02895-6195
Tel (401) 765-1500 *Founded/Ownrshp* 2007
Sales 46.5MM[E] *EMP* 3,602[E]
SIC 5912 Drug stores & proprietary stores
Prin: Zenon P Lankowsky

D-U-N-S 78-544-2591
RHODE ISLAND AND PROVIDENCE PLANTATIONS DEPARTMENT OF CORRECTIONS
(*Suby of* EXECUTIVE OFFICE OF STATE OF RHODE ISLAND) ★
40 Howard Ave, Cranston, RI 02920-3031
Tel (401) 462-2611 *Founded/Ownrshp* 1636
Sales NA *EMP* 1,609
SIC 9223 Prison, government;
IT Man: Deborah Marisi
Snr Mgr: Paul Kennedy

D-U-N-S 92-992-2706
RHODE ISLAND DEPT OF HUMAN SERVICES
(*Suby of* EXECUTIVE OFFICE OF STATE OF RHODE ISLAND) ★
57 Howard Ave Fl 2, Cranston, RI 02920-8404
Tel (401) 462-1000 *Founded/Ownrshp* 1900
Sales NA *EMP* 1,096
SIC 9441 Administration of social & manpower programs;
IT Man: Robert Farley

D-U-N-S 07-571-0996
RHODE ISLAND HOSPITAL
HASBRO CHILDREN'S HOSPITAL
593 Eddy St, Providence, RI 02903-4923
Tel (401) 444-4000 *Founded/Ownrshp* 1863
Sales 1.0MMM *EMP* 6,400
SIC 8062 General medical & surgical hospitals
CEO: Margaret Van Bree
**Pr:* Joseph F Amarald MD
CFO: Ann Kashmaniahn
CFO: Mamie Wakefield
Treas: Pamela Harrop
Ofcr: Beth Bailey
VP: Paul Pierannunzi
VP: Peter Snyder
Exec: Nancy Miller
Dir Lab: Marilyn McAllister
Assoc Dir: Nicholas Ward

D-U-N-S 36-100-3762
RHODE ISLAND HOSPITAL EMR
1 Hoppin St Ste 106, Providence, RI 02903-4141
Tel (401) 444-6237 Founded/Ownrshp 2005
Sales 1.1MMM EMP 8
SIC 8062 General medical & surgical hospitals
Prin: Deborah Lyon
Psych: Rebecca S Laptook

D-U-N-S 62-162-9021
RHODE ISLAND JOINT REINSURANCE ASSOC
2 Center Plz Ste 700, Boston, MA 02108-1906
Tel (617) 723-3800 Founded/Ownrshp 1968
Sales NA EMP 140
SIC 6331 Property damage insurance
Pr: John K Golembeski

D-U-N-S 07-570-5533
RHODE ISLAND SCHOOL OF DESIGN INC
RISD
2 College St, Providence, RI 02903-2717
Tel (401) 454-6100 Founded/Ownrshp 1877
Sales 158.4MM EMP 1,142E
Accts Pricewaterhousecoopers Llp Bo
SIC 8221 Colleges universities & professional schools
Pr: Rosanne Somerson
Pr: Anthony Gallonio
Treas: Robert Garzillo
Trst: Joan R Eeves
Trst: Richard Haining
Trst: Frederick C Lohrum
VP: Joseph J Bernier
VP: Willaim Hammer
Exec: Lynn McCarthy
Dir Soc: Patricia Brown
Ex Dir: Bill Foulkes

D-U-N-S 07-575-3756
RHODES COLLEGES INC
EVEREST COLLEGE
1815 Jet Wing Dr, Colorado Springs, CO 80916-2300
Tel (719) 638-6580 Founded/Ownrshp 1996
Sales NA EMP 10,064
SIC 8221 8222

D-U-N-S 07-917-9885
RHODES HOLDCO INC
800 Commonwealth Dr # 100, Warrendale, PA 15086-7525
Tel (724) 776-9780 Founded/Ownrshp 2013
Sales 450.1MME EMP 11,124E
SIC 6719 Investment holding companies, except banks
CFO: Keith McDonough

RHODES HOMES
See SAGEBRUSH ENTERPRISES INC

D-U-N-S 83-192-8986
RHODES PHARMACEUTICALS LP
498 Washington St, Coventry, RI 02816-5467
Tel (401) 262-9200 Founded/Ownrshp 2007
Sales 136.7MM EMP 13
Accts Ronald Haberlin Conventry Ri
SIC 2834 Pharmaceutical preparations
Pr: Vincent P Mancinelli
VP: Robert Thebeau

RHODIA
See SOLVAY HOLDING INC

D-U-N-S 83-187-6573
RHONE CAPITAL LLC
(Suby of RHONE GROUP LLC) ★
45 Rockefeller Plz # 2710, New York, NY 10111-2702
Tel (212) 218-6700 Founded/Ownrshp 2002
Sales 670.9MME EMP 1,005
SIC 6799 Investors

D-U-N-S 95-846-4653
RHONE GROUP LLC
630 5th Ave Ste 2710, New York, NY 10111-2798
Tel (212) 218-6700 Founded/Ownrshp 1998
Sales 2.7MMME EMP 6,186E
SIC 6282 Investment advisory service
CEO: Vito Badalamenti
CFO: James Giangrasso
Ex Dir: Nancy Cooper
Mng Dir: Franz Buerstedde
Mng Dir: Baudoin Lorans
Mng Dir: Andrew Sweet

D-U-N-S 60-645-5616
RHS CORP
REDLANDS COMMUNITY HOSPITAL
350 Terracina Blvd, Redlands, CA 92373-4850
Tel (909) 335-5500 Founded/Ownrshp 1985
Sales 210.7M EMP 1,450
Accts Moss Adams Llp San Francisco
SIC 8741 Hospital management
Pr: James R Holmes
Obsttrcn: Samir Hage
Doctor: Vincent Dorsey
Doctor: Jacqueline Pitt

D-U-N-S 12-320-3643
■ RIA ENVIA INC
(Suby of EURONET WORLDWIDE INC) ★
6565 Knott Ave, Buena Park, CA 90620-1139
Tel (714) 543-8448 Founded/Ownrshp 2007
Sales 180.0MME EMP 1,000E
SIC 7389 Financial services
Pr: Juan Beanchi
Off Mgr: Luis Marin

RIA FINANCIAL SERVICE
See CONTINENTAL EXCHANGE SOLUTIONS INC

D-U-N-S 08-415-1786
RIALTO UNIFIED SCHOOL DISTRICT
182 E Walnut Ave, Rialto, CA 92376-3598
Tel (909) 820-7700 Founded/Ownrshp 1963
Sales 188.6MME EMP 2,833
Accts Vavrinek Trine Day & Co Ll
SIC 8211 Public elementary & secondary schools
Pr: Joanne T Gilbert

*VP: Joseph Ayala
VP: Dina Walker
CTO: Beth Scantleburg
Dir IT: Mike Medina
Teacher Pr: Aaron Rogers

RIC
See REHABILITATION INSTITUTE OF CHICAGO

RICART AUTOMOTIVE GROUP
See RICART PROPERTIES INC

D-U-N-S 01-788-3430
RICART PROPERTIES INC
RICART AUTOMOTIVE GROUP
4255 S Hamilton Rd, Groveport, OH 43125-9332
Tel (614) 836-6680 Founded/Ownrshp 1990
Sales 131.2MME EMP 395
SIC 5511

D-U-N-S 78-909-7086
RICCELLI ENTERPRISES INC
6131 E Taft Rd, North Syracuse, NY 13212-2525
Tel (315) 433-5115 Founded/Ownrshp 1991
Sales 100.5MME EMP 300
SIC 4213 Trucking, except local; Building materials transport; Heavy hauling
CEO: Joseph F Riccelli
*Pr: Richard J Riccelli Sr
Sr VP: Sam Chiodo
*Sr VP: Mike Relf
*VP: Tony Alu
*VP: Richard Riccelli
Dir Bus: Jim Giufre
Genl Mgr: Robert Madey
Sls Mgr: Tom Rozzano
Genl Couns: Frederick Micale

D-U-N-S 05-245-4337
RICCIARDI BROS INC
1915 Springfield Ave, Maplewood, NJ 07040-3419
Tel (973) 762-3830 Founded/Ownrshp 1929
Sales 708.1MME EMP 712
SIC 5198 5231 Paints; Paint
Pr: Walter Ricciardi
Sr Cor Off: Michael Zlotnitsky
*VP: Robert Ricciardi
Admn Mgr: Phillip Fillner

D-U-N-S 07-923-9472
▲ RICE ENERGY INC
2200 Rice Dr, Canonsburg, PA 15317-1001
Tel (724) 271-7200 Founded/Ownrshp 2008
Sales 502.1MM EMP 371E
Tkr Sym RICE Exch NYS
SIC 1311 Crude petroleum & natural gas
CEO: Daniel J Rice IV
*Ch Bd: Robert F Vagt
*Pr: Toby Z Rice
CFO: Grayson T Lisenby
Ex VP: Derek A Rice
Sr VP: William E Jordan
Sr VP: James W Rogers
Sr VP: Robert R Wingo
Genl Couns: Gina Banai
Board of Directors: Scott A Gieselman, John McCartney, Daniel J Rice III, James W Christmas

D-U-N-S 02-664-1654
RICE EPICUREAN MARKETS INC
5333 Gulfton St, Houston, TX 77081-2801
Tel (713) 662-7700 Founded/Ownrshp 1974
Sales 85.7MME EMP 550
SIC 5411 5812 Supermarkets, chain; Eating places
Co-Ch Bd: Joel M Levy
*Pr: Gary Friedlander
*CFO: Bruce Levy
*Co-Ch Bd: Alfred L Friedlander
*Treas: Thomas Friedlander
*Sec: Tommy Friedlander
*VP: Phil L Cohen
*VP: Scott A Silverman
Exec: Gary Finley
MIS Dir: Keith Haggott

RICE EXPRESSIONS
See SAGE V FOODS LLC

D-U-N-S 04-893-9404
RICE HEALTH CARE FACILITIES OF WISCONSIN INC
(Suby of KBWB OPERATIONS-RICE LLC) ★
1726 N Ballard Rd Ste 2, Appleton, WI 54911-2444
Tel (920) 991-9072 Founded/Ownrshp 2014
Sales 39.3MME EMP 1,094
Accts Wipfli Llc Green Bay Wiscons
SIC 8051 Skilled nursing care facilities
Pr: Otis Rice
Sec: Larry Rice

D-U-N-S 02-352-6783 IMP/EXP
RICE LAKE WEIGHING SYSTEMS INC
230 W Coleman St, Rice Lake, WI 54868-2404
Tel (715) 234-9171 Founded/Ownrshp 1946
Sales 116.1MME EMP 450
SIC 3596 3545 Counting scales; Scales, measuring (machinists' precision tools)
Pr: Mark O Johnson
CFO: Kraig Smith
VP: Bruce Schmidt
Prin: Mark Johnson Sr
Off Mgr: Hans Lawrence
Snr Sftwr: Travis Gibson
Dir IT: Joe Waldera
IT Man: Mark Butzler
IT Man: Marvin Stodola
Software D: Tom Kowalski
Sftwr Eng: Travis L Gibson

D-U-N-S 01-033-7533
RICE MEMORIAL HOSPITAL
(Suby of WILLMAR, CITY OF (INC))
301 Becker Ave Sw, Willmar, MN 56201-3395
Tel (320) 235-4543 Founded/Ownrshp 1937
Sales 99.2MM EMP 500
Accts Rsm Us Llp Minneapolis Minne
SIC 8062 General medical & surgical hospitals
CEO: Michael Schramm
Chf Rad: Scott S Nielsen
*CFO: William Fenske

*Treas: Michael Gardner DDS
*VP: Steven Cederstrom
Ex Dir: Kelly Magnuson
Ansthlgy: John Seifert
Plas Surg: Evelyn Erickson
Doctor: Larry Okerlund

D-U-N-S 07-961-1654
▲ RICE MIDSTREAM PARTNERS LP
400 Woodcliff Dr, Canonsburg, PA 15317-5851
Tel (724) 746-6720 Founded/Ownrshp 2013
Sales 114.4MM EMP 74E
Accts Ernst & Young Llp Pittsburgh
Tkr Sym RMP Exch NYS
SIC 4922 Natural gas transmission
CEO: Daniel J Rice IV
Genl Pt: Rice M LLC
COO: Robert R Wingo
Sr VP: Grayson T Lisenby

D-U-N-S 00-633-7166 IMP/EXP
RICELAND FOODS INC (AR)
2120 S Park Ave, Stuttgart, AR 72160-6822
Tel (870) 673-5500 Founded/Ownrshp 1921
Sales 1.0MMM EMP 1,646
Accts Bkd Llp Little Rock Arkansa
SIC 2044 2079 5153 2075 Rice milling; Milled rice; Polished rice; Bran, rice; Edible fats & oils; Vegetable shortenings (except corn oil); Cooking oils, except corn: vegetable refined; Grains; Soybean oil, cake or meal; Lecithin, soybean
Pr: Daniel Kennedy
Ch Bd: Roger E Pohlner
CFO: Sandra Morgan
Treas: Bill Bulloch
Treas: Jackie Huguenard
Sr VP: Carl W Brothers
VP: Andrew Dallas
VP: Scott Johnson
VP: Harry Loftis
VP: Rick Rorex
VP: John Ruff
VP: George M Vickers

D-U-N-S 15-526-9939
RICERCA BIOSCIENCES LLC
7528 Auburn Rd, Painesville, OH 44077-9603
Tel (440) 357-3300 Founded/Ownrshp 2014
Sales 97.0MME EMP 210
SIC 8731 Medical research, commercial
CEO: Clifford W Croley
*Treas: Dorothie L Okleson
Ofcr: Jennifer Beech
*Ex VP: Michael W Martell
VP: Michael Dougherty
VP: Michael Watson
Exec: Susan Branchick
QA Dir: Michael Keherly
Dir IT: Bob Martin
Sys Mgr: Bob Katona
Doctor: Phil Cassidy

D-U-N-S 00-210-8371 IMP/EXP
RICH PRODUCTS CORP (DE)
1 Robert Rich Way, Buffalo, NY 14213-1701
Tel (716) 878-8422 Founded/Ownrshp 1993
Sales 3.2MMM EMP 8,400
SIC 2053 2092 2023 2099 Frozen bakery products, except bread; Fresh or frozen packaged fish; Shrimp, frozen: prepared; Shellfish, frozen: prepared; Dry, condensed, evaporated dairy products; Whipped topping, dry mix; Cream substitutes; Dessert mixes & fillings
CEO: William G Gisel
*COO: Richard M Ferranti
*CFO: James R Deuschle
CFO: Charles R Tecgo
*Ch: Robert Rich Jr
*Treas: Ryan Trapper
*V Ch Bd: Melinda R Rich
Ex VP: Jonathan Dandes
Ex VP: Dwight Gram
*Ex VP: Maureen Hurley
Ex VP: Kevin R Malchoff
Ex VP: Edward Moore
VP: Gary Duszynski
VP: William E Grieshober
VP: Trish Hudson
VP: Marty Hurley
VP: Dave Konst
VP: Jose Lechon
VP: Dalina Paduano
VP: Bob Pavone
*VP: David A Rich
Board of Directors: Herb Kusche, Lorry Rich

D-U-N-S 11-969-0196
RICHARD HEATH & ASSOCIATES INC
R H A
590 W Locust Ave Ste 103, Fresno, CA 93650-1079
Tel (559) 447-7000 Founded/Ownrshp 1979
Sales 154.9MM EMP 309
SIC 8748

D-U-N-S 05-784-2122 EXP
RICHARD WOLF MEDICAL INSTRUMENTS CORP
(Suby of RICHARD WOLF GMBH)
353 Corporate Woods Pkwy, Vernon Hills, IL 60061-3110
Tel (847) 913-1113 Founded/Ownrshp 1972
Sales 114.2MME EMP 193
SIC 5047 3841 Medical equipment & supplies; Surgical & medical instruments
Pr: Juergen Pfab
*Pr: Alfons Notheis
*COO: Siegfried Karst
*Treas: Monika Knodel
Area Mgr: Lena Roller
Area Mgr: Markus Scharfen
Dir IT: Heidi Heldt
Tech Mgr: Marek Rast
Ql Cn Mgr: Larry Maye
Mktg Dir: Niels Schmidt
Mktg Dir: Ed Troike

D-U-N-S 08-908-3117 IMP
RICHARDS BUILDING SUPPLY CO
GREATER CHICAGOLAND CLOSEOUTS
12070 W 159th St, Homer Glen, IL 60491-7850
Tel (773) 586-7777 Founded/Ownrshp 1978
Sales 173.3MME EMP 100
SIC 5033 5211 Roofing, asphalt & sheet metal; Siding, except wood; Roofing material; Sand & gravel; Windows, storm: wood or metal; Cabinets, kitchen
Pr: David Brush
*CFO: David A Goss
*VP: Ron Guzior
*VP: Angelos Manolis
*VP: Jay Walsh
Brnch Mgr: Sara Knight
Brnch Mgr: Joseph Linn
Brnch Mgr: Ed Waxmansky
Genl Mgr: Joe Stoddard
Sls Dir: Michael Joyce
Sls Mgr: Randy Ellis

D-U-N-S 05-129-1268 IMP
RICHARDS ELECTRIC SUPPLY CO INC
4620 Reading Rd, Cincinnati, OH 45229-1297
Tel (513) 242-8800 Founded/Ownrshp 1970
Sales 179.5MME EMP 150E
SIC 5063 Electrical apparatus & equipment; Electrical construction materials; Lighting fixtures
Pr: Ivan S Misrach
*VP: Mark Schmidlin
*Prin: Richard Misrach
*Prin: Joseph Schwartz
*Prin: Norma Strelow
Sls Mgr: Rick Sebold

D-U-N-S 06-637-9207
RICHARDS GROUP INC
DESKTYPE
2801 N Cntl Expy Ste 100, Dallas, TX 75204
Tel (214) 891-5700 Founded/Ownrshp 1965
Sales 118.5MME EMP 600
SIC 7311 Advertising agencies
Pr: Stanford H Richards
*CFO: Stephen W Kay
*VP: Scot Dykema
VP: Kimmie Swan
VP: Michael Zinn
Creative D: Chad Berry
Creative D: Rob Hollenbeck
*Prin: Stacie Barnett
*Prin: Brian Schadt
*Prin: Rod Ulrich
CTO: Warren Stepler

RICHARDS MEMORIAL HOSPITAL
See ROCKDALE HOSPITAL AUTHORITY (INC)

D-U-N-S 02-547-8371
▲ RICHARDSON ELECTRONICS LTD
40w267 Keslinger Rd, Lafox, IL 60147
Tel (630) 208-2316 Founded/Ownrshp 1947
Sales 142.0MM EMP 373
Accts Bdo Usa Llp Chicago Illinois
Tkr Sym RELL Exch NGS
SIC 5065 7373 3671 Electronic parts & equipment; Electronic tubes: receiving & transmitting or industrial; Semiconductor devices; Closed circuit television; Computer integrated systems design; Value-added resellers, computer systems; Electronic tube parts, except glass blanks
Ch Bd: Edward J Richardson
COO: Wendy S Diddell
CFO: Robert J Ben
Ex VP: Robert Ben
Ex VP: Gregory J Peloquin
Sr VP: Kathleen M McNally
VP: Tom Spees
Mktg Dir: Bernhard Zimmermann
Manager: George Stauffer
Board of Directors: Jacques Belin, James Benham, Kenneth Halverson, Paul J Plante

D-U-N-S 04-108-7255
RICHARDSON INDEPENDENT SCHOOL DISTRICT
400 S Greenville Ave # 205, Richardson, TX 75081-4107
Tel (469) 593-0000 Founded/Ownrshp 1854
Sales 406.8MM EMP 4,500
Accts Hankins Eastup Deaton Tonn
SIC 8211 Public elementary school; Public junior high school; Public senior high school
Pr: Kim Quirk
*Treas: Kim Caston
Treas: David Tyson
*VP: Karen Holburn
Prin: Jobob Aanenson
Prin: Becky Barnum
Prin: Kirk Beard
Prin: Robert Bostic
Prin: Nancy Britton
Prin: Lorine Burrell
Prin: Estee Celebucki

D-U-N-S 00-642-7744 IMP
RICHARDSON INDUSTRIES INC
RICHARDSON WOOD PRESERVING
635 Old County Road Pp, Sheboygan Falls, WI 53085-1874
Tel (920) 467-2950 Founded/Ownrshp 1848
Sales 91.5MME EMP 500
SIC 2511 2439 5211 2491 2434 2426 Dining room furniture: wood; Wood bedroom furniture; Trusses, except roof: laminated lumber; Trusses, wooden roof; Millwork & lumber; Wood preserving; Wood kitchen cabinets; Hardwood dimension & flooring mills
Ch Bd: David Richardson Sr
*Pr: Joseph E Richardson II
*Ex VP: Joseph E Richardson III
*VP: Greg Busch
*VP: Marvin Debbink
*VP: Eugene Geurts
*VP: Merle Nett
*VP: James Richardson

D-U-N-S 02-697-5813 IMP
■ RICHARDSON TRIDENT CO LLC
ALTAIR COMPANY, THE
(*Suby of* METALS USA HOLDINGS CORP) ★
405 N Plano Rd, Richardson, TX 75081-2938
Tel (972) 231-5176 *Founded/Ownrshp* 2011
Sales 180.0MM^E *EMP* 157
SIC 5051 5085 5063 5065 3316 Nonferrous metal sheets, bars, rods, etc.: Industrial supplies; Seals, industrial; Electrical fittings & construction materials; Switchboards; Wire & cable; Electronic parts; Resistors, electronic; Cold finishing of steel shapes
Pr: David Martens
VP: Karla Lewis
VP: Robert McPherson
VP: Silva Yeghyayan
Genl Mgr: Mike Cooney

RICHARDSON WOOD PRESERVING
See RICHARDSON INDUSTRIES INC

D-U-N-S 18-653-7676
RICHELIEU FOODS INC
222 Forbes Rd Ste 401, Braintree, MA 02184-2717
Tel (781) 786-6800 *Founded/Ownrshp* 1997
Sales 242.9MM^E *EMP* 650
SIC 2038 Breakfasts, frozen & packaged
CEO: Tim O'Connor
CFO: Michael Morin
VP: Ron Zaleski

D-U-N-S 15-178-3511
RICHFIELD HOLDINGS INC
MILLENNIUM HOTELS & RESORTS
(*Suby of* MILLENNIUM HOTELS & RESORTS) ★
5775 Dtc Blvd Ste 300, Greenwood Village, CO 80111-3209
Tel (303) 220-2000 *Founded/Ownrshp* 2000
Sales NA *EMP* 2,300
SIC 6321 8712 7389 6331 7011 Accident & health insurance carriers; Architectural services; Purchasing service; Workers' compensation insurance; Hotels
Pr: Aik Hong Tan
**Sr VP:* Lyle L Boll

D-U-N-S 02-374-1049
RICHFIELD HOSPITALITY INC
(*Suby of* SWAN HOLDINGS LIMITED)
7600 E Orchard Rd 230s, Greenwood Village, CO 80111-2553
Tel (303) 220-2000 *Founded/Ownrshp* 2000
Sales 77.1MM^E *EMP* 1,054^E
SIC 8741 Hotel or motel management
CEO: Lee Rossiter
Pr: Will Loughran
CFO: Alan Baer
Sr VP: Mobashir Ahmed
Sr VP: Thomas Clearwater
Sr VP: Peter Nichols
VP: Allen Kramm
VP: Jeanne Lynch
VP: Mark Ozawa
VP: Bill Zollars
Mng Dir: John Beier

RICHFIELD TECHNICAL SERVICES
See M&C HOTEL INTERESTS INC

D-U-N-S 00-794-1263
■ RICHFOOD INC
(*Suby of* SUPERVALU INC) ★
8258 Richfood Rd, Mechanicsville, VA 23116-2008
Tel (804) 746-6000 *Founded/Ownrshp* 1935, 2000
Sales 221.8MM^E *EMP* 3,000
SIC 5141 5147 5142 5148 5143 2026 Groceries, general line; Meats & meat products; Packaged frozen goods; Fresh fruits & vegetables; Dairy products, except dried or canned; Fluid milk
CEO: John E Stokely
**Ch Bd:* Donald D Bennett
Pr: John Kalita
Pr: Mearl D Lynch
Pr: Julie A McManus
Pr: Richard H Myers
Pr: Russell W Reynolds Jr
Pr: William Sharkey
**Pr:* Gary Zimmerman
Ex VP: Michael C Bourgoine
Ex VP: Belknap John C
Ex VP: Gary L Conrad
Ex VP: William C Stocker
Sr VP: Larry A King
Sr VP: John Della Noce Jr
VP: Lawrence W Bagwell
VP: John Belknap
VP: Charles A Brown
VP: Joe Callahan
VP: Charlotte D Edwards
VP: Donald G Eipp

D-U-N-S 01-337-1596
RICHLAND COUNTY SCHOOL DISTRICT 1
1616 Richland St, Columbia, SC 29201-2634
Tel (803) 231-7000 *Founded/Ownrshp* 1881
Sales 363.1MM *EMP* 5,200
Accts Derricks Stubbs Steth Llp Co
SIC 8211 Public elementary & secondary schools
COO: Michael Bobby
Bd of Dir: Jasper Salmond
Prin: Jacpb Holmes
Ex Dir: Luke Cioch
MIS Dir: -Luke Fox
Teacher Pr: Sanita Savage-Cousar

D-U-N-S 00-615-4546
RICHLAND SCHOOL DISTRICT
615 Snow Ave, Richland, WA 99352-3851
Tel (509) 967-6000 *Founded/Ownrshp* 1943
Sales 85.4MM^E *EMP* 1,400
SIC 8211 Public elementary & secondary schools; Public elementary school; Public junior high school; Public senior high school
Treas: Noelle Akyol

D-U-N-S 08-863-4712
RICHLAND SCHOOL DISTRICT TWO FOUNDATION
6831 Brookfield Rd, Columbia, SC 29206-2205
Tel (803) 787-1910 *Founded/Ownrshp* 1950
Sales 251.5MM *EMP* 3,500
Accts Preparer Columbia Sc
SIC 8211 Public elementary & secondary schools
CFO: Bob Davis
**CFO:* Robert Davis
CFO: Kathy Tremblay
**Ch:* William R Flemming Jr
**Prin:* Susan Brill
Prin: Beth Elliott
**Prin:* Ralph Schmidt
Ex Dir: Karen Lovett
Ex Dir: Libby Roof
Genl Mgr: Harry Miley
Web Dev: Travis Cotton

D-U-N-S 01-774-8195
RICHLIEU ASSOCIATES
LIGHTHOUSE COUNTY COMMONS APTS
3338 Richlieu Rd, Bensalem, PA 19020-1549
Tel (215) 639-2800 *Founded/Ownrshp* 1972
Sales 44.1MM^E *EMP* 3,900
SIC 6513 Apartment building operators
Pt: Elena Linnik
Sr VP: Leeann Morein
Prin: Jennifer Hardee

D-U-N-S 80-226-8180 IMP
■ RICHLINE GROUP INC
(*Suby of* BERKSHIRE HATHAWAY INC) ★
1385 Broadway Fl 12, New York, NY 10018-6118
Tel (212) 886-6000 *Founded/Ownrshp* 2007
Sales 382.5MM^E *EMP* 1,500
SIC 5094 3911 Jewelry; Jewelry, precious metal
CEO: Dennis Ulrich
**Pr:* Dave Meleski
**CFO:* Betty Sou
Chf Mktg O: Mark Hanna
**Ex VP:* Ofer Azrielant
**Ex VP:* Ramona Genao
VP: Lauri Aronson
VP: Maria Cutaia
VP: Kim Jozwiak
VP: David Radcliffe
VP: Cindy Witting

RICHMOND AIRPORT
See DNC/MFS FOOD GROUP

D-U-N-S 62-191-9513
■ RICHMOND AMERICAN HOMES OF COLORADO INC
(*Suby of* MDC HOLDINGS INC) ★
4350 S Monaco St, Denver, CO 80237-3400
Tel (303) 773-1100 *Founded/Ownrshp* 1996
Sales 93.7MM^E *EMP* 197
SIC 1521 New construction, single-family houses
Pr: David Mandarich
Pr: Liesel W Cooper
**Pr:* Geri Sue Sichler
Pr: Peter R Thompson
**Ex VP:* Timothy R Garrelts
**VP:* James C Van Gelder
**VP:* Diane Wildrick

D-U-N-S 03-687-1838
RICHMOND CITY PUBLIC SCHOOLS
301 N 9th St Fl 17, Richmond, VA 23219-1933
Tel (804) 780-7775 *Founded/Ownrshp* 2001
Sales 13.7MM^E *EMP* 4,200
SIC 8211 Public combined elementary & secondary school
MIS Dir: Kavansa Gardner
Pr Dir: Canita Bowers
Pr Dir: Rebina Switzer-Enis
Instr Medi: Phyllis Gardner
HC Dir: Charlene Rodgers

D-U-N-S 11-853-9261
RICHMOND COUNTY BOARD OF EDUCATION
RICHMOND COUNTY SCHOOL DST
864 Broad St, Augusta, GA 30901-1215
Tel (706) 826-1000 *Founded/Ownrshp* 1872
Sales 206.1MM^E *EMP* 5,500
Accts Russell W Hinton Cpa Cgfm
SIC 8211 Public elementary & secondary schools
Bd of Dir: Jack Padgett
Bd of Dir: Patsy Scott
Genl Mgr: Suzanne Lentz
Pr Dir: Kaden Jacobs
HC Dir: Maria Brown

D-U-N-S 10-005-8973
RICHMOND COUNTY SCHOOL DISTRICT
118 Vance St, Hamlet, NC 28345-3359
Tel (910) 582-5860 *Founded/Ownrshp* 1967
Sales 60.2MM^E *EMP* 1,428
Accts Dixon Hughes Pllc Southern Pi
SIC 8211 Public elementary & secondary schools; School board
MIS Dir: Jeff Epps
Pr Dir: Michelle Tublin
Teacher Pr: Beth Shuler

RICHMOND COUNTY SCHOOL DST
See RICHMOND COUNTY BOARD OF EDUCATION

D-U-N-S 07-979-9728
RICHMOND COUNTY SCHOOL SYSTEM
864 Broad St, Augusta, GA 30901-1215
Tel (706) 826-1000 *Founded/Ownrshp* 2015
Sales 35.4MM^E *EMP* 5,216^E
SIC 8211 Public elementary & secondary schools

RICHMOND HONDA
See PEARSON COMPANIES INC

D-U-N-S 79-107-3674 IMP
RICHMOND MEDICAL CENTER
RICHMOND UNIVERSITY MEDICAL CE
355 Bard Ave, Staten Island, NY 10310-1664
Tel (718) 818-1234 *Founded/Ownrshp* 2006
Sales 285.7MM *EMP* 2,555^E
SIC 8062 General medical & surgical hospitals
Pr: Daniel J Messina
CFO: Joseph Saporito
Sr VP: Joseph Herbert
Sr VP: Lynn Jennings
VP: Patricia Caldari
VP: Nancy T Lnc
VP: Rita Magnuski
Assoc Dir: Deborah Rodriguez
Dir Rx: Lenny Shats
Sls&Mrk Ex: Mary Scullin
Pathlgst: Minsheng Zhuang

RICHMOND PEAK QUALITY
See RICHMOND WHOLESALE MEAT CO

RICHMOND RESTAURANT SERVICE
See J L CULPEPPER & CO INC

D-U-N-S 04-184-4002 IMP
■ RICHMOND SANITARY SERVICE INC
CROCKETT GARBAGE SERVICE
(*Suby of* REPUBLIC SERVICES INC) ★
3260 Blume Dr Ste 100, Richmond, CA 94806-1960
Tel (510) 262-7100 *Founded/Ownrshp* 2001
Sales 96.3MM^E *EMP* 250
SIC 4959 Sanitary services
Pr: Richard Granzella
**CFO:* Dennis Varni
**VP:* Mario Acquilino
**Prin:* Pina Barbiere
**Prin:* Loyd Bonfante
**Prin:* Eddie Menosse
**Prin:* Caesar Nuti
**Prin:* Pasquale Parenti
**Prin:* Joe Della Zoppa

RICHMOND UNIVERSITY MEDICAL CE
See RICHMOND MEDICAL CENTER

D-U-N-S 00-398-6643 IMP/EXP
RICHMOND WHOLESALE MEAT CO (CA)
RICHMOND PEAK QUALITY
2920 Regatta Blvd, Richmond, CA 94804-4528
Tel (510) 233-5111 *Founded/Ownrshp* 1959
Sales 100.0MM *EMP* 85
SIC 5147 Meats & meat products
Pr: Richard Doellstedt
**CFO:* Alan Bell
CFO: Laura Steinebach
**VP:* Carl Doellstedt
VP: Paul Guess
**Prin:* John Doellstedt
Opers Mgr: Shelia Arbour

D-U-N-S 04-028-6510
RICKER OIL CO INC
30 W 11th St, Anderson, IN 46016-1402
Tel (765) 643-3016 *Founded/Ownrshp* 1979
Sales 279.4MM^E *EMP* 700
SIC 5171 Petroleum bulk stations
Pr: Quinn B Ricker
**Pr:* Jay Ricker
CFO: Jarod Downing
**VP:* Nancy S Ricker
Genl Mgr: Dennis Williamson
Dir IT: David Hilderbrand

D-U-N-S 04-132-6641
RICO CLARO PUERTO
(*Suby of* AMERICA MOVIL, S.A.B. DE C.V.)
1515 Frnklin D Rsvelt Ave, Guaynabo, PR 00968
Tel (787) 766-2355 *Founded/Ownrshp* 2007
Sales 206.4MM^E *EMP* 759^E
SIC 4812 8748 Cellular telephone services; Telecommunications consultant
Pr: Enrique M Rangel
**Pr:* Christina Lambert
**Treas:* Maria Elena De La Cruz

D-U-N-S 14-073-9090
■ RICO FIRSTBANK PUERTO
FIRST BANK OF PUERTO RICO
(*Suby of* FIRST BANK) ★
1519 Ave Ponce De Leon, San Juan, PR 00909-1732
Tel (787) 729-8200 *Founded/Ownrshp* 1950
Sales NA *EMP* 2,000^E
SIC 6022 State commercial banks
Pr: Aurelio Aleman-Bermudez
Pr: Martin Cativa
COO: Aureleo Alemes
Ofcr: Carlos A Ortiz
Sr Ex VP: Aurelio Alemn
Sr VP: Lillian Arroyo
Sr VP: Erie Perez
Sr VP: Carlos Power
Sr VP: Hayde Rivera
Sr VP: Hector Santiago
Sr VP: Sheila I Ocasio
VP: Karim Alberty
VP: Sara Alvaraz
VP: Carlos Figueroa
VP: Tammy Halfmann
VP: Dennis Lebron
VP: Migda L Malbert
VP: Joaquin Negron
VP: Francisco Rivera
Dir Risk M: Nayda Rivera

D-U-N-S 00-506-5073 IMP/EXP
RICO INDUSTRIES INC
RICO INDUSTRIES TAG EXPRESS
7000 N Austin Ave, Niles, IL 60714-4602
Tel (312) 427-0313 *Founded/Ownrshp* 1944
Sales 87.4MM^E *EMP* 140
SIC 5199 3172 2396 3993 Leather goods, except footwear, gloves, luggage, belting; Wallets; Checkbook covers; Key cases; Automotive & apparel trimmings; Signs & advertising specialties
Pr: Cary S Schack
**Treas:* Bernard Schack

RICO INDUSTRIES TAG EXPRESS
See RICO INDUSTRIES INC

D-U-N-S 36-288-9144
RICO PUERTO TELEPHONE CO INC
VERIZEN
(*Suby of* TELPRI) ★
1515 Ave Fd Roosevelt, Guaynabo, PR 00968-2705
Tel (787) 781-1314 *Founded/Ownrshp* 1914
Sales 98.4MM^E *EMP* 4,649
SIC 8748 Telecommunications consultant
CEO: Enrique O De M Rangel
**Pr:* Enrique Ortiz
**CEO:* Enrique O De Montellano Rangel
COO: Aldo Figueroa
CFO: Maria Russo
**Treas:* Maria Elana Dela Cruz
Treas: Maria E Dela Cruz
**VP:* Mariano Doble
**VP:* Luis G Garcia
**VP:* Adail Ortiz
IT Man: Vilma Pagan

D-U-N-S 09-045-6716 IMP
RICO SOL PUERTO LIMITED
450 Ave De La Const 18c, San Juan, PR 00901-2310
Tel (787) 721-0150 *Founded/Ownrshp* 2006
Sales 600.0MM *EMP* 35^E
Accts Pricewaterhousecoopers Llp Sa
SIC 5171 Petroleum bulk stations
Genl Mgr: Bario Amadeo
**Pr:* Candido Rivera

D-U-N-S 06-107-9273 IMP/EXP
RICOH AMERICAS CORP
70 Valley Stream Pkwy, Malvern, PA 19355-1407
Tel (610) 296-8000 *Founded/Ownrshp* 2012
Sales 6.1MMM^E *EMP* 25,000
SIC 5044 5065 5045 5043 3861 3661

RICOH AMERICAS CORP RICOH USA
See RICOH AMERICAS HOLDINGS INC

D-U-N-S 07-844-8457 IMP
RICOH AMERICAS HOLDINGS INC
RICOH AMERICAS CORP RICOH USA
(*Suby of* RICOH COMPANY,LTD.)
5 Dedrick Pl, West Caldwell, NJ 07006-6304
Tel (973) 882-2000 *Founded/Ownrshp* 2010
Sales 5.9MMM^E *EMP* 25,000^E
SIC 5044 5065 5043 Photocopy machines; Facsimile equipment; Photographic cameras, projectors, equipment & supplies
Pr: Frank Shibuno
Sr VP: Hede Nonaka
VP: Eric Norman
VP: Dave Williams
Exec: Julie Kinker
Dir IT: Dan Mensonides
IT Man: Noel Ayson
Opers Mgr: Chris Hill
Opers Mgr: Eduardo Ponce
VP Mktg: Shun Sato
VP Sls: David Greene

D-U-N-S 80-769-4828 IMP/EXP
RICOH CORP
(*Suby of* RICOH COMPANY,LTD.)
5 Dedrick Pl, West Caldwell, NJ 07006-6398
Tel (973) 882-2000 *Founded/Ownrshp* 2007
Sales 221.8MM^E *EMP* 648^E
SIC 5065 Facsimile equipment
CEO: Martin Brodigan
Pr: Curt Albrecht
Top Exec: Wayne Mize
VP: Mike Duciewicz
**VP:* Allen Hans
VP: Allen A Hans
**VP:* Robert Ingoglia
**VP:* Debbie Patskey
VP: Debbie Patsky
VP: Ron Potesky
VP: Tom Sicarddi
**VP:* Hugh Urabe
Exec: Leonard Harris
Exec: Rachna Seth
Dir Surg: Charles Matrai
Dir Teleco: Patricia N Rokosh

RICOH DEVELOPMENT CALIFORNIA
See RICOH ELECTRONICS INC

D-U-N-S 06-446-7996 IMP
RICOH ELECTRONICS INC
RICOH DEVELOPMENT CALIFORNIA
(*Suby of* RICOH USA INC) ★
1100 Valencia Ave, Tustin, CA 92780-6450
Tel (714) 566-2500 *Founded/Ownrshp* 1973
Sales 425.6MM^E *EMP* 1,550
SIC 3861 3695 Photocopy machines; Toners, prepared photographic (not made in chemical plants); Magnetic & optical recording media
Pr: Jeffrey A Briwick
**CEO:* Yoshinori Yamashita
**CFO:* Howard Suzuki
VP: Mesaki Gertz
Dir Risk M: Cristin McAllister
Genl Mgr: John Fickenscher
Dir IT: Ecker Yang
IT Man: Erik Finefield
Mfg Dir: Steve Sarg
Plnt Mgr: Tim Ohno
Ql Cn Mgr: Donald Nguyen

D-U-N-S 80-046-8311
RICOH PRODUCTION PRINT SOLUTIONS LLC
INFOPRINT
6300 Diagonal Hwy, Boulder, CO 80301-9270
Tel (303) 924-9348 *Founded/Ownrshp* 2007
Sales NA *EMP* 2,800^E
SIC 7389

D-U-N-S 04-396-4519 IMP/EXP
RICOH USA INC
(*Suby of* RICOH COMPANY,LTD.)
70 Valley Stream Pkwy, Malvern, PA 19355-1407
Tel (610) 296-8000 *Founded/Ownrshp* 1952
Sales 7.3MMM^E *EMP* 25,000
SIC 5044 5065 7359 5112 7334 6159 Office equipment; Copying equipment; Facsimile equipment; Office machine rental, except computers; Photocopying supplies; Photocopying & duplicating services; Machinery & equipment finance leasing
CEO: Zenji Miura
**COO:* Tracey Rothenberger
**CFO:* Gary Crowe
**Genl Couns:* Bill Lasalle

RICOS PRODUCTS
See LIBERTO SPECIALTY CO INC

D-U-N-S 04-709-9933 IMP/EXP
RIDA INTERNATIONAL INVESTMENTS LLC
1774 S Barranca Ave, Glendora, CA 91740-5421
Tel (626) 712-4776 *Founded/Ownrshp* 2012
Sales 270.0MM *EMP* 10
SIC 6221 Commodity contracts brokers, dealers
Pr: Dan Rabati
Pt: Nick Oyyoub

RIDDELL ALL AMERICAN SPORT
See ALL AMERICAN SPORTS CORP

D-U-N-S 00-512-8830 IMP
RIDDELL INC (IL)
RIDDELL SPORTS
(*Suby of* BRG SPORTS INC) ★
9801 W Higgins Rd Ste 800, Rosemont, IL 60018-4706
Tel (847) 292-1472 *Founded/Ownrshp* 1929
Sales 91.1MM^E^ *EMP* 245
SIC 5091 3949 Athletic goods; Helmets, athletic
Pr: William Sherman
**Pr:* Paul E Harrigton
**CFO:* Lawrence F Simon
**Sr VP:* Robert Brasser
**VP:* Mike Devel
**VP:* Thad Ide
**VP:* Richard A Lester
**VP:* Don Shea

RIDDELL SPORTS
See RIDDELL INC

D-U-N-S 07-162-7178
RIDDLE MEMORIAL HOSPITAL
1068 W Baltimore Pike, Media, PA 19063-5177
Tel (610) 566-9400 *Founded/Ownrshp* 1963
Sales 187.8MM *EMP* 1,350^E^
SIC 8062 General medical & surgical hospitals
**COO:* Robert Santilli
Ofcr: Gary Perecko
Phys Thrpy: Brian Murphy

D-U-N-S 96-961-7997
RIDDLE MEMORIAL HOSPITAL
950 E Haverford Rd, Bryn Mawr, PA 19010-3850
Tel (484) 337-8480 *Founded/Ownrshp* 2011
Sales 182.6MM *EMP* 8^E^
Accts Pricewaterhousecoopers Llp Ph
SIC 8062 General medical & surgical hospitals
Prin: Curt Whiteside

D-U-N-S 00-684-8923
■ **RIDDLEBERGER BROTHERS INC**
(*Suby of* COMFORT SYSTEMS USA INC) ★
6127 S Valley Pike, Mount Crawford, VA 22841-2352
Tel (540) 434-1731 *Founded/Ownrshp* 2008
Sales 162.8MM^E^ *EMP* 400
SIC 3444 1711 Sheet metalwork; Mechanical contractor
VP: Daniel Blosser
**CEO:* James P Young
**CFO:* Kelly Blosser
**VP:* Charles E Cline
**VP:* William George
**VP:* Trent McKenna
**VP:* Bill Tate
Board of Directors: Larry Atkins

D-U-N-S 15-168-1061 IMP
RIDDLES GROUP INC
MT RUSHMORE BLACK HILLS GOLD
2707 Mount Rushmore Rd, Rapid City, SD 57701-5324
Tel (605) 343-7099 *Founded/Ownrshp* 1959
Sales 232.9MM^E^ *EMP* 750
SIC 3873 3911 Watches, clocks, watchcases & parts; Medals, precious or semiprecious metal
Pr: Jesse Riddle
**Pr:* Brett Riddle
CFO: Rudolph Gatti
**CFO:* David Westerguard
**VP:* Lee Jensen

D-U-N-S 62-309-4893 IMP/EXP
RIDE CONTROL LLC
GABRIEL RIDE CONTROL
(*Suby of* MAT-AUTOMOTIVE) ★
39300 Country Club Dr, Farmington Hills, MI 48331-3473
Tel (248) 247-7600 *Founded/Ownrshp* 2009
Sales 239.4MM^E^ *EMP* 1,150
SIC 3714 Motor vehicle parts & accessories; Shock absorbers, motor vehicle
CEO: Lisa J Bahash
**CFO:* James Neelley
Dir IT: Scott Kim

D-U-N-S 07-611-9791
RIDEOUT MEMORIAL HOSPITAL
(*Suby of* FREEMONT RIDEOUT HEALTH GROUP) ★
726 4th St, Marysville, CA 95901-5656
Tel (530) 749-4416 *Founded/Ownrshp* 1955
Sales 324.1MM *EMP* 775
SIC 8062 8082 General medical & surgical hospitals; Home health care services
Ch: Ronald M Sweeney
**CEO:* Theresa Hamilton
**Treas:* John Cary
Doctor: Michael L Chin MD

D-U-N-S 06-988-4765
RIDER UNIVERSITY A NEW JERSEY NON-PROFIT CORP (NJ)
2083 Lawrenceville Rd, Lawrenceville, NJ 08648-3001
Tel (609) 896-5000 *Founded/Ownrshp* 1987
Sales 155.2MM *EMP* 740
Accts Kpmg Llp New York Ny
SIC 8221 College, except junior
Pr: Mordechai Rozanski
Treas: Carol Azoff
Assoc VP: Larry Bullock
VP: Jonathan Meer
VP: James Ohara
**VP:* Don Steven
Assoc Dir: Mary B Carstens
Assoc Dir: Christopher Foster
Assoc Dir: Jeffrey Kless
Assoc Dir: Shirley K Turner
Genl Mgr: John Mozes

D-U-N-S 15-693-8537
RIDERWOOD VILLAGE INC
3150 Gracefield Rd, Silver Spring, MD 20904-5896
Tel (301) 572-1300 *Founded/Ownrshp* 1998
Sales 110.0MM *EMP* 1,400
Accts Mcgladrey Llp Baltimore Md
SIC 8361 Geriatric residential care
Ex Dir: Donna Mason
**CEO:* Chip Warner
Podiatrist: Roberto Araujo
Doctor: John H Stuckey

D-U-N-S 00-455-0125 IMP/EXP
■ **RIDGE TOOL CO**
RIDGID
(*Suby of* EECO INC) ★
400 Clark St, Elyria, OH 44035-6100
Tel (440) 323-5581 *Founded/Ownrshp* 1966
Sales 367.7MM^E^ *EMP* 1,500
SIC 3541 3423 3547 3546 Machine tools, metal cutting type; Pipe cutting & threading machines; Hand & edge tools; Rolling mill machinery; Power-driven handtools
Prin: B J Jones
VP: Donna Calhoun
VP: Mark Downie
VP: Mark Hersh
VP: Toni Miller
VP: Cathy Raible
Info Man: Bruce Manning
Sls Mgr: David Dreher
Sales Asso: Aileen Beirne

D-U-N-S 78-476-4370
■ **RIDGE TOOL MANUFACTURING CO**
(*Suby of* RIDGID) ★
400 Clark St, Elyria, OH 44035-6100
Tel (440) 323-5581 *Founded/Ownrshp* 1990
Sales 70.7MM^E^ *EMP* 1,400
SIC 3541 3423 3547 3546 3545 3469 Machine tools, metal cutting type; Hand & edge tools; Rolling mill machinery; Power-driven handtools; Machine tool accessories; Metal stampings
Pr: Fred Pond
**CFO:* Ralph Shaw
**VP:* Scott Garfield
MIS Dir: Kevin Jakubec

D-U-N-S 06-668-8011
RIDGECREST REGIONAL HOSPITAL
SOUTHERN SIERRA MEDICAL CLINIC
1081 N China Lake Blvd, Ridgecrest, CA 93555-3130
Tel (760) 446-3551 *Founded/Ownrshp* 1962
Sales 86.0MM *EMP* 500
SIC 8062 General medical & surgical hospitals
CEO: James A Suver
Pr: Michelle Whalley
CFO: Donna Kiser
Bd of Dir: Paul Cooper
Bd of Dir: Charles Pietrangelo
VP: Darrell Eddins
Dir Lab: Scott Davis
Dir Sec: Matt Lilley
Genl Mgr: Tamara Khalifeh
Off Mgr: Tammy Lilly
CIO: Michael Grant

D-U-N-S 18-966-1296
RIDGESIDE CONSTRUCTION INC
RIDGESIDE FINISHING
4345 E Lowell St Ste A, Ontario, CA 91761-2223
Tel (909) 218-7593 *Founded/Ownrshp* 2005
Sales 125.2MM *EMP* 65
SIC 1521 Single-family housing construction
Pr: Dan Zita
**VP:* Kevin Hammond

RIDGESIDE FINISHING
See RIDGESIDE CONSTRUCTION INC

D-U-N-S 19-464-7103 IMP
RIDGEVIEW INDUSTRIES INC
3093 Northridge Dr Nw, Grand Rapids, MI 49544-9132
Tel (616) 453-8636 *Founded/Ownrshp* 1988
Sales 100.1MM^E^ *EMP* 425
SIC 3469 7692 Metal stampings; Welding repair
Pr: David Nykamp
Pr: Jerry Deshaw
IT Man: Steve Leppink
Ql Cn Mgr: Whitney Shorb

D-U-N-S 01-092-8740
RIDGEVIEW MEDICAL CENTER
500 S Maple St, Waconia, MN 55387-1791
Tel (952) 442-2191 *Founded/Ownrshp* 1990
Sales 201.0MM *EMP* 1,200
SIC 8062 General medical & surgical hospitals
Pr: Robert Stevens
COO: Mike Phelps
COO: Robert Welch
CFO: Gordon Gablenz
Ofcr: Shannon Mattson
VP: Pat Michaelson
Exec: Nancy Greenwood
Exec: Lynette Rettig
Dir Inf Cn: Chris Vos
Dir Rx: Stephanie J Svoboda
Ex Dir: Hauser Julie

RIDGEWOOD CENTER
See 25 RIDGEWOOD ROAD OPERATIONS LLC

D-U-N-S 15-394-0499 IMP
RIDGEWOOD MANOR INC
1624 Highland Dr, Washington, NC 27889-8761
Tel (252) 946-9570 *Founded/Ownrshp* 1996
Sales 584.3MM *EMP* 125
SIC 8051 8052 Skilled nursing care facilities; Intermediate care facilities
Pr: Mike Kelly
**Sec:* Alisa Kelly
Off Mgr: Judy Lilley

D-U-N-S 00-171-2090
RIDGEWOOD SAVINGS BANK
7102 Forest Ave Ste 1, Ridgewood, NY 11385-5697
Tel (718) 240-4800 *Founded/Ownrshp* 1921
Sales NA *EMP* 634
SIC 6036 State savings banks, not federally chartered
CFO: Leonard Sekol
**Pr:* Peter M Boger
Pr: Victor Padilla
CFO: Kenneth Ceonzo
**Treas:* Hala Elbedewe
**Ofcr:* Edward F O'Brien
Ofcr: Glenn Reyber
**Assoc VP:* Laura Camelo
**Sr VP:* Norman L McNamee
**Sr VP:* Rosemarie Mignogna
**Sr VP:* Walter J Reese
**VP:* Bruce Behrend
**VP:* Geraldine Brennan
**VP:* Joseph Curcio
**VP:* Vito Dibona
VP: Ann Freese
**VP:* Lisa Funaro
**VP:* Francis P O'Hagan
VP: Francis P Ohagan
**VP:* Laura Peters
**VP:* Melissa Riccardo

RIDGID
See RIDGE TOOL CO

RIDLEY FEED INGREDIENTS
See RIDLEY USA INC

D-U-N-S 07-162-8408
RIDLEY SCHOOL DISTRICT AUTHORITY
901 Morton Ave Unit A, Folsom, PA 19033-2997
Tel (610) 534-1900 *Founded/Ownrshp* 1830
Sales 100.4MM *EMP* 750
Accts Leitzell & Economidis Pc Med
SIC 8211 Public elementary & secondary schools; High school, junior or senior

D-U-N-S 11-122-3996
RIDLEY USA INC
RIDLEY FEED INGREDIENTS
(*Suby of* FORTNIGHT PRODUCTIONS) ★
111 W Cherry St Ste 500, Mankato, MN 56001-6992
Tel (507) 388-9400 *Founded/Ownrshp* 2015
Sales 153.0MM *EMP* 600
SIC 2048

RIDLEY'S FAMILY MARKETS
See RIDLEYS FOOD CORP

D-U-N-S 36-222-4479
RIDLEYS FOOD CORP
RIDLEY'S FAMILY MARKETS
621 Washington St S, Twin Falls, ID 83301-5519
Tel (208) 324-4633 *Founded/Ownrshp* 1988
Sales 277.3MM^E^ *EMP* 2,000
SIC 5411 2099 Grocery stores; Salads, fresh or refrigerated
Pr: Donald Mark Ridley
VP: Brian Hansen

D-U-N-S 01-816-4145
RIESBECK FOOD MARKETS INC
VALUE FRESH
48661 National Rd W, Saint Clairsville, OH 43950-9701
Tel (740) 695-7050 *Founded/Ownrshp* 1936
Sales 195.5MM *EMP* 1,300
Accts Bdo Usa Llp Pittsburgh Penns
SIC 5411 Supermarkets, independent
CEO: Richard L Riesbeck
COO: Dave Orr
**Treas:* Jennifer Kiger
**VP:* William B Riesbeck
VP: Jay Ropietski
CIO: Maok Kemp

RIESE ORGANIZATION
See NATIONAL RESTAURANTS MANAGEMENT INC

RIESE ORGANIZATION
See NATIONAL RESTAURANTS MANAGEMENT INC

D-U-N-S 02-318-2231
RIESTERER & SCHNELL INC
JOHN DEERE AUTHORIZED DEALER
N2909 State Highway 32, Pulaski, WI 54162-7905
Tel (920) 775-4146 *Founded/Ownrshp* 1931
Sales 155.5MM *EMP* 135
Accts Schenck Sc Green Bay Wiscons
SIC 5083 5261 Farm implements; Lawn & garden equipment
Pr: Raphael Riesterer
**Treas:* Delmar Riesterer
**VP:* Kenneth Riesterer

D-U-N-S 00-693-7445 IMP
RIETH-RILEY CONSTRUCTION CO INC
3626 Elkhart Rd, Goshen, IN 46526-5819
Tel (574) 875-5183 *Founded/Ownrshp* 1986
Sales 222.2MM^E^ *EMP* 303
SIC 1611 1771 1622

D-U-N-S 01-183-0635
RIGGINS INC
RIGGINS OIL
3938 S Main Rd, Vineland, NJ 08360-7743
Tel (856) 825-7600 *Founded/Ownrshp* 1984
Sales 249.9MM *EMP* 105
Accts Kenneth E Yeutter Cpa Millv
SIC 5171 Petroleum bulk stations
Pr: Paul Riggins
**CFO:* Steven D Riggins
**VP:* Richard E Cummines

RIGGINS OIL
See RIGGINS INC

D-U-N-S 06-732-8336 IMP
RIGGIO DISTRIBUTION CO
AUNT MID PRODUCE CO.
7939 Lafayette Blvd, Detroit, MI 48209-1987
Tel (313) 841-7911 *Founded/Ownrshp* 1984
Sales 109.7MM^E^ *EMP* 150
SIC 5148 Fruits, fresh; Vegetables, fresh
Pr: Philip D Riggio
**VP:* Vincent J Riggio
Prd Mgr: Bob Sheroian

RIGGS CA
See JA RIGGS TRACTOR CO

D-U-N-S 06-938-5813
RIGGS COUNSELMAN MICHAELS & DOWNES INC
RCM&D
555 Fairmount Ave, Baltimore, MD 21286-5417
Tel (410) 339-7263 *Founded/Ownrshp* 1969
Sales NA *EMP* 260
SIC 6411 Insurance agents; Insurance brokers
CEO: Albert R Counselman
**Pr:* Jason E Mulligan
**CEO:* Richard B Mulligan
**CFO:* Barbara Labuskes
CFO: Pete Poore
**V Ch Bd:* Thomas P Healy
**V Ch Bd:* Francis Riggs
VP: Michael Goode
VP: Samuel Hoyle
VP: David Johnson
VP: Brian Mueller
VP: Karen Randazzo
VP: Amanda Smith

D-U-N-S 00-695-0406
RIGGS DISTLER & CO INC (MD)
(*Suby of* NAPEC INC)
4 Esterbrook Ln, Cherry Hill, NJ 08003-4002
Tel (856) 433-6000 *Founded/Ownrshp* 1909, 1999
Sales 210.0MM *EMP* 850
SIC 1731 General electrical contractor
Pr: Stephen Zemaitatis Jr
CFO: Stephan R Thomas
**VP:* Paul Bizon
**VP:* Manfred Konrath
**VP:* Joseph Seaman
Exec: Denise Fearon
Genl Mgr: Dave Miller
IT Man: Thang Doan
Sfty Dirs: James Bross
Sfty Dirs: Dave White
Sfty Mgr: Michael Burnham

D-U-N-S 15-375-0237
RIGGS INDUSTRIES INC
2478 Lincoln Hwy, Stoystown, PA 15563-7821
Tel (814) 629-5621 *Founded/Ownrshp* 1985
Sales 119.8MM *EMP* 478
SIC 3713 3441 Truck & bus bodies; Fabricated structural metal
Pr: William B Friedline
**Treas:* David F Lowry
**VP:* S William Riggs
Dir IT: David McCahan

D-U-N-S 15-418-4667
RIGHT HUMAN RESOURCE CONSULTANTS INC
4445 Lake Forest Dr # 470, Blue Ash, OH 45242-3739
Tel (513) 733-1313 *Founded/Ownrshp* 1983
Sales 17.0MM^E^ *EMP* 1,000
SIC 8742 7361 Human resource consulting services; Employment agencies
Pr: Alvin N Hainline
Off Admin: Bonnie Billingsely

D-U-N-S 08-023-6401
RIGHT LIGHT ENERGY SERVICES LLC
811 Court St Ste 214, Utica, NY 13502-4054
Tel (315) 723-2329 *Founded/Ownrshp* 2012
Sales 140.0MM *EMP* 3
SIC 8748 Lighting consultant
Pt: Steve Couture
Pt: Kurt Benziger

D-U-N-S 05-346-9102
■ **RIGHT MANAGEMENT INC**
MANPOWER
(*Suby of* MANPOWERGROUP INC) ★
1600 Jf Kennedy Blvd # 610, Philadelphia, PA 19103-2812
Tel (952) 837-0955 *Founded/Ownrshp* 2004
Sales 205.5MM^E^ *EMP* 3,275
SIC 7363 Manpower pools
CEO: Owen J Sullivan
Pr: Bob Carlson
Pr: Douglas Matthews
Pr: Paul Straub
CFO: Morgan Ed
Ofcr: Luis Quismorio
Ofcr: Albert Tiede
Ex VP: Mike Evans
Ex VP: George Herrmann
Ex VP: Keiji Miyaki
Ex VP: Gilbert Wetzel
Ex VP: Theodore A Young
Sr VP: Romayne Berry
Sr VP: Joe Catrino
Sr VP: Gail Landazuri
Sr VP: Susan Palombo
Sr VP: John Schreitmueller
VP: Dianne Bond
VP: Katie Cummings
VP: Anabelle Fedora
VP: Jeff Gerkin

D-U-N-S 07-947-5206
▲ **RIGHTSIDE GROUP LTD**
5808 Lake Washington Blvd, Kirkland, WA 98033-7350
Tel (425) 298-2500 *Founded/Ownrshp* 2013
Sales 212.4MM *EMP* 275
Tkr Sym NAME *Exch* NGS
SIC 7374 7375 Data processing & preparation; Information retrieval services
CEO: Taryn J Naidu
**Ch Bd:* David E Panos
CFO: Tracy Knox
CTO: Wayne M Maclaurin
Genl Couns: Rick Danis
Board of Directors: Diane M Irvine, Robert J Majteles, James R Quandt, Richard C Spalding

D-U-N-S 03-037-1335 EXP
▲ RIGNET INC
1880 S Dairy Ashford Rd # 300, Houston, TX 77077-4746
Tel (281) 674-0100 *Founded/Ownrshp* 2000
Sales 271.2MM *EMP* 546[E]
Tkr Sym RNET *Exch* NGS
SIC 4899 4813 Data communication services;
Pr: Steven E Pickett
* *Ch Bd:* James H Browning
CFO: Charles Schneider
* *V Ch Bd:* Kevin J O'Hara
Ofcr: Jay T Hilbert
Sr VP: Morten Hagland Hansen
Sr VP: William Sutton
VP: Gerry Gutierrez
VP: Hector Maytorena
VP: Curtis McGee
VP: Keith Stewart
Board of Directors: Charles L Davis, Kevin Mulloy, Keith Olsen, Brent K Whittington

D-U-N-S 17-540-9676
■ RIH ACQUISITIONS IN LLC
RESORTS EAST CHICAGO
(*Suby of* AMERISTAR EAST CHICAGO HOLDINGS LLC) ★
777 Resorts Blvd, East Chicago, IN 46312-1847
Tel (219) 378-3000 *Founded/Ownrshp* 2007
Sales 11.0MM[E] *EMP* 1,200
SIC 7999 Gambling & lottery services
VP: Troy Stremming
Netwrk Mgr: Steve Labowski

D-U-N-S 80-003-8671
RIH ACQUISITIONS MS I LLC
RESORTS TUNICA CASINO
(*Suby of* COLONY MANAGEMENT) ★
1100 Casino Strip Resort, Robinsonville, MS 38664-9138
Tel (662) 363-7777 *Founded/Ownrshp* 2004
Sales 31.9MM[E] *EMP* 1,200
SIC 7999 Gambling & lottery services

D-U-N-S 19-835-1442
RIH ACQUISITIONS MS II LLC
BALLY'S TUNICA
(*Suby of* COLONY MANAGEMENT) ★
1450 Ballys Blvd, Robinsonville, MS 38664-9721
Tel (800) 382-2559 *Founded/Ownrshp* 2004
Sales 21.6MM[E] *EMP* 1,200
SIC 7999 Gambling & lottery services
CEO: Michael Frawley

D-U-N-S 83-090-2735 IMP/EXP
RIL USA INC
(*Suby of* RELIANCE INDUSTRIES LIMITED)
2000 W Sam Houston Pkwy S # 1155, Houston, TX 77042-3649
Tel (713) 430-8700 *Founded/Ownrshp* 2009
Sales 1.5MMM *EMP* 15
Accts Deloitte Haskins & Sells Llp
SIC 1382 Oil & gas exploration services
CEO: John Fitzereld
* *CFO:* Sanjeev Kedia

D-U-N-S 02-581-1704 IMP
RILCO INC
ROCK ISLAND LUBRICANTS & CHEM
1320 1st St, Rock Island, IL 61201-3218
Tel (309) 788-5631 *Founded/Ownrshp* 1979
Sales 157.7MM[E] *EMP* 90[E]
SIC 5172 5169 Engine fuels & oils; Chemicals & allied products
Pr: Conrad Wagner
* *VP:* Craig Wagner
Opers Mgr: Greg Bansteckelman
Sls Mgr: Michael Miller

D-U-N-S 00-296-0631
RILEY CONSTRUCTION CO INC (WI)
5301 99th Ave, Kenosha, WI 53144-2296
Tel (262) 658-4381 *Founded/Ownrshp* 1965
Sales 121.3MM[E] *EMP* 200
Accts Clifton Larson Allen Llp Raci
SIC 1542 1541 Commercial & office building contractors; Institutional building construction; Industrial buildings & warehouses
Pr: Dave Riley
* *CFO:* Peter Sinsky
IT Man: Michael Borst
VP Opers: Matt Prince
Mktg Mgr: Mary Pawlowski
Snr Mgr: Blanca Abend

D-U-N-S 04-663-1578
RILEY CREEK LUMBER CO
30 Riley Creek Rd, Laclede, ID 83841
Tel (208) 255-3200 *Founded/Ownrshp* 2008
Sales 159.5MM[E] *EMP* 280
SIC 5099 Timber products, rough
Ch Bd: Marc A Brinkmeyer
CFO: Suzanne Cullinane
* *Sec:* Kevin A Esser
* *VP:* Robert Boeh
IT Man: Bonnie Glazier

D-U-N-S 07-619-3015
RILEY GROUP INC
17522 Bthell Way Ne Ste A, Bothell, WA 98011
Tel (425) 415-0551 *Founded/Ownrshp* 1999
Sales 114.3MM *EMP* 8[E]
SIC 8748 Environmental consultant
Pr: Paul Riley

D-U-N-S 00-112-7455 IMP/EXP
RILEY POWER INC (MA)
(*Suby of* BABCOCK POWER CAPITAL CORPORATION)
5 Neponset St, Worcester, MA 01606-2714
Tel (508) 852-7100 *Founded/Ownrshp* 1913
Sales 135.3MM *EMP* 320
Accts Deloitte & Touche Llp Hartfor
SIC 3569 3443 3433 1711 3564 3511 Generators: steam, liquid oxygen or nitrogen; Fuel tanks (oil, gas, etc.): metal plate; Burners, furnaces, boilers & stokers; Boiler maintenance contractor; Blowers & fans; Turbines & turbine generator sets
CEO: Michael D Leclair
Pr: Edward C Dean
CFO: Anthony A Brandano
Sr VP: William J Ferguson Jr
Sr VP: Robert G Pierson
Sr VP: David Slack
VP: W Burke Allred
VP: Donna Anderson
VP: Donna D Anderson
VP: Joseph A Green
VP: Michael Kelly
VP: Joseph A Langone
VP: Earl Mason
VP: Earl B Mason
VP: Robert Pierson
Board of Directors: William J Ferguson Jr, Michael Leclair, Earl B Mason

D-U-N-S 86-931-3585
RIM CORP
RIM HOSPITALITY
915 17th St, Modesto, CA 95354-1207
Tel (209) 523-8331 *Founded/Ownrshp* 1983
Sales 98.4MM[E] *EMP* 3,000
SIC 8741

RIM HOSPITALITY
See RIM CORP

D-U-N-S 93-160-8913 IMP/EXP
RIM LOGISTICS LTD
200 N Gary Ave Ste B, Roselle, IL 60172-1681
Tel (630) 595-0610 *Founded/Ownrshp* 1996
Sales 121.7MM[E] *EMP* 250
Accts Plante & Moran Pllc Chicago
SIC 4731 Freight transportation arrangement
CEO: Robert J Mueller III
* *Pr:* Robert J Mueller IV
* *CFO:* Jim McGregor
Ex VP: Jason Steinke
VP: Mike Powell
* *VP:* Sheila J Serafin
Admn Mgr: James Sharpe
Brnch Mgr: Joe Logsdon
CIO: Tom McNulty
Dir IT: Shaun Saturno
* *VP Sls:* Brandon Mueller

RIMC
See REPUBLIC MORTGAGE INSURANCE CO INC

D-U-N-S 62-107-6715
RIMINI STREET INC
3993 Howard Hughes Pkwy, Las Vegas, NV 89169-0961
Tel (702) 839-9671 *Founded/Ownrshp* 2005
Sales 125.3MM[E] *EMP* 600[E]
SIC 7379 7373 Computer related consulting services; Systems software development services
Ch Bd: Seth Ravin
* *Pr:* Sebastian Grady
* *CFO:* Ed Schaffer
* *CFO:* Pieter Van Der Vorst
Sr VP: Keith Costello
* *Sr VP:* Nancy Lyskawa
Sr VP: Kevin Maddock
* *Sr VP:* Thomas Shay
Sr VP: Brian J Slepko
Sr VP: Daniel B Winslow
* *VP:* Meyleen Beichler
* *VP:* James Benge
* *VP:* Shelley Blackmarr
VP: William Carey
* *VP:* Shawn Dplessis
VP: Ray Grigsby
VP: Beth Lester
VP: George Lester
* *VP:* Michelle McGlocklin
VP: Naomi Miller
VP: Jennifer Perry
Board of Directors: Jack L Acosta, Thomas Ashburn, Steve Capelli, Brian J Slepko, Margaret Taylor

D-U-N-S 16-168-3651
RIMKUS CONSULTING GROUP INC
8 Greenway Plz Ste 500, Houston, TX 77046-0899
Tel (713) 621-3550 *Founded/Ownrshp* 1983
Sales 185.6MM[E] *EMP* 388
SIC 8711 Engineering services
Ch Bd: S Frank Culberson
* *Pr:* Curtis R Brown
* *COO:* Robert P Kocher
CFO: Gary W Markham
* *Sr VP:* Ralph S Graham
VP: Gary Lee Bell
VP: Duncan E Doss
VP: Harmon L Kirkpatrick
VP: Pe Kocher
VP: Walter R Reifel Jr
VP: Gregory Schuelke
VP: Dirk E Smith
VP: Reifel Walter
VP: Barbara Worsham
Board of Directors: Robert Kocher

D-U-N-S 00-933-0877
RIMROCK PARTNERS LLC
2415 E Camelback Rd # 700, Phoenix, AZ 85016-4288
Tel (602) 954-7085 *Founded/Ownrshp* 2006
Sales 323.7MM[E] *EMP* 9,000[E]
SIC 6531 6519 6552 Real estate leasing & rentals; Real property lessors; Subdividers & developers; Land subdividers & developers, commercial; Land subdividers & developers, residential

D-U-N-S 00-220-8627 IMP/EXP
RINCHEM CO INC
5131 Masthead St Ne, Albuquerque, NM 87109-4367
Tel (505) 998-4300 *Founded/Ownrshp* 1976
Sales 143.5MM[E] *EMP* 400
Accts Grant Thornton Llp Phoenix A
SIC 4789 4225 Pipeline terminal facilities, independently operated; General warehousing
CEO: William Moore
* *VP:* Shane Candelaria
Site Mgr: Paul Boisvert

D-U-N-S 12-161-4838
RINECO CHEMICAL INDUSTRIES INC
819 Vulcan Rd, Benton, AR 72015-8981
Tel (501) 778-9089 *Founded/Ownrshp* 1984
Sales 88.6MM *EMP* 335
SIC 4953 Hazardous waste collection & disposal; Chemical detoxification
Pr: Harry C Erwin
* *Sec:* Steven M Keith
Dir Lab: Paul Humburg
Plnt Mgr: Jim Brown
Plnt Mgr: Ryan Dossey
VP Sls: Dale Welch
Sls Mgr: Jose Cruz
Sls Mgr: Patrick Howell
Sls Mgr: Robert Hutchison

D-U-N-S 02-956-5454
RINEHART OIL INC
RINO
2401 N State St, Ukiah, CA 95482-3020
Tel (707) 462-8811 *Founded/Ownrshp* 1969
Sales 122.7MM[E] *EMP* 100
SIC 5172 5541 Petroleum products; Filling stations, gasoline
Pr: Robert Reed Rinehart
* *VP:* Mike Babcock

RING CAN
See RINGWOOD CONTAINERS LP

D-U-N-S 04-792-5607 IMP
RING CONTAINER TECHNOLOGIES LLC
1 Industrial Park, Oakland, TN 38060-4048
Tel (901) 465-6333 *Founded/Ownrshp* 1969
Sales 306.4MM[E] *EMP* 580
SIC 3085 Plastics bottles
CEO: Benjamin J Livingston
Pr: Carl D Ring
Pr: Jeffrey Ullrich
* *CFO:* T Wayne Drake
CFO: John Varvel
VP: Jeff Ulrich
VP: Scott P Wuerfel
Genl Mgr: David Wilson
Off Mgr: Judy Cook
Off Mgr: Delores Hedge
Off Mgr: Mildred Lacosta
Board of Directors: James S Gilliand Sr

D-U-N-S 00-281-2089 IMP/EXP
RING POWER CORP (FL)
RING POWER LIFTTRUCK RING
(*Suby of* RPC INC) ★
500 World Commerce Pkwy, Saint Augustine, FL 32092-3788
Tel (904) 201-7400 *Founded/Ownrshp* 1961
Sales 1.0MMM *EMP* 2,000
SIC 5082 5084 7353 Construction & mining machinery; Engines & transportation equipment; Heavy construction equipment rental
Pr: Randal L Ringhaver
COO: David Alban
* *CFO:* Ronald T Roy
Bd of Dir: John Grubb
Ex VP: Kevin Robbins
Sr VP: Sue Miller
* *VP:* Timothy Maguire
VP: James Rockenbach
* *VP:* Dennis Steed
Sales Exec: Stephen Smith
Manager: Scott Brassard

RING POWER LIFTTRUCK RING
See RING POWER CORP

D-U-N-S 14-921-5928
▲ RINGCENTRAL INC
20 Davis Dr, Belmont, CA 94002-3002
Tel (650) 472-4100 *Founded/Ownrshp* 1999
Sales 296.2MM *EMP* 759
Accts Kpmg Llp Santa Clara Califo
Tkr Sym RNG *Exch* NYS
SIC 7372 4899 Prepackaged software; Data communication services
Ch Bd: Vladimir Shmunis
Pt: Marty Piombo
COO: Dave Sipes
CFO: Clyde Hosein
Chf Mktg O: Riadh Dridi
Ex VP: Kira Makagon
Ex VP: David Sipes
Sr VP: John Marlow
Sr VP: Praful Shah
VP: Richard Borenstein
VP: Mitesh Dhruv
VP: Carson Hostetter
VP: David Marler
VP: Ramin Missaghieh
VP: Erich Ziegler
Board of Directors: Michael Kourey, Robert Theis, Allan Thygesen, Niel Williams

RINGLING BRS-BRNUM BLEY CIRCUS
See FELD ENTERTAINMENT INC

D-U-N-S 00-797-1146
RINGS END INC (CT)
RINGS END OF LEWISBORO
181 West Ave, Darien, CT 06820-4312
Tel (203) 655-2525 *Founded/Ownrshp* 1902, 1966
Sales 266.0MM[E] *EMP* 250
SIC 5031 5211 Building materials, exterior; Building materials, interior; Lumber & other building materials
Pr: David Campbell
* *Pr:* Douglas G Campbell
* *CFO:* Lou Reda
Sr VP: Claude Hirsch
* *VP:* Robert Campbell
* *VP:* Elliot Greenberg
* *VP:* Kel Tyler
Genl Mgr: Michael Loya
Genl Mgr: Pete McDonald
Genl Mgr: Matt Rich
Genl Mgr: David Rohr

RINGS END OF LEWISBORO
See RINGS END INC

D-U-N-S 94-294-9975
RINGWOOD CONTAINERS LP
RING CAN
1 Industrial Park, Oakland, TN 38060-4048
Tel (901) 465-3607 *Founded/Ownrshp* 1994
Sales 128.0MM[E] *EMP* 580
SIC 3085 Plastics bottles
Pt: Carl D Ring
Pt: T Wayne Drake
Pt: Benjamin J Livingston
Pt: Jeffrey Ullrich
Pt: Scott P Wuerfel
Plnt Mgr: Tim Hruby

D-U-N-S 18-136-7087
■ RINGWOOD GATHERING CO
CROSS TIMBERS OPERATING CO
(*Suby of* XTO ENERGY INC) ★
810 Houston St Ste 2000, Fort Worth, TX 76102-6223
Tel (817) 870-2800 *Founded/Ownrshp* 1967
Sales 297.4MM[E] *EMP* 242
SIC 4922 Pipelines, natural gas
Pr: Nick Dungey

D-U-N-S 01-838-0381
RINK MANAGEMENT SERVICES CORP
9414 Charter Crossing Dr, Mechanicsville, VA 23116-5120
Tel (804) 550-7002 *Founded/Ownrshp* 1999
Sales 47.7MM[E] *EMP* 1,800
SIC 7999 Skating rink operation services
Pr: Thomas W Hillgrove
* *VP:* Glen Danischewski

RINO
See RINEHART OIL INC

D-U-N-S 03-883-1160 IMP/EXP
RIO ENERGY INTERNATIONAL INC
5718 Westheimer Rd # 1806, Houston, TX 77057-5780
Tel (713) 977-5718 *Founded/Ownrshp* 1980
Sales 167.5MM[E] *EMP* 34
SIC 5172 Petroleum products
CEO: Carlos A Abello
* *VP:* Raul Abello
* *VP:* Jose J Iglesias
* *VP:* John P Thornton
CTO: Lewis Watson
Dir IT: Timothy Donvan

D-U-N-S 05-512-9910
RIO FRESH INC (TX)
6504 S Stewart Rd, San Juan, TX 78589
Tel (956) 787-0023 *Founded/Ownrshp* 1970
Sales 164.1MM[E] *EMP* 250
SIC 5148 Vegetables
Pr: Christine Morley
* *Sec:* Jeanette Brown
* *VP:* Fred Schuster

D-U-N-S 04-628-1127
RIO GRANDE CITY CONSOLIDATED INDEPEDENT SCHOOL DISTRICT
1 S Fort Ringgold St, Rio Grande City, TX 78582-4701
Tel (956) 716-6700 *Founded/Ownrshp* 1955
Sales 84.1MM[E] *EMP* 2,000
SIC 8211 Public elementary school; Public junior high school; Public senior high school; Public special education school
Dir Sec: Javier Garcia
Dir Sec: Hernan Garza
Dir IT: Vilma Garza
Schl Brd P: Daniel J Garcia
HC Dir: Diana A Solis

D-U-N-S 03-570-0483 IMP
RIO GRANDE INC
SONIC MILL CO
7500 Bluewater Rd Nw, Albuquerque, NM 87121-1962
Tel (505) 839-3550 *Founded/Ownrshp* 1944
Sales 97.0MM[E] *EMP* 114[E]
SIC 5094 5049 3915 Precious stones & metals; Precision tools; Jewelers' findings & materials; Jewelry parts, unassembled; Jewel preparing: instruments, tools, watches & jewelry
CEO: Marlene Richey
* *Treas:* Alan Bell
Ex VP: Clyde Treadwell
* *VP:* Louis Bell
* *VP:* Danny Cox
IT Man: Charles Wilhite
Software D: Paula Jones
Snr Mgr: Herb Benedic

D-U-N-S 02-428-4666
RIO GRANDE REGIONAL HOSPITAL
101 E Ridge Rd, McAllen, TX 78503-1847
Tel (956) 632-6000 *Founded/Ownrshp* 2008
Sales 213.3MM *EMP* 2
SIC 8062 General medical & surgical hospitals
Dir IT: Carlos Leal
Doctor: Kip Owen

D-U-N-S 06-644-7418 IMP
RIO GRANDE VALLEY SUGAR GROWERS INC
RGVSG
2.5 Miles W Hwy 107, Santa Rosa, TX 78593
Tel (956) 636-1411 *Founded/Ownrshp* 1970
Sales 149.8MM[E] *EMP* 500
SIC 2061 Raw cane sugar; Blackstrap molasses made from sugar cane
Ch: Dale Murden
* *Pr:* Steven Bearden
* *CEO:* James Russell
* *Treas:* Randy Rolando
* *Sec:* Tudor Uhlhorn

D-U-N-S 13-414-5932
RIO HOLDINGS INC
600 Congress Ave Ste 200, Austin, TX 78701-2995
Tel (512) 917-1742 *Founded/Ownrshp* 1988
Sales 115.4MM[E] *EMP* 10

SIC 4813 4841 Local & long distance telephone communications; ; Cable & other pay television services
Pr: Michael Wilfley
**Ch Bd:* Duncan T Butler Jr
**CIO:* Henry Jacobsen

D-U-N-S 15-272-3565
■ RIO HOTEL & CASINO INC
(*Suby of* HARRAHS) ★
3700 W Flamingo Rd, Las Vegas, NV 89103-4046
Tel (702) 777-7777 *Founded/Ownrshp* 1986
Sales 133.2MM^E *EMP* 4,000^E
SIC 7011 7997 Casino hotel; Golf club, membership
COO: David Hanlon
CFO: Harlan D Braaten
VP: Karen Brasier
VP: Mark Fioravanti
VP: Michael Massari
VP: Cary Rehm
Board of Directors: Thomas Y Hartley, John A Stuart, Peter M Thomas

D-U-N-S 84-740-7723
RIO MAR RESORT-WHG HOTEL PROPERTY LLC
6000 Rio Mar Blvd, Rio Grande, PR 00745-4661
Tel (787) 888-6000 *Founded/Ownrshp* 1994
Sales 24.6MM^E *EMP* 1,000
Accts Kpmg Llp San Juan Pr
SIC 7011 Resort hotel
Mng Pt: Tom Anderson
VP: Larry M Vitale

D-U-N-S 60-552-4461
■ RIO PROPERTIES INC
RIO SUITE HOTEL & CASINO
(*Suby of* RIO HOTEL & CASINO INC) ★
3700 W Flamingo Rd, Las Vegas, NV 89103-4043
Tel (702) 777-7777 *Founded/Ownrshp* 1999
Sales 133.5MM^E *EMP* 3,236
SIC 7011 5812 Casino hotel; Eating places
Sr VP: Tom Jenkin
Exec: Susan Ferreira

D-U-N-S 83-560-4810
RIO RANCHO PUBLIC SCHOOLS
500 Laser Rd Ne, Rio Rancho, NM 87124-4517
Tel (505) 896-0667 *Founded/Ownrshp* 1991
Sales 77.6MM^E *EMP* 2,000
SIC 8211 Public elementary & secondary schools
Bd of Dir: Mexico RE
VP: Joyce Picard
VP: Michelle Sotelo
**Prin:* Traci Kasten
**Prin:* Jayne Mitchell
**Prin:* Phyllis Sepulveda
Ex Dir: Cathy Ferris
MIS Dir: Karen Boulanger
Pr Dir: Marilyn L Dellangelo
Teacher Pr: Sue Passell
Psych: Monique Chavez

RIO SUITE HOTEL & CASINO
See RIO PROPERTIES INC

D-U-N-S 02-503-2330
RIO TINTO AMERICA INC
(*Suby of* RIO TINTO LONDON LIMITED)
8051 E Maplewood Ave # 100, Greenwood Village, CO 80111-4857
Tel (303) 713-5000 *Founded/Ownrshp* 1973
Sales 11.4MM^E *EMP* 3,071
SIC 3412 5082 1044

RIO TINTO REGIONAL CENTER
See KENNECOTT UTAH COPPER LLC

D-U-N-S 01-332-9254
■ RIO TINTO SERVICES INC
(*Suby of* CLOUD PEAK ENERGY SERVICES CO) ★
4700 W Daybreak Pkwy, South Jordan, UT 84009-5120
Tel (801) 204-2000 *Founded/Ownrshp* 1989
Sales 158.5MM^E *EMP* 1,200^E
SIC 8721 8741 Accounting, auditing & bookkeeping; Business management
Pr: R Antal
**CFO:* Jeff Birtcher
**Treas:* Jack R Welch
**VP:* Richard E Pierce Jr
**VP:* S Singer
**VP:* A P Slentz
**VP:* J D Tygesen
Genl Mgr: Andrew Broad
Genl Mgr: Clay Collins
Genl Mgr: Peter Mannion
Genl Mgr: Duncan White

D-U-N-S 04-094-3102 IMP
RIO VISTA VENTURES LLC
GIUMARRA COMPANIES
15651 Old Milky Way, Escondido, CA 92027-7104
Tel (760) 480-8502 *Founded/Ownrshp* 1975
Sales 91.1MM^E *EMP* 115
SIC 5141 Food brokers
Ch: Don Corsaro
Pr: Timothy Riley

D-U-N-S 00-216-3139
RIOT GAMES INC
(*Suby of* TENCENT HOLDINGS LIMITED)
12333 W Olympic Blvd, Los Angeles, CA 90064-1021
Tel (310) 828-7953 *Founded/Ownrshp* 2006, 2011
Sales 656.9MM^E *EMP* 902^E
SIC 7371 7993 Custom computer programming services; Video game arcade
CEO: Brandon Beck
**Pr:* Mark Marrill
CFO: A Dyoan Jadeja
VP: Dustin Beck
VP: Sean Bender
VP: Scott Gelb
VP: Nicolo Laurent
Prgrm Mgr: Christopher Wyatt
Genl Mgr: Bruno Schirch
Snr Sftwr: Javier Blazquez
Snr Sftwr: Scott Delap

D-U-N-S 02-677-8084
RIP GRIFFIN TRUCK SERVICE CENTER INC
GRIFFIN OIL CO
(*Suby of* R G B LP)
4710 4th St, Lubbock, TX 79416-4900
Tel (806) 795-8785 *Founded/Ownrshp* 1958
Sales 145.7MM *EMP* 88
Accts Garrett And Swann Llp Lubbock
SIC 6719 Investment holding companies, except banks
**Pt:* Don Hayden

D-U-N-S 82-477-8948
RIPPLEWOOD ADVISORS LLC
920 Broadway Fl 6, New York, NY 10010-8304
Tel (212) 218-2705 *Founded/Ownrshp* 2013
Sales 69.7MM^E *EMP* 5,150^E
SIC 6799 Venture capital companies

D-U-N-S 83-675-4309 IMP
RIPPLEWOOD HOLDINGS LLC
1 Rockefeller Plz Fl 10, New York, NY 10020-2108
Tel (212) 218-2705 *Founded/Ownrshp* 2001
Sales 204.2MM^E *EMP* 5,150
SIC 7389 6211

D-U-N-S 96-772-4613
RIPPLEWOOD INVESTMENTS LLC
(*Suby of* RIPPLEWOOD ADVISORS LLC) ★
920 Broadway Fl 6, New York, NY 10010-8304
Tel (212) 218-2705 *Founded/Ownrshp* 1996
Sales 396.6M^E *EMP* 4,847^E
SIC 6282 Investment advice
CEO: Timothy C Collins

RISD
See RHODE ISLAND SCHOOL OF DESIGN INC

D-U-N-S 86-697-0015
RISE INC
4554 E Inverness Ave # 134, Mesa, AZ 85206-4639
Tel (480) 497-1889 *Founded/Ownrshp* 1988
Sales 59.5MM *EMP* 2,000
Accts Full Forsberg & Olson Phoenix
SIC 8322 Social services for the handicapped
Pr: Gerald J Nebeker
CEO: Joshua Auer
CFO: Archie Fitzgerald
VP: Ruth Simmoneau
Ex Dir: Kirsten Walker
CTO: Matthew Dee

D-U-N-S 00-794-4325 IMP/EXP
RISH EQUIPMENT CO (VA)
6384 Airport Rd, Bluefield, WV 24701-9560
Tel (304) 327-5124 *Founded/Ownrshp* 1934, 2011
Sales 119.8MM^E *EMP* 298
SIC 5082 7699 Excavating machinery & equipment; Graders, motor; Mining machinery & equipment, except petroleum; Aircraft & heavy equipment repair services
CEO: Garrett Jones
**Pr:* Wesley D Burke
**COO:* Dale Hall
**CFO:* D Steven Hamilton
VP: Myron G Jones
**VP:* Ralph McGlothin

RISK MANAGEMENT DEPARTMENT
See SCHOOL BOARD OF BROWARD COUNTY

D-U-N-S 61-098-2845
RISK MANAGEMENT SOLUTIONS INC
(*Suby of* DMGI LAND & PROPERTY EUROPE LTD)
7575 Gateway Blvd, Newark, CA 94560-1193
Tel (510) 505-2500 *Founded/Ownrshp* 1998
Sales 247.5MM^E *EMP* 500
SIC 6794 6411 Patent owners & lessors; Insurance information & consulting services
CEO: Hemant Shah
Ch Bd: Paul Dali
CFO: Stephen Robertson
Sr VP: John Kapitan
Sr VP: Brad Nichols
VP: Alex Barnett
VP: Mike Dickey
VP: Paris Georgallis
VP: Joseph Kim
VP: Inas Martens
Exec: Debbie Byron

D-U-N-S 14-444-5892
RISK MANAGEMENT STRATEGIES INC
TRUST EMPLOYEE ADM & MGT
8530 La Mesa Blvd Ste 200, La Mesa, CA 91942-0966
Tel (619) 281-1100 *Founded/Ownrshp* 2003
Sales 98.4MM^E *EMP* 2,500
SIC 8748 Employee programs administration
Pr: Terence J Keating
**CFO:* Arthur D Candland
**VP:* Cheryl Doss
Opers Mgr: Denise Bryant

D-U-N-S 10-400-0823
■ RISK PLACEMENT SERVICES INC
GALLAGER BASSETT SERVICES
(*Suby of* ARTHUR J GALLAGHER & CO) ★
2 Pierce Pl Fl 25, Itasca, IL 60143-1203
Tel (630) 773-3800 *Founded/Ownrshp* 1997
Sales NA *EMP* 801
SIC 6411 Insurance agents & brokers
CEO: Phil Rellinger
**Pr:* Linda Abell
**Pr:* Joel D Cavaness
Pr: Karen Hammer
Pr: Jim Kennedy
Pr: Janine Worland
Sr VP: Susan Dunne
VP: Diana Butts
VP: Scott Hudson
Brnch Mgr: Fred Newren
IT Man: Eugene Hamm

RISK STRATEGIES COMPANY
See RSC INSURANCE BROKERAGE INC

D-U-N-S 06-800-6456
■ RISKMETRICS GROUP INC
(*Suby of* MSCI INC) ★
1 Chase Manhattan Plz F, New York, NY 10005-1401
Tel (212) 981-7475 *Founded/Ownrshp* 2010
Sales 56.8MM^E *EMP* 1,140
SIC 8742 Management consulting services
CEO: Henry A Fernandez
**CFO:* David M Obstler
Software D: Alex Hradouski
Sls Dir: Alkesh Gianchandani

D-U-N-S 83-194-2029
RITA RESTAURANT CORP
DON PABLO'S
(*Suby of* ALAMORITA RESTAURANT COMPANY, LLC)
120 Chula Vis, San Antonio, TX 78232-2234
Tel (210) 403-3725 *Founded/Ownrshp* 2007
Sales 139.0MM^E *EMP* 4,000
SIC 5812 6794 Mexican restaurant; Grills (eating places); Franchises, selling or licensing
Pr: Paul J Seidman
VP: Robyn Cook

RITCHIE BROS AUCTIONEERS
See RITCHIE BROS AUCTIONEERS (AMERICA) INC

D-U-N-S 16-142-7299
RITCHIE BROS AUCTIONEERS (AMERICA) INC
RITCHIE BROS AUCTIONEERS
(*Suby of* RITCHIE BROS. AUCTIONEERS INCORPORATED)
4000 Pine Lake Rd, Lincoln, NE 68516-5484
Tel (402) 421-3631 *Founded/Ownrshp* 1962
Sales 376.6MM *EMP* 1,500
SIC 7389 Auctioneers, fee basis
Ch Bd: David Ritchie
**CEO:* Ravi Saligram
**CFO:* Sharon Driscoll
**CFO:* Rob McLeod

RITE AID
See MAXI DRUG INC

D-U-N-S 01-457-8892 IMP
▲ RITE AID CORP
30 Hunter Ln, Camp Hill, PA 17011-2400
Tel (717) 761-2633 *Founded/Ownrshp* 1962
Sales 30.7MMM *EMP* 89,500
Accts Deloitte & Touche Llp Philade
Tkr Sym RAD *Exch* NYS
SIC 5912 7384 5963 Drug stores & proprietary stores; Photofinish laboratories; Direct selling establishments
Ch Bd: John T Standley
Pr: Kenneth A Martindale
Pr: Lori Pelphrey
CFO: Darren W Karst
Treas: Matthew Schroeder
Ex VP: David Abelman
Ex VP: Dedra N Castle
Ex VP: Enio Anthony Montini Jr
Ex VP: Tony Montini
Ex VP: Robert I Thompson
Ex VP: Marc A Strassler
Sr VP: Douglas E Donley
VP: Ken Black
VP: Jerry Cardinale
VP: Tracey Diehl
VP: Jeffery Ellison
VP: Alison Farrell
VP: Terry Halbur
VP: David Kelly
VP: Paul Krueger
VP: David Mahan
Board of Directors: Joseph B Anderson Jr, Bruce G Bodaken, David R Jessick, Kevin E Lofton, Myrtle S Potter, Michael N Regan, Frank A Savage, Marcy Syms

D-U-N-S 36-111-7435
■ RITE AID OF KENTUCKY INC
(*Suby of* RITE AID CORP) ★
30 Hunter Ln, Camp Hill, PA 17011-2400
Tel (717) 761-2633 *Founded/Ownrshp* 1977
Sales 122.5MM^E *EMP* 1,100
SIC 5912 Drug stores & proprietary stores
Ch Bd: Robert Miller
**Pr:* Mary Sammons
Opers Mgr: Scott Wilson

D-U-N-S 07-741-5271 IMP
■ RITE AID OF MARYLAND INC
(*Suby of* RITE AID CORP) ★
30 Hunter Ln, Camp Hill, PA 17011-2400
Tel (717) 761-2633 *Founded/Ownrshp* 1975
Sales 181.5MM^E *EMP* 2,000
SIC 5912 Drug stores & proprietary stores
Pr: Mary Sammons
**Ch Bd:* Robert Miller
**Ex VP:* Franklin Brown
Snr Mgr: Jennifer Wagnor

D-U-N-S 11-514-0287 IMP
■ RITE AID OF MICHIGAN INC
(*Suby of* RITE AID CORP) ★
30 Hunter Ln, Camp Hill, PA 17011-2400
Tel (717) 761-2633 *Founded/Ownrshp* 1984
Sales 308.0MM^E *EMP* 3,500
SIC 5912 Drug stores & proprietary stores
Ch Bd: John T Standley
**Pr:* Kenneth Martindale
Sr VP: Chris Hall

D-U-N-S 07-282-9807
■ RITE AID OF NEW JERSEY INC
(*Suby of* RITE AID CORP) ★
30 Hunter Ln, Camp Hill, PA 17011-2400
Tel (717) 761-2633 *Founded/Ownrshp* 1975
Sales 192.0MM^E *EMP* 2,100
SIC 5912 Drug stores & proprietary stores
CEO: Mary Sammons

D-U-N-S 07-282-9567 IMP
■ RITE AID OF NEW YORK INC
(*Suby of* RITE AID CORP) ★
30 Hunter Ln, Camp Hill, PA 17011-2400
Tel (717) 761-2633 *Founded/Ownrshp* 1975
Sales 320.9MM^E *EMP* 3,500
SIC 5912 Drug stores & proprietary stores
Pr: Mary Sammons
**CFO:* Frank Vitrano

D-U-N-S 07-282-9633
■ RITE AID OF OHIO INC
(*Suby of* RITE AID CORP) ★
30 Hunter Ln, Camp Hill, PA 17011-2400
Tel (717) 761-2633 *Founded/Ownrshp* 1988
Sales 459.9MM^E *EMP* 5,000
SIC 5912 Drug stores & proprietary stores
CEO: John Standley
**Pr:* Christopher Hall
**Treas:* Matthew Schroeder
**Ex VP:* Brian Fiala
**Ex VP:* Tony Montini
**Ex VP:* Robert I Thompson
**Ex VP:* Marc A Strassler
**Sr VP:* Ken Martindale
**VP:* Susan Lowell

D-U-N-S 07-119-8881
■ RITE AID OF PENNSYLVANIA INC
(*Suby of* RITE AID CORP) ★
30 Hunter Ln, Camp Hill, PA 17011-2400
Tel (717) 761-2633 *Founded/Ownrshp* 1975
Sales 605.5MM^E *EMP* 4,000
SIC 5912 Drug stores & proprietary stores
Pr: Christopher Hall
CFO: Frank Bergonzi
**Treas:* Matthew Schroeder
Ex VP: Franklin Brown
**VP:* Susan Lowell
VP: Steve Parsons
Genl Mgr: Ron Allen
MIS Dir: Kent Whiting
Dir IT: Chris Pandelaras

D-U-N-S 05-042-2591
■ RITE AID OF SOUTH CAROLINA INC (VT)
(*Suby of* RITE AID CORP) ★
30 Hunter Ln, Camp Hill, PA 17011-2400
Tel (717) 761-2633 *Founded/Ownrshp* 1975
Sales 155.6MM^E *EMP* 2,000
SIC 5912 Drug stores & proprietary stores
Pr: John Stanley
**Pr:* Mary Sammons
VP: Chuck Kibler
VP: James Krahulec
VP: Wayne Leclair
VP: Stephanie Naito

D-U-N-S 07-284-8435
■ RITE AID OF VIRGINIA INC (VA)
(*Suby of* RITE AID CORP) ★
30 Hunter Ln, Camp Hill, PA 17011-2400
Tel (717) 761-2633 *Founded/Ownrshp* 1975
Sales 92.3MM^E *EMP* 1,312
SIC 5912 Drug stores & proprietary stores
Pr: Mary Sammons
**Ch Bd:* Martin Grass
**CFO:* Frank Bergonzi
**VP:* Franklin Brown

D-U-N-S 07-283-6968 IMP
■ RITE AID OF WEST VIRGINIA INC
(*Suby of* RITE AID CORP) ★
30 Hunter Ln, Camp Hill, PA 17011-2400
Tel (717) 761-2633 *Founded/Ownrshp* 1975
Sales 139.8MM^E *EMP* 1,500
SIC 5912 Drug stores & proprietary stores
Ch Bd: Robert Miller
**Pr:* Doug Donley
**Pr:* Mary Sammons
**CFO:* John Standley
**Treas:* Richard Varmecky
Ofcr: David Jessec

RITE HITE
See RITE-HITE CO LLC

D-U-N-S 79-442-2568 EXP
RITE STUFF FOODS INC
2155 S Lincoln Ave, Jerome, ID 83338-6106
Tel (208) 324-8410 *Founded/Ownrshp* 1989
Sales 95.6MM^E *EMP* 200
SIC 5149 Groceries & related products
Pr: Tom Madden
**CFO:* Jerry Anderson
Ofcr: Martin Berry
**Ex VP:* James Madden

D-U-N-S 03-511-2028
RITE WAY INVESTMENTS INC
SPEEDEE MART
8400 I St, Omaha, NE 68127-1614
Tel (402) 331-6400 *Founded/Ownrshp* 1964
Sales 141.6MM *EMP* 150
SIC 5172 5541 5411 Gasoline; Filling stations, gasoline; Convenience stores, independent
Pr: Rex Ekwall
**VP:* Rick Ekwall

RITE WAY SERVICE
See LS1 LLC

RITE WAY SERVICE, LLC
See LS1 LLC

D-U-N-S 04-261-4677 IMP/EXP
RITE-HITE CO LLC
RITE HITE
(*Suby of* RITE-HITE HOLDING CORP) ★
8900 N Arbon Dr, Milwaukee, WI 53223-2451
Tel (414) 355-2600 *Founded/Ownrshp* 1965
Sales 220.4MM^E *EMP* 290
SIC 5084 3842 3448 Industrial machinery & equipment; Surgical appliances & supplies; Prefabricated metal buildings
Pr: Mark Petri
Owner: Michael White
CFO: Mark S Kirkish
VP: Tim Anderson

VP: Doug Campbell
VP: Ellen Everson
VP: Christa Gensler
VP: Matthew C McNeill
VP: Angie Moore
VP: Jim Oates
VP: Todd Paul
VP: Brad Stone
VP: Kim Wagner
VP: Chuck Waugaman

D-U-N-S 01-715-6329 IMP
RITE-HITE HOLDING CORP
8900 N Arbon Dr, Milwaukee, WI 53223-2451
Tel (414) 355-2600 *Founded/Ownrshp* 1998
Sales 376.5MM^E *EMP* 1,000
SIC 5084 3449 3537 Industrial machinery & equipment; Miscellaneous metalwork; Loading docks: portable, adjustable & hydraulic
Ch Bd: Michael H White
**Pr:* Mark Petri
VP: Antonio Catalano
VP: Todd Fagerstrom
VP: Christa Gensler
VP: Dave Haugh
VP: Ellen Kosidowski
**VP:* Clem Maslowski
VP: Kyle Nelson
VP: Brad Stone
VP: Kim Wagner
VP: Charles S Waugaman

D-U-N-S 03-299-8085
RITESCREEN CO LLC
4314 State Route 209, Elizabethville, PA 17023-8438
Tel (717) 362-7483 *Founded/Ownrshp* 2014
Sales 129.2MM^E *EMP* 500
SIC 3442 2431 Metal doors, sash & trim; Millwork; Door screens, metal covered wood; Door screens, wood frame
CEO: Randy Iles
Pr: Robert Williams
Treas: Jay K Poppleton
VP: Janet L Fasenmyer
Sls Dir: Jerry Pino

D-U-N-S 07-384-3047
RITEWAY BUS SERVICE INC
GORITEWAY
W201 N13900 Fond Du Lac, Richfield, WI 53076-9501
Tel (262) 677-3282 *Founded/Ownrshp* 1957
Sales 108.4MM^E *EMP* 800
SIC 4151 4142 4141 School buses; Bus charter service, except local; Local bus charter service
Pr: Ronald R Bast
**Sec:* Rochelle Bast
**VP:* James O Christian

D-U-N-S 02-242-3537 IMP
RITTAL CORP
(*Suby of* RITTAL GMBH & CO. KG)
425 N Martingale Rd # 400, Schaumburg, IL 60173-2202
Tel (847) 240-4600 *Founded/Ownrshp* 1981
Sales 172.7MM^E *EMP* 700
SIC 3469 5065 Electronic enclosures, stamped or pressed metal; Electronic parts & equipment
Pr: Douglas E Peterson
CFO: Terry Ray
CFO: Steven Sessel
Sr VP: John Boudreaux
Sr VP: James Wiest
VP: Tony Varga
Brnch Mgr: Sandeep Ayyappa
CTO: Michael Beyer
IT Man: David Schaller
IT Man: Jeremiah Stikeleather
Natl Sales: David Lee

D-U-N-S 01-479-8433
RITTENHOUSE BOOK DISTRIBUTORS INC (PA)
511 Feheley Dr, King of Prussia, PA 19406-2611
Tel (800) 345-6425 *Founded/Ownrshp* 1966, 1965
Sales 104.0MM^E *EMP* 85
SIC 5192 Books
CEO: Timothy Foster
**Pr:* Clark Morrell
**Treas:* Daniel Foster
Sls Mgr: Nicole Gallo

D-U-N-S 92-958-7546
RITTER AGRIBUSINESS
10 Elm St, Marked Tree, AR 72365-2211
Tel (870) 336-7310 *Founded/Ownrshp* 2009
Sales NA *EMP* 2
Accts Kpmg Llp Memphis Tn
SIC 6411 Insurance agents
Prin: Ritter Arnold

D-U-N-S 61-538-3242
RITTER CONSTRUCTION CO
(*Suby of* US SHALE SOLUTIONS INC) ★
671 Ritter Dr, Carthage, TX 75633-2560
Tel (903) 693-2397 *Founded/Ownrshp* 2014
Sales 137.7MM^E *EMP* 625
SIC 1623 Oil & gas pipeline construction
Pr: Robert W Ritter
**CFO:* Robert H Ritter
VP: Michael W Ritter

RITTLEWOOD HOLDING CO
See RDA HOLDING CO

RITZ CAMERA
See C & A MARKETING INC

D-U-N-S 13-473-1541 IMP/EXP
■ **RITZ-CARLTON HOTEL CO LLC**
(*Suby of* MI HOLDING, L.P.)
4445 Willard Ave Ste 800, Chevy Chase, MD 20815-3699
Tel (301) 547-4700 *Founded/Ownrshp* 1955
Sales 25.7MM^E *EMP* 20,000
SIC 7011 Hotels & motels
CEO: Herve Humler
CFO: Kathleen K Oberg
Ofcr: Bob Kharazmi
Ex VP: Randall Catt
Sr VP: John Cottrill
VP: John Anstey
VP: Doug Garfield
VP: George McNeill
VP: Page Petry
VP: Sue Stevenson
Exec: Sheldon Millett
Exec: Yves Samake
Dir Soc: Robert Morton

D-U-N-S 01-055-5845
RITZ-CRAFT CORP OF PENNSYLVANIA INC (PA)
MEDALLION HOMES
15 Industrial Park Rd, Mifflinburg, PA 17844-7992
Tel (570) 966-1053 *Founded/Ownrshp* 1954, 1976
Sales 87.6MM^E *EMP* 424
SIC 2452 Modular homes, prefabricated, wood
Opers Mgr: Dale Dixon
Prd Mgr: Stew Fitton
Prd Mgr: Terry Landis

D-U-N-S 00-895-7722
RITZVILLE WAREHOUSE CO
201 E 1st Ave, Ritzville, WA 99169-2393
Tel (509) 659-0130 *Founded/Ownrshp* 1893
Sales 86.4MM *EMP* 65
Accts Leffel Otis & Warwick Ps D
SIC 5153 4221 Grains; Farm product warehousing & storage
CEO: John Anderson
**Pr:* Grant Miller
**CFO:* Jeff Milner
**Treas:* Brian Gordon
Ofcr: Mark Cameron
**VP:* Don Dirks

D-U-N-S 11-747-9402
RIVER CITY CONSTRUCTION LLC
101 Hoffer Ln, East Peoria, IL 61611-9334
Tel (309) 694-3120 *Founded/Ownrshp* 1984
Sales 186.6MM^E *EMP* 250
SIC 1542 1629 Commercial & office building, new construction; Commercial & office buildings, renovation & repair; Institutional building construction; Industrial plant construction; Waste water & sewage treatment plant construction
Pr: Bernard J Koch
**VP:* Eric Bursott
**VP:* Stephen Dorris
VP: Bernie Koch
**VP:* John Sutherland
Dir IT: Greg Bachler
IT Man: Dan Taylor
Prd Mgr: Robert Schieber

D-U-N-S 05-113-4112 IMP
RIVER CITY PETROLEUM INC
3775 N Freeway Blvd # 101, Sacramento, CA 95834-1959
Tel (916) 371-4960 *Founded/Ownrshp* 1981
Sales 589.4MM *EMP* 55
Accts Bfba Llp Sacramento Califor
SIC 5172 Petroleum products
CEO: Jeanne Haskell
**CFO:* Kurt Schmidl
CFO: Kurt Schmidt
VP: Barry Cline
Genl Mgr: Brad Folkins
Genl Mgr: Len Robinson
IT Man: John Kreidler
Sls&Mrk Ex: Adam Gilbert
Mktg Mgr: Brian Rosser

D-U-N-S 02-307-6045
RIVER COUNTRY COOPERATIVE
9072 Cahill Ave, Inver Grove Heights, MN 55076-3543
Tel (651) 451-1151 *Founded/Ownrshp* 1935
Sales 135.9MM *EMP* 180
Accts Cliftonlarsonallen Llp Tomah
SIC 5171 5172 5191 Petroleum bulk stations; Gases, liquefied petroleum (propane); Gasoline; Fertilizer & fertilizer materials; Feed; Seeds: field, garden & flower
CEO: John Duchscherer

D-U-N-S 04-654-8470 IMP/EXP
■ **RIVER METALS RECYCLING LLC**
(*Suby of* DAVID J JOSEPH CO) ★
334 Beechwood Rd Ste 401, Fort Mitchell, KY 41017-2086
Tel (859) 292-8400 *Founded/Ownrshp* 1998
Sales 111.9MM^E *EMP* 280
SIC 5093 3341 Metal scrap & waste materials; Secondary nonferrous metals
Opers Mgr: Arvil Pennington
Plnt Mgr: Jeff Davis

RIVER MOUNTAIN QUARRIES
See PINE BLUFF SAND AND GRAVEL CO

RIVER OAKS HEALTH SYSTEM
See RIVER OAKS HOSPITAL LLC

D-U-N-S 18-659-0881
■ **RIVER OAKS HOSPITAL LLC**
RIVER OAKS HEALTH SYSTEM
(*Suby of* HMA) ★
1030 River Oaks Dr, Flowood, MS 39232-9553
Tel (601) 932-1030 *Founded/Ownrshp* 1998
Sales 134.3MM *EMP* 1,200
SIC 8062 General medical & surgical hospitals
Ch Bd: Dr Glenn Warren
**Pr:* Jack Cleary
**Pr:* Dianne Henley
**CEO:* Dwayne Blaylock
COO: Doug Self
COO: Joan Strayham
Treas: Jeffrey T Bedford
**VP:* Georgia Voyiatzis
Dir Rad: Beverly Greenhill
Obsttrcn: Missy M Minn

D-U-N-S 79-345-0552
RIVER PALMS RESORT CASINO
2121 S Casino Dr, Laughlin, NV 89029-1519
Tel (702) 298-2242 *Founded/Ownrshp* 1992
Sales 30.5MM^E *EMP* 1,200
SIC 7011 Casino hotel
Pr: Allen E Paulson
Genl Mgr: Allen Crombert

D-U-N-S 80-913-4674
RIVER POINT FARMS LLC
115 W Hermiston Ave # 240, Hermiston, OR 97838-1759
Tel (541) 567-4781 *Founded/Ownrshp* 2007
Sales 130.6MM^E *EMP* 500^E
SIC 0723 Vegetable crops market preparation services
Pr: Bob Hale
CFO: Craig Green
**VP:* Delbert Gehrke
**VP:* Craig Reeder

D-U-N-S 83-611-9073 IMP
RIVER RANCH FRESH FOODS LLC
(*Suby of* TAYLOR FRESH FOODS INC) ★
911 Blanco Cir Ste B, Salinas, CA 93901-4449
Tel (831) 758-1390 *Founded/Ownrshp* 2010
Sales 167.2MM^E *EMP* 900
SIC 5148 Vegetables, fresh
CEO: Bruce Knobeloch
**Pr:* John Bowman
**CFO:* Tom Welch
Admn Mgr: Debbie Anderson

D-U-N-S 07-506-1069
■ **RIVER REGION BEHAVIORAL HEALTH**
COLUMBIA VICKSBURG MEDICAL CTR
(*Suby of* HOSPITAL COPORATION OF AMERICA) ★
1111 N Frontage Rd, Vicksburg, MS 39180-5102
Tel (601) 619-3838 *Founded/Ownrshp* 1996
Sales 47.1MM^E *EMP* 1,800
SIC 8062 General medical & surgical hospitals
CEO: Philip Clendenin
**COO:* William Fulcher
**CFO:* Cynthia Clements
DP Dir: J White

D-U-N-S 08-031-1838
RIVER ROCK ENERGY LLC
211 N Robinson Ave S1525, Oklahoma City, OK 73102-7101
Tel (405) 606-7481 *Founded/Ownrshp* 2016
Sales 200.0MM^E *EMP* 75
SIC 1382 Oil & gas exploration services

D-U-N-S 00-798-8603
RIVER VALLEY COOPERATIVE
102 S Main St, Walcott, IA 52773-7761
Tel (563) 284-6223 *Founded/Ownrshp* 1932
Sales 125.9MM^E *EMP* 84
SIC 5153 5191 Grains; Chemicals, agricultural
CEO: Tom Leiting
Pr: Lonnie Mayne
Pr: William Pieper
Bd of Dir: Brian Corkill
Bd of Dir: Royce Johnson
**VP:* Tim Burress
**Genl Mgr:* Thomas Leiting
VP Mktg: Cindy Bergevin
VP Mktg: John Collins
VP Mktg: Tom Myers
Mktg Dir: Tom Capozzi

D-U-N-S 14-460-9724
RIVER VALLEY FOODS INC
5881 Court Street Rd # 2, Syracuse, NY 13206-1732
Tel (315) 437-4636 *Founded/Ownrshp* 1985
Sales 133.7MM^E *EMP* 160
SIC 5142 Packaged frozen goods; Dinners, frozen; Bakery products, frozen; Vegetables, frozen
Ch: Gerard Redmond
**Ch Bd:* John Redmond Jr
Area Mgr: Jeff Faries

D-U-N-S 17-830-5751 EXP
RIVER VALLEY PAPER CO
120 E Mill St Ste 337, Akron, OH 44308-1745
Tel (330) 535-1001 *Founded/Ownrshp* 1987
Sales 119.7MM^E *EMP* 120
SIC 5113 Industrial & personal service paper
Pr: John Sharp
**CFO:* Frank Satink
**Treas:* Mary K Pamer
Mktg Mgr: Rachel Stover

D-U-N-S 06-254-6262
RIVERBAY CORP
2049 Bartow Ave, Bronx, NY 10475-4613
Tel (718) 320-3300 *Founded/Ownrshp* 1965
Sales 178.5MM^E *EMP* 900^E
SIC 6513 Apartment building operators
Sr Cor Off: George Rogers
Bd of Dir: Ricardo Cabodevilla
Bd of Dir: Andrea Leslie
Bd of Dir: Evelyn Santiago
Genl Mgr: Debra Vanzandt
Sfty Mgr: Kevin Keenan
Plnt Mgr: Brian Reardon

D-U-N-S 05-546-7892
RIVERBED HOLDINGS INC
300 N La Salle Dr # 4350, Chicago, IL 60654-3406
Tel (312) 254-3300 *Founded/Ownrshp* 2014
Sales 1.1MMM^E *EMP* 10,000
SIC 6719 Investment holding companies, except banks
CEO: Orlando Bravo

D-U-N-S 13-735-4390 IMP
RIVERBED TECHNOLOGY INC
(*Suby of* RIVERBED HOLDINGS INC) ★
680 Folsom St Ste 500, San Francisco, CA 94107-2160
Tel (415) 247-8800 *Founded/Ownrshp* 2015
Sales 1.0MMM^E *EMP* 2,555
SIC 3577 5045 Computer peripheral equipment; Computer software
CEO: Jerry M Kennelly
**CFO:* Ernest E Maddock
**Chf Mktg O:* Subbu Iyer
Sr VP: Bjorn Engelhardt
**Sr VP:* Phil Harris
Sr VP: Keith Hoskison
**Sr VP:* Brett A Nissenberg
Sr VP: Paul O'Farrell
Sr VP: Rob Rosiello
Sr VP: Mike Sargent
Sr VP: Eric Wolford
VP: Frank Beltran
VP: Bill Bragg
VP: Jack Denn
VP: Matt Macarthur
VP: Thomas Masles
VP: Karl Meulema
VP: Debashish Nag
VP: Dave Olson
VP: David M Peranich
VP: Cecil Perez

D-U-N-S 79-211-3524
■ **RIVERBOAT CORP OF MISSISSIPPI**
ISLE OF CAPRI BILOXI
(*Suby of* ISLE OF CAPRI CASINOS INC) ★
151 Beach Blvd, Biloxi, MS 39530-4708
Tel (228) 435-5400 *Founded/Ownrshp* 1990
Sales 44.8MM^E *EMP* 1,100
SIC 7011 Hotels & motels
Pr: Virginia M McDowell
**CFO:* Donn Mitchel
**Ex VP:* Allan B Solomon

D-U-N-S 78-794-5042
RIVERDALE CENTER FOR NURSING AND REHABILITATION LLC
HUDSON POINTE AT RIVERDALE CEN
(*Suby of* NHCA) ★
3220 Henry Hudson Pkwy, Bronx, NY 10463-3211
Tel (718) 514-2000 *Founded/Ownrshp* 2006
Sales 21.7MM^E *EMP* 3,380^E
SIC 8051 Convalescent home with continuous nursing care
Dir Recs: Shona Kelly
Dir Soc: Amy Schwartz
Off Mgr: Laura Canty
Nrsg Dir: Cheikh Fall

D-U-N-S 07-743-1633
RIVERFRONT STEEL INC
10310 S Medallion Dr, Cincinnati, OH 45241-4836
Tel (513) 769-9999 *Founded/Ownrshp* 1985
Sales 138.7MM^E *EMP* 95
SIC 5051 Steel
Owner: Bradley Kuhr
**VP:* Rick Tenenholtz
Sls Dir: David Treglia
Sales Asso: Mark Kinder

D-U-N-S 00-892-2395
RIVERHEAD BUILDING SUPPLY CORP
JT'S LUMBER COMPANY
250 David Ct, Calverton, NY 11933-3052
Tel (631) 727-1400 *Founded/Ownrshp* 1948
Sales 207.5MM^E *EMP* 510
SIC 5031 5211 Lumber, plywood & millwork; Lumber & other building materials
Ch: Edgar Goodale
**Pr:* John Callahan
**COO:* Ted Sadowski
**CFO:* Tom Carberry
**Treas:* Laura Van Houten
**Ex VP:* John Wade Callahan
**VP:* Tracey Kappenberj
Sales Asso: Alan Duarte
Sales Asso: Greg Pignolet
Sales Asso: Brad Vanhouten
Sales Asso: Brian Wilkinson

D-U-N-S 80-640-7537 IMP
RIVERLAND AG CORP
(*Suby of* CERES GLOBAL AG CORP)
1660 Highway 100 S # 350, Minneapolis, MN 55416-1531
Tel (952) 746-6800 *Founded/Ownrshp* 2010
Sales 115.6MM^E *EMP* 75
SIC 5153 4221 Grain elevators; Grain elevator, storage only
Pr: Robert Day
**CFO:* Mark Kucala

D-U-N-S 16-090-7437 IMP
RIVERS END HOLDINGS LLC
RIVER'S END TRADING COMPANY
301 N Broom St Fl 2, Madison, WI 53703-5207
Tel (952) 912-2500 *Founded/Ownrshp* 2004
Sales 225.9MM^E *EMP* 330^E
SIC 5137 5136 Women's & children's clothing; Women's & children's outerwear; Caps & gowns; Sportswear, women's & children's; Men's & boys' hats, scarves & gloves; Shirts, men's & boys'; Sportswear, men's & boys'
CEO: John Maher
CFO: Dick Merhar
**Chf Mktg O:* Bret Slane

RIVER'S END TRADING COMPANY
See RIVERS END HOLDINGS LLC

RIVERSIDE BRICK & SUPPLY
See PINE HALL BRICK CO INC

D-U-N-S 55-755-5997
RIVERSIDE CARE CENTER LLC
856 Riverside Dr S, Mc Connelsville, OH 43756
Tel (740) 962-5303 *Founded/Ownrshp* 2004
Sales 380.8MM *EMP* 62
SIC 8051 Skilled nursing care facilities
Pr: Brian Colleran

RIVERSIDE CO, THE
See RIVERSIDE PARTNERS LLC

D-U-N-S 62-165-7196
RIVERSIDE COMMUNITY CARE INC
270 Bridge St Ste 301, Dedham, MA 02026-1883
Tel (617) 969-4925 *Founded/Ownrshp* 1990
Sales 60.3MM *EMP* 1,000
Accts Feeley & Driscoll Pc Boston
SIC 8322 Individual & family services
CEO: Scott M Bock
**CFO:* Debra Blair
**Ex VP:* Marsha Medalie
VP: Paul Block
**VP:* Edward Follen
VP: Melissa Kogut

Brnch Mgr: Nick Schibelli
Off Mgr: Sydney Szmonko
Board of Directors: Rita Dimartino, Edmund Ferrara, Renee Fixler, Frances Newton, Laura Olton, Janet Sharpe, Paul Sheiber, Alan West, David Wormley

D-U-N-S 07-360-2724
RIVERSIDE COMMUNITY COLLEGE DISTRICT (CA)
RCCD
(*Suby of* CALIFORNIA COMMUNITY COLLEGES SYSTEM) ★
3801 Market St, Riverside, CA 92501-3225
Tel (951) 328-3663 *Founded/Ownrshp* 1964
Sales 1.6MM *EMP* 2,651^E
Accts Ahern Adcock Devlin Llp River
SIC 8222 Community college
Pr: Virginia Blumenthal
Ofcr: Jim Beckham
Ofcr: Jason Johnston
Ofcr: Ray Placencia
Ofcr: Octavio Rojas
Ofcr: Arlen Verdehyou
**VP:* Janet Green
VP: Rachel Stone
Exec: Diana Meza
Admn Mgr: Gina Salazar
Sls Mgr: Stephen Rioux

D-U-N-S 07-606-6299
■ **RIVERSIDE COMMUNITY HEALTH SYSTEMS**
RIVERSIDE COMMUNITY HOSPITAL
(*Suby of* HOSPITAL COPORATION OF AMERICA) ★
4445 Magnolia Ave Fl 6, Riverside, CA 92501-4135
Tel (951) 788-3000 *Founded/Ownrshp* 1997
Sales 435.8MM *EMP* 1,200^E
SIC 8062 8011 General medical & surgical hospitals; Offices & clinics of medical doctors
Pr: Partrick Brilliant
**COO:* Doug Long
**CFO:* Tracey Fernandez
Dir Lab: May Kim
VP Mktg: Tracy Dallarda

RIVERSIDE COMMUNITY HOSPITAL
See RIVERSIDE COMMUNITY HEALTH SYSTEMS

RIVERSIDE COMMUNITY HOSPITAL
See RIVERSIDE HEALTHCARE SYSTEM LP

D-U-N-S 08-115-9865
RIVERSIDE COUNTY OFFICE OF EDUCATION
3939 13th St, Riverside, CA 92501-3505
Tel (951) 826-6530 *Founded/Ownrshp* 1893
Sales 211.3MM *EMP* 1,594
Accts Nigro & Nigro Pc Murrieta C
SIC 8211 8249 Public elementary & secondary schools; Vocational schools
Bd of Dir: Bruce Dennis
Dir Bus: Rollin Edmunds
Ex Dir: Ann Vessey
Ex Dir: Ronald Vito
Prgrm Mgr: Deirdre Edwards
DP Dir: Michael Wibben
IT Man: Richard D'Souza
IT Man: Robert Fazio
Snr Mgr: Lanelle Gordin

D-U-N-S 94-339-8941
RIVERSIDE COUNTY SCHOOLS
11840 Magnolia Ave Ste G, Riverside, CA 92503-4900
Tel (951) 788-7274 *Founded/Ownrshp* 2000
Sales 23.1MM^E *EMP* 6,000
Accts Vavrinektrineday & Co Llp
SIC 8211 Elementary & secondary schools

D-U-N-S 12-887-9868
RIVERSIDE FOOD DISTRIBUTORS LLC
F CHRISTIANA & CO
7251 River Rd, Marrero, LA 70072-1140
Tel (504) 328-7383 *Founded/Ownrshp* 2003
Sales 127.0MM^E *EMP* 120
SIC 5142 Packaged frozen goods
Genl Mgr: Frank Christiana

D-U-N-S 00-633-9931 IMP
RIVERSIDE FURNITURE CORP
RIVERSIDE LOGISTICS
1400 S 6th St, Fort Smith, AR 72901-4398
Tel (479) 785-8100 *Founded/Ownrshp* 1946
Sales 138.1MM^E *EMP* 900
SIC 2511 Wood household furniture; Wood bedroom furniture
Pr: Fred Henjes
Ch Bd: Howard J Spradlin
CFO: Beth Brown
CFO: Ronald E Powell
Sr VP: David H Dixon
Sr VP: Bernie Holly
VP: Jim Marshall
IT Man: Kirk Hoobs
VP Opers: Greg Adams

D-U-N-S 06-930-2925
RIVERSIDE HEALTH CARE SYSTEM INC (NY)
967 N Broadway, Yonkers, NY 10701-1301
Tel (914) 964-4444 *Founded/Ownrshp* 1870, 1981
Sales 224.0MM *EMP* 1,100^E
SIC 8062 General medical & surgical hospitals
Pr: Ronald J Corti
Chf Rad: Eugene M Farraro
**COO:* Lynn Nelson
CFO: David Scarpino
Bd of Dir: Kay Scott
Ex VP: Edward F Leonard
VP: Paul Antonecchio
Dir Soc: Elizabeth Ingeles
Dir Rad: Frances Dietz
Dir Rx: John Masi
Dir Rx: Joann B Stenstrom

RIVERSIDE HEALTH SYSTEM
See RIVERSIDE HEALTHCARE ASSOCIATION INC

D-U-N-S 10-219-9841
RIVERSIDE HEALTH SYSTEM
350 N Wall St, Kankakee, IL 60901-2901
Tel (815) 933-1671 *Founded/Ownrshp* 1964
Sales 467.8MM^E *EMP* 2,000
Accts Crowe Horwath Llp Chicago Il
SIC 8082 8062 5912 5047 Home health care services; General medical & surgical hospitals; Drug stores & proprietary stores; Medical equipment & supplies
Pr: Phillip M Kambic
**Pr:* Phillip Kambic
**CFO:* Bill Douglas
**Ch:* Connie Ashline
VP: Keith Moss
Dir Rx: Curtis Hebert
Dir Rx: James Shafer
CIO: Jeffrey Pollock
IT Man: Shaun Beckman
Sfty Dirs: Philip Crouch
Mtls Dir: David Legris

RIVERSIDE HEALTHCARE ASSN
See RIVERSIDE MIDDLE PENINSULA HOSPITAL INC

D-U-N-S 06-601-7922
RIVERSIDE HEALTHCARE ASSOCIATION INC
RIVERSIDE HEALTH SYSTEM
701 Town Center Dr # 1000, Newport News, VA 23606-4283
Tel (757) 534-7000 *Founded/Ownrshp* 2001
Sales 1.0MMM *EMP* 8,000
Accts Ernst & Young Llp Richmond V
SIC 8741 Hospital management; Nursing & personal care facility management
Ch: Alan S Witt
**Pr:* William B Downey
CFO: Bill Douglas
**Treas:* Walter W Austin Jr
**Ex VP:* Wade D Broughman
VP: William Austin
Adm Dir: Maria Bird
Adm Dir: Jennifer Carpenter
Adm Dir: Bonnie Cross
Adm Dir: Kim Johnson
Adm Dir: Melody Livengood

D-U-N-S 96-723-9869
RIVERSIDE HEALTHCARE SERVICES INC
(*Suby of* RIVERSIDE HEALTH SYSTEM) ★
608 Denbigh Blvd Ste 800, Newport News, VA 23608-4487
Tel (757) 856-7038 *Founded/Ownrshp* 1982
Sales 22.3MM *EMP* 8,000
Accts Ernst & Young Us Llp Saint Lo
SIC 8741 Hospital management; Nursing & personal care facility management
Pr: William B Downey
**Treas:* Walter William Austin
**VP:* Keith Percic

D-U-N-S 96-954-8119
■ **RIVERSIDE HEALTHCARE SYSTEM LP**
RIVERSIDE COMMUNITY HOSPITAL
(*Suby of* HOSPITAL COPORATION OF AMERICA) ★
4445 Magnolia Ave, Riverside, CA 92501-4135
Tel (951) 788-3000 *Founded/Ownrshp* 2012
Sales 36.8MM^E *EMP* 1,600
SIC 8062 General medical & surgical hospitals
Mng Pt: Patrick Brilliant

RIVERSIDE HOME HEALTH
See RIVERSIDE MEDI-CENTER INC

D-U-N-S 15-449-0619
RIVERSIDE HOSPITAL INC
RIVERSIDE REGIONAL MEDICAL CTR
(*Suby of* RIVERSIDE HEALTH SYSTEM) ★
500 J Clyde Morris Blvd, Newport News, VA 23601-1929
Tel (757) 594-2000 *Founded/Ownrshp* 1982
Sales 388.2MM^E *EMP* 8,000
Accts Ernst Young Richmond Va
SIC 8062 General medical & surgical hospitals
Pr: William B Downey
**Treas:* Walter W Austin Jr
Ofcr: Sherron Ware
Sr VP: Patrick R Parcells
**VP:* Mike J Doucette
Dir Risk M: Jody Friend
Off Mgr: Cindy Hogge
CIO: Dennis Loftus
Mktg Dir: Andrea Staskiel
Mktg Mgr: Garnet Gilmore
Doctor: Paul Evans

RIVERSIDE LOGISTICS
See RIVERSIDE FURNITURE CORP

RIVERSIDE MED CLNIC PTIENT CTR
See RIVERSIDE MEDICAL CLINIC INC

D-U-N-S 17-353-6269
RIVERSIDE MEDI-CENTER INC
RIVERSIDE HOME HEALTH
(*Suby of* RIVERSIDE HEALTH SYSTEM) ★
350 N Wall St, Kankakee, IL 60901-2901
Tel (815) 933-1671 *Founded/Ownrshp* 1983
Sales 209.0MM *EMP* 2,000
SIC 8082 5912 5999 Home health care services; Drug stores; Medical apparatus & supplies
Pr: Philip Kambic
Sr VP: William W Douglas III
Doctor: Mehmet Sipahi MD

D-U-N-S 07-142-9765
RIVERSIDE MEDICAL CENTER (IL)
(*Suby of* RIVERSIDE HEALTH SYSTEM) ★
350 N Wall St, Kankakee, IL 60901-2991
Tel (815) 933-1671 *Founded/Ownrshp* 1959, 1962
Sales 258.1MM *EMP* 2,000
SIC 8062 General medical & surgical hospitals
Pr: Phillip Kambik
Act CFO: Gary Zmrhal
Sr VP: William W Douglas III
**Sr VP:* David A Duda
Sr VP: Margaret Frogge
VP: Kyle Benoit
**VP:* Bill W Douglas
VP: John Jurica
VP: Brent Mallek
VP: Andrea McKay
VP: Michael Mutterer
VP: Tanya Stringer
Dir OR: Mary Kohl
Dir Lab: Stephanie Mitchell
Dir Rad: Corbin Asbury

D-U-N-S 07-815-0984
RIVERSIDE MEDICAL CLINIC INC
RIVERSIDE MED CLNIC PTIENT CTR
3660 Arlington Ave, Riverside, CA 92506-3987
Tel (951) 683-6370 *Founded/Ownrshp* 1993
Sales 110.0MM^E *EMP* 750
SIC 8011 Clinic, operated by physicians
Pr: Steven E Larson
**Pr:* Judy Carpenter
COO: Susan Marinaro
VP: Debbie Church
VP: Tony Lazcano
VP: Steven Schaerrer
Exec: Ruben Muradyan MD
Genl Mgr: Irma Vasquez
Off Mgr: Cathy Coiscer
VP Opers: Lynette Anthony
Obsttrcn: Kenneth E Dozir

D-U-N-S 96-723-5834
RIVERSIDE MERCY HOSPITAL
3404 W Sylvania Ave, Toledo, OH 43623-4467
Tel (419) 407-2663 *Founded/Ownrshp* 2011
Sales 93.6MM *EMP* 14^E
Accts Bkd Llp Cincinnati Oh
SIC 8062 General medical & surgical hospitals
Prin: Samatha Platzke

D-U-N-S 04-377-1450 IMP
RIVERSIDE MFG LLC
14510 Lima Rd, Fort Wayne, IN 46818-9537
Tel (260) 637-4470 *Founded/Ownrshp* 1992
Sales 93.5MM^E *EMP* 500
SIC 3714 Motor vehicle parts & accessories
CEO: Fred Merritt
CFO: Pam Meissner
Exec: Randy Young
Genl Mgr: Kurt Schneider
IT Man: Jeff Styf
Plnt Mgr: Paul Hopwood
Sls&Mrk Ex: Angie Triplett

D-U-N-S 84-749-9506
RIVERSIDE MIDDLE PENINSULA HOSPITAL INC
RIVERSIDE HEALTHCARE ASSN
7519 Hospital Dr, Gloucester, VA 23061-4178
Tel (757) 875-7545 *Founded/Ownrshp* 1982
Sales 948.0MM *EMP* 50
Accts Ernest Young Richmond Va
SIC 8062 General medical & surgical hospitals
Pr: William Downey

D-U-N-S 03-843-9738
RIVERSIDE PARTNERS LLC
RIVERSIDE CO, THE
45 Rockefeller Plz # 400, New York, NY 10111-0501
Tel (212) 265-6575 *Founded/Ownrshp* 1995
Sales 4.0MMM^E *EMP* 13,218
SIC 6799 Investors
Mng Pt: Hal R Greenberg
**VP:* George Cole
VP: Yu Miyake
VP: Jay Reynolds

D-U-N-S 01-648-2433
RIVERSIDE PHYSICIAN SVCS INC
608 Denbigh Blvd, Williamsburg, VA 23185
Tel (757) 442-6600 *Founded/Ownrshp* 2011
Sales 161.2MM *EMP* 1
Accts Ernst & Young Us Llp Richmond
SIC 8011 General & family practice, physician/surgeon
Prin: James Lenick

RIVERSIDE RECYCLING
See QRS INC

D-U-N-S 15-547-9541
RIVERSIDE REGIONAL MEDIAL CENTER
LIFELINE
500 J Clyde Morris Blvd, Newport News, VA 23601-1929
Tel (757) 856-7030 *Founded/Ownrshp* 2000
Sales 544.5MM *EMP* 1
SIC 5999 Alarm signal systems
Prin: Debbie Davis
VP: Susan Mc Andrews
VP: Christoper P Stolle
Ansthlgy: Clyde Pray

RIVERSIDE REGIONAL MEDICAL CTR
See RIVERSIDE HOSPITAL INC

D-U-N-S 04-682-2615
RIVERSIDE RESEARCH INSTITUTE
156 William St Fl 9, New York, NY 10038-5325
Tel (212) 563-4545 *Founded/Ownrshp* 1967
Sales 84.5MM *EMP* 550
Accts Baker Tilly Virchow Krause Llp
SIC 8733 Research institute
Ch Bd: Thomas G Pitts
**CEO:* Richard Annas
**CFO:* Michael F Cade
Ofcr: Iraida Hernandez
**VP:* Frank Falco
**VP:* Joel Rieman
Assoc Dir: Dominic Baca
Dir Bus: John Boylan
Prgrm Mgr: Myra Mills
Off Mgr: Kevin Harris
Software D: Nathan Sweeney

RIVERSIDE RESORT AND HOTEL
See DONALD J LAUGHLIN

D-U-N-S 00-479-7262
■ **RIVERSIDE TELECOM LLC**
TDS
(*Suby of* TDS TELECOMMUNICATIONS CORP) ★
121 Depot St, Johnson Creek, WI 53038
Tel (608) 831-1000 *Founded/Ownrshp* 1907
Sales 853.0MM *EMP* 2,700
SIC 4813 Local telephone communications
**Treas:* Noel Hutton
Sec: Debbie Meier

D-U-N-S 84-065-2473
RIVERSIDE TRANSPORT INC
5400 Kansas Ave, Kansas City, KS 66106-1143
Tel (913) 233-5500 *Founded/Ownrshp* 1993
Sales 112.0MM^E *EMP* 175^E
SIC 4212 4213 Local trucking, without storage; Trucking, except local
Pr: Bill Grojean
Dir Bus: Kenton Geghan
Dir IT: Brian Hedge
IT Man: Erik Snyder

D-U-N-S 06-615-8890
RIVERSIDE UNIFIED SCHOOL DISTRICT
3380 14th St, Riverside, CA 92501-3810
Tel (951) 788-7135 *Founded/Ownrshp* 1963
Sales 428.6MM *EMP* 3,740
Accts Nigro & Nigro Pc Murrieta C
SIC 8211 Public elementary & secondary schools; Secondary school
**Pr:* Lynn Carmen Day
Trst: Kathy Allavie
**VP:* Charles L Beaty PHD
Ex Dir: Timothy Walker
Dir Sec: Brian Caldwell
Genl Mgr: Sandra Meekins
CIO: Jesse Staton
IT Man: Kitty Smith
Sys Mgr: Karen Stevenson
Schl Brd P: Patricia Lock-Dawson
Psych: Patricia Miller

D-U-N-S 04-952-9035
■ **RIVERSOURCE LIFE INSURANCE CO**
(*Suby of* AMERIPRISE FINANCIAL INC) ★
1099 Ameriprise Fincl Ctr, Minneapolis, MN 55474-0010
Tel (612) 671-3131 *Founded/Ownrshp* 1957
Sales NA *EMP* 23
SIC 6311 6321 Life insurance carriers; Accident & health insurance
Ch Bd: John R Worner
**Ch Bd:* John R Woerner
**CFO:* Brian J McGrane
Sr VP: David K Stewart
VP: Mark Keeling

D-U-N-S 00-693-4798
RIVERSTONE GROUP INC (IL)
1701 5th Ave, Moline, IL 61265-7900
Tel (309) 757-8250 *Founded/Ownrshp* 1893, 1917
Sales 3.9MMM^E *EMP* 300
SIC 1422

D-U-N-S 13-076-8674
RIVERSTREET MANOR
440 N River St, Wilkes Barre, PA 18702-2631
Tel (570) 825-5611 *Founded/Ownrshp* 1985
Sales 1.1MMM *EMP* 120
SIC 8361 8059 8051 Rehabilitation center, residential: health care incidental; Nursing home, except skilled & intermediate care facility; Skilled nursing care facilities
Board of Directors: Richard Howard

RIVERVIEW HEALTH
See RIVERVIEW HOSPITAL

D-U-N-S 07-204-8481
RIVERVIEW HOSPITAL
RIVERVIEW HEALTH
395 Westfield Rd, Noblesville, IN 46060-1434
Tel (317) 773-0760 *Founded/Ownrshp* 1909
Sales 162.1MM *EMP* 949
SIC 8062 General medical & surgical hospitals
Pr: Seth Warren
**Treas:* T H Lee
Treas: William Wunder
Bd of Dir: Sarah Cookman
Ofcr: Ronald Reitenour
Ex VP: Nicole Klein
Ex VP: Joyce Woods
**VP:* Brenda Baker
**VP:* Brant Bucciarelli
VP: Jae Ebert
VP: Amy Kollars
**VP:* John Paris
VP: Dennis Pippenger
VP: Mary Valdez
**VP:* Joyce Wood
Exec: Amy Williams
Dir Rx: Brian Peters

D-U-N-S 07-478-3291
RIVERVIEW HOSPITAL ASSOCIATION
410 Dewey St, Wisconsin Rapids, WI 54494-4715
Tel (715) 423-6060 *Founded/Ownrshp* 1967
Sales 98.9MM *EMP* 641
Accts Wipfli Llp Wausau Wi
SIC 8062 General medical & surgical hospitals
Pr: Celse Berard

RIVERVIEW MEDICAL CENTER
See RIVERVIEW MEDICAL HOSPITAL

RIVERVIEW MEDICAL CENTER
See MERIDIAN HOSPITALS CORP

D-U-N-S 62-320-9517
RIVERVIEW MEDICAL HOSPITAL
RIVERVIEW MEDICAL CENTER
(*Suby of* MERIDIAN HOSPITAL) ★
1 Riverview Plz, Red Bank, NJ 07701-1864
Tel (732) 741-2700 *Founded/Ownrshp* 1984
Sales 276.1MM *EMP* 3^E
SIC 8093 Rehabilitation center, outpatient treatment
COO: Kelli O'Brien
Chf Rad: Robert Wold

*VP: Kathy McKean
Assoc Dir: Robert Bransfield
Nurse Mgr: Kim Pfeifer
QA Dir: Cathy Cutone
Obsttrcn: Garland Herron

D-U-N-S 07-210-5984
RIVERVIEW REGIONAL MEDICAL CENTER INC
(Suby of PRIME HEALTHCARE SERVICES INC) ★
600 S 3rd St, Gadsden, AL 35901-5304
Tel (256) 543-5200 Founded/Ownrshp 1991
Sales 108.5MM[E] EMP 750
SIC 8062 General medical & surgical hospitals
CEO: David Fuller
Ex VP: Sandra Lee
Exec: Tammy Harlow
Dir Rad: John Nichols

D-U-N-S 14-716-0956 IMP/EXP
RIVIANA FOODS INC
(Suby of EBRO FOODS, SA)
2777 Allen Pkwy Fl 15, Houston, TX 77019-2133
Tel (713) 529-3251 Founded/Ownrshp 2004
Sales 613.7MM[E] EMP 2,752
SIC 2044 2052 2033 5141 Rice milling; Milled rice; Polished rice; Cookies; Saltine crackers; Fruit juices: packaged in cans, jars, etc.; Tomato products: packaged in cans, jars, etc.; Groceries, general line
Pr: Bastiaan G De Zeeuw
*Ch Bd: Joseph A Hafner Jr
*CFO: Troy De Rouen
CFO: Carolyn Galfione
Treas: E W Ray Jr
*V Ch Bd: Charles R Godchaux
*VP: Brett L Beckfield
*VP: R Shane Faucett
*VP: Gerard J Ferguson
*VP: Paul A Galvani
VP: M Noungburg
VP: Paul R Stevens

D-U-N-S 80-729-0101
RIVIERA HOLDINGS CORP
2901 Las Vegas Blvd S, Las Vegas, NV 89109-1933
Tel (702) 794-9237 Founded/Ownrshp 1993
Sales 82.8MM EMP 1,063[E]
SIC 7011

RIVIERA UTILITIES
See UTILITIES BOARD OF CITY OF FOLEY

D-U-N-S 07-336-3350 IMP/EXP
RIVULIS IRRIGATION INC
JOHN DEERE WATER
(Suby of RIVULIS IRRIGATION LTD)
7545 Carroll Rd, San Diego, CA 92121-2401
Tel (858) 578-1860 Founded/Ownrshp 2014
Sales 307.0MM[E] EMP 300[E]
SIC 3523

D-U-N-S 04-790-5708
RJ OBRIEN & ASSOCIATES LLC
(Suby of RJ OBRIEN HOLDINGS INC) ★
222 S Riverside Plz # 1200, Chicago, IL 60606-5905
Tel (312) 373-5000 Founded/Ownrshp 1950
Sales 116.5MM[E] EMP 307
SIC 6221 6211 Commodity contracts brokers, dealers; Brokers, security; Dealers, security
CEO: Gerald F Corcoran
V Ch: Robert J O'Brien
Pr: Lawrence Hansen
Pr: Charmine Ll
Pr: Colleen M Mitchell
Pr: Joseph Murphy
Pr: Garry Rovner
CEO: David Mudie
COO: Karen Northup
CFO: Jim Gabriele
CFO: Jason Manumaleuna
Ofcr: Jamal Oulhadj
Ofcr: Nancy A Westwick
Ex VP: Mark B Sachs
Sr VP: John Aiello
Sr VP: Kirk R Bonniwell
Sr VP: Anthony Croce
Sr VP: Ron Epstein
Sr VP: Paul Goodhew
Sr VP: Richard Mayhew
Sr VP: Tod Mitchell

D-U-N-S 82-922-7722
RJ OBRIEN HOLDINGS INC
222 S Riverside Plz # 900, Chicago, IL 60606-5808
Tel (312) 373-5000 Founded/Ownrshp 2006
Sales 116.5MM[E] EMP 307[E]
SIC 6282 Investment advisory service
CEO: Gerald F Corcoran
*Pr: Robert O'Brien Jr
Ofcr: Steve Andrews
Sr VP: John Coleman
Sr VP: Tim Horan
Sr VP: Thomas Kurinsky
Sr VP: Anthony Pecoraro
VP: Dominic Colanuono
VP: Thomas Forte
VP: Andrew Geiser
VP: Ryan Turner

D-U-N-S 11-132-5945
■ RJE TELECOM LLC
(Suby of DYCOM INDUSTRIES INC) ★
4315 Metro Pkwy Ste 300, Fort Myers, FL 33916-7949
Tel (239) 454-1944 Founded/Ownrshp 2004
Sales 83.9MM[E] EMP 350
SIC 4899 Radio broadcasting operated by cab companies
Pr: Marvin Glaser
*Ch: Robert J Ennis
VP: Al Berg

D-U-N-S 79-070-7731
■ RJF AGENCIES INC
GALLAGHER & ASSOCIATES
(Suby of MARSH & MCLENNAN AGENCY LLC) ★
7225 Northland Dr N, Minneapolis, MN 55428-1571
Tel (763) 746-8000 Founded/Ownrshp 2011
Sales NA EMP 198
SIC 6411 Property & casualty insurance agent
CEO: Bill Jeatran
*Pr: Tim Fleming
*COO: Jill Lowder
Ex VP: Bruce Humphrey
Ex VP: Mary Setter
*VP Sls: Jim Johnson

D-U-N-S 19-490-2185 IMP/EXP
RJF INTERNATIONAL CORP
MATTING PRODUCTS DIV
3875 Embassy Pkwy Ste 110, Fairlawn, OH 44333-8342
Tel (330) 668-2069 Founded/Ownrshp 1988
Sales 188.5MM[E] EMP 850
SIC 3081 3089 3069

D-U-N-S 02-948-1140 IMP
RJMS CORP
TOYOTA MATERIAL HDLG NTHRN CAL
31010 San Antonio St, Hayward, CA 94544-7904
Tel (510) 675-0500 Founded/Ownrshp 1997
Sales 120.0MM[E] EMP 210
Accts Moss Adams Llp San Francisco
SIC 5084 5085 7699 Materials handling machinery; Industrial supplies; Industrial machinery & equipment repair
CEO: Richard Andres
*VP: Mark Andres
Trfc Dir: Rochelle Woolaver
VP Sls: Tim Agnew
Manager: David Mills
Manager: Tom Salata
Sls Mgr: Bill Parks

D-U-N-S 80-801-9512
RJR CONSULTING GROUP INC
JENSEN, RALPH L JR
707 Dover Park Trl # 200, Mansfield, TX 76063-8833
Tel (817) 992-0124 Founded/Ownrshp 2003
Sales 350.0M EMP 1,000
SIC 7379 Computer related consulting services
Pr: Ralph L Jensen Jr
*VP: Romualdas J Rutkauskas

D-U-N-S 10-318-7571
RJW LOGISTICS INC
11240 Katherines Xing, Woodridge, IL 60517-5054
Tel (630) 424-2400 Founded/Ownrshp 1981
Sales 91.1MM[E] EMP 250
SIC 4731 Brokers, shipping
Ch: Ronald Williamson
*Pr: Kevin Williamson
COO: Rich Rudpolf
*CFO: Randy Chapple
*VP: Wilma J Williamson
MIS Dir: James Walker

D-U-N-S 07-842-4547
RK HALL LLC
(Suby of SUMMIT MATERIALS LLC) ★
1114 Lost Creek Blvd # 410, Austin, TX 78746-6300
Tel (903) 784-7280 Founded/Ownrshp 2012
Sales 140.7MM[E] EMP 410[E]
SIC 1611 Highway & street construction

D-U-N-S 14-829-8797 IMP/EXP
RK MECHANICAL INC
RK MECHANICAL INC SVC GROUP
3800 Xanthia St, Denver, CO 80238-3306
Tel (303) 576-9696 Founded/Ownrshp 1985
Sales 385.3MM[E] EMP 1,000
Accts Bauerle And Company Pc Den
SIC 1711 3498 3441 Plumbing, heating, air-conditioning contractors; Ventilation & duct work contractor; Process piping contractor; Fabricated pipe & fittings; Fabricated structural metal
Pr: Rick L Kinning
VP: David Albertsen
VP: Brandon Evans
VP: Jeff Gucker
VP: Don Hirschfield
*VP: Jon Kinning
VP: Marc Paolicelli
Dir IT: Sreenivas Atluri
Dir IT: Jim Geraud
VP Opers: Stephen Donnelly
Opers Mgr: Luke Chambers

RK MECHANICAL INC SVC GROUP
See RK MECHANICAL INC

RK&K
See RUMMEL KLEPPER & KAHL LLP

D-U-N-S 01-674-9376
RKA PETROLEUM COMPANIES INC
28340 Wick Rd, Romulus, MI 48174-2639
Tel (734) 946-2199 Founded/Ownrshp 1979
Sales 151.3MM[E] EMP 100
SIC 5172 Petroleum products
CEO: Roger Albertie

D-U-N-S 07-975-4152
■ RL VENTURE LLC
(Suby of RLHC) ★
201 W North River Dr # 100, Spokane, WA 99201-2284
Tel (509) 459-6100 Founded/Ownrshp 2014
Sales 36.6MM[E] EMP 1,003[E]
SIC 7011 Hotels & motels

D-U-N-S 13-108-6001
RL2 INC
10802 Parkridge Blvd, Reston, VA 20191-4334
Tel (703) 390-1899 Founded/Ownrshp 2010
Sales 130.2MM[E] EMP 330[E]
SIC 4899

D-U-N-S 14-444-9683 IMP
RLB FOOD DISTRIBUTORS LP
FRESHPRO FOOD DISTRIBUTORS
2 Dedrick Pl Cn2285, West Caldwell, NJ 07006-6303
Tel (973) 575-9526 Founded/Ownrshp 1985
Sales 91.1MM[E] EMP 160
SIC 5148 5141 Fresh fruits & vegetables; Groceries, general line
Pt: Floyd Avillo
Pt: Pat Mele
VP: Jeff Shilling
Sls Mgr: Joey Granata
Sales Asso: Gregory Morante

D-U-N-S 13-107-5921 IMP/EXP
RLC INDUSTRIES CO
10599 Old Hwy 99 S, Dillard, OR 97432
Tel (541) 679-3311 Founded/Ownrshp 1936
Sales 887.1MM[E] EMP 3,400
SIC 2493 2436 2421 Particleboard products; Plywood, softwood; Lumber: rough, sawed or planed; Wood chips, produced at mill
Pr: Allyn C Ford

D-U-N-S 01-331-6278 IMP/EXP
RLE CORP
ATLANTIC INTERNATIONAL PDTS
1301 Broad St, Utica, NY 13501-1605
Tel (315) 724-4189 Founded/Ownrshp 1976
Sales 137.0MM[E] EMP 150
SIC 5141 Groceries, general line
Ch Bd: Vito Dalessandro
*CFO: Brian Suba
*Sec: Philip Casamento
*VP: John Fornino
Software D: Jon Lamb

RLHC
See RED LION HOTELS CORP

D-U-N-S 07-563-3412
▲ RLI CORP
9025 N Lindbergh Dr, Peoria, IL 61615-1499
Tel (309) 692-1000 Founded/Ownrshp 1965
Sales NA EMP 902[E]
Tkr Sym RLI Exch NYS
SIC 6411 Property & casualty insurance agent
Ch Bd: Jonathan E Michael
CFO: Thomas L Brown
Treas: Aaron P Diefenthaler
Ex VP: Craig W Kliethermes
VP: Kathleen M Kappes
VP: Daniel O Kennedy
Board of Directors: Michael J Stone, Barbara R Allen, Robert O Viets, Michael E Angelina, John T Baily, Calvin G Butler Jr, Jordan W Graham, Charles M Linke, F Lynn McPheeters, Robert P Restrepo Jr, James J Scanlan

D-U-N-S 03-841-1591
■ RLI INSURANCE CO (INC)
(Suby of RLI CORP) ★
9025 N Lindbergh Dr, Peoria, IL 61615-1499
Tel (309) 692-1000 Founded/Ownrshp 1965
Sales NA EMP 724
SIC 6331 Property damage insurance; Fire, marine & casualty insurance: stock
CEO: Jonathan E Michael
*Pr: Michael J Stone
*CFO: Joseph E Dondanville
VP: Donald J Driscol
VP: Jeffrerey Fick
VP: Eric Galisdorfer
VP: Kim Hensey
CIO: Jamie Baldock
VP Opers: Andrew B McCray
Mktg Dir: Becky Lundberg
Mktg Mgr: John Fee

D-U-N-S 07-853-1107
▲ RLJ ENTERTAINMENT INC
8515 Georgia Ave Ste 650, Silver Spring, MD 20910-3497
Tel (301) 608-2115 Founded/Ownrshp 2012
Sales 124.9MM EMP 109[E]
Accts Bdo Usa Llp Los Angeles Cal
Tkr Sym RLJE Exch NAS
SIC 7822 Motion picture & tape distribution
CEO: Miguel Penella
*Ch Bd: Robert L Johnson
CFO: Mark Nunis
CFO: Nazir Rostom
Ex VP: Mike Pears
Mktg Mgr: Karen Gordon
Snr Mgr: Sheila Velazquez
Board of Directors: Tyrone Brown, John Hsu, Dayton Judd, Andor M Laszlo, Arlene Manos, Scott Royster, John Ziegelman

D-U-N-S 01-208-3360
RLJ LODGING TRUST (MD)
3 Bethesda Metro Ctr, Bethesda, MD 20814 5330
Tel (301) 280-7777 Founded/Ownrshp 2000
Sales 1.1MMM EMP 56[E]
SIC 6798 Real estate investment trusts
Pr: Ross H Bierkan
*Ch Bd: Robert L Johnson
COO: Leslie D Hale
VP: Anita C Cookewells
VP: Carl Mayfield
Genl Mgr: Sharon Chism
Genl Mgr: Howard Isaacson
Board of Directors: Thomas J Baltimore, Evan Bayh, Nathaniel A Davis, Robert M La Forgia, Glenda G McNeal, Joseph Ryan

RM THORNTON
See HARRIS CONTRACTING CO

RMC
See ROOSEVELT MANAGEMENT CO LLC

D-U-N-S 06-453-6227
RMC JACKSONVILLE
PEDIATRIC ASSOCIATES
1701 Pelham Rd S, Jacksonville, AL 36265-3353
Tel (256) 782-4256 Founded/Ownrshp 2011
Sales 64.3MM[E] EMP 1,700
SIC 8011 Pediatrician
Prin: Vullaganti Ramarao
CEO: Joseph Weaver

D-U-N-S 19-587-1843 IMP
RMC USA INC
(Suby of CEMEX INC) ★
920 Memorial City Way, Houston, TX 77024-2649
Tel (713) 650-6200 Founded/Ownrshp 2005
Sales 208.8MM[E] EMP 2,380[E]
SIC 3273 3272 3271 5031 Ready-mixed concrete; Concrete products, precast; Pipe, concrete or lined with concrete; Concrete block & brick; Building materials, exterior; Building materials, interior
Pr: Gilberto Perez
VP: Hendrik Van Brenk

D-U-N-S 18-672-3128
RMD CORP
HOOTERS
2509 Plantside Dr, Louisville, KY 40299-2529
Tel (502) 499-9991 Founded/Ownrshp 1988
Sales 63.1MM[E] EMP 2,500
SIC 5812 5813 American restaurant; Bar (drinking places)
VP: Mike Gregory
Ofcr: Julia Owen

D-U-N-S 04-988-8084 IMP/EXP
RMET HOLDINGS INC
GOLD COAST BEVERAGE
133 Sevilla Ave, Coral Gables, FL 33134-6006
Tel (305) 567-3582 Founded/Ownrshp 1995
Sales 274.4MM[E] EMP 650
SIC 5181 5182 Beer & other fermented malt liquors; Wine & distilled beverages
Ch: Stephen Levin
*COO: Alfonso Fernandez
*CFO: Fernando Anon
*Sec: Martin Sweren

D-U-N-S 00-422-8631 IMP/EXP
■ RMI TITANIUM CO LLC
RTI NILES
(Suby of ALCOA TITANIUM ENGINEERED PDTS) ★
1000 Warren Ave, Niles, OH 44446-1168
Tel (330) 652-9952 Founded/Ownrshp 1998
Sales 150.4MM[E] EMP 500
SIC 3399 3356 1741 3533 Powder, metal; Titanium; Masonry & other stonework; Oil & gas drilling rigs & equipment
Pr: Dawn S Hickton
*Pr: Timothy Rupert
*Treas: Lawrence W Jacobs
*Ex VP: John H Odle
*Sr VP: Stephen R Giangiordano
Sr VP: William Hull
CIO: Ernie Crist
VP Opers: Richard R Vandegift

RMIS
See RALEIGH MINE AND INDUSTRIAL SUPPLY INC

D-U-N-S 00-943-0161
RML HEALTH PROVIDERS LIMITED PARTNERSHIP
RML SPECIALTY HOSPITAL
5601 S County Line Rd, Hinsdale, IL 60521-4875
Tel (708) 783-5800 Founded/Ownrshp 1997
Sales 98.7MM EMP 740
Accts Crowe Horwath Llp Chicago Il
SIC 8062 General medical & surgical hospitals
CEO: James R Prister
Pt: Irfan N Hafiz
Pt: Kieran J Nicholson
Pt: Abd A Noghnogh
Pt: Thomas M Pater
Pt: Tricia Vaisvila
COO: Ken Pawola
Chf Mktg O: Kathleen Mikrut
Dir OR: Kathy Hamzik
Dir QC: Karen Finerty
Phys Thrpy: Carl Burdinie

RML SPECIALTY HOSPITAL
See RML HEALTH PROVIDERS LIMITED PARTNERSHIP

D-U-N-S 15-314-2513
▲ RMR GROUP INC
255 Washington St Ste 300, Newton, MA 02458-1634
Tel (617) 928-1300 Founded/Ownrshp 1986
Sales 266.9MM EMP 400[E]
Tkr Sym RMR Exch NAS
SIC 8742 Real estate consultant
Pr: Adam D Portnoy
CFO: Matthew P Jordan
Ex VP: Jennifer B Clark
Mng Dir: Barry M Portnoy

RMS
See RECEIVABLE MANAGEMENT SERVICES INTERNATIONAL INC

RMS
See RESIDENTIAL MORTGAGE SERVICES INC

D-U-N-S 00-645-3872
RMS CO
(Suby of CRETEX COMPANIES INC) ★
8600 Evergreen Blvd Nw, Minneapolis, MN 55433-6036
Tel (763) 786-1520 Founded/Ownrshp 1966
Sales 146.4MM[E] EMP 700
SIC 3841 Surgical & medical instruments
CEO: Lee Zachman
*Treas: Steve Ragaller
Ex VP: Lawrence Raia
*VP: Lynn Schuler
Genl Mgr: Brian Archerd
CTO: John Klinkenborg
Prd Mgr: Dave Thompson

RMT
See ROSENBOOM MACHINE & TOOL INC

D-U-N-S 11-129-0417
RN INDUSTRIES TRUCKING
RNI DALBO
188 W 200 N, Roosevelt, UT 84066-2302
Tel (435) 722-2800 Founded/Ownrshp 1990
Sales 123.1MM[E] EMP 100
SIC 1389 Oil field services
Pr: Roger Chapman
*Pr: Chance Massey

RNDC
See REPUBLIC NATIONAL DISTRIBUTING CO LLC

D-U-N-S 00-895-2657 IMP
RNDC TEXAS LLC
REPUBLIC NATIONAL DISTRG CO
6511 Tri County Pkwy, Schertz, TX 78154-3219
Tel (210) 224-7531 *Founded/Ownrshp* 1939
Sales 900.3MM^E *EMP* 430^E
SIC 5182 Liquor; Wine
CFO: Paul Fine
CFO: Susan Talley
Ex VP: Scott Lammert
Ex VP: Keith Neill
Ex VP: David Ritch
VP: Steve Dyer
VP: Laura Karrer
VP: Joel Polichene
VP: Jug Rohlich
VP: Irwin Sivin
Area Mgr: Carl Vanwinkle

D-U-N-S 05-338-5811 IMP
RNGLNG BRS BRNM & BLY COMB SHO
GREATEST SHOW ON EARTH, THE
(*Suby of* RINGLING BRS-BRNUM BLEY CIRCUS) ★
8607 Westwood Center Dr # 500, Vienna, VA 22182-7506
Tel (703) 448-4000 *Founded/Ownrshp* 1982
Sales 34.4MM^E *EMP* 1,500
SIC 7999 Circus company
Pr: Kenneth Feld
Pr: Tom Albert
Pr: Stephen Payne
Ex VP: Nicole Feld
Sr VP: Robert McHugh
Sr VP: Jeff Meyer
Sr VP: Vicki Silver
VP: Lorraine Buck
VP: Sam Gomez
VP: Tim Hoist
VP: Ryan McSpadden

RNI DALBO
See RN INDUSTRIES TRUCKING

D-U-N-S 78-709-2279
RO HO HO INC
PAPA JOHN'S
1479 Tobias Gadson Blvd, Charleston, SC 29407-4794
Tel (877) 547-7272 *Founded/Ownrshp* 1991
Sales 48.6MM^E *EMP* 1,200
SIC 5812 Pizzeria, chain
Pr: Philip Horn Jr
Sec: Caroline Horn
VP: Don Bauer
Prin: Martin Boudreaux
Prin: Joe Dixon
Prin: Philip L Horn
Prin: Jory Mc Gee
Mktg Dir: Liz Bauer

D-U-N-S 03-244-1651
RO-MAC LUMBER & SUPPLY INC
RO-MAC LUMBER AND SUPPLY
700 E Main St, Leesburg, FL 34748-5318
Tel (352) 787-4545 *Founded/Ownrshp* 1947
Sales 86.4MM^E *EMP* 385
SIC 5211 5031 Lumber products; Door & window products; Building materials, exterior; Doors & windows
Pr: Dan Robuck III
**CEO:* Don Magruder
Genl Mgr: Alice Higgins
CIO: Brad Johnson
**Dir IT:* Susan Adams
Dir IT: Nic Nowlan
Manager: Donna Gaff
Opers Mgr: Gary Padgett
Sales Exec: Bart Lucas
Mktg Dir: Joe Czabajszki
Sales Asso: Jon Alley

RO-MAC LUMBER AND SUPPLY
See RO-MAC LUMBER & SUPPLY INC

ROACH CONVEYORS
See ROACH MANUFACTURING CORP

D-U-N-S 00-702-0183 IMP
ROACH MANUFACTURING CORP (AR)
ROACH CONVEYORS
808 Highway 463 N, Trumann, AR 72472-1635
Tel (870) 483-7631 *Founded/Ownrshp* 1953, 1970
Sales 103.3MM^E *EMP* 300
SIC 3535 Conveyors & conveying equipment; Belt conveyor systems, general industrial use
Pr: Gay W Roach Jr
**Treas:* Margaret Parks
VP: Brad Owen
**VP:* Charlie W Parks
**Prin:* Gay W Roach Sr
Ex Dir: Leslie Mitchell
**VP Mfg:* Mike Roach
Sales Exec: Hal Stewart
Sales Asso: Chris Breaker

D-U-N-S 18-116-9665
ROAD & RAIL SERVICES INC
4233 Bardstown Rd Ste 200, Louisville, KY 40218-3282
Tel (502) 365-5361 *Founded/Ownrshp* 1987
Sales 140.6MM^E *EMP* 900
SIC 4789 4013

D-U-N-S 14-797-9579 EXP
ROAD BUILDERS MACHINERY & SUPPLY CO INC
1001 S 7th St, Kansas City, KS 66105-2007
Tel (913) 371-3822 *Founded/Ownrshp* 1985
Sales 120.1MM^E *EMP* 103
Accts Larson & Company Pa Wichita
SIC 5082 7353 7699 General construction machinery & equipment; Heavy construction equipment rental; Construction equipment repair
Pr: Phil Mc Coy
**Sec:* M Nicole Argard
**Sr VP:* Gerry Buser
**VP:* Bryan Mc Coy
VP: Bryan McCoy
Sfty Dirs: Jamie Morche
Sls Mgr: Randy Frank
Sls Mgr: Randy Held

D-U-N-S 00-621-4654 IMP/EXP
ROAD MACHINERY & SUPPLIES CO
5633 Highway 13 W, Savage, MN 55378-1215
Tel (952) 895-9595 *Founded/Ownrshp* 1926
Sales 135.2MM^E *EMP* 204
SIC 5082 General construction machinery & equipment; Road construction equipment; Mining machinery & equipment, except petroleum; Logging equipment & supplies
Pr: Mike M Sill II
COO: David Johnson
Treas: William T Holte
VP: Mike Mencel
Genl Mgr: Jon Anderson
Genl Mgr: Marc Bottari
Genl Mgr: Chuck Gallagher
Mtls Mgr: Scott Kropiwka
Manager: J J Bunn
Manager: Chad Hein
Manager: Gordon Johnson

D-U-N-S 00-901-1644 IMP
ROAD MACHINERY LLC
(*Suby of* MITSUI & CO., LTD.)
4710 E Elwood St Ste 6, Phoenix, AZ 85040-1995
Tel (602) 256-5128 *Founded/Ownrshp* 2005
Sales 134.8MM^E *EMP* 315
SIC 5082 7359 7699 7353 7629 Mining machinery & equipment, except petroleum; General construction machinery & equipment; Road construction & maintenance machinery; Equipment rental & leasing; Industrial machinery & equipment repair; Heavy construction equipment rental; Electrical repair shops
Pr: Dan Roush
CFO: Bill Hoke
VP: Joseph Scalmato
IT Man: Carlos Padilla
IT Man: Luis Ramos
Opers Mgr: Becky Lucio
Sales Exec: Steve Morico
VP Sls: Daniel McGhuth
Mktg Dir: Charlie Bell
Sls Dir: Sloan Brooks

ROAD RANGER
See REOPCO INC

D-U-N-S 16-154-3467 IMP
ROAD RUNNER SPORTS INC
5549 Copley Dr, San Diego, CA 92111-7904
Tel (858) 974-4200 *Founded/Ownrshp* 1925
Sales 84.8MM^E *EMP* 280^E
SIC 5961 3949 5661 Mail order house; Sporting & athletic goods; Footwear, athletic
Pr: Michael Gotfredson
**CFO:* Scott Campbell
Off Mgr: Dawn Porter
Store Mgr: Jay Cytryn
Store Mgr: Allison Gavin
Store Mgr: Telan Nichols
Store Mgr: Gordon Richmond
Web Dev: Cindy Laterra
Mktg Mgr: Darren Moradian
Sls Mgr: Brian Simpson
Snr Mgr: Dane Bradley

D-U-N-S 07-964-4827
ROADHOUSE INTERMEDIATE INC
(*Suby of* ROADHOUSE HOLDING INC)
3011 Armory Dr Ste 300, Nashville, TN 37204-3721
Tel (615) 885-9056 *Founded/Ownrshp* 2010
Sales 614.3MM^E *EMP* 16,700^E
SIC 5812 Eating places; Steak restaurant
Pr: Samuel N Borgese

D-U-N-S 07-964-4731
ROADHOUSE MIDCO INC
(*Suby of* ROADHOUSE INTERMEDIATE INC) ★
3011 Armory Dr Ste 300, Nashville, TN 37204-3721
Tel (615) 885-9056 *Founded/Ownrshp* 2010
Sales 614.3MM^E *EMP* 16,700^E
SIC 5812 6794 Eating places; Steak & barbecue restaurants; Franchises, selling or licensing
Pr: Samuel N Borgese

D-U-N-S 07-964-4880
ROADHOUSE PARENT INC
(*Suby of* ROADHOUSE MIDCO INC) ★
3011 Armory Dr Ste 300, Nashville, TN 37204-3721
Tel (615) 885-9056 *Founded/Ownrshp* 2010
Sales 614.3MM^E *EMP* 16,700^E
SIC 5812 6794 Eating places; Steak restaurant; Franchises, selling or licensing
Pr: Samuel N Borgese

D-U-N-S 12-710-3989
ROADLINK USA INC
(*Suby of* FENWAY PARTNERS LLC) ★
1 Kelleway Dr, Randolph, MA 02368-5074
Tel (888) 622-6076 *Founded/Ownrshp* 2008
Sales 167.9MM^E *EMP* 2,788
SIC 4212 Delivery service, vehicular
Pr: Mike Shelton
**Ch Bd:* John Anderson
**Pr:* Mark Fornasiero
**Pr:* Mike Haley
**Pr:* L Michael Shelton
**COO:* David McLaughlin
**Prin:* Ken Kellaway
Admn Mgr: Joyce Smith
VP Opers: Craig Probe
VP Sls: Michael Donnelly

D-U-N-S 55-755-7944
ROADLINK USA NATIONAL LLC
(*Suby of* ROADLINK USA INC) ★
1240 Win Dr, Bethlehem, PA 18017-7061
Tel (215) 333-4444 *Founded/Ownrshp* 2004
Sales 32.8MM^E *EMP* 1,239^E
SIC 4212 Local trucking, without storage
Pr: Ronald T Sorrow
VP: Micheal Albert

ROADRUNNER MARKETS
See MOUNTAIN EMPIRE OIL CO

D-U-N-S 96-285-5917
■ **ROADRUNNER TRANSPORTATION SERVICES INC**
(*Suby of* ROADRUNNER TRANSPORTATION SYSTEMS INC) ★
4900 S Pennsylvania Ave, Cudahy, WI 53110-1347
Tel (414) 615-1500 *Founded/Ownrshp* 2005
Sales 91.1MM^E *EMP* 1,000
SIC 4731 Freight transportation arrangement
Pr: Mark Diblasi
Off Mgr: Ann Bissett
Off Mgr: Alisha Greer
Off Mgr: Lydia Lopez
DP Exec: Pam Latherow
Opers Mgr: Bill Bowes
Opers Mgr: Lynn Moore

D-U-N-S 11-411-4531
▲ **ROADRUNNER TRANSPORTATION SYSTEMS INC**
4900 S Pennsylvania Ave, Cudahy, WI 53110-1347
Tel (414) 615-1500 *Founded/Ownrshp* 2005
Sales 2.0MMM *EMP* 4,502
Tkr Sym RRTS *Exch* NYS
SIC 4731 Freight transportation arrangement; Customhouse brokers; Freight forwarding; Freight consolidation
Pr: Mark A Diblasi
**Ch Bd:* Scott D Rued
**Pr:* Curtis Stoelting
CFO: Peter R Armbruster
Dir Risk M: Robert Milane
CIO: Jason Descamps
Opers Mgr: Matthew Tylicki
Board of Directors: Christopher L Doerr, John G Kennedy III, Brian Murray, James D Staley, William S Urkiel, Judith A Vijums, Michael P Ward

D-U-N-S 80-846-1615
ROADSAFE TRAFFIC SYSTEMS INC
8750 W Bryn Mawr Ave # 400, Chicago, IL 60631-3655
Tel (773) 724-3300 *Founded/Ownrshp* 2007
Sales 838.5MM^E *EMP* 900^E
SIC 1721 1611 7389 Pavement marking contractor; Highway & street sign installation; Flagging service (traffic control)
CEO: David Meirick
Treas: Ronald Emmons
Rgnl VP: Dave Meirick
Rgnl VP: Robert Toomey
VP: Margaret Bennett
Brnch Mgr: Wil Martin
Off Mgr: Sharon Majewski
Off Mgr: Angelic Schropp
Off Admin: Connie Harris
Opers Mgr: Tom Busta
Opers Mgr: Adam Johnson

D-U-N-S 01-070-8329 IMP/EXP
■ **ROADTEC INC**
(*Suby of* ASTEC INDUSTRIES INC) ★
800 Manufacturers Rd, Chattanooga, TN 37405-3706
Tel (423) 265-0600 *Founded/Ownrshp* 1981
Sales 89.0MM^E *EMP* 325
SIC 3531 Planers, bituminous; Pavers
Pr: Jeff Richmond
Pr: Dave Swearingen
Treas: Don Brock
**Treas:* J Don Brock
Sr VP: Michael Kvach
IT Man: Kirk Phillips
Sftwr Eng: David Hales
Plnt Mgr: Darrell Duncan
Natl Sales: Frank Reiland
Manager: Scott Chalmers
Manager: Dave Miller

D-U-N-S 02-530-9241
■ **ROADWAY LLC**
(*Suby of* YRC WORLDWIDE INC) ★
10990 Roe Ave, Overland Park, KS 66211-1213
Tel (913) 344-3000 *Founded/Ownrshp* 2003
Sales 4.5MMM^E *EMP* 22,000
SIC 4213 Trucking, except local; Less-than-truckload (LTL) transport
CEO: James Welch
VP: Phil Gaines
VP: Terry Gerrond
Sls Mgr: Celeste Christian

D-U-N-S 06-220-5281
ROANE COUNTY
200 E Race St Ste 1, Kingston, TN 37763-2860
Tel (865) 376-3184 *Founded/Ownrshp* 1801
Sales NA *EMP* 1,139
SIC 9111 County supervisors' & executives' offices;
Prin: Ken Yager

D-U-N-S 07-979-8791
ROANE COUNTY SCHOOLS (TN)
105 Bluff Rd, Kingston, TN 37763-7209
Tel (865) 376-5592 *Founded/Ownrshp* 2015
Sales 13.0MM^E *EMP* 2,035^E
SIC 8211 Public elementary & secondary schools
Teacher Pr: Jodi McCloud
Instr Medi: Brenda Branson

D-U-N-S 87-893-4835
ROANOKE CITY PUBLIC SCHOOL DISTRICT
40 Douglas Ave Nw, Roanoke, VA 24012-4611
Tel (540) 853-2502 *Founded/Ownrshp* 1998
Sales 83.2MM^E *EMP* 2,024
SIC 8211 Public elementary & secondary schools
Off Mgr: Stacy Billon
IT Man: James Smith
Schl Brd P: Suzanne Moore
Instr Medi: David Baker
HC Dir: Karen Switzer

D-U-N-S 07-979-8722
ROANOKE CITY PUBLIC SCHOOLS
40 Douglas Ave Nw, Roanoke, VA 24012-4611
Tel (540) 853-2381 *Founded/Ownrshp* 2015
Sales 58.8MM^E *EMP* 1,286^E
SIC 8211 Public elementary & secondary schools
Dir IT: David Baker

D-U-N-S 14-367-7057
ROANOKE COMPANIES INC
(*Suby of* MUNICH RE HOLDING COMPANY (UK) LIMITED)
1475 E Woodfield Rd, Schaumburg, IL 60173-4980
Tel (847) 969-1420 *Founded/Ownrshp* 2008
Sales NA *EMP* 170
SIC 6411 Property & casualty insurance agent
Pr: William Stereitt
VP: Ron Gee

D-U-N-S 00-312-2553 IMP/EXP
■ **ROANOKE ELECTRIC STEEL CORP**
STEEL DYNAMICS ROANOKE BAR DIV
(*Suby of* SDI) ★
102 Westside Blvd Nw, Roanoke, VA 24017-6757
Tel (540) 342-1831 *Founded/Ownrshp* 2006
Sales 341.4MM^E *EMP* 500
SIC 3312 Bars, iron: made in steel mills; Billets, steel
Pr: T Joe Crawford
Chf Mktg O: Michael Levin
**VP:* Millett Mark D
**VP:* Wagler Theresa
Genl Mgr: Jim Carr
Sfty Mgr: Lynn Akers
Sales Exec: Parker Arthur

D-U-N-S 01-940-6644
ROANOKE INSURANCE GROUP INC (IL)
ROANOKE TRADES
(*Suby of* ROANOKE COMPANIES INC) ★
1475 E Wdfield Rd Ste 500, Schaumburg, IL 60173
Tel (847) 969-1420 *Founded/Ownrshp* 1935, 1973
Sales NA *EMP* 160
SIC 6411 Insurance agents, brokers & service
Pr: William A Sterrett
**Pr:* Janet Ciesko
Pr: Richard Councill
COO: Melissa Pyles
Treas: William Broderick
Ex VP: Paul Amstutz
**Ex VP:* James Cahalan
Ex VP: Rhonda Chuoke
**Ex VP:* Lewis M Moeller
**Ex VP:* Sean Walsh
**Ex VP:* Kathleen A Wilson
**Sr VP:* Ronald Bethke
**Sr VP:* Gerard Dooner
**Sr VP:* William B Florio
VP: Amanda Barlow
VP: Richard Bridges
VP: Oliver Corky
VP: Terry Cummings
VP: Timothy Danford
VP: David Esqueda
VP: Theresa Garcia

ROANOKE TRADES
See ROANOKE INSURANCE GROUP INC

D-U-N-S 00-432-9264 IMP/EXP
ROARING SPRING BLANK BOOK CO
ROARING SPRING PAPER PRODUCTS
740 Spang St, Roaring Spring, PA 16673-1924
Tel (814) 224-2306 *Founded/Ownrshp* 1887
Sales 96.4MM^E *EMP* 410
SIC 2678 5149 2653 7389 Tablets & pads, book & writing: from purchased materials; Notebooks: made from purchased paper; Mineral or spring water bottling; Boxes, corrugated: made from purchased materials; Coffee service
Pr: Daniel B Hoover
**VP:* Robert J Allen
Genl Mgr: James B Lucey

ROARING SPRING PAPER PRODUCTS
See ROARING SPRING BLANK BOOK CO

D-U-N-S 12-125-0232
ROARK CAPITAL GROUP INC
1180 Peachtree St Ne # 2500, Atlanta, GA 30309-7524
Tel (404) 591-5200 *Founded/Ownrshp* 2000
Sales 4.3MMM^E *EMP* 37,972
SIC 6726 3993 7331 6794 5261 Investment offices; Signs & advertising specialties; Mailing service; Franchises, selling or licensing; Nursery stock, seeds & bulbs
CEO: Neal K Aronson
Pr: Jeffrey J Keenan
COO: Neal Aronson
Ofcr: Julie McEwen
VP: Thomas Owens
Mng Dir: Timothy Armstrong
Mng Dir: Stephen Aronson

D-U-N-S 03-229-5479 IMP/EXP
ROBB & STUCKY LIMITED LLLP
14550 Plantation Rd, Fort Myers, FL 33912-4328
Tel (239) 437-7997 *Founded/Ownrshp* 1979
Sales NA *EMP* 1,400
SIC 5712 5713 5714 5231

D-U-N-S 07-545-0882
ROBBIE D WOOD INC (AL)
1051 Old Warrior River Rd, Dolomite, AL 35061
Tel (205) 744-8440 *Founded/Ownrshp* 1965
Sales 96.1MM^E *EMP* 140
SIC 4953 Hazardous waste collection & disposal
Pr: Robbie D Wood Jr
**VP:* Todd White
**VP:* J Brett Wood
IT Man: Jennifer Brooks
Sfty Dirs: Tiffany Wood

D-U-N-S 94-929-2759 IMP/EXP
■ **ROBBIN & MEYERS ENERGY SYSTEMS LP**
R&M ENERGY SYSTEMS
(*Suby of* ROBBINS & MEYERS INC) ★
10586 N Highway 75, Willis, TX 77378-5715
Tel (936) 890-1064 *Founded/Ownrshp* 1997
Sales 165.2MM^E *EMP* 400
SIC 3491 3533 Industrial valves; Oil & gas field machinery
Pr: Saeid Rahimian
Pt: Joseph M Rigot
Software D: Darrell Walker
Sftwr Eng: Luyang Chen
Mfg Mgr: James Mueller

D-U-N-S 00-428-3990 IMP
■ ROBBINS & MYERS INC (OH)
(Suby of NOV) ★
10586 N Highway 75, Willis, TX 77378-5715
Tel (936) 890-1064 Founded/Ownrshp 1878, 2013
Sales 777.1MM[E] EMP 3,473[E]
SIC 3533 3443 3823 5084 Oil & gas field machinery; Reactor containment vessels, metal plate; Industrial process control instruments; Hydraulic systems equipment & supplies
Pr: Peter C Wallace
Pr: Clay C Williams
CFO: Kevin J Brown
CFO: Randy Spurcz
Sr VP: Saeid Rahimian
VP: Craig C Goss
VP: Daniel L Molinaro
VP: Aaron H Ravenscroft

D-U-N-S 14-421-6587 EXP
ROBBINS CO
(Suby of NORTHERN HEAVY INDUSTRIES GROUP CO., LTD.)
29100 Hall St Ste 100, Solon, OH 44139-3926
Tel (440) 248-3303 Founded/Ownrshp 2016
Sales 161.1MM[E] EMP 400
Accts Meaden & Moore Ltd
SIC 3535 3541 3531 Conveyors & conveying equipment; Machine tools, metal cutting type; Tunnelling machinery
Pr: Lok Home
CFO: Clark Lubaski
VP: Douglas Harding
VP: Brian Khalighi
VP: Dean Workman
Genl Mgr: Martin Eckert
Dir IT: Mike Aemisegger

ROBBINS LUMBER
See ROBBINS MANUFACTURING CO INC

D-U-N-S 00-408-9231 IMP/EXP
ROBBINS MANUFACTURING CO INC (FL)
ROBBINS LUMBER
13001 N Nebraska Ave, Tampa, FL 33612-4456
Tel (813) 971-3030 Founded/Ownrshp 1938
Sales 181.8MM[E] EMP 450
SIC 2491 Wood preserving
Ch: Laurence W Hall Jr
*Pr: Dionel E Cotanda
CFO: Charlie Robbins
*Treas: Charles M Robbins
Ofcr: John Wilerson
*VP: William E Brown
*VP: Jerome Robbins II
Dir IT: John Wilkerson
VP Mktg: Gary Hurst

ROBBINS NISSAN-OLDS
See NISSAN ROBBINS INC

ROBBINSDALE AREA SCHOOL DST
See INDEPENDENT SCHOOL DISTRICT 281

D-U-N-S 03-219-2494
■ ROBBYS SPORTING GOODS INC
CHAMPS
(Suby of KINNEY) ★
311 Manatee Ave W, Bradenton, FL 34205-8842
Tel (941) 748-0577 Founded/Ownrshp 1988
Sales 120.0MM EMP 1,000
SIC 5941 Sporting goods & bicycle shops
Pr: Harold C Rowen
Treas: John H Cannon
*Sr VP: George J Konogeris
VP: William L De Vries
*VP: Philip W Richards
VP: William C Robinson

D-U-N-S 12-247-5945
ROBECO USA INC
(Suby of ROBECO GROEP N.V.)
909 3rd Ave, New York, NY 10022-4731
Tel (212) 908-9500 Founded/Ownrshp 2001
Sales 84.8MM[E] EMP 425
SIC 6282 Manager of mutual funds, contract or fee basis; Investment advisory service
CEO: William J Kelley
CFO: Jurgen Stegmann
Chf Cred: Elizabeth Roenker
Assoc VP: Alyson Tarquinio
Sr VP: Jacqueline Wong
CIO: Alfred Flanagan

D-U-N-S 03-620-3354
ROBERT A WILLIAMS ENTERPRISES
BOBBIE STVES AUTO WRLD RCHFELD
3701 Central Ave Ne, Minneapolis, MN 55421-3928
Tel (763) 788-1113 Founded/Ownrshp 1963
Sales 96.1MM[E] EMP 300
SIC 5541 6519 Filling stations, gasoline; Landholding office
Pt: Keith Ostendorf
Pt: Steve Anderson
Pt: Jeff Bahe
Pt: Jon Junch
Pt: Arlan Williams
Pt: Mellisa Williams
Pt: Robert A Williams
CFO: Mike Munns

D-U-N-S 00-142-5552 IMP/EXP
ROBERT ALLEN GROUP INC
BEACON HILL
(Suby of DECOR HOLDINGS INC) ★
2 Hampshire St Ste 300, Foxboro, MA 02035-2973
Tel (508) 339-9151 Founded/Ownrshp 1986, 2002
Sales 295.3MM[E] EMP 600
SIC 5023 Home furnishings; Bedspreads
Pr: Phil Kowalczyk
*Pr: Jeff Cordover
Pr: Kathryn Westman
*CFO: Chuck Cioffi
VP: Don Greene
VP: William Hargreaves
VP: Sandra Jordan
VP: Kim Vasquez
Exec: Jennie Wilde

CIO: Dean Riviera
CTO: Amron Alrai

D-U-N-S 93-937-0214
ROBERT B DAUGHERTY FOUNDATION INC
1 Valmont Plz, Omaha, NE 68154-5301
Tel (402) 933-4663 Founded/Ownrshp 2009
Sales 95.3MM EMP 3
Accts Bkd Llp Omaha Ne
SIC 8641 Civic social & fraternal associations
Prin: Robert B Daugherty

ROBERT B. GREEN CAMPUS
See UNIVERSITY HEALTH SYSTEM

D-U-N-S 82-590-2385 IMP
ROBERT BOSCH AUTOMOTIVE STEERING LLC
(Suby of ROBERT BOSCH AUTOMOTIVE STEERING BREMEN GMBH)
15 Spiral Dr, Florence, KY 41042-1357
Tel (859) 568-1143 Founded/Ownrshp 1998
Sales 312.3MM[E] EMP 1,295
SIC 3714 Steering mechanisms, motor vehicle
CEO: Christian Sobottka
*CFO: Mark Bugajski
*Ex VP: Hanns Bernd Ketteler
*Ex VP: Marcus Parche
*Ex VP: Henning Wagner

D-U-N-S 03-704-1076 IMP/EXP
ROBERT BOSCH LLC
AUTOMOTIVE GROUP
(Suby of R O B E R T B O S C H S T I F T U N G GESELLSCHAFT MIT BESCHRANKTER HAFTUNG)
2800 S 25th Ave, Broadview, IL 60155-4532
Tel (248) 876-1000 Founded/Ownrshp 1886
Sales 10.8MMM EMP 12,986
SIC 3714 3694 5013 5064 3565 3541 Motor vehicle parts & accessories; Motor vehicle brake systems & parts; Motor vehicle electrical equipment; Motors, starting: automotive & aircraft; Distributors, motor vehicle engine; Automotive supplies & parts; Automotive engines & engine parts; Automotive brakes; Radios, motor vehicle; Packaging machinery; Deburring machines
Ch: Werner Struth
Pr: Bernd Boisten
Pr: Tim Frasier
*Pr: Mike Mansuetti
CFO: Max Siegmann
*CFO: Maximiliane Straub
Treas: Mike McKenna
Ofcr: Laura Papenhagen
Ex VP: Reiner Emig
Ex VP: Peter Kilgenstein
VP: Donald R Chauncey
VP: Kurt Person
VP: Christine M Zimmerman

D-U-N-S 79-637-8024 IMP/EXP
ROBERT BOSCH TOOL CORP
GARDEN WATERING
(Suby of SCINTILLA AG)
1800 W Central Rd, Mount Prospect, IL 60056-2230
Tel (224) 232-2000 Founded/Ownrshp 1996
Sales 1.3MMM[E] EMP 5,007
SIC 3546 Cartridge-activated hand power tools
*Pr: Heiko Fischer
*CFO: Katina Xouria
VP: David Klein
VP: Peter Nueman
Exec: Chris Carlson
Prgrm Mgr: Manuel Hernandez
MIS Dir: Patricia Cox
Opers Mgr: Joffe Chuck
Opers Mgr: Donna Wolf
Snr Mgr: Noel Diaz

D-U-N-S 10-392-7257
ROBERT CO INC J E
J E ROBERT
1250 Connecticut Ave Nw # 700, Washington, DC 20036-2657
Tel (703) 714-8000 Founded/Ownrshp 1981
Sales 133.2MM[E] EMP 4,732
SIC 7011 Hotels & motels
CEO: Barden Gale
Ch Bd: Joseph E Robert Jr
Pr: Michael Pralle
VP: Gary Baron

ROBERT CO INC J E MCLEAN VA
See JER PARTNERS LLC

ROBERT COMPANY MARYLAND, J. E
See JAMESON INNS INC

D-U-N-S 82-631-0398
ROBERT FAMILY HOLDINGS INC
R F H
12430 Tesson Ferry Rd, Saint Louis, MO 63128-2702
Tel (314) 821-5665 Founded/Ownrshp 2008
Sales 145.9MM[E] EMP 553
SIC 2671 3572 3491 3498 7699 3494 Packaging paper & plastics film, coated & laminated; Computer storage devices; Pressure valves & regulators, industrial; Pipe fittings, fabricated from purchased pipe; Valve repair, industrial; Valves & pipe fittings
CEO: David Gilchrist
Pr: Jay Longbottom
Treas: Robert Bowron
Sec: C J Hagemann
Prin: Richard Schwartze

ROBERT GRAHAM
See RG PARENT LLC

D-U-N-S 12-101-8886 IMP/EXP
■ ROBERT GRAHAM DESIGNS LLC
(Suby of ROBERT GRAHAM) ★
264 W 40th St Fl 10, New York, NY 10018-1516
Tel (212) 869-8001 Founded/Ownrshp 2001
Sales 212.5MM[E] EMP 100
SIC 5137 5136 Apparel belts, women's & children's; Men's & boys' clothing
CEO: Michael F Buckley

D-U-N-S 04-325-6403 IMP
▲ ROBERT HALF INTERNATIONAL INC
2884 Sand Hill Rd Ste 200, Menlo Park, CA 94025-7059
Tel (650) 234-6000 Founded/Ownrshp 1948
Sales 5.0MMM EMP 16,100
Tkr Sym RHI Exch NYS
SIC 7363 7361 8748 8721 Temporary help service; Placement agencies; Business consulting; Auditing services
Ch Bd: Harold M Messmer Jr
Pr: Paul F Gentzkow
*Pr: M Keith Waddell
Ofcr: Michael C Buckley
Ex VP: Mike Buckley
Ex VP: Andy Denka
Ex VP: Robert W Glass
Ex VP: Lynn Justin
Ex VP: David King
Sr VP: Sean Perry
VP: Gregg Brandon
VP: Jill Crowe
VP: David Ezra
VP: Jean Gauthier
VP: Stan Godbehere
VP: Jen Green
VP: Frank Karlinski
VP: Tami McEldowney
VP: Anne Meehan
VP: John Owen
VP: Kirk Schwerzler
Board of Directors: Andrew S Berwick Jr, Marc H Morial, Barbara J Novogradac, Robert J Pace, Frederick A Richman

ROBERT HEELY CONSTRUCTION
See ROBERT HEELY INC

D-U-N-S 09-786-2189
ROBERT HEELY INC
ROBERT HEELY CONSTRUCTION
5401 Woodmere Dr, Bakersfield, CA 93313-2777
Tel (661) 617-1400 Founded/Ownrshp 1974
Sales 133.8MM[E] EMP 350
SIC 1623 Oil & gas pipeline construction
Ch: Robert Heely
*Pr: Craig Bonna
*CFO: Scott Erwin
*VP: Jeff Hanesworth
IT Man: Joe Carnevali

ROBERT HILL CONSTRUCTION CO
See HILLCO LTD

D-U-N-S 03-485-3010
ROBERT J YOUNG CO INC
R. J. YOUNG COMPANY
809 Division St, Nashville, TN 37203-4108
Tel (615) 255-8551 Founded/Ownrshp 1985
Sales 243.0MM[E] EMP 369
SIC 5044 Duplicating machines; Photocopy machines
Ch Bd: John T Crunk
*CEO: Chip Crunk
*COO: Hunter McCarty
*CFO: Frank Norfleet Abston
*VP: Phil Kirby
Dir IT: Joey Lush
Opers Mgr: Doug Montgomery
Opers Mgr: Rj Young
Mktg Dir: Chasity Fox
Sls Dir: Brantley Pearce
Sls Dir: Kerry Pelham

D-U-N-S 09-798-6236 IMP/EXP
ROBERT MADDEN INDUSTRIES LTD
PASCHAL HARPER
6021 43rd St, Lubbock, TX 79407-3712
Tel (806) 797-4251 Founded/Ownrshp 1979
Sales 131.1MM EMP 140
SIC 5075

D-U-N-S 09-485-1250
ROBERT N KARPP CO INC
480 E 1st St, Boston, MA 02127-1320
Tel (617) 269-5880 Founded/Ownrshp 1979
Sales 106.9MM[E] EMP 114
SIC 5031 1799

ROBERT ORR SYSCO
See SYSCO NASHVILLE LLC

D-U-N-S 06-959-8332
ROBERT PACKER HOSPITAL
(Suby of GUTHRIE CLINIC) ★
1 Guthrie Sq Ste B, Sayre, PA 18840-1698
Tel (570) 888-6666 Founded/Ownrshp 1885, 2001
Sales 324.7MM EMP 1,400
Accts Lb Pricewaterhousecoopers Llp
SIC 8062 General medical & surgical hospitals
Prin: Joseph A Scopelliti
*CFO: Minh Dang
Dir Lab: Ceil Miller
Pathlgst: Ricky Heartman
Pharmcst: Karen Leonard

D-U-N-S 03-424-3579
ROBERT R MCCORMICK FOUNDATION
205 N Michigan Ave # 4300, Chicago, IL 60601-5983
Tel (312) 445-5000 Founded/Ownrshp 2009
Sales 106.3MM EMP 35[E]
SIC 8641 8699 Civic social & fraternal associations; Charitable organization
CEO: David Hiller

D-U-N-S 13-121-1229
ROBERT V ROHRMAN INC
SCHAUMBURG HONDA AUTOMOBILE
750 E Golf Rd, Schaumburg, IL 60173-4512
Tel (847) 884-6632 Founded/Ownrshp 1984
Sales 235.5MM[E] EMP 1,000
SIC 5511 6159 Automobiles, new & used; Automobile finance leasing
Pr: Robert V Rohrman
*Prin: Crystal Jones
*Genl Mgr: Ryan Rohrman
Sls Mgr: Roger Love

D-U-N-S 05-529-6347
ROBERT W BAIRD & CO INC
(Suby of BAIRD FINANCIAL CORP) ★
777 E Wisconsin Ave Fl 29, Milwaukee, WI 53202-5391
Tel (414) 765-3500 Founded/Ownrshp 2004
Sales 1.4MMM[E] EMP 2,212[E]
SIC 6719 Investment holding companies, except banks
Pr: Steve Booth
CFO: Terrance Maxwell
Ch: Paul E Purcell
Ex VP: Peter Banzhaf
VP: John P Abels
VP: Clifford Asmuth
VP: Joseph Bosko
VP: David Bowman
VP: Philip Dallman
VP: Bryce Edwards
VP: Dennis B Engel
VP: Anton Faupl
VP: Joshua Fiedler
VP: Kenneth A Fox
VP: Paula Reichardt Garcia
VP: George J Gaspar
VP: Thomas J Gerger
VP: Kate Gough
VP: William Gray
VP: Frederick R Jetter
VP: Stephen Keane

D-U-N-S 04-303-1525
ROBERT W BAKER NURSERY INC
1700 Mountain Rd, West Suffield, CT 06093-3305
Tel (860) 668-7371 Founded/Ownrshp 1966
Sales 105.9MM[E] EMP 490
SIC 5193 5261 Nursery stock; Nurseries & garden centers
Ch Bd: Robert W Baker Sr
*Pr: Dale A Baker
*VP: Robert W Baker Jr
VP: Thomas Dlugos

D-U-N-S 96-702-5177
ROBERT W WILSON CHARITABLE TRUST
520 83rd St, Brooklyn, NY 11209-4559
Tel (718) 748-6113 Founded/Ownrshp 2011
Sales 105.4MM EMP 2
Accts Anchin Block & Anchin Llp New
SIC 8699 Charitable organization
Prin: Robert W Wilson

D-U-N-S 06-917-7194 IMP
ROBERT W WOODRUFF ARTS CENTER INC
ATLANTA SYMPHONY ORCHESTRA
1280 Peachtree St Ne, Atlanta, GA 30309-3502
Tel (404) 733-4200 Founded/Ownrshp 1905
Sales 105.2MM EMP 524
Accts Smith & Howard Pc Atlanta Ga
SIC 7929 8412 6512 8299 Symphony orchestras; Museum; Theater building, ownership & operation; Arts & crafts schools
CEO: Virginia A Hepner
*CFO: Noel M Barnes
Trst: Tim Bentsen
Trst: Brad Branch
*Ex VP: Stephen P Merz
Store Mgr: Mary B Megrew
VP Opers: Michael Flood

D-U-N-S 80-863-9343
ROBERT W WOODRUFF ARTS CENTER INC
1280 Peachtree St Ne, Atlanta, GA 30309-3502
Tel (404) 733-4200 Founded/Ownrshp 1905
Sales 113.1MM EMP 19[E]
SIC 8412 Museums & art galleries
CEO: Joseph R Bankoff
*CFO: Stephen P Merz

D-U-N-S 79-044-7150
ROBERT W WOODRUFF FOUNDATION INC
191 Peachtree St Ne, Atlanta, GA 30303-1740
Tel (404) 522-6755 Founded/Ownrshp 2007
Sales 89.9MM EMP 2
SIC 6733 Trusts
Pr: Charles McTier
Treas: Lee J Tribble
Ofcr: Jenny Morgan

D-U-N-S 04-153-4132 IMP
ROBERT WEED PLYWOOD CORP
705 Maple St, Bristol, IN 46507-9103
Tel (574) 848-7631 Founded/Ownrshp 1966
Sales 221.8MM[E] EMP 350
SIC 5031 2435 2431 Plywood; Panels, hardwood plywood; Moldings & baseboards, ornamental & trim; Moldings, wood: unfinished & prefinished
Pr: David Weed
COO: Mark Fiquett
VP: Matt Bunner
*VP: Thomas Longworth
Sls Mgr: Dave Ramundo

D-U-N-S 02-078-4906
ROBERT WOOD JOHNSON UNIVERSITY HOSPITAL
1 Robert Wood Johnson Pl, New Brunswick, NJ 08901-1928
Tel (732) 828-3000 Founded/Ownrshp 1884
Sales 1.2MMM EMP 4,674[E]
SIC 8062 Hospital, medical school affiliated with residency
Pr: Stephen K Jones
*Ch Bd: John Hoffman
Pr: Julie Arsenault
Pr: Kari Mastro
*CFO: John Gantner
Ex VP: Vincent Josephs
*Sr VP: Judith Burgis
VP: Lori Colineri
VP: Anirban Dass
VP: David Fernandez
VP: Larry Garinello
Exec: Timothy Gee
Exec: Elizabeth Maldonado
Dir Risk M: Doug Kimball
Dir Lab: Sue Chinery
Assoc Dir: Jack Jegou
Dir Soc: Rachael Fonseca
Dir Soc: Elizabeth Kleber

Dir Rad: James Cucco
Dir Rx: Pam Hildebrandt

D-U-N-S 07-551-6435
ROBERT WOOD JOHNSON UNIVERSITY HOSPITAL AT HAMILTON
1 Hamilton Health Pl # 2, Hamilton, NJ 08690-3542
Tel (609) 586-7900 *Founded/Ownrshp* 1941
Sales 191.8MM *EMP* 1,548
SIC 8062 General medical & surgical hospitals
CEO: Anthony J Cimino
V Ch: Barkat Jaferi
V Ch: Richard Siderits
Pr: Frederick Jacobs
COO: Barbara Smith
CFO: Gil Cottle
CFO: James Maher
CFO: Pete Newell
Treas: Lasanta Horana
Ofcr: Jan Stout
Sr VP: Rick Lovering
VP: Bruce Colligan
VP: Karyn Kaplan
VP: Javier Villota
Dir Lab: Barbara Dotsey
Dir Lab: Carol Kennedy
Dir Rad: Jim Kilmer

D-U-N-S 09-926-8567
ROBERT WOOD JOHNSON UNIVERSITY HOSPITAL AT RAHWAY
865 Stone St, Rahway, NJ 07065-2742
Tel (732) 381-4200 *Founded/Ownrshp* 1917
Sales 109.7MM *EMP* 700^E
SIC 8062 General medical & surgical hospitals
Pr: Kirk C Tice
Chf Rad: Gary Kronfeld
CFO: Pete Bihunaik
**VP:* Peter P Bihuniak
**VP:* Lynn M Kearney
**VP:* Barbara Mullery
VP: Arleen Tomchic
VP: Arlene Tomchik
Dir Rad: Bob White
Ex Dir: Irena Kaler
Ex Dir: Kathy Young

ROBERTS COMPANY, THE
See ROBERTS CO FIELD SERVICES INC

D-U-N-S 83-222-4229
■ ROBERTS CO FIELD SERVICES INC
ROBERTS COMPANY, THE
(*Suby of* ARGAN INC) ★
133 Forlines Rd, Winterville, NC 28590-8508
Tel (252) 355-9353 *Founded/Ownrshp* 2015
Sales 272.5MM^E *EMP* 800
SIC 1541 Industrial buildings, new construction
Pr: D Chris Bailey
**COO:* Rm Monty Glover
**CFO:* D Lee Barnett
**Ex VP:* T Jason Dunaway
VP: Kevin F Bryan
VP: Russell Roberson
VP: William Smyth
Sfty Mgr: Tim Coltrain
Sales Exec: Tom Harvey
VP Sls: Charles Mullinax

D-U-N-S 04-274-6537
ROBERTS DAIRY CO LLC (IL)
HILAND DAIRY FOOD
2901 Cuming St, Omaha, NE 68131-2108
Tel (402) 344-4321 *Founded/Ownrshp* 1906, 1981
Sales 146.6MM^E *EMP* 320
SIC 2026 5812 Milk processing (pasteurizing, homogenizing, bottling); Cream, aerated; Cottage cheese; Eating places
Div Mgr: Garry Bond
Off Mgr: Donald Fisher
Dir IT: Norvin Bunselmeyer
Sfty Dirs: Richard Dimon

ROBERTS HAWAII
See ROBERTS HAWAII INC

D-U-N-S 09-463-6297
ROBERTS HAWAII INC
ROBERTS HAWAII
680 Iwilei Rd Ste 700, Honolulu, HI 96817-5392
Tel (808) 523-7750 *Founded/Ownrshp* 1978
Sales 133.5MM^E *EMP* 1,400
SIC 4119 4724 7011 4489 Sightseeing bus; Travel agencies; Resort hotel; Sightseeing boats
**CEO:* Robert N Jr Iwamoto
**CFO:* Shari A Komo-Matsueda
VP: Roy Pfund
**VP:* Pfund Roy
Exec: Roger Dikon
Genl Mgr: Aaron Kimura
Genl Mgr: Teri Takamura
Sls Mgr: Alex Tolhurst

D-U-N-S 04-264-6877 IMP
ROBERTS OXYGEN CO INC
15830 Redland Rd, Rockville, MD 20855-2203
Tel (301) 315-9090 *Founded/Ownrshp* 1966
Sales 121.7MM^E *EMP* 286
Accts Strack Stanfield Llc Rockvill
SIC 5085 5169 5047 Cans for fruits & vegetables; Compressed gas; Oxygen; Medical & hospital equipment
Pr: William P Roberts III
CFO: Martin Begley
VP: Jim Davis
**VP:* Margaret L Roberts
Exec: Wayne Ferber
Brnch Mgr: Andre Butler
Brnch Mgr: Mark Eades
Genl Mgr: Ruth Castro
Store Mgr: Brian Hickman
Store Mgr: Michael Post
QA Dir: James Burns

D-U-N-S 09-463-6354
ROBERTS TOURS AND TRANSPORTATION INC
(*Suby of* ROBERTS HAWAII) ★
680 Iwilei Rd Ste 700, Honolulu, HI 96817-5392
Tel (808) 523-7750 *Founded/Ownrshp* 1986
Sales 63.8MM^E *EMP* 1,800
SIC 4119 Sightseeing bus
Pr: Robert Iwamoto Jr
**Treas:* Roy Phund

D-U-N-S 80-541-2921
ROBERTS TRUCK CENTER HOLDING CO LLC
SUMMIT HOLDINGS
1825 Lakeway Dr Ste 700, Lewisville, TX 75057-6047
Tel (469) 645-7111 *Founded/Ownrshp* 1974
Sales 268.2MM^E *EMP* 1,212
SIC 5012 7513 7538 Trucks, commercial; Trailers for trucks, new & used; Truck rental & leasing, no drivers; General truck repair
CEO: Blair N Roberts
**Pr:* Justin Fink

D-U-N-S 08-006-7102
ROBERTS TRUCK CENTER OF OKLAHOMA LLC (OK)
SUMMIT TRUCK GROUP
1023 N Garnett Rd, Tulsa, OK 74116-2002
Tel (918) 438-2000 *Founded/Ownrshp* 2007
Sales 42.4MM^E *EMP* 1,400
SIC 3713 Truck & bus bodies; Truck bodies & parts

D-U-N-S 05-255-6677
ROBERTS-GIBSON INC (TN)
BP
115 Highway 51 Byp, Dyersburg, TN 38024-4538
Tel (731) 285-4941 *Founded/Ownrshp* 1970
Sales 104.0MM *EMP* 25
SIC 5171 5541 Petroleum bulk stations; Filling stations, gasoline
Pr: Larry Gibson
**CFO:* Brad Carraway
**Sec:* Timothy Gibson
**VP:* Jane R Gibson

D-U-N-S 00-210-6466 IMP
ROBERTS-GORDON LLC
RG
(*Suby of* SPECIFIED AIR SOLUTIONS)
1250 William St, Buffalo, NY 14206-1819
Tel (716) 852-4400 *Founded/Ownrshp* 1998, 2014
Sales 90.4MM^E *EMP* 370
SIC 3675 3433 Condensers, electronic; Unit heaters, domestic
Pr: Mark J Dines
**CFO:* Richard G Jasiura
VP: Mark Murdoch
Sfty Mgr: Kevin Shamrock
Snr Mgr: Paul Sullivan

D-U-N-S 61-033-6708 IMP/EXP
ROBERTSHAW CONTROLS CO
(*Suby of* SUN CAPITAL PARTNERS INC) ★
1222 Hamilton Pkwy, Itasca, IL 60143-1160
Tel (630) 260-3400 *Founded/Ownrshp* 1986
Sales 665.5MM^E *EMP* 5,400
SIC 3823 3822 3492 Industrial instrmnts msrmnt display/control process variable; Auto controls regulating residntl & coml environmt & applncs; Control valves, aircraft: hydraulic & pneumatic
Pr: Mark Balcunas
Ql Cn Mgr: Rick Delvaux

D-U-N-S 18-418-6633
ROBERTSON COUNTY SCHOOL DISTRICT
800 Ms Couts Blvd Ste 2, Springfield, TN 37172-2799
Tel (615) 384-5588 *Founded/Ownrshp* 1950
Sales 72.7MM^E *EMP* 1,350
SIC 8211 Public elementary & secondary schools
V Ch: Jeff White
Top Exec: Brenda Gainous
Dir IT: Jeff Crawford
Dir IT: Melinda Thompson
Schl Brd P: Stoney Crockett

D-U-N-S 08-003-8216
ROBERTSON FOUNDATION
101 Park Ave Fl 48, New York, NY 10178-4799
Tel (212) 984-5714 *Founded/Ownrshp* 1961
Sales 98.9MM *EMP* 2^E
SIC 8699 Charitable organization
Founder: Julian Robertson
Ex Dir: Julia Bator

D-U-N-S 79-902-5171 EXP
■ ROBERTSON-CECO II CORP
(*Suby of* NCI BUILDING SYSTEMS INC) ★
10943 N Sam Huston Pkwy W, Houston, TX 77064-5758
Tel (281) 897-7788 *Founded/Ownrshp* 2006
Sales 289.6MM^E *EMP* 1,700^E
SIC 3448 Prefabricated metal buildings
Pr: Norman C Chambers
Pr: Michelle Barreda
**Treas:* Mark E Johnson
Bd of Dir: Gary Forbes
Bd of Dir: George Martinez
Ex VP: Leonard George
Ex VP: Kelly Ginn
VP: Patrick Griffin
VP: William Lawrence
VP: Al Richey
VP: Stephen Theall
VP: R Todd

D-U-N-S 08-117-6885 IMP
ROBERTSONS READY MIX LTD A CALIFORNIA LIMITED PARTNERSHIP
200 S Main St Ste 200, Corona, CA 92882-2212
Tel (951) 493-6500 *Founded/Ownrshp* 1991
Sales 655.9MM^E *EMP* 1,760
SIC 3273 3531 5032 2951 1442 Ready-mixed concrete; Bituminous, cement & concrete related products & equipment; Asphalt plant, including gravel-mix type; Concrete plants; Asphalt mixture; Paving mixtures; Concrete mixtures; Asphalt paving mixtures & blocks; Construction sand & gravel
Pt: Jon Troesh
Genl Mgr: Kaye Bennett
IT Man: Curt Perales

D-U-N-S 62-655-9660
ROBIN HOOD FOUNDATION
826 Broadway Fl 9, New York, NY 10003-4826
Tel (212) 227-6601 *Founded/Ownrshp* 1988
Sales 142.4MM *EMP* 77^E
Accts Grant Thornton Llp New York
SIC 8699 8322 Charitable organization; Individual & family services
Ch Bd: David Einhorn
**Pr:* Reynold Levy
**Pr:* Deborah Winshel
CFO: Beth Zolkind
**Sr VP:* Michael Weinstein
**Prin:* Laura Arnold
**Prin:* Emma Bloomberg
**Prin:* Laurence D Fink
**Prin:* Roland G Fryer Jr
**Prin:* Philippe Laffont
Ex Dir: Doris Cadoux
Board of Directors: Laura Arnold, Emma Bloomberg, Laurence D Fink, Roland G Fryer Jr, Philippe Laffont

D-U-N-S 10-682-8085 EXP
ROBINDALE ENERGY SERVICES INC
1 Lloyd Ave Fl 2, Latrobe, PA 15650
Tel (814) 446-6700 *Founded/Ownrshp* 2000
Sales 145.0MM^E *EMP* 100^E
SIC 5052 Coal
Pr: Martin Powers
**CFO:* James R Martin
**Treas:* Marie McCombs
**VP:* John Blohm
**VP:* Scott Kroh

D-U-N-S 79-869-6928
ROBINS & MORTON GROUP
400 Shades Creek Pkwy, Birmingham, AL 35209-4454
Tel (205) 870-1000 *Founded/Ownrshp* 2004
Sales 912.3MM^E *EMP* 875
SIC 1542 Commercial & office building contractors; Hospital construction
Pr: Bill Morton
**Ch Bd:* Barry Morton
**COO:* Robin Savage
**CFO:* Edward Cassady
CFO: John Connor
**Sr VP:* Bryson Edmonds
Sr VP: Bryson G Edmonds
**Sr VP:* Robert Gambrell
**Sr VP:* Rocky McMichen
**Sr VP:* Jim Poole
**VP:* Phil Yance
Exec: Michael Corwin

ROBINS KAPLAN MILLER & CIRESI
See LLP ROBINS KAPLAN

D-U-N-S 05-557-6813
ROBINSON & COLE LLP
280 Trumbull St Fl 28, Hartford, CT 06103-3597
Tel (860) 275-8200 *Founded/Ownrshp* 1845
Sales 84.1MM^E *EMP* 499
SIC 8111

ROBINSON CONSTRUCTION COMPANY
See ROBINSON MECHANICAL CONTRACTORS INC

ROBINSON CUSTOM ENCLOSURES
See ROBINSON METAL INC

D-U-N-S 07-777-9304
ROBINSON HEALTH SYSTEM INC
UNIVERSITY HOSPITAL PORTAGE MEDICAL CENTER
(*Suby of* UNIVERSITY HOSPITALS HEALTH SYSTEM INC) ★
6847 N Chestnut St, Ravenna, OH 44266-3929
Tel (330) 297-0811 *Founded/Ownrshp* 1905
Sales 160.5MM *EMP* 26,000
SIC 8062 8011 General medical & surgical hospitals; Offices & clinics of medical doctors
Pr: Stephen Colecchi
**Pr:* Bradley Raum
Trst: Norman Sandvoss
Trst: Larry Wright
Trst: Mark Yankovich
**VP:* Linda Breedlove
**VP:* Neil Everett
VP: Stephen Francis
VP: Robert J Sinsheimer
VP: Deborah C Small
Ex Dir: Deborah Solan

D-U-N-S 07-963-0414 IMP/EXP
ROBINSON HELICOPTER CO INC (CA)
2901 Airport Dr, Torrance, CA 90505-6115
Tel (310) 539-0508 *Founded/Ownrshp* 1973
Sales 228.8MM^E *EMP* 970
SIC 3721 Helicopters
CEO: Kurt L Robinson
**Pr:* Frank Robinson
**CFO:* Tim Goetz
VP: Jim Strom
Dir IT: Dennis Dyer
**VP Mfg:* P Wayne Walden
Ql Cn Mgr: David Hanners
Sls Dir: Terry Hane

D-U-N-S 00-332-8986 IMP/EXP
ROBINSON MANUFACTURING CO (TN)
798 Market St, Dayton, TN 37321-1473
Tel (423) 775-8331 *Founded/Ownrshp* 1927
Sales 113.0MM^E *EMP* 380
Accts Lattimore Black Morgan & Cain
SIC 2322 2339 2329 Underwear, men's & boys': made from purchased materials; Athletic clothing: women's, misses' & juniors'; Athletic (warmup, sweat & jogging) suits: men's & boys'
Pr: Patrick Robinson
**Sec:* Richard Ferrell
**VP:* Ray Griffin
VP: Stan Henderson
MIS Dir: Fred Coulter
Mktg Mgr: Cathy Griffin

D-U-N-S 03-735-7571
ROBINSON MECHANICAL CONTRACTORS INC
ROBINSON CONSTRUCTION COMPANY
2411 Walters Ln, Perryville, MO 63775-3320
Tel (573) 547-8397 *Founded/Ownrshp* 1979
Sales 103.6MM *EMP* 200
Accts Stanley Dirnberger Hopper An
SIC 1629 1711 Industrial plant construction; Waste water & sewage treatment plant construction; Mechanical contractor
Pr: Francis Robinson
**Treas:* Kevin Schade
**VP:* Paul Findlay

D-U-N-S 07-477-4860 EXP
ROBINSON METAL INC
ROBINSON CUSTOM ENCLOSURES
1740 Eisenhower Rd, De Pere, WI 54115-8148
Tel (920) 494-7411 *Founded/Ownrshp* 1975
Sales 130.1MM^E *EMP* 310
SIC 3444 3443 3599 Sheet metalwork; Fabricated plate work (boiler shop); Machine & other job shop work; Machine shop, jobbing & repair
Pr: Darrell Lacrosse
**VP:* Todd Robinson
IT Man: Jim Pelishek
Ql Cn Mgr: Joe Arttus
VP Sls: Tom Verboncouer

D-U-N-S 06-913-7685
ROBINSON OIL CORP
ROTTEN ROBBIE
955 Martin Ave, Santa Clara, CA 95050-2608
Tel (408) 327-4300 *Founded/Ownrshp* 1964
Sales 468.7MM *EMP* 250
SIC 5541 5411 Filling stations, gasoline; Convenience stores, independent
Pr: Thomas L Robinson
**CFO:* Stephen F White
IT Man: Brian Watson

D-U-N-S 05-579-4762
ROBINSON OIL SUPPLY & TRANSPORT INC
(*Suby of* ROTTEN ROBBIE) ★
955 Martin Ave, Santa Clara, CA 95050-2608
Tel (408) 327-4300 *Founded/Ownrshp* 2000
Sales 278.6MM *EMP* 15
SIC 5172 Petroleum products
Pr: Thomas L Robinson
**CFO:* Stephen F White

D-U-N-S 83-156-0578 IMP
ROBINSON PHARMA INC
3330 S Harbor Blvd, Santa Ana, CA 92704-6831
Tel (714) 241-0235 *Founded/Ownrshp* 1994
Sales 116.6MM^E *EMP* 420
SIC 2834 Pharmaceutical preparations
CEO: Tam H Nguyen
**Pr:* Tuong Nguyen
Sr VP: Suliman Jahangiri
VP: Zue Delaney
VP: David Gao
VP: Gerard McCann
VP: Neil Shah
VP: Jahangiri Suliman
Exec: Michelle Nguyen
QA Dir: Tuan Tran
QA Dir: Tiffany Yang

D-U-N-S 92-843-6005
■ ROBINSON PROPERTY GROUP LIMITED PARTNERSHIP
(*Suby of* CAESARS ENTERTAINMENT CORP) ★
1021 Casino Center Dr, Robinsonville, MS 38664-9708
Tel (662) 357-5500 *Founded/Ownrshp* 2000
Sales 27.3MM^E *EMP* 3,000
SIC 7011 5813 5812 Hotels; Drinking places; Eating places
Genl Mgr: Bob Mc Queen

D-U-N-S 07-983-6020
ROC HOLDINGS LLC
(*Suby of* CORAL REEF CAPITAL GROUP LLC) ★
191 Energy Way, Bridgeport, TX 76426
Tel (940) 683-0159 *Founded/Ownrshp* 2015
Sales 124.5MM^E *EMP* 600^E
SIC 1794 1731 6719 Excavation & grading, building construction; Energy management controls; Investment holding companies, except banks
Pr: Michael Richey
**CFO:* Paul Coscia

D-U-N-S 83-140-1786
ROC SERVICE CO LLC
(*Suby of* ROC HOLDINGS LLC) ★
191 Energy Way, Bridgeport, TX 76426
Tel (940) 683-0109 *Founded/Ownrshp* 2009
Sales 129.3MM^E *EMP* 600^E
SIC 1794 1731 1389 Excavation & grading, building construction; Energy management controls; Building oil & gas well foundations on site; Roustabout service; Servicing oil & gas wells
Pr: Michael Richey
**CFO:* Paul Coscia
Sr VP: Robert Johnson

D-U-N-S 07-975-5312
ROCTX LAKESIDE LLC (UT)
(*Suby of* BRIDGE INVESTMENT GROUP PARTNERS LLC) ★
1455 Lakeside Estates Dr, Houston, TX 77042-2225
Tel (801) 284-5960 *Founded/Ownrshp* 2011
Sales 16.8MM^E *EMP* 1,000
SIC 8741 Management services
Prin: Danuel R Stanger

D-U-N-S 01-950-3812 IMP
ROCHE BROS SUPERMARKETS INC
SUDBURY FARMS
70 Hastings St Ste 1, Wellesley, MA 02481-5439
Tel (781) 235-9400 *Founded/Ownrshp* 1952
Sales 446.0MM^E *EMP* 3,300
SIC 5411 Supermarkets, chain
Pr: Gary Pfeil
Recvr: Ray Coakley
**Pr:* Edward Roche

*CEO: Patrick E Roche Jr
*CFO: Dale Shores
*Ch: Patrick E Roche Sr
Div Mgr: Charlie Shanks
Store Mgr: Peter Keenan
VP Merchng: Paul McGillivray
Merch Mgr: Bob Stanton

D-U-N-S 00-182-4663 IMP/EXP
■ ROCHE DIAGNOSTICS CORP
(Suby of ROCHE HOLDINGS INC) ★
9115 Hague Rd, Indianapolis, IN 46256-1045
Tel (800) 428-5076 Founded/Ownrshp 1998
Sales 1.5MMM^E EMP 4,400
SIC 2835 In vitro & in vivo diagnostic substances
CEO: Jack Phillips
*CFO: Wayne Burris
*Treas: Scott Wilson
VP: Henry Bennett
VP: Tom Kegley
*VP: Steve A Oldham
VP: URS Schleuniger
Exec: Stephen Flynn
Genl Mgr: Kyle Fox
IT Man: Travis Knapp
VP Opers: Robert Yates

D-U-N-S 96-630-2585
ROCHE EMPLOYEE WELFARE BENEFIT TRUST
340 Kingsland St, Nutley, NJ 07110-1150
Tel (973) 235-5000 Founded/Ownrshp 2011
Sales 374.9MM EMP 2
SIC 6733 Trusts

D-U-N-S 18-907-5674 IMP/EXP
■ ROCHE HOLDINGS INC
(Suby of ROCHE HOLDING AG)
1 Dna Way, South San Francisco, CA 94080-4918
Tel (625) 225-1000 Founded/Ownrshp 1987
Sales 7.4MMM^E EMP 16,760
SIC 2834 2833 2835 2869 Pharmaceutical preparations; Druggists' preparations (pharmaceuticals); Veterinary pharmaceutical preparations; Medicinal chemicals; Radioactive diagnostic substances; Industrial organic chemicals
Pr: Franz B Humer
*Treas: Scott D Wilson
*VP: Carol Fiederlein
*VP: Dr Erich Hunziker
Dir Bus: Mike Macnulty
Snr Mgr: Amy Bachrodt

D-U-N-S 96-430-3945
■ ROCHE LABORATORIES INC
(Suby of HOFFMANN-LA ROCHE INC) ★
340 Kingsland St, Nutley, NJ 07110-1150
Tel (973) 235-5000 Founded/Ownrshp 1995
Sales 59.8MM^E EMP 2,800
SIC 8071 Medical laboratories
Pr: George Abercrombie
Top Exec: David C Fry
VP: Ernest Knesel
VP: Michelle Zupancic
Assoc Dir: Edward Conti
Genl Mgr: Becky Butler
CIO: Karl H Koelker
IT Man: Charlie Poynter
Mfg Dir: Christiane Rast
Mktg Mgr: Aime Chidester
Counsel: Marc E Fishman

D-U-N-S 88-323-8743 IMP/EXP
■ ROCHE MOLECULAR SYSTEMS INC
(Suby of ROCHE HOLDINGS INC) ★
4300 Hacienda Dr, Pleasanton, CA 94588-2722
Tel (925) 730-8000 Founded/Ownrshp 1991
Sales 201.4MM^E EMP 1,000
SIC 8731 Biotechnical research, commercial
Pr: Paul Brown
Software D: Fidel Fampo

ROCHE TISSUE DIAGNOSTICS
See VENTANA MEDICAL SYSTEMS INC

D-U-N-S 80-632-1089
■ ROCHELLE FOODS LLC
(Suby of HORMEL FOODS CORP) ★
1001 S Main St, Rochelle, IL 61068-2190
Tel (815) 562-4141 Founded/Ownrshp 2005
Sales 98.2MM^E EMP 700
SIC 2013 2011 Sausages & other prepared meats; Meat packing plants
IT Man: Meg Smith
Sfty Dirs: Paul Hardcastel

D-U-N-S 11-405-8175
ROCHESTER CITY SCHOOL DISTRICT
CENTRAL ADMINISTRATIVE OFFICES
131 W Broad St, Rochester, NY 14614-1103
Tel (585) 262-8100 Founded/Ownrshp 1841
Sales 756.9MM EMP 5,470
Accts Freedmaxick Cpas Pc Roches
SIC 8211 Public elementary & secondary schools
*Pr: Malik Evans
Treas: Kathleen Lamb
*VP: Jose Cruz
VP: Ed O'Machelley
*VP: Van Henri White
Dir Sec: Lori Baldwin
Telecom Ex: Angelo Palmerini
Software D: Todd Zdanowski
Teacher Pr: Harry Kennedy
Board of Directors: Shirley Jung

D-U-N-S 00-221-9939
■ ROCHESTER COCA COLA BOTTLING CORP
COCA-COLA
(Suby of COCA-COLA REFRESHMENTS USA INC) ★
300 Oak St, Pittston, PA 18640-3719
Tel (570) 655-2874 Founded/Ownrshp 1906, 1986
Sales 113.7MM^E EMP 1,200
SIC 2086 5962 Soft drinks: packaged in cans, bottles, etc.; Merchandising machine operators
Pr: Roger D Williams
*Treas: Michael B Melnic

D-U-N-S 07-277-5356
ROCHESTER COMMUNITY SCHOOLS
501 W University Dr, Rochester, MI 48307-1944
Tel (248) 726-3000 Founded/Ownrshp 1949
Sales 57.8MM^E EMP 1,225
Accts Doeren Mayhew Troy Michigan
SIC 8211 Public elementary & secondary schools
Ex Dir: Melinda C Callahan
Ex Dir: Carrie Lawler
Genl Mgr: Jamie Kendall-Dent
CIO: Jeff Moz
Psych: Jennifer Otoole-Seyka

D-U-N-S 00-983-2023
ROCHESTER DRUG CO-OPERATIVE INC
R D C
50 Jetview Dr, Rochester, NY 14624-4900
Tel (585) 271-7220 Founded/Ownrshp 1928
Sales 576.7MM^E EMP 124^E
SIC 5122 Drugs & drug proprietaries; Druggists' sundries
CEO: Lawrence Doud
CFO: Kim Perry
IT Man: Lynn Crane
Software D: Thomas Hamilton
Opers Mgr: Bill Pietruszewski
Sls Mgr: Bill Wood

D-U-N-S 00-699-4040
■ ROCHESTER GAS AND ELECTRIC CORP
RG&E
(Suby of AVANGRID INC) ★
89 East Ave, Rochester, NY 14649-0002
Tel (800) 295-7323 Founded/Ownrshp 2012
Sales 631.8MM^E EMP 865
Accts Pricewaterhousecoopers Llp P
SIC 4911 4924 Electric services; Distribution, electric power; Generation, electric power; Transmission, electric power; Natural gas distribution
Pr: Mark S Lynch
CFO: Daniel Alcain
CFO: J B Stokes
CFO: Mary Stokes
Treas: Mark Keogh
Treas: Joseph J Syta
Ofcr: Jessica S Raine
Sr VP: Michael T Tomaino
VP: Louis Bellina
VP: Douglas Herling
VP: David Irish
VP: Clifton Olson
VP: Paul Ruganis
Board of Directors: Robert E Rude,wesley W Von

D-U-N-S 87-994-5863
ROCHESTER GENERAL HEALTH SYSTEM
1425 Portland Ave, Rochester, NY 14621-3001
Tel (585) 922-4000 Founded/Ownrshp 2006
Sales 1.0MMM^E EMP 6,000
Accts Ernst & Young Us Llp Buffal
SIC 8741 8093 8059 Hospital management; Mental health clinic, outpatient; Rest home, with health care
CEO: Mark Clement
CFO: Robert Nesselbush
Sr VP: Cheryl Sheridan
VP: Jonathan C Comune
VP: Katherine Rogala
Prgrm Mgr: Cara Klein
Nurse Mgr: Diana Blauw
Nurse Mgr: Susan Breese
Nurse Mgr: Lynda Dinolfo
CTO: Karen Humbert
Dir IT: Ortia Fortia

D-U-N-S 04-307-8385
ROCHESTER GENERAL HOSPITAL INC (NY)
(Suby of ROCHESTER GENERAL HEALTH SYSTEM) ★
1425 Portland Ave, Rochester, NY 14621-3095
Tel (585) 922-4101 Founded/Ownrshp 1847
Sales 847.5MM EMP 3,100
SIC 8062 Hospital, medical school affiliated with residency
CEO: Mark Clement
Dir Vol: Eva Polito
CFO: Richard Hogg
*CFO: Robert Nesselbush
CFO: Paula Tinch
Sr VP: Joseph McCormick
Sr VP: Bridgette Wiefling
VP: Amy Craib
VP: Patricia Houghton
VP: Katherine Rogala
Dir Lab: Joseph Foti
Dir Rx: Douglas Hosie

D-U-N-S 00-222-3642
ROCHESTER INSTITUTE OF TECHNOLOGY (INC) (NY)
R I T
1 Lomb Memorial Dr, Rochester, NY 14623-5698
Tel (585) 475-2411 Founded/Ownrshp 1829
Sales 643.0MM EMP 3,300
Accts Pricewaterhousecoopers Llp A
SIC 8221 University
Pr: William Destler
Pr: Kate Caliel
Ch Bd: Frank Romano
V Ch: Christine B Whitman
Pr: Howard Ward
Trst: Daniel J Bader
Trst: Donald N Boyce
Trst: Charles S Brown Jr
Trst: William A Buckingham
Trst: David J Burns
Trst: Arunas A Chesonis
Trst: Mark C Clement
Trst: Thomas Curley
Trst: Sudhakar G Dixit
Trst: Arthur A Gosnell
Trst: Bart G Guerreri
Trst: Frank S Hermance
Trst: Susan R Holliday
Trst: Samuel T Hubbard Jr
Trst: Thomas F Judson Jr
Trst: Kraig H Kayser

D-U-N-S 60-544-0718 IMP
ROCHESTER MEDICAL CORP
1 Rochester Medical Dr Nw, Stewartville, MN 55976-1647
Tel (507) 533-9600 Founded/Ownrshp 1988
Sales 83.7MM^E EMP 344
SIC 3841 Catheters
Ch Bd: Anthony J Conway
*CFO: David A Jonas
VP: Rob M Anglin
VP: Philip J Conway
VP: Sarah L Grinde
VP: Dara L Horner
VP: Martyn R Sholtis
Exec: Marissa Anderson
Exec: Trisha Brackpool
Info Man: Randy Stockwell
VP Prd: Philip Conway
Board of Directors: Darnell L Boehm, Peter H Shepard

D-U-N-S 00-542-2209
ROCHESTER METAL PRODUCTS CORP
616 Indiana Ave, Rochester, IN 46975-1418
Tel (574) 223-3164 Founded/Ownrshp 1937, 1965
Sales 108.3MM^E EMP 370
SIC 3321 Gray iron castings; Ductile iron castings
Pr: Robert E Kersey
*CFO: Patrick D Hellman
*Sr VP: Greg Loving
Sfty Dirs: Michael Boucher

D-U-N-S 00-661-6940
ROCHESTER METHODIST HOSPITAL AUXILIARY INC
(Suby of MAYO CLINIC) ★
1216 2nd St Sw, Rochester, MN 55902-1906
Tel (507) 255-5123 Founded/Ownrshp 1968
Sales 330.9MM^E EMP 25,000^E
SIC 8062 Hospital, AMA approved residency
Pr: Glenn Forbes

D-U-N-S 00-220-7041 IMP/EXP
ROCHESTER MIDLAND CORP
155 Paragon Dr, Rochester, NY 14624-1167
Tel (585) 336-2200 Founded/Ownrshp 1888
Sales 130.5MM^E EMP 425
Accts Davie Kaplan Cpa Pc Rochest
SIC 2842 2676 2899 Specialty cleaning, polishes & sanitation goods; Floor waxes; Cleaning or polishing preparations; Disinfectants, household or industrial plant; Feminine hygiene paper products; Chemical preparations
Ch Bd: Harlan D Calkins
*Pr: Glenn A Paynter
*CEO: H Bradley Calkins
*CFO: Douglas M Miller
VP: Doug Bergen
VP: Kevin Cormick
VP: Jim Hayden
*VP: Mary Kay Ingersoll
VP: Donald Wyman
Dir Lab: Michael Kondolf
Assoc Dir: Tracey Lewis

ROCHESTER PUBLIC SCHOOLS
See INDEPENDENT SCHOOL DISTRICT #535

ROCHESTER REGIONAL HEALTH
See UNITY HEALTH SYSTEM

ROCHESTER REGIONAL HEALTH
See RU SYSTEM INC

ROCHESTER TELEPHONE
See GLOBAL CROSSING NORTH AMERICA INC

D-U-N-S 07-366-9749
ROCHESTER-GENESEE REGIONAL TRANSPORTATION AUTHORITY
RGRTA
1372 E Main St, Rochester, NY 14609-6912
Tel (585) 654-0200 Founded/Ownrshp 1969
Sales 104.9MM EMP 800
SIC 4111 Bus line operations
CEO: Bill Carpenter
*COO: Daniele Coll-Gonzalez
COO: Steven Hindershott
*CFO: Scott Adair
Genl Mgr: Eric Farr
Dir IT: Miguel Velazquez
IT Man: Manquel Velaquez
Mktg Dir: Jacqueline Halldow

D-U-N-S 05-761-3296 IMP/EXP
ROCHLING AUTOMOTIVE USA LLP
(Suby of ROCHLING AUTOMOTIVE SE & CO.KG)
245 Parkway E, Duncan, SC 29334-9489
Tel (864) 486-0888 Founded/Ownrshp 1998
Sales 157.4MM EMP 450
SIC 3089 Automotive parts, plastic
Pr: Justin White
Sec: Eric Brenneman
VP: Terry Moore
VP: Juergen Peters
Prd Mgr: Don Shepherd

D-U-N-S 18-914-7937 IMP/EXP
ROCHLING ENGINEERED PLASTICS LIMITED PARTNERSHIP
ROCHLING ENGINEERING
(Suby of ROCHLING ENGINEERING PLASTICS SE & CO. KG)
903 Gastonia Tech Pkwy, Dallas, NC 28034-7791
Tel (704) 922-7814 Founded/Ownrshp 1987
Sales 97.0MM EMP 180
SIC 3081 3082 Unsupported plastics film & sheet; Unsupported plastics profile shapes
Pr: Timothy Charles Brown
VP: Clete O'Dell
Plnt Mgr: Lloyd Moore
Sls Mgr: Maggie Cuenca

ROCHLING ENGINEERING
See ROCHLING ENGINEERED PLASTICS LIMITED PARTNERSHIP

ROCK BOTTOM REST & BREWRY
See ROCK BOTTOM RESTAURANTS INC

D-U-N-S 86-119-2599
ROCK BOTTOM RESTAURANTS INC
ROCK BOTTOM REST & BREWRY
(Suby of CRAFTWORKS RESTAURANTS & BREWERIES GROUP INC) ★
8001 Arista Pl Unit 500, Broomfield, CO 80021-4135
Tel (303) 664-4000 Founded/Ownrshp 2010
Sales 186.0MM^E EMP 6,500
SIC 5812 5813 American restaurant; Beer garden (drinking places)
Prin: Frank B Day
*Pr: Gary Foreman
*CFO: Brian T Armstrong
Genl Mgr: Matthew Kennedy
Netwrk Mgr: Jan Cri
Genl Couns: Courtney Mowry

ROCK COMMUNICATIONS
See MITTERA GROUP INC

ROCK CREEK RESTAURANT & TAVERN
See MCMENAMINS INC

ROCK FINANCIAL
See QUICKEN LOANS INC

D-U-N-S 07-450-0380
ROCK HILL SCHOOL DISTRICT 3
660 Anderson Rd N, Rock Hill, SC 29730-3324
Tel (803) 981-1000 Founded/Ownrshp 1892
Sales 90.7MM^E EMP 1,800^E
SIC 8211 Elementary & secondary schools
Adm Dir: Scott Allan
Adm Dir: George M Hapton
Pr Dir: Mychal Frost
HC Dir: Saddie Kirell

D-U-N-S 14-052-4138
ROCK HOLDINGS INC
20555 Victor Pkwy, Livonia, MI 48152-7031
Tel (313) 373-7700 Founded/Ownrshp 2002
Sales 553.1MM^E EMP 10,500^E
SIC 6719 Investment holding companies, except banks
Ch: Daniel Gilbert
*Pr: Patrick McInnis
*CEO: William Emerson
Dir IT: Linglong He
Dir IT: Patrick Sluck
Software D: Dan Jones
Software D: Janet Mihas
Sftwr Eng: Mel Findley

ROCK ISLAND ARGUS
See MOLINE DISPATCH PUBLISHING CO

ROCK ISLAND LUBRICANTS & CHEM
See RILCO INC

D-U-N-S 07-143-6224
ROCK ISLAND/MILAN SCHOOL DISTRICT 41
2101 6th Ave, Rock Island, IL 61201-8909
Tel (309) 793-5900 Founded/Ownrshp 1857
Sales 94.9MM EMP 908
Accts Bohnsack & Frommelt Llp Taylo
SIC 8211 Public elementary school; Public junior high school; Public senior high school
*Pr: Bill Cleaver
*Pr: Linda Dothard
*VP: Dave Rockwell
*Prin: Kim Armstrong
*Prin: Jim Bishop
*Prin: Katty Taylor
Ex Dir: Cosette Thoms
Pr Dir: Holly Sparkman
HC Dir: Alicia Sierra-Sanders

ROCK REVIVAL
See RCRV INC

ROCK SHOP
See HARD ROCK CAFE INTERNATIONAL (USA) INC

ROCK TENN
See WESTROCK MILL CO LLC

D-U-N-S 17-087-2626
ROCKAWAY HOME ATTENDANT SERVICES INC
ROCKAWAY HOME ATTENDENT SVCES
1603 Central Ave 100, Far Rockaway, NY 11691-4003
Tel (718) 327-1850 Founded/Ownrshp 1979
Sales 16.6MM EMP 1,200
Accts Rolando A Blancocpa Pllc Bald
SIC 8082 8361 Home health care services; Geriatric residential care
Ex Dir: Enosa Aibangbeeee

ROCKAWAY HOME ATTENDENT SVCES
See ROCKAWAY HOME ATTENDANT SERVICES INC

D-U-N-S 82-972-8042
ROCKBRIDGE GROWTH EQUITY LLC
1078 Woodward Ave, Detroit, MI 48226-1906
Tel (313) 373-7000 Founded/Ownrshp 2007
Sales 124.4MM^E EMP 710^E
SIC 6282 Investment advisory service
Pt: Daniel R Gilbert
Pt: Brian Hermelin
Pt: Kevin J Prokop
VP: Kenan Basha
VP: Scott Elkins
VP: Steve Linden

D-U-N-S 07-585-7375
ROCKDALE COUNTY BOARD OF EDUCATION
954 N Main St Nw, Conyers, GA 30012-4457
Tel (770) 483-4713 Founded/Ownrshp 1920
Sales 166.9MM^E EMP 2,400
SIC 8211 School board
Ch Bd: Jim Mc Brayer

D-U-N-S 07-979-8975
ROCKDALE COUNTY PUBLIC SCHOOLS
954 N Main St Nw, Conyers, GA 30012-4457
Tel (770) 483-4713 Founded/Ownrshp 2015
Sales 33.3MM^E EMP 2,069^E

SIC 8211 Public elementary & secondary schools
Dir IT: Grover Dailey
Teacher Pr: Cathy Smiley

D-U-N-S 07-417-6686
ROCKDALE HOSPITAL AUTHORITY (INC)
RICHARDS MEMORIAL HOSPITAL
(*Suby of* BLACKHAWK HEALTHCARE LLC) ★
1700 Brazos Ave, Rockdale, TX 76567-2517
Tel (512) 446-4500 *Founded/Ownrshp* 1973
Sales 96.6MM *EMP* 230
SIC 8062 8051 General medical & surgical hospitals; Skilled nursing care facilities
CEO: Jeff Madison
COO: Dr Lousie Grose
Exec: Sheila Lopez
Dir Sec: Joel Suits
Dir IT: Eric Matthews

D-U-N-S 96-324-2719
■ **ROCKDALE HOSPITAL LLC**
ROCKDALE MEDICAL CENTER
(*Suby of* LIFEPOINT HEALTH INC) ★
1412 Milstead Ave Ne, Conyers, GA 30012-3877
Tel (770) 918-3101 *Founded/Ownrshp* 2008
Sales 109.5MM *EMP* 99
SIC 8062 General medical & surgical hospitals
CIO: Paul Grulke
CTO: Reid Burch
Dir IT: Ch Green
Pharmcst: Todd D Mendsen

ROCKDALE MEDICAL CENTER
See ROCKDALE HOSPITAL LLC

D-U-N-S 03-005-1460
■ **ROCKDALE MEDICAL CENTER INC**
(*Suby of* LIFEPOINT HEALTH INC) ★
1412 Milstead Ave Ne, Conyers, GA 30012-3877
Tel (770) 918-3000 *Founded/Ownrshp* 1994
Sales 135.4MM *EMP* 1,600
SIC 8062 General medical & surgical hospitals
CEO: Deborah Armstrong
**COO:* James Atkins
**CFO:* Tom Arnold
CFO: Ann Finlon
CFO: Hal J Henderson
**VP:* Stuart Downs
Dir Lab: Sharon Potts
Chf Nrs Of: Michelle Epps
Chf Nrs Of: Eleanor Post
Off Mgr: Nealie Dodd
CTO: Michael Jones

D-U-N-S 07-279-6014
ROCKEFELLER FOUNDATION
420 5th Ave Fl 22, New York, NY 10018-2711
Tel (212) 869-8500 *Founded/Ownrshp* 1913
Sales 401.7MM *EMP* 150
SIC 8699 Charitable organization
Pr: Judith Rodin
CFO: Ellen Taus
**Treas:* Donna Dean
Ofcr: Vinson Cunningham
VP: Neill Coleman
**VP:* Richard J Tofel
Assoc Dir: Lorenzo Bernasconi
Assoc Dir: Samuel Carter
Assoc Dir: Ronald Chen
Assoc Dir: Brinda Ganguly
Assoc Dir: Caroline Kronley

ROCKEFELLER GROUP, THE
See ROCKEFELLER GROUP INTERNATIONAL INC

D-U-N-S 05-525-8193
ROCKEFELLER GROUP INC (NY)
(*Suby of* MITSUBISHI ESTATE COMPANY, LIMITED)
1221 Ave Of The Am Flr 17, New York, NY 10020
Tel (212) 282-2000 *Founded/Ownrshp* 1928
Sales 592.8MM^E *EMP* 11,000
SIC 6531 7389 Real estate leasing & rentals; Office facilities & secretarial service rental
Ch Bd: Kevin R Hackett
**CEO:* Atsushi Nakajima
**COO:* Vincent E Silvestri
**Treas:* Sam Pallotta
Chf Inves: Masahiro Kobayashi
Ofcr: Parkin Lee
Sr VP: John Bottomley
Sr VP: Robert Shults
**VP:* Santo F Curro
VP: Dwayne Doherty
VP: Edward Guiltinan
Assoc Dir: Heath Abramsohn

D-U-N-S 07-101-4740
ROCKEFELLER GROUP INTERNATIONAL INC
ROCKEFELLER GROUP, THE
(*Suby of* ROCKEFELLER GROUP INC) ★
1221 Avenue Of The Americ, New York, NY 10020-1001
Tel (212) 282-2000 *Founded/Ownrshp* 1991
Sales 136.5MM^E *EMP* 1,000
SIC 6512 6552 4813 Nonresidential building operators; Subdividers & developers; Telephone communication, except radio
Chf Inves: Atsushi Nakajima
Pr: Tc Cgung
**Pr:* Kevin R Hackett
**Treas:* Sam Pallotta
Ex VP: Leslie Smith
VP: Stephen R Caoll
**VP:* Santo F Curro
**VP:* Masahiro Kobayashi
**VP:* Parkin Lee
VP: Michael Salz
**VP:* Vincent E Silvestri
VP: Bill Stoddard
VP: Howard Watler

D-U-N-S 07-103-7113
ROCKEFELLER UNIVERSITY (NY)
ROCKEFELLER UNIVERSITY HOSPITA
1230 York Ave, New York, NY 10065-6399
Tel (212) 327-8078 *Founded/Ownrshp* 1901
Sales 537.0MM *EMP* 1,700
Accts Kpmg Llp New York Ny
SIC 8733 8221 8062 Noncommercial research organizations; Colleges universities & professional schools; General medical & surgical hospitals
Ch: Russell L Carson
**Pr:* Marc Tessier Lavigne
**CFO:* James H Lappie
**Ch:* David Rockefeller
**Ch:* Richard E Salomon
Trst: Willard J Overlock
Chf Inves: Amy Falls
**VP:* Barry S Coller
**VP:* Lisa Danzig
**VP:* Virginia Huffman
**VP:* Maren E Imhoff
**VP:* Timothy Oconnor
**VP:* Harriet Rabb
VP: Michael W Young
Dir Lab: Henrik Molina

ROCKEFELLER UNIVERSITY HOSPITA
See ROCKEFELLER UNIVERSITY

D-U-N-S 82-853-4649
▲ **ROCKET FUEL INC**
1900 Seaport Blvd, Redwood City, CA 94063-5587
Tel (650) 595-1300 *Founded/Ownrshp* 2008
Sales 461.6MM *EMP* 954^E
Tkr Sym FUEL *Exch* NGS
SIC 7379 Computer related consulting services
CEO: E Randolph Wootton III
CFO: Rex S Jackson
Ofcr: Rick Song
**Ex VP:* Richard A Frankel
Sr VP: Joann C Covington
Sr VP: Rock Pittenger
VP: Shobhana Ahluwalia
Comm Dir: Elaine Wu
Mng Dir: Oliver Hulse
CTO: Mark Torrance
Software D: Randy Harmon
Board of Directors: Susan L Bostrom, Ronald E F Codd, William W Ericson, Clark M Kokic, John J Lewis, Monte Zweben

D-U-N-S 62-000-1388
ROCKET SOFTWARE INC
77 4th Ave Ste 101, Waltham, MA 02451-7565
Tel (781) 577-4323 *Founded/Ownrshp* 2002
Sales 270.0MM *EMP* 1,077
SIC 7371 Computer software development
Pr: Andy Youniss
**CFO:* Kevin Thimble
**Sr VP:* Sam Elias
**Sr VP:* P Gary Gregory
**Sr VP:* Jay Leader
VP: Gary P Gregory
Mng Dir: Joseph Devlin
Snr Sftwr: Steve Able
Snr Sftwr: Kevin Baynes
Snr Sftwr: Darryl Madison
Snr Sftwr: Mike Nguyen

D-U-N-S 01-010-5883
ROCKETTECH FUEL CORP (NY)
20 Corbin Ave, Bay Shore, NY 11706-1004
Tel (516) 810-8947 *Founded/Ownrshp* 2004
Sales 90.0MM *EMP* 10
SIC 1311 Crude petroleum & natural gas
Pr: Richard Miller
**VP:* Joseph Silhan

D-U-N-S 07-479-2065
ROCKFISH SEAFOOD GRILL INC
801 E Campbell Rd Ste 300, Richardson, TX 75081-1867
Tel (214) 887-9400 *Founded/Ownrshp* 2008
Sales 46.2MM^E *EMP* 1,200
SIC 5812 5813 Seafood restaurants; Drinking places
CEO: Thomas A Lee
**CEO:* Henry Leonard
CFO: Frank Leonard
**Prin:* Eric Rasmussen
Genl Mgr: Eric Leon
IT Man: James Gonzales

ROCKFON
See CHICAGO METALLIC CO LLC

D-U-N-S 08-204-5204
ROCKFORD BOARD OF EDUCATION
ROCKFORD SCHOOL DST NUMBER 205
501 7th St, Rockford, IL 61104-1242
Tel (815) 966-3000 *Founded/Ownrshp* 1910
Sales 446.1MM *EMP* 4,200
Accts Sikich Llp Rock Illinois
SIC 8211 Public elementary & secondary schools
**Pr:* Harmon Mitchell
**VP:* Jude Makulec
MIS Dir: Margret Ryan
Dir IT: Todd Schmidt
Teacher Pr: Pilar Peigh
Teacher Pr: Matthew Zeidiker
Psych: Kim Driscoll
Psych: Cassandra Glover

ROCKFORD COMPANIES
See ROCKFORD CONSTRUCTION CO

D-U-N-S 11-604-8885 IMP
ROCKFORD CONCENTRIC INC
(*Suby of* CONCENTRIC AB)
2222 15th St, Rockford, IL 61104-7313
Tel (815) 398-4400 *Founded/Ownrshp* 2011
Sales 97.6MM^E *EMP* 871
SIC 3594 3629

D-U-N-S 18-708-9826
ROCKFORD CONSTRUCTION CO
ROCKFORD COMPANIES
601 1st St Nw, Grand Rapids, MI 49504-5517
Tel (616) 285-6933 *Founded/Ownrshp* 1987
Sales 187.9MM *EMP* 200
Accts Crowe Horwath Llp South Bend
SIC 1542 Commercial & office building, new construction
CEO: Mike Vangessel
Pr: Jennifer Boezwinkle
**Pr:* Tom McGovern
**COO:* Kurt Hassberger
**CFO:* Julie Towner
**Ex VP:* Ken Bailey
VP: Dan Bailey
VP: William Culhane
VP: Mike Meyers
Dir IT: Mike Gessel
Mktg Dir: Adam Jones

D-U-N-S 03-843-9477 IMP
ROCKFORD CORP
ROCKFORD-FOSGATE
600 S Rockford Dr, Tempe, AZ 85281-3022
Tel (480) 967-3565 *Founded/Ownrshp* 1980
Sales 217.7MM^E *EMP* 1,118
SIC 3651 Amplifiers: radio, public address or musical instrument; Audio electronic systems; Loudspeakers, electrodynamic or magnetic; Sound reproducing equipment
CFO: James M Thoson
**CFO:* Richard G Vasek
**VP:* Mark W Matson
VP: Jacqueline M Ott
Sls&Mrk Ex: Chris Parvin
**VP Sls:* Brian M Carlsness
Sls Mgr: Heath Lundsford
Board of Directors: Nicholas G Bartol, Mark A Riser

ROCKFORD HEALTH MEDICAL LABORATORIES
See ROCKFORD MEMORIAL HOSPITAL

D-U-N-S 02-580-3297
ROCKFORD HEALTH PHYSICIANS (IL)
(*Suby of* MERCY HEALTH CORP) ★
2300 N Rockton Ave, Rockford, IL 61103-3619
Tel (815) 971-2000 *Founded/Ownrshp* 1951, 1993
Sales 121.6MM *EMP* 1,354
Accts Pricewaterhousecoopers Philad
SIC 8011 Clinic, operated by physicians; Health maintenance organization
Pr: Gary Kaatz
Ch Bd: James Breckenridge MD
CFO: Sue Petro
Doctor: Sarah Beaves
Doctor: Mark Hornbach
Doctor: Romulo Ortega

D-U-N-S 86-709-2603
ROCKFORD HEALTH SYSTEM
2400 N Rockton Ave, Rockford, IL 61103-3655
Tel (815) 971-5000 *Founded/Ownrshp* 1982
Sales 428.9MM *EMP* 3,700
SIC 8741

ROCKFORD INTL IMPORTERS
See BILL DORAN CO

D-U-N-S 07-457-8949
ROCKFORD MEMORIAL HOSPITAL
ROCKFORD HEALTH MEDICAL LABORATORIES
(*Suby of* MERCY HEALTH CORP) ★
2400 N Rockton Ave, Rockford, IL 61103-3681
Tel (815) 971-5000 *Founded/Ownrshp* 1883
Sales 186.3MM *EMP* 2,200
SIC 8062 8011 8071 8099 General medical & surgical hospitals; Medical centers; Medical laboratories; Health screening service
CEO: Gary E Kaatz
Chf Rad: John Lind
Sr VP: Henry Seybold
Dir Risk M: Nancy Harvey
Dir Case M: Evelyn Pagan
Mtls Dir: Stuart Wasilewski
Pathlgst: James Harker
Pathlgst: Matthew Twohig
Doctor: Roger Bohn
Doctor: Todd Chaffin
Doctor: Avani M Doshi MD

D-U-N-S 07-457-1456
ROCKFORD PARK DISTRICT
401 S Main St Ste 101, Rockford, IL 61101-1321
Tel (815) 987-8800 *Founded/Ownrshp* 1979
Sales 39.8MM *EMP* 1,600
Accts Sikich Llp Rockford Illinois
SIC 7999 Recreation services
Ex Dir: Tim Dimke
**Pr:* Tyler Smith
COO: Debbie Brooks
**CFO:* Penny Christians
Ofcr: Brandon Bradbury
Ofcr: Jeff Kuhls
**VP:* Ian K Linnabary
Dir Risk M: Pete Stankiewicz
Off Admin: Christine Didier
Off Admin: Destiny Hannah
CIO: Sue Cichock

D-U-N-S 80-848-1985
ROCKFORD PRODUCTS LLC
707 Harrison Ave, Rockford, IL 61104-7162
Tel (815) 397-6000 *Founded/Ownrshp* 2013
Sales 192.7MM^E *EMP* 390^E
SIC 3462

D-U-N-S 08-034-4047
ROCKFORD PUBLIC SCHOOLS
350 N Main St, Rockford, MI 49341-1092
Tel (616) 863-6320 *Founded/Ownrshp* 1935
Sales 91.0MM *EMP* 895
Accts Hungerford Nichols Llp Grand
SIC 8211 Public elementary & secondary schools
Ex Dir: Colleen Cyrus
Ex Dir: Kirsten Myers
Ex Dir: Jill Silverman
Ex Dir: Travis Woulfe
MIS Dir: Peter Young
Psych: Judy Cunningham
Psych: Deb Longuski
Art Dir: Kyle Kennett

ROCKFORD SCHOOL DST NUMBER 205
See ROCKFORD BOARD OF EDUCATION

ROCKFORD-FOSGATE
See ROCKFORD CORP

D-U-N-S 00-787-3466
ROCKINGHAM CO-OPERATIVE FARM BUREAU INC (VA)
1040 S High St, Harrisonburg, VA 22801-1604
Tel (540) 434-3856 *Founded/Ownrshp* 1921
Sales 99.6MM *EMP* 180
SIC 5999 5251 Farm equipment & supplies; Hardware
Pr: Richard Morris
**CFO:* John Rosenberger
**Bd of Dir:* Anthony Beery
Bd of Dir: Maurice Cupp
Bd of Dir: Elizabeth Hefner
VP: Robert Coffman
**VP:* Joseph Lam

D-U-N-S 03-476-7869
ROCKINGHAM COOPERATIVE
1044 S High St, Harrisonburg, VA 22801-1604
Tel (540) 434-3856 *Founded/Ownrshp* 2012
Sales 99.6MM^E *EMP* 1
SIC 0191

ROCKINGHAM COUNTY PUB SCHOOLS
See ROCKINGHAM COUNTY SCHOOL DISTRICT

D-U-N-S 14-533-9255
ROCKINGHAM COUNTY SCHOOL DISTRICT
ROCKINGHAM COUNTY PUB SCHOOLS
100 Mount Clinton Pike, Harrisonburg, VA 22802-2507
Tel (540) 564-3200 *Founded/Ownrshp* 1777
Sales 127.8MM *EMP* 1,600
Accts Holden Moss Knott Clark & C
SIC 8211 Public elementary & secondary schools
Pr: Bill Gamble
MIS Dir: Oskar Schiekl
Teacher Pr: Suzan Guynn

D-U-N-S 19-301-7050
ROCKINGHAM COUNTY SCHOOLS
511 Harrington Hwy, Eden, NC 27288-7547
Tel (336) 627-2600 *Founded/Ownrshp* 1800
Sales 79.0MM^E *EMP* 1,853
SIC 8211 Public elementary & secondary schools
MIS Dir: Kacey Sensenich
Info Man: Jan McGuire
Pr Dir: Karen Hyler
Teacher Pr: Jonathan Craig

D-U-N-S 01-896-2217
ROCKINGHAM ELECTRICAL SUPPLY CO INC
437 Shattuck Way, Portsmouth, NH 03801-7871
Tel (603) 436-7731 *Founded/Ownrshp* 1959
Sales 103.0MM^E *EMP* 135
SIC 5063 Electrical apparatus & equipment
Pr: James E Pender Sr
**VP:* Dan Pender
**VP:* James E Pender Jr
Brnch Mgr: Chris Miller
Brnch Mgr: Dave Shallow
IT Man: Gino Milne

D-U-N-S 82-464-3001
ROCKINGHAM HEALTH CARE INC
SENTARA RMH MEDICAL CENTER
(*Suby of* SENTARA CNCER NTWRK NORFOLK CI) ★
2010 Health Campus Dr, Rockingham, VA 22801-8679
Tel (540) 433-4100 *Founded/Ownrshp* 1983
Sales 60.4MM^E *EMP* 2,400
Accts Sb Hoover & Company Llp
SIC 8062 General medical & surgical hospitals; Hospital, medical school affiliation
Pr: T Carter Melton Jr
Pr: Kay Harrison
Pr: Mike Rozmus
Ofcr: Sherrill Glanzer
Ofcr: Ryan Thornton
VP: Donna Hahn
Dir Risk M: Monica Rutledge
Dir Lab: Joyce Kuhns
Dir Rx: Betsy Early
**Prin:* Joseph K Funkhouser II
Nurse Mgr: Tena Bibb

D-U-N-S 05-029-0923
ROCKLAND BAKERY INC (NY)
94 Demarest Mill Rd W, Nanuet, NY 10954-2989
Tel (845) 623-5800 *Founded/Ownrshp* 1986
Sales 143.2MM^E *EMP* 450
SIC 2051 Bread, cake & related products
CEO: Ignazio Battaglia
**Treas:* Mario Battaglia
Ex VP: Antony Luna
**VP:* Philip Battaglia
CTO: Sal Battaglia
Manager: Ron Warner
Sls Mgr: Bill Doran

D-U-N-S 00-189-0458
■ **ROCKLAND ELECTRIC CO**
(*Suby of* ORANGE AND ROCKLAND UTILITIES INC) ★
1 Blue Hill Plz Ste 20, Pearl River, NY 10965-3100
Tel (845) 352-6000 *Founded/Ownrshp* 1899
Sales 102.2MM^E *EMP* 225
SIC 4911 Electric services
CEO: D Louis Peoples

D-U-N-S 00-406-5264 IMP/EXP
ROCKLAND INC (PA)
ROCKLAND MANUFACTURING COMPANY
152 Weber Ln, Bedford, PA 15522-7782
Tel (814) 623-1115 *Founded/Ownrshp* 1947, 1965
Sales 150.8MM^E *EMP* 256^E
SIC 3531 Construction machinery attachments; Blades for graders, scrapers, dozers & snow plows; Plows: construction, excavating & grading
Pr: Samuel J Pratt
**Sec:* Anne E Pratt
**VP:* Daniel D Shaffer III
Exec: Rocky Cambrea
Mktg Dir: Clara Kline
Sls Mgr: Bo Pratt

ROCKLAND MANUFACTURING COMPANY
See ROCKLAND INC

D-U-N-S 00-142-2997 IMP
■ ROCKLAND TRUST CO (MA)
(*Suby of* INDEPENDENT BANK CORP) ★
288 Union St, Rockland, MA 02370-1896
Tel (781) 878-6100 *Founded/Ownrshp* 1907
Sales NA *EMP* 1,110
SIC 6022 State trust companies accepting deposits, commercial
Pr: Christopher Oddleifson
**Ch Bd:* Donna L Abelli
COO: Denis K Sheahan
CFO: Robert D Cozzone
Ofcr: Bernadette Conneely
Ofcr: Karianne Golemme
Trst Ofcr: Jeffrey Mead
Ex VP: Ferdinand T Kelley
Ex VP: Jane L Lundquist
Ex VP: Gerard Nadeau
Sr VP: Raymond G Fuerschbach
Sr VP: James Rizzo
VP: Amanda Buckley
VP: Thomas Burton
VP: David Chamberlain
VP: Thomas Connolly
VP: Rholyn Dayrit
VP: Karen Delprete
VP: Maureen Demacedo
VP: Susan Dewsnap
VP: Geniene Elliott
Board of Directors: Mary L Lentz, Frederick Taw

D-U-N-S 36-098-9318
■ ROCKLEDGE HMA LLC
(*Suby of* HMA) ★
110 Longwood Ave, Rockledge, FL 32955-2828
Tel (321) 636-2211 *Founded/Ownrshp* 2010
Sales 188.0MM *EMP* 2,500
SIC 8062 General medical & surgical hospitals
CEO: Tim Cerullo
**Pr:* Emil Miller
Dir Rad: Jay Greer
Doctor: Freda A Nime MD
Doctor: Douglas R Smith MD

D-U-N-S 06-651-5156 IMP/EXP
ROCKLER COMPANIES INC
ROCKLER WOODWORKING & HARDWARE
4365 Willow Dr, Medina, MN 55340-4522
Tel (763) 478-8201 *Founded/Ownrshp* 1955
Sales 126.5MM[E] *EMP* 500
SIC 5251 5961 2721 Tools, hand; Tools, power; Builders' hardware; Mail order house; Tools & hardware, mail order; Periodicals
Ch Bd: Norton Rockler
**Pr:* Ann Rockler Jackson
**Pr:* David Laporte
**CEO:* Ann Jackson
Store Mgr: Scott Baumeister
Store Mgr: Pat Jones
CTO: Joe Fahey
IT Man: Gary Harris
Mktg Dir: Robert Jackson

ROCKLER WOODWORKING & HARDWARE
See ROCKLER COMPANIES INC

D-U-N-S 08-992-6893
ROCKLIN UNIFIED SCHOOL DISTRICT
2615 Sierra Meadows Dr, Rocklin, CA 95677-2126
Tel (916) 624-2428 *Founded/Ownrshp* 1860
Sales 66.2MM[E] *EMP* 1,000
Accts Perry-Smith Llp
SIC 8211 Public elementary school; Public junior high school; Public senior high school
**VP:* Steve Paul
CTO: Mike Fury
Schl Brd P: Todd Lowell

D-U-N-S 06-688-6102 IMP/EXP
ROCKLINE INDUSTRIES INC
4343 S Taylor Dr, Sheboygan, WI 53081-8485
Tel (800) 558-7790 *Founded/Ownrshp* 1991
Sales 319.4MM[E] *EMP* 1,500
SIC 2679 2297

D-U-N-S 07-837-6669
ROCKPILE ENERGY SERVICES LLC
(*Suby of* WHITE DEER ENERGY LP II) ★
1200 17th St Ste 2700, Denver, CO 80202-5827
Tel (303) 825-8170 *Founded/Ownrshp* 2016
Sales 95.3MM[E] *EMP* 80[E]
SIC 1389 Oil field services
CEO: Curt Dacar
Pr: James Evans
COO: Paul George
Opers Mgr: Bryan Harris
Sls Mgr: Tyler Pittenger

D-U-N-S 96-218-8517
ROCKROSE DEVELOPMENT CORP
15 E 26th St Fl 7, New York, NY 10010-1503
Tel (212) 847-3700 *Founded/Ownrshp* 1970
Sales 100.6MM[E] *EMP* 136[E]
SIC 6552 Subdividers & developers
Ch Bd: H Henry Elghanayan

ROCKTENN RETAIL SOLUTIONS CO
See WESTROCK CONVERTING CO

D-U-N-S 02-809-9653 IMP/EXP
ROCKVIEW DAIRIES INC
MOTIVE NATION
7011 Stewart And Gray Rd, Downey, CA 90241-4347
Tel (562) 927-5511 *Founded/Ownrshp* 1927
Sales 249.3MM[E] *EMP* 250[E]
SIC 5149 5143 2026 Dried or canned foods; Milk; Fluid milk
CEO: Egbert Jim Degroot
Pr: Valarie Cooke
COO: Floyd Maderis
**CFO:* Joe Valadez
Exec: Mark McGrath
Exec: Lyle McVicar
Dir Lab: Carlos Lopez
CIO: Ralph Gallardo
Dir IT: Egbert De
IT Man: Gary Musser
IT Man: Glenn Parker

ROCKVILLE BANK FOUNDATION INC
See UNITED BANK FOUNDATION CONNECTICUT INC

D-U-N-S 01-048-7296
ROCKWALL INDEPENDENT SCHOOL DISTRICT PUBLIC FACILITY CORP
1050 Williams St, Rockwall, TX 75087-2600
Tel (972) 771-0605 *Founded/Ownrshp* 1954
Sales 66.5MM[E] *EMP* 1,650
Accts Weaver And Tidwell Llp Dallas
SIC 8211 School board
Pr: Gene Burton
**VP:* James Crow
Exec: Marsha Mason
Ex Dir: Joey Byrum
Ex Dir: Bart Rosebure
Pr Dir: Renee Murphy
Teacher Pr: Mark Speck
HC Dir: Nicole Smithers

ROCKWATER ENERGY SOLUTIONS
See BENCHMARK PERFORMANCE GROUP INC

D-U-N-S 96-860-5175
ROCKWATER ENERGY SOLUTIONS INC
515 Post Oak Blvd Ste 200, Houston, TX 77027-9408
Tel (713) 235-9500 *Founded/Ownrshp* 2011
Sales 418.3MM[E] *EMP* 620[E]
SIC 8731 8748 Energy research; Environmental consultant
Pr: Larry Odonnell III
**Ex VP:* Holli C Ladhani
**Ex VP:* David Nightingale
**Sr VP:* J Kevin Blodgett
**Sr VP:* David J Isaac
Genl Mgr: Matt Smiley
CTO: Christopher Gallagher
Mktg Mgr: Thomas Erwin
Sls Mgr: Tommy Johnson

D-U-N-S 96-194-1531 IMP
▲ ROCKWELL AUTOMATION INC
1201 S 2nd St, Milwaukee, WI 53204-2410
Tel (414) 382-2000 *Founded/Ownrshp* 1903
Sales 6.3MMM *EMP* 22,500
Accts Deloitte & Touche Llp Milwauk
Tkr Sym ROK *Exch* NYS
SIC 3625 3621 3566 3661 Relays & industrial controls; Motors, electric; Speed changers (power transmission equipment), except auto; Telephone & telegraph apparatus
Ch Bd: Keith D Nosbusch
CFO: Theodore D Crandall
Treas: Steven W Etzel
Sr VP: Sujeet Chand
Sr VP: Douglas M Hagerman
Sr VP: Frank C Kulaszewicz
Sr VP: John P McDermott
Sr VP: Susan J Schmitt
Sr VP: Martin Thomas
VP: Jeff Banaszynski
VP: Thomas Denato
VP: David M Dorgan
VP: Edward Hill
VP: Marc Kartman
VP: John M Miller
VP: Lee Tschanz
VP: Desiree Welborn
Board of Directors: Betty C Alewine, J Phillip Holloman, Steven R Kalmanson, James P Keane, Lawrence D Kingsley, William T McCormick Jr, Donald R Parfet, Lisa A Payne, Thomas W Rosamilia

D-U-N-S 96-296-0589 IMP/EXP
▲ ROCKWELL COLLINS INC
400 Collins Rd Ne, Cedar Rapids, IA 52498-0505
Tel (319) 295-1000 *Founded/Ownrshp* 1933
Sales 5.2MMM *EMP* 19,500[E]
Tkr Sym COL *Exch* NYS
SIC 3812 3663 Search & navigation equipment; Aircraft control systems, electronic; Navigational systems & instruments; Radar systems & equipment; Receivers, radio communications
Ch Bd: Robert K Ortberg
COO: Philip J Jasper
COO: Kent L Statler
CFO: Patrick E Allen
Treas: Heather Stansberry
Treas: Douglas E Stenske
Sr VP: Bruce M King
Sr VP: Jeffrey D Maclauchlan
Sr VP: Colin R Mahoney
Sr VP: Nan Mattai
Sr VP: Martha L May
Sr VP: David J Nieuwsma
Sr VP: Robert J Perna
Sr VP: Jeffrey A Standerski
Sr VP: Robert A Sturgell
VP: John Borghese
VP: Tatum J Buse
VP: Todd Davis
VP: Amy McDonald
VP: Alan Prowse
VP: Leann Ridgeway
Board of Directors: Anthony J Carbone, Chris A Davis, Ralph E Eberhart, John A Edwardson, David Lilley, Andrew J Policano, Cheryl L Shavers, Jeffrey Turner

ROCKWELL COLLINS INFO MGT SVCS
See ARINC INC

D-U-N-S 78-853-0017
■ ROCKWELL COLLINS SALES & SERVICES INC
(*Suby of* ROCKWELL COLLINS INC) ★
400 Collins Rd Ne, Cedar Rapids, IA 52498-0505
Tel (319) 295-8899 *Founded/Ownrshp* 2007
Sales 93.4MM[E] *EMP* 200
SIC 5065 Communication equipment
Prin: Shawn Krenz

D-U-N-S 80-923-8447 IMP
■ ROCKWELL COLLINS SIMULATION & TRAINING SOLUTIONS LLC
(*Suby of* ROCKWELL COLLINS INC) ★
400 Collins Rd Ne, Cedar Rapids, IA 52498-0505
Tel (319) 295-1000 *Founded/Ownrshp* 2003
Sales 116.1MM[E] *EMP* 650
SIC 3699 8744 Electronic training devices; Facilities support services
Pr: J Anthony Syme
**Ch Bd:* Harold Gregory
**VP:* Donald P McDougall
Prgrm Mgr: Steve Tanner

D-U-N-S 07-876-8229
ROCKWELL FUNDING LLC
310 Maple Ave Ste L04, Barrington, RI 02806-3431
Tel (401) 466-4755 *Founded/Ownrshp* 2013
Sales NA *EMP* 6
SIC 6153 Factoring services
CEO: Patrick Churchville

D-U-N-S 07-039-3079
ROCKWOOD CLINIC PS (WA)
400 E 5th Ave Frnt, Spokane, WA 99202-1336
Tel (509) 838-2531 *Founded/Ownrshp* 1930
Sales 113.9MM[E] *EMP* 1,300
SIC 8011 Clinic, operated by physicians
CEO: Michael Patmas
**Pr:* Craig Whiting
COO: Thomas Moser
**CFO:* Christopher McGoldrick
Bd of Dir: Amy Anderson
Bd of Dir: Tom Richardson
Exec: Laura Hill
**Prin:* Dennis Barts
**Prin:* C Dan Henderson
Off Mgr: Colleen Kirk
Software D: Laurie Riches

D-U-N-S 01-616-4399 IMP/EXP
■ ROCKWOOD HOLDINGS INC
(*Suby of* ALBEMARLE CORP) ★
100 Overlook Ctr Ste 101, Princeton, NJ 08540-7814
Tel (609) 514-0300 *Founded/Ownrshp* 2015
Sales 1.3MMM *EMP* 10,200[E]
SIC 2819 2816 Industrial inorganic chemicals; Iron oxide pigments (ochers, siennas, umbers)
CEO: Seifi Ghasemi
**Pr:* Monika Engel-Bader
**Pr:* Andrew M Ross
**CFO:* Robert J Zatta
**Ex VP:* Thomas J Riordan
VP: Cary Hall

D-U-N-S 00-232-9456 IMP/EXP
■ ROCKWOOD LITHIUM INC
(*Suby of* ROCKWOOD SPECIALTIES GROUP INC) ★
348 Holiday Inn Dr, Kings Mountain, NC 28086-3615
Tel (704) 739-2501 *Founded/Ownrshp* 1876, 2004
Sales 160.5MM[E] *EMP* 500
SIC 2819 Industrial inorganic chemicals; Lithium compounds, inorganic
Ch: Steffen Haber
**CFO:* Marcus Brune
CFO: Ron France
**VP:* Thomas J Riordan
**VP:* Robert J Zatta
Genl Mgr: Kenneth Davis

D-U-N-S 04-011-5610
ROCKWOOD SCHOOL DISTRICT R-6 (INC)
111 E North St, Eureka, MO 63025-1229
Tel (636) 733-2000 *Founded/Ownrshp* 1948
Sales 181.1MM[E] *EMP* 3,328[E]
Accts Kerber Eck & Braeckel Llp S
SIC 8211 Public elementary & secondary schools; Secondary school
CFO: David Glaser
**Ex Dir:* Shirley Broz
Ex Dir: Linda Smith
Schl Brd P: Matt Doell

D-U-N-S 15-738-1757
ROCKWOOD SERVICE CORP
43 Arch St, Greenwich, CT 06830-6512
Tel (203) 869-6734 *Founded/Ownrshp* 1990
Sales 507.3MM[E] *EMP* 3,009
SIC 6719 Investment holding companies, except banks
Pr: Peter Scannell
**Treas:* John Lockwood

D-U-N-S 03-845-1386
■ ROCKWOOD SPECIALTIES CONSOLIDATED INC
(*Suby of* ROCKWOOD HOLDINGS INC) ★
100 Overlook Ctr Ste 101, Princeton, NJ 08540-7814
Tel (609) 514-0300 *Founded/Ownrshp* 2001
Sales 149.7MM[E] *EMP* 2,500
SIC 5169

D-U-N-S 10-679-3433 IMP/EXP
■ ROCKWOOD SPECIALTIES GROUP INC
(*Suby of* ROCKWOOD HOLDINGS INC) ★
100 Overlook Ctr Ste 101, Princeton, NJ 08540-7814
Tel (609) 514-0300 *Founded/Ownrshp* 2000
Sales 476.6MM[E] *EMP* 2,760
SIC 5169 2899 Industrial chemicals; Chemical preparations
CEO: Seifi Ghasemi
**CFO:* Bob Zatta

D-U-N-S 07-942-1384 IMP
▲ ROCKY BRANDS INC
39 E Canal St, Nelsonville, OH 45764-1247
Tel (740) 753-1951 *Founded/Ownrshp* 1932
Sales 269.3MM *EMP* 2,447[E]
Tkr Sym RCKY *Exch* NGS
SIC 3143 3144 2329 2331 2339 2389 Men's footwear, except athletic; Women's footwear, except athletic; Men's & boys' sportswear & athletic clothing; Women's & misses' blouses & shirts; Women's & misses' accessories; Men's miscellaneous accessories
CEO: Mike Brooks
Pr: Gary Adam
Pr: Jason Brooks
Pr: Richard Simms
CFO: James E McDonald
VP: Dennis Bleile
VP: Brian Gerrain
VP: Mary Lorenz
VP: James McLaughlin
VP: Jim Murphy
IT Man: Kandy Giffin
Board of Directors: Glenn E Corlett, Michael L Finn, G Courtney Haning, Harley E Rouda Jr, James L Stewart

ROCKY MOUNTAIN ASPHALT
See ROCKY MOUNTAIN MATERIALS AND ASPHALT INC

D-U-N-S 09-311-0757 IMP
ROCKY MOUNTAIN FABRICATION INC
R M F
(*Suby of* CANERECTOR INC)
1125 W 2300 N, Salt Lake City, UT 84116-1261
Tel (801) 532-5400 *Founded/Ownrshp* 2006
Sales 100.4MM[E] *EMP* 300
SIC 3443 Tanks, standard or custom fabricated: metal plate; Vessels, process or storage (from boiler shops): metal plate
Pr: Randy R Guest

D-U-N-S 83-108-6702
ROCKY MOUNTAIN HEALTH MAINTENANCE ORGANIZATION INC
ROCKY MOUNTAIN HEALTH PLANS
2775 Crossroads Blvd, Grand Junction, CO 81506-8712
Tel (970) 243-7050 *Founded/Ownrshp* 1970
Sales NA *EMP* 400
Accts Dalby Wendland &Amp Co Pc Gra
SIC 6321 Accident & health insurance
CEO: Patrick J Duncan
**CEO:* Steven Erkenbrack
**COO:* Lorell Walters

ROCKY MOUNTAIN HEALTH PLANS
See ROCKY MOUNTAIN HEALTH MAINTENANCE ORGANIZATION INC

D-U-N-S 18-777-1456
ROCKY MOUNTAIN MATERIALS AND ASPHALT INC
ROCKY MOUNTAIN ASPHALT
1910 Rand Ave, Colorado Springs, CO 80905-2862
Tel (719) 473-3100 *Founded/Ownrshp* 1977
Sales 98.1MM[E] *EMP* 340
SIC 1611 1771 1794 5032

ROCKY MOUNTAIN NEWS
See DENVER POST LLC

ROCKY MOUNTAIN PIES
See LAYTON COMPANIES INC

ROCKY MOUNTAIN POST TIME
See WEMBLEY USA INC

ROCKY MOUNTAIN POWER
See PACIFICORP

D-U-N-S 09-804-2661 EXP
ROCKY MOUNTAIN RECYCLING LLC (UT)
2950 W 900 S, Salt Lake City, UT 84104-4532
Tel (801) 975-1820 *Founded/Ownrshp* 1999
Sales 97.8MM[E] *EMP* 200
SIC 5093 Waste paper
Pr: John Sasine
**CFO:* Marvin Acey
VP: Chuck Jongert
Genl Mgr: Robert Mace
Web Dev: John Wilson
Mtls Mgr: Terry Hughes
Mktg Dir: Teresa Disera

D-U-N-S 00-647-2641
ROCKY MOUNTAIN SUPPLY INC
350 Jackrabbit Ln Stop 1, Belgrade, MT 59714-3035
Tel (406) 388-4008 *Founded/Ownrshp* 1935
Sales 86.4MM *EMP* 94
Accts Hennen & Associates Plc Sout
SIC 5171 5191 5541 5411 Petroleum bulk stations; Farm supplies; Fertilizer & fertilizer materials; Feed; Gasoline service stations; Convenience stores, independent
Pr: Kin Flikkema
**Treas:* John Jackson
**VP:* Ed Malesich
IT Man: Joydeep Choudhury

D-U-N-S 06-961-8363
ROCKY QCD MOUNTAIN LLC
MILE HI FROZEN FOODS
(*Suby of* QUALITY CUSTOM DISTRIBUTION SERVICES INC) ★
4770 E 51st Ave, Denver, CO 80216-3112
Tel (303) 399-6066 *Founded/Ownrshp* 1998, 2016
Sales 131.4MM[E] *EMP* 3[E]
SIC 5141 Food brokers
Pr: Ali Seyedi
Pt: Kristy Taddonio

D-U-N-S 05-044-7093
ROCKYTEP MOUNTAIN LLC
(*Suby of* TERRA ENERGY PARTNERS LLC) ★
1001 17th St Ste 1200, Denver, CO 80202-2056
Tel (303) 572-3900 *Founded/Ownrshp* 2016
Sales 150.1MM[E] *EMP* 196
SIC 5172 Petroleum brokers
CEO: Michael Land
Plnt Mgr: Joe Jaggers

D-U-N-S 01-964-8831
ROCKYS HARDWARE INC (MA)
ACE HARDWARE
40 Island Pond Rd, Springfield, MA 01118-1097
Tel (413) 781-1650 *Founded/Ownrshp* 1930, 1926
Sales 96.0MM[E] *EMP* 450
SIC 5251 Hardware
Ch Bd: James J Falcone
Pr: Fred Allen
**CEO:* Rocco J Falcone
**CFO:* Bob Ostrander
Treas: Michael Scavotto
**VP:* Claire M Falcone
VP: Karen M Gravelin
Dist Mgr: Jeff Baars

ROCON COMPANY CALIF ONLY
See R & O CONSTRUCTION CO INC

ROCS
See R M ROACH & SONS INC

D-U-N-S 00-440-1360
ROD GOLDEN HATCHERY INC (AL)
85 13th St Ne, Cullman, AL 35055-5907
Tel (256) 734-0941 *Founded/Ownrshp* 1959
Sales 64.7MM[E] *EMP* 1,010
SIC 0251 Broiling chickens, raising of
Pr: William Ingram
**VP:* Jim Howard
**Prin:* Forrest H Ingram

D-U-N-S 00-239-0607 IMP
RODALE INC (PA)
400 S 10th St, Emmaus, PA 18049-3622
Tel (800) 848-4735 *Founded/Ownrshp* 1953
Sales 458.7MM[E] *EMP* 1,200
SIC 2721 2731 Magazines: publishing only, not printed on site; Books: publishing only
Pr: Maria Rodale
CEO: Rosalba Messina
**Treas:* Gary Pave
Bd of Dir: George Bird
Chf Mktg O: Gregg Michaelson
**Ofcr:* Ardath Rodale
Assoc VP: Allison Hobson Falkenberry
**Ex VP:* Paul A McGinley
Ex VP: Gregg T Michaelson
**Ex VP:* Thomas A Pogash
**Ex VP:* David Zinczenko
Sr VP: Anne Alexander
**Sr VP:* Richard Alleger
**Sr VP:* Anthony Astarita
**Sr VP:* Chris Lambiase
**Sr VP:* Todd Leiser
**Sr VP:* Robert Novick
**Sr VP:* Tracey Simon-Durden Pierce
**Sr VP:* Karen Rinaldi
Sr VP: Howard Weill
**Sr VP:* David Willey
Board of Directors: Fabiola Arredondo, Placido Corpora, Anthony Rodale, Heather Stoneback, David Widenmyer

D-U-N-S 00-902-0470
RODDA PAINT CO (WA)
(*Subsy of* CLOVERDALE PAINT INC)
6107 N Marine Dr Ste 3, Portland, OR 97203-6443
Tel (503) 521-4300 *Founded/Ownrshp* 1932, 2004
Sales 169.6MM[E] *EMP* 400
SIC 2851 5198 5023 5231 5719 Paints & paint additives; Paints; Paint brushes, rollers, sprayers; Wallcoverings; Window furnishings; Window covering parts & accessories; Paint; Paint brushes, rollers, sprayers & other supplies; Wallcoverings; Window furnishings
CEO: Tim Vogel
Pr: Bill Danielson
**Pr:* David Wolf
COO: Bill Boone
VP: Jeff Pellatz
VP: George Stavnes
VP: Lis Weller
Rgnl Mgr: Jason Lawrence
Genl Mgr: Steve Barrese
Store Mgr: Todd Lightfield
Site Mgr: Dave Gantt

D-U-N-S 00-344-6986
RODGERS BUILDERS INC (NC)
5701 N Sharon Amity Rd, Charlotte, NC 28215-3998
Tel (704) 537-6044 *Founded/Ownrshp* 1963
Sales 260.7MM[E] *EMP* 350
SIC 1542 1541 Institutional building construction; Industrial buildings, new construction
Pr: Patricia A Rodgers
**Ch Bd:* B D Rodgers
**COO:* Eric Reichard
**CFO:* J Bennett Dellinger III
**Sr VP:* Robert J Glusenkamp AIA
**Sr VP:* J Steven Phifer
VP: Ron Cohn
VP: Todd Joyce
**VP:* Jason Money
**VP:* David C Page
**VP:* Lisa Perkins
**VP:* Phyllis Primm

D-U-N-S 01-736-4188
ROEBBELEN CONTRACTING INC
1241 Hawks Flight Ct, El Dorado Hills, CA 95762-9648
Tel (916) 939-4000 *Founded/Ownrshp* 1997
Sales 158.5MM[E] *EMP* 350
SIC 1542 1541 8741 Commercial & office building, new construction; Industrial buildings & warehouses; Construction management
Pr: Kenneth Wenham
COO: Kenneth Debruhl
**COO:* Robert McLean
**CFO:* Dennis Daniel
**CFO:* Greg Hill
**CFO:* Bruce Stimson
**VP:* Angela Mills Dixon
**VP:* Frank Lindsay
VP: Bryan Todd
Snr Sftwr: Denny Roberson
Snr PM: Andy Brophy

D-U-N-S 00-644-3071
ROEHL TRANSPORT INC (WI)
1916 E 29th St, Marshfield, WI 54449-5401
Tel (715) 591-3795 *Founded/Ownrshp* 1962
Sales 390.0MM *EMP* 2,500
SIC 4213 Trucking, except local
CEO: Richard Roehl
VP: Greg Koepel
VP: John Paape
**VP:* Tammara Roehl
VP: Phil Trierweiler
Genl Mgr: Rob Frazier
Opers Mgr: Shaun Glass

D-U-N-S 00-978-0180 IMP
ROEL CONSTRUCTION CO INC (CA)
(*Subsy of* SUFFOLK CONSTRUCTION CO INC) ★
1615 Murray Canyon Rd # 1000, San Diego, CA 92108-4319
Tel (619) 297-4156 *Founded/Ownrshp* 1998, 2011
Sales 85.3MM[E] *EMP* 570
SIC 1541 8741 Industrial buildings, new construction; Construction management
CEO: Wayne Hickey
**Pr:* Andrew Ball
**Pr:* Kevin Elliott
**COO:* Michael Dinapoli
**COO:* Steve Gray
**CFO:* Craig Koehler
Snr PM: Ben Briggs

D-U-N-S 78-391-7578
■ **ROFAN SERVICES INC**
(*Subsy of* DOW CHEMICAL CO) ★
2030 Dow Ctr, Midland, MI 48674-1500
Tel (989) 636-6943 *Founded/Ownrshp* 1989
Sales 209.2MM[E] *EMP* 3,105
SIC 7359 Equipment rental & leasing
Pr: J Pedro Reinhard
**Treas:* Fernando Ruiz
Ex VP: Heinz Haller
**VP:* Charles Kalil
**VP:* Stephane Paquier
**VP:* Margaret Walker

D-U-N-S 96-066-1775
■ **ROFIN-SINAR TECHNOLOGIES INC**
(*Subsy of* COHERENT INC) ★
40984 Concept Dr, Plymouth, MI 48170-4252
Tel (734) 416-0206 *Founded/Ownrshp* 2016
Sales 519.6MM *EMP* 10[E]
SIC 3699 Laser systems & equipment; Laser welding, drilling & cutting equipment
Pr: Thomas Merk
COO: Louis Molnar
Genl Mgr: Dino Chece
CTO: Ulrich Hefter
Sls Mgr: Yannick Galais
Sls Mgr: Stefan Quandt

D-U-N-S 06-174-2193
ROGAN SHOES INC
ROGAN'S SHOES
1750 Ohio St, Racine, WI 53405-3626
Tel (262) 637-3613 *Founded/Ownrshp* 1971
Sales 98.2MM[E] *EMP* 600
SIC 5661 Shoe stores; Men's shoes; Women's shoes; Children's shoes
Pr: Pat Rogan
**VP:* David M Rogan
**Prin:* Dan Donaldson
**Prin:* Dave Rogan
**Prin:* Pat Wolf
Dir IT: Eric Hammond
Sales Asso: Whitney Kallenbach
Sales Asso: Cody Witt

ROGAN'S SHOES
See ROGAN SHOES INC

ROGER DEAN CHEVROLET
See ROGER DEAN ENTERPRISES INC

D-U-N-S 05-268-6367 EXP
ROGER DEAN ENTERPRISES INC (WV)
ROGER DEAN CHEVROLET
2235 Okeechobee Blvd, West Palm Beach, FL 33409-4112
Tel (561) 683-8100 *Founded/Ownrshp* 1980
Sales 100.3MM[E] *EMP* 403
SIC 5511 5521 7538 7532 7515 Automobiles, new & used; Used car dealers; General automotive repair shops; Top & body repair & paint shops; Passenger car leasing
Pr: Paty Dean
**Prin:* Dean Patricia B

D-U-N-S 07-568-7665
ROGER WILLIAMS MEDICAL CENTER
825 Chalkstone Ave, Providence, RI 02908-4728
Tel (401) 456-2000 *Founded/Ownrshp* 1925
Sales 142.9MM *EMP* 1,350
SIC 8062 General medical & surgical hospitals
Pr: Kenneth H Belcher
COO: Karen Burke
CFO: John Schibler
Treas: Michael E Conklin Jr
Ofcr: Barbara O'Neil
VP: Joanne Dooley
VP: Richard Gamache
VP: Frank Renzulli
Exec: Gerald Colvin
Exec: Brenda Ketner
Dir OR: Darlene Pereira
Dir Lab: Mark Dooner
Board of Directors: Cynthia M Alves, Mark Baun, Louis J Marlorenzi, Charles E Maynard, James Melfi, Gary R Pannone, Rev Kenneth R Sicard, Sheri L Smith

D-U-N-S 62-589-9281
ROGER WILLIAMS MEDICAL CENTER
825 Chalkstone Ave, Providence, RI 02908-4728
Tel (401) 456-2000 *Founded/Ownrshp* 1982
Sales 45.7MM[E] *EMP* 1,500
Accts Kpmg Llp Providence Ri
SIC 8062 General medical & surgical hospitals
Pr: Kenneth Belcher
V Ch: Edward Hjerpe
V Ch: Donald C McQueen
COO: Guy Medeglia
CFO: John Hanley
CFO: Addy Kane
CFO: John Schibler
Ofcr: Barbara Oneil
Top Exec: James R Koness
VP: Brandon Clar
VP: Richard Gamache
VP: Guy Medaglia
VP: Roger Williams
Dir Lab: Bill Auerbach
Dir Rx: Jim Melfi

D-U-N-S 06-392-6380
ROGER WILLIAMS UNIVERSITY
1 Old Ferry Rd, Bristol, RI 02809-2921
Tel (401) 253-1040 *Founded/Ownrshp* 1919
Sales 197.3MM *EMP* 425
SIC 8221 University
Pr: Donald J Farish
Pr: Kathleen Chrupcala
**Treas:* David Gilmore
Ofcr: Warren A Brown
Ofcr: Gerald Lorden
Assoc VP: Peter Wilbur
**Ex VP:* Jerome Williams
VP: James Noonan
Assoc Dir: Lori Johnston
Assoc Dir: Francis McGovern III
Ex Dir: Chelsie Horne
Board of Directors: John Bo

D-U-N-S 00-330-7345
ROGER WOOD FOODS INC
RW
7 Alfred St, Savannah, GA 31408-3229
Tel (912) 652-9600 *Founded/Ownrshp* 1989
Sales 93.8MM[E] *EMP* 250
SIC 2013 5147 Sausages from purchased meat; Frankfurters from purchased meat; Meats, fresh; Meats, cured or smoked
Pr: David W Solana
**Treas:* Mark F Solana
**VP:* Joseph M Solana III

D-U-N-S 04-808-0378 IMP
ROGER ZATKOFF CO
ZATKOFF SEALS & PACKINGS
23230 Industrial Park Dr, Farmington Hills, MI 48335-2850
Tel (248) 478-2400 *Founded/Ownrshp* 1959
Sales 117.5MM[E] *EMP* 176
SIC 5085 5072 3053 Seals, industrial; Hardware; Gaskets & sealing devices; Packing materials
Pr: Gary Zatkoff
COO: Larry Cholody
**VP:* David Zatkoff
Brnch Mgr: Art Steitz
Genl Mgr: Patty Anson
Genl Mgr: Brian Gilboy
MIS Dir: Cliff Gary
MIS Dir: Sebring Gary
MIS Dir: Gary Sebring
IT Man: Norb Heban
IT Man: Cliff Sebling

ROGERS & HOLLANDS JEWELERS
See ROGERS ENTERPRISES INC

D-U-N-S 19-952-9140 IMP
ROGERS BENEFIT GROUP INC
5110 N 40th St Ste 234, Phoenix, AZ 85018-2151
Tel (612) 332-8866 *Founded/Ownrshp* 1988
Sales NA *EMP* 350
SIC 6411 Insurance agents, brokers & service

ROGER'S CARTAGE
See TANKSTAR USA INC

D-U-N-S 00-114-1167 IMP
▲ **ROGERS CORP** (MA)
1 Technology Dr, Rogers, CT 06263
Tel (860) 774-9605 *Founded/Ownrshp* 1832
Sales 641.4MM *EMP* 2,930
Accts Pricewaterhousecoopers Llp H
Tkr Sym ROG *Exch* NYS
SIC 2891 2821 2824 Adhesives & sealants; Laminating compounds; Polyurethane resins; Silicone resins; Elastomeric fibers
Pr: Bruce D Hoechner
Pr: Helen Zhang
COO: Roger Kenigson
CFO: Janice E Stipp
Ofcr: Gary M Glandon
Sr VP: Robert C Daigle
VP: Jeffrey M Grudzien
VP: Jay Knoll
VP: John C Quinn
VP: Dale Shepard
Exec: Craig Huffine
Board of Directors: Keith L Barnes, Michael F Barry, Carol R Jensen, William E Mitchell, Robert G Paul, Helene Simonet, Peter C Wallace

D-U-N-S 05-944-3614
ROGERS ENTERPRISES INC
ROGERS & HOLLANDS JEWELERS
20821 S Cicero Ave, Matteson, IL 60443-1201
Tel (708) 679-7588 *Founded/Ownrshp* 1987
Sales 106.4MM[E] *EMP* 700
SIC 5944 Jewelry, precious stones & precious metals
Ch Bd: Alan I Kadet
**Pr:* Craig Stern
Pr: Laurie Stern
**VP:* Joseph Hartl
**VP:* Juell Kadet
Dir IT: Kim Schunke

D-U-N-S 00-102-5113 IMP/EXP
ROGERS FOAM CORP (MA)
20 Vernon St Ste 1, Somerville, MA 02145-3699
Tel (617) 623-3010 *Founded/Ownrshp* 1947
Sales 196.8MM[E] *EMP* 500
SIC 3086 Plastics foam products
Pr: David P Marotta
Ch: Mathew Rogers
Board of Directors: Ann Rogers, Brenda R Rogers, Dorothy K Rogers, James H Rogers, Sheila A Rogers

D-U-N-S 05-791-3287
ROGERS GROUP INC
421 Great Circle Rd, Nashville, TN 37228-1495
Tel (615) 242-0585 *Founded/Ownrshp* 1908
Sales 1.2MMM[E] *EMP* 1,600
Accts Ernst & Young Llp Nashville
SIC 1611 1422 General contractor, highway & street construction; Crushed & broken limestone
CEO: Jerry Geraghty
Pr: Darin Matson
COO: Gerard Geraghty
**Treas:* James A Patton Jr
Treas: Joe Whitehouse
VP: Chet Foster
Dir: Larry Cox
Off Mgr: Elizabeth Lenning
MIS Dir: Fran Bellant
Mtls Mgr: Cameron Druyor
Sfty Mgr: Davey Thompson
Board of Directors: Jim Beard, Laura R Harper, Benjamin R Rechter, Benjamin L Rechter, David W Rechter, Richard P Rechter, Samuel R Rechter, Ray Richelson, Don Williamson

D-U-N-S 07-615-4749
ROGERS MEMORIAL HOSPITAL INC
34700 Valley Rd, Oconomowoc, WI 53066-4599
Tel (800) 767-4411 *Founded/Ownrshp* 1970
Sales 113.9MM *EMP* 600
Accts Wipfli Llp Wausau Wi
SIC 8063 Psychiatric hospitals
CEO: Paul A Mueller
**CFO:* Jerry Noll
Treas: Roger Cohen
Bd of Dir: William Mulligan
Bd of Dir: James Wahner
VP: James E Ledbetter
Dir IT: Wayne Mattson
HC Dir: Jamie Lewiston
HC Dir: Anthony Meyer

D-U-N-S 03-790-6096
ROGERS PETROLEUM INC
1634 W 1st North St, Morristown, TN 37814-3709
Tel (423) 581-7460 *Founded/Ownrshp* 1980
Sales 425.8MM *EMP* 200
SIC 5171 Petroleum bulk stations
Ch: Donald C Rogers
Pr: Scott Matherly
**CEO:* Chris Liposky
VP: Brent Cooper
**Prin:* Penney P Rogers
Genl Mgr: Tim Pruitt
Netwrk Eng: Fred Myers
VP Sls: Craig Kramer

D-U-N-S 02-948-0139
ROGERS PUBLIC SCHOOLS
ENGLISH AS A SECOND LANGUAGE
220 S 5th St, Rogers, AR 72756-4467
Tel (479) 631-3696 *Founded/Ownrshp* 1995
Sales 15.5MM[E] *EMP* 1,400
SIC 8299 Language school

D-U-N-S 03-041-6895
ROGERS SCHOOL DISTRICT 30
500 W Walnut St, Rogers, AR 72756-3774
Tel (479) 636-3910 *Founded/Ownrshp* 1920
Sales 82.0MM *EMP* 1,600
Accts Bkd Llp Fort Smith/Little Ro
SIC 8211 Public combined elementary & secondary school
Pr Dir: Ashley Kelley Siwiec
Schl Brd P: Jerry Carmichael

D-U-N-S 11-600-9457
ROGOSIN INSTITUTE INC
505 E 70th St Fl 2, New York, NY 10021-4872
Tel (212) 746-1551 *Founded/Ownrshp* 1963
Sales 100.0MM *EMP* 450
Accts Maier Markey & Justic Llp Whi
SIC 8733 8399 Medical research; Health & welfare council
Pr: Albert L Rubin MD
**Ch Bd:* Richard Hall
**COO:* Kurt Stenzel MD
**Sr VP:* Barry Smith MD
Doctor: Bruce R Godon
Doctor: Allen W Mead
Doctor: Jeffrey Silberzweig

D-U-N-S 61-619-2746
ROGUE WAVE SOFTWARE INC
1315 W Century Dr Ste 150, Louisville, CO 80027-9560
Tel (303) 473-9118 *Founded/Ownrshp* 2001
Sales 97.9MM[E] *EMP* 284
SIC 7371 7372 Computer software development; Prepackaged software
CEO: Bryan Pierce
CFO: Steve Scheudle
**Sr VP:* Frank Roe
VP: Christine Bottagaro
**VP:* Harold E Julsn
VP: David Rice
VP: Gregory J Schumacher
**VP:* Ted Smith
VP: Mary Walker
**Prin:* Rod Cope
**Prin:* Ian McLeod

ROHM AMERICA
See EVONIK CYRO LLC

D-U-N-S 00-229-2043 IMP/EXP
■ **ROHM AND HAAS CO**
(*Subsy of* DOW CHEMICAL CO) ★
100 N Independence Mall W, Philadelphia, PA 19106-1521
Tel (215) 592-3000 *Founded/Ownrshp* 1917
Sales 4.9MMM[E] *EMP* 15,710
SIC 2819 2851 2891 2899 Chemicals, high purity: refined from technical grade; Paints & paint additives; Adhesives & sealants; Salt
Pr: I M Peribere
**Pr:* Pierre R Brondeau
**CFO:* Jacques M Croisetiere
CFO: Dave Perkins
CFO: Jacques M Croiseti RE
Treas: Colleen Johnson
**Treas:* Edward E Liebert
Bd of Dir: S Stewart
**Ex VP:* Robert A Lonergan
**Ex VP:* Anne M Wilms
**VP:* I A Barbour
VP: Neil Carr
VP: Ruby Chandy
VP: Joseph J Forish
VP: Marisa L Guerin
VP: Bruce Hoechner
VP: Phil Louis
VP: Richard R Lovely

D-U-N-S 00-106-0615 IMP/EXP
■ ROHM AND HAAS ELECTRONIC MATERIALS LLC
(*Suby of* DOW CHEMICAL CO) ★
455 Forest St, Marlborough, MA 01752-3001
Tel (508) 481-7950 *Founded/Ownrshp* 1994
Sales 180.5MM^E *EMP* 1,000
SIC 2819 2869 Industrial inorganic chemicals; Industrial organic chemicals
CFO: Robert Harrer
Brnch Mgr: Jim Graham
Dir IT: Joseph Zarate
Sales Asso: Michael Condon
Counsel: Jonathan Baskin

D-U-N-S 06-509-6273 IMP/EXP
■ ROHM AND HAAS TEXAS INC (TX)
(*Suby of* ROHM AND HAAS CO) ★
6600 La Porte Fwy, Deer Park, TX 77536
Tel (281) 476-8304 *Founded/Ownrshp* 1948
Sales 204.9MM^E *EMP* 1,000^E
SIC 2869 2899 2819 Industrial organic chemicals; Chemical preparations; Industrial inorganic chemicals
Ch Bd: Rajiv L Gupta
**Pr:* Robert W Brinly
**Pr:* Pierre R Brondeau
**Pr:* Jacques M Croisetiere
**Pr:* John E Cubertson
Bd of Dir: Richard Keyser
Bd of Dir: Sandra Moose
Bd of Dir: Gilbert Omenn
Bd of Dir: Gary Rogers
Bd of Dir: George Whitesides
Bd of Dir: Mama Whittington
**VP:* James Fahey

D-U-N-S 00-838-2053 IMP
■ ROHR INC
GOODRICH AEROSTRUCTURES GROUP
(*Suby of* UNITED TECHNOLOGIES CORP) ★
850 Lagoon Dr, Chula Vista, CA 91910-2001
Tel (619) 691-4111 *Founded/Ownrshp* 1997
Sales 1.1MMM^E *EMP* 4,600
SIC 3728 Aircraft parts & equipment; Nacelles, aircraft; Aircraft landing assemblies & brakes; Research & dev by manuf., aircraft parts & auxiliary equip
Pr: Greg Peters
**Pr:* Curtis Reusser
**CFO:* Laurence A Chapman
Treas: Kenneth W Scholz
**VP:* Brian Broderick
**VP:* Robert A Gustafson
VP: Stephen Huggins
**VP:* Richard W Madsen
**VP:* Graydon A Wetzler
**VP:* Kenneth Wood
**VP:* Fred Zahn

D-U-N-S 00-421-4870 IMP
ROHRER CORP (OH)
GATEWAY PRINTING
717 Seville Rd, Wadsworth, OH 44281-1091
Tel (330) 335-1541 *Founded/Ownrshp* 1953
Sales 130.6MM^E *EMP* 495
SIC 3089 2675 Blister or bubble formed packaging, plastic; Die-cut paper & board
Pr: Scot D Adkins
**CFO:* Bob Stopar
**VP:* David W Rohrer
Exec: Mark Russo
Genl Mgr: Troy Eckstine
Genl Mgr: Carmine Lombardi
Genl Mgr: Scott Nagel
Off Mgr: Karen Wolfe
Plnt Mgr: Michael McDaniel
Sls&Mrk Ex: Alane Updegraff
Mktg Mgr: James Dalton

D-U-N-S 05-344-4840 IMP
ROHTSTEIN CORP (MA)
ORCHARD FOOD DIV
70 Olympia Ave, Woburn, MA 01801-2036
Tel (781) 935-8300 *Founded/Ownrshp* 1970
Sales 118.4MM^E *EMP* 95
SIC 5149 2099 2087 2062 2041 2033 Groceries & related products; Sugar, refined; Flour; Food preparations; Flavoring extracts & syrups; Cane sugar refining; Flour & other grain mill products; Canned fruits & specialties
Pr: Steven Rohtstein
Genl Mgr: Marty Braun

D-U-N-S 60-644-5674 IMP
ROKI AMERICA CO LTD
(*Suby of* ROKI HOLDINGS CO.,LTD.)
2001 Production Dr, Findlay, OH 45840-5450
Tel (419) 424-9713 *Founded/Ownrshp* 1989
Sales 186.7MM^E *EMP* 350
SIC 3714 Filters: oil, fuel & air, motor vehicle; Power transmission equipment, motor vehicle
CEO: Takaya Shimada
**Pr:* Toshifumi Sasamori
**Ch:* Hiromitsu Shimada Jr
**VP:* Bob Funkhouser
CTO: Steve Senn
Plnt Mgr: Akira Terada

D-U-N-S 18-710-1399 IMP/EXP
ROKR DISTRIBUTION US INC
KMC MUSIC
(*Suby of* FENDER MUSICAL INSTRUMENTS CORP) ★
310 W Newberry Rd, Bloomfield, CT 06002-1393
Tel (860) 509-8888 *Founded/Ownrshp* 1977
Sales 92.6MM^E *EMP* 400
SIC 5099 3931 Musical instruments parts & accessories; Musical instruments; Strings, musical instrument; Guitars & parts, electric & nonelectric
Pr: Mark Terry
**Pr:* Edward G Miller
**CFO:* Larry Dunn
**CFO:* Robert Garano
**CFO:* Mark Morneau
**Treas:* James Broenen
**VP:* Charles E Bashaw
VP: Robert Crescitelli
**VP:* Paul J Damiano

D-U-N-S 82-836-6836 IMP
ROKU INC
150 Winchester Cir, Los Gatos, CA 95032-1812
Tel (408) 556-9040 *Founded/Ownrshp* 1997
Sales 163.1MM^E *EMP* 400
SIC 4841 Cable & other pay television services
Pr: Anthony Wood
**CFO:* Steve Louden
**Chf Mktg O:* Matthew Anderson
VP: Mary E Broganer
VP: Mark Goodwin
VP: Scott D Haas
VP: Mark Lieblein
Creative D: Cheryl Singletary
Comm Dir: Brian Jaquet
Dir Rx: Barbara Shih
Snr Sftwr: Mike Kobb
Board of Directors: Ravi Ahuja, Shawn Carolan, Daniel V Leff Phd, Anthony Wood

D-U-N-S 06-384-4807 IMP/EXP
ROLAND CORP US
(*Suby of* ROLAND CORPORATION)
5100 S Eastern Ave, Los Angeles, CA 90040-2938
Tel (323) 890-3700 *Founded/Ownrshp* 1978
Sales 114.0MM^E *EMP* 350
Accts Deloitte & Touche Llp Los Ang
SIC 5099 5045 3931 Musical instruments; Computer peripheral equipment; Organs, all types: pipe, reed, hand, electronic, etc.
CEO: Christopher Bristol
Pr: Fumie Wolff
CFO: Thai Ngo
**VP:* Dennis M Houlihan
**VP:* Mark S Malbon
VP: Yoshi Shibata
**VP:* Charles L Wright
**VP:* Junpei Yamato
Dir IT: Paul Ward
Dir IT: David Williams
Web Dev: Jeff Gibbs

D-U-N-S 08-218-4300 IMP/EXP
ROLAND DGA CORP
(*Suby of* ROLAND DG CORPORATION)
15363 Barranca Pkwy, Irvine, CA 92618-2216
Tel (949) 727-2100 *Founded/Ownrshp* 2008
Sales 119.4MM *EMP* 105^E
Accts Deloitte & Touche Llp Los An
SIC 5045 8741 Computer peripheral equipment; Management services
Pr: David Goward
**Pr:* Andrew Oransky
COO: Ron Ball
**CFO:* Bruce Lauper
Exec: Connie Caigoy
Creative D: Patrick Kersey
CIO: Bob Castle
Natl Sales: Stephanie Andrews
Natl Sales: Grant Davis
Manager: Barry Lachance
Manager: Sid Lambert

D-U-N-S 01-223-1924 IMP/EXP
ROLAND FOODS LLC
AMERICAN FOOD
(*Suby of* VESTAR CAPITAL PARTNERS INC) ★
71 W 23rd St, New York, NY 10010-4102
Tel (212) 741-8290 *Founded/Ownrshp* 2013
Sales 119.1MM^E *EMP* 150
SIC 5149 Canned goods: fruit, vegetables, seafood, meats, etc.
CEO: James Wagner
Pr: Bhawani Katyal
Pr: George Steiner
CFO: Ted McCormick
VP: Joseph Gozzi
Rgnl Mgr: Barry Gertz
Dist Mgr: Kesi Wright
Dir IT: Steve Adler
Trfc Mgr: Steve Orlinsky
Manager: Tom Doughty
Genl Couns: Holly Passantino

D-U-N-S 06-524-1580 EXP
ROLAND MACHINERY CO
816 N Dirksen Pkwy, Springfield, IL 62702-6115
Tel (217) 789-7711 *Founded/Ownrshp* 1994
Sales 225.0MM *EMP* 325
Accts Sikich Llp Springfield Illin
SIC 7353 5082 Heavy construction equipment rental; General construction machinery & equipment
Ch Bd: Edwin Earl Roland
**Pr:* Matthew Roland
**Pr:* Raymond E Roland
**CFO:* Michael Armstrong
VP: Jerry Eastburn
Genl Mgr: James Jesuit
Genl Mgr: Dan Smith
Off Admin: Tammy Neil

D-U-N-S 02-887-9856
ROLEX INDUSTRIES INC
(*Suby of* ROLEX HOLDING SA)
665 5th Ave Fl 6, New York, NY 10022-5342
Tel (212) 758-7700 *Founded/Ownrshp* 1977
Sales 120.6MM^E *EMP* 500^E
SIC 5094 7631 6512 Watches & parts; Watch repair; Commercial & industrial building operation
Pr: Walter Fischer
**Ch Bd:* Patrick Harrigen
**CFO:* Michael Elms
**Treas:* Thomas Snowden
VP: Lawrence Camarda
VP: Stephen Hodgkins
VP: Heinz Imhof
VP: W Stoeber
IT Man: Ron Snaider

ROLFS
See TANDY BRANDS ACCESSORIES INC

ROLL III, WILLIAM J F
See SHEARMAN & STERLING LLP

ROLL-O-SHEETS
See PLIANT LLC

D-U-N-S 05-483-4288 IMP/EXP
ROLLED ALLOYS INC
125 W Sterns Rd, Temperance, MI 48182-9567
Tel (800) 521-0332 *Founded/Ownrshp* 1953
Sales 507.1MM^E *EMP* 166
SIC 5051 3369 3341 3317 2899 2851 Metals service centers & offices; Nonferrous foundries; Secondary nonferrous metals; Steel pipe & tubes; Chemical preparations; Paints & allied products
Prin: Thomas Nichol
CFO: Dave Nault
Sr VP: Nicole Cousino
VP: Woody Stephens
**Prin:* Alex Briceno
**Prin:* Richard W Colburn
**Prin:* Shaun A Hussey
**Prin:* Dale G Kuntz
**Prin:* David J Nault
**Prin:* Kenneth Reinke
Rgnl Mgr: Todd Brown

D-U-N-S 00-232-5991 IMP
■ ROLLER BEARING CO OF AMERICA INC
R B C
(*Suby of* RBC BEARINGS INC) ★
102 Willenbrock Rd, Oxford, CT 06478-1033
Tel (203) 267-7001 *Founded/Ownrshp* 1934
Sales 344.5MM^E *EMP* 1,746
SIC 3562 Ball & roller bearings; Roller bearings & parts; Ball bearings & parts
Ch Bd: Michael J Hartnett
**CFO:* Daniel A Bergeron
**Ex VP:* Michael S Gostomski
**VP:* Richard J Edwards
**VP:* Christopher Thomas
Board of Directors: Robert Anderson, Richard R Crowell, Kurt B Larsen, William E Myers Jr, Mitchell I Quain

D-U-N-S 00-636-6926
ROLLER DIE AND FORMING CO INC
1172 Industrial Blvd, Louisville, KY 40219-1804
Tel (502) 969-1327 *Founded/Ownrshp* 1931
Sales 84.1MM^E *EMP* 265^E
SIC 3355 3544 Structural shapes, rolled, aluminum; Special dies, tools, jigs & fixtures
Exec: Robert Koestel
Ex Dir: Glenn Nelson
Off Mgr: Angela Hemmons
Opers Mgr: Bill Thorsby
Sls Mgr: Doug Lange

D-U-N-S 00-510-1670
ROLLEX CORP (IL)
800 Chase Ave, Elk Grove Village, IL 60007-4806
Tel (847) 437-3000 *Founded/Ownrshp* 1950, 1951
Sales 105.1MM^E *EMP* 400
SIC 3444 Gutters, sheet metal; Siding, sheet metal
Pr: James L Brittingham
**Ch Bd:* Bruce Stevens
**CFO:* John Foley
CFO: Mark Mieszala
VP: Bill Smith
Exec: Robert Hattinger
Mfg Dir: Mike Shield
Sls Dir: Dan Summers
Sls Mgr: Brian Butz
Sls Mgr: Chris Danielson
Sls Mgr: Ryan Yeakley

ROLLING STONE
See WENNER MEDIA LLC

D-U-N-S 00-407-6667 IMP
ROLLINS COLLEGE (FL)
1000 Holt Ave 2718, Winter Park, FL 32789-4409
Tel (407) 646-2000 *Founded/Ownrshp* 1885
Sales 141.1MM *EMP* 645
Accts Cherry Bekaert Llp Orlando F
SIC 8221 Colleges universities & professional schools
Ch Bd: Francis H Barker
**Pr:* Lewis M Duncan
**Treas:* George H Herbst
VP: Mamta Accapadi
VP: Carol Bresnahan
VP: Ronald Korvas
VP: Lori Lovell
Assoc Dir: Jennifer Dewitt
Assoc Dir: Whitney McDonald
Creative D: Tom May
Store Mgr: Mary Vitelli

D-U-N-S 00-691-9088 IMP
▲ ROLLINS INC
2170 Piedmont Rd Ne, Atlanta, GA 30324-4135
Tel (404) 888-2000 *Founded/Ownrshp* 1948
Sales 1.4MMM *EMP* 11,000
Tkr Sym ROL *Exch* NYS
SIC 7342 Disinfecting & pest control services; Pest control in structures; Termite control
Ch Bd: R Randall Rollins
Pr: Pat Murray
Pr: Ken Poinsette
Pr: John F Wilson
CEO: Gary W Rollins
CFO: Paul E Northen
Ex VP: Chuck Summers
VP: Elizabeth Chandler
VP: Clyde Cobb
VP: Ralph D'Ambrosio
VP: Edward Donoghue
VP: Jerry Gahlhoff
VP: Tom Hutchins
VP: Eugene Iarocci
VP: Pamela A Nance
VP: Harry Sargent
VP: Thomas Tesh
VP: Eugene Weaver

D-U-N-S 05-142-4000 IMP
ROLLINS LEASING LLC
(*Suby of* PENSKE TRUCK LEASING CO LP) ★
2200 Concord Pike, Wilmington, DE 19803-2909
Tel (302) 426-2700 *Founded/Ownrshp* 2001
Sales 81.6MM^E *EMP* 2,446
Accts Kpmg Llp
SIC 7513 Truck rental, without drivers; Truck leasing, without drivers
Ch Bd: David Burr
**CEO:* I Larry Brown
**Treas:* Jim Mc Caughan
**Ex VP:* Terry Scott
**Ex VP:* Neil Vonnahme
**VP:* Ron Fijalkowski
**VP:* Carlisle Peet

ROLLINS RANCHES
See LOR INC

D-U-N-S 04-068-2858
■ ROLLINS SUPPLY INC
ORKIN
(*Suby of* ROLLINS INC) ★
2170 Piedmont Rd Ne, Atlanta, GA 30324-4135
Tel (404) 888-2000 *Founded/Ownrshp* 1975
Sales 77.4MM *EMP* 1,000
SIC 7389 Purchasing service
Pr: Gary W Rollins
**CFO:* Harry Cynkus
VP: Henry Anthony
**VP:* Tom Luczynsky
VP: Kathleen Mayton
Exec: Gordon Crenshaw
Exec: Nelson Jackson
Exec: Roxanne White
Mktg Dir: Kevin Whitehead
Sls Mgr: Robert Barr
Genl Couns: Katleen Maiton

D-U-N-S 80-475-4141 IMP
ROLLS-ROYCE CORP
(*Suby of* ROLLS-ROYCE NORTH AMERICA HOLDINGS INC) ★
450 S Meridian St, Indianapolis, IN 46225-1103
Tel (317) 230-2000 *Founded/Ownrshp* 1915
Sales 2.0MMM^E *EMP* 6,225
SIC 3724 3443 3462 3731 3743 3732 Aircraft engines & engine parts; Industrial vessels, tanks & containers; Nuclear power plant forgings, ferrous; Submarines, building & repairing; Railroad locomotives & parts, electric or nonelectric; Yachts, building & repairing
Pr: Marion C Blakey
**Pr:* Lawrie Haynes
**Pr:* Mark King
Pr: Daniel Longbottom
COO: John Cheffins
COO: Mark Wilson
Ofcr: Joseph Krok
Ex VP: Ronald Bates
VP: Kevin L Bell
VP: James R Bogan
**VP:* David Evans
VP: Kenneth Roberts
VP: Allan Swan
**VP:* Gary Swartz
VP: David Waggoner
Dir Rx: Graeme Waddell
Dir Bus: Jim Payton
Dir Bus: Cristal Rice
Comm Man: Steffi Anders

D-U-N-S 12-129-5372 IMP/EXP
ROLLS-ROYCE ENERGY SYSTEMS INC
105 N Sandusky St, Mount Vernon, OH 43050-2447
Tel (740) 393-8888 *Founded/Ownrshp* 1999
Sales 69.4M^E *EMP* 1,000
SIC 3511 5084 8711

D-U-N-S 00-100-6311 IMP/EXP
ROLLS-ROYCE MARINE NORTH AMERICA INC
(*Suby of* ROLLS-ROYCE NORTH AMERICA HOLDINGS INC) ★
110 Norfolk St, Walpole, MA 02081-1704
Tel (508) 668-9610 *Founded/Ownrshp* 1999
Sales 110.5MM^E *EMP* 250
SIC 3599 3446 3429 Propellers, ship & boat: machined; Acoustical suspension systems, metal; Manufactured hardware (general)
CEO: Jim Guyette
**Pr:* Don Roussinos
**CFO:* Mark Morris
**Treas:* William T Powers III
Ofcr: Brian Semle
VP: Christopher Cikanovich
VP: Joseph Riley
Ex Dir: Lames Guyette
Prgrm Mgr: Mark Mittle
Prgrm Mgr: Richard Olobri
Genl Mgr: Phyllis Craine

D-U-N-S 18-453-3227 IMP/EXP
ROLLS-ROYCE MOTOR CARS NA LLC
(*Suby of* BMW (US) HOLDING CORP) ★
300 Chestnut Ridge Rd, Woodcliff Lake, NJ 07677-7739
Tel (201) 307-4117 *Founded/Ownrshp* 2002
Sales 228.8MM^E *EMP* 4,293^E
SIC 3711 Motor vehicles & car bodies
Pr: Pedro Moto
Genl Mgr: Ethan Forchette

ROLLS-ROYCE N SCOTTSDALE
See PAG WEST LLC

D-U-N-S 18-839-3854 IMP
ROLLS-ROYCE NORTH AMERICA (USA) HOLDINGS CO
(*Suby of* ROLLS-ROYCE OVERSEAS HOLDINGS LIMITED)
1875 Explorer St Ste 200, Reston, VA 20190-6022
Tel (703) 834-1700 *Founded/Ownrshp* 1992
Sales 3.4MMM^E *EMP* 7,013^E
SIC 5088 8741 6159 3724 Aircraft & parts; Aircraft engines & engine parts; Business management; Machinery & equipment finance leasing; Aircraft engines & engine parts
Ch: Ian Davis
**Pr:* James Guyette
**Pr:* Lawrie Haynes
**Pr:* Andrew Heath
Pr: Dan Korte
**CEO:* John Rishton
**COO:* Mike Terrett
**Treas:* Michael Elliott
Sr VP: Robert Carpenter

VP: Louis Baviello
**VP:* T P Dale
VP: Steve Friedrich
VP: Tim McGrath
VP: Thomas Sacco
VP: Pete Torralbas
Dir Risk M: Maneesh Kessop
Comm Dir: Joel Reuter
Dir Bus: Robert Ivy

D-U-N-S 07-280-2317 IMP/EXP
ROLLS-ROYCE NORTH AMERICA HOLDINGS INC
(*Suby of* ROLLS-ROYCE NORTH AMERICA (USA) HOLDINGS CO) ★
1875 Explorer St Ste 200, Reston, VA 20190-6022
Tel (703) 834-1700 *Founded/Ownrshp* 1968
Sales 3.3MMM^E *EMP* 7,000
SIC 5088 8741 7699 Aircraft & parts; Business management; Aircraft & heavy equipment repair services
Pr: James M Guyette
CFO: William T Powers
Treas: Michael Elliott
Ex VP: James Bogan
VP: Chris Cyr
VP: Thomas Dale
Exec: Mike Stubbs
Sls&Mrk Ex: Mark Wilford
VP Sls: Randy Gordon
VP Sls: David Meeker

D-U-N-S 02-949-4056 IMP
ROLLS-ROYCE NORTH AMERICA INC
(*Suby of* ROLLS-ROYCE NORTH AMERICA HOLDINGS INC) ★
1875 Explorer St Ste 200, Reston, VA 20190-6022
Tel (703) 834-1700 *Founded/Ownrshp* 1999
Sales 1.2MMM^E *EMP* 700
SIC 5088 8741 1731 Transportation equipment & supplies; Management services; Electric power systems contractors
Pr: James S Guyette
Pr: Wayne Moni
Treas: Michael Elliott
**Ex VP:* Thomas P Dale
**Ex VP:* Kirk Larson
**Ex VP:* Thomas O Loehr
Sr VP: Bob Reding
VP: Rebecca Blackman
VP: Chris Cyr
VP: Mike Elliott
Dir Bus: Chris Floyd

ROLOK PRODUCTS
See TEMP-CONTROL MECHANICAL CORP

D-U-N-S 60-883-0915
ROLTA ADVIZEX TECHNOLOGIES LLC
(*Suby of* ROLTA INTERNATIONAL INC) ★
6480 S Rockside Woods, Independence, OH 44131-2233
Tel (216) 901-1818 *Founded/Ownrshp* 2005
Sales 210.6MM^E *EMP* 326
SIC 7373 Value-added resellers, computer systems; Systems software development services
CEO: Fred Traversi
CFO: Nick Colagiovanni
**CFO:* Mark Woelke
Ex VP: Dale M Constantino
**Ex VP:* Marc Sarazin
**VP:* John Brier
**VP:* Patrick Fettuccia
Sales Asso: Rebecca Sigler

D-U-N-S 79-344-4852
ROLTA INTERNATIONAL INC
(*Suby of* ROLTA INDIA LIMITED)
5865 N Point Pkwy Ste 300, Alpharetta, GA 30022-1113
Tel (678) 942-5000 *Founded/Ownrshp* 1992
Sales 237.7MM^E *EMP* 328
SIC 7389 7371 7372 Mapmaking or drafting, including aerial; Computer software development; Software programming applications; Prepackaged software
Pr: Preetha Pulusani
Pr: Chris Atkinson
Pr: Jason M Cory
**Pr:* Benedict Eazzetta
Pr: Ravi Shankar Pandey
**CFO:* Hiranya Ashar
**Ch:* Kamal K Singh
Ex VP: D T Kapadia
Ex VP: Jack Leahey
Ex VP: Blane Schertz
Sr VP: Anthony Catalano
Sr VP: David Kingsbury
Sr VP: Richard Martin
Sr VP: Anand Pitre
Sr VP: Ravi Puri
Sr VP: Jimmy Rushing
**Sr VP:* Sk Shirguppi
Sr VP: Joseph Ung
Sr VP: Jonathan Vivar
**VP:* Laxmidhar Gaopande
VP: Vipan Khanna

D-U-N-S 04-628-1846
ROMA INDEPENDENT SCHOOL DISTRICT
ROMA ISD
608 N Garcia St, Roma, TX 78584
Tel (956) 849-1377 *Founded/Ownrshp* 1930
Sales 71.1MM^E *EMP* 1,100
SIC 8211 Public elementary & secondary schools
Prin: Carlos Guzman
Dir Sec: Oscar Ramirez
IT Man: Leticia Cadena
IT Man: Manuel Garcia
IT Man: Eusebio Lopez
Schl Brd P: Arturo Perez

ROMA ISD
See ROMA INDEPENDENT SCHOOL DISTRICT

D-U-N-S 79-609-2450
ROMACORP INC
TONY ROMA'S
11315 Corp Blvd Ste 100, Orlando, FL 32817
Tel (214) 343-7800 *Founded/Ownrshp* 2006
Sales 136.6MM^E *EMP* 3,500
SIC 5812 Restaurant, family: chain
Pr: Stephen K Judge
Pr: John Brisco
Ch: John Morgan
VP: Sarah Jackson
VP: Kenneth Myres
VP: Miranda V Pulliam
VP: Bradley Smith
Dir Surg: Laura Hansen
Dir Surg: John Looney
Dir Surg: Shane Womack
Ex Dir: Bob Gallagher

D-U-N-S 00-896-3985
ROMAN CATHOLIC ARCHBISHOP OF BOSTON
ARCHDIOCESE OF BOSTON
66 Brooks Dr, Braintree, MA 02184-3839
Tel (617) 254-0100 *Founded/Ownrshp* 1800
Sales 95.5MM^E *EMP* 3,400
Accts Grant Thornton Llp Boston Ma
SIC 8661 Catholic Church
Pr: Sean Patrick O'Malley
Prin: Richard M Erikson
Snr Ntwrk: Dan Michaelis
Dir IT: George Clemens
Dir IT: Steven McDevitt
Genl Couns: Beirne Lovely

D-U-N-S 06-456-7084
ROMAN CATHOLIC ARCHBISHOP OF LOS ANGELES
ARCHDIOCESE OF LOS ANGELES
3424 Wilshire Blvd, Los Angeles, CA 90010-2263
Tel (213) 637-7000 *Founded/Ownrshp* 1904
Sales 373.2MM^E *EMP* 12,000
Accts Mcgladrey Llp Los Angeles Ca
SIC 8661 Catholic Church
**CFO:* Randolph E Stinr
Mktg Mgr: Joerg Stadler

D-U-N-S 08-859-5574
ROMAN CATHOLIC ARCHBISHOP OF PORTLAND IN OREGON AND SUCCESSORS A CORP SOLE
ARCHDIOCESE PORTLAND IN OREGON
2838 E Burnside St, Portland, OR 97214-1830
Tel (503) 234-5334 *Founded/Ownrshp* 1874
Sales 165.0MM *EMP* 2,500
SIC 8661 Catholic Church
Pr: Archbishop J Vlazny
**Pr:* Alexander K Sample
**CFO:* Joanne Willhite
VP: Maureen Maag

ROMAN CATHOLIC ARCHDIOCESE OF
See ST BARNABAS SCHOOL

D-U-N-S 00-653-3863
ROMAN CATHOLIC ARCHDIOCESE OF DETROIT
12 State St, Detroit, MI 48226-1823
Tel (313) 237-5800 *Founded/Ownrshp* 1833
Sales 277.1MM^E *EMP* 8,350
SIC 8661 Religious organizations

D-U-N-S 07-206-0205
ROMAN CATHOLIC ARCHDIOCESE OF INDIANAPOLIS INC
1400 N Meridian St, Indianapolis, IN 46202-2305
Tel (317) 236-1400 *Founded/Ownrshp* 1834
Sales 176.9MM^E *EMP* 5,475^E
SIC 8661 8211 Catholic Church; Elementary & secondary schools
Pr: Most Rev Joseph Tobin
**Sec:* Bishop Christopher Coyne
Bd of Dir: Stefanie Anderson
Ex Dir: William Bruns
Ex Dir: John Elcesser
Ex Dir: Charles Gardner
Ex Dir: Greg Otolski
Ex Dir: Mary Schaefer
Pr Dir: Robin Andrews

D-U-N-S 07-515-8253
ROMAN CATHOLIC ARCHDIOCESE OF NEWARK (NJ)
171 Clifton Ave, Newark, NJ 07104-1019
Tel (973) 497-4000 *Founded/Ownrshp* 1853
Sales 48.5MM^E *EMP* 1,000
SIC 8661 Catholic Church
Pr: John Myers
CFO: Dennis Obrien
**CFO:* George Peralta
**CFO:* Joseph Pescetore
**Ex Dir:* Nancy Lystash
Corp Couns: Janice Falivena

D-U-N-S 07-186-8574 EXP
ROMAN CATHOLIC ARCHDIOCESE OF SAN FRANCISCO
1 Peter Yorke Way 1, San Francisco, CA 94109-6602
Tel (415) 614-5500 *Founded/Ownrshp* 1853
Sales 57.9MM^E *EMP* 3,000
SIC 8299

ROMAN CATHOLIC BISHOP FRESNO
See DIOCESE OF FRESNO EDUCATION CORP

D-U-N-S 60-302-0884
ROMAN CATHOLIC BISHOP MONTEREY
485 Church St, Monterey, CA 93940-3207
Tel (831) 373-4666 *Founded/Ownrshp* 1967
Sales 18.0MM^E *EMP* 1,000^E
SIC 8661 Catholic Church
Prin: Richard Garcia

D-U-N-S 02-199-2110
ROMAN CATHOLIC BISHOP OF HELENA MONTANA
DIOCESE OF HELENA
515 N Ewing St, Helena, MT 59601-4002
Tel (406) 442-5820 *Founded/Ownrshp* 1884
Sales 51.8MM^E *EMP* 2,000
Accts Anderson Zurmuehlen & Co Pc
SIC 8661 8211 8221 2741 Catholic Church; Catholic combined elementary & secondary school; Colleges universities & professional schools; Miscellaneous publishing
Pr: George Leo Thomas
**Treas:* Peter L McNamee
**Genl Mgr:* Msgr Kevin S O'Neill

D-U-N-S 08-101-6438
ROMAN CATHOLIC BISHOP OF LOUISVILLE
ARCHDIOCESE OF LOUISVILLE
212 E College St, Louisville, KY 40203-2334
Tel (502) 585-3291 *Founded/Ownrshp* 1808
Sales 100.8MM^E *EMP* 3,500
Accts Mountjoy Chilton Medley Llp J
SIC 8661 Catholic Church
Pr: Joseph E Kurtz
Treas: Carolyn Kupper
Ofcr: Robert C Ash
Assoc Dir: Karl Dolson
Ex Dir: Sue Brodfehrer
Board of Directors: Juanita Bisig, Joseph E Curtz, Lori Massey, William Zoeller

D-U-N-S 04-862-0678
ROMAN CATHOLIC BISHOP OF MANCHESTER (NH)
ROMAN CTHLIC DOCESE MANCHESTER
153 Ash St, Manchester, NH 03104-4348
Tel (603) 669-3100 *Founded/Ownrshp* 1800
Sales 12.5MM *EMP* 1,200
SIC 8661 Religious organizations
Prin: Peter Anthony Libasci

D-U-N-S 07-653-6432
ROMAN CATHOLIC BISHOP OF OAKLAND
DIOCESE OF OAKLAND
2121 Harrison St Ste 100, Oakland, CA 94612-3788
Tel (510) 893-4711 *Founded/Ownrshp* 1962
Sales 21.9MM *EMP* 1,600
Accts Moss-Adams Llp San Francisco
SIC 8661 Catholic Church
COO: George Mockel
**CFO:* Sj Michael C Barber

D-U-N-S 07-174-3819
ROMAN CATHOLIC BISHOP OF PORTLAND
510 Ocean Ave, Portland, ME 04103-4936
Tel (207) 773-6471 *Founded/Ownrshp* 1853
Sales 39.0MM^E *EMP* 1,200
SIC 8052 8661 Intermediate care facilities; Catholic Church

D-U-N-S 07-571-6688
ROMAN CATHOLIC BISHOP OF PROVIDENCE (INC)
BLESSED SACRAMENT SCHOOL
1 Cathedral Sq, Providence, RI 02903-3601
Tel (401) 278-4616 *Founded/Ownrshp* 1830
Sales 88.2MM^E *EMP* 4,000
SIC 8661 Catholic Church
Pr: Most Rev Thomas J Tobin
Prin: Christopher Weber

D-U-N-S 07-155-5551
ROMAN CATHOLIC BISHOP OF SACRAMENTO
2110 Broadway, Sacramento, CA 95818-2518
Tel (916) 733-0100 *Founded/Ownrshp* 1897
Sales 48.1MM^E *EMP* 2,500
SIC 8661

D-U-N-S 05-794-4787
ROMAN CATHOLIC BISHOP OF SAN BERNARDINO (CA)
DIOCESE OF SAN BERNARDINO
1201 E Highland Ave, San Bernardino, CA 92404-4607
Tel (909) 475-5300 *Founded/Ownrshp* 1978
Sales 71.4MM^E *EMP* 2,400
SIC 8661 Catholic Church
Pr: Gerald R Barnes
**CFO:* Maryrose Wallace
Off Mgr: Susan Orem

D-U-N-S 06-616-9848
ROMAN CATHOLIC BISHOP OF SAN DIEGO
3888 Paducah Dr, San Diego, CA 92117-5349
Tel (858) 490-8200 *Founded/Ownrshp* 1800
Sales 103.7MM^E *EMP* 3,000
SIC 8661 Catholic Church
CEO: Robert H Brom
VP: John Borgia
Admn Mgr: Ann Anderson
Dir IT: Matt Dolan

D-U-N-S 13-163-1467
ROMAN CATHOLIC BISHOP OF SAN JOSE
DIOCESE OF SAN JOSE
1150 N 1st St Ste 100, San Jose, CA 95112-4966
Tel (408) 983-0100 *Founded/Ownrshp* 1981
Sales 57.7MM *EMP* 2,000
Accts Berger Lewis Accountancy Corpo
SIC 8661 Catholic Church
Dir Risk M: Lupe Warre
Prgrm Mgr: Anna M Cruz
MIS Dir: Sharon Johnson
Dir IT: Carl Silva

D-U-N-S 06-697-6101 IMP
ROMAN CATHOLIC BISHOP OF SPRINGFIELD
DIOCESE OF SPRINGFIELD
65 Elliot St, Springfield, MA 01105-1713
Tel (413) 732-3175 *Founded/Ownrshp* 1870
Sales 43.1MM^E *EMP* 1,500
SIC 8661 Catholic Church
Pr Dir: Stacy Dibbern

D-U-N-S 07-534-8664
ROMAN CATHOLIC BISHOP OF WORCESTER
DIOCESE OF WORCESTER
49 Elm St, Worcester, MA 01609-2514
Tel (508) 791-7171 *Founded/Ownrshp* 1950
Sales 40.4MM^E *EMP* 1,200
Accts O Connor Maloney & Company P
SIC 8661 Catholic Church
VP: Paul Gannon
VP: John Smithhisler

ROMAN CATHOLIC CHURCH
See CENTRAL SERVICES OF ROMAN CATHOLIC ARCHBISHOP OF BALTIMORE (INC)

D-U-N-S 07-767-0487 IMP
ROMAN CATHOLIC CHURCH IN STATE OF HAWAII
1184 Bishop St, Honolulu, HI 96813-2859
Tel (808) 536-7036 *Founded/Ownrshp* 1924
Sales 67.8MM^E *EMP* 1,800
SIC 8661 Catholic Church
**Pr:* Clarence Silva
**VP:* Gary L Secor

D-U-N-S 06-952-5244
ROMAN CATHOLIC CHURCH OF DIOCESE OF BATON ROUGE
CATHOLIC DIOCESE BATON ROUGE
1800 S Acadian Thruway, Baton Rouge, LA 70808-1663
Tel (225) 387-0561 *Founded/Ownrshp* 1961
Sales 66.5MM^E *EMP* 2,000
SIC 8661 Catholic Church
Pr: Most Rev Robert W Muench
**Treas:* Joseph E Ingraham
**VP:* Rev Thomas Rancino
**VP:* Very Rev Than Ngoc Vu

D-U-N-S 00-962-6060
ROMAN CATHOLIC CHURCH OF DIOCESE OF HOUMA THIBODAUX
HT PUBLISHING CO
2779 Highway 311, Schriever, LA 70395-3273
Tel (985) 868-7720 *Founded/Ownrshp* 1977
Sales 24.3MM^E *EMP* 1,100
SIC 8661 Catholic Church
Pr: Sam G Jacobs
**Sec:* Glenn J Landry Jr
**VP:* Jay Baker

D-U-N-S 02-012-7528
ROMAN CATHOLIC CHURCH OF DIOCESE OF PHOENIX (AZ)
DIOCESE PHOENIX SCHOOL OFFICE
400 E Monroe St, Phoenix, AZ 85004-2336
Tel (602) 257-0030 *Founded/Ownrshp* 1969
Sales 43.5MM^E *EMP* 1,200
SIC 8661

D-U-N-S 07-444-2062
ROMAN CATHOLIC CHURCH OF DIOCESE OF TUCSON (AZ)
ROMAN CATHOLIC DIOCESE TUCSON
64 E Broadway Blvd, Tucson, AZ 85701-1720
Tel (520) 792-3410 *Founded/Ownrshp* 1868, 1960
Sales 22.6MM^E *EMP* 1,000
SIC 8661

D-U-N-S 02-066-0346
ROMAN CATHOLIC DIOCESE OF ALBANY INC
HISPANIC OUTREACH SERVICES
40 N Main Ave Ste 4, Albany, NY 12203-1481
Tel (518) 453-6600 *Founded/Ownrshp* 1847
Sales 38.3MM^E *EMP* 1,387
SIC 8661 Catholic Church
Ex Dir: Elain Escobales
Assoc Dir: Stephen M Mawn

D-U-N-S 00-167-3763
ROMAN CATHOLIC DIOCESE OF BROOKLYN
310 Prospect Park W, Brooklyn, NY 11215-6214
Tel (718) 399-5900 *Founded/Ownrshp* 1853
Sales 162.7MM^E *EMP* 6,000
SIC 8661 Religious organizations
CEO: Donald Hackford
**Pr:* Frank Galligan
**VP:* Monsignor Otto Garcia
**VP:* Monsigor Viccari
Sls&Mrk Ex: Julio Gonzalez

D-U-N-S 07-906-5629
ROMAN CATHOLIC DIOCESE OF CHARLOTTE
PASTORAL CENTER
1123 S Church St, Charlotte, NC 28203-4003
Tel (704) 370-6299 *Founded/Ownrshp* 1972
Sales 56.4MM^E *EMP* 2,300
SIC 8661

D-U-N-S 07-137-5828
ROMAN CATHOLIC DIOCESE OF DALLAS
3725 Blackburn St, Dallas, TX 75219-4404
Tel (214) 528-2240 *Founded/Ownrshp* 1890
Sales 75.6MM^E *EMP* 2,000
SIC 8661 Catholic Church

D-U-N-S 06-391-2802
ROMAN CATHOLIC DIOCESE OF FALL RIVER OFFICE OF AIDS MINISTR
ST VINCENT HOME
47 Underwood St, Fall River, MA 02720-5427
Tel (508) 235-1184 *Founded/Ownrshp* 1994
Sales 48.8MM^E *EMP* 2,200
SIC 8661 8211 Catholic Church; Convent; Elementary & secondary schools
**Pr:* Sean P O'Malley

D-U-N-S 02-088-9044
ROMAN CATHOLIC DIOCESE OF GRAND RAPIDS
360 Division Ave S, Grand Rapids, MI 49503-4501
Tel (616) 243-0491 *Founded/Ownrshp* 1882
Sales 34.2MM^E *EMP* 1,100
SIC 8661 Catholic Church
Pgrm Dir: Debra Gutowski

D-U-N-S 01-046-0202
ROMAN CATHOLIC DIOCESE OF GREENSBURG
723 E Pittsburgh St, Greensburg, PA 15601-2636
Tel (724) 837-0901 *Founded/Ownrshp* 1951

Sales 3.4MM *EMP* 1,400
SIC 8661 Catholic Church
**CFO:* Michael J McGee

D-U-N-S 06-978-2340
ROMAN CATHOLIC DIOCESE OF HARRISBURG
4800 Union Deposit Rd, Harrisburg, PA 17111-3710
Tel (717) 657-4804 *Founded/Ownrshp* 1868
Sales 88.0MM^E *EMP* 2,500
Accts Mckonly & Asbury Llp Harrisbu
SIC 8661 8211 Catholic Church; Catholic senior high school; Catholic elementary school
Prin: Ronald W Gainer
CFO: Patrick Miorin
**Prin:* Diocese of Harrisburg
Off Mgr: Lynn Falcone
Pgrm Dir: Kelly Bolton

D-U-N-S 07-442-1199
ROMAN CATHOLIC DIOCESE OF JOLIET
425 Summit St, Joliet, IL 60435-7155
Tel (815) 722-6606 *Founded/Ownrshp* 1949
Sales 53.7MM^E *EMP* 2,100^E
SIC 8661

D-U-N-S 09-436-8032
ROMAN CATHOLIC DIOCESE OF MADISON INC
702 S High Point Rd, Madison, WI 53719-4925
Tel (608) 821-3000 *Founded/Ownrshp* 1946
Sales 26.7MM^E *EMP* 1,200
SIC 8661 Catholic Church
**VP:* Kathy Stellrecht

D-U-N-S 03-874-8034
ROMAN CATHOLIC DIOCESE OF ORANGE
13280 Chapman Ave, Garden Grove, CA 92840-4414
Tel (714) 282-3000 *Founded/Ownrshp* 1860
Sales 204.4MM^E *EMP* 6,000
SIC 8661 Catholic Church
VP: Tony Jennison
Ex Dir: Cindy Bobruk
Ex Dir: Roxanna Payton
Info Man: Yolanda Wright

D-U-N-S 07-517-2239
ROMAN CATHOLIC DIOCESE OF PATERSON (INC)
PATERSON DIOCESE CENTER
777 Valley Rd, Clifton, NJ 07013-2205
Tel (973) 777-8818 *Founded/Ownrshp* 1939
Sales 152.5MM^E *EMP* 2,000
SIC 8211 8661 Catholic elementary school; Religious organizations
Pr: Arthur J Serratelli
**CFO:* Paul Rubacky
Netwrk Mgr: Bernard Burney

D-U-N-S 06-541-6166
ROMAN CATHOLIC DIOCESE OF RICHMOND
CATHEDRAL SACRED HEART
7800 Carousel Ln, Richmond, VA 23294-4201
Tel (804) 359-5661 *Founded/Ownrshp* 1820
Sales 77.9MM^E *EMP* 2,100
Accts Cherry Bekaert & Holland Llp
SIC 8661 Catholic Church
CFO: John Barrett

D-U-N-S 07-674-4754
ROMAN CATHOLIC DIOCESE OF YOUNGSTOWN
144 W Wood St, Youngstown, OH 44503-1030
Tel (330) 744-8451 *Founded/Ownrshp* 1943
Sales 23.6MM *EMP* 2,927
Accts Anness Gerlach & Williams You
SIC 8661 Catholic Church
Prin: Thomas J Tobin
**CEO:* Meg Andersen
**CFO:* Mr Patrick Kelly
Treas: John Demarinis
Genl Mgr: Robert Gavalier
Genl Mgr: Robert G Purdy
DP Dir: Louis C Orbin

ROMAN CATHOLIC DIOCESE TUCSON
See ROMAN CATHOLIC CHURCH OF DIOCESE OF TUCSON

D-U-N-S 07-907-9034
ROMAN CATHOLIC WELFARE CORP OF OAKLAND
3014 Lakeshore Ave, Oakland, CA 94610-3615
Tel (510) 893-4711 *Founded/Ownrshp* 1962
Sales 29.6MM^E *EMP* 1,700
SIC 8211 Catholic elementary & secondary schools

ROMAN CTHLIC DIOCESE COVINGTON
See DIOCESE OF COVINGTON

ROMAN CTHLIC DOCESE MANCHESTER
See ROMAN CATHOLIC BISHOP OF MANCHESTER

ROMAN CTHLIC DOCESE WILMINGTON
See CATHOLIC DIOCESE OF WILMINGTON INC

D-U-N-S 03-446-0458
ROMAN JAMES DESIGN BUILD INC
3535 E Coast Hwy 145, Corona Del Mar, CA 92625-2404
Tel (949) 375-8618 *Founded/Ownrshp* 2010
Sales 100.0MM *EMP* 35
SIC 7389 Design services
CEO: Roman James

ROMANO'S MACARONI GRILL
See REDROCK PARTNERS LLC

D-U-N-S 02-124-5504
ROMARK LOGISTICS LLC
822 South Ave W, Westfield, NJ 07090-1460
Tel (908) 789-2800 *Founded/Ownrshp* 2009
Sales 83.2MM^E *EMP* 336^E
SIC 4225 4789 2631 General warehousing; Cargo loading & unloading services; Container, packaging & boxboard
Prin: Marc D Lebovitz
CFO: Howard Berlly
**Prin:* Beth Lebovitz

D-U-N-S 04-546-9467
ROME CITY SCHOOL DISTRICT
409 Bell Rd S, Rome, NY 13440-5298
Tel (315) 338-6500 *Founded/Ownrshp* 1870
Sales 52.1MM^E *EMP* 1,200
Accts D Archangelo & Co Llp Rome
SIC 8211 Public elementary & secondary schools
Prin: Mark Benson
Genl Mgr: Chris Whitmore
Dir IT: Pamela Mazzaferro

D-U-N-S 92-617-8229 IMP
ROME MEMORIAL HOSPITAL INC
1500 N James St, Rome, NY 13440-2899
Tel (315) 338-7000 *Founded/Ownrshp* 1994
Sales 73.4MM *EMP* 1,050
SIC 8062 8051 General medical & surgical hospitals; Skilled nursing care facilities
CEO: Basil Ariglio
Chf Rad: John Restivo
**Pr:* Basil Arigilio
**CFO:* Nick Mayhew
Treas: David Nolan
Bd of Dir: Gerald McDonald
Trst: Sally Hinman
Ofcr: Lynn Owens
Ex VP: Glady Jacob
VP: Dewey Rowlands
Dir Rx: Scott Burns

D-U-N-S 18-544-8420 IMP
ROMEO & JULIETTE INC
BEARPAW SHOES
7524 Old Auburn Rd, Citrus Heights, CA 95610-3806
Tel (916) 726-4413 *Founded/Ownrshp* 1985
Sales 86.5MM *EMP* 15
Accts Fineman West & Company Llp Lo
SIC 5139 Boots; Shoes
CEO: Thomas Romeo
COO: Wayne Cottrell
**CFO:* Jason Martini
Opers Mgr: Jessica Rennie

D-U-N-S 87-766-8244
ROMMEL HOLDINGS INC
ROMMELS ACE HOME CENTER
103 E Main St, Fruitland, MD 21826-1604
Tel (410) 749-3600 *Founded/Ownrshp* 1985
Sales 97.3MM^E *EMP* 412
SIC 5211 8741 Home centers; Restaurant management
Pr: Mike Cottingham
Treas: Suzanne Bowman
**VP:* Mike Rommel

ROMMELS ACE HOME CENTER
See ROMMEL HOLDINGS INC

D-U-N-S 10-515-7221
ROMULUS KEWADIN CASINO LLC
2186 Shunk Rd, Sault Sainte Marie, MI 49783-9467
Tel (906) 632-0530 *Founded/Ownrshp* 1953
Sales 29.9MM^E *EMP* 1,181
SIC 7011 Casino hotel
Ofcr: Rick Mc Dowell
Exec: Douglas Hartley

RON TONKIN ACURA
See RON TONKIN IMPORTS INC

D-U-N-S 02-775-9638
RON TONKIN CHEVROLET CO
122 Ne 122nd Ave, Portland, OR 97230-2103
Tel (503) 255-4100 *Founded/Ownrshp* 1960
Sales 293.5MM^E *EMP* 600
SIC 5511 Automobiles, new & used
Pr: Bradley E Tonkin
VP: Brad Tonkin
**VP:* Bradley Tonkin
VP: Edward Tonkin
Sls Mgr: Martin Parr
Sls Mgr: Art Smith
Sales Asso: Matthew Kim

D-U-N-S 15-765-7222 IMP
RON TONKIN IMPORTS INC
RON TONKIN ACURA
(*Suby of* RON TONKIN CHEVROLET CO) ★
9655 Sw Canyon Rd, Portland, OR 97225-2909
Tel (503) 292-0662 *Founded/Ownrshp* 1985
Sales 83.0MM^E *EMP* 231
SIC 5511 Automobiles, new & used
Pr: Ronald B Tonkin
**CFO:* John Cady
**VP:* Barry M Tonkin
Sales Asso: Joe Hughey

D-U-N-S 03-040-2242
RON WEBER AND ASSOCIATES INC
SERVICOM
1127 High Ridge Rd, Stamford, CT 06905-1203
Tel (203) 268-1725 *Founded/Ownrshp* 1980
Sales 21.4MM^E *EMP* 1,231
SIC 7389 Telemarketing services
Pr: Ronald Weber
VP Mktg: Jared Weber

RONALD WILLIAMS LIBRARY
See NORTHEASTERN ILLINOIS UNIVERSITY

D-U-N-S 01-744-0207
RONCELLI INC (MI)
6471 Metropolitan Pkwy, Sterling Heights, MI 48312-1027
Tel (586) 264-2060 *Founded/Ownrshp* 1966
Sales 126.3MM^E *EMP* 250^E
SIC 1541 8711 Industrial buildings & warehouses; Industrial buildings, new construction; Engineering services
Ch: Gary E Roncelli
**Pr:* Thomas Wickersham
VP: David Ladomer
**VP:* Scott Roncelli
VP: Jim Tressmer

D-U-N-S 03-812-9516
RONCO CONSULTING CORP
G4S
(*Suby of* G4S HOLDING ONE INC) ★
1395 University Blvd, Jupiter, FL 33458-5289
Tel (571) 551-2934 *Founded/Ownrshp* 2008
Sales 69.9MM^E *EMP* 2,000
SIC 1794 7389 7382 Excavation work; Explosives recovery or extraction services; Security systems services
Pr: Michael O'Connell
Ofcr: Ian Green
Ofcr: Jeff Morrow
Comm Dir: Stacy Smith

D-U-N-S 05-811-0735
RONELL INDUSTRIES INC
298 Cox St, Roselle, NJ 07203-1798
Tel (908) 245-5255 *Founded/Ownrshp* 1970
Sales 16.5MM^E *EMP* 1,000
SIC 7349 2842 Janitorial service, contract basis; Specialty cleaning preparations
Pr: Ronald Globerman
**VP:* Neil Salerno

D-U-N-S 01-147-1497
RONETCO SUPERMARKETS INC
SHOP RITE
1070 Us Highway 46 Ste 1, Ledgewood, NJ 07852-9735
Tel (973) 927-8300 *Founded/Ownrshp* 1937, 1961
Sales 158.9MM^E *EMP* 1,000
SIC 5411 5921 Supermarkets, chain; Liquor stores; Wine & beer
Pr: Dominick V Romano
Exec: Jeff Baker

D-U-N-S 12-182-4023 IMP/EXP
RONILE INC
701 Orchard Ave, Rocky Mount, VA 24151-1848
Tel (540) 483-0261 *Founded/Ownrshp* 1984
Sales 182.8MM^E *EMP* 1,383^E
SIC 2269 5949 2273 Finishing plants; Finishing: raw stock, yarn & narrow fabrics; Dyeing: raw stock yarn & narrow fabrics; Sewing, needlework & piece goods; Carpets & rugs
Ch Bd: Abe W Essig
**Pr:* Ronald W Martin
**CEO:* Phillip C Essig
**VP:* Elinor H Essig
**VP:* Rodney Lane Leonard
Sfty Dirs: Donna Essig
Sls Dir: Steve Wrigley

D-U-N-S 82-593-8467
ROOFERS SUPPLY INC
3359 S 500 W, Salt Lake City, UT 84115-4201
Tel (801) 266-1311 *Founded/Ownrshp* 1994
Sales 101.2MM^E *EMP* 95
SIC 5033 Roofing & siding materials
Pr: Dino Pappas
**CFO:* Stephanie Pappas
**Treas:* John Pappas
**VP:* George Pappas
Exec: Holly Henrie

D-U-N-S 82-954-7905
ROOFING SUPPLY GROUP HOLDINGS INC
3890 W Northwest Hwy # 400, Dallas, TX 75220-8108
Tel (214) 956-5100 *Founded/Ownrshp* 2006
Sales NA *EMP* 1,000
SIC 5211

D-U-N-S 79-716-0913
■ **ROOFING SUPPLY GROUP LLC**
(*Suby of* BEACON ROOFING SUPPLY INC) ★
3890 W Northwest Hwy # 400, Dallas, TX 75220-5166
Tel (214) 956-5100 *Founded/Ownrshp* 2015
Sales 688.0MM^E *EMP* 1,200
SIC 5033 Roofing, siding & insulation
CEO: Peter Arvan
Mng Pt: Mike Pease
**CFO:* Les Vines
VP: Wes Schlenker
Exec: Matt Disantis
Dist Mgr: Damien Katzenmeyer
Opers Mgr: David Pfeiffer
VP Sls: Jeff Willis
Mktg Mgr: Ryan Bills
Sales Asso: Darren Brett
Sales Asso: David Clifford

D-U-N-S 07-915-0922
■ **ROOFING SUPPLY GROUP-TUSCALOOSA LLC**
(*Suby of* ROOFING SUPPLY GROUP LLC) ★
3890 W Northwest Hwy # 400, Dallas, TX 75220-8108
Tel (214) 956-5100 *Founded/Ownrshp* 2013
Sales 7.6MM^E *EMP* 1,000
SIC 5033 Roofing, siding & insulation
CEO: Peter Arvan
CFO: Shaun Mara

D-U-N-S 00-900-9952 IMP
ROOFING WHOLESALE CO INC
RWC BUILDING PRODUCTS
1918 W Grant St, Phoenix, AZ 85009-5991
Tel (602) 258-3794 *Founded/Ownrshp* 1981
Sales 117.1MM *EMP* 225
Accts Johnson Lawdahl Pplc Phoenix
SIC 5033 Roofing & siding materials
Ch Bd: Harley Lisherness
**Pr:* Steven Binder
**CFO:* Stephen K Rold
Ofcr: Mark Wogernese
VP: Michael O'Day
Dir IT: Basil Farooq

D-U-N-S 08-025-3511 IMP/EXP
ROOM & BOARD INC
4600 Olson Memorial Hwy, Minneapolis, MN 55422-4815
Tel (763) 588-7525 *Founded/Ownrshp* 1980
Sales 167.5MM^E *EMP* 700
Accts Baker Tilly Virchow Krause Llp
SIC 5712 Furniture stores
CFO: Mark Miller
Genl Mgr: Dana Backer
Genl Mgr: Mary Gergen
Genl Mgr: Preston Long
DP Dir: Josh Bosma
QA Dir: Latinka Braianova
Dir IT: Susan Taets
Web Dev: Jeff Johnston
Web Dev: Diana Sharrow
Software D: Jordan Price
Site Mgr: Steven Rosengren

ROOM PLACE, THE
See OLD HF LLC

ROOM PLACE, THE
See TRP ACQUISITION CORP

ROOM STORE
See ROOMSTORES OF PHOENIX LLC

ROOMS TO GO
See RTG FURNITURE CORP OF GEORGIA

ROOMS TO GO FURNITURE
See RTG FURNITURE CORP

ROOMS TO GO KIDS
See RTG FURNITURE OF TEXAS LP

D-U-N-S 80-754-1479 IMP
ROOMSTORES OF PHOENIX LLC
ROOM STORE
3011 E Broadway Rd # 100, Phoenix, AZ 85040-2785
Tel (602) 268-1111 *Founded/Ownrshp* 1993
Sales 135.7MM^E *EMP* 520
SIC 5712 Furniture stores
Off Mgr: Brian Harsh

D-U-N-S 10-712-5957
ROONEY HOLDINGS INC
3705 Westview Dr Ste 1, Naples, FL 34104-4033
Tel (239) 403-0375 *Founded/Ownrshp* 1984
Sales 1.1MMM *EMP* 1,550
SIC 1542 Institutional building construction
Ch Bd: Francis Rooney
**CFO:* Kevin P Moore
**Treas:* Jim Lawson
Sr VP: Curtis Ferguson
CTO: Kevin Moore

D-U-N-S 00-487-7241
ROOSEVELT MANAGEMENT CO LLC
RMC
1540 Broadway Ste 1500, New York, NY 10036-4083
Tel (212) 704-4106 *Founded/Ownrshp* 2008
Sales 128.6MM *EMP* 100
SIC 8741 Management services
Sr VP: Stephen Zindler
VP: William Baird
VP: Mike Clifford
VP: Gary Graffagnino
Ex Dir: Bill Bell
Ex Dir: Linda Genneken
Mng Dir: Thomas Walsh
Off Mgr: Pam Paschall
IT Man: Chris Zito
Genl Couns: Karen Manson

D-U-N-S 00-229-3926 IMP/EXP
ROOSEVELT PAPER CO (PA)
1 Roosevelt Dr, Mount Laurel, NJ 08054-6312
Tel (856) 303-4100 *Founded/Ownrshp* 1932
Sales 191.5MM *EMP* 270
SIC 2679

D-U-N-S 03-762-1257
ROOSEVELT SCHOOL DISTRICT NO 66
6000 S 7th St, Phoenix, AZ 85042-4209
Tel (602) 243-2624 *Founded/Ownrshp* 1912
Sales 62.7MM^E *EMP* 1,500
SIC 8211 Public elementary school
Exec: Alma Ramos
Genl Mgr: Jacqueline Jackson
Genl Mgr: Kerre Laabs
Pr Dir: Joe Ortiz

D-U-N-S 04-253-1418
ROOSEVELT UNIVERSITY
430 S Michigan Ave, Chicago, IL 60605-1394
Tel (312) 341-3500 *Founded/Ownrshp* 1945
Sales 154.4MM *EMP* 1,200
Accts Crowe Horwath Llp Chicago Il
SIC 8221 University
Pr: Charles R Middleton
CFO: Hilda Mabon
**Ch:* James J Mitchell III
**Sr VP:* Paul Reis
Assoc Dir: Susan Fay
Assoc Dir: Raja Iqbal
Assoc Dir: Vickey Velazquez
Dir Soc: Jeanne Barnas
Ex Dir: Lauren Chill
Ex Dir: Michael Elliott
Genl Mgr: Joe Pietrie

D-U-N-S 07-945-1318
ROOSEVELT WIND HOLDINGS LLC
15445 Innovation Dr, San Diego, CA 92128-3432
Tel (888) 903-6926 *Founded/Ownrshp* 2013
Sales 232.7MM^E *EMP* 826
SIC 4911 Electric services; Generation, electric power
Pr: Tristan Grimbert
VP: Ryan Pfaff

ROOT, THE
See UNIVISION COMMUNICATIONS INC

D-U-N-S 08-651-7737 IMP/EXP
ROPAK CORP
ROPAK PACKAGING
(*Suby of* BWAY CORP) ★
10540 Talbert Ave 200w, Fountain Valley, CA 92708-6027
Tel (714) 845-2845 *Founded/Ownrshp* 2013
Sales 273.2MM^E *EMP* 1,100
SIC 3089 Plastic containers, except foam
CEO: Greg A Toft
VP: Dale Balough
Sftwr Eng: Fred Low
Sls Dir: Elaine Sonoda

ROPAK PACKAGING
See ROPAK CORP

D-U-N-S 19-729-1941 IMP
■ ROPER CORP
GE APPLIANCE DIV
(*Suby of* GENERAL ELECTRIC CO) ★
1507 Broomtown Rd, La Fayette, GA 30728-3407
Tel (706) 638-3559 *Founded/Ownrshp* 1988
Sales 276.2MM[E] *EMP* 1,800
SIC 3631 3634 Indoor cooking equipment; Gas ranges, domestic; Electric ranges, domestic; Electric housewares & fans
Pr: Scott Ossewaarde
**Ch Bd:* Richard F Segalini
**Treas:* Tamra Koshewa
Sales Exec: Rodney Walker
Snr Mgr: Wayne Vanlandingham

D-U-N-S 07-799-0729
ROPER HOSPITAL INC
(*Suby of* ROPER ST FRANCIS HEALTHCARE) ★
316 Calhoun St, Charleston, SC 29401-1125
Tel (843) 724-2000 *Founded/Ownrshp* 1986
Sales 369.5MM *EMP* 2,100[E]
SIC 8062 General medical & surgical hospitals
Pr: David L Dunlap
COO: Blake Ohlson
Exec: Ellen Brown
Dir Inf Cn: Cile Guerry
Dir Risk M: Gretchen Ring
Ex Dir: Emma Chambers
IT Man: Carolyn Brown
Netwrk Eng: Doug Laing
VP Sls: Robert H Bowles
Mktg Dir: Doug Bowling
Mktg Dir: Nicole Cassels

D-U-N-S 04-758-7766 IMP
■ ROPER PUMP CO
(*Suby of* ROPER TECHNOLOGIES INC) ★
3475 Old Maysville Rd, Commerce, GA 30529-1397
Tel (706) 336-3459 *Founded/Ownrshp* 1986
Sales 91.6MM[E] *EMP* 180
SIC 3823 3561 Industrial process control instruments; Pumps & pumping equipment
Pr: Walt Stadnisky
VP: Tate Coghlan
Dir IT: David Quinn

ROPER ST FRANCIS HEALTHCARE
See CAREALLIANCE HEALTH SERVICES

ROPER ST. FRANCIS PHYSICIAN PA
See ROPER ST FRANCIS PHYSICIANS NETWORK

D-U-N-S 96-654-9904
ROPER ST FRANCIS PHYSICIANS NETWORK
ROPER ST. FRANCIS PHYSICIAN PA
125 Doughty St Ste 760, Charleston, SC 29403-5785
Tel (843) 724-2903 *Founded/Ownrshp* 2008
Sales 134.7MM *EMP* 930
Accts Dixon Hughes Pllc Asheville
SIC 8011 Offices & clinics of medical doctors
CEO: Douglas Bowling
**CFO:* Molly Alexander

D-U-N-S 00-326-4850
▲ ROPER TECHNOLOGIES INC
6901 Prof Pkwy E Ste 200, Sarasota, FL 34240
Tel (941) 556-2601 *Founded/Ownrshp* 1981
Sales 3.5MMM *EMP* 10,806
Tkr Sym ROP *Exch* NYS
SIC 3823 3563 3491 3826 3829 Industrial instrmnts msrmnt display/control process variable; Temperature instruments: industrial process type; Differential pressure instruments, industrial process type; Pressure gauges, dial & digital; Air & gas compressors; Valves, automatic control; Process control regulator valves; Solenoid valves; Petroleum product analyzing apparatus; Vibration meters, analyzers & calibrators
Ch Bd: Brian D Jellison
CFO: John Humphrey
VP: Nigel Crocker
VP: Paul J Soni
VP: John Stipancich
VP: Ben Wood
Exec: Greg L Anderson
Genl Mgr: Larry Ritter
CTO: Tim Simmons
Corp Couns: Jeff Grinnell

D-U-N-S 07-171-4067
ROPES & GRAY LLP
800 Prudential Tower # 3600, Boston, MA 02199-3600
Tel (617) 951-7000 *Founded/Ownrshp* 1865
Sales 302.4MM[E] *EMP* 1,375
SIC 8111 General practice law office
Pt: Alyson Gal Allen
Pt: Peter A Alpert
Pt: John B Ayer
Pt: Mark Barnes
Pt: Brian R Bassett
Mng Pt: James R Batchelder
Mng Pt: David Chapin
Mng Pt: Douglass Ellis
Mng Pt: Laurel Fitzpatrick
Mng Pt: Asheesh Goel
Mng Pt: Mike Goetz
Mng Pt: Michael G McGovern
Pr: Mary Oconnell
COO: Hugh Simons
VP: Rina Burgey
VP: Daniel Routh
VP: Francis Sennott
VP: Patricia Teixeira
VP: Rom Watson
VP: Dalila Wendlandt

D-U-N-S 00-417-6905 IMP
ROPPE HOLDING CO
1602 N Union St, Fostoria, OH 44830-1958
Tel (419) 435-8546 *Founded/Ownrshp* 1955, 1999
Sales 155.2MM[E] *EMP* 650
SIC 3089 3069

ROPPONGI
See LADEKI RESTAURANT GROUP

D-U-N-S 62-798-4446 IMP/EXP
ROQUETTE AMERICA INC
(*Suby of* ROQUETTE FRERES)
1003 S 5th St, Keokuk, IA 52632-5463
Tel (319) 524-5757 *Founded/Ownrshp* 1991
Sales 176.9MM[E] *EMP* 575
SIC 2046 2869 Corn syrup, dried or unmixed; Corn starch; Gluten feed; Industrial organic chemicals
Pr: Dominique Baumann
**Treas:* Paul D Janicki
VP: Ivan Hasselbusch
VP: Ben Moser
Dir Risk M: Owen Morton
DP Dir: Tom Porter
QA Dir: Clark McGrew
Dir IT: Rodney Boyle
IT Man: Dave Fincher
Sls Mgr: Narhesh Mehta
Snr Mgr: Kumar Anil

D-U-N-S 60-381-3119
ROSA MEXICANO MIAMI LLC
846 7th Ave Fl 4, New York, NY 10019-5221
Tel (212) 397-0666 *Founded/Ownrshp* 2005
Sales 48.1MM[E] *EMP* 1,500
SIC 5812 Mexican restaurant
Ch Bd: Doug Griebel
**Pr:* Tom Dillon
**VP:* Cory Bronson
**VP:* Elvira Ryder
Genl Mgr: Mario Bernal
Genl Mgr: George Figares
Genl Mgr: Sean Maddrey
Genl Mgr: Michael Williams
Snr Mgr: Teresita Gingold

D-U-N-S 96-502-6271
ROSALIND AND JOSEPH GURWIN JEWISH GERIATRIC CENTER OF LONG ISLAND INC
GURWIN JEWISH NURSING AND REHA
68 Hauppauge Rd, Commack, NY 11725-4403
Tel (631) 499-6500 *Founded/Ownrshp* 1988
Sales 77.8MM *EMP* 1,000
Accts Loeb & Troper Llp New York N
SIC 8059 Nursing home, except skilled & intermediate care facility
CEO: Herbert H Freidman
**Ch Bd:* Larry Simon
**Pr:* Berst Drodsky
**Treas:* David Schachne

D-U-N-S 06-950-1252
ROSALIND FRANKLIN UNIVERSITY OF MEDICINE AND SCIENCE
DR WILLIAM SCHOLL COLLEGE OF P
3333 Green Bay Rd, North Chicago, IL 60064-3037
Tel (847) 578-3000 *Founded/Ownrshp* 1912
Sales 114.0MM *EMP* 800
Accts Crowe Horwath Llp Chicago Il
SIC 8221 University
Ch: Ruth Rothstein
**Pr:* K Michael Welch
Treas: Nutan Vaidya
Assoc VP: Maryann Decaire
**Ex VP:* Roberta Lane
VP: Gene Daun
**VP:* Rebecca Durkin
**VP:* Tina M Erickson
**VP:* Timothy Hansen
Dir Lab: Sangseop Kim
Dir Lab: Letia Peterson

ROSARY COLLEGE
See DOMINICAN UNIVERSITY

D-U-N-S 00-794-3681
ROSAUERS SUPERMARKETS INC (WA)
HUCKLEBERRY'S FRESH MARKETS
(*Suby of* URM STORES INC) ★
1815 W Garland Ave, Spokane, WA 99205-5015
Tel (509) 326-8900 *Founded/Ownrshp* 1940, 2000
Sales 262.7MM[E] *EMP* 2,100
SIC 5411 Supermarkets, 66,000-99,000 square feet
Pr: Jeffery Philipps
VP: Terry Grimes
VP: Ken Grogh
**VP:* Michael Shirts
Dir IT: Steve Lee
Sftwr Eng: Terri Norton
Sfty Mgr: Jamie Haun

D-U-N-S 00-902-3920
ROSBORO LLC (OR)
2509 Main St, Springfield, OR 97477-5162
Tel (541) 746-8411 *Founded/Ownrshp* 1940, 1950
Sales 88.4MM[E] *EMP* 400
SIC 2436 2421 2439 3441 2435 Plywood, softwood; Lumber: rough, sawed or planed; Trusses, except roof: laminated lumber; Trusses, wooden roof; Fabricated structural metal; Hardwood veneer & plywood
CTO: Lynn Damon
Sales Asso: Jon Howard

ROSCOE MEDICAL
See COMPASS HEALTH BRANDS CORP

D-U-N-S 01-624-5896 IMP/EXP
ROSE ACRE FARMS INC
6874 N Base Rd, Seymour, IN 47274-8934
Tel (812) 497-2557 *Founded/Ownrshp* 1944
Sales 794.1MM[E] *EMP* 1,900
SIC 0252 Chicken eggs
Pr: Marcus Rust
**COO:* Tony Wesner
**CFO:* Greg Marshall
**Ch:* Lois Rust
Ofcr: Bethany Klimek
Ofcr: Donna Seagroves
VP: Larry Isaacs
**VP:* Mike McCory
**VP:* Victor Rigterink
**VP:* Mark Whittington
Off Mgr: Kim Allman

ROSE ART INDUSTRIES
See MEGA BRANDS AMERICA INC

D-U-N-S 01-221-6321 IMP/EXP
ROSE BRAND WIPERS INC (NY)
4 Emerson Ln, Secaucus, NJ 07094-2504
Tel (201) 809-1730 *Founded/Ownrshp* 1921
Sales 113.3MM[E] *EMP* 239
SIC 5049 2399 Theatrical equipment & supplies; Emblems, badges & insignia
Pr: George M Jacobstein
**VP:* Rita Shapiro
Genl Mgr: Robert Bertrand
Sls Mgr: Jeff Flowers
Snr PM: Michael Cucciarre

D-U-N-S 87-626-2023
ROSE CASUAL DINING INC
APPLEBEE'S
826 Newtown Yardley Rd, Newtown, PA 18940-1797
Tel (215) 579-9220 *Founded/Ownrshp* 1994
Sales 99.2MM[E] *EMP* 3,000
SIC 5812 Restaurant, family: chain
CEO: Harry T Rose

D-U-N-S 07-284-6017
■ ROSE CITY HMA LLC
(*Suby of* HMA) ★
250 College Ave, Lancaster, PA 17603-3363
Tel (717) 291-8211 *Founded/Ownrshp* 1877
Sales 120.5MM *EMP* 1,100[E]
SIC 8062 General medical & surgical hospitals
CEO: Bradley Nurkin
CFO: Fred Ashworth
Chf Nrs Of: Joanne Lucas
Surgeon: Matthew D Bacharach
Board of Directors: Joe Legenstein

ROSE GROUP, THE
See ROSE MANAGEMENT SERVICES

ROSE HILL FARM
See BAY FOODS INC

D-U-N-S 06-667-4797
ROSE HILLS CO
ROSE HILLS MEM PK & MORTUARY
(*Suby of* ROSE HILLS MEM PK & MORTUARY) ★
3888 Workman Mill Rd, Whittier, CA 90601-1626
Tel (562) 699-0921 *Founded/Ownrshp* 2006
Sales 206.0MM[E] *EMP* 600
SIC 6553 Real property subdividers & developers, cemetery lots only
Ch Bd: Dennis Poulsen
**Pr:* Kenton Woods
Ofcr: Jackie Jung
Ex VP: Derrick Stover
VP: Shawn Aylesworth
VP: Ophelia Camero
**VP:* Mary Guzman
Ex Dir: Bruce Lazenby
Ex Dir: Ernesto Morales
Dir IT: Gordon Kelly
IT Man: Merrill Mefford

D-U-N-S 14-230-8928
ROSE HILLS HOLDINGS CORP
ROSE HILLS MEM PK & MORTUARY
3888 Workman Mill Rd, Whittier, CA 90601-1626
Tel (562) 699-0921 *Founded/Ownrshp* 1996
Sales 206.0MM[E] *EMP* 680
SIC 6553 Cemetery subdividers & developers
CEO: Pat Monroe

ROSE HILLS MEM PK & MORTUARY
See ROSE HILLS CO

ROSE HILLS MEM PK & MORTUARY
See ROSE HILLS HOLDINGS CORP

D-U-N-S 80-304-1466
ROSE INTERNATIONAL INC
16401 Swingley Ridge Rd, Chesterfield, MO 63017-0757
Tel (636) 812-4000 *Founded/Ownrshp* 1993
Sales 248.9MM *EMP* 6,000
Accts Brown Smith Wallace Llc St L
SIC 7371 8748 Computer software development; Systems engineering consultant, ex. computer or professional
CEO: Himanshu Bhatia
**Pr:* Gulab Bhatia
**Sr VP:* Eric Token
**VP:* Phil Black
**VP:* Hans De Bruijn
**VP:* Harish Vakharia
Assoc Dir: Brett Giarratano
Software D: Manish Jhamb

D-U-N-S 05-518-2016
ROSE L BRAND & ASSOCIATES PC
7301 Jefferson St Ne, Albuquerque, NM 87109-4355
Tel (505) 833-3036 *Founded/Ownrshp* 2014
Sales 88.1M[E] *EMP* 1,962
SIC 8111 Specialized law offices, attorneys
Pr: Rose Brand

D-U-N-S 96-867-4528
ROSE LANE HOME
LOUP CITY HEALTH
1005 N 8th St, Loup City, NE 68853-8215
Tel (308) 745-0303 *Founded/Ownrshp* 2000
Sales 337.4MM *EMP* 70
SIC 8051 6411 Skilled nursing care facilities; Insurance agents, brokers & service
Pr: Jack Vetter

D-U-N-S 78-868-9847
ROSE MANAGEMENT SERVICES
ROSE GROUP, THE
29 Friends Ln, Newtown, PA 18940-1803
Tel (215) 867-1802 *Founded/Ownrshp* 1993
Sales 181.0MM[E] *EMP* 5,000[E]
SIC 5812 Fast-food restaurant, chain
CEO: Harry T Rose
**Pt:* Philip Warden
**CFO:* Christopher J Tobia
VP: Jason Rose
Dir Risk M: Paul Trzaska
Off Admin: Leslie Casey
Off Admin: Linda Taormina
Dir IT: Robert Fuller

IT Man: Dave Corrigan
Mktg Mgr: Jeffrey Browne

D-U-N-S 07-645-3356
■ ROSE MEDICAL GROUP
HEALTH ONE
(*Suby of* HOSPITAL CORPORATION OF AMERICA) ★
4900 S Monaco St Ste 204, Denver, CO 80237-3487
Tel (303) 320-2101 *Founded/Ownrshp* 1995
Sales 150.3MM[E] *EMP* 1,201
SIC 8062 8011 8099 General medical & surgical hospitals; General & family practice, physician/surgeon; Blood related health services; Physical examination & testing services; Medical services organization
Pr: Kenneth Feiler
Dir Recs: Colleen Simianer
**COO:* Mary White
**CFO:* Jac Connly
VP: Ken Feiler
VP: Judy Hatch
VP: Kevin Kucera
Dir IT: Scott Wagner
Plnt Mgr: Bill Buxton
Sls Dir: Sarah Michel
Pathlgst: Carol Trujillo

D-U-N-S 07-835-3689
ROSE ROCK MIDSTREAM LP
6120 S Yale Ave Ste 1500, Tulsa, OK 74136-4231
Tel (918) 524-7700 *Founded/Ownrshp* 2016
Sales 844.7MM *EMP* 400[E]
SIC 1311 4612

D-U-N-S 02-073-0164
ROSE STATE COLLEGE
6420 Se 15th St, Oklahoma City, OK 73110-2799
Tel (405) 733-7673 *Founded/Ownrshp* 1967
Sales 10.0MM *EMP* 1,100
Accts Eidebailly Oklahoma City Ok
SIC 8222 Junior college; Technical institute
Pr: Jeanie Webb
**VP:* Francis Hendrix
VP: Kent Lashley
Dir Soc: Richard Charnay
Ex Dir: William Bernhardt
Off Mgr: Kelly Orr
CIO: John Primo
Dir IT: Ken Roper
IT Man: Joy Cole
Sfty Dirs: Isabelle Billen

ROSETREE CORPORATE CENTER II
See FXI INC

D-U-N-S 05-200-8414
ROSE-HULMAN INSTITUTE OF TECHNOLOGY INC
5500 Wabash Ave, Terre Haute, IN 47803-3999
Tel (812) 877-1511 *Founded/Ownrshp* 1874
Sales 89.0MM *EMP* 460
Accts Bkd Llp Indianapolis In
SIC 8221 College, except junior
Pr: James Conwell
Trst: Anton George
Trst: Niles Noblitt
**VP:* Robert Coons
VP: Robert A Coons
VP: James Goecker
VP: Peter Gustafson
VP: Elaine Kirkpatrick
VP: William Kline
Comm Dir: Michael Davids

D-U-N-S 02-654-4247
ROSEBUD MINING CO
301 Market St, Kittanning, PA 16201-1504
Tel (724) 545-6222 *Founded/Ownrshp* 1994
Sales 747.3MM[E] *EMP* 820
SIC 1222 1221 Bituminous coal-underground mining; Strip mining, bituminous
Pr: J Clifford Forrest III
**VP:* James R Barker
**VP:* Clifford Forest
Genl Mgr: Jerry Nassar
CIO: David Elkin
Sfty Dirs: Rick Peppel
Sfty Mgr: Stan Popich
Sls Mgr: Scott Rogers
Board of Directors: David Acerni

D-U-N-S 13-107-5863 IMP/EXP
ROSEBURG FOREST PRODUCTS CO
(*Suby of* RLC INDUSTRIES CO) ★
3660 Gateway St Ste A, Springfield, OR 97477-6010
Tel (541) 679-3311 *Founded/Ownrshp* 1985
Sales 887.1MM[E] *EMP* 2,000
SIC 2436 2421 2493 5031 5211 0811 Plywood, softwood; Lumber: rough, sawed or planed; Wood chips, produced at mill; Particleboard, plastic laminated; Lumber, plywood & millwork; Lumber products; Timber tracts
Pr: Allyn C Ford
**CFO:* Marty Daley
VP: David Cramsey
VP: Richard Dybevik
**VP:* Scott Folk
**VP:* Grady Mulbery
CIO: Richard Ryder
IT Man: Ron Fuentes
Sfty Mgr: John Mikkelson
Plnt Mgr: Mark Allen
S&M/VP: Steve Killgore

D-U-N-S 14-720-5074
ROSEMARK PAPER INC
1845 Progress Ave, Columbus, OH 43207-1726
Tel (614) 443-0303 *Founded/Ownrshp* 1985
Sales 128.9MM[E] *EMP* 98
SIC 5111 5199 Printing paper; Packaging materials
Pr: Robert A Rosenfeld
**Treas:* David Gurenberg
**VP:* Howard Simons

D-U-N-S 87-959-1105
ROSEMOND NURSING CENTER INC
(*Suby of* HMR ADVANTAGE HEALTH SYSTEMS INC) ★
138 Rosemond St, Pickens, SC 29671-2434
Tel (864) 878-9620 *Founded/Ownrshp* 1995

Sales 250.8MM EMP 45
SIC 8051 Skilled nursing care facilities
Pr: Michael McBride

D-U-N-S 80-482-8556
ROSEMONT EXPOSITION SERVICES INC
9291w Bryn Mawr Ave, Rosemont, IL 60018-5215
Tel (847) 696-2208 Founded/Ownrshp 1988
Sales 47.0MM[E] EMP 1,500
SIC 7389 Convention & show services
Pr: David D Houston
*VP: Grant Bailey
Creative D: Phil Hantak
Off Mgr: Linda Talaber
Sls Mgr: Ben Shahriari

ROSEMONT PRESBYTERIAN VILLAGE
See PHILADELPHIA PRESBYTERY HOMES INC

D-U-N-S 06-110-7236
ROSEMORE HOLDINGS INC
(Suby of ROSEMORE INC) ★
1 N Charles St Ste 2200, Baltimore, MD 21201-3759
Tel (410) 347-7090 Founded/Ownrshp 1999
Sales 164.0MM[E] EMP 2,656
Accts Ellin & Tucker Chartered
SIC 2911 5171 5541 5411 Petroleum refining; Petroleum terminals; Gasoline service stations; Convenience stores, chain
Pr: Ken Trout
*Treas: Barry L Miller
*Ex VP: Kenneth H Trout

D-U-N-S 05-821-5497
ROSEMORE INC
1 N Charles St Ste 2200, Baltimore, MD 21201-3759
Tel (410) 347-7080 Founded/Ownrshp 1999
Sales 497.0MM[E] EMP 3,000
Accts Ellin & Tucker Chartered
SIC 5541 Filling stations, gasoline
Pr: Edward L Rosenberg
*Ch Bd: Henry A Rosenberg Jr
*COO: Kenneth H Trout
*CFO: Barry L Miller
*Sr VP: Tommie E Yates
*VP: Lisa J Bertelsen
*VP: Jeffrey A Hoffberger

D-U-N-S 80-481-7070
■ **ROSEMOUNT AEROSPACE INC**
A UTC AEROSPACE SYSTEMS CO
(Suby of GOODRICH ARCFT WHEELS & BRAKES) ★
14300 Judicial Rd, Burnsville, MN 55306-4890
Tel (952) 892-4000 Founded/Ownrshp 1992
Sales 114.5MM[E] EMP 1,100
SIC 3812

D-U-N-S 00-647-7467 IMP/EXP
■ **ROSEMOUNT INC** (MN)
ROSEMOUNT MEASUREMENT
(Suby of EMERSON ELECTRIC (US) HOLDING CORP) ★
8200 Market Blvd, Chanhassen, MN 55317-9687
Tel (952) 906-8888 Founded/Ownrshp 1956, 1976
Sales 966.0MM[E] EMP 3,425
SIC 3823 3824 3545 5084 3829 Industrial instrmnts msrmnt display/control process variable; Temperature instruments: industrial process type; Analyzers, industrial process type; Pressure measurement instruments, industrial; Fluid meters & counting devices; Machine tool accessories; Industrial machinery & equipment; Measuring & controlling devices
CEO: Edward L Monser
*CFO: Tracy Thompson
VP: Richard Ballintine
VP: Dwight Bohm
VP: Jim Davis
*VP: Frank J Dellaquila
VP: Michael Hoffmann
VP: Dennis Hyland
VP: Kathleen P Iverson
VP: Terrance Krouth
VP: Kevin Kruse
VP: Kevin Oriley
VP: Curtis Petersen
VP: Jeffrey W Schmitt

ROSEMOUNT MEASUREMENT
See ROSEMOUNT INC

D-U-N-S 07-868-8355
ROSEMOUNT-APPLE VALLEY-EAGAN SCHOOL BOARD
3455 153rd St W, Rosemount, MN 55068-4946
Tel (651) 423-7700 Founded/Ownrshp 1858
Sales 339.4MM EMP 3,600
Accts Malloy Montague Karnowski R
SIC 8211 School board
Ch Bd: Rob Duchscher

D-U-N-S 17-685-0139
ROSEMOUNT-APPLE VALLEY-EAGAN SCHOOL DISTRICT
DISTRICT 196
3455 153rd St W, Rosemount, MN 55068-4946
Tel (651) 423-7700 Founded/Ownrshp 1959
Sales 173.4M EMP 5,981[E]
SIC 8211 Public elementary & secondary schools
VP: Kathy Hall
HC Dir: Deb Mehr

D-U-N-S 13-626-1216 IMP
ROSEN 9939 INC
ROSEN SHINGLE CREEK
(Suby of ROSEN HOTELS AND RESORTS INC) ★
9840 International Dr, Orlando, FL 32819-8111
Tel (407) 996-9939 Founded/Ownrshp 2006
Sales 136.0MM EMP 1,401
SIC 7011 5812 5813 7992 7389 Hotels; Eating places; Drinking places; Public golf courses; Trade show arrangement
Pr: Harris Rosen
*Sec: Frank Santos

ROSEN HONDA
See ROSEN MOTOR SALES INC

D-U-N-S 06-786-0320
ROSEN HOTELS AND RESORTS INC
9840 International Dr, Orlando, FL 32819-8111
Tel (407) 996-1706 Founded/Ownrshp 1974
Sales 13.4MM EMP 3,420
SIC 7011 5812 5813 7389 8011 7992 Hotels & motels; Eating places; Drinking places; Trade show arrangement; Offices & clinics of medical doctors; Public golf courses
Pr: Harris Rosen
CFO: Frank A Santos
*Sec: Frank Santos
VP: Daniel Gutierrez
*VP: Daniel Guttierez
Dir IT: Mike Lewis
S&M/VP: Leslie Menichini

D-U-N-S 01-926-3511
ROSEN MOTOR SALES INC
ROSEN HONDA
7000 Grand Ave, Gurnee, IL 60031-1626
Tel (847) 856-8439 Founded/Ownrshp 1990
Sales 91.9MM[E] EMP 240
SIC 5511 Automobiles, new & used
Pr: Saul Rosen
Genl Mgr: Terry Lumpkins

ROSEN NISSAN & KIA
See FOUR KEYS LLC

ROSEN SHINGLE CREEK
See ROSEN 9939 INC

ROSENBAUER AMERICA GEN SAFETY
See ROSENBAUER MOTORS LLC

D-U-N-S 02-447-3584 IMP/EXP
ROSENBAUER AMERICA LLC
(Suby of ROSENBAUER BETEILIGUNGSVERWALTUNG GMBH)
100 3rd St, Lyons, SD 57041-8000
Tel (605) 543-5591 Founded/Ownrshp 1998
Sales 271.4MM EMP 600
SIC 3711 Fire department vehicles (motor vehicles), assembly of
CEO: Harold Boer
Bd of Dir: Kevin Kirvida
Off Mgr: Helen Boer
Dir IT: Chris Blackwelder
IT Man: Monty Gearhart
Natl Sales: Donley Fredrickson

D-U-N-S 00-616-5682 EXP
ROSENBAUER MINNESOTA LLC
5181 260th St, Wyoming, MN 55092-8018
Tel (651) 462-1000 Founded/Ownrshp 1995
Sales 101.3MM EMP 163
Accts Lloyd Arends
SIC 3713 7699 3711 Specialty motor vehicle bodies; Aircraft & heavy equipment repair services; Motor vehicles & car bodies
CEO: Harold Boer
Dir IT: Chris Welder

D-U-N-S 02-443-4677
ROSENBAUER MOTORS LLC
ROSENBAUER AMERICA GEN SAFETY
(Suby of ROSENBAUER INTERNATIONAL AG)
5181 260th St, Wyoming, MN 55092-8018
Tel (651) 408-9304 Founded/Ownrshp 2003
Sales 93.1MM EMP 204
SIC 6719 Personal holding companies, except banks
Pr: Kevin Kirvida
*CEO: Harold Boer
*Treas: Mary Kay

D-U-N-S 10-229-2117 IMP/EXP
ROSENBAUER SOUTH DAKOTA LLC
(Suby of ROSENBAUER AMERICA LLC) ★
100 3rd St, Lyons, SD 57041-8000
Tel (605) 543-5591 Founded/Ownrshp 1998
Sales 151.9MM EMP 275
SIC 3711

D-U-N-S 07-290-0483 IMP
ROSENBOOM MACHINE & TOOL INC
RMT
1530 Western Ave, Sheldon, IA 51201-1950
Tel (712) 324-4854 Founded/Ownrshp 1974
Sales 93.0MM[E] EMP 600
SIC 3593 3492 3594

D-U-N-S 00-796-8621
ROSENDIN ELECTRIC INC (CA)
880 Mabury Rd, San Jose, CA 95133-1021
Tel (408) 286-2800 Founded/Ownrshp 1919
Sales 1.1MMM[E] EMP 3,300
SIC 1731 General electrical contractor
Ch Bd: Tom Sorley
Mng Pt: Kyle Louis
*Pr: Larry Beltramo
*CFO: Lorne Rundquist
Bd of Dir: Rich Calia
Bd of Dir: George Perez
Ex VP: Ron Schwarzenbach
VP: John Brown
VP: Bill Mazzetti
VP: Marty Rouse
VP: Cliff Thompson
Board of Directors: Hugh Rice, Dick Rolla

D-U-N-S 60-395-2581
ROSENS DIVERSIFIED INC
LONG PRAIRIE PACKING
1120 Lake Ave, Fairmont, MN 56031-1939
Tel (507) 238-4201 Founded/Ownrshp 1946
Sales 3.7MMM[E] EMP 8,000
SIC 2011 8748 5149 2879 Meat packing plants; Agricultural consultant; Pet foods; Agricultural chemicals
Pr: Thomas J Rosen
*CFO: Robert A Hovde
CFO: Robert Hovde
VP: Bruce Bollinger
VP: Steve Guetter
VP: Dan Rentschler
VP: Randy Young
VP Mktg: Philip Ladner
Mktg Dir: Kent Woodall

D-U-N-S 00-483-5401
ROSENS INC (MN)
(Suby of LONG PRAIRIE PACKING) ★
1120 Lake Ave, Fairmont, MN 56031-1939
Tel (507) 238-4201 Founded/Ownrshp 1946
Sales 95.4MM[E] EMP 75
SIC 5191 Chemicals, agricultural
CEO: Thomas J Rosen
*Pr: Ivan Wells
Mktg Mgr: Kent Woodall

D-U-N-S 04-769-8659
ROSENTHAL & ROSENTHAL INC
ROSENTHAL BUSINESS CREDIT
1370 Broadway, New York, NY 10018-7399
Tel (212) 356-1400 Founded/Ownrshp 1964
Sales NA EMP 206
SIC 6153 Factoring services; Working capital financing
*Pr: Peter Rosenthal
*CFO: James Occhiogrosso
*Treas: Franz Gritsch
Ex VP: Sheldon Kaye
*Ex VP: Michael Stanley
*Sr VP: Robert Prizer
VP: Eric Bader
VP: Omar Barbero
VP: David Bobby
VP: Michael Corcoran
VP: Deane Davis
VP: Andrew Matza
VP: Charles Sharf
VP: Tony Verrilli

ROSENTHAL BUSINESS CREDIT
See ROSENTHAL & ROSENTHAL INC

D-U-N-S 05-541-6481
ROSENTHAL COLLINS GROUP LLC
RCG
216 W Jackson Blvd # 400, Chicago, IL 60606-6980
Tel (312) 460-9200 Founded/Ownrshp 1970
Sales 151.8MM[E] EMP 350
SIC 6221 6289 6231 6211 Commodity brokers, contracts; Commodity dealers, contracts; Exchange clearinghouses, commodity; Security & commodity exchanges; Security brokers & dealers
CEO: Scott Gordon
COO: Greg Troyanowski
Ofcr: Sandy Morowitz
Ex VP: Brian S Adams
VP: Megan Hovey
*VP: George Recchia
Exec: S Adams
Admn Mgr: Jeffrey Fox
Snr Ntwrk: John Raisanen
CIO: S B Adams
CTO: Kris Patel

D-U-N-S 14-448-0753 IMP/EXP
ROSES SOUTHWEST PAPERS INC
1701 2nd St Sw, Albuquerque, NM 87102-4505
Tel (505) 842-0134 Founded/Ownrshp 1984
Sales 93.4MM[E] EMP 225
SIC 2676 2674 2621 Napkins, paper: made from purchased paper; Toilet paper: made from purchased paper; Towels, paper: made from purchased paper; Paper bags: made from purchased materials; Paper mills
CEO: Roberto E Espat
*Pr: Robert S Espat
*Sec: Rose Marie Espat
*VP: Amin Espat

ROSES STORES
See VARIETY STORES INC

D-U-N-S 83-016-4674
ROSETTA LLC
(Suby of PUBLICIS GROUPE S A)
100 American Metro Blvd # 201, Hamilton, NJ 08619-2319
Tel (609) 689-6100 Founded/Ownrshp 2003
Sales 152.7MM[E] EMP 1,065
SIC 8742 Marketing consulting services
Pt: Nigel Adams
Pt: Steve Gustafson
Pt: Kieran Walsh
Mng Pt: Hari Madadevan
CFO: Joan McManus
Sr VP: John Baglivo
Exec: Danielle Beerson
Exec: Lisa Morris
Prgrm Mgr: Kristin Levin
Prgrm Mgr: Zasha Morales-Jose
Prgrm Mgr: Maria Topping

D-U-N-S 60-216-7061
ROSETTA RESOURCES INC
1111 Bagby St Ste 1600, Houston, TX 77002-2547
Tel (713) 335-4000 Founded/Ownrshp 2005
Sales 1.3MMM EMP 252[E]
SIC 1311 1381

D-U-N-S 60-209-0552
■ **ROSETTA RESOURCES OFFSHORE LLC**
(Suby of NBL TEXAS LLC) ★
1111 Bagby St Ste 1600, Houston, TX 77002-2547
Tel (713) 335-4000 Founded/Ownrshp 2005
Sales 270.0MM[E] EMP 110
SIC 1382 Oil & gas exploration services

D-U-N-S 83-034-5422
▲ **ROSETTA STONE INC**
1621 N Kent St Ste 1200, Arlington, VA 22209-2131
Tel (703) 387-5800 Founded/Ownrshp 1992
Sales 217.6MM EMP 1,148[E]
Tkr Sym RST Exch NYS
SIC 7372 4813 7371 Educational computer software; ; Computer software development & applications
Ch Bd: A John Hass III
Pr: Judy K Verses
CFO: Thomas M Pierno
Snr Sftwr: Khanh Nguyen
Snr Sftwr: Clay Stewart
Opers Mgr: Jodi Hale
Board of Directors: Laurence Franklin, Patrick W Gross, David Nierenberg, Caroline J Tsay, Laura L Witt, Steven P Yankovich

D-U-N-S 07-933-7876
■ **ROSETTA STONE INTL LTD**
(Suby of ROSETTA STONE INC) ★
1919 N Lynn St Fl 7, Arlington, VA 22209-1742
Tel (540) 236-7719 Founded/Ownrshp 2008
Sales 227.5MM[E] EMP 1,200[E]
SIC 7372 Educational computer software
CEO: Stephen M Swad
VP: Nino Ninov
Dir Soc: Edward Rodriguez
Off Mgr: David Tucker
Snr Ntwrk: Scott Hardy
IT Man: Vinoth John

D-U-N-S 79-928-0128
■ **ROSETTA STONE LTD**
(Suby of ROSETTA STONE INC) ★
135 W Market St, Harrisonburg, VA 22801-3710
Tel (540) 432-6166 Founded/Ownrshp 1992
Sales 216.1MM[E] EMP 1,140
SIC 7372 Educational computer software
CEO: John Hass
*CFO: Thomas M Pierno
VP: Alex Herron
Dir Risk M: Catherine B Runion
Creative D: Andy Steenberge
QA Dir: Dennis Catt
QA Dir: Robert Frysinger
QA Dir: Miranda Kilby
Software D: Rob Lineweaver
VP Mktg: Andy Mead
Pr Dir: Michelle Alvarez

ROSEVILLE AREA SCHOOLS
See INDEPENDENT SCHOOL DISTRICT 623 (INC)

ROSEVILLE TOYOTA
See JOHN L SULLIVAN INVESTMENTS INC

D-U-N-S 13-955-9728
ROSEWOOD CORP
ROSEWOOD PRIVATE INVESTMENTS
2101 Cedar Springs Rd # 1600, Dallas, TX 75201-1878
Tel (214) 849-9000 Founded/Ownrshp 1976
Sales 63.1MM[E] EMP 1,456
SIC 6531 7382 Real estate managers; Security systems services
Pr: John Dziminski
Pr: Schuyler Marshall
Ch: Don W Crisp
Sr VP: Loren Greaves
Sr VP: C Jedson Nau
Board of Directors: Stephen H Sands

D-U-N-S 03-284-6805
ROSEWOOD HEALTH CARE CENTER
SUB OF KENDERD
550 High St, Bowling Green, KY 42101-1746
Tel (270) 843-3296 Founded/Ownrshp 1969
Sales 1.2MMM EMP 4
SIC 8051 8093 Convalescent home with continuous nursing care; Rehabilitation center, outpatient treatment
CFO: Byrd La Donna
Sls&Mrk Ex: Newman Sherri

ROSEWOOD PRIVATE INVESTMENTS
See ROSEWOOD CORP

D-U-N-S 83-275-7525
ROSEWOOD PRIVATE INVESTMENTS INC
2101 Cedar Springs Rd # 1600, Dallas, TX 75201-2104
Tel (214) 849-9000 Founded/Ownrshp 2009
Sales 83.3MM[E] EMP 212[E]
SIC 6799 3423 Investors; Cutting dies, except metal cutting
Ch Bd: Schuyler Marshall
*Treas: Marti D Chalk
*Sr VP: John M Dziminski
*Sr VP: Loren Greaves
Sr VP: Dennis King
*Sr VP: C Jedson Nau

ROSEWOOD WORKS
See LUMBERMENS INC

D-U-N-S 00-602-3162 IMP
ROSKAM BAKING CO (MI)
STARR PUFF FACTORY
4880 Corp Exch Blvd Se, Grand Rapids, MI 49512
Tel (616) 574-5757 Founded/Ownrshp 1918, 2006
Sales 477.9MM[E] EMP 1,000
SIC 2051 2043 7389 Bread, cake & related products; Cereal breakfast foods; Packaging & labeling services
Pr: Robert Roskam
Ql Cn Mgr: Rick Riva

ROSLYN PUBLIC SCHOOL
See ROSLYN UNION FREE SCHOOL DISTRICT

D-U-N-S 05-094-1608
ROSLYN UNION FREE SCHOOL DISTRICT
ROSLYN PUBLIC SCHOOL
300 Harbor Hill Rd, Roslyn, NY 11576
Tel (516) 801-5000 Founded/Ownrshp 1883
Sales 104.2MM EMP 600
Accts O Connor Davies Llp Harrison
SIC 8211 Public elementary school; Public junior high school; Public senior high school
Teacher Pr: Michael Goldspiel

D-U-N-S 61-599-2849 IMP
ROSS ACQUISITION CO
GALERIE AU CHOCOLAT
3380 Langley Dr, Hebron, KY 41048-9105
Tel (859) 538-8000 Founded/Ownrshp 1989
Sales 205.5MM[E] EMP 350
SIC 5145 6211 Confectionery; Brokers, security
Pr: Richard G Ross
*COO: Mark L Hilgeford

ROSS DRESS FOR LESS
See ROSS STORES INC

D-U-N-S 96-788-6425
ROSS GROUP CONSTRUCTION CORP
510 E 2nd St, Tulsa, OK 74120-1809
Tel (918) 878-2838 Founded/Ownrshp 1996
Sales 87.3MM[E] EMP 125
SIC 1542 Nonresidential construction

CEO: David Thomas
**Pr:* Warren Ross
**COO:* William Edmiston
**CFO:* Brandon Brown
Sfty Dirs: Brandon Robins

D-U-N-S 06-982-0421
ROSS MORTGAGE CORP
2075 W Big Beaver Rd # 700, Troy, MI 48084-3446
Tel (248) 968-1800 *Founded/Ownrshp* 1983
Sales NA *EMP* 170
SIC 6162 Mortgage bankers
Ch: Hugh C Ross
**Pr:* Timothy Ross
**Treas:* Betsy Corkum
VP: Ken Panosian
VP: Kelley Ross
VP: Mark Wiedemann
Brnch Mgr: James Bouscher
Off Mgr: Patrick Bingaman
Off Mgr: Kim Hickson
Off Mgr: David Poynter
Off Mgr: Connie Smith

D-U-N-S 02-908-9711 IMP
▲ ROSS STORES INC
ROSS DRESS FOR LESS
5130 Hacienda Dr, Dublin, CA 94568-7635
Tel (925) 965-4400 *Founded/Ownrshp* 1957
Sales 11.9MMM *EMP* 77,800
Accts Deloitte & Touche Llp San Fra
Tkr Sym ROST *Exch* NGS
SIC 5651 5661 5944 5632 5611 5999 Family clothing stores; Shoe stores; Women's shoes; Men's shoes; Children's shoes; Jewelry, precious stones & precious metals; Apparel accessories; Lingerie (outerwear); Men's & boys' clothing stores; Clothing accessories: men's & boys'; Haberdashery stores; Suits, men's; Cosmetics; Perfumes & colognes
CEO: Barbara Rentler
**Ch Bd:* Michael Balmuth
Pr: Bernie Brautigan
Pr: James Fassio
**Pr:* Michael O'Sullivan
Pr: Lisa Panattoni
CFO: Michael Hartshorn
CFO: Michael J Hartshorn
Chf Mktg O: Brian Morrow
Ex VP: Robert Bernard
Ex VP: John G Call
Sr VP: Pamela Smith
VP: Christina Cordoza
VP: Peter Laudeman
VP: Nancy Osborne
VP: Deon Riley
VP: Marjan Voit
Dir Soc: Jessica Burns
Board of Directors: J Gunnar Bjorklund, Michael J Bush, Norman A Ferber, Sharon D Garrett, Stephen D Milligan, George P Orban, Larry S Peiros, Gregory L Quesnel

ROSS-SIMONS
See LUXURY BRAND HOLDINGS INC

D-U-N-S 06-896-6431
■ ROSWELL HOSPITAL CORP
EASTERN NEW MEXICO MEDICAL CENTER
(*Suby of* COMMUNITY HEALTH SYSTEMS INC) ★
405 W Country Club Rd, Roswell, NM 88201-5209
Tel (575) 622-8170 *Founded/Ownrshp* 1998
Sales 122.7MM *EMP* 750
SIC 8062 General medical & surgical hospitals
Pr: W Larry Cash
Chf Rad: Phillip Durand
**Pr:* Martin G Schweinhart
**CEO:* Maridel Acosta
**CEO:* Brad McGrath
**COO:* Warren Yehl
CFO: Leann Hacker
**Treas:* James W Doucette
Sr VP: Teresa Spurny
**VP:* Kevin J Hammons
Exec: Sam Pettit
Dir Inf Cn: Brent Crabtree

D-U-N-S 07-138-5249
ROSWELL INDEPENDENT SCHOOL DISTRICT (INC)
300 N Kentucky Ave, Roswell, NM 88201-4636
Tel (575) 627-2500 *Founded/Ownrshp* 1890
Sales 68.7MM^E *EMP* 1,400
Accts Hector H Balderas New Mexico
SIC 8211 Public elementary school; Public junior high school; Public senior high school
Pr Dir: Royce Braggs
HC Dir: Brandy Samuell

D-U-N-S 02-704-2941
ROSWELL PARK CANCER INSTITUTE
UROLOGY
Elm And Carlton St, Buffalo, NY 14263-0001
Tel (716) 845-2300 *Founded/Ownrshp* 2010
Sales 528.6MM *EMP* 3,450^E
Accts Freedmaxick Cpas Pc Buffalo
SIC 8733 Noncommercial research organizations
CEO: Candice Johnson
Ofcr: Boris Kuvshinoff II
Dir Risk M: Marianne Hanley
Dir Lab: Richard Cheney
Telecom Ex: Colleen Sarick
Netwrk Mgr: Kenneth Sobzzak
Info Man: Kimberly Bonds
Sfty Dirs: Carl Thomas
Mktg Dir: Laurel Dibrog
Pathlgst: Mihai Merzianu
Pathlgst: Lourdes R Ylagan

D-U-N-S 04-238-6672
ROSWIL INC
RAMEY'S SUPER MARKET 1-29
1878 S State Highway 125, Rogersville, MO 65742-8357
Tel (417) 667-7530 *Founded/Ownrshp* 1966
Sales 132.3MM^E *EMP* 1,400
SIC 5411 Supermarkets, independent
Pr: Richard Cohen
**VP:* Joe Yates

ROTADYNE
See ROTATION DYNAMICS CORP

D-U-N-S 04-998-3737 IMP/EXP
ROTARY CORP
DURAMATIC PRODUCTS
801 W Barnard St, Glennville, GA 30427-3030
Tel (912) 654-3433 *Founded/Ownrshp* 1966
Sales 283.0MM^E *EMP* 375
SIC 5083 3469 5013 Lawn machinery & equipment; Metal stampings; Automotive engines & engine parts
CEO: Edward L Nelson
Pr: Todd McMahon
**CFO:* Don Martin
VP: Gerald Cox
VP: Donald Fountain
Exec: Jodonne Folsom
Genl Mgr: Dennis Lamb
Manager: Doug Stayton
Sls Mgr: Clarke Baum
Sls Mgr: Robert Smartt
Sls Mgr: Jason Wiggins

D-U-N-S 78-128-0941
ROTARY FOUNDATION OF ROTARY INTERNATIONAL
1560 Sherman Ave Ste 1111, Evanston, IL 60201-4810
Tel (847) 866-3000 *Founded/Ownrshp* 2006
Sales 232.9MM *EMP* 14^E
Accts Grant Thornton Llp Chicago I
SIC 8699 Membership organizations
Prin: Jeff H Wing

D-U-N-S 07-440-1712
ROTARY INTERNATIONAL (IL)
1 Rotary Ctr, Evanston, IL 60201-4422
Tel (847) 866-3000 *Founded/Ownrshp* 1905
Sales 92.9MM *EMP* 800
Accts Grant Thornton Llp Evanston
SIC 8641 Civic associations
CEO: John Hewko
**Pr:* Kalyan Banerjee
**CFO:* Lori O Carlson
**CFO:* David Jensen
Treas: Bernard L Rosen
Bd of Dir: Carl-Wilhelm Stenhammar
Ofcr: Karena Bierman
Exec: Shirley Kirschner
Genl Mgr: Michele Berg
Genl Mgr: Peter Markos
CIO: May Li

D-U-N-S 06-439-8712 IMP/EXP
ROTATION DYNAMICS CORP
ROTADYNE
8140 Cass Ave, Darien, IL 60561-5013
Tel (630) 769-9255 *Founded/Ownrshp* 1983
Sales 128.8MM^E *EMP* 550
SIC 3069

D-U-N-S 14-455-6222
ROTECH HEALTHCARE INC
3600 Vineland Rd Ste 114, Orlando, FL 32811-6460
Tel (407) 822-4600 *Founded/Ownrshp* 1981
Sales 375.0MM *EMP* 1,750
Accts Mcgladrey Llp Fort Lauderdale
SIC 7352 Medical equipment rental
Pr: Timothy Pigg
Chf Cred: Robin L Menchen
VP: Richard Dickerson
VP: Tami Seifert
Area Mgr: Carla Ard
Area Mgr: Buck Caulley
Area Mgr: Christine Ermento
Area Mgr: Kevin Harmison
Area Mgr: Shawna Morton
Area Mgr: Jacob Newby
Area Mgr: Judy Ratcliff
Board of Directors: James H Bloem, Edward L Kuntz, Timothy P Lavelle, Richard E Newsted, David A Reganato, Micheal J Wartell

D-U-N-S 00-725-9740 IMP
ROTELLAS ITALIAN BAKERY INC (NE)
6949 S 108th St, La Vista, NE 68128-5703
Tel (402) 592-6600 *Founded/Ownrshp* 1921
Sales 129.0MM^E *EMP* 350
SIC 2051 Bakery: wholesale or wholesale/retail combined
Pr: Louis J Rotella Jr
**Treas:* Helen Rotella
IT Man: Steve Frankenfield
Manager: Norm Peters

D-U-N-S 00-987-2888
ROTH BROS INC
(*Suby of* SODEXO INC) ★
3847 Crum Rd, Youngstown, OH 44515-1414
Tel (330) 793-5571 *Founded/Ownrshp* 2006
Sales 116.3MM^E *EMP* 400
SIC 1711 1761 Warm air heating & air conditioning contractor; Roofing contractor; Sheet metalwork
VP: Michael A Wardle
**CFO:* Christine Henderson
**Ex VP:* Thomas E Froelich
**Ex VP:* Stephen P Koneval
**Ex VP:* Richard M Wardle
Ex Dir: Paul Feezel
Snr Sftwr: Paul Harahuc

ROTH EQUIPMENT
See STRAUB INTERNATIONAL INC

D-U-N-S 02-779-0559
ROTH IGA FOODLINER INC
4895 Indian School Rd Ne, Salem, OR 97305-1126
Tel (503) 393-7684 *Founded/Ownrshp* 1962
Sales 117.7MM^E *EMP* 650
SIC 5411 Supermarkets, chain
Pr: Michael Roth
**Treas:* Melinda Roth
Art Dir: Will Hawkins

D-U-N-S 87-875-0785
ROTH STAFFING COMPANIES LP
ULTIMATE STAFFING SERVICES
450 N State College Blvd, Orange, CA 92868-1708
Tel (714) 939-8600 *Founded/Ownrshp* 1994
Sales 258.6MM *EMP* 500
SIC 7363 Help supply services
CEO: Ben Roth
Ofcr: Adam Roth
Ex VP: Pam Sexauer
Sr VP: Julie Hagan
Sr VP: Kristi Kennedy
Sr VP: Jennifer J Simonson
VP: Mary Boland
VP: Pauline Francis
VP: Brett Roth
VP: Mimi Taylor
Exec: Carolyn Andrews
Exec: Theresa Del Vecchio
Exec: Richard Gottron

D-U-N-S 17-848-9019
ROTHBURY FARMS INC
3061 Shaffer Ave Se, Grand Rapids, MI 49512-1709
Tel (616) 574-5757 *Founded/Ownrshp* 1985
Sales 128.9MM^E *EMP* 1,000
SIC 5149 2051 2043 Bakery products; Bread, cake & related products; Cereal breakfast foods
Pr: Robert O Roskam

ROTHCO
See MORRIS ROTHENBERG & SON INC

ROTHRIST TUBE
See BENTELER STEEL & TUBE

D-U-N-S 05-155-0564
ROTHSCHILD INC
(*Suby of* ROTHSCHILD NORTH AMERICA INC) ★
1251 Avenue Of The Americ, New York, NY 10020-1104
Tel (212) 403-3500 *Founded/Ownrshp* 1987
Sales 100.1MM^E *EMP* 213
SIC 6282 6211 Investment advisory service; Investment bankers
Ch Bd: Raymond Smith
COO: Bob Bicknese
CFO: Fabrice Guillard
CFO: Paul Jensen
Chf Mktg O: Michael Tamasco
Chf Inves: Daniel Oshinskie
Top Exec: David R Rothschild
Sr VP: Don McLoughlin
Sr VP: Richard Vasquez
VP: Nicholas Barnes
VP: William Bertolino
VP: Kunal Bhalla
VP: George Bryant
VP: Matthew Chou
VP: Peter Giallias
VP: Mary Kalambay
VP: Elizabeth Keegan
VP: Michael Kehoe
VP: Charles Mussat
VP: Matthew Narlinger
VP: Anna Niziol

D-U-N-S 36-204-6633
ROTHSCHILD NORTH AMERICA INC
(*Suby of* ROTHSCHILDS CONTINUATION HOLDINGS AG)
1251 Ave Of The Ave Fl 51, New York, NY 10020
Tel (212) 403-3500 *Founded/Ownrshp* 1987
Sales 159.9MM^E *EMP* 705
SIC 6211 6159 8742 6221 6282 8741 Investment bankers; Traders, security; Loan institutions, general & industrial; Business consultant; Commodity traders, contracts; Investment advisory service; Management services
Ch Bd: Baron David De Rothschild
V Ch Bd: Yves Andre Istel
V Ch Bd: Christopher R Lawrence
VP: Andy Freitas

D-U-N-S 04-266-7303 IMP
ROTO-DIE CO INC
ROTOMETRICS
800 Howerton Ln, Eureka, MO 63025-1027
Tel (636) 587-3600 *Founded/Ownrshp* 2014
Sales 203.9MM^E *EMP* 500
SIC 3544 3555 3312 Die sets for metal stamping (presses); Printing trades machinery; Tool & die steel & alloys
CEO: Robert Spiller
COO: Paul Clark
VP: Melissa Hughes
VP: Keith Laakko
VP: Rick Meuser
Exec: Nancy Moore
Mng Dir: Peter Emerson
Genl Mgr: Phil Taylor
IT Man: Peter Marmura
Software D: Tim Harris
Software D: Chris Rethemeyer

D-U-N-S 12-252-8763
■ ROTO-ROOTER DEVELOPMENT CO
(*Suby of* CHEMED CORP) ★
255 E 5th St Ste 2600, Cincinnati, OH 45202-4138
Tel (513) 762-6690 *Founded/Ownrshp* 1983
Sales 218.6MM^E *EMP* 2,500
SIC 7699 1711 Sewer cleaning & rodding; Gas appliance repair service; Plumbing contractors; Septic system construction
CEO: Spencer S Lee
**Ch Bd:* Edward L Hutton
**Pr:* Rick Arquilla
**CFO:* David Williams
**V Ch Bd:* Kevin J McNamara
Sr VP: Mark A Conners
Sr VP: Robert P Goldschmidt
VP: Fred L Carothers
VP: Robert B Carroll
VP: Dan Craig
VP: Charles Dale
VP: Adam Kantor
VP: Ken Kiesch
VP: David J Lohbeck
VP: Gulio Matthew
VP: Juan F Mendez
VP: Fred Smithauser
VP: Thomas Sullivan
VP: James Taylor
VP: Keith Vadas
VP: James Weiberg

D-U-N-S 04-447-0458
■ ROTO-ROOTER SERVICES CO
(*Suby of* ROTO-ROOTER DEVELOPMENT CO) ★
2500 Chemed Ctr 255e5th, Cincinnati, OH 45202-4725
Tel (513) 762-6690 *Founded/Ownrshp* 1980
Sales 207.3MM^E *EMP* 2,500
SIC 7699 1711 Sewer cleaning & rodding; Plumbing contractors
CEO: Spencer S Lee
**Pr:* Rick L Arquilla
**CFO:* David Williams
Board of Directors: Edward L Hutton, Kevin McNamara

D-U-N-S 05-479-5877
ROTOLO CHEVROLET INC
16666 S Highland Ave, Fontana, CA 92336-1213
Tel (866) 756-9776 *Founded/Ownrshp* 1971
Sales 155.8MM *EMP* 137
SIC 5511 5521 7538 Automobiles, new & used; Used car dealers; General automotive repair shops
Pr: Marie Waddingham
**Treas:* Nina Rotolo
**Sec:* Darinda Madeiros
VP: Don McCarty
Genl Mgr: Bernie Acosta
Genl Mgr: Lilia Cardona
Genl Mgr: Lucy Sanchez
Genl Mgr: Danielle York
Sls&Mrk Ex: Mike Caposio

ROTOMETRICS
See ROTO-DIE CO INC

ROTOPLAS
See MOLDING ACQUISITION CORP

ROTOR CLAMP
See ROTOR CLIP CO INC

D-U-N-S 00-152-7464 IMP
ROTOR CLIP CO INC
ROTOR CLAMP
187 Davidson Ave, Somerset, NJ 08873-4192
Tel (732) 469-7707 *Founded/Ownrshp* 1957
Sales 126.4MM^E *EMP* 300
SIC 3429 Metal fasteners; Clamps & couplings, hose
Pr: Robert Slass
CFO: Bennett Goldstein
Ofcr: Evita Jones
VP: Craig Slass
VP: Henry Yates
Div Mgr: Jonathan Slass
IT Man: James Cunningham
QI Cn Mgr: Bruce Rudin
VP Mktg: Lisa Coiro
Mktg Dir: Joe Cappello
Sls Mgr: Tom Baatz

D-U-N-S 00-122-3692 IMP
■ ROTRON INC
AMETEK ROTRON
(*Suby of* AMETEK SENSOR TECHNOLOGY BUS) ★
55 Hasbrouck Ln, Woodstock, NY 12498-1894
Tel (845) 679-2401 *Founded/Ownrshp* 1998
Sales 199.7MM^E *EMP* 1,137
SIC 3564 Blowers & fans
Pr: Robert J Vogel
**VP:* Michael Denicola
CIO: Alan Whitney
IT Man: Linda Moseman
Board of Directors: John W Hardin, Robert R Mandos, Robert J Vogel

ROTTEN ROBBIE
See ROBINSON OIL CORP

D-U-N-S 55-656-8855
ROTTINGHAUS CO INC
SUBWAY
510 Gillette St, La Crosse, WI 54603-3600
Tel (608) 784-2774 *Founded/Ownrshp* 1988
Sales 156.0MM *EMP* 3,200
SIC 5812 Sandwiches & submarines shop
CEO: Dennis Rottinghaus
**CFO:* Donald Rottinghaus

D-U-N-S 82-856-2228 IMP
ROUND GROUND METALS INC
RGM
4825 Turnberry Dr, Hanover Park, IL 60133-5493
Tel (630) 539-5300 *Founded/Ownrshp* 1988
Sales 85.3MM^E *EMP* 90
SIC 5051 7389 Bars, metal; Grinding, precision: commercial or industrial
Pr: Andrew Strzalkowski
Exec: Anna Bolanowski
Genl Mgr: John Pechan
IT Man: Greg Fore
IT Man: Greg Wardawy
Prd Mgr: Scott Stroup
QI Cn Mgr: Piotr Domalik

D-U-N-S 09-510-1986 IMP
ROUND ROCK INDEPENDENT SCHOOL DISTRICT (INC)
RRISD
1311 Round Rock Ave, Round Rock, TX 78681-4941
Tel (512) 464-5000 *Founded/Ownrshp* 1920
Sales 523.4MM *EMP* 4,500
Accts Maxwell Locke & Ritter Llp Au
SIC 8211 8748 Public elementary school; Public junior high school; Public senior high school; Public special education school; Business consulting
Bd of Dir: Jason Dimiceli
Assoc VP: Kimberly Kirby
**Prin:* Georgia Mill
Ex Dir: Marianne Reap
DP Exec: Vickie Bradford
Dir IT: Mike Bergeron
Trfc Dir: Brian Romanowski
Pr Dir: Albert Hernandez
Teacher Pr: Corey Ryan
Psych: Angela Padilla

ROUND TABLE HP
See ANGIOTECH PHARMACEUTICALS (US) INC

D-U-N-S 06-913-7396
ROUNDTABLE PIZZA INC
1320 Willow Pass Rd # 600, Concord, CA 94520-5292
Tel (925) 969-3900 *Founded/Ownrshp* 1972, 1992
Sales 94.4MM^E *EMP* 2,200
SIC 5812 6794 Pizzeria, chain; Franchises, selling or licensing
CEO: Robert McCourt
**Ch Bd:* James F Fletcher
**CFO:* Keith Davis
CFO: Rebecca Parlette
VP: Tinka Gordon
**VP:* Ted Storey
Snr Mgr: Darrah Shively

D-U-N-S 60-537-0498
ROUND-THE-WORLD LOGISTICS (USA) CORP
333 Cantor Ave Unit C, Linden, NJ 07036-6230
Tel (908) 862-3535 *Founded/Ownrshp* 2005
Sales 90.0MM^E *EMP* 8
SIC 8999 Personal services
Pr: Alan LI
Genl Mgr: Steven Yeh

D-U-N-S 10-126-3874 IMP/EXP
ROUNDTABLE HEALTHCARE PARTNERS LP
272 E Deerpath Ste 350, Lake Forest, IL 60045-5326
Tel (847) 482-9275 *Founded/Ownrshp* 2001
Sales 389.3MM^E *EMP* 710
SIC 6722 3699 2834 Management investment, open-end; Electrical equipment & supplies; Pills, pharmaceutical
Mng Pt: Lester Knight
Pt: Joseph Damico
Pt: Leonard G Kuhr
Pt: Jack McGinley
Pt: Todd Warnock

D-U-N-S 80-867-6832
ROUNDTOWER NORTHEAST LLC
200 Quannapowitt Pkwy, Wakefield, MA 01880-1312
Tel (781) 621-8600 *Founded/Ownrshp* 2007
Sales 93.0MM *EMP* 36
SIC 5734 Software, business & non-game
CEO: Gary Halloran
**VP:* Chris Clark
**VP:* Sean Daly
**VP:* Chris Tedesco
Mktg Mgr: Sara Lehmer

D-U-N-S 18-333-3095
ROUNDTREE AUTOMOTIVE GROUP LLC
7607 Fern Ave Ste 401, Shreveport, LA 71105-5699
Tel (318) 798-6500 *Founded/Ownrshp* 1985
Sales 125.9MM^E *EMP* 500
SIC 5511 Automobiles, new & used; Vans, new & used; Pickups, new & used
Pr: Frank Stinson
**Treas:* Brooke W Samuelson
**VP:* Brenda B Stinson

D-U-N-S 07-271-9144
ROUNDTREE OF SHREVEPORT LLC
(*Suby of* ROUNDTREE AUTOMOTIVE GROUP LLC) ★
910 Pierremont Rd Ste 312, Shreveport, LA 71106-2063
Tel (318) 798-6500 *Founded/Ownrshp* 1997
Sales 85.0MM^E *EMP* 253
SIC 5511 Automobiles, new & used

D-U-N-S 13-638-8530
■ **ROUNDYS INC**
(*Suby of* KROGER CO) ★
875 E Wisconsin Ave, Milwaukee, WI 53202-5404
Tel (414) 231-5000 *Founded/Ownrshp* 1872
Sales 3.8MMM *EMP* 21,802
SIC 5411 Grocery stores
Pr: Christine S Wheatley
Treas: Timothy M Terrell
VP: Daniel Farrell
VP: Gary Fryda
VP: Don Hamblen
VP: Stacey M Heiser
VP: Colleen Stenholt
Prgrm Mgr: Ken Koceja
IT Man: Mark Brazell
Snr PM: Robert Schmidt

D-U-N-S 00-794-7195
■ **ROUNDYS SUPERMARKETS INC** (WI)
PICK 'N SAVE
(*Suby of* ROUNDYS INC) ★
875 E Wscnsin Ave Ste 100, Milwaukee, WI 53202
Tel (414) 231-5000 *Founded/Ownrshp* 1872, 2002
Sales 3.1MMM^E *EMP* 18,029
SIC 5411 5141 Grocery stores; Grocery stores, chain; Groceries, general line
Ch Bd: Robert A Mariano
Pr: Ed Kitz
Bd of Dir: Jeffrey Beyer
**Ex VP:* Darren W Karst
VP: Roger Alswager
VP: Jason Benish
VP: Ron Cooper
VP: James Fenzel
VP: Larry Goddard
VP: Don Hamblen
VP: Mark Nolan
VP: Jess Terry
Exec: Joan Christianson

D-U-N-S 00-190-9852
■ **ROUSE CO LP**
(*Suby of* GGP INC) ★
10221 Wincopin Cir # 300, Columbia, MD 21044-3455
Tel (410) 992-6000 *Founded/Ownrshp* 1956
Sales 303.6MM^E *EMP* 1,660
Accts Deloitte & Touche Llp Chicago
SIC 6798 6512 Realty investment trusts; Commercial & industrial building operation; Shopping center, property operation only
Pr: Robert Michaels
**Ex VP:* Bernard Freibaum
Ex VP: Douglas A McGregor
**Sr VP:* Ronald Gern
Sr VP: Richard G McCauley
**Sr VP:* Jean Schlemmer
VP: Stephen E Pospisil
VP: Robert Rubenkonig
VP: Andrew C Tilmont

D-U-N-S 07-838-6028
ROUSE PROPERTIES LLC
(*Suby of* BSREP II RETAIL POOLING LLC)
1114 Avenue Of The Americ, New York, NY 10036-7711
Tel (212) 608-5108 *Founded/Ownrshp* 2016
Sales 305.3MM *EMP* 1,750
SIC 6799 Real estate investors, except property operators
CEO: Brian L Harper
Ofcr: Michael Grant
Ex VP: Eric Dinenberg
Ex VP: Susan Elman
Ex VP: Gary Yanosick
VP: Steve Bolger
VP: Jennifer Brigham
VP: Missy Heanue
Genl Mgr: Cindy Banister
Genl Mgr: Kenneth Cecil
Genl Mgr: Ric Jimenez

D-U-N-S 07-508-5688
ROUSES ENTERPRISES LLC
1301 Saint Mary St, Thibodaux, LA 70301-6527
Tel (985) 447-5998 *Founded/Ownrshp* 1959
Sales 760.2MM^E *EMP* 5,200
Accts Ts Kearns & Co Thibodaux
SIC 5411 Supermarkets, independent
Genl Mgr: Dave Daroca
Genl Mgr: Scott Miller
Dir IT: Tommy Rouse

D-U-N-S 78-725-9217
ROUSH ENTERPRISES INC
12447 Levan Rd, Livonia, MI 48150-1405
Tel (734) 779-7006 *Founded/Ownrshp* 1976
Sales 537.4MM^E *EMP* 2,400
SIC 8711 3714 7948 8734 Engineering services; Motor vehicle engines & parts; Motor vehicle transmissions, drive assemblies & parts; Race car owners; Stock car racing; Automobile proving & testing ground
Ch: Jack Roush
**Pr:* Geoffrey Smith
**CEO:* Evan Lyall
**COO:* Doug Smith
**CFO:* Andy Wozniacki
IT Man: Judy Childs

D-U-N-S 07-632-7295 IMP
ROUSH INDUSTRIES INC
(*Suby of* ROUSH ENTERPRISES INC) ★
12447 Levan Rd, Livonia, MI 48150-1405
Tel (734) 779-7006 *Founded/Ownrshp* 1990
Sales 450.1MM^E *EMP* 2,400
SIC 8734 8711 Automobile proving & testing ground; Engineering services
CEO: Evan Lyall
**Ch Bd:* Jack Roush
**Pr:* Douglas Smith
VP: John Carney
Comm Dir: Maureen Crowley
Opers Mgr: Paul Darrah
S&M/VP: Tim Wheeler
Corp Couns: Robin Johnson

D-U-N-S 02-995-2822
ROUSSEAU SONS LLC
102 S 95th Ave, Tolleson, AZ 85353-3418
Tel (623) 936-7100 *Founded/Ownrshp* 1985
Sales 74.3MM^E *EMP* 1,800
SIC 0161 0191 Vegetables & melons; General farms, primarily crop

ROUSSELOT DUBUQUE INC.
See ROUSSELOT DUBUQUE INC

D-U-N-S 11-406-6421 IMP
ROUSSELOT DUBUQUE INC
ROUSSELOT DUBUQUE INC.
(*Suby of* ROUSSELOT B.V.)
2350 Kerper Blvd, Dubuque, IA 52001-2220
Tel (262) 363-6050 *Founded/Ownrshp* 2002
Sales 140.2MM^E *EMP* 75
SIC 2899 Gelatin
Pr: Larry Jeske
**CFO:* Stephen Smith
VP: Martine Maryns
Dir Lab: Blake Pickel
IT Man: Steve Graham
Sfty Dirs: Jake Riniker

D-U-N-S 02-611-1612
ROUST CORP
CENTRAL EUROPEAN DIST CORP
(*Suby of* KOMPANIYA RUSSKI STANDART, AO)
3000 Atrium Way Ste 265, Mount Laurel, NJ 08054-3926
Tel (856) 273-6980 *Founded/Ownrshp* 1997
Sales 815.6MM *EMP* 4,100
SIC 5181 2085 5182 Beer & other fermented malt liquors; Vodka (alcoholic beverage); Wine
CEO: Grant Winterton
**Ch Bd:* Roustam Tariko
CEO: Vladimir Filiptsev
**CFO:* Ryan Lee
CFO: Goran Ljubicic
Sales Exec: Peter Schulte

D-U-N-S 13-201-4957
ROUTEONE LLC
31500 Nrthwstrn Hwy 200, Farmington Hills, MI 48334
Tel (866) 768-8301 *Founded/Ownrshp* 2002
Sales NA *EMP* 130
SIC 6141 7379 Personal credit institutions; Computer related consulting services
**COO:* Brad Rogers
**CFO:* Janice Basile
**VP:* Daniel J Doman
Software D: Brian Csonka
Snr Mgr: Jayaram Srinivasan

D-U-N-S 04-598-2667 IMP/EXP
ROUX LABORATORIES INC
COLOMER USA
5344 Overmyer Dr, Jacksonville, FL 32254-3645
Tel (904) 366-2602 *Founded/Ownrshp* 2016
Sales 96.4MM^E *EMP* 500^E
SIC 2844 Hair preparations, including shampoos
Pr: Mike Powell
**CFO:* Henry Wernars
CFO: Rannel Westberry
**Treas:* Etta Milner
**VP:* Timothy Buckingham

D-U-N-S 11-329-4870 IMP
■ **ROVI CORP**
(*Suby of* TIVO CORP) ★
2 Circle Star Way, San Carlos, CA 94070-6200
Tel (408) 562-8400 *Founded/Ownrshp* 2016
Sales 526.2MM *EMP* 19^E
SIC 7372 Home entertainment computer software
Pr: Thomas Carson
Pr: Pete Thompson
CFO: Peter Halt
Chf Mktg O: Ted Schremp
Ex VP: Samir Amaly
Ex VP: Bill Corry
Ex VP: Pamela Sergeeff
Sr VP: Michael Hawkey
VP: Kris Krishan
VP: Amy Slater
Snr Sftwr: Gregory Zaraysky

D-U-N-S 05-819-3707
ROVIN INC
BUBBA'S
1332 Paisley St, Denton, TX 76209-4534
Tel (940) 383-0300 *Founded/Ownrshp* 1981
Sales 37.0MM^E *EMP* 1,100
SIC 5812 Chicken restaurant
CEO: Paul Vinyard

D-U-N-S 60-607-4076
ROVISYS CO
1455 Danner Dr, Aurora, OH 44202-9273
Tel (330) 562-8600 *Founded/Ownrshp* 1989
Sales 89.3MM^E *EMP* 175^E
SIC 8711 Engineering services
Pr: John W Robertson
VP: Freda Keelin

D-U-N-S 00-793-0050 IMP/EXP
ROWAN COMPANIES INC
(*Suby of* ROWAN COMPANIES PLC)
2800 Post Oak Blvd # 5450, Houston, TX 77056-6189
Tel (713) 621-7800 *Founded/Ownrshp* 1948
Sales 2.2MMM^E *EMP* 2,719
SIC 1381 3531 3533 Drilling oil & gas wells; Loaders, shovel: self-propelled; Trucks, off-highway; Drill rigs
Pr: Thomas P Burke
CFO: William Well
**Ch:* W Matt Ralls
**Treas:* William H Wells
Ofcr: George Jones
**Ex VP:* J Kevin Bartol
VP: Barbara Carroll
**VP:* Gregory M Hatfield
VP: C W Johnson
**VP:* Mark A Keller
VP: William D Provine
Board of Directors: Robert G Croyle, William T Fox III, Graham Hearne, Thomas R Hix, Henry E Lentz, Lord Moynihan, Suzanne P Nimocks, P Dexter Peacock, John J Quicke

D-U-N-S 88-395-3713 IMP
ROWAN DRILLING CO INC
(*Suby of* ROWAN COMPANIES PLC)
2800 Post Oak Blvd # 5450, Houston, TX 77056-6100
Tel (713) 621-7800 *Founded/Ownrshp* 1923
Sales 153.8MM^E *EMP* 500
SIC 1381 Directional drilling oil & gas wells
CEO: Thomas P Burke
CFO: J Kevin Bartol
Ch: W Matt Ralls
Ex VP: John L Buvens
Ex VP: Mark A Keller
Prin: Mathew Ralls

D-U-N-S 13-141-6919
ROWAN HEALTH SERVICES CORP
(*Suby of* LAKESIDE FAMILY PHYSICIANS) ★
612 Mocksville Ave, Salisbury, NC 28144-2732
Tel (704) 210-5000 *Founded/Ownrshp* 1933
Sales 46.3MM^E *EMP* 1,200
SIC 8062 General medical & surgical hospitals
CEO: Charles Elliot
**Pr:* Wayne A Cline
**VP:* Dwight Messinger
IT Man: Shannon Sheppard

D-U-N-S 07-105-6535
ROWAN REGIONAL MEDICAL CENTER INC
(*Suby of* LAKESIDE FAMILY PHYSICIANS) ★
612 Mocksville Ave, Salisbury, NC 28144-2799
Tel (704) 210-5000 *Founded/Ownrshp* 2008
Sales 196.9MM *EMP* 1,196
SIC 8062 General medical & surgical hospitals
CEO: Carl Armato
Chf OB: Lynn B Anderson
Chf Rad: James C Johnson
**Pr:* Darise Caldwell
VP: Thomas F Trahey
Dir Inf Cn: Robert Pierce
Dir Rx: Julie Lippard
Dir Env Sv: Mike Lindsey
Chf Nrs Of: Catrina King
Dir QC: Shannon Shepherd
Dir IT: Delphine McCullough
Board of Directors: Carl Armato

D-U-N-S 13-920-3145 IMP/EXP
ROWAN UNIVERSITY
201 Mullica Hill Rd, Glassboro, NJ 08028-1702
Tel (856) 256-4000 *Founded/Ownrshp* 1923
Sales 291.7MM *EMP* 1,932
Accts Kpmg Llp Short Hills Nj
SIC 8221 University
Pr: Dr Ali Houshmand
Exec: Lafferty Clare
Assoc Dir: Gregory Biren
Assoc Dir: Joanne Fisher
Assoc Dir: Maria McCall
Ex Dir: Barry Kramer
Ex Dir: Donald Stoll
DP Exec: Craig Katz
HC Dir: Catherine Dayton

D-U-N-S 07-938-1306
ROWAN UNIVERSITY/RUTGERS-CAMDEN BOARD OF GOVERNORS
201 Mullica Hill Rd, Glassboro, NJ 08028-1702
Tel (856) 256-4121 *Founded/Ownrshp* 2014
Sales 4.5MM^E *EMP* 2,000
SIC 8221 Colleges universities & professional schools
Pr: Ali Houshmand

D-U-N-S 06-926-6930
ROWE BROTHERS (CT)
DAVIDSON COMPANY
367 Alumni Rd, Newington, CT 06111-1867
Tel (203) 265-5533 *Founded/Ownrshp* 1967
Sales 219.7MM^E *EMP* 300
Accts Konowitz Kahn & Company Pc
SIC 5141 Groceries, general line
CEO: Michael Davidson
**Pr:* Robert Rowe
**Sr VP:* James Rowe
**VP:* Stephen Rowe
Sls Dir: Joe Montano

D-U-N-S 79-127-5261 IMP/EXP
ROWE FINE FURNITURE INC
(*Suby of* SUN CAPITAL PARTNERS INC) ★
2121 Gardner St, Elliston, VA 24087-3055
Tel (540) 444-7693 *Founded/Ownrshp* 2007
Sales 222.7MM^E *EMP* 575
SIC 2512 2511 Upholstered household furniture; Wood household furniture
CEO: Stefanie J Lucas
**Pr:* Bob Choppa
**CFO:* Mark Freitas
Opers Mgr: Steve Dokus
Board of Directors: Christopher T Metz, Don Mueller

D-U-N-S 00-312-7750 EXP
ROWE FURNITURE CORP
(*Suby of* SUN CAPITAL PARTNERS INC) ★
2121 Gardner St, Elliston, VA 24087-3055
Tel (540) 444-7693 *Founded/Ownrshp* 1985
Sales 228.8MM^E *EMP* 2,400
SIC 2512 5712 Upholstered household furniture; Living room furniture: upholstered on wood frames; Chairs: upholstered on wood frames; Recliners: upholstered on wood frames; Furniture stores
CEO: Gerald M Birnbach
Pr: Bruce M Birnbach
**Treas:* Garry W Angle
Bd of Dir: Gerald Birnhach
Bd of Dir: Allan Tofias
**Sr VP:* Timothy J Fortune
Sr VP: Stefanie Lucas
**VP:* Barry A Birnbach
MIS Dir: Henry Bucklin
Dir IT: Mark Tokarc
IT Man: Taki Gikakis

D-U-N-S 78-618-5256 EXP
ROWE FURNITURE INC
(*Suby of* SUN CAPITAL PARTNERS INC) ★
2121 Gardner St, Elliston, VA 24087-3055
Tel (540) 389-8671 *Founded/Ownrshp* 2006
Sales 191.6MM^E *EMP* 1,500
SIC 2512 2511 2421 Upholstered household furniture; Wood household furniture; Kiln drying of lumber
CEO: Gerald M Birnbach
**Pr:* Rowe Cos

D-U-N-S 03-964-6591
ROWELL CHEMICAL CORP
15 Salt Creek Ln Ste 205, Hinsdale, IL 60521-8610
Tel (630) 920-8833 *Founded/Ownrshp* 1980
Sales 114.2MM^E *EMP* 60
SIC 5169 Acids; Alcohols; Caustic soda; Chlorine
**Pr:* Nat J Rowell
**VP:* Kyle Kohlhaas

D-U-N-S 07-723-3849
ROWLAND UNIFIED SCHOOL DISTRICT
RUSD
1830 Nogales St, Rowland Heights, CA 91748-2945
Tel (626) 854-8317 *Founded/Ownrshp* 1970
Sales 71.9MM^E *EMP* 1,180
Accts Vavrinek Trine Day & Co Ll
SIC 8211 Public combined elementary & secondary school
Bd of Dir: Gilbert Garcia
Bd of Dir: Mary Maxwell
Genl Mgr: Silvia Rivas

D-U-N-S 09-985-7286 IMP
ROWMAN & LITTLEFIELD PUBLISHING GROUP INC
4501 Forbes Blvd Ste 200, Lanham, MD 20706-4346
Tel (301) 459-3366 *Founded/Ownrshp* 2001
Sales 228.7MM^E *EMP* 500
SIC 2731 5192 Textbooks: publishing only, not printed on site; Books
Pr: James Lyons
**Pr:* Paul Konowitch
**CFO:* George Franzak
**Sec:* Stanley Plotnick
**Ex VP:* Robert Marsh
**VP:* Mike Cornell
VP: Michael Dorr
**VP:* Linda May
**VP:* Carla Quental
Sls&Mrk Ex: Mihela Kralj

D-U-N-S 83-349-0464
ROXANE LABORATORIES INC
(*Suby of* EUROHEALTH (USA) INC) ★
1809 Wilson Rd, Columbus, OH 43228-9579
Tel (614) 276-4000 *Founded/Ownrshp* 2005

Sales 500.0MM *EMP* 127
SIC 2834 Druggists' preparations (pharmaceuticals)
CEO: Michael Raya
**Pr:* Brian Hoffmann
**CFO:* Mohammed Obeidat
**Treas:* George J Muench III
VP: Glenn Marina
VP: Randy Wilson
Assoc Dir: Stephen Lieber
Assoc Dir: Mark Warner
Ex Dir: Kerri Finnegan
Board of Directors: Hussein Arkhagha, Ali Al Husry, Michael Raya

D-U-N-S 62-268-0130 IMP
ROXBORO HOLDINGS INC
(*Suby of* DIALIGHT PLC)
1501 State Route 34, Wall Township, NJ 07727-3932
Tel (732) 919-3119 *Founded/Ownrshp* 1990
Sales 270.5MM^E *EMP* 1,041
SIC 3643 3679 3993 3823 3674 Current-carrying wiring devices; Electronic circuits; Signs & advertising specialties; Industrial instrmnts msrmnt display/control process variable; Semiconductors & related devices
Pr: Roy Burton
**VP:* Nick Gallogly
Ex Dir: Bill Whiteley
IT Man: Sam Tooma

ROY ANDERSON
See ANDERSON COMPANIES INC

D-U-N-S 00-785-0530 IMP
■ **ROY ANDERSON CORP** (MS)
(*Suby of* ROY ANDERSON) ★
11400 Reichold Rd, Gulfport, MS 39503-6008
Tel (228) 896-4000 *Founded/Ownrshp* 1955
Sales 160.4MM^E *EMP* 300
SIC 1542 1541 1522 Commercial & office building contractors; Industrial buildings, new construction; Multi-family dwelling construction
Pr: Roy Anderson III
VP Bus Dev: Charles McLemore
Dir IT: Jason Taylor
Mktg Dir: Gina Davis
Board of Directors: Gina Dambrino Davis

ROY ROGERS
See PLAMONDON ENTERPRISES INC

ROYAL & SUNALLIANCE
See ARROWOOD INDEMNITY CO

D-U-N-S 08-464-4710 IMP/EXP
ROYAL ADHESIVES AND SEALANTS LLC
ROYAL ELASTOMERS
2001 W Washington St, South Bend, IN 46628-2032
Tel (574) 246-5000 *Founded/Ownrshp* 2015
Sales 615.9MM^E *EMP* 1,220
SIC 2891 7389 8711 Adhesives & sealants; Packaging & labeling services; Building construction consultant
Pr: Ted Clark
Pr: Richard Foukes
Pr: Mark S Masters
**CFO:* Gary Stenke
Bd of Dir: John Televantos
Bd of Dir: Tim Zappala
VP: Mark Ericson
**VP:* Randy Greenlee
VP: Ronald Vollmer
Genl Mgr: Karl Huelsenbeck
Genl Mgr: Timothy O'Neil

D-U-N-S 60-992-2695
ROYAL ALLIANCE ASSOCIATES INC
(*Suby of* ADVISOR GROUP INC) ★
1 Wrld Fncl Ctr Fl 14, New York, NY 10281-2100
Tel (212) 786-0235 *Founded/Ownrshp* 1997
Sales 219.0MM^E *EMP* 200
SIC 6211 Brokers, security
Ch Bd: Gary Krat
Pr: John Chitwood
**Pr:* Mark Goldberg
CFO: Betty Ann Sullivan
Assoc VP: Bob Aguanno
Assoc VP: Dayla Rodriguez
**Sr VP:* Vincent Cloud
Sr VP: Al Grill
Sr VP: Al Grilli
**Sr VP:* Barbara McInerney
**Sr VP:* Arthur Tambaro
VP: Kevin Beard
VP: Gwenn Kalow
VP: Paul Largo
VP: Rosemary Magee
VP: Betty Osborn
VP: Shaun Rose
VP: Matthew Schlueter
VP: Timothy Valento
Exec: Janelle Heck

ROYAL APPLIANCE MANUFACTURING
See TTI FLOOR CARE NORTH AMERICA INC

D-U-N-S 00-416-4836 IMP/EXP
ROYAL APPLIANCE MFG CO
TTI FLOOR CARE NORTH AMERICA
(*Suby of* TECHTRONIC INDUSTRIES COMPANY LIMITED)
7005 Cochran Rd, Cleveland, OH 44139-4303
Tel (440) 996-2000 *Founded/Ownrshp* 2003
Sales 356.4MM^E *EMP* 550
SIC 5064 Vacuum cleaners, household
Pr: Chris Gurreri
**CFO:* Matthew Shene
**CFO:* Richard Vasek
Sr VP: Gary Dieterich
**VP:* Dave Brickner
**VP:* Richard C Farone
VP: Keith T Moone
Off Mgr: Bill Moore
Dir IT: Ron Godeen
VP Mfg: David M Brickner
VP Mktg: Dave Schiever

D-U-N-S 15-763-7039
ROYAL BANK OF SCOTLAND PLC
RBS BANK
(*Suby of* THE ROYAL BANK OF SCOTLAND GROUP PUBLIC LIMITED COMPANY)
600 Washington Blvd, Stamford, CT 06901-3726
Tel (203) 897-2700 *Founded/Ownrshp* 1977
Sales NA *EMP* 300^E
SIC 6029 Commercial banks
Sr VP: Gavin Smyth
VP: Dennis Dimauro
VP: Michael Graziano
VP: Alec Matt
VP: David Trofi
VP: Andrew Wynn
Assoc Dir: John Copping
Assoc Dir: Rob Laurens
Mng Dir: Steven F Killilea
Mng Dir: Charles Randolph
Admn Mgr: Peter Fenwick

D-U-N-S 17-756-9688
ROYAL BATHS MANUFACTURING CO LTD
14635 Chrisman Rd, Houston, TX 77039-1116
Tel (281) 442-3400 *Founded/Ownrshp* 2013
Sales 186.2MM^E *EMP* 571
SIC 3842 3949 3432 3281 Whirlpool baths, hydrotherapy equipment; Sporting & athletic goods; Plumbing fixture fittings & trim; Cut stone & stone products
Dir Risk M: Mark Kieber
Dir IT: Shane Guyton
Mktg Dir: Bryce Boyd
Sls Mgr: Bill Carter
Sls Mgr: Eric Johnson

D-U-N-S 00-513-0315
ROYAL BOX GROUP LLC
ROYAL CONTINENTAL BOX COMPANY
(*Suby of* SCHWARZ PARTNERS LP) ★
1301 S 47th Ave, Cicero, IL 60804-1598
Tel (708) 656-2020 *Founded/Ownrshp* 1922
Sales 178.0MM^E *EMP* 737^E
SIC 2653 Boxes, corrugated: made from purchased materials
Ch: J Jordan Nerenberg
Pr: Robert L Mc Ilvaine
VP: Tim Benecke
Creative D: Marco Zamora
Creative D: Bryan Zander
Admn Mgr: Ron Mikol
Genl Mgr: Jay King
Opers Mgr: Scott Miller
Plnt Mgr: John Rockman
Plnt Mgr: Fernando Santana
Mktg Mgr: Cheryl Kinser

D-U-N-S 11-838-8552 IMP
ROYAL CABINETS INC
1299 E Phillips Blvd, Pomona, CA 91766-5429
Tel (909) 629-8565 *Founded/Ownrshp* 1984
Sales 99.6MM^E *EMP* 600
SIC 2434 2511 Wood kitchen cabinets; Wood household furniture
Pr: Clay Smith
**COO:* Bill Roan
Ofcr: Gus Danjoi

D-U-N-S 03-889-9951 IMP
ROYAL CANIN USA INC
(*Suby of* MARS INC) ★
500 Fountain Lakes Blvd # 100, Saint Charles, MO 63301-4341
Tel (636) 724-1692 *Founded/Ownrshp* 2003
Sales 93.4MM^E *EMP* 196
SIC 2047 0752 Dog food; Cat food; Animal specialty services
Pr: Stan Howton
VP: Brent Mayabb
Rgnl Mgr: Raymond Schultz
CIO: Pamela Welker
IT Man: Timothy Connolly
Opers Mgr: Tammy Lindner
Sls Mgr: Joe Taylor

D-U-N-S 96-728-4886
ROYAL CAPITAL CORP
255 E Paces Ferry Rd Ne # 300, Atlanta, GA 30305-2244
Tel (404) 239-0808 *Founded/Ownrshp* 1996
Sales 114.6MM^E *EMP* 755
SIC 6719 Investment holding companies, except banks
CEO: David Davoudpour

D-U-N-S 60-584-4232
▲ **ROYAL CARIBBEAN CRUISES LTD**
1050 Caribbean Way, Miami, FL 33132-2028
Tel (305) 539-6000 *Founded/Ownrshp* 1968
Sales 8.3MMM *EMP* 66,000
Tkr Sym RCL *Exch* NYS
SIC 4481 Deep sea passenger transportation, except ferry
Ch Bd: Richard D Fain
Pr: Adam M Goldstein
CFO: Jason T Liberty
Treas: Russ Bogue
Chf Cred: Bradley H Stein
Assoc VP: Claire Mason
Ex VP: Lisa Lutoff-Perlo
Sr VP: Michael Giresi
Sr VP: Henry L Pujol
VP: Vijay Duggal
VP: Tony Faso
VP: Steve Hancock
VP: Minas Miliaras
Board of Directors: John F Brock, William L Kimsey, Ann S Moore, Thomas J Pritzker, William K Reilly, Bernt Reitan, Donald Thompson, Arne Alexander Wilhelmsen

ROYAL CONTINENTAL BOX COMPANY
See ROYAL BOX GROUP LLC

D-U-N-S 00-636-9235
■ **ROYAL CROWN BOTTLING CORP** (KY)
RC COLA
(*Suby of* DR PEPPER SNAPPLE GROUP INC) ★
1100 Independence Ave, Evansville, IN 47714-4549
Tel (812) 424-7978 *Founded/Ownrshp* 1938, 2000
Sales 119.7MM^E *EMP* 315
SIC 2086 Soft drinks: packaged in cans, bottles, etc.
Pr: Nancy King Hodge
**Sec:* Gail L King
**VP:* Chad Metten
**CIO:* David Palmer
Plnt Mgr: Danny Hill
Mktg Mgr: Dave Brown

ROYAL CUP COFFEE
See ROYAL CUP INC

D-U-N-S 00-400-1541 IMP/EXP
ROYAL CUP INC
ROYAL CUP COFFEE
160 Cleage Dr, Birmingham, AL 35217-1461
Tel (205) 849-5836 *Founded/Ownrshp* 1951
Sales 321.8MM^E *EMP* 840
SIC 2095 5149 Roasted coffee; Groceries & related products; Soft drinks
CEO: William E Smith III
**Pr:* Hatton Cv Smith
**CFO:* Lamar C Bagby
**VP:* Eugene M Lewis
VP: Marc Schonland
Exec: Samantha Paliescheskey
Rgnl Mgr: Mike Powell
Rgnl Mgr: Scotty Scott
Brnch Mgr: Paul Atkisson
Brnch Mgr: Jerry Barber
Brnch Mgr: Jason Coln

ROYAL ELASTOMERS
See ROYAL ADHESIVES AND SEALANTS LLC

ROYAL FARMS
See TWO FARMS INC

D-U-N-S 87-981-7104
ROYAL FOOD SERVICE CO INC
3720 Zip Indus Blvd Se, Atlanta, GA 30354-2937
Tel (404) 366-4299 *Founded/Ownrshp* 1994
Sales 156.3MM^E *EMP* 220
SIC 5148 5142 Fresh fruits & vegetables; Packaged frozen goods
CEO: Craig Fleming
**CFO:* Mark McClendon
CIO: Jerry Maze III
Mktg Mgr: Reed Crouch
Sales Asso: Steve Ely

D-U-N-S 04-268-8416
▲ **ROYAL GOLD INC**
1660 Wynkoop St Ste 1000, Denver, CO 80202-1161
Tel (303) 573-1660 *Founded/Ownrshp* 1981
Sales 359.7MM *EMP* 20^E
Tkr Sym RGLD *Exch* NGS
SIC 6211 Mineral royalties dealers
Pr: Tony A Jensen
CFO: Stefan L Wenger
VP: Karli S Anderson
VP: William H Heissenbuttel
VP: Bruce C Kirchhoff
VP Opers: Mark Isto

D-U-N-S 80-919-6277
ROYAL HOLDINGS INC
(*Suby of* ARSENAL CAPITAL PARTNERS LP) ★
2001 W Washington St, South Bend, IN 46628-2032
Tel (574) 246-5000 *Founded/Ownrshp* 2003
Sales 186.6MM^E *EMP* 1,440
SIC 2891 Adhesives & sealants
CEO: Ted Clark
**CFO:* Gary Stenke
**VP:* Randy Greenlee
**VP:* Steve Zens

D-U-N-S 80-080-6304
ROYAL HOSPITALITY CORP
255 E Paces Ferry Rd Ne # 300, Atlanta, GA 30305-2233
Tel (404) 239-0329 *Founded/Ownrshp* 2004
Sales 324.7MM^E *EMP* 2,805^E
SIC 6794 8741 5812 Franchises, selling or licensing; Restaurant management; Fast-food restaurant, chain
CEO: David Davoudpour

D-U-N-S 80-905-8761
ROYAL MANAGEMENT CORP
LEXINGTON HEALTH NETWORK
665 W North Ave Ste 500, Lombard, IL 60148-1135
Tel (630) 495-1700 *Founded/Ownrshp* 1990
Sales 96.2MM^E *EMP* 2,500
SIC 8059 Nursing home, except skilled & intermediate care facility
Pr: John Samatas
COO: Daniel Wood
**CFO:* Karen I Gillis
VP: Christopher Dusza
Off Mgr: Sheila Tumpach
MIS Dir: Allen Fazzari
Dir IT: Carrie Deato
IT Man: Allen Pindell
IT Man: Patti Pyzynski

D-U-N-S 00-722-0882 EXP
ROYAL MFG CO LP (OK)
TROCO OIL COMPANY
516 S 25th West Ave, Tulsa, OK 74127-8406
Tel (918) 584-2671 *Founded/Ownrshp* 1914
Sales 98.0MM *EMP* 119
SIC 2992 2911 Oils & greases, blending & compounding; Greases, lubricating
Pr: William R Mallory Jr
Sec: Kari Mallory
VP: Jim Gott
Dir Lab: Paul Salter
Ql Cn Mgr: Jerril Billy
Sales Asso: Brad Flechtner

D-U-N-S 05-580-4595
ROYAL NEIGHBORS OF AMERICA
230 16th St, Rock Island, IL 61201-8645
Tel (309) 788-4561 *Founded/Ownrshp* 1895
Sales NA *EMP* 120
Accts Royal Neighbors Of America Ro
SIC 6411 6311 Insurance agents, brokers & service; Life insurance
Ch: Mary Clare Radke
**Pr:* Cynthia Tidwell
**CFO:* Brian Haynes
CFO: Marc Schoenfeld
Chf Mktg O: Jodii Zimmerman
Chf Inves: Jon Lucia
Rgnl Mgr: Philip McBee
QA Dir: Jodie Schau
Software D: Jeff Hugus
Sales Exec: Jay Csipkes
Mktg Dir: Connie O'Brien

D-U-N-S 00-623-0593 IMP/EXP
ROYAL OAK ENTERPRISES LLC
1 Royal Oak Ave, Roswell, GA 30076-7583
Tel (678) 461-3200 *Founded/Ownrshp* 1962
Sales 122.4MM^E *EMP* 933^E
SIC 2999 2899

ROYAL OAKS HEALTH CARE & REHAB
See KINDRED NURSING CENTERS LIMITED PARTNERSHIP

ROYAL POULTRY
See GOLDEN WEST TRADING INC

ROYAL PRESTIGE
See HY CITE ENTERPRISES LLC

D-U-N-S 03-239-1609
ROYAL SERVICES INC
WATCHMAN MARKETING
4526 Lenox Ave, Jacksonville, FL 32205-5418
Tel (904) 386-6436 *Founded/Ownrshp* 1914
Sales 18.6MM^E *EMP* 1,075
SIC 7349 7371 Janitorial service, contract basis; Computer software development
Pr: Percy Rosenbloom Jr
**Sec:* Paul A Grant
**VP:* Percy Rosenbloom III

ROYAL STAMP CO
See TERUYA BROS LIMITED

D-U-N-S 17-831-3383 IMP
ROYAL TECHNOLOGIES CORP
HI-TECH PLASTICS
3765 Quincy St, Hudsonville, MI 49426-8408
Tel (616) 669-3393 *Founded/Ownrshp* 2007
Sales 232.2MM^E *EMP* 700
SIC 3089 Injection molded finished plastic products
Pr: James H Vanderkolk
CFO: Dick Klamer
**VP:* Perry Franco
**VP:* Richard C Klamer
**VP:* Kirk Lambers
QA Dir: Pamela Gilsdorf
IT Man: French Williams
Tech Mgr: Chaunda Devries
Tech Mgr: Tracy Fields
VP Opers: Rick Kimber
Mtls Mgr: Adalberto Hernandez

D-U-N-S 19-690-5111 IMP/EXP
ROYAL TEN CATE (USA) INC
(*Suby of* KONINKLIJKE TEN CATE B.V.)
365 S Holland Dr, Pendergrass, GA 30567-4625
Tel (706) 693-2226 *Founded/Ownrshp* 1985
Sales 640.6MM *EMP* 1,500
SIC 2299 Fabrics: linen, jute, hemp, ramie
CEO: Loek De Vries
**CFO:* Joseph W Averette
VP: Todd Anderson
Board of Directors: Louis Loek De Vries, Jaap Lock, Pieter Van Der-Vorm

D-U-N-S 17-503-4925 IMP
ROYAL VENDORS INC
(*Suby of* COINCO) ★
300 Hunter Ave Fl 2, Saint Louis, MO 63124-2081
Tel (304) 728-7056 *Founded/Ownrshp* 1996
Sales 198.7MM^E *EMP* 1,150^E
SIC 3581 Automatic vending machines
Pr: Jack Thomas Jr
Pr: Kevin Ward
Treas: Daniel Ring
VP: Steve Anderson
VP: William Peterson

D-U-N-S 04-138-0594
ROYALTY CAPITAL INC
1010 N Central Ave, Glendale, CA 91202-2937
Tel (888) 210-0332 *Founded/Ownrshp* 2009
Sales 100.0MM *EMP* 15
SIC 4213 Trucking, except local
Pr: Alfred Megrabyan

D-U-N-S 05-009-0695 IMP
ROYALTY CARPET MILLS INC
17111 Red Hill Ave, Irvine, CA 92614-5607
Tel (949) 474-4000 *Founded/Ownrshp* 1963
Sales 163.7MM^E *EMP* 800
SIC 2273 Carpets, hand & machine made
CEO: Andrea Greenleaf
**Pr:* Mike Derderian
CFO: Steve Piwnica
Dir IT: Kien Trinh
Opers Mgr: Alan Voller
VP Sls: Lou Calangelo
Sls Dir: Paul Engle
Mktg Mgr: Katherine Vanderpool
Sls Mgr: Jonathan Bingham
Sls Mgr: Mike Mason
Sls Mgr: James Wofford

D-U-N-S 00-146-6119 IMP
ROYCE TOO LLC
(*Suby of* OKAMOTO CORPORATION)
3330 Healy Dr Ste 200, Winston Salem, NC 27103-2024
Tel (212) 356-1627 *Founded/Ownrshp* 2004, 2008
Sales 107.0MM^E *EMP* 100

SIC 5137 5136 Hosiery: women's, children's & infants'; Hosiery, men's & boys'
Pr: Bob Boglioli
**VP:* Ben Carson
VP Sls: Gary Silversteen

ROYOMARTIN
See MARTIN SUSTAINABLE RESOURCES LLC

ROYOMARTIN
See MARTCO LLC

ROY'S
See OS PRIME INC

D-U-N-S 94-243-2274
ROYSTON HOLDING LLC
111 Center St Ste 2500, Little Rock, AR 72201-4453
Tel (770) 735-3456 *Founded/Ownrshp* 2007
Sales 112.4MM[E] *EMP* 599[E]
SIC 7389 1751 2542 Design, commercial & industrial; Ship joinery; Showcases (not refrigerated): except wood; Counters or counter display cases: except wood; Shelving, office & store: except wood
Pr: Earl I Seekins
**CFO:* David Frost

D-U-N-S 05-864-5800
ROYSTON LLC
(*Suby of* ROYSTON HOLDING LLC) ★
1 Pickroy Rd, Jasper, GA 30143-5045
Tel (770) 735-3456 *Founded/Ownrshp* 2008
Sales 112.4MM[E] *EMP* 599
SIC 7389 2542 1751 Design, commercial & industrial; Showcases (not refrigerated): except wood; Counters or counter display cases: except wood; Shelving, office & store: except wood; Ship joinery
Pr: David Storey
Ex VP: Wes Barker
VP: Doug Mabeus
Plnt Mgr: Doug Mavius
Plnt Mgr: Bert Stephens

D-U-N-S 00-810-5926
ROYWELL SERVICES INC
4545 Bissonnet St Ste 104, Bellaire, TX 77401-3008
Tel (713) 661-4747 *Founded/Ownrshp* 1965
Sales 110.0MM[E] *EMP* 150
SIC 1389

D-U-N-S 07-870-7043
RP CROWN PARENT LLC
15059 N Scottsdale Rd # 400, Scottsdale, AZ 85254-2666
Tel (480) 308-3000 *Founded/Ownrshp* 2012
Sales 1.2MMM[E] *EMP* 6,204[E]
SIC 7371 Computer software development & applications

D-U-N-S 11-827-2517 IMP
▲ RPC INC
2801 Buford Hwy Ne # 520, Brookhaven, GA 30329-2143
Tel (404) 321-2140 *Founded/Ownrshp* 1984
Sales 1.2MMM *EMP* 3,100
Tkr Sym RES *Exch* NYS
SIC 1389 Oil field services; Pumping of oil & gas wells; Servicing oil & gas wells; Fire fighting, oil & gas field
Pr: Richard A Hubbell
**Ch Bd:* R Randall Rollins
CFO: Ben M Palmer
**VP:* Linda H Graham

D-U-N-S 16-183-5475 EXP
RPC INC
500 World Commerce Pkwy, Saint Augustine, FL 32092-3788
Tel (904) 448-1055 *Founded/Ownrshp* 1986
Sales 1.0MMM[E] *EMP* 2,400
SIC 5082 Construction & mining machinery
Ch Bd: Lance Ringhaver
**CEO:* Randal Ringhaver
**Ex VP:* Ronald Roy

D-U-N-S 04-538-2186
RPD HOTELS 18 LLC
VAGABOND INNS
2361 Rosecrans Ave # 150, El Segundo, CA 90245-7906
Tel (213) 746-1531 *Founded/Ownrshp* 1998
Sales 30.2MM[E] *EMP* 1,310
SIC 7011 Motels
Pr: Juan Sanchez Llaca
VP: Les Biggins
VP: Mark Sekelick
Genl Mgr: Jana Gage

D-U-N-S 08-329-5725
RPE INC (WI)
RPE TRANSPORTATION
8550 Central Sands Rd, Bancroft, WI 54921-8909
Tel (715) 335-8050 *Founded/Ownrshp* 1973
Sales 250.0MM *EMP* 36
SIC 7389 Brokers' services
CEO: Russell Wysocki
Manager: Mark Bucek
Board of Directors: Jeff Sommers, Kirk Wille, Gary Wysocki, William Wysocki

RPE TRANSPORTATION
See RPE INC

RPI
See RANBAXY INC

D-U-N-S 00-415-5651 IMP/EXP
▲ RPM INTERNATIONAL INC
2628 Pearl Rd, Medina, OH 44256-7623
Tel (330) 273-5090 *Founded/Ownrshp* 1947
Sales 4.8MMM *EMP* 12,962
Tkr Sym RPM *Exch* NYS
SIC 2851 2891 3069 2899 2865 2842 Paints & allied products; Lacquers, varnishes, enamels & other coatings; Lacquer: bases, dopes, thinner; Varnishes; Adhesives & sealants; Sealants; Adhesives; Roofing, membrane rubber; Waterproofing compounds; Concrete curing & hardening compounds; Corrosion preventive lubricant; Dyes & pigments; Specialty cleaning preparations
Ch Bd: Frank C Sullivan
Pr: Ronald A Rice
CFO: Russell L Gordon
Ch: John J McLaughlin
Chf Cred: Edward W Moore
Ex VP: Terry Horan
VP: Lonny R Dirusso
VP: Janeen B Kastner
VP: Barry M Slifstein
VP: Keith Smiley
Exec: Matthew Ratajczak

D-U-N-S 07-156-5444
RPM LUXURY AUTO SALES INC (CA)
LEXUS OF SACRAMENTO
5112 Madison Ave Ste 201, Sacramento, CA 95841-3000
Tel (916) 485-3987 *Founded/Ownrshp* 1982
Sales 171.9MM *EMP* 228
SIC 5511 Automobiles, new & used
Pr: Patrick Frink
**Ch Bd:* Robert L Frink
**Sec:* Richard G Hill
Sls Dir: Dick Hill
Sls Mgr: Bryon Burdette
Sls Mgr: Rick Rodell
Sls Mgr: Ernie Wassersleben

RPM MANAGEMENT
See BOB FRINK MANAGEMENT INC

RPM MARKETING
See SYNAGRO TECHNOLOGIES INC

D-U-N-S 01-120-4904
RPM MORTGAGE INC
3240 Stone Valley Rd W, Alamo, CA 94507-1555
Tel (925) 295-9300 *Founded/Ownrshp* 2007
Sales NA *EMP* 262[E]
SIC 6162 Mortgage bankers & correspondents
Pr: Erwin R Hirt
**Pr:* Tracey Hirt
**CEO:* Rob Hirt
Ex VP: Cindy Ertman
**Ex VP:* Donny Isaak
Ex VP: Lynne Lundgren
Ex VP: Joe Polizzi
Sr VP: Jill Sonderby
VP: Sue Carlson
VP: Megan Doonan
VP: Josh Lemos
VP: Anthony Scoma

D-U-N-S 11-305-4266
RPM PIZZA LLC
DOMINO'S
15384 5th St, Gulfport, MS 39503-3199
Tel (228) 832-4000 *Founded/Ownrshp* 2003
Sales 167.9MM[E] *EMP* 3,500
SIC 5812 Pizzeria, chain

D-U-N-S 03-745-1080 IMP
■ RPM WOOD FINISHES GROUP INC
(*Suby of* RPM INTERNATIONAL INC) ★
2220 Hwy 70 Se Ste 100, Hickory, NC 28602
Tel (828) 261-0325 *Founded/Ownrshp* 1997
Sales 242.1MM[E] *EMP* 745
SIC 2851 Paints & allied products
Pr: Ronnie G Holman
**Treas:* Wesley Harris
Treas: Gregor A Webb
VP: Jim Stoffer
Dir Lab: Gary Shore

RPS
See REVENUE PROCESSING SOLUTIONS INC

RPS MANAGEMENT
See REAL PROPERTY SERVICES CORP

D-U-N-S 82-885-3106
▲ RPX CORP
1 Market Plz Ste 800, San Francisco, CA 94105-1008
Tel (866) 779-7641 *Founded/Ownrshp* 2008
Sales 291.8MM *EMP* 161[E]
Tkr Sym RPXC *Exch* NGS
SIC 6794 8741 Patent owners & lessors; Business management
Pr: John A Amster
CEO: Trevor Campion
CFO: Robert H Heath
Ex VP: Mallun Yen
Sr VP: Martin E Roberts
Sr VP: Steven S Swank
Pgrm Dir: Tatiana Soldak
Board of Directors: Andrew D Africk, Shelby W Bonnie, Frank E Dangeard, Steven L Fingerhood, Gilbert S Palter, Sanford R Robertson, Thomas O Ryder

D-U-N-S 07-834-7094
RR ACQUISITION HOLDING LLC
1345 Avenue Of The Americ, New York, NY 10105-3101
Tel (212) 479-7116 *Founded/Ownrshp* 1992
Sales 28.7MM[E] *EMP* 1,836
SIC 4011 Railroads, line-haul operating
Pr: John E Giles

RR DONNELLEY
See RR DONNELLEY & SONS CO

D-U-N-S 00-511-9573
▲ RR DONNELLEY & SONS CO
RR DONNELLEY
35 W Wacker Dr Ste 3650, Chicago, IL 60601-1840
Tel (312) 326-8000 *Founded/Ownrshp* 1864
Sales 11.2MMM *EMP* 68,400[E]
Tkr Sym RRD *Exch* NYS
SIC 2754 2759 2752 2732 7331 7336 Commercial printing, gravure; Catalogs: gravure printing, not published on site; Magazines: gravure printing, not published on site; Directories: gravure printing, not published on site; Commercial printing; Letterpress printing; Commercial printing, offset; Books: printing & binding; Direct mail advertising services; Graphic arts & related design
Pr: Thomas J Quinlan III
**Ch Bd:* John C Pope
COO: Daniel L Knotts
CFO: Daniel N Leib
Chf Cred: Suzanne S Bettman
Sr VP: Andrew B Coxhead
Board of Directors: Susan M Cameron, Richard L Crandall, Susan M Gianinno, Judith H Hamilton, Jeffrey M Katz, Richard K Palmer, Michael T Riordan, Oliver R Sockwell

RR DONNELLEY FINANCIAL, INC.
See DONNELLEY FINANCIAL LLC

D-U-N-S 05-504-8532 IMP
■ RR DONNELLEY PRINTING CO LP
R R DONNELLEY
(*Suby of* RR DONNELLEY) ★
111 S Wacker Dr Ste 3500, Chicago, IL 60606-4304
Tel (312) 326-8000 *Founded/Ownrshp* 1864
Sales 626.9MM[E] *EMP* 2,500
SIC 2754 2752 5085 Rotogravure printing; Commercial printing, offset; Industrial supplies
Pr: Ronald Daly
CFO: Thomas Quinlan
CFO: Kevin Smith
**VP:* Monica Forhmann

RRCH HEALTHCARE PARTNERS
See ST MARYS REGIONAL MEDICAL CENTER

RRCH HEALTHCARE PARTNERS
See CAPELLA HEALTHCARE INC

RRCH HEALTHCARE PARTNERS
See CAPITAL MEDICAL CENTER

D-U-N-S 11-334-2187
RREMC LLC
DENNY'S
1800 Okeechobee Rd # 100, West Palm Beach, FL 33409-5207
Tel (561) 684-2101 *Founded/Ownrshp* 2002
Sales 45.0MM[E] *EMP* 1,000
SIC 5812 Restaurant, family: chain
CEO: John C Metz
CFO: Michael Lubitz
Treas: Alan Hartstein
Exec: Bill Howard

D-U-N-S 07-914-6568
RRERF REGENCY PARK LLC
NORTHHAMPTON CROSSING
64 Regency Dr, Mount Holly, NJ 08060-1300
Tel (856) 848-6700 *Founded/Ownrshp* 2014
Sales 27.5MM[E] *EMP* 1,828
SIC 6531 Real estate agents & managers
Prin: Jim Brooks
Prin: Tesa Doleman

D-U-N-S 07-247-7144
RRH CORP
1900 N Akard St, Dallas, TX 75201-2300
Tel (214) 978-8000 *Founded/Ownrshp* 1976
Sales 9.8MMM[E] *EMP* 2,571
SIC 1382 1311 2911 0212 6799

D-U-N-S 96-490-0349
■ RRI ENERGY BROADBAND INC
(*Suby of* NRG) ★
1000 Main St, Houston, TX 77002-6336
Tel (713) 537-3000 *Founded/Ownrshp* 2000
Sales 97.8MM[E] *EMP* 121[E]
SIC 4911 Electric services
Pr: D Rogers Herndon

RRISD
See ROUND ROCK INDEPENDENT SCHOOL DISTRICT (INC)

D-U-N-S 00-969-0538
RS HUGHES CO INC
SAUNDERS
1162 Sonora Ct, Sunnyvale, CA 94086-5378
Tel (408) 739-3211 *Founded/Ownrshp* 1954
Sales 323.7MM *EMP* 505
Accts Moss Adams Llp Campbell Cali
SIC 5085 Abrasives & adhesives; Abrasives; Adhesives, tape & plasters
CEO: Robert McCollum
**Pr:* Peter Biocini
**CFO:* Gail Zimmerman
VP: Michael Page
**VP:* Joseph Vargas

D-U-N-S 00-801-2635 EXP
RS LEGACY CORP
300 Radioshack Cir, Fort Worth, TX 76102-1901
Tel (817) 415-3011 *Founded/Ownrshp* 1963
Sales 4.1MMM[E] *EMP* 27,500
SIC 5731 5999 5734 Radio, television & electronic stores; Video cameras & accessories; Video recorders, players, disc players & accessories; Audio-visual equipment & supplies; Telephone equipment & systems; Personal computers; Software, computer games
CFO: Carlin Adrianopoli
COO: Diane Clinton
COO: David Edmondson
CFO: Holly F Etlin
CFO: Jim Gooch
Treas: Amy Brown
Treas: Martin Moad
Chf Mktg O: Carroll Don
Chf Mktg O: Paul Rutenis
Ofcr: Edmond Chan
Ex VP: Joe Formichelli
Ex VP: Scott E Young
Sr VP: Martin B Amschler
Sr VP: Marty Amschler
Sr VP: Michael S Defazio
Sr VP: Michael Defazio
Sr VP: Janet Fox
Sr VP: William Nebes III
VP: Tony Andrews
VP: Jeff Bland
VP: Len Clegg
Board of Directors: Robert A Abernathy, Frank J Belatti, Julie A Dobson, Daniel R Feehan, H Eugene Lockhart, Jack L Messman, Edwina D Woodbury

D-U-N-S 61-338-7281
RS&H INC
10748 Deerwood Park Blvd, Jacksonville, FL 32256-4842
Tel (904) 256-2500 *Founded/Ownrshp* 1990
Sales 124.3MM *EMP* 901
Accts Pricewaterhousecoopers Llp J
SIC 8711 8712 Engineering services; Architectural services
CEO: David T Sweeney
**Ch Bd:* Leerie T Jenkins Jr
Pr: Jack Haynes
COO: Doug Geiger
**CFO:* Kenneth R Jacobson
Ex VP: Joseph Debs
Sr VP: Brian Reed
Sr VP: Lisa Robert
VP: James Avitabile
VP: John Crump
VP: Richard Hammett
VP: Jim Hawkes
VP: Bill Hogan
VP: Keith Jackson
VP: Jeff Mishler
VP: Laura Reid
VP: Ben Searight
VP: Michael Vascellaro
VP: Andrew Wheeler
Comm Dir: Jennifer Stutts

R.S.A.
See TECHNOLOGY TRANSFER INC

D-U-N-S 00-783-9561
■ RSA MEDICAL LLC
(*Suby of* XEROX CORP) ★
2135 City Gate Ln Ste 600, Naperville, IL 60563-3064
Tel (630) 416-7150 *Founded/Ownrshp* 1992, 2015
Sales NA *EMP* 350
SIC 6321 Assessment associations, accident & health insurance
Pr: Rocco Salviola
CFO: Jeff Wink
VP: Gregg Antenen
Snr Sftwr: Stephen Halm
QA Dir: Jim Wazorick
Dir IT: Dale Eisenhardt
Software D: Juan Chavarriaga
Software D: Curt Petersen
Software D: Vinay Thotakura
Snr PM: Anitha Narayan

RSA, THE SECURITY DIVISION EMC
See RSA SECURITY LLC

D-U-N-S 12-161-5538 IMP
■ RSA SECURITY LLC
RSA, THE SECURITY DIVISION EMC
(*Suby of* DELL EMC) ★
174 Middlesex Tpke, Bedford, MA 01730-1445
Tel (781) 515-5000 *Founded/Ownrshp* 2006
Sales 4.5MM[E] *EMP* 2,146
SIC 3577 7372 7373 Computer peripheral equipment; Prepackaged software; Computer integrated systems design
CEO: Joseph M Tucci
Sr Pt: Daniel Pintal
**Pr:* Howard D Elias
COO: Mark Quigley
**Treas:* William J Teuber Jr
Bd of Dir: Richard Demillo
Ex VP: Jeremy Burton
**Ex VP:* Paul T Dacier
Ex VP: Timothy McKnight
**Ex VP:* Harry L You
Sr VP: Holly Rollo
VP: Tom Corn
VP: Sam Curry
VP: Jim Ducharme
VP: Burton S Kaliski Jr
VP: Carol Macura
VP: David Thompson
Dir Lab: Jim Johnston
Board of Directors: Alexander Volanis

D-U-N-S 92-762-4775 IMP
RSC EQUIPMENT RENTAL INC
6929 E Greenway Pkwy # 200, Scottsdale, AZ 85254-2171
Tel (480) 905-3300 *Founded/Ownrshp* 2006
Sales NA *EMP* 4,153
SIC 7353

D-U-N-S 14-083-6664
RSC INSURANCE BROKERAGE INC
RISK STRATEGIES COMPANY
(*Suby of* DEWITT STERN GROUP INC) ★
160 Federal St, Boston, MA 02110-1700
Tel (617) 330-5700 *Founded/Ownrshp* 2003
Sales NA *EMP* 181
SIC 6411 Insurance agents, brokers & service
CEO: Mike Christian
Pr: John Wilcox
CFO: John Vaglica
VP: Mark Vallucci
VP: Carol Wiek

D-U-N-S 95-911-2012 IMP
■ RSCC WIRE & CABLE LLC
(*Suby of* MARMON HOLDINGS INC) ★
20 Bradley Park Rd, East Granby, CT 06026-9789
Tel (860) 653-8300 *Founded/Ownrshp* 2010
Sales 166.3MM[E] *EMP* 540
SIC 3357 3315 Nonferrous wiredrawing & insulating; Cable, steel: insulated or armored
**VP:* Gary J Gagnon
Dir IT: Dennis Sprouse
Tech Mgr: David Petraska
Opers Mgr: Glenn Salvas
Natl Sales: Michael Brennan

RSCI
See RECORD STEEL AND CONSTRUCTION INC

RSD NEW ORLEANS
See RECOVERY SCHOOL DISTRICT

D-U-N-S 07-643-7615 IMP
RSG FOREST PRODUCTS INC
GRAM LUMBER COMPANY
985 Nw 2nd St, Kalama, WA 98625-9647
Tel (360) 673-2825 *Founded/Ownrshp* 1973
Sales 133.5MM^E *EMP* 800
SIC 2421 2499 Lumber: rough, sawed or planed; Fencing, wood
Pr: Robert C Sanders
**Sec:* Samuel E Sanders
Sls Mgr: Bob Redd

D-U-N-S 36-168-7130 IMP
RSI HOME PRODUCTS INC
400 E Orangethorpe Ave, Anaheim, CA 92801-1046
Tel (714) 449-2200 *Founded/Ownrshp* 1994
Sales 998.8MM^E *EMP* 3,500
SIC 2514 2541 3281 2434 Kitchen cabinets: metal; Medicine cabinets & vanities: metal; Counter & sink tops; Cut stone & stone products; Wood kitchen cabinets
CEO: Alex Calabrese
**Pr:* Jeff Hoeft
**CFO:* David Lowrie
Software D: Carlos Hernandez
VP Opers: Alan Dean
Mfg Dir: Damian Leduff
Sls Dir: Eric Vanderheyden
Sls Mgr: Kevin Houle
Board of Directors: Harold Kitay

D-U-N-S 15-088-1407
RSI LOGISTICS INC
2419 Science Pkwy, Okemos, MI 48864-2562
Tel (517) 349-7713 *Founded/Ownrshp* 2001
Sales 100.0MM^E *EMP* 140
SIC 8742 4231 Transportation consultant; Trucking terminal facilities
Pr: Robert Tuchek
CFO: Joseph Irish
**VP:* Kelley Minnehan
Opers Mgr: Richard Pastors

RSI PRECISION CONTROLS
See RADIATION SYSTEMS PRECISION CONTROLS INC

D-U-N-S 07-348-2424
RSM US LLP
1 S Wacker Dr Ste 800, Chicago, IL 60606-4650
Tel (312) 634-3400 *Founded/Ownrshp* 1999
Sales 1.8MMM *EMP* 9,000
SIC 8721 8742 7291 Accounting, auditing & bookkeeping; Certified public accountant; Management consulting services; Tax return preparation services
Pt: Tom Ferreira
Pt: Tom Losey
Pt: Don Natenstedt
Pt: Ron Pierson
Pt: Kevin Prien
Pt: Donna Sciarappa
COO: Bill Gorman
CFO: Dan Delauter
CFO: Doug Opheim
Ofcr: Bruce Jorth
VP: Sherry Dodd
Dir Surg: Celeste Johnson
Dir Bus: Mike Adkins
Dir Bus: Rod Reimann

D-U-N-S 07-921-4183
▲ RSP PERMIAN INC
3141 Hood St Ste 500, Dallas, TX 75219-5020
Tel (214) 252-2700 *Founded/Ownrshp* 2010
Sales 283.9MM *EMP* 99^E
Tkr Sym RSPP *Exch* NYS
SIC 1311 Crude petroleum & natural gas
CEO: Steven Gray
**Ch Bd:* Michael Grimm
COO: Zane Arrott
**CFO:* Scott McNeill
Ex VP: Tamara Pollard
VP: Erik B Daugbjerg
VP: William Huck
VP: James Mutrie

D-U-N-S 96-583-6799
■ RSP PERMIAN LLC
(*Suby of* RSP PERMIAN INC) ★
3141 Hood St Ste 700, Dallas, TX 75219-5022
Tel (214) 252-2700 *Founded/Ownrshp* 2010
Sales 83.0MM *EMP* 79
SIC 1382 Oil & gas exploration services

D-U-N-S 05-867-8517 IMP
RSR CORP
(*Suby of* QUEXCO INC) ★
2777 N Stemmons Fwy, Dallas, TX 75207-2500
Tel (317) 247-1303 *Founded/Ownrshp* 1970
Sales 258.2MM^E *EMP* 640
SIC 3341 Lead smelting & refining (secondary)
Pr: Robert E Finn
**CFO:* Joe Dugger
**Sr VP:* John De Paul
VP: Robert Guire
VP: Terry Simmons

D-U-N-S 61-213-4106
RSR GROUP INC
4405 Metric Dr, Winter Park, FL 32792-6904
Tel (407) 677-6114 *Founded/Ownrshp* 1989
Sales 223.3MM^E *EMP* 220
SIC 5099 Firearms, except sporting
Ch Bd: Robert C Steger
**Pr:* Joann Weisenford
**CFO:* John Slogar
**Sr VP:* Christa Bass
**Sr VP:* Christina Fisher
**Sr VP:* Kristen Sundermann
**VP:* Richard Blews
VP: Christina Marotta
IT Man: Sharon Trego
Site Mgr: Scott Christiaansen
Sales Asso: Paul Heberger

RSSC
See REGENT SEVEN SEAS CRUISES INC

D-U-N-S 13-369-1951
■ RSUI GROUP INC
(*Suby of* ALLEGHANY INSURANCE HOLDINGS LLC) ★
945 E Paces Ferry Rd Ne # 1800, Atlanta, GA 30326-1160
Tel (404) 231-2366 *Founded/Ownrshp* 1988
Sales NA *EMP* 370
SIC 6331 6321 Fire, marine & casualty insurance; Accident & health insurance
CEO: David E Leonard
**Pr:* Greg Buonocore
Pr: Sonny Burgess
Pr: Melvin Keith
Pr: Trey Kirven
Pr: Vicki Rubel
Treas: Bebe Daher
Bd of Dir: Diane Robertson
**Ex VP:* Phillip McCrorie
VP: Michael Adamson
VP: Tracy Carroll
VP: Steven Forrest
VP: John Gerdts
VP: John Graham
VP: Chuck Hawk
VP: Doug Johnson
VP: Nolan Kevin
VP: Scott Klemens
VP: Donna Mall
VP: Julie Perry
VP: Mark L Schwartz
Board of Directors: Erin Dolan E

D-U-N-S 07-870-9973 IMP/EXP
RT VANDERBILT HOLDING CO INC
30 Winfield St, Norwalk, CT 06855-1329
Tel (203) 295-2141 *Founded/Ownrshp* 2012
Sales 239.0MM *EMP* 415
Accts Deloitte & Touche Llp Stamfo
SIC 5169 2869 2819 1499 1459 Chemicals, industrial & heavy; Laboratory chemicals, organic; Industrial inorganic chemicals; Talc mining; Clays (common) quarrying
Pr: Roger K Price
**Ch Bd:* Hugh B Vanderbilt Jr
**Pr:* Randall L Johnson
**Treas:* Joseph Denaro

D-U-N-S 00-509-0741 IMP
RTC INDUSTRIES INC (IL)
RTC USA WORLD HEADQUARTERS
2800 Golf Rd, Rolling Meadows, IL 60008-4023
Tel (847) 640-2400 *Founded/Ownrshp* 1951
Sales 250.0MM^E *EMP* 800
SIC 2599 5211 Boards: planning, display, notice; Closets, interiors & accessories
Ch Bd: Walter Nathan
**Pr:* Richard Nathan
CFO: Ken Bloom
CFO: Martha Leonard
**Sr VP:* Gary Cohen
VP: Jean Carlson
VP: Andy Cremer
VP: Steve Gorman
VP: Larry O'Neill
Prgrm Mgr: Michelle Casteleyn
Prgrm Mgr: Adam Gold

RTC USA WORLD HEADQUARTERS
See RTC INDUSTRIES INC

RTD
See REGIONAL TRANSPORTATION DISTRICT

D-U-N-S 62-162-0830 IMP
RTG FURNITURE CORP
ROOMS TO GO FURNITURE
11540 E Us Highway 92, Seffner, FL 33584-7346
Tel (813) 623-5400 *Founded/Ownrshp* 1990
Sales 488.9MM^E *EMP* 1,850
SIC 5712 Furniture stores
Ch Bd: Jeffrey Seaman
**Pr:* Steve Buckley
**CFO:* Lewis Stein
**Sr VP:* Jeffrey Finkel
VP: Jack Barlia
**VP:* Michael Kettle
**VP:* Peter Weitzner

D-U-N-S 01-525-6738 IMP/EXP
RTG FURNITURE CORP OF GEORGIA
ROOMS TO GO
11540 E Us Highway 92, Seffner, FL 33584-7346
Tel (813) 623-5400 *Founded/Ownrshp* 1994
Sales 1.1MMM^E *EMP* 5,000
SIC 5712 Furniture stores
Pr: Jeffrey Seaman
Pr: Jon Studner
Ofcr: Richard Miller
**Sr VP:* Janis Altshuler
VP: Ennis Alvarez
VP: Christian Chiovarelli
VP: Manny Delgado
**VP:* Jeffrey Finkel
**VP:* J Michael Kettle
**VP:* Janice Latshuler
VP: Sue Meadows
**VP:* Sally Seiden
**VP:* Lewis Stein
**VP:* Peter Weitzner
Exec: Rodolfo Teodosio
Exec: Terri Thiro
Dir Risk M: Donna Reagan

D-U-N-S 01-189-5633 IMP/EXP
RTG FURNITURE OF TEXAS LP
ROOMS TO GO KIDS
11540 E Us Highway 92, Seffner, FL 33584-7346
Tel (813) 628-9724 *Founded/Ownrshp* 1991
Sales 185.5MM^E *EMP* 1,200
SIC 5712 5021 Furniture stores; Furniture
Pr: Jeff Seaman
CFO: Lewis Stein
Treas: Jeffrey Finkel
VP: Mike Kettle

RTI
See RESTAURANT TECHNOLOGIES INC

D-U-N-S 95-913-6169 IMP
■ RTI ENERGY SYSTEMS INC
WELD-TECH ENGINEERING
(*Suby of* ALCOA TITANIUM ENGINEERED PDTS) ★
7211 Spring Cypress Rd, Spring, TX 77379-3216
Tel (281) 379-4289 *Founded/Ownrshp* 2000
Sales 228.8MM *EMP* 1,117
SIC 3533 3498 Oil field machinery & equipment; Fabricated pipe & fittings
VP: James L McCarley
**Treas:* William F Strome
VP: Tom Dummer
**VP:* Dawne S Hickton

D-U-N-S 04-522-4347 IMP/EXP
■ RTI INTERNATIONAL METALS INC
ALCOA TITANIUM ENGINEERED PDTS
(*Suby of* ARCONIC INC) ★
5th Fl 1550 Crplis Hts Rd, Coraopolis, PA 15108
Tel (412) 893-0026 *Founded/Ownrshp* 2015
Sales 809.7MM^E *EMP* 2,575
SIC 3356 3441 Titanium; Titanium & titanium alloy bars, sheets, strip, etc.; Titanium & titanium alloy: rolling, drawing or extruding; Fabricated structural metal
CEO: Klaus Kleinfield
V Ch: Dawne Hickton
**COO:* Eric V Roegner
**COO:* Vitaliy V Rusakov
**COO:* Tmas Mr Sigurdsson
**CFO:* Ken Giacobbe
**CFO:* Glenn Miller
**Chf Cred:* Libby Archell
Ex VP: Graeme W Bottger
Ex VP: Roy Harvey
**Ex VP:* Raymond J Kilmer
Ex VP: Christoph Kollatz
Ex VP: James McCarley
Ex VP: Audrey Strauss
VP: Nahla Azmy

RTI NILES
See RMI TITANIUM CO LLC

D-U-N-S 00-616-6607
■ RTI REMMELE ENGINEERING INC (MN)
(*Suby of* ALCOA TITANIUM ENGINEERED PDTS) ★
10 Old Highway 8 Sw, Saint Paul, MN 55112-7709
Tel (651) 635-4100 *Founded/Ownrshp* 1949, 2012
Sales 137.9MM^E *EMP* 466
SIC 3728 3569 3812 3761 3842 Aircraft parts & equipment; Aircraft body & wing assemblies & parts; Aircraft body assemblies & parts; Empennage (tail) assemblies & parts, aircraft; Gas generators; Search & navigation equipment; Guided missiles & space vehicles; Surgical appliances & supplies
CEO: Richard Pogue
**Treas:* Theresa Short
**VP:* John Bowden
**VP:* Jim Frazer
**VP:* Terry Johnson
Genl Mgr: Leonard Huray
IT Man: Marc Williams
Prd Mgr: Mike Anderson

D-U-N-S 01-452-0584
▲ RTI SURGICAL INC
11621 Research Cir, Alachua, FL 32615-6825
Tel (386) 418-8888 *Founded/Ownrshp* 1998
Sales 282.2MM *EMP* 1,169^E
Tkr Sym RTIX *Exch* NGS
SIC 3842 Surgical appliances & supplies; Implants, surgical; Grafts, artificial: for surgery
Pr: Brian K Hutchison
**Ch Bd:* Curtis M Selquist
CFO: Robert P Jordheim
Ex VP: Caroline A Hartill
Ex VP: Roger W Rose
VP: John N Varela
Dir Bus: Mark Wagner
DP Exec: Brian Hutchinson
Netwrk Mgr: Mike Michael
Netwrk Eng: Chris Hairston
Snr PM: Amy Lovelady
Board of Directors: Shirley A Weis, Peter G Gearen, Frank R Williams Jr, Jeffrey D Goldberg, Darren P Lehrich, Thomas A McEachin, Jonathan M Singer, Mark D Stolper, Christopher R Sweeney, Paul G Thomas, Nicholas J Valeriani

RTP COMPANY
See MILLER WASTE MILLS INC

RTP FRANCE
See RTP INTERNATIONAL HOLDINGS INC

D-U-N-S 88-436-7202 IMP
RTP INTERNATIONAL HOLDINGS INC
RTP FRANCE
(*Suby of* RTP CO) ★
580 E Front St, Winona, MN 55987-4256
Tel (507) 454-6900 *Founded/Ownrshp* 1994
Sales 128.3MM^E *EMP* 599^E
SIC 2299 Fibers, textile: recovery from textile mill waste & rags
CEO: Hugh L Miller
**CFO:* Brian Evenson

D-U-N-S 17-651-7555 IMP
■ RTS PACKAGING LLC
(*Suby of* WESTROCK RKT CO) ★
504 Thrasher St, Norcross, GA 30071-1967
Tel (800) 558-6984 *Founded/Ownrshp* 1997
Sales 183.0MM^E *EMP* 800
SIC 2493 Particleboard products
CEO: Richard E Steed
Sfty Dirs: Patrick Mulcahy
Sales Asso: Malcolm Leniar

D-U-N-S 36-061-0414 IMP
RTU INC
RTUI
1445 Langham Creek Dr, Houston, TX 77084-5012
Tel (800) 247-4793 *Founded/Ownrshp* 1989
Sales 99.1MM *EMP* 400
Accts Robertson & Robertson Pllc H
SIC 7319 2752 Distribution of advertising material or sample services; Promotional printing, lithographic
Pr: Edward D Endsley
**COO:* Ashley Mate
**CFO:* Kenneth Griffith
**VP:* Gordon Miller

RTUI
See RTU INC

D-U-N-S 07-974-3207
RU SYSTEM INC
ROCHESTER REGIONAL HEALTH
100 Kings Hwy S, Rochester, NY 14617-5504
Tel (585) 922-1053 *Founded/Ownrshp* 2014
Sales 1.5MM^E *EMP* 8,000
SIC 8062 General medical & surgical hospitals
Pr: Eric Bieber
Ex VP: John Foley

D-U-N-S 10-737-7780
RUAN LOGISTICS CORP
(*Suby of* RUAN TRANSPORTATION MANAGEMENT SYSTEMS INC) ★
666 Grand Ave Ste 3100, Des Moines, IA 50309-2500
Tel (515) 245-2500 *Founded/Ownrshp* 1985
Sales 82.1MM^E *EMP* 1,100
SIC 8742 Transportation consultant
Pr: Steven Chapman
**Ch Bd:* John Ruan III
**CEO:* Mike Kandris
**CFO:* Tracy Ball
**Treas:* Steven Wood
**Sr VP:* Marty Wadle
VP: Bob Brown
**VP:* Steve Larson
Board of Directors: Elizabeth Ruan

D-U-N-S 00-694-1371
RUAN TRANSPORT CORP (IA)
(*Suby of* RUAN TRANSPORTATION MANAGEMENT SYSTEMS INC) ★
666 Grand Ave Ste 3100, Des Moines, IA 50309-2500
Tel (515) 245-2500 *Founded/Ownrshp* 1934, 1932
Sales 1.0MMM^E *EMP* 3,000
SIC 4213 Contract haulers
Ch: John Ruan III
**Pr:* Steve Chapman
**CFO:* Tracey Ball
**CFO:* Mitch Poole
**Sr VP:* Roger Mason
**Sr VP:* Ben McLean
VP: Susan Fitzsimmons
**VP:* Ron Hanson
VP: Tara Meier
**VP:* Laverne Milbrandt
Opers Mgr: Connie Weiss

D-U-N-S 03-660-8552
RUAN TRANSPORTATION MANAGEMENT SYSTEMS INC (IA)
666 Grand Ave Ste 3100, Des Moines, IA 50309-2500
Tel (515) 245-2500 *Founded/Ownrshp* 1996
Sales 2.0MMM^E *EMP* 3,800
SIC 4213 7513 Contract haulers; Truck leasing, without drivers
Ch Bd: John Ruan IV
V Ch: Steven G Chapman
**Pr:* Steven Chapman
**Pr:* Mike Kandris
**CFO:* Tracey Ball
**Treas:* Steven Wood
Ex VP: John Flies
VP: Wayne Ashley
VP: Lance Cheney
VP: Roger Mason
VP: Rachel McLean
**VP:* Tara Meier
VP: Martin Wadle
VP: Chris Walkup

D-U-N-S 04-992-4368 IMP/EXP
■ RUBBERMAID COMMERCIAL PRODUCTS LLC
(*Suby of* RUBBERMAID INC) ★
3124 Valley Ave, Winchester, VA 22601-2694
Tel (540) 667-8700 *Founded/Ownrshp* 1988, 2000
Sales 275.9MM^E *EMP* 1,350
SIC 3089 2673 Plastic containers, except foam; Bags: plastic, laminated & coated
Pr: Neil Eibeler
Ex Dir: William Slezak
Dir IT: Michael W Moorefield
IT Man: Terri Foote
IT Man: Robert OH

D-U-N-S 00-446-9193 IMP/EXP
■ RUBBERMAID INC
(*Suby of* NEWELL BRANDS INC) ★
3 Glenlake Pkwy, Atlanta, GA 30328-3447
Tel (770) 418-7000 *Founded/Ownrshp* 1920, 1999
Sales 275.9MM^E *EMP* 12,360
SIC 3089 2519 3944 2369 2392 Plastic kitchenware, tableware & houseware; Plastic hardware & building products; Buckets, plastic; Trays, plastic; Fiberglass & plastic furniture; Furniture, household: glass, fiberglass & plastic; Games, toys & children's vehicles; Girls' & children's outerwear; Mops, floor & dust
CEO: William A Burke
**CFO:* Ronald L Hardnock

D-U-N-S 06-253-2205 IMP
RUBBERMAID SPECIALTY PRODUCTS INC
29 E Stephenson St, Freeport, IL 61032-4235
Tel (815) 235-4171 *Founded/Ownrshp* 1993
Sales NA *EMP* 1,460
SIC 3089

D-U-N-S 80-641-7205
▲ RUBICON PROJECT INC
12181 Bluff Creek Dr Fl 4, Los Angeles, CA 90094-3234
Tel (310) 207-0272 *Founded/Ownrshp* 2007
Sales 248.4MM *EMP* 699[E]
Tkr Sym RUBI *Exch* NYS
SIC 7311 Advertising agencies
Ch Bd: Frank Addant
**Pr:* Gregory R Raifman
**Ofcr:* David L Day
Sr VP: Mari Kim Novak
Sr VP: Justin Thomas
VP: Adam Chandler
VP: Josh Durst
VP: Matt Greenberg
VP: Brad Holcenberg
VP: Dallas Lawrence
VP: Ryan Polley
VP Bus Dev: Todd Smith
Board of Directors: Lewis Coleman, Robert J Frankenberg, Robert F Spillane, Lisa L Troe

D-U-N-S 01-242-7605 IMP/EXP
RUBIES COSTUME CO INC
12008 Jamaica Ave, Richmond Hill, NY 11418-2521
Tel (718) 846-1008 *Founded/Ownrshp* 1973
Sales 429.9MM[E] *EMP* 1,700
SIC 2389 7299 Costumes; Costume rental
Ch Bd: Marc P Beige
**VP:* Howard Beige
Div Mgr: Joanne Rudis
Mktg Mgr: Sandy Fernandez

D-U-N-S 00-422-2900
RUBIN INSTITUTE FOR ADVANCED ORTHOPEDICS
SINAI HOSPITAL OF BALTIMORE
(*Suby of* SINAI HOSPITAL OF BALTIMORE INC) ★
2401 W Belvedere Ave, Baltimore, MD 21215-5216
Tel (410) 601-9000 *Founded/Ownrshp* 2009
Sales 6.6MM[E] *EMP* 2,334[E]
SIC 8062 General medical & surgical hospitals
Prin: Joel I Suldan
Chf Rad: Roy Moss
Dir Health: Angela Niparko

RUBIO'S FRESH MEXICAN GRILL
See RUBIOS RESTAURANTS INC

D-U-N-S 14-435-9262 IMP
RUBIOS RESTAURANTS INC
RUBIO'S FRESH MEXICAN GRILL
(*Suby of* MRRC HOLD CO) ★
2200 Faraday Ave Ste 250, Carlsbad, CA 92008-7234
Tel (760) 929-8226 *Founded/Ownrshp* 2010
Sales 188.7MM[E] *EMP* 3,800[E]
SIC 5812 Mexican restaurant
Pr: Daniel E Pittard
**CEO:* Marc Simon
**CFO:* Frank Henigman
**Sr VP:* Ken Hull
**Sr VP:* Lawrence Rusinko
VP: Jaime Ogus
Dist Mgr: Yvonne Brown
Opers Mgr: Gabe Hosler
Mktg Dir: Christy Geiling
Snr Mgr: Adam Zabzdyr

D-U-N-S 36-293-3012
RUBLOFF CONSTRUCTION INC
P.R.U. BUILDING SYSTEMS
6723 Weaver Rd Ste 108, Rockford, IL 61114-8021
Tel (815) 316-5410 *Founded/Ownrshp* 1988
Sales 106.5MM[E] *EMP* 812
SIC 1542 Commercial & office building, new construction
CEO: Joseph Kopcio
**Pr:* Gerald H Weber Jr
**VP:* Ron Swenson

D-U-N-S 04-658-1294
RUBY ROBINSON CO INC
100 Lexington Dr Ste 201, Buffalo Grove, IL 60089-6937
Tel (847) 808-3030 *Founded/Ownrshp* 1991
Sales 117.8MM *EMP* 50
SIC 5148

D-U-N-S 00-690-1102 IMP
▲ RUBY TUESDAY INC
150 W Church Ave, Maryville, TN 37801-4936
Tel (865) 379-5700 *Founded/Ownrshp* 1972
Sales 1.0MMM *EMP* 32,100[E]
Tkr Sym RT *Exch* NYS
SIC 5812 5813 6794 Restaurant, family: chain; Bar (drinking places); Franchises, selling or licensing
CEO: F Lane Cardwell Jr
Mng Pt: Tony Lankford
Mng Pt: Faheem Memon
Pr: Brett A Patterson
CFO: Sue Briley
Chf Mktg O: David W Skena
Chf Mktg O: David Skena
Ofcr: Rhonda Parish
VP: Sandra Belcher
VP: Edmond Bordelon
Dist Mgr: Ann Davis
Board of Directors: Mark W Addicks, F Lane Cardwell Jr, Kevin T Clayton, Donald E Hess, Bernard Lanigan Jr, Jeffrey J O'neill, Stephen I Sadove

D-U-N-S 11-349-9792
RUBYS DINER INC
RUBY'S RESTAURANT GROUP
201 Shipyard Way Ste E, Newport Beach, CA 92663-4452
Tel (949) 644-7829 *Founded/Ownrshp* 1982
Sales 67.4MM[E] *EMP* 1,300
SIC 5812 Diner
CEO: Douglas Cavanaugh
**Pr:* Fred Lefranc
**CFO:* Ralph Kosmides
Dist Mgr: Michael Berumen
Genl Mgr: Moses Cardoso
Genl Mgr: Jamie Corbett
Genl Mgr: Jose Melero
Genl Mgr: Ruben Rodriguez
CTO: Richard Rogers

RUBY'S RESTAURANT GROUP
See RUBYS DINER INC

RUCKER'S CANDY
See RUCKERS WHOLESALE & SERVICE CO

D-U-N-S 13-158-9418
RUCKERS WHOLESALE & SERVICE CO
RUCKER'S CANDY
777 E State St, Bridgeport, IL 62417
Tel (618) 945-2411 *Founded/Ownrshp* 1994
Sales 124.8MM[E] *EMP* 150
SIC 5145 Candy
Pr: Richard Rucker
**CFO:* Ernest Hoh
**Sr VP:* Delbert Parrott
**VP:* Dee Diggs
**VP:* Chad Rucker
DP Exec: Larry Miller

D-U-N-S 60-939-6721 IMP
■ RUCKUS WIRELESS INC
(*Suby of* BROCADE COMMUNICATIONS SYSTEMS INC) ★
350 W Java Dr, Sunnyvale, CA 94089-1026
Tel (650) 265-4200 *Founded/Ownrshp* 2016
Sales 373.3MM *EMP* 948[E]
SIC 4813
CEO: Selina Lo
COO: Daniel Rabinovitsj
CFO: Seamus Hennessy
Chf Cred: Ian Whiting
Sr VP: Barton Burstein
VP: Chloe Chan
VP: Bart Giordano
VP: Louis Au Kwok-Leung
VP: Kash Shaikh
Exec: Nancy Leroux
Genl Mgr: Sudarhsan Boosupalli
Board of Directors: Georges Antoun, Bart Burstein, Stewart Grierson, Mohan Gyani, Richard Lynch

D-U-N-S 00-700-2462 IMP/EXP
RUDD EQUIPMENT CO INC
4344 Poplar Level Rd, Louisville, KY 40213-1841
Tel (502) 456-4050 *Founded/Ownrshp* 1939
Sales 122.8MM[E] *EMP* 300
SIC 5082 7353 Construction & mining machinery; General construction machinery & equipment; Mining machinery & equipment, except petroleum; Heavy construction equipment rental
Ch Bd: Michael D Rudd
Pr: Mark Burris
Genl Mgr: Toni McQueen
Dir IT: Phillip George

D-U-N-S 82-837-8633
■ RUDDICK OPERATING CO LLC
(*Suby of* HARRIS TEETER SUPERMARKETS INC) ★
301 S Tryon St Ste 1800, Charlotte, NC 28282-1905
Tel (704) 372-5404 *Founded/Ownrshp* 2000
Sales 71.8MM[E] *EMP* 20,000
SIC 5411 2284 Supermarkets, chain; Cotton thread
Ch Bd: Thomas W Dickson
**VP:* John B Woodlief

D-U-N-S 96-192-0035
RUDER FINN GROUP INC
301 E 57th St, New York, NY 10022-5997
Tel (212) 593-5838 *Founded/Ownrshp* 1956
Sales 129.5MM[E] *EMP* 580[E]
SIC 8743 6799 8741 Public relations services; Investors; Management services
Ch: David Finn
Grp VP: James Walker
VP: Susan Slack

D-U-N-S 00-166-9464
RUDER FINN INC (NY)
(*Suby of* RUDER FINN GROUP INC) ★
425 E 53rd St, New York, NY 10022-5120
Tel (212) 593-6400 *Founded/Ownrshp* 1948
Sales 100.2MM[E] *EMP* 400
SIC 8743 7311 2752 Public relations & publicity; Advertising agencies; Commercial printing, offset
Ch Bd: Peter Finn
**CEO:* Kathy Bloomgarden
**CFO:* Peggy Walsh
**Ch:* David Finn
Sr Cor Off: David Katzive
Chf Mktg O: Brian Feinblumb
**Ofcr:* Scott Schneider
Ex VP: Sarah Anderson
Ex VP: Mary Conway
**Ex VP:* Christine Dusek
Ex VP: Ed Harnaga
Ex VP: Charles Lankester
Ex VP: Lisa Duszak Novak
Ex VP: Helen C Shelton
Ex VP: Deirdre Taylor
Sr VP: Marty McGough
Sr VP: John McInerney
Sr VP: Alice Sofield
Sr VP: Rachel Spielman
Sr VP: Michael Van Lewen
**Sr VP:* Jon Vidar
Board of Directors: William Ruder

D-U-N-S 00-284-5360
■ RUDOLPH AND SLETTEN INC (CA)
(*Suby of* TUTOR PERINI CORP) ★
1600 Seaport Blvd Ste 350, Redwood City, CA 94063-5575
Tel (650) 216-3600 *Founded/Ownrshp* 1960, 2005
Sales 940.3MM *EMP* 400
Accts Deloitte & Touche Llp Los An
SIC 1542 1541 Nonresidential construction; Industrial buildings & warehouses
Pr: Martin B Sisemore
CFO: Norma Swinger
Ex VP: Dan Dolinar
VP: Paul Aherne
VP: Nevan Elam
VP: Jonathan Foad
VP: Michael Mohrman
VP: Mike Mohrman
VP: Marcus Staniford
VP: Martin Ward
Exec: Tim Albiani
Exec: John Elwood
Exec: Gregory Palmer
Board of Directors: Robert Band, Mark Caspers, Ronald W Tutor

D-U-N-S 00-840-5607 IMP
RUDOLPH CHEVROLET LLC (TX)
5625 S Desert Blvd, El Paso, TX 79932-1158
Tel (915) 544-4321 *Founded/Ownrshp* 1934, 1960
Sales 91.8MM[E] *EMP* 250[E]
SIC 5511 Automobiles, new & used; Pickups, new & used
Pr: Dennis R Neessen
**Pr:* Matthew D Neessen
**Sec:* Donna R Neessen
Exec: Rosemary Garcia
Genl Mgr: Mike Miles
Sls Mgr: Rick Armijo

D-U-N-S 15-727-3673 IMP/EXP
RUDOLPH FOODS CO INC
6575 Bellefontaine Rd, Lima, OH 45804-4415
Tel (909) 383-7463 *Founded/Ownrshp* 1987
Sales 124.5MM[E] *EMP* 400
SIC 2096 2099 Pork rinds; Food preparations
CEO: James Rudolph
**Pr:* Richard Rudolph
**Sec:* Philip Rudolph
**VP:* Barbara Snyder
S&M/VP: Mark Singleton

D-U-N-S 00-480-6980
RUDOLPH LIBBE INC (OH)
(*Suby of* RUDOLPH/LIBBE COMPANIES INC) ★
6494 Latcha Rd, Walbridge, OH 43465-9788
Tel (419) 241-5000 *Founded/Ownrshp* 1955
Sales 246.5MM *EMP* 500
SIC 1541 1542 Industrial buildings & warehouses; Nonresidential construction
Pr: Timothy Alter
CFO: Robert Prueger
**Ch:* William Rudolph
Treas: Allan J Libbe
VP: Jim Buchanan
VP: Bradley Deal
VP: Ronald Dulay
VP: James Philo
**VP:* Philip J Rudolph
VP: Jeffery A Schaller
IT Man: Keith St John

D-U-N-S 00-216-5843
▲ RUDOLPH TECHNOLOGIES INC
16 Jonspin Rd, Wilmington, MA 01887-1093
Tel (973) 691-1300 *Founded/Ownrshp* 1940, 1996
Sales 221.6MM *EMP* 572[E]
Tkr Sym RTEC *Exch* NYS
SIC 3823 3827 Industrial process measurement equipment; Optical test & inspection equipment
CEO: Michael P Plisinski
**Ch Bd:* Thomas G Greig
**CEO:* Michael O Plisinski
CFO: Steven R Roth
VP: Debbora Ahlgren
VP: Mike Colgan
VP: Michael F Goodrich
VP: Robert A Koch
VP: Rajiv Roy
VP Mfg: Pete Vaillant
Board of Directors: Jeffrey A Aukerman, Leo Berlinghieri, Daniel H Berry, David B Miller, Richard F Spanier, John R Whitten

D-U-N-S 15-133-8688
RUDOLPH/LIBBE COMPANIES INC
6494 Latcha Rd, Walbridge, OH 43465-9788
Tel (419) 241-5000 *Founded/Ownrshp* 1986
Sales 425.3MM *EMP* 600[E]
Accts Rehmann Robson Toledo Oh
SIC 1541 1542 Industrial buildings & warehouses; Commercial & office building contractors
Ch: Bill Rudolph
**Pr:* Allan J Libbe
**Pr:* Frederick W Rudolph
**CFO:* Robert Pruger

RUDY'S COUNTRY STR & BAR-B-QUE
See K & N MANAGEMENT INC

RUE LA LA
See RUELALA INC

D-U-N-S 06-684-9282 IMP
RUE21 INC
(*Suby of* RHODES HOLDCO INC) ★
800 Commonwealth Dr, Warrendale, PA 15086-7525
Tel (724) 776-9780 *Founded/Ownrshp* 2013
Sales 1.7MMM[E] *EMP* 11,124
SIC 5611 5621 Men's & boys' clothing stores; Ready-to-wear apparel, women's
CEO: Keith McDonough
Sr VP: Michael A Holland
Sr VP: Kim A Reynolds
Sr VP: Michael Sablowski
Sr VP: Stacy B Siegal
Sr VP: Robert R Thomson
Dist Mgr: Valerie Basilio
Dist Mgr: Christina Floyd
Dist Mgr: Rhonda Graff
Dist Mgr: Kim Simmons
Store Mgr: Calli Artrip
Board of Directors: Arnold S Barron, Macon F Brock, Bruce A Hartman, Harlan Kent, John F Megrue Jr, Alex S Pellegrini, Laura Sen

D-U-N-S 14-395-1577 IMP/EXP
RUELALA INC
RUE LA LA
(*Suby of* KYNETIC LLC) ★
20 Channel Ctr St, Boston, MA 02210-3437
Tel (617) 695-7300 *Founded/Ownrshp* 2009
Sales 117.3MM[E] *EMP* 300
SIC 5961 General merchandise, mail order
CEO: Mark McWeeny
**Pr:* Steven Davis
**Treas:* Philip Roizin
Sr VP: Mark Weinberg
VP: Jim Barrett
**Prin:* Ben Fischman
Sftwr Eng: Laura Lynch

D-U-N-S 78-167-0443
RUFFALO NOEL LEVITZ LLC
1025 Kirkwood Pkwy Sw, Cedar Rapids, IA 52404-8629
Tel (800) 876-1117 *Founded/Ownrshp* 2001
Sales 252.1MM[E] *EMP* 3,000
SIC 7389 Telemarketing services; Fund raising organizations
CEO: Stephen J Meyer
**Pr:* Duane Jasper
**CEO:* Al Ruffalo
**CFO:* Joe Cunningham
Assoc VP: Doug Swartz
Prgrm Mgr: Bryan Curran
Prgrm Mgr: Sam Walling
CIO: Bruce Lahram

D-U-N-S 83-235-5791
RUFFIN ACQUISITION LLC
3300 Las Vegas Blvd S, Las Vegas, NV 89109-8916
Tel (800) 944-7444 *Founded/Ownrshp* 2008
Sales 315.0MM[E] *EMP* 4,510[E]
SIC 8732 Merger, acquisition & reorganization research

D-U-N-S 05-959-9282 IMP/EXP
RUG DOCTOR LLC
4701 Old Shepard Pl, Plano, TX 75093-5250
Tel (972) 673-1400 *Founded/Ownrshp* 1988
Sales 140.4MM[E] *EMP* 630
SIC 2842 3589 5087

D-U-N-S 01-181-6533
RUGBY ACQUISITION
RUGBY ARCHITECTURAL BLDG PDTS
(*Suby of* HARDWOODS DISTRIBUTION INC)
1 Pillsbury St Ste 302, Concord, NH 03301-3556
Tel (603) 369-4710 *Founded/Ownrshp* 1988
Sales 145.5MM[E] *EMP* 560[E]
SIC 5031 Structural assemblies, prefabricated: wood
**COO:* Drew Dickinson
**CTO:* Angie Wallert

RUGBY ARCHITECTURAL BLDG PDTS
See RUGBY ACQUISITION

RUGBY ARCHITECTURAL BLDG PDTS
See RUGBY IPD CORP

D-U-N-S 11-980-6714 IMP/EXP
RUGBY IPD CORP
RUGBY ARCHITECTURAL BLDG PDTS
(*Suby of* RUGBY HOLDINGS LLC)
1 Pillsbury St Ste 302, Concord, NH 03301-3556
Tel (603) 369-4710 *Founded/Ownrshp* 2016
Sales 156.9MM[E] *EMP* 400
SIC 5031 Building materials, exterior; Building materials, interior; Millwork; Lumber: rough, dressed & finished
CEO: David Hughes
COO: Drew H Dickinson
VP: Derek A Herman
VP: John Peery

D-U-N-S 13-080-5906 IMP/EXP
RUGBY USA INC
1440 S Priest Dr Ste 103, Tempe, AZ 85281-6954
Tel (480) 968-2208 *Founded/Ownrshp* 1986
Sales NA *EMP* 1,570
SIC 5031

RUGGED WEARHOUSE
See AMCP RETAIL ACQUISITION CORP

RUGGED WEARHOUSE
See AMCP RETAIL HOLDINGS CORP

D-U-N-S 00-419-3405
RUHLIN CO (OH)
6931 Ridge Rd, Sharon Center, OH 44274
Tel (330) 239-2800 *Founded/Ownrshp* 1915
Sales 121.8MM[E] *EMP* 250[E]
SIC 1542 1541 1622 1611 Commercial & office building, new construction; Industrial buildings, new construction; Bridge construction; General contractor, highway & street construction
Pr: James L Ruhlin
CFO: William Gantz
**Treas:* Russell F Gregory
VP: Mike Ciammaichella
**VP:* Michael Deiwert
Exec: Kent Crytzer
Genl Mgr: George Seanor
Dir IT: Scott McCarthy
Sfty Dirs: Ryan Berkhouse
Sfty Dirs: Ryan Nicholson
Board of Directors: Dean A Collura, Jeffrey O Evans, William J Laux, Michael S Lipscomb

D-U-N-S 00-947-6938
RUIZ FOOD PRODUCTS INC
501 S Alta Ave, Dinuba, CA 93618-2100
Tel (559) 591-5510 *Founded/Ownrshp* 1965
Sales 527.5MM[E] *EMP* 2,600
SIC 2038 2099 Ethnic foods, frozen; Food preparations
Pr: Rachel Cullen
**Ch Bd:* Kim R Beck
**CFO:* Forrest Chandler
CFO: Glenn McClaren
VP: Dave Norby
VP: George Turner
Mng Dir: Maribel Ortega
Genl Mgr: Erin Romero
Dir IT: Steve Miley
IT Man: Harry Wright
Netwrk Eng: Reggie Matthews

D-U-N-S 04-498-1322
RUMMEL KLEPPER & KAHL LLP
RK&K
81 Mosher St, Baltimore, MD 21217-4243
Tel (410) 728-2900 *Founded/Ownrshp* 1987
Sales 256.9MM[E] *EMP* 1,048
SIC 8711 8741 1623 8999 8713 1611 Engineering services; Management services; Construction management; Water, sewer & utility lines; Earth science services; Surveying services; Highway & street construction

Genl Pt: Mark M Dumler
Pt: Thomas E Mohler
Pt: Michael W Myers
Pt: J Michael Potter
Pt: David W Wallace
Mng Pt: William Hellmann
VP: Jimmy Norris
Assoc Dir: John Depagnier
Prgrm Mgr: Byung Song
Dir IT: Daniel Neal
IT Man: Brian Dial

D-U-N-S 04-878-5729
RUMPF CORP
JOB1USA
701 Jefferson Ave Ste 201, Toledo, OH 43604-6957
Tel (419) 255-5005 *Founded/Ownrshp* 1982
Sales 33.0MM^E *EMP* 1,012
SIC 7361 7363 7381 Employment agencies; Temporary help service; Employee leasing service; Security guard service; Protective services, guard
CEO: Bruce F Rumpf

D-U-N-S 78-199-9818
RUMPKE CONSOLIDATED COMPANIES INC
RUMPKE WASTE AND RECYCL SVCS
10795 Hughes Rd, Cincinnati, OH 45251-4598
Tel (800) 582-3107 *Founded/Ownrshp* 2014
Sales 1.4MMM^E *EMP* 2,107
SIC 4953 Recycling, waste materials
Pr: William Rumpke Jr
**CFO:* Phil Wehrman
**VP:* Jeff Rumpke
**VP:* Todd Rumpke
Comm Dir: Amanda Pratt
Sales Exec: Toni Moore
Sls&Mrk Ex: Brad Warman
Sls Mgr: Wilson Brian

D-U-N-S 08-185-5181
RUMPKE OF INDIANA INC
(*Suby of* RUMPKE WASTE AND RECYCL SVCS) ★
3800 Struble Rd, Cincinnati, OH 45251-4954
Tel (513) 851-0122 *Founded/Ownrshp* 1973
Sales 110.3MM^E *EMP* 371
SIC 4953 Garbage: collecting, destroying & processing; Sanitary landfill operation
Pr: William J Rumpke
COO: William Terry
**VP:* Thomas Rumpke

D-U-N-S 08-185-5264
RUMPKE OF KENTUCKY INC
(*Suby of* RUMPKE WASTE AND RECYCL SVCS) ★
10795 Hughes Rd, Cincinnati, OH 45251-4598
Tel (513) 851-0122 *Founded/Ownrshp* 1998
Sales 116.1MM^E *EMP* 291
SIC 4953 Refuse collection & disposal services
Pr: Thomas Rumpke
**CFO:* Phil E Wehrman
**VP:* William J Rumpke

D-U-N-S 05-309-0234
RUMPKE OF OHIO INC (OH)
(*Suby of* RUMPKE WASTE AND RECYCL SVCS) ★
3800 Struble Rd, Cincinnati, OH 45251-4954
Tel (513) 851-0122 *Founded/Ownrshp* 1999, 1998
Sales 211.4MM^E *EMP* 270
SIC 4953 4212 Refuse collection & disposal services; Recycling, waste materials; Local trucking, without storage
CEO: William J Rumpke
CFO: Phil Wehrman
Dir IT: Larry Ochs
IT Man: Brian Lincon
Opers Mgr: Travis Martin

D-U-N-S 05-309-2800
RUMPKE TRANSPORTATION CO LLC
(*Suby of* RUMPKE WASTE AND RECYCL SVCS) ★
10795 Hughes Rd, Cincinnati, OH 45251-4598
Tel (513) 851-0122 *Founded/Ownrshp* 1999
Sales 145.8MM^E *EMP* 800
SIC 3561 5084 7537 4953 Pumps & pumping equipment; Hydraulic systems equipment & supplies; Automotive transmission repair shops; Refuse systems
Pr: William J Rumpke
**CFO:* Phil Wehrman
Bd of Dir: Todd B Rumpke
Div Mgr: Tim Kemper

RUMPKE WASTE AND RECYCL SVCS
See RUMPKE CONSOLIDATED COMPANIES INC

D-U-N-S 10-856-9492
RUMPKE WASTE INC
(*Suby of* RUMPKE WASTE AND RECYCL SVCS) ★
10795 Hughes Rd, Cincinnati, OH 45251-4598
Tel (513) 851-0122 *Founded/Ownrshp* 1978
Sales 845.8MM^E *EMP* 1,800
SIC 4953 Garbage: collecting, destroying & processing
Pr: Bill Rumpke Jr
**Pr:* William J Rumpke
CFO: Phil Wehrman
VP: Bob Viox
Ex Dir: Danney Saylor
Prgrm Mgr: Jason Cozad
Genl Mgr: Gina Schueler
IT Man: Joe Rogan
Opers Mgr: Gary Lederer
Opers Mgr: Todd Wielinski
Opers Mgr: Tim Wolford

D-U-N-S 00-791-4807
RUMSEY ELECTRIC CO (PA)
15 Colwell Ln, Conshohocken, PA 19428-1878
Tel (610) 832-9000 *Founded/Ownrshp* 1895, 1959
Sales 230.5MM *EMP* 284
Accts Rainer & Company Newton Squar
SIC 5063 Electrical supplies
Pr: Gerald Lihota
**CFO:* Scott M Cutler
VP: Steven Cabibbo
**VP:* John R Graham
VP: Larry Hagarty
VP: John Thorn

RUN ADS
See RUN INC

D-U-N-S 07-945-8260
RUN INC
RUN ADS
(*Suby of* STAR.COM WORLWIDE) ★
375 Hudson St Fl 8, New York, NY 10014-3658
Tel (212) 244-3200 *Founded/Ownrshp* 2014
Sales 96.5MM^E *EMP* 1,665^E
SIC 7311 7319 Advertising agencies; Bus card advertising
CEO: Seth Hittman
**COO:* Dan Schwartz
**Ex VP:* Duke Barnett
VP: Ned Campion
VP: Brian Hopkins
VP: Matt Kershaw
VP: Chris Outram
VP: David Vitelli
**Dir Risk M:* Jason Askinasi
**CTO:* Michael Celona

D-U-N-S 02-286-5307 IMP/EXP
RUNNING SUPPLY INC
RUNNINGS
901 Highway 59, Marshall, MN 56258-2744
Tel (507) 532-9566 *Founded/Ownrshp* 1988
Sales 243.6MM^E *EMP* 750
SIC 5999

RUNNINGS
See RUNNING SUPPLY INC

D-U-N-S 83-016-0433
RUPPERT LANDSCAPE INC
23601 Laytonsville Rd, Laytonsville, MD 20882-2525
Tel (301) 482-0300 *Founded/Ownrshp* 2004
Sales 293.0MM^E *EMP* 800
SIC 0781 0783 0782 Landscape counseling & planning; Horticulture services; Landscape services; Ornamental shrub & tree services; Planting, pruning & trimming services; Lawn & garden services
CEO: Craig Ruppert
**Pr:* Phil Key
CFO: Lee Clark
VP: Tom Barry
**VP:* Doug Halsey
VP: Dean Rasco
Area Mgr: Brandon Simmons
Brnch Mgr: Eric Blevins
Brnch Mgr: Matt Davidson
Brnch Mgr: Steve Faber
Brnch Mgr: John Harich

D-U-N-S 02-528-9620 IMP/EXP
RUPRECHT CO
1301 Allanson Rd, Mundelein, IL 60060-3835
Tel (312) 829-4100 *Founded/Ownrshp* 1963
Sales 221.8MM^E *EMP* 289
SIC 5147 Meats, fresh
CEO: Carl Sommers
**Pr:* Walter Sommers
**CFO:* Todd Perry
**Sec:* Joyce Sommers
Sr VP: Dimitrios Apostolopoulos
VP: Pat Barry
Exec: Richard Thompson
Genl Mgr: Joyce Thompson
Off Mgr: John Morrison
VP Opers: Patrick Everett
Ql Cn Mgr: Silvia Peralta

D-U-N-S 02-024-7920
RURAL ALASKA COMMUNITY ACTION PROGRAM INC
RURAL CAP
731 E 8th Ave, Anchorage, AK 99501-3772
Tel (907) 279-2511 *Founded/Ownrshp* 1859
Sales 171.7M *EMP* 1,558
Accts Kpmg Llp Anchorage Ak
SIC 8399 Social change association
Ex Dir: David Hardenbergh
**Pr:* Andrew Ebona
**Sec:* Benna Hughey
**VP:* Steve Longley
Comm Dir: Janet Hall
Sls Mgr: Sarah Scanlan

RURAL CAP
See RURAL ALASKA COMMUNITY ACTION PROGRAM INC

D-U-N-S 79-472-4054
■ **RURAL CELLULAR CORP**
UNICEL
(*Suby of* VERIZON WIRELESS) ★
4133 Iowa St Ste 200, Alexandria, MN 56308-3383
Tel (320) 808-2111 *Founded/Ownrshp* 2008
Sales 171.3MM^E *EMP* 1,107
SIC 4812 5999 Cellular telephone services; Paging services; Mobile telephones & equipment
CEO: Daniel S Mead
**Pr:* Paul Martin
**Pr:* Jack D Plating
**COO:* Fredric Hibbler
**CFO:* Wesley Schultz
**CFO:* John Townsend
Treas: Suzanne Allen
**Sr VP:* Anthony J Melone
VP: Cynthia Degeorge
VP: David Del Zoppo
**VP:* Margaret P Feldman
**VP:* Elizabeth Kohler
VP: Robert Moore
**VP:* Michael T Stefanski
VP: Michael Stefanski
VP: W A Wilkinson Jr
VP: William A Wilkinson

D-U-N-S 00-896-0601
RURAL ELECTRIC SUPPLY COOPERATIVE
RESCO
2250 Pinehurst Dr, Middleton, WI 53562-2539
Tel (608) 831-2600 *Founded/Ownrshp* 1936
Sales 94.7MM^E *EMP* 54
SIC 5063 Electrical construction materials
CEO: Matt Brandrup
Pr: Steve Gebhardt
Pr: Chris Pederson
Pr: Drew Primrose
**CFO:* Jeffrey Kuhnle
VP: Butch Akers
**VP:* Jeff Kuhnle
IT Man: Nick Fallow
Sales Asso: Steve Brietzman
Sales Asso: Gary Toboyek

D-U-N-S 07-615-5951
RURAL MUTUAL INSURANCE CO
1241 John Q Hammons Dr # 200, Madison, WI 53717-1929
Tel (608) 836-5525 *Founded/Ownrshp* 1934
Sales NA *EMP* 195
SIC 6411 Insurance agents, brokers & service
CEO: Peter Pelizza
**Pr:* William C Bruins
**Treas:* Mary S Vena
Mktg Dir: Tom Thieding
Sls Mgr: Bill Kriese
Sls Mgr: Jim Ranta

D-U-N-S 00-388-9888
RURAL TELEPHONE SERVICE CO INC (KS)
NEX-TECH
145 N Main St, Lenora, KS 67645
Tel (785) 567-4281 *Founded/Ownrshp* 1951
Sales 180.9MM^E *EMP* 395
Accts Sartain Fischbein + Co
SIC 4813 5734 5045 Local & long distance telephone communications; Computer peripheral equipment; Computer software & accessories; Computers, peripherals & software
Pr: F C Brungardt
Pr: Jim Harries
CEO: Jimmy Todd
COO: Michael Pollock
CFO: Rhonda Goddard
Genl Mgr: Jan Jackson
Genl Mgr: Larry E Sevier
IT Man: Mindy Bieker
Mktg Mgr: Dustin Schlaefli
Sls Mgr: Dustin Schlaefli
Sales Asso: Eian Wagner

RURAL-METRO
See METRO CARE CORP

D-U-N-S 05-145-2183
■ **RURAL/METRO CORP**
(*Suby of* RURAL/METRO OPERATING CO LLC) ★
8465 N Pima Rd, Scottsdale, AZ 85258-4489
Tel (480) 606-3886 *Founded/Ownrshp* 2011
Sales 602.3MM^E *EMP* 400
SIC 4119 7389 Ambulance service; Fire protection service other than forestry or public
CEO: Scott A Bartos
V Ch: Louis G Jekel
**COO:* M Bryan Gibson
**CFO:* Kristine B Ponczak
**Treas:* Kevin Moore
Ofcr: Jamie Pienkowski
VP: Gary August
**VP:* Donna Berlinski
**VP:* Robert Fisher
VP: Mark Lashley
**VP:* Jorge A Perez
**VP:* Jeffrey Perry
VP: Maureen E Thompson
VP Bus Dev: David Lindberg
Exec: Lashay Harris
Exec: Renee Sandberg
Dir Risk M: John Rusinski

D-U-N-S 07-992-0320
■ **RURAL/METRO CORP**
(*Suby of* ENVISION HEALTHCARE) ★
8465 N Pima Rd, Scottsdale, AZ 85258-4489
Tel (480) 606-3345 *Founded/Ownrshp* 2015
Sales 641.6MM^E *EMP* 8,152^E
SIC 4119 7389 Ambulance service; Fire protection service other than forestry or public

D-U-N-S 80-143-3868
■ **RURAL/METRO OPERATING CO LLC**
(*Suby of* RURAL/METRO CORP) ★
8465 N Pima Rd, Scottsdale, AZ 85258-4489
Tel (480) 606-3886 *Founded/Ownrshp* 2007
Sales 641.6MM^E *EMP* 441
SIC 4119 Ambulance service

D-U-N-S 07-148-2132 IMP
RUSAL AMERICA CORP
UC RUSAL MKTG & MGT LTD CYPRUS
(*Suby of* RUSAL, AO)
500 Mmaroneck Ave Ste 102, Harrison, NY 10528
Tel (914) 670-5771 *Founded/Ownrshp* 1999
Sales 539.4MM *EMP* 11
SIC 5051 Aluminum bars, rods, ingots, sheets, pipes, plates, etc.
CEO: Sergey Bubnov
**Treas:* Sergei Korshun
**VP:* Susan Scarinci
Opers Mgr: Lisa Matthews
Sls Mgr: Jason Lapointe

RUSCHE DISTRIBUTING
See SUSSER PETROLEUM CORP

RUSD
See ROWLAND UNIFIED SCHOOL DISTRICT

D-U-N-S 06-759-8271
■ **RUSH ADMINISTRATIVE SERVICES INC**
(*Suby of* RUSH ENTERPRISES INC) ★
555 S Interstate 35 # 500, New Braunfels, TX 78130-4889
Tel (830) 626-5286 *Founded/Ownrshp* 1996
Sales 168.3MM^E *EMP* 500
SIC 5012 7538 5531 5014 7513 Automobiles & other motor vehicles; General automotive repair shops; Automotive & home supply stores; Tires & tubes; Truck rental & leasing, no drivers
Ch Bd: W M Rush
**CFO:* Martin A Naegelin Jr
**Ex VP:* Robin M Rush
**VP:* J M Lowe Jr

D-U-N-S 06-212-4110 IMP
▲ **RUSH ENTERPRISES INC**
555 S Ih 35 Ste 500, New Braunfels, TX 78130-4889
Tel (830) 302-5200 *Founded/Ownrshp* 1965
Sales 4.9MMM *EMP* 6,297
Tkr Sym RUSHA *Exch* NGS
SIC 5012 7538 5531 5014 7513 Automobiles & other motor vehicles; General automotive repair shops; Automotive & home supply stores; Tires & tubes; Truck rental & leasing, no drivers
Ch Bd: W M Rush
COO: Michael J McRoberts
CFO: Steven L Keller
Ex VP: Martin A Naegelin Jr
Sr VP: Scott Anderson
Sr VP: Corey H Lowe
Sr VP: Richard J Ryan
Sr VP: Derrek Weaver
VP: David Corf
Genl Mgr: Charlie Jones
Natl Sales: Robert Holt
Board of Directors: Thomas A Akin, William H Cary, Raymond J Chess, W Marvin Rush, James C Underwood

RUSH FITNESS COMPLEX, THE
See RUSH FITNESS CORP

D-U-N-S 01-887-9499
RUSH FITNESS CORP
RUSH FITNESS COMPLEX, THE
10708 Kingston Pike, Knoxville, TN 37934-3001
Tel (865) 671-6444 *Founded/Ownrshp* 2000
Sales 51.8MM^E *EMP* 1,700
SIC 7991 Physical fitness facilities
CEO: Steve Saxton
**Ch Bd:* Larry Gurney
**Pr:* David Carney
**CFO:* Mike Nanning
**VP:* Lori Anderson

RUSH FOUNDATION HOSPITAL
See RUSH MEDICAL FOUNDATION

D-U-N-S 10-798-4700
RUSH HEALTH SYSTEMS INC
1314 19th Ave, Meridian, MS 39301-4116
Tel (601) 703-9607 *Founded/Ownrshp* 1981
Sales 66.6MM *EMP* 1,982^E
Accts Horne Llp Ridgeland Ms
SIC 8741 Hospital management
CEO: J C Mc Elroy Jr
**Pr:* Wallace Strickland
**COO:* Chuck Reece
**Treas:* Darrell Wildman
VP: Dale Armour
VP: Arlie Ramsey
VP: Cathy Robinson
Adm Dir: Jimmy Cowan
Phys Thrpy: Lynn Holifield

RUSH INTL TRCK CTR SALT LK CY
See RUSH TRUCK CENTERS OF UTAH INC

D-U-N-S 07-208-5236
RUSH MEDICAL FOUNDATION
RUSH FOUNDATION HOSPITAL
1314 19th Ave, Meridian, MS 39301-4116
Tel (601) 483-0011 *Founded/Ownrshp* 1947
Sales 124.6MM *EMP* 1,400
SIC 8062 General medical & surgical hospitals
**CFO:* Darrell Wildman
Ofcr: Ken Purvis
VP: Libby Mitchell
Dir Case M: Faye Martin
Dir Rad: Tony Gore
Dir Rx: Jason Payne
Chf Nrs Of: Sheryl L Allen
Admn Mgr: Latonya Alford
CTO: Susan Stegall
IT Man: Terry Redmond
Mktg Dir: Jerome Pickard

D-U-N-S 06-745-1393
RUSH OAK PARK HOSPITAL INC
520 S Maple Ave, Oak Park, IL 60304-1022
Tel (708) 383-9300 *Founded/Ownrshp* 1990
Sales 124.8MM *EMP* 706
SIC 8051 8062

RUSH OVERLAND MANUFACTURING
See RUSH SALES CO

D-U-N-S 19-220-1267 IMP
RUSH SALES CO
RUSH OVERLAND MANUFACTURING
2700 E I 20 Service Rd, Odessa, TX 79766
Tel (432) 337-2397 *Founded/Ownrshp* 1987
Sales 83.1MM^E *EMP* 220
SIC 3533 5511 Oil field machinery & equipment; New & used car dealers
CEO: Jim Poer
**Pr:* Chad Spooner
**COO:* Herman Adams
**CFO:* Nina Valles
**VP:* Jana Rush
Off Mgr: Sherry Wester

D-U-N-S 17-911-8930
RUSH SERVICE CO INC
(*Suby of* RUSH HEALTH SYSTEMS INC) ★
1314 19th Ave, Meridian, MS 39301-4116
Tel (601) 483-0011 *Founded/Ownrshp* 1983
Sales 45.8MM^E *EMP* 1,980
SIC 8741 7371 Administrative management; Custom computer programming services
CEO: Wallace Strickland
**CEO:* J C Mc Elroy Jr

D-U-N-S 96-523-6987
RUSH SYSTEM FOR HEALTH
1645 W Jackson Blvd Ste 5, Chicago, IL 60612-3276
Tel (312) 942-4061 *Founded/Ownrshp* 1995
Sales 1.7MM *EMP* 10,109^E
Accts Deloitte Tax Llp Chicago Il
SIC 8741 8062 Restaurant management; General medical & surgical hospitals
Pr: Brent J Estes
V Ch: Michael Simpson
**Pr:* Leo M Henikoff MD

**CEO:* Larry Goodman
**Ch:* Robert Decresce
**Ch:* Richard M Jaffee
**Treas:* John Mordach
**Chf Mktg O:* Michael K Raymond
VP: Mick Zdeblick
Dir Risk M: Susan O'Leary
**CIO:* Julie A Bonello

D-U-N-S 82-555-4140 IMP
■ RUSHTRUCK CENTERS OF CALIFORNIA INC
(*Suby of* RUSH ENTERPRISES INC) ★
555 S Interstate 35 # 500, New Braunfels, TX 78130-4888
Tel (830) 626-5200 *Founded/Ownrshp* 1996
Sales 89.9MM^E *EMP* 310
SIC 5511 5012 Pickups, new & used; Trucks, tractors & trailers: new & used; Trucks, commercial
Pr: W M Rusty Rush
**Ch:* W Marvin Rush
**Ex VP:* Martin A Naegelin Jr
Off Mgr: John Schmitz

D-U-N-S 07-927-7449
■ RUSHTRUCK CENTERS OF ILLINOIS INC
(*Suby of* RUSH ENTERPRISES INC) ★
555 S Interstate 35 # 500, New Braunfels, TX 78130-4888
Tel (830) 626-5200 *Founded/Ownrshp* 2014
Sales 154.8MM^E *EMP* 709^E
SIC 5012 Trucks, commercial

D-U-N-S 01-792-2274 IMP
■ RUSHTRUCK CENTERS OF TEXAS INC
RUSH TRUCK CENTERS TEXAS, L.P.
(*Suby of* RUSH ENTERPRISES INC) ★
555 S Interstate 35 # 500, New Braunfels, TX 78130-4888
Tel (830) 626-5200 *Founded/Ownrshp* 1996
Sales 201.2MM^E *EMP* 221
SIC 5012 5511 Automobiles & other motor vehicles; Trucks, commercial; Trucks, tractors & trailers: new & used
CEO: Wm Rusty Rush
CFO: Steven L Keller
**Ch:* W Marvin Rush
**Ex VP:* Martin A Naegelin Jr

D-U-N-S 04-473-8581
■ RUSHTRUCK CENTERS OF UTAH INC
RUSH INTL TRCK CTR SALT LK CY
(*Suby of* RUSH ENTERPRISES INC) ★
964 S 3800 W, Salt Lake City, UT 84104-4567
Tel (801) 972-5320 *Founded/Ownrshp* 2010
Sales 93.5MM^E *EMP* 365
SIC 5012 7538 5531 Automobiles & other motor vehicles; General automotive repair shops; Automotive & home supply stores
Pr: W Marvin Rush
VP: Martin A Naegelin Jr

RUSHTRUCK CENTERS TEXAS, L.P.
See RUSHTRUCK CENTERS OF TEXAS INC

D-U-N-S 82-633-2525
■ RUSHTRUCK LEASING INC
RUSH TRUCK LEASING, NASHVILLE
(*Suby of* RUSH ENTERPRISES INC) ★
900 Expo Dr, Smyrna, TN 37167-5638
Tel (615) 220-7600 *Founded/Ownrshp* 2008
Sales 171.2MM^E *EMP* 653^E
SIC 5511 Trucks, tractors & trailers: new & used
Prin: Sandra Wood
**Prin:* Lee Slice
Genl Mgr: Troy Dickens
Plnt Mgr: Scott Looney

RUSHTRUCK LEASING, NASHVILLE
See RUSHTRUCK LEASING INC

D-U-N-S 13-126-9573
RUSHTRUCKING CORP
35160 E Michigan Ave, Wayne, MI 48184-3698
Tel (734) 641-1711 *Founded/Ownrshp* 1984
Sales 112.9MM^E *EMP* 350
SIC 4213 Trucking, except local
CEO: Andra M Rush
**Pr:* Greg Humes
COO: Ron Joseph
CFO: Paul Pew
Bd of Dir: Maynard Borowski
Sfty Mgr: Aaron Nussman
Opers Mgr: Bill Downing
Sls Dir: Paul Holmes
Board of Directors: Greg Humes, Daniel Piontek

D-U-N-S 06-861-0245
RUSH UNIVERSITY MEDICAL CENTER (IL)
RUSH-PRSBYTERIAN ST LUKES HOSP
(*Suby of* RUSH SYSTEM FOR HEALTH) ★
1653 W Congress Pkwy, Chicago, IL 60612-3833
Tel (312) 942-5000 *Founded/Ownrshp* 1837
Sales 1.4MMM *EMP* 8,000^E
SIC 8062 Hospital, medical school affiliated with residency
Pr: Larry J Goodman
Chf Rad: David Turner
CFO: Catherine Jacobson
Trst: Jerald Hoekstra
Ofcr: Cynthia Boyd
Assoc VP: Richard K Davis
Assoc VP: Patricia S O'Neil
Sr VP: Bobby Clapp Jr
Sr VP: Avery Miller
Sr VP: Lac Tran
VP: David Ansell MD
VP: Michele Flanagin
VP: Jane Grady
VP: Brad Hinrichs
VP: Jaime Parent
VP: Terry Peterson
VP: Patricia Skarulis
VP: Scott Sonnenschein
Exec: Sandra Cabral
Exec: Stanley Walker
Assoc Dir: Sharon Butler

D-U-N-S 14-478-3164
RUSH-COPLEY MEDICAL CENTER INC
COPLEY MEMORIAL HOSPITAL
(*Suby of* RUSH SYSTEM FOR HEALTH) ★
2000 Ogden Ave, Aurora, IL 60504-5893
Tel (630) 978-6200 *Founded/Ownrshp* 1996
Sales 311.3MM^E *EMP* 2,000
SIC 8062 General medical & surgical hospitals
Pr: Barry C Finn
**Sr VP:* Gail Bumgarner
**Sr VP:* John Diederich
**Sr VP:* Steve B Lowenthal
**Sr VP:* Brenda Van Wyhe
VP: Alexander F Pope
Exec: Diane Langston
Dir Lab: Gary Beck
Adm Dir: Patricia Gomez
Off Mgr: Matt Hearing
Dir IT: Katie Larbee

D-U-N-S 06-791-3129
RUSH-HENRIETTA CENTRAL SCHOOL DISTRICT
2034 Lehigh Station Rd, Henrietta, NY 14467-9616
Tel (585) 359-5000 *Founded/Ownrshp* 1946
Sales 110.0MM *EMP* 1,600
Accts Raymond F Wager Cpa Pc Hen
SIC 8211 Public combined elementary & secondary school
Dir Sec: Michael Paladino
MIS Dir: Brad Mallone

RUSH-PRSBYTERIAN ST LUKES HOSP
See RUSH UNIVERSITY MEDICAL CENTER

RUSHFURNITIURE.COM
See VRUSH INDUSTRIES INC

D-U-N-S 17-776-4362
RUSHLAKE HOTELS (USA) INC
(*Suby of* JIVJI HOLDINGS B.V.)
333 Clay St Ste 4980, Houston, TX 77002-4101
Tel (713) 759-0790 *Founded/Ownrshp* 1980
Sales 29.8MM^E *EMP* 1,160
SIC 7011 Hotel, franchised
Pr: Terry M Shaikh
**Treas:* Jacqueline M Looney
**VP:* Rustom B Kanga

RUSHMORE FOREST PRODUCTS
See NEIMAN ENTERPRISES INC

D-U-N-S 09-775-0525
RUSKEN PACKAGING INC
64 Walnut St Nw, Cullman, AL 35055-5928
Tel (256) 734-0092 *Founded/Ownrshp* 1979
Sales 117.5MM *EMP* 330
Accts Rsm Us Llp Birmingham Alabam
SIC 2652 Filing boxes, paperboard: made from purchased materials
Pr: Greg Rusk
**CFO:* Matt Parker
**VP:* Tim Rabon
Rgnl Mgr: John Ward
IT Man: Mike Campbell
Plnt Mgr: Tom Scannell
Sales Exec: Joey Jackson

RUSKIN AIR & SOUND CONTROL
See RUSKIN CO

D-U-N-S 08-551-0415 IMP
RUSKIN CO
RUSKIN AIR & SOUND CONTROL
(*Suby of* AIR DISTRIBUTION TECHNOLOGIES INC) ★
3900 Doctor Greaves Rd, Grandview, MO 64030-1134
Tel (816) 761-7476 *Founded/Ownrshp* 2014
Sales 383.4MM^E *EMP* 1,471
SIC 3822 3446 3585 Damper operators: pneumatic, thermostatic, electric; Louvers, ventilating; Air conditioning units, complete: domestic or industrial
Pr: Thomas Edwards
**VP:* David Hazelwood
**VP:* John Knapp
Software D: Jennifer Bui
Ql Cn Mgr: Stephen Hendrickson
Natl Sales: John Haukap

RUSS SUPERMARKETS
See B & R STORES INC

RUSSEL B M W-BUICK
See RUSSEL MOTOR CARS INC

D-U-N-S 80-804-1383 IMP
RUSSEL JMS METALS CORP
NORTON METALS
(*Suby of* RUSSEL METALS INC)
25 College Park Cv, Jackson, TN 38301-8706
Tel (731) 984-8121 *Founded/Ownrshp* 1990
Sales 246.5MM^E *EMP* 325
SIC 5051 Pipe & tubing, steel; Plates, metal; Sheets, metal; Tubing, metal
CEO: Brian R Hedges
**Ex VP:* Marion E Britton
**Ex VP:* John G Reid
VP: Lesley M Coleman
**VP:* Maureen A Kelly
Genl Mgr: Jerome Smith
Dir IT: Rob Lewis

D-U-N-S 14-773-4479
RUSSEL METALS WILLIAMS BAHCALL INC
(*Suby of* RUSSEL METALS INC)
999 W Armour Ave, Milwaukee, WI 53221-2419
Tel (414) 481-7100 *Founded/Ownrshp* 1916
Sales 112.9MM^E *EMP* 155
SIC 5051 Steel; Sheets, metal; Plates, metal; Structural shapes, iron or steel
Genl Mgr: Rod Smith
Genl Mgr: Brandon Ezell
Sfty Mgr: Allan Jakubowski
Sales Asso: Alicia Pereda
Sales Asso: Jennifer Schad
Sales Asso: Oscar Wright

D-U-N-S 05-394-8915
RUSSEL MOTOR CARS INC
RUSSEL B M W-BUICK
(*Suby of* MERCEDES-BENZ) ★
6700 Baltimore Nat Pike, Baltimore, MD 21228-3909
Tel (410) 788-8400 *Founded/Ownrshp* 1989
Sales 84.9MM^E *EMP* 250
SIC 5511 7538 7532 5521 Automobiles, new & used; General automotive repair shops; Top & body repair & paint shops; Used car dealers
Pr: F Steven Russel
CFO: Bong Lee
**Sec:* Robert C Russel
**VP:* Adella Russel
Genl Mgr: Greg Ryland

D-U-N-S 00-101-5429
RUSSELECTRIC INC
S Shore Park, Hingham, MA 02043
Tel (781) 749-6000 *Founded/Ownrshp* 1955
Sales 96.1MM^E *EMP* 422
SIC 3613 Power switching equipment
Pr: Dorian Alexandrescu
**Pr:* Raymond G Russell
VP: Ed Malley
**VP:* James Mandeville Jr
VP: Jim Mandiville Jr
VP: John Meuleman
CIO: Rob Zylinski
Sftwr Eng: Steve Harris
Sfty Mgr: Bill Shunstrum
Mktg Dir: Todd Grisdale
Mktg Mgr: John Stark

D-U-N-S 00-894-9760 EXP
RUSSELL & SMITH FORD INC
RUSSELL & SMITH HONDA
3440 South Loop W, Houston, TX 77025-5296
Tel (713) 663-4111 *Founded/Ownrshp* 1965
Sales 291.5MM *EMP* 310
Accts Svadlenak See & Company Pc
SIC 5511 Automobiles, new & used; Pickups, new & used
Ch: Michael G Smith
**Pr:* Charles M Smith Jr
**VP:* Daniel L Chernault
**VP:* Mark D Rehkopf
Sales Asso: Joe Rodriguez

RUSSELL & SMITH HONDA
See RUSSELL & SMITH FORD INC

D-U-N-S 00-339-5902 IMP/EXP
■ RUSSELL BRANDS LLC
A A I
(*Suby of* FRUIT OF LOOM) ★
1 Fruit Of The Loom Dr, Bowling Green, KY 42103-7932
Tel (270) 781-6400 *Founded/Ownrshp* 2001
Sales 2.0MMM^E *EMP* 14,288
SIC 2253 2211 2329 2339 3949 5091 Jerseys, knit; Jogging & warm-up suits, knit; T-shirts & tops, knit; Pants, slacks or trousers, knit; Cotton broad woven goods; Yarn-dyed fabrics, cotton; Men's & boys' athletic uniforms; Uniforms, athletic: women's, misses' & juniors'; Team sports equipment; Sporting & recreation goods
Pr: Richard D Medlin
Pr: Doug Kelly
COO: Dan Peterson
**CFO:* Richard C Price
Sr VP: Harm De Boer
VP: Michael L Dodge
VP: David P Major
VP Inf Sys: Thomas J Spraggins

RUSSELL CELLULAR & SATELLITE
See RUSSELL CELLULAR INC

D-U-N-S 82-969-1427
RUSSELL CELLULAR INC
RUSSELL CELLULAR & SATELLITE
5624 S Hwy Ff, Battlefield, MO 65619
Tel (417) 886-7542 *Founded/Ownrshp* 1993
Sales 680.7MM^E *EMP* 600
SIC 4812 Cellular telephone services
Pr: Jeffrey Russell
**VP:* Robert Lister
**VP:* Kim Russell
**VP:* Darin Wray
Sls Mgr: Heather Ryan

D-U-N-S 03-560-2630
RUSSELL CHEVROLET CO
RUSSELL HONDA
6100 Landers Rd, North Little Rock, AR 72117-1940
Tel (501) 835-8996 *Founded/Ownrshp* 1962
Sales 89.6MM *EMP* 156
Accts Dixon Hughes Goodman Llp Mem
SIC 5511 Automobiles, new & used
Pr: Bob Russell
COO: Russell Brett
**Sec:* Steve Martin
**VP:* Rick Russell
Genl Mgr: Brett Russell
Genl Mgr: Shan Russell
Sales Asso: Matt Fowles

D-U-N-S 10-737-4175
RUSSELL CONSTRUCTION CO INC
4600 E 53rd St, Davenport, IA 52807-3479
Tel (563) 355-1845 *Founded/Ownrshp* 1983
Sales 140.0MM *EMP* 150^E
SIC 1542 Commercial & office building, new construction
Pr: James Russell
**CFO:* Kathy Halter
**Ex VP:* Jim Simmons
**Sr VP:* Thomas Fennelly
**Sr VP:* Chris Krieg
**Sr VP:* Jerry Nieman
**Sr VP:* Scott Ward
VP: John Daly
VP: Terry Kilburg
VP: Matt Russell
VP: David Smith
Exec: Judy Cushman
Exec: Joel Purcell
Exec: Jay Wagner

RUSSELL HONDA
See RUSSELL CHEVROLET CO

RUSSELL INVESTMENT GROUP
See FRANK RUSSELL CO

D-U-N-S 06-369-8526
RUSSELL LANDS INC
WILLOW POINT GOLF & COUNTRY CL
2544 Willow Point Rd, Alexander City, AL 35010-6219
Tel (256) 329-0835 *Founded/Ownrshp* 1962
Sales 118.8MM^E *EMP* 450
SIC 5211 6514 4493 7997 7011 Lumber & other building materials; Dwelling operators, except apartments; Marinas; Country club, membership; Resort hotel
Ch Bd: Ben Russell
**Pr:* Thomas T Lamberth
COO: Jim Peace
**CFO:* David Sturdivant

D-U-N-S 06-453-2252 IMP/EXP
RUSSELL MCCALLS INC
GOURMET FOODS INTERNATIONAL
255 Ted Turner Dr Sw, Atlanta, GA 30303-3705
Tel (404) 954-7600 *Founded/Ownrshp* 1971
Sales 260.5MM^E *EMP* 200^E
SIC 5149 5143 5147 Bakery products; Cheese; Meats & meat products
Pr: Russell C McCall
**CFO:* Sherry Henry
**VP:* Douglas Jay
**VP:* Kenneth Swords
VP: Donnie Wade
Sls Mgr: Cameron Salmon

D-U-N-S 07-329-8424
RUSSELL REYNOLDS ASSOCIATES INC
200 Park Ave Fl 23, New York, NY 10166-2399
Tel (212) 309-1089 *Founded/Ownrshp* 1969
Sales 139.8MM^E *EMP* 990
Accts Pricewaterhousecoopers Llp Cp
SIC 7361 Executive placement
Ch Bd: Matthew J Wright
**Pr:* Clarke Murphy
CFO: Rose Mistri-Somers
**CFO:* Albert H Morris
**Treas:* Stephen R Scroggins
Chf Mktg O: Marcus Brauer
Chf Mktg O: Chris Shumake
Ofcr: Clare Metcalf
Ex VP: Dave Shull
VP: Susan Klug
Exec: Dana Allen
Exec: Marionne Barge
Exec: Eunice Bii
Exec: Margot Cierpinska
Exec: Kalpana Denzel
Exec: Melanie Heuser
Exec: Koen Heynssens
Exec: Sibylle Lane
Exec: Steven Martano
Exec: Sarah Schumacher
Exec: Michael Singleton

D-U-N-S 05-690-0616
RUSSELL SIGLER INC
9702 W Tonto St, Tolleson, AZ 85353-9703
Tel (623) 388-5100 *Founded/Ownrshp* 1971
Sales 513.4MM *EMP* 550
Accts Mcgladrey Llp Phoenix Arizon
SIC 5064 Air conditioning appliances
Pr: John J Sigler
CFO: Robert Orne
CFO: Robert D Osborne
Ch: Russell Sigler
Ofcr: Andy A Abbott
VP: Michelle Vogel
IT Man: Rich Unterbrink
Opers Mgr: James Olness
Sales Exec: Justin Sizemore
Mktg Dir: Ken Strum
Mktg Dir: Ken Sturm

D-U-N-S 00-439-2668
RUSSELL STANDARD CORP
HAMMAKER EAST
285 Kappa Dr Ste 300, Pittsburgh, PA 15238-2814
Tel (412) 449-0700 *Founded/Ownrshp* 1996
Sales 241.5MM^E *EMP* 300
SIC 1611 2951 Highway & street paving contractor; Resurfacing contractor; Concrete, bituminous; Road materials, bituminous (not from refineries)
CEO: James R Johnson
**Pr:* Mathew W Johnson
**CFO:* George E Leach

RUSSELL STOVER CANDIES, LLC
See RUSSELL STOVER CHOCOLATES LLC

D-U-N-S 00-712-5230 EXP
RUSSELL STOVER CHOCOLATES LLC (MO)
RUSSELL STOVER CANDIES, LLC
(*Suby of* LINDT & SPRUNGLI (INTERNATIONAL) AG)
4900 Oak St, Kansas City, MO 64112-2927
Tel (816) 842-9240 *Founded/Ownrshp* 1923, 1981
Sales 499.2MM^E *EMP* 3,000
SIC 2064 5441

D-U-N-S 09-885-5737
RUSSELLVILLE HEALTH CARE INC
705 Gandy St Ne, Russellville, AL 35653-1913
Tel (256) 332-3773 *Founded/Ownrshp* 1989
Sales 306.7MM *EMP* 66
SIC 8051 Convalescent home with continuous nursing care
Pr: John D Huie

D-U-N-S 05-807-5813
RUSSELLVILLE STEEL CO INC
280 Steel City Ln, Russellville, AR 72802-8975
Tel (479) 968-2211 *Founded/Ownrshp* 1961
Sales 87.3MM^E *EMP* 94
SIC 5051 Steel
Pr: Trish Henry
VP: Chris Knoles
Opers Mgr: Robert Chance
Ql Cn Mgr: Grover House

D-U-N-S 94-224-1134
RUST CONSULTING INC
(Suby of SOURCECORP LEGAL INC) ★
625 Marquette Ave Ste 900, Minneapolis, MN 55402-5616
Tel (612) 359-2000 Founded/Ownrshp 2013
Sales 84.1MM^E EMP 500
SIC 8741 8111 Administrative management; Legal services
Pr: Matthew Potter
*CFO: Paul Vogel
*Ex VP: Eric Hudgens
Sr VP: Eric Bishop
Sr VP: Julie Kline
VP: Julie Blascziek
VP: Kyle Coolbroth
*VP: David Holland
*VP: Daniel Marotto
VP: James Parks
VP: James Prutsman
Dir Bus: Jonathan Paul
Dir Bus: Kendall Zylstra

D-U-N-S 00-509-4420 IMP/EXP
■ **RUST-OLEUM CORP**
(Suby of RPM INTERNATIONAL INC) ★
11 E Hawthorn Pkwy, Vernon Hills, IL 60061-1499
Tel (847) 367-7700 Founded/Ownrshp 1932, 1994
Sales 635.3MM^E EMP 1,146
SIC 2891 2899 2816 2842 2851 Adhesives & sealants; Chemical preparations; Inorganic pigments; Specialty cleaning, polishes & sanitation goods; Paints, waterproof
Pr: Thomas E Reed
*CFO: Donald Harmeyer
VP: Herman Bacchus
VP: Kelly Bye
VP: Steve Deluca
VP: Kurt Hardy
VP: Ed Kay
VP: Lisa Stach
*VP: William Whiting
Prin: Tom Schweiger
*VP Admn: Steve Gillmann

D-U-N-S 03-141-9559
RUSTY ECK FORD INC
RUSTY ECK FORD OUTLET
7310 E Kellogg Dr, Wichita, KS 67207-1692
Tel (316) 685-9211 Founded/Ownrshp 1967
Sales 87.6MM^E EMP 212
SIC 5511 Automobiles, new & used
Pr: Leslie Eck
*CFO: Janet Cervantes
Genl Mgr: Craig Minten
Off Mgr: Vicky McMillin
Dir IT: Rob Wright
Sls Mgr: Erika Colgan
Sls Mgr: Ryan Long
Sales Asso: Mario Magnaye
Sales Asso: Nick Valentine

RUSTY ECK FORD OUTLET
See RUSTY ECK FORD INC

D-U-N-S 61-160-0318
RUTGER STATE UNIVERSITY
PURCHASING DEPT
(Suby of ERNEST MARIO SCHOOL PHARMACY) ★
Asb 3 Rutgers Pl, New Brunswick, NJ 08901
Tel (732) 932-4370 Founded/Ownrshp 2005
Sales 1.3MMM EMP 35^E
Accts Kpmg Llp Short Hills Nj
SIC 8221 University
VP: David Chapman

D-U-N-S 00-191-2864 IMP
RUTGERS STATE UNIVERSITY
ERNEST MARIO SCHOOL PHARMACY
96 Davidson Rd, Piscataway, NJ 08854-8062
Tel (732) 932-4636 Founded/Ownrshp 1766
Sales 1.3MMM EMP 10,000
SIC 8221

D-U-N-S 07-979-8727
RUTHERFORD COUNTY SCHOOLS
382 W Main St, Forest City, NC 28043-3027
Tel (828) 288-2200 Founded/Ownrshp 2015
Sales 19.8MM^E EMP 1,953^E
SIC 8211 Public elementary & secondary schools
Dir Sec: Ricky McKinney
MIS Dir: Darryl Smith
Cmptr Lab: Trina Caldwell
Dir IT: Donna Ledford
Dir IT: Steve Solomon
Dir IT: Michael Thompson
Teacher Pr: Martha Robinson
Psych: Matthew Taylor

D-U-N-S 00-577-1571
RUTHERFORD ELECTRIC MEMBERSHIP CORP
186 Hudlow Rd, Forest City, NC 28043-2575
Tel (704) 245-1621 Founded/Ownrshp 1940
Sales 134.3MM EMP 178
SIC 4911 Distribution, electric power
Pr: Joseph Quinn
Mng Pt: Jonathan W Pitman
*VP: Scott Culter
*VP: Matt Workman
*Mktg Dir: Bruce Simmons
Mktg Mgr: Steve Gibbs

RUTH'S CHRIS STEAK HOUSE
See RUTHS HOSPITALITY GROUP INC

D-U-N-S 03-438-0519
▲ **RUTHS HOSPITALITY GROUP INC**
RUTH'S CHRIS STEAK HOUSE
1030 W Canton Ave Ste 100, Winter Park, FL 32789-3050
Tel (407) 333-7440 Founded/Ownrshp 1965
Sales 373.4MM EMP 4,350^E
Tkr Sym RUTH Exch NGS
SIC 5812 6794 Eating places; Patent buying, licensing, leasing; Franchises, selling or licensing
CEO: Michael P O'Donnell
Pr: Cheryl Henry
COO: Peter Beaudrault
CFO: Arne G Haak
Treas: Brian Judge
Ex VP: Gil Fomaris
Ex VP: Hanne Olesen-Nahman
Sr VP: Robert Vincent
VP: Rick Crossland
VP: Stan Harris
VP: Rik Jenkins
VP: Helen Mackey
Exec: Brandon Bretz
Exec: Paul Cernansky
Exec: Jason Garcia
Exec: A Graf
Exec: Jason Ruderman
Exec: Yolanda Ruiz
Board of Directors: Carla R Cooper, Robert S Merritt, Robin P Selati, Alan Vituli

D-U-N-S 06-053-1506
RUTLAND HOSPITAL INC ACT 220
RUTLAND REGIONAL MEDICAL CTR
160 Allen St, Rutland, VT 05701-4595
Tel (802) 775-7111 Founded/Ownrshp 1983
Sales 228.3MM EMP 1,350
SIC 8062 General medical & surgical hospitals
CEO: Tom Huebner
Chf Rad: Daniel Mitchell
Chf Rad: James N Rademacher
CFO: Edward Ogorzalek
Ofcr: Michelle Cordeiro
Ofcr: John Wallace
VP: Barbara Robinson
VP: Allison Wollen
CIO: Sheri Ravlin
Software D: Lisa Mancini
Mtls Dir: Jim Greenough

D-U-N-S 10-661-5537
RUTLAND REGIONAL HEALTH SERVICES
160 Allen St, Rutland, VT 05701-4560
Tel (802) 775-7111 Founded/Ownrshp 1998
Sales 2.5MM EMP 1,000
Accts Bkd Llp Springfield Mo
SIC 8062 7352 8059 General medical & surgical hospitals; Medical equipment rental; Convalescent home
Ch: Mary E Moran
*Pr: Tom Huebner
CIO: John Kijewski

RUTLAND REGIONAL MEDICAL CTR
See RUTLAND HOSPITAL INC ACT 220

RUTTER'S FARM STORES
See C H R CORP

RV DEALERS MARKETPLACE
See CAMPING WORLD INC

RW
See ROGER WOOD FOODS INC

RWC BUILDING PRODUCTS
See ROOFING WHOLESALE CO INC

RWL WATER GROUP
See RWL WATER LLC

D-U-N-S 96-850-2653
RWL WATER LLC
RWL WATER GROUP
767 5th Ave Ste 4200, New York, NY 10153-0023
Tel (212) 572-5700 Founded/Ownrshp 2010
Sales 160.0MM EMP 160
SIC 1629 Waste water & sewage treatment plant construction
*CFO: Karl-Heinz Zorn
*Ch: Ronald S Lauder
Off Mgr: Donna O'Leary

D-U-N-S 62-165-4875
■ **RX PRO HEALTH LLC**
(Suby of AMN HEALTHCARE SERVICES INC) ★
12400 High Bluff Dr, San Diego, CA 92130-3077
Tel (858) 369-4050 Founded/Ownrshp 2007
Sales 93.5M^E EMP 1,800
SIC 7363 Medical help service
CEO: Susan R Salka

D-U-N-S 79-106-1190
RXR REALTY
625 Rxr Plz, Uniondale, NY 11556-3815
Tel (516) 506-6000 Founded/Ownrshp 2007
Sales 236.0MM^E EMP 300
SIC 6798 Real estate investment trusts
Ch Bd: Scott Rechler
*Pr: Michael Maturo
Pr: Seth Pinsky
*V Ch Bd: Jason Barnett
Assoc VP: Eric Shalem
Sr Ex VP: Frank Patafio
Ex VP: Frank Adipietro
*Ex VP: Tom Carey
Ex VP: David Frank
Ex VP: Michael McMahon
Ex VP: Philip Wharton
Sr VP: Carol Allen
*Sr VP: Kenneth W Bauer
Sr VP: Matthew D Frank
Sr VP: Scott Haegele
*Sr VP: Walt Smith
VP: Brian Cheeseman
VP: Greg Clancy
VP: Steven Fields
VP: Frank Haftel
VP: Joan Imbro

D-U-N-S 13-284-8198
RYAN AUTOMOTIVE LLC
OPEN ROAD AUTO GROUP
1120 Us Highway 22 Bldg 2, Bridgewater, NJ 08807-2962
Tel (732) 650-1550 Founded/Ownrshp 2000
Sales 194.0MM^E EMP 600^E
SIC 5511 New & used car dealers
CEO: Walter Rodman Ryan
Pr: Michael Morais
CFO: Martin Gross
VP: Robert Forcini
Genl Mgr: David Branch

D-U-N-S 06-818-3195
RYAN COMPANIES US INC (MN)
50 S 10th St Ste 300, Minneapolis, MN 55403-2012
Tel (612) 492-4000 Founded/Ownrshp 1938
Sales 631.0MM^E EMP 500
SIC 1542 1541 6552 6512 1522 Commercial & office building, new construction; Shopping center construction; Hospital construction; Industrial buildings, new construction; Land subdividers & developers, commercial; Nonresidential building operators; Apartment building construction
CEO: Patrick Ryan
CFO: Tim Gray
*CFO: Brian Murray
Sr Cor Off: Bob Ryan
Div VP: Norm Mead
Ex VP: Kent Carlson
VP: Richard E Brooks
*VP: Timothy M Gray
VP: Casey Hankinson
VP: Dan Levett
VP: Connor Lewis
VP: Peter Partipilo
VP: Paul Springthorpe
VP: Robert Wehner
VP: Brad Wilson
VP Bus Dev: Gary Robbins

D-U-N-S 04-452-0992 EXP
RYAN DIRECTIONAL SERVICES INC
I D L
(Suby of NABORS INDUSTRIES INC) ★
19510 Oil Center Blvd, Houston, TX 77073-3355
Tel (281) 443-1414 Founded/Ownrshp 2010
Sales 153.4MM^E EMP 120
SIC 1389 Well logging
Pr: Nigel Evans
*Treas: Andrew G Bruce
*VP: Stephen Krase
*Prin: Richard T Ryan

D-U-N-S 07-878-9944
RYAN GOVERNMENT SERVICES LLC
13155 Noel Rd Ste 100, Dallas, TX 75240-5050
Tel (972) 934-0022 Founded/Ownrshp 2012
Sales 29.5MM^E EMP 1,600
SIC 8742 Management consulting services
Prin: George Ryan
Prin: David English

RYAN HERCO FLOW SOLUTIONS
See RYAN HERCO PRODUCTS CORP

D-U-N-S 04-223-1654 IMP/EXP
RYAN HERCO PRODUCTS CORP (CA)
RYAN HERCO FLOW SOLUTIONS
3010 N San Fernando Blvd, Burbank, CA 91504-2524
Tel (818) 841-1141 Founded/Ownrshp 1948, 2011
Sales 230.5MM^E EMP 250
SIC 5074 5162 Pipes & fittings, plastic; Plastics materials & basic shapes
CEO: Stewart Howley
CFO: Carrie Blankenheim
Ex VP: Terry Obrien
*VP: Randy Beckwith
VP: Randall Finchum
VP: David Guardia
Exec: CJ J Mahoney
Exec: Fred Melnikoff
Genl Mgr: Sue Nickol
Off Mgr: Jeri Djokic
IT Man: Gregory M Garcia
Board of Directors: Brian Bowman

D-U-N-S 13-977-3022
RYAN INC CENTRAL
2700 E Racine St, Janesville, WI 53545-5216
Tel (608) 754-2291 Founded/Ownrshp 1985
Sales 93.8MM^E EMP 500
SIC 1794

D-U-N-S 78-888-0441
RYAN LLC
13155 Noel Rd Ste 100, Dallas, TX 75240-5050
Tel (972) 934-0022 Founded/Ownrshp 1991
Sales 394.7MM EMP 1,598
Accts Whitley Penn Llp Dallas Texa
SIC 8721 7291 7389 Accounting, auditing & bookkeeping; Tax return preparation services; Legal & tax services
CEO: G Brint Ryan
V Ch: Gerry L Ridgely Jr
V Ch: Jon C Sweet
Pr: Delta Emerson
Pr: Linda Falcone
*CFO: David English
*CFO: Brian Wing
Chf Mktg O: Jim Aubele
*Ofcr: Lee Ruiz
*Ofcr: Gregory S Weiss
Ex VP: Joe Mulcahy
*Sr VP: Ray Ann Cacheria
Sr VP: Adrianne Court
Sr VP: Blake K Holman
Sr VP: Whit Pepper
VP: Chris Belknap
VP: Luke Branyan
VP: Danny Ladouceur
VP: Marykay Manning
VP: Joe Mileti
VP: Richard Nearhood

D-U-N-S 07-616-3195
RYAN ROBERTSON AND ASSOCIATES INC
KEMPER INSURANCE
330 E Kilbourn Ave # 650, Milwaukee, WI 53202-3175
Tel (414) 271-3575 Founded/Ownrshp 1922
Sales NA EMP 260
SIC 6411 Insurance agents, brokers & service
CFO: Jay H Robertson
*Pr: Anthony Von Ruden
CFO: Bob Foster
*Treas: Thomas G Wells
Ofcr: Ron Hammerschlag
VP: Jeff Frank
*VP: Charles Johnson
VP: Patrick K Kuhnmuench
*VP: Steven R Kuhnmunch
VP: Mark Mason
*VP: Jack T Ryan
VP: Giovanna Vanwie

D-U-N-S 09-132-9268
RYANS RESTAURANT GROUP LLC
(Suby of OLD COUNTRY BUFFET RESTAURANTS) ★
120 Chula Vis, San Antonio, TX 78232-2234
Tel (651) 994-8608 Founded/Ownrshp 2006
Sales 269.1MM^E EMP 6,428^E
SIC 5812 Restaurant, family: chain; Steak restaurant
Pr: G Edwin McCranie
*Treas: Fred T Grant Jr
*Sr VP: Michal R Kirk

RYCAN
See HEALTHLAND INC

D-U-N-S 60-318-0118
RYCON CONSTRUCTION INC
2501 Smallman St Ste 100, Pittsburgh, PA 15222-4694
Tel (412) 392-2525 Founded/Ownrshp 1989
Sales 244.0MM EMP 375^E
SIC 1542 Commercial & office building contractors
CEO: Todd A Dominick
Pr: John W Sabatos
VP: David Semler
Genl Mgr: Kim Griffin
Dir IT: Pete Musulin
IT Man: Mark Ditullio
Sfty Mgr: Mike Penrod
Opers Mgr: Kevin Ahrens
Opers Mgr: Jim Celmo
Snr PM: Stephen Brunecz
Snr PM: James Gerdun

D-U-N-S 55-622-5175
RYDELL CO
2700 S Washington St, Grand Forks, ND 58201-6720
Tel (701) 780-1380 Founded/Ownrshp 1991
Sales 129.6MM^E EMP 471^E
SIC 5511 New & used car dealers
Pr: Randy Nehring
*Ch: Wes Rydell
*Sec: Duane Gilleland
*VP: Ivan Gandrud
Prd Mgr: Mark Steinke
Board of Directors: Wes Rydelling

RYDER
See TOTAL LOGISTICS ONLINE LLC

D-U-N-S 08-019-3097 IMP/EXP
■ **RYDER INTEGRATED LOGISTICS INC**
(Suby of RYDER TRUCK RENTAL INC) ★
11690 Nw 105th St, Medley, FL 33178-1103
Tel (305) 500-3726 Founded/Ownrshp 1973
Sales 1.2MMM^E EMP 7,571^E
SIC 7513 Truck rental, without drivers
Ch Bd: Gregory T Swienton
*Pr: Robert E Sanchez
*CFO: Art A Garcia
*Ex VP: Thomas E Mc Kinnon
Ex VP: Thomas Mc Mc Kinnon
*Ex VP: Vicki A O'Meara
*Exec: Edwin A Houston
Dir Bus: David Michael
Off Admin: Crystal Carlson
Off Admin: Vickie Navarro
Sls Dir: Delores Lail

D-U-N-S 00-692-2827 IMP/EXP
▲ **RYDER SYSTEM INC**
11690 Nw 105th St, Medley, FL 33178-1103
Tel (305) 500-3726 Founded/Ownrshp 1933
Sales 6.5MMM EMP 33,100
Tkr Sym R Exch NYS
SIC 7513 4212 Truck rental & leasing, no drivers; Truck rental, without drivers; Truck leasing, without drivers; Truck rental with drivers
Ch Bd: Robert E Sanchez
Pr: Dennis C Cooke
Pr: J Steven Sensing
CFO: Art A Garcia
Chf Mktg O: Karen M Jones
Ofcr: John Gleason
Ofcr: Gregory F Greene
Sr VP: Melvin L Kirk
Sr VP: Melvin Kirk
Sr VP: Frank Lopez
VP: Scott R Allen
VP: Amparo Bared
VP: Amparo Bravo
VP: Richard Cibos
VP: John Deris
VP: Greg Greene
VP: Stephen Hitchings
VP: Sanford Hodes
VP: Richard Jennings
VP: Tom Jones
VP: Karen Joness
Board of Directors: Hansel E Tookes II, John M Berra, Robert J Eck, Robert A Hagemann, L Patrick Hassey, Michael F Hilton, Tamara L Lundgren, Luis P Nieto Jr, Abbie J Smith, E Follin Smith

D-U-N-S 00-692-2835 IMP/EXP
■ **RYDER TRUCK RENTAL INC** (FL)
(Suby of RYDER SYSTEM INC) ★
11690 Nw 105th St, Medley, FL 33178-1103
Tel (305) 500-3726 Founded/Ownrshp 1934, 1955
Sales 1.5MMM^E EMP 12,500
SIC 7513 Truck rental, without drivers
Ex VP: Bobby J Griffin
Sr VP: Dana Fuller
VP: Glynis A Bryan
Dir Bus: Adriano Melluzzo
Counsel: Carlo Rodriguez

D-U-N-S 80-816-0985
▲ **RYERSON HOLDING CORP**
227 W Monroe St Fl 27, Chicago, IL 60606-5081
Tel (312) 292-5000 Founded/Ownrshp 2007
Sales 3.1MMM EMP 3,200^E
Tkr Sym RYI Exch NYS
SIC 5051 Metals service centers & offices; Iron & steel (ferrous) products; Aluminum bars, rods, ingots, sheets, pipes, plates, etc.; Nonferrous metal sheets, bars, rods, etc.
Pr: Edward J Lehner
V Ch: Victoria Zanutto

Pr: Michael J Burbach
Pr: Kevin D Richardson
CFO: Erich S Schnaufer
Ex VP: Mark S Silver
IT Man: Deb Salvaggio
Sales Asso: Jeremy Thomas
Board of Directors: Kirk K Calhoun, Eva M Kalawski, Stephen P Larson, Philip E Norment, Mary Ann Sigler

D-U-N-S 15-176-0600 IMP/EXP
RYERSON INC
227 W Monroe St Ste 2700, Chicago, IL 60606-5081
Tel (312) 292-5000 *Founded/Ownrshp* 2007
Sales 3.4MMM *EMP* 3,200[E]
SIC 5051

D-U-N-S 00-451-3896 IMP
■ RYERSON PROCUREMENT CORP
(*Suby of* JOSEPH T RYERSON & SON INC) ★
227 W Monroe St Fl 27, Chicago, IL 60606-5081
Tel (312) 292-5000 *Founded/Ownrshp* 1986
Sales 1.4MMM[E] *EMP* 2,678[E]
SIC 5051 Nonferrous metal sheets, bars, rods, etc.
Pr: Michael C Arnold
Pr: Mike Burbach
Pr: Roger W Lindsay
Pr: Kevin Richardson
CEO: Leong Fang
CFO: Edward Lehner

D-U-N-S 06-961-9641 IMP/EXP
RYKO SOLUTIONS INC
(*Suby of* TRIVEST FUND III LP) ★
1500 Se 37th St, Grimes, IA 50111-4951
Tel (515) 986-3700 *Founded/Ownrshp* 1973, 2010
Sales 133.7MM[E] *EMP* 447[E]
SIC 3589 1796 7699 Car washing machinery; Vacuum cleaners & sweepers, electric: industrial; Machinery installation; Industrial machinery & equipment repair
Ch: Troy Templeton
**Pr:* Steven L'Heureux
**CFO:* Jesse Wurth
**VP:* Russ Wilson
Genl Couns: Bill Raisch

D-U-N-S 05-123-9239
RYLA INC
RYLA TELESERVICES
2120 Barrett Park Dr Nw, Kennesaw, GA 30144-3673
Tel (678) 322-5000 *Founded/Ownrshp* 1995
Sales NA *EMP* 3,500[E]
SIC 7389

RYLA TELESERVICES
See RYLA INC

D-U-N-S 02-258-5913 EXP
RYLAND GROUP INC
3011 Townsgate Rd Ste 200, Westlake Village, CA 91361-5878
Tel (805) 367-3800 *Founded/Ownrshp* 1967
Sales 2.6MMM *EMP* 1,502
SIC 1531 1521 6162

D-U-N-S 07-857-0932
RYMAN HOSPITALITY PROPERTIES INC
1 Gaylord Dr, Nashville, TN 37214-1207
Tel (615) 316-6000 *Founded/Ownrshp* 2013
Sales 1.0MMM *EMP* 682[E]
SIC 6798 7011 Real estate investment trusts; Hotels & motels
Ch Bd: Colin V Reed
Pr: Mark Fioravanti
COO: Michael Guth
Sr VP: Patrick Chaffin
Sr VP: Jennifer Hutcheson
Sr VP: Scott J Lynn
Sr VP: Bennett Westbrook
VP: Shawn Smith
Comm Dir: Shannon Sullivan
Sales Exec: Candace Holden

D-U-N-S 15-209-1179 IMP
RYOBI DIE CASTING (USA) INC
(*Suby of* RYOBI LIMITED)
800 W Mausoleum Rd, Shelbyville, IN 46176-9719
Tel (317) 398-3398 *Founded/Ownrshp* 1988
Sales 240.2MM[E] *EMP* 900
SIC 3714 3444 3365 3363 Transmission housings or parts, motor vehicle; Sheet metalwork; Aluminum foundries; Aluminum die-castings
CEO: Takashi Yokoyama
**Pr:* Thomas L Johnson
**VP:* Hideki Tanyfuji
Genl Mgr: Yeou-Li Chu
Dir IT: Beth Neary
IT Man: Randy Burkett
IT Man: Sylvia Waters
Info Man: Randy Burket
Plnt Mgr: Tony Kuhn
Plnt Mgr: Harley Sheets
Plnt Mgr: George Umeda

D-U-N-S 96-578-7125
RYT-WAY ACQUISITION CO LLC
(*Suby of* WIND POINT PARTNERS VI LP) ★
21850 Grenada Ave, Lakeville, MN 55044-9076
Tel (952) 469-1417 *Founded/Ownrshp* 2008
Sales 24.3MM[E] *EMP* 1,239
SIC 7389 2023 3565 Packaging & labeling services; Labeling bottles, cans, cartons, etc.; Dried milk; Packaging machinery
CEO: David Finch

RYT-WAY FOOD PRODUCTS CO
See RYT-WAY INDUSTRIES LLC

D-U-N-S 02-297-5361
RYT-WAY INDUSTRIES LLC
RYT-WAY FOOD PRODUCTS CO
(*Suby of* RYT-WAY MIDCO LLC) ★
21850 Grenada Ave, Lakeville, MN 55044-9076
Tel (952) 469-1417 *Founded/Ownrshp* 2008
Sales 96.1MM[E] *EMP* 740
SIC 7389 2023 Packaging & labeling services; Labeling bottles, cans, cartons, etc.; Dried milk
CEO: Rich Scalise
**COO:* Larry Muma
**CFO:* Scott Edgcomb
**CFO:* Mary Beth Fong
**Prin:* David Finch
S&M/VP: Vicky Smitley

D-U-N-S 96-583-5296
RYT-WAY MIDCO LLC
(*Suby of* HEARTHSIDE FOOD SOLUTIONS LLC) ★
21850 Grenada Ave, Lakeville, MN 55044-9076
Tel (952) 469-1417 *Founded/Ownrshp* 2009
Sales 184.5MM[E] *EMP* 1,238
SIC 7389 2023 3565 Packaging & labeling services; Labeling bottles, cans, cartons, etc.; Dried milk; Packaging machinery
CEO: David Finch

D-U-N-S 08-001-3661
RYZE SYNTHETICS PORT ARTHUR LLC
20 Pacifica Ste 1010, Irvine, CA 92618-7462
Tel (310) 200-2081 *Founded/Ownrshp* 2015
Sales 100.0MM *EMP* 6
SIC 1311 Natural gas production
Prin: Nemo Perera
**Prin:* Matt Pierson

S

D-U-N-S 78-891-7995
S & A COMPUTER SERVICES INC
SA IT SERVICES
1125 Northmeadow Pkwy # 120, Roswell, GA 30076-3870
Tel (770) 569-2828 *Founded/Ownrshp* 1991
Sales 98.4MM[E] *EMP* 935
SIC 7379 Computer related consulting services
CEO: Anne Stevens
**Pr:* Stephen Bowker
**CFO:* Fritz Schlabach
**VP:* Christine House
**VP:* Chip White
**Prin:* Amy Easterday

D-U-N-S 14-736-3829
S & B HOLDINGS LTD
S&B ENGINEERS AND CONSTRUCTORS
7809 Park Place Blvd, Houston, TX 77087-4639
Tel (713) 645-4141 *Founded/Ownrshp* 1966
Sales 797.6MM *EMP* 4
Accts Ernst & Young Llp Houston T
SIC 1629 8711 Chemical plant & refinery construction; Civil engineering
Ch Bd: W A Brookshire
**Pr:* JG Slaughter Jr
VP: Sylvia Anderson
VP: Tommy Collins
S&M/VP: Rich L Akin

D-U-N-S 00-506-8895 IMP/EXP
S & C ELECTRIC CO
6601 N Ridge Blvd, Chicago, IL 60626-3997
Tel (773) 338-1000 *Founded/Ownrshp* 1911
Sales 867.9MM[E] *EMP* 2,500
SIC 3613 3643 3625 8711 Fuses, electric; Switches, electric power except snap, push button, etc.; Switchgear & switchgear accessories; Current-carrying wiring devices; Relays & industrial controls; Engineering services
Pr: Kyle Seymour
Pr: Mark Woods
COO: Anna Miranda
CFO: Susan C Keyes
Treas: John E Johann
Treas: John Johann
VP: Witold Bik
VP: John Blumenshine
VP: John Crain
VP: James Hart
VP: Dave Koepp
VP: David Myers
VP: Timothy Qualheim
VP: Christopher Roman
Board of Directors: Stanley F Slabas, Lynn O Conrad, Christopher Curtis, John W Estey, G Michael Horn, Barbara Jane Irwin, Frank Kelly, James Kelly, John E Kirkpatrick, Erle Nye

S & D COFFEE AND TEA
See S & D COFFEE INC

D-U-N-S 00-317-3085 IMP/EXP
S & D COFFEE INC (NC)
S & D COFFEE AND TEA
(*Suby of* S&D COFFEE HOLDING CO) ★
300 Concord Pkwy S, Concord, NC 28027-6702
Tel (704) 782-3121 *Founded/Ownrshp* 1927
Sales 358.3MM[E] *EMP* 1,100
SIC 2095 5149 2086 Roasted coffee; Coffee, green or roasted; Tea; Specialty food items; Tea, iced: packaged in cans, bottles, etc.
Ch Bd: C Ron Hinson
**COO:* Stephen F Cole
**Co-Ch Bd:* Alan P Davis
**Co-Ch Bd:* E Rhyne Davis
VP: Tracy Ging
VP: Eric Nakata
VP: Tom Robinson
Rgnl Mgr: Mark Uscilowski
Rgnl Mgr: Robert Whitcomb
Genl Mgr: Marc Seder
Off Mgr: Leo Kennon

D-U-N-S 00-129-0683 IMP
S & J SHEET METAL SUPPLY INC (NY)
608 E 133rd St, Bronx, NY 10454-4605
Tel (718) 993-0460 *Founded/Ownrshp* 1955
Sales 131.5MM[E] *EMP* 100
SIC 5033 3444 Roofing & siding materials; Sheet metalwork
Ch: Steven Schwartz
**CEO:* Michael Gotleib

S & K AMERICA'S MEN'S STORE
See S & K FAMOUS BRANDS INC

D-U-N-S 08-670-7119 IMP/EXP
S & K DISTRIBUTION LLC
NEW CASTLE BUILDING PRODUCTS
535 Old Tarrytown Rd, White Plains, NY 10603-2617
Tel (914) 948-6363 *Founded/Ownrshp* 2002
Sales 219.9MM[E] *EMP* 95
SIC 5031 2952 5033 Lumber, plywood & millwork; Roofing materials; Roofing & siding materials
Pr: Kristopher Steele
COO: Keith Haskell
**Sr VP:* Raymond Steele
Genl Mgr: Pat McNamara
Sls Mgr: Cary Ratner
Sales Asso: Doug Maclean

D-U-N-S 04-128-7210 IMP
S & K FAMOUS BRANDS INC
S & K AMERICA'S MEN'S STORE
20 N 8th St, Richmond, VA 23219-3302
Tel (804) 827-1000 *Founded/Ownrshp* 1967
Sales 127.8MM[E] *EMP* 2,090
Accts Bdo Seidman Llp Richmond Vi
SIC 5611 5661 Clothing accessories: men's & boys'; Men's shoes
Ch Bd: Stuart C Siegel
**CEO:* Joseph A Oliver III
**CFO:* Robert E Knowles
CFO: Robert E Knowls
Ofcr: J L Jorgensen
**Ofcr:* Jonathan M Tibus
**Ex VP:* Jarrod S Nadel
CTO: Bert Hardy

S & M MOVING SYSTEMS
See TORRANCE VAN & STORAGE CO

D-U-N-S 03-925-3372
S & N COMMUNICATIONS INC
636 Gralin St, Kernersville, NC 27284-3454
Tel (336) 992-5420 *Founded/Ownrshp* 1977
Sales 390.8MM[E] *EMP* 700
SIC 1623 1731 Telephone & communication line construction; Cable television installation
Pr: Allen Powell
**CFO:* George L Baer
CFO: Ronald Smith
Rgnl Mgr: Travis Haney

D-U-N-S 07-614-3320
S & R EGG FARM INC
N9416 Tamarack Rd, Whitewater, WI 53190-4015
Tel (262) 495-6220 *Founded/Ownrshp* 1958
Sales 129.0MM[E] *EMP* 75
SIC 0252

D-U-N-S 06-622-2639
S & S AUTOMOTIVE INC
S&S AUTOMOTIVE GROUP
740 N Larch Ave, Elmhurst, IL 60126-1569
Tel (630) 279-1613 *Founded/Ownrshp* 1960
Sales 105.0MM[E] *EMP* 250
SIC 5013 5999 5065 1731 Automotive supplies & parts; Telephone equipment & systems; Alarm signal systems; Telephone equipment; Fire detection & burglar alarm systems specialization
Pr: Ronald L Kushner
**Ex VP:* Jeremiah Chavoen
**VP:* Caryl Kushner

S & S CONSTRUCTION CO
See SHAPELL INDUSTRIES LLC

D-U-N-S 07-133-2365 IMP
S & S FIRESTONE INC
S & S TIRE CO
1475 Jingle Bell Ln, Lexington, KY 40509-4113
Tel (859) 281-8500 *Founded/Ownrshp* 1974
Sales 256.5MM[E] *EMP* 500[E]
SIC 5531 Automotive tires
Pr: Brooks Swentzel
**Treas:* Rick Skinner
**VP:* Paul Swentzel
**VP:* Paul Zurcher
Exec: Cindy Cheatham
Genl Mgr: Mike Cook
Genl Mgr: Mike Griffin
Genl Mgr: Jason Larkin
Genl Mgr: Daniel Maples
Genl Mgr: Greg Sebastian
Genl Mgr: Derek Sperzel

S & S FOOD STORES
See SCAFFS INC

S & STAGS
See TUG MANUFACTURING CORP

S & S TIRE CO
See S & S FIRESTONE INC

D-U-N-S 10-210-9345 IMP
S & STOOL & SUPPLY INC
S AND S SUPPLIES AND SOLUTIONS
2700 Maxwell Way, Fairfield, CA 94534-9708
Tel (925) 335-4000 *Founded/Ownrshp* 1983
Sales 134.5MM *EMP* 260
Accts She Labagh Dobberstein San Fr
SIC 5085 7699 5072 7359 Industrial supplies; Industrial equipment services; Tool repair services; Hand tools; Power handtools; Equipment rental & leasing; Tool rental
CEO: Tracy M Tomkovicz
**Pr:* Steven Tomkovicz
**CFO:* Tanya Powell
IT Man: Phil Jones
Sales Asso: Alison Hollman

D-U-N-S 00-114-0581 IMP/EXP
S & S WORLDWIDE INC (CT)
75 Mill St, Colchester, CT 06415-1263
Tel (860) 537-3451 *Founded/Ownrshp* 1906, 1969
Sales 221.8MM[E] *EMP* 235
SIC 5199 5049 3944 Art goods; School supplies; Games, toys & children's vehicles
CEO: Stephen L Schwartz
**Pr:* Adam L Schwartz
**COO:* Allen Dyer
**CFO:* Vin Pescosolido
**VP:* Audrey Bis
Creative D: Stephen Ross
MIS Dir: Robert Fuller
Web Dev: Tim Ahearn
Web Dev: James Jerram
Ql Cn Mgr: David Riccardi
Trfc Mgr: Robert Lambert

D-U-N-S 06-875-1148 IMP
■ S & T BANK
(*Suby of* S&T BANCORP INC) ★
800 Philadelphia St, Indiana, PA 15701-3908
Tel (724) 349-1800 *Founded/Ownrshp* 1983
Sales NA *EMP* 765
SIC 6022 State commercial banks
Pr: Todd Brice
COO: Edward C Hauck
COO: Caroline Raneri
CFO: Robert E Rout
Treas: Mark Kochvar
Chf Cred: Patrick J Haberfield
Chf Cred: Tony E Kallsen
Ofcr: Laurence S Christ
Ofcr: Kevin Conrad
Ofcr: Douglas A Hilditch
Ofcr: William Kametz
Ofcr: Tim McKee
Ofcr: Becky Stapleton
Ofcr: Tim Tyger
Assoc VP: Joshua Druce
Ex VP: David Antolik
Ex VP: George Basara
Ex VP: Joanne E Duggan
Ex VP: Rob Jorgenson
Ex VP: Thomas Kiral
Ex VP: Jim Mill

D-U-N-S 06-937-1193
S & W MANAGEMENT INC (MD)
PIZZA HUT
7070 Oakland Mills Rd, Columbia, MD 21046-1692
Tel (410) 720-6336 *Founded/Ownrshp* 1970
Sales 52.3MM[E] *EMP* 1,600
SIC 5812 Pizzeria, chain
Pr: Robert Schulze Jr
Ch Bd: Robert D Schulze Sr
Sec: John G Willias
VP: John F Schulze
Mktg Dir: Linda Schulze
Board of Directors: Anastasia W Simms

S A
See SAFE AUTO INSURANCE CO

S A C
See SAC CAPITAL ADVISORS LLC

D-U-N-S 07-775-9645
■ S A COMUNALE CO INC
SPRINKFAB
(*Suby of* EMCOR CONSTRUCTION SERVICES INC) ★
2900 Newpark Dr, Barberton, OH 44203-1050
Tel (330) 706-3040 *Founded/Ownrshp* 2015
Sales 199.0MM[E] *EMP* 700
SIC 1711

S A I
See SABIC AMERICAS INC

D-U-N-S 16-161-6842
S A ICTS-U INC
(*Suby of* ICTS INTERNATIONAL N.V.)
545 E John Carpenter Fwy, Irving, TX 75062-3931
Tel (972) 719-9180 *Founded/Ownrshp* 1995
Sales 88.9MM[E] *EMP* 2,805[E]
SIC 6719 Investment holding companies, except banks
CEO: Avraham Dan

S A M
See SURVEYING AND MAPPING LLC

S A S
See BAY ALARM CO

D-U-N-S 96-870-8581
S A TRINSEO
1000 Chesterbrook Blvd, Berwyn, PA 19312-1084
Tel (610) 240-3200 *Founded/Ownrshp* 2010
Sales 3.9MMM *EMP* 2,179
Tkr Sym TSE *Exch* NYS
SIC 2821 Plastics materials & resins
Pr: Christopher D Pappas
**Ch Bd:* Stephen M Zide
COO: Martin Pugh
CFO: John A Feenan
CFO: Barry J Niziolek
Treas: David Stasse
Sr VP: Marilyn N Horner
Sr VP: Timothy M Stedman
Sr VP: Hayati Yarkadas
VP: Jeff Denton

D-U-N-S 02-150-1325 IMP
S AND B ENGINEERS AND CONSTRUCTORS LTD
7825 Park Place Blvd, Houston, TX 77087-4697
Tel (713) 645-4141 *Founded/Ownrshp* 1991
Sales 10.1MMM[E] *EMP* 2,400
Accts Ernst & Young Llp Houston Tx
SIC 1629 8711 Chemical plant & refinery construction; Designing: ship, boat, machine & product
Ch: William A Brookshire
Pr: James G Slaughter Jr
Sr VP: Richard L Akin
Sr VP: Tommy H Collins
Sr VP: Charles R Reid
VP: Ronald Christy
VP: Mike Follett
VP: James Harrod
VP: K K Malone
VP: Frank Robertson
VP Bus Dev: Ken Collins

S AND S SUPPLIES AND SOLUTIONS
See S & STOOL & SUPPLY INC

D-U-N-S 04-344-9701
S B BALLARD CONSTRUCTION CO (VA)
2828 Shipps Corner Rd, Virginia Beach, VA 23453-2920
Tel (757) 440-5555 *Founded/Ownrshp* 1978
Sales 118.2MM[E] *EMP* 260

SIC 1542 1771 Nonresidential construction; Concrete work; Foundation & footing contractor
Pr: Stephen B Ballard
**CFO:* Ann Mason
VP: Wayne Barrett
VP: Curtis Griffin
VP: Paul Littlefield
VP: Tim Patterson
VP: Mark Payne
VP: Chuck Smith
VP Opers: Darrell Polokonis

S B C
See SOUTHERN NEW ENGLAND TELEPHONE CO INC

S B H
See ST BARNABAS HOSPITAL

D-U-N-S 06-059-3316
S B INC (OR)
SHERMAN BROS HEAVY TRUCKING
32921 Diamond Hill Dr, Harrisburg, OR 97446-9738
Tel (541) 995-7751 *Founded/Ownrshp* 1956, 1976
Sales 110.7MM^E *EMP* 503
SIC 4213 4731 Contract haulers; Heavy machinery transport; Freight transportation arrangement
Pr: Barton Sherman
**Sec:* Jeff Gunnarson
VP: Jeff Hannum
MIS Dir: Joe Arndt
VP Opers: Jerry Upchurch
Sfty Dirs: Don Thompson
Opers Mgr: Steve Chapman
Opers Mgr: Corey Moran

S B M
See SBM SITE SERVICES LLC

D-U-N-S 02-446-4505 IMP
S BAUCOM NURSERY CO
10020 John Russell Rd, Charlotte, NC 28213-5208
Tel (704) 596-3220 *Founded/Ownrshp* 1996
Sales 262.0MM^E *EMP* 170
SIC 0181 5193

D-U-N-S 04-470-2991 IMP
S BERTRAM INC
BERTRAM FOODS
3401 Tremley Point Rd, Linden, NJ 07036-3577
Tel (908) 862-8200 *Founded/Ownrshp* 1952
Sales 87.5MM^E *EMP* 87^E
SIC 5143 5141 Dairy products, except dried or canned; Groceries, general line
Ch Bd: Charles Bertram
VP Sls: Jerry Bertram
Sls Mgr: Juda Schwartz

D-U-N-S 17-448-7702 IMP
S BLACK TIRE SERVICE INC
BLACKS TIRE & AUTO SERVICE
30 Bitmore Rd, Whiteville, NC 28472-4928
Tel (910) 642-4123 *Founded/Ownrshp* 1986
Sales 254.8MM^E *EMP* 510
SIC 5531 5014

S C C
See SENIOR CARE COMMUNITIES INC

D-U-N-S 94-642-1799
S C INTERNATIONAL SERVICES INC
(*Suby of* LSG SKY CHEFS USA INC) ★
6191 N State Highway 161 # 100, Irving, TX 75038-2290
Tel (972) 793-9000 *Founded/Ownrshp* 1995
Sales 523.5MM^E *EMP* 7,300^E
SIC 5812 5962 Caterers; Contract food services; Coffee shop; Merchandising machine operators
Ch Bd: Hahns Rech
**CFO:* Patrick Tolbert
**Sr VP:* Randall Boyd

D-U-N-S 00-609-1417 IMP/EXP
S C JOHNSON & SON INC (WI)
SC JOHNSON PROFESSIONAL
1525 Howe St, Racine, WI 53403-2237
Tel (262) 260-2000 *Founded/Ownrshp* 1886
Sales 4.3MMM^E *EMP* 12,037
SIC 2842 2844 2879 2865 7342 7349 Floor waxes; Furniture polish or wax; Stain removers; Disinfectants, household or industrial plant; Shampoos, rinses, conditioners: hair; Shaving preparations; Face creams or lotions; Insecticides, agricultural or household; Exterminating products, for household or industrial use; Cyclic crudes & intermediates; Pest control in structures; Exhaust hood or fan cleaning; Air duct cleaning; Building maintenance, except repairs
Ch Bd: H F Johnson Jr
Pr: Frederick Martin
Pr: Joseph T Mallof
CFO: Neal Nottleson
Ex VP: John D Crabb
Ex VP: Mark H Eckhardt
Ex VP: Richard E Posey
Sr VP: James F Dimarco
Sr VP: Robert C Hart
Sr VP: Darcy D Massey
Sr VP: W Lee McCollum
Sr VP: M Garvin Shankster
VP: Larry L Beebe
VP: April Boisseau
VP: William J Freund
VP: Charles J Goldthwaite Jr
VP: David C Henry
VP: Cheryl Ho
VP: Scott Johnson
VP: Gayle P Kosterman
VP: Mark Miller

D-U-N-S 18-378-8991 EXP
S C S INC
SUNNYVALE SEAFOOD
(*Suby of* ZHANJIANG GUOLIAN AQUATIC PRODUCTS CO., LTD.)
2910 Faber St, Union City, CA 94587-1214
Tel (510) 477-0008 *Founded/Ownrshp* 2012
Sales 140.0MM *EMP* 47^E
SIC 5146 5147 Seafoods; Meats, fresh
CEO: Kevin Tang
Opers Mgr: Steven Zhao
Opers Mgr: Steven Zhou

D-U-N-S 03-740-7558
S C SAN ANTONIO INC
SOUTHWEST GENERAL HOSPITAL
(*Suby of* IASIS HEALTHCARE CORP) ★
7400 Barlite Blvd, San Antonio, TX 78224-1308
Tel (210) 921-2000 *Founded/Ownrshp* 1999
Sales 157.0MM *EMP* 225
SIC 8062 General medical & surgical hospitals
CEO: P Craig Desmond
**CFO:* Linda Kirks
Ofcr: Sara Rubio
Ofcr: Becky Tymrak
Dir OR: J Leal
Dir Inf Cn: Loretta Kent
Dir Case M: Chris Wagner
Chf Nrs Of: Pam Flentge
Netwrk Mgr: Joel Olivo
Plnt Mgr: Russell Bolner
HC Dir: Glenda Babineaux

S C U
See PRESIDENT AND BOARD OF TRUSTEES OF SANTA CLARA COLLEGE

S D I
See SOHEL DISTRIBUTORS NY LLC

S D I
See STANDARD DRYWALL INC

D-U-N-S 36-170-6708 IMP/EXP
S D WARREN CO
SAPPI FINE PAPER NORTH AMERICA
(*Suby of* SAPPI LTD)
255 State St Fl 4, Boston, MA 02109-2618
Tel (617) 423-7300 *Founded/Ownrshp* 1994
Sales 548.4MM^E *EMP* 2,321
SIC 2679 2674 2672 2621 Paper products, converted; Bags: uncoated paper & multiwall; Coated paper, except photographic, carbon or abrasive; Paper mills
Pr: Mark Gardner
**CFO:* Annette Luchene
Ofcr: Steve Binnie
VP: Michael Hall
**VP:* Sarah G Manchester
**VP:* Jennifer Miller
**VP:* Robert Weeden
Mng Dir: Bob Bertolami
Mng Dir: Flavio Ignacio
Mng Dir: Hugh Martin
CIO: James Fickett

S E D
See SED INTERNATIONAL INC

S E H
See SHORT-ELLIOTT-HENDRICKSON INC

S E H AMERICA
See SHIN-ETSU HANDOTAI AMERICA INC

S F
See SAINT FRANCIS HOSPITAL - BARTLETT INC

S F A
See STEPHEN F AUSTIN STATE UNIVERSITY

D-U-N-S 08-386-3159
S F ADMINISTRATORS INC
(*Suby of* ASSOCIATED THIRD PARTY ADMINISTRATORS INC)
642 Harrison St 306, San Francisco, CA 94107-1396
Tel (415) 777-3707 *Founded/Ownrshp* 1983
Sales NA *EMP* 35
SIC 6411 Insurance adjusters
Pr: Tom Weston
**Ch:* John Sweeney

S F M
See SFM MUTUAL INSURANCE CO

S F W
See SHOPPERS FOOD WAREHOUSE CORP

D-U-N-S 00-325-6427
S FREEDMAN & SONS INC
3322 Pennsy Dr, Landover, MD 20785-1626
Tel (301) 322-6400 *Founded/Ownrshp* 1934
Sales 162.8MM^E *EMP* 155
SIC 5113 5087 Industrial & personal service paper; Janitors' supplies
Pr: Mark Freedman
CFO: J J Thompson
**Sec:* Louis Sacks
**Ex VP:* Barry Perlis
MIS Dir: Robert Brown
Sales Exec: Jim Bortz
Board of Directors: Eileen Freedman, Linda Perlis

S H A
See SPECIALTY HOSPITAL OF AMERICA LLC

D-U-N-S 87-875-9240 IMP
S I L INC
JACK LINK'S BEEF JERKY
39210 221st St, Alpena, SD 57312-5402
Tel (605) 849-8800 *Founded/Ownrshp* 1994
Sales 96.1MM^E *EMP* 550
SIC 2013 Sausages & other prepared meats
Pr: Jack Link
**Ex VP:* Terry Smith
Sfty Mgr: Carl Kappel

S I T I
See SHELL INFORMATION TECHNOLOGY INTERNATIONAL INC

D-U-N-S 02-915-4101
S J AMOROSO CONSTRUCTION CO INC
390 Bridge Pkwy, Redwood City, CA 94065-1061
Tel (650) 654-1900 *Founded/Ownrshp* 1995
Sales 184.7MM^E *EMP* 400
SIC 1542 Commercial & office building contractors
Ch Bd: Dana McManus
**Pr:* Gilbert J Amoroso
VP: Robert Erskine
Exec: Mike Cleveland
Snr PM: Victoria Cotter
Snr PM: Bob Throckmorton

D-U-N-S 06-385-8500
S J FUEL CO INC
601 Union St, Brooklyn, NY 11215-1033
Tel (718) 855-6060 *Founded/Ownrshp* 1935
Sales 190.0MM *EMP* 35
SIC 5983 1711 Fuel oil dealers; Mechanical contractor
Pr: Constantine D'Arco
**Sec:* Joseph D'Arco
**VP:* Pete D'Arco

D-U-N-S 82-899-1153
S J LOUIS CONSTRUCTION OF TEXAS LTD
520 S 6th Ave, Mansfield, TX 76063-2301
Tel (817) 477-0320 *Founded/Ownrshp* 1998
Sales 110.4MM^E *EMP* 200^E
Accts Kern Dewenter Viere Ltd St
SIC 1623 Water & sewer line construction
Pt: James Schueller
Pt: Les Whiteman

D-U-N-S 02-210-0119
S J SMITH CO INC
S J SMITH WELDING SUPPLY
3707 W River Dr, Davenport, IA 52802-2411
Tel (563) 324-5237 *Founded/Ownrshp* 1950
Sales 83.4MM^E *EMP* 145
SIC 5169 5084 5999 Oxygen; Acetylene; Carbon dioxide; Welding machinery & equipment; Welding supplies
**VP:* John Hanlon
VP: Robin Saklar

S J SMITH WELDING SUPPLY
See S J SMITH CO INC

S J W
See SAN JOSE WATER CO

S K
See SERVICE KING MANUFACTURING INC

S K H WHOLESALE DISTRIBUTORS
See SKH MANAGEMENT CO

D-U-N-S 06-122-3269 IMP/EXP
S KATZMAN PRODUCE INC (NY)
Row A 153 157 Hnts Pt Mkt, Bronx, NY 10474
Tel (718) 991-4700 *Founded/Ownrshp* 1945, 1976
Sales 153.8MM^E *EMP* 260^E
SIC 5148 Fresh fruits & vegetables
Pr: Stephen Katzman
Exec: Ian Korr

S L
See SUPERIOR LUBRICANTS CO INC

S L E M C O
See SOUTHWEST LOUISIANA ELECTRIC MEMBERSHIP CORP

S M & P UTILITY RESOURCES
See USIC LOCATING SERVICES LLC

S M C
See SPECIALTY MFG CO

S M C
See SMART LIVING CO

S M C
See SERVICES MANAGEMENT CORP

S M C
See SCIENTIFIC MOLDING CORP LTD

S M C P S
See ST MARYS COUNTY PUBLIC SCHOOLS

D-U-N-S 00-780-2981
S M D C ST MARYS DULUTH CLINIC HEALTH SYSTEM HOSPICE & PALLIATIVE CARE
407 E 3rd St, Duluth, MN 55805-1950
Tel (218) 786-4020 *Founded/Ownrshp* 2001
Sales 73.2MM^E *EMP* 6,000
SIC 8062 General medical & surgical hospitals

S M I
See SPECIALTY MINERALS INC

S M S
See SCRAP METAL SERVICES LLC

S M U
See SOUTHERN METHODIST UNIVERSITY INC

S M U D
See SACRAMENTO MUNICIPAL UTILITY DISTRICT

D-U-N-S 00-285-1392
S M WILSON & CO
2185 Hampton Ave, Saint Louis, MO 63139-2904
Tel (314) 645-9595 *Founded/Ownrshp* 1989
Sales 262.0MM *EMP* 300
SIC 1541 1542

S N F
See SNF HOLDING CO

S O R T A
See SOUTHWEST OHIO REGIONAL TRANSIT AUTHORITY

S O S FUELS DIV
See M SPIEGEL & SONS OIL CORP

S P D I
See SUPERIOR PRODUCTS DISTRIBUTORS INC

D-U-N-S 36-123-6169 IMP
S P INDUSTRIES INC
SP SCIENTIFIC
(*Suby of* HARBOUR GROUP LTD) ★
935 Mearns Rd, Warminster, PA 18974-2811
Tel (215) 672-7800 *Founded/Ownrshp* 2015
Sales 209.5MM^E *EMP* 634
SIC 3826 3585 7699 3821 Instruments measuring thermal properties; Differential thermal analysis instruments; Refrigeration & heating equipment; Evaporative condensers, heat transfer equipment; Industrial machinery & equipment repair; Laboratory apparatus & furniture
Pr: Bill Downs
**COO:* Brian Wright
**CFO:* Mike Bonner
**Ex VP:* Ian Whitehall
VP: Ted Sutherland
Genl Mgr: Jay Oakley
Genl Mgr: Mary Seto
IT Man: Eric L Kratschmer
IT Man: Eric Kratschmer
Opers Mgr: Robert Weise
Plnt Mgr: Ron Petersen

S P L
See SOUTHERN PETROLEUM LABORATORIES INC

S P P D
See CREATIVE FOAM CORP

D-U-N-S 00-797-6384 IMP/EXP
■ **S P RICHARDS CO** (GA)
(*Suby of* GENUINE PARTS CO) ★
6300 Highlands Pkwy Se, Smyrna, GA 30082-7231
Tel (770) 434-4571 *Founded/Ownrshp* 1848, 1975
Sales 1.6MMM *EMP* 2,000
SIC 5112 5021 Office supplies; Manifold business forms; Stationery; Office furniture
Ch Bd: Wayne Beacham
**CFO:* J Philip Welch
Div VP: Ray Sreca
Sr VP: Steve Lynn
VP: Lester Christian
VP: Bob Kelly
VP: Henry Martin
VP: Donald C Mikolasy
VP: Craig Miller
VP: Gregory L Nissen
VP: Jim O'Brien

S P S
See SELECT PORTFOLIO SERVICING INC

S P X
See MARLEY CO LLC

S R A
See SRA INTERNATIONAL INC

S R M
See SPECIALTY ROLLED METALS LLC

S R U
See SLIPPERY ROCK UNIVERSITY

S S
See SHULTZ STEEL CO

S S F
See SSF IMPORTED AUTO PARTS LLC

S S I
See SURVEY SAMPLING INTERNATIONAL LLC

S S I
See SCHAEFER SYSTEMS INTERNATIONAL INC

S S I CONSTRUCTION MATERIALS
See SILICONE SPECIALTIES INC

D-U-N-S 03-500-9333
S S K CONSTRUCTORS JV
150 Meadowlands Pkwy Fl 3, Secaucus, NJ 07094-2304
Tel (201) 867-5070 *Founded/Ownrshp* 2010
Sales 125.0MM *EMP* 70
SIC 1622 Highway construction, elevated; Bridge construction; Tunnel construction
Genl Pt: Anthony Delvescovo
Pt: Kiewit Infrastructure Corp
Pt: Schiavone C LLC
Treas: Joe Patti

D-U-N-S 00-190-3889
S S KEMP & CO
TRIMARK SS KEMP
(*Suby of* TRIMARK UNITED EAST) ★
4567 Willow Pkwy, Cleveland, OH 44125-1052
Tel (216) 271-7062 *Founded/Ownrshp* 1926
Sales 109.1MM^E *EMP* 185^E
SIC 5046 Commercial cooking & food service equipment
Ch: Howard Fishman
**Pr:* Mark Fishman
**VP:* Steven Fishman
Off Mgr: Shannon Marchionda
Mktg Mgr: Stacey Cassidy
Manager: Carl Fazio
Manager: Doug Metzner
Sales Asso: Earl Bailey
Sales Asso: Rosie Puchalski
Sales Asso: Kristen Salay

S ST
See SYSTEMS & SERVICES TECHNOLOGIES INC

D-U-N-S 02-866-4076 EXP
S STAMOULES INC
STAMOULES PRODUCE CO
904 S Lyon Ave, Mendota, CA 93640-9735
Tel (559) 655-9777 *Founded/Ownrshp* 1992
Sales 100.0MM *EMP* 1,000
SIC 0723 Fruit (fresh) packing services; Vegetable packing services
Pr: Peggy Stefanopoulos
**Treas:* Chrisopher S Stefanopoulos
**VP:* Danny Stefanopoulos
**VP:* Tom Stefanopoulos

S T C
See STARK TRUSS CO INC

S T I
See SMITH TURF & IRRIGATION LLC

S T V
See STV GROUP INC

D-U-N-S 02-481-9682
S T WOOTEN CORP (NC)
3801 Black Creek Rd Se, Wilson, NC 27893-9568
Tel (252) 637-4294 Founded/Ownrshp 1956
Sales 586.2MM^E EMP 800
SIC 1611 3273 1623 General contractor, highway & street construction; Highway & street paving contractor; Grading; Resurfacing contractor; Ready-mixed concrete; Water main construction; Sewer line construction
Pr: Seth T Wooten Jr
*CFO: Keith H Merrick
*Ex VP: Nancy W Hammock
Ex VP: Nancy Hammock
*VP: Jonathan K Bivens
*VP: Henry D Butts Jr
*VP: Brian F Gurganus
*VP: Gregory N Nelson
*VP: George R Stickland
*VP: Richard E Vick
*VP: Christopher Wooten
Board of Directors: Nancy W Hammock, Seth T Wooten

S U S
See SERVICES FOR UNDERSERVED INC

S U U
See SOUTHERN UTAH UNIVERSITY FOUNDATION

S W R I
See SOUTHWEST RESEARCH INSTITUTE INC

D-U-N-S 03-773-5479
S W RODGERS CO INC
5816 Wellington Rd, Gainesville, VA 20155-1669
Tel (703) 591-8400 Founded/Ownrshp 1980
Sales 183.4MM^E EMP 750
SIC 1611 1799 6552 1771 1623 General contractor, highway & street construction; Building site preparation; Subdividers & developers; Concrete work; Water, sewer & utility lines
CEO: Steven W Rodgers
*Pr: Paul Kurt Rodgers
*CFO: Chris Jones
*Sec: Reta Rodgers

S W S
See SWS RE-DISTRIBUTION CO INC

S&B ENGINEERS AND CONSTRUCTORS
See S & B HOLDINGS LTD

D-U-N-S 06-108-9319 IMP/EXP
S&B INDUSTRIAL MINERALS NORTH AMERICA INC
(Suby of PERLITE INSTITUTE INC) ★
100 Mansell Ct E Ste 200, Roswell, GA 30076-4860
Tel (610) 647-1123 Founded/Ownrshp 1999, 2015
Sales 505.3MM^E EMP 49
SIC 5052 Coal & other minerals & ores
CEO: Gilles Michel
Pr: Efthimios O Vidalis

D-U-N-S 15-938-4721
S&C RESALE CO
(Suby of JBS USA HOLDINGS LLC) ★
1770 Promontory Cir, Greeley, CO 80634-9039
Tel (970) 506-8000 Founded/Ownrshp 2002
Sales 136.5MM^E EMP 39^E
SIC 5147 5421 Meats & meat products; Meats, cured or smoked; Meat & fish markets
CEO: Don Jackson
*Pr: John N Simons Jr
VP: Marshall Ernst
*VP: Dan V Halstrom

D-U-N-S 08-035-7423
S&D COFFEE HOLDING CO
(Suby of COTT CORPORATION)
300 Concord Pkwy S, Concord, NC 28027-6702
Tel (704) 782-3121 Founded/Ownrshp 2016
Sales 25.3MM^E EMP 1,100^E
SIC 6719 2095 5149 2086 Investment holding companies, except banks; Roasted coffee; Coffee, green or roasted; Tea; Specialty food items; Tea, iced: packaged in cans, bottles, etc.
CEO: Alan P Davis
Pr: C Ron Hinson
Sr VP: John W Robinson

D-U-N-S 79-006-2392
S&ME INC
3201 Spring Forest Rd, Raleigh, NC 27616-2821
Tel (919) 872-2660 Founded/Ownrshp 1992
Sales 133.5MM EMP 1,115
Accts Mcgladrey Llp Raleigh Nc
SIC 8711 Engineering services
Pr: Randall A Neuhaus
CFO: Bruce L Altstaetter
VP: Allen L Chestnut
VP: John 'brad' McLester
VP: M Howard Perry
Brnch Mgr: Jim McGirl

D-U-N-S 00-121-3206 EXP
▲ S&P GLOBAL INC (NY)
55 Water St Ste Conc2, New York, NY 10041-0016
Tel (212) 438-1000 Founded/Ownrshp 1888
Sales 5.3MMM EMP 20,400
Accts Ernst & Young Llp New York N
Tkr Sym SPGI Exch NYS
SIC 7323 6282 Credit reporting services; Commercial (mercantile) credit reporting bureau; Investment advice; Investment advisory service
Pr: Douglas L Peterson
Pr: John L Berisford
Pr: Michael Chinn
Pr: Martin Fraenkel
Pr: Imogen Dillon Hatcher
CEO: Alex J Matturri Jr
CEO: Ashu Suyash
CFO: Jack F Callahan Jr
CFO: Robert J Mackay
Ex VP: Courtney Geduldig
Ex VP: France M Gingras
Ex VP: Paul Sheard
VP: Gavin Chow
VP: Rosalind R Danner
VP: Geoffrey Dodge
VP: Michael Haddad
VP: Maryann Johnston
VP: Chip Merritt
VP: Anand Sahasram
Board of Directors: Richard E Thornburgh, Winfried Bischoff, Hilda Ochoa-Brillembourg, William D Green, Charles E Haldeman Jr, Rebecca Jacoby, Maria R Morris, Michael Rake, Edward B Rust Jr, Kurt L Schmoke

D-U-N-S 78-547-6016
S&R COMPRESSION LLC
4234 S Jackson Ave, Tulsa, OK 74107-7038
Tel (918) 447-1947 Founded/Ownrshp 2007
Sales 110.2MM^E EMP 164^E
SIC 5046 Commercial equipment
Ofcr: Venz Craddock
Sfty Dirs: Holly Fisher
Prd Mgr: Jerry Shackelford

D-U-N-S 06-982-7116
S&S ACTIVEWEAR LLC
581 Territorial Dr, Bolingbrook, IL 60440-3543
Tel (630) 679-9940 Founded/Ownrshp 1988
Sales 193.2MM^E EMP 50^E
SIC 5136 Men's & boys' outerwear
Sales Exec: Kari Caruso
Sales Exec: Mike Hanks
Manager: Blaise David
Sls Mgr: Mark Ketchem

S&S AUTOMOTIVE GROUP
See S & S AUTOMOTIVE INC

D-U-N-S 07-834-2296
S&S CULINARY MANAGEMENT LLC (GA)
(Suby of METZ CULINARY MANAGEMENT INC) ★
2 Woodland Dr, Dallas, PA 18612-9159
Tel (570) 675-8100 Founded/Ownrshp 2011
Sales 10.5MM^E EMP 1,498^E
SIC 5812 Concessionaire; Contract food services
*VP Opers: Grant Bennett

D-U-N-S 00-715-0212
S&S QUALITY MEATS LLC
FANESTIL MEATS
1542 S Highway 99, Emporia, KS 66801-7765
Tel (620) 342-6354 Founded/Ownrshp 1942
Sales 110.0MM EMP 65
SIC 2011 2013 Meat packing plants; Sausages & other prepared meats

D-U-N-S 15-513-6997
S&S STEEL SERVICES INC
444 E 29th St, Anderson, IN 46016-5319
Tel (765) 622-4545 Founded/Ownrshp 1986
Sales 155.7MM^E EMP 120
SIC 5051 3316

D-U-N-S 11-601-5140
▲ S&T BANCORP INC
800 Philadelphia St, Indiana, PA 15701-3908
Tel (800) 325-2265 Founded/Ownrshp 1983
Sales NA EMP 1,067
Tkr Sym STBA Exch NGS
SIC 6022 State commercial banks
Pr: Todd D Brice
*Ch Bd: Charles G Urtin
Pr: Stephanie Kline
COO: David P Ruddock
CFO: Mark Kochvar
*V Ch Bd: Christine J Toretti
Chf Cred: Patrick J Haberfield
Ofcr: Ernest J Draganza
Ex VP: George Basara
Sr VP: Melanie A Lazzari
Sr VP: Malcolm E Polley
VP: Robert Coleman
VP: Dennis Scott

D-U-N-S 03-812-2818 IMP/EXP
▲ S&W SEED CO
7108 N Fresno St Ste 380, Fresno, CA 93720-2953
Tel (559) 884-2535 Founded/Ownrshp 1980
Sales 96.0MM EMP 77^E
Accts Crowe Horwath Llp San Francis
Tkr Sym SANW Exch NAS
SIC 0139 0723 Alfalfa farm; Seed cleaning
Pr: Mark S Grewal
*Ch Bd: Mark J Harvey
COO: Dennis C Jury
CFO: Matthew K Szot
*V Ch Bd: Grover T Wickersham
Board of Directors: Glen D Bornt, David A Fischhoff, Michael M Fleming, Alexander C Matina, Charles B Seidler, William S Smith, Mark Wong

S-3
See SOCIAL & SCIENTIFIC SYSTEMS INC

D-U-N-S 16-121-6812
■ S-L DISTRIBUTION CO INC
(Suby of SOH) ★
1250 York St, Hanover, PA 17331-4503
Tel (717) 632-4477 Founded/Ownrshp 1999
Sales 155.0MM^E EMP 502^E
SIC 5145 Snack foods
Pr: Carl Lee Jr
*Treas: Charles Good
*VP: Michael C Hare
Board of Directors: M A Warehime

D-U-N-S 94-789-0906
■ S-L SNACKS NATIONAL LLC
(Suby of SOH) ★
13024 Ballantyne Pl 350, Charlotte, NC 28273
Tel (704) 554-1421 Founded/Ownrshp 2010
Sales 100.6MM^E EMP 750^E
SIC 2052 Cookies

D-U-N-S 02-945-9475
■ S-L SNACKS NC LLC
(Suby of S-L SNACKS PN, LLC)
13024 Balntyn Corp Pl, Charlotte, NC 28277-2113
Tel (717) 632-4477 Founded/Ownrshp 2011
Sales 91.1MM^E EMP 850
SIC 2052 Cookies
Pr: Carl Lee Jr
CFO: Rick D Puckett
Treas: Troy W Bryce
VP: Margarett Wicklund
VP Mfg: Patrick S McInerney

D-U-N-S 00-300-6590 EXP
■ S-L SNACKS REAL ESTATE INC (PA)
SOH
(Suby of SNYDERS-LANCE INC) ★
1250 York St, Hanover, PA 17331-4503
Tel (717) 632-4477 Founded/Ownrshp 1946, 2010
Sales 380.2MM^E EMP 2,400
SIC 2052 2096 Pretzels; Potato chips & other potato-based snacks; Corn chips & other corn-based snacks; Tortilla chips
Pr: Carl E Lee
*Treas: Charles E Good
VP: Tyler Cook
VP: Greg Flickinger
*VP: Ed Good
Exec: Steve Rager
Ql Cn Mgr: Johnny Evangelisti
Counsel: Paul McCleary

S-MART
See SAVE MART SUPERMARKETS

D-U-N-S 05-607-6433
S-N-GO STORES INC
STOP N GO FOODS
2701 University Dr S, Fargo, ND 58103-6027
Tel (701) 235-7531 Founded/Ownrshp 1974
Sales 104.0MM EMP 300
Accts Fiebiger Swanson West & Co
SIC 5541 5411 Filling stations, gasoline; Convenience stores, chain
Pr: Sheldon Ellig
*Sec: Sheila Carney

D-U-N-S 05-608-9030
S/S/G CORP
AUTO STOP
512 2nd St Ste 12, Hudson, WI 54016-1581
Tel (715) 386-8281 Founded/Ownrshp 1971
Sales 124.0MM^E EMP 440
SIC 5541 5411 Gasoline service stations; Convenience stores, chain
Pr: Burton L Nordstrand
Treas: Larry Hopkins
VP: Gail Dahlstrom

D-U-N-S 04-101-0856
■ S1 CORP
(Suby of ACI WORLDWIDE INC) ★
705 Westech Dr, Norcross, GA 30092-3506
Tel (678) 966-9499 Founded/Ownrshp 2012
Sales 107.4MM^E EMP 1,670
SIC 7372 7371 Prepackaged software; Computer software development
CEO: Johann J Dreyer
*Pr: Jan Kruger
*Pr: Pierre Naude
*CFO: Paul M Parrish
*Sr VP: Gregory D Orenstein
VP: David Morem
Sftwr Eng: Subapriya Nagarajan
S&M/VP: Robby Link
Board of Directors: Dennis P Byrnes, Ram Gupta, M Douglas Ivester, Thomas P Johnson Jr, Gregory J Owens, John W Spiegel, Edward Terino

D-U-N-S 03-756-9966
S2 HR SOLUTIONS 1A LLC
ENGAGE PEO
3001 Executive Dr Ste 340, Clearwater, FL 33762-3392
Tel (727) 565-2950 Founded/Ownrshp 2011
Sales 45.0MM EMP 4,000
SIC 8721 Payroll accounting service
Counsel: Ryan Hollander

S3
See SYSTEM STUDIES & SIMULATION INC

SA IT SERVICES
See S & A COMPUTER SERVICES INC

D-U-N-S 80-257-7283 IMP/EXP
SA RECYCLING LLC
2411 N Glassell St, Orange, CA 92865-2705
Tel (714) 632-2000 Founded/Ownrshp 2007
Sales 900.0MM^E EMP 1,200
SIC 5093 Scrap & waste materials; Ferrous metal scrap & waste; Nonferrous metals scrap
Rgnl Mgr: Sandie Moyers
Genl Mgr: Moises Figueroa
Genl Mgr: Francisco Mendoza
Tech Mgr: Norma Mata
Sfty Dirs: Tamara Deiro
Trfc Dir: Eddie Reyes

D-U-N-S 62-088-5806 IMP
SAAB NORTH AMERICA INC
(Suby of SAAB AB)
20700 Loudoun County Pkwy # 152, Ashburn, VA 20147-2930
Tel (703) 406-7277 Founded/Ownrshp 1990
Sales 250.0MM^E EMP 850
SIC 5088 3699 7371 Aircraft & parts; Electrical equipment & supplies; Custom computer programming services
Pr: Jonas Hjelm
*CFO: Stephen L Herbert
*CFO: Steve Herbert
Ex VP: Michael Anderson
*Ex VP: Joseph Evans
Ex VP: Patrick Palmer
*Ex VP: Mark Pugliese
*Ex VP: Mark D Pugliese
Ex VP: Wes Walters
Sr VP: John Belanger
Sr VP: Sharon Spaulding

D-U-N-S 15-137-5359
SAAB SENSIS CORP
(Suby of SAAB AB)
85 Collamer Crossings, East Syracuse, NY 13057-8800
Tel (315) 445-0550 Founded/Ownrshp 1985
Sales 90.9MM^E EMP 350^E
SIC 3699 7371 3728

D-U-N-S 16-138-7360
SAAD ENTERPRISES INC
SAAD'S HEALTHCARE SERVICES
1515 S University Blvd, Mobile, AL 36609-2958
Tel (251) 343-9600 Founded/Ownrshp 1986
Sales 0.1 EMP 2,584
SIC 8082 5047 7352 5912 5621 8741 Home health care services; Visiting nurse service; Medical equipment & supplies; Medical equipment rental; Drug stores; Ready-to-wear apparel, women's; Management services
Pr: Dorothy S Saad
*Pr: Barbara S Fulgham
*VP: Henry B Fulgham
*VP: Alexander J Saad

SAAD'S HEALTHCARE SERVICES
See SAAD ENTERPRISES INC

D-U-N-S 01-104-6682 IMP
SAARGUMMI TENNESSEE INC
200 Commerce Way, Pulaski, TN 38478-8751
Tel (931) 363-1363 Founded/Ownrshp 2011
Sales 110.6MM^E EMP 401
SIC 3061 Automotive rubber goods (mechanical)
COO: Markus Whittmann
*CFO: Daniel Truschel
Exec: Guenther Kegel
Ex Dir: Joseph Carney

D-U-N-S 80-188-2838
SAATCHI & SAATCHI ADVERTISING GROUP INC
SAATCHI STCHI CMPTON WORLDWIDE
(Suby of PUBLICIS GROUPE S A)
355 Park Ave S, New York, NY 10010-1706
Tel (212) 229-6403 Founded/Ownrshp 1986
Sales 98.4MM^E EMP 900
SIC 7311 Advertising agencies
CEO: Kevin Roberts
Chf Mktg O: Christine Prins
VP: Bruce Andreini
VP: Lynn Rossi
VP: Michael Webb
Exec: Gerald Boyle
Exec: Janet Ronga
Creative D: Chris Moreira
Creative D: Jessica Nandi
Ex Dir: Louise Burke
Ex Dir: Kevin Honey

SAATCHI STCHI CMPTON WORLDWIDE
See SAATCHI & SAATCHI ADVERTISING GROUP INC

D-U-N-S 15-991-7780
SABA SOFTWARE INC
(Suby of VECTOR TALENT II LLC) ★
2400 Bridge Pkwy, Redwood City, CA 94065-1166
Tel (650) 581-2500 Founded/Ownrshp 2015
Sales 276.2MM^E EMP 735
SIC 7372 7371 Application computer software; Computer software development & applications
CEO: Pervez Qureshi
*Pr: Phil Saunders
*CFO: Edward Hayden
*CFO: Mark Robinson
*Chf Cred: Paige Newcombe
*Chf Cred: Srinivasa Ogireddy
*Chf Mktg O: Emily He
*Ofcr: John Hiraoka
*Ex VP: Peter E Williams III
Sr VP: Oliver Ghezi
Sr VP: Dev Ghoshal
Sr VP: Leo Hanna
*Sr VP: Hemanth Puttaswamy
Sr VP: Karen Steele
VP: Bruce Allen
VP: Yvette Cameron
VP: Vincent Castiglione
VP: Theresa Damato
VP: Jae Evans
VP: Jason Hoffman
VP: Rajani Kolli

D-U-N-S 08-779-3774
SABADELL UNITED BANK NATIONAL ASSOCIATION
(Suby of BANCO DE SABADELL SA)
1111 Brickell Ave, Miami, FL 33131-3112
Tel (305) 358-4334 Founded/Ownrshp 2010
Sales NA EMP 420
SIC 6021 National commercial banks
Ch Bd: Fernando P Rez-Hickman
*Ch Bd: Gerald Katcher
*Pr: Dwight Hill
*Pr: Orlando Roche
*CEO: Mario Trueba
*CFO: Elliot Nunez
*CFO: Jordi Torras
Ex VP: Nicolas Young
Sr VP: Alessandro Bartolini
VP: Alexandra Londono
*VP: Luz Zuluaga

D-U-N-S 01-400-2934
SABAL FINANCIAL GROUP LP
4675 Macarthur Ct Fl 15, Newport Beach, CA 92660-1875
Tel (949) 255-2660 Founded/Ownrshp 2011
Sales 90.5MM^E EMP 160^E
SIC 6282 Investment advice
Pt: R Patterson Jackson
CFO: Ron Warwick
CIO: Matthew Stoehr
Dir IT: Jason Childers
Genl Couns: Mark E Foster

D-U-N-S 03-405-8503
SABEL STEEL SERVICE INC
MONTGOMERY IRON & METAL
749 N Court St, Montgomery, AL 36104-2301
Tel (334) 265-6771 Founded/Ownrshp 1856
Sales 110.8MM^E EMP 233
Accts Wilson Price Barranco Blank
SIC 5088 5051 Transportation equipment & supplies; Metals service centers & offices

Pr: Keith Sabel
**CFO:* Phillip Brown
**Treas:* Vickey Sanford
**VP:* Fred Callahan
VP: Truman Wallace
Sls Mgr: Bruce Esco
Sales Asso: Brennan Blanchard
Sales Asso: Pam Nance
Sales Asso: Rhonda Parrish

D-U-N-S 11-601-3079 IMP/EXP
SABERT CORP
2288 Main St, Sayreville, NJ 08872-1476
Tel (800) 722-3781 *Founded/Ownrshp* 1982
Sales 104.2MM^E *EMP* 560
SIC 3089 Trays, plastic; Plates, plastic; Food casings, plastic
Pr: Albert Salama
Sr VP: Tom Pasqualini
VP: Gary Ziznewski
Mfg Dir: Ron Seidel
VP Mktg: Nicole McLaughlin

D-U-N-S 17-722-9960 IMP/EXP
SABIC AMERICAS INC
SAI
(*Suby of* SAUDI BASIC INDUSTRIES CORPORATION (SABIC))
2500 Citywest Blvd, Houston, TX 77042-3000
Tel (713) 532-4999 *Founded/Ownrshp* 1987
Sales 409.1MM^E *EMP* 600
SIC 5172 5169 Gases, liquefied petroleum (propane); Chemicals, industrial & heavy; Industrial chemicals
VP: John Dearborn
CFO: Jeffrey Hebert
Sr Cor Off: Cathryn Eldridge
Ofcr: Allen Sather
Exec: Todd Washburn
Genl Mgr: Khalid Al-Turairi
Genl Mgr: Abdulaziz Alahmadi
**Genl Mgr:* Kahalid Almazyed
Genl Mgr: Othman Ghamdi
Genl Mgr: Abdulaziz A Habib
Genl Mgr: James Joubert

D-U-N-S 60-372-7103 IMP/EXP
SABIC INNOVATIVE PLASTICS MT VERNON LLC
(*Suby of* SABIC INNOVATIVE PLASTICS US LLC) ★
1 Lexan Ln, Mount Vernon, IN 47620-9367
Tel (812) 838-4385 *Founded/Ownrshp* 2000
Sales 228.8MM^E *EMP* 1,342
SIC 2821 3087 3081 Plastics materials & resins; Custom compound purchased resins; Unsupported plastics film & sheet
Pr: Joseph Castrale
**VP:* Michael L Walsh
Exec: Susan Metcalf
Prgrm Mgr: Michael Davis
Genl Mgr: Sandeep Dhawan
Genl Mgr: Michael Gilbert
Sfty Mgr: Judy D'Agostino
Opers Mgr: Tom Gibbs
Ql Cn Mgr: Suzanna Morris
Snr PM: David Bell
Snr Mgr: Jon Zwingelberg

D-U-N-S 79-953-3617 IMP/EXP
SABIC INNOVATIVE PLASTICS US LLC
(*Suby of* SAUDI BASIC INDUSTRIES CORPORATION (SABIC))
1 Plastics Ave, Pittsfield, MA 01201-3697
Tel (413) 448-7110 *Founded/Ownrshp* 2007
Sales 6.5MMM^E *EMP* 11,000
SIC 5049 Scientific & engineering equipment & supplies
CEO: Keith J Smith
CFO: Judith Kapernaros
CFO: Gail Sookey
Ofcr: Laurie Gallagher
**Ex VP:* Mohamed H Al-Mady
VP: Greg Adams
**VP:* Gregory A Adams
**VP:* Prince Saud Bin Abdullah Bin T
VP: Cynthia Hashim
Comm Man: David Cameron
Comm Man: Susan Lebourdais

D-U-N-S 07-861-2482 EXP
SABIC US HOLDINGS LP
(*Suby of* SAUDI BASIC INDUSTRIES CORPORATION (SABIC))
1 Plastics Ave, Pittsfield, MA 01201-3697
Tel (413) 448-7110 *Founded/Ownrshp* 2007
Sales 118.7M *EMP* 11,000
SIC 2821 Plastics materials & resins

D-U-N-S 07-931-6883
SABIN ROBBINS CONVERTING CO LLC
455 E 86th St Apt 5e, New York, NY 10028-6486
Tel (513) 874-5270 *Founded/Ownrshp* 2013
Sales 168.9MM^E *EMP* 140^E
SIC 5111 Fine paper

D-U-N-S 06-670-6938 IMP
■ SABINE MINING CO
(*Suby of* NORTH AMERICAN COAL CORP) ★
6501 Fm 968 W, Hallsville, TX 75650-7800
Tel (903) 660-4200 *Founded/Ownrshp* 1980
Sales 154.6MM *EMP* 163
Accts Ernst & Young Llp Richmond V
SIC 1241 8711 1221 Mining services: lignite; Engineering services; Bituminous coal & lignite-surface mining
Ch Bd: Clifford Miercort
Pr: Rick J Ziegler
Treas: K Donald Grischow
Exec: Dave Liffing

D-U-N-S 00-790-9948 IMP
▲ SABINE OIL & GAS CORP
1415 Louisiana St # 1600, Houston, TX 77002-7490
Tel (832) 242-9600 *Founded/Ownrshp* 1916
Sales 337.2MM *EMP* 146^E
Tkr Sym SOGC *Exch* OTO
SIC 1311 Crude petroleum & natural gas; Natural gas production; Crude petroleum production

Ch Bd: David J Sembrooks
COO: R Todd Levesque
CFO: Michael D Magilton Jr
Sr VP: Cheryl R Levesque
VP: Lindsay Bourg
VP: Rob Reasoner
Opers Mgr: Kim Hockabout
Board of Directors: Thomas N Chewning, Jonathan F Foster, Alex T Krueger, Patrick R McDonald, Duane C Radtke, Brooks M Shughart, John Yearwood

D-U-N-S 07-873-1670
■ SABINE PASS LIQUEFACTION LLC
(*Suby of* CHENIERE ENERGY PARTNERS LP) ★
700 Milam St Ste 1900, Houston, TX 77002-2835
Tel (713) 375-5000 *Founded/Ownrshp* 2010
Sales 270.0MM^E *EMP* 888
SIC 4924 Natural gas distribution
Pr: R Keith Teague
**CFO:* Michael J Wortley
Board of Directors: Sean T Klimczak

D-U-N-S 83-073-4872
■ SABINE PASS LNG LP
(*Suby of* SABINE PASS LNG-LP LLC) ★
700 Milam St Ste 1900, Houston, TX 77002-2835
Tel (713) 375-5000 *Founded/Ownrshp* 2003
Sales 523.0MM *EMP* 642
SIC 4922 Natural gas transmission
Pr: R K Teague
Genl Pt: Sabine Pass LNG-GP LLC

D-U-N-S 07-848-5147 EXP
■ SABINE PASS LNG-LP LLC
(*Suby of* CHENIERE ENERGY INVESTMENTS LLC) ★
700 Milam St Ste 800, Houston, TX 77002-2835
Tel (713) 375-5000 *Founded/Ownrshp* 2005
Sales 523.0MM^E *EMP* 642^E
SIC 4922 Natural gas transmission

D-U-N-S 96-188-7341
SABMD LLC
EASTERNS AUTOMOTIVE GROUP
22705 Commerce Center Ct, Sterling, VA 20166-2036
Tel (703) 790-1000 *Founded/Ownrshp* 2003
Sales 131.4MM *EMP* 200
Accts Crumback & Associates Llc Col
SIC 5521 Automobiles, used cars only
Genl Mgr: Tim Atkin

D-U-N-S 80-632-5804 IMP
SABRA DIPPING CO LLC
(*Suby of* STRAUSS GROUP LTD)
777 Westchester Ave Fl 3, White Plains, NY 10604-3520
Tel (914) 372-3900 *Founded/Ownrshp* 2008
Sales 202.2MM^E *EMP* 700
SIC 2035 Spreads, sandwich: salad dressing base
CEO: Shali Shalit-Shoval
**CFO:* Chris Hall
Chf Mktg O: Eugenio Perrier
Ex VP: John Boes
Ex VP: Luciano Lopez-May
VP: Doug Pearson
CTO: Tulin Tuzel
Sfty Dirs: Brandon Williams
Opers Supe: Betsy Gibson
Opers Supe: Matthew Stowell
Opers Mgr: Mendy Weiss

D-U-N-S 96-479-9642
SABRA HEALTH CARE REIT INC
18500 Von Karman Ave # 550, Irvine, CA 92612-0504
Tel (949) 255-7100 *Founded/Ownrshp* 2010
Sales 238.8MM *EMP* 10^E
Accts Pricewaterhousecoopers Llp Ir
SIC 6798 Real estate investment trusts
CFO: Harold W Andrews Jr
COO: Nick Cafferillo
Chf Inves: Talya Nevo-Hacohen
Sr VP: Peter W Nyland
VP: Tri Tran
CTO: Galen Warren

SABRE COMMUNICATIONS
See SABRE INDUSTRIES INC

D-U-N-S 08-462-1382 IMP/EXP
SABRE COMMUNICATIONS CORP
(*Suby of* SABRE COMMUNICATIONS) ★
7101 Southbridge Dr, Sioux City, IA 51111-1000
Tel (712) 258-6690 *Founded/Ownrshp* 2006
Sales 308.8MM^E *EMP* 1,000
SIC 3663 3441 1731 Radio & TV communications equipment; Tower sections, radio & television transmission; Communications specialization
Pr: James D Mack

D-U-N-S 78-633-8199
▲ SABRE CORP
3150 Sabre Dr, Southlake, TX 76092-2199
Tel (682) 605-1000 *Founded/Ownrshp* 2006
Sales 2.9MMM *EMP* 9,100
Tkr Sym SABR *Exch* NGS
SIC 4724 7375 Travel agencies; On-line data base information retrieval
Pr: Thomas Klein
**Ch Bd:* Lawrence W Kellner
V Ch: Gregory T Webb
Pr: Alexander S Alt
Pr: Hugh W Jones
Pr: Sean Menke
CFO: Richard A Simonson
Ofcr: William G Robinson
Ex VP: George Gonzalez
Ex VP: Rachel A Gonzalez
Ex VP: Deborah Kerr
Sr VP: Traci Mercer
VP: Ricardo Carreon
VP: Dolly Wagner-Wilkins
Board of Directors: George Bravante Jr, Renee James, Gary Kusin, Greg Mondre, Judy Odom, Joseph Osnoss, Karl Peterson, Zane Rowe

D-U-N-S 16-144-4740
■ SABRE GLBL INC
SABRE TRAVEL NETWORK
(*Suby of* SABRE TRAVEL INFO NETWORK) ★
3150 Sabre Dr, Southlake, TX 76092-2199
Tel (682) 605-1000 *Founded/Ownrshp* 1996
Sales 1.0MMM^E *EMP* 6,700
SIC 7375 7371 7374 7389 8748 Information retrieval services; Custom computer programming services; Data entry service; Telemarketing services; Business consulting
CEO: Tom Klein
**Pr:* Alex Alt
Pr: James F Hardee
Pr: Mark E Nixon
COO: Stephen Fitzgerald
CFO: David Devonshire
**CFO:* Jeffery Jackson
Ex VP: Pamela B Strobel
Sr VP: Sara Garrison
Sr VP: Hugh Jones
**Sr VP:* Jay Jones
Sr VP: Dolly Wagner-Wilkins
VP: Coleen Beacom
VP: Sharon Hall
VP: Barb Kotowski
VP: Kyle Moore
VP: R Murphy
VP: Jae L Rangel
VP: Michel Shahwan
Comm Man: Kathryn Hayden

D-U-N-S 94-930-3598
■ SABRE HOLDINGS CORP
SABRE TRAVEL INFO NETWORK
(*Suby of* SABRE CORP) ★
3150 Sabre Dr, Southlake, TX 76092-2199
Tel (682) 605-1000 *Founded/Ownrshp* 2007
Sales 1.1MMM^E *EMP* 9,000
SIC 4724 Travel agencies
Pr: Tom Klein
Ch Bd: Larry Kellner
Pr: Scott Alvis
CFO: Barbara Sabre
CFO: Rick Simonson
CFO: Shane Wood
Treas: Jeffrey M Jackson
Ofcr: Deborah Kerr
Ofcr: Bill Robinson
Ex VP: David A Schwarte
Sr VP: Clinton Anderson
Sr VP: Wade Jones
Sr VP: Leslie A Price
VP: Barb Kotowski
Exec: Gail Brooslin
Comm Dir: Faith Kuczaj
Comm Dir: Gilbert Montez
Dir Bus: Stephen Carroll
Dir Bus: Jenny Mays
Comm Man: Kim Creaven
Board of Directors: Michael Sam Gilliland

D-U-N-S 00-464-9073 EXP
SABRE INDUSTRIES INC
SABRE COMMUNICATIONS
(*Suby of* KOHLBERG & CO) ★
8653 E Highway 67, Alvarado, TX 76009-4012
Tel (817) 852-1700 *Founded/Ownrshp* 2012
Sales 681.2MM^E *EMP* 1,040
SIC 3441 Tower sections, radio & television transmission
Pr: Peter Sandore
CFO: Timothy Rossetti
VP: Patrick Cochran
VP: Brian D Newberg
Genl Mgr: Carroll Baynard

SABRE TRAVEL INFO NETWORK
See SABRE HOLDINGS CORP

SABRE TRAVEL NETWORK
See SABRE GLBL INC

D-U-N-S 17-678-5590
SAC & FOX TRIBAL OFFICES
SAC AND FOX TRIBE
349 Meskwaki Rd, Tama, IA 52339-9634
Tel (641) 484-4678 *Founded/Ownrshp* 1857
Sales NA *EMP* 1,300
SIC 9532 Rural planning & development agency, government
Ch: Frank Blackcloud
**CFO:* Ram Dhanwada
**Treas:* Lavern Jefferson
**Treas:* Tony Waseskuk
**Ex Dir:* Larry Lasley
IT Man: Leslie Barrett

SAC AND FOX TRIBE
See SAC & FOX TRIBAL OFFICES

D-U-N-S 01-617-3368
SAC CAPITAL ADVISORS LLC
SAC
(*Suby of* SAC CAPITAL ADVISORS LP) ★
72 Cummings Point Rd, Stamford, CT 06902-7912
Tel (203) 890-2000 *Founded/Ownrshp* 1995
Sales 181.8MM^E *EMP* 629
SIC 6799 Investors
COO: Peter Avellone
CFO: Brian Cohen
VP: Evan Frey
Assoc Dir: Chris Bloechle
Assoc Dir: Billy Shaw
Assoc Dir: Jordana Upton
Snr Ntwrk: Dominick Vanacore
Dir IT: Dan Jackson
Netwrk Mgr: Frances Baldwin
Counsel: Christopher Rosado

D-U-N-S 78-935-7779
SAC CAPITAL ADVISORS LP
72 Cummings Point Rd, Stamford, CT 06902-7912
Tel (203) 890-2000 *Founded/Ownrshp* 2008
Sales 186.3MM^E *EMP* 629
SIC 6282 Manager of mutual funds, contract or fee basis
Ofcr: Steven Kansky
VP: David Adler
VP: Torin Garrison

VP: Jiten Reddy
VP: Salvatore Salituro
Assoc Dir: Erick Berkowitz
Assoc Dir: Joe Moccia
Telecom Ex: Eric Schneider
IT Man: David Kelly
Netwrk Mgr: Victor Melgar
Genl Couns: Peter Nussbaum

D-U-N-S 00-247-2566
SAC WIRELESS LLC (CA)
(*Suby of* NOKIA SOLUTIONS AND NETWORKS US LLC) ★
540 W Madison St Ste 1600, Chicago, IL 60661-2551
Tel (847) 944-1600 *Founded/Ownrshp* 2009, 2014
Sales 168.0MM^E *EMP* 750
SIC 8741 8742 Construction management; Business consultant
Pr: Bill Koziel
**COO:* Jason Caliento
**Ofcr:* Scott Pomykalski
**Ex VP:* Nestor Popowych
**Ex VP:* Darrel Walker
**VP:* Randy Steines
Off Admin: Melissa Weeks
**CTO:* Joe Sanzo

D-U-N-S 06-594-7616
SACHEM CENTRAL SCHOOL DISTRICT AT HOLBROOK
51 School St, Lake Ronkonkoma, NY 11779-2231
Tel (631) 471-1336 *Founded/Ownrshp* 1950
Sales 290.3MM *EMP* 2,500
Accts Toski & Co Pc Cpas William
SIC 8211 Public elementary school; Public junior high school; Public senior high school
Dir Sec: Wayne Wilson
MIS Dir: Matt Demeo
HC Dir: Gary Beutel
HC Dir: Lori Hewlett

D-U-N-S 00-811-7400 IMP/EXP
SACHEM INC
821 Woodward St, Austin, TX 78704-7418
Tel (512) 421-4900 *Founded/Ownrshp* 1983
Sales 95.8MM^E *EMP* 300
SIC 2869 Industrial organic chemicals
Pr: John Mooney
**CFO:* Ron Morse
**VP:* Richard Goodin
**VP:* Louis Hunt
VP: Tom Mooney
VP: Eric Riden
VP: Brett Rodgers
**VP:* Jerry Windisch
CTO: Craig Allen
Ql Cn Mgr: Vicki Peters
Mktg Mgr: Cyril Coppel

D-U-N-S 00-980-9773
SACHS ELECTRIC CO (MO)
SACHS SYSTEM
(*Suby of* S. C. SACHS COMPANY, INC)
1572 Larkin Williams Rd, Fenton, MO 63026-3009
Tel (636) 532-2000 *Founded/Ownrshp* 1925
Sales 271.2MM *EMP* 875
SIC 1731

SACHS SYSTEM
See SACHS ELECTRIC CO

D-U-N-S 78-415-8560
SACHSE CONSTRUCTION AND DEVELOPMENT CO LLC
1528 Woodward Ave Ste 600, Detroit, MI 48226-2038
Tel (313) 481-8200 *Founded/Ownrshp* 1991
Sales 146.0MM *EMP* 125
SIC 1542 1522 Commercial & office building, new construction; Residential construction
Pr: Todd Sachse
**COO:* Steven R Berlage
CFO: Debbie M Date
VP: Jeremy Gershonowicz
VP: Chris Gould
**VP:* Frank Guirlinger
**VP:* Jeffrey Katkowsky
VP: Richard B Roder
VP Opers: Jay McKee
Sfty Dirs: Doug Henderson
Snr PM: Jim Ferguson

SACK N SAVE
See FOODLAND SUPER MARKET LIMITED

D-U-N-S 06-949-8749
SACO INDUSTRIES INC
17151 Morse St, Lowell, IN 46356-1433
Tel (219) 690-9900 *Founded/Ownrshp* 1977
Sales 85.0MM^E *EMP* 370
SIC 2434 Wood kitchen cabinets; Vanities, bathroom: wood
Pr: Ronald Bergstrom
**Sec:* Paulette Bergstrom
VP Sls: Douglas Newlin

D-U-N-S 00-204-8575
SACRAMENTO AREA SEWER DISTRICT
10060 Goethe Rd, Sacramento, CA 95827-3553
Tel (916) 876-6000 *Founded/Ownrshp* 2008
Sales 300.4MM^E *EMP* 391
Accts Vavrinek Trine Day & Co Ll
SIC 4953 Rubbish collection & disposal
CFO: Joseph Maestretti
COO: Claudia Goss
**Prin:* Prabhaker Somavarapu
Genl Mgr: Lisa Voight
CIO: Diane Lee
IT Man: Shannon Alley
IT Man: Glen Iwamura
IT Man: Diane Livingston

SACRAMENTO BEE
See MCCLATCHY NEWSPAPERS INC

D-U-N-S 06-069-7109
SACRAMENTO CITY UNIFIED SCHOOL DISTRICT
5735 47th Ave, Sacramento, CA 95824-4528
Tel (916) 643-7400 *Founded/Ownrshp* 1854
Sales 189.1MM^E *EMP* 6,500

Accts Crowe Horwath Llp Sacramento
SIC 8641 Veterans' organization; Environmental protection organization; Boy Scout organization
**CFO:* Tom Barrinson
Dir Sec: Nina Delgadillo
Admn Mgr: Mary Prather
Mktg Dir: Amari Watkins
Schl Brd P: Roy Grimes
Teacher Pr: Cancy McArn
HC Dir: Victoria Flores

D-U-N-S 00-797-3530
SACRAMENTO HOUSING AND REDEVELOPMENT AGENCY
REDEVELOPMENT AGENCY OF THE CI
801 12th St, Sacramento, CA 95814-2947
Tel (916) 440-1390 *Founded/Ownrshp* 1946
Sales NA *EMP* 1,182
Accts Macias Gini & O Connell Llp S
SIC 9532 Land redevelopment agency, government
Ex Dir: Lashelle Dozier
Bd of Dir: Sheri Grassinger
Bd of Dir: Bern Wikhammer

D-U-N-S 00-923-5342 IMP
SACRAMENTO MUNICIPAL UTILITY DISTRICT
S M U D
6201 S St, Sacramento, CA 95817-1818
Tel (916) 452-3211 *Founded/Ownrshp* 1946
Sales 1.5MMM *EMP* 2,213
Accts Baker Tilly Virchow Krause Ll
SIC 4911 Electric services
CEO: Arlen Orchard
CFO: James A Tracy
**CFO:* Jim Tracy
Treas: Noreen Roche
Treas: Noreen Roche-Carter
VP: Brad Gacke
Prgrm Mgr: Michael Deangelis
Prgrm Mgr: Jaspal Singh
CIO: Linda Dyer
CIO: Dell Pruett
IT Man: David Bitter

D-U-N-S 00-801-6008
SACRAMENTO REGIONAL COUNTY SANITATION DISTRICT (CA)
SRCSD
10060 Goethe Rd, Sacramento, CA 95827-3553
Tel (916) 876-6000 *Founded/Ownrshp* 1973
Sales 348.1MM^E *EMP* 700
SIC 4959 Sanitary services
CFO: Joe Maestretti
**Prin:* Phil Serna

D-U-N-S 04-894-7139 IMP
SACRAMENTO REGIONAL TRANSIT DIST
1400 29th St, Sacramento, CA 95816-6406
Tel (916) 726-2877 *Founded/Ownrshp* 1955
Sales 106.2MM^E *EMP* 850
SIC 4111 Bus line operations; Commuter rail passenger operation
CEO: Mike Wiley
Treas: Brent Bernegger

D-U-N-S 15-541-7520
SACRED HEART HEALTH CARE SYSTEM INC
SACRED HEART HOME CARE SERVICE
421 Chew St, Allentown, PA 18102-3430
Tel (610) 776-4900 *Founded/Ownrshp* 2001
Sales 23.2MM *EMP* 1,000
Accts Withumsmithbrown Pc Morristown
SIC 8741 5912 Hospital management; Drug stores
Pr: John Nespoli
**CFO:* Thomas Regner
**VP:* Valerie Downing
**VP:* Atty Stephen Lanshe
**VP:* Angela Long
**VP:* Ann Molesevich
Pharmcst: Hal Gooch
Pharmcst: Remesh Patel
Snr Mgr: Leo Clouser

SACRED HEART HEALTH CLINIC
See SACRED HEART HOSPITAL OF HOSPITAL SISTERS-3RD ORDER OF ST FRANCIS

D-U-N-S 05-522-1865
SACRED HEART HEALTH SERVICES (SD)
AVERA SACRED HEART HOSPITAL
501 Summit St, Yankton, SD 57078-3855
Tel (605) 668-8000 *Founded/Ownrshp* 1897
Sales 108.3MM *EMP* 1,200
Accts Eide Bailly Llp Minneapolis
SIC 8062 8011 General medical & surgical hospitals; Offices & clinics of medical doctors
Pr: Doug Ekeron
Dir Vol: Carla Hummel
VP: Barry Graham
**VP:* Mike Healy
Exec: Laurie McKee
Exec: Terri Mingo
Exec: Lisa Schroeder
Comm Man: Jay Gravholt
**Prin:* Pamela J Rezac
Adm Dir: Thomas Viereck
Dir IT: Kristen Gross

D-U-N-S 07-946-4053 IMP
SACRED HEART HEALTH SYSTEM INC
(*Suby of* ASCENSION HEALTH) ★
5151 N 9th Ave, Pensacola, FL 32504-8721
Tel (850) 416-1600 *Founded/Ownrshp* 1915
Sales 725.1MM *EMP* 2,310
Accts Deloitte Tax Llp Cincinnati
SIC 8062 8011 Hospital, affiliated with AMA residency; Offices & clinics of medical doctors
Pr: Irene Kraus
Chf Rad: Franklin D Abbott Jr
Pr: Susan L Davis
CEO: Laura S Kaiser
CFO: Buddy Elmore
Treas: Mary P Winters
VP: Carol Schmidt
VP: Brenda Shea
VP: Kim Shrewsbury
Chf Nrs Of: Deanie Lancaster
Dir Sec: Bruce Boggan

SACRED HEART HOME CARE SERVICE
See SACRED HEART HEALTH CARE SYSTEM INC

SACRED HEART HOSPITAL
See WESTERN MARYLAND HEALTH SYSTEM REHAB

D-U-N-S 06-047-7064
SACRED HEART HOSPITAL INC
900 W Clairemont Ave, Eau Claire, WI 54701-5105
Tel (715) 717-3926 *Founded/Ownrshp* 1890
Sales 234.1MM *EMP* 1,010
SIC 8062 General medical & surgical hospitals
CEO: Julie Manas
Chf Rad: Thomas Edwards
COO: Faye Deich
CFO: David Nelson
Ofcr: Adam Nichol
Exec: Thomas Hassemer
Dir Inf Cn: Donna Moraska
Dir Case M: Joanne Lee
Dir Lab: Debra Bloom
Dir Rx: John V Voort
Chf Nrs Of: Lynn Frank

D-U-N-S 06-049-8904
SACRED HEART HOSPITAL OF ALLENTOWN
421 Chew St, Allentown, PA 18102-3406
Tel (610) 776-4500 *Founded/Ownrshp* 1975
Sales 101.1MM *EMP* 1,058
SIC 8062 8011 Hospital, affiliated with AMA residency; Offices & clinics of medical doctors
Pr: James Seitzinger
**Pr:* John Nespoli
**CFO:* Thomas Regner
**Ch:* Paul Huck
VP: Valerie Downing
VP: Ann Molesevich
Dir Risk M: Michelle Haupt
Dir Risk M: Lucia Williams
Dir Lab: Diane Guerrero
Dir Rx: Paul Marino
**Prin:* Frank Sparenvero

D-U-N-S 02-279-0152
SACRED HEART HOSPITAL OF HOSPITAL SISTERS-3RD ORDER OF ST FRANCIS
SACRED HEART HEALTH CLINIC
1110 Oak Ridge Dr, Eau Claire, WI 54701-6133
Tel (715) 717-4131 *Founded/Ownrshp* 2009
Sales 176.5MM *EMP* 2
Accts Kpmg Llp Columbus Oh
SIC 8099 Health & allied services
Prin: Patricia R Huettl

D-U-N-S 07-494-6419
SACRED HEART HOSPITAL OF SISTERS OF CHARITY INC (MD)
12500 Willowbrook Rd, Cumberland, MD 21502-6393
Tel (240) 964-7000 *Founded/Ownrshp* 1914, 1967
Sales 154.9MM *EMP* 900
Accts Ernst & Young Llp Baltimore
SIC 8062 General medical & surgical hospitals
Pr: Barry Ronan
**CFO:* Kimberly Repac
Ofcr: Garry Miller
VP: Karen Ashby
VP: James A Patterson
**VP:* Frank Pommet
VP: Kevin Turley
Ex Dir: William T Bradel
VP Opers: James Delaney
VP Opers: R K Turley
Nrsg Dir: Sue Lindsay

D-U-N-S 15-147-3808
SACRED HEART MEDICAL CENTER
PROVIDENCE HEALTH AND SERVICES
(*Suby of* PROVIDENCE HEALTH & SERVICES) ★
101 W 8th Ave, Spokane, WA 99204-2364
Tel (509) 455-3131 *Founded/Ownrshp* 1886
Sales 166.9MM^E *EMP* 4,074
SIC 8062 8071 Hospital, AMA approved residency; Medical laboratories
Ch: Mike Reilly
Dir Recs: Jill Condon
Dir Recs: Carman Gramling
V Ch: Gary Livingston
Pr: Dianna Hollingsowrth
**Pr:* Michael Wilson
**CEO:* Dianne Doyle
**CFO:* Dan Goggin
CFO: Skip Kriz
VP: Stephen Hopkins
**VP:* Ann Hurst
Dir Lab: Dee Holm
Dir Rad: Jodi L Bailey
Dir Rad: Greg J Balmforth
Dir Rad: Gary V Bell
Dir Rad: Philip R Chapman
Dir Rx: Patricia Sohns

D-U-N-S 07-539-3348
SACRED HEART UNIVERSITY INC
5151 Park Ave, Fairfield, CT 06825-1000
Tel (203) 371-7999 *Founded/Ownrshp* 1963
Sales 267.1MM *EMP* 800
Accts Blum Shapiro & Company Pc Cpas
SIC 8221 University
Pr: John J Petillo
Ofcr: Kenneth Siegel
**Sr VP:* Michael J Kinney
VP: Thomas Forget
Exec: Vieux Leilo
Dir Risk M: Joseph Carrier
Assoc Dir: Celia Cruz
Ex Dir: Paul J Healy
Ex Dir: Jaya Kannan
Ex Dir: Jeffrey Rumpf
Phys Thrpy: Suzanne Kittredge

D-U-N-S 03-242-2453
SADDLE CREEK CORP
SADDLE CREEK LOGISTICS SVCS
3010 Saddle Creek Rd, Lakeland, FL 33801-9638
Tel (863) 665-0966 *Founded/Ownrshp* 1966
Sales 462.8MM^E *EMP* 1,130
SIC 4225 General warehousing
Ch: David Lyons
**Pr:* Bruce Abels
**Pr:* Cliff Otto
**CFO:* Mark Cabrera
**Treas:* Constance Lyons
Ofcr: Tracy Brown
**Sr VP:* Tom Patterson
Sr VP: Duane Sizemore
VP: Ellison Blaylock
VP: George Childs
VP: Doug Johnston
**VP:* Darrel Lake
**VP:* Thomas D Lyons
VP: Butch Riggleman
**VP:* Thornton W Scott
**VP:* Scott Thornton
Exec: Nicole Brown

SADDLE CREEK LOGISTICS SVCS
See SADDLE CREEK CORP

SADDLEBACK COLLEGE
See SOUTH ORANGE COUNTY COMMUNITY COLLEGE DISTRICT

D-U-N-S 06-762-0237
SADDLEBACK MEMORIAL MEDICAL CENTER
MEMORIAL CARE MEDICAL CENTERS
(*Suby of* MEMORIAL CARE MEDICAL CENTERS) ★
24451 Health Center Dr, Laguna Hills, CA 92653-3689
Tel (949) 837-4500 *Founded/Ownrshp* 1983
Sales 337.2MM *EMP* 1,209
SIC 8062 8011 8093 8099 8071 8069 General medical & surgical hospitals; Medical centers; Diabetes specialist, physician/surgeon; Cardiologist & cardio-vascular specialist; Pediatrician; Rehabilitation center, outpatient treatment; Blood related health services; Medical laboratories; Cancer hospital; Maternity hospital; Orthopedic hospital
CEO: Steve Geidt
**Pr:* Barry Arbuckle
**CFO:* Adolfo Chanez
**CFO:* Aaron Coley
**Sr VP:* Rick Graniere
**Sr VP:* Karen Testman
VP Mktg: Kathy Painter
Surgeon: Steven Becker
Surgeon: Chirag Patel
Obsttrcn: Hiren Patel
Ansthlgy: Dorming Wong

D-U-N-S 08-558-9141
SADDLEBACK VALLEY UNIFIED SCHOOL DISTRICT
25631 Peter Hartman Way, Mission Viejo, CA 92691
Tel (949) 586-1234 *Founded/Ownrshp* 1972
Sales 189.4MM^E *EMP* 3,975
SIC 8211

D-U-N-S 02-323-0089 EXP
SADOFF & RUDOY INDUSTRIES LLP
SADOFF IRON & METAL
240 W Arndt St 272, Fond Du Lac, WI 54935-2237
Tel (920) 921-2070 *Founded/Ownrshp* 2007
Sales 99.6MM^E *EMP* 250
SIC 5093 Ferrous metal scrap & waste; Nonferrous metals scrap
Genl Pt: Mark Lasky
Pt: Bradfrod Lasky
Pt: Jason Lasky
Pr: Frank Villaire
VP: Bradford Lasky

SADOFF IRON & METAL
See SADOFF & RUDOY INDUSTRIES LLP

D-U-N-S 96-539-1563
SAE TOWERS HOLDINGS LLC
(*Suby of* KEC INTERNATIONAL LIMITED)
16945 Northchase Dr # 1910, Houston, TX 77060-2135
Tel (281) 763-2282 *Founded/Ownrshp* 2010
Sales 142.6MM *EMP* 1,103
SIC 6719 Investment holding companies, except banks
CEO: Stanley Breitweiser
CEO: Gus Cedeno
CEO: Luigi Ruggieri
CFO: Yasaswy Kothari

D-U-N-S 96-960-0910
SAEXPLORATION INC
NORTHERN EXPLORATION SERVICES
(*Suby of* SAEXPLORATION HOLDINGS INC)
8240 Sandlewood Pl # 102, Anchorage, AK 99507-3159
Tel (907) 522-4499 *Founded/Ownrshp* 2011
Sales 333.0MM^E *EMP* 2,000^E
SIC 1389 Oil field services
Pr: Beatty Brian
**Pr:* Brian Beatty
**CFO:* Brent Whiteley
**Ch:* Jeff Hastings
**Ex VP:* Mike Scott
**Ex VP:* Darin Silvernagle
Opers Mgr: Tom Ainsworth

D-U-N-S 00-602-0879 IMP/EXP
SAF-HOLLAND INC
SAF-HOLLAND USA
1950 Industrial Blvd, Muskegon, MI 49442-6114
Tel (231) 773-3271 *Founded/Ownrshp* 2002
Sales 396.0MM^E *EMP* 146
SIC 5013

D-U-N-S 10-347-3179 IMP/EXP
SAF-HOLLAND INC
SAF-HOLLAND USA
(*Suby of* SAF-HOLLAND GMBH)
1950 Industrial Blvd, Muskegon, MI 49442-6114
Tel (231) 773-3271 *Founded/Ownrshp* 1921
Sales 34.3MM^E *EMP* 1,078^E
SIC 3714 3715 3568 3537 3452 Motor vehicle parts & accessories; Trailer hitches, motor vehicle; Truck trailers; Power transmission equipment; Industrial trucks & tractors; Bolts, nuts, rivets & washers
CEO: Richard W Muzzy Jr
**Pr:* Jack Gisinger
**Pr:* Steffen Schewerda
**CEO:* Detlef Borghardt
**CFO:* Wilfried Trepels
**Sec:* Kenneth Haveman
**Ex VP:* Samuel A Martin
Sr VP: Timothy Hemingway
VP: Michael Oconnell
VP: James Sykes
VP: John Wieringa
Exec: Dean Davis

SAF-HOLLAND USA
See SAF-HOLLAND INC

SAF-HOLLAND USA
See SAF-HOLLAND INC

SAFARILAND
See BAE SYSTEMS AH INC

SAFARILAND GROUP
See SAFARILAND LLC

D-U-N-S 09-016-1188 IMP
SAFARILAND LLC
SAFARILAND GROUP
(*Suby of* MAUI ACQUISITION CORP) ★
13386 International Pkwy, Jacksonville, FL 32218-2383
Tel (904) 741-5400 *Founded/Ownrshp* 1997, 2012
Sales 803.9MM^E *EMP* 2,280
SIC 3842 3199 Bulletproof vests; Holsters, leather
CEO: Warren Kanders
Pr: Scott T O'Brien
VP: Don Dutton
VP: David Levy
Dir Risk M: John Willim
Genl Mgr: Wanda Moody
Snr Ntwrk: Mike Lindblom
QA Dir: Jose Hernandez
QA Dir: Gloria Larson
QA Dir: Steven Yeh
IT Man: Jacqueline Beasley

D-U-N-S 96-481-4441
SAFAVIEH INC
40 Harbor Park Dr, Port Washington, NY 11050-4602
Tel (516) 945-1900 *Founded/Ownrshp* 2007
Sales 300.0MM *EMP* 500
SIC 2273 5712 Rugs, hand & machine made; Furniture stores
Ch Bd: Mohsen Yaraghi

D-U-N-S 09-690-6185 IMP/EXP
SAFC BIOSCIENCES INC
SAFC BIOSCIENCES LENEXA
(*Suby of* MILLIPORE SIGMA) ★
13804 W 107th St, Lenexa, KS 66215-2008
Tel (913) 469-5580 *Founded/Ownrshp* 2005
Sales 178.4MM^E *EMP* 600
SIC 2836 Culture media
Pr: Rod Kelley
VP: Tom Beil
QA Dir: Daniel Reed
Mktg Mgr: Carolyne Bailey

SAFC BIOSCIENCES LENEXA
See SAFC BIOSCIENCES INC

D-U-N-S 78-958-8431
SAFE AUTO INSURANCE CO
S A
(*Suby of* SAFE AUTO INSURANCE GROUP INC) ★
4 Easton Oval, Columbus, OH 43219-6010
Tel (614) 231-0200 *Founded/Ownrshp* 1993
Sales NA *EMP* 780
SIC 6411 Insurance agents, brokers & service
CEO: Ronald H Davies
**CFO:* Greg Sutton
Sr VP: Tara Baxley
VP: Jon Trickey
Prin: Shawn M Flahive
Prin: Anne C Griffin
Prin: James A Yano
Software D: Jeremy Furr
Software D: Dave Pugh
Software D: David Robertson
Mktg Mgr: Jennifer Klausman
Board of Directors: Britt Beemer, Ronald Davies, William H Graves

D-U-N-S 14-747-9724
SAFE AUTO INSURANCE GROUP INC
4 Easton Oval, Columbus, OH 43219-6010
Tel (614) 231-0200 *Founded/Ownrshp* 1993
Sales NA *EMP* 901^E
SIC 6331 6411 Automobile insurance; Insurance agents, brokers & service
CEO: Ronald H Davies
Ch Bd: ARI Deshe
Ch Bd: Jon P Diamond
V Ch: Jonathan P Diamond
CFO: Gregory A Sutton
CFO: Gregory Sutton
Sr VP: Jack H Coolidge
Sr VP: Jon L Trickey
VP: April Miller
Exec: Sandra Newton

D-U-N-S 08-127-0613
SAFE CREDIT UNION
2295 Iron Point Rd # 100, Folsom, CA 95630-8767
Tel (916) 979-7233 *Founded/Ownrshp* 1940
Sales NA *EMP* 348
Accts Crowe Horwath Llp Sacramento
SIC 6062 State credit unions
CEO: Henry Wirz
Pr: James Allen
Pr: David Pope
Ofcr: Jayne Anderson
Ofcr: Jason Cruce
Ofcr: Bill Erb
Ofcr: Matt Glasco
Ofcr: Regina Lott
Ofcr: Lorraine Paniagua
Ofcr: Shelly Sanada
Ofcr: Brandi Schaefer
Ofcr: Leslie Shull
Ofcr: Chris Singh
Ofcr: Ryan Smith

Ofcr: Zach Steele
Ofcr: Karen Swanson
Ex VP: Mark Lovewell
Sr VP: Michael Webber
VP: Faith Galati
VP: Paul Hersek
VP: Paul Rigdon

D-U-N-S 01-354-7857
SAFE ENVIRONMENT BUSINESS SOLUTIONS INC (NY)
8 Revolutionary Rd, Ossining, NY 10562-5911
Tel (914) 741-1000 *Founded/Ownrshp* 2007
Sales 40.0MM *EMP* 2,000
SIC 7381 Security guard service
CEO: Robert Dinozzi
**CFO:* Frank Newton

D-U-N-S 07-917-6817
SAFE FLEET HOLDINGS LLC
6800 E 163rd St, Belton, MO 64012-5462
Tel (816) 318-8000 *Founded/Ownrshp* 2013
Sales 155.7MM^E *EMP* 574^E
SIC 3089 3448 Injection molded finished plastic products; Prefabricated metal buildings
Pr: John Knox
**Pr:* Jeff Hupka
**CFO:* Michael Plunkett
Mktg Mgr: Cameron Blain

D-U-N-S 19-688-4287 IMP
SAFE SKIES LLC
TSA LUGGAGE LOCKS
954 3rd Ave Ste 504, New York, NY 10022-2013
Tel (888) 632-5027 *Founded/Ownrshp* 2004
Sales 106.4MM^E *EMP* 1,627
SIC 3429 Locks or lock sets

D-U-N-S 82-583-5085
■ **SAFE-GUARD PRODUCTS INTERNATIONAL LLC**
(*Suby of* GOLDMAN SACHS) ★
2 Concourse Pkwy Ste 500, Atlanta, GA 30328-5584
Tel (404) 816-3221 *Founded/Ownrshp* 2012
Sales NA *EMP* 230^E
SIC 6411 Insurance agents, brokers & service; Property & casualty insurance agent
CEO: Randy Barkowitz
Pr: Dave Duncan
COO: Jardon Bouska
CFO: Bruce Herman
CFO: Jeff Koenig
Chf Mktg O: David Pryor
VP: Brian Potter
Sls Dir: Tony Catania

D-U-N-S 80-748-9943
SAFECO ADMINISTRATIVE SERVICES INC
(*Suby of* SAFECO CORP) ★
1001 4th Ave, Seattle, WA 98154-1119
Tel (206) 545-5000 *Founded/Ownrshp* 1987
Sales NA *EMP* 2,000
SIC 6411 Insurance agents, brokers & service
Pr: Mike McGavick

D-U-N-S 00-794-2675
SAFECO CORP (WA)
(*Suby of* LIBERTY MUTUAL GROUP INC) ★
1001 4th Ave Ste 800, Seattle, WA 98185-9083
Tel (206) 545-5000 *Founded/Ownrshp* 1929
Sales NA *EMP* 7,208
SIC 6411 6311 6321 6324 6351 Insurance agents, brokers & service; Life insurance carriers; Health insurance carriers; Group hospitalization plans; Fidelity or surety bonding
Ch: J Paul Condrin III
Pr: Kim Garland
**Pr:* Michael Hughes
**COO:* Matthew D Nickerson
**Treas:* James Tuite
Ex VP: R Eric Martinez Jr
Sr VP: Gary Fischer
**Sr VP:* Kris L Hill
VP: Donald Asher
**VP:* Donald J Deshaw
VP: Lizbeth Englund
VP: Neal Fuller
VP: Robert McNichols
VP: Gregory Sears
VP: Chuck Stone
Comm Dir: Crista Walker

D-U-N-S 00-794-3152
SAFECO INSURANCE CO OF AMERICA
(*Suby of* SAFECO CORP) ★
1001 4th Ave Ste 800, Seattle, WA 98185-9083
Tel (206) 545-5000 *Founded/Ownrshp* 1953
Sales NA *EMP* 7,000
SIC 6411 Insurance agents, brokers & service; Fire insurance underwriters' laboratories; Patrol services, insurance
Pr: Matthew Nickerson
Pr: Melody Brown
**Pr:* Micheal Sean McGavick
**Treas:* Steve Bauer
Ex VP: Greg Davenport
VP: Michele Brooks
VP: Kris Hill
VP: Ray Hughes
VP: Mike Robon
**VP:* James H Ruddy
VP: Kristina Smith
Board of Directors: Don Chapman, James W Ruddy

D-U-N-S 00-251-5260 IMP/EXP
■ **SAFEGUARD BUSINESS SYSTEMS INC**
(*Suby of* DELUXE CORP) ★
8585 N Stemmons Fwy, Dallas, TX 75247-3824
Tel (214) 640-3916 *Founded/Ownrshp* 1967
Sales 129.5MM^E *EMP* 350^E
SIC 7374 2759 5112 5045 Data processing service; Commercial printing; Business forms; Computers
Pr: John J Sorrenli
VP: Dave Hebda
VP: Gretchen Luchsinger
Off Mgr: Kathy Rubin
Mktg Mgr: Jacqueline Schmidt
**Genl Couns:* Michael Dunlap

D-U-N-S 10-388-8400
■ **SAFEGUARD HEALTH ENTERPRISES INC**
(*Suby of* METLIFE INC) ★
95 Enterprise Ste 100, Aliso Viejo, CA 92656-2605
Tel (949) 425-4300 *Founded/Ownrshp* 2008
Sales NA *EMP* 360
SIC 6324 Dental insurance
Ch Bd: Steven J Baileys DDS
**Pr:* James E Buncher
COO: Stephen J Baker
**CFO:* Dennis L Gates
**Sr VP:* Ronald I Brendzel
VP: Kenneth E Keating
Mktg Dir: Bruce Cacciapaglia

D-U-N-S 14-428-4754
SAFEGUARD INTERNATIONAL FUND LP
435 Devon Park Dr Ste 200, Wayne, PA 19087-1937
Tel (610) 254-4110 *Founded/Ownrshp* 1997
Sales 128.5MM^E *EMP* 900
SIC 6282 Manager of mutual funds, contract or fee basis
Prin: Heinz Schimmelbusch

D-U-N-S 61-954-3846
SAFEGUARD PROPERTIES LLC
(*Suby of* SAFEGUARD PROPERTIES MANAGEMENT LLC) ★
7887 Safeguard Cir, Cleveland, OH 44125-5742
Tel (216) 739-2900 *Founded/Ownrshp* 1990
Sales 209.6MM^E *EMP* 900
SIC 8741 7382 7381 Management services; Security systems services; Detective & armored car services
CEO: Alan Jaffa
**Ch Bd:* Robert Klein
**CFO:* Gregory Robinson
**CIO:* George Mehok
Software D: Scott Mason
VP Opers: Michael Greenbaum
VP Opers: George Pilla

D-U-N-S 07-864-5250
SAFEGUARD PROPERTIES MANAGEMENT LLC
7887 Hub Pkwy, Cleveland, OH 44125
Tel (216) 739-2900 *Founded/Ownrshp* 2012
Sales 280.0MM^E *EMP* 1,500
SIC 1522 Residential construction; Remodeling, multi-family dwellings
CEO: Alan Jaffa
Pr: Pat Hoffman
Comm Dir: Gretchen Fri

SAFELITE AUTOGLASS
See SAFELITE GROUP INC

SAFELITE AUTOGLASS
See SAFELITE GLASS CORP

D-U-N-S 16-963-8488 IMP/EXP
SAFELITE FULFILLMENT INC
(*Suby of* SAFELITE AUTOGLASS) ★
7400 Safelite Way, Columbus, OH 43235-5086
Tel (614) 210-9747 *Founded/Ownrshp* 2004
Sales 479.6MM^E *EMP* 2,650
SIC 5231 Glass
CFO: Douglas A Herron
VP: Mark A Smolik

D-U-N-S 18-050-1108 IMP
SAFELITE GLASS CORP
SAFELITE AUTOGLASS
(*Suby of* SAFELITE AUTOGLASS) ★
7400 Safelite Way, Columbus, OH 43235-5086
Tel (614) 210-9000 *Founded/Ownrshp* 2000
Sales 1.7MMM^E *EMP* 5,950
SIC 3231 Windshields, glass: made from purchased glass
Pr: Dan Wislon
Ch Bd: George T Haymaker Jr
Pr: Dan H Wilson
CFO: Douglas A Herron
Ofcr: Thomas M Feeney
Sr VP: Douglas R Maehl
Sr VP: Stephen B Micheli
Sr VP: Elizabeth A Wolszon
VP: Garth R Beck
VP: Ronald H Duncan
VP: Don Giles
VP: James A Hammerschmidt
VP: Andrew J Kipker
VP: Dino D Lanno
VP: Brian D O'Mara
VP: James R Randolph
VP: Randy Randolph
VP: William J Rapp
VP: John Sadler
VP: David P Stagner
VP: Poe A Timmons

D-U-N-S 14-588-2069 IMP/EXP
SAFELITE GROUP INC
SAFELITE AUTOGLASS
(*Suby of* BELRON SA)
7400 Safelite Way, Columbus, OH 43235-5086
Tel (614) 210-9000 *Founded/Ownrshp* 1947
Sales 2.3MMM^E *EMP* 13,000
SIC 7536 3231 6411 Automotive glass replacement shops; Windshields, glass: made from purchased glass; Insurance claim processing, except medical
CEO: Thomas Feeney
Pr: Michelle Beiter
Pr: Ron Duncan
Pr: Paul Groves
Pr: Kerry Hurff
Pr: Randy Randolph
Pr: Ed Sprigler
**CFO:* Douglas Herron
Ex VP: Thomas M Feeney
**Sr VP:* Renee Cacchillo
**Sr VP:* Natalie Crede
**Sr VP:* Dino Lano
**Sr VP:* Steve Miggo
VP: Garth Beck
VP: Chad Flowers
VP: Dan Loyal
VP: Darci Ross
VP: Gary Strain

VP: Scot Zajic
Exec: Amy Lindner

D-U-N-S 78-436-4502
SAFELITE SOLUTIONS LLC
(*Suby of* SAFELITE AUTOGLASS) ★
7400 Safelite Way, Columbus, OH 43235-5086
Tel (614) 210-9000 *Founded/Ownrshp* 2003
Sales 98.4MM^E *EMP* 3,500
SIC 8742 Management consulting services
Pr: Dan Wislon
CFO: Douglas A Jenny Cain
CFO: Douglas A Herron

D-U-N-S 96-344-4661
SAFENET HOLDING CORP
(*Suby of* VECTOR STEALTH HOLDINGS II LLC) ★
4690 Millennium Dr, Belcamp, MD 21017-1523
Tel (410) 931-7500 *Founded/Ownrshp* 2010
Sales 64.5MM^E *EMP* 1,030
SIC 7371 Custom computer programming services
Pr: Ginney McAdams
CFO: John W Frederick
CFO: Charles J Neral
Snr Sftwr: Maneesh Anand
CTO: Bruce Devlin
CTO: Russell Dietz
Dir IT: Greg Critzer
Dir IT: Rick Smith
Dir IT: Michael Zunke
IT Man: Shawn Abbott
IT Man: Bill Becker

D-U-N-S 10-148-2511
SAFENET INC
(*Suby of* GEMALTO N.V.)
4690 Millennium Dr # 400, Belcamp, MD 21017-1526
Tel (410) 931-7500 *Founded/Ownrshp* 2015
Sales 486.9MM^E *EMP* 1,600
SIC 7371 Custom computer programming services
Pr: Prakash Panjwani
**CFO:* Jon McCabe
**Chf Mktg O:* Tsion Gonen
Ofcr: Ken Owens
Sr VP: Fred King
Sr VP: Steve Messick
Sr VP: Charles J Neral
Sr VP: Philip Saunders
VP: Eric Avigdor
VP: John Desmond
**VP:* Russell Dietz
VP: Chris Dunn
VP: Ron Grinfeld
VP: Terry Mahoney
VP: Ginney McAdams
VP: Todd Moore
VP: Joseph Rabick
VP: Ken Siegel
VP: Laurie Usewicz
Exec: Jill Pulliam

D-U-N-S 14-298-3266
■ **SAFETY & ECOLOGY HOLDINGS CORP**
(*Suby of* PERMA-FIX ENVIRONMENTAL SERVICES, INC.)
2800 Solway Rd, Knoxville, TN 37931-3015
Tel (865) 690-0501 *Founded/Ownrshp* 2011
Sales 98.5MM^E *EMP* 450
SIC 8744 8748 Facilities support services; Business consulting
Pr: Christopher Leichtwies
**COO:* Robert Szozda
**VP:* Jeff Scott

D-U-N-S 79-146-8044
■ **SAFETY INDEMNITY INSURANCE CO INC**
(*Suby of* SAFETY INSURANCE CO) ★
20 Custom House St # 400, Boston, MA 02110-3555
Tel (617) 951-0600 *Founded/Ownrshp* 1989
Sales NA *EMP* 68^E
SIC 6321 Disability health insurance
Pr: Richard B Simches
**Treas:* David F Brussard
Dir IT: Gabriel Arauz

D-U-N-S 13-186-4373 EXP
■ **SAFETY INSURANCE CO**
(*Suby of* THOMAS BLACK CORP) ★
20 Custom House St # 400, Boston, MA 02110-3516
Tel (617) 951-0600 *Founded/Ownrshp* 1979
Sales NA *EMP* 500
SIC 6331 Automobile insurance
Pr: David F Brussard
**CFO:* William Begley Jr
VP: Dan Laranger
VP Mktg: George Murphy

D-U-N-S 10-913-5249
▲ **SAFETY INSURANCE GROUP INC**
20 Custom House St # 400, Boston, MA 02110-3555
Tel (617) 951-0600 *Founded/Ownrshp* 1979
Sales NA *EMP* 622^E
Tkr Sym SAFT *Exch* NGS
SIC 6331 6411 Automobile insurance; Property & casualty insurance agent
Pr: George M Murphy
**Ch Bd:* David F Brussard
CFO: William J Begley Jr
VP: James D Berry
VP: David E Krupa
VP: Ann M McKeown
VP: Paul J Narciso
VP: Stephen A Varga
VP Mktg: John P Drago
Board of Directors: A Richard Caputo Jr, Frederic H Lindeberg, Peter J Manning, David K McKown

D-U-N-S 07-197-5601
SAFETY NATIONAL CASUALTY CORP
(*Suby of* TOKIO MARINE HOLDINGS, INC.)
1832 Schuetz Rd, Saint Louis, MO 63146-3540
Tel (314) 995-5300 *Founded/Ownrshp* 1996
Sales NA *EMP* 300
SIC 6331 Workers' compensation insurance
Ch Bd: Robert Rosenkranz
Pr: Edward M Breight Jr
Pr: Mike Harris
Pr: Sue Huckfeldt

Pr: Rob Leitner
Pr: Brad Ogle
**Pr:* Gerald Scott
**CEO:* Mark A Wilhelm
**COO:* Duane A Hercules
**CFO:* John Csik
Ex VP: Steven Luebbert
Sr VP: Steve Divine
Sr VP: Tom Grove
Sr VP: Raymond Harkins
**Sr VP:* Jeffrey Otto
VP: Ed Breight
VP: Steve Cotnoir
VP: Richard Gilmore
VP: Bob King
VP: Gene R Maier
VP: Bill Martin

D-U-N-S 05-780-8917
■ **SAFETY SOLUTIONS INC**
(*Suby of* WW GRAINGER INC) ★
6161 Shamrock Ct, Dublin, OH 43016-1293
Tel (614) 799-9900 *Founded/Ownrshp* 2013
Sales 91.6MM^E *EMP* 115
SIC 5084 5136 5139 Safety equipment; Gloves, men's & boys'; Shoes; Boots
Pr: David L Forsthoffer
**VP:* Mike Boone
**VP:* John Perrin
Sls&Mrk Ex: Ann Bauman

D-U-N-S 16-991-6546
■ **SAFETY-KLEEN (TULSA) INC**
(*Suby of* SAFETY-KLEEN INC) ★
1301 Gervais St Ste 300, Columbia, SC 29201-3332
Tel (800) 669-5740
Sales 1.6MM^E *EMP* 1,424^E
SIC 4953 Refuse systems
Pr: Robert M Craycraft II

D-U-N-S 80-936-8954
■ **SAFETY-KLEEN ENVIROSYSTEMS CO**
(*Suby of* SAFETY-KLEEN SYSTEMS INC) ★
2600 N Central Expy # 400, Richardson, TX 75080-2058
Tel (800) 323-5040 *Founded/Ownrshp* 1997
Sales 525.3MM^E *EMP* 1,000
SIC 4953 Recycling, waste materials
Pr: Robert M Craycraft II
**Pr:* Jerry E Correll
**Pr:* Dave Sprinkle
**CFO:* Jeff Richard
**Chf Cred:* Chip Duffie
**Chf Mktg O:* Curt Knapp
**Ex VP:* Dave Eckelbarger
Sr VP: Mark Bouldin
**Sr VP:* Jean Lee
**Sr VP:* Mark Stone
VP: Magnus Borg
VP: David Eckelbarger
VP: Paul T Lee
VP: Umesh Patel
VP: Mike Williams
VP: Eric Zimmer

D-U-N-S 05-397-6551 IMP/EXP
■ **SAFETY-KLEEN INC**
(*Suby of* CLEAN HARBORS INC) ★
2600 N Central Expy # 400, Richardson, TX 75080-2058
Tel (800) 669-5740 *Founded/Ownrshp* 2012
Sales 1.1MMM^E *EMP* 4,500
SIC 4953 3559 4212 5172 5085 7389 Recycling, waste materials; Degreasing machines, automotive & industrial; Hazardous waste transport; Petroleum products; Industrial supplies; Building scale models
Pr: Jerry E Correll
V Ch: James M Rutledge
Pr: Roy Dean Bullinger
**Pr:* Dave Sprinkle
**CFO:* Jeff Richard
Treas: Paul Lee
**Chf Cred:* Chip Duffie
**Chf Mktg O:* Curt Knapp
Chf Mktg O: Kurt Knapt
**Ex VP:* Dave Eckelbarger
Ex VP: David E Eckelbarger
Ex VP: Curtis C Knapp
Ex VP: Bruce Roberson
Ex VP: Michael J Smith
Sr VP: Danny Anderson
**Sr VP:* Jean Lee
**Sr VP:* Mark Stone
Sr VP: Mark A Stone
VP: Robert Perkins
VP: Carla Rolinc
VP: Troy Russell
Board of Directors: David Samuel Coats, R Randolph Devening, Richard B Neff

D-U-N-S 05-106-0408 IMP/EXP
■ **SAFETY-KLEEN SYSTEMS INC** (WI)
(*Suby of* SK HOLDING CO INC) ★
2600 N Central Expy # 400, Richardson, TX 75080-2058
Tel (972) 265-2000 *Founded/Ownrshp* 1963, 2003
Sales 1.0MMM^E *EMP* 4,500
SIC 3559 7359 5172 4212 7389 5085 Degreasing machines, automotive & industrial; Equipment rental & leasing; Petroleum products; Hazardous waste transport; Solvents recovery service; Industrial supplies
CEO: Robert M Craycraft II
**Pr:* Jerry E Orrell
**Pr:* Dave Sprinkle
**CFO:* Jeff Richard
**Chf Cred:* Chip Duffie
**Chf Mktg O:* Curt Knapp
**Ex VP:* Dave Eckelbarger
**Sr VP:* Jean Lee
**Sr VP:* Mark Stone
Board of Directors: R Randolph Devening

D-U-N-S 09-869-2130 IMP
SAFEWARE INC
SAFEWARE SUPPLY
4403 Forbes Blvd, Lanham, MD 20706-4328
Tel (301) 683-1234 *Founded/Ownrshp* 1979
Sales 99.8MM^E *EMP* 90

Accts Lanigan Bryan Malcolm & Doy
SIC 5084 Safety equipment
Ch Bd: Ed Simons
**CFO:* Keith Hyatt
**VP:* Edward Arthur Jr
**VP:* Tommy Nairnn
**VP:* Anne Petrenko
**VP:* Charles Radcliffe
Brnch Mgr: Diana Hyatt
Sls Mgr: Scott Simons

SAFEWARE SUPPLY
See SAFEWARE INC

D-U-N-S 61-783-1516
SAFEWAY CANADA HOLDINGS INC
(*Suby of* SAFEWAY INC) ★
5918 Stoneridge Mall Rd, Pleasanton, CA 94588-3229
Tel (925) 467-3000 *Founded/Ownrshp* 1986
Sales 71.8MM^E *EMP* 28,000
SIC 5411 Supermarkets, chain
Pr: Steve Burd
Pr: Linda Nordgren
**CFO:* Vasant Prabhu
**Treas:* Brad Fox
Mktg Mgr: Patricia Baker
Board of Directors: Harvey Naito

D-U-N-S 12-892-7774
SAFEWAY CONTRACTING INC
107 Trumbull St, Elizabeth, NJ 07206-2165
Tel (212) 627-8050 *Founded/Ownrshp* 2001
Sales 1.3MM *EMP* 1,998
SIC 5411 Supermarkets
Pr: Richie Greeley
**Prin:* Cara Greeley

D-U-N-S 78-691-9704
SAFEWAY DENVER INC
(*Suby of* SAFEWAY INC) ★
5918 Stoneridge Mall Rd, Pleasanton, CA 94588-3229
Tel (925) 467-3000 *Founded/Ownrshp* 1986
Sales 302.6MM^E *EMP* 9,000^E
SIC 5411 Supermarkets, chain
Pr: David Bond

D-U-N-S 00-913-7209 IMP
SAFEWAY INC
(*Suby of* ALBERTSONS COMPANIES LLC) ★
5918 Stoneridge Mall Rd, Pleasanton, CA 94588-3229
Tel (925) 467-3000 *Founded/Ownrshp* 2015
Sales 28.0MMM^E *EMP* 138,000^E
Accts Deloitte & Touche Llp San Fra
SIC 5411 5912 Supermarkets, chain; Supermarkets, 55,000-65,000 square feet (superstore); Drug stores
V Ch: Robert L Edwards
COO: Wayne A Denningham
**COO:* Kelly P Griffith
Ex VP: Justin Ewing
**Ex VP:* Robert A Gordon
**Ex VP:* Barry J Libenson
Ex VP: Jim Perkins
Ex VP: Jerry Tidwell
Ex VP: Lee Wilson
VP: Bruce Bower
VP: Stephen Flemming
VP: Michael Fox
VP: Kenneth Shachmut
Exec: Diane Stump
Board of Directors: Howard Cohen, Hersch Klaff, Ethan Klemperer, Ronald Kravit, Robert Miller, Jay Schottenstein

D-U-N-S 02-132-1500
SAFEWAY SELECT GIFT SOURCE INC
CARRS QUALITY CENTERS
(*Suby of* SAFEWAY INC) ★
6401 A St, Anchorage, AK 99518-1824
Tel (907) 561-1944 *Founded/Ownrshp* 1999
Sales 159.1MM^E *EMP* 3,200
SIC 5411 5141 5921 Supermarkets, chain; Groceries, general line; Liquor stores; Wine
Pr: Lawrence H Hayward
**Ch Bd:* John J Cairns
COO: Larry Walsh
**CFO:* Donald J Anderson
Sr VP: Gregory M Carr
**Sr VP:* Jeff L Philipps

D-U-N-S 55-706-9713
SAFEWAY STORES 46 INC
DENVER COUNTRY STORES
(*Suby of* SAFEWAY DENVER INC) ★
5918 Stoneridge Mall Rd, Pleasanton, CA 94588-3229
Tel (925) 467-3000 *Founded/Ownrshp* 1986
Sales 48.5MM^E *EMP* 1,000
SIC 5411 Supermarkets
Pr: Steve Burd

D-U-N-S 17-667-3432 IMP
SAFEWORKS LLC
SPIDER
(*Suby of* SAFWAY GROUP HOLDING LLC) ★
365 Upland Dr, Tukwila, WA 98188-3802
Tel (206) 575-6445 *Founded/Ownrshp* 2016
Sales 116.0MM^E *EMP* 300
SIC 3536 3531 3446 5082 Hoists; Construction machinery; Architectural metalwork; Cranes, construction
Pr: Scott Farrell
Pr: Erik Elzinga
CFO: Greg Kennelly
VP: David Beckett
VP: Vishnu Irigireddy
VP: Michael Moritz
Genl Mgr: Langton Machaya
Genl Mgr: Ken Pope
IT Man: Rick Weitz
Opers Mgr: Tavis Olson
Sls Mgr: Paul Frank

D-U-N-S 15-223-3222
■ **SAFG RETIREMENT SERVICES INC**
(*Suby of* AIG) ★
1 Sun America Ctr Fl 36, Los Angeles, CA 90067-6104
Tel (310) 772-6000 *Founded/Ownrshp* 1999
Sales NA *EMP* 20
SIC 6411 Insurance agents, brokers & service
Pr: Jay Wintrob

Pr: Jennifer D Cobbs
Ex VP: Howard Heitner
Sr VP: Anne M Franklin
VP: Gavin Friedman
VP: Lawrence Goldman
VP: Michelle Powers
Natl Sales: Shawn M Duffy

D-U-N-S 60-522-2272 IMP
SAFILO AMERICA INC
(*Suby of* SAFILO GROUP SPA)
801 Jefferson Rd, Parsippany, NJ 07054-3710
Tel (973) 952-2800 *Founded/Ownrshp* 1985
Sales 201.8MM^E *EMP* 758
SIC 5048 5099 5091 Frames, ophthalmic; Sunglasses; Goggles, sports
Pr: Vittorio Tabacchi
VP: Mark Ugenti

D-U-N-S 04-681-4760 IMP/EXP
SAFILO USA INC (NJ)
(*Suby of* SAFILO AMERICA INC) ★
801 Jefferson Rd, Parsippany, NJ 07054-3710
Tel (973) 952-2800 *Founded/Ownrshp* 1962, 1985
Sales 163.8MM^E *EMP* 338
SIC 5048 Frames, ophthalmic
CFO: Robert Risi

D-U-N-S 78-784-8928
SAFRA NATIONAL BANK OF NEW YORK
(*Suby of* SNBNY HOLDINGS LIMITED)
546 5th Ave, New York, NY 10036-5000
Tel (212) 382-9200 *Founded/Ownrshp* 1995
Sales NA *EMP* 237
SIC 6021 National commercial banks
CEO: Simone Morato
Pr: Melissa Bernstein
Pr: Diana Mento
**COO:* Luiz Bull
**CFO:* Carlos Bertaco
Ofcr: Nelson Dantas
Ex VP: Michell Brown
Sr VP: Elias Hadida
VP: Evelyn Allende
VP: Purna Bhattacharya
VP: Bernardo D'Orey
VP: Anthony Daddi
VP: Emily Dorris
VP: Isabelle Le Roch
VP: Cybele Marinello
VP: Martica Martinez
VP: Sergio Nakashima
VP: Albert Palacci
VP: Jorge Raab
VP: Joseph Safra
VP: Paulo Souza

SAFRAN
See MORPHOTRAK LLC

D-U-N-S 19-838-9678 IMP
SAFRAN USA INC
(*Suby of* SAFRAN)
700 S Washington St # 320, Alexandria, VA 22314-4291
Tel (703) 351-9898 *Founded/Ownrshp* 2000
Sales 991.4MM^E *EMP* 3,500
SIC 3643 3621 7699 3724 5013 5088 Connectors & terminals for electrical devices; Motors & generators; Engine repair & replacement, non-automotive; Aircraft engines & engine parts; Automotive supplies & parts; Aircraft equipment & supplies
Pr: Peter Lengyel
Mktg Dir: Michelle Lyle

D-U-N-S 06-315-2573 IMP/EXP
■ **SAFT AMERICA INC**
SAFT INDUSTRIAL BATTERY GROUP
(*Suby of* SAFT)
13575 Waterworks St, Jacksonville, FL 32221-8118
Tel (904) 861-1501 *Founded/Ownrshp* 2003
Sales 309.4MM^E *EMP* 800
SIC 3691 5063

SAFT INDUSTRIAL BATTERY GROUP
See SAFT AMERICA INC

D-U-N-S 07-879-9888
SAFWAY GROUP HOLDING LLC
N19w24200 Riverwood Dr, Waukesha, WI 53188-1179
Tel (262) 523-6500 *Founded/Ownrshp* 2012
Sales 1.9MMM^E *EMP* 7,300
SIC 1799 Insulation of pipes & boilers; Scaffolding construction
Pr: Bill Hayes

D-U-N-S 83-308-6874
SAFWAY HOLDINGS LLC
(*Suby of* ODYSSEY INVESTMENT PARTNERS LLC) ★
280 Park Ave Fl 38, New York, NY 10017-1216
Tel (212) 351-7900 *Founded/Ownrshp* 1936
Sales 75.6MM^E *EMP* 5,493^E
SIC 7359 5082 1799 Equipment rental & leasing; Scaffolding; Scaffolding construction
Pr: Marc J Wilson
**CFO:* Robert Sukalich
**Ex VP:* F Gerald Johns
**VP:* Curtis A Paulsen

D-U-N-S 87-971-8641 IMP/EXP
SAFWAY SERVICES LLC
(*Suby of* SAFWAY GROUP HOLDING LLC) ★
N19w24200 Riverwood Dr # 200, Waukesha, WI 53188-1179
Tel (262) 523-6500 *Founded/Ownrshp* 2009
Sales 1.6MMM^E *EMP* 5,000
SIC 5082 Scaffolding
Pr: Bill Hayes
**CFO:* Jim Walters
**Sr VP:* Marty McGee
**Sr VP:* Chris Wells
VP: Paul Amedee
VP: Danny Anderson
VP: Gary Duncan
VP: Stig Karlsen
VP: Larry Mickwee
VP: Chuck Thimm
VP: John Weber

Div/Sub He: Martin Carlson
Dir Bus: Brent Luedtke

D-U-N-S 79-807-3136
▲ **SAGA COMMUNICATIONS INC**
73 Kercheval Ave, Grosse Pointe Farms, MI 48236-3667
Tel (313) 886-7070 *Founded/Ownrshp* 1986
Sales 132.8MM *EMP* 1,086^E
Accts Uhy Llp Farmington Hills Mic
Tkr Sym SGA *Exch* ASE
SIC 4832 4833 Radio broadcasting stations; Television broadcasting stations
Ch Bd: Edward K Christian
COO: Warren S Lada
CFO: Samuel D Bush
CFO: Bush Samuel
Sr VP: Catherine A Bobinski
Sr VP: Marcia K Lobaito
Mktg Mgr: Jj Gerard
Mktg Mgr: Mark Jennings
Mktg Mgr: Michelle Matthews
Sls Mgr: Chris Hoffman
Sls Mgr: Tom Nankival
Board of Directors: Clarke R Brown Jr, Timothy J Clarke, Roy F Coppedge III, David B Stephens, Gary G Stevens

D-U-N-S 15-136-5558
■ **SAGA COMMUNICATIONS OF ILLINOIS LLC**
(*Suby of* SAGA COMMUNICATIONS OF NEW ENGLAND INC) ★
73 Kercheval Ave Ste 201, Grosse Pointe Farms, MI 48236-3559
Tel (313) 886-7070 *Founded/Ownrshp* 1992
Sales 140.7MM *EMP* 100
Accts Ernst & Young Llp Detroit Mi
SIC 4832 Radio broadcasting stations
Pr: Edward Christian
**CFO:* Sam Bush
**Ex VP:* Steven N Goldstein
**Sr VP:* Marcia Lobaito

D-U-N-S 15-126-5709
■ **SAGA COMMUNICATIONS OF NEW ENGLAND INC**
(*Suby of* SAGA COMMUNICATIONS INC) ★
73 Kercheval Ave Ste 201, Grosse Pointe Farms, MI 48236-3559
Tel (313) 886-7070 *Founded/Ownrshp* 1992
Sales 153.0MM^E *EMP* 400
SIC 4832 Radio broadcasting stations
Pr: Edward K Christian
CFO: Sam Bush
Ex VP: Steven J Goldstein
VP: Marcia K Lobaito

SAGAMORE APARTMENTS
See KBF AMSTERDAM PARTNERS

D-U-N-S 07-862-3459
SAGARD CAPITAL PARTNERS LP
280 Park Ave Fl 3ny, New York, NY 10017
Tel (203) 629-6700 *Founded/Ownrshp* 2005
Sales 234.0MM^E *EMP* 1,534^E
SIC 6799 Investors
Pt: Dan Friedberg

SAGE AND COMPANY
See TETERS FLORAL PRODUCTS INC

D-U-N-S 83-131-2553 IMP
SAGE AUTOMOTIVE INTERIORS INC
3 Research Dr Ste 300, Greenville, SC 29607-5272
Tel (864) 987-7778 *Founded/Ownrshp* 2014
Sales 483.8MM^E *EMP* 1,200
SIC 2399 Seat covers, automobile
Pr: Dirk Pieper
**COO:* Brian McSharry
**CFO:* Dave Gable
CFO: Paige Reed
VP: Mark Brezenski
VP Sls: Chris Heard
Snr Mgr: Leona Walfield

D-U-N-S 19-719-8158
SAGE CLIENT 283 LLC
(*Suby of* MARRIOTT) ★
3155 S Vaughn Way, Aurora, CO 80014-3505
Tel (303) 595-7200 *Founded/Ownrshp* 2005
Sales 2.1MM^E *EMP* 1,196^E
SIC 7011 8741 Hotels & motels; Management services
CEO: Walter Isenberg

D-U-N-S 62-140-7170
SAGE DINING SERVICES INC
1402 York Rd Ste 100, Lutherville, MD 21093-6018
Tel (410) 339-3950 *Founded/Ownrshp* 1990
Sales 41.1MM^E *EMP* 1,000
SIC 5812 Cafeteria
Pr: Paco Rodriguez
COO: Marcel Gallo
CFO: Christina J Rodriguez
CFO: Tina Rodriguez
Ex VP: Kenneth G Pensalfini
VP: Mark Benfield
VP: John S Downs
VP: Jon Hess
Dist Mgr: Tim Walsh

D-U-N-S 16-153-7758 IMP
SAGE HOLDING CO
UNIVERSAL CITY NISSAN
3550 Cahuenga Blvd W, Los Angeles, CA 90068-1304
Tel (310) 271-3476 *Founded/Ownrshp* 1970
Sales 139.0MM^E *EMP* 375
SIC 5511 Automobiles, new & used
CEO: Leonard Schrage
**Pr:* Morris Schrage
**VP:* Joseph Schrage
Exec: Carmen Straszewski
Mktg Dir: Robert Bailey

D-U-N-S 14-946-5536
SAGE HOSPITALITY RESOURCES LLC
MARRIOTT
1575 Welton St Ste 300, Denver, CO 80202-4218
Tel (303) 595-7200 *Founded/Ownrshp* 1984
Sales 426.9MM^E *EMP* 5,700
SIC 7011 Hotels & motels
Pr: Walter Isenberg
COO: Kenneth Widmaier
Chf Mktg O: Arthur Berg
Ofcr: Lisa Donovan
Ex VP: Kenneth J Geist
Ex VP: Kenneth Geist
VP: William Balinbin
VP: Robert Butler
VP: Michael Carr-Turnbough
VP: Bill Croke
VP: Jim Darter
VP: Ann Evans
VP: Courteney Fisher
VP: Jan Lucas
VP: Paul McCormick
VP: Matthew Sparks

D-U-N-S 00-918-1731 IMP/EXP
SAGE PARTS PLUS INC
30 Hub Dr Ste 1, Melville, NY 11747-3525
Tel (631) 501-1300 *Founded/Ownrshp* 1998
Sales 186.7MM^E *EMP* 375
SIC 5088 3812 3537 Aircraft equipment & supplies; Search & navigation equipment; Industrial trucks & tractors
Pr: Mark Pollack
**CFO:* Catherine Lucarelli
Chf Mktg O: Susan Fortel
**Ex VP:* Michael Bloomfield
VP: Thomas Artes
**VP:* Chris Damiano
**VP:* Harry Zuckerman
Rgnl Mgr: Carl Buchholz
Rgnl Mgr: Steve Derichsweiler
Site Mgr: Carlos Cabrera
Site Mgr: Ron Taggart

D-U-N-S 05-432-6178 IMP/EXP
■ **SAGE PRODUCTS LLC**
(*Suby of* STRYKER CORP) ★
3909 3 Oaks Rd, Cary, IL 60013-1804
Tel (815) 455-4700 *Founded/Ownrshp* 2016
Sales 147.5MM^E *EMP* 700^E
SIC 3842 5047 Surgical appliances & supplies; Medical & hospital equipment
Pr: Scott Brown
COO: Gary Ward
**CFO:* Richard Naponelli
**Treas:* Julie Mayer
VP: Paul H Hanifl
VP: Alan McCandless
VP: Richard Napponelli
QC Dir: Rod Manwill
Mktg Dir: Terry Boresma
Manager: Eric Cunningham

D-U-N-S 00-968-3194 IMP
SAGE PUBLICATIONS INC
2455 Teller Rd, Thousand Oaks, CA 91320-2234
Tel (805) 499-0721 *Founded/Ownrshp* 1966
Sales 96.6MM^E *EMP* 400^E
SIC 2731

D-U-N-S 11-916-3009
SAGE SOFTWARE HOLDINGS INC
(*Suby of* THE SAGE GROUP PLC.)
6561 Irvine Center Dr, Irvine, CA 92618-2118
Tel (866) 530-7243 *Founded/Ownrshp* 2003
Sales 464.0MM^E *EMP* 4,000
SIC 7372 7371 Business oriented computer software; Custom computer programming services
CEO: Stev Swenson
**CFO:* Mack Lout
**VP:* Doug Meyer

D-U-N-S 01-643-1660
SAGE SOFTWARE INC
(*Suby of* SAGE SOFTWARE HOLDINGS INC) ★
271 17th St Nw Ste 1100, Atlanta, GA 30363-6201
Tel (866) 996-7243 *Founded/Ownrshp* 1982
Sales 464.0MM^E *EMP* 1,311
Accts Pricewaterhousecoopers Llp
SIC 7372 Business oriented computer software; Application computer software
CEO: Pascal Houillon
CFO: Brandon Quigley
**CFO:* Marc Scheipe
Ofcr: Rich Spring
Ex VP: Gabie Boko
Ex VP: Connie Certusi
Ex VP: Nancy Harris
Ex VP: Joseph H Langner
Ex VP: Karen Mortham
VP: John Manry
VP: Alok Tyagi
VP: Jennifer Warawa
VP: Jon Witty

D-U-N-S 04-223-9991 IMP/EXP
SAGE V FOODS LLC (CA)
RICE EXPRESSIONS
1470 Walnut St Ste 202, Boulder, CO 80302-5335
Tel (303) 449-5626 *Founded/Ownrshp* 1998
Sales 110.0MM *EMP* 220
SIC 2044 Flour, rice

D-U-N-S 62-036-3478
SAGEBRUSH ENTERPRISES INC
RHODES HOMES
4730 S Fort Apache Rd, Las Vegas, NV 89147-7945
Tel (702) 873-5338 *Founded/Ownrshp* 1998
Sales 60.1MM^E *EMP* 1,000
Accts Deloitte & Touche Llp Las Veg
SIC 1522 1542 7992 6799 Residential construction; Commercial & office building contractors; Public golf courses; Real estate investors, except property operators
Ch Bd: James Rhodes
**CEO:* Paul Huygens

D-U-N-S 94-399-2289
■ SAGEBRUSH INC
(*Suby of* ADVANCE PIERRE FOODS) ★
112 Main St, Claremont, NC 28610
Tel (828) 459-0821 *Founded/Ownrshp* 1997
Sales 158.4MM *EMP* 1,230
SIC 5812 Eating places
Pr: L Dent Miller
**Treas:* Jammie Harris
**Ex VP:* Ken Moser
**Ex VP:* Jim Templetonn

SAGENET
See WOODARD TECHNOLOGY & INVESTMENTS LLC

D-U-N-S 79-685-2890 IMP
SAGENT PHARMACEUTICALS INC
(*Suby of* NICHI-IKO PHARMACEUTICAL CO.,LTD.)
1901 N Roselle Rd Ste 700, Schaumburg, IL 60195-3194
Tel (847) 908-1600 *Founded/Ownrshp* 2016
Sales 318.3MM *EMP* 440^E
SIC 2834 5122 Pharmaceutical preparations; Pharmaceuticals
CEO: Allan Oberman
CFO: Jonathon Singer
Ex VP: Lorin Drake
Ex VP: Frank Harmon
Ex VP: Albert Patterson
VP: Jeffrey Greve
VP: Peter Jensen
VP: Thomas Shea
Snr Mgr: Jeff Wojtynek

D-U-N-S 06-915-0092
■ SAGEPOINT FINANCIAL INC
(*Suby of* SUNAMERICA INC) ★
2800 N Central Ave # 2100, Phoenix, AZ 85004-1007
Tel (602) 744-3000 *Founded/Ownrshp* 1990
Sales NA *EMP* 240
SIC 6311 6211 Life insurance carriers; Security brokers & dealers
CEO: Jeffrey M Auld
COO: Lisa S Kubica
Ofcr: Mary Simonson
Sr VP: Dee Morgan
VP: Lester Helm
VP: Lexi Karsay
VP: Gamiel Randy
Genl Couns: Bridget M Gaughan

D-U-N-S 07-932-8898 IMP
SAGER CREEK FOODS INC
(*Suby of* DEL MONTE FOODS INC) ★
305 E Main St, Siloam Springs, AR 72761-3231
Tel (479) 524-6431 *Founded/Ownrshp* 2015
Sales 228.8MM^E *EMP* 1,000
SIC 2033 Vegetables & vegetable products in cans, jars, etc.
CEO: Chris L Kiser
**Pr:* Mike Zelkind
Dir IT: Steve Laverty

D-U-N-S 00-799-7653 IMP
■ SAGER ELECTRICAL SUPPLY CO INC (MA)
SAGER ELECTRONICS
(*Suby of* TTI INC) ★
19 Leona Dr, Middleboro, MA 02346-1404
Tel (508) 923-6600 *Founded/Ownrshp* 1980
Sales 106.4MM^E *EMP* 280
SIC 5065

SAGER ELECTRONICS
See SAGER ELECTRICAL SUPPLY CO INC

D-U-N-S 10-265-6030
SAGERS SEAFOOD PLUS INC
4802 Bridal Wreath Dr, Richmond, TX 77406-9172
Tel (281) 342-8833 *Founded/Ownrshp* 1984
Sales 120.0MM *EMP* 3
SIC 5146 Fish & seafoods; Fish, frozen, unpackaged; Seafoods
Pr: David E Sager
VP: Gail Sager

D-U-N-S 00-813-8570
SAGICOR LIFE INSURANCE CO
(*Suby of* SAGICOR FINANCIAL CORPORATION)
4343 N Scottsdale Rd # 300, Scottsdale, AZ 85251-3347
Tel (480) 425-5100 *Founded/Ownrshp* 2000
Sales NA *EMP* 140
Accts Pricewaterhousecoopers Llp Lo
SIC 6311 Life insurance carriers
CEO: Dodridge Miller
Pr: Bart Catmull
Bd of Dir: Stephen McNamara
Ofcr: Michael Stricker
Ex VP: Carl Formato
Sr VP: Ned Gaffney
VP: Sandy Clifford
VP: Steve Mills
VP: Leroy Pruitt
VP: Anabel Thomas
CTO: Catherine Hauck
Board of Directors: Arthur Bethell, Todd Campbell, Kendrick Marshall, Stephen McNamara, Ravi Rambarran, John F Shettle Jr, Beverly Sisson, William Lucie-Smith

D-U-N-S 08-231-8841
SAGINAW CHIPPEWA INDIAN TRIBE
7070 E Broadway Rd, Mount Pleasant, MI 48858-8970
Tel (989) 775-4000 *Founded/Ownrshp* 1934
Sales 203.3MM^E *EMP* 4,000
SIC 5812 Drive-in restaurant; Luncheonette
CEO: Steve Pego
**Pr:* Maynard Kahgegab Jr
CFO: Michael Johnson

D-U-N-S 00-652-0969 IMP
SAGINAW CONTROL & ENGINEERING INC (MI)
SCE
95 Midland Rd, Saginaw, MI 48638-5791
Tel (989) 799-6871 *Founded/Ownrshp* 1963
Sales 87.8MM^E *EMP* 320
SIC 3699 3444 Electrical equipment & supplies; Sheet metalwork
Pr: Frederick H May Jr
**Ch Bd:* Harold C Baldauf
**Treas:* David Baldauf
Exec: Dean Evans
Genl Mgr: Scott Baldeuf
Prd Mgr: John Garner
Prd Mgr: Rob Young
Ql Cn Mgr: Ron Zeitler
Sls&Mrk Ex: Dave Pankow

D-U-N-S 10-691-4260 EXP
SAGINAW PIPE CO INC
1980 Hwy 31 S, Saginaw, AL 35137
Tel (205) 664-3670 *Founded/Ownrshp* 1983
Sales 103.3MM *EMP* 140^E
Accts Jackson Howard And Whatley L
SIC 5051 Pipe & tubing, steel; Tubing, metal
CEO: Howard C Wise Jr
CFO: Bill Pitts
**CFO:* William F Pitts II
**Ex VP:* Richard F Olive
**VP:* James D Cates
**VP:* Greg Helms
VP: Dennis Ince
VP: Mary Laird
Exec: Steve Benton
Exec: Carl Lytle
Exec: Terry Pruet

SAHALIE
See NORM THOMPSON OUTFITTERS INC

SAI AUTOMOTIVE
See FAURECIA INTERIOR SYSTEMS INC

D-U-N-S 11-603-0698 IMP/EXP
▲ SAIA INC
11465 Johns Creek Pkwy # 400, Johns Creek, GA 30097-1574
Tel (770) 232-5067 *Founded/Ownrshp* 2000
Sales 1.2MMM *EMP* 8,700
Tkr Sym SAIA *Exch* NGS
SIC 4213 Trucking, except local; Less-than-truckload (LTL) transport
Pr: Richard D O'Dell
**Ch Bd:* Herbert A Trucksess III
Ofcr: Raymond R Ramu
VP: Brian A Balius
VP: Cris A Burgum
VP: Mike Parker
VP: Corey Thompson
Dir Bus: Billy Barnes
Mng Ofcr: Ray Ramu
Trfc Dir: Calvin Payne
Opers Mgr: Hever Bustos

SAIA LTL FRIEGHT
See SAIA MOTOR FREIGHT LINE LLC

D-U-N-S 00-278-1342 IMP
■ SAIA MOTOR FREIGHT LINE LLC
SAIA LTL FRIEGHT
(*Suby of* SAIA INC) ★
11465 Johns Creek Pkwy # 400, Duluth, GA 30097-1572
Tel (770) 232-5067 *Founded/Ownrshp* 2002
Sales 1.1MMM^E *EMP* 7,900
SIC 4213 Trucking, except local; Contract haulers; Heavy hauling
CEO: Richard D O'Dell
**Treas:* Douglas Col
**VP:* Brian Balius
**VP:* Frederick Holzgrefe
**VP:* Mark Robinson

SAIC
See SCIENCE APPLICATIONS INTERNATIONAL CORP

SAIC GEMINI, INC.
See SCIENCE APPLICATIONS INTERNATIONAL CORP

D-U-N-S 16-015-6212 IMP/EXP
SAIC USA INC
(*Suby of* SHANGHAI AUTOMOTIVE INDUSTRY CORPORATION (GROUP))
322 N Old Woodward Ave # 3, Birmingham, MI 48009-5318
Tel (248) 267-9117 *Founded/Ownrshp* 1994
Sales 200.0MM *EMP* 60
SIC 5013 Automotive supplies & parts
CEO: Yi Lu
**VP:* Jinan Dong Qian
Ql Cn Mgr: Jim Serafino

D-U-N-S 03-804-1778
SAIF CORP
400 High St Se, Salem, OR 97312-1000
Tel (503) 373-8000 *Founded/Ownrshp* 1997
Sales NA *EMP* 840
SIC 6321 8111 6331 Accident insurance carriers; Legal services; Fire, marine & casualty insurance
**Pr:* Brenda Rocklin
**CEO:* John Gilkey
CFO: Gina Manley
Bd of Dir: John Endicott
**VP:* Chris Davie
**VP:* Ryan Fleming
**VP:* Kathy Gehring
VP: Rick Hanson
Dir Soc: Erika Meier
IT Man: Marsha Malonson
Web Dev: Kimberly Kolb

D-U-N-S 96-446-9162
SAIIA CONSTRUCTION CO LLC
4400 Lewisburg Rd, Birmingham, AL 35207-1834
Tel (205) 290-0400 *Founded/Ownrshp* 2010
Sales 86.3MM^E *EMP* 380^E
SIC 1794 Excavation work
Pr: David Mathews
**Pr:* Lavaughn East
**Pr:* Frank Montgomery
**Pr:* Donald Stansberry
**Ch:* Joseph Saiia
DP Exec: Trent Phifer

D-U-N-S 01-166-1712
SAILORMEN INC
POPEYES CHICKEN & BISCUITS
(*Suby of* INTERFOODS OF AMERICA INC) ★
9500 S Dadeland Blvd # 800, Miami, FL 33156-2852
Tel (305) 670-4112 *Founded/Ownrshp* 1984
Sales 117.5MM^E *EMP* 2,200
SIC 5812 Fast-food restaurant, chain
Ch Bd: Robert S Berg
**Pr:* Steven Wemple
**VP:* Frank Maloney
VP: Mark Reineri

D-U-N-S 15-296-6276
SAILPOINT TECHNOLOGIES INC
11305 Four Points Dr 2-100, Austin, TX 78726-2367
Tel (512) 346-2000 *Founded/Ownrshp* 2014
Sales 134.8MM^E *EMP* 515^E
SIC 7372 Application computer software
CEO: Mark McClain
**Pr:* Kevin Cunningham
Pr: Dave Hildebrand
**CFO:* CAM McMartin
**Chf Mktg O:* Juliette Rizkallah
**Ofcr:* Kevin Hansel
**Sr VP:* Joe Gottlieb
**Sr VP:* Howard Greenfield
**Sr VP:* Dave Hendrix
**VP:* Troy Donley
VP: Trent Fitz
VP: Harry Gould
**VP:* Abby Payne
**VP:* Paul Trulove
Board of Directors: Mark McClain,kevin Cunning

SAINT AGNES HOSPITAL
See ST AGNES HEALTHCARE INC

D-U-N-S 05-842-6289
SAINT AGNES MEDICAL CENTER
(*Suby of* CATHOLIC HEALTH EAST) ★
1303 E Herndon Ave, Fresno, CA 93720-3309
Tel (559) 450-3000 *Founded/Ownrshp* 1978
Sales 478.5MM *EMP* 2,400
SIC 8062 General medical & surgical hospitals
CEO: Nancy R Hollingsworth
Chf Path: Tai-PO Tschang
Chf OB: Harold Groom
V Ch: Michael Martinez
CFO: David J Connor
CFO: Christine Sarrico
Treas: Andrea Lanier
Trst: Daniel G Hale
Trst: Lee Kolligian
Trst: Hilda C Montoy
Trst: Joan Marie Steadman
Trst: Veronique Wiedower
Ofcr: Beverly A Nelson
Ex VP: Michael Gallagher
VP: Richard Blanks
VP: Susie Kuszmar
VP: James Vandevelde
Exec: Marie Akin
Dir OR: Julie Lubeki
Dir Inf Cn: Christi Paradise
Dir Lab: Cathy Weston

SAINT ALEXIUS MEDICAL CENTER
See ST ALEXIUS MEDICAL CENTER

D-U-N-S 07-298-4867
SAINT ALPHONSUS MEDICAL CENTER - NAMPA HEALTH FOUNDATION INC
CHI
(*Suby of* CHI) ★
1512 12th Ave Rd, Nampa, ID 83686-6008
Tel (208) 467-1171 *Founded/Ownrshp* 1917
Sales 108.0MM *EMP* 650
SIC 8062 8011 General medical & surgical hospitals; Offices & clinics of medical doctors
CEO: Joseph Messmer
Chf Rad: Janice W Brooks
**CFO:* Lannie Checketts
Ofcr: Paul Feltz
Dir Rad: Peter Batchelor
Chf Nrs Of: Renee Mauriello
Mktg Mgr: Jeff Schaus
Surgeon: Jan Franko
Doctor: Diane Markus

D-U-N-S 18-549-9910
SAINT ALPHONSUS REGIONAL MEDICAL CENTER INC
CATHOLIC HEALTH EAST
(*Suby of* CATHOLIC HEALTH EAST) ★
1055 N Curtis Rd, Boise, ID 83706-1309
Tel (208) 367-2121 *Founded/Ownrshp* 1978
Sales 556.2MM *EMP* 3,500
SIC 8062 General medical & surgical hospitals
CFO: Kenneth Fry
Pr: Rodney Reider
COO: Rick Oconnell
Trst: Richard Oconnell
Trst: J K Sullivan
Ofcr: Nancy Powell
VP: Jean Basom
VP: Dina Ellwanger
VP: Karen Hodge
VP: James R Polk
VP: Robert Polk
VP: Pamela Thomas
VP: Stephanie Westermeier
Dir Rad: Terry Krogstad
Dir Rx: Mark T Phillips

SAINT ANNE'S HOSPITAL
See STEWARD ST ANNES HOSPITAL CORP

D-U-N-S 19-389-3914
SAINT ANNS HOSPITAL AUXILIARY
DIVERSIONS GIFT SHOP
500 S Cleveland Ave, Westerville, OH 43081-8971
Tel (614) 769-4459 *Founded/Ownrshp* 1958
Sales 210.0MM *EMP* 3
SIC 5947 5621 5611 5992 5441 Greeting cards; Gift shop; Ready-to-wear apparel, women's; Clothing, men's & boys': everyday, except suits & sportswear; Clothing, sportswear, men's & boys'; Flowers, fresh; Candy

D-U-N-S 07-396-9388
SAINT ANSELM COLLEGE
100 Saint Anselm Dr, Manchester, NH 03102-1310
Tel (603) 641-7000 *Founded/Ownrshp* 1889
Sales 111.1MM *EMP* 700
SIC 8221 College, except junior
Pr: Dr Steven Disalvo
**Pr:* Fr J Defelice
**Pr:* Fr Matthew Leavy
**Treas:* Fr Mark Cooper
**Treas:* Rev Mark A Cooper
Trst: John Healy
Trst: Michael Sheehan
Ex VP: Martha Dickerson
VP: Harry Dumay
Assoc Dir: Gerald Cournoyer
Assoc Dir: Christina Doyle
Assoc Dir: Sarah Goolkasian
Assoc Dir: Sarah Mockler
Creative D: Melinda Lott

D-U-N-S 06-858-0174 EXP
SAINT ANTHONY HOSPITAL
2875 W 19th St, Chicago, IL 60623-3596
Tel (773) 484-1000 *Founded/Ownrshp* 1897
Sales 105.1MM *EMP* 700
SIC 8062 General medical & surgical hospitals
CEO: Guy Medaglia
**CFO:* Charles R Brobst
CFO: Justin Bynum
VP: Neelam Bhardwaj
**VP:* Aileen Brooks
VP: Ellen Buke
VP: David Furst
VP: Irwin Katz
VP: Denise Leon
**VP:* Jill Stemmerman
VP: Jill Summerman
Dir Lab: Syed Husain

D-U-N-S 94-126-1158
SAINT ANTHONY MEMORIAL HEALTH CENTERS
301 W Homer St, Michigan City, IN 46360-4358
Tel (219) 877-1710 *Founded/Ownrshp* 1999
Sales 125.4MM *EMP* 1,000
SIC 8093 Rehabilitation center, outpatient treatment
VP Opers: Trish Weber

D-U-N-S 07-718-2251
SAINT BARNABAS CORP
SAINT BARNABAS HEALTH CARE SYS
95 Old Short Hills Rd, West Orange, NJ 07052-1008
Tel (973) 322-5000 *Founded/Ownrshp* 2016
Sales 1.8MMM^E *EMP* 24,600
SIC 8062 8082 General medical & surgical hospitals; Home health care services
Pr: Barry Ostrowsky

SAINT BARNABAS HEALTH CARE SYS
See SAINT BARNABAS CORP

SAINT BARNABAS HEALTH CARE SYS
See SAINT BARNABAS REALTY DEVELOP CORP

D-U-N-S 96-787-1083
SAINT BARNABAS REALTY DEVELOP CORP
SAINT BARNABAS HEALTH CARE SYS
(*Suby of* SAINT BARNABAS HEALTH CARE SYS) ★
94 Old Short Hills Rd, Livingston, NJ 07039-5672
Tel (732) 923-8072 *Founded/Ownrshp* 2011
Sales 9.5MM *EMP* 1,563^E
Accts Withumsmithbrown Pc Morristow
SIC 6531 Real estate agents & managers
Prin: Thomas G Scott CPA

D-U-N-S 14-307-4420
SAINT CHARLES MEDICAL CENTER REDMOND
(*Suby of* ST CHARLES HEALTH SYSTEM INC) ★
1253 Nw Canal Blvd, Redmond, OR 97756-1334
Tel (541) 548-8131 *Founded/Ownrshp* 2004
Sales 84.9MM *EMP* 1
SIC 8011 Medical centers
Pr: Dave Berman
VP: Rick Martin
VP: Pamela Steinke
Off Mgr: Tami Endicott

SAINT CLARE'S HEALTH SYSTEM
See SAINT CLARES HOSPITAL INC

D-U-N-S 01-089-8880
SAINT CLARES HOSPITAL INC (NJ)
SAINT CLARE'S HEALTH SYSTEM
(*Suby of* CHI) ★
25 Pocono Rd, Denville, NJ 07834-2954
Tel (973) 625-6000 *Founded/Ownrshp* 1994, 2008
Sales 273.0MM *EMP* 2,702
SIC 8062 General medical & surgical hospitals
Pr: Leslie D Hirsch
Off Mgr: Matthew Lucariello
Opers Mgr: Kimberly Donnenberg
Surgeon: Frank Capecci
Obsttrcn: Lawrence Boveri

D-U-N-S 18-542-7858
SAINT CLARES HOSPITAL OF WESTON INC
MINISTRY SAINT CLARES HOSPITAL
3400 Ministry Pkwy, Schofield, WI 54476-5220
Tel (715) 393-3000 *Founded/Ownrshp* 2002
Sales 104.6MM *EMP* 580
Accts Deloitte Tax Lp Milwaukee Wi
SIC 8062 General medical & surgical hospitals
Pr: Mary Krueger
**Chf Mktg O:* Larry Hegland
Nurse Mgr: Jennifer Rhea
CIO: Brian Kief
Mktg Dir: Tom Weaver

D-U-N-S 06-642-2098
SAINT EDWARDS UNIVERSITY INC
3001 S Congress Ave, Austin, TX 78704-6489
Tel (512) 448-8400 *Founded/Ownrshp* 1885
Sales 121.4MM *EMP* 964^E
Accts Bkd Llp Cpas & Advisors San A
SIC 8221 University
Pr: George E Martin

Pr: Christie Campbell
**CFO:* Rhonda Cartwright
**CFO:* Kimberly Kvaal
Trst: Michael Aviles
Trst: James Branigan
Trst: Timothy F Gavin
Trst: Margaret M Krasovec
Trst: Myra A McDaniel
Trst: Roy Peque O
Trst: Marilyn O'Neill
Trst: Duncan K Underwood
VP: Bill Clabby
VP: Mark Jacaman
VP: Taylor Johnson
VP: Robert Manzer
VP: Sandra Pacheco
VP: David Waldron
Dir Teleco: Dave Wilmot
Assoc Dir: Brenda Adrian
Assoc Dir: Ellisha D Isom

SAINT ELIZABETH HOSPITAL PHARM
See SAINT ELIZABETH REGIONAL MEDICAL CENTER

D-U-N-S 07-677-9651
SAINT ELIZABETH MEDICAL CENTER INC
CHANCELLOR SURGERY CENTER
1 Medical Village Dr, Edgewood, KY 41017-3403
Tel (859) 301-2000 *Founded/Ownrshp* 1868
Sales 633.5MM *EMP* 6,227[E]
SIC 8062 8069 8093 General medical & surgical hospitals; Hospital, AMA approved residency; Specialty hospitals, except psychiatric; Substance abuse hospitals; Specialty outpatient clinics
Pr: John Dubis
Dir Recs: Cindy Stroud
**COO:* Garren Colvin
**COO:* Marc Hoffman
**Treas:* Nathan Vanlaningham
VP: Glenda Harned
VP: Lori Ritchey
VP: Allen Zobay
Dir Rx: Andrea Schumann
Dir Rx: Paul Sinclair
Off Mgr: Lauren Jones

SAINT ELIZABETH REGIONAL HLTH
See GREATER LAFAYETTE HEALTH SERVICES INC

D-U-N-S 07-290-4782 IMP
SAINT ELIZABETH REGIONAL MEDICAL CENTER
SAINT ELIZABETH HOSPITAL PHARM
555 S 70th St, Lincoln, NE 68510-2462
Tel (402) 219-5200 *Founded/Ownrshp* 1889
Sales 212.4MM *EMP* 1,825
Accts Catholic Health Initiatives E
SIC 8062 8082 General medical & surgical hospitals; Home health care services
Pr: Robert J Lanik
Dir Recs: Elizabeth Bechtle
**Pr:* Kim Moore
Chf Mktg O: Kary Ward
**VP:* Libby Raetz
VP: Dan Schonlau
Dir Rad: Mike Hopkins
Dir Rad: John Speaker
Dir Sec: Steve Imes
Prac Mgr: Danielle Funcke
DP Dir: Rick Bohaty

D-U-N-S 07-373-1440
SAINT EUGENE MEDICAL CENTER
MCLEOD REGIONAL MED CNTR OF
(*Suby of* MCCLEOD MED CENTER-DARLINGTON) ★
301 E Jackson St, Dillon, SC 29536-2509
Tel (843) 774-4111 *Founded/Ownrshp* 1972
Sales 514.5MM *EMP* 300
SIC 8062 General medical & surgical hospitals
Pr: Donald Sandoval
Ansthlgy: Zizette Gabriel

D-U-N-S 10-407-8258
SAINT FRANCIS COMMUNITY SERVICES INC
509 E Elm St, Salina, KS 67401-2353
Tel (785) 825-0541 *Founded/Ownrshp* 1945
Sales 91.3MM *EMP* 926
Accts Kcoe Isom Llp Salina Kansas
SIC 8741 8361 Hospital management; Residential care
CEO: Fr Edward Fellhauer
**CFO:* Melanie Owens
Ex VP: Janet Atteberry
**VP:* Trish Bryant
VP: Cory Rathbun
Comm Dir: Shane Schneider
Adm Dir: Susan Montague
Ex Dir: Mike Dobson
Ex Dir: Rachel Marsh
**Ex Dir:* Revrobert Nelson Smith
Dept Mgr: Krista Patrick

SAINT FRANCIS HEALTH SYSTEM
See WARREN CLINIC INC

D-U-N-S 19-461-3949
SAINT FRANCIS HEALTH SYSTEM INC
ST FRANCIS HEALTH SYSTEMS
6161 S Yale Ave, Tulsa, OK 74136-1902
Tel (918) 494-2200 *Founded/Ownrshp* 1955
Sales 1.1MMM *EMP* 8,200
Accts Ernst & Young Llp Tulsa Ok
SIC 8011 Clinic, operated by physicians
CEO: Jake Henry
**CFO:* Barry Steinchen
**VP:* Jeffrey Sacra

SAINT FRANCIS HOSP & MED CTR
See SAINT FRANCIS HOSPITAL AND MEDICAL CENTER FOUNDATION INC

D-U-N-S 14-566-8740
■ **SAINT FRANCIS HOSPITAL - BARTLETT INC**
S F
(*Suby of* TENET HEALTHCARE CORP) ★
2986 Kate Bond Rd, Bartlett, TN 38133-4003
Tel (901) 820-7000 *Founded/Ownrshp* 2004
Sales 123.0MM *EMP* 700[E]
SIC 8062 General medical & surgical hospitals
CEO: Jeremy Clark
Doctor: Pamela Davis

D-U-N-S 07-731-4656
SAINT FRANCIS HOSPITAL AND MEDICAL CENTER FOUNDATION INC
SAINT FRANCIS HOSP & MED CTR
114 Woodland St, Hartford, CT 06105-1208
Tel (860) 714-4006 *Founded/Ownrshp* 1897
Sales 670.2MM *EMP* 3,270
SIC 8062 8011 8069 Hospital, professional nursing school; Offices & clinics of medical doctors; Cancer hospital
CEO: Christopher M Dadlez
Dir Recs: Allison Nicklas
V Ch: Thomas J Barry
**Pr:* John Rodis
COO: Mary Iguanti
COO: Kathleen Rocke
CFO: John Giamalis
**CFO:* Steven H Rosenberg
Ofcr: Marilyn Bogues
Ofcr: Sally Hodgdon
Ex VP: Angelo S Carrabba
Sr VP: Edward S Johnson
Sr VP: Jim Schepker
**VP:* Karen Beauchesne
VP: Teresa Bolton
VP: Bob Falaguerra
VP: Christopher C Hartley
**VP:* Nicole J Schulz
**VP:* Donald Straceski
Exec: Linda Bessette
Exec: Paul Pendergast

D-U-N-S 06-454-8175
SAINT FRANCIS HOSPITAL INC
(*Suby of* ST FRANCIS HEALTH SYSTEMS) ★
6161 S Yale Ave, Tulsa, OK 74136-1992
Tel (918) 502-2050 *Founded/Ownrshp* 1955
Sales 877.4MM *EMP* 4,000
SIC 8062 7352 5999 Hospital, medical school affiliation; Medical equipment rental; Medical apparatus & supplies
Ex Dir: Mike Russo
Pr: Mike Wilson
CFO: Stacie Mason
Ofcr: Jeffrey Sacra
Ofcr: David Weil
Sr VP: Lynn Sund
Dir Risk M: Sandra Shirley
Dir Rad: Pam Mitchell
Ex Dir: Doug A Williams
Off Mgr: Rick Gillis
CTO: Mark Weber
Board of Directors: Andria Stolhand

D-U-N-S 13-541-9252
SAINT FRANCIS HOSPITAL SOUTH LLC
(*Suby of* SAINT FRANCIS HOSPITAL INC) ★
10501 E 91st St, Tulsa, OK 74133-5790
Tel (918) 307-6000 *Founded/Ownrshp* 2002
Sales 91.1MM *EMP* 310
SIC 8062 General medical & surgical hospitals
Sfty Mgr: Ellen Bettinger
Obsttrcn: Amy Golden

D-U-N-S 07-800-6442
SAINT FRANCIS MEDICAL CENTER INC (NE)
CHI
(*Suby of* CHI) ★
2620 W Faidley Ave, Grand Island, NE 68803-4297
Tel (308) 384-4600 *Founded/Ownrshp* 1887, 1980
Sales 133.0MM *EMP* 1,200
SIC 8062 8069

D-U-N-S 07-464-7959
SAINT FRANCIS MEMORIAL HOSPITAL
(*Suby of* DIGNITY HEALTH) ★
900 Hyde St, San Francisco, CA 94109-4899
Tel (415) 353-6000 *Founded/Ownrshp* 1905
Sales 221.9MM *EMP* 1,100
Accts Kpmg Llp San Francisco Ca
SIC 8062 General medical & surgical hospitals
CEO: Thomas G Hennessy
**Pr:* John G Williams
**COO:* Cheryl A Fama Rn
CFO: Alan Fox
CFO: Craig Rucker
Ofcr: Malissa Karsseboom
Dir Rx: Ray Miller
Prin: Robert Durealt
Surgeon: James Garrick
Surgeon: Victor Prieto
Doctor: Susan L Lewis MD

D-U-N-S 04-125-5993
SAINT FRANCIS UNIVERSITY
117 Evergreen Dr, Loretto, PA 15940-9704
Tel (814) 472-3000 *Founded/Ownrshp* 1847
Sales 93.0MM *EMP* 420
Accts Baker Tilly Virchow Krause Llp
SIC 8221 College, except junior
Pr: Rev Malachi Van Tassell
Bd of Dir: Brent Ottaway
VP: Richard Crawford
VP: Jeffery Savino
VP: Patricia Serotkin
Assoc Dir: Jim Brazill
Assoc Dir: Paul Girardi
Genl Mgr: Leo Cavanaugh
Dir IT: Kent Tonkin
Mktg Dir: Laura Papcunik
Mktg Dir: Marie Young

SAINT FRANCIS-POUGHKEEPSIE
See ST FRANCIS HOSPITAL POUGHKEEPSIE NEW YORK

D-U-N-S 82-874-7175 IMP
SAINT GOBAIN GRAINS & POWDERS
(*Suby of* SAINT-GOBAIN CORP) ★
6600 Walmore Rd, Niagara Falls, NY 14304-1638
Tel (716) 731-8200 *Founded/Ownrshp* 2008
Sales 102.5MM[E] *EMP* 1,608[E]
SIC 3221 3269 2891 Glass containers; Food containers, glass; Bottles for packing, bottling & canning: glass; Vials, glass; Laboratory & industrial pottery; Chemical porcelain; Adhesives; Adhesives, plastic; Cement, except linoleum & tile; Epoxy adhesives
Prin: Tom Vincent

SAINT JAMES HOSP & HLTH CTRS
See ST JAMES HOSPITAL & HEALTH CENTERS INC

SAINT JAMES HOSPITAL
See FRANCISCAN ALLIANCE INC

SAINT JHNS BHAVIORAL HLTH CARE
See MERCY HEALTH SPRINGFIELD COMMUNITIES

SAINT JHNS VCTRIA NRSING FCLTY
See ST JOHNS REST HOME INC

D-U-N-S 07-294-5850
SAINT JOHNS HEALTH CENTER FOUNDATION
(*Suby of* SCL HEALTH SYSTEM) ★
2121 Santa Monica Blvd, Santa Monica, CA 90404-2303
Tel (310) 829-8424 *Founded/Ownrshp* 1975
Sales 330.2MM *EMP* 1,300
SIC 8062

D-U-N-S 06-456-7124
SAINT JOHNS HEALTH CTR D6
500 Eldorado Blvd # 6300, Broomfield, CO 80021-3422
Tel (913) 895-2800 *Founded/Ownrshp* 2013
Sales 313.2MM *EMP* 9[E]
SIC 8099 Health & allied services
Prin: Barry Harding

SAINT JOHN'S HOSPITAL
See ST JOHNS HOSPITAL SISTERS OF THIRD ORDER OF ST FRANCIS

SAINT JOHN'S MEDICAL SUPPLIES
See ST VINCENT ANDERSON REGIONAL HOSPITAL INC

SAINT JOSEPH HEALTH CENTER
See CARONDELET HEALTH

D-U-N-S 96-937-5588
SAINT JOSEPH HEALTH SYSTEM INC
KENTUCKYONE HEALTH SOURCE
(*Suby of* KENTUCKYONE HEALTH SOURCE) ★
1 Saint Joseph Dr, Lexington, KY 40504-3742
Tel (859) 313-1000 *Founded/Ownrshp* 2012
Sales 274.0MM *EMP* 99[E]
Accts Catholic Health Initiatives E
SIC 8062 8099 8011 General medical & surgical hospitals; Blood related health services; Offices & clinics of medical doctors
Ch: Doug Hacker
**Pr:* Ruth Brinkley
Pr: Jennie Rockidge
COO: Carmel Jones
**Treas:* Brutus Clay
Sr VP: Rose Patrick
VP: Kim Hite
VP: Christine Mays
VP: Ron Skarka
Dir Lab: Theresa Maberly
Dir Lab: Dennis Netzel
Dir Rx: Michael D Deluca
Dir Rx: Dana L Foster

SAINT JOSEPH HOSPITAL & HEALTH
See ST JOSEPH MEMORIAL HOSPITAL

D-U-N-S 05-579-2063 IMP
SAINT JOSEPH HOSPITAL INC
(*Suby of* SISTERS OF CHARITY OF LEAVENWR) ★
1375 E 19th Ave, Denver, CO 80218-1114
Tel (303) 812-2000 *Founded/Ownrshp* 1998
Sales 465.8MM *EMP* 2,300
SIC 8062 Hospital, medical school affiliated with residency; Hospital, AMA approved residency
Pr: Bain Farris
Chf OB: Gerald V Zarlengo
Ch Bd: William Jessee
Pr: Bain J Farris
COO: Margo Carsten
COO: Barbara Jahn
CFO: Buzz Binder
VP: Al Davis
VP: Shawn Dufford
VP: Sean Gregory
VP: Barb Jahn
VP: Brad Ludford
VP: Barbara Manor
VP: Mary Shepler
Dir Case M: Maureen Murphy
Dir Lab: Jerome Schroeder
Dir Rx: Donald Tillman
Dir Bus: Ann Wilcox

D-U-N-S 06-470-7425
SAINT JOSEPH MEDICAL CENTER INC
SAINT JOSEPH REGIONAL
5215 Holy Cross Pkwy, Mishawaka, IN 46545-1469
Tel (574) 335-5000 *Founded/Ownrshp* 2005
Sales 300.9MM *EMP* 3,000
SIC 8062 General medical & surgical hospitals
Pr: Albert L Gutierrez
**COO:* Christopher Karam
**CFO:* Janice Dunn
**VP:* Steven Gable
**VP:* Pamela Henderson
**Prin:* Nancy Hellyer
Off Mgr: Bonnie Hosinski
Doctor: Joseph G Glazier MD

SAINT JOSEPH REGIONAL
See SAINT JOSEPH MEDICAL CENTER INC

D-U-N-S 11-739-8453
SAINT JOSEPH REGIONAL MEDICAL CENTER-SOUTH BEND CAMPUS INC
SR. MAURA BRANNICK DENTAL CENT
(*Suby of* CATHOLIC HEALTH EAST) ★
5215 Holy Cross Pkwy, Mishawaka, IN 46545-1469
Tel (574) 335-5000 *Founded/Ownrshp* 1958
Sales 324.8MM *EMP* 680
SIC 8011 Medical centers
CEO: Albert Gutierrez
Chf Rad: Robert Burke
**Pr:* Nancy Helleyer
**CFO:* Janice Dunn
**Treas:* Charles Viater
VP: Steven Gable
Exec: Cliff Martin
Dir Lab: Kim Lamar
Ex Dir: Linda Zeese
Off Mgr: Bonnie Hosinski
CIO: Gary Miller

D-U-N-S 07-615-8179 IMP
SAINT JOSEPHS COMMUNITY HOSPITAL
SYNERGY HEALTH OF ST JOSEPH'S
3200 Pleasant Valley Rd, West Bend, WI 53095-9274
Tel (262) 334-5533 *Founded/Ownrshp* 1967
Sales 126.2MM *EMP* 688
Accts Kpmg Llp Columbus Oh
SIC 8062 General medical & surgical hospitals
Pr: Dennis Pollard
**Ch Bd:* Greg Miller
Pr: Johnstone Candice
Pr: David Olson
CFO: Scott Hauge
Ofcr: Karen Ernisse
VP: Mike Malzewiski
VP: Dana Seflow
Dir Rad: Gary Rogaczewsky
CIO: Robert Degrand
QA Dir: Jan Giedd

D-U-N-S 07-248-1476
SAINT JOSEPHS HOSPITAL INC
5353 Reynolds St, Savannah, GA 31405-6015
Tel (912) 355-9967 *Founded/Ownrshp* 1875
Sales 185.9MM *EMP* 1,145
Accts Draffin & Tucker Llp Albany
SIC 8062 General medical & surgical hospitals
Pr: Paul P Hinchey
**Pr:* Paul Hinchey
**COO:* John Adkins
**CFO:* Gregory Schaack
**VP:* Danny Brown
Dir Bus: Celeste Shearouse
Nurse Mgr: Judy Boykin
Netwrk Mgr: Angela Hathaway
Snr Mgr: Suzanne White

D-U-N-S 82-893-2090
SAINT JOSEPHS HOSPITAL INC
11705 Mercy Blvd, Savannah, GA 31419-1791
Tel (912) 819-4100 *Founded/Ownrshp* 1946
Sales 192.0MM *EMP* 19
SIC 8062 General medical & surgical hospitals
CEO: Paul P Hinchey
Chf Rad: David Estle
COO: Kyle McCann
Chf Mktg O: Menzanna Blakley
VP: Bill Mahler
VP: Peter Schenk
VP: Robert Smith
Dir Inf Cn: Leigh Craft
Dir Rx: Ray Maddox
CIO: George Evans
CIO: Nolan Hennessee

D-U-N-S 84-315-3610
SAINT JOSEPHS HOSPITAL INC
300 Werner St, Hot Springs, AR 71913-6448
Tel (501) 622-1000 *Founded/Ownrshp* 1994
Sales 63.1MM[E] *EMP* 1,400[E]
SIC 8011 Clinic, operated by physicians
CEO: Tim Johnson

D-U-N-S 07-938-0481
SAINT JOSEPHS HOSPITAL OF ATLANTA INC
SAINT JOSEPH'S PRMRY CRE NTWRK
(*Suby of* EMORY HEALTHCARE INC) ★
5665 Peachtree Dunwoody Rd Ne, Atlanta, GA 30342-1764
Tel (404) 851-7001 *Founded/Ownrshp* 2011
Sales 178.9MM[E] *EMP* 2,300[E]
SIC 8062 General medical & surgical hospitals
CEO: Craig McCoy
Chf Rad: Charles J Fulp
Pr: John Banks
COO: Paul Johnson
CFO: Michael Gardenier
**CFO:* Joann Manning
CFO: Tim Pollard
Bd of Dir: Timothy Cambias
Bd of Dir: Douglas Murphy
Ex VP: Maureen Deblois
**VP:* Heather Dexter
Dir Risk M: Renee D Allison
Dir Lab: Marilyn Kenyon
Dir Lab: Dennis Kmetz

D-U-N-S 07-477-8846
SAINT JOSEPHS HOSPITAL OF MARSHFIELD INC
SAINTS JOSEPH'S HOSPITAL
611 N Saint Joseph Ave, Marshfield, WI 54449-1832
Tel (715) 387-1713 *Founded/Ownrshp* 1890
Sales 382.1MM *EMP* 2,200[E]
Accts Deloitte Tax Lp Milwaukee Wi
SIC 8062 Hospital, affiliated with AMA residency
CEO: Michael Kryda
**Pr:* Michael A Schmidt
**CFO:* John Skadin
Dir Inf Cn: Celeste Hilgart
Ex Dir: Judy Riedel
Dir IT: Jerry Hubbard
Mtls Mgr: Stan Swedburg

SAINT JOSEPHS MERCY HEALTH CTR
See ST JOSEPHS REGIONAL HEALTH CENTER (INC)

D-U-N-S 15-062-8931
SAINT JOSEPHS PRIMARY CARE NETWORK INC
(*Suby of* EMORY HEALTHCARE INC) ★
5673 Peachtree Dunwdy, Atlanta, GA 30342-1731
Tel (404) 778-6100 *Founded/Ownrshp* 1985
Sales 3.3MM *EMP* 2,315

Accts Pricewaterhousecoopers Llp Ha
SIC 8741 Hospital management
Sr VP: Sr Jane Gerety

SAINT JOSEPH'S PRMRY CRE NTWRK
See SAINT JOSEPHS HOSPITAL OF ATLANTA INC

D-U-N-S 60-449-2702
SAINT JOSEPHS SERVICE CORP
(*Suby of* SAINT JOSEPHS PRIMARY CARE NETWORK INC) ★
5665 Peachtree Dunwoody Rd, Atlanta, GA 30342-1764
Tel (404) 851-7001 *Founded/Ownrshp* 1989
Sales 3.3MM^E *EMP* 2,315
SIC 8062 General medical & surgical hospitals
CEO: Paul Johnson
CFO: Kevin Brenan
**CFO:* Kevin Brennan
Ofcr: Laura Roberts
Ex VP: Maureen Deblois
VP: Leslie Brothers
**VP:* Heather Dexter
VP: Amparo Gonzalez
Exec: Cindi Bailey
Exec: Carissa Hawkins
**Prin:* Paul Justice

D-U-N-S 07-549-5937
SAINT JOSEPHS UNIVERSITY
5600 City Ave, Philadelphia, PA 19131-1376
Tel (610) 660-1000 *Founded/Ownrshp* 1851
Sales 307.8MM *EMP* 1,138
Accts Deloitte Tax Llp Philadelphia
SIC 8221 University
Pr: Timothy Lannon
**Ch Bd:* Robert D Falese Jr
Pr: Joseph Cassidy
**Pr:* Daniel J Hilferty III
**Pr:* C Kevin Gillespie S J
**Pr:* Timothy Lannon
Pr: Joe Lunardi
**CFO:* Edward W Moneypenny
**Treas:* Louis Mayer
Ofcr: Megan Mangefrida
Ofcr: Joseph F Reilly
Ex VP: Dennis Sheehan
Ex VP: Sean Sweeney
VP: Cary Anderson
VP: Joan Chrestay
VP: Stephanie Pricken
VP: Theresa Travis
Assoc Dir: Laura Dietz
Assoc Dir: Kristin Heasley
Assoc Dir: Kevin Kaufman
Assoc Dir: Maria L Mooney

SAINT JOSEPH'S WAYNE HOSPITAL
See ST JOSEPHS WAYNE HOSPITAL INC

D-U-N-S 02-098-7020
SAINT LEO UNIVERSITY INC
33701 State Road 52, Saint Leo, FL 33574-9700
Tel (352) 588-8200 *Founded/Ownrshp* 1890
Sales 193.6MM *EMP* 819
Accts Kpmg Llp Tampa Fl
SIC 8221 College, except junior
Pr: William Lennox
VP: Zachary Harris
Assoc Dir: Amanda Black
Assoc Dir: Peter Gressick
Assoc Dir: Daniel Stutzman
Ex Dir: Elihu Ohara
Dir IT: Vyas Krishnan
Netwrk Eng: David A Carr

SAINT LOUIS BREAD CO
See TRADITIONAL BAKERY INC

D-U-N-S 05-022-0722
SAINT LOUIS UNIVERSITY
1 N Grand Blvd, Saint Louis, MO 63103-2006
Tel (314) 977-2500 *Founded/Ownrshp* 1818
Sales 649.7MM^E *EMP* 7,500
Accts Kpmg Llp Columbus Oh
SIC 8221 University
Pr: Fred P Pestello
CFO: Robert Woodruff
Treas: Gary L Whitworth
VP: Tim Brooks
VP: William R Kauffman
VP: Frank Reale
VP: Raymond Tait
Off Mgr: Sue Debarry
Off Admin: Sheila Arnold
IT Man: Kirk Fortune
Doctor: Mark Herbers

D-U-N-S 36-100-8993
SAINT LOUISE HOSPITAL
9400 N Name Uno, Gilroy, CA 95020-3528
Tel (408) 848-2000 *Founded/Ownrshp* 2005
Sales 90.6MM *EMP* 500
Accts Grant Thornton Llp San Franci
SIC 8062 General medical & surgical hospitals
CEO: Jim Dober
**VP:* Terry Curley
Dir Lab: Ernest Spencer
**Prin:* Joanne Allan

D-U-N-S 04-789-1903
SAINT LUKES HEALTH SYSTEM INC
901 E 104th St, Kansas City, MO 64131-4517
Tel (816) 932-2000 *Founded/Ownrshp* 1996
Sales 140.4MM *EMP* 5,111
SIC 8062 General medical & surgical hospitals
CEO: Cliff A Robertson
Dir Recs: Melinda Hanaway
**Ch Bd:* Robert West
COO: Joann C Mdonough
COO: Will Staron
CFO: Sally Border
CFO: Shelby Frigon
**CFO:* Charles Robb
**Treas:* John Holland
Treas: Graham Hunt
**Ofcr:* William C Daniel
Ofcr: Katherine A Howell
Sr VP: Leonardo J Lozada
Sr VP: Julie L Quirin
Sr VP: Chuck Robb
VP: Bob Bonney
VP: Nancy Seelen
VP: Debbie White
Exec: Brad Hoffman
Dir Risk M: Bonnie Johnson
Dir Lab: Christy Gibson

SAINT LUKE'S HOSPITAL
See ST LUKES METHODIST HOSPITAL INC

SAINT LUKES HOSPITAL KANSAS CY
See SAINT LUKES HOSPITAL OF KANSAS CITY

D-U-N-S 07-366-4039
SAINT LUKES HOSPITAL OF BETHLEHEM PENNSYLVANIA
ST LUKES HOSP & HLTH NETWRK
(*Suby of* ST LUKES HOSPITAL & HEALTH NETWORK INC) ★
801 Ostrum St, Bethlehem, PA 18015-1000
Tel (484) 526-4000 *Founded/Ownrshp* 1872
Sales 629.4MM *EMP* 2,958
Accts Withumsmithbrown Pc Morristow
SIC 8062 8249 Hospital, professional nursing school; Medical training services
Pr: Richard A Anderson
**Pr:* Thomas P Lichtenwalner
COO: John J Haney
CFO: Tom Lichtenwalner
Sr VP: Jeffrey Jahre
Sr VP: Evan Jones
Sr VP: Seymour Traub
VP: Patrick J Bower
VP: Kevin M Fache
Dir Lab: Cynthia McKellin
Rgnl Mgr: Dave Capuano

D-U-N-S 07-303-9653 IMP
SAINT LUKES HOSPITAL OF KANSAS CITY
SAINT LUKES HOSPITAL KANSAS CY
(*Suby of* SAINT LUKES HEALTH SYSTEM INC) ★
4401 Wornall Rd, Kansas City, MO 64111-3241
Tel (816) 932-2000 *Founded/Ownrshp* 1984
Sales 561.5MM *EMP* 5,000
SIC 8062 8742 8011 6512 8082 7322 General medical & surgical hospitals; Management consulting services; Offices & clinics of medical doctors; Nonresidential building operators; Home health care services; Adjustment & collection services
CEO: Julie Quirin
**COO:* Brad Simmons
**CFO:* Amy Nachtigal
Treas: John Holland
Sr VP: Dawn Murphy
Dir Risk M: Sally Thieman
Dir Lab: Kristy Gibson
Dir Rad: Steve Bollin
Dir Rad: John H McMillan
**Ex Dir:* Debbie Wilson
Dir Sec: David Young

D-U-N-S 07-570-4932
SAINT LUKES HOSPITAL OF NEW BEDFORD INC
ST LUKE'S HOSPITAL
101 Page St, New Bedford, MA 02740-3464
Tel (508) 997-1515 *Founded/Ownrshp* 1884
Sales 124.8MM^E *EMP* 1,872
SIC 8062 8082 8093 General medical & surgical hospitals; Home health care services; Specialty outpatient clinics
Pr: Alfred J Smialek
**Ch Bd:* John Hodgson
**Pr:* Kieth Shozan
**CFO:* Linda Bodenmann
**Treas:* Leslie V Belken
**Treas:* Joseph Iannoni
Doctor: Catherine A Kiley MD
Pharmcst: Haylie Carvalho
Pharmcst: Christopher Goncalo
Pharmcst: Doug Haskins

D-U-N-S 95-650-0466
SAINT LUKES METHODIST HOSPITAL INC
OCCUPATIONAL THERAPY
1026 A Ave Ne, Cedar Rapids, IA 52402-5036
Tel (319) 369-7209 *Founded/Ownrshp* 1900
Sales 3.0MM^E *EMP* 1,300
SIC 8049 Occupational therapist
Prin: Steven Vanourny

D-U-N-S 07-628-3175
SAINT LUKES NORTHLAND HOME CARE
601 S Us Highway 169, Smithville, MO 64089-9317
Tel (816) 532-3700 *Founded/Ownrshp* 1993
Sales 111.0MM *EMP* 900
SIC 8062 8051 8069 8063 General medical & surgical hospitals; Skilled nursing care facilities; Substance abuse hospitals; Psychiatric hospitals
CEO: Gary Wages
Sr VP: Kevin Trimble
Dir Rad: Lawrence E Lee
Genl Mgr: Craig Williams
Mtls Mgr: Cheryl Lee

D-U-N-S 01-283-8244
SAINT LUKES SOUTH HOSPITAL INC
12300 Metcalf Ave, Shawnee Mission, KS 66213-1324
Tel (913) 317-7000 *Founded/Ownrshp* 1998
Sales 104.2MM *EMP* 310
SIC 8062 General medical & surgical hospitals
Pr: Charles Horner
**CFO:* Amy Nachtegal
Treas: William Roche
VP: Marie Griffin
Dir Lab: Ellen Deshone
Dir QC: Erica Hudson
Opers Mgr: Kathy Gover
Obsttrcn: Richard F Hill
Ansthlgy: Ralph W Richardson
Doctor: Gerald Staab
Nrsg Dir: Gary Christian

SAINT MARGARET MERCY
See ST MARGARET MERCY HEALTHCARE CENTERS INC

D-U-N-S 84-826-7696
SAINT MARGARET MERCY HEALTHCARE CENTER
(*Suby of* SAINT JAMES HOSPITAL) ★
24 Joliet St, Dyer, IN 46311-1799
Tel (219) 865-2141 *Founded/Ownrshp* 1942
Sales 96.8MM^E *EMP* 3,000
SIC 8062 8063 General medical & surgical hospitals; Psychiatric hospitals
Pr: Gene Diamond
Ansthlgy: Dipak Shah
Ansthlgy: Timothy White
Pharmcst: Diane Guba

D-U-N-S 07-652-6599
SAINT MARYS COLLEGE OF CALIFORNIA
1928 Saint Marys Rd, Moraga, CA 94575-2744
Tel (925) 631-4000 *Founded/Ownrshp* 1863
Sales 178.5MM *EMP* 1,000
Accts Baker Tilly Virchow Krause Llp
SIC 8221 College, except junior
Pr: Ronald Gallagher
Ofcr: Mark Chiarucci
Ofcr: Karrie Hagedorn
VP: Keith Brandt
VP: Bethami Dobkin
VP: Peter A Michell
VP: Lisa M Moore
Assoc Dir: Maria Flores
Assoc Dir: Jennifer Pigza
Ex Dir: Steve Kennedy
Prgrm Mgr: Sara Mumolo

D-U-N-S 80-361-9733
SAINT MARYS HEALTH CARE CORP
ST MARY'S HEALTH NETWORK
235 W 6th St, Reno, NV 89503-4548
Tel (775) 770-3000 *Founded/Ownrshp* 1981
Sales 165.6MM^E *EMP* 2,300
SIC 8062 General medical & surgical hospitals
CEO: Larry O'Brien
COO: Helen Lidholm
CFO: Dan Galles
Chf Nrs Of: Katie Grimm
CIO: Mike Montgomery
Psych: Kerry Roberts-Manson
Doctor: Brian Barnes

D-U-N-S 36-139-3994
SAINT MARYS HEALTH SYSTEM INC
56 Franklin St, Waterbury, CT 06706-1253
Tel (203) 709-6000 *Founded/Ownrshp* 1984
Sales 156.5M *EMP* 1,566
SIC 8062 7011 General medical & surgical hospitals; Hotel, franchised
Pr: Chad W Wable
CFO: Ralph Becker
VP: Clark Kennedy
Dir Sec: Mark Casey
QA Dir: James Tucker
Mktg Dir: Joseph Connolly
Mktg Dir: Clark Kearney
Surgeon: Robert Wetmore
Doctor: Winston Magno
Nrsg Dir: William Frederick

SAINT MARY'S HOSPITAL
See MERCY HOSPITAL ROGERS

D-U-N-S 07-136-3246
SAINT MARYS HOSPITAL
(*Suby of* MAYO CLINIC) ★
1216 2nd St Sw, Rochester, MN 55902-1970
Tel (507) 255-5123 *Founded/Ownrshp* 1968
Sales 1.9MMM *EMP* 3,250
SIC 8062 General medical & surgical hospitals
Pr: Robert R Waller
CFO: Stan Hofbauer
Pharmcst: Nancy Ollenburger

SAINT MARYS HOSPITAL & MED CTR
See ST MARYS HOSPITAL & MEDICAL CENTER INC

D-U-N-S 01-014-5811
SAINT MARYS HOSPITAL INC
56 Franklin St Ste 1, Waterbury, CT 06706-1281
Tel (203) 709-6000 *Founded/Ownrshp* 1984
Sales 294.3MM *EMP* 1,520
Accts Kpmg Llp Hartford Ct
SIC 8062 General medical & surgical hospitals
COO: Phillip Candito
VP: Thomas Senker
VP: Chad Wable
Dir Case M: Mary Phelan
Dir Rx: Daniel Sullivan
CTO: Lindsey Donato
Telecom Mg: Mark Casey
IT Man: Sharon Costa
Surgeon: Robert Hendrikson
Surgeon: Robert Wetmore
Surgeon: Donna Wysocki

SAINT MARYS MICHIGAN MED CTR
See ST MARYS MEDICAL CENTER OF SAGINAW INC

SAINT MARYS REGIONAL MED CTR
See PRIME HEALTHCARE SERVICES - RENO LLC

D-U-N-S 07-404-7093
SAINT MARYS RIVERSIDE
ST. MARY'S RIVERSIDE
(*Suby of* ST MARYS HOSPITAL) ★
37 Washington Ave, Evansville, IN 47713-1317
Tel (812) 485-8000 *Founded/Ownrshp* 1999
Sales 26.7MM^E *EMP* 1,691
SIC 8062 Hospital, professional nursing school
Ex Dir: Marc Chircop

D-U-N-S 06-817-8425
SAINT MARYS UNIVERSITY OF MINNESOTA
700 Terrace Hts 8, Winona, MN 55987-1321
Tel (507) 457-1436 *Founded/Ownrshp* 1928
Sales 77.4MM *EMP* 1,000
Accts Baker Tilly Virchow Krause Ll
SIC 8221 College, except junior
Pr: William Mann
Pr: Mark Kormann
**Ex VP:* Anne Merchlewitz
VP: Chris Kendall
**VP:* Cynthia Marek
VP: Scott McMahon
VP: Joseph Sweeney
Exec: Grace Engen
Exec: John Pyle
Pgrm Dir: Heather Wegwerth

D-U-N-S 02-067-5930
SAINT MICHAELS COLLEGE INC
1 Winooski Park, Colchester, VT 05439-1000
Tel (802) 654-2000 *Founded/Ownrshp* 1903
Sales 124.5MM *EMP* 460
Accts Kpmg Llp Colchester Vermont
SIC 8221 College, except junior
Pr: Dr John J Neuhauser
Treas: Neal E Robinson
Ofcr: Jamie Benson
Ofcr: Stacy Fender
VP: Nicole Corneau
VP: Dawn Ellinwood
Assoc Dir: Allison Gardner
Genl Mgr: Hank Strashnick
Off Admin: Renee R Davitt
CTO: Venessa Luck
Advt Mgr: Angela Baldacci

SAINT MICHAEL'S MEDICAL CENTER
See PRIME HEALTHCARE SERVICES - ST MICHAELS LLC

D-U-N-S 04-400-1410
SAINT MICHAELS MEDICAL CENTER INC
111 Center Ter, Newark, NJ 07114-2209
Tel (973) 877-5000 *Founded/Ownrshp* 2008
Sales 192.6MM *EMP* 1,400
Accts Withumsmithbrown Pc Morristow
SIC 8062
CEO: David Ricci
Pr: Caroline Pires
COO: Lowell Johnson
Comm Dir: Ann Liloia
Dir Rx: Kathleen Ryan
Comm Man: Bari Adelman
Adm Dir: Lois Greene
Ex Dir: Kenneth Waller
QA Dir: Ellie Anderson
Plnt Mgr: John Westervelt
Sls&Mrk Ex: Brendan Middleton

D-U-N-S 15-751-8507
SAINT PAUL FOUNDATION INC
MINNESOTA COMMUNITY FOUNDATION
101 5th St E Ste 2400, Saint Paul, MN 55101-1797
Tel (651) 224-5463 *Founded/Ownrshp* 1940
Sales 87.7MM^E *EMP* 84
Accts Akins Henke And Company Saint
SIC 8641 8399 Community membership club; Fund raising organization, non-fee basis
Pr: Carleen Rhodes
Sr Pt: E G Obrien II
Ofcr: Gerald C Timian
VP: Robert Engebretsen
VP: Ann Mulholland
VP: Christine Searson
Ex Dir: William L Collins Jr
Ex Dir: Jennifer Hoffman

D-U-N-S 04-579-0045
SAINT PETERS UNIVERSITY HOSPITAL INC
254 Easton Ave, New Brunswick, NJ 08901-1766
Tel (732) 745-8600 *Founded/Ownrshp* 1907
Sales 405.8MM *EMP* 3,000
SIC 8062 Hospital, affiliated with AMA residency
CEO: Ronald Rak
CFO: John Calondriello
**CFO:* Garrick Stoldt
Trst: Kathleen Killion
VP: Karel Raska
Dir Rad: Lauris Beam
**Int Pr:* Leslie Hirsch
Nurse Mgr: Beth Braconi
CTO: Bill Rears
Pathlgst: Elmer Gamboa
Pathlgst: Karl Schwarz

D-U-N-S 92-665-4286
SAINT STEPHEN NURSING FACILITY INC
LAKE MOULTRIE NURSING HOME
1038 Mcgill Ln, Saint Stephen, SC 29479-3196
Tel (843) 567-2307 *Founded/Ownrshp* 1992
Sales 474.9MM *EMP* 90
SIC 8051 8059 Skilled nursing care facilities; Nursing home, except skilled & intermediate care facility

D-U-N-S 06-953-3768
SAINT TAMMANY PARISH HOSPITAL SERVICE DISTRICT 1
ST TAMMANY PARISH HOSPITAL
1202 S Tyler St, Covington, LA 70433-2330
Tel (985) 898-4000 *Founded/Ownrshp* 1954
Sales 246.9MM *EMP* 1,520
SIC 8062 Hospital, affiliated with AMA residency
Pr: Patti Ellish
CFO: Robert J Barousse Jr
**CFO:* David Mabe
Ex Dir: Charley Strickland
Mng Dir: Tiquanna Gatlin
Genl Mgr: Paul D Cordes
Off Mgr: Stacy M Foster
Off Mgr: Maria Knox
Off Mgr: Barbara A Oakes
Off Admin: Stefanie Alford
Mktg Dir: Kelly Beckendorf

D-U-N-S 10-002-8471
SAINT TAMMANY PARISH SCHOOL BOARD
321 N Theard St, Covington, LA 70433-2835
Tel (985) 892-2276 *Founded/Ownrshp* 1905
Sales 475.5MM *EMP* 4,400^E
Accts La Porte Apac Covington La
SIC 8211 School board
Pr: Stephen Loup
**Pr:* Elizabeth B Heintz
VP: Robin Mullett
**VP:* Robert R Womack
VP: Robert Womack
**Prin:* Cheryl Arabie
Genl Mgr: Kim Taylor

Dir IT: Susan Grantham
Dir IT: Darlene Ochsner
IT Man: John Swang
Pr Dir: Meredith Mendez
Board of Directors: Suzanne - Public Info Dept

D-U-N-S 78-862-7503
SAINT THOMAS HEALTH SERVICES INC
SETON LODGE
(*Suby of* ST THOMAS HOSPITAL) ★
4220 Harding Pike, Nashville, TN 37205-2005
Tel (615) 222-2111 *Founded/Ownrshp* 1986
Sales 226.7MM *EMP* 4,650ᴱ
Accts Deloitte Tax Lp Cincinnati O
SIC 6512 6513 7011 Commercial & industrial building operation; Apartment building operators; Hotels & motels
Pr: Thomas Beeman
COO: Mark M Guinness
VP: Jessica Wells

D-U-N-S 02-026-1603
SAINT THOMAS HOSPITAL
4220 Harding Pike, Nashville, TN 37205-2095
Tel (615) 222-5976 *Founded/Ownrshp* 1898
Sales 493.9MM *EMP* 99
Accts Deloitte Tax Llp Cincinnati
SIC 8062 General medical & surgical hospitals
CEO: Tom Beeman
CFO: Craig Polkow
Dir Lab: Amanda Austin
Dir Rx: Marty Kelvas
Dir Sec: Michael Dossett
Dir Pat Ac: Wally Vinson
CTO: David Van Hooser

D-U-N-S 07-765-5975
SAINT THOMAS RUTHERFORD HOSPITAL
(*Suby of* ASCENSION HEALTH) ★
1700 Medical Center Pkwy, Murfreesboro, TN 37129-2245
Tel (615) 849-4100 *Founded/Ownrshp* 2007
Sales 279.4MM *EMP* 1,100ᴱ
SIC 8062 General medical & surgical hospitals
CEO: Gordon B Ferguson
CFO: Tom Maey
CFO: Thomas Massey
CFO: Ken Venuto
Dir IT: Dan West
VP Opers: Ryan Simpson

SAINT VINCENT CATHLIC MED CTRS
See SAINT VINCENTS CATHOLIC MEDICAL CENTERS OF NEW YORK

D-U-N-S 07-216-9378
SAINT VINCENT HEALTH CENTER INC
232 W 25th St, Erie, PA 16544-0001
Tel (814) 452-5000 *Founded/Ownrshp* 2001
Sales 94.6Mᴱ *EMP* 3,000
Accts Carbis Walker Llp Pittsburgh
SIC 8062 General medical & surgical hospitals
Pr: Scott Whalen
Chf Rad: Matthew Thomas
COO: Tom Fucci
COO: Ken Haynes
CFO: Alfred Manfield
CFO: Al Mansfield
Treas: Bob Cox
Ex VP: Joseph Cacchione
Sr VP: Christopher Clark
Sr VP: Richard Cogley
Sr VP: Janice Hamscher
Sr VP: Edward Malindzak
VP: Peter Lund
VP: Paul Matters
VP: Steve Osborn
VP: Debbie Tamilin
Exec: Keith Henderson
Dir Risk M: Jill Sonnenberg
Dir Rad: Bharath Chinta
Dir Rad: Matt Shebel
Dir Rx: Pete Pascale

D-U-N-S 60-449-9962
SAINT VINCENT HEALTH SYSTEM
232 W 25th St, Erie, PA 16544-0002
Tel (814) 452-5000 *Founded/Ownrshp* 1981
Sales 129.0MMᴱ *EMP* 2,300
Accts Carbis Walker Llp Pittsburgh
SIC 8741 8011 Hospital management; Offices & clinics of medical doctors
Pr: C Angela Bontempo
Dir Vol: Tony Bruno
V Ch: Michael Redlawsk
V Ch: Gretchen Stearns
CFO: Stephen Gary
Treas: Susan Sutto
Trst: Mary Ellen Dwyer
Ofcr: Janice Hamscher
Ex VP: Joseph Cacchione
Sr VP: Thomas Elliott
**Sr VP:* Graham C Lund
VP: Debbie Tamilin
Dir Risk M: Jill Sonnenberg

SAINT VINCENT HOSPITAL
See ST VINCENT HOSPITAL OF HOSPITAL SISTERS OF THIRD ORDER OF S

D-U-N-S 11-071-2668 EXP
■ **SAINT VINCENT HOSPITAL LLC**
WORCESTER MEDICAL CENTER
(*Suby of* VANGUARD HEALTH SYSTEMS INC) ★
123 Summer St, Worcester, MA 01608-1216
Tel (508) 363-5000 *Founded/Ownrshp* 2005
Sales 295.4MMᴱ *EMP* 2,200
SIC 8062 Hospital, affiliated with AMA residency
CEO: Cynthia Monahan
CEO: John E Smithhisler
CFO: Aileen Clemente
Ofcr: Jane Hurd
Assoc Dir: Kelly Chandley
Assoc Dir: Candy Gammal
Dir Rad: Jerome Fischer
Off Mgr: Karen Haddad
Off Admin: Elaine A Gavin
Telecom Mg: Barbara Ings
Mktg Dir: Judy Mackey

SAINT VINCENT'S
See JUBILEE CENTER

D-U-N-S 07-105-0132 IMP
SAINT VINCENTS CATHOLIC MEDICAL CENTERS OF NEW YORK
SAINT VINCENT CATHLIC MED CTRS
5 Penn Plz Ste 900, New York, NY 10001-1829
Tel (212) 356-4792 *Founded/Ownrshp* 1849
Sales 100.3MMᴱ *EMP* 70
SIC 8062 General medical & surgical hospitals
CEO: Steven R Korf
Sr VP: Brian Fitzsimmons PHD
Sr VP: Michelle Napier
Sr VP: Anthony Napoli
Sr VP: Virginia Sweeny
CTO: Elvira Agustin
Dir IT: Mark McConkey
Snr Mgr: Anthony Cartagena

SAINT VINCENT'S MEDICAL CENTER
See ST VINCENTS MEDICAL CENTER INC

D-U-N-S 07-234-9004
SAINT XAVIER UNIVERSITY
3700 W 103rd St, Chicago, IL 60655-3105
Tel (773) 298-3000 *Founded/Ownrshp* 1847
Sales 99.4MMᴱ *EMP* 758
SIC 8221 University
Pr: Christine M Wiseman JD
**VP:* Susan Piros
VP: Brenda Ruiz
VP: Robert C Tenczar Jr
Assoc Dir: Amanda Fijal
Assoc Dir: Therese Johnson
Off Mgr: Janice McMahon
Off Mgr: Bridget Stevens
Snr Ntwrk: Brian Goebel
DP Exec: Bill Rogers
Dir IT: Kathy Giordano

SAINT-GOBAIN
See CERTAINTEED CORP

D-U-N-S 00-112-6234 IMP/EXP
SAINT-GOBAIN ABRASIVES INC (MA)
BONDED ABRASIVES
(*Suby of* SAINT-GOBAIN DELAWARE CORP) ★
1 New Bond St, Worcester, MA 01606-2614
Tel (508) 795-5000 *Founded/Ownrshp* 1885, 1990
Sales 2.7MMMᴱ *EMP* 11,446
SIC 3291 3559 3545 3297 3082 2891 Wheels, abrasive; Coated abrasive products; Sandpaper; Concrete products machinery; Diamond cutting tools for turning, boring, burnishing, etc.; Dressers, abrasive wheel: diamond point or other; Graphite refractories: carbon bond or ceramic bond; Tubes, unsupported plastic; Sealing compounds, synthetic rubber or plastic
CEO: Patrick Millot
Pr: John Crowe
CFO: George B Amoss
Treas: John J Sweeney III
VP: John R Mesher
VP: Steven F Messmer
VP: M Shawn Puccio
VP: Robert Smith

D-U-N-S 09-246-9519 IMP
SAINT-GOBAIN ADFORS AMERICA INC
SAINT-GOBAIN-PARIS FRANCE
(*Suby of* SAINT-GOBAIN CORP) ★
1795 Baseline Rd, Grand Island, NY 14072-2010
Tel (716) 775-3900 *Founded/Ownrshp* 1976
Sales 146.9MMᴱ *EMP* 414
SIC 2297 Nonwoven fabrics
CEO: John Bedell
Genl Mgr: Rudy Coetzee

D-U-N-S 85-872-6011 IMP
SAINT-GOBAIN CERAMICS & PLASTICS INC
SAINT-GOBAIN CRYSTALS
(*Suby of* BONDED ABRASIVES) ★
750 E Swedesford Rd, Valley Forge, PA 19482
Tel (610) 341-7000 *Founded/Ownrshp* 1991
Sales 768.2MM *EMP* 5,668
SIC 2819 3679 3544 3297 Industrial inorganic chemicals; Electronic crystals; Special dies & tools; Nonclay refractories
Pr: John J Sweeney III
**VP:* M Shawn Puccio
Exec: Robert Konetzny
Brnch Mgr: Howard Wallar
IT Man: Kamel Mabrouki
Sls Dir: Steve Crittenden

D-U-N-S 07-956-8396
SAINT-GOBAIN CORP
(*Suby of* SAINT-GOBAIN CORP) ★
1 New Bond St, Worcester, MA 01606-2614
Tel (508) 795-5000 *Founded/Ownrshp* 1990
Sales 71.8MMᴱ *EMP* 4,262ᴱ
SIC 5945 Ceramics supplies

D-U-N-S 87-932-1644 IMP
SAINT-GOBAIN CORP
(*Suby of* SPAFI SOC PARTICIP FINANCIERE IN)
20 Moores Rd, Malvern, PA 19355-1114
Tel (610) 893-6000 *Founded/Ownrshp* 1990
Sales 8.9MMMᴱ *EMP* 25,836
SIC 2891 3269 3221 Adhesives; Laboratory & industrial pottery; Glass containers
Pr: John Crowe
V Ch: Ian Manter
COO: Christian Meyerhentschel
Ofcr: Josef Guesman
Sr VP: Gilles Colas
**Sr VP:* John R Mesher
**Sr VP:* Shawn Puccio
Sr VP: Shawn M Puccio
VP: Donna Dickinson
VP: Catherine Ferrante
**VP:* Rose Lee
VP: Robert Pierce

SAINT-GOBAIN CRYSTALS
See SAINT-GOBAIN CERAMICS & PLASTICS INC

D-U-N-S 83-642-3509 IMP/EXP
SAINT-GOBAIN DELAWARE CORP
(*Suby of* SAINT-GOBAIN CORP) ★
750 E Swedesford Rd, Valley Forge, PA 19482
Tel (610) 341-7000 *Founded/Ownrshp* 1990
Sales 5.4MMMᴱ *EMP* 11,474
SIC 3291 3269 2891 3296 3084 3221 Abrasive products; Laboratory & industrial pottery; Adhesives & sealants; Fiberglass insulation; Plastics pipe; Glass containers
Pr: Jean F Phelizon
**VP:* James F Harkins Jr
IT Man: Toke Godiksen

D-U-N-S 00-838-2947 IMP
SAINT-GOBAIN PERFORMANCE PLASTICS CORP
(*Suby of* BONDED ABRASIVES) ★
31500 Solon Rd, Solon, OH 44139-3528
Tel (440) 836-6900 *Founded/Ownrshp* 1999
Sales 1.2MMMᴱ *EMP* 4,437
SIC 3089 3053 Thermoformed finished plastic products; Gaskets, packing & sealing devices
Pr: Tom Kinisky
**CFO:* Laurent Guillot
VP: Mark Barter
Div/Sub He: Josehp Grewe

D-U-N-S 13-789-1441
SAINT-GOBAIN SEMICONDUCTOR COMPONENTS
(*Suby of* SAINT-GOBAIN CRYSTALS) ★
1 New Bond St, Worcester, MA 01606-2614
Tel (508) 795-5400 *Founded/Ownrshp* 2003
Sales 92.6MMᴱ *EMP* 1ᴱ
SIC 5085 Refractory material
Prin: Joseph Menendez

D-U-N-S 01-998-5355 IMP/EXP
SAINT-GOBAIN STRUCTURAL CERAMICS
(*Suby of* SAINT-GOBAIN CORP) ★
23 Acheson Dr, Niagara Falls, NY 14303-1555
Tel (716) 278-6233 *Founded/Ownrshp* 1990
Sales 172.9MMᴱ *EMP* 2,413ᴱ
SIC 3255 Brick, clay refractory
Pr: John Crowe

D-U-N-S 79-886-9046 IMP
SAINT-GOBAIN VETROTEX AMERICA INC
(*Suby of* SAINT-GOBAIN) ★
20 Moores Rd, Valley Forge, PA 19482
Tel (610) 893-6000 *Founded/Ownrshp* 1991
Sales 182.0MMᴱ *EMP* 1,000
SIC 3089 Spouting, plastic & glass fiber reinforced
Pr: David L Mascarin
**Treas:* John J Sweeney
**VP:* Steven F Messmer
Manager: Pablo Velarde

SAINT-GOBAIN-PARIS FRANCE
See SAINT-GOBAIN ADFORS AMERICA INC

SAINTS JOSEPH'S HOSPITAL
See SAINT JOSEPHS HOSPITAL OF MARSHFIELD INC

D-U-N-S 07-382-8444
SAINTS MEDICAL CENTER INC
1 Hospital Dr, Lowell, MA 01852-1311
Tel (978) 458-1411 *Founded/Ownrshp* 1930
Sales 104.2MM *EMP* 1,500
SIC 8051 8062 Skilled nursing care facilities; General medical & surgical hospitals
CEO: Norm Deschene
COO: Judy Casagrande
CFO: Stephen J Guimond
VP: Seve O Connoer
VP: Deborah Crady
VP: Balajee Thangavelu
Dir Case M: Deborah M Crady
Dir Lab: Jennifer M Carthy
Off Mgr: Glenna Scannell
CTO: Marygail Donohue
CTO: Greg Smith

D-U-N-S 55-631-6966
SAIPEM AMERICA INC
(*Suby of* SAIPEM SPA)
15950 Park Row, Houston, TX 77084-5102
Tel (281) 552-5600 *Founded/Ownrshp* 1990
Sales 462.9MMᴱ *EMP* 350
Accts Ernst & Young Llp Houston Tx
SIC 8711 1389 Marine engineering; Oil field services
Ch Bd: Massimo Ferraris
**Sec:* Vincenvo Auciello
Ofcr: Fermin Blum
Ofcr: Juan Estrada
Top Exec: Jobouy Thomson
**Prin:* Fabio Bini
Opers Mgr: Maria C Vanegas
Prd Mgr: Jody Thompson
Doctor: Robert Corkren

SAISD
See SAN ANGELO INDEPENDENT SCHOOL DISTRICT

D-U-N-S 01-974-2368
SAK CONSTRUCTION LLC (MO)
864 Hoff Rd, O Fallon, MO 63366-1922
Tel (636) 674-9104 *Founded/Ownrshp* 2006, 2008
Sales 162.2MMᴱ *EMP* 300
SIC 1623 1622 Sewer line construction; Tunnel construction
**VP:* Steve Hirtz
**VP:* Charlie Kuhnmuench
Sfty Dirs: Harry Miller

D-U-N-S 08-641-3028 IMP/EXP
SAKAR INTERNATIONAL INC (NY)
CSI IMPORTS
195 Carter Dr, Edison, NJ 08817-2068
Tel (732) 248-1306 *Founded/Ownrshp* 1977
Sales 98.6MMᴱ *EMP* 100
SIC 5043 Photographic cameras, projectors, equipment & supplies
CEO: Charles Saka
**Pr:* Jeffrey Saka
**COO:* Ralph Sasson
**VP:* Liza Abrams
VP: Carey Berg
VP: Stefan Betesh
**VP:* Howie Davis
**VP:* Allan Saka
**Prin:* Raymond Saka
Sales Asso: Yue Xu

D-U-N-S 08-660-6175 IMP
SAKATA SEED AMERICA INC
(*Suby of* SAKATA SEED CORPORATION)
18095 Serene Dr, Morgan Hill, CA 95037-2833
Tel (408) 778-7758 *Founded/Ownrshp* 1977
Sales 84.2MMᴱ *EMP* 162
SIC 5191 0182 Seeds: field, garden & flower; Vegetable crops grown under cover
CEO: David Armstrong
**VP:* Koichi Matsunaga
Area Mgr: Cory Dombrowski
Prd Mgr: Justin Davis
Mktg Dir: Susie Gunther
Sls Mgr: Mitsu Fukuda
Sls Mgr: Kevin Townsend

D-U-N-S 80-137-4609
SAKER HOLDINGS CORP
922 State Route 33 Bldg 1, Freehold, NJ 07728-8453
Tel (732) 462-4700 *Founded/Ownrshp* 2006
Sales 605.9MMᴱ *EMP* 6,850
SIC 5411 5261 5921 Supermarkets, chain; Nurseries & garden centers; Liquor stores
Pr: Richard J Saker
Ch Bd: Joseph J Saker
CFO: Michael Shapiro
Sr VP: Joseph C Troilo

D-U-N-S 83-255-2389
SAKER SHOPRITES INC
922 Hwy 33 Bldg 1, Freehold, NJ 07728-8453
Tel (732) 462-4700 *Founded/Ownrshp* 1958
Sales 1.0MMM *EMP* 7,200ᴱ
SIC 5411 Supermarkets, chain
CEO: Richard Saker

SAKS
See ALSAKER CORP

D-U-N-S 00-698-9867 EXP
SAKS & CO
SAKS IMPORT OFFICE
611 5th Ave, New York, NY 10022-6813
Tel (212) 753-4000 *Founded/Ownrshp* 1998
Sales NA *EMP* 12,000
SIC 5621 5311 5651

SAKS FIFTH AVENUE
See SAKS INC

D-U-N-S 96-699-2260
SAKS FIFTH AVENUE LLC
(*Suby of* SAKS FIFTH AVENUE) ★
12 E 49th St Fl 2, New York, NY 10017-1088
Tel (212) 940-5013 *Founded/Ownrshp* 2014
Sales 1.9MMMᴱ *EMP* 12,000ᴱ
SIC 5311 Department stores
CEO: Gerald Storch
Pr: Mari Landers
Treas: Michael Vincent
Chf Mktg O: Denise Incandela
Ex VP: Michael Brizel
Sr VP: Joseph Boitano
Sr VP: Tracy Haffner
Sr VP: Ernest La Porte
VP: Larry Bruce
VP: Larry Butts
VP: Meredith Fogel
VP: Theresa Gladstein
VP: Lewis Hopkins
VP: Jerry Kirby
VP: Kinjil Mathur
VP: Ramona Messore
VP: Fred Muse
VP: Anthony Nicola
VP: Gretchen Pace
VP: Kathleen Ruiz

SAKS IMPORT OFFICE
See SAKS & CO

D-U-N-S 00-894-2252 IMP/EXP
SAKS INC
SAKS FIFTH AVENUE
(*Suby of* HUDSON'S BAY COMPANY)
12 E 49th St Fl 2, New York, NY 10017-8299
Tel (212) 940-5305 *Founded/Ownrshp* 2013
Sales 2.3MMMᴱ *EMP* 13,900
SIC 5311 5611 5621 5641 Department stores; Men's & boys' clothing stores; Women's clothing stores; Children's & infants' wear stores
CEO: Richard Baker
Pr: Ron Frasch
**Pr:* Don Watros
**CFO:* Mike Culhane
**Treas:* Lucas Evans
Treas: Sarah Griffin
Treas: Michael Vincent
Ofcr: James Coggin
Ofcr: Robert Wallstrom
Ex VP: Michael A Brizel
**Sr VP:* Marc Metrick
Sr VP: Karolyn Wangstad
VP: Greg Fitting
VP: Teri Gakos
VP: Tracy Haffner
VP: Juan Lopez
VP: Gail Marone
VP: Tom Massey
VP: Anthony Nicola
VP: Robert Tonk
VP: Cathie Wilson

D-U-N-S 09-564-0736
SALADINOS INC
3325 W Figarden Dr, Fresno, CA 93711-3909
Tel (559) 271-3700 *Founded/Ownrshp* 1947
Sales 380.4MMᴱ *EMP* 250
SIC 5141 2099 Groceries, general line; Food preparations
CEO: Craig A Saladino
Pr: Owen Escola

**COO:* Patrick Peters
CFO: Mark Schuh
**Ch:* Don Saladino
VP: John Muro
Genl Mgr: Jeff Earl
Sfty Mgr: Robert Hunter
Sls Dir: Frank Giovanni Jr
Sls Mgr: Randy Norvelle

D-U-N-S 04-672-4714
SALARY.COM LLC
610 Lincoln St Ste 200, Waltham, MA 02451-2189
Tel (781) 989-9488 *Founded/Ownrshp* 2015, 2016
Sales 206.6MME *EMP* 2,564E
SIC 7371 7375 Computer software development & applications; Data base information retrieval
CEO: Kent Plunkett
**COO:* Yong Zhang
**CFO:* Anne Huemme
Sr VP: Robert Merklinger
**Prin:* Wendy Ryan

D-U-N-S 96-351-7532
SALEM CARE CENTER
2361 E 29th St, Oakland, CA 94606-3511
Tel (510) 534-3637 *Founded/Ownrshp* 2010
Sales 963.8MM *EMP* 10E
SIC 8051 Skilled nursing care facilities

D-U-N-S 10-789-4115
SALEM CARRIERS INC
(*Suby of* SALEM HOLDING CO) ★
175 Charlois Blvd, Winston Salem, NC 27103-1521
Tel (336) 768-6800 *Founded/Ownrshp* 1982
Sales 83.4MM *EMP* 650
SIC 4213 4212 Trucking, except local; Local trucking, without storage
Ch Bd: Kenneth G Langone
**Pr:* Thomas L Teague
Ex VP: Ken Adkins
Ex VP: Scott O'Brien
VP: Juan Correa
VP: C Stephen Dula
VP: Alan R Oakley

D-U-N-S 07-453-6996
SALEM COMMUNITY HOSPITAL
SALEM HOME MEDICAL
1995 E State St, Salem, OH 44460-2400
Tel (330) 332-1551 *Founded/Ownrshp* 1969
Sales 105.5MM *EMP* 1,000
SIC 8062 8051 General medical & surgical hospitals; Skilled nursing care facilities
CEO: Anita Hackstedde MD
**CFO:* Michael Giangardella

D-U-N-S 80-403-3715
SALEM FIVE BANCORP
210 Essex St, Salem, MA 01970-3705
Tel (978) 745-5555 *Founded/Ownrshp* 2007
Sales NA *EMP* 450E
SIC 6712 Bank holding companies
Prin: Joseph Gibbons
Sr VP: Bruce Potter
VP: Annis Miller

D-U-N-S 00-695-5827
SALEM FIVE CENTS SAVINGS BANK
(*Suby of* SALEM FIVE BANCORP) ★
210 Essex St, Salem, MA 01970-3705
Tel (978) 745-5555 *Founded/Ownrshp* 1855
Sales NA *EMP* 450
SIC 6022 State commercial banks
CEO: Joseph M Gibbons
**CFO:* Pingyin Chai
CFO: Kenneth Klipper
Chf Mktg O: Martha Acworth
Ofcr: Paula Kahr
Ofcr: Joe Rooney
Ex VP: Kim A Meader
Sr VP: Clifford Boggis
Sr VP: Diana Carito
Sr VP: Kenneth Ellis
Sr VP: David Fanikos
Sr VP: Joseph Greenough
Sr VP: Ryan Hayes
Sr VP: Bill Kelly
Sr VP: Jeffrey Letendre
Sr VP: John Malloy
Sr VP: Paul Oreilly
Sr VP: Elaine Paglia
Sr VP: Paul Passeri
Sr VP: Helen Topor
Sr VP: Doris J Waldman

D-U-N-S 04-980-2135
SALEM HEALTH
890 Oak St Se, Salem, OR 97301-3905
Tel (503) 561-5200 *Founded/Ownrshp* 1896
Sales 667.5MM *EMP* 3,400E
Accts Kpmg Llp Portland Oregon
SIC 8062 Hospital, AMA approved residency
Pr: Norman Gruber
Chf Rad: Jose Novoa
Dir Recs: Debra Harris
**COO:* Cheryl Nester Wolfe
**CFO:* Aaron Crane
Chf Mktg O: Anne Theis
**VP:* Laurie Barr
**VP:* Robert Brannigan
VP: Thomas Kahn
Dir Risk M: Ellen Hampton
**Off Mgr:* Kelli Fussell

D-U-N-S 79-819-0021
SALEM HOLDING CO
175 Charlois Blvd, Winston Salem, NC 27103-1521
Tel (336) 768-6800 *Founded/Ownrshp* 1991
Sales 246.0MM *EMP* 1,000
Accts Pricewaterhousecoopers Llp G
SIC 7513 4213 Truck leasing, without drivers; Contract haulers
Pr: Thomas L Teague
**Ch Bd:* Kenneth G Langone
VP: C Stephen Dula

SALEM HOME MEDICAL
See SALEM COMMUNITY HOSPITAL

D-U-N-S 07-657-4730
SALEM HOSPITAL
81 Highland Ave, Salem, MA 01970-2768
Tel (978) 741-1200 *Founded/Ownrshp* 1985
Sales NA *EMP* 2,322E
SIC 8062

D-U-N-S 02-489-3976 EXP
SALEM LEASING CORP
NATIONALEASE
(*Suby of* SALEM HOLDING CO) ★
175 Charlois Blvd, Winston Salem, NC 27103-1521
Tel (336) 768-6800 *Founded/Ownrshp* 1975
Sales 129.5MM *EMP* 420
SIC 7513 Truck leasing, without drivers
Pr: Thomas L Teague
**Ch Bd:* Kenneth G Langone
Treas: C Stephen Dula
Ex VP: Dennis M Giff
Sr VP: E Stephen Teague
VP: Richard Childers
VP: John M Egan
VP: Ernest Hanington
VP: John Holton
VP: Mitzi Keller
VP: Raymond Keller
VP: Jay Kiser
VP: Gary Murchison
VP: Tommy R Sides

D-U-N-S 10-307-5636
▲ SALEM MEDIA GROUP INC
4880 Santa Rosa Rd, Camarillo, CA 93012-5190
Tel (818) 956-0400 *Founded/Ownrshp* 1986
Sales 265.7MM *EMP* 1,198
Tkr Sym SALM *Exch* NGM
SIC 4832 2731 4813 Radio broadcasting stations; Book publishing;
CEO: Edward G Atsinger III
Ch Bd: Stuart W Epperson
Pr: David A R Evans
Pr: David P Santrella
CFO: Evan D Masyr
Ex VP: Evan Masyr
Sr VP: Christopher J Henderson
VP: Andrew Pino
VP: Linnae Young
Mktg Dir: Sara Westafer
Board of Directors: Eric H Halvorson, Roland S Hinz, James Keet Lewis, Richard A Riddle, Jonathan Venverloh

D-U-N-S 87-804-3561
SALEM STATE UNIVERSITY
352 Lafayette St, Salem, MA 01970-5348
Tel (978) 542-6000 *Founded/Ownrshp* 1854
Sales 98.0MM *EMP* 1,200
Accts O Connor & Drew Pc Braintr
SIC 8221 College, except junior
Pr: Patricia Maguire Meservey
Pr: Richard Delorey
**CFO:* Karen House
Treas: Joan Boudreau
Sr VP: Pete Kaznoski
Exec: Nancy Harrington
Assoc Dir: Rosa Arsuaga
Assoc Dir: Andrea Swirka
Assoc Dir: Nelly Wadsworth
VP Admn: Joe Donovan
Ex Dir: Linda Malek-Jones

D-U-N-S 62-037-3456
■ SALEM TELEPHONE CO
TDS
(*Suby of* TDS TELECOMMUNICATIONS CORP) ★
221 E Main St, Salem, KY 42078-8071
Tel (608) 831-1000 *Founded/Ownrshp* 1958
Sales 853.0MM *EMP* 2,700
SIC 4813 Local & long distance telephone communications
Pr: David Wittwer
**Genl Mgr:* Brian Mc Daniel

D-U-N-S 05-318-1442
SALEM TOOLS INC
STSOLUTIONS
1602 Midland Rd, Salem, VA 24153-6427
Tel (540) 389-0726 *Founded/Ownrshp* 1978
Sales 83.3MM *EMP* 92
Accts Brownedwards Roanoke Virgini
SIC 5085 Industrial supplies
Pr: William N Powell Jr
**Treas:* Dennis C Montgomery
VP: Alvin Montgomery

D-U-N-S 04-918-0191
SALEM WINSTON FORSYTH COUNTY SCHOOLS
475 Corporate Square Dr, Winston Salem, NC 27105-9100
Tel (336) 748-4000 *Founded/Ownrshp* 2010
Sales 59.9MME *EMP* 7,600
SIC 8211 Elementary & secondary schools
Prin: Donald Martin Jr
Genl Mgr: Kathy Jordan
IT Man: Mary A Weatherman

D-U-N-S 07-073-1690
SALEM-KEIZER SCHOOL DISTRICT 24J
DISTIRC24J-MRYNNE CNTRY-OREGON
2450 Lancaster Dr Ne # 100, Salem, OR 97305-1200
Tel (503) 399-3000 *Founded/Ownrshp* 1900
Sales 428.8MM *EMP* 4,000
Accts Grove Mueller & Swank Pc
SIC 8211 Public elementary & secondary schools
Dir Sec: John Van Dreal
Off Mgr: Tracy Fitzke
Off Mgr: Blanca Ochoa
Pr Dir: Jay Remy
Teacher Pr: John Beight
Teacher Pr: Mary Paulson
Instr Medi: Stephan Cox
HC Dir: Eric Richards

SALES & USE TAX
See DEPARTMENT OF REVENUE MINNESOTA

D-U-N-S 07-214-8831
▲ SALESFORCE.COM INC
1 Market Ste 300, San Francisco, CA 94105-5188
Tel (415) 901-7000 *Founded/Ownrshp* 1999
Sales 6.6MMM *EMP* 19,002
Accts Ernst & Young Llp San Jose C
Tkr Sym CRM *Exch* NYS
SIC 7372 7375 Business oriented computer software; Information retrieval services
Ch Bd: Marc Benioff
V Ch: Keith G Block
Pr: Keith Block
Pr: Alexandre Dayon
CFO: Mark J Hawkins
Ex VP: Suzanne Dibianca
Ex VP: Cindy Robbins
Ex VP: Amy Weaver
VP: Allyson Fryhoff
VP: Tony Rodoni
Co-Founder: Parker Harris
Board of Directors: Craig Conway, Alan Hassenfeld, Colin Powell, Sanford R Robertson, John V Roos, Lawrence Tomlinson, Robin Washington, Maynard Webb, Susan Wojcicki

D-U-N-S 17-433-5828
■ SALESLINK CORP
(*Suby of* MODUSLINK CORP) ★
425 Medford St, Charlestown, MA 02129-1408
Tel (617) 886-4800 *Founded/Ownrshp* 2004
Sales 55.8MME *EMP* 3,000
Accts Kpmg Peat Marwick Llp Boston
SIC 7379 8744 7331 Computer related consulting services; Facilities support services; Direct mail advertising services
Pr: Bryce C Boothby Jr
**CFO:* Thomas Oberdorf
**Sr VP:* Mike Mancini
Sr VP: John Rice
**Sr VP:* Patrick Ring
Sr VP: Joe Wester
VP: Susan Lincoln
Dir IT: James Cosier
Dir IT: Bob Oneil
Web Prj Mg: Greg Saltzman
Prd Mgr: Paul Watts

D-U-N-S 08-000-6028
SALIENT CRGT HOLDINGS INC
4000 Legato Rd Ste 600, Fairfax, VA 22033-4055
Tel (703) 891-8200 *Founded/Ownrshp* 2015
Sales 593.1MME *EMP* 2,654E
SIC 7371 8748 Computer software writing services; Systems analysis or design
CEO: Brad Antle
Pr: Tom Ferrando
Sr VP: Mark Colturi

D-U-N-S 84-955-0983
SALIENT CRGT INC
(*Suby of* SALIENT CRGT HOLDINGS INC) ★
4000 Legato Rd Ste 600, Fairfax, VA 22033-4055
Tel (703) 891-8200 *Founded/Ownrshp* 2015
Sales 245.8MME *EMP* 1,900
SIC 7373 8748 Computer integrated systems design; Systems analysis or design
CEO: Brad Antle
**Pr:* Tom Ferrando
**CFO:* JD Kuhn
**Sr VP:* John Edgar
Sr VP: Sal Fazzolari
Sr VP: Linda Harris
Sr VP: Tom Pettit
Sr VP: Ken Raffel
**Sr VP:* Laurence Rose
**VP:* Kevin Bahumian
**VP:* Paul Bander
VP: Ian Graham
VP: David Leach
**VP:* Anuj Mathur
VP: Sheri Neely
VP: Mary Slade
VP: Howard Zach
Dir Bus: JW Funkhouser

D-U-N-S 96-268-6031
SALIENT FEDERAL SOLUTIONS INC
(*Suby of* SALIENT CRGT HOLDINGS INC) ★
4000 Legato Rd Ste 600, Fairfax, VA 22033-4055
Tel (703) 891-8200 *Founded/Ownrshp* 2015
Sales 347.2MME *EMP* 1,194E
SIC 7371 Computer software writing services
CEO: Brad Antle
**COO:* Bill Parker
**CFO:* Ted Dunn
**Chf Mktg O:* Tim May
**Sr VP:* Kay R Curling
Sr VP: Larry Rose
Sr VP: Charles Sowell
VP: Paul Bander
VP: Matthew Carabia
VP: Sujey Edward
VP: Sheri Neely
VP: Scott Seavers

D-U-N-S 11-269-3358
SALIENT FEDERAL-SGIS INC
(*Suby of* SALIENT FEDERAL SOLUTIONS INC) ★
8255 Greensboro Dr # 400, Mc Lean, VA 22102-4943
Tel (703) 891-8200 *Founded/Ownrshp* 2010
Sales 200.0MM *EMP* 650E
SIC 7373 8711 7382 Systems integration services; Engineering services; Security systems services
CEO: Brad Antle
Mng Pt: Jason Lipton
**CFO:* Ted Dunn
Assoc VP: Kelly Strukoff
Sr VP: Linda Beardsley
**Sr VP:* Kay R Curling
**Sr VP:* Tim May
VP: Paul Bander
**VP:* Tom Lloyd
VP: Mark Moore
**VP:* Tom Pettit

SALINA AREA VCTIONAL TECHNICAL
See SALINA PUBLIC SCHOOLS

D-U-N-S 07-090-0592
SALINA PUBLIC SCHOOLS
SALINA AREA VCTIONAL TECHNICAL
1511 Gypsum Ave, Salina, KS 67401-3221
Tel (785) 309-4700 *Founded/Ownrshp* 1996
Sales 306.8MM *EMP* 1,750
SIC 8211 Public elementary & secondary schools; High school, junior or senior; Public vocational/technical school
Prin: Jerry Baxa
Prin: Cary Brinegar
Prin: Tina Daniels
Prin: Juanita Erickson
Prin: Carmen Flax
Prin: Myron Graber
Prin: James Hughes
Prin: Gail Konzem
Prin: Sue McCormick
Prin: Reuben Montoy
Prin: Gilbert K Quackenbush
Board of Directors: Cindy Foley

D-U-N-S 07-332-7892
SALINA REGIONAL HEALTH CENTER INC
400 S Santa Fe Ave, Salina, KS 67401-4144
Tel (785) 452-7000 *Founded/Ownrshp* 1995
Sales 184.3MM *EMP* 1,500
SIC 8062 General medical & surgical hospitals
Pr: Randy Peterson
Chf Rad: William Garlow
CFO: Joe Tallon
Sr Cor Off: Brian Weisel
VP: Heather Fuller
**VP:* Cheryl Mason
Exec: Janice Struble
Ex Dir: Tom Bell
Ex Dir: Terry Hauschel
Genl Mgr: Janelle Martin
Telecom Ex: Cecie Perez

D-U-N-S 09-598-8739
SALINAS UNION HIGH SCHOOL DISTRICT SCHOOL BUILDING CORP
431 W Alisal St, Salinas, CA 93901-1669
Tel (831) 796-7000 *Founded/Ownrshp* 1882
Sales 61.1MME *EMP* 1,000
SIC 8211 Public elementary & secondary schools
CEO: Teresa Santamaria
MIS Dir: Steven Peters

D-U-N-S 07-718-1071 IMP
SALINAS VALLEY MEMORIAL HEALTHCARE SYSTEMS
SALINAS VALLEY MEMORIAL HOSP
450 E Romie Ln, Salinas, CA 93901-4029
Tel (831) 757-4333 *Founded/Ownrshp* 1947
Sales 344.2MM *EMP* 1,480E
SIC 8062 General medical & surgical hospitals
CEO: Sam Downing
**COO:* Beverly Ranzenberger
CFO: Augustine Lopez
Treas: Chris Orman
Bd of Dir: Christopher Carver
Bd of Dir: Gregory M Chilton
Bd of Dir: Rick Deserpa
Bd of Dir: Myrle Maclaughlin
Bd of Dir: Bryan Mansour
Bd of Dir: Susan Merrill
Bd of Dir: Clarence Reed
Bd of Dir: Thomas E Verga
Bd of Dir: Joan Vincenz
Bd of Dir: John Wilkinson
Bd of Dir: Inge Ypina
**Sr VP:* John Fletcher
VP: James Brennan
VP: Pauline Monteith
VP: Irene Neumeister
VP: Julia Orozco
Board of Directors: Leonard Breschini, Thomas Mill, Deborah Nelson, Nathan Olivas

SALINAS VALLEY MEMORIAL HOSP
See SALINAS VALLEY MEMORIAL HEALTHCARE SYSTEMS

D-U-N-S 07-909-7222
SALINE COUNTY MEDICAL CENTER
SALINE MEMORIAL HOSPITAL
1 Medical Park Dr, Benton, AR 72015-3353
Tel (501) 776-6000 *Founded/Ownrshp* 1955
Sales 94.9MM *EMP* 1,900
Accts Bkd Llp Benton Ar
SIC 8062 General medical & surgical hospitals
Prin: Bob Trautman
Dir Vol: Tammy Batchelor
CFO: Carla Robertson
Dir Risk M: Sherry Jensen
Dir Lab: Dwayne Gentry
Dir Rx: Patti Vance
**Prin:* Robert Trautman
Off Mgr: Brian Fowler
Nurse Mgr: Tanya Shelnut
Off Admin: Regina Edmonson
Off Admin: Sharon Pledger

SALINE MEMORIAL HOSPITAL
See SALINE COUNTY MEDICAL CENTER

SALISBURY BY HONEYWELL
See SALISBURY ELECTRICAL SAFETY LLC

D-U-N-S 83-111-3662 IMP
■ SALISBURY ELECTRICAL SAFETY LLC
SALISBURY BY HONEYWELL
(*Suby of* HONEYWELL INTERNATIONAL INC) ★
101 E Crssrads Pkwy Ste A, Bolingbrook, IL 60440
Tel (877) 406-4501 *Founded/Ownrshp* 2006
Sales 121.7MME *EMP* 420
SIC 3842 Clothing, fire resistant & protective
Genl Mgr: Mate Olds
Plnt Mgr: Jim Sabo

D-U-N-S 78-953-8159
SALISBURY SCHOOL ROWAN SYSTEM
500 N Main St, Salisbury, NC 28144-4350
Tel (704) 630-6026 *Founded/Ownrshp* 2006
Sales 168.8MM *EMP* 3,000E
Accts Dixon Hughes Goodman Llp Wins
SIC 8211 Public elementary & secondary schools
**CFO:* Robin Leslie

CFO: Anthony Vann
Bd of Dir: Jean Kennedy
Ofcr: Pam York
Ex Dir: Alesia Burnette
Info Man: Cindy Graham
Teacher Pr: Kristi Rhone

D-U-N-S 01-277-5685
SALIX PHARMACEUTICALS INC
(*Suby of* SALIX PHARMACEUTICALS LTD) ★
8540 Colonnade Center Dr # 401, Raleigh, NC 27615-3052
Tel (919) 862-1000 *Founded/Ownrshp* 1989
Sales 137.3MM^E *EMP* 700
SIC 2834 Pharmaceutical preparations
Ch: John F Chappell
Assoc Dir: Michael Bullock
Genl Mgr: Bill Bertrand
Manager: Bob Jackson
Snr Mgr: Jennifer Woodbury

D-U-N-S 79-310-8036 IMP
SALIX PHARMACEUTICALS LTD
(*Suby of* VALEANT PHARMACEUTICALS INTERNATIONAL CORP) ★
400 Somerset Corp Blvd, Bridgewater, NJ 08807-2867
Tel (919) 862-1000 *Founded/Ownrshp* 2015
Sales 249.9MM^E *EMP* 887^E
SIC 2834 Drugs acting on the gastrointestinal or genitourinary system
Pr: Joseph Papa
V Ch: Kai-Fong Lo
Ex VP: William P Forbes
Ex VP: Jeff Tomlinson
Sr VP: Timothy J Creech
Sr VP: Dan Dalton
Sr VP: Lorin Johnson
Assoc Dir: Ryan Craig
Assoc Dir: Karen Lai
QA Dir: Marschall R White
Info Man: Bernadette Brown

D-U-N-S 07-873-1668
SALK INSTITUTE FOR BIOLOGICAL STUDIES SAN DIEGO CALIFORNIA (CA)
SALK INSTITUTE, THE
10010 N Torrey Pines Rd, La Jolla, CA 92037-1099
Tel (858) 453-4100 *Founded/Ownrshp* 1960, 1996
Sales 151.2MM *EMP* 1,100
SIC 8731

SALK INSTITUTE, THE
See SALK INSTITUTE FOR BIOLOGICAL STUDIES SAN DIEGO CALIFORNIA

SALLIE MAE
See SLM CORP

D-U-N-S 60-719-4888
■ SALLIE MAE BANK
(*Suby of* SALLIE MAE) ★
175 S West Temple Ste 600, Salt Lake City, UT 84101-4218
Tel (801) 320-3700 *Founded/Ownrshp* 2005
Sales NA *EMP* 30
SIC 6021 National commercial banks
Pr: Paul F Thome
**Treas:* Michael Blackham
Board of Directors: Raymond J Quinlan

D-U-N-S 79-055-4724
▲ SALLY BEAUTY HOLDINGS INC
3001 Colorado Blvd, Denton, TX 76210-6802
Tel (940) 898-7500 *Founded/Ownrshp* 1964
Sales 3.9MMM *EMP* 28,330^E
Tkr Sym SBH *Exch* NYS
SIC 5999 5087 Cosmetics; Hair care products; Beauty parlor equipment & supplies
Pr: Christian A Brickman
**Ch Bd:* Robert R McMaster
CFO: Mark J Flaherty
Chf Mktg O: Ashley Sheetz
Ofcr: Brian E Walker
Sr VP: Matthew O Haltom
VP: Thomas Bledsoe
VP: Barbara Clement
VP: Stacy Gaspard
VP: Mark Johnston
VP: Ryan Linders
VP: Janna Minton
VP: Susan Walker
Exec: Debbie Middleton
Board of Directors: Katherine Button Bell, Erin Nealy Cox, Marshall E Eisenberg, David W Gibbs, Robert R McMaster, John A Miller, Susan R Mulder, Edward W Rabin, Gary G Winterhalter

D-U-N-S 05-251-9881 IMP/EXP
■ SALLY BEAUTY SUPPLY LLC
(*Suby of* SALLY BEAUTY HOLDINGS INC) ★
3001 Colorado Blvd, Denton, TX 76210-6802
Tel (940) 898-7500 *Founded/Ownrshp* 1969
Sales 2.4MMM^E *EMP* 10,000
SIC 5999 5122 5087 Cosmetics; Cosmetics; Service establishment equipment
Pr: Michael G Spinozzi
**CFO:* Mark J Flaherty
**Sr VP:* Matthew O Haltom
**VP:* Janna S Minton

D-U-N-S 80-025-6138 IMP
■ SALLY HOLDINGS LLC
(*Suby of* SALLY INVESTMENT HOLDINGS LLC) ★
3001 Colorado Blvd, Denton, TX 76210-6802
Tel (940) 898-7500 *Founded/Ownrshp* 2001
Sales 1.5MMM^E *EMP* 24,615
Accts Kpmg Llp Dallas Texas
SIC 5087 Beauty salon & barber shop equipment & supplies
CFO: Mark J Flaherty
VP: Janna S Minton
Board of Directors: Richard J Schnall, Kathleen J Affeldt, James G Berges, Marshall E Eisenberg, Kenneth A Giuriceo, Robert R McMaster, Walter L Metcalfe Jr, John A Miller, Martha J Miller, Edward W Rabin

D-U-N-S 08-040-2922
■ SALLY INVESTMENT HOLDINGS LLC
(*Suby of* SALLY BEAUTY HOLDINGS INC) ★
3001 Colorado Blvd, Denton, TX 76210-6802
Tel (940) 898-7500 *Founded/Ownrshp* 2006
Sales 1.5MMM^E *EMP* 24,617^E
SIC 7389

D-U-N-S 96-681-6758
SALLYPORT GLOBAL LLC
27200 Riverview Ste 309, Bonita Springs, FL 34134
Tel (239) 390-1900 *Founded/Ownrshp* 2011
Sales 950.0M *EMP* 1,100
SIC 8999 Services
Pr: John P Deblasio Tr

D-U-N-S 19-948-8359
SALMON LEGACY CREEK HOSPITAL
(*Suby of* LEGACY HEALTH) ★
2211 Ne 139th St, Vancouver, WA 98686-2742
Tel (360) 487-1000 *Founded/Ownrshp* 2003
Sales 286.9MM *EMP* 700
SIC 8062 General medical & surgical hospitals
Pr: Lee Domanico
**Sr VP:* P Campbell Groner III
VP: Jodi Joyce
VP: Juan Millan

D-U-N-S 10-668-8484
SALO INC
INTERIM SERVICES
960 Checkrein Ave Ste A, Columbus, OH 43229-1107
Tel (614) 436-9404 *Founded/Ownrshp* 2002
Sales 26.1MM *EMP* 5,500^E
Accts Flagel Huber Flagel Certified
SIC 8082 Home health care services
CEO: Kathleen Gilmartin
**Ch Bd:* Michael Hartshorn
**CFO:* Thomas Dimarco
**CFO:* Michael Slupecki
**VP:* Max Hahnen
**VP:* Sonya Hinds
**VP:* Christine Oswald
**VP:* Lloyd Strothman
CIO: Tony Ott

SALON CENTRIC
See SALONCENTRIC INC

SALONBIZ
See NEILL CORP

D-U-N-S 03-022-9178 IMP/EXP
SALONCENTRIC INC
(*Suby of* LOREAL USA PRODUCTS) ★
575 5th Ave, New York, NY 10017-2422
Tel (800) 282-2843 *Founded/Ownrshp* 2007
Sales 769.2MM^E *EMP* 3,300
SIC 5087 Beauty parlor equipment & supplies
VP: Robert Kinnally
**Pr:* Bertrand Fontaine
**CEO:* Frederic Roze
CFO: Alan Kirschner
**Treas:* Anthony Elvedt
Treas: Barbara Hough
**Treas:* Marc Parenteau
VP: Craig Miller
VP: Darrell Neer
**VP:* Thomas Sarakatsannis
**VP:* Paul Sharnsky

D-U-N-S 85-854-1092 IMP
SALONCENTRIC INC
SALON CENTRIC
(*Suby of* LOREAL USA PRODUCTS) ★
50 Connell Dr, Berkeley Heights, NJ 07922-2705
Tel (212) 984-4000 *Founded/Ownrshp* 2007
Sales 1.9MM^E *EMP* 3,000
SIC 5122 Cosmetics, perfumes & hair products
Pr: Paul Sharnsky
**Treas:* Anthony Elvedt
Sls Mgr: Jeff Espinoza

D-U-N-S 01-443-4505
SALSON LOGISTICS INC
888 Doremus Ave, Newark, NJ 07114-3026
Tel (973) 986-0200 *Founded/Ownrshp* 1997
Sales 196.0MM^E *EMP* 900
SIC 4213 Trucking, except local
CEO: Anthony Berritto
**Pr:* David Wallach
Ex VP: Dominick Gustino
VP: Anna Brant
Exec: Dennis Murphy
VP Sls: Edy Sheng
Sls Dir: Douglas Elwell

D-U-N-S 13-588-2681
SALT FORK RESORT CLUB INC
74978 Broadhead Rd, Kimbolton, OH 43749-9747
Tel (740) 498-8116 *Founded/Ownrshp* 2010
Sales 1.8MM *EMP* 1,000
Accts Jmac Services Cambridge Oh
SIC 7011 7997 Resort hotel; Membership sports & recreation clubs
Pr: Karl Larue

D-U-N-S 07-867-6851
SALT LAKE CITY CORP
4380 W 2100 S, Salt Lake City, UT 84120-1216
Tel (801) 535-7704 *Founded/Ownrshp* 2012
Sales NA *EMP* 2,600
Accts Eide Bailly Llp Salt Lake Ci
SIC 9111 Mayors' offices

SALT LAKE CITY OPEN CLASSROOM
See SALT LAKE CITY SCHOOL DISTRICT

D-U-N-S 01-784-0950
SALT LAKE CITY SCHOOL DISTRICT
SALT LAKE CITY OPEN CLASSROOM
440 E 100 S, Salt Lake City, UT 84111-1841
Tel (801) 578-8307 *Founded/Ownrshp* 1890
Sales 266.3MM *EMP* 3,200
Accts Squire & Company Pc Orem Ut
SIC 8211 Public elementary & secondary schools; Public elementary school
Pr Dir: Jason Olsen
Schl Brd P: Heather Bennet
Teacher Pr: Mozelle Orton
HC Dir: Mindi Holndahl

D-U-N-S 07-301-2304
SALT LAKE COMMUNITY COLLEGE (INC)
4600 S Redwood Rd, Salt Lake City, UT 84123-3145
Tel (801) 957-4111 *Founded/Ownrshp* 1948
Sales 85.4MM *EMP* 3,200^E
Accts Office Of The Utah State Audit
SIC 8222 8221 Community college; Technical institute; Colleges universities & professional schools
Pr: Cynthia A Bioteau
Pr: Alison McFarlane
Pr: Robert Teague
CFO: Jim Lawson
Ex VP: Connor Holt
VP: Sydney Cahoon
VP: Amber Caine
VP: Barbara Grover
VP: Nancy Ho
**VP:* Deneece Huftalin
VP: Lori Ili
**VP:* Dennis Klaus
VP: Larry Landward
VP: Charles Lepper
VP: Brandi Mair
VP: David Richardson
**VP:* Tim Sheehan
**VP:* Chris Ticard

D-U-N-S 10-271-8459
SALT LAKE REGIONAL MEDICAL CENTER LP
(*Suby of* IASIS HEALTHCARE CORP) ★
1050 E South Temple, Salt Lake City, UT 84102-1507
Tel (801) 350-4631 *Founded/Ownrshp* 1999
Sales 109.5MM *EMP* 600
SIC 8062 General medical & surgical hospitals
CEO: Jeff Frandsen
Chf Rad: Robert D Grealy
Dir Vol: Anne Hunter
COO: Craig Wagoner
VP: Wanda S Updike
Dir Lab: Michael H Ferguson
Dir Rx: Andrew Steffen
Dir Sec: Scott Linford
CIO: Mark Runyon
Mktg Dir: Tammy Clark
Surgeon: David J Howe

D-U-N-S 00-694-4557
SALT RIVER ELECTRIC COOPERATIVE CORP
111 W Brashear Ave, Bardstown, KY 40004-1645
Tel (502) 348-3931 *Founded/Ownrshp* 1937
Sales 100.9MM *EMP* 73
Accts Alan Zumstein Lexington Ky
SIC 4911 Distribution, electric power
Pr: Jimmy Longmire
**CEO:* Larry Hicks
**Treas:* Gayle Troutman
**VP:* Eddie Boone
VP: Randy Burba
VP Opers: Tim Sharp

SALT RIVER MATERIALS GROUP
See SALT RIVER SAND & ROCK

D-U-N-S 10-858-8716
SALT RIVER PIMA-MARICOPA INDIAN COMMUNITY EDUCATIONAL SE
SALT RIVER PRIMA MARIC INDIA C
10005 E Osborn Rd, Scottsdale, AZ 85256-4019
Tel (480) 362-7400 *Founded/Ownrshp* 1978
Sales NA *EMP* 4,200
SIC 9131 Indian reservation;
Pr: Diane Enos
**VP:* Martin Harvier
Genl Mgr: Kathrn Kandas
Genl Mgr: Chris McIntier
Psych: Treves Tsosie

SALT RIVER PRIMA MARIC INDIA C
See SALT RIVER PIMA-MARICOPA INDIAN COMMUNITY EDUCATIONAL SE

D-U-N-S 00-901-1487 IMP
SALT RIVER PROJECT AGRICULTURAL IMPROVEMENT AND POWER DISTRICT
1521 N Project Dr, Tempe, AZ 85281-1206
Tel (602) 236-5900 *Founded/Ownrshp* 1937
Sales 2.8MMM^E *EMP* 4,336
Accts Pricewaterhousecoopers Llp La
SIC 4911 ; Generation, electric power; Distribution, electric power
Pr: David Rousseau
Pr: Clifford Rushton
CFO: Kathy Kotin
**Treas:* Dean R Duncan
**Treas:* Steven Hulet
Bd of Dir: Deborah Hendrickson
Bd of Dir: Wendy Marshall
Bd of Dir: Mario Rickert
Bd of Dir: Keith Woods
VP: Gary Harper
**VP:* John R Hoopes
VP: Colleen Pellegrin

D-U-N-S 04-676-3983
SALT RIVER SAND & ROCK
SALT RIVER MATERIALS GROUP
8800 E Chaparral Rd # 155, Scottsdale, AZ 85250-2603
Tel (480) 850-5757 *Founded/Ownrshp* 1959
Sales 84.6MM^E *EMP* 160
SIC 5032 1442 Sand, construction; Construction sand & gravel
Pr: Roger R Smith Jr
VP: Jeff Hearne
VP: Verle Martz
VP: Tom Vanderwalker
CTO: Chris Osborn
IT Man: Gilbert Hernandez
Opers Mgr: Helms Ron

D-U-N-S 07-510-8902 IMP/EXP
SALTCHUK RESOURCES INC (WA)
1111 Fairview Ave N, Seattle, WA 98109-4418
Tel (206) 652-1111 *Founded/Ownrshp* 1982
Sales 2.2MMM^E *EMP* 4,500
SIC 4492 4412 4499

D-U-N-S 79-082-8164
SALTGRASS INC
SALTGRASS STEAK HOUSE
(*Suby of* LSRI HOLDINGS INC) ★
1510 West Loop S, Houston, TX 77027-9505
Tel (713) 850-1010 *Founded/Ownrshp* 2002
Sales 1.2MMM *EMP* 15,000
SIC 5812 Steak restaurant
Pr: Tilman J Fertitta
**VP:* Steven Scheinthal

SALTGRASS STEAK HOUSE
See SALTGRASS INC

SALTGRASS STEAK HOUSE
See FSI RESTAURANT DEVELOPMENT LIMITED

D-U-N-S 05-103-7950
SALVATION ARMY
(*Suby of* SALVATION ARMY NATIONAL CORP) ★
1424 Northeast Expy Ne, Brookhaven, GA 30329-2088
Tel (404) 728-1300 *Founded/Ownrshp* 1865
Sales 1.2MMM *EMP* 16,168
Accts Ernst & Young Llp Atlanta Ge
SIC 8661 8322 Miscellaneous denomination church; Disaster service; Multi-service center
Ch Bd: David Jeffrey
**Pr:* Donald Bell
**Treas:* James Seiler
**Ex VP:* James Allison
**VP:* F Bradford Bailey
Corp Couns: Melanie M Brackett
Board of Directors: Debora Bell, John Needham, margaret McGo, Heidi Bailey William Moc

D-U-N-S 06-251-7941
SALVATION ARMY
(*Suby of* SALVATION ARMY NATIONAL CORP) ★
440 W Nyack Rd Ofc, West Nyack, NY 10994-1739
Tel (845) 620-7200 *Founded/Ownrshp* 1865
Sales 1.0MMM *EMP* 10,447^E
Accts Grant Thornton Llp New York
SIC 8661 Religious organizations
Pr: Barry C Swanson
**Ch:* William Roberts
**Treas:* Thomas O Henson
**Treas:* James W Reynolds
**Trst:* Glenn C Bloomfield
**Trst:* William Carlson
**Trst:* Janice A Howard
**Trst:* Steven M Howard
**Trst:* Kenneth W Maynor
**Trst:* Thomas A Schenk

D-U-N-S 07-462-9460
SALVATION ARMY
(*Suby of* SALVATION ARMY NATIONAL CORP) ★
180 E Ocean Blvd Fl 2, Long Beach, CA 90802-4709
Tel (562) 491-8464 *Founded/Ownrshp* 1865
Sales 485.1MM^E *EMP* 320
Accts Deloitte & Touche Llp Los Ang
SIC 8661 Non-church religious organizations
Prin: James M Knaggs
**Pr:* Commissioner Carolyn R Knaggs
**Ex Dir:* Susan Lawrence
Genl Mgr: Gwen Joyce
Board of Directors: Major Paul Seiler

D-U-N-S 12-486-3999
SALVATION ARMY NATIONAL CORP
615 Slaters Ln, Alexandria, VA 22314-1112
Tel (703) 684-5500 *Founded/Ownrshp* 1880
Sales 4.3MMM *EMP* 16,170
SIC 8661 8699 Religious organizations; Charitable organization
Pr: William A Robert
CFO: Mark Knecht
CFO: William H Urula
**Treas:* Sandra L Defibaugh
Bd of Dir: Gayle Horton
Ofcr: Michael Lutcher
Ex VP: Charlotte Anderson
**VP:* William Harfoot
VP: Clifford Marshall
Ex Dir: Harden H White
Ex Dir: Harden White

SALVATORE FERRAGAMO
See FERRAGAMO U S A INC

D-U-N-S 11-103-5015 IMP
SAM ASH MEGASTORES LLC
278 Duffy Ave Unit A, Hicksville, NY 11801-3642
Tel (516) 932-6400 *Founded/Ownrshp* 2002
Sales 132.4MM^E *EMP* 1,650
SIC 5736 Musical instrument stores

D-U-N-S 02-924-9350
SAM ASH MUSIC CORP
278 Duffy Ave Unit A, Hicksville, NY 11801-3642
Tel (516) 932-6400 *Founded/Ownrshp* 2014
Sales 43.9MM^E *EMP* 1,800
SIC 5099 5736 Musical instruments; Musical instrument stores
Pr: Richard Ash
CEO: David Ash
COO: Sammy Ash

D-U-N-S 07-750-4603 IMP/EXP
SAM ASH MUSIC CORP
278 Duffy Ave Unit A, Hicksville, NY 11801-3642
Tel (516) 932-6400 *Founded/Ownrshp* 1924
Sales 264.4MM^E *EMP* 1,700
SIC 5736 5731 5734 5961 7359 8741 Musical instrument stores; Radio, television & electronic stores; Computer & software stores; Mail order house; Musical instrument rental services; Management services
CEO: D Richard Ash
**Pr:* Paul Ash
**Pr:* Chris Konys
**Pr:* Clay Rigdon
**Pr:* Dave Stumacher
**CEO:* Richard Ash
**CFO:* Stuart Leibowitz
**Ch:* David C Ash
Sr Cor Off: Richard Augustin

*Ex VP: Sam M Ash
*VP: Steven Bender
Dir Bus: Tim Bradshaw

D-U-N-S 03-229-8150
SAM GALLOWAY FORD INC
1800 Boy Scout Dr, Fort Myers, FL 33907-2113
Tel (239) 936-3673 Founded/Ownrshp 1951
Sales 152.8MM[E] EMP 380
SIC 5511 Automobiles, new & used
Pr: Sam M Galloway Jr
COO: Jerry Toney
CFO: Brooke Samuelson
*VP: Robert W Galloway Jr
Sls&Mrk Ex: Bonnie Mason
Sls Mgr: Billy Todd

D-U-N-S 05-626-7867
SAM HOUSTON ELECTRIC COOPERATIVE INC
1157 E Church St, Livingston, TX 77351-3360
Tel (936) 327-5711 Founded/Ownrshp 1939
Sales 179.6MM EMP 152
Accts Axley & Rode Llp Lufkin Tx
SIC 4911 Electric services; Distribution, electric power
CEO: Kyle Kuntz
*Pr: Truett Thomson
*Treas: Katherine Hardin
*Sec: R C Thomas
Bd of Dir: Robert E Leisner
Bd of Dir: Thomas J Lucher
*VP: Ernie Miles

D-U-N-S 00-814-5005
SAM KANE BEEF PROCESSORS LLC
9001 Leopard St, Corpus Christi, TX 78409-2599
Tel (361) 241-5000 Founded/Ownrshp 1949
Sales 328.0MM[E] EMP 700
Accts Collier Johnson & Woods Pc
SIC 2011 Meat packing plants
CEO: Lou Waters Jr
*Pr: Charles R Jackson
*CEO: Alfred Bausch
VP: Brian Huesers
Genl Couns: David Kane

D-U-N-S 01-443-1043 IMP
SAM LEVIN INC
LEVIN'S FURNITURE
301 Fitz Henry Rd, Smithton, PA 15479-8715
Tel (724) 872-2055 Founded/Ownrshp 1946
Sales 202.6MM EMP 400
Accts Schneider Downs & Co Inc P
SIC 5712 Furniture stores
Pr: Robert Levin
Sec: Sally Levin
VP: Ward Dingman
VP: Basil Hawanchak
Exec: Carrie Isaac
Genl Mgr: Gene Sasso
Off Mgr: Eugene Forbes
Off Mgr: Trish Snider
Store Mgr: Ken Coury
Store Mgr: John Nymick
Dir IT: Joe Knouse

D-U-N-S 03-596-9039 IMP
SAM LEVITZ FURNITURE CO INC
3430 E 36th St, Tucson, AZ 85713-5207
Tel (520) 624-7443 Founded/Ownrshp 1951
Sales 100.5MM[E] EMP 400
SIC 5712 Furniture stores
Ch: Lee Levitz
*Pr: Sam R Levitz
*VP: Eric R Creson
*VP: Richard Marcus
VP: Rick Marcus
*VP: Karen Vactor
Genl Mgr: Dave Nelson
Manager: Francisco Orozco
Mktg Mgr: Bob Carter
Sls Mgr: Ali Rustempasic

D-U-N-S 02-612-7548
SAM PACKS FIVE STAR FORD LTD (TX)
1635 S Interstate 35e, Carrollton, TX 75006-7415
Tel (972) 447-0606 Founded/Ownrshp 1956, 2002
Sales 91.0MM[E] EMP 180
SIC 5511 Automobiles, new & used
Pr: Sam Cack
*Pt: Tony Pack
*Genl Mgr: Trey Russell
Sls Mgr: Justin Compton
Sls Mgr: Bobby Richardson
Sales Asso: Otilio Hernandez

D-U-N-S 87-743-7632
SAM RAYBURN G & T ELECTRIC COOPERATIVE INC
2905 Westward Dr, Nacogdoches, TX 75964-1231
Tel (936) 560-9532 Founded/Ownrshp 1979
Sales 149.3MM EMP 11
Accts Axley & Rode Llp Lufkin Tx
SIC 4911 Distribution, electric power
Pr: Fred Solly
*CFO: Ryan Thomas
*Treas: Roy Claud Thomas
*VP: Kyle Kuntz
Genl Mgr: John Butts

D-U-N-S 02-408-8650 IMP
SAM SWOPE AUTO GROUP LLC (KY)
ALLSTATE
10 Swope Autocenter Dr, Louisville, KY 40299-1806
Tel (502) 499-5000 Founded/Ownrshp 1960
Sales 287.8MM[E] EMP 900
SIC 5511 5012 7532 Automobiles, new & used; Pickups, new & used; Vans, new & used; Automobiles; Collision shops, automotive
Ch: Patricia G Swope
Sls Mgr: Jason McCurry
Sales Asso: Andres Magallanes

D-U-N-S 15-257-3010
■ **SAM-WILL INC**
FREMONT HOTEL AND CASINO
(Suby of CALIFORNIA HOTEL AND CASINO) ★
200 Fremont St, Las Vegas, NV 89101-5622
Tel (702) 385-3232 Founded/Ownrshp 1984
Sales 51.0MM[E] EMP 2,500
Accts Deloitte & Touche Llp
SIC 7011 Casino hotel
Pr: William S Boyd
*Sr VP: Robert Boughner
*Sr VP: Don Snyder

SAMARITAN ALBANY GENERAL HOSP
See ALBANY GENERAL HOSPITAL

D-U-N-S 83-038-8828
SAMARITAN ALBANY GENERAL HOSPITAL
1046 6th Ave Sw, Albany, OR 97321-1916
Tel (541) 812-4732 Founded/Ownrshp 2005
Sales 120.4MM EMP 29[E]
SIC 8062 General medical & surgical hospitals
Prin: David Triebes
CFO: Dan Smith

D-U-N-S 07-273-0179
SAMARITAN DAYTOP VILLAGE INC
13802 Queens Blvd Fl 1, Briarwood, NY 11435-2642
Tel (718) 206-2000 Founded/Ownrshp 1965
Sales 87.8MM EMP 550
Accts Withumsmithbrown Pc New Bruns
SIC 8322 8093 Emergency shelters; Drug clinic, outpatient
Pr: Tino Hernandez
*COO: Douglas Apple
*CFO: John Iammatteo
*Treas: Axel Graf
CIO: Sheila Greene
IT Man: Michael Pikman
Sls Mgr: Steven Rockman

D-U-N-S 12-254-7979
SAMARITAN HEALTH PARTNERS
(Suby of CHI) ★
2222 Philadelphia Dr, Dayton, OH 45406-1813
Tel (937) 208-8400 Founded/Ownrshp 1985
Sales 354.6MM[E] EMP 2,386
Accts Ernst & Young Llp Us Indiana
SIC 8062 General medical & surgical hospitals
Pr: K Douglas Deck
CFO: Tom Curtin
*CFO: Thomas M Duncan
Treas: Janet Rogers

D-U-N-S 83-605-3483
SAMARITAN HEALTH SERVICES
990 Nw Circle Blvd # 201, Corvallis, OR 97330-1967
Tel (541) 768-4773 Founded/Ownrshp 2010
Sales 159.1MM EMP 1
SIC 8099 Health & allied services
Prin: Bruce Madsen
CFO: Dan Smith
Exec: Linda Schader
IT Man: Dawn Miller
Mktg Dir: Brad Canfield

D-U-N-S 60-306-7463
SAMARITAN HEALTH SERVICES INC
GOOD SAMARITAN HOSPITAL
3600 Nw Samaritan Dr, Corvallis, OR 97330-3737
Tel (541) 757-5111 Founded/Ownrshp 1986
Sales 687.3MM[E] EMP 4,300[E]
SIC 8741 8062 Hospital management; General medical & surgical hospitals
Pr: Larry Mullins
CFO: Dan Smith
Ofcr: Colleen Fair
VP: Dawnell Buell
VP: Kathy Hale
VP: Ed Knecht
VP: Robert Power
VP: Ronald Stevens
Dir Lab: Harlan Akers
Dir Rad: Chris Clark
Dir Rx: Penny Reher

D-U-N-S 02-067-5211
SAMARITAN HOSPITAL OF TROY NEW YORK
2215 Burdett Ave, Troy, NY 12180-2475
Tel (518) 271-3300 Founded/Ownrshp 1983
Sales 142.6MM EMP 1,403
Accts Deloitte Tax Llp Philadelphia
SIC 8062 General medical & surgical hospitals
CEO: Norman Dascher
Dir Vol: Carol Favreau
COO: Karen Tassey
Ex VP: Dascher Norman
VP: Susan McDonough
Dir Lab: Loma Tan
Off Mgr: April Stevens
CIO: Jim Mormann
MIS Dir: James Banagan
Dir IT: Sonia McGrath
IT Man: Scott Flagel

D-U-N-S 07-728-6243
SAMARITAN MEDICAL CENTER
830 Washington St, Watertown, NY 13601-4099
Tel (315) 785-4000 Founded/Ownrshp 1881
Sales 192.7MM EMP 1,300
SIC 8062 5047 General medical & surgical hospitals; Medical & hospital equipment
Pr: Thomas Carman
Chf Path: Shahandeh Haghir
Dir Vol: Jennifer Young
COO: Deborah Vink
CFO: Sean Mills
VP: Anthony Joseph
Exec: Linda Golden
Ex Dir: Leslie Krensky
Admn Mgr: Julie Cannan
Off Mgr: Cindy Stean
Nurse Mgr: Pamela Denney

D-U-N-S 00-415-1668 IMP/EXP
SAMARITANS PURSE (NC)
801 Bamboo Rd, Boone, NC 28607-8721
Tel (828) 262-1980 Founded/Ownrshp 1970
Sales 599.8MM EMP 525
Accts Dixon Hughes Goodman Llp Char
SIC 8322 6732 Temporary relief service; Charitable trust management
Ch Bd: Franklin Graham
COO: Virgil Gottfried
VP: Jim Dailey
VP: Hugh Elder
VP: Ken Isaacs
VP: Merrill Littlejohn
*VP: Phyllis Payne
Exec: Rusty Faulks
Dir Sec: Humphrey Hayes
Prgrm Mgr: Todd Taylor
IT Man: Brad Harmon

SAMBA
See SPECIAL AGENTS MUTUAL BENEFIT ASSOCIATION INC

SAMBA ROOM
See E-BRANDS RESTAURANTS LLC

D-U-N-S 06-997-4376
SAMC INC
ST ANTHONY MEDICAL CENTER
(Suby of SAINT JAMES HOSPITAL) ★
1201 S Main St, Crown Point, IN 46307-8481
Tel (219) 738-2100 Founded/Ownrshp 1999
Sales 86.0MM[E] EMP 1,045
SIC 8062 General medical & surgical hospitals
Pr: Seth Warren
*CFO: Larry Stazinski
VP: John King
Phys Thrpy: Kevin Debraal

D-U-N-S 00-790-5458
SAMEDAN OIL CORP
NOBLE ENERGY
1001 Noble Energy Way, Houston, TX 77070-1435
Tel (580) 223-4110 Founded/Ownrshp 1932
Sales 310.9MM[E] EMP 500[E]
SIC 1311 Crude petroleum production; Natural gas production
CEO: Charles D Davidson

D-U-N-S 02-463-7373
SAMET CORP (NC)
309 Gallimore Dairy Rd # 102, Greensboro, NC 27409-9316
Tel (336) 544-2600 Founded/Ownrshp 1961
Sales 265.2MM EMP 140[E]
SIC 1541 1542 Industrial buildings & warehouses; Nonresidential construction
Ch: Norman G Samet
*Pr: Rick Davenport
*Pr: Arthur Samet
CFO: Arthur L Samet
Sr Cor Off: Arthur Samet
*VP: Marshal Tuck
Exec: Charles Blankinship
IT Man: Pam Hillerby

D-U-N-S 07-545-5410
SAMFORD UNIVERSITY
800 Lakeshore Dr, Birmingham, AL 35229-0002
Tel (205) 726-2011 Founded/Ownrshp 1841
Sales 153.8MM EMP 1,000[E]
SIC 8221

D-U-N-S 04-329-6060 IMP/EXP
SAMMONS ENTERPRISES INC
5949 Sherry Ln Ste 1900, Dallas, TX 75225-8015
Tel (214) 210-5000 Founded/Ownrshp 1962
Sales 1.9MMM[E] EMP 2,600
SIC 5084 6311 Industrial machinery & equipment; Life insurance
Pr: Esfandyar E Dinshaw
*CEO: Heather Kreager
*CFO: Pam Doeppe
*Ch: Thomas Corcoran
VP: Curt Foody
*Prin: Darron Ash
*Genl Couns: Linda Newman
Corp Couns: Yolanda Brown
Corp Couns: Cheryl Gosch
Board of Directors: Mary Ann Cree

D-U-N-S 15-453-8417
SAMMONS FINANCIAL GROUP INC
(Suby of SAMMONS ENTERPRISES INC) ★
525 W Van Buren St # 1200, Chicago, IL 60607-3838
Tel (312) 648-7600 Founded/Ownrshp 1996
Sales NA EMP 1,200
SIC 6311 Life insurance
CEO: Esfand Dinshaw
Pr: Bill Lowe
Ch: Mike Masterson
Treas: Thomas M Eyer
Ofcr: Brian Hansen
Sr VP: Gary J Gaspar
Sr VP: Stephen P Horvat Jr
IT Man: Greg Caffarelli

SAMMONS PRESTON
See PATTERSON MEDICAL PRODUCTS INC

D-U-N-S 03-507-4632
SAMPSON CONSTRUCTION CO INC (NE)
3730 S 14th St, Lincoln, NE 68502-5396
Tel (308) 865-1375 Founded/Ownrshp 1971
Sales 172.6MM[E] EMP 200
SIC 1542 1541 Commercial & office building, new construction; Industrial buildings, new construction
Pr: John Sampson
*Treas: Rodney M Sampson
Treas: Rodney Sapson
*Treas: Cori Vokoun
*VP: Sam Sampson

D-U-N-S 02-453-6658
SAMPSON-BLADEN OIL CO INC (NC)
HANDEE HUGO'S
510 Commerce St, Clinton, NC 28328-4300
Tel (910) 592-4177 Founded/Ownrshp 1936
Sales 323.8MM[E] EMP 280
SIC 5171 5411 5983 Petroleum bulk stations; Convenience stores, chain; Fuel oil dealers
Pr: Rogers H Clark
CFO: Jeff Smith
*Sec: David K Clark
*VP: Haddon M Clark
Prin: H Manly Clark Jr
Genl Mgr: Fred Jensen
Dir IT: Scotty Westbrook
Mktg Dir: Ed Wazney

SAM'S CLUB HOME OFFICE
See SAMS WEST INC

SAM'S TOWN CASINO
See RED RIVER ENTERTAINMENT OF SHREVEPORT

SAM'S TOWN GMBLING HALL CASINO
See BOYD TUNICA INC

D-U-N-S 78-624-2185 IMP/EXP
■ **SAMS WEST INC**
SAM'S CLUB HOME OFFICE
(Suby of WALMART) ★
2101 Se Simple Savings Dr, Bentonville, AR 72712-4304
Tel (479) 273-4000 Founded/Ownrshp 1999
Sales 708.8MM[E] EMP 261[E]
SIC 5399 Warehouse club stores
Pr: Donald Frieson
CFO: Michael Dastugue
*Treas: Jeff Davis
Treas: Charles Holley Jr
Ex VP: John Collier
Ex VP: Johnnie Dobbs Jr
Ex VP: Don Frieson
*Ex VP: P Todd Harbaugh
Ex VP: Phyllis Harris
Ex VP: Kerry Kilker
Ex VP: Greg S Spragg
Ex VP: Celia Swanson
Ex VP: Rick Weinstein
VP: Catherine Corely
VP: Racquel Harris
VP: Judy Hobbs
VP: Edward Kolodzieski
VP: Jose Laparte
*VP: J Councill Leak
VP: Carly McCarty
Exec: Arthur Brown

SAMSON CONTOUR
See SAMSON RESOURCES CO

D-U-N-S 07-880-5366
SAMSON ENERGY CO LLC
110 W 7th St Ste 2000, Tulsa, OK 74119-1076
Tel (918) 879-0279 Founded/Ownrshp 2011
Sales 84.3MM[E] EMP 183[E]
SIC 1389 1741 Building oil & gas well foundations on site; Chimney construction & maintenance
Netwrk Eng: Aaron Turner
Opers Mgr: Kurt P Primeaux

D-U-N-S 15-352-0663
SAMSON INVESTMENT CO
(Suby of SAMSON RESOURCES CORP) ★
2 W 2nd St Ste 1500, Tulsa, OK 74103-3135
Tel (918) 583-1791 Founded/Ownrshp 1986
Sales 1.2MMM[E] EMP 1,480
SIC 1311 7353 5082 Crude petroleum production; Natural gas production; Oil field equipment, rental or leasing; Oil field equipment
Pr: Randy Limbacher
Treas: John McCready
Treas: Phil C Tholen
Ex VP: Philip Cook
Ex VP: Richard Fraley
Ex VP: Louis Jones

D-U-N-S 80-366-3413 IMP/EXP
SAMSON INVESTMENT HOLDING INC
UNIVERSAL FURNITURE INTL
2575 Penny Rd, High Point, NC 27265-8334
Tel (336) 449-4600 Founded/Ownrshp 2008
Sales 123.6MM[E] EMP 451
SIC 2512 Upholstered household furniture
CEO: Jeffrey R Scheffer
*CFO: Victor Hsu
VP: Joanne Cutrer
QA Dir: Loren Morse

D-U-N-S 05-594-3096
SAMSON RESOURCES CO
SAMSON CONTOUR
(Suby of SAMSON INVESTMENT CO) ★
2 W 2nd St Ste 1500, Tulsa, OK 74103-3103
Tel (918) 583-1791 Founded/Ownrshp 1971
Sales 183.3MM[E] EMP 137
SIC 1311 2911 Crude petroleum production; Natural gas production; Petroleum refining
CEO: Randy Limbacher
Pr: Paul Smolarchuk
COO: Louis Jones
CFO: Philip Cook
Co-Pr: Thomas R Dimelow
Co-Pr: C Phil Tholen
Sr VP: Steven E Area
Sr VP: Sam D Parker
VP: Judith K Baird
VP: Richard Fraley
VP: Bill H McLaughlin
Exec: Gregg E Fairbrothers

D-U-N-S 07-883-0520
SAMSON RESOURCES CORP
2 W 2nd St Ste 1600, Tulsa, OK 74103-3104
Tel (918) 591-1791 Founded/Ownrshp 1971
Sales 1.7MMM[E] EMP 1,501[E]
SIC 1311 Crude petroleum production
*CEO: Randy L Limbacher
*COO: Louis Jones
*Ex VP: Richard Fraley

D-U-N-S 15-453-7724 IMP/EXP
SAMSONITE LLC
(Suby of SAMSONITE INTERNATIONAL S.A.)
575 West St Ste 110, Mansfield, MA 02048-1160
Tel (508) 851-1400 Founded/Ownrshp 2007
Sales 459.2MM[E] EMP 5,000
SIC 5948 5199 Luggage & leather goods stores; Leather goods, except footwear, gloves, luggage, belting

Pr: Tom Korbas
**CFO:* Kyle Gendreau
VP: Robert Cooper
VP: Tom Loba
**VP:* John B Livingston
Exec: Ada Li
Opers Mgr: Fred Peirce
VP Mktg: Lynne Berard
Mktg Dir: Cheryl Cotterman
Sls Dir: Carl Engelbourg

D-U-N-S 02-810-8483 IMP/EXP
SAMSUNG AUSTIN SEMICONDUCTOR LLC
(*Suby of* SAMSUNG SEMICONDUCTOR INC) ★
12100 Samsung Blvd, Austin, TX 78754-1903
Tel (512) 672-1000 *Founded/Ownrshp* 2000
Sales 228.8MM^E *EMP* 950
SIC 3674 Microprocessors; Microcircuits, integrated (semiconductor); Computer logic modules; Memories, solid state
Pr: Dr Youngwook Yw Park
**Pr:* Young Bum Koh
**Pr:* Gregory Lee
**CFO:* Nam Ho Park
Sls Mgr: Michael Phillips

D-U-N-S 04-006-1301 IMP/EXP
SAMSUNG C&T AMERICA INC
(*Suby of* SAMSUNG C&T CORPORATION)
105 Challenger Rd Fl 3, Ridgefield Park, NJ 07660-2100
Tel (201) 229-4000 *Founded/Ownrshp* 1975
Sales 696.4MM^E *EMP* 250
SIC 5169 6799 8742 Chemicals & allied products; Commodity investors; Marketing consulting services
CEO: Soohee Han
V Ch: Jason Kim
**CFO:* Know-Kook Park
Ex VP: John Pleasants
**Sr VP:* Sookee Lee
Sr VP: Mark Ramsey
VP: Scott Birnbaum
VP: Jeremy Choi
VP: Steven Cook
VP: Ronald Hulse
VP: Km Park
VP: Nicholas H Yoo
Dir Bus: Jack Woo

D-U-N-S 07-701-0254 IMP/EXP
SAMSUNG ELECTRONICS AMERICA INC
(*Suby of* SAMSUNG ELECTRONICS CO., LTD.)
85 Challenger Rd, Ridgefield Park, NJ 07660-2112
Tel (201) 229-4000 *Founded/Ownrshp* 1978
Sales 2.4MMM^E *EMP* 2,337
Accts Pricewaterhousecoopers Llp
SIC 5064 5065 5045 Electrical appliances, television & radio; Television sets; Video cassette recorders & accessories; Microwave ovens, non-commercial; Telephone & telegraphic equipment; Telephone equipment; Computers; Computer peripheral equipment
Pr: Gregory Lee
Pr: Young Hoon Eom
Pr: Iksung Hur
**Pr:* Yangkyu Kim
CFO: Jong M Bae
CFO: Minyong Choi
CFO: Edward Kim
CFO: J Lee
CFO: Young Min
Chf Mktg O: Todd Pendleton
**Chf Mktg O:* Ralph Santana
**Ofcr:* Jesse Coulter
**Ofcr:* Marc Mathieu
Ex VP: Alfred Koh
Sr VP: Michael Abary
**Sr VP:* Steven Cook
Sr VP: Dennis McGlynn
Sr VP: Rajiv Mehta
Sr VP: Tod Pike
**Sr VP:* Peter Weedfald
VP: Chris Franey

D-U-N-S 93-906-3293 IMP/EXP
SAMSUNG OPTO-ELECTRONICS AMERICA INC
SAMSUNG TECHWIN AMERICA
(*Suby of* HANWHA TECHWIN CO., LTD.)
100 Challenger Rd Ste 700, Ridgefield Park, NJ 07660-2119
Tel (201) 325-2612 *Founded/Ownrshp* 1989
Sales 177.4MM *EMP* 150
SIC 5043 7699 3861 Photographic cameras, projectors, equipment & supplies; Photographic & optical goods equipment repair services; Photographic instruments, electronic
Pr: Soon Hong Ahn

D-U-N-S 03-702-8524
SAMSUNG SDS AMERICA INC
(*Suby of* SAMSUNG SDS CO., LTD.)
100 Challenger Rd, Ridgefield Park, NJ 07660-2108
Tel (201) 229-4456 *Founded/Ownrshp* 1997
Sales 131.7MM^E *EMP* 310
SIC 7372 7371 Prepackaged software; Computer software development
CEO: Sean Seung Gyo Kae
**Pr:* Ki Hyung Cho
**CFO:* Jong Moo Bae
VP: John Godfrey
Snr Mgr: Dave Ko
Snr Mgr: Duhee Lee

D-U-N-S 10-210-8958 EXP
SAMSUNG SEMICONDUCTOR INC
(*Suby of* SAMSUNG ELECTRONICS AMERICA INC) ★
3655 N 1st St, San Jose, CA 95134-1707
Tel (408) 544-4000 *Founded/Ownrshp* 1979
Sales 745.7MM^E *EMP* 1,176
SIC 5065 5045 Semiconductor devices; Computers, peripherals & software
Pr: Young Chang Bae
**CFO:* Damian Huh
**Sr VP:* Tom Quinn
VP: Bob Brennan
VP: Chris Byrne
VP: Meng Chee
VP: Byung Cho
VP: Eui-Suk Chung
VP: Mike Crawley
VP: Bryan Hopkins
VP: Jon Kang
VP: Kiho Kim
VP: Yong Park
VP: David Shim
VP: Joe Virginia

SAMSUNG TECHWIN AMERICA
See SAMSUNG OPTO-ELECTRONICS AMERICA INC

D-U-N-S 78-759-2567 IMP
SAMSUNG TELECOMMUNICATIONS AMERICA LLC
1301 E Lookout Dr, Richardson, TX 75082-4107
Tel (972) 761-7000 *Founded/Ownrshp* 2002
Sales 19.5MMM *EMP* 600
SIC 5065

D-U-N-S 02-042-1905 IMP
SAMTEC INC
520 Park East Blvd, New Albany, IN 47150-7251
Tel (812) 944-6733 *Founded/Ownrshp* 1975
Sales 775.8MM^E *EMP* 4,000
SIC 3679

D-U-N-S 96-257-6489 IMP
SAMUEL ADAMS PENNSYLVANIA BREWERY CO
7880 Penn Dr, Breinigsville, PA 18031-1508
Tel (610) 391-4700 *Founded/Ownrshp* 2008
Sales 113.1MM^E *EMP* 746^E
SIC 2082

D-U-N-S 09-682-5997
SAMUEL PRESSURE VESSEL GROUP INC
(*Suby of* SAMUEL, SON & CO., LIMITED)
2121 Cleveland Ave, Marinette, WI 54143-3711
Tel (715) 735-9311 *Founded/Ownrshp* 2006
Sales 110.0MM *EMP* 792
SIC 3443 Industrial vessels, tanks & containers; Tanks, standard or custom fabricated: metal plate; Vessels, process or storage (from boiler shops): metal plate
Pr: Barry Bergquist
Sales Exec: William Wenzel

D-U-N-S 04-437-5236
SAMUEL ROBERTS NOBLE FOUNDATION INC
2510 Sam Noble Pkwy, Ardmore, OK 73401-2124
Tel (580) 226-2178 *Founded/Ownrshp* 1952
Sales 203.2MM *EMP* 374
Accts Grant Thornton Llp Oklahoma C
SIC 8733 Noncommercial research organizations; Bacteriological research
CEO: Michael A Cawley
**CEO:* Bill Buckner
**CFO:* A J Wallace
Top Exec: Pat Weaver
**Sr VP:* E Charles Brummer
**Sr VP:* Billy Cook
**Sr VP:* Richard A Dixon
Sr VP: Ji He
**Sr VP:* Michael Udvardi
**VP:* Steven P Rhines
Prgrm Mgr: Hugh Aljoe

D-U-N-S 80-919-1109 IMP
SAMUEL SON & CO INC
(*Suby of* SAMUEL, SON & CO., LIMITED)
4334 Walden Ave, Lancaster, NY 14086-9716
Tel (716) 681-4200 *Founded/Ownrshp* 1993
Sales 358.5MM^E *EMP* 500
SIC 5085 5051 Industrial supplies; Metals service centers & offices
CEO: William Chisholm
**Pr:* Bill Chisholm
**VP:* Bob Carter
VP: Paula Orlowski
Genl Mgr: Samuel Atlanta
Genl Mgr: Bruce Buzza
Off Admin: Andrea Mackenzie

D-U-N-S 05-674-2349 IMP/EXP
SAMUEL STRAPPING SYSTEMS INC
STEEL FAB
(*Suby of* SAMUEL, SON & CO., LIMITED)
1401 Davey Rd Ste 300, Woodridge, IL 60517-4991
Tel (630) 783-8900 *Founded/Ownrshp* 1971
Sales 128.9MM^E *EMP* 350
SIC 3499 5085 Strapping, metal; Industrial supplies
Pr: Robert Hickey
VP: Mark Menning
Exec: Peggy U Pfeifer
Genl Mgr: Victoria Peat
Dir IT: Joe Capoccio
Manager: Brian Wilson

D-U-N-S 07-947-4217
SAMUEL VAZQUEZ
DS SCREEN PRINTING & EMB
108 Calle Mendez Vigo E, Mayaguez, PR 00680-4955
Tel (787) 598-6107 *Founded/Ownrshp* 2014
Sales 86.0MM *EMP* 6
SIC 5699 T-shirts, custom printed
Owner: Samuel Vazquez

D-U-N-S 36-075-3529 IMP
SAMUELS AND SON SEAFOOD CO INC
SAMUELS SEAFOOD
3400 S Lawrence St, Philadelphia, PA 19148-5623
Tel (215) 336-7810 *Founded/Ownrshp* 1989
Sales 162.3MM^E *EMP* 250
SIC 5146 Seafoods
Pr: Samuel D'Angelo
**CFO:* John Harty

SAMUELS SEAFOOD
See SAMUELS AND SON SEAFOOD CO INC

SAMVARDHANA MTHERSON REFLECTEC
See SMR AUTOMOTIVE SYSTEMS USA INC

D-U-N-S 09-854-1444
SAN ANDREAS REGIONAL CENTER
300 Orchard Cy Dr Ste 170, Campbell, CA 95008
Tel (408) 374-9960 *Founded/Ownrshp* 1969
Sales 310.1MM *EMP* 272
Accts Elizabeth B Bacungan-Chief Ac
SIC 8322 Association for the handicapped
CEO: Mary Lu Gonzalez
**CFO:* Yoshiharu Kuroiwa
**VP:* Lisa Lopez

SAN ANGELO COMMUNITY MEDICAL CENTER
See SAN ANGELO HOSPITAL LP

D-U-N-S 08-579-3776
■ **SAN ANGELO HOSPITAL LP**
SAN ANGELO COMMUNITY MEDICAL CENTER
(*Suby of* COMMUNITY HEALTH SYSTEMS INC) ★
3501 Knickerbocker Rd, San Angelo, TX 76904-7610
Tel (325) 949-9511 *Founded/Ownrshp* 2000
Sales 130.8MM *EMP* 840^E
SIC 8062 General medical & surgical hospitals
CEO: Jeremy Rinney
Owner: David Lupton
Pt: Eric Becker
Mng Pt: Brad Holland
Dir Inf Cn: Nancy White
Dir Risk M: Cindy Tschudi
Dir Rad: Ann Peterson
QA Dir: Becky Brandon
Obsttrcn: Rosalinda Carrizales
Obsttrcn: Charles Harzke
Doctor: John Granaghan

D-U-N-S 07-079-9721
SAN ANGELO INDEPENDENT SCHOOL DISTRICT
SAISD
1621 University Ave, San Angelo, TX 76904-5164
Tel (325) 947-3700 *Founded/Ownrshp* 1900
Sales 103.0MM *EMP* 2,000
Accts Webb & Webb San Angelo Tx
SIC 8211 Public elementary & secondary schools
Pr: Lanny Layman
Prin: Cindy Lee
Prin: Elaine Stribling
Prin: Bill Waters
Prin: Connie Williams
Ex Dir: Brent McCallie
MIS Dir: Charlyn Doyle
HC Dir: Melissa Schumpert

SAN ANTONIO AIRLIFE
See AIR METHODS CORP

SAN ANTONIO COLLEGE
See ALAMO COMMUNITY COLLEGE DISTRICT

D-U-N-S 07-251-4060 IMP
SAN ANTONIO COMMUNITY HOSPITAL (CA)
999 San Bernardino Rd, Upland, CA 91786-4920
Tel (909) 985-2811 *Founded/Ownrshp* 1906
Sales 290.5MM *EMP* 2,000
Accts Ernst & Young Us Llp Irvine
SIC 8062 5912 General medical & surgical hospitals; Drug stores & proprietary stores
Ch: Jim Milhiser
Chf Rad: Carl Schultz
Chf Rad: Peter Yoo
**Pr:* Harris F Koenig
CFO: Linda Joslyn
**CFO:* Roger Parsons
Trst: Robert Sherwood
Ofcr: Peter Aprato
VP: Liz Aragon
Exec: Yu-Sheng Wu
Dir Lab: Anne Hendricks-Jones
Dir: William Ravenkamp
Dir Rx: Ken Saltgaver

D-U-N-S 01-055-0267
SAN ANTONIO FEDERAL CREDIT UNION (TX)
6061 W Ih 10 Fl 3, San Antonio, TX 78201-2104
Tel (210) 258-1414 *Founded/Ownrshp* 1935
Sales NA *EMP* 554
SIC 6062 State credit unions, not federally chartered
Pr: Jeffrey H Farver
**Ch:* Franklin W Burk
**Treas:* John W Hayes
VP: Dale Marroquin
Dir Bus: James Munsey
Admn Mgr: Carlos Cruz
Brnch Mgr: Salina Cannon-Ruiz
Brnch Mgr: David Guidry
Genl Mgr: Janet Espinoza
IT Man: Justin Collins
Tech Mgr: Juan Alfaro

D-U-N-S 02-224-7886
SAN ANTONIO FOOD BANK
PEARSALL PACKING SAGE
5200 Enrique M Barrera Pa, San Antonio, TX 78227-2209
Tel (210) 337-3663 *Founded/Ownrshp* 1980
Sales 123.4MM *EMP* 130^E
Accts Padgett Stratemann & Co Llp S
SIC 4225 8322 General warehousing; Individual & family services
Ex Dir: Eric Cooper
CFO: Kevin Brown
Treas: Don Specht
Exec: Joshua Schwencke
Comm Man: Dawn A Thurmond

D-U-N-S 06-945-1631
SAN ANTONIO INDEPENDENT SCHOOL DISTRICT FAC
141 Lavaca St, San Antonio, TX 78210-1039
Tel (210) 554-2200 *Founded/Ownrshp* 1884
Sales 624.1MM *EMP* 7,600
Accts Garza/Gonzalez & Associates S
SIC 8211 Public elementary & secondary schools
**Pr:* Ed Garza
**VP:* Olga M Hernandez
VP: Arthur Valdez
Exec: Margie Cisneros
Ex Dir: Leslie Price
Dir Sec: Lt S Slate
Dir Sec: Stan Slate
Admn Mgr: Homer Rivera
MIS Dir: Patti Holub
IT Man: Larry Garza
IT Man: Jeff Ward

D-U-N-S 01-054-6323 IMP
SAN ANTONIO SHOE INC
SAN ANTONIO SHOEMAKERS
1717 Sas Dr, San Antonio, TX 78224-1042
Tel (877) 727-7463 *Founded/Ownrshp* 1976
Sales 258.0MM^E *EMP* 2,000
SIC 3131 5661 5139 5632 3144

SAN ANTONIO SHOEMAKERS
See SAN ANTONIO SHOE INC

D-U-N-S 10-707-5343
SAN ANTONIO STATE HOSPITAL
6711 S New Braunfels Ave, San Antonio, TX 78223-3005
Tel (210) 532-8811 *Founded/Ownrshp* 1892
Sales 68.8MM *EMP* 1,309
SIC 8063 Hospital for the mentally ill

D-U-N-S 05-758-2603
SAN ANTONIO WATER SYSTEM
SAWS
(*Suby of* CITY OF SAN ANTONIO) ★
2800 Us Highway 281 N, San Antonio, TX 78212-3106
Tel (210) 233-3814 *Founded/Ownrshp* 1925
Sales 462.3MM *EMP* 1,700
Accts Padgett Stratemann & Co Llp
SIC 4941 Water supply
CEO: Robert R Puente
**COO:* Steve Clouse
COO: Steven Clouse
**CFO:* Doug Evanson
CFO: Douglas Evanson
Treas: Sergio Molina
Trst: Phil Hardberger
Trst: Willie Mitchell
Trst: Elizabeth Provencio
VP: Chuck Ahrens
VP: Mike Brinkmann
VP: Greg Flores
VP: Karen Guerrero
VP: Stacey Isenberg
VP: Ruben Moncivaiz
VP: Daryl D Spillmann
Exec: Neirta South-White
Comm Man: Anne Hayden

SAN BENITO CISD
See SAN BENITO CONSOLIDATED INDEPENDENT SCHOOL DISTRICT PUBLIC FACILITIES

D-U-N-S 08-313-7463
SAN BENITO CONSOLIDATED INDEPENDENT SCHOOL DISTRICT PUBLIC FACILITIES (TX)
SAN BENITO CISD
240 N Crockett St, San Benito, TX 78586-4608
Tel (956) 361-6100 *Founded/Ownrshp* 1907
Sales 115.2MM^E *EMP* 1,700
Accts Long Chilton Llp Harlingen
SIC 8211 Public elementary & secondary schools
**Pr:* Anna Cruz
Trst: Oscar De La Fuente
**VP:* Oscar Medrano
Dir Sec: Santiago Garcia
Schl Brd P: Arnold Padilla
HC Dir: Rosie Longoria

D-U-N-S 08-291-7626 IMP
SAN BENITO HEALTH CARE DISTRICT
HAZEL HAWKINS MEMORIAL HOSPITA
911 Sunset Dr Ste A, Hollister, CA 95023-5608
Tel (831) 637-5711 *Founded/Ownrshp* 1957
Sales 105.0MM *EMP* 435
Accts Tca Partners Llp Fresno Cal
SIC 8062 8051 8059 General medical & surgical hospitals; Skilled nursing care facilities; Convalescent home
CEO: Ken Underwood
**Pr:* Beth Ivy
**CFO:* Mark Robinson
VP: Lois Owens
Dir OR: Denette Perrien
Dir Inf Cn: Mindy Trites
Dir Rad: Darlene Debrito
Ex Dir: Julio Gill
IT Man: Shelly Baldwin
Netwrk Eng: Salomon Mercado
VP Mktg: Frankie Gallagher

D-U-N-S 07-358-2702
SAN BERNARDINO CITY UNIFIED SCHOOL DISTRICT
777 N F St, San Bernardino, CA 92410-3017
Tel (909) 381-1100 *Founded/Ownrshp* 1964
Sales 331.5MM^E *EMP* 6,000
SIC 8211 Public elementary & secondary schools
Dir Sec: Eric Vetere
Pr Dir: Linda R Bardere

D-U-N-S 07-359-4228
SAN BERNARDINO COMMUNITY COLLEGE DISTRICT
SAN BERNARDINO VALLEY COLLEGE
114 S Del Rosa Dr, San Bernardino, CA 92408-0108
Tel (909) 382-4000 *Founded/Ownrshp* 1926
Sales 62.5MM^E *EMP* 1,446
Accts Christy White Associates San
SIC 8222 4832 4833 Junior college; Radio broadcasting stations; Television broadcasting stations
Pr: Cheryl Marshall
**Ex VP:* Rebeccah Warren-Marlatt
**VP:* Bryan Reece
Off Admin: Treesa Oliver
CIO: Carl Dury
CIO: Gary Vanvoorhis
Dir IT: Glen Clark
Telecom Mg: Noemi Elizalde

D-U-N-S 17-926-6937
SAN BERNARDINO COUNTY SCHOOL DISTRICT
601 N E St, San Bernardino, CA 92415-0020
Tel (909) 386-2417 *Founded/Ownrshp* 1997
Sales 50.4MM^E *EMP* 1,700

Section I
Businesses Alphabetically

SIC 8211 Public elementary & secondary schools

D-U-N-S 60-278-0546
SAN BERNARDINO HILTON
(*Suby of* CARPENTERS SOUTHWEST ADMINISTRATIVE CORP) ★
285 E Hospitality Ln, San Bernardino, CA 92408-3411
Tel (909) 889-0133 *Founded/Ownrshp* 1984
Sales 37.0MM^E *EMP* 1,152
SIC 7011 6512 5812 Hotels & motels; Commercial & industrial building operation; Eating places
Pr: Douglas McCarron
Exec: Tina Gardy
**Ex Dir:* Morgan McPherson
Mktg Dir: Dael Strange

SAN BERNARDINO VALLEY COLLEGE
See SAN BERNARDINO COMMUNITY COLLEGE DISTRICT

SAN DIEGO CITY COLLEGE
See SAN DIEGO COMMUNITY COLLEGE DISTRICT

SAN DIEGO CITY SCHOOLS
See SAN DIEGO UNIFIED SCHOOL DISTRICT

D-U-N-S 07-335-7048
SAN DIEGO COMMUNITY COLLEGE DISTRICT
SAN DIEGO CITY COLLEGE
3375 Camino Del Rio S, San Diego, CA 92108-3807
Tel (619) 388-6500 *Founded/Ownrshp* 1970
Sales 145.1MM^E *EMP* 4,000
Accts Christy White Associates San
SIC 8222 8249 8221 Community college; Vocational apprentice training; Colleges universities & professional schools
Bd of Dir: Roma Weaver
Trst: Bernie Rhinerson
Ofcr: Claudia Perkins
VP: Kelly Rosas
Dir IT: Kent Keyser
Dir IT: Neelu Neelaka
IT Man: Lisa Dold
Counsel: Jennifer Gianera

D-U-N-S 03-210-4531
SAN DIEGO CONVENTION CENTER CORP INC
111 W Harbor Dr, San Diego, CA 92101-7822
Tel (619) 525-5000 *Founded/Ownrshp* 1984
Sales 101.2MM^E *EMP* 500^E
SIC 6512 Nonresidential building operators
Pr: Carol Wallace
CFO: Mark Emch
Ofcr: Alfonso Sanchez
Ofcr: Michael Vile
Sr VP: Andy Mikschl
VP: Dana Edward
Exec: Janie Breckenridge
Dir Soc: Valerie Lotz
Dir Soc: Kristina McCoy
Dir Soc: Daren Smylie
Comm Dir: Barbara Moreno
Dir Bus: Bess Eberhardt

D-U-N-S 05-361-0023
SAN DIEGO COUNTY CAPITAL ASSET LEASING C
1600 Pacific Hwy Ste 163, San Diego, CA 92101-2422
Tel (336) 733-2728 *Founded/Ownrshp* 2001
Sales 133.2MM *EMP* 2
SIC 6799 Investors
Pr: Michael Anderson

D-U-N-S 06-616-2785 IMP
SAN DIEGO COUNTY CREDIT UNION INC
6545 Sequence Dr, San Diego, CA 92121-4363
Tel (877) 732-2848 *Founded/Ownrshp* 1938
Sales NA *EMP* 529
SIC 6062 State credit unions
Pr: Irene Oberbauer
**Pr:* Theresa Halleck
**CFO:* Robert Marchand
**Ex VP:* Heather Moshier
Sr VP: Larry Crawley
Exec: Roberto Luna
Snr PM: Eric Stone

SAN DIEGO COUNTY OFF EDUCATN
See SAN DIEGO COUNTY OFFICE OF EDUCATION

D-U-N-S 08-758-1153
SAN DIEGO COUNTY OFFICE OF EDUCATION
SAN DIEGO COUNTY OFF EDUCATN
6401 Linda Vista Rd, San Diego, CA 92111-7319
Tel (858) 292-3500 *Founded/Ownrshp* 1970
Sales 75.6MM^E *EMP* 1,441
SIC 8211 Public vocational/technical school
**CFO:* Lora Duzyk
Ex Dir: Linda Visnick
Genl Mgr: David Dick
Dir IT: Joan Birdwell
Psych: Jorge Ley

D-U-N-S 08-424-1033 IMP
SAN DIEGO COUNTY WATER AUTHORITY
4677 Overland Ave, San Diego, CA 92123-1233
Tel (858) 522-6600 *Founded/Ownrshp* 1944
Sales 588.7MM *EMP* 280
Accts Macias Gini & O Connell Llp S
SIC 4941 Water supply
Genl Mgr: Maureen Stapleton
COO: Tina Gonzalez
**CFO:* Eric Sandler
**Ch:* Thomas V Wornham
Bd of Dir: Gary Croucher
Bd of Dir: Dana Friehauf
Bd of Dir: Wade Griffis
Bd of Dir: Nona Yang
**Genl Mgr:* Frank Belock
Genl Mgr: Sandra Kerl
**Genl Mgr:* Sandy Kerl

D-U-N-S 09-823-5401
SAN DIEGO DATA PROCESSING CORP INC
(*Suby of* CITY OF SAN DIEGO) ★
202 C St Fl 3, San Diego, CA 92101-4806
Tel (858) 581-9600 *Founded/Ownrshp* 1979
Sales 461.2M *EMP* 11,130
SIC 7374 Data processing service
CEO: Larry Morgan
**Ch Bd:* Reed Vickerman
CFO: Mary Erlenborn
Ofcr: Bill Martin
Dir IT: Ron Barone
Telecom Mg: Ron Scott
Software D: Gabor Nagy
Board of Directors: Charles Connoy, Diane Gallo, Chris Goodman, Debra Jensen, Gary Perlmutter, Steve Romeo, Alex Ruiz, Nader Tirandazi, Edward Wong

D-U-N-S 17-059-6795
SAN DIEGO FOUNDATION
2508 Historic Decatur Rd # 200, San Diego, CA 92106-6138
Tel (619) 235-2300 *Founded/Ownrshp* 1975
Sales 85.6MM *EMP* 48
Accts Cbiz Mhm Llc San Diego Ca
SIC 8322 Community center
Ex Dir: Robert Kelly
CFO: Jo A Anderson
CFO: Dennis V Arriola
**CFO:* Sarah Slaughter
Bd of Dir: James Cowley
Bd of Dir: Pablo Farias
Bd of Dir: Laura Fleming
Bd of Dir: Bill Hahn
Bd of Dir: Thomas Hall
Bd of Dir: Jerome S Katzin
Bd of Dir: Richard Kiy
Bd of Dir: Arzo Mansury
Bd of Dir: Marion Paul
Bd of Dir: Cheryl A Phelps
Bd of Dir: Carisa M Wisniewski
Assoc VP: Keely Bamberg
VP: Theresa M Mendoza

D-U-N-S 00-691-1457 IMP/EXP
■ **SAN DIEGO GAS & ELECTRIC CO**
(*Suby of* ENOVA CORP) ★
8326 Century Park Ct, San Diego, CA 92123-1530
Tel (619) 696-2000 *Founded/Ownrshp* 1905
Sales 4.2MMM *EMP* 4,300^E
SIC 4931 4911 4924 Electric & other services combined; Generation, electric power; Transmission, electric power; Distribution, electric power; Natural gas distribution
CEO: J Walker Martin
**Ch Bd:* Jessie J Knight Jr
**Pr:* Steven D Davis
CFO: Robert M Schlax
Ofcr: J Chris Baker
Sr VP: Doug Beshoof
Sr VP: Erbin B Keith
Board of Directors: Joseph A Householder, Martha B Wyrsch

D-U-N-S 15-368-2703
SAN DIEGO METROPOLITAN TRANSIT SYSTEM
1255 Imperial Ave # 1000, San Diego, CA 92101-7490
Tel (619) 231-1466 *Founded/Ownrshp* 1976
Sales 91.1MM^E *EMP* 1,600
SIC 4111 Local & suburban transit
CEO: Paul Jadlonski
**CEO:* Stan Abrams
CFO: Cliff Telfer
Exec: Jeff Stumbo
IT Man: Peter Thompson
Mktg Dir: Rob Schupp
Mktg Mgr: Jessica Krieg

SAN DIEGO PADRES
See PADRES LP

D-U-N-S 87-714-4592
SAN DIEGO STATE UNIVERSITY
SDSU
(*Suby of* CALIFORNIA STATE UNIVERSITY SYSTEM) ★
5500 Campanile Dr, San Diego, CA 92182-0003
Tel (619) 594-7985 *Founded/Ownrshp* 1897
Sales 206.1MM^E *EMP* 3,000
SIC 8221 9411 Colleges universities & professional schools; State education department
Pr: Elliot Hirshman
Genl Pt: Sommay Kongmalay
Assoc VP: Jane K Smith
Assoc Dir: Lorraine Freitas
Ex Dir: Tamara McLeod
Mng Dir: Mark J Ballam
IT Man: Javier Medina
IT Man: Connie Rhea
IT Man: Connie Rhea-English
Mktg Dir: Carol Schenke
Snr Mgr: Donna Tusack

D-U-N-S 07-337-1346
SAN DIEGO STATE UNIVERSITY FOUNDATION
(*Suby of* CALIFORNIA STATE UNIVERSITY SYSTEM) ★
5250 Campanile Dr Mc1947, San Diego, CA 92182-1901
Tel (619) 594-1900 *Founded/Ownrshp* 1943
Sales 161.2MM *EMP* 2,500
Accts Mcgladrey Llp Los Angeles Ca
SIC 8221 9411 University; Administration of educational programs;
Pr: Elliot Hirshman
**CFO:* Melinda Coil
**Treas:* Sally F Roush
Assoc Dir: Lisa Lamb
Brnch Mgr: Juanita Brents
CIO: David Todd

D-U-N-S 00-959-2825
SAN DIEGO UNIFIED PORT DISTRICT (CA)
PORT OF SAN DIEGO
3165 Pacific Hwy, San Diego, CA 92101-1128
Tel (619) 686-6200 *Founded/Ownrshp* 1962
Sales 160.2MM *EMP* 604
Accts Macias Gini & O Connell Llp S
SIC 4491 Marine cargo handling
CEO: John Bolduc
**CFO:* Robert Deangelis
CFO: Lori Poore
Treas: Georgina Carbajal
**Ex VP:* Randa Coniglio
**Ex VP:* Karen Porteous
Dir IT: Tom Lockwood
Mktg Mgr: Jackie Williams
**Genl Couns:* Thomas Russell

D-U-N-S 07-336-2543
SAN DIEGO UNIFIED SCHOOL DISTRICT
SAN DIEGO CITY SCHOOLS
4100 Normal St, San Diego, CA 92103-2653
Tel (619) 725-8000 *Founded/Ownrshp* 1936
Sales 863.2MM^E *EMP* 17,000
Accts Mayer Hoffman Mccann Pc Irvin
SIC 8211 Public elementary & secondary schools
**CFO:* Stanley Dobbs
VP: Paul Villar
Exec: Tim Asfazadour
Prin: Bob Morris
Ex Dir: Mary R Cannie
Prgrm Mgr: Beth Hannaman
Telecom Ex: Amanda White
Pr Dir: Steven Baratte
Instr Medi: Margo Denton
Board of Directors: Miles Durfee

SAN DIEGO UNION TRIBUNE
See SAN DIEGO UNION-TRIBUNE LLC

D-U-N-S 83-116-0812
■ **SAN DIEGO UNION-TRIBUNE LLC**
SAN DIEGO UNION TRIBUNE
(*Suby of* MLIM LLC) ★
600 B St, San Diego, CA 92101-4501
Tel (619) 299-3131 *Founded/Ownrshp* 2009
Sales 155.0MM *EMP* 650
SIC 2711 7313 7383 Newspapers: publishing only, not printed on site; Newspaper advertising representative; News reporting services for newspapers & periodicals
Ch: Douglas Manchester
Pr: Jeff Light
CFO: Ryan Kiesel
VP: Bill Yawman
IT Man: Joseph Clauson
VP Sls: Robert York
Sls Mgr: Cliff Chandler

SAN DIEGO WELDERS SUPPLY
See WESTAIR GASES & EQUIPMENT INC

SAN DIEGO WHOLESALE ELECTRIC
See ONESOURCE DISTRIBUTORS LLC

D-U-N-S 10-316-1758
SAN DIEGO-IMPERIAL COUNTIES DEVELOPMENTAL SERVICES INC
4355 Ruffin Rd Ste 220, San Diego, CA 92123-4308
Tel (858) 576-2996 *Founded/Ownrshp* 1982
Sales 288.8MM *EMP* 474
Accts Windes Inc Long Beach Ca
SIC 8322 Social services for the handicapped
Ex Dir: Carlos Flores
**CFO:* Edward Kenney
**Treas:* Judy Wallace Patton
Prgrm Mgr: Peggie Webb
Off Mgr: Myrtle Mark

SAN FELIPE DEL RIO CISD
See SAN FELIPE DEL RIO CONSOLIDATED INDEPENDENT SCHOOL DISTRICT

D-U-N-S 06-945-2118
SAN FELIPE DEL RIO CONSOLIDATED INDEPENDENT SCHOOL DISTRICT
SAN FELIPE DEL RIO CISD
315 Griner St, Del Rio, TX 78840-5533
Tel (830) 778-4000 *Founded/Ownrshp* 1920
Sales 104.3MM *EMP* 1,300
Accts Belt Harris Pechacek Lllp Hou
SIC 8211 Public elementary & secondary schools
Prin: Maria Gonzalez-Ramirez
Bd of Dir: Fernando Quiz
Ofcr: Amanda Calderon
Ofcr: Norma Gonzalez
Ofcr: Maria Hidalgo
VP: Joshua Overfelt
Cmptr Lab: Terri Arons
IT Man: Laura Douglas
IT Man: Pat Mills
Psych: Selina Cienega-Randez
Psych: Alda Zuniga

D-U-N-S 07-082-7068
SAN FRANCISCO BASEBALL ASSOCIATES LLC
SAN FRANCISCO GIANTS
24 Willie Mays Plz, San Francisco, CA 94107-2134
Tel (415) 972-2000 *Founded/Ownrshp* 1992
Sales 72.7MM^E *EMP* 1,300
SIC 7941 5947

D-U-N-S 04-740-9107 IMP
SAN FRANCISCO BAY AREA RAPID TRANSIT DISTRICT
BART
300 Lakeside Dr, Oakland, CA 94604
Tel (510) 464-6000 *Founded/Ownrshp* 1957
Sales 423.3MM^E *EMP* 3,347
SIC 4111 Local railway passenger operation
Genl Mgr: Grace Crunican
**Treas:* Scott Schroeder
Exec: Luna Salaver
Dept Mgr: Elaine Kurtz
Dept Mgr: Aaron Weinstein
Genl Mgr: Bart Blog
IT Man: Cindy Church
Sftwr Eng: Jonathan Hourany
Netwrk Eng: Jeff Martz
Opers Supe: Bart Ross
Mktg Mgr: Imara Yokely
Board of Directors: Carol Ward Allen, Thomas Blalock, James Fang V Pres, Roy Nakadegawa, Tom Radulovich, Dan Richard, Pete Snyder Pres, Lynette Sweet

SAN FRANCISCO CHRONICLE
See HEARST COMMUNICATIONS INC

D-U-N-S 18-743-1549
SAN FRANCISCO FOOD BANK
SF-MARIN FOOD BANK
900 Pennsylvania Ave, San Francisco, CA 94107-3498
Tel (415) 282-1900 *Founded/Ownrshp* 1987
Sales 94.2MM *EMP* 80
Accts Armanino Llp San Jose Ca
SIC 8322 Individual & family services
Ex Dir: Paul Ash
**COO:* Leslie Bacho
**CFO:* Michael Braude

D-U-N-S 07-188-6113
SAN FRANCISCO FORTY NINERS
4949 Mrie P Debartolo Way, Santa Clara, CA 95054-1156
Tel (408) 562-4949 *Founded/Ownrshp* 1977
Sales 216.8MM^E *EMP* 6,200
Accts Sweeney Kovar Llp Danville
SIC 7941 Football club
Ch Bd: Denise Debartolo York
**Pr:* Peter Harris
**CFO:* Larry Macneil
VP: Robert Alberino
VP: Edward Goines
Genl Mgr: Doug Garland
Genl Mgr: Scot McCloughan
Genl Mgr: Lou Spadia
CTO: Bill Duffy
CTO: Chrissy Mauck

D-U-N-S 07-467-6511
SAN FRANCISCO FOUNDATION
1 Embarcadero Ctr # 4150, San Francisco, CA 94111-3740
Tel (415) 733-8500 *Founded/Ownrshp* 1948
Sales 182.8MM *EMP* 60
Accts Hood & Strong Llp San Francis
SIC 7389 Fund raising organizations
Bd of Dir: Jeremy Madsen
Ex Dir: Raquel Donoso
Ex Dir: Teresa Mejia
DP Dir: Brian Harter
Dir IT: Fred Jacobs

SAN FRANCISCO GIANTS
See SAN FRANCISCO BASEBALL ASSOCIATES LLC

D-U-N-S 06-299-7309 IMP
SAN FRANCISCO MUSEUM OF MODERN ART
SFMOMA MUSEUM STORE
151 3rd St, San Francisco, CA 94103-3107
Tel (415) 357-4035 *Founded/Ownrshp* 1921
Sales 97.0MM *EMP* 363^E
Accts Deloitte Tax Llp San Jose Ca
SIC 8412 5942 Museum; Book stores
Pr: Robert J Fisher
Pr: Sandra Eggers
**Ch:* Charles R Schwab
**Treas:* Dennis J Wong
Bd of Dir: Katherine Abbey
Assoc Dir: Denise Marica
Assoc Dir: Elizabeth Waller

D-U-N-S 02-002-1044 IMP
SAN FRANCISCO OPERA ASSOCIATION (CA)
301 Van Ness Ave, San Francisco, CA 94102-4509
Tel (415) 861-4008 *Founded/Ownrshp* 1932
Sales 37.4MM *EMP* 1,050
Accts Armanino Llp San Ramon Calif
SIC 7922 Opera company
Ch: John A Gunn
Dir Vol: Megan McDonald
**Pr:* Keith B Geeslin
**CEO:* David Gockley
**CFO:* Michael Simpson
Bd of Dir: Nancy Reilly
Bd of Dir: Maria Trujillo
**Ex VP:* Paul Crane Dorfman
**VP:* Lisa Erdberg
VP: Noelle Ray
CIO: Jarrod Bell
Board of Directors: Reid W Dennis, Thomas Tilton

D-U-N-S 10-923-7669
SAN FRANCISCO REINSURANCE CO
(*Suby of* FIREMANS FUND INSURANCE CO) ★
1465 N Mcdowell Blvd, Petaluma, CA 94954-6516
Tel (415) 899-2000 *Founded/Ownrshp* 1964
Sales NA *EMP* 70
SIC 6321 Reinsurance carriers, accident & health
Pr: Joe Beneducci
Board of Directors: Jeffery F Johnson, Sally B Narey, D Andrew Torrance, Kevin E Walker

D-U-N-S 78-944-5934
SAN FRANCISCO STATE UNIVERSITY
(*Suby of* CALIFORNIA STATE UNIVERSITY SYSTEM) ★
1600 Holloway Ave, San Francisco, CA 94132-1740
Tel (415) 338-1111 *Founded/Ownrshp* 1899
Sales 14.7MM *EMP* 3,500^E
Accts Hood & Strong Llp San Francis
SIC 8221 9411 University; Administration of educational programs;
Pr: Robert A Corrigan
**VP:* Leroy Morishita
VP: Robert Nava
VP: Jo Volkert
Assoc Dir: Karen Johnson-Brennan
Prgrm Mgr: Drew McAdams
Genl Mgr: Rob Strong
Off Mgr: Sylvia Leng
DP Exec: Holden Leung
Psych: Lin Greer

D-U-N-S 07-466-5571 IMP
SAN FRANCISCO SYMPHONY INC (CA)
201 Van Ness Ave, San Francisco, CA 94102-4585
Tel (415) 552-8000 *Founded/Ownrshp* 1911
Sales 91.1MM *EMP* 400
Accts Armanino Llp San Ramon Ca
SIC 7929 Symphony orchestras
CEO: Brent Assink
**CFO:* Mark Koenig

CFO: John Prunty
Bd of Dir: Sam Yamada
Ofcr: Michael Lawrence
VP: Ruth Goldfine
VP: Richard Kovacevich
VP: Eff Martin
VP: Glynn Robert
VP: Patrick Talamantes
Exec: Marina Kennedy
Exec: Carol Sebelius
Dir: Robert Lasher

D-U-N-S 04-132-0532
SAN FRANCISCO UNIFIED SCHOOL DISTRICT
ADMINISTRATION OFFICE
555 Franklin St, San Francisco, CA 94102-4456
Tel (415) 241-6000 *Founded/Ownrshp* 1856
Sales 445.0MM^E *EMP* 8,000
SIC 8211 8741 Public elementary & secondary schools; Administrative management
Bd of Dir: Jill Wynns
Exec: Susan Ortega-Resurrec
Exec: Lori Swihart
Exec: Kim Walker
Dir Sec: Walter Patrick
Prgrm Mgr: Mary Jue
Off Mgr: Kathy Doherty
Snr Ntwrk: David Burns
Teacher Pr: Angie Sagastume
Teacher Pr: Monica Vasquez
Psych: Orlando Beltran

D-U-N-S 07-983-6500
SAN FRANCISCO UNIFIED SCHOOL DISTRICT BOARD OF EDUCATION
555 Franklin St, San Francisco, CA 94102-4456
Tel (415) 241-6000 *Founded/Ownrshp* 2015
Sales 123.1MM^E *EMP* 56^E
SIC 8211 School board
Pr: Emily Murase

SAN FRANSISCO SPECIALITY PROD
See LA SPECIALTY PRODUCE CO

D-U-N-S 04-442-7045
SAN GABRIEL VALLEY WATER CO (CA)
FONTANA WATER COMPANY
11142 Garvey Ave, El Monte, CA 91733-2498
Tel (626) 448-6183 *Founded/Ownrshp* 1936, 2011
Sales 133.3MM^E *EMP* 247
SIC 4941 Water supply
Ch Bd: R H Nicholson Jr
Pr: Michael L Whitehead
Treas: David Batt
VP: Frank A Lo Guidice

D-U-N-S 15-272-3763
SAN GABRIEL/POMONA VALLEYS DEVELOPMENTAL SERVICES INC
SAN GBRIEL/POMONA REGIONAL CTR
75 Rancho Camino Dr, Pomona, CA 91766-4728
Tel (909) 620-7722 *Founded/Ownrshp* 1986
Sales 196.2MM *EMP* 323
Accts Windes Inc Long Beach Cali
SIC 8322 Social service center
Ex Dir: R Keith Penman
**CFO:* John Hunt

SAN GBRIEL/POMONA REGIONAL CTR
See SAN GABRIEL/POMONA VALLEYS DEVELOPMENTAL SERVICES INC

D-U-N-S 07-742-2798
SAN JACINTO COMMUNITY COLLEGE DISTRICT
4624 Fairmont Pkwy # 106, Pasadena, TX 77504-3323
Tel (281) 998-6306 *Founded/Ownrshp* 1961
Sales 81.8MM^E *EMP* 2,220
Accts Mfr Pc Houston Tx
SIC 8222 Junior college

D-U-N-S 07-415-5771
SAN JACINTO METHODIST HOSPITAL
METHODIST HOSPITAL SYSTEM, THE
(*Suby of* METHODIST HOSPITAL SYSTEM) ★
4401 Garth Rd, Baytown, TX 77521-2122
Tel (281) 420-8600 *Founded/Ownrshp* 1948
Sales 225.0MM *EMP* 1,480
SIC 8062 8063 8051 General medical & surgical hospitals; Psychiatric hospitals; Skilled nursing care facilities
CEO: Jeffery Ackernan
VP: Jane Destefano
VP: Lauren Rykert
CIO: Beverly Cline
IT Man: Brian Schwinger

D-U-N-S 07-432-8048
SAN JOAQUIN COMMUNITY HOSPITAL (CA)
2615 Chester Ave, Bakersfield, CA 93301-2014
Tel (661) 395-3000 *Founded/Ownrshp* 1910
Sales 367.1MM *EMP* 2,200
SIC 8062 8011 General medical & surgical hospitals; Offices & clinics of medical doctors
Pr: Sharlet Briggs
CFO: Mike Lukens
Ofcr: Greg McGovern
Top Exec: Tracey S Stewart
VP: Matt Clark
Dir OR: Kelly Barber
Dir Rad: Brad Taylor
Adm Dir: Chris Maupin
CIO: Adrian McReynolds
CTO: Nancy Garcia
Dir IT: Brandi Evans

D-U-N-S 79-084-5051
SAN JOAQUIN COUNCIL OF GOVERNMENTS
555 E Weber Ave, Stockton, CA 95202-3016
Tel (209) 235-0600 *Founded/Ownrshp* 1967
Sales 300.0MM *EMP* 33
SIC 8742 Transportation consultant
Ex Dir: Andrew Chesely

**CFO:* Steve Dial
Comm Man: Dianne Barth

D-U-N-S 85-856-7951
SAN JOAQUIN HILLS TRANSPORTATION CORRIDOR AGENCY
TRANSPRTTION CORRIDOR AGENCIES
125 Pacifica Ste 100, Irvine, CA 92618-3324
Tel (949) 754-3400 *Founded/Ownrshp* 1986
Sales 151.2MM *EMP* 71^E
Accts Kpmg Llp Irvine Ca
SIC 1611 General contractor, highway & street construction
CEO: Michael Kraman
Exec: Linda Lindholm
Exec: Kathleen Loch
Exec: Lance Maclean
Dir IT: Jim Rhodes

D-U-N-S 04-066-9058
SAN JOAQUIN HOSPITAL
HEALTHCARE SERVICES
500 W Hospital Rd, French Camp, CA 95231-9693
Tel (209) 468-6000 *Founded/Ownrshp* 2005
Sales 313.0MM *EMP* 1,300
SIC 8062 General medical & surgical hospitals
CEO: David Colberson
**CFO:* Ronald Kruetner

SAN JOAQUIN VLY CONCENTRATES
See E & J GALLO WINERY

D-U-N-S 78-962-9821
SAN JOSE MEDICAL SYSTEMS LP
REGIONAL MEDICAL CTR SAN JOSE
225 N Jackson Ave, San Jose, CA 95116-1603
Tel (408) 259-5000 *Founded/Ownrshp* 1984
Sales 308.9MM *EMP* 1,200^E
SIC 8062 General medical & surgical hospitals
Pt: Mike Johnson
COO: Trey Abshier
CFO: Richard Canning
CFO: Joseph Hirt
VP: Nicole Diem
VP: Paul Estes
VP: Gary Goeringer
Dir Lab: Lisa Vanwyk
Ex Dir: Rhonda Brown
DP Dir: Robert Hallett
DP Dir: Gary Kalus

D-U-N-S 13-161-6542
SAN JOSE MERCURY-NEWS LLC
(*Suby of* DIGITAL FIRST MEDIA) ★
4 N 2nd St Fl 8, San Jose, CA 95113-1317
Tel (408) 920-5000 *Founded/Ownrshp* 2006
Sales 107.7MM^E *EMP* 1,400
SIC 2711 Newspapers, publishing & printing
COO: Parnell F Delcham
CFO: Raju Iyer
Ch: George Riggs
VP: Dave Bauer
VP: David Butler
VP: Mary S Evans
VP: Jeff Keil
VP: Glenn Nardi
VP: Kathleen Slattery
VP: Harry Woldt
Exec: Carol Scholl

D-U-N-S 05-052-0840 IMP
SAN JOSE STATE UNIVERSITY
(*Suby of* CALIFORNIA STATE UNIVERSITY SYSTEM) ★
1 Washington Sq, San Jose, CA 95192-0001
Tel (408) 924-1000 *Founded/Ownrshp* 1857
Sales 190.0MM^E *EMP* 3,186
SIC 8221 9411

D-U-N-S 06-912-5136
SAN JOSE UNIFIED SCHOOL DISTRICT
855 Lenzen Ave, San Jose, CA 95126-2736
Tel (408) 535-6000 *Founded/Ownrshp* 1900
Sales 300.0MM *EMP* 4,500
SIC 8211 Public elementary & secondary schools
**Pr:* Sandra Engel
**Pr:* Pamela Foley
**Pr:* Richard Garcia
Dir IT: Paul Rischee
Sys Mgr: George Oneel
Sys Mgr: Brenda Stone
Psych: Megan Warter

D-U-N-S 11-329-1694
■ **SAN JOSE WATER CO**
S J W
(*Suby of* SJW CORP) ★
110 W Taylor St, San Jose, CA 95110-2131
Tel (408) 288-5314 *Founded/Ownrshp* 1985
Sales 268.6MM^E *EMP* 300
SIC 4941 Water supply
CEO: W Richard Roth
**Ch Bd:* Charles Toeniskoetter
**CFO:* Angela Yip
Sr VP: George J Belhumeur
**VP:* Richard Balocco
**VP:* Geaorge Belhumeur
VP: Dana R Drysdale
VP: Carol Naes
**VP:* Scott Yoo
Admn Mgr: Stephanie Orosco
CIO: Sandy Freeman

D-U-N-S 02-927-6342
SAN JOSE/EVERGREEN COMMUNITY COLLEGE DISTRICT FOUNDATION
SJECCD
40 S Market St, San Jose, CA 95113-2367
Tel (408) 918-6131 *Founded/Ownrshp* 1963
Sales 22.9MM *EMP* 1,200
Accts Crowe Horwath Llp Sacramento
SIC 8222 Community college
CEO: Autumn Young
COO: Ron Lind
Bd of Dir: Joy Pace
Bd of Dir: Mike Rendler
Trst: Rudy Nasol
VP: Marie Burns

Assoc Dir: Ingrid Thompson
Ex Dir: Tamela Hawley
Board of Directors: Carol Coen

SAN JUAN CENTER
See PEAK MEDICAL FARMINGTON LLC

SAN JUAN CITY HALL
See MUNICIPIO DE SAN JUAN

D-U-N-S 03-043-4567
SAN JUAN REGIONAL MEDICAL CENTER INC
801 W Maple St, Farmington, NM 87401-5630
Tel (505) 609-2000 *Founded/Ownrshp* 1994
Sales 252.3MM *EMP* 1,700
Accts Ernst & Young Us Llp Phoenix
SIC 8062 General medical & surgical hospitals
Ch Bd: Mike Jakino
**Pr:* Rick Wallace
**CFO:* Michael Philips
**Chf Mktg O:* Robert Fabrey
Ofcr: Charles Hoffman MD
VP: Doug Frary
**VP:* J Michael Philips
Exec: Teresa Becker
**Chf Nrs Of:* Suzanne Smith
**Dir Sec:* John Buffington
Genl Mgr: Cynthia Remshak

D-U-N-S 07-378-7962
SAN JUAN UNIFIED SCHOOL DISTRICT
3738 Walnut Ave, Carmichael, CA 95608-3099
Tel (916) 971-7700 *Founded/Ownrshp* 1960
Sales 226.9MM^E *EMP* 4,200
Accts Crowe Horwath Llp Sacramento
SIC 8211 Public elementary & secondary schools; Public adult education school
Bd of Dir: Thomaysa Glover
Exec: Jinne Horger
Exec: Doreen Lenhart
Exec: Norman Ryan
Comm Dir: Trent Allen
Prgrm Mgr: Dominic Covello
Genl Mgr: Bill Rugg
Dir IT: Jeri De Witt
Dir IT: Timothy Glasgow
IT Man: Peter Cazanis
IT Man: Nina Mancina

SAN LORENZO ITALIAN RESTAURANT
See TEXAS STATION GAMBLING HALL & HOTEL INC

D-U-N-S 08-184-2049
SAN LORENZO UNIFIED SCHOOL DISTRICT
15510 Usher St, San Lorenzo, CA 94580-1641
Tel (510) 317-4600 *Founded/Ownrshp* 1890
Sales 94.6MM^E *EMP* 1,700
SIC 8211 Public elementary & secondary schools; Public senior high school
**VP:* Dr Helen Foster
IT Man: Victoria Zuber

D-U-N-S 96-408-8194
SAN LUIS VALLEY HEALTH REGIONAL MEDICAL CENTER
106 Blanca Ave, Alamosa, CO 81101-2340
Tel (719) 589-2511 *Founded/Ownrshp* 1927
Sales 70.0MM^E *EMP* 1,270
SIC 8062 Hospital, affiliated with AMA residency
CEO: Konnie Martin
Chf Rad: Edward Carter

D-U-N-S 15-373-3266 IMP
SAN MANUEL INDIAN BINGO & CASINO
SAN MANUEL INDIAN BINGO CASINO
777 San Manuel Blvd, Highland, CA 92346-6713
Tel (909) 864-5050 *Founded/Ownrshp* 1986
Sales 183.2MM^E *EMP* 3,000
SIC 7999 Bingo hall; Card & game services
Ch: James Ramos
**CFO:* Rebecca Spalding
VP: Andy Marquez
VP: Samira Sayegh
Exec: Stephen Fliss
Comm Man: Janet S Nakamura
Ex Dir: Steve Lengel
**Ex Dir:* Steve Lengeo
**Ex Dir:* Jimmy Starcher
CIO: JB King
Dir IT: Ed Bustamente

SAN MANUEL INDIAN BINGO CASINO
See SAN MANUEL INDIAN BINGO & CASINO

SAN MANUEL MINING DIVISION
See BHP COPPER INC

D-U-N-S 08-628-9618
SAN MARCOS CONSOLIDATED INDEPENDENT SCHOOL DISTRICT
SAN MARCOS PUBLIC SCHOOLS
501 S Lbj Dr, San Marcos, TX 78666-6821
Tel (512) 393-6700 *Founded/Ownrshp* 1920, 1986
Sales 89.5MM *EMP* 1,020
Accts Alonzo Bacarisse Irvine & Pa
SIC 8211 Public elementary & secondary schools
Dir IT: Greg Hubenak
HC Dir: Dyanna Eastwood

SAN MARCOS PUBLIC SCHOOLS
See SAN MARCOS CONSOLIDATED INDEPENDENT SCHOOL DISTRICT

D-U-N-S 02-051-8072
SAN MARCOS UNIFIED SCHOOL DISTRICT
255 Pico Ave Ste 250, San Marcos, CA 92069-3712
Tel (760) 744-4776 *Founded/Ownrshp* 1946
Sales 177.0MM *EMP* 1,500
Accts Christy White Associates San
SIC 8211 Public elementary school; Public junior high school; Public senior high school
Bd of Dir: Camille Burks
Bd of Dir: Corine Foster
Bd of Dir: Maria Harte
Bd of Dir: Sharon Jenkins
Bd of Dir: Karrie Laatsch
Bd of Dir: Sandra Orozco
Bd of Dir: Caroline Reyes

Bd of Dir: Marla Rosenthal
Bd of Dir: Kendal Salisbury
Bd of Dir: Peter Tashjian
Bd of Dir: Brenda Thompson

D-U-N-S 04-132-0797
SAN MATEO COUNTY COMMUNITY COLLEGE DISTRICT
COLLEGE OF SAN MATEO
3401 Csm Dr, San Mateo, CA 94402-3651
Tel (650) 358-6742 *Founded/Ownrshp* 1922
Sales 69.8MM^E *EMP* 2,000
Accts Vavrinek Trine Day & Company
SIC 8222 Community college
CFO: Kathy Blackwood
VP: James W Keller
**VP:* Karen Schwarz
VP: Theresa Tentes
VP: Dennis Tordesillas

D-U-N-S 10-000-8580
SAN MATEO-FOSTER CITY SCHOOL DISTRICT
1170 Chess Dr, Foster City, CA 94404-1107
Tel (650) 312-7700 *Founded/Ownrshp* 1908
Sales 86.7MM^E *EMP* 1,200
SIC 8211 Public elementary & secondary schools
Ex Dir: Jean Abeles
Netwrk Mgr: Pat Armanino
Schl Brd P: Colleen Sullivan
Teacher Pr: Michelle Harmeier
Psych: Kelly Nystrom

D-U-N-S 08-848-4852 IMP
SAN MIGUEL ELECTRIC COOPERATIVE INC
6200 Fm 3387, Christine, TX 78012
Tel (830) 784-3411 *Founded/Ownrshp* 1977
Sales 137.6MM *EMP* 175
Accts Gowland Strealy Morales & Co
SIC 4911 ; Generation, electric power
Pr: Leroy Skloss
Genl Mgr: Marshall Darby
**Genl Mgr:* Mike Kezar
Sfty Mgr: Ben Garza

D-U-N-S 06-770-1859
■ **SAN RAMON REGIONAL MEDICAL CENTER INC**
(*Suby of* TENET HEALTHCARE CORP) ★
6001 Norris Canyon Rd, San Ramon, CA 94583-5400
Tel (925) 275-0634 *Founded/Ownrshp* 1990
Sales 156.9MM *EMP* 600
Accts Williams & Olds Cpas Sacramen
SIC 8062 8093 General medical & surgical hospitals; Rehabilitation center, outpatient treatment
CEO: Gary J Sloan
**COO:* Susan Micheletti
Exec: Dennis Mills
Dir Lab: Vera Foster
Dir Rad: Tim Jefferson
CIO: Jay Juarez
Pathlgst: Harris Goodman
Pathlgst: Meena Tandon

D-U-N-S 08-183-8856
SAN RAMON VALLEY UNIFIED SCHOOL DISTRICT
699 Old Orchard Dr, Danville, CA 94526-4331
Tel (925) 552-5500 *Founded/Ownrshp* 1953
Sales 201.2MM^E *EMP* 3,000
SIC 8211 Public elementary & secondary schools
VP: Ann Katzburg
Off Admin: Lorre Heyes
Pr Dir: Liz Graswich
Teacher Pr: Melanie Jones
Psych: Lori Balleza
HC Dir: Lisa Ward

SAN YSIDRO HEALTH CENTER
See CENTRO DE SALUD DE LA COMUNIDAD DE SAN YSIDRO INC

D-U-N-S 06-883-6466
SANARE LLC
3620 Enterprise Way, Miramar, FL 33025-6616
Tel (305) 438-9696 *Founded/Ownrshp* 2010
Sales 83.9MM^E *EMP* 445^E
SIC 5047 Medical equipment & supplies
Ch Bd: Tim Hargarten

D-U-N-S 07-831-8568
▲ **SANCHEZ ENERGY CORP**
1000 Main St Ste 3000, Houston, TX 77002-6342
Tel (713) 783-8000 *Founded/Ownrshp* 2011
Sales 475.7MM *EMP* 200^E
Tkr Sym SN *Exch* NYS
SIC 1311 Crude petroleum & natural gas; Natural gas production
Pr: Antonio R Sanchez III
Mng Pt: Gerry Willinger
Ch Bd: A R Sanchez Jr
Pr: Eduardo Sanchez
COO: Christopher D Heinson
CFO: Garrick A Hill
CFO: Michael G Long
CFO: Howard Thill
Ofcr: Ramsey Cruz
Sr VP: Jaime Brito
Sr VP: Kirsten A Hink
Sr VP: Gregory B Kopel
VP: Robert Ramsey

D-U-N-S 02-154-8011
SANCHEZ OIL & GAS CORP
1000 Main St Ste 3000, Houston, TX 77002-6342
Tel (956) 722-8092 *Founded/Ownrshp* 1972
Sales 114.7MM^E *EMP* 50
SIC 1311 Crude petroleum production; Natural gas production
CEO: A R Sanchez Jr
**Pr:* Franks Guerra
**CFO:* Michael G Long
CFO: Michael Long
**Sr VP:* Charles W Macleod
**Sr VP:* Patrick Talamas
VP: Glenn Adcock
VP: John Happ
VP: C W Macleod

VP: Robert Ramsey
Snr Mgr: Ryan Bayer

D-U-N-S 83-891-4013
SANCTUARY AT HOLY CROSS
TRINITY SNIOR LVING CMMUNITIES
17475 Dugdale Dr, South Bend, IN 46635-1545
Tel (574) 247-7500 *Founded/Ownrshp* 2009
Sales 978.4MM *EMP* 2
SIC 8322 8052 Rehabilitation services; Personal care facility

D-U-N-S 96-267-3245
SANCTUS LLC
SHIFT DIGITAL
348 E Maple Rd, Birmingham, MI 48009-6313
Tel (248) 594-2396 *Founded/Ownrshp* 2008
Sales 287.0MM *EMP* 250
SIC 8741 7319 8742 Business management; Transit advertising services; Marketing consulting services
CEO: Stephen St Andre

D-U-N-S 80-227-2880
■ **SAND CANYON CORP**
(*Suby of* H&R BLOCK INC) ★
7595 Irvine Center Dr # 100, Irvine, CA 92618-2958
Tel (949) 727-9425 *Founded/Ownrshp* 2011
Sales NA *EMP* 500
SIC 6163 6162 Loan brokers; Mortgage bankers & correspondents
Pr: Robert Dubrish
**CEO:* Dale M Sugimoto
**COO:* Steve Nadon
**CFO:* William O'Neill

D-U-N-S 02-938-1238 IMP
SAND DOLLAR HOLDINGS INC
1022 Bay Marina Dr # 106, National City, CA 91950-6398
Tel (619) 477-0185 *Founded/Ownrshp* 1998
Sales 349.5MM^E *EMP* 250
SIC 5147 Meats & meat products
Pr: John Leavy
**CFO:* Eric Doan
**VP:* Kevin Leavy
Sales Exec: Mike Pepin

D-U-N-S 00-695-8896 IMP/EXP
SAND PRODUCTS CORP (MI)
TYLER CREEK GOLF CLB CMPGROUND
13495 92nd St Se, Alto, MI 49302-9615
Tel (231) 722-6691 *Founded/Ownrshp* 1924, 1930
Sales 444.1MM^E *EMP* 100
SIC 1446

D-U-N-S 09-330-8591
SANDATA HOLDINGS INC (NY)
26 Harbor Park Dr, Port Washington, NY 11050-4602
Tel (516) 484-4400 *Founded/Ownrshp* 1978, 2003
Sales 121.6MM^E *EMP* 401^E
SIC 7374 7373 Data processing service; Turnkey vendors, computer systems
CEO: Tom Underwood
Pt: Jamie Richardson
Ch Bd: Bert E Brodsky
Pr: Stephen Silverstein
COO: Mark S Rangell
CFO: Stuart Diamond
CFO: David Gershen
Ex VP: David Birnbaum
Ex VP: Kenneth D Faltischek
Sr VP: Stephen Kennedy
VP: Richard Clark
VP: Karen Erickson
VP: Brian Lawson
VP: Adrienne Woodward

D-U-N-S 00-828-7674 IMP
SANDBERG FURNITURE MANUFACTURING CO INC
5685 Alcoa Ave, Vernon, CA 90058-3728
Tel (323) 582-0711 *Founded/Ownrshp* 1918
Sales 102.6MM^E *EMP* 445
SIC 2511 Wood bedroom furniture
CEO: John Sandberg
**COO:* Mark Nixon
VP: Bill Hall
CIO: Thong Cao
VP Mfg: Michael Bagwell

D-U-N-S 17-592-6344
SANDEL AVIONICS INC
2401 Dogwood Way, Vista, CA 92081-8409
Tel (760) 727-4900 *Founded/Ownrshp* 1997
Sales 90.0MM *EMP* 200
SIC 3812 Aircraft control instruments; Aircraft flight instruments; Air traffic control systems & equipment, electronic; Antennas, radar or communications
Pr: Gerald Block
**CFO:* Grant Miller
Snr Sftwr: Bret Strain
Snr Sftwr: Kevin Vap
IT Man: Erik Mortensen
Sftwr Eng: Patric Fitzsimmons
S&M/VP: Pat Gordon

D-U-N-S 07-487-7556 IMP
SANDEN INTERNATIONAL (USA) INC (TX)
(*Suby of* SANDEN OF AMERICA INC) ★
601 Sanden Blvd, Wylie, TX 75098-4923
Tel (972) 442-8941 *Founded/Ownrshp* 1974
Sales 271.5MM^E *EMP* 897
SIC 3714 1711 3585 3563 Air conditioner parts, motor vehicle; Plumbing, heating, air-conditioning contractors; Refrigeration & heating equipment; Air & gas compressors
CEO: Mark Olfig
COO: Yoshihiro Cachikawa
Ofcr: Nettie Couch
**VP:* Andrew Kennedy
VP: Jimmye Phaup
VP: Scott Poorman
VP: Vivian Tu
VP: Ryuhei Ushikubo
Genl Mgr: Kumar Coimbatore
Genl Mgr: Gregory Gorski
QA Dir: Joseph Rigali

D-U-N-S 80-597-0907
SANDEN NORTH AMERICA INC
MINER TECHNOLOGIES
(*Suby of* SANDEN OF AMERICA INC) ★
9900 Pflumm Rd Ste 22, Shawnee Mission, KS 66215-1231
Tel (913) 888-6667 *Founded/Ownrshp* 2003
Sales 12.0MM^E *EMP* 1,098^E
SIC 7389
Opers Mgr: Mika Seever

D-U-N-S 19-234-3630 IMP/EXP
SANDEN OF AMERICA INC
(*Suby of* SANDEN HOLDINGS CORPORATION)
601 Sanden Blvd, Wylie, TX 75098-4923
Tel (972) 442-8400 *Founded/Ownrshp* 1995
Sales 283.6MM^E *EMP* 2,003
SIC 3585 3581 Air conditioning, motor vehicle; Automatic vending machines
Pr: Mitsuya Yamamoto
**Treas:* Tsutomu Nomono

D-U-N-S 19-643-0719 IMP
SANDENVENDO AMERICA INC
(*Suby of* SANDEN HOLDINGS CORPORATION)
10710 Sanden Dr, Dallas, TX 75238-1335
Tel (800) 344-7216 *Founded/Ownrshp* 2005
Sales 896.5MM^E *EMP* 10,000
SIC 3581 Automatic vending machines
Pr: Frank Kabei
Ql Cn Mgr: Mike Gann

D-U-N-S 87-768-7020
SANDERS BROTHERS ELECTRIC INC
8195 Kipling St, Pensacola, FL 32514-7441
Tel (850) 857-0701 *Founded/Ownrshp* 1995
Sales 4.9MMM *EMP* 80
Accts Warren Averett Llc Pensacola
SIC 1731 General electrical contractor
VP: Edward J Sanders
**Pr:* Albert Simmons
**Sec:* Gary A Garza
**VP:* Thomas G Sanders

D-U-N-S 08-938-5285 IMP
SANDERS INDUSTRIES
(*Suby of* INDUSTRIAL GROWTH PARTNERS) ★
3701 E Conant St, Long Beach, CA 90808-1783
Tel (562) 354-2920 *Founded/Ownrshp* 2014
Sales 128.3MM^E *EMP* 350
SIC 2824 Elastomeric fibers
CEO: Larry O'Toole
**CFO:* Rick Ginsburgh
**VP:* Adam Gilbert
**VP:* Tim Shanahan

D-U-N-S 04-648-1032 IMP
SANDERS LEAD CO INC
1 Sanders Rd, Troy, AL 36079-2504
Tel (334) 566-1563 *Founded/Ownrshp* 1966
Sales 112.9MM^E *EMP* 400
SIC 3341 Lead smelting & refining (secondary)
Ch Bd: Wiley C Sanders Sr
**Pr:* Wiley C Sanders Jr
CFO: Wayne Turberville
VP: Roy Bray
Plnt Mgr: Bart Sanders

D-U-N-S 09-604-3708 IMP/EXP
▲ **SANDERSON FARMS INC**
127 Flynt Rd, Laurel, MS 39443-9062
Tel (601) 649-4030 *Founded/Ownrshp* 1947
Sales 2.8MMM *EMP* 12,264
Accts Ernst & Young Llp New Orleans
Tkr Sym SAFM *Exch* NGS
SIC 0251 2015 Broiling chickens, raising of; Chicken, slaughtered & dressed; Chicken, processed: fresh; Chicken, processed: frozen
Ch Bd: Joe F Sanderson Jr
**Pr:* Lampkin Butts
**CFO:* Mike Cockrell
Div Mgr: Donnie Peters
Sls Mgr: Glenn Caves
Sls Mgr: Heath Graham
Board of Directors: Charles W Ritter Jr, John H Baker III, Fred Banks Jr, John Bierbusse, Toni Cooley, Beverly Wade Hogan, Robert C Khayat, Phil K Livingston, Dianne Mooney, Gail Jones Pittman

D-U-N-S 04-729-6603 EXP
■ **SANDERSON FARMS INC (FOODS DIVISION)**
(*Suby of* SANDERSON FARMS INC) ★
127 Flynt Rd, Laurel, MS 39443-9062
Tel (601) 649-4030 *Founded/Ownrshp* 1986
Sales 151.6MM^E *EMP* 1,300
SIC 2038 2092 Dinners, frozen & packaged; Ethnic foods, frozen; Seafoods, frozen: prepared
Pr: Joe Frank Sanderson Jr
**CFO:* D Michael Cockrell
VP: Dianne Mooney

D-U-N-S 00-817-2512 EXP
■ **SANDERSON FARMS INC (PROCESSING DIVISION)**
(*Suby of* SANDERSON FARMS INC) ★
127 Flynt Rd, Laurel, MS 39443-9062
Tel (601) 649-4030 *Founded/Ownrshp* 1961
Sales 550.0MM^E *EMP* 5,500
SIC 2015 Chicken, slaughtered & dressed; Chicken, processed: fresh; Chicken, processed: frozen
Pr: Joe F Sanderson Jr
**Pr:* Lampkin Butts
**CFO:* D Michael Cockrell
**Treas:* Mike Cockrell
Board of Directors: John H Baker III, Phil Livingston, Charles W Ritter, D R Sanderson Jr, Robert Buck Sanderson, Rowan Taylor, Donald W Zacharias

D-U-N-S 11-277-4864
■ **SANDERSON FARMS INC (PRODUCTION DIVISION)**
(*Suby of* SANDERSON FARMS INC) ★
127 Flynt Rd, Laurel, MS 39443-9062
Tel (601) 425-2552 *Founded/Ownrshp* 1947
Sales 230.0MM^E *EMP* 9,000
SIC 0251 Broiling chickens, raising of
Pr: Lampkin Butts
**Treas:* D Michael Cockrell

SANDERSON FORD
See DON FORD SANDERSON INC

D-U-N-S 07-157-5146
SANDHILL CENTER LME/MCO
1120 7 Lakes Dr, West End, NC 27376-9082
Tel (910) 673-9111 *Founded/Ownrshp* 1963
Sales 336.1MM *EMP* 395
Accts Dixon Hughes Goodman Llp Pine
SIC 8011 Health maintenance organization
Comm Dir: Sid Linton

D-U-N-S 00-711-3228
■ **SANDIA CORP**
SANDIA NATIONAL LABORATORIES
(*Suby of* LOCKHEED MARTIN CORP) ★
1515 Eubank Blvd Se, Albuquerque, NM 87123-3453
Tel (505) 284-4784 *Founded/Ownrshp* 1993
Sales 1.9MMM^E *EMP* 8,150
SIC 8733 Noncommercial research organizations
Pr: Jill M Hruby
Treas: Patricia Taylor
**Ex VP:* Kim Sawyer
VP: Andrew Allerman
**VP:* James Chavez
VP: Duane B Dimos
VP: Christine Mitchell
VP: Mark Overberg
**Prin:* Jerry McDowell
Dept Mgr: Sylvia Saltzstein
Brnch Mgr: Fran Current

SANDIA NATIONAL LABORATORIES
See SANDIA CORP

SANDIA NATIONAL LABORATORY
See UNITED STATES DEPARTMENT OF ENERGY ALBUQUERQUE OFFICE

D-U-N-S 07-876-2188
SANDIS DINER LLC (TX)
704 Ayers St, Corpus Christi, TX 78404-1913
Tel (361) 334-3850 *Founded/Ownrshp* 2013
Sales 200.0MM *EMP* 5
SIC 7221 Photographic studios, portrait

SANDISK
See FUSION-IO INC

D-U-N-S 36-240-7041 IMP
■ **SANDISK CORP**
WESTERN DIGITAL
(*Suby of* WD) ★
951 Sandisk Dr, Milpitas, CA 95035-7933
Tel (408) 801-1000 *Founded/Ownrshp* 2016
Sales 5.5MMM^E *EMP* 8,696
SIC 3572 Computer storage devices
Pr: Sanjay Mehrotra
**Ch Bd:* Michael Marks
**CFO:* Judy Bruner
**Treas:* John Joy
**Ex VP:* Sumit Sadana
Ex VP: Siva Sivaram
Sr VP: Manish Bhatia
**Sr VP:* Mark Brazeal
Sr VP: Drew Henry
**Sr VP:* Shuki Nir
Sr VP: Khandker Nazrul Quader
Sr VP: Gursharan Singh
VP: Pascal De Boer
VP: Bob France
VP: Doug Hauck
VP: Noam Kedem
VP: Lisa Kho
VP: Mike Lakowicz
VP: Sharo McAfee-Hunter
VP: Juha Raisanen
VP: Eric S Whitaker

D-U-N-S 19-477-1796
SANDLER ONEILL & PARTNERS LP
1251 Ave Of Americas 6t, New York, NY 10020
Tel (212) 466-7800 *Founded/Ownrshp* 1988
Sales 134.6MM^E *EMP* 262
Accts Bdo Seidman Llp
SIC 6211 Brokers, security; Dealers, security
Prin: Judith Lynn Beizer
**Pt:* Sandler O'Neill Corp
**COO:* Fred Price
**CFO:* May F Della Pietra
VP: Joseph Adams
VP: Steven Alexopoulos
VP: Paul Barrese
VP: Reid Brewer
VP: Matt Brunner
VP: Eric Ferdinand
VP: Joseph Fiorito
VP: Amanda Gilman
VP: Robert Haderer
VP: Kathleen Haigood
VP: Patricia Koch
VP: Nathan Mittag
VP: Sumeet Mody
VP: Joseph Peri
VP: Michael Piper
Assoc Dir: John Brown
Assoc Dir: Bernie Krock

D-U-N-S 12-624-8173 IMP
SANDOW MEDIA LLC
3651 Nw 8th Ave Ste 200, Boca Raton, FL 33431-6489
Tel (561) 961-7700 *Founded/Ownrshp* 2002
Sales 89.9MM^E *EMP* 320
SIC 2721 Magazines: publishing only, not printed on site
CEO: Adam I Sandow
Pr: James Dimonekas
**Pr:* Erica Holborn
CEO: Paul Blum
COO: Chris Fabian
**COO:* Peter Fain
**CFO:* Chris Frabian
**CFO:* Paul Suh
VP: Steffanie Attenberg
Comm Man: Rachel Lexier-Nagle
**Prin:* Cindy Allen

D-U-N-S 00-538-7188 IMP
SANDOZ INC
(*Suby of* NOVARTIS AG)
100 College Rd W, Princeton, NJ 08540-6604
Tel (609) 627-8500 *Founded/Ownrshp* 1960
Sales 441.5MM^E *EMP* 1,730
SIC 2834 5122 Tablets, pharmaceutical; Pills, pharmaceutical; Pharmaceuticals
Pr: Benhard Hamel
**Pr:* Don Degolyer
**Pr:* Peter Goldschmidt
COO: Joe Reener
**CFO:* Eric Evans
**CFO:* Kevin Plummer
CFO: Sierk Poetting
Ofcr: Giuseppe Daprano
**VP:* Robin Adelstein
VP: Pranab Bhattacharyya
VP: Samuele Butera
VP: Jesus Corchero
VP: Patrik Florencio
VP: Rathnam Kumar
VP: Anthony Maffia
VP: Martha Manning
VP: Marie McCarthy
VP: Dave Picard
VP: Eric Pomerantz
VP: Leon Shargel
Assoc Dir: Satarupa Basu

D-U-N-S 17-778-0509
▲ **SANDRIDGE ENERGY INC**
123 Robert S Kerr Ave, Oklahoma City, OK 73102-6406
Tel (405) 429-5500 *Founded/Ownrshp* 1984
Sales 768.7MM *EMP* 1,165
Tkr Sym SD *Exch* NYS
SIC 1311 Crude petroleum & natural gas; Crude petroleum production; Natural gas production
Pr: James D Bennett
**Ch Bd:* Jeffrey S Serota
COO: Steve Turk
CFO: Julian Bott
Treas: Trent M Richey
Ex VP: Duane M Grubert
Ex VP: Craig A Johnson
Ex VP: Rodney E Johnson
Ex VP: Todd Tipton
Sr VP: Randall D Cooley
Sr VP: R Scott Griffin
Sr VP: John Suter
Sr VP: Philip Warman
VP: Mark T Arra
VP: Gregory Dewey
VP: Robert M Potts
VP: Trent Richey
Board of Directors: Stephen C Beasley, Jim J Brewer, Everett R Dobson, Edward W Moneypenny, J Michael Stice, Alan J Weber, Dan A Westbrook

D-U-N-S 19-872-1409 IMP
SANDRIDGE FOOD CORP
SANDRIDGE GOURMET SALADS
133 Commerce Dr, Medina, OH 44256-1333
Tel (330) 725-2348 *Founded/Ownrshp* 1988
Sales 113.5MM^E *EMP* 396
SIC 2099 Salads, fresh or refrigerated
CEO: Mark D Sandridge
**Pr:* William G Frantz
Pr: Frank Sidari
COO: Bill Holmes
VP: Dale Fortner
VP: Matthew S Harris
Genl Mgr: Jordan Sandridge
QA Dir: Al Moneypenny
IT Man: Thomas Novak
Ql Cn Mgr: Allison Cramer
Ql Cn Mgr: Ahmad Tahajod

SANDRIDGE GOURMET SALADS
See SANDRIDGE FOOD CORP

D-U-N-S 96-862-3053
SANDRIDGE PERMIAN TRUST
919 Congress Ave, Austin, TX 78701-2102
Tel (512) 236-6599 *Founded/Ownrshp* 2011
Sales 87.7MM *EMP* 2
SIC 6733 Trusts
Prin: Jon Brumley

D-U-N-S 00-276-4998
■ **SANDS BETHWORKS GAMING LLC**
SANDS CASINO RESORT BETHLEHEM
(*Suby of* LAS VEGAS SANDS CORP) ★
77 Sands Blvd, Bethlehem, PA 18015-7705
Tel (877) 726-3777 *Founded/Ownrshp* 2008
Sales 136.0MM^E *EMP* 2,400
SIC 7011 Casino hotel
Pr: Douglas S Niethold
Ofcr: Marco Lou
VP: Derinda Brown
VP: Michele Trageser
Exec: Sonia Lei
IT Man: Robin Bohrer
IT Man: Cindy Brinton
Sls&Mrk Ex: Julia Corwin
Sls&Mrk Ex: Karen Kwong
Snr PM: Pam Frebel

SANDS CASINO RESORT BETHLEHEM
See SANDS BETHWORKS GAMING LLC

D-U-N-S 09-988-0221
SANDS PROPERTIES INC
SANDS VILLA RESORT
201 74th Ave N, Myrtle Beach, SC 29572-3832
Tel (843) 449-4431 *Founded/Ownrshp* 1984
Sales 34.0MM^E *EMP* 1,000
SIC 6531 Real estate managers; Rental agent, real estate; Time-sharing real estate sales, leasing & rentals
Pr: Frans N Mustert

SANDS VILLA RESORT
See SANDS PROPERTIES INC

D-U-N-S 00-446-5894
SANDUSKY NEWSPAPERS INC
314 W Market St, Sandusky, OH 44870-2410
Tel (419) 625-5500 *Founded/Ownrshp* 1957

Sales 97.2MM^E *EMP* 500
SIC 4832 2711 2752 Radio broadcasting stations; Newspapers; Commercial printing, lithographic
Ch Bd: Dudley A White Jr
**Pr:* David A Rau

SANDVIK & COROMANT
See SANDVIK INC

D-U-N-S 00-147-9369 IMP/EXP
SANDVIK INC
SANDVIK & COROMANT
(*Suby of* SANDVIK FINANCE B.V.)
17-02 Nevins Rd, Fair Lawn, NJ 07410-2886
Tel (201) 794-5000 *Founded/Ownrshp* 1919
Sales 932.7MM^E *EMP* 4,000
SIC 3316 3317 3356 3315 3545 3533 Strip steel, cold-rolled: from purchased hot-rolled; Wire, flat, cold-rolled strip: not made in hot-rolled mills; Tubes, seamless steel; Zirconium & zirconium alloy: rolling, drawing or extruding; Titanium & titanium alloy: rolling, drawing or extruding; Wire products, ferrous/iron: made in wiredrawing plants; Machine tool accessories; Bits, oil & gas field tools: rock; Drilling tools for gas, oil or water wells
Pr: Rick Askin
COO: Troy Montgomery
Ofcr: Ulf Hermansson
Ex VP: Peter Larson
Ex VP: Norman Margolin
VP: Lars Blomberg
VP: Magnus Eriksson
VP: Robert Roth
VP: Janne Uotila
Dir Bus: Anna Relius
Comm Man: Madelene Hammar

D-U-N-S 09-277-4850 IMP/EXP
SANDVIK MINING AND CONSTRUCTION USA LLC
(*Suby of* SANDVIK AB)
300 Technology Ct Se, Smyrna, GA 30082-5235
Tel (404) 589-3800 *Founded/Ownrshp* 1997
Sales 140.7MM^E *EMP* 240
SIC 5082 Mining machinery & equipment, except petroleum
Pr: Lars Olof Josefsson
Pr: Dan Allan
Pr: Gary Hughes
VP: John Walsh

D-U-N-S 07-952-3720
SANDY PAGES
1794 S Kihei Rd Ste 4, Kihei, HI 96753-8058
Tel (808) 205-0321 *Founded/Ownrshp* 2014
Sales 200.0MM *EMP* 1
SIC 5192 5092 Books; Toys & games; Puzzles
Owner: Rodney Saunders

D-U-N-S 19-043-1726
▲ SANDY SPRING BANCORP INC
17801 Georgia Ave, Olney, MD 20832-2233
Tel (301) 774-6400 *Founded/Ownrshp* 1988
Sales NA *EMP* 737^E
Tkr Sym SASR *Exch* NGS
SIC 6411 National commercial banks; Insurance agents, brokers & service
Pr: Daniel J Schrider
**Ch Bd:* Robert L Orndorff
CFO: Philip J Mantua
Ofcr: Victoria Kalantar
Ex VP: Ronald E Kuykendall
Ex VP: Joseph J O'Brien Jr
VP: Larry Arch
VP: Douglas Greene
VP: Cathy Jeary
VP: Lisa Johnson
VP: Robert Mann
VP: Barbara Mulitz
VP: Bradley Preisinger
VP: Noel Shepherd
VP: Mark Slatin
VP: Joyce Vance
VP: Sandra Workman
Board of Directors: Dennis A Starliper, Mona Abutaleb, Ralph F Boyd Jr, Mark E Friis, Susan D Goff, Robert E Henel Jr, Pamela A Little, James J Maiwurn, Gary G Nakamoto, Craig A Ruppert

D-U-N-S 03-582-4218
■ SANDY SPRING BANK (MD)
(*Suby of* SANDY SPRING BANCORP INC) ★
17801 Georgia Ave, Olney, MD 20832-2267
Tel (301) 774-6400 *Founded/Ownrshp* 1868, 1987
Sales NA *EMP* 439
SIC 6021 National commercial banks
Pr: Daniel J Schrider
Pr: Lynn Mason
**COO:* Frank H Small
Treas: Sheldon Mandel
Ofcr: Gretchen Harris
Ofcr: Roy Manuel
Ofcr: Melissa Schulze
Ex VP: William W Hill
Ex VP: Philip Mantua
Ex VP: Diana Matthews
Ex VP: Ronda McDowell
**Ex VP:* Sara Watkins
**Ex VP:* Jeffrey A Welch
Sr VP: John Bell
Sr VP: George Cave
Sr VP: Joseph Dennis
**Sr VP:* James R Farmer
Sr VP: Don Haasen
Sr VP: Lauretta Kramer
Sr VP: Sharon L McGrail
**Sr VP:* Stanley L Merson

SANEL AUTO PARTS
See AUTOMOTIVE SUPPLY ASSOCIATES INC

D-U-N-S 04-772-4802
SANESE SERVICES INC
2590 Elm Rd Ne, Warren, OH 44483-2904
Tel (614) 436-1234 *Founded/Ownrshp* 1946
Sales 111.7MM^E *EMP* 850
Accts Gbq Partners Llc Columbus Oh
SIC 5962 5812 7389 Food vending machines; Eating places; Cafeteria; Caterers; Coffee service
Pr: Ralph Sanese
**CFO:* William Z Esch
**CFO:* Steve Hoffman
**Exec:* Victoria Steck
**Prin:* Doris Sanese

D-U-N-S 83-271-9376
SANFORD
SANFORD HEALTH
801 Broadway N, Fargo, ND 58102-3641
Tel (701) 234-6000 *Founded/Ownrshp* 2009
Sales 3.9MM *EMP* 17,400^E
Accts Deloitte Tax Lp Minneapolis
SIC 8062 8011 8051 General medical & surgical hospitals; Offices & clinics of medical doctors; Skilled nursing care facilities
Pr: Kelby K Krabbenhoft
V Ch: James Volk
**COO:* Becky Nelson
COO: Jeff Sandene
**CFO:* Joann Kunkel
**Treas:* Bill Marlette
Trst: Ellen E Chaffee
Trst: Nancy Jordheim
Trst: Jack Reynolds
Ofcr: Julia Beaton
Ofcr: Cindy Haugrud
**Ex VP:* Rich Adcock
**Ex VP:* Andrew Richburg
**VP:* Mike Begeman
VP: Jesse Tischer
Exec: Lloyd Galloway
**Exec:* Dave Link
Exec: Julie Marsh
Dir Lab: Judy Adamson
Dir Rad: Jason Asheim
Dir Rad: William Ausin

D-U-N-S 78-319-7650 IMP
SANFORD AUTO DEALERS EXCHANGE INC
2851 Saint Johns Pkwy, Sanford, FL 32771-4825
Tel (407) 328-7300 *Founded/Ownrshp* 1991
Sales 103.9MM^E *EMP* 300
SIC 5012

SANFORD BEMIDJI MEDICAL CENTER
See SANFORD HEALTH OF NORTHERN MINNESOTA

D-U-N-S 07-149-4348
SANFORD BISMARCK
MEDCENTER ONE HEALTH SYSTEMS
300 N 7th St, Bismarck, ND 58501-4439
Tel (701) 323-6000 *Founded/Ownrshp* 1907
Sales 224.7MM^E *EMP* 2,781
Accts Eide Bailly Llp Minneapolis
SIC 8011 8062 Primary care medical clinic; Hospital, professional nursing school with AMA residency
Pr: Craig Lambrecht
Ex Dir: Carrol M Dobler
CIO: John Miller
IT Man: Bob Quintus
Mktg Dir: Jamie L Christensen
Surgeon: William D Canham
Surgeon: Michael L Schmit
Obsttrcn: James Zuberneis
Doctor: Sylvia M Anderson MD
Doctor: Al Bitar
Doctor: Steffen Christensen

SANFORD BRANDS
See SANFORD LP

SANFORD BROADWAY PHARMACY
See SANFORD CLINIC NORTH

D-U-N-S 02-052-0466
SANFORD BURNHAM PREBYS MEDICAL DISCOVERY INSTITUTE
SBP
10901 N Torrey Pines Rd, La Jolla, CA 92037-1005
Tel (858) 795-5000 *Founded/Ownrshp* 1976
Sales 122.0MM *EMP* 1,000
Accts Deloitte & Touche Llp San Di
SIC 8733 Research institute
CEO: Perry Nisen
**Pr:* Kristiina Vuori
**CFO:* Gary Chessum
CFO: Nicole Deberg
CFO: Robert Walsh
Trst: Howard Cohen
Trst: Leon Kassel
Trst: Marvin Levine
Trst: Alan Stanford
Trst: Eugene Step
Trst: Victor Vilaplana
VP: Paul Baker
VP: Edgar M Gillenwaters
VP: Craig Hauser
VP: Michael R Jackson
VP: Michael J Jackson
**VP:* Robin Ryan
VP: Robert H Zaugg
VP: Robert Zaugg
Assoc Dir: Sylvie E Blondelle
Assoc Dir: Mehrak Kiankarimi

D-U-N-S 80-573-3490 IMP
SANFORD CLINIC NORTH
SANFORD BROADWAY PHARMACY
(*Suby of* SANFORD NORTH) ★
737 Broadway N, Fargo, ND 58102-4421
Tel (701) 234-2000 *Founded/Ownrshp* 1980
Sales 538.4MM^E *EMP* 7,000
Accts Eide Bailly Llp Minneapolis
SIC 5912 Drug stores & proprietary stores
Pr: Kelby Krabbenhote
VP: Martha Leclerc
Off Mgr: Morey Leiseth
Anesthlgy: Steven Daniels
Doctor: Paul J Carson MD
Doctor: Weimin Hao MD
Doctor: Bhargav Mistry MD
Doctor: Vishnupriy Parvathareddy MD
Doctor: Alan J Rosenbloom

D-U-N-S 96-715-7061
SANFORD CLINIC NORTH
SANFORD CLINIC NORTH FARGO
(*Suby of* SANFORD NORTH) ★
801 Broadway N, Fargo, ND 58102-3641
Tel (701) 234-2000 *Founded/Ownrshp* 2010
Sales 65.3MM^E *EMP* 2,500
SIC 8741 8721 Hospital management; Nursing & personal care facility management; Accounting, auditing & bookkeeping
Pr: Roger L Gilbertson
**VP:* Douglas Okland
Genl Mgr: Roni Smart

SANFORD CLINIC NORTH FARGO
See SANFORD CLINIC NORTH

D-U-N-S 04-984-5993
SANFORD CONTRACTORS INC
628 Rocky Fork Church Rd, Sanford, NC 27332-0835
Tel (919) 775-7882 *Founded/Ownrshp* 1969
Sales 106.6MM^E *EMP* 250
Accts Williams Overman Pierce Llp
SIC 1611 1622 1629 6552 1794 1623 Grading; Bridge, tunnel & elevated highway; Land clearing contractor; Subdividers & developers; Excavation work; Water, sewer & utility lines
Pr: Donald T Oldham
**Sec:* Thomas M Haislip
VP: Randall Gattis
**VP:* Vicky Oldham Haislip
VP: Rich Holshouser
**VP:* David Stike
Off Mgr: Annette Scott

SANFORD HEALTH
See SANFORD

D-U-N-S 07-291-8303
SANFORD HEALTH
(*Suby of* SANFORD HEALTH) ★
1305 W 18th St, Sioux Falls, SD 57105-0401
Tel (605) 333-1720 *Founded/Ownrshp* 2009
Sales 4.2MMM *EMP* 2,939^E
Accts Deloitte & Touche Llp Minnea
SIC 8062 8011 8051 General medical & surgical hospitals; Offices & clinics of medical doctors; Skilled nursing care facilities
Pr: Kelby K Krabbenhoft
Chf Rad: Thomas Free
**Pr:* Dan Blue MD
**Pr:* Ruth Krystopolski
**Pr:* Brian Mortensen
**Pr:* Ed Weiland
COO: Randy Bury
COO: Rob Lovejoy
**COO:* Becky Nelson
**CFO:* Michelle Bruhn
CFO: Duane Coulter
CFO: Jim Frank
CFO: Merrilee Schultz
CFO: Bruce Viessmann
Ofcr: Bill Marlette
Ex VP: Rich Adcock
**Ex VP:* Dave Link
Sr VP: David Danielson
VP: Arlene Biberdorf
VP: Mike Christianson
VP: Daniel Heinemann

D-U-N-S 18-706-4027
SANFORD HEALTH NETWORK
1305 W 18th St, Sioux Falls, SD 57105-0401
Tel (605) 328-2929 *Founded/Ownrshp* 1985
Sales 78.0MM^E *EMP* 2,200
Accts Deloitte & Touche Llp
SIC 8741 8011 Hospital management; Offices & clinics of medical doctors
Pr: Kelby K Krabbenhoft
**COO:* Nate White
**Ex VP:* David Link
Exec: Michele Bruhn

D-U-N-S 03-690-9278
SANFORD HEALTH OF NORTHERN MINNESOTA
SANFORD BEMIDJI MEDICAL CENTER
1300 Anne St Nw, Bemidji, MN 56601-5103
Tel (218) 751-5430 *Founded/Ownrshp* 1977
Sales 215.5MM *EMP* 900
SIC 8082 Home health care services
Pr: Paul Hanson
COO: Joy Johnson
Pathlgst: Arif Azam

D-U-N-S 00-506-7574 EXP
■ SANFORD LP
SANFORD BRANDS
(*Suby of* NEWELL BRANDS INC) ★
3500 Lacey Rd, Downers Grove, IL 60515-5422
Tel (770) 418-7000 *Founded/Ownrshp* 1992
Sales 445.3MM^E *EMP* 2,425
SIC 2891 3951 3952 Adhesives; Pens & mechanical pencils; Lead pencils & art goods
Pr: Michael Colk
VP: Rusty Snow
Genl Mgr: Debra Svennizik
IT Man: Neil Lancarte
VP Sls: Maureen Wolthuis
Sales Asso: Leslie Hoalt

D-U-N-S 06-815-7668
SANFORD MEDICAL CENTER FARGO
(*Suby of* SANFORD NORTH) ★
720 4th St N, Fargo, ND 58122-4520
Tel (701) 234-6000 *Founded/Ownrshp* 2010
Sales 656.5MM^E *EMP* 7,000
SIC 8062 General medical & surgical hospitals
Pr: Paul Richard
**COO:* Nate White
CFO: Lisa Carlson
**CFO:* Joann Kunkel
CFO: Doug Okland
CIO: Jo Burdick
CIO: Craig Hewitt
IT Man: Todd Morken
Anesthlgy: Nicole Abrahamson
Opthamlgy: Steven Anderson

D-U-N-S 07-649-0945
SANFORD MEDICAL CENTER THIEF RIVER FALLS
(*Suby of* SANFORD NORTH) ★
120 Labree Ave S Ste A, Thief River Falls, MN 56701-2819
Tel (218) 681-4240 *Founded/Ownrshp* 2010
Sales 100.0MM *EMP* 600
SIC 8062 General medical & surgical hospitals
CEO: Chris Harff
**Pr:* Paul Hanson
**COO:* Rob Lovejoy
CFO: Eddie Klein
Mtls Dir: Floyd Hageman Jr
Sls Mgr: Thomas Wang

D-U-N-S 14-758-1615
SANFORD NORTH
(*Suby of* SANFORD HEALTH) ★
801 Broadway N, Fargo, ND 58102-3641
Tel (701) 234-2000 *Founded/Ownrshp* 1984
Sales 1.4MMM^E *EMP* 7,200
SIC 8011 Medical centers
Prin: Roger L Gilbertson
**CFO:* Lisa Carlson

SANGAMON TRANSPORTATION
See LOUIS DREYFUS US LLC

D-U-N-S 07-738-5185
SANGER UNIFIED SCHOOL DISTRICT
1905 7th St, Sanger, CA 93657-2897
Tel (559) 237-3171 *Founded/Ownrshp* 1889
Sales 81.0MM^E *EMP* 1,200
SIC 8211 Public elementary school; Public combined elementary & secondary school; Public senior high school; Public adult education school
VP: Peter Fillippi
Dir IT: Kim Jacobsen
Schl Brd P: James Karle
Instr Medi: Katherine Panasco
HC Dir: Kimberly Salomonson

D-U-N-S 07-003-2610
SANGUINE GAS EXPLORATION LLC
110 W 7th St Ste 2700, Tulsa, OK 74119-1199
Tel (918) 494-6070 *Founded/Ownrshp* 2003
Sales 115.9MM^E *EMP* 30
SIC 1311

D-U-N-S 80-204-9010
SANIMAX CORP
(*Suby of* INDUSTRIES SANIMAX INC)
2099 Badgerland Dr, Green Bay, WI 54303-4831
Tel (920) 494-5233 *Founded/Ownrshp* 2005
Sales 292.3MM^E *EMP* 405
SIC 5199 2077 Greases, animal or vegetable; Tallow rendering, inedible; Grease rendering, inedible
CEO: Martin Couture
**Ch Bd:* Andr Couture
Treas: Robert Pfeil
CIO: Paul Van Learhoven
Plnt Mgr: Tim Kedrowski

D-U-N-S 09-733-5616 IMP
SANIMAX USA LLC
(*Suby of* SANIMAX CORP) ★
2099 Badgerland Dr, Green Bay, WI 54303-4831
Tel (920) 494-5233 *Founded/Ownrshp* 2009
Sales 184.0MM^E *EMP* 405
SIC 5199 2077

D-U-N-S 06-776-1700
SANITATION DISTRICT OF LOS ANGELES COUNTY DISTRICT 2
L.A.CO.
1955 Workman Mill Rd, Whittier, CA 90601-1415
Tel (562) 699-7411 *Founded/Ownrshp* 1924
Sales NA *EMP* 1,700
Accts Moss Levy & Hartzheim Llp Cu
SIC 9511
Genl Mgr: Stephen Maguin
Bd of Dir: Rechelle Asperin
VP: Kristen Ruffell
VP: Kim Schulze
Ex Dir: Gina Schmitt
CTO: Thomas Tran
Dir IT: Daniel Lee
IT Man: William Barbe
IT Man: Robyn Beach
IT Man: Guy Clark
Plnt Mgr: Greg Osburne

D-U-N-S 80-227-6191
SANITATION DISTRICTS OF LOS ANGELES COUNTY
1955 Workman Mill Rd, Whittier, CA 90601-1415
Tel (562) 908-4288 *Founded/Ownrshp* 2007
Sales 576.0MM *EMP* 1,698
SIC 4953 Refuse systems; Rubbish collection & disposal
Bd of Dir: Phil Markle
Top Exec: CHI-Chung Tang
Genl Mgr: Grace Robinson Chan
IT Man: Melissa Brown

D-U-N-S 79-054-7587 IMP
SANJEL (USA) INC
1630 Welton St Ste 400, Denver, CO 80202-4239
Tel (303) 893-6866 *Founded/Ownrshp* 1998
Sales 605.9MM^E *EMP* 300
SIC 1389 Oil field services
Pr: Don Macdonald
CFO: Susan Morris
**Treas:* Darin Macdonald
Ex VP: Stephen Lipari

D-U-N-S 07-926-8702 IMP/EXP
SANMAR CORP
22833 Se Black Nugget Rd, Issaquah, WA 98029-3621
Tel (206) 727-3200 *Founded/Ownrshp* 1962
Sales 1.3MMM^E *EMP* 595
SIC 5136 5137 Shirts, men's & boys'; Women's & children's clothing
**Pr:* Jeremy Lott
**CFO:* Jerry Magnani
**VP:* Jordan Lott
**VP:* Sharon Lott

Dir IT: Jan Mosher
IT Man: Kile Froisland
IT Man: Paul Harvey
Opers Mgr: Larry Batson
Opers Mgr: Marty Rask
Natl Sales: Sean Lee
Natl Sales: Dan Tushar

D-U-N-S 79-877-8395

▲ SANMINA CORP
2700 N 1st St, San Jose, CA 95134-2015
Tel (408) 964-3500 *Founded/Ownrshp* 1980
Sales 6.4MMM *EMP* 45,397
Accts Pricewaterhousecoopers Llp Sa
Tkr Sym SANM *Exch* NGS
SIC 3672 3674 Printed circuit boards; Semiconductors & related devices; Light emitting diodes
Ch Bd: Jure Sola
CFO: Robert Eulau
Ex VP: Alan Reid
Ex VP: Dennis Young
Board of Directors: Neil R Bonke, Michael J Clarke, Eugene A Delaney, John P Goldsberry, Rita S Lane, Joseph G Licata Jr, Mario M Rosati, Wayne Shortridge, Jackie M Ward

SANMINA SCI
See SCI SYSTEMS INC

D-U-N-S 00-921-0175

■ SANMINA-SCI SYSTEMS (ALABAMA) INC
(*Suby of* SANMINA CORP) ★
13000 Memorial Pkwy Sw, Huntsville, AL 35803-6000
Tel (256) 882-4800 *Founded/Ownrshp* 1980
Sales 886.6MM^E *EMP* 5,677
SIC 6719 Investment holding companies, except banks
Ch Bd: Jure Sola
**Pr:* Randy Furr
CFO: Rick Ackle
**CFO:* Bob Eulau
Treas: Ronald Sibolio
Bd of Dir: Gwen Munroe
Bd of Dir: Rich Reed
**Ex VP:* Michael Tyler
Sr VP: Ken Haney
VP: Robert Swift
Exec: Denny Disbrow

D-U-N-S 08-672-3285 IMP

SANOFI PASTEUR INC
(*Suby of* SANOFI)
1 Discovery Dr, Swiftwater, PA 18370-9100
Tel (570) 839-7187 *Founded/Ownrshp* 1977
Sales 465.0MM^E *EMP* 2,200
SIC 2836 Biological products, except diagnostic; Vaccines
Pr: Damian A Braga
Pr: Jean Cappelli
Sr VP: Damian A Braga
VP: Bill Averbeck
VP: Tony Damore
VP: Daniel Gordon
VP: David P Greenberg
VP: Allan Jarvis
**VP:* Charles Montgomery
VP: Charles S Montgomery
VP: David Pankow
VP: Jean Renard
VP: Olivier Selignan
VP: Maggie Shafmaster
Comm Dir: Arne Naeeke

D-U-N-S 00-711-9555 IMP

SANOFI US SERVICES INC
(*Suby of* SANOFI)
55 Corporate Dr, Bridgewater, NJ 08807-1265
Tel (336) 407-4994 *Founded/Ownrshp* 1950, 1999
Sales 4.7MMM^E *EMP* 16,508
SIC 2834 Pharmaceutical preparations; Drugs acting on the cardiovascular system, except diagnostic; Drugs acting on the central nervous system & sense organs; Drugs acting on the gastrointestinal or genitourinary system
CEO: Christopher A Viehbacher
**Ch Bd:* Timothy Rothwell
Pr: Bhavesh Ashar
Pr: Gerald P Belle
Pr: Mark Kwiatek
Pr: Margaret Sparks
**Pr:* Anne Whitaker
Treas: Gloria Gilbert
Ofcr: Gary Nabel
Assoc VP: Mike Capaldi
Assoc VP: Anthony Casciano
Assoc VP: Elizabeth Colarossi
Assoc VP: Frank Harrison
Assoc VP: Carolyn Kircher
Assoc VP: Kevin Malobisky
Assoc VP: Mark C Nelligan
Assoc VP: Sabrina Spitaletta
**Ex VP:* David Meeker
Ex VP: Heinz-Werner Meier
**Sr VP:* Damian Braga
Sr VP: Damian A Braga

D-U-N-S 82-467-6584 IMP

SANOFI-AVENTIS US LLC
(*Suby of* SANOFI-SYNTHELABO INC) ★
55 Corporate Dr, Bridgewater, NJ 08807-1265
Tel (908) 981-5000 *Founded/Ownrshp* 2006
Sales 718.0MM^E *EMP* 616
SIC 5122 2834 Pharmaceuticals; Pharmaceutical preparations
Pr: Joseph Palladino
Treas: Richard Thomson
Assoc VP: Barbara Fanelli
Assoc VP: Rima Nassar
Ex VP: Charles F Rouse
Sr VP: Gregory Irace
Assoc Dir: Ed Eisenberg
Assoc Dir: Noemi Guma
Natl Sales: Charles Hyde
Natl Sales: Lauren Rendino
Mktg Dir: Hee Kim

D-U-N-S 80-442-4612 IMP/EXP

SANOFI-SYNTHELABO INC
(*Suby of* SANOFI)
55 Corporate Dr, Bridgewater, NJ 08807-1265
Tel (908) 981-5000 *Founded/Ownrshp* 1994
Sales 724.6MM^E *EMP* 16,000
SIC 8011 Health maintenance organization
Pr: George Doherty
**Treas:* Richard Thomson
**Sr VP:* Jack Dean
Board of Directors: Kurt Briner, Gerard Le Fur

D-U-N-S 17-832-3614 IMP

SANOH AMERICA INC
(*Suby of* SANOH INDUSTRIAL CO.,LTD.)
1849 Industrial Dr, Findlay, OH 45840-5440
Tel (419) 425-2600 *Founded/Ownrshp* 1986
Sales 274.9MM^E *EMP* 1,270
SIC 3498 Tube fabricating (contract bending & shaping)
Pr: Masahiko Mizukami
**CFO:* Ronald Frisch
**VP:* Eric Carroll
**VP:* Jeff Hook
Dir IT: Brian Aller
**VP Mktg:* Ronald J Curry

SANS INSTITUTE
See ESCAL INSTITUTE OF ADVANCED TECHNOLOGIES INC

D-U-N-S 01-188-5584

■ SANSPAN CORP
(*Suby of* BLACKSTONE GROUP L P) ★
1500 Orange Ave, Coronado, CA 92118-2918
Tel (619) 435-6611 *Founded/Ownrshp* 2011
Sales 13.9MM^E *EMP* 1,000
SIC 7011 Hotels & motels
Pr: Todd Shallan
CFO: Bob Antes
Admn Mgr: Howart Cho
Admn Mgr: Marvin Tayag
VP Opers: Susan Drechsler
VP Opers: John Spomer
Mktg Mgr: Kelly Carpenter
Sls Mgr: Anne Roetzer

D-U-N-S 07-882-2939

SANSUM CLINIC
470 S Patterson Ave, Santa Barbara, CA 93111-2404
Tel (805) 681-7700 *Founded/Ownrshp* 1972
Sales 223.5MM *EMP* 900
Accts Moss Adams Llp San Francisco
SIC 8011 Clinic, operated by physicians
Pr: Kurt Ransohoff MD
**CFO:* Chad Hine
Genl Mgr: Joanne Stokes
**CIO:* Tom Colbert
IT Man: Nellie Mendoza
Surgeon: Gregory C Greaney
Doctor: Nancy Alex
Doctor: Tom Beamer
Doctor: Victor H Carabba MD
Doctor: Mark Wilson
Doctor: James Zmolek

SANTA ANA COLLEGE
See RANCHO SANTIAGO COMMUNITY COLLEGE DISTRICT INC

D-U-N-S 07-606-1712

SANTA ANA UNIFIED SCHOOL DISTRICT PUBLIC FACILITIES CORP
1601 E Chestnut Ave, Santa Ana, CA 92701-6322
Tel (714) 558-5501 *Founded/Ownrshp* 1889
Sales 11.7MM^E *EMP* 4,965
SIC 8211

SANTA BARBARA CITY COLLEGE
See SANTA BARBARA COMMUNITY COLLEGE DISTRICT

D-U-N-S 07-963-2592

SANTA BARBARA COMMUNITY COLLEGE DISTRICT
SANTA BARBARA CITY COLLEGE
721 Cliff Dr, Santa Barbara, CA 93109-2312
Tel (805) 965-0581 *Founded/Ownrshp* 1908
Sales 64.0MM^E *EMP* 2,091
SIC 8222 Community college
Pr: Lori Gaskin
**Pr:* John Romo
Trst: Morris Jurkowitz
Trst: Joan Livingston
Admn Mgr: Steven Lewis
Off Mgr: Yoli Contreras
DP Exec: Paula Coffey
DP Exec: Alan McKenzie
DP Dir: Brandon Lovelace
DP Dir: Richard Shultz
Dir IT: Kent Richards

SANTA BARBARA COTTAGE HOSPITAL
See COTTAGE HEALTH

D-U-N-S 07-882-9900

SANTA BARBARA COTTAGE HOSPITAL
COTTAGE HOSPITAL CHILDRENS CTR
400 W Pueblo St, Santa Barbara, CA 93105-4353
Tel (805) 682-7111 *Founded/Ownrshp* 1982
Sales 610.4MM *EMP* 1,786^E
SIC 8062 General medical & surgical hospitals; Hospital, AMA approved residency
Ch: Gretchen Milligan
**Pr:* Ronald C Werft
**Ex VP:* Steven Fellows
Dir Lab: Charlene Fernandez
**Prin:* Karen Jones Grandidier
Genl Mgr: Tiana Riskowski
Off Mgr: Pat Keay
Dir IT: Gary Gill
VP Opers: Susanne Peterson
Secur Mgr: Debbie Welterlen
Surgeon: Lisa Ferrigno
Board of Directors: Michael Towbes, Patricia Dillion Bliss, Frederick W Clough, Bob Ferguson, Betty Mazzetti Hatch, Karl J Kassity, Robert A Reid, J Robert Schrieffer, George E Scott, David W Spainhour

D-U-N-S 10-889-1748

SANTA BARBARA TRANSPORTATION CORP
(*Suby of* STUDENT TRANSPORTATION OF AMERICA INC) ★
6414 Hollister Ave, Goleta, CA 93117-3145
Tel (805) 681-8355 *Founded/Ownrshp* 1983
Sales 42.0MM^E *EMP* 1,000
SIC 4151 4141 School buses; Local bus charter service
CEO: Denis J Hallagher
**CFO:* Patrick Walker
Brnch Mgr: Lynn Buckley

D-U-N-S 09-838-5982

SANTA BARBARA UNIFIED SCHOOL DISTRICT
720 Santa Barbara St, Santa Barbara, CA 93101-2232
Tel (805) 963-4338 *Founded/Ownrshp* 1899
Sales 69.7MM^E *EMP* 1,175
Accts Christy White Accountancy Corp
SIC 8211 Public elementary school
Prin: David E Cash
**Pr:* Annette Cordero
**VP:* Susan C Deacon
Genl Mgr: Laci Preston
Off Admin: Elizabeth Sandoval
Dir IT: Teresa Koontz
Pr Dir: Barbara Keyani
Psych: Susan Snyder

D-U-N-S 60-285-8441

SANTA CLARA COUNTY OFFICE OF EDUCATION
1290 Ridder Park Dr, San Jose, CA 95131-2304
Tel (408) 453-6500 *Founded/Ownrshp* 1967
Sales 89.9MM^E *EMP* 1,800
Accts Vavrinek Trine Day & Co Ll
SIC 8211 Public elementary & secondary schools
CIO: Teo Anley
MIS Dir: David Wu

D-U-N-S 06-912-8148

SANTA CLARA UNIFIED SCHOOL DISTRICT
1889 Lawrence Rd, Santa Clara, CA 95051-2166
Tel (408) 423-2000 *Founded/Ownrshp* 1987
Sales 125.0MM *EMP* 2,000
SIC 8211 Public elementary school; Public junior high school; Public senior high school; Public adult education school
Prgrm Mgr: Joy Bartol
Prgrm Mgr: Nancy Morin
IT Man: Min Chae
Pr Dir: Jennifer Dericco
Schl Brd P: Albert Gonzalez
Psych: Nuzhath Quadri

D-U-N-S 96-446-1482

SANTA CLARA VALLEY MEDICAL CENTER
SCVMC
751 S Bascom Ave, San Jose, CA 95128-2699
Tel (408) 885-5000 *Founded/Ownrshp* 2010
Sales 417.7MM *EMP* 2,059^E
SIC 8062 6324 General medical & surgical hospitals; Hospital & medical service plans
CEO: Paul E Lorenz
CFO: Kim Roberts
Ofcr: Cheryl Bernard-Shaw
VP: Tom Bush
Chf Nrs Of: Alice N Mugler
Off Mgr: Celia Radcliffe
Sys Mgr: Kris Manian
Netwrk Eng: Lili Jafari
Pathlgst: Raymond L Azzi
Pathlgst: Dawn Darbone
Pathlgst: Michael Deftos

D-U-N-S 09-220-2837 IMP

SANTA CLARA VALLEY TRANSPORTATION AUTHORITY
3331 N 1st St, San Jose, CA 95134-1906
Tel (408) 321-2300 *Founded/Ownrshp* 1972
Sales NA *EMP* 2,053
Accts Vavrinek Trine Day & Co Ll
SIC 9621
Genl Mgr: Michael Burns
V Ch: Warren Smith
Pr: Theresa Boston
CFO: Raj Srinath
Sr Cor Off: Dan Robertson
Exec: Dieu Nguyen
Genl Mgr: Grace Salandanan
CIO: Glenn Loo
CIO: Gary Miskell
DP Exec: Richard Kurk
DP Exec: Dennis Mellon

D-U-N-S 06-912-8999 IMP

SANTA CLARA VALLEY WATER DISTRICT PUBLIC FACILITIES FINANCING CORP (CA)
SANTA CLARA VALLEY WATER DST
5750 Almaden Expy, San Jose, CA 95118-3614
Tel (408) 265-2600 *Founded/Ownrshp* 1951
Sales 130.5MM *EMP* 850
Accts Vavrinek Trine Day & Co Ll
SIC 4941 Water supply
CEO: Beau Goldie
Bd of Dir: Roderick Jefferson
Bd of Dir: Carol Presley
VP: Debra Osikominu
Exec: Meenakshi Ganjoo
Exec: Fe Hernandez
Exec: Katharine Oven
Dir Lab: Jim Scott
Prgrm Mgr: Denise Uriarte
Dir IT: Zuberi White
Sys Mgr: Emmanuel Aryee

SANTA CLARA VALLEY WATER DST
See SANTA CLARA VALLEY WATER DISTRICT PUBLIC FACILITIES FINANCING CORP

D-U-N-S 03-755-9127

SANTA CLARITA COMMUNITY COLLEGE DISTRICT
COLLEGE OF THE CANYONS
(*Suby of* CALIFORNIA COMMUNITY COLLEGES SYSTEM) ★
26455 Rockwell Canyon Rd, Santa Clarita, CA 91355-1803
Tel (661) 259-7800 *Founded/Ownrshp* 1969
Sales 11.7MM *EMP* 1,100^E
Accts Vavrinek Trine Day & Co Ll
SIC 8222 8221 Community college; Colleges universities & professional schools
Pr: Dr Diane Van Hook
Pr: Dennis Chuning
Dir: Cathy Ritz
Dir IT: James Temple
Psych: Julie Visner
HC Dir: Jasmine Ruys
Art Dir: Nick Pavik

D-U-N-S 14-767-6480

SANTA CLARITA HEALTH CARE ASSOCIATION INC
23845 Mcbean Pkwy, Santa Clarita, CA 91355-2001
Tel (661) 253-8000 *Founded/Ownrshp* 1983
Sales 22.6MM^E *EMP* 1,000
SIC 8741 Hospital management; Nursing & personal care facility management
Pr: Roger Seaver
**COO:* Paul Salomon
**CFO:* C R Hudson
**Treas:* James D Hicken
Software D: Bob Hudson

SANTA CRUZ NUTRITIONALS
See HARMONY FOODS CORP

D-U-N-S 00-691-3925 IMP

SANTA CRUZ SEASIDE CO INC
400 Beach St, Santa Cruz, CA 95060-5416
Tel (831) 423-5590 *Founded/Ownrshp* 1915
Sales 55.2MM *EMP* 1,000
SIC 7996 7011 7933 6531 Pier, amusement; Motels; Bowling centers; Real estate agents & managers
Pr: Charles L Canfield
VP: Jo Anne Dlott
VP: Marq Lipton
Mng Dir: Regina Smith
Genl Mgr: Brigid Fuller
IT Man: Frank Gemignani
Secur Mgr: Don Hutchison
Art Dir: Jill James
Board of Directors: Robert Millslagle DDS, Albert W Rice, Jeffrey Rice MD, James Van Houten

SANTA CRUZ SPORTS MEDICINE CEN
See DOMINICAN HOSPITAL

D-U-N-S 08-877-6307

SANTA FE COLLEGE
3000 Nw 83rd St, Gainesville, FL 32606-6210
Tel (352) 395-5000 *Founded/Ownrshp* 1966
Sales 2.3MM *EMP* 1,200
Accts Purvis Gray & Company Llp Gai
SIC 8222 8221 Community college; Colleges universities & professional schools
Pr: Stefan M Davis
**Pr:* Jackson N Sasser
**Treas:* Charles W Clemons
**VP:* Ginger Gibson
**VP:* Alan Hitchcock
**VP:* Anne Kress
Assoc Dir: Doug Bagby
Store Mgr: Mary J Mahoney
Off Admin: Sarah Eiland
Off Admin: Rebecca Morgan
Pgrm Dir: Bobbie Konter

D-U-N-S 10-661-0793

SANTA FE COMMUNITY COLLEGE
SFCC
6401 S Richards Ave, Santa Fe, NM 87508-4887
Tel (505) 428-1000 *Founded/Ownrshp* 1983
Sales 91.4MM^E *EMP* 850
Accts Moss Adams Llp Albuquerque N
SIC 8222 8221 Community college; Colleges universities & professional schools
Pr: Randy Grissom
Assoc VP: Jill Douglass
VP: Orlando Griego
VP: Bruce McAllister

SANTA FE MUNICPL SCHOOLS DST C
See BOARD OF EDUCATION OF CITY OF SANTA FE (INC)

D-U-N-S 07-980-2451

SANTA FE PUBLIC SCHOOLS
610 Alta Vista St, Santa Fe, NM 87505-4149
Tel (505) 467-2000 *Founded/Ownrshp* 2015
Sales 26.2MM^E *EMP* 1,890^E
SIC 8211 Public elementary & secondary schools
Bd of Dir: Lorraine Price
Ex Dir: Richard Halford
Ex Dir: Kristy Janda
Schl Brd P: Steven Carrillo
Teacher Pr: Theresa Baca
Teacher Pr: Tracie Oliver
HC Dir: Susan Lujan

SANTA FE STATION HT & CASINO
See SANTA FE STATION INC

D-U-N-S 80-142-6532

SANTA FE STATION INC
SANTA FE STATION HT & CASINO
4949 N Rancho Dr, Las Vegas, NV 89130-3505
Tel (702) 658-4900 *Founded/Ownrshp* 2000
Sales 77.6MM^E *EMP* 1,500
SIC 7011 Casino hotel
Pr: Kevin L Kelley
**Treas:* Thomas M Friel

SANTA MARIA NURSING & REHAB
See SANTA MARIA NURSING HOME INC

D-U-N-S 08-049-3828
SANTA MARIA NURSING HOME INC (WI)
SANTA MARIA NURSING & REHAB
430 S Clay St, Green Bay, WI 54301-3896
Tel (920) 432-5231 *Founded/Ownrshp* 1965
Sales 296.2MM *EMP* 70
SIC 8051 Skilled nursing care facilities
Pr: Ronald Desotell
**Sec:* Helen Desotell

D-U-N-S 10-064-4848
SANTA MARIA-BONITA SCHOOL DIST
708 S Miller St, Santa Maria, CA 93454-6230
Tel (805) 928-1783 *Founded/Ownrshp* 1900
Sales 81.0MM[E] *EMP* 1,200
SIC 8211 Public elementary school
**Pr:* Paula Elkins
**Ofcr:* Maggie White
Schl Brd P: Linda Cordero
Teacher Pr: Patty Grady
HC Dir: Mark Muller

D-U-N-S 18-721-3715
SANTA MONICA COMMUNITY COLLEGE DISTRICT
1900 Pico Blvd, Santa Monica, CA 90405-1628
Tel (310) 434-4000 *Founded/Ownrshp* 1929
Sales 41.3MM[E] *EMP* 1,300
SIC 8222 Community college
V Ch: Joy Abbott
Trst: Margaret R Quiones-Perez
Assoc VP: David Muller
VP: Bob Isomoto
VP: Randal Lawson
**Prin:* Tom Donner
Ex Dir: Debbie Adler
Cmptr Lab: Joshi John
IT Man: Jocelyn Chong
Snr Mgr: Teresa Garcia
Snr Mgr: Maria Martinez

D-U-N-S 02-942-0874 IMP
SANTA MONICA SEAFOOD CO
18531 S Broadwick St, Rancho Dominguez, CA 90220-6440
Tel (310) 886-7900 *Founded/Ownrshp* 1981
Sales 101.4MM[E] *EMP* 431
SIC 5421 5146 5142 Fish & seafood markets; Fish & seafoods; Packaged frozen goods
CEO: Roger O'Brien
COO: Fernando Gonzalez
Sr VP: Dave Litle
**VP:* Michael Cigliano II
VP: Lisa Hogan
CIO: Khai Vuong

D-U-N-S 07-187-9464
SANTA ROSA CITY OF
100 Santa Rosa Ave, Santa Rosa, CA 95404-4959
Tel (707) 543-3010 *Founded/Ownrshp* 1863
Sales NA *EMP* 1,400
SIC 9121 City council;
Ofcr: Eric McHenry

D-U-N-S 06-013-6009
SANTA ROSA CITY SCHOOL DIST
SANTA ROSA CITY SCHOOLS
211 Ridgway Ave, Santa Rosa, CA 95401-4320
Tel (707) 528-5409 *Founded/Ownrshp* 1900
Sales 115.4MM[E] *EMP* 1,780
SIC 8211 Public elementary & secondary schools
Prin: Rich Raphael
Ex Dir: Carolyn Bischof
Prgrm Mgr: April Santos
MIS Dir: Al Merkrebs
IT Man: Javier Descalzo
IT Man: Gwen Soares
Schl Brd P: Bill Carle
Schl Brd P: Donna Jeye
Psych: Nancy Allsup
Psych: Yvonne Martinez
Psych: Robin Wilkins

SANTA ROSA CITY SCHOOLS
See SANTA ROSA CITY SCHOOL DIST

D-U-N-S 14-556-0442
SANTA ROSA INDIAN COMMUNITY OF SANTA ROSA RANCHERIA
16835 Alkali Dr, Lemoore, CA 93245-9463
Tel (559) 924-1278 *Founded/Ownrshp* 1984
Sales NA *EMP* 1,663
SIC 9131 Indian reservation;
Pr: Clarence Atwell Jr
**Ch:* Ruben Barrios
**Treas:* Rosa Hernandez
**Treas:* Dena Vaga
IT Man: Christian Douandphouxay

SANTA ROSA JUNIOR COLLEGE
See SONOMA COUNTY JUNIOR COLLEGE DISTRICT

D-U-N-S 06-885-6053
SANTA ROSA MEMORIAL HOSPITAL INC
SJHS SONOMA COUNTY
(*Suby of* ST JOSEPH HEALTH SYSTEM) ★
1165 Montgomery Dr, Santa Rosa, CA 95405-4897
Tel (707) 546-3210 *Founded/Ownrshp* 1948
Sales 489.4MM *EMP* 2,100
Accts Ernst & Young Us Llp San Dieg
SIC 8062 General medical & surgical hospitals
CEO: Todd Salnas
**CFO:* Mich Riccioni
**VP:* Gary Greensweig
Dir Rx: Larry Munkelt
**Chf Nrs Of:* Kathrine Hardin
CIO: Stephanie Olivier
Opers Mgr: Joanne Bell
Doctor: C Burke

SANTA SWEETS
See AG-MART PRODUCE INC

D-U-N-S 02-091-2358
SANTAFE HEALTHCARE INC
4300 Nw 89th Blvd, Gainesville, FL 32606-5688
Tel (352) 372-8400 *Founded/Ownrshp* 1982
Sales 5.5MM *EMP* 1,900[E]
Accts Pricewaterhousecoopers Llp Ja
SIC 8741 Hospital management
Pr: Robert C Hudson
**CFO:* Randy Stuart
**Exec:* Robert McNichols
Dir Surg: Terry Bohlke

D-U-N-S 14-141-3166
■ **SANTANDER BANCORP**
(*Suby of* BANCO SANTANDER SA)
B7 Calle Tabonuco Fl 18, Guaynabo, PR 00968-3342
Tel (787) 777-4100 *Founded/Ownrshp* 1999
Sales NA *EMP* 1,764
SIC 6021 6411 6211 National commercial banks; Insurance agents, brokers & service; Security brokers & dealers
Pr: Juan S Moreno
V Ch: Jos R Gonz Lez
V Ch: Jost R Gonz Lez
Pr: Roman Blanco
Treas: Manuel Aya
Ofcr: Mar A Calero
Ofcr: Marivelisse Diaz
Ofcr: Juan D Vila
Ex VP: Jose Alvarez
Ex VP: Roberto Jara
Ex VP: Bartolom V Lez
Ex VP: Justo Mu Oz
Ex VP: Roberto E C Rdova
Ex VP: Tom S E Torres
Sr VP: Maria L Garc A
Sr VP: Rafael S Bonilla
Sr VP: M Nica Loma
Sr VP: Jos Santoni
Sr VP: Frank Serra
Sr VP: Juan M Diaz Soutaire
Sr VP: Laura V Zquez
Board of Directors: Stephen A Ferriss, Jos R Gonzlez, Roberto H Valentn, Jess M Zabalza

D-U-N-S 08-162-6947
■ **SANTANDER BANK NA**
(*Suby of* SANTANDER HOLDINGS USA INC) ★
28 State St Fl 5, Boston, MA 02109-1775
Tel (617) 757-3410 *Founded/Ownrshp* 1988
Sales NA *EMP* 7,100
SIC 6035 Federal savings banks
CEO: Scott Powell
**Pr:* T Timothy Ryan
CFO: James D Hogan
Sr Cor Off: Mark McCollom
**Chf Mktg O:* Robert W Galea
Ofcr: Barbara Burkes
Ofcr: Randy Fromm
Ofcr: William Habalow
Ofcr: Sandie Luber
Ofcr: Lisa Miller
Ofcr: Samuel Salant
Assoc VP: Gabrielle K Zerb
Ex VP: Alison Rourke
Ex VP: John Watson
Sr VP: Alison Berman
Sr VP: Paul Black
Sr VP: Marc Feigenbaum
Sr VP: William Latham
Sr VP: Lisa Maronski
Sr VP: Kurt Swartz
VP: Jeff Bonner

D-U-N-S 07-908-8900
■ **SANTANDER CONSUMER USA HOLDINGS INC**
(*Suby of* SANTANDER HOLDINGS USA INC) ★
1601 Elm St Ste 800, Dallas, TX 75201-7260
Tel (214) 634-1110 *Founded/Ownrshp* 1995
Sales NA *EMP* 5,100[E]
Tkr Sym SC *Exch* NYS
SIC 6141 Personal credit institutions
Pr: Jason A Kulas
**Ch Bd:* William Rainer
COO: Richard Morrin
CFO: Ismail Dawood
**V Ch Bd:* Stephen A Ferriss
Ofcr: Lisa Vanroekel
Genl Couns: Christopher Pfirrman

D-U-N-S 94-915-2987
■ **SANTANDER CONSUMER USA INC FOUNDATION**
DRIVE FINANCIAL SERVICES
(*Suby of* SANTANDER CONSUMER USA HOLDINGS INC) ★
8585 N Stemmons Fwy, Dallas, TX 75247-3822
Tel (214) 634-1110 *Founded/Ownrshp* 2014
Sales NA *EMP* 3,300[E]
SIC 6141

D-U-N-S 18-815-1336 IMP
■ **SANTANDER HOLDINGS USA INC**
(*Suby of* BANCO SANTANDER SA)
75 State St, Boston, MA 02109-1827
Tel (617) 346-7200 *Founded/Ownrshp* 2009
Sales NA *EMP* 14,000
Accts Deloitte & Touche Llp Boston
SIC 6021 6035 National commercial banks; Savings institutions, federally chartered
Pr: Scott Powell
Ch Bd: James Lynch
CFO: Gerald Plush
Ofcr: Wayne Benner
Ofcr: Juan D Vila
Ex VP: Thomas D Cestare
Ex VP: Jesse O Villarreal
VP: George Demoulias
VP: Cathleen Ingersoll
VP: Michael Jones
VP: Daniel M Sossaman
Exec: Christopher K Pfirrman
Exec: Guillermo Sabater
Dir Risk M: John Corston

SANTEE COOPER
See SOUTH CAROLINA PUBLIC SERVICE AUTHORITY (INC)

D-U-N-S 00-792-0010
SANTEE ELECTRIC COOPERATIVE INC (SC)
424 Sumter Hwy, Kingstree, SC 29556-4980
Tel (843) 355-6187 *Founded/Ownrshp* 1939, 1986
Sales 134.6MM *EMP* 147
SIC 4911

D-U-N-S 07-053-1587
SANTEE SCHOOL DISTRICT
9625 Cuyamaca St, Santee, CA 92071-2674
Tel (619) 258-2300 *Founded/Ownrshp* 1995
Sales 53.8MM *EMP* 1,050
Accts Vavrinek Trine Day & Co Ll
SIC 8211 Public elementary school
Pr: Ken Fox
**VP:* Dustin Burns
MIS Dir: Brenard Yeo
Teacher Pr: Minnie Malin

D-U-N-S 18-330-3478
SANTEK ENVIRONMENTAL INC
650 25th St Nw Ste 100, Cleveland, TN 37311-1353
Tel (423) 476-9160 *Founded/Ownrshp* 1987
Sales 186.2MM[E] *EMP* 250
SIC 4953 Air, water & solid waste management
CEO: Kenneth Higgins
**Pr:* Edward Caylor
**CFO:* James P Gleeson IV
**CFO:* Greg Hamilton
**Ex VP:* Matt Dillard
Genl Mgr: Lisa Humphres

D-U-N-S 01-794-2145
SANTMYER OIL CO INC
3000 Old Airport Rd, Wooster, OH 44691-9520
Tel (330) 262-6501 *Founded/Ownrshp* 1983
Sales 116.9MM[E] *EMP* 95
SIC 5172 5983 4212 5531 Fuel oil; Gasoline; Fuel oil dealers; Petroleum haulage, local; Automotive parts
VP: Randy Ruggles
Genl Mgr: Zach Santmyer

SANTROL
See TECHNISAND INC

D-U-N-S 60-900-1243
SANTRONICS INC
3010 Lee Ave, Sanford, NC 27332-6210
Tel (919) 775-1223 *Founded/Ownrshp* 1987
Sales 87.9MM[E] *EMP* 980
SIC 3679 3674 Electronic loads & power supplies; Semiconductors & related devices
Pr: Edwin H Swartz
VP: Denise Bost

SANWA GREENHOUSES
See SANWA GROWERS INC

D-U-N-S 10-755-7654 IMP
SANWA GROWERS INC
SANWA GREENHOUSES
2801 E Hillsborough Ave, Tampa, FL 33610-4410
Tel (813) 642-5159 *Founded/Ownrshp* 1981
Sales 88.4MM[E] *EMP* 200
SIC 5147 5148 Meats, fresh; Fresh fruits & vegetables
Pr: Tony Leung
**Sec:* Connie Leung
Genl Mgr: Fizal Mukaddam
Store Mgr: Stacy Frankson
Store Mgr: Kenneth Wright
IT Man: James Letchworth
IT Man: Charles Williams
Opers Mgr: Eugenio Alvarado
Opers Mgr: Katie Chu
Opers Mgr: Susie Sum

D-U-N-S 96-117-2848 IMP/EXP
SANWA USA INC
(*Suby of* SANWA HOLDINGS CORPORATION)
4020 Mcewen Rd Ste 118, Dallas, TX 75244-5014
Tel (972) 503-3031 *Founded/Ownrshp* 1996
Sales 639.3MM[E] *EMP* 4,544[E]
SIC 3442 2431 3699 3537 Garage doors, overhead: metal; Rolling doors for industrial buildings or warehouses, metal; Metal doors; Doors, wood; Door opening & closing devices, electrical; Industrial trucks & tractors
Pr: Ryoichi Yamaji
**Prin:* Brian Bolton

D-U-N-S 18-361-6317
SAP AMERICA INC
(*Suby of* SAP SE)
3999 West Chester Pike, Newtown Square, PA 19073-2305
Tel (610) 661-1000 *Founded/Ownrshp* 1988
Sales 1.0MMM *EMP* 13,888
SIC 7371 Computer software development
CEO: William McDermott
Pt: Aaron Ang
Pt: Amjad Zarrad
Pr: Robert Courteau
**Pr:* Robert Enslin
Pr: Robert C Resanti
Pr: Sam Wee
**COO:* Rasmiah Alawwad
**COO:* Steven Birdsall
**COO:* Steven Sussman
COO: Thomas Wienke
**COO:* Steve Winter
CFO: Joel Bernstein
**CFO:* Peter David
**CFO:* Mark R White
CFO: Thomas Wrede
**Co-CEO:* Jim Hagemann Snabe
Chf Mktg O: Kay Kienast
Ofcr: Andreas Hube
**Ex VP:* Pat Bakey
**Sr VP:* Richard A Knowles

D-U-N-S 83-151-9652 IMP
SAPA EXTRUDER INC
(*Suby of* SAPA EXTRUSIONS INC) ★
Airport Offc Park, Moon Township, PA 15108
Tel (412) 299-7600 *Founded/Ownrshp* 2009
Sales 212.1MM[E] *EMP* 900[E]
SIC 3354 Aluminum extruded products
CEO: Patrick Lawlor
**CFO:* Todd Presnick
**Treas:* Robert Kavanaugh
**VP:* Geir Kvernmo
**VP:* Robert Rubicky

D-U-N-S 93-954-1129 IMP
SAPA EXTRUSIONS INC
(*Suby of* SAPA PROFILER AB)
6250 N River Rd Ste 5000, Rosemont, IL 60018-4214
Tel (877) 710-7272 *Founded/Ownrshp* 2013
Sales 1.1MMM[E] *EMP* 3,000
SIC 3354 Aluminum extruded products
CEO: Timothy R J Stubbs
VP: Geir Kvernmo
VP: Lonnie Nicol
**Prin:* Belcastro Jacquelyne
**Prin:* Kavanaugh Robert
**Prin:* Robert Rubicky
Mng Dir: Jacques Podszun
Mktg Mgr: Alex Cole
Snr Mgr: Robert McCaffrey

D-U-N-S 00-510-6810 IMP/EXP
SAPA EXTRUSIONS NORTH AMERICA LLC
(*Suby of* SAPA AS)
999 Corporate Blvd # 100, Linthicum Heights, MD 21090-2272
Tel (410) 487-4500 *Founded/Ownrshp* 2000
Sales 257.8MM[E] *EMP* 2,000
SIC 3354

D-U-N-S 83-151-9801 IMP
SAPA NORTH AMERICA INC
(*Suby of* SAPA EXTRUSIONS INC) ★
400 Rouser Rd Ste 300, Moon Township, PA 15108-2749
Tel (877) 922-7272 *Founded/Ownrshp* 2000
Sales 133.9MM[E] *EMP* 400[E]
SIC 3354 Aluminum extruded products
CEO: Patrick Lawlor
**CFO:* Todd Presnick
**VP:* Geir Kvernmo

D-U-N-S 00-941-6462 IMP
SAPA PROFILES INC (OR)
7933 Ne 21st Ave, Portland, OR 97211-1909
Tel (503) 285-0404 *Founded/Ownrshp* 1964
Sales 228.8MM[E] *EMP* 820
SIC 3354 3471 Aluminum extruded products; Anodizing (plating) of metals or formed products
Pr: John Noordwijk
**Pr:* Patrick Lawlor
**Sec:* Albert Christensen
**Ex VP:* Lennart Evrell
**Ex VP:* Hilde Myrberg
**Ex VP:* Paul Thomas
**Sr VP:* Baard Haugen
**VP:* Paul Hogg
**VP:* Rudi Huber
**VP:* Bob Huckvale
**VP:* Derek Phillips
**VP:* Paul Wharton
**VP:* Don Willis
**VP:* Magnus Wittbom

D-U-N-S 79-016-6219
SAPIENT CORP
(*Suby of* PUBLICIS GROUPE S A)
131 Dartmouth St Ste 301, Boston, MA 02116-5385
Tel (617) 621-0200 *Founded/Ownrshp* 2015
Sales 1.3MMM *EMP* 11,945
SIC 7373 7374 7371 8742 Computer integrated systems design; Systems software development services; Data processing & preparation; Computer graphics service; Custom computer programming services; Computer software development & applications; Management consulting services
Pr: Alan J Herrick
**CFO:* Joseph S Tibbetts Jr
Ex VP: Paul Digiammarino
Sr VP: Christopher R Davey
Sr VP: Steven J Hoffman
Sr VP: William Kanarick
**Sr VP:* Joseph A Lasala Jr
**Sr VP:* Laurie W Maclaren
Sr VP: Christian Oversohl
Sr VP: Harry Register
Sr VP: Nigel Vaz
VP: Alana Barnett
VP: Mark Berler
VP: Robert F Binder
VP: Teresa Bozzelli
VP: Brian Carter
VP: Donald Chestnut
VP: Patricia K Cohen
VP: Mike Collins
VP: Scott Criddle
VP: David Donovan
Board of Directors: James M Benson, Eva M Sage-Gavin, Silvia Lagnado, J Stuart Moore, Robert L Rosen, Ashok Shah, Curtis R Welling

D-U-N-S 19-771-2573 IMP
SAPP BROS INC
9915 S 148th St, Omaha, NE 68138-3876
Tel (402) 895-7038 *Founded/Ownrshp* 1971
Sales 1.1MMM *EMP* 1,115
Accts Kpmg Llp Omaha Ne
SIC 5812 Pizza restaurants
CEO: William Sapp
**CFO:* Allen J Marsh
**VP:* Keith Crandall
**VP:* Donald Quinn
Genl Mgr: Dan Adams
Genl Mgr: Roy Kranz
Genl Mgr: Mike Porter
Genl Mgr: Jared Reorda
CIO: Tyler Marsh
Dir IT: John Miller
Mktg Dir: Mark Stevenson

D-U-N-S 96-826-8354 IMP
SAPP BROS TRAVEL CENTERS INC
(*Suby of* SAPP BROS INC) ★
9915 S 148th St, Omaha, NE 68138-3876
Tel (402) 895-2202 *Founded/Ownrshp* 2010
Sales 1.0MMM *EMP* 1,000
SIC 5541 Gasoline service stations
CEO: William Sapp
**CFO:* Allen Marsh
Chf Mktg O: Mark Stevenson
Store Mgr: Jennifer Adams
Dir IT: Daniel Adams
Dir IT: John Miller

SAPPHIRE COAL COMPANY
See UNITED COAL CO LLC

D-U-N-S 07-834-7628
■ SAPPHIRE POWER FINANCE LLC
(*Suby of* SAPPHIRE POWER LLC) ★
2901 Via Fortuna Ste 600, Austin, TX 78746-7710
Tel (512) 314-8600 *Founded/Ownrshp* 2011
Sales 90.0MM *EMP* 100
SIC 4911 Electric services
CEO: Chuck Cook
**Genl Couns:* Janet Janieson

D-U-N-S 03-528-1874
■ SAPPHIRE POWER LLC
(*Suby of* TALEN ENERGY SUPPLY LLC) ★
2901 Via Fortuna Ste 600, Austin, TX 78746-7710
Tel (512) 314-8600 *Founded/Ownrshp* 2015
Sales 90.0MM[E] *EMP* 188[E]
SIC 4911 Generation, electric power

SAPPI FINE PAPER NORTH AMERICA
See S D WARREN CO

D-U-N-S 05-399-8071 EXP
SAPUTO CHEESE USA INC
(*Suby of* SAPUTO INC)
800 E Paige Ave, Tulare, CA 93274-6863
Tel (559) 687-8411 *Founded/Ownrshp* 2007
Sales 118.9MM[E] *EMP* 300
SIC 2022 Cheese, natural & processed; Whey, raw or liquid
Pr: Terry Brockman
CTO: Lee Blakly
Natl Sales: Phil Palermo

D-U-N-S 79-642-6286 IMP/EXP
SAPUTO CHEESE USA INC
(*Suby of* SAPUTO INC)
1 Overlook Pt Ste 300, Lincolnshire, IL 60069-4327
Tel (847) 267-1100 *Founded/Ownrshp* 1997
Sales 8.0MMM[E] *EMP* 4,580
SIC 2022 Cheese spreads, dips, pastes & other cheese products
Pr: Lino A Saputo Jr
VP: Terry Brockman
VP: Ernie Carreiro
VP: Jeff Cockrell
**VP:* Emanuele Saputo
Plnt Mgr: Eric Rickman
Sls&Mrk Ex: Lavonne Dietrich
Manager: Rebecca Low
Snr Mgr: Corey Brower

D-U-N-S 18-508-8770 IMP
SAPUTO DAIRY FOODS USA LLC
SULPHUR SPRINGS CULTURED SPC
(*Suby of* SAPUTO CHEESE USA INC) ★
2711 N Haskell Ave Ste 3700, Dallas, TX 75204
Tel (214) 863-2300 *Founded/Ownrshp* 2013
Sales 8.0MMM *EMP* 2,500
SIC 2023 2015 2026 Cream substitutes; Egg substitutes made from eggs; Cream, sour; Milk, reconstituted; Whipped topping, except frozen or dry mix; Cottage cheese
Pr: Kevin Yost
**Treas:* Timothy A Smith
VP: Nick Adame
**VP:* Rachel A Gonzalez
VP: David Rothstein
MIS Dir: Ivan Rojas
IT Man: Kaye Bushdiecker
VP Opers: Shaun Young
Opers Mgr: Ken Miller
Natl Sales: Jay Price

SARA LEE FOOD & BEVERAGE
See HILLSHIRE BRANDS CO

D-U-N-S 07-142-9054
SARAH BUSH LINCOLN HEALTH CENTER
1000 Health Center Dr, Mattoon, IL 61938-9261
Tel (217) 258-2525 *Founded/Ownrshp* 1970
Sales 223.8MM *EMP* 1,543
SIC 8011 8062 Offices & clinics of medical doctors; Hospital, affiliated with AMA residency
Pr: Timothy A Ols
Ofcr: Cathy Alexander
Ex VP: Maggie Ratliff
VP: Babatunde Alao
VP: Jerry Esker
VP: James Hildebrandt
**VP:* Dennis Pouard
VP: Maggie Ratliss
Dir Inf Cn: Ramona Tomshack
CTO: Rich Fanelli
Cmptr Lab: Dave Sowers

SARAHCARE HOME HEALTH AGENCY
See ARSENS HOME CARE INC

D-U-N-S 07-979-8954
SARALAND CITY SCHOOLS
943 Highway 43 S, Saraland, AL 36571-3608
Tel (251) 375-5420 *Founded/Ownrshp* 2015
Sales 2.6MM[E] *EMP* 2,853[E]
SIC 8211 Public elementary & secondary schools
Sr VP: Eric Vollmer
Teacher Pr: Stacy Skinner

D-U-N-S 07-920-8849
SARASOTA COUNTY PUBLIC HOSPITAL DISTRICT
SARASOTA MEMORIAL HOSPITAL
1700 S Tamiami Trl, Sarasota, FL 34239-3509
Tel (941) 917-9000 *Founded/Ownrshp* 1925, 1949
Sales 590.8MM *EMP* 4,200
SIC 8062 7372 General medical & surgical hospitals; Application computer software
Pr: David Verinder
Chf Path: J Robert Spencer
Chf OB: Michael Swor
**Ch Bd:* Gregory Carter
V Ch: Thomas Kelly
V Ch: Richard C Merritt
**COO:* Lorrie Liang
**CFO:* William Woeltjen
**Treas:* Joseph J Devirgilio Jr
Bd of Dir: Donna Desisto
Trst: Katherine Keeley
Ofcr: Lisa Totten
VP: Denis Baker
Dir Lab: Charlene Harris
Dir Rad: Debbie Bohanon
Dir Env Sv: Jim Hesemann

D-U-N-S 07-979-9018
SARASOTA COUNTY SCHOOLS
1960 Landings Blvd, Sarasota, FL 34231-3300
Tel (941) 927-9000 *Founded/Ownrshp* 1950
Sales 55.5MM[E] *EMP* 4,097
SIC 8211 Public elementary & secondary schools
V Ch: Shirley Brown
MIS Dir: Joe Binswanger
MIS Dir: Wayne Johnson
Pr Dir: Gary Leatherman
HC Dir: Sherri Reynolds

D-U-N-S 60-991-6721
■ SARASOTA DOCTORS HOSPITAL INC
ABLE CARE HOME HEALTH
(*Suby of* HOSPITAL COPORATION OF AMERICA) ★
5731 Bee Ridge Rd, Sarasota, FL 34233-5056
Tel (941) 342-1100 *Founded/Ownrshp* 1967
Sales 113.3MM *EMP* 700
SIC 8062 General medical & surgical hospitals
CEO: Robert Meade
Chf Path: Kevin M McCormack
**Pr:* Samuel N Hazen
**CFO:* Robert Billings
**CFO:* Chuck Schwaner
**Treas:* David G Anderson
VP: Jean Opsut
**VP:* Donald W Stinnett
Dir Rx: Jennifer Rawley
IT Man: Pam Carroll
IT Man: Dave Young

D-U-N-S 08-194-2245
SARASOTA FAMILY YOUNG MENS CHRISTIAN ASSOCIATION INC
YMCA
1 S School Ave Ste 301, Sarasota, FL 34237-6052
Tel (941) 951-2916 *Founded/Ownrshp* 1945
Sales 41.2MM *EMP* 1,150
Accts Kerkering Barberio & Co Saras
SIC 8641 8351 8322 7997 7991 Youth organizations; Child day care services; Individual & family services; Membership sports & recreation clubs; Physical fitness facilities
Ch: Ed Landis
**CEO:* Carl Weinreich
**CFO:* Steven Bourne
CFO: Rtheresa White
**Treas:* Rick McDaniel

SARASOTA MEMORIAL HOSPITAL
See SARASOTA COUNTY PUBLIC HOSPITAL DISTRICT

D-U-N-S 78-786-6367
SARATOGA CARE INC
SARATOGA HOSPITAL AND NURSING
211 Church St Ste 1, Saratoga Springs, NY 12866-1003
Tel (518) 587-3222 *Founded/Ownrshp* 1985
Sales 1.6MM *EMP* 1,200
SIC 8062 8741 General medical & surgical hospitals; Hospital management
Dir Recs: Loralei Barrett
CFO: Gary Foster
Treas: Michael Iacolucci
VP: Mary Jo Laposta
VP: Kevin P Ronayne
Dir Soc: Rachel Wheatley
Dir Rx: Mary A Davis
Ex Dir: Amy V Raimo
Nurse Mgr: Amy Hulse
CTO: Scott White
Site Mgr: Julie Sipperly

D-U-N-S 06-052-3602
SARATOGA HOSPITAL
211 Church St, Saratoga Springs, NY 12866-1090
Tel (518) 587-3222 *Founded/Ownrshp* 1985
Sales 259.9MM *EMP* 1,500
SIC 8062 8051 General medical & surgical hospitals; Skilled nursing care facilities
CEO: Angelo G Calbone
**Ch:* Janice M White
**Treas:* Michael H Iacolucci
Treas: Julie Sipperly
Trst: Theresa Skaine
Dir Lab: Richard Vandell
Ex Dir: Amy Raimo
Nurse Mgr: Carol Howard
Sfty Dirs: John Dinovo
Nutrtnst: Kathy Mennillo
Doctor: Sanjay Chaudhry

SARATOGA HOSPITAL AND NURSING
See SARATOGA CARE INC

D-U-N-S 16-855-5683 IMP
SARATOGA LIGHTING HOLDINGS LLC
535 Madison Ave Fl 4, New York, NY 10022-4291
Tel (212) 906-7800 *Founded/Ownrshp* 2003
Sales 218.1MM[E] *EMP* 1,483
SIC 3641 3645 3646 3648 Electric lamps & parts for generalized applications; Residential lighting fixtures; Commercial indusl & institutional electric lighting fixtures; Lighting equipment

SARATOGA SPRINGS CITY SCHL DST
See SARATOGA SPRINGS CITY SCHOOL DISTRICT

D-U-N-S 09-835-5597
SARATOGA SPRINGS CITY SCHOOL DISTRICT
SARATOGA SPRINGS CITY SCHL DST
3 Blue Streak Blvd, Saratoga Springs, NY 12866-5967
Tel (518) 583-4708 *Founded/Ownrshp* 1900
Sales 118.3MM *EMP* 1,023
Accts Marvin And Company Pc Latham
SIC 8211 Public elementary school; Public junior high school; Public senior high school
Prin: Stuart F Byrne
Prin: Daniel J O'Rourke
Prin: Deborah Winters
Dir Sec: Mark Sullivan

D-U-N-S 07-498-2869
SARES REGIS GROUP
18802 Bardeen Ave, Irvine, CA 92612-1521
Tel (949) 756-5959 *Founded/Ownrshp* 1993
Sales 137.8MM[E] *EMP* 650
SIC 6552 Land subdividers & developers, commercial; Land subdividers & developers, residential
Prin: Geoffrey L Stack
Pr: Greg Albert
Pr: John Gregory
Pr: Christopher L Payne
Pr: Sandy Pedersen
Ofcr: Michael H Heiken
Sr VP: Kenneth M Coatsworth
Sr VP: Gail Duke
Sr VP: Kenneth Gladstein
Sr VP: Patrick Russell
VP: Joseph Blair
VP: Ron Dyer
VP: Steven Fedde
VP: Jeff Holzman
VP: Mark Khatoonian
VP: Andrea Le Claire
VP: Andrea Leclaire
VP: Larry Lukanish
VP: Lynda Mellor
VP: Susan Whitney
Dir Risk M: Pene Mariner

D-U-N-S 00-175-0090
SARGENT & LUNDY LLC (TX)
55 E Monroe St Ste 2700, Chicago, IL 60603-5780
Tel (312) 269-2000 *Founded/Ownrshp* 1891
Sales 721.0MM[E] *EMP* 2,600
SIC 8711 Consulting engineer
CEO: Thomas Whit
COO: Kenneth Snell
Ex VP: Gregory Anderson
Ex VP: Larry Jacques
Ex VP: Thomas White
Ex VP: William Zaretsky
Sr VP: Bill Depriest
Sr VP: Thomas R Eisenbart
Sr VP: Ira Owens Jr
Sr VP: Warren Vahle
VP: Todd Baumbach
VP: Tom Behringer
VP: Farid Berry
VP: Delfo Bianchini
VP: David Cohn
VP: Jack Daly
VP: Kurt Dietzen
VP: Tom Eisenb
VP: Raj Gaikwad
VP: Robert Herbster
VP: Michael Knaszak

D-U-N-S 07-961-6433
■ SARGENT AEROSPACE & DEFENSE LLC
SARGENT CONTROLS & AEROSPACE
(*Suby of* R B C) ★
5675 W Burlingame Rd, Tucson, AZ 85743-9453
Tel (520) 744-1000 *Founded/Ownrshp* 2013, 2015
Sales 198.5MM[E] *EMP* 800
SIC 3728 3724 3568 3492 Aircraft assemblies, subassemblies & parts; Aircraft engines & engine parts; Power transmission equipment; Valves, hydraulic, aircraft; Control valves, fluid power: hydraulic & pneumatic
Pr: Jeffrey Post
Pr: Jeff Kijak
**VP:* Garry Spangenberg
QA Dir: Ron Gryniewicz
QA Dir: Oscar Ruiz
Dir IT: Dewayne Pitts
IT Man: Jorge Herrera
Software D: Nick Tridico
Ql Cn Mgr: Elizabeth Harris
**S&M/VP:* Vijay Sundharam
Sls Mgr: Paul Gold

SARGENT CONTROLS & AEROSPACE
See SARGENT AEROSPACE & DEFENSE LLC

D-U-N-S 36-171-4657 IMP
SARGENT CORP
H. E. SARGENT
(*Suby of* SC HOLDINGS INC) ★
378 Bennoch Rd, Stillwater, ME 04489-5105
Tel (207) 827-4435 *Founded/Ownrshp* 2006
Sales 202.7MM[E] *EMP* 400
SIC 1629 Land preparation construction
Pr: Herbert R Sargent
**VP:* Timothy M Folster
**VP:* George Thomas
Mtls Mgr: Tim Richards

D-U-N-S 00-893-8961
SARGENT ELECTRIC CO (PA)
2767 Liberty Ave, Pittsburgh, PA 15222-4703
Tel (412) 338-8480 *Founded/Ownrshp* 1907
Sales 98.6MM *EMP* 400
Accts Lally & Co Llc Pittsburgh P
SIC 1731 General electrical contractor
CEO: Stephan H Dake
**COO:* Gary W Groom
**CFO:* Elizabeth Lawrence
**VP:* Charles J Peckham
Dir IT: Bryan Dally

D-U-N-S 83-556-7322 IMP
SARGENT GROUP INC
TODD & SARGENT
2905 Se 5th St, Ames, IA 50010-7716
Tel (515) 232-0442 *Founded/Ownrshp* 1961
Sales 137.1MM *EMP* 250
SIC 1541 1796 Warehouse construction; Industrial buildings, new construction; Food products manufacturing or packing plant construction; Millwright
Ch Bd: Lee M Sargent
Pr: William Bokhoven
Sec: Jerry Murphy
Ex VP: Philip B Sargent
Sr VP: Phil Sargent
VP: Jon Sargent
VP: Clint Steele
Board of Directors: Don Newbrough

D-U-N-S 16-198-6740 IMP/EXP
SARGENT MANUFACTURING CO
ASSA ABLOY USA
(*Suby of* ASSA ABLOY USA) ★
100 Sargent Dr, New Haven, CT 06511-5943
Tel (203) 562-2151 *Founded/Ownrshp* 1985
Sales 155.4MM[E] *EMP* 900[E]
SIC 3429 Locks or lock sets; Builders' hardware
CEO: Thanasis Molokotos
**Treas:* David M Ambrosini
Exec: Jeff Mereschuk
Genl Mgr: Bill Grambo
Dir IT: Dominic Viscuso
Web Dev: Woody Sharp
Plnt Mgr: Ron Rubano
Sls&Mrk Ex: Julie Panagoulias

D-U-N-S 14-361-7389
■ SARGENT TRUCKING INC
SARGENT'S TRUCKING
(*Suby of* ROADRUNNER TRANSPORTATION SYSTEMS INC) ★
64 Main St, Mars Hill, ME 04758-3402
Tel (207) 429-8106 *Founded/Ownrshp* 1983
Sales 115.0MM *EMP* 110
SIC 4213 Contract haulers
Pr: Joshua Tweedie

D-U-N-S 02-321-8233 IMP/EXP
SARGENTO FOODS INC
1 Persnickety Pl, Plymouth, WI 53073-3544
Tel (920) 893-8484 *Founded/Ownrshp* 1953
Sales 1.7MMM *EMP* 1,700
SIC 2022 Natural cheese; Processed cheese
CEO: Louie Gentine
Pr: Michael Gordy
CFO: George H Hoff
Ch: Louis P Gentine
Ex VP: Kristine M Jankowski
Ex VP: Mike McElvoy
Sr VP: Karri J Neils
VP: Jeremy Behler
VP: Mike McEvoy
VP: Janet Raddatz
VP: Marcy Stanczyk
VP: Gary Vissers
Dir Soc: Barbara Gannon
Creative D: Heidi Haack

SARGENT'S TRUCKING
See SARGENT TRUCKING INC

D-U-N-S 82-932-0808
SARNOVA INC
5000 Tuttle Crossing Blvd, Dublin, OH 43016-1534
Tel (614) 760-5000 *Founded/Ownrshp* 2008
Sales 153.7MM[E] *EMP* 495
SIC 5999 5047 Medical apparatus & supplies; Medical equipment & supplies
CEO: Dan Connors
**CFO:* Mark Dougherty
Prgrm Mgr: Robert Seidel
VP Mktg: Fred Hunter
Mktg Dir: Lizbeth Scott
Sales Asso: Paula White
Genl Couns: Darrell Hughes

D-U-N-S 00-610-4525 IMP/EXP
SARTORI CO
SARTORI FOODS
107 N Pleasant View Rd, Plymouth, WI 53073-4948
Tel (920) 893-6061 *Founded/Ownrshp* 1939
Sales 94.6MM[E] *EMP* 252
Accts Schenck Sc Sheboygan Wi
SIC 2022 Natural cheese
Ch Bd: James C Sartori
Pr: Jeffrey R Schwager
CFO: Mark Schwechel
Chf Mktg O: Chad T Vincent
VP: Rob Donnelly
VP: Phillip W Kramer
VP: Bill Michel
VP: Pat Mugan
VP: Patrick H Mugan
VP: Bradley J Nicholson
VP: Rana F Shehadeh PHD

SARTORI FOODS
See SARTORI CO

D-U-N-S 04-953-2807 IMP
SARTORIUS STEDIM FILTERS INC
(*Suby of* SARTORIUS STEDIM BIOTECH GMBH)
Intersection 376 Rr 128, Yauco, PR 00698
Tel (787) 856-5020 *Founded/Ownrshp* 2004
Sales 91.2MM *EMP* 240
Accts Llm&D Psc San Juan Puerto R
SIC 3569 Filters
Pr: Mary Lavin
**Treas:* Jorge L Salamo
**VP:* Marcos Lopez

D-U-N-S 79-653-2971 IMP
SARTORIUS STEDIM NORTH AMERICA INC
(*Suby of* SARTORIUS STEDIM BIOTECH)
5 Orville Dr Ste 200, Bohemia, NY 11716-2535
Tel (631) 254-4249 *Founded/Ownrshp* 2007
Sales 163.7MM[E] *EMP* 130
SIC 5085 Filters, industrial
CEO: Joachim Kreuzburg
**Pr:* Mary Lavin
**Treas:* Rainer Lehnann
**VP:* Alan Burns
**VP:* Maik Jornitz

D-U-N-S 04-004-6724
SAS INSTITUTE INC
100 Sas Campus Dr, Cary, NC 27513-8617
Tel (919) 677-8000 *Founded/Ownrshp* 1994
Sales 2.6MMM[E] *EMP* 13,147
Accts Bdo Usa Llp Raleigh Nc
SIC 8243 7372 Software training, computer; Application computer software; Business oriented computer software; Educational computer software
Ch Bd: James H Goodnight
Pr: Marianna Suciu
CFO: Don Parker
CFO: Ralph Wolfe
Chf Mktg O: James C Davis

Ex VP: Keith Collins
Ex VP: Mikael Haegstrom
Ex VP: Mikael Hagstr M
Ex VP: John P Sall
Ex VP: Armistead Sapp
Sr VP: Keith V Collins
Sr VP: Allan Russell
VP: John G Boswell
VP: Stuart Bowden
VP: Kathy Council
VP: Charles H Dunham
VP: Suzanne Gordon
VP: Barrett R Joyner
VP: Herbert Kirk
VP: Paul Lovell
VP: Ron Reed

SAS SUPPLY
See TACONIC BIOSCIENCES INC

D-U-N-S 14-602-7250
SASCO
2750 Moore Ave, Fullerton, CA 92833-2563
Tel (714) 870-0217 *Founded/Ownrshp* 1997
Sales 884.1MM[E] *EMP* 4,000
SIC 1731 General electrical contractor
Pr: Larry Smead
Treas: Kay Udry
VP: Tom Diomartich
VP: Billy Flanagan
Exec: Bennie Barker
CIO: Matt Saikkonen
Dir IT: David Buford
Netwrk Mgr: Rudy Ruiz
Sfty Dirs: Anthony Pennington
Mktg Dir: Mike Ochoa
Sls Dir: David Weir

D-U-N-S 07-722-8849
SASCO ELECTRIC INC
(*Suby of* SASCO) ★
2750 Moore Ave, Fullerton, CA 92833-2563
Tel (714) 870-0217 *Founded/Ownrshp* 1968
Sales 182.2MM[E] *EMP* 1,500
SIC 7373 1731 Computer integrated systems design; General electrical contractor
Ch Bd: L H Smead
VP: Jason Brooks
VP: Mike Korthals

D-U-N-S 62-370-3774
SASKER REPAIR
27535 460th Ave, Chancellor, SD 57015-5717
Tel (605) 647-5766 *Founded/Ownrshp* 1990
Sales 8.0MM[E] *EMP* 1,989
SIC 7699 Farm machinery repair; Tractor repair
Owner: Robert Sasker

D-U-N-S 07-878-0682
SASOL (USA) CORP
(*Suby of* SASOL LTD)
12120 Wickchester Ln, Houston, TX 77079-1211
Tel (281) 588-3000 *Founded/Ownrshp* 2013
Sales 356.8MM[E] *EMP* 573[E]
SIC 1382 Oil & gas exploration services
Pr: Mike Thomas

D-U-N-S 10-266-6872 IMP/EXP
SASOL CHEMICALS (USA) LLC
CERALOX DIVISION
(*Suby of* SASOL (USA) CORP) ★
12120 Wickchester Ln, Houston, TX 77079-1211
Tel (281) 588-3000 *Founded/Ownrshp* 1983
Sales 348.4MM[E] *EMP* 553[E]
SIC 2869 5169 Alcohols, industrial: denatured (non-beverage); Detergents & soaps, except specialty cleaning
CEO: David Constable
IT Man: Debbie Eng
IT Man: Dortha White
Sales Exec: Joseph Lopez

D-U-N-S 62-706-1948 IMP/EXP
SASOL WAX NORTH AMERICA CORP
3563 Inv Blvd Ste 2, Hayward, CA 94545
Tel (510) 783-9295 *Founded/Ownrshp* 1989
Sales 130.0MM[E] *EMP* 100
SIC 5172 5169

D-U-N-S 60-280-0872 IMP
SATAIR USA INC
(*Suby of* AINA HOLDINGS) ★
3993 Tradeport Blvd, Atlanta, GA 30354-3731
Tel (404) 675-6333 *Founded/Ownrshp* 1987
Sales 96.1MM[E] *EMP* 65
SIC 5088 Aircraft & parts
CEO: John Stear
CFO: Marko Enderlein
**CFO:* Michael Hojgaard
**VP:* Anette Hagelsten
**VP:* Morten Olsen
VP: Rick Tonney
Mng Dir: Rene Frandsen
**VP Mktg:* Steen Karsbo
VP Sls: Peter Lundberg

D-U-N-S 07-897-5807
SATCOM DIRECT INC
SD
1050 Satcom Ln, Melbourne, FL 32940-7010
Tel (321) 777-3000 *Founded/Ownrshp* 1999
Sales 107.9MM *EMP* 200
SIC 3663 Satellites, communications
CEO: James W Jensen
Pr: David Greenhill
Pr: Dale Holland
Treas: Paul A Newman
Ofcr: Whitney Coyle
VP: Renae Matteson
VP: Chris Moore
VP: Greg Romano
Prgrm Mgr: Tammy Moschetti
Genl Mgr: Stefan Tilliard
Snr Sftwr: Bill Brennan
Board of Directors: David Greenhill, James Jensen

SATELLITE DIALYSIS CENTERS
See SATELLITE HEALTHCARE INC

D-U-N-S 07-717-7947
SATELLITE HEALTHCARE INC
SATELLITE DIALYSIS CENTERS
300 Santana Row Ste 300, San Jose, CA 95128-2424
Tel (650) 404-3600 *Founded/Ownrshp* 1973
Sales 188.9MM *EMP* 570
Accts Kpmg Llp San Francisco Ca
SIC 8092 Kidney dialysis centers
Pr: Rick J Barnett
**Ch Bd:* Norman S Coplon
**COO:* Dave Carter
COO: Rosemary Fox
CFO: Mark Branson
**CFO:* Susan Del Bene
**Ofcr:* Brigitte Schiller
**Ex VP:* Marc Branson
Sr VP: Sergio O Fernandez
**VP:* Robert A Lunbeck Jr
VP: Pamela Molano
**VP:* Estrella Parker
VP: Miten Sampat
VP: Tobias Speckbacher
Board of Directors: Robert Fahlman

D-U-N-S 36-193-7378
SATELLITE SHELTERS INC
2530 Xenium Ln N Ste 150, Minneapolis, MN 55441-4591
Tel (763) 553-1900 *Founded/Ownrshp* 1972
Sales 96.9MM[E] *EMP* 110[E]
SIC 1542 7353 Commercial & office building contractors; Heavy construction equipment rental
CEO: Marty Mullaney
**Pr:* James M Mullaney
**Sec:* Thomas Vickman
VP: Chris Peterson
**Prin:* Al Hilde
Brnch Mgr: Chuck Walen
IT Man: Duane Jasco
Opers Mgr: Alan Rupp

SATICOY FRUIT EXCHANGE
See SATICOY LEMON ASSOCIATION

D-U-N-S 00-691-4170 IMP
SATICOY LEMON ASSOCIATION (CA)
SATICOY FRUIT EXCHANGE
103 N Peck Rd, Santa Paula, CA 93060-3099
Tel (805) 654-6500 *Founded/Ownrshp* 1933
Sales 155.7MM *EMP* 300
Accts Soren Mcadam Llp Redlands Ca
SIC 0723 Fruit crops market preparation services
Pr: Glenn A Miller
**CFO:* Jerry Pogorzelski

D-U-N-S 00-692-4583
SATILLA RURAL ELECTRIC MEMBERSHIP CORP (GA)
928 Ga Highway 32 E, Alma, GA 31510-3307
Tel (912) 632-7222 *Founded/Ownrshp* 1937
Sales 116.9MM *EMP* 147
Accts Nichols Cauley & Associates Ll
SIC 4911 Distribution, electric power
Pr: Romeo A Reyes
**Treas:* Kenneth Vickers

D-U-N-S 04-973-4833 IMP
SATISLOH NORTH AMERICA INC
(*Suby of* SATISLOH HOLDING AG)
N106w13131 Bradley Way # 200, Germantown, WI 53022-4442
Tel (262) 255-6001 *Founded/Ownrshp* 2005
Sales 121.5MM[E] *EMP* 159
SIC 5049 5072 Precision tools; Optical goods; Hardware
Pr: Peter Lothes
**Pr:* Lawrence Clarke
Pr: Chris Seifert
Genl Mgr: Subodh Modhe
Dir IT: Ann Compton
Web Prj Mg: Candy Lang
Sales Exec: Will Daniels
Sls Dir: Tomasz Michalak
Mktg Mgr: Amy Halloran
Sls Mgr: Steve Schneider
Snr Mgr: Bruno Fischer

D-U-N-S 12-978-5598
SATTERBERG FOUNDATION
1904 3rd Ave Ste 825, Seattle, WA 98101-1196
Tel (206) 441-3045 *Founded/Ownrshp* 1990
Sales 101.2MM[E] *EMP* 12
SIC 8641 Social associations
Pr: Mashanda Lazarus
**Treas:* Peter Helsell

D-U-N-S 61-843-0904
SATTERFIELD AND PONTIKES CONSTRUCTION INC
11000 Equity Dr Ste 100, Houston, TX 77041-8235
Tel (713) 996-1393 *Founded/Ownrshp* 1989
Sales 395.1MM[E] *EMP* 400
SIC 1542 1541 Commercial & office building contractors; Industrial buildings, new construction
Ch Bd: George A Pontikes Jr
CFO: Salinas Anjy
**CFO:* Angela Salinas
Ex VP: Lori Volan
**VP:* Charles Fote
VP: Jason Haralson
VP: Pete Lozada
**VP:* John S Marshall
VP: Frank Roetzel
VP: Kenneth Smith
Exec: Tom Langley
Dir Risk M: Janet Chamberlin

SATURN
See COVERT BUICK INC

SATURN
See FINDLAY AUTOMOTIVE INC

SAU 16
See SCHOOL ADMINISTRATIVE UNIT 16

SAU 42
See SCHOOL ADMINISTRATIVE UNIT 42

D-U-N-S 00-504-8111 IMP/EXP
SAUDER MANUFACTURING CO (OH)
WIELAND
(*Suby of* SAUDER WOODWORKING CO) ★
930 W Barre Rd, Archbold, OH 43502-9385
Tel (419) 445-7670 *Founded/Ownrshp* 1945
Sales 91.9MM[E] *EMP* 425
SIC 2531 Church furniture; Chairs, portable folding
Pr: Virgil L Miller
**Pr:* Phil Bontrager
VP: Luther Gaupsche
VP: Willaim Ogden
**VP:* William Ogden
VP: Blair Wieland
Genl Mgr: Beth Ehinger
Mtls Mgr: Kyle Batt
Prd Mgr: Troy McDaniel
S&M/VP: Kelvin Friesen
Mktg Dir: Rick Mueller

D-U-N-S 00-503-5167 IMP/EXP
SAUDER WOODWORKING CO
502 Middle St, Archbold, OH 43502-1500
Tel (419) 446-3828 *Founded/Ownrshp* 1940
Sales 500.0MM[E] *EMP* 2,600
SIC 2519 5021 Furniture, household: glass, fiberglass & plastic; Furniture
Pr: Kevin J Sauder
Pr: Dan Sauder
**Ch:* Maynard Sauder
Ex VP: Brent Gingerich
**Ex VP:* Arnold Moshier
VP: Gerritt Tinsman
**Prin:* Amy Robison
Dir IT: Jan Arvay
IT Man: Philip Rupp
Opers Mgr: Val Stites
Natl Sales: Todd Nafziger

D-U-N-S 06-259-4069
SAUER HOLDINGS INC (PA)
30 51st St, Pittsburgh, PA 15201-2708
Tel (412) 687-4100 *Founded/Ownrshp* 1999
Sales 122.1MM[E] *EMP* 736
SIC 1711 Mechanical contractor
Pr: William Steitz
**CFO:* Terence R Kiliany
**Ex VP:* Timothy Steitz
**VP:* Judy Campbell
VP: Eugene Moody
**VP:* Charles Steitz
IT Man: Dan Dulik
Sfty Mgr: John Harrington
VP Mktg: Brian Franco

SAUER-DANFOSS US COMPANY
See DANFOSS POWER SOLUTIONS (US) CO

D-U-N-S 08-006-0023
SAUGUS UNION SCHOOL DISTRICT
24930 Avenue Stanford, Santa Clarita, CA 91355-1272
Tel (661) 294-5300 *Founded/Ownrshp* 1908
Sales 118.6MM *EMP* 1,373[E]
Accts Brown Armstrong Accountancy Co
SIC 8211 Public elementary school
Dir Sec: Keith Karzin
Off Mgr: Jill McCarty
Pr Dir: Lee Morrell
Psych: Lauralinda Mendenhall
HC Dir: Diane D Elia

D-U-N-S 83-025-1112
▲ SAUL CENTERS INC
7501 Wisconsin Ave 1500e, Bethesda, MD 20814-6522
Tel (301) 986-6200 *Founded/Ownrshp* 1993
Sales 209.0MM *EMP* 61
Tkr Sym BFS *Exch* NYS
SIC 6798 Real estate investment trusts
Ch Bd: B Francis Saul II
**Pr:* J Page Lansdale
CFO: Scott V Schneider
**V Ch Bd:* Philip D Caraci
Ex VP: Christine N Kearns
Sr VP: John F Collich
Sr VP: Joel A Friedman
Sr VP: Christopher H Netter
Sr VP: Charles W Sherren Jr
VP: Steve Brand
VP Opers: Lynn Phillips
Board of Directors: John R Whitmore, John E Chapoton, George P Clancy Jr, Gilbert M Grosvenor, Philip C Jackson Jr, Patrick F Noonan, H Gregory Platts, Andrew M Saul II, Mark Sullivan III, James W Symington

D-U-N-S 06-989-4384
SAUL EWING LLP
1500 Market St Fl 38, Philadelphia, PA 19102-2128
Tel (215) 972-7777 *Founded/Ownrshp* 1998
Sales 111.2MM[E] *EMP* 542
SIC 8111 General practice law office
Pt: Nancy S Cleveland
Pt: William A Destefano
Pt: Martin J Doyle
Pt: Saul Ewing
Pt: Steven A Goldfield
Pt: Robert M Greenbaum
Pt: Jeffrey C Hampton
Pt: Linda Hill
Pt: Timothy E Hoeffner
Pt: Adam H Isenberg
Pt: James F Kilcur
Pt: Seth J Lapidow
Pt: Mark C Levy
Pt: Robert H Louis
Pt: Suzanne S Mayes
Pt: Gary A Rosen
Pt: Gary Arlen Smith
Pt: James J O Toole
Pt: Virginia G White
COO: Jennifer Peterson
Dir Soc: Mary F Brightman

D-U-N-S 05-020-5251
SAULSBURY ELECTRIC CO LTD
2951 E Interstate 20, Odessa, TX 79766-8835
Tel (432) 366-3686 *Founded/Ownrshp* 1968
Sales 474.8MM[E] *EMP* 1,500
SIC 1629 Chemical plant & refinery construction; Oil refinery construction; Power plant construction
Pr: Charles R Saulsbury Sr
**CEO:* Michael Mangum
**CFO:* Thomas Saunders
CFO: Chat York
**Sec:* Amelia D Saulsbury Zugg
**Sr VP:* Mark Saulsbury
VP: Norman Hood
**VP:* Larry Molinar
**VP:* Amelia Saulsbury
**VP:* Bubba Saulsbury
Genl Couns: Frank A Hunold

D-U-N-S 07-861-2352
SAULSBURY INDUSTRIES INC
2951 E Interstate 20, Odessa, TX 79766-8835
Tel (432) 366-3686 *Founded/Ownrshp* 1967
Sales 600.0MM *EMP* 30[E]
SIC 1629 Industrial plant construction
CEO: Rick Graves
Pr: Kim Combs
**COO:* Tracy Frazier
Sr VP: David Clem
**Sr VP:* Mark Saulsbury
Sr VP: C R Soulsbury Jr
VP: David Dool
VP: Jim Lemarr
VP: Jimmy Matthews
Exec: Randy Walker
Dir Bus: Rich Cecil
Dir Bus: David Sandberg

D-U-N-S 08-617-7086
SAULT SAINTE MARIE TRIBE OF CHIPPEWA INDIANS
NORTHERN HOSPITILITY
523 Ashmun St, Sault Sainte Marie, MI 49783-1907
Tel (906) 635-6050 *Founded/Ownrshp* 1953
Sales NA *EMP* 1,200
Accts Anderson Tackman & Company P
SIC 9131 Indian reservation
Ch Bd: Aaron Payment
**Treas:* Tricia Gough
**Treas:* Fred Paquin
Exec: Douglas Hartley
Ex Dir: Tony Nertoli
IT Man: Sam Gurnoe
VP Mktg: Alan Bouschor

D-U-N-S 96-167-8609
SAUMIL DIAM LLC
CAPPUCCINO COLLECTION
15 W 47th St Ste 1707, New York, NY 10036-5700
Tel (212) 575-3655 *Founded/Ownrshp* 2009
Sales 112.4MM *EMP* 14
Accts Saumil Diam Llc New York Ny
SIC 5094 Diamonds (gems); Jewelry

SAUNDERS
See RS HUGHES CO INC

D-U-N-S 08-402-9057 EXP
SAUNDERS CONSTRUCTION INC
6950 S Jordan Rd, Centennial, CO 80112-4211
Tel (303) 699-9000 *Founded/Ownrshp* 1972
Sales 158.5MM[E] *EMP* 400
SIC 1542 Commercial & office building, new construction
CEO: John P Beeble
**Pr:* Gregory A Schmidt
**CFO:* David E Alberts
**VP:* W Scott Bonner
VP: Graham Coddington
**VP:* W Dennis Disney
**VP:* Darrell L Eastwood
**VP:* David F Hoffman
VP: Dennis Nolan
**VP:* Dennis A Noland
VP: Trae Rigby
**VP:* Susan M Stewart
**VP:* James L Weber

SAVA SENIOR CARE
See SAVASENIORCARE LLC

SAVAGE ARMS
See CALIBER CO

D-U-N-S 04-870-4480 IMP/EXP
■ SAVAGE ARMS INC
(*Suby of* SAVAGE SPORTS CORP) ★
140 Apremont Way, Westfield, MA 01085-1359
Tel (413) 642-4135 *Founded/Ownrshp* 1896, 1995
Sales 99.9MM[E] *EMP* 415
SIC 3484 Rifles or rifle parts, 30 mm. & below; Shotguns or shotgun parts, 30 mm. & below
Ch Bd: Ronald Coburn
**Pr:* Albert F Kasper
VP Sls: Bud Fini

D-U-N-S 15-078-4759
SAVAGE BMW INC
1301 Auto Center Dr, Ontario, CA 91761-2211
Tel (909) 390-7888 *Founded/Ownrshp* 1974
Sales 93.6MM *EMP* 54
SIC 5511

D-U-N-S 10-270-4954
SAVAGE COMPANIES
RAILCAR TRACKING COMPANY LLC
901 W Legacy Center Way, Midvale, UT 84047-5765
Tel (801) 944-6600 *Founded/Ownrshp* 1982
Sales 910.7MM[E] *EMP* 1,800
SIC 4212 4213 Local trucking, without storage; Coal haulage, local; Petroleum haulage, local; Trucking, except local; Liquid petroleum transport, non-local
Ch Bd: Allen B Alexander
Ex VP: Kelly J Flint
Ex VP: Gary L Plant
Ex VP: Todd L Savage
**Sr VP:* Curtis C Dowd
VP: Sharon Broadwater
VP: Beau Harris
VP: Butch Jentzsch
VP: Michael Klein
VP: Scott Smith
VP Bus Dev: Kent Avery
Board of Directors: J Kimo Esplin, Crystal Call Maggelet, David Winder

D-U-N-S 62-075-1078
SAVAGE SERVICES CORP
(*Suby of* RAILCAR TRACKING CO LLC) ★
901 W Legacy Center Way, Midvale, UT 84047-5765
Tel (801) 944-6600 *Founded/Ownrshp* 1995
Sales 467.8MM^E *EMP* 1,600
SIC 4212 Animal & farm product transportation services
CEO: Allen Alexander
**Pr:* Kirk Aubry
Treas: Dean Rees
Sr VP: Donald W Alexander
Genl Mgr: Kenneth Cooper

D-U-N-S 05-940-7689
■ **SAVAGE SPORTS CORP**
(*Suby of* SAVAGE ARMS) ★
100 Springdale Rd, Westfield, MA 01085-1624
Tel (413) 568-7001 *Founded/Ownrshp* 1995
Sales 101.9MM^E *EMP* 415^E
SIC 3484 Rifles or rifle parts, 30 mm. & below; Shotguns or shotgun parts, 30 mm. & below
Ch Bd: Ronald Coburn
**Pr:* Albert F Kasper
**CFO:* David Pacentini
VP Sls: Bud Fini

D-U-N-S 02-251-2669
SAVAL FOODS CORP
SAVAL FOODSERVICE
6740 Dorsey Rd, Elkridge, MD 21075-6205
Tel (410) 379-5100 *Founded/Ownrshp* 1932
Sales 113.2MM^E *EMP* 225^E
SIC 5141 2013

SAVAL FOODSERVICE
See SAVAL FOODS CORP

D-U-N-S 01-683-2240
SAVANNA ENERGY SERVICES (USA) CORP
(*Suby of* SAVANNA ENERGY SERVICES CORP)
2445 Technology Ste 200, The Woodlands, TX 77381-5261
Tel (281) 907-4800 *Founded/Ownrshp* 2005
Sales 197.7MM^E *EMP* 300
SIC 1381 1389 Drilling oil & gas wells; Bailing, cleaning, swabbing & treating of wells
CEO: Ken Mullen
**Ex VP:* George Chow
**Ex VP:* John Cooper
**Ex VP:* Darcy Draudson
**Ex VP:* Dwayne Lamontagne
VP: Jay Canizaro
**VP:* Evan Russell

D-U-N-S 07-846-5355
SAVANNA-CHATHAM COUNTY PUBLIC SCHOOL SYSTEM
208 Bull St, Savannah, GA 31401-3843
Tel (912) 395-5600 *Founded/Ownrshp* 2012
Sales 11.8MM^E *EMP* 5,033^E
SIC 8211 Public elementary & secondary schools
Pr Dir: Kurt Hetager

D-U-N-S 04-761-1954
SAVANNAH CITY WATER SUPPLY
6183 Hwy 21 N, Savannah, GA 31407
Tel (912) 964-4473 *Founded/Ownrshp* 1982
Sales 162.0MM^E *EMP* 30
SIC 4941 Water supply

D-U-N-S 09-931-2266 IMP
SAVANNAH COLLEGE OF ART AND DESIGN INC
SCAD
126 E Gaston St, Savannah, GA 31401-5604
Tel (912) 525-5000 *Founded/Ownrshp* 1978
Sales 392.6MM *EMP* 1,200
Accts Mauldin & Jenkins Llc Atlanta
SIC 8221 Professional schools
Pr: Paula Wallace
**CFO:* Joseph P Manory
Bd of Dir: Antoinette Parris
Assoc VP: Hannah Crockett
**Ex VP:* Brian Murphy
VP: John Joseph Hoey
VP: Scott Linzey
VP: Darrell Naylor-Johnson
**VP:* Roger Ross
VP: John Rowan
VP: Cathy Turbiville
VP: Judith Van Baron
Exec: Pat Helbig
Comm Man: Katie Brown

D-U-N-S 14-471-1160
SAVANNAH COLLEGE OF ART AND DESIGN INC
115 E York St, Savannah, GA 31401-3718
Tel (912) 525-5800 *Founded/Ownrshp* 2004
Sales 365.1MM *EMP* 2
SIC 8748 Educational consultant

D-U-N-S 00-692-6539
■ **SAVANNAH ELECTRIC AND POWER CO**
(*Suby of* GEORGIA POWER CO) ★
600 E Bay St, Savannah, GA 31401-1286
Tel (912) 644-7171 *Founded/Ownrshp* 2014
Sales 444.9MM *EMP* 549
SIC 4911 Generation, electric power
Pr: Craig Barrs
Ch Bd: Anthony R James
CFO: Kirby R Willis
Sr VP: Arthur M Gignilliat
VP: W Miles Greer
VP: Leonard Haynes
VP: Ellen Lindemann
VP: Christopher C Womack
Genl Mgr: Janet Galloway
Board of Directors: Gus H Bell III, Archie Davis, Walter D Gnann, Robert B Miller III, Arnold M Tenenbaum

D-U-N-S 79-886-1048
SAVANNAH RIVER NUCLEAR SOLUTIONS LLC
SRNS
203 Laurens St Sw Frnt, Aiken, SC 29801-2422
Tel (803) 643-4570 *Founded/Ownrshp* 2007
Sales 0.0 *EMP* 6,000^E
SIC 8731 Commercial physical research
Pr: Carol Johnson
**COO:* Fred Dohse
VP: David Eyler

D-U-N-S 80-837-6193
■ **SAVANNAH RIVER REMEDIATION LLC**
SAVANNAH RVER BUS UNT-LIVEWIRE
(*Suby of* URS FEDERAL SVCS INC AN AECOM) ★
Savannah River Site, Aiken, SC 29808-0001
Tel (803) 952-9630 *Founded/Ownrshp* 2007
Sales 617.4MM^E *EMP* 1,737
SIC 4953 Liquid waste, collection & disposal
Genl Mgr: David Pethick

SAVANNAH RVER BUS UNT-LIVEWIRE
See SAVANNAH RIVER REMEDIATION LLC

D-U-N-S 00-329-3156 EXP
SAVANNAH WOOD PRESERVING CO INC (GA)
501 Stiles Ave, Savannah, GA 31415-3141
Tel (912) 236-4875 *Founded/Ownrshp* 1954, 1978
Sales 300.0MM *EMP* 7
SIC 2491 Wood preserving
Pr: Herbert Guerry
**Pr:* Wen-Chuan Huang

SAVANNAH-CHATHAM BOARD OF EDUC
See BOARD OF EDUCATION FOR CITY OF SAVANNAH AND COUNTY OF CHATHAM (INC)

SAVANNAH-CHATHAM CNTY SCHL SYS
See CHATHAM COUNTY BOARD OF EDUCATION

D-U-N-S 19-321-0841
SAVASENIORCARE LLC
SAVA SENIOR CARE
1 Ravinia Dr Ste 1500, Atlanta, GA 30346-2115
Tel (770) 829-5100 *Founded/Ownrshp* 2004
Sales 1.7MMM^E *EMP* 23,000^E
SIC 8742 Administrative services consultant
CEO: Tony Oglesby
**CFO:* Kevin Sceramaur
Ofcr: Brent Snelgrove
**Ex VP:* Stefano Miele
Sr VP: Julie Purcell
VP: Candace Gunderson
VP: Stacey Hallissey
**VP:* Wynn Sims
Snr Ntwrk: Robert Sebastian
Software D: John Dunlap
VP Opers: Brent A Snelgrove

SAVE A TREE
See NATURESTREES INC

D-U-N-S 07-212-9919 IMP/EXP
SAVE CHILDREN FEDERATION INC
501 Kings Hwy E Ste 400, Fairfield, CT 06825-4861
Tel (203) 221-4000 *Founded/Ownrshp* 1932
Sales 657.8MM *EMP* 3,000
Accts Kpmg Llp Hartford Ct
SIC 8322 5947 Individual & family services; Gift shop
CEO: Carolyn Miles
Pr: Rick Trowbridge CPA
**Ex VP:* Carlos Carrazana
**VP:* Michael Klosson
**VP:* Tom Krift
**VP:* Ken Murdoch
VP: Greg Ramm
VP: Mark Shriver
VP: Brian White
Exec: Vicki Banks
Exec: Kim Snell
Assoc Dir: Gail Arcamone
Assoc Dir: Penny Crump
Assoc Dir: Carolyn Davis
Assoc Dir: Lynne Lebarron
Assoc Dir: Thulo Shrestha
Assoc Dir: Sarah Thompson
Comm Dir: Dara McLeod

D-U-N-S 00-787-4480
SAVE MART SUPERMARKETS (CA)
S-MART
1800 Standiford Ave, Modesto, CA 95350-0180
Tel (209) 577-1600 *Founded/Ownrshp* 1952
Sales 4.0MMM^E *EMP* 17,500
SIC 5411 5141 4213 4212 Supermarkets, chain; Groceries, general line; Refrigerated products transport; Local trucking, without storage
CEO: Robert M Piccinini
CFO: Greg Hill
**CFO:* Ronald Riesenbeck
Ofcr: James Orr
**VP:* Art Patch
VP: Ron Riesenbeck
**VP:* Cecil Russell
**VP:* Michael Silvera
VP: James Sims
VP: Paul Tidwell
**VP:* Jim Watt
Board of Directors: Jay L Margulies

D-U-N-S 08-103-2666
SAVE MORE INC
9405 Livingston Rd, Fort Washington, MD 20744-4917
Tel (301) 372-1000 *Founded/Ownrshp* 1986
Sales 93.7MM *EMP* 50
Accts Elliott Davis Cpa Anderson
SIC 5531 5015 Automotive parts; Automotive parts & supplies, used
Pr: Stephen M Meinhardt
**Treas:* Henry Alvin Meinhardt
**VP:* Walter M Meinhardt

D-U-N-S 09-551-2484 EXP
■ **SAVE-A-LOT FOOD STORES LTD**
SAVE-A-LOT LIMITED
(*Suby of* MORAN FOODS LLC) ★
100 Corporate Office Dr, Earth City, MO 63045-1511
Tel (314) 592-9261 *Founded/Ownrshp* 1999
Sales 279.2MM^E *EMP* 1,015
SIC 5411 Grocery stores
Pr: Bill Shaner
Dist Mgr: Helio Camilli
Div Mgr: Bob Dwane
Genl Mgr: Fred Malinosky
IT Man: Chris Oestereich
Mktg Dir: Mark Kotcher

SAVE-A-LOT LIMITED
See SAVE-A-LOT FOOD STORES LTD

SAVEBIG RX
See HEALTHSOURCE DISTRIBUTORS LLC

D-U-N-S 00-568-5941 IMP/EXP
SAVERS INC
VALUE VILLAGE STORES
11400 Se 6th St Ste 220, Bellevue, WA 98004-6423
Tel (425) 462-1515 *Founded/Ownrshp* 2000
Sales 3.1MMM^E *EMP* 20,000
SIC 5932 5311 5331 Used merchandise stores; Department stores; Variety stores
Prin: Thomas Ellison
**Pr:* Kenneth Alterman
COO: David Johnston
**CFO:* Robert C Houglund
Treas: Michael Daily
Chf Mktg O: Karin Koonings
Ofcr: Mark Rodocker
VP: Chad Buscho
VP: Shannon Vernerey
Prgrm Mgr: Dominic Franza
Dist Mgr: Brian Clearman

D-U-N-S 07-943-0183
SAVILLS AMERICA LIMITED
(*Suby of* SAVILLS PLC)
399 Park Ave Fl 11, New York, NY 10022-4609
Tel (212) 326-1000 *Founded/Ownrshp* 2007
Sales 105.8MM^E *EMP* 587^E
SIC 6531 6799 Real estate brokers & agents; Investors
Snr Mgr: Alexandria Faiz

D-U-N-S 07-522-2091
SAVILLS STUDLEY INC
(*Suby of* SAVILLS AMERICA LIMITED) ★
399 Park Ave Fl 11, New York, NY 10022-4609
Tel (212) 326-1000 *Founded/Ownrshp* 2014
Sales 105.8MM^E *EMP* 587
SIC 6531 6799 Real estate brokers & agents; Investors
Pr: Mitchel S Steir
V Ch: George J Martin
V Ch: Peter M Speier
V Ch: Lois A Zambo
**Pr:* Michael D Colacino
COO: John Pantazis
CFO: Alfonso Petrillo
Ex VP: Steve Barker
**Ex VP:* Matthew Barlow
Ex VP: Matthew P Barlow
Ex VP: Bill Bauman
**Ex VP:* Peter Capuciati
Ex VP: Thomas Fulcher
**Ex VP:* David J Goldstein
Ex VP: Arthur Greenberg
Ex VP: Daniel Horowitz
Ex VP: Gregory Katz
Ex VP: David Lipson
Ex VP: Jim McGrath
Ex VP: Mark O'Donnell
Ex VP: Mark Odonnell

D-U-N-S 07-659-2641
SAVINGS BANK LIFE INSURANCE CO OF MASSACHUSETTS
1 Linscott Rd, Woburn, MA 01801-2001
Tel (781) 938-3500 *Founded/Ownrshp* 1991
Sales NA *EMP* 220
SIC 6311 Life insurance
Pr: James Morgan
**Ch Bd:* Gerald Mulligan
**CEO:* Robert K Sheridan
**CFO:* James P Loring
VP: Maria Cianfichi
VP: Paul Lynch
IT Man: Leanne Downey
IT Man: Bill Oliver
Sls Mgr: Richard Benoit

D-U-N-S 78-065-3713 EXP
SAVINO DEL BENE USA INC
(*Suby of* TRASPORTI INTERNAZIONALI AGENZIA MARITTIMA SAVINO DEL BENE SPA)
34 Engelhard Ave, Avenel, NJ 07001-2217
Tel (347) 960-5568 *Founded/Ownrshp* 1973
Sales 481.5MM^E *EMP* 2,600
SIC 3799 4731 All terrain vehicles (ATV); Freight forwarding
Ch Bd: Andrea Fanti
Pr: Silvano Brandani
CFO: Fred Sheinblum
Sr Cor Off: Silvano Drandani
VP: Massimilliano Brandani
Brnch Mgr: Jarred Varanelli
Mktg Dir: Marcela Schaub
Sls Dir: Fabrizio Giugno
Board of Directors: Umberto Cella, Andrea Fanti, Paolo Nocentini

D-U-N-S 00-233-3672 IMP
SAVOR STREET FOODS INC
1 Park Plz, Wyomissing, PA 19610-1301
Tel (610) 320-7800 *Founded/Ownrshp* 1980
Sales 89.2MM^E *EMP* 350
SIC 2052 2096 2099 Pretzels; Potato chips & other potato-based snacks; Cheese curls & puffs; Popcorn, already popped (except candy covered); Corn chips & other corn-based snacks; Food preparations
Pr: Scott R Carpenter
**Treas:* Joseph F Welch
**Sec:* Marcia Welch
**V Ch Bd:* John J Mastromarino
**VP:* Roy Emery

D-U-N-S 04-224-2508
■ **SAVVIS COMMUNICATIONS CORP** (MO)
CENTURYLINK TS
(*Suby of* CENTURYLINK INC) ★
1 Solutions Pkwy, Town and Country, MO 63017-5827
Tel (314) 628-7000 *Founded/Ownrshp* 1995, 1998
Sales 146.1MM^E *EMP* 1,000
SIC 4813 7375 ; Information retrieval services
CEO: Jim Ousley
**Pr:* Pete Bazil
Pr: Jim Clancy
**Pr:* Bill Fathers
**Pr:* James Parker
**Pr:* Jeffery Von Deylen
CFO: Greg Freiberg
Bd of Dir: Jeanine Drumright
**Sr VP:* Marc Capri
**VP:* Siobhan De Leeuw
VP: Jim Kozlowski
VP: Drew Leonard
VP: Aj Matel
VP: Michelle McWhorter
VP: Craig Mertz
**VP:* James Mori
VP: Jeff Myers
**VP:* Daniel Patton
VP: Betty Smith
Assoc Dir: Michele Oehlbert

D-U-N-S 78-650-2778
■ **SAVVIS FEDERAL SYSTEMS INC**
CENTURYLINK TS
(*Suby of* CENTURYLINK TS) ★
4250 Fairfax Dr, Arlington, VA 22203-1665
Tel (703) 667-6000 *Founded/Ownrshp* 2004
Sales 108.0MM^E *EMP* 1,000
SIC 4813 7379 ; Computer related consulting services
CEO: Jeffrey H Von Deylen
**Pr:* Glen F Post III
Treas: Lisa B Bruch
**Treas:* Gregory W Freiberg
Sr VP: Harsch Bhatnagar
VP: David Shacochis
Sls Mgr: Bob Sahagun
Snr Mgr: Elissa Homenock

D-U-N-S 03-551-9235
SAVVIS INC
CENTURYLINK TECH SOLUTIONS
1 Solutions Pkwy, Town and Country, MO 63017-5827
Tel (314) 628-7000 *Founded/Ownrshp* 2011
Sales 425.3MM^E *EMP* 2,440
SIC 7373 7379 4813 7375

D-U-N-S 84-474-8145
SAW MILL CAPITAL LLC
555 Pleasantville Rd 220s, Briarcliff Manor, NY 10510-1963
Tel (914) 741-2426 *Founded/Ownrshp* 1997
Sales 399.2MM^E *EMP* 1,785
SIC 6726 6282 Investment offices; Investment advisory service
Mng Pt: Howard D Unger
**Pt:* Scott A Budoff
**Pt:* William M Gerstner
Mng Pt: Howard Unger
**CFO:* Blinn M Cirella
CFO: Blinn Cirella
**VP:* Jason W Mueller
VP: Jason Mueller
VP: Scott Rivard
**VP:* Scott A Vandekerkhoff

D-U-N-S 00-692-5937
SAWNEE ELECTRIC MEMBERSHIP CORP (GA)
SAWNEE EMC
543 Atlanta Rd, Cumming, GA 30040-2701
Tel (770) 887-2363 *Founded/Ownrshp* 1938
Sales 337.2MM *EMP* 300
Accts Mcnair Mclemore Middlebrooks &
SIC 4911 Distribution, electric power
Pr: Michael A Goodroe
**COO:* Gary Mauldin
**CFO:* Ginny J Ellis
**CFO:* Sandra Fraro
**VP:* Carl Badgett
**VP:* Greg Farr
**VP:* Jack Hylton
VP: Bill Parsons
Board of Directors: Frank Coker, Larry Evans, Jimmy Fagan, Preston Martin, Marshall Millwood, Lee Pittman, Rodney Reese, Lamar Sexton

SAWNEE EMC
See SAWNEE ELECTRIC MEMBERSHIP CORP

SAWS
See SAN ANTONIO WATER SYSTEM

D-U-N-S 17-364-9109
■ **SAXON CAPITAL INC**
MORGAN STANLEY MORTGAGE
(*Suby of* MORGAN STANLEY MORTGAGE CAPITAL HOLDINGS LLC) ★
4860 Cox Rd Ste 300, Glen Allen, VA 23060-9250
Tel (804) 270-1468 *Founded/Ownrshp* 2006
Sales 94.2MM^E *EMP* 1,127
SIC 6798 Real estate investment trusts; Mortgage investment trusts
Pr: Michael L Sawyer
**CFO:* Robert B Eastep
**Ex VP:* David L Dill
**Ex VP:* Richard D Shepherd
VP: Frederick Elflein
Dir Soc: Paniccia Caron

D-U-N-S 02-069-8330
■ **SAXON MORTGAGE SERVICES INC**
(*Suby of* MORGAN STANLEY) ★
3701 Regent Blvd Ste 100, Irving, TX 75063-2295
Tel (972) 570-6000 *Founded/Ownrshp* 2008
Sales NA *EMP* 1,250
SIC 6162 Mortgage bankers & correspondents
Pr: David L Dill
**COO:* Joe Healan
**CFO:* Larry Spangler
**Ex VP:* Robert Meachum
**Sr VP:* Joe Moran
**Sr VP:* Jennifer Sebastian

D-U-N-S 85-890-3727
SAXTON GROUP INC
MCALISTER'S DELI
7859 Walnut Hill Ln # 325, Dallas, TX 75230-5606
Tel (214) 373-3400 *Founded/Ownrshp* 1991
Sales 78.3MM *EMP* 3,000
SIC 5812 Restaurant, family: chain
Ch: Kelly Saxton
**Pr:* Kelly G Saxton
COO: Matt Saxton
**Ch:* Kirk Lanier
**VP:* James E Robertson

D-U-N-S 04-241-6495
SAYBOLT LP
(*Suby of* CORE LABORATORIES LP) ★
6316 Windfern Rd, Houston, TX 77040-4916
Tel (713) 328-2673 *Founded/Ownrshp* 1997
Sales 797.5MM^E *EMP* 5,000
SIC 1389

D-U-N-S 04-551-5145
SAYCO CONTAINER INC
(*Suby of* COI GRAPHICS) ★
13400 Nelson Ave, City of Industry, CA 91746-2331
Tel (619) 440-4411 *Founded/Ownrshp* 1998
Sales 64.2MM^E *EMP* 1,000
SIC 2653 3089 3086 Corrugated & solid fiber boxes; Plastic containers, except foam; Plastics foam products
Pr: Michael G Feterik
COO: Greg Hall
**VP:* Jerry Verst
Genl Mgr: Randy Nelson
Opers Mgr: Dan Domino

D-U-N-S 07-982-2348
SAYERS TECHNOLOGY LLC
825 Corporate Woods Pkwy, Vernon Hills, IL 60061-3158
Tel (847) 391-4802 *Founded/Ownrshp* 2015
Sales 100.0MM *EMP* 105
SIC 5734 7378 Computer peripheral equipment; Computer maintenance & repair
VP: Jim Locke
**CEO:* Christopher Callahan
Sr VP: Al Bibergall

SAYGUS
See AMERICAN SMARTPHONE INC

D-U-N-S 03-326-7287
SAYLE OIL CO INC
GAS MART
410 W Main St, Charleston, MS 38921-2125
Tel (800) 844-8120 *Founded/Ownrshp* 1947
Sales 109.0MM^E *EMP* 300
SIC 5541 5171 5411 Filling stations, gasoline; Petroleum bulk stations; Convenience stores, independent
Pr: Isaac E Sayle
**CFO:* Caroline Taylor
**Treas:* Linda Allison
VP: Michael Brasell
Mktg Mgr: Bobby Burns
Manager: Jerry Graham
Manager: Keasler Meeks

D-U-N-S 00-818-6033 IMP/EXP
SAZERAC CO INC
MONSIEUR HENRI WINE
3850 N Causeway Blvd # 1695, Metairie, LA 70002-8177
Tel (504) 831-9450 *Founded/Ownrshp* 1919
Sales 274.9MM^E *EMP* 350
SIC 5182 2085

D-U-N-S 07-829-0455
SB CAPITAL ACQUISITIONS LLC
JC'S 5 STAR OUTLET
(*Suby of* RETAIL 4 LESS) ★
4010 E 5th Ave, Columbus, OH 43219-1811
Tel (614) 443-4080 *Founded/Ownrshp* 2011
Sales 353.4M *EMP* 1,500
Accts Jb Plante & Moftan Pllc Col
SIC 5399 Army-Navy goods

D-U-N-S 96-591-1217
SB CAPITAL GROUP LLC
RETAIL 4 LESS
4300 E 5th Ave, Columbus, OH 43219-1816
Tel (516) 829-2400 *Founded/Ownrshp* 1996
Sales 96.5MM^E *EMP* 1,525
SIC 7389 Merchandise liquidators
Ch Bd: Jay L Schottenstein
**Pr:* David Bernstein
VP: Dirk E Greene
VP: Stephen Jenkins
Ex Dir: Bob Marsh
Off Mgr: Susan Levan

D-U-N-S 55-687-9799
SB RESTAURANT CO
ELEPHANT BAR RESTAURANT
(*Suby of* APAX PARTNERS OF NEW YORK) ★
18900 Dallas Pkwy Ste 125, Dallas, TX 75287-6922
Tel (800) 227-5454 *Founded/Ownrshp* 2005
Sales 157.7MM^E *EMP* 5,000
SIC 5812 5813 American restaurant; Bar (drinking places)
Pr: Robert Holden
**CFO:* Paul Potvin
**Ex VP:* Reinhard Dorfhuber
Genl Mgr: Leo Gilleran
Genl Mgr: Randy Sharpe

D-U-N-S 00-959-4552
▲ SBA COMMUNICATIONS CORP
8051 Congress Ave Ste 100, Boca Raton, FL 33487-1311
Tel (561) 995-7670 *Founded/Ownrshp* 1989
Sales 1.6MMM *EMP* 1,310^E
Tkr Sym SBAC *Exch* NGS
SIC 4899 Television antenna construction & rental; Communication signal enhancement network system
Pr: Jeffrey A Stoops
**Ch Bd:* Steven E Bernstein
Pr: Kurt L Bagwell
CFO: Brendan T Cavanagh
CFO: Brendon Cavanagh
Ofcr: Thomas P Hunt
Ex VP: Mark R Ciarfella
Ex VP: Jason V Silberstein
Sr VP: Jorge Grau
Sr VP: Brian D Lazarus
Sr VP: Neil H Seidman
VP: Mark Derussy
VP: Josh Koenig
VP: Vickie Tillman
Exec: Kathryn Adler
Board of Directors: Kevin L Beebe, Brian C Carr, Mary S Chan, Duncan H Cocroft, George R Krouse Jr, Jack Langer

D-U-N-S 01-092-9482
■ SBA COMMUNICATIONS INC
SBA NETWORK SERVICES
(*Suby of* SBA COMMUNICATIONS CORP) ★
8051 Congress Ave Ste 100, Boca Raton, FL 33487-1311
Tel (561) 995-7670 *Founded/Ownrshp* 1998
Sales 99.9MM^E *EMP* 350^E
SIC 4899 Communication signal enhancement network system
CEO: Jeffrey Stoops
COO: Paul Estes
Sr Cor Off: Rudolph Coleman
Sr VP: John Marino
VP: Kurt Bagwell
VP: Randy M Henderson
VP: Bryce Rankin
Genl Mgr: Walter J Hinkle
Dir IT: Robert Gonzales
S&M/VP: Jeff Langdon

SBA GLOBAL LOGISTICS SERVICES
See SERVICE BY AIR INC

SBA NETWORK SERVICES
See SBA COMMUNICATIONS INC

D-U-N-S 60-254-1844
■ SBA SENIOR FINANCE II LLC
(*Suby of* SENIOR SBA FINANCE INC) ★
8051 Congress Ave Ste 100, Boca Raton, FL 33487-1311
Tel (561) 995-7670 *Founded/Ownrshp* 2005
Sales 93.3MM^E *EMP* 307
SIC 6519 Real property lessors
CEO: Jeffrey A Stoops

D-U-N-S 80-667-9184
SBARRO HOLDINGS LLC
401 Broadhollow Rd Ll10, Melville, NY 11747-4720
Tel (631) 715-4100 *Founded/Ownrshp* 2007
Sales 64.4MM^E *EMP* 5,500
SIC 5812 6794

D-U-N-S 09-878-7849
SBARRO INC
SBARRO LICENSING INC.
401 Broadhollow Rd Ll10, Melville, NY 11747-4720
Tel (631) 715-4100 *Founded/Ownrshp* 2007
Sales NA *EMP* 5,300
SIC 5812 6794

SBARRO LICENSING INC.
See SBARRO INC

D-U-N-S 07-920-5194
SBARRO LLC
(*Suby of* NEW SBARRO INTERMEDIATE HOLDINGS INC) ★
1328 Dublin Rd Ste 21, Columbus, OH 43215-1054
Tel (614) 769-9911 *Founded/Ownrshp* 2011
Sales 89.9MM^E *EMP* 2,162^E
SIC 5812 Italian restaurant
Pr: Tony Missano
**CFO:* Carolyn Spatafora
**Treas:* Stuart Steinberg

D-U-N-S 01-115-5769 IMP
SBARS INC
14 Sbar Blvd, Moorestown, NJ 08057-1058
Tel (856) 234-8220 *Founded/Ownrshp* 1952
Sales 143.3MM^E *EMP* 200
SIC 5092 Arts & crafts equipment & supplies
Pr: A J Piperno
**Prin:* Debbie Burger
**Prin:* Charlie Moffa
**Prin:* Bob Young
**Genl Mgr:* Joe Scappa

SBC
See AMERITECH

SBC
See AMERITECH PAYPHONE SERVICES OF MICHIGAN INC

SBC
See AMERITECH PUBLISHING INC

SBC
See AMERITECH SERVICES INC

SBC
See PACIFIC BELL DIRECTORY

SBC
See AT&T LABS INC

SBHPP
See SUMITOMO BAKELITE NORTH AMERICA INC

SBI
See SHORT BARK INDUSTRIES INC

D-U-N-S 08-302-9769
SBI INC
8500 Valcour Ave, Saint Louis, MO 63123-2257
Tel (314) 615-2000 *Founded/Ownrshp* 1976
Sales 142.0MM^E *EMP* 577
SIC 5199 5122 7334 5084 Chamois leather; Leather goods, except footwear, gloves, luggage, belting; Drugs, proprietaries & sundries; Blueprinting service; Engines & parts, diesel
Pr: John G Wilmsen
**VP:* Elizabeth Wilmsen

D-U-N-S 07-850-6799
SBM MANAGEMENT SERVICES LP
5241 Arnold Ave, McClellan, CA 95652-1025
Tel (866) 855-2211 *Founded/Ownrshp* 2007
Sales 98.4MM^E *EMP* 6,000
SIC 7349 Janitorial service, contract basis
CEO: Charles Somers
CFO: Ken Silva
Ex VP: Donald Tracy
Prin: Don Tracy
Site Mgr: Aresio Rodriguez

D-U-N-S 82-506-0908
SBM SITE SERVICES LLC
S B M
5241 Arnold Ave, McClellan, CA 95652-1025
Tel (916) 922-7600 *Founded/Ownrshp* 1994
Sales 264.3MM^E *EMP* 5,500
SIC 7349 Building maintenance services
COO: Chris Geyer
**Ofcr:* Ken Silva
Exec: Mary B Fort
Rgnl Mgr: Darin Morino
Area Mgr: Albert Barrera
Area Mgr: Richard Fisher
Area Mgr: Adam M Simmons
Opers Mgr: Nick Galiszewski

D-U-N-S 05-422-3075
SBMC HEALTHCARE LLC
SPRING BRANCH MEDICAL CENTER
1301 Mckinney St Ste 2025, Houston, TX 77010-3089
Tel (713) 953-1055 *Founded/Ownrshp* 2010
Sales 62.4MM^E *EMP* 1,120^E
SIC 8011 Health maintenance organization

SBP
See SANFORD BURNHAM PREBYS MEDICAL DISCOVERY INSTITUTE

D-U-N-S 07-945-9854
SBP HOLDING LP
(*Suby of* AEA INVESTORS LP) ★
125 Mccarty St, Houston, TX 77029-1135
Tel (713) 953-1113 *Founded/Ownrshp* 2012
Sales 228.3MM^E *EMP* 712
SIC 5085 3496 Industrial supplies; Slings, lifting: made from purchased wire
CEO: Otis Dufarene

SBP HOLDINGS
See SINGER EQUITIES INC

SBS
See SPANISH BROADCASTING SYSTEM INC

D-U-N-S 07-972-1250
SBS SERVICES CORP
3091 Holcomb Bridge Rd, Norcross, GA 30071-1335
Tel (678) 534-4861 *Founded/Ownrshp* 2014
Sales 400.0MM *EMP* 130
SIC 8741 Management services
CEO: David Levitan
**CFO:* Gary Hahn

D-U-N-S 13-979-3061
SC COMPANIES INC
225 Iowa Ave, Muscatine, IA 52761-3730
Tel (563) 264-6600 *Founded/Ownrshp* 1986
Sales 149.9MM *EMP* 1,053
Accts Deloitte & Touche Llp Cedar R
SIC 8711 Consulting engineer
Pr: Gayle A Roberts
Treas: Richard C Smith
Tech Mgr: William Karunaratne

D-U-N-S 07-616-2676
SC DATA CENTER INC
1112 7th Ave, Monroe, WI 53566-1364
Tel (608) 328-8600 *Founded/Ownrshp* 1969
Sales 102.0MM^E *EMP* 1,200
SIC 7374 Data processing service; Data punch service
Pr: John Baumann
**Treas:* Raymond R Kubly
VP Mktg: Al Asber
Snr Mgr: Andrew Sefcik
Board of Directors: Shirley A Kubly

D-U-N-S 01-865-0980
SC DJJ PIEDMONT REGIONAL OFFICE
(*Suby of* STATE OF SOUTH CAROLINA) ★
300 E Courthouse Pub Sq, Laurens, SC 29360-2973
Tel (864) 681-1035 *Founded/Ownrshp* 2008
Sales 2.5MM^E *EMP* 2,939^E
SIC 8322 Youth self-help agency

SC FUELS
See PECOS INC

SC FUELS
See SOUTHERN COUNTIES OIL CO

D-U-N-S 08-041-5703
SC HOLDINGS INC
378 Bennoch Rd, Stillwater, ME 04489-5105
Tel (207) 827-4435 *Founded/Ownrshp* 2005
Sales 203.4MM^E *EMP* 450^E
SIC 1629 Land preparation construction
Pr: Herbert R Sargent
VP Opers: Tim Folster

SC JOHNSON PROFESSIONAL
See S C JOHNSON & SON INC

D-U-N-S 05-134-2568
SC PUBLIC CHARTER SCHOOL DISTRICT
3700 Forest Dr Ste 406, Columbia, SC 29204-4010
Tel (803) 734-8322 *Founded/Ownrshp* 2011
Sales 98.9MM *EMP* 19
Accts Mcgregor & Company Llp Colum
SIC 8211 Public elementary & secondary schools
Ch: D McLaurin Charleston
Ch: Don McLaurin Charleston
IT Man: Wayne Brazell

SC PUBLIC CHARTER SCHOOL DST
See SOUTH CAROLINA PUBLIC CHARTER SCHOOL DISTRICT

SC REGION OFFICE
See PROGRESSIVE WASTE SOLUTIONS LTD

D-U-N-S 09-276-0669
SC STATE BOARD FOR TECHNICAL AND COMPREHENSIVE EDUCATION
SC TECHNICAL COLLEGE SYST
(*Suby of* SOUTH CAROLINA DEPARTMENT OF EDUCATION) ★
111 Executive Center Dr # 1, Columbia, SC 29210-8414
Tel (803) 896-5280 *Founded/Ownrshp* 2007
Sales NA *EMP* 1,300
SIC 9411 Administration of educational programs;
Pr: Barry Russell
Genl Mgr: Vanessa Gill
IT Man: Cindy Hoogenboom

SC TECHNICAL COLLEGE SYST
See SC STATE BOARD FOR TECHNICAL AND COMPREHENSIVE EDUCATION

SC2
See SUPERIOR CONSOLIDATED INDUSTRIES INC

SCA AMERICAS
See SCA TISSUE NORTH AMERICA LLC

D-U-N-S 78-785-0148 IMP
SCA AMERICAS INC
TENA
(*Suby of* SVENSKA CELLULOSA AB SCA)
2929 Arch St Ste 2600, Philadelphia, PA 19104-2863
Tel (610) 499-3700 *Founded/Ownrshp* 2007
Sales 1.3MMM^E *EMP* 4,650
SIC 2621 3086 2676 Towels, tissues & napkins: paper & stock; Wrapping & packaging papers; Packaging & shipping materials, foamed plastic; Sanitary paper products
Pr: Sune Lundin
Treas: Johan Rydin
VP: Fred Albrecht
VP: Michael C Feenan
**VP:* Kevin Gorman
VP: Andreas Koch
VP: Russ Macchione
Exec: Irina Mosur
Comm Man: Tim Viola
CIO: Stephan Sinning
IT Man: Julio Elizondo

D-U-N-S 00-569-4349 IMP/EXP
SCA TISSUE NORTH AMERICA LLC
SCA AMERICAS
(*Suby of* TENA) ★
984 Winchester Rd, Neenah, WI 54956-2047
Tel (920) 725-7031 *Founded/Ownrshp* 2001
Sales 726.6MM^E *EMP* 2,460
SIC 2621 Paper mills
Pr: Don Lewis
**CFO:* Joseph Fahley
VP: Mark Phiscator
Sfty Mgr: Neal Richter
Opers Mgr: Jaann Dudenas
Mktg Dir: Cindy Stilp
Sls Mgr: Lisa Forbes
Sls Mgr: Bonni Sennett
Sls Mgr: Michael Wicklund
Sales Asso: Lisa Schaaf
Snr Mgr: Ryan Morgan

SCAD
See SAVANNAH COLLEGE OF ART AND DESIGN INC

D-U-N-S 06-388-2161 EXP
SCAFCO CORP
SCAFCO STEEL STUD MFG
2800 E Main Ave, Spokane, WA 99202-7004
Tel (509) 343-9000 *Founded/Ownrshp* 1954
Sales 146.6MM^E *EMP* 325
SIC 3523 5065 6531 3444 Farm machinery & equipment; Electronic parts & equipment; Real estate managers; Sheet metalwork
Ch: Lawrence Stone
**Pr:* Lawrence B Stone
**VP:* Arthur Mell
Brnch Mgr: Susan McCleary
Brnch Mgr: Roman Shevchuk
Brnch Mgr: Brad Tanneberg
IT Man: Adam Lester
Sfty Mgr: Lewis Boggs
Opers Mgr: Kimberlee Danard
Plnt Mgr: Greg Lewis
Prd Mgr: Leroy Utecht

SCAFCO STEEL STUD MFG
See SCAFCO CORP

D-U-N-S 03-241-3304
SCAFFS INC
S & S FOOD STORES
134 Se Colburn Ave, Lake City, FL 32025-4714
Tel (386) 752-7344 *Founded/Ownrshp* 1961
Sales 209.6MM *EMP* 400
Accts Richard E Parker Cpa Pllc
SIC 5411 Convenience stores, independent
Pr: Stafford L Scaff Jr
**Sec:* Anne C Scaff
CIO: Jenny Drawdy

SCAG POWER EQUIPMENT DIV
See METALCRAFT OF MAYVILLE INC

D-U-N-S 05-773-1812
■ SCALED COMPOSITES LLC
(*Suby of* NORTHROP GRUMMAN SYSTEMS CORP) ★
1624 Flight Line, Mojave, CA 93501-1663
Tel (661) 824-4541 *Founded/Ownrshp* 2007
Sales 181.3MM^E *EMP* 500
SIC 3721 3999 8711 Aircraft; Models, except toy; Aviation &/or aeronautical engineering
Pr: Kevin Mickey
CFO: Mark Taylor
Ofcr: Elbert L Rutan
VP: Cory Bird
VP: Dean Clarktt
VP: Ben Diachun
VP: Jason Kelley
VP: Jay Kelley

VP: Trish Mills
Exec: Elizabeth Serrano
Prgrm Mgr: Luke Goossen

D-U-N-S 08-357-3014
SCAN DRILLING CO INC
11777 Katy Fwy Ste 470, Houston, TX 77079-1781
Tel (281) 496-5571 *Founded/Ownrshp* 1922
Sales 113.0MM^E *EMP* 300
SIC 1381 Directional drilling oil & gas wells
Pr: Nils M Mosvold
**VP:* Torrey Mosvold

SCAN HEALTH PLAN
See SENIOR CARE ACTION NETWORK FOUNDATION

D-U-N-S 11-965-5434
SCAN HEALTH PLAN
3800 Kilroy Airport Way # 100, Long Beach, CA 90806-6818
Tel (562) 989-5100 *Founded/Ownrshp* 1983
Sales NA *EMP* 530^E
Accts Bdo Usa Llp Costa Mesa Ca
SIC 6324 Hospital & medical service plans
Ch: Ryan Trimble
**Pr:* Dave Schmidt
**CEO:* Chris Wing
**COO:* Bill Roth
**CFO:* Vinod Mohan
**Ofcr:* Nancy Monk
Sr VP: Sherry Stanislaw
VP: Holly Ackman
VP: Gene Dameron
VP: Hans Eckardt
VP: James Hendrickson
VP: Roger Lapp
VP: Kwan Leung
VP: Nick Milazzo
VP: Gil Miller
VP: Michael Montevideo
VP: Bevann Moreland
VP: Rajeev Narula
**VP:* Dan Osterweil
VP: Lisa Roth
VP: Ren Seidel
Board of Directors: Leo F Estrada, Jennie Chin Hansen

D-U-N-S 07-914-3133
SCAN HEALTH PLAN ARIZONA
3800 Kilroy Airport Way # 100, Long Beach, CA 90806-6818
Tel (602) 778-3300 *Founded/Ownrshp* 1998
Sales 209.1MM *EMP* 3
SIC 8099 Physical examination & testing services
CEO: Chris Wing
**COO:* Bill Roth
**CFO:* Randy Stone

D-U-N-S 96-757-1964
SCAN LONG TERM CARE
3800 Kilroy Airport Way, Long Beach, CA 90806-2494
Tel (562) 989-5100
Sales 120.3MM *EMP* 7^E
Accts Bdo Usa Llp Costa Mesa Ca
SIC 8051 Skilled nursing care facilities
Prin: Jay Greenberg

D-U-N-S 10-190-4845
▲ SCANA CORP
100 Scana Pkwy, Cayce, SC 29033-3714
Tel (803) 217-9000 *Founded/Ownrshp* 1924
Sales 4.3MMM *EMP* 5,829
Tkr Sym SCG *Exch* NYS
SIC 4931 4911 4924 4922 Electric & other services combined; Generation, electric power; Distribution, electric power; Transmission, electric power; Natural gas distribution; Natural gas transmission; Storage, natural gas
Ch Bd: Kevin B Marsh
CFO: Jimmy E Addison
Ex VP: Jimmy Addison
Ex VP: Stephen A Byrne
Sr VP: D Russell Harris
Sr VP: Kenneth R Jackson
Sr VP: W Keller Kissam
Sr VP: Ronald T Lindsay
Sr VP: Martin K Phalen
VP: Randal M Senn
Netwrk Eng: Lee Tackett

D-U-N-S 13-984-6559
■ SCANA SERVICES INC
(*Suby of* SCANA CORP) ★
220 Operation Way, Cayce, SC 29033-3713
Tel (803) 217-9000 *Founded/Ownrshp* 1999
Sales 168.9MM^E *EMP* 2,037^E
SIC 8741 Business management
CEO: Kevin Marsh

D-U-N-S 02-935-7183 IMP/EXP
SCANDINAVIAN DESIGNS INC
PLUMMERS FURNITURE
2250 S Mcdowell Blvd Ext, Petaluma, CA 94954-5659
Tel (707) 778-1600 *Founded/Ownrshp* 1963
Sales 193.3MM^E *EMP* 980^E
SIC 5712 Furniture stores
CEO: Erling Eide

D-U-N-S 78-041-2177 EXP
▲ SCANSOURCE INC
6 Logue Ct Ste G, Greenville, SC 29615-5785
Tel (864) 288-2432 *Founded/Ownrshp* 1992
Sales 3.5MMM *EMP* 2,000
Tkr Sym SCSC *Exch* NGS
SIC 5045 Computers, peripherals & software; Computers; Computer software; Computer peripheral equipment
CEO: Michael L Baur
**Ch Bd:* Steven R Fischer
CFO: Charles A Mathis
Ex VP: John J Ellsworth
Sr VP: Gerald Lyons
VP: John Harrison
Snr Sftwr: Jonathan Patton
CIO: Blake Zemp
Tech Mgr: Juan Hidalgo

Sftwr Eng: Heather Turner
Sales Exec: Rigg Zelaya
Board of Directors: Peter C Browning, Michael J Grainger, John P Reilly, Charles R Whitchurch

D-U-N-S 08-757-7680 IMP
SCANTIBODIES LABORATORY INC
9336 Abraham Way, Santee, CA 92071-2861
Tel (619) 258-9300 *Founded/Ownrshp* 1976
Sales 88.0MM^E *EMP* 620
SIC 2835 In vitro & in vivo diagnostic substances; Pregnancy test kits; In vitro diagnostics
CEO: Thomas L Cantor
**COO:* John Van Duzer
**VP:* Cheryl Cantor
Dist Mgr: Hal Bowerfind
QA Dir: Myriel Evangelista
IT Man: Jorge Escasan
IT Man: Julio Garcia
Info Man: Kris Timmerman
Web Dev: Carlos Castro
Ql Cn Mgr: Julio Padilla

D-U-N-S 05-924-3436 IMP/EXP
SCANTRON CORP
(*Suby of* HARLAND CLARKE HOLDINGS CORP) ★
1313 Lone Oak Rd, Eagan, MN 55121-1334
Tel (651) 683-6000 *Founded/Ownrshp* 1988
Sales 217.5MM^E *EMP* 980
SIC 3577 7372 2752 3575 2761 Optical scanning devices; Readers, sorters or inscribers, magnetic ink; Prepackaged software; Educational computer software; Commercial printing, lithographic; Computer terminals; Manifold business forms
CEO: Kevin Brueggeman
**Pr:* William D Hansen
**COO:* David Porter
Sr VP: Denise Schuenke
VP: Stephanie Nellons
Prin: Angie Weadge
CTO: Ramana Mantravadi
CTO: Cheryl McKaig
CTO: John Ohair
CTO: Gerald Svenby
DP Exec: Bob Ellett

D-U-N-S 00-407-1809 EXP
SCAPA NORTH AMERICA INC (CT)
(*Suby of* SCAPA GROUP PUBLIC LIMITED COMPANY)
111 Great Pond Dr, Windsor, CT 06095-1527
Tel (860) 688-8000 *Founded/Ownrshp* 1955, 1990
Sales 97.1MM^E *EMP* 300
SIC 2231 3069 2211 2824 2672 Papermakers' felts, woven: wool, mohair or similar fibers; Rubber rolls & roll coverings; Printers' rolls & blankets: rubber or rubberized fabric; Filter cloth, cotton; Textured yarns, non-cellulosic; Coated & laminated paper
CEO: Heejae Chae
Ex VP: Steve Lennon
VP: Jim Ding
**VP:* Margaret Gilmartin
VP: Andy Woodward
Assoc Dir: John Bobo
MIS Mgr: Larry Smitley

SCC
See SOUTHERN COPPER CORP

SCC
See SOFT COMPUTER CONSULTANTS INC

SCC DISTRIBUTION
See SOURCE CODE CORP

D-U-N-S 12-837-2633
SCC HOLDING CO LLC
150 Saunders Rd Ste 150, Lake Forest, IL 60045-2523
Tel (847) 444-5000 *Founded/Ownrshp* 2004
Sales 734.8MM^E *EMP* 19,500
SIC 3089 2656 3421 Cups, plastic, except foam; Plates, plastic; Plastic containers, except foam; Straws, drinking: made from purchased material; Cutlery

D-U-N-S 92-639-4230
■ SCCI HOSPITALS OF AMERICA INC
SPECIALIZED COMPLEX CARE
(*Suby of* TRIUMPH HEALTHCARE HOLDINGS INC) ★
7333 North Fwy Ste 500, Houston, TX 77076-1322
Tel (713) 807-8686 *Founded/Ownrshp* 2005
Sales 21.5MM^E *EMP* 1,300
SIC 8062 General medical & surgical hospitals
Pr: Charles Allen
**CFO:* Larry Humphrey
MIS Dir: Kitty Sibayan

SCDC
See SOUTH CAROLINA DEPARTMENT OF CORRECTIONS (INC)

SCDOT
See SOUTH CAROLINA DEPARTMENT OF TRANSPORTATION

SCE
See SAGINAW CONTROL & ENGINEERING INC

SCE
See KEY COOPERATIVE

D-U-N-S 01-001-1453 IMP/EXP
SCENTSY INC (ID)
2701 E Pine Ave, Meridian, ID 83642-5924
Tel (208) 472-0800 *Founded/Ownrshp* 2004
Sales 380.5MM^E *EMP* 1,090
SIC 3999 Candles
Pr: Heidi Thompson
**CEO:* Orville R Thompson
COO: Tabb Compton
**CFO:* Charles Thompson
Chf Mktg O: Mark Stastny
Ofcr: Phil Broadbent
VP: Richard Steel
Dir Sec: Mike Perkins
Prgrm Mgr: Keyth Bauer
CIO: Matt Cooley
QA Dir: Modou Alieu

SCF ARIZONA
See COPPERPOINT MUTUAL INSURANCE CO

SCF PARTNERS
See L E SIMMONS & ASSOCIATES INC

D-U-N-S 00-302-7273
SCHAEDLER/YESCO DISTRIBUTION INC (PA)
3982 Paxton St, Harrisburg, PA 17111-1423
Tel (717) 843-9991 *Founded/Ownrshp* 1924
Sales 155.3MM^E *EMP* 150^E
SIC 5063 Electrical supplies
CEO: Jim Schaedler
**Pr:* Matt Brnik
**CFO:* Dave Davis
**VP:* Dean Krout
**VP:* Kurt Suchar
Brnch Mgr: Ryan Reighard
Brnch Mgr: Tom Robson
Brnch Mgr: Greg Schaedler
Brnch Mgr: Allen Toth
Genl Mgr: Ken Dapp
VP Opers: James Hoffman

D-U-N-S 14-733-1342 IMP/EXP
SCHAEFER SYSTEMS INTERNATIONAL INC
S S I
(*Suby of* FRITZ SCHAFER GMBH & CO KG, EINRICHTUNGSSYSTEME)
10021 Westlake Dr, Charlotte, NC 28273-3787
Tel (704) 944-4500 *Founded/Ownrshp* 1968
Sales 146.7MM^E *EMP* 473
SIC 3089 5046 5084 5099 7372

D-U-N-S 00-627-1308 IMP/EXP
SCHAEFFER MFG CO (MO)
102 Barton St, Saint Louis, MO 63104-4729
Tel (314) 865-4100 *Founded/Ownrshp* 1839, 1981
Sales 138.0MM *EMP* 150^E
SIC 2992 2879

D-U-N-S 04-912-8598 IMP/EXP
SCHAEFFLER GROUP USA INC
(*Suby of* IHO VERWALTUNGS GMBH)
308 Springhill Farm Rd, Fort Mill, SC 29715-9784
Tel (803) 548-8500 *Founded/Ownrshp* 1964
Sales 1.8MMM^E *EMP* 7,700
SIC 3562 Roller bearings & parts
CEO: Klaus Rosenfeld
Pr: Lynn Kier
**COO:* Oliver Jung
**Treas:* Timothy U Zygmont
VP: Shoukat A Bhamani
VP: Larry Pitchard
Prgrm Mgr: Justin Laporte
Dist Mgr: Jay Smith
Genl Mgr: Wayne Proctor
Genl Mgr: Tim Shamblin
MIS Dir: Bill Smith

D-U-N-S 03-103-2738
SCHAETZEL CENTER-SCRIPPS MEMORIAL HOSPITAL
9890 Genesee Ave, La Jolla, CA 92037-1205
Tel (858) 626-7712 *Founded/Ownrshp* 1991
Sales 530.4MM *EMP* 4
SIC 8062 General medical & surgical hospitals
Pr: Mike Krucky

D-U-N-S 06-934-1303
SCHAFER GOVERNMENT SERVICES LLC
(*Suby of* SCHAFER INTERMEDIATE HOLDINGS, LLC)
101 Billerica Ave, North Billerica, MA 01862-1271
Tel (978) 256-2070 *Founded/Ownrshp* 1972
Sales 99.6MM^E *EMP* 284
SIC 7389
Ch Bd: Michael D Griffin
**Pr:* John Gilligan
Pr: Gary Sauer
**CFO:* Stephen Hughes
Sr VP: Timothy Tamerler
**VP:* Thomas Lynch
Exec: Desyree Dixon
Netwrk Mgr: Susan Baker
Sys Mgr: Rett Benedict
Snr Mgr: Len Smith

D-U-N-S 84-755-2213
SCHAUMBOND GROUP INC
225 S Lake Ave Ste 300, Pasadena, CA 91101-3009
Tel (626) 215-4998 *Founded/Ownrshp* 1996
Sales 2.2MMM *EMP* 550^E
SIC 6726 Investment offices
Pr: Baohua Zheng

D-U-N-S 06-744-4760
SCHAUMBURG COMMUNITY CONSOLIDATED SCHOOL DISTRICT 54
524 E Schaumburg Rd, Schaumburg, IL 60194-3510
Tel (847) 357-5000 *Founded/Ownrshp* 1952
Sales 179.2M *EMP* 2,500
SIC 8211 Public elementary school
MIS Dir: Paul Goldberg
IT Man: Judy Hays
IT Man: John Wilms
Psych: Liz Perez

SCHAUMBURG HONDA AUTOMOBILE
See ROBERT V ROHRMAN INC

D-U-N-S 07-140-0469 IMP
SCHEELS ALL SPORTS INC
4550 15th Ave S, Fargo, ND 58103-8959
Tel (701) 364-0572 *Founded/Ownrshp* 1902
Sales 988.3MM^E *EMP* 6,000
SIC 5661 5941 5699 5251 5261 Footwear, athletic; Sporting goods & bicycle shops; Hunting equipment; Fishing equipment; Specialty sport supplies; Sports apparel; Hardware; Builders' hardware; Tools, power; Tools, hand; Lawn & garden equipment; Lawnmowers & tractors; Garden supplies & tools
CEO: Steve D Scheel
Ofcr: Michelle Killoran
Ex VP: Matt Bowman
VP: Jane Mc Goldrick
VP: David Revier
VP: Byron Snider
Genl Mgr: Louie Sikich
Off Admin: Tammy Mollet
CIO: Marc Windahl

Site Mgr: Bill Nelson
Sales Asso: Tanner Hills

D-U-N-S 00-309-7862
SCHENCK FOODS CO INC
3578 Valley Pike, Winchester, VA 22602-2452
Tel (540) 869-1870 *Founded/Ownrshp* 1952
Sales 89.9MM^E *EMP* 125
SIC 5141 5142 5087 5147 5148 Groceries, general line; Packaged frozen goods; Janitors' supplies; Meats & meat products; Fresh fruits & vegetables
Pr: David C Huntsberry
COO: Alan Barker
**Treas:* Scott Ball
**Treas:* Kenneth P Smiy
**Ex VP:* Marshall De Haven
**VP:* Edna Huntsberry
**VP:* Gordette S Huntsberry
MIS Dir: Tom Miller

D-U-N-S 03-064-0098 IMP
SCHENCK PROCESS LLC
(*Suby of* SCHENCK PROCESS BETEILIGUNGS GMBH)
7901 Nw 107th Ter, Kansas City, MO 64153-1910
Tel (816) 891-9300 *Founded/Ownrshp* 2008
Sales 263.7MM^E *EMP* 378
SIC 5084 Pneumatic tools & equipment
Pr: Jay Brown
CFO: Rob Spaedy
**CFO:* Rob Speady
**Sr VP:* Joe Stallbaumer
VP: Joseph Stallbaumer
Dir Lab: Andy Harrell
Dir IT: Jeannie Rethman
Dir IT: Jonathan Thorn
Opers Mgr: Glenn Hicks
Plnt Mgr: Dennis Thome
Sls Dir: Mike Oberrieder
Board of Directors: Norbert Geilen

D-U-N-S 07-856-5158
SCHENKER (BAX) HOLDING CORP
(*Suby of* DB US HOLDING CORP) ★
120 White Plains Rd, Tarrytown, NY 10591-5526
Tel (914) 366-7200 *Founded/Ownrshp* 2005
Sales 51.9MM^E *EMP* 1,520
SIC 4731 Freight forwarding
Pr: Dr Christoph Bohl
**CFO:* Joseph L Groneman

D-U-N-S 08-045-2825
SCHENKER AMERICAS INC
RHO AMERICAS
(*Suby of* SCHENKER AG)
1000 Nw 57th Ct Ste 700, Miami, FL 33126-3287
Tel (786) 388-4300 *Founded/Ownrshp* 2016
Sales 1.9MMM^E *EMP* 6,225
SIC 4731 Foreign freight forwarding
CEO: Philippe Gilbert
**CFO:* Brent Blake
**Ex VP:* Steven Gundlach
**Sr VP:* Daniel Bergman
**Sr VP:* Geoff Mansell
**Sr VP:* Andreas Pohl
**Sr VP:* Trond Prestroenning
**Sr VP:* Marta Ramirez

D-U-N-S 00-182-6692 IMP/EXP
SCHENKER INC (NY)
(*Suby of* RHO AMERICAS) ★
150 Albany Ave, Freeport, NY 11520-4702
Tel (516) 377-3000 *Founded/Ownrshp* 1947, 2016
Sales 1.9MMM^E *EMP* 6,200
SIC 4731 4225 Foreign freight forwarding; Customhouse brokers; General warehousing & storage
CEO: Malcolm Heath
**CFO:* Jan Dekempe
CFO: Lutz Freytag
Top Exec: Andrew Seah
VP: Jay Arnold
VP: Dawn Boulden
VP: Steve Grier
VP: Karsten Kollmeier
VP: Barry McNeil
VP: Andreas Pohl
Comm Dir: Brenda Kelly

D-U-N-S 03-795-3388
SCHENKER INTERNATIONAL INC
(*Suby of* DB US HOLDING CORP) ★
3501 Island Ave, Philadelphia, PA 19153-3227
Tel (724) 695-7886 *Founded/Ownrshp* 2010
Sales 212.7M^E *EMP* 1,224^E
SIC 4731 Freight forwarding
Prin: Toni Groover

D-U-N-S 00-219-0643
■ SCHER CHEMICALS INC (NJ)
(*Suby of* LUBRIZOL ADVANCED MATERIALS INC) ★
Industrial West, Clifton, NJ 07012
Tel (973) 471-1300 *Founded/Ownrshp* 1932
Sales 175.6MM^E *EMP* 2,780
SIC 2869 Industrial organic chemicals; Fatty acid esters, aminos, etc.
Pr: Stephen K Scher
**VP:* Judith Donner
Opers Mgr: Janie Woo

D-U-N-S 01-053-3941
SCHERTZ-CIBOLO-UNIVERSAL CITY INDEPENDENT SCHOOL DISTRICT
S.C.U.C.I.S.D
1060 Elbel Rd, Schertz, TX 78154-2037
Tel (210) 945-6200 *Founded/Ownrshp* 1950
Sales 137.9MM *EMP* 411
Accts Pattillo Brown & Hill Llp
SIC 8211 Public elementary school; Public junior high school; Public special education school; Public senior high school
**Pr:* Kenneth E Ratcliff
Teacher Pr: Linda Cannon
Instr Medi: Kelley Mosley

D-U-N-S 00-794-0448 IMP
SCHEWEL FURNITURE CO INC (VA)
1031 Main St, Lynchburg, VA 24504-1800
Tel (434) 522-0200 *Founded/Ownrshp* 1897

Sales 117.5MM *EMP* 850
Accts Cherry Bekaert Llp Lynchburg
SIC 5712 5722 5713 Furniture stores; Household appliance stores; Floor covering stores
Pr: Marc A Schewel
Treas: William S Sprinkle Jr
VP: Wes Moreland
VP: Orville R Westmoreland Jr
Sls Dir: Steve Campbell

D-U-N-S 07-921-5497
■ SCHF NOT-FOR-PROFIT WIND-DOWN INC
WUESTHOFF HOSPITAL
(*Suby of* HMA) ★
110 Longwood Ave, Rockledge, FL 32955-2828
Tel (321) 636-2211 *Founded/Ownrshp* 1941
Sales 203.0MM[E] *EMP* 2,400
Accts Kpmg Llp Greensboro Nc
SIC 8062 General medical & surgical hospitals
CEO: Tim Cerullo
**Pr:* Emil P Miller
**COO:* Rich Kolleda
**CFO:* George Fayer
**CFO:* Theresa Mouton
Dir Lab: Sumant Pandya
Ex Dir: Gordon Hessie
Pathlgst: Julie Bell
Pathlgst: Shondell Bouie
Doctor: James Nimocks
Doctor: Brian Ziegler

D-U-N-S 00-379-1852 IMP
SCHIAVONE CONSTRUCTION CO LLC
(*Suby of* DRAGADOS USA INC) ★
150 Meadowlands Pkwy # 2, Secaucus, NJ 07094-2300
Tel (201) 867-5070 *Founded/Ownrshp* 1956, 2007
Sales 235.0MM *EMP* 600
SIC 1622 1629 Highway construction, elevated; Subway construction
Pr: Jose Miguel Ibanez Rojo
COO: Carl J Cosenzo
**VP:* James Maranino
Dir Risk M: Robert Blanda

D-U-N-S 19-386-6378 IMP/EXP
■ SCHICK MANUFACTURING INC
SCHICK-WILKINSON SWORD
(*Suby of* EDGEWELL PERSONAL CARE CO) ★
10 Leighton Rd, Milford, CT 06460-3552
Tel (203) 882-2100 *Founded/Ownrshp* 2003
Sales 118.1MM[E] *EMP* 300[E]
SIC 3421 Razor blades & razors
Pr: David Hatfield
**Ex VP:* Daniel J Sescleifer
VP: Jacqueline Burwitz
**VP:* William C Fox
**VP:* Mark S Lavigne
**VP:* David R Wegner
**Prin:* Joseph Lynch
Brnch Mgr: Karen Tosado
Dir IT: Mike Mormile

SCHICK-WILKINSON SWORD
See SCHICK MANUFACTURING INC

D-U-N-S 02-355-9545
SCHIERL INC
SCHIERL TIRE AND SERVICE CTRS
2201 Madison St, Stevens Point, WI 54481-3835
Tel (715) 345-5060 *Founded/Ownrshp* 1956
Sales 152.0MM[E] *EMP* 400
SIC 5171 5014 5531 5983 Petroleum bulk stations; Automobile tires & tubes; Automotive tires; Fuel oil dealers
CEO: Bill Schierl
**Pr:* Timothy Schierl
**CEO:* Frederick Schierl
**CEO:* William Schierl
**Co-CEO:* Fritz Gerald

SCHIERL TIRE AND SERVICE CTRS
See SCHIERL INC

SCHILLI AVIATION
See SCHILLI LEASING INC

D-U-N-S 06-471-4843
SCHILLI LEASING INC
SCHILLI AVIATION
6358 W Us Highway 24, Remington, IN 47977-8618
Tel (888) 233-1919 *Founded/Ownrshp* 1968
Sales 64.5MM[E] *EMP* 1,000
SIC 7513 7359 Truck leasing, without drivers; Equipment rental & leasing
Genl Mgr: Tom Schilli
**Ch Bd:* Thomas R Schilli
**Pr:* Floyd D Melchi

D-U-N-S 02-205-4985 IMP
SCHIMBERG CO
1106 Shaver Rd Ne, Cedar Rapids, IA 52402-4500
Tel (319) 365-9421 *Founded/Ownrshp* 1977
Sales 222.0MM[E] *EMP* 170
SIC 5074 3498 Plumbing fittings & supplies; Fabricated pipe & fittings
Pr: Charles Schimberg
COO: Paul Kearney
**VP:* David Schimberg
**Prin:* Joseph R Schimberg
Brnch Mgr: Dave Schimberg
Off Mgr: Monica Price
CIO: Weigel Jim
MIS Dir: Jamie Reider
IT Man: Scott McMurrin

D-U-N-S 96-520-6345
SCHIMENTI CONSTRUCTION CO LLC
650 Danbury Rd Ste 4, Ridgefield, CT 06877-2739
Tel (914) 244-9100 *Founded/Ownrshp* 1996
Sales 142.0MM *EMP* 135
Accts Caposella Cohen Llc Southpo
SIC 1542 Commercial & office building contractors
Pr: Matthew C Schimenti
Off Admin: Monica Mulvihill

D-U-N-S 09-480-9993 IMP/EXP
SCHINDLER ELEVATOR CORP
(*Suby of* SCHINDLER ENTERPRISES INC) ★
20 Whippany Rd, Morristown, NJ 07960-4539
Tel (973) 397-6500 *Founded/Ownrshp* 1979
Sales 1.1MMM[E] *EMP* 4,970
SIC 3534 7699 1796 Elevators & equipment; Elevators: inspection, service & repair; Miscellaneous building item repair services; Elevator installation & conversion
Pr: Greg Ergenbright
V Ch: Luc Bonnard
Pr: John Kenner
CFO: Erich Amman
CFO: Michael Bickel
Treas: Jujudhan Jena
Treas: R H Watanabe
Bd of Dir: Chris Novella
Ex VP: David Clymo
Ex VP: Carlos Guembe
VP: Paul Bloom
VP: Jeff Borland
VP: Michael Fergus
VP: Bill Fiacco
VP: Rod Hoyng
VP: Frank Resch
VP: Keith Rodgers
Exec: Erich Ammann

D-U-N-S 19-901-1024 IMP/EXP
SCHINDLER ENTERPRISES INC
(*Suby of* SCHINDLER HOLDING AG)
20 Whippany Rd, Morristown, NJ 07960-4539
Tel (973) 397-6500 *Founded/Ownrshp* 1988
Sales 1.2MMM[E] *EMP* 5,010
SIC 3534 7699 1796 Elevators & moving stairways; Elevators: inspection, service & repair; Elevator installation & conversion
VP: John R Impellizeeri
**Pr:* David J Bauhs
**Treas:* Jujudhan Jena
IT Man: Michael Maloy

D-U-N-S 00-911-1212 IMP/EXP
SCHLAGE LOCK CO LLC
(*Suby of* ALLEGION PUBLIC LIMITED COMPANY)
11819 N Pennsylvania St, Carmel, IN 46032-4555
Tel (317) 810-3700 *Founded/Ownrshp* 2013
Sales 559.3MM[E] *EMP* 3,150
SIC 3429

D-U-N-S 00-996-6461 IMP
SCHLEGEL CORP
(*Suby of* HENNIGS AUTOMOBILES) ★
2750 High Meadow Cir, Auburn Hills, MI 48326-2796
Tel (248) 340-4100 *Founded/Ownrshp* 1990
Sales 222.9MM[E] *EMP* 2,960
SIC 5013 7539 Motor vehicle supplies & new parts; Automotive repair shops
CEO: Doug Delgrosso
**VP:* Larry Williams

D-U-N-S 00-886-5466 IMP/EXP
SCHLEGEL SYSTEMS INC (DE)
(*Suby of* TYMAN MANAGEMENT LIMITED)
1555 Jefferson Rd, Rochester, NY 14623-3109
Tel (585) 427-7200 *Founded/Ownrshp* 1885
Sales 326.4MM[E] *EMP* 2,423
SIC 3053 3089 3069 Gaskets, packing & sealing devices; Plastic hardware & building products; Pillows, sponge rubber
CEO: Jeff Grady
**Ch Bd:* Jonathan Petromelis
Off Mgr: Susan Sim
MIS Dir: Tom Ruganis
Opers Mgr: Dave Franco
Opers Mgr: Scott Paige
Trfc Mgr: Steven Burley

D-U-N-S 01-953-6795 IMP/EXP
SCHLETTER INC
(*Suby of* SCHLETTER GMBH)
1001 Commerce Center Dr, Shelby, NC 28150-7728
Tel (704) 595-4200 *Founded/Ownrshp* 2007
Sales 89.1MM[E] *EMP* 200
SIC 3441 3999 Fabricated structural metal; Atomizers, toiletry
CEO: Dennis Brice
Pr: Steve Buchanan
Pr: Ed Grover
**COO:* Guy Roberts
Chf Cred: Peter Denapoli
Dir IT: Folko Kleinitzke
VP Sls: Ryan Kelly
Manager: Michael Mularski
Sales Asso: Christian Savaia
Board of Directors: Ludwig Schletter

D-U-N-S 05-384-8610 IMP/EXP
SCHLOSSER FORGE CO
ARCONIC FSTENING SYSTEMS RINGS
(*Suby of* FIRTH RIXSON MONROE) ★
11711 Arrow Rte, Rancho Cucamonga, CA 91730-4998
Tel (909) 987-4760 *Founded/Ownrshp* 1970
Sales 103.3MM[E] *EMP* 370
SIC 3463 3462

SCHLUMBERGER
See SMITH INTERNATIONAL INC

D-U-N-S 00-807-4213
SCHLUMBERGER INTERNATIONAL INC
REED TOOL
(*Suby of* SCHLUMBERGER OILFIELD SERVICES) ★
7030 Ardmore St, Houston, TX 77054-2302
Tel (713) 747-4000 *Founded/Ownrshp* 1998
Sales 1.2MMM[E] *EMP* 5,500
SIC 1389 3561 3492 3533 Oil field services; Pumps, oil well & field; Fluid power valves & hose fittings; Oil & gas field machinery; Bits, oil & gas field tools: rock
Ch Bd: Gilbert H Tausch
**Pr:* Robert J Caldwell
**Pr:* Rene Huck
**Pr:* Merle C Muckleroy
**Pr:* Stephen D Smith
**CFO:* Herbert S Yates
**VP:* Thomas W Everitt
**VP:* Bruce F Longaker Jr
**VP:* Ronald R Randall
VP: W Reiss
MIS Dir: Ken Altendorf

D-U-N-S 00-185-4546
SCHLUMBERGER LIMITED
(*Suby of* SCHLUMBERGER N.V.)
5599 San Felipe St Fl 17, Houston, TX 77056-2790
Tel (713) 513-2000 *Founded/Ownrshp* 1926
Sales 35.7MMM *EMP* 95,000
Accts Pricewaterhousecoopers Llp Ho
SIC 1381 1389 1382 3825 3824 3823 Directional drilling oil & gas wells; Well logging; Geophysical exploration, oil & gas field; Geological exploration, oil & gas field; Measuring instruments & meters, electric; Meters: electric, pocket, portable, panelboard, etc.; Controls, revolution & timing instruments; Counters, revolution; Data loggers, industrial process type
Ch Bd: Paal Kibsgaard
Pr: Richard Lewis
Pr: Rex Mennem
Pr: Mark Morley
Pr: Gleb Ovsyannikov
Pr: Lianne Qvale
CFO: Simon Ayat
Ex VP: Chakib Sbiti
VP: Ashok Belani
VP: Stephane Biguet
VP: Mohammed Saadat
VP: Depinder Sandhu
VP: Mike Skibicki
VP: Jeff Stellas
VP: Malcolm Theobald
Board of Directors: Peter L S Currie, Maureen Kempston Darkes, Michael E Marks, Indra K Nooyi, Leo Rafael Reif, Tore I Sandvold, Henri Seydoux

SCHLUMBERGER OILFIELD SERVICES
See SCHLUMBERGER TECHNOLOGY CORP

D-U-N-S 87-978-6945
SCHLUMBERGER OMNES INC
(*Suby of* SCHLUMBERGER N.V.)
5599 San Felipe St Fl 17, Houston, TX 77056-2790
Tel (713) 375-3400 *Founded/Ownrshp* 2001
Sales 33.5MMM *EMP* 38,916
SIC 1382 1389 Oil & gas exploration services; Construction, repair & dismantling services
CEO: Paal Kibsgaard
**Pr:* Xavier Flinois
**CFO:* Simon Ayat
**Ch:* Andrew Gould
Ex VP: Ashok Belani
Ex VP: Jean-Francois Poupeau
Rgnl Mgr: Bill Matthews
Admn Mgr: Sajid Khan
Brnch Mgr: Attilio Tisoni
IT Man: Alejandro Del Villar
Netwrk Eng: Craig Moore

D-U-N-S 00-592-6100 IMP/EXP
SCHLUMBERGER TECHNOLOGY CORP
SCHLUMBERGER OILFIELD SERVICES
(*Suby of* SCHLUMBERGER OMNES INC) ★
100 Gillingham Ln, Sugar Land, TX 77478-3135
Tel (281) 285-8500 *Founded/Ownrshp* 1961
Sales 15.7MMM[E] *EMP* 16,800
SIC 1382 1389 3825 3824 3533 3586 Geophysical exploration, oil & gas field; Geological exploration, oil & gas field; Well logging; Cementing oil & gas well casings; Pumping of oil & gas wells; Oil field services; Instruments to measure electricity; Meters: electric, pocket, portable, panelboard, etc.; Fluid meters & counting devices; Counters, revolution; Oil & gas field machinery; Measuring & dispensing pumps
CEO: Paal Kibsgaard
Treas: Terry Keller
**Ex VP:* Simon Ayat
**Ex VP:* Ashok Belani
**Ex VP:* Satish Pai
**Ex VP:* Jean-Francois Poupeau
VP: Jean F Poupeau
CIO: Stuart Richards
Dir IT: Philip Savundar
Counsel: William Rice

D-U-N-S 00-306-1124 IMP
SCHMIDT BAKING CO INC
7801 Fitch Ln, Baltimore, MD 21236-3998
Tel (410) 668-8200 *Founded/Ownrshp* 1926
Sales 333.4MM[E] *EMP* 650
SIC 2051 Bread, all types (white, wheat, rye, etc): fresh or frozen; Rolls, bread type: fresh or frozen; Buns, bread type: fresh or frozen
CEO: John Paterakis
**VP:* John Stewart
Sfty Mgr: Joseph Xavier

D-U-N-S 04-381-6842
SCHMITT SALES INC
2101 Saint Ritas Ln, Buffalo, NY 14221-2055
Tel (716) 639-1500 *Founded/Ownrshp* 1964
Sales 99.9MM[E] *EMP* 66
SIC 5172 5541 Gasoline; Filling stations, gasoline
Pr: Peter G Glor

D-U-N-S 00-166-3533 IMP
SCHMOLZ + BICKENBACH USA INC (IL)
SCHMOLZ BICKENBACH
(*Suby of* SCHMOLZ+BICKENBACH AG)
365 Village Dr, Carol Stream, IL 60188-1828
Tel (630) 682-3900 *Founded/Ownrshp* 1987
Sales 1.1MMM[E] *EMP* 10,000[E]
SIC 5051

SCHMOLZ BICKENBACH
See SCHMOLZ + BICKENBACH USA INC

D-U-N-S 00-325-4414 IMP
SCHNABEL FOUNDATION CO INC (DC)
45240 Business Ct Ste 250, Sterling, VA 20166-6723
Tel (703) 742-0020 *Founded/Ownrshp* 1959
Sales 108.7MM[E] *EMP* 350
SIC 1741 Foundation & retaining wall construction
CEO: Kevin W Cargill
**VP:* Ernest D Brandl
**VP:* K Ronald Chapman
**VP:* Charles Conlon
**VP:* Norman Garfield
**VP:* Claus J Ludwig
**VP:* Harry W Schnabel
**VP:* David E Weatherby
Sfty Dirs: Ryan McKavish
Snr PM: Mark Goudschaal

SCHNECK MEDICAL CENTER
See JACKSON COUNTY SCHNECK MEMORIAL HOSPITAL

D-U-N-S 19-447-5141 IMP
SCHNEIDER AUTOMATION INC
SCHNEIDER ELECTRIC
800 Federal St Ste 1, Andover, MA 01810-1068
Tel (978) 794-0800 *Founded/Ownrshp* 1996
Sales 175.4MM[E] *EMP* 1,337
SIC 3822 Auto controls regulating residntl & coml environmt & applncs
Pr: Ellen L Irving
CFO: Ellen Irving
CFO: Phillip Macy
VP: Dave Guidette
VP: Gordon Quigley
VP: Michael Sullivan
Genl Mgr: Tracy Vogt
IT Man: Herve Bregent
Mfg Dir: Bruce Boardman
VP Mktg: Paul Hamilton
Mktg Mgr: Richard Medley

SCHNEIDER ELECTRIC
See INVENSYS SYSTEMS INC

SCHNEIDER ELECTRIC
See TELVENT DTN LLC

SCHNEIDER ELECTRIC
See SCHNEIDER AUTOMATION INC

D-U-N-S 15-469-5530 EXP
SCHNEIDER ELECTRIC BUILDINGS AMERICAS INC
(*Suby of* SCHNEIDER ELECTRIC HOLDINGS INC) ★
1650 W Crosby Rd, Carrollton, TX 75006-6628
Tel (972) 323-1111 *Founded/Ownrshp* 2000
Sales 626.3MM[E] *EMP* 2,619
SIC 3822 1731 Auto controls regulating residntl & coml environmt & applncs; Air conditioning & refrigeration controls; Electric heat controls; Energy cutoff controls, residential or commercial types; Electronic controls installation
Pr: James Sandlan
**CFO:* Pierre Gunnarrson
Exec: Donna Lee
Opers Mgr: Edward Keller
Manager: Mike Willover

D-U-N-S 00-514-5958 IMP/EXP
SCHNEIDER ELECTRIC BUILDINGS LLC (DE)
INVENSYS ENVIRONMENTAL CONTRLS
(*Suby of* SCHNEIDER ELECTRIC HOLDINGS INC) ★
839 N Perryville Rd, Rockford, IL 61107-6202
Tel (815) 381-5000 *Founded/Ownrshp* 1836
Sales 328.5MM[E] *EMP* 2,000
SIC 3822 1711 3625 3823 3621 Building services monitoring controls, automatic; Mechanical contractor; Relays & industrial controls; Motor control accessories, including overload relays; Motor controls, electric; Actuators, industrial; Industrial process control instruments; Motors, electric
CEO: Jean-Pascal Tricoire
**Ex VP:* Clemens Blum
**Ex VP:* Annette Clayton
**Ex VP:* Michel Crochon
**Ex VP:* Laurent Vernerey
VP: Bob Jones
**VP:* E J Meyers
**Prin:* Barry Coflan
**Prin:* Aurelie Richard
DP Exec: Ed Klein
IT Man: Larry J Anderson

D-U-N-S 83-308-9860 IMP
SCHNEIDER ELECTRIC HOLDINGS INC
(*Suby of* SCHNEIDER ELECTRIC SE)
200 N Martingale Rd # 100, Schaumburg, IL 60173-2033
Tel (717) 944-5460 *Founded/Ownrshp* 1996
Sales 7.3MMM[E] *EMP* 22,954
SIC 3822 1711 3625 3823 3621 Building services monitoring controls, automatic; Mechanical contractor; Relays & industrial controls; Motor control accessories, including overload relays; Motor controls, electric; Industrial process control instruments; Motors, electric
CEO: Jean-Pascal Tricoire
Pr: Martin Hanna
Pr: Bobby Rogers
COO: Chris Richardson
CFO: Karen Miranda
Ex VP: Laurent Vernerey
VP: Russ Brown
VP: Mark Feasel
VP: Peggy Frett
VP: Tammy Fulop
VP: Paul Hamilton
VP: Daniel Kelly
VP: Kevin Sweeney
Dir Risk M: Barbara Naus
Comm Man: Jeannie Birdwell

D-U-N-S 00-520-7816 IMP/EXP
SCHNEIDER ELECTRIC IT CORP
A P C M G E
(*Suby of* SCHNEIDER ELECTRIC INDUSTRIES SA)
132 Fairgrounds Rd, West Kingston, RI 02892-1511
Tel (401) 789-5735 *Founded/Ownrshp* 1981
Sales 2.2MMM[E] *EMP* 7,580
SIC 3629 3612 3677 3585 7372 2542 Power conversion units, a.c. to d.c.: static-electric; Transformers, except electric; Line voltage regulators; Voltage regulators, transmission & distribution; Filtration devices, electronic; Refrigeration & heating equipment; Prepackaged software; Racks, merchandise display or storage: except wood
CEO: Harold Grant
**Pr:* Cyril Helbert

**COO:* Edward W Machala
**CFO:* Richard J Thompson
**Treas:* Michael Ricci
**Chf Mktg O:* Aaron L Davis
**Sr VP:* Jean-Yves Mouttet
**Sr VP:* Neil E Rasmussen
VP: Paul T Goldman III
VP: Dave Guidette
VP: Dave Johnson
**VP:* Robert Murray
VP: Alistair Pim
**VP:* Peter Wexler

D-U-N-S 82-700-1236 IMP/EXP
SCHNEIDER ELECTRIC IT USA INC
AMERICAN POWER CONVERSION
(*Suby of* A P C M G E) ★
132 Fairgrounds Rd, West Kingston, RI 02892-1511
Tel (401) 789-5735 *Founded/Ownrshp* 2008
Sales 160.0MM^E *EMP* 650^E
SIC 3679 Power supplies, all types: static
Pr: Laurent Vernerey
CFO: Harvey Couveil
Treas: Herve Coureil Jr
Treas: Angela Felty
VP: Chris Grant
VP: David Johnson
VP: Ben Smith
Exec: Timothy Tolman
Dir Bus: Ayo Labadie
Prgrm Mgr: Ken Belanger
Prgrm Mgr: Allan Braish

D-U-N-S 96-892-8841
SCHNEIDER ELECTRIC SOFTWARE LLC
26561 Rancho Pkwy S, Lake Forest, CA 92630-8301
Tel (949) 727-3200 *Founded/Ownrshp* 2014
Sales 260.0MM *EMP* 700
SIC 7373 Computer integrated systems design
Pr: Ravi Gopinath
**Treas:* James Danley
VP: Paul Forney
**VP:* Jim Griffith
**VP:* Robert Murray
**VP:* Steve Zalfa
Snr Sftwr: Chetankumar Katariya
Snr Sftwr: Jim Ohearn
Sls&Mrk Ex: Pat Cupo
Mktg Mgr: Helen Lindros

D-U-N-S 00-128-8364 IMP/EXP
SCHNEIDER ELECTRIC USA INC
(*Suby of* SCHNEIDER ELECTRIC HOLDINGS INC) ★
800 Federal St, Andover, MA 01810-1067
Tel (978) 975-9600 *Founded/Ownrshp* 1991
Sales 6.2MMM^E *EMP* 18,085
SIC 3613 3643 3612 3823 3625 5063 Switchgear & switchboard apparatus; Power circuit breakers; Switches, electric power except snap, push button, etc.; Switchboards & parts, power; Bus bars (electrical conductors); Connectors & terminals for electrical devices; Power transformers, electric; Controllers for process variables, all types; Relays & industrial controls; Motor controls, electric; Relays, electric power; Switches, electronic applications; Electrical apparatus & equipment
Pr: Laurent Vernerey
Genl Pt: Jean-Marc Bally
Pr: Kevin Sweeney
**CEO:* Jean Pascal Tricoire
**CFO:* Dorinda Abendschein
CFO: Antoine G D'Estai
**Treas:* James Danley
Treas: Stephen Laham
**Ex VP:* Olivier Blum
**Ex VP:* Annette Clayton
**Ex VP:* Herve Coureil
Ex VP: Zhu Hai
Ex VP: Eric Rondolat
Ex VP: Peter Wexler
VP: Shon Anderson
VP: David Goidette
VP: Ralph Harris
VP: Scott Harris
VP: Vincent A Inendino
VP: Edward Mueskes
**VP:* Robert Murray

D-U-N-S 86-798-7596 IMP/EXP
SCHNEIDER LOGISTICS INC
(*Suby of* SCHNEIDER NATIONAL INC) ★
3101 Packerland Dr, Green Bay, WI 54313-6187
Tel (920) 592-0000 *Founded/Ownrshp* 1994
Sales 320.4MM^E *EMP* 1,750
SIC 4731 4225 4789 4212 Freight forwarding; General warehousing; Cargo loading & unloading services; Delivery service, vehicular
CEO: Christopher B Lofgren PHD
**Pr:* Tom Escott
**CFO:* Bohn Crain
**Sr VP:* Steve Matheys
**Sr VP:* Wayne Messman
**Sr VP:* Rodger W Mullen

D-U-N-S 00-121-7165
SCHNEIDER MILLS INC
1430 Broadway Rm 1202, New York, NY 10018-3390
Tel (212) 768-7500 *Founded/Ownrshp* 1921, 1946
Sales 110.1MM^E *EMP* 350
SIC 2221 Manmade & synthetic broadwoven fabrics; Acetate broadwoven fabrics; Nylon broadwoven fabrics; Polyester broadwoven fabrics
Pr: Peter M Campanelli
**VP:* Mark A Labbe
Off Mgr: Eva Pang

D-U-N-S 15-730-4676
SCHNEIDER NATIONAL CARRIERS INC
(*Suby of* SCHNEIDER NATIONAL INC) ★
3101 Packerland Dr, Green Bay, WI 54313-6187
Tel (920) 592-2000 *Founded/Ownrshp* 1978
Sales 1.0MMM^E *EMP* 20,000
SIC 4731 Truck transportation brokers; Domestic freight forwarding
CEO: Christopher Lofgren
**Pr:* Bill Matheson
**Pr:* Mark Rourke
**Sec:* Michael F Gasick
**Ex VP:* Judy Lemke
**Ex VP:* Steven Matheys
Sr VP: Jon Johnson
VP: Mark Aurig
VP: Jerry Demeuse
Genl Mgr: Michelle Becker
Genl Mgr: Trena Booth

D-U-N-S 08-617-5221
SCHNEIDER NATIONAL INC
3101 Packerland Dr, Green Bay, WI 54313-6187
Tel (920) 592-2000 *Founded/Ownrshp* 1976
Sales 4.2MMM^E *EMP* 23,350
SIC 8742 4213 Transportation consultant; Trucking, except local
CEO: Christopher B Lofgren
Owner: Nuno Gomes
V Ch: Thomas A Gannon
Pr: David Bennett
Pr: Bill Matheson
Pr: Mark Rourke
CFO: Lori Lutey
Ex VP: Timothy S Fliss
Ex VP: Judith A Lemke
Ex VP: Steve Matheys
Ex VP: Steven J Matheys
Ex VP: Steven Matheys
Sr VP: Dan Van Alstine
VP: Mark Deprey
VP: J N Leyland
VP: Paul Mueller
VP: Don Osterberg
VP: Marc Rogers
VP: Greg Sanders
VP: Jared Stedl
VP: Jim Van Hefty

D-U-N-S 12-995-1042
SCHNEIDER RESOURCES INC
(*Suby of* SCHNEIDER NATIONAL INC) ★
3101 Packerland Dr, Green Bay, WI 54313-6187
Tel (920) 592-2000 *Founded/Ownrshp* 1998
Sales 91.1MM^E *EMP* 16,700
SIC 4213 Trucking, except local
CEO: Christopher Lofgren
**Ch Bd:* Don Schneider
**Pr:* Patrick C Costello
**CFO:* Dave Vanderploeg

D-U-N-S 10-785-6056 IMP
■ SCHNELLER LLC
VERITAS
(*Suby of* TRANSDIGM GROUP INC) ★
6019 Powdermill Rd, Kent, OH 44240-7109
Tel (330) 676-7183 *Founded/Ownrshp* 2011
Sales 89.0MM^E *EMP* 200
SIC 2295 Resin or plastic coated fabrics; Laminating of fabrics
Exec: Verla Gray
QA Dir: Kathleen Higgins
IT Man: Dominic Aliperti
Info Man: Dominic Aliberti
QC Dir: Dale Marshall
Plnt Mgr: Eric Custis
Sls Dir: Alex Feil

D-U-N-S 61-284-7991 EXP
■ SCHNITZER SOUTHEAST LLC
(*Suby of* SCHNITZER STEEL INDUSTRIES INC) ★
906 Adamson St Sw, Atlanta, GA 30315-2140
Tel (404) 332-1750 *Founded/Ownrshp* 2005
Sales 146.2MM^E *EMP* 455^E
SIC 5093 Scrap & waste materials
VP Sls: Lenny Fina

D-U-N-S 02-775-4084 IMP/EXP
▲ SCHNITZER STEEL INDUSTRIES INC
299 Sw Clay St Ste 350, Portland, OR 97201-5819
Tel (503) 224-9900 *Founded/Ownrshp* 1906
Sales 1.9MMM *EMP* 2,955
Tkr Sym SCHN *Exch* NGS
SIC 5093 3312 3449 3441 3433 5015 Ferrous metal scrap & waste; Automotive wrecking for scrap; Junk & scrap; Blast furnaces & steel mills; Bar, rod & wire products; Fence posts, iron & steel; Miscellaneous metalwork; Fabricated structural metal; Heating equipment, except electric; Motor vehicle parts, used
Pr: Tamara L Lundgren
**Ch Bd:* John D Carter
CFO: Richard D Peach
Sr VP: Peter Saba
VP: Richard Bettencourt
VP: Stefano Gaggini
VP: John Hare
VP: Belinda Hyde
VP: Mike Ryan
Exec: Steve Robinson
Ex Dir: Byron Kopman
Board of Directors: David J Anderson, Wayland R Hicks, David L Jahnke, Judith A Johansen, William D Larsson, Michael W Sutherlin

D-U-N-S 00-890-8956 IMP/EXP
SCHNUCK MARKETS INC
SCHNUCKS
11420 Lackland Rd, Saint Louis, MO 63146-3559
Tel (314) 994-9900 *Founded/Ownrshp* 1939
Sales 3.6MMM^E *EMP* 15,600
SIC 5411 5912 5812 7841 Supermarkets, chain; Drug stores & proprietary stores; Eating places; Video tape rental
CEO: Scott C Schnuck
**Pr:* Todd R Schnuck
**CFO:* David Bell
**Ch:* Craig D Schnuck
**Treas:* Gary J Meyer
**Ofcr:* Debra Ogston
**Sr VP:* Mark Schnuck
VP: Melissa Bunch
VP: Richard T Frede
VP: Charlotte Jensen
VP: Bergman Jim
VP: Mike Juergensmeyer
VP: Donald L Minton
VP: David M Steck
VP: Mark Zimmerman

SCHNUCKS
See SCHNUCK MARKETS INC

D-U-N-S 00-622-4471
SCHOENECKERS INC (MN)
BI WORLDWIDE
7630 Bush Lake Rd, Edina, MN 55439-2805
Tel (952) 835-4800 *Founded/Ownrshp* 1950
Sales 545.0MM *EMP* 1,400^E
SIC 8742 7361 Incentive or award program consultant; Training & development consultant; Employment agencies
Ch Bd: Guy Schoenecker
Pr: Greg Hoglund
**Pr:* Lawrence G Schoenecker
Div VP: Linda McCormick
**Ex VP:* Larry Schoenecker
**VP:* James Anderson
VP: Chris Awes
VP: Fred Baumer
VP: Joel Breeggemann
VP: Todd Crane
VP: Bruce Fredrickson
VP: Marie Hilliard
**VP:* Tim Houlihan
VP: John Jack
VP: Peder Jacobsen
VP: Dawn Martin
VP: Brad Reinders
VP: Betsy Schneider
VP: Art Swanson
VP: Tom Vicarel
VP: Anne Worrell

D-U-N-S 62-063-7504
SCHOENMANN PRODUCE CO INC
(*Suby of* SYNDEX CORP) ★
6950 Neuhaus St, Houston, TX 77061-4607
Tel (713) 923-2728 *Founded/Ownrshp* 1990
Sales 201.4MM^E *EMP* 180
SIC 5148 Fruits, fresh; Vegetables, fresh
Ch Bd: Cary Hoffman
**VP:* Mark Steakley
CIO: Jack Harris
QA Dir: Cirilo Zuniga
Dir IT: Larry Haig
VP Sls: John Pope

D-U-N-S 13-154-0817
SCHOLARSHIP AMERICA INC
7900 Intl Dr Ste 500, Minneapolis, MN 55425
Tel (800) 537-4180 *Founded/Ownrshp* 1961
Sales 166.4MM *EMP* 150
Accts B Baker Tilly Virc W Krause
SIC 8399 Fund raising organization, non-fee basis
Pr: Lauren A Segal
Pr: Susan Ponwith
CFO: Richard S Greene
Sr VP: Donald Lassere
VP: Debra Behrens
VP: Marilee Hedberg
VP: Barbara McBee
VP: Paul Vo
Ex Dir: Richard Millerick
Prgrm Mgr: Christy Borseth
Prgrm Mgr: Dawn Lehtinen

D-U-N-S 11-850-7128 IMP
■ SCHOLASTIC BOOK FAIRS INC
(*Suby of* SCHOLASTIC CORP) ★
1080 Greenwood Blvd, Lake Mary, FL 32746-5425
Tel (407) 829-7300 *Founded/Ownrshp* 2002
Sales 338.3MM^E *EMP* 1,800
SIC 5192 5199 5942 Books; Posters; Book stores
Pr: Alan Boyko
**CFO:* Maureen O'Connell
**Treas:* Vincent Marzano
Ex VP: Barbara A Marcus
**VP:* Kerry Collins
**VP:* R Anthony Hopkins
VP: Karen A Maloney
VP: Kevin J McEnery
VP: William Wegner
Ex Dir: Angela Im
Brnch Mgr: Jeffrey Bittner

D-U-N-S 15-428-7767 IMP
▲ SCHOLASTIC CORP
557 Broadway Lbby 1, New York, NY 10012-3999
Tel (212) 343-6100 *Founded/Ownrshp* 1920
Sales 1.6MMM *EMP* 8,900
Tkr Sym SCHL *Exch* NGS
SIC 2731 2721 7372 7812 6794 7311 Book publishing; Books: publishing only; Textbooks: publishing only, not printed on site; Magazines: publishing only, not printed on site; Educational computer software; Non-theatrical motion picture production, television; Video production; Motion picture production; Copyright buying & licensing; Advertising agencies
Ch Bd: Richard Robinson
Pr: Alan Boyko
Ofcr: Maureen O'Connell
**Ex VP:* Andrew S Hedden
Ex VP: Judith A Newman
VP: Ellie Berger
Snr Sftwr: Richard Dye

D-U-N-S 00-150-3580 IMP/EXP
■ SCHOLASTIC INC (NY)
(*Suby of* SCHOLASTIC CORP) ★
557 Broadway Lbby 1, New York, NY 10012-3999
Tel (800) 724-6527 *Founded/Ownrshp* 1920
Sales 1.5MMM^E *EMP* 8,250
SIC 2731 2721 7372 7812 Books: publishing only; Textbooks: publishing only, not printed on site; Magazines: publishing only, not printed on site; Statistical reports (periodicals): publishing only; Educational computer software; Video production; Television film production; Motion picture production & distribution
Ch Bd: Richard Robinson
Pr: Neal Goff
Ofcr: Gene Benkelman
**Ofcr:* Ken Cleary
**Ex VP:* Deborah A Forte
Ex VP: Linda Keene
**Ex VP:* Barbara A Marcus
**Ex VP:* Margery W Mayer
Ex VP: Maureen Oconnell
**Ex VP:* Hugh Roome
Sr VP: Ernest Fleishman
Sr VP: Kyle Good
Sr VP: Andrea Sporer
VP: Becky Bone
VP: Lois Bridges
VP: Charles B Deull
VP: Jean L Feiwel
VP: Linda Gadsby
VP: Leslie Garych
VP: Jazan Higgins
VP: Karen A Maloney
Board of Directors: Richard Spaulding, Ramon C Cortines, John L Davies, Charles T Harris III, Andrew S Hedden, Mae C Jemison, Linda Keene, Peter Mayer, John G Mc Donald, Augustus K Oliver

D-U-N-S 00-149-5902 IMP
■ SCHOLASTIC LIBRARY PUBLISHING INC (DE)
(*Suby of* SCHOLASTIC CORP) ★
90 Sherman Tpke, Danbury, CT 06816-0002
Tel (203) 797-3500 *Founded/Ownrshp* 1988
Sales 343.5MM^E *EMP* 1,828
SIC 2731 5963 5192 2721 5961 7371 Books: publishing only; Textbooks: publishing only, not printed on site; Encyclopedias, house-to-house; Encyclopedias & publications, direct sales; Books; Magazines; Periodicals; Magazines: publishing only, not printed on site; Statistical reports (periodicals): publishing only; Books, mail order (except book clubs); Magazines, mail order; Computer software development
Pr: Dick Robinson
**Ch Bd:* Dominique D'Hinnin
**Ch Bd:* Arnaud Lagardere
Pr: David M Arganbright
**CFO:* Lester Rackoff
Ex VP: Dante Cirilli
Ex VP: Stephen E Toman
Sr VP: Barry Jones
VP: Lawrence J Cianciolo
VP: Edward M Kabak

D-U-N-S 01-137-5193
SCHOLES ELECTRIC & COMMUNICATIONS
1021 Centennial Ave, Piscataway, NJ 08854-4178
Tel (732) 562-1900 *Founded/Ownrshp* 1954
Sales 131.2MM *EMP* 450
Accts De Falco & Co Certified Publ
SIC 1731 General electrical contractor
Pr: Tom Demcsak
**Pr:* Edward Welsh III
**CEO:* Gina Addeo
CFO: Erwin Moskowitz
VP: John Ferrugiaro
VP: Ramon Gonzalez
Dir IT: Steven Demcsak

D-U-N-S 00-174-6684 IMP/EXP
SCHOLLE IPN CORP
SCHOLLE PACKAGING
200 W North Ave, Northlake, IL 60164-2402
Tel (708) 562-7290 *Founded/Ownrshp* 1945
Sales 564.9MM^E *EMP* 2,100
SIC 2819 3081 2821 3089 Industrial inorganic chemicals; Packing materials, plastic sheet; Cellulose derivative materials; Plastic processing
CEO: Leon Gianneschi
Pr: Thomas Bickford
Treas: Jerry Trousdale
VP: Jim Middendorf
Dir Bus: Jim Kolar
Dir IT: Chris Ther
IT Man: Randy Weaver
Software D: Jeremy Biros
Opers Mgr: Kevin Mekaru
Sales Exec: Randy Austin
Sales Asso: Carson Heims

D-U-N-S 79-102-4255 IMP/EXP
SCHOLLE IPN PACKAGING INC
SCHOLLE PACKAGING
(*Suby of* SCHOLLE PACKAGING) ★
200 W North Ave, Northlake, IL 60164-2402
Tel (708) 562-7290 *Founded/Ownrshp* 2005
Sales 230.5MM^E *EMP* 807
SIC 3089 Plastic processing
Pr: Thomas Bickford
CFO: Jerry Trousdale
Sr VP: Alec Marketos
VP: Melania Craddock
VP: David Mondrus
Genl Mgr: Kent Kisselle
Genl Mgr: Xaverie Plashar

SCHOLLE PACKAGING
See SCHOLLE IPN CORP

SCHOLLE PACKAGING
See SCHOLLE IPN PACKAGING INC

SCHOLL'S
See DISTRIBUTION ALTERNATIVES INC

D-U-N-S 19-487-0432
SCHONFELD SECURITIES LLC
SCHONFELD TOOLS
2 Jericho Plz Ste 300, Jericho, NY 11753-1681
Tel (646) 735-3180 *Founded/Ownrshp* 1988
Sales 134.1MM^E *EMP* 867
SIC 6211 Traders, security
CEO: Steven Schonfeld
**Pr:* Andrew Fishman
**CFO:* Joseph Avantario
Ofcr: Michael Wilson
**Ex VP:* William Vidro
VP: Ryan Alder
**VP:* Howie Brammen
IT Man: Thomas Mullhey
Software D: Steve Harmon
Software D: Jim Petrizzi
Software D: Bob Pisani

SCHONFELD TOOLS
See SCHONFELD SECURITIES LLC

SCHOOL ADMINISTRATIVE UNIT
See TIMBERLANE REGIONAL SAU

D-U-N-S 80-315-6371
SCHOOL ADMINISTRATIVE UNIT 16
SAU 16
30 Linden St, Exeter, NH 03833-2622
Tel (603) 775-8400 *Founded/Ownrshp* 1970

Sales 68.3MM^E *EMP* 1,200
SIC 8211 Public elementary & secondary schools
**Prin:* Paul Flynn
Ex Dir: Eric Kobb
Dir IT: Darrel McKinnon
Psych: Kim Felch

D-U-N-S 08-032-6509
SCHOOL ADMINISTRATIVE UNIT 42
SAU 42
141 Ledge St, Nashua, NH 03060-3073
Tel (603) 966-1000 *Founded/Ownrshp* 2016
Sales 99.7MM^E *EMP* 2,002
SIC 8211 Public elementary & secondary schools

D-U-N-S 36-462-2886
SCHOOL BOARD OF BREVARD COUNTY
2700 Jdge Fran Jmeson Way, Viera, FL 32940-6699
Tel (321) 633-1000 *Founded/Ownrshp* 1900
Sales 626.9MM *EMP* 9,031
Accts Ernst & Young Llp Orlando Fl
SIC 8211 School board
Ch Bd: Andy Ziegler
**Ch Bd:* Amy Kneessy
Treas: Lalanya Wilson

D-U-N-S 00-832-2633
SCHOOL BOARD OF BROWARD COUNTY
RISK MANAGEMENT DEPARTMENT
600 Se 3rd Ave, Fort Lauderdale, FL 33301-3125
Tel (754) 321-0000 *Founded/Ownrshp* 1994
Sales 2.5MMM *EMP* 31,174
SIC 8211 Public elementary & secondary schools
COO: Donnie Carter
Bd of Dir: Robert Parks
Exec: Joy Emerson
Dir Risk M: Jeffrey Moquin
Ex Dir: Dildra Martin
Ex Dir: Claudia Munroe
Mng Dir: Adele Taylor
Off Mgr: Tammy Flanders
Off Mgr: Angela Linhart
Off Mgr: Kathryn McArthur
Off Mgr: Sharard Walker

D-U-N-S 07-728-3471
SCHOOL BOARD OF BROWARD COUNTY (INC)
SCHOOL DISTRICT BROWARD COUNTY
(*Suby of* BOARD OF COUNTY COMMISSIONERS) ★
600 Se 3rd Ave, Fort Lauderdale, FL 33301-3125
Tel (754) 321-0000 *Founded/Ownrshp* 1948
Sales 3.0MMM^E *EMP* 6,500
Accts Moore Stephens Lovelace Pa
SIC 8211 8222 Public elementary & secondary schools; Elementary school; Finishing school, secondary; High school, junior or senior; Technical institute
CFO: Benjamin Leong
VP: Dave Marcus
Dir Sec: Robert Krickovich Jr
Admn Mgr: Debi Mulford
Dir IT: Teresa Macri
IT Man: Ivonne Coronado
IT Man: Joe Kirkman
Pr Dir: Tracy Clark
Teacher Pr: Amanda Bailey
Instr Medi: Jeanine Gendron
Instr Medi: Lynne Oakvik
Board of Directors: Carol Andrews, Judy Budnick, Darla Carter, Beverly Gallagher, Stephanie Kraft, Robert Parks, Marty Rubinstein, Lois Wexler, Benjamin J Williams

D-U-N-S 10-224-2745
SCHOOL BOARD OF CHARLOTTE COUNTY FLORIDA
1445 Education Way, Port Charlotte, FL 33948-1052
Tel (941) 255-0808 *Founded/Ownrshp* 1963
Sales 165.5MM *EMP* 2,000
SIC 8211 School board
Ch Bd: Barbara Rendell
**Ch Bd:* Ian Vincent
**Prin:* Barbara Kendall
**Prin:* Alleen Miller
**Prin:* Lee Swift

D-U-N-S 84-967-9634
SCHOOL BOARD OF CITY OF NORFOLK
NORFOLK PUBLIC SCHOOLS
800 E City Hall Ave # 1201, Norfolk, VA 23510-2731
Tel (757) 628-3830 *Founded/Ownrshp* 1682
Sales 158.2MM^E *EMP* 6,527
SIC 8211 Public elementary & secondary schools
**CFO:* John Maniscalco
Dir Surg: Patricia Dillard
**Dir Surg:* Vizel Townsend
Ex Dir: Cathy Lassiter
**CIO:* Pat Salvin
IT Man: Tifany Speight
Netwrk Mgr: David Feliciano

D-U-N-S 82-723-4121
SCHOOL BOARD OF CITY OF VIRGINIA BEACH
ADMINISTATION DEPT
2512 George Mason Dr, Virginia Beach, VA 23456-9105
Tel (757) 263-1033 *Founded/Ownrshp* 1963
Sales 185.7MM^E *EMP* 5,000
Accts Cherry Bekaet & Holland Llp
SIC 8211 Public elementary & secondary schools
Ch: Daniel D Edwards
V Ch: William J Brunke IV
**COO:* Dale R Holt
**CFO:* Farrell E Hanzaker
Dir Sec: Richard Ponti
Admn Mgr: Pamela Bennis
Admn Mgr: Nanocie Diggs
Admn Mgr: Edward Schrecengost
IT Man: Dave Foster
IT Man: Tom Shearer
IT Man: Nikki Smead

D-U-N-S 06-588-6327
SCHOOL BOARD OF FLAGLER COUNTY (FL)
FLAGLER COUNTY SCHOOL DISTRICT
1769 E Moody Blvd Bldg 2f, Bunnell, FL 32110-5991
Tel (386) 437-7526 *Founded/Ownrshp* 1917
Sales 92.8MM^E *EMP* 1,800^E
Accts David W Martin Cpa Tallahas
SIC 8211 8222 School board; Junior colleges & technical institutes
MIS Dir: Mark Saltmarsh
Teacher Pr: James Wood

D-U-N-S 10-001-2863
SCHOOL BOARD OF HIGHLANDS COUNTY
426 School St, Sebring, FL 33870-4048
Tel (863) 471-5555 *Founded/Ownrshp* 1921
Sales 108.6MM^E *EMP* 1,463
SIC 8211 School board
Ch: William Brantley II
**Prin:* Donna Howerton
Dir IT: Lois Miners
IT Man: Bob Perry
Board of Directors: Margaret Cooper, Rob Fitzgerald, Ned Hancock, Donna Howeton, Wendy Rensro

D-U-N-S 82-841-1616
SCHOOL BOARD OF LAKE COUNTY (INC)
201 W Burleigh Blvd, Tavares, FL 32778-2407
Tel (352) 253-6500 *Founded/Ownrshp* 2008
Sales 342.3MM *EMP* 10^E
Accts Purvis Gray And Company Llp
SIC 8211 School board
Ex Dir: Carman Cullen
CFO: Carol Macleod
Dir Sec: Sebrina Dillon-Banks
CTO: Ken Osman III
MIS Dir: Harris Jacobs
Pr Dir: Chris Patton
Teacher Pr: Laurie Marshall
Instr Medi: Faith Harris
Psych: Richard Griffith
Psych: Loretta Jones
Psych: Anne Shutze

D-U-N-S 10-596-4068
SCHOOL BOARD OF MIAMI-DADE COUNTY
M-DCPS SCHOOL BOARD
1450 Ne 2nd Ave, Miami, FL 33132-1308
Tel (305) 995-1000 *Founded/Ownrshp* 2009
Sales 3.5MMM *EMP* 9
Accts Mcgladrey Llp Miami Florida
SIC 8211 School board
Ch Bd: Perla Tabares Hantman
Ofcr: Ivo Gomez
Ex Dir: Marla Berenson

D-U-N-S 19-041-4359
SCHOOL BOARD OF ORANGE COUNTY FLORIDA
445 W Amelia St Lbby, Orlando, FL 32801-1153
Tel (407) 317-3200 *Founded/Ownrshp* 1869
Sales 2.1MMM *EMP* 25,000
Accts Ernst & Young Llp Orlando Fl
SIC 8211 School board
Ch Bd: Bill Sublette
**CFO:* Toni Greene
Ex Dir: Rhonda Scott
Psych: Peggy Donovan
Doctor: Joan Flewelling MD
Snr Mgr: Pamela Carson

D-U-N-S 13-202-6527
SCHOOL BOARD OF PALM BEACH COUNTY
3300 Forest Hill Blvd C316, West Palm Beach, FL 33406-5813
Tel (561) 434-8000 *Founded/Ownrshp* 1909
Sales 897.3MM^E *EMP* 21,000
SIC 8211 Public elementary & secondary schools
Ch: Chuck Shaw

D-U-N-S 07-831-2907
SCHOOL BOARD OF POLK COUNTY
1915 S Floral Ave, Bartow, FL 33830-7124
Tel (863) 534-0500 *Founded/Ownrshp* 1895
Sales 206.1MM^E *EMP* 19,000
SIC 8211 Public elementary & secondary schools
Admn Mgr: Sheryl Gentry
CTO: Brenda Smith
MIS Dir: Judy Roberts
Snr Mgr: Linda Babington
Snr Mgr: Anna Carter
Snr Mgr: Brittney Oakes

D-U-N-S 00-340-7293
SCHOOL BOARD OF SARASOTA COUNTY
(*Suby of* ADULT & CMNTY ENRICHMENT ACE) ★
1960 Landings Blvd, Sarasota, FL 34231-3304
Tel (941) 927-9000 *Founded/Ownrshp* 1950
Sales 233.9MM^E *EMP* 141^E
SIC 8211 School board
Ch Bd: Frank Kobach
**Ch Bd:* Jane Goodwin
Prin: Jeff Hradek
Prin: Candace Millington

D-U-N-S 05-054-1754
SCHOOL CITY OF EAST CHICAGO
1401 E 144th St, East Chicago, IN 46312-3046
Tel (219) 391-4100 *Founded/Ownrshp* 1888
Sales 56.3MM^E *EMP* 1,000
SIC 8211 Elementary & secondary schools
Prin: Javier Abrego
Prin: Michael Milich
Dir IT: Laura Hubinger
Dir IT: Mary Jensen

SCHOOL DISTRICT 17
See MILLARD PUBLIC SCHOOLS

D-U-N-S 09-575-0014
SCHOOL DISTRICT 27J CAPITAL FACILITY FEE FOUNDATION
18551 E 160th Ave, Brighton, CO 80601-8519
Tel (303) 655-2900 *Founded/Ownrshp* 1896
Sales 319.8M *EMP* 1,200^E
Accts Flewelling & Mitton Pc Louisv
SIC 8211 Public combined elementary & secondary school
Dir Sec: Nancy Ross
MIS Dir: Jeremy Heidi
IT Man: Karen Shima
Pr Dir: Kevin Denke
Teacher Pr: Michael Cloud

SCHOOL DISTRICT BROWARD COUNTY
See SCHOOL BOARD OF BROWARD COUNTY (INC)

D-U-N-S 08-863-6113
SCHOOL DISTRICT FIVE OF LEXINGTON AND RICHLAND COUNTIES
1020 Dutch Fork Rd, Irmo, SC 29063-8822
Tel (803) 476-8000 *Founded/Ownrshp* 1952
Sales 201.3MM *EMP* 2,500
Accts Derrick Stubbs & Stith Llp
SIC 8211 Public elementary & secondary schools; Public elementary school; Public junior high school; Public senior high school
Pr Dir: Mark Bounds
Teacher Pr: Allison Jacques

D-U-N-S 09-626-1177
SCHOOL DISTRICT OF CITY OF ALLENTOWN
31 S Penn St, Allentown, PA 18102-5409
Tel (484) 765-4001 *Founded/Ownrshp* 1900
Sales 178.8MM^E *EMP* 2,000
SIC 8211 Public elementary & secondary schools
Bd of Dir: Janine Allen
Bd of Dir: Julie Ambrose
Bd of Dir: David Zimmerman
VP: Ce-Ce Gerlach
Ex Dir: Christina Mazzella
Ex Dir: Stacey Prohaska
Dir Sec: Barry Rodenbagh
Site Mgr: William Penn
Pr Dir: Kimberly Golden-Benner
Board of Directors: Patrick Brennen, Patricia Hoffman, James Levan, Edith Lindenmuth

D-U-N-S 02-008-9256
SCHOOL DISTRICT OF CITY OF BIRMINGHAM
BIRMINGHAM PUBLIC SCHOOLS
31301 Evergreen Rd, Beverly Hills, MI 48025-3800
Tel (248) 203-3000 *Founded/Ownrshp* 1882
Sales 85.3MM^E *EMP* 1,400
Accts Yeo & Yeo Pc Flint Michig
SIC 8211 Public elementary & secondary schools
Adm Dir: Jeanne Asch
**Ex Dir:* Kelly Friedland-Lovik
Ex Dir: Kelly Lovik
Genl Mgr: Deborah Piesz
Off Admin: Gail Frederickson
Off Admin: Maria Reilly
Off Admin: Jacquie Stephenson
MIS Dir: Kevin Galbraith
VP Mktg: Stephen King
Schl Brd P: Geri Rinschler
Teacher Pr: Dandridge Floyd

D-U-N-S 06-685-5016
SCHOOL DISTRICT OF CITY OF ERIE
ERIE'S PUBLIC SCHOOL
148 W 21st St, Erie, PA 16502-2834
Tel (814) 874-6000 *Founded/Ownrshp* 1945
Sales 121.3MM^E *EMP* 1,700
SIC 8211 Public combined elementary & secondary school
Adm Dir: Tony Casey
IT Man: Joseph Sulkowskie
Pr Dir: Darla Devlin
Board of Directors: John C Harkins, Richard Hilinski

D-U-N-S 01-088-0227
SCHOOL DISTRICT OF CITY OF FLINT
FLINT COMMUNITY SCHOOLS
923 E Kearsley St, Flint, MI 48503-1974
Tel (810) 760-1000 *Founded/Ownrshp* 1905
Sales 190.2MM^E *EMP* 3,371
SIC 8211 Public elementary & secondary schools
**Pr:* Antoinette Lockett
**Treas:* Vera Julie Perry
**VP:* Isaiah Oliver
Ex Dir: Bernadean Clothier
Cmptr Lab: Lois Mengel
Teacher Pr: Rick Lee

D-U-N-S 02-009-3449
SCHOOL DISTRICT OF CITY OF PONTIAC
PONTIAC SCHOOL DISTRICT
47200 Woodward Ave, Pontiac, MI 48342-5008
Tel (248) 451-6800 *Founded/Ownrshp* 1849
Sales 70.6MM^E *EMP* 1,800
Accts Alan C Young & Associates P
SIC 8211 Public senior high school; Public junior high school; Public elementary school
Brnch Mgr: Ernie Russell
Genl Mgr: Laura Bohr

D-U-N-S 01-731-1168
SCHOOL DISTRICT OF CLAY COUNTY
SCHOOLS OF CLAY COUNTY
900 Walnut St, Green Cove Springs, FL 32043-3129
Tel (904) 284-6500 *Founded/Ownrshp* 1916
Sales 322.0MM *EMP* 5,000
SIC 8211 School board; Public elementary & secondary schools; Specialty education
**Ch:* Carol Studdard
DP Exec: Chris Phillips
IT Man: Scott Kerr
Teacher Pr: Cathy Richardson
Teacher Pr: Brenda Troutman
Instr Medi: Karen Robinson
HC Dir: Terry Roth

D-U-N-S 80-467-1105
SCHOOL DISTRICT OF HERNANDO COUNTY FLORIDA
919 N Broad St, Brooksville, FL 34601-2397
Tel (352) 797-7000 *Founded/Ownrshp* 1993
Sales 198.8MM *EMP* 2,900
SIC 8211 Public elementary & secondary schools
**CFO:* George Gall
**Ch:* Charles Fagan
Dir Sec: Bill Hall
Pr Dir: Karen Jordan

D-U-N-S 04-934-1507
SCHOOL DISTRICT OF HILLSBORUGH COUNTY
129 Glen Ridge Ave, Temple Terrace, FL 33617-4101
Tel (813) 817-4507 *Founded/Ownrshp* 2010
Sales 1.9MMM *EMP* 6^E
SIC 8211 Public elementary & secondary schools
Prin: Patricia Velazquez

D-U-N-S 12-075-4676
SCHOOL DISTRICT OF INDIAN RIVER COUNTY
6500 57th St, Vero Beach, FL 32967-6002
Tel (772) 564-3000 *Founded/Ownrshp* 1925
Sales 141.4MM *EMP* 2,000
SIC 8211 Public elementary & secondary schools; Public vocational/technical school
Ofcr: Angela McCutchen
VP: Christopher Hiser
VP: Raubin Pierce
Ex Dir: Denise Roberts
HC Dir: Lillian Martinez

D-U-N-S 03-164-2572
SCHOOL DISTRICT OF LACROSSE
HOGAN ADMINISTRATIVE CENTER
807 East Ave S, La Crosse, WI 54601-4982
Tel (608) 789-7600 *Founded/Ownrshp* 2012
Sales 57.1MM^E *EMP* 1,147
SIC 8211 Public elementary & secondary schools
Bd of Dir: Steve Kipp
Bd of Dir: Dave Rudolph
Bd of Dir: Tom Thompson
VP: Jan Correll
Prin: Dave Gluch
Prin: Tarry Hall
Prin: Tucky Skemp
Pr Dir: Nicholas Maricou
HC Dir: Carla Beneke

D-U-N-S 06-978-3140
SCHOOL DISTRICT OF LANCASTER (PA)
251 S Prince St, Lancaster, PA 17603-5396
Tel (717) 299-2700 *Founded/Ownrshp* 1800
Sales 111.3MM^E *EMP* 1,400
SIC 8211 Public elementary & secondary schools
COO: Matt R Przywara

D-U-N-S 07-937-6010
SCHOOL DISTRICT OF MANATEE COUNTY FLORIDA
215 Manatee Ave W, Bradenton, FL 34205-8840
Tel (941) 708-8770 *Founded/Ownrshp* 2014
Sales 34.0MM^E *EMP* 5,500^E
SIC 8211 Public elementary & secondary schools
Dir Sec: Sally Hull
MIS Dir: Patrick Fletcher
Teacher Pr: Sarah Brown
HC Dir: Willie Clark

D-U-N-S 07-804-5275
SCHOOL DISTRICT OF OCONEE COUNTY
414 S Pine St, Walhalla, SC 29691-2146
Tel (864) 886-4400 *Founded/Ownrshp* 1953
Sales 80.6MM^E *EMP* 1,700
Accts Stancil Cooley Estep & Stamey
SIC 8211 Public elementary & secondary schools
VP: Cathy Plowden
Genl Mgr: Scott Hood
IT Man: Joy Waller
Pr Dir: Karen Powell
Teacher Pr: Rosemary Wise

D-U-N-S 10-001-3036
SCHOOL DISTRICT OF OSCEOLA COUNTY FL
817 Bill Beck Blvd, Kissimmee, FL 34744-4492
Tel (407) 870-4600 *Founded/Ownrshp* 1887
Sales 545.2MM *EMP* 6,250^E
Accts Moore Stephens Lovelace Pa
SIC 8211 Public elementary & secondary schools
CFO: Pat Alderman
Prin: George Sullivan
Ex Dir: Beth Rattie
Dir Sec: Randy Schuttera
MIS Dir: Robert Curran
Pr Dir: Dana Lee Schafer
Teacher Pr: Tammy Cope-Otterson
Teacher Pr: Heather Day
HC Dir: Ken Debord
Pgrm Dir: Marcie Hill

D-U-N-S 04-882-5962
SCHOOL DISTRICT OF PHILADELPHIA
440 N Broad St, Philadelphia, PA 19130-4090
Tel (215) 400-4000 *Founded/Ownrshp* 1818
Sales 216.9M^E *EMP* 21,065
SIC 8211 Public elementary & secondary schools
CEO: Paul G Vallas
**CFO:* Matthew E Stanski
Dir Sec: Brendan Lee
Pr Dir: Kevin Geary
Pr Dir: Evelyn Sample-Oates
Teacher Pr: Louis Bellardine
Teacher Pr: Leslie Lindsey
Teacher Pr: Kendra-Lee Rosati
Teacher Pr: Naomi Wyatt
HC Dir: Bettyann Creighton
Pgrm Dir: Kineret Shakow

D-U-N-S 03-010-1547
SCHOOL DISTRICT OF PICKENS COUNTY
1348 Griffin Mill Rd, Easley, SC 29640-6997
Tel (864) 397-1000 *Founded/Ownrshp* 1826
Sales 156.0MM *EMP* 1,600
Accts Greene Finney & Horton Llp
SIC 8211 Public elementary & secondary schools; Public elementary school; Public junior high school; Public senior high school
Genl Mgr: Terri Smith
Pr Dir: John EBY
Schl Brd P: Brian Swords
Teacher Pr: Stephanie Lackey
HC Dir: Angela Watson

D-U-N-S 01-051-2135
SCHOOL DISTRICT OF PUTNAM COUNTY FLORIDA
PUTNAM COUNTY SCHOOL DISTRICT
200 Reid St Ste 1, Palatka, FL 32177-3737
Tel (386) 329-0653 *Founded/Ownrshp* 1885
Sales 92.2MM^E *EMP* 1,600
SIC 8211 Public elementary & secondary schools
Exec: Joe Warren
Dir Sec: Travis Weaver
MIS Dir: Jim Yopp
Dir IT: Dee Swamer
IT Man: Phil McWhirt
Schl Brd P: Nikki Cummings
Teacher Pr: Debbie Decubellis

D-U-N-S 07-930-7878
SCHOOL DISTRICT OF WEST ALLIS-WEST MILWAUKEE ET AL
1205 S 70th St Ste 440, West Allis, WI 53214-3167
Tel (414) 604-3000 *Founded/Ownrshp* 2014
Sales 116.2MM *EMP* 13^E
Accts Rpb Cpas Milwaukee Wi
SIC 8211 Elementary & secondary schools

D-U-N-S 07-979-8995
SCHOOL DISTRICT OF WEST PALM BEACH COUNTY
PALM BEACH COUNTY PUBLIC SCHL
3300 Forest Hill Blvd, West Palm Beach, FL 33406-5813
Tel (561) 434-8747 *Founded/Ownrshp* 2015
Sales 1.9MMM *EMP* 40,294^E
Accts Rsm Us Llp West Palm Beach F
SIC 8211 Public elementary & secondary schools
Treas: Jenny Okoee
Exec: Gary Swaye
Ex Dir: Margarita Pinkos
Genl Mgr: Steve Backhus
Psych: Juliana Davis

D-U-N-S 03-961-5307
SCHOOL DISTRICT U-46
355 E Chicago St, Elgin, IL 60120-6500
Tel (847) 888-5000 *Founded/Ownrshp* 1840
Sales 503.5MM *EMP* 4,250
SIC 8211

SCHOOL DST OF OSCEOLA CNTY FLA
See OSCEOLAK12FL

D-U-N-S 08-443-3838
SCHOOL EMPLOYEES RETIREMENT SYSTEM OF OHIO
(*Suby of* EXECUTIVE OFFICE STATE OF OHIO) ★
300 E Broad St Ste 100, Columbus, OH 43215-3747
Tel (614) 222-5853 *Founded/Ownrshp* 1937
Sales NA *EMP* 166
Accts Mcgladrey Llp Cleveland Ohi
SIC 6371 9441 Pension, health & welfare funds; Administration of social & manpower programs;
Ex Dir: James R Winfree
**CFO:* Virginia Briszendine
Ofcr: Joe Bell
Ofcr: Elizabeth Homeier
Sr Inv Off: Steve Price
Sr Inv Off: Tim Steitz
VP: Alan Tharp
Ex Dir: Thomas Anderson
Ex Dir: Carla Marshall
Dir IT: Jay Patel
IT Man: Adam Furmkin

SCHOOL FOR INTL TRAINING
See WORLD LEARNING INC

SCHOOL OF FILM AND TELEVISION
See CHAPMAN UNIVERSITY

SCHOOL OF NURSING
See SHARON REGIONAL HEALTH SYSTEM

D-U-N-S 07-629-1152
SCHOOL OF OZARKS
COLLEGE OF THE OZARKS
100 Opportunity Ave, Point Lookout, MO 65726
Tel (417) 239-1900 *Founded/Ownrshp* 1906
Sales 92.1MM *EMP* 300^E
Accts The Whitlock Company Llp Spri
SIC 8221 College, except junior
Pr: Jerry C Davis
**CFO:* Charles Hughes
VP: Kurt McDonald
Ex Dir: Sue Head
Genl Mgr: Craig Ernsting
Genl Mgr: Lori Miller
Pr Dir: Ben Carson

D-U-N-S 07-524-7148 IMP
SCHOOL OF VISUAL ARTS INC
209 E 23rd St Frnt 1, New York, NY 10010-3901
Tel (212) 592-2000 *Founded/Ownrshp* 1947
Sales 131.5MM *EMP* 1,400
SIC 8221 5734 5999 College, except junior; Computer & software stores; Artists' supplies & materials
CEO: David Rhodes
**CFO:* Gary Shillet
**Ex VP:* Anthony Rhodes
Assoc Dir: Jim Cavaliere
Assoc Dir: Elaine Chow
Assoc Dir: Vennette Jones
Ex Dir: Javier Vega
Off Mgr: Rebecca Fowler
Off Admin: Chloe R Bush
CIO: Tomescu Cosmin
Dir IT: Cosmin Tomescu

D-U-N-S 06-577-6031
SCHOOL SERVICES AND LEASING INC
(*Suby of* NATIONAL EXPRESS GROUP PLC)
9011 Mtn Rdg Dr Ste 200, Austin, TX 78759-7251
Tel (512) 241-7050 *Founded/Ownrshp* 1965, 1975
Sales 71.3MM^E *EMP* 2,978
SIC 4151 4141 School buses; Local bus charter service
Pr: Don Kincaid
**CFO:* Joe Jahnke
**VP:* Kathy Hall
Web Prj Mg: Ty Smith

D-U-N-S 00-614-4026 IMP/EXP
SCHOOL SPECIALTY INC
W6316 Design Dr, Greenville, WI 54942-8404
Tel (920) 734-5712 *Founded/Ownrshp* 2013
Sales 675.0MM *EMP* 1,750
SIC 5049 5021

D-U-N-S 07-911-8224 IMP/EXP
▲ SCHOOL SPECIALTY INC
W6316 Design Dr, Greenville, WI 54942-8404
Tel (920) 734-5712 *Founded/Ownrshp* 1959
Sales 1.6MMM^E *EMP* 1,450^E
Tkr Sym SCOO *Exch* OTO
SIC 5049 5021 5961 School supplies; Furniture; Office & public building furniture; School desks; Educational supplies & equipment, mail order
Pr: Joseph Yorio
**Ch Bd:* James Henderson
CFO: Ryan M Bohr
Ex VP: Edward J Carr Jr
Ex VP: Rick Holden
Ex VP: Todd A Shaw
Ex VP: Todd Shaw
Sr VP: Laura J Vartanian
VP: Mark Christopher
VP: Allen Hoeppner
Exec: Sheri Yerges
Board of Directors: Gus D Halas, Justin Lu, Andrew E Schultz

D-U-N-S 16-966-7305
SCHOOL UNION 42 CSD 10
45 Millard Harrison Dr, Readfield, ME 04355-3583
Tel (207) 685-3336 *Founded/Ownrshp* 2004
Sales 1.3MM^E *EMP* 1,412^E
SIC 8211 Public elementary & secondary schools

D-U-N-S 06-881-8335
SCHOOLCRAFT COLLEGE
18600 Haggerty Rd, Livonia, MI 48152-2696
Tel (734) 462-4400 *Founded/Ownrshp* 1961
Sales 44.8MM *EMP* 1,000
Accts Plante & Moran Pllc Clinton
SIC 8222 Community college
Pr: Conway A Jeffress
**CFO:* Glenn Cerny
Trst: Kevin McNamara
Trst: Gregory J Stempien
**VP:* Cheryl Hagen
**VP:* Richard Weinkauf
Ex Dir: Cindy Koenigsknecht
Ex Dir: Regina Mosley
Ex Dir: James Polkowski
**Ex Dir:* James Ryan
Ex Dir: Laura Sensing

SCHOOLS OF CLAY COUNTY
See SCHOOL DISTRICT OF CLAY COUNTY

D-U-N-S 07-608-5505
SCHOOLSFIRST FEDERAL CREDIT UNION
2115 N Broadway, Santa Ana, CA 92706-2613
Tel (714) 258-4000 *Founded/Ownrshp* 2014
Sales NA *EMP* 743
SIC 6061 Federal credit unions
Pr: Bill Cheney
V Ch: Kary Bemoll
Ex VP: Martha Monzon
VP: Terri Agius
VP: Emilio Arenas
VP: Jose Lara
VP: Mark Rapp
VP: Trisha Rome
VP: Bryan Wallace
VP: Brenda Zimmerman
Exec: Cary Heton

D-U-N-S 07-659-9398
SCHOONER CAPITAL LLC
60 South St, Boston, MA 02111-2759
Tel (617) 963-5200 *Founded/Ownrshp* 1971
Sales NA *EMP* 12
SIC 6159 Small business investment companies

D-U-N-S 16-163-2757 IMP
SCHOTT CORP
(*Suby of* SCHOTT AG)
555 Taxter Rd Ste 470, Elmsford, NY 10523-2363
Tel (914) 831-2200 *Founded/Ownrshp* 1986
Sales 1.0MMM^E *EMP* 3,101
SIC 3211 3829 3221 3229 Flat glass; Measuring & controlling devices; Glass containers; Vials, glass; Glass fiber products
Ch Bd: Linda S Mayer
**Ch Bd:* Greg Wolters
**Pr:* Dr Andreas F Liebenberg
COO: Michael Landi
**VP:* George Giatras
**VP:* Manfred Jaeckel
Genl Mgr: Robert Galante
IT Man: Ashley Bartow
Tech Mgr: Ronald Klimek
QC Dir: Bill Long
Opers Mgr: David Alunni

D-U-N-S 06-672-0434 IMP
SCHOTT GEMTRON CORP
VINCENNES DIVISION
(*Suby of* SCHOTT CORP) ★
615 Highway 68, Sweetwater, TN 37874-1911
Tel (423) 337-3522 *Founded/Ownrshp* 1972
Sales 185.1MM^E *EMP* 1,000
SIC 3211 Flat glass
Pr: Douglas Roberts
CFO: Greg Willig
**Treas:* Gary Miller
**VP:* Mark Dale
**VP:* Lester Delp
**Prin:* Gene Farmer
**Prin:* Julie White
Natl Sales: Steven Leek
Sls Dir: Tim Dye

D-U-N-S 00-955-2220 IMP
SCHOTT NORTH AMERICA INC
(*Suby of* SCHOTT CORP) ★
555 Taxter Rd Ste 470, Elmsford, NY 10523-2352
Tel (914) 831-2200 *Founded/Ownrshp* 1998
Sales 744.3MM^E *EMP* 2,700
SIC 5099 Containers: glass, metal or plastic
CEO: Greg Wolters
CFO: Michael Kitts
VP Admn: Stefan Spengler
IT Man: Dan Bergman
Board of Directors: Gerald Fine

D-U-N-S 06-358-6036 IMP/EXP
SCHOTTENSTEIN STORES CORP
VALUE CITY
4300 E 5th Ave, Columbus, OH 43219-1816
Tel (614) 221-9200 *Founded/Ownrshp* 1972
Sales 2.7MMM^E *EMP* 30,050
SIC 5311 5712 5912 5999 Department stores, discount; Furniture stores; Proprietary (non-prescription medicine) stores; Toiletries, cosmetics & perfumes
Ch Bd: Jay Schottenstein
Pr: Steve Rabe
**CFO:* Jeffrey Swanson
Treas: Benton E Kraner
Ex VP: Jim Frasso
**Ex VP:* David Thompson
VP: Michael Broidy
VP: Steve Haffer
Genl Mgr: Shawn Beavin
Dir IT: Jerry Sprout
Site Mgr: Ron Stogner

D-U-N-S 10-401-3388 IMP
SCHRADER-BRIDGEPORT INTERNATIONAL INC
AIRAWARE
(*Suby of* AUGUST LUX HOLDING COMPANY SARL)
205 Frazier Rd, Altavista, VA 24517-1020
Tel (434) 369-4741 *Founded/Ownrshp* 2014
Sales 484.1MM^E *EMP* 2,117
SIC 3492 3714 3491 3011 Hose & tube couplings, hydraulic/pneumatic; Motor vehicle wheels & parts; Tire valve cores; Industrial valves; Tire & inner tube materials & related products; Tire sundries or tire repair materials, rubber
Pr: Hugh W Charvat
**CEO:* Kersi Dordi
**VP:* Dave Berg
**VP:* Ronald Klump
VP: Drew Leftwich
VP: Trevor Potter
**VP:* Gary Spanos
Dir IT: Paul Greene
Mtls Mgr: Mark Migliozzi

D-U-N-S 09-752-1199 IMP
SCHRATTER FOODS INC
ANCO FINE CHEESE
(*Suby of* EUREXPAN B.V.)
333 Fairfield Rd Ste 2, Fairfield, NJ 07004-1961
Tel (973) 461-2400 *Founded/Ownrshp* 1990
Sales 123.8MM^E *EMP* 180
SIC 5143 5149 Cheese; Chocolate
Pr: Alain Voss
COO: Sandy Bodi
CFO: Bertrand Proust
**Ex VP:* Carmen Messina

D-U-N-S 00-281-2865 IMP/EXP
SCHREIBER FOODS INC (WI)
400 N Washington St, Green Bay, WI 54301-5111
Tel (920) 437-7601 *Founded/Ownrshp* 1945, 1962
Sales 2.2MMM^E *EMP* 5,500
SIC 2022 3556 3565 Processed cheese; Natural cheese; Cheese making machinery; Vacuum packaging machinery
Ch Bd: Larry P Fergusen
**Pr:* Michael J Haddad
Pr: Steve Theurer
**CFO:* Matt P Mueller
CFO: Matt Mueller
Ex VP: Ted Christiansen
Sr VP: Frank Eckstein
Sr VP: Frederick J Parker
VP: James Allen
VP: Tom Andreoli
VP: Nancy Armbrust
VP: Dennis Clark
VP: John D Connor
VP: Rob Dilworth
VP: Helmut Felder
VP: Michael Koval
VP: Staci Kring
VP: Alfred Ottolino
VP: Stephen Shelley
**VP:* Harley Skidmore
VP: Jerry Smyth

D-U-N-S 79-066-7885 EXP
SCHREIBER INTERNATIONAL INC
(*Suby of* SCHREIBER FOODS INC) ★
425 Pine St, Green Bay, WI 54301-5137
Tel (920) 437-7601 *Founded/Ownrshp* 1979
Sales 166.9MM^E *EMP* 120^E
SIC 5143 Dairy products, except dried or canned
Pr: Tim T Opel
**Sec:* Brian P Liddy
**VP:* Raj Narasimmon
VP: Stephen Shelley
Dir IT: Troy Gibson
Mktg Dir: Terry Moeller

D-U-N-S 96-120-5440
SCHREINER CORP
28210 Se 440th St, Enumclaw, WA 98022-9216
Tel (253) 736-5774 *Founded/Ownrshp* 1983
Sales 14.5MM *EMP* 2,700
SIC 7374 Data processing & preparation
CEO: Brenda Darlene Schreiner
Pr: Albert W Schreiner

D-U-N-S 04-436-2564
SCHRODER US HOLDINGS INC
(*Suby of* SCHRODER INTERNATIONAL HOLDINGS LIMITED)
875 3rd Ave Fl 21, New York, NY 10022-7253
Tel (212) 641-3800 *Founded/Ownrshp* 1968
Sales 215.3MM^E *EMP* 1,646
SIC 6282 6719 6211 6799 Investment advisory service; Investment holding companies, except banks; Brokers, security; Dealers, security; Investment bankers; Venture capital companies
Pr: George W Mallinckrodt
VP: Mona Yee
Dir IT: Henry Broom
IT Man: Steven Henkle
Mktg Dir: Jennifer Manser

D-U-N-S 80-837-2536
SCHRYVER MEDICAL SALES AND MARKETING LLC
12075 E 45th Ave Ste 600, Denver, CO 80239-3136
Tel (303) 371-0073 *Founded/Ownrshp* 1993
Sales 71.7MM^E *EMP* 1,000
Accts Londer & Associates Pc Den
SIC 8071 8011 Medical laboratories; Radiologist
CEO: Mark Schryver
**Ex VP:* Todd Hubbard
VP: Jay Bruckner
**VP:* Jay Schryver

SCHUECK STEEL
See LEXICON INC

D-U-N-S 08-372-2850
■ SCHUFF STEEL CO
(*Suby of* DBM GLOBAL INC) ★
1841 W Buchanan St, Phoenix, AZ 85007-3335
Tel (602) 252-7787 *Founded/Ownrshp* 1976
Sales 524.8MM^E *EMP* 1,359
SIC 3441 Building components, structural steel
Ch: David A Schuff
**Pr:* Rustin Roach
COO: Tracy Metzger
VP: Les Dias
**VP:* Michael R Hill
VP: Rik Kempton
**VP:* Scott Sherman
Exec: Will Trujillo
IT Man: Greg Shapley
Board of Directors: Michael Hill, James Roach, David Schuff

D-U-N-S 06-628-5768
■ SCHULER HOMES INC
(*Suby of* DR HORTON INC) ★
828 Fort Street Mall 4th, Honolulu, HI 96813-4332
Tel (808) 521-5661 *Founded/Ownrshp* 2002
Sales 94.5MM^E *EMP* 500
Accts Ernst & Young Llp Honolulu H
SIC 6552 Land subdividers & developers, residential
Ch Bd: James K Schuler
**CFO:* Pamela Jones
**Ex VP:* Michael T Jones
Sr VP: Harvey Goth
VP: Peter Aiello
VP Sls: Mary K Flood
Board of Directors: Thomas Bevilacqua, Martin Hart, Bert Kobayashi

D-U-N-S 00-428-9096 IMP/EXP
SCHULER INC (OH)
(*Suby of* SCHULER AG)
7145 Commerce Blvd, Canton, MI 48187-4288
Tel (734) 207-7200 *Founded/Ownrshp* 1961, 1992
Sales 111.5MM *EMP* 100
Accts Clayton And Mckervey Southfie
SIC 5084 3444 3599 Industrial machinery & equipment; Sheet metal specialties, not stamped; Custom machinery
CEO: Stefan Klebert
**COO:* Peter Jost
**CFO:* Norbert Broger
CFO: Marcus Ketter
**CFO:* Alexander Nitsche
VP: Tim Quinn
VP: Bob Rich
**VP:* Robert Rich
Mng Dir: Martin Habert
Genl Mgr: Linda Florance
IT Man: Paul Dixon

D-U-N-S 00-384-9973
SCHULL CONSTRUCTION CO
405 1st Ave Ne, Watertown, SD 57201-2701
Tel (605) 886-3495 *Founded/Ownrshp* 1946
Sales 135.7MM^E *EMP* 350
SIC 5072 Hardware
Pr: Lee E Schull

D-U-N-S 17-792-1538
SCHULTE BUILDING SYSTEMS INC
17600 Badtke Rd, Hockley, TX 77447-7818
Tel (281) 304-6111 *Founded/Ownrshp* 2007
Sales 150.0MM *EMP* 564
Accts Fitts Roberts & Co Pc Ho
SIC 3448 Prefabricated metal buildings
Pr: Fred Koetting
**Ex VP:* Frank Rosales
Ex VP: Robert Smith
VP: Mike Giacomo
**VP:* Eric Masterson
**VP:* Ronnie Peters
**VP:* Matt Stone
Dist Mgr: Joe Arnold
Dist Mgr: Brad Cook
Dist Mgr: Tommy Crouch
Dist Mgr: Jeff Timme

D-U-N-S 09-296-4444
SCHULTE ROTH & ZABEL LLP
919 3rd Ave Frnt 2, New York, NY 10022-3905
Tel (212) 756-2000 *Founded/Ownrshp* 1969
Sales 160.3MM^E *EMP* 1,000
SIC 8111 General practice law office
Pt: Paul Weber
Pt: Philippe Benedict
Pt: Eric A Bensky
Pt: Andrew J Dady
Pt: Marc E Elovitz
Pt: Nancy Finkelstein
Pt: Stuart Freedman
Pt: Kenneth S Gerstein
Pt: Peter J Halasz
Pt: Adam Harris
Pt: Christopher S Harrison
Pt: David J Karp
Pt: Robert R Kiesel
Pt: Eleazer Klein
Pt: Robert Benton Loper
Pt: Joel E Lutzker
Pt: Leonard Sorgi

Pt: Robert J Ward
CFO: Richard Piotrowicz
VP: Maureen Chandra
VP: Maria Osmanski

D-U-N-S 00-510-5960 IMP
SCHULZE AND BURCH BISCUIT CO
1133 W 35th St, Chicago, IL 60609-1485
Tel (773) 927-6622 *Founded/Ownrshp* 1976, 1923
Sales 96.2MM^E *EMP* 350^E
SIC 2051 2052 2099 Bread, cake & related products; Cookies & crackers; Food preparations
Pr: Kevin M Boyle
**Treas:* Patricia Boyle Wheeler
**VP:* David Hensler
VP: Joseph Lynch
**VP:* James McBride
**VP:* Steve Podracky
**VP:* Paul Salina
VP: William Stuart
VP: Grace Yao
Genl Mgr: Sorrell John
DP Dir: Thomas Thaus

D-U-N-S 00-512-4516 IMP/EXP
SCHUMACHER ELECTRIC CORP
801 E Business Center Dr, Mount Prospect, IL 60056-2179
Tel (847) 385-1600 *Founded/Ownrshp* 1947
Sales 142.6MM *EMP* 125
SIC 3629 3677 Battery chargers, rectifying or nonrotating; Transformers power supply, electronic type
Ch Bd: Donald A Schumacher
**Pr:* John Waldron
**Pr:* Cory Watkins
**CFO:* Daniel Frano
CTO: Chris Hadsall
DP Exec: Robb Hyland
Dir IT: Robert Gorny
VP Sls: Norman Patinka
Board of Directors: Bill Stephens

D-U-N-S 13-236-7389
SCHUMACHER GROUP OF DELAWARE INC
(*Suby of* ONEX CORPORATION)
200 Corporate Blvd # 201, Lafayette, LA 70508-3870
Tel (337) 237-1915 *Founded/Ownrshp* 1996
Sales 324.5MM^E *EMP* 1,888^E
SIC 7363 Medical help service
CEO: Rich D'Amaro
**Pr:* Gary Keller
Pr: Vicky Romero
**COO:* Jim Guidry
**COO:* Lee White
**CFO:* Marie Bourque
**CFO:* David P Dempsey
**CFO:* Thomas Dolan
**Ch:* William C Schumacher
**Chf Mktg O:* Randy L Pilgrim
Ofcr: Keith Cantrell
Ofcr: Donna Landry
Ofcr: Timothy Quattrone
Ofcr: Bob Wright
Sr VP: Jeffrey Curtis
Sr VP: Bill Hayden
Sr VP: Mike Pawlowski
Sr VP: Karen Reynolds
VP: Jessica Berthelot
VP: Rena Cottam
Exec: Marie Bourke

D-U-N-S 01-143-3989
SCHUMACHER GROUP OF LOUISIANA INC (CT)
EMBCC
(*Suby of* SCHUMACHER GROUP OF DELAWARE INC) ★
200 Corporate Blvd # 201, Lafayette, LA 70508-3870
Tel (337) 237-1915 *Founded/Ownrshp* 1994, 1996
Sales 51.9MM^E *EMP* 1,888^E
SIC 8741 Management services
CEO: William Schumacher
**Pr:* Randy Pilgrim
**COO:* Jim Guidry
**CFO:* William D Crays
Ofcr: Donna Landry
**Sr VP:* Karen Reynolds
**VP:* Janet Courvillion
**VP:* Jeff Curtis
**VP:* Gretchen Guidry
VP: Ricardo Martinez
**VP:* Kathleen Schexnaider
Exec: Lindsey Summerhill

SCHUMACHER HOMES
See 50 X 20 HOLDING CO INC

SCHUMAN CHEESE
See ARTHUR SCHUMAN INC

D-U-N-S 08-034-4203 IMP
SCHUPAN & SONS INC
SCHUPAN ALUMINUM & PLASTIC SLS
2619 Miller Rd, Kalamazoo, MI 49001-4138
Tel (269) 382-0000 *Founded/Ownrshp* 1968
Sales 87.2MM^E *EMP* 210
SIC 5093 5051 3341

SCHUPAN ALUMINUM & PLASTIC SLS
See SCHUPAN & SONS INC

D-U-N-S 00-922-8883 IMP/EXP
SCHURMAN FINE PAPERS
PAPYRUS
500 Chadbourne Rd, Fairfield, CA 94534-9656
Tel (707) 425-8006 *Founded/Ownrshp* 1950
Sales 1.2MMM^E *EMP* 3,005
SIC 5113 2679 2771 5947 Industrial & personal service paper; Paper & products, wrapping or coarse; Gift wrap & novelties, paper; Greeting cards; Gift, novelty & souvenir shop; Greeting cards
CEO: Dominique Schurman
Ch: Marcel Schurman
VP: Christian Carlsson
VP: Diana Ruhl
Creative D: Anna Bower
Art Dir: Jennifer Lew

D-U-N-S 00-521-3269
■ **SCHURZ COMMUNICATIONS INC**
(*Suby of* GRAY TELEVISION INC) ★
1301 E Douglas Rd, Mishawaka, IN 46545-1732
Tel (574) 247-7237 *Founded/Ownrshp* 1872, 2016
Sales 472.3MM^E *EMP* 3,020
SIC 4833 2711 Television broadcasting stations; Newspapers, publishing & printing
Pr: Todd Schurz
**CFO:* Gary N Hoipkemier
VP: Jeesie Augstino
VP: Sally Brown
VP: Jim Pagano
CTO: John Petersen
Sls Mgr: Carol Agee
Sls Mgr: Lolly Quigley
Sls Mgr: Gregg Richardson

SCHUSTER CONCRETE
See DANIEL G SCHUSTER LLC

D-U-N-S 04-760-9367
SCHUSTER ENTERPRISES INC
BURGER KING
3530 Macon Rd, Columbus, GA 31907-2530
Tel (706) 568-2657 *Founded/Ownrshp* 1968
Sales 74.3MM^E *EMP* 2,400
SIC 5812 Fast-food restaurant, chain
Pr: Bruce Walker
**Ch Bd:* Marvin R Schuster
**CEO:* Todd Schuster

D-U-N-S 61-033-4898 IMP
SCHUTZ CONTAINER SYSTEMS INC
(*Suby of* SCHUTZ CORP) ★
200 Aspen Hill Rd, Branchburg, NJ 08876-3564
Tel (908) 429-1637 *Founded/Ownrshp* 1991
Sales 145.1MM^E *EMP* 300
SIC 2655 Fiber cans, drums & containers; Containers, laminated phenolic & vulcanized fiber; Drums, fiber: made from purchased material
Pr: Frederick Wenzel
Plnt Mgr: David Farenden
Plnt Mgr: David Fredkin
Plnt Mgr: Chris Price
Sales Exec: Ted Jones
Manager: Bill Tifft
Sls Mgr: John Millard

D-U-N-S 80-104-8661 IMP/EXP
SCHUTZ CORP
(*Suby of* SCHUTZ-WERKE GMBH & CO. KG)
200 Aspen Hill Rd, Branchburg, NJ 08876-3564
Tel (908) 526-6161 *Founded/Ownrshp* 1982
Sales 131.9MM^E *EMP* 300
SIC 2655 Fiber cans, drums & similar products
Ch Bd: Udo Schutz
**Pr:* Peter Schafer
**CFO:* Norman Burke
**Treas:* Jur Juergen Huebbe

D-U-N-S 05-471-8630
SCHUYLKILL VALLEY SPORTS INC
118 Industrial Dr Ste 1, Pottstown, PA 19464-3462
Tel (610) 495-8813 *Founded/Ownrshp* 1990
Sales 130.8MM^E *EMP* 250
SIC 5091 5941 Sporting & recreation goods; Sporting goods & bicycle shops
Ch Bd: Randall R Ruch
**Pr:* Gerald V Williams
VP: Greg Baldwin
Dist Mgr: Jen Alles
Dist Mgr: Matt Hirsch
Dist Mgr: Nate Moyer
VP Opers: Mike Renninger
VP Sls: Ron Bacchi

D-U-N-S 14-003-5333
SCHWAB CHARITABLE FUND
211 Main St, San Francisco, CA 94105-1905
Tel (415) 667-9131 *Founded/Ownrshp* 1999
Sales 722.4MM *EMP* 26
Accts Deloitte & Touche Llp San Fra
SIC 8699 Charitable organization
Ex Dir: Susan Heldman
**Ch Bd:* Carrie Schwab-Pomerantz
Pr: Kim Laughton
Off Mgr: Michael Smithwick

D-U-N-S 18-062-7549
■ **SCHWAB HOLDINGS INC**
CHARLES SCHWAB
(*Suby of* CHARLES SCHWAB CORP) ★
211 Main St, San Francisco, CA 94105-1905
Tel (415) 636-7000 *Founded/Ownrshp* 1987
Sales 789.7MM^E *EMP* 5,000
SIC 6211 Brokers, security; Dealers, security; Investment firm, general brokerage
Ch Bd: Charles R Schwab
CFO: Chris Dodds
Ofcr: Daren Free
VP: Lauren Ozuna
VP: Fred Potts
VP: Lisa Scibetta
Mng Dir: Fred De Jesus
Mng Dir: Steven Ruddy
Dir IT: Vic Vinogradov
IT Man: Kathy Anson
IT Man: CAM Lee

D-U-N-S 11-269-8691
■ **SCHWAB RETIREMENT PLAN SERVICES CO**
(*Suby of* CHARLES SCHWAB CORP) ★
12401 Res Blvd Bldg 2, Austin, TX 78759
Tel (512) 344-3000 *Founded/Ownrshp* 2007
Sales NA *EMP* 290
SIC 6371 Pension funds
Pr: Gerald Bramlett
**Sr VP:* Barbara Driscoll
**Sr VP:* Debbie Matustik
**Sr VP:* Holly Nance
**Sr VP:* Steve Slade
**VP:* Debbie Ebner
**VP:* Donald Figer
**VP:* Steve Hale
**VP:* Danny Ischy
**VP:* Melissa Janda

**VP:* Ken Robertson
**VP:* Melissa Sandberg

D-U-N-S 83-115-3908 IMP/EXP
SCHWABE NORTH AMERICA INC
NATURE'S WAY PRODUCTS
(*Suby of* SCHWABE INTERNATIONAL GMBH)
825 Challenger Dr, Green Bay, WI 54311-8328
Tel (920) 469-1313 *Founded/Ownrshp* 1982
Sales 439.5MM^E *EMP* 1,150
Accts Deloitte & Touche Llp
SIC 2834 2099 Pharmaceutical preparations; Food preparations
CEO: Mike Devereux
CFO: Mike Winkler
Sr VP: Rory Mahony
Sr VP: Chad Wiegand
Genl Mgr: John Thornton
Opers Supe: Andrea Reyment
Prd Mgr: Adam Lee
Sls Mgr: Rick Woeckener
Board of Directors: Dirk Reischig, Rainer Skrotzki

D-U-N-S 07-837-9636 IMP
SCHWAN COSMETICS USA INC (TN)
COSMOLAB, INC.
(*Suby of* SCHWAN-STABILO COSMETICS GMBH & CO. KG)
3202 Elam Farms Pkwy, Murfreesboro, TN 37127-7786
Tel (931) 359-6253 *Founded/Ownrshp* 2009
Sales 99.7MM^E *EMP* 299
SIC 2844 Cosmetic preparations
Pr: Holli Montgomery
VP: Tom Byrne
VP: Hugh Hasty
Exec: Bobby Henson
VP Opers: Bill Zebick
Ql Cn Mgr: Kim Helton
VP Sls: Debra McDonough

D-U-N-S 02-286-5398 IMP/EXP
SCHWAN FOOD CO
115 W College Dr, Marshall, MN 56258-1747
Tel (507) 532-3274 *Founded/Ownrshp* 1952
Sales 4.8MMM^E *EMP* 14,000
SIC 2038 2024 2037 Pizza, frozen; Ethnic foods, frozen; Ice cream, packaged: molded, on sticks, etc.; Ice milk, packaged: molded, on sticks, etc.; Fruit juice concentrates, frozen
Ch Bd: Allan Schuman
**CEO:* Dimitrios Smyrnios
**CFO:* Irobin Galloway
**Treas:* Heidi Dirckx
Sr Cor Off: Kristy Hansen
Ex VP: David Bunnell
**Ex VP:* Brian Sattler
Sr VP: Kristy Griffin
VP: Brian Green
VP: Bill Humlan
VP: Bernadette Kruk
**VP:* Don Miller
VP: Brian Nau
VP: Tracy Welch
Exec: William O McCrmick
Creative D: Nicole Deboer
Board of Directors: Mike McFadden

D-U-N-S 11-344-0965 EXP
SCHWANS CONSUMER BRANDS INC
(*Suby of* SCHWAN FOOD CO) ★
8500 Normandale Lake Blvd, Bloomington, MN 55437-3813
Tel (952) 346-0100 *Founded/Ownrshp* 1978
Sales 761.8MM^E *EMP* 3,100
SIC 5142 Packaged frozen goods
CEO: Bob Waldron
**CFO:* Steve Fuechtmann
Sls Dir: Mark Rehborg
Sls Mgr: Jim Hatzer

D-U-N-S 12-594-4244 IMP
SCHWANS HOME SERVICE INC
(*Suby of* SCHWAN FOOD CO) ★
115 W College Dr, Marshall, MN 56258-3810
Tel (507) 532-3274 *Founded/Ownrshp* 1964
Sales 662.0MM^E *EMP* 6,523^E
SIC 5411 Frozen food & freezer plans, except meat
CEO: David Muscato
CFO: Dan Herrmann
Mktg Mgr: Dusty Halverson

D-U-N-S 00-190-3327 IMP/EXP
SCHWARZ PAPER CO LLC (VA)
SEMPER/EXETER
(*Suby of* ARCH LOGISTICS) ★
8338 Austin Ave, Morton Grove, IL 60053-3209
Tel (847) 966-2550 *Founded/Ownrshp* 1907, 2012
Sales 172.4MM^E *EMP* 400
SIC 2621 5199 4225 Packaging paper; Packaging materials; General warehousing
CEO: Christopher J Donnelly Jr
**CFO:* Ken A Thomson
**Ch:* Andrew Mc Kenna
**Treas:* Denise M Jakubowski
Treas: Denise Jakubowski
**Sr VP:* Bruce B Barton
**Sr VP:* Paul R Frantz
VP: Meridith Adams
VP: Paul France
**VP:* Jean A Luber
Snr Ntwrk: Mike Sells

D-U-N-S 04-677-4753
SCHWARZ PARTNERS LP
3600 Woodview Trce # 300, Indianapolis, IN 46268-3123
Tel (317) 290-1140 *Founded/Ownrshp* 1995
Sales 210.8MM^E *EMP* 35
SIC 2679 Paper products, converted
Pt: Jack Schwarz
**Pt:* Gaye H Schwarz
**Pt:* Jeff Schwarz
CFO: Thomas Bennett

D-U-N-S 03-016-0951
SCHWARZ PARTNERS PACKAGING LLC
2808 New Tampa Hwy, Lakeland, FL 33815-3438
Tel (863) 682-0123 *Founded/Ownrshp* 1998
Sales 217.7MM *EMP* 48

Accts Bkd Llp Indianapolis In
SIC 2653 Corrugated boxes, partitions, display items, sheets & pad

SCHWARZKOPF HOLDING CORP
See PSE HOLDING CORP

SCHWARZOPF
See HENKEL CORP

D-U-N-S 00-417-0130
SCHWEBEL BAKING CO (WV)
965 E Midlothian Blvd, Youngstown, OH 44502-2869
Tel (330) 783-2860 *Founded/Ownrshp* 1906
Sales 170.0MM *EMP* 1,290
SIC 2051 Bread, cake & related products
Pr: Paul Schwebel
**Treas:* David Alter
VP: Barry Solomon
**VP:* Alyson Winick
Dist Mgr: Bruce Reber
Div Mgr: Zach Gross
Off Mgr: Holly Ankeney
Off Mgr: Maryn Schwebel
IT Man: Mike Illes
VP Opers: Rick Terhenko
Site Mgr: Rich Hollis

D-U-N-S 11-895-2159 IMP/EXP
SCHWEITZER ENGINEERING LABORATORIES INC
2440 Ne Hopkins Ct, Pullman, WA 99163-5616
Tel (509) 332-1890 *Founded/Ownrshp* 1982
Sales 1.1MMM^E *EMP* 3,500
SIC 1731 Electric power systems contractors
Pr: Edmund O Schweitzer III
**COO:* Luis D'Acosta
**Treas:* Joseph Nestegard
**Sr VP:* Ronald Schwartz
**VP:* Kevin Fritch
VP: Ali Kazemi
VP: Bob Morris
Exec: Tyson Salewske
Dir Risk M: Susan Pfeifer
Dir Bus: Beatriz Schweitzer
Snr Sftwr: Joe Casebolt

D-U-N-S 92-978-5616 IMP/EXP
▲ **SCHWEITZER-MAUDUIT INTERNATIONAL INC**
SWM INTL
100 N Point Ctr E Ste 600, Alpharetta, GA 30022-8263
Tel (800) 514-0186 *Founded/Ownrshp* 1995
Sales 764.1MM *EMP* 3,100
Tkr Sym SWM *Exch* NYS
SIC 2141 2111 2621 Tobacco stemming & redrying; Cigarettes; Paper mills; Cigarette paper; Printing paper; Wrapping & packaging papers
Ch Bd: Frederic P Villoutreix
CFO: Allison Aden
Bd of Dir: Richard Jackson
Ex VP: Michel Fievez
Ex VP: Daniel Lister
Board of Directors: Claire L Arnold, Karl C Caldabaugh, William A Finn, Heinrich Fischer, Jeffrey J Keenan, John D Rogers, Anderson D Warlick

D-U-N-S 00-794-7229
SCHWERMAN TRUCKING CO (WI)
(*Suby of* ROGERS CARTAGE) ★
611 S 28th St, Milwaukee, WI 53215-1200
Tel (414) 671-1600 *Founded/Ownrshp* 1913
Sales 92.3MM^E *EMP* 750
SIC 4213 Trucking, except local; Building materials transport; Liquid petroleum transport, non-local; Heavy machinery transport
Pr: Geoffrey M Redman
**Treas:* Kelly A Leibham
**VP:* Terrance P Lacasse
VP Opers: Scott Pearce
Sales Exec: Leonard Mulanax

D-U-N-S 07-150-3247 IMP/EXP
SCHWING AMERICA INC
(*Suby of* SCHWING GMBH)
5900 Centerville Rd, Saint Paul, MN 55127-6899
Tel (651) 429-0999 *Founded/Ownrshp* 1974
Sales 90.9MM^E *EMP* 300^E
SIC 3531 3561 3999 Bituminous, cement & concrete related products & equipment; Construction machinery attachments; Industrial pumps & parts; Atomizers, toiletry
CEO: Brian Hazelton
Pr: Aaron Lian
**CFO:* Bill Murray
**CFO:* Gerhard Schwing
**CFO:* Patrick Widmaier
**Treas:* J Andy Anderson
**VP:* Jose Amezaga
Rgnl Mgr: Matt Donnelly
MIS Dir: Kenneth Meyers
Ql Cn Mgr: Tom Eggert
Manager: Andy Conway

D-U-N-S 08-513-2629
SCHWOB BUILDING CO LTD
2349 Glenda Ln, Dallas, TX 75229-3318
Tel (972) 243-7674 *Founded/Ownrshp* 2001
Sales 158.5MM^E *EMP* 250
Accts Cornwell Jackson Pllc Plano
SIC 1542 Nonresidential construction
Pt: Scott Schwob
**Pt:* Andy Erickson
**Pt:* Harlan Smith
**VP:* Scott Knepper
**VP:* James Robinet
VP: Curtis Stanley
Mtls Mgr: Jerry Gann
Sfty Mgr: Robert Henley
Opers Mgr: Adam McInnes
Opers Mgr: Robert Taylor
Secur Mgr: Tim Mayner

SCI
See SERVICE CORP INTERNATIONAL

SCI
See SUAREZ CORP INDUSTRIES

SCI
See CRAIG F SORENSEN CONSTRUCTION INC

SCI
See SMITH COOPER INTERNATIONAL INC

D-U-N-S 55-716-9323
■ SCI FUNERAL SERVICES OF NEWYORK INC
(Suby of SCI) ★
1929 Allen Pkwy, Houston, TX 77019-2506
Tel (713) 522-5141 Founded/Ownrshp 1992
Sales 108.5MM^E EMP 700
SIC 7261 Funeral service & crematories
Pr: Curtis G Briggs

SCI MANAGEMENT
See SCI SHARED RESOURCES LLC

D-U-N-S 14-725-1511
■ SCI SHARED RESOURCES LLC
SCI MANAGEMENT
(Suby of SCI) ★
1929 Allen Pkwy, Houston, TX 77019-2506
Tel (713) 522-5141 Founded/Ownrshp 2002
Sales 339.6MM^E EMP 20,000
SIC 7261 6553 Funeral home; Cemetery subdividers & developers
Ch: Robert L Waltrip
*Pr: Kenneth J Russell
*Pr: Thomas L Ryan
*COO: Michael R Webb
Treas: James Faubion
Treas: Sonja Horn
*VP: Sara F Beaves
*VP: Janet L Riley

D-U-N-S 00-401-6960 IMP
SCI SYSTEMS INC
SANMINA SCI
13000 Memorial Pkwy Sw, Huntsville, AL 35803-6000
Tel (256) 882-4800 Founded/Ownrshp 2001
Sales NA EMP 40,000
SIC 3571

D-U-N-S 14-458-8951
■ SCI TECHNOLOGY INC
(Suby of SANMINA CORP) ★
13000 Memorial Pkwy Sw, Huntsville, AL 35803-6000
Tel (256) 882-4800 Founded/Ownrshp 2001
Sales 92.7MM EMP 564^E
SIC 3672 3829 8711 3663 Printed circuit boards; Aircraft & motor vehicle measurement equipment; Engineering services; Radio & TV communications equipment
Pr: Furr Randy
*Pr: Michael W Underwood
Sr VP: G J King
IT Man: Bill Thornton

D-U-N-S 79-885-7934
■ SCI VIRGINIA FUNERAL SERVICES INC
(Suby of SCI) ★
1929 Allen Pkwy, Houston, TX 77019-2506
Tel (713) 522-5141 Founded/Ownrshp 1990
Sales 41.8MM^E EMP 2,000
SIC 8741 Management services
Ch Bd: Robert L Waltrip
*Pr: Marc Watts
*CEO: Thomas L Ryan

SCI-FI
See USA CABLE INC

D-U-N-S 78-593-9141
▲ SCICLONE PHARMACEUTICALS INC
950 Tower Ln Ste 900, Foster City, CA 94404-2125
Tel (650) 358-3456 Founded/Ownrshp 1990
Sales 157.2MM EMP 590^E
Tkr Sym SCLN Exch NGS
SIC 2834 Pharmaceutical preparations
Pr: Friedhelm Blobel
*Ch Bd: Jon S Saxe
CEO: Hong Zhao
CFO: Wilson W Cheung
CFO: Lan Xie
Sr VP: Robert King
IT Man: Jason Wan
Genl Couns: Carey Chern
Board of Directors: Nancy T Chang, Richard J Hawkins, Gregg A Lapointe, Simon Li

D-U-N-S 78-319-6348
SCIENCE AND ENGINEERING SERVICES LLC
SES
6992 Columbia Gateway Dr # 200, Columbia, MD 21046-2986
Tel (443) 539-0139 Founded/Ownrshp 2011
Sales 213.1MM^E EMP 700
SIC 8711 8731 3826 Aviation &/or aeronautical engineering; Commercial physical research; Laser scientific & engineering instruments
Pr: Hyo Sang Lee
*Ex VP: Russell Chunn
VP: Millard Jernigan
Dir IT: Jeff Rosen
Dir IT: Thomas Sarsfield

D-U-N-S 00-527-2365
■ SCIENCE APPLICATIONS INTERNATIONAL CORP
SAIC GEMINI, INC.
(Suby of SAIC) ★
1049 W 5th Ave, Anchorage, AK 99501-1965
Tel (907) 792-2700 Founded/Ownrshp 2007, 2013
Sales 14.1MM^E EMP 2,683^E
SIC 7389 Inspection & testing services
Prin: Shane Taylor
Div Mgr: Mike Cimino

D-U-N-S 07-874-5061
▲ SCIENCE APPLICATIONS INTERNATIONAL CORP
SAIC
1710 Saic Dr Ste B, Mc Lean, VA 22102-3701
Tel (703) 676-6942 Founded/Ownrshp 1969
Sales 4.3MMM EMP 15,000^E
Tkr Sym SAIC Exch NYS
SIC 7373 7374 Computer integrated systems design; Data processing & preparation
CEO: Anthony J Moraco
*Ch Bd: Edward J Sanderson Jr
Pr: Cheryl Francisco
Pr: Gayle M Godfrey
Pr: Nazzic S Keene
Pr: Karl Kropp
Pr: Mike Sanoian
Pr: John Stiles
Pr: John Szymanski
Pr: Gail Turk
Pr: Douglas M Wagoner
Pr: James Younts
Pr: Annette Zimmermann
CFO: Maria M Bishop
CFO: Rohrer Kelly
Bd of Dir: Steve Shane
Ofcr: Kimberly S Admire
Ex VP: Steven G Mahon
Ex VP: Robert Rosenberg
VP: Sarah Allen
VP: Ashok Arora
Board of Directors: Robert A Bedingfield, Deborah B Dunie, Thomas F Frist III, John J Hamre, Timothy J Mayopoulos, Donna S Morea, Steven R Shane

D-U-N-S 04-682-5337 IMP
SCIENTIFIC COMPONENTS CORP
MINI-CIRCUITS
13 Neptune Ave, Brooklyn, NY 11235-4404
Tel (718) 934-4500 Founded/Ownrshp 1968
Sales 109.0MM^E EMP 500
SIC 3679 Electronic switches; Electronic circuits
Pr: Harvey Kaylie
*Sec: Gloria Kaylie
VP: Stephen Sherman
CTO: Wayne Shum
QA Dir: Amul Christian
IT Man: Ron Beagle
Sftwr Eng: Arkady Veyts

D-U-N-S 04-875-7843 IMP/EXP
SCIENTIFIC DRILLING INTERNATIONAL INC
16071 Greenspoint Park Ste 200, Houston, TX 77060
Tel (281) 443-3300 Founded/Ownrshp 1986
Sales 24.6MM^E EMP 1,300
SIC 1381 1389 Directional drilling oil & gas wells; Surveying wells
Pr: Phil N Longorio
*CFO: Dana Armstrong
Sr VP: Chip Abrant
*Sr VP: William R Abrant
*Sr VP: Daniel R Carter
*Sr VP: P David Cotten Jr
*Sr VP: Dr Gerald Heisig
*Sr VP: Douglas McGregor
*VP: Gordon Thomson
QA Dir: Balaji Vemula
Dir IT: Duane Morris
Board of Directors: Phillip Gobe, Philip N Longorio, Joseph P McCoy, Pamela Pierce, Elizabeth Van Steenwyk

SCIENTIFIC GAMES AND RACING
See AUTOTOTE SYSTEMS INC

D-U-N-S 11-349-1252 IMP/EXP
▲ SCIENTIFIC GAMES CORP
6650 El Camino Rd, Las Vegas, NV 89118-2601
Tel (702) 897-7150 Founded/Ownrshp 1984
Sales 2.7MMM EMP 8,500
Tkr Sym SGMS Exch NGS
SIC 7999 7373 Gambling & lottery services; Lottery operation; Computer integrated systems design
Pr: Kevin M Sheehan
Ch Bd: Ronald O Perelman
V Ch: Richard M Haddrill
CEO: James C Kennedy
CEO: Derik J Mooberry
CFO: Michael A Quartieri
CFO: Michael Quartieri
V Ch Bd: Peter A Cohen
V Ch Bd: David L Kennedy
Ofcr: Larry A Potts
Ofcr: Dan Savage
Ofcr: David Smail
VP: Edward Cornell

D-U-N-S 12-760-3269 IMP/EXP
SCIENTIFIC GAMES FINANCE CORP
(Suby of SPORTECH RACING LLC) ★
1500 Bluegrass Lakes Pkwy, Alpharetta, GA 30004-7754
Tel (770) 664-3700 Founded/Ownrshp 1998
Sales 99.0MM^E EMP 1,000
SIC 2754 Commercial printing, gravure
CEO: Gavin Isaacs
*Ex VP: William J Huntley
*Ex VP: James C Kennedy Jr
*Sr VP: Jeffrey S Lipkin

D-U-N-S 55-722-1280 IMP/EXP
■ SCIENTIFIC GAMES INTERNATIONAL INC
(Suby of SCIENTIFIC GAMES CORP) ★
1500 Bluegrass Lakes Pkwy, Alpharetta, GA 30004-7754
Tel (770) 664-3700 Founded/Ownrshp 1998
Sales 186.8MM^E EMP 1,000
SIC 7389 7999 Printed circuitry graphic layout; Lottery tickets, sale of
Pr: Jordan Levin
*CFO: Michael Quartieri
VP: David Bausch
VP: Robert Becker
VP: C G Bethea
*VP: Susan Cartwright
VP: Effective February
Dist Mgr: George Brannen
Dist Mgr: Chris Friedrich
Dist Mgr: Dennis Steiger
MIS Dir: Ron Taylor

D-U-N-S 18-542-1518 IMP
SCIENTIFIC MOLDING CORP LTD
S M C
330 Smc Dr, Somerset, WI 54025-9050
Tel (715) 247-3500 Founded/Ownrshp 1988
Sales 592.3MM^E EMP 1,750
SIC 3089 3544 Injection molding of plastics; Special dies, tools, jigs & fixtures
Pr: Chetan N Patel
Comm Man: Christie Wanderer
Prgrm Mgr: John Lefavour
Genl Mgr: Jason B Larocco
Opers Supe: Mark Comeau
Plnt Mgr: Roy Gruel
Prd Mgr: Eric Malmgren
Prd Mgr: Rohit Tandon
Ql Cn Mgr: Robert McDonald
Ql Cn Mgr: Ron Schalk
Ql Cn Mgr: Dennis Schendel

D-U-N-S 06-524-0319 IMP
SCIENTIFIC PROTEIN LABORATORIES LLC
(Suby of SHENZHEN HEPALINK PHARMACEUTICAL CO., LTD.)
700 E Main St, Waunakee, WI 53597-1440
Tel (608) 849-5944 Founded/Ownrshp 2004
Sales 134.0MM^E EMP 175
SIC 2834 2833 Proprietary drug products; Vitamin preparations; Animal based products
CEO: Yan Wang
Ofcr: Denise Kwiatkowski
VP: Bob Garreau
VP: Michael Reardon
CIO: Thomas Kittle
Dir IT: Matt Ginter
Mktg Mgr: Gregg Steinhauer

D-U-N-S 19-713-8274
SCIENTIFIC RESEARCH CORP
2300 Windy Ridge Pkwy Se 400s, Atlanta, GA 30339-8431
Tel (770) 859-9161 Founded/Ownrshp 1988
Sales 293.8MM EMP 1,006
Accts Dixon Hughes Goodman Llp Atla
SIC 8732 8711 Research services, except laboratory; Engineering services
CEO: Michael L Watt
COO: Rich Kniskern
Ch: Charles K Watt
Ex VP: James Ward
Ex VP: Steven Watt
VP: Elizabeth Nettles
VP Bus Dev: Mark Pelletier
Prgrm Mgr: Tyler Angel
Prgrm Mgr: Beason Bill
Prgrm Mgr: Jon Boucher
Prgrm Mgr: Charles Cathey

D-U-N-S 00-326-5022 IMP/EXP
■ SCIENTIFIC-ATLANTA LLC (GA)
CISCO SYSTEMS INTERNATIONAL
(Suby of CISCO SYSTEMS INC) ★
5030 Sugarloaf Pkwy, Lawrenceville, GA 30044-2869
Tel (678) 277-1000 Founded/Ownrshp 1951, 2006
Sales 639.1MM^E EMP 9,900
SIC 3663 3661 3577 3825 Radio & TV communications equipment; Space satellite communications equipment; Cable television equipment; Antennas, transmitting & communications; Telephone & telegraph apparatus; Fiber optics communications equipment; Computer peripheral equipment; Encoders, computer peripheral equipment; Decoders, computer peripheral equipment; Instruments to measure electricity; Test equipment for electronic & electrical circuits; Spectrum analyzers; Energy measuring equipment, electrical
Ch Bd: James F McDonald
Ex VP: H Allen Ecker
Sr VP: Brad Boston
Sr VP: Wallace G Haislip
Sr VP: John H Levergood
Sr VP: Robert C McIntyre
Sr VP: Michael C Veysey
VP: Steven D Boyd
VP: Jonathan Chadwick
VP: Michael Cowan
VP: Ward Dickson
VP: Wall Haislip
VP: David K Holland
VP: Robert Johnson
VP: Bill Katherman
VP: Jim Lysaker
VP: Dennis D Powell
VP: Michael Stolorena
Board of Directors: Marion H Antonini, James I Cash Jr, David W Dorman, William E Kassling, Terence F McGuirk, David J McLaughlin, James V Napier, Sam Nunn

SCION
See TOYOTA MOTOR SALES USA INC

D-U-N-S 06-358-6408
■ SCIOTO DOWNS INC
(Suby of MTR GAMING GROUP INC) ★
6000 S High St, Columbus, OH 43207
Tel (614) 295-4700 Founded/Ownrshp 2003
Sales 1.8MM^E EMP 1,000
SIC 7948 Horse race track operation; Harness horse racing
Pr: Edward T Ryan
Mgt/VP: Troy Buswell

SCIOTO MEMORIAL HOSPITAL CAMPU
See SOUTHERN OHIO MEDICAL CENTER

D-U-N-S 01-599-6366
SCIQUEST INC
(Suby of SCIQUEST PARENT LLC) ★
3020 Carrington Mill Blvd # 100, Morrisville, NC 27560-5433
Tel (919) 659-2100 Founded/Ownrshp 2016
Sales 105.3MM EMP 510^E
SIC 7372 Business oriented computer software
CEO: Robert Bonavito
VP: Brad Stevens
Off Admin: Teresa Lassiter
Software D: Jason Johns
Software D: John Sun
Board of Directors: Thomas Barnds, Dean Jacobson

D-U-N-S 08-035-7068
SCIQUEST PARENT LLC
3020 Carrington Mill Blvd, Morrisville, NC 27560-5432
Tel (919) 659-2100 Founded/Ownrshp 2016
Sales 105.3MM^E EMP 510^E
SIC 7372 Business oriented computer software

D-U-N-S 10-798-1305 IMP
SCIS AIR SECURITY CORP
(Suby of S C INTERNATIONAL SERVICES INC) ★
1521 N Cooper St Ste 300, Arlington, TX 76011-5537
Tel (817) 792-4500 Founded/Ownrshp 2001
Sales 114.9MM^E EMP 800^E
SIC 5063 7382 Light bulbs & related supplies; Security systems services
Pr: Moe Kamyab
*Pr: Steve Skoglund
Prgrm Mgr: Joe Hailey
Dir IT: Joshua Irvin
IT Man: Jacob Margolis
Mktg Dir: Sharon Schmitz

D-U-N-S 03-988-5421
■ SCITOR CORP
(Suby of SCITOR HOLDINGS INC) ★
12010 Sunset Hills Rd, Reston, VA 20190-5856
Tel (703) 961-4000 Founded/Ownrshp 1979
Sales 257.6MM^E EMP 1,158
SIC 8711 Consulting engineer
CEO: Jim Hoskins
*Pr: Tim Dills
COO: Eric Richardson
*CFO: Robert J Kosinski
Chf Mktg O: Terry Hanshaw
*VP: Kathleen T Dickman
VP: Danny Pophin
*VP: James R Waldo
Exec: Tom Heffernan
Exec: Steven McKay
*Prin: Kenneth Pomietto
Board of Directors: Jim Hoskins, Robert Kosinski

D-U-N-S 82-742-9973
■ SCITOR HOLDINGS INC
(Suby of SAIC) ★
12010 Sunset Hills Rd # 800, Reston, VA 20190-5856
Tel (703) 481-5892 Founded/Ownrshp 2015
Sales 286.2MM^E EMP 1,158^E
SIC 7382 5065 7373 Security systems services; Security control equipment & systems; Systems engineering, computer related
Pr: Timothy Dills
Sftwr Eng: Donovan Marsh
Sls Mgr: Susan Crawford

D-U-N-S 05-560-4896
SCL HEALTH - FRONT RANGE INC
SISTERS OF CHARITY OF LEAVENWR
(Suby of SCL HEALTH SYSTEM) ★
8300 W 38th Ave, Wheat Ridge, CO 80033-6005
Tel (303) 813-5000 Founded/Ownrshp 1905
Sales 586.0MM^E EMP 5,300
Accts Ernst & Young Us Llp Phoenix
SIC 8062 8011 8051 General medical & surgical hospitals; Medical centers; Skilled nursing care facilities
Pr: Mike Slubowski
*Ch Bd: Jo Ann Soker
V Ch: Koger L Propst
*Pr: Jeffrey Selberg
COO: Ralph L Dean
CFO: Lydia W Jumonville
*CFO: William Pack
Ex VP: Richard T Lopes
Sr VP: Christine Woolsey
VP: Pat Jolitz
VP: Susan Kerschen
VP: Benjamin Malanga
VP: Allen Mitzel
VP: Amy Pacey
VP: Debbie Welle-Powell
Exec: Bob Powell
Comm Dir: Sarah Ellis

SCL HEALTH SYSTEM
See SISTERS OF CHARITY OF LEAVENWORTH HEALTH SYSTEM INC

SCLARC
See SOUTH CENTRAL LOS ANGELES REGIONAL CENTER FOR DEVELOPMENTALLY DISABLED PERSONS INC

D-U-N-S 13-926-9617
SCO FAMILY OF SERVICES
1 Alexander Pl, Glen Cove, NY 11542-3745
Tel (516) 671-1253 Founded/Ownrshp 2011
Sales 253.2MM EMP 3,500
Accts Bdo Usa Llp New York Ny
SIC 8322 Individual & family services
Ex Dir: Gail B Nayowith
Bd of Dir: Photeine Anagnostopoulos
Bd of Dir: Madonna Heights
Bd of Dir: Craig Treiber
Dir Soc: Anjali Mathai
Ex Dir: J McMahon
Off Mgr: Janet Santiago
Off Mgr: Patricia Smith
Nurse Mgr: Victor Spivey
CIO: Joe Fatuzzo
CTO: Dillon Wright

SCOLARI'S DISTRIBUTION CENTER
See SCOLARIS WAREHOUSE MARKETS INC

D-U-N-S 03-496-5798
SCOLARIS WAREHOUSE MARKETS INC
SCOLARI'S DISTRIBUTION CENTER
950 Holman Way, Sparks, NV 89431-2125
Tel (775) 355-8568 Founded/Ownrshp 1992
Sales 204.4MM^E EMP 1,400
SIC 5411 Supermarkets, chain
CEO: Joey E Scolari
Sec: Robert W Nugent
VP: Rob Dornberger
VP: Robert E Dornberger
VP: Pierra M Sundland
Dir IT: Mark Stimac

D-U-N-S 79-430-8585 IMP/EXP
SCOMI EQUIPMENT INC
(*Suby of* SCOMI GROUP BHD.)
6607 Theall Rd, Houston, TX 77066-1213
Tel (281) 260-6016 *Founded/Ownrshp* 1992
Sales 108.4MM[E] *EMP* 200
SIC 1389 Oil field services
CEO: Shah Hakim Zain
**Pr:* Michael Kent Walker
**VP:* Stephen Fredrick Bracker
VP: Dan Farrar

SCOOTER STORE, THE
See SCOOTER STORE LTD

D-U-N-S 03-267-5949
SCOOTER STORE LTD
SCOOTER STORE, THE
1650 Independence Dr, New Braunfels, TX 78132-3942
Tel (877) 841-8159 *Founded/Ownrshp* 1996
Sales NA *EMP* 2,500
SIC 5999

D-U-N-S 10-900-1552
SCOPE INC
100 Lawrence Ave Ste 105, Smithtown, NY 11787-3618
Tel (631) 360-0800 *Founded/Ownrshp* 1964
Sales 14.1MM *EMP* 1,100
SIC 8299 Educational services
Ex Dir: Joseph J Delrosso
**CFO:* Patricia Walsh
Assoc Dir: George Duffy

D-U-N-S 00-690-8842
SCOPE INDUSTRIES
SCOPE PRODUCTS
2811 Wilshire Blvd # 410, Santa Monica, CA 90403-4805
Tel (310) 458-1574 *Founded/Ownrshp* 1938
Sales 203.7MM *EMP* 300[E]
Accts Cohn Reznick Llp Los Angeles
SIC 4953 Recycling, waste materials
Ch Bd: Meyer Luskin
**COO:* David Luskin
CFO: Eric Iwafuchi
**Ex VP:* Rida Hamed
VP: Gerald Truelove
Genl Mgr: Steve Alvarez
Genl Mgr: Joseph Giustra
Genl Mgr: Braden McLeish
Plnt Mgr: Douglas Dunn
Plnt Mgr: Martin Kline

SCOPE PRODUCTS
See SCOPE INDUSTRIES

D-U-N-S 13-211-3981
SCOR GLOBAL LIFE USA REINSURANCE CO
(*Suby of* SCOR GLOBAL LIFE SE)
11625 Rosewood St Ste 300, Leawood, KS 66211-2000
Tel (913) 901-4600 *Founded/Ownrshp* 2013
Sales NA *EMP* 130[E]
SIC 6311 6321 Life reinsurance; Reinsurance carriers, accident & health
CEO: Edward Ritter
**Sr VP:* Bill Crouch
**Sr VP:* Terry Dickinson
**Sr VP:* Jay Kinnimon
**VP:* Mike Lynch
**VP:* Randy Makin
**VP:* Randy Meyer
VP: Tequila Wright

SCOR RE-INSURANCE COMPANY
See SCOR US CORP

D-U-N-S 07-761-3271
SCOR REINSURANCE CO
(*Suby of* SCOR RE-INSURANCE CO) ★
199 Water St Fl 21, New York, NY 10038-3536
Tel (212) 884-9000 *Founded/Ownrshp* 1984
Sales NA *EMP* 116
SIC 6331 Fire, marine & casualty insurance & carriers
Pr: Henry Klecan Jr
Pr: Chaim Markowitz
**CFO:* Mark Kociancic
CFO: Mark Kociancik
Ex VP: Mary Bahna-Nolan
**Sr VP:* Steve Desner
**Sr VP:* John Fitzpatrick
**Sr VP:* Andrew Flasko
**Sr VP:* Sarah Krutov
**Sr VP:* Peter Rizacos
**Sr VP:* Lee Routledge
VP: Hugh Barbanell
VP: Jonathan Beerman
VP: Daniel Carreras
VP: Rose Golz
VP: Mindy Spry
VP: Terry Spry
VP: Clif Stone
VP: Manny Villa

D-U-N-S 14-464-2741
SCOR US CORP
SCOR RE-INSURANCE COMPANY
(*Suby of* SCOR)
199 Water St Fl 21, New York, NY 10038-3536
Tel (212) 884-9667 *Founded/Ownrshp* 1981
Sales NA *EMP* 125
SIC 6411 Property & casualty insurance agent
Pr: Henry Klecan Jr
**CFO:* Mark Kociancic
**Ch:* Denis Kessler
**Sr VP:* Maxine Verne
VP: Dennis Helewa
VP Inf Sys: Bob Robertson
VP Opers: Aparna Varma
Mktg Mgr: Shimpei Saito

D-U-N-S 96-757-4968 IMP/EXP
■ **SCORPIO ACQUISITION CORP**
(*Suby of* AVINTIV INC) ★
9335 Harris Corners Pkwy, Charlotte, NC 28269-3818
Tel (704) 697-5100 *Founded/Ownrshp* 2010
Sales 259.2MM[E] *EMP* 4,000[E]
SIC 2297 Nonwoven fabrics
Pr: J Joel Hackney Jr

D-U-N-S 00-512-3252 IMP/EXP
SCOT FORGE CO (NV)
8001 Winn Rd, Spring Grove, IL 60081-9687
Tel (815) 675-1000 *Founded/Ownrshp* 1893, 1976
Sales 145.7MM[E] *EMP* 600
SIC 3462 Aircraft forgings, ferrous
Pr: John L Cain
Pr: Michelle Riedel
COO: Ron Hahn
**COO:* Ronald E Hahn
**CFO:* Lisa Kieres
CFO: Todd Leistner
Comm Dir: David Fallon
Ex Dir: Jim Merkel
Genl Mgr: Matt Nowakowski
CTO: Peter I Georgeson
Cmptr Lab: Tim Spooner
Board of Directors: James C Anderson, Michael W Klingenberg, Thomas I Rodhouse, James E Wanserski, Edward J Zajac

D-U-N-S 00-611-5182 IMP/EXP
SCOT INDUSTRIES INC
3756 Fm 250 N, Lone Star, TX 75668
Tel (903) 639-2551 *Founded/Ownrshp* 1949
Sales 196.9MM[E] *EMP* 450
SIC 7389 5051 3498 3471

D-U-N-S 10-409-9411
SCOTIABANK DE PUERTO RICO
(*Suby of* BANK OF NOVA SCOTIA, THE)
290 Ave Jesus T Pinero, San Juan, PR 00918-4002
Tel (787) 766-4999 *Founded/Ownrshp* 1979
Sales NA *EMP* 1,400
SIC 6022 State commercial banks
Pr: Troy Wright
**Pr:* Bruce Bowen
Sr VP: John Oliver
**VP:* Maria De Lourdes Garcia

SCOTLAND COUNTY BOARD EDUCATN
See SCOTLAND COUNTY SCHOOL SYSTEM

D-U-N-S 08-416-4854
SCOTLAND COUNTY SCHOOL SYSTEM
SCOTLAND COUNTY BOARD EDUCATN
322 S Main St, Laurinburg, NC 28352-3834
Tel (910) 276-1138 *Founded/Ownrshp* 1940
Sales 75.0MM *EMP* 1,155
SIC 8211 Public elementary & secondary schools
Ex Dir: Larry Johnson
Dir Sec: Julius Dockery
IT Man: Laura B Urie
Pr Dir: Meredith Bounds
Teacher Pr: Cory Satterfield

D-U-N-S 83-569-7350
SCOTLAND HEALTH CARE SYSTEM
SCOTLAND MEMORIAL HOSPITAL
500 Lauchwood Dr, Laurinburg, NC 28352-5501
Tel (910) 291-7000 *Founded/Ownrshp* 1989
Sales 109.1MM *EMP* 600
SIC 8062 8011 8082 General medical & surgical hospitals; Offices & clinics of medical doctors; Home health care services
CEO: Gregory C Wood
Chf Path: Donna Richardson
Sr VP: Sheila McNulty
**VP:* Hugh Fulton
**VP:* Ruth Glaser
**VP:* Terry Seladon
VP: Greg Stanley
**VP:* Matthew Tracht
Exec: Susan Hardy
Dir Lab: Pat Gentry
Dir Lab: Janet Hankins
Dir Rad: Zim Townsend

SCOTLAND MEMORIAL HOSPITAL
See SCOTLAND HEALTH CARE SYSTEM

D-U-N-S 07-558-4235
SCOTLAND MEMORIAL HOSPITAL INC
500 Lauchwood Dr, Laurinburg, NC 28352-5599
Tel (910) 291-7680 *Founded/Ownrshp* 1989
Sales 126.1MM *EMP* 900
SIC 8062 General medical & surgical hospitals
Pr: Gregory C Wood
Chf Path: Donna Richardson
Pr: Ruth Glaser
**Sr VP:* Sheila McNulty
**VP:* Ann Locklear
**VP:* Gray Mills
**VP:* Matt Pracht
VP: Matthew D Pracht
MIS Dir: Chip Reklis
VP Mktg: Barbara Barnas

D-U-N-S 36-446-6284 IMP
SCOTSMAN INDUSTRIES INC
SCOTSMAN OF LOS ANGELES
(*Suby of* ALI SPA)
101 Corporate Woods Pkwy, Vernon Hills, IL 60061-3109
Tel (847) 215-4501 *Founded/Ownrshp* 2009
Sales 263.1MM[E] *EMP* 800
SIC 3585 3632 Refrigeration equipment, complete; Ice making machinery; Ice boxes, industrial; Cold drink dispensing equipment (not coin-operated); Ice boxes, household: metal or wood; Refrigerators, mechanical & absorption: household
VP: Mark Hardy
Rgnl Mgr: Ken Harris
S&M/VP: Denis Griesmer
S&M/VP: Jim Weaks
Sls Dir: Larry Lozar
Manager: Vince Dattolo

SCOTSMAN OF LOS ANGELES
See SCOTSMAN INDUSTRIES INC

D-U-N-S 04-219-6014
■ **SCOTT & STRINGFELLOW LLC**
BB & T CAPITAL MARKETS
(*Suby of* BB&T CORP) ★
901 E Byrd St Ste 300, Richmond, VA 23219-4066
Tel (804) 643-1811 *Founded/Ownrshp* 1999
Sales 137.9MM[E] *EMP* 825
SIC 6211 Investment firm, general brokerage
Pr: Walter S Robertson III
**Ch Bd:* S Buford Scott
**Ch Bd:* John Sherman
Pr: Staci Goins
Pr: Rebecca Springer
Bd of Dir: Matt Gilman
Bd of Dir: Sidney Scott
Ofcr: Gordon Plancon
Ex VP: Ken Goodyear
Ex VP: Roger Vaden
Ex VP: Rufus W Yates
Sr VP: Cory P Boyte
**Sr VP:* Randy Saufley
VP: Brian Blomeke
VP: John Boehling
VP: Arch Brown
VP: John Conrad
VP: Jay Donlin
VP: Bernard M Donnelly
VP: James Elliott
VP: Peter Faherty

D-U-N-S 60-388-4136
SCOTT & WHITE CLINIC
BAYLOR SCOTT & WHITE
(*Suby of* BAYLOR SCOTT & WHITE HEALTH) ★
2401 S 31st St, Temple, TX 76508-0001
Tel (254) 724-2111 *Founded/Ownrshp* 2013
Sales 1.1MMM *EMP* 300[E]
SIC 8062 General medical & surgical hospitals
Pr: Robert W Pryor
Ex VP: Calvin Eshbaugh
VP: Peter Brumleve
VP: Doeothy Gonzales
VP: Pasquale Montanaro
VP: Amy Perkins
Dir Lab: Alicia Gale
Dir Lab: Dan Koss
Ex Dir: Gail Vanzyl
Dir Sec: Stephen F Sullivan
Dir IT: Don Helms

D-U-N-S 07-669-7960
SCOTT & WHITE MEMORIAL HOSPITAL
KING'S DAUGHTERS HOSPITAL
(*Suby of* BAYLOR SCOTT & WHITE HEALTH) ★
2401 S 31st St, Temple, TX 76508-0001
Tel (254) 724-2111 *Founded/Ownrshp* 1897
Sales 1.1MMM *EMP* 8,000[E]
SIC 8062 6512 7352 7363 General medical & surgical hospitals; Hospital, medical school affiliated with residency; Commercial & industrial building operation; Medical equipment rental; Medical help service
CEO: Robert Pryor
**Pr:* Shahin Motakef
COO: Linda M Burke
COO: Patti Ellisor
**COO:* Donny Sequin
**CFO:* Ken Johnson
VP: Martin Prince
VP: Jay Yellott
Dir Risk M: Lisa Havens
Dir Lab: Dan Koss
Assoc Dir: Angela McGehee

D-U-N-S 08-019-8087
SCOTT + CORMIA ARCHITECTURE AND INTERIORS LLC
429 S Keller Rd Ste 200, Orlando, FL 32810-7187
Tel (407) 660-2766 *Founded/Ownrshp* 2015
Sales 420.0MM *EMP* 28
SIC 8712 Architectural services

SCOTT AIR CONDITIONING & HTG
See SCOTT ELECTRIC CO

D-U-N-S 00-685-0663 IMP
SCOTT BRIDGE CO INC (FL)
2641 Interstate Dr, Opelika, AL 36801-1527
Tel (334) 749-5045 *Founded/Ownrshp* 1958
Sales 120.3MM[E] *EMP* 250
Accts Bartlett Gunder & Yeager Cpas
SIC 1622 Bridge construction
CEO: I J Scott
**VP:* Charles S Davis
**VP:* William Scott
**VP:* Michael E Terrell
**Prin:* David Scott
IT Man: Craig Bacheler
Mtls Mgr: Mark Guin
Snr PM: Stephen Summers

SCOTT COMMUNITY COLLEGE
See EASTERN IOWA COMMUNITY COLLEGE DISTRICT

D-U-N-S 03-138-8960
SCOTT COOPERATIVE ASSOCIATION INC
410 E 1st St, Scott City, KS 67871-1065
Tel (620) 872-5823 *Founded/Ownrshp* 1957
Sales 134.1MM *EMP* 42
SIC 5153 5541 5191 4221 Grains; Filling stations, gasoline; Farm supplies; Chemicals, agricultural; Fertilizer & fertilizer materials; Feed; Grain elevator, storage only
Pr: Tony Wienter

D-U-N-S 07-285-9721
SCOTT COUNTY BOARD OF EDUCATION
2168 Frankfort Rd, Georgetown, KY 40324-9434
Tel (502) 863-3663 *Founded/Ownrshp* 1900
Sales 76.3MM *EMP* 1,000
Accts Stiles Carter & Associates P
SIC 8211 School board
Ch Bd: Haley Conway
IT Man: Sherry Robison

D-U-N-S 07-982-7315
SCOTT COUNTY SCHOOLS
2168 Frankfort Rd, Georgetown, KY 40324-9434
Tel (502) 863-3663 *Founded/Ownrshp* 2015
Sales 86.3MM *EMP* 1,069[E]
SIC 8211 Public elementary & secondary schools
HC Dir: Lynne Switzer

D-U-N-S 00-884-4177
SCOTT ELECTRIC CO (TX)
SCOTT AIR CONDITIONING & HTG
2001 N Port Ave, Corpus Christi, TX 78401-1205
Tel (361) 884-6326 *Founded/Ownrshp* 1920
Sales 106.5MM[E] *EMP* 350
SIC 1731 General electrical contractor
Pr: Sarah Moore
**Treas:* Tino Vasquez
**VP:* B W Diegel
**VP:* Diana Hope
**VP:* Michael Hope
VP: Lonnie M Robisheaux

D-U-N-S 01-416-0501 IMP
SCOTT ELECTRIC CO
1000 S Main St, Greensburg, PA 15601-4868
Tel (800) 442-8045 *Founded/Ownrshp* 1930
Sales 392.2MM[E] *EMP* 433
SIC 5063 Boxes & fittings, electrical; Conduits & raceways; Electrical construction materials; Electrical supplies
Pr: Samuel Scott
**VP:* Joseph Dastafo
Div Mgr: Grant Kern
Sls Dir: Dick Smith
Sales Asso: Scott Allan
Sales Asso: Shannon Kulyk
Sales Asso: Alynn Martin
Sales Asso: Tom McDonough

D-U-N-S 09-033-7010
SCOTT ENTERPRISES INC (PA)
1000 S Main St, Greensburg, PA 15601-4868
Tel (814) 868-9500 *Founded/Ownrshp* 1957
Sales 105.2MM[E] *EMP* 1,500
SIC 8741 Management services
Pr: Samuel Z Scott
**VP:* Joseph Dastolfo
VP: Alison Scott
Genl Mgr: Linda Holland
Mktg Dir: Melanie Whaley
Sls Dir: Pamela Wolff

D-U-N-S 10-210-3194 IMP/EXP
SCOTT EQUIPMENT CO LLC
1000 M L King Jr Dr J, Monroe, LA 71203
Tel (318) 387-4160 *Founded/Ownrshp* 1939
Sales 350.0MM *EMP* 525[E]
SIC 7353 5082 Heavy construction equipment rental; Construction & mining machinery
Pr: Jim Bershen
**Pr:* Scott Cummins
**CEO:* George J Bershen Sr
**COO:* Stephen Harrison
**Ch:* Bobbie Williams
Treas: Laura Culp
VP: Lance Pankey
Genl Mgr: Thomas Soileau

D-U-N-S 07-877-3603 IMP/EXP
SCOTT FARMS INC
7965a Simpson Rd, Lucama, NC 27851-9371
Tel (919) 284-4030 *Founded/Ownrshp* 1976
Sales 175.0MM *EMP* 12
SIC 0132 0115 0116 0161 0139 Tobacco; Corn; Soybeans; Cucumber farm; Sweet potato farm
Pr: Linwood Sonny Scott Jr
**Pr:* Linwood H Scott
**VP:* Dewey R Scott

D-U-N-S 00-418-6706 IMP/EXP
■ **SCOTT FETZER CO**
KIRBY VACUUM CLEANER
(*Suby of* BHSF INC) ★
28800 Clemens Rd, Westlake, OH 44145-1197
Tel (440) 892-3000 *Founded/Ownrshp* 1986
Sales 381.5MM[E] *EMP* 500
SIC 7699 Industrial equipment services
Ch Bd: Kenneth J Semelsberger
**COO:* Vince Nardy
**Treas:* John Grepta
VP: David Lamb
VP: Patricia Scanlon
**Prin:* Bob McBride
Genl Mgr: Bryan Telepak
DP Exec: Bob Schulte
Genl Couns: Ilah Adkins
Corp Couns: Steven Baden
Corp Couns: Lori Kosakowski

D-U-N-S 82-997-9715
SCOTT KRAMER
COEUR D ALENE TRIBAL BINGO
Hwy 95, Worley, ID 83876
Tel (800) 523-2464 *Founded/Ownrshp* 1993
Sales 9.3MM[E] *EMP* 1,200
SIC 7011 Casino hotel
Owner: Scott Kramer

D-U-N-S 03-333-6025
SCOTT PETROLEUM CORP (MS)
102 Main St, Itta Bena, MS 38941-2712
Tel (662) 254-9024 *Founded/Ownrshp* 1935, 1950
Sales 103.1MM[E] *EMP* 239
SIC 5171 5984 5411

D-U-N-S 10-150-4876 IMP/EXP
SCOTT PROCESS SYSTEMS INC
SPSI
(*Suby of* INDUSTRIAL PIPING INC) ★
1160 Sunnyside St Sw, Hartville, OH 44632-9098
Tel (330) 877-2350 *Founded/Ownrshp* 2014
Sales 97.5MM[E] *EMP* 240
SIC 3498 Piping systems for pulp paper & chemical industries
VP: Frank Diener
Plnt Mgr: Jason Kinsley

SCOTT SAFETY
See SCOTT TECHNOLOGIES INC

D-U-N-S 10-569-2602 IMP/EXP
SCOTT TECHNOLOGIES INC
SCOTT SAFETY
(*Suby of* TYCO INTERNATIONAL MANAGEMENT CO LLC) ★
4320 Goldmine Rd, Monroe, NC 28110-7355
Tel (800) 247-7257 *Founded/Ownrshp* 2001
Sales 162.3MM[E] *EMP* 580
SIC 3842 3728 3569 Surgical appliances & supplies; Oxygen systems, aircraft; Firefighting apparatus
Pr: Mark A Kirk
Genl Mgr: Tabatha Williams

D-U-N-S 00-240-7161
SCOTT-MCRAE AUTOMOTIVE GROUP INC (FL)
SCOTT-MCRAE GROUP
701 Riverside Park Pl # 120, Jacksonville, FL 32204-3364
Tel (904) 354-4000 *Founded/Ownrshp* 1980
Sales 339.1MM[E] *EMP* 900[E]
SIC 5511 7515 6159 Automobiles, new & used; Passenger car leasing; Automobile finance leasing
Ch Bd: Walter A Mc Rae Jr
**Ch Bd:* Diane Graham
**Pr:* John Fricks
**Pr:* Henry H Graham Jr
**CEO:* David C Hodges Jr
COO: James B Morgan
**CFO:* Lawrence M Matheny Jr
**Ex VP:* Jeffery S Curry
**Ex VP:* William A Long
**VP:* Monica Hillin
**VP:* Bruce D Ivey
VP: Brian Lynskey
**VP:* R Glynn Wimberly

SCOTT-MCRAE GROUP
See SCOTT-MCRAE AUTOMOTIVE GROUP INC

SCOTTISH HOSPITAL FOR CHILDREN
See TEXAS SCOTTISH RITE HOSPITAL FOR CHILDREN

D-U-N-S 79-727-5625
SCOTTISH RITE TEMPLE
200 Plato Blvd E, Saint Paul, MN 55107-1618
Tel (651) 222-2676 *Founded/Ownrshp* 1859
Sales 4.7M *EMP* 1,000
SIC 8641 Fraternal associations
Prin: Larry Wert

D-U-N-S 83-276-7771
SCOTTRADE BANK
(*Suby of* SCOTTRADE FINANCIAL) ★
12800 Corp Hill Dr, Saint Louis, MO 63131
Tel (314) 965-1555 *Founded/Ownrshp* 2011
Sales NA *EMP* 75
SIC 6035 Federal savings banks
CFO: Rodney Stanley

SCOTTRADE FINANCIAL
See SCOTTRADE INC

D-U-N-S 02-165-3860
SCOTTRADE INC
SCOTTRADE FINANCIAL
12800 Corporate Hill Dr, Saint Louis, MO 63131-1845
Tel (314) 965-1555 *Founded/Ownrshp* 1980
Sales 984.6MM[E] *EMP* 1,600
Accts Deloitte & Touche Llp St Loui
SIC 6211 Stock brokers & dealers
CEO: Rodger O Riney
Pr: Steve Evans
Pr: Mike Garrity
Pr: Matthew Raye
Pr: Matt Wilson
CFO: Drew Dennison
Chf Mktg O: Kim Wells
Ofcr: Andrew Small
VP: Charles Abbitt
VP: Ryan Davidson
VP: Jim Denning
VP: Gary Disalvo
VP: Roy Hinkamper
VP: Ginny Kienstra
VP: Debbie Martensen
VP: Jennifer Myers
VP: Jeffrey Prelle
VP: Wendelynn Rhodes
VP: Jim Ruszala
VP: Mike Shamia
VP: Jason Welker

SCOTTS, THE
See SCOTTS MIRACLE-GRO CO

D-U-N-S 14-721-1270 IMP/EXP
■ SCOTTS CO LLC
SCOTTS MIRACLE-GRO PRODUCTS
(*Suby of* SCOTTS) ★
14111 Scottslawn Rd, Marysville, OH 43040-7801
Tel (937) 644-0011 *Founded/Ownrshp* 1986
Sales 2.1MMM[E] *EMP* 4,900
SIC 2873 2874 2879 0782 2499 3524 Fertilizers: natural (organic), except compost; Phosphates; Fungicides, herbicides; Insecticides, agricultural or household; Lawn services; Mulch, wood & bark; Lawn & garden equipment; Lawnmowers, residential: hand or power
CEO: James Hagedorn
CFO: David Evans
Treas: Phalla Sauers
Bd of Dir: Horace Hagedorn
Bd of Dir: Joseph Rice
Chf Mktg O: Claude Lopez
Ofcr: Rich Martinez
Ex VP: Mike Lukemire
Sr VP: Randy Coleman
Sr VP: Tom Feusse
Sr VP: Michel Gasnier
Sr VP: Brian Kura
Sr VP: Dan Paradiso
Sr VP: Christian Ringuet
VP: Bonny Beetham
VP: Craig Izzo
VP: Korbin Riley
VP: Pete Supron
VP: Robert Walter
VP: Mark Weaver

D-U-N-S 19-690-4069 IMP/EXP
▲ SCOTTS MIRACLE-GRO CO
SCOTTS, THE
14111 Scottslawn Rd, Marysville, OH 43040-7801
Tel (937) 644-0011 *Founded/Ownrshp* 1868
Sales 3.0MMM *EMP* 7,900[E]
Tkr Sym SMG *Exch* NYS
SIC 3542 0782 7342 Machine tools, metal forming type; Lawn & garden services; Pest control services
Ch Bd: James Hagedorn
Pr: Michael C Lukemire
CFO: Thomas R Coleman
Treas: Paul Desantis
Ex VP: Ivan C Smith
Ex VP: Denise S Stump
Mktg Mgr: Phil Jones
Board of Directors: Brian D Finn, Adam Hanft, Michelle A Johnson, Stephen L Johnson, Thomas N Kelly Jr, Katherine Hagedorn Littlef, James F McCann, Nancy G Mistretta, John R Vines

SCOTTS MIRACLE-GRO PRODUCTS
See SCOTTS CO LLC

D-U-N-S 07-834-3364
SCOTTS PEEK N PEAK LLC
PEEK'N PEAK RESORT AND SPA
2225 Downs Dr, Erie, PA 16509-4793
Tel (814) 868-9518 *Founded/Ownrshp* 2011
Sales 245.6MM[E] *EMP* 12,300
SIC 7011 7992 Ski lodge; Public golf courses
**CFO:* Anne Marie Renze

SCOTTS- HYPONEX
See HYPONEX CORP

SCOTTSDALE, CITY OF
See CITY OF SCOTTSDALE MUNICIPAL PROPERTY CORP

SCOTTSDALE HALTHCARE HOSPITALS
See SCOTTSDALE HEALTHCARE CORP

D-U-N-S 06-842-4472
SCOTTSDALE HEALTHCARE CORP (AZ)
SCOTTSDALE HALTHCARE HOSPITALS
8125 N Hayden Rd, Scottsdale, AZ 85258-2463
Tel (480) 882-4000 *Founded/Ownrshp* 1981
Sales 88.2MM *EMP* 17,000
Accts Ernst & Young Us Llp Phoenix
SIC 8062 General medical & surgical hospitals
CEO: Thomas J Sadvary
Chf Path: Ted Allred
Ch Bd: Harrison Whitman
V Ch: Brad Gazaway
Pr: John N Ferree Jr
Pr: Rhonda Forsyth
Pr: Michael Hildebrandt
Ch: Mike Welborn
Treas: Drew Brown
V Ch Bd: Phillip F Schneider
Assoc VP: Anthony Parker
Ex VP: Todd Laporte
Sr VP: Gary Baker
VP: James Burke
VP: Christine Kontgas
VP: Peggy Reiley
VP: Thomas Sadvary
VP: Mark Slater
VP: Kathy Zarubi
Dir Risk M: Mary Bachhuber
Dir Lab: Susan Bittikofer

D-U-N-S 11-553-3069
SCOTTSDALE HEALTHCARE HOSPITALS
HONORHEALTH
(*Suby of* SCOTTSDALE HALTHCARE HOSPITALS) ★
8125 N Hayden Rd, Scottsdale, AZ 85258-2463
Tel (480) 324-7215 *Founded/Ownrshp* 1981
Sales 900.0MM *EMP* 14,000
Accts Lb Ernst & Young Us Llp Phoen
SIC 8062 Hospital, AMA approved residency
CEO: Tom Sadvary
**Ch Bd:* Robert C Johnson
**Pr:* Max Poll
**CEO:* Thomas J Sadvary
**Treas:* F Michael Geddes
**V Ch Bd:* Gary J Goodman
Assoc VP: Scott Sheldon
**Ex VP:* Gary Baker
**Ex VP:* Todd Laporte
**Sr VP:* James F Burke
**Sr VP:* Alan B Kelly
VP: Jim Cramer
VP: Teresa Read
VP: Brian Steines
Dir Risk M: Jan Ross

SCOTTSDALE INDEMNITY COMPANY
See SCOTTSDALE INSURANCE CO

SCOTTSDALE INDEMNITY COMPANY
See SCOTTSDALE INSURANCE CO

D-U-N-S 05-702-8185
SCOTTSDALE INSURANCE CO
SCOTTSDALE INDEMNITY COMPANY
(*Suby of* NATIONWIDE MUTUAL INSURANCE CO) ★
8877 N Gainey Center Dr, Scottsdale, AZ 85258-2108
Tel (480) 365-4000 *Founded/Ownrshp* 1982
Sales NA *EMP* 1,350
SIC 6331 Fire, marine & casualty insurance: stock
**Ch Bd:* R Max Williamson
Pr: Larry Goodyear
Pr: Michael D Miller
COO: Michael Dmiller
Sr VP: John E Goodloe
VP: Rick Aune
VP: Kyle English
VP: Judy Howard
VP: Kenneth Levine
VP: Alesia Martin
VP: Randy Orr
VP: Gary Piepelman
VP: George Suprenant
VP: Matt Thompson
Comm Man: Gay Leon

D-U-N-S 78-582-2003
SCOTTSDALE INSURANCE CO
SCOTTSDALE INDEMNITY COMPANY
(*Suby of* SCOTTSDALE INDEMNITY CO) ★
1 Nationwide Plz 13207, Columbus, OH 43215-2226
Tel (480) 365-4000 *Founded/Ownrshp* 1987
Sales NA *EMP* 1[E]
SIC 6411 Insurance agents, brokers & service

D-U-N-S 02-013-4276
SCOTTSDALE UNIFIED SCHOOL DISTRICT
7575 E Main St, Scottsdale, AZ 85251-4522
Tel (480) 484-6100 *Founded/Ownrshp* 1896
Sales 122.4MM[E] *EMP* 3,000
SIC 8211 Public elementary & secondary schools
Ch: Price Nosky
CFO: Daniel O'Brien
**VP:* Shonna James
Dir Sec: James Dorer
Off Admin: Kristine Smith
Dir IT: Derrick Tutt
IT Man: Paul Goldstein
Netwrk Eng: Elden Cozort
Pr Dir: Kristine Harrington
Genl Couns: Michelle Marshall
Snr Mgr: Tony Batrof

D-U-N-S 06-834-0835
SCOTTYS CONTRACTING AND STONE LLC (KY)
(*Suby of* HOUCHENS INDUSTRIES INC) ★
2300 Barren River Rd, Bowling Green, KY 42101-9483
Tel (270) 781-3998 *Founded/Ownrshp* 1972, 2004
Sales 144.8MM[E] *EMP* 350
SIC 1629 1611 2951 Drainage system construction; Highway & street paving contractor; Asphalt paving mixtures & blocks
CFO: Todd Dyer
**CFO:* Rod England
VP: Gary Hopkins
**VP:* Mike Law
Dir IT: George Walenga
Plnt Mgr: Ronnie Bryant

D-U-N-S 14-715-8661 IMP/EXP
SCOULAR CO
INDUSTRIAL FOOD INGREDIENTS
2027 Dodge St Ste 200, Omaha, NE 68102-1229
Tel (402) 342-3500 *Founded/Ownrshp* 1967
Sales 4.6MMM *EMP* 801[E]
Accts Kpmg Llp Omaha Ne
SIC 5153 Grain & field beans; Corn; Wheat; Soybeans
Ch Bd: Marshall E Faith
Pr: Eric Jackson
CEO: Chuck Elsea
COO: Bob Ludington
CFO: Richard A Cogdill
Treas: Roger Barber
Ex VP: David Faith
Ex VP: John Heck
Ex VP: Joan Maclin
Sr VP: John M Heck
Sr VP: Joan C Maclin
Sr VP: George Schieber
VP: Roger L Barber
VP: Tim Dingman
VP: Curt Engel
VP: Randall Foster
VP: Arthur Huskey
VP: Jim Konz
VP: Todd McQueen
VP: Omer Sagheer
VP: George Schieber

SCP
See STANDARD CONCRETE PRODUCTS INC

D-U-N-S 05-764-4247 IMP/EXP
■ SCP DISTRIBUTORS LLC
SOUTH CENTRAL POOL
(*Suby of* POOL CORP) ★
109 Northpark Blvd, Covington, LA 70433-5005
Tel (985) 892-5521 *Founded/Ownrshp* 1993
Sales 1.6MMM[E] *EMP* 2,650
SIC 5091 Swimming pools, equipment & supplies
CFO: Craig Hubbard
CFO: Donald Meyer
VP: David Cook
Brnch Mgr: David Beyersdorf
Genl Mgr: Stephen Nelson
Sls Mgr: Bryce McElroy

SCRA TECHNOLOGY VENTURES
See SOUTH CAROLINA RESEARCH AUTHORITY INC

D-U-N-S 78-137-3683
■ SCRANTON HOSPITAL CO LLC
REGIONAL HOSPITAL OF SCRANTON
(*Suby of* COMMUNITY HEALTH SYSTEMS INC) ★
746 Jefferson Ave, Scranton, PA 18510-1624
Tel (570) 348-7100 *Founded/Ownrshp* 2010
Sales 70.7MM[E] *EMP* 1,231
SIC 8062 General medical & surgical hospitals
CEO: Brooks Turkel
**Pr:* John Starcher
Dir IT: Tom Ranella
Nrsg Dir: Patricia Deltos

D-U-N-S 07-915-8523
SCRANTON SCHOOL DISTRICT
425 N Washington Ave, Scranton, PA 18503-1396
Tel (570) 348-3474 *Founded/Ownrshp* 1870
Sales 124.9MM *EMP* 1,200
Accts Michael A Barbetti Llc Dunm
SIC 8211 Public elementary & secondary schools
CFO: Gregg Sunday
**Ofcr:* Jeff Brazil
MIS Dir: Megan Barrett
Pr Dir: Nancy Lavarty
Schl Brd P: Said Douaihy

D-U-N-S 05-844-2492
SCRANTON TIMES L P
CITY PAPER OF BALTIMORE
149 Penn Ave Ste 1, Scranton, PA 18503-2094
Tel (570) 348-9100 *Founded/Ownrshp* 1895
Sales 124.9MM[E] *EMP* 691
SIC 2711 4832 Newspapers, publishing & printing; Radio broadcasting stations
Mng Pt: Edward J Lynett Jr
Pt: Cecelia Lynett Haggerty
Pt: George V Lynett
Pt: Lynda Mulligan Lynett
Pt: Mary Jean Foley Lynett
COO: Hal Marion

D-U-N-S 60-985-1675
SCRAP METAL SERVICES LLC
S M S
13830 S Brainard Ave, Burnham, IL 60633-1638
Tel (708) 730-1400 *Founded/Ownrshp* 2005
Sales 556.0MM[E] *EMP* 150[E]
SIC 5093 Metal scrap & waste materials
CFO: Jolynn Gosser
**Ex VP:* Richard Gertler
Ex VP: Ralph Pinkert

D-U-N-S 83-189-5219
SCREEN ACTORS GUILD-PRODUCERS ADMINISTRATIVE CORP
3601 W Olive Ave Ste 200, Burbank, CA 91505-4697
Tel (818) 954-9400 *Founded/Ownrshp* 1994
Sales NA *EMP* 19[E]
Accts Bernard Kotkin & Company Llp
SIC 6371 Pension, health & welfare funds
CEO: Bruce L Dow

D-U-N-S 82-802-3387
SCRIBEAMERICA LLC
(*Suby of* CHICAGO GROWTH PARTNERS II LP) ★
1200 E Las Olas Blvd # 201, Fort Lauderdale, FL 33301-2367
Tel (786) 279-1057 *Founded/Ownrshp* 2014
Sales 77.5MM *EMP* 5,000[E]
SIC 8099 Medical services organization
**COO:* Sarah Lamb
**CFO:* Michael Welch
**Ex VP:* Jennifer Larsen
**Ex VP:* Jackie McDonald
Dir IT: Daniel Tehrani
Snr Mgr: Anthony Ramirez

D-U-N-S 04-845-4412
SCRIP ADVANTAGE INC
4273 W Richert Ave # 110, Fresno, CA 93722-6333
Tel (559) 320-0052 *Founded/Ownrshp* 2000
Sales 136.0MM *EMP* 54
SIC 7389 Fund raising organizations
Pr: John Coyle
**CFO:* Robert Coyle
**VP:* Bob Coyle

D-U-N-S 82-961-4309 IMP/EXP
SCRIP HOLDING CORP
360 Veterans Pkwy Ste 115, Bolingbrook, IL 60440-4673
Tel (630) 771-7400 *Founded/Ownrshp* 2006
Sales 113.7MM[E] *EMP* 175[E]
SIC 5047 Physician equipment & supplies; Therapy equipment; X-ray machines & tubes
Pr: Kray Kibler
**VP:* John Matusiewicz

D-U-N-S 04-876-7953
SCRIPPS CLINIC FOUNDATION
(*Suby of* SCRIPPS HEALTH) ★
12395 El Camino Real, San Diego, CA 92130-3082
Tel (858) 554-9000 *Founded/Ownrshp* 2000
Sales 96.5MM[E] *EMP* 1,600
SIC 8741 Management services
CEO: Dr Hugh Greenway
Surgeon: Giacomo Delaria

D-U-N-S 13-118-5241
SCRIPPS HEALTH
4275 Campus Point Ct, San Diego, CA 92121-1513
Tel (858) 678-7000 *Founded/Ownrshp* 1924
Sales 1.4MMM[E] *EMP* 13,445
Accts Ernst & Young Us Llp San Dieg
SIC 8051 8082 8062 8049 8042 8043 Skilled nursing care facilities; Home health care services; General medical & surgical hospitals; Physical therapist; Psychologist, psychotherapist & hypnotist; Offices & clinics of optometrists; Offices & clinics of podiatrists
Pr: Chris D Van Gorder
Dir Vol: Carrie Cushman
**CFO:* Richard K Rothberger
Trst: Mary J Anderson
Trst: Westcott W Price
Ofcr: Jan Coughlin
**Ofcr:* A B Eastman MD
Ofcr: Kelly Hardiman
**Sr VP:* Robin B Brown Jr
**Sr VP:* Victor V Buzachero
**Sr VP:* John B Engle
**Sr VP:* Richard Sheridan
VP: Peter D Aldrich
VP: Vic Buzachero
VP: David Cohn
VP: Richard McKeown
VP: Gary W Williams MD
Dir Rad: William Marshall
Dir Rx: Christine Low

SCRIPPS NETWORK
See TELEVISION FOOD NETWORK GP

D-U-N-S 82-526-5726
▲ SCRIPPS NETWORKS INTERACTIVE INC
9721 Sherrill Blvd, Knoxville, TN 37932-3330
Tel (865) 694-2700 *Founded/Ownrshp* 2007
Sales 3.0MMM *EMP* 3,500[E]
Tkr Sym SNI *Exch* NGS
SIC 4841 Cable & other pay television services; Closed circuit television services; Direct broadcast satellite services (DBS)
Ch Bd: Kenneth W Lowe
COO: Burton Jablin
CFO: Lori A Hickok
Ofcr: Nello-John Pesci Jr
Ex VP: Mark S Hale
Ex VP: Beth Lawrence
Sr VP: Katherine Alford
Sr VP: Melissa Mick
VP: Chad Boydston

VP: Tim Harty
Mng Dir: Marcio Fonseca
Board of Directors: Ronald W Tysoe, Gina L Bianchini, Michael R Costa, David A Galloway, Donald E Meihaus, Richelle P Parham, Nicholas B Paumgarten, Mary McCabe Peirce, Jeffrey Sagansky, Wesley W Scripps

D-U-N-S 87-859-6220 IMP
SCRIPTPRO LLC
5828 Reeds Rd, Shawnee Mission, KS 66202-2740
Tel (913) 384-1008 *Founded/Ownrshp* 1994
Sales 118.7MM[E] *EMP* 600
SIC 3559 3586 Pharmaceutical machinery; Measuring & dispensing pumps
Prin: Mike Coughlin
Pr: Shafi Shilad
CFO: Annette Slade
Ex VP: Joe Courtright
Dir Bus: Kasie Waters
Genl Mgr: Renee Dye
CIO: Christopher Duffy
CTO: Frank Grange
IT Man: Elizabeth Brooks
Sftwr Eng: Mike Daugherty
Sftwr Eng: Bradley Lockard

D-U-N-S 02-448-2296
SCRIPTPRO USA INC
(*Suby of* SCRIPTPRO LLC) ★
5828 Reeds Rd, Shawnee Mission, KS 66202-2740
Tel (913) 384-1008 *Founded/Ownrshp* 1997
Sales 107.4MM[E] *EMP* 415
SIC 5087 Vending machines & supplies
Ch Bd: Michael E Coughlin
* *CFO:* Doug Maughan
* *VP:* Sharon Coughlin
* *VP:* Joseph N McCormack
* *VP:* Tracy Thomas

SCS ENGINEERS
See STEARNS CONRAD AND SCHMIDT CONSULTING ENGINEERS INC

SCTR
See CHINA SUTONG TIRE RESOURCES INC

S.C.U.C.I.S.D
See SCHERTZ-CIBOLO-UNIVERSAL CITY INDEPENDENT SCHOOL DISTRICT

D-U-N-S 11-869-5527
SCULL CONSTRUCTION SERVICE INC
SCULL J CONSTRUCTION
803 Industrial Ave, Rapid City, SD 57702-0337
Tel (605) 342-2379 *Founded/Ownrshp* 1985
Sales 87.4MM[E] *EMP* 125
Accts Ketel Thorstenson Llp Rapid
SIC 1542 Commercial & office building, new construction
Pr: James L Scull Jr
* *Treas:* Andrew Scull
VP: Dan Wegner
* *VP:* Danny Wegner

SCULL J CONSTRUCTION
See SCULL CONSTRUCTION SERVICE INC

D-U-N-S 94-859-6700
SCULLY SERVICES LLC
(*Suby of* TAS) ★
19319 Oil Center Blvd, Houston, TX 77073-3354
Tel (281) 230-7500 *Founded/Ownrshp* 2008
Sales 97.8MM[E] *EMP* 785[E]
Accts Hidalgo Banfill Zlotnik & Ke
SIC 1771 Concrete work
Pr: Mark Scully

SCVMC
See SANTA CLARA VALLEY MEDICAL CENTER

SD
See SATCOM DIRECT INC

SD 271
See COEUR D ALENE SCHOOL DISTRICT 271

D-U-N-S 10-297-8207
SD DEACON CORP
7745 Greenback Ln Ste 250, Citrus Heights, CA 95610-5865
Tel (916) 969-0900 *Founded/Ownrshp* 1999
Sales 391.5MM *EMP* 340
Accts Bfba Llp Sacramento Califor
SIC 1542 Commercial & office building, new construction
CEO: Steven D Deacon
Pt: Bob Miller
* *Pr:* Richard Smith
VP: Paul Cunha
VP: Bill Townsend
Prin: Pete Snook
Genl Mgr: Mitch Parker
Off Mgr: Cynthia Hulliger
VP Opers: Bob Aroyan
Sfty Mgr: Roger Dale-Moore
Sfty Mgr: Glen Kuntz

S.D. FURNITURE MART
See FURNITURE MART USA INC

SDB GROUP, THE
See SDB TRADE INTERNATIONAL LP

D-U-N-S 10-282-2681
SDB INC
810 W 1st St, Tempe, AZ 85281-2676
Tel (480) 967-5810 *Founded/Ownrshp* 1980
Sales 127.3MM[E] *EMP* 300[E]
SIC 1542 Nonresidential construction
CEO: Dominic Spagnuolo
* *CFO:* Edward W Riccio
* *VP:* Brian Bohnsack
Dir IT: Jeffrey Bingham
Dir IT: Adobe Mechanical
Sfty Dirs: David Dopp

D-U-N-S 80-568-5380 IMP
SDB TRADE INTERNATIONAL LP
SDB GROUP, THE
817 Southmore Ave Ste 301, Pasadena, TX 77502-1130
Tel (713) 475-0048 *Founded/Ownrshp* 2003
Sales 94.7MM[E] *EMP* 12
SIC 3317 Steel pipe & tubes
Pr: Dilip Bhargava

D-U-N-S 08-004-1797
SDH EDUCATION WEST LLC
(*Suby of* SODEXO AMERICA LLC) ★
9801 Washington Blvd, Gaithersburg, MD 20878
Tel (301) 987-4000 *Founded/Ownrshp* 2000
Sales 13.5MM[E] *EMP* 2,468[E]
SIC 8741 Management services

SDI
See SPECIAL DEVICES INC

SDI
See STEEL DYNAMICS INC

D-U-N-S 05-330-2709
SDI INC
(*Suby of* SDH NEW INTERMEDIATE HOLDCO, INC.)
1414 Radcliffe St Ste 300, Bristol, PA 19007-5497
Tel (215) 633-1900 *Founded/Ownrshp* 1971
Sales 232.9MM[E] *EMP* 275
SIC 7374 7389 8711 8748 Data processing service; Inventory computing service; Engineering services; Business consulting
Pr: Andy Cvitanov
* *Ch:* John Gavin
* *Treas:* Louay Khatib
VP: Thomas Liberta
VP: Tina Merrell
VP: Scott Morehous
VP: Chris Shaffer
VP: Chuck Wallace
Prgrm Mgr: Vee Browne
Prgrm Mgr: David Gulaitis
CTO: Kurt Meiers

SDI TELECOM
See FISK TELECOM LLC

D-U-N-S 02-512-0243
SDM&R INC
SENN DUNN INSURANCE
3625 N Elm St, Greensboro, NC 27455-2604
Tel (336) 272-7161 *Founded/Ownrshp* 1927
Sales NA *EMP* 150
SIC 6321 Accident & health insurance carriers
Pr: Tim Templeten
CFO: Danielle L Hoversten
Dir IT: Neda J Pitt
Sls Mgr: Angela Reynolds

SDP/SI
See DESIGNATRONICS INC

D-U-N-S 36-110-4888 IMP
SDR PLASTICS INC
STAR PLASTICS
1 Plastics Ave, Ravenswood, WV 26164-4610
Tel (304) 273-5326 *Founded/Ownrshp* 1988
Sales 100.8MM[E] *EMP* 140[E]
SIC 5093 Plastics scrap
Pr: Doug Ritchie
* *Sec:* Ray Ritchie
CIO: Mike Watson
DP Exec: John Burge
IT Man: James Holland

SDSU
See SAN DIEGO STATE UNIVERSITY

SDV USA
See BOLLORE LOGISTICS USA INC

D-U-N-S 87-930-1059 IMP/EXP
SDW HOLDINGS CORP
255 State St Fl 7, Boston, MA 02109-2618
Tel (617) 423-5400 *Founded/Ownrshp* 1994
Sales 498.5MM[E] *EMP* 2,500
SIC 2621

SE REGION OFFICE
See PROGRESSIVE WASTE SOLUTIONS OF FL INC

D-U-N-S 15-237-8670
SE SCHER CORP
ACROBAT STAFFING
665 3rd St Ste 415, San Francisco, CA 94107-1968
Tel (415) 431-8826 *Founded/Ownrshp* 2005
Sales 19.8MM *EMP* 2,000
SIC 7361 Employment agencies
Pr: Steve Scher
Off Mgr: Pia Harris
Off Admin: Arlene Deleon
Opers Mgr: Alyssa Hardy
Opers Mgr: Debbie McKee
VP Sls: Marc Caplan

SEA
See SOUTHEAST AEROSPACE INC

D-U-N-S 11-793-6547
SEA CREST HEALTH CARE MANAGEMENT LLC
LAVIE CARE CENTER
800 Concourse Pkwy S, Maitland, FL 32751-6152
Tel (813) 744-2800 *Founded/Ownrshp* 2002
Sales 142.1MM[E] *EMP* 5,000
SIC 8059 Convalescent home
Pr: Jeffrey K Jellerson
* *VP:* Troy M Antonik

D-U-N-S 00-227-5600 IMP/EXP
SEA GULL LIGHTING PRODUCTS LLC
WOODRIVER INDUSTRIES
(*Suby of* QUALITY HOME BRANDS HOLDINGS LLC) ★
1829 Underwood Blvd Ste 2, Delran, NJ 08075-4135
Tel (856) 764-0500 *Founded/Ownrshp* 1919, 2006
Sales 177.4MM[E] *EMP* 600
SIC 3645 Residential lighting fixtures

CFO: Bruce Hawkins
Sls Dir: Srinivasa Krishna

D-U-N-S 96-610-8248
SEA ISLAND ACQUISITION LP
100 Cloister Dr, Sea Island, GA 31561-9705
Tel (912) 638-3611 *Founded/Ownrshp* 2010
Sales 173.4MM[E] *EMP* 1,800[E]
SIC 7011 0781 7992 Resort hotel; Landscape planning services; Public golf courses
Pt: Bill Jones III
* *Pt:* David Bansmer

D-U-N-S 96-732-4935
SEA ISLAND ACQUISITIONS LLC
100 Cloister Dr, Sea Island, GA 31561-9705
Tel (912) 638-3611 *Founded/Ownrshp* 2008
Sales 25.7MM[E] *EMP* 1,234
SIC 7011 Hotels & motels

D-U-N-S 00-692-6562
SEA ISLAND CO (GA)
5 STAR RESORT
(*Suby of* SEA ISLAND ACQUISITION LP) ★
100 Cloister Dr, Sea Island, GA 31561-9701
Tel (888) 732-4752 *Founded/Ownrshp* 1926, 2010
Sales 173.4MM[E] *EMP* 1,800
SIC 7011 0781 7992 Resort hotel; Landscape planning services; Public golf courses
Prin: Scott Steilen
CFO: Ron Roberts
VP: Yates Anderson
Exec: Holly Hersey
Exec: Maurice Richards
Genl Mgr: Gerald Lott
* *Mktg Dir:* Merry Tipton
Sls Mgr: Amanda Biffle
Genl Couns: Carl Alexander

D-U-N-S 03-788-6876
SEA ISLAND SERVICES INC
(*Suby of* 5 STAR RESORT) ★
100 Hudson Pl, Sea Island, GA 31561
Tel (912) 638-3611 *Founded/Ownrshp* 1992
Sales 16.7MM[E] *EMP* 1,500
SIC 4111 4941 Local & suburban transit; Water supply
Ch: William Jones III
* *Sec:* Dennie L McCrary
* *Sec:* William C Smith
* *VP:* J Dewey Benefield Jr
Board of Directors: Edward T Wright

SEA MAR
See SEA-MAR COMMUNITY HEALTH CENTER

D-U-N-S 86-951-3028
SEA MAR COMMUNITY CARE CENTER
SEA MAR SKILLED NURSING FCILTY
1040 S Henderson St, Seattle, WA 98108-4720
Tel (206) 763-5210 *Founded/Ownrshp* 1994
Sales 8.1MM *EMP* 1,000
Accts Sea Mar Community Health Cente
SIC 8051 8351 Skilled nursing care facilities; Head start center, except in conjunction with school
CEO: Rogelio Riojas
CFO: Zachary Smulski

SEA MAR SKILLED NURSING FCILTY
See SEA MAR COMMUNITY CARE CENTER

D-U-N-S 06-108-7029 IMP/EXP
■ **SEA RAY BOATS INC**
(*Suby of* BRUNSWICK CORP) ★
800 S Gay St Ste 1200, Knoxville, TN 37929-9729
Tel (865) 522-4181 *Founded/Ownrshp* 1978
Sales 247.0MM[E] *EMP* 1,782
SIC 3732 Boats, fiberglass: building & repairing
Pr: Rick Stones
CFO: Tom Okley
* *VP:* Terry McKnew
Exec: Rhonda Auten
Genl Mgr: Mike Fritts
Telecom Ex: Steve Schneider
IT Man: Darrell Bivens
Opers Mgr: Craig Laboranti
VP Mktg: Michael Berk
S&M/VP: Jeff Gayer
Mktg Mgr: Chris Helton

D-U-N-S 12-134-5565 IMP
SEA WATCH INTERNATIONAL LTD
OLD SALT SEAFOOD
8978 Glebe Park Dr, Easton, MD 21601-7004
Tel (410) 822-7501 *Founded/Ownrshp* 1999
Sales 111.0MM[E] *EMP* 450
SIC 2092 2091 Shellfish, frozen: prepared; Shrimp, frozen: prepared; Shellfish: packaged in cans, jars, etc.; Shrimp: packaged in cans, jars, etc.
Pr: Robert J Brennan
* *Sr VP:* Micheal Wyatt
* *VP:* Bernie Carr
MIS Mgr: Janice Bain
Sfty Mgr: Jose Alicea
VP Sls: Joe Moock
Sls Mgr: Dan McAuliffe
Sls Mgr: Sandy Thompson

D-U-N-S 13-347-3819 IMP
■ **SEA WORLD LLC**
SWC, AQC
(*Suby of* SEAWORLD PARKS & ENTERTAINMENT INC) ★
9205 Southpark Ctr Loop, Orlando, FL 32819-8651
Tel (407) 226-5011 *Founded/Ownrshp* 1976
Sales 115.1MM[E] *EMP* 2,588[E]
SIC 7996 Theme park, amusement
VP Mktg: Marilyn Hannes
* *Pr:* John T Reilly
* *COO:* Donnie Mills
* *CFO:* Peter Crage
VP: Fred Jacobs
* *VP:* Roy Rieve
IT Man: Steve Voss
Mktg Dir: Brandon Gregory
Snr Mgr: Lori Ello

D-U-N-S 78-154-5777 IMP
■ **SEA WORLD OF FLORIDA LLC**
SWF, DCO, AQF
(*Suby of* SWC AQC) ★
9205 Southpark Ctr Loop, Orlando, FL 32819-8651
Tel (407) 226-5011 *Founded/Ownrshp* 1990
Sales 113.4MM[E] *EMP* 2,306[E]
SIC 7996 Theme park, amusement
Pr: Donald Mills
VP: Brad Andrews
Sls Mgr: Steve Vinciguerra
Art Dir: Helen Bryner

D-U-N-S 07-777-4149 IMP/EXP
SEA-LAND CHEMICAL CO
821 Westpoint Pkwy, Westlake, OH 44145-1545
Tel (440) 871-7887 *Founded/Ownrshp* 1980
Sales 92.3MM[E] *EMP* 54[E]
SIC 5169 Chemicals & allied products
Pr: Joseph Clayton
* *CFO:* Mark Getsay
* *Ex VP:* Mark Christeon
VP: Jack McKenna
Genl Mgr: Rob Stubbs
IT Man: Mike Jasien
Sales Asso: Buck Evans
Sales Asso: Scot Wahl
Doctor: Linda Pascali

D-U-N-S 09-724-5658
SEA-MAR COMMUNITY HEALTH CENTER
SEA MAR
1040 S Henderson St, Seattle, WA 98108-4720
Tel (206) 763-5277 *Founded/Ownrshp* 1978
Sales 162.6MM *EMP* 850
SIC 8322 8082 8093 8051 Individual & family services; Old age assistance; Home health care services; Specialty outpatient clinics; Skilled nursing care facilities
CEO: Rogelio Riojas
* *Sr VP:* Carolina Lucero
* *VP:* Mary Bartolo
VP: Michael Leong
VP: Ricardo Sanchez
Dir Rx: Gea Caballero
Nutrtnst: Sandra Aramburu
Nutrtnst: Kolleen Bump
Nutrtnst: Abrey Weidman
Pharmcst: Monica Serrano

D-U-N-S 00-104-2472 IMP/EXP
▲ **SEABOARD CORP**
9000 W 67th St, Merriam, KS 66202-3638
Tel (913) 676-8800 *Founded/Ownrshp* 1928
Sales 5.5MMM *EMP* 10,772
Accts Kpmg Llp Kansas City Missour
Tkr Sym SEB *Exch* ASE
SIC 2011 0133 4412 6221 0723 0213 Pork products from pork slaughtered on site; Sugarcane farm; Deep sea foreign transportation of freight; Commodity traders, contracts; Flour milling custom services; Hogs
Ch Bd: Steven J Bresky
Pr: David M Dannov
Pr: Edward A Gonzalez
Pr: Terry J Holton
CFO: Robert L Steer
Treas: David S Oswalt
Sr VP: David M Becker
Sr VP: James L Gutsch
Sr VP: Ralph L Moss
Sr VP: David H Rankin
VP: Gary Louis
VP: Stephen Summerlin
VP: Michael D Trollinger
VP: Ty A Tywater
Dir Risk M: Will Franken

D-U-N-S 82-593-6321 IMP
■ **SEABOARD FARMS INC**
(*Suby of* SEABOARD CORP) ★
424 N Main St Ste 200, Guymon, OK 73942-4316
Tel (580) 338-1470 *Founded/Ownrshp* 1992
Sales 144.0MM[E] *EMP* 865
SIC 0213 2011 Hogs; Pork products from pork slaughtered on site
Ch Bd: H Harry Bresky
Sfty Mgr: Keith Henry

D-U-N-S 00-695-5421 IMP/EXP
SEABOARD FLOUR LLC
1320 Centre St Ste 200, Newton, MA 02459-2487
Tel (617) 928-6040 *Founded/Ownrshp* 1928
Sales 449.3MM[E] *EMP* 10,500
SIC 5046 Bakery equipment & supplies
COO: Paul Squires

D-U-N-S 12-849-9121 IMP/EXP
■ **SEABOARD FOODS LLC**
(*Suby of* SEABOARD CORP) ★
9000 W 67th St Ste 200, Shawnee Mission, KS 66202-3656
Tel (913) 261-2600 *Founded/Ownrshp* 1995
Sales 153.8MM[E] *EMP* 450
SIC 0213 5147 2011 Hogs; Meats & meat products; Meat packing plants
Pr: Terry Holton
VP: John Allis
VP: Brad Hamilton
VP: Dave Oswalt
VP: Stephen Summerlin
VP Bus Dev: David A Oswalt
Exec: Greg Mangan
Exec: Richard Watt
Genl Mgr: Terry Mahan
Genl Mgr: Stan Scott
IT Man: Lee Christina

D-U-N-S 10-194-7984 IMP/EXP
■ **SEABOARD MARINE LTD INC**
(*Suby of* SEABOARD CORP) ★
8001 Nw 79th Ave, Medley, FL 33166-9113
Tel (305) 863-4444 *Founded/Ownrshp* 1983
Sales 167.9MM[E] *EMP* 800
SIC 4412

D-U-N-S 61-856-7358 IMP
■ SEABOURN CRUISE LINE LIMITED
YACHTS OF SEABOURN, THE
(Suby of CARNIVAL CORP) ★
300 Elliott Ave W Ste 100, Seattle, WA 98119-4122
Tel (206) 626-9179 *Founded/Ownrshp* 1998
Sales 91.1MM^E *EMP* 3,500
SIC 4481 Deep sea passenger transportation, except ferry
Pr: Pamela C Conover
**Pr:* Richard D Meadows
**CFO:* Lourdes Pineda
**Ch:* Stein Kruse
**VP:* Kelly W Clark
VP: John Delaney
**VP:* Daniel S Grausz
VP: Rapp Lawrence
VP: Helen Panagos
VP: Larry Rapp
**Prin:* Larry D Calkins

D-U-N-S 16-752-5273
SEABRIGHT HOLDINGS INC
SEABRIGHT INSURANCE COMPANY
(Suby of ENSTAR GROUP LIMITED)
1111 3rd Ave Ste 1450, Seattle, WA 98101-3292
Tel (206) 269-8500 *Founded/Ownrshp* 2013
Sales NA *EMP* 225^E
SIC 6331 Workers' compensation insurance
VP: Steve Kelley
Pr: Gene Gerrard
COO: Jeffrey D Miller
Sr VP: William O Courtney
VP: James L Borland
Snr Ntwrk: Jeff Wilkinson

SEABRIGHT INSURANCE COMPANY
See SEABRIGHT HOLDINGS INC

D-U-N-S 15-048-6736 IMP/EXP
SEABRING MARINE INDUSTRIES INC
MONTEREY BOATS
1579 Sw 18th St, Williston, FL 32696-2477
Tel (352) 529-9161 *Founded/Ownrshp* 1985
Sales 121.0MM^E *EMP* 200
SIC 5091 3732 Boats, canoes, watercrafts & equipment; Motorboats, inboard or outboard: building & repairing
Pr: Robert A Pita
**VP:* James M Ducharme

D-U-N-S 08-643-4040 IMP
SEABROOK BROTHERS & SONS INC
85 Finley Rd, Bridgeton, NJ 08302-6078
Tel (856) 455-8080 *Founded/Ownrshp* 1978
Sales 100.8MM *EMP* 200
Accts Athey & Company Bridgeton Ne
SIC 2037 Vegetables, quick frozen & cold pack, excl. potato products
Pr: James M Seabrook Jr
COO: Andrew Carpenter
**V Ch Bd:* Charles F Seabrook II
**VP:* William Seabrook
QA Dir: Burgos Edeidy
Ql Cn Mgr: Barbara Michalkiewicz
VP Sls: Brian Seabrook
S&M/VP: Ivin Seabrook

SEABROOK NUCLEAR POWER PROJECT
See NORTH ATLANTIC ENERGY SERVICE CORP

D-U-N-S 87-755-4584
■ SEABULK INTERNATIONAL INC
SEABULK OFFSHORE
(Suby of SEACOR HOLDINGS INC) ★
2200 Eller Dr, Fort Lauderdale, FL 33316-3069
Tel (954) 828-1701 *Founded/Ownrshp* 2005
Sales 240.4MM^E *EMP* 2,502
SIC 4424 4492 Deep sea domestic transportation of freight; Marine towing services; Tugboat service
CFO: Richard J Ryan
CFO: J Nouss
Bd of Dir: Peter H Cressy
Sr VP: John O Cnnell
**Sr VP:* Alice N Gran
**Sr VP:* Kenneth M Rogers
Sr VP: Alan R Twaits
**Sr VP:* L Stephen Willrich
**VP:* A Thomas Denning
**VP:* John Gellert
Dir Risk M: Steve Moglia

SEABULK OFFSHORE
See SEABULK INTERNATIONAL INC

D-U-N-S 15-276-8875
■ SEABURY & SMITH (DELAWARE) INC
(Suby of MARSH & MCLENNAN COMPANIES INC) ★
1166 Ave Of The Americas, New York, NY 10036-2708
Tel (212) 345-9049 *Founded/Ownrshp* 1982
Sales NA *EMP* 4,600
SIC 6411 6331 6321 6311 Insurance brokers; Fire, marine & casualty insurance; Accident & health insurance; Life insurance
Pr: Claude Mercier
CFO: Thomas R Hopkins
**Treas:* Jeff Schlingbaum
**VP:* Jody Chessman
Dept Mgr: Tom Delcor
IT Man: Ellen Clarke
IT Man: Nathalie Vanheusden

SEACATCH SEAFOODS
See ATLANTIS SEAFOOD LLC

D-U-N-S 80-749-9595
▲ SEACHANGE INTERNATIONAL INC
50 Nagog Park, Acton, MA 01720-3409
Tel (978) 897-0100 *Founded/Ownrshp* 1993
Sales 106.9MM *EMP* 660^E
Tkr Sym SEAC *Exch* NGS
SIC 3663 7822 7371 Television broadcasting & communications equipment; Television & video tape distribution; Television tape distribution; Computer software development
CEO: Edward Terino
**Ch Bd:* Steven Craddock
CFO: Peter Faubert
Sr VP: David McEvoy
Prgrm Mgr: Maria Gaibor
Snr Sftwr: Nur Malonzo
Snr Sftwr: Vincent Ruiz
Dir IT: Shay Moles
Tech Mgr: Francis Villaluz
Sftwr Eng: Peter Gibbons
Corp Couns: Sean Gusmini
Board of Directors: Mary Palermo Cotton, William Francis Markey III, Thomas F Olson, Royce E Wilson

D-U-N-S 07-699-2197 IMP
■ SEACOAST BANK OF FLORIDA INC
SEACOAST NATIONAL BANK
(Suby of SEACOAST BANKING CORP OF FLORIDA) ★
815 Colorado Ave Lbby, Stuart, FL 34994-3060
Tel (772) 221-2760 *Founded/Ownrshp* 1983
Sales NA *EMP* 579
SIC 6021 National trust companies with deposits, commercial
CEO: Dennis S Hudson II
**Pr:* A Douglas Gilbert
**CFO:* William R Hahl
Bd of Dir: Laura Petersen
Bd of Dir: Shirley Weems
Ofcr: Jamie Adams
Ofcr: Maria Frias
**Ofcr:* H Russell Holland III
Ofcr: Kevin Sargent
Ofcr: Debbie Skidmore
Ofcr: Robert Stillwell
Ex VP: Leonard Hoag
Ex VP: Thomas Wilkinson
**Sr VP:* Susan Bergstrom
Sr VP: Cathy Cavicchioli
**Sr VP:* Patricia Cucchiara
Sr VP: Teresa Idzior
Sr VP: Jeff Lee
Sr VP: Charles Olsson
Sr VP: Kevin Picart
Sr VP: Fred Roxas
Board of Directors: Dennis Arczynski, Julie H Daum, Maryann Goebel

D-U-N-S 11-296-3608
▲ SEACOAST BANKING CORP OF FLORIDA
815 Colorado Ave, Stuart, FL 34994-3053
Tel (772) 287-4000 *Founded/Ownrshp* 1983
Sales NA *EMP* 665
Tkr Sym SBCF *Exch* NGS
SIC 6022 State commercial banks
Ch Bd: Dennis S Hudson III
Pr: Frances Portalatin
CFO: Stephen A Fowle
Ex VP: William R Hahl
Ex VP: David D Houdeshell
Board of Directors: Dennis S Hudson Jr, Dennis J Arczynski, Timothy S Huval, Stephen E Bohner, Herbert Lurie, Jacqueline L Bradley, Thomas E Rossin, T Michael Crook, H Gilbert Culbreth Jr, Julie H Daum, Christopher E Fogal, Maryann Goebel, Roger O Goldman

SEACOAST NATIONAL BANK
See SEACOAST BANK OF FLORIDA INC

SEACOAST REGIONAL
See ANNA JAQUES HOSPITAL

D-U-N-S 61-033-7990
▲ SEACOR HOLDINGS INC
2200 Eller Dr, Fort Lauderdale, FL 33316-3069
Tel (954) 523-2200 *Founded/Ownrshp* 1989
Sales 1.0MMM *EMP* 4,849
Tkr Sym CKH *Exch* NYS
SIC 4412 4424 4449 4959 8748 Deep sea foreign transportation of freight; Deep sea domestic transportation of freight; Intracoastal (freight) transportation; Environmental cleanup services; Environmental consultant
Ch Bd: Charles Fabrikant
COO: Eric Fabrikant
CFO: Matthew Cenac
**V Ch Bd:* Oivind Lorentzen
Sr VP: Bruce Weins
VP: Michael Campbell
VP: Andrew Strachan
Opers Mgr: Armond Batiste
Board of Directors: David R Berz, Pierre De Demandolx, Andrew R Morse, R Christopher Regan, David M Schizer

D-U-N-S 05-748-1939 IMP
■ SEACOR MARINE LLC
(Suby of SEACOR HOLDINGS INC) ★
7910 Main St Ste 200, Houma, LA 70360-3427
Tel (985) 858-6427 *Founded/Ownrshp* 1982
Sales 88.7MM^E *EMP* 800
SIC 4424 Deep sea domestic transportation of freight
Pr: John Gellert

D-U-N-S 01-062-1303 IMP/EXP
SEAGATE TECHNOLOGY (US) HOLDINGS INC
(Suby of SEAGATE TECHNOLOGY PUBLIC LIMITED COMPANY)
10200 S De Anza Blvd, Cupertino, CA 95014-3029
Tel (831) 438-6550 *Founded/Ownrshp* 2000
Sales 9.4MMM^E *EMP* 46,018
SIC 3572 Computer storage devices; Magnetic storage devices, computer
Ch Bd: Stephen J Luczo
COO: Steven Markowski
COO: James Orr
**CFO:* David H Morton Jr
**CFO:* Charles C Pope
Ex VP: Robert Whitemore
Ex VP: Bob Whitmore
Sr VP: Pornchai Piemsomboon
VP: Johor Bahru
VP: Glen Peterson
Comm Man: Lori Johnson

SEAGATE TECHNOLOGY HDD HLDGS
See SEAGATE TECHNOLOGY LLC

D-U-N-S 03-847-6441 IMP
SEAGATE TECHNOLOGY LLC
SEAGATE TECHNOLOGY HDD HLDGS
(Suby of SEAGATE TECHNOLOGY (US) HOLDINGS INC) ★
10200 S De Anza Blvd, Cupertino, CA 95014-3029
Tel (408) 658-1000 *Founded/Ownrshp* 2000
Sales 9.4MMM^E *EMP* 43,000
SIC 3572 Computer storage devices
Pr: Stephen J Luczo
**Pr:* Terry Cunningham
COO: Robert Whitemore
**COO:* Robert Whitmore
COO: David A Wickershm
CFO: Patrick O Malley
CFO: Patrick J O'Malley
**CFO:* Bob Whitmore
**Treas:* David H Morton Jr
Bd of Dir: Kristen M Onken
Ex VP: William L Hudson
Ex VP: Kenneth M Massaroni
**Ex VP:* Dave Mosley
**Ex VP:* Patrick Omalley
**Ex VP:* Albert Rocky Pimentel
Ex VP: Albert A Pimentel
Sr VP: Kenneth M Assaroni
Sr VP: John D Griec
Sr VP: John Grieci
VP: Rich Becks
VP: Rod Cooper

D-U-N-S 13-191-1120 IMP
SEAGRAVE FIRE APPARATUS LLC
SWD SEAGRAVE
(Suby of SEAGRAVES FIRE APPARATUS) ★
105 E 12th St, Clintonville, WI 54929-1590
Tel (715) 823-2141 *Founded/Ownrshp* 2003
Sales 137.8MM^E *EMP* 275
SIC 5012 3713 8711 Fire trucks; Truck & bus bodies; Engineering services
CEO: A Joseph Neiner
**CFO:* Ulisses Parmeziani
CFO: Mark Proctor
Ofcr: Tom Nuthals
VP: McMorran Matt
VP: Tom Shand
IT Man: Dwight McMillan
VP Sls: Matt Macmorra
Mktg Dir: George Kanugh
Sls Mgr: Tom Camp

SEAGRAVES FIRE APPARATUS
See FWD SEAGRAVE HOLDINGS LP

SEAHAWKS STADIUM
See FIRST & GOAL INC

D-U-N-S 12-203-2006
SEAKR ENGINEERING INC
6221 S Racine Cir, Centennial, CO 80111-6427
Tel (303) 662-1449 *Founded/Ownrshp* 1982
Sales 105.8MM^E *EMP* 400^E
SIC 3674 8711 Random access memory (RAM); Aviation &/or aeronautical engineering
Pr: Raymond Anderson
Ofcr: Susan Haake
**VP:* Eric Anderson
Prgrm Mgr: Scot Sommer
QA Dir: Chris Mercer
IT Man: Mike Chenoweth
Sftwr Eng: Steve Zimmermann
Mfg Mgr: Michael Clawson
Sls Mgr: Steve Koritnik

D-U-N-S 14-534-5401
SEALTECH INC
GUARDIAN COMPLIANCE
28420 Hardy Toll Rd # 220, Spring, TX 77373-8084
Tel (281) 475-4770 *Founded/Ownrshp* 1983
Sales 274.9MM^E *EMP* 1,040
Accts Briggs & Veselka Co Bellaire
SIC 5169 Sealants
Pr: James Craig
**CEO:* Thomas McMullen
**CFO:* Jennifer Buhigas

D-U-N-S 02-806-1257 IMP/EXP
SEAL123 INC
WET SEAL
26972 Burbank, Foothill Ranch, CA 92610-2506
Tel (949) 699-3900 *Founded/Ownrshp* 1962
Sales 530.1MM *EMP* 7,413
SIC 5621 5632 5961

D-U-N-S 05-231-6494
SEALAND CONTRACTORS CORP
85 High Tech Dr, Rush, NY 14543-9746
Tel (704) 522-1102 *Founded/Ownrshp* 1977
Sales 87.9MM^E *EMP* 205
SIC 1622 1611 1623 Bridge construction; General contractor, highway & street construction; Water main construction; Sewer line construction
Pr: Daniel Bree
**CFO:* George Dietz
VP: Joseph Bree
VP: Vinnie Diprospero

D-U-N-S 07-819-9049 IMP/EXP
SEALASKA CORP
1 Sealaska Plz Ste 400, Juneau, AK 99801-1276
Tel (907) 586-1512 *Founded/Ownrshp* 1972
Sales 109.4MM *EMP* 1,400
Accts Kpmg Llp Anchorage Ak
SIC 5099 8744 7371 8748 1542 Timber products, rough; Logs, hewn ties, posts & poles; ; Custom computer programming services; Systems engineering consultant, ex. computer or professional; Nonresidential construction
Pr: Anthony Mallott
COO: Terry Downes
COO: Lewis Ivers
CFO: Doug Morris
VP: Russell Adick
VP: Jaeleen Araujo
VP: Joleen Araujo
VP: Nicole Hallingstad
VP: Richard Harris
Off Mgr: Lori Simanton
Board of Directors: Ross Soboleff, Michael Beasley, Bill Thomas, Sidney Edenshaw, Edward Thomas, A M Kookesh, Rosita Worl, J Tate London, Jodi Mitchell, Barbara Cadiente-Nelson, Joe Nelson, Jacqueline Pata, Richard Rinehart

D-U-N-S 00-245-7638 IMP/EXP
▲ SEALED AIR CORP
8215 Forest Point Blvd # 100, Charlotte, NC 28273-5509
Tel (980) 221-3235 *Founded/Ownrshp* 1960
Sales 7.0MMM *EMP* 23,000
Accts Ernst & Young Llp Charlotte
Tkr Sym SEE *Exch* NYS
SIC 2673 2671 3087 3086 3089 Plastic & pliofilm bags; Packaging paper & plastics film, coated & laminated; Custom compound purchased resins; Plastics foam products; Plastic processing
Pr: Jerome A Peribere
Pr: Ilham Kadri
Pr: Colleen Ryan
CFO: Carol P Lowe
Sr VP: Emile Z Chammas
VP: Norman D Finch Jr
VP: Edwina Payne
VP: Ram Ramesh
VP: Barbara Seale
VP: Brian Sharp
VP: Robert L Tatterson
Board of Directors: Michael Chu, Lawrence R Codey, Patrick Duff, Jacqueline B Kosecoff, Neil Lustig, Kenneth P Manning, William J Marino, Richard L Wambold, Jerry R Whitaker

D-U-N-S 79-093-3183 EXP
■ SEALED AIR CORP (US)
(Suby of SEALED AIR CORP) ★
200 Riverfront Blvd # 301, Elmwood Park, NJ 07407-1038
Tel (201) 791-7600 *Founded/Ownrshp* 1969
Sales NA *EMP* 7,500
SIC 2673 2671 3087 3086 3089 Plastic & pliofilm bags; Packaging paper & plastics film, coated & laminated; Custom compound purchased resins; Plastics foam products; Plastic processing
Pr: Jerome Peribere
**CFO:* David H Kelsey
**Treas:* Tod Christie
**Sr VP:* Robert A Pesci
VP: Anthony Caspio
VP: Mary A Coventry
VP: David B Crosier
VP: Keith Galbraith
VP: Brian Luburgh
VP: James P Mix
VP: Jim Mize
VP: Carol O Neill
VP: Ruth Roper
VP: Hugh L Sargant
VP: James D Tate
VP: Jeffrey S Warren
**VP:* H Katherine White
VP: Chris Woodbridge
Dir Bus: Martin Klein

D-U-N-S 04-516-8879 IMP/EXP
SEALING DEVICES INC
4400 Walden Ave, Lancaster, NY 14086-9751
Tel (716) 684-7600 *Founded/Ownrshp* 1963
Sales 103.0MM^E *EMP* 164
Accts Lumsden Mccormick Cpas
SIC 5085 3069 3053 Gaskets; Seals, industrial; Hard rubber & molded rubber products; Gaskets & sealing devices
Pr: Terry S Galanis Jr
Treas: Gregory Delduce
Genl Mgr: Tammie Rost
Software D: Matt Kelly
Ql Cn Mgr: Michael Barnard
Sales Exec: Vincent Andolina
Sls Mgr: Stephen Glynn
Sls Mgr: Michael Moretti
Sls Mgr: Gary Reitmeier
Sls Mgr: Ray Szkutak
Sales Asso: Mark Andolina

SEALMASTER
See THORWORKS INDUSTRIES INC

SEALY & COMPANY
See SEALY CORP

D-U-N-S 12-179-2154 IMP
■ SEALY CORP
SEALY & COMPANY
(Suby of TEMPUR SEALY INTERNATIONAL INC) ★
1 Office Parkway Rd, Trinity, NC 27370-9449
Tel (336) 861-3500 *Founded/Ownrshp* 2013
Sales 1.2MMM^E *EMP* 4,267
SIC 2515 Mattresses, innerspring or box spring; Box springs, assembled
Pr: Lawrence J Rogers
COO: Tony Smith
CFO: Jeffrey C Ackerman
CFO: E Leewyatt
Treas: Steven Benrubi
Treas: Mark D Boehmer
Ofcr: Jodi Allen
Ex VP: Louis R Bachicha
Ex VP: Michael G Hofmann
Sr VP: Salvadore Gomez
Sr VP: Michael Q Murray
VP: Nat Bernstein
VP: Carmen Dabiero
VP: Roy Finke
VP: James Goughenour
VP: Don Pflug
VP: Derek Ritzel
VP: Chris Spano
Board of Directors: Simon Brown, Deborah G Ellinger, James W Johnston, Gary E Morin, Dean B Nelson, Paul J Norris, John B Replogle, Richard W Roedel

D-U-N-S 13-046-5867
■ SEALY INC
(Suby of SEALY MATTRESS CO) ★
1 Office Parkway Rd, Trinity, NC 27370-9449
Tel (336) 861-3500 *Founded/Ownrshp* 1984
Sales 52.5MM^E *EMP* 2,500

SIC 8741 Administrative management
VP: Kenneth L Walker
Plnt Mgr: John Kocaja

D-U-N-S 05-151-6979 IMP/EXP
■ SEALY MATTRESS CO (OH)
(Suby of SEALY & CO) ★
1 Office Parkway Rd, Trinity, NC 27370-9449
Tel (336) 861-3500 Founded/Ownrshp 1881, 1912
Sales 454.9MM[E] EMP 2,500
SIC 2515 Mattresses, innerspring or box spring; Box springs, assembled
Ch Bd: Ronald L Jones
Pr: Mike Campbell
Pr: Randy Cowart
*Pr: Dave Mcilquham
*CEO: Lawrence J Rogers
*CFO: Jeffrey C Ackerman
*CFO: Jim Hirshorn
*Treas: Mark D Boehmer
VP: Richard Moss
*VP: David V Sherman
Dir IT: Ben Kuchel

D-U-N-S 06-041-2939 EXP
■ SEALY MATTRESS MANUFACTURING CO INC (DE)
(Suby of TEMPUR SEALY INTERNATIONAL INC) ★
1 Office Parkway Rd, Trinity, NC 27370-9449
Tel (336) 861-3500 Founded/Ownrshp 1982, 2016
Sales 257.8MM[E] EMP 1,375
SIC 2515 Mattresses, innerspring or box spring
CEO: Laurence Rogers
*Sr VP: Kenneth Walker
*VP: David V Sherman
Genl Mgr: Barbara Simmons

D-U-N-S 00-421-1124 IMP/EXP
SEAMAN CORP
1000 Venture Blvd, Wooster, OH 44691-9358
Tel (330) 262-1111 Founded/Ownrshp 1951
Sales 127.2MM[E] EMP 290
SIC 2221 Nylon broadwoven fabrics; Polyester broadwoven fabrics
Pr: Richard N Seaman
*COO: James E Dye
VP: Scott Gipson
VP: Carol Momchilou
IT Man: Susan Uhler
Plnt Mgr: Johnny Henson

D-U-N-S 14-471-6219 IMP/EXP
■ SEAMLESS TEXTILES LLC
(Suby of HANESBRANDS INC) ★
Km 86 3 Rr 3, Humacao, PR 00791
Tel (787) 850-3440 Founded/Ownrshp 1995
Sales 133.8MM[E] EMP 725
SIC 5137 Lingerie
Prin: Ricardo Perez

SEAPORT STEEL
See ISSC INC

SEARHC
See SOUTHEAST ALASKA REGIONAL HEALTH CONSORTIUM

D-U-N-S 62-111-4750 EXP
SEARLES VALLEY MINERALS INC
(Suby of SVM MINERALS HOLDINGS INC) ★
9401 Indn Crk Pkwy # 1000, Overland Park, KS 66210-2091
Tel (913) 344-9500 Founded/Ownrshp 2003
Sales 554.2MM[E] EMP 648
SIC 1479 Salt & sulfur mining
Pr: Avinash Puri
*CFO: Emanuel Teresi
Treas: Janet Kapin
*VP: Burnell Blanchard
*VP: Stephen W Cole
*VP: Matthew Dowd
*VP: Pamela Hasty
*Prin: Don Pemberton
*Prin: John F Tancredi

SEARS DENTAL CENTER
See DENTALCARE PARTNERS INC

D-U-N-S 19-122-2244 IMP/EXP
▲ SEARS HOLDINGS CORP
3333 Beverly Rd, Hoffman Estates, IL 60179-0001
Tel (847) 286-2500 Founded/Ownrshp 2004
Sales 25.1MMM EMP 178,000
Accts Deloitte & Touche Llp Chicago
Tkr Sym SHLD Exch NGS
SIC 5311 5411 5531 5961 Department stores; Grocery stores; Automotive & home supply stores; Catalog & mail-order houses
Ch Bd: Edward S Lampert
Pr: Girish Lakshman
Pr: Tom Park
Pr: Lynn Pendergrass
Pr: Sean Skelley
CFO: Jason Hollar
Ex VP: Jeffrey A Balagna
Sr VP: Kristin M Coleman
Sr VP: Leena Munjal
VP: Jonathan Carpenter
VP: Don Fotsch
VP: Perianne Grignon
VP: Amy Higgins
VP: Christopher Kraft
VP: Mac Mcllvried
VP: Robert A Riecker
VP: David Schauble
VP: Les Townsend
Dir Bus: Judy Byrnes
Board of Directors: Cesar L Alvarez, Bruce R Berkowitz, Paul G Depodesta, William C Kunkler III, Ann N Resse, Thomas J Tisch

D-U-N-S 78-734-9815
■ SEARS HOLDINGS MANAGEMENT CORP
SHC REALTY
(Suby of SEARS ROEBUCK AND CO) ★
3333 Beverly Rd, Hoffman Estates, IL 60179-0001
Tel (847) 286-2500 Founded/Ownrshp 2005
Sales 6.2MMM[E] EMP 45,004[E]
SIC 6531 6719 Real estate managers; Investment holding companies, except banks
Pr: Ronald D Moire
Pr: Alasdair James
CFO: Robert A Schriesheim
Ex VP: Jeffrey A Balagna
Sr VP: Arun D Arora
VP: Peter Evans
VP: Valerie Johnson
Prin: Lou D'Ambrosio
Dist Mgr: Richard Schmitt
Dist Mgr: Scott Stanislaw
Dist Mgr: Janis Taylor

D-U-N-S 02-035-4101 EXP
■ SEARS HOME IMPROVEMENT PRODUCTS INC
(Suby of SEARS ROEBUCK AND CO) ★
1024 Florida Central Pkwy, Longwood, FL 32750-7579
Tel (407) 767-0990 Founded/Ownrshp 1999
Sales 910.0MM[E] EMP 2,900
Accts Philip Hansen Contrl By Fax O
SIC 1521 General remodeling, single-family houses
Pr: Stuart Reed
*Pr: Mark C Good
Pr: Anne Hand
*CEO: Allywn Lewis
*CFO: Christine Menges
VP: Jack Grau
*VP: Laurence Macdowell
*VP: Joseph J Steenbeke
*VP: James H Williams
Dept Mgr: Susan Borowicz
Dist Mgr: Tim Conner

D-U-N-S 07-834-8322
▲ SEARS HOMETOWN AND OUTLET STORES INC
5500 Trillium Blvd # 501, Hoffman Estates, IL 60192-3401
Tel (847) 286-2500 Founded/Ownrshp 2012
Sales 2.2MMM EMP 3,634[E]
Accts Bdo Usa Llp Chicago Illinoi
Tkr Sym SHOS Exch NAS
SIC 5251 5261 5722 Hardware; Nurseries & garden centers; Lawn & garden equipment; Lawn & garden supplies; Household appliance stores
Pr: William A Powell
*Ch Bd: Ephraim J Bird
Chf Mktg O: David J Buckley Jr
Ofcr: Ryan D Robinson
Sr VP: Michael A Gray
VP: Charles J Hansen
VP: Michael P McCarthy
Sls Mgr: Gary Altieri
Board of Directors: Jeffrey Flug, James F Gooch, Josephine Linden, William K Phelan

D-U-N-S 00-526-3801 IMP/EXP
SEARS MANUFACTURING CO
SEARS SEATING
1718 S Concord St, Davenport, IA 52802-2999
Tel (563) 383-2800 Founded/Ownrshp 1855
Sales 225.0MM[E] EMP 1,000
SIC 2531

D-U-N-S 84-866-9313
SEARS METHODIST RETIREMENT SYSTEM INC
1 Village Dr Ste 400, Abilene, TX 79606-8232
Tel (325) 691-5519 Founded/Ownrshp 1993
Sales 4.8MM EMP 1,600
SIC 8361

D-U-N-S 00-162-9955 IMP/EXP
■ SEARS ROEBUCK AND CO
(Suby of SEARS HOLDINGS CORP) ★
3333 Beverly Rd, Hoffman Estates, IL 60179-0002
Tel (847) 286-2500 Founded/Ownrshp 1886
Sales 25.1MMM[E] EMP 178,000
SIC 5311 Department stores, non-discount
Pr: Joelle Maher
Pr: Beryl Buley
CFO: Atul Kavthekar
*CFO: Glenn R Richter
*CFO: Glenn Richter
CFO: Robert A Schriesheim
Ex VP: Jeffrey A Balagna
Ex VP: Scott Freidheim
Sr VP: Leslie Mann
Sr VP: William G Paonis
VP: Tony Brown
*VP: Gerald F Kelly
VP: Linda Knapp
VP: Frank Kneller
VP: Dan Laughlin
VP: Paul J Liska
VP: Robert J O'Leary
*VP: William G Pagonis
VP: Richard F Westenberger
*VP: Andrea L Zopp
Board of Directors: Jean Haley, Rory Herriman

D-U-N-S 09-012-7648 IMP/EXP
■ SEARS ROEBUCK DE PUERTO RICO INC
(Suby of SEARS ROEBUCK AND CO) ★
383 Ave Fd Roosevelt # 105, San Juan, PR 00918-2143
Tel (787) 773-7000 Founded/Ownrshp 1961
Sales 147.9MM[E] EMP 3,500
SIC 5311 Department stores, non-discount
Pr: Gary Salvatore

SEARS SEATING
See SEARS MANUFACTURING CO

D-U-N-S 10-670-0060
SEASIDE TRANSPORTATION SERVICES LLC
389 Terminal Way, San Pedro, CA 90731-7430
Tel (310) 241-1760 Founded/Ownrshp 2001
Sales 210.6MM[E] EMP 13
SIC 4231 Trucking terminal facilities
Ch: Teche Lee

SEASONS
See BLUE GOLD EQUITIES LLC

SEASONS, THE
See 331 HOLT LANE OPERATIONS LLC

D-U-N-S 05-420-8574 IMP
SEASONS-4 INC
4500 Industrial Access Rd, Douglasville, GA 30134-3949
Tel (770) 489-0716 Founded/Ownrshp 1985
Sales 89.1MM[E] EMP 230
SIC 3585 3567 Air conditioning equipment, complete; Heating equipment, complete; Industrial furnaces & ovens
CEO: Lewis B Watford
*Treas: Stephen L Watford
VP: Lee Churchill
VP: Shapour Nassiri
Sfty Mgr: Dan Kochan
Plnt Mgr: Ray Rollins

D-U-N-S 07-984-2984
▲ SEASPINE HOLDINGS CORP
5770 Armada Dr, Carlsbad, CA 92008-4608
Tel (760) 727-8399 Founded/Ownrshp 2015
Sales 133.1MM EMP 295
Tkr Sym SPNE Exch NGS
SIC 3841 Surgical & medical instruments; Surgical instruments & apparatus
Pr: Keith C Valentine
CFO: John J Bostjancic
VP: Brian Baker
VP: Paul Benny
VP: Colin Smith
VP Mktg: Troy Woolley
VP Sls: John J Winge

SEASTAR SOLUTIONS
See MARINE ACQUISITION CORP

SEASTAR SOLUTIONS
See MARINE ACQUISITION (US) INC

D-U-N-S 03-764-1487 IMP/EXP
SEATEL INC
COBHAM SATCOM
(Suby of COBHAM AROSPC COMMUNICATIONS) ★
4030 Nelson Ave, Concord, CA 94520-1200
Tel (925) 798-7979 Founded/Ownrshp 1981
Sales 86.0MM EMP 175
SIC 3663

SEATING TECHNOLOGIES
See ZIEMAN MANUFACTURING CO INC

D-U-N-S 78-765-2411 IMP/EXP
SEATRAX INC
(Suby of POWER WELL SERVICE) ★
13223 Fm 529 Rd, Houston, TX 77041-2532
Tel (713) 896-6500 Founded/Ownrshp 1990
Sales 137.7MM[E] EMP 325
SIC 3531 3536 Cranes, ship; Hoists, cranes & monorails
Pr: William D Morrow
*Sec: Tom McKinney
*VP: John Hale
QA Dir: Maurice Gilby
Dir IT: Tim Young
Netwrk Mgr: Vicki Smith
Prd Mgr: Neville Boakes
Genl Couns: Jill Czapla

D-U-N-S 00-610-5506 IMP
SEATS INC
A NORDIC GROUP COMPANY
(Suby of NORDIC GROUP OF COMPANIES LTD) ★
1515 Industrial St, Reedsburg, WI 53959-2153
Tel (608) 524-8261 Founded/Ownrshp 1952
Sales 100.3MM[E] EMP 378
SIC 2531

D-U-N-S 96-375-4478
SEATTLE AIRPORT HOSPITALITY LLC
5847 San Felipe St # 4650, Houston, TX 77057-3000
Tel (713) 787-6222 Founded/Ownrshp 1996
Sales 18.8MM[E] EMP 1,030
SIC 7011 Hotels & motels
Prin: Olivier Santos

D-U-N-S 80-643-3145
SEATTLE CANCER CARE ALLIANCE
825 Eastlake Ave E, Seattle, WA 98109-4405
Tel (206) 288-7222 Founded/Ownrshp 1998
Sales 464.1MM EMP 1,300[E]
Accts Clark Nuber Ps Bellevue Wa
SIC 8069 Cancer hospital
Pr: Fred Appelbaum
Dir Vol: Erica Karlovits
*Ch Bd: Richard McCune
*V Ch: Mike Delman
*VP: David Ackerson
*VP: Debby Gentzen
*VP: Norman Hubburd
*VP: Barbara Jagels
*VP: Angelique Richard
*VP: Jonathan Tingstad
Assoc Dir: Lori Klebeck

D-U-N-S 14-424-6253
SEATTLE CHILDRENS HEALTHCARE SYSTEM
4800 Sand Point Way Ne, Seattle, WA 98105-3901
Tel (206) 987-2000 Founded/Ownrshp 1981
Sales 79.6MM[E] EMP 3,000
SIC 8069 Children's hospital
Pr: Thomas Hansen
*Pr: Jim Ladd
*CFO: Kelly Wallace
*Treas: Mike Delman
Ofcr: Susan Heath
Sr VP: David Fisher
Sr VP: Sanford M Melzer
VP: Jennifer Abermanis
VP: Cara Bailey
VP: Ruth Benfield
VP: Cindy Evans
*VP: Bob Flowers
*VP: Treuman Katz
VP: Erik Lausund
VP: David Perry
VP: Suzanne Petersen

D-U-N-S 96-226-7873
SEATTLE CHILDRENS HEALTHCARE SYSTEM
P.O. Box 5371 (98145-5005)
Tel (206) 987-4846 Founded/Ownrshp 2010
Sales 115.2MM EMP 7[E]
Accts Clark Nuber Ps Bellevue Wa
SIC 8062 General medical & surgical hospitals

D-U-N-S 04-868-2157
SEATTLE CHILDRENS HOSPITAL
SEATTLE CHILDRENS RES INST
4800 Sand Point Way Ne, Seattle, WA 98105-3901
Tel (206) 987-2000 Founded/Ownrshp 1981
Sales 1.0MMM EMP 2,800
SIC 8062 8069 General medical & surgical hospitals; Children's hospital
Pr: Jim Ladd
COO: Senait Abraham
COO: Cliff Coe
COO: Richard Ellenbogen
COO: Gabriel Haddad
COO: Douglas Hawkins
COO: Karen Kropp
COO: Hagan Patrick
COO: Kathleen Patterson
*CFO: Kelly Wallace
*Treas: Bob Flowers
*Sec: Patrick Hagan
Bd of Dir: John Iacuone
Ofcr: Susan Heath
Ex VP: Sandy Melzer
*Sr VP: Jeff Brown
Sr VP: Mark A Del Beccaro
VP: Cindy E Gazecki
VP: Joshua Greenberg
Exec: Maneesh Batra
Exec: Don Cotter

SEATTLE CHILDRENS RES INST
See SEATTLE CHILDRENS HOSPITAL

D-U-N-S 04-302-2045
SEATTLE COLLEGES
WASHINGTON CC DISTRICT 6
1500 Harvard Ave, Seattle, WA 98122-3803
Tel (206) 934-4100 Founded/Ownrshp 1966
Sales 5.0MM EMP 1,496
SIC 8222 Community college
Ch: Albert Shen
*Ch Bd: Carmen Gayton
*CFO: Kurt Buttleman
Ex VP: Warren Brown
*Ex Dir: Dawn Vinberg
Prgrm Mgr: Joy Gulmon-Huri
Dir IT: Michael Lock
Board of Directors: Paul Kilpatrick

D-U-N-S 18-024-1648
SEATTLE FOUNDATION
1200 5th Ave Ste 1300, Seattle, WA 98101-3151
Tel (206) 622-2294 Founded/Ownrshp 1946
Sales 115.3MM EMP 22
Accts Clark Nuber Ps Bellevue Wa
SIC 8399 Community development groups
Owner: Phyllis Campbell
Pt: Stewart M Landefeld
Ofcr: Maggie Wykowski
Sr VP: Jane Repensek
VP: Michael Brown
VP: Patti Dill
VP: Fidelma McGinn
VP: Jared Watson
Comm Dir: Mary Roske
Off Mgr: Barb Peterson
Off Admin: Daphanie Randle

D-U-N-S 02-848-4371
▲ SEATTLE GENETICS INC
21823 30th Dr Se, Bothell, WA 98021-3907
Tel (425) 527-4000 Founded/Ownrshp 1997
Sales 336.8MM EMP 759[E]
Tkr Sym SGEN Exch NGS
SIC 2836 Biological products, except diagnostic
Ch Bd: Clay B Siegall
COO: Eric L Dobmeier
CFO: Todd E Simpson
Chf Mktg O: Jonathan Drachman
Ex VP: Darren S Cline
Ex VP: Vaughn B Himes
Ex VP: Jean I Liu
Sr VP: Dennis Benjamin
Sr VP: Robert J Lechleider
Exec: Stan Brown
Exec: Rajesh Surapaneni
Exec: Tracy Wolniewicz
Assoc Dir: Michael Young
Board of Directors: Felix Baker, David W Gryska, Marc E Lippman, John P McLaughlin, John A Orwin, Nancy A Simonian, Daniel G Welch

D-U-N-S 00-794-3210
SEATTLE GOODWILL INDUSTRIES INC (WA)
700 Dearborn Pl S, Seattle, WA 98144-2736
Tel (206) 329-1000 Founded/Ownrshp 1923
Sales 103.1MM EMP 985
SIC 5932

SEATTLE HUMAN SERVICES
See CITY OF SEATTLE

SEATTLE LIGHTING FIXTURE
See DOLAN NORTHWEST LLC

SEATTLE MARINERS BASEBALL CLUB
See BASEBALL CLUB OF SEATTLE LLLP

D-U-N-S 00-121-9153 IMP
SEATTLE PACIFIC INDUSTRIES INC
UNIONBAY SPORTSWEAR
1633 Westlake Ave N # 300, Seattle, WA 98109-6227
Tel (253) 872-8822 Founded/Ownrshp 1980
Sales 118.0MM[E] EMP 220
SIC 5136 5137 Sportswear, men's & boys'; Women's & children's clothing
Pr: Stephen Ritchey
*COO: Douglas Sellin
Sr VP: Christina Briant
VP: Pat Hutchins
VP: Amanda Kendall

VP: Cathie Underwood
Genl Mgr: Rod Leung
Sls Mgr: Mini Black
Board of Directors: Tony Lau, Brian Leung

D-U-N-S 07-185-3477
SEATTLE PACIFIC UNIVERSITY INC
3307 3rd Ave W, Seattle, WA 98119-1997
Tel (206) 281-2000 *Founded/Ownrshp* 1891
Sales 107.1MM *EMP* 500
SIC 8221 8661

D-U-N-S 07-819-9965
SEATTLE PUBLIC SCHOOLS
2445 3rd Ave S, Seattle, WA 98134-1923
Tel (206) 252-0000 *Founded/Ownrshp* 1871
Sales 362.0MM[E] *EMP* 4,650
Accts Brian Sonntag Cgfm State Aud
SIC 8211 Public elementary school; Public junior high school; Public senior high school; Public special education school
Bd of Dir: Darlene Flynn
Exec: Gary Davis
Exec: Donna Good
Adm Dir: Dave Anderson
Ex Dir: Shauna Heath
Prgrm Mgr: Conny Spann
Area Supr: Sharon Giri
Genl Mgr: Gregg Neilson
Dir IT: Amy Markishtum
Dir IT: Ryan Yeh
IT Man: Kristin Nichols

D-U-N-S 14-978-3243
SEATTLE TIMES CO
TIMES COMMUNICATIONS CO
(*Suby of* BLETHEN CORP) ★
1000 Denny Way Ste 501, Seattle, WA 98109-5323
Tel (206) 464-2111 *Founded/Ownrshp* 1971
Sales 188.9MM[E] *EMP* 990
SIC 2711 Newspapers
Ch Bd: Frank A Blethen
**Pr:* Carolyn S Kelly
**COO:* Alayne Fardella
CFO: Phil Metka
**Treas:* William K Blethen Jr
**Ex VP:* Alan Fisco
VP: Nancy Bruner
VP: Michael Fapcher
VP: Brian Kokes
Exec: Molly Wangerin
Creative D: Laura McAdoo

D-U-N-S 05-124-1875
SEATTLE UNIVERSITY
901 12th Ave, Seattle, WA 98122-4411
Tel (206) 296-6150 *Founded/Ownrshp* 1891
Sales 265.1MM *EMP* 1,100
Accts Kpmg Llp Seattle Wa
SIC 8221 University
Pr: Steve Sundborg
**Pr:* Steve Sundborg Sj
Ofcr: Danielle Mar
VP: Scott McClellan
VP: Andrew O'Boyle
VP: Robert Schwartz
Assoc Dir: Dhorea Brown
Ex Dir: Marilyn Gist
Mng Dir: Richard Wood
Opers Mgr: Lane Gerber
Opers Mgr: Richard Hansen

D-U-N-S 02-150-6068
▲ SEAWORLD ENTERTAINMENT INC
9205 Southpark Center Loo, Orlando, FL 32819-8651
Tel (407) 226-5011 *Founded/Ownrshp* 2009
Sales 1.3MMM *EMP* 11,300[E]
Tkr Sym SEAS *Exch* NYS
SIC 7996 Amusement parks; Theme park, amusement
Pr: Joel K Manby
**Ch Bd:* David F D'Alessandro
V Ch: Jim Atchison
Pr: Jim Dean
Pr: David Hammer
Pr: John T Reilly
COO: Daniel B Brown
COO: Donald W Mills Jr
CFO: Peter J Crage
Chf Cred: Anthony Esparza
Ofcr: Brad Andrews
Ofcr: Dave Hammer
VP: Howard Demsky
Board of Directors: Ron Bension, William Gray, Judith A McHale, Thomas E Moloney, Ellen O Tauscher, Deborah M Thomas, Peter F Wallace

D-U-N-S 07-872-1161
■ SEAWORLD PARKS & ENTERTAINMENT INC
(*Suby of* SEAWORLD ENTERTAINMENT INC) ★
9205 Southpark Center Loo, Orlando, FL 32819-8651
Tel (407) 226-5011 *Founded/Ownrshp* 2009
Sales 187.5MM[E] *EMP* 3,528[E]
SIC 7996 Amusement parks
CEO: Joel K Manby

D-U-N-S 80-075-6848
■ SEBASTIAN RIVER MEDICAL CENTER
(*Suby of* HMA) ★
13695 Us Highway 1, Sebastian, FL 32958-3230
Tel (772) 589-3186 *Founded/Ownrshp* 2007
Sales 111.0MM *EMP* 500
SIC 8062 General medical & surgical hospitals
CEO: Steven Salyer
Mktg Dir: Angela Dickens

D-U-N-S 88-473-7057
■ SEBESTA INC
(*Suby of* VERTICAL V INC) ★
1450 Energy Park Dr # 300, Saint Paul, MN 55108-5274
Tel (651) 634-0775 *Founded/Ownrshp* 2016
Sales 104.5MM[E] *EMP* 156
SIC 8711 Engineering services
CEO: Robert Costello
**CFO:* Todd Gilles
CFO: Daniel M Tollman
**VP:* Abbe Bjorklund
**VP:* Nathan Germolus
VP: Paul Ham
**VP:* David Harrison
**VP:* Randy Lorenz
**VP:* Maryam Peters
**VP:* Thomas Schubbe
VP: William Tippin
Dir Bus: David Mannix

D-U-N-S 14-868-0858 IMP
■ SEC ENERGY PRODUCTS & SERVICES LP
(*Suby of* ENERGY TRANSFER PARTNERS LP) ★
9523 Frbanks N Houston Rd, Houston, TX 77064-6212
Tel (281) 890-9977 *Founded/Ownrshp* 2009
Sales 114.4MM[E] *EMP* 206[E]
SIC 3563 Air & gas compressors
Pt: Mr L Thomas Stone
Pt: Ralph Gates
Pt: Robert Pierce
Pt: E Randall West
Pt: Randall West
Sfty Dirs: Ulysses Garcia

D-U-N-S 02-426-2044
SECHLER FAMILY FOODS INC
154 W Main St, Fredericksburg, PA 17026-9510
Tel (717) 865-6626 *Founded/Ownrshp* 2009
Sales 154.9MM[E] *EMP* 1,050[E]
SIC 2015 Chicken, slaughtered & dressed
Pr: Scott I Sechler
**Treas:* Daniel P Chirico
**Prin:* Mark Blazek

SECO
See SUMTER ELECTRIC COOPERATIVE INC

D-U-N-S 19-487-2214 IMP
SECO HOLDING CO INC
CARBOLOY
(*Suby of* SECO TOOLS AB)
2805 Bellingham Dr, Troy, MI 48083-2046
Tel (248) 528-5200 *Founded/Ownrshp* 1987
Sales 99.2MM[E] *EMP* 600
SIC 3545 Cutting tools for machine tools
Pr: Bruce E Belden
**Sec:* Michael L Neel
Mktg Mgr: Dave Yared

D-U-N-S 17-806-8433 IMP/EXP
SECO TOOLS LLC
(*Suby of* CARBOLOY) ★
2805 Bellingham Dr, Troy, MI 48083-2046
Tel (248) 528-5200 *Founded/Ownrshp* 1987
Sales 99.2MM[E] *EMP* 500
SIC 5084 3545

D-U-N-S 09-248-3791
SECOND BAPTIST CHURCH
SECOND BAPTIST CHURCH WOODWAY
6400 Woodway Dr, Houston, TX 77057-1699
Tel (713) 465-3408 *Founded/Ownrshp* 1927
Sales 69.0MM *EMP* 1,100[E]
SIC 8661 Baptist Church
Pr: H Edwin Young
**Ch:* Moulton Goodrum

SECOND BAPTIST CHURCH WOODWAY
See SECOND BAPTIST CHURCH

D-U-N-S 14-743-5960
SECOND HARVEST FOOD BANK OF CENTRAL FLORIDA INC
411 Mercy Dr, Orlando, FL 32805-1019
Tel (407) 295-1066 *Founded/Ownrshp* 1981
Sales 91.2MM *EMP* 95[E]
Accts Schafer Tschopp Whitcomb Mi
SIC 8699 Food co-operative
Ch: Brad M Butterstein
**Pr:* Jean Bauman
**Pr:* Christian E Hart
CFO: Dawn Koffarnus
**Treas:* Sherri Avara
Treas: Leigh N Horto
**Ex VP:* Matt E Beal
**Sr VP:* Jim Thomas
VP: Greg Higgerson
**Ex Dir:* Dave Krepcho
Opers Mgr: Ricardo Robledo

D-U-N-S 11-831-8518
SECOND HARVEST FOOD BANK OF METROLINA INC
500 Spratt St Ste B, Charlotte, NC 28206-3235
Tel (704) 376-1785 *Founded/Ownrshp* 1981
Sales 83.7MM *EMP* 28
Accts C Dewitt Foard & Company Pa
SIC 8699 Food co-operative
Dir Vol: Nancy Hagerman

D-U-N-S 09-853-2294
SECOND HARVEST FOOD BANK OF SANTA CLARA & SAN MATEO COUNTIES (CA)
750 Curtner Ave, San Jose, CA 95125-2118
Tel (408) 266-8866 *Founded/Ownrshp* 1974
Sales 124.2MM *EMP* 120
Accts Armanino Llp San Jose Ca
SIC 8322 Meal delivery program
CEO: Kathryn Jackson
VP: Bruno Pillet
Ex Dir: Keith Flager
Ex Dir: Susan Takalo
Genl Mgr: Larry Diskin
Off Admin: Emily Donoho
CTO: Michael Enos
IT Man: Steve Mangold
VP Opers: Ralph Maltese

D-U-N-S 13-499-5448
SECOND HARVEST HEARTLAND
1140 Gervais Ave, Saint Paul, MN 55109-2042
Tel (651) 484-5117 *Founded/Ownrshp* 1974
Sales 129.4MM *EMP* 130
Accts Schechter Dokken Kanter Andrew
SIC 8322 Individual & family services
Pr: Rob Zeaske
Dir Vol: Jessica Hultgren
**COO:* Bob Chatmas
CFO: Patrick Boran
**Ch:* Jim Gilliam
Ofcr: Kelly Retka
VP: Kathleen McKown
Ex Dir: Emily Moore

SECOR GROUP
See SECURITY STORAGE CO OF WASHINGTON

SECRETARY OF THE COMMONWEALTH
See EXECUTIVE OFFICE OF COMMONWEALTH OF PUERTO RICO

D-U-N-S 36-074-4247
SECRETARY OF STATE OHIO
(*Suby of* EXECUTIVE OFFICE STATE OF OHIO) ★
180 E Broad St Fl 16, Columbus, OH 43215-3726
Tel (614) 466-2655 *Founded/Ownrshp* 1803
Sales NA *EMP* 1,300[E]
SIC 9111 9611 Executive offices, state & local; ; Administration of general economic programs
Prin: J Kenneth Blackwell
Genl Mgr: Stacey Morgan
Pr Mgr: Matthew Christman

SECU
See STATE EMPLOYEES CREDIT UNION OF MARYLAND INC

D-U-N-S 00-794-5595
SECURA INSURANCE A MUTUAL CO (INC) (WI)
SECURA INSURANCE COMPANIES
2401 S Memorial Dr, Appleton, WI 54915-1406
Tel (920) 739-3161 *Founded/Ownrshp* 1986
Sales NA *EMP* 550
SIC 6331 Fire, marine & casualty insurance: mutual; Automobile insurance; Burglary & theft insurance
Ch Bd: John A Bykowski
**Pr:* David D Gross
**CFO:* Kathryn J Sieman
Treas: Laurie A Lamers
**Sr VP:* Scott M Huiras
**VP:* Jeffrey J Bemis
VP: Jean Brandt
VP: Diana Buechel
**VP:* Daniel P Ferris
VP: Daniel Ferris
VP: Shane A Roh
VP: Shane Roh
VP: Richard E Voelzke
**VP:* Garth Wicinsky
Exec: Richelle Cuomo
Exec: Sarah Krause
Exec: Michelle Welch
Dir Teleco: Gary Wichman
Board of Directors: Douglas Pinter, Catherine J Tierney

SECURA INSURANCE COMPANIES
See SECURA INSURANCE A MUTUAL CO (INC)

D-U-N-S 18-407-3547
SECURAMERICA LLC
3399 Peachtree Rd Ne # 1050, Atlanta, GA 30326-2812
Tel (404) 926-4222 *Founded/Ownrshp* 2004
Sales 68.2MM[E] *EMP* 1,700
SIC 7381 Security guard service
**Pr:* John Adams
Pr: John Fratolillo
CFO: Mark Adams
**Sr VP:* John Garrigan
Sr VP: Ted O'Donnell
**Sr VP:* Carlos Villarreal
VP: Soames D Navarro
VP: Pat Soucy
VP: Bob Varga
VP: Greg Wilson
Mng Dir: Terri Sands

D-U-N-S 62-302-8409
SECURE ENERGY SOLUTIONS LLC
12 Somers Rd 14, East Longmeadow, MA 01028-2918
Tel (413) 733-2571 *Founded/Ownrshp* 2006
Sales 200.0MM *EMP* 26
SIC 8711 Energy conservation engineering

D-U-N-S 83-225-3723
SECURE MISSION SOLUTIONS INC
(*Suby of* PARSONS GOVERNMENT SERVICES INC) ★
5875 Trinity Pkwy Ste 300, Centreville, VA 20120-1971
Tel (703) 230-2804 *Founded/Ownrshp* 2014
Sales 122.7MM[E] *EMP* 550
SIC 7382 Security systems services
Pr: Phillip E Lacombe
**CFO:* Michael J McDermott
**Ex VP:* Jon B Dorrick
**Ex VP:* Michael McDermott
Sr VP: Mark McIntosh
VP: Doug Chabot
VP: Paul Decker
VP: Dave Glovier PHD
Prgrm Mgr: Christopher R Goforth
Genl Mgr: Melissa Seabrook
Genl Mgr: Janice Shannon

D-U-N-S 12-850-2130
SECURE MISSION SOLUTIONS LLC
(*Suby of* SECURE MISSION SOLUTIONS INC) ★
5875 Trinity Pkwy Ste 300, Centreville, VA 20120-1971
Tel (703) 245-1300 *Founded/Ownrshp* 2004
Sales 105.0MM *EMP* 130
SIC 7382 Security systems services
CEO: Thomas D Sundling
**Pr:* Mark A McIntosh
**COO:* Warren Higbie
**CFO:* William Davis
**CFO:* Michael McDermott
**VP:* Mike Bonheim
**VP:* Doug Chabot
**VP:* Paul Decker
**VP:* Phillip E Lacombe
**VP:* Marianne Meins
Off Mgr: Todd Paul

D-U-N-S 01-049-2651
■ SECUREWORKS CORP (GA)
(*Suby of* DELL COMPUTER) ★
1 Concrse Pkwy Ne Ste 500, Atlanta, GA 30328
Tel (404) 327-6339 *Founded/Ownrshp* 1999, 2011
Sales 339.5MM *EMP* 2,047
Tkr Sym SCWX *Exch* NGS
SIC 7371 Computer software development & applications
Pr: Michael R Cote
**Ch Bd:* Michael S Dell
CFO: R Wayne Jackson
VP: Tyler T Winkler
Board of Directors: Pamela Daley, David W Dorman, Egon Durban, Mark J Hawkins, William R McDermott, James M Whitehurst

D-U-N-S 12-675-2265
■ SECUREWORKS INC
DELL SECUREWORKS
(*Suby of* DELL COMPUTER) ★
1 Concourse Pkwy Ste 500, Atlanta, GA 30328-5346
Tel (770) 396-5767 *Founded/Ownrshp* 2011
Sales 260.6MM[E] *EMP* 700[E]
SIC 7371 Computer software development & applications
CEO: Michael R Cote
Pr: Jeffrey Longoria
**CFO:* Brian Gladden
**CFO:* Michael R Vandiver
**Chf Mktg O:* Kathy Jaques
**Sr VP:* Jeff Browning
**VP:* Stacie Hagan
**VP:* Kevin Hanes
**VP:* Jim Ulam
**VP:* Tyler T Winkler
Exec: Jeff Multz

SECURIAN
See MINNESOTA LIFE INSURANCE CO

D-U-N-S 82-529-1060
SECURIAN FINANCIAL GROUP INC
MINNESOTA LIFE INSURANCE CO
400 Robert St N Ste A, Saint Paul, MN 55101-2098
Tel (651) 665-3500 *Founded/Ownrshp* 1998
Sales 991.6MM[E] *EMP* 5,000
SIC 7389 6399 Financial services; Deposit insurance
Pr: Christopher M Hilger
V Ch: Randy F Wallake
Pr: Christopher M Hilger
CFO: Warren Zaccaro
Treas: Leah Reckin-Mahoney
Ofcr: Leslie J Chapman
Ofcr: Nancy R Swanson
Sr VP: Leslie Chapman
Sr VP: Bill Kavanaugh
Sr VP: Dave Leplavy
Sr VP: Jean D Nelson
Sr VP: Gregory S Trong
VP: Rick Ayers
VP: Marc Cabral
VP: Gary Christensen
VP: Larry Cochrane
VP: William M Gould
VP: Brent Lesmeister
VP: Richard L Manke
VP: Michael Webster
VP: Gerald Woelfel
Board of Directors: Eric B Goodman, Paul Snyder

D-U-N-S 04-550-9338
SECURIGUARD INC
6858 Old Dominion Dr # 307, Mc Lean, VA 22101-3832
Tel (703) 821-6777 *Founded/Ownrshp* 1982
Sales 54.3MM[E] *EMP* 1,300
Accts Goodman & Company Mclean Vir
SIC 7381 8744 Security guard service; Facilities support services
Pr: Patricia Delmarvil
CFO: Jason Blandford
**Sec:* Roger Bruley
**VP:* Patrick C Marvil

D-U-N-S 94-799-0511
SECURITAS CRITICAL INFRASTRUCTURE SERVICES INC
(*Suby of* SECURITAS HOLDINGS INC) ★
6850 Versar Ctr Ste 400, Springfield, VA 22151-4148
Tel (703) 750-1098 *Founded/Ownrshp* 1989
Sales 360.0MM[E] *EMP* 12,000
SIC 7381 Detective & armored car services; Guard services; Detective services
Pr: Kevin M Sandkuhler
**Ch:* James Freeze
Ofcr: Scott Graham
VP: John Lee
**VP:* Robert Maydoney
VP: Nick RE
Mng Dir: Miguel Martinez
Mng Dir: Richard Zarzana
IT Man: Hai Hoang
IT Man: Chris Wilson
Natl Sales: Connie Latal

D-U-N-S 08-015-6033
SECURITAS ELECTRONIC SECURITY INC
(*Suby of* SECURITAS SECURITY SERVICES USA INC) ★
1790 Graybill Rd Ste 100, Uniontown, OH 44685-7993
Tel (855) 331-0359 *Founded/Ownrshp* 2015
Sales 14.8MM[E] *EMP* 1,100
SIC 7382 Security systems services
CEO: Santiago Galaz
Pr: Tony Byerly
Treas: Thomas C Cantlon
VP: Frederick W London

D-U-N-S 02-231-4178
SECURITAS HOLDINGS INC
(*Suby of* SECURITAS AB)
9 Campus Dr Ste 1, Parsippany, NJ 07054-4412
Tel (973) 267-5300 *Founded/Ownrshp* 1989
Sales 7.2MMM[E] *EMP* 250,000[E]
SIC 7381 Security guard service
Pr: Alf Goransson
Sr VP: Arun Agarwal
VP: Perry Clarke
IT Man: Rod Heatwole

D-U-N-S 13-328-7206
SECURITAS SECURITY SERVICES USA INC
(*Suby of* SECURITAS SERVICES INC) ★
9 Campus Dr, Parsippany, NJ 07054-4408
Tel (973) 267-5300 *Founded/Ownrshp* 2002
Sales 7.2MMM^E^ *EMP* 100,000
SIC 7381 Security guard service
Pr: Santiago Galaz
Pr: Anthony Sabatino
Pr: Ty Stafford
Pr: Jeff Winter
COO: William Barthelemy
COO: Bart Kraft
Treas: Tom Cantlon
Ex VP: Rocco De Felice
Ex VP: Joseph Vinciguerra
VP: Douge Bryant
VP: Jerry Herzog
VP: Josh Letourneau
VP: Bob Marone
VP: Peter Robbins
VP: Bill Siple
VP: Mats Wahlsrom
Comm Man: Nancy Schwander

D-U-N-S 08-040-8525
SECURITAS SERVICES INC
(*Suby of* SECURITAS HOLDINGS INC) ★
9 Campus Dr Ste 1, Parsippany, NJ 07054-4412
Tel (973) 267-5300 *Founded/Ownrshp* 2003
Sales 7.2MMM^E^ *EMP* 60,830^E^
SIC 7381 Security guard service
Pr: Santiago Galaz
* *Treas:* Thomas C Cantlon
* *VP:* Richard Ferens
* *VP:* Frederick W London

D-U-N-S 00-347-5175
■ **SECURITIES AND EXCHANGE COMMISSION US**
(*Suby of* EXECUTIVE OFFICE OF UNITED STATES GOVERNMENT) ★
100 F St Ne, Washington, DC 20549-2000
Tel (202) 942-8088 *Founded/Ownrshp* 1934
Sales NA *EMP* 2,883
Accts Pkf San Diego California
SIC 9651 Securities regulation commission, government;
COO: Jeff Heslop
Pt: James Burk
Pt: Charles Demoulin
Pt: Kathleen Derose
Pt: Steffen Dietz
Pt: Fernando Igartua
Pt: Erich Kandler
Pt: Vanessa Knapp
Pt: Georg Lanfermann
Pt: Jorge Marrao
Pt: Karen Morris
Pt: Mark Otto
Pt: Ira Schochet
Pt: Edward Waitzer
Pt: Daniela Weber-Rey
Pt: Jaap Winter
Pr: Hong Chu
Pr: Everardo De Armas
Pr: Mark Dowell
Pr: Dan Gordon
Pr: Holly Hunter-Ceci

SECURITIES EDUCATION INSTITUTE
See REGED INC

D-U-N-S 07-483-3146
SECURITIES INVESTOR PROTECTION CORP
1667 K St Nw Ste 1000, Washington, DC 20006-1620
Tel (202) 371-8300 *Founded/Ownrshp* 1970
Sales 477.3MM *EMP* 35
Accts Grant Thornton Mclean Va
SIC 6289 Protective committees
Pr: Stephen P Harbeck
COO: Armando J Bucelo
Sr Cor Off: Michael Don
* *VP:* Joseph S Furr Jr
* *VP:* Karen L Saterstein
Dir Risk M: Albert Caviness
Genl Couns: Kevin H Bell
Genl Couns: Kenneth Caputo
Genl Couns: Chris Larosa
Counsel: Hemant Sharma
Board of Directors: Anthony D'agostino, Matthew Eichner, William Jasien, Gregory Karawan, Mark Kaufman

SECURITY & EMERGENCY MANAGMENT
See MAGNOLIA REGIONAL HEALTH CENTER FOUNDATION INC

D-U-N-S 19-506-5503
SECURITY AND DATA TECHNOLOGIES INC
101 Pheasant Run, Newtown, PA 18940-1820
Tel (215) 579-7000 *Founded/Ownrshp* 1988
Sales 88.4MM^E^ *EMP* 100
SIC 5063 Fire alarm systems; Alarm systems; Wire & cable
Pr: Jerome Paley
* *VP:* Jeffrey S Miles
* *VP:* Byron Pratt
* *VP:* Wayne S Randall
* *VP:* Kenneth R Spressart

D-U-N-S 80-142-7951
SECURITY BENEFIT CORP
(*Suby of* GUGGENHEIM PARTNERS LLC) ★
1 Sw Security Benefit Pl, Topeka, KS 66636-1000
Tel (785) 438-3000 *Founded/Ownrshp* 2010
Sales 225.4MM^E^ *EMP* 4,538^E^
SIC 6211 Security brokers & dealers
CEO: Howard Fricke
Pr: Michael Burbach
Ch: Michael Reidy
Bd of Dir: Wayne Diviney
Bd of Dir: Donna Walsh
Ofcr: Laura Anderson
Sr VP: Malcolm E Robinson
Sr VP: Donald Schepker
VP: Deborah Bartuccio
VP: Joe Bilsborough
VP: Ken Difrancesca
VP: Christine Dobbins
VP: John Ference
VP: Jamal Ford
VP: Jackie Fox
VP: John Guyot
VP: George Kelly
VP: Andrew J Maliskas
VP: Dale McAllister
VP: Jake Moore
VP: Bill Nestel

D-U-N-S 12-216-2845
SECURITY BENEFIT GROUP INC
SECURITY BNEFT GROUP COMPANIES
(*Suby of* SECURITY BENEFIT LIFE INSURANCE CO) ★
1 Sw Security Benefit Pl, Topeka, KS 66636-1000
Tel (785) 438-3000 *Founded/Ownrshp* 1970
Sales 375.7MM^E^ *EMP* 500
SIC 6211 7311 6411 Security brokers & dealers; Advertising agencies; Insurance agents, brokers & service
Pr: Kris A Robbins
* *Pr:* James F Mullery
* *CFO:* John F Frye
* *CFO:* Thomas Swank
* *Ch:* Howard R Fricke
Ofcr: Errol Williams
* *Sr VP:* John F Guyot
VP: Craig Anderson
VP: Ken Difrancesca
VP: James Schmank
* *CTO:* John Keddy
Board of Directors: George D Webb II

D-U-N-S 00-694-3856
SECURITY BENEFIT LIFE INSURANCE CO
(*Suby of* GUGGENHEIM PARTNERS LLC) ★
1 Sw Security Benefit Pl, Topeka, KS 66636-1000
Tel (785) 438-3000 *Founded/Ownrshp* 1892, 2010
Sales NA *EMP* 625
SIC 6311 6722 6091 6211 8748 Life insurance; Management investment, open-end; Nondeposit trust facilities; Brokers, security; Business consulting
Pr: Kris Robbins
* *Ch Bd:* Howard R Fricke
* *Pr:* Eric REA
* *CFO:* Jim Schmank
* *CFO:* Thomas Swank
Bd of Dir: Robert Wheeler
* *Sr VP:* Malcolm E Robinson
VP: Natalie Haag
VP: Dave Keith
VP: Carolyn Samuel
VP: Donald Schepker

SECURITY BNEFT GROUP COMPANIES
See SECURITY BENEFIT GROUP INC

D-U-N-S 05-294-4659
SECURITY CAPITAL CORP (DE)
(*Suby of* SEDGWICK CMS HOLDINGS INC) ★
8 Greenwich Office Park # 2, Greenwich, CT 06831-5149
Tel (203) 625-0770 *Founded/Ownrshp* 1979, 2006
Sales NA *EMP* 1,470
SIC 6411 8211 Insurance agents, brokers & service; Private elementary school
Pr: Brian D Fitzgerald
CFO: William R Schlueter

D-U-N-S 78-840-4085
■ **SECURITY CAPITAL GROUP INC**
(*Suby of* GENERAL ELECTRIC CAPITAL CORP) ★
292 Long Ridge Rd, Stamford, CT 06902-1627
Tel (203) 373-2211 *Founded/Ownrshp* 2002
Sales 108.3MM^E^ *EMP* 687
SIC 6799 8742 Real estate investors, except property operators; Real estate consultant
VP: Harri Singh

D-U-N-S 79-623-8491
SECURITY CONSULTANTS GROUP INC
WESTERN DIVISION SCG
(*Suby of* PARAGON SYSTEMS INC) ★
13655 Dulles Tech Dr, Herndon, VA 20171-4633
Tel (703) 263-7176 *Founded/Ownrshp* 2011
Sales 33.1MM^E^ *EMP* 2,040
SIC 7381 Security guard service
CEO: Timothy A Frank
* *Pr:* Leslie Kaciban Jr
Treas: Richard J Lang
* *Prin:* Kevin Sandkuhler
Board of Directors: W Ralph Basham Jr, James E Freeze, W Asa Hutchinson, Thomas R Jolly, Michael G Oxley

D-U-N-S 80-883-3289
SECURITY ENGINEERS INC
SEI
1617 3rd Ave N, Birmingham, AL 35203-1935
Tel (205) 251-0566 *Founded/Ownrshp* 1993
Sales 70.0MM^E^ *EMP* 1,450
SIC 7381 Protective services, guard
CEO: Donald L Bottom
CFO: Michael Golden
* *CFO:* Gary Sexton
* *Treas:* Wray Pierce
Bd of Dir: Samuel Upchurch
VP: Martin Harm
Rgnl Mgr: Timothy Brumlow
Brnch Mgr: Rodney Clark
Dist Mgr: Tracie Firebaugh
Dist Mgr: Cedric Freeman
Dist Mgr: Robert Reid

D-U-N-S 03-626-6096
SECURITY FINANCE CORP OF SPARTANBURG
(*Suby of* SECURITY GROUP INC) ★
181 Security Pl, Spartanburg, SC 29307-5450
Tel (864) 582-8193 *Founded/Ownrshp* 1990
Sales NA *EMP* 2,500
Accts Elliott Davis Decosimo Llc G
SIC 6141 Licensed loan companies, small
Pr: A Raymond Biggs
* *Ch Bd:* Susan A Bridges
* *COO:* Judy Perkins
* *CFO:* A Greg Williams
* *V Ch Bd:* C H Edwards
Snr Ntwrk: Joey Hilliard

D-U-N-S 00-696-9828
SECURITY FINANCIAL LIFE INSURANCE CO
(*Suby of* ASG INC) ★
4000 Pine Lake Rd, Lincoln, NE 68516-5484
Tel (402) 434-9500 *Founded/Ownrshp* 1895
Sales NA *EMP* 130
SIC 6311 Life insurance carriers

D-U-N-S 36-450-1718
SECURITY GROUP INC
181 Security Pl, Spartanburg, SC 29307-5450
Tel (864) 582-8193 *Founded/Ownrshp* 1981
Sales NA *EMP* 2,500
Accts Elliott Davis Decosimo Llc G
SIC 6141 Licensed loan companies, small
Ch Bd: Susan A Bridges
Pr: Ray Biggs
Treas: Beadie H Townsel
* *V Ch Bd:* Clarence Edwards
VP: A Greg Williams
IT Man: Stacy Jordon
Board of Directors: Margaret Bridges

D-U-N-S 80-017-0532
SECURITY HEALTH PLAN OF WISCONSIN INC
1515 N Saint Joseph Ave, Marshfield, WI 54449-1343
Tel (715) 221-9555 *Founded/Ownrshp* 1986
Sales 1.1MMM *EMP* 1,006^E^
Accts Kpmg Llp Minneapolis Mn
SIC 8011 Health maintenance organization
CEO: Steve Youso
* *Pr:* Dr Fredrick Wesbrook
* *CEO:* John Smylie
Ofcr: Lisa Boero
Exec: Joan Berlin
Off Mgr: Sandra Smith
CIO: Dave Marksteiner
QA Dir: Lon Wilkosz
Sales Asso: Dean Hoffman
Doctor: Ellen Schumann

D-U-N-S 00-697-6328
SECURITY MUTUAL LIFE INSURANCE CO OF NEW YORK
100 Court St, Binghamton, NY 13901-3406
Tel (607) 723-3551 *Founded/Ownrshp* 1886
Sales NA *EMP* 350
SIC 6311 6321 Life insurance carriers; Health insurance carriers
Pr: Bruce Boyea
Mng Pt: Carson E Beadle
Mng Pt: Robert H Linn
* *Pr:* Bruce W Boyea
Pr: Dolly Fox
Pr: Barb Parker
Pr: Joseph Rideout
* *CFO:* Howell M Palmer
Ex VP: Ray F Barnard
Ex VP: Marc Novotney
Ex VP: Frederick Wortman
Sr VP: George B Kozol
* *VP:* Michael A Cohen
VP: Stephen M Garnder
VP: Kevin McKeown
* *VP:* Frank D Mistretta
VP: Rich Novak
* *VP:* Gregory Simonelli Jr
VP: Martin Smith
Comm Dir: Colleen Kenny-Kuk

D-U-N-S 11-974-6188
▲ **SECURITY NATIONAL FINANCIAL CORP**
5300 S 360 W Ste 250, Salt Lake City, UT 84123-2647
Tel (801) 264-1060 *Founded/Ownrshp* 1979
Sales NA *EMP* 1,271^E^
Tkr Sym SNFCA *Exch* NGM
SIC 6311 6531 6162 Life insurance; Cemetery management service; Mortgage bankers & correspondents
Ch Bd: Scott M Quist
CFO: Garrett S Sill
Sr VP: Christie Q Overbaugh
VP: Stephen C Johnson
* *VP:* Jason G Overbaugh
* *VP:* S Andrew Quist
Counsel: Andrew Quist
Board of Directors: John L Cook, Gilbert A Fuller, Robert G Hunter, Norman G Wilbur

D-U-N-S 00-243-0957
SECURITY PLUMBING & HEATING SUPPLY CO (NY)
(*Suby of* WSS- DAYTON) ★
196 Maple Ave, Selkirk, NY 12158-1712
Tel (518) 767-2226 *Founded/Ownrshp* 1934, 2015
Sales 99.7MM^E^ *EMP* 150
SIC 5074 Plumbing & hydronic heating supplies; Plumbing fittings & supplies
Pr: Kim Willey
Sales Exec: Joe Contois
Sales Exec: Steve Ricco
Sales Exec: Todd Smith
S&M/VP: Brian Fowler
Sales Asso: Tom Evans

D-U-N-S 36-357-8878
SECURITY SERVICE CUSO LLC
SECURITY SERVICE INVESTMENT GROUP
(*Suby of* SECURITY SERVICE FEDERAL CREDIT UNION) ★
16211 La Cantera Pkwy, San Antonio, TX 78256-2419
Tel (210) 476-4151 *Founded/Ownrshp* 2007
Sales NA *EMP* 353^E^
SIC 6061 7381 Federal credit unions; Detective & armored car services
Pr: David Reynolds
Sr VP: Brian Ziemba
Exec: John Worthington
Web Dev: Robert Galan

D-U-N-S 07-460-1824
SECURITY SERVICE FEDERAL CREDIT UNION
15000 W Interstate 10, San Antonio, TX 78249-3528
Tel (210) 476-4000 *Founded/Ownrshp* 1956
Sales NA *EMP* 1,700
SIC 6061 Federal credit unions
Pr: Jim Laffoon
Pr: Charlene Bowlin
Pr: Renae Cunningham
Pr: Garth Erickson
Pr: Yvonne Fernandez
Pr: Henry Ibarra
Pr: Rick Ramirez
* *Pr:* David Reynolds
COO: Robert Chamberlain
COO: Cindy Moran
Treas: Allen Snyder
Sr Cor Off: Natalie Garza
Bd of Dir: Mary Holub
Ofcr: Angela Marin
Ofcr: Cheri Whitacre
Sr VP: Carlo Ienna
Sr VP: Mike Martinez
VP: Lori Allen
VP: Jt Cody
VP: John Dallahan
VP: Kathleen Himes

SECURITY SERVICE INVESTMENT GROUP
See SECURITY SERVICE CUSO LLC

SECURITY SERVICES OF AMERICA
See SSA SECURITY INC

D-U-N-S 00-692-0375 IMP/EXP
SECURITY STORAGE CO OF WASHINGTON
SECOR GROUP
1701 Florida Ave Nw, Washington, DC 20009-2621
Tel (202) 797-5659 *Founded/Ownrshp* 2003
Sales 102.3MM^E^ *EMP* 350
SIC 4213 4226 4214 4731

D-U-N-S 07-245-3368
■ **SECURITY TITLE AGENCY INC**
(*Suby of* CHICAGO TITLE AND TRUST CO) ★
3636 N Central Ave # 140, Phoenix, AZ 85012-1971
Tel (602) 230-6271 *Founded/Ownrshp* 1999
Sales NA *EMP* 387
SIC 6411 6541 Insurance agents, brokers & service; Title abstract offices
Pr: Henry Fajkowski
* *Treas:* Patrick Farenga
Ofcr: Mies Angie
* *Sr VP:* Ron Erhardt
* *VP:* Barbara McDugald
VP: Mary Stults

D-U-N-S 96-686-0665
SECURUS HOLDINGS INC
(*Suby of* ABRY PARTNERS INC) ★
14651 Dallas Pkwy Ste 600, Dallas, TX 75254-8815
Tel (972) 241-1535 *Founded/Ownrshp* 2010
Sales 314.1MM^E^ *EMP* 1,071^E^
SIC 4813 Telephone communication, except radio
CEO: Richard A Smith
CFO: William Markert

D-U-N-S 19-285-8954 IMP/EXP
SECURUS TECHNOLOGIES INC
(*Suby of* SECURUS HOLDINGS INC) ★
14651 Dallas Pkwy Ste 600, Dallas, TX 75254-8815
Tel (972) 241-1535 *Founded/Ownrshp* 2005
Sales 314.1MM^E^ *EMP* 717
SIC 4813 Telephone communication, except radio
CEO: Richard A Smith
* *Pr:* Robert E Pickens
CFO: Bill Markert
* *CFO:* William D Markert
Chf Mktg O: Bob Pickens
Sr VP: John Bell
VP: Patrick Brolsma
VP: Randy Hoffman
* *VP:* Dennis Reinhold
VP: Robert Rob
VP: Jon Secrest
VP: Dan Wigger

D-U-N-S 13-116-9070 IMP/EXP
▲ **SED INTERNATIONAL HOLDINGS INC**
2150 Cedars Rd Ste 200, Lawrenceville, GA 30043-4781
Tel (678) 878-2600 *Founded/Ownrshp* 1980
Sales 517.3MM *EMP* 327
Accts Cohn Reznick Llp Roseland N
Tkr Sym MIHI *Exch* OTO
SIC 5045 5065 Computers, peripherals & software; Telephone & telegraphic equipment
Ch Bd: Hesham M Gad
COO: Ronell Rivera
CFO: Juan O Bravo
CFO: Lyle Dickler
Sr VP: Derrek P Hallock
Sr VP: Eddie Lageyre
Sr VP: Lou Leonardo
VP: Carla Giussani
VP: Frank Gonzalez
VP: Peter Seltzberg
Dir Risk M: Dan Scouler
Board of Directors: Dennis L Chandler, Jim Illson, Arnold Kezsbom, Samuel S Weiser

D-U-N-S 03-787-9764 IMP/EXP
■ **SED INTERNATIONAL INC**
S E D
(*Suby of* SED INTERNATIONAL HOLDINGS INC) ★
2150 Cedars Rd Ste 200, Lawrenceville, GA 30043-4781
Tel (844) 501-5858 *Founded/Ownrshp* 1986
Sales 177.3MM^E^ *EMP* 320
SIC 5045 Computers, peripherals & software
CEO: Hesham Gad
* *CFO:* Juan Orlando Bravo
Sr VP: Stan Baumgartner Jr
VP Opers: Mark Divito
Mktg Mgr: Stacy Gileo
Sls Mgr: Doc Beadiun
Board of Directors: Jean A Diamond, Arthur Goldberg, Stephen Greenspan, J K Hage III, Samuel A

Kidston

D-U-N-S 84-480-5734 IMP
SEDANOS MANAGEMENT INC
SEDANO'S SUPERMARKETS
3140 W 76th St, Hialeah, FL 33018-3803
Tel (305) 824-1034 *Founded/Ownrshp* 1962
Sales 234.1MM[E] *EMP* 2,500
SIC 5411 5912 Supermarkets, chain; Drug stores
CEO: Agustin Herran
**VP:* Jose Herran
VP: Juan Mora
Genl Mgr: Eddie Fernandez
Genl Mgr: Dan Prasertlum
Dir IT: Javier Herran
IT Man: Larry Rodriguez

SEDANOS SUPERMARKET 42
See 3801 FLAGLE SUPERMARKET LLC

SEDANO'S SUPERMARKETS
See SEDANOS MANAGEMENT INC

D-U-N-S 08-058-9166
SEDGWICK CLAIMS MANAGEMENT SERVICES INC (IL)
(*Suby of* SEDGWICK CMS HOLDINGS INC) ★
1100 Ridgeway Loop Rd # 200, Memphis, TN 38120-4057
Tel (901) 415-7400 *Founded/Ownrshp* 1997, 1999
Sales NA *EMP* 14,000
SIC 6411 Insurance claim adjusters, not employed by insurance company
Pr: David North
Pr: Richard Grew
Pr: John Koval
Pr: Sean McKelley
Pr: Mark Niedt
Pr: Marcia Nigro
Pr: Christopher Nykiel
Pr: Jay Scott
Pr: Denise Wimbiscus
**COO:* Steven E Penman
**CFO:* Henry C Lyons
Treas: Susan Wolf
**Ofcr:* Darrell Brown
Ofcr: Stephen Elliot
**Ofcr:* Jason P Hood
Assoc VP: Cheryl Van Gee
**Ex VP:* Terri Browne
Ex VP: William P Foley II
Ex VP: Darryl Hammann
Ex VP: Robert A Johnson
**Ex VP:* Bob Peterson

D-U-N-S 61-013-5399
SEDGWICK CMS HOLDINGS INC
1100 Ridgeway Loop Rd # 200, Memphis, TN 38120-4057
Tel (901) 415-7400 *Founded/Ownrshp* 1999
Sales 3.3MMM[E] *EMP* 14,001[E]
SIC 6719 Investment holding companies, except banks
Pr: David North
Pr: Michael Arena
**COO:* James B Wiertelak
**CFO:* Bill Brewer
**Ex VP:* William P Foley II
**Ex VP:* Alan L Stinson
Sr VP: Doug Bennett
Sr VP: Brent B Bickett
**VP:* Bryon E Bass
VP: Sharon Christian
VP: Richard L Cox
VP: Mary V Hunter
VP: Brenda Lott
VP: Peter T Sadowski
Exec: Gary Keirce

D-U-N-S 05-107-9994
■ **SEDGWICK JAMES INC**
(*Suby of* MARSH & MCLENNAN COMPANIES INC) ★
1000 Ridgeway Loop Rd # 4, Memphis, TN 38120-4045
Tel (901) 415-7400 *Founded/Ownrshp* 1998
Sales NA *EMP* 52,306
SIC 6411 Insurance agents; Insurance brokers
Ch Bd: Michael Cherkasky
**Treas:* Joe Meyers
Ofcr: Yolanda Dewberry
Ex VP: Alan Stinson
Sr VP: Rick Ackerman
Sr VP: Darrell Brown
Sr VP: Stan Tofil
VP: Lynn Thayer
Mng Dir: Lisa Payne
CIO: Paul Holden
Dir IT: Milind Ganoo

D-U-N-S 07-017-5120
SEDGWICK LLP
333 Bush St Fl 30, San Francisco, CA 94104-2834
Tel (415) 781-7900 *Founded/Ownrshp* 1932, 1933
Sales 191.8MM[E] *EMP* 834
SIC 8111 Specialized law offices, attorneys
Mng Pt: Michael F Healy
Pt: Michael H Bernstein
Pt: Bruce D Celebrezze
**Pt:* Gregory H Halliday
**Pt:* Mark J Hancock
Pt: Curtis Parvin
Pt: W Neil Rambin
Pt: Lilliam G Stenfeldt
Mng Pt: Michael Davisson
Mng Pt: James Keale
Ofcr: Margaret Morasca
VP: Matthew Goedert
Exec: Barry Marsh
Exec: David Sanders
Exec: Cherie Zeier

D-U-N-S 10-267-8364
SEDKO GROUP INC
5847 San Felipe St # 4650, Houston, TX 77057-3000
Tel (713) 782-9100 *Founded/Ownrshp* 1975
Sales 19.2MM[E] *EMP* 1,948
SIC 7011 Hotels
Pr: A Majid Mangalji
**VP:* Moez Mangalji

SEE OPTICAL
See GOLDEN OPTICAL CORP

SEED RESEARCH OF OREGON
See DLF PICKSEED USA INC

D-U-N-S 61-325-2618
SEED RESTAURANT GROUP INC
FAZOLI'S
2470 Palumbo Dr, Lexington, KY 40509-1117
Tel (859) 268-1668 *Founded/Ownrshp* 1990
Sales 203.3MM *EMP* 5,600
Accts Kpmg Llp Louisville Ky
SIC 6794 5812 Franchises, selling or licensing; Italian restaurant
Pr: Kunihide Toyoda
**CFO:* David Smith
Board of Directors: Richard Furst, Ernest Renaud, Hiroshi Yamagishi

D-U-N-S 00-583-1987
SEEDORFF MASONRY INC (IA)
SMI
408 W Mission St, Strawberry Point, IA 52076-9434
Tel (563) 933-2296 *Founded/Ownrshp* 1957
Sales 91.3MM[E] *EMP* 317
SIC 1741 2448

D-U-N-S 12-884-9457 IMP
SEEDWAY LLC
AGWAY
(*Suby of* GROWMARK INC) ★
1734 Railroad Pl, Hall, NY 14463-9005
Tel (585) 526-6391 *Founded/Ownrshp* 2002
Sales 120.0MM *EMP* 205
SIC 5261 Nurseries & garden centers
Pr: Jeffrey Solberge
**COO:* Donald Wertman
**CFO:* Richard Malcolm
Exec: Scott Rushe
Exec: Jenkins Sherrie

D-U-N-S 05-470-3319 IMP/EXP
SEEMAC INC
11350 N Meridian St # 450, Carmel, IN 46032-4558
Tel (317) 844-3995 *Founded/Ownrshp* 1971
Sales 116.1MM *EMP* 20
Accts Bkd Llp Indianapolis Indian
SIC 5031 Molding, all materials
Pr: Elliott Savage
**Ch Bd:* Thomas Kohlmeier
**Sec:* Susan Hassfurder
**Ex VP:* Dan Nickander
**Sr VP:* Lester E Canter
Dir IT: Lance Lawson
Manager: George Merriam

SEE'S CANDIES
See SEES CANDY SHOPS INC

D-U-N-S 00-911-8357 IMP
■ **SEES CANDIES INC**
(*Suby of* SEES CANDIES) ★
210 El Camino Real, South San Francisco, CA 94080-5998
Tel (650) 761-2490 *Founded/Ownrshp* 1972
Sales 587.5MM[E] *EMP* 2,500
SIC 2064 5441 Candy & other confectionery products; Candy
Ch Bd: Warren E Buffett
**Pr:* Bradley D Kinstler
**CFO:* Ken Scott
Treas: Daryl Wollenburg
VP: Tracy Cioffi
VP: Eileen Duag
Dir IT: Shirley Fraser
IT Man: Nancy Halper
Info Man: Michael Tran
Manager: Gordon McNally

D-U-N-S 00-828-6155 IMP
■ **SEES CANDY SHOPS INC** (CA)
SEE'S CANDIES
(*Suby of* BERKSHIRE HATHAWAY INC) ★
210 El Camino Real, South San Francisco, CA 94080-5968
Tel (650) 761-2490 *Founded/Ownrshp* 1922, 1921
Sales 637.4MM[E] *EMP* 2,500
SIC 2064 5441 Candy & other confectionery products; Candy; Confectionery
Pr: Brad Kinstler
**Ch Bd:* Warren E Buffet
Treas: Marc Hamburg
Ex VP: David Conn
VP: Janelle Kay
VP Sls: Marie Griffith

D-U-N-S 03-721-9045
SEFA GROUP INC
217 Cedar Rd, Lexington, SC 29073-8871
Tel (803) 520-9000 *Founded/Ownrshp* 1976
Sales 106.6MM[E] *EMP* 185
SIC 5093 Scrap & waste materials
Pr: Thomas C Hendrix
**CFO:* Bret J Harris
CFO: Bret Harris
**Ex VP:* Gregg T Hendrix
**VP:* Jim Clayton
**VP:* Jennie S Hendrix
**VP:* Jimmy C Knowles
**VP:* Walter E Nunn III

D-U-N-S 00-182-5850 IMP
SEFAR INC (NY)
(*Suby of* SEFAR HOLDING AG)
111 Calumet St, Depew, NY 14043-3734
Tel (716) 683-4050 *Founded/Ownrshp* 1929
Sales 88.0MM[E] *EMP* 150
SIC 5131 5051 5084 3496 2297 2221 Piece goods & other fabrics; Silk piece goods, woven; Synthetic fabrics; Wire screening; Screening machinery & equipment; Miscellaneous fabricated wire products; Nonwoven fabrics; Broadwoven fabric mills, manmade
Ch Bd: David S Koebcke
Chf Mktg O: Frank Edwards
Exec: Mike Branson
Mng Dir: Andy Burgess

QA Dir: Patrick Badame
Dir IT: Claudio Zollet
VP Opers: Tom Welch
Opers Mgr: Mario Grima
Sls Mgr: Gerald Morkisz

SEFCU
See STATE EMPLOYEES FEDERAL CREDIT UNION

D-U-N-S 17-143-8299
SEFNCO COMMUNICATIONS INC
4610 Tacoma Ave, Sumner, WA 98390-2200
Tel (877) 385-2903 *Founded/Ownrshp* 1999
Sales 172.8MM[E] *EMP* 500[E]
SIC 1623 Communication line & transmission tower construction
CEO: Scott Nall
**VP:* Todd Krieger
**VP:* Daham Pham
**VP:* Seth Sherwood
**VP:* Clint Sweetser
Genl Mgr: Joe Knackstedt

D-U-N-S 19-729-8198 IMP
SEGA ENTERTAINMENT USA INC
(*Suby of* SEGA HOLDINGS USA INC) ★
600 N Brand Blvd Fl 5, Glendale, CA 91203-4207
Tel (310) 217-9500 *Founded/Ownrshp* 2004
Sales 34.2MM[E] *EMP* 1,550
SIC 7993 Coin-operated amusement devices
Pr: Cory Haynes
Sls Dir: Mark Wiley
Mktg Mgr: Tiffany Ballard

D-U-N-S 12-545-5654 IMP/EXP
SEGA HOLDINGS USA INC
(*Suby of* SEGA GAMES CO., LTD.)
9737 Lurline Ave, Chatsworth, CA 91311-4404
Tel (415) 701-6000 *Founded/Ownrshp* 2002
Sales 168.1MM[E] *EMP* 1,880
SIC 3999 5045 Coin-operated amusement machines; Computers & accessories, personal & home entertainment
CEO: Naoya Tsurumi
**Pr:* Tetsu Kayama
COO: Simon Jeffery
**CFO:* John Cheng
Sr VP: Raymond Goldsmith
VP: Sue Hughes
Dept Mgr: Masaru Igarashi
Dir IT: Jake Salgado
IT Man: Miyuki Friedman
Sls Dir: Frank Chiechi

D-U-N-S 13-163-1988 IMP
SEGA OF AMERICA INC
(*Suby of* SEGA HOLDINGS USA INC) ★
6400 Oak Cyn Ste 100, Irvine, CA 92618-5204
Tel (415) 806-0169 *Founded/Ownrshp* 2007
Sales 129.4MM[E] *EMP* 180
SIC 3999 5092 Coin-operated amusement machines; Video games
CEO: Tatsuyuki Miyazaki
**Ch Bd:* Hayao Nakayama
**Pr:* Howell Ivy
**Sr VP:* Yukio Aoyama
Sr VP: Raymond Goldsmith

D-U-N-S 15-510-5422
SEGA OF AMERICA INC
(*Suby of* SEGA OF AMERICA INC) ★
350 Rhode Island St # 400, San Francisco, CA 94103-5188
Tel (415) 701-6000 *Founded/Ownrshp* 1985
Sales 129.4MM[E] *EMP* 165
SIC 5045 5092 Computers & accessories, personal & home entertainment; Video games
CEO: Mike Hayes
**Pr:* Masanao Maeda
**CFO:* John Cheng
**Ch:* Naoya Tsurumi
Ex VP: Shinobu Toyoda
Comm Man: Jasmine Ramos
CIO: Joaquin Salgado
QA Dir: Michael Sanders
IT Man: George Bueno
IT Man: Irene Gregorio
VP Mktg: Peter Moore

D-U-N-S 00-171-0136
SEGAL GROUP INC
333 W 34th St, New York, NY 10001-2417
Tel (212) 251-5000 *Founded/Ownrshp* 1939
Sales 167.8MM[E] *EMP* 960
SIC 8742 Human resource consulting services
Pr: Joseph A Locicero
**Ch:* Howard Fluhr
**Ch:* Robert D Krinsky
**Ch:* Martin E Segal
Sr VP: Jason M Adwin
Sr VP: Randolph Carter
Sr VP: John Coyle
Sr VP: Cathie Eitelberg
Sr VP: Mary L Feldman
Sr VP: Aldwin P Frias
**Sr VP:* Margery Sinder Friedman
Sr VP: Christopher D Heppner
Sr VP: Frederick Herberich
Sr VP: Richard S Hiss
Sr VP: Norman Jacobson
Sr VP: Karen M Johnson
Sr VP: Rick Johnson
Sr VP: Mary P Kirby
Sr VP: Margaret T Lennon
Sr VP: Deborah Marcotte
Sr VP: Judith F Mazo

D-U-N-S 00-506-5164
SEGERDAHL CORP (IL)
SG360
1351 Wheeling Rd, Wheeling, IL 60090-5997
Tel (847) 541-1080 *Founded/Ownrshp* 1956
Sales 298.0MM[E] *EMP* 640
SIC 2752 Commercial printing, offset
Pr: Richard D Joutras
**Pr:* Mary Lee Schneider
**CFO:* Gary Gardner
**Ex VP:* Jeff Reimers
**Ex VP:* Paul White
**Sr VP:* Hans Kollinger

VP: Ed Anderson
VP: Russell C Brown
VP: Ken Gile
VP: Wood Kevin
VP: Brian Pell
**VP:* John Romita

D-U-N-S 03-963-6592
SEGERDAHL GRAPHICS INC
(*Suby of* SG360) ★
1351 Wheeling Rd, Wheeling, IL 60090-5913
Tel (847) 541-1080 *Founded/Ownrshp* 2002
Sales 127.2MM[E] *EMP* 350
SIC 2752 8742 Commercial printing, offset; Marketing consulting services
Pr: Richard D Joutras
Sr VP: Hans Kollinger
Genl Mgr: Phil Parrish
IT Man: Vince Dante
VP Sls: Terry McLaughlin

D-U-N-S 08-737-7891 IMP
SEGERSTROM CENTER FOR ARTS (CA)
600 Town Center Dr, Costa Mesa, CA 92626-1916
Tel (714) 556-2122 *Founded/Ownrshp* 1973
Sales 83.9MM *EMP* 47
SIC 7922

D-U-N-S 07-848-6198
SEGUIN INDEPENDENT SCHOOL DISTRICT (TX)
1221 E Kingsbury St, Seguin, TX 78155-2152
Tel (830) 372-5771 *Founded/Ownrshp* 1901
Sales 74.6MM *EMP* 1,231
Accts Armstrong Vaughan & Associate
SIC 8211 Public elementary & secondary schools
**CFO:* Sandra Hill
CFO: Sandra K Hill
Ofcr: Ellie Cisneros
Ofcr: Armando Gonzales
Exec: Sean Hoffmann
Dir Risk M: Denise Erlanson
Ex Dir: Denise Roane
Dir IT: Jerry Belmarez
Dir IT: Richard Mejia
Schl Brd P: Louis Reyes

D-U-N-S 96-963-1969
SEGUNDO NAVARRO DRILLING LTD
10101 Reunion Pl Ste 1000, San Antonio, TX 78216-4157
Tel (210) 384-3200 *Founded/Ownrshp* 1995
Sales 118.0MM *EMP* 40
Accts Hanke Group Pc San Antonio
SIC 1382 4925 Oil & gas exploration services; Gas production and/or distribution
Pt: Rod Lewis
CFO: Mark Stavinoha

SEI
See SENIOR HOLDINGS INC

SEI
See SECURITY ENGINEERS INC

SEI GIVING FUND
See RENAISSANCE CHARITABLE FOUNDATION INC

D-U-N-S 07-837-7409
SEI HOLDING I CORP
(*Suby of* AEA INVESTORS LP) ★
11233 Shadow Creek Pkwy # 235, Pearland, TX 77584-7367
Tel (410) 553-9192 *Founded/Ownrshp* 2011
Sales 172.0MM[E] *EMP* 583
SIC 8741 Business management
Pr: Otis Dufrene

D-U-N-S 88-436-0926
SEI INC
SERVICE EXPRESS
3854 Broadmoor Ave Se # 101, Grand Rapids, MI 49512-3967
Tel (616) 698-2221 *Founded/Ownrshp* 1993
Sales 107.0MM[E] *EMP* 250
SIC 7378 Computer peripheral equipment repair & maintenance
Pr: Ron Alvesteffer
**COO:* Dwight Strayer
**CFO:* Kraig Harper
Manager: Debra Swann
Sls Mgr: Chuck Rush
Sls Mgr: Rob Somers

D-U-N-S 06-437-8086
▲ **SEI INVESTMENTS CO**
1 Freedom Valley Dr, Oaks, PA 19456-9989
Tel (610) 676-1000 *Founded/Ownrshp* 1968
Sales 1.3MMM *EMP* 2,985
Tkr Sym SEIC *Exch* NGS
SIC 6722 8742 Management investment, open-end; Management consulting services
Ch Bd: Alfred P West Jr
CFO: Dennis J McGonigle
Ex VP: Kevin P Barr
Ex VP: Robert F Crudup
Ex VP: N Jeffrey Klauder
Ex VP: Paul F Klauder
Ex VP: Stephen G Meyer
Ex VP: Joseph P Ujobai
Ex VP: Wayne M Withrow
VP: Ross Ellis
VP: Scott Morgan
VP: Robert Rinicella
VP: Muse Robb
Board of Directors: Sarah W Blumenstein, William M Doran, Carl A Guarino, Kathryn M McCarthy, Carmen V Romeo

SEI OILFIELDS
See SITTON ENTERPRISES LLC

D-U-N-S 78-882-3909
■ **SEI PRIVATE TRUST CO**
(*Suby of* SEI INVESTMENTS CO) ★
1 Freedom Valley Dr, Oaks, PA 19456-9989
Tel (610) 676-1000 *Founded/Ownrshp* 2000
Sales 254.1MM *EMP* 10

SIC 6733 6211 Trusts, except educational, religious, charity: management; Security brokers & dealers
Prin: Barbara B Rushing
COO: Robert Caton
CFO: Dennis McGonigle
Ex VP: Carmen Romeo
Sr VP: Mark Nagle
VP: Edward Loughlin
Prin: Jeff Klauder
Dir IT: Steven Zeh
IT Man: Jim Warren
IT Man: Scott Wilson
Info Man: Corey Moscoe

D-U-N-S 92-821-6662
SEIDLE ENTERPRISES INC
SEIDLE SUZUKI
2900 Nw 36th St, Miami, FL 33142-5156
Tel (305) 635-8000 *Founded/Ownrshp* 1992
Sales 150.0MM *EMP* 300
SIC 5511 7538 7532 Automobiles, new & used; General automotive repair shops; Top & body repair & paint shops
Pr: William D Seidle

SEIDLE SUZUKI
See SEIDLE ENTERPRISES INC

D-U-N-S 01-223-7772 IMP/EXP
SEIKO CORP OF AMERICA
PULSAR
(*Suby of* SEIKO WATCH CORPORATION)
1111 Macarthur Blvd # 101, Mahwah, NJ 07430-2321
Tel (201) 529-3316 *Founded/Ownrshp* 2001
Sales 87.3MM^E *EMP* 400
SIC 5094

SEIKO EPSON
See EPSON AMERICA INC

SEIRRA TELEPHONE
See SIERRA TEL COMMUNICATIONS GROUP

D-U-N-S 82-879-5562 IMP
SEISA MEDICAL INC
9005 Montana Ave, El Paso, TX 79925-1313
Tel (915) 774-4321 *Founded/Ownrshp* 1983
Sales 201.0MM^E *EMP* 1,500
SIC 3841 Surgical & medical instruments
CEO: Julio Chiu
COO: Aaron Chiu
CFO: Salvador Almeida
VP: Isaac Chiu
VP: Jocobo Chiu

D-U-N-S 80-732-4699 IMP
SEITEL HOLDINGS INC
10811 S Westview Circle D, Houston, TX 77043-2748
Tel (713) 881-8900 *Founded/Ownrshp* 2006
Sales 100.2MM^E *EMP* 148^E
SIC 1382 Seismograph surveys
Pr: Robert D Monson

D-U-N-S 02-590-0671 IMP
SEITEL INC
(*Suby of* SEITEL HOLDINGS INC) ★
10811 S Westvw Cir Dr 100, Houston, TX 77043-2748
Tel (713) 881-8900 *Founded/Ownrshp* 2007
Sales 100.2MM *EMP* 129^E
Accts Bkd Llp Houston Texas
SIC 1382 Seismograph surveys; Geophysical exploration, oil & gas field
Pr: Robert D Monson
**Ch Bd:* Gregory P Spivy
**COO:* Kevin P Callaghan
CFO: Marcia H Kendrick
Sr VP: Joann Lippman
IT Man: Chris Hanson
Board of Directors: Allison A Bennington, Ryan M Birtwell, Dalton J Boutte, Kyle N Cruz, Jay H Golding, John E Jackson, Daniel R Osnoss

D-U-N-S 07-603-2150
SEITLIN & CO
MARSH
1000 Corp Dr Ste 400, Fort Lauderdale, FL 33334
Tel (305) 591-0090 *Founded/Ownrshp* 1946
Sales NA *EMP* 148
SIC 6411 8742 Insurance agents; Management consulting services
Sr VP: Ned Black
**Pr:* Shannon Alfonso
**Pr:* Roxana F Sora
**COO:* Eric Donahoe
**CFO:* Darlene Merino
**Ch:* Stephen Jackman
**Ex VP:* Kelly E Bleeker
Sr VP: Kevin White
IT Man: Christy Garcia

D-U-N-S 96-930-8415
SEIU HEALTHCARE NW HEALTH BENEFITS TRUST
215 Columbia St Ste 300, Seattle, WA 98104-1511
Tel (425) 771-7359 *Founded/Ownrshp* 2011
Sales 168.6MM *EMP* 3^E
Accts Schoedel & Schoedel Cpas Pllc
SIC 6733 Trusts

SEIU LOCAL 25 WELFARE FUND
See LOCAL 25 SEIU WELFARE FUND

D-U-N-S 02-388-4356
SEIU UNITED HEALTHCARE WORKERS-WEST LOCAL 2005
560 Thomas L Berkley Way, Oakland, CA 94612-1602
Tel (510) 251-1250 *Founded/Ownrshp* 1923
Sales 104.3MM *EMP* 325
Accts Hood & Strong Llp San Franci
SIC 8631 Labor union
Pr: Dave Regan
**CFO:* Edgard Tajina
**Trst:* Eliseo Medina
**Trst:* Debbie M Schneider
VP: Laphonza Butler
**VP:* Stanley Lyles
Comm Man: Shawn Masten
Board of Directors: Fred Seavey, Phyllis Willett

SEJIN AMERICA
See SJA INC

D-U-N-S 80-867-6485 IMP
SEJONG ALABAMA LLC
(*Suby of* SEJONG INDUSTRIAL CO., LTD.)
450 Old Fort Rd E, Fort Deposit, AL 36032-4038
Tel (334) 227-0821 *Founded/Ownrshp* 2003
Sales 227.5MM *EMP* 167
SIC 3714 Mufflers (exhaust), motor vehicle

D-U-N-S 00-192-6708 IMP/EXP
SEKISUI AMERICA CORP
VOLTEK DIVISION
(*Suby of* SEKISUI CHEMICAL CO., LTD.)
666 5th St Fl 12t, Secaucus, NJ 07094-3005
Tel (201) 423-7960 *Founded/Ownrshp* 1987
Sales 500.4MM^E *EMP* 850
SIC 3086 Plastics foam products
Pr: Naofumi Negishi
**Treas:* Hirmou Mitsui
Genl Mgr: Dave Metro

D-U-N-S 96-681-2344
SEKISUI DIAGNOSTICS LLC
(*Suby of* VOLTEK DIVISION) ★
4 Hartwell Pl, Lexington, MA 02421-3122
Tel (781) 652-7800 *Founded/Ownrshp* 2008
Sales 136.1MM^E *EMP* 650^E
SIC 3841 Diagnostic apparatus, medical
Pr: Bob Schruender
**CEO:* Mitsuhisa Manabe
VP: Peter Lawsky
Site Mgr: Yoichi Tamenori

D-U-N-S 18-002-0901 IMP/EXP
SEKISUI POLYMER INNOVATIONS LLC
SEKISUI SPI
(*Suby of* VOLTEK DIVISION) ★
6685 Low St, Bloomsburg, PA 17815-8613
Tel (570) 387-6997 *Founded/Ownrshp* 2003
Sales 126.5MM^E *EMP* 450
SIC 2821 Plastics materials & resins
Opers Mgr: Liane Klobe
Plnt Mgr: Dave Hebda

D-U-N-S 83-085-8309 IMP/EXP
SEKISUI SPECIALTY CHEMICALS AMERICA LLC
(*Suby of* VOLTEK DIVISION) ★
1501 Lyndo B Johns Fwy St Ste 530, Dallas, TX 75234
Tel (972) 277-2900 *Founded/Ownrshp* 1963
Sales 117.7MM^E *EMP* 173
SIC 2899 Chemical preparations

SEKISUI SPI
See SEKISUI POLYMER INNOVATIONS LLC

D-U-N-S 08-014-3351
SEKO GLOBAL LOGISTICS NETWORK LLC
(*Suby of* GREENBRIAR EQUITY GROUP LLC) ★
1100 Arlington Ste 600, Itasca, IL 60143-3111
Tel (630) 919-4800 *Founded/Ownrshp* 2003
Sales 427.0MM^E *EMP* 171
SIC 4731 Freight transportation arrangement
CFO: Dan Sarna
CIO: Tom Madzy
IT Man: Dana Maes

D-U-N-S 06-998-6644
SEKO WORLDWIDE LLC
(*Suby of* SEKO GLOBAL LOGISTICS NETWORK LLC) ★
1100 N Arlingtn Hts 600, Itasca, IL 60143-3111
Tel (630) 919-4800 *Founded/Ownrshp* 2003
Sales 427.0MM *EMP* 170
SIC 4731 Freight transportation arrangement
Pr: William J Wascher
COO: James T Gagne
COO: Rick Lee
COO: Keith O'Brien
COO: Randy Sinker
CFO: Dan Sarna
CFO: Dan Serna
VP: Jose Quesada
VP: Tom Szwaja
VP: John Weir
VP: Rick White
VP Bus Dev: Rhonda Moon
Exec: David Emerson

D-U-N-S 17-730-2858 IMP/EXP
▲ SELECT COMFORT CORP
9800 59th Ave N, Minneapolis, MN 55442-3274
Tel (763) 551-7000 *Founded/Ownrshp* 1987
Sales 1.2MMM *EMP* 3,484
Tkr Sym SCSS *Exch* NGS
SIC 2515 Mattresses & foundations
Pr: Shelly R Ibach
CFO: David R Callen
Bd of Dir: Michael Peel
Chf Mktg O: Kevin K Brown
Chf Mktg O: Catherine Bur-Hall
Ofcr: Bob Poirier
Ex VP: Kathryn V Roedel
Sr VP: Tracey T Breazeale
Sr VP: Andrew P Carlin
Sr VP: Patricia Dirks
Sr VP: Hunter Saklad
VP: Melissa Barra
VP: Annie Bloomquist
VP: Christine M Day
VP: Ernest Erne
VP: James D Gaboury
VP: Kathleen Graber
VP: Robert Hawthorne
VP: Heather Somer
VP: Mark Sponsler
Board of Directors: Daniel Alegre, Stephen L Gulis Jr, Michael J Harrison, David T Kollat, Brenda J Lauderback, Barbara R Matas, Kathleen L Nedorostek, Vicki A O'meara, Micheal A Peel

D-U-N-S 94-553-9690 EXP
■ SELECT COMFORT RETAIL CORP
(*Suby of* SELECT COMFORT CORP) ★
9800 59th Ave N, Minneapolis, MN 55442-3274
Tel (763) 551-7000 *Founded/Ownrshp* 1987
Sales 220.0MM^E *EMP* 1,501
SIC 5712 Mattresses
CEO: Shelly Ibach
**CFO:* David Callen
Bd of Dir: Christopher Krichen
Chf Mktg O: Doug Collier
Ex VP: Christine M Day
Sr VP: Kathryn V Roedel
Dist Mgr: Wesley R Leuck
Genl Mgr: David E Karr
Mktg Dir: Tom Laier
**Genl Couns:* Mark A Kimball

D-U-N-S 01-875-5979
SELECT ENERGY SERVICES LLC
ALICE SOUTHERN EQUIPMENT
(*Suby of* SES HOLDINGS LLC) ★
1820 N Interstate 35, Gainesville, TX 76240-2179
Tel (940) 668-1818 *Founded/Ownrshp* 2007
Sales 2.1MMM^E *EMP* 3,700
SIC 1389 Oil field services

D-U-N-S 02-277-3585 IMP/EXP
SELECT HARVEST USA LLC (CA)
SPYCHER BROTHERS
14827 W Harding Rd, Turlock, CA 95380-9012
Tel (209) 668-2471 *Founded/Ownrshp* 2008
Sales 200.0MM^E *EMP* 124
SIC 5159 0173 Nuts & nut by-products; Almond grove
CFO: Shelly Broumas
Ofcr: Juan-Carlos Veraza
Sls Dir: Dinesh Bajaj

D-U-N-S 19-238-8697 IMP
■ SELECT HOTELS GROUP LLC
HYATT SELECT HOTELS GROUP
(*Suby of* HYATT HOTELS CORP) ★
71 S Wacker Dr, Chicago, IL 60606-4637
Tel (312) 750-1234 *Founded/Ownrshp* 2004
Sales 269.3MM^E *EMP* 2,800
SIC 7011 Hotels & motels
Pr: Mark S Hoplamazian
Pr: Matt Sanders
VP: Jerry Anderson
VP: Brian Kallish
Dir: Jason Gregorek
Genl Mgr: Sandra Betancourt
Genl Mgr: Shelley Carroll
Genl Mgr: Anthony Conte
Genl Mgr: Drew Dawson
Genl Mgr: Allyson Englishman
Genl Mgr: Patti Hansen

D-U-N-S 07-834-8301
SELECT INCOME REIT
255 Washington St Ste 300, Newton, MA 02458-1634
Tel (617) 796-8303 *Founded/Ownrshp* 2011
Sales 428.3MM *EMP* 407^E
SIC 6798 Real estate investment trusts
Pr: David M Blackman
CFO: Tim Bonang
CFO: John C Popeo

D-U-N-S 03-058-3814
SELECT MANAGEMENT RESOURCES LLC
ATLANTA TITLE LOANS
3440 Preston Ridge Rd # 500, Alpharetta, GA 30005-3823
Tel (678) 823-4700 *Founded/Ownrshp* 1998
Sales 115.6MM^E *EMP* 923^E
SIC 8741 Management services
Owner: Rod Aycox
Off Mgr: Sarah Johnson
CTO: Austin Cherry

D-U-N-S 00-748-2334
■ SELECT MEDICAL CORP
SELECT PHYSICAL THEREPAHY
(*Suby of* SELECT MEDICAL HOLDINGS CORP) ★
4714 Gettysburg Rd, Mechanicsburg, PA 17055-4325
Tel (717) 972-1100 *Founded/Ownrshp* 2005
Sales 3.7MMM *EMP* 29,900
SIC 8093 8051 8069 Rehabilitation center, outpatient treatment; Skilled nursing care facilities; Specialty hospitals, except psychiatric
Ch: Robert A Ortenzio
Chf Rad: Robert McGhee
Dir Recs: Stacey Gebo
Ch Bd: Rocco A Ortenzio
Pr: Lucasd Fields
Pr: Patricia A Rice
CEO: David Chernow
COO: Jeff Denney
COO: Paul Livingston
COO: Frank Schneider
COO: James J Talalai
CFO: Martin F Jackson
Treas: Joel Veit
Ex VP: Maggie Frye
Ex VP: Marty Jackson
Sr VP: Scott A Romberger
VP: Mary Barker
VP: Steve Byers
VP: Carolyn Cumane
VP: John Duggan
VP: David Elledge

D-U-N-S 18-745-9545 IMP
▲ SELECT MEDICAL HOLDINGS CORP
4714 Gettysburg Rd, Mechanicsburg, PA 17055-4325
Tel (717) 972-1100 *Founded/Ownrshp* 1997
Sales 3.7MMM *EMP* 41,000
Tkr Sym SEM *Exch* NYS
SIC 8093 8069 Rehabilitation center, outpatient treatment; Specialty hospitals, except psychiatric
Pr: David S Chernow
**Ch Bd:* Robert A Ortenzio
**V Ch:* Rocco A Ortenzio
CFO: Martin F Jackson
Ofcr: John A Saich
Ex VP: Michael E Tarvin
Sr VP: Scott A Romberger
VP: Robert G Breighner Jr
VP: Kevin Oswald
Exec: Lori Retzler-Zimmer
CIO: Brian Rusignuolo

SELECT PHYSICAL THEREPAHY
See SELECT MEDICAL CORP

SELECT PHYSICAL THEREPAHY AND
See SELECT SPECIALTY HOSPITAL-BATTLE CREEK INC

SELECT PHYSICAL THEREPAHY AND
See KESSLER INSTITUTE FOR REHABILITATION INC

D-U-N-S 78-691-5553
SELECT PORTFOLIO SERVICING INC
S P S
(*Suby of* SPS HOLDINGS CORP) ★
3217 Decker Lake Dr, West Valley City, UT 84119-3284
Tel (800) 258-8602 *Founded/Ownrshp* 1989
Sales NA *EMP* 1,000
SIC 6162 Loan correspondents
CEO: Timothy O'Brien
Ex VP: Craig A Bullock
**Sr VP:* Lester L Cheng
VP: Joe Arico
VP: Dennis Cook
VP: Michele Crampton
**VP:* Andrew De Jong
**VP:* Lee Ervin
VP: Randhir Gandhi
VP: Nathan Green
VP: Scott Hansen
VP: Bud Hertig
VP: Jacqueline Johnson
VP: Mike Maynard
VP: Candice Pitcher
VP: Kevin Rucci
**VP:* Michelle Simon
VP: Dustin Stephenson
VP: Jeff Young

SELECT PRODUCT GROUP
See SPG HOLDINGS LLC

D-U-N-S 17-195-0160 EXP
SELECT PRODUCT GROUP LP
(*Suby of* SELECT PRODUCT GROUP) ★
8214 Westchester Dr # 800, Dallas, TX 75225-6114
Tel (214) 363-7427 *Founded/Ownrshp* 2010
Sales 158.8MM^E *EMP* 190
SIC 5199 Novelties, paper
Pt: Bobby Cheney
Pt: Bennie Bray
Pt: Miguel Leal
Pt: John Waghorne
CFO: John Olsen
Ex VP: Jonathan Dyer
Sls Mgr: Mike Henderson

D-U-N-S 07-864-9451
SELECT REHABILITATION-MIDWEST LLC
550 W Frontage Rd # 2415, Northfield, IL 60093-1202
Tel (847) 441-5593 *Founded/Ownrshp* 1998
Sales 46.1MM^E *EMP* 1,000^E
SIC 8093 Rehabilitation center, outpatient treatment
Pr: Neil Deutsch
Off Mgr: Marie Fulton

D-U-N-S 05-136-4404
SELECT SIRES INC
11740 U S 42 N, Plain City, OH 43064
Tel (614) 873-4683 *Founded/Ownrshp* 1965
Sales 269.4MM^E *EMP* 181
SIC 0751

D-U-N-S 00-812-5036
■ SELECT SPECIALTY HOSPITAL-BATTLE CREEK INC
SELECT PHYSICAL THEREPAHY AND
(*Suby of* SELECT PHYSICAL THEREPAHY) ★
300 North Ave, Battle Creek, MI 49017-3307
Tel (269) 245-4675 *Founded/Ownrshp* 1998
Sales 155.9MM *EMP* 300
SIC 8069 Specialty hospitals, except psychiatric
CEO: David Gehinger
Pr: Sue Taylor
Nrsg Dir: Terry Hunter

SELECT STAFFING
See EMPLOYBRIDGE HOLDING CO

SELECT STAFFING
See EMPLOYBRIDGE LLC

D-U-N-S 12-659-5003
■ SELECTBUILD CONSTRUCTION INC
BMC CONSTRUCTION
(*Suby of* BMC STOCK HOLDINGS INC) ★
720 E Park Blvd Ste 115, Boise, ID 83712-7756
Tel (208) 331-4300 *Founded/Ownrshp* 2016
Sales 985.4MM^E *EMP* 6,000
SIC 1521 1771 1751 2431 5031 5211 Single-family housing construction; Concrete work; Foundation & footing contractor; Framing contractor; Windows & window parts & trim, wood; Lumber, plywood & millwork; Doors & windows; Door frames, all materials; Windows; Lumber & other building materials
Pr: Stanley M Wilson
CFO: William Smartt
Dir IT: Paula Sheldon
Board of Directors: Robert E Mellor, William M Smartt, Paul S Street, Stanley M Wilson

D-U-N-S 13-126-0242
SELECTCARE INC
SELECTCARE P P O
2401 W Big Beaver Rd, Troy, MI 48084-3306
Tel (248) 358-2560 *Founded/Ownrshp* 1984
Sales NA *EMP* 187
Accts Deloitte & Touche Llp
SIC 6324 8741 Health maintenance organization (HMO), insurance only; Group hospitalization plans; Administrative management
Pr: Roman T Kulich
COO: Bobby Jones
Ofcr: James D Forshee MD
Sr VP: Denise Christy
VP: Edward Bornoty
VP: Paul Browne
VP: Colleen McClorey
Board of Directors: Barbara E Allushuski, Stephen A George MD, Barbara M Littles Esq, Lester W Robinson, Donald C Wegmiller, Gary M Wetstein, Tracey A Yokich, Allen Wayne Jacobs D O Phd

SELECTCARE P P O
See SELECTCARE INC

D-U-N-S 61-848-1621
SELECTHEALTH BENEFIT ASSURANCE
(*Suby of* SELECTHEALTH INC) ★
5381 S Green St, Murray, UT 84123-4661
Tel (801) 442-5000 *Founded/Ownrshp* 2006
Sales NA *EMP* 1,165E
SIC 6321 Accident & health insurance
Pr: Patricia Richards
**CFO:* Mark Brown
**VP:* Jerry Edgington
**VP:* Lisa Fallert
**VP:* Bob White
**VP:* Murphy Winfield
**Doctor:* Stephen Barlow

D-U-N-S 80-586-0517
SELECTHEALTH INC
(*Suby of* IHC HEALTH SERVICES) ★
5381 S Green St, Murray, UT 84123-4661
Tel (801) 442-5000 *Founded/Ownrshp* 1983
Sales NA *EMP* 1,200
Accts Ernst & Young Us Llp Salt Lak
SIC 6321 Accident & health insurance
Pr: William H Nelson
**CFO:* Mark Brown
**Sec:* Mark L Baird
**Chf Mktg O:* Russ Kuzel
**VP:* Dr Stephen L Barlow
**VP:* Jerry Edgington
**VP:* Lisa Fallert
**VP:* Bob White
**VP:* Murphy Winfield
Off Admin: Tracey N Snelson
QA Dir: James Cahoon

D-U-N-S 00-697-1816
■ **SELECTIVE INSURANCE CO OF AMERICA**
(*Suby of* SELECTIVE INSURANCE GROUP INC) ★
40 Wantage Ave, Branchville, NJ 07890-0002
Tel (973) 948-3000 *Founded/Ownrshp* 1926, 1977
Sales NA *EMP* 1,900
Accts Kpmg Llp New York New York
SIC 6411 6351 Insurance agents, brokers & service; Surety insurance
Pr: Gregory E Murphy
**Pr:* John J Marchioni
**CFO:* Dale Thatcher
**Chf Mktg O:* Rohit Mull
Ofcr: Dennis L Barger
**Ofcr:* George Neale
Assoc VP: Robin Bullock
Assoc VP: Zachary Kramer
**Ex VP:* Kimberly Burnett
**Ex VP:* Angelique Carbo
**Ex VP:* Gordon J Gaudet
**Ex VP:* Michael H Lanza
**Ex VP:* Dale A Thatcher
Ex VP: Steven B Woods
**Ex VP:* Ronald J Zaleski Sr
Sr VP: Jeffrey Beck
Sr VP: Andrew S Becker
Sr VP: John Bresney
Sr VP: Teresa Caro
Sr VP: Brenda M Hall
**Sr VP:* Anthony Harnett

D-U-N-S 09-497-2106
▲ **SELECTIVE INSURANCE GROUP INC**
40 Wantage Ave, Branchville, NJ 07890-0001
Tel (973) 948-3000 *Founded/Ownrshp* 1977
Sales NA *EMP* 2,200E
Tkr Sym SIGI *Exch* NGS
SIC 6331 Fire, marine & casualty insurance
Ch Bd: Gregory E Murphy
Pr: John J Marchioni
CFO: Dale A Thatcher
Chf Cred: Michael H Lanza
Ex VP: Angelique Carbo
Board of Directors: Philip H Urban, Paul D Bauer, John C Burville, Robert Kelly Doherty, Michael J Morrissey, Cynthia S Nicholson, Ronald L O'kelley, William M Rue, John S Scheid, J Brian Thebault

D-U-N-S 15-765-7016
SELECTQUOTE INSURANCE SERVICES
595 Market St Fl 10, San Francisco, CA 94105-2899
Tel (415) 543-7338 *Founded/Ownrshp* 2001
Sales NA *EMP* 322
SIC 6411 Life insurance agents
Pr: Charan J Singh
**COO:* Robert Edwards
**VP:* Steven H Gerber
Off Mgr: Kellie Stewart
**CTO:* Michael L Feroah
Dir IT: Ian Kirwan
Dir IT: Paulette Slattery
Opers Mgr: Andrea Hatch
Sales Exec: Julia Arant
Sales Exec: Cisar Ocana
Sales Exec: William Walley

D-U-N-S 05-376-4879 IMP
SELECTRANSPORTATION RESOURCES LLC
9550 North Loop E, Houston, TX 77029-1230
Tel (713) 672-4115 *Founded/Ownrshp* 1998
Sales 371.5MME *EMP* 366
Accts Doerenmayhew Cpas And Advisor
SIC 5012 5013 5511 7538 Trucks, commercial; Trucks, noncommercial; Truck parts & accessories; Trucks, tractors & trailers: new & used; Truck engine repair, except industrial
VP: Robert Garwood
IT Man: Josh Howe
Sls Mgr: John Hernandez
Genl Couns: Roger Poser

D-U-N-S 06-667-9531
SELEY & CO
1515 Hope St, South Pasadena, CA 91030-2610
Tel (626) 799-1196 *Founded/Ownrshp* 1934
Sales 100.0MM *EMP* 14
SIC 5191 Feed
Pr: James C Seley
**CFO:* Michael Seley
**VP:* Ronald J Seley

SELF ESTEEM
See ALL ACCESS APPAREL INC

D-U-N-S 07-371-3885 IMP
SELF REGIONAL HEALTHCARE
GREENWOOD COUNTY HOSPITAL
1325 Spring St, Greenwood, SC 29646-3875
Tel (864) 725-4150 *Founded/Ownrshp* 1969
Sales 305.4MM *EMP* 1,551
SIC 8062 General medical & surgical hospitals
Pr: Jim Pfeiffer
Ofcr: Martin Lester
**Sr VP:* Camie Patterson
**VP:* Bill Keith
**VP:* Greg Mappin MD
**VP:* Craig White
Ex Dir: Robert Helfrich
**Ex Dir:* Jack Schwartz
Snr Ntwrk: Jason Goldman
CIO: Chuck McDeritt
Dir IT: Andy Hartong

D-U-N-S 03-462-9662
SELF-INSURED SCHOOLS OF CALIFORNIA
SISC
1300 17th St 5, Bakersfield, CA 93301-4504
Tel (661) 636-4000 *Founded/Ownrshp* 2002
Sales NA *EMP* 400E
SIC 6371 Pension, health & welfare funds
Pr: Russell E Bigler

D-U-N-S 80-564-5512 IMP
SELKIRK CORP
(*Suby of* JOHNSON CONTROLS INC) ★
5030 Corp Exch Blvd Se, Grand Rapids, MI 49512
Tel (616) 656-8200 *Founded/Ownrshp* 1920
Sales 157.8MME *EMP* 800
SIC 3444 Metal ventilating equipment

D-U-N-S 18-677-3990
SELL-THRU SERVICES INC
4807 Spicewd Spgs Rd # 3120, Austin, TX 78759-8442
Tel (512) 346-5075 *Founded/Ownrshp* 1987
Sales 171.1MME *EMP* 1,000
SIC 5141 8742 Groceries, general line; Marketing consulting services
Pr: Ted Lusher
**VP:* Valerie Schweers

D-U-N-S 00-282-4159 IMP
SELLEN CONSTRUCTION CO INC
227 Westlake Ave N, Seattle, WA 98109-5217
Tel (206) 682-7770 *Founded/Ownrshp* 1952
Sales 396.3MM *EMP* 761
Accts Moss Adams
SIC 1542 8741 Commercial & office building contractors; Institutional building construction; Construction management
CEO: Robert P McCleskey
**Pr:* Scott B Redman
**COO:* Wilfrid Wainhouse
**CFO:* Andrew J Aiken
**Ch:* Robert E Barrett
**Treas:* Nancy Stratton
Ex VP: Andrew Akin
Sr VP: Lori Carlson
Sr VP: Lori Daigle
**Sr VP:* Michael Morris
**VP:* John Avery
VP: James Hunter
VP: Adam Kriefall
**VP:* David J Scalzo
VP: Mark D Summers

D-U-N-S 02-664-7693 IMP
SELLERS BROS INC
SELLERS BROS' SUPER DRIVE IN
4580 S Wayside Dr, Houston, TX 77087-1112
Tel (713) 640-1611 *Founded/Ownrshp* 1946
Sales 116.3MME *EMP* 1,000
SIC 5411 Grocery stores, chain; Supermarkets, chain; Convenience stores, chain
Pr: George Sellers
**Sec:* John L Sellers
**VP:* Charles D Sellers
Dir Risk M: Ross Cantril

SELLERS BROS' SUPER DRIVE IN
See SELLERS BROS INC

SELLERS PETROLEUM
See SNAKEBITE LEASING INC

D-U-N-S 07-511-3402
SELLETHICS MARKETING GROUP INC
941 Matthews Mint Hill Rd, Matthews, NC 28105-1777
Tel (704) 847-4450 *Founded/Ownrshp* 1999
Sales 92.8MME *EMP* 332E
SIC 5141 Groceries, general line
Pr: Joel Barham
**VP:* Jeff Hensley
**VP:* John Mann
**VP:* Wendy Mason
VP: John Nolan
Snr Ntwrk: Rick Helton
IT Man: Jordan Zell
VP Sls: Ken Hestley
VP Sls: Ronnie Rudd
Sls Dir: Tommy Fincher
Sls Dir: Steve Johnson

SELMA CITY SCHOOL DISTRICT
See SELMA PUBLIC SCHOOLS

D-U-N-S 07-897-4136
SELMA PUBLIC SCHOOLS
SELMA CITY SCHOOL DISTRICT
2194 Broad St, Selma, AL 36701-4101
Tel (334) 874-1600 *Founded/Ownrshp* 1845
Sales 46.1MME *EMP* 1,185
SIC 8211 Public elementary & secondary schools

SELMER PARIS
See CONN-SELMER INC

D-U-N-S 62-388-2495
SEMA CONSTRUCTION INC
7353 S Eagle St, Centennial, CO 80112-4223
Tel (303) 627-2600 *Founded/Ownrshp* 1991
Sales 401.6MME *EMP* 550
SIC 1622 1771 Bridge, tunnel & elevated highway; Concrete work
CEO: Thomas G Ames
**Pr:* Bradley J Spies
**Sec:* Steven R Graves
**Sr VP:* Thomas C Clark
**VP:* Melvin L Browning
Brnch Mgr: Don Bernhoft
Off Mgr: Nichole Chafpy
IT Man: Randy Brownfield
Sfty Mgr: Jason James

SEMAFOR TECHNOLOGIES USA
See IDHASOFT INC

SEMCO ENERGY
See CONTINENTAL ENERGY SYSTEMS LLC

D-U-N-S 08-971-2079
SEMCO ENERGY INC (MI)
(*Suby of* SEMCO HOLDING CORP) ★
1411 3rd St Ste A, Port Huron, MI 48060-5480
Tel (810) 987-2200 *Founded/Ownrshp* 1977, 2007
Sales 674.0MM *EMP* 500
Accts Ernst & Young Llp Detroit M
SIC 4924 Natural gas distribution
CEO: David M Harris
**Pr:* John D O'Brien
**CFO:* Mark Moses
VP: Tracy Vincent
VP: Steven Warsinske
Comm Dir: Timothy Lubbers
**Prin:* James C Larsen
Tech Mgr: Stephen Makowski
Opers Supe: Doug Hulst

D-U-N-S 82-784-5574
SEMCO HOLDING CORP
(*Suby of* ALTAGAS LTD)
1411 3rd St Ste A, Port Huron, MI 48060-5480
Tel (810) 987-2200 *Founded/Ownrshp* 2008
Sales 674.0MME *EMP* 500
SIC 4924 Natural gas distribution
VP: Steven W Warsinske
**Treas:* Mark A Moses
**VP:* James C Larsen
**VP:* Michael Olson
**VP:* M Colleen Starring

D-U-N-S 05-147-5853
■ **SEMCO INSTRUMENTS INC**
(*Suby of* AEROCONTROLEX) ★
25700 Rye Canyon Rd, Valencia, CA 91355-1148
Tel (661) 257-2000 *Founded/Ownrshp* 2012
Sales 86.4MME *EMP* 495
SIC 3829 Thermometers & temperature sensors
Pr: Michael G Moore
**CEO:* Vincent Sandoval

D-U-N-S 78-278-5489 IMP
SEMCO LLC
186 Jean Lafitte Blvd, Lafitte, LA 70067-5100
Tel (504) 689-2054 *Founded/Ownrshp* 1989
Sales 95.3MME *EMP* 421
SIC 3441 3731 Boat & barge sections, prefabricated metal; Offshore supply boats, building & repairing
Sec: Tom McKinney
**VP:* Allen Moore
Sfty Dirs: Steve Juul

D-U-N-S 80-807-4939
■ **SEMGAS LP**
(*Suby of* SEMGROUP CORP) ★
6120 S Yale Ave Ste 700, Tulsa, OK 74136-4216
Tel (918) 524-7100 *Founded/Ownrshp* 2001
Sales 295.8MME *EMP* 400E
SIC 4923 Gas transmission & distribution
Pr: Timothy R O'Sullivan
VP: Wayne Ziegler

D-U-N-S 02-050-9027 IMP
▲ **SEMGROUP CORP**
6120 S Yale Ave Ste 700, Tulsa, OK 74136-4216
Tel (918) 524-8100 *Founded/Ownrshp* 2000
Sales 1.4MMM *EMP* 1,160
Tkr Sym SEMG *Exch* NYS
SIC 1389 4612 5171 2951 Oil field services; Crude petroleum pipelines; Petroleum bulk stations & terminals; Asphalt paving mixtures & blocks
Pr: Carlin G Conner
Ch Bd: John F Chlebowski
COO: Peter L Schwiering
CFO: Robert N Fitzgerald
VP: Candice L Cheeseman
VP: Timothy R O'Sullivan
VP: Thomas D Sell
Opers Mgr: Remi Petit
Board of Directors: Ronald A Ballschmiede, Sarah M Barpoulis, Karl F Kurz, James H Lytal, Thomas R McDaniel

D-U-N-S 04-414-9362 IMP
■ **SEMICONDUCTOR COMPONENTS INDUSTRIES LLC**
ON SEMICONDUCTOR
(*Suby of* ON SEMICONDUCTOR CORP) ★
5005 E Mcdowell Rd, Phoenix, AZ 85008-4229
Tel (602) 244-6600 *Founded/Ownrshp* 1999
Sales 1.6MMME *EMP* 5,599
SIC 3674 3823 Semiconductors & related devices; Industrial instrmnts msrmnt display/control process variable
CEO: Keith D Jackson
**COO:* William A Schromm
Ofcr: John Nelson
**Ex VP:* Paul Rolls
**VP:* George H Cave
**VP:* Bernard Gutmann
**VP:* Robert A Klosterboer
VP: Joe R Pemberton
VP: Chandra Subramaniam
**VP:* Peter J Zdebel
IT Man: Mario Robles

D-U-N-S 94-836-5861
■ **SEMINIS INC**
(*Suby of* MONSANTO CO) ★
2700 Camino Del Sol, Oxnard, CA 93030-7967
Tel (805) 485-7317 *Founded/Ownrshp* 2005
Sales 83.0MME *EMP* 2,798
SIC 8731 8742 2099 Agricultural research; Food research; Productivity improvement consultant; Marketing consulting services; Food preparations
Pr: Bruno Ferrari
V Ch: W Paine
Pr: Eugenio N Solorzano
CFO: Andy Kuchan
**Sr VP:* Charles E Green
**Sr VP:* Oscar J Velasco
VP: Gasper Alvarez
**VP:* Enrique Lopez
VP: Gaspar A Martinez
VP: Amerique D Nord
VP: Enrique Osorio
Exec: Kevin Lane

D-U-N-S 04-116-2140 IMP/EXP
■ **SEMINIS VEGETABLE SEEDS INC** (CA)
(*Suby of* MONSANTO CO) ★
2700 Camino Del Sol, Oxnard, CA 93030-7967
Tel (855) 733-3834 *Founded/Ownrshp* 1962
Sales 500.4MME *EMP* 2,700
SIC 5191 0723 Seeds: field, garden & flower; Crop preparation services for market
CEO: Michael J Frank
**Pr:* Kerry Preete

D-U-N-S 03-214-4698
SEMINOLE COUNTY PUBLIC SCHOOLS
400 E Lake Mary Blvd, Sanford, FL 32773-7125
Tel (407) 320-0000 *Founded/Ownrshp* 2004
Sales 585.2MM *EMP* 7,000E
Accts Moore Stephens Lovelace Pa
SIC 8211 Public elementary & secondary schools
Dir Sec: Rick Francis
CIO: Rosmac George
MIS Dir: Tim Harper
IT Man: Phyllis McKeeon
IT Man: Mary Werner
Teacher Pr: Ron Pinnell

D-U-N-S 07-833-2657 IMP
SEMINOLE ELECTRIC COOPERATIVE INC (FL)
16313 N Dale Mabry Hwy, Tampa, FL 33618-1427
Tel (813) 963-0994 *Founded/Ownrshp* 1948
Sales 1.0MMM *EMP* 528
SIC 4911
CEO: Lisa Johnson
COO: Wm Reid
**CFO:* Jo Fuller
Trst: John W Drake
Trst: W F Hart
Trst: R D Lundy
VP: Al Garcia
**VP:* David Gerhart
**VP:* Mark Sherman
IT Man: Dennis Lee
Opers Supe: Leroy Hunter

SEMINOLE ENERGY SERVICES
See CONTINUUM MIDSTREAM LLC

SEMINOLE GAMING
See SEMINOLE TRIBE OF FLORIDA HARD ROCK

D-U-N-S 87-775-9220
SEMINOLE HARD ROCK HOTEL & CASINO
1 Seminole Way, Fort Lauderdale, FL 33314-6407
Tel (954) 327-7625 *Founded/Ownrshp* 2007
Sales 95.1MME *EMP* 3,000
SIC 7011 Casino hotel
CEO: James Allen
**Pr:* Phillip Maydow
Sr VP: Jeanine Repa
VP: James Fair
VP: Michael Maclean
Exec: Arturo Camargo
Exec: Alex Hernandez
Exec: Kristina Valente
Exec: Tanya Williams
Dir Sec: John McDonal
Off Mgr: Kami Dietz

D-U-N-S 13-655-8566
SEMINOLE SCHOOL DISTRICT I01
617 Timmons St, Seminole, OK 74868-3813
Tel (405) 382-5085 *Founded/Ownrshp* 1900
Sales 95.0MM *EMP* 325
SIC 8211 Public elementary school; Public junior high school; Public senior high school

D-U-N-S 04-665-7123
SEMINOLE STATE COLLEGE OF FLORIDA
100 Weldon Blvd, Sanford, FL 32773-6132
Tel (407) 708-4722 *Founded/Ownrshp* 1967
Sales 117.6MME *EMP* 1,550
Accts David W Martin Cpa Tallahas
SIC 8221 Colleges & universities
Ch: Scott D Howat
**Pr:* E Ann McGee
Pr: Lynn Powers
VP: Carol Hawkins
Comm Dir: Jay Davis
Ex Dir: John Gyllin
Site Mgr: Ken Moore
Site Mgr: Michael Weber
Snr Mgr: Mila Ecle

D-U-N-S 14-648-9781
SEMINOLE TRIBE OF FLORIDA HARD ROCK
SEMINOLE GAMING
(*Suby of* SEMINOLE WHOLESALE DISTRS) ★
1 Seminole Way, Fort Lauderdale, FL 33314-6407
Tel (954) 327-7625 *Founded/Ownrshp* 2004
Sales 48.2MME *EMP* 2,125
SIC 7011 Casino hotel
Pr: Michael Volkert
CFO: John R Eder
Prin: Michael Bloom

D-U-N-S 07-845-6860
SEMINOLE TRIBE OF FLORIDA INC
SEMINOLE WHOLESALE DISTRS
6300 Stirling Rd, Hollywood, FL 33024-2198
Tel (954) 966-6300 *Founded/Ownrshp* 1957
Sales 397.4MME *EMP* 4,000

SIC 7999 5194 2011 5182 2911 Tourist attraction, commercial; Cigarettes; Beef products from beef slaughtered on site; Corned beef from meat slaughtered on site; Bottling wines & liquors; Diesel fuels; Oils, fuel
Ch Bd: James E Billie
V Ch: Richard Bowers Jr
**Pr:* Mitchell Cypress
Dir Risk M: Victor Marrero
Ex Dir: Tina Osceola
Dir Sec: Chris Osceola
Dir IT: Mario Silva
Pharmcst: Monica Oban

D-U-N-S 14-627-1718
SEMINOLE TRIBE OF FLORIDA T V INC
3107 N State Road 7, Hollywood, FL 33021-2102
Tel (954) 966-6300 *Founded/Ownrshp* 2007
Sales 153.6MM^E *EMP* 6,000
SIC 5812 Eating places
Ch Bd: Mitchell Cypress
**Pr:* James E Billie
**Treas:* Priscilla D Sayen
**VP:* Sam Kravetz

SEMINOLE WHOLESALE DISTRS
See SEMINOLE TRIBE OF FLORIDA INC

D-U-N-S 09-620-0175 IMP
■ **SEMITOOL INC** (MT)
(*Suby of* APPLIED MATERIALS INC) ★
655 W Reserve Dr, Kalispell, MT 59901-2127
Tel (406) 752-2107 *Founded/Ownrshp* 2009
Sales 151.6MM^E *EMP* 1,155^E
SIC 3559 Semiconductor manufacturing machinery
CEO: Raymon F Thompson
Pr: Ed Le Cesne Byrne
Pr: Larry E Murphy
CFO: Larry A Viano
CFO: Larry A Vino
Ex VP: Timothy Dodkin
Ex VP: Timothy C Dodkin
VP: Ed Lecesne Byrne
VP: James Gordley
VP: Fabio Gualandris
VP: Jurek Koziol
VP: Nancy Ludgus
VP: Kathy Woods
Board of Directors: Howard E Bateman, Donald P Baumann, Daniel J Eigeman, Charles P Grenier, Steven C Stahlberg, Steven R Thompson

SEMPER/EXETER
See SCHWARZ PAPER CO LLC

SEMPERIAN COLLECTION CENTER
See ALLY SERVICING LLC

D-U-N-S 02-271-5408
▲ **SEMPRA ENERGY**
488 8th Ave, San Diego, CA 92101-7123
Tel (619) 696-2000 *Founded/Ownrshp* 1996
Sales 10.2MMM *EMP* 17,387
Tkr Sym SRE *Exch* NYS
SIC 4932 4911 5172 4922 Gas & other services combined; Electric services; Distribution, electric power; Generation, electric power; Transmission, electric power; Petroleum products; Natural gas transmission; Pipelines, natural gas; Storage, natural gas
Ch Bd: Debra L Reed
V Ch: Justice Urbas
Pr: Mark A Snell
CFO: Joseph A Householder
Treas: Kate Collier
Treas: Tim Ransdell
Ofcr: G Joyce Rowland
Ex VP: Mike Iammarino
Ex VP: Martha B Wyrsch
Sr VP: Trevor I Mihalik
VP: Karen L Sedgwick
VP: Michael Sliwowski
VP: Caroline Winn
Board of Directors: James C Yardley, Alan L Boeckmann, Kathleen L Brown, Pablo A Ferrero, William D Jones, William G Ouchi, William C Rusnack, William P Rutledge, Lynn Schenk, Jack T Taylor

D-U-N-S 12-652-0365
■ **SEMPRA ENERGY GLOBAL ENTERPRISES**
(*Suby of* SEMPRA ENERGY) ★
101 Ash St, San Diego, CA 92101-3017
Tel (619) 696-2000 *Founded/Ownrshp* 1997
Sales 64.9MM^E *EMP* 1,000
SIC 4924 4911 Natural gas distribution; Generation, electric power
Pr: Mark Snell
**CFO:* Michael Allman
Chf Cred: Randall Peterson
Sr VP: Frank Ault
**VP:* Mark Fisher
VP: Joseph Householder
VP: Charles McMonagle
VP: Mark Randle
VP: Thomas Sayles
Mktg Dir: Jeffrey Reed

D-U-N-S 84-805-4727
■ **SEMPRA ENERGY INTERNATIONAL**
SEMPRA ENERGY UTILITIES
(*Suby of* SEMPRA ENERGY) ★
101 Ash St, San Diego, CA 92101-3017
Tel (619) 696-2000 *Founded/Ownrshp* 1998
Sales 753.8MM^E *EMP* 1,200
SIC 4911 Electric services
CEO: Luis Eduardo Pawluszek
**Pr:* Mark A Snell
**Ch:* Donald E Felsinger
**Ex VP:* Javade Chaudhri
Ex VP: Vicki Zeiger
**VP:* Randall L Clark
**VP:* Kathryn J Collier
Ex Dir: Michael Shaffer
Dir IT: Dawn Welch
Tech Mgr: David Jeon
Netwrk Eng: David Lennon

SEMPRA ENERGY UTILITIES
See SEMPRA ENERGY INTERNATIONAL

D-U-N-S 01-425-6379
■ **SEMPRA GENERATION LLC**
(*Suby of* SEMPRA ENERGY) ★
101 Ash St, San Diego, CA 92101-3017
Tel (619) 696-2000 *Founded/Ownrshp* 2008
Sales 226.1MM^E *EMP* 350
SIC 4931 Electric & other services combined
CEO: Debra L Reed
Pr: Michael Niggli
Pr: Mark A Snell
Ex VP: Joseph A Householder
VP: William R Engelbecht
VP: William Engelbrecht
VP: William Keller
VP: Jim Sahagian
VP: Oct Vio M Simoes
VP: Kevin Swartz
VP: Michael Walker
Dir: Tim Allen

D-U-N-S 00-847-9941 IMP
▲ **SEMTECH CORP**
200 Flynn Rd, Camarillo, CA 93012-8790
Tel (805) 498-2111 *Founded/Ownrshp* 1960
Sales 490.2MM *EMP* 1,335
Tkr Sym SMTC *Exch* NGS
SIC 3674 Semiconductors & related devices
Pr: Mohan R Maheswaran
**Ch Bd:* Rockell N Hankin
CFO: Emeka N Chukwu
**V Ch Bd:* James P Burra
Ofcr: Alberto Guerra
Ex VP: Charles B Ammann
Ex VP: Gary M Beauchamp
Ex VP: J Michael Wilson
Sr VP: Alain Dantec
Sr VP: Sharon Faltemier
Sr VP: James J Kim
Sr VP: Asaf Silberstein
Sr VP: Ross Teggatz
VP: Alan Bennett
VP: Roger Levinson
Exec: Justin Abbott
Board of Directors: Glen M Antle, Bruce C Edwards, Ye Jane Li, James T Lindstrom, John L Piotrowski, Carmelo J Santoro, Sylvia Summers

D-U-N-S 93-335-1207
■ **SENATE UNITED STATES**
(*Suby of* CONGRESS UNITED STATES) ★
111 Russell Senate Bldg, Washington, DC 20510-0001
Tel (202) 224-3121 *Founded/Ownrshp* 1787
Sales NA *EMP* 6,200^E
SIC 9121 Congress;
VP: Joseph Biden

D-U-N-S 06-183-2825 IMP
SENATOR INTERNATIONAL FREIGHT FORWARDING LLC (FL)
(*Suby of* SENATOR INTERNATIONAL HOLDING LLC) ★
10201 Nw 112th Ave Ste 10, Medley, FL 33178-1057
Tel (305) 593-5520 *Founded/Ownrshp* 1999
Sales 93.0MM *EMP* 160
SIC 4731 Freight transportation arrangement; Customhouse brokers
**COO:* Ralf Schneider
**CFO:* Kay Oster

D-U-N-S 13-572-9304
SENATOR INTERNATIONAL HOLDING LLC
(*Suby of* SENATOR GMBH)
10201 Nw 112th Ave Ste 10, Medley, FL 33178-1057
Tel (305) 593-5520 *Founded/Ownrshp* 2001
Sales 93.0MM^E *EMP* 200^E
SIC 4731 Freight forwarding; Customhouse brokers
CEO: Tim Oliver Kirschbaum
CFO: Kay Oster
Mng Dir: Berndt Lindenmayer
Genl Mgr: Alexander Forward
IT Man: Guillermo Almendarez

D-U-N-S 83-136-9447 IMP
SENCO BRANDS INC
NEXICOR
(*Suby of* WYNNCHURCH CAPITAL LTD) ★
4270 Ivy Pointe Blvd # 300, Cincinnati, OH 45245-0003
Tel (513) 388-2000 *Founded/Ownrshp* 2009
Sales 172.7MM^E *EMP* 400
SIC 3546 Power-driven handtools
CEO: Ben Johansen
Manager: Preston Kaufman

SEND LIGHT
See SEND LIGHT DISTRIBUTION LLC

D-U-N-S 07-859-8650 IMP
SEND LIGHT DISTRIBUTION LLC
SEND LIGHT
212 Industrial Dr, Bristol, TN 37620-5424
Tel (423) 547-5100 *Founded/Ownrshp* 2012
Sales 119.9MM^E *EMP* 130
SIC 5192

D-U-N-S 08-011-9181
SENECA COAL RESOURCES LLC
15 Appledore Ln, Natural Bridge, VA 24578-3602
Tel (304) 369-8175 *Founded/Ownrshp* 2015
Sales 396.1MM^E *EMP* 1,029^E
SIC 1222 Bituminous coal-underground mining

D-U-N-S 08-014-7274
SENECA COAL RESOURCES LLC
Shaffer Rd Exit, Madison, WV 25130
Tel (304) 369-8316 *Founded/Ownrshp* 2015
Sales 200.0MM *EMP* 800^E
SIC 1241 Coal mining services

D-U-N-S 05-718-6504 IMP/EXP
■ **SENECA DATA DISTRIBUTORS INC**
(*Suby of* ARROW ELECTRONICS INC) ★
6040 Tarbell Rd Ste 103, Syracuse, NY 13206-1324
Tel (315) 433-1160 *Founded/Ownrshp* 2014
Sales 86.0MM *EMP* 140
SIC 5045 Computers, peripherals & software
CEO: Kevin Conley
Pr: Lourdes Bedoya
**Pr:* Greg Masingill
**CFO:* Jim Petrie
**VP:* Steve Maser
**VP:* Mike Smith
Exec: David Mitchell
Exec: Ron Tassel
Exec: Ron Vantassel
Dir IT: Scott Harte
Sftwr Eng: Eric Luke

D-U-N-S 17-842-0030
SENECA FAMILY OF AGENCIES
SENECA RESIDENTIAL
15942 Foothill Blvd, San Leandro, CA 94578-2102
Tel (510) 317-1444 *Founded/Ownrshp* 1985
Sales 88.8MM *EMP* 1,000
Accts Gilmore & Associates San Mate
SIC 8322 8299 8082 Social service center; Educational services; Home health care services
CEO: Ken Berrick
**CFO:* Kanwar Singh
**Ex Dir:* Catherine West
Psych: Bobby Coleman
Psych: Toshia Mears

D-U-N-S 00-220-7322 IMP/EXP
▲ **SENECA FOODS CORP** (NY)
3736 S Main St, Marion, NY 14505-9751
Tel (315) 926-8100 *Founded/Ownrshp* 1949
Sales 1.2MMM *EMP* 3,500
Accts Bdo Usa Llp Milwaukee Wisco
Tkr Sym SENEA *Exch* NGS
SIC 2033 2037 Vegetables: packaged in cans, jars, etc.; Fruits: packaged in cans, jars, etc.; Vegetables, quick frozen & cold pack, excl. potato products; Fruits, quick frozen & cold pack (frozen); Fruit juices, frozen
Pr: Kraig H Kayser
**Ch Bd:* Arthur S Wolcott
COO: Paul L Palmby
CFO: Timothy J Benjamin
Ofcr: Cynthia L Fohrd
Sr VP: Carl A Cichetti
Sr VP: Dean E Erstad
Sr VP: Aaron M Girard
Sr VP: Matt J Henschler
VP: Mike Bliek
VP: Mark Gavigan
VP: Jeffrey L Van Riper
Board of Directors: Arthur H Baer, Peter R Call, John P Gaylord, Susan A Henry, Samuel T Hubbard Jr, Thomas Paulson, Susan W Stuart

SENECA MEDICAL
See CONCORDANCE HEALTHCARE SOLUTIONS LLC

D-U-N-S 60-663-8203 IMP
SENECA MEDICAL LLC
(*Suby of* SENECA MEDICAL) ★
85 Shaffer Park Dr, Tiffin, OH 44883-9290
Tel (419) 447-0236 *Founded/Ownrshp* 2016
Sales 423.7MM^E *EMP* 475
SIC 5047 Medical equipment & supplies; Surgical equipment & supplies
CEO: Roger Benz
**Pr:* Buddy Wert
**CFO:* Todd Howell
**Chf Cred:* Dave Myers
Dir Bus: Jeff Lawing
**Dir Sec:* Lisa Hohman
Sls Mgr: Sonya Kimmet
Sales Asso: Jo Seery
Sales Asso: Lori Wise

D-U-N-S 07-929-0205
SENECA MORTGAGE INVESTMENTS LP
375 Park Ave Ste 3401, New York, NY 10152-3402
Tel (888) 601-6718 *Founded/Ownrshp* 2013
Sales 211.0MM^E *EMP* 595
SIC 6799 6719 Real estate investors, except property operators; Investment holding companies, except banks
Founder: Ivan Kaufman
VP Mktg: Erica Mileo

D-U-N-S 82-826-0179
SENECA MORTGAGE SERVICING LLC
(*Suby of* SENECA MORTGAGE INVESTMENTS LP) ★
611 Jamison Rd Ste 1201, Elma, NY 14059-9392
Tel (716) 204-3601 *Founded/Ownrshp* 2014
Sales NA *EMP* 355
SIC 6162 Mortgage bankers
CEO: Steve Katz
Ex VP: Craig Lindauer
Sr VP: Kevin J Cooke
VP: Thomas Przybyla

D-U-N-S 07-403-8266
SENECA NATION OF INDIANS
90 Ohiyo Way, Salamanca, NY 14779
Tel (716) 945-1790 *Founded/Ownrshp* 1848
Sales NA *EMP* 4,300
SIC 9131 Indian reservation;
Pr: Barry E Snyder Sr
COO: Suzanne Kettle
**Treas:* Maurice A John Sr
Ofcr: Will Miller
Genl Mgr: Theresa Ray
Genl Mgr: Cheryl Watts
Snr PM: Murray Williams
Assoc Ed: Stephanie Crowley

D-U-N-S 13-358-6615 EXP
SENECA NORTH AMERICAN COAL LLC
CLIFFS NORTH AMERICAN COAL LLC
(*Suby of* SENECA COAL RESOURCES LLC) ★
15 Appledore Ln, Natural Bridge, VA 24578-3602
Tel (304) 369-8175 *Founded/Ownrshp* 2015
Sales 394.2MM^E *EMP* 1,000
SIC 1222 Bituminous coal-underground mining
CEO: Ronald G Stovash
**Ch:* Benjamin Statler

SENECA RESIDENTIAL
See SENECA FAMILY OF AGENCIES

D-U-N-S 00-791-2918
■ **SENECA RESOURCES CORP** (PA)
(*Suby of* NATIONAL FUEL GAS CO) ★
1201 Louisiana St Ste 400, Houston, TX 77002-5613
Tel (713) 654-2600 *Founded/Ownrshp* 1913, 1976
Sales 137.4MM^E *EMP* 250
SIC 1382 Oil & gas exploration services
Pr: Matt Cabell
Treas: Thomas Atkins
**Sr VP:* John P McGinnis
**Sr VP:* Barry L McMahan
IT Man: Shawn Rogers

D-U-N-S 00-902-2526
SENECA SAWMILL CO (OR)
90201 Highway 99 N, Eugene, OR 97402-9769
Tel (541) 689-1011 *Founded/Ownrshp* 1954
Sales 146.7MM^E *EMP* 370
SIC 2421 Sawmills & planing mills, general
Ch Bd: Aaron U Jones
Pr: Diana Ebersbacher
**CFO:* Gary Brokaw
VP: Dale Riddle
IT Man: Daniel Vance
Sls Mgr: Terri Adair

D-U-N-S 83-127-3987 IMP
SENESCO MARINE LLC
(*Suby of* REINAUER TRANSPORTATION COMPANIES LLC) ★
10 Macnaught St, North Kingstown, RI 02852-7414
Tel (401) 295-0373 *Founded/Ownrshp* 2006
Sales 110.7MM^E *EMP* 300
SIC 3731 Shipbuilding & repairing
**VP:* Michael J Foster
Exec: Cynthia Carpenter
Dir IT: Rob Anthony
Ol Cn Mgr: Mike Day

SENGENUITY
See VECTRON INTERNATIONAL INC

D-U-N-S 18-043-4797
SENIOR AEGIS COMMUNITIES LLC
AEGIS LIVING
17602 Ne Union Hill Rd, Redmond, WA 98052-3324
Tel (866) 688-5829 *Founded/Ownrshp* 1997
Sales 99.9MM^E *EMP* 2,000
SIC 8082 Home health care services
CEO: Dwayne Clark
**Pr:* Judy Meleliat
**COO:* Jerry Meyer
**CFO:* Rich Lange
**Chf Mktg O:* Sharon McCarthy
Sr VP: Michael Grisar
VP: Tracee Degrande
VP: Michael Derr
VP: Polly Miller
Ex Dir: John Carpentier
Mktg Dir: Joan Rettmann

D-U-N-S 96-819-2617
SENIOR BRANDYWINE CARE INC
525 Fellowship Rd Ste 360, Mount Laurel, NJ 08054-3406
Tel (856) 813-2000 *Founded/Ownrshp* 2004
Sales 95.7MM^E *EMP* 1,500
Accts Kpmg Llp
SIC 8741 8322 8051 Nursing & personal care facility management; Rehabilitation services; Skilled nursing care facilities
CEO: Brenda J Bacon
CFO: Steven Carmine
**CFO:* Keith Phillips
VP: Steven Heaney
**VP:* Maria Nadelstumph
Ex Dir: Christopher Gillies
MIS Dir: Dan Lawson
Dir IT: Mark Marshall
Pr Dir: Charlene Loglisci
Pr Dir: Amy Willner

D-U-N-S 14-474-5486
■ **SENIOR BROOKDALE LIVING COMMUNITIES INC**
ALTERNATIVE LIVING SERVICES
(*Suby of* BROOKDALE SENIOR LIVING) ★
6737 W Wa St Ste 2300, Milwaukee, WI 53214-5650
Tel (414) 918-5000 *Founded/Ownrshp* 2005
Sales 483.5MM^E *EMP* 9,000
SIC 8059 8051 8361 Rest home, with health care; Extended care facility; Home for the aged
CEO: Bill Sheriff
**Pr:* Mark W Ohlendorf
Ex VP: G Faye Godwin
Sr VP: Paul C Pebley

D-U-N-S 79-911-3266
SENIOR BROOKDALE LIVING INC
6737 W Wa St Ste 2300, Milwaukee, WI 53214-5650
Tel (941) 625-1220 *Founded/Ownrshp* 2005
Sales 175.2MM^E *EMP* 1,372^E
SIC 8059 Convalescent home
CEO: T Andrew Smith
**Pr:* Mark W Ohlendorf
Pr: Sheri Strobel
**COO:* Gregory B Richard
**Ex VP:* Kristin A Ferge
**Ex VP:* H Todd Kaestner
Sr VP: Geri Krupp-Gordon
VP: Timothy Cesar
VP: Tonya Cloutier
Ex Dir: Kristi Breakell
Ex Dir: Kelly Costello

SENIOR CARE
See ACTIVE DAY INC

D-U-N-S 13-051-9531
SENIOR CARE ACTION NETWORK FOUNDATION
SCAN HEALTH PLAN
3800 Kilroy Airport Way, Long Beach, CA 90806-2494
Tel (562) 989-5100 *Founded/Ownrshp* 1978
Sales NA *EMP* 857
Accts Deloitte & Touche Llp Los Ang
SIC 6324 Hospital & medical service plans
CEO: David Schmidt
COO: Susan Cameron

Section I Businesses Alphabetically

*CFO: Dennis Eder
CFO: William Rice
Ofcr: Rebecca M Learner
Sr VP: Douglas Jaques
Sr VP: Roger Lapp
Sr VP: Sherry Stanislaw
VP: David Meyer
VP: Bevann Moreland
VP: Karen Sugano
VP: Christian Zorn
Exec: Diane Yates

D-U-N-S 96-217-7858
SENIOR CARE CENTERS LLC
600 N Pearl St Ste 1100, Dallas, TX 75201-7495
Tel (214) 252-7600 Founded/Ownrshp 2009
Sales 576.5MME EMP 11,000
SIC 8741 Nursing & personal care facility management
CEO: Mark McKenzie
Pr: Mark Carden
*Pr: Andrew Kerr
Pr: Christopher Long
Pr: Brandon Tappan
*COO: Mike Brandley
COO: Ana Pico
CFO: Laurence Daspit
Ofcr: Harold Hammond
Ofcr: Kraig Turpen
VP: Sherri Harris
Dir Soc: Itoya Collins
Dir Bus: Kelly Brennan
Dir Bus: Ann Passino
Dir Bus: Jennifer Pelham
Dir Bus: Kelly Wilson

D-U-N-S 80-816-1496
SENIOR CARE COMMUNITIES INC
S C C
161 Saint Anthony Ave # 825, Saint Paul, MN 55103-2457
Tel (651) 287-6408 Founded/Ownrshp 1995
Sales 59.0MM EMP 1,000
Accts Larsonallen Llp Minneapolis
SIC 8059 Nursing home, except skilled & intermediate care facility
CEO: Susan M Landwehr
*Sec: Sandra Hesse
*VP: Richard Martin

D-U-N-S 04-421-0990
SENIOR CARE GROUP INC (PA)
1240 Marbella Plaza Dr, Tampa, FL 33619-7906
Tel (813) 341-2700 Founded/Ownrshp 1983
Sales 90.1MM EMP 2,200
Accts Pdr Certified Public Accountan
SIC 8051 Skilled nursing care facilities
Ch: David R Vaughan
*Pr: Kevin Goyer
*CFO: Katherine Chudow
Sfty Mgr: Sara Charrett

D-U-N-S 79-178-4890
SENIOR CARE INC
ELMCROFT SENIOR LIVING
700 N Hurstbourne Pkwy # 200, Louisville, KY 40222-5395
Tel (502) 753-6000 Founded/Ownrshp 2006
Sales 147.9MME EMP 1,500E
SIC 8082 Home health care services
Pr: Patrick Mulloy
Ex VP: John Wesley
Sr VP: Mike Kirzinger
*VP: Timothy Wesley
VP Sls: Melissa Owens
Mktg Dir: Robin Barich
Pr Dir: Carol Bruno
Pr Dir: Tina Lamaison
Pr Dir: Jennifer Marentette

D-U-N-S 09-435-5401
■ **SENIOR CONSECO HEALTH INSURANCE CO**
(Suby of CNO FINANCIAL GROUP INC) ★
11825 N Pennsylvania St, Carmel, IN 46032-4604
Tel (317) 817-6100 Founded/Ownrshp 1996
Sales NA EMP 374
SIC 6321 Accident & health insurance carriers
CEO: John A Powell
*Treas: Benedict J Iacovetti
Treas: Daniel Murphy
VP: Russell Bostick

SENIOR FLEXONICS
See SENIOR OPERATIONS LLC

D-U-N-S 00-609-6184 IMP
SENIOR FLEXONICS GA PRECISION
(Suby of SENIOR PLC)
5215 W Airways Ave, Franklin, WI 53132-8860
Tel (414) 817-5300 Founded/Ownrshp 1951, 2012
Sales 91.1MME EMP 400
SIC 3714 Motor vehicle engines & parts
Pr: Tom Amhardt
Treas: Lynn Hajdu

SENIOR FLEXONICS PTHWY
See WAHLCOMETROFLEX INC

D-U-N-S 10-097-7847
SENIOR HEALTH PARTNERS INC
HEALTH FIRST
(Suby of HEALTH FIRST) ★
100 Church St Fl 17, New York, NY 10007-2607
Tel (646) 273-4610 Founded/Ownrshp 2011
Sales NA EMP 50E
Accts Ernst & Young Llp New York
SIC 6321 Health insurance carriers
Pr: Gerry Polony
Treas: Randolph Guggenheimer

D-U-N-S 18-184-2337
SENIOR HOLDINGS INC
SEI
(Suby of SENIOR PLC)
300 E Devon Ave, Bartlett, IL 60103-4608
Tel (630) 837-1811 Founded/Ownrshp 2000
Sales 446.0MME EMP 2,800E
SIC 3599 2821 Hose, flexible metallic; Tubing, flexible metallic; Bellows, industrial: metal; Polytetrafluoroethylene resins (teflon)
CEO: Michael W Sheppard
Pr: Jim Mestan
COO: Ross Huntley
*CFO: Tom Baird
VP: Paul Henderson
VP: Joseph Mockus
VP: Baird Tom
*VP: Kevin R Williams
Dir Rx: Scott Cwik
Prgrm Mgr: Chuck Furst

D-U-N-S 87-886-9171
■ **SENIOR HOME CARE INC**
(Suby of KINDRED HEALTHCARE INC) ★
680 S 4th St, Louisville, KY 40202-2407
Tel (502) 596-7300 Founded/Ownrshp 2013
Sales 23.8MME EMP 1,000
SIC 8082 Home health care services
CEO: Robert Fusco
*COO: Lynne Hebert
*CFO: Mitch Morel
*Sr VP: Helen Roybal

D-U-N-S 10-336-3367
SENIOR HOUSING PROPERTIES TRUST
255 Washington St Ste 300, Newton, MA 02458-1634
Tel (617) 796-8350 Founded/Ownrshp 1998
Sales 998.7MM EMP 400E
Accts Ernst & Young Llp Boston Mas
SIC 6798 Real estate investment trusts
Pr: David J Hegarty
Mng Trst: Adam D Portnoy
CFO: Richard A Doyle Jr
CFO: Doyle Richard
CFO: Richard W Siede Jr

SENIOR INDEPENDENCE ADULT DAY
See NEBRASKA INDUSTRAIL COMPETITIVENESS SERVICE

D-U-N-S 12-575-3959
SENIOR KISCO LIVING LLC
5790 Fleet St Ste 300, Carlsbad, CA 92008-4703
Tel (760) 804-5900 Founded/Ownrshp 1997
Sales 135.3MME EMP 1,456
SIC 8322 8741 Senior citizens' center or association; Management services
Pr: Andrew S Kohlberg
*COO: Terri Novak
*CFO: Kimberly Hynek
*VP: Brenda Post
Prin: Mitchell K Brown
Ex Dir: Carole Bush
VP Mktg: Robin Craig
S&M/VP: Bob Ogle
Sls Dir: Erin Clem
Nrsg Dir: Ruth Jones

D-U-N-S 15-514-9511
SENIOR LIFESTYLE CORP
303 E Wacker Dr Ste 2400, Chicago, IL 60601-7800
Tel (312) 673-4333 Founded/Ownrshp 1985
Sales 322.4MME EMP 3,000
SIC 8052 Intermediate care facilities
Ch Bd: William B Kaplan
*Pr: John Deluca
*COO: Keven J Bennema
*COO: Lisa A Fordyce
COO: Larry Murphy
CFO: David Deeds
*CFO: Steven T Hippel
*V Ch Bd: James B Klutznick
*Ex VP: Jerrold H Frumm
Ex VP: Kayda Johnson
*Ex VP: Matthew Phillips
Sr VP: Sean Carney
Sr VP: Cherie Dupor
*Sr VP: Adam Kaplan
*Sr VP: Steven Levy
VP: Robert Gawronski

D-U-N-S 78-650-8965
SENIOR LIVING COMMUNITES LLC
3530 Toringdon Way # 204, Charlotte, NC 28277-3436
Tel (704) 246-1620 Founded/Ownrshp 2005
Sales 57.0MME EMP 1,300
SIC 8052 Intermediate care facilities
CEO: Donald O Thompson Jr
*Pr: Wallace M Saunders
COO: Mary Bowers
CFO: Micah Gerber
*Ex VP: Chris Rio
VP: Harris Ader
*VP: Stacy Carter
VP: Annette Goodwin
*VP: Katie Huffstetler
VP: Stewart Wiley
Sls Dir: Marti Ditaranto

D-U-N-S 00-801-9734
SENIOR LIVING PROPERTIES LLC (IN)
ANAHUAC HEALTHCARE CENTER
1316 S Florida St, Borger, TX 79007-6306
Tel (806) 273-3785 Founded/Ownrshp 1998, 1997
Sales 116.8MME EMP 1,850
SIC 8051 Convalescent home with continuous nursing care
CEO: James O Rogers
*Pr: James E Eden
*CFO: Larry Martin

D-U-N-S 79-060-7027
SENIOR MANAGEMENT SERVICES OF NORMANDY AT SAN ANTONIO INC
NORMANDY TERRACE NURSING REHAB
841 Rice Rd, San Antonio, TX 78220-3513
Tel (210) 648-0101 Founded/Ownrshp 2007
Sales 1.1MMM EMP 22E
SIC 8051 Skilled nursing care facilities
Pr: Troy Clanton

D-U-N-S 80-423-8108
SENIOR MBK LIVING LLC
4 Park Plz Ste 400, Irvine, CA 92614-2507
Tel (949) 242-1400 Founded/Ownrshp 2004
Sales 64.1MME EMP 1,500E
SIC 8322 Old age assistance
Pr: Terry Howard

D-U-N-S 10-694-4788 IMP
SENIOR OPERATIONS LLC
SENIOR FLEXONICS
(Suby of SENIOR PLC)
300 E Devon Ave, Bartlett, IL 60103-4608
Tel (630) 837-1811 Founded/Ownrshp 1992
Sales 799.5MME EMP 3,000
SIC 3599 Hose, flexible metallic; Tubing, flexible metallic; Bellows, industrial: metal
CEO: David Squires
CFO: Tom Baird
VP: Gerald Goodwin
VP: Amy Legenza

D-U-N-S 02-946-3796
SENIOR PHS LIVING INC
PRESBYTERIAN HOMES & SERVICES
13 Roszel Rd Ste C120, Princeton, NJ 08540-6292
Tel (609) 426-6802 Founded/Ownrshp 1916
Sales 8.4MME EMP 1,300
Accts Ernst & Young Llp
SIC 8361 8052 8051 Residential care; Intermediate care facilities; Skilled nursing care facilities
Pr: Gary Puma
*COO: Charles Mooney
*CFO: Eric Gurley

D-U-N-S 55-625-4592
SENIOR RELATED WORLD LLC
LANSING MANOR APARTMENTS
5600 Mall Dr W, Lansing, MI 48917-3253
Tel (517) 321-5058 Founded/Ownrshp 2005
Sales 17.6MME EMP 1,828
SIC 6513 Apartment building operators
Prin: Larry Lipton

D-U-N-S 12-562-1818
SENIOR RESOURCE GROUP LLC
SRG LAVIDA OPS NW SERIES
500 Stevens Ave Ste 100, Solana Beach, CA 92075-2055
Tel (858) 792-9300 Founded/Ownrshp 2000
Sales 70.7MME EMP 1,328
SIC 6513 6512 6531 6553 Apartment building operators; Nonresidential building operators; Real estate agents & managers; Cemetery subdividers & developers
CEO: Michael S Grust
*CFO: Kayda Johnson
*Ch: Martin Fenton
Ex VP: Timothy J Fox
*VP: Ron Mead
*VP: J Wickliffe Peterson
Ex Dir: Kare Valliere
Dir IT: Tony Villone
Mktg Dir: Amy Coppens
Sls Dir: Monika Einsporn

D-U-N-S 00-470-6854
SENIOR RESURRECTION SERVICES
(Suby of PRESENCE HEALTH NETWORK) ★
7435 W Talcott Ave, Chicago, IL 60631-3707
Tel (773) 774-8000 Founded/Ownrshp 2013
Sales 35.2MME EMP 1,041
SIC 8059 Nursing home, except skilled & intermediate care facility
CEO: Joseph Petoomey
Ex Dir: Matthew A Brown

D-U-N-S 61-748-6076
■ **SENIOR SBA FINANCE INC**
(Suby of SBA NETWORK SERVICES) ★
8051 Congress Ave Ste 100, Boca Raton, FL 33487-1311
Tel (561) 995-7670 Founded/Ownrshp 2003
Sales 93.6MME EMP 325
SIC 4899 6519 Television antenna construction & rental; Real property lessors
CEO: Jeffrey A Stoops

D-U-N-S 01-552-8920
SENIOR SILVERADO LIVING INC (CA)
6400 Oak Cyn Ste 200, Irvine, CA 92618-5233
Tel (949) 240-7200 Founded/Ownrshp 1996
Sales 182.6MME EMP 2,300
SIC 8059 Personal care home, with health care
CEO: George L Chapman
Pr: Rick Barker
Pr: Kathy Greene
*Pr: Loren B Shook
*CFO: Thomas Croal
Sr VP: John T Peters
Sr VP: Randy Platt
*Sr VP: Stephen Winner
VP: Michelle Egerer
VP: Ray Oborn
Off Mgr: Millie Alexander

D-U-N-S 07-144-9748
SENIOR SPRINGPOINT LIVING INC
PRESBYTERIAN HOMES & SERVICES
4814 Outlook Dr Ste 201, Wall Township, NJ 07753-6812
Tel (609) 987-8900 Founded/Ownrshp 1916
Sales 128.8MM EMP 1,279
Accts Baker Tilly Virchow Krause Llp
SIC 8059 8741 Rest home, with health care; Management services
Pr: Gary Puma
*CFO: Eric Gurley
CFO: Garrett Midget
CFO: Garett Midgett
Sr VP: Maureen Cafferty
Sr VP: Joseph T Claffey
Sr VP: Garrett Midgett III
Sr VP: Linda Rose
Sr VP: Pamela L Smith
Dir Risk M: Jim McGrath
Dir IT: Ray Leenig

D-U-N-S 36-293-7138
SENIOR TEALWOOD LIVING
TEALWOOD CARE CENTERS
7400 W 109th St, Minneapolis, MN 55438-2374
Tel (952) 888-2923 Founded/Ownrshp 1989
Sales 50.6MME EMP 1,300
SIC 8051 8741 Skilled nursing care facilities; Nursing & personal care facility management
Pr: Howard A Groff
*COO: Greg Brown
*CFO: Molly Toulouse
*VP: Tim Bush
*VP: Steven L Harl
*VP: Gail Sheridan

SENIOR VILLAGE NURSING HOME
See LOUISIANA EXTENDED CARE CENTERS INC

D-U-N-S 80-321-6261
SENIOR VINTAGE MANAGEMENT INC
VINTAGE SENIOR LIVING
23 Corporate Plaza Dr # 190, Newport Beach, CA 92660-7943
Tel (949) 719-4080 Founded/Ownrshp 2002
Sales 69.9MME EMP 1,710E
SIC 8059 Rest home, with health care
CEO: Brian Flornes
*Pr: Vicki Clark
*CFO: Mark Schulz
*VP: Eric Davidson
Exec: Jay Pagaduan
Off Mgr: Shirley Durham
CTO: Mike Post
Sales Exec: Jenny McFarland

SENN DUNN INSURANCE
See SDM&R INC

D-U-N-S 61-009-9744 IMP/EXP
SENSATA TECHNOLOGIES INC
(Suby of SENSATA TECHNOLOGIES HOLDING N.V.)
529 Pleasant St, Attleboro, MA 02703-2421
Tel (508) 236-3800 Founded/Ownrshp 2006
Sales 2.0MMME EMP 19,000E
SIC 3679 Electronic circuits
Pr: Martha Sullivan
*COO: Jeffrey Cote
*CFO: Paul Vasington
Treas: Bill Perry
*Ex VP: Steven Beringhause
*Sr VP: Allisha Elliott
VP: Harry Fox
VP: Jacob Sayer
Dir Rx: Mike Bennett
Dir Bus: Klaus Rost
Prgrm Mgr: Eric Alsfeld

D-U-N-S 96-156-0898
SENSATA TECHNOLOGIES INDIANA INC
(Suby of SENSATA TECHNOLOGIES INC) ★
529 Pleasant St, Attleboro, MA 02703-2421
Tel (508) 236-3245 Founded/Ownrshp 2008
Sales 245.5MME EMP 615E
SIC 3676 3625 Thermistors, except temperature sensors; Flow actuated electrical switches
Pr: Steven Dow
*CFO: James Butler

D-U-N-S 93-794-1052 IMP/EXP
■ **SENSIENT COLORS LLC**
SENSIENT PHARMACEUTICAL
(Suby of SENSIENT TECHNOLOGIES CORP) ★
2515 N Jefferson Ave, Saint Louis, MO 63106-1939
Tel (314) 889-7600 Founded/Ownrshp 2010
Sales 166.4MME EMP 350E
SIC 2816 Color pigments
Pr: Paul Manning
*CFO: John Crumrine
*CFO: Peter Spears
Opers Mgr: Vince Ciaramitaro

D-U-N-S 04-685-8572 IMP/EXP
SENSIENT DEHYDRATED FLAVORS CO
151 S Walnut Rd, Turlock, CA 95380-5127
Tel (209) 667-2777 Founded/Ownrshp 1992
Sales 118.1MME EMP 550
SIC 2034

D-U-N-S 03-252-2864 IMP/EXP
■ **SENSIENT FLAVORS LLC**
(Suby of SENSIENT TECHNOLOGIES CORP) ★
5600 W Raymond St, Indianapolis, IN 46241-4343
Tel (317) 243-3521 Founded/Ownrshp 1986
Sales 348.7MME EMP 1,500
SIC 2087 Flavoring extracts & syrups
Pr: Ralph Pickles
CTO: Mark Austin
CTO: Peter Morelli
Dir IT: Miguel Graniello
Mktg Mgr: Eric Dick
Sales Asso: Rechelle Huck

SENSIENT PHARMACEUTICAL
See SENSIENT COLORS LLC

D-U-N-S 00-608-8884 IMP/EXP
▲ **SENSIENT TECHNOLOGIES CORP**
777 E Wisconsin Ave # 1100, Milwaukee, WI 53202-5304
Tel (414) 271-6755 Founded/Ownrshp 1882
Sales 1.3MMM EMP 4,032
Accts Ernst & Young Llp Milwaukee
Tkr Sym SXT Exch NYS
SIC 2087 2099 Flavoring extracts & syrups: Beverage bases; Food colorings; Food preparations; Yeast; Seasonings: dry mixes
Ch Bd: Paul Manning
CFO: Stephen J Rolfs
Treas: John F Collopy
Treas: John Collopy
VP: Jeff Makal
VP: Jeffrey T Makal
VP: John J Manning
CTO: Kurt Burmeister
QA Dir: Alexander Guerrero
Opers Mgr: Matt Thomas
Plnt Mgr: Tushar Patel
Board of Directors: Hank Brown, Joseph Carleone, Edward H Cichurski, Fergus M Clydesdale, Deborah McKeithan-Gebhardt, Donald W Landry, Scott Morrison, Elaine R Wedral, Essie Whitelaw

D-U-N-S 78-398-6086 IMP
■ **SENSITECH INC**
(*Suby of* UNITED TECHNOLOGIES CARRIER) ★
800 Cummings Ctr Ste 258x, Beverly, MA 01915-6197
Tel (978) 927-7033 *Founded/Ownrshp* 1991
Sales 120.8MM^E *EMP* 430
SIC 3826 3823 3822 Environmental testing equipment; Industrial instrmnts msrmnt display/control process variable; Auto controls regulating residntl & coml environmt & applncs
Pr: Mike Hurton
**Treas:* Joseph Gest
**Treas:* Christopher Witzky
Ex VP: John C Carr
**VP:* Tom Chase
VP: Robin Olson
Prgrm Mgr: Hanan S Hassan
Prgrm Mgr: Craig Marotz
CIO: Tung Nguyen
MIS Dir: Mohamed Hassim
IT Man: Ross Blum

D-U-N-S 04-492-4769
SENSORMATIC ELECTRONICS LLC
(*Suby of* TYCO INTEGRATED SECURITY LLC) ★
6600 Congress Ave, Boca Raton, FL 33487-1213
Tel (561) 912-6000 *Founded/Ownrshp* 2001
Sales 252.5MM^E *EMP* 2,500
SIC 7382 Security systems services; Confinement surveillance systems maintenance & monitoring
VP: Kevin Dasilva

D-U-N-S 18-833-7356
SENSORMATIC INTERNATIONAL INC
TYCO
(*Suby of* SENSORMATIC ELECTRONICS LLC) ★
6600 Congress Ave, Boca Raton, FL 33487-1213
Tel (561) 912-6000 *Founded/Ownrshp* 1976
Sales 252.5MM^E *EMP* 700
Accts Pricewater House Coopers Llp
SIC 5065 Electronic parts; Closed circuit television
Ch Bd: Ronald G Assaf
**COO:* Bob Vanourek
**VP:* Richard Decook
**VP:* James P Forman
VP: Hubert Patterson
**VP:* Gerd Witter
Rgnl Mgr: Michael Upton
Web Dev: Kurt Miller

D-U-N-S 80-923-9622
■ **SENSORYEFFECTS INC**
(*Suby of* BALCHEM CORP) ★
13723 Rverport Dr Ste 201, Maryland Heights, MO 63043
Tel (314) 291-5444 *Founded/Ownrshp* 2014
Sales 278.0MM *EMP* 300
SIC 2087 Extracts, flavoring
CEO: Charles Nicolais
Exec: Kathy Singler
Dir Rx: Jeff Borchers

D-U-N-S 83-141-1793
SENSUS (BERMUDA 2) LTD
8601 Six Forks Rd, Raleigh, NC 27615-5276
Tel (919) 845-4000 *Founded/Ownrshp* 1986
Sales 227.8MM^E *EMP* 3,691
SIC 3824 3363 3491 Gas meters, domestic & large capacity: industrial; Water meters; Aluminum die-castings; Industrial valves
Pr: Joseph McCormick
COO: Mike Tracy
CFO: Courtney Enghauser
Ex VP: Jose Hernandez
Ex VP: William Yeates
**VP:* Jonathan F Boucher
Board of Directors: J Jack Watson, Nicole V Agnew, David W Zalaznick, Gerald J Cardinale, Louis D'ambrosio, Daniel W Harness, John W Jordan II, Bryan Kelln, H Russel Lemcke, Eugene R McGrath, Thomas H Quinn

D-U-N-S 36-117-4139 IMP
SENSUS METERING SYSTEMS-NORTH AMERICA INC
450 N Gallatin Ave, Uniontown, PA 15401-2458
Tel (724) 439-7700 *Founded/Ownrshp* 2003
Sales 137.1MM^E *EMP* 739
SIC 3824 Water meters
Pr: Dan W Harness
CFO: Ken Saska
CIO: Walter Kirkland
Netwrk Mgr: Theresa Dubos
Mktg Mgr: Tim Harriger
Mktg Mgr: Rick Straley
Sls Mgr: Doug Neely
Board of Directors: Edgar P De Vylder, Jon Thompson

D-U-N-S 62-066-4599 IMP/EXP
SENSUS USA INC
8601 Six Forks Rd Ste 700, Raleigh, NC 27615-5277
Tel (919) 845-4000 *Founded/Ownrshp* 2003
Sales 600.1MM^E *EMP* 3,691
SIC 3824 3363 2891 3491

D-U-N-S 15-105-8336
SENTAGE CORP
DSG PITTSBURGH
801 12th Ave N, Minneapolis, MN 55411-4211
Tel (412) 431-3353 *Founded/Ownrshp* 1989
Sales 100.0MM *EMP* 600
SIC 8072 Dental laboratories; Crown & bridge production; Denture production; Artificial teeth production
CEO: Kirby Picle
VP: Kim Jones
VP: Charlie Meneguzzo
**VP:* Ojars A Papedis
Genl Mgr: Donna Jordon

SENTARA BELLEHARBOUR
See SENTARA LOUISE OBICI MEMORIAL HOSPITAL

SENTARA CANCER NETWORK (NORFOL
See SENTARA ENTERPRISES

SENTARA CANCER NETWORK (NORFOL
See SENTARA LIFE CARE CORP

SENTARA CANCER NETWORK (NORFOL
See OPTIMA HEALTH PLAN

SENTARA CANCER NETWORK (NORFOL
See SENTARA PRINCESS ANNE HOSPITAL

D-U-N-S 04-359-7440
SENTARA CAREPLEX HOSPITAL
3000 Coliseum Dr, Hampton, VA 23666-5963
Tel (757) 736-1000 *Founded/Ownrshp* 2010
Sales 220.6MM *EMP* 11^E
SIC 8062 General medical & surgical hospitals
Prin: Kathleen E Carlson

SENTARA CNCER NTWRK NORFOLK CI
See SENTARA HEALTHCARE

D-U-N-S 07-857-1921
SENTARA ENTERPRISES
SENTARA CANCER NETWORK (NORFOL
(*Suby of* SENTARA CNCER NTWRK NORFOLK CI) ★
6015 Poplar Hall Dr, Norfolk, VA 23502-3819
Tel (757) 455-7000 *Founded/Ownrshp* 2012
Sales 123.2MM *EMP* 6^E
SIC 8011 Offices & clinics of medical doctors
Prin: David L Bernd

D-U-N-S 10-171-8138 IMP
SENTARA HEALTHCARE
SENTARA CNCER NTWRK NORFOLK CI
6015 Poplar Hall Dr, Norfolk, VA 23502-3819
Tel (757) 455-7976 *Founded/Ownrshp* 1982
Sales 4.8MMM *EMP* 28,000
Accts Kpmg Llp Norfolk Va
SIC 8062 6324 General medical & surgical hospitals; Hospital, medical school affiliation; Hospital & medical service plans
Pr: David L Bernd
**Pr:* Howard Kern
**Pr:* Kern Howard P
CFO: Robert A Broerman
**CFO:* Robert A Broermann
Ofcr: Phyllis Stoneburner
Sr VP: Terry Gilliland
Sr VP: Bertram S Reese
VP: Mary L Blunt
VP: Michael Gentry
VP: Vicky Gray
VP: Grace Hines
VP: Ken Krakaur
VP: Vikki Lorenz
VP: Sylvia Richendollar
VP: Fred Schriever
VP: Douglas Thompson
VP: Lance Torcom
VP Bus Dev: Katherine Harrison
Dir Risk M: Jacque Mitchell
Dir Rx: Betsy Early

D-U-N-S 96-736-0475
SENTARA HOSPITALS - NORFOLK
SENTARA NORFOLK GENERAL HOSP
(*Suby of* SENTARA CNCER NTWRK NORFOLK CI) ★
600 Gresham Dr, Norfolk, VA 23507-1904
Tel (757) 388-3000 *Founded/Ownrshp* 1972
Sales 791.4MM *EMP* 159^E
Accts Kpmg Llp Norfolk Va
SIC 8062 General medical & surgical hospitals
CEO: David L Bernd
**Pr:* Howard Kern
**Pr:* Kern Howard P
**CFO:* Robert A Broermann
VP: Peggy Evans
Surgeon: Stephen D Wohlgemuth

D-U-N-S 14-823-2150
SENTARA LIFE CARE CORP
SENTARA CANCER NETWORK (NORFOL
(*Suby of* SENTARA CNCER NTWRK NORFOLK CI) ★
249 S Newtown Rd, Norfolk, VA 23502-5718
Tel (757) 892-5500 *Founded/Ownrshp* 1982
Sales 91.2MM *EMP* 1,191
SIC 8051 Convalescent home with continuous nursing care
Pr: Steven Gold
**Pr:* Mary Blunt

D-U-N-S 04-459-7909
SENTARA LOUISE OBICI MEMORIAL HOSPITAL
SENTARA BELLEHARBOUR
2800 Godwin Blvd, Suffolk, VA 23434-8038
Tel (757) 934-4827 *Founded/Ownrshp* 1959
Sales 38.0MM^E *EMP* 1,200
SIC 8062 General medical & surgical hospitals
Pr: Kurt Hofelich

D-U-N-S 10-171-8195
SENTARA MEDICAL GROUP
NDC MEDICAL CENTER
(*Suby of* SENTARA CNCER NTWRK NORFOLK CI) ★
835 Glenrock Rd, Norfolk, VA 23502-3767
Tel (757) 252-3070 *Founded/Ownrshp* 1983
Sales 258.1MM *EMP* 331
Accts Kpmg Llp Norfolk Virginia
SIC 8093 8082 Specialty outpatient clinics; Home health care services
Ch Bd: Kenneth R Perry
**Ch Bd:* Catherine S Brisland
**Pr:* Donald V Jellig
**Pr:* Maizel MD David R
**Ch:* Rose MD Meredith B

SENTARA NORFOLK GENERAL HOSP
See SENTARA HOSPITALS - NORFOLK

SENTARA NORTHERN VA MED CTR
See POTOMAC HOSPITAL CORP OF PRINCE WILLIAM

D-U-N-S 85-978-7207
SENTARA PRINCESS ANNE HOSPITAL
SENTARA CANCER NETWORK (NORFOL
(*Suby of* SENTARA CNCER NTWRK NORFOLK CI) ★
1925 Glenn Mitchell Dr, Virginia Beach, VA 23456-0170
Tel (757) 507-1660 *Founded/Ownrshp* 2010
Sales 228.7MM *EMP* 1,100
SIC 8062 General medical & surgical hospitals; Hospital, medical school affiliation
Pr: Howard R Kern
**Ch:* David L Bernd
**Treas:* Robert Broermann
**VP:* Bruce Robertson

SENTARA RMH MEDICAL CENTER
See ROCKINGHAM HEALTH CARE INC

D-U-N-S 06-600-1892
SENTARA RMH MEDICAL CENTER
(*Suby of* SENTARA CNCER NTWRK NORFOLK CI) ★
2010 Health Campus Dr, Rockingham, VA 22801-8679
Tel (540) 433-4100 *Founded/Ownrshp* 1908
Sales 408.9MM *EMP* 1,892
Accts Kpmg Llp Norfolk Va
SIC 8062 General medical & surgical hospitals
Pr: James D Krauss
**Ch:* Ann E C Homan
**Treas:* J Michael Burris
VP: Mark Zimmerman
Dir Rx: Laura Adkins
Genl Mgr: Katherine Robinson
Off Mgr: Steve Hall
IT Man: Portia Gibson
Netwrk Mgr: Brett Lykins
Opers Mgr: Darla Macdonald
Obsttrcn: Teresa Boshart-Yoder

D-U-N-S 07-476-0331
SENTARA WILLIAMSBURG REGIONAL MEDICAL CENTER
WILLIAMSBURG COMMUNITY HOSP
(*Suby of* SENTARA CNCER NTWRK NORFOLK CI) ★
100 Sentara Cir, Williamsburg, VA 23188-5713
Tel (757) 984-6000 *Founded/Ownrshp* 2002
Sales 142.8MM *EMP* 1,150
Accts Kpmg Llp Norfolk Va
SIC 8062 General medical & surgical hospitals
VP: Robert Graves
**Pr:* Kenneth M Krakaur
**Ch:* David L Bernd
**Sec:* Howard P Kern
Doctor: Megan Reuter

D-U-N-S 36-063-8902
SENTEL CORP
(*Suby of* R&R ENTERPRISES INC) ★
2800 Eisenhower Ave # 300, Alexandria, VA 22314-5209
Tel (571) 481-2000 *Founded/Ownrshp* 1986
Sales 94.0MM *EMP* 350
SIC 8711 8742 8741

SENTINEL
See SPRINT WASTE SERVICES LP

D-U-N-S 96-800-2589
SENTINEL ACQUISITION HOLDINGS INC
2000 Avenue Of The Stars, Los Angeles, CA 90067-4700
Tel (310) 201-4100 *Founded/Ownrshp* 2011
Sales 291.4MM^E *EMP* 1,463
SIC 7371 7379 Computer software systems analysis & design, custom;
Pr: Matt Cwiertnia

D-U-N-S 93-889-1470
SENTINEL CAPITAL PARTNERS LLC
330 Madison Ave Fl 27, New York, NY 10017-5019
Tel (212) 688-3100 *Founded/Ownrshp* 1995
Sales 801.7MM^E *EMP* 6,403
SIC 5812 Restaurant, family: chain
Mng Pt: David S Lobel
**Pt:* Eric D Bommer
**Pt:* James D Coady
**Pt:* Michael J Fabian
**Pt:* John F McCormack
**Pt:* Paul F Murphy
**Pt:* C Scott Perry
**CFO:* Douglas G Levy
Mng Dir: Joseph J Catalano

D-U-N-S 00-408-1964
■ **SENTINEL COMMUNICATIONS NEWS VENTURES INC**
ORLANDO SENTINNEL MEDIA GROUP
(*Suby of* TRIBUNE MEDIA CO) ★
633 N Orange Ave, Orlando, FL 32801-1325
Tel (407) 420-5000 *Founded/Ownrshp* 1885, 1893
Sales 95.2MM^E *EMP* 779
SIC 2711 Commercial printing & newspaper publishing combined
CEO: Howard Greenberg
Pr: John Dorlando
CFO: Thomas Brown
Sr VP: Avido Khahaifa
VP: Bonita Burton
VP: Bert Ortiz
Admn Mgr: Donna Maddamma
Dir IT: Mike Sutton
Plnt Mgr: Charlotte Hall
Prd Mgr: Frank Busby
Sales Exec: Stephanie Covatta

SENTINEL COMPUTER SERVICES
See SENTINEL TECHNOLOGIES INC

D-U-N-S 14-490-9553
SENTINEL TECHNOLOGIES INC
SENTINEL COMPUTER SERVICES
2550 Warrenville Rd, Downers Grove, IL 60515-1723
Tel (630) 769-4300 *Founded/Ownrshp* 1985
Sales 105.4MM^E *EMP* 400
SIC 7378 1731

D-U-N-S 94-762-9754
■ **SENTINEL TRANSPORTATION LLC**
(*Suby of* E I DU PONT DE NEMOURS AND CO) ★
3521 Silverside Rd Ste 2a, Wilmington, DE 19810-4914
Tel (302) 477-1640 *Founded/Ownrshp* 2002
Sales 92.8MM^E *EMP* 600
SIC 4212 Local trucking, without storage

D-U-N-S 96-342-6262
SENTIO HEALTHCARE PROPERTIES INC
189 S Orange Ave Ste 1700, Orlando, FL 32801-3260
Tel (407) 999-7679 *Founded/Ownrshp* 2006
Sales 115.3MM *EMP* 2^E
Accts Kpmg Llp Orlando Florida
SIC 6798 Real estate investment trusts
Pr: John Mark Ramsey
CFO: Sharon C Kaiser

SENTRY GROUP
See SENTRY SAFE INC

D-U-N-S 05-766-6877
SENTRY INSURANCE A MUTUAL CO
1800 Northpoint Dr, Stevens Point, WI 54481-1283
Tel (715) 346-6000 *Founded/Ownrshp* 1914
Sales NA *EMP* 4,830
SIC 6331 6311 6411 6321 Fire, marine & casualty insurance: mutual; Life insurance carriers; Insurance agents, brokers & service; Accident & health insurance
CEO: Dale R Schuh
Pr: Michael Dietry
Pr: Peter McPartland
Pr: Elisha Robinson
Pr: Rob Yeiser
CFO: Dewey A Gantz
Treas: William J Lohr
Ofcr: Mark R Trautschold
Ex VP: James J Weishan
Sr VP: Mark R Hackl
Sr VP: James D Stitzlein
Sr VP: James Weishan
VP: Ken Erler
VP: Jim Frank
VP: David E Hartman
VP: WEI Huang
VP: Kalin Lamp
VP: Jane Laux
VP: Michael J Williams
VP: Dan Wuest
Exec: Peter G Anhalt
Board of Directors: Edmund R Steinike

D-U-N-S 00-794-7732
SENTRY LIFE INSURANCE CO
(*Suby of* SENTRY INSURANCE A MUTUAL CO) ★
1800 Northpoint Dr, Stevens Point, WI 54481-1253
Tel (715) 346-6000 *Founded/Ownrshp* 1958
Sales NA *EMP* 2,000
SIC 6411 6321 Insurance agents, brokers & service; Accident insurance carriers; Health insurance carriers
Pr: Dale Schuh
VP: Susan E Phillips

D-U-N-S 00-220-6480 IMP/EXP
■ **SENTRY SAFE INC** (NY)
SENTRY GROUP
(*Suby of* MASTER LOCK CO LLC) ★
137 W Forest Hill Ave, Oak Creek, WI 53154-2901
Tel (585) 381-4900 *Founded/Ownrshp* 1954, 2014
Sales 162.5MM^E *EMP* 600
SIC 3089 3499 2522 Plastic containers, except foam; Boxes, plastic; Safes & vaults, metal; Safe deposit boxes or chests, metal; Office furniture, except wood
Ch: James B Brush
**CFO:* Robert Fetterman
DP Dir: Terri Mentzer
QA Dir: Adina Goltsman
Dir IT: John Matrachisia
Web Dev: Anthony Desalvo
Mfg Dir: Nancy Hoyt
Manager: Michael Sanguinito
Natl Sales: Bill Gefteas
Sls&Mrk Ex: Sondra Stegemann
VP Mktg: Bill Bean

D-U-N-S 18-338-7885 IMP
SENTRY SUPPLY INC
SUPERIOR SUPPLY & STEEL
318 S Cities Service Hwy, Sulphur, LA 70663-6406
Tel (337) 625-2300 *Founded/Ownrshp* 1980
Sales 301.7MM^E *EMP* 250
SIC 5085 5051 Industrial supplies; Valves, pistons & fittings; Pipe & tubing, steel; Steel
Pr: C Steve Mitchell
**CFO:* John Ezernack
**Sec:* Cathy C Mitchell
**Ex VP:* Wayne Lebert
VP: Bill Kotcher
Dist Mgr: Kelly Broussard
Dist Mgr: Veronica Orr
CIO: Paul Lancaster
IT Man: Jennifer Guillory
Sales Asso: Yvonne Anderson
Sales Asso: Brent Brock

D-U-N-S 14-626-5173
SENTURE LLC
460 Industrial Blvd, London, KY 40741-7285
Tel (606) 878-4205 *Founded/Ownrshp* 2003
Sales 85.0MM^E *EMP* 340
SIC 7379 7389 7374 7373 8742 Computer related maintenance services; Telephone services; Telemarketing services; Data entry service; Computer systems analysis & design; Management consulting services
Sr VP: Jim Gayhart
Genl Mgr: Randall Cobb
Genl Mgr: Stephanie Fouts
Dir IT: Scott Noble

D-U-N-S 07-862-8121
SEOHAN-NTN DRIVESHAFT USA CORP (AL)
(*Suby of* SEOHAN INDUSTRY CO.,LTD)
246 Teague Ct, Auburn, AL 36832-4362
Tel (334) 707-6863 *Founded/Ownrshp* 2007
Sales 104.9MM *EMP* 64
SIC 3559 Automotive related machinery
CEO: Seon Kae Kim

SEOYAN E-HWA
See SEOYON E-HWA INTERIOR SYSTEMS ALABAMA LLC

D-U-N-S 61-037-1564 IMP
SEOYON E-HWA INTERIOR SYSTEMS ALABAMA LLC
SEOYAN E-HWA
(Suby of SEOYON CO., LTD.)
200 Craig Industrial Park, Selma, AL 36701-8103
Tel (334) 410-7100 Founded/Ownrshp 1972
Sales 134.0MM EMP 406
Accts Choi Kim & Park Llp Montgom
SIC 3089 Automotive parts, plastic
Ql Cn Mgr: In Jang

D-U-N-S 17-132-8193 IMP
SEPHORA USA INC
(Suby of LVMH MOET HENNESSY LOUIS VUITTON INC) ★
525 Market St Fl 32, San Francisco, CA 94105-2740
Tel (415) 284-3300 Founded/Ownrshp 1999
Sales 1.1MMM^E EMP 5,000
SIC 5999 Toiletries, cosmetics & perfumes
Pr: Calvin McDonald
*CFO: Alexis Rollier
*Ex VP: Julie Bornstein
*Ex VP: Mary Herald
*Ex VP: Satish Malhotra
Sr VP: Margarita Arriagata
*Sr VP: Christie Jack
*Sr VP: Mary Beth Laughton
Sr VP: Osh O'Crowley
*Sr VP: Artemis Patrick
*Sr VP: Philippe Pinatel
*Sr VP: Mike Racer
*Sr VP: Savio Thattil

SEPTA
See SOUTHEASTERN PENNSYLVANIA TRANSPORTATION AUTHORITY

D-U-N-S 00-137-4727 IMP/EXP
■ **SEQUA CORP**
KOLLSMAN INSTRUMENT DIVISION
(Suby of CARLYLE GROUP L P) ★
3999 Rca Blvd, Palm Beach Gardens, FL 33410-4219
Tel (201) 343-1122 Founded/Ownrshp 1929, 2007
Sales 1.1MMM^E EMP 1,300
SIC 3724 3764 3812 3699 3845 3542 Aircraft engines & engine parts; Airfoils, aircraft engine; Rocket motors, aircraft; Guided missile & space vehicle propulsion unit parts; Rocket motors, guided missiles; Propulsion units for guided missiles & space vehicles; Search & navigation equipment; Infrared object detection equipment; Missile guidance systems & equipment; Aircraft flight instruments; Flight simulators (training aids), electronic; Electromedical apparatus; Automated blood & body fluid analyzers, except laboratory; Metal container making machines: cans, etc.
CEO: Armand F Lauzon
Pr: Gerard M Dombek
Pr: Carlo Luzzatto
Pr: Kathleen Peskens
CEO: Martin Weinstein
CFO: Donna Costello
CFO: Keith Howe
Ex VP: Kenneth J Binder
Sr VP: John J Dowling III
Sr VP: Robert F Ellis
VP: Michael E Goodin
VP: William P Ksiazek
VP: Dunlap Marie
VP: Leonard P Pasculli
VP: Steven Sehuas
VP: James Sides
Board of Directors: Mark V Rosenker, Stefan Weingartner

D-U-N-S 00-484-1086
SEQUACHEE VALLEY ELECTRIC COOPERATIVE INC (TN)
SVEC
512 S Cedar Ave, South Pittsburg, TN 37380-1310
Tel (423) 837-8605 Founded/Ownrshp 1939
Sales 85.3MM EMP 74
Accts Sequachee Valley Electric Coop
SIC 4911 Distribution, electric power
*CFO: Floyd Hatfield
*Ch: Michael Jordon
VP: Beth Duggar
VP: Danny Kirkendoll
VP: Bobby Skyles
*Prin: Bob Matheny

SEQUEL SCHOOLS
See SEQUEL YOUTH AND FAMILY SERVICES LLC

D-U-N-S 96-278-6351
SEQUEL TSI HOLDINGS LLC
SEQUEL YOUTH AND FAMILY SVCS
(Suby of SEQUEL SCHOOLS) ★
1131 Eagletree Ln Sw # 300, Huntsville, AL 35801-6491
Tel (256) 880-3339 Founded/Ownrshp 2009
Sales 25.3MM^E EMP 1,100
SIC 8361 8322 Residential care for children; Child related social services
CEO: John Stupak
*Ch Bd: John Ripley
*Ch Bd: Adam Shapiro
*CFO: Sybil Potts
*VP: Steve Gilbert
*VP: Mandy Moses
Ex Dir: Paula Garay

D-U-N-S 07-854-4890
SEQUEL YOUTH AND FAMILY SERVICES LLC (IA)
SEQUEL SCHOOLS
1131 Eagletree Ln Sw, Huntsville, AL 35801-6491
Tel (256) 880-3339 Founded/Ownrshp 2006
Sales 154.0MM EMP 2,500
SIC 8322 8361 Individual & family services; Residential care
CEO: John Stupak
*CFO: Sybil Potts
*Ch: Jay Ripley
*Ch: John Ripley
*Chf Cred: Jack Rachk
Bd of Dir: Mandy Moses Board
Ofcr: Ed Irby
Sr VP: Beverly Richard
*VP: Steve Gilbert
Mktg Dir: Yvonne Gurule

SEQUEL YOUTH AND FAMILY SVCS
See SEQUEL TSI HOLDINGS LLC

D-U-N-S 80-883-9968 IMP/EXP
■ **SEQUENOM CENTER FOR MOLECULAR MEDICINE LLC**
SEQUENOM LABORATORIES
(Suby of SEQUENOM INC) ★
3595 John Hopkins Ct, San Diego, CA 92121-1121
Tel (858) 202-9051 Founded/Ownrshp 2008
Sales 89.7MM EMP 400
SIC 8071 Medical laboratories
*Treas: Carolyn D Beaver
*VP: Daniel Grosu
Dir IT: Ryan Blitz
Ql Cn Mgr: Marty R Young
Board of Directors: Daniel S Grosu

D-U-N-S 96-000-4026
■ **SEQUENOM INC**
(Suby of LABORATORY CORP OF AMERICA HOLDINGS) ★
3595 John Hopkins Ct, San Diego, CA 92121-1121
Tel (858) 202-9000 Founded/Ownrshp 2016
Sales 128.2MM EMP 434
SIC 8731 Biological research
Pr: Dirk Van Den Boom
CFO: Carolyn D Beaver
Chf Mktg O: Daniel S Grosu
Ofcr: Mathias Ehrich
Sr VP: Jeffrey D Linton
Sr VP: Rob Lozuk
Sr VP: Robert J Lozuk
Sr VP: Robin G Weiner

SEQUENOM LABORATORIES
See SEQUENOM CENTER FOR MOLECULAR MEDICINE LLC

D-U-N-S 61-207-5846
■ **SEQUENT ENERGY MANAGEMENT LP**
(Suby of SOUTHERN CO GAS) ★
1200 Smith St, Houston, TX 77002-4313
Tel (832) 397-1700 Founded/Ownrshp 2001
Sales 113.6MM^E EMP 150
SIC 4924 Natural gas distribution
Pr: Peter Tumminello
CFO: Brian Little
Sr VP: Marshall Lang
VP: Ben Abramson
VP: Kelly Adams
VP: Berney Aucoin
VP: Lance J Roth
Mng Dir: John Childers
Off Mgr: Consuelo Lujan
Sls Mgr: Bill Kickert
Corp Couns: Jacques Hodges

D-U-N-S 08-011-0917
▲ **SEQUENTIAL BRANDS GROUP INC**
5 Bryant Park Fl 30, New York, NY 10001
Tel (646) 564-2577 Founded/Ownrshp 2015
Sales 183.7MM^E EMP 279^E
Tkr Sym SQBG Exch NAS
SIC 7389 Advertising, promotional & trade show services
CEO: Yehuda Shmidman
Pr: Andrew Cooper
CFO: Gary Klein
Ex VP: Chad Wagenheim
Dir IT: Joe Wertz

D-U-N-S 07-466-5258
SEQUOIA HEALTH SERVICES
SEQUOIA HOSPITAL
(Suby of DIGNITY HEALTH) ★
170 Alameda De Las Pulgas, Redwood City, CA 94062-2751
Tel (650) 369-5811 Founded/Ownrshp 1998
Sales 258.7MM EMP 1,167^E
Accts Maze & Associates Pleasant Hi
SIC 8062 General medical & surgical hospitals
Bd of Dir: Kim Griffin
Bd of Dir: Malcolm Macnaughton
Dir Rad: Michael D Hollett
Sfty Dirs: Debi Simon
Ansthlgy: Michael Fahmy
Ansthlgy: Thomas A Gaffey
Ansthlgy: Mark Gjolaj
Ansthlgy: Nichole R Herbert
Ansthlgy: Shirley X Liu
Ansthlgy: Lewis S Margolis
Ansthlgy: Daniel J McFarland

SEQUOIA HOSPITAL
See SEQUOIA HEALTH SERVICES

D-U-N-S 96-549-4490
■ **SEQUOIA SPRINGS COTTAGES**
SEQUOIA SPRNG ASSISTED LIVING
(Suby of BROOKDALE SENIOR LIVING) ★
3131 Elliott Ave Ste 500, Seattle, WA 98121-1032
Tel (206) 298-2909 Founded/Ownrshp 2010
Sales 4.5MM^E EMP 2,012^E
SIC 8051 Skilled nursing care facilities
Prin: Robert Bateman
VP: Randy Cyphers
Exec: Liberty Stansberry
Prin: Eric Mendelsohn

SEQUOIA SPRNG ASSISTED LIVING
See SEQUOIA SPRINGS COTTAGES

D-U-N-S 08-721-0787
SEQUOIA UNION HIGH SCHOOL DISTRICT
480 James Ave, Redwood City, CA 94062-1041
Tel (650) 369-1411 Founded/Ownrshp 1895
Sales 150.4MM EMP 626
SIC 8211 Public senior high school; Public special education school; Public adult education school
Treas: Jayne Smith
Off Admin: Susie Hendrick
Off Admin: Natasha Rivera
IT Man: Julio Calles
Trfc Dir: Sandy Wagerman
Plnt Mgr: Cherry Stephens
Psych: Edith Bennett

D-U-N-S 07-417-8351 IMP/EXP
SERCEL INC
(Suby of SERCEL HOLDING)
17200 Park Row, Houston, TX 77084-4925
Tel (281) 492-6688 Founded/Ownrshp 1982
Sales 126.5MM^E EMP 600
SIC 3829 Geophysical & meteorological testing equipment
CEO: Thierry Le Rou
*Pr: George Wood
*CEO: Thierry Le Roux
*CFO: Kenneth Fitts
VP: Robin Eillis
Exec: Richard Miles
Exec: Amy Vierling
IT Man: Jeff Owens
IT Man: Serge Poupis
Sftwr Eng: Bill Roche
Sftwr Eng: Brett Thompson

D-U-N-S 03-668-2813
SERCO GROUP INC
(Suby of SERCO GROUP PLC)
1818 Library St Ste 1000, Reston, VA 20190-6276
Tel (703) 939-6000 Founded/Ownrshp 1996
Sales 232.0MM^E EMP 16,000
SIC 8744 Facilities support services
CEO: Dan Allen
CFO: Richard Galanis
*CFO: Gary Shankman
Sr VP: Mike Becraft
Sr VP: Leslee Belluchie
Sr VP: Jim Daniel
Sr VP: Harry D Gatanas
Sr VP: Michael Plymack
Sr VP: Steve Sieke
Sr VP: Mark Wrigley
VP: Louis Addeo
VP: Stephanie Ambrose
VP: Dorian Anderson
VP: Maureen A Baginski
VP: Phil Breddy
VP: Deborah Brunetti
VP: Dan Cooley
VP: Paul Dalglish
VP: Paul Danglish
VP: Al Debenedictis
VP: Tracy Denny

D-U-N-S 92-885-9149
SERCO INC
(Suby of SERCO NORTH AMERICA LIMITED)
1818 Library St Ste 1000, Reston, VA 20190-6276
Tel (703) 939-6000 Founded/Ownrshp 1988
Sales 1.2MMM^E EMP 10,500^E
Accts Deloitte Llp Mclean Va
SIC 8999 Information bureau
CEO: Daniel D Allen
COO: Louis Addeo
CFO: Brian Johnson
*CFO: Gary A Shankman
CFO: Gary Shankman
Treas: Paul Martinez
Sr Cor Off: Eva Garzadewae
Chf Mktg O: Leslee Velluchie
Sr VP: Mike Becraft
Sr VP: David Cummins
*Sr VP: Candy M Curtin
*Sr VP: David Goldberg
*Sr VP: J Alan Hill
Sr VP: Louis Montgomery
*Sr VP: Al Pisani
Sr VP: Lee Stratton
Sr VP: Chris Sullivan
*Sr VP: Christopher M Sullivan
VP: Kent Brown
*VP: Tom Carter
VP: David Dacquino
Board of Directors: Daniel D Allen, Edward Casey, Guy Leach, Riley D Mixson, T Wood Parker, Robert F Reynolds

D-U-N-S 96-702-6803
SERCO NORTH AMERICA (HOLDINGS) INC
(Suby of SERCO HOLDINGS LIMITED)
1818 Library St Ste 1000, Reston, VA 20190-6276
Tel (703) 939-6000 Founded/Ownrshp 1964
Sales 529.1MM^E EMP 20,000^E
SIC 8744 Facilities support services
Ch: Alastair Lyons Cbe
*Pr: Edward J Casey Jr
*COO: Bo Durickovic
CFO: James Morgan
*CFO: Gary Shankman
Sr VP: Leslee Belluchie
Sr VP: Ashley Bianchini
Sr VP: Bob Hahn
Sr VP: Ron Lewis
Sr VP: Mark Wrigley
VP: Stephanie Ambrose
VP: Kent Brown
VP: Steve Christmas
VP: Kay Curling
VP: Lisa Douds
VP: Don Eich
VP: Tom Enright
VP: Bill Fischer
*VP: Harry Gatanas
VP: Walt Grabowski
VP: Kim Hintzman

D-U-N-S 01-438-7489
SERCO SERVICES INC
(Suby of SERCO INC) ★
1818 Library St Ste 1000, Reston, VA 20190-6276
Tel (703) 939-6000 Founded/Ownrshp 2008
Sales 160.8MM^E EMP 4,054
SIC 7371 Computer software systems analysis & design, custom
CEO: Dan Allen
*Pr: Edward J Casey Jr
CFO: Thomas Dunn
*CFO: Dirk Smith
Ex VP: Bo Durickovic
Sr VP: Harry Gatanas
Sr VP: Ronald Lewis
Sr VP: Louis Montgomery
Sr VP: Robert Mutchler
Sr VP: Mike Plymack
Sr VP: Steve Sieke
Sr VP: Marylynn Stowers
Sr VP: Mark Wrigley
VP: P Michael Becraft
VP: Deborah A Brunetti
*VP: James E Daniel
VP: J Alan Hill
VP: James D Kuhn

D-U-N-S 12-016-9321 IMP
SERENA SOFTWARE INC
(Suby of MICRO FOCUS (US) INC) ★
2345 Nw Amberbrook Dr # 200, Beaverton, OR 97006-6969
Tel (650) 481-3400 Founded/Ownrshp 2015
Sales 176.2MM EMP 400^E
Accts Kpmg Llp
SIC 7372 Prepackaged software
Pr: Greg Hughes
*CFO: Robert Pender Jr
*Sr VP: Edward Malysz
VP: Alison Edge
VP: Shane Hanel
VP: Kevin Parker

SERENADE FOODS
See MAPLE LEAF FARMS INC

D-U-N-S 02-882-1135 IMP/EXP
SERENGETI TRADING CO LP
19100 Hamilton Pool Rd, Dripping Springs, TX 78620-2871
Tel (512) 358-9593 Founded/Ownrshp 2001
Sales 170.0MM^E EMP 10
SIC 5149 Coffee, green or roasted; Coffee & tea
CEO: Bert Von Roemer
CFO: Marc Carlson
VP: Jessica Sellers

D-U-N-S 87-699-5171 IMP/EXP
SERGEANTS PET CARE PRODUCTS INC
PERRIGO ANIMAL HEALTH
(Suby of PERRIGO CO) ★
10077 S 134th St, Omaha, NE 68138-3710
Tel (402) 938-7000 Founded/Ownrshp 2012
Sales 180.0MM EMP 188
SIC 2834 5199 2048 Drugs acting on the central nervous system & sense organs; Drugs acting on the gastrointestinal or genitourinary system; Drugs affecting parasitic & infective diseases; Pet supplies; Prepared feeds
Pr: Gary Coffey
VP: Mark Levin
VP: Patsy Sumner
Genl Mgr: Neal Wilmore
Dir IT: Josh Haggin
VP Opers: Nick Gubser
Sfty Mgr: Robbin Hostetter
Manager: Joe Kaschmitter
Plnt Mgr: Ben Conkey
Plnt Mgr: Kevin Harmon
Ql Cn Mgr: Jamie Davis

D-U-N-S 00-608-1574 IMP
SERIGRAPH INC (DE)
3801 Decorah Rd, West Bend, WI 53095-9597
Tel (262) 335-7200 Founded/Ownrshp 1949, 1987
Sales 472.5MM^E EMP 1,400
SIC 2759 2752 2396 Screen printing; Commercial printing, offset; Automotive & apparel trimmings
CEO: Sean Torinus
*Ch Bd: John Torinus Jr
COO: Mike Kincaide
*COO: Michael Palm
*CFO: Todd Schneider
VP: Rob Averkamp
VP: John Barrett
*VP: Dan Haas
Netwrk Mgr: Mike Snyder
Mktg Mgr: Nancy Kane

SERIVCE CORP INTERNATIONAL
See KEYSTONE AMERICA INC

D-U-N-S 15-528-3864
SERRA AUTOMOTIVE INC
3118 E Hill Rd, Grand Blanc, MI 48439-8106
Tel (810) 695-1451 Founded/Ownrshp 2000
Sales 435.1MM^E EMP 1,400^E
SIC 5511 8742 Automobiles, new & used; Industry specialist consultants
Pr: Joseph O Serra
*CFO: Matthew S Daugherty
*Treas: Matt Daugherty
Genl Mgr: Jerry Colten
Dir IT: Will Kelley
Sls Mgr: Christopher Bard
Sales Asso: Dawn Laborde
Sales Asso: Dave Simonson

SERRA CHEVROLET BUICK GMC
See NASHVILLE AUTOMOTIVE LLC

D-U-N-S 06-034-7721 IMP
SERTA INC (DE)
SERTA INTERNATIONAL
(Suby of SERTA SIMMONS BEDDING LLC) ★
2600 Forbs Ave, Hoffman Estates, IL 60192-3723
Tel (847) 645-0200 Founded/Ownrshp 1931
Sales 950.1MM^E EMP 3,100
SIC 2515 Mattresses & foundations
Pr: Michael Traub
*CEO: Gary T Fazio
VP: Maria Balistreri
VP: Susan Ebaugh
VP: Al Klancnik
*VP: Alan Klancnik
VP: John Rachid
Ex Dir: Richard Yulman
MIS Dir: April Roggers
Dir IT: Donna Zett
IT Man: Carlos Canjura

SERTA INTERNATIONAL
See SERTA INC

SERTA MATTRESS CO
See AW INDUSTRIES INC

SERTA MATTRESS COMPANY
See NATIONAL BEDDING CO LLC

D-U-N-S 96-187-8662
SERTA SIMMONS BEDDING LLC
(Suby of ADVENT INTERNATIONAL CORP) ★
1 Concourse Pkwy Ste 800, Atlanta, GA 30328-6188
Tel (770) 512-7700 Founded/Ownrshp 2012
Sales 2.4MMM^E EMP 5,000^E
SIC 2515 Mattresses, innerspring or box spring
Pr: Gary T Fazio
Ex VP: Daren Couture
*Ex VP: Kristen K McGuffey
*Sr VP: Robert M Carstens
Sr VP: Brad Hill

SERVCO LIFE INSURANCE CO
See GULF STATES FINANCIAL SERVICES INC

D-U-N-S 00-692-7099
SERVCO PACIFIC INC (HI)
2850 Pukoloa St Ste 300, Honolulu, HI 96819-4475
Tel (808) 564-1300 Founded/Ownrshp 1919
Sales 1.0MMM EMP 925
SIC 5013 5064 5511 Automotive supplies & parts; Electric household appliances; New & used car dealers
Ch Bd: Mark H Fukunaga
*Pr: Eric Fukunaga
*CFO: Jeffery A Bell
*Ex VP: Patrick D Ching
*Sr VP: Brian K Horikami
*VP: Sheryl Delsol
VP: Peter Eldridge
VP: Eugene Harada
*VP: John Harris
*VP: Glenn K Inouye
VP: Glenn Inouye
VP: Robert Inouye
VP: William Kawashima
VP: Raymond Lum
VP: Rebecca Moore
VP: Russ Robertson
VP: Dean Takazawa
*VP: Alan Young

SERVE SOURCE STAFFING
See DEFENDER SERVICES INC

D-U-N-S 80-843-3234 IMP
SERVICE AMERICA ENTEPRISE INC
2755 Nw 63rd Ct, Fort Lauderdale, FL 33309-1711
Tel (954) 979-1100 Founded/Ownrshp 2004
Sales 122.3MM^E EMP 380
SIC 1711 1731 Plumbing, heating, air-conditioning contractors; Electrical work
Pr: David J Crawford
*Ch Bd: Gene Gomberg
*COO: Mark D Miller
*COO: Alberto Soto
*CFO: Vivian Psinakis
*VP: Nancy R Donegan
VP: Klaus Leitzsch
*VP: Richard M Levinson
*Prin: Steven Christensen
IT Man: E Decker

D-U-N-S 05-857-9061 IMP/EXP
■ **SERVICE BY AIR INC**
SBA GLOBAL LOGISTICS SERVICES
(Suby of RADIANT LOGISTICS INC) ★
222 Crossways Park Dr, Woodbury, NY 11797-2015
Tel (800) 243-5545 Founded/Ownrshp 1972
Sales 119.7MM^E EMP 166
SIC 4731 Domestic freight forwarding; Foreign freight forwarding
Pr: Joseph Poliseno
Pr: Philippe Gabay
VP: Michael Poliseno
Exec: Anthony Deltuva
Dir Bus: Matthew Newman
Mng Dir: Lyn Rothmeyer
Rgnl Mgr: Kim Gabehart
Rgnl Mgr: Tim Gabehart
Brnch Mgr: Brandon Dvorak
Dist Mgr: Joe Carter
Dist Mgr: David Naman

D-U-N-S 11-522-1954
SERVICE CHAMP INC
180 New Britain Blvd, Chalfont, PA 18914-1832
Tel (215) 822-8500 Founded/Ownrshp 2005
Sales 142.8MM^E EMP 250
SIC 5013 Automotive supplies & parts
Pr: Fred Berman
*Sec: Marc Berman
*Sec: Thomas Janis
Ofcr: Ted Hubiak
*Sr VP: Kevin Gibbons
*VP: Kirk Gustie
VP Opers: Steven Moretti
Sales Exec: Kathy Atkinson
Sales Exec: Scott Gustie
Sales Exec: Jeffrey Players
Sales Exec: Julie Williams

D-U-N-S 04-575-6715 IMP/EXP
▲ **SERVICE CORP INTERNATIONAL**
SCI
1929 Allen Pkwy, Houston, TX 77019-2500
Tel (713) 522-5141 Founded/Ownrshp 1962
Sales 2.9MMM EMP 23,785
Tkr Sym SCI Exch NYS
SIC 7261 Funeral service & crematories; Funeral home; Crematory
Ch Bd: Thomas L Ryan
Pr: Michael R Webb
CFO: Eric D Tanzberger
Sr VP: Gregory T Sangalis
Sr VP: Steven A Tidwell
Sr VP: Sumner J Waring
VP: Nockels David
VP: Mohn Del Mixon
VP: John Del-Mixon
VP: John Delmixon
VP: Richard Havens
VP: Phil Jacobs
VP: Tammy R Moore
VP: Darin Sommer
VP: Steve Tidwell
Board of Directors: Edward E Williams, Alan R Buckwalter III, Anthony L Coelho, Victor L Lund, John W Mecom Jr, Clifton H Morris Jr, Ellen Ochoa, R L Waltrip, W Blair Waltrip, Marcus A Watts

SERVICE ELC CBLETV CMMNCTIONS
See SERVICE ELECTRIC CABLETV INC

D-U-N-S 00-791-2330
SERVICE ELECTRIC CABLETV INC
SERVICE ELC CBLE TV CMMNCTIONS
2200 Avenue A Ste 101, Bethlehem, PA 18017-2157
Tel (610) 865-9100 Founded/Ownrshp 1948
Sales 182.0MM^E EMP 489
SIC 4841 6719 Cable television services; Investment holding companies, except banks
Pr: Edward Walson
*VP: John Walson
Genl Mgr: William Brayford
Genl Mgr: Larry Shewack

D-U-N-S 96-637-4589
■ **SERVICE ELECTRIC CO**
(Suby of QUANTA SERVICES INC) ★
1631 E 25th St, Chattanooga, TN 37404-4198
Tel (423) 894-4336 Founded/Ownrshp 2012
Sales 185.4MM^E EMP 600^E
SIC 1629 1731 1541 Power plant construction; General electrical contractor; Industrial buildings, new construction
Pr: Jody Shea
*Sr VP: Keith Sheppard
*VP: Jim Bowen
*VP: Brian Imsand
*VP: Joshua Post
*VP: J Tyre Williamson

D-U-N-S 07-484-5389
SERVICE EMPLOYEES INTERNATIONAL UNION
SERVICE EMPLOYEES INTL
1800 Massachusetts Ave Nw, Washington, DC 20036-1806
Tel (202) 730-7000 Founded/Ownrshp 1921
Sales 299.2MM EMP 35,000
Accts Bond Beebe Pc Bethesda Md
SIC 8631 Labor unions & similar labor organizations
Pr: Mary Kay Henry
*Sec: Anna Burger
*Ex VP: Elseo Medina
*Ex VP: Tom Woodruff
VP: Andrea Dehlendorf
VP: Carol Harris-Davis
Dir Soc: Donna Alston
Comm Dir: Nathan Hoffmann
Ex Dir: Molly Ringo
Snr Ntwrk: Allen Brown
Snr Ntwrk: Amardeep Singh

D-U-N-S 85-989-7969
SERVICE EMPLOYEES INTERNATIONAL UNION LOCAL 1
(Suby of SERVICE EMPLOYEES INTL) ★
111 E Wacker Dr Ste 2500, Chicago, IL 60601-4200
Tel (312) 240-1600 Founded/Ownrshp 1928
Sales 27.1MM EMP 35,000
SIC 8631 Labor union
Pr: Tom Balanoff
VP: Maria Barrera
*VP: Nancy Cross
Genl Mgr: Leone Bicchieri

SERVICE EMPLOYEES INTL
See SERVICE EMPLOYEES INTERNATIONAL UNION

D-U-N-S 07-850-6955
SERVICE EXPERTS HEATING & AIR CONDITIONING LLC
(Suby of SERVICE EXPERTS LLC) ★
2140 Lake Park Blvd, Richardson, TX 75080-2252
Tel (972) 535-3800 Founded/Ownrshp 2004
Sales 118.9MM^E EMP 2,010^E
SIC 1711 5074 5075 8742 Plumbing, heating, air-conditioning contractors; Plumbing & hydronic heating supplies; Warm air heating & air conditioning; Management consulting services
Pr: Michael J Blatz
*VP: Charles E Donnelly
*VP: John D Torres

D-U-N-S 96-020-5870
SERVICE EXPERTS LLC
(Suby of SEHAC HOLDINGS LLC)
3820 American Dr Ste 200, Plano, TX 75075-6110
Tel (972) 231-5468 Founded/Ownrshp 2016
Sales 163.8MM^E EMP 291
SIC 1711 5074 5075 8742 Heating & air conditioning contractors; Warm air heating & air conditioning contractor; Ventilation & duct work contractor; Heating equipment (hydronic); Furnaces, except electric & warm air; Heating equipment & panels, solar; Air conditioning & ventilation equipment & supplies; Warm air heating equipment & supplies; Air conditioning equipment, except room units; Ventilating equipment & supplies; Industry specialist consultants
Pr: Michael Blatz
VP: Paul Adams
*VP: John Torres
Exec: Mary Kimball
Genl Mgr: Christopher Overton
Netwrk Eng: Stacy Dodson
Trfc Dir: Jonathan Neesmith
Trfc Dir: Bill Stallings
Opers Mgr: Jonathan Gipson

SERVICE EXPRESS
See SEI INC

SERVICE GROUP
See SERVICE LLOYDS INSURANCE CO

D-U-N-S 80-768-6709
SERVICE GROUP INVESTMENTS LLC
6005 Century Oaks Dr # 100, Chattanooga, TN 37416-3677
Tel (423) 643-2600 Founded/Ownrshp 2004
Sales 284.5MM^E EMP 1,475
SIC 6282 Investment advice
Prin: Murray Taylor

SERVICE KING CLLSION REPR CTRS
See SERVICE KING HOLDINGS LLC

SERVICE KING CLLSION REPR CTRS
See SERVICE KING PAINT & BODY LLC

D-U-N-S 07-835-6583
SERVICE KING HOLDINGS LLC
SERVICE KING CLLSION REPR CTRS
2600 N Central Expy # 400, Richardson, TX 75080-2058
Tel (972) 960-7595 Founded/Ownrshp 2012
Sales 239.2MM^E EMP 5,058
SIC 7532 Body shop, automotive
CEO: Patrick C James
VP: William M Johnston
VP: Brent McKinney
VP: Justin Regan
Area Mgr: Bryan Wendt
Genl Mgr: Kevin Lipscomb
CTO: Bob Byrd
IT Man: Mitchel Hayes
VP Opers: Danny McKinley
Site Mgr: Perry Alexander
Site Mgr: Steve Feltner

D-U-N-S 62-146-6064 EXP
SERVICE KING MANUFACTURING INC
S K
2100 W Hgwy 66, Stroud, OK 74079
Tel (918) 968-2899 Founded/Ownrshp 2005
Sales 89.3MM^E EMP 230
SIC 3533 Oil & gas drilling rigs & equipment
Pr: Robert L Gordon
*VP: Dixie L Gordon
Sls Mgr: Mike Goodman

D-U-N-S 07-934-1848
■ **SERVICE KING PAINT & BODY LLC**
SERVICE KING CLLSION REPR CTRS
(Suby of BLACKSTONE GROUP L P) ★
2600 N Central Expy, Richardson, TX 75080-2055
Tel (972) 960-7595 Founded/Ownrshp 2014
Sales 194.7MM^E EMP 1,076
SIC 7532 Body shop, automotive
CEO: Chris Abrham
*CFO: Daniel Mangini
*VP: Jeff McFadden
*VP Opers: Danny McKinley
*VP Advt: Jennifer Kirk

D-U-N-S 13-182-4922
SERVICE LLOYDS INSURANCE CO
SERVICE GROUP
6907 N Capital Of Texas, Austin, TX 78731-1795
Tel (512) 343-0600 Founded/Ownrshp 1982
Sales NA EMP 100
SIC 6331 Workers' compensation insurance
Pr: J Kelly Gray
*Sr VP: Gary Holiday
Sr VP: Bob Newton
VP: Scott Sloan

SERVICE LOGIC
See MSHC INC

SERVICE OIL
See J & H OIL CO

D-U-N-S 02-296-0546
SERVICE OIL INC
STAMART
1718 Main Ave E, West Fargo, ND 58078-2204
Tel (701) 277-1050 Founded/Ownrshp 1946
Sales 106.9MM^E EMP 250
Accts Widmer Roel Pc Fargo Nd
SIC 5541 5411 Filling stations, gasoline; Convenience stores, chain
Pr: Steven Lenthe

D-U-N-S 07-579-3518 IMP
■ **SERVICE PARTNERS LLC**
(Suby of TOPBUILD SERVICES GROUP CORP) ★
1029 Technology Park Dr, Glen Allen, VA 23059-4500
Tel (804) 515-7400 Founded/Ownrshp 2015
Sales 2.0MMM^E EMP 790
SIC 5033 Insulation materials
Pr: Mark Moore
Ex VP: Bob Hoffman
Ex VP: Allan Neill
VP: Mike Herbert
VP: Matt Kowal
Brnch Mgr: Danton Delans
Brnch Mgr: Chad Maxcy
Genl Mgr: James Cole
Genl Mgr: John Garland
Genl Mgr: John Holland
CIO: Timothy Monteith

D-U-N-S 06-911-4952
SERVICE SOLUTIONS US LLC
(Suby of AUTOMOTIVE GROUP) ★
7121 N Haggerty Rd, Canton, MI 48187-2452
Tel (734) 582-2382 Founded/Ownrshp 1998, 2012
Sales 102.5MM^E EMP 4,200
SIC 8711 Engineering services
Pr: Tanvir Arfi
Ofcr: Laura Papenhagen
VP: Kevin Mull

D-U-N-S 13-108-1135 IMP/EXP
SERVICE STEEL INC
5555 N Channel Ave Bldg 2, Portland, OR 97217-7666
Tel (503) 224-9500 Founded/Ownrshp 1996
Sales 107.8MM^E EMP 70
Accts Maginnis & Carey Llp Portland
SIC 5051 3711 Steel; Personnel carriers (motor vehicles), assembly of
CEO: Edward G Westerdahl III
*VP: Troy Westerdahl

D-U-N-S 02-648-1788 IMP/EXP
SERVICE STEEL WAREHOUSE CO LP
8415 Clinton Dr, Houston, TX 77029-3613
Tel (713) 675-2631 Founded/Ownrshp 1965
Sales 181.8MM^E EMP 125
SIC 5051 Steel
Owner: Gabe Siegel
*Ch: Jon Osborne
VP Opers: Seth White
Sales Asso: Chad Hudgens
Sales Asso: Austin Moore

D-U-N-S 19-962-3588
SERVICE SYSTEMS ASSOCIATES INC
4699 Marion St, Denver, CO 80216-2118
Tel (417) 746-0242 Founded/Ownrshp 1989
Sales 224.3MM^E EMP 2,000
SIC 5947 5812 Gift shop; Concessionaire
Pr: T Kevin Mc Nicholas
*CFO: Mark Schroeder
Ex VP: Kevin Eldredge
*VP: Timothy Brantley
Genl Mgr: Annie Fedora
Genl Mgr: Chris Hepp
Genl Mgr: Christine Jamison
Genl Mgr: Paul Karros
Genl Mgr: Marty Marcely
Genl Mgr: Jake Pugh
VP Mktg: David Goetz

D-U-N-S 04-513-8245 IMP
SERVICE TIRE TRUCK CENTER INC
2255 Avenue A, Bethlehem, PA 18017-2165
Tel (610) 691-8473 Founded/Ownrshp 1955
Sales 132.9MM^E EMP 600
SIC 7534 5531 Tire recapping; Automotive tires
Pr: Ronald Bennett
*COO: Walter J Dealtrey
*VP: Edward I Betz
VP: Kristofer Harmes
Exec: Earl Gassmann
Brnch Mgr: Jim Calabrese
Brnch Mgr: Leo Dasilva
Brnch Mgr: Rich Despins
Brnch Mgr: Jeff England
Brnch Mgr: Scott Ferri
Brnch Mgr: Bill Hogan

D-U-N-S 07-932-1457
■ **SERVICELINK HOLDINGS LLC**
(Suby of BLACK KNIGHT HOLDINGS INC) ★
601 Riverside Ave Bldg 5, Jacksonville, FL 32204-2945
Tel (904) 854-8100 Founded/Ownrshp 2013
Sales NA EMP 30^E
SIC 6361 6331 6531 8741 3699 Title insurance; Fire, marine & casualty insurance; Escrow agent, real estate; Restaurant management; Electrical equipment & supplies

D-U-N-S 07-951-8745
■ **SERVICELINK NLS LLC**
(Suby of SERVICELINK HOLDINGS LLC) ★
1400 Cherrington Pkwy, Moon Township, PA 15108-4356
Tel (800) 777-8759 Founded/Ownrshp 2014
Sales NA EMP 3,796
SIC 6361 Title insurance
CEO: Chris Azur

D-U-N-S 04-160-8162
■ **SERVICEMAGIC INC**
(Suby of IAC/INTERACTIVECORP) ★
14023 Denver West Pkwy # 2, Lakewood, CO 80401-3253
Tel (303) 963-7200 Founded/Ownrshp 2004
Sales 131.5MM^E EMP 265
SIC 4813
CEO: Chris Terrill
Genl Pt: Terrence Torn
*Pr: Craig Smith
*Co-Ch Bd: Michael Beaudoin
*Co-Ch Bd: Rodney Rice
Sr VP: Ryan Sullivan
VP: Dave Eren
VP: Nick Tacquard
VP: Robert Whitehead
VP: Gerry Wienholt
Exec: Shahana Ali

SERVICEMASTER
See ARAMARK MANAGEMENT SERVICES LIMITED PARTNERSHIP

SERVICEMASTER BY STRATOS
See STRATOS INC

D-U-N-S 16-197-2237 IMP/EXP
■ **SERVICEMASTER CO LLC**
(Suby of CDRSVM HOLDING LLC) ★
860 Ridge Lake Blvd Fl 3, Memphis, TN 38120-9422
Tel (901) 597-1400 Founded/Ownrshp 2014
Sales 2.6MMM^E EMP 13,000
SIC 7349 7342 1711 1731 7641 Building maintenance services; Termite control; Pest control in structures; Heating & air conditioning contractors; Plumbing contractors; Electrical work; Reupholstery & furniture repair
CEO: Robert J Gillette
Pr: Katrina Helmkamp
CFO: Alan J M Haughie
Sr VP: Susan K Hunsberger
Sr VP: Mark W Peterson
VP: Giovanni Cueto
VP: John P Mullen
VP: Bradley Mundt
CIO: Linda Goodspeed
Prd Mgr: Connie Wiederin
VP Mktg: Stephen Burnett
Board of Directors: Sarah Kim, David H Wasserman

D-U-N-S 78-373-4205 IMP/EXP
■ **SERVICEMASTER CONSUMER SERVICES LIMITED PARTNERSHIP**
(Suby of SERVICEMASTER CO LLC) ★
889 Ridge Lake Blvd Fl 2, Memphis, TN 38120-9425
Tel (901) 597-7574 Founded/Ownrshp 2001
Sales 2.5MMM EMP 13,000
SIC 0782 6351 7349 Lawn care services; Warranty insurance, home; Building maintenance services
Pt: Ernest Mrozek
Dir Soc: Julie Rule

D-U-N-S 07-938-0105
▲ SERVICEMASTER GLOBAL HOLDINGS INC
860 Ridge Lake Blvd, Memphis, TN 38120-9434
Tel (901) 597-1400 *Founded/Ownrshp* 1947
Sales 2.5MMM *EMP* 13,000E
Tkr Sym SERV *Exch* NYS
SIC 7342 7629 7641 Disinfecting & pest control services; Pest control services; Electrical household appliance repair; Furniture repair & maintenance
CEO: Robert J Gillette
Ch Bd: Mark E Tomkins
Pr: Timothy M Haynes
Pr: Mary Kay Wegner
COO: Marty Wick
CFO: Alan J M Haughie
Sr VP: Susan K Hunsberger
Sr VP: James T Lucke

D-U-N-S 80-564-8552
SERVICEMASTER HOLDING CORP
860 Ridge Lake Blvd, Memphis, TN 38120-9434
Tel (901) 597-1400 *Founded/Ownrshp* 2007
Sales NA *EMP* 39,000E
SIC 0782 7342 1711 1731 7349 7641

D-U-N-S 60-621-9744
▲ SERVICENOW INC
2225 Lawson Ln, Santa Clara, CA 95054-3311
Tel (408) 501-8550 *Founded/Ownrshp* 2004
Sales 1.0MMM *EMP* 3,686
Tkr Sym NOW *Exch* NYS
SIC 7379 7372 Computer related maintenance services; Prepackaged software
Pr: Frank Slootman
**Ch Bd:* Paul V Barber
COO: Daniel R McGee
CFO: Michael P Scarpelli
VP: Pat Calhoun
VP: Sridhar Chandrashekar
VP: Tom Hannigan
VP: Tristan Munday
VP: Craig Pratt
VP: John Sapone
VP: Matt Schvimmer
VP: Mark Thompson
VP: Gadi Yedwab
Dir Risk M: David L Schneider
Board of Directors: Susan L Bolstrom, Ronald E G Codd, Charles H Giancarlo, Jeffrey A Miller, Anita M Sands, William L Strauss

D-U-N-S 10-367-5559
SERVICES FOR UNDERSERVED INC
S U S
305 7th Ave Fl 10, New York, NY 10001-6146
Tel (212) 633-6900 *Founded/Ownrshp* 1980
Sales 10.2MM *EMP* 1,500
Accts Bdo Usa Llp New York Ny
SIC 8322 Individual & family services
Pr: John A McKesson
**V Ch:* Carolyn P Powell
**CEO:* Donna Colonna
**CFO:* Neil Flynn
CFO: Perry Perlmutter
**Treas:* Edward Semler
Ex VP: Terence G Blackwell
**Sr VP:* Louis Cavaliere
**Sr VP:* Priscilla Fuller
**VP:* Yves Ades
VP: Yves Ades
VP: Nancy Southwell

D-U-N-S 04-133-6785 IMP/EXP
SERVICES GROUP OF AMERICA INC
16100 N 71st St Ste 500, Scottsdale, AZ 85254-2232
Tel (480) 927-4000 *Founded/Ownrshp* 1954
Sales 5.9MMME *EMP* 3,600E
SIC 5141 5148 6331 6552 Groceries, general line; Fresh fruits & vegetables; Workers' compensation insurance; Subdividers & developers
Pr: Peter Smith
CFO: Jim Keller
Sr VP: Lee Clark
**VP:* Steven Twist
VP Opers: Larry Boyer

D-U-N-S 08-112-7607
SERVICES MANAGEMENT CORP
S M C
(*Suby of* NTCA RURAL BROADBAND ASSN) ★
4121 Wilson Blvd Fl 10, Arlington, VA 22203-1839
Tel (703) 351-2074 *Founded/Ownrshp* 1980
Sales 293.4MM *EMP* 15
SIC 8741 Administrative management
Pr: Michael E Brunner

D-U-N-S 06-927-4009
SERVICESOURCE INC (VA)
10467 White Granite Dr # 100, Oakton, VA 22124-2763
Tel (703) 461-6000 *Founded/Ownrshp* 1971
Sales 98.0MM *EMP* 1,900
Accts Mcgladrey Llp Mc Lean Va
SIC 8331 7331 Sheltered workshop; Mailing service
CEO: Janet Samuelson
Dir Vol: Maureen Andretta
**COO:* Bruce Patterson
CFO: John Adams
CFO: Edward Carse
Ofcr: Kareem Franklin
Assoc VP: Donald Pincus
Ex VP: Jay Ackerman
Ex VP: Rich Baldyga
**Ex VP:* Mark Hall
**Ex VP:* David Hodge
Ex VP: Katy Keim
Ex VP: Kevin Maddock
Ex VP: Rob Sturgeon
**Ex VP:* Lisa Ward
VP: Tom Chang
VP: Dave Dunlap
VP: Linda GE
**VP:* Nate Hoover
VP: Jack Johnson
VP: Natalie McCullough

D-U-N-S 78-598-2344
▲ SERVICESOURCE INTERNATIONAL INC
760 Market St Fl 4, San Francisco, CA 94102-2306
Tel (415) 901-6030 *Founded/Ownrshp* 2002
Sales 252.2MM *EMP* 2,745E
Tkr Sym SREV *Exch* NGS
SIC 8742 Business consultant
CEO: Christopher M Carrington
COO: Brian J Delaney
CFO: Robert N Pinkerton
Ex VP: Rob Sturgeon
Sr VP: Patricia Elias
Sls Mgr: Annie Barraza
Sls Mgr: Ashley Deal
Sls Mgr: Alexandra Price
Sales Asso: Elicia Anderson
Sales Asso: Karen Carlson
Corp Couns: Bernard Gajos
Board of Directors: Robert G Ashe, Steven M Cakebread, Bruce W Dunlevie, James C Madden, Thomas F Mendoza, Gary B Moore, Barry D Reynolds

D-U-N-S 94-157-7707
SERVICEXPRESS CORP
120 N Ray St, Georgetown, DE 19947
Tel (302) 856-3500 *Founded/Ownrshp* 2007
Sales 10.0MM *EMP* 1,116E
SIC 7361 Labor contractors (employment agency)
Pr: Bamdad Bahar

SERVICIO DE BOMBEROS DE PR
See PUERTO RICO FIREFIGHTERS CORPS

SERVICOM
See RON WEBER AND ASSOCIATES INC

D-U-N-S 10-909-2759
SERVICON SYSTEMS INC
PACIFICA CONSULTING SERVICES
3965 Landmark St, Culver City, CA 90232-2399
Tel (310) 204-5040 *Founded/Ownrshp* 1973
Sales 74.9MME *EMP* 1,500
SIC 8744 7349 1771 Facilities support services; Building maintenance services; Flooring contractor
Ch: Michael Mahdesian
**Pr:* Laurie Sewell
**CFO:* Maritza Aguilar
**VP:* Enio Martinez
VP: Gary O'Brien
**VP:* Mark Rossiter
VP: Rick Tate
Dist Mgr: Danilo Esquivel
Dist Mgr: Hector Vasquez
Genl Mgr: Richard J Mahdesian
CIO: Paul Walters

SERVIS1ST
See SERVISFIRST BANK

SERVISAIR GROUP HANDLING
See SERVISAIR USA & CARRIBEAN

D-U-N-S 15-991-1569
SERVISAIR LLC
151 Northpoint Dr, Houston, TX 77060-3207
Tel (281) 260-3900 *Founded/Ownrshp* 2005
Sales NA *EMP* 5,500
SIC 4581

D-U-N-S 00-753-1614
SERVISAIR USA & CARRIBEAN
SERVISAIR GROUP HANDLING
(*Suby of* SWISSPORT USA INC) ★
6065 Nw 18th St Bldg 716d, Miami, FL 33126-7332
Tel (305) 262-4059 *Founded/Ownrshp* 1999
Sales 67.2MME *EMP* 1,639E
SIC 4581 Airport terminal services
CEO: Michael Hancock

D-U-N-S 82-765-5825
▲ SERVISFIRST BANCSHARES INC
850 Shades Creek Pkwy, Mountain Brk, AL 35209-4460
Tel (205) 949-0302 *Founded/Ownrshp* 2007
Sales NA *EMP* 371E
Tkr Sym SFBS *Exch* NGS
SIC 6022 State commercial banks
Pr: Thomas A Broughton III
**Ch Bd:* Stanley M Brock
COO: Clarence C Pouncey III
CFO: William M Foshee

D-U-N-S 61-628-1106
■ SERVISFIRST BANK
SERVIS1ST
(*Suby of* SERVISFIRST BANCSHARES INC) ★
850 Shades Creek Pkwy, Mountain Brk, AL 35209-4460
Tel (205) 949-0302 *Founded/Ownrshp* 2005
Sales NA *EMP* 273
SIC 6022 State commercial banks
Pr: Thomas A Broughton III
Pr: Tom Trouche
Bd of Dir: James Filler
Ofcr: Melissa Britton
Ofcr: Angelique Densmore
Ofcr: Buzz Fowler
Ofcr: Delynn Gower
Ofcr: David Lee
Ofcr: Cory Sims
Ex VP: Bud Foshee
Ex VP: Rodney Rushing
Ex VP: Paul Schabacker
Sr VP: Alex Arendall
Sr VP: Ryland Craft
Sr VP: Allen Farr
Sr VP: Seth Horton
Sr VP: Christopher Houtchens
Sr VP: Jeff Johnson
Sr VP: Paula Renfroe
Sr VP: Steve Shelton
Sr VP: Bradford Vieira

D-U-N-S 00-450-9787
SERVPRO INDUSTRIES INC
801 Industrial Blvd, Gallatin, TN 37066-3742
Tel (615) 451-0200 *Founded/Ownrshp* 1977
Sales 141.7MM *EMP* 350
Accts Kraft Cpas Pllc Nashville Te
SIC 5087 Cleaning & maintenance equipment & supplies
Pr: Randall Isaacson
**CEO:* Susan L Steen
COO: Rich Quinn
CFO: Tara Brown
**Ex VP:* Richard Isaacson
Off Mgr: Delvia Lesa-Garza
Mktg Mgr: Chad Lewis

D-U-N-S 04-623-1601
SERVPRO INTELLECTUAL PROPERTY INC
(*Suby of* SERVPRO INDUSTRIES INC) ★
801 Industrial Blvd, Gallatin, TN 37066-3742
Tel (615) 451-0200 *Founded/Ownrshp* 1967
Sales 136.0MM *EMP* 111
Accts Kraft Cpas Pllc Nashville T
SIC 7349 8741 5087 Building maintenance services; Management services; Cleaning & maintenance equipment & supplies
CEO: Sue Isaacson Steen
**Pr:* Randall Isaacson
**CFO:* Rick Forster
**Ex VP:* Richard Isaacson
CIO: Mike Matheny

D-U-N-S 05-583-3834
SERVUS
DENNY'S
4201 Mannheim Rd Ste A, Jasper, IN 47546-9617
Tel (812) 482-3212 *Founded/Ownrshp* 1964
Sales 142.0M *EMP* 3,200
SIC 5812 Restaurant, family: chain
Ch Bd: Robert Ruckriegel
**Pr:* Jason Kelly
IT Man: Ann Sochulte
Mktg Dir: Brooke Richards
Pr Dir: Rebecca Wheaton

SES
See SCIENCE AND ENGINEERING SERVICES LLC

D-U-N-S 08-198-0286 IMP
SES AMERICOM INC
(*Suby of* SES- WORLD SKIES) ★
4 Research Way, Princeton, NJ 08540-6686
Tel (609) 987-4000 *Founded/Ownrshp* 2001
Sales 194.8MME *EMP* 298
SIC 4899 Satellite earth stations
CEO: Edward D Horowitz
**COO:* Jim Ducay
**CFO:* Rob Kisilywicz
CFO: Mark Rigolle
**Ex VP:* Alan Young
Sr VP: Daniel Harel
**Sr VP:* Bryan A McGuirk
Sr VP: Dieter Schweinle
Sr VP: Mary Kathryn Uhl
VP: Romain Bausch
VP: U Bouwsma
VP: Steve Bunke
VP: Kevin Parks
VP: Orlando Skelton

D-U-N-S 03-634-3437
SES GLOBAL- AMERICAS INC
SES- WORLD SKIES
(*Suby of* SES SA)
4 Research Way, Princeton, NJ 08540-6618
Tel (609) 987-4000 *Founded/Ownrshp* 1986
Sales 197.4MME *EMP* 341
SIC 4899 Data communication services
Pr: Robert Benarek
Mng Dir: Mike Chandler
Prgrm Mgr: Molly Meske
Snr Sftwr: Brian Hathaway

D-U-N-S 03-927-4332
SES GOVERNMENT SOLUTIONS INC
(*Suby of* SES AMERICOM INC) ★
11790 Sunrise Valley Dr # 300, Reston, VA 20191-1441
Tel (703) 610-1000 *Founded/Ownrshp* 2001
Sales 192.1MM *EMP* 45E
Accts Pricewaterhousecoopers Llp Mc
SIC 7389 3663 Personal service agents, brokers & bureaus; Space satellite communications equipment
Pr: Peter F Hoene
**CFO:* John Strand
Sr Cor Off: Robert Kisilywicz
Ofcr: Linda Mila
Ofcr: James Scheimer
VP: William Flynn
VP: Scott Galus
VP: Peter Hoene
VP: David S Jackson
VP: Jeffrey Rowlison
**Prin:* Robert Osterthaler

D-U-N-S 02-639-9509
SES HOLDINGS LLC
114 E Foreline St, Gainesville, TX 76240-3320
Tel (940) 668-0251 *Founded/Ownrshp* 2008
Sales 843.8MM *EMP* 4,200
Accts Kpmg Llp Dallas Tx
SIC 6719 5084 Investment holding companies, except banks; Oil well machinery, equipment & supplies
**Pr:* Kelly Stanley
**CFO:* Eric Mattson
**VP:* Faye McCarrell

SES- WORLD SKIES
See SES GLOBAL- AMERICAS INC

D-U-N-S 05-456-1469 IMP
SESAME WORKSHOP
1 Lincoln Plz Fl 2, New York, NY 10023-7163
Tel (212) 595-3456 *Founded/Ownrshp* 1970, 2000
Sales 104.7MM *EMP* 330
SIC 7812 2731

SESCO
See STATE ELECTRIC SUPPLY CO

SESH
See SOUTHEAST SUPPLY HEADER LLC

D-U-N-S 96-558-4217
■ SESI LLC
(*Suby of* SUPERIOR ENERGY SERVICES INC) ★
1001 Louisiana St, Houston, TX 77002-5089
Tel (504) 587-7374 *Founded/Ownrshp* 2000
Sales 2.7MMME *EMP* 3,873E
SIC 7353 1389 Oil field equipment, rental or leasing; Servicing oil & gas wells
CEO: Terence Hall

D-U-N-S 18-915-7261
SET AND SERVICE RESOURCES LLC
8303 Six Forks Rd Ste 207, Raleigh, NC 27615-3094
Tel (919) 787-5571 *Founded/Ownrshp* 2008
Sales 78.8MME *EMP* 1,500
SIC 7361 Executive placement

D-U-N-S 60-582-1149
SET ENTERPRISES INC
30500 Van Dyke Ave # 701, Warren, MI 48093-2114
Tel (586) 573-3600 *Founded/Ownrshp* 1989
Sales 98.6MME *EMP* 400
SIC 7389 3465 3544 3312 Metal cutting services; Automotive stampings; Special dies, tools, jigs & fixtures; Blast furnaces & steel mills
Pr: Sidney Taylor
CFO: Ken Pachla
Exec: Robert Falco
Genl Mgr: Jim Smith

D-U-N-S 18-109-3741
SETECH INC
410 New Salem Hwy Ste 106, Murfreesboro, TN 37129-3361
Tel (615) 890-1758 *Founded/Ownrshp* 1986
Sales 201.6MME *EMP* 858
SIC 8742 8748 5085 Management consulting services; Business consulting; Industrial supplies; Power transmission equipment & apparatus; Mill supplies
CEO: Thomas N Eisenman
**CFO:* Richard M Eddinger
**VP:* Trevor R Finger
**VP:* Cindy Rollins
Dir IT: Richard Christy
IT Man: Brent Nothan

D-U-N-S 18-730-1924 IMP
SETEX INC
(*Suby of* TACHI-S ENGINEERING USA INC) ★
1111 Mckinley Rd, Saint Marys, OH 45885-1816
Tel (419) 394-7800 *Founded/Ownrshp* 1987
Sales 110.3MME *EMP* 470
SIC 2531 Seats, automobile
Pr: Shinichirou Shirahama
CFO: Robert Bowlin

D-U-N-S 07-932-4315
SETON HALL UNIVERSITY
400 S Orange Ave, South Orange, NJ 07079-2697
Tel (973) 761-9000 *Founded/Ownrshp* 1856
Sales 272.3MM *EMP* 2,700E
Accts Grantthornton Llp Iselin Nj
SIC 8221 University
Pr: Rev Monsignor R Sheeran
**Pr:* A Gabriel Esteban
CFO: Stephen A Graham
CFO: Thomas Nydegger
VP: Catherine A Kiernan
Off Mgr: Maribel Landrau
CIO: Stephen G Landry
MIS Dir: Stephanie Hauge
IT Man: Bryan Dwyer
Web Dev: Gary Clark
Pgrm Dir: Vivienne Carr

D-U-N-S 87-808-2213
SETON HEALTH SYSTEM INC
ST. MARY'S CAMPUS
(*Suby of* ASCENSION HEALTH) ★
1300 Massachusetts Ave, Troy, NY 12180-1695
Tel (518) 268-5000 *Founded/Ownrshp* 1994
Sales 112.0MM *EMP* 1,288
Accts Deloitte Tax Llp Philadelphia
SIC 8062 8011 General medical & surgical hospitals; Offices & clinics of medical doctors
Pr: Matthias Maguire
**CFO:* Scott St George
Ofcr: Reen Carnevale
VP: Margaret Holcomb
Exec: Irene Griffith
Dir Rx: Joseph Goss
Ex Dir: Mary Russo
Ex Dir: Marcia M Steiner
Pathlgst: Jihong Tang
Plas Surg: Vladimir Kalas
Doctor: Yun Kim

D-U-N-S 07-849-5868 IMP
SETON HEALTHCARE FAMILY (TX)
(*Suby of* ASCENSION HEALTH) ★
1201 W 38th St, Austin, TX 78705-1056
Tel (512) 324-1000 *Founded/Ownrshp* 1900
Sales 816.4MME *EMP* 5,741
Accts Deloitte Tax Llp Cincinnati
SIC 8062 General medical & surgical hospitals
Pr: Jesus Garza
**COO:* Pat Hayes
COO: David Weigle
**CFO:* Alan Strauss
**CFO:* Doug Waite
Bd of Dir: Debra Rodriguez
Ofcr: Delia Presley
Ofcr: Mark Sorensen
**Sr VP:* Ray Anderson
**Sr VP:* Teresa Burroff
Sr VP: Gregory Hartman
VP: Raymond Anderson
**VP:* Joe Canales
VP: Ashton Cumberbatch
VP: Herb Dyer
VP: Lawrence Eul Sr
VP: Hugh Gilmore
VP: Chris Hartle
VP: Gerald W Hill
VP: Tim Lafrey
VP: Cyndy Perkins

SETON IDENTIFICATION PRODUCTS
See TRICOR DIRECT INC

SETON LODGE
See THOMAS SAINT MIDTOWN HOSPITAL

SETON LODGE
See SAINT THOMAS HEALTH SERVICES INC

D-U-N-S 07-188-0116
SETON MEDICAL CENTER
(Suby of VERITY HEALTH SYSTEM OF CALIFORNIA INC) ★
1900 Sullivan Ave, Daly City, CA 94015-2229
Tel (650) 992-4000 Founded/Ownrshp 2002
Sales 246.5MM EMP 1,231
Accts Grant Thornton Llp San Franci
SIC 8062 8051 General medical & surgical hospitals; Skilled nursing care facilities
Pr: John Ferrelli
Chf Rad: Christopher Yoo
Ex VP: Patricia White
VP: John Thomas
Dir Lab: Mary Paulson
Dir Rad: Vida A Campbell
Telecom Mg: Dametra Jefferson
IT Man: Gail Keikoan
Opers Mgr: Joseph B McElmurry
Pathlgst: Ana Quiroga
Opthamlgy: Francisco Garcia

D-U-N-S 08-020-3307
SETON MEDICAL CENTER WILLIAMSON
201 Seton Pkwy, Round Rock, TX 78665-8000
Tel (512) 324-4000 Founded/Ownrshp 2016
Sales 156.3MM EMP 15^E
SIC 8011 Medical centers

D-U-N-S 12-269-4185 IMP
SETPOINT INTEGRATED SOLUTIONS INC
(Suby of PVI HOLDINGS INC) ★
19011 Highland Rd, Baton Rouge, LA 70809-6118
Tel (225) 753-3290 Founded/Ownrshp 2008
Sales 182.4MM EMP 459
SIC 5085 5084 Industrial supplies; Valves & fittings; Instruments & control equipment
Pr: Jack Guidr
*Pr: Jack Guidry
*COO: Jeff Birch
CFO: Chris Elliott
*Sec: David Watkins
VP: Shelby Coleman
*VP: David Ross
Genl Mgr: Larry Guillot
Genl Mgr: Michael Loisel
Genl Mgr: Stuart Prestridge
Dir IT: Cherie Bliss

D-U-N-S 05-140-4735
SEURAT HOLDINGS INC
(Suby of STRATASYS LTD)
5 Fortune Dr, Billerica, MA 01821-3923
Tel (877) 489-9449 Founded/Ownrshp 2012
Sales 317.6MM^E EMP 339^E
SIC 3544 5084 Forms (molds), for foundry & plastics working machinery; Plastic products machinery

D-U-N-S 04-419-8729
SEVEN COUNTIES SERVICES INC
101 W Muhammad Ali Blvd, Louisville, KY 40202-1451
Tel (502) 589-8600 Founded/Ownrshp 1978
Sales 92.6MM EMP 1,300
Accts Mountjoy Chilton Medley Llp L
SIC 8399 8011 8093 8322 8031 Health systems agency; Psychiatric clinic; Specialty outpatient clinics; Mental health clinic, outpatient; Family counseling services; Offices & clinics of osteopathic physicians
CEO: Anthony Zipple
COO: Kelley Gannon
VP: Don Harris
VP: Jean Russell
Admn Mgr: Beth Burden
Off Mgr: Sarah Davenport
Off Mgr: Sonia Livers
Off Admin: John Spivey
CIO: Gerald Brazeau
IT Man: Lisa Mivelaz
Netwrk Eng: Bryan Elam

D-U-N-S 13-241-0684
SEVEN D WHOLESALE OF PA LP
(Suby of DE GOL BROS CARPET DIV) ★
3229 Pleasant Valley Blvd, Altoona, PA 16602-4435
Tel (814) 941-7777 Founded/Ownrshp 1973
Sales 107.8MM^E EMP 72
Accts Richard Burgan Gallitzin Pa
SIC 5031 Building materials, exterior
Genl Pt: Donald A Degol Sr
Pt: Bruno Degol Jr
Pt: David Degol

D-U-N-S 60-425-7654 IMP
SEVEN FOR ALL MANKIND LLC
7 FOR ALL MANKIND
(Suby of WUNDIES KICKAWAY INNER SECRETS) ★
4440 E 26th St, Vernon, CA 90058-4318
Tel (323) 406-5300 Founded/Ownrshp 2016
Sales 111.8MM^E EMP 438
SIC 2325 Men's & boys' jeans & dungarees
Exec: Rosie Rivera
Mktg Mgr: Liat Mazor
Snr Mgr: Neil Laukat

D-U-N-S 07-061-1504
SEVEN HILLS FOUNDATION INC
81 Hope Ave, Worcester, MA 01603-2299
Tel (508) 755-2340 Founded/Ownrshp 1950
Sales 173.6MM EMP 3,900
Accts Bollus Lynch Llp Worcester M
SIC 8211 8361 School for the retarded; Residential care
Pr: David Jordan
*Ch Bd: Melvin Gordon
*COO: Joe Tosches
*CFO: Mike Matthews
*Treas: Claire Swan
VP: Sharon Bacon
VP: Cliff Cabral
VP: Leslie Courtney
VP: Lee Dalphonse
VP: Robin Foley
VP: Sharon Goldberg
VP: Christine Mahoney
VP: Joseph Realbuto

SEVEN ONE SEVEN PARKING ENTPS
See SEVEN-ONE-SEVEN PARKING SERVICES INC

D-U-N-S 61-379-4379 IMP
SEVEN-ELEVEN HAWAII INC
7-ELEVEN
(Suby of SEVEN-ELEVEN JAPAN CO., LTD.)
1755 Nuuanu Ave Fl 2, Honolulu, HI 96817-3207
Tel (808) 526-1711 Founded/Ownrshp 1989
Sales 94.1MM^E EMP 730
SIC 5411 Convenience stores, chain
Ch Bd: Toshifumi Suzuki
*CEO: Gregory Ayres Hanna
*Ex VP: Masaaki Asakura
Ex VP: Jesus H Delgado-Jenkins
Exec: Garrick Carter
Genl Mgr: Glenn Nagatori

D-U-N-S 93-374-1597
SEVEN-ONE-SEVEN PARKING SERVICES INC
SEVEN ONE SEVEN PARKING ENTPS
1410 N Florida Ave, Tampa, FL 33602-2612
Tel (813) 228-7722 Founded/Ownrshp 1994
Sales 67.6MM^E EMP 2,500
SIC 7299 6519 7521 4119 8742 Valet parking; Real property lessors; Automobile parking; Local passenger transportation; Transportation consultant
Pr: Jason Accardi
*VP: John Accardi
Mktg Mgr: Katie Hosier

D-U-N-S 08-353-5773
SEVENSON ENVIRONMENTAL SERVICES INC (NY)
2749 Lockport Rd, Niagara Falls, NY 14305-2229
Tel (716) 284-0431 Founded/Ownrshp 1917, 2002
Sales 200.0MM EMP 500
Accts Chiampou Travis Besaw & Kershn
SIC 4959 1795 Toxic or hazardous waste cleanup; Environmental cleanup services; Demolition, buildings & other structures
CEO: Alan Elia
Pr: Michael Elia
CFO: William McDermott
Treas: Dena M Armstrong
Ex VP: Richard A Eli
Ex VP: Richard A Elia
VP: Laurence A Elia
VP: M Lock
VP: John Robbins

D-U-N-S 07-827-3392
SEVENTY SEVEN ENERGY INC
777 Nw 63rd St, Oklahoma City, OK 73116-7601
Tel (405) 608-7777 Founded/Ownrshp 2001
Sales 1.1MMM EMP 1,700^E
SIC 1389 Hydraulic fracturing wells; Gas compressing (natural gas) at the fields
Pr: Jerry L Winchester
*Ch Bd: Edward J Dipaolo
Pr: James Minmier
Pr: William Stanger
*Pr: Jerry Winchester
COO: Karl Blanchard
CFO: Cary Baetz
Snr PM: Everett Bates
Snr PM: Jill Heitert
Board of Directors: Bob G Alexander, Ronnie Irani, Alvin Bernard Krongard, Tucker Link

D-U-N-S 07-947-1466
SEVENTY SEVEN OPERATING LLC
(Suby of SEVENTY SEVEN ENERGY INC) ★
777 Nw 63rd St, Oklahoma City, OK 73116-7601
Tel (405) 608-7777 Founded/Ownrshp 2014
Sales 711.9MM^E EMP 1,600^E
SIC 3533 1389 Drill rigs; Hydraulic fracturing wells; Gas compressing (natural gas) at the fields
Pr: Jerry L Winchester
*CEO: Jerry Winchester
*COO: Karl Blanchard
*CFO: Cary Baetz

D-U-N-S 80-414-3691 IMP/EXP
SEVERN TRENT (DEL) INC
(Suby of SEVERN TRENT OVERSEAS HOLDINGS LIMITED)
1011 Centre Rd Ste 320, Wilmington, DE 19805-1266
Tel (302) 427-5990 Founded/Ownrshp 1990
Sales 360.5MM^E EMP 1,700^E
SIC 3589 7371 8741 Sewage & water treatment equipment; Computer software writing services; Management services
CEO: Ken Kelly
*Pr: Leonard F Graziano
*CFO: David L Chester
*Treas: Peter Winnington

D-U-N-S 00-530-4782 IMP
SEVERN TRENT SERVICES INC
(Suby of SEVERN TRENT PLC)
220 Gibraltar Rd Ste 200, Fort Washington, PA 19034
Tel (215) 646-9201 Founded/Ownrshp 1991, 2007
Sales 98.1MM^E EMP 281
SIC 8748 3589 Business consulting; Water treatment equipment, industrial
Pr: Leonard F Graziano
*Pr: Stephane Bouvier
*CFO: David L Chester
*Treas: Kenneth J Kelly
*VP: Terry Pearce
Comm Dir: Tracey Rotan
Dist Mgr: Cal Teague
Opers Mgr: Ron Bywaters

D-U-N-S 78-372-3273
SEVERSON GROUP INC
3601 Serpentine Dr, Los Alamitos, CA 90720-2440
Tel (562) 493-3611 Founded/Ownrshp 1990
Sales 288.7MM^E EMP 76
Accts Syme & Fletke Laguna Hills C
SIC 1542 1541 Commercial & office building, new construction; Hospital construction; Institutional building construction; Industrial buildings, new construction
Pr: Jonathan Edward Severson
*Treas: Brian Cresap
*VP: Scott Feest
*VP: Robert Severson

D-U-N-S 17-531-0916 IMP/EXP
SEVERSTAL US HOLDINGS II INC
ESMARK
(Suby of SEVERSTAL, PAO)
907 N Elm St Ste 100, Hinsdale, IL 60521-3644
Tel (708) 756-0400 Founded/Ownrshp 2008
Sales 196.3MM^E EMP 3,929^E
SIC 3291 Abrasive metal & steel products
CEO: James P Bouchard
*Pr: Craig T Bouchard
Pr: Joel Mazur
*CFO: J Gregory Pilewicz
*Co-CEO: David A Luptak
*Co-CEO: Thomas A Modrowski
Area Mgr: Jim Shaffer
Manager: Ted Wozny
Sales Asso: Natalie Bouchard

D-U-N-S 92-995-3727
SEVIER COUNTY BOARD OF EDUCATION
226 Cedar St, Sevierville, TN 37862-3803
Tel (865) 453-4671 Founded/Ownrshp 1890
Sales 69.5MM^E EMP 2,500^E
SIC 8211 School board
Ch Bd: Mike Oakley
*Ex Dir: Donna Koester

D-U-N-S 06-670-7167
SEVIER COUNTY ELECTRIC SYSTEM INC
315 E Main St, Sevierville, TN 37862-3527
Tel (865) 453-2887 Founded/Ownrshp 1940
Sales 153.2MM EMP 98
Accts Brown Jake 7 Mcdaniel Pc Kno
SIC 4911 Distribution, electric power
*Sec: Allen Robbins
CTO: Joe Green
IT Man: Joe Greene
IT Man: Mark Woodham

D-U-N-S 79-459-1482
SEVIER COUNTY SCHOOL SYSTEM
226 Cedar St, Sevierville, TN 37862-3803
Tel (865) 453-4671 Founded/Ownrshp 2012
Sales 30.6MM^E EMP 2,500
SIC 8211 Public elementary & secondary schools; Public elementary school; Public junior high school; Public senior high school
Instr Medi: Nikki Hensley
Psych: Audrea Potter
HC Dir: Don Best

D-U-N-S 83-929-8502 IMP
SEVILLE FARMS INC
8805 Levy County Line Rd, Mansfield, TX 76063
Tel (817) 473-2249 Founded/Ownrshp 1993
Sales 162.3MM^E EMP 350^E
SIC 5193 Nursery stock
Pr: William A Brentlinger
Sr VP: Angela Otts
*VP: Robert J Brentlinger
Dir Soc: Heather Carlson
Dir IT: Angela Hernandez

D-U-N-S 61-756-9640
SEVONE INC
800 Boylston St Bsmt 5, Boston, MA 02199-7060
Tel (617) 982-7700 Founded/Ownrshp 2003
Sales 116.2MM^E EMP 316^E
SIC 7373 Systems integration services
CEO: Jack Sweeney
*CFO: Rafe Brown
*Chf Mktg O: Jim Melvin
*Sr VP: Tanya Bakalov
Sr VP: William J Conners Jr
Sr VP: Ed Zaval
VP: Bart Kelly
VP: Jeff Melvin
VP: Shiva Pillay
*Prin: Kevin Denuccio
*CTO: Vess Bakalov
Board of Directors: Robert Adelson, Ben Holzman, Ben Nye, Michael Phelan, Misha Sanwal

D-U-N-S 07-944-5607 IMP/EXP
SEW-EURODRIVE INC
(Suby of SEW-EURODRIVE GMBH & CO KG)
1295 Old Spartanburg Hwy, Lyman, SC 29365-1820
Tel (864) 439-7537 Founded/Ownrshp 1983
Sales 110.8MM^E EMP 470
SIC 3566 Gears, power transmission, except automotive; Speed changers (power transmission equipment), except auto
CEO: Juergen Blickle
COO: Bruce King
*VP: Christopher Blickle
Sfty Mgr: Dan Raney
Sls Dir: Tom Youngblood
Manager: Ric Henderson
Sls Mgr: David Buccellato
Sls Mgr: Scott Eno
Sls Mgr: Ryan Hill
Sls Mgr: Lance Hornberger
Sls Mgr: John Mikovsky

SEWANEE
See UNIVERSITY OF SOUTH

D-U-N-S 03-915-6237
SEWANHAKA CENTRAL HIGH SCHOOL DISTRICT
77 Landau Ave, Floral Park, NY 11001-3603
Tel (516) 488-9810 Founded/Ownrshp 1926
Sales 47.5MM^E EMP 1,075
SIC 8211 Public senior high school
*Pr: Jean Fichel
HC Dir: Paul Klimuszko

SEWARD FISHERIES
See ICICLE SEAFOODS INC

D-U-N-S 60-293-3673 IMP
SEWELL CORP
SEWELL LEXUS
6421 Lemmon Ave, Dallas, TX 75209-5721
Tel (214) 352-8100 Founded/Ownrshp 1989
Sales 136.4MM^E EMP 430^E
SIC 5511 Automobiles, new & used
Ch Bd: Carl Sewell III
*Pr: Jerry Griffin
CFO: Mark McCants
*VP: Barry Pryor
*VP: Peggy Sewell
*Prin: Mark Smith
Sales Asso: John Abbott
Sales Asso: Ken Brown
Sales Asso: Kevin Bush
Sales Asso: Anthony Contreras
Sales Asso: Roy Harp

D-U-N-S 06-422-9636
SEWELL FAMILY OF COMPANIES INC
2425 E 8th St, Odessa, TX 79761-4901
Tel (432) 498-0421 Founded/Ownrshp 1935
Sales 131.8MM^E EMP 320
SIC 5511 Automobiles, new & used; Pickups, new & used
CEO: Ronald R Sewell
*Pr: Collin M Sewell
*CFO: Carla Rowell
*VP: Paul Crump Jr
*VP: Canda Sewell
Exec: Chris Garrett
IT Man: Andrew Petersen
Sls Mgr: Joe Fee
Sales Asso: Daniel Bright
Sales Asso: Jacob Landrum
Snr Mgr: Johnny Harrell

SEWELL INFINITI
See SEWELL VILLAGE CADILLAC CO INC

SEWELL LEXUS
See SEWELL CORP

D-U-N-S 02-629-6392
SEWELL VILLAGE CADILLAC CO INC
SEWELL INFINITI
7310 Lemmon Ave, Dallas, TX 75209-3014
Tel (214) 350-2000 Founded/Ownrshp 1946
Sales 514.8MM^E EMP 1,350
SIC 5511 Automobiles, new & used
Ch Bd: Carl Sewell
COO: Ken Clayton
*COO: Mark Smith
*CFO: Rich Clonts
*VP: Jerry Griffin
*VP: Peggy Sewell
Exec: Paul Cyr
Sales Exec: Baden Rowland
VP Mktg: Stephen Tolerico
Mktg Mgr: Ken Slataper
Sales Asso: Kathryn Brkovich

D-U-N-S 03-058-1255
SEWICKLEY CAPITAL INC
501 Silverside Rd Ste 67, Wilmington, DE 19809-1394
Tel (302) 793-4964 Founded/Ownrshp 1999
Sales 158.8MM^E EMP 631
SIC 3559 3822 Plastics working machinery; Temperature controls, automatic
CEO: G Watts Humphrey

D-U-N-S 00-470-3353 IMP
SEWON AMERICA INC (GA)
(Suby of SEWON PRECISION INDUSTRY CO., LTD.)
1000 Sewon Blvd, Lagrange, GA 30240-5758
Tel (706) 298-5800 Founded/Ownrshp 2008
Sales 359.2MM EMP 800
SIC 3711 Motor vehicles & car bodies
Pr: Chang Joo Lee
Exec: Eun Lee
Genl Mgr: Junho Jung
*Genl Mgr: Seok Ha You
Snr Mgr: Michael Terry

SEWS
See SUMITOMO ELECTRIC WIRING SYSTEMS INC

D-U-N-S 07-235-8559
SEYFARTH SHAW LLP
131 S Dearborn St # 2400, Chicago, IL 60603-5863
Tel (312) 460-5000 Founded/Ownrshp 2003
Sales 328.5MM^E EMP 1,608
SIC 8111 General practice law office; Corporate, partnership & business law; Administrative & government law; Labor & employment law
Mng Pt: David J Rowland
Pt: John H Anderson
Pt: David S Baffa
Pt: Michael H Baniak
Pt: Edward W Bergmann
Pt: James S Cochran
Pt: Maura B O Connor
Pt: Lisa Damon
Pt: William J Dritsas
Pt: Joel H Kaplan
Pt: Edward Karlin
Pt: Kenwood C Youmans
Mng Pt: Lorie E Almon
Mng Pt: Robert L Bodansky
Mng Pt: Mark W Coffin
Mng Pt: Steven L Kennedy
Mng Pt: Aaron R Lubeley
Mng Pt: Richard Mendelson
Mng Pt: John P Napoli
Mng Pt: Laura W Shelby
Mng Pt: Russell B Swapp

D-U-N-S 60-780-1065 IMP
SEYMOUR TUBING INC
(Suby of NIPPON STEEL & SUMIKIN PIPE CO., LTD.)
1515 E 4th Street Rd, Seymour, IN 47274-4301
Tel (812) 523-0842 Founded/Ownrshp 1988
Sales 89.2MM^E EMP 425
SIC 3312 Tubes, steel & iron
Pr: Toru Nishikado
*Treas: Yasutaka Nakano
Genl Mgr: Hirokazu Ajima

D-U-N-S 01-327-3375 EXP
SF HOLDINGS GROUP INC
SOLO CUP
(*Suby of* SOLO CUP CO LLC) ★
300 Tr State Intl Ste 200, Lincolnshire, IL 60069
Tel (847) 831-4800 *Founded/Ownrshp* 1997
Sales 77.6MM[E] *EMP* 1,763[E]
SIC 2656 Plates, paper: made from purchased material; Food containers (liquid tight), including milk cartons
CEO: Robert M Korzenski
COO: Julie Harvey
Ex VP: Robert D Koney Jr
Ex VP: Robert Koney
Ex VP: Susan Marks
Ex VP: Anil Shan
VP: Rick Bowdle
VP: Tom Pasqualini
VP: Bill Rickert
**VP:* Linda Ridgley
VP: Jeff Seidman

SF-MARIN FOOD BANK
See SAN FRANCISCO FOOD BANK

D-U-N-S 00-834-6140 IMP/EXP
SFC GLOBAL SUPPLY CHAIN INC (MN)
(*Suby of* SCHWAN FOOD CO) ★
115 W College Dr, Marshall, MN 56258-1747
Tel (507) 532-3274 *Founded/Ownrshp* 1962, 1985
Sales 1.0MMM[E] *EMP* 4,670
SIC 2045 2038 Pizza doughs, prepared: from purchased flour; Pizza, frozen
Pr: Douglas Olsem
Exec: Helen Andries

SFCC
See SANTA FE COMMUNITY COLLEGE

D-U-N-S 05-232-7983
SFG MANAGEMENT LIMITED LIABILITY CO
3114 S Haskell Ave, Dallas, TX 75223-3121
Tel (214) 824-8163 *Founded/Ownrshp* 1994
Sales 211.0MM[E] *EMP* 6,000
SIC 2026 Milk processing (pasteurizing, homogenizing, bottling)

SFI GRAY STEEL
See SFI-GRAY STEEL LLC

D-U-N-S 01-050-2479 IMP
■ **SFI-GRAY STEEL LLC**
SFI GRAY STEEL
(*Suby of* JOSEPH T RYERSON & SON INC) ★
3511 W 12th St, Houston, TX 77008-6005
Tel (713) 864-6450 *Founded/Ownrshp* 2011
Sales 16.1MM[E] *EMP* 3,000
SIC 3325 5051 Steel foundries; Metals service centers & offices
CEO: Edward J Lehner
**CFO:* Terence Rogers
**Prin:* Micheal Arnold
Sales Exec: Gene Bellman

D-U-N-S 11-286-6678
SFM MUTUAL INSURANCE CO
S F M
3500 Amrcn Blvd W Ste 700, Bloomington, MN 55431
Tel (952) 838-4200 *Founded/Ownrshp* 1983
Sales NA *EMP* 200
Accts Strohm Ballweg Llp Madison
SIC 6331 Workers' compensation insurance
Pr: Robert T Lund
**CFO:* Terrence Miller
Bd of Dir: Truman Jeffers
**Sr VP:* M Scott Brener
**Sr VP:* Michael L Happe
**Sr VP:* David E Kaiser
VP: Scott Brener
**VP:* Steven T Sandilla
QA Dir: Laurie Weatbrook
Web Dev: Peter Raih
Software D: Jared Lane

SFMC
See ST FRANCIS MEDICAL CENTER

SFMOMA MUSEUM STORE
See SAN FRANCISCO MUSEUM OF MODERN ART

D-U-N-S 05-303-2074
SFN GROUP INC
MERGIS GROUP, THE
(*Suby of* RANDSTAD NORTH AMERICA INC) ★
2050 Spectrum Blvd, Fort Lauderdale, FL 33309-3008
Tel (954) 308-7600 *Founded/Ownrshp* 1946, 2011
Sales 19.3MMM[E] *EMP* 171,000
SIC 6794 7363 Franchises, selling or licensing; Temporary help service
CEO: Roy G Krause
Pr: Kelly Cartwright
Pr: Brian Kraner
**COO:* William J Grubbs
**CFO:* Mark W Smith
Ex VP: Carleen Mackay
Ex VP: Sharon Wienandt
Sr VP: Ian Dawson
VP: Linda Perneau
VP: Michael Winwood
Exec: Phil Smith

D-U-N-S 03-695-5966
SFN PROFESSIONAL SERVICES LLC
TODAYS OFFICE PROFESSIONALS
(*Suby of* MERGIS GROUP) ★
2050 Spectrum Blvd, Fort Lauderdale, FL 33309-3008
Tel (954) 938-7600 *Founded/Ownrshp* 1999
Sales 61.6MM[E] *EMP* 3,275
SIC 7363 Help supply services
CFO: Roy Krause
Sr VP: Teri Miller
VP: Kelly Cartwright
VP: Karen Turner
Prin: Robert Livonus
Brnch Mgr: Lisa Dickerson
Opers Mgr: Kim Gorczynski

D-U-N-S 14-644-0326 IMP/EXP
SFS INTEC INC
FASTENING SYSTEMS
(*Suby of* SFS INTEC HOLDING AG)
1045 Spring St, Wyomissing, PA 19610-1747
Tel (610) 376-5751 *Founded/Ownrshp* 1986
Sales 87.2MM[E] *EMP* 550
SIC 7699 5012 5085 Industrial equipment services; Automobiles; Fasteners & fastening equipment
Pr: Michael A Mullen
**Treas:* Tim Myers
**VP:* Jens Breu
VP: Richard Cohen
**VP:* URS Langenauer
**VP:* Eric D Murray
Rgnl Mgr: Ken Deck
Dist Mgr: Keith Ammerman
Dist Mgr: Earl Hernandez
Dist Mgr: Kevin Keith
Dist Mgr: Doug Palmer

SFWMD
See SOUTH FLORIDA WATER MANAGEMENT DISTRICT LEASING CORP

D-U-N-S 07-872-9567 IMP
▲ **SFX ENTERTAINMENT INC**
902 Broadway Fl 8, New York, NY 10010-6037
Tel (646) 561-6400 *Founded/Ownrshp* 2012
Sales 354.4MM *EMP* 450[E]
Tkr Sym SFXEQ *Exch* OTC
SIC 7929 Entertainment service
Ch Bd: Robert F X Sillerman
**Pr:* Gregory Consiglio
CFO: Tim Clyne
**CFO:* Richard Rosenstein
**V Ch Bd:* Joseph F Rascoff
**Sr VP:* Robert Damon
VP: Shawn Kent
VP: Frank Lopresti
VP: Eliron Ozarko
VP: Rama Poola
VP: Veenerick Vos
Board of Directors: D Geoff Armstrong, Andrew N Bazoz, Pasquale Manocchia, Michael Meyer, John Miller, Edward Simon, Mitchell Slater

D-U-N-S 78-057-2223
SG AMERICAS SECURITIES HOLDINGS LLC
SGAS
245 Park Ave Fl 5, New York, NY 10167-0002
Tel (212) 278-6000 *Founded/Ownrshp* 2003
Sales 333.8MM[E] *EMP* 530
SIC 6211 Brokers, security; Dealers, security
CEO: Craig Overlander
**CFO:* Andrew Wohl
**Mng Dir:* Kim Fennebresque

D-U-N-S 16-787-3939
SG AMERICAS SECURITIES LLC
(*Suby of* SOCIETE GENERALE)
245 Park Ave, New York, NY 10167-0002
Tel (212) 278-6000 *Founded/Ownrshp* 2005
Sales 796.8MM *EMP* 18
Accts Deloitte & Touche Llp New Yor
SIC 6211 Investment bankers
COO: Vincent Gay-Forest
CFO: Karim Hajjaji
VP: John Correnti
VP: Elina Zak
Mng Dir: Mark Johnson
Dir IT: Julian Ku
VP Opers: Dean Hagler
Snr Mgr: Craig Overlander

D-U-N-S 96-849-8696 IMP
SG SEAFOOD HOLDINGS INC
225 Southampton St, Boston, MA 02118-2715
Tel (617) 442-5800 *Founded/Ownrshp* 2010
Sales 166.0MM[E] *EMP* 192[E]
SIC 5146 Fish, fresh; Fish, frozen, unpackaged; Seafoods
Pr: Kimberly Gorton
COO: Michael Richard
**Treas:* Michael C Gorton
VP: Patrice Flanagan

SG360
See SEGERDAHL CORP

SGAS
See SG AMERICAS SECURITIES HOLDINGS LLC

D-U-N-S 07-587-0225 IMP
■ **SGD NORTH AMERICA INC**
(*Suby of* SGD S A)
9141 Technology Dr, Covington, GA 30014-0971
Tel (770) 385-3800 *Founded/Ownrshp* 1995
Sales 97.0MM[E] *EMP* 450
SIC 3221 Glass containers
**VP:* David Shan
Dir IT: John Hsu
Board of Directors: Frederic Brunet, Ashok Sudan

D-U-N-S 00-520-0662
■ **SGK LLC**
(*Suby of* MATTHEWS INTERNATIONAL CORP) ★
1600 Sherwin Ave, Des Plaines, IL 60018-3013
Tel (847) 827-9494 *Founded/Ownrshp* 2014
Sales 519.0MM[E] *EMP* 3,600[E]
SIC 8748 Business consulting
CEO: David Schawk
**Pr:* Eric Ashworth
CFO: Timothy J Cunningham
**Ex VP:* Carol Campagnolo
**Ex VP:* Tim Cunningham
Ex VP: Gary Kohl
**Ex VP:* Brad Wills
Sr VP: Michael Leeds
VP: Jerry Habeck
VP: Otto Hektor
VP: Eric Schultz
**Exec:* A Alex Sarkisian

D-U-N-S 00-146-7976 IMP/EXP
SGL CARBON LLC (NV)
(*Suby of* SGL CARBON BETEILIGUNG GMBH)
10130 Perimeter Pkwy # 500, Charlotte, NC 28216-2447
Tel (704) 593-5100 *Founded/Ownrshp* 1939, 1998
Sales 630.0MM[E] *EMP* 565
SIC 3624

D-U-N-S 78-380-4185
SGS INTERNATIONAL LLC
(*Suby of* SOUTHERN GRAPHICS INC) ★
626 W Main St Ste 500, Louisville, KY 40202-4269
Tel (502) 637-5443 *Founded/Ownrshp* 2005
Sales 590.0MM[E] *EMP* 2,400
SIC 6719 Investment holding companies, except banks
CEO: Aidan Tracey
COO: Michael C Jackson Jr
CFO: David Scheve
Ex VP: Luca C Naccarato
Sr VP: Michael L Shannon
VP: Benjamin F Harmon IV
VP: Todd Santo
CTO: Phillip Acosta

D-U-N-S 05-360-0573
SGS NORTH AMERICA INC
(*Suby of* SGS US HOLDING INC) ★
301 Route 17, Rutherford, NJ 07070-2575
Tel (201) 508-3000 *Founded/Ownrshp* 1980
Sales 1.3MMM[E] *EMP* 5,100
SIC 8734 7389 8071 4499 4785 Testing laboratories; Industrial & commercial equipment inspection service; Building inspection service; Testing laboratories; Marine surveyors; Inspection services connected with transportation
Pr: Kimmo Fuller
CFO: Michael Brigant
CFO: Michael Brigante
Ex VP: Mike Belton
VP: Fadia Alkhalil
VP: Elvis Calixto
VP: Anita Changur
VP: Ronald Mathis
VP: Michelle Smith
VP Bus Dev: Bob Gapinski
Exec: Luciano Rebello
Dir Teleco: Bill Bauer

D-U-N-S 08-030-6455
SGS US HOLDING INC
(*Suby of* SGS SA)
201 Route 17, Rutherford, NJ 07070-2574
Tel (201) 508-3000 *Founded/Ownrshp* 2003
Sales 1.3MMM[E] *EMP* 5,324[E]
SIC 8734 6719 7389 Testing laboratories; Investment holding companies, except banks; Industrial & commercial equipment inspection service
CEO: Christopher Kirk

SGT
See STEAM GENERATING TEAM LLC

D-U-N-S 87-890-1396
SGT INC
7701 Greenbelt Rd Ste 400, Greenbelt, MD 20770-6521
Tel (301) 614-8600 *Founded/Ownrshp* 1994
Sales 570.8MM *EMP* 2,300
Accts Dixon Hughes Goodman Llp Tyso
SIC 7371 7373 7376 Custom computer programming services; Computer integrated systems design; Computer facilities management
Ch Bd: Harold Stinger
**Pr:* Kamal S Ghaffarian
Pr: Michael T Suffredini
COO: Dave Wolt
CFO: Joe Morway
Sr VP: Wayne Friedman
VP: Joy Colucci
VP: Mike Gigliotti
VP: Doug Woodward
VP Bus Dev: James King
Exec: Wayne Rustin

D-U-N-S 08-039-1542
SGWSNHC LLC
(*Suby of* SOUTHERN GLAZERS WINE AND SPIRITS LLC) ★
1600 Nw 163rd St, Miami, FL 33169-5641
Tel (305) 625-4171 *Founded/Ownrshp* 2016
Sales 195.0MM[E] *EMP* 75[E]
SIC 5182 Liquor

D-U-N-S 83-320-5870
SH GROUP INC
SYSCA
1515 Broadway, New York, NY 10036-8901
Tel (212) 921-2300 *Founded/Ownrshp* 2005
Sales 100.4MM *EMP* 500
Accts Anchin Block & Anchin Llp Ne
SIC 8748 8711 1542 Business consulting; Engineering services; Commercial & office building contractors
Co-Pr: Gary Brennan
**Co-Pr:* Cyrus Izzo

D-U-N-S 18-603-2694
SHA LLC
FIRSTCARE
12940 N Hwy 183, Austin, TX 78750-3203
Tel (512) 257-6000 *Founded/Ownrshp* 1995
Sales NA *EMP* 270
SIC 6324 6311 6321 Hospital & medical service plans; Life insurance; Accident & health insurance
**CEO:* Keith Lundien
**COO:* Mark Huntley
CFO: Velann Anderson
**CFO:* Keenan Freeman
Assoc VP: Will Rodriguez
Assoc VP: Tony Rourke
Sr VP: Ashley Allen
Sr VP: Sonya Henderson
VP: Barbara Berger
VP: Brianna Braden
**CIO:* Gerald Shields

D-U-N-S 07-873-3877
SHACKLEFORDS CONSTRUCTION & CONTRACTING LTD
303 Lexington Ave, New York, NY 10016-3165
Tel (646) 771-4470 *Founded/Ownrshp* 2013
Sales 150.0MM *EMP* 300
SIC 1522 1542 1541 7389 Residential construction; Nonresidential construction; Industrial buildings, new construction;
Pr: Johnathon Shackleford

D-U-N-S 14-184-0186
SHADE STRUCTURES INC
USA SHADE & FABRIC STRUCTURES
(*Suby of* PLAYPOWER INC) ★
8505 Chancellor Row, Dallas, TX 75247-5519
Tel (214) 905-9500 *Founded/Ownrshp* 2013
Sales 123.1MM[E] *EMP* 349[E]
SIC 2394 Shades, canvas: made from purchased materials
Pr: John Saunders
**VP:* George Ochs
S&M/VP: DOT Haymann

D-U-N-S 36-116-5509
SHADOW HOLDINGS LLC
BOCCHI LABORATORIES
26455 Ruether Ave, Santa Clarita, CA 91350-2621
Tel (661) 252-3807 *Founded/Ownrshp* 2008
Sales 184.9MM[E] *EMP* 500[E]
SIC 2844 Hair preparations, including shampoos; Cosmetic preparations
CEO: Joe Pender
CFO: Patrick Kelley
VP: Steve Dugdale
Dir IT: David Carpenter

D-U-N-S 07-833-5973
SHADOW MOUNTAIN MANAGEMENT CORP (CO)
HILDEBRAND CARE CENTER
(*Suby of* PIKES PEAK LODGE 38) ★
1401 Phay Ave, Canon City, CO 81212-2303
Tel (719) 275-8656 *Founded/Ownrshp* 1973
Sales 514.7MM *EMP* 138
SIC 8051 Convalescent home with continuous nursing care
Pr: John Havill
**VP:* Ammon Scott
Exec: Chris Abraas
Telecom Ex: Candice T Foraker
Mktg Mgr: Bev Smith
Sls Mgr: Lawrence Cowan
Nrsg Dir: Phyllis Hall

SHADY GROVE MEDICAL CENTER
See ADVENTIST HEALTHCARE INC

D-U-N-S 01-642-4476
SHAFT DRILLERS INTERNATIONAL LLC
130 Madow Ridge Rd Ste 23, Mount Morris, PA 15349
Tel (800) 331-0175 *Founded/Ownrshp* 2011
Sales 115.4MM[E] *EMP* 797
SIC 1781 Water well drilling
Pr: Scott Kiger
**CFO:* Casie Shaner
Off Mgr: Tammie Peters
IT Man: Michael Brown
Genl Couns: Jim Cunningham

D-U-N-S 07-976-0012
▲ **SHAKE SHACK INC**
24 Union Sq E Fl 5, New York, NY 10003-3201
Tel (646) 747-7200 *Founded/Ownrshp* 2014
Sales 190.5MM *EMP* 2,215[E]
Tkr Sym SHAK *Exch* NYS
SIC 5812 American restaurant
CEO: Randy Garutti
**Ch Bd:* Daniel Meyer
CFO: Jeff Uttz
VP: Ronald Palmese Jr
Genl Mgr: Carlos Casian
Board of Directors: Jeff Flug, Evan Guillemin, Jonathan D Sokoloff, Robert Vivian

D-U-N-S 12-385-4346 IMP/EXP
SHAKE-N-GO FASHION INC
85 Harbor Rd, Port Washington, NY 11050-2535
Tel (516) 944-7777 *Founded/Ownrshp* 1991
Sales 301.5MM *EMP* 200[E]
Accts Friedman Llp New York Ny
SIC 3999 Hairpin mountings; Wigs, including doll wigs, toupees or wiglets
Ch Bd: James K Kim
**Treas:* Betty Kim
**VP:* Mike Kim
IT Man: Yunsung Han

D-U-N-S 05-354-0845 IMP
■ **SHAKESPEARE CO LLC**
JARDEN APPLIED MATERIALS
(*Suby of* NEWELL BRANDS) ★
6111 Shakespeare Rd, Columbia, SC 29223-7323
Tel (803) 754-7011 *Founded/Ownrshp* 1980
Sales 430.1MM[E] *EMP* 850
SIC 3089 3949 3679 3663 Monofilaments, nontextile; Fishing tackle, general; Reels, fishing; Rods & rod parts, fishing; Antennas, receiving; Marine radio communications equipment
CFO: Diana Crawford
Treas: Nyle Miyamoto
Dir IT: Gina Waller
VP Sls: Brian Searfoss
S&M/Dir: Gary Remensnyder

SHAKEY'S PIZZA
See JACMAR COMPANIES

D-U-N-S 02-028-4076 IMP
SHAKLEE CORP
4747 Willow Rd, Pleasanton, CA 94588-2763
Tel (925) 924-2000 *Founded/Ownrshp* 2004
Sales 119.1MM[E] *EMP* 500
SIC 5499 Health & dietetic food stores
CEO: Roger Barnett
**Pr:* Dan Rajczak
**CFO:* Mike Batesole
**Sr VP:* Justin Rose

*Sr VP: Todd Tucker
VP: Shobhna Asthana
VP: Craig Cushman
VP: Laura Evans
VP: Chris Jensen
VP: Cathy Keating
VP: Jill Miller
VP: Brad Muise
VP: Jeff Olson
VP: Elena Panos
VP: Robert Young
Exec: Alice Coker
Exec: Jack Wolf
Exec: Jennifer Wyckoff

D-U-N-S 02-028-4282 IMP
SHAKLEE US INC
4747 Willow Rd, Pleasanton, CA 94588-2763
Tel (925) 924-2000 Founded/Ownrshp 2004
Sales 103.0MM^E EMP 300^E
SIC 5122 Vitamins & minerals
Pr: Bob Schults
*VP: John Rim

D-U-N-S 07-867-0411
SHAKOPEE MDEWAKANTON SIOUX COMMUNITY
SMSC
2330 Sioux Trl Nw, Prior Lake, MN 55372-9077
Tel (952) 445-8900 Founded/Ownrshp 1973
Sales 92.3MM^E EMP 1,500
SIC 7999 Gambling establishment
Ch: Stanley Crooks
*Treas: Lori Beaulieu
*Treas: Charlie Vig
*Sec: Lori K Watso
Bd of Dir: Linda Brown
Genl Mgr: William Rudnicki
Off Mgr: Nina Hatling
Snr Mgr: Eric Zimmerman

SHALE-INLAND
See FLOWORKS INTERNATIONAL LLC

D-U-N-S 00-555-2187
■ **SHAMBAUGH & SON LP** (TX)
(Suby of EMCOR GROUP INC) ★
7614 Opportunity Dr, Fort Wayne, IN 46825-3363
Tel (260) 487-7777 Founded/Ownrshp 1926, 2002
Sales 429.5MM EMP 1,800
SIC 1711 1799 1731 1796 1629

D-U-N-S 07-879-9303
SHAMBAUGH & SON LP
7614 Opportunity Dr, Fort Wayne, IN 46825-3363
Tel (260) 487-7814 Founded/Ownrshp 1999
Sales 50.8MM^E EMP 1,600
SIC 8711 3556 5122 Construction & civil engineering; Smokers, food processing equipment; Pharmaceuticals
CEO: Mark Shambaugh
Pr: Paul R Meyers Jr
CFO: Mark Veerkamp
Sr VP: Ken Bitner
Sr VP: Jeff Johns
Prin: Scott Simon

D-U-N-S 08-031-2928
SHAMI MEDIA GROUP INC
1395 Brickell Ave Ste 800, Miami, FL 33131-3302
Tel (347) 549-2710 Founded/Ownrshp 2013
Sales 900.0MM EMP 6
SIC 7389 Music distribution systems
Pr: Bob Shami

D-U-N-S 07-449-0632
SHAMIN HOTELS INC
SHAMIN MANAGEMENT
2000 Ware Btm Spring Rd, Chester, VA 23836-4200
Tel (804) 777-9000 Founded/Ownrshp 1997
Sales 142.8MM^E EMP 1,800
SIC 7011 8051 6512 6513 Hotels & motels; Extended care facility; Shopping center, property operation only; Apartment building operators
Pr: Pramod C Amin
Rgnl Mgr: Margaret Akins
Genl Mgr: Badal Patel
VP Opers: Leigh Burke
VP Opers: Mark Yardis
Sls Dir: Delinda Carter
Sls Mgr: Jaclyn Lester

SHAMIN MANAGEMENT
See SHAMIN HOTELS INC

D-U-N-S 13-944-2573
SHAMROCK ACQUISITION CORP
SHAMROCK CLEAN
10540 Belcher Rd S, Seminole, FL 33777-1447
Tel (727) 209-0553 Founded/Ownrshp 2001
Sales 22.4MM^E EMP 1,500
SIC 7349 Building maintenance, except repairs
Pr: Carl Shanahan Jr
*VP: Kevin Shanahan

D-U-N-S 08-197-8876 IMP/EXP
SHAMROCK BUILDING MATERIALS INC
SHAMROCK TRADING CO
4725 Village Plaza Loop # 201, Eugene, OR 97401-6677
Tel (877) 426-2341 Founded/Ownrshp 1997
Sales 163.4MM^E EMP 55
Accts Isler Cpa Eugene Oregon
SIC 5031 5051 Lumber, plywood & millwork; Pipe & tubing, steel
Pr: Michael D Gambee
*VP: Gregory J Gambee

SHAMROCK CLEAN
See SHAMROCK ACQUISITION CORP

D-U-N-S 96-542-2306
SHAMROCK CO
KFC
15 Spinning Wheel Rd # 110, Hinsdale, IL 60521-7653
Tel (630) 655-8274 Founded/Ownrshp 1986
Sales 35.3MM^E EMP 1,000
SIC 5812 Fast-food restaurant, chain
Pr: Stephen C Mc Gue
*VP: Kevin Wallace

D-U-N-S 00-881-2786
SHAMROCK COAL CO INC (TN)
(Suby of JAMES RIVER COAL SERVICE CO) ★
1374 Highway 192 E, London, KY 40741-3123
Tel (606) 878-7411 Founded/Ownrshp 1944
Sales 47.3MM^E EMP 1,018
SIC 1222 Bituminous coal-underground mining
Pr: Timothy Frasure
Ch Bd: James Crawford
Pr: Tim Frasure
Treas: Elmer Ison

D-U-N-S 61-145-2970 IMP
SHAMROCK COMPANIES INC
24090 Detroit Rd, Westlake, OH 44145-1513
Tel (440) 899-9510 Founded/Ownrshp 1982
Sales 91.0MM^E EMP 140
SIC 5112 5199 7336 7389 2754 2395 Business forms; Advertising specialties; Art design services; Brokers' services; Commercial printing, gravure; Pleating & stitching
Ch Bd: Robert E Troop
*CEO: Tim Connor
*COO: Dave Fechter
*CFO: Gary A Lesjak
Treas: Joseph B Knezevich
Dir IT: SAI Totapally
Plnt Mgr: Matthew Balmer
Sales Exec: Bill Fischer
Sales Exec: Dustin Resar
Mktg Dir: Caryn Harknett
Sls Mgr: John Arnold

D-U-N-S 86-781-1689
SHAMROCK ENVIRONMENTAL CORP
6106 Corporate Park Dr, Browns Summit, NC 27214-9700
Tel (336) 375-1989 Founded/Ownrshp 1994
Sales 96.6MM^E EMP 150
SIC 4953 4212 8748 7699 Non-hazardous waste disposal sites; Local trucking, without storage; Environmental consultant; Tank repair & cleaning services
CEO: George Oliver
*Pr: Gregory Kiser
*VP: Dennis Snead
VP: Dennis R Snead Jr
VP: Steven A Thackston
VP: Mark Wise
Mktg Mgr: Rick Wigal

D-U-N-S 04-237-0734 IMP
SHAMROCK FOODS CO
3900 E Camelback Rd # 300, Phoenix, AZ 85018-2615
Tel (602) 477-2500 Founded/Ownrshp 1922
Sales 2.7MMM EMP 2,600
SIC 5146 5149 5147 5148 5142 2026 Fish, fresh; Fish, frozen, unpackaged; Groceries & related products; Canned goods: fruit, vegetables, seafood, meats, etc.; Meats, fresh; Fruits, fresh; Vegetables, fresh; Packaged frozen goods; Milk processing (pasteurizing, homogenizing, bottling)
Pr: W Kent McClelland
*Ch Bd: Norman P McClelland
COO: Kent Mc Clelland
*Treas: Michael Garnreiter
*Sr VP: Michael Krueger
*Sr VP: Kent Mullison
*Sr VP: Larry Yancy
VP: F Giltne
VP: Ed Reinhart
VP: Mark Sherman
Area Mgr: Brett Baczkowski

SHAMROCK PLANK FLOORING
See JT SHANNON LUMBER CO INC

SHAMROCK TRADING CO
See SHAMROCK BUILDING MATERIALS INC

D-U-N-S 18-615-8569
SHAMROCK TRADING CORP
9300 Metcalf Ave, Overland Park, KS 66212-1463
Tel (913) 310-2200 Founded/Ownrshp 2005
Sales 113.3MM^E EMP 300
Accts Bkd Llp
SIC 4731 6153 8742 7323 Freight transportation arrangement; Short-term business credit; Management consulting services; Credit reporting services
Pr: William Ryan
*CFO: Ken Bowman
*VP: Patrick Kellerman
VP: Martin Ryan
CIO: Bill Ryan

SHANDS AT THE UNIVERSITY FLA
See SHANDS TEACHING HOSPITAL AND CLINICS INC

D-U-N-S 96-403-2325
SHANDS JACKSONVILLE HEALTHCARE INC
(Suby of SHANDS AT UNIVERSITY FLA) ★
655 W 8th St, Jacksonville, FL 32209-6511
Tel (904) 244-0411 Founded/Ownrshp 1984
Sales 522.8MM EMP 1^E
SIC 8062 General medical & surgical hospitals
Prin: Susan Brownie
CFO: William J Ryan
VP: Gregory Fache
VP: Michael Lawton
VP: Greg Miller
Obsttrcn: Nikki J Rowan
Ansthlgy: Kristen Vanderhoef
Ansthlgy: Matthew Warrick
Podiatrist: Sadia M Ali
Doctor: Julie Cassells
Doctor: Malcolm T Foster

D-U-N-S 14-705-6410 IMP
SHANDS JACKSONVILLE MEDICAL CENTER INC
UNIVERSITY HEALTH GROUPS
655 W 8th St, Jacksonville, FL 32209-6511
Tel (904) 244-5576 Founded/Ownrshp 1981
Sales 663.3MM EMP 3,000
Accts Pricewaterhousecoopers Llp T
SIC 8062 General medical & surgical hospitals
CEO: David S Guzick
*Pr: Russell E Armistead Jr
*CFO: William J Ryan
VP: Steven Blumberg
*VP: Greg Miller
VP: Penny Thompson
Dir Risk M: Debbie Monnseratt
Dir Rx: Marci Delossantos
Dir Sec: Paul Reis
Genl Mgr: Neal McMahon
IT Man: Shawn Clark

D-U-N-S 03-918-3736 IMP
SHANDS TEACHING HOSPITAL AND CLINICS INC
SHANDS AT THE UNIVERSITY FLA
(Suby of UNIVERSITY HEALTH GROUPS) ★
1600 Sw Archer Rd, Gainesville, FL 32610-3003
Tel (352) 265-0111 Founded/Ownrshp 1979
Sales 1.2MMM EMP 3,160^E
SIC 8011 Medical centers
CEO: Marvin Dewar
*Pr: David S D
*Pr: David S Guzick
*CEO: Russell E Armistead
*CEO: Timothy Goldfarb
*CFO: Michael E Gleason
CFO: Bill Robinson
CFO: William J Robinson
*Treas: James J Kelly
Ex VP: Timothy M Goldfarb
Sr VP: Kari Cassel
*Sr VP: Greg Miller
*Sr VP: Daniel R Wilson
VP: Irene Alexaitis
VP: Janet Christie
VP: Mary A Kiely
VP: Melanie F Ross
Assoc Dir: Brad Kowal
Dir Rad: Anthony Mancuso

D-U-N-S 17-950-1911
SHANER HOTEL GROUP LIMITED PARTNERSHIP
1965 Waddle Rd, State College, PA 16803-1639
Tel (814) 234-4460 Founded/Ownrshp 1995
Sales 262.6MM^E EMP 4,000
SIC 7011 Hotels & motels
Pt: Lance T Shaner
Pt: J B Griffin
Pt: Patrick Landy
Pt: Bill Mabrey
Pt: Brian McMahon
Pt: Fred Shaner
Pt: George Wolfe
CFO: Bruce Benner
CFO: Amanda Droll
VP: William Hoy
Ex Dir: Barbara Eslick

D-U-N-S 09-247-0962
SHANER OPERATING CORP
1965 Waddle Rd, State College, PA 16803-1639
Tel (814) 234-4460 Founded/Ownrshp 1976
Sales 71.1MM^E EMP 2,500
SIC 8741 Hotel or motel management
Ch Bd: Lance T Shaner
*CFO: Patrick Landy
*VP: Goerge Wolfe
Board of Directors: Elizabeth Shaner

D-U-N-S 87-428-3153
SHANGHAI FOXBORO CO
33 Commercial St, Foxboro, MA 02035-5309
Tel (508) 543-8750 Founded/Ownrshp 1981
Sales 113.3MM^E EMP 500
SIC 3699 Electrical equipment & supplies
Pr: Henry Metcalf
Pr: Shanghai Electronic Instrument
Pr: John Eva
VP: Mike Flint
Ql Cn Mgr: Rick Rehberg

D-U-N-S 07-854-4400
SHANNON CLINIC
VISTA GERDE MEDICAL PLAZA
(Suby of SHANNON HEALTH SYSTEM) ★
120 E Beauregard Ave, San Angelo, TX 76903-5919
Tel (325) 658-1511 Founded/Ownrshp 1995
Sales 122.4MM EMP 700
Accts Bkd Llp Houston Tx
SIC 8011 Clinic, operated by physicians
Pr: Bryan Horner
COO: Gary Bowen
CFO: John Gilbreath
Dir Lab: Lynn Youngblood
Genl Mgr: Sheryl Moon
CIO: Tom Perkin
Dir IT: Connie Dodson
Surgeon: Glen H Henderson
Ansthlgy: Brandan Hernandez
Opthamlgy: Kenton H Fish
Opthamlgy: Ames White

SHANNON DISTRIBUTION CENTER
See SHANNON PRECISION FASTENER LLC

D-U-N-S 92-932-7195
SHANNON HEALTH SYSTEM
120 E Harris Ave, San Angelo, TX 76903-5904
Tel (325) 653-6741 Founded/Ownrshp 1995
Sales 18.1M EMP 1,500^E
SIC 8011 Offices & clinics of medical doctors
CEO: Brayn Horner
Dir Recs: Margaret Benson
Treas: Steven Cainelli
Ofcr: Deborah Harder
Ofcr: Ronald Kelly
Genl Mgr: Trish Aldridge
CIO: Tom Perkin
QA Dir: Diane Zeitler
Dir IT: Chris Scott
Mktg Dir: Shelly Ladden
Nrsg Dir: Wilma Powell

D-U-N-S 07-315-0963
SHANNON MEDICAL CENTER
SHANNON WEST TEXAS MEM HOSP
120 E Harris Ave, San Angelo, TX 76903-5904
Tel (325) 653-6741 Founded/Ownrshp 1999
Sales 251.3MM EMP 1,568
SIC 8062 General medical & surgical hospitals
Ch: Len Mertz
Chf Rad: Chris Cole
*Pr: Bryan Horner
*CFO: Shane Plymell
*Treas: Robert Eckert
*VP: Wilma Stuart
Exec: Jo Feist
Exec: Cheridan Lyons
Dir Inf Cn: Peggy Creel
Dir Case M: Diane Sattler
Dir Lab: Billy Moore
Dir Lab: Carla Schwartz

D-U-N-S 16-751-8773 IMP
SHANNON PRECISION FASTENER LLC
SHANNON DISTRIBUTION CENTER
31600 Stephenson Hwy, Madison Heights, MI 48071-1642
Tel (248) 589-9670 Founded/Ownrshp 2004
Sales 100.0MM EMP 179
SIC 3452 Bolts, nuts, rivets & washers
*CFO: Joe Ankley
Treas: Jack G Rankin
*VP: Glenn Purvin
*VP: Robb Thompson
IT Man: Joe Peplinski
Plnt Mgr: Scott Mayer
Prd Mgr: Bill Cleland
Ql Cn Mgr: Bob Allison
Ql Cn Mgr: Matt Bruce

SHANNON WEST TEXAS MEM HOSP
See SHANNON MEDICAL CENTER

D-U-N-S 13-051-6909 IMP
SHAPCO INC
1666 20th St Ste 100, Santa Monica, CA 90404-3828
Tel (310) 264-1666 Founded/Ownrshp 1984
Sales 87.4MM EMP 312
Accts Armanino Llp
SIC 5051 3317 6799 Iron & steel (ferrous) products; Pipe & tubing, steel; Steel pipe & tubes; Real estate investors, except property operators
Pr: Leonard Shapiro
*Ch Bd: Bernard J Shapiro
*VP: Jaime Gesundheidt
*VP: Steve Teller

D-U-N-S 06-585-9555 IMP/EXP
SHAPE CORP
1900 Hayes St, Grand Haven, MI 49417-8937
Tel (616) 846-8700 Founded/Ownrshp 1974
Sales 425.0MM EMP 1,700
SIC 3449 3089 Miscellaneous metalwork; Molding primary plastic
Ch Bd: Gary Verplank
*V Ch: Peter Sturrus
COO: John Boese
*Treas: Lurelle J Verplank
VP: Bill Andrews
VP: Rob Weykamp
Exec: Molly Hunting
Prgrm Mgr: Ryan Vanderweele
Plnt Mgr: Andy Rosenberg
Prd Mgr: Sean Herman
Prd Mgr: Shawn McPherson

D-U-N-S 07-928-5575
SHAPE TECHNOLOGIES GROUP INC
(Suby of SHAPE TECHNOLOGIES GROUP PARENT HOLDINGS INC) ★
23500 64th Ave S, Kent, WA 98032-2618
Tel (253) 246-3200 Founded/Ownrshp 2015
Sales 114.5MM^E EMP 800^E
SIC 6719 Investment holding companies, except banks
CEO: David Savage

D-U-N-S 08-015-5303
SHAPE TECHNOLOGIES GROUP PARENT HOLDINGS INC
23500 64th Ave S, Kent, WA 98032-2618
Tel (253) 850-3500 Founded/Ownrshp 2015
Sales 123.1MM^E EMP 823^E
SIC 7379 Computer related consulting services

D-U-N-S 05-147-6992
■ **SHAPELL INDUSTRIES LLC**
S & S CONSTRUCTION CO
(Suby of TOLL BROTHERS INC) ★
8383 Wilshire Blvd # 700, Beverly Hills, CA 90211-2425
Tel (323) 655-7330 Founded/Ownrshp 2014
Sales 87.2MM^E EMP 302
SIC 6552 6514 1522 Land subdividers & developers, residential; Residential building, four or fewer units: operation; Residential construction
CEO: Nathan Shapell
CFO: Margaret F Leong
Ex VP: David Shapell
Sr VP: Max Webb
VP: John Critikos
IT Man: Karen Synesiou

D-U-N-S 95-837-2708 IMP
SHAPES/ARCH HOLDINGS LLC
ARCH AMERICA
9000 River Rd, Delair, NJ 08110-3204
Tel (856) 662-5500 Founded/Ownrshp 2008
Sales 103.4MM^E EMP 375^E
SIC 3354 3365 Aluminum extruded products; Aluminum foundries
CEO: Thomas Riddle
CFO: Paul Sorensen
VP: John Anning
Genl Mgr: Frank Wimmersberge

D-U-N-S 08-105-6087
SHAPIRO & DUNCAN INC
14620 Rothgeb Dr, Rockville, MD 20850-5311
Tel (240) 453-0280 Founded/Ownrshp 1993

Sales 106.2MM^E *EMP* 250
SIC 1711 Mechanical contractor
CEO: Sheldon Shapiro
**Pr:* Jerry Shapiro
**CFO:* Dave Holmes
CFO: David Holmes
VP: Charlie Ayres
Exec: Ron Chazin
Netwrk Eng: Jerry Freeman
Sfty Dirs: Daniel Dan
Snr PM: Dave Britschge

SHAPIRO METALS
See SHAPIRO SALES CO

D-U-N-S 03-109-5375 IMP/EXP
SHAPIRO SALES CO
SHAPIRO METALS
9666 Olive Blvd Ste 500, Saint Louis, MO 63132-3026
Tel (314) 381-9300 *Founded/Ownrshp* 1990
Sales 98.0MM^E *EMP* 100
SIC 5093 4953 Ferrous metal scrap & waste; Refuse systems
Pr: Bruce Shapiro
**VP:* Rick Dobkin
IT Man: Jamie Dutton

SHARAGANO STUDIO
See E-LO SPORTSWEAR LLC

D-U-N-S 11-869-7242 IMP
SHARED SERVICE SYSTEMS INC
(*Suby of* NEBRASKA METHODIST HEALTH SYSTEM INC) ★
1725 S 20th St, Omaha, NE 68108-3889
Tel (402) 536-5300 *Founded/Ownrshp* 1984
Sales 90.4MM^E *EMP* 157
SIC 5047 5142 7211 5149 5113 7218 Medical equipment & supplies; Hospital equipment & furniture; Surgical equipment & supplies; Meat, frozen: packaged; Fish, frozen: packaged; Poultry, frozen: packaged; Laundry collecting & distributing outlet; Groceries & related products; Dried or canned foods; Baking supplies; Cups, disposable plastic & paper; Towels, paper; Bags, paper & disposable plastic; Napkins, paper; Industrial launderers
Pr: Alvin L Chemberlain
**Pr:* David Koraleski
**Treas:* Art N Burtscher
Treas: Art Burtscher
CIO: Jerome Kostal
Sls Mgr: Kevin Giles

SHARED SOLUTIONS AND SERVICES
See ARROW SYSTEMS INTEGRATION INC

D-U-N-S 61-195-3683
SHARED TECHNOLOGY SERVICES GROUP INC
(*Suby of* PLYMOUTH ROCK CO INC) ★
695 Atlantic Ave, Boston, MA 02111-2623
Tel (617) 720-1620 *Founded/Ownrshp* 1995
Sales 77.8MM^E *EMP* 1,000
SIC 1521 General remodeling, single-family houses
Pr: Paul D Luongo

SHARI'S CAFE & PIES
See SHARIS MANAGEMENT CORP

D-U-N-S 09-848-9503
SHARIS MANAGEMENT CORP
SHARI'S CAFE & PIES
(*Suby of* CIRCLE PEAK CAPITAL MANAGEMENT LLC) ★
9400 Sw Gemini Dr, Beaverton, OR 97008-7105
Tel (503) 605-4299 *Founded/Ownrshp* 1978
Sales 3.9MM^E *EMP* 4,000
SIC 5812 Restaurant, family: chain
Pr: Bruce Macdiarmid
Sr Cor Off: Peter Damelio
**VP:* Craig Kessler
Dir Soc: Heather Clark
Dist Mgr: Mark Denise
Genl Mgr: Ruth Pedroso
VP Mktg: Michael Kiriazis

D-U-N-S 08-018-9107
■ **SHARK ACQUISITION SUB II LLC**
(*Suby of* SNYDERS-LANCE INC) ★
13515 Balntyn Corp Pl, Charlotte, NC 28277-2706
Tel (704) 554-1421 *Founded/Ownrshp* 2016
Sales 123.0MM^E *EMP* 275^E
SIC 2099

D-U-N-S 06-104-3741
SHARKEY TRANSPORT SERVICES INC
3803 Dye Rd, Quincy, IL 62305-9002
Tel (217) 228-6555 *Founded/Ownrshp* 1971
Sales 107.7MM^E *EMP* 1,168^E
SIC 4213

SHARON JOHNSTON PARK RESV
See MADISON COUNTY COMMISSIONS

D-U-N-S 06-874-2121
■ **SHARON REGIONAL HEALTH SYSTEM**
SCHOOL OF NURSING
(*Suby of* COMMUNITY HEALTH SYSTEMS INC) ★
740 E State St, Sharon, PA 16146-3328
Tel (724) 983-3911 *Founded/Ownrshp* 2014
Sales 138.9MM *EMP* 1,850
SIC 8062 8063 8069 General medical & surgical hospitals; Psychiatric hospitals; Specialty hospitals, except psychiatric
CEO: John R Jack Janoso Jr
Dir Recs: Ginny Catterson
**Pr:* Wayne W Johnston
**CFO:* Jeffrey Chrobak
Bd of Dir: James P Epstein
Bd of Dir: Diane Gardner
Bd of Dir: John M Hudson
VP: Susan Gibson
VP: Patricia Hillebrand
VP: Jack Janosa
VP: Bob Leiter
VP: Ed Newmyer
Dir Rx: Jodi Shrawder

D-U-N-S 08-180-7828
SHARP CHULA VISTA AUXILIARY INC
SHARP CHULA VISTA MEDICAL CTR
751 Medical Center Ct, Chula Vista, CA 91911-6617
Tel (619) 421-6110 *Founded/Ownrshp* 1966
Sales 319.4MM *EMP* 29^E
SIC 8062 General medical & surgical hospitals
CEO: Chris Boyd

D-U-N-S 07-333-4666
SHARP CHULA VISTA MEDICAL CENTER
SHARP CHULA VISTA MEDICAL CTR
(*Suby of* SHARP REES-STEALY PHARMACY) ★
751 Medical Center Ct, Chula Vista, CA 91911-6617
Tel (619) 502-5800 *Founded/Ownrshp* 1990
Sales 367.2MM *EMP* 1,600
SIC 8062 General medical & surgical hospitals
CEO: Chris Boyd
**Pr:* Michael Murphy
**CFO:* Rick King
Genl Mgr: Vennie Henderson
HC Dir: Glenell Rutkoff

D-U-N-S 79-673-5483
SHARP CHULA VISTA MEDICAL CENTER
8695 Spectrum Center Blvd, San Diego, CA 92123-1489
Tel (858) 499-5150 *Founded/Ownrshp* 2007
Sales 315.6MM *EMP* 99
Accts Lb Ernst & Young Us Llp San D
SIC 8062 General medical & surgical hospitals
CEO: Chris Boyd
Bd of Dir: Tomas Romero
HC Dir: Karen Simpson

SHARP CHULA VISTA MEDICAL CTR
See SHARP CHULA VISTA MEDICAL CENTER

SHARP CHULA VISTA MEDICAL CTR
See SHARP CHULA VISTA AUXILIARY INC

D-U-N-S 06-761-6557
SHARP CORONADO HOSPITAL & HEALTHCARE CENTER
SHARP REES-STEALY PHARMACY
(*Suby of* SHARP REES-STEALY PHARMACY) ★
250 Prospect Pl, Coronado, CA 92118-1943
Tel (619) 522-3600 *Founded/Ownrshp* 1994
Sales 93.8MM *EMP* 550
SIC 8062

D-U-N-S 00-234-6625 IMP
SHARP CORP (PA)
SHARP PACKAGING SOLUTIONS
(*Suby of* UDG HEALTHCARE PUBLIC LIMITED COMPANY)
22-23 Carland Rd, Conshohocken, PA 19428
Tel (610) 395-5800 *Founded/Ownrshp* 1952, 2008
Sales 158.9MM^E *EMP* 800
SIC 7389 Packaging & labeling services
Pr: George K Burke
VP: Jeffrey A Benedict
**VP:* David Thomson
Ex Dir: Elizabeth Newman
QA Dir: Mercelena Callejas
IT Man: Rebecca Kornek
Sfty Dirs: Jeremy Edris
Prd Mgr: Tom Magilton
Mktg Mgr: Bob Macadangdang
Snr PM: Marcia McClellan

D-U-N-S 00-181-8012 IMP/EXP
SHARP ELECTRONICS CORP (NY)
SHARP MANUFACTURING CO AMER
(*Suby of* SHARP CORPORATION)
1 Sharp Plz Ste 1, Mahwah, NJ 07495-1163
Tel (201) 529-8200 *Founded/Ownrshp* 1965
Sales 1.1MMM^E *EMP* 2,500
SIC 5044 5064 3651 3631 3861 3674 Office equipment; Calcvlators, electronic; Photocopy machines; Cash registers; Electrical appliances, television & radio; Television sets; Tape players & recorders; High fidelity equipment; Television receiving sets; Microwave ovens, including portable: household; Projectors, still or motion picture, silent or sound; Semiconductors & related devices
Ch Bd: Toshiyki Osawa
**Ch Bd:* Kozo Takahashi
Pr: John Herrington
**CFO:* William Flynn
**CFO:* Mamoru Kondo
**Chf Mktg O:* Bob Scaglione
VP: Ken Aldred
VP: Oflaherty Paul
VP: Michael Pietrunti
VP: Tim Polega
VP: Kevin Procter
VP: Bruce Tripido
VP: Hideto Yamaji
Assoc Dir: Jerry Bunone
Assoc Dir: Tom Cunningham
Dir: Cliff Quiroga
Dir Bus: Gary Eyen
Board of Directors: Robert Becker, Todd Farin, Larry Kriebel, Richard Mowtier, Susan Osgood, Arthur Rudin, Mike Weathers

D-U-N-S 80-983-7750
SHARP HEALTH PLAN
8520 Tech Way Ste 200, San Diego, CA 92123-1450
Tel (858) 499-8300 *Founded/Ownrshp* 1992
Sales NA *EMP* 98
Accts Ernst & Young Us Llp San Dieg
SIC 6324 Health maintenance organization (HMO), insurance only
Pr: Melissa Hayden-Cook
**COO:* Leslie Pels-Beck
**CFO:* Rita Datko
**VP:* Michael Byrd
VP: Janet Hoy
**VP:* Dr Cary Shames
VP: Cary B Shames
Dir Bus: Susan Levy

D-U-N-S 07-336-5579
SHARP HEALTHCARE
SHARP REES-STEALY PHARMACY
8695 Spectrum Center Blvd, San Diego, CA 92123-1489
Tel (858) 499-4000 *Founded/Ownrshp* 1946
Sales 3.4MMM *EMP* 13,000
Accts Ernst & Young Llp San Diego
SIC 8062 8741 6324 General medical & surgical hospitals; Hospital management; Nursing & personal care facility management; Hospital & medical service plans
Pr: Michael Murphy
V Ch: Teri Featheringill
**CFO:* Ann Pumpian
Treas: Joanne Boyle
Treas: James Brown
Bd of Dir: Dee Ammon
Bd of Dir: Connie Conard
Bd of Dir: Shawna Fallon
Bd of Dir: Ann Goldberg
Bd of Dir: Elizabeth W Morgante
Bd of Dir: William L Pogue
Bd of Dir: Barry Uhl
**Ex VP:* Daniel L Gross
**Sr VP:* Alison J Fleury
**Sr VP:* Carlisle KY C Lewis III
Sr VP: Carlisle C Lewis
**Sr VP:* William A Spooner
Sr VP: William A Spooner
VP: Patty Atkins
VP: Paul Belton
VP: Anne Davis

SHARP HTG VENTILATION DIV DMG
See DMG CORP

SHARP MANUFACTURING CO AMER
See SHARP ELECTRONICS CORP

D-U-N-S 01-052-2758
SHARP MEMORIAL HOSPITAL
(*Suby of* SHARP REES-STEALY PHARMACY) ★
7901 Frost St, San Diego, CA 92123-2701
Tel (858) 939-3636 *Founded/Ownrshp* 1957
Sales 1.2MMM *EMP* 3,500
SIC 8062 General medical & surgical hospitals
CEO: Tim Smith
VP: Kathryn Hanna
Dir Lab: Cheryl Balderas
Netwrk Mgr: Mario Grozdanovic
VP Opers: Robert Wherry
Opers Supe: Kelly Tirado
Psych: Frank Ogle
Surgeon: Tabitha Rozebloom
Doctor: Jamie Lavender
Doctor: Aimee Lopes
Doctor: David Marsh

SHARP PACKAGING SOLUTIONS
See SHARP CORP

SHARP REES-STEALY PHARMACY
See SHARP CORONADO HOSPITAL & HEALTHCARE CENTER

SHARP REES-STEALY PHARMACY
See SHARP HEALTHCARE

D-U-N-S 05-461-2601 IMP/EXP
SHARPER IMAGE CORP (DE)
350 The Embarcadero Fl 6, San Francisco, CA 94105-1259
Tel (877) 714-7444 *Founded/Ownrshp* 1971
Sales 316.6MM^E *EMP* 2,500
SIC 5731 5941 5999 5719 5945 5961 Consumer electronic equipment; Exercise equipment; Toiletries, cosmetics & perfumes; Housewares; Toys & games; Catalog & mail-order houses
CEO: Robert Conway
**CFO:* Rebecca L Roedell
Bd of Dir: Richard J Thalheimer
**Ex VP:* William Feroe
Ex VP: Joyce Maruniak
**Sr VP:* Gary Chant
Sr VP: Davia Kimmey
Sr VP: Shannon King
**Sr VP:* James M Sander
Sr VP: Robert Thompson
VP: Barry Jacobsen
VP: Harvey Johnson
VP: Brian Pack
VP: Steve Renzelmann
Board of Directors: Morton E David, William R Fields, Howard Gross, George B James, Michael S Koeneke, Marc J Leder, Howard M Liebman, David M Meyer

D-U-N-S 10-139-9405
SHARYLAND UTILITIES LP
1807 Ross Ave Ste 460, Dallas, TX 75201-8078
Tel (214) 978-8958 *Founded/Ownrshp* 1998
Sales 123.5MM^E *EMP* 95
SIC 4911 Electric services
Pr: Hunter Hunt
IT Man: Gabriela Canales

D-U-N-S 10-340-1972 IMP/EXP
■ **SHASTA BEVERAGES INC**
NATIONAL BEVPAK
(*Suby of* NEWBEVCO INC) ★
26901 Indl Blvd, Hayward, CA 94545
Tel (954) 581-0922 *Founded/Ownrshp* 1985
Sales 109.2MM^E *EMP* 600
SIC 2086 Soft drinks: packaged in cans, bottles, etc.; Carbonated beverages, nonalcoholic: bottled & canned
CEO: Joseph G Caporella
**Pr:* John Minton
Chf Mktg O: Bob Halsey
VP: Grace Keene
**VP:* Dean McCoy
VP: Raymond J Smith
Exec: Cesca Schwan
**Prin:* Nick Caporella
Ex Dir: Ray Notarantonio
Manager: Tony Mucci

D-U-N-S 04-145-6567 IMP
SHASTA INDUSTRIES INC
SHASTA POOLS
6031 N 16th St, Phoenix, AZ 85016-1801
Tel (602) 532-3750 *Founded/Ownrshp* 1962
Sales 134.7MM^E *EMP* 570
SIC 1799 1771 5169 7389 3088 5091 Swimming pool construction; Gunite contractor; Swimming pool & spa chemicals; Swimming pool & hot tub service & maintenance; Plastics plumbing fixtures; Sporting & recreation goods
Pr: Edward E AST
**CFO:* Mike Wagner
**VP:* Jeffrey AST
Dir IT: Chris Lake
Dir IT: Christine Ricke
IT Man: Steven Albinda
IT Man: Phillip Alger
IT Man: Jim Sheerin
Opers Mgr: Lori Gonzales
Sls&Mrk Ex: Joan Roth
Mktg Mgr: Erin Terjesen

SHASTA POOLS
See SHASTA INDUSTRIES INC

SHASTA REGIONAL MEDICAL CENTER (SRMC)
See PRIME HEALTHCARE SERVICES - SHASTA LLC

D-U-N-S 00-890-8964 IMP
SHAUGHNESSY-KNIEP-HAWE-PAPER CO
(*Suby of* PAPERS UNLIMITED) ★
2355 Ball Dr, Saint Louis, MO 63146-8605
Tel (314) 810-8100 *Founded/Ownrshp* 1878, 2015
Sales 137.2MM^E *EMP* 155
SIC 5111 Printing paper
Pr: Edward Kniep IV
**CFO:* Larry Guess
**Ch:* Edward Kniep III
**VP:* Joe Reich
Genl Mgr: Jeff Alexander
**CIO:* Jim Thome

SHAVER MILLWORK
See SHAVER PROPERTIES INC

D-U-N-S 19-854-5865 EXP
SHAVER PROPERTIES INC
SHAVER MILLWORK
6010 Old Dixie Hwy Ste K, Vero Beach, FL 32967-7539
Tel (772) 569-3466 *Founded/Ownrshp* 1987
Sales 132.1MM^E *EMP* 2,025
SIC 2431 Millwork; Blinds (shutters), wood
Pr: Robert A Shaver
**Sec:* Jason A Shaver
VP: Clayton Shaver
**VP:* Mark A Shaver

SHAVLIK
See LANDESK SOFTWARE INC

D-U-N-S 03-202-1875
SHAW CONSTRUCTION LLC
300 Kalamath St, Denver, CO 80223-1150
Tel (303) 825-4740 *Founded/Ownrshp* 1962
Sales 93.2MM^E *EMP* 110
SIC 1542 Commercial & office building, new construction; Commercial & office buildings, renovation & repair
CEO: Steve Meyer
**Pr:* Clark Atkinson
**VP:* Doug Grogan
Exec: Jim Carter
Dir IT: Jack Hamm

D-U-N-S 01-563-3241 IMP
■ **SHAW CONTRACT FLOORING SERVICES INC**
SPECTRA CONTRACT FLOORING
(*Suby of* SHAW INDUSTRIES GROUP INC) ★
616 E Walnut Ave, Dalton, GA 30721-4409
Tel (706) 278-3812 *Founded/Ownrshp* 1996
Sales 343.8MM^E *EMP* 1,100
SIC 1752 Carpet laying
Pr: Timothy L Baucom
**CFO:* Scott E Hampton
VP: Dhruvi Patel
VP: Chip Sellers
Plng Mgr: Gregory Mullins
IT Man: Vonda Davis
VP Mktg: Tim Baucom
VP Sls: Bob Chandler
Sls Mgr: Becky Appleton

D-U-N-S 78-886-8722
SHAW ENVIRONMENTAL & INFRASTRUCTURE
1326 N Market Blvd, Sacramento, CA 95834-1912
Tel (916) 928-3300 *Founded/Ownrshp* 2006
Sales 86.8MM^E *EMP* 6,000
SIC 8711 Engineering services
Prin: Patricia Olson

D-U-N-S 18-003-8382
SHAW GROUP INC
(*Suby of* CHICAGO BRIDGE & IRON CO (DELAWARE)) ★
4171 Essen Ln, Baton Rouge, LA 70809-2157
Tel (225) 932-2500 *Founded/Ownrshp* 2013
Sales 4.3MMM^E *EMP* 25,000
SIC 8711 8734 1629 3498 Construction & civil engineering; Consulting engineer; Pollution testing; Soil analysis; Hazardous waste testing; Water testing laboratory; Industrial plant construction; Power plant construction; Fabricated pipe & fittings
Ex VP: Brian K Ferraioli
Pr: Dave Barry
Pr: Frederick W Buckman
CEO: Clarence Ray
COO: Remi Bonnecaze
COO: Gary P Graphia
CFO: Michael Dillman
CFO: Timothy J Poche
Ex VP: Robert Belk
Ex VP: Dave Brannen
Ex VP: John W Dalton Sr
Ex VP: John Donofrio
Ex VP: Walter R Rhodes

Sr VP: Paul Bridges
Sr VP: Dick Dwyer
Sr VP: Michael J Kershaw
Sr VP: Jeffrey S Merrifield
Sr VP: Mitchell A Ryner
Sr VP: Michael Wootton
VP: Sean Clancy
VP: Sergio Lopez

D-U-N-S 04-584-0055 IMP/EXP
■ SHAW INDUSTRIES GROUP INC
(*Suby of* BERKSHIRE HATHAWAY INC) ★
616 E Walnut Ave, Dalton, GA 30721-4409
Tel (800) 441-7429 *Founded/Ownrshp* 1946
Sales 5.0MMM^E *EMP* 6,800
SIC 5023 Floor coverings
COO: William Fry IV
**CFO:* Kenneth G Jackson
VP: Jim Carew
VP: James Coker
VP: John Davis
VP: Tony Graef
VP: Jon Jewell
VP: Doug Kenney
VP: Brenda Knowles
VP: Lisa Quady
VP: Linda Reynolds
VP: Carl P Rollins
VP: Kevin Sanders
VP: Bob Spahn
VP: Darrell Swilling
VP: Chris Vlach
VP: Kirk Wessells
Exec: Debbie Roy

D-U-N-S 78-637-1393 IMP/EXP
■ SHAW INDUSTRIES INC
EXECUTIVE OFFICES
(*Suby of* SHAW INDUSTRIES GROUP INC) ★
616 E Walnut Ave, Dalton, GA 30721-4409
Tel (706) 278-3812 *Founded/Ownrshp* 1946
Sales 4.5MMM^E *EMP* 1,100
SIC 2273 Carpets & rugs
CEO: Vance D Bell
**Pr:* Percy Merritt
COO: William Fry IV
**CFO:* Kenneth Jackson
CFO: Kenneth G Jackson
**VP:* Gerald Embry
VP: Kent Lusk
VP: Scott Robertson
Dir Risk M: Bill Whitmire
Dir Sec: Mike Leonard
Prgrm Mgr: Dawn Beard

D-U-N-S 01-033-3946
SHAW-LUNDQUIST ASSOCIATES INC
2757 W Service Rd, Saint Paul, MN 55121-1230
Tel (651) 454-0670 *Founded/Ownrshp* 1974
Sales 121.3MM *EMP* 75
SIC 1542 1541 Commercial & office building, new construction; Industrial buildings, new construction
CEO: Hoyt Hsiao
**VP:* Holden Hsiao
**VP:* Thomas Meyers

D-U-N-S 82-528-9932 IMP
SHAW-ROSS INTERNATIONAL IMPORTERS INC
(*Suby of* SOUTHERN GLAZERS WINE AND SPIRITS LLC) ★
2900 Sw 149th Ave Ste 200, Miramar, FL 33027-6612
Tel (954) 430-5020 *Founded/Ownrshp* 2004
Sales 316.4MM^E *EMP* 91^E
SIC 5182 Bottling wines & liquors
CEO: Harvey R Chaplin
**Pr:* Wayne E Chaplin
**Sec:* Herbert S Joseph
**Ex VP:* Lee F Hager
**Sr VP:* Melvin A Dick
**VP:* Elliot W Dinnerstein
**VP:* Becker R Steven
**VP:* Jay W Weiss
IT Man: Juana Polanco
Opers Mgr: Ana Mole
Opers Mgr: Ana Moli

D-U-N-S 08-029-0988
SHAW-ROSS INTERNATIONAL IMPORTERS LLC
2900 Sw 149th Ave Ste 200, Miramar, FL 33027-6612
Tel (954) 430-5020 *Founded/Ownrshp* 2011
Sales 100.0MM *EMP* 50
SIC 5182 Bottling wines & liquors
Mng Dir: Bruce Hunter

D-U-N-S 07-949-7770
SHAWCOR INC
(*Suby of* SHAWCOR CANADA HOLDINGS LTD)
3838 N Sam Houston Pkwy E # 300, Houston, TX 77032-3405
Tel (281) 886-2350 *Founded/Ownrshp* 1989
Sales 224.5MM^E *EMP* 1,479
SIC 8734 X-ray inspection service, industrial
VP: Michael Cockrell

D-U-N-S 83-567-8574 IMP/EXP
SHAWCOR PIPE PROTECTION LLC
(*Suby of* SHAWCOR INC) ★
3838 N Sam Houston Pkwy E # 300, Houston, TX 77032-3405
Tel (281) 886-2350 *Founded/Ownrshp* 2002
Sales 91.9MM^E *EMP* 287
SIC 3479 Coating or wrapping steel pipe
Prin: Bredero Shaw
**Ex VP:* John D Tikkanen
**VP:* Carlos I Escobar
**VP:* Michael B Cockrell
VP: Michael Cockrell

D-U-N-S 08-465-2171 IMP
SHAWMUT CORP
208 Manley St, West Bridgewater, MA 02379-1044
Tel (508) 588-3300 *Founded/Ownrshp* 1916
Sales 196.9MM^E *EMP* 380
SIC 2295 Laminating of fabrics
CEO: James H Wyner
Pr: Wade Martin
Treas: Giang T H Wyner
VP: Suzanne Claus
VP: Sherri Harrington
Dir Lab: Robert Medeiros
CIO: Jim Schenck
CIO: Jim Slavin
IT Man: Wayne Pavao
Opers Mgr: Monique Carter
Plnt Mgr: Eric Finn

SHAWMUT DESIGN & CONSTRUCTION
See SHAWMUT WOODWORKING & SUPPLY INC

D-U-N-S 04-705-6460 IMP
SHAWMUT WOODWORKING & SUPPLY INC
SHAWMUT DESIGN & CONSTRUCTION
560 Harrison Ave Ste 200, Boston, MA 02118-2632
Tel (617) 338-6200 *Founded/Ownrshp* 1982
Sales 957.6MM *EMP* 711
Accts Crowe Horwath Llp Oak Brook
SIC 1542 Commercial & office building contractors; Institutional building construction
Pr: Thomas E Goemaat
**Pr:* Lester Hiscoe
CFO: Thomas J McBride
CFO: Ira B Morgenstern
CFO: Roger C Tougas
**Treas:* Roger Tougas
Ofcr: Doug Lareau
VP: Paul Doherty
Exec: Brad Cadieux
Exec: Steven Ham
Exec: Kyle Lloyd
Exec: Robert Motta
Exec: Vytas Sipas
Exec: William Sweeney
Exec: John Tobin
Dir Bus: Jay Gibson
Dir Bus: Bryan Gubbins

D-U-N-S 07-993-1185
SHAWNEE MISSION BOARD OF EDUCATION
7235 Antioch Rd, Shawnee Mission, KS 66204-1758
Tel (913) 993-6200 *Founded/Ownrshp* 2014
Sales 317.6MM *EMP* 3^E
Accts Mize Houser & Company Pa Law
SIC 8211 School board
Pr: Sara Goodburn
Dir IT: Lori Oneal

D-U-N-S 06-796-2134
SHAWNEE MISSION MEDICAL CENTER INC
ADVENTIST HEALTH SYSTEM SUNBEL
(*Suby of* ADVENTST HLTH SYSTM SUNBELT H) ★
9100 W 74th St, Shawnee Mission, KS 66204-4004
Tel (913) 676-2000 *Founded/Ownrshp* 2001
Sales 435.4MM *EMP* 1,850
SIC 8062 General medical & surgical hospitals
CEO: Ken Bacon
Pr: Sam Turner
CFO: Jack Wagnar
Ofcr: William Robertson
Sr VP: Robin Harrold
VP: Peggy Todd
VP: Andrew Weston
Exec: Red Hoffman
Exec: Michael Quarles
Dir Rad: Lyle Ackerman
Chf Nrs Of: Sheri Hawkins

D-U-N-S 07-303-4332
SHAWNEE MISSION SCHOOL DISTRICT
7235 Antioch Rd, Shawnee Mission, KS 66204-1758
Tel (913) 993-6200 *Founded/Ownrshp* 1969
Sales 316.3MM *EMP* 4,132
Accts Mize Houser & Company Pa Law
SIC 8211 Public elementary & secondary schools; Elementary school; Public special education school; Vocational high school
Ofcr: Richard Pacheco
Off Admin: Jody Evert
Dir IT: Lori O'Neal
Pr Dir: Leigh Anne Neal
Teacher Pr: Doug Sumnber
Psych: Elizabeth Franey
HC Dir: Shelby Rebeck

D-U-N-S 96-596-1498
SHAWNEE MISSION UNIFIED SCHOOL DISTRICT
7235 Antioch Rd, Overland Park, KS 66204-1758
Tel (913) 993-6200 *Founded/Ownrshp* 1969
Sales 92.9MM^E *EMP* 4,087^E
SIC 8211 Elementary & secondary schools
MIS Dir: Richard Cavallaro
Teacher Pr: Amy Dillon
Psych: Laura Carter

D-U-N-S 07-921-7195
SHAWNEE VILLAGE PRESERVATION LP
1304 W Boulevard St, Marion, IL 62959-4415
Tel (618) 997-5365 *Founded/Ownrshp* 2013
Sales 23.3MM^E *EMP* 1,828
SIC 6531 Real estate agents & managers

D-U-N-S 03-962-2506
SHAWS HOLDINGS INC
750 W Center St, West Bridgewater, MA 02379-1518
Tel (508) 313-4000 *Founded/Ownrshp* 2013
Sales 998.5MM^E *EMP* 26,064^E
SIC 5411 Supermarkets, chain; Supermarkets, 55,000-65,000 square feet (superstore)
Pr: Carl Jablonski
VP: John Nieman
VP: Jack Traynor
Ex Dir: Irwin Cohen

D-U-N-S 00-695-3525
SHAWS SUPERMARKETS INC
(*Suby of* SHAWS HOLDINGS INC) ★
750 W Center St, West Bridgewater, MA 02379-1518
Tel (508) 313-4000 *Founded/Ownrshp* 1987
Sales 998.5MM^E *EMP* 5,800
SIC 5411 Supermarkets, chain; Supermarkets, 55,000-65,000 square feet (superstore)
Pr: Jim Rice
**COO:* Justin Dye
Treas: John Flaherty
**Treas:* Scott Ramsay
**Ex VP:* H Verne Powell
Sr VP: Thomas Farello
**Sr VP:* Scott Santos
**VP:* Michael Bessent
VP: Brian Pijanowski
MIS Dir: Alan Joughin
Board of Directors: Harry Beckner, Ruth Bramson, David Brenner, Stephen M Du Brul Jr, H Peter Gunderson, Robert C Nakasone

D-U-N-S 13-978-7949
SHAZAM INC
6700 Pioneer Pkwy, Johnston, IA 50131-1605
Tel (515) 288-2828 *Founded/Ownrshp* 1976
Sales 91.1MM *EMP* 780
SIC 7374 Data processing service
Pr: Mike Hollinger
Sr VP: Scott Dobesh
Sr VP: Peter Szabo
VP: Gina Amos
VP: Elissa Coughlin
Exec: David Hecker
Ex Dir: Kathy Siefken
IT Man: Leo Doyle
Sftwr Eng: Ameen Abed
Sftwr Eng: Michael Jacobson
Sls Dir: Darren Klein

D-U-N-S 61-209-8053
SHAZZAM INC
1001 25th St N, Fargo, ND 58102-3116
Tel (701) 237-3330 *Founded/Ownrshp* 1996
Sales 98.1MM *EMP* 3,000
SIC 6719 Investment holding companies, except banks
Pr: James R McLeod
**Pr:* James R McLeod
CFO: Jill Motschenbacher

D-U-N-S 96-794-1480
SHC HOLDING INC
311 Park Place Blvd, Clearwater, FL 33759-4904
Tel (727) 533-9700 *Founded/Ownrshp* 2006
Sales 150.0MM *EMP* 2,000
SIC 6719 Investment holding companies, except banks
Ch: Robert Fusco
**CFO:* Mitchel Morel

SHC REALTY
See SEARS HOLDINGS MANAGEMENT CORP

D-U-N-S 19-368-8876
SHC SERVICES INC
SUPPLEMENTAL HEALTH CARE
1640 Redstone Center Dr # 200, Park City, UT 84098-7607
Tel (435) 645-0788 *Founded/Ownrshp* 2016
Sales 272.3MM^E *EMP* 3,000
SIC 7361 Placement agencies
CEO: Janet Elkin
**Pr:* Laura Magner
**CFO:* Steve Ure
VP: Missy Blankenship
VP: Travis Furlow
VP: Christopher Long
VP: Linda McDonnell
VP: Ron Murphy
VP: Cheryl Wilhelm
Exec: Natalie Ehlenbeck
Exec: Ella Oerther
Exec: Jamie Veno

SHEA HOMES FOR ACTIVE ADULTS
See JF SHEA CONSTRUCTION INC

D-U-N-S 94-506-3865
SHEA HOMES LIMITED PARTNERSHIP A CALIFORNIA LIMITED PARTNERSHIP
(*Suby of* J F SHEA CO INC) ★
655 Brea Canyon Rd, Walnut, CA 91789-3078
Tel (909) 594-9500 *Founded/Ownrshp* 1989
Sales 1.1MMM *EMP* 1,200
Accts Ernst & Young Llp Los Angeles
SIC 1521 Single-family housing construction
Pt: Jim Shontere
Pt: John F Shea LP
Treas: Robert Odell
CIO: Bruce Verker
Dir IT: Steve Rilee
Sales Exec: Adam Heib
Sales Exec: Ken Peterson
Sales Exec: Eric Snider
Sales Exec: Heather Stevenson
Sls Dir: Janet Benavidez

D-U-N-S 00-336-7208
SHEALY ELECTRICAL WHOLESALERS INC (SC)
E D I
120 Saxe Gotha Rd, West Columbia, SC 29172-3002
Tel (803) 252-5668 *Founded/Ownrshp* 1945
Sales 419.1MM^E *EMP* 300
SIC 5063 Electrical apparatus & equipment
Ch Bd: William Deloache III
Bd of Dir: Christopher N Union
**Ex VP:* David White
VP: Dan Culicerto
**VP:* Todd Ferrell
**VP:* Earl Jones
VP: Barclay Ryan
VP: James Sipe
Mktg Dir: Jana Case
Sales Asso: Kyle Ledbetter
Sales Asso: Angela Vinson

D-U-N-S 07-953-6204
SHEARERS FOODS BURLINGTON LLC
(*Suby of* SHEARERS FOODS LLC) ★
3000 Mount Pleasant St, Burlington, IA 52601-2064
Tel (319) 754-6551 *Founded/Ownrshp* 2014
Sales 300.0MM *EMP* 750
SIC 2052 Bakery products, dry
CEO: CJ Fraleigh
**Treas:* Alan Fritts

D-U-N-S 05-459-9659 IMP/EXP
SHEARERS FOODS LLC
100 Lincoln Way E, Massillon, OH 44646-6634
Tel (330) 834-4030 *Founded/Ownrshp* 2012
Sales 198.5MM *EMP* 1,600
SIC 2096 5145 Potato chips & similar snacks; Snack foods
CEO: C J Fraleigh
**CEO:* Christopher Fraleigh
**CFO:* Fritz Kohmann
**Treas:* Alan Fritts
Top Exec: John Stephenson
**Ex VP:* Montgomery Pooley
Sr VP: Walter Fink
VP: James Allan
VP: Coleman Caldwell
VP: Steve Surmay
QA Dir: Julie Phelps

D-U-N-S 07-520-8868 IMP/EXP
SHEARMAN & STERLING LLP
ROLL III, WILLIAM J F
599 Lexington Ave Fl 16, New York, NY 10022-6069
Tel (212) 848-4000 *Founded/Ownrshp* 2003
Sales 733.1MM^E *EMP* 3,478
SIC 8111 General practice attorney, lawyer
Pt: David J Beveridge
Pt: Michael W Benjamin
Pt: Lisa M Brill
Pt: Fabio Fauceglia
Pt: Kristen M Garry
Pt: Craig J Gibian
Pt: Adam M Givertz
Pt: Geoffrey B Goldman
Pt: Monica L Holland
Pt: Colin Law
Pt: Kyungwon Lee
Pt: Marc O Plepelits
Pt: Benjamin R F Shorten
Pt: Marco A Sustmann
Pt: Michael H Torkin
Mng Pt: Matthew Bersani
Mng Pt: Robert Ellison
Mng Pt: Masahisa Ikeda
Mng Pt: Jason Lehner
Mng Pt: Andrew B J Nszky
Mng Pt: Andrew Ruff

D-U-N-S 03-287-8456
SHEBOYGAN AREA SCHOOL DISTRICT
830 Virginia Ave, Sheboygan, WI 53081-4427
Tel (920) 459-3500 *Founded/Ownrshp* 1982
Sales 80.2MM^E *EMP* 1,600
Accts Schenck Sc Sheboygan Wiscons
SIC 8211 8741 Public elementary & secondary schools; Public junior high school; Public elementary school; Management services
Pr Dir: Nicole Sondalli

D-U-N-S 09-173-5852
SHEE ATIKA INC
315 Lincoln St Ste 300, Sitka, AK 99835-7579
Tel (907) 747-3534 *Founded/Ownrshp* 1974
Sales 147.0MM *EMP* 20
Accts Peterson Sullivan Llp Seattle
SIC 6514 6552 Dwelling operators, except apartments; Subdividers & developers
CEO: Elliott Wimberly
**CFO:* Sandi Dalton
Treas: Donnelly Harold

D-U-N-S 96-489-8014
SHEET METAL WORKERS LOCAL 104 HEALTH CARE PLAN
2610 Crow Canyon Rd, San Ramon, CA 94583-1768
Tel (925) 208-9999 *Founded/Ownrshp* 2010
Sales 86.3MM *EMP* 9^E
Accts Lindquist Llp San Ramon Ca
SIC 8631 Labor unions & similar labor organizations
Prin: Bruce Ward

D-U-N-S 61-809-4254
SHEET METAL WORKERS LOCAL 124
3717 Nw 63rd St Ste 100, Oklahoma City, OK 73116-1925
Tel (405) 848-4848 *Founded/Ownrshp* 2002
Sales NA *EMP* 500
SIC 6371 Pension funds

SHEETZ CONVENIENCE STORE
See SHEETZ INC

D-U-N-S 07-843-4762
SHEETZ DISTRIBUTION SERVICES LLC (PA)
(*Suby of* SHEETZ CONVENIENCE STORE) ★
242 Sheetz Way, Claysburg, PA 16625-8345
Tel (814) 239-1600 *Founded/Ownrshp* 2006
Sales 90.9MM^E *EMP* 788
SIC 5411 Grocery stores
Pr: Raymond Ryan

D-U-N-S 01-381-8448 IMP
SHEETZ INC
SHEETZ CONVENIENCE STORE
5700 6th Ave, Altoona, PA 16602-1111
Tel (814) 946-3611 *Founded/Ownrshp* 1956
Sales 2.1MMM^E *EMP* 9,300
SIC 5411 Convenience stores
VP: Joseph S Sheetz
**Pr:* Stanton R Sheetz
Pr: Jim Wenner
**V Ch Bd:* G Robert Sheetz
**Ex VP:* Charles Sheetz
Ex VP: Louie Sheetz
**Ex VP:* Randall Sheetz
Ex VP: David Woodley
VP: Michael Cortez
VP: Stephanie Doliveira
VP: Dave Woodley

SHEFFIELD MERCHANT BNKG GROUP
See CRT CAPITAL GROUP LLC

D-U-N-S 10-241-7342 IMP
SHEFFIELD STEEL CORP
GERDAU AMERISTEEL
(*Suby of* GERDAU LONG STEEL NORTH AMER) ★
2300 S State Highway 97, Sand Springs, OK 74063-6516
Tel (918) 245-1335 *Founded/Ownrshp* 2006
Sales 110.1MM^E *EMP* 672
SIC 3312 Bars & bar shapes, steel, cold-finished: own hot-rolled; Bars & bar shapes, steel, hot-rolled; Billets, steel
CEO: Mario Longhi
Ch Bd: Philip Casey
VP: William Macormic
VP: Neil McCullouhs
Genl Mgr: Rick Howard
Genl Mgr: Dwain Marple

D-U-N-S 60-794-4766
SHELBURNE CORP
20001 Shelburne Rd, Shaker Heights, OH 44118-5013
Tel (216) 321-9177 *Founded/Ownrshp* 1989
Sales 86.0MM^E *EMP* 336
SIC 3443 3823 3544 3769 Industrial vessels, tanks & containers; Heat exchangers: coolers (after, inter), condensers, etc.; Temperature measurement instruments, industrial; Forms (molds), for foundry & plastics working machinery; Bellows assemblies, missiles: metal
Pr: Edward S Young
**VP:* Dave Young

SHELBY BAPTIST MEDICAL CENTER
See BAPTIST HEALTH SYSTEM INC

D-U-N-S 80-015-6718
SHELBY CO SCHOOL DISTRICT
410 E College St, Columbiana, AL 35051-9301
Tel (205) 682-7000 *Founded/Ownrshp* 2007
Sales 6.2MM^E *EMP* 3,324^E
SIC 8211 Public elementary & secondary schools
Off Mgr: Tina Etress
Pr Dir: Cindy Warner
Instr Medi: Michelle Hall
Psych: Jamie Payne

SHELBY COUNTY BD COMMISSIONERS
See COUNTY OF SHELBY

D-U-N-S 01-759-5153
SHELBY COUNTY BOARD OF EDUCATION
160 S Hollywood St, Memphis, TN 38112-4801
Tel (901) 321-2500 *Founded/Ownrshp* 1867
Sales 285.4MM^E *EMP* 24^E
Accts Watkins Uiberall Pllc/Banks
SIC 8211 School board
Dir Bus: Faye Morrison
Dir Sec: Marjorie Douglas
CTO: Mary Green
IT Man: Michael T Murphy
Plnt Mgr: Derron Dowell

D-U-N-S 07-050-8932
SHELBY COUNTY BOARD OF EDUCATION
410 E College St, Columbiana, AL 35051-9301
Tel (205) 682-7000 *Founded/Ownrshp* 1925
Sales 204.8MM *EMP* 4,139
Accts Ronald L Jones Montgomery A
SIC 8211 Public elementary & secondary schools
**CFO:* Gary McCombs
Bd of Dir: Peg Hill
Comm Dir: Vincent Higgins
IT Man: Jeff Yallope
Netwrk Eng: Cecil Bunn

D-U-N-S 12-161-3186
SHELBY COUNTY HEALTH CARE CORP
MED, THE
877 Jefferson Ave, Memphis, TN 38103-2807
Tel (901) 545-7928 *Founded/Ownrshp* 1981
Sales 316.6MM *EMP* 2,800
SIC 8062

D-U-N-S 07-288-6591
SHELBY COUNTY MEMORIAL HOSPITAL ASSOCIATION
WILSON HEALTH
915 Michigan St, Sidney, OH 45365-2401
Tel (937) 498-2311 *Founded/Ownrshp* 1930
Sales 101.5MM *EMP* 700
Accts Blue & Co Llc Columbus Ohi
SIC 8062 General medical & surgical hospitals
Pr: Thomas Boecker
**COO:* Craig Lannoye
**CFO:* Douglas Bomba
VP: Linda Maurer
Dir Rad: Eric Charlton
Ex Dir: Bonnie Faulkner
Nurse Mgr: Carol W Johnston
CIO: Larry Meyers

SHELBY COUNTY SCHOOLS
See BOARD OF EDUCATION-MEMPHIS CITY SCHOOLS

D-U-N-S 07-979-8742
SHELBY COUNTY SCHOOLS
160 S Hollywood St, Memphis, TN 38112-4801
Tel (901) 321-2500 *Founded/Ownrshp* 1867
Sales 136.9MM^E *EMP* 4,800
SIC 8211 Public elementary & secondary schools
Ofcr: Sharryl Hall
Ofcr: Keith Peete
Dir Sec: Gary W Gitchell
Genl Mgr: Stefani Everson
Pr Dir: Natalia Powers
Teacher Pr: Roderick Richmond

D-U-N-S 07-351-2550 IMP/EXP
SHELBY GROUP INTERNATIONAL INC
MCR SAFETY
1255 W Schilling Blvd, Collierville, TN 38017-7190
Tel (901) 795-5810 *Founded/Ownrshp* 1984
Sales 182.7MM^E *EMP* 700
SIC 3842 2381 3851 5137

D-U-N-S 08-990-2563
SHELCO LLC (NC)
2320 Cascade Pointe Blvd # 100, Charlotte, NC 28208-6700
Tel (704) 367-5600 *Founded/Ownrshp* 1978, 2013
Sales 99.7MM^E *EMP* 125^E
Accts Elliott Davis Decosimo Charlo
SIC 1541 1542 Industrial buildings, new construction; Commercial & office building, new construction
Pr: D Edwin Rose
**CFO:* J Scott Bengel
**Ex VP:* Barry W Gardner
**Ex VP:* Howard N Peabody
**Ex VP:* Gerard J Reid
**VP:* Susan F Campbell
**VP:* Earl R Hiatt
**VP:* Daniel W Perry
Genl Mgr: Scott Harton

D-U-N-S 01-216-1487
SHELF DRILLING DISTRIBUTION LTD
(*Suby of* SHELF DRILLING OFFSHORE HOLDINGS LIMITED (DMCC BRANCH))
1 Riverway, Houston, TX 77056-1920
Tel (713) 457-8220 *Founded/Ownrshp* 2012
Sales NA *EMP* 3,900
SIC 6719 Investment holding companies, except banks

D-U-N-S 17-697-9446 IMP
SHELF RELIANCE LLC
THRIVE LIFE
691 S Auto Mall Dr, American Fork, UT 84003-2495
Tel (801) 756-9902 *Founded/Ownrshp* 2004
Sales 100.7MM^E *EMP* 150
SIC 5021 Shelving
**COO:* Jeremy Taeoalii
**CFO:* Rich Fankhauser
Rgnl Mgr: Seth Adams
Opers Mgr: Shannon Peterson

SHELL
See EQUIVA SERVICES LLC

SHELL
See EMPIRE PETROLEUM PARTNERS LLC

SHELL
See SWEPI LP

D-U-N-S 16-167-7778 IMP
SHELL CATALYST VENTURES INC
(*Suby of* SHELL OIL CO) ★
910 Louisiana St, Houston, TX 77002-4916
Tel (713) 241-5766 *Founded/Ownrshp* 1985
Sales 104.1MM^E *EMP* 2,000^E
SIC 2819 Catalysts, chemical
Pr: Steven Miller
**Pr:* Dick Schimbar
**Treas:* Rick Cooper
**VP:* Warren Ache

D-U-N-S 01-777-4071 IMP/EXP
SHELL CHEMICAL LP
SHELL CHEMICALS
(*Suby of* SHELL OIL CO) ★
910 Louisiana St, Houston, TX 77002-4916
Tel (855) 697-4355 *Founded/Ownrshp* 1929
Sales 530.2MM^E *EMP* 1,449
SIC 2869 Industrial organic chemicals
Pt: Michael Marr
Pt: John Hofmeiscer
Ex VP: Thomas Casparie
Ex VP: Ben Van Beurden
VP: Brian Davis
VP: Alexander Farina
VP: Cindy Gaddis
VP: Sven Royall
Sales Exec: David Byrne
Sls Mgr: Terry Schieber
Genl Couns: Hans Van Der Linde

SHELL CHEMICALS
See SHELL CHEMICAL LP

D-U-N-S 83-756-5548 IMP/EXP
SHELL ENERGY NORTH AMERICA (US) LP
(*Suby of* SHELL OIL CO) ★
1000 Main St, Houston, TX 77002-6336
Tel (713) 230-3822 *Founded/Ownrshp* 1998
Sales 990.0MM^E *EMP* 600
SIC 1311 Crude petroleum & natural gas
Pr: Frans Everts
Ofcr: Melissa R Ihrig
VP: Troy Bailey
VP: Scott Campbell
VP: Mark Gill
VP: Danny A Martin
VP: Danny Meyer
VP: Tim Pickering
VP: Mark Viola
Brnch Mgr: David Niederkrome

D-U-N-S 06-538-1345 IMP
SHELL ENERGY RESOURCES INC
(*Suby of* SHELL OIL CO) ★
1105 N Market St Ste 1300, Wilmington, DE 19801-1241
Tel (302) 658-3676 *Founded/Ownrshp* 1981
Sales 792.6MM^E *EMP* 5,000^E
SIC 1311 1382 Crude petroleum & natural gas production; Geological exploration, oil & gas field
Pr: R L Howard
**Treas:* Nick J Caruso

D-U-N-S 83-078-0404
SHELL EXPLORATION & PRODUCTION CO
(*Suby of* SHELL OIL CO) ★
200 N Dairy Ashford Rd, Houston, TX 77079-1101
Tel (832) 337-0369 *Founded/Ownrshp* 1995
Sales 254.0MM^E *EMP* 95^E
SIC 4922 Pipelines, natural gas
CEO: Marvin E Odum
IT Man: Michiele Bosschert
IT Man: Carl H Svenning

D-U-N-S 11-213-9733 IMP
SHELL GLOBAL SOLUTIONS (US) INC
(*Suby of* SHELL OIL CO) ★
3333 Highway 6 S, Houston, TX 77082-3101
Tel (281) 544-7709 *Founded/Ownrshp* 2001
Sales 1.1MMM^E *EMP* 1,449^E
SIC 1311 Crude petroleum & natural gas
Pr: Graeme Sweeney
CFO: David Rodriguez
**VP:* Edward D Daniels
**Prin:* Tzu Yang Lee
**Prin:* Mr Armand Lumens
Sls Mgr: Jose Bravo

D-U-N-S 15-992-9249
SHELL INFORMATION TECHNOLOGY INTERNATIONAL INC
S I T I
(*Suby of* SHELL OIL CO) ★
910 Louisiana St, Houston, TX 77002-4916
Tel (855) 697-4355 *Founded/Ownrshp* 1995
Sales 85.0MM^E *EMP* 1,440^E
SIC 8742 7371 Management consulting services; Computer software development
Ch: Erik T Betz
**Treas:* Deborah D Smith
**VP:* Cynthia Deere
**VP:* Julie L Sturm

SHELL MARTINEZ REFINERY
See SHELL MARTINEZ REFINING CO

D-U-N-S 96-357-3175 IMP
SHELL MARTINEZ REFINING CO
SHELL MARTINEZ REFINERY
(*Suby of* SHELL OIL CO) ★
3485 Pacheco Blvd, Martinez, CA 94553-2120
Tel (925) 313-3000 *Founded/Ownrshp* 1996
Sales 200.2MM^E *EMP* 900
SIC 2911 Petroleum refining
Genl Mgr: Alicia Igarraraz
VP: Glenn Gilcrest
VP: Bill Klein
Mktg Mgr: Laura Brown

D-U-N-S 96-680-2725
SHELL MEDICAL PLAN
P.O. Box 53456 (85072-3456)
Tel (800) 352-3705 *Founded/Ownrshp* 2011
Sales 536.9MM *EMP* 2^E
Accts Pricewaterhousecoopers Llp P
SIC 8099 Health & allied services

D-U-N-S 07-944-7944
SHELL MIDSTREAM PARTNERS LP
910 Louisiana St, Houston, TX 77002-4916
Tel (713) 241-6161 *Founded/Ownrshp* 2014
Sales 326.5MM *EMP* 2
Tkr Sym SHLX *Exch* NYS
SIC 4612 Crude petroleum pipelines
Pr: John H Hollowell
**Genl Pt:* Shell M LLC
**CFO:* Susan M Ward

D-U-N-S 83-157-8583 IMP
SHELL OFFSHORE INC
(*Suby of* ROYAL DUTCH SHELL PLC)
200 N Dairy Ashford Rd, Houston, TX 77079-1101
Tel (281) 544-4800 *Founded/Ownrshp* 1981
Sales 108.2MM^E *EMP* 99
SIC 5172 Gasoline
Pr: John H Hollowell
**CEO:* Ben Van Beurden
**CFO:* Simon Henry
**VP:* Gregory L Andrews
**VP:* Len S Falsone
**VP:* Jan C Harrell
**VP:* Cade F Kohoutek
**VP:* Catherine D McRae

D-U-N-S 00-809-0938 IMP/EXP
SHELL OIL CO
(*Suby of* SHELL PETROLEUM INC) ★
910 Louisiana St Ste 1500, Houston, TX 77002-4934
Tel (713) 241-6161 *Founded/Ownrshp* 1922
Sales 5.8MMM^E *EMP* 8,449
SIC 5541 4612 1311 2821 2869 2911 Filling stations, gasoline; Crude petroleum pipelines; Crude petroleum production; Natural gas production; Epoxy resins; Polypropylene resins; Olefins; Alcohols, nonbeverage; Petroleum refining; Gasoline; Jet fuels; Kerosene
Pr: Marvin E Odum
CFO: J R Eagan
Treas: Susan Hodge
Treas: Takashi Kimura
**Ex VP:* Bruce B Culpepper
Ex VP: John Donovan
VP: Glen Cayley
VP: Leonard Falsone
VP: Lee Humphries
VP: Olivier Lazare
VP: Helaen Vanderklei
VP: Deborah F Witmer
Dir Bus: Andrea Jimenez

SHELL OIL PRODUCTS U S
See EQUILON ENTERPRISES LLC

D-U-N-S 13-148-9817 IMP/EXP
SHELL PETROLEUM INC
(*Suby of* SHELL PETROLEUM N.V.)
910 Louisiana St Ste 420, Houston, TX 77002-4985
Tel (713) 241-6161 *Founded/Ownrshp* 1984
Sales 9.0MMM^E *EMP* 22,000
SIC 2911 4613 5172 Gasoline; Oils, fuel; Refined petroleum pipelines; Petroleum products; Gasoline; Fuel oil
Pr: Cornelius A J Herkstrter
CFO: Judith Boynton
CFO: Dave Rietmann
VP: Harry De Grijs
VP: Michelle M McGrath
VP: Richard Sears
VP: William Welcher
Dir IT: Blake Hensley

D-U-N-S 00-793-2593 IMP
SHELL PIPE LINE CORP (MD)
(*Suby of* SHELL OIL CO) ★
2 Shell Plz Ste 1160, Houston, TX 77002
Tel (713) 241-6161 *Founded/Ownrshp* 1919
Sales 102.6MM^E *EMP* 540
SIC 4612 Crude petroleum pipelines
Pr: George M Rootes
Treas: Dennis A Keel
Exec: Volkan Candan

SHELL POINT VILLAGE
See CHRISTIAN AND MISSIONARY ALLIANCE FOUNDATION INC

SHELL SPEE-D-MART
See WALTERS-DIMMICK PETROLEUM INC

D-U-N-S 07-911-4335
SHELL TOPCO LP
(*Suby of* NOVA CAPITAL MANAGEMENT USA LLC) ★
2533 S West St, Wichita, KS 67217-1025
Tel (316) 942-7266 *Founded/Ownrshp* 2012
Sales 100.0MM *EMP* 400^E
SIC 3625 1711 Control equipment, electric; Mechanical contractor

D-U-N-S 12-271-2792 IMP
SHELL TRADING NORTH AMERICA CO
(*Suby of* SHELL PETROLEUM INC) ★
1000 Main St, Houston, TX 77002-6336
Tel (713) 241-6161 *Founded/Ownrshp* 2000
Sales 737.5MM^E *EMP* 525^E
SIC 5172 Petroleum products
CEO: Ben Van Beurden
**CFO:* Andrew P Roberts
**Ex VP:* Paul W Chung
**Ex VP:* Julian C Dalzell
**Ex VP:* Thomas E Mark
VP: Mark Gill

D-U-N-S 62-613-0272
SHELL US GAS & POWER LLC
(*Suby of* SHELL PETROLEUM INC) ★
1301 Mckinney St Ste 700, Houston, TX 77010-3030
Tel (713) 658-0509 *Founded/Ownrshp* 1998
Sales 227.8MM^E *EMP* 353^E
SIC 4922 Natural gas transmission
CEO: A Y Noojin III
Pr: Rene R Joyce

D-U-N-S 96-757-9512
SHELLPOINT PARTNERS LLC
140 E 45th St Fl 37, New York, NY 10017-9307
Tel (212) 850-7700 *Founded/Ownrshp* 2010
Sales NA *EMP* 463
SIC 6162 7389 Mortgage bankers;
Genl Couns: Shari Kushner

D-U-N-S 00-430-0158
SHELLY AND SANDS INC (OH)
3570 S River Rd, Zanesville, OH 43701-9052
Tel (740) 453-0721 *Founded/Ownrshp* 1942, 1944
Sales 301.4MM^E *EMP* 550
SIC 1611 1442 2951 Highway & street paving contractor; Construction sand mining; Gravel mining; Asphalt & asphaltic paving mixtures (not from refineries)
Pr: Richard H McClelland
**Pr:* Gerald N Little
**VP:* Larry E Young

SHELLY COMPANY, THE
See SHELLY MATERIALS INC

D-U-N-S 01-834-3152
SHELLY CO
SHELLY MATERIALS
(*Suby of* OLDCASTLE MATERIALS GROUP) ★
80 Park Dr, Thornville, OH 43076-9397
Tel (740) 246-6315 *Founded/Ownrshp* 2000
Sales 542.7MM^E *EMP* 800
SIC 1611

SHELLY MATERIALS
See SHELLY CO

D-U-N-S 02-518-8256
SHELLY MATERIALS INC (OH)
SHELLY COMPANY, THE
(*Suby of* SHELLY MATERIALS) ★
80 Park Dr, Thornville, OH 43076-9397
Tel (740) 246-6315 *Founded/Ownrshp* 1938
Sales 457.0MM^E *EMP* 800
SIC 1422 1442 2951 4492 Crushed & broken limestone; Construction sand & gravel; Concrete, asphaltic (not from refineries); Tugboat service
Pr: John Power
**Treas:* Doug Radabaugh
VP: Melissa Dozer
**VP:* Ted Lemon
VP: Bill Lentz
Off Mgr: Kelly Dunn

D-U-N-S 02-369-2734
SHELOR CHEVROLET CORP
SHELOR MOTOR MILE
2265 Roanoke St, Christiansburg, VA 24073-2513
Tel (540) 382-2981 *Founded/Ownrshp* 1974
Sales 174.8MM^E *EMP* 400
SIC 5511 Automobiles, new & used
Pr: Larry J Shelor
**VP:* David Hagan
Sls Mgr: Dwight Funk
Sales Asso: Danny Burkholder

SHELOR MOTOR MILE
See SHELOR CHEVROLET CORP

D-U-N-S 10-714-9221
SHELTER DEVELOPMENT LLC
218 N Charles St Ste 220, Baltimore, MD 21201-4002
Tel (410) 962-0595 *Founded/Ownrshp* 1995
Sales 233.9MM^E *EMP* 1,200
SIC 6552 Subdividers & developers
CEO: Marilynn Duker
**Ch:* Mark K Joseph
**Ch:* Arnold Richman
VP: Alan Siegfried

SHELTER INSURANCE
See SHELTER MUTUAL INSURANCE CO

D-U-N-S 00-633-4692
SHELTER MUTUAL INSURANCE CO
SHELTER INSURANCE
1817 W Broadway, Columbia, MO 65218-1000
Tel (573) 445-8441 *Founded/Ownrshp* 1945
Sales NA *EMP* 3,145
SIC 6331 6311 Fire, marine & casualty insurance; Life insurance
CEO: Rick Means
**Ch Bd:* Don Duello
**Pr:* John Moore
**Treas:* Jerry French
Treas: Brian Strickland
Ofcr: Jean Curry
**Ex VP:* Ray Jones
**Ex VP:* Don Mc Cubbin
**Ex VP:* Gary Myers
**VP:* Dan Clapp
**VP:* Teresa Magruder
**VP:* Matt Moore
VP: Tina Workman

D-U-N-S 96-981-3955 EXP
SHELTER PRODUCTS INC
1490 Se Gideon St Ste 100, Portland, OR 97202-2463
Tel (503) 872-3600 *Founded/Ownrshp* 1998
Sales 128.5MM^E *EMP* 101^E
SIC 5031 Lumber, plywood & millwork
Pr: George J Beechler
**CFO:* Kurt Hutton
Admn Mgr: Barb Rauchenstein
Genl Mgr: Judy Vaught
Off Mgr: Sue Hawley
DP Exec: Bruce Wilkanson
IT Man: Victor Voqui
Info Man: Chuck Hildenbrand
Trfc Mgr: Dave Hall
Mktg Dir: Joe Beechler
Sls Mgr: Arthur Morales

D-U-N-S 17-362-5807 IMP
SHELTERED WINGS INC
VORTEX OPTICS
2120 W Greenview Dr Ste 4, Middleton, WI 53562-2547
Tel (608) 664-9856 *Founded/Ownrshp* 1986
Sales 101.4MM^E *EMP* 125
SIC 5049 Optical goods
Pr: Daniel C Hamilton
**Sec:* Margaret A Hamilton
Genl Mgr: Amy Washa
Off Mgr: Barbara Baier
Mktg Mgr: Tami Newman
Sls Mgr: Ben Lizdas

D-U-N-S 07-286-7971
SHELTERING ARMS HOSPITAL FOUNDATION INC
OHIOHEALTH O'BLENESS HOSPITAL
(*Suby of* OHIOHEALTH CORP) ★
55 Hospital Dr, Athens, OH 45701-2302
Tel (740) 592-9300 *Founded/Ownrshp* 1948
Sales 83.0MM *EMP* 368
Accts Deloitte Tax Lp Cincinnati O
SIC 8062 General medical & surgical hospitals
Pr: Mark Seckinger
**Pr:* Greg Long
**CEO:* Larry Thornhill
**CFO:* Ken Dicken
Treas: Robert Norris
**VP:* Lynn Anastas
**VP:* Shawn Bail
**VP:* Kimberly Gettwiller
**VP:* Sandy Leasure
**VP:* Scott Mash
**VP:* Candace N Miller

D-U-N-S 92-679-9172
SHELTERPOINT GROUP INC
600 Northern Blvd Ste 310, Great Neck, NY 11021-5200
Tel (516) 829-8100 *Founded/Ownrshp* 1972
Sales NA *EMP* 89
SIC 6411 Advisory services, insurance
CEO: Richard White
**Ch Bd:* Seth Goldberg
**Treas:* Bruce Wallach
Sr VP: Robert Slack

SHELTON FIREWORKS
See SHELTON WHOLESALE INC

D-U-N-S 15-558-7512 IMP
SHELTON WHOLESALE INC
SHELTON FIREWORKS
24073 24th St, Eagleville, MO 64442-8181
Tel (660) 867-3354 *Founded/Ownrshp* 1975
Sales 88.2MM^E *EMP* 548
SIC 5092 Fireworks
Pr: Gregory Shelton

D-U-N-S 80-856-2714 IMP
■ **SHEMIN NURSERIES INC**
(*Suby of* SITEONE LANDSCAPE SUPPLY LLC) ★
42 Old Ridgebury Rd Ste 3, Danbury, CT 06810-5126
Tel (203) 207-5000 *Founded/Ownrshp* 2015
Sales 251.6MM^E *EMP* 499
SIC 5191 5193 Farm supplies; Fertilizer & fertilizer materials; Seeds & bulbs; Flowers & nursery stock
Pr: Steffan R Burns
CFO: Bob Curlett
**VP:* Robert L Curlett
**VP:* Frank J Derosa
**VP:* Ronald W Sentman
**VP:* Donald E Smedberg
Genl Mgr: Gregg Maybach
Genl Mgr: John Oakley
Genl Mgr: Andrew Sebor
CIO: Brian Lynch
Dir IT: Don ABRA
Board of Directors: L David Cardenas, James Conroy, Frank M Danziger, Robert S Morris, Emanuel Shemin

D-U-N-S 06-599-8742
SHENANDOAH LIFE INSURANCE CO
(*Suby of* PROSPERITY LIFE INSURANCE GROUP) ★
4415 Pheasant Ridge Rd # 300, Roanoke, VA 24014-5275
Tel (540) 985-4400 *Founded/Ownrshp* 2012
Sales NA *EMP* 100
SIC 6311 Life insurance
Pr: Michael Akker
CFO: Robert Damante
Sr VP: Kathleen Kronau
Sr VP: Ralph Meola
VP: Ed Machado
VP: Paulus W Moore Jr
VP: Lee B Mowry

D-U-N-S 05-673-0450
▲ **SHENANDOAH TELECOMMUNICATIONS CO**
SHENTEL
500 Shentel Way, Edinburg, VA 22824-3577
Tel (540) 984-4141 *Founded/Ownrshp* 1981
Sales 342.4MM *EMP* 730^E
Tkr Sym SHEN *Exch* NGS
SIC 4813 4812 4841 Local & long distance telephone communications; ; ; Cellular telephone services; Cable television services
Ch Bd: Christopher E French
COO: Earle A Mackenzie
CFO: Adele M Skolits
Sr VP: Edward H McKay
Sr VP: William L Pirtle
Sr VP: Thomas A Whitaker
VP: Raymond B Ostroski
Dir IT: Richard A Baughman
Board of Directors: Douglas C Arthur, Ken L Burch, Tracy Fitzsimmons, John W Flora, Richard L Koontz Jr, Dale S Lam, Leigh Ann Schultz, James E Zerkel II

D-U-N-S 07-492-0299
SHENANDOAH UNIVERSITY
1460 University Dr, Winchester, VA 22601-5195
Tel (540) 665-4500 *Founded/Ownrshp* 1875
Sales 116.7MM *EMP* 600
SIC 8221 University
Ch: Andrew U Ferrari
**Pr:* Tracy Fitzsimmons
**Treas:* Robert J Frogale
**Treas:* Frogale Robert J
Bd of Dir: John D Hill
VP: Mitch Moore
**VP:* Richard Shickle
Assoc Dir: Meredith C Cox
Assoc Dir: Andrea Schmahl
Ex Dir: Andy Woodall
Store Mgr: Mary Knupp

D-U-N-S 00-478-4807
SHENANDOAH VALLEY ELECTRIC COOPERATIVE INC (VA)
147 Dinkel Ave, Mount Crawford, VA 22841-2358
Tel (540) 434-2200 *Founded/Ownrshp* 1936
Sales 253.5MM *EMP* 221
SIC 4911 Electric services
Pr: Myron D Rummel
**Ch:* Steven Burkholder
**Sec:* Charles Huffman
**V Ch Bd:* Larry E Garber
**VP:* John A Coffey III
**VP:* Wayne Hannah Jr
**VP:* Allen R Ritchie
IT Man: Julie Fix

SHENANGO VALLEY MEDICAL CENTER
See U P M C HORIZON

D-U-N-S 06-052-3123
SHENENDEHOWA CENTRAL SCHOOL DISTRICT
5 Chelsea Pl, Clifton Park, NY 12065-3200
Tel (518) 881-0600 *Founded/Ownrshp* 1950
Sales 76.4MM^E *EMP* 1,600
Accts Cusack & Company Cpa S Llc L
SIC 8211 Public combined elementary & secondary school
Pr: Mary Blaauboer
CFO: Susan Martins
**VP:* Todd Gilbert
**Prin:* Gary Dilallo
Schl Brd P: Bill Casey
Teacher Pr: Anna Sugarman

SHENTEL
See SHENANDOAH TELECOMMUNICATIONS CO

SHENTEL
See NTELOS HOLDINGS CORP

D-U-N-S 06-922-5019 IMP
SHEPARD EXPOSITION SERVICES INC (GA)
1424 Hills Pl Nw, Atlanta, GA 30318-2821
Tel (404) 720-8600 *Founded/Ownrshp* 1905, 1982
Sales 116.3MM^E *EMP* 600
SIC 7389 Convention & show services
Pr: Carl Mitchell
Pr: Kevin Bird
**CFO:* Stephen Basch
VP: Susan Hall
Natl Sales: Mary A Rogers

D-U-N-S 04-067-9664
SHEPHERD CENTER INC
2020 Peachtree Rd Nw, Atlanta, GA 30309-1465
Tel (404) 352-2020 *Founded/Ownrshp* 1975
Sales 198.2MM *EMP* 800
Accts Bennett Thrasher Llp Atlanta
SIC 8069 Specialty hospitals, except psychiatric
Pr: Gary R Ulicny
Dir Recs: Lydia Williams
COO: Stephen Macciocchi
**CFO:* Stephen B Holleman
**Sec:* Stephen B Goot
Bd of Dir: Stephen Goot
Ofcr: Kristin Boggs
VP: Wilma Bunch
VP: Mitch Fillhaber
VP: Mitchell Fillhaber
VP: Sarah Morrison
Exec: Joshua Cauthen
Exec: Tim Elliott
Exec: Jill Koval
Dir Lab: Joe Barber
Assoc Dir: Brock K Bowman

D-U-N-S 06-322-3523 IMP
SHEPHERD ELECTRIC CO INC (MD)
SHEPHERD ELECTRIC SUPPLY
7401 Pulaski Hwy, Baltimore, MD 21237-2542
Tel (410) 866-6000 *Founded/Ownrshp* 1892, 1931
Sales 173.4MM *EMP* 185
Accts Stegman & Company Baltimore
SIC 5063 Electrical supplies
Ch Bd: Charles C Vogel III
**Pr:* Stuart L Vogel
CFO: Carmen Grieves
**VP:* David T Revella
**VP:* James Shearer
**VP:* Scott F Vogel
VP Mktg: Glenn Carroll
Sls Mgr: Mary Early
Sls Mgr: Mike Farinelli
Sls Mgr: Erik Sigmon
Sls Mgr: Blair Weitzel

SHEPHERD ELECTRIC SUPPLY
See SHEPHERD ELECTRIC CO INC

D-U-N-S 03-017-2613
SHEPHERD GOOD HOSPITAL INC (TX)
GOOD SHEPHERD MEDICAL CENTER
700 E Marshall Ave, Longview, TX 75601-5572
Tel (903) 315-2000 *Founded/Ownrshp* 1959
Sales 279.5MM *EMP* 2,200^E
SIC 8062 General medical & surgical hospitals
CEO: Edward D Banos
**Sr VP:* Ruby Brewer
**Sr VP:* Ken Cunningham
**VP:* Beth Chrismer
VP: Christi Hawkins
**VP:* Brenda Sanders
**VP:* Ron Short
**Prin:* Jerry D Adair
Ex Dir: Keith Creel
Prac Mgr: Jo L Crane
Mtls Mgr: Kristy Pierce

D-U-N-S 07-361-8142
SHEPHERD GOOD REHABILITATION NETWORK
850 S 5th St, Allentown, PA 18103-3308
Tel (610) 776-3100 *Founded/Ownrshp* 1982
Sales 55.9MM *EMP* 1,114
SIC 8051 8361 8322 Skilled nursing care facilities; Rehabilitation center, residential: health care incidental; Rehabilitation services
Pr: John Kristel
VP: Maryellen Dickey
QC Dir: Susan Lee

SHEPHERD INSUR & FINCL SVCS
See SHEPHERD INSURANCE LLC

D-U-N-S 13-630-1546
SHEPHERD INSURANCE LLC
SHEPHERD INSUR & FINCL SVCS
111 Congressional Blvd # 100, Carmel, IN 46032-5638
Tel (317) 846-5554 *Founded/Ownrshp* 1974
Sales NA *EMP* 160^E
SIC 6411 Insurance agents
CEO: David Shepherd
**Pr:* Jeff Kweder
VP: Andrew Denny
Exec: Steven Shepherd
Opers Mgr: Lori Brown
Sales Exec: Keith Allen
Sales Exec: Jacob Bartley
Sales Exec: Deborah Brooks
Sales Exec: Kenneth Brooks
Sales Exec: Jason Bukowski
Sales Exec: Dan Burt

D-U-N-S 03-288-8182
SHEPHERD OIL CO LLC
1831 S Main St, Blackwell, OK 74631-4926
Tel (580) 363-4280 *Founded/Ownrshp* 1949
Sales 300.0MM *EMP* 60^E
SIC 5411 5172 Convenience stores; Petroleum products
Pt: Mike Shepherd
VP: Scott Shepherd
Sls Mgr: Bob Niles

D-U-N-S 83-035-2741
■ **SHEPLERS HOLDING CORP**
(*Suby of* AMERICAN WORKER) ★
6501 W Kellogg Dr, Wichita, KS 67209-8900
Tel (316) 946-3800 *Founded/Ownrshp* 2015
Sales 111.3MM^E *EMP* 810^E
SIC 5699 5661 Western apparel; Men's boots; Women's boots
CEO: Mark Syrstad
**CFO:* Jim Ritter

D-U-N-S 04-306-4088
■ **SHEPLERS INC**
(*Suby of* SHEPLERS HOLDING CORP) ★
15345 Barranca Pkwy, Irvine, CA 92618-2216
Tel (316) 946-3835 *Founded/Ownrshp* 2007
Sales 111.3MM^E *EMP* 800
SIC 5699 5661 5961 5651 5632 5611 Western apparel; Men's boots; Women's boots; Catalog & mail-order houses; Family clothing stores; Women's accessory & specialty stores; Men's & boys' clothing stores
CEO: Mark Syrstad
**CFO:* John T Mosley
Exec: Michael Anop

D-U-N-S 09-218-6360
SHEPLEY WOOD PRODUCTS INC
216 Thornton Dr, Hyannis, MA 02601-8103
Tel (508) 862-6200 *Founded/Ownrshp* 1977
Sales 100.0MM *EMP* 167
SIC 5031

SHEPPARD MULLIN
See SHEPPARD MULLIN RICHTER & HAMPTON LLP

D-U-N-S 06-668-8342
SHEPPARD MULLIN RICHTER & HAMPTON LLP
SHEPPARD MULLIN
333 S Hope St Fl 43, Los Angeles, CA 90071-1422
Tel (213) 620-1780 *Founded/Ownrshp* 1960
Sales 215.7MM^E *EMP* 1,124
SIC 8111 General practice law office
Pt: Guy N Halgren
Pt: Charles Barker
Pt: Robert Beall
Pt: Lawrence Braun
Pt: Justine M Casey
Pt: Robert A Darwell
Pt: Curtis M Dombek
Pt: Dana Dunwoody
Pt: Robert Magielnicki
Pt: Benjamin Mulchany
Pt: David Sands
Pt: Joan Story
Pt: Christine L Swanick
Pt: Carlton A Varner
Pt: Robert Williams
Ch Bd: Nagendra Setty
COO: Ted Tinson
Bd of Dir: Jeryl Bowers

D-U-N-S 04-195-1526
SHEPPARD PRATT HEALTH SYSTEM INC
6501 N Charles St, Baltimore, MD 21204-6819
Tel (410) 938-3000 *Founded/Ownrshp* 1853
Sales 210.7MM *EMP* 2,000
Accts Sc&H Tax & Advisory Services L
SIC 8741 8062 Hospital management; General medical & surgical hospitals
Pr: Steven S Sharfstein
V Ch: Gayle Hurt
COO: Donna Corbett
COO: John Kent
**CFO:* Gerald Noll
CFO: Greg Weller
Ofcr: Susan Amrose
VP: Ernestine Cosby
VP: Vareen O Domaleski
VP: Catherine Doughty
VP: Debora Hagwood
VP: Bonnie Katz
VP: Robert Roca
Exec: Amy Coleman
Dir Risk M: Barbara Charen
Dir Rx: Ken Walters

SHERATON BOSTON
See HST LESSEE BOSTON LLC

D-U-N-S 00-192-7326 EXP
■ **SHERATON CORP**
(*Suby of* STARWOOD HOTELS & RESORTS WORLDWIDE LLC) ★
1111 Westchester Ave, White Plains, NY 10604-3525
Tel (800) 328-6242 *Founded/Ownrshp* 1998
Sales 2.4MMM^E *EMP* 145,000
SIC 7011 8741 6794 Hotels & motels; Casino hotel; Motor inn; Hotel or motel management; Franchises, selling or licensing
Ch Bd: Theodore W Darnall
**Pr:* Richard D Nanula
CFO: Clayton C Daley Jr
**Ex VP:* Ronald Brown
Genl Couns: Ken Siegel

D-U-N-S 83-457-4238
■ **SHERATON PHOENICIAN CORP**
STARWOOD HOTELS & RESORTS
(*Suby of* STARWOOD HOTELS & RESORTS WORLDWIDE LLC) ★
6000 E Camelback Rd, Scottsdale, AZ 85251-1949
Tel (480) 941-8200 *Founded/Ownrshp* 1998
Sales 67.4MM^E *EMP* 1,700
SIC 7011 5812 5813 7999 7992 Hotels & motels; Eating places; Cocktail lounge; Tennis club, non-membership; Public golf courses
Pr: Michael Dojlidko
**Treas:* Jason Creed
**VP:* Peter Houghton
Assoc Dir: Juliette Demma
**Genl Mgr:* Mark Vinciguerra
IT Man: Marvin Emert
Mktg Mgr: David Richard
Sls Mgr: Katelyn Timpani
Snr Mgr: David Mapel

SHERIDAN CHILDREN'S HEALTHCARE
See SHERIDAN HEALTHCARE INC

D-U-N-S 60-938-4169 IMP/EXP
SHERIDAN GROUP INC
11311 Mccormick Rd # 260, Hunt Valley, MD 21031-1437
Tel (410) 785-7277 *Founded/Ownrshp* 1989
Sales 267.2MM *EMP* 1,460^E
SIC 2752 2732 Commercial printing, offset; Books: printing & binding
Pr: John A Saxton
Pr: Gary Kittredge
CFO: Bob Jakobe
CFO: Robert M Jakobe
VP: Patricia Groft
VP: Thomson Joe
VP: Susan Wiercinski
Dept Mgr: Peter Olson
CIO: James Rausch
Dir IT: Ashlea Collins
Software D: Randy King
Board of Directors: Thomas J Baldwin, Nicholas Daraviras, Craig H Deery, Gary T Dicamillo, James L Luikart, Nicholas R Sheppard

D-U-N-S 93-224-4494
■ **SHERIDAN CHILDREN'S HEALTHCARE INC**
SHERIDAN CHILDREN'S HEALTHCARE
(*Suby of* ARIZONA II MERGER CORP) ★
1613 Harrison Pkwy # 200, Sunrise, FL 33323-2853
Tel (954) 838-2371 *Founded/Ownrshp* 2014
Sales 225.5MM^E *EMP* 3,000
SIC 8011 Medical centers
Pr: Robert J Coward
**CFO:* Thomas Kiraly
**Chf Cred:* Gilbert Drozdow

Ofcr: Robin Barton
**Ex VP:* Patrick Solomon
**Sr VP:* Ken Chatfield
VP: Richard Auerbach
VP: Donald Beuerle
VP: David Donnelly
VP: Ted Emmert
VP: Janet Gehring
VP: Gregg Goldenberg
VP: Brian Hoffson
VP: Lee Lipton
VP: Michael Lynch
VP: Patti McEwen
VP: Josh Miller
VP: Kara Munro
VP: Tom S Summerill

D-U-N-S 88-405-8223
SHERIDAN HEALTHCORP INC
1613 Nw 136th Ave, Sunrise, FL 33323-2896
Tel (954) 838-2371 *Founded/Ownrshp* 1962
Sales 255.2MM[E] *EMP* 2,380
SIC 8741 Hospital management
CEO: John Carlyle
**Pr:* Mitchell Eisenberg
**Treas:* Robert Coward
**Ex VP:* Louis Gold
**VP:* Jay Martus
IT Man: Michael Edgett
Web Prj Mg: Zamora Maria
Opers Mgr: Stacy Constantine
Ansthlgy: George Luck
Doctor: Bruce Schulman

D-U-N-S 80-021-0283
SHERIDAN PRODUCTION CO LLC
9 Greenway Plz Ste 1300, Houston, TX 77046-0922
Tel (713) 548-1000 *Founded/Ownrshp* 2007
Sales 830.0MM *EMP* 460
SIC 1381 Directional drilling oil & gas wells
Pr: Lisa A Stewart
**CFO:* Matthew Assiff
**Treas:* Ron McCauley
**Ex VP:* James K Bass
**Ex VP:* Eric L Harry
CIO: Tony Sepolio
Dir IT: Joyce Williams
IT Man: Patrick W Brown
VP Opers: Mark McCool

SHERIFF NEWELL NORMAND
See JEFFERSON PARISH SHERIFFS OFFICE

SHERIFFS DEPARTMENT
See HAMILTON COURT JUSTICE OFFICE

D-U-N-S 06-800-6824
SHERMAN ADVOCATE HOSPITAL
1425 N Randall Rd, Elgin, IL 60123-2300
Tel (847) 742-9800 *Founded/Ownrshp* 1991
Sales 277.7MM *EMP* 1,685
SIC 8062 General medical & surgical hospitals
Pr: Richard B Floyd
CFO: Eric Krueger
Exec: Claudia Larsen
Dir Env Sv: Tim Leverentz
MIS Dir: Steve Chapman
Ansthlgy: GE LI
Ansthlgy: Istvan Miko
Doctor: Jane Bradford
Doctor: Hina Patel

SHERMAN BROS HEAVY TRUCKING
See S B INC

D-U-N-S 00-920-1315
SHERMAN FINANCIAL GROUP LLC
200 Meeting St Ste 206, Charleston, SC 29401-3187
Tel (212) 922-1616 *Founded/Ownrshp* 1997
Sales NA *EMP* 1,500
SIC 6153 6726 Buying of installment notes; Investment offices
CFO: Rusty Kendall
Telecom Mg: Darren Thomas
IT Man: Adrian Mackaay
IT Man: Marvia Mitchell
Netwrk Eng: Stephen Lammers

D-U-N-S 08-946-4184
SHERMAN INDEPENDENT SCHOOL DISTRICT
2701 N Loy Lake Rd, Sherman, TX 75090-1701
Tel (903) 891-6400 *Founded/Ownrshp* 1878
Sales 77.7MM *EMP* 1,176
Accts Adami Lindsey & Company Ll
SIC 8211 Public elementary school; Public junior high school; Public senior high school
**Treas:* Keith Nathan
Ex Dir: Kathy Bickerstaff
Ex Dir: Sandi Froese
CTO: Bill Tredennick
Pr Dir: Emily Parks
HC Dir: Judy Hathcock

D-U-N-S 94-212-8232
SHERMAN V ALLEN INC
MAC'S CONVENIENCE STORES
126 Post St, Rutland, VT 05701-4413
Tel (802) 775-7421 *Founded/Ownrshp* 1982
Sales 99.0MM[E] *EMP* 230
SIC 5172 5984 5411 4923 Engine fuels & oils; Propane gas, bottled; Convenience stores; Gas transmission & distribution
Pr: Jennifer Allen
**Treas:* Edward E Eno
**VP:* Robert Wetherby
Admn Mgr: Kelly M Pratico

D-U-N-S 06-489-3257
SHERMAN/GRAYSON HOSPITAL LLC
WILSON N JONES REGIONAL MEDICAL CENTER
(*Suby of* ALECTO HEALTHCARE SERVICES LLC) ★
500 N Highland Ave, Sherman, TX 75092-7354
Tel (903) 870-4611 *Founded/Ownrshp* 2010
Sales 102.9MM *EMP* 597
SIC 8011 Medical centers
Prin: Mary E Womack
Exec: Grant Craig
Dir Risk M: Tracy Masson
Psych: Christian A Cooper
Psych: Gary Grafa
Psych: Jasyn Haney
Psych: Asad Karim
Psych: Mark Koone
Psych: Maneeb Mellem
Psych: John H Pulliam
Psych: Lynda Smith

D-U-N-S 06-896-2216 IMP
SHERMCO INDUSTRIES INC
2425 E Pioneer Dr, Irving, TX 75061-8919
Tel (972) 793-5523 *Founded/Ownrshp* 1974
Sales 174.4MM *EMP* 446
Accts Crowe Horwarth Llp Indianapol
SIC 8711 7694 5063 Electrical or electronic engineering; Rewinding services; Electric motor repair; Motors, electric
Pr: Ron A Widup
V Ch: John Waite
**Ex VP:* Thad Brown III
**VP:* Pat Beisert
**VP:* Thaddeus Brown III
**VP:* Scott Meador
**VP:* Lonnie Mullen
Sales Asso: Kenilyn Downs
Sales Asso: Henry Riley

SHERM'S FOOD 4 LESS
See THUNDERBIRD SHERMS MARKET INC

D-U-N-S 00-322-8350 IMP/EXP
SHERRILL FURNITURE CO INC (NC)
2405 Highland Ave Ne, Hickory, NC 28601-8164
Tel (828) 322-2640 *Founded/Ownrshp* 1943
Sales 322.1MM[E] *EMP* 1,400
SIC 2512 2511 Couches, sofas & davenports: upholstered on wood frames; Chairs: upholstered on wood frames; Wood household furniture
Pr: Harold W Sherrill
CFO: Walter Bost
VP: Jeffrey Behmer
VP: Steve Cartee
VP: Hw Sherrill
VP: William Smith
VP Admn: Michael E Powers
Genl Mgr: Dan Hall
Plnt Mgr: Andy Matton
VP Mktg: Steven Hagar
Sls Mgr: Dick Ferraguto
Board of Directors: Marshall Yount

D-U-N-S 17-186-8672 IMP/EXP
■ **SHERWIN-WILLIAMS AUTOMOTIVE FINISHES CORP**
(*Suby of* SHERWIN-WILLIAMS CO) ★
4440 Warrensville Ctr Rd, Cleveland, OH 44128-2837
Tel (216) 332-8330 *Founded/Ownrshp* 1866
Sales 355.7MM[E] *EMP* 3,000[E]
SIC 5231 2851 Paint & painting supplies; Paints & allied products
Pr: Thomas Havlitzel
**CEO:* Christopher Connor
Area Mgr: Jerry Frushour

D-U-N-S 00-420-6397
▲ **SHERWIN-WILLIAMS CO**
101 W Prospect Ave # 1020, Cleveland, OH 44115-1075
Tel (216) 566-2000 *Founded/Ownrshp* 1866
Sales 11.3MMM *EMP* 40,706
Tkr Sym SHW *Exch* NYS
SIC 5231 2851 Paint & painting supplies; Wallcoverings; Paints & allied products
Pr: John G Morikis
**Ch Bd:* Christopher M Connor
CFO: Sean P Hennessy
Treas: Narsi Bodapati
Treas: Scott McVeigh
Ex VP: Jim Shepard
Sr VP: Catherine M Kilbane
VP: Thomas Bergdahl
VP: Graham Buchan
VP: Michael Cummins
VP: Bill Desantis
VP: Jennie S Gerardot
VP: Thomas Hopkins
VP: Allen J Mistysyn
VP: Allen Mistysyn
VP: Ryan Rampton
VP: Bill Rauterkus
VP: Kerri Rodgers
VP: Nate Shinsky
Exec: Jim Kazimir
Board of Directors: Arthur F Anton, David F Hodnik, Thomas G Kadien, Richard J Kramer, Susan J Kropf, Christine A Poon, John M Stropki, Matthew Thornton III, Steven H Wunning

D-U-N-S 06-495-6204
SHERWOOD CONSTRUCTION CO INC
3219 W May St, Wichita, KS 67213-1540
Tel (316) 943-0211 *Founded/Ownrshp* 1981
Sales 107.9MM[E] *EMP* 500
SIC 1794 4522 Excavation & grading, building construction; Flying charter service
Ch Bd: Howard Sherwood
**Pr:* John R Curtis
**CEO:* David Sherwood
CFO: Lanny Gridley
**Sec:* Patrick Burns
VP: Rod Abbott
VP: Kyle Conaway
VP: Alan Farrington
VP: Sam Parker
VP: John D Sherwood
VP: Brian Welborn

D-U-N-S 18-053-8670 EXP
SHERWOOD FOOD DISTRIBUTORS LLC
12499 Evergreen Ave, Detroit, MI 48228-1059
Tel (313) 659-7300 *Founded/Ownrshp* 1987
Sales 1.8MM[E] *EMP* 1,100
SIC 5147 5144 5146 5142 5143 Meats, fresh; Poultry: live, dressed or frozen (unpackaged); Fish, frozen, unpackaged; Fish, frozen: packaged; Meat, frozen: packaged; Poultry, frozen: packaged; Dairy products, except dried or canned; Cheese
CEO: Earl D Ishbia
**Pr:* Jim Gell
**Pr:* Howard Ishbia
**Pr:* Jason Ishbia
**Pr:* Joel Ishbia
**Pr:* Gary Karp
**Pr:* Robert Lipson
**Ch:* Alexander Karp
VP: John Politowski
VP: Markus Rohtbart
Genl Mgr: Rob Zeman

D-U-N-S 93-140-0431
SHERWOOD FOUNDATION
3555 Farnam St, Omaha, NE 68131-3311
Tel (402) 341-1717 *Founded/Ownrshp* 2007
Sales 152.3MM *EMP* 3
SIC 8641 Civic social & fraternal associations
Prin: Susan A Buffett

SHETAKIS WHOLESALERS
See JIM L SHETAKIS DISTRIBUTING CO

D-U-N-S 78-373-4411 IMP
■ **SHFL ENTERTAINMENT INC**
(*Suby of* BALLY TECHNOLOGIES INC) ★
6650 El Camino Rd, Las Vegas, NV 89118-2601
Tel (702) 897-7150 *Founded/Ownrshp* 2013
Sales 96.1MM[E] *EMP* 805
SIC 3999 3949 3944 Coin-operated amusement machines; Darts & table sports equipment & supplies; Video game machines, except coin-operated
CEO: Ramesh Srinivasan
**CFO:* Linster W Fox
**Ofcr:* Louis J Castle II
**Ofcr:* Roger Snow
**Ex VP:* Kathryn S Lever
Ex VP: Katie Lever
VP: Randy Buschner
VP: Dana Kelly
VP: Kate Reinhart
VP: Ken Swanson
Exec: Gary Massey

D-U-N-S 96-664-7468
■ **SHG SERVICES INC**
(*Suby of* SUN HEALTHCARE GROUP INC) ★
101 Sun Ave Ne, Albuquerque, NM 87109-4373
Tel (505) 468-4973 *Founded/Ownrshp* 2002
Sales 55.8MM[E] *EMP* 4,000[E]
SIC 7363 Medical help service
Pr: William Mathies

D-U-N-S 61-142-9481
SHI INTERNATIONAL CORP
SOFTWARE HOUSE INTERNATIONAL
290 Davidson Ave, Somerset, NJ 08873-4145
Tel (732) 764-8888 *Founded/Ownrshp* 1989
Sales 6.5MMM *EMP* 2,850
Accts Cohn & Reznick Accounting Tax
SIC 7371 7374 Computer & software stores
CEO: Thai Lee
**Ch Bd:* Koguan Leo
**CFO:* Paul Ng
VP: Kevin Boyles
**VP:* Al Fitzgerald
**VP:* Melissa Graham
VP: Pete Hackett
**VP:* Hal Jagger
**VP:* Celeste Lee
Comm Man: Ed McNamara
Prgrm Mgr: Jim Sheridan

D-U-N-S 14-724-3096
SHI/GOVERNMENT SOLUTIONS INC
1301 St Mo Pac Expy Ste, Austin, TX 78746
Tel (512) 634-8100 *Founded/Ownrshp* 1999
Sales 289.6MM *EMP* 32[E]
SIC 5045 7372 Computer software; Prepackaged software; Business oriented computer software
Pr: Thai-HIT Lee
**Ch Bd:* Koguan Leo
Sls Dir: Philip Wilhelm
Sls Mgr: Cecily Doyle
Sales Asso: Justin Adoue
Sales Asso: Amy Byrd
Sales Asso: Shawn Cox
Sales Asso: Jeff D'Arienzo
Sales Asso: Michael Hartmann
Sales Asso: Jeremy Hubik
Sales Asso: Bill Mattrisch

D-U-N-S 05-962-7224
SHIEL SEXTON CO INC
902 N Capitol Ave, Indianapolis, IN 46204-1005
Tel (317) 423-6000 *Founded/Ownrshp* 1970
Sales 255.9MM *EMP* 380
Accts Somerset Cpas Pc Indianapo
SIC 1542 1541 Commercial & office building, new construction; Commercial & office buildings, renovation & repair; Industrial buildings, new construction; Renovation, remodeling & repairs: industrial buildings
Pr: Michael T Dilts
**Pr:* Ben Wilhelm
**CFO:* Daniel J Murphy
VP: Bob Groogan
**VP:* Richard Hennessey
VP: Tom Scheele
Exec: Heather Devocelle
**Exec:* Brian J Sullivan
CIO: Tim Malarney
Sfty Mgr: Wade Ison
Snr PM: Chris Metzger

D-U-N-S 07-882-9066
SHIELD SECURITY INC
(*Suby of* UNIVERSAL PROTECTION SERVICE LP) ★
1551 N Tustin Ave Ste 650, Santa Ana, CA 92705-8664
Tel (714) 210-1501 *Founded/Ownrshp* 2010
Sales 25.7MM[E] *EMP* 1,500
SIC 7381 Security guard service
Pr: Ed Klosterman Jr
**VP:* Kenneth Klosterman

SHIFT DIGITAL
See SANCTUS LLC

D-U-N-S 80-440-6106
SHILO MANAGEMENT CORP
11600 Sw Shilo Ln, Portland, OR 97225-5995
Tel (503) 641-6565 *Founded/Ownrshp* 1991
Sales 171.1MM[E] *EMP* 2,500
SIC 8741 Hotel or motel management
Pr: Shannon M Hemstreet
CFO: Jamie Duckworth
**VP:* Ivan McAffee
Genl Mgr: Tim Laib
Off Mgr: Lesleey Gemmill
CIO: Rich Morris

D-U-N-S 00-417-6194
■ **SHILOH CORP** (OH)
MANSFIELD BLANKING DIV
(*Suby of* SHILOH INDUSTRIES INC) ★
880 Steel Dr, Valley City, OH 44280-9736
Tel (330) 558-2600 *Founded/Ownrshp* 1950
Sales 97.5MM[E] *EMP* 615
SIC 3469 3544 Metal stampings; Special dies & tools
Pr: Robert Grissinger
Ex VP: G Loesch

D-U-N-S 80-995-3136 IMP/EXP
▲ **SHILOH INDUSTRIES INC**
880 Steel Dr, Valley City, OH 44280-9736
Tel (330) 558-2600 *Founded/Ownrshp* 1993
Sales 1.1MMM *EMP* 3,400
Tkr Sym SHLO *Exch* NGM
SIC 3465 3469 3544 Automotive stampings; Metal stampings; Special dies & tools
Pr: Ramzi Y Hermiz
**Treas:* Thomas M Dugan
**VP:* Gary Dethomas
VP Sls: Scott Borovich

D-U-N-S 79-962-8573 IMP
SHIMADZU AMERICA INC
(*Suby of* SHIMADZU CORPORATION)
7102 Riverwood Dr, Columbia, MD 21046-1245
Tel (410) 381-1227 *Founded/Ownrshp* 1997
Sales 243.3MM[E] *EMP* 300
SIC 5049 5047 5088 Analytical instruments; Medical equipment & supplies; Aircraft equipment & supplies
Pr: Katsuaki Kaito
**Treas:* Satoshi Honda
Snr Sftwr: John Uhler

SHIMADZU MEDICAL SYSTEMS DIV
See SHIMADZU PRECISION INSTRUMENTS INC

D-U-N-S 09-747-0595 IMP
SHIMADZU PRECISION INSTRUMENTS INC
SHIMADZU MEDICAL SYSTEMS DIV
(*Suby of* SHIMADZU AMERICA INC) ★
3645 N Lakewood Blvd, Long Beach, CA 90808-1797
Tel (562) 420-6226 *Founded/Ownrshp* 1979
Sales 152.1MM[E] *EMP* 140
SIC 5088 5047 5084 Aircraft equipment & supplies; Medical equipment & supplies; Industrial machinery & equipment
CEO: Yutaka Nakamura
**Pr:* Koki Aoyama
**Pr:* Atsushi Nishizaki
**Pr:* Akira Watanabe
Dir Bus: Tracie Matsudaira
Rgnl Mgr: Patrick Fromal
IT Man: Joe Lovegren
Ql Cn Mgr: Erik Geierman
Sls Mgr: Dan Odonnell

D-U-N-S 07-329-6345 IMP
SHIMANO AMERICAN CORP
(*Suby of* SHIMANO INC.)
1 Holland, Irvine, CA 92618-2597
Tel (949) 951-5003 *Founded/Ownrshp* 2007
Sales 86.1MM[E] *EMP* 170
SIC 5091 Bicycle parts & accessories; Fishing equipment & supplies
Pr: David Pfeiffer
**Ex VP:* Jim Lafrance
Sr VP: Koichi Shimazu
Area Mgr: Robert Bakker
Area Mgr: Robert Milne
CTO: June Wong
IT Man: Robby Gant
VP Opers: Sue Allan
Opers Mgr: Gary Napolitano
Opers Mgr: Tony Torok
Natl Sales: Robert Funk

D-U-N-S 60-821-0977
SHIMMICK CONSTRUCTION CO INC
8201 Edgewater Dr Ste 202, Oakland, CA 94621-2023
Tel (510) 777-5000 *Founded/Ownrshp* 1990
Sales 319.6MM *EMP* 1,020[E]
SIC 1629 1623 Earthmoving contractor; Sewer line construction
Ch Bd: Paul Cocotis
**Pr:* Paul Camaur
CFO: Scott Fairgrieve
Ex VP: Christian Fassari
**Ex VP:* Jeffrey Lessman
Area Mgr: Osama Martell

D-U-N-S 61-096-9578 IMP/EXP
SHIMS BARGAIN INC
J C SALES
2600 S Soto St, Vernon, CA 90058-8015
Tel (323) 881-0099 *Founded/Ownrshp* 1993
Sales 182.8MM *EMP* 250
Accts Kagw Llp Artesia California
SIC 5199 General merchandise, non-durable
Pr: K Kenneth Suh
**CFO:* BJ Chang
**Ch:* James Shim
Sales Exec: James Shime

D-U-N-S 09-598-3334 IMP
SHIN-ETSU HANDOTAI AMERICA INC
S E H AMERICA
(*Suby of* SHIN-ETSU HANDOTAI CO., LTD.)
4111 Ne 112th Ave, Vancouver, WA 98682-6776
Tel (360) 883-7000 *Founded/Ownrshp* 1979
Sales 370.3MM[E] *EMP* 850
SIC 3674 5065 Wafers (semiconductor devices); Semiconductor devices
Pr: Yashuhiko Saitoh
**Treas:* Todashi Okuyama
CTO: Jeff Stroud
Dir IT: Mohammad Shahrokh

VP Mktg: Parker Brinson
S&M/VP: Steven Shimada

D-U-N-S 02-233-7372 IMP
SHINE BROS CORP
225 10th Ave Se, Spencer, IA 51301-5278
Tel (712) 262-5579 *Founded/Ownrshp* 1902
Sales 90.4MM^E *EMP* 100
SIC 5093 3341 Scrap & waste materials; Secondary nonferrous metals
Pr: Toby Shine
Genl Mgr: Dan Wycoff
Off Mgr: Leah Studer

SHINER BOCK
See GAMBRINUS CO

D-U-N-S 87-907-3476
SHINGLE SPRINGS RANCHERIA
SHINGLE SPRNG BAND MWOK INDANS
5168 Honpie Rd, Placerville, CA 95667-8682
Tel (530) 672-8059 *Founded/Ownrshp* 1928
Sales NA *EMP* 1,872
SIC 9131 Indian reservation
Ch: Nicholas H Fonseca
V Ch: John Tayaba
**Prin:* Veronica Holmes
**Prin:* Hermo Olanio
**Prin:* Kimberly Stock
**Prin:* Malissa Tayaba

D-U-N-S 95-702-3125
SHINGLE SPRINGS TRIBAL GAMING AUTHORITY
RED HAWK CASINO
(*Suby of* SHINGLE SPRNG BAND MWOK INDANS) ★
1 Red Hawk Pkwy, Placerville, CA 95667-8639
Tel (530) 677-7000 *Founded/Ownrshp* 2008
Sales 64.0MM^E *EMP* 1,200
SIC 7999 Gambling establishment
Ch Bd: Nicholas Fonseca
Pr: Tyler Bila
Pr: Matthew Morgan
**CFO:* Tyrone Huff
VP: Evan Smith
VP: Kevin Tolliver
Exec: Mishell Barwis
Exec: Kristina Bonachita
Exec: James Chen
Exec: Ana Dominguez
Exec: Walter Hahn
Dir Risk M: Penny Sullivan
Dir Soc: Melody P Souza

SHINGLE SPRNG BAND MWOK INDANS
See SHINGLE SPRINGS RANCHERIA

SHINSHU
See TRUE WORLD FOODS NEW YORK LLC

D-U-N-S 06-509-5390 EXP
SHINTECH INC
(*Suby of* SHIN-ETSU CHEMICAL CO., LTD.)
3 Greenway Plz Ste 1150, Houston, TX 77046-0325
Tel (713) 965-0713 *Founded/Ownrshp* 1973
Sales 207.7MM^E *EMP* 462
SIC 2821 Polyvinyl chloride resins (PVC)
Ch Bd: Chihiro Kanagawa
**VP:* Y Saitoh
**VP Mfg:* Ervin E Schroeder
Manager: Kevin Joyce

D-U-N-S 80-272-8477 IMP
SHIONOGI PHARMA INC
(*Suby of* SHIONOGI & CO., LTD.)
300 Campus Dr Ste 300, Florham Park, NJ 07932-1039
Tel (678) 427-5359 *Founded/Ownrshp* 2008
Sales 255.2MM^E *EMP* 900^E
SIC 2834 Pharmaceutical preparations
Pr: Dr John A Keller
Ch Bd: Pierre Lapalme
Pr: Edward J Schutter
Pr: Bala Ventkataraman
CEO: Patrick P Fourteau
CFO: Darrell Borne
CFO: Tadashi Hara
Chf Cred: Emile A Williams
Ofcr: Larry M Dillaha MD
Ex VP: Deanne Melloy
Sr VP: Hideo Utsumi
Assoc Dir: Yohei Enomoto
Assoc Dir: John Hines

D-U-N-S 00-317-4273 IMP
SHIP COLONNAS YARD INC
STEEL AMERICA
400 E Indian River Rd, Norfolk, VA 23523-1799
Tel (757) 545-2414 *Founded/Ownrshp* 1875
Sales 150.0MM *EMP* 880
Accts Dixon Hughes Goodman Llp Virg
SIC 3731 3443 3499 Shipbuilding & repairing; Fabricated plate work (boiler shop); Fire- or burglary-resistive products
Ch Bd: Willoughby W Colonna Jr
**Pr:* Thomas W Godfrey Jr
COO: Eddie Hughes
CFO: Rebecca Wieters
**VP:* Ken Mebane
VP: Richard Sobocinski
IT Man: Cristina Cooper
VP Opers: Steve Walker
Sfty Mgr: Jimmy Nicastro
Sfty Mgr: Randy Wheatly
Opers Mgr: Kent Mayer

D-U-N-S 83-031-0830 IMP
SHIP L TAMPA L C
1130 Mcclosky Blvd, Tampa, FL 33605-6722
Tel (813) 248-9310 *Founded/Ownrshp* 2008
Sales 97.3MM^E *EMP* 327
SIC 3731 Shipbuilding & repairing
VP: Mark Gisclair
Off Mgr: George Raymon
Prd Mgr: Shari Olbon

D-U-N-S 60-760-2182
SHIPCO TRANSPORT INC
(*Suby of* SSNYC INC) ★
80 Washington St, Hoboken, NJ 07030-4506
Tel (973) 457-3300 *Founded/Ownrshp* 1988
Sales 137.4MM^E *EMP* 235
SIC 8742 4731 Transportation consultant; Freight forwarding
CEO: Klaus Jepsen
**Pr:* Christian Mogelvang
COO: Mario Marin
**Sr VP:* Kim Ekstroem
VP: Frank J Cozzarelli II
**VP:* Steen Dyrholm
VP: Fiona Govan
Mng Dir: Angela Avery
Mng Dir: Raymond Kotowski
Mng Dir: Jennifer Roman
Genl Mgr: Karen Elken

D-U-N-S 82-684-9486
SHIPSTON ALUMINUM TECHNOLOGIES INTERNATIONAL LLC
(*Suby of* BUSCHE PERFORMANCE GROUP) ★
1450 Commerce Pkwy, Franklin, IN 46131-6963
Tel (317) 738-0282 *Founded/Ownrshp* 2015
Sales 152.5MM^E *EMP* 550
SIC 3365 Aluminum & aluminum-based alloy castings
CEO: Nick Busche
**CFO:* Craig Conaty
CFO: Greg Taylor
VP Sls: Mike Weber

D-U-N-S 08-043-5161
SHIPSTON GROUP US INC
BUSCHE PERFORMANCE GROUP
363 Exeter Rd, Hampton, NH 03842-1004
Tel (603) 929-6811 *Founded/Ownrshp* 2014
Sales 303.1MM^E *EMP* 1,000
SIC 8741 Business management
Prin: David Dingman

D-U-N-S 62-611-9668
SHIRE HUMAN GENETIC THERAPIES INC
SHIRE PHARMACEUTICALS
(*Suby of* SHIRE PLC)
300 Shire Way, Lexington, MA 02421-2101
Tel (617) 349-0200 *Founded/Ownrshp* 1988
Sales 132.9MM^E *EMP* 250^E
SIC 8731 Biological research
CEO: Dr Flemming Ornskov
**Pr:* Bill Ciambrone
**Treas:* Jonathan Poole
**Ex VP:* David Pendergast
VP: Suzanne L Bruhn
VP: Robert Dempsey
**VP:* Wayne Eppinger
VP: John Flaherty
VP: Tamara Joseph
VP: Wendy Merrill
VP: Marcio Voloch
Assoc Dir: Paul Godding
Assoc Dir: Joe Kavka
Assoc Dir: Cathleen Oconnor
Assoc Dir: Praveen Prasanna
Assoc Dir: James Stout

SHIRE PHARMACEUTICALS
See SHIRE US INC

SHIRE PHARMACEUTICALS
See SHIRE HUMAN GENETIC THERAPIES INC

D-U-N-S 14-626-9753
SHIRE PHARMACEUTICALS LLC
(*Suby of* SHIRE BIOPHARMACEUTICALS HOLDINGS)
1200 Morris Dr, Chesterbrook, PA 19087-5507
Tel (484) 595-8800 *Founded/Ownrshp* 2005
Sales 671.2MM^E *EMP* 3,500^E
SIC 3826 Analytical instruments
Pr: John Miller
**Pr:* Michael Cola
**CFO:* Angus Russell
**Ch:* James Cavanaugh
**Ex VP:* John Lee
Sr VP: Howard Mayer
**VP:* Gary Casto
**VP:* Hugh Cole
**VP:* Wayne Eppinger
VP: Patrick Martin
**VP:* Gwendolyn Niebler
VP: Wolfram Nothaft
Exec: Renee Dekin
Assoc Dir: Pat Bankes
Assoc Dir: Josh Carver
Assoc Dir: Jessica Cotrone
Assoc Dir: Debbie Cummings
Assoc Dir: Ignatius D'Anna
Assoc Dir: Serene Josiah
Assoc Dir: Matt McLaughlin
Assoc Dir: Marlene Ross
Board of Directors: Janice Hall, Gene Hoffman, Maura Lane-Warner, Maura L Warner

D-U-N-S 62-246-7447 IMP
SHIRE US INC
SHIRE PHARMACEUTICALS
(*Suby of* SHIRE PLC)
300 Shire Way, Lexington, MA 02421-2101
Tel (781) 482-9222 *Founded/Ownrshp* 2004
Sales 810.9MM^E *EMP* 1,210
SIC 5122 Pharmaceuticals
Pr: John Miller
CFO: Chris Goddard
VP: Charlotte Sibley
Assoc Dir: Mert Aktar
Assoc Dir: Nathan Bryce
Assoc Dir: Hugh McLaughlin
Genl Mgr: Jamie Oates
Snr Ntwrk: Kevin Dekofski
QA Dir: Sara Burhans
QA Dir: Kelly Ohare
IT Man: Stewart Cummins

D-U-N-S 18-187-1427
SHIRE-NPS PHARMACEUTICALS INC
(*Suby of* SHIRE PHARMACEUTICAL HOLDINGS IRELAND LIMITED)
300 Shire Way, Lexington, MA 02421-2101
Tel (617) 349-0200 *Founded/Ownrshp* 2015
Sales 65.5MM^E *EMP* 5,207
SIC 2834 Drugs acting on the central nervous system & sense organs; Drugs acting on the gastrointestinal or genitourinary system; Thyroid preparations
CEO: Flemming Ornskov MD
Pr: Paul Firuta
**Pr:* John Miller
VP: John Caminis

D-U-N-S 06-928-5062
SHIRLEY CONTRACTING CO LLC
(*Suby of* CLARK CONSTRUCTION GROUP LLC) ★
8435 Backlick Rd, Lorton, VA 22079-1498
Tel (703) 550-8100 *Founded/Ownrshp* 2002
Sales 136.7MM^E *EMP* 400
SIC 1611 General contractor, highway & street construction
Pr: Michael E Post
**VP:* Christopher Bucher
VP: Tom Vitale
Snr PM: Adam Gortowski
Snr PM: Joe Maguire
Snr PM: Robbie Roberts

D-U-N-S 19-708-4635 IMP
SHIROKI NORTH AMERICA INC
(*Suby of* SHIROKI CORPORATION)
1111 W Broad St, Smithville, TN 37166-2504
Tel (615) 597-8870 *Founded/Ownrshp* 1946
Sales 121.9MM^E *EMP* 1,100
SIC 3711

SHIRT BY SHIRT USA
See JACHS NY LLC

D-U-N-S 78-267-7132 IMP
SHISEIDO AMERICA INC
(*Suby of* SHISEIDO COSMETICS) ★
366 Prncton Hightstown Rd, East Windsor, NJ 08520-1411
Tel (609) 371-5800 *Founded/Ownrshp* 1989
Sales 90.0MM^E *EMP* 168^E
SIC 5122 2844 Drugs, proprietaries & sundries; Cosmetic preparations
Pr: Tamaki Shimamoto
**Ch Bd:* Edward Houlihan
VP: Rosanne Aliperti
Sls Dir: Leslie Shiro

D-U-N-S 19-369-1821 IMP/EXP
SHISEIDO AMERICAS CORP
SHISEIDO COSMETICS
(*Suby of* SHISEIDO COMPANY, LIMITED)
900 3rd Ave Fl 15, New York, NY 10022-4792
Tel (212) 805-2300 *Founded/Ownrshp* 1988
Sales 430.6MM^E *EMP* 1,128
SIC 2844 5122 Cosmetic preparations; Toilet preparations; Cosmetics; Toilet preparations
CFO: Ronald Gee
**CFO:* George Grossi Jr
**CFO:* Pankaj Gupta
**VP:* Edward W Klause
VP: Takafumi Oba
**VP:* Tatsuya Toda
**CIO:* Deanna Johnston

SHISEIDO COSMETICS
See SHISEIDO AMERICAS CORP

D-U-N-S 01-704-8174
SHIVELY BROTHERS INC
2919 S Grand Traverse St, Flint, MI 48507-1697
Tel (810) 232-7401 *Founded/Ownrshp* 1947
Sales 191.8MM^E *EMP* 230
SIC 5084 5085 Machine tools & accessories; Abrasives
Pr: Scott Shively
**Sec:* Daniel Graves
**VP:* Martin Kenney
Sls Mgr: Ronald Corbett

D-U-N-S 10-200-6954 IMP
SHIVERS TRADING & OPERATING CO
(*Suby of* QUESTO INC) ★
725 Broad St, Augusta, GA 30901-1336
Tel (706) 724-0851 *Founded/Ownrshp* 1981
Sales 800.2MM^E *EMP* 6,000
SIC 2711 2721 2731 4832 7312 6512 Newspapers; Newspapers, publishing & printing; Periodicals; Books: publishing only; Radio broadcasting stations; Outdoor advertising services; Nonresidential building operators
CEO: W S Morris III
**Pr:* William S Morris IV
CIO: Paul V Buckley
CIO: Ryan Strubinger
CTO: Erin De Veaux
CTO: Bill McMillen
Dir IT: Max Guffy
IT Man: Joel Lefever
IT Man: James White

D-U-N-S 00-696-6675 IMP
SHO-ME POWER ELECTRIC COOPERATIVE
301 W Jackson St, Marshfield, MO 65706-2128
Tel (417) 859-2615 *Founded/Ownrshp* 1947
Sales 207.0MM *EMP* 150
Accts The Whitlock Co Llp Springfi
SIC 4911 Electric services
CEO: Gary L Fulks
**Pr:* Dan Singletary
COO: Debbie Martin
**CFO:* John Richards
**Sec:* Chris Hamon
**VP:* Jack Bybee
Dir IT: Jeff Rhein
Trfc Dir: Earl Stuart

D-U-N-S 09-539-1173 IMP
▲ SHOE CARNIVAL INC
7500 E Columbia St, Evansville, IN 47715-9127
Tel (812) 867-6471 *Founded/Ownrshp* 1993
Sales 983.9MM *EMP* 5,500^E
Tkr Sym SCVL *Exch* NGS
SIC 5661 Shoe stores
Pr: Clifton E Sifford
**Ch Bd:* J Wayne Weaver
COO: W Kerry Jackson
Chf Mktg O: Carl N Scibetta
Ex VP: Timothy T Baker
VP: Clint Pierce
VP: Tucker Robinson
Genl Mgr: Diana Boshears
IT Man: Erica Robb
IT Man: Jason Sullivan
Board of Directors: James A Aschleman, Jeffrey C Gerstel, Andrea R Guthrie, Kent A Kleeberger, Joseph W Wood

D-U-N-S 82-812-8368 IMP
SHOE SENSATION INC
UNDERGROUND ATTITUDE
253 America Pl, Jeffersonville, IN 47130-4285
Tel (812) 288-7659 *Founded/Ownrshp* 2007
Sales 111.2MM^E *EMP* 650^E
SIC 5661 Shoe stores
CEO: Michael Zawoysky
Pr: Mickey Marsee
**CFO:* Eddie Price
VP: Philip McElhinny
VP: Gordon Partin Sr
Store Mgr: Toni Henderson
Sls Mgr: Angela Jackson

D-U-N-S 04-227-0769
SHOE SHOW INC (NC)
BURLINGTON SHOES
2201 Trinity Church Rd, Concord, NC 28027-8421
Tel (704) 782-4143 *Founded/Ownrshp* 1963
Sales 888.2MM^E *EMP* 6,000
SIC 5661

D-U-N-S 13-197-0980 IMP
SHOEI FOODS USA INC
(*Suby of* SHOEI FOODS CORPORATION)
1900 Feather River Blvd, Olivehurst, CA 95961-9627
Tel (530) 742-7866 *Founded/Ownrshp* 1985
Sales 89.8MM^E *EMP* 100
SIC 5141 Food brokers
CEO: Don Soetaert
**Pr:* Sumio Kawanabe
**Pr:* Tall Matsushima
CFO: Paul Jones

D-U-N-S 82-787-4459 IMP/EXP
SHOES FOR CREWS LLC
250 S Australian Ave # 1700, West Palm Beach, FL 33401-7437
Tel (561) 683-5090 *Founded/Ownrshp* 2004
Sales 201.4MM^E *EMP* 386^E
SIC 5139 Shoes
CEO: Matthew K Smith
COO: William Wolz
Chf Mktg O: Alex Carballo
Ex VP: Nathan Crary
Ex VP: Jim Dugan
Board of Directors: Kurt Kimball, Zohar Ziv

D-U-N-S 00-180-1570 IMP/EXP
SHOJI JFE TRADE AMERICA INC
(*Suby of* JFE SHOJI TRADE CORPORATION)
301 E Ocean Blvd Ste 1750, Long Beach, CA 90802-4879
Tel (562) 637-3500 *Founded/Ownrshp* 1965
Sales 219.2MM^E *EMP* 290
Accts Shimomura & Co Cpas New Yor
SIC 5051 Steel
Pr: Itsuji Araki
Treas: Hitoshi Ino
Sr VP: Brion Talley

D-U-N-S 04-700-1128
SHONEYS NORTH AMERICA LLC
SHONEY'S RESTAURANT
(*Suby of* ROYAL HOSPITALITY CORP) ★
1717 Elm Hill Pike Ste B1, Nashville, TN 37210-3628
Tel (615) 231-2333 *Founded/Ownrshp* 2007
Sales 301.5MM^E *EMP* 2,500
SIC 6794 8741 5812 Franchises, selling or licensing; Restaurant management; Fast-food restaurant, chain
CEO: David Davoudpour
**Pr:* Kamran Habeeb
**COO:* Michael Wozniak
**CFO:* Steve Neuroth
**VP:* Catherine Hite
Info Man: Sean McAnally
**VP Opers:* G M Hissong

D-U-N-S 03-470-7166
SHONEYS OF KNOXVILLE INC
9720 Parkside Dr, Knoxville, TN 37922-2203
Tel (865) 690-6331 *Founded/Ownrshp* 1962
Sales 47.3MM^E *EMP* 1,300
SIC 5812 Restaurant, family: chain
Pr: Bill Baugh

D-U-N-S 02-389-3803
SHONEYS OF RICHMOND INC
7202 Glen Forest Dr # 104, Richmond, VA 23226-3781
Tel (804) 346-3414 *Founded/Ownrshp* 1961
Sales 35.3MM^E *EMP* 1,500
SIC 5812 Restaurant, family: chain
Pr: Mark A Sweeney
Genl Mgr: Tom Edenstrom
Mktg Mgr: Jennifer Ford

SHONEY'S RESTAURANT
See SHONEYS NORTH AMERICA LLC

D-U-N-S 00-982-8856
SHOOK & FLETCHER INSULATION CO INC
4625 Valleydale Rd, Birmingham, AL 35242-4608
Tel (205) 991-7606 *Founded/Ownrshp* 1967
Sales 98.8MM^E *EMP* 200
SIC 5033 1799 5085 Insulation materials; Insulation of pipes & boilers; Mill supplies
Pr: Wayne Killion Jr
CFO: Randall Long
**Sec:* Ricky Stricklin
Ex VP: Mike Bedford
**Ex VP:* J D Jackson

VP: David Jackson
**VP:* Paul Kennard
Sls Mgr: Michelle Lovelady

SHOOK CONSTRUCTION
See SHOOK NATIONAL CORP

D-U-N-S 00-386-1267
SHOOK CONSTRUCTION CO (OH)
(*Suby of* SHOOK CONSTRUCTION) ★
4977 Northcutt Pl, Dayton, OH 45414-3839
Tel (937) 276-6666 *Founded/Ownrshp* 1925
Sales 111.0MM[E] *EMP* 250
SIC 1629 1542 8741

SHOOK HARDY & BACON
See SHOOK HARDY & BACON LLP

D-U-N-S 01-066-8705
SHOOK HARDY & BACON LLP
SHOOK HARDY & BACON
2555 Grand Blvd, Kansas City, MO 64108-2613
Tel (816) 474-6550 *Founded/Ownrshp* 1947
Sales 310.0MM *EMP* 1,200
SIC 8111 General practice law office
Ch: John Fmurphy
Pt: Michael G Cameron
Pt: Stephen J Darmody
Pt: Kirk J Goza
Pt: Gregory B Kuhn
Pt: Madeline M McDonough
Pt: John F Murphy
**Pt:* Lynn H Murray
Pt: Dennis R Neutze
Pt: Kelley D Sears
Pt: Neil E Spague
**Pt:* Gene Mwilliams
Mng Pt: Simon J Castley
Mng Pt: Alicia Donahue
Mng Pt: William P Geraghty
Mng Pt: Michelle R Mangrum
Mng Pt: Daniel F Molony
Mng Pt: Doug W Robinson
Mng Pt: Samuel B Sebree II
Mng Pt: James Shepherd
Mng Pt: Sean P Wajert

D-U-N-S 12-254-7532
SHOOK NATIONAL CORP
SHOOK CONSTRUCTION
4977 Northcutt Pl, Dayton, OH 45414-3839
Tel (937) 276-6666 *Founded/Ownrshp* 1986
Sales 114.9MM[E] *EMP* 250[E]
SIC 8741 1542 1629 1541 Construction management; Commercial & office building, new construction; Waste water & sewage treatment plant construction; Industrial buildings, new construction
CEO: Frank Klein
**Pr:* Vincent Corrado
**CFO:* Dianne Brush
Snr PM: Chris Halapy

D-U-N-S 10-730-7712
■ **SHOOTING STAR**
SHOOTING STAR, INC.
(*Suby of* MARSH & MCLENNAN AGENCY LLC) ★
8144 Walnut Hill Ln Fl 16, Dallas, TX 75231-4388
Tel (972) 770-1600 *Founded/Ownrshp* 2015
Sales NA *EMP* 201
SIC 6411 8741 Insurance brokers; Financial management for business
**Pr:* Dan Browning
**COO:* Robert Smith
VP: Tiffany Parker
VP: Dan Weber

SHOOTING STAR, INC.
See SHOOTING STAR

D-U-N-S 80-088-1278
■ **SHOP N SAVE WAREHOUSE FOODS INC**
(*Suby of* SUPERVALU HOLDINGS INC) ★
10461 Manchester Rd, Saint Louis, MO 63122-1522
Tel (314) 984-0322 *Founded/Ownrshp* 1992
Sales 375.8MM[E] *EMP* 4,000
SIC 5411 Supermarkets
Pr: Marlene Gebhard
Pr: Don Lorimier
Ex VP: Janel Haugarth
Ex VP: David Pylipow
Ex VP: Peter Van Helden
**Prin:* Chuck Hentz
VP Opers: Russ Achelpohl

SHOP RITE
See FOODARAMA SUPERMARKETS INC

SHOP RITE
See DELAWARE SUPERMARKETS INC

SHOP RITE
See RONETCO SUPERMARKETS INC

D-U-N-S 04-217-8657
SHOP RITE INC
115 E 1st St, Crowley, LA 70526-5101
Tel (337) 785-2924 *Founded/Ownrshp* 1967
Sales 88.6MM[E] *EMP* 450
SIC 5411 Convenience stores, chain
Pr: John Dan Gielen
**Sec:* Lazar J Gielen
Dir IT: Louis Saab

SHOP RITE OF LAUREL HILL
See BERAT CORP

SHOP RITE OF ROCHELLE PARK
See GLASS GARDENS INC

D-U-N-S 04-412-4758 IMP/EXP
SHOP VAC CORP
2323 Reach Rd, Williamsport, PA 17701-5579
Tel (570) 326-0502 *Founded/Ownrshp* 1969
Sales 418.9MM[E] *EMP* 1,600
SIC 3589 Vacuum cleaners & sweepers, electric: industrial
Ch Bd: Jonathan Miller
COO: Ed Mungo
**CFO:* David Grill
**V Ch Bd:* Matthew Miller
**Sr VP:* Felice Miller
VP: Vincent Bungo
VP: Dean Bussler
VP: Ray Morrissey
VP: Richard Pincofski
Exec: Jason Martin
Exec: Robert Terry
Board of Directors: Janine Miller

SHOP-RITE
See INSERRA SUPERMARKETS INC

SHOP-RITE
See PERLMART INC

D-U-N-S 05-352-1852 IMP
SHOP-RITE SUPERMARKETS INC
(*Suby of* WAKEFERN GENERAL MERCHANDISE) ★
5000 Riverside Dr, Keasbey, NJ 08832-1209
Tel (908) 527-3300 *Founded/Ownrshp* 1970
Sales 477.1MM[E] *EMP* 3,000
SIC 5411 Grocery stores
Ch Bd: Dominick V Romano
Treas: Thomas Milner

D-U-N-S 96-253-7341
SHOPCORE PROPERTIES LP
EXCEL TRUST, L.P.
(*Suby of* BRE RETAIL CENTERS CORP)
17140 Bernardo Center Dr, San Diego, CA 92128-2093
Tel (858) 613-1800 *Founded/Ownrshp* 2015
Sales 130.3MM *EMP* 6[E]
SIC 6733 Trusts
Pt: Gary B Sabin
VP: Greg Davis
VP: Steven A Farnsworth
VP: John Langford
VP: Dagan Sutherland
Off Mgr: Kyle Clayton

SHOPKO
See SPECIALTY RETAIL SHOPS HOLDING CORP

D-U-N-S 05-035-7789 IMP
SHOPKO
8800 F St, Omaha, NE 68127-1507
Tel (402) 339-2400 *Founded/Ownrshp* 1986, 2006
Sales 154.0MM[E] *EMP* 1,000
SIC 5331 5912 Variety stores; Drug stores & proprietary stores
Prin: Larry Johnson
Dist Mgr: Bill Babiash

D-U-N-S 80-867-2377
SHOPKO HOLDING CO INC
(*Suby of* SHOPKO) ★
700 Pilgrim Way, Green Bay, WI 54304-5276
Tel (920) 429-2211 *Founded/Ownrshp* 2005
Sales 5.6MM[E] *EMP* 15,000
SIC 5311 Department stores, discount
CEO: Michael Macdonald
**Treas:* Gary Gibson

D-U-N-S 02-325-2638 IMP
SHOPKO STORES OPERATING CO LLC
(*Suby of* SUN CAPITAL PARTNERS INC) ★
700 Pilgrim Way, Green Bay, WI 54304-5276
Tel (920) 429-2211 *Founded/Ownrshp* 2005
Sales 4.8MMM[E] *EMP* 23,000
SIC 5311 5912 8042 Department stores, discount; Drug stores; Offices & clinics of optometrists
CEO: Peter McMahon
Pr: Jill Soltau
CFO: Ann Bushman
CFO: Larry Clark
CFO: Mary Meixelsperger
CFO: Mary H Meixelsperger
Treas: Gary Gibson
Treas: R Pindred
Sr VP: Brian W Bender
Sr VP: Danny Bolstad
Sr VP: Michael Cantrell
Sr VP: Michael B Cooper
Sr VP: Kevin Easton
Sr VP: Craig Gourley
Sr VP: Lynn Hempe
Sr VP: Matthew J Lynch
Sr VP: Douglas McHose
VP: Dale Adams
VP: Lee A Alexakos
VP: Douglas Bergan
VP: John Bulgarella

D-U-N-S 02-425-0367
■ **SHOPPERS FOOD WAREHOUSE CORP** (OH)
S F W
(*Suby of* SUPERVALU INC) ★
4600 Forbes Blvd, Lanham, MD 20706-4312
Tel (301) 306-8600 *Founded/Ownrshp* 1956, 1999
Sales 387.3MM[E] *EMP* 5,000
SIC 5411 Supermarkets, chain
Pr: William J White
**Ch Bd:* Jeffery Noddle
VP: Mark T Coffin
VP: George Guthridge
**VP:* Edward A Klig
VP: Ernie Smith
DP Dir: Charlie Bryant
Board of Directors: Keith E Alessi, Douglas M Bregman, Bonita A Wilson

SHOPPERS SUPPLY
See BOMGAARS SUPPLY INC

SHOPPERS WORLD
See SW GROUP LLC

SHOPRITE OF ROXBOROUGH
See BROWNS SUPER STORES INC

D-U-N-S 14-584-1297
SHOPWELL INC
FOOD EMPORIUM
(*Suby of* A & P) ★
42 W 39th St Fl 18, New York, NY 10018-2033
Tel (212) 915-2202 *Founded/Ownrshp* 1983
Sales 377.8MM[E] *EMP* 6,500
SIC 5411 Supermarkets, chain
Pr: Louis Ruggiero

SHOPZILLA.COM
See CONNEXITY INC

D-U-N-S 13-042-9368
SHORE HEALTH SYSTEM INC
EMERGENCY HOSPITAL EASTON MD
219 S Washington St, Easton, MD 21601-2913
Tel (410) 822-1000 *Founded/Ownrshp* 1906
Sales 241.6MM *EMP* 1,800
SIC 8741

SHORE MEDICAL CENTER
See SHORE MEMORIAL HOSPITAL

D-U-N-S 62-077-2350
SHORE MEMORIAL HEALTH FOUNDATION INC
SHORE MEMORIAL HOSPITAL
100 Medical Center Way, Somers Point, NJ 08244-2300
Tel (609) 653-3500 *Founded/Ownrshp* 1987
Sales 187.8MM *EMP* 1,600
Accts Ernst & Young Llp
SIC 8062 General medical & surgical hospitals
Pr: Albert Gutierrez
Treas: Frank Sindoni

SHORE MEMORIAL HOSPITAL
See SHORE MEMORIAL HEALTH FOUNDATION INC

D-U-N-S 07-162-8549
SHORE MEMORIAL HOSPITAL
SHORE MEDICAL CENTER
100 Medical Center Way, Somers Point, NJ 08244-2389
Tel (609) 653-3500 *Founded/Ownrshp* 1940
Sales 183.3MM *EMP* 1,600
SIC 8062 General medical & surgical hospitals
Pr: Ronald Johnson
Pr: Robin Keyack
COO: Linda Kenwood
CFO: David Hughes
Assoc Dir: Calla Waldron-Buck
Adm Dir: Harry Downs
Adm Dir: Karen Sharkey
Adm Dir: Derek Suragh
Dir Sec: Georgette Fox
Nurse Mgr: Annmarie Guerrieri
Nurse Mgr: Patty Hogan

D-U-N-S 79-458-1033 IMP
SHORE TO SHORE INC
(*Suby of* CHECKPOINT SYSTEMS INC) ★
8170 Washington Vlg Dr, Dayton, OH 45458-1848
Tel (937) 866-1908 *Founded/Ownrshp* 2011
Sales 135.5MM[E] *EMP* 1,700
SIC 2679 2241 Labels, paper: made from purchased material; Labels, woven
Pr: Howard Kurdin
**CFO:* Chuck Rowland
**Ex VP:* John Lau
Ql Cn Mgr: Jo Clark

SHOREGROUP I&W
See SHOREGROUP INC

D-U-N-S 09-144-4195
SHOREGROUP INC (NY)
SHOREGROUP I&W
460 W 35th St, New York, NY 10001-1505
Tel (212) 736-2915 *Founded/Ownrshp* 1999
Sales 114.2MM[E] *EMP* 300
SIC 7373 Systems software development services; Systems integration services
Ch Bd: Robert V Kennedy
**Pr:* John McCarthy
**CFO:* Alan L Bendes
**Ex VP:* Robert Bojanek
VP: Judith Brown
VP: Bharat Shah
Sls&Mrk Ex: Mike Smith

SHORELINE CENTRAL MARKET
See TOWN & COUNTRY MARKETS INC

D-U-N-S 05-181-9551
SHORELINE ENERGY PARTNERS LP
400 E Kaliste Saloom Rd # 2600, Lafayette, LA 70508-8516
Tel (281) 872-0051 *Founded/Ownrshp* 2010
Sales 120.0MM *EMP* 24
SIC 4911 Electric services
Pt: Daniel Hurley

SHORELINE PUBLIC SCHOOLS
See SHORELINE SCHOOL DISTRICT

D-U-N-S 04-018-8807
SHORELINE SCHOOL DISTRICT
SHORELINE PUBLIC SCHOOLS
18560 1st Ave Ne, Shoreline, WA 98155-2148
Tel (206) 367-6111 *Founded/Ownrshp* 1944
Sales 51.8MM[E] *EMP* 1,400
SIC 8211 Public elementary & secondary schools
Ex Dir: Brian Schultz
Off Mgr: Heather Hahn
MIS Dir: Jim Golubich
Teacher Pr: Tam Osborne

D-U-N-S 15-913-7843
SHORELINE SCHOOL DISTRICT
18560 1st Ave Ne, Shoreline, WA 98155-2148
Tel (206) 361-4208 *Founded/Ownrshp* 1950
Sales 6.2MM[E] *EMP* 1,400
SIC 8211 Public elementary & secondary schools; Public senior high school
Dir IT: James Golubich

D-U-N-S 96-838-7175 IMP
▲ **SHORETEL INC**
960 Stewart Dr, Sunnyvale, CA 94085-3912
Tel (408) 331-3300 *Founded/Ownrshp* 1996
Sales 360.2MM *EMP* 1,063
Tkr Sym SHOR *Exch* NGS
SIC 3661 3663 7372 Telephone & telegraph apparatus; Radio & TV communications equipment; Television broadcasting & communications equipment; Mobile communication equipment; Prepackaged software
Pr: Donald Joos
**Ch Bd:* Charles D Kissner
**Pr:* Don Joos
**CFO:* Michael E Healy
Sr VP: Bharath Oruganti
**Sr VP:* David Petts
VP: Pankaj Malhotra
VP: Katherine Mancuso
**VP:* Allen Seto
Software D: Eric Lockhart
Sftwr Eng: Taojie Chen
Board of Directors: Mark F Bregman, Kenneth D Denman, Shane Robison, Constance Skidmore, Edward F Thompson, Josef Vejvoda

D-U-N-S 94-746-1984
SHOREWOOD PACKAGING HOLDINGS LLC
AGI-SHOREWOOD U.S.
(*Suby of* AGI SHOREWOOD US) ★
100 Northfield St, Greenwich, CT 06830-4618
Tel (203) 541-8100 *Founded/Ownrshp* 2012
Sales 167.1MM[E] *EMP* 3,810
SIC 2671 Plastic film, coated or laminated for packaging; Wrapping paper, waterproof or coated; Waxed paper: made from purchased material
Pr: Mike Ukropina

SHORR PACKAGING
See HANCHETT PAPER CO

D-U-N-S 82-836-6604 IMP/EXP
SHORT BARK INDUSTRIES INC
SBI
139 Grand Vis, Vonore, TN 37885-2136
Tel (423) 884-2010 *Founded/Ownrshp* 2008
Sales 144.5MM[E] *EMP* 545
SIC 2311 Military uniforms, men's & youths': purchased materials
Pr: Lisa Held-Janke
**COO:* Mike Slate
**CFO:* Steve Crandall
**Genl Mgr:* Rigo Aponte

SHORT HILLS OFFICE PLAZA
See GARDEN PROPERTIES CORP

SHORT STOP
See LEISZLER OIL CO INC

D-U-N-S 07-177-6405
SHORT-ELLIOTT-HENDRICKSON INC
S E H
3535 Vadnais Center Dr # 200, Saint Paul, MN 55110-5108
Tel (651) 490-2000 *Founded/Ownrshp* 1927
Sales 90.0MM *EMP* 718
SIC 8711 8712 Civil engineering; Sanitary engineers; Consulting engineer; Architectural engineering
CEO: Sam L Claassen
CFO: James Fraser
Prin: Jim Hall
Prin: Miles Jensen
Prin: Brian Kent
Prin: Noel Vogen
Prin: Dan Zienty
Genl Mgr: Leanne Sedani
CIO: Bill Koster
Dir IT: Sheldon Hasse
IT Man: Donna Viland
Board of Directors: Daniel R Boxrud, Brian Davis, Bob Ellis, Kerry Keith, Scott Lange, Bruce Olson, Dave Simons, Terry Wotzka

SHORTLINE BUS SYSTEMS
See COACH USA INC

D-U-N-S 93-202-7758
SHOW PROS ENTERTAINMENT SERVICES INC
514 Springbrook Rd Ste A, Charlotte, NC 28217-2170
Tel (704) 525-3784 *Founded/Ownrshp* 1989
Sales 44.7MM[E] *EMP* 1,509
SIC 7363 7361 Labor resource services; Employment agencies
Pr: Paul Manley
Pr: Robert Reddick
Treas: Teresa Manley
VP: Robert Redick
Genl Mgr: Juan King

D-U-N-S 87-420-0645
SHOW SERVICES LLC
920 E Highway 199, Springtown, TX 76082-6038
Tel (800) 737-8757 *Founded/Ownrshp* 1984
Sales 10.0MM *EMP* 1,500[E]
SIC 7389 Advertising, promotional & trade show services; Decoration service for special events
**Pr:* Jon Ford

D-U-N-S 18-824-4651 IMP/EXP
SHOWA DENKO CARBON INC
(*Suby of* SHOWA DENKO K.K.)
478 Ridge Rd, Ridgeville, SC 29472-7830
Tel (843) 875-3200 *Founded/Ownrshp* 2008
Sales 226.0MM[E] *EMP* 500
SIC 3624 Electrodes, thermal & electrolytic uses: carbon, graphite
Pr: Robert C Whitten
CFO: James S Kahl
CFO: James Kahl
VP: Clint Lucas
VP: Shigeki Mizobata
IT Man: Mark Little
IT Man: Robert Park
IT Man: Stan Pickles
Tech Mgr: Benjamin Ayers
Mtls Mgr: Lisa Kirny
Mktg Mgr: Jeff Dahlberg

SHOWBOAT HOTEL & CASINO
See SHOWBOAT INC

D-U-N-S 15-413-0678
SHOWBOAT INC
SHOWBOAT HOTEL & CASINO
801 Boardwalk, Atlantic City, NJ 08401-7509
Tel (609) 343-4000 *Founded/Ownrshp* 1998
Sales 108.4MM^E *EMP* 3,600
SIC 7011 Casino hotel
Pr: Philip G Satre
Sr VP: Jay Snowden
Exec: Dina Peterson
VP Sls: Shelly Williams

D-U-N-S 78-680-4638
SHPS FULFILLMENT SERVICES
(*Suby of* WELSH CARSON ANDERSON & STOWE) ★
3900 Collins Ln, Louisville, KY 40245-1642
Tel (502) 267-3423 *Founded/Ownrshp* 2008
Sales 117.2MM^E *EMP* 4,723^E
SIC 3555 Printing presses

D-U-N-S 14-494-8192
SHPS HOLDINGS INC
(*Suby of* WELSH CARSON ANDERSON & STOWE) ★
9200 Shelbyville Rd # 100, Louisville, KY 40222-5144
Tel (502) 267-4900 *Founded/Ownrshp* 2003
Sales NA *EMP* 2,000^E
SIC 6411 8742 Medical insurance claim processing, contract or fee basis; Human resource consulting services; Compensation & benefits planning consultant
Pr: Rishabh Mehrotra
CFO: John McCarty
CFO: Merle Merleryland
VP: Paul Knittel
IT Man: Charles McHenry
IT Man: Bill Yock

D-U-N-S 79-985-2900
SHRED-IT DALLAS INC
825 W Sandy Lake Rd # 100, Coppell, TX 75019-7408
Tel (972) 556-0197 *Founded/Ownrshp* 1987
Sales 58.2MM^E *EMP* 1,500
SIC 7389 5093 5087 Document & office record destruction; Waste paper; Shredders, industrial & commercial
Pr: Greg Brophy

D-U-N-S 07-942-6985
■ **SHRED-IT US JV LLC**
(*Suby of* SHRED-IT JV LP)
11311 Cornell Park Dr # 125, Blue Ash, OH 45242-1889
Tel (513) 245-8659 *Founded/Ownrshp* 2014
Sales 544.1MM^E *EMP* 1,300
SIC 7389 Document & office record destruction
Pr: Vincent Depalma
* *Sr VP:* Brenda Frank

D-U-N-S 18-920-2463
■ **SHRED-IT USA LLC**
(*Suby of* SHRED-IT US JV LLC) ★
11311 Cornell Park Dr # 125, Blue Ash, OH 45242-1831
Tel (513) 699-0845 *Founded/Ownrshp* 2008
Sales 544.1MM^E *EMP* 1,249
SIC 3589 Shredders, industrial & commercial
CEO: Vincent R De Palma
* *CFO:* James Rudyk
* *Ex VP:* Colette Raymond
* *VP:* Brenda Frank

SHREVEPORT TRUCK CENTER
See LTG LONESTAR TRUCK GROUP EAST LLC

D-U-N-S 09-397-2602 IMP/EXP
SHRIEVE CHEMICAL CO (TX)
SHRIEVE CHEMICAL PRODUCTS
1755 Woodstead Ct, The Woodlands, TX 77380-0964
Tel (281) 367-4226 *Founded/Ownrshp* 1978
Sales 389.2MM *EMP* 77
Accts Briggs & Veselka Co Houston
SIC 5169 Chemicals & allied products; Acids; Ammonia
CEO: James W Shrieve
Pr: Tom Carlson
* *Pr:* Jerry Jackson
* *Treas:* James C Coffey
* *VP:* Jack Weaverling
Sls Mgr: Dave Archacki

SHRIEVE CHEMICAL PRODUCTS
See SHRIEVE CHEMICAL CO

D-U-N-S 07-442-5083 IMP
SHRINERS HOSPITALS FOR CHILDREN
(*Suby of* SHRINERS HSPITALS FOR CHILDREN) ★
12502 Usf Pine Dr, Tampa, FL 33612-9499
Tel (813) 972-2250 *Founded/Ownrshp* 1925
Sales 120.0MM *EMP* 6,100
Accts Cbiz Mhm Llc Clearwater Fl
SIC 8069 Children's hospital
Ex VP: Lewis K Molnar
CFO: Michael A Van Horne
Trst: Gene Bracewell
Trst: Charles A Claypool
Trst: Gary Dunwoody
Trst: Raoul L Frevel Sr
Chf Mktg O: Peter Armstrong
Ex VP: James Full
* *Ex VP:* John McCabe
* *VP:* Eugene R D'Amore
* *VP:* Kathy A Dean
VP: Don Eisenbrown
* *VP:* Scott R Laubisch
VP: Scott Laubisch
* *VP:* Sharon Russell
VP: Kent Southworth
Exec: Joseph Melchiorre
Dir Risk M: Rosemary Hargreaves
Dir Lab: John Benjamin
Dir Rx: Maria Perez

SHRINERS HSPITALS FOR CHILDREN
See SHRINERS INTERNATIONAL HEADQUARTERS INC

D-U-N-S 94-083-5002
SHRINERS INTERNATIONAL HEADQUARTERS INC
SHRINERS HSPITALS FOR CHILDREN
2900 N Rocky Point Dr, Rocky Point, FL 33607-1460
Tel (813) 281-0300 *Founded/Ownrshp* 1980
Sales 190.6MM^E *EMP* 6,100^E
SIC 8082 Home health care services
CEO: Louis A Molnar
Bd of Dir: Robert Bob
CTO: Cathy Dean

SHRM ONLINE
See SOCIETY FOR HUMAN RESOURCE MANAGEMENT

SHSU
See HOUSTON SAM STATE UNIVERSITY

D-U-N-S 08-039-8985
SHUBERT FOUNDATION INC
234 W 44th St Fl 6, New York, NY 10036-3909
Tel (212) 944-3777 *Founded/Ownrshp* 1945
Sales 49.4MM *EMP* 1,700
Accts Pricewaterhouse Coopers Llp N
SIC 8699 6512 Charitable organization; Nonresidential building operators; Theater building, ownership & operation
Pr: Phillip Smith

D-U-N-S 07-327-8376
SHUBERT ORGANIZATION INC
SHUBERT TICKETING SERVICES DIV
(*Suby of* SHUBERT FOUNDATION INC) ★
234 W 44th St Fl 6, New York, NY 10036-3979
Tel (212) 944-3700 *Founded/Ownrshp* 1973
Sales 48.7MM^E *EMP* 1,675
SIC 6512 7922 Theater building, ownership & operation; Theatrical producers & services
Ch Bd: Philip J Smith
CEO: Robert E Wankel
CFO: Elliot Greene
Sr VP: David Andrews
VP: Juan Calvo
VP: Cathy Cozens
VP: Charles Flateman
MIS Dir: Nina Mobileo
IT Man: Larry Yedwab

SHUBERT TICKETING SERVICES DIV
See SHUBERT ORGANIZATION INC

D-U-N-S 00-959-3567 IMP/EXP
■ **SHULTZ STEEL CO**
S S
(*Suby of* PCC) ★
5321 Firestone Blvd, South Gate, CA 90280-3629
Tel (323) 357-3200 *Founded/Ownrshp* 2016
Sales 165.7MM *EMP* 490
SIC 3463 3462

D-U-N-S 07-984-5313
SHUNA & CAM
805 Van Zandt Ave Apt G, Marshall, TX 75670-1557
Tel (903) 578-5478 *Founded/Ownrshp* 2015
Sales 1.8MM^E *EMP* 1,000
SIC 8299 Airline training
Owner: Shuna Sherow
Prin: Brad Cameron

D-U-N-S 00-523-1220 IMP/EXP
SHURE INC
5800 W Touhy Ave, Niles, IL 60714-4608
Tel (847) 600-2000 *Founded/Ownrshp* 1925
Sales 282.4MM^E *EMP* 1,000
SIC 3651 3679 3661

D-U-N-S 82-927-2496
SHURTAPE TECHNOLOGIES INC
1506 Highland Ave Ne, Hickory, NC 28601-5302
Tel (828) 322-2700 *Founded/Ownrshp* 2009
Sales 112.7MM^E *EMP* 900
SIC 2672 Tape, pressure sensitive: made from purchased materials
CEO: Jim Shuford

D-U-N-S 93-232-0336 IMP
SHURTAPE TECHNOLOGIES LLC
(*Suby of* SHURTECH BRANDS) ★
1712 8th Street Dr Se, Hickory, NC 28602-9656
Tel (828) 322-2700 *Founded/Ownrshp* 1996
Sales 359.8MM^E *EMP* 1,100
SIC 2672 Tape, pressure sensitive: made from purchased materials
Pr: James B Shuford
* *CFO:* Don Pomeroy

SHURTECH BRANDS
See STM INDUSTRIES INC

D-U-N-S 83-164-4419 IMP/EXP
SHURTECH BRANDS LLC
DUCK TAPE
(*Suby of* SHURTAPE TECHNOLOGIES LLC) ★
32150 Just Imagine Dr, Avon, OH 44011-1355
Tel (440) 937-7000 *Founded/Ownrshp* 2008
Sales 129.5MM^E *EMP* 350^E
SIC 2671 Packaging paper & plastics film, coated & laminated
CFO: Don Pomeroy
* *Prin:* C Hunt Shuford Jr
* *Prin:* James B Shuford
* *Prin:* Stephenson P Shuford
VP Mktg: Randy Lear
Mktg Dir: Shelley Price

D-U-N-S 01-424-3570 IMP
SHUSTERS BUILDERS SUPPLIES INC (PA)
SHUSTER'S BUILDING COMPONENTS
2920 Clay Pike, Irwin, PA 15642-3020
Tel (724) 446-7000 *Founded/Ownrshp* 1959
Sales 116.1MM^E *EMP* 200
SIC 5031 5211 Windows; Doors; Lumber & other building materials
Pr: Anthony J Shuster Jr
* *Treas:* Robert W Shuster
* *Ex VP:* James A Vogel Jr
* *VP:* James Mackanick

SHUSTER'S BUILDING COMPONENTS
See SHUSTERS BUILDERS SUPPLIES INC

D-U-N-S 10-604-5680
▲ **SHUTTERFLY INC**
2800 Bridge Pkwy Ste 100, Redwood City, CA 94065-1193
Tel (650) 610-5200 *Founded/Ownrshp* 1999
Sales 1.0MMM *EMP* 2,016^E
Tkr Sym SFLY *Exch* NGS
SIC 7384 Photofinish laboratories; Film developing & printing
Pr: Christopher North
CFO: Michael Pope
CFO: Michael W Pope
Bd of Dir: Jeffrey Housenbold
Chf Mktg O: John Boris
Sr VP: Dwayne A Black
Sr VP: Dwayne Black
Sr VP: Peter Elarde
Sr VP: Satish Menon
Sr VP: Jayne Spiegelman
Sr VP: Gautam Srivastava
Sr VP: Jeannine M Smith Thomas
Sr VP: Karl Wiley
VP: Nigel Johnson
VP: Jerry Ko
VP: Isabelle Steiner
Board of Directors: Thomas D Hughes, Eva Manolis, Ann Mather, Elizabeth Sartain, H Tayloe Stansbury, Brian T Swette, Michael P Zeisser

D-U-N-S 61-240-8976
SHUTTERSTOCK INC
350 5th Ave Fl 21, New York, NY 10118-2100
Tel (646) 766-1855 *Founded/Ownrshp* 2003
Sales 425.1MM *EMP* 627
Tkr Sym SSTK *Exch* NYS
SIC 7374 7335 Data processing & preparation; Commercial photography
Ch Bd: Jonathan Oringer
CFO: Steven Berns
VP: Paul Brennan
VP: Michael Lesser
VP: Dan McCormick
VP: Ben Pfeifer
CIO: David Giambruno
IT Man: Joanne Chan
IT Man: Belinda Fischer
Sftwr Eng: Paul Bellora
Sftwr Eng: Mike Crowl
Board of Directors: Deirdre M Bigley, Jeff Epstein, Thomas R Evans, Paul J Hennessy, Jeffrey Lieberman

SI
See CALIFORNIA STEEL INDUSTRIES INC

D-U-N-S 00-207-0100 IMP/EXP
SI GROUP INC (NY)
2750 Balltown Rd, Schenectady, NY 12309-1006
Tel (518) 347-4200 *Founded/Ownrshp* 1906
Sales 1.1MMM^E *EMP* 2,700
SIC 2865 3087 2851 Phenol, alkylated & cumene; Custom compound purchased resins; Enamels
CEO: Wallace A Graham
* *CFO:* Richard P Barlow
CFO: Richard Barlow
CFO: John C Obst
* *Sr VP:* Paul Tilley
VP: Emmanuel Hess
VP: Traci Hockstra
VP: Christopher T Roberts
Site Mgr: Jeff Prickett
Sls Mgr: Steven Daigle
Board of Directors: Greg Brown, Lee Edwards, Ashley Graham-Gardner, Alexander Mac Cormick, Heather M Ward, Aleda Wright

D-U-N-S 80-115-0009
SI HOLDINGS INC
111 Center St, Little Rock, AR 72201-4402
Tel (501) 688-8400 *Founded/Ownrshp* 2006
Sales 184.2MM^E *EMP* 475^E
SIC 6211 Investment bankers; Bond dealers & brokers
Ch Bd: Warren A Stephens
Treas: Todd Ferguson
VP: Kathy Bryant

D-U-N-S 96-878-1617
SI INTERNATIONAL ZEN TECHNOLOGY INC
(*Suby of* SERCO SERVICES INC) ★
1818 Library St, Reston, VA 20190-6242
Tel (703) 939-6671 *Founded/Ownrshp* 1994
Sales NA *EMP* 4,000
SIC 7379 Computer related consulting services
CEO: Donald E Reed
* *Pr:* Leslie W Butler
* *VP:* Cindy A Andre

D-U-N-S 06-895-1631
SIBCY CLINE INC
SIBCY CLINE REALTORS
8044 Montgomery Rd # 300, Cincinnati, OH 45236-2922
Tel (513) 984-4100 *Founded/Ownrshp* 1970
Sales 2.1MMM *EMP* 1,150
SIC 6531 Real estate brokers & agents
Pr: Robert N Sibcy
COO: Bill Borek
* *Sec:* William D Borek
* *Ex VP:* James A Stofko
IT Man: Lori Meadows
IT Man: Nickolas J Sakelos
VP Sls: Nat Comisar

SIBCY CLINE REALTORS
See SIBCY CLINE INC

SIBLEY MEMORIAL HOSPITAL
See LUCY W HAYES TRAINING SCHOOL FOR DECONESSES & MISSIONARIES INC

SICAR FARMS
See LIMEX SICAR LTD CO

D-U-N-S 60-676-7200 EXP
SICOM SYSTEMS INC
4434 Progress Meadow Dr, Doylestown, PA 18902-9868
Tel (215) 489-2500 *Founded/Ownrshp* 1987
Sales 89.9MM^E *EMP* 200^E
SIC 5045 3578 7379 Terminals, computer; Point-of-sale devices; Computer related consulting services
Pr: William Terry Doan
Ex VP: Barbara McGinnity
Sr VP: William Robert
Sr VP: Miguel Solares
Software D: David Overholtzer
Software D: Sean Wegeler
Sftwr Eng: David Horn
Mktg Mgr: Michael Schwartz
Manager: Jon McCall

D-U-N-S 00-801-6495 EXP
SID RICHARDSON CARBON & ENERGY CO (TX)
309 Main St, Fort Worth, TX 76102-4006
Tel (817) 336-0494 *Founded/Ownrshp* 1948
Sales 121.2MM^E *EMP* 350
SIC 2895 Carbon black
Ch Bd: Sid R Bass
* *Pr:* Craig F Strehl
* *CFO:* William Reimann
* *VP:* Nancy Lee Bass
VP: Riaz Bismilla
* *VP:* W Robert Cotha
VP: Gregory A King
* *VP:* Herb A Trulove
* *VP:* Herb Trulove
VP: Herb A Trulove
* *VP:* Wesley A Wampler
Exec: Candida Luman
Exec: Long Nguyen

D-U-N-S 00-241-2724 IMP/EXP
■ **SID TOOL CO INC** (NY)
M S C INDUSTRIAL SUPPLY
(*Suby of* MSC INDUSTRIAL DIRECT CO INC) ★
75 Maxess Rd, Melville, NY 11747-3151
Tel (516) 812-2000 *Founded/Ownrshp* 1942, 1995
Sales 1.5MMM^E *EMP* 2,853
SIC 5085 5084 Industrial supplies; Industrial machinery & equipment
Ch Bd: Erik Gershwind
* *Pr:* Mitchell Jacobson
* *COO:* James A Schroeder
CFO: Charles Boehlke Jr
* *CFO:* Shelley Boxer
* *Sr VP:* Charles Moyer
* *Sr VP:* David Sandler
Board of Directors: Roger Fradin, Michael Kaufmann, Denis Kelly, Ray Langton, Steven Paladino

SID WAINER & SON
See FRIENDLY FRUIT INC

D-U-N-S 13-133-3387 IMP/EXP
SIDEL INC
(*Suby of* SIDEL PARTICIPATIONS)
5600 Sun Ct, Norcross, GA 30092-2892
Tel (678) 221-3000 *Founded/Ownrshp* 1984
Sales 104.7MM^E *EMP* 350
SIC 5084 Plastic products machinery
Pr: Sebastian Geffrault
COO: Darron Thomas
* *Treas:* Angela Wideman
Ex VP: Paul Mayer
* *VP:* Kevin Andrzejak
CIO: Dick Mehlan
Opers Mgr: Jerome Blanc
Mktg Mgr: Lynn McCay
Sls Mgr: Philippe Bartissol
Sls Mgr: Yann L Goff

D-U-N-S 96-624-3164
SIDERA NETWORKS INC
RCN
(*Suby of* LTS GROUP HOLDINGS LLC) ★
196 Van Buren St Ste 250, Herndon, VA 20170-5345
Tel (703) 434-8500 *Founded/Ownrshp* 2013
Sales 188.5MM^E *EMP* 880
SIC 4841 4813 7375 Cable & other pay television services; Telephone communication, except radio; Local telephone communications; Long distance telephone communications; Information retrieval services
Pr: Robert J Shanahan
CFO: Bob Albrecht
CFO: Edward O'Hara
Treas: Jean Garbier
Treas: Eric Sandman
Sr Cor Off: Jessica Kaman
Trst: Ray Forlano
Ofcr: Gary Smith
Ex VP: Timothy J Dunne
Sr VP: Richard Ramlall
VP: Bruce Abbott
VP: Stephen A Bogiages
VP: Paul Eskildsen
VP: Jackie Heitman
VP: Baker John
VP: Mike O'Day
VP: William Shelley
Exec: Michael Tarlow
Dir Rx: Kathleen Macedo

D-U-N-S 96-882-1368
SIDEWINDER DRILLING INC
952 Echo Ln Ste 460, Houston, TX 77024-2816
Tel (832) 320-7600 *Founded/Ownrshp* 2011
Sales 586.9MM^E *EMP* 1,000
SIC 1381 Drilling oil & gas wells
CEO: Jon C Cole
* *Pr:* J Anthony Gallegos
* *COO:* F Bruce Humphries
Treas: Keith Gunst
* *VP:* Craig Dauterive

SIDING DEPOT
See PASSAIC METAL & BUILDING SUPPLIES CO

D-U-N-S 05-005-0988
SIDLEY AUSTIN LLP
1 S Dearborn St Ste 900, Chicago, IL 60603-2323
Tel (312) 853-7000 *Founded/Ownrshp* 1866

Sales 841.8MM^E *EMP* 3,280
SIC 8111 General practice attorney, lawyer
Pt: Charles W Douglas
Pt: David L Anderson
Pt: Thomas H Beck
Pt: Glen Bernstein
Pt: Sanjay Bhandari
Pt: Jeffrey Bjork
Pt: Bruce Braverman
Pt: Sandra A Bresnick
Pt: Curtin Elizabeth C
Pt: John A Chamberlin
Pt: Thomas A Cole
Pt: Duncan N Darrow
Pt: Karen Dreyfus
Pt: Michael O'Hara Duff
Pt: Vera M Elson
Pt: Joel S Feldman
Pt: Max C Fischer
Pt: Stephen P Fitzell
Pt: Brian C Flavell
Pt: Bruce W Fraser
Pt: Bruce Gardner

D-U-N-S 03-202-2691
SIEGEL OIL CO
TITAN OIL ANALYSIS LABORATORY
1380 Zuni St, Denver, CO 80204-3300
Tel (303) 893-5273 *Founded/Ownrshp* 1995
Sales 120.4MM^E *EMP* 108
Accts Feldhake & Associates Pc G
SIC 5172 8734 Gasoline; Diesel fuel; Fuel oil; Lubricating oils & greases; Testing laboratories
CEO: Don Siegel
**Pr:* Tom McClary
**CFO:* Dave Rogers
**CFO:* Ronald R Sims
VP: Dawn Miller
Exec: Tiffany Vincel
Off Mgr: Paula Sherrill
Sls Mgr: Michelle Walters

D-U-N-S 07-928-7826
SIEGESECURE LLC
111 Lindbergh Ave Ste E, Livermore, CA 94551-9342
Tel (925) 963-6548 *Founded/Ownrshp* 2013
Sales 200.0MM *EMP* 18
SIC 7389 Personal service agents, brokers & bureaus
CEO: Gordon Shevlin
Pr: Jeff Bennett

D-U-N-S 04-109-7422 IMP
SIEGFRIED USA HOLDING INC
(*Suby of* SIEGFRIED HOLDING AG)
33 Industrial Park Rd, Pennsville, NJ 08070-3244
Tel (856) 678-3601 *Founded/Ownrshp* 2012
Sales 190.0MM^E *EMP* 970^E
SIC 2834 Druggists' preparations (pharmaceuticals)
Ch: Michael Husler

D-U-N-S 06-499-5533 IMP/EXP
SIEMENS CORP
(*Suby of* SIEMENS AG)
300 New Jersey Ave Nw # 10, Washington, DC 20001-2030
Tel (202) 434-4800 *Founded/Ownrshp* 1954
Sales 20.0MMM *EMP* 60,000
SIC 3661 3641 3844 3612 3357

D-U-N-S 62-068-0298
SIEMENS CORPORATE RESEARCH INC
(*Suby of* SIEMENS CORP) ★
755 College Rd E, Princeton, NJ 08540-6632
Tel (609) 734-6500 *Founded/Ownrshp* 1988
Sales 95.9MM^E *EMP* 2,000
SIC 8731 7373 Commercial physical research; Systems software development services
Pr: Norbert Gaus
Sr VP: Kurt D Bettenhausen
Prgrm Mgr: Gianluca Paladini
Genl Mgr: Samuel Roods
DP Exec: Joseph Day
IT Man: Susan Demeo
Sftwr Eng: Edward Slavin

D-U-N-S 15-397-7632 IMP/EXP
SIEMENS ENERGY INC
(*Suby of* SIEMENS CORP) ★
4400 N Alafaya Trl, Orlando, FL 32826-2301
Tel (407) 736-5183 *Founded/Ownrshp* 1997
Sales 3.0MMM^E *EMP* 7,900
SIC 3511 Steam turbines
CFO: Steve Conner
Dir Bus: Dan Rowlings
Prgrm Mgr: James McQuiggan
CIO: Christy Woodruff
IT Man: Michael Ambrogio
IT Man: Chuck Bucher
IT Man: Randolph Smith
Sftwr Eng: Gary Marangoni
Opers Mgr: Kurt Berg
Opers Mgr: Eric Kok
Opers Mgr: Victor Quinones

D-U-N-S 13-221-3638
SIEMENS FINANCIAL SERVICES INC
(*Suby of* SIEMENS CORP) ★
170 Wood Ave S Fl 1, Iselin, NJ 08830-2726
Tel (609) 954-2489 *Founded/Ownrshp* 1982
Sales NA *EMP* 150
SIC 6159 Machinery & equipment finance leasing
Pr: Kirk Edelman
CFO: Robert J Knapp
Sr VP: Robert A Anderson
Sr VP: Guy Cirincione
Sr VP: Dave Kantes
Sr VP: Richard J Kershaw
VP: Joseph Accardi
VP: Scott Lamoreaux

D-U-N-S 10-516-2098
SIEMENS GOVERNMENT TECHNOLOGIES INC
DRESSER-RAND
(*Suby of* SIEMENS INDUSTRY INC) ★
2231 Crystal Dr Ste 700, Arlington, VA 22202-3724
Tel (703) 860-1574 *Founded/Ownrshp* 2001
Sales 166.4MM^E *EMP* 600
SIC 8711 7373 7376 7379 8712 7378 Engineering services; Computer integrated systems design; Computer facilities management; Computer related maintenance services; Architectural services; Computer maintenance & repair
CEO: Judith F Marks
**Ch Bd:* Stanley McChrystal
Bd of Dir: Lowell Brown
Sr VP: Clay Halec
Sr VP: Barbara Humpton
VP: Diana O Knapton
VP: Frederick Latrash
VP: Scott McCoy
VP: James Regan
VP: Lamont J Wells
Dir Surg: Douglas Norton
Board of Directors: Robert Coutts, John Sylvester

D-U-N-S 06-460-8573 IMP/EXP
SIEMENS HEALTHCARE DIAGNOSTICS INC
(*Suby of* NUCLEAR SYSTEMS GROUP) ★
511 Benedict Ave, Tarrytown, NY 10591-5005
Tel (914) 631-8000 *Founded/Ownrshp* 2006
Sales 1.0MMM^E *EMP* 2,406
SIC 5047 Medical & hospital equipment
CEO: Michael Reitermann
Bd of Dir: Maxwell H Salter
VP: Nicholaas Arnold
VP: Stacy Mengel
VP: Ira Ziering
Prgrm Mgr: Darius Daruwala
QA Dir: Wolfgang Zens
Dir IT: Cathy Rohm
IT Man: Bill Thompson
Sftwr Eng: Tony Pinho
Ql Cn Mgr: Elizabeth Beato

D-U-N-S 01-094-4650 IMP/EXP
SIEMENS INDUSTRY INC
(*Suby of* SIEMENS CORP) ★
1000 Deerfield Pkwy, Buffalo Grove, IL 60089-4547
Tel (847) 215-1000 *Founded/Ownrshp* 1988
Sales 3.0MMM^E *EMP* 7,422
SIC 3822 5063 3669 1731 7382 3625 Air conditioning & refrigeration controls; Thermostats & other environmental sensors; Electric alarms & signaling equipment; Emergency alarms; Safety & security specialization; Security systems services; Relays & industrial controls
Pr: Joe Kaeser
CFO: Klaus P Stegemann
Ofcr: Jason Mallace
Sr VP: Kay Meggers
**VP:* George T Burck
**VP:* Axel Meier
VP: Albrecht Neumann
**Prin:* Daryl Dean Dulaney
Prgrm Mgr: Kelly Sangston
Snr Sftwr: Steve Dover
Snr Sftwr: Heather Klem
Board of Directors: Daryl Dulaney, Heinrich Hiesinger, Johannes Milde, George Nolan, Rolf Renz, Garry Wagner

D-U-N-S 18-681-2384 IMP
SIEMENS MEDICAL SOLUTIONS DIAGNOSTICS
DPC INSTRUMENT SYSTEMS
(*Suby of* SIEMENS HEALTHCARE DIAGNOSTICS INC) ★
62 Flanders Bartley Rd, Flanders, NJ 07836-4715
Tel (973) 927-2828 *Founded/Ownrshp* 1992
Sales 228.8MM^E *EMP* 2,100
SIC 3826 Analytical instruments
Pr: Douglas R Olson
Ofcr: Jim Jacobson
**VP:* Jim Guille
**VP:* David Herzog
Snr Sftwr: Thomas Hanc
Sftwr Eng: Hitender Mittal
Snr Mgr: Dan Orsini

D-U-N-S 10-323-1817 IMP/EXP
SIEMENS MEDICAL SOLUTIONS USA INC
NUCLEAR SYSTEMS GROUP
(*Suby of* SIEMENS CORP) ★
40 Liberty Blvd, Malvern, PA 19355-1418
Tel (610) 219-6300 *Founded/Ownrshp* 1982
Sales 1.7MMM^E *EMP* 4,613
SIC 5047 3845 3842 3843 Medical & hospital equipment; Medical equipment & supplies; Diagnostic equipment, medical; Electromedical apparatus; Pacemaker, cardiac; Orthopedic appliances; Hearing aids; Dental equipment & supplies
Pr: Michael Reitermann
**CEO:* Jeffrey Bundy
**CEO:* Britta Fuenfstueck
**CEO:* John Glaser
**CFO:* Michael Beierwaltes
**CFO:* Thomas Rackow
**CFO:* Christian Rummel
**CFO:* Franz Wiehler
Sr VP: Christi Pedra
VP: Alex Cole
**VP:* Anthonie Goudemond
VP: Alexander Herold
VP: Thomas Kearney
VP: Robert W Miller
VP: William Mount
VP: Kevin Piccola
VP: Juergen Scholl
Board of Directors: Klaus Stegemann-Member, Thomas Miller, Michael Sen, Gregory Sorensen, Eric Spiegel

SIEMENS PLM SOFTWARE
See SIEMENS PRODUCT LIFECYCLE MANAGEMENT SOFTWARE INC

D-U-N-S 06-999-3942 IMP
SIEMENS POWER TRANSMISSION & DISTRIBUTION INC
110 Macalyson Ct, Cary, NC 27511-7912
Tel (919) 463-8702 *Founded/Ownrshp* 1997
Sales NA *EMP* 2,100
SIC 3613 3625

D-U-N-S 01-071-2847
SIEMENS PRODUCT LIFECYCLE MANAGEMENT SOFTWARE INC
SIEMENS PLM SOFTWARE
(*Suby of* SIEMENS INDUSTRY INC) ★
5800 Granite Pkwy Ste 600, Plano, TX 75024-6612
Tel (972) 987-3000 *Founded/Ownrshp* 1997, 2007
Sales 850.6MM^E *EMP* 7,200
SIC 7372 Business oriented computer software
Ch Bd: Anton S Huber
**Pr:* Charles C Grindstaff
**CFO:* Harry Volande
CFO: Thomas Wang
**Treas:* Paul Keetley
Ex VP: Mike Sayen
Ex VP: Paul J Vogel
Sr VP: Stephen M Bashada
Sr VP: Craig J Berry
Sr VP: Kevin J Eustace
Sr VP: Robert W Jones
Sr VP: Daniel D Malliet
Sr VP: James W Rusk
Sr VP: David S Shook
VP: Paul Au
**VP:* Steven Dietz Sr
VP: Raj Khoshoo
VP: Ruben D Kreimer
VP: Christopher Migura
VP: John F Miller
VP: Daryl A Rhodes

D-U-N-S 05-681-9642 IMP
SIEMENS RAIL AUTOMATION CORP
INVENSYS RAIL
(*Suby of* SIEMENS INDUSTRY INC) ★
2400 Nelson Miller Pkwy, Louisville, KY 40223-2192
Tel (502) 244-7400 *Founded/Ownrshp* 2013
Sales 169.6MM^E *EMP* 600
SIC 3743 3669 Railroad equipment; Railroad signaling devices, electric
CEO: Nick Crossfield
**Pr:* John J Paljug
VP: Kim Dickey
VP: Brad Hall
Dir IT: Richard Strange
IT Man: Steven Moore
Plnt Mgr: Donnie Bane

SIEMENS VAI METALS TECH
See PRIMETALS TECHNOLOGIES USA LLC

D-U-N-S 00-627-5648
SIEMER MILLING CO (IL)
111 W Main St, Teutopolis, IL 62467-1201
Tel (217) 857-3131 *Founded/Ownrshp* 1882
Sales 205.5MM *EMP* 130
SIC 2041

D-U-N-S 03-999-0718 IMP/EXP
SIEMON CO
SIEMON GLOBAL PROJECT SERVICES
101 Siemon Company Dr, Watertown, CT 06795-2651
Tel (860) 945-4200 *Founded/Ownrshp* 1903
Sales 155.0MM^E *EMP* 547
SIC 3643 3089 3679 3469 3613 3357 Electric connectors; Thermoformed finished plastic products; Harness assemblies for electronic use: wire or cable; Metal stampings; Switchgear & switchboard apparatus; Nonferrous wiredrawing & insulating
Pr: Carl N Siemon
**Pr:* CK Siemon
**Treas:* Thomas Costello
VP: Rob Galle
**VP:* John Siemon
Exec: Valerie Maguire
Exec: Andy Reynolds
QC Dir: Lou Beres
Plnt Mgr: Brian Wheelock
VP Mktg: Christina Marrone
VP Sls: Robert Carlson

SIEMON GLOBAL PROJECT SERVICES
See SIEMON CO

SIEMON LAKE VIEW MANOR ESTATE
See SIEMON NURSING HOME INC

D-U-N-S 01-044-2499
SIEMON NURSING HOME INC
SIEMON LAKE VIEW MANOR ESTATE
228 Siemon Dr, Somerset, PA 15501-7055
Tel (814) 443-2811 *Founded/Ownrshp* 1958
Sales 637.8MM *EMP* 118
SIC 8051 Skilled nursing care facilities
Pr: Martin O Siemon III

D-U-N-S 08-048-1351
SIENA COLLEGE
515 Loudon Rd, Loudonville, NY 12211-1462
Tel (518) 783-2300 *Founded/Ownrshp* 1938
Sales 97.1MM *EMP* 650^E
Accts Kpmg Llp Albany Ny
SIC 8221 College, except junior
Pr: Edward Coughlin
Ofcr: Ann Klotz
VP: Joe Fitzgerald
VP: Timoth Lederman
VP: Anthony Pondillo
Exec: Mary Burns
Assoc Dir: Pat Bradway
Assoc Dir: Lori Lasch
Off Mgr: Eileen Martino
Web Prj Mg: Mitzi Bianchi
Pgrm Dir: Dacey Bonney

D-U-N-S 00-196-6852
SIERRA CLUB (CA)
SIERRA CLUB BOOKS
2101 Webster St Ste 1300, Oakland, CA 94612-3011
Tel (415) 977-5500 *Founded/Ownrshp* 1892
Sales 98.1MM *EMP* 600
Accts Rk Taylor & Associates Walnut
SIC 8641 8399 Environmental protection organization; Advocacy group
Pr: Robin Mann
Dir Vol: Amy Schlotthauer
V Ch: Lynn Henning
V Ch: Craig Lubow
V Ch: Ted Manahan
V Ch: Ken Smokoska
COO: Deborah Soronda
CFO: Ginny Quick
**Treas:* Donna Buell
**Treas:* Allison Chin
Treas: Terry Davis
**Bd of Dir:* Rafael Reyes
Ofcr: Dave Thack
**VP:* Spencer Black
VP: Jan Oconnell
**VP:* David Scott
Exec: Robert Bernstein
Exec: Phil Busey
Assoc Dir: Annette Rizzo
Comm Dir: Dustin Bayard
Comm Dir: Dustin Chicurel-Bayard

SIERRA CLUB BOOKS
See SIERRA CLUB

D-U-N-S 03-496-1813
SIERRA DEVELOPMENT CO
CLUB CAL-NEVA
38 E 2nd St, Reno, NV 89501-1410
Tel (775) 323-1046 *Founded/Ownrshp* 1955
Sales 51.9MM^E *EMP* 1,300
SIC 7011 Casino hotel
Pr: Jeffery L Siri
**CEO:* Phil Kenny

SIERRA ENERGY
See TOMS SIERRA CO INC

D-U-N-S 02-012-0432
■ **SIERRA HEALTH AND LIFE INSURANCE CO INC**
(*Suby of* UNITED HEALTHCARE) ★
2720 N Tenaya Way, Las Vegas, NV 89128-0424
Tel (702) 242-7700 *Founded/Ownrshp* 1906, 1986
Sales NA *EMP* 500
SIC 6311 Life insurance carriers
Pr: Johnothan Bunker
**VP:* Donald Giancursio
**VP:* Wayne Haddad
**VP:* David Narlon

D-U-N-S 12-086-8807
■ **SIERRA HEALTH SERVICES INC**
UNITED HEALTHCARE
(*Suby of* UNITEDHEALTH GROUP INC) ★
2720 N Tenaya Way, Las Vegas, NV 89128-0424
Tel (702) 242-7000 *Founded/Ownrshp* 2008
Sales NA *EMP* 2,900
SIC 6324 6311 8082 8741 8093 Hospital & medical service plans; Life insurance carriers; Home health care services; Management services; Mental health clinic, outpatient; Substance abuse clinics (outpatient)
Ch Bd: Anthony M Marlon
**Pr:* Jonathon W Bunker
Pr: Michael Ehlman
**Pr:* Donald J Giancursio
**CFO:* Marc R Briggs
Treas: Tim Coulter
**Treas:* Robert Worth Oberrender
VP: Allan Ebbin
VP: Michael Motalvo
VP: Peter Neill
**Exec:* Frank E Collins

D-U-N-S 04-228-1014 IMP
SIERRA INTERNATIONAL INC
TELEFLEX MARINE
1 Sierra Pl, Litchfield, IL 62056-3029
Tel (217) 324-9400 *Founded/Ownrshp* 2014
Sales 117.6MM^E *EMP* 200
SIC 5088 3519 Marine crafts & supplies; Parts & accessories, internal combustion engines
Pr: Joe Holtschulte
VP: Joseph Holtschulte
**Prin:* Yvan Cote
Dir IT: June Jackson
Dir IT: Dennis Zirkelbach

SIERRA ITS
See SIERRA SYSTEMS INC

D-U-N-S 02-900-6947
SIERRA JOINT COMMUNITY COLLEGE DISTRICT
5000 Rocklin Rd, Rocklin, CA 95677-3337
Tel (916) 624-3333 *Founded/Ownrshp* 1960
Sales 43.4MM^E *EMP* 1,500
SIC 8222 8221 Community college; Colleges universities & professional schools
Pr: Leo Chavez
VP: Alan Shuttleworth
Ex Dir: Sonbol Aliabadi
Psych: Cheryl Axton

D-U-N-S 92-829-8983
SIERRA LOBO INC
102 Pinnacle Dr, Fremont, OH 43420-7400
Tel (419) 332-7101 *Founded/Ownrshp* 1993
Sales 137.8MM^E *EMP* 260
SIC 8711 Engineering services
Pr: George A Satornino
**VP:* Nabil Kattouah
**VP:* Daniel R Lowe

D-U-N-S 03-827-8578 IMP/EXP
SIERRA NEVADA BREWING CO
SIERRA NEVADA TAPROOM & REST
1075 E 20th St, Chico, CA 95928-6722
Tel (530) 893-3520 *Founded/Ownrshp* 1979
Sales 140.3MM^E *EMP* 400^E
SIC 2082 5812 Beer (alcoholic beverage); Eating places
Pr: Kenneth Grossman
Dir Soc: Megan Andrews
IT Man: Rob Gerrity
Natl Sales: Adam Lane
Art Dir: Jason C Roberson

D-U-N-S 09-437-3495 IMP/EXP
SIERRA NEVADA CORP
444 Salomon Cir, Sparks, NV 89434-9651
Tel (775) 331-0222 *Founded/Ownrshp* 1994
Sales 1.2MMM *EMP* 3,063
Accts Deloitte & Touche Llp Las Veg

SIC 3728 3812 Aircraft parts & equipment; Search & navigation equipment
CEO: Fatih Ozmen
*Pr: Eren Ozmen
Ex VP: Gerald Harvey
VP: Greg Burgess
VP: Steve Cass
VP: Joe Fucci
VP: Patrick Garman
VP: Wayne Killian
VP: Gordon Nash
VP: Allen Peterson
VP: Bill Shaver
VP: Jeff Summers
VP: Jim Voss
VP: Paul Zeisman
Dir Risk M: Leanne McCulley
Dir Bus: Mac Dorsey

SIERRA NEVADA MEMORIAL HOSPITAL
See SIERRA NEVADA MEMORIAL-MINERS HOSPITAL

D-U-N-S 01-098-2643
SIERRA NEVADA MEMORIAL-MINERS HOSPITAL
SIERRA NEVADA MEMORIAL HOSPITAL
(Suby of DIGNITY HEALTH) ★
155 Glasson Way, Grass Valley, CA 95945-5723
Tel (530) 274-6000 Founded/Ownrshp 1934
Sales 155.7MM EMP 300
Accts Kpmg Llp San Francisco Ca
SIC 8062 General medical & surgical hospitals
Pr: Katherine A Medeiros
*Ch Bd: Don Coots
VP: Timothy Stephens
Netwrk Eng: David Alfred

SIERRA NEVADA TAPROOM & REST
See SIERRA NEVADA BREWING CO

D-U-N-S 04-740-3696 IMP/EXP
SIERRA PACIFIC INDUSTRIES
19794 Riverside Ave, Anderson, CA 96007-4908
Tel (530) 378-8000 Founded/Ownrshp 1974
Sales 1.2MMM^E EMP 3,500
SIC 2421 2431 Lumber: rough, sawed or planed; Millwork; Windows, wood
Pr: George Emmerson
*Ch: Mark Emmerson
Treas: Dennis Young
VP: Kendall Pierson
VP: Aaron Sulzer
VP: Tom Takach
VP: Jared Tappero
Exec: Jim Blunt
Exec: Jane Hume
Rgnl Mgr: Gary Fenati
Rgnl Mgr: Scott Henson

D-U-N-S 16-150-8692
SIERRA PACIFIC MORTGAGE CO INC
1180 Iron Point Rd # 200, Folsom, CA 95630-8325
Tel (916) 932-1700 Founded/Ownrshp 1986
Sales NA EMP 800
SIC 6162 Mortgage bankers
Pr: James Coffrini
COO: Gary Clark
Ofcr: Jeffrey Kibbey
Ofcr: Lorae Oliver
*VP: Chuck Iverson
*VP: Janet Lewis
Rgnl Mgr: Angela Sykes
Brnch Mgr: Franco Manueli
Brnch Mgr: Brian McGinley
Brnch Mgr: Steve Peterson
Brnch Mgr: Florica Shepherd

D-U-N-S 00-697-1006 EXP
■ **SIERRA PACIFIC POWER CO**
NV ENERGY
(Suby of NV ENERGY INC) ★
6100 Neil Rd Ste 100, Reno, NV 89511-1137
Tel (775) 834-4011 Founded/Ownrshp 1965
Sales 904.0MM EMP 1,000^E
Accts Deloitte & Touche Llp Las Veg
SIC 4911 4924 4941 4971 Generation, electric power; Transmission, electric power; Distribution, electric power; Natural gas distribution; Water supply; Water distribution or supply systems for irrigation
Pr: Paul J Caudill
*CFO: E Kevin Bethel
Treas: William D Rogers
Bd of Dir: Walter M Higgins
*Sr VP: Douglas A Cannon
*Sr VP: Patrick S Egan
*Sr VP: Tony F Sanchez III
VP: Kevin Geraghty
VP: Gary L Lavey
VP: Walter Spansel
IT Man: Ruth Crispino
Board of Directors: Kevin C Geraghty, Francis P Gonzales, John C Owens

D-U-N-S 94-651-6325
SIERRA SYSTEMS INC
SIERRA ITS
200 S Prospect Ave, Park Ridge, IL 60068-4037
Tel (847) 384-2000 Founded/Ownrshp 1995
Sales 18.5MM^E EMP 1,016^E
SIC 7363 Help supply services
Pr: Leonard Wislow

D-U-N-S 05-121-6844
SIERRA TEL COMMUNICATIONS GROUP
SEIRRA TELEPHONE
49150 Road 426, Oakhurst, CA 93644-8702
Tel (559) 683-4611 Founded/Ownrshp 1895
Sales 102.3MM^E EMP 285^E
SIC 4813 Local telephone communications; Long distance telephone communications;
CEO: John H Baker
*Ch Bd: Harry H Baker

D-U-N-S 15-354-9357 IMP
■ **SIERRA TRADING POST INC**
(Suby of TJ MAXX) ★
5025 Campstool Rd, Cheyenne, WY 82007-1898
Tel (307) 775-8050 Founded/Ownrshp 2012
Sales 234.5MM^E EMP 780
SIC 5961 Clothing, mail order (except women's)
Pr: Ken Walter
Store Dir: John Williams
Store Mgr: Matthew Lafortune
Store Mgr: Scott Patton
QA Dir: John Soto
Software D: Travis Jeffries
Software D: Ted Tietjen
Software D: Thomas Wolf

D-U-N-S 07-295-2880
■ **SIERRA VISTA HOSPITAL INC**
SIERRA VISTA REGIONAL MEDICAL CENTER
(Suby of TENET HEALTHCARE CORP) ★
1010 Murray Ave, San Luis Obispo, CA 93405-8801
Tel (805) 546-7600 Founded/Ownrshp 1968
Sales 139.8MM EMP 700
SIC 8062 General medical & surgical hospitals
CEO: Joseph Deschryver
Chf OB: Kurt L Haupt
*Pr: Candace Markwith
*COO: Ikenna Mmeje
*CFO: Richard Phillips
*CFO: Rollie Pirkl
Dir Rx: Michael Amortegui
Pathlgst: Steven Jobst
Pharmcst: Shilpa Patel

SIERRA VISTA REGIONAL MEDICAL CENTER
See SIERRA VISTA HOSPITAL INC

D-U-N-S 10-591-3149 EXP
SIERRA-CASCADE NURSERY INC
472-715 Johnson Rd, Susanville, CA 96130-8727
Tel (530) 254-6867 Founded/Ownrshp 1975
Sales 120.3MM^E EMP 1,600
SIC 0181 Nursery stock, growing of
Pr: Steve Fortin
*COO: Randy Jertberg
*VP: Robert Akeson
*VP: Robert Murie
Genl Mgr: Seth Peterson
IT Man: Justin Whitaker
Sls Mgr: Bob Akeson

D-U-N-S 09-702-5779 IMP
■ **SIERRACIN CORP**
(Suby of PPG INDUSTRIES INC) ★
12780 San Fernando Rd, Sylmar, CA 91342-3796
Tel (818) 741-1656 Founded/Ownrshp 2006
Sales 90.9MM^E EMP 600
SIC 2851 Paints & allied products
CEO: Barry N Gillespie
*Ex VP: Michael H McGarry
*Ex VP: Viktoras R Sekmakas
*Ex VP: Frank S Sklarsky
*Sr VP: David B Navikas
VP: Barry Gillespie
VP: David Morris
CTO: Alexander Katchadourian

D-U-N-S 13-125-0862 IMP/EXP
■ **SIERRACIN/SYLMAR CORP**
PPG AEROSPACE
(Suby of PPG INDUSTRIES INC) ★
12780 San Fernando Rd, Sylmar, CA 91342-3728
Tel (818) 362-6711 Founded/Ownrshp 1988
Sales 181.9MM^E EMP 600
SIC 3089 3812 3621 3231 Windshields, plastic; Search & navigation equipment; Motors & generators; Products of purchased glass
CEO: Barry Gillespie
Board of Directors: Frank Corlin, E E Noneman

D-U-N-S 78-437-6493 EXP
SIERRAPINE A CALIFORNIA LIMITED PARTNERSHIP
1050 Melody Ln Ste 160, Roseville, CA 95678-5196
Tel (800) 676-3339 Founded/Ownrshp 1991
Sales 121.3MM^E EMP 447
SIC 2431

D-U-N-S 00-415-4407 IMP/EXP
▲ **SIFCO INDUSTRIES INC** (OH)
970 E 64th St, Cleveland, OH 44103-1694
Tel (216) 881-8600 Founded/Ownrshp 1916
Sales 119.1MM EMP 593^E
Tkr Sym SIF Exch ASE
SIC 3724 3462 3471 Aircraft engines & engine parts; Aircraft forgings, ferrous; Anodizing (plating) of metals or formed products
Pr: Peter W Knapper
*Ch Bd: Norman E Wells Jr
CFO: Salvatore Incanno
VP: John Glover
Cmptr Lab: Marilyn Wilson
Opers Mgr: Stephanie Schulze
Plnt Mgr: Steve Lacher
Board of Directors: John G Chapman Sr, Jeffrey P Gotschall, Michael S Lipscomb, Donald C Molten Jr, Alayne L Reitman, Mark J Silk, Hudson D Smith

SIG
See SUSQUEHANNA INTERNATIONAL GROUP LLP

D-U-N-S 12-230-2987 IMP/EXP
SIG SAUER INC
(Suby of SIG SAUER BETEILIGUNGS GMBH)
72 Pease Blvd, Newington, NH 03801-6801
Tel (603) 610-3000 Founded/Ownrshp 1853
Sales 208.4MM^E EMP 1,100
SIC 3484 7999 Small arms; Shooting facilities & archery lanes
Pr: Ron Cohen
CFO: Tim Scullin
VP: Amaro Goncalves
VP: Steven Shawver
VP: Scott Smith
Exec: Charlotte Casey
Rgnl Mgr: Brett Hilsmeyer
Rgnl Mgr: John Sheppard
Rgnl Mgr: Rich Verdi
Rgnl Mgr: Matt Willette
CIO: Sean Houlihan

D-U-N-S 17-783-6905
SIG STRUCTURED PRODUCTS LLLP
401 E City Ave Ste 220, Bala Cynwyd, PA 19004-1117
Tel (610) 617-2600 Founded/Ownrshp 1987
Sales 267.5MM^E EMP 1,753
SIC 6231 Stock option exchanges
COO: Andrew Frost

SIGECO
See SOUTHERN INDIANA GAS & ELECTRIC CO

D-U-N-S 07-848-7559
SIGHTSAVERS INTERNATIONAL INC
1000 N West St Ste 1200, Wilmington, DE 19801-1058
Tel (800) 707-9746 Founded/Ownrshp 2012
Sales 207.0MM EMP 1
SIC 8069 Eye, ear, nose & throat hospital

D-U-N-S 62-347-6434 IMP
SIGMA - ALDRICH CO LLC
SIGMA-ALDRICH
(Suby of MILLIPORE SIGMA) ★
3050 Spruce St, Saint Louis, MO 63103-2530
Tel (314) 771-5765 Founded/Ownrshp 1996
Sales 665.5MM^E EMP 6,140
SIC 2899 5169 Chemical preparations; Chemicals & allied products
CEO: Rakesh Sachdev

D-U-N-S 02-625-3856 EXP
SIGMA ALIMENTOS INTERNATIONAL INC
(Suby of SIGMA ALIMENTOS, S.A. DE C.V.)
1009 Black Diamond Cir, Laredo, TX 78045
Tel (956) 417-2693 Founded/Ownrshp 1971
Sales 232.0MM EMP 38^E
SIC 5147 Meats & meat products
Pr: Raul Sergio Graza
*Pr: Raul Castro
*Pr: Nilda Nelly Gonzalez
*Treas: Reynaldo Garza
*VP: Jaime Joel Villarrela

D-U-N-S 00-627-3726 IMP
SIGMA CHEMICAL CORP (MO)
(Suby of MILLIPORE SIGMA) ★
3050 Spruce St, Saint Louis, MO 63103-2564
Tel (314) 771-5765 Founded/Ownrshp 1935
Sales 426.0MM^E EMP 2,000
SIC 2836 2869 Biological products, except diagnostic; Industrial organic chemicals
Pr: Larry Hummel
Treas: Kirk A Richter

D-U-N-S 16-097-3848 IMP/EXP
SIGMA CORP
(Suby of SIGMA INTERNATIONAL GROUP INC) ★
700 Goldman Dr, Cream Ridge, NJ 08514-2599
Tel (609) 758-0800 Founded/Ownrshp 2008
Sales 94.9MM^E EMP 225
SIC 5074 5199 Pipes & fittings, plastic; General merchandise, non-durable
CEO: James McGivern
*Pr: Larry Rybacki
*CFO: Jeffery Marcus
Exec: Jessica Stohr
Off Mgr: Iona Shenoy
Dir IT: Andy Podner
Sales Exec: Kane Connor
Sls Mgr: Marty Carter

D-U-N-S 06-474-8635 IMP
▲ **SIGMA DESIGNS INC**
47467 Fremont Blvd, Fremont, CA 94538-6504
Tel (510) 897-0200 Founded/Ownrshp 1982
Sales 227.2MM EMP 717^E
Tkr Sym SIGM Exch NGS
SIC 3674 Semiconductors & related devices; Integrated circuits, semiconductor networks, etc.
Pr: Thinh Q Tran
COO: Sal Cobar
CFO: Elias N Nader
VP: Eran Schwartz
Snr Sftwr: Aaron Chen
Board of Directors: J Michael Dodson, Martin Manniche, Pete Thompson

D-U-N-S 10-680-8629 EXP
■ **SIGMA INTERNATIONAL GENERAL MEDICAL APPARATUS LLC**
(Suby of BAXTER INTERNATIONAL INC) ★
711 Park Ave, Medina, NY 14103-1078
Tel (585) 798-3901 Founded/Ownrshp 2012
Sales 209.2MM^E EMP 500
SIC 3841 IV transfusion apparatus
*Pr: Nelson Tatterson
Pr: Dan Wellington
VP: John Dutcher
VP: Mike Southworth
*VP: Jeff Wakefield
Opers Mgr: Todd Underwood
Sales Exec: David Wolski
Doctor: Nathan Way

D-U-N-S 12-656-7127 EXP
SIGMA INTERNATIONAL GROUP INC
700 Goldman Dr, Cream Ridge, NJ 08514-2528
Tel (609) 758-0800 Founded/Ownrshp 2007
Sales 94.9MM^E EMP 275
Accts Pellegrino & Sherwin Llp
SIC 3494 Valves & pipe fittings
Pr: Victor Pais
*VP: Siddharth Bhattacharji
*VP: Larry Rybacki
Off Mgr: Leona Shenoy
Manager: Gary Dwyer

SIGMA PLASTICS GROUP
See OMEGA PLASTICS CORP

SIGMA PLASTICS GROUP, THE
See ALPHA INDUSTRIES MANAGEMENT INC

SIGMA SOLUTIONS
See SIGMA TECHNOLOGY SOLUTIONS INC

D-U-N-S 04-329-6933
SIGMA SOLUTIONS GP INC
SIS TECHNOLOGIES
607 E Sonterra Blvd # 250, San Antonio, TX 78258-4282
Tel (210) 348-9876 Founded/Ownrshp 1998
Sales 94.0MM EMP 100
Accts Akin Doherty Klein & Feuge
SIC 7373 7379 Computer integrated systems design; Computer related consulting services
Pr: Scott E Gruendler
Pr: Ian Watts
*VP: Frank G Jarzombek
VP Sls: Mike Moates
Mktg Dir: Sandie Vega

D-U-N-S 07-852-4321
SIGMA TECHNOLOGY SOLUTIONS INC
SIGMA SOLUTIONS
607 E Sonterra Blvd # 250, San Antonio, TX 78258-4282
Tel (888) 895-0495 Founded/Ownrshp 2012
Sales 147.6MM^E EMP 200^E
SIC 7373 Value-added resellers, computer systems
CEO: Scott Gruendler
*COO: Elias Khnaser
*Ex VP: Frank Jarzombek
VP: Rick Eddings
*VP: John Flores
VP: Shannon Gillenwater
*VP: Bruce Gilmore
*VP: Brian Netties
Prin: Scott Gaspard
IT Man: Tom Prentice

SIGMA-ALDRICH
See SIGMA - ALDRICH CO LLC

D-U-N-S 07-992-8354 IMP/EXP
SIGMA-ALDRICH CORP
MILLIPORE SIGMA
(Suby of MERCK KG AUF AKTIEN)
3050 Spruce St, Saint Louis, MO 63103-2530
Tel (314) 771-5765 Founded/Ownrshp 2015
Sales 2.7MMM EMP 9,300
SIC 2899 5169 8099 Chemical preparations; Chemicals & allied products; Organic chemicals, synthetic; Physical examination & testing services
Pr: Rakesh Sachdev
Mng Pt: Ted Ruppert
Pr: Darryl Goss
CFO: Jan A Bertsch
Ex VP: Deborah Slagle
Sr VP: George L Miller
Sr VP: Karen J Miller
VP: Silji Abraham
VP: Jason T Apter
VP: Ed Austin
VP: Gerrit J Van Den Dool
VP: Michael F Kanan
VP: Richard Keffer
VP: Mark Reinholz
VP: Mark Robillard
Dir Lab: Len Sidisky

D-U-N-S 06-830-1431 IMP
SIGMA-TAU PHARMACEUTICALS INC
(Suby of SIGMA-TAU INDUSTRIE FARMACEUTICHE RIUNITE SPA)
9841 Wash Blvd Ste 500, Gaithersburg, MD 20878
Tel (301) 948-1041 Founded/Ownrshp 1981
Sales 87.9MM^E EMP 100
SIC 5122 Pharmaceuticals
CEO: Dave Lemus
VP: John Fornoseei
VP: Jeff Hackman
VP: Taha Keilani
VP: Brian Schreiber
VP: Giuseppe Testa
QA Dir: Mary Jane Marshall
Netwrk Eng: Tom Partosh
Mfg Dir: Jeff Perry
Natl Sales: Lana Donino
Natl Sales: Mike Waldron

D-U-N-S 62-451-0525
SIGMANET INC
(Suby of CONVERGEONE HOLDINGS CORP) ★
4290 E Brickell St, Ontario, CA 91761-1524
Tel (909) 230-7500 Founded/Ownrshp 2015
Sales 146.7MM^E EMP 210^E
SIC 5045 7373 Computers, peripherals & software; Computer integrated systems design
CEO: Ahmed Al Khatib
*Pr: Neil Wada
*Sr VP: Apo Hagopian

D-U-N-S 82-562-2327 IMP
▲ **SIGMATRON INTERNATIONAL INC**
2201 Landmeier Rd, Elk Grove Village, IL 60007-2616
Tel (847) 956-8000 Founded/Ownrshp 1990
Sales 253.9MM EMP 2,710
Tkr Sym SGMA Exch NAS
SIC 3672 3677 3679 3549 3825 Printed circuit boards; Electronic coils, transformers & other inductors; Electronic circuits; Assembly machines, including robotic; Engine electrical test equipment
Ch Bd: Gary R Fairhead
*CFO: Linda K Frauendorfer
Ex VP: Greg Fairhead
Ex VP: Gregory A Fairhead
Ex VP: Rajesh B Upadhyaya
VP: Daniel P Camp
VP: Hom-Ming Chang
VP: Steve McNulty
VP: John P Sheehan
Prgrm Mgr: Jane Wu

SIGN POST PROS
See MASTER-TEC FLOORS INC

SIGN WAREHOUSE.COM
See SIGNWAREHOUSE INC

D-U-N-S 79-461-5682
■ **SIGNAL**
(Suby of SIGNAL HOLDINGS LLC) ★
676 E Swedesford Rd # 300, Wayne, PA 19087-1631
Tel (610) 975-8901 Founded/Ownrshp 2002
Sales NA EMP 699

SIC 6411 Insurance agents
Pt: Thomas Cloetingh
VP: Steve Debusk
IT Man: Tom Lowy

D-U-N-S 83-041-4731
SIGNAL 88 FRANCHISE GROUP INC
SIGNAL 88 SECURITY
3880 S 149th St Ste 102, Omaha, NE 68144-5568
Tel (877) 498-8494 *Founded/Ownrshp* 2007
Sales 36.5MM[E] *EMP* 1,000
SIC 7381 Guard services
Pr: Reed Nyffeler
**VP:* Tim Conahan
**VP:* Ty Hughes
**VP:* Josh Minturn
**Co-Founder:* Shea M Degan
**Co-Founder:* Timothy Nass

D-U-N-S 07-975-6914
SIGNAL 88 LLC
SIGNAL 88 SECURITY
3880 S 149th St Ste 102, Omaha, NE 68144-5568
Tel (877) 498-8494 *Founded/Ownrshp* 2014
Sales 16.2MM[E] *EMP* 1,000
SIC 7381 Guard services
Pr: Reed Nyffeler
**VP:* Tim Conahan
VP: Danielle Holm
**VP:* Ty Hughes
**VP:* Josh Minturn
VP: Laura Vodvarka
Dir Bus: Jessica Hinnen
**Co-Founder:* Shea M Degan
**Co-Founder:* Timothy Nass
Rgnl Mgr: Truman Faeh
Rgnl Mgr: Dan Fiala

SIGNAL 88 SECURITY
See SIGNAL 88 LLC

SIGNAL 88 SECURITY
See SIGNAL 88 FRANCHISE GROUP INC

D-U-N-S 19-537-6632
SIGNAL ENERGY LLC
(*Suby of* EMJ CORP) ★
2034 Hamilton Place Blvd # 400, Chattanooga, TN 37421-6102
Tel (423) 443-4190 *Founded/Ownrshp* 2005
Sales 339.0MM *EMP* 38
SIC 1542 8731 Commercial & office building contractors; Energy research
Pr: Ben Fischer
VP: Julian Bell

D-U-N-S 13-194-7249
■ **SIGNAL HOLDINGS LLC**
(*Suby of* ASSURANT INC) ★
676 E Swedesford Rd # 300, Wayne, PA 19087-1631
Tel (610) 341-1300 *Founded/Ownrshp* 2008
Sales 107.6MM[E] *EMP* 1,500[E]
SIC 6719 Investment holding companies, except banks
CEO: Thomas K Cloetingh
CFO: Gregg Bien
VP: Paul Shiah

D-U-N-S 12-755-6772 IMP
SIGNAL INTERNATIONAL LLC
601 Bayou Casotte Pkwy, Pascagoula, MS 39581-9600
Tel (228) 762-0010 *Founded/Ownrshp* 2002
Sales 185.5MM[E] *EMP* 2,750
SIC 7699 3731 3441

D-U-N-S 86-815-9633 IMP
SIGNAL POINT SYSTEMS INC
LYNX POWER SYSTEMS
1270 Shiloh Rd Nw Ste 100, Kennesaw, GA 30144-1317
Tel (770) 499-0439 *Founded/Ownrshp* 1961
Sales 89.1MM[E] *EMP* 175
SIC 1623 Water, sewer & utility lines
Pr: Dennis H Parks
**CFO:* Gordon D Harris
**VP:* Michael Kelly
**VP:* Frank Lynch
**VP:* Mike Sciarappa
**VP:* Tim Thomas
Snr Mgr: Mike Scirappa

D-U-N-S 79-199-0658 IMP
SIGNAL PRODUCTS INC
SIGNAL PRODUCTS/GUESS HANDBAGS
320 W 31st St, Los Angeles, CA 90007-3806
Tel (213) 748-0990 *Founded/Ownrshp* 1992
Sales 260.0MM *EMP* 109[E]
SIC 5137

SIGNAL PRODUCTS/GUESS HANDBAGS
See SIGNAL PRODUCTS INC

D-U-N-S 18-198-6670
■ **SIGNAL SOLUTIONS LLC**
(*Suby of* GDIT) ★
3211 Jermantown Rd # 700, Fairfax, VA 22030-2844
Tel (703) 205-0500 *Founded/Ownrshp* 2007
Sales 308.3M[E] *EMP* 1,850
SIC 8711 7379 7374 4813 7373 8731 Engineering services; Computer related maintenance services; Data processing & preparation; Telephone communication, except radio; Systems engineering, computer related; Commercial physical research
CFO: Michael Garrity
Treas: David Fogg
VP: Scott Goss
VP: Ted Hengst

SIGNAL STAT PRODUCT LINE
See TRUCK-LITE CO INC

SIGNATR HLTHCR BRCTN HSPTL
See SIGNATURE HEALTHCARE CORP

D-U-N-S 19-829-3172 IMP
▲ **SIGNATURE BANK**
565 5th Ave Fl 8r, New York, NY 10017-2413
Tel (646) 822-1500 *Founded/Ownrshp* 2001
Sales NA *EMP* 994
Accts Kpmg Llp New York New York
Tkr Sym SBNY *Exch* NGS
SIC 6029 7389 Commercial banks; Financial services
Ch Bd: Scott A Shay
Pr: Joanne Neville
COO: Mark T Sigona
CFO: Eric R Howell
CFO: Vito Susca
Chf Cred: Michael J Merlo
Ex VP: Kai Dare
Ex VP: Bryan Duncan
Sr VP: Joseph Alexander
Sr VP: Avraham Azuolay
Sr VP: James Buck Jr
Sr VP: Pat V Capparelli
Sr VP: Andrew F Corrado
Sr VP: Drew S Crowley
Sr VP: Richard Desousa
Sr VP: Joseph L Festa
Sr VP: Carl M Gambino
Sr VP: Thomas Grippa
Sr VP: James Handal
Sr VP: Kevin Hardiman
Sr VP: Mohammed Omar Kamil
Board of Directors: Kathryn A Byrne, Derrick D Cephas, Alfonse M D'amato, Barney Frank, Judith Huntington, Jeffrey W Meshel, Michael Pappagallo, Frank R Selvaggi

D-U-N-S 00-406-9514 IMP
SIGNATURE BRANDS LLC
PAAS EASTER EGG
808 Sw 12th St, Ocala, FL 34471-0540
Tel (352) 622-3134 *Founded/Ownrshp* 1952, 1996
Sales 182.9MM[E] *EMP* 440[E]
SIC 2064 Cake ornaments, confectionery
CEO: Jerry Reardon
**CFO:* Gary Silver
**Treas:* Timothy J Kennedy
IT Man: John Kehoe

SIGNATURE COMMERCIAL SOLUTIONS
See SIGNATURE CONSULTANTS LLC

D-U-N-S 96-875-3277
SIGNATURE CONSULTANTS LLC
SIGNATURE COMMERCIAL SOLUTIONS
200 W Cypress Creek Rd # 400, Fort Lauderdale, FL 33309-2175
Tel (954) 677-1020 *Founded/Ownrshp* 1997
Sales 253.1MM *EMP* 1,450
Accts Grant Thornton Llp Fort Laude
SIC 7379 8742 Computer related consulting services; Financial consultant
CEO: Dr Jay L Cohen
Sr Pt: Will Schwerin
COO: Mark Nussbaum
CFO: Philip Monti
Brnch Mgr: Kelly Beam
Div Mgr: Pat Palmer
Genl Mgr: Josh Tobias
Off Admin: Debbie Meertins
Dir IT: Ron Charron
Sftwr Eng: Pete Key
Mktg Dir: Steven Speet

SIGNATURE FLIGHT SUPPORT
See LANDMARK FBO LLC

D-U-N-S 78-588-6375
SIGNATURE FLIGHT SUPPORT CORP
EXECUTIVE BEECHCRAFT
(*Suby of* BBA AVIATION PLC)
201 S Orange Ave Ste 1100, Orlando, FL 32801-3464
Tel (407) 648-7200 *Founded/Ownrshp* 1996
Sales 702.8MM[E] *EMP* 1,500
Accts Deloitte & Touche Llp
SIC 5541 Gasoline service stations
Pr: Maria Sastre
CFO: Sami T Teittinen
Sr Cor Off: Wanda El Assar
**Sr VP:* Geoff Heck
VP: John Farmer
VP: Melissa Hannan
VP: Eric Hietala
**VP:* Larry Jorash
VP: Jennifer Joseph
VP: Arlette Kopciak
VP: Ron Lance
VP: Mary Miller
Exec: Michael Harper

D-U-N-S 14-805-2645 EXP
SIGNATURE FOOD MARKETING LLC
5786 Us Highway 129 N, Pendergrass, GA 30567-4723
Tel (706) 693-0095 *Founded/Ownrshp* 2003
Sales 138.1MM[E] *EMP* 125[E]
SIC 5141 Groceries, general line

SIGNATURE HEALTHCARE COLUMBIA
See LP COLUMBIA LLC

D-U-N-S 07-382-7701
SIGNATURE HEALTHCARE CORP
SIGNATR HLTHCR BRCTN HSPTL
680 Centre St, Brockton, MA 02302-3308
Tel (508) 941-7000 *Founded/Ownrshp* 1890
Sales 248.5MM *EMP* 1,500[E]
SIC 8062 General medical & surgical hospitals
Pr: Kim Hollon
Chf Path: Desiree Carlson
COO: Jeffrey Russell
CFO: James Papadakos
Trst: Manthala George
Ex VP: Sandy Lafratta
VP: Pat Cullen
VP: Allen Davis
VP: Mitchell Selinger
VP: Kimberly Walsh
VP: Malcom Weiner
Dir OR: Gail Franzen
Dir Lab: Stephen Travassos

D-U-N-S 82-806-8689 IMP
SIGNATURE HEALTHCARE LLC
12201 Bluegrass Pkwy, Louisville, KY 40299-2361
Tel (502) 568-7800 *Founded/Ownrshp* 2007
Sales 359.1MM[E] *EMP* 4,037
SIC 8051 Skilled nursing care facilities
CEO: Joe Steier
COO: Kelly Atkins
**CFO:* John Harrison
**VP:* Sandra Adams
VP: Terry Clay
VP: Lynn Fieldhouse
Exec: Jeff Williams
Chf Nrs Of: Kathy Owens
Genl Mgr: Melody Shannon
CTO: Jim Orms
Dir IT: Bill Breitenbach

D-U-N-S 61-526-2537
SIGNATURE HOSPITAL CORP
363 N Sam Houston Pkwy E, Houston, TX 77060-2404
Tel (281) 598-9800 *Founded/Ownrshp* 2003
Sales 43.7MM[E] *EMP* 1,025
SIC 8062 General medical & surgical hospitals
Pr: Charles R Miller
VP: David Spencer
Dir Rad: Joy Janak

D-U-N-S 87-635-1953
SIGNATURE MEDICAL GROUP INC
12639 Old Tesson Rd # 115, Saint Louis, MO 63128-2786
Tel (314) 849-0311 *Founded/Ownrshp* 1994
Sales 87.1MM[E] *EMP* 800[E]
SIC 8011 Offices & clinics of medical doctors
Prin: Forbes A McMullin MD
**CFO:* Martin Vaegel
Sr VP: Chad Sackman
VP: John Tessier
Off Admin: Celia Lewis
Dir IT: Mike Magee
Surgeon: Dennis A Dusek
Surgeon: Stephen E Vierling
Podiatrist: Nicolas C Martin
Doctor: Mahesh R Bagwe
**Doctor:* George Schoedinger III

D-U-N-S 07-991-3057
SIGNET JEWELERS LIMITED
(*Suby of* SIGNET JEWELERS LIMITED)
375 Ghent Rd, Fairlawn, OH 44333-4601
Tel (330) 668-5785 *Founded/Ownrshp* 2015
Sales 71.8MM[E] *EMP* 3,000
SIC 5944 Jewelry stores
**Sr VP:* Clark McEwen
**VP:* James Grant

D-U-N-S 18-548-3583 EXP
SIGNET US HOLDINGS INC
(*Suby of* SIGNET GROUP LIMITED)
850 Library Ave, Newark, DE 19711-7170
Tel (302) 738-9652 *Founded/Ownrshp* 1987
Sales 304.2MM[E] *EMP* 9,900
SIC 5944 Jewelry stores
Ch Bd: Terry Burman
**VP:* Donald Puglisi

D-U-N-S 04-467-0222 IMP
SIGNICAST LLC
1800 Innovation Way, Hartford, WI 53027-9082
Tel (262) 673-2700 *Founded/Ownrshp* 1959
Sales 180.0MM *EMP* 850
SIC 3324 Commercial investment castings, ferrous
Pr: Todd McDonald
**COO:* Greg Gasper
VP: Tom Dottl
VP: Bill Jahn
VP: Christopher Kovach
VP: Brad Witte
Dir IT: Barry Dieser
Plnt Mgr: Keith Pleester

SIGNITY AMERICAS
See SWAROVSKI NORTH AMERICA LIMITED

D-U-N-S 02-938-1647 IMP/EXP
■ **SIGNODE CORP**
SIGNODE IPS
(*Suby of* CARLYLE GROUP L P) ★
3600 W Lake Ave, Glenview, IL 60026-1215
Tel (800) 527-1499 *Founded/Ownrshp* 2013
Sales 228.8MM[E] *EMP* 1,500
SIC 3565 3499 Packaging machinery; Strapping, metal
Pr: Russell Flaum
VP: John Hartnett
VP: Mike Potempa
VP: William Reeb
**VP:* David B Smith
Brnch Mgr: Jeff Wright
Genl Mgr: Regis Fraval
Genl Mgr: Barry Henderson
Genl Mgr: Gerard Young
CTO: William Jones
CTO: Tom King

D-U-N-S 07-932-8885 IMP
SIGNODE INDUSTRIAL GROUP LLC
INSULATED TRANSPORT PRODUCTS
(*Suby of* VAULT BERMUDA HOLDING CO LTD)
3650 W Lake Ave, Glenview, IL 60026-1215
Tel (847) 724-7500 *Founded/Ownrshp* 2013
Sales 252.0MM[E] *EMP* 450
SIC 2671 Resinous impregnated paper for packaging; Thermoplastic coated paper for packaging
CEO: Mark Burgees
**CFO:* Ron Kropp
**Treas:* Nils Stenger
**VP:* Chad Pisha

SIGNODE IPS
See SIGNODE CORP

D-U-N-S 11-864-8484 IMP
SIGNWAREHOUSE INC
SIGN WAREHOUSE.COM
2614 Texoma Dr, Denison, TX 75020-1053
Tel (903) 462-7700 *Founded/Ownrshp* 1981
Sales 25.0MM[E] *EMP* 1,003
SIC 7373 Value-added resellers, computer systems
Pr: Christopher Gripp
**COO:* Larry Adam
COO: Larry Adams
**Treas:* Erik A Gripp
Brnch Mgr: Todd Castle
Sales Asso: Greg Beavers

D-U-N-S 00-217-9893 IMP/EXP
SIKA CORP (NJ)
(*Suby of* SIKA AG)
201 Polito Ave, Lyndhurst, NJ 07071-3601
Tel (201) 933-8800 *Founded/Ownrshp* 1937
Sales 915.8MM *EMP* 1,067
SIC 2891 2899 2851 2821 3272 Epoxy adhesives; Chemical preparations; Epoxy coatings; Epoxy resins; Concrete products
Pr: Christoph Ganz
**CFO:* Stephen Lysik
**Treas:* Gail Pacifico
Bd of Dir: Millie Herman
**Ex VP:* Richard Montani
**Ex VP:* Brian Whelan
**Ex VP:* Herbert Zwartkruis
**Sr VP:* Bernhard Bosshard
**Sr VP:* Michael Campion
Sr VP: Scott Henry
**Sr VP:* Daniel Hilliard
**Sr VP:* Jacqueline Lumley
VP: Dean Cannarozzi
**VP:* Nicholas Romano
VP: Jim Walther
VP: Mark Yamout

D-U-N-S 60-920-8983
SIKESTON BOARD OF MUNICIPAL UTILITIES
107 E Malone Ave, Sikeston, MO 63801-2921
Tel (573) 471-5000 *Founded/Ownrshp* 1931
Sales 183.2MM[E] *EMP* 144
Accts Pricewaterhousecoopers Llp S
SIC 4911 1623 Transmission, electric power; Water, sewer & utility lines
CFO: Marsha Witt
IT Man: Doug Shaw
Opers Mgr: Wayne McSpadden
Opers Mgr: Jeff Winders
Plnt Mgr: Chester Cardwell

D-U-N-S 11-456-1160
SIKICH LLP
1415 W Diehl Rd Ste 400, Naperville, IL 60563-1197
Tel (630) 566-8400 *Founded/Ownrshp* 1982
Sales 121.3MM[E] *EMP* 501
SIC 8721 Accounting, auditing & bookkeeping
CEO: James A Sikich
Pt: Ryan Overtoom
Pt: Jeff Rudolph
Pt: Michael Sheehan
Chf Mktg O: Tara Giuliano
Sr VP: Kurt Estes
Off Admin: Megan Sikich
QA Dir: Christopher Rabin
Netwrk Eng: Don Nims

SIKORSKY AEROSPACE MAINTENANCE
See SIKORSKY SUPPORT SERVICES INC

D-U-N-S 83-555-1474 IMP/EXP
■ **SIKORSKY AIRCRAFT CORP**
(*Suby of* LOCKHEED MARTIN CORP) ★
6900 Main St, Stratford, CT 06614-1385
Tel (203) 386-4000 *Founded/Ownrshp* 2015
Sales 2.7MMM[E] *EMP* 8,735
SIC 3721 4581 5599 Helicopters; Aircraft maintenance & repair services; Aircraft dealers
Pr: Daniel Schultz
Pr: Kate Mason
**CFO:* Mary Gallagher
**Sr VP:* John Palumbo
VP: Gloria Addonizio
VP: David Adler
**VP:* Judith E Bankowski
VP: Paul Benedetto
VP: Mark Cherry
VP: Ariel R David
VP: Stephen B Estill
VP: Stephen Estill
VP: Bob Kokorda
VP: Peter G Lipperman
**VP:* Mark F Miller
VP: Mark Miller
VP: Doris Papcun
VP: Marc B Poland
VP: Scott Starrett
VP: Joe Triompo
Board of Directors: George David

SIKORSKY COMMERCIAL
See HELICOPTER SUPPORT INC

D-U-N-S 00-972-3404 IMP
SIKORSKY GLOBAL HELICOPTERS INC
110 Stewart Huston Dr, Coatesville, PA 19320-1646
Tel (610) 644-4430 *Founded/Ownrshp* 1961
Sales 142.5MM[E] *EMP* 1,000
SIC 3721

D-U-N-S 10-725-4062 IMP
■ **SIKORSKY SUPPORT SERVICES INC**
SIKORSKY AEROSPACE MAINTENANCE
(*Suby of* SIKORSKY AIRCRAFT CORP) ★
6900 Main St, Stratford, CT 06614-1378
Tel (203) 386-4000 *Founded/Ownrshp* 1984
Sales 224.8MM[E] *EMP* 989
SIC 5088 Aircraft & space vehicle supplies & parts; Aircraft equipment & supplies
Pr: Joe Coleman
**Prin:* Dean Borman
**Prin:* James A Falco
**Genl Mgr:* Robert Schulman

D-U-N-S 00-239-0284 IMP
SILBERLINE MANUFACTURING CO INC
130 Lincoln Dr, Tamaqua, PA 18252-4321
Tel (570) 668-6050 *Founded/Ownrshp* 1945, 1963
Sales 124.1MM[E] *EMP* 426
SIC 2816 2819 Metallic & mineral pigments; Industrial inorganic chemicals
Pr: Lisa J Scheller
**Ch Bd:* Ernest Scheller Jr
Tech Mgr: Colin McKay
VP Opers: Jim Mason
Ql Cn Mgr: Sheila Setcavage

D-U-N-S 01-820-5174 EXP
■ SILGAN CONTAINERS CORP
(*Suby of* SILGAN CONTAINERS LLC) ★
21800 Oxnard St Ste 600, Woodland Hills, CA 91367-3609
Tel (818) 348-3700 *Founded/Ownrshp* 1987
Sales 228.8MM[E] *EMP* 3,900
SIC 3411 Metal cans; Food containers, metal
CEO: Anthony J Allott
Ch Bd: Thomas J Snyder
Pr: James D Beam
V Ch Bd: R Phillip Silver
Ex VP: Adam J Greenlee
Sr VP: Frank W Hogan III
VP: Anthony P Andreacchi
VP: Joseph Heaney
VP: B Frederik Prinzen
Off Mgr: Jim Beckman
Web Dev: Joe Banach

D-U-N-S 17-827-7497 IMP/EXP
■ SILGAN CONTAINERS LLC
(*Suby of* SILGAN HOLDINGS INC) ★
21800 Oxnard St Ste 600, Woodland Hills, CA 91367-3654
Tel (818) 710-3700 *Founded/Ownrshp* 1997
Sales 1.9MMM[E] *EMP* 6,300
SIC 3411 Metal cans; Food containers, metal
**CFO:* Ron Ford
**Sr VP:* Richard Brewer
**Sr VP:* Daniel Carson
**VP:* Michael Beninato
**VP:* Anthony Cost
**VP:* Joseph Heaney
**VP:* John Mooers
Area Mgr: Steve Kaempf
Ql Cn Mgr: James Letzig
Board of Directors: Robert Owen, Robert Wagenaar

D-U-N-S 96-496-3974
■ SILGAN CONTAINERS MANUFACTURING CORP
(*Suby of* SILGAN CONTAINERS LLC) ★
21800 Oxnard St Ste 600, Woodland Hills, CA 91367-3654
Tel (818) 710-3700 *Founded/Ownrshp* 1997
Sales 313.7MM[E] *EMP* 1,000[E]
SIC 3411 Metal cans
Prin: Thomas Snyder

D-U-N-S 61-420-1895
▲ SILGAN HOLDINGS INC
4 Landmark Sq Ste 400, Stamford, CT 06901-2502
Tel (203) 975-7110 *Founded/Ownrshp* 1987
Sales 3.7MMM *EMP* 9,600[E]
Tkr Sym SLGN *Exch* NGS
SIC 3411 3085 3089 Food & beverage containers; Aluminum cans; Plastics bottles; Plastic containers, except foam; Plastic kitchenware, tableware & houseware
Pr: Anthony J Allott
**Ch Bd:* D Greg Horrigan
**Ch Bd:* R Philip Silver
COO: Adam J Greenlee
CFO: Robert B Lewis
Sr VP: Frank W Hogan III
Sr VP: B Frederik Prinzen
VP: Anthony P Andreacchi
VP: Kimberly I Ulmer
Board of Directors: John W Alden, William C Jennings, Joseph M Jordan, Edward A Lapekas

D-U-N-S 86-709-3270 IMP/EXP
■ SILGAN PLASTIC FOOD CONTAINERS CORP
REXAM CONTAINERS
(*Suby of* SILGAN HOLDINGS INC) ★
710 W Park Rd, Union, MO 63084-1088
Tel (636) 583-5550 *Founded/Ownrshp* 2012
Sales 88.7MM[E] *EMP* 200
SIC 3086 Packaging & shipping materials, foamed plastic
CEO: Robert McCoy

D-U-N-S 17-784-8710 IMP/EXP
■ SILGAN PLASTICS LLC
(*Suby of* SILGAN HOLDINGS INC) ★
14515 North Outer 40 Rd # 210, Chesterfield, MO 63017-5746
Tel (800) 274-5426 *Founded/Ownrshp* 1987
Sales 977.8MM[E] *EMP* 2,316[E]
SIC 3085 3089 Plastics bottles; Plastic processing
Pr: Jay A Martin
VP: Anne Carten
VP: Sherry Fransen
VP: John Silva
Opers Mgr: Cheryl Wilson
Natl Sales: George Mesaros

D-U-N-S 83-247-3875
■ SILGAN WHITE CAP CORP
(*Suby of* SILGAN HOLDINGS INC) ★
4 Landmark Sq Ste 400, Stamford, CT 06901-2502
Tel (630) 515-8383 *Founded/Ownrshp* 2003
Sales 85.1MM[E] *EMP* 1,121[E]
SIC 3411 Metal cans
CEO: Anthony J Allott
**VP:* Robert B Lewis

D-U-N-S 10-133-3573 EXP
■ SILGAN WHITE CAP LLC
(*Suby of* SILGAN CONTAINERS LLC) ★
1140 31st St, Downers Grove, IL 60515-1212
Tel (630) 515-8383 *Founded/Ownrshp* 2003
Sales 1.1MMM[E] *EMP* 1,800
SIC 5199 Packaging materials
Pr: Les Herold
**VP:* Robert Anderson
**VP:* Robert Rey
Manager: Dave Miller

D-U-N-S 84-132-2394 IMP
■ SILICON GRAPHICS INTERNATIONAL CORP
(*Suby of* HEWLETT PACKARD ENTERPRISE CO) ★
900 N Mccarthy Blvd, Milpitas, CA 95035-5128
Tel (669) 900-8000 *Founded/Ownrshp* 2016
Sales 532.9MM *EMP* 1,100[E]
Accts Deloitte & Touche Llp San Jos
SIC 3577 7371 Computer peripheral equipment; Computer software development & applications
Pr: Jorge L Titinger
COO: Cassio Conceicao
CFO: Mack Asrat
Sr VP: Eng Lim Goh
Sr VP: Peter E Hilliard
Sr VP: Liz King
Sr VP: Rick Rinehart
Sr VP: Kirk Williams
VP: Gabriel Broner
VP: Rod Evans
VP: Brian Freed

D-U-N-S 93-225-2893 IMP
■ SILICON IMAGE INC
(*Suby of* LATTICE SEMICONDUCTOR CORP) ★
2115 Onel Dr, San Jose, CA 95131-2032
Tel (408) 616-4000 *Founded/Ownrshp* 2015
Sales 132.6MM[E] *EMP* 640[E]
SIC 3674 7371 Semiconductors & related devices; Computer software development & applications; Computer software systems analysis & design, custom
Pr: Darin G Billerbeck
**Pr:* Kurt Thielen
**CFO:* Joe Bedewi
**VP:* Byron Milstead
VP: Peter Rado
VP: Terry Sutherland
VP: Sherif Sweha
VP: Tim Vehling
VP: Mark Wadlington
VP: Rick White
CTO: Hyung Kwon
Board of Directors: William George, Peter Hanelt, William Raduchel

D-U-N-S 96-563-5394
▲ SILICON LABORATORIES INC
400 W Cesar Chavez St, Austin, TX 78701-3883
Tel (512) 416-8500 *Founded/Ownrshp* 2016
Sales 644.8MM *EMP* 1,199[E]
Accts Ernst & Young Llp Austin Tex
Tkr Sym SLAB *Exch* NGS
SIC 3674 Integrated circuits, semiconductor networks, etc.
Pr: G Tyson Tuttle
Ch Bd: Navdeep S Sooch
CFO: John C Hollister
Chf Mktg O: Michele Grieshaber
Ofcr: Lori Knowlton
Sr VP: Sandeep Kumar
Sr VP: Alessandro Piovaccari
Sr VP: James Stansberry
Sr VP: Mark Thompson
Sr VP: Brandon Tolany
VP: Geir Forre
Board of Directors: William G Bock, R Ted Enloe III, Jack R Lazar, Nina Richardson, William P Wood

D-U-N-S 10-277-7836
■ SILICON VALLEY BANK
(*Suby of* SVB FINANCIAL GROUP) ★
3003 Tasman Dr, Santa Clara, CA 95054-1191
Tel (408) 654-7400 *Founded/Ownrshp* 1983
Sales NA *EMP* 1,100
SIC 6029 Commercial banks
CEO: Kenneth P Wilcox
**COO:* Michael Dreyer
CFO: Judy Lee
**CFO:* Cecilia Shea
Sr Cor Off: Jay Mc Neil
**V Ch Bd:* Harry Kellogg
**Chf Mktg O:* Michelle Draper
Ofcr: Chris Stedman
**Ofcr:* Bruce Wallace
Top Exec: Sean Stone
Ex VP: L Blake Baldwin
**Ex VP:* Christopher T Lues
Ex VP: Eric Yee
**Sr VP:* Nidd Paras
VP: John Atanasoff
VP: Larisa B Chilton
VP: Brittany Clements
VP: Ashley Fairon
VP: Quentin Falconer
VP: Patrick Gildea
**VP:* Laurita J Hernandez
Board of Directors: James R Porter, Gary K Barr, Ann R Wells, Gregory W Becker, Kenneth Wilcox, James F Burnes Jr, John C Dean, David M Dewilde, Alex W Hart, Stephen E Jackson, Daniel J Kelleher, Harry Kellogg

D-U-N-S 03-590-3343
SILICON VALLEY EDUCATION FOUNDATION (CA)
1400 Parkmoor Ave Ste 200, San Jose, CA 95126-3798
Tel (408) 790-9400 *Founded/Ownrshp* 1958
Sales 2.6MM *EMP* 1,000
Accts Maze & Associates Pleasant H
SIC 8399 Fund raising organization, non-fee basis
CEO: Muhammed Chaudhry

D-U-N-S 01-291-9703
SILICON VALLEY EXECUTIVE NETWORK
1336 Nelson Way, Sunnyvale, CA 94087-3135
Tel (408) 746-5803 *Founded/Ownrshp* 2012
Sales 15.1MM[E] *EMP* 1,001
SIC 8748 Business consulting
CEO: Brian Reynard

D-U-N-S 05-104-9260 EXP
SILICONE SPECIALTIES INC
S S I CONSTRUCTION MATERIALS
430 S Rockford Ave, Tulsa, OK 74120-3416
Tel (918) 587-5567 *Founded/Ownrshp* 1976
Sales 124.6MM[E] *EMP* 75
SIC 5072 Hardware
Ch Bd: Joe Cathey
**Pr:* Duane Barnett
CFO: Bob Poplin
**CFO:* Robert Poplin
**VP:* Brandon Cathey

D-U-N-S 00-913-1392 IMP
■ SILICONIX INC
(*Suby of* VISHAY INTERTECHNOLOGY INC) ★
2201 Laurelwood Rd, Santa Clara, CA 95054-1593
Tel (408) 988-8000 *Founded/Ownrshp* 2005
Sales 368.0MM[E] *EMP* 2,033
SIC 3674 Semiconductors & related devices; Transistors; Microcircuits, integrated (semiconductor); Switches, silicon control
CEO: Serge Jaunay
**Pr:* King Owyang
**COO:* Nick Bacile

D-U-N-S 13-583-6901
SILKROAD TECHNOLOGY INC
100 S Wacker Dr Ste 425, Chicago, IL 60606-4031
Tel (866) 329-3363 *Founded/Ownrshp* 2003
Sales 83.1MM[E] *EMP* 348
SIC 7371 Computer software development & applications
Pr: John Shackleton
Ch Bd: Andrew J Filipowski
COO: Brian Platz
CFO: Merri Bonino
Ch: Flip Filipowski
Ex VP: Edward Vesely
Ex VP: Steven Worth
Sr VP: Sherry Allred
VP: Mark Long
VP: Joe Weber
Exec: Shane Blatt
Exec: Kevin Gardner
Exec: Kevin Kinsella
Exec: Tony Preston
Exec: Joshua Rowell
Exec: Stephanie Sayer
Exec: Tracy Schmitz
Dir Risk M: Paul O'Donnell

D-U-N-S 09-625-3737 IMP/EXP
SILTRONIC CORP
(*Suby of* SILTRONIC HOLDING INTERNATIONAL B.V.)
7200 Nw Front Ave, Portland, OR 97210-3676
Tel (503) 243-2020 *Founded/Ownrshp* 2002
Sales 147.6MM[E] *EMP* 380
SIC 3674 Silicon wafers, chemically doped
Pr: Neil J Nelson
Ex VP: Tobias Ohler
Sr VP: Ruediger Schmolke
VP: Volker Braetsch
Exec: Tom Fahey
MIS Dir: Mark Chase
Software D: Tanya Estrina
Sls Dir: Dave Adelman
Sls Dir: David Liu
Snr Mgr: Karsen King
Snr Mgr: Kevin Lite

D-U-N-S 79-113-5705 IMP/EXP
SILVARIS CORP
LOWGRADE LUMBER
505 5th Ave S Ste 610, Seattle, WA 98104-3846
Tel (888) 856-6677 *Founded/Ownrshp* 2000
Sales 87.1MM[E] *EMP* 80[E]
SIC 5031 Lumber, plywood & millwork
Pr: Kurt Bray
Pr: Lynn Buckalew
Pr: Jody Craig
**COO:* Troy Lundquist
**CFO:* Kevin Amoth
VP: Scott Bean
VP: Eric Miller
Exec: Ray Winkels
IT Man: Brandon Hurtado
Mktg Mgr: Amy Cronin
Counsel: Teresa Resendiz

D-U-N-S 07-870-4216
SILVER BAY REALTY TRUST CORP (MD)
3300 Fernbrook Ln N, Plymouth, MN 55447-5338
Tel (952) 358-4400 *Founded/Ownrshp* 2012
Sales 113.6MM *EMP* 5
Accts Ernst & Young Llp Minneapolis
SIC 6798 6531 1521 Real estate investment trusts; Real estate leasing & rentals; Single-family housing construction
Pr: Thomas Brock
**Ch Bd:* Irvin R Kessler
COO: Lawrence B Shapiro
CFO: Christine Battist

D-U-N-S 86-097-8860 IMP/EXP
SILVER BAY SEAFOODS LLC
208 Lake St Ste 2e, Sitka, AK 99835-7582
Tel (907) 966-3110 *Founded/Ownrshp* 2006
Sales 259.4MM[E] *EMP* 1,700[E]
SIC 5146 Seafoods
CEO: Richard A Riggs
**Pr:* Troy A Denkinger
**COO:* Dave J Hambleton
**CFO:* Van E Kramer
Genl Mgr: Jon P Hickman
**Plnt Mgr:* Wayne Unger

D-U-N-S 10-106-5485 IMP
■ SILVER BELL MINING LLC
(*Suby of* AR SILVER BELL INC) ★
25000 W Avra Valley Rd, Marana, AZ 85653-8716
Tel (520) 682-2420 *Founded/Ownrshp* 2005
Sales 170.0MM *EMP* 500
SIC 1021 Copper ores
Genl Mgr: Richard Rhodes

D-U-N-S 09-788-1309
SILVER CINEMAS ACQUISITION CO
LANDMARK THEATRES
2222 S Barrington Ave, Los Angeles, CA 90064-1206
Tel (310) 473-6701 *Founded/Ownrshp* 2003
Sales 75.1MM[E] *EMP* 1,000
Accts Deloitte & Touche Llp
SIC 7832 Motion picture theaters, except drive-in
Pr: Mark Cuban
**CEO:* George T Mundorff
**CEO:* Todd Wagner
COO: Ted Mundorff
VP: Paul Duchouquette
VP: John McCauley
VP: Michael McClellan
VP: Brenda Ross
VP: Brian Well
Genl Mgr: Rita Gattegno
Genl Mgr: Laura Resnick

D-U-N-S 19-424-6620
SILVER CREEK INDUSTRIES INC
2830 Barrett Ave, Perris, CA 92571-3258
Tel (951) 943-5393 *Founded/Ownrshp* 2005
Sales 89.5MM[E] *EMP* 175
SIC 1542 2452 Nonresidential construction; Prefabricated wood buildings; Prefabricated buildings, wood
CEO: Brett D Bashaw
**Sec:* Micheal Rhodes

D-U-N-S 14-490-6757
SILVER CROSS HEALTH SYSTEM
SILVER CROSS HOSPITAL
1900 Silver Cross Blvd, New Lenox, IL 60451-9509
Tel (815) 300-1100 *Founded/Ownrshp* 1895
Sales 348.8MM *EMP* 1,600[E]
Accts Kpmg Llp Chicago Il
SIC 8059 Rest home, with health care
Pr: Paul Pawlak
**Ex VP:* Mary Bakken
**Sr VP:* Ruth Colby
**Sr VP:* John Krepps
**VP:* Wayne Aardsma
Off Admin: Mary Furst
Off Admin: Doreen Kirkwood
Off Admin: Xiomara Roebuck
Info Man: Brian Staniszeski
Trfc Dir: Kathleen Pucel

SILVER CROSS HOSPITAL
See SILVER CROSS HEALTH SYSTEM

D-U-N-S 07-443-5843
SILVER CROSS HOSPITAL AND MEDICAL CENTERS
1900 Silver Cross Blvd, New Lenox, IL 60451-9509
Tel (815) 300-1100 *Founded/Ownrshp* 1891
Sales 335.5MM *EMP* 1,700
Accts Kpmg Llp Chicago Il
SIC 8062 General medical & surgical hospitals
Pr: Paul Pawlak
**CFO:* William Brownlow
**Ex VP:* Mary Bakken
**VP:* Kevin Lane
**VP:* Geoffrey Tryon
Dir Sec: John Farrell
Genl Mgr: Kay Novak
Nurse Mgr: Teri Hoogstra
IT Man: Ahmed Vanek
Opers Supe: Bridget Depasquale

D-U-N-S 18-692-7372
SILVER DINER INC
SILVER DINER RESTAURANT
12276 Rockville Pike, Rockville, MD 20852-1664
Tel (301) 770-2828 *Founded/Ownrshp* 1987
Sales 42.2MM[E] *EMP* 1,100
SIC 5812 Diner
CEO: Bob Giaimo
**Pr:* Robert Giaimo
COO: Frank Mitolo
CFO: Greg Kendall
**VP:* Von Hengst
VP: John Huddle
Genl Mgr: Roberto Mantari

SILVER DINER RESTAURANT
See SILVER DINER INC

SILVER DOLLAR CITY
See HERSCHEND ENTERTAINMENT CO LLC

D-U-N-S 02-665-1802 IMP
SILVER EAGLE DISTRIBUTORS LIMITED PARTNERSHIP
7777 Washington Ave, Houston, TX 77007-1037
Tel (713) 869-4361 *Founded/Ownrshp* 1989
Sales 558.8MM[E] *EMP* 1,200
SIC 5181 Beer & other fermented malt liquors
CEO: John L Nau III
**Pt:* Robert Boblitt
**Pt:* Scott Emel
COO: Bobbi Bobblitt
VP: Mike Critelli
**VP:* David Davis
**VP:* Roxann Neumann
**VP:* Matt Soileau
VP: Andy Stepanian
Rgnl Mgr: Tyrone Boudreaux
Rgnl Mgr: Tony Bright

D-U-N-S 02-645-2224 IMP
SILVER EAGLE DISTRIBUTORS LLC
7777 Washington Ave, Houston, TX 77007-1037
Tel (713) 869-4361 *Founded/Ownrshp* 2010
Sales 130.3MM[E] *EMP* 209[E]
SIC 5181 Beer & ale
Pt: Robert Boblitt
COO: Bob Litt
**Sr VP:* Ed Pritchard
Rgnl Mgr: Tommy Henderson
CIO: Brian Kirk

D-U-N-S 61-390-3462
SILVER LAKE PARTNERS II LP
2775 Sand Hill Rd Ste 100, Menlo Park, CA 94025-7085
Tel (650) 233-8120 *Founded/Ownrshp* 1999
Sales 360.9MM[E] *EMP* 2,175
SIC 6726 6211 Investment offices; Security brokers & dealers
Pt: Jim Davidson
Pt: Glenn Hutchins
Pt: Dave Roux
Mng Pt: Mike Bingle
Mng Pt: Egon Durban
CFO: Yolande Jun
Exec: Teresa Foster
Mng Dir: Hollie Moore
Mktg Dir: Susannah Carrier
Corp Couns: Karen King
Snr Mgr: Linda Jiang

SILVER LEGACY RESORT CASINO
See CIRCUS AND ELDORADO JOINT VENTURE LLC

D-U-N-S 00-218-9058 IMP/EXP
SILVER LINE BUILDING PRODUCTS LLC (DE)
AMERICAN CRAFTSMAN
(*Suby of* ANDERSEN CORP) ★
1 Silverline Dr, North Brunswick, NJ 08902-3397
Tel (732) 435-1000 *Founded/Ownrshp* 1947, 2006
Sales 518.6MM^E *EMP* 6,300
SIC 3089 3442

D-U-N-S 62-334-0549
SILVER OAK SERVICES PARTNERS LLC
1560 Sherman Ave Ste 1200, Evanston, IL 60201-4811
Tel (847) 492-1700 *Founded/Ownrshp* 2006
Sales 100.0MM^E *EMP* 300
SIC 6722 Management investment, open-end

SILVER PLUMBING & SEWER SVC
See FIRST SERVICE RESIDENTIAL FLORIDA INC

D-U-N-S 12-283-8332
SILVER POINT CAPITAL LIMITED PARTNERSHIP
SPCP GROUP
2 Greenwich Plz, Greenwich, CT 06830-6353
Tel (203) 542-4200 *Founded/Ownrshp* 2002
Sales 81.6MM^E *EMP* 1,320
SIC 8741 6726

D-U-N-S 14-902-3215 IMP
▲ **SILVER SPRING NETWORKSINC**
230 W Tasman Dr, San Jose, CA 95134-1714
Tel (669) 770-4000 *Founded/Ownrshp* 2002
Sales 489.5MM *EMP* 576
Tkr Sym SSNI *Exch* NYS
SIC 4899 7372 Communication signal enhancement network system; Prepackaged software
Pr: Michael Bell
**Ch Bd:* Scott A Lang
**COO:* Ayse Ildeniz
Chf Mktg O: Ingrid Hoogen
**Ex VP:* Eric P Dresselhuys
Ex VP: Don Reeves
**Ex VP:* Donald L Reeves III
VP: Kenneth P Gianella
VP: Mark McKechnie
VP: Terri Stynes
Prgrm Mgr: Laila Kaiser
Board of Directors: Thomas R Kuhn, Jonathan Schwartz, Richard A Simonson, Laura D Tyson, Peter Van Camp, Warren M Weiss, Thomas H Werner

SILVER STAR HOTEL & CASINO
See PEARL RIVER RESORT

D-U-N-S 96-955-0727
SILVER STAR SOLUTIONS-KNIGHT PROTECTIVE SERVICE-JOINT VENTURE LLC
59 Osceola Rd, Wayne, NJ 07470-5001
Tel (201) 847-9148 *Founded/Ownrshp* 2011
Sales 5.0MM *EMP* 1,800
SIC 7381 Security guard service

D-U-N-S 04-852-7287
■ **SILVERTOWNE LP**
SILVERTOWNE MINT
(*Suby of* PRECIOUS A-MARK METALS INC) ★
120 E Union City Pike, Winchester, IN 47394-8383
Tel (765) 584-7481 *Founded/Ownrshp* 1949
Sales 342.8MM *EMP* 80
Accts Drumm & Company Cpa Muncie
SIC 5999 5094 Coins; Precious stones & metals; Coins, medals & trophies
Genl Pt: David Hendrickson
Pr: Jamie Meadows
VP: Brent McCormick
Dir IT: Jackie Hetzler
IT Man: Brian Feltis

D-U-N-S 00-315-4648 IMP/EXP
SILVER-LINE PLASTICS CORP
900 Riverside Dr, Asheville, NC 28804-3115
Tel (828) 252-8755 *Founded/Ownrshp* 1963
Sales 138.1MM *EMP* 187
SIC 3084 Plastics pipe
Pr: Ricky C Silver
**Ch Bd:* Charles J Silver
COO: Pam Gibson
CFO: William H Beard
Exec: Dean Michael
VP Mfg: James Rice
Sls Dir: Chuck Walker
Sls Mgr: Bill Beard

D-U-N-S 01-556-0402
SILVERLEAF RESORTS INC
1201 Elm St Ste 4600, Dallas, TX 75270-2112
Tel (214) 631-1166 *Founded/Ownrshp* 2011
Sales 135.8MM^E *EMP* 1,983
SIC 6531 Condominium manager
Pr: Thomas J Morris
**COO:* Joe W Conner
**CFO:* Robert M Sinnott
**Treas:* Harry J White Jr
VP: Robert R Levy
Exec: Melinda Capes
Genl Mgr: Steve Spiewak
**CIO:* Michael D Jones
Dir IT: Kelly Bell
IT Man: Phillip Hollen
Netwrk Mgr: Lyza Beaudreault

D-U-N-S 07-026-6836
SILVERPEAK REAL ESTATE PARTNERS LP
909 3rd Ave Fl 30, New York, NY 10022-5002
Tel (212) 716-2000 *Founded/Ownrshp* 2011
Sales 15.0MM *EMP* 60
SIC 6531 Real estate brokers & agents
Mng Pt: Brett Bossung
Mng Pt: Mark Walsh
Sr VP: Ji Chu
Mng Dir: Brad Lebovitz

D-U-N-S 15-797-4085
■ **SILVERPOP SYSTEMS INC**
(*Suby of* IBM) ★
6303 Barfield Rd, Atlanta, GA 30328-4233
Tel (404) 348-9600 *Founded/Ownrshp* 2014
Sales 107.4MM^E *EMP* 400
SIC 7374 Data processing & preparation
Pr: Bill Nussey
Pr: Eric Stablow
**CFO:* Jim McCormick
Sr VP: Jeff Browning
Sr VP: Todd McCormick
Sr VP: Will Schnabel
VP: Bryan Brown
VP: Jeff Dernavich
VP: Dave Faupel
VP: Loren McDonald
VP: Elaine O'Gprman
VP: Rachel Ooston
VP: Barry Schnur
VP: Stuart Small
VP: Kelly Thompson

D-U-N-S 05-460-7528
SILVERSTONE GROUP INC
11516 Miracle Hills Dr # 100, Omaha, NE 68154-5311
Tel (402) 964-5400 *Founded/Ownrshp* 1993
Sales NA *EMP* 160
SIC 6371 6311 8742 6411 Pension, health & welfare funds; Life insurance; Compensation & benefits planning consultant; Insurance agents, brokers & service
Pr: John H Nelson
CFO: Todd Rogge
**Ch:* John P Nelson
Chf Mktg O: Michelle Hansen
**Ex VP:* Laurie Harper
Ex VP: Mark A Weber
VP: Ryan Gebauer
VP: Tim Huber
**VP:* Mary Kramer
VP: Tom Kristensen
VP: Lizanne Lefler
**VP:* Grant Matthies
VP: Dan Myers
VP: Renee Nolte
VP: Chad Tremel

D-U-N-S 00-212-7673
SILVERTON CASINO LLC (NV)
3333 Blue Diamond Rd, Las Vegas, NV 89139-7888
Tel (702) 263-7777 *Founded/Ownrshp* 1991
Sales 100.0MM *EMP* 875
SIC 7011 7299 5813 Casino hotel; Banquet hall facilities; Bars & lounges
CFO: Pam Benson
Sr VP: Martha Ferguson
Sr VP: Vince Santiago
Exec: Chris Fearnow
**Prin:* Alison Victoria
Info Man: Andrew Morris

D-U-N-S 05-597-9710
SILVERTON HEALTH
342 Fairview St, Silverton, OR 97381-1917
Tel (503) 873-1500 *Founded/Ownrshp* 1918
Sales 104.6MM *EMP* 642
SIC 8062 General medical & surgical hospitals
CEO: Rick Cagen
Pr: Henry Nino
COO: Sarah Fronza
**CFO:* Jeff Fritsche
**Ch:* Gayle Goschie
**Ch:* Gary Simon
**Treas:* Cory Cross
Bd of Dir: Kate Robertson
**Ex VP:* Rob Johnson
VP: Jeff Lorenz
Exec: Pj Hardy
Dir Inf Cn: Suzanne McKenzie

SILVERTON HOSPITAL LIFELINE
See SILVERTON HOSPITAL NETWORK

D-U-N-S 96-332-1302
SILVERTON HOSPITAL NETWORK
SILVERTON HOSPITAL LIFELINE
342 Fairview St, Silverton, OR 97381-1993
Tel (503) 873-1782 *Founded/Ownrshp* 2006
Sales 96.1MM *EMP* 2
SIC 8062 General medical & surgical hospitals

SILVERTOWNE MINT
See SILVERTOWNE LP

D-U-N-S 01-481-8355 IMP
SIMCO LOGISTICS INC
JACK & JILL D.S.D.
101 Commerce Dr, Moorestown, NJ 08057-4212
Tel (856) 813-2300 *Founded/Ownrshp* 1929
Sales 481.6MM^E *EMP* 325
SIC 5143 Ice cream & ices
CEO: Jay Schwartz
Pr: Kenneth Schwartz
Pr: Robert Vanderijn
CFO: Mary Hamilton-Carey
VP: John Corrao
VP: Robert Van De Rijn

D-U-N-S 94-004-7959 IMP
SIMEX INC
SIMEX VINYL EXTRUSION
181 Pleasant Indus Ctr, Saint Marys, WV 26170-8011
Tel (304) 665-1104 *Founded/Ownrshp* 2000
Sales 89.4MM^E *EMP* 152
SIC 5039 2431 Interior flat glass: plate or window; Doors & door parts & trim, wood
Pr: Mark Savan
**Treas:* Matthew C Lenz
**VP:* Michael S Petersen
**VP:* Steve Wrubleski

SIMEX VINYL EXTRUSION
See SIMEX INC

D-U-N-S 79-138-0603
SIMI VALLEY HOSPITAL AND HEALTH CARE SERVICES
ADVENTIST HEALTH
(*Suby of* ADVENTIST HEALTH SYSTEM/WEST) ★
2975 Sycamore Dr, Simi Valley, CA 93065-1201
Tel (805) 955-6000 *Founded/Ownrshp* 1960
Sales 139.6MM *EMP* 824^E
SIC 8049 Physical therapist
Pr: Margaret Peterson
Chf Rad: Eric Cordes
**Pr:* Caroline Esparza
**CFO:* Clif Patten
Opers Mgr: Allen Oxonder
Mktg Mgr: Jeremy Brewer
Pharmcst: Kit Chang

D-U-N-S 07-617-9878
SIMI VALLEY UNIFIED SCHOOL DISTRICT
875 Cochran St, Simi Valley, CA 93065-1934
Tel (805) 306-4500 *Founded/Ownrshp* 1935
Sales 91.6MM^E *EMP* 1,250
Accts Vavrinek Trine Day & Co Ll
SIC 8211 Public elementary & secondary schools
Pr: Scott Blough
**Trst:* Rob Collins
**Trst:* Bill Daniels
**Trst:* Debbie Sandland
**Trst:* Dan White
VP: Doug King
Off Mgr: Constance Sherman
Dir IT: Doug Hoxmeier
Dir IT: Gaylord Joseph
Dir IT: Robin McGowan
Dir IT: Philip Scrivano

D-U-N-S 00-130-7594
■ **SIMMONDS PRECISION PRODUCTS INC**
GOODRICH CORPORATION
(*Suby of* GOODRICH ARCFT WHEELS & BRAKES) ★
100 Panton Rd, Vergennes, VT 05491-1008
Tel (802) 877-4000 *Founded/Ownrshp* 1941
Sales 114.1MM^E *EMP* 700
SIC 3829 3694 3724 3728 Aircraft & motor vehicle measurement equipment; Ignition systems, high frequency; Aircraft engines & engine parts; Aircraft parts & equipment
CEO: Justin Robert Keppy
**Treas:* Michael G McAuley
**VP:* Paul V Cappiello
Dir IT: Julia St George
IT Man: David Ploof
Ql Cn Mgr: Gary Andrews
Ql Cn Mgr: Richard Collins

D-U-N-S 09-200-6089
SIMMONDS RESTAURANT MANAGEMENT INC
3730 S 149th St Ste 107, Omaha, NE 68144-5557
Tel (402) 493-2300 *Founded/Ownrshp* 1977
Sales 68.0MM^E *EMP* 2,560
SIC 5812 Fast-food restaurant, chain
Pr: Michael Simmonds
COO: Shawn Simmonds
**CFO:* Paula Glissman
Software D: Joe Lukas

SIMMONS
See SSB MANUFACTURING CO

D-U-N-S 00-690-3678
■ **SIMMONS BANK**
(*Suby of* SIMMONS FIRST NATIONAL CORP) ★
501 S Main St, Pine Bluff, AR 71601-4327
Tel (870) 541-1000 *Founded/Ownrshp* 1903, 1968
Sales NA *EMP* 567^E
SIC 6021 National commercial banks
Ch Bd: J Thomas May
Pr: Travis J Liebig
Pr: Andrea Scarpelli
**V Ch Bd:* Tom Spillyards
Ofcr: R Williams
Ex VP: Robert C Dill
Ex VP: Craif Hunt
Sr VP: Amy Johnson
VP: Michael Childers
VP: Linda Hogaboom
VP: Brent Martin
VP: Bill Whitmore

D-U-N-S 07-952-2819
SIMMONS COLLEGE
300 Fenway, Boston, MA 02115-5898
Tel (617) 521-2000 *Founded/Ownrshp* 1899
Sales 161.0MM *EMP* 641^E
Accts Pricewaterhousecoopers Llp Bo
SIC 8221 College, except junior
Pr: Helen G Drinan
**Treas:* Stefano Falconi
Ofcr: Joanna Conroy
Ofcr: Mehrdad Kermani
Ofcr: Heather Patenaude
Ofcr: Linda Sechovicz
VP: Bert Alves
VP: Nephelie Bellos
Assoc Dir: Judith Benjamin
Assoc Dir: Diana Church
Assoc Dir: Timothy Rogers
Dir Soc: Nikki Vanderpol

D-U-N-S 82-972-3837
SIMMONS FEED INGREDIENTS INC
(*Suby of* SIMMONS FOODS INC) ★
601 N Hico St, Siloam Springs, AR 72761-2410
Tel (479) 254-8151 *Founded/Ownrshp* 2005
Sales 120.0MM *EMP* 157^E
SIC 2077 Rendering
Ch Bd: Mark Simmons
**Pr:* Jeff Webster
**CEO:* Todd Simmons
**CFO:* Mark Wiens
**Treas:* Kerry Hairston
Plnt Mgr: Terry Graham
Prd Mgr: Kevin Reece

D-U-N-S 10-364-9554
▲ **SIMMONS FIRST NATIONAL CORP**
501 S Main St, Pine Bluff, AR 71601-4327
Tel (870) 541-1000 *Founded/Ownrshp* 1968
Sales NA *EMP* 1,946^E
Accts Bkd Llp Little Rock Arkansa
Tkr Sym SFNC *Exch* NGS
SIC 6021 National commercial banks
Ch Bd: George A Makris Jr
Pr: Jym Fees
CFO: Robert A Fehlman
Chf Cred: Steve C Wade
Ofcr: Barry K Ledbetter
Ofcr: Stephen C Massanelli
Trst Ofcr: Robin Thornton
Ex VP: Patrick A Burrow
Ex VP: F Chris Dunn
Ex VP: David W Garner
VP: Deana Powell
Exec: Marty D Casteel
Board of Directors: Edward Drilling, Jay D Burchfield, William E Clark II, Steven A Cosse, Mark C Doramus, Eugene Hunt, Christopher R Kirkland, W Scott McGeorge, Joseph D Porter, Robert L Shoptaw

D-U-N-S 04-448-7833 IMP/EXP
SIMMONS FOODS INC
601 N Hico St, Siloam Springs, AR 72761-2410
Tel (479) 524-8151 *Founded/Ownrshp* 1949
Sales 1.5MM *EMP* 6,363
SIC 2015

D-U-N-S 03-971-5560 IMP/EXP
SIMMONS HAROLD C FAMILY TRUST
5430 Lyndon B Johnson Fwy # 1700, Dallas, TX 75240-2601
Tel (972) 233-1700 *Founded/Ownrshp* 1964
Sales NA *EMP* 8,501
SIC 2063

D-U-N-S 96-187-9058
SIMMONS HOLDINGS LLC
(*Suby of* AOT BEDDING INTERMEDIATE HOLDINGS LLC) ★
1 Concrs Pkwy Ne Ste 800, Atlanta, GA 30328-6188
Tel (770) 512-7700 *Founded/Ownrshp* 1998
Sales 219.2M^E *EMP* 2,293^E
SIC 2515 Mattresses, waterbed flotation
Pr: Stephen G Fendrich

SIMMONS KIDS
See SIMMONS MANUFACTURING CO LLC

D-U-N-S 10-250-7683 IMP/EXP
SIMMONS MANUFACTURING CO LLC
SIMMONS KIDS
(*Suby of* SIMMONS) ★
1 Concrse Pkwy Ne Ste 800, Atlanta, GA 30328
Tel (770) 512-7700 *Founded/Ownrshp* 1942
Sales 335.3MM^E *EMP* 2,000
SIC 2515 Mattresses & bedsprings; Mattresses & foundations
CEO: Stephen Robertson
**Pr:* Steve G Fendrick
**Sr VP:* Earl Brewer
**Sr VP:* Mark F Chambless
Sr VP: Kristin K McGuffey

D-U-N-S 14-406-0634 IMP/EXP
SIMMONS PET FOOD INC
(*Suby of* SIMMONS FOODS INC) ★
601 N Hico St, Siloam Springs, AR 72761-2410
Tel (479) 524-8151 *Founded/Ownrshp* 1959
Sales 167.9MM^E *EMP* 1,050
SIC 2047 Dog & cat food
Pr: Mark Simmons
**Pr:* David Jackson
Pr: Stacy Smith
**CEO:* Todd Simmons
CFO: Mike Jones
**CFO:* Mark Wiens
**Treas:* Kerry Hairston
Sr VP: Dan Houston
VP: Heather Bishop
Comm Dir: Donny Epp
Dir Bus: Bob Shade

D-U-N-S 01-389-7041 IMP
SIMMONS PET FOOD KS INC
(*Suby of* SIMMONS PET FOOD INC) ★
1400 E Logan Ave, Emporia, KS 66801-6822
Tel (620) 342-1323 *Founded/Ownrshp* 1997
Sales 166.0MM *EMP* 429
SIC 2047 Dog & cat food
CEO: Mark Simmons
**Pr:* David Jackson
**CEO:* Todd Simmons

D-U-N-S 02-408-9560 EXP
SIMMONS PREPARED FOODS INC (AR)
MAD WINGS
(*Suby of* SIMMONS FOODS INC) ★
601 N Hico St, Siloam Springs, AR 72761-2410
Tel (479) 524-8151 *Founded/Ownrshp* 2004
Sales 891.6MM^E *EMP* 3,863
SIC 2015 Poultry, processed
Ch Bd: Mark Simmons
**Pr:* M Todd Simmons
**COO:* Gary Murphy
**CFO:* Mark A Wiens
**Treas:* Kerry Hairston
VP: Jason Godsey
**VP:* Tom Roark
Sls Dir: Corey Rhodes

SIMMONS TRUCK TERMINAL
See PARKER OIL CO INC

D-U-N-S 00-149-5969 IMP/EXP
■ **SIMON & SCHUSTER INC**
(*Suby of* CBS CORP) ★
1230 Ave Of The Americas, New York, NY 10020-1586
Tel (212) 698-7000 *Founded/Ownrshp* 1994
Sales 181.4MM^E *EMP* 1,400
SIC 2731 2741 7372 8732

D-U-N-S 94-878-6900
SIMON CONTRACTORS
SIMON'S
(*Suby of* COLAS INC) ★
1103 Old Town Ln Ste 1a, Cheyenne, WY 82009-4359
Tel (307) 635-9005 *Founded/Ownrshp* 1994
Sales 103.6MM^E *EMP* 180

Accts Pricewaterhousecoopers Llp
SIC 1611 Highway & street paving contractor
Pr: Tim Grossman
*Ch Bd: James E Weeks
*Treas: Tami Hobbs
*VP: Timothy P Gentleman
Board of Directors: Georges Ausseil, Dominique Leveille

SIMON PRODUCTS CO
See MICHAEL LEWIS CO

D-U-N-S 80-835-9012
▲ SIMON PROPERTY GROUP INC
225 W Washington St, Indianapolis, IN 46204-3438
Tel (317) 636-1600 Founded/Ownrshp 1993
Sales 5.2MMM EMP 5,000
Tkr Sym SPG Exch NYS
SIC 6798 6512 Real estate investment trusts; Nonresidential building operators
Ch Bd: David Simon
V Ch: Steve Holden
Pr: David J Contis
*Pr: Richard S Sokolov
CFO: Andrew Juster
Treas: Brian J McDade
Sr Ex VP: Gary Lewis
Sr VP: Steven K Broadwater
Sr VP: Mark Hunter
VP: Greg Bradbury
VP: Tim Cutting
VP: Norman Finbloom
VP: Joe Gerardi
VP: Robert Guerra
VP: John Gumerson
VP: Cynthia Hall
VP: Ronald Hanson
VP: Ralph Higley
VP: Michael Horvath
VP: Cathy Iunghuhn
VP: Steven Kingsley
Board of Directors: Glyn F Aeppel, Larry C Glasscock, Karen N Horn, Allan Hubbard, Reuben S Leibowitz, Gary M Rodkin, Herbert Simon, Daniel C Smith, J Albert Smith Jr

D-U-N-S 15-060-8768
■ SIMON PROPERTY GROUP LP
(Suby of SIMON PROPERTY GROUP INC) ★
225 W Washington St, Indianapolis, IN 46204-3438
Tel (317) 636-1600 Founded/Ownrshp 1993
Sales 5.2MMM EMP 5,000
SIC 6798 6512 Real estate investment trusts; Nonresidential building operators; Property operation, retail establishment
Ch Bd: David Simon
Genl Pt: Simon Property Group
Pr: Richard S Sokolov
VP: Greg Kreegar

D-U-N-S 18-812-3996 IMP/EXP
SIMONDS INTERNATIONAL LLC
(Suby of WESPA METALLSAGENFABRIK SIMONDS INDUSTRIES GMBH)
135 Intervale Rd, Fitchburg, MA 01420-6519
Tel (978) 343-3731 Founded/Ownrshp 2014
Sales 431.0MM[E] EMP 960
SIC 3553 Woodworking machinery
Pr: Raymond J Martino
*Ch Bd: John Cosentino
*CFO: Henry J Botticello
CTO: Doug Rand
Board of Directors: Donald Bates, Rick Brult, Bernard Buonanno, Habib Gorgi, Eric Pfeiffer, Gary Simonds

SIMON'S
See SIMON CONTRACTORS

D-U-N-S 18-843-3507
SIMONS FOUNDATION INC
160 5th Ave Fl 7, New York, NY 10010-7037
Tel (646) 654-0066 Founded/Ownrshp 1995
Sales 223.5MM EMP 85
SIC 8399 Advocacy group
Pr: Marilyn Simons
*Pr: Leyla Ahari
*CFO: Maria Adler
*Sec: James H Simons
*VP: Mark Silver
Comm Dir: Anastasia Greenebaum
Comm Dir: Stacey Greenebaum
VP Admn: Marion Greenup
Prgrm Mgr: Elizabeth Roy
Snr Sftwr: Richard Marini
IT Man: Chris Fleisch

D-U-N-S 02-683-2600
SIMONS PETROLEUM
PILOT LOGISTICS SERVICES
(Suby of PILOT FLYING J) ★
201 N Rupert St Ste 101, Fort Worth, TX 76107-1460
Tel (405) 551-2403 Founded/Ownrshp 2004
Sales 238.5MM[E] EMP 125
SIC 5172 5171 5541 5411 Engine fuels & oils; Diesel fuel; Gasoline; Petroleum bulk stations; Filling stations, gasoline; Truck stops; Convenience stores
Pr: Roger Simons
*CFO: Jeff Roberts
*CFO: Michelle Salbaing
VP: Steven Cross
VP: Mary Daugherty
VP: Mike McLaughlin
VP: Bill Woolsey
Snr Ntwrk: Brandon Brown
CIO: Quinton Crenshaw
Tech Mgr: Jim Engelskirchen
Sls Mgr: Chad O'Neil

D-U-N-S 08-256-7058
SIMONS PETROLEUM INC
(Suby of PILOT LOGISTICS SERVICES) ★
201 N Rupert St Ste 101, Fort Worth, TX 76107-1460
Tel (405) 848-3500 Founded/Ownrshp 1946
Sales 206.7MM[E] EMP 125
SIC 5171 5172 Petroleum bulk stations; Petroleum products; Diesel fuel
Pr: Roger Simons
Treas: Craig Calle
*VP: Steve Cross
*VP: Stephen Hiatt
*VP: Brad Simons
Dir Risk M: David Mulroney
Trfc Dir: Brian Heim
Sls Mgr: Randy Ogden

D-U-N-S 09-403-8304
SIMONSON PROPERTIES CO
DO IT BEST
2455 12th St Se, Saint Cloud, MN 56304-9705
Tel (320) 252-9385 Founded/Ownrshp 1977
Sales 108.4MM[E] EMP 829
SIC 5211 Millwork & lumber; Prefabricated buildings
CEO: Kenneth Fuchs
*Pr: Richard F Hobbs
*VP: Michael Hobbs
IT Man: Ed Holen

D-U-N-S 04-137-8662 IMP/EXP
SIMONTON BUILDING PRODUCTS INC
SIMONTON WINDOWS
(Suby of SPECIALTY BUILDING RESOURCES) ★
5300 Briscoe Rd, Parkersburg, WV 26105-8125
Tel (304) 659-2851 Founded/Ownrshp 1977
Sales 1.5MM[E] EMP 1,868
SIC 3089 3442 3231 Window frames & sash, plastic; Sash, door or window: metal; Products of purchased glass
Pr: W S Simonton
*Pr: Mark Savan
CFO: Beth Taylor
Treas: Mark Hausberg
*Treas: Matthew C Lenz
*VP: Michael S Petersen
VP: Dennis Sellers
VP Sls: Steve Sullivan
Board of Directors: Robert Rector

D-U-N-S 05-909-1652 IMP/EXP
SIMONTON HOLDINGS INC
SPECIALTY BUILDING RESOURCES
(Suby of BEAM SUNTORY INC) ★
520 Lake Cook Rd, Deerfield, IL 60015-5611
Tel (304) 428-8261 Founded/Ownrshp 2006
Sales 172.7MM[E] EMP 2,200
SIC 3089 5961 3086 5963 Window frames & sash, plastic; Mail order house; Plastics foam products; Direct selling establishments
Ch Bd: Samuel B Ross II

SIMONTON WINDOWS
See SIMONTON BUILDING PRODUCTS INC

SIMONTON WINDOWS
See FORTUNE BRANDS WINDOWS INC

D-U-N-S 07-955-7327
■ SIMPLER NORTH AMERICA LLC
(Suby of TRUVEN HEALTH ANALYTICS INC) ★
1 N Dearborn St Ste 1400, Chicago, IL 60602-4336
Tel (312) 533-3500 Founded/Ownrshp 2014
Sales 40.9MM[E] EMP 2,100
SIC 8742 7379 Hospital & health services consultant; Data processing consultant

D-U-N-S 00-112-5954
SIMPLEXTIME RECORDER LLC (MA)
(Suby of SIMPLEXGRINNELL HOLDINGS LLC) ★
50 Technology Dr, Westminster, MA 01441-0001
Tel (978) 731-2500 Founded/Ownrshp 1902, 2005
Sales 1.9MMM[E] EMP 12,873
SIC 7382 3669 1711

D-U-N-S 79-991-4341
SIMPLEXGRINNELL HOLDINGS LLC
(Suby of TYCO INTERNATIONAL MANAGEMENT CO LLC) ★
1501 Nw 51st St, Boca Raton, FL 33431-4438
Tel (561) 988-7200 Founded/Ownrshp 2012
Sales 1.9MMM[E] EMP 12,876
SIC 3579 3669 3699 3822 Time clocks & time recording devices; Fire detection systems, electric; Fire alarm apparatus, electric; Security control equipment & systems; Sound signaling devices, electrical; Thermostats & other environmental sensors
Pr: James Spicer
Pr: Keith McKinney
VP: Peter Richards
VP: David Urban
Exec: Jean C Boutin
Exec: Darlene Clark
Creative D: Tom Akos
Brnch Mgr: Mike Brant
Genl Mgr: Barry Popoff
Genl Mgr: Paul Ragusa
Dir IT: Dale Wrightam

D-U-N-S 09-473-8007
SIMPLEXGRINNELL LP
(Suby of SIMPLEXTIME RECORDER LLC) ★
4700 Exchange Ct, Boca Raton, FL 33431-4450
Tel (561) 988-7200 Founded/Ownrshp 2001
Sales 1.8MMM EMP 9,500
SIC 5087 1711 3669 7382 Firefighting equipment; Sprinkler contractors; Emergency alarms; Security systems services
CEO: George R Oliver
Pr: Robert Chauvin
Ex VP: Larry Costello
VP: Chris Maxie
Dist Mgr: Tommy Higgins
Genl Mgr: Steven Baker
Genl Mgr: Randy Martin
CTO: Jay Haughn
Dir IT: Donna Fenchel
IT Man: Dina Garcia
IT Man: Nolan Selin

D-U-N-S 15-749-4006 IMP/EXP
SIMPLICITY CREATIVE GROUP INC
(Suby of EK SUCCESS BRANDS) ★
261 Madison Ave Fl 4, New York, NY 10016-3906
Tel (212) 686-7676 Founded/Ownrshp 2013
Sales 125.3MM[E] EMP 1,147
SIC 2241 2221 2396 2298 Narrow fabric mills; Fringes, woven; Trimmings, textile; Fabric tapes; Jacquard woven fabrics, manmade fiber & silk; Automotive & apparel trimmings; Cordage & twine
Ch Bd: J Cary Findlay
Ofcr: John Davis
*Sr VP: Konstance J K Findlay
*VP Mfg: William M Stewart
*VP Sls: David Sears
Mktg Mgr: Jennifer Pegram

D-U-N-S 36-425-9846
SIMPLIFIED BUSINESS SOLUTIONS INC
10201 S 51st St Ste 100, Phoenix, AZ 85044-5216
Tel (602) 414-0062 Founded/Ownrshp 1996
Sales 45.9MM[E] EMP 6,008
Accts Cbiz Miller Wagner Llc Phoen
SIC 8721 Payroll accounting service
Pr: Dean Lucente
*VP: Bradley Johnston

SIMPLOT CATTLE
See SIMPLOT LIVESTOCK CO

D-U-N-S 05-951-1170
SIMPLOT LIVESTOCK CO
SIMPLOT CATTLE
(Suby of SIMPLOT WESTERN STOCKMENS) ★
1301 Highway 67, Grand View, ID 83624-5062
Tel (208) 834-2231 Founded/Ownrshp 1961
Sales 100.0MM EMP 201
SIC 0211 Beef cattle feedlots
Pr: Tom Basabe
Genl Mgr: John Maggiore
Dir IT: John McGiffin
Site Mgr: Greg Mongrain

D-U-N-S 02-761-4919
SIMPLOT PHOSPHATES LLC
(Suby of SIMPLOT WESTERN STOCKMENS) ★
999 W Main St Ste 1300, Boise, ID 83702-9009
Tel (208) 336-2110 Founded/Ownrshp 1929
Sales 104.2MM[E] EMP 350
SIC 2874 Phosphates
Ch: Scott Simplot
VP: Terry Uhling
Dir IT: Barbara Limber
Dir IT: Willie Quasne
Dir IT: Vernon Wing
Genl Couns: David Spurling
Genl Couns: Paul Thompson
Genl Couns: Gray Young

SIMPLOT WESTERN STOCKMEN'S
See JR SIMPLOT CO

D-U-N-S 78-463-1780
SIMPLY FASHION STORES LTD
2500 Crestwood Blvd # 100, Irondale, AL 35210-2096
Tel (205) 951-1700 Founded/Ownrshp 1991
Sales 219.4MM[E] EMP 1,300
SIC 5621

D-U-N-S 07-974-0567
■ SIMPLY HEALTHCARE HOLDINGS INC (FL)
(Suby of ANTHEM INC) ★
9250 W Flagler St Ste 600, Miami, FL 33174-3460
Tel (877) 915-0551 Founded/Ownrshp 2009
Sales NA EMP 61[E]
SIC 6321 6719 Health insurance carriers; Investment holding companies, except banks
Pr: Marcio Cabrera
*VP: Jorge L Rico

D-U-N-S 96-265-4898
■ SIMPLY HEALTHCARE PLANS INC
(Suby of SIMPLY HEALTHCARE HOLDINGS INC) ★
9250 W Flagler St Ste 600, Miami, FL 33174-3460
Tel (305) 408-5700 Founded/Ownrshp 2009
Sales NA EMP 60
SIC 6321 Health insurance carriers
CEO: Lourdes Tome-Rivas
*Pr: Michael B Fernandez
*CFO: Holly Prince
*Treas: Marcio C Cabrera
Act CFO: Isabel Pena
Ex VP: Tomas Orozco
VP: Raylene Adams
VP: Efrain Duarte
VP: Dana Gryniuk
*VP: Jorge L Rico
Dir IT: Richard Smith

D-U-N-S 02-517-6921
SIMPLY WIRELESS INC
8484 Westpark Dr Ste 800, Mc Lean, VA 22102-5135
Tel (703) 343-2700 Founded/Ownrshp 1997
Sales 179.2MM[E] EMP 500
SIC 4812 Cellular telephone services
CEO: Steven Qureshi
Treas: Robert Qureshi
VP: Muzz Jones
Dir IT: Cesar Feghali
Dir IT: Raul Munoz
IT Man: Feghali Cesar
Software D: Rattanaphan Chavez

D-U-N-S 00-987-3043 EXP
SIMPSON & BROWN INC
119 North Ave W, Cranford, NJ 07016-2189
Tel (908) 276-2776 Founded/Ownrshp 2009
Sales 113.1MM EMP 120
Accts Caruso Thompson Llp Nutley
SIC 1629 1771 Dock construction; Pile driving contractor; Land preparation construction; Dams, waterways, docks & other marine construction; Foundation & footing contractor
Pr: Thatcher Simpson
*VP: Robert Branston
*VP: Michael Byrne
*VP: William D'Ambola
*VP: Christopher Simpson

D-U-N-S 05-180-6123
SIMPSON GUMPERTZ & HEGER INC
41 Seyon St Ste 500, Waltham, MA 02453-8355
Tel (781) 907-9000 Founded/Ownrshp 1958
Sales 126.0MM[E] EMP 430
SIC 8711 Consulting engineer
CEO: Glenn R Bell
Pr: Charles Russo
CFO: Martin Mullins
CFO: George W Reitter
Treas: Paul Millette
Treas: Joseph J Zona
VP: William Freet Jr
VP: Jason Heroux
VP: David P Kuivanen
VP: Julianne Nevins
VP: Beverly Tompkins

D-U-N-S 15-146-4633 IMP
SIMPSON INVESTMENT CO INC
(Suby of KAMILCHE CO) ★
1301 5th Ave Ste 2700, Seattle, WA 98101-2675
Tel (253) 272-0158 Founded/Ownrshp 1985
Sales 359.7MM[E] EMP 2,839
SIC 2621 2611 2421 2431 3084 Paper mills; Pulp mills; Lumber: rough, sawed or planed; Doors, wood; Plastics pipe
Pr: Douglas Reed
*Ch: Colin Moseley
Ofcr: Sharon Gartten
*Sr VP: Joseph R Breed
VP: James Brown
*VP: D M McEntee
*VP: B G Stauffer
*Prin: A Trinkwald
Opers Mgr: Stacy Conkle
Counsel: Betsy Stauffer
Board of Directors: Clifford Slade

D-U-N-S 00-915-6449 IMP/EXP
▲ SIMPSON MANUFACTURING CO INC
5956 W Las Positas Blvd, Pleasanton, CA 94588-8540
Tel (925) 560-9000 Founded/Ownrshp 1956
Sales 794.0MM EMP 2,498
Accts Pricewaterhousecoopers Llp Sa
Tkr Sym SSD Exch NYS
SIC 3441 3399 Fabricated structural metal; Building components, structural steel; Metal fasteners
Pr: Karen Colonias
*Ch Bd: Peter N Louras Jr
CFO: Brian J Magstadt
*V Ch Bd: Thomas J Fitzmyers
VP: Sunny H Leung
VP: Jeffrey E Mackenzie
Dir IT: Bruce Mahagan
Board of Directors: James S Andrasick, Jennifer A Chatman, Gary M Cusumano, Celeste Volz Ford, Robin G Macgillivray

D-U-N-S 06-974-7764 IMP/EXP
■ SIMPSON STRONG-TIE CO INC
(Suby of SIMPSON MANUFACTURING CO INC) ★
5956 W Las Positas Blvd, Pleasanton, CA 94588-8540
Tel (925) 560-9000 Founded/Ownrshp 1914
Sales 477.8MM[E] EMP 2,000
SIC 3449 2891 Joists, fabricated bar; Adhesives
CEO: Karen Colonias
*Pr: Phillip Kingsfather
*Pr: Terry Kingsfather
*VP: Michael Herbert
VP: Bruce Lewis
Genl Mgr: Gerald Hagel
Info Man: Nicolaj Christensen

D-U-N-S 07-682-7487 IMP
SIMPSON THACHER & BARTLETT LLP
425 Lexington Ave Fl 15, New York, NY 10017-3903
Tel (212) 455-2000 Founded/Ownrshp 1884
Sales 825.5M EMP 1,300
SIC 8111 6531 General practice attorney, lawyer; Real estate agents & managers
Pt: Richard Beattie
Pt: Maripat Alpuche
Pt: Kevin J Arquit
Pt: Elisha D Graff
Pt: Justin M Lungstrum
Pt: Peter Martelli
Pt: Stacie E McGinn
Pt: William B Sheehan
Pt: Adam Signy
Pt: Robert E Spatt
Pt: Marisa D Stavenas
Pt: Alan C Turner
Pt: Joyce Y Xu
Mng Pt: Daniel Clivner
Mng Pt: Gregory W Conway
Mng Pt: Peter C Thomas
CFO: Adrienne E Boa N
Exec: Tish O'Brien
Dir Soc: Oscar Orellana

D-U-N-S 00-925-1570 IMP
SIMPSON TIMBER CO
OREGON OVERLAYS
917 E 11th St, Tacoma, WA 98421-3039
Tel (253) 779-6400 Founded/Ownrshp 1984
Sales 140.0MM[E] EMP 1,500
SIC 2421 2439

D-U-N-S 04-367-5293
SIMS ENTERPRISES OF GEORGIA LLC
205 Creekview Blvd, Covington, GA 30016-7694
Tel (770) 385-3461 Founded/Ownrshp 2011
Sales 168.0MM EMP 3
SIC 3585 Heating & air conditioning combination units
Owner: Quincy Sims

D-U-N-S 18-543-2457 IMP/EXP
SIMS GROUP USA CORP
SIMSMETAL AMERICA
(Suby of SIMS METAL MANAGEMENT) ★
600 S 4th St, Richmond, CA 94804-3504
Tel (510) 412-5300 Founded/Ownrshp 1987
Sales 161.1MM[E] EMP 400
SIC 5093 4953 Ferrous metal scrap & waste; Nonferrous metals scrap; Recycling, waste materials
CEO: Galdino Claro
*Pr: Bob Kelman
*CFO: Myles Partridge
*Ex VP: Jimmie Buckland
Ex VP: Marie Burk
*Prin: John Crabb
*Prin: Ross Cunningham
*Prin: Rick Jansen
*Prin: Robert A Kelman
IT Man: Scott Campbell
Site Mgr: Leroy Fruchey

D-U-N-S 06-203-8708 IMP/EXP
SIMS GROUP USA HOLDINGS CORP
SIMS METAL MANAGEMENT
(*Suby of* SIMS GROUP AUSTRALIA HOLDINGS LIMITED)
16 W 22nd St Fl 10, New York, NY 10010-5967
Tel (212) 604-0710 *Founded/Ownrshp* 1967, 2005
Sales 373.3MM^E *EMP* 581
SIC 5093 Ferrous metal scrap & waste
CEO: Galdino Claro

SIMS METAL MANAGEMENT
See METAL MANAGEMENT MIDWEST INC

SIMS METAL MANAGEMENT
See SIMS GROUP USA HOLDINGS CORP

SIMS METAL MANAGEMENT
See METAL MANAGEMENT INC

SIMS-LOHMAN FINE KITCHENS GRAN
See SIMS-LOHMAN INC

D-U-N-S 06-395-9332 IMP
SIMS-LOHMAN INC
SIMS-LOHMAN FINE KITCHENS GRAN
6325 Este Ave, Cincinnati, OH 45232-1458
Tel (513) 651-3510 *Founded/Ownrshp* 1998
Sales 87.0MM^E *EMP* 500
SIC 5031 2435 Kitchen cabinets; Hardwood veneer & plywood
CEO: Steve Steinman
Pr: John Beiersdorfer

SIMSMETAL AMERICA
See SIMS GROUP USA CORP

D-U-N-S 02-258-0786 IMP
SIMU LTD
201 Mittel Dr, Wood Dale, IL 60191-1116
Tel (630) 350-1060 *Founded/Ownrshp* 1997
Sales 440.0MM^E *EMP* 257^E
Accts Lipschultz Levin & Gray Nort
SIC 5113 5141 5142 2782 2759 2621 Industrial & personal service paper; Groceries, general line; Packaged frozen goods; Looseleaf binders & devices; Menus: printing; Packaging paper
Pr: Michael L Simon
**VP:* Ira Epstein
**VP:* Craig Simon
Info Man: Carlos Calit

D-U-N-S 00-713-2183
SINAI CHILDRENS HOSPITAL
MOUNT SINAI HOSPITAL
1500 S Cal Ave K435 435 K, Chicago, IL 60608
Tel (773) 542-2000 *Founded/Ownrshp* 1990
Sales 206.1MM^E *EMP* 3,000
SIC 8011 8062 Medical centers; General medical & surgical hospitals
Prin: Allan Channing
V Ch: Abraham Morgan
COO: Carl Josehart
CFO: Eduardu Dejesus
CFO: Jay Schweikart
Ex VP: Rachel Dvorken
VP: David Berkey
VP: Trena Burke
VP: Nacny Cutler
VP: Mary Karr
VP: Laura Landmeier
VP: Ellen McKenny
VP: Ismene Munch
VP: Kathy Neely
VP: Lori Paccura
VP: Lori Pacura
Dir Bus: Margaret Pesares

D-U-N-S 12-148-5288
SINAI HEALTH SYSTEM
1500 S Fairfield Ave, Chicago, IL 60608-1782
Tel (773) 542-2000 *Founded/Ownrshp* 1981
Sales 599.8MM *EMP* 6,000
Accts Pricewaterhousecoopers Llp On
SIC 6512 8741 Nonresidential building operators; Hospital management
Pr: Alan Channing
COO: Loyd Mayer
COO: Karen C Teitelbaum
**CFO:* Charles Weiss
Assoc VP: David W Fache
VP: Claude Hall
Chf Nrs Of: Suzette Mahneke
Telecom Mg: Brent Spyrka
IT Man: Patricia Timmes
QI Cn Mgr: Begum Kutay

SINAI HOSPITAL OF BALTIMORE
See RUBIN INSTITUTE FOR ADVANCED ORTHOPEDICS

D-U-N-S 07-492-0364
SINAI HOSPITAL OF BALTIMORE INC
(*Suby of* LIFEBRIDGE HEALTH INC) ★
2401 W Belvedere Ave, Baltimore, MD 21215-5270
Tel (410) 601-5678 *Founded/Ownrshp* 1868
Sales 677.8MM *EMP* 4,497
SIC 8062 Hospital, professional nursing school with AMA residency
Pr: Neil Meltzer
**Ch:* Brian L Moffet
**Treas:* Barry F Levin
**Ofcr:* Daniel C Silverman
CIO: Kenrick Cough
IT Man: Steven Sandler
Doctor: Scott Brown

D-U-N-S 00-630-4877 IMP/EXP
SINCLAIR & RUSH INC
STOCKCAP
123 Manufacturers Dr, Arnold, MO 63010-4727
Tel (636) 282-6800 *Founded/Ownrshp* 1978
Sales 106.6MM^E *EMP* 314
SIC 3089 Plastic processing
CEO: Vincent T Gorguze
**Pr:* Bradford M Philip
**COO:* Troy Wesley
Exec: Jim Pitrak
Dir IT: Joseph Thomas
Natl Sales: Donald Daut
Manager: Ryan O'Keefe
Manager: Ryan Okeefe
Manager: Rob Strauser

D-U-N-S 17-551-6384
▲ SINCLAIR BROADCAST GROUP INC
10706 Beaver Dam Rd, Hunt Valley, MD 21030-2207
Tel (410) 568-1500 *Founded/Ownrshp* 1986
Sales 2.2MMM *EMP* 8,000^E
Tkr Sym SBGI *Exch* NGS
SIC 4833 Television broadcasting stations
Ch Bd: David D Smith
COO: David B Amy
CFO: Christopher S Ripley
Treas: Lucy A Rutishauser
Ex VP: Barry M Faber
Sr VP: David R Bochenek
Sr VP: M William Butler
Sr VP: Rebecca J Hanson
Sr VP: Robert F Malandra
Sr VP: Delbert R Parks III
Sr VP: Donald H Thompson
**VP:* Frederick G Smith
**VP:* J Duncan Smith
Board of Directors: Howard E Friedman, Daniel C Keith, Martin R Leader, Lawrence E McCanna, Robert E Smith

D-U-N-S 07-468-3822
SINCLAIR COMMUNITY COLLEGE
444 W 3rd St, Dayton, OH 45402-1453
Tel (937) 512-2525 *Founded/Ownrshp* 1965
Sales 63.8MM *EMP* 1,200
SIC 8222 8221 Community college; Colleges universities & professional schools
CEO: Steven L Johnson
**CFO:* Jeff Boudouris
VP: Mary Gaier
Prgrm Mgr: Cindra Phillips
Dir IT: David Curtis
Info Man: Brett Baylor
Netwrk Eng: Chad Rumbarger
Prd Mgr: Ron Estes
Psych: David Brown

D-U-N-S 07-995-9185 IMP
SINCLAIR COMPANIES
550 E South Temple, Salt Lake City, UT 84102-1005
Tel (801) 363-5100 *Founded/Ownrshp* 1952
Sales 6.2MMM^E *EMP* 7,000
Accts Kpmg Llp
SIC 2911 4612 1382 5541 7011 0212 Petroleum refining; Crude petroleum pipelines; Oil & gas exploration services; Filling stations, gasoline; Hotels & motels; Resort hotel; Beef cattle except feedlots
Ch: Carol Holding
Pr: Steven Holding
CFO: Charles Barlow
Ex VP: Kenneth Knight
VP: Peter Johnson
VP: George Odencrantz
VP Opers: Paul Moote
VP Mktg: Jack Barger

D-U-N-S 78-501-7604
SINCLAIR OIL CORP
(*Suby of* SINCLAIR COMPANIES) ★
550 E South Temple, Salt Lake City, UT 84102-1098
Tel (801) 524-2700 *Founded/Ownrshp* 1968
Sales 698.1MM^E *EMP* 2,300
SIC 2911 5172 Petroleum refining; Petroleum products
Pr: Peter Johnson
Treas: C E Barlow
VP: K W Brown
**VP:* Dave Crittenden
VP: Dave Donegan
**VP:* Lynn Hart
Exec: Marilyn Byrd
Exec: Lowell Hardy
Exec: Tanya Lewis
Rgnl Mgr: Katherine Chadey
Dir IT: Ray Hansen

D-U-N-S 78-501-7109
SINCLAIR SERVICES CO
(*Suby of* SINCLAIR COMPANIES) ★
550 E South Temple, Salt Lake City, UT 84102-1005
Tel (801) 363-5100 *Founded/Ownrshp* 2005
Sales 221.8MM^E *EMP* 1,572^E
SIC 5172 Crude oil
Pr: P M Johnson

D-U-N-S 78-610-5267
■ SINCLAIR TELEVISION GROUP INC
(*Suby of* SINCLAIR BROADCAST GROUP INC) ★
10706 Beaver Dam Rd, Hunt Valley, MD 21030-2207
Tel (410) 568-1500 *Founded/Ownrshp* 2006
Sales 274.1MM^E *EMP* 815^E
SIC 4832 Radio broadcasting stations
Pr: David D Smith
**Ex VP:* Barry M Faber
VP: Mark Aitken
VP: Michael Butler
VP: Scott Livingston
VP: Robert Malandra
**VP:* Frederick G Smith

D-U-N-S 36-290-5809 IMP
SINCLAIR WYOMING REFINING CO
(*Suby of* SINCLAIR OIL CORP) ★
100 E Lincoln Ave, Sinclair, WY 82334
Tel (307) 328-3539 *Founded/Ownrshp* 2005
Sales 211.7MM^E *EMP* 362
SIC 2911 Gasoline
CIO: Russ Murry
Sfty Mgr: Curt Church
**Plnt Mgr:* Demes McGuire

D-U-N-S 00-251-2622 IMP
SINGER EQUIPMENT CO INC
WORLD SANITARY SUPPLY
150 S Twin Valley Rd, Elverson, PA 19520-9387
Tel (610) 387-6400 *Founded/Ownrshp* 1918, 2004
Sales 230.0MM *EMP* 280
Accts Mcgladrey Llp
SIC 5046 Restaurant equipment & supplies
Ch Bd: Henry D Singer
**Pr:* Frederick Singer
**COO:* John Vozzo
VP: Ronna Meade
VP: Brian Morehead
Genl Mgr: Darlene Heffner
Store Mgr: Tom Curtin
Store Mgr: Barbara Frankhouser
Mtls Mgr: Joseph Gallagher
Manager: Blair Heppe
Sls Mgr: Scott Richman

D-U-N-S 82-869-1639
SINGER EQUITIES INC
SBP HOLDINGS
(*Suby of* SEI HOLDING I CORP) ★
125 Mccarty St, Houston, TX 77029-1135
Tel (713) 714-3610 *Founded/Ownrshp* 2011
Sales 172.0MM^E *EMP* 399
SIC 8741 Business management
Treas: Otis Dufrene
**CEO:* Sam Petillo
**CFO:* George Dappert
**CFO:* Craig Osborne
**Ch:* Don Fitzsinger

D-U-N-S 62-017-5356 IMP/EXP
SINGER SEWING CO
(*Suby of* SINGER WORLDWIDE LLC) ★
1224 Heil Quaker Blvd, La Vergne, TN 37086-3515
Tel (615) 213-0880 *Founded/Ownrshp* 2004
Sales 161.0MM *EMP* 118^E
SIC 5064 Sewing machines, household: electric
CEO: Paul Block
Pr: Gary Jones
**VP:* David Perez

D-U-N-S 01-136-3801
SINGER SUPERMARKETS INC
(*Suby of* SHOP-RITE) ★
20 Ridge Rd, Mahwah, NJ 07430-2010
Tel (201) 529-5900 *Founded/Ownrshp* 1994
Sales 72.8MM^E *EMP* 1,500
SIC 5411 5912 Supermarkets, chain; Drug stores; Proprietary (non-prescription medicine) stores
Ch: Lawrence R Inserra
**VP:* Laura Dupont

D-U-N-S 19-296-4471
SINGER WORLDWIDE LLC
295 Madison Ave Fl 6, New York, NY 10017-7731
Tel (615) 213-0880 *Founded/Ownrshp* 2006
Sales 161.0MM^E *EMP* 121^E
SIC 5064 Sewing machines, household: electric

D-U-N-S 15-657-3396
SINGH MANAGEMENT CO INC
7125 Orchard Lake Rd # 200, West Bloomfield, MI 48322-5306
Tel (248) 865-1600 *Founded/Ownrshp* 1973
Sales 10.3MM^E *EMP* 1,300
SIC 6531 6513 8742 Real estate managers; Apartment building operators; Real estate consultant
Pr: Gurmale S Grewal
**Treas:* Tahil Grewal
**VP:* Lushman Grewal

D-U-N-S 00-696-4613
SINGING RIVER ELECTRIC POWER ASSOCIATION
11187 Old 63 S, Lucedale, MS 39452-4982
Tel (601) 947-4211 *Founded/Ownrshp* 1938
Sales 161.6MM *EMP* 187
SIC 4911 Distribution, electric power
CEO: Mike Smith
**VP:* Trafix Baxter
Genl Mgr: Shellie Hudson

D-U-N-S 07-505-1706
SINGING RIVER HEALTH SYSTEM
SRHS
2101 Highway 90, Gautier, MS 39553-5340
Tel (228) 497-7900 *Founded/Ownrshp* 1959
Sales 326.7MM *EMP* 2,100
SIC 8062 General medical & surgical hospitals
CEO: Kevin Holland
**CFO:* Brian Argo
Ofcr: Pete Horn
Ex VP: Randy Ross
Exec: Leigh Boutwell
Chf Nrs Of: Marsha White
Nurse Mgr: Rendy Foster Do
IT Man: Marshall Hammond
Pharmcst: Gloria Graham
Pharmcst: Ramzi Maaya

D-U-N-S 04-903-8953 IMP
SINGLE SOURCE INC
8160 Cass Ave, Darien, IL 60561-5013
Tel (630) 324-5982 *Founded/Ownrshp* 1995
Sales 143.3MM *EMP* 20
SIC 5141 Groceries, general line
Pr: Darlene Zitko
**CFO:* Eileen Finn
**CIO:* Robert Newhart

D-U-N-S 88-352-7806
SINGLE SOURCE INC
601 W Crssvlle Rd Ste 100, Roswell, GA 30075
Tel (770) 840-7877 *Founded/Ownrshp* 1995
Sales 88.2MM^E *EMP* 180
SIC 5013 7532

D-U-N-S 60-572-1070
SINOHUB INC
3 Kensington Way, Upton, MA 01568-1511
Tel (508) 603-1085 *Founded/Ownrshp* 1999
Sales 46.5MM^E *EMP* 1,100
SIC 3663 Mobile communication equipment
CEO: Henry Cochran
CFO: De Hai Li

SINTERED SPECIALTIES DIV
See SSI TECHNOLOGIES INC

SINTERITE PRODUCTS DIVISION
See GASBARRE PRODUCTS INC

D-U-N-S 16-089-9324
SINTON DAIRY FOODS CO LLC
3801 Sinton Rd, Colorado Springs, CO 80907-5036
Tel (719) 633-3821 *Founded/Ownrshp* 1987
Sales 84.6MM^E *EMP* 205
SIC 2026 Fluid milk
Sfty Mgr: Mark Dale

D-U-N-S 04-091-2909
SIOUX CITY COMMUNITY SCHOOL DISTRICT INC
627 4th St Ofc, Sioux City, IA 51101-1608
Tel (712) 279-6667 *Founded/Ownrshp* 1869
Sales 77.2MM^E *EMP* 1,518
SIC 8211 Public senior high school; Public junior high school; Public elementary school
**CFO:* Bill Stoneberg
**CFO:* Gordon Winterlin
**Prin:* Linda Maddison
MIS Dir: Kathy Bottaro
Pr Dir: Alison Benson
Teacher Pr: Rita Vannatta

D-U-N-S 00-726-2611
SIOUX CITY FOUNDRY CO
801 Division St, Sioux City, IA 51105-2644
Tel (712) 252-4181 *Founded/Ownrshp* 1985
Sales 136.5MM^E *EMP* 200
SIC 5051 3443 3321 3316 3444 3441 Steel; Plate work for the metalworking trade; Tanks, lined: metal plate; Gray & ductile iron foundries; Cold finishing of steel shapes; Sheet metalwork; Fabricated structural metal
Pr: Andrew M Galinsky
Exec: Val L Corbin
Off Mgr: Mary Cain
Mktg Mgr: Lorraine Jacobson
Sales Asso: Blake Hughes
Board of Directors: Mark Wahlberg

D-U-N-S 02-233-1383
SIOUX CITY TRUCK SALES INC
PETERBILT OF SIOUX CITY
2601 Voyager Ave, Sioux City, IA 51111-1229
Tel (712) 234-2728 *Founded/Ownrshp* 1954
Sales 132.6MM *EMP* 250
Accts Henjes Conner & Williams Pc
SIC 5511 Trucks, tractors & trailers: new & used
Pr: Wilson B A
**Treas:* Mardella V Wilson
**VP:* Gerald L Wilson

D-U-N-S 07-801-5427
SIOUX FALLS SCHOOL DISTRICT NO 49-5
201 E 38th St, Sioux Falls, SD 57105-5815
Tel (605) 367-7900 *Founded/Ownrshp* 1880
Sales 222.6MM *EMP* 3,300
Accts Mcgladrey Llp Sioux Falls So
SIC 8211 Public elementary & secondary schools; Secondary school
Schl Brd P: Douglas Morrison

D-U-N-S 12-211-9555
SIOUX FALLS SPECIALTY HOSPITAL LLP
SIOUX FALLS SURGICAL CENTER
910 E 20th St, Sioux Falls, SD 57105-1012
Tel (605) 334-6730 *Founded/Ownrshp* 1985
Sales 88.5MM *EMP* 70^E
SIC 8062 General medical & surgical hospitals
Pt: G V Nelson
**Pt:* Michael W Pekas
VP: Jennifer Rusk
Orthpdst: Mitchell Johnson
Surgeon: Jon Ellenbecker
Surgeon: Daniel Goede
Surgeon: Joe Olsen
Surgeon: Joseph Skibinski
Surgeon: Melvin Thaler
Surgeon: Bradley Vance
Ansthlgy: David Munce

SIOUX FALLS SURGICAL CENTER
See SIOUX FALLS SPECIALTY HOSPITAL LLP

D-U-N-S 00-726-8055 IMP
SIOUX STEEL CO
EMPIRE CREDIT COMPANY
196 1/2 E 6th St, Sioux Falls, SD 57104-5929
Tel (605) 336-1750 *Founded/Ownrshp* 1948
Sales 150.0MM^E *EMP* 396
SIC 3523 3448 2221

D-U-N-S 15-610-7315
SIOUXLAND ETHANOL LLC
1501 Knox Blvd, Jackson, NE 68743-3060
Tel (402) 632-2676 *Founded/Ownrshp* 2004
Sales 144.0MM *EMP* 35
SIC 2869 2083 Ethyl alcohol, ethanol; Corn malt
Pr: Charles Hofland
CFO: Mark Rolfes

D-U-N-S 02-231-3134
SIOUXLAND FARMERS COOPERATIVE
317 3rd St Nw, Sioux Center, IA 51250-1856
Tel (712) 722-2671 *Founded/Ownrshp* 1906
Sales 105.2MM *EMP* 32
SIC 5153 5191 Grains; Feed; Fertilizer & fertilizer materials; Seeds: field, garden & flower; Chemicals, agricultural
Genl Mgr: Rod Winter

D-U-N-S 07-870-4539
SIRIS CAPITAL GROUP LLC
601 Lexington Ave Rm 5901, New York, NY 10022-4622
Tel (212) 231-0095 *Founded/Ownrshp* 2011
Sales 600.8MM^E *EMP* 2,692
SIC 6799 Investors

D-U-N-S 03-822-1180
SIRIUS AMERICA INSURANCE CO
(*Suby of* CM INTERNATIONAL HOLDING PTE. LTD.)
140 Broadway Fl 32, New York, NY 10005-1123
Tel (212) 312-2500 *Founded/Ownrshp* 2016
Sales NA *EMP* 191
SIC 6331 Fire, marine & casualty insurance
Pr: Daniel Wilson
**Ch Bd:* Michael E Tyburski

*COO: Brian Kensil
*Sr VP: Joann L Deblasis
*Sr VP: John S Game
*Sr VP: David Gilligan
*Sr VP: John H Haley
*Sr VP: Peter L Hudson
*Sr VP: Robert Robertson
*Sr VP: Rafael A Saer
*Sr VP: Edward J Stanco
*Sr VP: Warren J Trace
*Sr VP: James D Wickwire
VP: William Biegaj
VP: Mary Bradley
VP: Humberto Cabrera
VP: Keith Cartmell
VP: Steven Christopherson
VP: Jose Dieguez
VP: Jerry Farrell
VP: Gina Ferris
Board of Directors: Andres Henriksson

D-U-N-S 00-416-1712
SIRIUS COMPUTER SOLUTIONS INC (TX)
10100 Reunion Pl Ste 500, San Antonio, TX 78216-9599
Tel (210) 369-8000 Founded/Ownrshp 2000, 2015
Sales 767.7MM[E] EMP 1,233
SIC 7373 5045 Computer integrated systems design; Computer peripheral equipment
Pr: Joe Mertens
*Pr: Jim Simpson
*CFO: Terry Johnson
CFO: Terry L Johnson
Ex VP: Rick Bailer
*Ex VP: Muditha Karunatileka
*Ex VP: Craig Nelson
Sr VP: Sue Bonar
Sr VP: Dave Eaton
Sr VP: Michael Harwood
Sr VP: Becky Murphy
Sr VP: Thomas Neville
Sr VP: Imran Salim
VP: Joe Andersen
VP: Deborah L Bannworth
VP: Jerimiah Cook
VP: Brian Finzen
VP: Brandi Henderson
VP: Bonnie M Johnson
*VP: Karen Kochheiser
VP: Chris Lusk

D-U-N-S 87-841-7088
■ **SIRIUS XM CONNECTED VEHICLE SERVICES INC**
ATX NORTH AMERICA
(Suby of SIRIUS XM RADIO INC) ★
8550 Freeport Pkwy, Irving, TX 75063-2547
Tel (972) 753-6200 Founded/Ownrshp 1994
Sales 148.5MM[E] EMP 592
SIC 7375 Information retrieval services
Pr: Michael Saxton
*Pr: Enrique Rodriguez
*Treas: David Frear
Bd of Dir: Tomas Isaksson
*Sr VP: Thomas Metzger
VP: Fred Hoein
VP: Tom Metzger
*VP: Gary Wallace
*VP: Howard Wolk
Exec: Cindy B Gibbs
Prgrm Mgr: Charles Wang

D-U-N-S 02-782-5458
■ **SIRIUS XM HOLDINGS INC**
(Suby of LIBERTY MEDIA CORP) ★
1221 Avenue Of Americas Flr 36, New York, NY 10020
Tel (212) 584-5100 Founded/Ownrshp 1990
Sales 4.5MMM EMP 2,323[E]
Tkr Sym SIRI Exch NGS
SIC 4832 Radio broadcasting stations
CEO: James E Meyer
*Ch Bd: Gregory B Maffei
Pr: Greg Corley
Pr: Scott A Greenstein
CFO: David J Frear
Chf Mktg O: Katherine Kohler Thomson
Ofcr: Dara F Altman
Ex VP: James A Cady
Ex VP: Stephen Cook
Ex VP: Patrick L Donnelly
Ex VP: Joseph A Verbrugge
VP: Brian Hamilton
VP: Michael Moore
VP: Christa Petros
Dir Soc: Timothy Dolan
Board of Directors: Vanessa A Wittman, Joan L Amble, David M Zaslav, Anthony J Bates, George W Bodenheimer, Mark D Carleton, Eddy W Hartenstein, James P Holden, Evan D Malone, James F Mooney, Carl E Vogel

D-U-N-S 80-005-8992 IMP
■ **SIRIUS XM RADIO INC**
(Suby of SIRIUS XM HOLDINGS INC) ★
1221 Avenue Of The Americ, New York, NY 10020-1001
Tel (212) 584-5100 Founded/Ownrshp 2013
Sales 4.1MMM EMP 1,596
Accts Kpmg Llp New York New York
SIC 4832 Radio broadcasting stations
CEO: James E Meyer
Pr: Scott A Greenstein
Pr: Stephen Smith
CFO: David J Frear
Ex VP: Dara F Altman
Ex VP: Patrick L Donnelly
Ex VP: Stell Patsiokas
Sr VP: Jennifer Campbell
Sr VP: Gary Hahn
Sr VP: Andreas Lazar
Sr VP: Patrick Reilly
Sr VP: Bette Rockmore
VP: Donna Colorito
VP: Randy Dry
VP: Neil Leibowitz
VP: Cynthia Ricciardi
VP: Robert Shideleff
VP: Larry Simon
Exec: Paul Nugent
Board of Directors: Charles Y Tanabe, Joan L Amble, Carl Vogel, Anthony J Bates, Vanessa Wittman, George W Bodenheimer, David J A Flowers, Eddy W Hartenstein, James P Holden, Gregory B Maffei, John C Malone, James F Mooney

D-U-N-S 12-460-6315
SIRIUSDECISIONS INC
187 Danbury Rd, Wilton, CT 06897-4122
Tel (203) 665-4000 Founded/Ownrshp 2001
Sales 90.1MM[E] EMP 340[E]
SIC 6282 8742 Investment advisory service; Investment research; Marketing consulting services
Co-CEO: Richard Eldh
*CEO: John J Neeson
CFO: Martijn Tel
*CFO: Martijn Tel
*Sr VP: Tony Jaros
*Sr VP: Heather Loisel
*VP: Richard Benvenuto
VP: Bruce Brien
VP: Lynn Gaudio
*Prin: Richard E Eldh Jr
Off Mgr: Kerry Cuneo

D-U-N-S 09-450-2432
SIRNA & SONS INC
SIRNA'S MARKET & DELI
7176 State Route 88, Ravenna, OH 44266-9189
Tel (330) 298-2222 Founded/Ownrshp 1979
Sales 105.3MM[E] EMP 150
SIC 5148 Fruits, fresh; Vegetables, fresh
Pr: Tom Sirna
*CEO: Joseph Sirna
*Sec: Serena Wagner
*VP: Vince Sirna
Off Mgr: Debbie Michalski
IT Man: Serena Serna
Opers Mgr: Troy Bennington

SIRNA'S MARKET & DELI
See SIRNA & SONS INC

D-U-N-S 79-691-2350 IMP
■ **SIRONA DENTAL SYSTEMS INC**
(Suby of DENTSPLY SIRONA INC) ★
3030 47th Ave Ste 500, Long Island City, NY 11101-3492
Tel (718) 482-2011 Founded/Ownrshp 2015
Sales 1.1MMM EMP 3,458[E]
SIC 8021 3313 3843 3841 Offices & clinics of dentists; Electrometallurgical products; Dental equipment & supplies; Diagnostic apparatus, medical
Pr: Michael Augins
*Sec: Jonathan I Friedman
*Ex VP: Walter Petersohn
Ex VP: Jeffery Slovin
VP: Stefan Hehn
VP: Regina Kuhnert
VP: Roddy Macleod
VP: Susan Murphy
VP: ARI Neugroschl
Area Mgr: Christof Bissdorf
Area Mgr: Kristian Sandrini

D-U-N-S 03-503-6813
SIRSI CORP
SIRSIDYNIX
3300 N Ashton Blvd # 500, Lehi, UT 84043-5339
Tel (801) 223-5200 Founded/Ownrshp 2015
Sales 110.0MM[E] EMP 500
SIC 7371 Computer software development
CEO: Bill Davison
VP: Rick Branham
VP: Tim Hyde
VP: David King
VP: Berit Nelson
VP: Barbara Pacut
VP: Jeff Smith
VP: Brad Whittle
Snr Sftwr: Jeffrey Goodwin

SIRSIDYNIX
See SIRSI CORP

D-U-N-S 06-224-9128
SIRVA INC
1 Parkview Plz, Oakbrook Terrace, IL 60181-4400
Tel (630) 570-3047 Founded/Ownrshp 1997
Sales 2.1MMM[E] EMP 3,800
SIC 4213 4214 4731 7513 6331 Household goods transport; Household goods moving & storage, local; Domestic freight forwarding; Foreign freight forwarding; Truck leasing, without drivers; Property damage insurance; Fire, marine & casualty insurance: stock
Pr: Wes W Lucas
Pr: Jacob George
COO: Andrew P Coolidge
*CFO: Douglas V Gathany
CFO: Ron L Mienski
*CFO: Thomas Oberdorf
Ofcr: Matthew B Dickerson
Ex VP: John Kirk
Ex VP: Dennis Koziol
Sr VP: M Sean Fernandez
Sr VP: Douglas Gathany
Sr VP: Michelle M Guswiler
VP: John Anderson
VP: Lynn Brown
*VP: Margaret E Pais

D-U-N-S 14-078-4120
SIRVA WORLDWIDE INC
(Suby of SIRVA INC) ★
1 Parkview Plz Ste 300, Oakbrook Terrace, IL 60181-4491
Tel (630) 570-3047 Founded/Ownrshp 2003
Sales 241.4MM[E] EMP 3,800
SIC 4213 4214 4731 7513 6331 Household goods transport; Household goods moving & storage, local; Domestic freight forwarding; Foreign freight forwarding; Truck leasing, without drivers; Property damage insurance; Fire, marine & casualty insurance: stock
Pr: Wes W Lucas
*Pr: Deborah L Balli
*Pr: Michael T Wolfe
*COO: Andrew P Coolidge
*CFO: J Gordon Smith
*Treas: Douglas V Gathany
*Ofcr: Daniel P Mullin

SIS
See SOFTWARE INFORMATION SYSTEMS LLC

SIS TECHNOLOGIES
See SIGMA SOLUTIONS GP INC

SISC
See SELF-INSURED SCHOOLS OF CALIFORNIA

SISD
See SOCORRO INDEPENDENT SCHOOL DISTRICT

D-U-N-S 00-792-0887 IMP
■ **SISKIN STEEL & SUPPLY CO INC** (TN)
EAST TENNESSEE STEEL SUPPLY CO
(Suby of RELIANCE STEEL & ALUMINUM CO) ★
1901 Riverfront Pkwy, Chattanooga, TN 37408-1037
Tel (423) 756-3671 Founded/Ownrshp 1900, 1996
Sales 314.1MM[E] EMP 600
SIC 3312 5051 Bars & bar shapes, steel, cold-finished: own hot-rolled; Steel
Pr: Paul Loftin
*CFO: Betty Anne Nall
*VP: Nelson Burger
VP: Dave Garland
*VP: Dan Youngman
DP Exec: Kevin Sneary
Dir IT: Greg Browning
QC Dir: Greg Lanier
Sales Asso: John Burkett
Sales Asso: Scott Glasgow
Sales Asso: Ryan Graceffa
Board of Directors: Greg Browing, Rick England, James Morgan

D-U-N-S 09-045-6609 IMP
SISTEMA UNIVERSITARIO ANA G MENDEZ INC
UNIVERSIDAD METROPOLITANA
Carr 176 Km 0 3 Cpey Lowr St Ca, San Juan, PR 00928
Tel (787) 751-0178 Founded/Ownrshp 1949
Sales 300.8MM EMP 5,387[E]
Accts Ernst & Young Llp San Juan P
SIC 8221 4833 University; Professional schools; Television broadcasting stations
Pr: Jose F Mendez
CFO: Dorie Mendez
*Ex VP: Victoria De Jess
Dept Mgr: Maria Charneco

D-U-N-S 78-345-5322
SISTERS OF CHARITY HEALTH SYSTEMS
99 Campus Ave Ste 303, Lewiston, ME 04240-6045
Tel (207) 782-5424 Founded/Ownrshp 1989
Sales 61.2MM EMP 2,036
Accts William Steele & Associates P
SIC 8011 Surgeon
Pr: James Cassady
Owner: Maria Ikossi MD
Comm Dir: Rebecca Gallant
Off Mgr: Carol Sirois

D-U-N-S 03-732-8369
SISTERS OF CHARITY HOSPITAL OF BUFFALO
144 Genesee St, Buffalo, NY 14203-1560
Tel (716) 828-3723 Founded/Ownrshp 2014
Sales 390.3MM EMP 1[E]
SIC 8661 Religious organizations

D-U-N-S 07-402-3144
SISTERS OF CHARITY HOSPITAL OF BUFFALO NEW YORK
(Suby of CATHOLIC HEALTH SYSTEM INC) ★
2157 Main St, Buffalo, NY 14214-2692
Tel (716) 862-1000 Founded/Ownrshp 1848
Sales 83.9MM[E] EMP 1,329
SIC 8062 General medical & surgical hospitals
CEO: Peter U Bergmann
*Treas: Joseph J Castiglia
Dir IT: Susan Schack
Pr Mgr: Ann Schlifke

SISTERS OF CHARITY OF LEAVE
See ST VINCENT HEALTHCARE

D-U-N-S 06-795-6060
SISTERS OF CHARITY OF LEAVENWORTH
4200 S 4th St Traffic Way, Leavenworth, KS 66048
Tel (913) 682-5151 Founded/Ownrshp 1858
Sales 2.5MMM EMP 75
SIC 8661 Convent
Pr: Sister Joan Sue Miller
*Sec: Sister Katherine Franchett
Board of Directors: Sister Barbara Aldrich

D-U-N-S 09-380-7147
SISTERS OF CHARITY OF LEAVENWORTH HEALTH SYSTEM INC
SCL HEALTH SYSTEM
500 Eldorado Blvd # 6300, Broomfield, CO 80021-3422
Tel (303) 813-5000 Founded/Ownrshp 1972
Sales 2.4MMM EMP 15,000
SIC 8062 8011 5912 General medical & surgical hospitals; Offices & clinics of medical doctors; Drug stores
CEO: Michael Slubowski
*Ch Bd: William Starusburg
*Pr: William M Murray
*CFO: Lydia Jumonville
CFO: Lydia W Jumonville
Ex VP: Richard T Lopes
*Sr VP: Edward L Barker
*Sr VP: Rosland Fisher McLeod
VP: Bob Boysen
VP: Robert Fries
VP: Joseph B Heaton
VP: Ken Homan
VP: Barb Manor
VP: Mary E Shepler
VP: Christine Woolsey
VP: Jennifer Wrona

SISTERS OF CHARITY OF LEAVENWR
See SCL HEALTH - FRONT RANGE INC

D-U-N-S 05-287-8410
SISTERS OF CHARITY OF ST AUGUSTINE HEALTH SYSTEM INC (OH)
2475 E 22nd St, Cleveland, OH 44115-3221
Tel (216) 696-5560 Founded/Ownrshp 1982, 1851
Sales 309.9MM[E] EMP 80
SIC 8661 8733

SISTERS OF MERCY HEALTH SYSTEM
See MERCY HOSPITAL FORT SMITH

SISTERS OF MERCY HEALTH SYSTEM
See MERCY HOSPITAL JEFFERSON

SISTERS OF MERCY HEALTH SYSTEM
See MERCY HOSPITAL JOPLIN

SISTERS OF MERCY HEALTH SYSTEM
See MERCY HEALTH

SISTERS OF MERCY HEALTH SYSTEM
See ST JOHNS MERCY HEALTH CARE

D-U-N-S 07-554-6358
SISTERS OF MERCY OF AMERICAS MID-ATLANTIC COMMUNITY INC
515 Montgomery Ave, Merion Station, PA 19066-1297
Tel (610) 664-6650 Founded/Ownrshp 1861
Sales 44.3MM[E] EMP 1,315
SIC 8661 Religious organizations
Pr: Christine McCann
*Treas: Catharine McGrogary

D-U-N-S 06-894-8983
SISTERS OF MERCY OF CLERMONT COUNTY OHIO INC
CLERMONT MERCY HOSPITAL
3000 Hospital Dr, Batavia, OH 45103-1921
Tel (513) 732-8200 Founded/Ownrshp 1973
Sales 116.8MM EMP 720[E]
Accts Bkd Llp Cincinnati Oh
SIC 8062 8011 General medical & surgical hospitals; Clinic, operated by physicians
Pr: Mark Shuagerman
CFO: Mel Fritz
VP: Bonna Bauer
*VP: Arlene Cooper
CIO: Raytier Angeli

D-U-N-S 06-615-7165
SISTERS OF ST JOSEPH OF ORANGE
480 S Batavia St, Orange, CA 92868-3998
Tel (714) 633-8121 Founded/Ownrshp 1912
Sales 4.5MMM[E] EMP 22,000
SIC 8661 Convent
CEO: Jayne Helmlinger
Exec: Melinda Snyder
Pgrm Dir: Mary Anne Huepper

D-U-N-S 85-848-0932
SISTERS OF THIRD ORDER OF ST FRANCIS
1175 Saint Francis Ln, East Peoria, IL 61611-1298
Tel (309) 699-7215 Founded/Ownrshp 1877
Sales 13.5MM EMP 10,145
Accts Kpmg Llp Chicago Il
SIC 8661 Non-church religious organizations
Pr: Sister Mary Ellen
*Treas: Sister Diane Marie McGrew

SISTERS PROVIDENCE HEALTH SYS
See SPHS CORP

D-U-N-S 07-162-4407
SISTERS SERVANTS OF IMMACULATE HEART OF MARY INC (MI)
1140 King Rd, Immaculata, PA 19345
Tel (610) 647-2160 Founded/Ownrshp 1845
Sales 27.2MM[E] EMP 1,000
SIC 8661 Catholic Church
Genl Mgr: Lorraine McGrew

D-U-N-S 11-270-6499 IMP/EXP
SITA INFORMATION NETWORKING COMPUTING USA INC
(Suby of SOCIETE INTERNATIONALE DE TELECOMMUNICATIONS AERONAUTIQUES SCRL)
3100 Cumberland Blvd Se, Atlanta, GA 30339-5940
Tel (770) 850-4500 Founded/Ownrshp 1998
Sales 302.9MM[E] EMP 900
SIC 4899

SITE 264
See BFI WASTE SERVICES OF PENNSYLVANIA LLC

SITE 468
See ALLIED WASTE SERVICES OF INDEPENDENCE

D-U-N-S 15-119-7597
SITE CONCRETE INC
1544 Valwood Pkwy Ste 100, Carrollton, TX 75006-8427
Tel (972) 313-0733 Founded/Ownrshp 1984
Sales 54.4MM[E] EMP 1,000
SIC 1611 1771 1794 Surfacing & paving; Concrete work; Excavation work
Pr: Jean S Boney
*VP: James M Boney

SITE STORAGE
See UTILITY TRAILER SALES OF UTAH INC

D-U-N-S 15-064-3849
SITEL CORP
(Suby of SITEL LLC) ★
5601 N 103rd St, Omaha, NE 68134-1016
Tel (402) 963-6810 Founded/Ownrshp 2007
Sales 930.1MM[E] EMP 24,568
SIC 7389 Telemarketing services
CEO: Jim Lynch
Ex VP: Antoon Vanparys
Sr VP: Pete Weaklend
*VP: William Sims
Mktg Mgr: Virginie Sarazin
Snr Mgr: Nilesh Singh

D-U-N-S 79-631-2762
SITEL LLC
(Suby of SITEL WORLDWIDE CORP) ★
3102 West End Ave Ste 900, Nashville, TN 37203-1341
Tel (615) 301-7100 Founded/Ownrshp 2007

Sales 1.2MMM^E *EMP* 25,000
SIC 7389 Telephone services; Telemarketing services; Telephone solicitation service
Prin: Bert Quintana
Pr: Don Berryman
CFO: Paul Stone
Treas: Craig Jantzi
Sr Cor Off: Lisa Wallace
IT Man: Joemar Maglaqui

D-U-N-S 17-075-6618
SITEL OPERATING CORP
(*Suby of* SITEL LLC) ★
3102 West End Ave Ste 900, Nashville, TN 37203-1341
Tel (615) 301-7100 *Founded/Ownrshp* 1999
Sales 279.7MM^E *EMP* 6,000
SIC 7389 7375 Telephone services; Telemarketing services; Telephone solicitation service; Information retrieval services
Pr: Bert Quintana
**CFO:* Patrick Tolbert
VP: Raj Venkaty

D-U-N-S 61-616-2699
SITEL WORLDWIDE CORP
3102 West End Ave Ste 900, Nashville, TN 37203-1341
Tel (615) 301-7100 *Founded/Ownrshp* 2015
Sales 1.4MMM^E *EMP* 75,100
SIC 7389 7375 Telephone services; Telemarketing services; Information retrieval services
Pr: Dagoberto Quintana
COO: Olivier Camino
COO: Patrick Tolbert
Treas: Neal Miller
Chf Cred: Don Berryman
Chf Mktg O: Arnaud De Lacoste
Chf Mktg O: Sean Erickson
Ex VP: Steve Barker
VP: Paula D Walker
Genl Mgr: Nicholas Keca
CTO: David Slaviero

D-U-N-S 08-025-5239
■ **SITEONE LANDSCAPE SUPPLY HOLDING LLC**
(*Suby of* SITEONE LANDSCAPE SUPPLY INC) ★
300 Colonial Center Pkwy, Roswell, GA 30076-4899
Tel (770) 255-2100 *Founded/Ownrshp* 2013
Sales 1.6MMM^E *EMP* 2,850^E
SIC 5083 5191 5193 5032 5063 Irrigation equipment; Landscaping equipment; Herbicides; Pesticides; Soil, potting & planting; Flowers & nursery stock; Brick, stone & related material; Lighting fixtures
CEO: Doug Black

D-U-N-S 08-004-6723
▲ **SITEONE LANDSCAPE SUPPLY INC**
300 Colonial Center Pkwy, Roswell, GA 30076-4899
Tel (770) 255-2100 *Founded/Ownrshp* 2013
Sales 1.7MMM^E *EMP* 2,850
Tkr Sym SITE *Exch* NYS
SIC 5083 5191 5193 5032 5063 Irrigation equipment; Landscaping equipment; Herbicides; Pesticides; Soil, potting & planting; Flowers & nursery stock; Brick, stone & related material; Lighting fixtures
CEO: Doug Black
CFO: John Guthrie
Ex VP: Ross Anker
Ex VP: Briley Brisendine
Ex VP: Pascal Convers
Sr VP: Joseph Ketter
Board of Directors: William W Douglas III, Kenneth A Giuriceo, Jeri L Isbell, John Lagemann, Paul S Pressler, Wes Robinson, David H Wasserman, Jack L Wyszomierski

D-U-N-S 18-005-5774 IMP
■ **SITEONE LANDSCAPE SUPPLY LLC**
(*Suby of* SITEONE LANDSCAPE SUPPLY HOLDING LLC) ★
300 Colonial Center Pkwy # 600, Roswell, GA 30076-4899
Tel (770) 255-2100 *Founded/Ownrshp* 2013
Sales 1.6MMM^E *EMP* 2,850
SIC 5063 5193 5083 Light bulbs & related supplies; Nursery stock; Irrigation equipment; Landscaping equipment
CEO: Doug Black
**Treas:* James Davlin
**Sr VP:* Jeff Lanahan
VP: James Field
VP: Nathan J Jones
VP: Michael J McGrady
VP: Mark Nattinger
Brnch Mgr: Kurt Kisling
Brnch Mgr: Scott Martineau
Sls Mgr: Jim Weller

SITONIT
See EXEMPLIS LLC

D-U-N-S 14-494-9331
SITTON ENTERPRISES LLC
SEI OILFIELDS
4100 Intl Plz Ste 820, Fort Worth, TX 76109
Tel (940) 328-6000 *Founded/Ownrshp* 1998
Sales 84.6MM^E *EMP* 150
SIC 1389 Oil field services

SIU HEALTHCARE
See SIU PHYSICIANS & SURGEONS INC

D-U-N-S 15-339-8321
SIU PHYSICIANS & SURGEONS INC
SIU HEALTHCARE
801 N Rutledge St # 2050, Springfield, IL 62702-4933
Tel (217) 545-8065 *Founded/Ownrshp* 1997
Sales 100.6MM *EMP* 250
Accts Kerber Eck & Braeckel Llp Spr
SIC 8011 Specialized medical practitioners, except internal
CEO: Dr Jerry Kruse

SIUC
See SOUTHERN ILLINOIS UNIVERSITY INC

D-U-N-S 15-741-2271 IMP
SIVANTOS INC
(*Suby of* SIVANTOS PTE. LTD.)
10 Constitution Ave, Piscataway, NJ 08854-6145
Tel (732) 562-6600 *Founded/Ownrshp* 1991
Sales 249.9MM^E *EMP* 835
SIC 3842 Orthopedic appliances; Hearing aids
Pr: Christi Pedra
**CEO:* Scott Davis
CEO: Brian Kinnerk
**CFO:* Nicolau Gaeta
**CFO:* Tony Manuccia
**VP:* Thomas A Powers
VP: Tom Powers
IT Man: David McAvoy
VP Opers: Roger Talish
Sls Mgr: Johnathan Davis

D-U-N-S 60-672-6953
SIVICA HOMES INC
1640 Pwrs Fry Rd Se 18-300, Marietta, GA 30067-1474
Tel (770) 645-5559 *Founded/Ownrshp* 2004
Sales 100.0MM *EMP* 60
SIC 1521 Single-family housing construction
Pr: Bill Dennis

D-U-N-S 00-608-2069 IMP/EXP
SIVYER STEEL CORP
225 33rd St, Bettendorf, IA 52722-6403
Tel (563) 355-1811 *Founded/Ownrshp* 1909
Sales 140.6MM^E *EMP* 320
SIC 3325 Alloy steel castings, except investment
Pr: Arthur Gibeaut
**Pr:* Keith D Kramer
**COO:* Tim Mohs
CFO: Frank Johnson
**VP:* Tonya Burgess
**VP:* Hal Davis
QA Dir: Dennis Glaser
IT Man: Justin Heffe
IT Man: Ralph Janis
VP Sls: Karla McFarland

D-U-N-S 00-702-1066 IMP
SIX CONTINENTS HOTELS INC
I H G
(*Suby of* INTERCONTINENTAL HOTELS LIMITED)
3 Ravinia Dr Ste 100, Atlanta, GA 30346-2121
Tel (770) 604-2000 *Founded/Ownrshp* 2003
Sales 1.8MMM^E *EMP* 30,000
SIC 7011 6794 8741 Hotels & motels; Hotel, franchised; Franchises, selling or licensing; Hotel or motel management
CEO: Kirk Kinsell
Pr: Richard Cunningham
**CEO:* Jim Abrahamson
**CFO:* Robert Gunkel
Ex VP: Humberto Aburto
Ex VP: Carolyn Dinberg
Ex VP: Sally Jamara
VP: Jill Cady
Exec: Chad Bayless
Exec: Bart Hannah
Exec: Shankar Kotian
Dir Soc: Grace Dibenedetto
Comm Dir: Carolyn Hergert
Dir Bus: Jenni Butt
Comm Man: Francie Schulwolf

SIX CORNERS MEDICAL CENTER
See ILLINOIS MASONIC MEDICAL CENTER

D-U-N-S 06-227-3669 IMP
▲ **SIX FLAGS ENTERTAINMENT CORP**
924 E Avenue J, Grand Prairie, TX 75050-2622
Tel (972) 595-5000 *Founded/Ownrshp* 1970
Sales 1.2MMM *EMP* 1,900^E
Tkr Sym SIX *Exch* NYS
SIC 7996 Amusement parks; Theme park, amusement
Pr: John M Duffey
**Ch Bd:* James Reid-Anderson
CFO: Marshall Barber
CFO: Jeff Speed
Sr VP: Walter S Hawrylak
Sr VP: Michael S Israel
Sr VP: Tom Iven
Sr VP: Nancy A Krejsa
Sr VP: David McKillips
Sr VP: John Odum
Sr VP: Leonard A Russ
Comm Man: Katy Morris
Board of Directors: Kurt M Cellar, Charles A Koppelman, Jon L Luther, Stephen D Owens, Richard W Roedel

SIX FLAGS FESTA TEXAS THEME PK
See FIESTA TEXAS INC

D-U-N-S 06-456-8785 IMP
SIX FLAGS THEME PARKS INC
924 E Avenue J, Grand Prairie, TX 75050-2622
Tel (972) 595-5000 *Founded/Ownrshp* 2007
Sales 72.0MM^E *EMP* 2,000
SIC 7996 Theme park, amusement
Ch Bd: Larry D Bouts
**CEO:* Mark Shapiro
**CFO:* Jeff Speed
**Ch:* Daniel M Snyder
**V Ch Bd:* Larry B Cochran
**VP:* Andrew J Barkley
Dir IT: Tricia Holland
Software D: Peter Karaganis

SIX L'S PACKING
See LFC ENTERPRISES INC

D-U-N-S 03-235-4854 IMP/EXP
SIX LS PACKING CO INC
(*Suby of* SIX LS PACKING) ★
315 New Market Rd E, Immokalee, FL 34142-3509
Tel (239) 657-3117 *Founded/Ownrshp* 1953
Sales 91.0MM^E *EMP* 290
SIC 5148 Vegetables, fresh
**Treas:* Blake Gunn
**VP:* Peter Dessak
Board of Directors: Larry Lipman

SIX POINT BEVERAGES
See CAPITAL DISTRIBUTING LLC

D-U-N-S 05-476-3094
■ **SIX3 ADVANCED SYSTEMS INC**
BIT SYSTEMS
(*Suby of* SIX3 SYSTEMS HOLDINGS II INC) ★
45200 Business Ct Ste 100, Dulles, VA 20166-6715
Tel (703) 742-7660 *Founded/Ownrshp* 2009
Sales 165.4MM^E *EMP* 560^E
SIC 3825 4899 8099 4789 Signal generators & averagers; Data communication services; Blood related health services; Cargo loading & unloading services
CEO: Kenneth Asbury
**Ch Bd:* J P London
**Pr:* John Mengucci
**CFO:* Thomas Mutryn
**Ex VP:* J William Koegel Jr
**Ex VP:* Tom Ladd
VP: Roy Apseloff
**VP:* Michael Folkman
**VP:* Paul Schauer
Prgrm Mgr: Aaron Fleet
Prgrm Mgr: Erik Hunsaker

D-U-N-S 00-202-6363
■ **SIX3 SYSTEMS HOLDINGS II INC**
(*Suby of* CACI INC - FEDERAL) ★
1100 N Glebe Rd, Arlington, VA 22201-5798
Tel (703) 841-7800 *Founded/Ownrshp* 2009, 2013
Sales 253.6MM^E *EMP* 405^E
SIC 7373 Computer systems analysis & design
Ch Bd: J P London
**Pr:* John S Mengucci
**CEO:* Kenneth Asbury
**CFO:* Thomas A Mutryn
**Ex VP:* J William Koegel Jr
Ex VP: Tom Ladd
Ex VP: Robin Rhiner
Ex VP: Ryan Wagener
**VP:* Michael Folkman

D-U-N-S 83-151-6898
■ **SIX3 SYSTEMS INC**
(*Suby of* SIX3 SYSTEMS HOLDINGS II INC) ★
1430 Spring Hill Rd # 525, Mc Lean, VA 22102-3000
Tel (703) 442-6650 *Founded/Ownrshp* 2009
Sales 88.0MM^E *EMP* 225^E
SIC 7373 Computer systems analysis & design
CEO: Kenneth Asbury
Ch Bd: J P London
Pr: John Mengucci
Treas: Thomas Mutryn
Ofcr: Angela King
Ex VP: J William Koegel Jr
Ex VP: Tom Ladd
Ex VP: Ryan Wagener
VP: Michael Folkman
Exec: Tracy Ratermann
Snr Sftwr: Bhavesh Patel

D-U-N-S 04-759-5269
SIZEMORE INC
SIZEMORE SECURITY
2116 Walton Way, Augusta, GA 30904-4387
Tel (706) 736-1456 *Founded/Ownrshp* 1955
Sales 43.0MM *EMP* 2,200
SIC 7381 7363 7349 Security guard service; Help supply services; Building maintenance services
Ch Bd: Preston E Sizemore
Pr: Julie Cook
**COO:* Marc McClain
**CFO:* Matthew Kottyan
**Treas:* Kathryn A Anderson
Ofcr: Barry Lowe
**Sr VP:* Robert Cadarr
**VP:* Kim Barry
**VP:* Mike Eley
Brnch Mgr: Pat Kitchens
Brnch Mgr: Kent White

SIZEMORE SECURITY
See SIZEMORE INC

D-U-N-S 07-928-2350
SIZMEK INC
500 W 5th St Ste 900, Austin, TX 78701-3833
Tel (512) 469-5900 *Founded/Ownrshp* 2013
Sales 172.7MM *EMP* 1,204
SIC 7311 Advertising agencies
Pr: Neil H Nguyen
Ch Bd: John R Harris
CFO: Kenneth J Saunders
Board of Directors: Scott K Ginsburg, Xavier A Gutierrez, Adam Klein, Cecil H Moore Jr, Stephen E Recht

SIZZLER
See SIZZLING PLATTER LLC

D-U-N-S 06-623-7223
SIZZLER USA RESTAURANTS INC (DE)
25910 Acero Ste 350, Mission Viejo, CA 92691-7908
Tel (949) 273-4497 *Founded/Ownrshp* 1967, 2006
Sales 87.4MM^E *EMP* 2,000
SIC 5812 Steak restaurant
Pr: Kerry Kramp
CFO: Keith Wall
Sr Cor Off: John Bailey
VP: Mike Branigan
VP: Todd Peterson
VP: Richard Pineda
Genl Couns: Adela Espiritu

D-U-N-S 05-719-4698
SIZZLING PLATTER LLC
SIZZLER
348 E Winchester St # 200, Salt Lake City, UT 84107-8518
Tel (801) 268-3400 *Founded/Ownrshp* 1968
Sales 203.2MM^E *EMP* 5,000
SIC 5812 Steak restaurant
CFO: Emanuel M Hilario
Rgnl Mgr: Milio Mascaro
Genl Mgr: Jon Albritton
Genl Mgr: Connie Brown
Genl Mgr: Greg Waterhouse
Mktg Mgr: Gary Shatswell

D-U-N-S 60-085-1658
SJ DISTRIBUTORS INC
625 Vista Way, Milpitas, CA 95035-5433
Tel (888) 988-2328 *Founded/Ownrshp* 2005
Sales 102.1MM *EMP* 160
SIC 5142 5148 5149 Meat, frozen: packaged; Fresh fruits & vegetables; Canned goods: fruit, vegetables, seafood, meats, etc.
CEO: Scot Chun Ho Suen
**CFO:* Jerry Yeung

D-U-N-S 14-758-4296
SJ LOUIS CONSTRUCTION INC
1351 Broadway St W, Rockville, MN 56369
Tel (320) 685-4164 *Founded/Ownrshp* 1986
Sales 199.0MM^E *EMP* 550
Accts Kern Dewenter Viere Ltd St
SIC 1623 Water & sewer line construction
CEO: James L Schueller
**CFO:* Donald Meyer
**Ex VP:* Les V Whitman

D-U-N-S 36-101-4157
SJ MEDICAL CENTER LLC
ST. JOSEPH MEDICAL CENTER
(*Suby of* IASIS HEALTHCARE LLC) ★
1401 St Joseph Pkwy, Houston, TX 77002-8301
Tel (713) 757-1000 *Founded/Ownrshp* 2011
Sales 204.3MM *EMP* 2,100
SIC 8062 General medical & surgical hospitals
CEO: W Carl Whitmer
**COO:* Phillip J Mazzuca
**CFO:* John M Doyle
**CFO:* Pat Mathews
Ofcr: Laura Fortin
**VP:* William A Stokes

D-U-N-S 01-482-2508 IMP
SJA INC
SEJIN AMERICA
(*Suby of* SEJIN CO.,LTD)
274 Thweatt Indus Blvd, Dadeville, AL 36853-2610
Tel (256) 825-2290 *Founded/Ownrshp* 2007
Sales 147.0MM *EMP* 300
SIC 3089 Automotive parts, plastic
Pr: Seung Hwa Ahn
Plnt Mgr: S Kim

SJC
See TRUSTEES OF ST JOSEPHS COLLEGE

SJECCD
See SAN JOSE/EVERGREEN COMMUNITY COLLEGE DISTRICT FOUNDATION

SJHS SONOMA COUNTY
See SANTA ROSA MEMORIAL HOSPITAL INC

SJI
See SOUTH JERSEY INDUSTRIES INC

SJI
See SOUTH JERSEY GAS CO

D-U-N-S 00-691-3644
▲ **SJW CORP**
110 W Taylor St, San Jose, CA 95110-2131
Tel (408) 279-7800 *Founded/Ownrshp* 1866
Sales 305.0MM *EMP* 399
Accts Kpmg Llp Santa Clara Ca
Tkr Sym SJW *Exch* NYS
SIC 4941 6531 Water supply; Real estate agent, commercial
Ch Bd: W Richard Roth
COO: Suzy Papazian
CFO: James P Lynch
Ofcr: Andrew F Walters
Sfty Mgr: Thomas Petroni
Board of Directors: Katharine Armstrong, Walter J Bishop, Mark L Cali, Douglas R King, Debra Man, Daniel B More, Ronald B Moskovitz, George E Moss, Robert A Van Valer

D-U-N-S 02-555-1109
SK CAPITAL PARTNERS II LP
400 Park Ave Ste 820, New York, NY 10022-9481
Tel (212) 826-2700 *Founded/Ownrshp* 2010
Sales 1.2MMM^E *EMP* 3,800^E
SIC 6799 Investors
Genl Pt: Aaron Davenport

D-U-N-S 80-806-4724
SK CAPITAL PARTNERS LP
400 Park Ave Ste 820, New York, NY 10022-9481
Tel (212) 826-2700 *Founded/Ownrshp* 2015
Sales 389.5MM^E *EMP* 3,525
SIC 6211 Investment firm, general brokerage
Pr: Barry Siadat

D-U-N-S 02-748-1258
SK FOOD GROUP INC
(*Suby of* PREMIUM BRANDS HOLDINGS CORPORATION)
4600 37th Ave Sw Ste 300, Seattle, WA 98126-2720
Tel (206) 935-8100 *Founded/Ownrshp* 2010
Sales 319.7MM^E *EMP* 1,000
SIC 2099 Food preparations
Ch: George Paleologou
**Pr:* Stephen Sposari
**CFO:* Laurence Leslie
**VP:* David Meares
VP: Eric Schwartz
**Prin:* Steve Stosari
**VP Sls:* Rick Schultz

D-U-N-S 36-154-8915
■ **SK HOLDING CO INC**
(*Suby of* SAFETY-KLEEN INC) ★
5400 Legacy Dr Cluster Ii, Plano, TX 75024
Tel (972) 265-2000 *Founded/Ownrshp* 2005
Sales 127.6MM^E *EMP* 4,500^E
SIC 6719 Personal holding companies, except banks

D-U-N-S 10-211-4758 IMP
SK HYNIX AMERICA INC
(*Suby of* SK HYNIX INC.)
3101 N 1st St, San Jose, CA 95134-1934
Tel (408) 232-8000 *Founded/Ownrshp* 1983
Sales 460.1MM^E *EMP* 1,192

SIC 5065 5045 Electronic parts & equipment; Semiconductor devices; Computer peripheral equipment
CEO: Kun Chul Suh
**Pr:* Jae H Park
Chf Mktg O: Richard H Chin
VP: Halfred Hofherr
VP: David Yoo
IT Man: C Charles Cho
IT Man: Caroline Chow
VP Mktg: Byung Kim
Sls Dir: Ken Heller
Mktg Mgr: Wonwook Lee
Mktg Mgr: Ben Wu

D-U-N-S 04-111-3403 IMP/EXP
SK LUBRICANTS AMERICAS INC
(*Suby of* SK LUBRICANTS CO., LTD.)
11700 Katy Fwy Ste 900, Houston, TX 77079-1222
Tel (713) 341-5828 *Founded/Ownrshp* 1997
Sales 400.8MM^E *EMP* 18^E
Accts Deloitte & Touche Llp New Yor
SIC 5169 Silicon lubricants
Pr: Tony Jin
**Pr:* Keesu Ryu
Mktg Mgr: Eric Kim

D-U-N-S 04-186-0674
SK TITAN HOLDINGS LLC
(*Suby of* SK CAPITAL PARTNERS II LP) ★
400 Park Ave, New York, NY 10022-4406
Tel (212) 826-2700 *Founded/Ownrshp* 2009
Sales 1.2MMM *EMP* 3,780
SIC 6799 Investors

D-U-N-S 07-104-4069 IMP
SKADDEN ARPS SLATE MEAGHER & FLOM LLP
4 Times Sq Fl 24, New York, NY 10036-6522
Tel (212) 735-3000 *Founded/Ownrshp* 1996
Sales 578.9MM^E *EMP* 3,950
SIC 8111 General practice law office
Pt: Eric J Friedman
**Pt:* Bruce Goldner
**CFO:* Noah Puntus
Top Exec: David Goldman
Ex VP: Jeffrey Mishkin
VP: Don Longo
VP: Janet Mastronardi
**Ex Dir:* Claudia Joyce
Off Admin: Susan Mammele
Dir IT: Steve Alexander
Counsel: Carl Erdmann

SKAGGS COMMUNITY HEALTH CENTER
See SKAGGS COMMUNITY HOSPITAL ASSOCIATION

D-U-N-S 07-625-2857
SKAGGS COMMUNITY HOSPITAL ASSOCIATION
SKAGGS COMMUNITY HEALTH CENTER
251 Skaggs Rd, Branson, MO 65616-2031
Tel (417) 335-7000 *Founded/Ownrshp* 1906
Sales 161.0MM *EMP* 1,076
SIC 8062 8082 8011 7352 8051 General medical & surgical hospitals; Home health care services; Clinic, operated by physicians; Medical equipment rental; Skilled nursing care facilities
Pr: William K Mahoney
**CFO:* David Strong
**Ch:* Jim Kaneaster
**Treas:* Larry Schmitt
Chf Mktg O: Neil Frost
**VP:* Carol Murrow
Exec: Darin Talley
**Prin:* Lynn Allison MD
**Prin:* Michael Elley
Doctor: Narin Arunakul
Nrsg Dir: Sheryl Tilus

D-U-N-S 03-740-8952
SKAGIT COUNTY PUBLIC HOSPITAL DISTRICT 2
ISLAND HOSPITAL
1211 24th St, Anacortes, WA 98221-2562
Tel (360) 299-1300 *Founded/Ownrshp* 1962
Sales 92.4MM *EMP* 695^E
SIC 8062 General medical & surgical hospitals
CEO: Vincent Oliver
**Pr:* Jan Iversen
**CFO:* Elise Cutter
**CFO:* Peter Swanson
Dir Inf Cn: Gary Preston
Dir Lab: Michael Sharp
**Prin:* Cw Buzz Ely
Genl Mgr: Anita McCoy
Off Mgr: Sharon Horak
Cmptr Lab: Joann Fain
IT Man: Tom Bluhm

D-U-N-S 02-728-0619
SKAGIT FARMERS SUPPLY
AFCO DISTRIBUTION
1833 Park Ln, Burlington, WA 98233-4630
Tel (360) 757-6053 *Founded/Ownrshp* 1934
Sales 98.4MM *EMP* 300
Accts Moss Adams Llp Bellingham Wa
SIC 5191 5172 5983 5451 5331 5261 Farm supplies; Gasoline; Crude oil; Fuel oil dealers; Dairy products stores; Variety stores; Nurseries & garden centers
Pr: Ronald Muzzall
**Sec:* Steven Sakuma
**VP:* Richard Williams
Genl Mgr: Brian Duquaine
Genl Mgr: Ken Kadlec

SKAGIT VALLEY HOSPITAL
See PUBLIC HOSPITAL DISTRICT 1 SKAGIT COUNTY

D-U-N-S 96-167-7080
SKANSKA INC
(*Suby of* SKANSKA KRAFT AB)
350 5th Ave Fl 32, New York, NY 10118-3290
Tel (917) 438-4500 *Founded/Ownrshp* 1971
Sales 5.7MMM^E *EMP* 10,000^E
SIC 8741 1542 Construction management; Nonresidential construction
Pr: Richard Cavallaro
**Pr:* Michael McNally
Pr: Jim Turissini
Ofcr: John Coster
Ex VP: Shawn Hurley
Sr VP: Terry Daly
Sr VP: John O'Keefe
VP: Mike Benedetto
VP: Brian Best
VP: Jennifer McMullen
VP: James Robinson
VP: Jeff Rosser
VP: Joe Schneider
VP: John Sullivan
VP: Michael Toth
VP: Robert Walker
Dir Risk M: Tim Klein

D-U-N-S 00-697-8605 IMP
SKANSKA KOCH INC
(*Suby of* SKANSKA USA CIVIL INC) ★
400 Roosevelt Ave, Carteret, NJ 07008-3511
Tel (732) 969-1700 *Founded/Ownrshp* 1989
Sales 211.3MM^E *EMP* 500
SIC 1622 Bridge construction; Highway construction, elevated
Pr: Robert W Koch Jr
**Sec:* Stephen Hughes
**Ex VP:* Steven Koch
Sr VP: Mike Attardo
Sr VP: James M Becker
Sr VP: Dan Hoefling
Sr VP: Allen Jones
Sr VP: Ivette Vanas
VP: Steve Clem
VP: Tony Colonna
**VP:* Terry Daly
VP: Daniel Maldonado
VP: Marty Massey
**VP:* Thomas Sutton
Exec: Philip Carter
Exec: Blake Devine
Dir Risk M: Wendy Harris
Dir Bus: Steven Agor
Dir Bus: Cesar Souza

D-U-N-S 07-836-9326
SKANSKA US CIVIL MIDWEST INC
(*Suby of* SKANSKA USA CIVIL INC) ★
401 Nw 1st St, Evansville, IN 47708-1001
Tel (812) 423-7832 *Founded/Ownrshp* 2011, 2009
Sales 222.4MM^E *EMP* 2,400^E
SIC 1611 Highway & street construction; Concrete construction: roads, highways, sidewalks, etc.
Ex VP: Denny Quinn

D-U-N-S 01-427-5114 IMP
SKANSKA USA BUILDING INC
(*Suby of* SKANSKA USA INC) ★
389 Interpace Pkwy Ste 5, Parsippany, NJ 07054-1132
Tel (973) 753-3500 *Founded/Ownrshp* 2000
Sales 3.4MMM^E *EMP* 4,100
Accts Kpmg Llp New York Ny
SIC 1541 1542 8741 Industrial buildings & warehouses; Nonresidential construction; Management services
CEO: Michael McNally
**Pr:* Bill Flemming
**Pr:* Karl H Reichelt
CFO: Ron Oakley
**CFO:* Leo Sinicin
CFO: Rick Smith
Bd of Dir: Ronnie Campbell
**Ex VP:* Johan Karlstrom
Ex VP: Michael Leondi
Ex VP: Jim Link
Ex VP: Catherine Pfeiffenberger
Ex VP: K Reichelt
Ex VP: Chris Toher
Ex VP: Ross Vroman
Ex VP: Andrew Whiteley
Sr VP: Ronald Joneshas
VP: Wael Allan
VP: Brian Best
VP: Matt Damborsky
VP: Matt Daniel
VP: Steve Eustis

D-U-N-S 12-422-7443
SKANSKA USA CIVIL INC
(*Suby of* SKANSKA USA INC) ★
7520 Astoria Blvd Ste 200, East Elmhurst, NY 11370-1135
Tel (718) 340-0777 *Founded/Ownrshp* 2002
Sales 1.8MMM^E *EMP* 5,200^E
Accts Kpmg Llp New York Ny
SIC 1611 Highway & street construction
Pr: Salvatore Mancini
CFO: Hans Andersson
CFO: Conny Ek
Treas: David Rosenbaum
Ex VP: Alan Gillman
Sr VP: Tor Krusell
VP: David J Eastwood
VP: Peter Gimbe

D-U-N-S 01-243-5913 IMP/EXP
SKANSKA USA CIVIL NORTHEAST INC (NY)
(*Suby of* SKANSKA USA CIVIL INC) ★
7520 Astoria Blvd Ste 200, East Elmhurst, NY 11370-1135
Tel (718) 340-0811 *Founded/Ownrshp* 1958, 1989
Sales 526.4MM^E *EMP* 1,500
SIC 1622 Bridge construction; Tunnel construction
Ch Bd: Michael Viggiano
**CEO:* Michael Cobelli
**Sr VP:* Ralph Russo
Genl Mgr: Robert W Koch Jr
Genl Mgr: Micheal Lembo
Genl Mgr: Peter E Mackenna
MIS Dir: Scott Silverman

D-U-N-S 00-794-1958
SKANSKA USA CIVIL SOUTHEAST INC (VA)
(*Suby of* SKANSKA USA CIVIL INC) ★
295 Bendix Rd Ste 400, Virginia Beach, VA 23452-1295
Tel (757) 420-4140 *Founded/Ownrshp* 1932, 2006
Sales 394.0MM *EMP* 750
SIC 1622 1629 3272 1541 Bridge construction; Marine construction; Prestressed concrete products; Industrial buildings, new construction
Ex VP: Sal Taddeo
**CFO:* Kenneth J Johnson
**Sr VP:* Robert J Rose
**VP:* James P Goyer
VP: John Gray
**VP:* Wade H Watson
IT Man: Dan Frye
Board of Directors: Richard Cavallaro, Mike Cobelli, Peter Mac Kenna, Sal Taddeo

D-U-N-S 00-831-8503
SKANSKA USA CIVIL WEST CALIFORNIA DISTRICT INC
(*Suby of* SKANSKA USA CIVIL INC) ★
1995 Agua Mansa Rd, Riverside, CA 92509-2405
Tel (951) 684-5360 *Founded/Ownrshp* 1919
Sales 356.9MM^E *EMP* 900
SIC 1611 1622 1629 8711 2951 General contractor, highway & street construction; Bridge construction; Highway construction, elevated; Dam construction; Engineering services; Asphalt paving mixtures & blocks
CEO: Richard Cavallero
**COO:* Michael Cobelli
**CFO:* Joseph Nogues
**Ex VP:* Michael Aparicio
Ex VP: Lisa Picard
Ex VP: Chris Toher
Ex VP: Ross Vroman
Ex VP: Robert Ward
Sr VP: Thomas Henriksson
Sr VP: Mark Howell
Sr VP: Daniel Kolakowski
Sr VP: James Link
Sr VP: Randy McNeely
Sr VP: Catherine Pfeiffenberger
Sr VP: Andrew Quirk
VP: Pete Devoney
VP: Kayle Gastley
VP: Dan Howell
VP: Jeff Lage
VP: Eric Temp
Comm Man: Mary Humphreys

D-U-N-S 09-239-9013 IMP/EXP
SKANSKA USA INC
(*Suby of* SKANSKA INC) ★
350 5th Ave Fl 32, New York, NY 10118-3290
Tel (917) 438-4500 *Founded/Ownrshp* 1971
Sales 5.7MMM^E *EMP* 7,500
Accts Kpmg Llp New York Ny
SIC 8741 1542 Construction management; Nonresidential construction
Pr: Michael McNally
**Pr:* Bill Flemming
Pr: Richard Kennedy
**CEO:* Michael F McNally
**CFO:* Conny Ek
Treas: Carrie Key
**Treas:* Barry Ross
Co-COO: Scott Macleod
Ex VP: Kerim Evin
**Ex VP:* Karl H Reichelt
VP: John Coster
VP: James Melvin
VP: David Murawski
VP: Joe Palermo

SKAPS INDUSTRIES
See PBR INC

D-U-N-S 08-850-7173 IMP/EXP
SKB CORP
434 W Levers Pl, Orange, CA 92867-3605
Tel (714) 637-1252 *Founded/Ownrshp* 1975
Sales 89.8MM^E *EMP* 370
SIC 3089 3161 Cases, plastic; Luggage
CEO: Steven A Kottman
**VP:* David Sanderson
Exec: Glen Barney
Exec: Juana Hernandez
Creative D: Brian Torres
**VP Mfg:* Don Weber
Plnt Mgr: Robert Welks
Sls Dir: Ray Ellis
Sls Mgr: David Vie

D-U-N-S 07-083-8268
SKBHC HOLDINGS LLC
8723 E Via De Commercio, Scottsdale, AZ 85258-3588
Tel (480) 393-0562 *Founded/Ownrshp* 2009
Sales NA *EMP* 1,583^E
SIC 6712

D-U-N-S 15-044-0790 IMP
SKC COMMUNICATION PRODUCTS LLC
8320 Hedge Lane Ter, Shawnee Mission, KS 66227-3543
Tel (913) 422-4222 *Founded/Ownrshp* 1982
Sales 112.0MM *EMP* 216
SIC 5065 5999 Communication equipment; Communication equipment
CEO: Tray Vedock
**CFO:* Jennifer Lowe
**VP:* Jill Phillips
CIO: Darin Worthington
**CTO:* Jeff Holton
Sls Dir: John Chandler
Sls Dir: Kim Speckin
Mktg Mgr: Emily Dack
Mktg Mgr: Lacy Fox
Sls Mgr: Terry Sowers

D-U-N-S 79-054-5016
▲ SKECHERS USA INC
228 Manhattan Beach Blvd # 200, Manhattan Beach, CA 90266-5356
Tel (310) 318-3100 *Founded/Ownrshp* 1992
Sales 3.1MMM *EMP* 9,200
Accts Bdo Usa Llp Los Angeles Ca
Tkr Sym SKX *Exch* NYS
SIC 3021 3149 Rubber & plastics footwear; Shoes, rubber or plastic molded to fabric; Athletic shoes, except rubber or plastic
Ch Bd: Robert Greenberg
**Pr:* Michael Greenberg
COO: Gary Stern
**COO:* David Weinberg
Ex VP: Mark Nason
Ex VP: Philip Paccione
**Sr VP:* Jeffrey Greenberg
VP: Jennifer Clay
VP: Lynda Cumming
VP: Lynda Cummings
VP: Gary Patrick
VP: Marc Rooney
VP: Marc Rosko
VP: Kurt Stockbridge
Board of Directors: Morton Erlich, Richard Rappaport, Richard Siskind, Thomas Walsh

D-U-N-S 02-516-9475
SKENDER CONSTRUCTION CO
200 W Madison St Ste 1300, Chicago, IL 60606-3454
Tel (312) 781-0265 *Founded/Ownrshp* 1955
Sales 171.0MM^E *EMP* 100
SIC 1542

SKF AEROENGINE NORTH AMERICA
See MRC BEARINGS INC

SKF MOTION TECHNOLOGIES
See SKF USA INC

D-U-N-S 00-229-7661 IMP/EXP
SKF USA INC
SKF MOTION TECHNOLOGIES
(*Suby of* AB SKF)
890 Forty Foot Rd, Lansdale, PA 19446-4303
Tel (267) 436-6000 *Founded/Ownrshp* 1907, 1933
Sales 2.7MMM *EMP* 4,020
SIC 3562 3053 3829 Ball & roller bearings; Ball bearings & parts; Roller bearings & parts; Gaskets & sealing devices; Oil seals, rubber; Vibration meters, analyzers & calibrators
CFO: Drew Cross
**Pr:* John Schmidt
CFO: Carlos Johansson
Treas: Brian J Duffy
**Treas:* Terry Papincak
VP: Mike Riley
VP: Denise Scheib
VP: Otto Wieber
Mng Dir: Valeriy Konev
Area Mgr: Henrik Fritsche
Genl Mgr: Scott Brady

D-U-N-S 01-434-3313 IMP
SKH MANAGEMENT CO (PA)
S K H WHOLESALE DISTRIBUTORS
813 Lititz Pike, Lititz, PA 17543-8629
Tel (717) 627-0090 *Founded/Ownrshp* 1959, 1932
Sales 309.0MM^E *EMP* 850
SIC 5141 5092 5261 5411 Groceries, general line; Hobby goods; Nurseries & garden centers; Grocery stores
VP: Jere M Stauffer
**Treas:* Donovan S Oberholtzer
Genl Mgr: Jodie Morris
IT Man: Brian Davidson
Mktg Dir: Debi Drescher

D-U-N-S 02-067-0741
SKIDMORE COLLEGE
815 N Broadway, Saratoga Springs, NY 12866-1698
Tel (518) 580-5000 *Founded/Ownrshp* 1903
Sales 146.9MM *EMP* 720
Accts Uhy Llp Albany New York
SIC 8221 College, except junior
Pr: Philip A Glotzbach
Treas: Steve Otrembiak
Trst: Rosemary Bourne
Trst: John Morris
Trst: Oscar Tang
VP: Barbara E Beck
VP: Luca Mobilia
VP: Joseph Stankovich
VP: Michael D West
Assoc Dir: Beth Brucker-Kane
Assoc Dir: Lisa Rinaolo
Assoc Dir: Barbara Schallehn

D-U-N-S 04-194-1881
SKIDMORE OWINGS & MERRILL LLP
224 S Michigan Ave # 1000, Chicago, IL 60604-2526
Tel (312) 554-9090 *Founded/Ownrshp* 1969
Sales 124.2MM^E *EMP* 724
Accts Fgmk Llc Bannockburn Illino
SIC 8712 Architectural engineering
Mng Pt: Gene Schnair
Pt: Gary Haney
Pt: Jeffrey McCarthy
Mng Pt: Tj Gottesdiener
Mng Pt: Peter Magill
Ofcr: Latyce Earles
Ex VP: Charles Besjak
Assoc Dir: Edward Guerra
Assoc Dir: Eric D Long
Assoc Dir: Dane Rankin
Assoc Dir: Yue Zhu

D-U-N-S 01-768-3194 IMP/EXP
SKIDMORE SALES & DISTRIBUTING CO INC (OH)
9889 Cincinnati Dayton Rd, West Chester, OH 45069-3825
Tel (513) 755-4200 *Founded/Ownrshp* 1963
Sales 146.5MM^E *EMP* 68
SIC 5149 5169 Groceries & related products; Chemicals & allied products
Ch: Gerald Skidmore
**Pr:* Jim McCarthy
**CEO:* Douglas S Skidmore
**CFO:* Steppi Frey
**VP:* Mark Overbeck
**VP Sls:* Steve Jackson
Board of Directors: William W Victor, L D Williams

SKILLED CARE
See JORDAN HEALTHCARE HOLDINGS INC

D-U-N-S 05-076-6781
SKILLED CARE PHARMACY INC
6175 Hi Tek Ct, Mason, OH 45040-2603
Tel (513) 459-7626 *Founded/Ownrshp* 1981
Sales 117.8MM^E *EMP* 220

Section I
Businesses Alphabetically

SIC 5122 Drugs, proprietaries & sundries
CEO: Larry Galluzzo Rph
CFO: Chris Kuczek
CFO: Christopher S Kuczek
VP: Bill Bauza
VP: Joe Cesta
VP: Nancy Mlinarik
Dir Rx: Angela Sazraves
Ex Dir: Sandra McLellan
Ex Dir: Marilyn Rumbin
Dir IT: Garry Kelly
Trfc Dir: Anthony Ponikvar

D-U-N-S 06-280-3184
■ SKILLED HEALTHCARE LLC
(*Suby of* GENESIS HEALTHCARE LLC) ★
27442 Portola Pkwy # 200, Foothill Ranch, CA 92610-2822
Tel (949) 282-5800 *Founded/Ownrshp* 2015
Sales 111.7MM^E *EMP* 345^E
SIC 8051 6513 5122 Skilled nursing care facilities; Retirement hotel operation; Drugs, proprietaries & sundries
COO: Laurie Thomas
Ofcr: Alan Crommett
Ex VP: Roland Rapp
Sr VP: Carl Sebern
Sr VP: James Sims
VP: Huong Dang
**VP:* Richard Edwards
VP: Brad Gibson
VP: Kristiina Hintgen
Exec: Michele Kaufman
VP Opers: Amanda Burnett

D-U-N-S 01-149-6069
SKILLSOFT CORP
(*Suby of* SKILLSOFT LIMITED)
107 Northeastern Blvd, Nashua, NH 03062-1916
Tel (603) 821-3715 *Founded/Ownrshp* 1997
Sales 687.2MM^E *EMP* 2,133
Accts Ernst & Young Llp Boston Mas
SIC 7372 Educational computer software
Ch Bd: Charles E Moran
**COO:* Jerald A Nine Jr
COO: Jerry Nine
**CFO:* Thomas J McDonald
CFO: Tom McDonald
**Chf Mktg O:* Heather Loisel
**Ex VP:* Colm M Darcy
**Ex VP:* Mark A Townsend
Sr VP: John Ambrose
VP: Michael Bacher
VP: Chris Cohen
VP: Jerry Gatlin
VP: Julie Hall
VP: Gina Knollenberg
VP: Nute Laura
VP: Robin Lawrence
VP: Kate McCarthy
VP: Roger Mortimer
VP: George Neuss
VP: Donna Shiel
VP: Kerry Smith
Board of Directors: William J Boyce, P Howard Edelstein, Stewart K P Gross, James S Krzywicki, William F Meagher Jr, Ferdinand Von Prondzynski

D-U-N-S 13-117-1522
SKILSTAF INC
860 Airport Dr, Alexander City, AL 35010-3453
Tel (256) 234-6208 *Founded/Ownrshp* 1984
Sales 46.8MM^E *EMP* 5,000
Accts Don Thornell Cpa Inc Alaba
SIC 7363 Employee leasing service
Pr: Wayne Stark

SKITCH
See EVERNOTE CORP

D-U-N-S 04-160-3674 IMP
SKJODT-BARRETT CONTRACT PACKAGING LLC
401 S Enterprise Blvd, Lebanon, IN 46052-8888
Tel (765) 482-6856 *Founded/Ownrshp* 2011
Sales 100.0MM^E *EMP* 300
SIC 2099 Food preparations
Pr: Dan Skjodt

D-U-N-S 82-843-3826
SKO GROUP HOLDING LLC
8800 F St, Omaha, NE 68127-1507
Tel (920) 429-2211 *Founded/Ownrshp* 2005
Sales 326.2MM^E *EMP* 7,500^E
SIC 6719 Personal holding companies, except banks

D-U-N-S 04-265-7247
SKOGENS FOODLINER INC (WI)
IGA
3800 Emerald Dr E, Onalaska, WI 54650-2796
Tel (608) 783-5500 *Founded/Ownrshp* 1946, 1976
Sales 47.1MM^E *EMP* 5,000
SIC 5411 5461 5421 Supermarkets, chain; Grocery stores, independent; Bakeries; Meat markets, including freezer provisioners
Pr: David R Skogen
**VP:* Barbara Skogen
Dir Risk M: Brian Witt

D-U-N-S 07-689-1688 IMP
SKOKIE HOSPITAL
(*Suby of* EVANSTON HOSPITAL) ★
9600 Gross Point Rd, Skokie, IL 60076-1214
Tel (847) 677-9600 *Founded/Ownrshp* 2009
Sales 154.5MM *EMP* 1,400
SIC 8062 General medical & surgical hospitals
VP: Kerry Kerlin
Chf Rad: Robert R Edelman
V Ch: Leonard Berlin
COO: JP Gallagher
VP: Rich Casey
VP: Mary Keegan
Dir Lab: Margaret Langguth
Dir Rx: Carol Heunisch
Prgrm Mgr: Pam Ball
Surgeon: Jonathan Somers
Doctor: Ira A Oliff

SKOOKUM CONTRACT SERVICES
See SKOOKUM EDUCATIONAL PROGRAMS INC

D-U-N-S 79-178-0778
SKOOKUM EDUCATIONAL PROGRAMS INC
SKOOKUM CONTRACT SERVICES
4525 Auto Center Way, Bremerton, WA 98312-4312
Tel (360) 475-0756 *Founded/Ownrshp* 1988
Sales 91.7MM *EMP* 560
SIC 8744

D-U-N-S 13-961-5970
SKULLCANDY INC
1441 Ute Blvd Ste 250, Park City, UT 84098-7632
Tel (435) 940-1545 *Founded/Ownrshp* 2003
Sales 266.3MM *EMP* 300^E
SIC 3679 Headphones, radio
CEO: Jason Hodell
**Ch Bd:* Doug Collier
Chf Cred: Sam Paschel Jr
VP: Ron Ross
VP: Richard Sargente
Dir Risk M: David Raffone
Mktg Mgr: Eli Seddon
Genl Couns: Mitchell Edwards
Board of Directors: Rick Alden, Jeff Kearl, Heidi O'neill, Scott Olivet, Greg Warnock

D-U-N-S 82-906-6369
SKY ACQUISITION LLC
345 Park Ave, New York, NY 10154-0004
Tel (212) 583-5000 *Founded/Ownrshp* 1991
Sales 2.4MMM^E *EMP* 14,300^E
SIC 6799 Investors

D-U-N-S 00-699-0402 IMP
SKY CHEFS INC
LSG SKY CHEFS
(*Suby of* S C INTERNATIONAL SERVICES INC) ★
6191 N State Highway 161 # 100, Irving, TX 75038-2290
Tel (972) 793-9000 *Founded/Ownrshp* 1941, 1986
Sales 408.5MM^E *EMP* 7,100
SIC 5812 Caterers; Concessionaire; Coffee shop
Pr: Walter Gehl
**Pr:* Sondra Lehman
**CFO:* Arnd Schwierholz
**Sr VP:* Patrick Berkelbaugh
**Sr VP:* Chris Burt
**Sr VP:* Dale Easdon
**VP:* Thomas Berti
**VP:* Michael Mueller
Exec: Daniel M Klein
Exec: Isabelle Zeitz

D-U-N-S 05-096-3727 IMP
SKY LAKES MEDICAL CENTER FOUNDATION INC
2865 Daggett Ave, Klamath Falls, OR 97601-1106
Tel (541) 882-6311 *Founded/Ownrshp* 1986
Sales 2.2MM *EMP* 1,100
Accts Moss Adams Llp Portland Or
SIC 8062 General medical & surgical hospitals
Pr: Paul Stewart
Dir Rx: Todd Montgomery
Off Mgr: Vicki Collier
Ansthlgy: John Pattee
Doctor: Edward Vantassel

D-U-N-S 82-816-6962
SKYBRIDGE AMERICAS INC
SKYBRIDGE MARKETING GROUP
7600 69th Ave, Rockford, MN 55373-5400
Tel (763) 477-7600 *Founded/Ownrshp* 1953
Sales 98.4MM^E *EMP* 980
SIC 8742 Marketing consulting services
CEO: Kevin Cattoor
COO: Jeannine Peterson
Ofcr: Debi Steinkraus
Ex VP: Ron Schleper
Ex VP: Macy Seymour
VP: Robert Borman
VP: John Turner
CTO: Bruce Whitmore
Dir IT: Jim Aulick

SKYBRIDGE MARKETING GROUP
See SKYBRIDGE AMERICAS INC

SKYLAKES MEDICAL CENTER
See KLAMATH FALLS INTERCOMMUNITY HOSPITAL AUTHORITY

SKYLANE FARMS
See VALLEY FRESH FOODS INC

D-U-N-S 06-415-5773
■ SKYLAWN
CHAPEL OF CHIMES
(*Suby of* CAPITAL SOUTHWEST CORPORATION)
32992 Mission Blvd, Hayward, CA 94544-8257
Tel (510) 471-3363 *Founded/Ownrshp* 1969
Sales 125.1MM^E *EMP* 205
SIC 6553 7261 Mausoleum operation; Funeral service & crematories; Crematory
Pr: Andy Bryant

SKYLINE CHILI
See CAROCO INC

D-U-N-S 00-447-4870
SKYLINE CHILI INC (OH)
4180 Thunderbird Ln, Fairfield, OH 45014-2235
Tel (513) 874-1188 *Founded/Ownrshp* 1949
Sales 46.4MM^E *EMP* 1,000^E
SIC 5812 2038 6794 5149 2032 Restaurant, family: chain; Frozen specialties; Franchises, selling or licensing; Groceries & related products; Dried or canned foods; Canned goods: fruit, vegetables, seafood, meats, etc.; Canned specialties
Pr: Kevin R Mc Donnell
Sr VP: Philip M Lewis
VP: Kenneth E Davis
VP: Charles L Harnist
VP: Jim Konves
VP: Jim H Konves
VP Sls: Tom Allen
S&M/VP: Susan Fongheises
Mktg Mgr: Sarah Lapham
Board of Directors: Charles Schnatter, Ray Biondi Januarius Stal

D-U-N-S 96-477-8187
SKYLINE COMMERCIAL INTERIORS INC
SKYLINE CONSTRUCTION
731 Sansome St Fl 4, San Francisco, CA 94111-1723
Tel (415) 908-1020 *Founded/Ownrshp* 1996
Sales 136.0MM *EMP* 80^E
Accts Rina Accountancy Corporation
SIC 1542 Commercial & office buildings, renovation & repair
CEO: David Hayes
**Pr:* Rick Millitello
VP: Howard Fish
Mktg Mgr: Ali Bedwell
Snr PM: Jessica Callahan
Snr PM: Adam Chelini
Snr PM: Mike Higashi

SKYLINE CONSTRUCTION
See SKYLINE COMMERCIAL INTERIORS INC

D-U-N-S 00-507-0669
▲ SKYLINE CORP
2520 Bypass Rd, Elkhart, IN 46514-1584
Tel (574) 294-6521 *Founded/Ownrshp* 1951
Sales 211.7MM *EMP* 1,200^E
Tkr Sym SKY *Exch* ASE
SIC 2451 2452 3792 Mobile homes; Mobile homes, except recreational; Prefabricated buildings, wood; Travel trailers & campers
Pr: Richard W Florea
**Ch Bd:* John C Firth
CFO: Jon S Pilarski
Sr VP: Jeffrey A Newport
VP: Robert C Davis
CIO: Steven Katz
VP Mktg: Terrence M Decio
Board of Directors: Arthur J Decio, Jerry Hammes, William H Lawson, David T Link, Samuel S Thompson

D-U-N-S 00-538-9596
SKYLINE EXHIBITS INLAND NW INC
SKYLINE INLAND NORTHWEST
10102 E Knox Ave Ste 450, Spokane Valley, WA 99206-4124
Tel (509) 892-5354 *Founded/Ownrshp* 2006
Sales 39.4MM^E *EMP* 1,500
SIC 7389 Design services
Pr: Jeff Backstrom
Exec: David Byram
Exec: Louis Gonzalez

D-U-N-S 12-619-5205
■ SKYLINE HOMES INC
(*Suby of* SKYLINE CORP) ★
2520 Bypass Rd, Elkhart, IN 46514-1584
Tel (574) 294-6521 *Founded/Ownrshp* 1960
Sales 194.1MM^E *EMP* 1,100^E
SIC 2451 3792 Mobile homes; Travel trailers & campers; Travel trailer chassis
CFO: Jon Pilarski
VP: Tom McGillicuddy

SKYLINE INLAND NORTHWEST
See SKYLINE EXHIBITS INLAND NW INC

SKYLINE MAINSFIELD
See HOMETTE CORP

D-U-N-S 05-244-9576 IMP/EXP
■ SKYLINE STEEL LLC
(*Suby of* NUCOR CORP) ★
8 Woodhollow Rd Ste 102, Parsippany, NJ 07054-2829
Tel (973) 428-6100 *Founded/Ownrshp* 2012
Sales 110.3MM^E *EMP* 450^E
SIC 3317 5051

SKYRIDGE MEDICAL CENTER
See NATIONAL HEALTHCARE OF CLEVELAND INC

D-U-N-S 96-543-4819 IMP
SKYROCKET TOYS LLC
12910 Culver Blvd Ste F, Los Angeles, CA 90066-6729
Tel (310) 822-6155 *Founded/Ownrshp* 2010
Sales 103.2MM *EMP* 15
SIC 5945 Toys & games
Ex VP: Sherry Perry

SKYTEL
See VELOCITA WIRELESS LLC

D-U-N-S 18-758-7910 IMP
■ SKYWEST AIRLINES INC
(*Suby of* SKYWEST INC) ★
444 S River Rd, St George, UT 84790-2095
Tel (435) 634-3000 *Founded/Ownrshp* 1985
Sales 1.3MMM^E *EMP* 11,000
SIC 4512 Air passenger carrier, scheduled
Ch Bd: Jerry C Atkin
**Pr:* Russell A Childs
COO: Ron B Reer
**Treas:* Michael J Kraupp
Bd of Dir: Peg Billson
Bd of Dir: James L Welch
VP: Klen P Brooks
VP: Tracy Gallo
**VP:* Jim Jensen
VP: Bill N Mihu
VP: Sonya Wolford
**VP:* Eric Woodward
Board of Directors: Steve Albrecht, Ronald J Mittelstaedt, Robert G Sarver, Keith E Smith, James L Welch

D-U-N-S 06-797-3032
▲ SKYWEST INC
444 S River Rd, St George, UT 84790-2085
Tel (435) 634-3000 *Founded/Ownrshp* 1972
Sales 3.1MMM *EMP* 18,300^E
Tkr Sym SKYW *Exch* NGS
SIC 4512 Air transportation, scheduled
Pr: Russell A Childs
**Ch Bd:* Jerry C Atkin
COO: Terry Vais
CFO: Robert J Simmons
Chf Cred: Wade J Steel
Sftwr Eng: Casey Miller
Sftwr Eng: Allan Stevens
Board of Directors: W Steve Albrecht, Henry J Eyring, Steven F Udvar-Hazy, Meredith S Madden, Ronald J Mittelstaedt, Andrew C Roberts, Keith E Smith, James L Welch

D-U-N-S 00-103-0311
▲ SKYWORKS SOLUTIONS INC
20 Sylvan Rd, Woburn, MA 01801-1885
Tel (781) 376-3000 *Founded/Ownrshp* 1962
Sales 3.2MMM *EMP* 6,700
Accts Kpmg Llp Boston Massachusett
Tkr Sym SWKS *Exch* NGS
SIC 3674 Semiconductors & related devices
CEO: Liam K Griffin
CFO: Donald W Palette
CFO: Kris Sennesael
Ex VP: Bruce J Freyman
VP: Mitchell J Haws
VP: Nien-Tsu Shen
VP: Mark V B Tremallo
Plng Mgr: Bill Naille
CTO: Peter L Gammel
IT Man: Jorge Seldner
IT Man: Jerry Urdiales
Board of Directors: Kevin L Beebe, Timothy R Furey, Christine King, David P McGlade, David J McLachlan, Robert A Schriesheim

D-U-N-S 15-310-0511 IMP
SL ALABAMA LLC
(*Suby of* SL CORPORATION)
2481 Airport Blvd, Alexander City, AL 35010-3331
Tel (256) 397-8140 *Founded/Ownrshp* 2003
Sales 238.8MM *EMP* 400
SIC 3714 Motor vehicle parts & accessories
Prd Mgr: Bill Smith
Ql Cn Mgr: Brian Jeong

D-U-N-S 79-991-3939 IMP
SL AMERICA CORP
SL TENNESSEE
(*Suby of* SL CORPORATION)
312 Frank L Diggs Dr, Clinton, TN 37716-6956
Tel (865) 457-8511 *Founded/Ownrshp* 2000
Sales 355.5MM *EMP* 2,094
Accts Warren Averett Llc Montgomer
SIC 3714 Motor vehicle parts & accessories
Pr: C W Kim
Off Mgr: Erin Perrault
Opers Mgr: C P Smalling
Ql Cn Mgr: Al Daugherty
Ql Cn Mgr: Prasanna RAO

D-U-N-S 78-426-1021
SL GREEN OPERATING PARTNERSHIP LP
420 Lexington Ave Rm 1800, New York, NY 10170-1899
Tel (212) 594-2700 *Founded/Ownrshp* 1997
Sales 1.6MMM *EMP* 1,060
SIC 6798 Real estate investment trusts
CEO: Marc Holliday
Genl Pt: SL Green Realty Corp
Pr: Andrew W Mathias

D-U-N-S 01-127-1512
▲ SL GREEN REALTY CORP
420 Lexington Ave Rm 1824, New York, NY 10170-1881
Tel (212) 594-2700 *Founded/Ownrshp* 1997
Sales 1.6MMM *EMP* 1,177
Tkr Sym SLG *Exch* NYS
SIC 6798 Real estate investment trusts
CEO: Marc Holliday
**Ch Bd:* Stephen L Green
V Ch: Shelby Snodgrass
**Pr:* Andrew W Mathias
CFO: Matthew J Diliberto
Sr VP: Robert Dewitt
VP: Raymond Benemerito
VP: Young Hahn
VP: Courtney Haydon
VP: Tony Mastrolia
Genl Couns: Jeffrey Steiner
Board of Directors: John H Alschuler Jr, Betsy Atkins, Edward Thomas Burton III, Lauren Dillard, Craig M Hatkoff, John S Levy

D-U-N-S 00-234-4083 IMP
■ SL INDUSTRIES INC
(*Suby of* HANDY & HARMAN GROUP LTD) ★
520 Fellowship Rd A114, Mount Laurel, NJ 08054-3425
Tel (856) 727-1500 *Founded/Ownrshp* 1956, 2016
Sales 199.8MM *EMP* 1,400^E
SIC 3679 3643 Power supplies, all types: static; Electric connectors
Pr: William Fejes Jr
CFO: Louis Belardi
Ql Cn Mgr: Ron Strauss

D-U-N-S 09-703-4714 IMP/EXP
■ SL POWER ELECTRONICS CORP
(*Suby of* SL INDUSTRIES INC) ★
6050 King Dr Ste A, Ventura, CA 93003-7176
Tel (805) 228-3400 *Founded/Ownrshp* 1993
Sales 96.6MM^E *EMP* 677
SIC 3679 Power supplies, all types: static
Pr: Jim Taylor
**CEO:* Ken Owens
**VP:* Steven Miller
VP: Jim Morrissey
Genl Mgr: Patrick Crawford
QA Dir: Manuel Soriano
IT Man: Jim Hamblin
Plnt Mgr: Jose Casanova
Manager: Jay Johnson
Sales Asso: Pattie Schlesinger

SL TENNESSEE
See SL AMERICA CORP

D-U-N-S 83-004-9271 IMP
SL TENNESSEE LLC
(*Suby of* SL TENNESSEE) ★
312 Frank Diggs Dr, Clinton, TN 37716
Tel (865) 457-8511 *Founded/Ownrshp* 2003
Sales 211.2MM *EMP* 1,300
SIC 3714 Motor vehicle parts & accessories
Pr: C W Kim
Sls Mgr: Steven Brooks

D-U-N-S 07-648-4112
■ **SL-MONTEVIDEO TECHNOLOGY INC**
SL-MTI
(*Suby of* SL INDUSTRIES INC) ★
2002 Black Oak Ave, Montevideo, MN 56265-2400
Tel (320) 269-5583 *Founded/Ownrshp* 1985
Sales 179.4MM^E *EMP* 1,257
SIC 3625 Motor controls & accessories
Pr: Thomas Lemley
**VP:* Dave Scott
Genl Mgr: Neal Carstensen
Info Man: Jackie Lindvall
Ql Cn Mgr: Rene Garcia
Sls Dir: Dale Spaeth
Sls Mgr: Dennis Daisy

SL-MTI
See SL-MONTEVIDEO TECHNOLOGY INC

SLAIT CONSULTING
See SLAIT PARTNERS INC

D-U-N-S 79-347-3625
SLAIT PARTNERS INC
SLAIT CONSULTING
100 Landmark Sq, Virginia Beach, VA 23452-6822
Tel (757) 313-6500 *Founded/Ownrshp* 2005
Sales 432.1MM^E *EMP* 375
SIC 5045 3571 8748 7373 Computers, peripherals & software; Electronic computers; Business consulting; Computer integrated systems design
CEO: Casey F Robinson
**Pr:* Denise M Robinson

D-U-N-S 00-691-1119 IMP/EXP
SLAKEY BROTHERS INC
2215 Kausen Dr Ste 1, Elk Grove, CA 95758-7172
Tel (916) 478-2000 *Founded/Ownrshp* 1939
Sales 162.8MM^E *EMP* 500
SIC 5075 5074 5078

D-U-N-S 80-916-5145
SLALOM LLC
TWO DEGREES
821 2nd Ave Ste 1900, Seattle, WA 98104-1526
Tel (206) 374-4200 *Founded/Ownrshp* 1993
Sales 710.0MM^E *EMP* 4,000^E
SIC 8742 7373 Accounting, auditing & bookkeeping; Management consulting services
**Pr:* Anthony Rojas
VP: Jeff Slalom
Dir Bus: Haywood Eric
Dir Bus: Eric Haywood
Dir Bus: Colin Weeks
Mng Dir: Patty Brown
Mng Dir: Jeff Dillenburg
Mng Dir: George Ghali
Mng Dir: Jila Javdani
Mng Dir: Kory Kimball
Mng Dir: Alex Nelson

D-U-N-S 00-149-5134 IMP
SLANT/FIN CORP (NY)
100 Forest Dr, Greenvale, NY 11548-1295
Tel (516) 484-2600 *Founded/Ownrshp* 1949
Sales 102.8MM^E *EMP* 450
SIC 3433 3443 Heating equipment, except electric; Fabricated plate work (boiler shop)
Ch Bd: Melvin Dubin
**CFO:* Donald Brown
**Ch:* Adam Dubin
Plnt Mgr: Gary Golden
Plnt Mgr: Neil Segal

D-U-N-S 62-662-0897
SLAP SHOT HOLDINGS CORP
SPORTS AUTHORITY
(*Suby of* GREEN EQUITY INVESTORS IV LP) ★
11111 Santa Monica Blvd, Los Angeles, CA 90025-3333
Tel (310) 954-0444 *Founded/Ownrshp* 2006
Sales 2.9MMM^E *EMP* 15,000^E
SIC 5941 Sporting goods & bicycle shops
CEO: Michael E Foss
**Prin:* Jonathan D Sokoloff

SLASHPOINT SHARE DRIVE
See XMULTIPLE TECHNOLOGIES INC

D-U-N-S 07-945-9695
SLATE CREEK WIND PROJECT LLC
15445 Innovation Dr, San Diego, CA 92128-3432
Tel (888) 903-6926 *Founded/Ownrshp* 2013
Sales 351.8MM^E *EMP* 826
SIC 4911 Electric services
Pr: Tristan Grimbert
Treas: Kara Vongphakdy
VP: Ryan Pfaff

D-U-N-S 00-523-2743
SLATE PHARMACEUTICALS INC
1400 Atwater Dr, Malvern, PA 19355-8701
Tel (484) 321-5900 *Founded/Ownrshp* 2007
Sales 400.0MM *EMP* 65
SIC 2834 Pharmaceutical preparations
Prin: Bob Whitehead
**CFO:* Matt Tetzold

SLAY INDUSTRIES
See J S LEASING CO INC

D-U-N-S 00-985-5826 IMP
SLAY TRANSPORTATION CO INC (MO)
(*Suby of* SLAY INDUSTRIES) ★
1441 Hampton Ave, Saint Louis, MO 63139-3115
Tel (314) 647-7529 *Founded/Ownrshp* 1953, 1920
Sales 110.2MM^E *EMP* 400
SIC 4213 Trucking, except local
Pr: Gary Slay
Opers Mgr: Mark Wilcox

D-U-N-S 18-973-9464
SLAYDEN CONSTRUCTION GROUP INC
500 Willamette Ave, Stayton, OR 97383-9420
Tel (503) 769-1969 *Founded/Ownrshp* 1984
Sales 92.5MM^E *EMP* 125
SIC 1542 Nonresidential construction
Pr: Greg Huston
CFO: Matt Smith
VP: Jeremy Lawson
IT Man: Steven Clark
Mtls Mgr: Dave Strauss
Board of Directors: Greg Huston, Matt Smith

D-U-N-S 09-667-9659
SLAYMAKER GROUP INC
TONY ROMA'S
404 E 4500 S Ste A12, Salt Lake City, UT 84107-2777
Tel (801) 261-3700 *Founded/Ownrshp* 1976
Sales 49.0MM^E *EMP* 1,000
SIC 5812 Restaurant, family: chain
Ch Bd: Scott Slaymaker

D-U-N-S 04-636-6274 IMP
SLBS MANAGEMENT INC
SUMMIT DISTRIBUTING
3201 Rider Trl S, Earth City, MO 63045-1520
Tel (314) 874-0400 *Founded/Ownrshp* 1994
Sales 108.0MM^E *EMP* 140
SIC 5181 Beer & other fermented malt liquors
CEO: Thomas H Stillman
**Pr:* Kim Barrow
CFO: Brian Robinson
Ofcr: Debbie Wilson
IT Man: John Merchant
IT Man: James Tubbs
Opers Mgr: Rick Firmand
VP Sls: Johnathan Hummel

D-U-N-S 94-241-5183
■ **SLC OPERATING LIMITED PARTNERSHIP**
(*Suby of* STARWOOD HOTELS & RESORTS WORLDWIDE LLC) ★
2231 E Camelback Rd # 400, Phoenix, AZ 85016-3453
Tel (602) 852-3900 *Founded/Ownrshp* 1994
Sales 41.7MM^E *EMP* 1,345
SIC 6719 Personal holding companies, except banks

D-U-N-S 01-617-5309
SLEDD CO CHAS M
100 E Cove Ave, Wheeling, WV 26003-6078
Tel (800) 333-0374 *Founded/Ownrshp* 1996
Sales 203.1MM^E *EMP* 175
SIC 5194 5142 5149 Cigarettes; Cigars; Chewing tobacco; Packaged frozen goods; Groceries & related products
Pr: Robert Sincavich
**VP:* S Randall Emanuelson
Sales Asso: Becky Henry

D-U-N-S 03-446-5548
SLEDHEAD TRUCKING LLC
115 Denver Br, Hagerhill, KY 41222-8844
Tel (606) 297-5391 *Founded/Ownrshp* 2010
Sales 300.0MM *EMP* 2
SIC 4212 Local trucking, without storage

SLEEP INNOVATIONS
See INNOCOR INC

SLEEP STYLES
See JLJ HOME FURNISHINGS LLC

D-U-N-S 15-695-6716 IMP
SLEEP TRAIN INC
ON TRACK ADVERTISING
(*Suby of* MATTRESS FIRM HOLDING CORP) ★
2205 Plaza Dr, Rocklin, CA 95765-4404
Tel (916) 751-4300 *Founded/Ownrshp* 2014
Sales 163.8MM^E *EMP* 635
SIC 5712 Mattresses
CEO: Dale R Carlsen
Pr: Brian Burris
VP: Mike Estes
Store Mgr: Suzanne Hollaway
Dir IT: Mark Tseu
S&M/VP: Robert Kilgore
Sls Mgr: Brian Berruto
Sls Mgr: Menelik Holt
Sales Asso: Reyna Aguirre
Sales Asso: Eric Cardoza
Sales Asso: Darryl Miller

SLEEPY'S CORPORATE
See SLEEPYS REORGANIZATION INC

D-U-N-S 83-231-0556 EXP
SLEEPYS LLC
SLEEPYS MATTRESS PROFESSIONALS
1000 S Oyster Bay Rd, Hicksville, NY 11801-3527
Tel (516) 861-8800 *Founded/Ownrshp* 1957
Sales 1.0MMM *EMP* 3,188
SIC 5712 Mattresses
**COO:* Adam Blank
**CFO:* Ron Ristau
VP: Christopher Cucuzza
VP: Dan Sackrowitz
VP: Neil Zimmer
Dir Risk M: Hector Santiago
Creative D: Wendya Jacobs
IT Man: Greg Schumm
VP Opers: Jim Gaspa
VP Opers: Tom Gioiella
Mktg Dir: Max Vasser

SLEEPYS MATTRESS PROFESSIONALS
See SLEEPYS LLC

D-U-N-S 01-249-0009 EXP
SLEEPYS REORGANIZATION INC
SLEEPY'S CORPORATE
1000 S Oyster Bay Rd, Hicksville, NY 11801-3527
Tel (516) 861-8800 *Founded/Ownrshp* 1957
Sales 587.3MM^E *EMP* 2,900
SIC 5712 Mattresses
Pr: David Acker
**CEO:* Harold Acker
**COO:* Adam Blank
**CFO:* Joseph Graci
Mktg Mgr: Spencer Acker

D-U-N-S 00-582-3851 IMP
SLETTEN CONSTRUCTION CO (MT)
(*Suby of* SLETTEN INC) ★
1000 25th St N Ste 4, Great Falls, MT 59401-1394
Tel (406) 761-7920 *Founded/Ownrshp* 1928
Sales 130.5MM *EMP* 150
Accts Junkermier Clark Campanella
SIC 1541 1542 1611 Industrial buildings, new construction; Commercial & office building, new construction; Institutional building construction; Highway & street construction
CEO: Erik Sletten
**CFO:* Robert Nommensen
**Ex VP:* Martin Becker
**Ex VP:* Ronald McCullough
**Sr VP:* Robert Robertson
**VP:* Ronald Hagen
**VP:* Wade Robertson
**VP:* Paul Robinson
**VP:* Mark Visocan
Opers Mgr: Steve Garness

D-U-N-S 12-206-5287
SLETTEN INC
1000 25th St N Ste 4, Great Falls, MT 59401-1382
Tel (406) 761-7920 *Founded/Ownrshp* 1928
Sales 189.7MM *EMP* 375^E
Accts Junkermier Clark Campanella St
SIC 1542 1541 1611 Commercial & office building, new construction; Institutional building construction; Industrial buildings, new construction; General contractor, highway & street construction
Ch Bd: J Robert Sletten
**Pr:* Erik Sletten
**CFO:* Robert N Nommensen
**Ex VP:* Martin W Becker
**Ex VP:* Ron McCullough
**Sr VP:* Robert G Robertson
**VP:* Ron Hagen
**VP:* Ray Richardson
**VP:* Wade Robertson
**VP:* Paul Robinson
**VP:* Mark Visocan

SLIDE GO
See PRIME-LINE PRODUCTS CO

SLIDELL MEMORIAL HOSPITAL
See ST TAMMANY PARISH HOSPITAL SERVICE DISTRICT 2

SLIMFAST
See KSF ACQUISITION CORP

D-U-N-S 07-495-5113
SLIPPERY ROCK UNIVERSITY
S R U
(*Suby of* STATE SYSTEM HIGHER EDUCATN PA) ★
1 Morrow Way, Slippery Rock, PA 16057-1399
Tel (724) 738-9000 *Founded/Ownrshp* 1889
Sales 108.6MM^E *EMP* 877
Accts Parentebeard Llc State Colleg
SIC 8221 9411 University; Administration of educational programs;
Pr: Dr Cheryl Norton
**Pr:* Robert M Smith
**CFO:* Charles Curry
Ex Dir: Rita Abent
Web Dev: Darcy White
VP Opers: Simon Beeching
Board of Directors: Dr Dixon

D-U-N-S 16-000-2218
▲ **SLM CORP**
SALLIE MAE
300 Continental Dr Ste 1s, Newark, DE 19713-4339
Tel (302) 451-0200 *Founded/Ownrshp* 1972
Sales NA *EMP* 1,200^E
Tkr Sym SLM *Exch* NGS
SIC 6111 6141 7322 Student Loan Marketing Association; Personal credit institutions; Adjustment & collection services
Ch Bd: Raymond J Quinlan
CFO: Steven J McGarry
Chf Mktg O: Charles P Rocha
Ofcr: Paul F Thome
Ex VP: Laurent C Lutz
Sr VP: Jeffrey F Dale
VP: Christopher Lynch
VP: Anne Milem
VP: Tony Olivero
VP: Tina Vogel
Sftwr Eng: Jeffery Walton

SLOAN CONSTRUCTION COMPANY
See REEVES CONSTRUCTION CO

D-U-N-S 87-637-6864 EXP
SLOAN IMPLEMENT CO INC
JOHN DEERE AUTHORIZED DEALER
120 N Business 51, Assumption, IL 62510-1120
Tel (217) 226-4411 *Founded/Ownrshp* 1994
Sales 155.5MM^E *EMP* 350
SIC 5083 Farm & garden machinery
Pr: James L Steck
**Ch Bd:* Larry Sloan
Store Mgr: Mike Klein
Board of Directors: Howard Buffett, Jeff Sloan, Kevin Sloan

SLOAN INDUSTRY CENTERS
See ALFRED P SLOAN FOUNDATION

D-U-N-S 00-512-1033 IMP/EXP
SLOAN VALVE CO
10500 Seymour Ave, Franklin Park, IL 60131-1259
Tel (847) 671-4300 *Founded/Ownrshp* 1906
Sales 233.0MM^E *EMP* 600
SIC 3494 3432 Valves & pipe fittings; Pipe fittings; Plumbing fixture fittings & trim
Ch: Charles S Allen
Pr: James C Allen
CFO: Kevin A Mc Carthy
CFO: Bernard Peters
Ex VP: John Aykroyd
VP: Tom Coleman
VP: Jeff Krull
VP: Margie Rodino
Ex Dir: Kathy Volpi
Admn Mgr: Robert Briggs
Brnch Mgr: Tim Schiffbauer

D-U-N-S 06-493-1884
SLOAN-KETTERING INSTITUTE FOR CANCER RESEARCH
1275 York Ave, New York, NY 10065-6094
Tel (212) 639-2000 *Founded/Ownrshp* 1950
Sales 566.4MM *EMP* 2,096
SIC 8733 Medical research
Pr: Dr Craig B Thompson
COO: Kathryn Martin
CFO: Michael P Gutnick
Sr VP: Kerry Bessey
VP: Anne Thomas
Assoc Dir: Matthew Warshaw
Ex Dir: Frank Kalman
CIO: Patricia Skarulis
Doctor: Nadeem R Abu-Ustum MD

SLOANE AUTO GROUP
See RGS INC

D-U-N-S 01-286-9145
SLOMINS INC (NY)
125 Lauman Ln, Hicksville, NY 11801-6539
Tel (516) 932-7000 *Founded/Ownrshp* 1923
Sales 184.0MM^E *EMP* 1,000
SIC 5983 1731 1711 Fuel oil dealers; Fire detection & burglar alarm systems specialization; Heating systems repair & maintenance; Heating & air conditioning contractors
CEO: Ira Salzman
**Sec:* David McKenney
Ex VP: Mike Alfieri
Genl Mgr: David Olsen
Sales Asso: Frank Angrisani
Sales Asso: Allan Jacobowitz

SLOPAK
See PATTERSON PUMP CO

SLORA COMPANY
See TERTELING HOLDING CO INC

SLS LAS VEGAS
See LAS VEGAS RESORT HOLDINGS LLC

SLUMBERLAND FURNITURE
See SLUMBERLAND INC

D-U-N-S 04-178-1402 IMP
SLUMBERLAND INC
SLUMBERLAND FURNITURE
3060 Centerville Rd, Little Canada, MN 55117-1100
Tel (651) 482-7500 *Founded/Ownrshp* 1970
Sales 269.6MM^E *EMP* 1,000
SIC 5712 Beds & accessories; Mattresses; Bedding & bedsprings
CFO: Tammy Spinelli
Ex Dir: Wayne Deilke
Genl Mgr: Ron Ambrose
Genl Mgr: Daryl Cunningham
Off Mgr: Karen Feigal
Store Mgr: Kevin Fitzgerald
Store Mgr: Michelle Klein
IT Man: John Cleveland
Opers Mgr: Janet Gray
Opers Mgr: Jason Jensen
Opers Mgr: Shawn Kudrna
Board of Directors: Barbara J Larson, Barbara J Larson, Jeanette Wilacker

D-U-N-S 02-392-4582
SLURRY PAVERS INC
3617 Nine Mile Rd, Richmond, VA 23223-4811
Tel (804) 264-0707 *Founded/Ownrshp* 1966
Sales 94.3MM *EMP* 400
SIC 2951 1611

D-U-N-S 07-647-8155 IMP
▲ **SM ENERGY CO**
1775 N Sherman St # 1200, Denver, CO 80203-4339
Tel (303) 861-8140 *Founded/Ownrshp* 1908
Sales 1.5MMM *EMP* 786^E
Tkr Sym SM *Exch* NYS
SIC 1311 Crude petroleum production; Natural gas production
Pr: Javan D Ottoson
**Ch Bd:* William D Sullivan
CFO: A Wade Pursell
Ex VP: David W Copeland
Ex VP: Jay Ottoson
Ex VP: Awade Pursell
Ex VP: Herbert S Vogel
Sr VP: Kenneth J Knott
Sr VP: Mark D Mueller
Sr VP: Lehman E Newton III
VP: Newt Newton
VP: Mark T Solomon
Exec: Sue Adamson
Board of Directors: Larry W Bickle, Stephen R Brand, Loren M Leiker, Ramiro G Peru, Julio M Quintana, Rose M Robeson

SMA AMERICA
See SMA SOLAR TECHNOLOGY AMERICA LLC

D-U-N-S 01-148-0299 IMP
SMA AMERICA PRODUCTION LLC
(*Suby of* SMA AMERICA) ★
3801 Havana St, Denver, CO 80239-3252
Tel (720) 347-6000 *Founded/Ownrshp* 2009
Sales 111.6MM^E *EMP* 200
SIC 3433 Solar heaters & collectors
VP: Mark Smiens
Sls Mgr: Michael Mendik

D-U-N-S 09-734-4274 IMP/EXP
SMA SOLAR TECHNOLOGY AMERICA LLC (WV)
SMA AMERICA
(*Suby of* SMA SOLAR TECHNOLOGY AG)
6020 West Oaks Blvd, Rocklin, CA 95765-5472
Tel (916) 625-0870 *Founded/Ownrshp* 2000
Sales 229.6MM^E *EMP* 200^E
SIC 5065 Electronic parts
Ofcr: Maurice C Kemp
VP: Jurgen Reekers
Genl Mgr: Scott Crabtree
QC Dir: Ron Edmon
Opers Supe: Patrick Martin
Opers Mgr: Ken Paquin
Mktg Dir: Brad Dore
Manager: Peter Zullo
Sls Mgr: William Weisbecker
Sales Asso: Brett Dotson
Snr Mgr: Rick McKinnon

D-U-N-S 00-347-9748
■ SMALL BUSINESS ADMINISTRATION US
(Suby of EXECUTIVE OFFICE OF UNITED STATES GOVERNMENT) ★
409 3rd St Sw Ste 5000, Washington, DC 20416-0011
Tel (202) 205-6770 Founded/Ownrshp 1953
Sales NA EMP 6,241E
Accts Kpmg Llp Washington Dc
SIC 9611 Economic development agency, government;
COO: Eileen Harrington
CFO: Tom Dumaresq
CFO: Jonathan I Carver
*Ofcr: Tracy Terrill
*CIO: Maria Roat
CIO: Eric Won
Sys/Dir: Lawrence Barrett
*Genl Couns: Frank R Borchert III

SMALL BUSINESS AUTHORITY, THE
See NEWTEK BUSINESS SERVICES INC

D-U-N-S 15-397-2401
SMALL MINE DEVELOPMENT LLC
670 E Riverpark Ln # 100, Boise, ID 83706-6571
Tel (208) 338-8880 Founded/Ownrshp 1982
Sales 183.5MM EMP 250
Accts Eide Bailly Llp Boise Idaho
SIC 1081 Mine development, metal; Test boring, metal mining

D-U-N-S 14-432-4993
SMALL NEWSPAPER GROUP
JOURNAL
8 Dearborn Sq, Kankakee, IL 60901-3909
Tel (815) 937-3300 Founded/Ownrshp 1903
Sales 160.7MME EMP 1,000
SIC 2711 2791 2752 Newspapers, publishing & printing; Typesetting; Commercial printing, lithographic
Pr: Len R Small
*Treas: Joseph Lacaeyse
Sls&Mrk Ex: Bryan Corbin

D-U-N-S 00-507-9744 IMP/EXP
SMALL PARTS INC
(Suby of MPI) ★
600 Humphrey St, Logansport, IN 46947-4999
Tel (574) 753-6323 Founded/Ownrshp 1958
Sales 115.6MME EMP 660
SIC 3443 Metal parts
CEO: John E Barnes
*Pr: Clay T Barnes
*Pr: Clay Jackson
*Treas: John Farmani
*VP: Jim Bauer

SMALL TUBE PRODUCTS
See ST PRODUCTS LLC

D-U-N-S 05-925-6982
SMALLEY & CO
861 S Jason St, Denver, CO 80223-2817
Tel (303) 777-3435 Founded/Ownrshp 1967
Sales 115.6MME EMP 120
SIC 5169 Adhesives & sealants
Pr: Bruce E Coy
*VP: Joseph A Coy
*VP: Jeff Stickney
Manager: Jeff Albanese
Sls Mgr: Patrick Coy
Sls Mgr: Clifford Sharp

SMART
See SUBURBAN MOBILITY AUTHORITY FOR REGIONAL TRANSPORATION

D-U-N-S 80-054-6702
SMART & FINAL HOLDINGS LLC
10205 Constellation Blvd, Los Angeles, CA 90067-6201
Tel (310) 843-1900 Founded/Ownrshp 2007
Sales 162.3MME EMP 5,910
SIC 5141 5411 Groceries, general line; Grocery stores

D-U-N-S 00-690-9048 IMP
■ SMART & FINAL INC
(Suby of SMART & FINAL STORES INC) ★
600 Citadel Dr, Commerce, CA 90040-1562
Tel (323) 869-7500 Founded/Ownrshp 2012
Sales 2.9MMME EMP 2E
SIC 5141 5411 Groceries, general line; Grocery stores
CEO: George Golleher
Sr VP: Norah Morley
*VP: Jan Berger
VP: Anthony V Bernardini
VP: Michael Paul
VP: Ed Puskas
VP: Gary Somes
Genl Mgr: Carlos Aguilar
Telecom Mg: Bob Halverson

D-U-N-S 07-957-5020
▲ SMART & FINAL STORES INC
600 Citadel Dr, Commerce, CA 90040-1562
Tel (323) 869-7500 Founded/Ownrshp 2012
Sales 3.9MMM EMP 10,956
Tkr Sym SFS Exch NYS
SIC 5411 Grocery stores, chain
Pr: David G Hirz
*Ch Bd: David B Kaplan
Pr: Martin J Trtek
CFO: Richard N Phegley
Treas: Eugene M Smith
Chf Mktg O: Eleanor E Hong
Ex VP: Scott R Drew
Ex VP: Scott Drew
Sr VP: Michael M Laddon
Sr VP: Michael Laddon
Sr VP: Michael A Mortensen
Sr VP: Leland P Smith
Sr VP: Jeffrey D Whynot
VP: Richard A Link

Board of Directors: Norman H Axelrod, Andrew A Giancamilli, Dennis T Gies, Paul N Hopkins, Elaine Rubin, Adam L Stein, Joseph S Tesoriero, Kenneth I Tuchman

D-U-N-S 55-694-8354
■ SMART & FINAL STORES LLC
(Suby of SMART & FINAL INC) ★
600 Citadel Dr, Commerce, CA 90040-1562
Tel (323) 869-7500 Founded/Ownrshp 1991
Sales 3.1MMME EMP 3,713
SIC 5411 Grocery stores, chain
CEO: Etienne P Snollaerts
*Ch Bd: Ross E Roeder
Pr: Diane Godfrey
*CFO: Martin Lynch
*Ex VP: Dennis L Chiavelli
*Sr VP: Donald G Alvarado
Sr VP: Sonia Iglesis
*Sr VP: Suzanne Mullins
*Sr VP: James E Robinson
*VP: Abdul S Mirza
VP: Dan Reams
*VP: Timothy M Snee
VP: Jeff Whynot
Exec: Michael Paul
Comm Dir: Randall Oliver

SMART ALABAMA
See STAMPED METAL AMERICAN RESEARCH TECHNOLOGY INC

D-U-N-S 13-075-1469 IMP
SMART ALABAMA LLC
(Suby of SHIN YOUNG CO., LTD.)
121 Shin Young Dr, Luverne, AL 36049-6536
Tel (334) 335-5800 Founded/Ownrshp 2003
Sales 238.0MM EMP 700
SIC 3469 3465 Metal stampings; Automotive stampings
CFO: Kwang Twung Kim

D-U-N-S 02-564-3560
■ SMART CHOICE AUTOMOTIVE GROUP INC
ECKLERS
(Suby of AMERICAS CAR-MART INC) ★
5130 S Washington Ave, Titusville, FL 32780-7318
Tel (321) 269-9680 Founded/Ownrshp 1999
Sales 89.0MME EMP 386
SIC 5521 3714 6141 Used car dealers; Motor vehicle parts & accessories; Automobile & consumer finance companies; Automobile loans, including insurance
Pr: Brian T Scher
*Ch Bd: Edward R McMurphy
*COO: Ronald W Anderson
*CFO: Joseph B Cavalier
CFO: Matt Jordan
VP: Amitava Bose
*VP: Larry W Lange
*VP: Gary R Smith
Board of Directors: Robert J Abrahams

SMART CIRCLE, THE
See SMART CIRCLE INTERNATIONAL LLC

D-U-N-S 79-696-3978
SMART CIRCLE INTERNATIONAL LLC
SMART CIRCLE, THE
4490 Von Karman Ave, Newport Beach, CA 92660-2008
Tel (949) 587-9207 Founded/Ownrshp 2007
Sales 355.4MM EMP 95E
SIC 5963 Direct selling establishments
CEO: Michael Meryash
*Pr: George Graffy
*CFO: Michael Shimada
*VP: Chad Powers

D-U-N-S 07-961-5911
SMART CITY LOCATING INC
5555 Smu Blvd, Dallas, TX 75206-5015
Tel (214) 586-0519 Founded/Ownrshp 2014
Sales 1.0MMM EMP 3
SIC 6531 Real estate agents & managers
CEO: Cassandra Brown

D-U-N-S 84-901-3842 IMP
■ SMART ELECTRONICS AND ASSEMBLY INC
(Suby of SECURE COMMUNICATION SYSTEMS, INC.)
2000 W Corporate Way, Anaheim, CA 92801-5373
Tel (714) 772-2651 Founded/Ownrshp 1994
Sales 100.2MM EMP 120
SIC 3672 Circuit boards, television & radio printed
Pr: Robert Swelgin
*CEO: Shou-Lee Wang
COO: Patrick Huang
*CFO: Dave Wopschall
CFO: David Wopschall
*VP: Getaneh Bekele
Prgrm Mgr: Fadi Aoun
Genl Mgr: Steiner Chen
CTO: Kevin Ffeiff
Ql Cn Mgr: Jacques Bojoh
Ql Cn Mgr: Vincent Pham

D-U-N-S 05-009-7583 IMP/EXP
SMART LIVING CO (CA)
S M C
4100 Guardian St, Simi Valley, CA 93063-6717
Tel (805) 578-5500 Founded/Ownrshp 1955
Sales 110.4MME EMP 400
SIC 5199 Gifts & novelties
CEO: Mark Schelbert
*CFO: Scott Palladino
Sr Cor Off: Joe Wu
Ex Dir: Ron Hein
CTO: Charles Serian
IT Man: Cecilia Torres
VP Merchng: Mindy Suk

SMART MACHINES
See TEKSERVE CORP

D-U-N-S 19-596-2543 IMP
SMART MODULAR TECHNOLOGIES (WWH) INC
39870 Eureka Dr, Newark, CA 94560-4809
Tel (510) 623-1231 Founded/Ownrshp 2011
Sales 434.0MME EMP 1,200
SIC 3674 3577 3679 Integrated circuits, semiconductor networks, etc.; Computer peripheral equipment; Liquid crystal displays (LCD)
Pr: Iain Mackenzie
*COO: Jack Pacheco
COO: Jack A Pacheco
*CFO: Barry Zwarenstein
*VP: Alan Marten
VP: Anjali Reddy
VP: Mike Rubino
Prin: Mike Maynard
Manager: Jack Carney
Counsel: Erin Williams

SMART SOURCE
See NEWS AMERICA MARKETING IN-STORE SERVICES LLC

D-U-N-S 01-626-6620
■ SMART-TEK AUTOMATED SERVICES INC
(Suby of TRUCEPT INC) ★
11838 Bernardo Plaza Ct # 250, San Diego, CA 92128-2413
Tel (858) 798-1644 Founded/Ownrshp 2009
Sales 27.7MME EMP 7,000
SIC 7372 Business oriented computer software
COO: Kelly Mowrey
*CEO: Bryan Bonar

D-U-N-S 62-108-7407 IMP
SMARTDRIVE SYSTEMS INC
9450 Carroll Park Dr, San Diego, CA 92121-5201
Tel (866) 933-9930 Founded/Ownrshp 2005
Sales 162.1MME EMP 362
SIC 5099 Safety equipment & supplies
CEO: Steve Mitgang
*Pr: Jason Palmer
Sr VP: Kenneth Colby
*VP: Michael J Baker
VP: Michael Baker
*VP: Mark Freitas
*VP: Slaven Sljivar
VP: Wendy Wyatt
Prgrm Mgr: Craig Bilderback
Prgrm Mgr: Mark Woody
Snr Sftwr: Ramon Henares

D-U-N-S 06-108-1477 IMP/EXP
SMARTHEALTH INC
SMARTPRACTICE
3400 E Mcdowell Rd, Phoenix, AZ 85008-3884
Tel (602) 225-9090 Founded/Ownrshp 1972
Sales 304.6MME EMP 550
SIC 5047 Dentists' professional supplies; Medical equipment & supplies
Pr: Curtis P Hamann MD
*Ch Bd: James A Rhode
*CFO: Dan Nahom
*VP: Meg Burke
*VP: David Kline
VP: Kathy Pfister
*VP: Naomi Rhode
*VP: David Spresser
Creative D: Kimberly Metivier
Dir Bus: Tina Strickler
Genl Mgr: James Lanphere

SMARTPAC
See SUPERIOR FIBERS INC

SMARTPRACTICE
See SMARTHEALTH INC

D-U-N-S 01-002-4300
SMARTREVENUE.COM INC
60 Twin Ridge Rd, Ridgefield, CT 06877-5825
Tel (203) 733-9156 Founded/Ownrshp 2000
Sales 48.5MME EMP 1,028
SIC 8732 Market analysis or research
Pr: John Dranow
Pr: Candace Adams
*CFO: Adam Mustafa

D-U-N-S 96-509-1606
SMARTRONIX INC
44150 Smartronix Way, Hollywood, MD 20636-3172
Tel (301) 373-6000 Founded/Ownrshp 1995
Sales 218.8MME EMP 566
SIC 7371 8731 7373 Computer software development; Computer (hardware) development; Value-added resellers, computer systems
Pr: Arshed Javaid
*CEO: John C Parris
*CFO: Joseph Gerczak
VP: Brian Brown
*VP: Alan Parris
Assoc Dir: Dave Swicegood
Prgrm Mgr: Jim Crowe
Prgrm Mgr: Jesse Morrell
Prgrm Mgr: Robbi Muller
Prgrm Mgr: Eric Walters
Prgrm Mgr: Donnie Wathen

SMARTSTOP SELF STORAGE
See STRATEGIC STORAGE TRUST INC

SMC PACKAGING GROUP
See SOUTHERN MISSOURI CONTAINERS INC

D-U-N-S 93-752-5376
SMCL LLC
(Suby of LIFECARE FAMILY OF HOSPITALS) ★
5340 Legacy Dr, Plano, TX 75024-3178
Tel (469) 241-2100 Founded/Ownrshp 1994
Sales 149.4MME EMP 678
SIC 8062 8069 General medical & surgical hospitals; Chronic disease hospital
Pr: Jake Socha
*CEO: Phillip B Douglasm
COO: Bryan Burklow
Sr VP: Bridget Gallagher
Sr VP: Timothy L Hunt
*VP: Maegan Bowman
*VP: Stephanie Carpenter
*VP: Ann Corrigan
Dir Rx: Lori Breckheimer
Off Mgr: Richard Yutzy
QA Dir: Susan Weaver

SMDC
See ST MARYS DULUTH CLINIC HEALTH SYSTEM

D-U-N-S 06-818-7871
SMDC MEDICAL CENTER
ESSENTIA HEALTH
(Suby of ESSENTIA HEALTH) ★
502 E 2nd St, Duluth, MN 55805-1913
Tel (218) 726-4000 Founded/Ownrshp 2001
Sales 502.6MM EMP 750
SIC 8062 General medical & surgical hospitals
CEO: Peter Person
*CEO: John Smylie
CIO: Dennis Dassenko
*Genl Couns: James N Abelsen
Genl Couns: Teresa Otto

D-U-N-S 12-278-1743 IMP/EXP
SME HOLDING CO LLC
EASTERN MOUNTAIN SPORTS
(Suby of VESTIS RETAIL GROUP LLC) ★
160 Corporate Ct, Meriden, CT 06450-7177
Tel (603) 924-9571 Founded/Ownrshp 2012
Sales 229.3MME EMP 1,000
SIC 5941 Sports apparel; Camping equipment
VP: Dorey Cutting
VP: Ken Mamak
Dir IT: Bill Houlihan
Opers Mgr: Chris Fisher
VP Mktg: Maile Buker

D-U-N-S 85-872-9098 IMP
SME INDUSTRIES INC
SME STEEL CONTRACTORS
5801 W Wells Park Rd, West Jordan, UT 84081-5665
Tel (801) 280-3960 Founded/Ownrshp 1992
Sales 220.1MME EMP 850
SIC 1791 3441 Structural steel erection; Building components, structural steel
CEO: Wayne Searle
Ch Bd: Jerry Moyes
Sec: Gordon K Holladay
VP: Justin Pitts
Prin: Craig Moyes
Opers Mgr: Mark Mundy
Ql Cn Mgr: Richard Cook
Manager: Angie Jones

SME STEEL CONTRACTORS
See SME INDUSTRIES INC

D-U-N-S 00-616-6797 IMP
SMEAD MANUFACTURING CO INC (MN)
600 Smead Blvd, Hastings, MN 55033-2219
Tel (651) 437-4111 Founded/Ownrshp 1907
Sales 280.8MME EMP 1,200
SIC 2675 7372 2789 2759 2752 2542 Cards, folders & mats: die-cut; Folders, filing, die-cut: made from purchased materials; Manila folders; Index cards, die-cut: made from purchased materials; Business oriented computer software; Bookbinding & related work; Commercial printing; Commercial printing, lithographic; Partitions & fixtures, except wood
Pr: Sharon L Avent
*COO: Robert Karrick
*Sr VP: David Fasbender
VP: Elbert Arends
VP: Dale Olson
MIS Dir: Ron Gilbertson
VP Opers: John Behrens
Opers Mgr: Dawn L Finholdt
Sls Mgr: Michael Bauer

D-U-N-S 09-640-7622
SMEAL FIRE APPARATUS CO (NE)
610 W 4th St, Snyder, NE 68664-2429
Tel (402) 568-2224 Founded/Ownrshp 1978
Sales 92.5MME EMP 300E
SIC 3711 Fire department vehicles (motor vehicles), assembly of
CEO: Delwin Smeal
*Pr: Mark Huber
*Treas: Jeffrey M Scherer
*VP: Gary M Hasemann
*VP: Jeff Hunke
*VP: Jeff Wegner
Dept Mgr: David Volpp
IT Man: Frank Barrett
IT Man: Jason Coe
IT Man: Brenda Larsen
Sls Dir: Chuck Glagola

SMECO
See MARYLAND SOUTHERN ELECTRIC COOPERATIVE INC

SMEMC
See PRESENCE SAINTS MARY AND ELIZABETH MEDICAL CENTER

D-U-N-S 11-413-9074
SMF ENERGY CORP
STREICHER MOBILE FUELING
200 W Cypress Creek Rd # 400, Fort Lauderdale, FL 33309-2175
Tel (954) 308-4200 Founded/Ownrshp 1996
Sales 236.4MM EMP 248E
SIC 5172

D-U-N-S 78-331-8991
SMG HOLDINGS INC
300 Cnshohckn State Rd # 450, Conshohocken, PA 19428-3801
Tel (610) 729-7900 Founded/Ownrshp 2007
Sales 410.9MME EMP 4,500
SIC 6512 8742 7922 Nonresidential building operators; Real estate consultant; Entertainment promotion
CEO: Wes Westley
*CFO: John Burns
*Ex VP: Gregg Caren
*Ex VP: Maureen Ginty
*Ex VP: Doug Thornton
VP: Michael Evans
*Prin: Harold L Westley Jr
Ex Dir: Michael Godoy
Ex Dir: Bill Helmig
Corp Couns: Bruce Hanson

D-U-N-S 14-740-3547
SMG-PREMIER FOOD SERVICES INC
(*Suby of* SMG HOLDINGS INC) ★
8555 Aero Dr Ste 205, San Diego, CA 92123-1745
Tel (858) 621-5151 *Founded/Ownrshp* 2014
Sales 36.7MME *EMP* 1,100
SIC 5812 Concessionaire; Cafeteria; Caterers; Contract food services
CEO: Harold Westley
**Pr:* George E Karetas
**Sec:* John Burns

SMHC
See SOUTHERN MAINE HEALTH CARE

SMI
See SEEDORFF MASONRY INC

D-U-N-S 06-712-3570 IMP
■ **SMI STEEL LLC**
CMC STEEL ALABAMA
(*Suby of* COMMERCIAL METALS CO) ★
101 50th St S, Birmingham, AL 35212-3525
Tel (205) 592-8981 *Founded/Ownrshp* 2012
Sales 153.6MME *EMP* 430
SIC 3312 Structural shapes & pilings, steel
CEO: Russ Rinn
**Treas:* David Sudbury
**VP:* Mike Buckentin
**VP:* Murray McClean
Genl Mgr: Robert Unfried
VP Sls: Ray Bauer

D-U-N-S 96-196-4884
SMI-FUEL LLC
(*Suby of* SCHNUCKS) ★
11420 Lackland Rd, Saint Louis, MO 63146-3559
Tel (314) 994-9900 *Founded/Ownrshp* 2008
Sales 179.7MME *EMP* 1E
SIC 5172 Fuel oil

D-U-N-S 02-310-6722
SMILE BRANDS GROUP INC
BRIGHT NOW DENTAL
100 Spectrum Center Dr # 1500, Irvine, CA 92618-4962
Tel (714) 668-1300 *Founded/Ownrshp* 2016
Sales 538.4MME *EMP* 4,100
SIC 8741 8021 Management services; Dental clinics & offices
CEO: Steven C Bilt
Pr: Stan Andrakowicz
CFO: Bradley Schmidt
VP: Mazin Alayssami
VP: Rick Brown
VP: Marlin Clark
VP: Jeff Hamill
VP: John Magrann
VP: Lorilee Schmidt
Exec: Christopher Meier
Exec: Kim Seiling

SMILE KEEPERS
See INTERDENT INC

D-U-N-S 07-787-0520
SMILE TRAIN INC
41 Madison Ave Ste 2801, New York, NY 10010-2325
Tel (212) 689-9199 *Founded/Ownrshp* 1999
Sales 98.2MM *EMP* 16
Accts Lb Grant Thornton Llp New Yor
SIC 8699 Charitable organization
Ofcr: Janet Blackwood
**Ofcr:* Mohamed Fakhreldin Attia Hassa
**Sr VP:* Dr Shell Xue
VP: Beatriz G Day
VP: Beatriz Gonzalez
VP: William Horan
**VP:* Troy Reinhart
VP: Pamela Wren
IT Man: Ewa Rumprecht

D-U-N-S 85-873-3306 IMP
SMITH & NEPHEW HOLDINGS INC
(*Suby of* SMITH & NEPHEW (OVERSEAS) LIMITED)
1201 N Orange St Ste 788, Wilmington, DE 19801-1173
Tel (302) 884-6720 *Founded/Ownrshp* 1996
Sales 657.9MME *EMP* 1,850E
SIC 5047 3841 Medical equipment & supplies; Surgical & medical instruments
Pr: Cliff Lomax

D-U-N-S 04-548-3575 IMP/EXP
SMITH & NEPHEW INC
SMITH&NEPHEW
(*Suby of* SMITH & NEPHEW HOLDINGS INC) ★
1450 E Brooks Rd, Memphis, TN 38116-1804
Tel (901) 396-2121 *Founded/Ownrshp* 1975
Sales 648.4MME *EMP* 1,849E
SIC 3842 5047 Surgical appliances & supplies; Splints, pneumatic & wood; Dressings, surgical; Surgical equipment & supplies; Orthopedic equipment & supplies
CEO: Olivier Bohuon
**Pr:* Rodrigo Bianchi
Pr: Mark Buckley
**CFO:* Julie Brown
CFO: Douglas Wickstead
Ofcr: Arjun Rajaratnam
Ofcr: Derryl Robinson
Sr VP: Todd Durniak
Sr VP: Alain Tranchemontagne
Sr VP: Todd Usen
VP: Michael Barnett
VP: Dwayne Montgomery
VP: Neil Ryding
VP: Bill Sho
Dir Lab: Patrick Aldinger
Dir Lab: Carla Crockett
Dir Lab: Mark Gorman
Dir Lab: Jody Stallings
Dir Lab: Agata Walas-Maenhoudt
Comm Man: Susan Myers

D-U-N-S 18-681-2236 IMP
■ **SMITH & WESSON CORP**
(*Suby of* SMITH & WESSON HOLDING CORP) ★
2100 Roosevelt Ave, Springfield, MA 01104-1698
Tel (413) 781-8300 *Founded/Ownrshp* 2001
Sales 99.7MME *EMP* 800
SIC 3484 3429 3999 5091

D-U-N-S 04-687-2417 IMP/EXP
▲ **SMITH & WESSON HOLDING CORP**
2100 Roosevelt Ave, Springfield, MA 01104-1698
Tel (800) 331-0852 *Founded/Ownrshp* 1852
Sales 722.9MM *EMP* 1,853
Accts Deloitte & Touche Llp Hartfo
Tkr Sym SWHC *Exch* NGS
SIC 3482 Small arms ammunition; Shotgun ammunition: empty, blank or loaded; Pellets & BB's, pistol & air rifle ammunition
Ch Bd: Barry M Monheit
Pr: Matthew W Buckingham
**Pr:* P James Debney
Pr: Mark P Smith
CFO: Jeffrey D Buchanan
**V Ch Bd:* Robert L Scott
Chf Cred: Robert J Cicero
Dist Mgr: Larry Flatley
Board of Directors: Robert H Brust, John B Furman, Gregory J Gluchowski Jr, Michael F Golden, Mitchell A Saltz, I Marie Wadecki

D-U-N-S 11-298-8068
SMITH & WOLLENSKY RESTAURANT GROUP INC
260 Franklin St Ste 240, Boston, MA 02110-3143
Tel (617) 600-3500 *Founded/Ownrshp* 2015
Sales 61.7MME *EMP* 1,676
SIC 5812 Restaurant, family: chain
Pr: Michael Feighery
**CFO:* Cathy Tsoukalas
VP: Kim Lapine
Genl Mgr: Ned Mirkovic
Off Mgr: Karissa Dadario

D-U-N-S 01-886-8543
SMITH ACADEMY FOR EXCELLENCE INC
LEONA GROUP ARIZONA
(*Suby of* LEONA GROUP ARIZONA) ★
2625 Belvedere Dr Ste 108, Fort Wayne, IN 46802
Tel (260) 749-5832 *Founded/Ownrshp* 1994
Sales 647.2M *EMP* 1,477E
SIC 8211 Elementary & secondary schools
Prin: Thomas Smith

D-U-N-S 01-836-9041 EXP
SMITH AND LOVELESS INC
14040 Santa Fe Trail Dr, Shawnee Mission, KS 66215-1284
Tel (913) 888-5201 *Founded/Ownrshp* 2009
Sales 141.6MME *EMP* 496
SIC 3589 5074 Water treatment equipment, industrial; Sewage treatment equipment; Plumbing & hydronic heating supplies
Pr: Frank Rebori
VP: William Flores
VP: Mason Donald G
**VP:* Stuart Marschall
VP: Jodel Wickham
IT Man: Kathleen Honey
Trfc Mgr: Dena Demoret
Manager: Martin Paredes
Sls Mgr: George Sajwaj

D-U-N-S 78-058-6509
■ **SMITH BARNEY CONSULTING CORP**
(*Suby of* CITIGROUP INC) ★
388 Greenwich St Ofc 1, New York, NY 10013-2339
Tel (212) 816-6000 *Founded/Ownrshp* 1989
Sales 55.5MME *EMP* 2,000
SIC 7389 Personal service agents, brokers & bureaus
Dir IT: Bharath Raju

SMITH CLINIC
See HARRIS HEALTH SYSTEM

D-U-N-S 80-970-9835 IMP/EXP
SMITH COOPER INTERNATIONAL INC
SCI
2867 Vail Ave, Commerce, CA 90040-2613
Tel (323) 890-4455 *Founded/Ownrshp* 1993
Sales 91.5MME *EMP* 220
SIC 5085 3494 Industrial supplies; Valves & pipe fittings
CEO: Jason Hild
**Pr:* Robert E Cooper
**CFO:* George Bullock
VP: Frank Connelley
Rgnl Mgr: Bill Small
Genl Mgr: Paul Youngren
VP Opers: Keith Shadrick
Manager: Jeff Mullavey
Sales Asso: Alicia Johnson

D-U-N-S 04-996-3416
SMITH COOPER/T CORP
118 N Royal St Ste 1000, Mobile, AL 36602-3608
Tel (251) 431-6100 *Founded/Ownrshp* 1983
Sales 502.5MME *EMP* 900
SIC 4499 4492 2421 7692 4491 Marine salvaging; Marine towing services; Sawmills & planing mills, general; Welding repair; Stevedoring
Ch Bd: Angus R Cooper II
**COO:* Michael G Johnson
**Treas:* Jamie K Davidson
**Sr VP:* George Brown
**VP:* Eric Hansen
Mng Dir: George Yurcisin
CIO: Gerald Carter
CTO: Dominic Trione
Opers Mgr: Clifford Mosby
Sls Mgr: Lucian Lott

D-U-N-S 05-707-0674 IMP/EXP
SMITH FROZEN FOODS INC
101 Depot St, Weston, OR 97886-5020
Tel (541) 566-3515 *Founded/Ownrshp* 1919
Sales 91.5MME *EMP* 307
SIC 2037 Vegetables, quick frozen & cold pack, excl. potato products
**Pr:* Kelly W Brown
CFO: Garry Crowder
Genl Mgr: Roy Rocker
Opers Mgr: Jim Brannon
Plnt Mgr: Barb Byerly
Plnt Mgr: Aaron Ware

D-U-N-S 02-181-7895 IMP
SMITH GARDENS INC
PACFIC PLUG LINER
4164 Meridian St Ste 400, Bellingham, WA 98226-5583
Tel (800) 755-6256 *Founded/Ownrshp* 1903
Sales 108.6MME *EMP* 550
SIC 0181 Ornamental nursery products
Ch Bd: Harry C Smith
**VP:* Mark Smith
**VP:* Doug Ward
Sales Exec: Dave Edenfield

D-U-N-S 07-987-1835
SMITH GREENTECH TANNERY LLC (TX)
2233 Vantage St, Dallas, TX 75207-6101
Tel (214) 566-8392 *Founded/Ownrshp* 2014
Sales 115.0MM *EMP* 7
SIC 3111 Tanneries, leather
CEO: Jon Deweik

SMITH INSTRUMENT
See JO GALLOUP CO

D-U-N-S 00-838-3362 IMP
SMITH INTERNATIONAL INC
SCHLUMBERGER
(*Suby of* SCHLUMBERGER LIMITED) ★
1310 Rankin Rd, Houston, TX 77073-4802
Tel (281) 443-3370 *Founded/Ownrshp* 1937, 2010
Sales 5.5MMME *EMP* 21,931
SIC 3532 3533 Drills, bits & similar equipment; Oil & gas field machinery
CEO: Andrew Gould
**Pr:* Paal Kibsgaard
**CFO:* Simon Ayat
CFO: Margaret K Dorman
Treas: Mark Chambers
**Ex VP:* Ashok Belani
Ex VP: Mike Pearce
**VP:* Gerard Martellozo
VP: Peter Pintar
VP: Christina Ptasinski
VP: Jay Roueche
VP: Gerard Ryan
VP: Chad Taylor

D-U-N-S 82-485-2859
SMITH JOHNSON LAVEY AND BELL INC
2025 1st Ave Ste 1150, Seattle, WA 98121-2158
Tel (206) 443-8846 *Founded/Ownrshp* 1989
Sales 500.5MM *EMP* 30
SIC 8743 Public relations services
Pr: Dan Lavey
**Ch:* Gary Smith
**VP:* Julia Weisenburger

SMITH MEDICAL PARTNERS DIV
See H D SMITH LLC

SMITH METAL PRODUCTS
See PLASTIC PRODUCTS CO INC

D-U-N-S 08-550-1349 IMP
SMITH MOUNTAIN INDUSTRIES OF VIRGINIA INC
BLUE RIDGE CANDLE COMPANY
1000 Dillard Dr, Forest, VA 24551-2760
Tel (800) 827-2231 *Founded/Ownrshp* 2009
Sales 111.5MME *EMP* 95E
SIC 5199 5947 Candles; Gift, novelty & souvenir shop
Pr: John Fontana
**CEO:* James Ramaker
Mktg Dir: Jamey White
Snr PM: Jon Irvan

SMITH PIPE OF ABILENE
See PETROSMITH EQUIPMENT LP

D-U-N-S 00-909-2396 IMP/EXP
SMITH POWER PRODUCTS INC
3065 W California Ave, Salt Lake City, UT 84104-4586
Tel (801) 262-2631 *Founded/Ownrshp* 1960, 1979
Sales 93.9MM *EMP* 275
Accts Traveller & Company Llc Cente
SIC 5084 7538 3714 5063 Engines & parts, diesel; Diesel engine repair: automotive; Transmissions, motor vehicle; Generators
Pr: Michael B Smith
CFO: Tyson Williams
**Treas:* Brent D Sandberg
**VP:* Christopher W Fleming
**VP:* Darrell Manuel

D-U-N-S 06-897-3718
SMITH PROTECTIVE SERVICES INC (TX)
4440 Beltway Dr, Addison, TX 75001-3705
Tel (972) 960-8481 *Founded/Ownrshp* 1903, 1972
Sales 37.6MME *EMP* 1,295
SIC 7381 Protective services, guard; Security guard service; Private investigator; Lie detection service
CEO: Clayton J Smith
**Pr:* Mark L Smith
**Ex VP:* Bill Cue
Opers Mgr: John Robertson

D-U-N-S 04-979-3763 IMP/EXP
SMITH SEED SERVICES LLC
26890 Powerline Rd, Halsey, OR 97348-9736
Tel (541) 369-2831 *Founded/Ownrshp* 1976
Sales 99.5MM *EMP* 100
SIC 5191

D-U-N-S 12-544-2298 IMP
SMITH TANK & STEEL INC
42422 Highway 30, Gonzales, LA 70737-8409
Tel (225) 644-8747 *Founded/Ownrshp* 1997
Sales 142.6MME *EMP* 300
SIC 1541 Steel building construction
Pr: Sam J Smith Jr
**CFO:* David Hubbard
**Sec:* Karen S Guidry
**VP:* Billy S Smith

D-U-N-S 96-416-1855
SMITH TEMPORARIES INC
CORNERSTONE STAFFING
1200 Summit Ave Ste 518, Fort Worth, TX 76102-4408
Tel (817) 332-5882 *Founded/Ownrshp* 1991
Sales 53.2MME *EMP* 1,500
SIC 7363 Temporary help service
Pr: Stephen Michael Smith
**Ex VP:* Michael Phillips
Brnch Mgr: Loris Montenegro
Brnch Mgr: Kara Thornberg
VP Opers: Heather Stroh

D-U-N-S 79-912-9309
SMITH TRANSPORT INC
153 Smith Transport Rd, Roaring Spring, PA 16673-2247
Tel (814) 224-5155 *Founded/Ownrshp* 1987
Sales 91.1MME *EMP* 1,200
SIC 4213 Contract haulers; Heavy hauling
Owner: Barry F Smith
CFO: Ivan Fetzer
VP: Jeffrey Musselman
**VP:* Tommy D Smith
IT Man: John Norwood
Sls Mgr: Jack Kissell

D-U-N-S 11-831-4731 EXP
SMITH TURF & IRRIGATION LLC
S T I
4355 Golf Acres Dr, Charlotte, NC 28208-5874
Tel (704) 393-8873 *Founded/Ownrshp* 1984
Sales 87.4MM *EMP* 280
SIC 5083

SMITH&NEPHEW
See SMITH & NEPHEW INC

D-U-N-S 10-175-4612
SMITH-ROWE LLC
639 Old Us 52 S, Mount Airy, NC 27030-8042
Tel (336) 789-8221 *Founded/Ownrshp* 1979
Sales 141.1MME *EMP* 530
Accts Smith Kesler & Company Spart
SIC 1622 Bridge construction
**VP:* David Locke Rowe
Genl Mgr: David Rowe
Board of Directors: Cleve May

D-U-N-S 06-849-9110
SMITHBUCKLIN CORP
330 N Wabash Ave, Chicago, IL 60611-3586
Tel (312) 644-6610 *Founded/Ownrshp* 1949
Sales 165.1MME *EMP* 766
SIC 8742 8743 4724 Management consulting services; Marketing consulting services; Labor & union relations consultant; Financial consultant; Public relations services; Travel agencies
CEO: Henry S Givray
COO: Julie Siverstein
CFO: Wesley W Christensen
Treas: Al Koob
Chf Mktg O: David Schulte
Ofcr: Kevin M Hinton
Ex VP: Carolyn Dolezal
Ex VP: Michael L Payne
Ex VP: David Schmahl
Sr VP: Michael Silverman
VP: Megan Cohen
VP: Tom Myers
VP: Brian Teague
VP: Leslie Thornton
Exec: Colette Huzinec
Assoc Dir: Doug Fesler
Creative D: Bill Wargo

D-U-N-S 00-311-0913 IMP/EXP
SMITHFIELD FARMLAND CORP
(*Suby of* SMITHFIELD FOODS INC) ★
111 Commerce St, Smithfield, VA 23430-1201
Tel (757) 357-3131 *Founded/Ownrshp* 1939, 1971
Sales 5.1MMME *EMP* 22,465
SIC 2011 2013 Hams & picnics from meat slaughtered on site; Sausages & other prepared meats
Pr: Tim Shellpeper
**Sr VP:* Kurt Dellos
Sr VP: George Knierbein
**Sr VP:* Shelly Phalen
Sr VP: Dennis Treacy
VP: Todd Scott
Dir Teleco: Jeff Yedinak
**CIO:* Dan Sabin
CTO: Mansour Zadeh
QA Dir: Stephen Melton
Dir IT: Jeff Thomas

D-U-N-S 07-939-5619
SMITHFIELD FARMLAND SALES CORP
(*Suby of* SMITHFIELD FARMLAND CORP) ★
111 Commerce St, Smithfield, VA 23430-1201
Tel (757) 357-3131 *Founded/Ownrshp* 2014
Sales 130.6MME *EMP* 400
SIC 5147 8743 5963 Meats & meat products; Sales promotion; Food services, direct sales
Pr: Timothy O Schellpeper
**Sr VP:* Shelly Phalen

D-U-N-S 04-320-5053 IMP/EXP
SMITHFIELD FOODS INC
(*Suby of* WH GROUP LIMITED)
200 Commerce St, Smithfield, VA 23430-1204
Tel (757) 365-3000 *Founded/Ownrshp* 2013
Sales 14.4MMM *EMP* 50,236
SIC 2011 2013 2015 Meat packing plants; Boxed beef from meat slaughtered on site; Hams & picnics from meat slaughtered on site; Sausages & other prepared meats; Poultry slaughtering & processing; Poultry slaughtering & processing
Pr: Kenneth M Sullivan
Genl Pt: Doug Shisler
**Ch Bd:* Long Wan
Pr: Jerry Frizzell
Pr: Dariusz Nowakowski
Pr: Joseph B Sebring
CFO: Glenn T Nunziata
Treas: Landon Moore

Chf Mktg O: Bob Weber
Chf Mktg O: Tim Zimmer
Ex VP: Robert Manly
Ex VP: Dhamu Thamodaran
Ex VP: Dennis H Treacy
Sr VP: Chuck Gitkin
VP: Timothy Dykstra
VP: Mark Garrett
VP: Craig Harlow
VP: Stewart T Leeth

D-U-N-S 00-154-7835 EXP
SMITHFIELD PACKING CO INC (DE)
GWALTNEY OF SMITHFIELD
(*Suby of* SMITHFIELD FOODS INC) ★
601 N Church St, Smithfield, VA 23430-1221
Tel (757) 357-3131 *Founded/Ownrshp* 1981
Sales 347.0MM^E *EMP* 3,000
SIC 2011 2013 Meat packing plants; Sausages & other prepared meats
Pr: Timothy O Schellpeper
**CFO:* Kurt Dellos
**VP:* Michael H Cole
IT Man: Mike Paddon
Opers Mgr: Charles Darrow

SMITHFIELDS HOG PRODUCTION DIV
See MURPHY-BROWN LLC

D-U-N-S 00-421-3930
SMITHFOODS ORRVILLE INC (OH)
1381 Dairy Ln, Orrville, OH 44667-2503
Tel (330) 683-8710 *Founded/Ownrshp* 1909
Sales 122.9MM^E *EMP* 500
SIC 2026 2024

D-U-N-S 09-696-2261
SMITHGROUP COMPANIES INC
500 Griswold St Fl 1700, Detroit, MI 48226-8011
Tel (313) 442-8351 *Founded/Ownrshp* 1979
Sales 86.6MM^E *EMP* 823
SIC 8712 8711 Architectural services; Engineering services
Ch Bd: David King
Pr: Michael Medici
Treas: Joseph Lordon
VP: Randal Swiech
Comm Man: Sandra Knight
Prin: Russell Sykes
Prin: Troy Thompson
Board of Directors: David King, Carl Roehling

D-U-N-S 00-538-1660 IMP/EXP
SMITHGROUPJJR INC (MI)
(*Suby of* SMITHGROUP COMPANIES INC) ★
1700 New York Ave Nw # 100, Washington, DC 20006-5201
Tel (602) 265-2200 *Founded/Ownrshp* 1903, 2007
Sales 86.2MM^E *EMP* 817
SIC 8712 Architectural engineering
Pr: Michael Medici
**Treas:* Joseph Lordon
Dir Bus: Kathleen Hudson-Beitz
Board of Directors: William Patek, Timothy Tracey, Kathleen Hudson-Beitz, Mark Patterson, David Varner, Heather Chung, Russell Perry, A Bradley Woodman, Jeffrey Hausman, Joyce Polhamus, Bonnie Khang-Keating, Christopher Purdy, David Rh King, Carl Roehling, William Kline, Sven Shockey, Mark Kranz, Randal Swiech, Thomas Mroz Jr, Russell Sykes, Lise Newman, Troy Thompson

SMITH'S
See FRYS FOOD STORES OF ARIZONA INC

D-U-N-S 19-423-9018 IMP/EXP
SMITHS DETECTION INC
(*Suby of* SMITHS GROUP PLC)
2202 Lakeside Blvd, Edgewood, MD 21040-1102
Tel (410) 510-9100 *Founded/Ownrshp* 1997
Sales 136.5MM^E *EMP* 550
SIC 3824 3823 3829 8731

D-U-N-S 04-370-0194 IMP
■ **SMITHS FOOD & DRUG CENTERS INC**
(*Suby of* KROGER CO) ★
1550 S Redwood Rd, Salt Lake City, UT 84104-5105
Tel (801) 974-1400 *Founded/Ownrshp* 1999
Sales 1.9MMM^E *EMP* 14,500
SIC 5912 5499 Drug stores; Coffee
Pr: Mark C Tuffin
Bd of Dir: Katherine Ortega
Bd of Dir: Ronald Sargent
**VP:* Peter Barth
**VP:* Colleen Juergensen
VP: Ken Kimball
VP: Bill Ross
VP: Steve Sorensen
VP: Jeff Talbot
Genl Mgr: Rich Bylski
Telecom Mg: Doug Summers

D-U-N-S 04-710-8485 IMP/EXP
SMITHS GROUP NORTH AMERICA INC
(*Suby of* SMITHS GROUP PLC)
101 Lindenwood Dr Ste 125, Malvern, PA 19355-1755
Tel (772) 286-9300 *Founded/Ownrshp* 1958
Sales 738.7MM^E *EMP* 10,125
SIC 3812 3841 3679 Aircraft control systems, electronic; Navigational systems & instruments; Surgical instruments & apparatus; Harness assemblies for electronic use: wire or cable
VP: R C Albrecht
Treas: R C Albeht
**VP:* Ronald C Albrecht
VP: Michael Jones
VP: Kathy Niness
Tech Mgr: Jay Pruiett
Sftwr Eng: Douglas Lewis

D-U-N-S 79-043-4620
SMITHS INTERCONNECT INC
(*Suby of* SMITHS INTERCONNECT GROUP LIMITED)
4726 Eisenhower Blvd, Tampa, FL 33634-6309
Tel (813) 901-7200 *Founded/Ownrshp* 2007
Sales 197.9MM^E *EMP* 1,162
SIC 3679 Antennas, receiving
Pr: David Moorehouse
**Prin:* Serge Taylor

D-U-N-S 05-632-9097 IMP
SMITHS MEDICAL ASD INC
(*Suby of* SMITHS GROUP PLC)
6000 Nathan Ln N Ste 100, Plymouth, MN 55442-1691
Tel (763) 383-3000 *Founded/Ownrshp* 1985
Sales 363.4MM^E *EMP* 1,125
SIC 3842 Surgical appliances & supplies
CEO: Jeff McCaulley
**Pr:* Stuart Morris-Hipkins
**Pr:* Srini Seshadri
CFO: Robert James
**CFO:* Ted Melo
**VP:* Bob Armstrong
VP: John Baranski
**VP:* Jeffrey Brown
**VP:* Russ Davies
**VP:* Tommy Johns
**VP:* Ron Leonhardt
VP: Gretchen Rawdon
**VP:* Ben Sommerness
**VP:* Carl Stamp
**VP:* Richard Thomas
VP: Edward Yoxen
Exec: Kathleen Preston

D-U-N-S 10-671-2748 IMP
SMITHS MEDICAL MD INC
(*Suby of* SMITHS GROUP PLC)
6000 Nathan Ln N Ste 100, Minneapolis, MN 55442-1691
Tel (651) 633-2556 *Founded/Ownrshp* 1994
Sales 228.8MM^E *EMP* 2,580
SIC 3841 3586 3561 Surgical & medical instruments; Measuring & dispensing pumps; Pumps & pumping equipment
CEO: Stuart Morris-Hipkins
Pr: Jim Stitt
CFO: Mark Barrenechea
CFO: Karen Linnard
Sr Cor Off: Kawada San
Sr VP: John Bordin
VP: John Baranski
VP: Carlos Santos
Exec: Steven Bledsoe
Dir Lab: Jerome Kernes
Prgrm Mgr: Lyle V Peterson

D-U-N-S 00-108-3609 IMP
SMITHS TUBULAR SYSTEMS-LACONIA INC (NH)
TITEFLEX AEROSPACE
(*Suby of* SMITHS GROUP PLC)
93 Lexington Dr, Laconia, NH 03246-2935
Tel (603) 524-2064 *Founded/Ownrshp* 1913, 2002
Sales 117.5MM^E *EMP* 300
SIC 3463 3498 8734 7692 3441 3398 Machinery forgings, nonferrous; Tube fabricating (contract bending & shaping); Testing laboratories; Welding repair; Fabricated structural metal; Metal heat treating
Pr: William T Smith
COO: Ron Mowery
COO: Mowery Ron
**Treas:* Martin Hough
**VP:* Patrick D McCaffrey
**VP:* Robert M Speer
Genl Mgr: Jeremy Beck
Genl Mgr: David Bonisteel
Dir IT: Kathe Turner
IT Man: Teri Thibeault
VP Opers: Michael Sandahl

D-U-N-S 00-326-1880 IMP/EXP
■ **SMITHSONIAN INSTITUTION** (DC)
(*Suby of* EXECUTIVE OFFICE OF UNITED STATES GOVERNMENT) ★
1000 Jefferson Dr Sw, Washington, DC 20560-0009
Tel (202) 633-1000 *Founded/Ownrshp* 1846
Sales 1.4MMM *EMP* 6,100
Accts Kpmg Llp Mclean Va
SIC 8412 8422 Museum; Zoological garden, noncommercial
CEO: Gary M Beer
V Ch: John W McCarter Jr
V Ch: Patricia Q Stonesifer
**Pr:* Christopher Liedel
CFO: Gregory Bokman
**CFO:* Albert Horvath
**CFO:* Alice C Maroni
**Treas:* Sudeep Anand
Sr Cor Off: Rafael Lemaitre
Ofcr: Maura Reidy
VP: Linda St Thomas
Exec: Ann Sekeres
Exec: Laura C Steele
Assoc Dir: Greg Bettwy
Dir Soc: Emily Chamberlin
Comm Dir: Jennifer Northrop

D-U-N-S 06-806-5309
SMITHTOWN CENTRAL SCHOOL DISTRICT
26 New York Ave Unit 1, Smithtown, NY 11787-3435
Tel (631) 382-2000 *Founded/Ownrshp* 1920
Sales 65.9MM^E *EMP* 1,090
SIC 8211 Public elementary & secondary schools
Dir Vol: David Parsick
Ex VP: Carie Bodo
VP: Ann Devito
Exec: Deborah Smith
Prin: Paul Graf
Prin: Jeanne Kull
Prin: John Nocero
Prin: Ireen Westrack
Mng Dir: Kimberly Williams
Area Mgr: Nicole Mogil
Genl Mgr: Andrew Tobin

SMITTY'S
See R H SMITH DISTRIBUTING CO INC

D-U-N-S 04-973-5434 IMP/EXP
SMITTYS SUPPLY INC
63399 Highway 51, Roseland, LA 70456-1801
Tel (985) 748-9687 *Founded/Ownrshp* 2001
Sales 301.9MM^E *EMP* 245^E
SIC 5172 5531 Lubricating oils & greases; Automotive parts
CEO: David A Smith
**Pr:* Ed Smith III

**CFO:* Michael Estay
**Treas:* Gary Hamilton
**Sec:* George D Smith
**VP:* Joshua Adam Beech
**VP:* Mitchell S Smith
Trfc Dir: John Pierce
Manager: Jimmy Ellis
VP Sls: Chad Tate

SMMPA
See SOUTHERN MINNESOTA MUNICIPAL POWER AGENCY

D-U-N-S 08-004-1746
SMO FINANCE CORP
(*Suby of* SODEXO AMERICA LLC) ★
9801 Washington Blvd, Gaithersburg, MD 20878
Tel (301) 987-4000 *Founded/Ownrshp* 1998
Sales 14.8MM^E *EMP* 2,468^E
SIC 8741 Management services

D-U-N-S 00-695-1032
SMO INC (MD)
(*Suby of* WILLS GROUP INC) ★
6355 Crain Hwy, La Plata, MD 20646-4267
Tel (301) 932-3600 *Founded/Ownrshp* 1926
Sales 496.9MM *EMP* 50
SIC 5172 Petroleum products
CEO: Mel Strine
**Pr:* Lock Wills
CFO: Jennifer Popescu
**Prin:* Charles Boyers

D-U-N-S 00-525-3364 EXP
SMOKER CRAFT INC
68143 Clunette St, New Paris, IN 46553-3700
Tel (574) 831-2103 *Founded/Ownrshp* 1869, 1964
Sales 165.0MM *EMP* 525
SIC 3732 5551 3731 Motorized boat, building & repairing; Boat dealers; Ferryboats, building & repairing
Pr: Douglas Smoker
CFO: Joe Blackburn
Sr VP: Peter Barrett
**VP:* Byron Smoker
IT Man: Troy Pippenger
Board of Directors: Sara Barrett, Susan Graff, Cinda Mc Kinney

SMOKEY BONE'S BAR & FIRE GRILL
See BARBEQUE INTEGRATED INC

D-U-N-S 02-131-4265
SMOKEY POINT DISTRIBUTING INC
(*Suby of* DASEKE INC) ★
19201 63rd Ave Ne, Arlington, WA 98223-6357
Tel (360) 435-5737 *Founded/Ownrshp* 1979
Sales 91.1MM^E *EMP* 310
SIC 4213 4212 4214 Trucking, except local; Local trucking, without storage; Local trucking with storage
Pr: Dan Wirkkala
**CFO:* Steve Sams
**VP:* Troy Fuller
**VP:* Greg Hirsch
IT Man: David Lemasters
Opers Mgr: Patrick Bacon
Opers Mgr: Derek Dietrich

SMP
See STURGIS MOLDED PRODUCTS CO

D-U-N-S 00-338-9561 IMP
SMR AUTOMOTIVE MIRROR INTERNATIONAL USA INC
(*Suby of* SMR AUTOMOTIVE TECHNOLOGY HOLDINGS USA PARTNERS LLP) ★
1855 Busha Hwy, Marysville, MI 48040-1892
Tel (810) 364-4141 *Founded/Ownrshp* 1990, 2000
Sales 321.0MM^E *EMP* 750
SIC 3231 Products of purchased glass
Pr: Char Zawadzinski
Treas: John Jesionowski

D-U-N-S 60-755-7782 IMP
SMR AUTOMOTIVE SYSTEMS USA INC
SAMVARDHANA MTHERSON REFLECTEC
(*Suby of* SMR AUTOMOTIVE MIRROR INTERNATIONAL USA INC) ★
1855 Busha Hwy, Marysville, MI 48040-1892
Tel (810) 364-4141 *Founded/Ownrshp* 1989
Sales 321.0MM^E *EMP* 725
SIC 3231 Mirrors, truck & automobile: made from purchased glass
COO: Char Zawadzinski
**Treas:* John Jesionowski
**VP:* SAI Tatineni
QA Dir: Paul Bouverette
Netwrk Mgr: Randall Mrock
QI Cn Mgr: Kimberly Nolte
Board of Directors: Andreas Heuser

D-U-N-S 00-338-9009 IMP
SMR AUTOMOTIVE TECHNOLOGY HOLDINGS USA PARTNERS LLP
(*Suby of* SMR AUTOMOTIVE MIRROR PARTS AND HOLDINGS UK LIMITED)
1855 Busha Hwy, Marysville, MI 48040-1892
Tel (810) 364-4141 *Founded/Ownrshp* 2000
Sales 321.0MM^E *EMP* 750^E
SIC 3231 Products of purchased glass
Treas: Jeff Dolbee

D-U-N-S 09-535-0484
SMS DATA PRODUCTS GROUP INC
1751 Pinnacle Dr Ste 1200, Mc Lean, VA 22102-3881
Tel (703) 288-8100 *Founded/Ownrshp* 1976
Sales 422.5MM^E *EMP* 295
SIC 5045 7373 Word processing equipment; Computer software; Systems integration services
CEO: Albert Rosecan
**Pr:* Juan Hernandez
**CFO:* Juan Morales
**VP:* John Cordeiro
**VP:* John Ladd
**VP:* Jose Nabielsky
VP: Rakesh Patel
VP Bus Dev: Luis Laranjeira
Genl Mgr: Scott Lang

Netwrk Eng: Cary Quintana
Netwrk Eng: Joshua Snyder

D-U-N-S 12-231-2288
SMS HOLDINGS CORP
7135 Charlotte Pike # 100, Nashville, TN 37209-5015
Tel (615) 399-1839 *Founded/Ownrshp* 2006
Sales 891.5MM^E *EMP* 15,100^E
SIC 7349 Building maintenance services
CEO: Keith Walken
**Pr:* Dan Rakestraw
**Pr:* Mike Wein
**CFO:* Hiram Cox
CFO: Hiram A Cox
Div VP: Dan Hickey
Div VP: Gregory Moore
**Ex VP:* Jim Burnett
Sr VP: T S Emerson
VP: Scott Emerson
Creative D: Levi Watson

D-U-N-S 93-841-1824 IMP
SMS INFOCOMM CORP
WISTRON INFOCOMM
(*Suby of* WISTRON CORPORATION)
4051 N Highway 121 # 100, Grapevine, TX 76051-2327
Tel (972) 906-7800 *Founded/Ownrshp* 2002
Sales 96.0MM^E *EMP* 750
SIC 7378 Computer maintenance & repair
Pr: Jerry Wang
Sec: Sandy Peng
Prin: Hung-Kuei Hsu
IT Man: Alfonso Romero

SMS MILLCRAFT
See SMS TECHNICAL SERVICES LLC

D-U-N-S 00-541-9148
SMS SYSTEMS MAINTENANCE SERVICES INC (MA)
10420 Harris Oak Blvd C, Charlotte, NC 28269-7513
Tel (704) 921-1620 *Founded/Ownrshp* 1981, 2005
Sales 237.4MM^E *EMP* 631
SIC 7378 Computer maintenance & repair
**Pr:* Joe Scordino
**CFO:* Steve Favory
Ex VP: Vince Cavell
Ex VP: Jim Kleeman
CTO: Greg Hoogerland
IT Man: Bill Hable
Netwrk Eng: Aubrey Kipp
Sls Dir: Steve Forsey
Sls Mgr: Jim Stanton
Snr Mgr: Chris Vollo

D-U-N-S 11-137-1733 IMP/EXP
SMS TECHNICAL SERVICES LLC
SMS MILLCRAFT
(*Suby of* SMS HOLDING GMBH)
210 W Kensinger Dr # 300, Cranberry Township, PA 16066-3435
Tel (724) 553-3420 *Founded/Ownrshp* 2002
Sales 159.9MM^E *EMP* 500
SIC 3569 7539 Assembly machines, non-metalworking; Machine shop, automotive
CEO: Doug Dunworth
**Pr:* George Born
**Ex VP:* Scott Sander
**VP:* Steve Winger
Exec: Donna Brophy
Exec: Dieter Stotski
Genl Mgr: Ronald Lewis
Genl Mgr: Jim Mulhern
Genl Mgr: Christina Salera
Genl Mgr: Ken Sharrer
CIO: Dennis Stecko

D-U-N-S 17-503-2036 IMP
SMS USA LLC
(*Suby of* SMS GROUP GMBH)
100 Sandusky St, Pittsburgh, PA 15212-5822
Tel (412) 231-1200 *Founded/Ownrshp* 1992
Sales 182.8MM^E *EMP* 800
SIC 3547 3542 Rod mills (rolling mill equipment); Finishing equipment, rolling mill; Extruding machines (machine tools), metal
Pr: Joseph Dzierzawski
Pr: Thomas Isajiw
**Pr:* Keith Watson
**COO:* Thomas Fest
**CFO:* Peter Fernie
Chf Mktg O: Gail Sunderland
Ex VP: Scott Sander
Ex VP: Rudiger Zerbe
VP: Matthew Korzi
Exec: Donna Brophy
Exec: Cathy Stanyard
Exec: Dieter Stotski
Board of Directors: Kay Mayland

D-U-N-S 83-268-5007
SMSA PALESTINE ACQUISITION CORP
174 E Fm 1830, Argyle, TX 76226-4300
Tel (972) 233-0300 *Founded/Ownrshp* 2009
Sales 125.7MM *EMP* 2^E
SIC 6799 Investors
Prin: Orsolya Peresztegi

SMSC
See STANDARD MICROSYSTEMS CORP

SMSC
See SHAKOPEE MDEWAKANTON SIOUX COMMUNITY

D-U-N-S 78-977-9147 IMP
SMSC GAMING ENTERPRISE
MYSTIC LAKE CASINO
(*Suby of* SMSC) ★
2400 Mystic Lake Blvd, Prior Lake, MN 55372-9004
Tel (952) 445-9000 *Founded/Ownrshp* 1982
Sales 41.8MM^E *EMP* 1,500^E
SIC 7999 7011 Gambling establishment; Bingo hall; Casino hotel
CEO: Edward Stevenson
CFO: Lawrence Kovach
**Treas:* Loretta Zacharias
Ex VP: Angela Heikes
VP: Kyle Kool
VP: Kyle Kossol

*VP: Tom Polusny
VP: Scott Scepaniak
Exec: Andrea Olsen
Exec: Marshall Rosenthal
Genl Mgr: Tom Johnson

D-U-N-S 07-914-7003
SMT TELECOM INC
5219 N Harlem Ave, Chicago, IL 60656-1803
Tel (773) 842-4412 Founded/Ownrshp 2011
Sales 110.0MM EMP 15
SIC 8748 Telecommunications consultant
Pr: Sadruddin Harmani
*VP: Azim Hemani

D-U-N-S 10-914-9190
SMTC MANUFACTURING CORP OF CALIFORNIA
(Suby of SMTC MANUFACTURING CORPORATION OF CANADA)
2302 Trade Zone Blvd, San Jose, CA 95131-1819
Tel (408) 934-7100 Founded/Ownrshp 1994
Sales 224.8MM^E EMP 1,875
SIC 3672 Printed circuit boards
CEO: Larry Silber
*Pr: John Caldwell
*Pr: Claude Germain
*Pr: Alex Walker
*CFO: Jane Todd
*Ex VP: Paul Blom
*VP: Frank Gerber
*VP: David Sandberg
VP: Don Simpson
*VP: Betsy Smith
*Prin: Clarke Bailey

D-U-N-S 05-021-4741 IMP/EXP
■ SMUCKER NATURAL FOODS INC
(Suby of J M SMUCKER CO) ★
37 Speedway Ave, Chico, CA 95928-9554
Tel (530) 899-5000 Founded/Ownrshp 1971
Sales 256.7MM^E EMP 2,000
SIC 2086 2033 2087 Iced tea & fruit drinks, bottled & canned; Carbonated beverages, nonalcoholic: bottled & canned; Canned fruits & specialties; Syrups, drink
CEO: Richard K Smucker
*Pr: Timothy P Smucker
*VP: Julia Sabin
VP: Albert Yeagley
Mktg Mgr: Jasen Cusick
Snr Mgr: Gary Royer
Snr Mgr: Dewayne Williams

D-U-N-S 00-803-8549 IMP
SMURFIT KAPPA BATES LLC (TX)
(Suby of SMURFIT KAPPA PACKAGING LIMITED)
6433 Davis Blvd, North Richland Hills, TX 76182-4717
Tel (817) 498-3200 Founded/Ownrshp 1963, 2007
Sales 124.6MM^E EMP 325
SIC 2653 5113 Boxes, corrugated: made from purchased materials; Display items, corrugated: made from purchased materials; Bags, paper & disposable plastic
VP: Ron Welch
Genl Mgr: Jim Horvath
VP Sls: Mortiz Deford

D-U-N-S 05-576-0722 IMP
SMURFIT KAPPA NORTH AMERICA LLC
COI GRAPHICS
(Suby of SMURFIT KAPPA GROUP PUBLIC LIMITED COMPANY)
13400 Nelson Ave, City of Industry, CA 91746-2331
Tel (626) 333-6363 Founded/Ownrshp 2012
Sales 638.5MM^E EMP 1,700
SIC 2653 2671 2657 Boxes, corrugated: made from purchased materials; Packaging paper & plastics film, coated & laminated; Folding paperboard boxes
Pr: Greg Hall
CFO: Kevin McDonald
*Sr VP: David Ortiz
VP: John Murphy
*Prin: David Capanash
*Prin: Forest Felvey
*Prin: Michael Feterik
*Prin: David Graham
*Prin: Richard Lockwood
Dir IT: Steve Kinney
Sls Mgr: Dave Capanash

D-U-N-S 05-451-2640
SMX LLC
860 W Evergreen Ave, Chicago, IL 60642-2634
Tel (312) 915-0900 Founded/Ownrshp 2011
Sales 98.4MM^E EMP 6,050
SIC 7361 Executive placement
CEO: Patrick Beharelle
CFO: Christopher Averill

D-U-N-S 01-819-5214
SMYTH AUTOMOTIVE INC (OH)
4275 Mt Carmel Tobasco Rd, Cincinnati, OH 45244-2319
Tel (513) 528-2800 Founded/Ownrshp 1963
Sales 131.6MM^E EMP 375
SIC 5013 5531 Automotive supplies & parts; Automotive parts
Pr: Joseph M Smyth
*Sec: Lynette Smithson
*VP: Jim Smyth
Mktg Dir: Natalie Hansman

D-U-N-S 00-615-3415 IMP
SMYTH COMPANIES LLC
(Suby of GG MCGUIGGAN CORP) ★
1085 Snelling Ave N, Saint Paul, MN 55108-2705
Tel (651) 646-4544 Founded/Ownrshp 1877
Sales 129.3MM^E EMP 480
SIC 2679 2752 3993 7389 5084 7699 Labels, paper: made from purchased material; Commercial printing, lithographic; Commercial printing, offset; Displays & cutouts, window & lobby; Laminating service; Processing & packaging equipment; Industrial machinery & equipment repair
CEO: John Hickey
Pr: James Lundquist
CFO: David K Baumgardner
Ex VP: Daniel E Hickey
VP: Larry Brandes
VP: Steve Yokanovich
Genl Mgr: Bill Denzen
Ql Cn Mgr: Donna Niedenfuer

SMYTH JEWELERS
See ALBERT S SMYTH CO INC

D-U-N-S 96-074-5032 IMP/EXP
SNACK ALLIANCE INC
(Suby of SHEARERS FOODS LLC) ★
100 Lincoln Way E, Massillon, OH 44646-6634
Tel (330) 767-3426 Founded/Ownrshp 2010
Sales 144.4MM^E EMP 1,600^E
SIC 2096 Potato chips & similar snacks
CEO: Robert Shearer
*Pr: Scott Smith
*CFO: Fredric Kohmann
*Ex VP: Thomas Shearer

D-U-N-S 02-745-5633 IMP/EXP
SNAK-KING CORP
16150 Stephens St, City of Industry, CA 91745-1718
Tel (626) 336-7711 Founded/Ownrshp 1980
Sales 108.2MM^E EMP 577
SIC 2096

D-U-N-S 17-202-2162
SNAKE RIVER SUGAR CO
1951 S Saturn Way Ste 100, Boise, ID 83709-2924
Tel (208) 383-6500 Founded/Ownrshp 1897
Sales 722.4MM^E EMP 2,500
Accts Eidebailly Llp Boise Idaho
SIC 8611 2063 Growers' associations; Dry beet sugar products, except refining
*Pr: Vic Jaro
*CFO: Wayne Neely
*Ex Dir: Terry L Ketterling
Dir IT: Dennis Costesso
IT Man: Ano Sundara

D-U-N-S 78-279-7695
SNAKEBITE LEASING INC
SELLERS PETROLEUM
821 S Pacific Ave, Yuma, AZ 85365-2117
Tel (928) 276-3328 Founded/Ownrshp 1976
Sales 114.8MM EMP 42
Accts Terkelsen Smith Tyree & Snell
SIC 5171
Pr: Dave Sellers
*VP: John Sellers
*VP: Reed Sellers

D-U-N-S 07-156-1105
SNAP INC
SNAPCHAT
63 Market St, Venice, CA 90291-3603
Tel (310) 399-3339 Founded/Ownrshp 2012
Sales 8.1MM^E EMP 1,101^E
SIC 7372 Application computer software
CEO: Evan T Spiegel
Pr: Mary Ritti
*CFO: Drew Vollero
Exec: Chris Handman
CTO: Bobby Murphy
Sftwr Eng: Alexander Grytsiuk
Sftwr Eng: Yunao Liu
Sftwr Eng: Ruoyu Li
Sftwr Eng: Gowrishankar Sunder
Sftwr Eng: Khoi Tran
Sftwr Eng: Anthony Urso

D-U-N-S 80-808-0618
■ SNAP-ON BUSINESS SOLUTIONS INC
(Suby of SNAP-ON TOOLS) ★
4025 Kinross Lakes Pkwy, Richfield, OH 44286-9371
Tel (330) 659-1600 Founded/Ownrshp 2006
Sales 162.0MM^E EMP 700
SIC 2741 Miscellaneous publishing
Pr: Timothy Chambers
*CEO: Bruce Rhoades
CFO: Jerry Baracz
*Ofcr: Michael Maddison
VP: Simon Beale
VP: Elliot Forsyth
VP: Lynda Gilboe
VP: Gary Marcus
VP: Corey Roberts
Prgrm Mgr: Jay Raymond
Area Mgr: Rhett Scully

D-U-N-S 82-572-8223
SNAP-ON CREDIT LLC
950 Technology Way # 301, Libertyville, IL 60048-5339
Tel (847) 782-7700 Founded/Ownrshp 1999
Sales NA EMP 225^E
SIC 6153 Short-term business credit
*Pr: Jack Kania
Treas: Jeffrey F Kostrzewa
VP: Ken Shamblen
Prgrm Mgr: Jennifer Gussarson
*VP Opers: Jack Munnelly
Mktg Dir: Michael Columbia
Mktg Dir: Michael Dilallo

D-U-N-S 00-609-0294 IMP
▲ SNAP-ON INC
SNAP-ON TOOLS
2801 80th St, Kenosha, WI 53143-5656
Tel (262) 656-5200 Founded/Ownrshp 1920
Sales 3.3MMM EMP 11,500
Tkr Sym SNA Exch NYS
SIC 3546 3559 3825 Power-driven handtools; Hammers, portable: electric or pneumatic, chipping, etc.; Drill attachments, portable; Automotive related machinery; Wheel balancing equipment, automotive; Internal combustion engine analyzers, to test electronics
Pr: Nicholas T Pinchuk
Pr: Jean-Pierre Levrey
CFO: Aldo J Pagliari
Treas: Eric Ormson
Chf Mktg O: Charlene M Dreyer
Ex VP: Bradley Lewis
VP: Govind Arora
VP: Anup Banerjee
VP: Mary Bauerschmidt
VP: Mike Biggs
VP: Samuel E Bottum
VP: Jim Godby
VP: Gary S Henning
VP: Constance R Johnsen
VP: Leslie Kratcoski
VP: Jim McKibbin
VP: Jeanne M Moreno
VP: Gerald Seebeck
VP: Irwin M Shur
VP: Irene Sudac
VP: John Watters
Board of Directors: Donald J Stebbins, David C Adams, Karen L Daniel, John F Fiedler, Ruth Ann M Gillis, James P Holden, Nathan J Jones, Henry W Knueppel, W Dudley Lehman, Gregg M Sherrill

SNAP-ON INDUSTRIAL
See IDSC HOLDINGS LLC

SNAP-ON TOOLS
See SNAP-ON INC

SNAP-ON TOOLS
See SNAP-ON-TOOLS CORP

D-U-N-S 94-141-8741 IMP/EXP
■ SNAP-ON-TOOLS CORP
SNAP-ON TOOLS
(Suby of SNAP-ON TOOLS) ★
2801 80th St, Kenosha, WI 53143-5699
Tel (262) 656-5200 Founded/Ownrshp 1995
Sales 111.1MM^E EMP 295
SIC 5251 Hardware
Pr: Dale Elliott
Treas: Andrew D Tressler
VP: Jerry Baracz
VP: Ned Brooks
*VP: Nicholas Loffredo
Exec: Terri Crangle
IT Man: Vince Caputa
IT Man: Alex Pasrons
Sfty Mgr: Kathy Reddel
Sls Mgr: Luke Rollins

SNAPCHAT
See SNAP INC

SNAPPING SHOALS ELC MEMBERSHIP
See SNAPPING SHOALS ELECTRIC TRUST INC

D-U-N-S 96-630-4490
SNAPPING SHOALS ELECTRIC MEMBERSHIP CORP
14750 Brown Bridge Rd, Covington, GA 30016-4113
Tel (770) 786-3484 Founded/Ownrshp 1930
Sales 168.2MM EMP 2^E
Accts Mcnair Mclemore Middlebrooks
SIC 1731 Electrical work
CEO: Bradley Kent Thomas
CFO: Randall W Shaw

D-U-N-S 00-980-3396
SNAPPING SHOALS ELECTRIC TRUST INC
SNAPPING SHOALS ELC MEMBERSHIP
14750 Brown Bridge Rd, Covington, GA 30016-4113
Tel (770) 786-3484 Founded/Ownrshp 1953
Sales 168.2MM EMP 270
Accts Mcnair Mclemore Middlebrooks
SIC 4911 Distribution, electric power
CEO: Bradley Kent Thomas
*CFO: Carl Smith
VP: Robert Steele
Exec: Jackie Johnson
DP Dir: John Taylor

SNC LAVALIN CONSTRUCTOR
See SNC-LAVALIN CONSTRUCTORS INC

D-U-N-S 08-461-8144 IMP/EXP
SNC-LAVALIN CONSTRUCTORS INC
SNC LAVALIN CONSTRUCTOR
(Suby of GROUPE SNC-LAVALIN INC)
19015 North Creek Pkwy # 300, Bothell, WA 98011-8029
Tel (425) 489-3300 Founded/Ownrshp 1911
Sales 1.5MMM^E EMP 5,000
SIC 1629 Power plant construction
Pr: Michael Ranz
*CEO: Robert G Card
*COO: John H Gillis
*CFO: Alain-Pierre Raynaud
*Ex VP: Ian Edwards
*Sr VP: Steven L Daniels
*Sr VP: James Zapke
*VP: Paul Cutrona
VP: Steven Daniels
VP: David H Lund Jr
VP: Greg Tardanico

D-U-N-S 60-170-1469
SNEAKER VILLA INC
(Suby of GOODE PARTNERS LLC) ★
1926 Arch St Fl 3, Philadelphia, PA 19103-1444
Tel (215) 279-5600 Founded/Ownrshp 2013
Sales 120.0MM EMP 371^E
SIC 5699 5661 Sports apparel; Footwear, athletic
CEO: Jason Lutz
COO: David Rhoads
*CFO: Larry Long
VP: Jared Sadlowski
Store Mgr: Natasha Tate
IT Man: John Goy

D-U-N-S 07-753-5490
SNELL & WILMER LLP
400 E Van Buren St Fl 10, Phoenix, AZ 85004-0908
Tel (602) 382-6000 Founded/Ownrshp 1938
Sales 105.9MM^E EMP 922
SIC 8111 Legal services
Pt: John J Bouma
Pt: Jon S Cohen
Pt: Matt Feeney
Pt: Thomas R Hoecker
Pt: Warren E Platt
CFO: David Boden
Treas: Erica Warne
IT Man: Barry Ewart
Web Dev: Cindy Marquis
Counsel: Neil Peck

D-U-N-S 18-565-7538
SNELLING STAFFING LLC
(Suby of PATRIARCH PARTNERS LLC) ★
4055 Valley View Ln # 700, Dallas, TX 75244-5074
Tel (972) 239-7575 Founded/Ownrshp 2005
Sales 106.5MM^E EMP 1,200
SIC 7363 Temporary help service
VP: Larry Offutt
VP: Karen Taylor
Brnch Mgr: Justin Hall
IT Man: Caren Coffel
Sls Dir: Julia Stephens

D-U-N-S 00-382-3648
SNELSON COMPANIES INC
(Suby of POWER LINE SERVICES INC) ★
601 W State St, Sedro Woolley, WA 98284-1560
Tel (360) 856-6511 Founded/Ownrshp 2012
Sales 171.3MM^E EMP 350
SIC 1623 Pipeline construction
Pr: Greg Gapinski
Treas: Jerry W Iseman
Treas: Gerald Wiseman
*Treas: Mike Woodmansee
*Ex VP: Brian L Ganske
VP: Tony Anderson
*VP: Kevin Gundersen
*VP: Dale Lappe
VP: Steve Massey
Prgrm Mgr: Brandon Itzel
Mtls Mgr: Tom Howard

D-U-N-S 87-893-0965 IMP/EXP
SNF HOLDING CO
S N F
(Suby of SNF SAS)
1 Chemical Plant Rd, Riceboro, GA 31323
Tel (912) 884-3366 Founded/Ownrshp 1978
Sales 711.3MM^E EMP 1,600
SIC 2822 2899 Ethylene-propylene rubbers, EPDM polymers; Water treating compounds
CEO: Peter W Nichols
*CFO: Mark Schlag
VP: James R Calson
Opers Mgr: David Hancock

D-U-N-S 96-249-6738 EXP
SNF INC
(Suby of SNF SAS)
1 Chemical Plant Rd, Riceboro, GA 31323
Tel (912) 884-3366 Founded/Ownrshp 2002
Sales 170.7MM^E EMP 700
SIC 2822 Ethylene-propylene rubbers, EPDM polymers
Pr: Peter Nichols
Dir IT: Tracy L McBride

SNHU
See SOUTHERN NEW HAMPSHIRE UNIVERSITY

D-U-N-S 01-307-4552
SNI COMPANIES
4500 Westown Pkwy Ste 120, West Des Moines, IA 50266-6717
Tel (727) 577-4294 Founded/Ownrshp 2009
Sales 166.5MM^E EMP 9,000^E
SIC 7361 Employment agencies
Ch Bd: Ron Smith
Mng Dir: Anthony Mancini
Mng Dir: Jan Tobin
Brnch Mgr: Nathan Lee

SNIDER FLEET SOLUTIONS
See SNIDER TIRE INC

D-U-N-S 02-459-0051
SNIDER TIRE INC (NC)
SNIDER FLEET SOLUTIONS
200 E Meadowview Rd, Greensboro, NC 27406-4521
Tel (336) 691-5480 Founded/Ownrshp 1954, 1976
Sales 551.0MM^E EMP 900
SIC 5531 7534

D-U-N-S 61-000-7825
■ SNL FINANCIAL LC
(Suby of S&P GLOBAL INC) ★
1 Snl Plz, Charlottesville, VA 22902-5150
Tel (434) 977-1600 Founded/Ownrshp 2015
Sales 471.9MM^E EMP 1,956
SIC 7374 Data processing & preparation
Pr: Mike Chinn
*COO: Nick Cafferillo
*CFO: Adam Hall
*Chf Cred: Dan Oakey
Ex VP: John Fletcher
VP: Lisa Fontanella
VP: Thomas Serzan
Assoc Dir: Adnan Afzal
Assoc Dir: Lynn Bachstetter
Assoc Dir: Scott Dovel
Assoc Dir: Adam Fehd
Assoc Dir: Carlo Hontiveros
Assoc Dir: Chris Lewis
Assoc Dir: Matt Morton
Assoc Dir: Abby Newton
Assoc Dir: John-Patrick O'Sullivan
Assoc Dir: Lance Pickett
Assoc Dir: Brian Shullow
Assoc Dir: Arpita Trivedi

SNOHOMISH CNTY PUB UTILITY DST
See PUBLIC UTILITY DISTRICT 1 OF SNOHOMISH COUNTY

D-U-N-S 07-574-0332
SNOHOMISH SCHOOL DISTRICT 201
1601 Avenue D, Snohomish, WA 98290-1799
Tel (360) 563-7263 Founded/Ownrshp 1920
Sales 63.1MM^E EMP 1,283
Accts Brian Sonntag Cgfm
SIC 8211 Public elementary school; Public junior high school; Public senior high school; School board
*Ex Dir: Karen Riddle
Genl Mgr: Thomas Laufmann
Pr Dir: Kristin Foley

SNOQUALMIE CASINO
See SNOQUALMIE ENTERTAINMENT

D-U-N-S 82-702-7892
SNOQUALMIE ENTERTAINMENT
SNOQUALMIE CASINO
37500 Se North Bend Way, Snoqualmie, WA 98065-9260
Tel (425) 888-1234 Founded/Ownrshp 2008
Sales 50.1MM[E] EMP 1,000
SIC 7993 7011 Gambling establishments operating coin-operated machines; Casino hotel
CEO: Jon Jenkins
*CFO: James McDermott
Ofcr: Kyle Dropp
Ofcr: Timothy Gilliam
Ofcr: Rocky Martinez
Ofcr: Russell Ross
Exec: Kari White
Dir Soc: Carolyn McCoy
Sfty Dirs: Tim Bollig
Secur Mgr: Ken Hooper

D-U-N-S 00-416-0326 IMP/EXP
SNORKEL INTERNATIONAL INC
(Suby of TANFIELD GROUP PLC)
2009 Roseport Rd, Elwood, KS 66024
Tel (785) 989-3000 Founded/Ownrshp 1997, 2007
Sales 124.4MM[E] EMP 400[E]
SIC 3537 Trucks, tractors, loaders, carriers & similar equipment; Forklift trucks; Lift trucks, industrial: fork, platform, straddle, etc.; Stackers, power (industrial truck stackers)
Pr: Dave Smith
Pr: Richard Hoffelmeyer
*CFO: Ron Layfield
*VP: Steve Watts
Sls Mgr: David Kane
Sls Mgr: Lisa Williams

D-U-N-S 61-163-4150
SNOW PHIPPS GROUP LLC
667 Madison Ave Fl 18, New York, NY 10065-8029
Tel (212) 508-3300 Founded/Ownrshp 2005
Sales 762.6MM[E] EMP 3,000
SIC 6799 Investment clubs
Mng Pt: Ian Snow
*Pt: Halsey M Minor
*Pt: Ogden Phipps
*CFO: Steven Schwinger

D-U-N-S 04-365-3773
SNOW SUMMIT SKI CORP
880 Summit Blvd, Big Bear Lake, CA 92315
Tel (909) 866-5766 Founded/Ownrshp 1963
Sales 59.0MM[E] EMP 1,000
SIC 7011 5812 Ski lodge; American restaurant
Pr: Richard C Kun
*CFO: Robert Tarras
*Treas: Alan Macquoid
*VP: Robert Law
Admn Mgr: Janet Evans

D-U-N-S 07-296-2475 IMP
SNOWBIRD CORP
SNOWBIRD SKI & SUMMER RESORT
3165 E Millrock Dr # 150, Holladay, UT 84121-4732
Tel (801) 742-2222 Founded/Ownrshp 1965
Sales 147.6MM[E] EMP 1,200[E]
SIC 6531 7011 Condominium manager; Ski lodge
Ch Bd: Richard Bass
*Pr: Bob Bonar
*CFO: Thomas Jones
VP: Jack Cole
*VP: Tom Jones
Genl Mgr: Rob Sogard
MIS Dir: Bruce Galleskan
Dir IT: Bruce Golskin
Web Dev: Matt Crawley
Manager: Mike Ewing
Natl Sales: Jim Dixon

D-U-N-S 12-844-0604
SNOWBIRD HOLDINGS LLC
2721 E Kelly Ln, Salt Lake City, UT 84117-5521
Tel (801) 277-2840 Founded/Ownrshp 2002
Sales NA EMP 1,102
SIC 6719 Investment holding companies, except banks

D-U-N-S 05-951-2509
SNOWBIRD LTD (UT)
SNOWBIRD SKI AND SUMMER RESORT
State Rd 210, Snowbird, UT 84092
Tel (801) 742-2222 Founded/Ownrshp 1965
Sales 160.8MM[E] EMP 900
SIC 1531 6519 Condominium developers; Real property lessors
Pt: Richard D Bass
Pt: Bob Bonar
Pt: Tom Jones
Dir IT: Bruce Goluskin
IT Man: Matt Crawley

D-U-N-S 08-031-8179
SNOWBIRD RESORT LLC
SNOWBIRD SKI & SUMMER RESORT
9385 S Snowbird Center Dr, Snowbird, UT 84092-6249
Tel (801) 933-4670 Founded/Ownrshp 2014
Sales 1.0MM[E] EMP 1,100
SIC 7011 Resort hotel
Pr: Bob Bonar

SNOWBIRD SKI & SUMMER RESORT
See SNOWBIRD CORP

SNOWBIRD SKI & SUMMER RESORT
See SNOWBIRD RESORT LLC

SNOWBIRD SKI AND SUMMER RESORT
See SNOWBIRD LTD

D-U-N-S 85-849-0949
SNOWSHOE MOUNTAIN INC
SNOWSHOE MTN RESPONSE TEAM
10 Snowshoe Dr, Slatyfork, WV 26291-1201
Tel (304) 572-5601 Founded/Ownrshp 1996
Sales 159.5M EMP 1,400
SIC 8741 7011 5813 5812 Hotel or motel management; Hotels & motels; Drinking places; Eating places
Pr: Frank Deberry
*Pr: Joe Houssain
Pr: Bruce Pittet
*Treas: Patti Duncan
*VP: J F Hodges
VP: George Murphy
*Genl Mgr: Bill Rock
IT Man: Daniel Seme
Sls Dir: Rebecca B Furee
Sls Mgr: Kaie McGann
Sls Mgr: Grada Vandavander

SNOWSHOE MTN RESPONSE TEAM
See SNOWSHOE MOUNTAIN INC

SNWA
See SOUTHERN NEVADA WATER AUTHORITY

D-U-N-S 10-159-6310 IMP/EXP
SNYDER ASSOCIATED COMPANIES INC
SYLVAN
1 Glade Park Dr, Kittanning, PA 16201-7001
Tel (724) 548-8101 Founded/Ownrshp 1975
Sales 983.5MM[E] EMP 2,592
SIC 1442 3281 1222 Sand mining; Gravel mining; Limestone, cut & shaped; Bituminous coal-underground mining
Ch Bd: Charles H Snyder Jr
*Pr: Monir K Elzalaki
*Pr: David E Snyder
CFO: Mark Karenchak
Treas: Ronald Piechowicz
*Treas: Thomas C Snyder

D-U-N-S 00-726-6992 IMP/EXP
SNYDER INDUSTRIES INC
(Suby of LEONARD GREEN & PARTNERS LP) ★
6940 O St Ste 100, Lincoln, NE 68510-2458
Tel (402) 465-1206 Founded/Ownrshp 2012
Sales 124.5MM[E] EMP 500
SIC 3089 Pallets, plastic
Pr: Thomas O'Connell
*Sec: David W Gentry
Genl Mgr: Mike Isner
Dir IT: Vicky Wilson
VP Opers: Alan Markowski
Plnt Mgr: Brad Beckman
Natl Sales: Jason Harrington
S&M/VP: Mike Spurrier
Manager: Greg Weddle
Snr Mgr: John Surman

D-U-N-S 11-314-3747
SNYDER OIL CORP
777 Main St Ste 1400, Fort Worth, TX 76102-5356
Tel (817) 338-4043 Founded/Ownrshp 1978
Sales 141.1MM EMP 83
Accts Arthur Andersen Llp
SIC 1311 4922 Crude petroleum production; Natural gas production; Pipelines, natural gas
Ch Bd: John C Snyder
*Pr: William G Hargett
CFO: Mark A Jackson
Treas: Rodney L Waller
Sr VP: Jay H Smith
VP: John J Karnes
VP: H Richard Pate
VP: David M Posner
Board of Directors: Roger W Brittain, John A Hill, William J Johnson, B J Kellenberger, Harold R Logan Jr, James E McCormick, Edward T Story

D-U-N-S 00-352-0020 IMP
SNYDER PAPER CORP
250 26th Street Dr Se, Hickory, NC 28602-1456
Tel (828) 328-2501 Founded/Ownrshp 1946
Sales 151.1MM[E] EMP 350
SIC 5199 5085

D-U-N-S 00-315-9100
▲ **SNYDERS-LANCE INC** (NC)
13515 Balntyn Corp Pl, Charlotte, NC 28277-2706
Tel (704) 554-1421 Founded/Ownrshp 1909
Sales 1.6MMM EMP 5,000
Tkr Sym LNCE Exch NGS
SIC 2052 2064 2068 2096 5145 Cookies; Crackers, dry; Soda crackers; Candy bars, including chocolate covered bars; Granola & muesli, bars & clusters; Nuts: dried, dehydrated, salted or roasted; Potato chips & other potato-based snacks; Corn chips & other corn-based snacks; Tortilla chips; Cheese curls & puffs; Snack foods
Pr: Carl E Lee Jr
*Ch Bd: Wilbur J Prezzano
*Chf Mktg O: Rodrigo F Troni Pena
*Ofcr: Rick D Puckett
*Sr VP: Patrick S McInerney
VP: Mark Carter
VP: Kelly McBride
*VP: Margaret E Wicklund
Dist Mgr: Henry Bonavia
IT Man: Greg Dyksma
Mfg Dir: Andre Boom
Board of Directors: Isaiah Tidwell, Jeffrey A Atkins, Patricia A Warehime, Peter P Brubaker, C Peter Carlucci Jr, John E Denton, Brian J Driscoll, Lawrence V Jackson, James W Johnston, David C Moran, Dan C Swander

D-U-N-S 04-245-4249 IMP/EXP
SO-PAK-CO INC
(Suby of UNAKA CO INC) ★
118 S Cypress St, Mullins, SC 29574-3004
Tel (423) 639-1163 Founded/Ownrshp 1944, 1989
Sales 100.0MM EMP 600
SIC 2099 4226 Food preparations; Special warehousing & storage
Pr: Lonnie Thompson
*Treas: L A Budy Yonz
Exec: Dominick Jackson
Tech Mgr: Ed Smith
Pgrm Dir: David L Dubose

D-U-N-S 19-347-7775
SOAVE ENTERPRISES LLC
3400 E Lafayette St, Detroit, MI 48207-4962
Tel (313) 567-7000 Founded/Ownrshp 1998
Sales 152.3MM[E] EMP 492
SIC 6719 Investment holding companies, except banks
Pr: Anthony Soave
COO: William Fox
COO: Howard Sherman
*CFO: Michael L Piesko
*Treas: Richard Brockhaus
Ex VP: Dick Kenny
*Ex VP: Yale Levin
*Sr VP: Michael D Hollarbach
VP: Rob Bakotich
VP: Tysen McCarthy
VP: Ed Schwartz
VP: Thomas Turnbull

D-U-N-S 17-269-5025
SOBOBA BAND OF LUISENO INDIANS
NOLI INDIAN SCHOOL
23906 Soboba Rd, San Jacinto, CA 92583
Tel (951) 654-2765 Founded/Ownrshp 1883
Sales NA EMP 1,000
SIC 9131 Indian reservation;
Ch: Rose Mary Morillow
*Pr: Chester Arthur
*Ch: Scott Cozart
Exec: Isaura Avalos

D-U-N-S 80-715-2397
SOC LLC
(Suby of DAY & ZIMMERMANN GROUP INC) ★
15002 Northridge Dr # 100, Chantilly, VA 20151-3850
Tel (703) 955-5700 Founded/Ownrshp 2015
Sales 91.1MM[E] EMP 1,200
SIC 7382 1731 Security systems services; Protective devices, security; Safety & security specialization
Pr: Steve Selfridge
Pr: Todd Bryer
*CFO: Kathleen King
*Sr VP: Derek Johnson
Sr VP: Michael McAreavy
*CIO: John K Hess II
Snr Mgr: Javier Angulo

SOCH
See SOUTHERN OCEAN COUNTY HEALTH SYSTEM INC

D-U-N-S 09-134-0943
SOCIAL & SCIENTIFIC SYSTEMS INC
S-3
8757 Georgia Ave Ste 1200, Silver Spring, MD 20910-3739
Tel (301) 628-3000 Founded/Ownrshp 1978
Sales 123.3MM[E] EMP 500
SIC 7374 7371 Data processing & preparation; Custom computer programming services
Pr: James J Lynch
*COO: Donna Bareis
*CFO: Bruce Beddow
*Ch: Dan R Bannister
Ex VP: Howard Ruddell
VP: Taylor Abernathy
*VP: Kevin Beverly
*VP: Charles Chesson
VP: Lori Golino
VP: Jim Maat
VP: Peggy Vanness
Exec: Aaron Aamodt
Exec: Irving Gwynn
Exec: Veronica Harris
Exec: Hemant Patel
Dir Lab: Susan Baker
Creative D: Katie Bryan

D-U-N-S 92-764-5598
■ **SOCIAL SECURITY ADMINISTRATION**
(Suby of EXECUTIVE OFFICE OF UNITED STATES GOVERNMENT) ★
6401 Security Blvd, Baltimore, MD 21235-6401
Tel (410) 965-8882 Founded/Ownrshp 1974
Sales NA EMP 65,000
SIC 9441 Social security administration, government;
Bd of Dir: Ted Beard
Ofcr: Mark Lassiter
Ex Dir: Jonathan R Cantor
Ex Dir: Shirley Todd
Dist Mgr: Jose Cotera
Dist Mgr: Evelyn Rosario-Martine
CIO: Franklin H Baitman
CIO: Lester P Diamond
CIO: Gregory C Pace
CIO: Marsha Young
Genl Couns: David F Black

D-U-N-S 80-857-5708
SOCIAL SERVICES SOUTH CAROLINA DEPARTMENT
DSS
(Suby of BUDGET & CTRL BD EXEC DIRS OFF) ★
1535 Confederate Ave, Columbia, SC 29201-1915
Tel (803) 898-7601 Founded/Ownrshp 1937
Sales NA EMP 4,000
SIC 9441 Administration of social & manpower programs;
Ex Dir: Kathleen Hayes
*CEO: Lillian B Coller
IT Man: Latonya Rish

D-U-N-S 09-514-9589
SOCIAL VOCATIONAL SERVICES INC
EMPLOY AMERICA
3555 Torrance Blvd, Torrance, CA 90503-4802
Tel (310) 944-3303 Founded/Ownrshp 1977
Sales 87.2MM EMP 1,400
SIC 8361

SOCIEDAD ESPANOLA DE AUXILIO
See HOSPITAL ESPANOL AUXILIO MUTUO DE PUERTO RICO INC

D-U-N-S 09-010-6444 IMP
SOCIEDAD ESPAOLA DE AUXILIO MUTUO Y BENEFICENCIA DE PUERTO RICO
Ponce De Leon Ave, San Juan, PR 00917
Tel (787) 758-2000 Founded/Ownrshp 1883
Sales 29.3MM EMP 2,100[E]
SIC 8062 General medical & surgical hospitals
Pr: Enrique Fierres Gonzalez
*CFO: Maria Bell Marti
*Treas: Emilio Torres Antuano
*VP: Valentin Valderrabano Barcena
*VP: Bruno Herrerias Diaz
*VP: Juan Leizan Lopez
*VP: Amador Falcon Perdido
*VP: Angel Cocero Sanchez

D-U-N-S 07-777-1640
SOCIETY FOR HUMAN RESOURCE MANAGEMENT
SHRM ONLINE
1800 Duke St, Alexandria, VA 22314-3494
Tel (703) 548-3440 Founded/Ownrshp 1949
Sales 113.0MM EMP 450
Accts Raffa Pc Washington Dc
SIC 8621 Professional membership organizations
Ch: Brian D Silva
Pr: Henry G Jackson
CEO: Achal Khanna
CFO: Mary Mohney
Ofcr: Jeaneen Andrews-Feldman
Sr VP: J Robert Carr
Sr VP: Deb Cohen
Sr VP: Brian K Dickson
Sr VP: Brian Dickson
Sr VP: Jessica Perry
VP: Mike Aitken
VP: Tony Lee
Board of Directors: Jeffrey M Cava, Jorge Consuega, Thomas W Derry, Bette J Francis, Jose Tomas, Scott Washburn, David Windley, Patrick Wright Phd, Gretchen Zech

D-U-N-S 07-617-2824
SOCIETY INSURANCE A MUTUAL CO
150 Camelot Dr, Fond Du Lac, WI 54935-8030
Tel (920) 922-1220 Founded/Ownrshp 1915
Sales NA EMP 263[E]
SIC 6411 Insurance brokers; Patrol services, insurance; Fire insurance underwriters' laboratories
CEO: Rick Parks
*Treas: Edwin W Storer
VP: Dominic Weber
IT Man: Quinn Gudex
IT Man: Shane Guyette
Netwrk Eng: Paul Brockman
Sales Exec: Brad Korkow
VP Sls: Dina Schultz
Manager: Scott Weber
Board of Directors: Rick W Porks, Edwin Storer

D-U-N-S 07-373-7793
SOCIETY OF CATHOLIC MEDICAL MISSIONARIES INC (MD)
MEDICAL MISSION SISTER'S
8400 Pine Rd Ste A, Philadelphia, PA 19111-1385
Tel (215) 742-6100 Founded/Ownrshp 1925
Sales 17.7MM[E] EMP 1,250
SIC 8661 Religious organizations
Pr: Helen Lembeck
*VP: Maria Hornung
*VP: Patricia Lowery
Sales Exec: Joan Foley

D-U-N-S 01-265-3853
SOCORRO INDEPENDENT SCHOOL DISTRICT
SISD
12440 Rojas Dr, El Paso, TX 79928-5261
Tel (915) 937-0100 Founded/Ownrshp 1961
Sales 376.8MM[E] EMP 6,000
Accts Gibson Ruddock Patterson Llc
SIC 8211 Public elementary school; Public junior high school; Public senior high school
*CFO: Tony Reza
IT Man: Heriberto Martinez
Snr Mgr: Ivonne Jacobs

D-U-N-S 55-667-7214 IMP
SODASTREAM USA INC
(Suby of SODASTREAM INTERNATIONAL LTD)
200 E Park Dr Ste 600, Mount Laurel, NJ 08054-1297
Tel (800) 763-2258 Founded/Ownrshp 1999
Sales 218.1MM EMP 72
SIC 2087 3585 Syrups, drink; Soda fountain & beverage dispensing equipment & parts
CEO: Daniel Birnbaum
*Pr: Scott Guthrie
*COO: Yossi Azarzar
*CFO: Daniel Erdreich
Ofcr: Kristen Kaminski
Ofcr: Eyal Shohat
Sr VP: Jack Thompson
Ex Dir: Yonah Lloyd
Off Admin: Kristie Correll
CIO: Tom Jacobsen
VP Opers: Gerry Cantwell

SODECIA GROUP
See SODECIA USA AUTOMOTIVE CORP

D-U-N-S 11-293-4927 IMP
SODECIA USA AUTOMOTIVE CORP
SODECIA GROUP
(Suby of SODECIA - PARTICIPACOES SOCIAIS, SGPS, S.A.)
24331 Sherwood, Center Line, MI 48015-1060
Tel (586) 759-2200 Founded/Ownrshp 2010
Sales 168.8MM[E] EMP 650
SIC 3465 Body parts, automobile: stamped metal
CEO: Rui Montero
CFO: Jack Carter
Genl Mgr: Gary Easterly
Dir IT: Lori May
Sys Mgr: Vicky Valente
Sls Dir: Tom Spagnuolo
Sls Dir: Rick Sutter
Snr Mgr: Brenda White

D-U-N-S 07-994-2435
SODEXO AMERICA LLC
(Suby of SODEXO INC & AFFILIATES) ★
9801 Washington Blvd, Gaithersburg, MD 20878
Tel (301) 987-4000 Founded/Ownrshp 2000
Sales 40.4MM[E] EMP 5,021[E]
SIC 8741 Management services

D-U-N-S 18-554-6207
SODEXO INC
(*Suby of* SODEXO)
9801 Washingtonian Blvd # 1, Gaithersburg, MD 20878-5355
Tel (301) 987-4000 *Founded/Ownrshp* 2001
Sales 7.1MMM^E *EMP* 126,120
SIC 5812 7349 Contract food services; Lunchrooms & cafeterias; Caterers; Building maintenance services; Building cleaning service; Janitorial service, contract basis
Pr: Lorna Donatone
**Pr:* Patrick E Connolly
Pr: Lorna Donatone
**Pr:* Michael Norris
Pr: Humberto A Patorniti
Pr: James Taylor
**CFO:* Olivier Poirot
CFO: Debbie White
**Treas:* Marc Blass
**Treas:* Paul Brock
Div VP: Mark Bickford
Div VP: Jay Peverley
Ex VP: Anthony Alibrio
Ex VP: Dana Johnston
Sr VP: Rohini Anand
Sr VP: Allan Bentley
Sr VP: Peri Bridger
Sr VP: Reginald E Gilliam
Sr VP: Husein Kitabwalla
Sr VP: Jay Marvin
Sr VP: Michael Montelongo

SODEXO, INC & AFFILIATES
See SODEXO MANAGEMENT INC

SODEXO, INC. AND AFFILIATES
See SODEXO OPERATIONS LLC

D-U-N-S 08-003-9219
SODEXO LAUNDRY SERVICES INC
(*Suby of* SODEXO INC & AFFILIATES) ★
9801 Washington Blvd, Gaithersburg, MD 20878
Tel (301) 987-4000 *Founded/Ownrshp* 1971
Sales 26.7MM^E *EMP* 3,318^E
SIC 8741 Management services

D-U-N-S 78-365-1011
SODEXO MANAGEMENT INC
SODEXO, INC & AFFILIATES
(*Suby of* SODEXO INC AND AFFILIATES) ★
9801 Washingtonian Blvd, Gaithersburg, MD 20878-5355
Tel (301) 987-4000 *Founded/Ownrshp* 1986
Sales 1.5MMM^E *EMP* 99,000
SIC 8741 6552 Management services; Subdividers & developers
Pr: Michel Landel
**Ch Bd:* George Chavel
Ex VP: Charles P O'Dell
VP: Ollie Lawrence Jr

D-U-N-S 13-068-3001
SODEXO OPERATIONS LLC
SODEXO, INC. AND AFFILIATES
(*Suby of* SODEXO INC) ★
9801 Washingtonian Blvd, Gaithersburg, MD 20878-5355
Tel (301) 987-4000 *Founded/Ownrshp* 1998
Sales 4.2MMM^E *EMP* 100,000
SIC 8741 5812 7349 Restaurant management; Lunchrooms & cafeterias; Building maintenance services
CEO: Michael Landel
VP: Linda Bryant
VP: Liz Clark
VP: Scott Freeman
VP: Gerri Hall
VP: Peter A Mellin
Genl Mgr: Wayne Crawford
Genl Mgr: Michael Fleming
Genl Mgr: Karen Mosher
VP Opers: Grant Colby
Snr Mgr: Mary Riley

D-U-N-S 61-982-2075 IMP
SODEXO REMOTE SITES PARTNERSHIP
(*Suby of* SODEXO)
5749 Susitna Dr, New Orleans, LA 70123-4136
Tel (504) 733-5761 *Founded/Ownrshp* 2001
Sales 34.3MM^E *EMP* 1,100
SIC 5812 Caterers
Pt: Nicholas Japy
**Pt:* Bruno De Reneville

D-U-N-S 08-011-8442
SODEXO SERVICES OF TX LTD PARTNERSHIP
(*Suby of* CORPORATE FOOD SERVICES INC) ★
9801 Washington Blvd, Gaithersburg, MD 20878
Tel (301) 987-4000 *Founded/Ownrshp* 1998
Sales 25.9MM^E *EMP* 5,005^E
SIC 8741 Management services

D-U-N-S 83-075-4904
SODEXOMAGIC LLC
9801 Washingtonian Blvd, Gaithersburg, MD 20878-5355
Tel (301) 987-4433 *Founded/Ownrshp* 2006
Sales 56.9MM^E *EMP* 4,890
SIC 8742 Restaurant & food services consultants
**Treas:* Marc Blass
VP: Antonio Hunter
Dir Surg: Stacey Wrazen
Ex Dir: Michael Sheehy
Genl Mgr: Karen Spann

SOEX GROUP
See SOEX WEST USA LLC

D-U-N-S 03-164-0782 IMP/EXP
SOEX WEST USA LLC
SOEX GROUP
3294 E 26th St, Vernon, CA 90058-8008
Tel (323) 264-8300 *Founded/Ownrshp* 2006
Sales 102.0MM^E *EMP* 300
SIC 5136 Men's & boys' clothing

SOFA MART
See BIG SUR WATERBEDS INC

D-U-N-S 06-211-5472 EXP
SOFEC INC
MODEC SOFEC
(*Suby of* MODEC INTERNATIONAL INC) ★
15011 Katy Fwy Ste 500, Houston, TX 77094-0010
Tel (713) 510-6600 *Founded/Ownrshp* 2006
Sales 119.0MM^E *EMP* 160^E
SIC 3533 8742 Oil & gas drilling rigs & equipment; Construction project management consultant
Pr: Rick Hall
VP: Terry Boatman
Dir IT: John Wright
IT Man: Chris Newlands
Opers Mgr: Giny George
VP Sls: James Hodges
Snr PM: Scott Binnion
Board of Directors: Brent Konstanzer

D-U-N-S 01-618-5279 IMP/EXP
SOFIDEL AMERICA CORP (FL)
(*Suby of* SOFIDEL SPA)
1006 Marley Dr, Haines City, FL 33844-8464
Tel (863) 547-3920 *Founded/Ownrshp* 1988, 2012
Sales 221.8MM^E *EMP* 406
SIC 5113 Towels, paper
CEO: Anthony Curtis
**Pr:* Luigi Lazzareschi
**Pr:* EMI Stefani
Treas: Todd Banes
Exec: Jorge Altieri
Board of Directors: Luigi Lazzareschi, Angelo Della Maggiora

D-U-N-S 13-131-1409
SOFT COMPUTER CONSULTANTS INC
SCC
5400 Tech Data Dr, Clearwater, FL 33760-3116
Tel (727) 789-0100 *Founded/Ownrshp* 1980
Sales 156.5MM *EMP* 900
SIC 7373 7371 Computer systems analysis & design; Custom computer programming services
CEO: Gilbert Hakim
**Ch Bd:* Jean Hakim
VP: Laurel Estabrooks
Prgrm Mgr: Pmp V Churilov CSM
IT Man: Mike Ivanics
IT Man: Cheryl Kerr
IT Man: Liliane Saberin
Software D: Polina Grozina
Sftwr Eng: Krzysztof Hippe
VP Sls: Ellie Hakim
S&M/VP: Ellie Vahman

SOFT SURROUNDINGS
See TRIAD CATALOG CO LLC

D-U-N-S 00-417-7895
SOFT-LITE LLC
SOFT-LITE WINDOWS
(*Suby of* CLARITY INDUSTRIES LLC) ★
10250 Philipp Pkwy, Streetsboro, OH 44241-4765
Tel (330) 528-3400 *Founded/Ownrshp* 1937
Sales 114.1MM^E *EMP* 450
SIC 3089 Windows, plastic
CFO: Kyle Pozek
VP: Arnold Levitt
VP: Michael Rempel
VP: Rick Robson
VP Opers: Rich Bonney
Ql Cn Mgr: Ken Miller
Natl Sales: Steve Cespedes
VP Sls: Tyson Schwartz
Mktg Mgr: Dennis Ragan
Manager: Randy Lamotte
Manager: Furman Raine

SOFT-LITE WINDOWS
See SOFT-LITE LLC

SOFTBALL.COM
See TEAM EXPRESS DISTRIBUTING LLC

D-U-N-S 83-932-0223
■ **SOFTBANK HOLDINGS INC**
(*Suby of* SOFTBANK GROUP CORP.)
1188 Centre St Ste 2, Newton, MA 02459-1556
Tel (617) 928-9300 *Founded/Ownrshp* 1995
Sales 61.0MM^E *EMP* 3,025
SIC 8741 Management services
Ch Bd: Masayoshi Sain
Genl Pt: Charley Lax
Pr: Shevrin Phil
Doctor: Anthony R Castellanos

D-U-N-S 92-902-2028
SOFTCHOICE CORP
(*Suby of* SOFTCHOICE HOLDINGS INC)
314 W Superior St Ste 400, Chicago, IL 60654-3538
Tel (416) 588-9002 *Founded/Ownrshp* 2016
Sales 277.4MM^E *EMP* 1,300
SIC 5045

D-U-N-S 60-301-0864
SOFTLAYER TECHNOLOGIES INC
14001 Dallas Pkwy M100, Dallas, TX 75240-4350
Tel (214) 442-0600 *Founded/Ownrshp* 2013
Sales 98.4MM^E *EMP* 555
SIC 7374 4813

D-U-N-S 12-699-0980
SOFTSCRIPT INC
2215 Campus Dr, El Segundo, CA 90245-0001
Tel (310) 451-2110 *Founded/Ownrshp* 1997
Sales 60.4MM^E *EMP* 1,200
SIC 7338 Secretarial & court reporting
CEO: Howard Wisnicki
Ex VP: Ruien Shu
Sr VP: Brandon Phillips
Software D: Michael Iverson
VP Opers: Carla Rigdon

D-U-N-S 14-472-6747
SOFTSERVE INC
111 Congress Ave, Austin, TX 78701-4050
Tel (512) 516-8880 *Founded/Ownrshp* 2002
Sales 93.5MM^E *EMP* 1,800
SIC 7371 Computer software development
CEO: Alan Harlan
**Pr:* Taras Vervega
**Ex VP:* Neil Fox
**Ex VP:* Juan Turruellas

D-U-N-S 01-186-1478
SOFTTEK INTEGRATION SYSTEMS INC
(*Suby of* VALORES CORPORATIVOS SOFTTEK, S.A. DE C.V.)
2002 Summit Blvd Ste 300, Brookhaven, GA 30319-6403
Tel (404) 460-5040 *Founded/Ownrshp* 1997
Sales 185.8MM *EMP* 330^E
SIC 7379 7371 7373 Computer related consulting services; Custom computer programming services; Computer software development; Computer integrated systems design
CEO: Benigno Lopez
**CFO:* Rosa M Delgado
**CFO:* Marcos Jimenez
Chf Mktg O: Alberto Cortes
**VP:* Jorge Best
VP: Roberto Montelongo
QA Dir: Alexandra Ledezma
Sales Exec: Eduardo Guerrero
Snr Mgr: Julio Solares

D-U-N-S 17-388-5450
SOFTWARE AG INC
(*Suby of* SOFTWARE AG)
11700 Plaza America Dr # 700, Reston, VA 20190-4739
Tel (703) 860-5050 *Founded/Ownrshp* 2015
Sales 300.0MM^E *EMP* 800
Accts Bdo Seidman Llp
SIC 7372 Application computer software; Business oriented computer software; Operating systems computer software; Word processing computer software
Pr: Mark Edwards
Top Exec: Rohit Aggarwal
VP: Marc Beckers
VP: Dave Brooks
VP: Jay Gauthier
VP: Robin Riedel
VP: Frank Simon
Exec: Andrea Kelley
**Prin:* Johnson Jay
Prac Mgr: Bharath Vutukuru
Genl Mgr: Jim Carahan

D-U-N-S 01-518-8162
SOFTWARE AG USA INC
(*Suby of* SOFTWARE AG INC) ★
11700 Plaza America Dr # 700, Reston, VA 20190-4739
Tel (703) 860-5050 *Founded/Ownrshp* 2007
Sales 300.0MM *EMP* 800
SIC 7371 Computer software development & applications
Pr: Jay Johnson
Sr VP: Joe Gentry
**Sr VP:* Smith W Stanford
VP: Eeshan Rairkar
**VP:* Robin Riedel
**Prin:* John Johnson
Manager: Gene Mallett

D-U-N-S 60-550-4158 IMP/EXP
■ **SOFTWARE BROKERS OF AMERICA INC**
INTCOMEX
(*Suby of* INTCOMEX INC) ★
3505 Nw 107th Ave Ste 1, Doral, FL 33178-9800
Tel (305) 477-5993 *Founded/Ownrshp* 1999
Sales 176.2MM^E *EMP* 135
SIC 5045 Computers; Computer peripheral equipment; Computer software
Pr: Anthony Shalom
**COO:* Leopoldo Coronado
**VP:* Michael Shalom

D-U-N-S 61-267-4457
SOFTWARE FORENSICS INC
384 S 400 W Ste 200, Lindon, UT 84042-1959
Tel (801) 377-5410 *Founded/Ownrshp* 1992
Sales 83.1MM^E *EMP* 150^E
SIC 7371 8243 Computer software development; Software training, computer

SOFTWARE HOUSE INTERNATIONAL
See SHI INTERNATIONAL CORP

D-U-N-S 13-036-2346
SOFTWARE INFORMATION SYSTEMS LLC
SIS
165 Barr St, Lexington, KY 40507-1321
Tel (859) 977-4747 *Founded/Ownrshp* 2000
Sales 213.7MM^E *EMP* 126
SIC 5045 7379 Computers, peripherals & software; Computer related consulting services
COO: Steve Sigg
Pr: Pat Sigg
**CFO:* Chris Sigg
CFO: Christopher Sigg
**Ex VP:* Roger Finney
**Ex VP:* Mike Hardy
**Ex VP:* Chris Henry
Ex VP: Maria Veyon
Snr Ntwrk: Zach Johnstone
Software D: Nick Loghides
Software D: Jeff Randolph

D-U-N-S 12-159-3552
SOFTWARE ONE INC
SOFTWAREONE
(*Suby of* SOFTWAREONE AG)
20875 Crssroads Cir Ste 1, Waukesha, WI 53186
Tel (262) 317-5555 *Founded/Ownrshp* 1984
Sales 1.3MMM^E *EMP* 650
SIC 5045 Computer software; Computers
CEO: Patrick Winter
Ofcr: Rachayathip Sangphosuk
Mng Dir: Rafael Burgos
IT Man: Johann Coulon
Opers Mgr: David Papak
Sales Exec: Dan Doerr
Sls Dir: Andrea Sanchez
Sls Mgr: Teresa Lewis
Sls Mgr: Kevin Stannis
Sales Asso: John Carity
Sales Asso: Celine Nury

D-U-N-S 96-863-0785
SOFTWARE PARADIGMS INTERNATIONAL GROUP LLC
(*Suby of* SOFTVISION SRL)
5 Concourse Pkwy Ste 500, Atlanta, GA 30328-6101
Tel (770) 904-7720 *Founded/Ownrshp* 2008
Sales 67.0MM *EMP* 1,500
SIC 7379 Computer related consulting services
CFO: John M Toma

D-U-N-S 10-259-5865
■ **SOFTWARE SPECTRUM INC**
(*Suby of* INSIGHT ENTERPRISES INC) ★
3480 Lotus Dr, Plano, TX 75075-7850
Tel (469) 443-3900 *Founded/Ownrshp* 2006
Sales 1.1MMM^E *EMP* 1,200
SIC 5045 7373 Computer software; Computer integrated systems design
VP: Rebecca E G Tankersley
IT Man: David Brenner

SOFTWAREONE
See SOFTWARE ONE INC

SOGA FOODS
See PULMUONE USA INC

D-U-N-S 03-050-1071
SOGETI USA LLC
(*Suby of* CAPGEMINI CONSULTING) ★
10100 Innovation Dr # 200, Miamisburg, OH 45342-4966
Tel (937) 291-8100 *Founded/Ownrshp* 1971
Sales 378.3MM^E *EMP* 2,200
SIC 7379
CEO: Rajnish Nath
VP: William Blaxton
VP: Paban Sarma
Off Mgr: Amy Chinchilla
QA Dir: Philip Tia
Web Dev: Munavvar Ahmed
Software D: Henry Minh
Software D: Eric Moderbacher
Snr Mgr: Ryan Green
Snr Mgr: Arunkumar Keserla
Snr Mgr: Amarish Tripathi

SOGIMEX
See MYERS GROUP L L C

SOH
See S-L SNACKS REAL ESTATE INC

D-U-N-S 01-185-5462
SOHEL DISTRIBUTORS NY LLC
S D I
1091 Yonkers Ave, Yonkers, NY 10704-3220
Tel (914) 476-2073 *Founded/Ownrshp* 2011
Sales 100.0MM *EMP* 42
Accts Rosenberg Rich Baker Berman &
SIC 4812 Cellular telephone services
CEO: Sohel Kapadia
**Pr:* Shakil Kathawala

D-U-N-S 96-408-1827
SOI HOLDINGS INC
3023 Hsbc Way Ste 100, Fort Mill, SC 29707-7203
Tel (704) 523-2191 *Founded/Ownrshp* 2005
Sales 270.0MM^E *EMP* 175
SIC 7361 Employment agencies
CEO: Carl Guidice
**CFO:* Mike Willson

D-U-N-S 02-023-7140
SOIN INTERNATIONAL LLC
1129 Miamsbg Ctrvl Rd 1 Ste, Dayton, OH 45449
Tel (937) 427-7646 *Founded/Ownrshp* 1998
Sales 148.3MM^E *EMP* 1,092
SIC 8741 Management services
CEO: Rajesh Raj K Soin
**Pr:* Vishal Soin
VP: Michael Cauldwell
**VP:* Kevin Robie
VP: Kevin A Robie

D-U-N-S 00-698-8448 IMP/EXP
SOJITZ CORP OF AMERICA (NY)
(*Suby of* SOJITZ CORPORATION)
1120 Ave Of The, New York, NY 10036
Tel (212) 704-6500 *Founded/Ownrshp* 1952
Sales 245.8MM^E *EMP* 380
SIC 5065 5084 5169 5051 5099 5052 Electronic parts & equipment; Electronic parts; Industrial machinery & equipment; Industrial chemicals; Ferrous metals; Nonferrous metal sheets, bars, rods, etc.; Steel; Logs, hewn ties, posts & poles; Coal
Ch Bd: Shinichi Teranishi
Chf Cred: Shinichi Taniguchi
Ex VP: William R Hammock
Ex VP: Hiroyuki Tanabe
VP: Toni Buono
VP: Daisuke Fukumoto
VP: SEI Nakayama
VP: Richard C Paice
VP: Shinichi Uchiyama
Genl Mgr: Maritza Diaz
Genl Mgr: Gary Ferraro

D-U-N-S 18-050-2684 IMP/EXP
■ **SOLAE LLC**
(*Suby of* E I DU PONT DE NEMOURS AND CO) ★
4300 Duncan Ave, Saint Louis, MO 63110-1110
Tel (314) 659-3000 *Founded/Ownrshp* 2003
Sales 370.1MM^E *EMP* 1,600
SIC 2075 2076 Soybean oil mills; Vegetable oil mills
CEO: Tony L Arnold
Mng Pt: Peter Mallers
COO: Andrea Burr
COO: Joseph Chelsvig
COO: Paul Greg
CFO: Steve Fray
CFO: Robert Richter
**Ch:* Craig F Binetti
Sr Cor Off: Michael Skeans
Ex VP: Terry B Hatfield
Ex VP: Gregory Kesel
**VP:* Lindell R Bean
VP: Paul Bossert
VP: Kent Cipollo

*VP: Michele Fite
VP: Paul Graham
VP: James Holbrook
VP: Kathy Min
Exec: Gregory Bates
Exec: Greg Kasel
Dir Surg: Tom Damiano

D-U-N-S 07-965-6481
SOLAERO TECHNOLOGIES CORP
10420 Res Rd Se Bldg 1, Albuquerque, NM 87123
Tel (505) 332-5000 Founded/Ownrshp 2014
Sales 157.6MM^E EMP 376^E
SIC 3679 3674 Electronic circuits; Solar cells
Pr: Marvin Clevenger
*Pr: Brad Clevenger
*CFO: Jeffrey Lassiter
Sr VP: Navid Fatemi
*VP: Hugh Evans
VP: Paul Sharps
Prgrm Mgr: Kevin Crist
Opers Mgr: Jerry Winton
Snr Mgr: Robert Little

D-U-N-S 83-180-9780
SOLAR CAPITAL LTD
500 Park Ave Fl 3, New York, NY 10022-1606
Tel (212) 993-1670 Founded/Ownrshp 2007
Sales 115.5MM EMP 4
Accts Kpmg Llp New York New York
Tkr Sym SLRC Exch NGS
SIC 6799 Investors
Ch Bd: Michael S Gross
*COO: Bruce Spohler
Ofcr: Guy Talarico

SOLAR DATA
See SOLAR SUPPLY INC

SOLAR POWER, INC.
See SPI SOLAR INC

D-U-N-S 07-207-1533 IMP
SOLAR SOURCES INC
6755 Gray Rd, Indianapolis, IN 46237-3254
Tel (317) 788-0084 Founded/Ownrshp 1974
Sales 154.0MM^E EMP 250
SIC 1221 Strip mining, bituminous
Pr: Felson Bowman
*VP: Fred Bowman
*VP: David Bricker
*VP: Donald A Keller
IT Man: Peggy Stevens
Genl Couns: Jacqueline Ponder

D-U-N-S 00-289-4814
SOLAR SUPPLY INC
SOLAR DATA
1212 12th St, Lake Charles, LA 70601-6376
Tel (337) 310-1000 Founded/Ownrshp 1954
Sales 90.4MM^E EMP 200
SIC 5075 5078 Warm air heating equipment & supplies; Air conditioning equipment, except room units; Refrigeration equipment & supplies
Pr: Ronald R Dingler
Treas: Charlotte Guillory
Ex VP: Charmayne Yelverton
*VP: Charmayne Yulverton

D-U-N-S 04-226-1099 IMP/EXP
■ **SOLAR TURBINES INC**
(Suby of CATERPILLAR INC) ★
2200 Pacific Hwy, San Diego, CA 92101-1773
Tel (619) 544-5000 Founded/Ownrshp 1981
Sales 1.9MMM^E EMP 4,800
SIC 3511 Gas turbine generator set units, complete
Pr: Thomas Pellette
*CFO: C K Scott-Stanfel
*Treas: Daniel Boylan
*VP: P F Browning
*VP: D W Esbeck
*VP: K K Nolen
*VP: D J Umpleby
Dist Mgr: Monty Reed
IT Man: Frank Wasserman
Tech Mgr: Jason Kepler
Software D: Li Wang

D-U-N-S 78-515-6410
■ **SOLARCITY CORP**
(Suby of TESLA MOTORS INC) ★
3055 Clearview Way, San Mateo, CA 94402-3709
Tel (650) 638-1028 Founded/Ownrshp 2016
Sales 399.6MM EMP 12,000
SIC 1711 Solar energy contractor
CEO: Lyndon R Rive
Pr: Toby Corey
*CFO: J Radford Small
*Ex VP: Marco Krapels
*Ex VP: Brendon Merkley
*Ex VP: Seth R Weissman
VP: John Frampton
VP: Anurag Malik
VP: Michael Mullen
*CTO: Peter J Rive
Sftwr Eng: Travis Brier

D-U-N-S 04-098-1165
SOLAREDGE TECHNOLOGIES INC
47505 Seabridge Dr, Fremont, CA 94538-6546
Tel (877) 360-5292 Founded/Ownrshp 2006
Sales 89.7MM^E EMP 440
SIC 3629 Power conversion units, a.c. to d.c.: static-electric
CEO: Guy Sella
*CFO: Ronen Faier
VP: Yoav Galin
*VP: Lior Handelsman
*VP: Cliff Kalinowski
*VP: Zvi Lando
*VP: Rachel Prishkolnik
*VP: Alon Shapira
*Dir Surg: Alex Bronfer
Sls Dir: Manny Lugos
Mktg Mgr: Michael Rogerson

D-U-N-S 07-360-3335
SOLARIS FOUNDATION INC
D SOLARIS FOUNDATION
9520 Bonita Beach Rd Se, Bonita Springs, FL 34135-4517
Tel (239) 919-1142 Founded/Ownrshp 2012
Sales 197.6MM EMP 3,000
SIC 8051 8059 Skilled nursing care facilities; Personal care home, with health care
CEO: John Helsel
*CFO: Patti Goodling

D-U-N-S 62-386-6741 IMP
SOLARIS PAPER INC
13415 Carmenita Rd, Santa Fe Springs, CA 90670-4906
Tel (562) 376-9717 Founded/Ownrshp 2005
Sales 197.4MM^E EMP 231
Accts D S Lin Cpa Lake Forest Ca
SIC 5093 Waste paper
Pr: Andre Soetjahja
Pr: Mike Murphy
VP: Corey Rodriguez
Dist Mgr: Edward Cody
Dist Mgr: Peggy Litwin
Dist Mgr: Lisa Pollinger
Dir IT: Chia Yoh
Opers Mgr: Mark Muir
VP Mktg: Mike Motherwell
Manager: Quetzaly Dumas
Sls Mgr: Scott Miller

D-U-N-S 08-016-6736
SOLARWINDS HOLDINGS INC
7171 Southwest Pkwy # 400, Austin, TX 78735-6140
Tel (512) 682-9300 Founded/Ownrshp 2015
Sales 428.7MM^E EMP 1,646^E
SIC 7372 Prepackaged software
Pr: Kevin B Thompson

D-U-N-S 09-598-1176
SOLARWINDS INC
(Suby of SOLARWINDS HOLDINGS INC) ★
7171 Southwest Pkwy # 400, Austin, TX 78735-6140
Tel (512) 682-9300 Founded/Ownrshp 1999, 2016
Sales 428.7MM EMP 1,646^E
SIC 7372 Prepackaged software
Pr: Kevin B Thompson
CFO: Jason Ream
Ex VP: Douglas G Hibberd
Ex VP: J Barton Kalsu
Ex VP: Paul Strelzick
Sr VP: John F Rizzo
Sr VP: Geeta Sachdev
VP: Gary Angel
VP: Sanjay Castelino
VP: Sandy Ensminger
VP: Doug Hibberd
VP: Lee McClendon
VP: David Owenns
VP: Doug Rogers
VP: Wendy Shepperd
VP: Mark Szygenda
Exec: Mike Bennett

D-U-N-S 83-067-5323 IMP/EXP
SOLARWORLD AMERICAS INC
(Suby of SOLARWORLD AG)
25300 Nw Evergreen Rd, Hillsboro, OR 97124-5768
Tel (503) 844-3400 Founded/Ownrshp 2007
Sales 259.6MM^E EMP 750^E
SIC 3674 Solar cells
Pr: Mukesh Dulani
IT Man: Michael Perelli-Minetti
IT Man: Brad Taylor
Snr PM: Rick Moats
Snr Mgr: Joanne Swyers

D-U-N-S 09-269-8521 IMP/EXP
SOLARWORLD INDUSTRIES AMERICA LP
(Suby of SOLARWORLD AMERICAS INC) ★
25300 Nw Evergreen Rd, Hillsboro, OR 97124-5768
Tel (805) 482-6800 Founded/Ownrshp 1989
Sales 133.8MM^E EMP 350
SIC 3674 Solar cells
Genl Pt: Mukesh Dulani
*Pt: Robert Beisner
*Pt: Phillip Koecke
Dir IT: Brad Taylor

D-U-N-S 07-950-6907
SOLENIS INTERNATIONAL LP
(Suby of SOLENIS LLC) ★
500 Hercules Rd, Wilmington, DE 19808-1513
Tel (302) 994-1698 Founded/Ownrshp 2014
Sales 221.8MM^E EMP 915^E
SIC 2911 2611 1382 Petroleum refining; Pulp mills; Oil & gas exploration services
CEO: John Panichella

D-U-N-S 07-943-6434
SOLENIS LLC
3 Beaver Valley Rd # 500, Wilmington, DE 19803-1129
Tel (866) 337-1533 Founded/Ownrshp 2014
Sales 402.1MM^E EMP 3,500
SIC 2899 Chemical preparations; Sizes; Gum sizes; Water treating compounds
Pr: John Panichella
*Chf Mktg O: Jeff Fulgham

D-U-N-S 80-002-8677
SOLERA HOLDINGS INC
(Suby of SUMMERTIME HOLDING CORP) ★
1301 Solana Blvd Ste 2100, Westlake, TX 76262-1675
Tel (817) 961-2100 Founded/Ownrshp 2015
Sales 1.1MMM EMP 5,442
SIC 7371 Custom computer programming services; Computer software development & applications; Software programming applications
CEO: Tony Aquila
*CFO: Renato Giger
VP: Richard Heppenstall
Opers Mgr: Jennifer White
Genl Couns: Jason Brady
Snr Mgr: Morgan Jones

D-U-N-S 08-021-0001
SOLERA LLC
1301 Solana Blvd Ste 2100, Westlake, TX 76262-1675
Tel (817) 961-2100 Founded/Ownrshp 2015
Sales 34.0MM^E EMP 5,442
SIC 7371 Custom computer programming services
CEO: Tony Aquila
COO: Mark Miola

D-U-N-S 19-411-4914 IMP/EXP
SOLETANCHE INC
(Suby of SOLETANCHE BACHY FRANCE)
2400 Ansys Dr Ste 303, Canonsburg, PA 15317-0403
Tel (412) 221-4500 Founded/Ownrshp 1960
Sales 108.6MM EMP 200
Accts Schneider Downs Pittsburgh Pa
SIC 1771 Foundation & footing contractor
CEO: Andrew Walker
*Treas: Timothy Mitchell
*Ex VP: Laurent Lefebvre
*Sr VP: John Wise
*VP: Roger Baldwin
*VP: Richard Deschamps

SOLID OAK
See HERITAGE ENVIRONMENTAL SERVICES LLC

D-U-N-S 01-452-0604
SOLID RESOURCES INC
2200 Eller Dr, Fort Lauderdale, FL 33316-3069
Tel (941) 928-0958 Founded/Ownrshp 2000
Sales 28.0MM EMP 2,300
SIC 8742 Management consulting services
CEO: K Tim Perkins
*Pr: Gary J Stankovich
*CFO: Keith R Forster
Ex VP: Jon Hamrick
*VP: Randall Blank
VP: Pam Devaul
*VP: Charles Fabrikant
*VP: Alice N Gran
VP: Duane Holt
Off Mgr: Bennisa Gatto

SOLID WASTE SERVICES
See EDCO WASTE & RECYCLING SERVICES INC

D-U-N-S 07-916-9523
SOLIGENT DISTRIBUTION LLC
(Suby of SOLIGENT HOLDINGS INC) ★
1500 Valley House Dr # 210, Rohnert Park, CA 94928-4924
Tel (707) 992-3100 Founded/Ownrshp 2013
Sales 199.0MM^E EMP 137^E
SIC 5065 Electronic parts & equipment
CEO: Jonathan Doochin
*Pr: Thomas Enzendorfer
VP: Justin Davidson
Exec: Patti Gutleben
Brnch Mgr: Jeffrey Carroll
Mktg Dir: Conor Farese
Sls Dir: Chris Brown
Sls Dir: Hollis Miles

D-U-N-S 07-914-1991 EXP
SOLIGENT HOLDINGS INC
1500 Valley House Dr, Rohnert Park, CA 94928-4924
Tel (707) 992-3100 Founded/Ownrshp 2013
Sales 212.1MM^E EMP 172
SIC 5074 7359 1711 Heating equipment & panels, solar; Equipment rental & leasing; Solar energy contractor
CEO: Jonathan Doochin

D-U-N-S 88-301-1392
SOLIS HEALTHCARE LP
5800 Ridge Ave, Philadelphia, PA 19128-1737
Tel (215) 483-9900 Founded/Ownrshp 2007
Sales 30.4MM^E EMP 1,254^E
SIC 8062 Hospital, medical school affiliated with nursing & residency
CEO: Robert G Souaid
COO: Jack Donnelly

SOLLEY'S
See JERRYS FAMOUS DELI INC

SOLO CUP
See SF HOLDINGS GROUP INC

D-U-N-S 00-514-4399 EXP
SOLO CUP CO
(Suby of SOLO CUP CO LLC) ★
300 Tri State Intl # 200, Lincolnshire, IL 60069-4415
Tel (847) 831-4800 Founded/Ownrshp 2004
Sales 701.5MM^E EMP 6,400^E
SIC 3089 3421 2656 Cups, plastic, except foam; Plates, plastic; Plastic containers, except foam; Cutlery; Straws, drinking: made from purchased material
Pr: Robert M Korzenski
IT Man: Enrique Bonilla
IT Man: Joseph Dimichele
IT Man: Mathew Talaga
IT Man: Stefanie Whiteman
Sfty Mgr: Wade Beall

D-U-N-S 60-366-1302 IMP
SOLO CUP CO LLC
300 Tri State Intl # 200, Lincolnshire, IL 60069-4415
Tel (847) 444-5000 Founded/Ownrshp 2012
Sales 1.3MMM^E EMP 6,400
SIC 3089 2656 3421 Cups, plastic, except foam; Plates, plastic; Plastic containers, except foam; Straws, drinking: made from purchased material; Cutlery
Prin: Robert C Dart
Ex VP: Robert D Koney
Sr VP: Steve Jungmann
VP: Jan Stern Reed
VP: Ronald E Wesel
Exec: Jose Ochoa
Brnch Mgr: William Rickert
Snr Ntwrk: Robert N Jones
Snr Ntwrk: Laurentiu N Suciu
QA Dir: Shalini Javvaji
Sfty Mgr: Barbara Flowers
Board of Directors: R James Alexy, Jeffrey M Greene, Neil Harrison, James R Hulseman, John D Hulseman, Paul J Hulseman, Kevin A Mundt, Daniel S O'connell, Brian P O'connor

D-U-N-S 18-675-4276 EXP
SOLO CUP INVESTMENT CORP
(Suby of SCC HOLDING CO LLC) ★
1700 Old Deerfield Rd, Highland Park, IL 60035-3000
Tel (847) 831-4800 Founded/Ownrshp 2004
Sales 654.2MM^E EMP 11,500^E
SIC 3089 2656 3421 Cups, plastic, except foam; Plates, plastic; Plastic containers, except foam; Straws, drinking: made from purchased material; Cutlery
CEO: Robert M Korzenski
CFO: Robert D Koney
Ex VP: Hans H Heinsen
*Prin: Ronald Whaley
QI Cn Mgr: Jessie Whiting

D-U-N-S 02-782-2048 IMP/EXP
SOLO CUP OPERATING CORP
(Suby of SOLO CUP) ★
300 Tr State Intl Ste 200, Lincolnshire, IL 60069
Tel (847) 444-5000 Founded/Ownrshp 1981
Sales 11.9MM^E EMP 4,370
SIC 3089 2656 3556 Plastic kitchenware, tableware & houseware; Cups, plastic, except foam; Plates, plastic; Plastic containers, except foam; Paper cups, plates, dishes & utensils; Cups, paper: made from purchased material; Plates, paper: made from purchased material; Straws, drinking: made from purchased material; Food products machinery
Pr: Robert C Dart
COO: Jim Kallikragas
CFO: James W Nellen
Treas: Linda Ridgley

SOLOMON ELECTRIC COMPANY
See SOLOMON TRANSFORMERS LLC

D-U-N-S 07-682-7666 IMP
SOLOMON R GUGGENHEIM FOUNDATION
1071 5th Ave, New York, NY 10128-0112
Tel (212) 423-3500 Founded/Ownrshp 1937
Sales 89.1MM EMP 281
SIC 8412 Museum
Ex Dir: William Mack
*Pr: Peter Lawson Johnston
*COO: Marc Steglitz
*Treas: Howard W Lutnick
*VP: Frederick B Henry
*VP: Wendy L-J Mc Neil
*VP: Jennifer Stockman
*VP: Stephen G Swid
*VP: John Wadsworth
*VP: Mark R Walter
CIO: Robert Rosenthal

D-U-N-S 05-475-7646 IMP/EXP
SOLOMON TRANSFORMERS LLC (KS)
SOLOMON ELECTRIC COMPANY
103 W Main St, Solomon, KS 67480-9760
Tel (785) 655-2191 Founded/Ownrshp 1971, 2000
Sales 140.5MM^E EMP 489
SIC 3612 5093 Voltage regulating transformers, electric power; Scrap & waste materials
CEO: Thomas M Hemmer
*COO: Phillip E Hemmer
*COO: Jerry Newton
*CFO: Lance Allen
*CFO: Joseph C Hemmer
Ofcr: Marsha Hartung
*VP: Katherine M Platten
Genl Mgr: Rj Ladenburger
IT Man: Joyce Young
Mktg Mgr: Cindy Curry
Sls Mgr: Keith Kenney

D-U-N-S 78-718-4167
SOLOMON-PAGE GROUP LLC
SPG
260 Madison Ave Fl 3, New York, NY 10016-2401
Tel (212) 403-6100 Founded/Ownrshp 1994
Sales 154.4MM EMP 200
Accts Grassi & Co Cpas Pc Jerich
SIC 7361 Employment agencies
CFO: Eric Davis
Sr VP: Jeffrey Kleiman
VP: Lisa Arty
VP: Brandon Barlow
VP: Dave Bruder
VP: Laura Cassidy
VP: Nicole Dantzler
VP: Ron Degasperis
VP: Howard Hecht
VP: John Patterson
VP: Scott Selover
VP: Bob Sugar
VP: Lisa Terry
VP: Richard Walsh
VP: Jennifer Williamson

D-U-N-S 78-803-0851
SOLPAC CONSTRUCTION INC
SOLTEK PACIFIC CONSTRUCTION CO
2424 Congress St, San Diego, CA 92110-2819
Tel (619) 296-6247 Founded/Ownrshp 2005
Sales 121.2MM EMP 235
Accts Gendron And Henriksen La Mesa
SIC 8741 1542 1611 Construction management; Commercial & office building contractors; Design & erection, combined: non-residential; General contractor, highway & street construction
CEO: Steven Thompson
*Pr: Dave Carlin
*Sr VP: John Myers
*VP: Kevin Cammall
*VP: William Naylor

D-U-N-S 01-938-5819
■ **SOLSTAS LAB PARTNERS GROUP LLC**
(Suby of QUEST DIAGNOSTICS INC) ★
4380 Federal Dr Ste 100, Greensboro, NC 27410-8149
Tel (336) 664-6100 Founded/Ownrshp 2014
Sales 71.2MM^E EMP 1,022
SIC 8071 Medical laboratories
CEO: David C Weavil
*Pr: Michael Hanbury
Ex VP: Carmine Capuccio
VP: Eugene Bustria

Genl Mgr: Steven Harris
Off Mgr: Teresa Powell
IT Man: Amy Gayle
IT Man: Stephen Macconnell
Pathlgst: Jerald Winter

D-U-N-S 80-981-0968
SOLSTICE BENEFITS INC
7901 Sw 6th Ct Ste 400, Plantation, FL 33324-3283
Tel (954) 370-1700 *Founded/Ownrshp* 2004
Sales NA *EMP* 130
SIC 6324 Hospital & medical service plans
Pr: Michael D Flax
COO: Carlos Ferrera
Dir Bus: Brian M Correia
Dir IT: Ted Vukelich
Netwrk Mgr: Kimberly Thomas
Software D: Michael Bloch
Sales Exec: Maria Rodriguez
Mktg Dir: Alissa Gavrilescu
Sales Asso: Carlos Henriquez
Genl Couns: Jamie Horne

D-U-N-S 62-511-0007
SOLSTICE HOLDINGS INC
ALTICOR
(*Suby of* ALTICOR GLOBAL HOLDINGS INC) ★
7575 Fulton St E, Ada, MI 49355-0001
Tel (616) 787-1000 *Founded/Ownrshp* 2002
Sales 9.4MMM^E^ *EMP* 14,000
SIC 4731 Freight transportation arrangement; Customs clearance of freight
Pr: Mr Doug L Devos
**COO:* Alvin Koop
**CFO:* Russ Evans
**Ch:* Stephen Van Andel
**VP:* Mr Michael Mohr

D-U-N-S 14-747-8528 IMP
SOLTA MEDICAL INC
(*Suby of* VALEANT PHARMACEUTICALS INTERNATIONAL CORP) ★
25881 Industrial Blvd, Hayward, CA 94545-2991
Tel (510) 786-6946 *Founded/Ownrshp* 2014
Sales 101.3MM^E^ *EMP* 371^E^
SIC 3845 Electromedical equipment
Pr: J Michael Pearson
**Treas:* Howard B Schiller
VP: Mingo Ku
VP: Thomas Yorkey
Area Mgr: Nick Blake
Area Mgr: Jacqueline Luby
Area Mgr: Melanie Mullen
Area Mgr: Porter Tiller
Plng Mgr: Paul Culver
IT Man: Pinakinn Purohit
Mktg Dir: Vladimir Paul-Blanc

SOLTEK PACIFIC CONSTRUCTION CO
See SOLPAC CONSTRUCTION INC

D-U-N-S 04-085-3731 IMP/EXP
■ **SOLUTIA INC**
(*Suby of* EASTMAN CHEMICAL CO) ★
575 Maryville Centre Dr, Saint Louis, MO 63141-5813
Tel (423) 229-2000 *Founded/Ownrshp* 1997
Sales 221.9MM^E^ *EMP* 3,400^E^
SIC 2824 2821 3081 2869 Organic fibers, noncellulosic; Acrylic fibers; Nylon fibers; Polyvinylidene chloride fibers; Plastics materials & resins; Nylon resins; Polyvinylidene chloride resins; Plasticizer/additive based plastic materials; Unsupported plastics film & sheet; Industrial organic chemicals
Ch Bd: Jeffry N Quinn
Pr: Kent Davies
Pr: Craig Ivey
Pr: Greta Senn
**COO:* D Michael Donnelly
COO: Luc D Temmerman
**CFO:* James M Sullivan
**Sr VP:* Paul J Berra III
**Sr VP:* Gary M Glandon
Sr VP: James R Voss
VP: Russell J Belle
VP: Christopher Bray
VP: Ricardo Coutino
VP: Sheila B Feldman
VP: Todd B Imhoff
VP: Eric Nichols
Exec: Bruce Elliston

SOLUTIAS PERFORMANCE FILMS DIV
See CPFILMS INC

D-U-N-S 00-648-9186
SOLUTIONARY INC
9420 Underwood Ave # 300, Omaha, NE 68114-6608
Tel (402) 361-3000 *Founded/Ownrshp* 2013
Sales 98.0MM^E^ *EMP* 350
SIC 7379

D-U-N-S 83-148-7363 IMP
SOLUTIONS 2 GO LLC
111 Theory Ste 250, Irvine, CA 92617-3041
Tel (949) 825-7700 *Founded/Ownrshp* 2009
Sales 300.0MM *EMP* 56
SIC 5092 Toys & hobby goods & supplies
**Pr:* Wayne Yodzio

D-U-N-S 07-970-6845
■ **SOLUTIONSTAR HOLDINGS LLC**
(*Suby of* NATIONSTAR MORTGAGE LLC) ★
750 Hwy 121 Byp Ste 100, Lewisville, TX 75067-8199
Tel (888) 321-2192 *Founded/Ownrshp* 2013
Sales 350.0MM *EMP* 1,000
SIC 6531 Real estate listing services
CEO: Kal Raman
**Pr:* Shawn Stone
Chf Mktg O: Prem Luthra
Ofcr: Parag Pandya
Ofcr: Angelo Rossi
Ex VP: Jay Gaskill
CTO: John Hensley
Genl Couns: Arash Mostafavipour

D-U-N-S 00-210-5914 IMP/EXP
SOLVAIRA SPECIALTIES INC
50 Bridge St, North Tonawanda, NY 14120-6842
Tel (716) 693-4040 *Founded/Ownrshp* 1917, 2013
Sales 129.4MM^E^ *EMP* 230
SIC 2823 2299 Cellulosic manmade fibers; Flock (recovered textile fibers)
CEO: L J Baillargeon
Ex VP: Dean Newby
VP: Jit Ang
VP: Lawrence A McKee
VP: Peter Vogt
IT Man: Lisa Fritz
Sfty Mgr: Scott Olick
Plnt Mgr: Martin Terry
Ql Cn Mgr: Whitney Baker
Sls&Mrk Ex: Mike Bailey

D-U-N-S 19-464-8705
SOLVATION INC
885 3rd Ave Fl 34, New York, NY 10022-4881
Tel (212) 888-5500 *Founded/Ownrshp* 1980
Sales NA *EMP* 1,020
SIC 6153 1611 3272 Factoring services; Highway & street construction; Prestressed concrete products
Pr: John W Adams

SOLVAY AMERICA
See SOLVAY CHEMICALS INC

D-U-N-S 15-173-4506 IMP/EXP
SOLVAY AMERICA INC
SOLVAY NORTH AMERICA
(*Suby of* SOLVAY SA)
3737 Buffalo Ste 800, Houston, TX 77098
Tel (713) 525-4000 *Founded/Ownrshp* 1957
Sales 1.2MMM^E^ *EMP* 3,960
SIC 2819 Industrial inorganic chemicals
Pr: Rene Degreve
CFO: Guy Mercier
Treas: Edgar H Case
Sr VP: Dick Hogan
VP: E J Buckingham
VP: James Daly
VP: Paul Harding
VP: Steve Kovar
VP: Michael Lacey
VP: Mark Looney
Dir Rx: David Henry

D-U-N-S 13-086-8656 IMP/EXP
SOLVAY CHEMICALS INC
SOLVAY AMERICA
(*Suby of* SOLVAY NORTH AMERICA) ★
3737 Buffalo Speedway, Houston, TX 77098-3099
Tel (713) 525-6800 *Founded/Ownrshp* 1992
Sales 564.8MM^E^ *EMP* 680
SIC 1474 2819 Soda ash (natural) mining; Peroxides, hydrogen peroxide
CEO: Richard Hogan
**Pr:* Michael Lacey
**Ex VP:* Ron Hughes
**Sr VP:* Vance Erickson
**Sr VP:* Paul Hogan
**Sr VP:* Marc Nuchelmans
VP: Bill Barnes
**VP:* William Barnes
**VP:* Cameron Berry
**VP:* Heather Hajdik
Sls Mgr: Rodrigo Elizondo

D-U-N-S 87-474-8937 IMP/EXP
SOLVAY HOLDING INC
RHODIA
(*Suby of* RHODIA HOLDINGS LIMITED)
8 Cedarbrook Dr, Cranbury, NJ 08512-3612
Tel (609) 860-4000 *Founded/Ownrshp* 2007
Sales 228.8MM^E^ *EMP* 14,250
SIC 2819 2812 2865 2869 Boric acid; Phosphates, except fertilizers: defluorinated & ammoniated; Soda ash, sodium carbonate (anhydrous); Phenol, alkylated & cumene; Diphenylamines; Isocyanates; Fluorinated hydrocarbon gases; Silicones
Ch: Jean Pierre Clamadieu
**Pr:* James Harton
**CFO:* Karim Hajjar
**Sr VP:* John P Donahue
Board of Directors: Harold F Boardman Jr, David D Eckert

D-U-N-S 09-397-1430
SOLVAY INTEROX INC
(*Suby of* SOLVAY NORTH AMERICA) ★
3737 Buffalo Speedway, Houston, TX 77098-3099
Tel (713) 525-6500 *Founded/Ownrshp* 1978
Sales 140.0MM *EMP* 20
SIC 2819 2899 Industrial inorganic chemicals; Peroxides, hydrogen peroxide; Sodium compounds or salts, inorg., ex. refined sod. chloride; Chemical preparations
Pr: Gary L Hall
**Pr:* David Burney
**Treas:* Robert L Swann
VP: Carl E Johnson
**VP:* Robert M Monsen
**VP:* Carl G Widerquist
VP Mktg: Peter Lai

SOLVAY NORTH AMERICA
See SOLVAY AMERICA INC

D-U-N-S 09-473-1705 IMP/EXP
SOLVAY SPECIALTY POLYMERS USA LLC
(*Suby of* SOLVAY NORTH AMERICA) ★
4500 Mcginnis Ferry Rd, Alpharetta, GA 30005-2203
Tel (770) 772-8200 *Founded/Ownrshp* 2001
Sales 247.2MM^E^ *EMP* 500
SIC 3089 Plastic processing
CEO: George Corbin
**VP:* Joe Greulich
**VP:* Satchit Srinivasan
**VP:* Tom Wood
Genl Mgr: Vincenzo Morici
Mktg Dir: Chuck Roney
Mktg Mgr: Edgar Benjamin

D-U-N-S 00-295-9810 IMP/EXP
SOLVAY USA INC
(*Suby of* SOLVAY SA)
504 Carnegie Ctr, Princeton, NJ 08540-6241
Tel (609) 860-4000 *Founded/Ownrshp* 1995, 2012
Sales 804.0MM^E^ *EMP* 1,800
SIC 2899 2869 2821 2087 2865 Chemical preparations; Fluorinated hydrocarbon gases; Silicones; Plastics materials & resins; Flavoring extracts & syrups; Phenol, alkylated & cumene; Diphenylamines; Isocyanates
Pr: James Harton
**CFO:* Mark Dahlinger
**Sr VP:* John P Donahue
Dir Rx: Jean L Joye
IT Man: Boris Foiselle
Sls Mgr: Bob Dollinger

SOLVE ALL FACILITY SERVICES
See BERGENSONS PROPERTY SERVICES INC

D-U-N-S 06-296-3279
SOLVIS STAFFING SERVICES INC
500 La Terraza Blvd # 110, Escondido, CA 92025-3875
Tel (858) 230-8920 *Founded/Ownrshp* 2013
Sales 100.0MM *EMP* 10,000^E^
SIC 7361 Employment agencies
CEO: Ronald Carr

D-U-N-S 15-103-8247 IMP
SOMEBODY CARES INC
57 N Court St, Fairfield, IA 52556-3212
Tel (641) 472-5352 *Founded/Ownrshp* 2000
Sales 23.2MM^E^ *EMP* 1,015
SIC 5947 7699 5999 Gift shop; Picture framing, custom; Art dealers
Pr: Mark Welch
**Pr:* Martin Davis
**VP:* Janice Overholtzer

D-U-N-S 10-284-2598
SOMERS BUILDING MAINTENANCE INC
5241 Arnold Ave, McClellan, CA 95652-1025
Tel (916) 922-3300 *Founded/Ownrshp* 1982
Sales 91.6MM^E^ *EMP* 5,000
SIC 7349 Building maintenance, except repairs
CEO: Ken Silva
**COO:* Don Tracy
Ofcr: Ron Alvarado
**Ex VP:* Charles Somers
VP: D Tracey
Site Mgr: Aaron Jenkins
Site Mgr: Meg Minasian

SOMERS POINT VILLAGE I & II
See SOMERS RELATED POINT LLC

D-U-N-S 00-799-3950
SOMERS RELATED POINT LLC
SOMERS POINT VILLAGE I & II
50 Mays Landing Rd # 226, Somers Point, NJ 08244-1123
Tel (609) 927-0441 *Founded/Ownrshp* 2007
Sales 13.1MM^E^ *EMP* 1,828
SIC 7299 6531 Apartment locating service; Real estate agents & managers
Prin: Larry Lipton

D-U-N-S 13-153-1139 IMP/EXP
SOMERSET HARDWOOD FLOORING INC
SOMERSET HARDWOOD PELLETS
70 W Racetrack Rd, Somerset, KY 42503-3934
Tel (606) 678-2842 *Founded/Ownrshp* 1985
Sales 85.6MM^E^ *EMP* 400
SIC 2426 Flooring, hardwood
Pr: Stephen D Merrick
**VP:* Timothy Bullock
**VP:* George Crawford
**VP:* Paul Stringer
**VP:* Jason Webster
**Prin:* S L Sears
Sls Mgr: Scott Burega
Board of Directors: Jeffrey Eads

SOMERSET HARDWOOD PELLETS
See SOMERSET HARDWOOD FLOORING INC

D-U-N-S 62-077-3937
SOMERSET HEALTH CARE CORP
110 Rehill Ave, Somerville, NJ 08876-2519
Tel (908) 685-2200 *Founded/Ownrshp* 1985
Sales 334.0M *EMP* 1,700
Accts Withumsmithbrown Pc Morristow
SIC 8093 8011 Rehabilitation center, outpatient treatment; Health maintenance organization
CEO: Kenneth Bateman

D-U-N-S 06-314-1972
SOMERSET MEDICAL CENTER
110 Rehill Ave, Somerville, NJ 08876-2598
Tel (908) 685-2200 *Founded/Ownrshp* 2006
Sales 245.2MM *EMP* 1,743
SIC 8062

D-U-N-S 10-066-0591
SOMERSET NEIGHBORHOOD SCHOOL INC
12425 Sw 53rd St, Miramar, FL 33027-5493
Tel (305) 829-2406 *Founded/Ownrshp* 2001
Sales 97.3MM *EMP* 9^E^
SIC 8211 Elementary & secondary schools
Prin: Shannine Sadesky-Hunt

D-U-N-S 07-854-5234
SOMERSET OPERATING CO LLC
7725 Lake Rd, Barker, NY 14012-9611
Tel (716) 795-9501 *Founded/Ownrshp* 2012
Sales 101.3MM^E^ *EMP* 103
SIC 4911 Generation, electric power
Prin: Jack White

D-U-N-S 00-191-5545 IMP
SOMERSET TIRE SERVICE INC (NJ)
STS TIRE & AUTO SERVICE CTRS
(*Suby of* MAVIS DISCOUNT TIRE) ★
358 Saw Mill River Rd # 5, Millwood, NY 10546-1051
Tel (732) 356-8500 *Founded/Ownrshp* 1958
Sales 369.7MM^E^ *EMP* 1,000
SIC 5531 5014 5013 7538 Automotive tires; Automobile tires & tubes; Tire & tube repair materials; Automotive supplies & parts; Truck parts & accessories; General automotive repair shops
CEO: William Caulin
**CFO:* Anthony Losardo
**Sr VP:* Robert Howardson
**VP:* Michael Cardali
**VP:* Robert Glotfelty
**VP:* Robert T Haase
**VP:* Mark S Reiner
**VP:* Kevin B Traier

D-U-N-S 07-812-0276
SOMMERS CO
EL CHEAPO FUEL STOPS
1000 Sommers Blvd, Richmond Hill, GA 31324-8817
Tel (800) 654-6466 *Founded/Ownrshp* 1976
Sales 296.7MM *EMP* 30
Accts Tjs Deemer Dana Llp Savannah
SIC 5172 5541 7033 Fuel oil; Gasoline; Filling stations, gasoline; Campgrounds
Pr: Jimmy F Sommers
**COO:* Randy Sommers
**Sec:* Sarah W Sommers
**VP:* Wynelle Sommers

D-U-N-S 07-525-8319
SOMPO AMERICA INSURANCE SERVICES LLC
(*Suby of* SOMPO JAPAN NIPPONKOA INSURANCE INC.)
777 3rd Ave Fl 24, New York, NY 10017-1412
Tel (212) 416-1200 *Founded/Ownrshp* 1962
Sales NA *EMP* 194
SIC 6331 Fire, marine & casualty insurance
CEO: Hiroyuki Yamaguchi
**Pr:* Hideo Haraguchi
**Treas:* Richard A Tafro
**Sr VP:* John J McElroy
Sr VP: John Ritter
Board of Directors: Takeo Akiyama, Leonard Cummings, Stanley Dorf, Donald D Gabay, Hiroshi Kawakami, Harry Kefe, Frank Palotta, William James Robinson

D-U-N-S 07-731-7766 IMP
SONALYSTS INC
215 Parkway N, Waterford, CT 06385
Tel (860) 442-4355 *Founded/Ownrshp* 1973
Sales 100.3MM^E^ *EMP* 432
SIC 8711 7373 8748 8732 3993 Consulting engineer; Systems engineering, computer related; Systems engineering consultant, ex. computer or professional; Business research service; Displays & cutouts, window & lobby
Ch Bd: Lawrence F Clark
**Pr:* Milton L Stretton
**Pr:* Andrew N Toriello
CFO: Marik Sol
**Treas:* Miroslaw Fal
Ofcr: Katie Coleman
Ofcr: Catherine Vincent
**Ex VP:* David R Samuelson
VP: Robert Amundson
VP: George Banta
VP: Dan Bouchard
VP: Rip Coleman
VP: Donald Estes
VP: Steve Juskiewicz
VP: Bob Kurzawa
VP: Jeffrey Lemmon
VP: Gaylord Liby
VP: Rich Miller
VP: Brad Perrin
VP: William Stone
VP: Brian Vanvolkenburg

SONDRA ROBERTS
See BECARRO INTERNATIONAL CORP

D-U-N-S 00-196-9591
SONEPAR DISTRIBUTION NEW ENGLAND INC
NORTHEAST ELECTRICAL DISTRS
(*Suby of* SONEPAR USA) ★
560 Oak St, Brockton, MA 02301-1346
Tel (508) 998-8900 *Founded/Ownrshp* 1998
Sales 169.7MM^E^ *EMP* 390
SIC 5063 Electrical supplies; Motor controls, starters & relays: electric
Pr: Donald M Block
**Treas:* Andrew J Waring
VP: Frank Marandino
VP: Gregg Richards
Brnch Mgr: Andrew Macwalter
Brnch Mgr: Stephen Massey
Brnch Mgr: Eric McCue
Brnch Mgr: Chris Ronaghan
Brnch Mgr: Mike Shannahan
Brnch Mgr: Scott Terceiro
Manager: Joel Flaherty

D-U-N-S 04-878-1830 IMP/EXP
SONEPAR MANAGEMENT US INC
SONEPAR USA
(*Suby of* SOCIETE DE NEGOCE ET DE PARTICIPATION)
510 Walnut St Ste 400, Philadelphia, PA 19106-3625
Tel (215) 399-5900 *Founded/Ownrshp* 1998
Sales 4.5MMM^E^ *EMP* 2,172
SIC 5063 Electrical apparatus & equipment
Pr: Halsey Cook
**CFO:* Andy Waring
VP: Jim Brzezinski
VP: Jeff Davidson
VP: Karen Dunn
VP: Mark Linder
VP: Karen Monte
CIO: Doug Lauer
Dir IT: Brande Kloster
IT Man: Brad Bachmann
IT Man: Patricia Kridlow

SONEPAR USA
See SONEPAR MANAGEMENT US INC

D-U-N-S 05-014-1865 IMP/EXP
SONEPAR USA HOLDINGS INC
(*Suby of* SONEPAR)
1011 Centre Rd Ste 327, Wilmington, DE 19805-1203
Tel (302) 573-3807 *Founded/Ownrshp* 1998
Sales 4.0MMM^E^ *EMP* 6,480
SIC 5063 Electrical apparatus & equipment
Pr: Tony Burr
**CFO:* Kathleen Rusko

Section I

Businesses Alphabetically

*Treas: Paul Trudel
VP: Franois Chatin

SONESTA HOTELS & RESORTS
See SONESTA INTERNATIONAL HOTELS CORP

D-U-N-S 00-194-5922
SONESTA INTERNATIONAL HOTELS CORP (MD)
SONESTA HOTELS & RESORTS
255 Washington St Ste 270, Newton, MA 02458-1634
Tel (770) 923-1775 Founded/Ownrshp 1963
Sales 252.3MM^E EMP 2,500
SIC 7011 Hotels
Pr: Carlos Flores
*Ch Bd: Bill Sheehan
*Ch Bd: Peter J Sonnabend
*Pr: Stephanie Sonnabend
*Treas: Boy Van Riel
Ex VP: John J Depaul
*Ex VP: Jacqueline Sonnabend
*VP: Carol Beggs
VP: El Maghraby
VP: David Sanclemente
VP: Hans U Wandfluh
Exec: Christopher Cramer
Board of Directors: George S Abrams, Joseph L Bower, Charles J Clark, Clarence A Davis, Irma Fisher Mann, Stephen Sonnabend, Jean C Tempel

SONGER STEEL SERVICES
See SSSI INC

D-U-N-S 09-736-4715 IMP/EXP
▲ SONIC AUTOMOTIVE INC
4401 Colwick Rd, Charlotte, NC 28211-2311
Tel (704) 566-2400 Founded/Ownrshp 1997
Sales 9.6MMM EMP 9,800
Tkr Sym SAH Exch NYS
SIC 5511 7538 New & used car dealers; Automobiles, new & used; General automotive repair shops
Pr: B Scott Smith
*Ch Bd: O Bruton Smith
CFO: Heath R Byrd
*V Ch Bd: David Bruton Smith
Ex VP: Frank J Dyke
Ex VP: Jeff Dyke
Ex VP: John Rush
VP: Edd D Bryant
VP: Raymond Valentine
VP: Jay Winston
Exec: Doug Morgan
Comm Man: Shannon Kendall
Board of Directors: William I Belk, William R Brooks, Victor H Doolan, John W Harris III, H Robert Heller, R Eugene Taylor

D-U-N-S 06-127-8735
■ SONIC AUTOMOTIVE OF TEXAS LP
LONE STAR FORD
(Suby of SONIC AUTOMOTIVE INC) ★
8477 North Fwy, Houston, TX 77037-2807
Tel (281) 931-3300 Founded/Ownrshp 1997
Sales 125.1MM^E EMP 500
SIC 5511 7538 Automobiles, new & used; Trucks, tractors & trailers: new & used; Vans, new & used; General automotive repair shops
Pr: B Scott Smith
CFO: Heath R Byrd
CFO: David Cosper
VP: Jeff Dy Ke
VP: David Smith
Sls Mgr: Javier Medina

D-U-N-S 60-945-6033
▲ SONIC CORP
300 Johnny Bench Dr, Oklahoma City, OK 73104-2471
Tel (405) 225-5000 Founded/Ownrshp 1953
Sales 606.3MM EMP 10,863
Tkr Sym SONC Exch NGS
SIC 5812 6794 Drive-in restaurant; Franchises, selling or licensing
Ch Bd: J Clifford Hudson
Pr: Harold A Caron
Pr: Steve Young
CFO: Claudia S San Pedro
Treas: Corey R Horsch
Chf Mktg O: Todd W Smith
Ofcr: Stephen C Vaughan
Ex VP: Mark Ely
Sr VP: Paige S Bass
Sr VP: John H Budd III
Sr VP: Craig J Miller
VP: Tanishia Beacham
VP: Michelle E Britten
VP: Carolyn C Cummins
VP: Carolyn Cummins
VP: Bill Klearman
VP: Patrick Lenow
VP: Larry Morton
VP: Claudia Pedro
VP: Sandy Piscitello
VP: Diane Prem
Board of Directors: Susan E Thronson, Tony D Bartel, R Neal Black, Lauren R Hobart, Kate S Lavelle, J Larry Nichols, Federico F Pena, Frank E Richardson, Jeffrey H Schutz, Kathryn L Taylor

SONIC DRIVE-IN
See M & D INDUSTRIES CORP

SONIC DRIVE-IN
See MCCLAIN SONICS INC

SONIC DRIVE-IN
See SONIC INDUSTRIES SERVICES INC

SONIC DRIVE-IN
See B & B CONSULTANTS INC

SONIC DRIVE-IN
See D L ROGERS CORP

D-U-N-S 06-267-2915
▲ SONIC FINANCIAL CORP
5401 E Independence Blvd, Charlotte, NC 28212-0503
Tel (704) 536-5600 Founded/Ownrshp 1987
Sales 496.4MM^E EMP 1,171^E
SIC 7948 6321 6311 Racing, including track operation; Accident & health insurance; Life insurance
Pr: O Bruton Smith
*VP: William R Brooks
Genl Mgr: Charles Hutto
CTO: Shannon Keit

D-U-N-S 94-172-7344
SONIC HEALTHCARE USA INC
9737 Great Hills Trl # 100, Austin, TX 78759-6417
Tel (512) 439-1600 Founded/Ownrshp 2007
Sales 543.2MM^E EMP 16,000^E
SIC 8099 Health screening service
CEO: David W Bryant
VP: Bill Sledge
Off Admin: Nancy Lunsford
IT Man: Adrian Fonseca
Mktg Dir: Gloria Armellin

D-U-N-S 07-121-8739
■ SONIC INDUSTRIES SERVICES INC
SONIC DRIVE-IN
(Suby of SONIC CORP) ★
300 Johnny Bench Dr # 400, Oklahoma City, OK 73104-2472
Tel (405) 225-5000 Founded/Ownrshp 1953
Sales 487.7MM^E EMP 8,750
SIC 6794 5812 Franchises, selling or licensing; Drive-in restaurant
Pr: W S McLain
*Ch Bd: Cliff Hudson
Pr: Doug Cook
*Pr: Scott McLain
*CFO: Steven Vaughan
*Treas: Claudia San Pedro
Sr VP: Craig Miller
Sr VP: James O'Reilly
Sr VP: Nancy Robertson
VP: Larry Archibald
*VP: Paige S Bass
*VP: Paul Macaluso
VP: Dino Medina
*VP: Drew Ritger
VP: John Salama
Dir Risk M: Doug Wohletz

D-U-N-S 96-376-4576 IMP
SONIC MANUFACTURING TECHNOLOGIES INC
47951 Westinghouse Dr, Fremont, CA 94539-7483
Tel (510) 580-8500 Founded/Ownrshp 1996
Sales 123.3MM^E EMP 300
SIC 3672 Printed circuit boards
Pr: Kenneth Raab
VP: Dave Ginsberg
*VP: Robert Pereyda
VP: Bob Tolan
*VP: Henry Woo
Prgrm Mgr: Don Kou
Sfty Mgr: Henry Wu
Prd Mgr: Norma Hirle

SONIC MILL CO
See RIO GRANDE INC

SONICCARE
See PHILIPS ORAL HEALTHCARE LLC

D-U-N-S 62-320-3684 IMP
■ SONICWALL LLC
DELL SONICWALL
(Suby of DELL COMPUTER) ★
5455 Great America Pkwy, Santa Clara, CA 95054-3645
Tel (800) 509-1265 Founded/Ownrshp 1991
Sales 113.8MM^E EMP 820^E
SIC 7373 Computer integrated systems design; Systems software development services; Computer systems analysis & design
Pr: Matt Medeiros
*CFO: Robert D Selvi
CFO: Robert Selvi
*VP: Gary Bacon
*VP: Marvin Blough
*VP: Edward Cohen
VP: Brandon Conley
*VP: Atul Dhablania
*VP: John Gmuender
*VP: Michael M Stewart
VP: Mike Stuart
*VP: Michael Valentine

D-U-N-S 10-229-2851 IMP
SONIFI SOLUTIONS INC
3900 W Innovation St, Sioux Falls, SD 57107-7066
Tel (605) 988-1000 Founded/Ownrshp 2013
Sales 87.0MM^E EMP 700^E
SIC 7812 8082 Motion picture production & distribution, television; Home health care services
CEO: Ahmad Ouri
*Pr: Tom Storey
*CFO: John Chang
VP: Eric Aasen
VP: Kelly Boyd
VP: Stephen Guzzetta
VP: Matthew Harmon
VP: John Johnson
VP: Thomas McAdaragh
VP: Michael McClain
VP: Rob Tash

D-U-N-S 03-869-9930 IMP/EXP
SONNYS ENTERPRISES INC
5605 Hiatus Rd, Tamarac, FL 33321-6408
Tel (954) 720-4100 Founded/Ownrshp 1978
Sales 94.9MM^E EMP 155
SIC 5087 3589 Carwash equipment & supplies; Car washing machinery
Pr: Paul Fazio
*CFO: Mike Bauer
CFO: David Shield
Sr VP: Jon Simmons
VP: Robert Picard
VP: Barbara Piccirilli
VP: Katie Pierce
Creative D: Sergio Martinengo
Mng Dir: Reginald Flanagan
Genl Mgr: Nick Fazio
CTO: Kevin Collette

SONOCO ALLOYD
See TEGRANT ALLOYD BRANDS INC

SONOCO CORRFLEX
See SONOCO DISPLAY & PACKAGING LLC

D-U-N-S 79-947-4655 IMP
■ SONOCO DISPLAY & PACKAGING LLC
SONOCO CORRFLEX
(Suby of SONOCO PRODUCTS CO) ★
555 Aureole St, Winston Salem, NC 27107-3201
Tel (336) 784-0445 Founded/Ownrshp 1997
Sales 251.9MM^E EMP 1,200
SIC 3086 Packaging & shipping materials, foamed plastic
Genl Mgr: Ken Kesler
Dir IT: Theodore Topalu
IT Man: Ted Topalo
Mktg Mgr: Greg Powell

D-U-N-S 07-933-8432
■ SONOCO PLASTICS INC
(Suby of SONOCO PRODUCTS CO) ★
1 N 2nd St, Hartsville, SC 29550-3305
Tel (843) 383-7000 Founded/Ownrshp 2002
Sales 554.9MM^E EMP 2,300
SIC 3082 Unsupported plastics profile shapes
CEO: Jack Sanders
VP: John M Colyer
*VP: Jeffrey Di Pasquale
VP: Ginny Jones
Dir IT: Steve Wyatt
Prd Mgr: Nigel Rhodes
Ql Cn Mgr: Bob Lundy
Snr Mgr: Edward Short

D-U-N-S 00-335-4230
▲ SONOCO PRODUCTS CO (SC)
1 N 2nd St, Hartsville, SC 29550-3305
Tel (843) 383-7000 Founded/Ownrshp 1899
Sales 4.9MMM EMP 21,000
Accts Pricewaterhousecoopers Llp C
Tkr Sym SON Exch NYS
SIC 2631 2671 2653 2655 3089 2499 Paperboard mills; Packaging paper & plastics film, coated & laminated; Corrugated & solid fiber boxes; Fiber cans, drums & similar products; Injection molded finished plastic products; Extruded finished plastic products; Reels, plywood
Pr: M Jack Sanders
Ch Bd: Harris E Deloach Jr
CFO: Barry L Saunders
Sr VP: John M Colyer Jr
Sr VP: Robert C Tiede
VP: John Florence
Exec: Josh Haen
Cmptr Lab: Jan Grady
Prd Mgr: Dave Morrison
Sls Mgr: Rick Turner
Board of Directors: Thomas E Whiddon, Harry A Cockrell, Pamela L Davies, John R Haley, Richard G Kyle, Edgar H Lawton III, John E Linville, Blythe J McGarvie, James M Micali, Marc D Oken

SONOCO PROTECTIVE SOLUTION
See TEGRANT CORP

D-U-N-S 00-433-3423 IMP/EXP
■ SONOCO PROTECTIVE SOLUTIONS INC (PA)
(Suby of SONOCO PROTECTIVE SOLUTION) ★
1 N 2nd St, Hartsville, SC 29550-3305
Tel (843) 383-7000 Founded/Ownrshp 1962
Sales 611.4MM^E EMP 2,470^E
SIC 3086 2679 Plastics foam products; Packaging & shipping materials, foamed plastic; Insulation or cushioning material, foamed plastic; Building, insulating & packaging paperboard
Pr: William M Kelly
*Treas: Ritchie L Bond
VP: Scott Novak
*VP: Jack Sanders

D-U-N-S 02-482-3072
■ SONOCO RECYCLING LLC
PAPER STOCK
(Suby of SONOCO PRODUCTS CO) ★
1 N 2nd St, Hartsville, SC 29550-3305
Tel (843) 383-0273 Founded/Ownrshp 1951, 1972
Sales 139.3MM^E EMP 334
SIC 5093 Waste paper
Pr: Ray Howard
*Sec: Ritchie L Bond
VP: Roger Schrum
Sls&Mrk Ex: Andrew Bell

D-U-N-S 15-738-8661 IMP
■ SONOCO-CRELLIN INTERNATIONAL INC
(Suby of SONOCO PRODUCTS CO) ★
87 Center St, Chatham, NY 12037-1032
Tel (518) 392-2000 Founded/Ownrshp 2001
Sales 119.6MM^E EMP 900
SIC 3089 Molding primary plastic
VP: Bob Puechl
CFO: Ralph Tassone
*VP: David Marche
*VP: Michael Tucker

SONOMA CELLAR STEAKHOUSE
See SUNSET STATION HOTEL AND CASINO

D-U-N-S 02-002-0533
SONOMA COUNTY JUNIOR COLLEGE DISTRICT
SANTA ROSA JUNIOR COLLEGE
1501 Mendocino Ave, Santa Rosa, CA 95401-4332
Tel (707) 527-4011 Founded/Ownrshp 1919
Sales 53.7MM^E EMP 2,100
Accts Gilbert Associates Inc Sacra
SIC 8222 8221 Junior college; Colleges universities & professional schools
Pr: Frank Chong
*VP: Ricardo Navarrett
*VP: Doug Roberts
*VP: Mary Kay Rudolph
Plng Mgr: Curtis L Groninga
Telecom Ex: Ben Toyeda
CIO: Ian Baker
Info Man: Robert Flaa
Netwrk Eng: Stephen Wilder
Psych: Anthonytony Vasquez

D-U-N-S 17-098-8815 IMP
SONORA MILLS FOODS INC
POP CHIPS
3064 E Maria St, E Rncho Dmngz, CA 90221-5804
Tel (310) 639-5333 Founded/Ownrshp 1991
Sales 92.0MM^E EMP 200^E
SIC 2052 Rice cakes
CEO: Patrick Turpin
*VP: Martin Basch
Exec: Sara Ortiz
Plnt Mgr: Ruben Calzada

D-U-N-S 01-443-8001
SONORA QUEST LABORATORIES LLC
(Suby of LABORATORY SCIENCES OF ARIZONA LLC) ★
1255 W Washington St, Tempe, AZ 85281-1210
Tel (602) 685-5000 Founded/Ownrshp 1997
Sales 88.9MM^E EMP 1,200
SIC 8071 Medical laboratories
VP: Steve Burton
VP: Mary Gregg
VP: David Norgard
Dir Risk M: Kim Fleurquin
Genl Mgr: Michelle Brown
CIO: Robert Dowd
Dir IT: Jackie Carlisle
Dir IT: Calley McCoy
IT Man: Cindy Fizzard
Mktg Mgr: Jef Wright

D-U-N-S 96-442-3987
SONORA REGIONAL HOSPITAL
1000 Greenley Rd, Sonora, CA 95370-5200
Tel (209) 736-0249 Founded/Ownrshp 2010
Sales 236.8MM EMP 4^E
SIC 8011 Medical centers

D-U-N-S 07-187-7575
SONORA REGIONAL MEDICAL CENTER
ADVENTIST HEALTH
(Suby of ADVENTIST HEALTH SYSTEM/WEST) ★
1000 Greenley Rd, Sonora, CA 95370-5200
Tel (209) 532-5000 Founded/Ownrshp 1957
Sales 249.4MM EMP 720
SIC 8062 8051 General medical & surgical hospitals; Skilled nursing care facilities
Chf OB: Felix A Conte
*CFO: David Larsen
Dir OR: Andi Coniglio
*Prin: Jeff Eler
CIO: Cheri Bailey
Netwrk Eng: Mark Gosney
Mtls Mgr: Carolyn Ayers
Opers Mgr: Mary L Mearsman
Pr Mgr: Ilena Grycel
Orthpdst: Kevin Booth
Orthpdst: Christine Elder

D-U-N-S 15-454-9059
SONSTEGARD FOODS CO
5005 S Bur Oak Pl, Sioux Falls, SD 57108-2228
Tel (605) 338-4642 Founded/Ownrshp 1972
Sales 117.9MM^E EMP 400
SIC 5144 Poultry & poultry products
Pr: Philip Sonstegard
Sls Mgr: Diane Lakee

D-U-N-S 01-611-9765
▲ SONUS NETWORKS INC
4 Technology Park Dr, Westford, MA 01886-3140
Tel (978) 614-8100 Founded/Ownrshp 1997
Sales 249.0MM EMP 1,089^E
Tkr Sym SONS Exch NGS
SIC 7373 Systems software development services
Pr: Raymond P Dolan
Ch Bd: Howard E Janzen
CFO: Susan M Villare
Ofcr: Jeffrey M Snider
Ex VP: Todd Abbott
Sr VP: Kevin Riley
Sr VP: Michael Swade
VP: Gail England
VP: Beth Frazier
VP: Sean King
Sls Dir: Hal Deutsch
Board of Directors: Beatriz V Infante, Richard J Lynch, Pamela D A Reeve, John A Schofield, Scott E Schubert, Matthew W Bross

D-U-N-S 96-221-9234
SONUS-USA INC
(Suby of AMPLIFON (USA) INC) ★
5000 Cheshire Pkwy N # 1, Minneapolis, MN 55446-4104
Tel (763) 268-4065 Founded/Ownrshp 1996
Sales 99.0MM^E EMP 800
SIC 5999 Hearing aids
Pr: Scott Klein
*VP: Randall Drullinger
*VP: Gregory Frazer PHD
*VP: Dan Quall
*VP: Jeff Weiss
VP Bus Dev: John Grana
Board of Directors: Brandon M Dawson, Greg Schott Nd Scott Klein

D-U-N-S 62-198-8955 IMP
SONY BROADBAND ENTERTAINMENT CORP
(Suby of SONY MUSIC ENTERTAINMENT) ★
550 Madison Ave Fl 6, New York, NY 10022-3211
Tel (212) 833-6800 Founded/Ownrshp 1991
Sales 1.3MMM^E EMP 17,000
SIC 3652 7812 5734 7832 5735 Pre-recorded records & tapes; Motion picture production & distribution; Motion picture production & distribution, television; Software, computer games; Motion picture theaters, except drive-in; Video discs & tapes, prerecorded
Ch Bd: Howard Stringer
*CFO: Robert Wiesenthal
VP Mktg: Flory Bramnick
VP Sls: Andy Wiswell

D-U-N-S 60-213-8570 IMP/EXP
SONY CORP OF AMERICA
SONY MUSIC ENTERTAINMENT
(*Suby of* SONY CORPORATION)
25 Madison Ave Fl 27, New York, NY 10010-8601
Tel (212) 833-8000 *Founded/Ownrshp* 1988
Sales 12.0MMM[E] *EMP* 33,234
SIC 3695 3652 3651 3577 3572 Optical disks & tape, blank; Compact laser discs, prerecorded; Household audio & video equipment; Computer peripheral equipment; Computer storage devices
Ch Bd: Kazuo Hirai
**Pr:* Howard Stringer
CFO: Joe Gorman
CFO: Kevin Kelleher
**CFO:* Rob Weisenthal
Bd of Dir: Roger Vercammen
Ofcr: Masaru Kato
Ex VP: Mike Fasulo
Ex VP: Bob Ishida
Ex VP: Mark E Khalil
Ex VP: Ann McClanathan
**Ex VP:* Nicole Seligman
**Sr VP:* Mary Jo V Green
**Sr VP:* Steven E Kober
Sr VP: Emily H Susskind
VP: Sam Levenson
VP: Stuart Redsun
Exec: David Andronofsky
Exec: Paul Barnabee
Exec: Miles Braffet
Exec: Filipe Hermosillo

D-U-N-S 10-363-1131 IMP
SONY DADC US INC
(*Suby of* SONY MUSIC ENTERTAINMENT) ★
1800 N Fruitridge Ave, Terre Haute, IN 47804-1780
Tel (812) 462-8100 *Founded/Ownrshp* 1988
Sales 188.2MM[E] *EMP* 1,200
SIC 3695 3652 3651 3577 3572 Optical disks & tape, blank; Compact laser discs, prerecorded; Household audio & video equipment; Computer peripheral equipment; Computer storage devices
Pr: David Rubenstein
**Pr:* Michael Frey
**Treas:* Wallace R Page
VP: John Daly
VP: Robert Hurley
**VP:* Warren Maccaroni
CTO: Jim Krouse
IT Man: Joseph Kallubhavi
Netwrk Eng: Jim McNair
Netwrk Eng: Ty Taylor
Sfty Mgr: Debra King

D-U-N-S 00-590-2150 IMP/EXP
SONY ELECTRONICS INC
(*Suby of* SONY MUSIC ENTERTAINMENT) ★
16535 Via Esprillo Bldg 1, San Diego, CA 92127-1738
Tel (858) 942-2400 *Founded/Ownrshp* 1960
Sales 4.4MMM[E] *EMP* 26,150
SIC 3651 5064 3695 3671 3572 3674 Household audio & video equipment; Television receiving sets; Radio receiving sets; Tape recorders: cassette, cartridge or reel: household use; Electrical appliances, television & radio; Television sets; Radios; Video cassette recorders & accessories; Video recording tape, blank; Audio range tape, blank; Television tubes; Computer tape drives & components; Semiconductors & related devices
Pr: Phil Molyneux
**Ch Bd:* Hideki Komiyama
Pr: Charles Gregory
**CFO:* Rintaro Miyoshi
**Ex VP:* Frank M Lesher
Sr VP: Tim Baxter
**Sr VP:* William A Glaser
Sr VP: Alec Shapiro
VP: Takashi Akimoto
VP: Marc Birnkrant
VP: Neal Manowitz
VP: David Migdal
VP: Hiroshi Takahashi
Exec: Bob Lofland

D-U-N-S 11-151-9336 IMP
SONY INTERACTIVE ENTERTAINMENT AMERICA LLC
(*Suby of* SONY MUSIC ENTERTAINMENT) ★
2207 Bridgepointe Pkwy, Foster City, CA 94404-5060
Tel (650) 655-8000 *Founded/Ownrshp* 1996
Sales 2.3MMM[E] *EMP* 1,500
SIC 5092 Video games
Sr VP: Peter Dille
Sr VP: Andrew J House
Sr VP: Guy W Longworth
VP: Philip Rosenberg
VP: Scott A Steinberg
VP: Takashi Usuki
IT Man: Brian Peck
IT Man: Dean Richmond
IT Man: Vinh Tran
IT Man: Luciana Yamaguchi
Netwrk Mgr: Mike Pigoncelli

D-U-N-S 61-291-8396 IMP
SONY MOBILE COMMUNICATIONS (USA) INC
(*Suby of* SONY MOBILE COMMUNICATIONS MANAGEMENT LIMITED)
2207 Bridgepoint Pkwy, San Mateo, CA 94404
Tel (866) 766-9374 *Founded/Ownrshp* 2001
Sales 182.2MM[E] *EMP* 170
SIC 3663 5999 Mobile communication equipment; Mobile telephones & equipment
CEO: Kunihiko Shiomi
**Pr:* Hideki Komiyama
**CFO:* Francisco Lazardi
VP: Paul Hamnett
VP: Ron Louks
**VP:* Ravi Nookala
**VP:* Anders Runevad
VP: Joe Wray
**Prin:* Cherie Hary
**Prin:* Najmi Jarwala
IT Man: Hubert Lin

SONY MUSIC ENTERTAINMENT
See SONY CORP OF AMERICA

D-U-N-S 17-295-7508 IMP
SONY MUSIC ENTERTAINMENT INC
SONY WONDER
(*Suby of* SONY BROADBAND ENTERTAINMENT CORP) ★
25 Madison Ave Fl 19, New York, NY 10010-8601
Tel (212) 833-8500 *Founded/Ownrshp* 2004
Sales 1.4MMM[E] *EMP* 9,500
SIC 3652 5064 Pre-recorded records & tapes; Electrical appliances, television & radio
Ch Bd: Robert Sorrentino
**CEO:* Hartwig Masuch
COO: Kathy Moreno
CFO: Carmine Coppola
CFO: Ken Dopher
CFO: Peter Hellar
Treas: Jonathan Spicehandler
Bd of Dir: Clive Davis
Ex VP: Liz Young
Sr VP: Kaz Ambe
Sr VP: Adam Block
Sr VP: Mark Flaherty
Sr VP: David Griffith
Sr VP: David Levin
Sr VP: Cece McClendon
Sr VP: Yaz Noya
Sr VP: Lee Stimmel
Sr VP: Thomas C Tyrrell
Sr VP: Barry Wine
VP: Tom Bernard
VP: Skip Bishop

D-U-N-S 14-980-6945 IMP/EXP
SONY MUSIC HOLDINGS INC
(*Suby of* SONY MUSIC ENTERTAINMENT) ★
550 Madison Ave Fl 16, New York, NY 10022-3211
Tel (212) 833-8000 *Founded/Ownrshp* 2008
Sales 354.6MM[E] *EMP* 3,000
SIC 3652 5099 2741 Pre-recorded records & tapes; Phonograph records; Tapes & cassettes, prerecorded; Compact discs; Miscellaneous publishing
Pr: Steven E Kober
Pt: Ariola Eurodisc
Pt: Bertelsmann Music Group
Pr: Charles Goldstuck
Pr: Richard Griffiths
Pr: Robert Jamieson
Pr: Bogdan Roscic
CEO: Douglas P Morris
COO: Michael Smellie
CFO: Joe Gorman
Treas: Terriann Regan
Ex VP: Konrad Hilbers
VP: Vincent Birbes
VP: Thomas McIntyre

D-U-N-S 11-292-3511 IMP
SONY PICTURES ENTERTAINMENT INC
SONY PICTURES STUDIOS
(*Suby of* SONY MUSIC ENTERTAINMENT) ★
10202 Washington Blvd, Culver City, CA 90232-3119
Tel (310) 244-4000 *Founded/Ownrshp* 1991
Sales 507.3MM[E] *EMP* 4,200
SIC 7812 7822 7832 Motion picture production & distribution; Motion picture production & distribution, television; Distribution, exclusive of production: motion picture; Distribution for television: motion picture; Motion picture theaters, except drive-in
Ch Bd: Michael Lynton
**Pr:* Doug Belgrad
Pr: Kristine Belson
Pr: David Bishop
Pr: Rory Bruer
Pr: Dwight Caines
Pr: Randy Lake
Pr: Hannah Minghella
Pr: Bob Osher
Pr: Peter Schlessel
Pr: Valerie Van Galder
Pr: Marc Weinstock
Pr: Mark Zucker
CFO: John Needham
CFO: Philip Rowley
**Co-Ch Bd:* Amy Pascal
**V Ch Bd:* Jeff Blake
**V Ch Bd:* Yair Landau
Ex VP: Matt Brown
Ex VP: Paul Culberg
Ex VP: Peter Iacono
Board of Directors: Howard Stringer

D-U-N-S 05-463-4022
SONY PICTURES IMAGEWORKS INC (CA)
(*Suby of* SONY PICTURES STUDIOS) ★
9050 Washington Blvd, Culver City, CA 90232-2518
Tel (310) 840-8000 *Founded/Ownrshp* 1992
Sales 98.4MM[E] *EMP* 1,000
SIC 7374 Computer graphics service
Pr: Bob Osher
**Pr:* Ken Ralston
Ex VP: Pam Marsden
VP: Jay Dellostretto
Dept Mgr: Stephanie Greco
Snr Sftwr: Larry Gritz
Sftwr Eng: Al Ibrahim
Snr Mgr: Regaye Fulcher

SONY PICTURES STUDIOS
See SONY PICTURES ENTERTAINMENT INC

SONY WONDER
See SONY MUSIC ENTERTAINMENT INC

D-U-N-S 12-270-8340
SOO LINE CORP
CANADIAN PACIFIC RAILWAY
(*Suby of* CANADIAN PACIFIC RAILWAY COMPANY)
14327 Huntington Ave, Savage, MN 55378-2678
Tel (952) 895-5277 *Founded/Ownrshp* 2015
Sales 307.5MM[E] *EMP* 3,200
SIC 4011 Railroads, line-haul operating
CEO: Fred J Green
**Ch Bd:* Robert J Ritchie
**Pr:* Edwin V Dodge
**Treas:* M Jerry Patava
**VP:* John C Miller

D-U-N-S 00-696-2641
SOO LINE RAILROAD CO
CANADIAN PACIFIC RAILWAY
(*Suby of* CANADIAN PACIFIC RAILWAY) ★
120 S 6th St Ste 900, Minneapolis, MN 55402-1812
Tel (800) 234-0013 *Founded/Ownrshp* 1949
Sales 305.1MM[E] *EMP* 2,800
SIC 4011 Railroads, line-haul operating
CEO: E Hunter Harrison
COO: Patrick A Pender
Treas: J Joseph Doolan
Treas: William D Gantous
Sr VP: Brian Grassby
VP: Peter Edwards
VP: Cathryn Frankenberg
VP: John P Lynch
VP: Jane O'Hagan
VP: Michael Redeker
VP: Marcella M Szel

D-U-N-S 17-665-8227
SOPHOS INC
(*Suby of* SOPHOS LIMITED)
3 Van De Graaff Dr Ste 2, Burlington, MA 01803-5131
Tel (781) 494-5800 *Founded/Ownrshp* 1996
Sales 159.3MM[E] *EMP* 843
SIC 7371 Computer software development
CEO: Kris Hagerman
**CFO:* Nicholas Paul Seaton Bray
**Sr VP:* Gerhard Eschelbeck
**VP:* David ARI Buchler
VP: Chris Doggett
VP: Steve Hale
VP: John Keenan
**VP:* Bruce McDonald
VP: Jason Richards
Snr Mgr: Peter Lukomskyj

D-U-N-S 62-333-8274 IMP/EXP
SOPREMA INC
(*Suby of* HOLDING SOPREMA)
310 Quadral Dr, Wadsworth, OH 44281-9571
Tel (330) 334-0066 *Founded/Ownrshp* 1990
Sales 110.7MM[E] *EMP* 115
SIC 5033 Roofing, siding & insulation
Pr: P-E Bindschedler
**VP:* Gilbert Lorenzo
Tech Mgr: Curtis Liscum
Plnt Mgr: Kent Furcron
Ql Cn Mgr: Molly Dravenstott
Manager: Chris Jolliff
Manager: Jeff Valentine
Sls Mgr: Bryan Beth
Sls Mgr: Amato Dilauro
Sls Mgr: Fay Jarrett
Sls Mgr: Tim Loftus

SOPUS PRODUCTS
See PENNZOIL-QUAKER STATE CO

SORC
See STRANDED OIL RESOURCES CORP

D-U-N-S 01-337-2342
■ SOREL CORP
(*Suby of* COLUMBIA SPORTSWEAR CO) ★
14375 Nw Science Park Dr, Portland, OR 97229-5418
Tel (503) 978-2300 *Founded/Ownrshp* 2000
Sales 66.8MM[E] *EMP* 1,600
SIC 5699 Sports apparel
Pr: Timothy Boyle
Ex Dir: Dan Dougherty

SORENSEN SYSTEMS
See THG CORP

D-U-N-S 62-199-5802 IMP/EXP
SORIN GROUP USA INC
CARDIAC SURGERY BUSINESS UNIT
14401 W 65th Way, Arvada, CO 80004-3599
Tel (303) 425-5508 *Founded/Ownrshp* 2013
Sales 136.6MM *EMP* 750
SIC 3845 Electrotherapeutic apparatus
Pr: Sean McNerney
VP: Tim Dougherty
VP: Sharon Thompson
Exec: Mark Englade
Exec: Chris Kelley
Sales Exec: Ron Gerhart
Snr Mgr: Peter Bergsma
Snr Mgr: Scott Sterling
Board of Directors: Sean McNerney, Jim Trevor

D-U-N-S 07-526-1776
SOROS FUND MANAGEMENT LLC
250 W 55th St Fl 28, New York, NY 10019-7664
Tel (212) 872-1054 *Founded/Ownrshp* 1996
Sales 88.6MM[E] *EMP* 160[E]
SIC 6282 Investment advisory service
Ch: George Soros
CFO: Tracie Ahern
**CFO:* Abbas Eddy Zuaiter
**Ch:* Robert Soros
Treas: John Dischiavi
**Chf Inves:* Ted Burdick
Top Exec: Lou Tang
Mng Dir: David Wassong
CTO: Daniel Longmuir
Dir IT: Kevin Baldwin
IT Man: Ash Chhaniara

SORRENTO LACTALIS
See LACTALIS AMERICAN GROUP INC

D-U-N-S 16-809-3602 IMP
SOS CUETARA USA INC
(*Suby of* DEOLEO SA)
10700 North Fwy Ste 800, Houston, TX 77037-1158
Tel (281) 272-8800 *Founded/Ownrshp* 2003
Sales 470.0MM *EMP* 250
SIC 2044 Rice milling
Pr: Jesus Salazar-Bello
**VP:* Lee Adams
**VP:* Raul Jaime Salazar-Bello
**VP:* Bronson Schultz

D-U-N-S 07-840-4891
SOS INTERNATIONAL LLC
SOSI
(*Suby of* SOS INTERNATIONAL LTD) ★
40 Fulton St Fl 26, New York, NY 10038-5007
Tel (212) 742-2410 *Founded/Ownrshp* 2011
Sales 95.0MM *EMP* 490[E]
SIC 3724 8711 7389 8732 Aircraft engines & engine parts; Engineering services; Translation services; Opinion research
Pr: Sosi Setian
**CFO:* Bruce Crowell
Ofcr: Pandora Setian
VP: Jim Edwards
VP: Frank Helmick
**VP:* Julian Setian

D-U-N-S 86-919-0355
SOS INTERNATIONAL LTD
40 Fulton St Fl 26, New York, NY 10038-5007
Tel (212) 742-2410 *Founded/Ownrshp* 1992
Sales 100.0MM *EMP* 490
SIC 7389 Inspection & testing services
CEO: Julian M Setian
**Pr:* Sosi Setian
**CFO:* Bruce M Crowell
**VP:* Frank G Helmick
**VP:* Pandora A Setian
Dir IT: Jorge Dana
IT Man: Steve Thornton
Snr Mgr: Matthew Mead

D-U-N-S 08-172-6069 IMP/EXP
■ SOS METALS INC
(*Suby of* PCC) ★
201 E Gardena Blvd, Gardena, CA 90248-2813
Tel (310) 217-8848 *Founded/Ownrshp* 2014
Sales 92.8MM[E] *EMP* 236
Accts Green Hasson & Janks Llp Los
SIC 5093 5051 Ferrous metal scrap & waste; Ferroalloys
CEO: Kenneth Buck
VP: Patsy Siu
Sls Mgr: Michael Lytton

D-U-N-S 00-684-9277
SOS SECURITY INC (GA)
1915 Us Highway 46 Ste 1, Parsippany, NJ 07054-1300
Tel (973) 402-6600 *Founded/Ownrshp* 1970, 1982
Sales 100.0MM[E] *EMP* 3,200
SIC 7381 Security guard service; Detective agency
CEO: Edward B Silverman
Pr: Lou Dilorenzo
**Pr:* Kenneth M Fisher
Pr: Mj Manno
**COO:* Marc Bognar
CFO: Anthony Gerardi
CFO: Thomas Gustafson
Ex VP: Eugene Chan
**Ex VP:* Barry A Frank
**Ex VP:* Eugene McDonald
Sr VP: Jim Bush
Sr VP: Bob Larkin
**VP:* Scott Alswang
VP: Robert Steffman

D-U-N-S 07-910-5023
SOS SECURITY LLC
1915 Us Highway 46, Parsippany, NJ 07054-1300
Tel (973) 402-6600 *Founded/Ownrshp* 2012
Sales 107.0MM *EMP* 3,400[E]
SIC 7381 Protective services, guard; Detective agency
CEO: Edward B Silverman
Pr: Kenneth M Fisher
COO: Marc Bognar
CFO: Thomas Gustafson
Ex VP: Eugene McDonald
VP: Scott Alswang

SOSI
See SOS INTERNATIONAL LLC

D-U-N-S 83-246-1755
SOTERA DEFENSE SOLUTIONS INC
(*Suby of* SENTINEL ACQUISITION HOLDINGS INC) ★
2121 Coop Way Ste 400, Herndon, VA 20171
Tel (703) 230-8200 *Founded/Ownrshp* 2008
Sales 291.4MM[E] *EMP* 1,128
Accts Pricewaterhousecoopers Llp Mc
SIC 7371 7379 Computer software systems analysis & design, custom;
Pr: Deb Alderson
**CFO:* John C Pitsenberger
**Ex VP:* Kirk Herdman
Sr VP: Alex Drew
Sr VP: Jack Hess
Sr VP: Steve Niezgoda
Sr VP: Mark Savarese
**Sr VP:* Matt Talbot
**Sr VP:* Jesse D Watters
**VP:* John Pitsenberger
**VP:* Robert Pugh

D-U-N-S 14-785-2693
▲ SOTHEBYS
1334 York Ave, New York, NY 10021-4806
Tel (212) 606-7000 *Founded/Ownrshp* 1744
Sales 961.4MM *EMP* 1,596[E]
Tkr Sym BID *Exch* NYS
SIC 6531 6111 5921 Real estate brokers & agents; Federal mortgage credit agencies; Wine
Pr: Thomas S Smith Jr
**Ch Bd:* Domenico De Sole
CFO: Michael Goss
Ofcr: Lisa Nadler
Ofcr: Lorena Sferlazza
Assoc VP: Jeannie Gill
Ex VP: David Goodman
Sr VP: Kevin M Delaney
Sr VP: Jane A Levine
Sr VP: Jonathan A Olsoff
VP: Louise Beit
VP: Michael Zolfo
Board of Directors: Jessica M Bibliowicz, Linus Wing Lam Cheung, Kevin C Conroy, Daniel S Loeb, Olivier Reza, Marsha E Simms, Diana L Taylor, Dennis M Weibling, Harry J Wilson

D-U-N-S 16-722-0560
▲ SOTHERLY HOTELS INC
410 W Francis St, Williamsburg, VA 23185-4046
Tel (757) 229-5648 *Founded/Ownrshp* 2004
Sales 124.6MM^E *EMP* 13
Tkr Sym SOHO *Exch* NGM
SIC 6798 Real estate investment trusts
Ch Bd: Andrew M Sims
**Pr:* David R Folsom
CFO: Anthony E Domalski
VP Opers: Scott Kucinski

D-U-N-S 94-570-9637
SOULCYCLE INC
609 Greenwich St Fl Grnd, New York, NY 10014-3691
Tel (212) 787-7685 *Founded/Ownrshp* 2006
Sales 66.6MM^E *EMP* 1,000
SIC 7991 Physical fitness clubs with training equipment
CEO: Melanie Whelan
**CEO:* Julie Race
Area Mgr: Laura Mozur
Area Mgr: Tanysha Smith
IT Man: Noni Manzano
Mktg Mgr: Laura Cox
Mktg Mgr: Tori Johnston
Mktg Mgr: Sophia Stich

D-U-N-S 08-028-1685
SOUND INPATIENT PHYSICIANS HOLDINGS LLC
(*Suby of* FRESENIUS MEDICAL CARE NORTH) ★
1498 Pacific Ave Ste 400, Tacoma, WA 98402-4208
Tel (253) 682-1710 *Founded/Ownrshp* 2014
Sales 90.2MM^E *EMP* 720^E
SIC 8011 6719 General & family practice, physician/surgeon; Physicians' office, including specialists; Investment holding companies, except banks
CEO: Ronald Kuerbitz

D-U-N-S 19-669-6814
SOUND INPATIENT PHYSICIANS INC
HOSPITLIST MEDICINE PHYSICIANS
(*Suby of* SOUND INPATIENT PHYSICIANS HOLDINGS LLC) ★
1498 Pacific Ave Ste 400, Tacoma, WA 98402-4208
Tel (253) 682-1710 *Founded/Ownrshp* 2014
Sales 90.2MM^E *EMP* 720
SIC 8011 General & family practice, physician/surgeon; Physicians' office, including specialists
CEO: Robert Bessler
Pr: Jennifer Grande
**Pr:* Jess Parks
Pr: Juhie Parnami
Pr: Lynn Purdy
**CFO:* Dena Parker
**Ch:* Edward G Murphy
Chf Mktg O: Michael Kedansky
Chf Mktg O: Brian Macaulay
Ofcr: Scott Enderby Do
Ofcr: Julie L Seitz
Rgnl VP: Alan Himmelstein
Ex VP: Jason Howard
**Sr VP:* JD Fitz
Sr VP: Scott Sears
VP: Dianna Budgeon
VP: Debbie Faulkner
VP: Josh Kermisch

D-U-N-S 92-630-7901 IMP
SOUND PACKAGING LLC
260 N Roosevelt Ave, Chandler, AZ 85226-2622
Tel (480) 940-2010 *Founded/Ownrshp* 1995
Sales 95.9MM^E *EMP* 300
SIC 2653 Corrugated & solid fiber boxes
VP: Mark Riley
**Pr:* Tyler Howland
**CFO:* Troy Gale
Dir IT: Linda Hansen
Ql Cn Mgr: Andy Jones
Sales Exec: Leon Gale
Sales Asso: Linda Johnson

D-U-N-S 80-539-2706
SOUND PUBLISHING HOLDING INC
(*Suby of* BLACK PRESS GROUP LTD)
19351 8th Ave Ne Ste 106, Poulsbo, WA 98370-8710
Tel (360) 394-5800 *Founded/Ownrshp* 2001
Sales 245.8MM^E *EMP* 1,544
SIC 2711 Newspapers, publishing & printing
CEO: David Black

D-U-N-S 00-947-9270
SOUND PUBLISHING INC
EVERETT/KITSAP PRESS
(*Suby of* SOUND PUBLISHING HOLDING INC) ★
11323 Commando Rd W Main, Everett, WA 98204-3532
Tel (360) 394-5800 *Founded/Ownrshp* 1987
Sales 99.7MM^E *EMP* 609
SIC 2711 Newspapers; Newspapers, publishing & printing
Pr: Gloria G Fletcher
**VP:* Lori Maxim
**VP:* Josh Oconnor
IT Man: Dan Grover
IT Man: John Wulff

D-U-N-S 13-589-3878
SOUND SHORE HEALTH SYSTEM INC
16 Guion Pl, New Rochelle, NY 10801-5502
Tel (914) 632-5000 *Founded/Ownrshp* 1998
Sales 62.9MM^E *EMP* 3,000
SIC 8062 General medical & surgical hospitals
Pr: John R Spicer
Dir IT: Rich Orourke
Doctor: Robert Cristofaro

SOUND SHORE MEDICAL CENTER
See NRHMC INC

D-U-N-S 07-543-1502
SOUND SHORE MEDICAL CENTER OF WESTCHESTER
16 Guion Pl, New Rochelle, NY 10801-5502
Tel (914) 632-5000 *Founded/Ownrshp* 1892
Sales NA *EMP* 1,400
SIC 8062

SOUNDVIEW PAPER COMPANY
See MARCAL MANUFACTURING LLC

D-U-N-S 07-912-9543 IMP
SOUNDVIEW PAPER HOLDINGS LLC
1 Market St, Elmwood Park, NJ 07407-1401
Tel (201) 796-4000 *Founded/Ownrshp* 2011
Sales 478.3MM^E *EMP* 1,000
SIC 2676 2656 Sanitary paper products; Towels, paper: made from purchased paper; Napkins, paper: made from purchased paper; Toilet paper: made from purchased paper; Sanitary food containers; Straws, drinking: made from purchased material
CEO: Karl Meyers
**Pr:* Rob Baron
**CFO:* Jim Andrews
**CFO:* John Sickler
**Ex VP:* John Glaze
**Sr VP:* Carrie Williamson

D-U-N-S 07-854-9215
SOUNDVIEW PAPER MILLS LLC
(*Suby of* SOUNDVIEW PAPER HOLDINGS LLC) ★
1 Sound Shore Dr Ste 203, Greenwich, CT 06830-7251
Tel (201) 796-4000 *Founded/Ownrshp* 2012
Sales 478.3MM^E *EMP* 800^E
SIC 2676 Sanitary paper products
CEO: George Wurtz
**Pr:* Karl Meyers
**CFO:* Kimberly Knotts
**Sr VP:* Tim Crawford
**VP:* John McLean

D-U-N-S 03-722-2254
SOUPER SALAD INC
4004 Belt Line Rd Ste 100, Addison, TX 75001-4320
Tel (972) 761-1790 *Founded/Ownrshp* 2005
Sales 90.9MM^E *EMP* 2,300
SIC 5812 Restaurant, family: independent
Pr: Ward T Olgreen
**Pr:* Hazen Ouf
**COO:* Danny K Meisenheimer
**VP:* Dan Patel
Exec: Lynn Brazee
Genl Mgr: Nicole Moore

SOUPLANTATION
See GARDEN FRESH RESTAURANT CORP

SOUPPLANTATION SWEET TOMATOES
See GARDEN FRESH HOLDINGS INC

D-U-N-S 96-804-5570
SOURCE CAPITAL BACKYARD LLC
1000 Ternes Dr, Monroe, MI 48162-5224
Tel (734) 242-6900 *Founded/Ownrshp* 2009
Sales 85.0MM *EMP* 2^E
SIC 2511 2452 Play pens, children's: wood; Prefabricated wood buildings

D-U-N-S 79-119-4715
SOURCE CODE CORP
SCC DISTRIBUTION
159 Overland Rd Ste 3, Waltham, MA 02451-1703
Tel (781) 255-2022 *Founded/Ownrshp* 1992
Sales 92.6MM^E *EMP* 106^E
SIC 5045 Computer peripheral equipment; Computer software
Pr: Hassan N Yazdi
Exec: David Lebov
Ql Cn Mgr: Steve Drugas

D-U-N-S 82-604-6273
SOURCE HOME ENTERTAINMENT LLC
(*Suby of* SOURCE INTERLINK COMPANIES INC) ★
8251 Greensboro Dr # 400, Mc Lean, VA 22102-3817
Tel (239) 949-4450 *Founded/Ownrshp* 2005
Sales NA *EMP* 8,500
SIC 5192 5099 8742 2541 Books; Magazines; Compact discs; Retail trade consultant; Bar fixtures, wood

D-U-N-S 07-487-6087
SOURCE INC
SOURCE, INC - MIDWEST
4550 Spring Valley Rd # 200, Dallas, TX 75244-3705
Tel (972) 371-2600 *Founded/Ownrshp* 1971
Sales 102.8MM^E *EMP* 160
SIC 5065 7629

SOURCE, INC - MIDWEST
See SOURCE INC

D-U-N-S 55-637-0831
SOURCE INTERLINK COMPANIES INC
27200 Riverview Center Bl, Bonita Springs, FL 34134-4317
Tel (866) 276-5584 *Founded/Ownrshp* 2007
Sales 1.3MMM^E *EMP* 8,500
SIC 4731 Freight transportation arrangement; Transportation agents & brokers
CEO: Michael L Sullivan
Pr: David G Algire
Pr: Chris H Argentieri
Pr: Frank Bishop
Pr: Michael Porche
Ex VP: Doug Evans
Ex VP: Stephanie S Justice
Sr VP: Brad Gerber
VP: Sharmila Aroskar
VP: John B Bode
VP: David Buck
VP: Chris Butler
VP: Tom Cornack
VP: David Harris
VP: Mike Karsting
VP: Robert Krepps
VP: Ryan Payne
Dir Risk M: Todd Busby

D-U-N-S 60-217-6716 IMP
SOURCE INTERLINK DISTRIBUTION LLC
27500 Riverview Center Bl, Bonita Springs, FL 34134-4328
Tel (239) 949-4450 *Founded/Ownrshp* 2008
Sales NA *EMP* 4,872
SIC 5192

D-U-N-S 95-905-4933 IMP
SOURCE MEDIA INC
(*Suby of* OBSERVER CAPITAL LLC)
1 State St Fl 26, New York, NY 10004-1561
Tel (212) 803-8200 *Founded/Ownrshp* 2004
Sales 193.0MM^E *EMP* 803^E
SIC 2721 Magazines: publishing & printing
CEO: Douglas J Manoni
**CFO:* Michael P Caruso
CFO: Rebecca Knoop
Ofcr: Dean Anason
Ofcr: Marianne Collins
Ex VP: Rob Whitaker
VP: Robert Akert
**VP:* John Delmauro
VP: Sphr Wong
Dir Soc: Patrice Deza-Castillo
Dir Soc: Kristen Mulieri
Dir Soc: Melissa Vasquez

D-U-N-S 94-339-3736
SOURCE ONE STAFFING LLC
5312 Irwindale Ave Ste 1h, Baldwin Park, CA 91706-2076
Tel (626) 337-0560 *Founded/Ownrshp* 1995
Sales 167.4MM^E *EMP* 9,500
SIC 7363 Temporary help service
Pr: Gwen Gordon
CFO: Paulina Kuroki

D-U-N-S 96-586-5660
SOURCE REFRIGERATION & HVAC INC
800 E Orangethorpe Ave, Anaheim, CA 92801-1123
Tel (714) 578-2300 *Founded/Ownrshp* 2007
Sales 428.5MM^E *EMP* 1,100
SIC 1711 1731 Plumbing, heating, air-conditioning contractors; Electrical work
Pr: Adam Coffey
**Ch Bd:* Bradley Norman Howard
Pr: Steve Cook
Pr: Hal Kolp
**COO:* Andrew Mandell
**CFO:* Scott Rosner
Sr VP: Mike Ochoa
VP: Brian Beitler
IT Man: Renae Hess
IT Man: Todd Walsh
Trfc Dir: Barry Hall

D-U-N-S 11-392-8654 IMP/EXP
SOURCE-RAY INC
50 Fleetwood Ct, Ronkonkoma, NY 11779-6907
Tel (631) 244-8200 *Founded/Ownrshp* 2002
Sales 86.4MM^E *EMP* 31
SIC 5047 Medical & hospital equipment
Ch Bd: Raymond Manez
**VP:* Vasilios Milonas
Mtls Mgr: Joel Miller

D-U-N-S 07-480-9377
SOURCEAMERICA
8401 Old Courthouse Rd, Vienna, VA 22182-3820
Tel (888) 411-8424 *Founded/Ownrshp* 1974
Sales 142.9MM *EMP* 350
Accts Lb Calibre Cpa Group Pllc Bet
SIC 8399 Fund raising organization, non-fee basis
CEO: E Robert Chamberlin
**COO:* Dennis Fields
**CFO:* Elizabeth Goodman
Ofcr: Raquel Tamez
Sr VP: Bruce Hafner
VP: Nancyellen Gentile
VP: Martin Williams
Dir Bus: Bill Allen
Ex Dir: Richard Gazaway
Ex Dir: Rick Van Hoose
Prgrm Mgr: Sue Elwell

D-U-N-S 07-879-0277
SOURCECORP HEALTHSERVE RADIOLOGY INC
(*Suby of* SOURCECORP INC) ★
602 N English Station Rd, Louisville, KY 40223-4724
Tel (502) 244-0035 *Founded/Ownrshp* 2013
Sales 44.2MM^E *EMP* 1,109^E
SIC 7334 8748 8721 Photocopying & duplicating services; Business consulting; Accounting, auditing & bookkeeping
CEO: Steve Grieco

D-U-N-S 93-203-7344
SOURCECORP INC
(*Suby of* CORPSOURCE HOLDINGS LLC) ★
2701 E Grauwyler Rd, Irving, TX 75061-3414
Tel (866) 321-5854 *Founded/Ownrshp* 2006
Sales 340.3MM *EMP* 4,512
Accts Deloitte & Touche Llp Dallas
SIC 7375 7334 7374 Information retrieval services; Photocopying & duplicating services; Data processing service
CEO: Ron Cogburn
CFO: Katy Murray
CFO: Mark Trivette
Treas: Russell Birk
Treas: Sara Richardson
VP: Gayle Clark
VP: Karen Emerick
VP: Gene Marzano
VP: John Peschier
VP: Ron Young
VP Bus Dev: Kevin Wert
Exec: Ralph Canfield
Exec: Carl York
Dir Bus: Bill McKeon
Board of Directors: Marc Becker, Matt Nord

D-U-N-S 07-878-0281
SOURCECORP LEGAL INC
(*Suby of* SOURCECORP INC) ★
625 Marquette Ave Ste 880, Minneapolis, MN 55402-2469
Tel (612) 359-2822 *Founded/Ownrshp* 1999
Sales 141.8MM^E *EMP* 1,783^E
SIC 8748 Business consulting
CEO: Steve Grieco
**CFO:* Katy Murray
**Treas:* Russell Birk
**Genl Couns:* Charles Gilber

D-U-N-S 79-665-3678
■ SOURCEGAS LLC
(*Suby of* BLACK HILLS CORP) ★
1515 Wynkoop St Ste 500, Denver, CO 80202-2062
Tel (303) 243-3400 *Founded/Ownrshp* 2006
Sales 266.1MM^E *EMP* 564
SIC 4924 Natural gas distribution
Pr: William N Cantrell
**CFO:* Manjit Cheema
**VP:* Michael Noone
VP: Douglas D Whitefoot
Exec: Alder David
Div Mgr: Jason Cox
Div Mgr: Kelly Spitz
Dir IT: Rick Lathrop

D-U-N-S 07-878-7121
SOURCEHOV HOLDINGS INC
2701 E Grauwyler Rd, Irving, TX 75061-3414
Tel (972) 821-4000 *Founded/Ownrshp* 2011
Sales 2.0MMM^E *EMP* 15,000^E
SIC 6719 Investment holding companies, except banks
CEO: Ronald Cogburn
Ch: Jim Reynolds
CTO: Sanjay Kulkarni
VP Mktg: Chuck Corbin

D-U-N-S 96-930-4190
SOURCEHOV LLC
(*Suby of* SOURCEHOV HOLDINGS INC) ★
2701 E Grauwyler Rd, Irving, TX 75061-3414
Tel (866) 321-5854 *Founded/Ownrshp* 2013
Sales 870.2MM^E *EMP* 15,000^E
SIC 8748 Business consulting
CEO: Ron Cogburn
Pr: Kevin Wert
**Pr:* Suresh Yannamani
**CFO:* Michael Henricks
**CFO:* Katy Murray
**Ex VP:* Ronald Cogburn
Sr VP: Jim Stephenson
Sls Mgr: Minerva Parras

D-U-N-S 07-888-8848
SOURCEHOV TAX INC
(*Suby of* SOURCECORP LEGAL INC) ★
4150 International Plz, Fort Worth, TX 76109-4892
Tel (817) 732-5494 *Founded/Ownrshp* 2013
Sales 30.4MM^E *EMP* 1,125^E
SIC 8748 Business consulting
Mng Dir: Deb Roth
VP Opers: Chris Henderson

D-U-N-S 61-240-8190
SOURCELINK ACQUISITION LLC
500 Park Blvd Ste 1425, Itasca, IL 60143-1215
Tel (866) 947-6872 *Founded/Ownrshp* 2015
Sales 135.3MM^E *EMP* 500
SIC 7374 7331 Data processing service; Direct mail advertising services
Pr: Don Landrum
Pr: Pat Obrien
**CFO:* Phil Hoey
VP: David Funsten
VP: Brent Tartar
VP: Tom Taylor
VP: Jim Wisnionski
Creative D: Dennis Heckler
Dir Bus: Craig Blake
Dir Bus: Steve Streibel
Mng Dir: Tom Roth

D-U-N-S 12-754-7037
SOURCEONE HEALTHCARE TECHNOLOGIES INC
MXR SOURCEONE
(*Suby of* M X R) ★
8020 Tyler Blvd, Mentor, OH 44060-4825
Tel (440) 701-1200 *Founded/Ownrshp* 2005
Sales 133.7MM^E *EMP* 150^E
SIC 5047 Medical laboratory equipment
CEO: Leo Zuckerman
**Pr:* Larry Lawson
VP: Ted Sloan
Genl Mgr: Frank Krashoc
Telecom Mg: Dave Rock

D-U-N-S 83-983-3100
SOUTH AFRICAN AIRWAYS SOC LIMITED INC
1200 S Pine Isl Rd 650, Plantation, FL 33324
Tel (800) 722-9675 *Founded/Ownrshp* 1999
Sales 250.0MM *EMP* 75
SIC 4512 Air passenger carrier, scheduled
CEO: Monwabisi Kalawe
Ofcr: Salome Karamalidis
Ex VP: Marc S Cavaliere
VP: Zuhre Canligil
Mktg Mgr: James Chikaonda
Mktg Mgr: Amy Chow

SOUTH ATL TRI-CITY ELEC CONTRS
See TRI-CITY ELECTRICAL CONTRACTORS INC

SOUTH BALDWIN REGIONAL MED CTR
See FOLEY HOSPITAL CORP

D-U-N-S 05-420-0266 IMP
SOUTH BAY CIRCUITS INC
99 N Mckemy Ave, Chandler, AZ 85226-3447
Tel (480) 940-3125 *Founded/Ownrshp* 1981
Sales 88.4MM^E *EMP* 550
SIC 3672

SOUTH BAY CONSTRUCTION COMPANY
See B C C S INC

D-U-N-S 08-600-8117
SOUTH BAY UNION SCHOOL DISTRICT (CA)
601 Elm Ave, Imperial Beach, CA 91932-2029
Tel (619) 628-1600 *Founded/Ownrshp* 1920
Sales 63.4MM^E *EMP* 1,200
Accts Wilkinson Hadley King & Co
SIC 8211 Public elementary & secondary schools
**Pr:* Elvia Aguilar
**VP:* Chris Brown
**Prin:* Melanie Ellsworth
Teacher Pr: Maria Verdugle

D-U-N-S 93-223-5492 IMP
SOUTH BEND CHOCOLATE CO INC
3300 W Sample St Ste 110, South Bend, IN 46619-3077
Tel (574) 233-2577 *Founded/Ownrshp* 1994
Sales 84.7MM[E] *EMP* 240
SIC 5149 2066 5441 5812 Chocolate; Chocolate; Candy; Cafe
Pr: Mark Tarner
**Sec:* Julie Tarner
**Prin:* S Eric Marshall
Plnt Mgr: Justin Weidner
Sls Dir: Jeff Zielinski
Sales Asso: Kristina Tressler

D-U-N-S 07-430-7216 IMP
SOUTH BEND COMMUNITY SCHOOL CORP
RILEY SCHOOL BUILDING
215 S Saint Joseph St, South Bend, IN 46601-2003
Tel (574) 283-8000 *Founded/Ownrshp* 1993
Sales 144.7MM[E] *EMP* 3,000
SIC 8211 Public elementary & secondary schools
**Pr:* Gene F Stockdale
Treas: Bob Orlowski
Treas: Fred Stump
**Prin:* Dr Robert Zimmerman
Dir Sec: Erik Crittendon
Genl Mgr: Sue Coney
MIS Dir: Patrick Stalvey
Dir IT: Dave Jozwiak
IT Man: David Mette
Pr Dir: Susan Coney
Teacher Pr: Cheryl Greene

D-U-N-S 06-470-2889
SOUTH BEND MEDICAL FOUNDATION INC
CENTRAL BLOOD BANK
530 N Lafayette Blvd, South Bend, IN 46601-1004
Tel (574) 234-4176 *Founded/Ownrshp* 1912
Sales 95.8MM *EMP* 800
Accts Crowe Horwath Llp South Bend
SIC 8071 Pathological laboratory
Pr: Robert Tomec
COO: Luis Gatup
**Treas:* Ann M Sullivan
VP: Diane Janowiak
VP: Ray Krass
**VP:* Joyce Simpson
Exec: Francisco Deogracias
Admn Mgr: Betty Y Lerner
Admn Mgr: Betty Y Woodburn
IT Man: Robert Pennoni
Netwrk Eng: Bill Hallman

D-U-N-S 14-857-7166
SOUTH BROWARD HOSPITAL DISTRICT
MEMORIAL HOSPITAL WEST
3501 Johnson St, Hollywood, FL 33021-5421
Tel (954) 987-2000 *Founded/Ownrshp* 1947
Sales 1.9MMM *EMP* 9,200
SIC 8062 8051 General medical & surgical hospitals; Skilled nursing care facilities
CEO: Frank V Sacco
Chf OB: Nigel Spier
Chf Rad: Mark Schwimmer
Dir Vol: David Reinmund
COO: Aurelio M Fernandez
CFO: Jeffrey Crudele
**CFO:* Matthew Muhart
**Ofcr:* Anthony C Krayer III
Sr VP: Stanley Marks
VP: Zeff Ross
Dir OR: Pat Collins
Assoc Dir: Daren Grosman
Dir Rx: Irvin Alfonzo

D-U-N-S 17-248-1715
SOUTH BRUNSWICK TOWNSHIP BOARD OF EDUCATION
4 Executive Dr, Monmouth Junction, NJ 08852-2406
Tel (732) 297-7800 *Founded/Ownrshp* 1870
Sales 127.9MM[E] *EMP* 1,205
SIC 8211 Public elementary & secondary schools
Genl Mgr: Kimberly Ahern

D-U-N-S 87-870-1374
SOUTH CAROLINA DEPARTMENT OF COMMERCE
(*Suby of* BUDGET & CTRL BD EXEC DIRS OFF) ★
1201 Main St Ste 1600, Columbia, SC 29201-3261
Tel (803) 737-0400 *Founded/Ownrshp* 1920
Sales NA *EMP* 1,039
SIC 9611 Economic development agency, government;
**CFO:* Chris Huffman
VP: Julie Horton
**Prin:* Robert M Hitt III
**Prin:* George B Patrick III

D-U-N-S 04-397-4567
SOUTH CAROLINA DEPARTMENT OF CORRECTIONS (INC)
SCDC
(*Suby of* BUDGET & CTRL BD EXEC DIRS OFF) ★
4444 Broad River Rd, Columbia, SC 29210-4012
Tel (803) 896-8500 *Founded/Ownrshp* 1865
Sales NA *EMP* 5,800
SIC 9223 Prison, government;
Dir IT: Trevis Shealy

D-U-N-S 80-838-5447
SOUTH CAROLINA DEPARTMENT OF DISABILITIES AND SPECIAL NEEDS
(*Suby of* BUDGET & CTRL BD EXEC DIRS OFF) ★
3440 Harden Street Ext, Columbia, SC 29203-6835
Tel (803) 898-9600 *Founded/Ownrshp* 1967
Sales NA *EMP* 4,250
SIC 9431 Mental health agency administration, government;

D-U-N-S 06-931-3609
SOUTH CAROLINA DEPARTMENT OF EDUCATION
(*Suby of* BUDGET & CTRL BD EXEC DIRS OFF) ★
1429 Senate St, Columbia, SC 29201-3730
Tel (803) 734-8500 *Founded/Ownrshp* 1950
Sales NA *EMP* 1,400
Accts Deloach & Williamson Llp
SIC 9411 Administration of educational programs;

D-U-N-S 94-300-0203
SOUTH CAROLINA DEPARTMENT OF EMPLOYMENT AND WORKFORCE
(*Suby of* BUDGET & CTRL BD EXEC DIRS OFF) ★
1550 Gadsden St, Columbia, SC 29201-2713
Tel (803) 737-2400 *Founded/Ownrshp* 1936
Sales NA *EMP* 1,200
SIC 9441 Administration of social & manpower programs;
Ex Dir: Abraham Turner
Genl Mgr: Angela Daniels
IT Man: Felix Childs

D-U-N-S 80-838-5892
SOUTH CAROLINA DEPARTMENT OF HEALTH AND ENVIRONMENTAL CONTROL
(*Suby of* BUDGET & CTRL BD EXEC DIRS OFF) ★
2600 Bull St, Columbia, SC 29201-1708
Tel (803) 898-3510 *Founded/Ownrshp* 1976
Sales NA *EMP* 5,200
SIC 9431 Environmental health program administration, government;
Prin: Gwendolyn Thompson
IT Man: Roger L Heck

D-U-N-S 87-870-5631
SOUTH CAROLINA DEPARTMENT OF LAW ENFORCEMENT
(*Suby of* BUDGET & CTRL BD EXEC DIRS OFF) ★
4400 Broad River Rd, Columbia, SC 29210-4012
Tel (803) 737-9000 *Founded/Ownrshp* 2000
Sales NA *EMP* 1,000
SIC 9221 State police;
Ofcr: David Caldwell
Prgrm Mgr: Bettina Jones

D-U-N-S 04-398-0093
SOUTH CAROLINA DEPARTMENT OF MENTAL HEALTH
(*Suby of* BUDGET & CTRL BD EXEC DIRS OFF) ★
2414 Bull St, Columbia, SC 29201-1906
Tel (803) 898-8581 *Founded/Ownrshp* 1895
Sales NA *EMP* 4,500
SIC 9431 Mental health agency administration, government;
Ch Bd: John H Maggiol
**CFO:* David Schaefer
Dir Teleco: Dian Hornsby
**Prin:* Douglas Gay
IT Man: Charlie Zeberlein

D-U-N-S 78-027-8474
SOUTH CAROLINA DEPARTMENT OF MOTOR VEHICLES
(*Suby of* BUDGET & CTRL BD EXEC DIRS OFF) ★
10311 Wilson Blvd, Blythewood, SC 29016-9018
Tel (803) 896-5000 *Founded/Ownrshp* 2006
Sales NA *EMP* 1,351[E]
SIC 9621 Regulation, administration of transportation;

D-U-N-S 09-868-8513
SOUTH CAROLINA DEPARTMENT OF PUBLIC SAFETY
(*Suby of* BUDGET & CTRL BD EXEC DIRS OFF) ★
10311 Wilson Blvd, Blythewood, SC 29016-9018
Tel (803) 896-9000 *Founded/Ownrshp* 2001
Sales NA *EMP* 1,039
SIC 9229 Public order & safety statistics centers;
Ex Dir: Leroy Smith
Genl Mgr: Stephen Fulmer

D-U-N-S 80-833-5251
SOUTH CAROLINA DEPARTMENT OF TRANSPORTATION
SCDOT
(*Suby of* BUDGET & CTRL BD EXEC DIRS OFF) ★
955 Park St, Columbia, SC 29201-3959
Tel (803) 737-1243 *Founded/Ownrshp* 1925
Sales NA *EMP* 4,500
Accts Scott And Company Llp Columbi
SIC 9621 Regulation, administration of transportation;
Ex Dir: Elizabeth S Mabry
Ofcr: Janet M Tucker
VP: R J Bean
Exec: Stan Shealy
Ex Dir: H B Limehouse
Prgrm Mgr: Tucker S Creed
Prgrm Mgr: Kevin Gantt
Prgrm Mgr: Chris Jordan
Sys Mgr: Todd Anderson
Tech Mgr: Lee Foster
Software D: Hance Mary

D-U-N-S 00-791-9517 IMP
■ **SOUTH CAROLINA ELECTRIC & GAS CO** (SC)
(*Suby of* SCANA CORP) ★
100 Scana Pkwy, Cayce, SC 29033-3712
Tel (803) 217-9000 *Founded/Ownrshp* 1924, 1984
Sales 2.9MMM *EMP* 3,213
SIC 4931 4911 4922 4924 Electric & other services combined; Distribution, electric power; Generation, electric power; Transmission, electric power; Natural gas transmission; Natural gas distribution
Ch Bd: Kevin B Marsh
COO: Stephen A Byrne
CFO: Jimmy E Addison
Sr VP: Jeffrey B Archie
Sr VP: Keller Kissam

D-U-N-S 06-700-7062
SOUTH CAROLINA FARM BUREAU MUTUAL INSURANCE CO (INC)
FARM BUREAU INSURANCE
724 Knox Abbott Dr, Cayce, SC 29033-3340
Tel (803) 796-6700 *Founded/Ownrshp* 1955
Sales NA *EMP* 245
SIC 6331 Automobile insurance; Fire, marine & casualty insurance & carriers; Agricultural insurance
Pr: David M Winkles
CFO: Bob Fallaw
**CFO:* Mike Myers
**Ex VP:* Phillip E Love Jr
**VP:* Carl E Derrick
**VP:* Ben Gramling II
**VP:* Mike Hooks
**VP:* Lee P Jedziniak
VP: Wilkins Lee
**VP:* D Bruce Mackay
VP: Dwayne Smalls
**VP:* David C Wylie
**VP:* Elbert L Young

SOUTH CAROLINA PORTS AUTHORITY
See SOUTH CAROLINA STATE PORTS AUTHORITY

D-U-N-S 07-979-8897
SOUTH CAROLINA PUBLIC CHARTER SCHOOL DISTRICT
SC PUBLIC CHARTER SCHOOL DST
3710 Landmark Dr Ste 203, Columbia, SC 29204-4034
Tel (803) 734-8322 *Founded/Ownrshp* 2015
Sales 133.9MM *EMP* 19[E]
Accts Mcgregor & Company Llp Colum
SIC 8211 Public elementary & secondary schools
Ch: Don McLaurin
MIS Dir: Zenobia Ealy
Teacher Pr: Paula Gray
HC Dir: Robert Compton

D-U-N-S 05-681-2456 IMP
SOUTH CAROLINA PUBLIC SERVICE AUTHORITY (INC)
SANTEE COOPER
1 Riverwood Dr, Moncks Corner, SC 29461-2998
Tel (843) 761-4121 *Founded/Ownrshp* 1934
Sales 1.8MMM *EMP* 1,748
Accts Cherry Bekaert Llp Raleigh N
SIC 4911 Generation, electric power
CEO: Lonnie N Carter
**COO:* Bill McCall Jr
**CFO:* Jeff Armfield
**CFO:* Elaine Peterson
**Ch:* O L Thompson
Bd of Dir: Jeff Thomas
**Ex VP:* Jim Brogdon
Sr VP: Michael Crosby
Sr VP: Robert Fleming Jr
Sr VP: Lewis Pierce
Sr VP: Rennie M Singletary
VP: Tom Abrams
VP: Thomas Kierspe
VP: Phil Pierce
VP: Ray Smith
VP: Laura Varn
VP: Elizabeth Warner
Exec: Sandra Starks
Dir Risk M: Jennifer Wadford

D-U-N-S 18-301-3333
SOUTH CAROLINA RESEARCH AUTHORITY INC
SCRA TECHNOLOGY VENTURES
1000 Catawba St Ste 100, Columbia, SC 29201-5706
Tel (803) 799-4070 *Founded/Ownrshp* 1983
Sales 399.6MM *EMP* 218
Accts Bdo Usa Llp Raleigh Nc
SIC 8733 Noncommercial research organizations
CEO: Bill Mahoney
COO: Greg Frank
COO: Bob Kiggans
**CFO:* Julia A Martin
Ex VP: Marvin Davis
VP: Mark Aukamp
VP: Tom McCord
Ex Dir: Jon Tirpak
Prgrm Mgr: Polly Graham
Prgrm Mgr: Justin Montague
Dir IT: Blaine Nielson

D-U-N-S 03-647-9699 IMP
SOUTH CAROLINA STATE PORTS AUTHORITY
SOUTH CAROLINA PORTS AUTHORITY
176 Concord St, Charleston, SC 29401-2642
Tel (843) 723-8651 *Founded/Ownrshp* 1942
Sales 117.8MM[E] *EMP* 493
Accts Pricewaterhousecoopers Llp Sp
SIC 4491 8111 2721 Docks, piers & terminals; Legal services; Periodicals
CEO: James I Newsome III
**CFO:* Peter N Hughes
**Ofcr:* Paul G McClintock
**Sr VP:* Jack Ellenberg
**Sr VP:* William A McLean
**Sr VP:* Barbara L Melvin
CIO: Pamela A Everitt
Software D: Tina Grady
Secur Mgr: Mark Lester
Mktg Mgr: Marion Bull
Board of Directors: Harry J Butler Jr, Karen K Floyd, S Richard Hagins, John F Hassell III, Robert M Hitt III, David J Posek, Douglas M Robertson, Robert J St Onge Jr, Bill H Stern

D-U-N-S 07-799-4770
SOUTH CAROLINA STATE UNIVERSITY
(*Suby of* SOUTH CAROLINA DEPARTMENT OF EDUCATION) ★
300 College Ave, Orangeburg, SC 29115-4427
Tel (803) 536-7000 *Founded/Ownrshp* 1896
Sales 102.3MM[E] *EMP* 1,342
SIC 8221 9411 University; Administration of educational programs;
Pr: Thomas J Elzey
**Pr:* Andrew Hugine Jr
**Pr:* Dr Rita J Teal
CFO: Felicia P Dickerson
Treas: Thomas Cassidy
Trst: John T Bowden
Trst: Earl A Bridges
Trst: Lumus Byrd
Trst: Charles H Williams
VP: Betty Boatwright
**VP:* Mr Anthony L Holloman
**VP:* Charlene Johnson
VP: Learie Luke
VP: Charles Smith
**VP:* Dr G Dale Wesson

D-U-N-S 07-372-0567
SOUTH CAROLINA STUDENT LOAN CORP
EDMANAGE
8906 Two Notch Rd, Columbia, SC 29223-6366
Tel (803) 798-0916 *Founded/Ownrshp* 1974
Sales NA *EMP* 162
SIC 6111

D-U-N-S 12-927-4663
SOUTH CAROLINA TELECOMMUNICATIONS GROUP HOLDING LLC
SPIRIT TELECOM
1500 Hampton St Ste 100, Columbia, SC 29201-2984
Tel (803) 726-7000 *Founded/Ownrshp* 2000
Sales 135.9MM[E] *EMP* 190
SIC 4813
CEO: Robert M Keane
CFO: Tim Geyer
VP: Julie Cathcart
VP: Greg Guerra
VP: Larry Sims

D-U-N-S 00-691-7876
SOUTH CENTRAL CONNECTICUT REGIONAL WATER AUTHORITY (CT)
90 Sargent Dr, New Haven, CT 06511-5918
Tel (203) 562-4020 *Founded/Ownrshp* 1864, 1980
Sales 325.0MM[E] *EMP* 299
SIC 4941 Water supply
Pr: Larry L Bingaman
Treas: Thomas Clifford
Bd of Dir: Anthony Disalvo
**VP:* Linda Discepolo
VP: Darrell Smith
Genl Mgr: Stephanie Cucurello
CIO: Jean Dyer
Mktg Dir: Peter Gaewski

D-U-N-S 00-798-1608
SOUTH CENTRAL FS INC (IL)
NAHC
405 S Banker St, Effingham, IL 62401-2570
Tel (217) 342-9231 *Founded/Ownrshp* 1944
Sales 118.3MM[E] *EMP* 250
SIC 5171 5191 2875

D-U-N-S 17-365-1449
SOUTH CENTRAL LOS ANGELES REGIONAL CENTER FOR DEVELOPMENTALLY DISABLED PERSONS INC
SCLARC
2500 S Western Ave, Los Angeles, CA 90018-2609
Tel (213) 744-7000 *Founded/Ownrshp* 1983
Sales 160.5MM *EMP* 235[E]
Accts Windes Inc Long Beach Ca
SIC 8399 Health & welfare council
CEO: Dexter Henderson
**COO:* Roy Doronila

SOUTH CENTRAL POOL
See SCP DISTRIBUTORS LLC

D-U-N-S 00-790-3248 IMP
SOUTH CENTRAL POWER CO INC
2780 Coonpath Rd Ne, Lancaster, OH 43130-9343
Tel (740) 653-4422 *Founded/Ownrshp* 1936
Sales 273.8MM *EMP* 235
Accts Gbq Partners Llc Columbus Oh
SIC 4911 Distribution, electric power
Pr: Rick Lemonds
**CFO:* Rebecca Witt
**Treas:* Kenneth Davis
**VP:* Cathy Bitler
**VP:* Tom Musick
**Prin:* James Evans
**Prin:* Mike Hummel
**Prin:* Richard Poling
CIO: Jay Donahue

D-U-N-S 07-193-1919
SOUTH CENTRAL REGIONAL MEDICAL CENTER
1220 Jefferson St, Laurel, MS 39440-4355
Tel (601) 426-4000 *Founded/Ownrshp* 1949
Sales 154.4MM *EMP* 1,750
Accts Hornellp Ridgeland Mississip
SIC 8062 General medical & surgical hospitals
Pr: Doug Higginbotham
**CFO:* James Thomas Canizaro
Dir Risk M: Carol Prevost
Dir Lab: Pamela Shores
Dir Rad: Ronald W Gateood
Dir Rad: Ronald W Gatewood
Dir Rad: Peeler G Lacey
Dir Rad: Frederick D Vial
Ex Dir: Linda Gavin
Ex Dir: Douglas Higginbotham
Dir Sec: Steve Earnest

D-U-N-S 06-441-2851 EXP
SOUTH CHICAGO PACKING LLC
16250 Vincennes Ave, South Holland, IL 60473-1260
Tel (708) 589-2400 *Founded/Ownrshp* 1982
Sales 101.5MM[E] *EMP* 100
SIC 2079 Compound shortenings
Pr: David J Miniat
**Ch Bd:* Ron Miniat
**VP:* Tim Meyer
**VP:* Charles Nalon

SOUTH COAST AUTO INSURANCE
See FREEWAY INSURANCE

SOUTH COAST BAKING CO.
See SOUTH COAST BAKING LLC

D-U-N-S 60-448-1960 IMP/EXP
SOUTH COAST BAKING LLC
SOUTH COAST BAKING CO.
(*Suby of* LE PETIT PAIN HOLDINGS LLC) ★
1722 Kettering, Irvine, CA 92614-5616
Tel (949) 851-9654 *Founded/Ownrshp* 2015
Sales 110.3MM *EMP* 255
Accts Wright Ford Young & Co Irvin
SIC 2052 5149 Cookies & crackers; Cookies
CEO: Kent Hayden

COO: Rick Ptak
CFO: James Bergeson

D-U-N-S 08-046-7061
SOUTH COLONIE CENTRAL SCHOOLS DISTRICT
SOUTH COLONIE SCHOOLS
102 Loralee Dr, Albany, NY 12205-2223
Tel (518) 869-6481 *Founded/Ownrshp* 1949
Sales 102.0MM *EMP* 892
Accts Cusack & Company Cpa Llc La
SIC 8211 Public elementary & secondary schools; Public junior high school; Public senior high school
Dir Sec: David Perry
Dir IT: Henry Kaiser
IT Man: Jane Cuddeback
Pr Dir: John Noetzel
Psych: Nancy Marmet

SOUTH COLONIE SCHOOLS
See SOUTH COLONIE CENTRAL SCHOOLS DISTRICT

D-U-N-S 78-541-7718
SOUTH COUNTY HOSPITAL HEALTHCARE SYSTEM
(*Suby of* HEALTHCARE SYTEMS) ★
100 Kenyon Ave, Wakefield, RI 02879-4216
Tel (401) 782-8000 *Founded/Ownrshp* 1989
Sales 136.5MM *EMP* 600
SIC 8062 General medical & surgical hospitals
CEO: Louis Giancola
Chf Path: James Carlsten
Chf Rad: Richard Black
Dir Vol: Nadine McCauley
**Ch Bd:* Eve Keenan
Pr: Victoria Pawlak
Treas: James Stone
Bd of Dir: Margaret Cunnie
Trst: John Heffernan
**VP:* Thomas Breen
VP: Elaine Desmarais
VP: Susan McCauley
**VP:* Anne Schmidt
**VP:* Barbara Seagrave
VP: Elaine Vieira
Exec: Diane Haley
Exec: Maggie Thomas
Dir Soc: Nicole Manfredo

D-U-N-S 07-567-8706
SOUTH COUNTY HOSPITAL HEALTHCARE SYSTEM ENDOWMENT AND AFFILIATES (RI)
HEALTHCARE SYTEMS
100 Kenyon Ave, Wakefield, RI 02879-4299
Tel (401) 782-8000 *Founded/Ownrshp* 1920, 1927
Sales 136.5MM *EMP* 1,389
SIC 8062 General medical & surgical hospitals
Pr: Louis Giancola
Treas: Joe Laplume
**VP:* Michael Koziol

D-U-N-S 92-953-8999
SOUTH DAKOTA BOARD OF REGENTS
BOARD OF REGENTS, SOUTH DAKOTA
306 E Capitol Ave Ste 200, Pierre, SD 57501-2545
Tel (605) 773-3455 *Founded/Ownrshp* 1862
Sales 302.0MM^E *EMP* 4,250
SIC 8221 Colleges universities & professional schools
CEO: Michael G Rush
**Pr:* Dean Krogman
VP: Matt Dahle
VP: Rohit Dulal
VP: Matteo Knox
**VP:* Rady Morris
VP: Jordan Stewart
VP: Paul Turman
VP: Elizabeth Williams
Exec: Barbara Christensen
Adm Dir: Cody Folden

D-U-N-S 80-958-7678
SOUTH DAKOTA DEPARTMENT OF HUMAN SERVICES
HUMAN SERVICES, DEPARTMENT OF
(*Suby of* EXECUTIVE OFFICE OF STATE OF SOUTH DAKOTA) ★
500 E Capitol Ave, Pierre, SD 57501-5007
Tel (605) 773-5990 *Founded/Ownrshp* 1989
Sales NA *EMP* 1,232
Accts Martin L Guindon Cpa Auditor
SIC 9441 Administration of social & manpower programs;
V Ch: Kristie Fiegen
Sr VP: David Hillard
Snr Mgr: Steven Esser
Snr Mgr: Casey Glines
Snr Mgr: Cody Griffee
Snr Mgr: Jay Wickham

D-U-N-S 80-958-7900
SOUTH DAKOTA DEPARTMENT OF SOCIAL SERVICES
(*Suby of* EXECUTIVE OFFICE OF STATE OF SOUTH DAKOTA) ★
700 Governors Dr, Pierre, SD 57501-2291
Tel (605) 773-3165 *Founded/Ownrshp* 1973
Sales NA *EMP* 1,100
SIC 9441 Administration of social & manpower programs;
Genl Mgr: Doug Dix

D-U-N-S 80-958-8098
SOUTH DAKOTA DEPARTMENT OF TRANSPORTATION
(*Suby of* EXECUTIVE OFFICE OF STATE OF SOUTH DAKOTA) ★
700 E Broadway Ave, Pierre, SD 57501-2586
Tel (605) 773-3265 *Founded/Ownrshp* 1917
Sales NA *EMP* 1,000
SIC 9621 Regulation, administration of transportation;
Exec: Darin Bergquist
Genl Mgr: Patty Thompson
Nutrtnst: Larissa Skjonsberg

SOUTH DAKOTA FURNITURE MART
See FURNITURE OUTLETS USA INC

D-U-N-S 06-219-7517
SOUTH DAKOTA HOUSING DEVELOPMENT AUTHORITY
3060 E Elizabeth St, Pierre, SD 57501-5876
Tel (605) 773-3181 *Founded/Ownrshp* 2007
Sales 90.4MM *EMP* 65
Accts Eide Bailly Llp Aberdeen So
SIC 8748 Urban planning & consulting services
Ex Dir: Mark Lauseng
Ofcr: Heather Stoeser

D-U-N-S 92-930-1653
SOUTH DAKOTA SOYBEAN PROCESSORS LLC
100 Caspian Ave, Volga, SD 57071-9006
Tel (605) 627-9240 *Founded/Ownrshp* 1996
Sales 367.5MM *EMP* 94^E
Accts Eide Bailly Llp Greenwood Vil
SIC 2075 Soybean oil, cake or meal
CEO: Thomas J Kersting
CFO: Mark Hyde
CFO: James A Seurer
Prgrm Mgr: Angel Chen
Board of Directors: Gary Kruggel, Gary Wertish, Paul Barthel, Robert Nelsen, David Driessen, Robert Nelson, Paul Dummer, Maurice Odenbrett, Wayne Enger, Doyle Renaas, Gary Goplen, Randy Tauer, Ronald J Gorder, Dennis Timmerman, Kent Howell, Lyle R Trautman, Jerome L Jerzak, Delbert Tschakert, Jonathan Kleinjan, Ardon Wek

D-U-N-S 92-992-9743
SOUTH DAKOTA STATE UNIVERSITY
(*Suby of* BOARD OF REGENTS SOUTH DAKOTA) ★
2201 Administration Lane, Brookings, SD 57007-0001
Tel (605) 688-6101 *Founded/Ownrshp* 1881
Sales 44.0MM *EMP* 2,000
SIC 8221 Colleges universities & professional schools
Pr: David Chicoina
**VP:* Wesley Tschetter
Doctor: John Hnsen

D-U-N-S 00-792-0267
SOUTH DAKOTA WHEAT GROWERS ASSOCIATION
908 Lamont St S, Aberdeen, SD 57401-5515
Tel (605) 225-5500 *Founded/Ownrshp* 1923
Sales 1.2MMM *EMP* 638
Accts Gardiner Thomsen Pc Des Mo
SIC 5153 Grain elevators
Pr: Hal Clemensen
**CFO:* Robert Porter
**Treas:* Todd Bushong
**Treas:* Dale Locken
**VP:* Dave Thorson

SOUTH EASTERN ORTHAPEDIC CTR
See ORTHOPEDIC SURGERY CENTER L P

D-U-N-S 78-764-1935 IMP
SOUTH EASTERN REGIONAL MEDICAL INC
YELLOW JACKET GIFT SHOP
300 W 27th St, Lumberton, NC 28358-3075
Tel (910) 671-5543 *Founded/Ownrshp* 1995
Sales 270.8MM *EMP* 4
SIC 5947 Gift shop
Pr: Bonnie Biggs
CFO: Thomas Johnson
**Prin:* David Sumners

D-U-N-S 07-919-6093
SOUTH FLORIDA BAPTIST HOSPITAL INC
(*Suby of* BAYCARE EDUCATION SERVICES) ★
301 N Alexander St, Plant City, FL 33563-4303
Tel (813) 757-1200 *Founded/Ownrshp* 1947
Sales 107.1MM *EMP* 350^E
SIC 8062 General medical & surgical hospitals
Pr: Karen Kerr
Mktg Mgr: Shannon Mitchell
Surgeon: Susan Musser
Plas Surg: Shreekant K Tripathi

SOUTH FLORIDA LEASING & RENTAL
See HOLMAN AUTOMOTIVE INC

SOUTH FLORIDA TEST SERVICE DIV
See ATLAS MATERIAL TESTING TECHNOLOGY LLC

D-U-N-S 00-454-4862 IMP/EXP
SOUTH FLORIDA WATER MANAGEMENT DISTRICT LEASING CORP
SFWMD
3301 Gun Club Rd, West Palm Beach, FL 33406-3007
Tel (561) 686-8800 *Founded/Ownrshp* 1949
Sales 720.0MM *EMP* 1,200^E
SIC 4941 Water supply
Ch Bd: Daniel O'Keefe
**VP:* Mitch Hutchcraft
Dir IT: Les Pearson
IT Man: Orlowski Stanley

SOUTH GEORGIA MEDICAL CENTER
See HOSPITAL AUTHORITY OF VALDOSTA AND LOWNDES COUNTY GEORGIA

D-U-N-S 07-938-9435
SOUTH GEORGIA MEDICAL CENTER
2501 N Patterson St, Valdosta, GA 31602-1785
Tel (229) 333-1000 *Founded/Ownrshp* 2014
Sales 310.3MM *EMP* 10^E
SIC 8062 General medical & surgical hospitals

D-U-N-S 06-803-3919
SOUTH HUNTINGTON UNION FREE SCHOOL DISTRICT
60 Weston St, Huntington Station, NY 11746-4031
Tel (631) 425-5300 *Founded/Ownrshp* 1925
Sales 60.3MM^E *EMP* 1,000
SIC 8211 Private combined elementary & secondary school
VP: Nicholas Ciappetta

D-U-N-S 05-140-9605
■ **SOUTH JERSEY GAS CO**
SJI
(*Suby of* SJI) ★
1 S Jersey Plz, Hammonton, NJ 08037-9109
Tel (609) 561-9000 *Founded/Ownrshp* 1910
Sales 534.2MM *EMP* 475^E
SIC 4923 4924 4922 Gas transmission & distribution; Natural gas distribution; Natural gas transmission
Pr: Jeffrey E Dubois
CFO: Stephen H Clark
Treas: Stephen Clark
Board of Directors: Thomas A Bracken, Victor A Fortkiewicz, Edward J Graham, Frank L Sims

D-U-N-S 05-140-9498
▲ **SOUTH JERSEY INDUSTRIES INC**
SJI
1 S Jersey Plz, Hammonton, NJ 08037-9109
Tel (609) 561-9000 *Founded/Ownrshp* 1910
Sales 959.5MM *EMP* 720^E
Tkr Sym SJI *Exch* NYS
SIC 4911 4922 4924 Electric services; Natural gas transmission; Natural gas distribution
Pr: Michael J Renna
**Ch Bd:* Walter M Higgins III
CFO: Stephen H Clark
Ofcr: Kathleen A McEndy
Ex VP: Jeffrey E Dubois
Sr VP: Gina Merritt-Epps
Sr VP: Gregory M Nuzzo
Sr VP: David Robbins Jr
Off Admin: Latricia Quarles
Opers Mgr: Brad Kienzle
Opers Mgr: Brian J Ritz
Board of Directors: Sarah M Barpoulis, Thomas A Bracken, Keith S Campbell, Sheila Hartnett-Devlin, Victor A Fortkiewicz, Joseph H Petrowski, Joseph M Rigby, Frank L Sims

SOUTH KENTUCKY RECC
See SOUTH KENTUCKY RURAL ELECTRIC CO-OPERATIVE CORP

D-U-N-S 00-694-6214
SOUTH KENTUCKY RURAL ELECTRIC CO-OPERATIVE CORP
SOUTH KENTUCKY RECC
925-929 N Main St, Somerset, KY 42503
Tel (606) 678-4121 *Founded/Ownrshp* 1938
Sales 146.8MM *EMP* 163
Accts Alan Zumst Lexington Ky
SIC 4911 Electric services
CEO: Allen Anderson
**Ch Bd:* Rick Halloran
**CFO:* Michelle Herrman
**Ch:* Cathy Crew Epperson
Bd of Dir: Greg Beard
Bd of Dir: Charles Gore
Genl Mgr: Kevin Newton
IT Man: Mary L Henderlight
Sfty Mgr: Eddie Black
Snr Mgr: Tony Tupman

D-U-N-S 07-097-1916
SOUTH KITSAP SCHOOL DISTRICT 402
2689 Hoover Ave Se, Port Orchard, WA 98366-3013
Tel (360) 874-7000 *Founded/Ownrshp* 1941
Sales 61.6MM *EMP* 1,150
SIC 8211 Public elementary school; Public junior high school
Off Mgr: Kim Ellis
IT Man: Barb Tyner

D-U-N-S 07-256-6326
SOUTH LAKE HOSPITAL INC
1900 Don Wickham Dr Lbby, Clermont, FL 34711-1999
Tel (352) 394-4071 *Founded/Ownrshp* 1942
Sales 161.8MM *EMP* 1,150
SIC 8062 General medical & surgical hospitals
CEO: Leslie Longacre
**CEO:* John Moore
**COO:* Paul Johns
**Ch:* Susan McLean
**Treas:* Cary D'Ortona
**Treas:* Catherine Hoechst
**VP:* Sherrie Sitarik
Dir Lab: Carol Fornier
Dir Rx: Erica Thompson
**Prin:* Kasey Kesselring
Off Mgr: Shanda Vann

D-U-N-S 05-191-8993
SOUTH LYON COMMUNITY SCHOOLS
345 S Warren St, South Lyon, MI 48178-1317
Tel (248) 573-8127 *Founded/Ownrshp* 1966
Sales 83.8MM *EMP* 650
Accts Plante & Moran Pllc Ann Arbo
SIC 8211 Public elementary school; Public junior high school; Public senior high school

D-U-N-S 07-221-4018 IMP
SOUTH MIAMI HOSPITAL INC
(*Suby of* BAPTIST HEALTH SOUTH FLORIDA INC) ★
6200 Sw 73rd St, South Miami, FL 33143-4679
Tel (786) 662-4000 *Founded/Ownrshp* 1995
Sales 495.3MM *EMP* 2,205
SIC 8062 General medical & surgical hospitals
CEO: Lincoln S Mendez
Chf Path: Ronald A Goerss
Chf OB: Rene A Paez
Chf Rad: Jonathan M Messinger
**Pr:* Javier Hermandev-Lichto
COO: Jeanette Stone
CFO: Berta Rufat
**Treas:* George M Corrigan
Ofcr: Mercedes Delrey
VP: Carol Biggs
VP: George Shoffner
Dir Rad: Eileen Loring

SOUTH MILL INTERNATIONAL FOODS
See SOUTH MILL MUSHROOM SALES INC

D-U-N-S 17-552-2192 IMP
SOUTH MILL MUSHROOM SALES INC
SOUTH MILL INTERNATIONAL FOODS
649 W South St, Kennett Square, PA 19348-3417
Tel (610) 444-4800 *Founded/Ownrshp* 1982
Sales 202.7MM^E *EMP* 1,000^E
SIC 5148 Vegetables, fresh
Pr: John Pia
CFO: Robert Severi
**Sec:* Michael Pia
Opers Mgr: Mark Moran

SOUTH MISSISSIPPI ELECTRIC PWR
See COOPERATIVE ENERGY A MISSISSIPPI ELECTRIC COOPERATIVE

D-U-N-S 04-432-7617 EXP
SOUTH MOTOR CO OF DADE COUNTY (FL)
SOUTH MOTORS HONDA
16165 S Dixie Hwy, Miami, FL 33157-1840
Tel (888) 418-3508 *Founded/Ownrshp* 1956, 1989
Sales 176.8MM^E *EMP* 439^E
SIC 5511 5521 Automobiles, new & used; Used car dealers
Ch Bd: Charles Dascal
**Pr:* Manuel Villamanan
**CFO:* John Hilton
CFO: Christopher Lopez
**Sec:* Larry Hoffman
**VP:* Jonathan Chariff
**VP:* Ricardo Lujan
Genl Mgr: Joe Canaves
Genl Mgr: Gil Suquet
IT Man: Donnie Snyder
Sls Mgr: Fernando Ortiz

SOUTH MOTORS HONDA
See SOUTH MOTOR CO OF DADE COUNTY

D-U-N-S 05-059-5933 IMP
SOUTH NASSAU COMMUNITIES HOSPITAL INC
1 Healthy Way, Oceanside, NY 11572-1551
Tel (516) 632-3000 *Founded/Ownrshp* 1927
Sales 423.8MM *EMP* 2,800
SIC 8062 General medical & surgical hospitals
CEO: Richard J Murphy
Pr: Lori Allocca
COO: Opal McPartlin
CFO: Mark Bogan
CFO: Mark Bogen
**CFO:* Gerard Haas
Ofcr: Ann H Amato
VP: William Allison
VP: Stephen P Jieniewicz
VP: Ruth Ragusa
VP: Richard Rosenhagen
Exec: Stephen Bello
Dir Lab: Marian Sarli
Assoc Dir: Asif Rehman MD
Dir Rad: Sydney S Yoon

D-U-N-S 87-994-1433
SOUTH OKLAHOMA CITY HOSPITAL CORP
4401 S Western Ave, Oklahoma City, OK 73109-3413
Tel (405) 636-7000 *Founded/Ownrshp* 1994
Sales 27.0MM^E *EMP* 1,457
Accts Kpmg Llp Oklahoma City Ok
SIC 8741 Hospital management
Pr: Stanley F Hupfeld
**CFO:* Wentz Miller
Doctor: Naeem Tahirkheli

D-U-N-S 07-606-0169
SOUTH ORANGE COUNTY COMMUNITY COLLEGE DISTRICT
SADDLEBACK COLLEGE
28000 Marguerite Pkwy, Mission Viejo, CA 92692-3635
Tel (949) 582-4500 *Founded/Ownrshp* 1967
Sales 107.6MM^E *EMP* 2,752
SIC 8222 8221 Community college; Colleges universities & professional schools
Pr: T J Prendergast III
Trst: Marcia Milchiker
VP: David Bugay
**VP:* Nancy M Padberg
Comm Man: Lisa Cavallaro
Ex Dir: Teddi Lorch
Ex Dir: Kimberly McCord
Dir IT: Mark Schiffelbein
Psych: Phong Luong
Board of Directors: Beth Mueller

D-U-N-S 00-793-4185
SOUTH PLAINS ELECTRIC COOPERATIVE INC (TX)
4727 S Loop 289 Ste 200, Lubbock, TX 79424-2263
Tel (806) 775-7732 *Founded/Ownrshp* 1937
Sales 150.8MM *EMP* 144
SIC 4911 Distribution, electric power
Ex Dir: James C Driver
**CFO:* Ronnie Rucker
VP: Rd McCallister

D-U-N-S 83-554-5559
SOUTH PLAINS FINANCIAL INC
5219 City Bank Pkwy # 55, Lubbock, TX 79407-3544
Tel (806) 792-7101 *Founded/Ownrshp* 1993
Sales NA *EMP* 385
SIC 6712 Bank holding companies
Pr: Cory Newsom
**Ch Bd:* Curtis Griffith

D-U-N-S 07-353-1840
SOUTH PLAZA CO
100 Peabody Pl Ste 1400, Memphis, TN 38103-3648
Tel (901) 260-7400 *Founded/Ownrshp* 1985
Sales 99.2MM^E *EMP* 2,800
SIC 6531

SOUTH POINT HOTEL & CASINO SPA
See GAUGHAN SOUTH LLC

SOUTH RIVER ELC MEMBERSHIP
See SOUTH RIVER ELECTRIC MEMBERSHIP CORP

D-U-N-S 00-699-6391
SOUTH RIVER ELECTRIC MEMBERSHIP CORP
SOUTH RIVER ELC MEMBERSHIP
17494 Us Highway 421 S, Dunn, NC 28334-0013
Tel (910) 892-8071 *Founded/Ownrshp* 1940
Sales 92.4MM[E] *EMP* 110
SIC 4911 Distribution, electric power
CEO: Robert Butler
**Pr:* Francis Clifton
COO: Andy Howard
**Treas:* Carlton Martin
**Ex VP:* Buddy G Creed
VP: Charles Collier
**VP:* Kelly Harrington
VP: Kathy McPhail
Tech Mgr: Brian Linens

D-U-N-S 08-959-3818 IMP
SOUTH SAN ANTONIO INDEPENDENT SCHOOL DISTRICT
5622 Ray Ellison Blvd, San Antonio, TX 78242-2214
Tel (210) 977-7000 *Founded/Ownrshp* 1922
Sales 71.9MM[E] *EMP* 1,400
SIC 8211 Public elementary & secondary schools
Bd of Dir: Wanda Gutierrez
Prin: Sharon Liskow
**Ex Dir:* David Landeros
Dir IT: Frank Harmier
Teacher Pr: Monica Lopez

D-U-N-S 08-155-6888
SOUTH SAN FRANCISCO UNIFIED SCHOOL DISTRICT
398 B St, South San Francisco, CA 94080-4423
Tel (650) 877-8700 *Founded/Ownrshp* 1936
Sales 67.7MM[E] *EMP* 1,143
SIC 8211 Public junior high school; School board
Bd of Dir: John Baker
Bd of Dir: Daina Lujan
Psych: Christina S Johnson
Psych: Kathleen Kenney

D-U-N-S 15-726-3856
SOUTH SHORE HEALTH AND EDUCATIONAL CORP
55 Fogg Rd, South Weymouth, MA 02190-2432
Tel (781) 340-8000 *Founded/Ownrshp* 1922
Sales 2.2MM *EMP* 3,000
Accts Deloitte Tax Llp Boston Ma
SIC 8062 General medical & surgical hospitals
Pr: David T Hannan
V Ch: James Devin
V Ch: Robert Driscoll
V Ch: Peter Ferlisi
V Ch: Michael Hayes
V Ch: Brian W Hotarek
V Ch: Darlyne Johnson
V Ch: Jeffrey Johnson
V Ch: Jon Pehrson
V Ch: Benjamin Ryan
V Ch: Christo Shakr
V Ch: James Suojanen
V Ch: David Wong
**Treas:* John W Burns
Trst: Gary E Adams
Trst: Warren Baker
Trst: Richard Bonner
Trst: Thomas Cataldo
Trst: Jack Conway
Trst: Edmund Corvelli
Trst: Kevin Courtney

D-U-N-S 07-659-1353
SOUTH SHORE HOSPITAL INC
SOUTH SHORE VSITING NURSE ASSN
55 Fogg Rd, South Weymouth, MA 02190-2455
Tel (781) 624-8000 *Founded/Ownrshp* 1922
Sales 522.1MM *EMP* 2,375
SIC 8062 8049 General medical & surgical hospitals; Physical therapist; Nurses & other medical assistants
Pr: Richard Aubut
Dir Vol: Diane Downs
V Ch: Jon Pehrson
**COO:* Joseph Cahill
CFO: Joseph Cuhill
**CFO:* Michael Cullen
**Ch:* Brian Hotorek
Ch: Richard Sullivan
Bd of Dir: John Doucette
Trst: John O'Connor
Trst: Alec Petro
**Sr VP:* Margaret Holda
Sr VP: Judith McTiernan
**Sr VP:* Christopher J Oconnor
Sr VP: Paul J Taylor
VP: Margaret Holda
VP: Patrice Lynch
VP: Christopher O'Connor
VP: Rose Pietro
VP: Paul Sullivan
VP: John Walsh

D-U-N-S 06-010-5798
SOUTH SHORE MEDICAL CENTER INC
75 Washington St Ste 1, Norwell, MA 02061-1795
Tel (781) 878-5200 *Founded/Ownrshp* 1962
Sales 131.6MM *EMP* 150
Accts Pkf Pc Quincy Ma
SIC 8011 Medical centers
Pr: Edward W Nalband
CFO: Mike Kaplan
**VP:* Dr W Robert Prouty
Obsttrcn: Christine Skiadus
Doctor: David Chiang
Doctor: Joseph H Scwartz
Doctor: Ginter Sotrel

SOUTH SHORE VSITING NURSE ASSN
See SOUTH SHORE HOSPITAL INC

D-U-N-S 00-792-0127
■ **SOUTH STATE BANK** (SC)
(*Suby of* SOUTH STATE CORP) ★
520 Gervais St Ste 310, Columbia, SC 29201-3071
Tel (803) 771-2265 *Founded/Ownrshp* 1934, 1985
Sales NA *EMP* 383
SIC 6022 State commercial banks
Pr: John F Windley
**Ch Bd:* Robert R Horger
Pr: John Boretti
Pr: Greg A Lapointe
Ex VP: Hobson Busby
Ex VP: Jeff Fulp
**Ex VP:* Allen M Hay
**Ex VP:* Don Kerr
**Ex VP:* F Gene McConnell Jr
Ex VP: Bill Medich
**Ex VP:* Rodney W Overby
Sr VP: Susan Amick
**Sr VP:* Veronica H Bailey
Sr VP: Nate Barber
**Sr VP:* Jim Boyd
Sr VP: Cynthia Cain
Sr VP: Donna Cameron
Sr VP: Chrissie Casas
Sr VP: Chris Claussen
**Sr VP:* Michael Coggin
Sr VP: Lee Fryland

D-U-N-S 14-484-1715
▲ **SOUTH STATE CORP**
520 Gervais St Ste 310, Columbia, SC 29201-3071
Tel (800) 277-2175 *Founded/Ownrshp* 1985
Sales NA *EMP* 2,058[E]
Tkr Sym SSB *Exch* NGS
SIC 6712 6022 Bank holding companies; State commercial banks
CEO: Robert R Hill Jr
**Ch Bd:* Robert R Horger
**COO:* John C Pollok
**V Ch Bd:* Paula Harper Bethea
Chf Cred: Joseph E Burns
Ofcr: John F Windley

D-U-N-S 07-538-0113
SOUTH TENNESSEE OIL CO INC
QUIK MART CONVENIENCE STORES
105 Helton Dr, Lawrenceburg, TN 38464-2253
Tel (931) 762-9600 *Founded/Ownrshp* 1971
Sales 180.0MM *EMP* 415
Accts Ad Regeon & Associates Colu
SIC 5541 5411 Filling stations, gasoline; Convenience stores, independent
Pr: Jonathan Edwards
COO: Doug Holden
**Sec:* Connie Lynn Cooper
Area Supr: Rickey Dodd
Genl Mgr: Oneal Stanford
Site Mgr: Angela Montijo

D-U-N-S 17-165-4346
SOUTH TEXAS COLLEGE
3201 Pecan Blvd, McAllen, TX 78501-6661
Tel (956) 872-8311 *Founded/Ownrshp* 1993
Sales 56.3MM[E] *EMP* 1,200[E]
SIC 8222 Junior colleges & technical institutes
Pr: Shirley A Reed
**VP:* Anahid Petrosian
Store Mgr: Kristin Buck
DP Exec: Guadalupe Martinez

SOUTH TEXAS ELECTRIC CO OP
See SOUTH TEXAS ELECTRIC COOPERATIVE INC

D-U-N-S 00-386-6332 IMP/EXP
SOUTH TEXAS ELECTRIC COOPERATIVE INC (TX)
SOUTH TEXAS ELECTRIC CO OP
2849 Fm 447, Nursery, TX 77976
Tel (361) 575-6491 *Founded/Ownrshp* 1944
Sales 416.1MM *EMP* 253[E]
Accts Bumgardner Morrison And Compa
SIC 4911 Generation, electric power; Transmission, electric power
Pr: Gary Raybon
Pr: Darryl Klinitchek
**Sec:* Tommy Ermis
**VP:* Larry Huesser
VP: Burt O'Connell
Exec: Randy Snider
IT Man: Darrell Klimitchek
Plnt Mgr: Roger Bishop
Board of Directors: Blaine Warzecha, Bobby Bauch, Don Wehmeyer, Brad Bierstedt, Paul Brysch, James Coleman, Bruce Elliot, John Herrera, Ron Hughes, Leroy Kaspar, Mark Rollans

SOUTH TEXAS HEALTH SYSTEM
See MCALLEN MEDICAL CENTER LP

SOUTH TXAS PRJ ELC GNRTING STN
See STP NUCLEAR OPERATING CO

D-U-N-S 60-971-7090
SOUTH UNIVERSITY ONLINE
1400 Penn Ave Ste 201, Pittsburgh, PA 15222-4342
Tel (412) 995-7424 *Founded/Ownrshp* 2004
Sales 21.8MM[E] *EMP* 1,125
SIC 8221 Colleges universities & professional schools
Pr: Todd Nelson
**CFO:* Ed West
VP: Andrew Hurst
Assoc Dir: Matthew Horne
HC Dir: Michael Buric

D-U-N-S 78-343-3568
SOUTH VALLEY CARE CENTER
1629 Bowe Ln Sw, Albuquerque, NM 87105-3772
Tel (505) 877-2200 *Founded/Ownrshp* 1976
Sales 338.2MM *EMP* 60
SIC 8051 8059 Skilled nursing care facilities; Rest home, with health care
Prin: Hunter Greene

SOUTH WASHINGTON CNTY SCHOOLS
See SOUTH WASHINGTON COUNTY SCHOOLS ISD 833

D-U-N-S 08-449-5266
SOUTH WASHINGTON COUNTY SCHOOLS ISD 833 (MN)
SOUTH WASHINGTON CNTY SCHOOLS
7362 E Point Douglas Rd S, Cottage Grove, MN 55016-3025
Tel (651) 458-6300 *Founded/Ownrshp* 1951
Sales 200.0MM *EMP* 3,200
SIC 8211 Public elementary school; Public junior high school; Public senior high school; School board
**Sec:* Laurel Dalluhn
Teacher Pr: Denise Griffith

SOUTH WEST GRAIN
See FRENCHMAN VALLEY FARMERS COOPERATIVE INC

SOUTH WEST KEY YOUNGTOWN
See SOUTHWEST KEY PROGRAMS INC

D-U-N-S 05-993-9298
SOUTH- WESTERN CITY SCHOOL DISTRICT
3805 Marlane Dr, Grove City, OH 43123-9224
Tel (614) 801-3000 *Founded/Ownrshp* 1956
Sales 261.1MM *EMP* 2,600
Accts Balestra Harr & Scherer Cpas
SIC 8211 Public elementary & secondary schools
**Treas:* Hugh Garside
Ex Dir: Brian Bowser
Ex Dir: Linda Kuhn
IT Man: Karen New
Pr Dir: Sandra Nekoloff
Sls Mgr: Dale Daniels
HC Dir: Amber Hutford

D-U-N-S 06-594-0579
SOUTHAMPTON HOSPITAL ASSOCIATION
240 Meeting House Ln, Southampton, NY 11968-5090
Tel (631) 726-8200 *Founded/Ownrshp* 1909
Sales 135.5MM *EMP* 750
SIC 8062 General medical & surgical hospitals
CEO: Robert S Chaloner
Chf OB: Vito Alamia
**Pr:* Steve Bernstein
Pr: Christine Cassamassino
CFO: Chris Schulteis
**CFO:* Chris J Schultheis
**Ch:* Peter Larsen
Ex VP: Fredric Weinbaum
**VP:* Patricia A Darcey
VP: Patricia Darcey
VP: Sharon Disunno
VP: Andrea Dowd
**VP:* Robert I Ross
VP: Robert Ross
VP: Howard Sklarek
Dir Lab: Victoria Moller
Dir Rx: Jerry West
Board of Directors: Florence Rolston

D-U-N-S 08-713-8129
SOUTHBORO MEDICAL GROUP INC
24-28 Newton St, Southborough, MA 01772
Tel (508) 481-5500 *Founded/Ownrshp* 1972
Sales 102.8MM *EMP* 400
SIC 8011

D-U-N-S 15-487-0638
SOUTHCENTRAL FOUNDATION
4501 Diplomacy Dr, Anchorage, AK 99508-5919
Tel (907) 729-4955 *Founded/Ownrshp* 1982
Sales 307.4MM *EMP* 1,600
Accts Altman Rogers & Co Anchorag
SIC 8093 8021 8042 Substance abuse clinics (outpatient); Mental health clinic, outpatient; Offices & clinics of dentists; Offices & clinics of optometrists
CEO: Katherine Gottlieb
**Bd of Dir:* Lee Olson
Bd of Dir: James Segura
Ofcr: Kahoney M Monsen
**VP:* Chanda Aloysius
**VP:* Douglas EBY
**VP:* Kevin Gottlieb
**VP:* Ileen Sylvester
Exec: Leanndra Ross
Dir: Fred Kopacz
Nurse Mgr: Arica Carpenter

D-U-N-S 02-457-4287
SOUTHCO DISTRIBUTING CO (NC)
2201 S John St, Goldsboro, NC 27530-7163
Tel (919) 735-8012 *Founded/Ownrshp* 1981, 1996
Sales 397.2MM *EMP* 225
Accts Parker & Parker Pa Goldbor
SIC 5194 5141 5131 Cigarettes; Groceries, general line; Notions
CEO: Sherwin Herring
**Pr:* Marvin Wooten
**CFO:* Chris Wise
**VP:* April Garver

D-U-N-S 00-232-8797 IMP
SOUTHCO INC
(*Suby of* TOUCHPOINT INC) ★
210 N Brinton Lake Rd, Concordville, PA 19331
Tel (610) 459-4000 *Founded/Ownrshp* 1899
Sales 601.9MM[E] *EMP* 2,800
SIC 3965 Fasteners
Pr: Brian M Mc Neill
CFO: Paul Brown
Treas: David Montgomery
VP: Raymond Canzanese
VP: Paul Houle
VP: Michael Mc Philmy
VP: Thomas Mehler
Exec: Theresa Mongiello
Mng Dir: Mike Zhang
Genl Mgr: Shane Oconnor
Genl Mgr: Pascal Testeil

D-U-N-S 18-756-3721
SOUTHCOAST HEALTH SYSTEM INC
101 Page St, New Bedford, MA 02740-3464
Tel (508) 997-1515 *Founded/Ownrshp* 1983
Sales 4.4MM *EMP* 6,000[E]
Accts Pricewaterhousecoopers Llp Bo
SIC 8741 8062 Hospital management; Nursing & personal care facility management; General medical & surgical hospitals
Pr: Keith Hovan
Dir Vol: Agatha St Amour
**Pr:* John D Day
**Treas:* Linda A Bodenmann
**Treas:* Kristofer Lindeman
Sr Cor Off: Mary Vieira
Bd of Dir: Debbie Chmiel
Trst: William H Lapointe
Dir Risk M: Stephen Pires
Ex Dir: Greg Robinson
Nurse Mgr: Judith Baulier

D-U-N-S 94-757-8753
SOUTHCOAST HOSPITALS GROUP INC
TOBEY HOSPITAL
(*Suby of* SOUTHCOAST HEALTH SYSTEM INC) ★
363 Highland Ave, Fall River, MA 02720-3703
Tel (508) 679-3131 *Founded/Ownrshp* 1984
Sales 743.5MM *EMP* 3,853
SIC 8062

D-U-N-S 18-762-7807
SOUTHCOAST PHYSICIAN SERVICES INC
101 Page St, New Bedford, MA 02740-3464
Tel (508) 961-5555 *Founded/Ownrshp* 1986
Sales 125.3MM *EMP* 9
SIC 8741 Management services
Pr: Ronald Goodspeed MD

D-U-N-S 07-845-2749
SOUTHCOAST PHYSICIANS GROUP INC
200 Mill Rd Ste 180, Fairhaven, MA 02719-5255
Tel (508) 758-3781 *Founded/Ownrshp* 2012
Sales 125.3MM *EMP* 1,000[E]
Accts Pricewaterhousecoopers Llp Bo
SIC 8011 Offices & clinics of medical doctors
Pr: Warren Wood
**Treas:* Kristofer Linderman

D-U-N-S 07-847-0182
▲ **SOUTHCROSS ENERGY PARTNERS LP**
1717 Main St Ste 5200, Dallas, TX 75201-7365
Tel (214) 979-3720 *Founded/Ownrshp* 2012
Sales 698.4MM *EMP* 291[E]
Tkr Sym SXE *Exch* NYS
SIC 4922 Natural gas transmission
Pr: John E Bonn
Genl Pt: Southcross E GP
CFO: Bret M Allan

D-U-N-S 15-982-0190 IMP/EXP
SOUTHEAST AEROSPACE INC
SEA
1399 General Aviation Dr, Melbourne, FL 32935-6310
Tel (321) 255-9877 *Founded/Ownrshp* 1993
Sales 105.2MM[E] *EMP* 120
SIC 5088 3812 3728 3721 4581 Transportation equipment & supplies; Search & navigation equipment; Aircraft parts & equipment; Aircraft; Aircraft maintenance & repair services
Pr: John Braddock IV
CFO: Greg Rodriguez
**Treas:* John B Braddock IV
**VP:* Marianne Braddock
Exec: Jenny Gibbons
Comm Dir: Christina Mennen
Prgrm Mgr: Steve White
Genl Mgr: Jason Hicks
Sls Mgr: Nathan Hernandez
Sales Asso: Jessica Costa

SOUTHEAST ALABAMA MEDICAL CTR
See HOUSTON COUNTY HEALTHCARE AUTHORITY

D-U-N-S 08-372-7826
SOUTHEAST ALASKA REGIONAL HEALTH CONSORTIUM
SEARHC
3100 Channel Dr Ste 300, Juneau, AK 99801-7837
Tel (907) 463-4000 *Founded/Ownrshp* 1975
Sales 111.2MM *EMP* 900
Accts Elgee Rehfeld Mertz Llc Junea
SIC 8011 8062 Medical centers; General medical & surgical hospitals
Pr: Roald Helgesen
CFO: Jim Slater
**VP:* David Edwards
Exec: Diana Colbert
Exec: Brenda Sturm
Surgeon: Kim N Hort
Pharmcst: Cole Dysinger

D-U-N-S 07-697-3361
SOUTHEAST COMMUNITY COLLEGE AREA
301 S 68th Street Pl, Lincoln, NE 68510-2449
Tel (402) 323-3400 *Founded/Ownrshp* 1973
Sales 31.9MM *EMP* 1,075
Accts Dana F Cole & Company Llp L
SIC 8222 Community college
Pr: Jack J Huck
CFO: Theodore Suhr
Bd of Dir: Lynn Schluckebier
Assoc Dir: Rebecca Carr
Ex Dir: Ruby Uzzle
Sales Asso: Nathan Smith

D-U-N-S 06-039-9594
SOUTHEAST CONNECTIONS LLC
2720 Dogwood Dr Se, Conyers, GA 30013-1558
Tel (678) 509-0165 *Founded/Ownrshp* 2006
Sales 190.8MM[E] *EMP* 680
SIC 1623 Water, sewer & utility lines
Pr: Billy Campbell
**VP:* Kevin Adams
**VP:* Josh Evans
VP: Daniel Ragsdale
Opers Mgr: Scott Warren

D-U-N-S 09-607-7805
SOUTHEAST FOODS INC
SUNFLOWER FOOD STORE
1001 N 11th St, Monroe, LA 71201-5633
Tel (318) 388-1884 *Founded/Ownrshp* 1974
Sales 139.6MM[E] *EMP* 1,100
SIC 5411

D-U-N-S 62-757-0575 IMP/EXP
SOUTHEAST FROZEN FOODS CO LP
TALG
3261 Executive Way, Miramar, FL 33025-3931
Tel (954) 882-1044 *Founded/Ownrshp* 1991
Sales 897.9MM[E] *EMP* 600
SIC 5142 4222 5411 Packaged frozen goods; Warehousing, cold storage or refrigerated; Co-operative food stores
Pt: Richard A Bauer

Genl Pt: Southeast Frozen Foods Corp
Pt: Jackson Hole Investment Acquis
COO: Marc Goodman
Exec: Julio Diaz
VP Opers: Lyndon Valerie

D-U-N-S 14-260-4722 IMP/EXP
SOUTHEAST FROZEN FOODS INC
SOUTHEAST WHOLESALE FOODS
3261 Executive Way, Miramar, FL 33025-3931
Tel (866) 289-1198 *Founded/Ownrshp* 1958
Sales 215.6MM^E *EMP* 600
SIC 2038 Ethnic foods, frozen
Pr: Rich Bauer
**CFO:* Marc Goodman
**VP:* Bob Dernbach
**VP:* Danny Payne
Rgnl Mgr: Dave Miller
Dir IT: Brian Cass
Dir IT: Brian Gass
IT Man: Carol Loftus
VP Mktg: Tim Martis
VP Sls: Gary Cogwell
Sls Mgr: David Levine

SOUTHEAST HEALTH
See SOUTHEAST MISSOURI HOSPITAL ASSOCIATION

D-U-N-S 83-798-6462
SOUTHEAST INDUSTRIAL EQUIPMENT INC
12200 Steele Creek Rd, Charlotte, NC 28273-3736
Tel (704) 363-6432 *Founded/Ownrshp* 1994
Sales 131.6MM *EMP* 290
Accts Arrowood & Associates Pa Gas
SIC 7353 7359 5084 Heavy construction equipment rental; Industrial truck rental; Industrial machine parts; Lift trucks & parts; Materials handling machinery
CEO: Steven H Thorne
**Pr:* Cory Thorne
Genl Mgr: Lauren Hunke
IT Man: Jamele Hall
Trfc Dir: Linda Keith
Opers Mgr: Harry Scott
Manager: Mike Brown
Manager: Thomas Chandler
Manager: Ron Davison
Manager: Ryan Desroches
Manager: Scott Stephens

D-U-N-S 04-955-5741
SOUTHEAST MILK INC
1950 Se County Hwy 484, Belleview, FL 34420-8620
Tel (352) 245-2437 *Founded/Ownrshp* 1998
Sales 378.7MM^E *EMP* 340
SIC 5143 2048 Milk; Livestock feeds
CEO: Calvin Covington
**Pr:* Joe Wright
**CFO:* Albert Antoine
**Treas:* Doyle Weltzbarker
**VP:* Dale Eade
IT Man: Danielle Weaver

D-U-N-S 07-696-9583
SOUTHEAST MISSOURI HOSPITAL ASSOCIATION
SOUTHEAST HEALTH
1701 Lacey St, Cape Girardeau, MO 63701-5230
Tel (573) 334-4822 *Founded/Ownrshp* 1927
Sales 289.9MM *EMP* 2,000^E
SIC 8062 Hospital, AMA approved residency
CEO: Wayne Smith
Pr: Brian Gilliland
**Pr:* James W Wente
COO: Sly Moore
**CFO:* David Storm
Ofcr: Rodney Gibson
VP: Dan Berry
**VP:* Karen Hendrickson
VP: Hugh King
Dir Rx: Nicole Allcock
Dir Sec: Keith May

D-U-N-S 02-034-7944
SOUTHEAST MISSOURI STATE UNIVERSITY
ACCOUNTS PAYABLE DEPT
1 University Plz, Cape Girardeau, MO 63701-4710
Tel (573) 651-2000 *Founded/Ownrshp* 1873
Sales 109.6MM *EMP* 941
Accts Rubinbrown Llp Saint Louis M
SIC 8221 University
Pr: Kenneth W Dobbins
VP: Caitlyn Blanton
VP: Chanel Blount
VP: Hannah Gordon
VP: William Holland
VP: Dylan Kennedy
VP: Dmitri Kozak
VP: Kelsey Orf
VP: Christine Paige
Ex Dir: Zahir Ahmed
Prgrm Mgr: David Probst

D-U-N-S 80-091-3428
SOUTHEAST MISSOURI STATE UNIVERSITY
1 University Plz, Cape Girardeau, MO 63701-4710
Tel (573) 651-2000 *Founded/Ownrshp* 1998
Sales 121.2MM *EMP* 6
SIC 8351 Child day care services

D-U-N-S 03-498-3551
SOUTHEAST NEBRASKA COOPERATIVE CO
403 S 3rd St, Beatrice, NE 68310-3824
Tel (402) 228-3458 *Founded/Ownrshp* 1919
Sales 107.0MM *EMP* 50
SIC 5191 5153 2048

D-U-N-S 93-885-5293
SOUTHEAST PETRO DISTRIBUTORS INC
402 High Point Dr Ste A, Cocoa, FL 32926-6600
Tel (321) 631-0245 *Founded/Ownrshp* 1993
Sales 553.3MM *EMP* 12
Accts James Moore & Co Pl Gaine
SIC 5172 Gasoline
Pr: Mahesh Shah
**VP:* Rashmi Shah
**VP:* Shah Summit

D-U-N-S 04-759-8446
■ **SOUTHEAST POWER CORP**
(*Suby of* GOLDFIELD CORP DEL) ★
1805 Hammock Rd, Titusville, FL 32796-7820
Tel (321) 268-0540 *Founded/Ownrshp* 1984
Sales 93.4MM *EMP* 226
Accts Kpmg Llp Orlando Fl
SIC 1731 General electrical contractor
CEO: John R Davis III
**Pr:* Robert Jones
**CEO:* John R Davis III
**CEO:* John H Sottile
**CFO:* Steve Wherry
VP: Jack E Brady
VP: John W Davis
VP: Add For

D-U-N-S 02-487-6153
SOUTHEAST SERVICE CORP
SSC SERVICE SOLUTIONS
(*Suby of* COMPASS GROUP PLC)
1845 Midpark Rd Ste 201, Knoxville, TN 37921-5951
Tel (865) 546-8880 *Founded/Ownrshp* 2010
Sales 283.9MM^E *EMP* 6,500
SIC 7349

D-U-N-S 00-562-1248
■ **SOUTHEAST SERVICES INC** (VA)
(*Suby of* ANTHEM SOUTHEAST INC) ★
2015 Staples Mill Rd, Richmond, VA 23230-3108
Tel (804) 354-7000 *Founded/Ownrshp* 1995, 2002
Sales NA *EMP* 4,122^E
SIC 6324 Health maintenance organization (HMO), insurance only
CEO: Thomas R Byrd
**Sr VP:* J Christopher Wiltshire

D-U-N-S 80-826-4746
SOUTHEAST SUPPLY HEADER LLC
SESH
5400 Westheimer Ct, Houston, TX 77056-5353
Tel (713) 627-5400 *Founded/Ownrshp* 2006
Sales 110.1MM *EMP* 15
Accts Deloitte & Touche Llp Housto
SIC 4923 Gas transmission & distribution
VP: Richard Kruse Jr

D-U-N-S 00-782-2471
SOUTHEAST TELEPHONE CO OF WISCONSIN LLC
TDS
311 Elizabeth St, Waterford, WI 53185-4366
Tel (608) 831-1000 *Founded/Ownrshp* 1946
Sales 853.0MM *EMP* 2,700
SIC 4813 Local telephone communications; Long distance telephone communications
Pr: David Wittwer

D-U-N-S 79-592-1613
SOUTHEAST TESTING & ENGINEERING INC
2870 N Berkeley Lk Rd Nw, Duluth, GA 30096-4346
Tel (678) 377-1234 *Founded/Ownrshp* 2003
Sales 90.0MM *EMP* 1
SIC 7389 Inspection & testing services
CEO: Charles Radev

D-U-N-S 96-667-1679
SOUTHEAST TEXAS CLASSIC AUTOMOTIVE INC
CLASSIC ACURA
1000 Interstate 10 N, Beaumont, TX 77702-1003
Tel (409) 898-8001 *Founded/Ownrshp* 1999
Sales 216.6MM^E *EMP* 350
SIC 5511 7515 Automobiles, new & used; Pickups, new & used; Passenger car leasing
Pr: Ken Ruddy
**VP:* Roane Ruddy

SOUTHEAST TEXAS INDUS SVCS
See STIS INC

D-U-N-S 62-651-5829 IMP
SOUTHEAST TEXAS INDUSTRIES INC
STI GROUP
35911 Us Highway 96 S, Buna, TX 77612-4031
Tel (409) 994-3570 *Founded/Ownrshp* 1990
Sales 235.8MM^E *EMP* 850
SIC 3312 3443 Structural shapes & pilings, steel; Hot-rolled iron & steel products; Fabricated plate work (boiler shop)
Pr: Paul T Spence
**CFO:* James Parsley
Treas: Stacy Spence
**VP:* Richard E Purkey Jr
Genl Mgr: Marc Sammons
QA Dir: Kirsten Colley
QA Dir: Pam Reeves
Dir IT: Kevin Brocato

D-U-N-S 04-601-9360 EXP
SOUTHEAST TOYOTA DISTRIBUTORS LLC
JM FAMILY ENTERPRISES
(*Suby of* JM & A GROUP) ★
100 Jim Moran Blvd, Deerfield Beach, FL 33442-1702
Tel (954) 429-2000 *Founded/Ownrshp* 1969
Sales 286.1MM^E *EMP* 944
SIC 5012 Automobiles & other motor vehicles
CEO: Colin Brown
Pr: Sonya Deen
Pr: Brent Sergot
Top Exec: Tom Bentley
Ex VP: Brent Burns
Ex VP: Forrest Heathcott
Ex VP: Ed Sheehy
VP: Deborah Battisto
VP: Tom Blanton
VP: Mike Casey
VP: Charles Gordon
VP: Billy Hayes
VP: David Reid
VP: Eduardo Rivera
Board of Directors: Colin W Brown, Janice M Moran

SOUTHEAST TOYOTA FINANCE
See WORLD OMNI FINANCIAL CORP

D-U-N-S 10-799-8049
SOUTHEAST VOLUSIA HEALTHCARE CORP
FLORIDA HOSPITAL NEW SMYRNA
(*Suby of* ADVENTST HLTH SYSTM SUNBELT H) ★
401 Palmetto St, New Smyrna Beach, FL 32168-7322
Tel (386) 424-5000 *Founded/Ownrshp* 2015
Sales 86.1MM *EMP* 700
SIC 8062 General medical & surgical hospitals
Pr: Daryl Tol
**Treas:* Debora Thomas
Dir Risk M: Patty Graham
Board of Directors: Al Allred, Pat Card, Pat Corbett, Nancy Evolga, Jacqueline Herchek

SOUTHEAST WHOLESALE FOODS
See SOUTHEAST FROZEN FOODS INC

D-U-N-S 03-748-9747
SOUTHEAST WOOD TREATING INC
3077 Carter Hill Rd, Montgomery, AL 36111-1801
Tel (321) 631-1003 *Founded/Ownrshp* 1980
Sales 115.9MM^E *EMP* 375
SIC 2421 2491 Sawmills & planing mills, general; Wood preserving
Pr: Guice M Slawson
**CFO:* Charles Morello
VP: Ed Galt
**VP:* Stinson Slawson
CTO: Greg Graham
MIS Dir: Randy Chester

D-U-N-S 06-615-0806
SOUTHEASTERN CALIFORNIA CONFERENCE OF SEVENTH-DAY ADVENTISTS
(*Suby of* PACIFIC UNION ASSOCIATION OF SEVENTH-DAY ADVENTISTS) ★
11330 Pierce St, Riverside, CA 92505-3303
Tel (951) 509-2200 *Founded/Ownrshp* 1917
Sales 142.8MM^E *EMP* 2,100
SIC 8211 8661 Private elementary school; Private senior high school; Seventh Day Adventist Church
Pr: Sandra E Roberts
**CEO:* Gerald Penick
**Treas:* Verlon Strauss
**VP:* Alberto E Ingleton
**VP:* George M King

D-U-N-S 07-547-0740
SOUTHEASTERN CONFERENCE
2201 Richard Arringtn Jr, Birmingham, AL 35203-1103
Tel (205) 949-8960 *Founded/Ownrshp* 1933
Sales 527.3MM *EMP* 30
Accts Barfield Murphy Shank & Smith
SIC 8699 Athletic organizations
**Exec:* Mark Womack

D-U-N-S 10-691-2488
SOUTHEASTERN FOOD MERCHANDISERS INC
201 Parker Dr, Pelham, AL 35124-1924
Tel (205) 664-3322 *Founded/Ownrshp* 1988
Sales 141.8MM^E *EMP* 126
SIC 5141 Food brokers
Pr: Charles Mizarany
**Pr:* Benny M La Russa
**VP:* James Acomb
Dir IT: Steve Kendrick

D-U-N-S 00-379-3569 IMP/EXP
SOUTHEASTERN FREIGHT LINES INC (SC)
420 Davega Dr, Lexington, SC 29073-7485
Tel (803) 794-7300 *Founded/Ownrshp* 1950
Sales 1.2MMM^E *EMP* 7,000
SIC 4213 Trucking, except local
Ch: W T Cassels III
Sr VP: J Russell Burleson Jr
VP: Dean Baker
VP: Keith Heaton
VP: Dave Robinson
Admn Mgr: Kevin Taylor
Snr Sftwr: Daniel Ellis
Snr Sftwr: Jasper Rozinski
Dir IT: Woody Lovelace
IT Man: Chris Harley
Info Man: Billy Reardon
Board of Directors: W T Cassels Jr

D-U-N-S 07-920-9922
SOUTHEASTERN GROCERS LLC
(*Suby of* WINN-DIXIE) ★
8928 Prominence Pkwy # 200, Jacksonville, FL 32256-8264
Tel (904) 783-5000 *Founded/Ownrshp* 2010
Sales 12.8MMM^E *EMP* 177,938^E
SIC 5411 Convenience stores, chain
CEO: Ian McLeod
**CFO:* Brian P Carney
Ex VP: Sharry Cramond
**Ex VP:* D Mark Prestidge
**Ex VP:* Lawrence A Stablein
Sr VP: Ricardo S Coro
VP: Holly Angell
VP: Bert Dumars
Snr Mgr: Scott Fraser
Snr Mgr: Karyn Keppel
Snr Mgr: Amy Lindsey

D-U-N-S 05-339-3299
SOUTHEASTERN HEALTHCARE SYSTEM INC
111 Brewster St, Pawtucket, RI 02860-4474
Tel (401) 729-2000 *Founded/Ownrshp* 1996
Sales 140.0MM *EMP* 1,653
SIC 8748 Business consulting
Pr: Francis R Dietz

D-U-N-S 04-035-1047
SOUTHEASTERN ILLINOIS ELECTRIC COOPERATIVE
P.O. Box 251 (62930-0251)
Tel (618) 273-2611 *Founded/Ownrshp* 2012
Sales 108.2MM *EMP* 25^E
Accts Alan Zumst Lexington Ky
SIC 4911 Electric services
CEO: Dustin Tripp
Exec: Eric Jung

D-U-N-S 00-693-3766
SOUTHEASTERN ILLINOIS ELECTRIC COOPERATIVE INC (IL)
100 Cooperative Way, Carrier Mills, IL 62917-2275
Tel (618) 273-2611 *Founded/Ownrshp* 1938
Sales 94.2MM *EMP* 80^E
Accts Dreyer & Kelso Pc Pa Mission
SIC 4911 Distribution, electric power
Pr: Bill Richardson
**CFO:* Greg Cruse
**Sec:* Jamie Scherrer
**Ex VP:* James M Cummins
Board of Directors: Jamie Scherrer, Jim Smith, Robert Tiberend

SOUTHEASTERN LIFESTYLES FITNES
See SOUTHEASTERN REGIONAL MEDICAL CENTER

D-U-N-S 06-547-0684
SOUTHEASTERN LOUISIANA UNIVERSITY
500 Ned Mcgehee Dr, Hammond, LA 70402-0001
Tel (985) 549-2068 *Founded/Ownrshp* 1925
Sales 91.3MM *EMP* 1,831
SIC 8221 University
Pr: John Crain
**VP:* Stephen Smith
Exec: Wendy Johns

SOUTHEASTERN MED
See SOUTHEASTERN OHIO REGIONAL MEDICAL CENTER

D-U-N-S 00-777-3823
SOUTHEASTERN MICHIGAN RURAL ELECTRIC COOPERATIVE
1610 E Maumee St, Adrian, MI 49221-3584
Tel (517) 263-1808 *Founded/Ownrshp* 1937
Sales 167.4MM^E *EMP* 395
SIC 4911 Distribution, electric power
Pr: Les Teel
**Pr:* Les Steel

SOUTHEASTERN MILLS DIVISION
See SOUTHEASTERN MILLS INC

D-U-N-S 00-332-2229 IMP
SOUTHEASTERN MILLS INC
SOUTHEASTERN MILLS DIVISION
333 Old Lindale Rd Se, Rome, GA 30161-6769
Tel (706) 291-6528 *Founded/Ownrshp* 1972
Sales 89.6MM^E *EMP* 215
SIC 2099 2041 5149 2045 Gravy mixes, dry; Wheat flour; Corn meal; Bread & bread-type roll mixes; Flour; Prepared flour mixes & doughs
CEO: Vernon D Grizzard
**Pr:* Linda G Owens
Pr: Tim Tejada
**CFO:* Peter W Hjort
Ch: Ken Bingham
Sr VP: Trena Keys
VP: Ralph Byers
VP: Bruce Crist
VP Opers: Lon Peterson
Mtls Mgr: Coni Carey
Prd Mgr: Greg Lane

D-U-N-S 00-328-1862 IMP
SOUTHEASTERN NEWSPAPERS CO LLC (GA)
AUGUSTA CHRONICLE, THE
(*Suby of* BESTREADGUIDE.COM) ★
725 Broad St, Augusta, GA 30901-1336
Tel (706) 722-0011 *Founded/Ownrshp* 1955, 1970
Sales 129.5MM^E *EMP* 1,700
SIC 2711 Newspapers, publishing & printing
Ch Bd: William S Morris III
**Pr:* William S Morris IV
VP: Edward Skinner
Genl Mgr: John Winter
MIS Dir: Lowell Dorn
Prd Dir: Pat McCue
Sales Exec: Will McCranie
Sls&Mrk Ex: Lark Lux
Mktg Mgr: Larry Younginer

D-U-N-S 07-502-6468
SOUTHEASTERN OHIO REGIONAL MEDICAL CENTER
SOUTHEASTERN MED
1341 Clark St, Cambridge, OH 43725-9614
Tel (740) 439-3561 *Founded/Ownrshp* 1985
Sales 198.6MM^E *EMP* 660
Accts Tucker & Tucker Cpas Llc Camb
SIC 8062 General medical & surgical hospitals
Pr: Raymond Chorey
**Pr:* Raymond Chorey
**CFO:* Donald Huelskamp
IT Man: Jeff Hayes
Mtls Dir: Doug Gotschall
Nutrtnst: Sneha Patadia
Nrsg Dir: Tim Sinfield
HC Dir: Ron Cobb

D-U-N-S 04-912-3987 IMP
SOUTHEASTERN PAPER GROUP INC
50 Old Blackstock Rd, Spartanburg, SC 29301-5571
Tel (800) 858-7230 *Founded/Ownrshp* 1969
Sales 313.4MM^E *EMP* 339
SIC 5113 Industrial & personal service paper; Bags, paper & disposable plastic; Boxes, paperboard & disposable plastic; Containers, paper & disposable plastic
Ch Bd: E Lewis Miller Sr
**Pr:* E Lewis Miller Jr
CFO: Jim Heatherly
Ex VP: Andrew Miller
VP: Patrick Rourke
Rgnl Mgr: David Anderson
Dir IT: Lewis Mann
Dir IT: Eric Moe
Sls Dir: Taylor Smith
Manager: Bill Clayton
Manager: Eric Palmer

D-U-N-S 04-454-3841
SOUTHEASTERN PENNSYLVANIA TRANSPORTATION AUTHORITY
SEPTA
1234 Market St Fl 4, Philadelphia, PA 19107-3701
Tel (215) 580-7800 *Founded/Ownrshp* 1964
Sales 479.6MM^E^ *EMP* 9,000
SIC 4111 Local & suburban transit
Ch: Deon T Pasquale Sr
**CFO:* Richard Burnfield
CFO: Richard G Burnfield
Treas: Faye L Mitchell Moore
Ofcr: John McGee
Ofcr: Heather Redfern
**VP:* Thomas E Babcock
VP: Mark Camerote
**Prin:* Daniel Kubik
**Prin:* Faye L M Moore
Ex Dir: Howard Patton
Board of Directors: Wallace Nunn, Linda K Caracappa Esq, Michael J O'donoghue Esq, Pasquale T Deon Sr, James J Rohn, Stewart Greenleaf, James C Schwartzman, Thomas Killion, Richard Voith, Daniel J Kubik, Herman M Wooden, Karen L Martynick, Robert T Wooten, Frank G Mc Cartney, Mario Mele, Jettie D Newkirk Esq

D-U-N-S 07-201-0028 IMP
SOUTHEASTERN REGIONAL MEDICAL CENTER
SOUTHEASTERN LIFESTYLES FITNES
300 W 27th St, Lumberton, NC 28358-3075
Tel (910) 671-5000 *Founded/Ownrshp* 1946
Sales 267.5MM *EMP* 2,000
SIC 8062 General medical & surgical hospitals
CEO: Joann Anderson
**CFO:* Charles Thomas Johnson III
CFO: Thomas C Johnson
VP: Teresa B Fache
VP: Andrew Schwartz
Exec: Natalie Russ
Dir IT: Rhonda Carter
IT Man: Lauren Metzger
Mtls Mgr: Ronald Allen
Psych: Jason Godaire
Pathlgst: Walter B Walek

D-U-N-S 13-194-9422
SOUTHEASTERN UNIVERSITIES RESEARCH ASSOCIATION INC
SURA
1201 New York Ave Nw # 430, Washington, DC 20005-3917
Tel (202) 408-7872 *Founded/Ownrshp* 1980
Sales 161.3MM *EMP* 700
Accts Kpmg Llp Mclean Va
SIC 8741 Management services
Pr: Jerry P Draayer
**CFO:* Peter Bjonerud
VP: Clair Goldsmith
CIO: Betty Leydon

D-U-N-S 83-854-0342
SOUTHEASTERN VENTURES INC
DIRECTTV HOME SVCS SOUTHEAST
4803 29th Ave Ste B, Meridian, MS 39305-2675
Tel (601) 693-0900 *Founded/Ownrshp* 1992
Sales 87.5MM *EMP* 350
SIC 1799 Antenna installation
Pr: Herbert Bruister

D-U-N-S 01-994-9341
SOUTHEASTRANS INC
4751 Best Rd Ste 140, Atlanta, GA 30337-5616
Tel (404) 209-4000 *Founded/Ownrshp* 2000
Sales 103.8MM *EMP* 200
Accts Porter Keadle Moore Llc Atlan
SIC 8742 Transportation consultant
CEO: Steve R Adams
**COO:* Moreland Adams
**CFO:* Gary Kinard
**VP:* Benjie Alexander
CIO: Jim Degliumberto
Opers Mgr: Deardra Gaines

SOUTHERN ABRASIVES
See INDUSTRIAL FINISHES & SYSTEMS INC

D-U-N-S 80-860-2929
■ SOUTHERN AIR HOLDINGS INC
(*Suby of* ATLAS AIR WORLDWIDE HOLDINGS INC) ★
7310 Turfway Rd Ste 400, Florence, KY 41042-4911
Tel (859) 568-9200 *Founded/Ownrshp* 2016
Sales 93.7MM^E^ *EMP* 305^E^
SIC 4522 4581 Air cargo carriers, nonscheduled; Airports, flying fields & services
CEO: Daniel McHugh
**COO:* Paul Chase

D-U-N-S 00-681-2820
SOUTHERN AIR INC
2655 Lakeside Dr, Lynchburg, VA 24501-6944
Tel (434) 385-6200 *Founded/Ownrshp* 1946
Sales 216.4MM^E^ *EMP* 800
SIC 1711 1731 Mechanical contractor; General electrical contractor
Pr: Paul R Denham
**CFO:* Robert W Burrill Jr
Ofcr: Lisa Phillips
**VP:* Charles T Cardwell
VP: Bill Hankins
Sfty Dirs: Tom Stafford
Opers Mgr: Chris Blankenship
S&M/VP: Jeff Lindsay
Board of Directors: Gregory A Graham, William P Hankins, Ronald G Kidd, William E Maddox, James E Moses, Lester B Wilkinson

D-U-N-S 07-251-2101
■ SOUTHERN AIR INC
(*Suby of* WORLDWIDE AIR LOGISTICS GROUP INC) ★
7310 Turfway Rd Ste 400, Florence, KY 41042-4911
Tel (859) 568-9200 *Founded/Ownrshp* 2007
Sales 85.0MM^E^ *EMP* 300^E^
SIC 4522 Air cargo carriers, nonscheduled
CEO: Daniel McHugh
COO: Paul Chase
CFO: Fred Deleeuw
Sr VP: Jon Olin
Board of Directors: Hank Halter, Caitlin H Melchior, Jonathan G Ornstein, Robert A Peiser

D-U-N-S 95-997-2522
■ SOUTHERN ASSISTED LIVING INC
(*Suby of* BROOKDALE SENIOR LIVING) ★
6737 W Wa St Ste 2300, Milwaukee, WI 53214-5650
Tel (414) 588-0431 *Founded/Ownrshp* 2006
Sales 38.1MM^E^ *EMP* 2,000
SIC 6513 Apartment building operators
CEO: Christopher Hollister
**Pr:* Stephen Morton
Ex Dir: Karen Mosley
Ex Dir: Dennis Toney
S&M/VP: Doug Whitman
Board of Directors: Christopher Hollister, Stephen Morton, Chris Rio

SOUTHERN AUTO AUCTION
See SOUTHERN AUTO SALES INC

D-U-N-S 01-884-7210
SOUTHERN AUTO SALES INC
SOUTHERN AUTO AUCTION
161 S Main St, East Windsor, CT 06088-9702
Tel (860) 292-7500 *Founded/Ownrshp* 1955
Sales 221.8MM^E^ *EMP* 900
SIC 5012 Automobile auction
Pr: Lawrence G Tribble
**VP:* Carolyn Tribble Hudkins
**VP:* Garrison Hudkins
**VP:* Rick Nadeau
Genl Mgr: Lauren Giaccone
Dir IT: Michael Penda
Software D: William Saltzgiver
Sftwr Eng: David Crockett
Opers Mgr: Steve Phillips
Board of Directors: Candace Tribble

D-U-N-S 12-262-6187
■ SOUTHERN BAKERIES INC
BUTTERKRUST BAKERIES
(*Suby of* FLOWERS FOODS INC) ★
3355 W Memorial Blvd, Lakeland, FL 33815-1084
Tel (863) 682-1155 *Founded/Ownrshp* 2008
Sales 277.3MM^E^ *EMP* 800
SIC 2051 5149 Breads, rolls & buns; Bakery products
Pr: Doug Wimberly
**VP:* Rob Hancock
Exec: Shea Brock
VP Sls: George Abel

D-U-N-S 36-198-6412
SOUTHERN BAKERIES LLC
(*Suby of* HARLAN BAKERIES LLC) ★
2700 E 3rd St, Hope, AR 71801-6237
Tel (870) 777-9031 *Founded/Ownrshp* 2005
Sales 192.1MM^E^ *EMP* 425
SIC 5149 Bakery products
COO: Albert S Gaton

D-U-N-S 18-908-8883
SOUTHERN BANCSHARES (NC) INC
116 E Main St, Mount Olive, NC 28365-2113
Tel (919) 658-7000 *Founded/Ownrshp* 1986
Sales NA *EMP* 432
Accts Dixon Hughes Pllc Greenville
SIC 6022 State commercial banks
CEO: J Grey Morgan
**Pr:* Drew M Covert
**CFO:* Davis A Bean
**CFO:* Dan R Ellis Jr
VP: Jerry Alexander
**VP:* Michael T Bryant
**VP:* R D Ray
VP: Brandon Strickland

D-U-N-S 07-758-2369
SOUTHERN BAPTIST HOSPITAL OF FLORIDA INC
WOLFSON CHILDREN'S HOSPITAL
800 Prudential Dr, Jacksonville, FL 32207-8202
Tel (904) 202-2000 *Founded/Ownrshp* 1983
Sales 442.1MM^E^ *EMP* 4,000
Accts Ernst & Young Llp Jacksonvil
SIC 8062 Hospital, medical school affiliated with residency
Pr: Hugh Greene
**COO:* Johm Wilbanks
**Ch:* M C Harden
**Sec:* Richard L Sisisky
Ex VP: Carol Thompson
**VP:* Harvey Granger
**VP:* John Wilbanks
Snr Ntwrk: Rich Gassett
Snr Ntwrk: Mark Green
Dir IT: Jim Bilsky
Dir IT: Maribeth Brannan

SOUTHERN BATH & KITCHEN CENTER
See SOUTHERN PIPE & SUPPLY CO INC

D-U-N-S 96-452-8496
SOUTHERN CAL SCHOOLS VOL EMP BENEFITS ASSOC
8885 Rio San Diego Dr # 327, San Diego, CA 92108-1624
Tel (619) 278-0021 *Founded/Ownrshp* 2010
Sales 598.3MM *EMP* 8^E^
Accts Rosner Brown Touchstone & Kell
SIC 8211 Elementary & secondary schools
Prin: George McGregor

D-U-N-S 07-529-1633
SOUTHERN CAL UNITED FOOD & COMMERCIAL WORKERS UNIONS & FOOD EMPLOYERS PENSION TRUST FUND
U F C PENSION TRUST FUND
6425 Katella Ave, Cypress, CA 90630-5246
Tel (714) 220-2297 *Founded/Ownrshp* 1957
Sales NA *EMP* 240
Accts Hemming Morse Cpa S And Consul
SIC 6371 Pension funds

D-U-N-S 17-497-2224 IMP
SOUTHERN CALIFORNIA DISCOUNT TIRE CO INC
(*Suby of* DISCOUNT TIRE) ★
5310 E Shea Blvd, Scottsdale, AZ 85254-4700
Tel (480) 606-6000 *Founded/Ownrshp* 1985
Sales 21.9M^E^ *EMP* 9,430
SIC 5531 Automotive tires
Ch Bd: Bruce T Halle
**CEO:* Thomas Englert
**CFO:* Christian Roe
**Prin:* Robert Holman Jr
IT Man: Michael Smith
IT Man: Trevor Spears

D-U-N-S 00-690-8818
■ SOUTHERN CALIFORNIA EDISON CO
(*Suby of* EDISON INTERNATIONAL) ★
2244 Walnut Grove Ave, Rosemead, CA 91770-3714
Tel (626) 302-1212 *Founded/Ownrshp* 1909
Sales 11.4MMM *EMP* 12,678
SIC 4911 Generation, electric power; Transmission, electric power; Distribution, electric power
CEO: Kevin M Payne
Pr: Ronald O Nichols
CFO: William Petmecky
Sr VP: Peter T Dietrich
Sr VP: Stuart R Hemphill
Sr VP: Russell C Swartz
VP: Connie J Erickson
VP: Marc Ulrich
Board of Directors: Brett White, Vanessa C L Chang, Louis Hernandez Jr, James T Morris, Pedro J Pizarro, Richard T Schlosberg III, Linda G Stuntz, William P Sullivan, Ellen Tauscher, Peter J Taylor

D-U-N-S 00-690-8826
■ SOUTHERN CALIFORNIA GAS CO (CA)
GAS COMPANY, THE
(*Suby of* PACIFIC ENTERPRISES) ★
555 W 5th St Fl 31, Los Angeles, CA 90013-1018
Tel (213) 244-1200 *Founded/Ownrshp* 1910
Sales 3.4MMM *EMP* 8,196^E^
SIC 4924 4922 4932 Natural gas distribution; Natural gas transmission; Gas & other services combined
CEO: Debra L Reed
Pr: Mark A Snell
CFO: Robert M Schlax
Ex VP: Steven D Davis
Ex VP: Joseph A Householder
Sr VP: Erbin B Keith
Sr VP: Anne S Mith
Sr VP: Anne Mith
VP: Justin C Bird
VP: Lee Schavrien
Software D: Ronald Johnson
Board of Directors: Joseph A Householder, Martha B Wyrsch

D-U-N-S 79-822-3624
■ SOUTHERN CALIFORNIA GAS TOWER INC
(*Suby of* GAS COMPANY THE) ★
555 W 5th St Ste 1700, Los Angeles, CA 90013-1083
Tel (213) 244-1200 *Founded/Ownrshp* 1987
Sales 115.7MM^E^ *EMP* 1,000
SIC 4924 Natural gas distribution
Pr: Ed Guiles
VP: Margot Kyd

D-U-N-S 80-199-5239
SOUTHERN CALIFORNIA HEALTHCARE SYSTEM INC
3415 S Sepulveda Blvd # 9, Los Angeles, CA 90034-6060
Tel (310) 943-4500 *Founded/Ownrshp* 1998
Sales 32.6MM^E^ *EMP* 1,000
SIC 8062 General medical & surgical hospitals
CEO: David R Topper

D-U-N-S 06-380-6194
SOUTHERN CALIFORNIA HOSPITAL AT CULVER CITY
BROTMAN MEDICAL PARTNERS
(*Suby of* PROSPECT MEDICAL HOLDINGS INC) ★
3828 Delmas Ter, Culver City, CA 90232-2713
Tel (310) 836-7000 *Founded/Ownrshp* 2005
Sales 157.2MM^E^ *EMP* 1,000^E^
SIC 8062 General medical & surgical hospitals
CEO: Barbara Schneider
Chf Rad: Peter Pop
**Pr:* Howard H Levine
Pathlgst: Inderjit Deol
Surgeon: Joseph Page
Surgeon: Rajan Patel
Opthamlgy: Casimiro Gonzalez
Opthamlgy: Melinda Hakim
Nrsg Dir: Katherine Cass
HC Dir: Larry L Smith

D-U-N-S 07-226-6448
SOUTHERN CALIFORNIA PERMANENTE MEDICAL GROUP
KAISER PERMANENTE
393 Walnut Dr, Pasadena, CA 91107-4922
Tel (626) 405-5704 *Founded/Ownrshp* 1945
Sales NA *EMP* 7,969
SIC 6324 Hospital & medical service plans

D-U-N-S 06-992-5345
SOUTHERN CALIFORNIA PRESBYTERIAN HOMES
516 Burchett St, Glendale, CA 91203-1014
Tel (818) 247-0420 *Founded/Ownrshp* 1955
Sales 79.2MM *EMP* 1,500
SIC 8051 Skilled nursing care facilities
CEO: John H Cochrane
**CEO:* Gerald W Dingivan
CFO: Howard Korwes
**Treas:* Ruben Grigorians
Bd of Dir: Dan Hutson
Bd of Dir: Tom Le
VP: Benjamin F Beckler III
Mktg Dir: Randy Allison

D-U-N-S 12-691-0079
SOUTHERN CALIFORNIA RISK MANAGEMENT ASSOCIATES INC
YORK
(*Suby of* ODYSSEY INVESTMENT PARTNERS LLC) ★
99 Cherry Hill Rd Ste 102, Parsippany, NJ 07054-1102
Tel (973) 541-1330 *Founded/Ownrshp* 2006
Sales NA *EMP* 670
SIC 6411 Insurance agents, brokers & service
Pr: Anthony Galioto
**Pr:* Mark Aussicker
**Pr:* Doug Markham
**Pr:* Richard H Taketa
**CFO:* Jeffrey H Marshall
CFO: David Panico
**Ex VP:* Jim Sweeney
**Sr VP:* Ritchie Vener
VP: Gary Arabian
VP: Tom Baber
VP: Terry Camp

D-U-N-S 94-723-7616
SOUTHERN CARE INC
1000 Urban Center Dr # 115, Vestavia, AL 35242-2532
Tel (205) 868-4400 *Founded/Ownrshp* 1987
Sales 43.4MM^E^ *EMP* 1,700
SIC 8082 Home health care services
Pr: Marie A King
**Sr VP:* Richard Duren
**Sr VP:* Jeff Lang
**VP:* Theresa Bush
**VP:* Robert Smoot

SOUTHERN CARLSON
See CARLSON SYSTEMS HOLDINGS INC

SOUTHERN CASEARTS
See SOUTHERN STORE FIXTURES INC

SOUTHERN CENTRIFUGAL DIV
See METALTEK INTERNATIONAL INC

D-U-N-S 80-713-8768 IMP/EXP
SOUTHERN CHAMPION TRAY LP
220 Compress St, Chattanooga, TN 37405-3724
Tel (423) 756-5121 *Founded/Ownrshp* 1998
Sales 133.9MM^E^ *EMP* 550
SIC 2675 Paperboard die-cutting
Ch Bd: Chuck Zeiser
Pt: John M Zeiser
Pr: Bruce Zeiser
CFO: Mark Longnecker
VP: Pat McKinney
Exec: Martha Martinez
Exec: Marty Miller
Dist Mgr: Ron Couvillon
Dist Mgr: Steve Gibson
Genl Mgr: James Miller
CTO: Curt Rowel

D-U-N-S 00-692-5341
▲ SOUTHERN CO (GA)
30 Ivan Allen Jr Blvd Nw, Atlanta, GA 30308-3055
Tel (404) 506-5000 *Founded/Ownrshp* 1945
Sales 17.4MMM *EMP* 27,196^E^
Tkr Sym SO *Exch* NYS
SIC 4911 Generation, electric power; Transmission, electric power; Distribution, electric power
Ch Bd: Thomas A Fanning
V Ch: Michael Christie
Pr: Stephen Bennett
Pr: Ron Bertasi
Pr: Oscar C Harper
COO: Kimberly S Greene
CFO: Art P Beattie
Bd of Dir: Henry Clark
Bd of Dir: Jeff Orgeron
Bd of Dir: Euel J Wood
Ex VP: W Paul Bowers
Ex VP: Martin B Davis
Ex VP: Michael D Garrett
Ex VP: James Y Kerr II
Ex VP: Penny M Manuel
Ex VP: Charles D McCrary
Ex VP: David M Ratcliffe
Sr VP: Bryan D Anderson
Sr VP: Ronnie Bates
Sr VP: James P Heilbron
Sr VP: Doug Jones
Board of Directors: William G Smith Jr, Juanita Powell Baranco, Steven R Specker, Jon A Boscia, Larry D Thompson, Henry A Clark III, Jennifer Wood III, Veronica M Hagen, David J Grain, Warren A Hood Jr, Linda P Hudson, Donald M James, John D Johns, Dale E Klein

D-U-N-S 93-395-6211
■ SOUTHERN CO GAS
(*Suby of* SOUTHERN CO) ★
10 Peachtree Pl Ne, Atlanta, GA 30309-4497
Tel (404) 584-4000 *Founded/Ownrshp* 2016
Sales 3.9MMM *EMP* 5,203
SIC 4922 4924 Natural gas transmission; Pipelines, natural gas; Storage, natural gas; Natural gas distribution
Pr: Andrew W Evans
Pr: Melvin D Williams
**CFO:* Elizabeth W Reese
**Treas:* Steve Cave
**Ex VP:* Henry P Linginfelter
**Ex VP:* Paul R Shlanta
**Ex VP:* Peter Tumminello
Sr VP: Bryan Batson
Sr VP: Jim Kibler
Sr VP: Marshall Lang
**Sr VP:* Ron Lepionka
**Sr VP:* Joseph A Surber III
Sr VP: Jay Sutton
VP: Jeffrey Howell
VP: Dan Lambright
VP: Jorge Martinez
**Exec:* Scott Carter

D-U-N-S 07-546-3174
■ SOUTHERN CO SERVICES INC
(*Suby of* SOUTHERN CO) ★
30 Ivan Allen Jr Blvd Nw, Atlanta, GA 30308-3055
Tel (404) 506-5000 *Founded/Ownrshp* 1963
Sales 614.3MM^E^ *EMP* 3,021
SIC 8711 Engineering services

Pr: Mark S Lantrip
**Ch:* Thomas A Fanning
Bd of Dir: John Ward
**Ofcr:* Theodore J McCullough
**Ex VP:* Martin B Davis
Ex VP: Paula M Marino
**Sr VP:* Larry S Monroe
**VP:* Tommy Chisolm
**VP:* Tom Wilson
Dir IT: Steven Gray
Software D: Linda Middleton

D-U-N-S 87-754-3462
■ SOUTHERN COMMUNICATIONS SERVICES INC
SOUTHERN L
(*Suby of* SOUTHERN CO) ★
5555 Glenridge Connector, Atlanta, GA 30342-4759
Tel (678) 443-1500 *Founded/Ownrshp* 1996
Sales 163.5MM^E *EMP* 500
SIC 4813 4812 Telephone communication, except radio; Radio telephone communication
Pr: Donald Horsley
CFO: Carmine Reppucci
**CFO:* Carmine Rettucci
**VP:* Rodney Johnson
VP: Julie Pigot
**VP:* Julie T Pigott
IT Man: Robert Bennett
VP Sls: Rodney H Johnson

D-U-N-S 00-494-5259
■ SOUTHERN CONNECTICUT GAS CO
(*Suby of* UIL HOLDINGS CORP) ★
77 Hartland St Ste 405, East Hartford, CT 06108-3259
Tel (800) 659-8299 *Founded/Ownrshp* 1967, 2010
Sales 176.9MM^E *EMP* 275^E
SIC 4924 Natural gas distribution
Pr: Robert M Allessio
VP: Don Hannibal
VP: Earnest Karkut
VP: Peter Loomis
Pr Mgr: David McGill

D-U-N-S 00-128-8455 IMP/EXP
■ SOUTHERN COPPER CORP
SCC
(*Suby of* AMERICAS MINING CORP) ★
1440 E Missouri Ave # 160, Phoenix, AZ 85014-2458
Tel (602) 264-1375 *Founded/Ownrshp* 1960
Sales 5.0MMM *EMP* 13,024^E
Accts Galaz Yamazaki Ruiz Urquiza
Tkr Sym SCCO *Exch* NYS
SIC 1021 3331 1031 1061 1044 Copper ore mining & preparation; Open pit copper ore mining; Primary copper; Zinc ores mining; Molybdenum ores mining; Silver ores mining
Pr: Oscar Gonzalez Rocha
**Ch Bd:* German Larrea Mota-Velasco
CFO: Raul Jacob Ruisanchez
VP: Javier Gomez Aguilar
VP: Juan Rodriguez Arriaga
VP: Vidal Muhech Dip
Exec: Edgard Corrales Aguilar

D-U-N-S 04-659-2507
SOUTHERN COUNTIES OIL CO
SC FUELS
1800 W Katella Ave # 400, Orange, CA 92867-3449
Tel (714) 744-7140 *Founded/Ownrshp* 1969
Sales 1.0MMM^E *EMP* 624
SIC 5171 5541 5172 Petroleum bulk stations; Gasoline service stations; Petroleum products
CEO: Frank P Greinke
**Pr:* Steve Greinke
**COO:* David Larimer
**CFO:* Mimi Taylor
CFO: Mimi S Taylor
VP: Rick Bullock
VP: Frank Hyson
Rgnl Mgr: Mark Scheerer
CIO: Charles Lee
CTO: Stephen Deal
Manager: Christopher Willig

SOUTHERN CRES BHVORAL MEDICINE
See SOUTHERN REGIONAL MEDICAL CENTER

D-U-N-S 94-310-9777 IMP
SOUTHERN EAGLE SALES & SERVICE LP
(*Suby of* SOUTHERN EAGLE SALES MANAGEMENT LLC) ★
5300 Blair St, Metairie, LA 70003-2406
Tel (504) 733-8656 *Founded/Ownrshp* 2009
Sales 114.5MM^E *EMP* 207
SIC 5181 Beer & other fermented malt liquors
Pt: Joel C Champagne
VP: Gary Penzato
VP: Gerard Peters
VP Opers: Herman Scallan
Natl Sales: Lou Provenzano
VP Sls: Bert Bahlinger
Sls Mgr: Jamie Caldcleugh

D-U-N-S 07-844-4768
SOUTHERN EAGLE SALES MANAGEMENT LLC
5300 Blair St, Metairie, LA 70003-2406
Tel (504) 733-8656 *Founded/Ownrshp* 2009
Sales 114.5MM^E *EMP* 207
SIC 5181 Beer & other fermented malt liquors
Pt: Patrick Mockler

D-U-N-S 00-690-0492 IMP
■ SOUTHERN ELECTRIC GENERATING CO (AL)
(*Suby of* ALABAMA POWER CO) ★
600 18th St N, Birmingham, AL 35203-2206
Tel (205) 257-1000 *Founded/Ownrshp* 1956
Sales 2.2MMM^E *EMP* 29^E
SIC 4911 Generation, electric power
Pr: Charles McCrary
Pr: Julia Segars
**Treas:* Randy Derieux
VP: Ephraim Stockdale
Genl Mgr: Don Roberts
IT Man: Glenn Barr
IT Man: Cheryl Thompson
Netwrk Mgr: Mark Kuester
Sfty Dirs: Christopher Fitzgerald
Secur Mgr: Wooten Keith
Mktg Dir: Catherine Staggs
Board of Directors: Earl B Parsons Jr, Robert Boyer, Randy Derieux, H Allen Franklin, B M Guthrie, Elmer Harris, Robert Haubein Jr, Bruce Hutchins, Warren Y Jobe, Charles D McCrary

D-U-N-S 00-983-6271 EXP
SOUTHERN ELECTRIC SUPPLY CO INC
REXEL
301 46th Ct, Meridian, MS 39305-2812
Tel (601) 693-4141 *Founded/Ownrshp* 1946
Sales NA *EMP* 1,608
SIC 5063

SOUTHERN ENERGY DIVISION
See COUGAR OIL INC

D-U-N-S 04-298-3148
■ SOUTHERN ENERGY HOMES INC
SOUTHERN ESTATES
(*Suby of* CMH MANUFACTURING INC) ★
144 Corporate Way, Addison, AL 35540
Tel (256) 747-8589 *Founded/Ownrshp* 1982, 2006
Sales 585.0MM^E *EMP* 2,304
SIC 2451 5271 Mobile homes; Mobile homes
Pr: Keith O Holdbrooks
**Ex VP:* Dan Batchelor
VP: Dan Bathelor
Genl Mgr: John Tedder
Genl Mgr: Ralph Trallo

D-U-N-S 18-755-0330
SOUTHERN ENVIRONMENTAL INC
6690 W Nine Mile Rd, Pensacola, FL 32526-3211
Tel (850) 944-4475 *Founded/Ownrshp* 1973
Sales 128.6MM *EMP* 30
Accts Saltmarsh Cleaveland & Gund
SIC 3822 Thermostats & other environmental sensors
Pr: Michael W Hatsfelt
VP: John Cain
**VP:* Johnny L Jernigan
Ql Cn Mgr: Anthony Bennett
Snr PM: John Carson

SOUTHERN EQUIPMENT COMPANY INC
See ARGOS READY MIX (CAROLINAS) CORP

SOUTHERN ESTATES
See SOUTHERN ENERGY HOMES INC

D-U-N-S 36-380-4217
SOUTHERN FAMILY MARKETS LLC
PIGGLY WIGGLY
7 Corporate Dr, Keene, NH 03431-5042
Tel (973) 605-6381 *Founded/Ownrshp* 2005
Sales 67.6MM^E *EMP* 1,500
SIC 5411 Supermarkets, chain

D-U-N-S 00-696-4480
SOUTHERN FARM BUREAU CASUALTY INSURANCE CO
FARM BUREAU INSURANCE
1800 E County Line Rd, Ridgeland, MS 39157-1916
Tel (601) 957-3200 *Founded/Ownrshp* 1947
Sales NA *EMP* 1,500
SIC 6411 Insurance agents, brokers & service
CEO: Robert Jaratt
**Treas:* Judy Blackburn
Treas: Judy G Blackburn
Treas: Mack Stallings
Bd of Dir: E F Dunton
**Sr VP:* Dennis Griffin
**Sr VP:* Steve Ingram
VP: Kimberly Blackburn
VP: Carl Derrick
VP: Tommy Lee
VP: Frank Leonard
VP: Bill Lepine
VP: Geoff Mercer
VP: Matt Packham
VP: Laura W Sphr
VP: Lydia Warren
VP: Steve Williams
VP: David Wylie
VP: Elbert Young
Assoc Dir: Scott Catington

D-U-N-S 00-696-4498
SOUTHERN FARM BUREAU LIFE INSURANCE CO INC (MS)
FARM BUREAU INSURANCE
1401 Livingston Ln, Jackson, MS 39213-8098
Tel (601) 981-7422 *Founded/Ownrshp* 1946
Sales NA *EMP* 600
SIC 6411 Insurance agents, brokers & service
CEO: Larry Favreau
**Pr:* Carl B Loop Jr
Ex VP: Wynne Jacobs
**Sr VP:* Gino Gianfrancesco
VP: Gail Chisum
VP: Walter J Olson
**VP:* Joe Purvis
Mktg Dir: Matt Ginn
Corp Couns: Chadwick Russell

D-U-N-S 18-796-5439 IMP
SOUTHERN FASTENING SYSTEMS LLC
SOUTHERNCARLSON
(*Suby of* SOUTHERNCARLSON) ★
635 Fairgrounds Rd, Muscle Shoals, AL 35661-3598
Tel (256) 381-3628 *Founded/Ownrshp* 2006
Sales 100.0MM^E *EMP* 347^E
SIC 5084 5085 5251 5072 Compressors, except air conditioning; Staplers & tackers; Tools, hand; Hardware
CEO: K G Sims
**Pr:* Jim Whitley
**CFO:* Philip Fowler
Genl Mgr: Bobby Strickland
Sales Exec: Steve Lee
Sls Mgr: James Frye

SOUTHERN FOODS
See MEAT AND SEAFOOD SOLUTIONS LLC

D-U-N-S 17-412-7555
■ SOUTHERN FOODS GROUP LLC
(*Suby of* DEAN FOODS CO) ★
3114 S Haskell Ave, Dallas, TX 75223-3121
Tel (214) 824-8163 *Founded/Ownrshp* 2000
Sales 293.1MM^E *EMP* 1,000^E
SIC 2026 Cream, sour; Cottage cheese
CEO: Gregg A Tanner
**CFO:* Patrick Ford
**VP:* Rachel A Gonzalez
**VP:* Timothy A Smith

D-U-N-S 00-323-0240
SOUTHERN FOODS INC
CULINAIRE FLAIR
3500 Old Battlegrd Rd A, Greensboro, NC 27410-2498
Tel (336) 545-3800 *Founded/Ownrshp* 1992
Sales 134.1MM^E *EMP* 600
SIC 5147 5143 5146 5148 5142 Meats & meat products; Cheese; Seafoods; Vegetables, fresh; Meat, frozen: packaged; Fish, frozen: packaged; Vegetables, frozen
CEO: Mac Sullivan
**Pr:* H Trey Pounders
**CFO:* Steven Elliot
**Prin:* Keith Kantor

D-U-N-S 03-153-1387
SOUTHERN FOODSERVICE MANAGEMENT INC
500 Office Park Dr # 210, Mountain Brk, AL 35223-2441
Tel (205) 871-8000 *Founded/Ownrshp* 1951
Sales 56.3MM^E *EMP* 1,000
SIC 5812 5962

D-U-N-S 78-508-2509
SOUTHERN FULFILLMENT SERVICES LLC
HALE INDIAN RIVER GROVES
1650 90th Ave, Vero Beach, FL 32966-6614
Tel (772) 226-3500 *Founded/Ownrshp* 2006
Sales 377.8MM^E *EMP* 1,000^E
SIC 5148 5149 Fruits, fresh; Food gift baskets
CEO: Don Wright
Pr: Michael Hickey
**CEO:* Alex Brown
Bd of Dir: Tom Mitchell
**Ex VP:* Andy Graham
**VP:* Bob Daberkow
**VP:* John Schepers
VP: Keith Tyson
IT Man: Dave Brumit
IT Man: Jamie Dixon
Ql Cn Mgr: John Dorst

D-U-N-S 05-855-5897 IMP/EXP
SOUTHERN GLAZERS WINE AND SPIRITS LLC (FL)
1600 Nw 163rd St, Miami, FL 33169-5641
Tel (305) 625-4171 *Founded/Ownrshp* 1968
Sales 5.1MMM^E *EMP* 10,300
SIC 5182 5181 Wine & distilled beverages; Wine; Liquor; Bottling wines & liquors; Beer & ale
CEO: Wayne E Chaplin
**Ch Bd:* Harvey R Chaplin
**Pr:* Shelly Stein
**COO:* Brad Vassar
**Treas:* Steven R Becker
Ofcr: George Fisher
Ex VP: Jack Brennan
Ex VP: Will Conniff
**Ex VP:* Lee Hager
**Ex VP:* Rudolf Ruiz
Ex VP: Chuck Silio
Ex VP: John Wittig
Sr VP: Kevin Fennessey
Sr VP: Barry Goldberg
Sr VP: Michael W Head
Sr VP: W Michael Head
VP: James Allen
VP: Randy Barnhart
VP: Steve Bonavita
VP: Tom Collins
VP: Daniel Daul

D-U-N-S 82-891-6960 IMP
SOUTHERN GLAZERS WINE AND SPIRITS OF ARIZONA LLC
(*Suby of* SGWSNHC LLC) ★
2375 S 45th Ave, Phoenix, AZ 85043-3900
Tel (602) 533-8000 *Founded/Ownrshp* 1999
Sales 179.4MM^E *EMP* 1^E
SIC 5181 5182 Beer & ale; Wine & distilled beverages

D-U-N-S 07-943-3425
SOUTHERN GLAZERS WINE AND SPIRITS OF CANADA LLC
(*Suby of* SOUTHERN GLAZERS WINE AND SPIRITS LLC) ★
14911 Quorum Dr Ste 150, Dallas, TX 75254-7003
Tel (972) 392-8200 *Founded/Ownrshp* 2013
Sales 1.1MMM^E *EMP* 6,000^E
SIC 5182 Wine & distilled beverages
CEO: Sheldon Stein
COO: Robert Swartz
CFO: Thomas Greenlee
Ex VP: Pete Carr
Ex VP: Mike McLaughlin

D-U-N-S 11-908-2928 IMP
SOUTHERN GLAZERS WINE AND SPIRITS OF ILLINOIS LLC
SOUTHERN WINE SPIRITS ILL INC
(*Suby of* SOUTHERN GLAZERS WINE AND SPIRITS LLC) ★
300 E Crossroads Pkwy, Bolingbrook, IL 60440-3516
Tel (630) 685-3000 *Founded/Ownrshp* 2001
Sales 250.0MM^E *EMP* 710
SIC 5182 Wine; Liquor
Pr: Wayne Chaplin
Ex VP: Will Conniff
VP: Terry Brick
VP: Steven J Taylor
VP: Michael J Thompson
Genl Mgr: Will Conniss
VP Mktg: Ron Foster
Sls Mgr: John McFadden

D-U-N-S 00-792-6538 IMP/EXP
SOUTHERN GLAZERS WINE AND SPIRITS OF TEXAS LLC
GLAZERS WHOLESALE DISTRIBUTORS
(*Suby of* SOUTHERN GLAZERS WINE AND SPIRITS LLC) ★
14911 Quorum Dr Ste 150, Dallas, TX 75254-7003
Tel (972) 392-8200 *Founded/Ownrshp* 1909
Sales 1.8MMM^E *EMP* 6,000
SIC 2082 5182 5199 Beer (alcoholic beverage); Ale (alcoholic beverage); Wine & distilled beverages; General merchandise, non-durable; Art goods & supplies
Pr: Bennett Glazer
**COO:* Robert M Swartz
CFO: Stacy Brown
CFO: Thomas Greenlee
Ex VP: Pete Carr
Ex VP: Alan Greenspan
Ex VP: Mike McLaughlin
VP: Ray Bessinger
VP: Tom Brannen
VP: Ryan Chandler
VP: Matt Metz
VP: Gary Schwartz
VP: Wilemia Shaw
**VP:* Betty Silverman
**VP:* Barkley Stuart
VP: Matt Swilling

D-U-N-S 00-637-7030 IMP
SOUTHERN GRAPHIC SYSTEMS LLC (KY)
KWIKEE
(*Suby of* SGS INTERNATIONAL LLC) ★
626 W Main St Ste 500, Louisville, KY 40202-4269
Tel (502) 637-5443 *Founded/Ownrshp* 1946, 2005
Sales 434.1MM^E *EMP* 1,200
SIC 2796 Platemaking services; Plates & cylinders for rotogravure printing
CEO: Aidan Tracey
**COO:* Luca Naccarato
Ofcr: Karen Scot
**Ex VP:* Marriott Winchester
VP: Greg Horsman
Mng Dir: Cresenciano Maramot
Off Mgr: Cathy Adkins
Opers Mgr: Kristina Makarova
Prd Mgr: Sioux Johannsen
Prd Mgr: Steve Murphy
Mktg Mgr: Jennifer Dwyer

D-U-N-S 04-045-6839
SOUTHERN GRAPHICS INC
(*Suby of* LOGO HOLDINGS II CORP) ★
626 W Main St, Louisville, KY 40202-2972
Tel (502) 637-5443 *Founded/Ownrshp* 2012
Sales 590.0MM^E *EMP* 2,400^E
SIC 7336 7389 Commercial art & graphic design; Printed circuitry graphic layout
Pr: Henry Baughman
Pr: David Gordon
Sr VP: Brian Weissmann
VP: Vic Baranowski
**VP:* James Dahmus
VP: Joe O'Connor
VP: Joe Rebeschi
VP: Ray Shackelford
Genl Mgr: Pat Ryan
CIO: Glenn West
Opers Mgr: Allen McDowell

D-U-N-S 78-617-4649
SOUTHERN HENS INC
327 Moselle Seminary Rd, Moselle, MS 39459-8935
Tel (601) 582-2262 *Founded/Ownrshp* 1989
Sales 148.1MM^E *EMP* 600
SIC 3556 Meat processing machinery
Pr: Ken Primm
**Pr:* Bob Kenney
**Treas:* Mark Kaminsky
**Genl Mgr:* John Comino

D-U-N-S 18-358-2097
SOUTHERN HOSPITALITY INC
3202 1st St, Woodward, OK 73801-6707
Tel (580) 256-7600 *Founded/Ownrshp* 1988
Sales 38.9MM^E *EMP* 1,120
SIC 7011 Hotels & motels
Pr: Robert Slater
Off Mgr: Glenn Krausser
VP Opers: James T Wheeler

D-U-N-S 07-887-8281
SOUTHERN ILLINOIS HEALTHCARE E
2370 N Mcroy Dr, Carbondale, IL 62901-5629
Tel (618) 457-5200 *Founded/Ownrshp* 2013
Sales 528.0MM *EMP* 14^E
Accts Mcgladrey Llp Springfield Il
SIC 8099 Health & allied services

D-U-N-S 13-158-2470
SOUTHERN ILLINOIS HEALTHCARE ENTERPRISES INC
1239 E Main St Ste C, Carbondale, IL 62901-3176
Tel (618) 457-5200 *Founded/Ownrshp* 1983
Sales 1.6MM *EMP* 3,493
Accts Rsm Us Llp Springfield Illin
SIC 8062 General medical & surgical hospitals
CEO: Rex Budde
**CFO:* Mike Kasser
VP: Julie Firman
VP: Phillip Schaefer
VP: Scott Seaborn
**Prin:* Jerry Hickam
Adm Dir: Jim Osborn
Off Mgr: Abby Robinson
CTO: Dena Cook
Surgeon: David Clutts
Doctor: Tandy Korte

D-U-N-S 06-854-8403
SOUTHERN ILLINOIS HOSPITAL SERVICES
MEMORIAL HOSPITAL CARBONDALE
(*Suby of* SOUTHERN ILLINOIS HEALTHCARE ENTERPRISES INC) ★
1239 E Main St Ste C, Carbondale, IL 62901-3176
Tel (618) 457-5200 *Founded/Ownrshp* 1946, 1983
Sales 562.9MM *EMP* 1,200

SIC 8062

D-U-N-S 00-781-3900 IMP
SOUTHERN ILLINOIS POWER CO-OPERATIVE
11543 Lake Of Egypt Rd, Marion, IL 62959-8500
Tel (618) 964-1448 *Founded/Ownrshp* 1948
Sales 204.7MM *EMP* 125E
Accts Baker Tilly Virchow Krause Llp
SIC 4911 ; Generation, electric power
VP: Todd Gallenbach
Exec: Diane Karnes
Genl Mgr: James Webb
Dir IT: Paul Furtak
Opers Mgr: Greg Bain

D-U-N-S 07-196-5214 IMP
SOUTHERN ILLINOIS UNIVERSITY INC
SIUC
(*Suby of* SOUTHERN ILLINOIS UNIVERSITY SYSTEM) ★
1400 Douglas Dr, Carbondale, IL 62901-4332
Tel (618) 536-3475 *Founded/Ownrshp* 1869
Sales 597.8MM *EMP* 9,576
Accts Cliftonlarsonallen Llp Peoria
SIC 8221 University
Pr: Randy J Dunn
Ofcr: Ryan Rosiak
**Sr VP:* Duane Stucky
VP: Elaine Hyden
Genl Mgr: Will Patterson
DP Exec: Rudy Amaro
DP Exec: Carol Clutts
DP Exec: Robert Eads
DP Exec: Paul Lannom
DP Exec: Brenda Lindsey
DP Exec: Joshua Morrison

D-U-N-S 14-394-1909
SOUTHERN ILLINOIS UNIVERSITY SYSTEM
1400 Douglas Dr, Carbondale, IL 62901-4332
Tel (618) 536-3331 *Founded/Ownrshp* 2004
Sales 600.2MME *EMP* 9,576
SIC 8221 Colleges universities & professional schools
Pr: James E Walker
CFO: Duane Stucky
VP: Tracey Jarrell
Exec: Sherri Thomas-Rich
Off Mgr: Janice Swearingen

D-U-N-S 00-517-9411 IMP
SOUTHERN IMPERIAL INC
SUNBELT PLASTIC EXTRUSIONS
1400 Eddy Ave, Rockford, IL 61103-3198
Tel (815) 877-7041 *Founded/Ownrshp* 1962
Sales 132.8MME *EMP* 395
SIC 5046 2542 Store fixtures & display equipment; Fixtures: display, office or store: except wood; Racks, merchandise display or storage: except wood
Pr: Stanley Valiulis
**Pr:* Steven Vandemore
**CFO:* Dale S Thomas
**CFO:* Frank S Wojtowicz
Chf Mktg O: Tracy Bilyeu
Dist Mgr: Gary Rothmeyer
Dir IT: Bruce Browning
VP Opers: Paul Quinn
Opers Mgr: Dale Carroll
Opers Mgr: Todd Miller
Sales Exec: Brian Conroy

D-U-N-S 00-693-7015 IMP
■ **SOUTHERN INDIANA GAS & ELECTRIC CO**
SIGECO
(*Suby of* VECTREN UTILITY HOLDINGS INC) ★
1 Vectren Sq, Evansville, IN 47708-1209
Tel (812) 424-6411 *Founded/Ownrshp* 2000
Sales 460.4MME *EMP* 779
SIC 4911 4924 4932 Electric services; Generation, electric power; Transmission, electric power; Natural gas distribution; Gas & other services combined
CEO: Carl L Chapman
**Pr:* William S Doty
**CEO:* Niel C Ellerbrook
**CFO:* Jerome A Benkert Jr
**Treas:* Robert Goocher
**Sr VP:* Ronald E Christian
**VP:* Daniel Bugher
**VP:* M Susan Hardwick
**VP:* Ellis S Redd
**VP:* Eric J Schach

D-U-N-S 62-287-5339
SOUTHERN INDIANA WASTE SYSTEMS LLC
6108 Sable Mill Ct, Jeffersonville, IN 47130-9250
Tel (502) 935-1130 *Founded/Ownrshp* 2005
Sales 2.7MMM *EMP* 15
SIC 5722 Garbage disposals

D-U-N-S 00-783-6836 IMP
■ **SOUTHERN INDUSTRIAL CONSTRUCTORS INC** (NC)
(*Suby of* EMCOR GROUP INC) ★
6101 Triangle Dr, Raleigh, NC 27617-4835
Tel (919) 782-4600 *Founded/Ownrshp* 1962, 2012
Sales 274.7MME *EMP* 750
SIC 1629 1799 1731 1796 1791 7353

D-U-N-S 04-969-1876
SOUTHERN INSURANCE UNDERWRITERS INC
CENTURY CASUALTY COMPANY
4500 Mansell Rd, Alpharetta, GA 30022-8265
Tel (678) 498-4500 *Founded/Ownrshp* 1964
Sales NA *EMP* 140
SIC 6411 Insurance agents & brokers
Ch Bd: W C Duesenberg Sr
**Ch Bd:* Wesley C Duesenberg Sr
**Pr:* Wesley C Duesenberg Jr
**CFO:* John W Lamay
Ex VP: Sam Pritchard
Sr VP: Bill Nelson
VP: Thomas Albrecht
VP: Marcelo Araujo
VP: Trip Duesenberg
VP: Paul Wilson
IT Man: Marcelo Arauio

D-U-N-S 04-910-9440 IMP
SOUTHERN IONICS INC
180 W Broad St, West Point, MS 39773-2802
Tel (662) 494-3055 *Founded/Ownrshp* 1990
Sales 150.3MME *EMP* 260
SIC 2819 Industrial inorganic chemicals; Alums; Aluminum compounds
Pr: Milton O Sundbeck Jr
CFO: Steve Mitchener
**CFO:* Steven D Mitchener
VP: Joe Stevens
**VP:* Randy Weimer
Plnt Mgr: Craig Gill

SOUTHERN L
See SOUTHERN COMMUNICATIONS SERVICES INC

D-U-N-S 07-746-8270
SOUTHERN MAINE HEALTH CARE
SMHC
1 Medical Center Dr, Biddeford, ME 04005-9422
Tel (207) 283-7000 *Founded/Ownrshp* 1899
Sales 171.8MM *EMP* 1,000E
Accts Mainehealth Portland Me
SIC 8062 General medical & surgical hospitals
Pr: Edward McGeachey
**CFO:* Norm Belair
Ex VP: Frank Lavoie
VP: Patricia Aprile
VP: Lorraine Bouchard
Exec: Timothy Haley
Genl Mgr: Kathy Constantine
Off Mgr: Judy Jacques
Off Mgr: Suzanne Menard
CIO: Ralph Johnson
Secur Mgr: Michael Harriman

D-U-N-S 05-780-5343
SOUTHERN MANAGEMENT CORP
1950 Old Gallows Rd # 600, Vienna, VA 22182-3970
Tel (703) 902-2000 *Founded/Ownrshp* 1981
Sales 334.7M *EMP* 1,200
SIC 6531 Real estate managers
CEO: David Hillman
**COO:* Ronald Frank
VP: Richard Hillman
Ex Dir: Rick Holt
Rgnl Mgr: Hilary Krubsack
Pr Mgr: Pamela Martin
Mktg Mgr: Matt Cabaniss

D-U-N-S 15-750-1024
SOUTHERN MANAGEMENT CORP
101 N Main St Ste 600, Greenville, SC 29601-4846
Tel (864) 233-9033 *Founded/Ownrshp* 2012
Sales NA *EMP* 958
SIC 6141 Consumer finance companies
CEO: Bob Bloom
**Pr:* Roy D Little
**CFO:* James A Cantley
CFO: Jim Cantley
**Treas:* James E Ashcraft
IT Man: Michael Oakes

D-U-N-S 60-820-7122
■ **SOUTHERN MANAGEMENT CORP**
(*Suby of* ABM INDUSTRIES INC) ★
5751 Uptain Rd Ste 408, Chattanooga, TN 37411-5674
Tel (423) 510-0010 *Founded/Ownrshp* 2008
Sales 57.8MME *EMP* 2,400
SIC 7349 Janitorial service, contract basis
Pr: Randall Steele
**VP:* Trey Brock
VP: Roy Neeley
VP: Donald Toole
Brnch Mgr: Charle Denton
Dist Mgr: Butch Cordell
Dist Mgr: Andrew Jordan
Genl Mgr: Charles Denton
Dir IT: Jade Greeson

SOUTHERN MARYLAND ORTHOPAEDICS
See CENTERS FOR ADVANCED ORTHOPAEDICS LLC

SOUTHERN MARYLAND SANITATION
See UNITED SITE SERVICES OF MARYLAND INC

D-U-N-S 14-457-7384
SOUTHERN MEDICAL HEALTH SYSTEMS INC
3632 Dauphin St Ste 101b, Mobile, AL 36608-1246
Tel (251) 460-5280 *Founded/Ownrshp* 1983
Sales 180.7MME *EMP* 1,732
SIC 8741 8011 7374 7322 Hospital management; Nursing & personal care facility management; Offices & clinics of medical doctors; Data processing & preparation; Adjustment & collection services
CEO: Celia A Wallace
**Pr:* Bill A Mason
**Ex VP:* Randy Sucher
VP: Paul Read
VP: Bill Wood

D-U-N-S 00-198-1133
SOUTHERN METHODIST UNIVERSITY INC (TX)
S M U
6425 Boaz Ln, Dallas, TX 75205
Tel (214) 768-2000 *Founded/Ownrshp* 1911
Sales 571.9MM *EMP* 2,200
Accts Kpmg Llp Dallas Tx
SIC 8221 University
Pr: R Gerald Turner
Mng Pt: Kathy Brooks
**Ch:* Caren Prothro
**Treas:* Michael Condon
Ofcr: Roxanne Crowley
Ofcr: Linda Hervey
Assoc VP: Ernie Barry
**VP:* Thomas Barry
**VP:* Chris Casey
VP: James E Caswll
**VP:* Brad Cheves
VP: George Chrisman
VP: Cindy Gautreaux
VP: Alex Munoz
VP: Ross Murfin
VP: Cchea Nugent
VP: Ellen Small
VP: Andrea Smith
**VP:* Paul Ward
VP: Paul J Ward
**VP:* Lori White

D-U-N-S 00-329-1382 IMP/EXP
SOUTHERN MILLS INC (GA)
TENCATE PROTECTIVE FABRICS
(*Suby of* KONINKLIJKE TEN CATE B.V.)
6501 Mall Blvd, Union City, GA 30291-1519
Tel (770) 969-1000 *Founded/Ownrshp* 1925, 2004
Sales 218.7MME *EMP* 530
SIC 2221 2297 Broadwoven fabric mills, manmade; Nonwoven fabrics
Pr: Donald M Olsen
CFO: Bob Shimkus
**Sec:* Mark Christman
VP: Peggy Holcomb
VP: Frank Lee
VP: Michael Stanhope
VP: Mary Sullivan
Software D: Mark Murphy
VP Sls: John Shadinger
Sls Mgr: Chris Corner
Sls Mgr: Tara Glover

D-U-N-S 06-285-9814 IMP
SOUTHERN MINNESOTA BEET SUGAR COOPERATIVE
83550 County Road 21, Renville, MN 56284-2319
Tel (320) 329-8305 *Founded/Ownrshp* 1975
Sales 350.0MM *EMP* 610
Accts Pricewaterhousecoopers Llp Mi
SIC 2063 Granulated sugar from sugar beets; Beet pulp, dried: from beet sugar refinery; Molasses from sugar beets
CEO: Kelvin Thompsen
**Treas:* Harlan Ruiter
VP: Todd Geselius
Exec: Blake Klinger
Exec: Carol Maurice
Dir IT: Jeffrey Carlson
Software D: Paul Sorenson
Sftwr Eng: Thomas McDonnell
Sftwr Eng: Nick Wulf
VP Opers: John Dean
VP Opers: Robert Strickland

D-U-N-S 05-575-3735 IMP
SOUTHERN MINNESOTA MUNICIPAL POWER AGENCY
SMMPA
500 1st Ave Sw, Rochester, MN 55902-3303
Tel (507) 285-0478 *Founded/Ownrshp* 1977
Sales 231.6MM *EMP* 41
Accts Kpmg Llp Minneapolis Mn
SIC 4911 Generation, electric power; Distribution, electric power
Pr: Richard D Kittelson
**VP:* Lewis G Giesking
Counsel: Jeff Ihrke
Board of Directors: Lewis Giesking

D-U-N-S 05-789-4065
SOUTHERN MISSOURI CONTAINERS INC
SMC PACKAGING GROUP
3131 E Division St, Springfield, MO 65802-2493
Tel (417) 831-2685 *Founded/Ownrshp* 1972
Sales 91.8MM *EMP* 330
Accts Kpm Cpas Pc Springfield Mis
SIC 2671 2653 Packaging paper & plastics film, coated & laminated; Boxes, corrugated: made from purchased materials
CEO: Kevin R Ausburn
**Pr:* Richard R Bachus
**Ch:* Ross B Ausburn
**Sr VP:* Randall M Bachus
**Sr VP:* William M McNay
**VP:* Vernon L Bennett
**VP:* Benjamin Jones
**VP:* Gary N Turner
Genl Mgr: David Bykowski
Genl Mgr: Brad Tabor
VP Opers: Mark McNay

D-U-N-S 13-805-6671
SOUTHERN MONTANA ELECTRIC GENERATION AND TRANSMISSION COOPERATIVE INC
7250 Entryway Dr, Billings, MT 59101-6236
Tel (406) 294-9527 *Founded/Ownrshp* 2003
Sales 109.9MM *EMP* 8
Accts Douglas Wilson & Company Pc G
SIC 4911 Generation, electric power; Transmission, electric power
Prin: Lee A Freeman
**Pr:* Bill Fitzgerald
**CEO:* Tim Gregori
Genl Mgr: Allan Sze

D-U-N-S 94-950-8733 IMP/EXP
SOUTHERN MOTION INC
298 Henry Southern Dr, Pontotoc, MS 38863
Tel (662) 488-4007 *Founded/Ownrshp* 1996
Sales 118.7MME *EMP* 1,400E
SIC 2512 Recliners: upholstered on wood frames
Pr: Roger Bland
**Ch Bd:* H Guy Lipscomb Sr
**CFO:* Wayne Patterson
**VP:* Guy Lipscomb
IT Man: Trent Brazeal
Manager: Sean McCabe
Sls Mgr: Aaron Cooley
Sls Mgr: Jack Tidwell

D-U-N-S 08-760-2363
SOUTHERN MULTIFOODS INC
TACO BELL
101 E Cherokee St, Jacksonville, TX 75766-4807
Tel (903) 586-1524 *Founded/Ownrshp* 1977
Sales 110.0MM *EMP* 2,000
SIC 5812 Fast-food restaurant, chain
Pr: Larry Durrett
**Sec:* Kenneth Durrett
**VP:* Dennis Durrett
Brnch Mgr: Gabriel Alvera
VP Opers: Martin Riggs

D-U-N-S 00-883-5894
SOUTHERN NEBRASKA RURAL PUBLIC POWER DISTRICT
4550 W Husker Hwy, Grand Island, NE 68803-6555
Tel (402) 725-3370 *Founded/Ownrshp* 1940, 1974
Sales 83.4MME *EMP* 100
SIC 4911 Electric services
Pr: Neal Niedfeldt
**Ch Bd:* Marin Fishler
**Pr:* Gary Hedmen
**Treas:* Dean Klute
IT Man: James Erbes
IT Man: Brad Kool

D-U-N-S 13-596-5650
SOUTHERN NEVADA WATER AUTHORITY
SNWA
100 N City Pkwy Ste 700, Las Vegas, NV 89106-4615
Tel (702) 862-3400 *Founded/Ownrshp* 1991
Sales 169.6MME *EMP* 230E
Accts Piercy Bowler Taylor & Kern L
SIC 4941 Water supply
Ch Bd: Shari Buck
Pr: Rose Addison
Treas: Don Boettcher
**V Ch Bd:* Steven Kirk
VP: Karen Griffin
Exec: Nicole Lise
**Prin:* Mary Beth Scow
Genl Couns: Gregory Walch

D-U-N-S 15-118-0593
■ **SOUTHERN NEW ENGLAND TELECOMMUNICATIONS CORP**
AT&T
(*Suby of* AT&T INC) ★
2 Science Park, New Haven, CT 06511-1963
Tel (203) 771-5200 *Founded/Ownrshp* 1998
Sales 1.7MMME *EMP* 9,841
SIC 4813 4812 5065 6159 2741 4822 Local & long distance telephone communications; Local telephone communications; Cellular telephone services; Paging services; Telephone equipment; Machinery & equipment finance leasing; Directories, telephone: publishing & printing; Electronic mail
Pr: William Blase
CFO: James Lindner
CFO: Donald McGregor
Sr VP: Alfred Richter
VP: Michelle Macauda
VP: Al Porta
Exec: David Browne
Exec: Tim O'Connell
Exec: Kevin Wheat
Assoc Dir: Arthur Paquette
Ex Dir: John Emra

D-U-N-S 00-691-7926
■ **SOUTHERN NEW ENGLAND TELEPHONE CO INC**
S B C
(*Suby of* FRONTIER COMMUNICATIONS CORP) ★
310 Orange St, New Haven, CT 06510-1719
Tel (203) 771-5200 *Founded/Ownrshp* 2014
Sales 1.9MMME *EMP* 6,791
SIC 4813 4822 Local & long distance telephone communications; Local telephone communications; Electronic mail
Pr: Michele Macauda
CFO: Donald McGregor

D-U-N-S 07-397-1772
SOUTHERN NEW HAMPSHIRE MEDICAL CENTER
8 Prospect St, Nashua, NH 03060-3925
Tel (603) 577-2000 *Founded/Ownrshp* 1892
Sales 215.7MM *EMP* 1,200
Accts Baker Newman & Noyes Limited
SIC 8062 8011 General medical & surgical hospitals; Offices & clinics of medical doctors
Pr: Tom Wilhelmsen
Ex VP: Eugene Lesser
**VP:* Gary P Marlow
VP: Stephanie W Rosenblum
VP: Stephanie Wolf-Rosenblum
Exec: Ashima Handa
Exec: Stephanie L Wolf-Rosenb
Exec: Melissa Wu
Prac Mgr: Jean Foley
CTO: Ann McLaughlin
IT Man: John Szyszlo

D-U-N-S 06-990-8192
SOUTHERN NEW HAMPSHIRE UNIVERSITY
SNHU
2500 N River Rd, Manchester, NH 03106-1018
Tel (603) 668-2211 *Founded/Ownrshp* 1932
Sales 449.5MM *EMP* 1,000
Accts Kpmg Llp Boston Ma
SIC 8221 Colleges universities & professional schools
Pr: Paul La Blanc
Treas: William McGarry
Assoc Dir: Domenic Gioioso
Ex Dir: Anthony Siciliano
Off Mgr: Wendy Marquis
Snr Sftwr: Al Swisher
Board of Directors: Jeanette Goldberg

D-U-N-S 01-081-2436
SOUTHERN NEWSPAPERS INC
BRAZOSPORT FACTS
5701 Woodway Dr Ste 131, Houston, TX 77057-1589
Tel (713) 266-5481 *Founded/Ownrshp* 1969
Sales 120.8MME *EMP* 687
SIC 2711

D-U-N-S 79-077-8997
■ SOUTHERN NUCLEAR OPERATING CO INC
(Suby of SOUTHERN CO) ★
42 Inverness Center Pkwy, Birmingham, AL 35242-4809
Tel (205) 992-5000 Founded/Ownrshp 1990
Sales 209.3MM^E EMP 2,960
SIC 8741 Management services
CEO: Thomas A Fanning
Ch: Barnie Beasley
Ex VP: Joseph A Miller
VP: Bradley J Adam
VP: Bradley Adams
VP: J W Averett
VP: Brian Ivey
VP: Kathleen King
VP: Kerry Kline
VP: Dennis Madison
VP: J O Meier

D-U-N-S 17-377-7533
SOUTHERN OCEAN COUNTY HEALTH SYSTEM INC
SOCH
(Suby of MERIDIAN HOSPITAL) ★
1140 Route 72 W, Manahawkin, NJ 08050-2412
Tel (609) 597-6011 Founded/Ownrshp 2010
Sales 161.8MM EMP 900
SIC 8062 General medical & surgical hospitals
Pr: Joseph P Coyle
*CFO: Richard Hand
Ofcr: John Brede
Exec: Raymond Green
Dir Case M: Marilyn Butler
Dir Rad: Linda Liana
Nurse Mgr: Cindy Stagg
QA Dir: Michele F De Noia
Doctor: Michael I Bleiman

D-U-N-S 07-501-9810 IMP
SOUTHERN OHIO MEDICAL CENTER (OH)
SCIOTO MEMORIAL HOSPITAL CAMPU
1805 27th St, Portsmouth, OH 45662-2640
Tel (740) 354-5000 Founded/Ownrshp 1954, 1984
Sales 351.0MM EMP 2,100
SIC 8062 General medical & surgical hospitals
Pr: Randal M Arnett
*Ch Bd: Robert E Dever
*VP: Claudia Burchett
Dir Risk M: Desiree Hess
Adm Dir: Amy Fraulini
Adm Dir: Tom Greene
Adm Dir: Shawn Jordan
Adm Dir: Kara Redoutey
Off Mgr: Zoe Richards
Nurse Mgr: Linda Horner
Telecom Ex: John Schaefer

D-U-N-S 60-774-0222
SOUTHERN PAN SERVICES CO
CADENCE STRUCTURES DIV
2385 Lithonia Indus Blvd, Lithonia, GA 30058-4692
Tel (678) 301-2400 Founded/Ownrshp 1987
Sales 366.3MM^E EMP 1,000
SIC 1542 Commercial & office building contractors
Pr: Brack Maggard
CFO: Linda Burgess
*CFO: Carrie Harris
*Sec: Gerry P Harkins
Ofcr: Chris Alexander
VP: David Bobbitt
VP: Jeremy Cantrill

D-U-N-S 00-958-3878
SOUTHERN PETROLEUM INC
600 Monticello St, Somerset, KY 42501-2974
Tel (606) 678-5127 Founded/Ownrshp 1997
Sales 158.7MM^E EMP 100^E
SIC 5171 Petroleum bulk stations & terminals
Pr: Jonathan Arnett
CFO: Darin Jones
*VP: Roger Todhunter

D-U-N-S 02-665-1422
SOUTHERN PETROLEUM LABORATORIES INC
S P L
8850 Interchange Dr, Houston, TX 77054-2511
Tel (713) 660-0901 Founded/Ownrshp 2016
Sales 148.9MM^E EMP 357
SIC 5172 8999 8734 Gases, liquefied petroleum (propane); Geological consultant; Testing laboratories; Water testing laboratory; Soil analysis
CEO: Ian Milne
V Ch: Joe Landes
COO: Steve Grenda
CFO: David Rowland
VP: Robert Bienvenu
VP: Christopher Brown
VP: Royce Miller
Sales Exec: Joe Credeur
VP Sls: Craig Falgout

D-U-N-S 00-282-0488
SOUTHERN PINE ELECTRIC POWER ASSOCIATION
SOUTHERN PINE EPA
110 Risher St, Taylorsville, MS 39168-5555
Tel (601) 785-6511 Founded/Ownrshp 1938
Sales 226.2MM EMP 260
Accts Jackson Thornton & Co Pc Mont
SIC 4911 Electric services
Pr: Billy M Berry
*VP: Marcus H Martin
Genl Mgr: Donald Jordan
Board of Directors: Robert Fillingham, Paula Makar, Wayne Olsen, Sheppard Root

SOUTHERN PINE EPA
See SOUTHERN PINE ELECTRIC POWER ASSOCIATION

D-U-N-S 00-402-7280
SOUTHERN PIPE & SUPPLY CO INC
SOUTHERN BATH & KITCHEN CENTER
4330 Highway 39 N, Meridian, MS 39301-1082
Tel (601) 693-2911 Founded/Ownrshp 1925
Sales 495.1MM^E EMP 767
Accts Horne Cpa Llp
SIC 5074 1711 1623 Plumbing fittings & supplies; Plumbing, heating, air-conditioning contractors; Water, sewer & utility lines
Pr: Jay Davidson
*Ch Bd: Martin D Davidson
*CFO: Marc Ransier
*VP: Mark Roebuck
Brnch Mgr: Tom Cameron
Brnch Mgr: Brent Gooding
Brnch Mgr: Susan Walden

D-U-N-S 06-209-2457
SOUTHERN POLYTECHNIC STATE UNIVERSITY FOUNDATION INC
(Suby of GEORGIA BOARD OF REGENTS) ★
1100 S Marietta Pkwy Se, Marietta, GA 30060-2855
Tel (678) 915-7778 Founded/Ownrshp 1980
Sales 102.8MM^E EMP 1,100
Accts Mauldin & Jenkins Llc Atlanta
SIC 8221 College, except junior
Pr: Lisa A Rossbacher
Ex VP: Brad Reid
VP: Trish Buchanan
*VP: Ron Dempsey
VP: Randy Hinds
Dir Lab: Jessica McNally
Admn Mgr: Callie Melton
Admn Mgr: Denise Stover
Genl Mgr: Robin Wade
Off Mgr: Madison Giddens
IT Man: Temika Boucaud

D-U-N-S 06-578-6043
■ SOUTHERN POWER CO
(Suby of SOUTHERN CO) ★
30 Ivan Allen Jr Blvd Nw, Atlanta, GA 30308-3055
Tel (404) 506-5000 Founded/Ownrshp 2001
Sales 1.3MMM EMP 3^E
Accts Deloitte & Touche Llp Atlanta
SIC 4911 Electric services
Pr: Oscar C Harper IV
COO: John G Trawick
CFO: William C Grantham
Bd of Dir: Henry A Clark
Ofcr: Chief F Fanning
Ex VP: Mickey A Brown
VP: Michael Anderson
VP: Susan B Ortenstone
VP: Patricia Roberts
Dir IT: Misty Blizzard

D-U-N-S 08-021-4125
SOUTHERN POWER DISTRICT
101 16th Ave, Franklin, NE 68939-1050
Tel (308) 425-6217 Founded/Ownrshp 1946
Sales 89.5MM EMP 6
SIC 4911 Electric services

D-U-N-S 00-892-4136
SOUTHERN PUMP & TANK CO LLC
4800 N Graham St, Charlotte, NC 28269-4885
Tel (704) 596-4373 Founded/Ownrshp 2006
Sales 111.2MM^E EMP 262
SIC 5084 1799 Petroleum industry machinery; Processing & packaging equipment; Service station equipment installation & maintenance
CEO: Charles E Tew
*Pr: Sandy Samways
*Treas: Chris Elrod
VP: John Force
Brnch Mgr: Alan Tapscott
Dir IT: Mike Snowdy
VP Opers: Steve Childers
Mtls Mgr: Tonia Ballard

D-U-N-S 92-673-7321 IMP/EXP
SOUTHERN RECYCLING LLC
EMR
(Suby of EUROPEAN METAL RECYCLING LIMITED)
902 Julia St, New Orleans, LA 70113-1114
Tel (504) 636-7200 Founded/Ownrshp 2006
Sales 168.6MM^E EMP 385
SIC 5093 Scrap & waste materials
Pr: Joel Dupre
Ofcr: David Farnsworth
Genl Mgr: Chris Covington
Genl Mgr: Tony Schultz
IT Man: Daryl Marvel
Sfty Dirs: Paul Martin
Site Mgr: Matt Moody
Opers Mgr: Tony Torricelli

D-U-N-S 78-248-3911
SOUTHERN REGIONAL HEALTH SYSTEM INC
SOUTHERN REGIONAL MEDICAL CTR
11 Upper Riverdale Rd Sw, Riverdale, GA 30274-2615
Tel (770) 991-8175 Founded/Ownrshp 1991
Sales 238.9MM EMP 2,315
Accts Dixon Hughes Goodman Llp Ashe
SIC 8062 General medical & surgical hospitals
CEO: Kim Ryan
*Pr: Clint Matthews
COO: John R McLain
CFO: Jean Barnes
*CFO: G E Hoffman
*CFO: John Schibler
VP: Gina Dickson
Dir Rx: Dana Fox
VP Admn: Paul Casbergue
Doctor: David Goodman
Doctor: Carl Sutton
Board of Directors: Jean

SOUTHERN REGIONAL MEDICAL CENTER
See PRIME HEALTHCARE FOUNDATION - SOUTHERN REGIONAL LLC

D-U-N-S 17-939-8714
SOUTHERN REGIONAL MEDICAL CENTER
SOUTHERN CRES BHVORAL MEDICINE
11 Upper Riverdale Rd Sw, Riverdale, GA 30274-2615
Tel (770) 991-8520 Founded/Ownrshp 1995
Sales 252.7MM EMP 5
SIC 8011 Psychiatrist

SOUTHERN REGIONAL MEDICAL CTR
See SOUTHERN REGIONAL HEALTH SYSTEM INC

SOUTHERN SALES COMPANY
See TENCARVA MACHINERY CO LLC

SOUTHERN SIERRA MEDICAL CLINIC
See RIDGECREST REGIONAL HOSPITAL

SOUTHERN STAR
See ARGOS READY MIX (SOUTH CENTRAL) CORP

D-U-N-S 12-360-3644
SOUTHERN STAR CENTRAL CORP
(Suby of MSIP-SSCC HOLDINGS LLC) ★
4700 Highway 56, Owensboro, KY 42301-9303
Tel (270) 852-5000 Founded/Ownrshp 2012
Sales 216.1MM EMP 498
SIC 4923 Gas transmission & distribution
Pr: Jerry L Morris
CEO: Carol Cruise
CFO: Susanne W Harris

D-U-N-S 00-790-6233
SOUTHERN STAR CENTRAL GAS PIPELINE INC
(Suby of SOUTHERN STAR CENTRAL CORP) ★
4700 Highway 56, Owensboro, KY 42301-9303
Tel (270) 852-5000 Founded/Ownrshp 1922
Sales 255.7MM EMP 469
SIC 4923 Gas transmission & distribution
Pr: Jerry L Morris
Pr: David L Finley
*CFO: Susanne W Harris
*Sr VP: Robert S Bahnick
VP: Rob Carlton
*VP: Beverly H Griffith

SOUTHERN STAR CONCRETE
See HANSON AGGREGATES LLC

D-U-N-S 12-681-2366
SOUTHERN STAR INC
DISH NETWORK
306 Kerr Ave, Poteau, OK 74953-5246
Tel (918) 647-8383 Founded/Ownrshp 1999
Sales 166.7MM^E EMP 550
SIC 4841 Direct broadcast satellite services (DBS)
CEO: Jeremy Fields
*COO: Jeff Fesperman
*VP: Josh Bhatia
Rgnl Mgr: William Holden
Admn Mgr: Sharon Ming

D-U-N-S 00-896-4637 IMP
SOUTHERN STATES COOPERATIVE INC
6606 W Broad St Ste B, Richmond, VA 23230-1731
Tel (804) 281-1000 Founded/Ownrshp 1923
Sales 1.8MMM^E EMP 4,000
Accts Kpmg Llp Richmond Va
SIC 2048 0181 2873 2874 5191 5172 Prepared feeds; Bulbs & seeds; Nitrogenous fertilizers; Phosphatic fertilizers; Farm supplies; Feed; Seeds & bulbs; Fertilizer & fertilizer materials; Petroleum products
Pr: Thomas R Scribner
*CFO: Leslie T Newton
Ex VP: Wesley Wright
Sr VP: C A Miller
*VP: Curry A Roberts
Pr Dir: Jimmie Loftis
Board of Directors: Daniel M King, Cecil D Bell Jr, Doug Langley, Laird Bowman, Eddie A Melton, Mark H Burkett, Norman W Messick, William F Covington, Curry A Roberts, John B East, John Henry Smith, Daryl Grannis, William W Vanderwende, Mason R Hopkins Sr, Raleigh O Ward Jr, R Bruce Johnson, Wilber C Ward, Johnny Jordan, Charles A Wilfong

D-U-N-S 60-738-2348
SOUTHERN STATES HOLDINGS INC
(Suby of SOUTHERN STATES COOPERATIVE INC) ★
6606 W Broad St Ste B, Richmond, VA 23230-1731
Tel (804) 281-1206 Founded/Ownrshp 1923
Sales 221.8MM^E EMP 3,000
SIC 5191 5261 0724 Farm supplies; Garden supplies & tools; Cotton ginning
Pr: Thomas Scribner
*Treas: Leslie T Newton

D-U-N-S 08-008-4361 IMP
SOUTHERN STATES LLC
SOUTHERN STATES SS
30 Georgia Ave, Hampton, GA 30228-2950
Tel (770) 946-4562 Founded/Ownrshp 1983
Sales 128.6MM^E EMP 300
SIC 3613 4013 1731 Time switches, electrical switchgear apparatus; Switching & terminal services; Electrical work
Pr: Raj Anand
Pr: Neil McCord
CFO: David Shelly
Treas: Laurie Hilliard
VP: Billy Watson
Area Mgr: Bob Maresca
Genl Mgr: Willie Watson
MIS Dir: Rick Toland
MIS Dir: Rick Towland
IT Man: Jeff Gallimore
VP Mfg: Thomas Uhl

D-U-N-S 11-440-7950 EXP
SOUTHERN STATES PACKAGING CO
180 Brooks Blvd, Spartanburg, SC 29307-5447
Tel (864) 579-3911 Founded/Ownrshp 1984
Sales 86.4MM EMP 120
Accts Deanne Shehan
SIC 2679 Paper products, converted
Prin: Michael Lyon
Ex VP: Michael L Yon
VP: Elida Karyshyn
*VP: Robert B Lyon
Exec: Mike Dorsey
IT Man: Steve Witt
VP Sls: Gil Copeland
*VP Sls: David C Lyon
Sls Mgr: Jennifer Ivey

SOUTHERN STATES SS
See SOUTHERN STATES LLC

SOUTHERN STATES TOYOTA LIFT
See FLORIDA LIFT SYSTEMS LLC

D-U-N-S 04-864-6475
SOUTHERN STATES UTILITY TRAILER SALES INC
550 Highway 49 S, Jackson, MS 39218-9486
Tel (601) 939-9000 Founded/Ownrshp 1982
Sales 83.3MM^E EMP 85^E
SIC 5012 Trailers for trucks, new & used
Pr: Michael Lee Thornton
*Treas: Margie Thornton
*VP: Andy Chandler
Exec: DOT Stuart

D-U-N-S 07-887-8087
SOUTHERN STORE FIXTURES INC (AL)
SOUTHERN CASEARTS
275 Drexel Rd Se, Bessemer, AL 35022-6416
Tel (205) 428-4800 Founded/Ownrshp 2012
Sales 96.8MM^E EMP 362
SIC 6719 Investment holding companies, except banks
Pr: William Cary Jr
CFO: Jimmy Brandon
*Sec: Connie L Cary
VP: Daniel McMurray

D-U-N-S 13-046-0806
SOUTHERN THEATRES LLC
GRAND THEATER, THE
935 Gravier St Ste 1200, New Orleans, LA 70112-1677
Tel (504) 297-1133 Founded/Ownrshp 2002
Sales 128.7MM^E EMP 2,002^E
SIC 7832 Motion picture theaters, except drive-in
*Pr: Ronald Krueger II
VP: Doug Whitford

D-U-N-S 14-383-0128
SOUTHERN TIRE MART LLC
800 Us 98, Columbia, MS 39429
Tel (601) 424-3200 Founded/Ownrshp 2003
Sales 370.4MM^E EMP 1,300
SIC 7534 5014 Tire retreading & repair shops; Automobile tires & tubes
*Pt: Jim Duff
*Mng Pt: Thomas Duff

D-U-N-S 00-792-8013
■ SOUTHERN UNION CO (TX)
SOUTHERN UNION GAS
(Suby of ENERGY TRANSFER EQUITY LP) ★
1300 Main St, Houston, TX 77002-6803
Tel (713) 989-2000 Founded/Ownrshp 1932, 2012
Sales 2.0MMM^E EMP 2,437
SIC 4924 Natural gas distribution
Ch Bd: George L Lindemann
*Pr: Eric D Herschmann
COO: David Black
CFO: Richard N Marshall
Ofcr: Hack Robert
Sr VP: Robert O Bond
Sr VP: Monica M Gaudiosi
Sr VP: Steve J Hotte
VP: Willie C Johnson
VP: John Kelly
VP: Rob Kerrigan
Board of Directors: Michal Barzuza, David Brodsky, Frank W Denius, Kurt A Gitter MD, Herbert H Jacobi, Thomas N McCarter III, George Rountree III, Allan D Scherer

D-U-N-S 07-246-1395
SOUTHERN UNION CONFERENCE ASSOCIATION OF SEVENTH-DAY ADVENTISTS (GA)
302 Research Dr, Norcross, GA 30092-2934
Tel (404) 299-1832 Founded/Ownrshp 1910
Sales 57.4MM^E EMP 2,500
SIC 8661 Seventh Day Adventist Church
Pr: Gordon Retzer
*Treas: Richard Centor
VP: Jim Etterson
MIS Dir: Todd Mace
Mktg Dir: Gerald Bond

SOUTHERN UNION GAS
See SOUTHERN UNION CO

SOUTHERN UNION GAS
See PANHANDLE EASTERN PIPE LINE CO LP

D-U-N-S 13-579-4456
■ SOUTHERN UNION PANHANDLE LLC
(Suby of SOUTHERN UNION GAS) ★
1 Ugi Ctr Fl 2, Wilkes Barre, PA 18711-0600
Tel (570) 820-2400 Founded/Ownrshp 1996
Sales 44.2MM^E EMP 1,100
SIC 4922 Pipelines, natural gas
Pr: Thomas Karam
*Pr: David W Stevens

D-U-N-S 00-820-1410
SOUTHERN UNIVERSITY AGRICULTURAL & MECHANICAL COLLEGE
(Suby of SOUTHERN UNIVERSITY SYSTEM) ★
G Leon Netherville Dr, Baton Rouge, LA 70813-0001
Tel (225) 771-5021 Founded/Ownrshp 1880
Sales 86.7MM^E EMP 2,300
SIC 8221 9411 University; Administration of educational programs;
Pr: Ronald Mason

D-U-N-S 93-788-6471
SOUTHERN UNIVERSITY AND A&M COLLEGE SYSTEM
SOUTHERN UNIVERSITY SYSTEM
J S Clark Adm Bldg 3rd Fl, Baton Rouge, LA 70813-0001
Tel (225) 771-4680 Founded/Ownrshp 1914
Sales 114.5MM^E EMP 2,300
SIC 8221 University
Pr: Ray L Belton
*VP: Kevin Appleton
IT Man: Jesse Smith
Psych: Edwin H Walker

SOUTHERN UNIVERSITY SYSTEM
See SOUTHERN UNIVERSITY AND A&M COLLEGE SYSTEM

D-U-N-S 02-091-7670
SOUTHERN UTAH UNIVERSITY FOUNDATION
SUU
351 W University Blvd, Cedar City, UT 84720-2415
Tel (435) 586-7700 *Founded/Ownrshp* 1996
Sales 110.7MM[E] *EMP* 1,727
Accts Auston G Johnson Cpa Salt L
SIC 8221 University
Pr: Michael T Benson
**VP:* Stuart Jones
**VP:* Dorian G Page
Exec: Renee Ballenger
Assoc Dir: Ed Meyer
Off Mgr: Malinda Rhodes
Netwrk Eng: Larry Gardner
Opers Mgr: John S Gholdston
HC Dir: Emily Phillips

D-U-N-S 07-835-3919
SOUTHERN UTE INDIAN TRIBE (CO)
LAKE CAPOTE PARK
356 Ouray Dr, Ignacio, CO 81137
Tel (970) 563-0100 *Founded/Ownrshp* 1936
Sales NA *EMP* 1,500
SIC 9131 Indian reservation
Ch: Jimmy R Newton Jr
**Pr:* Ben Shelly
**Treas:* Mishelle Taylor Olguin
Ex Ofcr: Byron Red
Exec: Lena Atencio
Div/Sub He: Steve Whiteman
Ex Dir: Lynn Brittner
CTO: Mathew Box
MIS Dir: Aaron Torres
IT Man: Esther Rima
Sls Mgr: Mark Torres

D-U-N-S 82-969-5654 IMP
SOUTHERN WINE & SPIRITS-PACIFIC NORTHWEST HOLDINGS LLC
10500 Ne 8th St Ste 2000, Bellevue, WA 98004-4369
Tel (425) 456-3535 *Founded/Ownrshp* 2008
Sales 318.9MM[E] *EMP* 1,500[E]
SIC 5182 Wine & distilled beverages
CFO: Jeff Edwards
**Co-Pr:* Wayne Chaplin

SOUTHERN WINE SPIRITS ILL INC
See SOUTHERN GLAZERS WINE AND SPIRITS OF ILLINOIS LLC

SOUTHERNCARLSON
See FASTENER HOLDINGS INC

SOUTHERNCARLSON
See SOUTHERN FASTENING SYSTEMS LLC

D-U-N-S 02-569-7343 EXP
SOUTHFIELD CORP
ILLINOIS BRICK COMPANY
8995 W 95th St, Palos Hills, IL 60465-5030
Tel (708) 344-1000 *Founded/Ownrshp* 1981
Sales 257.1MM[E] *EMP* 1,500
SIC 3273 1442 3241 4212 4213 5032

D-U-N-S 01-086-1417
SOUTHFIELD PUBLIC SCHOOL DISTRICT
24661 Lahser Rd, Southfield, MI 48033-3238
Tel (248) 746-8500 *Founded/Ownrshp* 1947
Sales 105.0MM *EMP* 1,200
Accts Plante & Moran Pllc Detroit
SIC 8211 Public elementary school; Public junior high school; Public senior high school
Trst: Nathaniel Lewis
Trst: Rance D Williams
VP: Betty Robinson

D-U-N-S 05-994-8406 IMP/EXP
SOUTHLAND CONTAINER CORP
CONCEPT PACKAGING GROUP
60 Fairview Church Rd, Spartanburg, SC 29303-5218
Tel (864) 578-0085 *Founded/Ownrshp* 1983
Sales 1.2MMM[E] *EMP* 4,501
SIC 2653 3086 Boxes, corrugated: made from purchased materials; Plastics foam products
Pr: David Katt
**Sec:* Larry Cantrell
VP: Bill O'Hearn
VP: Carolyn Stanton
Genl Mgr: Mark Parker
MIS Dir: Aaron Dame
Plnt Mgr: Don Nygren

D-U-N-S 02-456-6036 IMP
SOUTHLAND CONTRACTING INC (TX)
(*Suby of* SOUTHLAND HOLDINGS LLC) ★
608 Henrietta Creek Rd, Roanoke, TX 76262-6339
Tel (817) 293-4263 *Founded/Ownrshp* 1974
Sales 158.5MM[E] *EMP* 356
SIC 1799 1622 Boring for building construction; Tunnel construction
Pr: Clay Griffith
**Treas:* Teresa Longsdon

D-U-N-S 87-827-7995
■ **SOUTHLAND ENVIRONMENTAL SERVICES INC**
(*Suby of* REPUBLIC SERVICES INC) ★
8619 Western Way, Jacksonville, FL 32256-0360
Tel (904) 731-2456 *Founded/Ownrshp* 1999
Sales 164.3MM[E] *EMP* 500
SIC 4953 Refuse systems
CEO: James E O Connor

D-U-N-S 01-403-4465
SOUTHLAND HOLDINGS LLC (TX)
608 Henrietta Creek Rd, Roanoke, TX 76262-6339
Tel (817) 293-4263 *Founded/Ownrshp* 2006
Sales 273.3MM[E] *EMP* 356
SIC 1629 Dams, waterways, docks & other marine construction
CEO: Frank Renda
VP: Teressa Logsdon

SOUTHLAND IDEALEASE
See SOUTHLAND INTERNATIONAL TRUCKS INC

D-U-N-S 04-116-2926
SOUTHLAND INDUSTRIES
7390 Lincoln Way, Garden Grove, CA 92841-1427
Tel (800) 613-6240 *Founded/Ownrshp* 1949
Sales 362.5MM *EMP* 2,150
Accts Moss Adams Llp Irvine Califo
SIC 1711 Plumbing, heating, air-conditioning contractors
Ch Bd: Theodore D Lynch
**COO:* Charles M Allen
**CFO:* Kevin J Coghlan
CFO: Jon Spallino
**Treas:* Tony SF Wang
**Ofcr:* Brian Boutte
**Ofcr:* Joseph G Cvetas
Ofcr: Peter Pobjoy
**Ofcr:* Lisa Hoffman Starr
**Sr VP:* Peter C Pobjoy
VP: Chris Lofaso
VP: Gregory Michaud
VP: Michael Miller
VP: Linda Smart
Exec: Glenn Brandon

D-U-N-S 07-790-1932
SOUTHLAND INTERNATIONAL TRUCKS INC
SOUTHLAND IDEALEASE
200 Oxmoor Blvd, Birmingham, AL 35209-4749
Tel (205) 942-6226 *Founded/Ownrshp* 1997
Sales 114.2MM[E] *EMP* 235
SIC 5511 5531 7538 7513

D-U-N-S 06-897-9624
■ **SOUTHLAND LIFE INSURANCE CO**
(*Suby of* SECURITY LIFE OF DENVER INSURANCE COMPANY)
5780 Powers Ferry Rd, Atlanta, GA 30327-4347
Tel (770) 980-5100 *Founded/Ownrshp* 1960
Sales NA *EMP* 900
SIC 6311 Life insurance
CEO: Tom McInerney
**Ch Bd:* R Glenn Hilliard
**Pr:* James D Thompson
COO: Jerry Cwiok
**Treas:* David Pendergrass
Chf Mktg O: Tom Daniel
Sr VP: Jeff McClellan
**VP:* William S Adams Jr
VP: Harold Cohen
VP: Craig Collins
VP: Mark Halloran
**VP:* Ken Hunbt
**VP:* Alan Jeglinski
Board of Directors: Michael W Cunningham, Linda B Emory, P Randall Lowry, Francis Mulcahy, Robert St Jacques

SOUTHLAND READY MIX CONCRETE
See SUPERIOR READY MIX CONCRETE LP

D-U-N-S 18-109-6678 IMP
SOUTHLAND TUBE INC
3525 Richard Arringt, Birmingham, AL 35234-2307
Tel (205) 251-1884 *Founded/Ownrshp* 1995
Sales 91.2MM[E] *EMP* 275
SIC 3317 Steel pipe & tubes
Pr: John R Montgomery Jr
**CFO:* Craig T Hill
CFO: Craig Hill
VP: Joseph Carley
VP: Tony Mc Gough
VP: Louis Montgomery
Telecom Ex: Louis Montgovery
DP Exec: Willard Groover
IT Man: David Langsdales
**VP Sls:* Joe Carley
VP Sls: Gary Day

SOUTHPOLE
See WICKED FASHIONS INC

D-U-N-S 96-883-0831
SOUTHPORT LANE MANAGEMENT LLC
350 Madison Ave Fl 21, New York, NY 10017-3714
Tel (212) 729-3247 *Founded/Ownrshp* 2011
Sales 160.3MM[E] *EMP* 200[E]
SIC 6799 Investors
**COO:* Brandon Young
Sr Cor Off: Michael Morrow
Ofcr: Jim McNichols
Mng Dir: Andrew B Scherr
Off Mgr: Lauren Adelman
Genl Couns: Darren Fortunato
Genl Couns: Hugh Hill

SOUTHPORT MEWS APARTMENTS
See SOUTHPORT MEWS HOUSING PRESERVATION

D-U-N-S 02-089-3045
SOUTHPORT MEWS HOUSING PRESERVATION
SOUTHPORT MEWS APARTMENTS
50 S Main St, Port Chester, NY 10573-4656
Tel (914) 937-1681 *Founded/Ownrshp* 2008
Sales 14.1MM[E] *EMP* 1,828
SIC 6513 Apartment building operators
Prin: Larry Lipton
Prin: Novelette Duncan

D-U-N-S 10-260-7496
▲ **SOUTHSIDE BANCSHARES INC**
1201 S Beckham Ave, Tyler, TX 75701-3320
Tel (903) 531-7111 *Founded/Ownrshp* 1982
Sales NA *EMP* 813[E]
Tkr Sym SBSI *Exch* NGS
SIC 6022 State commercial banks
Pr: Sam Dawson
CFO: Lee R Gibson
CFO: Julie N Shamburger
Bd of Dir: Joe Norton
Bd of Dir: William Sheehy
Ex VP: Tim Alexander
Ex VP: Ashley Fettig
Ex VP: Randall Hendrix
Ex VP: Randall R Hendrix
Ex VP: Brian K McCabe
Ex VP: Lonny Uzzell
VP: Vonna Crowley
VP: Michael L Custer
VP: Cindy Davis
VP: Justin Hargrove
VP: Randi Mitchell
VP: Kim Partin
VP: Jeff Quesenberry
Board of Directors: Donald W Thedford, Lawrence Anderson, S Elaine Anderson, Herbert C Buie, Alton Cade, Patricia A Callan, Melvin B Lovelady, Paul W Powell, William Sheehy, Preston L Smith

D-U-N-S 03-632-5876
■ **SOUTHSIDE BANK** (TX)
(*Suby of* SOUTHSIDE BANCSHARES INC) ★
1201 S Beckham Ave, Tyler, TX 75701-3320
Tel (903) 531-7111 *Founded/Ownrshp* 1960, 1983
Sales NA *EMP* 591
SIC 6022 State trust companies accepting deposits, commercial
CEO: Bill G Hartley
**CFO:* Lee R Gibson CPA
**V Ch Bd:* Robbie N Edmonson
Bd of Dir: Alton Cade
Ofcr: Jill Kinsley
Ofcr: Kathy Williamson
Ex VP: Joel Adams
Ex VP: Tim Alexander
Ex VP: Ashley Fettig
Ex VP: Jared Green
Ex VP: Randal Hendrix
Ex VP: Stephen Manley
**Ex VP:* Jeryl Story
**Ex VP:* Lonny R Uzzell
**Ex VP:* H Andy Wall
Sr VP: Shannon Bettis
Sr VP: Trent Dawson
Sr VP: Renee Hollingsworth
Sr VP: Keith Miller
Sr VP: Julie Shamburger
VP: Robyn Coffey

D-U-N-S 00-794-0067
SOUTHSIDE ELECTRIC COOPERATIVE INC (VA)
2000 W Virginia Ave, Crewe, VA 23930-1072
Tel (800) 552-2118 *Founded/Ownrshp* 1936
Sales 123.3MM *EMP* 151
Accts Adams Jenkins Cheatham Pc Mid
SIC 4911 Electric services
Pr: Jeffrey S Edwards
**CFO:* Danny Hammond
**Ch:* Frank W Bacon
**Treas:* Winn Herbert E
Comm Dir: Allan Sharrett

D-U-N-S 06-800-9935
SOUTHSIDE HOSPITAL
NSLIJ-SOUTHSIDE HOSPITAL
(*Suby of* NSLIJ) ★
301 E Main St, Bay Shore, NY 11706-8458
Tel (631) 968-3000 *Founded/Ownrshp* 1913
Sales 381.9MM *EMP* 1,900[E]
SIC 8062 General medical & surgical hospitals
Chf Rad: David Weltman
Dir Recs: Sondra Murdaugh
CFO: Robert Powers
Sr VP: Shapiro S Robert
VP: Robert Castano
VP: Cecelia Fullam
Assoc Dir: Alex Hellinger
Dir Rad: Eric Godin
Adm Dir: Mike Eller
**Ex Dir:* Winifred Mack
Opers Mgr: Paul Ronning

SOUTHSIDE REGIONAL MEDICAL CTR
See PETERSBURG HOSPITAL CO LLC

D-U-N-S 00-229-9212
SOUTHWARK METAL MANUFACTURING CO (PA)
2800 Red Lion Rd, Philadelphia, PA 19114-2312
Tel (215) 735-3401 *Founded/Ownrshp* 1946
Sales 103.8MM[E] *EMP* 800
SIC 3444

D-U-N-S 80-857-4032
■ **SOUTHWEST A B Q RES CENTER**
(*Suby of* SOUTHWEST AIRLINES CO) ★
2702 Love Field Dr, Dallas, TX 75235-1908
Tel (214) 792-4000 *Founded/Ownrshp* 1971
Sales 34.0MM[E] *EMP* 1,889[E]
SIC 4724 Tourist agency arranging transport, lodging & car rental
Pr: Herb Kelleher

D-U-N-S 05-532-9262
▲ **SOUTHWEST AIRLINES CO**
2702 Love Field Dr, Dallas, TX 75235-1908
Tel (214) 792-4000 *Founded/Ownrshp* 1971
Sales 19.8MMM *EMP* 49,600
Accts Ernst & Young Llp Dallas Tex
Tkr Sym LUV *Exch* NYS
SIC 4512 Air transportation, scheduled; Air cargo carrier, scheduled; Air passenger carrier, scheduled
Ch Bd: Gary C Kelly
COO: Michael G Van De Ven
CFO: Tammy Romo
V Ch Bd: Ron Ricks
Chf Cred: Robert E Jordan
Ex VP: Deborah Ackerman
Ex VP: Jeff Lamb
Ex VP: Thomas M Nealon
Sr VP: Randolph J Babbit
Sr VP: Craig Drew
Sr VP: Ginger C Hardage
Sr VP: Brian Hirshman
Sr VP: Daryl Krause
Sr VP: Teresa Laraba
Sr VP: Mark R Shaw
Sr VP: Randy Sloan
Sr VP: Jack Smith
VP: Reid Grandle
VP: Justin Jones
Dir Bus: Bert Craus
Board of Directors: David W Biegler, J Veronica Biggins, Douglas H Brooks, William H Cunningham, John G Denison, Thomas W Gilligan, Nancy B Loeffler, John T Montford

D-U-N-S 12-258-2687
▲ **SOUTHWEST BANCORP INC**
608 S Main St, Stillwater, OK 74074-4059
Tel (405) 742-1800 *Founded/Ownrshp* 1981
Sales NA *EMP* 402[E]
Accts Bkd Llp Oklahoma City Oklaho
Tkr Sym OKSB *Exch* NGS
SIC 6021 National commercial banks
Pr: Mark W Funke
Ch Bd: Russell W Teubner
Pr: Matt Cassell
COO: Priscilla Barnes
CFO: Joe T Shockley Jr
Treas: Charles H Westerheide
Ex VP: Brent A Bates
Ex VP: Nick Boinpally
Ex VP: James D Bygland
Ex VP: John T Danielson
Ex VP: Rusty Laforge
Ex VP: Rusty N Laforge
Sr VP: Elaine Skillman
VP: Laura Briscoe
VP: Penny Holt
VP: Jerre Taylor
VP: Gary Teel

D-U-N-S 08-515-7964
SOUTHWEST BUSINESS CORP
SWBC
9311 San Pedro Ave # 600, San Antonio, TX 78216-4458
Tel (210) 525-1241 *Founded/Ownrshp* 1976
Sales NA *EMP* 1,800
SIC 6411 6162 6282 Insurance agents, brokers & service; Mortgage bankers & correspondents; Investment advice
Ch: Charles Amato
**Pr:* Gary Dudley
CEO: Joan Cleveland
CEO: Linda Hummel
**CFO:* Cindy Jorgensen
**Ex VP:* David Horne
Ex VP: Mark Ulmer
Sr VP: Timothy Anderson
Sr VP: Mark Berger
Sr VP: Jason O'Brien
VP: Nancy Ayotte
VP: Debby Divich
VP: Andrew Grove
VP: Scott McCabe
VP: Jeff Mortenson

D-U-N-S 05-564-9248
SOUTHWEST CANNING & PACKAGING INC (AZ)
(*Suby of* KALIL BOTTLING CO) ★
931 S Highland Ave, Tucson, AZ 85719-6728
Tel (520) 622-5811 *Founded/Ownrshp* 1969
Sales 88.1MM[E] *EMP* 780
SIC 2086 Carbonated beverages, nonalcoholic: bottled & canned
Pr: George Kalil
**VP:* John Kalil
Sales Exec: Steve Yankovick
Board of Directors: Frank Kalil

D-U-N-S 16-153-0308
SOUTHWEST CATHOLIC HEALTH NETWORK CORP
MERCY CARE PLAN
4350 E Cotton Center Blvd, Phoenix, AZ 85040-8852
Tel (602) 263-3000 *Founded/Ownrshp* 1985
Sales 1.8MMM *EMP* 500
SIC 8011 Health maintenance organization
CEO: Mark Fisher
Pr Dir: Jim Grosso

D-U-N-S 15-618-7465 EXP
SOUTHWEST CHEESE CO LLC
(*Suby of* GLANBIA PUBLIC LIMITED COMPANY)
1141 Cr N Ste 4, Clovis, NM 88101-9477
Tel (575) 742-9200 *Founded/Ownrshp* 2007
Sales 221.8MM[E] *EMP* 305
SIC 5143 2022 Cheese; Natural cheese
Dir Lab: Mary McWilliams

D-U-N-S 78-663-7405
SOUTHWEST COMMUNITY HEALTH SYSTEMS (INC)
SOUTHWEST GENERAL HOSPITAL
18697 Bagley Rd, Cleveland, OH 44130-3417
Tel (440) 816-8000 *Founded/Ownrshp* 1984
Sales 14.7M *EMP* 1,982
SIC 8062 General medical & surgical hospitals
Ch: Vasu Pandrangi
**Pr:* Thomas A Selden
**Treas:* James Bastian

D-U-N-S 00-843-8327
■ **SOUTHWEST CONVENIENCE STORES LLC**
7-ELEVEN
(*Suby of* ALON USA ENERGY INC) ★
4001 Penbrook St Ste 400, Odessa, TX 79762-5977
Tel (432) 580-8850 *Founded/Ownrshp* 2001
Sales 198.2MM[E] *EMP* 1,300[E]
SIC 5411 Convenience stores, chain
**CFO:* Claire Hart
Sr VP: Jonathan Ketchum
Dist Mgr: Deborah Fowler

D-U-N-S 06-226-9543
SOUTHWEST ELECTRIC CO
6503 Se 74th St, Oklahoma City, OK 73135-1100
Tel (800) 364-4445 *Founded/Ownrshp* 1946
Sales 103.7MM[E] *EMP* 370
Accts John Kmaranch
SIC 3825 3612 Transformers, portable: instrument; Specialty transformers
CEO: Roy Townsdin
**Pr:* Keith Nesbit
**CFO:* Mike Wilky
**VP:* John Maravich

Genl Mgr: Bruce Forsyth
Mktg Mgr: John Zink
Board of Directors: Eugene Gillespie, Norma Townsdin

D-U-N-S 15-722-1362
SOUTHWEST ELECTRICAL CONTRACTING SERVICES LTD
9435 E Loop 1604 N, Converse, TX 78109-9754
Tel (210) 568-1632 *Founded/Ownrshp* 2004
Sales 120.0MM *EMP* 195^E
SIC 1731 Electrical work
Pr: Ernie Ward
Genl Mgr: Joe Davis

SOUTHWEST FDSERVICE EXCELLENCE
See SOUTHWEST FOODSERVICE EXCELLENCE LLC

D-U-N-S 03-930-2259
SOUTHWEST FOODSERVICE EXCELLENCE LLC
SOUTHWEST FDSERVICE EXCELLENCE
9366 E Raintree Dr 101, Scottsdale, AZ 85260-2098
Tel (480) 551-6550 *Founded/Ownrshp* 2004
Sales 100.0MM *EMP* 20
SIC 5812 Concessionaire
Exec: Neal Cunningham
Assoc Dir: Nichole Emery
Assoc Dir: Sarah Stoudt

D-U-N-S 00-697-0917
▲ SOUTHWEST GAS CORP
5241 Spring Mountain Rd, Las Vegas, NV 89150-0002
Tel (702) 876-0711 *Founded/Ownrshp* 1931
Sales 2.4MMM *EMP* 2,219^E
Accts Pricewaterhousecoopers Llp La
Tkr Sym SWX *Exch* NYS
SIC 4923 1623 1389 Gas transmission & distribution; Water, sewer & utility lines; Construction, repair & dismantling services
Pr: John P Hester
**Ch Bd:* Michael J Melarkey
CFO: Roy R Centrella
Treas: Kenneth J Kenny
Ex VP: William N Moody
Sr VP: Eric Debonis
Sr VP: Karen S Haller
Sr VP: Edward A Janov
VP: Randall P Gabe
**VP:* Gregory J Peterson
VP: Anita M Romero
VP: Frank J Stanbrough
Board of Directors: Robert L Boughner, Jose A Cardenas, Thomas E Chestnut, Stephen C Comer, Leroy C Hanneman Jr, Anne L Mariucci, A Randall Thoman, Thomas A Thomas, Terrence L Wright

D-U-N-S 07-692-0859
SOUTHWEST GENERAL HEALTH CENTER
18697 Bagley Rd, Cleveland, OH 44130-3417
Tel (440) 816-8000 *Founded/Ownrshp* 1920
Sales 303.9MM *EMP* 2,500
SIC 8062 General medical & surgical hospitals
Pr: L Jon Schurmeier
Bd of Dir: Jason Fronek
Trst: Donald Williams
Ex VP: Janice Dunn
VP: Harry Hoyen
VP: Albert Matyas
VP: Ferdinand Plecha
VP: Susan Scheutzow
VP: Ajit Shah
Dir Lab: John Eschnauer
Dir Rx: Stacey Zorska

SOUTHWEST GENERAL HOSPITAL
See S C SAN ANTONIO INC

SOUTHWEST GENERAL HOSPITAL
See SOUTHWEST COMMUNITY HEALTH SYSTEMS (INC)

D-U-N-S 04-297-1457
SOUTHWEST GEORGIA OIL CO INC
TOTAL PETROLEUM
1711 E Shotwell St, Bainbridge, GA 39819-4349

Tel (229) 246-1553 *Founded/Ownrshp* 1990
Sales 295.8MM^E *EMP* 350
SIC 5171 5541 5411 5921 Petroleum bulk stations; Gasoline service stations; Convenience stores, independent; Beer (packaged); Wine
Pr: Michael Harrell
**VP:* Glennie Bench
**VP:* Aaron Goodman

D-U-N-S 80-132-8626 IMP
■ SOUTHWEST HEALTHCARE SYSTEM AUXILIARY
RANCHO SPRINGS MEDICAL CENTER
(*Suby of* UNIVERSAL HEALTH SERVICES INC) ★
25500 Medical Center Dr, Murrieta, CA 92562-5965
Tel (951) 696-6000 *Founded/Ownrshp* 1989
Sales 60.6M *EMP* 1,162
Accts John B Austin Temecula Ca
SIC 8062 8051 8059 4119 General medical & surgical hospitals; Skilled nursing care facilities; Convalescent home; Ambulance service
CEO: Brad Neet
**CFO:* Diane Moon
**CFO:* Barry Thorfenson
Chf Nrs Of: Anne Marie Watkins
Opers Mgr: Illya Esposito
Pathlgst: Duyet Vo

SOUTHWEST HEALTHCARE SYSTEMS INLAND VALLEY
See UNIVERSAL HEALTH SERVICES OF RANCHO SPRINGS INC

D-U-N-S 09-510-5029
SOUTHWEST INDEPENDENT SCHOOL DISTRICT
11914 Dragon Ln, San Antonio, TX 78252-2612
Tel (210) 622-4300 *Founded/Ownrshp* 1951
Sales 147.1MM *EMP* 1,500
Accts Coleman Horton & Company Llp
SIC 8211 Public elementary school; Public junior high school; Public senior high school
Pr Dir: Janice Hernandez

D-U-N-S 05-116-7559
SOUTHWEST INTERNATIONAL TRUCKS INC
3722 Irving Blvd, Dallas, TX 75247-5979
Tel (214) 689-1400 *Founded/Ownrshp* 1982
Sales 126.5MM^E *EMP* 200
SIC 5511 5531 Trucks, tractors & trailers: new & used; Truck equipment & parts
Pr: Gilbert R Trimble
**Sec:* Jane C Roth
**VP:* Shane R McBee

D-U-N-S 19-854-2214
SOUTHWEST IOWA RENEWABLE ENERGY LLC
10868 189th St, Council Bluffs, IA 51503-6925
Tel (712) 366-0392 *Founded/Ownrshp* 2005
Sales 319.5MM *EMP* 60
SIC 2869 2085 2046 Industrial organic chemicals; Ethyl alcohol, ethanol; Distillers' dried grains & solubles & alcohol; Corn syrup, dried or unmixed
Pr: Brian T Cahill
Ch Bd: Karol D King
CFO: Brett L Frevert
Sec: Theodore V Bauer
V Ch Bd: Matthew K Gibson
Sfty Mgr: Daniel Velasquez
Opers Mgr: Matt O'Grady
Plnt Mgr: Daniel D Wych
Board of Directors: Andrew J Bulloch, Michael K Guttau, Eric J Heismeyer, Hubert M Houser

D-U-N-S 19-977-8358
SOUTHWEST KEY PROGRAMS INC
SOUTH WEST KEY YOUNGTOWN
6002 Jain Ln, Austin, TX 78721-3104
Tel (512) 462-2181 *Founded/Ownrshp* 1987
Sales 159.1MM *EMP* 1,232
SIC 8361 Residential care for children; Halfway home for delinquents & offenders
Pr: Juan J Sanchez
**Treas:* Melody Chung
Comm Dir: Layla Fry
Prgrm Mgr: Aleah Penn
Genl Mgr: Billy Linson
Genl Mgr: Wan Sanchez
Dir IT: James Van
Pgrm Dir: Josie Cedillo
Pgrm Dir: Paulette Chambers
Pgrm Dir: Rachel Maldonado
Pgrm Dir: Clarissa Mitchell

D-U-N-S 00-694-6974
SOUTHWEST LOUISIANA ELECTRIC MEMBERSHIP CORP
SLEMCO
3420 Ne Evangeline Trwy, Lafayette, LA 70507-2554
Tel (337) 896-5384 *Founded/Ownrshp* 1937
Sales 198.4MM *EMP* 270
Accts Briscoe Burke & Grigsby Llp T
SIC 4911 Distribution, electric power
CEO: J U Gajan
**Pr:* Jerry F Meaux
**CFO:* Katherine Domingue
**Treas:* Dave L Aymond
**VP:* William R Huval
Comm Man: Mary Laurent
Comm Man: Mary A Lurent
CIO: Chris Smith

D-U-N-S 07-416-9962
SOUTHWEST LOUISIANA HOSPITAL ASSOCIATION
LAKE CHARLES MEMORIAL HOSPITAL
(*Suby of* SWLHS INC) ★
1701 Oak Park Blvd, Lake Charles, LA 70601-8911
Tel (337) 494-2121 *Founded/Ownrshp* 1950
Sales 262.8MM *EMP* 1,500
SIC 8062 General medical & surgical hospitals
Pr: Larry M Graham
CFO: Charles Whitson
Bd of Dir: Louis Todd
VP: Sherry Haley
VP: Bernita Loyd
Dir Risk M: David Usher
Dir Lab: Mary Stoma
Ex Dir: Erich Metcalf
CIO: Belinda Summers
Dir IT: Kevin Haymon
Netwrk Eng: Mike Prestridge

D-U-N-S 92-985-7548
SOUTHWEST LOUISIANA MEMORIAL FOUNDATION
1701 Oak Park Blvd, Lake Charles, LA 70601-8911
Tel (337) 494-3204 *Founded/Ownrshp* 1994
Sales 9.8MM^E *EMP* 1,400
Accts Price Waterhouse
SIC 8062 General medical & surgical hospitals
Pr: Larry Graham
**CFO:* Charles Witson

D-U-N-S 06-543-8822 IMP
SOUTHWEST MEDICAL CENTER OF OKLAHOMA (OK)
4401 S Western Ave, Oklahoma City, OK 73109-3413
Tel (405) 636-7000 *Founded/Ownrshp* 1964, 1986
Sales 77.2MM^E *EMP* 3,030
SIC 8062 General medical & surgical hospitals
Pr: Patricia Dorris

D-U-N-S 05-874-6574 IMP/EXP
SOUTHWEST METAL INDUSTRIES LLC
4708 W Pasadena Ave, Glendale, AZ 85301-7617
Tel (623) 760-9014 *Founded/Ownrshp* 2001
Sales 108.0MM^E *EMP* 15
SIC 5051 4953 Nonferrous metal sheets, bars, rods, etc.; Recycling, waste materials
Mng Pt: Mike Jaap
**Mng Pt:* Henry Fleet
CFO: Brian Walker

D-U-N-S 07-262-7599
SOUTHWEST MISSISSIPPI REGIONAL MEDICAL CENTER
215 Marion Ave, McComb, MS 39648-2705
Tel (601) 249-5500 *Founded/Ownrshp* 1969
Sales 139.7MM *EMP* 1,100
Accts Wm F Horne & Company Pllc
SIC 8062 Hospital, affiliated with AMA residency
CEO: Norman Price
CFO: Dan Jessup
**CFO:* Reece Nunnery
VP: Katie Wall
Dir Rad: Charles Regan
Doctor: Jeanny Gillory
HC Dir: Gary Heim

D-U-N-S 80-931-3450
SOUTHWEST NETWORK
2700 N Central Ave # 1050, Phoenix, AZ 85004-1217
Tel (602) 266-8402 *Founded/Ownrshp* 1999
Sales 86.0MM *EMP* 217^E
Accts Lb Mcgladrey Llp Phoenix Az
SIC 8741 Business management
CEO: Amy B Henning
VP: Vicki Gonzalez
Genl Mgr: Michelle Fornoff

D-U-N-S 18-691-9759 IMP
SOUTHWEST OFFSET PRINTING CO INC
13650 Gramercy Pl, Gardena, CA 90249-2453
Tel (310) 965-9154 *Founded/Ownrshp* 1990
Sales 94.7MM^E *EMP* 300
SIC 2752 Commercial printing, offset
CEO: Greg McDonald
COO: Dutch Greve
**CFO:* Art Spear
**VP:* Jennifer McDonald
VP: John Vigil
Exec: Brian Kelshaw
Exec: Robert Shennan
Genl Mgr: Rick West
CTO: Warren Dow
Mfg Dir: Ryan McDonald
Plnt Mgr: Bob Rohl

D-U-N-S 07-128-3832
SOUTHWEST OHIO REGIONAL TRANSIT AUTHORITY
SORTA
602 Main St Ste 1100, Cincinnati, OH 45202-2549
Tel (513) 621-4455 *Founded/Ownrshp* 1880, 1973
Sales 91.0MM^E *EMP* 865
Accts Clifton Gunderson Llp Toledo
SIC 4111 Bus line operations
CEO: Terry Garcia Cruz
V Ch: William L Mallory Sr
MIS Mgr: Thomas Vogelphl
Trfc Dir: Tom Lay

D-U-N-S 00-807-4072 IMP/EXP
SOUTHWEST OILFIELD PRODUCTS INC
(*Suby of* AMERICAN BLOCK MFG CO) ★
10340 Wallisville Rd, Houston, TX 77013-4138
Tel (713) 675-7541 *Founded/Ownrshp* 2015
Sales 119.3MM^E *EMP* 474
SIC 3533 3561

D-U-N-S 07-739-6224
SOUTHWEST POWER POOL INC
201 Worthen Dr, Little Rock, AR 72223-4936
Tel (501) 614-3200 *Founded/Ownrshp* 1941
Sales 164.1MM *EMP* 166^E
SIC 4911 Electric services
**Pr:* John J Marschewski
**Sr VP:* Nicolas Brown
IT Man: Tom Burdic
IT Man: Robert Garcia
IT Man: Todd Liles
Board of Directors: Graham Edwards, Bruce Scherr

D-U-N-S 00-793-6842 IMP
SOUTHWEST RESEARCH INSTITUTE INC (TX)
SWRI
6220 Culebra Rd, San Antonio, TX 78238-5100
Tel (210) 684-5111 *Founded/Ownrshp* 1947, 1966
Sales 592.3MM *EMP* 2,754
Accts Ernst & Young Llp San Antonio
SIC 8731 8711 Commercial physical research; Engineering services
Pr: Adam L Hamilton
CFO: Beth Ann Rafferty
Treas: Linda M Boehme
Treas: Beth Rafferty
Ex VP: Walter D Downing
Ex VP: Walter Downing
VP: Jack Ballard
VP: Kenneth H Bennett Jr
VP: Kenneth Bennett
VP: Jim Burch
VP: Susan Crumrine
VP: Danny Deffenbaugh
VP: Steve Dellenback
VP: Paul Easley
VP: Nigel Gale
VP: Lee Grant
VP: Mike Macnaughton
VP: Steve Marty
VP: Mary Massey
VP: David McComas
VP: John W McLeod
Board of Directors: Mary Ann Rankin, Wayne S Alexander, John B Roberts, Eugene L Ames Jr, Ricardo Romo, J Dan Bates, David S Zachry, Walter D Downing, A Baker Duncan, Roger R Hemminghaus, John C Korbell, Milton B Lee, Philip J Pfeiffer

D-U-N-S 11-877-4025
■ SOUTHWEST ROYALTIES INC
(*Suby of* CLAYTON WILLIAMS ENERGY INC) ★
6 Desta Dr Ste 2100, Midland, TX 79705-5556
Tel (432) 688-3008 *Founded/Ownrshp* 1983
Sales 109.0MM *EMP* 462
SIC 1311 6211 1389 Crude petroleum production; Natural gas production; Oil royalties dealers; Roustabout service
COO: Mel G Riggs
COO: R Keathley
**CFO:* Bill Coggin
**Sec:* H Allen Corey
**Sr VP:* Michael L Pollard
**VP:* Robert C Lyon
**VP:* T Mark Tisdale
Dir IT: Britt Priddy
Board of Directors: William P Nicoletti

SOUTHWEST SOUVENIRS
See PC INTERNATIONAL SALES INC

SOUTHWEST SOUVENIRS
See PRODUCT CENTRE - SW INC

D-U-N-S 96-482-3959 IMP/EXP
SOUTHWEST STAINLESS LP
SOUTHWEST STAINLESS, SUNBELT
(*Suby of* SHALE-INLAND) ★
515 Post Oak Blvd Ste 800, Houston, TX 77027-9432
Tel (713) 943-3544 *Founded/Ownrshp* 2012
Sales 657.7MM *EMP* 840
SIC 3498 5051 5085 Fabricated pipe & fittings; Pipe & tubing, steel; Valves & fittings
CEO: Frank Riddick
Pr: Michael L Stanwood
CFO: Gary Haire
Treas: Rick Hawthorne
Ex VP: Rob Broyles
Sr VP: Suzanne Mailes-Dineff
VP: Keith Barnard
VP: Larry Feld
VP: Jeff Legrand
Genl Mgr: EMI Sentell

SOUTHWEST STAINLESS, SUNBELT
See SOUTHWEST STAINLESS LP

D-U-N-S 06-770-5285
SOUTHWEST TENNESSEE ELECTRIC MEMBERSHIP CORP (TN)
STEMC
1009 E Main St, Brownsville, TN 38012-2652
Tel (731) 772-1322 *Founded/Ownrshp* 1936
Sales 109.2MM *EMP* 134
SIC 4911 Distribution, electric power
Pr: Kevin Murphy
**Pr:* Jack Fox
**Ch:* Alan Ferguson
**Sec:* Audrey Blue
**VP:* Billy Gordon
VP: Douglas Jonnida
**VP:* Phillip Mullins
**VP:* Mark Only
**VP:* Scott Sims

D-U-N-S 62-239-8154 IMP
SOUTHWEST TEXAS EQUIPMENT DISTRIBUTORS INC
MISSION RESTAURANT SUPPLY CO
1126 S Saint Marys St, San Antonio, TX 78210-1244
Tel (210) 354-0691 *Founded/Ownrshp* 1990
Sales 99.7MM^E *EMP* 145
SIC 5078 Ice making machines
Pr: A J Lewis III
**Treas:* John A Triplett
**VP:* Sherry Kruciak
**VP:* Liza B Lewis

D-U-N-S 08-498-1950 IMP
SOUTHWEST TRADERS INC
SWT STOCKTON
27565 Diaz Rd, Temecula, CA 92590-3411
Tel (951) 699-7800 *Founded/Ownrshp* 1977
Sales 492.3MM^E *EMP* 350
Accts Mayer Hoffman Mccann Pc Sa
SIC 5141 Food brokers
CEO: Ken Smith
**CFO:* Lynne Bredemeier
VP: Mike Bredemeier
VP: Karen Smith
VP Opers: Wayne Sullens
Opers Supe: Chris Dias
Opers Supe: Mike Osborne

SOUTHWEST TUBE MFG DIV
See WEBCO INDUSTRIES INC

D-U-N-S 80-174-7965
SOUTHWEST VOLUSIA HEALTHCARE CORP
ADVENTIST HEALTH SYSTEM SUNBEL
(*Suby of* ADVENTST HLTH SYSTM SUNBELT H) ★
1055 Saxon Blvd, Orange City, FL 32763-8468
Tel (386) 917-5000 *Founded/Ownrshp* 1999
Sales 158.5MM *EMP* 943^E
SIC 8062 General medical & surgical hospitals
CEO: Ed Noseworthy
Chf Path: Pedro N Yepes-Hoyos
Dir Risk M: Jill Pace
Dir Rx: Eugene Porvan
Off Admin: Susan Smith
CIO: Trish Stebbins
Dir IT: Jackie Adkins
Doctor: Daniel Garlick
Doctor: Williams Geers
Doctor: Steven Knight
Doctor: Winston Lightburn

D-U-N-S 15-116-1312
SOUTHWEST WASHINGTON HEALTH SYSTEM
PEACEHEALTH SOUTHWEST MED CTR
400 Ne Mother Joseph Pl, Vancouver, WA 98664-3200
Tel (360) 514-2000 *Founded/Ownrshp* 1983
Sales 7.9MM *EMP* 3,500^E
SIC 8741 Hospital management
Pr: Joe Kortum
Off Mgr: Susan Pagel
Dir IT: Peter Harvey
IT Man: Eric Rafferty

D-U-N-S 01-017-9716
SOUTHWEST WASHINGTON MEDICAL CENTER
CANCER CENTER
400 Ne Mother Joseph Pl, Vancouver, WA 98664-3200
Tel (360) 514-1900 *Founded/Ownrshp* 2001
Sales 573.7MM *EMP* 12
SIC 8011 Oncologist

CEO: Joe Kortum
Dir IT: Paul Dickson
Mktg Mgr: Chad Dillard

D-U-N-S 00-277-8694
SOUTHWEST WATER CO
(*Suby of* SW MERGER ACQUISITION CORP) ★
1325 N Grand Ave Ste 100, Covina, CA 91724-4044
Tel (626) 543-2500 *Founded/Ownrshp* 1954, 2010
Sales 602.3MM^E *EMP* 1,224
SIC 4941 4952 Water supply; Sewerage systems
CEO: Robert Carroll
Pr: Stephen C Held
**CFO:* Ben Smith
VP: John Brettl
**VP:* William K Dix
VP: Shelley Farnham
VP: Robert Kelly
VP: Keith C Rice
VP: Steven E Richardson
VP: Joe R Zimmeman
Mng Dir: Keith Fischer

D-U-N-S 07-314-8108
SOUTHWESTERN BAPTIST THEOLOGICAL SEMINARY
2001 W Seminary Dr, Fort Worth, TX 76115-1153
Tel (817) 923-1921 *Founded/Ownrshp* 1908
Sales 92.9MM^E *EMP* 1,250
SIC 8221 Theological seminary
Pr: Paige Patterson
**Pr:* Leighton P Patterson
Ex VP: Craig Blaising
**VP:* Michael C Hughes
**VP:* Greg Kingrey
VP: Thomas White
Exec: Dale Ford
Assoc Dir: Daniel Haase
Assoc Dir: Ryan Mulvaney
Assoc Dir: Tony Price
Assoc Dir: Andrew Selking

D-U-N-S 12-145-2809 IMP
■ **SOUTHWESTERN BELL MOBILE SYSTEMS LLC**
CINGULAR WIRELESS
(*Suby of* AT&T MOBILITY LLC) ★
5601 Legacy Dr, Plano, TX 75024-3504
Tel (972) 712-7305 *Founded/Ownrshp* 2002
Sales 510.3MM^E *EMP* 4,810
SIC 4812 Cellular telephone services
Pr: John T Stupka
COO: Pat Parker
VP: Wayne Watts
Plng Mgr: Bill Cotton
Snr Mgr: Mike Evans

D-U-N-S 12-175-8478
■ **SOUTHWESTERN BELL TELECOMMUNICATIONS INC**
AT&T
(*Suby of* AT&T INC) ★
1651 N Collins Blvd, Richardson, TX 75080-3658
Tel (972) 705-7658 *Founded/Ownrshp* 1983
Sales 96.9MM^E *EMP* 599
SIC 5065 5999 Telephone equipment; Telephone equipment & systems
Pr: Richard E Moore
**CFO:* Kelly R Waite
Assoc Dir: Robert Vrshek

SOUTHWESTERN COMPANY, THE
See SOUTHWESTERN/GREAT AMERICAN INC

D-U-N-S 00-694-8764
■ **SOUTHWESTERN ELECTRIC POWER CO**
AEP
(*Suby of* AEP) ★
1 Riverside Plz, Columbus, OH 43215-2355
Tel (614) 716-1000 *Founded/Ownrshp* 1912
Sales 1.7MMM *EMP* 1,468^E
SIC 4911 Generation, electric power; Distribution, electric power; Transmission, electric power
Ch Bd: Nicholas K Akins
**CFO:* Brian X Tierney
Board of Directors: Lisa M Barton, David M Feinberg, Lana L Hillebrand, Mark C McCullough, Robert P Powers, Dennis E Welch

D-U-N-S 00-690-2936
▲ **SOUTHWESTERN ENERGY CO INC**
10000 Energy Dr, Spring, TX 77389-4954
Tel (832) 796-1000 *Founded/Ownrshp* 1929
Sales 3.1MMM *EMP* 2,597
Tkr Sym SWN *Exch* NYS
SIC 1311 1382 Crude petroleum production; Oil & gas exploration services
CEO: William J Way
**Ch Bd:* Steven Mueller
**Pr:* Mark K Boling
CFO: Gregory Kerley
**CFO:* R Craig Owen
**Ex VP:* Jeffrey B Sherrick
Ex VP: William J Stein
**Sr VP:* John C Ale
Sr VP: John E Bergeron Jr
Sr VP: Randy L Curry
Sr VP: John D Thaeler
Sr VP: Doug Van Slambrouck
Sr VP: James W Vick
VP: Jim Bolander
VP: Paul Geiger
VP: Sheila Green
VP: Roy Hartstein
VP: Joanne Hresko
VP: Amber Kinnard
VP: John R Lee III
VP: Jenny McCauley
Board of Directors: John D Gass, Catherine A Kehr, Greg D Kerley, Kenneth R Mourton, Elliott Pew, Terry W Rathert, Alan H Stevens

D-U-N-S 06-226-4759
■ **SOUTHWESTERN ENERGY PRODUCTION CO INC**
(*Suby of* SOUTHWESTERN ENERGY CO INC) ★
2350 N Sam Houston Pkwy E, Houston, TX 77032-3100
Tel (281) 618-4700 *Founded/Ownrshp* 1959
Sales 538.8MM^E *EMP* 784
SIC 1382 1311 Oil & gas exploration services; Crude petroleum production; Natural gas production
Pr: Steven L Mueller
CFO: Greg D Kerley
CFO: Alan Stevens
Treas: William N Banks
Sr VP: Jeffrey B Sherrick
VP: Bill Banks
VP: Gene Hammons
VP: Jennifer Stewart
VP: John Thaeler
IT Man: Manuel Rodriguez
IT Man: Jamie Salinas

D-U-N-S 00-792-8104
SOUTHWESTERN FINANCIAL SERVICES CORP
SOUTHWESTERN LIFE INSURANCE CO
(*Suby of* LIFE RE CORP) ★
12001 N Cntl Expy Ste 800, Dallas, TX 75243
Tel (800) 792-4368 *Founded/Ownrshp* 1903, 2001
Sales NA *EMP* 473^E
SIC 6311 Life insurance
Pr: Chris C Stroup
**Treas:* Raymond A Eckert

D-U-N-S 06-854-7256
SOUTHWESTERN ILLINOIS COLLEGE COMMUNITY COLLEGE DISTRICT NO 522
2500 Carlyle Ave, Belleville, IL 62221-5899
Tel (618) 235-2700 *Founded/Ownrshp* 1947, 1967
Sales 15.2MM *EMP* 1,800
Accts Clifton Larson Allen Llp Bell
SIC 8222 8221 Junior colleges & technical institutes; Colleges universities & professional schools
Pr: Georgia Costello
Dir Vol: Pat Etling
**CFO:* Bernie Ysursa
VP: Staci Clayborne
VP: Mark Eichenlaub
Assoc Dir: Kelly Turner
CIO: James Riha
Dir IT: Ron Durrer
Dir IT: Austin Winkleman
IT Man: Lindaann Stork
Snr Mgr: Christie Stennett

D-U-N-S 08-226-1314
SOUTHWESTERN ILLINOIS HEALTH FACILITIES INC
ANDERSON HOSPITAL
6800 State Route 162, Maryville, IL 62062-8500
Tel (618) 288-5711 *Founded/Ownrshp* 1929
Sales 126.6MM *EMP* 900
SIC 8062 General medical & surgical hospitals
Pr: Keith Page
Chf Rad: Tom Hill
Ofcr: Patrick Smith
Comm Dir: Natalie Head
Dir Rx: Lynn Fromm
Adm Dir: Lisa Klaustermeier
Dir Sec: Norm Wilson
Nurse Mgr: Bernie Gisher
IT Man: Donna Wendel
Secur Mgr: Paul Head
Pr Dir: Lori St John

SOUTHWESTERN LIFE INSURANCE CO
See SOUTHWESTERN FINANCIAL SERVICES CORP

SOUTHWESTERN MEDICAL SCHOOL
See UNIVERSITY OF TEXAS SOUTHWESTERN MEDICAL CENTER

D-U-N-S 00-736-9713 IMP/EXP
■ **SOUTHWESTERN PUBLIC SERVICE CO** (NM)
XCEL ENERGY
(*Suby of* XCEL ENERGY INC) ★
Tyler At Sixth, Amarillo, TX 79101
Tel (303) 571-7511 *Founded/Ownrshp* 1921
Sales 1.7MMM *EMP* 1,282^E
SIC 4911 Electric services; Distribution, electric power; Generation, electric power; Transmission, electric power
Ch Bd: Ben Fowke
**Pr:* David T Hudson
**CFO:* Teresa S Madden
VP: Jeffrey S Savage
Board of Directors: Marvin E McDaniel Jr

D-U-N-S 83-803-6069
SOUTHWESTERN REGIONAL MEDICAL CENTER INC
CANCER TREATMENT CENTER TULSA
10109 E 79th St, Tulsa, OK 74133-4564
Tel (918) 286-5000 *Founded/Ownrshp* 1991
Sales 100.8MM^E *EMP* 400
SIC 8069 Cancer hospital
CEO: Richard Haldeman
**Ch Bd:* Richard J Stephenson
**Pr:* Steve Mackin
**COO:* John Jay Foley
COO: John McNeil
**Prin:* Morris J Coff
Off Mgr: Sandy Nassar
Cmptr Lab: Lori Maner
Dir QC: Debbie Allen
Mktg Dir: Eric Magnussen
Ansthlgy: Christopher Schmidt

D-U-N-S 07-460-2939
SOUTHWESTERN UNIVERSITY
1001 E University Ave, Georgetown, TX 78626-6107
Tel (512) 863-6511 *Founded/Ownrshp* 1835
Sales 89.5MM *EMP* 357^E
Accts Grant Thornton Lp Wichita Ks
SIC 8221 University
Pr: Dr Edward Burger
VP: Richard L Anderson
VP: Richard Anderson
VP: Elma Benavides
VP: Gerald Brody
VP: Julie Cowley
VP: Monty Curtis
VP: Craig Erwin
VP: Octivia Marcel
VP: Bob Mathis
VP: Bob Paver
Exec: Erika Berroth
Assoc Dir: Taylor Kidd
Assoc Dir: Jennifer O'Daniel
Assoc Dir: Grace Pyka
Assoc Dir: Scott Sandoval
Assoc Dir: Todd Watson

D-U-N-S 14-451-0864
SOUTHWESTERN VERMONT HEALTH CARE CORP
SOUTHWESTERN VERMONT MED CTR
100 Hospital Dr, Bennington, VT 05201-5004
Tel (802) 442-6361 *Founded/Ownrshp* 1910
Sales 9.4MM^E *EMP* 1,200^E
SIC 8741 Hospital management; Nursing & personal care facility management
CEO: Thomas A Dee
Pr: Michael Brady
COO: Mary Wicker
CFO: Thomas Lenkowski
CFO: Stephen D Majetich
CFO: Frank Skala
Ofcr: Judd Gregory
VP: Kevin Dailey
VP: Jennifer Fels
VP: Wayne Kachman
VP: Leslie Keefe
VP: Steve McClafferty
VP: Kevin McDonald
VP: Mark Novotny
VP: Rich Ogilvie
VP: Dianne Prpola
Exec: Jeff Morgan
Dir Soc: Virginia Cuddihy
Dir Rx: Michael Iglinski

SOUTHWESTERN VERMONT MED CTR
See SOUTHWESTERN VERMONT HEALTH CARE CORP

D-U-N-S 06-052-7645
SOUTHWESTERN VERMONT MEDICAL CENTER INC
100 Hospital Dr, Bennington, VT 05201-5004
Tel (802) 442-6361 *Founded/Ownrshp* 1910
Sales 142.7MM *EMP* 750
SIC 8062 General medical & surgical hospitals
CEO: Mark Novotny
**VP:* Thomas Lenkowski
Dir Rad: Terrell L Coffield

D-U-N-S 04-812-0711 IMP/EXP
SOUTHWESTERN/GREAT AMERICAN INC
SOUTHWESTERN COMPANY, THE
2451 Atrium Way, Nashville, TN 37214-5102
Tel (615) 391-2717 *Founded/Ownrshp* 1982
Sales 573.9MM^E *EMP* 1,000
SIC 5192 Books
CEO: Henry Bedford
Sr Pt: Dave Brown
Sr Pt: Amanda Johns
Sr Pt: Emmie Young
**Pr:* Daniel Moore
CFO: Bob Sircy
VP: David Causer
**VP:* Cynthia Johnstone
Genl Mgr: Jeff Young
IT Man: Derek Preston
Software D: John Palmer

SOUTHWICK
See GOLDEN FLEECE MANUFACTURING GROUP LLC

D-U-N-S 10-445-5618 IMP
SOUTHWIND FOODS LLC
GREAT AMERCN SEAFOOD IMPORT CO
20644 S Fordyce Ave, Carson, CA 90810-1018
Tel (323) 262-8222 *Founded/Ownrshp* 1999
Sales 232.6MM^E *EMP* 250
SIC 5146 5147 Fish & seafoods; Meats & meat products
Pr: Buddy Galletti
**CFO:* Don Sutherland
**VP:* Jim Elie
**VP:* Paul Galletti
**VP:* Sal Perri
Div Mgr: Ken Engasser
Div Mgr: Terry Veenendaal
Off Mgr: Claudia Guerra
Plnt Mgr: Alex Barajas
Sales Asso: Maria Vasquez

D-U-N-S 00-326-4421 IMP/EXP
SOUTHWIRE CO LLC (GA)
1 Southwire Dr, Carrollton, GA 30119-4400
Tel (770) 832-4242 *Founded/Ownrshp* 1952
Sales 2.1MMM^E *EMP* 7,000
SIC 3351 3355 3357 3599

SOUTHWIRE COLEMAN
See COLEMAN CABLE LLC

D-U-N-S 00-262-5721 IMP/EXP
SOUTHWORTH-MILTON INC (NH)
CATERPILLAR AUTHORIZED DEALER
100 Quarry Dr, Milford, MA 01757-1729
Tel (508) 634-3400 *Founded/Ownrshp* 1960
Sales 719.9MM^E *EMP* 1,300
SIC 5082 7353 General construction machinery & equipment; Heavy construction equipment rental
CEO: Christopher G Milton
**CEO:* Jack W Milton
**VP:* Stephen Boyd
VP: Scott Martel
Genl Mgr: Erik Sveden
IT Man: David Convery
IT Man: Brian Saucier
Sls Dir: Larry Cutliffe
Sls Mgr: Johnathan Davis

SOUTHWSTRN ELEC SERV COMPANY
See PXU ELECTRIC DELIVERY

D-U-N-S 03-185-6195
SOUTO FOODS LLC (GA)
3077 Mccall Dr Ste 5, Atlanta, GA 30340-2832
Tel (404) 317-0674 *Founded/Ownrshp* 2010
Sales 87.0MM *EMP* 20
SIC 5141 Food brokers

D-U-N-S 78-782-6072 IMP
SOVENA USA INC
(*Suby of* SOVENA OILSEEDS PORTUGAL, S.A.)
1 Olive Grove St, Rome, NY 13441-4815
Tel (315) 797-7070 *Founded/Ownrshp* 1991
Sales 220.5MM *EMP* 165
SIC 5149 Cooking oils
Ch Bd: Luis Arriba
**Ch Bd:* Jorge Demello
**Pr:* Antonio Simoes
**CEO:* Luis Gato
**Treas:* Jennifer Kiehn
**VP:* Frank Talarico
Plnt Mgr: Steven Barnes

D-U-N-S 60-701-2143 IMP/EXP
SOVEREIGN DISTRIBUTORS INC
AVALON FLOORING
2030 Springdale Rd, Cherry Hill, NJ 08003-2052
Tel (856) 489-4996 *Founded/Ownrshp* 1992
Sales 103.7MM^E *EMP* 315
SIC 5713 Floor covering stores
Pr: Maryanne Adams
**CFO:* Ron Martignoni
Bd of Dir: Mary Millar
Sr VP: Jason Paradis
Opers Mgr: Frederick Beach

D-U-N-S 13-920-8677
SOVEREIGN HEALTHCARE LLC
5887 Glenridge Dr Ste 150, Atlanta, GA 30328-5577
Tel (404) 574-2033 *Founded/Ownrshp* 2003
Sales 102.2MM^E *EMP* 2,500
SIC 8051 Skilled nursing care facilities

D-U-N-S 93-259-1761
■ **SOVRAN ACQUISITION LIMITED PARTNERSHIP**
(*Suby of* LIFE STORAGE INC) ★
6467 Main St, Williamsville, NY 14221-5856
Tel (716) 633-1850 *Founded/Ownrshp* 1995
Sales 291.4MM^E *EMP* 1,051^E
SIC 6798 Real estate investment trusts
Ch Bd: Robert J Attea
**Pr:* Kenneth F Myszka
**CFO:* David L Rogers
Board of Directors: James R Boldt, John Burns, Anthony P Gammie, Charles E Lannon

D-U-N-S 07-862-2322 IMP/EXP
■ **SP FIBER TECHNOLOGIES SOUTHEAST LLC**
(*Suby of* WESTROCK SP CO) ★
709 Papermill Rd, Dublin, GA 31027-2494
Tel (478) 272-1600 *Founded/Ownrshp* 2012
Sales 201.3MM^E *EMP* 351^E
SIC 2621 Catalog, magazine & newsprint papers
CEO: Allen Byrd

D-U-N-S 02-064-5206
▲ **SP PLUS CORP**
200 E Randolph St # 7700, Chicago, IL 60601-7702
Tel (312) 274-2000 *Founded/Ownrshp* 1929
Sales 1.6MMM *EMP* 21,974
Tkr Sym SP *Exch* NGS
SIC 7521 7514 Automobile parking; Parking lots; Rent-a-car service
Pr: G Marc Baumann
**Ch Bd:* James A Wilhelm
Pr: Tracy Pelham
Pr: Robert M Toy
CFO: Vance C Johnston
Ofcr: Gerard M Klaisle
Ex VP: William H Bodenhamer Jr
Ex VP: Hector O Chevalier
Ex VP: Thomas L Hagerman
Ex VP: John Ricchiuto
Ex VP: Robert N Sacks
Sr VP: Mike Drow
Sr VP: Jeff Eckerling
Sr VP: Vincent Raguseo
VP: Andrew Tedrick
VP Bus Dev: Jim Wilhelm
Dir Bus: Roamy Valera
Board of Directors: Karen M Garrison, Paul Halpern, Robert S Roath, Wyman T Roberts, Douglas R Waggoner, Jonathan P Ward, Gordon H Woodward

SP SCIENTIFIC
See S P INDUSTRIES INC

D-U-N-S 02-396-0755
SP WIND DOWN INC
(*Suby of* MMODAL SERVICES INC) ★
9009 Carothers Pkwy # 303, Franklin, TN 37067-1704
Tel (615) 261-1500 *Founded/Ownrshp* 2010
Sales 58.2MM^E *EMP* 5,382
Accts Securities And Exchange Commis
SIC 7338 Stenographic services
Pr: Steven E Simpson
Sr VP: Alan Whorton
VP: Michael McKee
VP: John Rhome
VP: Kim Vernon
Opers Supe: Sandra Jacobson
Corp Couns: Diana Sandoval
Board of Directors:

D-U-N-S 16-190-4102
SPA RESORT CASINO
401 E Amado Rd, Palm Springs, CA 92262-6403
Tel (888) 999-1995 *Founded/Ownrshp* 1960
Sales 57.2MM^E *EMP* 1,000^E
SIC 7011 Resort hotel
Genl Mgr: Kato Moy
Owner: Agvahgue Eahilla Indian
Exec: Maria Mendoza
Snr Mgr: Jeff Pepple

D-U-N-S 07-919-2969
SPACE COAST CREDIT UNION (FL)
EASTERN FINANCIAL FLORIDA CRED
8045 N Wickham Rd, Melbourne, FL 32940-7920
Tel (321) 259-6219 *Founded/Ownrshp* 1951
Sales NA *EMP* 320
SIC 6062 State credit unions, not federally chartered
Pr: Douglas R Samuels
COO: Tony Tomlinson
CFO: Thomas Baldwin
Bd of Dir: Donna Mascolo
Ex VP: Tom Baldwin
Sr VP: Tanya R Boggs
VP: David P Avone
VP: David Pavone Gone
VP: Linda Hart
VP: Donna Johnson
VP: Steve Koniecki

D-U-N-S 13-056-6375
■ SPACE COAST HEALTH FOUNDATION INC
HMA
(*Suby of* HMA) ★
6905 N Wickham Rd Ste 301, Melbourne, FL 32940-7551
Tel (321) 241-6600 *Founded/Ownrshp* 2010
Sales 4.2MM *EMP* 2,391
SIC 8399 Community action agency
Ex Dir: Johnette Gindling
COO: Rick Brown
COO: Rich Koleda
Ofcr: Kelly Sullivan
Comm Man: Debbie Bohacs
Chf Nrs Of: Sue Beauregard
**Prin:* Bill Bancroft
**Prin:* James Dwight
**Prin:* Fran Pickett
**Prin:* Larry Schultz
Ex Dir: Charles Biehl

SPACE COMPONENTS
See ATK SPACE SYSTEMS INC

SPACE DESIGNS
See PIVOT INTERIORS INC

SPACE DYNAMICS LABORATORY
See UTAH STATE UNIVERSITY RESEARCH FOUNDATION

D-U-N-S 12-040-6462 IMP/EXP
SPACE EXPLORATION TECHNOLOGIES CORP
SPACEX
Rocket Rd, Hawthorne, CA 90250
Tel (310) 363-6000 *Founded/Ownrshp* 2002
Sales 1.1MMM^E *EMP* 3,000
SIC 3761 Rockets, space & military, complete
CEO: Elon R Musk
**Pr:* Gwynne Shotwell
**CFO:* Bret Johnsen
Sr VP: Mark Bitterman
VP: Bulent Altan
VP: Tim Buzza
VP: Jinnah Hosein
VP: Mark Juncosa
VP: Hans Koenigsmann
VP: Andrew Lambert
VP: Barry Matsumori
VP: Tom Mueller
VP: Bob Reagan
VP: Robert Reagan

D-U-N-S 03-572-6319
SPACE GATEWAY SUPPORT LLC
1235 Evans Rd, Melbourne, FL 32904-2314
Tel (321) 853-3393 *Founded/Ownrshp* 2000
Sales 85.4MM^E *EMP* 1,500
SIC 1531 Operative builders

D-U-N-S 00-227-9123 IMP/EXP
SPACE SYSTEMS/LORAL LLC
SSL
(*Suby of* MACDONALD, DETTWILER AND ASSOCIATES LTD)
3825 Fabian Way, Palo Alto, CA 94303-4604
Tel (650) 852-7320 *Founded/Ownrshp* 2012
Sales 443.8MM^E *EMP* 1,400
SIC 4899 3663 Satellite earth stations; Satellites, communications
Pr: John Celli
Pr: Barbara Ellis
Pr: Ed McFarlane
CFO: Ron Haley
CFO: Ronald A Hley
CFO: Michael Santoro
Ex VP: Paul Estey
Ex VP: Alexis Livanos
Sr VP: David Bernstein
Sr VP: Richard Currier
Sr VP: Arnold Friedman
Sr VP: Bill McCombe
Sr VP: Richard White
VP: Julie Bannerman
VP: Hampton Chan
VP: Tony Colucci
VP: Mouctar Diallo
VP: Michael Gold
VP: Chris Goodman
VP: Brian Kosinski
VP: Don McClure

SPACELABS HEALTH CARE
See SPACELABS HEALTHCARE (WASHINGTON) INC

D-U-N-S 14-558-1588 IMP/EXP
■ SPACELABS HEALTHCARE (WASHINGTON) INC
SPACELABS HEALTH CARE
(*Suby of* OSI SYSTEMS INC) ★
35301 Se Center St, Snoqualmie, WA 98065-9216
Tel (425) 396-3300 *Founded/Ownrshp* 2004
Sales 154.3MM^E *EMP* 1,250
SIC 3845 3841 3575 7699 7378 Patient monitoring apparatus; Diagnostic apparatus, medical; Computer terminals, monitors & components; Hospital equipment repair services; Computer peripheral equipment repair & maintenance
CEO: Deepak Chopra
Pr: Eugene Defelice
**Pr:* Kujit Sumar
**CFO:* Alan Edrick
**Treas:* Patrick Ip
Sr VP: Timothy Miskimon
VP: Wolfgang Schraml
Dir IT: Mark Bryant
IT Man: Vikram Balaji
IT Man: Beth Bennett
IT Man: Julie Larson

D-U-N-S 36-338-0036
■ SPACELABS HEALTHCARE INC
(*Suby of* OSI SYSTEMS INC) ★
35301 Se Center St, Snoqualmie, WA 98065-9216
Tel (425) 396-3302 *Founded/Ownrshp* 2005
Sales 100.1MM^E *EMP* 1,250^E
SIC 3841 3845 3575 7699 7378 Surgical & medical instruments; Ultrasonic medical equipment, except cleaning; Patient monitoring apparatus; Computer terminals, monitors & components; Hospital equipment repair services; Computer peripheral equipment repair & maintenance
CEO: Deepak Chopra
**Pr:* Nicholas Ong
**CFO:* Alan Edrick
VP: Pat Cline
VP: Scott Dalebout
VP: David Hinton
VP: Leslie Honda
VP: Timothy Miskimon
VP: Brandt Sonzongi
VP: Ron Tobia
Genl Mgr: Bob Brooks

D-U-N-S 00-643-2918 IMP/EXP
SPACESAVER CORP (WI)
(*Suby of* KI) ★
1450 Janesville Ave, Fort Atkinson, WI 53538-2798
Tel (920) 563-6362 *Founded/Ownrshp* 1963
Sales 165.1MM^E *EMP* 520
SIC 2542 Partitions & fixtures, except wood
Pr: Paul Olsen
VP: Nicki Johnson
**VP:* Mary Schrimpf
Exec: Rhonda Cunningham
Snr Sftwr: Eric Wipperfurth
Dir IT: Matthew Bergman
Dir IT: Kristy Dobel
Dir IT: Erik Schmidt
Sfty Dirs: Jake Lowell
Prd Mgr: Clate Bogan
Prd Mgr: Marty Weber

SPACEX
See SPACE EXPLORATION TECHNOLOGIES CORP

D-U-N-S 09-289-9137
SPADA PROPERTIES INC
UNITED SALAD CO.
8448 Ne 33rd Dr Ste 100, Portland, OR 97211-2105
Tel (503) 288-8300 *Founded/Ownrshp* 1965
Sales 244.4MM^E *EMP* 500
SIC 5148 Fresh fruits & vegetables
Pr: Ernest Spada

SPAGHETTI WAREHOUSE ITLN GRILL
See CONSOLIDATED RESTAURANT OPERATIONS INC

D-U-N-S 80-138-7171
SPAGHETTI WAREHOUSE RESTAURANTS INC
(*Suby of* SWRI AQUISITION COMPANY, LLC)
1815 N Market St, Dallas, TX 75202-1809
Tel (949) 336-5111 *Founded/Ownrshp* 2007
Sales 31.7MM^E *EMP* 1,387
SIC 5812 Italian restaurant
CEO: Doug Pak
V Ch: John D Harkey Jr
**Pr:* Azam Malik
**CFO:* Robert Trebing
Site Mgr: Patrick Wager

D-U-N-S 12-724-3298 IMP/EXP
SPANCRETE GROUP INC
N16 W 23415 Stone Rdge Dr St N 16, Waukesha, WI 53188
Tel (414) 290-9000 *Founded/Ownrshp* 2000
Sales 109.0MM^E *EMP* 325
SIC 3272 3531 Concrete products; Construction machinery
CEO: John Nagy
**Pr:* Alan Antoniewicz
**CFO:* Todd Backus
Treas: Lyle Norman
**VP:* Scott Bertschinger
**VP:* Jim Clapper
**VP:* Robert S McCormack
VP: John Wang
Prgrm Mgr: Jenni Burgmeier
Genl Mgr: Edward Gross
Genl Mgr: Rick Vandesand

D-U-N-S 00-433-4694 IMP/EXP
SPANG & CO
SPANG POWER ELECTRONICS
110 Delta Dr, Pittsburgh, PA 15238-2806
Tel (412) 963-9363 *Founded/Ownrshp* 1894, 1908
Sales 106.8MM^E *EMP* 450
SIC 3672 3944 3612 3613 3312 Printed circuit boards; Games, toys & children's vehicles; Power transformers, electric; Panelboards & distribution boards, electric; Blast furnaces & steel mills
Pr: Frank E Rath Jr
**CFO:* Robert C Harbage
**Treas:* Frederick J Artz
VP: Lowell Bosley
**VP:* Michael J Reilly
Dir IT: Brian Buddemeyer
Dir IT: Brian Huddle
Dir IT: Gary Williams
IT Man: Richard Durham
Sftwr Eng: Steven Ammerman
Netwrk Eng: Michael Amurgis
Board of Directors: David F Rath

SPANG POWER ELECTRONICS
See SPANG & CO

D-U-N-S 05-516-5518
SPANGLER COMPANIES INC
1110 E Morehead St, Charlotte, NC 28204-2815
Tel (704) 372-4500 *Founded/Ownrshp* 1966
Sales 618.8MM^E *EMP* 2,100
SIC 6799 Venture capital companies
Ch Bd: Anna Spangler Nelson
**Pr:* W D Cornwell Jr
**Pr:* William D Cornwell
**Sr VP:* Stephen Cornwell
**Sr VP:* Steven W Dixon

D-U-N-S 01-993-5444 EXP
▲ SPANISH BROADCASTING SYSTEM INC
SBS
7007 Nw 77th Ave, Miami, FL 33166-2836
Tel (305) 441-6901 *Founded/Ownrshp* 1983
Sales 146.9MM *EMP* 567^E
Tkr Sym SBSA *Exch* NGM
SIC 4832 4833 Radio broadcasting stations; Television broadcasting stations
Ch Bd: Raul Alarcon
COO: Albert Rodriguez
**CFO:* Joseph A Garcia
Board of Directors: Manuel E Machado, Alan B Miller, Jason L Shrinsky, Gary B Stone, Jose A Villamil, Mitchell A Yelen

D-U-N-S 60-711-7942
SPANLINK COMMUNICATIONS INC
(*Suby of* CONVERGEONE HOLDINGS CORP) ★
5940 Golden Hills Dr, Minneapolis, MN 55416-1040
Tel (763) 971-2000 *Founded/Ownrshp* 2014
Sales 85.2MM^E *EMP* 122
SIC 7373 7371 Value-added resellers, computer systems; Computer software development & applications
Pr: Paul Maier
**CFO:* Terry Brill
**Ex VP:* Mark Langanki
**Ex VP:* Scott Vincent
VP: Paul Martin
Snr Sftwr: Andy Bauer
Dir IT: Gary Mahle
IT Man: Skip Singer
VP Sls: Ralph Flamini
Mktg Mgr: Terri Kocon
Manager: August Baecker

D-U-N-S 61-905-1761 IMP
■ SPANSION INC
(*Suby of* CYPRESS SEMICONDUCTOR CORP) ★
198 Champion Ct, San Jose, CA 95134-1709
Tel (408) 962-2500 *Founded/Ownrshp* 2015
Sales 940.8MM^E *EMP* 3,893
SIC 3674 Semiconductors & related devices; Integrated circuits, semiconductor networks, etc.; Semiconductor diodes & rectifiers
Pr: John H Kispert
Pr: Akinori Kobayashi
Pr: Gary Wang
**CFO:* Randy W Furr
Ex VP: Jeffrey W Davis
Ex VP: Glenda Dorchak
Ex VP: Glenda M Dorchak
Ex VP: Tom EBY
Ex VP: Jose Mejia
Ex VP: Louis Parrillo
Ex VP: Jim Reid
Sr VP: Robin J Jigour
Sr VP: Jay Legenhausen
Sr VP: Joseph T Rauschmayer
VP: SL Chan
VP: Doug Duval
VP: Jean-Marc Julia
VP: Steve Kwon
VP: George Minassian
VP: Carmine Renzulli
VP: Stephan Rosner

D-U-N-S 07-270-2004
▲ SPAR GROUP INC
333 Westchester Ave S204, White Plains, NY 10604-2932
Tel (914) 332-4100 *Founded/Ownrshp* 1943
Sales 119.2MM *EMP* 17,100^E
Tkr Sym SGRP *Exch* NAS
SIC 7389 8732 Inventory stocking service; Market analysis or research
Pr: Scott Popaditch
**Ch Bd:* Robert G Brown
COO: Kori G Belzer
CFO: James R Segreto
**V Ch Bd:* William H Bartels
Sr VP: Dave Manchester
Board of Directors: Arthur B Drogue, R Eric McCarthey, Jack W Partridge

D-U-N-S 02-376-8880
■ SPAR MARKETING FORCE INC
(*Suby of* SPAR GROUP INC) ★
333 Westc Ave South Build, White Plains, NY 10604
Tel (914) 332-4100 *Founded/Ownrshp* 2002
Sales 27.3MM^E *EMP* 1,000
SIC 8742 Merchandising consultant
CEO: Robert Brown
**Pr:* William H Bartels

D-U-N-S 09-173-2545
SPARBOE FARMS INC (MN)
23577 Mn Hwy 22, Litchfield, MN 55355
Tel (320) 693-7241 *Founded/Ownrshp* 1946, 2005
Sales 105.4MM^E *EMP* 450
SIC 2015 Egg processing
CEO: Beth Sparboe Schnell

D-U-N-S 00-224-7067 IMP
SPARBOE FOODS LLC (MN)
23577 Minnesota Hwy 22, Litchfield, MN 55355-5841
Tel (320) 593-9600 *Founded/Ownrshp* 1996
Sales 83.0MM^E *EMP* 500
SIC 2015 Egg processing
Pr: Beth Sparboe Schnell
**Prin:* Robert Schnell
VP Opers: Ross Sharp

D-U-N-S 07-941-7907
▲ SPARK ENERGY INC
12140 Wickchester Ln, Houston, TX 77079-1219
Tel (713) 600-2600 *Founded/Ownrshp* 1999
Sales 358.1MM *EMP* 189^E
Tkr Sym SPKE *Exch* NGS
SIC 4931 4911 Electric & other services combined; Electric services
Ch Bd: W Keith Maxwell III
Pr: Nathan Kroeker
CFO: Robert Lane
Ex VP: Jason Garrett
VP: Gil Melman

D-U-N-S 03-759-7437
■ SPARK ENERGY LLC
(*Suby of* SPARK ENERGY INC) ★
12140 Wickchester Ln, Houston, TX 77079-1219
Tel (713) 977-5634 *Founded/Ownrshp* 2002
Sales 156.0MM^E *EMP* 146^E
SIC 4911 Distribution, electric power
Pr: Nathan Kroeker
Pt: Waters Davis
Pt: Terry Guth
Pt: Terry D Jones
Pt: Nathen Kroeker
Pr: Dennis Vermette
CEO: William Keith Maxwell III
COO: Allison Wall
CFO: Mandy Bush
CFO: Georganne Hodges
Ex VP: Jason Garrett
VP: Gil Melman

SPARKLING IMAGE
See WASH DEPOT HOLDINGS INC

SPARKS HEALTH SYSTEM
See FORTH SMITH HMA LLC

SPARKS HEALTH SYSTEMS
See SPARKS REGIONAL MEDICAL CENTER

D-U-N-S 80-651-1361
SPARKS MARKETING GROUP INC
2828 Charter Rd, Philadelphia, PA 19154-2111
Tel (800) 925-7727 *Founded/Ownrshp* 2006
Sales 89.9MM^E *EMP* 400^E
Accts Mc Gladrey & Pullen Llp Blue
SIC 7389 Advertising, promotional & trade show services
Ch: Jeffrey Harrow
CEO: Scott Tarte
CFO: Bob Ginsberg
Treas: Art Augugliaro
VP: Geoff Albro
VP: Angel Carra
VP: Karolyn Chebookjian
VP: Jane Hawley
VP: Paul Martin
VP: Cynthia McArthur
Dir Soc: Angeline Merlitti
Dir Soc: Alexandra Weiss
Creative D: Rod Morton
Creative D: Autumn Oser
Board of Directors: Robert B Ginsburg

D-U-N-S 03-496-6523
SPARKS NUGGET INC
JOHN ASCUAGA'S NUGGET
(*Suby of* COLORADO BELL AND CASINO) ★
1100 Nugget Ave, Sparks, NV 89431-5750
Tel (775) 356-3300 *Founded/Ownrshp* 2016
Sales 226.5MM^E *EMP* 2,800
SIC 7011 Casino hotel
Pr: John J Ascuaga
**COO:* Stephen Ascuaga
**Sec:* Rose Ascuaga
**Exec:* Vern Sohrt
Exec: John Spillman
Advt Mgr: Randy Kennedy

D-U-N-S 07-567-5447
■ SPARKS REGIONAL MEDICAL CENTER
SPARKS HEALTH SYSTEMS
(*Suby of* HMA) ★
1001 Towson Ave, Fort Smith, AR 72901-4992
Tel (479) 441-4000 *Founded/Ownrshp* 1887
Sales 281.9MM *EMP* 2,300
SIC 8062 General medical & surgical hospitals
CEO: Jeremy Drinkwitz
Prin: Dennis Bauer
Brnch Mgr: Teresa Thornton
Genl Mgr: Alisa Simmons
Off Mgr: Jennifer Dobbs
Off Mgr: Courtney Phelan
Off Mgr: Lisa Williams
Off Admin: Ouida Pillstrom
Mktg Dir: Jillian Waters
Sls Mgr: Kay Underwood
Doctor: Manar S Ibrahim

SPARKS SANITATION
See RENO DISPOSAL CO

D-U-N-S 14-796-3599
SPARROW HEALTH SYSTEM
1215 E Michigan Ave, Lansing, MI 48912-1811
Tel (517) 364-1000 *Founded/Ownrshp* 1984
Sales 1.1MMM *EMP* 3,400
Accts Ernst & Young Llp
SIC 8062 7991 General medical & surgical hospitals; Athletic club & gymnasiums, membership
Pr: Dennis A Swan
V Ch: Jae Evans
V Ch: Johathan Raven
COO: Sandra Moore
CFO: Paula Reichle
Treas: Patrick Burns
Bd of Dir: Patricia Hollenbeck
Bd of Dir: Beth Jungel
**Ex VP:* Andrea Price
Sr VP: Ira R Ginsburg
VP: Richard Allen
VP: Thomas A Bres
**VP:* Mark Brett
VP: James A Budzinski

VP: Ira Gewolb
VP: Peter Graham
VP: David Johnson
VP: Ron Swenson
Dir Lab: R Horowitz
Dir Rx: John A Piasecki

D-U-N-S 00-503-6728 IMP/EXP
SPARTAN CHEMICAL CO INC (OH)
1110 Spartan Dr, Maumee, OH 43537-1725
Tel (419) 897-5551 *Founded/Ownrshp* 1956
Sales 98.4MM^E *EMP* 231^E
SIC 2842 Specialty cleaning, polishes & sanitation goods; Floor waxes; Disinfectants, household or industrial plant
CEO: Stephen H Swigart
**Pr:* John Swigart
**CFO:* Scott M Libbe
**VP:* Kenneth G Ford
**VP:* James R Lenardson
**VP:* Jim Lenardson
**VP:* William J Schalitz
CIO: Kelly Designore
IT Man: Tina Etts-Serio
Board of Directors: James R Lenardson, Scott M Libbe, John W Swigart, Stephen H Swigart

D-U-N-S 00-629-7493 IMP/EXP
SPARTAN LIGHT METAL PRODUCTS INC (IL)
510 E Mcclurken Ave, Sparta, IL 62286-1850
Tel (618) 443-4346 *Founded/Ownrshp* 1961
Sales 137.0MM *EMP* 600
Accts Uhy Llp St Louis Missouri
SIC 3363 3364 3369 3365 Aluminum die-castings; Magnesium & magnesium-base alloy die-castings; Nonferrous foundries; Aluminum foundries
Pr: Donald A Jubel
CFO: Ed Bean
Ex VP: Mike Sparks
VP: Mike Dierks
VP: Scott Homan
VP: Kevin Monahan
Genl Mgr: Jeremy Long
IT Man: Jennifer Hanna
Tech Mgr: Bob Sandre
Sfty Mgr: Bill Reed
Ql Cn Mgr: Erica Agley

D-U-N-S 61-055-5554 IMP
SPARTAN LIGHT METAL PRODUCTS LLC
(*Suby of* SPARTAN LIGHT METAL PRODUCTS INC) ★
2510 Lakeview Rd, Mexico, MO 65265-1391
Tel (573) 581-2272 *Founded/Ownrshp* 1994
Sales 99.0MM *EMP* 225^E
Accts Uhy Llp St Louis Missouri
SIC 3363 3364 3369 3365 Aluminum die-castings; Magnesium & magnesium-base alloy die-castings; Nonferrous foundries; Aluminum foundries
CEO: Donald Jubel

D-U-N-S 06-017-8811 IMP/EXP
▲ SPARTAN MOTORS INC
1541 Reynolds Rd, Charlotte, MI 48813-2099
Tel (517) 543-6400 *Founded/Ownrshp* 1975
Sales 550.4MM *EMP* 1,900
Tkr Sym SPAR *Exch* NGS
SIC 3711 3714 7519 Chassis, motor vehicle; Fire department vehicles (motor vehicles), assembly of; Ambulances (motor vehicles), assembly of; Motor vehicle parts & accessories; Utility trailer rental
Pr: Daryl M Adams
**Ch Bd:* Hugh W Sloan Jr
Pr: John A Forbes
Pr: Steve Guillaume
Pr: John W Slawson
CFO: Frederick J Sohm
CFO: Lori Wade
Treas: Greg Salchow
Ex Ofcr: Arthur D Ickes
VP: Thomas T Kivell
Exec: Dee Clements
Board of Directors: Richard R Current, Richard F Dauch, Ronald Harbour, Andrew M Rooke, James A Sharman, James C Orchard

D-U-N-S 61-538-0420
SPARTAN OFFSHORE DRILLING LLC
(*Suby of* SPARTAN OFFSHORE INTERMEDIATE LLC) ★
516 J F Smith Ave, Slidell, LA 70460-4686
Tel (504) 885-7449 *Founded/Ownrshp* 2002
Sales 133.1MM *EMP* 337
SIC 3533 Gas field machinery & equipment; Oil field machinery & equipment
CEO: Paul Butler
**CFO:* Chris Hellyer

D-U-N-S 07-915-8779
SPARTAN OFFSHORE INTERMEDIATE LLC
(*Suby of* SPARTAN OFFSHORE HOLDINGS, LLC)
516 J F Smith Ave, Slidell, LA 70460-4686
Tel (504) 885-7449 *Founded/Ownrshp* 2007
Sales 133.1MM^E *EMP* 338^E
SIC 3533 Gas field machinery & equipment
CEO: Paul Butler
CFO: Doy Dugan

D-U-N-S 06-193-5839
SPARTAN SECURITY SERVICES INC
(*Suby of* TEMCO FACILITY SERVICES) ★
417 5th Ave Fl 9, New York, NY 10016-2204
Tel (212) 251-7888 *Founded/Ownrshp* 2014
Sales 12.4MM^E *EMP* 1,250^E
SIC 7381 Security guard service; Detective agency; Guard dog rental; Lie detection service
Pr: Herman J Hellman

D-U-N-S 82-807-6807
■ SPARTAN STORES FUEL LLC
(*Suby of* SPARTANNASH CO) ★
850 76th St Sw, Grand Rapids, MI 49518
Tel (616) 878-2000 *Founded/Ownrshp* 2004
Sales 150.0MM *EMP* 100
SIC 5541 5411 Gasoline service stations; Convenience stores
Treas: Bill Jacobs

D-U-N-S 05-527-6380 IMP
SPARTANBURG AUTOMOTIVE INC
SPARTANBURG STEEL PRODUCTS
1290 New Cut Rd, Spartanburg, SC 29303-4733
Tel (864) 585-5211 *Founded/Ownrshp* 2011
Sales 175.2MM^E *EMP* 650
SIC 3465 3412 3411 Automotive stampings; Metal barrels, drums & pails; Food & beverage containers
Pr: Mark Hamlin Jr
**Ch Bd:* Richard M Hamlin
**CFO:* Richard Mallett
**Treas:* Jim Van Tiem
Exec: Raul Cavanna
Exec: Karen Lecroy
Prgrm Mgr: Chris Griffith
CIO: Keith Bailey
Dir IT: Maurice Rice
Software D: Joseph Hawk
Ql Cn Mgr: Daniel Dawson

D-U-N-S 04-655-2365 IMP
SPARTANBURG AUTOMOTIVE STEEL INC
SPARTANBURG STEEL PRODUCTS
(*Suby of* SPARTANBURG STEEL PRODUCTS) ★
1290 New Cut Rd, Spartanburg, SC 29303-4733
Tel (864) 585-5211 *Founded/Ownrshp* 1998
Sales 93.3MM^E *EMP* 618
SIC 3465 Automotive stampings
Pr: Bryan Bickimer
**CEO:* John Byers
**CFO:* Barry Whipple

SPARTANBURG COUNTY COUNCIL
See COUNTY OF SPARTANBURG

D-U-N-S 04-548-1868
SPARTANBURG COUNTY SCHOOL DISTRICT NO 7
610 Dupre Dr, Spartanburg, SC 29307-2980
Tel (864) 594-4400 *Founded/Ownrshp* 1951
Sales 107.4MM *EMP* 1,250
Accts Mcabee Schwartz Halliday & C
SIC 8211 Public elementary & secondary schools
**Prin:* Pam Hogan
**Ex Dir:* Lynn Batten
MIS Dir: Eric Levitt
Dietician: Mary Freeman

D-U-N-S 05-207-2048
SPARTANBURG REGIONAL HEALTH SERVICES DISTRICT INC
SPARTANBURG REGIONAL MED CTR
101 E Wood St, Spartanburg, SC 29303-3040
Tel (864) 560-6000 *Founded/Ownrshp* 1917
Sales 1.0MMM *EMP* 5,000
SIC 8062 General medical & surgical hospitals
CEO: Ingo Angermeier
COO: Randy Nyp
COO: Randy Nyt
**CFO:* Larry Barnette
Bd of Dir: Sam Kleckley
Trst: Lizzie Staggs
Ofcr: Ken Hollifield
VP: James D Bearden
VP: David Church
VP: Brian Earnest
VP: Tim Fagan
VP: Sara Hammond
VP: Ray Shingler
Exec: Sara Beth Hammond
Dir Risk M: Michelle Patton
Dir Lab: Susan Gilbert
Dir: Elizabeth Fletcher
Dir Rx: Rene Brown
Dir Rx: Alex McDonald
Dir Rx: Vashti Ray
Board of Directors: W Dewey Tullis Sr, Ronnie Allison, Mark Visk MD, Wendell G Cantrell, William M Cooper, Ron Fields, Bobby Ivey, Julian C Josey MD, William Monroe, Danny R Smith, Frank Stone

D-U-N-S 04-484-2579
SPARTANBURG REGIONAL HEALTHCARE SYSTEM
411 Woodsberry Shoals Dr, Duncan, SC 29334-8862
Tel (864) 560-1406 *Founded/Ownrshp* 2010
Sales 1.1MMM *EMP* 1^E
SIC 7389 Business services
Prin: Heather Bendyk

SPARTANBURG REGIONAL MED CTR
See SPARTANBURG REGIONAL HEALTH SERVICES DISTRICT INC

D-U-N-S 01-388-6882
SPARTANBURG SCHOOL DISTRICT 6
1390 Cavalier Way, Roebuck, SC 29376-3367
Tel (864) 576-4212 *Founded/Ownrshp* 1933
Sales 95.5MM^E *EMP* 1,240
SIC 8211 Public elementary & secondary schools; School board
Dir IT: Sally Dover

SPARTANBURG STEEL PRODUCTS
See SPARTANBURG AUTOMOTIVE STEEL INC

SPARTANBURG STEEL PRODUCTS
See SPARTANBURG AUTOMOTIVE INC

D-U-N-S 08-342-2097
SPARTANBURG WATER SYSTEM
200 Commerce St, Spartanburg, SC 29306-5159
Tel (864) 582-6375 *Founded/Ownrshp* 1900
Sales 130.4MM^E *EMP* 250
SIC 4941 4952 Water supply; Sewerage systems
CEO: Sue G Schneider
**COO:* Rebecca F West
**CFO:* G Newton Pressley
Off Mgr: Trish Heatherington
CTO: Barbara Barnes
Dir IT: Adam Rochelle
IT Man: Kevin Brown

D-U-N-S 00-695-9613
▲ SPARTANNASH CO (MI)
850 76th St Sw, Byron Center, MI 49315-8510
Tel (616) 878-2000 *Founded/Ownrshp* 1917
Sales 7.6MMM *EMP* 15,200^E
Accts Deloitte & Touche Llp Grand
Tkr Sym SPTN *Exch* NGS
SIC 5141 5411 5912 Groceries, general line; Grocery stores; Drug stores
Ch Bd: Dennis Eidson
Pr: David M Staples
CFO: Chris Meyers
CFO: Christopher P Meyers
Treas: Bill Jacobs
Ofcr: Tammy Hurley
Div VP: Bruce Emery
Ex VP: Larry Pierce
VP: David Des Couch
VP: Tom Luidens
VP: Joe McQuesten
VP: Stephanie Naito
VP: Jeanne Norcross
VP: Francis Wong
Board of Directors: Mickey P Foret, Frank M Gambino, Douglas A Hacker, Yvonne R Jackson, Elizabeth A Nickels, Timothy J O'donovan, Hawthorne L Proctor, William R Voss

D-U-N-S 08-692-6250 IMP/EXP
SPARTECH CORP
120 S Central Ave # 1700, Saint Louis, MO 63105-1735
Tel (314) 721-4242 *Founded/Ownrshp* 2013
Sales NA *EMP* 2,600
SIC 3081 2821 3089

SPARTECH TECHNOLOGY CENTER.
See POLYONE DESIGNED STRUCTURES AND SOLUTIONS LLC

D-U-N-S 00-535-6548 IMP
▲ SPARTON CORP (OH)
425 N Martingale Rd, Schaumburg, IL 60173-2406
Tel (847) 762-5800 *Founded/Ownrshp* 1900
Sales 419.3MM *EMP* 2,009^E
Accts Bdo Usa Llp Grand Rapids Mi
Tkr Sym SPA *Exch* NYS
SIC 3674 3672 Microprocessors; Printed circuit boards
CEO: Joseph J Hartnet
**Ch Bd:* James R Swartwout
CFO: Joseph G McCormack
Sr VP: Steven M Korwin
Sr VP: Gordon B Madlock
VP: Michael A Gaul
VP: James M Lackemacher
VP: Christopher A Ratliff
VP: James D Shaddix II
Board of Directors: Alan L Bazaar, James D Fast, John A Janitz, Charles R Kummeth, David P Molfenter, Frank A Wilson

D-U-N-S 07-948-3738
■ SPARTON EMT LLC
(*Suby of* SPARTON CORP) ★
425 N Martingale Rd Ste 2, Schaumburg, IL 60173-2406
Tel (800) 772-7866 *Founded/Ownrshp* 2014
Sales 255.1MM^E *EMP* 1,300^E
SIC 3674 Microprocessors

D-U-N-S 07-952-0862
SPAULDING REHABILITATION HOSPITAL (SRH) VOLUNTEER SERVICES
300 1st Ave, Charlestown, MA 02129-3109
Tel (617) 952-5000 *Founded/Ownrshp* 1970, 1996
Sales 108.3MM *EMP* 1,087
SIC 8069 8011 Specialty hospitals, except psychiatric; Medical centers
Pr: David E Storto
**Ch Bd:* Diana Barett
**CFO:* Kathleen Murphy
CFO: Joyce Speakmen
Treas: Costas C Christodoulakismd
**Treas:* John Mulcahey
**VP:* Joseph Castellana
**VP:* Bob McCall
**VP:* Karen S Nelson
**VP:* Steven Patrick
VP: Cathy Williams
Dir Case M: Denise Moretti

D-U-N-S 00-165-5393
SPAULDING REHABILITATION HOSPITAL CORP
300 1st Ave, Charlestown, MA 02129-3109
Tel (617) 952-5000 *Founded/Ownrshp* 2000
Sales 98.5MM *EMP* 3
SIC 8062 General medical & surgical hospitals
Pr: David E Storto
CFO: Mary Shaughnessy
Trst: Norton Sloan
Trst: Jacquelynne Stepanian
Off Mgr: Nancy Schmidt
Site Mgr: Timothy Needham
Opers Supe: Jennifer Stornelli
Secur Mgr: Eric Ditonno
Psych: Stephanie Machell
Orthpdst: Chris Diehl
Pathlgst: Barbara Barresi

D-U-N-S 80-672-3847
SPAW GLASS CONSTRUCTION CORP
(*Suby of* SPAW GLASS HOLDING LP) ★
13800 West Rd, Houston, TX 77041-1114
Tel (281) 970-5300 *Founded/Ownrshp* 1953
Sales 126.3MM^E *EMP* 220
SIC 1542 1522 1541 Commercial & office building contractors; Institutional building construction; Hotel/motel, new construction; Industrial buildings, new construction
Ch Bd: Fred Raley
**Pr:* Michael Emmons
**CEO:* Joel Stone
**Sec:* Dan Hinson
**Sr VP:* John English
MIS Dir: Debbie Hodgkins
Mktg Mgr: Casey Cowman

D-U-N-S 84-705-2479
SPAW GLASS CONTRACTORS INC
(*Suby of* SPAW GLASS HOLDING LP) ★
9331 Corporate Dr, Selma, TX 78154-1250
Tel (210) 651-9000 *Founded/Ownrshp* 1993
Sales 164.9MM^E *EMP* 351
Accts Padgett Stratemann & Co Llp
SIC 1522 Multi-family dwellings, new construction
Pr: Fred Raley
**CEO:* Joel Stone
**CFO:* Robert Blalock
**Sec:* Robert Friedel
**VP:* Chuck Calvin
Genl Mgr: Stephanie Dixon
IT Man: Richard Evans

D-U-N-S 82-540-9501
SPAW GLASS HOLDING LP
9331 Corporate Dr, Selma, TX 78154-1250
Tel (210) 651-9000 *Founded/Ownrshp* 1994
Sales 442.5MM *EMP* 450^E
Accts Padgett Stratemann & Co Ll
SIC 1542 1522 1541 Institutional building construction; Hotel/motel, new construction; Industrial buildings, new construction
Ch Bd: Fred Raley
**CEO:* Joel Stone
Exec: Weston Voss
IT Man: Richard Evans

SPC HEATING & COOLING
See SPC MECHANICAL CORP

D-U-N-S 05-852-3325
SPC MECHANICAL CORP
SPC HEATING & COOLING
1908 Baldree Rd S, Wilson, NC 27893-9509
Tel (252) 237-9035 *Founded/Ownrshp* 1970
Sales 121.5MM^E *EMP* 415
SIC 3494 1711 3444 Valves & pipe fittings; Plumbing contractors; Warm air heating & air conditioning contractor; Sheet metalwork
Pr: S Christopher Williford
**VP:* Larry Bissette
**VP:* George Dail
**VP:* Mark Williford
**VP:* Peggy Williford
**VP:* Tim Williford
**VP:* Curtis T Williford
Div Mgr: Arthur Crocker

SPCP GROUP
See SILVER POINT CAPITAL LIMITED PARTNERSHIP

D-U-N-S 17-124-8102
■ SPD ELECTRICAL SYSTEMS INC
L-3 SPD ELECTRICAL SYSTEMS
(*Suby of* L-3 COMMUNICATIONS CORP) ★
13500 Roosevelt Blvd, Philadelphia, PA 19116-4201
Tel (215) 698-6426 *Founded/Ownrshp* 2000
Sales 112.8MM^E *EMP* 480
SIC 3612 3699 3613 Transformers, except electric; Electrical equipment & supplies; Switchgear & switchboard apparatus
Pr: J C Wilcox
VP: Patrick Oconner
VP: Lawrence Wasnock
Genl Mgr: Kevin Torpey
IT Man: Justin Rylak

D-U-N-S 06-666-7221 IMP/EXP
SPEARS MANUFACTURING CO
15853 Olden St, Sylmar, CA 91342-1293
Tel (818) 364-7306 *Founded/Ownrshp* 1970
Sales 1.2MMM^E *EMP* 3,800
SIC 3494 5083 Valves & pipe fittings; Irrigation equipment
CEO: Robert W Spears
**Pr:* Wayne Spears
**Sec:* Ken Ruggles
Ofcr: Stella Stand
**VP:* Michael Valasquez
Brnch Mgr: Debbie Meagley
Sfty Mgr: Robert Kirkelie
Plnt Mgr: Al Hoffman

SPEC ADV SPEC PROD GRP
See SPECTRUM MICROWAVE INC

SPEC ROOFING CONTRACTORS SUP
See MEL STEVENSON & ASSOCIATES INC

D-U-N-S 07-781-6783
SPECIAL AGENTS MUTUAL BENEFIT ASSOCIATION INC
SAMBA
11301 Old Georgetown Rd, Rockville, MD 20852-2860
Tel (301) 984-1440 *Founded/Ownrshp* 1948
Sales NA *EMP* 57^E
Accts Bond Beebe Bethesda Md
SIC 6411 Insurance agents
Ex Dir: Walter Wilson
COO: Lynn Chang
Mng Dir: Pamela Cummings

D-U-N-S 09-106-7405
SPECIAL CARE PHARMACY SERVICES INC
1221 Ave Americo Miranda, San Juan, PR 00921-1619
Tel (787) 783-8579 *Founded/Ownrshp* 2009
Sales 206.0MM *EMP* 100
SIC 5912 8082 Drug stores; Home health care services
Pr: Rey F Vega

D-U-N-S 60-980-8811
SPECIAL COUNSEL
(*Suby of* ADECCO TECHNICAL) ★
1400 I St Nw Ste 325, Washington, DC 20005-6523
Tel (202) 737-3436 *Founded/Ownrshp* 2003
Sales 32.5MM^E *EMP* 1,500
SIC 7363 8111 7361 Temporary help service; Legal services; Employment agencies
Pr: John Marshall
IT Man: Daniel Hurd

D-U-N-S 80-097-0824
SPECIAL COUNSEL INC
(*Suby of* ADECCO TECHNICAL) ★
10201 Centurion Pkwy N, Jacksonville, FL 32256-4100
Tel (904) 360-2251 *Founded/Ownrshp* 1995
Sales 106.6MM^E *EMP* 1,982
SIC 7363 Temporary help service
CEO: Robert Crouch

*Pr: Laurie Chamberlin
*Pr: John I Marshall
*CFO: J Todd King
*Sr VP: David J Maldonado
VP: Robert Elias
*VP: Diane S Howell
Dir Bus: Brent Gustafson
Ex Dir: Marya Brancio
Ex Dir: Marciann Dunnagan

D-U-N-S 00-826-2529 IMP
SPECIAL DEVICES INC
SDI
(Suby of DAICEL CORPORATION)
2655 1st St Ste 300, Simi Valley, CA 93065-1580
Tel (805) 387-1000 Founded/Ownrshp 1991
Sales 118.7MM^E EMP 600
SIC 3714 Motor vehicle parts & accessories
Pr: Satoshi Sakamoto
COO: Mike Mendonca
*CFO: Harry Rector
*Chf Cred: Nicholas J Bruge
Dir IT: Nicholas Bruge
Board of Directors: Kenichi Tanaka, Kenichi Yamada

D-U-N-S 00-224-1669 IMP
■ **SPECIAL METALS CORP**
(Suby of PCC) ★
4832 Richmond Rd Ste 100, Warrensville Heights, OH 44128-5993
Tel (216) 755-3030 Founded/Ownrshp 2006
Sales 662.0MM^E EMP 2,500
SIC 3356 Nickel & nickel alloy: rolling, drawing or extruding
Pr: Ken Buck
Pr: Joseph Snowden
CFO: Douglas D Watts
Sr Cor Off: Gregory De Vito
VP: James M Hensler
VP: Stanton D Kirk
VP: Roderick C McDonald
Genl Mgr: Chris Strok
Opers Mgr: Dave Janosko

D-U-N-S 03-775-6293 IMP
SPECIAL OLYMPICS INC
1133 19th St Nw Ste 1200, Washington, DC 20036-3645
Tel (202) 628-3630 Founded/Ownrshp 1968
Sales 108.2MM EMP 160
Accts Lb Raffa Pc Washington Dc
SIC 8322 Social services for the handicapped
CEO: Mary Davis
*Ch Bd: Timothy P Shriver
Pr: Lonnie Snyder
*CEO: Janet Froetscher
COO: John Dow
*CFO: Michael Meenan
CFO: Douglas K Stevens Jr
*Treas: William Alford
Treas: Andrew Robertson
*Sr VP: Richard S Allen
*Sr VP: Stephen Corbin
Sr VP: Stephen B Corbin
*Sr VP: Stephen Neill
*Sr VP: Christa White
*VP: Beth Alldridge
*VP: Denis Doolan
Board of Directors: Eddie Barbanell, Loretta Claiborne, Vivian Fernandez De Torrij, Yolanda De Varela, Kevin Farr, Muhtar Kent, Angelo Moratti

D-U-N-S 04-063-3174
SPECIAL SCHOOL DISTRICT OF FORT SMITH
FORT SMITH SCHOOL DISTRICT
3205 Jenny Lind Rd, Fort Smith, AR 72901-7101
Tel (479) 785-2501 Founded/Ownrshp 1875
Sales 149.7MM EMP 1,800
Accts Przybysz & Associates Cpas P
SIC 8211 Public elementary & secondary schools; High school, junior or senior
Bd of Dir: Martha Gunter
Bd of Dir: Malinda Larey
Bd of Dir: Ana Minden
Bd of Dir: Stephen Smith
Dir Risk M: Bettye Laborn
Off Mgr: Nadine Brooks
MIS Dir: Todd Cross
Dir IT: Vance Gregory
IT Man: Donna Buccella
IT Man: Linda Holland
IT Man: Carole Lee

D-U-N-S 07-711-9055
SPECIAL SCHOOL DISTRICT OF ST LOUIS COUNTY
12110 Clayton Rd, Saint Louis, MO 63131-2599
Tel (314) 989-8100 Founded/Ownrshp 1957
Sales 405.8MM^E EMP 5,204
Accts Schowalter & Jabouri Pc St
SIC 8211 Public special education school
CIO: Nancy Ide
Dir IT: Daniel Burrus
Telecom Mg: Sharon Bond

D-U-N-S 17-331-3651
SPECIAL TOUCH HOME HEALTH CARE SERVICES INC
2091 Coney Island Ave, Brooklyn, NY 11223-2334
Tel (718) 627-1122 Founded/Ownrshp 1987
Sales 22.9MM^E EMP 1,000
SIC 8082 Home health care services
Pr: Roni Ostrovsky
*VP: Rose Kamalhar

D-U-N-S 07-717-1932 IMP/EXP
SPECIALIZED BICYCLE COMPONENTS INC
15130 Concord Cir, Morgan Hill, CA 95037-5428
Tel (408) 779-6229 Founded/Ownrshp 1974
Sales 388.7MM^E EMP 1,350
SIC 5091

SPECIALIZED COMPLEX CARE
See SCCI HOSPITALS OF AMERICA INC

SPECIALIZED CRANE & RIGGING CO
See TFORCE ENERGY SERVICES INC

D-U-N-S 13-596-3408
SPECIALIZED LOAN SERVICING LLC
(Suby of SPECIALIZED LOAN SERVICING HOLDINGS LLC)
8742 Lucent Blvd Ste 300, Highlands Ranch, CO 80129-2386
Tel (720) 241-7200 Founded/Ownrshp 2011
Sales NA EMP 1,500
Accts Pricewaterhousecoopers Llp De
SIC 6162 Loan correspondents
Pr: Toby Wells
Pr: Shawn Stroud
*COO: Ali Haralson
Ex VP: Rob Brennan
Sr VP: Darren Bronaugh
Sr VP: Ryan Conser
Sr VP: Oscar Southall
VP: Andy Beggins
VP: Anthony Forsberg
VP: Samantha Gramsas
VP: Debi Kelly
VP: Hunter Robinson
VP: Evan Thomas
VP: Jennie Thornton
VP: Mark Volosov
Exec: Amy White
Exec: Tara Wilson

D-U-N-S 79-113-6141
■ **SPECIALTY BENEFITS LLC**
(FOMERLY: OPTUMHEALTH, LLC)
(Suby of UNITED HEALTHCARE SERVICES INC) ★
11000 Optum Cir, Eden Prairie, MN 55344-2503
Tel (866) 427-6845 Founded/Ownrshp 1998
Sales NA EMP 1,000^E
SIC 6321 Accident & health insurance
CEO: Larry Renfro
*COO: John Prince
CFO: Randall B Odzer
*Ex VP: Karen Erickson
*Ex VP: Jack Larsen
*Sr VP: Lynn Myhran
VP: Amy Joy

D-U-N-S 83-237-6185
■ **SPECIALTY BLENDING CO LLC**
(Suby of FLOWERS FOODS INC) ★
1000 Wenig Rd Ne, Cedar Rapids, IA 52402-4514
Tel (319) 298-3360 Founded/Ownrshp 2009
Sales NA EMP 1,093^E
SIC 6163 Loan brokers

D-U-N-S 55-707-1552
SPECIALTY BRANDS INC
4200 Concours Ste 100, Ontario, CA 91764-4982
Tel (909) 477-4851 Founded/Ownrshp 1968
Sales NA EMP 1,900
SIC 2038 5142

SPECIALTY BUILDING RESOURCES
See SIMONTON HOLDINGS INC

D-U-N-S 80-199-3192
SPECIALTY CARE SERVICES GROUP LLC
3100 West End Ave Ste 400, Nashville, TN 37203-5800
Tel (615) 345-5400 Founded/Ownrshp 2006
Sales 55.6MM^E EMP 1,238^E
SIC 8071 Neurological laboratory
CEO: Mr J Michael Mauldin
Pr: Mr J Toby Gray
Ex VP: Susan L Crutchfield
Ex VP: Jim Lordeman
Ex VP: David Maloney
Ex VP: D Chris Wells
Sr VP: John Lovelace
VP: Ms Christi Griffin
VP: Dawn Zangara

D-U-N-S 60-208-5714 IMP/EXP
■ **SPECIALTY COMMODITIES INC**
(Suby of ARCHER-DANIELS-MIDLAND CO) ★
1530 47th St N, Fargo, ND 58102-2858
Tel (701) 282-8222 Founded/Ownrshp 2014
Sales 113.0MM^E EMP 100^E
SIC 5149 5153 Groceries & related products; Grains
CEO: Manda Tweten
*Pr: Ken Campbell
Exec: Seth Novak
Plnt Mgr: Ricardo Mendez
Ql Cn Mgr: Elsbeth Colon
Sales Exec: Carole Inman
Natl Sales: Maggi Keller

SPECIALTY FOODS GROUP
See FIELD PACKING CO LLC

SPECIALTY FOODS GROUP
See SPECIALTY FOODS HOLDINGS INC

D-U-N-S 82-521-5924
SPECIALTY FOODS HOLDINGS INC
SPECIALTY FOODS GROUP
6 Dublin Ln, Owensboro, KY 42301-0545
Tel (757) 952-1200 Founded/Ownrshp 2003
Sales 234.0MM EMP 529
SIC 2013 Prepared beef products from purchased beef; Sausages & related products, from purchased meat
Pr: Steven P Wright
CFO: John Williams
Sr Cor Off: David Shaplin
Off Mgr: Laura Davis

D-U-N-S 04-941-1262
■ **SPECIALTY HEALTHCARE SERVICES INC**
(Suby of KINDRED HEALTHCARE OPERATING INC) ★
680 S 4th St, Louisville, KY 40202-2407
Tel (502) 596-7300 Founded/Ownrshp 2002
Sales 109.3MM^E EMP 1,500
SIC 8741 Hospital management
Pr: Tye Richardson
*Ex VP: George Burkley
*Ex VP: Denise Chamberlin
*VP: Rich McCarthy
*VP: Howard Mintz

D-U-N-S 19-153-4085
SPECIALTY HOSPITAL OF AMERICA LLC
S H A
155 Fleet St, Portsmouth, NH 03801-4050
Tel (603) 570-4888 Founded/Ownrshp 2005
Sales 65.8MM^E EMP 1,200^E
SIC 8062 General medical & surgical hospitals
Ch: Jim Rappaport
*Chf Inves: Robert E Rummler Sr
*Sr VP: Susan P Bailey

D-U-N-S 00-615-9651 IMP/EXP
SPECIALTY MFG CO (MN)
S M C
5858 Centerville Rd, Saint Paul, MN 55127-6804
Tel (651) 653-0599 Founded/Ownrshp 1947
Sales 100.0MM^E EMP 404
Accts Mc Gladrey & Pullen
SIC 3494 Valves & pipe fittings
CEO: Daniel McKeown
*Ch Bd: Heidi Mc Keown
COO: Joe Boyle
Treas: Kent Brunner
Genl Mgr: Roman Neubauer
IT Man: Aaron Hecker
IT Man: Dennis Johnson
IT Man: Debbie Zaiger
Plnt Mgr: Joel Howlett
Ql Cn Mgr: Connie Walerius

D-U-N-S 62-488-0274 IMP/EXP
■ **SPECIALTY MINERALS INC**
S M I
(Suby of MTI) ★
622 3rd Ave Fl 38, New York, NY 10017-6729
Tel (212) 878-1800 Founded/Ownrshp 1992
Sales 314.5MM^E EMP 1,978
SIC 2819 5032 1422 5169 2899 Industrial inorganic chemicals; Calcium carbide; Lime building products; Crushed & broken limestone; Chemical additives; Chemical preparations
Ch Bd: Paul R Saueracker
Mng Pt: Timothy South
*Prin: Dj Monagle
Mktg Dir: Paul Petrignani
Sls Dir: Markku Pelto
Sls Mgr: Michael Sowinski

SPECIALTY PRINTING COMPANY
See SPECIALTY PROMOTIONS INC

SPECIALTY PRODUCE
See TOMATOES EXTRAORDINAIRE INC

D-U-N-S 96-512-1445 IMP
SPECIALTY PROMOTIONS INC
SPECIALTY PRINTING COMPANY
6019 W Howard St, Niles, IL 60714-4801
Tel (847) 588-2580 Founded/Ownrshp 1996
Sales 148.4MM^E EMP 325^E
SIC 2752 Commercial printing, lithographic
CEO: Paul B Lefebvre
*Pr: Adam M Lefebvre
CFO: Robert Guertin
Sr VP: William Mattran
VP: Gil Bathgate
QA Dir: Anant Osburn
IT Man: Marcos Nunez
VP Mfg: John Gaspari
VP Mfg: Jack Kenney
VP Prd: Garry Nielsen
VP Sls: Edward Bork

D-U-N-S 04-724-5761
SPECIALTY RESTAURANT DEVELOPMENT LLC
APPLEBEE'S
2600 Westhall Ln Ste 100, Maitland, FL 32751-7123
Tel (407) 661-3151 Founded/Ownrshp 1998
Sales 39.0MM^E EMP 1,500
SIC 8741 Restaurant management

D-U-N-S 04-935-2743
SPECIALTY RESTAURANTS CORP
CRAWDADDY'S
8191 E Kaiser Blvd, Anaheim, CA 92808-2214
Tel (714) 279-6100 Founded/Ownrshp 1958
Sales 224.7MM^E EMP 4,500
SIC 5812 5813 American restaurant; Bars & lounges
CEO: John Pallichet
*Pr: John Tallichet
*CEO: David Tallichet Jr
*CFO: John Kenny
CFO: Charles Ochoa
VP: Tyler Thomas
Genl Couns: Francis Drelling

D-U-N-S 55-749-9303
SPECIALTY RETAIL SHOPS HOLDING CORP
SHOPKO
700 Pilgrim Way, Green Bay, WI 54304-5263
Tel (920) 429-2211 Founded/Ownrshp 2005
Sales 1.4MMM^E EMP 15,000
SIC 6719 Personal holding companies, except banks
CEO: Michael Bettiga
*CFO: Mary Meixelsperger
*Treas: Gary Gibson

D-U-N-S 00-895-0008 IMP
■ **SPECIALTY RETAILERS INC**
PEEBLES
(Suby of STAGE STORES INC) ★
2425 West Loop S Ste 110, Houston, TX 77027-4207
Tel (713) 331-4970 Founded/Ownrshp 1928
Sales 160.0MM EMP 13,500
SIC 5651 Family clothing stores
Pr: Michael Glazer
*Ex VP: Ernie Cruse
Ex VP: Steven Hunter
*Ex VP: Ron Lucas
Sr VP: Bill Gentner
VP: Bob Aronson
VP: Tim Moyer
Exec: Timothy Moyer

D-U-N-S 94-490-5231
SPECIALTY RISK SERVICES INC
(Suby of SEDGWICK CLAIMS MANAGEMENT SERVICES INC) ★
100 Corporate Dr Ste 211, Windsor, CT 06095-2173
Tel (860) 520-2500 Founded/Ownrshp 2011
Sales 4.9MM^E EMP 1,400
SIC 8741 Financial management for business
Pr: Joseph Boures
*CFO: John Hess
Sr VP: James Leonards
*Sr VP: Pam Rippens
*Sr VP: Jim Ryan
*Sr VP: Mike Ryan
*VP: Rob Dietz
*VP: Betsy Enloe
VP: Michael Krause
VP: Scott Westman
Dir Bus: Joseph Wilson

D-U-N-S 19-767-0602 IMP
SPECIALTY ROLLED METALS LLC
S R M
423 Saint Paul Blvd, Carol Stream, IL 60188-5207
Tel (630) 871-5765 Founded/Ownrshp 2000
Sales 227.1MM^E EMP 50
Accts Rohit Trivedi Cpa
SIC 5051 Iron & steel (ferrous) products; Sheets, metal
Sales Asso: Darren Phillips
Genl Couns: William Ross

D-U-N-S 13-757-6547
SPECIALTY RX INC
2 Bergen Tpke, Ridgefield Park, NJ 07660-2340
Tel (908) 241-6337 Founded/Ownrshp 2003
Sales 96.5MM^E EMP 218
SIC 5122 Pharmaceuticals
Pr: Cheskel Berkowitz
*COO: Joe Kubulak
*VP: Joe Zopnick
Ex Dir: Joe Friedman

SPECIALTY STEEL SERVICE
See PDM STEEL SERVICE CENTERS INC

D-U-N-S 80-848-9707
SPECIALTYCARE INC
3100 West End Ave Ste 800, Nashville, TN 37203-1378
Tel (615) 345-5405 Founded/Ownrshp 2011
Sales 65.0MM^E EMP 1,508
SIC 8099 Medical services organization
CEO: Melvin F Hall
*Pr: Samuel Weinstein
*COO: Bill Elliot
*CFO: Jeffrey Gray
*Chf Cred: Brett Burrell
Sr VP: Susan Byrd
Sr VP: David Peterson
VP: Jonathan R Walker
Mng Dir: Marc L Saiontz

D-U-N-S 02-660-9214
SPECS FAMILY PARTNERS LTD
2410 Smith St, Houston, TX 77006-2316
Tel (713) 526-8787 Founded/Ownrshp 1965
Sales 148.9MM^E EMP 500
SIC 5921

D-U-N-S 03-060-3836
SPECTAGUARD ACQUISITION LLC
ALLIEDBARTON SECURITY SERVICES
(Suby of ALLIEDBARTON SECURITY SERVICES) ★
161 Washington St Ste 600, Conshohocken, PA 19428-2083
Tel (484) 351-1300 Founded/Ownrshp 1997
Sales 207.1MM^E EMP 1,585
SIC 7381 Guard services; Security guard service
CEO: William C Whitmore
*CFO: William Torzolini
VP: Jeffrey Lampinski

D-U-N-S 13-579-5834
SPECTAGUARD HOLDING CORP
(Suby of MACANDREWS & FORBES HOLDINGS INC) ★
161 Washington St Ste 600, Conshohocken, PA 19428-2083
Tel (610) 239-1100 Founded/Ownrshp 2000
Sales 24.7MM^E EMP 5,006^E
SIC 7381 Guard services
CEO: Ronald Perelman
Dist Mgr: Gene Cummings
Dist Mgr: Gary Jones
Off Admin: Yanit Pineiro

SPECTRA CONTRACT FLOORING
See SHAW CONTRACT FLOORING SERVICES INC

D-U-N-S 60-376-9753
■ **SPECTRA ENERGY CAPITAL LLC**
(Suby of SPECTRA ENERGY CORP) ★
526 S Church St, Charlotte, NC 28202-1802
Tel (704) 594-6200 Founded/Ownrshp 2007
Sales 1.2MMM^E EMP 7,000
SIC 4922 Natural gas transmission

D-U-N-S 78-956-7430
▲ **SPECTRA ENERGY CORP**
5400 Westheimer Ct, Houston, TX 77056-5353
Tel (713) 627-5400 Founded/Ownrshp 2006
Sales 5.2MMM EMP 6,000
Tkr Sym SE Exch NYS
SIC 4922 4924 Natural gas transmission; Pipelines, natural gas; Storage, natural gas; Natural gas distribution
Ch Bd: Gregory L Ebel
Pr: William T Yardley
CFO: J Patrick Reddy
Treas: Laura Buss Sayavedra
Ofcr: Dorothy M Ables
Ofcr: Guy G Buckley
Ofcr: Julie A Dill
VP: Allen C Capps
CTO: Janice Devers
Genl Couns: Reginald D Hedgebeth

D-U-N-S 80-040-1098
■ **SPECTRA ENERGY PARTNERS LP**
(*Suby of* SPECTRA ENERGY TRANSMISSION LLC) ★
5400 Westheimer Ct, Houston, TX 77056-5353
Tel (713) 627-5400 *Founded/Ownrshp* 2007
Sales 2.4MMM *EMP* 2,300ᴱ
Accts Deloitte & Touche Llp Houston
Tkr Sym SEP *Exch* NYS
SIC 4922 4924 Natural gas transmission; Pipelines, natural gas; Storage, natural gas; Natural gas distribution
Ch Bd: Gregory L Ebel
Genl Pt: Spectra E GP
CFO: J Patrick Reddy

D-U-N-S 80-787-2903
■ **SPECTRA ENERGY TRANSMISSION LLC**
(*Suby of* SPECTRA ENERGY CORP) ★
5400 Westheimer Ct, Houston, TX 77056-5353
Tel (713) 627-5400 *Founded/Ownrshp* 2007
Sales 2.4MMMᴱ *EMP* 5,110ᴱ
SIC 4922 4924 Natural gas transmission; Pipelines, natural gas; Storage, natural gas; Natural gas distribution
Pr: Greg Ebel
**CFO:* Reddy J Patrick
Treas: Lindsay A Hall
Sr VP: Richard J Kruse
VP: Patrick T Gibson
VP: Joseph E Ramsey
VP: William T Yardley
Exec: A N Harris
Exec: Gregory J Rizzo
Mktg Mgr: Mark Homestead
Counsel: Dan Jones

D-U-N-S 15-737-5416
SPECTRA HEALTHCARE ALLIANCE INC
(*Suby of* GOLDEN LIVING CTRS COMMUNITIES) ★
1000 Fianna Way, Fort Smith, AR 72919-9008
Tel (479) 201-2000 *Founded/Ownrshp* 1996
Sales 34.7MMᴱ *EMP* 2,900
SIC 8741 Nursing & personal care facility management
CEO: William R Floyd

D-U-N-S 09-701-9442
SPECTRA LABORATORIES INC
(*Suby of* FRESENIUS MEDICAL CARE NORTH) ★
525 Sycamore Dr, Milpitas, CA 95035-7429
Tel (408) 571-1290 *Founded/Ownrshp* 1982
Sales 57.0MMᴱ *EMP* 1,257
SIC 8071

D-U-N-S 19-709-8718 IMP/EXP
SPECTRA METAL SALES INC
ALUMCO
6104 Boat Rock Blvd Sw, Atlanta, GA 30336-2706
Tel (404) 344-4305 *Founded/Ownrshp* 1997
Sales 297.2MMᴱ *EMP* 400
SIC 5051 3354 3355 3479 3444 2952 Aluminum bars, rods, ingots, sheets, pipes, plates, etc.; Aluminum extruded products; Aluminum rolling & drawing; Coating of metals & formed products; Aluminum coating of metal products; Sheet metalwork; Asphalt felts & coatings
CEO: Andrew M Snell
**Pr:* Thomas Snell Sr
**CFO:* Nancy A Snell

D-U-N-S 01-407-2821
SPECTRA PREMIUM (USA) CORP
(*Suby of* INDUSTRIES SPECTRA PREMIUM INC, LES)
3052 N Distribution Way, Greenfield, IN 46140-6602
Tel (317) 891-1700 *Founded/Ownrshp* 2007
Sales 150.0MM *EMP* 300
SIC 5013 Motor vehicle supplies & new parts
Pr: Jason Best
Ex VP: Kerry Best
Ex VP: Denis Poirier
Prin: Jacques Mombleau

D-U-N-S 78-661-2481
■ **SPECTRA-PHYSICS INC**
LASER DIVISION
(*Suby of* NEWPORT CORP) ★
3635 Peterson Way, Santa Clara, CA 95054-2809
Tel (650) 961-2550 *Founded/Ownrshp* 2002
Sales 101.7MMᴱ *EMP* 800
SIC 3699 8731 Laser systems & equipment; Commercial physical research
CEO: Robert J Phillippy
CFO: Charles F Cargile
Sr VP: George M Balogh
Genl Mgr: David J Allen
Sls Dir: Keith McCurdy

D-U-N-S 79-064-3720
SPECTRACARE INC
9000 Wessex Pl Ste 100, Louisville, KY 40222-5070
Tel (800) 467-5410 *Founded/Ownrshp* 1988
Sales 13.1MMᴱ *EMP* 1,400
SIC 8082 Home health care services
Ch Bd: J David Grissom
**Pr:* Richard D Hogan
**CFO:* John Dadds

D-U-N-S 61-687-1828 IMP
SPECTRALINK CORP
2560 55th St, Boulder, CO 80301-5804
Tel (303) 441-7500 *Founded/Ownrshp* 2012
Sales 97.1MMᴱ *EMP* 422
SIC 3663 Radio & TV communications equipment; Cellular radio telephone
CEO: Doug Werking
Pt: Candice Narajka
CFO: Bill Robertson
Chf Mktg O: Ashish Sharma
Ex VP: Leah Maher
VP: Jay Andersen
VP: Kc Forward
VP: Matthew Nauertz
IT Man: Phil Elser
IT Man: Kurt Mensch
VP Mktg: Mike Lanciloti

D-U-N-S 15-104-7370
▲ **SPECTRANETICS CORP**
9965 Federal Dr Ste 100, Colorado Springs, CO 80921-3823
Tel (719) 633-8333 *Founded/Ownrshp* 1984
Sales 245.9MM *EMP* 892ᴱ
Tkr Sym SPNC *Exch* NGS
SIC 3845 Electromedical equipment; Laser systems & equipment, medical
Pr: Scott Drake
**Ch Bd:* R John Fletcher
COO: Shahriar Matin
CFO: Stacy McMahan
Ex VP: Bruce Ross
Sr VP: Donna Ford-Serbu
Sr VP: Jason Hein
Sr VP: Udo Scheiner
VP: Larry Adighije
VP: Don Fletcher
VP: Robert Fuchs
VP: Gabe Szabo
Dir Bus: Peter Jimenez
Board of Directors: William C Jennings, B Kristine Johnson, Daniel A Pelak, Joseph M Ruggio, Maria Sainz, Todd C Schermerhorn

D-U-N-S 14-956-7252 IMP
■ **SPECTRASITE COMMUNICATIONS LLC**
(*Suby of* AMERICAN TOWER CORP) ★
400 Regency Forest Dr # 300, Cary, NC 27518-7702
Tel (919) 468-0112 *Founded/Ownrshp* 2005
Sales 152.5MMᴱ *EMP* 500
SIC 4812 8748 1623 3661 4813 4899 Radio telephone communication; Cellular telephone services; Business consulting; Transmitting tower (telecommunication) construction; Telephone & telegraph apparatus; Telephone communication, except radio; Data communication services
CEO: James D Taiclet
**Pr:* Stephen Clark
**COO:* Timothy Biltz
CFO: Mark A Slaven
**CFO:* David Tomick
Treas: James S Felman
**Treas:* Steven C Lilly
**Ex VP:* Richard Byrne
**Ex VP:* Calvin Payne
**Sr VP:* Terry Armant
**VP:* Dan Hunt
**VP:* Glen F Spivak

D-U-N-S 14-600-6429
SPECTRIS INC
(*Suby of* SPECTRIS PLC)
117 Flanders Rd, Westborough, MA 01581-1042
Tel (508) 768-6400 *Founded/Ownrshp* 1915
Sales 413.2MMᴱ *EMP* 940ᴱ
SIC 3674 3829 3826 3821 Infrared sensors, solid state; Thermometers & temperature sensors; Thermal analysis instruments, laboratory type; Calibration tapes for physical testing machines
Pr: Clive Graeme Watson

D-U-N-S 00-826-2602
■ **SPECTROLAB INC**
(*Suby of* BOEING SATELLITE SYSTEMS INC) ★
12500 Gladstone Ave, Sylmar, CA 91342-5373
Tel (818) 365-4611 *Founded/Ownrshp* 2000
Sales 122.5MMᴱ *EMP* 400
SIC 3674 3679 Solar cells; Power supplies, all types: static
Pr: David Lillington
**CFO:* Paul Ballew
VP: Chris Fetzer
**VP:* Nasser Karam
**VP:* Jeff Peacock
**VP:* Edward Ringo
Prgrm Mgr: Don Aldrich
Prgrm Mgr: Jeff Treptow
IT Man: Leonard Hoskinn
Opers Mgr: Robert Cravens
Mktg Mgr: Silver Alexander

D-U-N-S 09-621-4473
■ **SPECTRUM ARENA LIMITED PARTNERSHIP**
(*Suby of* COMCAST SPECTACOR INC) ★
3601 S Broad St, Philadelphia, PA 19148-5250
Tel (215) 389-9524 *Founded/Ownrshp* 1996
Sales 96.0MMᴱ *EMP* 1,000ᴱ
SIC 6512 7941 Property operation, auditoriums & theaters; Stadium event operator services
Genl Mgr: Kevin Boryczki
Genl Mgr: Scott Warren
VP Mktg: Shawn Tilger

SPECTRUM BRANDS HDWR HM IMPRV
See KWIKSET CORP

D-U-N-S 96-452-0717
■ **SPECTRUM BRANDS HOLDINGS INC**
(*Suby of* HRG GROUP INC) ★
3001 Deming Way, Middleton, WI 53562-1431
Tel (608) 275-3340 *Founded/Ownrshp* 2010
Sales 5.0MMM *EMP* 15,500ᴱ
Tkr Sym SPB *Exch* NYS
SIC 3692 2879 3999 3648 Primary batteries, dry & wet; Agricultural chemicals; Barber & beauty shop equipment; Lighting equipment
CEO: Andreas Rouve
**Ch Bd:* David M Maura
CFO: Douglas L Martin
**V Ch Bd:* Omar M Asali
Ex VP: Merrell Tomlin
Sr VP: Nathan E Fagre
Sr VP: Stacey L Neu
Sr VP: Phil Szuba
Board of Directors: Kenneth C Ambrecht, Eugene I Davis, Norman S Matthews, Terry L Polistina, Hugh R Rovit, Joseph S Steinberg

D-U-N-S 00-195-1946 IMP/EXP
■ **SPECTRUM BRANDS INC**
RAYOVAC
(*Suby of* SPECTRUM BRANDS HOLDINGS INC) ★
3001 Deming Way, Middleton, WI 53562-1431
Tel (608) 275-3340 *Founded/Ownrshp* 1906
Sales 4.2MMMᴱ *EMP* 13,400
Accts Kpmg Llp Milwaukee Wisconsi
SIC 3692 3634 2879 3999 3648 Primary batteries, dry & wet; Razors, electric; Agricultural chemicals; Barber & beauty shop equipment; Pet supplies; Lighting equipment
Pr: David R Lumley
Pr: Amy J Yoder
Ofcr: Rodney Mackenzie
Sr VP: Gregory Brady
**Sr VP:* Nathan E Fagre
Sr VP: Timothy Simmone
Sr VP: Tom Walzer
VP: Hans-Peter Kuebler

SPECTRUM CHILD AND FAMILY SERV
See SPECTRUM COMMUNITY SERVICES

SPECTRUM CHILD AND FAMILY SVCS
See SPECTRUM HUMAN SERVICES INC

D-U-N-S 00-358-1340
SPECTRUM CLUBS INC (CA)
840 Apollo St Ste 100, El Segundo, CA 90245-4641
Tel (310) 727-9300 *Founded/Ownrshp* 2005
Sales 59.9MMᴱ *EMP* 1,600
SIC 7991

D-U-N-S 62-650-0946
SPECTRUM COMMUNITY SERVICES
SPECTRUM CHILD AND FAMILY SERV
(*Suby of* SPECTRUM CHILD AND FAMILY SVCS) ★
28303 Joy Rd, Westland, MI 48185-5524
Tel (734) 453-8804 *Founded/Ownrshp* 1976
Sales 32.6MM *EMP* 1,000
Accts Yeo & Yeo Pc Saginaw Mi
SIC 8361 Home for the mentally retarded
Pr: Roger I Swaninger
**CFO:* Lawrence G Poupard
Treas: Jeffrey Sherbow
VP: Carla Giles
Prgrm Mgr: Matthew Elgersma
Dir IT: Cory Truesdell
Pgrm Dir: Tajuanda Carey

D-U-N-S 04-576-4453 IMP
SPECTRUM CONTROL INC
API TECHNOLOGIES
(*Suby of* API TECHNOLOGIES CORP) ★
8061 Avonia Rd, Fairview, PA 16415-2899
Tel (814) 474-2207 *Founded/Ownrshp* 1968
Sales 195.0MMᴱ *EMP* 1,631ᴱ
SIC 3677 3663 3612 3676 Filtration devices, electronic; Amplifiers, RF power & IF; Transformers, except electric; Thermistors, except temperature sensors
CEO: Robert E Tavares
**Pr:* Bel Lazar
**CFO:* Phil Rehkemper
**Treas:* J Siegel
Ofcr: James R Foster
**VP:* Andrew Laurence
**VP:* Robert McKenna
**VP:* James Toohey
Div Mgr: Don Powell
Genl Mgr: Andy Rusonck
QA Dir: Sandra Russell

D-U-N-S 80-666-6475
▲ **SPECTRUM GROUP INTERNATIONAL INC**
1063 Mcgaw Ave Ste 250, Irvine, CA 92614-5506
Tel (949) 748-4800 *Founded/Ownrshp* 1981
Sales 7.4MMM *EMP* 149
Tkr Sym SPGZ *Exch* OTO
SIC 7389 5094 5944 Auction, appraisal & exchange services; Precious metals; Jewelry, precious stones & precious metals
Pr: Gregory N Roberts
Pr: Corey Maita
Pr: Chris Napolitano
CFO: Paul Soth
Ex VP: Arthur Hamilton
Ex VP: Carol Meltzer
VP: Rafael Guiti N
Creative D: Bryan Stoughton
CIO: Bernie Jimenez

SPECTRUM HEALTH BLODGETT CAMPU
See SPECTRUM HEALTH HOSPITALS

D-U-N-S 07-929-2512
SPECTRUM HEALTH HOSPITALS
SPECTRUM HEALTH BLODGETT CAMPU
(*Suby of* SPECTRUM HEALTH SYSTEM) ★
100 Michigan St Ne Mc-498, Grand Rapids, MI 49503-2560
Tel (616) 391-1774 *Founded/Ownrshp* 2001
Sales 1.7MMM *EMP* 11,000
Accts Crowe Horwath Llp Chicago Il
SIC 8062 6351 8082 6331 General medical & surgical hospitals; Liability insurance; Home health care services; Fire, marine & casualty insurance
Pr: Kevin R Splaine
**Pr:* David M Krhovsky
Treas: Lori Smith
**VP:* William L Bush MD
**VP:* Joseph J Fifer
VP: Shari Schwanzl
VP: Nancy Tait
Dir Lab: Sue Memmina
Ex Dir: Aly Mageed
Dir IT: Edward Koller
Telecom Mg: Larry Walter

SPECTRUM HEALTH MEDICAL GROUP
See SPECTRUM HEALTH PRIMARY CARE PARTNERS DBA

D-U-N-S 96-937-0084
SPECTRUM HEALTH PRIMARY CARE PARTNERS DBA
SPECTRUM HEALTH MEDICAL GROUP
1840 Wealthy St Se, Grand Rapids, MI 49506-2921
Tel (616) 774-7322 *Founded/Ownrshp* 2011
Sales 391.6MMᴱ *EMP* 14ᴱ
Accts Crowe Horwath Llp Chicago Il
SIC 8011 Offices & clinics of medical doctors

D-U-N-S 04-759-3173
SPECTRUM HEALTH SYSTEM
100 Michigan St Ne, Grand Rapids, MI 49503-2560
Tel (616) 391-1774 *Founded/Ownrshp* 1997
Sales 4.1MMMᴱ *EMP* 16,996ᴱ
SIC 8062 General medical & surgical hospitals
Pr: Richard C Breon
COO: Diane Hummel
COO: Kevin Splaine
CFO: Vicki Weaver
Ch: Matt Davis
Treas: Lori Smith
Trst: Dan Hurwitz
Ex VP: Lowell Bursch
Ex VP: Bruce Hagen
Ex VP: Philip Johnson
Ex VP: John Mackeigan
Sr VP: Roger E Jansen
Sr VP: John Mosley
Sr VP: Patrick J O'Hare
Sr VP: Patrick Ohare
VP: Christopher Baskel
VP: Scott Berman
VP: Jonathan Flyte
Dir Lab: Cindy Stitt
Dir Lab: Susan Wood
Dir Rx: Alison Potter

D-U-N-S 07-657-1785
SPECTRUM HEALTH SYSTEMS INC
10 Mechanic St Ste 302, Worcester, MA 01608-2419
Tel (508) 792-1508 *Founded/Ownrshp* 1971
Sales 4.6MMM *EMP* 1,000
Accts Ernst & Young Llp
SIC 8361 8093 Rehabilitation center, residential: health care incidental; Specialty outpatient clinics
CEO: Charles Faris
**Ch Bd:* David Grenier
**COO:* Kurt Isaacson
**CFO:* Janet Langlois
**V Ch Bd:* Verilyn Mitchell
Trst: John Renner Jr
**Sr VP:* Brad Greenstein
**VP:* Romas Buivydas
VP: Cindy Buraczynski
VP: Peter Paolantonio
Rgnl Mgr: Tracy Desruisseaux

D-U-N-S 03-773-9810
SPECTRUM HUMAN SERVICES INC
SPECTRUM CHILD AND FAMILY SVCS
28303 Joy Rd, Westland, MI 48185-5524
Tel (734) 458-8736 *Founded/Ownrshp* 1975
Sales 3.8MM *EMP* 1,000
Accts Baker Tilly Virchow Krause Llp
SIC 8361 Residential care; Residential care for children
Pr: Roger Swaninger
COO: Shirley Edwards
CFO: Barbara Fowkes
**CFO:* Lawrence Poupard
Prgrm Mgr: Kimberly Payne
Dir IT: Song Cheng
VP Mktg: Kari Klinski

D-U-N-S 13-027-3803
■ **SPECTRUM MANAGEMENT HOLDING CO LLC**
TIME WARNER
(*Suby of* CHARTER COMMUNICATIONS INC) ★
400 Atlantic St, Stamford, CT 06901-3512
Tel (203) 905-7801 *Founded/Ownrshp* 2016
Sales 6.5MMMᴱ *EMP* 16,000ᴱ
SIC 4841 Cable television services; Subscription television services
CEO: Tom Rutledge

D-U-N-S 16-878-7344 IMP/EXP
SPECTRUM MICROWAVE INC
SPEC ADV SPEC PROD GRP
(*Suby of* API TECHNOLOGIES) ★
8061 Avonia Rd, Fairview, PA 16415-2829
Tel (814) 474-4300 *Founded/Ownrshp* 2004
Sales 63.8MM *EMP* 1,314
SIC 3679 Microwave components
Pr: Richard Southworth
**CFO:* John Freeman
**Treas:* Jim Seagul
Opers Mgr: Diane Ohman

D-U-N-S 79-177-3948
■ **SPECTRUM NUMISMATICS INTERNATIONAL INC**
(*Suby of* SPECTRUM GROUP INTERNATIONAL INC) ★
1063 Mcgaw Ave Ste 250, Irvine, CA 92614-5506
Tel (949) 955-1250 *Founded/Ownrshp* 1991
Sales 130.0MM *EMP* 40
SIC 5094 Coins
Pr: Gregory N Roberts
**CFO:* Andrew Glassman

SPECTRUM PAINT & DECORATING
See SPECTRUM PAINT CO INC

D-U-N-S 14-832-1326
SPECTRUM PAINT CO INC
SPECTRUM PAINT & DECORATING
15247 E Skelly Dr, Tulsa, OK 74116-2620
Tel (918) 836-9911 *Founded/Ownrshp* 1986
Sales 248.7MMᴱ *EMP* 150
SIC 5198 5231 Paints; Paint
Pr: Travis Detter
**Sec:* Roddy Russo
Mng Dir: Dennis Grace
IT Man: John Detter
Sls Mgr: Tony Johnson
Sls Mgr: Chris Lancaster

D-U-N-S 79-088-8002
▲ **SPECTRUM PHARMACEUTICALS INC**
11500 S Estrn Ave Ste 240, Henderson, NV 89052
Tel (702) 835-6300 *Founded/Ownrshp* 1987
Sales 162.5MM *EMP* 212ᴱ
Tkr Sym SPPI *Exch* NGS
SIC 2834 Pharmaceutical preparations
Ch Bd: Rajesh C Shrotriya
Pr: Joseph W Turgeon

CFO: Kurt A Gustafson
Opers Mgr: Gene Menendez
Board of Directors: Raymond W Cohen, Gilles R Gagnon, Stuart M Krassner, Luigi Lenaz, Anthony E Maida III

SPEECH CENTER
See JTD HEALTH SYSTEMS INC

D-U-N-S 10-227-6177 IMP
SPEED COMMERCE INC
1303 E Arapaho Rd Ste 200, Richardson, TX 75081-2444
Tel (866) 377-3331 *Founded/Ownrshp* 1983
Sales 120.0MM *EMP* 1,609
SIC 5045 5099 Computer software; Video & audio equipment
CEO: Dalton Edgecomb
COO: Matthew Konkle

D-U-N-S 95-969-3425 IMP
SPEEDCO INC
(*Suby of* BANDAG EQUIPMENT CO) ★
535 Marriott Dr, Nashville, TN 37214-5092
Tel (866) 773-3326 *Founded/Ownrshp* 2004
Sales 102.3MME *EMP* 1,100
SIC 7549 Lubrication service, automotive
Pr: Chris Ripany
**VP:* Jim Dudley

SPEEDEE MART
See RITE WAY INVESTMENTS INC

D-U-N-S 18-311-2879 IMP/EXP
SPEEDLINE TECHNOLOGIES INC
16 Forge Pkwy, Franklin, MA 02038-3150
Tel (508) 541-4867 *Founded/Ownrshp* 1979
Sales 104.6MME *EMP* 465
SIC 3565 3569

D-U-N-S 07-757-0158
■ **SPEEDWAY LLC**
(*Suby of* MARATHON PETROLEUM CORP) ★
500 Speedway Dr, Enon, OH 45323-1056
Tel (937) 864-3000 *Founded/Ownrshp* 2011
Sales 3.5MMME *EMP* 19,828
SIC 5411 5541 2869 Convenience stores, chain; Filling stations, gasoline; Fuels
Pr: Anthony R Kenney
**VP:* Cindy E Peebles
Prgrm Mgr: Abbey Henninger
Rgnl Mgr: Michael Eargood
Rgnl Mgr: Mark Redicker
Genl Mgr: Mary Johnson
Genl Mgr: Seth Rostoser
Genl Mgr: Richard Worley
VP Opers: M E Mittleman

D-U-N-S 87-893-8893
■ **SPEEDWAY MOTORSPORTS INC**
(*Suby of* SONIC FINANCIAL CORP) ★
5555 Concord Pkwy S, Concord, NC 28027-4600
Tel (704) 455-3239 *Founded/Ownrshp* 1994
Sales 496.4MM *EMP* 1,087E
Tkr Sym TRK *Exch* NYS
SIC 7948 Automotive race track operation
CEO: Marcus G Smith
**Ch Bd:* O Bruton Smith
**CFO:* William R Brooks

D-U-N-S 96-378-6038
SPEEDY CASH HOLDINGS CORP
3527 N Ridge Rd, Wichita, KS 67205-1212
Tel (316) 722-3801 *Founded/Ownrshp* 2013
Sales NA *EMP* 286E
SIC 6162 Bond & mortgage companies
CEO: Don Gayhardt
**CFO:* J Douglas Maxwell
Chf Mktg O: Bill Baker
VP: Ryan Rathje
Mktg Dir: John Wulf
Mktg Mgr: Lacey Frazier

D-U-N-S 03-251-0690
SPEEDY STOP FOOD STORES LLC
SUBWAY
8701 N Navarro St, Victoria, TX 77904-2601
Tel (361) 573-7662 *Founded/Ownrshp* 1993
Sales 47.2MME *EMP* 1,006
SIC 5812 5541 5411 Sandwiches & submarines shop; Gasoline service stations; Convenience stores
Prin: Clifton Lthomas Jr
**Pr:* Jeff Johanson
**CFO:* Bonnie Reeves
**Treas:* Berni McBroom
VP: Carlton Labeff
Exec: Jan Hanslik
CTO: Dennis Garich

D-U-N-S 07-951-7790
SPELL CAPITAL PARTNERS FUND III FOR QUALIFIED PURCHASERS LP (MN)
222 S 9th St Ste 2880, Minneapolis, MN 55402-3359
Tel (612) 371-9650 *Founded/Ownrshp* 2006
Sales 23.7MME *EMP* 1,041
SIC 6799 Investors
Pr: William H Spell

D-U-N-S 11-088-2024 IMP/EXP
SPELL CAPITAL PARTNERS LLC
222 S 9th St Ste 2880, Minneapolis, MN 55402-3359
Tel (612) 371-9650 *Founded/Ownrshp* 1997
Sales 113.1MME *EMP* 1,041
SIC 3599 3469 3444 Custom machinery; Metal stampings; Sheet metalwork
Pt: William H Spell
**Pt:* Bruce A Richard
**Pt:* Kristin Waddell
VP: Thomas Morgan

D-U-N-S 04-544-2993 IMP
SPELLMAN HIGH VOLTAGE ELECTRONICS CORP
475 Wireless Blvd, Hauppauge, NY 11788-3951
Tel (631) 630-3000 *Founded/Ownrshp* 1947
Sales 273.1MME *EMP* 1,000
SIC 3612 Transformers, except electric
Pr: Loren Skeist
CFO: Rosalie Casarona
VP: Mitch Alexander
VP: Robert Barone
Dir Bus: Jim Willsey
Mng Dir: Dennis Bay
IT Man: Donna Scott
VP Opers: David Gillispie
VP Opers: Godrej Mehta
Sls Dir: Eric Mako
Sls Mgr: John Coppola

D-U-N-S 06-917-4407
SPELMAN COLLEGE
350 Spelman Ln Sw 589, Atlanta, GA 30314-4399
Tel (404) 681-3643 *Founded/Ownrshp* 1881
Sales 90.4MM *EMP* 550
Accts Kpmg Llp/Martin Harps Syphoe
SIC 8221 College, except junior
Pr: Mary Schmidt Campbell
Pr: Kassandra Jolley
CFO: Robert D Flanigan
Ofcr: Willis Perry
Ofcr: Cynthia Willingham
VP: Myra Burnett
VP: Helga Greenfield
VP: Ingrid Hayes
VP: Darnita Killian
Assoc Dir: Chardina Choate
Dir Soc: Maya N Cody
Mng Ofcr: Marian Parker

D-U-N-S 03-540-8830 IMP
■ **SPENARD BUILDERS SUPPLY LLC**
GALCO BUILDING PRODUCTS
(*Suby of* PROBUILD HOLDINGS LLC) ★
300 E 54th Ave Ste 201, Anchorage, AK 99518-1230
Tel (907) 261-9126 *Founded/Ownrshp* 1952, 1978
Sales 177.5MME *EMP* 680
SIC 5211 Lumber & other building materials
Brnch Mgr: Ray Foster
Genl Mgr: Greg Nelson
Sales Exec: Steve Lusk

D-U-N-S 08-446-6812
SPENCE DRISCOLL & CO LLC
5050 N 40th St Ste 350, Phoenix, AZ 85018-2197
Tel (602) 957-7155 *Founded/Ownrshp* 1974, 1990
Sales NA *EMP* 50
SIC 6411 Life insurance agents
Pt: John M Driscoll
Pt: Dwight Spence
Exec: Alex Stivrins

D-U-N-S 07-210-7139
SPENCER COMPANIES INC
120 Woodson St Nw, Huntsville, AL 35801-5521
Tel (256) 533-1150 *Founded/Ownrshp* 1964
Sales 136.7MM *EMP* 235
Accts Beason & Nalley Inc Huntsvi
SIC 5541 5172 Filling stations, gasoline; Petroleum products
Ch Bd: Guy J Spencer Jr
**Pr:* Michael Segrest
**CFO:* Gary Tucker
**CFO:* W Gary Tucker Jr
**VP:* Sarah Spencer Chappell
**VP:* Guy J Spencer III
**VP:* J Spencer

D-U-N-S 14-949-7435
SPENCER GIFTS HOLDINGS INC
6826 Black Horse Pike, Egg Harbor Township, NJ 08234-4197
Tel (609) 645-3300 *Founded/Ownrshp* 2007
Sales 71.8MME *EMP* 4,202
SIC 5947 Gift shop; Novelties
CEO: Steven Silverstein
**Treas:* Isaac Silvera

D-U-N-S 01-107-2642 IMP
SPENCER GIFTS LLC
SPIRIT HALLOWEEN SUPERSTORES
(*Suby of* SPENCER SPIRIT HOLDINGS INC) ★
6826 Black Horse Pike, Egg Harbor Township, NJ 08234-4197
Tel (609) 645-3300 *Founded/Ownrshp* 1971
Sales 743.1MME *EMP* 4,200
SIC 5947 5944 Gift shop; Novelties; Jewelry stores
CEO: Steven Silverstein
Treas: Gregory T Moulton
VP: Michele Kensey
VP: Bill Miller
Dir Surg: Karen Humphery
Plng Mgr: Ingrid Retto
CIO: Kelly Grotheer
CTO: Bill Winkel
Dir IT: Donna Matteucci
VP Merchng: Anthony Graziosi
Merch Mgr: Gina Bowman

SPENCER HOSPITAL'S
See SPENCER MUNICIPAL HOSPITAL

D-U-N-S 02-019-8388
SPENCER MUNICIPAL HOSPITAL
SPENCER HOSPITAL'S
1200 1st Ave E Ste 1, Spencer, IA 51301-4342
Tel (712) 264-6198 *Founded/Ownrshp* 1935
Sales 93.9MME *EMP* 439
Accts Wither Stave & Co
SIC 8062 8011 General medical & surgical hospitals; Offices & clinics of medical doctors
CEO: Bill Bumgarner
V Ch: Chuck Gass
CFO: Mark Gaworski
**CFO:* Lois Morris
Sr Cor Off: Renee Tuzzio
Exec: Donald Nordstrom
Dir Lab: Lacey Dokken
Dir Lab: Lacey Proctor
Ex Dir: Mindy Gress
DP Exec: Lynn Scharn
VP Mktg: Susan Zulk

D-U-N-S 83-050-6221
SPENCER SPIRIT HOLDINGS INC
6826 Black Horse Pike, Egg Harbor Township, NJ 08234-4132
Tel (609) 645-3300 *Founded/Ownrshp* 2007
Sales 815.0MME *EMP* 2E
SIC 5699 6719 Uniforms & work clothing; Investment holding companies, except banks
Pr: Steven Silverstein

D-U-N-S 06-841-8243
SPENCERS AIR CONDITIONING & APPLIANCE INC
SPENCER'S TV & APPLIANCE
525 W 21st St, Tempe, AZ 85282-2027
Tel (480) 505-2355 *Founded/Ownrshp* 1974
Sales 105.8MME *EMP* 190E
SIC 5064 Electrical appliances, major
Pr: Richard C Biederbeck
**Sec:* Nancy Biederbeck
**VP:* Richard J Biederbeck

SPENCER'S TV & APPLIANCE
See SPENCERS AIR CONDITIONING & APPLIANCE INC

D-U-N-S 87-695-1021 IMP
■ **SPERIAN PROTECTION USA INC**
HONEYWELL SAFETY PRODUCTS
(*Suby of* HONEYWELL SAFETY PRODUCTS USA INC) ★
900 Douglas Pike, Smithfield, RI 02917-1879
Tel (401) 232-1200 *Founded/Ownrshp* 2010
Sales 398.1MME *EMP* 2,460
SIC 3851 3842 2311 7218 5999 Protective eyeware; Ear plugs; Firemen's uniforms: made from purchased materials; Safety glove supply; Safety supplies & equipment
Pr: Mark Levy
**CFO:* Erik Loch
Plnt Mgr: Alberto Arce

D-U-N-S 00-768-0945
SPF ENERGY INC (ND)
100 27th St Ne, Minot, ND 58703-5164
Tel (701) 852-1194 *Founded/Ownrshp* 1996
Sales 1.0MMM *EMP* 300
SIC 5541 5411 Filling stations, gasoline; Convenience stores, independent
Pr: Jeffrey Farstad
**CFO:* Bruce Hest
**VP:* Dennis Krueger
Trfc Dir: Rusty Krall
Advt Mgr: Alyssa Staggs

D-U-N-S 96-768-3488
■ **SPF HOLDINGS II LLC**
(*Suby of* J M SMUCKER CO) ★
9 W 57th St Ste 4200, New York, NY 10019-2707
Tel (212) 750-8300 *Founded/Ownrshp* 2015
Sales 2.1MMME *EMP* 7,600E
SIC 2033 5149 6719 2099 Fruits & fruit products in cans, jars, etc.; Vegetables & vegetable products in cans, jars, etc.; Tomato products: packaged in cans, jars, etc.; Canned goods: fruit, vegetables, seafood, meats, etc.; Pet foods; Personal holding companies, except banks; Syrups; Frosting, ready-to-use; Sandwiches, assembled & packaged: for wholesale market; Peanut butter
Pr: Dave West

D-U-N-S 11-170-9192 IMP
SPFM LP
TIENDAS SINDICALES
4310 West Ave, San Antonio, TX 78213-3033
Tel (210) 805-8931 *Founded/Ownrshp* 1995
Sales 133.9MME *EMP* 150
Accts Padgett Stratemann & Co Llp
SIC 5122 5149 2834 2833 2841 2844 Cosmetics, perfumes & hair products; Specialty food items; Pharmaceutical preparations; Medicinals & botanicals; Soap & other detergents; Toilet preparations
Pt: Fred M Battah
Pt: Shalimar Maakar
VP: Randy Chugnow
Dir IT: Brandon Grant

SPG
See SOLOMON-PAGE GROUP LLC

D-U-N-S 96-826-2274
SPG HOLDINGS LLC
SELECT PRODUCT GROUP
(*Suby of* GEORGIA-PACIFIC LLC) ★
133 Peachtree St Se, Atlanta, GA 30303
Tel (404) 652-4000 *Founded/Ownrshp* 2014
Sales 158.8MME *EMP* 500
SIC 2621 5199 Packaging paper; Wrapping & packaging papers; Packaging materials
Pr: Kathleen Walters

D-U-N-S 79-744-1099
SPG-FCM VENTURES LLC
225 W Washington St, Indianapolis, IN 46204-3435
Tel (317) 636-1600 *Founded/Ownrshp* 2007
Sales 128.0MME *EMP* 1,150
SIC 6798 Real estate investment trusts
Pr: Richard B Fried
**Treas:* Mark C Wehrly
**VP:* David Simon

D-U-N-S 07-879-2799
▲ **SPH GROUP HOLDINGS LLC**
590 Madison Ave Fl 32, New York, NY 10022-2524
Tel (212) 520-2300 *Founded/Ownrshp* 2013
Sales 782.0MME *EMP* 2,125E
SIC 3339 3011 3312 Precious metals; Tire & inner tube materials & related products; Wire products, steel or iron
CEO: Jack L Howard

D-U-N-S 07-843-8779
■ **SPH GROUP LLC**
(*Suby of* SPLP) ★
590 Madison Ave, New York, NY 10022-2524
Tel (212) 520-2300 *Founded/Ownrshp* 2011
Sales NA *EMP* 3,514E
SIC 6141 Consumer finance companies

D-U-N-S 07-844-0884
■ **SPH SERVICES INC**
(*Suby of* SPH GROUP LLC) ★
590 Madison Ave Fl 32, New York, NY 10022-2524
Tel (212) 520-2300 *Founded/Ownrshp* 2011
Sales NA *EMP* 3,449E
SIC 6141 Consumer finance companies
Prin: Warren G Lichtenstein

D-U-N-S 10-165-0844
SPHERION OF LIMA INC
216 N Elizabeth St, Lima, OH 45801-4303
Tel (419) 224-8367 *Founded/Ownrshp* 1972
Sales 59.0MME *EMP* 4,500
SIC 7363 Temporary help service
Pr: Grace Schulte
**VP:* Robert Schulte

SPHERIS
See TOTAL EMED INC

D-U-N-S 78-067-6305
SPHERIS HOLDING III INC
(*Suby of* WARBURG PINCUS PRIVATE EQUITY VIII LP) ★
720 Cool Springs Blvd, Franklin, TN 37067-2626
Tel (615) 261-1500 *Founded/Ownrshp* 2004
Sales 21.0MME *EMP* 5,000
SIC 7338 Stenographic services; Word processing service
CEO: Steven Simpson
**Mng Dir:* Joel Ackerman

D-U-N-S 17-359-4086
SPHS CORP
SISTERS PROVIDENCE HEALTH SYS
(*Suby of* CATHOLIC HEALTH EAST) ★
271 Carew St, Springfield, MA 01104-2377
Tel (413) 748-9000 *Founded/Ownrshp* 1984
Sales NA *EMP* 4,000
SIC 8741 Hospital management
Pr: Vincent McCorcell
CFO: Michael Hammond
Ofcr: Megan Duffy
Ofcr: Lisa McCusker
VP: Mark Fulco
Dir Lab: Margaret Serra
Dir Rad: David B Mernoff
Dir Rx: Melissa Burke
Off Mgr: Lynn Shewchuk
IT Man: Paul Malouin

D-U-N-S 80-838-3454 EXP
SPI PHARMA INC
(*Suby of* ASSOCIATED BRITISH FOODS PLC)
503 Carr Rd Ste 210, Wilmington, DE 19809-2864
Tel (302) 576-8500 *Founded/Ownrshp* 1994
Sales 168.1MME *EMP* 300
SIC 5122 Pharmaceuticals
Pr: Rana Kayal
VP: Sarath Chandar
QA Dir: Steve Hughes

D-U-N-S 78-394-0757
SPI SOLAR INC
SOLAR POWER, INC.
3500 Douglas Blvd Ste 240, Roseville, CA 95661-4280
Tel (916) 770-8100 *Founded/Ownrshp* 2006
Sales 91.6MM *EMP* 566E
SIC 3433 Solar heaters & collectors
CEO: Roger Dejun Ye
**Ch Bd:* Xiaofeng Peng
COO: Hoong Khoeng Cheong
CFO: Amy Jing Liu
Dir Sec: Stephen C Kircher

D-U-N-S 60-448-3198 IMP/EXP
SPICERS PAPER INC
(*Suby of* LINDENMEYR CENTRAL) ★
12310 Slauson Ave, Santa Fe Springs, CA 90670-2629
Tel (562) 698-1199 *Founded/Ownrshp* 2012
Sales 530.4MME *EMP* 370
SIC 5111 Fine paper; Printing paper; Writing paper
CEO: Janice L Gottesman
**VP:* Rick Anderson
Sls Dir: Rhonda Lomas
Board of Directors: Andrew Wallach, Kenneth Wallach

SPIDER
See SAFEWORKS LLC

D-U-N-S 80-848-1522
SPIN HOLDCO INC
(*Suby of* CSC SERVICEWORKS INC) ★
303 Sunnyside Blvd # 70, Plainview, NY 11803-1597
Tel (516) 349-8555 *Founded/Ownrshp* 2007
Sales 164.2MME *EMP* 805
SIC 3633 5087 Household laundry equipment; Laundry equipment & supplies
Prin: Bob Doyl

D-U-N-S 02-719-3114 IMP/EXP
SPINIELLO COMPANIES
354 Eisenhower Pkwy # 1200, Livingston, NJ 07039-1036
Tel (973) 808-8383 *Founded/Ownrshp* 1998
Sales 229.3MME *EMP* 350
SIC 1623 Water, sewer & utility lines
CEO: Emil W Solimine
**CFO:* Bill Black
**Treas:* Anthony Desiena
VP: V J Spiniello III
CIO: William Peters
Mtls Mgr: Jerry Tobia

D-U-N-S 03-616-2865
SPINX CO INC
1414 E Washington St N, Greenville, SC 29607-1859
Tel (864) 233-5421 *Founded/Ownrshp* 1973
Sales 430.8MME *EMP* 961
Accts Pope Smith Brown & King Pa
SIC 5541 5411 5812 Gasoline service stations; Convenience stores; Fast food restaurants & stands
CEO: Lester S Spinks
**Ch Bd:* Stewart Spinks
**Pr:* Steve Spinks
COO: Dave Deserio
**CFO:* Stan Storti

Treas: Stan Stewarty
Chf Mktg O: Jim Weber
Ofcr: Tracie Lilly
VP: Adam Marcus
VP: Greg Minton
Exec: Phill Sill
Dir Risk M: Raymond Hargrave

SPIRA-LOC
See UNIVERSITY MECHANICAL & ENGINEERING CONTRACTORS INC

D-U-N-S 00-202-2655 IMP/EXP
SPIRAL BINDING CO INC (NY)
SPIRAL JAMES BURN
1 Maltese Dr, Totowa, NJ 07512-1413
Tel (973) 256-0666 Founded/Ownrshp 1932, 1965
Sales 89.3MM^E EMP 210
SIC 2789 3083 5112 2891 Binding & repair of books, magazines & pamphlets; Laminated plastics plate & sheet; Stationery & office supplies; Adhesives & sealants
CEO: Robert Roth
*CFO: Bob D'Alessio
*Ex VP: Matthew Roth
Brnch Mgr: Joe Cicalese
CTO: Doris Dytchel
Web Dev: Thomas Gorgolione
Netwrk Eng: Bob Dalessio
Mfg Mgr: Jeff Pendleton
Manager: Kevin Redwood
Sls Mgr: Anthony Maglio

SPIRAL JAMES BURN
See SPIRAL BINDING CO INC

D-U-N-S 15-344-7722
SPIRE HOSPITALITY LLC
111 S Pfingsten Rd # 425, Deerfield, IL 60015-4994
Tel (847) 498-6650 Founded/Ownrshp 1980
Sales 9.0MM^E EMP 3,000^E
SIC 8741 Hotel or motel management
CEO: Bill Deforrest
*COO: Greg Horeph
*Ex VP: Bill Keating
*VP: Chad Cooley
*VP: Bernard Michael
*VP: Virginia 'ginny' Morrison
*VP: Jonathan Rosenfeld
*VP: Russell Slicker
*VP: Debra W Stinson
Sls Dir: Jina Ellison

D-U-N-S 05-947-0943
▲ SPIRE INC
700 Market St, Saint Louis, MO 63101-1829
Tel (314) 342-0500 Founded/Ownrshp 1857
Sales 1.5MMM EMP 3,344
Tkr Sym SR Exch NYS
SIC 4924 Natural gas distribution
Pr: Suzanne Sitherwood
*Ch Bd: Edward L Glotzbach
Pr: Ellen Theroff
COO: Steven L Lindsey
CFO: Steven P Rasche
Chf Cred: Mark C Darrell
Sr VP: L Craig Dowdy
Sr VP: Michael C Geiselhart
Sfty Mgr: Sheryl Payne

D-U-N-S 55-584-3192 IMP
SPIRENT COMMUNICATIONS INC
(Suby of SPIRENT COMMUNICATIONS PLC)
27349 Agoura Rd, Calabasas, CA 91301-2413
Tel (818) 676-2300 Founded/Ownrshp 1999
Sales 249.5MM^E EMP 1,100
SIC 3663 3829 3825 Radio & TV communications equipment; Measuring & controlling devices; Instruments to measure electricity
CEO: Eric G Hutchinson
*Pr: Bill Burns
COO: Christopher Wiese
CFO: Frank Pizzi
Dir Bus: David Crossley
Snr Sftwr: Tim Dellinger
Sftwr Eng: Jojan Vazhaeparampil
Prd Mgr: Mark Gile
Manager: Andrew Hart

D-U-N-S 14-473-9059 IMP
SPIRENT INC
(Suby of SPIRENT COMMUNICATIONS PLC)
303 Griffing Ave, Riverhead, NY 11901-3010
Tel (631) 208-0680 Founded/Ownrshp 1991
Sales 105.9MM^E EMP 1,879
SIC 3699 High-energy particle physics equipment
Pr: L John Knox
Treas: Frank V Pizzi

D-U-N-S 79-005-0020 IMP
▲ SPIRIT AEROSYSTEMS HOLDINGS INC
3801 S Oliver St, Wichita, KS 67210-2112
Tel (316) 526-9000 Founded/Ownrshp 2005
Sales 6.6MMM EMP 15,200
Tkr Sym SPR Exch NYS
SIC 3728 3724 Aircraft parts & equipment; Aircraft body assemblies & parts; Fuselage assembly, aircraft; Wing assemblies & parts, aircraft; Engine mount parts, aircraft
Pr: Thomas C Gentile
*Ch Bd: Robert Johnson
CFO: Sanjay Kapoor
Ofcr: Samantha J Marnick
Sr VP: Stacy Cozad
Sr VP: Duane Hawkins
Sr VP: Duane F Hawkins
Sr VP: Krisstie Kondrotis
Sr VP: Michelle J Lohmeier
Sr VP: John Pilla
Sr VP: Ron Rabe

D-U-N-S 36-217-6773 IMP
■ SPIRIT AEROSYSTEMS INC
(Suby of SPIRIT AEROSYSTEMS HOLDINGS INC) ★
3801 S Oliver St, Wichita, KS 67210-3000
Tel (316) 526-9000 Founded/Ownrshp 2004
Sales 3.3MMM^E EMP 11,000^E
SIC 3728 Aircraft parts & equipment
Pr: Tom Gentile
*CFO: Sanjay Kapoor
Treas: Barbara Borg
*Ex VP: Sam Marnick
Sr VP: William Brown
Sr VP: Buck Buchanan
Sr VP: David Coleal
*Sr VP: Duane Hawkins
*Sr VP: Krisstie Kondrotis
Sr VP: Alex Kummant
Sr VP: John Lewelling
*Sr VP: Michelle J Lohmeier
*Sr VP: John Pilla
*Sr VP: Ron Rabe
Sr VP: David Walker
Sr VP: Robert Waner
Sr VP: Heidi Wood
Exec: Donna Barkley
Board of Directors: Christopher E Kubasik, John L Plueger

D-U-N-S 06-097-9986 IMP
▲ SPIRIT AIRLINES INC
2800 Executive Way, Miramar, FL 33025-6542
Tel (954) 447-7920 Founded/Ownrshp 1974
Sales 2.1MMM EMP 4,847
Tkr Sym SAVE Exch NGS
SIC 4512 Air passenger carrier, scheduled
Pr: Robert L Fornaro
Ch Bd: H McIntyre Gardner
COO: John Bendoraitis
CFO: Edward M Christie III
Chf Cred: Matt Klein
Ofcr: Martha Laurie Villa
Sr VP: Theodore C Botimer
Sr VP: Thomas C Canfield
Sr VP: Rocky Wiggins
VP: Edmundo Miranda
VP: Charlie Rue
VP: Patricia Willis
Board of Directors: Carlton D Donaway, David G Elkins, Robert D Johnson, Barclay G Jones III, Horacio Scapparone, Myrna M Soto, Dawn M Zier

D-U-N-S 60-279-8936
SPIRIT CONSTRUCTION SERVICES INC
(Suby of VHC INC) ★
118 Coleman Blvd, Savannah, GA 31408-9565
Tel (912) 748-8055 Founded/Ownrshp 1989
Sales 113.9MM^E EMP 250
SIC 1541 1542 Industrial buildings, new construction; Institutional building construction; Commercial & office building contractors
*Treas: Doug Barone

D-U-N-S 07-908-1958
SPIRIT HALLOWEEN SUPER STORES LLC (NC)
(Suby of SPENCER SPIRIT HOLDINGS INC) ★
6826 Black Horse Pike, Egg Harbor Township, NJ 08234-4132
Tel (609) 645-5691 Founded/Ownrshp 2002
Sales 71.8MM^E EMP 5,000
SIC 5311 Department stores
CEO: Steven B Silverstein

SPIRIT HALLOWEEN SUPERSTORES
See SPENCER GIFTS LLC

D-U-N-S 13-658-5374
SPIRIT REALTY CAPITAL INC
16767 N Perimeter Dr # 210, Scottsdale, AZ 85260-1062
Tel (480) 606-0820 Founded/Ownrshp 2003
Sales 282.7MM EMP 38^E
SIC 6798

D-U-N-S 78-651-7099
SPIRIT REALTY CAPITAL INC
2727 N Harwood St Ste 300, Dallas, TX 75201-2407
Tel (480) 606-0820 Founded/Ownrshp 2003
Sales 667.3MM EMP 71^E
SIC 6798 Real estate investment trusts
Ch Bd: Thomas H Nolan Jr
Pr: Jackson Hsieh
CFO: Phillip D Joseph Jr
Ofcr: Michelle M Greenstreet
Ex VP: Mark L Manheimer
Ex VP: Boyd Messmann
Sr VP: Prakash J Parag
VP: Pierre Revol
Board of Directors: Kevin M Charlton, Todd A Dunn, David J Gilbert, Richard I Gilchrist, Diane M Morefield, Thomas D Senkbeil, Nicholas P Shepherd

SPIRIT TELECOM
See SOUTH CAROLINA TELECOMMUNICATIONS GROUP HOLDING LLC

D-U-N-S 55-652-9493
SPIRIT TRUCK LINES INC
200 W Nolana, San Juan, TX 78589-3694
Tel (956) 781-7715 Founded/Ownrshp 1990
Sales 90.8MM^E EMP 250
SIC 4731 Truck transportation brokers
Pr: Raul Garza
*Treas: Juan Garza
*VP: Leonel E Garza
Exec: Steve Garza
DP Exec: Joe David
Dir IT: Mario Rosa
Sfty Mgr: Larry Elizondo
Sls&Mrk Ex: Michelle Garza

D-U-N-S 10-264-5215 IMP
SPITZER INDUSTRIES INC
12141 Wickc Ln Ste 750, Houston, TX 77079
Tel (713) 466-1518 Founded/Ownrshp 2006
Sales 471.6MM^E EMP 505
SIC 1389 Processing service, gas
Ch: Cullen R Spitzer
*Pr: Brian Groody
*COO: Milo Thibeadeau
Treas: Shirley Spitzer
*Sec: Ted Johnson
*Sr VP: David Kotzebue

SPLASH AUTOWASH
See WASH DEPOT AUTO CENTERS LP

SPLITCO
See EAGLE SPINCO INC

SPLP
See STEEL PARTNERS HOLDINGS LP

D-U-N-S 19-947-2668
▲ SPLUNK INC
250 Brannan St, San Francisco, CA 94107-2007
Tel (415) 848-8400 Founded/Ownrshp 2003
Sales 668.4MM EMP 2,100
Accts Pricewaterhousecoopers Llp Sa
Tkr Sym SPLK Exch NGS
SIC 7372 Prepackaged software
Pr: Doug Merritt
*Ch Bd: Godfrey Sullivan
*Pr: Douglas Merritt
CFO: David F Conte
Chf Mktg O: Brian Goldfarb
Chf Mktg O: Steven R Sommer
Ofcr: Richard Campione
Ofcr: Susan St Ledger
Sr VP: Guido R Schroeder
Sr VP: Guido Schroeder
Sr VP: Leonard R Stein
VP: Kevin Davis
VP: Declan Morris
VP: Vishal RAO
VP: Guido Schroder
VP: Sendur Sellakumar
Board of Directors: Mark Carges, Amy L Chang, John G Connors, David M Hornik, Patricia B Morrison, Thomas M Neustaetter, Stephen G Newberry

SPM
See BACE MANUFACTURING INC

D-U-N-S 00-801-9366 IMP/EXP
SPM FLOW CONTROL INC (TX)
WEIR SPM
(Suby of WEIR GROUP PLC(THE))
601 Weir Way, Fort Worth, TX 76108-2508
Tel (817) 246-2461 Founded/Ownrshp 1958, 2007
Sales 211.2MM^E EMP 321
SIC 3533 3599 Oil & gas field machinery; Machine shop, jobbing & repair
Pr: Paul M Coppinger
*Pr: Gavin Nicol
*Sr VP: Tommy Wall
VP: Stephen Christie
*VP: Doug Lawrie
*VP: Andrew Newell
Genl Mgr: Craig Ralston
Sls Mgr: Mark Feldstein

SPOHN MEMORIAL HOSPITAL
See CHRISTUS SPOHN HEALTH SYSTEM CORP

D-U-N-S 17-072-9870 IMP
▲ SPOK HOLDINGS INC
6850 Versar Ctr Ste 420, Springfield, VA 22151-4148
Tel (800) 611-8488 Founded/Ownrshp 2004
Sales 189.6MM EMP 605^E
Tkr Sym SPOK Exch NGS
SIC 4812 4822 7372 Cellular telephone services; Paging services; Photographic message services; Nonvocal message communications; Prepackaged software
Pr: Vincent D Kelly
*Ch Bd: Royce Yudkoff
CFO: Shawn E Endsley
Treas: Sharon Woods Keisling
Ex VP: Bonnie K Culp-Fingerhut
CIO: Thomas G Saine
Board of Directors: N Blair Butterfield, Nicholas A Gallopo, Stacia A Hylton, Brian O'reilly, Matthew Oristano

D-U-N-S 13-962-4829
■ SPOK INC
(Suby of SPOK HOLDINGS INC) ★
6850 Versar Ctr Ste 420, Springfield, VA 22151-4148
Tel (703) 269-6850 Founded/Ownrshp 2004
Sales 192.7MM^E EMP 615^E
SIC 4812 Paging services
Pr: Vincent D Kelly
*CFO: Shawn Endsley
Off Mgr: Eve Shelton

D-U-N-S 02-751-9248
SPOKANE PRODUCE INC
1905 S Geiger Blvd, Spokane, WA 99224-5498
Tel (509) 455-8970 Founded/Ownrshp 1971
Sales 155.0MM^E EMP 250
SIC 5148 Fruits; Vegetables
Pr: Craig Higashi
*Sec: Ramona Higashi
Mktg Dir: Barry Lauderdale
Sls Dir: Dan Zoesch
Sls Mgr: John Laughery

D-U-N-S 06-754-7826
SPOKANE PUBLIC SCHOOLS
200 N Bernard St, Spokane, WA 99201-0206
Tel (509) 354-5900 Founded/Ownrshp 1900
Sales 403.7MM EMP 3,880
Accts Troy Kelley Olympia Wa
SIC 8211 Public elementary & secondary schools
Pr: Deana Brower
Bd of Dir: Robert Douthitt
VP: Susan Chapin
Prin: John Andes
Dir Sec: Scott Mullennix
Off Mgr: Donna Cozza
Off Mgr: Carol Mack
MIS Dir: Clay Gering
Schl Brd P: Jeffrey Bierman
Teacher Pr: Tennille Jeffries-Simmo
HC Dir: Rebecca Doughty

D-U-N-S 82-954-3888
■ SPOKANE VALLEY WASHINGTON HOSPITAL CO LLC
VALLEY HOSPITAL AND MEDICAL CENTER
(Suby of COMMUNITY HEALTH SYSTEMS INC) ★
12606 E Mission Ave, Spokane Valley, WA 99216-3421
Tel (509) 924-6650 Founded/Ownrshp 2008
Sales 114.7MM EMP 600
SIC 8062 General medical & surgical hospitals
CEO: Dennis Parts
Chf Rad: Dale Neilson
CEO: Greg Repetti
Podiatrist: Richard Frost
Podiatrist: Kirk Herring
HC Dir: Ann Armstrong

D-U-N-S 15-381-2797 IMP
■ SPOKANE WASHINGTON HOSPITAL CO LLC
DEACONESS HOSPITAL
(Suby of COMMUNITY HEALTH SYSTEMS INC) ★
800 W 5th Ave, Spokane, WA 99204-2803
Tel (509) 458-5800 Founded/Ownrshp 2008
Sales 253.2MM^E EMP 1,300^E
SIC 8062 General medical & surgical hospitals
Pr: Dan Engle
COO: Gregory Repetti
CFO: Dan Houghton
*CFO: Rod Schumacher
Ofcr: Connie Stamper
CIO: Bryan Hillstaead
Pathlgst: Karl Anders
Pathlgst: Dennis Small
Plas Surg: Elizabeth L Peterson

SPONSORED PROGRAMS
See UNIVERSITY OF WYOMING

SPONSRED PRGRAMS OFF - SYS ADM
See RESEARCH FOUNDATION FOR STATE UNIVERSITY OF NEW YORK

D-U-N-S 80-970-5424
SPORT & HEALTH CLUBS LC
1760 Old Madow Rd Ste 300, Mc Lean, VA 22102
Tel (703) 556-6556 Founded/Ownrshp 1999
Sales 11.7MM^E EMP 2,100
SIC 7991 Physical fitness facilities

D-U-N-S 02-834-0883 IMP
SPORT CHALET LLC
(Suby of EVEREST MERGER SUB INC) ★
160 Corporate Ct, Meriden, CT 06450-7177
Tel (818) 790-2717 Founded/Ownrshp 2014
Sales 553.7MM^E EMP 2,800
SIC 5699 Sports apparel
*CFO: Howard K Kaminsky
*Chf Mktg O: Thomas H Tennyson
*Ex VP: Tim A Anderson
*Ex VP: Dennis D Trausch
Dept Mgr: Dave Crigger
Dist Mgr: Darren Paxton
Dist Mgr: Dave Worden
Genl Mgr: Meghan Brown
Genl Mgr: Lisa Hall
Genl Mgr: Judith Hardy
Genl Mgr: Jennifer Talarico

D-U-N-S 78-482-3742
SPORTECH RACING LLC
(Suby of SPORTECH PLC)
1095 Windward Ridge Pkwy, Alpharetta, GA 30005-1728
Tel (678) 566-1021 Founded/Ownrshp 2010
Sales 100.7MM^E EMP 1,000^E
SIC 7373 Computer integrated systems design
Pr: Books Pierce

SPORTS AUTHORITY
See TSA STORES INC

SPORTS AUTHORITY
See SLAP SHOT HOLDINGS CORP

D-U-N-S 83-498-6812 IMP/EXP
SPORTS AUTHORITY INC
(Suby of SPORTS AUTHORITY) ★
1050 W Hampden Ave, Englewood, CO 80110-2118
Tel (303) 200-5050 Founded/Ownrshp 2008
Sales 2.9MMM^E EMP 15,000
SIC 5941 Sporting goods & bicycle shops
Ch Bd: John Douglas Morton
CEO: Michael Foss
CFO: Jeremy J Aguilar
CFO: Thomas T Hendrickson
CFO: Johanna G Remster
Ch: Martin Hanaka
Chf Mktg O: Stephen Binkle
Chf Mktg O: Paul M Okimoto
Chf Mktg O: Jeffrey Schumacher
Chf Mktg O: Ron Stoupa
Ofcr: Stephen Binkley
Ex VP: Paul Gaudet
Ex VP: Nesa E Hassanein
Ex VP: Greg Waters
Sr VP: Fred Argir
Sr VP: Kathy Persian
Sr VP: Emily White-Keating
VP: Thomas Albright
VP: Mark Johns
VP: Patrick Koreck
VP: Bob Lynch

SPORTS CLUB LA, THE
See MILLENNIUM PARTNERS SPORTS CLUB MANAGEMENT LLC

D-U-N-S 10-914-2695 IMP/EXP
SPORTS ENDEAVORS INC
EURO SPORT
431 Us Highway 70a E, Hillsborough, NC 27278-9262
Tel (919) 644-6800 Founded/Ownrshp 1984
Sales 94.2MM^E EMP 800^E
SIC 5941 Soccer supplies; Specialty sport supplies
CEO: Cheryl Ekstrom
*Pr: Mike Moylan
*CEO: Roger Parro
*COO: Brendan Moylan
*CFO: Frank Durham
VP: Jim Covington
*Prin: Bernard Frei
Web Dev: Michael Arribage
Software D: Scott Poteat
Sftwr Eng: Peter Neurohr
Prd Dir: John Kenan

SPORTS FRST FTNES WELLNESS CTR
See CULLMAN REGIONAL MEDICAL CENTER INC

Section I Businesses Alphabetically

D-U-N-S 62-369-9345 IMP
SPORTS IMAGES INC
1000 Franklin Village Dr # 104, Franklin, MA 02038-4015
Tel (508) 530-3225 Founded/Ownrshp 2014
Sales 116.2MM^E EMP 65
SIC 5199

D-U-N-S 03-526-6543
SPORTS INC
333 2nd Ave N, Lewistown, MT 59457-2700
Tel (406) 538-3496 Founded/Ownrshp 1965
Sales 841.4MM EMP 38
Accts Junkermier Clark Campanella
SIC 5091 Sporting & recreation goods
Pr: John Valiero
*Pr: Barry Cory
*Treas: Nancy Wilson
VP: Todd Adams
*VP: Chad Wyffels
Mktg Mgr: Andy Eames
Mktg Mgr: Travis Elam

D-U-N-S 80-841-4044 IMP/EXP
SPORTS LICENSED DIVISION OF ADIDAS GROUP LLC
(Suby of REEBOK INTERNATIONAL LTD) ★
1895 J W Foster Blvd, Canton, MA 02021-1099
Tel (781) 401-5000 Founded/Ownrshp 2001
Sales 58.9MM^E EMP 1,298^E
SIC 2329 Athletic (warmup, sweat & jogging) suits: men's & boys'; Men's & boys' athletic uniforms; Knickers, dress (separate): men's & boys'
CFO: John Warren
Ex Dir: Claire Fahie
Ex Dir: Paul Fisher
Ex Dir: Greg Mingels
Dir IT: Jeremy Meier
Dir IT: Ramani Sakamuri
Opers Mgr: Joe Fleury
Opers Mgr: Bob Lyle
Trfc Mgr: Bruce Neff
Sls&Mrk Ex: Liam Devoy
Sls&Mrk Ex: Gregg Nebel

SPORTS MEDICINE PRFMCE CTR
See ST FRANCIS HOSPITAL INC

D-U-N-S 06-973-2857
SPORTS SOUTH LLC (LA)
1039 Kay Ln, Shreveport, LA 71115-3602
Tel (318) 797-4848 Founded/Ownrshp 1974, 1952
Sales 155.8MM^E EMP 70^E
SIC 5091 Firearms, sporting
Ch Bd: Markham A Dickson Sr
*Pr: Markham A Dickson Jr
Pr: Walter Frederick
*VP: C Markham Dickson
DP Exec: Chris Beatty
Dir IT: Ezra Weinstein
Software D: Stephen Waller
Sls Dir: Ronnie Whitten
Mktg Mgr: Tony Ocon

D-U-N-S 80-702-5580
SPORTSMANS DISTRIBUTION CO
(Suby of BASS PRO SHOPS) ★
2500 E Kearney St, Springfield, MO 65898-0001
Tel (417) 873-5000 Founded/Ownrshp 1992
Sales 46.0MM^E EMP 1,400
SIC 4225 General warehousing
Pr: John L Morris

SPORTSMAN'S SUPPLY
See HARVEST SPORTING GROUP INC

D-U-N-S 14-848-4868
SPORTSMANS SUPPLY INC
(Suby of SPORTSMANS SUPPLY) ★
2219 Hitzert Ct, Fenton, MO 63026-2562
Tel (636) 600-9301 Founded/Ownrshp 1995
Sales 107.8MM EMP 35
Accts Abeles And Hoffman Pc Saint
SIC 5091 Sporting & recreation goods
Pr: Tom Siegmund

D-U-N-S 12-859-9482
▲ **SPORTSMANS WAREHOUSE HOLDINGS INC**
7035 S High Tech Dr # 100, Midvale, UT 84047-3706
Tel (801) 566-6681 Founded/Ownrshp 1986
Sales 729.9MM EMP 4,200
Tkr Sym SPWH Exch NGS
SIC 5941 5699 5661 Hunting equipment; Archery supplies; Fishing equipment; Camping equipment; Sports apparel; Shoe stores
Pr: John V Schaefer
*Ch Bd: Christopher Eastland
CFO: Kevan P Talbot
Board of Directors: Kent V Graham, Gregory P Hickey, Joseph P Schneider, Kay L Toolson

D-U-N-S 17-793-1482 IMP
■ **SPORTSMANS WAREHOUSE INC**
(Suby of SPORTSMANS WAREHOUSE HOLDINGS INC) ★
7035 S High Tech Dr, Midvale, UT 84047-3706
Tel (801) 566-6681 Founded/Ownrshp 2009
Sales 341.6MM^E EMP 2,000
SIC 5941 5699 5661 Hunting equipment; Archery supplies; Fishing equipment; Camping equipment; Sports apparel; Footwear, athletic
CEO: John V Schaefer
*CFO: Kevan P Talbot
*Ex Ofcr: Darren Lester
VP: Matt French
VP: Larry Knight
VP: Jeremy Sage
Genl Mgr: Jeremy Williams
Store Mgr: Ben Bodmer
Store Mgr: Dave Nitzel
CTO: Michael Van Orden
Mktg Dir: Ritz Coles

SPORTSNET NEW YORK
See STERLING ENTERTAINMENT ENTERPRISES LLC

D-U-N-S 19-667-0301
SPOTLESS PLASTICS (USA) INC
(Suby of SPOTLESS GROUP LIMITED)
100 Motor Pkwy Ste 155, Hauppauge, NY 11788-5165
Tel (631) 951-9000 Founded/Ownrshp 1987
Sales 111.8MM^E EMP 730
SIC 3089 Clothes hangers, plastic
Pr: Peter Wilson
*VP: Stanley Gouldson

D-U-N-S 07-979-9759
SPOTSYLVANIA COUNTY PUBLIC SCHOOLS
8020 River Stone Dr, Fredericksburg, VA 22407-8761
Tel (540) 834-2500 Founded/Ownrshp 2016
Sales 19.9MM^E EMP 3,268^E
SIC 8211 Public elementary & secondary schools
CFO: Lashahn Gaines
Ex Dir: Michelle Colbert
Ex Dir: Don Upperco
Genl Mgr: Melissa Webster
Psych: Pamela Hall
Psych: Mary Nelson
Psych: Maria Way

D-U-N-S 78-334-8212
SPOTSYLVANIA COUNTY SCHOOL BOARD
8020 River Stone Dr, Fredericksburg, VA 22407-8761
Tel (540) 898-6032 Founded/Ownrshp 1975
Sales 93.7MM^E EMP 3,000
SIC 8211 Public elementary & secondary schools
V Ch: Henry Connors
CFO: John Reader
Bd of Dir: James Meyer
Exec: Kathy Smith
Brnch Mgr: Linda Johnson
Genl Mgr: Douglas Boggs
Plng Mgr: Patrick Mulhern
MIS Dir: Janice Sterch
Dir IT: Sue Burgess
Opers Mgr: Shawn Hockaday

D-U-N-S 00-210-5645
■ **SPOTSYLVANIA MEDICAL CENTER INC** (VA)
COLUMBIA HCA
(Suby of HOSPITAL COPORATION OF AMERICA) ★
4600 Spotsylvania Pkwy, Fredericksburg, VA 22408-7762
Tel (540) 498-4000 Founded/Ownrshp 2005
Sales 93.6MM EMP 500
SIC 8011 Medical centers
CEO: Greg Madsen
*CEO: Tim Tobin
*COO: Terika Richardson
*CFO: Sean Thomson

D-U-N-S 13-136-2733 IMP/EXP
■ **SPRAGUE OPERATING RESOURCES LLC**
(Suby of SPRAGUE RESOURCES LP) ★
185 International Dr, Portsmouth, NH 03801-6836
Tel (603) 431-1000 Founded/Ownrshp 2013
Sales 3.4MMM EMP 580
SIC 5172 5052 5171 Petroleum products; Diesel fuel; Fuel oil; Coal; Petroleum terminals
Pr: Dave Glendon
Pr: Marilyn Driver
CFO: John Moore
*CFO: Gary A Rinaldi
Treas: Kevin Henry
Ex VP: Ben Hennelly
VP: Miles Allen
VP: John Bischoff
VP: Frank Easton
VP: Don Simposon
Plnt Mgr: Scott Johnson

D-U-N-S 96-894-9599
▲ **SPRAGUE RESOURCES LP**
185 International Dr, Portsmouth, NH 03801-6836
Tel (800) 225-1560 Founded/Ownrshp 2011
Sales 3.4MMM EMP 580^E
Accts Ernst & Young Llp Hartford
Tkr Sym SRLP Exch NYS
SIC 5172 4922 Petroleum products; Storage, natural gas
Pr: David C Glendon
Genl Pt: Sprague Resources GP LLC
COO: Gary A Rinaldi
Ofcr: Steven D Scammon
VP: Thomas F Flaherty
VP: John W Moore
VP: Joseph S Smith

D-U-N-S 80-004-1097
■ **SPRAGUE VISHAY INC**
(Suby of VISHAY INTERTECHNOLOGY INC) ★
111 Gilbane St, Warwick, RI 02886-6901
Tel (401) 738-9150 Founded/Ownrshp 1993
Sales 179.6MM^E EMP 1,393
SIC 3629 Capacitors, a.c., for motors or fluorescent lamp ballasts; Capacitors, fixed or variable
Pr: Donald Alfson
*Treas: Richard N Grubb
*Sr VP: Robert A Freece

D-U-N-S 00-507-1071 IMP
SPRAYING SYSTEMS CO
AUTOJET TECHNOLOGIES
200 W North Ave, Glendale Heights, IL 60139-3408
Tel (630) 665-5000 Founded/Ownrshp 1984
Sales 345.8MM^E EMP 903
SIC 3499 Nozzles, spray: aerosol, paint or insecticide
Pr: James E Bramsen
CFO: Marty Hynes
Exec: Joe Ruelas
Area Mgr: David Yates
Dept Mgr: James Valenta
Brnch Mgr: Brent Baltzer
Genl Mgr: Jim McGarrey
Tech Mgr: Tony Chadwick
Snr Mgr: Benny Orozco

D-U-N-S 01-887-4921
SPREDFAST INC
200 W Cesar Chavez St # 600, Austin, TX 78701-3819
Tel (512) 823-2320 Founded/Ownrshp 2008
Sales 107.0MM^E EMP 600^E
SIC 7371 Computer software development & applications
Pr: Rod Favaron
Pr: Brian Dainton
*CFO: Tim Barker
Ofcr: Olivier Gachot
Ex VP: Virginia Miracle
VP: Ashley Brown
*VP: Dan Doman
*VP: Jay Harry
*VP: Carol Howard
VP: Jeff Luttrull
VP: Kevin Morris
Exec: Benjamin Hardy
Board of Directors: Bill Bock, Sue Bostrom, Michael Dodd, Rod Favaron, Chris Harrington, Adam Marcus, Doug Pepper

D-U-N-S 80-179-6681
SPRENGER ENTERPRISES INC
2198 Gladstone Ct, Glendale Heights, IL 60139-1514
Tel (630) 529-0700 Founded/Ownrshp 1989
Sales 106.4MM^E EMP 1,320
Accts Howard Wershbale & Co Cleve
SIC 8741 Nursing & personal care facility management
Pr: Kenneth Malanowski
*CEO: Nicole Sprenger
*VP: Sandra Kaiser
*VP: Chris Mallett
*VP: Mark A Sprenger
Nrsg Dir: Kris Mead

SPRING HARBOR HOSPITAL
See MAINE BEHAVIORAL HEALTHCARE

D-U-N-S 07-390-1662
SPRING BRANCH INDEPENDENT SCHOOL DISTRICT (INC)
955 Campbell Rd, Houston, TX 77024-2803
Tel (713) 464-1511 Founded/Ownrshp 1946
Sales 380.6MM EMP 4,484
Accts Whitley Penn Houston Texas
SIC 8211 Public elementary & secondary schools
Pr Dir: Linda Buchman
Pr Dir: Patricia Waldrop
Schl Brd P: Chris Vierra
Teacher Pr: Lori Cummings
HC Dir: Rebecca Fuchs

SPRING BRANCH MEDICAL CENTER
See SBMC HEALTHCARE LLC

D-U-N-S 92-652-5049
SPRING BRANCH MEDICAL CENTER INC
(Suby of SPRING BRANCH MEDICAL CENTER) ★
6060 Richmond Ave Ste 315, Houston, TX 77057-6269
Tel (713) 722-3799 Founded/Ownrshp 2011
Sales 62.4MM^E EMP 1,114
SIC 8062 General medical & surgical hospitals
CEO: Patricia Curry
*COO: David Huffstutler
*CFO: Ray Grenier
CFO: Gale Piledgi
*VP: Mary Ann Euliarte
Exec: Richard Vera

D-U-N-S 06-071-6685
SPRING INDEPENDENT SCHOOL DISTRICT
16717 Ella Blvd, Houston, TX 77090-4213
Tel (281) 891-6000 Founded/Ownrshp 1932
Sales 383.7MM EMP 5,000
SIC 8211 Public elementary & secondary schools; High school, junior or senior; Public special education school
*CFO: Ann Westbrooks
Trst: Deborah Jensen
*Ofcr: Tiffany Dunne-Oldfield
VP: Chris Bell
Ex Dir: Irene Darby
Dir Sec: Victor Mitchell
Psych: Velma Moss
Psych: Jocelyn Stokes
Doctor: Scott Rand
HC Dir: Jeanne Parker

SPRING VALLEY HOSPITAL
See SPRING VALLEY MEDICAL CENTER INC

D-U-N-S 07-982-5305
SPRING VALLEY HOSPITAL MEDICAL CENTER
5400 S Rainbow Blvd, Las Vegas, NV 89118-1825
Tel (702) 853-3000 Founded/Ownrshp 2015
Sales 300.7MM EMP 4^E
SIC 8011 Medical centers
CEO: Leonard Freehof
CIO: Allen Woratschek

D-U-N-S 13-351-0227
■ **SPRING VALLEY MEDICAL CENTER INC**
SPRING VALLEY HOSPITAL
(Suby of VALLEY HOSPITAL MEDICAL CENTER) ★
5400 S Rainbow Blvd, Las Vegas, NV 89118-1859
Tel (702) 853-3000 Founded/Ownrshp 1989
Sales 285.4MM EMP 15
SIC 8062 General medical & surgical hospitals
Pr: Jerry Engel
*CEO: Karla Perez
Doctor: Larry Denny
Doctor: James Dettling

D-U-N-S 09-434-4058
SPRING-FORD AREA SCHOOL DISTRICT
857 S Lewis Rd, Royersford, PA 19468-2711
Tel (610) 705-6000 Founded/Ownrshp 1940
Sales 134.7M EMP 1,000
Accts Maillie Falconiero & Company
SIC 8211 Public elementary & secondary schools
Schl Brd P: Mark P Dehnert
HC Dir: Debbie Zelle

D-U-N-S 96-640-4241
SPRING-FORD AREA SCHOOL DISTRICT OFFICE
857 S Lewis Rd, Royersford, PA 19468-2711
Tel (610) 705-6000 Founded/Ownrshp 2011
Sales 128.5MM EMP 37^E
Accts Maillie Llp Oaks Pennsylvani
SIC 8211 Elementary & secondary schools
MIS Dir: Sandra Bernat
Teacher Pr: Elizabeth Leiss

SPRINGBROOK GOLF COURSE
See PARK NAPERVILLE DISTRICT

D-U-N-S 02-067-3471
SPRINGBROOK NY INC
UPSTATE HOME FOR CHILDREN & AD
105 Campus Dr, Oneonta, NY 13820-6175
Tel (607) 286-7171 Founded/Ownrshp 1923
Sales 49.4MM EMP 1,200
Accts Bryans & Gramuglia Cpas Llc A
SIC 8211 School for physically handicapped
CEO: Patricia E Kennedy
*Pr: Rev William Carlsen
*COO: Seth Haight
*CFO: Richard Carnrike
*Treas: Les Sittler
*VP: Margaret Savoie

D-U-N-S 18-387-3413
SPRINGDALE PUBLIC SCHOOL DISTRICT 50
804 W Johnson Ave, Springdale, AR 72764-4159
Tel (479) 750-8800 Founded/Ownrshp 1900
Sales 76.5MM^E EMP 1,800
SIC 8211 Public elementary school; Public junior high school; Public senior high school
Exec: Hartzell Jones
*Prin: Allison Byford
*Prin: Kelly Koons
*Prin: Michael Shepherd
Genl Mgr: Dee Hobbs
HC Dir: Robert Ferguson

D-U-N-S 00-677-2776
SPRINGFIELD BOARD OF EDUCATION
1500 W Jefferson St, Springfield, OH 45506-1224
Tel (937) 505-2800 Founded/Ownrshp 1855
Sales 75.1MM^E EMP 1,923
Accts Clark Schaefer Hackett & Co
SIC 8211 School board
Pr: Ed Leventhal
*CFO: Penelope Rucker
*Treas: Dale Miller
Teacher Pr: Mattie White

D-U-N-S 06-698-5920
SPRINGFIELD CITY OF (INC)
36 Court St, Springfield, MA 01103-1687
Tel (413) 736-3111 Founded/Ownrshp 1636
Sales NA EMP 6,107
Accts Powers & Sullivan Llc Wakefi
SIC 9111 City & town managers' offices;
CFO: Mary Tzambazakis
*Treas: Ehsanul Bhuiya
Treas: Salvatore Calvanese
Treas: Susan Fielding
Prgrm Mgr: Richard Griffin
Web Dev: Eileen Foley

D-U-N-S 07-982-7323
SPRINGFIELD CITY SCHOOL DISTRICT
1500 W Jefferson St, Springfield, OH 45506-1224
Tel (937) 505-2800 Founded/Ownrshp 2015
Sales 67.0MM^E EMP 1,410^E
SIC 8211 Public elementary & secondary schools
Dir Sec: Dave Lyle
Pr Dir: Kim Fish
Teacher Pr: Stacie Tipler

D-U-N-S 04-703-2875
SPRINGFIELD CLINIC LLP
1025 S 6th St, Springfield, IL 62703-2499
Tel (217) 528-7541 Founded/Ownrshp 1939
Sales 188.4MM^E EMP 1,530
SIC 8011 Clinic, operated by physicians
Genl Pt: Michael A Pick MD
CFO: Alan Nerone
Bd of Dir: James Fullerton
Dir Lab: Tina Reno
Dir Lab: Susan Weber
Off Mgr: Ann Hunt
Off Mgr: Bonnie Lynch
Off Mgr: Stevie Stoneking
Off Mgr: Dawn Willison
IT Man: David Kiel
Netwrk Mgr: Todd Kelzer

D-U-N-S 06-697-9188
SPRINGFIELD COLLEGE
263 Alden St, Springfield, MA 01109-3788
Tel (413) 748-3000 Founded/Ownrshp 1885
Sales 160.3MM EMP 579
SIC 8221 College, except junior
Pr: Dr Mary-Beth Cooper
*Pr: Richard B Flynn
*Treas: Mike Dobise
Ofcr: Brian Toohey
Assoc VP: Scott Berg
*VP: John Mailhot
CIO: Danny Davis
Netwrk Mgr: Dave Linnehan
Web Dev: Nathan Larkin
Web Dev: Brian Page
Prd Mgr: Kelly Gonya

D-U-N-S 00-175-6139
SPRINGFIELD ELECTRIC SUPPLY CO (IL)
700 N 9th St, Springfield, IL 62702-6307
Tel (217) 788-2100 Founded/Ownrshp 1932
Sales 267.6MM^E EMP 290
SIC 5063 5719 Electrical construction materials; Electrical supplies; Lighting fixtures; Transformers, electric; Lighting fixtures; Lamps & lamp shades
Pr: J Michael Barker
*Pr: Mark Barthel
*COO: Nikki Baker
*CFO: Greg Lutchka
*Sr VP: Daniel Dungan
*Sr VP: Randall S Germeraad
VP: Drew McMinn
*Prin: William R Schnirring
Brnch Mgr: Shawn Schalk
Opers Mgr: Heath Stinebaker
Sls Mgr: Gwynn Lawson

D-U-N-S 00-696-8929
SPRINGFIELD GROCER CO (MO)
2415 W Battlefield St, Springfield, MO 65807-4005
Tel (417) 883-4230 *Founded/Ownrshp* 1885, 1969
Sales 169.4MM^E^ *EMP* 130^E^
SIC 5142 5141 5149 Packaged frozen goods; Groceries, general line; Groceries & related products
Pr: William M Tynes
CFO: Tommy Wohlgemuth
VP: Brendon O'Doherty

D-U-N-S 04-730-6217 IMP/EXP
SPRINGFIELD LLC
100 Jericho Quadrangle # 340, Jericho, NY 11753-2710
Tel (516) 861-6250 *Founded/Ownrshp* 1998
Sales 114.4MM^E^ *EMP* 300
SIC 2221 Broadwoven fabric mills, manmade
CEO: Ed Shogan
**Pr:* James C Tennyson
**CFO:* Aby Snyder
CFO: James Tennyson
**VP:* Lenard Fishman

SPRINGFIELD PUBLIC SCHOOL
See SPRINGFIELD SCHOOL DISTRICT 19

SPRINGFIELD PUBLIC SCHOOL SYST
See SPRINGFIELD SCHOOL DISTRICT R12

D-U-N-S 06-939-6575
SPRINGFIELD PUBLIC SCHOOLS
1550 Main St Fl 2, Springfield, MA 01103-1446
Tel (413) 787-7100 *Founded/Ownrshp* 1800
Sales 184.6MM^E^ *EMP* 4,000
SIC 8211 Public elementary & secondary schools
Ofcr: Martha Mering
Dir Sec: Bill Baker

SPRINGFIELD REGIONAL MEDICAL C
See COMMUNITY MERCY HEALTH PARTNERS

D-U-N-S 00-563-7814 IMP
SPRINGFIELD REMANUFACTURING CORP
SRC AUTOMOTIVE DIVISION
(*Suby of* SRC HOLDINGS CORP) ★
650 N Broadview Pl, Springfield, MO 65802-5839
Tel (417) 862-3501 *Founded/Ownrshp* 1997
Sales 93.2MM^E^ *EMP* 495
SIC 3519 3714 3713 3561 Diesel, semi-diesel or duel-fuel engines, including marine; Fuel pumps, motor vehicle; Truck & bus bodies; Pumps & pumping equipment
Pr: Marty Callison
COO: Diana Devore
**CFO:* Beth Marsh
CFO: Elizabeth Marsh
**Treas:* Beverly Willis
**VP:* William D Sheppard
**Genl Mgr:* Jeff Payne
**Genl Mgr:* Ryan Stack
QA Dir: Catherine Crockett
IT Man: Eric Bein
Sys Mgr: Brandon Gray

D-U-N-S 07-141-8438
SPRINGFIELD SCHOOL DISTRICT 186
1900 W Monroe St, Springfield, IL 62704-1531
Tel (217) 525-3000 *Founded/Ownrshp* 1850
Sales 216.7MM *EMP* 2,300
Accts Sikich Llp Springfield Illin
SIC 8211 Public elementary & secondary schools
VP: Lara James
Dir Sec: Jon Filbrun
IT Man: Michael Holinga
Pr Dir: Gina Schurman
Instr Medi: Karen Thompson

D-U-N-S 03-078-5836
SPRINGFIELD SCHOOL DISTRICT 19
SPRINGFIELD PUBLIC SCHOOL
525 Mill St, Springfield, OR 97477-4548
Tel (541) 726-3331 *Founded/Ownrshp* 1949
Sales 73.0MM^E^ *EMP* 1,550
SIC 8211 Public elementary & secondary schools
Pr Dir: Devon Ashridge
Pr Dir: John Saraceno
Teacher Pr: Michael Henry

D-U-N-S 08-312-0477
SPRINGFIELD SCHOOL DISTRICT R12
SPRINGFIELD PUBLIC SCHOOL SYST
1359 E Saint Louis St, Springfield, MO 65802-3409
Tel (417) 523-0000 *Founded/Ownrshp* 1875
Sales 281.5MM *EMP* 3,000
Accts Westbrook & Co Pc Richmon
SIC 8211 Public elementary & secondary schools; Public elementary school; Public junior high school; Public senior high school
MIS Dir: Bruce Douglas
Teacher Pr: Lisa Turner
HC Dir: Jean Grabeel

D-U-N-S 00-287-0434
SPRINGFIELD TERMINAL RAILWAY CO INC
(*Suby of* PAN AM RAILWAYS INC) ★
1700 Iron Horse Park, North Billerica, MA 01862-1641
Tel (978) 663-1050 *Founded/Ownrshp* 1983
Sales 55.4MM^E^ *EMP* 1,000
SIC 4011 Railroads, line-haul operating
Pr: David A Fink
**Treas:* Eric H Lawler
**VP:* Stephen Ryan
**VP:* Cynthia S Scarano

D-U-N-S 07-181-9981
SPRINGFIELD UTILITY BOARD (INC)
250 A St, Springfield, OR 97477-4513
Tel (541) 746-8451 *Founded/Ownrshp* 1950
Sales 115.4MM^E^ *EMP* 141
Accts Julie Desimone Partner For Mo
SIC 4931 4941 Electric & other services combined; Water supply
Genl Mgr: Robert C Linahan

D-U-N-S 04-532-2286
SPRINGFIELD WATER & SEWER COMMISSION
250 M St, Agawam, MA 01001-2043
Tel (413) 787-6060 *Founded/Ownrshp* 1880
Sales 109.0MM^E^ *EMP* 250
SIC 4941 Water supply
Ex Dir: Joseph Supeneau

D-U-N-S 07-791-6674
SPRINGHILL HOSPITALS INC
SPRINGHILL MEMORIAL HOSPITAL
(*Suby of* SOUTHERN MEDICAL HEALTH SYSTEMS INC) ★
3719 Dauphin St Frnt, Mobile, AL 36608-1750
Tel (251) 344-9630 *Founded/Ownrshp* 1979
Sales 179.4MM *EMP* 900
SIC 8062 General medical & surgical hospitals
Pr: Jeffery M St Clair
**Pr:* William Mason
**COO:* Rene J Areaux
**COO:* Randy Sucher
**CFO:* Stephen Grigsby
Ofcr: James Evans
Dir Inf Cn: Beth Beck
CIO: Mark Kilborn
IT Man: Pam Shedd
Obsttrcn: Erin Saucier
Ansthlgy: Stephen R Snypes

SPRINGHILL MEMORIAL HOSPITAL
See SPRINGHILL HOSPITALS INC

D-U-N-S 00-693-6918
■ **SPRINGLEAF FINANCE CORP**
(*Suby of* SPRINGLEAF FINANCE INC) ★
601 Nw 2nd St, Evansville, IN 47708-1013
Tel (812) 424-8031 *Founded/Ownrshp* 2010
Sales NA *EMP* 3,239
Accts Pricewaterhousecoopers Llp Ch
SIC 6141 Consumer finance companies
Pr: Jay N Levine
**Ch Bd:* Wesley R Edens
CFO: Minchung Kgil
Treas: David McManigal
Ofcr: John Biederman
Ex VP: Brad Borchers
Sr VP: Raymond S Brown
VP: Jeanne Balczewski
VP: Daniel Barrett
VP: Sean P Donnelly
VP: Jeanne Dressel
VP: Dave Gutscher
VP: Ed Jackson
VP: Jane Maher
VP: Tom Peake
VP: George Roach
VP: Kevin Small
VP: David Smith
Exec: Crystal Reidford
Assoc Dir: Laura Johnston
Assoc Dir: Eileen Mayes
Board of Directors: Roy A Guthrie, Douglas L Jacobs, Ronald M Lott

D-U-N-S 07-131-4934
■ **SPRINGLEAF FINANCE INC**
(*Suby of* OMH) ★
601 Nw 2nd St, Evansville, IN 47708-1013
Tel (812) 424-8031 *Founded/Ownrshp* 2013
Sales NA *EMP* 4,500
SIC 6153 6351 6331 7389 Working capital financing; Credit & other financial responsibility insurance; Property damage insurance; Financial services
Pr: Jay N Levine
**CFO:* Donald R Breivogel Jr
Treas: Bryan Binyon
**Ex VP:* Bradford D Borchers
**Sr VP:* Raymond S Brown
Sr VP: Timothy Hayes
Sr VP: Donald Tennenhouse
VP: Clay Spires
**VP:* Leonard J Winiger
Exec: George Boehm
Dir IT: Jeff Kohut
Board of Directors: Robert A Cole, Wesley R Edens, Susan Givens, Douglas L Jacobs, Randal A Nardone, Peter M Smith

D-U-N-S 07-960-2732
■ **SPRINGLEAF MORTGAGE LOAN TRUST 2012-2**
(*Suby of* OMH) ★
601 Nw 2nd St, Evansville, IN 47708-1013
Tel (812) 424-8031 *Founded/Ownrshp* 2014
Sales 14.4MM^E^ *EMP* 2,493^E^
SIC 6733 Trusts

D-U-N-S 79-155-7627 IMP/EXP
SPRINGS CREATIVE PRODUCTS GROUP LLC
300 Chatham Ave Ste 100, Rock Hill, SC 29730-5395
Tel (803) 324-6300 *Founded/Ownrshp* 2006
Sales 90.5MM *EMP* 220
SIC 5949 2759 Bridal fabrics; Commercial printing
CEO: Derick Close
**Pr:* Travis Blackwood
**CFO:* Doug McIlvaine
**VP:* Dannielle Heinrichs
**VP:* Brian Wacaster
Exec: Mike Boylin
Plng Mgr: Debra Hess
Opers Mgr: David Seagroves

D-U-N-S 61-172-4613 IMP/EXP
SPRINGS GLOBAL US INC
(*Suby of* SPRINGS GLOBAL PARTICIPACOES S/A.)
205 N White St, Fort Mill, SC 29715-1654
Tel (803) 547-1500 *Founded/Ownrshp* 2005
Sales 377.6MM^E^ *EMP* 1,000
SIC 2299 5023 Linen fabrics; Sheets, textile
CEO: Josu Christiano G D Silva
Pr: Tom O'Connor
Treas: Alan McManus
VP: Shari Gold
VP: Richard Langone
Mfg Dir: Steve Decubellis
Plnt Mgr: Gene Quesinberry
Prd Mgr: Marco Hernandez
Merch Mgr: Emily Kelly

D-U-N-S 00-316-3102 IMP/EXP
SPRINGS INDUSTRIES INC
(*Suby of* SPRINGS GLOBAL PARTICIPACOES S/A.)
7549 Graber Rd, Middleton, WI 53562-1001
Tel (608) 836-1011 *Founded/Ownrshp* 2005
Sales 657.9MM^E^ *EMP* 4,610
SIC 2591 Drapery hardware & blinds & shades; Shade, curtain & drapery hardware; Window blinds; Window shades
CEO: Scott Fawcett
Ch Bd: Crandall C Bowles
CFO: Philip Garton
CTO: Toshiaki Ikoma
S&M/VP: Ted Matthews
Mktg Mgr: Jill Kerttula
Board of Directors: Bob Lee, Dan Tredwell

D-U-N-S 06-632-5507
SPRINGS MEMORIAL HOSPITAL (SC)
COMMUNITY HEALTH SYSTEMS
800 W Meeting St, Lancaster, SC 29720-2298
Tel (803) 286-1477 *Founded/Ownrshp* 1940
Sales 161.9MM *EMP* 600^E^
Accts Thompson & Davis Cpas Lancast
SIC 8062 8069 8049 General medical & surgical hospitals; Alcoholism rehabilitation hospital; Physical therapist
CEO: Janice Dabney
**COO:* Parkes B Coggins
**CFO:* Nathan Crabdree
Dir Rx: Skip Ghantt
Mktg Mgr: Ashley Shannon
Doctor: Tooba Khan

D-U-N-S 09-855-0437 IMP/EXP
SPRINGS WINDOW FASHIONS LLC
(*Suby of* GOLDEN GATE CAPITAL) ★
7549 Graber Rd, Middleton, WI 53562-1001
Tel (608) 836-1011 *Founded/Ownrshp* 2013
Sales 1.4MMM^E^ *EMP* 5,183
SIC 2591 Drapery hardware & blinds & shades; Curtain & drapery rods, poles & fixtures; Blinds vertical; Window shade rollers & fittings
CEO: Scott Fawcett
**CFO:* Philip Garton
**VP:* Doug Olstad
Sftwr Eng: Kevin Ballweg

D-U-N-S 80-088-7262
■ **SPRINGSTONE FINANCIAL LLC**
(*Suby of* LENDINGCLUB CORP) ★
1700 W Park Dr Ste 310, Westborough, MA 01581-3976
Tel (800) 630-1663 *Founded/Ownrshp* 2014
Sales 64.5MM^E^ *EMP* 1,291^E^
SIC 6282 Investment advice
COO: Jim Donovan

SPRINKFAB
See S A COMUNALE CO INC

D-U-N-S 17-909-1660 IMP
SPRINKLES CUPCAKES INC
9635 Santa Monica Blvd, Beverly Hills, CA 90210-4401
Tel (310) 274-8765 *Founded/Ownrshp* 2004
Sales 37.3MM^E^ *EMP* 1,000
SIC 5441 Confectionery
Pr: Charles E Nelson II
Genl Mgr: Lauren Randol
Dir IT: James Szeto

D-U-N-S 96-339-3488
SPRINKLR INC
29 W 35th St Fl 7, New York, NY 10001-2299
Tel (917) 933-7800 *Founded/Ownrshp* 2011
Sales 109.4MM^E^ *EMP* 325^E^
SIC 8742 7372 Marketing consulting services; Business oriented computer software
CEO: Ragy Thomas
**COO:* Carlos Dominguez
**COO:* Tim Page
**COO:* Murali Swaminathan
**CFO:* Chris Lynch
**Ofcr:* Thomas Butta
Ofcr: Jan Zlotnick
**Sr VP:* Scott Doniger
VP: Elizabeth Closmore
**VP:* Jeremy Epstein
VP: Rob Peacock
VP: Marc Silberstrom
VP: Pavitar Singh
Dir Bus: Kathrin Schneider

SPRINT
See NEXTEL OF CALIFORNIA INC

D-U-N-S 15-422-9660
■ **SPRINT COMMUNICATIONS CO LP**
(*Suby of* SPRINT COMMUNICATIONS INC) ★
6391 Sprint Pkwy, Overland Park, KS 66251-6100
Tel (800) 829-0965 *Founded/Ownrshp* 1988
Sales 3.6MMM^E^ *EMP* 22,000
SIC 4813 Long distance telephone communications; Voice telephone communications; Data telephone communications
Pt: Dan Hesse
Pt: Daniel R Hesse
Pt: Christie A Hill
Pt: Jerry Usry
Mng Pt: Timothy Kelly
Treas: Richard Lindahl
VP: William Arendt

D-U-N-S 00-694-2395 IMP
■ **SPRINT COMMUNICATIONS INC**
(*Suby of* SPRINT CORP) ★
6200 Sprint Pkwy, Overland Park, KS 66251-6117
Tel (855) 848-3280 *Founded/Ownrshp* 2013
Sales 13.5MMM^E^ *EMP* 29,050
SIC 4813 4812 5999 Local & long distance telephone communications; Long distance telephone communications; Voice telephone communications; Data telephone communications; Cellular telephone services; Telephone & communication equipment; Telephone equipment & systems
Pr: Brian S Miller
**Pr:* Matt Carter
Pr: Keith Cowan
Pr: Steven L Elfman
**CFO:* Joseph J Euteneuer
Ofcr: Thomas N Kelly
Sr VP: Charles L Hall
Sr VP: Sandra J Price
Sr VP: William White
Snr Ntwrk: Eric Kratz
Dir IT: Marvis Aleem

D-U-N-S 07-908-2747
■ **SPRINT CORP**
(*Suby of* GALAXY INVESTMENT HOLDINGS INC) ★
6200 Sprint Pkwy, Overland Park, KS 66251-6117
Tel (855) 848-3280 *Founded/Ownrshp* 2012
Sales 32.1MMM *EMP* 30,000^E^
Accts Deloitte & Touche Llp Kansas
Tkr Sym S *Exch* NYS
SIC 4813 4812 Local & long distance telephone communications; Data telephone communications; ; ; Cellular telephone services
Pr: Marcelo Claure
V Ch: Ronald D Fisher
Pr: Brandon Dow Draper
Pr: Jerry Gallegos
Pr: Brian Hedlund
Pr: Claudio Hidalgo
Pr: Annette Jacobs
Pr: Jaime Jones
Pr: Michael Miess
Pr: Brian S Miller
Pr: John Stevens
Pr: Gabriel Torres
COO: G Nther Ottendorfer
COO: Guenther Ottendorfer
CFO: Tarek Robbiati
Ofcr: Robert L Johnson
Ofcr: Rob Roy
Ex VP: Jeff Moore
Sr VP: Ismat Aziz
Sr VP: Jorge Gracia
Sr VP: Doug Michelman
Board of Directors: Robert Bennett, Gordon Bethune, Patrick T Doyle, Ronald Fisher, Julius Genachowski, Michael Mullen, Sara Martinez Tucker

D-U-N-S 00-121-9174 IMP
■ **SPRINT INTERNATIONAL INC**
(*Suby of* UTELCOM, INC.)
2330 Shawnee Mission Pkwy, Westwood, KS 66205-2005
Tel (913) 624-3000 *Founded/Ownrshp* 1986
Sales 1.5MMM^E^ *EMP* 4,930
SIC 4813 Long distance telephone communications; Telephone cable service, land or submarine
CEO: William T Esrey
Netwrk Eng: Charles Pittman

SPRINT PIPELINE SERVICES
See PRIMORIS ENERGY SERVICES CORP

D-U-N-S 95-682-2274
■ **SPRINT SPECTRUM HOLDING CO LP**
(*Suby of* SPRINT COMMUNICATIONS INC) ★
6160 Sprint Pkwy, Shawnee Mission, KS 66251-6115
Tel (800) 829-0965 *Founded/Ownrshp* 1996
Sales 1.9MMM^E^ *EMP* 13,000
SIC 4813 Telephone communication, except radio
Prin: Charles Levine
Pt: Comcast Telephony Services
Pt: TCI Telephony Services

D-U-N-S 83-945-1796 IMP
■ **SPRINT SPECTRUM LP**
(*Suby of* SPRINT CORP) ★
6800 Sprint Pkwy, Overland Park, KS 66251-0001
Tel (703) 433-4000 *Founded/Ownrshp* 1995
Sales 9.5MMM^E^ *EMP* 13,000^E^
SIC 4813 Telephone communication, except radio
Mng Pt: Timothy Kelly
Pt: William Arendt
Pt: Christie A Hill
Pt: Samuel Mayson

D-U-N-S 80-057-1551
SPRINT WASTE SERVICES LP
SENTINEL
16011 W Bellfort St, Sugar Land, TX 77498-8538
Tel (281) 491-7775 *Founded/Ownrshp* 2006
Sales 93.0MM^E^ *EMP* 130
SIC 5093 4953 Metal scrap & waste materials; Liquid waste, collection & disposal
Pt: William J Swinbank
Pt: Joe Swinbank
Pt: Reagan Swinbank
Pr: William Swinbank
CFO: James Goodyear
IT Man: Barbara Johns
VP Sls: Raegan P Swinbank

D-U-N-S 78-638-3869
■ **SPRINT/UNITED MANAGEMENT CO**
(*Suby of* SPRINT COMMUNICATIONS INC) ★
6200 Sprint Pkwy, Overland Park, KS 66251-6117
Tel (800) 697-6000 *Founded/Ownrshp* 1989
Sales 132.1MM^E^ *EMP* 469^E^
SIC 8741 Management services
Pr: Len J Lauer
CEO: Gary Forsee
Ex VP: Robert Dellinger
Ex VP: Tom Gerke
Sr VP: John P Meyer
VP: Paul R Buchanan
VP: Don A Jensen
DP Dir: Keet Hornbuckle

D-U-N-S 11-143-1545
▲ **SPROUTS FARMERS MARKET INC**
5455 E High St Ste 111, Phoenix, AZ 85054-5464
Tel (480) 814-8016 *Founded/Ownrshp* 2002
Sales 3.5MMM *EMP* 20,000

Tkr Sym SFM *Exch* NGS
SIC 5411 Grocery stores
CEO: Amin N Maredia
**Ch Bd:* J Douglas Sanders
Pr: James L Nielsen
CFO: Bradley S Lukow
Chf Mktg O: Shawn R Gensch
Ofcr: Theodore E Frumkin
Brnch Mgr: Mike McMaster
Store Mgr: Vincent Powell
CIO: Daniel J Bruni
Site Mgr: Scott Darley
Counsel: Carlos Rojas
Board of Directors: Kristen Blum, Joseph Fortunato, Terri Funk Graham, Lawrence P Molloy, Steven H Townsend

SPS
See SUMMIT PACKAGING SYSTEMS INC

D-U-N-S 18-110-5065
▲ SPS COMMERCE INC
333 S 7th St Ste 1000, Minneapolis, MN 55402-2421
Tel (612) 435-9400 *Founded/Ownrshp* 1987
Sales 158.5MM *EMP* 1,046E
Tkr Sym SPSC *Exch* NGM
SIC 7374 7372 Data processing & preparation; Prepackaged software
Pr: Archie C Black
**Ch Bd:* Philip E Soran
COO: James J Frome
CFO: Kimberly K Nelson
VP: Stephen Byrnes
Prac Mgr: Sarah Rogstad
Prac Mgr: Nikki Stephens
CTO: Lisa Pamblanco
IT Man: Michael Mahoney
Software D: Alexander Yegorov
Sls Mgr: Anna Meyer
Board of Directors: Martin J Leestma, James B Ramsey, Tami L Reller, Michael A Smerklo, Sven A Wehrwein

D-U-N-S 00-622-1063
SPS COMPANIES INC (MN)
INTERSTATE MFG & SUPPLY DIV
6363 Highway 7, Minneapolis, MN 55416-2346
Tel (952) 929-1377 *Founded/Ownrshp* 1951
Sales 109.2MME *EMP* 210
SIC 5074 5075 3498 Plumbing & hydronic heating supplies; Warm air heating equipment & supplies; Air conditioning & ventilation equipment & supplies; Pipe sections fabricated from purchased pipe; Pipe fittings, fabricated from purchased pipe
CEO: William Weber
**Pr:* Ralph Gross
CFO: Bill Weber
**Brnch Mgr:* Kevin Robinson
Genl Mgr: Dustin Gunderson
Genl Mgr: Eric Hoihjelle
Genl Mgr: Mike Kahnke
MIS Dir: Anthony Fritz
Dir IT: Gregg Kapsalis
IT Man: Chris Clauss

D-U-N-S 95-829-9570
SPS HOLDINGS CORP
(*Suby of* CREDIT SUISSE (USA) INC) ★
3815 S West Temple, Salt Lake City, UT 84115-4412
Tel (801) 293-1883 *Founded/Ownrshp* 2005
Sales NA *EMP* 1,000
SIC 6162 6798 Loan correspondents; Real estate investment trusts
CEO: Matthew L Hollingsworth
CFO: Bryan M Marshall
Treas: Peter J Feeney
Ofcr: Frank J Decongelio
Ex VP: Craig A Bullock
Ex VP: Robert J Holz
Ex VP: Bruce Kaiserman
Ex VP: Timothy J O'Brien
Ex VP: John Pataky
Ex VP: Brent Rasmussen
Ex VP: Patrick Remmert
VP: Edward W Flynn
VP: Thomas Prevost
VP: Doug Roseman
VP: Albert Scarola

D-U-N-S 00-234-4117 IMP/EXP
■ SPS TECHNOLOGIES LLC (PA)
PCC SPS FASTENER DIVISION
(*Suby of* PCC) ★
301 Highland Ave, Jenkintown, PA 19046-2692
Tel (215) 572-3000 *Founded/Ownrshp* 2003
Sales 1.3MMME *EMP* 5,065
SIC 3452 3423 3499 3264 3679 3341 Bolts, nuts, rivets & washers; Screws, metal; Dowel pins, metal; Nuts, metal; Hand & edge tools; Magnets, permanent: metallic; Magnets, permanent: ceramic or ferrite; Cores, magnetic; Secondary nonferrous metals
CEO: John S Thompson
CFO: James Dee
CFO: Thomas W McDonnell
Ex VP: Kevin M Stein
VP: Thomas Cross
VP: Joe Dunleavy
VP: Vincent Harris
VP: Ryan Hinkle
IT Man: Paul Lewis
IT Man: Linda Welty
Mktg Dir: Bill Young

SPSI
See SCOTT PROCESS SYSTEMS INC

D-U-N-S 03-088-0488
SPSS INC
200 W Madison St Ste 2300, Chicago, IL 60606-3416
Tel (312) 651-3000 *Founded/Ownrshp* 2009
Sales NA *EMP* 1,246
SIC 7372

D-U-N-S 07-626-5917 IMP/EXP
■ SPX COOLING TECHNOLOGIES INC (DE)
(*Suby of* SPX CORP) ★
7401 W 129th St, Overland Park, KS 66213-2694
Tel (913) 664-7400 *Founded/Ownrshp* 1981
Sales 373.1MME *EMP* 2,000
SIC 3443 Cooling towers, metal plate; Heat exchangers: coolers (after, inter), condensers, etc.
Pr: Gene Lowe
CFO: Mary Sczudlo
**CFO:* Scott Sproule
**Treas:* Pat Kellerman
Sr VP: Wayne Struchtemeyer
VP: Robert Foster
VP: Mike Vessels
Prgrm Mgr: Carlos Galhardo
Rgnl Mgr: Johnny Dawson
Genl Mgr: Jose Carlos
Software D: Thomas Cleary

D-U-N-S 00-602-4129 IMP
▲ SPX CORP
13320a Balntyn Corp Pl, Charlotte, NC 28277-3607
Tel (980) 474-3700 *Founded/Ownrshp* 1912
Sales 1.7MMM *EMP* 6,000
Tkr Sym SPXC *Exch* NYS
SIC 3443 3599 3829 3559 3545 Heat exchangers, condensers & components; Air coolers, metal plate; Cooling towers, metal plate; Heat exchangers, plate type; Air intake filters, internal combustion engine, except auto; Measuring & controlling devices; Aircraft & motor vehicle measurement equipment; Automotive related machinery; Machine tool accessories
Ch Bd: Christopher J Kearney
Ch Bd: Patrick J O'Leary
Pr: J Randall Data
Pr: Eugene J Lowe III
Pr: John W Swann III
CFO: Scott W Sproule
Ofcr: Natausha H White
VP: John W Nurkin
VP: Barbara Pitts
Natl Sales: Jay Francis
S&M/VP: Trevor Hartman
Board of Directors: Christopher J Kearney, Ricky D Puckett, David A Roberts, Ruth G Shaw, Tana L Utley

D-U-N-S 07-980-0324
▲ SPX FLOW INC
13320 Balntyn Corp Pl, Charlotte, NC 28277-3607
Tel (704) 752-4400 *Founded/Ownrshp* 2015
Sales 2.3MMM *EMP* 2,026E
Tkr Sym FLOW *Exch* NYS
SIC 3556 Food products machinery
Ch Bd: Christopher J Kearney
CFO: Jeremy W Smeltser
Ch: Scott Sproule
Ofcr: Belinda G Hyde
Ofcr: Michael Swanzy
VP: Michael Chill
VP: Sue Dupuis
VP: Kevin J Eamigh
VP: Bruce Knuth
VP: Stephen A Tsoris
VP: Tim Wells
Board of Directors: Anne K Altman, Patrick D Campbell, Emerson U Fullwood, Robert F Hull Jr, Terry S Lisenby, David V Singer

D-U-N-S 05-942-5496 IMP
■ SPX FLOW TECHNOLOGY SYSTEMS INC
APV CREPACO
(*Suby of* SPX FLOW INC) ★
105 Crosspoint Pkwy, Getzville, NY 14068-1603
Tel (716) 692-3000 *Founded/Ownrshp* 1972
Sales 342.5MME *EMP* 1,000
SIC 3556 8742 Food products machinery; Food & beverage consultant
CEO: Christopher J Kearney
**Pr:* Marc Michael
**Pr:* Patrick J O'Leary
**CFO:* Brian Goff
**CFO:* Jeremy Smeltser

D-U-N-S 79-619-9818 IMP/EXP
■ SPX FLOW TECHNOLOGY USA INC
KEMP
(*Suby of* SPX FLOW INC) ★
4647 Se 40th Ave, Ocala, FL 34474
Tel (352) 237-1220 *Founded/Ownrshp* 2015
Sales 84.8MME *EMP* 8E
SIC 3569 Filters, general line: industrial
Pr: Marc Michael
**Pr:* Dwight Gibson
**Pr:* David Kowalski
**Pr:* Tony Renzi
**Pr:* David J Wilson
**CFO:* Keith Miller
**Ex VP:* Jeremy Smelster
VP: James Doughty
VP: Cochran Fant
**CIO:* Kevin Eamigh
IT Man: Debra Mager

D-U-N-S 05-368-2712 IMP/EXP
■ SPX TRANSFORMER SOLUTIONS INC
WAUKESHA ELECTRIC
(*Suby of* SPX CORP) ★
400 S Prairie Ave, Waukesha, WI 53186-5969
Tel (262) 547-0121 *Founded/Ownrshp* 1998
Sales 500.0MM *EMP* 1,100
SIC 7629 3612 Electronic equipment repair; Power transformers, electric
Pr: Brian G Mason
Pr: Sandeep Arora
Pr: Troy D Kabrich
Pr: Brian Regan
Pr: Michael Skowronek
Pr: Dharam Vir
IT Man: Jon Schepke
Sfty Mgr: Bill Meekma
Ql Cn Mgr: David Bandow
Secur Mgr: Melvin P Rhodes
Sls&Mrk Ex: Mary Dahms

SPYCHER BROTHERS
See SELECT HARVEST USA LLC

D-U-N-S 83-653-3500
SQS USA INC
545 E John Carpenter Fwy, Irving, TX 75062-3931
Tel (630) 596-6001 *Founded/Ownrshp* 2007
Sales 40.4MME *EMP* 2,100
SIC 7373 Systems software development services
CEO: Gireendra Kasmalkar
**VP:* Suresh Pabba

D-U-N-S 60-325-1575
SQUARE 1 BANK
406 Blackwell St Ste 240, Durham, NC 27701-3984
Tel (919) 314-3040 *Founded/Ownrshp* 2005
Sales NA *EMP* 160
SIC 6021

D-U-N-S 80-045-9625
SQUARE 1 FINANCIAL INC
406 Blackwell St Ste 240, Durham, NC 27701-3984
Tel (866) 355-0468 *Founded/Ownrshp* 2005
Sales NA *EMP* 258
SIC 6022 6799

SQUARE BUTTE ELECTRIC COOPS
See MINNKOTA POWER COOPERATIVE INC

SQUARE DEAL BUILDING SUPPLY
See CIRAULO BROTHERS BUILDING CO

D-U-N-S 96-193-6593 IMP
SQUARE ENIX OF AMERICA HOLDINGS INC
(*Suby of* SQUARE ENIX HOLDINGS CO., LTD.)
999 N Sepulveda Blvd Fl 3, El Segundo, CA 90245-2731
Tel (310) 846-0400 *Founded/Ownrshp* 2007
Sales 300.0MM *EMP* 120E
SIC 5045 Computer software
CEO: Yoichi Wada
**VP:* Jim Burley

D-U-N-S 96-366-5638
▲ SQUARE INC
1455 Market St Ste 600, San Francisco, CA 94103-1357
Tel (415) 375-3176 *Founded/Ownrshp* 2009
Sales 1.2MMM *EMP* 1,449
Tkr Sym SQ *Exch* NYS
SIC 7372 Prepackaged software
Ch Bd: Jack Dorsey
CFO: Sarah Friar
Genl Couns: Sydney Schaub
Genl Couns: Sivan Whiteley
Board of Directors: Paul Deighton, Jim McKelvey, Mary Meeker, Ruth Simmons, Lawrence Summers, David Viniar

D-U-N-S 05-171-0636
SQUARESPACE INC
225 Varick St Fl 12, New York, NY 10014-4383
Tel (646) 580-3456 *Founded/Ownrshp* 2006
Sales 117.4MME *EMP* 407
SIC 7371 Computer software development
CEO: Anthony Casalena
CFO: Nicole Anasenes
**CFO:* Peter Kyviakidis
VP: Andrew Bartholomew
VP: John Colton
QA Dir: Laurence Cruz
Tech Mgr: Gilbert Iancu
Sls Mgr: Michelle Spelman
Board of Directors: Anton Levy

D-U-N-S 96-450-4422
SQUARETRADE INC
360 3rd St Fl 6, San Francisco, CA 94107-2154
Tel (415) 541-1000 *Founded/Ownrshp* 1999
Sales NA *EMP* 292E
SIC 6411 Pension & retirement plan consultants
Pr: Ahmedulla Khaishgi
Pr: Mark Harris
**CFO:* Michael Adler
CFO: Randy Heppner
CFO: Mike Liberatore
**Ch:* Steve Abernethy
Sr VP: Dina Furash
Sr VP: Raj Kapoor
**Sr VP:* Vince Tseng
**VP:* Susheel Bhasin
VP: Beverley Chadwick
**VP:* Manoj Jain
VP Bus Dev: Michael Costanza
Creative D: Chelsea Wickline

D-U-N-S 94-195-0321
SQUARETWO FINANCIAL CORP
4340 S Monaco St Fl 2, Denver, CO 80237-3485
Tel (877) 944-5715 *Founded/Ownrshp* 1994
Sales 202.6MM *EMP* 440
Accts Ernst & Young Llp Denver Co
SIC 7322 Adjustment & collection services
Ch Bd: Christopher J Lane
**CEO:* Paul A Larkins
CFO: Mike Jones
**CFO:* John D Lowe
Ofcr: Sarah Bowes
Ex VP: John Curry
**Ex VP:* Brian W Tuite
Sr VP: Kristin A Dickey
Sr VP: Mark Erickson
Sr VP: Julie Fellows
Sr VP: Bethany Parker
**Sr VP:* James B Richardson Jr
**Sr VP:* Alan Singer
**Sr VP:* William A Weeks
VP: Andrea Bollefer
VP: David Colson
VP: Trevor Giampietro
VP: Eric Hayes
VP: Michael Heinze
VP: Dan Parks
VP: JB Richardson Jr
Board of Directors: Kim Patmore, Thomas R Sandler

D-U-N-S 60-646-0475
SQUAXIN ISLAND TRIBE OF SQUAXIN ISLAND RESERVATION
10 Se Squaxin Ln, Shelton, WA 98584-9200
Tel (360) 426-9781 *Founded/Ownrshp* 1965
Sales 227.2MME *EMP* 1,190
SIC 5411 5146 7011 0132 Convenience stores; Fish & seafoods; Casino hotel; Tobacco
CFO: Deborah Stoehr
Sr VP: Erica Thale

D-U-N-S 07-675-7939
SQUIRE PATTON BOGGS (US) LLP
4900 Key Tower 127 Pub Sq, Cleveland, OH 44114
Tel (216) 479-8500 *Founded/Ownrshp* 1890
Sales 439.5MME *EMP* 2,198
SIC 8111

D-U-N-S 83-248-3890
SR BRAY LLC
POWER PLUS
1210 N Red Gum St, Anaheim, CA 92806-1820
Tel (714) 765-7551 *Founded/Ownrshp* 2009
Sales 120.3MME *EMP* 360
SIC 1731 7359 Standby or emergency power specialization; Equipment rental & leasing
Pr: Steven R Bray
COO: Mike Lang
CFO: Keith Bjelajac
Sr VP: Brian Bates
Genl Mgr: William Kehrer
Sales Exec: David Lambert
Sales Asso: Jeff Lamb

D-U-N-S 09-265-8160
SR CORPORATE SOLUTIONS AMERICA HOLDING CORP
SWISS REINSURANCE AMERICA
(*Suby of* SCHWEIZERISCHE RUCKVERSICHERUNGS-GESELLSCHAFT AG)
175 King St, Armonk, NY 10504-1606
Tel (914) 828-8000 *Founded/Ownrshp* 2011
Sales NA *EMP* 1,651
SIC 6331 6311 Fire, marine & casualty insurance; Property damage insurance; Life insurance carriers
Ch: Walter B Kielholz
VP: David Assenza
Dir Risk M: Raj Singh
Dir Sec: Anthony Passaniti
CIO: Guido Fuerer
IT Man: Venkat Narayan

D-U-N-S 03-269-9994
SR MARY PHILIPPA HEALTH CENTER
2235 Hayes St Fl 5, San Francisco, CA 94117-1012
Tel (415) 750-5500 *Founded/Ownrshp* 2010
Sales 8.7MMM *EMP* 2
SIC 8099 Health & allied services
Prin: Barry Lawlor

SR. MAURA BRANNICK DENTAL CENT
See SAINT JOSEPH REGIONAL MEDICAL CENTER-SOUTH BEND CAMPUS INC

D-U-N-S 07-994-4404
SRA COMPANIES INC
15036 Conference Ctr Dr, Chantilly, VA 20151-3848
Tel (703) 803-1500 *Founded/Ownrshp* 2011
Sales 1.3MMM *EMP* 5,600
SIC 7372 8742 Prepackaged software; Management consulting services
Pr: William L Ballhaus
**Ch Bd:* Ernst Volgenau
CFO: David F Keffer
Ofcr: Timothy J Atkin
Ex VP: George Batsakis
Ex VP: Paul Nedzbala
Ex VP: Clyde T Nixon
Board of Directors: Charles E Gottdiener, Christopher C Ragona

D-U-N-S 96-883-8909
SRA COMPANIES INC
50 Kennedy Plz 18, Providence, RI 02903-2393
Tel (401) 277-1000 *Founded/Ownrshp* 2011
Sales 269.9ME *EMP* 7,300
SIC 6211 Investment firm, general brokerage
Prin: Jonathan M Nelson

SRA INTERNATIONAL
See CONSTELLA GROUP LLC

D-U-N-S 09-777-9698 IMP
■ SRA INTERNATIONAL INC
S R A
(*Suby of* STAR SECOND MERGER SUB LLC) ★
15036 Conference Ctr Dr, Chantilly, VA 20151-3848
Tel (703) 803-1500 *Founded/Ownrshp* 2015
Sales 1.3MMM *EMP* 6,000E
SIC 7373 8748 Computer integrated systems design; Business consulting
CEO: William L Ballhaus
COO: Deborah Alderson
COO: Timothy Atkin
CFO: David Keffer
CFO: Richard J Nadeau
Chf Mktg O: Marc Solomon
Ofcr: David Fisher
Ofcr: Tom Nixon
VP: Beth Bartholomew
VP: Scott Bennett
VP: Christopher Bishop
VP: Timothy A Campen
VP: Mike Dandrea
VP: John Dankowski
VP: Michael B Fisher
VP: Theresa Golinvaux
VP: Ronald Gornto
VP: Chris McGoff
VP: Todd Morris
Dir Bus: Bill Hassler
Comm Man: Dave Nemer
Board of Directors: Charles E Gottdiener

D-U-N-S 09-021-0515
SRA TRANSPORT INC (CA)
1041 N Willow Ave, Rialto, CA 92376-4245
Tel (909) 510-2481 *Founded/Ownrshp* 2015
Sales 240.0MM *EMP* 3
SIC 4789 Pipeline terminal facilities, independently operated
Prin: Arturo F Solorzano

D-U-N-S 18-606-5843 IMP/EXP
SRAM LLC
1000 W Fulton Market # 400, Chicago, IL 60607-1299
Tel (312) 664-8800 *Founded/Ownrshp* 1987
Sales 629.8MME *EMP* 2,500
SIC 3751 Gears, motorcycle & bicycle
Pr: Stanley R Day Jr

*CFO: Mike Herr
*Ex VP: Fk Day
*VP: Michael D Mercuri
*VP: John Nedeau
Ql Cn Mgr: Edward Herrington

SRC AUTOMOTIVE DIVISION
See SPRINGFIELD REMANUFACTURING CORP

D-U-N-S 80-814-7263 IMP
SRC AUTOMOTIVE INC
4431 W Calhoun St, Springfield, MO 65802-6706
Tel (417) 829-2400 Founded/Ownrshp 1999
Sales 152.3MM^E EMP 206
SIC 5012 Automobiles
CFO: David Cruts
Dir Bus: Clark Wilson
IT Man: Richard Cooper

D-U-N-S 06-532-0145 IMP/EXP
SRC HOLDINGS CORP
531 S Union Ave, Springfield, MO 65802-2659
Tel (417) 862-2337 Founded/Ownrshp 1983
Sales 403.2MM EMP 1,000
Accts Kpm Cpas Pc Springfield Mis
SIC 3519 3714 Diesel, semi-diesel or duel-fuel engines, including marine; Fuel pumps, motor vehicle
Pr: John P Stack
Pr: Don Ross
CFO: Jo Miles
*Treas: Beverly Willis
VP: Craig Keeling
*VP: Dennis Sheppard
CTO: David Scott
IT Man: Eric Bein
IT Man: Rich Williams
Sfty Dirs: Kathy Choate

D-U-N-S 06-305-3771
SRC INC
7502 Round Pond Rd, North Syracuse, NY 13212-2558
Tel (315) 452-8000 Founded/Ownrshp 2011
Sales 153.2MM EMP 1,160
SIC 8733

D-U-N-S 00-427-7893 IMP/EXP
SRC LIQUIDATION LLC
600 Albany St, Dayton, OH 45417-3405
Tel (937) 221-1000 Founded/Ownrshp 1912
Sales 1.2MMM^E EMP 3,700
SIC 2761 2672 2677 2759 Manifold business forms; Labels (unprinted), gummed: made from purchased materials; Envelopes; Promotional printing
Pr: Landen Williams
*Ch Bd: F David Clarke III
COO: Joseph Morgan
CFO: Benjamin T Cutting
Treas: James M Vaughn
CIO: Diana Tullio
Board of Directors: Frederic F Brace, R Eric McCarthey, Robert A Peiser, John J Schiff Jr, John Q Sherman II

SRCSD
See SACRAMENTO REGIONAL COUNTY SANITATION DISTRICT

SRG GLOBAL EVANSVILLE
See SRG GLOBAL TRIM INC

D-U-N-S 00-626-4675 IMP/EXP
SRG GLOBAL INC (NV)
(Suby of CARLEX GLASS OF INDIANA INC) ★
800 Stephenson Hwy, Troy, MI 48083-1123
Tel (586) 757-7800 Founded/Ownrshp 1946, 2016
Sales 610.8MM^E EMP 3,400
SIC 3089 3571 3494 2522 3826 3825 Blow molded finished plastic products; Injection molded finished plastic products; Thermoformed finished plastic products; Electronic computers; Valves & pipe fittings; Office furniture, except wood; Analytical instruments; Instruments to measure electricity
Pr: Jim Davis
COO: Bob Plummer
CFO: Ken Kershaw
Prgrm Mgr: Phil Zhang
Dir IT: Eric Ordona
Opers Mgr: Tom Bell
Ql Cn Mgr: Keith L Krider

D-U-N-S 82-967-1473
SRG GLOBAL INC
(Suby of GUARDIAN INDUSTRIES CORP) ★
800 Stephenson Hwy, Troy, MI 48083-1123
Tel (248) 509-1100 Founded/Ownrshp 2000
Sales 1.7MMM^E EMP 3,400^E
SIC 2396 Automotive & apparel trimmings
Pr: Kevin Baird
Dir IT: Eric Ordoa A

D-U-N-S 00-700-1050 IMP
SRG GLOBAL TRIM INC (NV)
SRG GLOBAL EVANSVILLE
(Suby of SRG GLOBAL INC) ★
601 N Congress Ave, Evansville, IN 47715-2448
Tel (812) 473-6200 Founded/Ownrshp 1964, 1988
Sales 174.0MM^E EMP 790
SIC 3089 Injection molded finished plastic products
Pr: Kevin Baird
*Treas: Doug Girdler
Opers Mgr: Shelby Evans

SRG LAVIDA OPS NW SERIES
See SENIOR RESOURCE GROUP LLC

SRHS
See SINGING RIVER HEALTH SYSTEM

D-U-N-S 07-822-6792
■ **SRHS BANKRUPTCY INC**
SUMNER REGIONAL MEDICAL CENTER
(Suby of LIFEPOINT HEALTH INC) ★
555 Hartsville Pike, Gallatin, TN 37066-2400
Tel (615) 452-4210 Founded/Ownrshp 1959
Sales 47.0MM EMP 1,000
SIC 8062 General medical & surgical hospitals
CEO: Susan Peach
*COO: Michael S Herman

*CFO: Kevin Rinks
*CFO: David H Wilhoite
*VP: William D Mize
*Dir Risk M: S Waite Popejoy
Mktg Mgr: Tawnya Lassiter

D-U-N-S 00-923-2752 IMP
SRI INTERNATIONAL
333 Ravenswood Ave, Menlo Park, CA 94025-3493
Tel (650) 859-2000 Founded/Ownrshp 1946
Sales 507.7MM EMP 2,437
Accts Pricewaterhousecoopers Llp Sa
SIC 8733 8748 Scientific research agency; Noncommercial social research organization; Business consulting
Pr: William Jeffrey
Ch Bd: Mariann Byerwalter
CEO: John Prausa
CFO: Luther Lau
Bd of Dir: Richard B Brewer
Sr VP: Michael Page
VP: Richard Abramson
VP: Denise Borders
VP: Stephen Ciesinski
VP: Mark A Clifton
VP: Mark Clifton
VP: Grit Denker
VP: Katie Keating
VP: Manish Kothari
VP: Walter Moos
VP: Eric Pearson
VP: John W Prausa
VP: Alice Resnick
VP: Scott Seaton
VP: Jean Tooker
Assoc Dir: Nancy Adelman
Board of Directors: David Liddle, Samuel Armacost, Phillip Quigley, Curtis Carlson, Laura Wright, Vernon Clark, John Young, Vern Clark, John J Young Jr, Charles Holloway, David Hoyt, Robert L Joss, Leslie Kenne, Henry Kressel

SRNS
See SAVANNAH RIVER NUCLEAR SOLUTIONS LLC

D-U-N-S 82-523-8715 EXP
SRS DISTRIBUTION INC
SUNCOAST ROOFER'S SUPPLY
5900 S Lake Forest Dr # 400, McKinney, TX 75070-2193
Tel (214) 491-4149 Founded/Ownrshp 2013
Sales 1.1MMM^E EMP 750
SIC 5033 Roofing & siding materials
Pr: Ronald R Ross
Mng Pt: Rogerryan Esparza
*Ch Bd: Alan W Wilkinson
Pr: John S Davis
*COO: Daniel R Tinker
*CFO: Garold E Swan
*VP: John Bradberry
VP: Timothy Hanks
*VP: Eric J Hinkle
VP: Eric Hinkle
*VP: Thomas Miller
VP: Lonnie R Peterson
VP: Sonya K Wells

D-U-N-S 96-249-1416 IMP/EXP
SRS INDUSTRIES LLC
WHITEHALL INDUSTRIES
5175 W 6th St, Ludington, MI 49431-9322
Tel (231) 845-5101 Founded/Ownrshp 2009
Sales 169.7MM^E EMP 550
SIC 3354

SS BODY ARMOR I, INC.
See POINT BLANK SOLUTIONS INC

D-U-N-S 19-583-5736
▲ **SS&C TECHNOLOGIES HOLDINGS INC**
80 Lamberton Rd, Windsor, CT 06095-2136
Tel (860) 298-4500 Founded/Ownrshp 1986
Sales 1.0MMM EMP 4,674^E
Tkr Sym SSNC Exch NGS
SIC 7372 7371 Prepackaged software; Custom computer programming services
Ch Bd: William C Stone
*Pr: Normand A Boulanger
CFO: Patrick J Pedonti
Sr VP: Adam Hall
Sr VP: Paul G Igoe
Sr VP: Rahul Kanwar
Sr VP: Stephanie Miller
Board of Directors: Michael E Daniels, William A Etherington, Jonathan E Michael, David A Varsano, Michael J Zamkow

D-U-N-S 16-134-1383
■ **SS&C TECHNOLOGIES INC**
(Suby of SS&C TECHNOLOGIES HOLDINGS INC) ★
80 Lamberton Rd, Windsor, CT 06095-2136
Tel (860) 298-4500 Founded/Ownrshp 2005
Sales 405.4MM^E EMP 1,399
SIC 7372 7371 8741 Prepackaged software; Custom computer programming services; Management services
Ch Bd: William C Stone
*Pr: Normand A Boulanger
CFO: Patrick J Pedonti
Treas: Stephan Petrov
Sr VP: James Ramenda
Sr VP: Stephen V R Whitman
VP: Alan Grate
VP: Heinmiller John
VP: Beth Mercier
VP: Bob Moitoso
VP: Marshall Pimenta
VP: David Reid
VP: Henry Toy
VP: Karen Zaffanella
Dir Bus: Dicky Yuen
Board of Directors: Campbell R Dyer, William A Etherington, Claudius E Watts IV, Allan M Holt Jonathan E Mi

SSA
See SYSTEM SOFTWARE ASSOCIATES INC DEL

D-U-N-S 09-493-1198
SSA HOLDINGS II LLC
1207 Arendell St Ste C, Morehead City, NC 28557-4167
Tel (252) 808-3185 Founded/Ownrshp 1999
Sales 23.3MM^E EMP 4,610
SIC 7381 Detective & armored car services
CFO: Jeff Johnson

D-U-N-S 15-535-9037 IMP
SSA MARINE INC
(Suby of CARRIX INC) ★
1131 Sw Klickitat Way, Seattle, WA 98134-1108
Tel (206) 623-0304 Founded/Ownrshp 1970
Sales 1.3MMM^E EMP 10,000
SIC 4491 4731 Stevedoring; Freight transportation arrangement
Pr: Knud Stubkjaer
VP: Jim Darnley
*VP: Edward A Denike
VP: Brian Frennea
VP: Marty Greco
VP: Bill Helms
VP: David Mazzella
VP: Jim Pederson
VP: Chad Pittman
VP: Jon Rosselle
VP: Thomas Rucker
VP: Jeff Swanson
VP: Tommy Taylor
*VP: Robert E Watters
VP Bus Dev: Joe Ritzman

SSA PHOENIX
See SYSTEMS SERVICES OF AMERICA INC

D-U-N-S 03-627-6405
■ **SSA SECURITY INC**
SECURITY SERVICES OF AMERICA
(Suby of ABM INDUSTRIES INC) ★
5447 Hwy 70 W Ste 200, Morehead City, NC 28557-4511
Tel (252) 808-3185 Founded/Ownrshp 2004
Sales 36.0MM^E EMP 4,600
SIC 7381 Security guard service
Pr: Larry T Smith
Board of Directors: Neil Mayzic

D-U-N-S 96-359-0096 IMP
SSAB ENTERPRISES LLC
(Suby of SSAB US HOLDING INC) ★
801 Warrenville Rd # 800, Lisle, IL 60532-1396
Tel (630) 810-4800 Founded/Ownrshp 2007
Sales 2.0MMM EMP 1,100
SIC 3312 Blast furnaces & steel mills
Pr: Chuck Schmitt
*CFO: Phillip Marusarz
*Treas: Gregory Burnett
*Ex VP: Helena Stalnert
*VP: Michele Klebuc-Simes
VP: Greg Maindonald

D-U-N-S 96-303-2677 IMP
SSAB IOWA INC
MONTPELIER STEELWORKS
(Suby of SSAB ENTERPRISES LLC) ★
1770 Bill Sharp Blvd, Muscatine, IA 52761-9419
Tel (563) 381-5300 Founded/Ownrshp 1993
Sales 127.4MM^E EMP 450^E
SIC 3312 Blast furnaces & steel mills
Pr: David Britten
*CFO: Phillip Marusarz
*Treas: Gregory Burnett

D-U-N-S 82-758-6491
SSAB US HOLDING INC
(Suby of SSAB AB)
801 Warrenville Rd # 800, Lisle, IL 60532-1396
Tel (630) 810-4800 Founded/Ownrshp 2008
Sales 2.0MMM^E EMP 1,101
SIC 3312 Blast furnaces & steel mills
Pr: David Britten
*CFO: Phillip Marusarz
*Treas: Gregory Burnett
*VP: Michele Klebuc-Simes
CIO: Eric Kroeger

D-U-N-S 00-416-2454 IMP
SSB HOLDINGS INC (TX)
PROTEC LABORATORY
4300 Fm 2225, Quitman, TX 75783-3529
Tel (903) 878-7513 Founded/Ownrshp 2002
Sales 187.7MM^E EMP 180
SIC 5122 Vitamins & minerals
Pr: Sail Ricks
*Treas: Sue Ricks
VP: Sarah Quigley-Ricks
*VP: Sarah Quigley Ricks

D-U-N-S 03-820-4020 IMP/EXP
SSB MANUFACTURING CO
SIMMONS
(Suby of SERTA SIMMONS BEDDING LLC) ★
1 Concourse Pkwy Ste 800, Atlanta, GA 30328-6188
Tel (770) 512-7700 Founded/Ownrshp 2004
Sales 757.1MM^E EMP 2,000
SIC 2515 Mattresses, innerspring or box spring; Box springs, assembled; Mattresses, waterbed flotation
CEO: Gary T Fazio
Pr: Matt Anderson
COO: Mark Parrish
*CFO: William S Creekmuir
Ex VP: Joseph Ulicny
Ex VP: Jeff Willard
*Sr VP: Tom Burns
*Sr VP: Francis Jan
*Sr VP: Kristen K McGuffey
VP: Brian Boen
VP: Rob Brown
VP: Bob Carrol
VP: Bruce Dibert
VP: Michelle Montgomery
*VP: Kevin Odiorne
VP: Kevin Osborne
VP: Ron Richmond
Creative D: Matt Schachte

D-U-N-S 36-153-8882
SSC ATHENS OPERATING CO LLC
PARK HIGHLAND NURSING CENTER
(Suby of SAVA SENIOR CARE) ★
711 Lucas Dr, Athens, TX 75751-3445
Tel (903) 675-8538 Founded/Ownrshp 2005
Sales 669.2MM EMP 99
SIC 8051 Skilled nursing care facilities
Prin: Mark H Duncan

D-U-N-S 36-150-0734
SSC GOLDSBORO OPERATING CO LLC
(Suby of SAVA SENIOR CARE) ★
1700 Wayne Memorial Dr, Goldsboro, NC 27534-2240
Tel (919) 731-2805 Founded/Ownrshp 2004
Sales 2.5MM^E EMP 1,385^E
SIC 8051 Skilled nursing care facilities
*Prin: Gregory Goode

D-U-N-S 55-608-5459
SSC LAREDO WEST OPERATING CO LLC
RETAMA MNOR NRSING CNTR/LRDO-W
(Suby of SAVA SENIOR CARE) ★
1200 E Lane St, Laredo, TX 78040-7210
Tel (956) 722-0031 Founded/Ownrshp 2005
Sales 655.3MM EMP 99
SIC 8051 Skilled nursing care facilities
Dir Recs: Guerilimina Esquevel

D-U-N-S 36-157-2956
SSC MCALLEN RETAMA OPERATING CO LLC
RETAMA MNOR NRSING CNTR/MCLLEN
(Suby of SAVA SENIOR CARE) ★
900 S 12th St, McAllen, TX 78501-5037
Tel (956) 682-4171 Founded/Ownrshp 2005
Sales 2.0MM^E EMP 1,880^E
SIC 8051 Skilled nursing care facilities
Mktg Mgr: Sandra Ortiz

D-U-N-S 05-996-6513
SSC PITTSBURG OPERATING CO LP
DIAMOND RIDGE HEALTHCARE CTR
(Suby of SAVA SENIOR CARE) ★
2351 Loveridge Rd, Pittsburg, CA 94565-5117
Tel (925) 427-4444 Founded/Ownrshp 2011
Sales 14.0MM EMP 2,473^E
SIC 8059 Nursing home, except skilled & intermediate care facility

D-U-N-S 55-683-1902
SSC SAN ANTONIO NORTHGATE OPERATING CO LLC
NORTHGATE HLTH RHBLITATION CTR
(Suby of SAVA SENIOR CARE) ★
5757 N Knoll, San Antonio, TX 78240-2239
Tel (210) 694-7951 Founded/Ownrshp 2005
Sales 5.6MM EMP 1,286^E
SIC 8051 Skilled nursing care facilities
Sls&Mrk Ex: Heidi Wear

SSC SERVICE SOLUTIONS
See SOUTHEAST SERVICE CORP

D-U-N-S 36-146-4535
SSC WINSTON-SALEM OPERATING CO LLC
BRIAN CENTER HEALTH/RETIREMENT
4911 Brian Center Ln, Winston Salem, NC 27106-6423
Tel (336) 744-5674 Founded/Ownrshp 2006
Sales 440.4MM EMP 80
SIC 8051 Skilled nursing care facilities
CEO: H Paul Schrank II
Exec: Pat Granzik
Nrsg Dir: Debra Moser

D-U-N-S 01-277-8232
SSCG GROUP LLC
220 E 42nd St, New York, NY 10017-5806
Tel (212) 907-4300 Founded/Ownrshp 2008
Sales 98.4MM^E EMP 1,084
SIC 7311 Advertising agencies
Sr VP: Juliet Lee
VP: Lisa Healy

D-U-N-S 08-155-7126 IMP
SSF IMPORTED AUTO PARTS LLC
S S F
466 Forbes Blvd, South San Francisco, CA 94080-2015
Tel (800) 203-9287 Founded/Ownrshp 2012
Sales 137.0MM^E EMP 200
SIC 5013 Automotive supplies & parts
Dir IT: Nancy Sanguinetti
Sales Exec: Vince Ortisi
Manager: Bill Foxworthy
Sales Asso: Jeff Gregg

D-U-N-S 16-183-6820
SSI GROUP INC
4721 Morrison Dr, Mobile, AL 36609-3350
Tel (251) 345-0000 Founded/Ownrshp 1991
Sales 94.3MM^E EMP 417
SIC 7371 7372 Custom computer programming services; Prepackaged software
CEO: Bob E Smith
Genl Pt: Len Jordan
*Ch Bd: Celia A Wallace
*Pr: James Lyons
Pr: Bryan Pearce
*COO: Deborrah J Short
CFO: Cory Delello
*CFO: James M Lyons
*CFO: Terry Pefanis
CFO: Mark Williamson
*Sec: Robbie Hansen
Ex VP: Jay Colfer
*Ex VP: David Watson
*VP: Mary Hyland
*VP: Tom Myers
VP: Scott Oneill
VP: Mike Ruggles
VP: Debbie Short-Rodrick
VP: Lamar Windham
Dir Risk M: Walter Bracewell

D-U-N-S 96-641-2707
SSI INVESTMENTS I LIMITED
(*Suby of* SSI POOLING LP)
107 Northeastern Blvd, Nashua, NH 03062-1916
Tel (603) 324-3000 *Founded/Ownrshp* 2010
Sales 413.5MM^E *EMP* 1,106^E
SIC 7372 Prepackaged software
Pr: Charles E Moran

D-U-N-S 96-631-7880
SSI INVESTMENTS II LIMITED
(*Suby of* SSI INVESTMENTS I LIMITED) ★
107 Northeastern Blvd, Nashua, NH 03062-1916
Tel (603) 324-3000 *Founded/Ownrshp* 2010
Sales 413.5MM *EMP* 1,103^E
Accts Ernst & Young Llp Boston Mas
SIC 7372 Prepackaged software
Pr: Charles E Moran
**COO:* Jerald A Nine Jr
**CFO:* Thomas J McDonald
**Ex VP:* Colm M Darcy
**Ex VP:* Mark A Townsend
Board of Directors: Michael C Ascione, Mark Commins, David W Humphrey, John Maldonado, Eugene Regan, Imelda Shine, Ferdinand Von Prondzynski

D-U-N-S 04-649-2963 IMP
SSI TECHNOLOGIES INC (WI)
SINTERED SPECIALTIES DIV
3200 Palmer Dr, Janesville, WI 53546-2308
Tel (608) 758-1500 *Founded/Ownrshp* 1974, 1982
Sales 125.5MM *EMP* 700
Accts Baker Tilly Virchon Krause Llp
SIC 3399 3825 Powder, metal; Test equipment for electronic & electric measurement
Pr: David S Baum
COO: William R Coon
CFO: Bruce E Corner
CFO: Bruce E Cornr
VP: Sue Koch
VP: Lawrence Reimer
Dir Bus: Rainer Utz
Prgrm Mgr: Mike Britton
Natl Sales: Shawn King
Sls Dir: Bill Day
Manager: Josh Bardwell

D-U-N-S 80-998-2911 IMP
SSI-TURLOCK DAIRY DIVISION
SUNNYSIDE FARMS
2600 Spengler Way, Turlock, CA 95380-8591
Tel (209) 668-2100 *Founded/Ownrshp* 1988
Sales 188.1MM^E *EMP* 195
Accts Moss-Adams Llp Cpa Sacrament
SIC 5143 2024 5144 2022 Dairy products, except dried or canned; Ice cream & ice milk; Eggs; Cheese, natural & processed
CFO: Tracy Nicholl
**CFO:* Tracy Twomey
Sls Dir: Todd Hager

SSL
See SPACE SYSTEMS/LORAL LLC

D-U-N-S 07-590-4839
SSM CARDINAL GLENNON CHILDRENS HOSPITAL
(*Suby of* SSM HEALTH CARE CORP) ★
1465 S Grand Blvd, Saint Louis, MO 63104-1003
Tel (314) 577-5600 *Founded/Ownrshp* 1956
Sales 1.7MM^E *EMP* 1,500
SIC 8069

D-U-N-S 07-711-0021
SSM HEALTH CARE CORP
10101 Woodfield Ln # 100, Saint Louis, MO 63132-2944
Tel (314) 994-7800 *Founded/Ownrshp* 1986
Sales 1.1MMM *EMP* 24,230
Accts Deloitte Tax Llp Houston Tx
SIC 8062 8082 8011 8051 General medical & surgical hospitals; Home health care services; Offices & clinics of medical doctors; Skilled nursing care facilities
CEO: Bill Thompson
**COO:* William C Schoenhard
CFO: Suzanne M Petru
**Sr VP:* Lynn Bruchhof
**Sr VP:* Paula J Friedman
Sr VP: Phillip Loftus
**Sr VP:* Michael Panicola
**Sr VP:* William P Thompson
**Sr VP:* Kris A Zimmer
VP: Tom Ahr
VP: Ken Bade
VP: Cheryl Champoux
VP: Filippo Ferrigni
VP: Candace Jennings
VP: Lisa D Jones
VP: Louis C Rotter
VP: R Vanconia
VP: R B Vanconia
VP: Debbie Walkenhorst
VP: Jan Wesley
VP: Lynn Widmer
Board of Directors: Kris Zimmer

D-U-N-S 07-123-6103
SSM HEALTH CARE OF OKLAHOMA INC
ST ANTHONY HOSPITAL
(*Suby of* SSM HEALTH CARE CORP) ★
1000 N Lee Ave, Oklahoma City, OK 73102-1036
Tel (405) 272-7000 *Founded/Ownrshp* 1982
Sales 444.7MM *EMP* 3,000
SIC 8062 General medical & surgical hospitals
CEO: Joe Hodges
Pr: Donna Retter
**CFO:* Garrick Muller
**VP:* Cynthia Brundige
VP: Marti Jourden
**VP:* Shasta Manuel
**VP:* Kersey Winfree
Exec: Barbara Baker
Exec: Teresa Carter
IT Man: Darla Wilson
Doctor: Michael Klein

D-U-N-S 12-961-5931
SSM HEALTH CARE OF WISCONSIN INC
(*Suby of* SSM HEALTH CARE CORP) ★
1808 W Beltline Hwy, Madison, WI 53713-2334
Tel (608) 258-6551 *Founded/Ownrshp* 1999
Sales 3.5MM^E *EMP* 3,000
SIC 8062 General medical & surgical hospitals
Pr: Damond Boatwright
VP: Michael G Heifetz
VP: Jonathan P Lewis
Ex Dir: Carole Halberg
Ex Dir: Sandra Lampman
Pharmcst: Greg Bauer
Pharmcst: Ron Baumgart

SSM HEALTH GOOD SAMARITAN HOSP
See GOOD SAMARITAN REGIONAL HEALTH CENTER

D-U-N-S 84-425-2549
SSM HEALTH ST JOSEPH HOSPITAL-ST CHARLES
SSM ST. JOSEPH HEALTH CENTER
(*Suby of* SSM HEALTH CARE CORP) ★
300 1st Capitol Dr, Saint Charles, MO 63301-2844
Tel (636) 947-5000 *Founded/Ownrshp* 1914
Sales 5.7MM^E *EMP* 1,567^E
SIC 8062 General medical & surgical hospitals
CEO: Christopher Howard
**Pr:* Sherlyn Hailstone
CFO: Chuck Chervitz
Adm Dir: Brenda Peterson
Doctor: William T Schnarr MD

SSM ST. JOSEPH HEALTH CENTER
See SSM HEALTH ST JOSEPH HOSPITAL-ST CHARLES

D-U-N-S 00-966-7932 EXP
SSMB PACIFIC HOLDING CO INC (CA)
BAY AREA KENWORTH
1755 Adams Ave, San Leandro, CA 94577-1001
Tel (510) 836-6100 *Founded/Ownrshp* 1942, 1999
Sales 181.5MM^E *EMP* 170
SIC 5012 7699 Trucks, commercial; Industrial truck repair
Pr: Harry Mamizuka
CFO: Thomas Parodi
**VP:* Tom Bertolino
VP: Mike Lee
VP: Bruce Nobles
VP: Wade Sperry
Sales Exec: Xavier Martinez

D-U-N-S 08-573-3335
SSNYC INC
(*Suby of* SCAN GROUP A/S)
80 Washington St, Hoboken, NJ 07030-4506
Tel (201) 216-1500 *Founded/Ownrshp* 1980
Sales 137.4MM^E *EMP* 330
SIC 4731 6512 Freight forwarding; Nonresidential building operators
Pr: Arne Simonsen
**VP:* Steen Dyrhlom
**VP:* Klaus Jepsen
**VP:* Hans Mikkelsen

SSOE GROUP
See SSOE INC

D-U-N-S 05-162-9301
SSOE INC
SSOE GROUP
1001 Madison Ave Ste A, Toledo, OH 43604-5585
Tel (419) 255-3830 *Founded/Ownrshp* 1948
Sales 138.2MM *EMP* 1,077
SIC 8711 8712 8742 1541 7389

D-U-N-S 06-662-1178
SSP AMERICA INC
SSP CANADA FOOD SERVICES
(*Suby of* SSP GROUP PLC)
19465 Drfield Ave Ste 105, Lansdowne, VA 20176
Tel (703) 723-7235 *Founded/Ownrshp* 2006
Sales 116.3MM^E *EMP* 3,000
SIC 5812 Caterers
Pr: Les Cappetta
COO: Pat Banducci
**CFO:* Roger Worrell
Ex VP: Roderick McOwan
VP: Palmer Brown
VP: Patrick Gleason
VP: Paul Heflin
VP: Anthony Montepare
Exec: Franco Maffettone
Exec: Dean Matsushita
Opers Mgr: Bill Guynn

SSP CANADA FOOD SERVICES
See SSP AMERICA INC

D-U-N-S 14-554-7571
SSSI INC
SONGER STEEL SERVICES
2755a Park Ave, Washington, PA 15301-8147
Tel (724) 743-5815 *Founded/Ownrshp* 1984
Sales 175.0MM^E *EMP* 500
SIC 1611 3312 4925 General contractor, highway & street construction; Blast furnaces & steel mills; Coke oven gas, production & distribution
CEO: Paul Songer
**Pr:* Joseph C Meneskie
**CEO:* Paul J Songer
**CFO:* Richard J Kline
**Ex VP:* Jo Stright
VP: Elaine Reihner
**VP:* John P Songer
Off Mgr: Mark Cokain
Opers Mgr: Bill Yockel

D-U-N-S 02-383-9421 IMP/EXP
SSW HOLDING CO INC
3501 Tulsa St, Fort Smith, AR 72903-6809
Tel (479) 646-1651 *Founded/Ownrshp* 1998
Sales 474.7MM^E *EMP* 1,476
SIC 3496 6719 Miscellaneous fabricated wire products; Shelving, made from purchased wire; Investment holding companies, except banks
Ch Bd: Paul Kara

**Pr:* Mark A Gritton
**CFO:* Steve Koss

D-U-N-S 80-186-3168
ST AEROSPACE MOBILE INC
(*Suby of* SINGAPORE TECHNOLOGIES AEROSPACE LTD)
2100 Aerospace Dr Brkley Brookley Complex, Mobile, AL 36615
Tel (251) 438-8888 *Founded/Ownrshp* 1990
Sales 250.0MM *EMP* 1,400
SIC 4581 Aircraft maintenance & repair services
Pr: Joseph Ng
Div Mgr: Khay Lee
Genl Mgr: Yip Hin
Genl Mgr: Chai Keat

D-U-N-S 06-938-0160
ST AGNES HEALTHCARE INC
SAINT AGNES HOSPITAL
(*Suby of* ASCENSION HEALTH) ★
900 S Caton Ave, Baltimore, MD 21229-5201
Tel (667) 234-6000 *Founded/Ownrshp* 1862
Sales 438.1MM *EMP* 2,506
SIC 8062 Hospital, affiliated with AMA residency; Hospital, medical school affiliated with nursing & residency
Pr: Keith Vander Kolk
**CFO:* Rhonda Anderson
**CFO:* Scott Furniss
Exec: John Kersheskey
Dir Rx: Gregory Smith
Dir Sec: Stanley Netwwski
Nurse Mgr: Carol Gallaher
CIO: William Gersgovitch
Mktg Mgr: Lisa Winterton
Doctor: Hope Allen
Doctor: Elizabeth Bower

D-U-N-S 07-895-1555
ST AGNES HOSPITAL OF FOND DU LAC WISC INC
AGNESIAN HALTHCARE FOND DU LAC
430 E Division St, Fond Du Lac, WI 54935-4597
Tel (920) 929-2300 *Founded/Ownrshp* 1896
Sales 312.1MM *EMP* 2,700
Accts Wipfli Llp Wausau Wisconsin
SIC 8062 General medical & surgical hospitals
Pr: Robert Fale
CFO: William Fenske
Off Admin: Debra Aird
Opers Supe: Mary J Menzies
Nrsg Dir: Carol Mueller

D-U-N-S 08-047-8589
ST ALBANS COOPERATIVE CREAMERY INC
VERMONT FAMILY FARMS
140 Federal St, Saint Albans, VT 05478-2000
Tel (802) 524-9366 *Founded/Ownrshp* 1919
Sales 387.0MM^E *EMP* 70
Accts Dopkins & Company Llp Buffal
SIC 2026 2023 Fluid milk; Dried milk
Ex Dir: Leon Berthiaume
**Pr:* Ralph McNall
COO: Robert Hirss
**CFO:* Michael Janson
Genl Mgr: Leon Berthiemu
Sfty Mgr: Allen Yanney
Plnt Mgr: Steve Machia

D-U-N-S 06-654-2846
ST ALEXIUS MEDICAL CENTER
CHI ST. ALEXIUS HEALTH
900 E Broadway Ave, Bismarck, ND 58501-4520
Tel (701) 530-7000 *Founded/Ownrshp* 1885
Sales 289.3MM *EMP* 1,947
SIC 8062 General medical & surgical hospitals
CEO: Gary P Miller
Chf Path: Ward D Fredickson
CFO: Gary Miller
**VP:* Amy Hornbacher
**VP:* Shiraz Hyder
VP: Shiraz S Hyder
**VP:* Julie Jeske
VP: Frank Kilzer
**VP:* Rosanne Schmidt
Dir Rad: Douglas Peterson
Doctor: Shelley Killen

D-U-N-S 09-475-2706
ST ALEXIUS MEDICAL CENTER
SAINT ALEXIUS MEDICAL CENTER
1555 Barrington Rd Bldg 1, Hoffman Estates, IL 60169-1099
Tel (847) 884-9800 *Founded/Ownrshp* 1999
Sales 351.5MM *EMP* 1,500
Accts Deloitte Tax Llp Chicago Il
SIC 8062 General medical & surgical hospitals
CEO: Len Wilk
**CFO:* Robin Chopp
VP: John Sullivan
Dir Sec: Eric Swanson
Obsttrcn: Anna Bobba
Pharmcst: Gita Patel
Pharmcst: Joanne Yoo

D-U-N-S 06-325-4395
ST AMBROSE UNIVERSITY
518 W Locust St, Davenport, IA 52803-2898
Tel (563) 333-6000 *Founded/Ownrshp* 1882
Sales 111.5MM *EMP* 500
Accts Mcgladrey Llp Davenport Iowa
SIC 8221 University
CEO: Joan Lescinski
**Pr:* Sister Joan Lescinski
CFO: Edward Henkhaus
VP: Kaley Brouwer
VP: John Cooper
Assoc Dir: Sheila Deluhery
Dir Sec: Robert Christopher
IT Man: Irene Kremer
Mktg Dir: Angela Elliott

D-U-N-S 96-777-1077
ST ANDREWS ACQUISITION INC
9720 South Tacoma Way, Tacoma, WA 98499-4456
Tel (253) 584-2170 *Founded/Ownrshp* 2013
Sales 5.5MM^E *EMP* 1,600
Accts Moss Adams Llp Spokane Washi
SIC 8322 8361 Social service center; Rehabilitation center, residential: health care incidental
CEO: Cheryl Borden
COO: Heather K Okeefe

D-U-N-S 07-830-6366
ST ANNE MERCY HOSPITAL
3404 W Sylvania Ave, Toledo, OH 43623-4480
Tel (419) 407-2663 *Founded/Ownrshp* 2011
Sales 113.2MM *EMP* 35^E
SIC 8062 General medical & surgical hospitals
CEO: Richard Evans
**Prin:* Mahjabeen M Islam MD
**Prin:* Agha Shahid MD

D-U-N-S 62-158-3087
ST ANNES HEALTH CARE SYSTEM INC
795 Middle St, Fall River, MA 02721-1733
Tel (508) 674-5741 *Founded/Ownrshp* 1985
Sales 123.5MM *EMP* 4
Accts Deloitte & Touche Llp Boston
SIC 8741 Hospital management; Nursing & personal care facility management
Pr: Micheal Metzler
**CFO:* Robert Guyon Jr
Treas: Sister Irene Vroder
DP Exec: Mary O'Brien
Ansthlgy: Henry Korzeniowski

ST ANNE'S HOSPITAL
See TAS-SAHC INC

ST ANN'S COMMUNITY HOME
See ST ANNS HOME FOR AGED

D-U-N-S 04-307-6256
ST ANNS HOME FOR AGED
ST ANN'S COMMUNITY HOME
287 Flower City Park # 2, Rochester, NY 14615-3699
Tel (585) 697-6086 *Founded/Ownrshp* 1874
Sales 64.1MM *EMP* 1,000
Accts Efp Rotenberg Llp Rochester
SIC 8051 Skilled nursing care facilities
Pr: Elizabeth Mullin-Diprosa
**Ch Bd:* Robert Ryan
**Treas:* Rayman De Posgutino
Sr VP: Michael McRae
VP: Barbara Joyce
VP: Debra Metzger
Exec: Pasquale Conca
Exec: Daryl Cronk
Dir Rx: Christine Freeley
Ex Dir: Tony Coccitto
MIS Dir: Marie Peartree

ST ANTHONY CENTRAL HOSPITAL
See CATHOLIC HEALTH INITIATIVES COLORADO

ST ANTHONY HOME
See FRANCISCAN COMMUNITIES INC

ST ANTHONY HOSPITAL
See LINNEA BASEY CANCER RESOURCE CENTER

ST ANTHONY HOSPITAL
See SSM HEALTH CARE OF OKLAHOMA INC

ST ANTHONY MEDICAL CENTER
See SAMC INC

ST. ANTHONY'S HEALTH CARE
See ST ANTHONYS HOSPITAL INC

D-U-N-S 06-279-3955
ST ANTHONYS HOSPITAL INC
ST. ANTHONY'S HEALTH CARE
(*Suby of* BAYCARE EDUCATION SERVICES) ★
1200 7th Ave N, Saint Petersburg, FL 33705-1388
Tel (727) 825-1100 *Founded/Ownrshp* 1931
Sales 252.1MM *EMP* 1,076
Accts Ernst & Young Us Llp Atlanta
SIC 8062 General medical & surgical hospitals
Pr: William Uobricht
V Ch: Charles J Osterholt
**Ofcr:* Carl Tremonti
Dir Risk M: Isabelle Smith
Dir Lab: Rickie M Jones
Dir Rx: Walter Inman
Pathlgst: Kern Davis
Surgeon: Rose Ellen Lucarell
Doctor: Francois Guimond MD
Doctor: Todd Letzring
Doctor: Steven Schirm

D-U-N-S 11-090-9186
ST ANTHONYS MEDICAL CENTER
10010 Kennerly Rd, Saint Louis, MO 63128-2106
Tel (314) 525-1000 *Founded/Ownrshp* 1900
Sales 482.5MM *EMP* 3,900^E
Accts Bkd Llp St Louis Missouri
SIC 8062 General medical & surgical hospitals
Ch: David M Sindelar
CFO: Kenneth Venuto
Ex VP: Michalene Maringer
VP: Patrick Garrett
VP: Robert Griesbaum
Chf Nrs Of: Beverly Bokovitz
Snr Ntwrk: Joseph Barron
CIO: Jim Weldon
CTO: Gary Holzem
Dir IT: Ed Wichmann
Telecom Mg: Don Armstron

D-U-N-S 07-588-8081
ST ANTHONYS MEMORIAL HOSPITAL OF HOSPITAL SISTERS OF THETHIRD ORDER OF ST FRANCIS
(*Suby of* HOSPITAL SISTERS HEALTH SYSTEM) ★
503 N Maple St, Effingham, IL 62401-2099
Tel (217) 342-2121 *Founded/Ownrshp* 1954
Sales 126.3MM *EMP* 900^E
SIC 8062 General medical & surgical hospitals
CEO: Theresa Rutherford
**CEO:* Dan Woods
COO: Bob Esker
**CFO:* Dave Storm
Ex Dir: Michael Wall
CIO: Jan Schuette
Surgeon: Josue Gabriel

Ansthlgy: Shane R Fancher
HC Dir: Teri Phillips

D-U-N-S 19-426-7407
ST BARNABAS COMMUNITY ENTERPRISES
4422 3rd Ave, Bronx, NY 10457-2545
Tel (718) 960-6100 *Founded/Ownrshp* 1986
Sales 45.3MM^E *EMP* 2,000
SIC 8062 General medical & surgical hospitals
Ch: Victor Wright

D-U-N-S 06-811-7787
ST BARNABAS HOSPITAL
S B H
4422 3rd Ave, Bronx, NY 10457-2594
Tel (718) 960-9000 *Founded/Ownrshp* 1986
Sales 333.2MM *EMP* 2,119
SIC 8062 General medical & surgical hospitals
Ch Bd: Victor Wright
**Pr:* Scott Cooper
**CFO:* Todd Gorlewski
Sr VP: Keith Wolf
VP: Catherine Graham
VP: Ann M McDonald
Plnt Mgr: Frank Conti
Ansthlgy: David S Marhak
Opthamlgy: Laura Klein
Doctor: Fareed Ali
Doctor: Sheryl G Kho

D-U-N-S 06-752-0759 IMP
ST BARNABAS MEDICAL CTR
(*Suby of* SAINT BARNABAS HEALTH CARE SYS) ★
94 Old Short Hills Rd # 1, Livingston, NJ 07039-5668
Tel (973) 322-5000 *Founded/Ownrshp* 1865
Sales 728.3MM *EMP* 4,000
SIC 8062 General medical & surgical hospitals
Ch Bd: Ronald J Del Mauro
Chf Path: Selwyn J Baptist
Chf Rad: Robert Goodman
**Ch Bd:* Ronald J Del Mauro
COO: Patrick Ahern
**CFO:* Patrick Aheran
CFO: Dick Davis
CFO: Mary Duffy
Ofcr: Anna Burian
Assoc VP: Bonnie Geissler
VP: Thomas Scott
VP: Tony Soriano
Dir Rad: William Qiu
Dir Env Sv: Jane Mc Gill

D-U-N-S 79-896-7050
ST BARNABAS SCHOOL
ROMAN CATHOLIC ARCHDIOCESE OF
(*Suby of* ROMAN CATHOLIC ARCHDIOCESE OF INDIANAPOLIS INC) ★
8300 Rahke Rd, Indianapolis, IN 46217-4951
Tel (317) 881-7422 *Founded/Ownrshp* 2007
Sales 18.4MM^E *EMP* 1,266^E
SIC 8211 Catholic elementary & secondary schools
Prin: Debbie Perkins

D-U-N-S 05-057-3195
ST BERNARD HOSPITAL (IL)
326 W 64th St, Chicago, IL 60621-3146
Tel (773) 962-3900 *Founded/Ownrshp* 1904
Sales 94.8MM *EMP* 875
Accts Crowe Horwath Llp Chicago Il
SIC 8062 General medical & surgical hospitals
Pr: Charles Holland
Chf Path: Kirkor Karachorlu
Chf Rad: Henry Wiggins
Pr: Ken Spiewak
**CFO:* Guy Alton
Trst: Bridget Ross
**VP:* Roland Abellera
**VP:* Ronald Campbell
**VP:* Evelyn Jones
VP: Danny Rollins
Dir Lab: Barbara Lee
Comm Man: Gale Sykes

D-U-N-S 13-020-1267 IMP/EXP
ST BERNARD SOAP CO
(*Suby of* TRILLIUM HEALTH CARE PRODUCTS INC)
5177 Spring Grove Ave, Cincinnati, OH 45217-1050
Tel (513) 242-2227 *Founded/Ownrshp* 2003
Sales 209.0MM^E *EMP* 301
SIC 2841 Soap & other detergents
Pr: William Biedenharm

D-U-N-S 07-355-5146
ST BERNARDS HOSPITAL INC
ST BERNARD'S MEDICAL CENTER
225 E Jackson Ave, Jonesboro, AR 72401-3119
Tel (870) 207-7300 *Founded/Ownrshp* 1900
Sales 270.4MM *EMP* 2,000
SIC 8062 General medical & surgical hospitals
CEO: Chris B Barber
**Pr:* Ben E Owens
CFO: Harry Hutchinson
VP: Jimmy Cooper
VP: David Pyle
Exec: Tommy Rohlfing
Dir Case M: Susan Greenwood
Dir Rad: Chris Copeland
Dir Rad: Mark S Newman
Ex Dir: Keith Johnson
CIO: Mark Odom

ST BERNARD'S MEDICAL CENTER
See ST BERNARDS HOSPITAL INC

D-U-N-S 17-260-2950
ST BERNARDS PROVIDENCE HOSPITA
901 E Virgil Ave, Milbank, SD 57252-2124
Tel (605) 432-4538 *Founded/Ownrshp* 2004
Sales 757.5MM *EMP* 10^E
Accts Eide Bailly Llp Sioux Falls
SIC 8062 General medical & surgical hospitals
Prin: Genevieve Karels

D-U-N-S 07-331-3744
ST CATHERINE HOSPITAL
CHI
(*Suby of* CHI) ★
401 E Spruce St, Garden City, KS 67846-5672
Tel (620) 272-2222 *Founded/Ownrshp* 1931
Sales 92.8MM *EMP* 500
Accts Catholic Health Initiatives E
SIC 8062 General medical & surgical hospitals
Dir Recs: Linda Pickering
**Pr:* Mark Steadham
**CFO:* Amanda Vaughan
**Sr VP:* John Yox
**VP:* Margie Prewitt
Ex Dir: Kevin Gallagher
**Ex Dir:* Kathy Morrison
Software D: Edward Brown

D-U-N-S 06-858-5785
ST CATHERINE HOSPITAL INC
(*Suby of* COMMUNITY FOUNDATION OF NORTHWEST INDIANA INC) ★
4321 Fir St, East Chicago, IN 46312-3097
Tel (219) 392-1700 *Founded/Ownrshp* 2001
Sales 157.5MM *EMP* 900
Accts Ernst & Young Us Llp Indianap
SIC 8062 General medical & surgical hospitals
CEO: Jo Ann Birdzell
Chf Rad: Thomas Hoess
**COO:* Lou Molina
**CFO:* Art Vasquez
CFO: Joseph Winterhaler
**VP:* David Berkey
Dir Rad: Dave Padilla
Ex Dir: Robert Bertrand
Off Mgr: Kathleen Deneau
CIO: Vernon Goeber
CIO: Vernon Grober

D-U-N-S 79-715-7422
ST CATHERINE OF SIENA MEDICAL CENTER
50 Route 25a, Smithtown, NY 11787-1348
Tel (631) 862-3000 *Founded/Ownrshp* 1999
Sales 257.1MM *EMP* 1,500
SIC 8062 General medical & surgical hospitals
CEO: Alan D Guerci
**Prin:* Paul Rowland
Off Mgr: Tammy Arnnaczisi

D-U-N-S 07-176-3676
ST CATHERINE UNIVERSITY
2004 Randolph Ave, Saint Paul, MN 55105-1750
Tel (651) 690-6000 *Founded/Ownrshp* 1913
Sales 128.0MM *EMP* 318^E
Accts Cliftonlarsonallen Llp Minnea
SIC 8221 College, except junior
Pr: Andrea J Lee
**Sr VP:* Colleen Hegranes
**VP:* Brian Bruess
**VP:* Marjorie Mathison Hance
**VP:* Thomas Rooney
Assoc Dir: Tina Wagner
Prgrm Mgr: Valerie Krech
IT Man: Sadie Hiedler
IT Man: Mary Kleinberg
Pgrm Dir: Alan Bode
Art Dir: Carol Evans-Smith

D-U-N-S 07-458-8260
ST CHARLES COMMUNITY UNIT SCHOOL DISTRICT 303
ST. CHARLES CUSD 303
201 S 7th St, Saint Charles, IL 60174-2664
Tel (331) 228-2000 *Founded/Ownrshp* 1949
Sales 111.9M *EMP* 1,700
SIC 8211 Public elementary school; Public junior high school; Public senior high school
Bd of Dir: Edward McNally
**Ex Dir:* Laurel O'Brien
**Genl Mgr:* Kathy Litts
MIS Dir: Phil Morris
Psych: Williams Jean

D-U-N-S 83-596-8421
ST CHARLES CORP
200 Belle Terre Rd, Port Jefferson, NY 11777-1928
Tel (631) 474-6260 *Founded/Ownrshp* 1984
Sales 30.1MM^E *EMP* 1,700
Accts Jh Cohn Llp Roseland Nj
SIC 8741 Hospital management
Pr: Jim Oconner

ST. CHARLES CUSD 303
See ST CHARLES COMMUNITY UNIT SCHOOL DISTRICT 303

D-U-N-S 87-811-0717
■ **ST CHARLES GAMING CO INC**
(*Suby of* ISLE OF CAPRI CASINOS INC) ★
100 Lake St, Lake Charles, LA 70607-8825
Tel (337) 430-0711 *Founded/Ownrshp* 1996
Sales 21.3MM^E *EMP* 2,000
SIC 7011 Casino hotel
Prin: Jay Luchun

D-U-N-S 06-149-2740
ST CHARLES HEALTH SYSTEM INC (OR)
2500 Ne Neff Rd, Bend, OR 97701-6015
Tel (541) 382-4321 *Founded/Ownrshp* 1971
Sales 664.7MM *EMP* 3,200
SIC 8062 8011 General medical & surgical hospitals; Offices & clinics of medical doctors
CEO: Jim Diegel
CFO: Roger Highland
CFO: Beverly Minor
CFO: Karen Sheppard
VP: Scott Brown
Dir Risk M: Caludia Macdonald
Mktg Dir: Todd Sprague
Opthamlgy: Michael D Stauer

ST CHARLES HOSPITAL
See ST CHARLES HOSPITAL AND REHABILITATION CENTER

D-U-N-S 06-801-7110
ST CHARLES HOSPITAL AND REHABILITATION CENTER
ST CHARLES HOSPITAL
200 Belle Terre Rd, Port Jefferson, NY 11777-1928
Tel (631) 474-6000 *Founded/Ownrshp* 1950
Sales 173.5MM *EMP* 1,400
SIC 8062 8011 General medical & surgical hospitals; Medical centers
Pr: James O'Connor
Pharmcst: John Bruno

D-U-N-S 01-040-7518
ST CHARLES PARISH PUBLIC SCHOOLS
13855 River Rd, Luling, LA 70070-6220
Tel (985) 785-6289 *Founded/Ownrshp* 1875
Sales 89.6MM^E *EMP* 1,700
SIC 7991 Physical fitness facilities
Bd of Dir: Ellis Alexander
IT Man: Wendy Duhe
IT Man: Gwendolyn Lee
HC Dir: Jerry Smith

D-U-N-S 62-534-2373
ST CLAIR HEALTH CORP
1000 Bower Hill Rd, Pittsburgh, PA 15243-1873
Tel (412) 561-4900 *Founded/Ownrshp* 1985
Sales 81.4M *EMP* 1,504
SIC 8062 General medical & surgical hospitals
CEO: James Collins
VP: Rick Chesnos
Ex Dir: Barb Girod
Doctor: Karl Bushman
Doctor: Harshad Mehta
Pharmcst: John Lytwak
Pharmcst: Len Spicuzza
Diag Rad: Joseph Lenkey
Diag Rad: Scott Patterson
Diag Rad: Frank Torok

ST CLAIR HOSPITAL
See ST CLAIR MEMORIAL HOSPITAL

ST. CLAIR HOSPITAL
See ST CLAIR MEMORIAL HOSPITAL FOUNDATION

D-U-N-S 07-748-4665
ST CLAIR MEMORIAL HOSPITAL
ST CLAIR HOSPITAL
1000 Bower Hill Rd, Pittsburgh, PA 15243-1899
Tel (412) 561-4900 *Founded/Ownrshp* 1991
Sales 168.2MM^E *EMP* 1,500
Accts St Clair Memorial Hospital P
SIC 8062 General medical & surgical hospitals
Pr: James M Collins
**Treas:* Virginia Goldbach
**Sr VP:* Richard C Chesnos
**Sr VP:* Michael J Flanagan
**Sr VP:* G Alan Yeasted
**VP:* Andrea L Kalina
VP: Richard J Schaeffer
Nurse Mgr: Beth Reedy
Info Man: Terry McFetridge
Nutrtnst: Joy Palonis

D-U-N-S 87-738-1814
ST CLAIR MEMORIAL HOSPITAL FOUNDATION
ST. CLAIR HOSPITAL
1000 Bower Hill Rd, Pittsburgh, PA 15243-1873
Tel (412) 942-4000 *Founded/Ownrshp* 1981
Sales 172.9MM^E *EMP* 2,025^E
Accts Ernst & Young Us Llp Fl Pi
SIC 8062 General medical & surgical hospitals
Pr: James Collins
Dir Vol: Williams Georgianne
COO: Tom Ague
Bd of Dir: Adiba Ahmed
Bd of Dir: Michael Ban
Bd of Dir: David Catalane
Bd of Dir: Mario Fatigati
Bd of Dir: Leo Fatur
Bd of Dir: Gregory Habib
Bd of Dir: Edward Kaliman
Bd of Dir: Eric Nabors
Bd of Dir: Daniel Nalin
Bd of Dir: E D Newton
Bd of Dir: David Palko
Bd of Dir: Linda Range
Bd of Dir: Brenda Walther
Bd of Dir: John Yankura
Bd of Dir: Mary Zervos
Ofcr: Chris Miller
Sr VP: Michael Flanagan
Sr VP: Barry S Zaiser

ST CLAIRE FLORAL BROKERS
See ST CLAIRE FLORAL CO INC

D-U-N-S 87-840-6768
■ **ST CLAIRE FLORAL CO INC**
ST CLAIRE FLORAL BROKERS
(*Suby of* 1-800-FLOWERS.COM INC) ★
1600 Stewart Ave, Westbury, NY 11590-6696
Tel (516) 237-6000 *Founded/Ownrshp* 1994
Sales 28.2MM^E *EMP* 2,000
SIC 7389 Florist telegraph service
CEO: James McCann

ST CLAIRE MATERNITY CENTER
See ST CLAIRE MEDICAL CENTER INC

D-U-N-S 06-813-5029
ST CLAIRE MEDICAL CENTER INC
ST CLAIRE MATERNITY CENTER
222 Medical Cir, Morehead, KY 40351-1179
Tel (606) 783-6500 *Founded/Ownrshp* 1963
Sales 130.3MM *EMP* 2,527
Accts Blue & Co Llc Indianapolis I
SIC 8062 8011 General medical & surgical hospitals; Medical centers
Pr: Mark J Neff
Pr: David A Burns
**CFO:* G R Jones Jr
**Ch:* Robert G Stevens
VP: Linda Fultz
VP: Lerae Wilson
Dir: Tom Lewis
Dept Mgr: Rosemary Curtis

VP Sls: Clarence Clayton
Pharmcst: Janie Wills

D-U-N-S 07-867-2821
ST CLOUD AREA SCHOOL DISTRICT (MN)
ST CLOUD AREA SCHOOL DST 742
1000 44th Ave N Ste 100, Saint Cloud, MN 56303-2034
Tel (320) 253-9333 *Founded/Ownrshp* 1890
Sales 142.6MM *EMP* 1,500
Accts Bergankdv Ltd St Cloud Mi
SIC 8211 Public elementary & secondary schools
MIS Dir: Kevin Januszewski
Dir IT: Gary Ganje
IT Man: Mike Gritman
Info Man: Jim Tasto

ST CLOUD AREA SCHOOL DST 742
See ST CLOUD AREA SCHOOL DISTRICT

ST CLOUD COLLISION CENTER
See GILLELAND CHEVROLET CADILLAC INC

D-U-N-S 06-478-1396 IMP
ST CLOUD HOSPITAL
CENTRACARE CLINIC RIVER CAMPUS
(*Suby of* CENTRACARE CLINIC RIVER CAMPUS) ★
1406 6th Ave N, Saint Cloud, MN 56303-1901
Tel (320) 251-2700 *Founded/Ownrshp* 1928
Sales 767.0MM *EMP* 4,957
Accts Mcgladrey Llp Minneapolis Mn
SIC 8062 General medical & surgical hospitals
Pr: Craig Broman
COO: Philip Boyle
**CFO:* Greg Klugherz
Ofcr: Julie Grams
Dir Lab: Cynthia Johnson
Assoc Dir: Kevin Switzer
Dir Rx: Mary Phipps
Ex Dir: Mark Larkin
Off Mgr: Tim Dalton
Psych: Finneman Sherry
Doctor: Jon Bowar

ST. CLOUD STATE UNIVERSITY
See MINNESOTA STATE COLLEGES AND UNIVERSITIES

ST COLUMBA PRE-SCHOOL
See ARCHDIOCESE OF MOBILE ED OFF

D-U-N-S 02-158-1681
ST CROIX CHIPPEWA INDIANS OF WISCONSIN
TRIBAL GOVERNMENT
24663 Angeline Ave, Webster, WI 54893-9246
Tel (715) 349-2195 *Founded/Ownrshp* 1934
Sales NA *EMP* 1,500
SIC 9131 Indian reservation;
Ch Bd: Lewis Taylor
Genl Mgr: Ricky Petersen
Secur Mgr: Patrick McCready

D-U-N-S 15-722-6267
ST DAVIDS COMMUNITY HEALTH FOUNDATION INITIATIVE
1303 San Antonio St, Austin, TX 78701-1685
Tel (512) 879-6240 *Founded/Ownrshp* 1925
Sales 708.4MM^E *EMP* 621
SIC 8062 General medical & surgical hospitals
CEO: Earl Maxwell
CFO: Jim Ries
Ofcr: Becky Pastner
Dir: Cara Abazari

ST. DAVID'S FOUNDATION
See ST DAVIDS HEALTH CARE FOUNDATION

D-U-N-S 07-999-8200
ST DAVIDS FOUNDATION
1303 San Antonio St, Austin, TX 78701-1685
Tel (512) 879-6600 *Founded/Ownrshp* 2015
Sales 118.4MM *EMP* 9^E
SIC 8062 General medical & surgical hospitals
CEO: Earl Maxwell
**Pr:* Becky Pastner
**CFO:* James Ries
Ofcr: Deborah Durham
Ofcr: Andrew Levack
Ofcr: Kim McPherson
Comm Man: Shannon Hartigan
Genl Mgr: Carol Clark

D-U-N-S 07-748-9818
ST DAVIDS HEALTH CARE FOUNDATION
ST. DAVID'S FOUNDATION
811 Barton Springs Rd # 600, Austin, TX 78704-8702
Tel (512) 879-6600 *Founded/Ownrshp* 1981
Sales 94.7MM^E *EMP* 4
Accts Flieller Kruger Skelton & Plyl
SIC 8621 Health association
Pr: Carol Clark
**VP:* Luke Doyle

D-U-N-S 00-406-4577
ST DAVIDS HEALTHCARE PARTNERSHIP LLP
ST DAVIDS ROUND ROCK MED CTR
(*Suby of* ST DAVIDS COMMUNITY HEALTH FOUNDATION INITIATIVE) ★
2400 Round Rock Ave, Round Rock, TX 78681-4004
Tel (512) 341-1000 *Founded/Ownrshp* 1991
Sales 95.7MM^E *EMP* 610
SIC 8062 General medical & surgical hospitals
CEO: Deborah Ryl
Chf Rad: Ken Trevino
**Pr:* David Husfftueler
Chf Nrs Of: Loraine E Ondrj
MIS Dir: Rob Graham
Mktg Dir: Celeste Lismeister
Mktg Mgr: Celeste Muenzler

D-U-N-S 00-735-8612
ST DAVIDS HEALTHCARE PARTNERSHIP LP LLP
COLUMBIA ST DAVIDS DIV OFF
98 San Jacinto Blvd, Austin, TX 78701-4082
Tel (512) 708-9700 *Founded/Ownrshp* 1996

Sales 419.0MM^E *EMP* 5,500^E
SIC 8062 General medical & surgical hospitals
Pr: David Huffstutler
Pt: Jack Brown
Pt: Jack Campbell
Pt: C W Heatherly
Pt: David R Wilson
COO: Carol Clark
Ofcr: Caroline Murphy
VP: Mark Clayton
VP: Lisa Doyle
VP: David Thomsen
VP: Lisa Wang-Doyle
Dir: Tom Coefield

D-U-N-S 07-849-4333
ST DAVIDS HOSPITAL (INC)
ST DAVIDS MEDICAL CENTER
(*Suby of* ST DAVIDS COMMUNITY HEALTH FOUNDATION INITIATIVE) ★
919 E 32nd St, Austin, TX 78705-2709
Tel (512) 476-7111 *Founded/Ownrshp* 1925
Sales 612.7MM *EMP* 610
Accts Ernst & Young Austin Tx
SIC 8062 General medical & surgical hospitals
Pr: Jack Campbell
COO: Cole Eslyn
Sr VP: Deborah Ryle
VP: Jane Lewis
Dir IT: Debbie Castleberry
HC Dir: Cynthia Clovas

ST DAVIDS MEDICAL CENTER
See ST DAVIDS HOSPITAL (INC)

D-U-N-S 87-862-5490
ST DAVIDS NORTH AUSTIN MEDICAL CENTER
(*Suby of* COLUMBIA ST DAVIDS DIV OFF) ★
12221 N Mo Pac Expy, Austin, TX 78758-2401
Tel (512) 901-1000 *Founded/Ownrshp* 1995
Sales 100.9MM^E *EMP* 1,000
SIC 8062 8011 8069 8049 General medical & surgical hospitals; Offices & clinics of medical doctors; Cancer hospital; Nutritionist
CEO: Allen Harrison
Chf Rad: Joe Volpe
COO: Sheri Wallace
**CFO:* Cindy Frickston
**CFO:* Kenneth W Mitchell MD
**Sr VP:* Mark W Clayton
Exec: David Joseph
Exec: Joseph Volpe
Dir Risk M: Eileen Dunne
Dir Rad: Joe Lopez
Dir Pat Ac: Carly Barker

ST DAVIDS ROUND ROCK MED CTR
See ST DAVIDS HEALTHCARE PARTNERSHIP LLP

D-U-N-S 05-751-8342
■ ST DAVIDS SOUTH AUSTIN MEDICAL CENTER
COLUMBIA HCA
(*Suby of* HOSPITAL COPORATION OF AMERICA) ★
901 W Ben White Blvd, Austin, TX 78704-6903
Tel (512) 447-2211 *Founded/Ownrshp* 1981
Sales 260.4MM *EMP* 1,400^E
SIC 8062 8011 General medical & surgical hospitals; Offices & clinics of medical doctors
CEO: Erol Akdamar
**COO:* Charles Gressle
**COO:* Brett Natens
CFO: Dwayne Benefield
**Sr VP:* Carol Gregory
VP: A Moore
Dir Teleco: Darren Garza
Chf Nrs Of: Dawn Johnson
Dir Sec: Carl Craddock
CIO: Richard Lear
Opers Mgr: Robert Gross

D-U-N-S 18-140-8865
ST DOMINIC HEALTH SERVICES INC
ST DOMINIC HOSPITAL
969 Lakeland Dr, Jackson, MS 39216-4606
Tel (601) 200-2000 *Founded/Ownrshp* 1985
Sales 422.0MM^E *EMP* 2,500^E
Accts Horne Llp Ridgeland Ms
SIC 8741 8093 8069 8062 Hospital management; Nursing & personal care facility management; Mental health clinic, outpatient; Alcoholism rehabilitation hospital; General medical & surgical hospitals
Ch Bd: Mary Dorothea
**Pr:* Claude W Harbarger
CFO: Deidra Bell
Ex VP: Robert Mobley
VP: Steve Chamblee
VP: Kevin Flynn
Dir Risk M: Jerry Farr
Dir Lab: Tom Birkbeck
Dir Rx: Mary Bowen
Dir Rx: John Cleary
Ex Dir: Mary Judy

ST DOMINIC HOSPITAL
See ST DOMINIC HEALTH SERVICES INC

D-U-N-S 07-790-1924
ST DOMINIC-JACKSON MEMORIAL HOSPITAL
(*Suby of* ST DOMINIC HOSPITAL) ★
969 Lakeland Dr, Jackson, MS 39216-4606
Tel (601) 200-6776 *Founded/Ownrshp* 1985
Sales 418.7MM *EMP* 2,400
SIC 8062 General medical & surgical hospitals
Pr: Claude W Harbarger
**Pr:* Lester Diamond
**Sec:* Sister Mary Trinita

ST. EDMOND'S HOME FOR CRIPPLED
See ARCHDIOCESE OF PHILADELPHIA

D-U-N-S 07-933-2004
ST ELIZABETH BOARDMAN HEALTH CENTER
8401 Market St, Boardman, OH 44512-6725
Tel (330) 729-4580 *Founded/Ownrshp* 2014
Sales 166.2MM *EMP* 23^E
SIC 8099 8062 Childbirth preparation clinic; General medical & surgical hospitals
Genl Mgr: Gary Kabetso

D-U-N-S 07-609-5801
ST ELIZABETH COMMUNITY HOSPITAL
(*Suby of* DIGNITY HEALTH) ★
2550 Sster Mary Clumba Dr, Red Bluff, CA 96080-4327
Tel (530) 529-7760 *Founded/Ownrshp* 1901
Sales 93.2MM *EMP* 450^E
SIC 8062 6513 General medical & surgical hospitals; Retirement hotel operation
CEO: Todd Smith
**Pr:* John Halfhide
Dir Lab: Sally Guiney
Mktg Dir: Tammy Fuller
Pharmcst: John D'Luisse
HC Dir: Charlene Almocera

ST ELIZABETH HEALTH CENTER
See MERCY HEALTH YOUNGSTOWN LLC

ST ELIZABETH HOSPITAL
See OUR LADY OF LAKE ASCENSION COMMUNITY HOSPITAL

D-U-N-S 07-477-8754
ST ELIZABETH HOSPITAL INC
(*Suby of* AFFINITY HEALTH SYSTEM) ★
1506 S Oneida St, Appleton, WI 54915-1396
Tel (920) 738-2000 *Founded/Ownrshp* 1930
Sales 195.6MM *EMP* 1,368
SIC 8062 General medical & surgical hospitals
Pr: Monica Hilp
**CFO:* Jeff Badger
Sr VP: Sarah Giolando
VP: Mary Lefevre

D-U-N-S 07-159-5474
ST ELIZABETH MEDICAL CENTER (NY)
2209 Genesee St, Utica, NY 13501-5999
Tel (315) 798-8100 *Founded/Ownrshp* 1870
Sales 197.2MM *EMP* 1,700
SIC 8062 General medical & surgical hospitals
CEO: Richard Ketcham
Dir Vol: Grace Garro
Dir Vol: Cathy Southwick-Lee
Dir Vol: Susan Warwick
**Pr:* Sister Dylaiss
COO: Jacob Bast
CFO: Sherry Gibson
Ofcr: Dave Carlson
Ofcr: Michelle Fredsell
VP: Jim Engel
VP: Helen Harrington
VP: Robert Scholefield

D-U-N-S 80-801-9954
ST ELIZABETH PHYSICIAN SERVICES LLC
ST ELIZABETH PHYSICIANS
334 Thomas More Pkwy, Crestview Hills, KY 41017-3464
Tel (859) 344-3737 *Founded/Ownrshp* 1995
Sales 206.2MM *EMP* 1,150
Accts Crowe Horwath Llp Louisville
SIC 8011 General & family practice, physician/surgeon
CEO: Glenn A Loomis
V Ch Bd: Robert Baker

ST. ELIZABETH PHYSICIANS
See SUMMIT MEDICAL GROUP INC

ST ELIZABETH PHYSICIANS
See ST ELIZABETH PHYSICIAN SERVICES LLC

ST ELIZABETH REGIONAL HEALTH
See GREATER LAFAYETTE HEALTH SERVICES

D-U-N-S 07-588-8370
ST ELIZABETHS HOSPITAL OF BELLEVILLE INC (IL)
211 S 3rd St, Belleville, IL 62220-1915
Tel (618) 234-2120 *Founded/Ownrshp* 1875
Sales 169.5MM *EMP* 1,200
SIC 8062 General medical & surgical hospitals
CEO: Maryann L Reese Rn
**Pr:* Shelley Harris
**Pr:* Kevin L Shrake
**COO:* Robert Miller
Info Man: Bill Davis
Pharmcst: Maria Massey

D-U-N-S 96-962-7517
ST ELIZABETHS HOSPITAL OF THIRD ORDER OF ST FRANCIS
211 S 3rd St, Belleville, IL 62220-1915
Tel (618) 234-2120 *Founded/Ownrshp* 2011
Sales 177.0MM *EMP* 3
Accts Kpmg Llp Columbus Oh
SIC 8641 Civic associations
Prin: Mark S Peters

D-U-N-S 10-707-2274
ST ENVIRONMENTAL SERVICES INC (I)
(*Suby of* SEVERN TRENT (DEL) INC) ★
5726 Corporation Cir, Fort Myers, FL 33905-5008
Tel (239) 690-0175 *Founded/Ownrshp* 1993
Sales 107.1MM^E *EMP* 750
SIC 4959 4941 Sanitary services; Water supply
Pr: Rennie Quin
**VP:* Ivan S Burrows
**VP:* Jim Gullam

D-U-N-S 02-120-5448 IMP/EXP
ST FRANCIS HEALTH CENTER INC (KS)
TOPEKA FAMILY PRACTICE
(*Suby of* SCL HEALTH SYSTEM) ★
1700 Sw 7th St, Topeka, KS 66606-2489
Tel (785) 295-8000 *Founded/Ownrshp* 1909
Sales 259.7MM *EMP* 1,700
Accts Bruce E Bernstien & Assoc Pc
SIC 8062 8011 General medical & surgical hospitals; Offices & clinics of medical doctors
Pr: Robert J Erickson
Chf OB: Dallas Thompson
Ofcr: Stuart Moore
VP: Shirley Heintz
VP: Mike Kongs
Exec: Laura Moyer
Dir Inf Cn: Nancy Krohe
Dir Rx: Jane Henry
Ex Dir: Jason Fizell
Dir QC: Darrell Dodge
Pathlgst: Paul Pettavel

D-U-N-S 17-540-5927
ST FRANCIS HEALTH SERVICES CORP
ST FRANCIS HOSPITAL
(*Suby of* CATHOLIC HEALTH EAST) ★
7th N Clayton St, Wilmington, DE 19805
Tel (302) 575-8301 *Founded/Ownrshp* 1963
Sales 60.4MM *EMP* 1,200
SIC 8062

D-U-N-S 61-363-8402
ST FRANCIS HEALTH SERVICES OF MORRIS INC
801 Nevada Ave, Morris, MN 56267-1865
Tel (320) 589-2004 *Founded/Ownrshp* 1984
Sales 7.2MM *EMP* 2,000
Accts Conway Deuth & Schmiesing Pllp
SIC 8741 Hospital management; Nursing & personal care facility management
Pr: Luverne Hoffman
VP: Scot Allen
VP: Debra Grio
**VP:* Carol Raw
Dir Soc: Britney Dyke
Dir IT: Koehntop Lucas
Nrsg Dir: Jody Cunningham
Nrsg Dir: Shelly S Herron
Nrsg Dir: Stephanie Nelson
Nrsg Dir: Stacy Oberstar
Nrsg Dir: Cameo Pallesen

ST FRANCIS HEALTH SYSTEMS
See SAINT FRANCIS HEALTH SYSTEM INC

D-U-N-S 06-627-5660
ST FRANCIS HEALTHCARE SYSTEM OF HAWAII
2226 Liliha St Ste 227, Honolulu, HI 96817-1600
Tel (808) 547-6883 *Founded/Ownrshp* 2008
Sales 5.3MM *EMP* 1,500
Accts Ernst & Young Us Llp San Dieg
SIC 8051 8082 Skilled nursing care facilities; Home health care services
CEO: Ching Agnelle Sister
Dir Vol: Patty Martin
VP: Becki Murashige
Ex Dir: Suanne Morikuni
Ex Dir: Gary Simon
CIO: Diane Smith
QA Dir: Angie Ronduen

ST FRANCIS HOSPITAL
See CHARLESTON HOSPITAL INC

ST FRANCIS HOSPITAL
See ST FRANCIS HEALTH SERVICES CORP

D-U-N-S 06-283-4949
ST FRANCIS HOSPITAL
333 Laidley St, Charleston, WV 25301-1628
Tel (304) 347-6860 *Founded/Ownrshp* 2011
Sales 99.7MM *EMP* 69^E
SIC 8742 Hospital & health services consultant
CEO: Lawrence E McManus
**Ch:* Richard J J Sullivan Jr
Dir Lab: Steven Ewers
CIO: Jane Harless

D-U-N-S 14-833-4659
ST FRANCIS HOSPITAL
ST JOSEPH MEDICAL CENTER
(*Suby of* ST JOSEPH MEDICAL CENTER) ★
34515 9th Ave S, Federal Way, WA 98003-6799
Tel (253) 944-8100 *Founded/Ownrshp* 1987
Sales 231.4MM *EMP* 1,062
SIC 8062 General medical & surgical hospitals
CEO: Ketul Patel
**Pr:* Tony McLean
**CFO:* Mike Fitzgerald
Admn Mgr: Lindsay Baker
Ansthlgy: Sivaprasad M Reddy

D-U-N-S 03-949-6344
■ ST FRANCIS HOSPITAL INC
(*Suby of* LIFEPOINT HEALTH INC) ★
2122 Manchester Expy, Columbus, GA 31904-6804
Tel (706) 596-4000 *Founded/Ownrshp* 2016
Sales 317.2MM^E *EMP* 1,527^E
SIC 8062 General medical & surgical hospitals
CEO: David Koontz
**CFO:* Greg Hembree
**Treas:* Mark Holladay
**Chf Mktg O:* Bobbi A Farber MD
**Sr VP:* Debbie Bostic
Sr VP: Rick Lowe
Sr VP: Deborah Saylor
VP: Patty Simmons
Adm Dir: Rita Hooker
Telecom Ex: Tammy Foster
Pathlgst: Frank Willett

D-U-N-S 07-352-0447
■ ST FRANCIS HOSPITAL INC
(*Suby of* TENET HEALTHCARE CORP) ★
5959 Park Ave, Memphis, TN 38119-5198
Tel (901) 765-1000 *Founded/Ownrshp* 1995
Sales 267.9MM *EMP* 2,000
SIC 8062 8051 General medical & surgical hospitals; Skilled nursing care facilities
Pr: Dave Archer
Dir Inf Cn: Judy Baker
Sls&Mrk Ex: Marilyn Robinson
Doctor: Martha Tibbs
Pharmcst: Karen Summers
HC Dir: Vicki Thayer

D-U-N-S 07-384-2056
ST FRANCIS HOSPITAL INC
SPORTS MEDICINE PRFMCE CTR
3237 S 16th St, Milwaukee, WI 53215-4592
Tel (414) 647-5000 *Founded/Ownrshp* 1956
Sales 126.0MM^E *EMP* 1,600
SIC 8062 General medical & surgical hospitals
Pr: Debra Standridge
Treas: Marge McGinn
Ofcr: Lynn Grudzielanek
VP: Gregory A Banaszynski
**VP:* Sister Mary Jendras
Dir IT: Debora Standridge
Anesthlgy: Rachel Belits
Doctor: Arthur Arena
Doctor: Gregory Kuhr

D-U-N-S 07-805-8344
ST FRANCIS HOSPITAL INC
ST FRANCIS WOMEN'S HOSPITAL
(*Suby of* BON SECOURS HEALTH SYSTEM INC) ★
1 Saint Francis Dr, Greenville, SC 29601-3955
Tel (864) 255-1000 *Founded/Ownrshp* 1983
Sales 534.3MM *EMP* 2,105
Accts Deloitte Tax Lp Atlanta Ga
SIC 8062 General medical & surgical hospitals
CEO: Greg McCoy
**Pr:* Valinda Reutledge
**VP:* Ronnie Hyatt
VP: Lisa Slaton
**Prin:* Mark Nantz
Dir Sec: Bruce Spaulding
CIO: Rita Hooker
IT Man: Jan Murphy
Doctor: Terrence Clark
HC Dir: Chris Foster
Genl Couns: Jeff Sacra
Board of Directors: Karen Riley

D-U-N-S 07-947-6503
ST FRANCIS HOSPITAL INC
CATHOLIC HEALTH EAST
(*Suby of* CATHOLIC HEALTH EAST) ★
701 N Clayton St, Wilmington, DE 19805-3155
Tel (302) 421-4100 *Founded/Ownrshp* 2015
Sales 133.4MM *EMP* 1,000
SIC 8062 General medical & surgical hospitals
CEO: Brian Dietz
Pr: Margaret M Lewis
**CFO:* Bernard Citerone
VP: Marilyn Curtis
VP: George J Miller
VP: Sally B Thomas
Dir Risk M: Joan Caruso
Dir Lab: Bao Huynh
Dir Rx: Cheri Briggs
Off Mgr: Grace Anderson
QA Dir: Maureen Jewell

ST. FRANCIS HOSPITAL OF CHARLE
See HERBERT J THOMAS MEMORIAL HOSPITAL ASSOCIATION

ST. FRANCIS HOSPITAL OF CHARLE
See THOMAS HEALTH SYSTEM INC

D-U-N-S 08-046-8044
ST FRANCIS HOSPITAL POUGHKEEPSIE NEW YORK
SAINT FRANCIS-POUGHKEEPSIE
241 North Rd, Poughkeepsie, NY 12601-1154
Tel (845) 483-5000 *Founded/Ownrshp* 1914
Sales NA *EMP* 1,490
SIC 8062 8069 8011 8351

D-U-N-S 06-597-4990
ST FRANCIS HOSPITAL ROSLYN NEW YORK
CATHOLIC HLTH SYS LONG ISLAND
(*Suby of* CATHOLIC HLTH SVCS LONG ISLAND) ★
100 Port Washington Blvd, Roslyn, NY 11576-1347
Tel (516) 627-3813 *Founded/Ownrshp* 1964
Sales 9.3MM *EMP* 2,184
Accts Pricewaterhousecoopers Llp Ne
SIC 8069 Specialty hospitals, except psychiatric
Pr: Alan Guerci MD
**COO:* Martin A Bieber
COO: Beiber Martin
COO: Suzanne McLaughlin
**CFO:* William C Arms
CFO: Ronnie Hyatt
**Ex VP:* Ruth Hennessey
**Sr VP:* Ann Cella Rn
Sr VP: Ruth Henneey
**Sr VP:* Jack Soterakis
**VP:* Linda Cavallo-Miller
VP: Anthony Pellicano

ST. FRANCIS MEDICAL CENTER
See FRANCIS SAINT MEDICAL CENTER

D-U-N-S 04-084-1306
ST FRANCIS MEDICAL CENTER
(*Suby of* CATHOLIC HEALTH EAST) ★
601 Hamilton Ave, Trenton, NJ 08629-1915
Tel (609) 599-5000 *Founded/Ownrshp* 1996
Sales 1.0MMM *EMP* 1,150
SIC 8062 General medical & surgical hospitals
CEO: Christy Stephenson
**Ofcr:* Vincent M Costantino
Dir Inf Cn: Irene Taylor
Dir Rx: Joseph Latini
Ex Dir: Judith L Dibartolo
QA Dir: Susan Farber
Software D: Veronica Smith
Surgeon: Karen J Kish
Doctor: Vinuta Mohan
Doctor: Fredric Seinfeld
Doctor: Sangeeta Tyerech

D-U-N-S 06-131-2535
ST FRANCIS MEDICAL CENTER
SFMC
3630 E Imperial Hwy, Lynwood, CA 90262-2609
Tel (310) 900-8900 *Founded/Ownrshp* 2001
Sales 500.1MM *EMP* 114^E
SIC 8011 Medical centers
CEO: Gerald Kozai
CFO: Nancy Wilson
Telecom Ex: Anne Schlick
Pathlgst: Philip Gruskin
Ansthlgy: David H Daneshvar

D-U-N-S 78-877-4631
ST FRANCIS MEDICAL CENTER INC
(*Suby of* FMOL HEALTH SYSTEM) ★
309 Jackson St, Monroe, LA 71201-7407
Tel (318) 966-4000 *Founded/Ownrshp* 1941
Sales 271.1MM *EMP* 99[E]
SIC 8062 General medical & surgical hospitals
Pr: Scott K Wester
**Pr:* Kristin Wolkart
COO: Ashish Agarwal
**CFO:* Ron Hogan
CFO: Frank Shiffer
**VP:* Aimee Kane
**VP:* Sabrina Ramsey
**VP:* Butch Tolbert
**VP:* Eve Van Sickle
Nurse Mgr: Jeni Wiltcher
CIO: Shane Coleman

D-U-N-S 07-796-8014
ST FRANCIS MEDICAL CENTER OF LYNWOOD FOUNDATION
3630 E Imperial Hwy, Lynwood, CA 90262-2609
Tel (310) 900-8900 *Founded/Ownrshp* 1945
Sales 79.9MM[E] *EMP* 1,684
Accts Grant Thornton Llp San Franci
SIC 8062 General medical & surgical hospitals
CEO: Mary Eileen Drees
**Pr:* Gerald T Kozai
**CEO:* Arnold J Simoni
Pharmcst: Dien Ton

D-U-N-S 07-762-6083 IMP/EXP
ST FRANCIS REGIONAL MEDICAL CENTER
ALLINA HOSPITALS & CLINICS
(*Suby of* ALLINA HOSPITALS & CLINICS) ★
1455 Saint Francis Ave, Shakopee, MN 55379-3374
Tel (952) 428-3000 *Founded/Ownrshp* 1993
Sales 139.3MM *EMP* 840
SIC 8062 General medical & surgical hospitals
Pr: Michael Baumgartner
Dir Vol: Katie Lawrence
Treas: Kelly O'Neill
Treas: Sharon Torodor
**VP:* Alan Lem
Dir OR: Bilal Rabai

D-U-N-S 02-032-6641
ST FRANCIS SPECIALTY HOSPITAL INC
FMOL HEALTH SYSTEM
(*Suby of* FMOL HEALTH SYSTEM) ★
309 Jackson St, Monroe, LA 71201-7407
Tel (318) 966-4196 *Founded/Ownrshp* 1913
Sales 88.0MM[E] *EMP* 1,700
Accts Kpmg Llp Baton Rouge La
SIC 8062 General medical & surgical hospitals
CEO: Louis H Bremer Jr
**Ch:* J Stewart Gentry
Dir IT: Barry Leblanc
Dir IT: Barbara Schlichtman
Tech Mgr: Carol Perry
Pr Mgr: Beverly Busher

ST FRANCIS WOMEN'S HOSPITAL
See ST FRANCIS HOSPITAL INC

ST GABRIEL'S HOSPITAL
See UNITY FAMILY HEALTHCARE

D-U-N-S 07-297-6368
ST GEORGE CITY GOVERNMENT (INC)
CITY OF SAINT GEORGE
175 E 200 N, St George, UT 84770-2845
Tel (435) 627-4000 *Founded/Ownrshp* 1862
Sales NA *EMP* 1,190
Accts Hinton Burdick Pllc St Geor
SIC 9532 Urban & community development
Treas: Tiffany Lajoice
Ofcr: Greg Baldwin
Ofcr: Travis Brown
Ofcr: Kenneth Childs
Ofcr: Jeff Cottam
Ofcr: Brandon Dunbar
Ofcr: Ivor Fuller
Ofcr: Johnny Heppler
Ofcr: Brett Huish
Ofcr: Wade Johnson
Ofcr: Seth Lefevre
Ofcr: Derek Lewis
Ofcr: Steve Linton
Ofcr: Jonathan McInnes
Ofcr: Jordan Minnick
Ofcr: Matthew Orr
Ofcr: Todd Pitcher
Ofcr: Steven Powell
Ofcr: Andrew Priest
Ofcr: David Slack
Ofcr: Christopher Smith

D-U-N-S 79-648-3167
ST GEORGE WAREHOUSE OF DELAWARE INC
(*Suby of* WIND POINT PARTNERS LP) ★
5 Logistics Dr, Kearny, NJ 07032-6550
Tel (973) 578-8400 *Founded/Ownrshp* 2003
Sales 94.2MM *EMP* 300[E]
SIC 6719 Investment holding companies, except banks
CEO: Denis Reilly
**Pr:* Linda Kuper
**CFO:* Anthony Perrella
**Ex VP:* Marie Costa
**Ex VP:* Anthony Mayor
**VP:* Brian Galik

D-U-N-S 02-927-2606
ST HELENA HOSPITAL
DEER PARK PHARMACY
10 Woodland Rd, Saint Helena, CA 94574-9554
Tel (707) 963-1882 *Founded/Ownrshp* 1878
Sales 208.2MM *EMP* 900
SIC 8062 8063 General medical & surgical hospitals; Psychiatric hospitals
CEO: Steven Herber
**Sr VP:* Edward Buck McDonald
VP: Tricia Williams
Exec: Jay Whitcomb
Dir Case M: Bruce F Singer
Dir Rad: Chuck Adams
VP Admn: Patricia Williams
Genl Mgr: Hossein Razavi
Mktg Dir: Lynn Wallace
Pathlgst: Randy P Hausted
Opthamlgy: Erin K Jacobson

D-U-N-S 05-005-9674
ST JAMES HEALTHCARE INC
ST JAMES SPICE LIFE SENIOR SVC
(*Suby of* SCL HEALTH SYSTEM) ★
400 S Clark St, Butte, MT 59701-2328
Tel (406) 723-2484 *Founded/Ownrshp* 1881
Sales 120.0MM *EMP* 514
Accts Ernst & Young Us Llp Saint Lo
SIC 8062 General medical & surgical hospitals
CEO: Chuck Wright
**CFO:* Jay Doyle
**VP:* Kevin Dennehy
**VP:* Shannon Holland
Dir Lab: Mary A Jones
Mktg Dir: Linda McGullean

D-U-N-S 80-303-8249
ST JAMES HOSPITAL & HEALTH CENTERS INC
SAINT JAMES HOSP & HLTH CTRS
(*Suby of* SAINT JAMES HOSPITAL) ★
20201 Crawford Ave, Olympia Fields, IL 60461-1010
Tel (708) 747-4000 *Founded/Ownrshp* 2000
Sales 932.5MM *EMP* 2,200
SIC 8062 5912 General medical & surgical hospitals; Drug stores
CEO: Seth Warren
**Prin:* Terry Brown

D-U-N-S 07-637-5385 IMP
ST JAMES INC
AMERICAN SPECIALTY CARS
18500 Walnut St, Southgate, MI 48195-3046
Tel (734) 285-4911 *Founded/Ownrshp* 2002
Sales NA *EMP* 1,100
SIC 3714 3711 3465

D-U-N-S 09-119-5305
ST JAMES SECURITY SERVICES INC
NATIONAL INVESTIGATION & PROTE
1604 Ave Ponce De Leon, San Juan, PR 00909-1844
Tel (787) 754-8448 *Founded/Ownrshp* 2004
Sales 71.2MM[E] *EMP* 3,400
SIC 7381 Protective services, guard
Pr: Marcos Rivera
**VP:* Adriana Cortina
**VP:* Raul Matos
VP: Hector Rivera
**VP:* Carlos Diaz Vivo

ST JAMES SPICE LIFE SENIOR SVC
See ST JAMES HEALTHCARE INC

D-U-N-S 00-405-9614
▲ ST JOE CO (FL)
133 S Watersound Pkwy A, Watersound, FL 32461-7280
Tel (850) 231-6400 *Founded/Ownrshp* 1936
Sales 103.8MM *EMP* 55[E]
Accts Kpmg Llp Jacksonville Flori
Tkr Sym JOE *Exch* NYS
SIC 6531 6552 6512 0811 0851 Real estate managers; Land subdividers & developers, commercial; Commercial & industrial building operation; Timber tracts; Forestry services
Pr: Jorge L Gonzalez
**Ch Bd:* Bruce R Berkowitz
CFO: Marek Bakun
Sr VP: Kenneth M Borick
Sr VP: Jorge Gonzalez
Sr VP: David S Harrelson
Sr VP: Patrick W Murphy
CTO: Christine McClure
Board of Directors: Cesar L Alvarez, Howard S Frank, Stanley Martin, Thomas P Murphy Jr, Vito S Portera

D-U-N-S 01-039-3551
ST JOHN BAPTIST PARISH PUBLIC SCHOOLS
118 W 10th St, Reserve, LA 70084-6202
Tel (985) 536-1106 *Founded/Ownrshp* 1900
Sales 90.1MM *EMP* 1,000
Accts Carr Riggs & Ingram Llc Met
SIC 8211 Public elementary & secondary schools
**Prin:* Herbert Smith
MIS Dir: Bonnie Dinvant
IT Man: Monica Jackson
Teacher Pr: Paige Eschette
Instr Medi: Jennifer Boquet
HC Dir: Dr Stacey Spies

D-U-N-S 07-970-2452
ST JOHN FISHER COLLEGE
3690 East Ave Ofc, Rochester, NY 14618-3597
Tel (585) 385-8000 *Founded/Ownrshp* 1951
Sales 130.1MM *EMP* 574
Accts Bonadio & Co Llp Pittsford N
SIC 8221 College, except junior
Pr: Donald E Bain
**Ex VP:* Ronald Ambrosetti
VP: Brendan Hughes
**VP:* Thomas E O'Neil
VP: Richard Dejesa S-Rueff
VP: Jordan Staiti
VP: Olivia Thomas
Dir IT: Mike Allington
Mktg Dir: Anne Geer
Pr Dir: Sally J Vaughan

D-U-N-S 18-549-4465
ST JOHN HEALTH SYSTEM INC
1923 S Utica Ave, Tulsa, OK 74104-6520
Tel (918) 744-2180 *Founded/Ownrshp* 1926
Sales 1.1MMM *EMP* 4,011
SIC 7991 6512 7389 8361 8071 8062 Physical fitness facilities; Nonresidential building operators; Fund raising organizations; Home for the aged; Testing laboratories; General medical & surgical hospitals
Pr: Sister Mary T Gottschalk
**Ch Bd:* Robert Lafortune
Treas: Donna Butler
VP: William Allred
VP: Dewey Davis
VP: Randy Hamil
VP: Gwen Moudry
Chf Nrs Of: Pamela Kiser
Ex Dir: Tiari Harris
Netwrk Mgr: Greg Brooks
Doctor: Douglas Brown

D-U-N-S 14-732-3273
ST JOHN HOLDINGS INC
320 King Of Prussia Rd, Radnor, PA 19087-4440
Tel (610) 964-8702 *Founded/Ownrshp* 1984
Sales 117.0MM[E] *EMP* 1,000
Accts Kreischer Miller Horsham Pa
SIC 6211 Investment bankers
Pr: Gregory I Russell
**Treas:* Gilbert J Guim
Sr VP: John Greenebaum
**VP:* Michael J Quigg

ST JOHN HOSPITAL
See DETROIT-MACOMB HOSPITAL CORP

ST JOHN HOSPITAL
See ST JOHN MEDICAL CENTER INC

D-U-N-S 07-420-9875
ST JOHN HOSPITAL AND MEDICAL CENTER
(*Suby of* ST JOHN PROVIDENCE HEALTH SYSTEM) ★
28000 Dequindre Rd, Warren, MI 48092-2468
Tel (313) 343-4000 *Founded/Ownrshp* 2000
Sales 753.3MM *EMP* 5,000
SIC 8062 Hospital, affiliated with AMA residency
CEO: Mark Taylor
COO: Christopher Palazzolo
VP: Donna Handley
VP: James Orosz
VP: Marie Rizzo
VP: David Sessions
CTO: Thomasine Marx
Dir IT: Raymond C Hilu
Pathlgst: Shilpa A Rungt
Surgeon: Rosemary Belz
Obsttrcn: Nathan V Wagstaff

D-U-N-S 16-619-3644
ST JOHN KNITS INC
(*Suby of* ST JOHN KNITS INTERNATIONAL INC) ★
17522 Armstrong Ave, Irvine, CA 92614-5726
Tel (949) 863-1171 *Founded/Ownrshp* 1962
Sales 127.8MM[E] *EMP* 1,000[E]
SIC 2339 2253 2389 Women's & misses' accessories; Knit outerwear mills; Men's miscellaneous accessories
CEO: Bruce Fetter
Sr VP: Claudia Slaughter
VP: Guillermo Lopez
VP: Sue Novak
Creative D: Kelly A Gray
Store Mgr: Kate Debernardi

D-U-N-S 05-659-9475 IMP/EXP
ST JOHN KNITS INTERNATIONAL INC
(*Suby of* GRAY VESTAR INVESTORS LLC) ★
17622 Armstrong Ave, Irvine, CA 92614-5728
Tel (949) 863-1171 *Founded/Ownrshp* 1999
Sales 509.6MM[E] *EMP* 4,000
SIC 2339 Sportswear, women's; Scarves, hoods, headbands, etc.: women's; Jackets, untailored: women's, misses' & juniors'; Slacks: women's, misses' & juniors'
CEO: Geoffroy Van Raemdonck
Pt: James Kelley
Ch Bd: Bernd Beetz
CEO: Glenn McMahon
COO: Bruce Fetter
CFO: Tammy Storino
VP: Linda Koontz
Board of Directors: Christopher Henderson, Sander Levy, Daniel O'connell

D-U-N-S 96-952-1801
ST JOHN MACOMB-OAKLAND HOSPITAL
28000 Dequindre Rd, Warren, MI 48092-2468
Tel (586) 753-0094 *Founded/Ownrshp* 2010
Sales 405.7MM *EMP* 23[E]
Accts Deloitte Tax Llp Cincinnati
SIC 8062 General medical & surgical hospitals
Prin: Kam Parekh
Surgeon: Roger Bigelow

D-U-N-S 96-215-5607
ST JOHN MEDICAL CENTER
29000 Center Ridge Rd, Westlake, OH 44145-5219
Tel (440) 835-8000 *Founded/Ownrshp* 1981
Sales 149.1MM *EMP* 99
SIC 8062 General medical & surgical hospitals
Pr: Cliff Coker
Pr: Donald Sheldon
**VP:* Eileen Hayes
Dir Rx: Michael Carlin
Pathlgst: Sonia Saracco
HC Dir: David Simkanin
Pgrm Dir: Gennaro Romanello
Snr Mgr: Kevin Smith

D-U-N-S 07-242-0581
ST JOHN MEDICAL CENTER INC
ST JOHN HOSPITAL
(*Suby of* ASCENSION HEALTH) ★
1923 S Utica Ave, Tulsa, OK 74104-6520
Tel (918) 744-2828 *Founded/Ownrshp* 2015
Sales 550.4MM *EMP* 3,187[E]
SIC 8062 General medical & surgical hospitals
Pr: Charles Anderson
VP: Dewey Davis
VP: Martha Mars
Dir OR: Patricia Wright
**Prin:* Magdalen Grellner
Genl Mgr: Lex Anderson
IT Man: Jim Burke

ST JOHN OAKLAND HOSPITAL
See OAKLAND HOSPITAL

D-U-N-S 02-109-9353
ST JOHN PROVIDENCE HEALTH SYSTEM
(*Suby of* ASCENSION HEALTH) ★
28000 Dequindre Rd, Warren, MI 48092-2468
Tel (586) 753-0500 *Founded/Ownrshp* 1978
Sales 255.0MM *EMP* 17,806
Accts Deloitte Tax Lp Cincinnati O
SIC 8062 General medical & surgical hospitals
Pr: Patricia Maryland
Chf Path: Martha Higgens
COO: Michael Beaubien
COO: Paul Tiem
COO: Paul Vantien
VP: Deborah Condino
VP: Elizabeth Granger
VP: Terence Hamilton
**VP:* Patrick M McGuire
Exec: Paul Gliesman
Dir Lab: Diane Whyte
Dir Rad: Holly Fitzpatrick
Comm Man: Rosemary Kluczynski

ST JOHN W SHORE HOSP AUXILLARY
See CSA ST JOHN MINISTRIES

ST JOHNS CLINIC
See INTERNAL MEDICINE GROUP FREMONT

D-U-N-S 96-939-0033
ST JOHNS CLINIC INC
1235 E Cherokee St, Springfield, MO 65804-2203
Tel (417) 820-2000 *Founded/Ownrshp* 2011
Sales 394.8MM *EMP* 63[E]
Accts Ernst & Young Us Llp Clayton
SIC 8062 General medical & surgical hospitals
Prin: Guy Ruddick
Chf Rad: Chris Chernesky
VP: Eric Fuhr
Ansthlgy: David Delahay Jr
Diag Rad: Julie A Alford
Diag Rad: Mark W Coburn

D-U-N-S 79-085-4806
ST JOHNS COUNTY SCHOOL BOARD
40 Orange St, Saint Augustine, FL 32084-3633
Tel (904) 547-7500 *Founded/Ownrshp* 1908
Sales 67.1M[E] *EMP* 2,460
SIC 8211 School board

D-U-N-S 01-050-0601
ST JOHNS COUNTY SCHOOL BOARD OF PUBLIC INSTRUCTION
2980 Collins Ave, Saint Augustine, FL 32084-1921
Tel (904) 824-4401 *Founded/Ownrshp* 1915
Sales 313.8MM *EMP* 3,002
Accts Dufresne & Associates Cpa Pa
SIC 8211 School board
Ch Bd: Patrick Canan
**Pr:* Sandra L Raburn
**CFO:* Sandy Marshall
CFO: Sandra N Raeburn

D-U-N-S 07-979-8982
ST JOHNS COUNTY SCHOOL DISTRICT
40 Orange St, Saint Augustine, FL 32084-3633
Tel (904) 547-7500 *Founded/Ownrshp* 1915
Sales 25.1MM[E] *EMP* 3,002
SIC 8211 Public elementary & secondary schools
CIO: Jessica Masters
Pr Dir: Christina Langston
Teacher Pr: Jewell Johnson
Instr Medi: Linda Thompson
HC Dir: Melissa Petty

D-U-N-S 07-962-9964
ST JOHNS EPISCOPAL HOSPITAL
327 Beach 19th St, Far Rockaway, NY 11691-4423
Tel (718) 869-7000 *Founded/Ownrshp* 2014
Sales 11.3MM[E] *EMP* 1,500
SIC 8062 General medical & surgical hospitals
CEO: Richard Brown
**CFO:* Will Moore
**Chf Mktg O:* Raymond Pastore MD
Sr VP: Natalie Schwartz MD
VP: Dr Rev Cecily Broderick Y Guer
VP: Suzanne Timmer
Assoc Dir: Elvin Anthony
Dir Rx: Kerry Muir
**Chf Nrs Of:* Gwen Pinckney Rn
**CIO:* Kelly Barland
CIO: Ted Bayack

ST JOHNS HOSPITAL & NURSING HM
See TETON COUNTY HOSPITAL DISTRICT

D-U-N-S 07-912-9623 IMP
ST JOHNS HOSPITAL SISTERS OF THIRD ORDER OF ST FRANCIS
SAINT JOHN'S HOSPITAL
800 E Carpenter St, Springfield, IL 62769-0002
Tel (217) 544-6464 *Founded/Ownrshp* 1955
Sales 500.5MM *EMP* 3,000
Accts Crowe Horwath Llp Chicago Il
SIC 8062 Hospital, medical school affiliated with residency
CEO: Dr Charles Lucore
COO: Lindsey Jarrell
**COO:* Dave Olejniczak
COO: Chris Palazzolo
CFO: Ron Dent
**CFO:* Larry Ragel
VP: Jacob Bast
VP: Gerald Dowdy
VP: Ted Fronczak
VP: Eric Fuhr
Dir Lab: Anne Cox

D-U-N-S 80-778-9511
ST JOHNS MERCY HEALTH CARE
SISTERS OF MERCY HEALTH SYSTEM
(*Suby of* SISTERS OF MERCY HEALTH SYSTEM) ★
645 Maryville Centre Dr # 100, Saint Louis, MO 63141-5846
Tel (314) 364-2400 *Founded/Ownrshp* 2007
Sales 180.1MM *EMP* 1[E]
SIC 8741 Hospital management; Nursing & personal care facility management
Prin: Alastair Wood

D-U-N-S 07-330-5534
ST JOHNS REST HOME INC
SAINT JHNS VCTRIA NRSING FCLTY
2225 Canterbury Dr, Hays, KS 67601-2300
Tel (785) 735-2208 *Founded/Ownrshp* 1962
Sales 280.5MM *EMP* 120
SIC 8361 Home for the aged

D-U-N-S 13-967-6803 IMP
ST JOHNS RIVER POWER PARK
21 W Church St, Jacksonville, FL 32202-3155
Tel (904) 751-7700 *Founded/Ownrshp* 1982
Sales 196.6MM^E *EMP* 414
Accts Price Waterhouse Llp
SIC 4911 Generation, electric power
CEO: Walter Bussells
Pt: Jacksonville Electric Authorit

D-U-N-S 04-566-6351
ST JOHNS RIVERSIDE HOSPITAL DOBBS FERRY PAVILION
COMMUNITY HOSP AT DOBBS FERRY
128 Ashford Ave, Dobbs Ferry, NY 10522-1924
Tel (914) 693-0700 *Founded/Ownrshp* 1893
Sales 134.0MM^E *EMP* 1,636
SIC 8062 General medical & surgical hospitals
CEO: Ronad Corti
VP: Cheryl Burke
VP: James Mahoney
VP: Ellen Weiner

D-U-N-S 07-313-4744
ST JOHNS UNIVERSITY NEW YORK
8000 Utopia Pkwy, Jamaica, NY 11439-9000
Tel (718) 990-6161 *Founded/Ownrshp* 1871
Sales 855.4MM^E *EMP* 3,310
Accts Kpmg Llp Greensboro Nc
SIC 8221 University
Pr: Conrado Gempesaw
**CFO:* Sharon Hewitt Watkins
Top Exec: Cynthia Chambers
**Ex VP:* Bernard M Tracey
**VP:* Robert Mangione
VP: Andr McKenzie
Assoc Dir: Theresa McNerney
Assoc Dir: Dominique Torres
Comm Man: Jennifer Vacchio
Ex Dir: Edward Kling
Ex Dir: Luis G Manzo

ST JOSEPH HEALTH SERVICES OF R
See FATIMA GIFT SHOP

D-U-N-S 10-310-3370 IMP
ST JOSEPH HEALTH SYSTEM
(*Suby of* SISTERS OF ST JOSEPH OF ORANGE) ★
3345 Michelson Dr Ste 100, Irvine, CA 92612-0693
Tel (949) 381-4000 *Founded/Ownrshp* 1981
Sales 4.5MMM^E *EMP* 21,500
Accts Ernst & Young Llp Irvine Ca
SIC 8082 8741 Home health care services; Hospital management
Pr: Annette Walker
COO: Carlos Trevino
**CFO:* Jo Ann Escasa-Haigh
CFO: Michel Riccioni
Treas: Garrett Kop
**Ofcr:* Jack L Cox
Assoc VP: Tricia Kassab
**Ex VP:* Shannon Dwyer
VP: Steve Gilbert
VP: Richard Green
VP: Don Kiceina
VP: Kevin Simes
Dir Risk M: Mia Bunch
Dir Risk M: Ann Warner
Dir Lab: Ard Roshan
Dir Rx: Debbie Lewellen
Dir Rx: Don Miller

D-U-N-S 14-352-6890
■ **ST JOSEPH HEALTH SYSTEM LLC**
ST. JOSEPH HOSPITAL
(*Suby of* COMMUNITY HEALTH SYSTEMS INC) ★
700 Broadway, Fort Wayne, IN 46802-1493
Tel (260) 425-3000 *Founded/Ownrshp* 1869
Sales 61.4MM^E *EMP* 1,100^E
SIC 8099 Medical services organization
CEO: Dawn Rudolph
CFO: Micheal Ruthkowski
Mtls Dir: Chuck Otis
Mktg Dir: Alice Robinson
Pharmcst: Renee Jarrett
HC Dir: Jill Cripe
HC Dir: Sandy Libben

ST. JOSEPH HEALTHCARE
See ST JOSEPH HOSPITAL

D-U-N-S 12-136-1794
ST JOSEPH HEALTHCARE FOUNDATION INC
ST JOSEPH HOSPITAL
360 Broadway, Bangor, ME 04401-3979
Tel (207) 907-1000 *Founded/Ownrshp* 1983
Sales 120.1MM *EMP* 900^E
Accts Baker Newman & Noyes Portland
SIC 8099 Physical examination & testing services
CEO: Mary Prybylo
**CEO:* Sister Mary Norbeta
Treas: Richard Hogan
VP: Lois Macias
VP: William Wood
Exec: Mark Miller
Ex Dir: Susan Sue
CIO: Karen Bowling
CIO: Ron Crall
Nrsg Dir: Matthew Flynn
Pharmcst: Irene Carroll

ST JOSEPH HOSP FOR SPCLTY CARE
See PROSPECT CHARTERCARE SJHSRI LLC

ST JOSEPH HOSPITAL
See ST JOSEPH HEALTHCARE FOUNDATION INC

ST. JOSEPH HOSPITAL
See ST JOSEPH HEALTH SYSTEM LLC

ST JOSEPH HOSPITAL
See WSNCHS NORTH INC

D-U-N-S 07-173-5286
ST JOSEPH HOSPITAL
ST. JOSEPH HEALTHCARE
360 Broadway, Bangor, ME 04401-3900
Tel (207) 262-1000 *Founded/Ownrshp* 1947
Sales 108.9MM *EMP* 950
SIC 8062 General medical & surgical hospitals
Pr: Sister Mary Norberta
Prac Mgr: Sue Rouleau
Mktg Mgr: Bethany Mc Mc Knight
Psych: Edward Cliff

D-U-N-S 07-396-2995
ST JOSEPH HOSPITAL
172 Kinsley St, Nashua, NH 03060-3688
Tel (603) 882-3000 *Founded/Ownrshp* 1908
Sales 173.6MM *EMP* 1,200
SIC 8062 General medical & surgical hospitals
Pr: Peter B Davis
COO: John Walsh
**CFO:* Richard Plamondon
Off Mgr: Mary Landry
Dir IT: Larry Krainz
Dir IT: Brian Murray
IT Man: Allen Goetz
IT Man: Mark Lacombe
IT Man: Mike Prater
IT Man: Keith Reynolds
Pathlgst: Constance Buttlar

D-U-N-S 07-466-5530 IMP
ST JOSEPH HOSPITAL (CA)
2700 Dolbeer St, Eureka, CA 95501-4799
Tel (707) 445-8121 *Founded/Ownrshp* 1920
Sales 248.2MM *EMP* 850^E
SIC 8062 General medical & surgical hospitals
CEO: Joseph Mark
Pr: David O'Brien
CFO: Terry Conrad
CFO: Andrew Rybolt
VP: Laurie W Stone
Plas Surg: Robert Green
Plas Surg: Mark Pardoe
Doctor: Marc Levin

D-U-N-S 07-179-6258
ST JOSEPH HOSPITAL INC
EXEMPLA SAINT JOSEPH HOSPITAL
1375 E 19th Ave, Denver, CO 80218-1114
Tel (303) 837-7111 *Founded/Ownrshp* 2011
Sales 498.1MM *EMP* 2,400^E
SIC 8062 General medical & surgical hospitals
CEO: Bain J Farris
COO: Barbara Jahn
VP: William B Gould
Comm Man: Mary F Jackson
**Prin:* Barb Jahn
Prgrm Mgr: Jan Notch
Prgrm Mgr: Rebecca Schoby
Pathlgst: Martin Potash
Pharmcst: Scott Cardona

D-U-N-S 07-154-4581
ST JOSEPH HOSPITAL OF EUREKA
(*Suby of* ST JOSEPH HOSPITAL OF ORANGE) ★
2700 Dolbeer St, Eureka, CA 95501-4736
Tel (707) 445-8121 *Founded/Ownrshp* 2011
Sales 254.8MM *EMP* 970^E
SIC 8062 General medical & surgical hospitals

D-U-N-S 06-760-7572
ST JOSEPH HOSPITAL OF ORANGE (CA)
(*Suby of* ST JOSEPH HEALTH SYSTEM) ★
1100 W Stewart Dr, Orange, CA 92868-3891
Tel (714) 633-9111 *Founded/Ownrshp* 1929
Sales 567.4MM *EMP* 3,300
SIC 8062 General medical & surgical hospitals
Pr: Larry K Ainsworth
**CFO:* Tina Nycroft
**Ch:* Jim Cora
**V Ch Bd:* Warren D Johnson
VP: Cory Rayyes
VP: Linda Simon
VP: Mary A Vincent
Exec: Patricia Brydges
Dir Lab: Val Grinenko
Dir Rx: Bich Nguyen
Mng Dir: Melvyn Sterling

ST JOSEPH MEDICAL CENTER
See ST JOSEPH REGIONAL HEALTH NETWORK

ST JOSEPH MEDICAL CENTER
See ST FRANCIS HOSPITAL

ST. JOSEPH MEDICAL CENTER
See SJ MEDICAL CENTER LLC

ST JOSEPH MEDICAL CENTER
See FRANCISCAN HEALTH SYSTEM

D-U-N-S 07-183-4287
ST JOSEPH MEDICAL CENTER
(*Suby of* CHI) ★
1717 S J St, Tacoma, WA 98405-4933
Tel (253) 627-4101 *Founded/Ownrshp* 1996
Sales 537.1MM^E *EMP* 3,761
SIC 8062 General medical & surgical hospitals
CEO: Katul Patel
Pr: Syd Bersante
CFO: Mike Fitzgerald
Exec: June C Bowman
Dir Health: Sylvia Zellmer
Board of Directors: Jane Russell

D-U-N-S 07-303-4811
ST JOSEPH MEDICAL CENTER
(*Suby of* PRIME HEALTHCARE SERVICES INC) ★
1000 Carondelet Dr, Kansas City, MO 64114-4673
Tel (816) 942-4400 *Founded/Ownrshp* 2014
Sales 156.3MM *EMP* 1,550
Accts Deloitte Tax Llp Cincinnati
SIC 8062 General medical & surgical hospitals
CEO: Robert J Erickson
**CFO:* Debra Catwright
VP: Deb Ohnoutka
Dir Rx: Melinda Carter
Secur Mgr: Mike Kruger

D-U-N-S 03-396-9549
ST JOSEPH MEDICAL CENTER CORP
(*Suby of* IASIS HEALTHCARE LLC) ★
1401 St Joseph Pkwy, Houston, TX 77002-8301
Tel (713) 757-1000 *Founded/Ownrshp* 2011
Sales 282.9MM^E *EMP* 1,500^E
SIC 8051 Skilled nursing care facilities
CEO: Patrick Matthews
Chf Path: Edwin Basden
**Pr:* Richard Joseph Steel
COO: Bo Beaudry
CFO: Brad Mitchell
Ofcr: Cucharras Martin
Exec: Brenda Ray
Dir Lab: Linda Myers
Assoc Dir: Mary Kowalski
Dir Rx: Jeff Buck
Chf Nrs Of: Glenda Newby

D-U-N-S 06-281-9339
ST JOSEPH MEMORIAL HOSPITAL
SAINT JOSEPH HOSPITAL & HEALTH
1907 W Sycamore St, Kokomo, IN 46901-5148
Tel (765) 456-5433 *Founded/Ownrshp* 1913
Sales 138.3MM *EMP* 900
Accts Deloitte Tax Llp Indianapolis
SIC 8062 General medical & surgical hospitals
CEO: Margaret Johnson
Dir Vol: Tiffani McLaurin
**Pr:* Kathy Young
**COO:* Michael Williams
CFO: Darrin Montalvo
CFO: Dennis Resserler
**CFO:* Dennis Ressler
Ofcr: Wallace Pippen
VP: Scott Sageman
VP: Eileen Wrobleski
Exec: Andrea Mattlock
Dir Lab: Shapour Khosravipour
Dir Rx: Diane Heine

D-U-N-S 12-627-3668
ST JOSEPH MERCY OAKLAND
(*Suby of* CATHOLIC HEALTH EAST) ★
44405 Woodward Ave, Pontiac, MI 48341-5023
Tel (248) 858-3000 *Founded/Ownrshp* 2003
Sales 288.1MM^E *EMP* 4,000^E
SIC 8062 General medical & surgical hospitals
CEO: Jack Weiner
VP: Jennifer Cobb
VP: Thomas Petingado
IT Man: Jeffrey Gillespie
Opers Supe: Elizabeth Shaker
Surgeon: John J Lee
Obsttrcn: Ashley M Lane
Doctor: Einas Joseph
Doctor: Kathy Sobanski
Doctor: Mary Verardi
Board of Directors: Jean Lacken

D-U-N-S 80-792-4803
ST JOSEPH MERCY OAKLAND HOSPITAL
44405 Woodward Ave, Pontiac, MI 48341-5023
Tel (248) 858-6186 *Founded/Ownrshp* 2007
Sales 950.0M *EMP* 2,601
SIC 8062 General medical & surgical hospitals
Treas: Todd Clark
VP: Cindy Harrison
IT Man: Jeffrey Gillespie
Doctor: Robert C Padilla

ST JOSEPH MERCY OF MACOMB
See HENRY FORD MACOMB HOSPITAL CORP

ST. JOSEPH MERCY POTU HURON
See TRINITY HEALTH-MICHIGAN

D-U-N-S 05-993-7255
ST JOSEPH PREFERRED HEALTHCARE INC
2500 Harbor Blvd, Port Charlotte, FL 33952-5000
Tel (941) 625-4122 *Founded/Ownrshp* 1994
Sales 26.5MM^E *EMP* 1,400
SIC 8741 Hospital management
CEO: Michael L Harrington

D-U-N-S 02-659-5467
ST JOSEPH REGIONAL HEALTH CENTER
2801 Franciscan Dr, Bryan, TX 77802-2544
Tel (979) 776-3777 *Founded/Ownrshp* 1998
Sales 250.9MM *EMP* 1,200^E
SIC 8062 8322 General medical & surgical hospitals; Rehabilitation services
CEO: Kathleen Krusie
V Ch: Mark Scarmardo
COO: Bob Just
COO: John Mason
Ofcr: Denise Goffney
**Sr VP:* Dan Goggin
**VP:* Steve Crichton
VP: Ricardo Diaz
VP: Donovan French
VP: Sam Fulton
VP: Mark Montgomery
VP: Thomas Pool
**Exec:* Mike Costa
Dir Rad: Mark Kicklighter

D-U-N-S 13-412-9118
ST JOSEPH REGIONAL HEALTH NETWORK
ST JOSEPH MEDICAL CENTER
(*Suby of* CHI) ★
2500 Bernville Rd, Reading, PA 19605-9453
Tel (610) 378-2000 *Founded/Ownrshp* 1998
Sales 213.3MM *EMP* 1,500^E
Accts Catholic Health Initiatives E
SIC 8062 General medical & surgical hospitals
Pr: John Morahan
COO: Doug Azar
**Treas:* George E Hoffman
Exec: Kathryn Obriant
Dir Rx: Marian Rhoads
Telecom Ex: Dan Mosser
QA Dir: Loretta Boyd
IT Man: Laura Welliver
Opers Mgr: Julia Jarrell
Opers Mgr: Mim Lambros
VP Mktg: Robert S Kniffin

D-U-N-S 16-821-6281 IMP
ST JOSEPH REGIONAL MEDICAL CENTER INC
415 6th St, Lewiston, ID 83501-2431
Tel (208) 743-2511 *Founded/Ownrshp* 1902
Sales 153.4MM *EMP* 1,000
Accts Lb Deloitte Tax Llp Cincinnat
SIC 8062 General medical & surgical hospitals
Ex Dir: Doug Barton
**Pr:* Troy Ledgerwood
**CEO:* Albert Gutierrez
COO: Tom Pflieger
**CFO:* Janice Dunn
Treas: Betty Riebe
Ofcr: Jose Alvarez
VP: Pat Rosholt
Chf Nrs Of: Sena Blickenstaff
Mtls Mgr: Leo Fitz
Mktg Dir: Christina Metcalf

D-U-N-S 04-164-2047
ST JOSEPH RESIDENCE INC
495 Mammoth Rd, Manchester, NH 03104-5463
Tel (603) 668-6011 *Founded/Ownrshp* 1980
Sales 151.7MM *EMP* 60
SIC 8059 Nursing home, except skilled & intermediate care facility

D-U-N-S 07-675-3169
ST JOSEPH RIVERSIDE HOSPITAL
667 Eastland Ave Se, Warren, OH 44484-4503
Tel (330) 841-4000 *Founded/Ownrshp* 1941
Sales 38.2M *EMP* 1,100
SIC 8062

D-U-N-S 07-302-3277
ST JOSEPH SCHOOL DISTRICT
925 Felix St, Saint Joseph, MO 64501-2788
Tel (816) 671-4000 *Founded/Ownrshp* 1860
Sales 121.7MM *EMP* 1,800^E
Accts Westbrook & Co Pc Richmon
SIC 8211 Public combined elementary & secondary school
**CFO:* Janet Pullen
**VP:* Cheri Patterson
**Ex Dir:* Melody Smith
Genl Mgr: Katie Guinn
Off Mgr: Megan McCamy
Dir IT: Ron Starks
Pr Dir: Joey Austin
Teacher Pr: Amy Todd
HC Dir: Maria Burnham

ST JOSEPH'S CANDLER HOSPITAL
See ST JOSEPHS/CANDLER HEALTH SYSTEM INC

D-U-N-S 06-827-9991
ST JOSEPHS COLLEGE NEW YORK
245 Clinton Ave, Brooklyn, NY 11205-3688
Tel (718) 940-5300 *Founded/Ownrshp* 1916
Sales 103.4MM *EMP* 800
Accts Grant Thornton Llp New York
SIC 8221 Colleges universities & professional schools
Pr: Rev William T Dillon
**Pr:* Jack P Calareso
**VP:* Sister Mary Florence Burns
Assoc Dir: Catherine Meehan
Ex Dir: D'Adra Crump
**CIO:* Joseph Spadaro
Sfty Mgr: Henry Dorta
Sfty Mgr: Mike McGrann

D-U-N-S 79-253-6422 EXP
ST JOSEPHS HEALTHCARE SYSTEM INC
703 Main St, Paterson, NJ 07503-2621
Tel (973) 754-4500 *Founded/Ownrshp* 1996
Sales 706.6MM *EMP* 12,217^E
Accts Deloitte Tax Llp Jericho Ny
SIC 8062 General medical & surgical hospitals
Prin: Marianne Lanno
CFO: Jack Robinson
Treas: Esther Polacci
Ofcr: William Segal
VP: John Bruno
VP: Kuimbo Genoso
VP: James Labagnara Jr
Exec: Jose Espinal
Dir Risk M: Laura Norton
Dir Rx: Mitch Sobel
Adm Dir: Linda Cronk

ST JOSEPH'S HOME CARE
See ST JOSEPHS HOSPITAL HEALTH CENTER

ST. JOSEPH'S HOSPITAL
See HEALTHEAST ST JOSEPHS HOSPITAL

D-U-N-S 05-793-6155
ST JOSEPHS HOSPITAL
(*Suby of* ARNOT HEALTH INC) ★
555 Saint Josephs Blvd, Elmira, NY 14901-3256
Tel (607) 733-6541 *Founded/Ownrshp* 1908
Sales 43.4MM *EMP* 1,050
SIC 8062 General medical & surgical hospitals; Hospital, affiliated with AMA residency
Pr: Fred Farley
CFO: Ronald Kintz
Sr VP: Wesley Blauvelt
Dir Lab: Lois Vanalstine
Dir Rx: Maryann Mahajan
Dir Env Sv: Denise Figueroa
Adm Dir: Lorri Youmans
Off Mgr: Janet Frost
CIO: Peter Kane
CIO: Gregg Martin
IT Man: Teresa Fletcher

D-U-N-S 06-427-9623
ST JOSEPHS HOSPITAL AND MEDICAL CENTER
(*Suby of* ST JOSEPHS HEALTHCARE SYSTEM INC) ★
703 Main St, Paterson, NJ 07503-2691
Tel (973) 754-2000 *Founded/Ownrshp* 1941
Sales 752.2MM *EMP* 4,000
SIC 8062 General medical & surgical hospitals
Pr: William A McDonald
Chf Path: Aquiles B Villacin
**CFO:* Jack Robinson
CFO: Jack D Robinson

CFO: Lisa Sacco
**Ch:* Rosemary Smith
Ofcr: William Segal
VP: Timothy Barr
VP: Maria Brennan
VP: James Cavanaugh
VP: Gloria A Kunze
VP: James Labagnara
Dir Soc: Elaine Silben
Dir Rx: Mitch Sobel
Dir Env Sv: John Di' Giovani

D-U-N-S 93-360-4860
ST JOSEPHS HOSPITAL CORPORATE SERVICES
(*Suby of* ST JOSEPH HOSPITAL) ★
172 Kinsley St, Nashua, NH 03060-3688
Tel (603) 882-3000 *Founded/Ownrshp* 1986
Sales 120.9MM *EMP* 2
Accts Pricewaterhousecoopers Llp
SIC 6719 Investment holding companies, except banks
Treas: Richard Plamondon
**Ex Dir:* Eileen Kelly

D-U-N-S 07-159-7637
ST JOSEPHS HOSPITAL HEALTH CENTER
ST JOSEPH'S HOME CARE
301 Prospect Ave, Syracuse, NY 13203-1899
Tel (315) 448-5113 *Founded/Ownrshp* 1869
Sales 542.1MM *EMP* 3,300
SIC 8062 General medical & surgical hospitals
Dir Recs: Michelle Degraff
**Ch Bd:* George Deptula
Bd of Dir: Paul Hudson
**Sr VP:* Mary W Brown
**VP:* Sallie Biittner
**VP:* Annemarie Czyz
**VP:* Charles J Fennell
Dir Lab: Debbie Yineman
**Prin:* Lucinda Drescher
**Prin:* Balasubramaniam Sivakumar
HC Dir: Sharon Goettel

D-U-N-S 06-966-3979
ST JOSEPHS HOSPITAL INC (FL)
ST JOSEPH'S WOMEN'S HOSPITAL
(*Suby of* BAYCARE EDUCATION SERVICES) ★
3001 W Dr Mrtn Lthr Kng B Martin Luther, Tampa, FL 33607
Tel (813) 554-8500 *Founded/Ownrshp* 1933
Sales 872.9MM *EMP* 300^E
SIC 8062 General medical & surgical hospitals
Pr: Lorraine Lutton
Chf Rad: Matthew Berlet
**Pr:* Kimberly Guy
**Pr:* Isaac Mallah
**Pr:* Paula McGuiness
**CFO:* Cathy Yoder
**VP:* Tommy Inzina
VP: Mark Vaaler
Orthpdst: Steven Knezevich
Obsttrcn: Alan E Smith
HC Dir: Elcylin Morgan

D-U-N-S 07-668-2723
ST JOSEPHS HOSPITAL YONKERS
ST JOSEPH'S MEDICAL CENTER
127 S Broadway, Yonkers, NY 10701-4080
Tel (914) 378-7000 *Founded/Ownrshp* 1888
Sales 190.9MM *EMP* 900
SIC 8062 8011 General medical & surgical hospitals; Medical centers
Pr: Michael J Spicer
COO: Kenneth Pierson
**CFO:* James Curcuruto
**Sr VP:* Frances Casola
**Sr VP:* Bernadette Kingham-Bez
**VP:* Dean Civitello
VP: Lorraine D Horgan
VP: Susan Obrien
Dir Rad: John Ohnacht
Off Mgr: Marie Parker
Off Mgr: Mia Rodriguez

D-U-N-S 07-964-2144
ST JOSEPHS HOSPITAL-NORTH
(*Suby of* BAYCARE EDUCATION SERVICES) ★
4211 Van Dyke Rd, Lutz, FL 33558-8005
Tel (813) 443-7000 *Founded/Ownrshp* 2014
Sales 3.4MM^E *EMP* 1,290^E
SIC 8099 Blood related health services

ST JOSEPH'S MEDICAL CENTER
See ST JOSEPHS HOSPITAL YONKERS

D-U-N-S 79-736-3520
ST JOSEPHS MEDICAL CENTER
ESSENTIA HLTH ST JSPHS MED CTR
(*Suby of* ESSENTIA HEALTH) ★
523 N 3rd St, Brainerd, MN 56401-3098
Tel (218) 829-2861 *Founded/Ownrshp* 1983
Sales 172.1MM *EMP* 1,400
SIC 8062 General medical & surgical hospitals
Pr: Adam Rees
CFO: Dave Pilot
Dir Rx: Jeff Swenson
Prin: Tracy Galles
Dir IT: Bonnie Groneberg
Dir IT: Pam Marlatt
Info Man: Pat Delong
Mktg Dir: Miranda Anderson
Pathlgst: Fred Hall
Pathlgst: Diane Kendell
Ansthlgy: Corey R Anderson

D-U-N-S 00-904-6082
ST JOSEPHS MEDICAL CENTER INC
(*Suby of* DIGNITY HEALTH) ★
1800 N California St, Stockton, CA 95204-6019
Tel (209) 943-2000 *Founded/Ownrshp* 1995
Sales 482.6MM *EMP* 150
SIC 8062 General medical & surgical hospitals
Pr: Donald J Wiley
Chf OB: Kevin E Rine
Dir Vol: Patti Wells
COO: Michael Ricks
CFO: Doreen Hartmann
Ofcr: Ray Sejas
**VP:* Dr Susan McDonald
VP: Abby Newton
VP: Mary Omara
**VP:* Terry Spring
**VP:* Kathy Tohrnan
**Exec:* Rae Charos
Dir Lab: Stephen Connolly
Dir Rad: Daniel Terry
Dir Rx: Bill Yee

D-U-N-S 07-879-6406
ST JOSEPHS MEDICAL CENTER OF STOCKTON
(*Suby of* DIGNITY HEALTH) ★
1800 N California St, Stockton, CA 95204-6019
Tel (209) 943-2000 *Founded/Ownrshp* 1899
Sales 4.2MM *EMP* 2,366
SIC 8062 General medical & surgical hospitals
Pr: Donald J Wiley
Dir Lab: Teresa Bryant
Dir IT: Randy Gamino

D-U-N-S 07-125-6218
ST JOSEPHS REGIONAL HEALTH CENTER (INC)
SAINT JOSEPHS MERCY HEALTH CTR
300 Werner St, Hot Springs, AR 71913-6406
Tel (501) 622-4500 *Founded/Ownrshp* 1888
Sales 130.4MM^E *EMP* 2,500
SIC 8062 General medical & surgical hospitals
CEO: Kim Day
COO: Timothy J Ohnsen
Dir Rad: Robert W Fore
Dir Rad: Michael P Hickman
Doctor: Larry Alford
Doctor: Mitchell H Kaufman

D-U-N-S 06-578-9240
ST JOSEPHS WAYNE HOSPITAL INC
SAINT JOSEPH'S WAYNE HOSPITAL
224 Hamburg Tpke, Wayne, NJ 07470-2124
Tel (973) 942-6900 *Founded/Ownrshp* 1871
Sales 99.3MM^E *EMP* 925
SIC 8062 General medical & surgical hospitals
Pr: Peter J Karl
Chf Rad: Michael Steinberg
VP: Gloria Kunze
VP: Ann Shears
Dir Lab: Jose Espinal
Ex Dir: Susan Spatt
CIO: Jim Cavanaugh
QA Dir: Laura Norton
IT Man: Melanie Kolesnikow
Netwrk Mgr: Michael Rightmire
Web Dev: Patricia Dipietro

ST JOSEPH'S WOMEN'S HOSPITAL
See ST JOSEPHS HOSPITAL INC

D-U-N-S 04-441-0814
ST JOSEPHS/CANDLER HEALTH SYSTEM INC (GA)
ST JOSEPH'S CANDLER HOSPITAL
5353 Reynolds St Ste 101, Savannah, GA 31405-6089
Tel (912) 819-6000 *Founded/Ownrshp* 1997
Sales 24.5MM *EMP* 3,684
Accts Draffin & Tucker Llp Albany
SIC 8062 General medical & surgical hospitals
Pr: Paul P Hinchey
V Ch: Robert H Demere
**Pr:* Gregory J Schaack
COO: Kyle McCann
CFO: Greg Schaack
CFO: Gregory J Schaak
Dir Rx: Steven Dufour
QA Dir: Cheryl Capers
Dir IT: Beth Patino
Netwrk Mgr: Angela Hathaway
Nrsg Dir: Sherry Danello
Board of Directors: Melissa Allen, Joe Loya, Linton Smith, Thomas White

D-U-N-S 06-771-7892
ST JUDE CHILDRENS RESEARCH HOSPITAL INC (TN)
262 Danny Thomas Pl, Memphis, TN 38105-3678
Tel (901) 595-3300 *Founded/Ownrshp* 1959
Sales 205.9MM *EMP* 2,500
Accts Deloitte & Touche Llp Memphis
SIC 8733 8062 Medical research; General medical & surgical hospitals
CEO: James Downing
CFO: Pat Keel
Chf Mktg O: Robert Sauer
Ex VP: Richard J Gilbertson
Ex VP: Larry E Kun
Ex VP: Dr Joseph Mirro
Sr VP: Robyn Diaz
Sr VP: Pam Dotson
VP: Galen Briggs
VP: Pamela Dotson
VP: Richard Gilbertson
VP: Michael Meagher
VP: Barry Whyte
Assoc Dir: Jessica Fisher
Assoc Dir: Jeff Harris
Assoc Dir: Shawn Hawkins

D-U-N-S 07-250-3634 IMP
ST JUDE HOSPITAL
ST JUDE MEDICAL CENTER
(*Suby of* ST JOSEPH HEALTH SYSTEM) ★
101 E Valencia Mesa Dr, Fullerton, CA 92835-3875
Tel (714) 871-3280 *Founded/Ownrshp* 1981
Sales 458.2MM *EMP* 2,600
Accts Ernst & Young Llp Irvine Ca
SIC 8062 General medical & surgical hospitals
Pr: Robert Fraschetti
Chf Path: Patrick L Fitzgibbons
Dir Recs: Pamela Frey
**CEO:* Doreen Dann
**CEO:* Lee Penrose
COO: Brian Helleland
CFO: Ed Salvador
VP: Teresa Frey
VP: Joseph S Lawton
Dir Rx: Donald A Miller
Dir Env Sv: EMD Ferdous

D-U-N-S 78-473-9310
■ **ST JUDE MEDICAL ATG INC**
(*Suby of* ST JUDE MEDICAL INC) ★
1 Lillehei Plz, Saint Paul, MN 55117-1799
Tel (651) 756-2000 *Founded/Ownrshp* 1994
Sales 50.0MM^E *EMP* 1,000
SIC 3842 Surgical appliances & supplies
Ch: Dan Starks
Pr: Terry L Shepherd

D-U-N-S 04-096-0379
■ **ST JUDE MEDICAL CARDIOVASCULAR DIVISION**
(*Suby of* ST JUDE MEDICAL INC) ★
14901 Deveau Pl, Minnetonka, MN 55345-2126
Tel (952) 933-4700 *Founded/Ownrshp* 1996
Sales 96.8MM^E *EMP* 950
SIC 3841 3842 Catheters; Surgical appliances & supplies
CEO: Daniel J Starks
**Pr:* David W Adinolfi
**VP:* Dean Bruhn-Ding
**VP:* James A Hassett
**VP:* David Kolstad
**Dir Surg:* Peter C Mc Lane

ST JUDE MEDICAL CENTER
See ST JUDE HOSPITAL

D-U-N-S 08-023-2168 IMP/EXP
▲ **ST JUDE MEDICAL INC**
1 Saint Jude Medical Dr, Saint Paul, MN 55117-1789
Tel (651) 756-2000 *Founded/Ownrshp* 1976
Sales 5.5MMM *EMP* 18,000
Tkr Sym STJ *Exch* NYS
SIC 3845 3842 3841 Electromedical equipment; Pacemaker, cardiac; Surgical appliances & supplies; Implants, surgical; Surgical & medical instruments; Surgical instruments & apparatus; Catheters; Medical instruments & equipment, blood & bone work
Pr: Michael T Rousseau
**Ch Bd:* Daniel J Starks
Pr: Joel D Becker
Pr: Eric S Fain
Pr: Denis M Gestin
CFO: Donald J Zurbay
Ofcr: Lisa M Andrade
Ex VP: John C Heinmiller
VP: I Paul Bae
VP: Mark D Carlson
VP: Jeffrey A Dallager
VP: Philip J Ebeling
VP: Rachel H Ellingson
VP: Jeff A Fecho
VP: Joel Friedman
VP: Michael T Moore
VP: Mark W Murphy
VP: Scott P Thome
VP: Ryan Walters
VP: Jason A Zellers
Exec: William Ivie
Board of Directors: John W Brown, Richard R Devenuti, David C Dvorak, Stuart M Essig, Barbara B Hill, Michael A Rocca, Stefan K Widensohler, Wendy L Yarno

D-U-N-S 78-473-9161
■ **ST JUDE MEDICAL SC INC**
(*Suby of* ST JUDE MEDICAL INC) ★
1 Lillehei Plz, Saint Paul, MN 55117-1799
Tel (651) 483-2000 *Founded/Ownrshp* 1988
Sales 917.6MM^E *EMP* 6,000
SIC 5047 Medical equipment & supplies
Ch Bd: Terry L Shepherd
**Pr:* Joel D Becker
Pr: Sharon Knutson
**COO:* Daniel J Starks
CFO: Robert Peterson
VP: Steven Brandt
VP: Paul Gam
VP: Scott Thome
VP: Jim Ufford
Ex Dir: John Fleischhacker
Snr Sftwr: Susan Miner

D-U-N-S 14-882-8036
ST LANDRY PARISH AIRPORT AUTHORITY
299 Hangar Rd, Opelousas, LA 70570-0003
Tel (337) 407-1551 *Founded/Ownrshp* 2004
Sales 125.0MM *EMP* 2
SIC 4581 Airports, flying fields & services

D-U-N-S 08-008-6657
ST LANDRY PARISH SCHOOLS
PORT BARRE HIGH SCHOOL
1013 Creswell Ln, Opelousas, LA 70570-5821
Tel (337) 948-3657 *Founded/Ownrshp* 1900
Sales 18.7MM^E *EMP* 2,600
SIC 8211 Public elementary & secondary schools
Pr Dir: Patricia Mason-Guillory
Teacher Pr: Matthew Scruggins
HC Dir: Jerome Robinson

D-U-N-S 07-580-6042
ST LAWRENCE COUNTY
BOARD OF LEGISLATORS
48 Court St, Canton, NY 13617-1169
Tel (315) 379-2276 *Founded/Ownrshp* 1802
Sales NA *EMP* 1,000
Accts Whittemore Dowen & Ricciardel
SIC 9111 Executive offices;
**Treas:* Bob McNeil
Ex Dir: Mike Cunningham
Ex Dir: Patrick Rourk
IT Man: Kevin Felt

D-U-N-S 00-225-5792 IMP
ST LAWRENCE UNIVERSITY (NY)
23 Romoda Dr, Canton, NY 13617-1501
Tel (315) 229-5011 *Founded/Ownrshp* 1856
Sales 125.8MM *EMP* 650
Accts Bonadio & Co Llp Cpas Pitt
SIC 8221 7011 University; Hotel, franchised
Pr: William L Fox
Trst: John M Finley
Trst: David B Laird
VP: Lisa Cania
VP: Grant H Cornwell Jr
VP: Laura Ellis
VP: Abbey Gardner
VP: Sean Kelly
VP: Melissa Richards
VP: Jeff Rickey
VP: Justin Sipher
VP: Robert Wells
Assoc Dir: Neal S Burdick
Assoc Dir: David Geleta
Assoc Dir: Joe Keniston
Assoc Dir: Dan McDonnell
Board of Directors: Susan M Pankey, Cynthia Y Atkins, Daniel B Seaman, Marguerite Cornwell, Margaret F Strait, Peter Feickert, Christine Zimmerman, Peter D Fieckert, Ronald J Ortiz Flores, Walter H Johnson, John M Meagher, Kim M Mooney, Ren M Murphy

ST. LKES REGIONAL MEDICAL CENT
See NORTHWEST IOWA HOSPITAL CORP

D-U-N-S 07-199-5203 IMP
ST LOUIS CHILDRENS HOSPITAL
(*Suby of* BJC HEALTHCARE) ★
1 Childrens Pl, Saint Louis, MO 63110-1081
Tel (314) 454-6000 *Founded/Ownrshp* 1879
Sales 527.4MM *EMP* 2,959
SIC 8069 Children's hospital
Pr: Joan Magruder
Ofcr: Charles Dougherty
**Sr VP:* Michael Dehaven
**VP:* David Aplington
Dir Rx: Christine L Pavlik
CIO: Feliciano Yu
Ansthlgy: Rania A Aziz
Opthamlgy: Rajendra S Apte

ST LOUIS CITY HALL
See CITY OF ST LOUIS

ST LOUIS COMMUNITY COLLEGE
See JUNIOR COLLEGE DISTRICT OF ST LOUIS

D-U-N-S 87-763-0319
ST LOUIS COMMUNITY COLLEGE
(*Suby of* ST LOUIS COMMUNITY COLLEGE) ★
5600 Oakland Ave, Saint Louis, MO 63110-1316
Tel (314) 644-9100 *Founded/Ownrshp* 2005
Sales 81.7MM^E *EMP* 1,516^E
SIC 8222 Community college
Pr: William Kennedy
Ofcr: Kurt Wagner
Ofcr: Byron Watson
VP: Kawaii Brown
VP: Devon Cook
VP: Allif Dove
VP: Jason Fossella
VP: Joyce Hodge
VP: Julie Howell
VP: Samuel Huddleston
VP: Cynthia Jenkins
VP: Vernon Kays
VP: Andrew Langrehr
VP: Amanda Mead-Roach
VP: Suzette Moore
VP: Leola Smith
VP: Keith Ware
VP: Elizabeth Wilcoxson

D-U-N-S 07-763-7726
ST LOUIS COUNTY OF (INC)
100 N 5th Ave W Rm 320, Duluth, MN 55802-1207
Tel (218) 726-2340 *Founded/Ownrshp* 1856
Sales NA *EMP* 2,300
Accts Rebecca Otto Saint Paul Mn
SIC 9131 Executive & legislative combined
Ex Dir: Marcus Hall

ST LOUIS DOWNTOWN AIRPORT
See BI-STATE DEVELOPMENT AGENCY OF MISSOURI-ILLINOIS METROPOLITAN DISTRICT (INC)

D-U-N-S 03-109-0343 IMP
ST LOUIS ELECTRIC SUPPLY INC
METRO ELECTRIC
6801 Hoffman Ave, Saint Louis, MO 63139-2529
Tel (314) 645-9000 *Founded/Ownrshp* 1994
Sales 116.2MM^E *EMP* 175
SIC 5063 5719 Electrical supplies; Lighting fixtures; Wire & cable; Lighting fixtures; Lamps & lamp shades
Pr: Bill Frisella
CFO: Brett Vollrath
Exec: Conrad Seibel
Brnch Mgr: Pat Buyers
Brnch Mgr: Ken Mauermann
Genl Mgr: Matt Gagnepain
Opers Mgr: Barbara Moynihan
VP Mktg: Steven Talbot
Sls Dir: Paul Frisella

D-U-N-S 07-864-9397
■ **ST LOUIS GAMING VENTURES LLC**
HOLLYWOOD CASINO ST LOUIS
(*Suby of* PENN NATIONAL GAMING INC) ★
777 Casino Center Dr, Maryland Heights, MO 63043-4821
Tel (314) 770-7629 *Founded/Ownrshp* 2012
Sales 38.3MM^E *EMP* 1,200
SIC 7999 7011 Gambling establishment; Casino hotel
Genl Mgr: Tony Carlucci
Sr VP: John D Smith
Comm Dir: Seth Palansky
Off Admin: Sherri Booth
IT Man: Chris Riley
Natl Sales: J Wills
Mktg Dir: Charley Puhr
Mktg Mgr: Joan Harris

ST. LOUIS POST-DISPATCH
See PULITZER INC

D-U-N-S 00-193-8414
■ **ST LOUIS POST-DISPATCH LLC**
(*Suby of* LP ACQUISITION) ★
900 N Tucker Blvd, Saint Louis, MO 63101-1069
Tel (314) 340-8000 *Founded/Ownrshp* 1932, 1999
Sales 83.2MM^E *EMP* 663
SIC 2711 Newspapers, publishing & printing

Pr: Nicholas G Penniman IV
VP: Jane Amari
VP: Connie Hoffman
Creative D: Gabe Hartwig
Dir IT: Jimmy Washington
VP Prd: Blake Dickie
Opers Mgr: Evans Judy
Mktg Dir: Lisa Clark
Sls Mgr: Susan Eckert

D-U-N-S 07-990-6178
ST LOUIS PUBLIC SCHOOLS
BOARD OF EDCATN OF CY ST LOUIS
801 N 11th St, Saint Louis, MO 63101-1015
Tel (314) 231-3720 *Founded/Ownrshp* 1833
Sales 395.3MM *EMP* 4,600
Accts Rubinbrown Llp Saint Louis M
SIC 8211 Public elementary & secondary schools
Treas: George Byron
Ex Dir: David Flieg
Ex Dir: Donna Johnson
Pr Dir: Patrick Wallace
Psych: Pearl Johnson

D-U-N-S 82-502-4987
ST LUCIE COUNTY SCHOOL BOARD
4204 Okeechobee Rd, Fort Pierce, FL 34947-5414
Tel (772) 429-3600 *Founded/Ownrshp* 1915
Sales 318.9MM^E *EMP* 159^E
Accts Cherry Bakaert Llp Orlando F
SIC 8211 School board
Ch Bd: Kathryn Hensley
* *V Ch:* Troy Ingersol

D-U-N-S 07-979-8846
ST LUCIE PUBLIC SCHOOLS
4204 Okeechobee Rd, Fort Pierce, FL 34947-5414
Tel (772) 429-3600 *Founded/Ownrshp* 2015
Sales 47.2MM^E *EMP* 4,638^E
SIC 8211 Public elementary & secondary schools
Dir Sec: Brian Reuther
MIS Dir: Terence O'Leary
Telecom Mg: Julie Kittrell
HC Dir: Barbara Casteen
HC Dir: Kim Pennington

D-U-N-S 14-002-8924
ST LUKES COMMUNITY HEALTH SERVICES
ST. LUKE'S THE WOODLANDS HOSPITAL
(*Suby of* CHI ST LUKES HEALTH BAYLOR COLLEGE OF MEDICINE MEDICAL CENTER) ★
17200 St Lukes Way, The Woodlands, TX 77384-8007
Tel (936) 266-2000 *Founded/Ownrshp* 1997
Sales 185.8MM *EMP* 900
SIC 8011 8062 Medical centers; General medical & surgical hospitals
Ch Bd: Michael Richmond
CFO: Mary S Lipnan
* *Treas:* Stephen Pickett
Dir Rad: Scott R Dorfman
Dir Rad: Parke F Gregg
Dir Rx: Kay Rarhmann
* *Prin:* Michael H Covert
Nurse Mgr: Teresa Oehler

D-U-N-S 07-869-9790
ST LUKES CORNWALL HOSPITAL
70 Dubois St, Newburgh, NY 12550-4851
Tel (845) 561-4400 *Founded/Ownrshp* 1997
Sales 165.9MM *EMP* 1,500^E
SIC 8062 General medical & surgical hospitals
Pr: Allan E Atzrott
Sr VP: Kathleen Bloss
* *VP:* Mary Elizabeth Duffy
VP: Mary Kelley
Prgrm Mgr: Babi Satzman
Prgrm Mgr: Suzanne Tremper
Dir IT: Jane Lake
IT Man: Clara Locey
Doctor: Rebecca L Loverso

D-U-N-S 96-774-6897
ST LUKES EPISCOPAL HOSPITAL
6624 Fannin St, Houston, TX 77030-2312
Tel (713) 610-9326 *Founded/Ownrshp* 2011
Sales 860.3MM *EMP* 37^E
SIC 8062 General medical & surgical hospitals
CEO: Angela Shippy
Dir Sec: Ron Kelemen
Psych: Peg Reiter
Psych: Debra Sukin
Plas Surg: David T Netscher

D-U-N-S 06-915-1293
ST LUKES EPISCOPAL HOSPITAL INDEPENDENT PRACTICE ASSOCIATION INC (TX)
ST LUKES HEALTH SYSTEMS
(*Suby of* CHI) ★
6720 Bertner Ave, Houston, TX 77030-2697
Tel (832) 355-1000 *Founded/Ownrshp* 1954, 2013
Sales 100.0MM *EMP* 4,500
SIC 8062 General medical & surgical hospitals
Pr: Michael K Jhin
* *CFO:* Alan F Koval
CFO: Howard Schramm
Treas: Ian Browning
VP: Richard H Shafer
VP: Charles R Swanson
Exec: Bueso Fernando
Exec: Osborne Kent
Dir Lab: Janet Sherrill
Chf Nrs Of: Maribel Castro
Adm Dir: Divya Varkey

D-U-N-S 07-196-0660
ST LUKES EPISCOPAL-PRESBYTERIAN HOSPITALS
ST. LUKE'S HOSPITAL
(*Suby of* ST LUKES HOSPITAL) ★
232 S Woods Mill Rd, Chesterfield, MO 63017-3406
Tel (314) 434-1500 *Founded/Ownrshp* 1868
Sales 470.6MM *EMP* 3,000
Accts Kpmg Llp Oklahoma City Ok
SIC 8062 General medical & surgical hospitals
Pr: Christine Candio
* *VP:* Brian Spillers
Dir Lab: David L Scrivner
Dir Rad: Reggie Hicks
Dir Rx: Christy Burrows
Dir Rx: Zachary A Stacy
QA Dir: Lisa Donnelly
Mktg Mgr: Jessica Dederer
Pathlgst: David Scrivner
Doctor: Zaheer Ahmed
Doctor: Alexander Bollis

D-U-N-S 05-618-8691
ST LUKES HEALTH CORP
ST. LUKE'S HOSPITAL
232 S Woods Mill Rd, Chesterfield, MO 63017-3406
Tel (314) 434-1500 *Founded/Ownrshp* 1981
Sales 437.4MM *EMP* 3,100
Accts Kpmg Llp Oklahoma City Ok
SIC 8741 Hospital management
Pr: Gary Olson
Dir Vol: Sue Smith
Mng Pt: Jonathan Vitsky
Assoc Dir: Mari Chollet
Dir Rx: Richard Fook
Ex Dir: James Walsh
Off Mgr: Sandra Krajcovic
Off Mgr: Michelle Overman
Off Mgr: Carol Ross
CIO: William Meyer
IT Man: Dinah Hayes
Board of Directors: Ed Heathcock, Rod Henning, Diane Jorgenson

D-U-N-S 96-768-6259
ST LUKES HEALTH NETWORK INC
ST LUKE'S HOSPITAL & HEALTH NE
(*Suby of* ST LUKES HOSP & HLTH NETWRK) ★
801 Ostrum St, Bethlehem, PA 18015-1000
Tel (610) 954-4000 *Founded/Ownrshp* 1985
Sales 67.4MM *EMP* 2,958^E
Accts Withumsmithbrown Pc Morristow
SIC 8062 Hospital, professional nursing school
Pr: Richard A Anderson
* *Sr VP:* Tom Lichpenwalner
HC Dir: Jenni Levy

D-U-N-S 96-800-3504
ST LUKES HEALTH SYSTEM CORP
CHI ST. LUKE'S HEALTH
(*Suby of* CHI) ★
6624 Fannin St Ste 1100, Houston, TX 77030-2323
Tel (832) 355-1000 *Founded/Ownrshp* 2013
Sales 128.3MM^E *EMP* 1^E
SIC 8062 General medical & surgical hospitals
Ch: Don A Wimberly
* *Pr:* Wayne Keathley
* *CEO:* Michael Covert
* *COO:* Deborah Lee-Eddie
* *CFO:* William Brosius
Sr VP: Beryl Vallejo
Adm Dir: Andrew Brown
Adm Dir: Craig Frost
Ex Dir: Megan Thomas
Admn Mgr: Will Lloyd
Opers Supe: George Gaitan

D-U-N-S 83-267-6899
ST LUKES HEALTH SYSTEM LTD
190 E Bannock St, Boise, ID 83712-6241
Tel (208) 381-2222 *Founded/Ownrshp* 2006
Sales 241.4MM *EMP* 7,891
SIC 8062 General medical & surgical hospitals
CEO: Chris Roth
Ex VP: Jeff Taylor
VP: Bart Hill
VP: Albert Sinisi
Dir IT: Sheryl Bell
Dir IT: David Blue
Dir IT: Brad Hild
IT Man: Rex Lagrone
Site Mgr: Nickole Oneida
Doctor: Avery Seifert
Nrsg Dir: Belinda Day

ST LUKES HEALTH SYSTEMS
See ST LUKES EPISCOPAL HOSPITAL INDEPENDENT PRACTICE ASSOCIATION INC

ST LUKES HOSP & HLTH NETWRK
See SAINT LUKES HOSPITAL OF BETHLEHEM PENNSYLVANIA

ST. LUKE'S HOSPITAL
See ST LUKES HEALTH CORP

ST. LUKE'S HOSPITAL
See ST LUKES EPISCOPAL-PRESBYTERIAN HOSPITALS

ST LUKE'S HOSPITAL
See SAINT LUKES HOSPITAL OF NEW BEDFORD INC

ST LUKE'S HOSPITAL
See ST LUKES HOSPITAL ASSOCIATION

D-U-N-S 05-416-5675
ST LUKES HOSPITAL (OH)
PROMEDICA
5901 Monclova Rd, Maumee, OH 43537-1899
Tel (419) 893-5911 *Founded/Ownrshp* 1906
Sales 188.3MM *EMP* 1,558
SIC 8062 5912 Hospital, affiliated with AMA residency; Drug stores
Pr: Frank J Bartell III
* *CFO:* Joseph J Zigray
Ofcr: Kerry Burmeister
VP: Stephen Bazeley
Dir Risk M: Bill Quinlan
Dir Lab: Thomas J Thompson
Prac Mgr: Broderick Lisa
CTO: Julie Punches
IT Man: Charles Hainy
Mktg Dir: David Dewey
Pathlgst: Shaila Fernandes

D-U-N-S 61-286-9151
ST LUKES HOSPITAL
3555 Cesar Chavez, San Francisco, CA 94110-4490
Tel (415) 647-8600 *Founded/Ownrshp* 1991
Sales 3.5MM *EMP* 23
SIC 8062 General medical & surgical hospitals
CEO: Warren S Browner
CIO: Craig Vercruysse
Telecom Mg: Cathy Courtney
Pathlgst: David Anderson
Pharmcst: Joey Low

ST LUKE'S HOSPITAL & HEALTH NE
See ST LUKES HEALTH NETWORK INC

D-U-N-S 07-986-6132
ST LUKES HOSPITAL & HEALTH NETWORK INC
801 Ostrum St, Bethlehem, PA 18015-1000
Tel (484) 526-4000 *Founded/Ownrshp* 2014
Sales 602.7MM *EMP* 3,101^E
SIC 8741 Hospital management
Pr: Richard A Anderson
COO: John J Haney
* *Sr VP:* Rthomas P Lichtenwalner
Rgnl Mgr: Dave Capuano
Genl Mgr: Thomas Lichtenwalner
Snr Ntwrk: Bryan Smith
IT Man: James Derr
IT Man: Diane Godshall
IT Man: James Schmutzler
Pgrm Dir: Scott Melanson
Snr PM: Patience Phillips

D-U-N-S 07-984-6458
ST LUKES HOSPITAL - ANDERSON CAMPUS
(*Suby of* ST LUKES HOSPITAL & HEALTH NETWORK INC) ★
1872 St Lukes Blvd, Easton, PA 18045-5669
Tel (484) 503-3000 *Founded/Ownrshp* 2011
Sales 155.9MM *EMP* 99
SIC 8062 General medical & surgical hospitals
Pr: Edward Nawrocki

D-U-N-S 07-758-4365
ST LUKES HOSPITAL ASSOCIATION
ST LUKE'S HOSPITAL
4201 Belfort Rd, Jacksonville, FL 32216-5898
Tel (904) 296-3700 *Founded/Ownrshp* 1984
Sales 86.1MM^E *EMP* 1,300^E
Accts Pricewaterhousecoopers By Fax
SIC 8062 General medical & surgical hospitals
CEO: Randy Hartley
Chf Rad: Mark McKinney
* *Pr:* Bob Walters
* *CFO:* Mary Hoffman
VP: Patrick Bower
Dir Rad: Gary Doyle
Off Mgr: Nancy Okeefe
IT Man: Jill Hilburn
Doctor: Wendell H Williams MD
Pharmcst: Robert Besser
Dir Health: Lucy Hedden

D-U-N-S 06-817-8268
ST LUKES HOSPITAL OF DULUTH (MN)
915 E 1st St, Duluth, MN 55805-2193
Tel (218) 726-5555 *Founded/Ownrshp* 1883
Sales 352.0MM *EMP* 2,200
SIC 8062 8011 Hospital, AMA approved residency; Offices & clinics of medical doctors
Pr: John Strange
Chf Path: Sarah J Lundeen
* *CFO:* James Wuellner
Dir Rx: Roger Young
Brnch Mgr: Jean Elton
MIS Dir: Richard Smith
Ansthlgy: Andrea L Benson
Doctor: Alan Spivack

D-U-N-S 96-385-6997
ST LUKES HOSPITAL OF KANSAS CITY
4401 Wornall Rd, Kansas City, MO 64111-3220
Tel (816) 932-2000 *Founded/Ownrshp* 2011
Sales 647.9MM *EMP* 4^E
SIC 8062 General medical & surgical hospitals
Pr: Julie Quirin
* *CFO:* Jama Johnson
* *VP:* Kevin Thorpe

D-U-N-S 07-297-7911
ST LUKES MAGIC VALLEY INC
ST LUKES VLY REGIONAL MED CTR
801 Pole Line Rd W, Twin Falls, ID 83301-5810
Tel (208) 737-2000 *Founded/Ownrshp* 2011
Sales 333.0MM *EMP* 1,580
SIC 8062 8063

D-U-N-S 00-517-4653
ST LUKES MEDICAL CENTER
1800 E Van Buren St, Phoenix, AZ 85006-3742
Tel (602) 251-8100 *Founded/Ownrshp* 1907
Sales 140.6MM *EMP* 4^E
SIC 8011 Medical centers
Prin: Paul Jenson

D-U-N-S 07-245-8912
ST LUKES MEDICAL CENTER LP
(*Suby of* IASIS HEALTHCARE CORP) ★
1800 E Van Buren St, Phoenix, AZ 85006-3742
Tel (602) 251-8535 *Founded/Ownrshp* 1997
Sales 175.0MM *EMP* 1,649
SIC 8062 8063 8051 General medical & surgical hospitals; Hospital for the mentally ill; Skilled nursing care facilities
CEO: Ed Myers
Adm Dir: Anthony Richard

D-U-N-S 06-522-3166
ST LUKES METHODIST HOSPITAL INC
SAINT LUKE'S HOSPITAL
(*Suby of* UNITYPOINT HEALTH) ★
1026 A Ave Ne, Cedar Rapids, IA 52402-5074
Tel (319) 369-7211 *Founded/Ownrshp* 1884
Sales 319.0MM *EMP* 2,000
SIC 8062 General medical & surgical hospitals
Pr: Theodore Townsend Jr
Chf Path: Ruth A Macke
* *Ch Bd:* James Sealy
COO: Rocklon Chapin
Dir Inf Cn: Julie Sturbaum
Off Mgr: Mary Trupld
CIO: Sue Ramm
Cmptr Lab: Sue Smith
Sfty Mgr: Janet Posekany
Mktg Mgr: Mike Humbert
Pathlgst: Lileah Harris

D-U-N-S 80-897-8829
ST LUKES PHYSICIAN GROUP INC
FOUNTAIN HILL MEDICAL SERVICES
(*Suby of* ST LUKES HOSP & HLTH NETWRK) ★
801 Ostrum St Ste 1, Bethlehem, PA 18015-1000
Tel (610) 954-4990 *Founded/Ownrshp* 1984
Sales 238.6MM *EMP* 135^E
Accts Withumsmithbrown Pc Morristow
SIC 8741 Administrative management
CEO: Richard Anderson
* *Pr:* Dean Evans
* *Treas:* Thomas P Lichtenwaher

D-U-N-S 10-716-1697
ST LUKES PHYSICIANS GROUP
7790 Easton Rd, Ottsville, PA 18942-1765
Tel (610) 847-2071 *Founded/Ownrshp* 1990
Sales 80.0MM *EMP* 8,900
SIC 8011 General & family practice, physician/surgeon
Pr: Joseph O Neill

D-U-N-S 07-835-0154
ST LUKES REGIONAL MEDICAL CENTER LTD
190 E Bannock St, Boise, ID 83712-6241
Tel (208) 381-5500 *Founded/Ownrshp* 1906
Sales 1.3MMM *EMP* 4,500
SIC 8062 8011 Hospital, affiliated with AMA residency; Offices & clinics of medical doctors
Pr: Edwin Dahlberg
VP: David Crane
* *VP:* Gary Fletcher
VP: John Kee
VP: Clarence Pomeroy
* *VP:* Clarence Pumeroy
Dir Sec: Cal Ledbetter
Genl Mgr: Mike Jones
Opers Mgr: Steve O'Toole
Doctor: Howard King
Doctor: Robert Lee
Board of Directors: Julie Eng, Armando Garcia, Angela Moser, Ken Price

ST. LUKE'S THE WOODLANDS HOSPITAL
See ST LUKES COMMUNITY HEALTH SERVICES

ST LUKES VLY REGIONAL MED CTR
See ST LUKES MAGIC VALLEY INC

D-U-N-S 10-511-8939
ST LUKES-ROOSEVELT HOSPITAL CENTER
1111 Amsterdam Ave, New York, NY 10025-1716
Tel (212) 523-4000 *Founded/Ownrshp* 1846
Sales 859.8MM *EMP* 6,000
Accts Ernst & Young Us Llp Indianap
SIC 8062 General medical & surgical hospitals
Pr: Frank Cracolici
Dir Vol: Amy Bush
COO: Gail Donovan
Treas: Steven Hochberg
* *Sr VP:* Robert Catalano
Dir Lab: Mary E Nusbaum
Ex Dir: Barbara Rothbart
Cmptr Lab: Fran McGorty
Sfty Dirs: Yvonne Guariglia
Opers Mgr: Patricia Nickelson
Pathlgst: Mark Friedman
Board of Directors: Ken Barritt

D-U-N-S 79-783-5444
ST MARGARET MERCY HEALTHCARE CENTERS INC
SAINT MARGARET MERCY
(*Suby of* SAINT JAMES HOSPITAL) ★
5454 Hohman Ave, Hammond, IN 46320-1999
Tel (219) 932-2300 *Founded/Ownrshp* 1991
Sales 183.0MM^E *EMP* 2,859
SIC 8062 8052 8051 General medical & surgical hospitals; Intermediate care facilities; Skilled nursing care facilities
* *Prin:* Thomas J Gryzbek
Mtls Mgr: Terry Wozniak
Doctor: Frank Hilvert

ST MARK'S HOSPITAL
See NORTHERN UTAH HEALTHCARE CORP

D-U-N-S 02-122-3743 IMP/EXP
■ **ST MARKS POWDER INC**
(*Suby of* GENERAL DYNAMICS ORDNANCE AND TACTICAL SYSTEMS INC) ★
7121 Coastal Hwy, Crawfordville, FL 32327-2918
Tel (850) 577-2824 *Founded/Ownrshp* 1998
Sales 125.6MM^E *EMP* 340
SIC 2869 Industrial organic chemicals
Pr: Michael S Wilson
* *VP:* Guy Cornwell

D-U-N-S 08-765-0123
ST MARTIN PARISH SCHOOL BOARD
625 Corporate Blvd, Breaux Bridge, LA 70517-4324
Tel (337) 394-6261 *Founded/Ownrshp* 1900
Sales 84.2MM *EMP* 1,100
Accts Kolder Champagne Slaven & Co
SIC 8211 School board
Pr: Mark Hebert
HC Dir: Adrean Huval

D-U-N-S 07-980-2902
ST MARTIN PARISH SCHOOL DISTRICT
P.O. Box 1000 (70517-1000)
Tel (337) 394-6261 *Founded/Ownrshp* 2015
Sales 30.5MM^E *EMP* 1,100^E
SIC 8211 Public elementary & secondary schools

D-U-N-S 78-733-6486
ST MARY HEALTH CORP
211 Pennington Ave, Passaic, NJ 07055-4617
Tel (973) 470-3000 *Founded/Ownrshp* 1987
Sales 58.1MM^E *EMP* 2,100
SIC 8741 Hospital management
Pr: Patricia Peterson
* *VP:* Stephen Cerra
* *VP:* Joanne Devine

CIO: Shafiq Rab
Mktg Mgr: Roseann Mazzeo

D-U-N-S 06-883-5057
ST MARY HOSPITAL OF LIVONIA
ST MARY MERCY GIFT SHOP
(*Suby of* CATHOLIC HEALTH EAST) ★
36475 5 Mile Rd, Livonia, MI 48154-1971
Tel (734) 655-4800 *Founded/Ownrshp* 1953
Sales 131.3MM[E] *EMP* 1,500
SIC 8062 8051 General medical & surgical hospitals; Skilled nursing care facilities
Pr: David Spivey
Pr: Caroline Hays
Ofcr: Karen Paison
VP: Richard Deloof
VP: Sister Janet Marie
DP Dir: Jerry Baj
Doctor: Tom Wood
Pgrm Dir: Paula Magid

D-U-N-S 07-020-8723
ST MARY MEDICAL CENTER
ST MARY'S SCHOOL OF NURSING
(*Suby of* DIGNITY HEALTH) ★
1050 Linden Ave, Long Beach, CA 90813-3321
Tel (562) 491-9000 *Founded/Ownrshp* 1953
Sales 273.5MM *EMP* 2,000
SIC 8062 Hospital, medical school affiliated with nursing & residency
CEO: Trammie McMann
**CEO:* Alan Garrett
**CEO:* Tammie McMann
COO: Joel Yuhaf
Dir Lab: Stephen Dunn
Mtls Dir: Tom Lees
HC Dir: Gail Daly
Snr Mgr: Chester Choi

D-U-N-S 07-710-7043
ST MARY MEDICAL CENTER
(*Suby of* CATHOLIC HEALTH EAST) ★
1201 Langhorne Newtown Rd, Langhorne, PA 19047-1295
Tel (215) 710-2000 *Founded/Ownrshp* 1974
Sales 443.8MM *EMP* 2,400[E]
SIC 8062 General medical & surgical hospitals
Ch Bd: Ron Gigliotti
Chf Path: Zenon Gibas
Dir Vol: Lil Schonewolf
**Pr:* Greg Wozniak
Sr VP: Brian Burgess
VP: Sharon Brown
VP: Robert Cardinale
VP: Terri Rivera
VP: Mary Sweeney
Dir Lab: Tom Flatley
Dir Rx: Suzette Rph

D-U-N-S 18-107-0442
ST MARY MEDICAL CENTER
18300 Us Highway 18, Apple Valley, CA 92307-2206
Tel (760) 242-2311 *Founded/Ownrshp* 1992
Sales 325.2MM *EMP* 1,350[E]
Accts Ernst & Young Us Llp San Diego
SIC 8062 General medical & surgical hospitals
Pr: Alan H Garrett
**COO:* Kelly Linden
**CFO:* Marilyn Drone
**CFO:* Tracey Fernandez
Bd of Dir: Joe Pizzorno
**Trst:* Diana Carloni - O'Malley
**VP:* Dennis Haghighat
**VP:* Paul Kaminski
**VP:* Judy Wagner
VP: Larry Woodward
Genl Mgr: Rosa Ramirez

D-U-N-S 01-439-1747
ST MARY MEDICAL CENTER INC
1500 S Lake Park Ave, Hobart, IN 46342-6699
Tel (219) 942-0551 *Founded/Ownrshp* 1996
Sales 233.8MM *EMP* 800
SIC 8062 General medical & surgical hospitals
CEO: Janice Ryba
Chf Rad: Jaime Cebedo
**CFO:* Mary Sudicky
CFO: Milton Triani
Chf Mktg O: Peter Mevrelis
Sr VP: John Gorski
VP: Betty Lane
Dir IT: Corey Alston
Pathlgst: Ruth D Goldberg
Doctor: Cindy Macko
Doctor: Evelyn Ryan

ST MARY MERCY GIFT SHOP
See ST MARY HOSPITAL OF LIVONIA

D-U-N-S 07-577-0156
■ ST MARY OPERATING CO
(*Suby of* SM ENERGY CO) ★
1775 N Sherman St # 1200, Denver, CO 80203-1100
Tel (303) 861-8140 *Founded/Ownrshp* 1994
Sales 125.4MM[E] *EMP* 600
SIC 1311 Crude petroleum production; Natural gas production
Ch Bd: Mark Hellerstein
Pr: Donna Grant
**Pr:* Jay Ottoson
**CEO:* Tony Best
VP: Robert T Hanley
VP: Michael Rosenzweig
Ex Dir: Malcolm Kintzing
Off Mgr: Debra Arroya
Off Mgr: Debra Arroyo
CIO: Kerin Todaro
VP Mktg: David Whitcomb

D-U-N-S 07-262-4224
ST MARY PARISH SCHOOL BOARD
474 Hwy 317, Centerville, LA 70522
Tel (337) 836-9661 *Founded/Ownrshp* 1900
Sales 67.1MM[E] *EMP* 1,500
Accts Darnall Sikes Gardes & Frede
SIC 8211 School board; Public elementary school; Public junior high school; Public senior high school
Ex Dir: Henry Lagr
IT Man: Clevon Self
HC Dir: Lydia Duval

D-U-N-S 07-980-2439
ST MARY PARISH SCHOOLS
474 Hwy 317, Centerville, LA 70522
Tel (337) 836-9661 *Founded/Ownrshp* 2015
Sales 39.3MM[E] *EMP* 1,594[E]
SIC 8211 Public elementary & secondary schools
MIS Dir: Debra Mitchell
MIS Dir: Irene Mouton
Teacher Pr: Ricky Armelin

ST MARY PHYSICIAN GROUP
See PROVIDENCE ST MARY MEDICAL CENTER

D-U-N-S 79-168-3923
ST MARY-CORWIN HOSPITAL OF PUEBLO CO (INC)
ST MARY-CRWIN REGIONAL MED CTR
(*Suby of* ST ANTHONY CENTRAL HOSPITAL) ★
1008 Minnequa Ave, Pueblo, CO 81004-3733
Tel (719) 557-4000 *Founded/Ownrshp* 1979
Sales 167.1MM *EMP* 1,208
SIC 8062 General medical & surgical hospitals
CEO: Rob Ryder
**CFO:* Kimberly Monjesky
**VP:* Mike Cafasso
**VP:* Larae Eggleston
**VP:* Donna Fisher
Surgeon: Gary E Lane
Anesthlgy: John R Sandoval

ST MARY-CRWIN REGIONAL MED CTR
See ST MARY-CORWIN HOSPITAL OF PUEBLO CO (INC)

ST. MARY'S CAMPUS
See SETON HEALTH SYSTEM INC

D-U-N-S 07-924-2946
ST MARYS COUNTY PUBLIC SCHOOLS
SMCPS
23160 Moakley St Ste 101, Leonardtown, MD 20650-2933
Tel (301) 475-5511 *Founded/Ownrshp* 2014
Sales 239.5MM *EMP* 1,688[E]
SIC 8211 Public elementary & secondary schools
Dir Sec: Michael Wyant
Prgrm Mgr: Sarah Tyson
Teacher Pr: Dale Farrell

D-U-N-S 95-813-7283
ST MARYS DEAN VENTURES INC
1808 W Beltline Hwy, Madison, WI 53713-2334
Tel (608) 250-1311 *Founded/Ownrshp* 1989
Sales 130.2MM *EMP* 11,000
SIC 8011 Offices & clinics of medical doctors
CEO: Stephen M Olson
**CFO:* Duan Etate

D-U-N-S 01-568-2615
ST MARYS DULUTH CLINIC HEALTH SYSTEM
SMDC
(*Suby of* ESSENTIA HEALTH) ★
400 E 3rd St, Duluth, MN 55805-1951
Tel (218) 786-8364 *Founded/Ownrshp* 1996
Sales 1.4MM[E] *EMP* 5,144
SIC 8093 8011 8062 Mental health clinic, outpatient; Offices & clinics of medical doctors; General medical & surgical hospitals
Pr: Thomas Patnoe
**CEO:* Peter E Person
COO: Laura Ackman
**CFO:* Bert Norman
Ex VP: Sandra McCarthy
VP: Carl Heltne
**VP:* Michael J Mahoney
VP: Carolyn Roller
VP: Kristi Schmidt
Dir Rad: Bruce Derauf
Pathlgst: Geoffrey A Witrak

D-U-N-S 14-456-9365
ST MARYS FOOD BANK ALLIANCE
FOOD CARE
2831 N 31st Ave, Phoenix, AZ 85009-1518
Tel (602) 242-3663 *Founded/Ownrshp* 1966
Sales 124.8MM *EMP* 76[E]
Accts Henry & Horne Llp Tempe Az
SIC 8322 Temporary relief service
Ex Dir: Terrance P Shannon
COO: Mike Hanosh
CFO: Sarah Stuckey
Ofcr: Susan Combe
Ofcr: Pat Fehlhaber
Prgrm Mgr: Laura Brill
Opers Mgr: Rob O'Brien
Pr Dir: Bryan Leeseberg

ST MARY'S GIFT SHOP
See MERCY REGIONAL HEALTH CENTRE AUXILIARY

D-U-N-S 07-344-5413
ST MARYS HEALTH CARE SYSTEM INC (GA)
CATHOLIC HEALTH EAST
(*Suby of* CATHOLIC HEALTH EAST) ★
1230 Baxter St, Athens, GA 30606-3712
Tel (706) 389-3000 *Founded/Ownrshp* 1938, 1998
Sales 174.1MM *EMP* 1,350
SIC 8062 8051 General medical & surgical hospitals; Skilled nursing care facilities
CEO: Don McKenna
Chf Rad: Phil Van Dyke
V Ch: Rodney Bennett
V Ch: Walter Jarrett
Exec: Nancy Argo
Dir Lab: Tina Cheek
Dir Rad: Jerry O Smith
**Prin:* Stephanie Walsh
Dir Sec: Joe Lockman
Genl Mgr: Mark Abbott
Off Mgr: Maxine Brown

D-U-N-S 05-456-3582
ST MARYS HEALTH CENTER
6420 Clayton Rd, Saint Louis, MO 63117-1872
Tel (228) 233-4998 *Founded/Ownrshp* 2010
Sales 604.9MM *EMP* 88[E]
SIC 8099 Health & allied services

D-U-N-S 05-681-9501
ST MARYS HEALTH INC
ST MARY'S HOSPITAL
3700 Washington Ave, Evansville, IN 47714-0541
Tel (812) 485-4000 *Founded/Ownrshp* 1872
Sales 471.6MM *EMP* 3,500
Accts Deloitte Tax Llp Indianapolis
SIC 8062 General medical & surgical hospitals
Pr: Timothy Flesch
Chf Rad: Killol Thakore
Dir Recs: Alice Long
Mng Pt: Paul Wallace
**COO:* Gwen Sandefur
Bd of Dir: Prasad Gade
Bd of Dir: Bruce Haskins
Bd of Dir: Stewart Phillips
Bd of Dir: Anthony Stephens
Sr VP: Thomas R Lilly
VP: Barbara K Clayton
VP: John Gallagher
VP: Wathen Robert
Dir Rad: Julie Wolowitz
Dir Rx: Michael Whitmore

D-U-N-S 96-962-7574
ST MARYS HEALTH INC
ST MARY'S MEDICAL EQUIPMENT
3700 Washington Ave, Evansville, IN 47714-0541
Tel (812) 485-7623 *Founded/Ownrshp* 1998
Sales 487.3MM *EMP* 5[E]
SIC 8062 General medical & surgical hospitals
Pr: Keith Jewels
CFO: Kim Hodgkinson
**Prin:* Allison Taylor
Ex Dir: Eric Jost
Mktg Dir: Cathy Fulkerson
Pathlgst: Stephen Rose
Obsttrcn: Lora A Perry

ST MARY'S HEALTH NETWORK
See SAINT MARYS HEALTH CARE CORP

D-U-N-S 10-817-3659
ST MARYS HEALTH SYSTEM
96 Campus Ave, Lewiston, ME 04240-6019
Tel (207) 777-8546 *Founded/Ownrshp* 1983
Sales 176.2MM *EMP* 1,900
SIC 8062 8052 8051 8011 8361 General medical & surgical hospitals; Intermediate care facilities; Skilled nursing care facilities; Clinic, operated by physicians; Home for the aged
CEO: Leo Myles
**CEO:* Christopher Chekouras
**COO:* Susan Keiler
**CFO:* Carolyn Kasabian
QA Dir: Janet Smith

D-U-N-S 07-721-3619
ST MARYS HEALTHCARE (NY)
427 Guy Park Ave Ste 1, Amsterdam, NY 12010-1054
Tel (518) 842-1900 *Founded/Ownrshp* 1903
Sales 149.6MM *EMP* 1,002
Accts Lumsden Mccormikc Llp Buffalo
SIC 8062 General medical & surgical hospitals
Pr: Vic Giulianelli
Chf Rad: Tariq Gill
COO: Scott Bruce
VP: Albert Turo
Dir Rx: Alfred Mazur
Dir Sec: Joseph Puglisi
Dir IT: Peter Levine
Software D: Mark Romani
Mktg Dir: Jerri Cortese
Orthpdst: Nicholas Alexander
Doctor: Parul Saxena

ST MARY'S HOSPITAL
See ST MARYS HEALTH INC

ST. MARY'S HOSPITAL
See PRIME HEALTHCARE SERVICES - ST MARYS PASSAIC LLC

ST MARY'S HOSPITAL
See ST MARYS-GOOD SAMARITAN INC

D-U-N-S 06-831-9375
ST MARYS HOSPITAL
HOSPITAL SIS OF THE 3RD ORDER
(*Suby of* HOSPITAL SISTERS HEALTH SYSTEM) ★
1726 Shawano Ave, Green Bay, WI 54303-3282
Tel (920) 498-4200 *Founded/Ownrshp* 1905
Sales 120.0MM *EMP* 712
SIC 8011 8062 Offices & clinics of medical doctors; General medical & surgical hospitals
CEO: Therese B Pandl
**COO:* Larry Connors
Pathlgst: Patrick M McDonough
Surgeon: Jennifer Nehring
Anesthlgy: Brian L Johnson

D-U-N-S 11-576-7022
ST MARYS HOSPITAL
(*Suby of* HOSPITAL SISTERS HEALTH SYSTEM) ★
1800 E Lake Shore Dr, Decatur, IL 62521-3883
Tel (217) 464-2984 *Founded/Ownrshp* 1984
Sales 138.1MM *EMP* 1[E]
SIC 8062 General medical & surgical hospitals
CEO: Kevin Kast
Dir IT: Mark Krieger
Surgeon: Shane R Fancher

D-U-N-S 96-375-2402
ST MARYS HOSPITAL
ST. MARY'S MADISON
(*Suby of* SSM HEALTH CARE CORP) ★
700 S Park St, Madison, WI 53715-1893
Tel (608) 251-6100 *Founded/Ownrshp* 1927
Sales 420.6MM *EMP* 2,797
SIC 8062 General medical & surgical hospitals
Pr: Frank Byrne
VP: Kyle Martin
Comm Dir: Marsha Gahagan

D-U-N-S 06-971-5746
ST MARYS HOSPITAL & MEDICAL CENTER INC (OH)
SAINT MARYS HOSPITAL & MED CTR
(*Suby of* SCL HEALTH SYSTEM) ★
2635 N 7th St, Grand Junction, CO 81501-8209
Tel (970) 298-2013 *Founded/Ownrshp* 1896, 1972
Sales 436.3MM *EMP* 2,000[E]
SIC 8062 General medical & surgical hospitals
CEO: Brian Davidson
Chf Rad: Michael E Holt
**CFO:* Terri Chinn
Ofcr: Ryan Stringfellow
**Ex VP:* Reza Kaleel
**VP:* Sister Barbara Aldrich
VP: Judy W House
**VP:* Dan Prinster
Prgrm Mgr: Joan Cox
CIO: Todd Nicholson
Netwrk Eng: Allan Worley

D-U-N-S 04-103-8746
ST MARYS HOSPITAL DECATUR OF HOSPITAL SISTERS OF THIRD ORDER OF ST FRANCIS
HSHS SAINT MARY'S HOSPITAL
1800 E Lake Shore Dr, Decatur, IL 62521-3883
Tel (217) 464-2966 *Founded/Ownrshp* 1878
Sales 159.0MM[E] *EMP* 1,300[E]
Accts Kpmg Llp Decatur Il
SIC 8062 General medical & surgical hospitals
CEO: Daniel L Perryman
Exec: Julie Causey
Exec: Barbara Tate
Pr Mgr: Jessica Michael
HC Dir: Pam Craft

D-U-N-S 06-688-5245
ST MARYS HOSPITAL MEDICAL CENTER AUXILIARY (INC)
700 S Park St, Madison, WI 53715-1893
Tel (608) 251-6100 *Founded/Ownrshp* 1965
Sales NA *EMP* 120
SIC 6321 Accident & health insurance
Pr: Mary Quamme
Adm Dir: Kathleen Ambs
Dir IT: Heather Pinske
Pharmcst: Heidi Deforest

D-U-N-S 06-486-9860
ST MARYS HOSPITAL OF SAINT MARYS COUNTY INC
MEDSTAR HEALTH VNA
(*Suby of* MEDSTAR HEALTH VNA) ★
25500 Point Lookout Rd, Leonardtown, MD 20650-2015
Tel (301) 475-8981 *Founded/Ownrshp* 2009
Sales 147.7MM *EMP* 1,250[E]
Accts Kpmg Llp Mc Lean Va
SIC 8062 General medical & surgical hospitals
Pr: Christine Wray
VP: Donald M Fache
**VP:* Joan Gelrud
**Prin:* Richard Braam
Ex Dir: Christopher Steen
Off Mgr: Greg Matthews
Mktg Dir: Holly Meyer
Pathlgst: Yahia M Tagouri
Surgeon: Usman Zahir
HC Dir: Stephen Michaels

ST. MARY'S MADISON
See ST MARYS HOSPITAL

ST MARY'S MEDICAL CENTER
See CATHOLIC HEALTHCARE WEST

D-U-N-S 05-556-9545 IMP
ST MARYS MEDICAL CENTER
2900 1st Ave, Huntington, WV 25702-1241
Tel (304) 526-1234 *Founded/Ownrshp* 1928
Sales 311.7MM *EMP* 2,000
SIC 8062 Hospital, medical school affiliated with nursing & residency
Pr: Michael G Sellards
Bd of Dir: Karen Foster
**Sr VP:* Todd Campbell
Sr VP: David Sheils
VP: Ruth Cila
VP: Doug Korstanje
VP: Susan Robinson
VP: Vera Rose
VP: Lee Taylor MD
VP: Chris Trotter
VP: Lavona Turvey
VP: Judy Wagner
Dir Lab: Jane Roberts
Comm Dir: Gary Taylor
Dir Rad: Jamie Kellar

D-U-N-S 07-223-1954 IMP
■ ST MARYS MEDICAL CENTER
OUTPATIENT PROGRAM
(*Suby of* TENET HEALTHCARE CORP) ★
901 45th St, West Palm Beach, FL 33407-2413
Tel (561) 844-6300 *Founded/Ownrshp* 2001
Sales 320.1MM *EMP* 56,605
SIC 8062 Hospital, affiliated with AMA residency
CEO: Davide Carbone
**COO:* Joey Bulfin
CFO: Joel Dalva
CFO: Michael Loscalzo
**CFO:* Thomas Schlemmer
Dir Risk M: Ray Hibner
Opers Mgr: Glen McClean
Mktg Dir: Patti Patrick
Anesthlgy: Kimberly J Dugan
Anesthlgy: Dava L Grundhoefer
Doctor: Mukesh Kumar

D-U-N-S 60-413-2043
ST MARYS MEDICAL CENTER
ESSENTIA HEALTH
(*Suby of* ESSENTIA HEALTH) ★
407 E 3rd St, Duluth, MN 55805-1984
Tel (218) 786-4000 *Founded/Ownrshp* 2004
Sales 396.0MM *EMP* 4,209

SIC 8062 8082 8351 General medical & surgical hospitals; Home health care services; Group day care center
Ch Bd: SIS Kathleen Hofer
**Pr:* James Garvey
**Pr:* Kathleen Hofer
**VP:* Timothy Backous
**VP:* Hugh P Renier
Surgeon: Steven D Eyer
Surgeon: Vincent U Ohaju
Surgeon: John A Sauer
Ansthlgy: Scott A Eskuri
Ansthlgy: James P Gregory

D-U-N-S 05-191-7987
ST MARYS MEDICAL CENTER FOUNDATION (CA)
(*Suby of* DIGNITY HEALTH) ★
450 Stanyan St, San Francisco, CA 94117-1019
Tel (415) 668-1000 *Founded/Ownrshp* 1983
Sales 4.1MM *EMP* 1,067
Accts Kpmg Llp San Francisco Ca
SIC 8062 Hospital, professional nursing school
Pr: Ken Steele
**CFO:* James Wentz
Board of Directors: P Maudel, Sister L Murphy

D-U-N-S 06-983-8654
ST MARYS MEDICAL CENTER OF SAGINAW INC (MI)
SAINT MARYS MICHIGAN MED CTR
(*Suby of* ASCENSION HEALTH ALLIANCE) ★
800 S Washington Ave, Saginaw, MI 48601-2551
Tel (989) 907-8000 *Founded/Ownrshp* 1876
Sales 223.9MM *EMP* 1,869
SIC 8062 General medical & surgical hospitals
Pr: John Graham
**Sec:* Gina Butcher
Dir Inf Cn: Karen Hoover
**Prin:* Brian Eggers
**Prin:* Andrew Richards
Ex Dir: Gary Dunbar
**Ex Dir:* Karen Stiffler
Mktg Dir: Christine Bergman

ST MARY'S MEDICAL EQUIPMENT
See ST MARYS HEALTH INC

ST MARY'S PROPERTIES
See ARCHDIOCESE OF MIAMI INC

D-U-N-S 13-596-2975
ST MARYS REGIONAL HEALTH CENTER
(*Suby of* ESSENTIA HEALTH) ★
1027 Washington Ave, Detroit Lakes, MN 56501-3409
Tel (218) 847-5611 *Founded/Ownrshp* 2009
Sales 111.1MM *EMP* 400^E
SIC 8062 8051 General medical & surgical hospitals; Skilled nursing care facilities
Pr: Peter Jacobson
**CFO:* Ryan Hill
Dir Rx: Shelley Johnson
Genl Mgr: Lydia Kolofale

D-U-N-S 07-174-3694
ST MARYS REGIONAL MEDICAL CENTER
(*Suby of* ST MARYS HEALTH SYSTEM) ★
93 Campus Ave, Lewiston, ME 04240-6030
Tel (207) 777-8546 *Founded/Ownrshp* 1967
Sales 138.8MM *EMP* 1,374^E
SIC 8062 8052 8051 8011 8361 General medical & surgical hospitals; Intermediate care facilities; Skilled nursing care facilities; Clinic, operated by physicians; Home for the aged
CFO: Carolyn Kasabian
**CEO:* Christopher Chekouras
**CFO:* Michael Hendrix
Comm Man: Jennifer Radel
Plng Mgr: Lorrie J Potvin
CIO: Rene Dumont
CIO: Norm Rioux
Telecom Mg: Bill Marr

D-U-N-S 08-111-4415
ST MARYS REGIONAL MEDICAL CENTER
RRCH HEALTHCARE PARTNERS
(*Suby of* RRCH HEALTHCARE PARTNERS) ★
1808 W Main St, Russellville, AR 72801-2724
Tel (479) 968-2841 *Founded/Ownrshp* 1987
Sales 86.4MM *EMP* 700
SIC 8062 General medical & surgical hospitals
CEO: Mike McCoy
Pr: Lynn Sims
CFO: Carolyn Kasabien
**CFO:* Wendell Van Es
Dir Lab: Melanie Elmore
Dir Rx: Alan N Reams
Telecom Ex: Brenda Harrison
DP Exec: Lynn Simms
Dir QC: Tim Copeland
VP Opers: Danny J Aquilar
Nrsg Dir: Carol Gore

D-U-N-S 14-556-4238
■ **ST MARYS REGIONAL MEDICAL CENTER**
(*Suby of* UNIVERSAL HEALTH SERVICES INC) ★
305 S 5th St, Enid, OK 73701-5832
Tel (580) 233-6100 *Founded/Ownrshp* 2000
Sales 91.7MM *EMP* 645
SIC 8011 Medical centers
CFO: Vanessa Kocheyar
VP: Tracy Andersen
Dir OR: Terry Baartman
Dir Rad: Bob Brice
Mktg Mgr: Cindy Shepard
Mktg Mgr: Cindy Shephard
Doctor: Linda Hoag
Doctor: Joe Snodgrass
HC Dir: Frank Kribbs

D-U-N-S 07-423-2419
ST MARYS REGIONAL REHAB CENTER
201 Nw R D Mize Rd, Blue Springs, MO 64014-2513
Tel (816) 228-5900 *Founded/Ownrshp* 1990
Sales 89.8MM *EMP* 40
SIC 8093 Rehabilitation center, outpatient treatment
Ex Dir: Jim Scussel

ST. MARY'S RIVERSIDE
See SAINT MARYS RIVERSIDE

ST MARY'S SCHOOL OF NURSING
See ST MARY MEDICAL CENTER

ST MARY'S UNIVERSITY
See ST MARYS UNIVERSITY OF SAN ANTONIO TEXAS

D-U-N-S 07-850-0725
ST MARYS UNIVERSITY OF SAN ANTONIO TEXAS
ST MARY'S UNIVERSITY
1 Camino Santa Maria St, San Antonio, TX 78228-5433
Tel (210) 436-3506 *Founded/Ownrshp* 1852
Sales 99.9MM *EMP* 806
Accts Ernst & Young Llp San Antonio
SIC 8221 University
Pr: Thomas M Mengler
CFO: David Simpson
**VP:* Thomas Galvin
VP: Andre Hampton
**VP:* Rebeckah McCoy
**VP:* Katherine M Sisoian
Ex Dir: Daxing Chen
Telecom Mg: Matt Schultz
Pr Dir: Gina Farrell
Doctor: Dave Hatch

D-U-N-S 07-196-9877
ST MARYS-GOOD SAMARITAN INC
ST MARY'S HOSPITAL
(*Suby of* SSM HEALTH CARE CORP) ★
400 N Pleasant Ave, Centralia, IL 62801-3056
Tel (618) 436-8000 *Founded/Ownrshp* 1947
Sales 91.3MM *EMP* 950
SIC 8062 General medical & surgical hospitals
Pr: Bruce Merrel
**CFO:* Kay Tinsley
Mktg Dir: Julie Long

D-U-N-S 02-046-3196
ST MICHAEL HOSPITAL OF FRANCISCAN SISTERS MILWAUKEE INC
(*Suby of* WHEATON FRANCISCAN HEALTHCARE) ★
5000 W Chambers St, Milwaukee, WI 53210-1650
Tel (414) 447-2000 *Founded/Ownrshp* 1983
Sales 22.7MM^E *EMP* 1,027
SIC 8062 8011 General medical & surgical hospitals; Offices & clinics of medical doctors
Pr: Ron Gropper

D-U-N-S 07-477-3334
ST MICHAELS HOSPITAL INC
(*Suby of* MINISTRY HEALTH CARE INC) ★
900 Illinois Ave, Stevens Point, WI 54481-3196
Tel (715) 346-5000 *Founded/Ownrshp* 1913
Sales 20.9MM^E *EMP* 1,900^E
SIC 8062 General medical & surgical hospitals
Pr: Jeffery Martin
**Pr:* Bill Hinner
Bd of Dir: Karen Shurbert
Ofcr: Shirley Bailey
**VP:* Sharon Frazier
**VP:* Al Pennebecker
**VP:* Jane Schill
QA Dir: Crystal Kirschling
Web Dev: Dave Groen
Surgeon: Calvin K Selwyn
Ansthlgy: Dana D Doll

D-U-N-S 04-720-1728
ST MORITZ BUILDING SERVICES INC
4616 Clairton Blvd, Pittsburgh, PA 15236-2114
Tel (412) 885-2100 *Founded/Ownrshp* 1968
Sales 64.8MM^E *EMP* 1,250
SIC 7349 5087 Janitorial service, contract basis; Service establishment equipment
CEO: Philip L St Moritz
**CFO:* Brian K Fiscus
VP: Gregory Barker
VP: John Brady
VP: Jeromie Lauck
Area Mgr: Cheryl Devlin
Genl Mgr: Craig Bryant
VP Opers: Alex Russo
Opers Mgr: Lee Caton
Opers Mgr: Langston Logan
Opers Mgr: Rob Strickland

D-U-N-S 10-775-6470
ST MORITZ SECURITY SERVICES INC
4600 Clairton Blvd, Pittsburgh, PA 15236-2114
Tel (412) 885-3144 *Founded/Ownrshp* 1982
Sales 82.1MM^E *EMP* 1,424
SIC 7381 Security guard service; Detective services
Pr: Brian K Fiscus
**Pr:* Brian Fiscus
**Pr:* Paul L Harris
Ofcr: John Jones
VP: Mark Sheratsky
CTO: Grace Jones

D-U-N-S 95-924-2033
ST NICHOLAS LOCAL DEVELOPMENT CORP
11 Catherine St, Brooklyn, NY 11211-2706
Tel (718) 388-2233 *Founded/Ownrshp* 1979
Sales 25.0MM *EMP* 1,200
Accts Loeb & Troper Llp New York N
SIC 8322 Individual & family services
Ex Dir: Mike Rocksford
Ex Dir: Richard Macellaro

D-U-N-S 04-120-1070 IMP
ST OLAF COLLEGE
1520 Saint Olaf Ave, Northfield, MN 55057-1574
Tel (507) 786-2222 *Founded/Ownrshp* 1874
Sales 203.0MM *EMP* 800^E
SIC 8221 College, except junior
Pr: Craig Dunton
**Pr:* David R Anderson
**Treas:* Alan J Norton
Bd of Dir: Judith A Stoutland
**VP:* James May
VP: Craig Rice
VP: Theresa H Wise

Ex Dir: Jennifer Bader
Dir IT: Roberta Lembke
IT Man: Dana Thompson
HC Dir: Dan Franklin

D-U-N-S 11-868-2538
ST PATRICK HOSPITAL AND HEALTH SCIENCES CENTER
500 W Broadway St, Missoula, MT 59802-4096
Tel (406) 543-7271 *Founded/Ownrshp* 1991
Sales 37.1MM^E *EMP* 1,600
SIC 8062 General medical & surgical hospitals
Pr: Jeff D Fee
COO: Steven Whitz
Dir Rx: Jim Moran
Doctor: Gary Muskett
Doctor: Royce Pyette
Doctor: Mary A Sladich-Lantz
Doctor: Richard Vinglas
HC Dir: J Burke

D-U-N-S 79-404-4248
ST PATRICK HOSPITAL CORP
500 W Broadway St, Missoula, MT 59802-4008
Tel (406) 543-7271 *Founded/Ownrshp* 1873
Sales 159.9MM^E *EMP* 1,460
SIC 8062 General medical & surgical hospitals
Pr: Jeff Fee
COO: Craig Aasved
COO: Marianne Farr
COO: Paul Thormahlen
CFO: Kirk Bodlovic
CFO: Loren Jacobson
VP: Jinny Iverson
Exec: Jorge Reyno
Chf Nrs Of: Joyce Dombrouski
CIO: Paul Barber
IT Man: Brett Thorne

D-U-N-S 13-072-8751
ST PAUL ELECTRICAL ADMINISTRATIVE SERVICES CORP
ST PAUL ELECTRICAL CNSTR TR
1330 Conway St Ste 130, Saint Paul, MN 55106-5856
Tel (651) 772-8746 *Founded/Ownrshp* 1985
Sales 91.1MM *EMP* 9
SIC 6733 Trusts, except educational, religious, charity: management

ST PAUL ELECTRICAL CNSTR TR
See ST PAUL ELECTRICAL ADMINISTRATIVE SERVICES CORP

D-U-N-S 00-557-0460
■ **ST PAUL FIRE AND MARINE INSURANCE CO** (MN)
(*Suby of* TRAVELERS COMPANIES INC) ★
385 Washington St, Saint Paul, MN 55102-1309
Tel (651) 221-7911 *Founded/Ownrshp* 1925
Sales NA *EMP* 10,000
SIC 6331 6351 6321 6411 Fire, marine & casualty insurance; Workers' compensation insurance; Automobile insurance; Reciprocal interinsurance exchanges: fire, marine, casualty; Surety insurance; Liability insurance; Fidelity responsibility insurance; Reciprocal interinsurance exchanges: surety, fidelity; Accident & health insurance carriers; Reinsurance carriers, accident & health; Insurance agents, brokers & service
CEO: Brian W Maclean
CFO: Tom Bradley
CFO: Paul J Liska
Treas: Tom Berkman
Sr VP: Maria Olivo
VP: Gary Gillard
VP: Kerry Sparen
Prin: Douglas Leatherdale
Dir IT: Dean Collins
Dir IT: Bryan Eastep
Dir IT: Kevin Field

D-U-N-S 07-175-1440
■ **ST PAUL GUARDIAN INSURANCE CO**
(*Suby of* ST PAUL FIRE AND MARINE INSURANCE CO) ★
385 Washington St, Saint Paul, MN 55102-1309
Tel (651) 221-7911 *Founded/Ownrshp* 1970
Sales NA *EMP* 1,000^E
SIC 6331 Property damage insurance; Fire, marine & casualty insurance & carriers
CEO: Jay Fishman
VP: Alan Tuvin

D-U-N-S 00-693-5878
■ **ST PAUL PROTECTIVE INSURANCE CO** (IL)
(*Suby of* NORTHBROOK HOLDINGS, INC.)
Allstate S Barrington Plz, Northbrook, IL 60062
Tel (847) 402-5000 *Founded/Ownrshp* 1932, 1996
Sales NA *EMP* 1,475
SIC 6331 Fire, marine & casualty insurance
Pr: Bryan Anderson
**Ch:* Patrick A Thiele
**Treas:* Donald Swanson
**Ex VP:* Michael J Conroy
**Ex VP:* James Schulte
**Sr VP:* David Litzkow
**VP:* Bruce Backberg

ST. PAUL PUBLIC SCHOOLS
See INDEPENDENT SCHOOL DIST 625

D-U-N-S 07-421-1616
■ **ST PAUL SURPLUS LINES INSURANCE CO**
(*Suby of* ST PAUL FIRE AND MARINE INSURANCE CO) ★
385 Washington St, Saint Paul, MN 55102-1309
Tel (651) 310-7911 *Founded/Ownrshp* 1981
Sales NA *EMP* 29^E
SIC 6331 Fire, marine & casualty insurance
Pr: J Stephen Fishman
Sr VP: Bob Brody
Sr VP: Scott Haniford
VP: Julio Martinez
VP: John Charles Treacy

D-U-N-S 17-823-4407
ST PAUL TEACHERS RETMNT FUND ASSN
1619 Dayton Ave Ste 309, Saint Paul, MN 55104-6276
Tel (651) 642-2550 *Founded/Ownrshp* 2002
Sales NA *EMP* 17
SIC 6371 Pension funds
Ex Dir: Paul V Doane
Ofcr: Chris Macdonald

ST. PETER MIDDLE SCHOOL
See ST PETER PUBLIC SCHOOL DISTRICT

D-U-N-S 03-000-5615
ST PETER PUBLIC SCHOOL DISTRICT
ST. PETER MIDDLE SCHOOL
100 Lincoln Dr Ste 229, Saint Peter, MN 56082-1339
Tel (507) 934-5703 *Founded/Ownrshp* 1955
Sales 64.9MM^E *EMP* 1,959
Accts Peterson & Company Pa
SIC 8211 Public junior high school
CTO: Cbrischke Peterson
Instr Medi: Karen Shay

D-U-N-S 06-053-3031
ST PETERS HEALTH PARTNERS
ST PETER'S HOSPITAL
(*Suby of* CATHOLIC HEALTH EAST) ★
315 S Manning Blvd, Albany, NY 12208-1707
Tel (518) 525-1550 *Founded/Ownrshp* 2011
Sales 527.1MM *EMP* 6,000
SIC 8062 Hospital, AMA approved residency
CEO: Ann Errichettii
Chf Path: Russell Newkirk
Chf Mktg O: Robert Cella
Ofcr: Anne Simpson
VP: Charles Gianfagna
VP: Judy Gray
VP: Rosie Perez
VP: Ron Watson
Prgrm Mgr: Sandra Cummings
Nurse Mgr: Stephanie Fitzsimmons
Telecom Ex: George Seabury

D-U-N-S 07-868-8243
ST PETERS HEALTH PARTNERS (NY)
(*Suby of* CATHOLIC HEALTH EAST) ★
315 S Manning Blvd, Albany, NY 12208-1707
Tel (518) 525-1111 *Founded/Ownrshp* 2011
Sales 1.2MMM *EMP* 12,000
Accts Deloitte & Touche Llp Rochest
SIC 8062 General medical & surgical hospitals
Pr: James Reed MD
**CFO:* Thomas Schuhle

ST PETER'S HOSPITAL
See ST PETERS HEALTH PARTNERS

D-U-N-S 06-892-1535 IMP
ST PETERS HOSPITAL
2475 E Broadway St, Helena, MT 59601-4999
Tel (406) 442-2480 *Founded/Ownrshp* 1886
Sales 178.6MM *EMP* 1,200
SIC 8062 General medical & surgical hospitals
Ch Bd: Mark Taylor
Pr: Fred Olson
COO: Ann Kjosa
Treas: Guy Almquist
Ofcr: Samataha Williams
Prin: William Northey
CTO: Deb Jones
Mtls Mgr: Thom Kimbel
Obsttrcn: Michael Hay
Doctor: Andrew Cupino
Doctor: Thea Dalfino
Board of Directors: Sheila Hogan, William Northey, Mark Taylor

D-U-N-S 06-752-0585
ST PETERS UNIVERSITY
2641 John F Kennedy Blvd, Jersey City, NJ 07306-5943
Tel (201) 761-6000 *Founded/Ownrshp* 1872
Sales 108.9MM *EMP* 800
Accts Withumsmithbrown Pc Jersey Ci
SIC 8221 University
Pr: Eugene J Cornacchia
Ofcr: Daryl Levy
Assoc VP: Carla Tharp
**Prin:* Judy Hanley
Ex Dir: Nicholas A Chiaravalloti
Off Mgr: Louise Newman
CIO: Dale Hochstein
Netwrk Eng: Al-Rabb Lewis
Sfty Mgr: Arthur Youmans
Snr Mgr: Sharon Morrissey

ST PETERSBURG COLLEGE
See BOARD OF TRUSTEES ST PETERSBURG COLLEGE

ST. PETERSBURG GENERAL HOSP
See GALEN OF FLORIDA INC

D-U-N-S 11-829-4891 IMP
ST PRODUCTS LLC
SMALL TUBE PRODUCTS
200 Oliphant Dr, Duncansville, PA 16635
Tel (814) 693-6000 *Founded/Ownrshp* 2008
Sales 90.6MM^E *EMP* 200
SIC 3351 Copper pipe
CEO: Stephen L Drew
COO: Ned Oliphant
CFO: Jay Zimmerman
Ql Cn Mgr: James Barroner
Manager: Small Tube

D-U-N-S 03-736-5780
ST REGIS MOHAWK EDUCATION AND COMMUNITY FUND INC
ST REGIS MOHAWK TRIBE
412 State Route 37, Hogansburg, NY 13655-3109
Tel (518) 358-2272 *Founded/Ownrshp* 1890
Sales 46.2MM^E *EMP* 1,400
SIC 7929 Entertainment service
Ex Dir: Dawn Thompson
Exec: Debbie Francis
**Ex Dir:* Tsiorasa Barreiro
Ex Dir: Laura George
Genl Mgr: Harry Cook

ST REGIS MOHAWK TRIBE
See ST REGIS MOHAWK EDUCATION AND COMMUNITY FUND INC

ST REGIS RESORT MONARCH BEACH
See CPH MONARCH HOTEL LLC

ST REGIS SCHOOL
See ARCHDIOCESE OF DETROIT ED OFF

D-U-N-S 05-416-3464
ST RITAS MEDICAL CENTER (OH)
PUTNAM CNTY AMBLATORY CARE CTR
(*Suby of* MERCY HEALTH) ★
730 W Market St, Lima, OH 45801-4667
Tel (419) 227-3361 *Founded/Ownrshp* 1918
Sales 448.4MM *EMP* 2,850
SIC 8062 7352 General medical & surgical hospitals; Medical equipment rental
Ch Bd: Steve Walter
* *CFO:* John Renner
Doctor: Kenneth E Patick MD

ST ROSE HOSPITAL
See HAYWARD SISTERS HOSPITAL

D-U-N-S 96-353-0212
ST ROSE HOSPITAL
(*Suby of* ALECTO HEALTHCARE SERVICES LLC) ★
27200 Calaroga Ave, Hayward, CA 94545-4383
Tel (510) 264-4000 *Founded/Ownrshp* 1955
Sales 99.4MM *EMP* 1^E
SIC 8062 General medical & surgical hospitals
Pr: Lex Reddy
* *CEO:* Mak Nakayama
* *CFO:* Roger Krissman
* *Ex Dir:* Aman Dhuper

ST TAMMANY PARISH HOSPITAL
See SAINT TAMMANY PARISH HOSPITAL SERVICE DISTRICT 1

D-U-N-S 07-262-9777
ST TAMMANY PARISH HOSPITAL SERVICE DISTRICT 2
SLIDELL MEMORIAL HOSPITAL
1001 Gause Blvd, Slidell, LA 70458-2939
Tel (985) 280-2200 *Founded/Ownrshp* 1959
Sales 133.2MM *EMP* 1,200^E
SIC 8062 General medical & surgical hospitals
Pr: Robert Hawley
V Ch: Diego Espaillat
* *Pr:* Diana Clavin
* *CFO:* William Davis
Dir Lab: Michelle Bond
Dir IT: Holly Sanchez
Opers Mgr: Tom Cooks
Ansthlgy: Melvin A Ferlita
Anstlgy: Darren P Ruiz
Doctor: Elizabeth Teague

D-U-N-S 07-980-2910
ST TAMMANY PARISH PUBLIC SCHOOL SYSTEM
321 N Theard St, Covington, LA 70433-2835
Tel (985) 892-2276 *Founded/Ownrshp* 2015
Sales 97.0MM^E *EMP* 4,400^E
SIC 8211 Public elementary & secondary schools

D-U-N-S 07-869-5871
ST THERESE HOME INC (MN)
8000 Bass Lake Rd, Minneapolis, MN 55428-3118
Tel (763) 531-5000 *Founded/Ownrshp* 1968
Sales 37.5MM *EMP* 1,050
Accts Cliftonlarsonallen Llp Minnea
SIC 8051 Convalescent home with continuous nursing care
CEO: Barbara Rode
* *CFO:* Mike Warden
Comm Dir: Abby Dehmer
Ex Dir: Kym Fisher
Dir IT: Dave Bruess

D-U-N-S 05-525-2597
ST THOMAS HOSPITAL
4220 Harding Pike, Nashville, TN 37205-2095
Tel (615) 222-2111 *Founded/Ownrshp* 1898
Sales 405.7MM *EMP* 4,690
SIC 8062

D-U-N-S 07-890-4810
ST VINCENT ANDERSON REGIONAL HOSPITAL INC
SAINT JOHN'S MEDICAL SUPPLIES
(*Suby of* ST VINCENT HEALTH INC) ★
2015 Jackson St, Anderson, IN 46016-4337
Tel (765) 649-2511 *Founded/Ownrshp* 2013
Sales 141.9MM *EMP* 145^E
SIC 8062 5047

D-U-N-S 03-035-3704
ST VINCENT CARMEL HOSPITAL
(*Suby of* ASCENSION HEALTH ALLIANCE) ★
13500 N Meridian St, Carmel, IN 46032-1456
Tel (317) 582-7000 *Founded/Ownrshp* 2011
Sales 237.8MM *EMP* 72^E
Accts Deloitte Tax Lp Indianapolis
SIC 8093 Rehabilitation center, outpatient treatment
Pr: Barbara Carter
VP: Jennifer Fry
VP: Gwynn Perlich

D-U-N-S 15-118-1174
ST VINCENT CHARITY MEDICAL CENTER
2351 E 22nd St, Cleveland, OH 44115-3111
Tel (216) 861-6200 *Founded/Ownrshp* 1926
Sales 144.0MM *EMP* 974
SIC 8062 General medical & surgical hospitals
Ch Bd: Melvin G Pye Jr
* *Pr:* David F Perse MD
COO: Ross Joan
* *COO:* Joan Ross
* *CFO:* Patrick McMahon
* *CFO:* John Rusnaczyk
* *Treas:* Jeffery J Weaver
VP: Christina Walker
Adm Dir: Mario Markovic
Dir Sec: Ken Kozlowski
Dir IT: Loran Faulkner

D-U-N-S 14-545-1493
ST VINCENT HEALTH INC
(*Suby of* ASCENSION HEALTH) ★
10330 N Meridian St, Indianapolis, IN 46290-1024
Tel (317) 338-2345 *Founded/Ownrshp* 1998
Sales 219.9MM *EMP* 5^E
Accts Deloitte Tax Lp Indianapolis
SIC 8011 Health maintenance organization
CEO: Jonathan S Nalli
Dir Vol: Beth Dragoo
* *CEO:* Jonathan Nalli
CFO: Donald Apple
* *CFO:* Cheryl Harmon
* *CFO:* Fogel Richard I
Sr VP: Jean Meyer
Sr VP: Michael Wiemann
VP: Laura Cook
VP: Julie Embry
Dir Lab: Tamela Sample

D-U-N-S 06-767-8417
ST VINCENT HEALTH SERVICES INC
(*Suby of* CHI) ★
2 Saint Vincent Cir, Little Rock, AR 72205-5423
Tel (501) 552-2620 *Founded/Ownrshp* 1985, 1888
Sales 224.9MM^E *EMP* 3,640
SIC 8062 8099 General medical & surgical hospitals; Health screening service
* *Pr:* Steve Mansfield
* *CEO:* Ken D Haynes
* *CFO:* Pam Stoyanoff
* *Sec:* Rick Canady
* *VP:* John Hutton
Dir Rad: Ken Goad
Dir Rx: Jamie Dennis
Adm Dir: Julie Carpenter
Adm Dir: Susan Hapner
Ex Dir: Dawn Kregel
Ex Dir: Bryan Williams

ST. VINCENT HEALTH SYSTEM
See ST VINCENT INFIRMARY MEDICAL CENTER

D-U-N-S 04-593-4510
ST VINCENT HEALTHCARE (MT)
SISTERS OF CHARITY OF LEAVE
(*Suby of* SCL HEALTH SYSTEM) ★
1233 N 30th St, Billings, MT 59101-0127
Tel (406) 657-7000 *Founded/Ownrshp* 1896, 1972
Sales 439.4MM *EMP* 1,800
SIC 8062 General medical & surgical hospitals
Pr: Steve Loveless
* *COO:* Jack Bell
CFO: Ron Oldfield
VP: Steve Ballock
Dir IT: Cindy L Aprn
Mtls Dir: Jeff Morganflash
Psych: David Gumm
Doctor: Arnold R Christopher
Doctor: Joan L Huffman
Doctor: Patricia Lahaie
Doctor: Mark D Morasch

D-U-N-S 12-100-1718
ST VINCENT HEART CENTER OF INDIANA LLC
10580 N Meridian St, Indianapolis, IN 46290-1028
Tel (317) 583-5000 *Founded/Ownrshp* 2002
Sales 137.3MM *EMP* 496
SIC 8069 Specialty hospitals, except psychiatric
Pr: Blake Dye
* *COO:* Michael Schroyer
* *CFO:* Becky Jacobson
CFO: Al Mansfield
* *VP:* Jane Richardson
Exec: Edward Miller
Exec: Shelly Skinner
Dir Lab: Janet Gafkjen
Dir Env Sv: Luiz Dos Santos
CIO: Roger Strange
IT Man: Jason Hermann

ST VINCENT HOME
See ROMAN CATHOLIC DIOCESE OF FALL RIVER OFFICE OF AIDS MINISTR

D-U-N-S 06-942-1618
ST VINCENT HOSPITAL (NM)
CHRISTUS SAINT VINCENT
455 Saint Michaels Dr, Santa Fe, NM 87505-7663
Tel (505) 983-3361 *Founded/Ownrshp* 1865
Sales 374.3MM *EMP* 2,000
SIC 8062 General medical & surgical hospitals
CEO: Bruce Tassin
* *Pr:* Alex Valdez
* *COO:* Jason Adams
* *CFO:* Bob Moon
Ofcr: Martha Payne
* *VP:* Kathy Armijo Etre
* *VP:* Lillian Montoya
Ex Dir: Jan Goodwin
Off Mgr: Greta Graves
Off Mgr: Karen Lewis
Off Mgr: Ceila Lucero

D-U-N-S 07-203-5603 IMP
ST VINCENT HOSPITAL AND HEALTH CARE CENTER INC
ST VINCENT STRESS CENTER
2001 W 86th St Ste 200, Indianapolis, IN 46260-1902
Tel (317) 338-7000 *Founded/Ownrshp* 1881
Sales 1.1MMM^E *EMP* 5,500^E
Accts Deloitte Tax Lp Indianapolis
SIC 8062 General medical & surgical hospitals
CEO: Joel F D
* *Ch Bd:* Al Smith
* *Pr:* Kyle Defur
* *COO:* Darcey Burthay
* *CFO:* Tom Cook
VP: Joseph Murdock
VP: Nancy J Pitcock
Assoc Dir: Steve Knaus
Ex Dir: Loraine M Brown
Ex Dir: Melanie Holt
Ex Dir: Charles L Jeffras

ST. VINCENT HOSPITAL AND MEDIA
See MERCY HEALTH ST VINCENT MED LLC

D-U-N-S 07-477-6592
ST VINCENT HOSPITAL OF HOSPITAL SISTERS OF THIRD ORDER OF S
SAINT VINCENT HOSPITAL
835 S Van Buren St, Green Bay, WI 54301-3575
Tel (920) 433-0111 *Founded/Ownrshp* 1890
Sales 480.3MM *EMP* 2,360^E
Accts Crowe Horwath Llp Chicago Il
SIC 8062 8011 General medical & surgical hospitals; Offices & clinics of medical doctors
Ch Bd: Sr Mary Beth Culnan
* *CEO:* Theresa Shuck
* *VP:* Joseph J Neidenbach
Dir Rad: Gary Rogaczewski
Genl Mgr: Roger Breitrick
IT Man: Kate Umentum
Doctor: Sally Schlise
Doctor: Jane Seidl

D-U-N-S 12-787-8577
ST VINCENT INFIRMARY MEDICAL CENTER
ST. VINCENT HEALTH SYSTEM
(*Suby of* CHI) ★
2 Saint Vincent Cir, Little Rock, AR 72205-5423
Tel (501) 552-3000 *Founded/Ownrshp* 1998
Sales 358.8MM *EMP* 2,824
SIC 8011 Medical centers
CEO: Peter Banko
VP: Bubba Arnold
Dir Env Sv: Felix Addison
Adm Dir: Kevin Johnson
Off Mgr: Dana Chaney
Off Mgr: Mary Cotton
Dir IT: Mike Seastrom
VP Opers: Patrick McCruden
Doctor: Beverly Derrickson
Doctor: Mary B McDonald
Doctor: Alan Winkler

D-U-N-S 07-230-1195
ST VINCENT MEDICAL CENTER (CA)
(*Suby of* VERITY HEALTH SYSTEM OF CALIFORNIA INC) ★
2131 W 3rd St, Los Angeles, CA 90057-1901
Tel (213) 484-7111 *Founded/Ownrshp* 1856
Sales 237.2MM *EMP* 1,200
Accts Grant Thornton Llp San Franci
SIC 8062 General medical & surgical hospitals
Chf Rad: Michael McMongle
* *CFO:* Michael Garko
Chf Nrs Of: Joan Simon
Chf Nrs Of: Joan Simons
CIO: Dick Hutsell
Pathlgst: Hongying Tan
Pharmcst: Christrine Culver

D-U-N-S 07-976-7727
ST VINCENT MEDICAL CENTER EAST PAVILION LOBBY GIFT SHOP
PROVIDENCE ST VINCENT MEDICAL
9205 Sw Barnes Rd, Portland, OR 97225-6603
Tel (503) 216-2100 *Founded/Ownrshp* 2015
Sales 828.5MM *EMP* 135^E
SIC 8062 General medical & surgical hospitals
Ansthlgy: Mark P Haubrich
Ansthlgy: Stephen C Holmes
Ansthlgy: Matthew M Kellogg
Ansthlgy: Frank E Palmrose
Anstlgy: Wenonah L Usher

ST VINCENT MEDICAL GROUP
See CARE GROUP LLC

ST VINCENT STRESS CENTER
See ST VINCENT HOSPITAL AND HEALTH CARE CENTER INC

D-U-N-S 07-211-2618
ST VINCENTS BIRMINGHAM
ST. VINCENT'S HEALTH SYSTEM
810 Saint Vincents Dr, Birmingham, AL 35205-1601
Tel (205) 939-7000 *Founded/Ownrshp* 1898
Sales 382.0MM *EMP* 1,478
Accts Deloitte Tax Llp Cincinnati
SIC 8062 General medical & surgical hospitals
Pr: Curtis James
Ofcr: Eddie Kilgore
Ex VP: Doug Hughes
VP: Elizabeth Moore
VP: Cindy Williams
MIS Dir: Jacqueline Kennedy
Sfty Dirs: Donna Keith
Mktg Dir: Phillip Greene
Doctor: James Bailey
Doctor: Lauren Savage

D-U-N-S 11-837-1525
ST VINCENTS DEVELOPMENT INC
2800 Main St, Bridgeport, CT 06606-4201
Tel (203) 576-6000 *Founded/Ownrshp* 1984
Sales 72.6MM^E *EMP* 3,300
Accts Ernst & Young Llp Hartford C
SIC 8399 6531 Health systems agency; Real estate agents & managers
Pr: Susan Davis
* *Pr:* Stuart G Marcus
* *CFO:* John Gleckler
VP: Margaret Hardy

D-U-N-S 07-764-0100
ST VINCENTS EAST
(*Suby of* ST VINCENTS HEALTH SYSTEM) ★
50 Medical Park Dr E, Birmingham, AL 35235-3401
Tel (205) 838-3000 *Founded/Ownrshp* 2007
Sales 203.3MM *EMP* 1,550
Accts Deloitte Tax Llp Cincinnati
SIC 8062 8011 General medical & surgical hospitals; Offices & clinics of medical doctors
CEO: George McGowan
* *Pr:* Robert C Chapman
COO: Kim Shrewsbury
* *CFO:* Brian Carson
Ofcr: Jennifer Philpot
VP: Tony Byram
VP: Jennifer Kingry
* *VP:* Stephen Marino
* *VP:* B J Scharath
VP: Susan Sellers
Mfg Mgr: Larry Simpson

D-U-N-S 13-174-4419
ST VINCENTS HEALTH SERVICES CORP
2800 Main St, Bridgeport, CT 06606-4201
Tel (203) 576-6000 *Founded/Ownrshp* 1984
Sales 4.0MM *EMP* 2,000
SIC 8741 8062 Hospital management; Nursing & personal care facility management; Hospital, medical school affiliated with nursing & residency
Pr: William Riordan
* *Ch Bd:* Sister Margaret John Kelly
* *CFO:* John M Ahle
* *Treas:* George Taylor
* *V Ch Bd:* Josephe Maloney
Sr VP: Kerry Eaton
VP: Dale Danowski
Exec: Mike Summerer
Dir Risk M: Pamela Miller
Dir Lab: Jean Cayer
Dir Sec: Joe Laveneziana

ST. VINCENT'S HEALTH SYSTEM
See ST VINCENTS BIRMINGHAM

D-U-N-S 80-793-8506
ST VINCENTS HEALTH SYSTEM
(*Suby of* ASCENSION HEALTH) ★
810 Saint Vincents Dr, Birmingham, AL 35205-1601
Tel (205) 939-7000 *Founded/Ownrshp* 1986
Sales 113.9MM *EMP* 4,620
Accts Deloitte Tax Llp Cincinnati
SIC 8062 General medical & surgical hospitals
CEO: John O'Neil
V Ch: Robert Lewis
* *COO:* Neeysa Biddle
* *CFO:* Jeff Rooney
Ofcr: Eddie Kilgore
* *Ofcr:* Nan Priest
Ofcr: Dr Mark Williams
Sr VP: Wayne Carmello-Harper
Sr VP: Tim Stettheimer
Sr VP: Sister Dinah White
VP: Andrew Gnann Fache
* *VP:* Doug Hughes
VP: Nancy Lewis

D-U-N-S 83-702-9636
ST VINCENTS HEALTH SYSTEM INC
ST. VINCENT'S MEDICAL CENTER
4203 Belfort Rd Ste 155, Jacksonville, FL 32216-1408
Tel (904) 308-7300 *Founded/Ownrshp* 1995
Sales 274.8MM^E *EMP* 4,000
SIC 8741 Hospital management; Nursing & personal care facility management
CEO: Donnie Romine
Chf Rad: Michael Donohue
Chf Rad: Terence Hughes
* *Pr:* Jane R Lanier
COO: Gene Miyamoto
CFO: Dan Curran
CFO: Kim Hodgkinson
* *Ch:* David Kulik
* *VP:* Fernando Acosta-Rua
* *VP:* Debbie Gottlieb
Dir Risk M: Derek Merrill
Dir Lab: Lynette Chakkaphak
Dir Rx: Adam Bauman

ST. VINCENT'S MEDICAL CENTER
See FAIRFIELD COUNTRY RADIOOLOGY A

ST. VINCENT'S MEDICAL CENTER
See ST VINCENTS HEALTH SYSTEM INC

D-U-N-S 07-214-7259
ST VINCENTS MEDICAL CENTER FOUNDATION INC
ST. VNCNTS MLTISPECIALTY GROUP
2800 Main St, Bridgeport, CT 06606-4201
Tel (203) 576-6000 *Founded/Ownrshp* 1984
Sales 5.8MM *EMP* 1,900^E
Accts Deloitte Tax Llp Cincinnati
SIC 8062 Hospital, affiliated with AMA residency
Pr: William Riordan
Sr VP: Dianne Auger
Sr VP: Vincent Russello
VP: Michael C Bisciglia
VP: Jody Gerard
VP: Margaret Hardy
VP: Bill Hoey
VP: Stuart Marcus
VP: Brandon Schwarz
* *VP:* John Treleaven
Dir Risk M: Pamela Miller
Dir Case M: Karen Nefornes
Dir Lab: Jean Cayer
Dir Rx: Karen Sinto

D-U-N-S 07-832-0207
ST VINCENTS MEDICAL CENTER INC
SAINT VINCENT'S MEDICAL CENTER
4205 Belfort Rd Ste 4030, Jacksonville, FL 32216-1475
Tel (904) 308-7300 *Founded/Ownrshp* 1969
Sales 452.3MM *EMP* 3,535^E
Accts Deloitte Tax Llp Cincinnati
SIC 8062 General medical & surgical hospitals
Pr: Moody Chisolm
* *Pr:* Blain Claypool
* *COO:* Gene Miyamoto
* *COO:* Donnie Romine
* *VP:* Ann Carey
* *VP:* Sean Fitzpatrick
VP: Ken Perry
Exec: Jim Towler
Dir Lab: Wilma Fryer
Dir QC: Betsy Miller
Dir IT: Brian Leonard

ST. VNCNTS MLTISPECIALTY GROUP
See ST VINCENTS MEDICAL CENTER FOUNDATION INC

D-U-N-S 01-062-6331
ST VRAIN VALLEY SCHOOL DISTRICT RE-1J
ST. VRAIN VALLEY SCHOOLS
395 S Pratt Pkwy, Longmont, CO 80501-6436
Tel (303) 776-6200 *Founded/Ownrshp* 1961
Sales 286.5MM *EMP* 3,500

Accts Rubinbrown Llp Denver Co
SIC 8211 Public elementary & secondary schools; Public elementary school; Public junior high school; Public senior high school
Prin: Don Hedad
Treas: Sutyak Peter
Dir: Scott Toillion
Genl Mgr: Regina Renaldi
Genl Mgr: Terry Schueler
IT Man: Daniel Brauch
IT Man: Gregory Fieth
Web Dev: Jody Leffel
Schl Brd P: John Creighton
Schl Brd P: Bob Smith
Teacher Pr: Dina Perfetti-Deany

ST. VRAIN VALLEY SCHOOLS
See ST VRAIN VALLEY SCHOOL DISTRICT RE-1J

D-U-N-S 80-683-2457
STA-HOME HEALTH & HOSPICE INC
406 Briarwood Dr Ste 200, Jackson, MS 39206-3060
Tel (601) 956-5100 *Founded/Ownrshp* 1976
Sales 86.0MM *EMP* 968
SIC 8082 Visiting nurse service
CEO: Vincent Carracci

D-U-N-S 00-607-5022 IMP/EXP
STA-RITE INDUSTRIES LLC (WI)
(*Suby of* FLOW CONTROL US HOLDING CORP) ★
293 S Wright St, Delavan, WI 53115-2008
Tel (888) 782-7483 *Founded/Ownrshp* 2011
Sales 276.2MM^E *EMP* 1,182
SIC 3561 5084 5251 Pumps & pumping equipment; Water pumps (industrial); Pumps & pumping equipment
CFO: David Harrison
VP: Thomas Schuman
Board of Directors: Paul Donovan, Kristine Rappe

STAAB MANAGEMENT CO
See KWS INC

D-U-N-S 00-436-2355
STABILIS CAPITAL MANAGEMENT LP
767 5th Ave Fl 12, New York, NY 10153-0023
Tel (212) 256-8970 *Founded/Ownrshp* 2010
Sales 125.2MM^E *EMP* 572^E
SIC 6211 Investment firm, general brokerage
Prin: Salman Khan
CFO: Suzette Del Giudice
Mng Dir: Juan Robayo
Genl Couns: Karen Duong
Genl Couns: Joseph Tuso

D-U-N-S 06-739-2746 IMP/EXP
STABILUS INC
STABILUS STUS
(*Suby of* STABLE HOLDCO INC) ★
1201 Tulip Dr, Gastonia, NC 28052-1842
Tel (704) 865-7444 *Founded/Ownrshp* 2001
Sales 129.9MM^E *EMP* 400^E
SIC 3493 Steel springs, except wire
Pr: Anthony Haba
VP: Tony Haba
**VP:* Craig Pospiech
QA Dir: Alex Gurowski
**VP Mfg:* Tom Napoli
Prd Mgr: Edward Twist
Ql Cn Mgr: Jim Tallent
Sales Exec: Cindy Nichols
Natl Sales: Greg Sturwold

STABILUS STUS
See STABILUS INC

D-U-N-S 07-979-4675
STABLE HOLDCO INC
(*Suby of* STABLE BETEILIGUNGS GMBH)
1201 Tulip Dr, Gastonia, NC 28052-1842
Tel (704) 866-7140 *Founded/Ownrshp* 2008
Sales 129.9MM^E *EMP* 401
SIC 3493 Steel springs, except wire
Pr: Ansgar Kroetz

D-U-N-S 00-300-5220
STABLER COMPANIES INC
(*Suby of* BUFFALO CRUSHED STONE) ★
635 Lucknow Rd, Harrisburg, PA 17110-1635
Tel (717) 236-9307 *Founded/Ownrshp* 1955
Sales 183.6MM^E *EMP* 900^E
SIC 5032 3089 7359 3531 1611 3648 Paving mixtures; Concrete & cinder block; Stone, crushed or broken; Stock shapes, plastic; Work zone traffic equipment (flags, cones, barrels, etc.); Road construction & maintenance machinery; Highway & street paving contractor; Resurfacing contractor; Lighting equipment
Pr: James Van Buren
**CFO:* Thomas M Minori

D-U-N-S 62-182-3827 IMP
STACI CORP
VEXOS
(*Suby of* CLP ST INC) ★
110 Commerce Dr, Lagrange, OH 44050-9491
Tel (440) 355-5102 *Founded/Ownrshp* 2014
Sales 169.9MM^E *EMP* 569
SIC 3672 Circuit boards, television & radio printed
CEO: David M Buckley
**Pr:* Jim Thirkill
Sr VP: Greg Hebson
VP: Keith Mallery
VP: Joe Shero
IT Man: Franco Gutierrez
IT Man: Isaac Velez

D-U-N-S 03-518-9984
STACY AND WITBECK INC
2800 Harbor Bay Pkwy, Alameda, CA 94502-3040
Tel (510) 748-1870 *Founded/Ownrshp* 1981
Sales 162.6MM^E *EMP* 350
SIC 1629

D-U-N-S 80-185-9877
STAFF FORCE INC
STAFF FORCE PERSONNEL SERVICES
419 Mason Park Blvd, Katy, TX 77450-6187
Tel (281) 492-6044 *Founded/Ownrshp* 1989
Sales 104.8MM *EMP* 20,000
SIC 7363 Temporary help service
Pr: David L Howard
COO: Russell Potocki
**CFO:* Glenn T Van Dusen
**Ex VP:* Arthur L Busby
**VP:* Charles F Nowlin Jr
Exec: Patricia Nesbit
Brnch Mgr: David Martinez
Brnch Mgr: Manuel Peralta
VP Mktg: Hjalmer Danielson
Sls Dir: Rebecca Busby
Mktg Mgr: Mahn Tun

STAFF FORCE PERSONNEL SERVICES
See STAFF FORCE INC

D-U-N-S 00-949-6057
STAFF HUNTERS
1 Nh Ave Ste 125, Portsmouth, NH 03801-2907
Tel (603) 766-4909 *Founded/Ownrshp* 2007
Sales 2.5MM^E *EMP* 3,015^E
SIC 7361 Employment agencies
Prin: Anthony Stephen Manfredi
Exec: Joshua Woods

D-U-N-S 36-247-2789
STAFF LEASING OF CENTRAL NEW YORK INC
149 Northern Concourse # 3, Syracuse, NY 13212-4055
Tel (315) 641-3600 *Founded/Ownrshp* 1989
Sales 57.0MM^E *EMP* 2,500
SIC 7363 8721 Employee leasing service; Payroll accounting service
Pr: Thomas J Boell
VP: William Mullis
VP: James Roberts
**VP:* Mark C Roberts

D-U-N-S 07-853-7275
■ STAFF MANAGEMENT SOLUTIONS LLC
PEOPLESCOUT
(*Suby of* TRUEBLUE INC) ★
860 W Evergreen Ave, Chicago, IL 60642-2634
Tel (312) 915-0900 *Founded/Ownrshp* 1988
Sales 381.8MM^E *EMP* 3,850^E
SIC 7363 8741 Employee leasing service; Temporary help service; Management services
**Pr:* Joan Davison
**COO:* Jason Walker
VP: Jerry Grant
VP: Anne Osty
VP: Marcie Smith
VP: Janice Weiner
Mng Dir: Joe Solisbarba
Prgrm Mgr: Rebecca Chapman
Prgrm Mgr: Autumn Stockton
CIO: Dawn Gildenmeister
VP Opers: Roxanne Ramoutar

D-U-N-S 36-092-9236
STAFF ONE INC
8111 Lndn B Jnsn Fwy 13 Ste 1350, Dallas, TX 75251
Tel (214) 461-1140 *Founded/Ownrshp* 2008
Sales 72.5MM^E *EMP* 4,200
Accts Adami Lindsey & Company Llp
SIC 7363 Professional membership organizations
CEO: Robert Befidi Jr
**Pr:* Mark Sinatra
CFO: Kevin McGahey
Ex VP: Marty Scirratt
**VP:* Tj Carter
Dir Bus: Donna Meek
Sales Asso: Ashley Mullican

D-U-N-S 61-982-5722
STAFF PRO INC
15272 Jason Cir, Huntington Beach, CA 92649-1238
Tel (714) 230-7200 *Founded/Ownrshp* 1987
Sales 81.2MM^E *EMP* 2,200
SIC 7382 8741 Security systems services; Management services
CEO: Cory Meredith
CFO: Pete Wachob
VP: Michael Absher

D-U-N-S 14-855-7742
STAFFCHEX INC
790 The City Dr S Ste 180, Orange, CA 92868-4941
Tel (714) 912-7500 *Founded/Ownrshp* 2004
Sales 66.2MM^E *EMP* 2,000
SIC 7361 Employment agencies
CEO: Ruben Garza
**COO:* Peter Lugo
**CFO:* Patrick Brennen

D-U-N-S 07-882-8534
▲ STAFFING 360 SOLUTIONS INC
641 Lexington Ave, New York, NY 10022-4503
Tel (646) 507-5710 *Founded/Ownrshp* 2009
Sales 165.5MM *EMP* 4,180
Tkr Sym STAF *Exch* NAS
SIC 7363 Help supply services; Labor resource services; Manpower pools
Pr: Matthew Briand
**Ch Bd:* Brendan Flood
CFO: David Faiman

D-U-N-S 84-158-4647
STAFFING CONCEPTS INTERNATIONAL OF GEORGIA INC
2435 Tech Center Pkwy, Lawrenceville, GA 30043-1311
Tel (770) 623-9143 *Founded/Ownrshp* 1986
Sales 37.9MM^E *EMP* 2,500
SIC 7363 Help supply services
Pr: Henry C Hardin III

D-U-N-S 82-773-2905
STAFFING SOLUTIONS OF CENTRAL TEXAS INC
PROLOGISTIX
(*Suby of* PROLOGISTIX) ★
1040 Crown Pointe Pkwy, Atlanta, GA 30338-6908
Tel (770) 671-1900 *Founded/Ownrshp* 2002
Sales 35.5MM^E *EMP* 3,185^E
SIC 7363 Temporary help service
Pr: Thomas A Bickes
CFO: Shawn W Poole
Exec: Merri Hamrick
Exec: Julie Young
Opers Mgr: Laura Geier

D-U-N-S 12-506-6089
STAFFING SOLUTIONS SOUTHWEST INC
PROLOGISTIX
(*Suby of* EB SUPPLY CHAIN HOLDINGS LLC)
1040 Crown Pointe Pkwy, Atlanta, GA 30338-6908
Tel (678) 443-4200 *Founded/Ownrshp* 2000
Sales 93.4MM^E *EMP* 16,154^E
SIC 7361 7363 Labor contractors (employment agency); Help supply services
Pr: Thomas A Bickes
CFO: Shawn W Poole
Board of Directors: Chip Grissom Vp, Lisa Powell Vp, Sharon Greenbaum Assistan, Fred Herbert Vp, John Rosenbaum Vp, Michael Baer Vp, Keith Kislow Vp, Paul Seymour Vp, Ken Christensen Vp, Dan Lieblich Vp, Carolyn Silvey Vp, Jim Cleary Vp, Chris Loope Vp, Paul Sorensen Vp, Lisa Cooney Vp, Mark McComb Vp, Jeannie Davis Vp, Theresa McDannald Vp, Brian Devine Vp, Steve Mills Vp, Gunnar Gooding Vp, Michael Mitchell Vp, Steven Grimaud Vp, Melissa Porter Vp

STAFFIRST
See WORKERS TEMPORARY STAFFING INC

D-U-N-S 16-916-3560
STAFFMARK HOLDINGS INC
(*Suby of* RECRUIT HOLDINGS CO.,LTD.)
201 E 4th St Ste 800, Cincinnati, OH 45202-4248
Tel (513) 651-1111 *Founded/Ownrshp* 2001
Sales 149.8MM^E *EMP* 800
SIC 7361 7363 Placement agencies; Executive placement; Labor resource services; Temporary help service
CEO: Lesa J Francis
**COO:* Koji Sakamoto
**CFO:* William E Aglinsky
**Ch:* Hitoshi Motohara
Ofcr: Mary B Lucas
**Ex VP:* Kathryn S Bernard
Sr VP: Suzanne M Perry
Mng Dir: Anthony Fanzo

D-U-N-S 78-990-4765
STAFFMARK INVESTMENT LLC
(*Suby of* STAFFMARK HOLDINGS INC) ★
201 E 4th St Ste 800, Cincinnati, OH 45202-4248
Tel (513) 651-3600 *Founded/Ownrshp* 2008
Sales 99.4MM^E *EMP* 800
SIC 7361 Employment agencies
**Pr:* Clay Bullock
**CEO:* W David Bartholomew
**VP:* Kenny Berkemeyer
**VP:* Sally Berrier
Area Mgr: Heather Healy
**Genl Couns:* Abraham Bogoslavsky
Snr Mgr: Frances Burke

D-U-N-S 07-830-0332
STAFFORD COUNTY PUBLIC SCHOOL BOARD
31 Stafford Ave, Stafford, VA 22554-7246
Tel (540) 658-6000 *Founded/Ownrshp* 1865
Sales 83.6MM^E *EMP* 4,000
SIC 8211 School board
Ch Bd: Nanette Kidbys

D-U-N-S 07-843-4447
STAFFORD COUNTY PUBLIC SCHOOLS
31 Stafford Ave, Stafford, VA 22554-7246
Tel (540) 658-6000 *Founded/Ownrshp* 2012
Sales 144.8MM^E *EMP* 4,749^E
SIC 8211 Public elementary & secondary schools
Dir Sec: Gregory Martin
MIS Dir: Jay Cooke
Teacher Pr: Rick L Fitzgerald
Instr Medi: Karen Duffy
HC Dir: Barbara Platt

D-U-N-S 00-980-7942 EXP
STAFFORD-SMITH INC
KIRCHMAN BROTHERS
3414 S Burdick St, Kalamazoo, MI 49001-4888
Tel (269) 343-1240 *Founded/Ownrshp* 1940
Sales 152.7MM^E *EMP* 140
SIC 5046 5078 Commercial cooking & food service equipment; Commercial refrigeration equipment
Pr: David J Stafford
**VP:* Kyle Dekema
**VP:* Richard Harrison
Snr Mgr: Stafford Smith

D-U-N-S 96-520-3586
▲ STAG INDUSTRIAL INC
1 Federal St Fl 23, Boston, MA 02110-2031
Tel (617) 574-4777 *Founded/Ownrshp* 2010
Sales 218.6MM *EMP* 54^E
Accts Pricewaterhousecoopers Llp Bo
Tkr Sym STAG *Exch* NYS
SIC 6798 Real estate investment trusts
Ch Bd: Benjamin S Butcher
COO: Stephen C Mecke
CFO: William R Crooker
Ex VP: Peter S Fearey
Ex VP: David G King
Ex VP: Jeffrey M Sullivan
Board of Directors: Jeffrey D Furber, Larry T Guillemette, Francis X Jacoby III, Christopher P Marr, Hans S Weger

D-U-N-S 04-209-8681 IMP/EXP
STAG-PARKWAY INC (GA)
6320 Boat Rock Blvd Sw, Atlanta, GA 30336-2841
Tel (404) 349-7800 *Founded/Ownrshp* 1968, 2012
Sales 187.4MM^E *EMP* 320
Accts Deloitte & Touche Llp Atlant
SIC 5013 Trailer parts & accessories
Pr: Martin Street
**CFO:* Mick Becker
**Sr VP:* Bob Barra
**Sr VP:* Craig Mellor
**Sr VP:* Ken Russell
**Sr VP:* Tom Seath
**Sr VP:* John Spaulding

D-U-N-S 80-814-5536 IMP
▲ STAGE STORES INC
2425 West Loop S, Houston, TX 77027-4300
Tel (800) 579-2302 *Founded/Ownrshp* 1988
Sales 1.6MMM *EMP* 13,500^E
Accts Deloitte & Touche Llp Houston
Tkr Sym SSI *Exch* NYS
SIC 5651 5661 Family clothing stores; Shoe stores
Pr: Michael Glazer
**Ch Bd:* William J Montgoris
COO: Edward J Record
CFO: Oded Shein
Chf Mktg O: Steven P Lawrence
Chf Mktg O: Thorsten Weber
Ex VP: Steven L Hunter
Sr VP: Richard E Stasyszen
VP: Tim Duvic
VP: Regina Edwards
VP: Kim Hutton
VP: Todd McGuire
VP: Clark McNaught
VP: David Mosley
VP: Tim Moyer
VP: Don Stanley
VP: Sabrina Willingham
Exec: Natasha Dhuldhoya
Exec: Sue Howton
Dir: Greg Lurry
Board of Directors: Alan J Barocas, Elaine D Crowley, Diane M Ellis, Earl J Hesterberg, Lisa R Kranc, C Clayton Reasor, Ralph P Scozzafava

D-U-N-S 10-134-9285 IMP
STAHL (USA) INC
(*Suby of* STAHL HOLDINGS B.V.)
13 Corwin St, Peabody, MA 01960-5107
Tel (978) 531-0371 *Founded/Ownrshp* 2002
Sales 364.5MM^E *EMP* 36
SIC 2891 Adhesives & sealants
**Treas:* Ellen Joyce
**Sec:* Howard Farber
Ex VP: John Bouchard
Genl Mgr: Robert Mc Bride

D-U-N-S 00-712-3441 IMP
STAHL SPECIALTY CO (MO)
(*Suby of* LIGON INDUSTRIES LLC) ★
111 E Pacific St, Kingsville, MO 64061-2510
Tel (816) 597-3322 *Founded/Ownrshp* 1946, 2010
Sales 144.9MM^E *EMP* 450^E
SIC 5051 3544 3365 3567 3369 Foundry products; Forms (molds), for foundry & plastics working machinery; Aluminum foundries; Industrial furnaces & ovens; Nonferrous foundries
Pr: Jim Spaulding
MIS Dir: Jeff Elliott
MIS Mgr: Ken Mc Anich
Plnt Mgr: Clayton Bond
Plnt Mgr: Phil Frerking
Plnt Mgr: Walter Tuley
Ql Cn Mgr: George Waddle

D-U-N-S 78-784-6963 IMP/EXP
STAHLBUSH ISLAND FARMS INC
3122 Se Stahlbush Is, Corvallis, OR 97333-2709
Tel (541) 753-8942 *Founded/Ownrshp* 1985
Sales 168.7MM^E *EMP* 1,000
SIC 2037 0161 Vegetables, quick frozen & cold pack, excl. potato products; Vegetables & melons
Pr: William D Chambers
VP: Karla Bohr
**VP:* Karla S Chambers
Natl Sales: Chelsea Hartman

D-U-N-S 00-183-3086 IMP
STAINLESS SALES CORP
2301 W Windsor Ct Unit B, Addison, IL 60101-1462
Tel (773) 247-9060 *Founded/Ownrshp* 1946
Sales 116.0MM^E *EMP* 60
SIC 5051 Metals service centers & offices
Pr: Marilyn Kutzen
**Pr:* Brad Hite
CFO: Kurt Izydorek
Sls Dir: Polly Whitehouse
Manager: Jack Gallan
Board of Directors: Terry Newman

D-U-N-S 07-979-6019
STAINLESS STEEL ACQUISITION CO LLC
2615 E Highway 146, La Grange, KY 40031-9153
Tel (502) 805-1120 *Founded/Ownrshp* 2014
Sales 125.5MM *EMP* 30^E
SIC 4953 Recycling, waste materials

D-U-N-S 07-839-1735
STAINLESS STEEL MIDWEST LLC (KY)
ALLIED ALLOYS MIDWEST
(*Suby of* STAINLESS STEEL ACQUISITION CO LLC) ★
2615 E Highway 146, La Grange, KY 40031-9153
Tel (502) 805-1120 *Founded/Ownrshp* 2014
Sales 130.0MM *EMP* 20
SIC 5093 Nonferrous metals scrap
Pr: Steve Jones

D-U-N-S 02-494-5706
STAKER & PARSON COMPANIES (UT)
STAKER PAVING, JACK B PARSON
(*Suby of* OLDCASTLE MATERIALS GROUP) ★
2350 S 1900 W Ste 100, Ogden, UT 84401-3481
Tel (801) 298-7500 *Founded/Ownrshp* 2001
Sales 522.2MM^E *EMP* 777
SIC 1611 5032 3273 4212 2951 1771 General contractor, highway & street construction; Highway & street paving contractor; Asphalt mixture; Gravel; Ready-mixed concrete; Local trucking, without storage; Asphalt paving mixtures & blocks; Concrete work
CEO: Scott W Parson
**Sec:* Jared Hyde
**Ex VP:* John Parsons
**Ex VP:* Rocky Woodruff
VP: Chris Kinnersley

STAKER PAVING, JACK B PARSON
See STAKER & PARSON COMPANIES

D-U-N-S 60-120-7038 IMP/EXP
STALEY HOLDINGS INC
501 Silverside Rd Ste 55, Wilmington, DE 19809-1388
Tel (302) 793-0289 *Founded/Ownrshp* 2008
Sales NA *EMP* 2,100
SIC 2046

D-U-N-S 18-645-5093
STALEY INC
STALEY TECHNOLOGIES
8101 Fourche Rd, Little Rock, AR 72209-5567
Tel (501) 565-3006 *Founded/Ownrshp* 1986
Sales 98.8MM^E *EMP* 395
SIC 1731 Voice, data & video wiring contractor; Fiber optic cable installation
CEO: Brent Staley
* *Sr VP:* Gary G Ferrell
Mktg Mgr: Kelly Imhoff
Sls Mgr: Dan Christians
Snr PM: Bob Smith
Snr Mgr: Amy Pridgen

STALEY TECHNOLOGIES
See STALEY INC

D-U-N-S 83-240-5455
STALLION OILFIELD HOLDINGS LTD
950 Corbindale Rd Ste 300, Houston, TX 77024-2849
Tel (713) 528-5544 *Founded/Ownrshp* 2005
Sales 1.4MMM^E *EMP* 3,042^E
SIC 8999 Actuarial consultant
CEO: David C Mannon
* *Ex VP:* Hill Dishman
* *Ex VP:* David Schorlemer

D-U-N-S 14-144-5267
STALLION OILFIELD SERVICES LTD
(*Suby of* STALLION OILFIELD HOLDINGS LTD) ★
950 Corbindale Rd Ste 300, Houston, TX 77024-2849
Tel (713) 528-5544 *Founded/Ownrshp* 2002
Sales 1.4MMM^E *EMP* 3,000
SIC 1389 Oil field services
CEO: Craig Johnson
* *COO:* Hill Dishman
* *CFO:* David Schorlemer
* *VP:* Mike Moore
Opers Mgr: Justin Campbell
Opers Mgr: Chris Ingram

STAMART
See SERVICE OIL INC

D-U-N-S 88-478-4224
STAMFORD CAPITAL GROUP INC
1266 E Main St Ste 700r, Stamford, CT 06902-3507
Tel (800) 977-7837 *Founded/Ownrshp* 1994
Sales 79.0MM^E *EMP* 1,675
SIC 2741 6211 Guides: publishing only, not printed on site; Investment bankers
Pr: Patton Corrigan
* *VP:* Evan Tessler

D-U-N-S 60-232-3941
STAMFORD HEALTH SYSTEM INC
30 Shelburne Rd, Stamford, CT 06902-3628
Tel (203) 325-7000 *Founded/Ownrshp* 1983
Sales 6.6MM *EMP* 1,978^E
Accts Ernst & Young Us Llp Indianap
SIC 8741 Hospital management; Nursing & personal care facility management
Pr: Brian Grissler
COO: Ronald Turnbull
CFO: Dean Swindle
Sr VP: Darryl McCormick

D-U-N-S 06-986-2159
STAMFORD HOSPITAL
1 Hospital Plz, Stamford, CT 06902
Tel (203) 325-7000 *Founded/Ownrshp* 1989
Sales 493.6MM *EMP* 2,000
Accts Ernst & Young Llp New York N
SIC 8062 Hospital, AMA approved residency
Pr: Brian Grissler
* *Ex VP:* Kathleen Silard
Sr VP: Sharon Kiely
* *Sr VP:* Darryl McCormick
Sr VP: Chris Riendeau
Sr VP: Robert Scinto
Sr VP: David Smith
VP: Rohit Bhalla
VP: Ellen Komar
VP: Darren McCormick
VP: Andrew Snyder
VP: Steve Taylor
Exec: Sheila Smith
Dir Rad: James J McSweeney
Dir Rad: Frank A Msino
Dir Rx: Geoffrey Gittleson
Dir Env Sv: Jeffrey Wrigley

STAMOULES PRODUCE CO
See S STAMOULES INC

D-U-N-S 07-849-9136
STAMPED METAL AMERICAN RESEARCH TECHNOLOGY INC
SMART ALABAMA
(*Suby of* HYUNDAI MOTOR AMERICA) ★
121 Shin Young Dr, Luverne, AL 36049-6536
Tel (334) 296-5126 *Founded/Ownrshp* 2004
Sales 238.0MM *EMP* 7^E
Accts Pk Llp Opelika Alabama
SIC 3469 Stamping metal for the trade
CEO: Ho CA Kang
* *Pr:* Jong Cheol Kim

D-U-N-S 87-937-5590 IMP
STAMPEDE MEAT INC
7351 S 78th Ave, Bridgeview, IL 60455-1185
Tel (773) 376-4300 *Founded/Ownrshp* 2007
Sales 320.0MM *EMP* 1,100
SIC 2013 Prepared beef products from purchased beef; Prepared pork products from purchased pork
CEO: Brock Furlong
Pr: Bill Kulach
* *CFO:* Vito Giustino
* *Sr VP:* Raymond McKiernan
VP: John Cikowski
* *VP:* Dennis Gruber
VP: Krys Harbut
Exec: Bill Asleson
QA Dir: Elizabeth Fiecko
QA Dir: Adam Miller
Opers Mgr: Marty Cocorikis

D-U-N-S 79-953-3823 IMP
STAMPEDE PRESENTATION PRODUCTS INC
(*Suby of* MURCELL, INC.)
55 Woodridge Dr, Amherst, NY 14228-2221
Tel (716) 635-9474 *Founded/Ownrshp* 2004
Sales 156.1MM^E *EMP* 75
SIC 5065 Electronic parts & equipment; Video equipment, electronic
Ch Bd: Mark R Wilkins
* *Pr:* Kevin Kelly
* *VP:* Michael V Brylinski
VP: Craig Werynski
VP: Jeff Willis
Trfc Mgr: Michele Huffman
VP Mktg: Beth Clune
Sls Dir: Peter Hurley
Sls Dir: Chris Lubick
Manager: Bill Wood
Sls Mgr: Dan O'Brasky

D-U-N-S 80-599-5974 IMP
STAMPIN UP INC
12907 S 3600 W, Riverton, UT 84065-6972
Tel (801) 257-5400 *Founded/Ownrshp* 1998
Sales 122.9MM^E *EMP* 450
SIC 3953 Embossing seals & hand stamps; Postmark stamps, hand: rubber or metal
Pr: Shelli Gardner
* *Pr:* Richard Jutkins
* *CFO:* J Scott Nielsen
* *Treas:* Curtis Lamb
* *VP:* David Baugh
* *VP:* Amy Swartz
Dir Soc: Katie Robertson
Creative D: Sean Douglass
Creative D: Monica Livingston
Creative D: Jordan Tregeagle
Dir Bus: Jason Howes

D-U-N-S 01-052-1297
▲ STAMPS.COM INC
1990 E Grand Ave, El Segundo, CA 90245-5013
Tel (310) 482-5800 *Founded/Ownrshp* 1996
Sales 213.9MM *EMP* 600^E
Tkr Sym STMP *Exch* NGS
SIC 7331 5961 4813 Mailing service; Catalog & mail-order houses;
Ch Bd: Kenneth McBride
Pr: James Bortnak
Pr: Kyle Huebner
Bd of Dir: Brad Jones
VP: John DOE
Creative D: Steve Mueller
QA Dir: Jason Eberlin
QA Dir: Eva Guzman
QA Dir: Raynard Japor
Software D: Rajkumar Narkhede
Mktg Mgr: CHI Tran
Board of Directors: Mohan P Ananda, David Habiger, G Bradford Jones, Lloyd I Miller

D-U-N-S 05-035-8837
STAN BOYETT & SON INC
BOYETT PETROLEUM
601 Mchenry Ave, Modesto, CA 95350-5411
Tel (209) 577-6000 *Founded/Ownrshp* 1977
Sales 383.0MM^E *EMP* 170
SIC 5172 5541 Gasoline; Filling stations, gasoline
CEO: Carl Boyett
* *Pr:* Dale Boyett
* *VP:* Scott Castle
Off Admin: Martha Garcia
Dir IT: David Zellman
Sls&Mrk Ex: John Duncan
Sls&Mrk Ex: Seth T Terry
Mktg Dir: Art Bond
Manager: Clark Nakamura
Genl Couns: Katie Hollowell
Snr Mgr: Sherman Kris

D-U-N-S 61-930-1757
STAN KOCH & SONS TRUCKING INC
KOCH COMPANIES
4200 Dahlberg Dr Ste 100, Minneapolis, MN 55422-4842
Tel (763) 302-5400 *Founded/Ownrshp* 1978
Sales 275.0MM *EMP* 1,100
SIC 4213 4731 Trucking, except local; Freight transportation arrangement
CEO: Scott A Shephard
Pr: Randy Koch
CFO: John Tillman
CFO: John Tillmann
VP: Dave Koch
VP: Michael Patrick
VP: Mike Wasko
Genl Mgr: Robert Buss

D-U-N-S 61-512-3791 IMP
STANADYNE INTERMEDIATE HOLDINGS LLC
(*Suby of* STANADYNE PARENT HOLDINGS INC) ★
92 Deerfield Rd, Windsor, CT 06095-4200
Tel (860) 525-0821 *Founded/Ownrshp* 2014
Sales 210.0MM *EMP* 1,400
SIC 3714 3492 Fuel systems & parts, motor vehicle; Control valves, fluid power: hydraulic & pneumatic
CEO: David P Galuska
* *Pr:* John A Pinson
* *CFO:* Stephen S Langin
CFO: Stephen Langin
* *Treas:* Steve Rodgers

D-U-N-S 19-854-7390 IMP
STANADYNE LLC
(*Suby of* STANADYNE INTERMEDIATE HOLDINGS LLC) ★
92 Deerfield Rd, Windsor, CT 06095-4200
Tel (860) 525-0821 *Founded/Ownrshp* 2004
Sales 267.8MM *EMP* 1,730
Accts Pricewaterhousecoopers Llp Ha
SIC 3714 Fuel pumps, motor vehicle; Fuel systems & parts, motor vehicle
CEO: David P Galuska
Ch Bd: Robert G Isaman
Pr: John A Pinson
CFO: Stephen S Langin
VP: Jacquie L Boyer
VP: Titus Iwaszkiewicz
VP: David B Vanderford
Board of Directors: Samuel P Frieder, James D Wiggins, Evan Wildstein, Gordon H Woodward

D-U-N-S 07-973-5670
STANADYNE PARENT HOLDINGS INC
92 Deerfield Rd, Windsor, CT 06095-4200
Tel (860) 525-0821 *Founded/Ownrshp* 2014
Sales 210.0MM^E *EMP* 1,732
SIC 3714 Fuel pumps, motor vehicle; Fuel systems & parts, motor vehicle
CEO: David P Galuska

D-U-N-S 05-322-4098
STANCORP FINANCIAL GROUP INC
1100 Sw 6th Ave, Portland, OR 97204-1020
Tel (971) 321-7000 *Founded/Ownrshp* 2015
Sales NA *EMP* 2,702^E
Accts Deloitte & Touche Llp Portlan
SIC 6311 6321 Life insurance; Accident & health insurance
Pr: J Greg Ness
Pr: Sherri Borgmeyer
Pr: Raghu Crowley
Pr: Rob Ericson
Pr: Dayna V Kirk
Pr: Greg List
* *CFO:* Floyd F Chadee
Sr VP: Cindy J McPike
Sr VP: David M O'Brien
VP: Katherine Durham
VP: Jim Harbolt
VP: Scott A Hibbs
VP: Dan McMillan
VP: Daniel J McMillan
VP: Cherri Roden
VP: Mike Roy
VP: Mark Temme
VP: Alex M Terry
Assoc Dir: Shirley Ingram
Comm Dir: Will Carter
Board of Directors: Virginia L Anderson, Frederick W Buckman, Timothy A Holt, Debora D Horvath, Duane C McDougall, Kevin Murai, Eric E Parsons, Mary F Sammons, E Kay Stepp

D-U-N-S 10-445-5238
STANCORP MORTGAGE INVESTORS LLC
(*Suby of* STANCORP FINANCIAL GROUP INC) ★
19225 Nw Tanasbourne Dr, Hillsboro, OR 97124-5836
Tel (503) 321-7785 *Founded/Ownrshp* 1966
Sales NA *EMP* 2,630
SIC 6311 Life insurance
Mng Dir: Mark Fisher

D-U-N-S 12-129-3039
STAND ENERGY CORP
1077 Celestial St Ste 110, Cincinnati, OH 45202-1629
Tel (513) 621-1113 *Founded/Ownrshp* 1984
Sales 110.3MM *EMP* 34
Accts Novikoff Manheimer Co Cinc
SIC 4924 Natural gas distribution
Ch: Matth Toebben
* *Pr:* Judith Phillips
CFO: Robert Embry
* *Ex VP:* Lawrence Freeman
VP: Matthew Milligan
VP: John Phillips
Genl Couns: John Dosker

D-U-N-S 00-136-7697
■ STANDARD & POORS FINANCIAL SERVICES LLC
(*Suby of* S&P GLOBAL INC) ★
55 Water St Fl 49, New York, NY 10041-0004
Tel (212) 438-2000 *Founded/Ownrshp* 1906, 2008
Sales 509.9MM^E *EMP* 1,226
SIC 6282 Investment advisory service
CEO: Douglas Peterson
Mng Pt: Charles Davidson
* *Ofcr:* Demetrios Lefakis
* *Ex VP:* Pat Milano
* *Sr VP:* Edward J Haran
* *Sr VP:* Joseph D Sniado
VP: Chris Atkins
VP: Michael Privitera
VP: Ram Ranganath
VP: James Wiemken
Exec: Peter De Boer
Assoc Dir: Tim Bartl
Assoc Dir: Pablo Feldman
Assoc Dir: Ronan Fox
Assoc Dir: Christian Green
Assoc Dir: Maren Josefs
Assoc Dir: Laura A Kuffler
Assoc Dir: Simon Marshall

D-U-N-S 05-539-1908
■ STANDARD & POORS SECURITIES EVALUATIONS INC
(*Suby of* S&P GLOBAL INC) ★
55 Water St Fl 44, New York, NY 10041-0004
Tel (212) 438-3388 *Founded/Ownrshp* 2005
Sales 98.4MM^E *EMP* 5,000
SIC 7323 6289 Credit reporting services; Commercial (mercantile) credit reporting bureau; Financial reporting
Pr: James W Mitos
* *VP:* Deborah Branagan
VP: Michael Haddad

D-U-N-S 08-215-6642
STANDARD AERO (ALLIANCE) INC
(*Suby of* STANDARDAERO AVIATION HOLDINGS INC) ★
1029 Ross Dr, Maryville, TN 37801-8272
Tel (865) 983-2992 *Founded/Ownrshp* 2004
Sales 330.0MM *EMP* 350
SIC 3724 Aircraft engines & engine parts
CEO: Russell Ford
* *Pr:* James Colleary
* *Pr:* Robert Cords
* *CFO:* Mike Scott
VP: Richard Mingle
VP: Mark L Ratliff
Manager: Ron Gilleland
Snr Mgr: Robert Blackorby
Snr Mgr: Jason Junot
Snr Mgr: Bob Laginess

D-U-N-S 12-270-8464 EXP
STANDARD AERO HOLDINGS INC
(*Suby of* STANDARDAERO AVIATION HOLDINGS INC) ★
6710 N Scottsdale Rd # 250, Paradise Valley, AZ 85253-4444
Tel (480) 377-3100 *Founded/Ownrshp* 1982
Sales 63.1MM^E *EMP* 3,500
SIC 7699 Aircraft & heavy equipment repair services
CEO: Russell Ford
* *Pr:* James Colleary
* *COO:* Jack Lawless
* *CFO:* Mike Scott

D-U-N-S 61-437-1003
STANDARD AERO INC
STANDARDAERO
(*Suby of* STANDARDAERO AVIATION HOLDINGS INC) ★
3523 General Hudnell Dr, San Antonio, TX 78226-2030
Tel (210) 704-1100 *Founded/Ownrshp* 1987
Sales 48.6MM^E *EMP* 1,050^E
SIC 7699 Aircraft & heavy equipment repair services
CEO: Russell Ford
* *CFO:* Michael Scott
VP: Rob Higby
Ql Cn Mgr: Erwin Hechter
Manager: Gene Elzinga
Sls Mgr: Frank Garcia

STANDARD AIR SUPPLY
See STANDARD PLUMBING SUPPLY CO INC

D-U-N-S 55-563-0107
STANDARD AMERICAS INC
(*Suby of* THE STANDARD BANK OF SOUTH AFRICA LTD)
520 Madison Ave Fl 28, New York, NY 10022-4368
Tel (212) 407-5000 *Founded/Ownrshp* 1997
Sales NA *EMP* 48,000
SIC 6081 6082 Agencies of foreign banks; Foreign trade & international banking institutions
Pr: Albert Maartens
Sr VP: Angel M Solorio
VP: Leonardo Jafet

D-U-N-S 00-174-9449 IMP
STANDARD BANK & TRUST CO (INC)
(*Suby of* STANDARD BANCSHARES, INC)
7800 W 95th St Ste 101, Hickory Hills, IL 60457-2298
Tel (708) 499-2062 *Founded/Ownrshp* 1984
Sales NA *EMP* 296
SIC 6022 State commercial banks
Ch Bd: Alfred J O Malley
Pr: Michael J Helsdingen
* *Pr:* Lawrence P Kelly
Sr Cor Off: Tim Gallagher
Ofcr: Brandon Akins
Ex VP: Tom Dockweiler
* *Sr VP:* H Patrick Berg
Sr VP: Thomas G Clifford
* *Sr VP:* Dennis O'Malley
Sr VP: Dennis Omalley
* *Sr VP:* Charla A Wright
VP: Keith M Behrens
VP: William Evens
VP: Robert E Gallagher
VP: Terry Hackett
VP: Dann Zimmer
Board of Directors: William McEnery

D-U-N-S 05-540-3752 IMP/EXP
■ STANDARD CAR TRUCK CO INC
(*Suby of* WABTEC GLOBAL SERVICES) ★
6400 Shafer Ct Ste 450, Rosemont, IL 60018-4948
Tel (847) 692-6050 *Founded/Ownrshp* 2008
Sales 127.6MM^E *EMP* 400
SIC 3743 3321 Freight cars & equipment; Ductile iron castings; Gray iron castings
Pr: Richard A Mathes
* *Sec:* Donald Popernik
* *VP:* Daniel Schroeder
VP: David Watson

D-U-N-S 78-206-4224
STANDARD CHARTERED HOLDINGS INC
(*Suby of* STANDARD CHARTERED HOLDINGS (INTERNATIONAL) B.V.)
1095 Ave Of The Americas, New York, NY 10036-6797
Tel (212) 667-0700 *Founded/Ownrshp* 2006
Sales 205.1MM^E *EMP* 1,200
SIC 6221 6211 6531 Commodity dealers, contracts; Security brokers & dealers; Real estate agents & managers
Pr: James McCabe
COO: Nancy Wisniewski
Assoc Dir: Asad Ahmed
Mng Dir: Justin Crane
Mng Dir: Lars Hubinette
Mng Dir: Kaushik Rudra
Snr Mgr: John Peace

D-U-N-S 04-435-1674
STANDARD CHARTERED INTERNATIONAL (USA) LTD
AMERICAN EXPRESS BANK LTD.
(*Suby of* STANDARD CHARTERED PLC)
200 Vesey St, New York, NY 10285-1000
Tel (212) 640-2000 *Founded/Ownrshp* 2008
Sales NA *EMP* 3,500
SIC 6082 6021 6099 Foreign trade & international banking institutions; Edge act corporations; National commercial banks; Foreign currency exchange; Travelers' checks issuance
Ch Bd: James M Cracchiolo
* *CEO:* W Richard Holmes
* *CFO:* Alan P Gallo
Top Exec: William J Blomquist
Sr VP: William Harper
VP: Susan Atran

VP: Susan Evers
VP: Ruth Gorski
VP: Steve Heim
Exec: Donna Wasdyke
Dir Risk M: Ash Gupta

D-U-N-S 96-682-2678 IMP
STANDARD CONCRETE PRODUCTS INC
SCP
(*Suby of* LEHIGH CEMENT CO LLC) ★
945 Broadway Ste 300, Columbus, GA 31901-2746
Tel (706) 322-3274 *Founded/Ownrshp* 1996
Sales 112.6MM^E *EMP* 475
SIC 3272 Prestressed concrete products
Pr: Mason H Lampton
**COO:* Larry Paul
**CFO:* Fred J Dodelin
**CFO:* Fred Dodelin
**Treas:* Steven Wilson
Plnt Mgr: Hunter Moye
Prd Mgr: David Hennessee

STANDARD DRY WALL
See E M P INTERIORS INC

D-U-N-S 02-943-9247
STANDARD DRYWALL INC
S D I
(*Suby of* STANDARD DRY WALL) ★
9902 Channel Rd, Lakeside, CA 92040-3042
Tel (619) 443-7034 *Founded/Ownrshp* 1955
Sales 133.7MM^E *EMP* 1,250
SIC 1742 Drywall; Acoustical & ceiling work
Prin: Robert E Caya
**VP:* Blaine Caya

D-U-N-S 00-890-2850
STANDARD ELECTRIC CO
UP ELECTRIC/WITTA SUPPLY
2650 Trautner Dr, Saginaw, MI 48604-9599
Tel (989) 497-2100 *Founded/Ownrshp* 1929
Sales 176.1MM *EMP* 250
Accts Gordon Advisors Pc Troy Mi
SIC 5063 Electrical apparatus & equipment; Electrical fittings & construction materials; Electrical construction materials
Pr: Laverne N Weber
**Sec:* Benjamin F Rosenthal
**VP:* Bill Gray
**VP:* Scott Leemaster
**VP:* Richard Sonenklar
Brnch Mgr: Marlin Brush
Brnch Mgr: Ron Daniels
IT Man: Craig Halm
Opers Mgr: Tim Fitzgerald
Ql Cn Mgr: Ron Simpson
Manager: Don Padgett

D-U-N-S 00-176-4216
STANDARD ELECTRIC SUPPLY CO INC
(*Suby of* ELECTRICAL WHOLESALERS) ★
14 Jewel Dr, Wilmington, MA 01887-3361
Tel (978) 658-5050 *Founded/Ownrshp* 1952
Sales 88.5MM^E *EMP* 250
SIC 5063

D-U-N-S 12-087-2127 IMP
STANDARD FIBER LLC
577 Airport Blvd Ste 200, Burlingame, CA 94010-2052
Tel (650) 872-6528 *Founded/Ownrshp* 2005
Sales 175.6MM *EMP* 200
Accts Stayner Bates & Jensen Pc Sa
SIC 5021 Beds & bedding

D-U-N-S 00-691-7389
■ STANDARD FIRE INSURANCE CO
(*Suby of* TRI STATE BUSINESS SYSTEMS INC) ★
1 Tower Ave, Hartford, CT 06120-1034
Tel (860) 277-0111 *Founded/Ownrshp* 1910, 2000
Sales NA *EMP* 6,300
SIC 6331 Fire, marine & casualty insurance; Automobile insurance
V Ch Bd: Jay S Fishman
**CFO:* William P Hannon
**Ex VP:* Charles J Clarke
**Ex VP:* Ronald E Foley Jr
**Ex VP:* Joseph P Kiernan
**Ex VP:* Robert P Restrepo Jr
**Ex VP:* Alan M Silberstein

D-U-N-S 00-817-1522 IMP/EXP
STANDARD FURNITURE MANUFACTURING CO INC (AL)
801 S Us Highway 31, Bay Minette, AL 36507-2898
Tel (251) 937-6741 *Founded/Ownrshp* 1946
Sales 136.8MM^E *EMP* 700
SIC 2511 Wood bedroom furniture; Bed frames, except water bed frames: wood; Headboards: wood; Dressing tables: wood
Ch: William M Hodgson III
**Pr:* Todd Evans
**CFO:* Kerry Nickerson
VP: Richard Louise

D-U-N-S 82-724-2256 IMP/EXP
STANDARD INDUSTRIES INC
BMCA
(*Suby of* BUILDING MATERIALS CORP AMER) ★
1 Campus Dr, Parsippany, NJ 07054-4404
Tel (973) 628-3000 *Founded/Ownrshp* 1993
Sales 1.6MMM^E *EMP* 3,650
SIC 2493 Insulation & roofing material, reconstituted wood
Pr: Robert B Tafaro
**COO:* Richard A Nowak
**CFO:* John F Rebele
CFO: John Rebele
Ex VP: Frank Jalili
**Sr VP:* Daniel J Goldstein
**Sr VP:* Jan E Jerger-Stevens
**Sr VP:* Matti Kiik
VP: Jim Esposito
VP: Joseph Gary
Natl Sales: Chris Yeatts

D-U-N-S 00-790-9153
STANDARD INSURANCE CO
(*Suby of* STANCORP FINANCIAL GROUP INC) ★
920 Sw 6th Ave Ste 1100, Portland, OR 97204-1244
Tel (971) 321-7000 *Founded/Ownrshp* 1906
Sales NA *EMP* 2,702^E
SIC 6311 6321 6411

D-U-N-S 04-686-2116 IMP
■ STANDARD LIFE & ACCIDENT INSURANCE CO INC
(*Suby of* ANICO) ★
1 Moody Plz, Galveston, TX 77550-7947
Tel (409) 766-6036 *Founded/Ownrshp* 1976
Sales NA *EMP* 3^E
SIC 6324 6311 Hospital & medical service plans; Life insurance carriers
Pr: G Richard Ferdinandtsen
VP: Glenn Langley
VP: George Marchand
**VP:* James Edward Pozzi
Mktg Mgr: Amanda Feist

D-U-N-S 00-693-8674
STANDARD LIFE INSURANCE CO OF INDIANA
(*Suby of* CAPITAL ASSURANCE CORPORATION)
10689 N Pennsylvna St # 200, Indianapolis, IN 46280-1070
Tel (317) 574-6201 *Founded/Ownrshp* 1934
Sales NA *EMP* 100
SIC 6324 Hospital & medical service plans
Ch Bd: John Franco
CIO: Geoff Endris

D-U-N-S 05-498-8506 IMP
■ STANDARD MICROSYSTEMS CORP
SMSC
(*Suby of* MICROCHIP TECHNOLOGY INC) ★
80 Arkay Dr Ste 100, Hauppauge, NY 11788-3774
Tel (631) 435-6000 *Founded/Ownrshp* 2012
Sales 100.8MM^E *EMP* 1,064^E
SIC 3674 Integrated circuits, semiconductor networks, etc.
Pr: Christine King
Pr: Ian Harris
CFO: Kris Sennesael
Bd of Dir: Andrew Caggia
Sr VP: David Coller
Sr VP: Aaron L Fisher
Sr VP: Walter Siegel
Sr VP: Jeff Verheul
Sr VP: Roger Wendelken
VP: Richard Wahler
VP: Dean Zambelli
Exec: Nelson Saenz

D-U-N-S 00-131-5266 IMP/EXP
▲ STANDARD MOTOR PRODUCTS INC (NY)
3718 Northern Blvd # 600, Long Island City, NY 11101-1637
Tel (718) 392-0200 *Founded/Ownrshp* 1919
Sales 971.9MM *EMP* 3,400
Accts Kpmg Llp New York New York
Tkr Sym SMP *Exch* NYS
SIC 3714 3694 3585 3564 3052 Motor vehicle engines & parts; Fuel systems & parts, motor vehicle; Air conditioner parts, motor vehicle; Motor vehicle electrical equipment; Ignition systems, high frequency; Harness wiring sets, internal combustion engines; Battery cable wiring sets for internal combustion engines; Compressors for refrigeration & air conditioning equipment; Parts for heating, cooling & refrigerating equipment; Air conditioning equipment, complete; Blowers & fans; Rubber & plastics hose & beltings
Pr: Eric Sills
Ch Bd: Lawrence I Sills
CFO: James J Burke
Treas: Robert H Martin
Chf Mktg O: Michael Fitzgerald
Ex VP: Dale Burks
VP: Carmine J Broccole
VP: Phil Hutchens
VP: Bernard Mengus
VP: Ray Nicholas
VP: Rob Sweeney
Board of Directors: John P Gethin, Pamela Forbes Lieberman, Joseph W McDonnell, Alisa C Norris, Frederick D Sturdivant, William H Turner, Richard S Ward, Roger M Widmann

D-U-N-S 00-132-5604 IMP/EXP
STANDARD OIL CO
BP
(*Suby of* BP AMERICA INC) ★
4101 Winfield Rd Ste 100, Warrenville, IL 60555-3522
Tel (630) 836-5000 *Founded/Ownrshp* 1870
Sales 957.0MM^E *EMP* 8,000
SIC 2911 Petroleum refining; Gasoline; Intermediate distillates; Jet fuels
Prin: Brian Gilvary
**Prin:* Samuel Andrews
**Prin:* Henry M Flagler
**Prin:* John D Rockefeller

D-U-N-S 05-856-9005 IMP
STANDARD PLUMBING SUPPLY CO INC
STANDARD AIR SUPPLY
9150 S 300 W Bldg 5, Sandy, UT 84070-2643
Tel (801) 255-7145 *Founded/Ownrshp* 1992
Sales 311.2MM^E *EMP* 320
SIC 5074 Plumbing & hydronic heating supplies; Plumbing fittings & supplies
Pr: Richard N Reese

D-U-N-S 07-998-9980
STANDARD REGISTER INC
TAYLOR COMMUNICATIONS
(*Suby of* TAYLOR CORP) ★
600 Albany St, Dayton, OH 45417-3442
Tel (937) 221-1000 *Founded/Ownrshp* 2015
Sales 145.4MM^E *EMP* 2,860^E
SIC 8742 Management consulting services
CEO: Debra L Taylor
**CFO:* Thomas A Johnson
**Ex VP:* Gregory W Jackson

Sr VP: Rick Morgan
**VP:* Gregory J Greve
VP: Steve McDonell
VP: Gerard Sowar
**VP:* Suzanne M Spellacy
**VP:* Larry D Taylor
Prgrm Mgr: James Hamilton
Snr Sftwr: Daniel Baker

D-U-N-S 00-886-2641 IMP
STANDARD SALES CO LP (TX)
4800 E 42nd St Ste 400, Odessa, TX 79762-7249
Tel (432) 367-7662 *Founded/Ownrshp* 1952, 2001
Sales 144.4MM^E *EMP* 500
SIC 5181 Beer & other fermented malt liquors
CEO: Lanny Layman
Brnch Mgr: Brian Richardson
Sls Mgr: Steve Allen
Sls Mgr: Fidel Duron
Sls Mgr: Danny Gray
Sls Mgr: Jeff Horvat

D-U-N-S 12-862-7416 IMP
STANDARD STEEL LLC
(*Suby of* NIPPON STEEL & SUMITOMO METAL USA INC) ★
500 N Walnut St, Burnham, PA 17009-1644
Tel (717) 242-4615 *Founded/Ownrshp* 2006
Sales 128.4MM *EMP* 685^E
SIC 3312 3462 Wheels, locomotive & car: iron & steel; Railroad wheels, axles, frogs or other equipment: forged
CEO: Daniel J Condon
**Pr:* Yukinori Akimoto
Ex VP: Ed Ganssle
**Sr VP:* Takashi Fujimura
**Sr VP:* John M Hilton
**VP:* Alan M Majewski
VP: J O Parke
Sales Asso: Joe Ughetto

D-U-N-S 00-751-4904 IMP
STANDARD SUPPLY AND DISTRIBUTING CO INC
JOHNSON CONTRLS AUTHORIZED DLR
1431 Regal Row, Dallas, TX 75247-3617
Tel (214) 630-7800 *Founded/Ownrshp* 1946
Sales 227.9MM^E *EMP* 150
SIC 5075 Warm air heating & air conditioning
Pr: William B Shaw
Pr: Chris Dees
**Pr:* Lance Malone
**CEO:* Spencer Shaw
**CFO:* Mark Shaw
**Sec:* Phyllis Shaw
**VP:* Todd Day
**VP:* William R Dunn
Rgnl Mgr: Chris Reeves
Brnch Mgr: Jimmy Judkins
Brnch Mgr: Taylor Wynne

D-U-N-S 00-699-9858 IMP/EXP
STANDARD TEXTILE CO INC
PRIDECRAFT ENTERPRISES
1 Knollcrest Dr, Cincinnati, OH 45237-1608
Tel (513) 761-9255 *Founded/Ownrshp* 1940
Sales 982.2MM^E *EMP* 3,500
SIC 2389 2326 2337 2211 2391 5136 Hospital gowns; Medical & hospital uniforms, men's; Uniforms, except athletic: women's, misses' & juniors'; Bandages, gauzes & surgical fabrics, cotton; Surgical fabrics, cotton; Draperies, plastic & textile: from purchased materials; Uniforms, men's & boys'
Pr: Gary Heiman
**Pr:* Santa J Ono Lauds Gov John Kas
**CFO:* Chris Bopp
**Treas:* Edward Frankel
Ofcr: Erin Branscum
Ofcr: Kathy McCarthy
**Sr VP:* Norman Frankel
**Sr VP:* Kim Heiman
**Sr VP:* Steve Tracey
VP: Cathy Borgmeier
VP: Buddy Douglas
VP: Raymond Douglas
VP: Karen Fisher
VP: Tim Keith
VP: Michael Lean
VP: Michael McCarthy
VP: David Mizrachi
VP: Mike Newton
VP: Paul Poe
VP: David Rosenthal
VP: Walter Spiegel

D-U-N-S 09-387-1572
STANDARD WESTWOOD VENTURE LP
WESTWOOD TERRACE
2200 1st St Ste A, Moline, IL 61265
Tel (309) 797-4327 *Founded/Ownrshp* 2011
Sales 40.1MM^E *EMP* 3,900
SIC 6513 Apartment building operators
Pt: Sharon Brown
Sr VP: Leann Morein

STANDARDAERO
See STANDARD AERO INC

D-U-N-S 82-758-0197
STANDARDAERO AVIATION HOLDINGS INC
6710 N Scottsdale Rd # 250, Paradise Valley, AZ 85253-4405
Tel (480) 377-3100 *Founded/Ownrshp* 2015
Sales 1.7MMM^E *EMP* 3,500^E
Accts Ernst & Young Llp Winnipeg
SIC 3721 Aircraft
CEO: Russell Ford
**CFO:* Michael Scott

D-U-N-S 16-730-0131
STANDARDAERO BUSINESS AVIATION SERVICES LLC
(*Suby of* STANDARDAERO AVIATION HOLDINGS INC) ★
6710 N Scottsdale Rd, Scottsdale, AZ 85253-4405
Tel (480) 377-3100 *Founded/Ownrshp* 2015
Sales 172.0MM^E *EMP* 1,000
SIC 7363 Pilot service, aviation

CEO: Russell Ford
Pr: Robert Lummus
Pr: Marc McGowan
**CFO:* Michael Scott
Sr VP: Michele Grisez
VP: John Baker
VP: Troy Jonas
VP: Mark Larsen
VP: Melissa Maddox
VP: Leticia Sembera
VP: Juli West

D-U-N-S 00-420-1562 IMP
STANDBY SCREW MACHINE PRODUCTS CO (OH)
1122 W Bagley Rd, Berea, OH 44017-2908
Tel (440) 243-8200 *Founded/Ownrshp* 1939
Sales 88.7MM^E *EMP* 375
SIC 3451 Screw machine products
Ch Bd: Frederick W Marcell
**Pr:* Sal Caroniti
VP: William Horvath
VP: Ted Reynolds
VP: Russell Rybicki
VP: John Stricker
**Prin:* J Albert Lowell
**Prin:* William F Marcell
**Prin:* E J Miller
Sls Mgr: Andrew Rabkewych
Board of Directors: William Marcell

D-U-N-S 00-103-2002 IMP/EXP
▲ STANDEX INTERNATIONAL CORP
11 Keewaydin Dr, Salem, NH 03079-2840
Tel (603) 893-9701 *Founded/Ownrshp* 1955
Sales 751.5MM *EMP* 5,100^E
Tkr Sym SXI *Exch* NYS
SIC 3585 3549 3675 Refrigeration & heating equipment; Refrigeration equipment, complete; Metalworking machinery; Electronic capacitors
Pr: David A Dunbar
Ch Bd: Roger L Fix
CFO: Thomas D Debyle
Ofcr: Deborah A Rosen
VP: Paul Burns
Opers Mgr: Marty Rushing
Prd Mgr: Chris Brafford
Board of Directors: Charles H Cannon Jr, Thomas E Chorman, Jeffrey S Edwards, Gerald H Fickenscher, Roger L Fix, Thomas J Hansen, Daniel B Hogan

D-U-N-S 08-010-2412
STANDLEE HAY TRUCKING CO INC
990 S 1690 E, Eden, ID 83325
Tel (208) 825-5117 *Founded/Ownrshp* 2004
Sales 20.7MM^E *EMP* 2,000
SIC 5191 Hay

D-U-N-S 08-860-2917 IMP/EXP
STANDRIDGE COLOR CORP
1196 E Hightower Trl, Social Circle, GA 30025-2791
Tel (770) 464-3362 *Founded/Ownrshp* 1973
Sales 202.5MM^E *EMP* 350
SIC 2865 2816 3083 Color pigments, organic; Color pigments; Thermoplastic laminates: rods, tubes, plates & sheet
CEO: Richard Samuelson
**CFO:* Blane Allen
CFO: Johnny Rainey
**CFO:* Mable W Standridge
**Sec:* Henry Stowe
VP: Cathy McLean
**Prin:* Sherry Waters
Cmptr Lab: Donavan Day
Plnt Mgr: Barry Carter
Sales Exec: Don Guess
Sls Mgr: Doug Davis

D-U-N-S 15-676-7915 IMP
STANFORD HEALTH CARE
STANFORD LINEAR ACCELERATOR CE
(*Suby of* STANFORD LNEAR ACCELERATOR CTR) ★
300 Pasteur Dr, Stanford, CA 94305-2200
Tel (650) 723-4000 *Founded/Ownrshp* 1986
Sales 3.5MMM *EMP* 5,045
Accts Pricewaterhousecoopers Llp Sa
SIC 8062 Hospital, medical school affiliated with residency
CEO: David Entwistle
Pr: Barbara Clemons
COO: Betsy Williams
**CFO:* David Connor
Bd of Dir: Raksha Patel
Trst: Ying-Ying Goh
**Chf Mktg O:* Norman Rizk MD
VP: Deborah Italiano
VP: Barbara Ralston
VP: Helen Wilmot
VP Bus Dev: Jane Shannahan
Assoc Dir: Sara Tung
Dir Rx: Mike Brown

STANFORD LINEAR ACCELERATOR CE
See STANFORD HEALTH CARE

STANFORD LNEAR ACCELERATOR CTR
See LELAND STANFORD JUNIOR UNIVERSITY

D-U-N-S 87-897-0300
STANFORD UNIVERSITY
295 Galvez St, Stanford, CA 94305-6104
Tel (650) 723-2300 *Founded/Ownrshp* 1995
Sales 333.3MM *EMP* 2,118
SIC 8221 Colleges universities & professional schools
Prin: Kelley Skeff
Assoc VP: Roberta Katz
VP: Stephen Krasner
VP: David Laitin
VP: Martin Shell
Assoc Dir: Tom Cramer
Assoc Dir: Jonrie Davila
Assoc Dir: Dandre Desandies
Assoc Dir: Christine Timko
Assoc Dir: Randall Williams
Ex Dir: Jay Kohn

D-U-N-S 03-137-4853
STANION WHOLESALE ELECTRIC CO INC (KS)
812 S Main St, Pratt, KS 67124-2600
Tel (620) 672-5678 *Founded/Ownrshp* 1993
Sales 84.1MM *EMP* 197
SIC 5063 Electrical apparatus & equipment
Pr: Bill Keller
**VP:* Cynthia Keller
**VP:* Monty Mathews
Brnch Mgr: Flynn Harvey
Brnch Mgr: Willie Perez
Brnch Mgr: Jim Stewart
Sales Asso: Kevin Martin

D-U-N-S 02-869-0717
STANISLAUS FARM SUPPLY CO
WESTLINK
624 E Service Rd, Modesto, CA 95358-9451
Tel (860) 678-5160 *Founded/Ownrshp* 1949
Sales 91.4MM^{E} *EMP* 65
SIC 5191 Fertilizer & fertilizer materials; Insecticides; Seeds: field, garden & flower
CEO: Anselmo Bettencourt
CFO: Espiri Ixta
**CFO:* Espiridion Ixta
**V Ch Bd:* Stuart Bradley
IT Man: David Lemos
IT Man: Ed Tobler
Mktg Mgr: Tony Weatherred

D-U-N-S 80-196-4227 IMP/EXP
■ **STANLEY ACCESS TECHNOLOGIES LLC**
(*Suby of* STANLEY BLACK & DECKER INC) ★
65 Scott Swamp Rd, Farmington, CT 06032-2803
Tel (860) 409-6502 *Founded/Ownrshp* 2006
Sales 164.3MM^{E} *EMP* 900^{E}
SIC 1751 Garage door, installation or erection
Prd Mgr: Kevin Fitzgibbons

D-U-N-S 14-420-2843
STANLEY ASSOCIATES INC
(*Suby of* STANLEY INC) ★
12601 Fair Lakes Cir, Fairfax, VA 22033-4920
Tel (703) 227-6000 *Founded/Ownrshp* 2002
Sales 119.9MM^{E} *EMP* 1,166
SIC 7373 Systems integration services
Pr: George D Schindler
Treas: Mike Snodgrass
Web Dev: Eugene Phillips
Counsel: Lawrence Delaney

D-U-N-S 00-115-2461 IMP/EXP
▲ **STANLEY BLACK & DECKER INC**
1000 Stanley Dr, New Britain, CT 06053-1675
Tel (860) 225-5111 *Founded/Ownrshp* 1843
Sales 11.1MMM *EMP* 51,250
Accts Ernst & Young Llp Hartford C
Tkr Sym SWK *Exch* NYS
SIC 3429 3546 3423 3452 3699 Builders' hardware; Power-driven handtools; Hand & edge tools; Bolts, nuts, rivets & washers; Security devices; Door opening & closing devices, electrical
Ch Bd: John F Lundgren
Pr: James M Loree
Pr: Lee B McChesney
Pr: Jaime Ramirez
Pr: Ben S Sihota
Pr: William S Taylor
Pr: John H Wyatt
CFO: Donald Allan Jr
Treas: Craig A Douglas
Sr VP: Jeffery D Ansell
Sr VP: Bruce H Beatt
Sr VP: James J Cannon
Sr VP: Joseph Voelker
VP: Michael A Bartone
VP: Rhonda O Gass
VP: Steven J Stafstrom
Board of Directors: Andrea J Ayers, George W Buckley, Patrick D Campbell, Carlos M Cardoso, Robert B Coutts, Debra A Crew, Anthony Luiso, Marianne M Parrs, Robert L Ryan

D-U-N-S 00-798-9056 EXP
STANLEY CONSULTANTS INC
(*Suby of* SC COMPANIES INC) ★
225 Iowa Ave, Muscatine, IA 52761-3764
Tel (563) 264-6600 *Founded/Ownrshp* 1913
Sales 148.4MM *EMP* 1,000
SIC 8711 Consulting engineer
CEO: Gayle A Roberts
**Ch Bd:* Richard H Stanley
**COO:* Mike Hunzinger
**Ch:* Gregs G Thomopulos
**Sr VP:* Bennett D Reichauer
**Sr VP:* Richard C Smith
VP: Kevin Cavanaugh
VP: Monte Engelkemier
Exec: Tom Iannelli
Assoc Dir: Kevin Madsen
Prgrm Mgr: Michelle French

D-U-N-S 14-722-0672
■ **STANLEY CONVERGENT SECURITY SOLUTIONS INC**
STANLEY SECURITY
(*Suby of* STANLEY BLACK & DECKER INC) ★
55 Shuman Blvd Ste 900, Naperville, IL 60563-8488
Tel (630) 245-7100 *Founded/Ownrshp* 2007
Sales 126.8MM^{E} *EMP* 1,800
SIC 7382 Security systems services
Pr: Kyle Michael Dancho
**COO:* Kyle Dancho
**COO:* Jim Kopplin
CFO: Sean Forrest
VP: Raymond Radis
**Prin:* Brettt Bontrager
Off Mgr: Susan Flanegan

D-U-N-S 03-490-9358 IMP
STANLEY ELECTRIC US CO INC
420 E High St, London, OH 43140-9799
Tel (740) 852-5200 *Founded/Ownrshp* 2011
Sales 40.0MM *EMP* 1,450
Accts Kpmg Llp Columbus Oh
SIC 3647 3694 3089 Automotive lighting fixtures; Automotive electrical equipment; Injection molding of plastics
Pr: Shinomiya Masahiro
Plnt Mgr: Brian Boldman
Sls Mgr: Robert Farmwald
Sls Mgr: Matt Hoffman

STANLEY ENGINEERED FASTENING
See EMHART TEKNOLOGIES LLC

D-U-N-S 17-670-3122 IMP
■ **STANLEY FASTENING SYSTEMS LP**
(*Suby of* STANLEY BLACK & DECKER INC) ★
2 Briggs Dr, East Greenwich, RI 02818-1555
Tel (401) 884-2500 *Founded/Ownrshp* 1996
Sales 236.2MM^{E} *EMP* 1,100^{E}
SIC 3399 3579 Staples, nonferrous metal or wire; Stapling machines (hand or power)
Mng Pt: Stanley Works
VP: Judith Beacom
IT Man: John McCarthy

D-U-N-S 78-652-5621
STANLEY INC
(*Suby of* C G I) ★
12601 Fair Lakes Cir, Fairfax, VA 22033-4920
Tel (703) 684-1125 *Founded/Ownrshp* 1966
Sales 195.1MM^{E} *EMP* 4,800
SIC 7373 Systems integration services
Prin: Heather Poirier
CFO: Brian J Clark
Ex VP: George H Wilson
Sr VP: Brett Bontrager
Sr VP: Scott D Chaplin
Sr VP: James Peake
Sr VP: Chris J Torti
Comm Dir: Erin Herbig
Comm Man: Joelle Pozza
Prgrm Mgr: Laurie Carter
Prgrm Mgr: Phil Copeland

D-U-N-S 07-923-8372 IMP
■ **STANLEY INDUSTRIAL & AUTOMOTIVE LLC**
(*Suby of* STANLEY BLACK & DECKER INC) ★
505 N Cleveland Ave, Westerville, OH 43082-7130
Tel (614) 755-7000 *Founded/Ownrshp* 2013
Sales 257.8MM^{E} *EMP* 1,426
SIC 3429 3546 3423 3452 Builders' hardware; Power-driven handtools; Hand & edge tools; Bolts, nuts, rivets & washers
Pr: Joanna Sohovich
Pr: Larry Harper
Pr: Joe McCormack
Pr: James Ray
Pr: Brett Shaw
Pr: Christine Yingli Yan
CFO: James Ritter
Treas: Craig A Douglas
VP: Michael A Bartone
VP: Bruce H Beatt
VP: Anthony Buffum
VP: Darren G Pratt
VP: Gregory P Smulski
VP: Michael Vagnini
VP: Gary Wells

D-U-N-S 04-320-0906
STANLEY MARTIN COMPANIES INC (MD)
STANLEY MARTIN HOMES
11710 Plaza America Dr # 1100, Reston, VA 20190-4771
Tel (703) 964-5000 *Founded/Ownrshp* 1966
Sales 89.0MM^{E} *EMP* 200
SIC 1531

STANLEY MARTIN HOMES
See STANLEY MARTIN COMPANIES INC

D-U-N-S 83-320-1192
■ **STANLEY MORGAN DOMESTIC HOLDINGS INC**
(*Suby of* MORGAN STANLEY & CO LLC) ★
1585 Broadway Lowr B, New York, NY 10036-8200
Tel (212) 761-4000 *Founded/Ownrshp* 2008
Sales NA *EMP* 47^{E}
SIC 6021 National commercial banks

STANLEY NATIONAL HARDWARE
See NATIONAL MANUFACTURING CO

STANLEY SECURITY
See STANLEY CONVERGENT SECURITY SOLUTIONS INC

D-U-N-S 00-192-7961 IMP/EXP
■ **STANLEY SECURITY SOLUTIONS INC**
BEST LOCK
(*Suby of* STANLEY BLACK & DECKER INC) ★
9998 Crosspoint Blvd # 3, Indianapolis, IN 46256-3306
Tel (317) 849-2255 *Founded/Ownrshp* 2002
Sales 623.0MM^{E} *EMP* 1,520
SIC 3699 Security control equipment & systems
Pr: Jim Cannon
Exec: Richard Young
CIO: John Van Kirk
Mktg Mgr: Morgan Kucic

STANLEY STEEMER CARPET CLEANER
See STANLEY STEEMER INTERNATIONAL INC

D-U-N-S 01-787-6764 IMP
STANLEY STEEMER INTERNATIONAL INC
STANLEY STEEMER CARPET CLEANER
5800 Innovation Dr, Dublin, OH 43016-3271
Tel (614) 764-2007 *Founded/Ownrshp* 1947
Sales 234.1MM *EMP* 2,000
Accts Gbq Partners Llc Columbus Oh
SIC 7217 3635 6794 5713 Carpet & furniture cleaning on location; Upholstery cleaning on customer premises; Household vacuum cleaners; Franchises, selling or licensing; Carpets
CEO: Wesley C Bates
**Pr:* Jack A Bates
**Pr:* Justin Bates
**CFO:* Mark Bunner CPA
Sr Cor Off: Kevin Rogers
**Ex VP:* Philip P Ryser
Ex VP: Dean Scalera
VP: Dana Beck
**VP:* D Ryan Jankowski
VP: Ryan Jankowski
VP: Jeff Schneider
**VP:* Eric Smith
VP: Brenda Smittle

D-U-N-S 07-979-8852
STANLY COUNTY SCHOOLS
1000 N 1st St Ste 4, Albemarle, NC 28001-2819
Tel (704) 961-3000 *Founded/Ownrshp* 2015
Sales 17.0MM^{E} *EMP* 1,556^{E}
SIC 8211 Public elementary & secondary schools
MIS Dir: Harry Stogner
IT Man: Katrice Thomas
Schl Brd P: Jeff Chance
Schl Brd P: Angela Mills
Teacher Pr: Vicki Calvert

D-U-N-S 12-414-8362
STANLY COUNTY SCHOOLS EDUCATIONAL FOUNDATION INC
1000 N 1st St Ste 4, Albemarle, NC 28001-2819
Tel (704) 983-5151 *Founded/Ownrshp* 1875
Sales 122.0MM^{E} *EMP* 1,235
SIC 8399 Fund raising organization, non-fee basis
Ch Bd: Dr Angela Mills
**V Ch:* Todd Swaringen
Dir: Michael Sandy
Ex Dir: James Jones

D-U-N-S 17-402-3036
STANLY HEALTH SERVICES INC
STANLY MEM HOSP FOUNDATION
301 Yadkin St, Albemarle, NC 28001-3441
Tel (704) 982-3888 *Founded/Ownrshp* 1991
Sales 111.2MM *EMP* 3
SIC 8741 Hospital management; Nursing & personal care facility management
Int Pr: Roy Hinson
VP: Brian Freeman
Assoc Dir: Jane Boone
**Ex Dir:* Kathy Boyd
Ex Dir: Ginger Moser
Counsel: Ron Burris

STANLY MEM HOSP FOUNDATION
See STANLY HEALTH SERVICES INC

D-U-N-S 07-449-6142
STANLY REGIONAL MEDICAL CENTER
CAROLINAS HEALTHCARE
301 Yadkin St, Albemarle, NC 28001-3441
Tel (704) 982-3888 *Founded/Ownrshp* 1945
Sales 96.7MM *EMP* 750
SIC 8062 Hospital, AMA approved residency
Ch Bd: Joel Huneycutt
**Pr:* Al Taylor
**COO:* Debra Smith
**CFO:* Nick Samilo
**Treas:* Alan Bowers
VP: Dale Burris
VP: Kerry Burris
VP: Joseph Hunter
Dir Lab: Kelly Almond
**Prin:* Linda Carter
CIO: Keith Bray

STANT
See VAPOR ACQUISITION CORP

D-U-N-S 07-840-0180 IMP/EXP
STANT CORP
(*Suby of* HIG CAPITAL MANAGEMENT INC) ★
1620 Columbia Ave, Connersville, IN 47331-1672
Tel (765) 825-3121 *Founded/Ownrshp* 1898
Sales 176.1MM^{E} *EMP* 1,000
SIC 3714 Motor vehicle parts & accessories
CEO: Curt S Howell
**COO:* Inacio Moriguchi
**CFO:* Phillip Fitzpatrick
**VP:* Mike Boles
**VP:* John Allen Chamberlain

D-U-N-S 96-888-6700 IMP
STANT MANUFACTURING INC
1620 Columbia Ave, Connersville, IN 47331-1672
Tel (870) 247-5480 *Founded/Ownrshp* 1965
Sales 228.8MM^{E} *EMP* 1,400
SIC 3491

D-U-N-S 83-225-5819 IMP/EXP
STANT USA CORP
(*Suby of* HIG CAPITAL MANAGEMENT INC) ★
1620 Columbia Ave, Connersville, IN 47331-1672
Tel (765) 825-3121 *Founded/Ownrshp* 2009
Sales 166.6MM *EMP* 482
SIC 3714 Motor vehicle parts & accessories
CEO: Lou Braga
**COO:* Inacio Moriguchi
**CFO:* Michael Saccucci
**VP:* Mike Boles

D-U-N-S 96-868-3768
STANTEC ARCHITECTURE AND ENGINEERING PC
(*Suby of* STANTEC TECHNOLOGY INTERNATIONAL INC) ★
311 Summer St, Boston, MA 02210-1723
Tel (617) 234-3100 *Founded/Ownrshp* 2015
Sales 12.5MM^{E} *EMP* 1,242^{E}
SIC 8712 Architectural engineering
Pr: Richard Allen
Treas: Daniel J Lefaivre
Info Man: Reshma Panjanani

D-U-N-S 17-448-2208
STANTEC ARCHITECTURE INC
(*Suby of* STANTEC TECHNOLOGY INTERNATIONAL INC) ★
301 N Main St Ste 2452, Winston Salem, NC 27101-3844
Tel (336) 714-7413 *Founded/Ownrshp* 2000
Sales 114.0MM *EMP* 459
SIC 8712 7389 Architectural services; Interior decorating
Pr: Richard K Allen
**CFO:* Dan Lefaivre
**Sr VP:* Stanif Smith
**VP:* Jeff Lloyd
Info Man: Reshma Panjanani
**Counsel:* Jennifer Addison

D-U-N-S 07-345-8523
STANTEC CONSULTING SERVICES INC
(*Suby of* STANTEC TECHNOLOGY INTERNATIONAL INC) ★
50 W 23rd St Fl 8, New York, NY 10010-5272
Tel (212) 366-5600 *Founded/Ownrshp* 1954
Sales 612.8MM *EMP* 5,306
SIC 8731 8711 1541 Commercial physical research; Construction & civil engineering; Industrial buildings & warehouses
CEO: Robert Gomes
**Ch Bd:* Brian Larson
**CFO:* Daniel J Lefaivre
**Sr VP:* Rich Allen
**VP:* Tom Higgins
**VP:* Jeff Lloyd
**VP:* Scott Murray
VP: Frederick Sankey
VP: Rick Smilow
**VP:* Matt Tin
Info Man: Reshma Panjanani

D-U-N-S 17-931-1386
STANTEC TECHNOLOGY INTERNATIONAL INC
(*Suby of* STANTEC INC)
8211 S 48th St, Phoenix, AZ 85044-5355
Tel (602) 438-2200 *Founded/Ownrshp* 1991
Sales 739.3MM^{E} *EMP* 5,475
SIC 8711 Engineering services
Pr: Orville Shah
Info Man: Reshma Panjanani

D-U-N-S 93-020-2044 IMP
STANTON OPTICAL FLORIDA LLC
3801 S Congress Ave, Palm Springs, FL 33461-4140
Tel (561) 275-2020 *Founded/Ownrshp* 2009
Sales 126.0MM^{E} *EMP* 838^{E}
SIC 5995 Optical goods stores
Genl Mgr: Kristy Bink
Mktg Mgr: Salena Youngman
Sls Mgr: Frank Pineiro
Sls Mgr: Kathryn Roche

D-U-N-S 01-663-4263
STANZ CHEESE CO INC
STANZ FOODSERVICE
1840 Commerce Dr, South Bend, IN 46628-1563
Tel (574) 232-6666 *Founded/Ownrshp* 1975
Sales 83.5MM^{E} *EMP* 180
SIC 5142 5141 5148 5113 5087 5085

STANZ FOODSERVICE
See STANZ CHEESE CO INC

STAPLCOTN
See STAPLE COTTON CO-OPERATIVE ASSOCIATION

D-U-N-S 04-313-8429 IMP/EXP
STAPLE COTTON CO-OPERATIVE ASSOCIATION
STAPLCOTN
214 W Market St, Greenwood, MS 38930-4329
Tel (662) 453-6231 *Founded/Ownrshp* 1921
Sales 984.0MM *EMP* 187
SIC 5159 4221 6159 Cotton, raw; Cotton compresses & warehouses; Agricultural loan companies
Ch Bd: Mike P Sturdivant III
**Ch Bd:* Ben Lamensdorf
**CEO:* Meredith Allen
COO: Billy Bridgforth
**CFO:* Mike Moffatt
**Ch:* Woods E Eastland
VP: David Camp
VP: Sterling Jones
Exec: Tunya Wells
Off Admin: Jeff McPhail

D-U-N-S 04-244-7644 IMP/EXP
■ **STAPLES CONTRACT & COMMERCIAL INC**
BUSINESS INTERIORS BY STAPLES
(*Suby of* STAPLES INC) ★
500 Staples Dr, Framingham, MA 01702-4474
Tel (508) 253-5000 *Founded/Ownrshp* 1997
Sales 176.1MM^{E} *EMP* 1,000
SIC 5943 Notary & corporate seals
Pr: Joe Doody
**Pr:* Shira Goodman
**Treas:* William Mayerson
VP: Mike Ramsey
VP Bus Dev: David Goldman
Dir Bus: Bill Crockett
Area Mgr: Deana Alegre
Snr Sftwr: Chris Weidert
Sales Asso: Tiffiny Greene
Sales Asso: Jared Shalek
Sales Asso: Jason Shaw

STAPLES ENTERPRISES
See STAPLES OIL CO INC

D-U-N-S 15-106-4821 IMP
▲ **STAPLES INC**
500 Staples Dr, Framingham, MA 01702-4474
Tel (508) 253-5000 *Founded/Ownrshp* 1985
Sales 21.0MMM *EMP* 75,371
Tkr Sym SPLS *Exch* NGS
SIC 5943 5999 7513 5961 5712 Stationery stores; Office forms & supplies; School supplies; Writing supplies; Typewriters & business machines; Business machines & equipment; Photocopy machines; Truck rental & leasing, no drivers; Catalog & mail-order houses; Computer equipment & electronics, mail order; Computer software, mail order; Computers & peripheral equipment, mail order; Furniture stores; Office furniture
Pr: Shira Goodman
**Ch Bd:* Ronald L Sargent
Pr: Marty Robertson
Pr: John Wilson
CFO: Christine T Komola
Ex VP: Tom Conophy
Ex VP: Shaira Goodman

Ex VP: Faisal Masud
Ex VP: Karen Pappas
Ex VP: Michael Williams
Sr VP: Mark Conte
VP: Scott Barron
VP: Ed Bonner
VP: Jean Cerulle
VP: Steve Chalas
VP: Jim Christianson
VP: Michael Dubose
VP: Laura Granahan
VP: Tom Heisroth
VP: Steven Mastrogiacomo
VP: Kevin Moss
Board of Directors: Drew Faust, Carol Meyrowitz, Robert Sulentic, Paul F Walsh

D-U-N-S 16-001-9832 IMP
■ STAPLES INTERNATIONAL INC
(*Suby of* STAPLES INC) ★
500 Staples Dr, Framingham, MA 01702-4474
Tel (508) 253-5000 *Founded/Ownrshp* 1992
Sales 1.8MMM^E *EMP* 43,048
SIC 5943 5712 5044 5021 5112 Stationery stores; Office forms & supplies; Office furniture; Office equipment; Office furniture; Office supplies
CEO: Ronald L Sargent
**Treas:* Nicholas Hotchkin
**Ex VP:* Tom Conophy
**Ex VP:* Mike Edwards
**Ex VP:* Faisal Masud
**Sr VP:* Michael T Williams
**VP:* Michael Devlin

D-U-N-S 07-026-3041
STAPLES OIL CO INC
STAPLES ENTERPRISES
1680 N Redding Ave, Windom, MN 56101-1297
Tel (507) 831-4450 *Founded/Ownrshp* 1972
Sales 100.0MM *EMP* 35
SIC 5411 Convenience stores, chain
Pr: Alan J Staples
**CEO:* Brent Staples
**Dir Bus:* Corey Maricle

D-U-N-S 14-255-4695
STAR BRANDS NORTH AMERICA INC
(*Suby of* YILDIZ HOLDING ANONIM SIRKETI)
30 Buxton Farm Rd Ste 100, Stamford, CT 06905-1206
Tel (203) 329-4545 *Founded/Ownrshp* 2013
Sales 137.0MM *EMP* 235
SIC 2066 Chocolate candy, solid
Pr: Nirmal Tripathy
CFO: Ali Derwish
CFO: Scott Hilley
Ex VP: David Clarke
Sr VP: James Gerbo
IT Man: Kevin Slusser
VP Opers: Colin Swift
Ql Cn Mgr: Korey Schaffer
Ql Cn Mgr: Joann Young

D-U-N-S 61-187-7804
STAR BUFFET INC
2501 N Hayden Rd Ste 103, Scottsdale, AZ 85257-2326
Tel (480) 425-0397 *Founded/Ownrshp* 1997
Sales 54.1MM^E *EMP* 1,770
Tkr Sym STRZ *Exch* OTO
SIC 5812 Buffet (eating places); Family restaurants; Fast-food restaurant, chain
Ch Bd: Robert E Wheaton
Treas: Ronald E Dowdy
Board of Directors: Todd S Brown, Thomas G Schadt, B Thomas M Smith Jr, Craig B Wheaton

D-U-N-S 15-472-0213
■ STAR CONSTRUCTION LLC
(*Suby of* DYCOM INDUSTRIES INC) ★
6621 Asheville Hwy, Knoxville, TN 37924-3704
Tel (865) 521-6795 *Founded/Ownrshp* 1990
Sales 181.8MM^E *EMP* 491
SIC 1623 Telephone & communication line construction
CFO: J Kimsey
IT Man: Chris Maples

STAR CUTTER COMPANY
See STAR CUTTER CO

D-U-N-S 00-532-0015 IMP
STAR CUTTER CO (MI)
STAR CUTTER COMPANY
23461 Industrial Park Dr, Farmington Hills, MI 48335-2855
Tel (248) 474-8200 *Founded/Ownrshp* 1927, 1940
Sales 228.1MM^E *EMP* 650
SIC 3545 3479 3546 3541 Cutting tools for machine tools; Hobs; Reamers, machine tool; Drilling machine attachments & accessories; Painting, coating & hot dipping; Power-driven handtools; Machine tools, metal cutting type
Pr: Bradley L Lawton
VP: Robert Allen
**VP:* Thomas Bel
**VP:* David W Goodfellow
VP: Richard Holder
**VP:* William Langendorfer
**VP:* Bryan Lawton
VP: Lapo Colonna Vivarelli
**VP:* Martin C Woodhouse
QC Dir: Andrew Bergquist
Manager: John Simpson
Board of Directors: Norman Lawton, Richard McLeod

D-U-N-S 01-863-7306 IMP/EXP
STAR DISTRIBUTORS INC (CT)
460 Frontage Rd, West Haven, CT 06516-4154
Tel (203) 932-3636 *Founded/Ownrshp* 1937, 1986
Sales 84.8MM^E *EMP* 200
SIC 5181 Beer & other fermented malt liquors
Pr: Anthony Gallo
**CFO:* James Wicks
**VP:* Peter Gallo
VP: Cathrine Molano
Dir IT: John Gravereaux
Opers Mgr: Jeffery Stasiak

D-U-N-S 15-282-1260
STAR FINANCIAL GROUP INC
127 W Berry St Fl 2, Fort Wayne, IN 46802-2328
Tel (260) 467-5500 *Founded/Ownrshp* 1986
Sales NA *EMP* 630
Accts Bkd Llp Fort Wayne Indiana
SIC 6712 Bank holding companies
Pr: Thomas M Marcuccilli
**Ch Bd:* Kenneth A Wright
**Ch Bd:* Robert L Wright
COO: Ralph Marcuccilli
**CFO:* Karen Gregerson
Ofcr: Ronald Sasche
Ex VP: J Campbell
**Ex VP:* James C Marcuccilli
Sr VP: Robin Wright
VP: Jo Blackburn
VP: Richard Buchanan
VP: Courtney Lloyd
VP: Goldman Mike

STAR FLOORING AND DECORATING
See STAR LUMBER & SUPPLY CO INC

D-U-N-S 00-322-2924 EXP
STAR FOOD PRODUCTS INC (NC)
2050 Willow Spring Ln A, Burlington, NC 27215-8854
Tel (336) 227-4079 *Founded/Ownrshp* 1953, 2008
Sales 93.1MM^E *EMP* 125
Accts Gilliam Coble & Moser Llp
SIC 5147 2099 Meats & meat products; Ready-to-eat meals, salads & sandwiches; Salads, fresh or refrigerated
CEO: George Bradford
**Pr:* Norman Mabry
**CFO:* Joyce Abbott
**VP:* Charles Caudle
VP: Jason Griffith
**VP:* Lee Harless
Off Mgr: Crystal Hill
CTO: Benny Kidd

D-U-N-S 80-718-3629
STAR FUEL CENTERS INC
11161 Overbrook Rd, Leawood, KS 66211-2299
Tel (913) 652-9400 *Founded/Ownrshp* 1992
Sales 149.6MM^E *EMP* 120
SIC 5172 7542 5541 5411 Petroleum products; Carwashes; Truck stops; Convenience stores
Pr: David A Selph
**CFO:* Dan Engle
**VP:* Lincoln O Clifton

STAR FURNITURE
See LUXURY HOME FURNISHINGS LLC

STAR GAS
See PETRO INC

D-U-N-S 93-243-9524
▲ STAR GAS PARTNERS LP
9 W Broad St Ste 3, Stamford, CT 06902-3734
Tel (203) 328-7310 *Founded/Ownrshp* 1995
Sales 1.6MMM *EMP* 3,101^E
Accts Kpmg Llp Stamford Connectic
Tkr Sym SGU *Exch* NYS
SIC 1711 5172 Heating & air conditioning contractors; Heating systems repair & maintenance; Gases, liquefied petroleum (propane)
Pr: Steven J Goldman
Genl Pt: Kestrel Heat
CFO: Richard F Ambury

D-U-N-S 01-683-7958
STAR GLOBE NETWORK ENTERPRISES INC
1331 Nw 80th Ter, Plantation, FL 33322-5739
Tel (561) 771-2053 *Founded/Ownrshp* 2003
Sales 115.0MM *EMP* 26^E
SIC 7389 Brokers, business: buying & selling business enterprises
COO: Bruce Rynearson

D-U-N-S 12-584-4063
STAR H-R
STAR STAFFING
3820 Cypress Dr Ste 2, Petaluma, CA 94954-6964
Tel (707) 762-4447 *Founded/Ownrshp* 2003
Sales 38.9MM^E *EMP* 2,070^E
SIC 7363 Temporary help service
Pr: Carla Shevchuk
**VP:* Lisa A Rogelstad
Rgnl Mgr: Letty Smith

D-U-N-S 84-975-3769 IMP/EXP
■ STAR INTERNATIONAL HOLDINGS INC
(*Suby of* NEW STAR HOLDINGS INTERNATIONAL INC) ★
10 Sunnen Dr, Saint Louis, MO 63143-3800
Tel (314) 781-2777 *Founded/Ownrshp* 1994
Sales 93.0MM *EMP* 613
SIC 3589 Commercial cooking & foodwarming equipment
Pr: Frank Ricchio
**VP:* Mike Barber
VP: Tom Hargis

D-U-N-S 00-885-9530 IMP
STAR LUMBER & SUPPLY CO INC
STAR FLOORING AND DECORATING
325 S West St, Wichita, KS 67213-2177
Tel (316) 942-2221 *Founded/Ownrshp* 1939
Sales 113.6MM *EMP* 300^E
Accts Agh Lc Wichita Ks
SIC 5211 5713 Lumber & other building materials; Home centers; Floor covering stores
Ch Bd: Chris Goebel
**Pr:* Patrick Goebel
**CFO:* Steven Briggs
**Treas:* Jennifer Stephens
**Sr VP:* Roger Voge
Sls Mgr: Tony Burk
Sales Asso: Sean Lunsford
Sales Asso: Frank Tobias

D-U-N-S 08-894-5738 IMP
STAR MICRONICS AMERICA INC
65 Clyde Rd Ste G, Somerset, NJ 08873-3485
Tel (732) 623-5500 *Founded/Ownrshp* 1976
Sales 88.8MM^E *EMP* 584^E
SIC 5065 5045 Electronic parts; Computer peripheral equipment
Ch Bd: Hiroya Mochizuki
**CEO:* Takayouki Aoki
**CEO:* Hajime Sato
**Sec:* Yasuhiro Yamada
IT Man: Didoy Francisco
Opers Mgr: Jeff St
Ql Cn Mgr: Salman Rizvi
S&M/VP: Michael Hanson
Mktg Dir: Christophe Naasz
Mktg Dir: Annette Tarlon
Sls Dir: Christine J Duffy
Board of Directors: Hideo Fujiwara, Shozo Kasuya

D-U-N-S 09-576-4031
STAR MULTI CARE SERVICES INC
115 Broadhollow Rd # 275, Melville, NY 11747-4990
Tel (631) 423-6689 *Founded/Ownrshp* 2004
Sales 33.7MM^E *EMP* 1,042
SIC 8082 7361 Home health care services; Nurses' registry
Ch Bd: Stephen Sternbach
**CFO:* David Schoenberg
Brnch Mgr: Lauren Scalcione

D-U-N-S 07-915-2285
STAR OF DAVID ARMS INDUSTRIES INC
304 Se 2nd St Apt B, Grimes, IA 50111-1186
Tel (888) 491-0307 *Founded/Ownrshp* 2015
Sales 136.0MM *EMP* 3
SIC 3484 7389 Guns (firearms) or gun parts, 30 mm. & below;
CEO: Patrick Binder
**Pr:* Nate McAninch
**VP:* Elizabeth Binder

D-U-N-S 00-890-1498 EXP
STAR OF WEST MILLING CO (MI)
121 E Tuscola St, Frankenmuth, MI 48734-1731
Tel (330) 673-2941 *Founded/Ownrshp* 1870
Sales 396.8MM *EMP* 239
Accts Yeo & Yeo Pc Saginaw Mi
SIC 2041 5153 5191 Flour; Grains; Beans, dry: bulk; Fertilizer & fertilizer materials; Seeds: field, garden & flower; Feed
Ch Bd: Gary Rummel
**Pr:* Arthur A Loeffler
**V Ch Bd:* William A Zehnder III
**VP:* Michael Fassezke
**VP:* James Howe

D-U-N-S 08-883-5996
STAR ONE CREDIT UNION
1306 Bordeaux Dr, Sunnyvale, CA 94089-1005
Tel (408) 543-5202 *Founded/Ownrshp* 1956
Sales NA *EMP* 133
SIC 6061 Federal credit unions
Pr: Rick Heldebrant
V Ch: Dan Abihider
COO: Bonnie Kramer
CFO: Scott Dunlap
Treas: Richard Aubrey
Treas: Brian Ross
Ofcr: Dorota Jaroszewska
VP: Lynn Brubaker
VP: Kevin Collins
VP: Koji Fukumoto
VP: Chuck Ingwell
VP: Regina Rutledge
VP: Ann Sebastian

STAR PLASTICS
See SDR PLASTICS INC

D-U-N-S 00-293-1231 IMP/EXP
STAR PLASTICS INC
(*Suby of* STAR PLASTICS) ★
326 Jack Burlingame Dr, Millwood, WV 25262-8577
Tel (304) 273-0352 *Founded/Ownrshp* 1977
Sales 100.8MM^E *EMP* 120
SIC 5162 2821 Plastics materials & basic shapes; Plastics materials & resins
Pr: S Doug Ritchie
VP: Ray R Ritchie

D-U-N-S 08-014-1099
■ STAR SECOND MERGER SUB LLC
(*Suby of* CSRA INC) ★
3170 Fairview Park Dr, Falls Church, VA 22042-4516
Tel (703) 876-1000 *Founded/Ownrshp* 2015
Sales 1.3MMM^E *EMP* 6,000^E
SIC 7373 8748 Computer integrated systems design; Business consulting

D-U-N-S 80-143-8255 IMP/EXP
STAR SNACKS CO LLC
105 Harbor Dr, Jersey City, NJ 07305-4505
Tel (201) 200-9820 *Founded/Ownrshp* 1992
Sales 212.4MM *EMP* 430
Accts Saul N Friedman & Co Brookl
SIC 2068 Nuts: dried, dehydrated, salted or roasted
Off Mgr: Dawn Diaz
Site Mgr: Jacob Fleischer
Ql Cn Mgr: Don Markey
Natl Sales: Joey Weinreich

STAR STAFFING
See STAR H-R

D-U-N-S 00-214-6785 IMP/EXP
STAR STAINLESS SCREW CO
30 W End Rd, Totowa, NJ 07512-1406
Tel (973) 256-2300 *Founded/Ownrshp* 1948
Sales 138.8MM^E *EMP* 400
SIC 5072 Hardware; Miscellaneous fasteners; Screws; Nuts (hardware)
Pr: Wayne Golden
CIO: Susan Raab
Dir IT: Susan Denicola

D-U-N-S 11-909-5177 IMP
STAR SU CO LLC
5200 Prairie Stone Pkwy, Hoffman Estates, IL 60192-3709
Tel (847) 649-1450 *Founded/Ownrshp* 2009
Sales 180.0MM *EMP* 450
SIC 5084 Machine tools & accessories
VP: Brian Cluff
VP: Rick Falgiatano
Manager: Rodney Howard
Manager: Jeff Jacobs
Manager: Pat Kirwan
Sls Mgr: Dan Kalafut
Sales Asso: Tessa Johnson

STAR TOYOTA
See BENSON - SABIN INC

STAR TRAC
See CORE INDUSTRIES LLC

STAR TRAC
See CORE HEALTH & FITNESS LLC

D-U-N-S 00-584-1580
STAR TRANSPORT INC
240 W Ashland St, Morton, IL 61550-1437
Tel (309) 266-7613 *Founded/Ownrshp* 1987
Sales NA *EMP* 1,050
SIC 4213 4731

D-U-N-S 83-267-2377
STAR TRIBUNE MEDIA CO LLC
650 3rd Ave S Ste 1300, Minneapolis, MN 55488-0001
Tel (612) 673-4000 *Founded/Ownrshp* 2009
Sales 431.1MM^E *EMP* 2,764
SIC 2711 Newspapers
CEO: Michael J Klingensmith
Treas: Mario Pedercini
**Sr VP:* Chuck Brown
VP: Steven H Alexander
VP: Jim Bernard
VP: Kevin Desmond
VP: David Diegnau
VP: Jon Ochetti
**VP:* Adrienne Sirany
Dir IT: Wayne Johnson

STAR WATER SYSTEMS
See FLINT & WALLING INC

D-U-N-S 17-282-1050
STAR-LO ELECTRIC INC
32 S Jefferson Rd, Whippany, NJ 07981-1001
Tel (973) 515-0500 *Founded/Ownrshp* 1951
Sales 86.6MM^E *EMP* 230
SIC 1731 General electrical contractor
Pr: Joe Stark
**VP:* Robert Delle Cava
VP: Robert Dellecava
**VP:* Joe Rinaldi
**VP:* Ted Stark
Sfty Dirs: Robert Jennings

D-U-N-S 19-508-0379
■ STAR-TELEGRAM OPERATING LTD
FORT WORTH STAR TELEGRAM
(*Suby of* CYPRESS MEDIA, INC)
808 Throckmorton St, Fort Worth, TX 76102-6315
Tel (817) 390-7400 *Founded/Ownrshp* 1997
Sales 204.9MM^E *EMP* 1,800
SIC 2711 Newspapers
Pr: Gary Wortel
**Pr:* Marhta Wilson
**CFO:* Roger Provost
Ex VP: James Michael
VP: Javier Aldape
VP: Randy Bridgeford
**VP:* Dolan Stidom
**VP:* Weldon Whiteman
VP: Mike Winter
VP Admn: David Ivory
Genl Mgr: Mark Williamson

STAR.COM WORLWIDE
See STARCOM MEDIAVEST GROUP INC

D-U-N-S 04-403-1326 IMP/EXP
STARBOARD CRUISE SERVICES INC (FL)
LVMH MOET HNNSSY LOUIS VUITTON
(*Suby of* LVMH MOET HENNESSY LOUIS VUITTON INC) ★
8400 Nw 36th St Ste 600, Doral, FL 33166-6620
Tel (786) 845-7300 *Founded/Ownrshp* 1958, 2007
Sales 100.9MM^E *EMP* 380
SIC 5399 Duty-free goods
VP: Maureen Johnson
**Treas:* Ares Michaelides
**Chf Mktg O:* Patrick Gates
**VP:* Ronnie Morrison
Brnch Mgr: Scott C Singer
Dist Mgr: Nikola Dimovski
Dir IT: Jose Carpio
Merch Mgr: Cecilia Gonzalez
Merch Mgr: Sherri Korman
Merch Mgr: Carolina Salcedo
Merch Mgr: Diane Treganza

STARBUCKS
See FRESH CHOICE LLC

D-U-N-S 78-947-7325 IMP/EXP
■ STARBUCKS COFFEE INTERNATIONAL INC
(*Suby of* STARBUCKS CORP) ★
2401 Utah Ave S Ste 800, Seattle, WA 98134-1435
Tel (206) 447-1575 *Founded/Ownrshp* 1963
Sales 4.1MMM^E *EMP* 186,582^E
SIC 5812 Coffee shop
CEO: Howard Schultz
**Pr:* Troy Alstead
**Sr VP:* Wendy Collie
**VP:* Clifford Burrows
**VP:* John Culver
**VP:* Annie Young-Scrivner
Prgrm Mgr: Susan Genoni
Prgrm Mgr: Aaron Hatch
Dist Mgr: Susan S Nixon
Store Mgr: Lea Brazee
Store Mgr: Evelyn Pineda

D-U-N-S 15-536-6107
▲ STARBUCKS CORP
2401 Utah Ave S, Seattle, WA 98134-1436
Tel (206) 447-1575 *Founded/Ownrshp* 1985
Sales 21.3MMM *EMP* 238,000
Tkr Sym SBUX *Exch* NGS
SIC 5812 5499 5461 5149 Coffee shop; Coffee; Pastries; Coffee, green or roasted; Tea

Ch Bd: Howard Schultz
Pr: Cliff Burrows
Pr: John Culver
**Pr:* Kevin R Johnson
CFO: Scott Maw
Ofcr: Leanne Fremar
Ex VP: Eduardo Garcia
Ex VP: Lucy Lee Helm
Ex VP: Frank Wubben
VP: Linda Barr
VP: Luigi Bonini
VP: Brady Brewer
VP: Rob Dilworth
VP: Julie Eisen
VP: Jennifer Gurtov
VP: Willard Hay
VP: Eric Jensen
VP: Dave Olsen
VP: Jim Olson
VP: Jim Spillane
VP: Brendan Weitzman
Board of Directors: William W Bradley, Mary N Dillon, Robert M Gates, Joshua Cooper Ramo, James G Shennan Jr, Clara Shih, Javier G Teruel, Myron E Ullman III, Craig E Weatherup

D-U-N-S 11-361-6689
STARCOM MEDIAVEST GROUP INC
STAR.COM WORLWIDE
(*Suby of* PUBLICIS GROUPE S A)
35 W Wacker Dr Fl 9, Chicago, IL 60601-1639
Tel (312) 220-3535 *Founded/Ownrshp* 2002
Sales 675.2MM^E *EMP* 5,800
SIC 7311 Advertising agencies
CEO: Jack Klues
**Pr:* Laura Desmond
CFO: Robin Chen
Ex VP: Brian Elwarner
Ex VP: Esther Franklin
Ex VP: Danielle Gonzales
Ex VP: Chris Harder
Ex VP: Matt Kain
Ex VP: Chris Rayner
Ex VP: Matt Rayner
Ex VP: Lia Silkworth
Sr VP: Shelby Saville
VP: Kris Allen
VP: Bethany Bayer
VP: Cecilia Bizon
VP: Bohb Blair
VP: Randy Carelli
VP: Rob Davis
VP: John Delaney
VP: Laurie Deprete
VP: Paul Furia

D-U-N-S 05-746-9504 IMP
STARCREST PRODUCTS OF CALIFORNIA INC
T-MICHAEL INTERNATIONAL
3660 Brennan Ave # 1000, Perris, CA 92599-1000
Tel (951) 943-2011 *Founded/Ownrshp* 1976
Sales 215.0MM^E *EMP* 1,000^E
SIC 5961 Gift items, mail order; Mail order house; Women's apparel, mail order
Pr: Timothy E Calandra
**Pr:* Michael Donnelly
COO: Becky Wolever
VP: Daniella Rosenthal
IT Man: Dave Branson
IT Man: Donald Smith
Sales Exec: Alex Angellar

D-U-N-S 07-310-3384
STARFIRE HOLDING CORP
445 Hamilton Ave Ste 1210, White Plains, NY 10601-1833
Tel (914) 614-7000 *Founded/Ownrshp* 1982
Sales 1.4MMM^E *EMP* 11,300
SIC 3743 4741 4789 Freight cars & equipment; Rental of railroad cars; Railroad car repair
Ch Bd: Carl Celian Icahn
VP: Keith Cozza

D-U-N-S 01-225-7549 IMP
STARK CARPET CORP
STARK U.S.A.
979 3rd Ave Fl 11, New York, NY 10022-1276
Tel (844) 407-8275 *Founded/Ownrshp* 1968
Sales 146.4MM^E *EMP* 450
SIC 5099 5131 5021 Brass goods; Piece goods & other fabrics; Furniture
CEO: John Stark
Pr: Steven Stark
Rgnl Mgr: Timothy Cohen
Genl Mgr: Edward Haleman
DP Exec: Eric Robespierre
Opers Mgr: Sandra Decastro
Opers Mgr: Steven Duncan
Sales Exec: Lisa Whetsell
Mktg Dir: Nyan Gabriel
Sls Dir: Richard Zolt
Sls Mgr: Robin Weiss

D-U-N-S 00-597-1841
STARK EXCAVATING INC (IL)
1805 W Washington St, Bloomington, IL 61701-3703
Tel (309) 828-5034 *Founded/Ownrshp* 1949, 1973
Sales 206.6MM^E *EMP* 625
SIC 1611 1794 Highway & street construction; Excavation work
Pr: David K Stark
CFO: Gary Mao
CFO: Gary Masso
**Treas:* Gary W Masso
**VP:* Joseph W Weishaar

D-U-N-S 07-689-7354
STARK STATE COLLEGE
6200 Frank Ave Nw, North Canton, OH 44720-7299
Tel (330) 494-6170 *Founded/Ownrshp* 1960
Sales 56.4MM^E *EMP* 1,000^E
Accts Balestra Harr & Scherer Cpas
SIC 8222 Technical institute
Pr: Para Jones
Pr: Michael Droney
Treas: Cindy Bruce
Bd of Dir: Monica Gwin
Bd of Dir: Ahmed Sabe
Bd of Dir: Ronald Wilkof

Ofcr: Hollis Burkes
VP: James Myers
Netwrk Mgr: Jack Freis
Netwrk Mgr: Gordon Gord

D-U-N-S 00-446-1612
STARK TRUSS CO INC
S T C
109 Miles Ave Sw, Canton, OH 44710-1261
Tel (330) 478-2100 *Founded/Ownrshp* 1963
Sales 256.1MM^E *EMP* 600
SIC 5031 2439 Lumber, plywood & millwork; Trusses, wooden roof
CEO: Abner Yoder
**Pr:* Stephen Yoder
CFO: Ron Groom
**Treas:* Esther Yoder
**Ex VP:* Javan Yoder
**VP:* Todd Pallotta

STARK U.S.A.
See STARK CARPET CORP

D-U-N-S 05-546-1479 IMP
STARKEY LABORATORIES INC (MN)
MICRO TECH
6600 Washington Ave S, Eden Prairie, MN 55344-3404
Tel (952) 941-6401 *Founded/Ownrshp* 1969
Sales 1.0MMM^E *EMP* 3,300
SIC 3842 Hearing aids
CEO: William F Austin
**Pr:* Jerry Ruzicka
CFO: Scott Nelson
Treas: Tani Austin
Ofcr: Ken Meyer
**Sr VP:* Rob Duchscher
Sr VP: Robert Erickson
Sr VP: Keith Guggenberger
**Sr VP:* Phil Lyons
Sr VP: Brandon Sawalich
Sr VP: Timothy D Trine
**VP:* Brent Edwards PH D
VP: Kenny Landherr
VP: Dale J Thorstad
Exec: Rachael Kuiken
Dir Soc: Jackie Larson

D-U-N-S 18-420-4790
STARKVILLE OKTIBBEHA CONSOLIDATED SCHOOL DISTRICT
401 Greensboro St, Starkville, MS 39759-2803
Tel (662) 324-4050 *Founded/Ownrshp* 1994
Sales 29.1MM^E *EMP* 1,000
SIC 8211 Public elementary & secondary schools
Schl Brd P: Lee Brand
HC Dir: Milton Smith

D-U-N-S 09-469-8321 IMP/EXP
■ **STARMARK CABINETRY**
(*Suby of* MID CONTINENT CABINETRY) ★
600 E 48th St N, Sioux Falls, SD 57104-0620
Tel (800) 755-7789 *Founded/Ownrshp* 1978
Sales 85.1MM^E *EMP* 600
SIC 2434 Wood kitchen cabinets; Vanities, bathroom: wood
Pr: John Swedeen
Dir IT: Michael Melvin
Dir IT: Brad Tieszen
Dir IT: Darin Wipf
VP Opers: Peter Bendix
Mktg Dir: Jennifer Thom
Manager: Mark Pyle
Sls Mgr: Bill Bowen
Sls Mgr: Antoine Hampton

D-U-N-S 10-255-2619 IMP
STARMARK MANAGEMENT HOLDINGS LLC
WELLBRIDGE COMPANY
6140 Greenwood Plaza Blvd, Greenwood Village, CO 80111-4803
Tel (303) 866-0800 *Founded/Ownrshp* 1982
Sales 101.4MM^E *EMP* 4,500
SIC 7997 Membership sports & recreation clubs
Rgnl Mgr: Steve Datte
Genl Mgr: Laurie A Smith
Mktg Dir: Glen Strandberg

D-U-N-S 80-464-0134
STARMOUNT LIFE INSURANCE CO INC
8485 Goodwood Blvd, Baton Rouge, LA 70806-7878
Tel (225) 400-9100 *Founded/Ownrshp* 1983
Sales NA *EMP* 160
SIC 6311 Life insurance
Ch: Hans J Sternberg
**Pr:* Erich Sternberg
**CFO:* Jeff Wild
**Sr VP:* Donna Sternberg

STARPAK
See ULTRAPAK LTD

D-U-N-S 18-039-8505
STARPLEX CORP
CROWD MANAGEMENT SERVICES
12722 Ne Airport Way, Portland, OR 97230-1027
Tel (503) 222-5957 *Founded/Ownrshp* 1979
Sales 38.2MM^E *EMP* 1,517
Accts L Phillip Paris Cpa Pc
SIC 7381 7363 7999 Security guard service; Usher service; Ticket sales office for sporting events, contract
Pr: James J Deloretto
COO: Debra Zawada
Opers Mgr: James Ryan
Opers Mgr: Bill Scott

STARQUEST PRODUCTS
See KINRO MANUFACTURING INC

STARQUEST SECURITIES
See POHLAD COMPANIES

D-U-N-S 07-950-0066
STARR COMPANIES
399 Park Ave Rm 1700, New York, NY 10022-4681
Tel (646) 227-6300 *Founded/Ownrshp* 2014
Sales NA *EMP* 232^E
SIC 6321 Accident & health insurance
CEO: Maurice R Greenberg

CFO: Michael J Castelli
CFO: Niraj Patel
Sr VP: Grant Saunders
Snr Mgr: John Sanchez

D-U-N-S 02-460-1239
STARR ELECTRIC CO INC (NC)
6 Battleground Ct, Greensboro, NC 27408-8007
Tel (336) 275-0241 *Founded/Ownrshp* 1928
Sales 160.1MM^E *EMP* 840
SIC 1731

D-U-N-S 02-321-5896
STARR INDEMNITY & LIABILITY CO
(*Suby of* STARR INSURANCE GROUP, INC.)
399 Park Ave Rm 1700, New York, NY 10022-4681
Tel (646) 227-6300 *Founded/Ownrshp* 2012
Sales NA *EMP* 2^E
SIC 6321 Accident & health insurance
Ch Bd: Maurice R Greenberg

D-U-N-S 07-886-5239
STARR INSURANCE HOLDINGS INC
(*Suby of* STARR INTERNATIONAL CO INC) ★
399 Park Ave Rm 1702, New York, NY 10022-4882
Tel (646) 227-6300 *Founded/Ownrshp* 2012
Sales 303.1MM^E *EMP* 434
SIC 6282 6411 Investment advice; Insurance brokers
CEO: Maurice R Greenberg
Ex VP: Allyson Vento

D-U-N-S 96-820-3039
STARR INTERNATIONAL CO INC
399 Park Ave Fl 8, New York, NY 10022-4877
Tel (646) 227-6300 *Founded/Ownrshp* 2011
Sales 303.1MM^E *EMP* 621
SIC 6531 Real estate agents & managers
V Ch Bd: Lord Peter Levene

STARR PUFF FACTORY
See ROSKAM BAKING CO

D-U-N-S 02-037-7388
STARR TECHNICAL RISKS AGENCY INC
(*Suby of* STARR INDEMNITY & LIABILITY CO) ★
90 Park Ave Fl 9, New York, NY 10016-1310
Tel (646) 227-6301 *Founded/Ownrshp* 2012
Sales NA *EMP* 150
SIC 6331 Property damage insurance
Pr: Richard Shaak
**Sr VP:* James J Regan

D-U-N-S 96-686-6431
STARRETT CITY ASSOCIATES LP
1230 Pa Ave Ste 1, Brooklyn, NY 11239-1119
Tel (718) 240-4112 *Founded/Ownrshp* 2007
Sales 122.0MM *EMP* 490^E
SIC 6513 Apartment building operators
Pt: Carol Deane

D-U-N-S 17-085-7015
STARRETT CITY INC
(*Suby of* STARRETT CITY ASSOCIATES LP) ★
1230 Pa Ave Ste 1, Brooklyn, NY 11239-1119
Tel (718) 642-8700 *Founded/Ownrshp* 1973
Sales 114.0MM *EMP* 200
SIC 6513 Apartment building operators
Pr: Carol Deane

D-U-N-S 01-225-7804
STARRETT CORP
70 E 55th St Fl 7, New York, NY 10022-3392
Tel (212) 350-9909 *Founded/Ownrshp* 2006
Sales 295.4MM^E *EMP* 1,800^E
SIC 6552 Land subdividers & developers, commercial; Land subdividers & developers, residential
CEO: Robert Birnbach
**VP:* Peter H Gray

D-U-N-S 83-090-6967
■ **STARSUPPLY PETROLEUM LLC**
(*Suby of* GFI GROUP INC) ★
55 Water St, New York, NY 10041-0004
Tel (212) 968-2920 *Founded/Ownrshp* 2001
Sales 94.8MM^E *EMP* 988^E
SIC 5172 Petroleum products
Prin: Mark Gaynor

D-U-N-S 09-085-7517
▲ **STARTEK INC**
8200 E Maplewood Ave # 100, Greenwood Village, CO 80111-4813
Tel (303) 262-4500 *Founded/Ownrshp* 1987
Sales 282.1MM *EMP* 14,500^E
Tkr Sym SRT *Exch* NYS
SIC 7374 7379 8742 Data processing service; Computer related consulting services; Business consultant
Pr: Chad A Carlson
**Ch Bd:* Ed Zschau
CFO: Donald Norsworthy
Sr VP: John Hoholik
Sr VP: Jaymes D Kirksey
VP: Eric Concepcion
VP Bus Dev: Lucas Anderson
Snr PM: Rebecca Surad
Board of Directors: Arnaud Ajdler, Benjamin L Rosenzweig, Robert Sheft, Jack D Plating

D-U-N-S 15-466-7125
■ **STARTEK USA INC**
(*Suby of* STARTEK INC) ★
8200 E Maplewood Ave # 100, Greenwood Village, CO 80111-4813
Tel (303) 262-4150 *Founded/Ownrshp* 1987
Sales 124.0MM^E *EMP* 3,000
SIC 7372 7379 5045 Business oriented computer software; Computer related consulting services; Computer software
Pr: Steve Butler
**Ch Bd:* A Emmet Stephenson Jr
**CFO:* Rodd Granger
CFO: Dennis M Swenson
**Sr VP:* Jim Farnsworth
Sr VP: Michael Griffith
Sr VP: Patrick M Hayes
VP: Grant Lomas

VP: Shelby Test-Peralta
MIS Dir: Debbie Grosskopf

D-U-N-S 07-413-8397
STARVING STUDENTS INC
6220 Kimberly Ave Ste 2, Las Vegas, NV 89122-7660
Tel (702) 900-4002 *Founded/Ownrshp* 1973
Sales 132.7MM^E *EMP* 600
SIC 4214 4213 Household goods moving & storage, local; Household goods transport
CEO: Chris Carlsson
**Pr:* Ethan Margalith
**CFO:* Jean Fria

D-U-N-S 80-948-9891
STARWOOD CAPITAL GROUP LLC
591 W Putnam Ave, Greenwich, CT 06830-6005
Tel (203) 422-7700 *Founded/Ownrshp* 1996
Sales 440.6MM^E *EMP* 535
SIC 6211 Investment firm, general brokerage
CEO: Barry S Sternlicht
Pr: Neil B Jacobs
Pr: James D Motta
Pr: C Scott Rohm
**COO:* Daniel Yih
CFO: James Allen
CFO: Stew Ward
Ofcr: Warren De Haan
**Ex VP:* Ellis F Rinaldi
**Ex VP:* Jerome C Silvey
Sr VP: David J Friedman
Sr VP: Heather Goldman
Sr VP: Neil Harris
VP: Ash Kapur
VP: Mark Keatley
VP: Roy G Paskow
VP: Joseph Rizzo
VP: Gary A Walker

STARWOOD HOTELS & RESORTS
See SHERATON PHOENICIAN CORP

D-U-N-S 03-775-8281
■ **STARWOOD HOTELS & RESORTS WORLDWIDE LLC**
(*Suby of* MARRIOTT INTERNATIONAL INC) ★
1 Star Pt, Stamford, CT 06902-8911
Tel (203) 964-6000 *Founded/Ownrshp* 2016
Sales 5.7MMM *EMP* 47^E
SIC 7011 8741 Hotels; Casino hotel; Resort hotel; Motor inn; Hotel or motel management
Ch Bd: JW Marriott Jr
Pr: Arne M Sorenson
CFO: Kathleen K Oberg
Ch: David A Rodriguez
Treas: Carolyn B Handlon
Ofcr: Bao Giang Val Bauduin
Ex VP: Anthony G Capuano
Ex VP: Leslie Fairbanks
Ex VP: Stephanie C Linnartz
Ex VP: Tricia Primrose
Ex VP: Edward Ryan
Sr VP: Laura E Paugh
Sr VP: Jim Petrus
VP: David Auerbach
VP: Emilio Consigliere
VP: Jim Crane
VP: Eve Dreher
VP: Kelly Frank
VP: Bancroft S Gordon
VP: Lance Johnson
VP: Jaime Leonti
Board of Directors: Charlene Barshefsky, Thomas E Clarke, Clayton C Daley Jr, Eric Hippeau, Aylwin B Lewis, Stephen R Quazzo, Thomas O Ryder

D-U-N-S 83-129-5899
STARWOOD PROPERTY TRUST INC
591 W Putnam Ave, Greenwich, CT 06830-6005
Tel (203) 422-7700 *Founded/Ownrshp* 2009
Sales 735.8MM *EMP* 948
Accts Deloitte & Touche Llp Miami
SIC 6798 Real estate investment trusts; Mortgage investment trusts
Ch Bd: Barry S Sternlicht
Pr: Jeffrey F Dimodica
COO: Andrew J Sossen
CFO: Rina Paniry
Ofcr: Dennis Schuh
Board of Directors: Richard D Bronson, Jeffrey G Dishner, Camille J Douglas, Solomon J Kumin

D-U-N-S 11-201-9005 EXP
■ **STARWOOD VACATION SERVICES INC**
(*Suby of* STARWOOD HOTELS & RESORTS WORLDWIDE LLC) ★
8801 Vistana Centre Dr, Orlando, FL 32821-6354
Tel (407) 903-4640 *Founded/Ownrshp* 1999
Sales 172.7MM^E *EMP* 3,800
SIC 7041 Membership-basis organization hotels
CEO: Sergio D Rivera
**Pr:* Frits Van Paasschen
**COO:* Matthew E Avril
**CFO:* Vasant M Prabhu
CFO: Michelle Srymire
**Ch:* Raymond L Gellein Jr
**Treas:* John Buckwalter
Treas: Lisa Casin
**Ex VP:* Jeff Cava
**Sr VP:* Roger Berry
**Sr VP:* Victoria H Carter
**Sr VP:* Thorp S Thomas
**Sr VP:* Susan Werth
**Sr VP:* Stephen G Williams
**VP:* Angela K Halladay
Board of Directors: James G Brocksmith Jr, Laurence S Geller, Steven J Heyer

D-U-N-S 07-828-7792
▲ **STARZ**
8900 Liberty Cir, Englewood, CO 80112-7057
Tel (720) 852-7700 *Founded/Ownrshp* 2007
Sales 1.7MMM *EMP* 772
Tkr Sym STRZA *Exch* NGS
SIC 4841 4813 Cable & other pay television services; Telephone communication, except radio
**Ch Bd:* Gregory B Maffei
**Pr:* Christopher P Albrecht
COO: Jeffrey Hirsch
CFO: Scott D Macdonald

Ex VP: David I Weil
Ex VP: Edward Huguez
VP: Melissa Harper
Mktg Mgr: Lynnette Holloway

D-U-N-S 62-249-1173
■ STARZ ENTERTAINMENT LLC
(*Suby of* STARZ LLC) ★
8900 Liberty Cir, Englewood, CO 80112-7057
Tel (720) 852-7700 *Founded/Ownrshp* 1998
Sales 1.3MMM *EMP* 692
Accts Kpmg Llp Denver Colorado
SIC 7812 Motion picture production & distribution, television
CEO: Chris Albrecht
**Pr:* Glenn Curtiz
**CFO:* Scott D Macdonald
Treas: Mandy Minnard
**Ofcr:* Michael Phorton
VP: Debbie Alther
VP: Janet Dickinson
VP: Todd Hoy
VP: James Porter
VP: Suzanne Sell
Creative D: Rama Wong

D-U-N-S 78-787-4796
■ STARZ LLC
(*Suby of* STARZ) ★
8900 Liberty Cir, Englewood, CO 80112-7057
Tel (720) 852-7700 *Founded/Ownrshp* 2006
Sales 1.7MMM *EMP* 916
SIC 7812 Cartoon motion picture production; Cartoon production, television
CEO: Chris Albrecht
**Pr:* Glenn Curtis
**CFO:* Scott D Macdonald
**Treas:* Mindy Jack
Ex VP: Dave Baldwin
Ex VP: Ray Milius
Ex VP: John Penney
Sr VP: Kelly Bumann
Sr VP: Christine Carrier
Sr VP: Richard Turner
Sr VP: Richard Waysdorf
VP: Debbie Alther
VP: Ryc Brownrigg

D-U-N-S 05-008-2643
STATCO ENGINEERING & FABRICATORS INC
INTERSTATE MNROE MCHY SUPS DIV
7595 Reynolds Cir, Huntington Beach, CA 92647-6752
Tel (714) 375-6300 *Founded/Ownrshp* 1982
Sales 102.0MM^E *EMP* 123
SIC 5084 3556 Processing & packaging equipment; Food products machinery; Meat, poultry & seafood processing machinery
CEO: Eric Perkins
Sales Asso: Elizabeth Martinez

D-U-N-S 80-678-0433
STATE ASSEMBLY NEW YORK
(*Suby of* NEW YORK STATE ASSEMBLY) ★
1 Enterprise Dr, Albany, NY 12204-2520
Tel (518) 455-4100 *Founded/Ownrshp* 1788
Sales NA *EMP* 2,000
SIC 9121 Legislative bodies, state & local;
**Prin:* Sheldon Silver
Web Prj Mg: Zimmerman Steve

D-U-N-S 78-282-0146
■ STATE AUTO FINANCIAL CORP
(*Suby of* STATE AUTO INSURANCE CO) ★
518 E Broad St, Columbus, OH 43215-3901
Tel (614) 464-5000 *Founded/Ownrshp* 1990
Sales NA *EMP* 2,274^E
Accts Ernst & Young Llp Columbus O
Tkr Sym STFC *Exch* NGS
SIC 6331 Fire, marine & casualty insurance
Pr: Michael E Larocco
**Ch Bd:* Robert P Restrepo Jr
Pr: Alp Can
Pr: Tom Mullaney
Pr: Rudy Palenik
CFO: Steven E English
Treas: Matthew R Pollak
Ofcr: Stephen P Hunckler
Ofcr: Steve Hunckler
Ofcr: Cynthia A Powell
Sr VP: Joel E Brown
Sr VP: Jessica E Buss
Sr VP: Melissa A Centers
Sr VP: Clyde H Fitch Jr
Sr VP: Kim Garland
Sr VP: Lyle D Rhodebeck
Sr VP: Paul Stachura
Sr VP: James A Yano
VP: Jack Abney
VP: Lester Brue
VP: Jay Carleton
Board of Directors: Robert E Baker, David J D'antoni, Michael J Fiorile, Eileen A Mallesch, Thomas E Markert, David R Meuse, S Elaine Roberts

STATE AUTO INSURANCE CO
See STATE AUTOMOBILE MUTUAL INSURANCE CO INC

D-U-N-S 00-486-8287
■ STATE AUTO PROPERTY AND CASUALTY INSURANCE CO (IA)
(*Suby of* STATE AUTO FINANCIAL CORP) ★
518 E Broad St, Columbus, OH 43215-3901
Tel (614) 464-5000 *Founded/Ownrshp* 1958
Sales NA *EMP* 2,059
SIC 6331 Fire, marine & casualty insurance & carriers; Automobile insurance
Pr: Robert P Restrepo Jr
VP: Terrence Bowshier
VP: Joel Brown
VP: David Dalton
VP: James Duemey
VP: Steven Hazelbaker
VP: Terrence Higerd
**VP:* Terry Higerd
**VP:* David J Hosler
VP: John Melvin
VP: Cathy Miley
VP: Paul Nordman
VP: John Petrucci
**VP:* Cynthia A Powell
VP: Jean Reynolds

D-U-N-S 00-790-2232
▲ STATE AUTOMOBILE MUTUAL INSURANCE CO INC
STATE AUTO INSURANCE CO
518 E Broad St, Columbus, OH 43215-3901
Tel (614) 464-5000 *Founded/Ownrshp* 1987
Sales NA *EMP* 2,488
SIC 6331 6411 6351 Fire, marine & casualty insurance & carriers; Automobile insurance; Insurance agents, brokers & service; Surety insurance
Ch Bd: Robert Restrepo Jr
**CFO:* Steven J Johnston
**Ofcr:* Stephen P Hunckler
Ofcr: Cynthia A Powell
Sr VP: Jessica E Buss
Sr VP: Lyle D Rhodebeck
Sr VP: James A Yano
VP: Steven R Hazelbaker
**VP:* David J Hosler
**VP:* John R Lowther
**VP:* Cynthia Powell
**VP:* Larry Williams

D-U-N-S 80-045-0228
■ STATE BANK AND TRUST CO
(*Suby of* STATE BANK FINANCIAL CORP) ★
3399 Peachtree Rd Ne # 1900, Atlanta, GA 30326-2836
Tel (800) 414-4177 *Founded/Ownrshp* 2004
Sales NA *EMP* 355
SIC 6022 State commercial banks
CEO: J Thomas Wiley Jr
V Ch: Kim M Childers
V Ch: J Saniel Speight Jr
Pr: Thomas M Bird
Pr: Remer Y Brinson III
CFO: Sheila E Ray
Ch: Joseph W Evans
VP: Cecilia Crutchfield

D-U-N-S 96-333-1538
▲ STATE BANK FINANCIAL CORP
3399 Peachtree Rd Ne, Atlanta, GA 30326-1120
Tel (404) 475-6599 *Founded/Ownrshp* 2010
Sales NA *EMP* 732^E
Tkr Sym STBZ *Exch* NAS
SIC 6022 6712 6311 6141 6331 State commercial banks; Bank holding companies; Life insurance; Automobile loans, including insurance; Automobile insurance
Ch Bd: Joseph W Evans
**Pr:* J Thomas Wiley Jr
CFO: Sheila E Ray
**V Ch Bd:* Kim M Childers
**V Ch Bd:* J Daniel Speight Jr
Ex VP: David F Black
Ex VP: David C Brown
Ex VP: David Brown
Ex VP: David W Cline
Ex VP: Steven G Deaton
Ex VP: Michael R Fitzgerald
Ex VP: Michael S Sims
Ex VP: Bradford L Watkins

D-U-N-S 93-267-1688
STATE BANKSHARES INC
3100 13th Ave S, Fargo, ND 58103-3507
Tel (701) 298-1500 *Founded/Ownrshp* 1989
Sales NA *EMP* 300
SIC 6022 State commercial banks
VP: Thomas Snortland
Bd of Dir: Billy M Nustad
Bd of Dir: Julie Peterson
Ex VP: John Aarsvold
Sr VP: Christine Christensen
Sr VP: Durinda Detar
Sr VP: Diane Kaiser
Sr VP: Kevin Prodoehl
Sr VP: Bob Willer
VP: Vikki Nielsen
Mng Dir: Seth Hove

D-U-N-S 79-549-3709
STATE BOARD FOR COMMUNITY COLLEGES AND OCCUPATIONAL EDUCATIONAL SYSTEM
COLORADO COMMUNITY COLLEGE SYS
9101 E Lowry Pl, Denver, CO 80230-6011
Tel (303) 595-1552 *Founded/Ownrshp* 1985
Sales 321.8M *EMP* 2,658
Accts Eks&H Lllp Denver Co
SIC 8222 Community college
Pr: Nancy McCallin
CFO: Kerri Nawrocki
VP: Geri Anderson
VP: Cliff Richardson
VP: Nancy Wahl
Ex Dir: Cynthia Hier
Genl Mgr: Jon Cermak
CTO: Kendra Rodriguez
QA Dir: Elizabeth Dzabic
Dir IT: Yvonne Gilstrap
IT Man: Ken Campion

D-U-N-S 06-886-9734
STATE CENTER COMMUNITY COLLEGE DISTRICT
CLOVIS COMMUNITY COLLEGE CTR
1525 E Weldon Ave, Fresno, CA 93704-6340
Tel (559) 226-0720 *Founded/Ownrshp* 1964
Sales 57.5MM *EMP* 1,266
Accts Crowe Horwath Llp Sacramento
SIC 8222 Community college
Ch: Tim Liermann
**CEO:* Gurdeep Sihota He'bert
Trst: John Leal
Ofcr: Chris Caldwell
Ofcr: Nick Hernandez
Ofcr: Felipe Uribe
Exec: Daine Clerou
CTO: Charles Francis
Dir IT: Ray Tjahjadi
Board of Directors: Gonzalez Patricia-Sec, Billings Glynna-Acct, Schofield Wil-Dir of Fin

STATE CHEMICAL MANUFACTURING
See STATE INDUSTRIAL PRODUCTS CORP

D-U-N-S 07-285-0779
STATE COLLEGE AREA SCHOOL DISTRICT (PA)
131 W Nittany Ave, State College, PA 16801-4899
Tel (814) 231-1016 *Founded/Ownrshp* 1966
Sales 100.4MM^E *EMP* 1,500
Accts Parentebeard Llc State Colleg
SIC 8211 Public combined elementary & secondary school
Exec: Andrea De Carle
Pr Dir: Chris Rosenblum
Teacher Pr: Linda Pierce
Psych: Danielle Deangelis
Psych: Daniel Duffy
Psych: Rachel Lago
Psych: Sarah Rochette

D-U-N-S 00-923-6100
STATE COMPENSATION INSURANCE FUND INC
STATE FUND
333 Bush St Fl 8, San Francisco, CA 94104-2845
Tel (888) 782-8338 *Founded/Ownrshp* 1914
Sales NA *EMP* 4,300
SIC 6331 Workers' compensation insurance
Pr: Vernon Steiner
COO: Judy Girdenis
COO: Beatriz Sanchez
CFO: Peter Guastamachio
CFO: Peter A Guastamachio
CFO: Daniel J Sevilla Jr
CFO: Jay Stewart
Bd of Dir: Scott Reid
Chf Inves: Peter Guastamichio
Ex VP: Darlyn Regan
Sr VP: Andreas Acker
Sr VP: Brian Watson
VP: Christina Castro
VP: Simon Chong
VP: Don Smith
VP: Cheryl Sutherland
VP: Jennifer Vargen
VP: William Zachry
Dir Risk M: Ken Van Laar
Board of Directors: Sheryl Chalupa, Daniel M Curtin, Donald Garcia, Lawrence Mulryan, Francis Quinlan, Steven Rank, Thomas Rankin, Scott Reid, William Zachry

STATE CONTROLLER DIVISION
See OREGON DEPARTMENT OF ADMINISTRATIVE SERVICES

D-U-N-S 04-089-8256
STATE COUNCIL OF HIGHER EDUCATION FOR VIRGINIA
(*Suby of* VIRGINIA SECRETARY OF EDUCATION) ★
101 N 14th St Fl 9, Richmond, VA 23219-3665
Tel (804) 225-2627 *Founded/Ownrshp* 1997
Sales NA *EMP* 6,900^E
SIC 9411
Ex Dir: Peter Blake
Ex VP: Arthur Garson Jr
VP: M D Shelton Jr
VP: Julius A Sigler Jr

STATE DATA CENTER
See EMPLOYMENT COMMISSION VIRGINIA

D-U-N-S 94-948-5445
STATE DEPARTMENT OF COMMUNITY AFFAIRS
(*Suby of* NEW JERSEY DEPT OF COMMUNITY AFFAIRS) ★
101 S Broad St, Trenton, NJ 08608-2401
Tel (609) 292-6420 *Founded/Ownrshp* 1999
Sales NA *EMP* 1,000
SIC 9441

D-U-N-S 00-501-6589 IMP
STATE ELECTRIC SUPPLY CO (WV)
SESCO
(*Suby of* STATE ELECTRIC SUPPLY CO) ★
2010 2nd Ave, Huntington, WV 25703-1108
Tel (304) 523-7491 *Founded/Ownrshp* 1952
Sales 557.8MM^E *EMP* 550
SIC 5063 3357 Lighting fixtures; Receptacles, electrical; Wire & cable; Fuses & accessories; Nonferrous wiredrawing & insulating
Pr: John Spoor
**VP:* Clarence Martin
Brnch Mgr: Nick Hall

D-U-N-S 15-762-7498 IMP/EXP
STATE ELECTRIC SUPPLY CO
2010 2nd Ave, Huntington, WV 25703-1108
Tel (304) 523-7491 *Founded/Ownrshp* 1986
Sales 637.1MM^E *EMP* 700
SIC 5063 3357 Electrical supplies; Nonferrous wiredrawing & insulating
Pr: Joan Weisberg
**VP:* Charles F Oldaker Jr
Exec: Kent Seaman
**Prin:* Robert M Levy
Brnch Mgr: Jason Bogacz
Brnch Mgr: Todd Burris
Brnch Mgr: Randall Caviness
Brnch Mgr: Bill Craven
Brnch Mgr: Dave Creed
Brnch Mgr: Tina Earhart
Brnch Mgr: Ralph Edwards

D-U-N-S 07-201-6967
STATE EMPLOYEES CREDIT UNION
119 N Salisbury St, Raleigh, NC 27603-1739
Tel (919) 839-5000 *Founded/Ownrshp* 1937
Sales NA *EMP* 5,000
SIC 6062 State credit unions, not federally chartered
Pr: Michael Lord
COO: Sue Douglas
CFO: Joan Collins
Bd of Dir: Jo Sanford
Ofcr: Annette Blanton
Ofcr: John Elliott
Ofcr: Leigh Pearson
Ofcr: Kelly Snipes
Trst Ofcr: Sara Trexler
**Ex VP:* Jamie Applequist
VP: Chris Ayer
VP: Phil Bethea
VP: Barclay Close
VP: Karen Daeke
VP: Will Dahmen
VP: Bobby Gardner
VP: Bill Hazle
VP: Rl Jones
VP: Sandra Jones
VP: Wesley Jones
VP: Josh Kelly

D-U-N-S 09-758-7190
STATE EMPLOYEES CREDIT UNION OF MARYLAND INC
SECU
971 Corporate Blvd # 100, Linthicum Heights, MD 21090-2234
Tel (410) 487-7920 *Founded/Ownrshp* 1951
Sales NA *EMP* 500
SIC 6062 State credit unions, not federally chartered
Pr: Rodney H Staatz
**CFO:* Anthony Caccese
Treas: Gayle Seward
**Ofcr:* Michael Gordy
Sr VP: Ed Hoffman
Sr VP: Kim Hollifield
VP: Paulette Bowden
VP: James Polcaro
Secur Mgr: Mark Yu
Snr Mgr: Joseli Wright

D-U-N-S 00-580-3812
STATE EMPLOYEES FEDERAL CREDIT UNION
SEFCU
575 Broadway, Albany, NY 12207-2911
Tel (518) 452-8183 *Founded/Ownrshp* 1934
Sales NA *EMP* 400
SIC 6061 Federal credit unions
CEO: Patrick Calhoun
**Pr:* Michael Castellana
**Ch:* Ron Rock
Ofcr: Cynthia Alaia
Ex VP: Robert J McLasco
Sr VP: Michelle Raymond
VP: Julie A Fancher
VP: Sally Porush
VP: Lisa Scott
Dir Risk M: Earl T Young
Brnch Mgr: Susan Klepadlo

D-U-N-S 78-702-2685
STATE EMPLOYEES FEDERAL CREDIT UNION
700 Patroon Creek Blvd, Albany, NY 12206-5010
Tel (518) 452-8183 *Founded/Ownrshp* 2006
Sales NA *EMP* 7^E
SIC 6061 Federal credit unions
Pr: Patrick Calhoun
Bd of Dir: Mary Warr-Cowans
Sr VP: Barbara Hess
Dir IT: Gwynn Jones

D-U-N-S 13-792-5421
STATE FARM BANK FSB
STATE FARM INSURANCE
(*Suby of* STATE FARM INSURANCE) ★
1 State Farm Plz E 6, Bloomington, IL 61701
Tel (877) 734-2265 *Founded/Ownrshp* 1998
Sales NA *EMP* 2,039
SIC 6411 Insurance agents, brokers & service
Pr: Stanley R Ommen

D-U-N-S 00-692-8071
STATE FARM FIRE AND CASUALTY CO
STATE FARM INSURANCE
(*Suby of* STATE FARM INSURANCE) ★
Three State Frm Plz S H-4, Bloomington, IL 61710-0001
Tel (309) 766-2311 *Founded/Ownrshp* 1935
Sales NA *EMP* 12,709
SIC 6411 Insurance agents & brokers
Ch Bd: Edward B Rust Jr
Ofcr: David Grizzle
Sys Mgr: Susan Bowles
Sys Mgr: Robin Scott
Sys Mgr: Ron Sendelbach
Board of Directors: Phillip G Buffinton, Robert S Eckley, William H Knight Jr, Kurt G Moser, Don D Rood, William D Sullivan, Vincent J Trosino, Charles R Wright

D-U-N-S 36-392-3298
STATE FARM FLORIDA INSURANCE CO
(*Suby of* STATE FARM INSURANCE) ★
1 State Farm Plaza D 2, Bloomington, IL 61701
Tel (309) 766-2311 *Founded/Ownrshp* 2005
Sales NA *EMP* 2
SIC 6411 Insurance agents, brokers & service
Prin: David Gilbert

D-U-N-S 07-141-9816
STATE FARM GENERAL INSURANCE CO INC
STATE FARM INSURANCE
(*Suby of* STATE FARM INSURANCE) ★
1 State Farm Plz, Bloomington, IL 61701
Tel (309) 766-2311 *Founded/Ownrshp* 1962
Sales NA *EMP* 2,736^E
SIC 6411 Insurance agents & brokers
Pr: Edward Rust Jr
**Treas:* Michael Leon Tipsord
VP: William Hudson
VP: Deb Traskell
Sls&Mrk Ex: Doug Waire
Mktg Mgr: Ben Daily

STATE FARM INSURANCE
See STATE FARM FIRE AND CASUALTY CO

STATE FARM INSURANCE
See STATE FARM LIFE INSURANCE CO INC

STATE FARM INSURANCE
See STATE FARM MUTUAL AUTOMOBILE INSURANCE CO

STATE FARM INSURANCE
See STATE FARM LIFE AND ACCIDENT ASSURANCE CO (INC)

STATE FARM INSURANCE
See STATE FARM GENERAL INSURANCE CO INC

STATE FARM INSURANCE
See STATE FARM BANK FSB

STATE FARM INSURANCE
See STATE FARM LLOYDS INC

D-U-N-S 07-171-8923
STATE FARM INSURANCE
(*Suby of* STATE FARM INSURANCE) ★
100 State Farm Pkwy, Birmingham, AL 35209-7186
Tel (205) 916-6000 *Founded/Ownrshp* 1999
Sales NA *EMP* 1,000
SIC 6411 Insurance agents & brokers
Pr: Tom Lakin
VP: Tyrone Smith

D-U-N-S 06-741-4417
STATE FARM LIFE AND ACCIDENT ASSURANCE CO (INC)
STATE FARM INSURANCE
(*Suby of* STATE FARM INSURANCE) ★
1 State Farm Plz, Bloomington, IL 61701
Tel (309) 766-2311 *Founded/Ownrshp* 1960
Sales NA *EMP* 1,001
SIC 6411 Insurance agents & brokers
Pr: Edward B Rust
**Pr:* Edward B Rust
**Treas:* Roger Tompkins
**VP:* Kurt G Moser
Board of Directors: Edward B Rust, Marvin Bower, Joe Bruce Callis, Robert S Eckley, Paul Holman, Roger S Joslin, Roger J Lehman, Vincent J Trosino, Charles R Wright

D-U-N-S 00-692-8089
STATE FARM LIFE INSURANCE CO INC
STATE FARM INSURANCE
(*Suby of* STATE FARM INSURANCE) ★
1 State Farm Plz, Bloomington, IL 61701
Tel (309) 766-2311 *Founded/Ownrshp* 1929
Sales NA *EMP* 2,374
SIC 6311 Life insurance carriers
Pr: Edward B Rust Jr
**Ch Bd:* Vincent Trosino
**CFO:* Michael Tipsord
VP: Darrell Kehl
VP: Charles Wright
Board of Directors: Darrell W Beernink, Robert S Eckley, Earle B Johnson, Roger S Joslin, Kurt G Moser, George Perry, Curtis Tarr, Vincent J Trosino

D-U-N-S 14-871-4421
STATE FARM LLOYDS INC
STATE FARM INSURANCE
(*Suby of* STATE FARM INSURANCE) ★
17301 Preston Rd, Dallas, TX 75252-5727
Tel (972) 732-5000 *Founded/Ownrshp* 1992
Sales NA *EMP* 1,000
SIC 6411 Insurance agents & brokers
Prin: Edward B Rust Jr
Exec: Dan Hering
Dir Soc: Heather Carter
Dir IT: Linda Allen
VP Sls: Ernest Day
Pr Mgr: Brenda Smith
Mktg Mgr: Joy Jackson-Ling

D-U-N-S 00-692-8097
STATE FARM MUTUAL AUTOMOBILE INSURANCE CO
STATE FARM INSURANCE
1 State Farm Plz, Bloomington, IL 61710-0001
Tel (309) 766-2311 *Founded/Ownrshp* 1922
Sales NA *EMP* 68,000[E]
SIC 6321 6311 6036 6331 Health insurance carriers; Accident insurance carriers; Life insurance carriers; State savings banks, not federally chartered; Automobile insurance
Ch: Edward B Rust Jr
V Ch: Ken Fischer
Pr: Carolyn Lee
**Pr:* Michael L Tipsord
**V Ch Bd:* Michael C Davidson
Bd of Dir: Arabella Martinez
Bd of Dir: Judith A Muhlberg
**Ex VP:* Kim Brunner
VP: John P Coffey
VP: Pam Ei
VP: Deborah Traskell
Board of Directors: W Steven Jones

STATE FIRE INSURANCE COMPANY
See MERRIMACK MUTUAL FIRE INSURANCE CO

STATE FUND
See STATE COMPENSATION INSURANCE FUND INC

STATE GAS & OIL DIVISION
See UNI-MARTS LLC

D-U-N-S 80-993-5679
STATE HAWAII DEPARTMENT OF HEALTH
DOH
(*Suby of* EXECUTIVE OFFICE OF STATE OF HAWAII) ★
1250 Punchbowl St, Honolulu, HI 96813-2416
Tel (808) 586-4400 *Founded/Ownrshp* 1966
Sales NA *EMP* 6,000
Accts Accuity Llp Honolulu Hawaii
SIC 9431 Administration of public health programs;
Bd of Dir: Eugene Bal
Bd of Dir: Andrew Don
Bd of Dir: Gary Fukuroku
Bd of Dir: Barry Shitamoto
Bd of Dir: Leslie A Yokouchi
VP: Saedene Y Ota
VP: R C Sutherland

STATE HIGHWAY PATROL
See MISSISSIPPI DEPARTMENT OF PUBLIC SAFETY

STATE HOUSE PRODUCE
See WUHL SHAFMAN & LIEBERMAN INC

D-U-N-S 00-452-0987 IMP/EXP
STATE INDUSTRIAL PRODUCTS CORP (OH)
STATE CHEMICAL MANUFACTURING
5915 Landerbrook Dr # 300, Cleveland, OH 44124-4039
Tel (877) 747-6986 *Founded/Ownrshp* 1911, 1916
Sales 107.9MM *EMP* 1,110
Accts Plante & Moran Pllc Cleveland
SIC 2841 5072 2842 2992 2952 2899 Soap: granulated, liquid, cake, flaked or chip; Bolts, nuts & screws; Specialty cleaning, polishes & sanitation goods; Degreasing solvent; Disinfectants, household or industrial plant; Lubricating oils & greases; Asphalt felts & coatings; Chemical preparations
Pr: Harold Uhrman
**Pr:* Robert M San Julian
**COO:* Brian Limbert
**CFO:* Dan Prugar
**Sec:* William Barnett
VP: Sean Sullivan
VP: Jeff Trattner
Dist Mgr: Jamie Montague
Mktg Dir: Trisha Cox
Sls Mgr: Kathy McNamara
Sls Mgr: Bianca Varela

D-U-N-S 00-403-6208 IMP
■ **STATE INDUSTRIES INC**
STATE WATER HEATERS
(*Suby of* A O SMITH CORP) ★
500 Tennessee Waltz Pkwy, Ashland City, TN 37015-1299
Tel (615) 792-4371 *Founded/Ownrshp* 2005
Sales 219.4MM[E] *EMP* 1,811
SIC 3639 3443 Hot water heaters, household; Fabricated plate work (boiler shop)
Pr: Ajita G Rajendra
**Pr:* Steve Anderson
VP: Jim Margoni
IT Man: Keith Auville
Sfty Dirs: Taylor Colby
Natl Sales: Tom Jackson
Mktg Dir: David Dixon

STATE INSURANCE FUND
See CORPORACION DEL FONDO DEL SEGURO DEL ESTADO

D-U-N-S 00-693-8690
STATE LIFE INSURANCE CO
(*Suby of* AMERICAN UNITED MUTUAL INSURANCE HOLDING CO) ★
1 American Sq, Indianapolis, IN 46282-0020
Tel (317) 285-2300 *Founded/Ownrshp* 1894
Sales NA *EMP* 43
SIC 6311 6321 Life insurance; Disability health insurance
Pr: Richard Merrill
**Ch:* Dayton Molendorp
VP: Christopher Greene
VP: Steven Ramsey
Dir IT: Darrell Kehrt

STATE NATIONAL COMPANIES
See TBA INSURANCE GROUP LIMITED PARTNERSHIP

D-U-N-S 07-938-4791
STATE NATIONAL COMPANIES INC
1900 L Don Dodson Dr, Bedford, TX 76021-5990
Tel (817) 265-2000 *Founded/Ownrshp* 2002
Sales 198.9MM *EMP* 1[E]
Accts Ernst & Young Llp Dallas Tex
Tkr Sym SNC *Exch* NGS
SIC 8742 Management consulting services
Pr: Matthew Freeman

D-U-N-S 60-708-3896
STATE NATIONAL INSURANCE CO INC
(*Suby of* STATE NATIONAL COMPANIES) ★
1900 L Don Dodson Dr, Bedford, TX 76021-5990
Tel (817) 265-2000 *Founded/Ownrshp* 1973
Sales NA *EMP* 400[E]
SIC 6331 Fire, marine & casualty insurance
CEO: Lonnie K Ledbetter
**Pr:* Terry Ledbetter
**COO:* Wyatt D Blackburn
**CFO:* David D Hale

D-U-N-S 00-402-7553
STATE OF ALABAMA
300 Dexter Ave, Montgomery, AL 36104-3741
Tel (334) 242-7100 *Founded/Ownrshp* 1819
Sales NA *EMP* 37,659
Accts Ronald L Jones Montgomery A
SIC 9111 Governors' offices;
Dir: Acquanetta Knight
Prgrm Mgr: Gale Richardson

D-U-N-S 07-819-8983
STATE OF ALASKA
120 4th St, Juneau, AK 99801-1162
Tel (907) 465-3500 *Founded/Ownrshp* 1959
Sales NA *EMP* 19,339
Accts Kris Curtis Cpa Cisa Juneau
SIC 9111
Ofcr: Marcia Coonce
Ofcr: Ellie Dash
Ofcr: John Maddy
Ofcr: Harry Moore
Ofcr: Marcus Parker
Assoc Dir: Patricia F Eckert
Comm Dir: Grace Jang
Ex Dir: Paul Dauphinais
Ex Dir: Shannon Daut
Prgrm Mgr: Jetta Whittaker

D-U-N-S 07-245-9266 IMP/EXP
STATE OF ARIZONA
GOVERNOR'S OFFICE
1700 W Washington St Fl 7, Phoenix, AZ 85007-2808
Tel (602) 542-4331 *Founded/Ownrshp* 1912
Sales NA *EMP* 34,161
Accts State Of Arizona Office Of The
SIC 9111 Governors' offices;
**Treas:* David Petersen
Ofcr: Dwayne Russell
Exec: Rebecca Wilder

D-U-N-S 06-532-0400
STATE OF ARKANSAS
4 Capitol Mall Rm 403a, Little Rock, AR 72201-1013
Tel (501) 682-2345 *Founded/Ownrshp* 1836
Sales NA *EMP* 28,272
Accts Roger A Norman Jd Cpa Cfe
SIC 9111 Governors' offices;
Dir IT: Courtney Baum
IT Man: Jacqueline Goodman
Pr Dir: Gail Morris
Snr Mgr: Lynda Lehing
Snr Mgr: Terita Williams

D-U-N-S 07-154-9000 IMP/EXP
STATE OF CALIFORNIA
State Capital, Sacramento, CA 95814
Tel (916) 445-2864 *Founded/Ownrshp* 1850
Sales NA *EMP* 208,580
Accts John F Collis Ii Cpa Sacram
SIC 9111 Governors' offices
Ofcr: Shell Culp
Ofcr: John Lane
CIO: Andrew Chin
CIO: Ed Lee
CIO: Steve Saks
CIO: Kevin See

D-U-N-S 07-643-8621
STATE OF COLORADO
200 E Colfax Ave Ste 91, Denver, CO 80203-1716
Tel (303) 866-5000 *Founded/Ownrshp* 1876
Sales NA *EMP* 81,349
Accts Dianne E Ray Cpa Denver Co
SIC 9111 Governors' offices;
COO: Michael Dillon
Treas: Jonathan Forbes
Comm Dir: Don Naccarato
Comm Dir: Eddie Stern
Plng Mgr: Pat Saffo
Dir IT: Kirk Teklits
Opers Mgr: Carol Reinboldt

D-U-N-S 00-453-4830
STATE OF CONNECTICUT
210 Capitol Ave Ste 1, Hartford, CT 06106-1568
Tel (860) 566-4840 *Founded/Ownrshp* 1788
Sales NA *EMP* 76,940
Accts John C Geragosian Hartford
SIC 9111 Governors' offices;
Ofcr: Lawrence Carlascio
**Ofcr:* Arthur House
Ofcr: Dennis Tovey
Prgrm Mgr: David Graves
Brnch Mgr: Charmaine Bostick
Off Mgr: Jamal Gartling
CIO: Robin Browne
Dir IT: Shane Powser
IT Man: Jim Grochowiski
IT Man: Chris Ideker
Netwrk Eng: Karen Douglas

STATE OF CONNECTICUT DMR
See CONNECTICUT DEPARTMENT OF DEVELOPMENTAL SERVICES

D-U-N-S 10-193-9978
STATE OF DELAWARE DNREC
(*Suby of* DIVISION OF ENERGY AND CLIMATE) ★
89 Kings Hwy, Dover, DE 19901-7305
Tel (302) 739-9903 *Founded/Ownrshp* 1987
Sales NA *EMP* 1,000
SIC 9512 Fish & wildlife conservation agency, government
CEO: Robert Zimmerman
**Pr:* David Small

D-U-N-S 80-965-5091
STATE OF DELAWARE DNREC
DIVISION OF ENERGY AND CLIMATE
(*Suby of* EXECUTIVE OFFICE OF GOVERNOR OF DELAWARE) ★
89 Kings Hwy, Dover, DE 19901-7305
Tel (302) 739-9101 *Founded/Ownrshp* 1970
Sales NA *EMP* 1,209
SIC 9511 9512 Air, water & solid waste management; ; Land, mineral & wildlife conservation;
Prin: Philip Cherry

D-U-N-S 00-407-8374 IMP/EXP
STATE OF FLORIDA
400 S Monroe St, Tallahassee, FL 32399-6591
Tel (850) 488-7146 *Founded/Ownrshp* 1845
Sales NA *EMP* 129,274
Accts David W Martin Cpa Tallahas
SIC 9111 Governors' offices
Ch: Jennifer Hritz
CIO: Diane Gish
CIO: Patricia Norris
CIO: Tony Powell
MIS Dir: Ray Cales
Dir IT: Frank Kerwick
IT Man: David Elliott
MIS Mgr: Darlene Bello
Software D: Shelby Watson
Software D: Hong Wen
Genl Couns: Isis Carbajal

D-U-N-S 36-070-6212
STATE OF FLORIDA OF JUDICIARY COURTS
FLORIDA STATE COURT SYSTEM
(*Suby of* STATE OF FLORIDA) ★
500 S Duval St, Tallahassee, FL 32399-6556
Tel (850) 922-5081 *Founded/Ownrshp* 1845
Sales NA *EMP* 2,288
Accts Johnson & Cate Rockport Texa
SIC 9211 State courts;

D-U-N-S 06-923-0183
STATE OF GEORGIA
206 Washington St Sw # 111, Atlanta, GA 30334-9007
Tel (404) 656-1776 *Founded/Ownrshp* 1788
Sales NA *EMP* 67,139
Accts Greg S Griffin Department Of
SIC 9111 Governors' offices;
Pr: Reggie Hawthorne
CFO: Debbie Dlugolenski
Ofcr: Kirby McClendon
Ofcr: Troy Scott
Ex Dir: Sallie Tanner
Off Mgr: Miranda Dunn
CTO: Paul S Goggin
Dir IT: Chris Hackett
Pgrm Dir: Kristina Martin
Pgrm Dir: Samantha Wolf
Pgrm Dir: Shontel Wright

D-U-N-S 07-767-6997 IMP
STATE OF HAWAII
201 Merchant St Ste 1805, Honolulu, HI 96813-2963
Tel (808) 586-1735 *Founded/Ownrshp* 1959
Sales NA *EMP* 44,201
Accts Accuity Llp Honolulu Hawaii
SIC 9111 Executive offices

D-U-N-S 06-523-2498
STATE OF ILLINOIS
207 State House, Springfield, IL 62706-0001
Tel (217) 782-6830 *Founded/Ownrshp* 1818
Sales NA *EMP* 59,659
Accts William G Holland
SIC 9111 Governors' offices;
V Ch: James Bruner
V Ch: Cinda Klickna
Bd of Dir: John Keith
Ex VP: David Parkhill
VP: Rhonda Johnson
VP: Molly Phalen
VP: Philip Wood
Exec: Bob Golasky
Comm Dir: Justin Dejong
Comm Dir: Abby Ottenhoff
Comm Dir: Lance Trover

D-U-N-S 07-204-2443
STATE OF INDIANA
200 W Washington St # 201, Indianapolis, IN 46204-2728
Tel (317) 232-4567 *Founded/Ownrshp* 1816
Sales NA *EMP* 33,000
Accts Paul D Joyce Cpa Indianapol
SIC 9111 Executive offices
Exec: Carlos Pettiford
Genl Mgr: Luke Kenworthy

D-U-N-S 05-374-5303
STATE OF IOWA
1007 E Grand Ave Rm 105, Des Moines, IA 50319-9003
Tel (515) 281-5211 *Founded/Ownrshp* 1846
Sales NA *EMP* 24,304
Accts Mary Mosiman Cpa Des Moines
SIC 9111 Executive offices
Ofcr: Tim Cook
Assoc Dir: Bradley Dirks
IT Man: Brian Maloney
Counsel: Aimee Clayton

D-U-N-S 07-313-2748
STATE OF KANSAS
300 Sw 10th Ave Ste 222s, Topeka, KS 66612-1514
Tel (785) 354-1388 *Founded/Ownrshp* 1861
Sales NA *EMP* 22,375
Accts Cliftonlarsonallen Llp Broom
SIC 9111 Governors' offices;
Prin: Sam Brownback
V Ch: Raymond Merrick
V Ch: Susan Wagle
IT Man: Jeff Hixon
IT Man: Richard Miller
Netwrk Mgr: Steve Roach
Surg Cl Rc: Clay Aurand
Surg Cl Rc: Les Donovan
Surg Cl Rc: Bill Feuerborn
Surg Cl Rc: John Vratil

D-U-N-S 06-123-8911
STATE OF LOUISIANA
900 N 3rd St Fl 4, Baton Rouge, LA 70802-5236
Tel (225) 342-0991 *Founded/Ownrshp* 1812
Sales NA *EMP* 47,937
Accts Daryl G Purpera Cpa Cfe Ba
SIC 9111 Executive offices
**Treas:* John Neely Kennedy
Ofcr: Richard L Stader

D-U-N-S 05-797-9312
STATE OF MAINE
1 State House Sta, Augusta, ME 04333-0001
Tel (207) 549-7182 *Founded/Ownrshp* 1820
Sales NA *EMP* 14,144
Accts Office Of The State Auditor P
SIC 9111 Governors' offices;
Ch: Paul R Lepage
V Ch: Patrick Reed
**CFO:* Richard Rosen
CFO: Steven Thebarge
Bd of Dir: Linda Ruman
VP: David Farmer
VP: Kay Rand
**Prin:* April Newman
Ex Dir: Kay Evans
Prgrm Mgr: David W Craford
Off Mgr: Gaye Mullen

D-U-N-S 00-196-9443
STATE OF MARYLAND
45 Calvert St Ste 1, Annapolis, MD 21401-1994
Tel (410) 974-3901 *Founded/Ownrshp* 1788
Sales NA *EMP* 58,020
Accts Sb & Company Llc Hunt Valley
SIC 9111 Governors' offices;
Dir IT: Mark Higby

D-U-N-S 78-068-3699
STATE OF MARYLAND
BALTIMORE CITY CMNTY COLLEGE
2901 Liberty Heights Ave, Baltimore, MD 21215-7807
Tel (410) 462-8300 *Founded/Ownrshp* 1947
Sales 186.6MM[E] *EMP* 14,000
SIC 8222 Community college
Pr: Carolyn Anderson
Assoc Dir: Juanita Catchings
Prin: Sabina Silkworth
Dir IT: Carolyn Townsend

Psych: Allenette Valentine
Psych: Frances Wilson

D-U-N-S 01-828-7046
STATE OF MARYLAND TREASURERS OFFICE
(*Suby of* STATE OF MARYLAND) ★
80 Calvert St, Annapolis, MD 21401-1907
Tel (800) 974-0468 *Founded/Ownrshp* 1851
Sales NA *EMP* 5,007[E]
SIC 9311 Treasurers' office, government
Treas: Nancy Kopp

D-U-N-S 05-469-8428
STATE OF MICHIGAN
111 S Capitol Ave, Lansing, MI 48933-1555
Tel (517) 373-3400 *Founded/Ownrshp* 1837
Sales NA *EMP* 55,416
Accts Doug A Ringler Lansing Mich
SIC 9111 Governors' offices;
Dir Lab: Alecia Lamb
Off Mgr: Laura Stoken
IT Man: Anne Brys

D-U-N-S 06-475-4757
STATE OF MINNESOTA
116 Veteran Service Bld, Saint Paul, MN 55155-0001
Tel (218) 828-2400 *Founded/Ownrshp* 1858
Sales NA *EMP* 35,217
Accts James R Nobles/Cecile M Ferk
SIC 9111 Executive offices
**Treas:* Carol C Johnson
Ofcr: Andrea Capaul
Comm Man: Naomi Rettke
IT Man: Jim Wehri

D-U-N-S 00-821-0692
STATE OF MISSISSIPPI
501 N West St, Jackson, MS 39201-1001
Tel (601) 359-3100 *Founded/Ownrshp* 1817
Sales NA *EMP* 27,775
Accts William R Doss Cpa Jackson
SIC 9111 Governors' offices;
Chf Mktg O: Marlo Dorsey
**Ex Dir:* Kevin J Upchurch
Prgrm Mgr: Lauren Von Foregger
Netwrk Mgr: Steve Walker

D-U-N-S 07-313-4579 IMP
STATE OF MISSOURI
201 W Capitol Ave Rm 216, Jefferson City, MO 65101-1556
Tel (573) 751-3222 *Founded/Ownrshp* 1821
Sales NA *EMP* 51,488
Accts Thomas A Schweich Jefferson
SIC 9111 Governors' offices;
Ofcr: Patsy Whitley
Exec: Wayne Berten
Exec: Michelle Branson
Exec: Kathy Jeffries
Exec: Gina Martin
Exec: Christine Slaughter
Counsel: Andrea Spillars

D-U-N-S 00-749-6631
STATE OF NEBRASKA
1445 K St Oom 2316, Lincoln, NE 68509
Tel (402) 471-2311 *Founded/Ownrshp* 1867
Sales NA *EMP* 18,653
Accts Don Dunlap Cpa Lincoln Nebr
SIC 9111 Governors' offices;
Treas: Don Stenberg
Ofcr: Scott Eveland
Ofcr: Staci Gaes
Ofcr: Melissa Martinez
Counsel: Chris Shubert

D-U-N-S 06-780-8063
STATE OF NEVADA
101 N Carson St Ste 1, Carson City, NV 89701-7011
Tel (775) 684-5670 *Founded/Ownrshp* 1864
Sales NA *EMP* 14,790
Accts Eidebailly Llp Reno Nevada
SIC 9111 Governors' offices;
CFO: Brian Krolicki
Treas: Al Kramer
**Treas:* Kate Marshall
Exec: David Fierro
IT Man: Jeffrey Cherpeski
IT Man: Linnette Ollson

D-U-N-S 06-676-0232
STATE OF NEW HAMPSHIRE
64 South St, Concord, NH 03301-3612
Tel (603) 271-1110 *Founded/Ownrshp* 1788
Sales NA *EMP* 12,280
Accts Kpmg Llp Boston Ma
SIC 9111 Governors' offices;
Ofcr: Darin Briggs
Ofcr: Eric Cornish
Ofcr: Michael Correia
Ofcr: Keith Croteau
Ofcr: Craig Drouin
Ofcr: Michael Dube
Ofcr: Michael Eaton
Ofcr: Marilyn Hunt
Ofcr: James Iseman
Ofcr: Chance Johnmeyer
Ofcr: Matthewj Laclair
Ofcr: Lynn McLain
Ofcr: Andrew Sargent
Ofcr: Eric Stone
Ofcr: Donald Tomlin
Ofcr: Denis Watson
Ofcr: Michele Watson
Ofcr: John Woolf

D-U-N-S 06-737-3258
STATE OF NEW JERSEY
125 W State St, Trenton, NJ 08608-1101
Tel (609) 396-4657 *Founded/Ownrshp* 1787
Sales NA *EMP* 85,898
Accts Stephen M Eells Trenton Nj
SIC 9111 Governors' offices;
Genl Mgr: Rosemary Iannacone
Genl Mgr: Kathryn Winfree
CIO: E Steven Emanuel
CTO: Charles S Dawon
MIS Dir: Donna Valla
IT Man: Christine Lewis
Snr Mgr: Brian Arena

D-U-N-S 00-711-1818
STATE OF NEW MEXICO
237 Don Gaspar Ave, Santa Fe, NM 87501-2178
Tel (505) 827-3000 *Founded/Ownrshp* 1850
Sales NA *EMP* 22,217
Accts Cliftonlarsonallen Llp Albuqu
SIC 9111 Governors' offices;
Exec: Mary Deets
Exec: Beverly Friedman
Genl Couns: Daniel Hill
Counsel: Arlene Strumor

D-U-N-S 04-100-2973
STATE OF NEW YORK
800 N Pearl St, Menands, NY 12204-1817
Tel (518) 473-6790 *Founded/Ownrshp* 1788
Sales NA *EMP* 154,954
SIC 9111

D-U-N-S 00-345-9047
STATE OF NORTH CAROLINA
20301 Mail Service Ctr, Raleigh, NC 27699-0300
Tel (919) 715-1411 *Founded/Ownrshp* 1789
Sales NA *EMP* 69,869
Accts Beth A Wood Cpa Raleigh No
SIC 9111 Executive offices
Pr: Jenny Steele
CFO: Caterri Woodrum
Ofcr: William Summer
Genl Mgr: Janet Rust

D-U-N-S 07-313-1823
STATE OF NORTH DAKOTA
600 E Boulevard Ave # 101, Bismarck, ND 58505-0601
Tel (701) 328-4905 *Founded/Ownrshp* 1889
Sales NA *EMP* 8,800[E]
Accts Robert R Peterson State Audi
SIC 9111 Governors' offices;
COO: John Halvorson
Ofcr: Sloan Thigpen
VP Bus Dev: Michael Strotheide
Exec: Cliff Heyne
Dir Risk M: Dawn Roppel
Ex Dir: Illona J Sacco
Dir Sec: Valerie Fischer
CIO: Curtis Wolfe
Dir IT: Darin Meschke
Dir IT: Dorothy Vetter
Telecom Mg: Brandi Peterson

D-U-N-S 00-430-5215
STATE OF OHIO
30 E Broad St Fl 40, Columbus, OH 43215-3414
Tel (614) 466-3455 *Founded/Ownrshp* 1803
Sales NA *EMP* 57,631[E]
Accts Dave Yost Columbus Ohio
SIC 9111 Governors' offices;
IT Man: Tina Collins

D-U-N-S 80-917-2653
STATE OF OHIO
OHIO DEPARTMENT YOUTH SERVICES
(*Suby of* EXECUTIVE OFFICE STATE OF OHIO) ★
30 W Spring St Fl 5, Columbus, OH 43215-2241
Tel (614) 466-8660 *Founded/Ownrshp* 1983
Sales NA *EMP* 2,200
SIC 9441 Administration of social & manpower programs;
Ex Dir: Harvey Reed
Board of Directors: Jeff Spear

D-U-N-S 80-884-7677
STATE OF OHIO OFFICE OF BUDGET AND MANAGEMENT STATE ACCOUNTING
OFFICE FISCAL ADMINISTRATION
(*Suby of* EXECUTIVE OFFICE STATE OF OHIO) ★
30 E Broad St, Columbus, OH 43215-3414
Tel (614) 466-4034 *Founded/Ownrshp* 1973
Sales NA *EMP* 1,240
SIC 9311 Finance, taxation & monetary policy;
Ex Dir: Chris Korleski
CFO: Chris Geyer
Genl Mgr: Kurtis Wingo
CIO: Alan Shellhause
Dir IT: Danelle Karvois
Dir IT: Tom Meyer
Dir IT: Fred Wortman
IT Man: Mark Barr
IT Man: Larry Congrove
IT Man: Christina Helm
IT Man: Kelly Kassor
Board of Directors: Astrid Arca

D-U-N-S 80-917-2372
STATE OF OHIO OFFICE OF BUDGET AND MANAGEMENT STATE ACCOUNTING
OHIO ENVMTL PROTECTION AGCY
(*Suby of* EXECUTIVE OFFICE STATE OF OHIO) ★
30 E Broad St Fl 34, Columbus, OH 43215-3414
Tel (614) 466-4034 *Founded/Ownrshp* 1972
Sales NA *EMP* 1,280
SIC 9511 Air, water & solid waste management;
V Ch: Timothy Young
Ofcr: Chris Geyer
VP: Monica Green
Comm Dir: Shaunte Russell
Psych: Rena Elliott
Genl Couns: Sarah Creedon

D-U-N-S 04-344-0601
STATE OF OKLAHOMA
421 Nw 13th St Ste 220, Oklahoma City, OK 73103-3784
Tel (405) 521-2342 *Founded/Ownrshp* 1907
Sales 2.3MMM[E] *EMP* 37,613
Accts Gary A Jones Cpa Cfe Oklah
SIC 7361 Placement agencies
IT Man: Robin Frank
IT Man: Timothy Webster

D-U-N-S 04-300-8317
STATE OF OREGON
900 Court St Ne Ste 160, Salem, OR 97301-4046
Tel (503) 378-3111 *Founded/Ownrshp* 1859
Sales NA *EMP* 36,176
Accts Office Of The Secretary Of Sta
SIC 9111 Governors' offices;
CFO: Darin Rand
Ofcr: Sandra F Aguinaga
Ofcr: Aaron P Baer
Ofcr: Brian Belleque
Ofcr: Dave L Bowman
Ofcr: Karl L Harry
Ofcr: Laura R Harsin
Ofcr: Robin M Hoffman
Ofcr: Jeanine M Hohn
Ofcr: Connie L Kyle
Ofcr: Ruby E McClorey
Ofcr: Shannon S Mecham
Ofcr: David J Nelson
Ofcr: Melissa J Northcutt
Ofcr: Khris M Nunnery
Ofcr: Cheryl L Olson
Ofcr: Garth D Olson
Ofcr: Rick E Ridderbusch
Ofcr: Janet L Ridgley
Ofcr: Ken Rocco
Ofcr: May S Saechao

D-U-N-S 04-455-2957
STATE OF RHODE ISLAND
114 Enfield Ave, Providence, RI 02908-1241
Tel (401) 351-8448 *Founded/Ownrshp* 2010
Sales 5.0MMM[E] *EMP* 3
SIC 7389
Owner: Linda Nelson

D-U-N-S 06-231-3077
STATE OF RHODE ISLAND AND PROVIDENCE PLANTATIONS
82 Smith St Ste 102, Providence, RI 02903-1121
Tel (401) 222-2080 *Founded/Ownrshp* 1790
Sales 6.7MMM *EMP* 13,535
Accts Dennis E Hoyle Cpa-Office Of
SIC 9111 Governors' offices;

D-U-N-S 95-792-5464
STATE OF RHODE ISLAND DEPARTMENT OF ADMINISTRATION
(*Suby of* EXECUTIVE OFFICE OF STATE OF RHODE ISLAND) ★
1 Capitol Hl Ste 1, Providence, RI 02908-5803
Tel (401) 222-2280 *Founded/Ownrshp* 1936
Sales NA *EMP* 1,785
SIC 9199 Personnel agency, government;
VP: Robert A Weygand
Genl Mgr: Karen Scott

D-U-N-S 06-700-6072
STATE OF SOUTH CAROLINA
1205 Pendleton St, Columbia, SC 29201-3756
Tel (803) 734-2100 *Founded/Ownrshp* 1788
Sales NA *EMP* 67,816
Accts Cliftonlarsonallen Llp
SIC 9111 Governors' offices;
Ofcr: Tracy Smith
IT Man: Annie Bryant
IT Man: Renee Graham
IT Man: Cynthia Popenhagen
IT Man: Denise Riley
Snr Mgr: Petula Hendley

D-U-N-S 07-762-6729 IMP
STATE OF SOUTH DAKOTA
500 E Capitol Ave, Pierre, SD 57501-5007
Tel (605) 773-3378 *Founded/Ownrshp* 1889
Sales NA *EMP* 8,256
Accts Martin L Guindon Cpa Pierre
SIC 9111 Governors' offices;
Ofcr: June Hansen
Ofcr: Andrea Meyers
Ofcr: Gene Stegeman
Sr VP: Brenda Gordon
Exec: Barb Buhler
Ex Dir: Norman Lingle
Ex Dir: Wayne Winter
Prgrm Mgr: Jan Talley
Genl Mgr: Merilee Beck
Genl Mgr: Scott Bollinger
Genl Mgr: Travis Dovre

D-U-N-S 04-143-8821
STATE OF TENNESSEE
312 Rosa L Prks Ave Fl 21, Nashville, TN 37243-0001
Tel (615) 741-2001 *Founded/Ownrshp* 1796
Sales NA *EMP* 37,737
Accts Deborah V Loveless Cpa Nash
SIC 9111 Governors' offices;
Prin: Bill Haslam
V Ch: Heather Hall
Bd of Dir: David Collier
Bd of Dir: Jack Gilpin
Chf Mktg O: Dan Strasser
Ofcr: Valisa Thompson
Ofcr: Trang Wadsworth
Exec: Allyson Sneed
Genl Mgr: George Ross
Dir IT: Russell Nicoll
IT Man: Skeet Owen

D-U-N-S 00-253-7595 IMP
STATE OF TEXAS
1100 San Jacinto Blvd, Austin, TX 78701-1935
Tel (512) 463-2000 *Founded/Ownrshp* 1845
Sales NA *EMP* 144,175
Accts John Keel Cpa Austin Texas
SIC 9111 Governors' offices
Ex Dir: Ginger Salone
Ex Dir: Glenn Shankle
CTO: Brian Rawson
Pgrm Dir: Eileen Alter

D-U-N-S 00-909-4301
STATE OF UTAH
GOVERNORS OFFICE
350 N State St Ste 200, Salt Lake City, UT 84114-0002
Tel (801) 538-1000 *Founded/Ownrshp* 1896
Sales NA *EMP* 29,821
Accts Office Of The Utah State Audit
SIC 9111 Governors' offices;
Ofcr: Bisera Habibija
Ofcr: Michael Labounty
Ofcr: Brent Moody
Trst Ofcr: Brent Bluth
Trst Ofcr: Kelli Jones
Trst Ofcr: Aaron Langston
Trst Ofcr: Bryan Torgerson
**Ex Dir:* Q Val Hale
Admn Mgr: Sonya White
CTO: David Fletcher
CTO: Steve Fletcher

D-U-N-S 06-676-0240
STATE OF VERMONT
109 State St Ste 4, Montpelier, VT 05609-0003
Tel (802) 828-1452 *Founded/Ownrshp* 1791
Sales NA *EMP* 8,795
Accts Kpmg Llp Colchester Vermont
SIC 9111 Governors' offices;
Treas: George B Spaulding
Ofcr: Austin Anderson
Ofcr: David Cohen
Ofcr: Georgia Cumming
Ofcr: Donald Gray
Ofcr: Andrea Hall
Ofcr: Donna Houghton
Ofcr: Jeanne Jean
Ofcr: Eric Johnson
Ofcr: Ingrid Jonas
Ofcr: David Kopacz
Ofcr: David Lajoice
Ofcr: Amy Lear
Ofcr: Janeen Morrison
Ofcr: Diane Nealy
Ofcr: Alison Ryan
Ofcr: Charles Thompson
Ofcr: Deborah Tremblay
Exec: Roberta Garrand
Exec: David Thurber
Comm Dir: Laura Peterson

STATE OF WASH OFFICE OF GVRNOR
See EXECUTIVE OFFICE OF STATE OF WASHINGTON

D-U-N-S 07-924-8936
STATE OF WASHINGTON
GOVERNOR'S OFFICE
106 Legislative Building, Olympia, WA 98504-0001
Tel (360) 902-4111 *Founded/Ownrshp* 1889
Sales NA *EMP* 57,659
Accts Jan M Jutte Cpa Cgfm Olymp
SIC 9111 Governors' offices;
**Treas:* Michael Murphy
Comm Dir: Hector Castro
Ex Dir: David Postman
Ex Dir: Ted Sturdevant
Pr Dir: Jaime Smith

D-U-N-S 06-812-6721
STATE OF WEST VIRGINIA
GOVERNOR'S OFFICE
1900 Kanawha Blvd E # 714, Charleston, WV 25305-0032
Tel (304) 558-2000 *Founded/Ownrshp* 1863
Sales NA *EMP* 19,357
Accts Ernst & Young Llp Charleston
SIC 9111 Governors' offices
Genl Mgr: Caryn Gresham
Genl Mgr: Jeff Pierson
Software D: Mike Mullins
Genl Couns: Meridith Johnstone

D-U-N-S 00-177-8349
STATE OF WISCONSIN
115 E Capitol, Madison, WI 53702-0015
Tel (608) 266-1212 *Founded/Ownrshp* 1848
Sales NA *EMP* 35,522
Accts Joe Chrisman Legislative Audi
SIC 9111 Executive offices
Sr Cor Off: Colleen Storck
Dir IT: Lee Hellickson
Opers Mgr: Terri Devine
Snr Mgr: Linda Richardson

D-U-N-S 08-002-9896
STATE OF WISCONSIN
DEPARTMENT OF REVENUE
2135 Rimrock Rd, Madison, WI 53713-1443
Tel (608) 266-6466 *Founded/Ownrshp* 2015
Sales NA *EMP* 1,000
SIC 9311 Taxation department, government

D-U-N-S 07-647-1994
STATE OF WYOMING
122 W 25th St Fl 4, Cheyenne, WY 82001-3004
Tel (307) 777-7758 *Founded/Ownrshp* 1890
Sales NA *EMP* 7,439
Accts Mcgee Hearne & Paiz Llp Che
SIC 9111 Executive offices;

D-U-N-S 83-500-5778
STATE POLICE MARYLAND
(*Suby of* EXECUTIVE OFFICE OF STATE OF MARYLAND) ★
1201 Reisterstown Rd, Pikesville, MD 21208-3802
Tel (410) 653-4219 *Founded/Ownrshp* 1997
Sales NA *EMP* 2,500
SIC 9221 State police;

D-U-N-S 04-254-3269
STATE POLICE NEW YORK
TROOP K
(*Suby of* EXECUTIVE OFFICE OF STATE OF NEW YORK) ★
1220 Washngtn Ave Bldg 22, Albany, NY 12226-1799
Tel (518) 457-6721 *Founded/Ownrshp* 1917
Sales NA *EMP* 6,820
SIC 9221 State police;
**Prin:* Andrew M Cuomo

D-U-N-S 03-731-9332 IMP/EXP
STATE SERVICE CO INC
1062 Harbor 2 Bishop Rd, Ingleside, TX 78362
Tel (281) 347-2500 *Founded/Ownrshp* 1976
Sales 83.4MM[E] *EMP* 220
Accts Johnson & Cate Rockport Texa
SIC 1629 Dams, waterways, docks & other marine construction

D-U-N-S 00-695-3228
■ STATE STREET BANK AND TRUST CO
(*Suby of* STATE STREET CORP) ★
1 Lincoln St Fl 1, Boston, MA 02111-2900
Tel (617) 786-3000 *Founded/Ownrshp* 1792
Sales NA *EMP* 15,416
SIC 6022 State trust companies accepting deposits, commercial
Pr: Joseph L Hooley
**Pr:* Jorg Ambrosius
**Pr:* Tracy Atkinson
**Pr:* Aunoy Banerjee
Pr: Lynn S Blake
Pr: Ronald P O'Hanley
**Pr:* Michael F Rogers
CEO: Jeff Conway
CEO: Wai-Kwong Seck
**CFO:* Michael W Bell
CFO: Mark R Keating
Ch: Alison Quirk
Chf Mktg O: Hannah Grove
Ofcr: Marc P Brown
Ofcr: Jeffrey N Carp
Ofcr: Cuan Coulter
Ofcr: Maria Dwyer
Ofcr: James Hardy
Ofcr: Karen C Keenan
Ofcr: Andrew Kuritzkes
Ofcr: Rick Lacaille

D-U-N-S 06-215-6427
▲ STATE STREET CORP
1 Lincoln St, Boston, MA 02111-2901
Tel (617) 786-3000 *Founded/Ownrshp* 1969
Sales NA *EMP* 32,356[E]
Tkr Sym STT *Exch* NYS
SIC 6022 6282 State commercial banks; Investment advisory service; Investment counselors
Ch Bd: Joseph L Hooley
Pr: Christina Bueno
Pr: Elaine Chen
Pr: Brian Harnett
Pr: Kristie Helms
Pr: Grace Liu
Pr: Debbie May
Pr: Michael F Rogers
COO: Anthony Carey
COO: Sharon E Donovan Hart
COO: Peter Leahy
COO: Otello Sturino
CFO: Michael W Bell
CFO: Edward J Resch
Treas: David J Gutschenritter
Ofcr: Robert Baillargeon
Ofcr: Marc P Brown
Ofcr: Karen C Keenan
Ofcr: Andrew Kuritzkes
Ofcr: Jacques M Longerstaey
Ofcr: Mark Marinella
Board of Directors: Patrick De Saint-Aignan, Lynn A Dugle, Amelia C Fawcett, William C Freda, Linda A Hill, Richard P Sergel, Ronald L Skates, Gregory L Summe, Thomas J Wilson

D-U-N-S 79-862-5562
■ STATE STREET HOLDING CO LLC
(*Suby of* STATE STREET BANK AND TRUST CO) ★
225 Franklin St Lbby 1, Boston, MA 02110-2800
Tel (617) 664-1029 *Founded/Ownrshp* 1984
Sales NA *EMP* 450
SIC 6082 Foreign trade & international banking institutions
Ch Bd: Marshall Carter
Ofcr: Alyssa A Albertelli
Sr VP: James Hardy
Sr VP: Jon Ricketson
Sr VP: David Saul
VP: Allison L Corbally
VP: Daniel Feeley
VP: Jason Gregerman
VP: Chuck Levine
VP: Kate E McCabe
VP: Christopher C McNeillie
VP: Michael Mulcahy
VP: Janet Nolin
VP: Trong Pham
VP: Marcus Schulmerich
VP: David Settles
VP: David Swiniarski

STATE STREET KANSAS CITY
See INVESTORS FIDUCIARY TRUST CO

STATE SYSTEM HIGHER EDUCATN PA
See STATE SYSTEM OF HIGHER EDUCATION OF COMMONWEALTH OF PENNSYLVANIA

STATE SYSTEM OF HGHR
See MILLERSVILLE UNIVERSITY OF PENNSYLVANIA

D-U-N-S 79-657-3764
STATE SYSTEM OF HIGHER EDUCATION OF COMMONWEALTH OF PENNSYLVANIA
STATE SYSTEM HIGHER EDUCATN PA
(*Suby of* GOVERNORS OFFICE) ★
2986 N 2nd St, Harrisburg, PA 17110-1200
Tel (717) 720-4000 *Founded/Ownrshp* 1982
Sales NA *EMP* 12,169[E]
SIC 9411

STATE SYSTM OF HGHR EDUC OF TH
See WEST CHESTER UNIVERSITY OF PENNSYLVANIA

STATE SYSTM OF HIGHER EDUC OF
See INDIANA UNIVERSITY OF PENNSYLVANIA

D-U-N-S 07-943-1631
STATE TEACHERS RETIREMENT SYSTEM OF OHIO
STRS OHIO
(*Suby of* STATE OF OHIO) ★
275 E Broad St, Columbus, OH 43215-3703
Tel (614) 227-4090 *Founded/Ownrshp* 1919
Sales NA *EMP* 480[E]
Accts Cliftonlarsonallen Llp Toledo
SIC 6371 Pension funds
Ch: Robert Stein
Ofcr: Evelio Rosario
Top Exec: Corey Geog
VP: Christine Leslie
**Exec:* David Tackett
Comm Dir: Nick Treneff
Ex Dir: Matthew Dietrich
**Ex Dir:* Sandra L Knoesel
**Ex Dir:* Stephen A Mitchell
**Ex Dir:* Michael J Nehf
**Ex Dir:* Robert A Slater

D-U-N-S 04-060-6808
STATE UNIVERSITY OF IOWA FOUNDATION
1 W Park Rd, Iowa City, IA 52242-2000
Tel (319) 335-3305 *Founded/Ownrshp* 1956
Sales 156.7MM *EMP* 180[E]
Accts Mcgladrey Llp Iowa City Iowa
SIC 8399 7371 7359 Fund raising organization, non-fee basis; Computer software development; Equipment rental & leasing
Pr: Lynette L Marshall
**Treas:* Sherri Furman
Bd of Dir: Mary Greiner
Bd of Dir: Scott Johnson
VP: Flynn Andrizzi
VP: David R Dierks
Assoc Dir: Erika Lueker-Tarango
Ex Dir: Dana Larson
Ex Dir: Randy Rumery

D-U-N-S 04-427-1604
STATE UNIVERSITY OF NEW YORK
SUNY ADMINISTRATION
(*Suby of* EXECUTIVE OFFICE OF STATE OF NEW YORK) ★
353 Broadway, Albany, NY 12246-2915
Tel (518) 320-1100 *Founded/Ownrshp* 1948
Sales 10.2MMM[E] *EMP* 88,024
Accts Kpmg Llp Albany Ny
SIC 8221 9411 University; Administration of educational programs;
Acting Pr: James Stellar
Pr: Brady Galan
Pr: Tina Good
Pr: Timothy Killeen
CFO: Kimberly R Cline
Trst: Thomas Mastro
Assoc Dir: Dan Flynn
Prin: John B King Jr
Prgrm Mgr: Donna Russo
Counsel: Kelly Lester

D-U-N-S 06-305-3656 IMP/EXP
STATE UNIVERSITY OF NEW YORK HEALTH SCIENCE CENTER AT SYRACUSE
UNIVERSITY HOSPITAL
750 E Adams St, Syracuse, NY 13210-2306
Tel (315) 464-5540 *Founded/Ownrshp* 1950
Sales 753.5MM *EMP* 9,000
SIC 8011 8062 Offices & clinics of medical doctors; Hospital, medical school affiliated with residency
Pr: Gregory L Eastwood
CFO: Gregory Eastwood
CFO: Stewrat Right
Ofcr: Claude Thauvette
VP: Erick Frost
**VP:* Philip Shinegold
VP: Jay Stein
Assoc Dir: Michele Estabrook
Assoc Dir: Lori Murphy
**Prin:* David Smith
Adm Dir: Roxanne Taylor

STATE WATER HEATERS
See STATE INDUSTRIES INC

STATE WATER RESOURCES
See WATER RESOURCES CONTROL BOARD CALIFORNIA

D-U-N-S 06-595-2921
STATE WIDE INSURANCE CO INC
20 Main St, Hempstead, NY 11550-4020
Tel (516) 564-8000 *Founded/Ownrshp* 2010
Sales NA *EMP* 105
SIC 6331 Fire, marine & casualty insurance
Pr: Gerral E Felson
**Treas:* Renan Asuncion Sr
**VP:* Ann B Looney
**VP:* Ronald I Lemberger
IT Man: Paul Cucinella

D-U-N-S 00-843-9234
STATELINE COOPERATIVE
120 Walnut St, Burt, IA 50522-7738
Tel (515) 885-2642 *Founded/Ownrshp* 1996
Sales 173.2MM[E] *EMP* 85
SIC 5191 5172 5031 Fertilizers & agricultural chemicals; Fuel oil; Composite board products, woodboard
CEO: Bill Beukema
**Pr:* Kim Ruby
**Prin:* Larry Sterk

D-U-N-S 17-513-8700
STATEN ISLAND UNIVERSITY HOSPITAL
NSLIJ
(*Suby of* NSLIJ) ★
475 Seaview Ave, Staten Island, NY 10305-3436
Tel (718) 226-9000 *Founded/Ownrshp* 1861
Sales 850.1MM *EMP* 5,700
SIC 8062 General medical & surgical hospitals
Pr: Anthony C Ferreri
Dir Vol: Angela Demarco
Dir Vol: Paula McAvoy
COO: Andrew J Passeri
**CFO:* Thomas Reca
Sr Cor Off: ADI Davidov
Sr Cor Off: Iris Dori
Ofcr: Michael Scognamiglio
**Ex VP:* Nicholas Caruselle
**Ex VP:* Robin Wittenstein
**Sr VP:* Margaret Dialto
VP: Al Cancellieri
VP: Raimonda Clark
VP: Michael Coyne
**VP:* John P Demoleas
VP: Thomas Neglia
VP: John Pullano
**VP:* John Steiger
Dir Lab: Arthur Philipps

D-U-N-S 60-693-6045 IMP
STATER BROS HOLDINGS INC
301 S Tippecanoe Ave, San Bernardino, CA 92408-0121
Tel (909) 733-5000 *Founded/Ownrshp* 1989
Sales 3.8MMM *EMP* 16,100[E]
SIC 5411 Supermarkets, chain
Ch Bd: Jack H Brown
V Ch: Thomas W Field
CFO: David J Harris
Board of Directors: Thomas W Field Jr, Ronald G Skipper, Phillip J Smith

D-U-N-S 05-498-6104
STATER BROS MARKETS INC
(*Suby of* STATER BROS HOLDINGS INC) ★
301 S Tippecanoe Ave, San Bernardino, CA 92408-0121
Tel (909) 733-5000 *Founded/Ownrshp* 1936
Sales 1.5MMM[E] *EMP* 7,000
SIC 5411 Supermarkets, chain
Ch: Jack H Brown
**Pr:* Keith Venholden
**CEO:* Pete Van Helden
**CFO:* David Harris
Ex VP: George Frahm
Ex VP: Dennis McIntyre
Ex VP: Dan Meyer
Sr VP: Darold Fero
VP: Gil Salazar
VP: Mike Slaton

D-U-N-S 07-249-0584
■ STATESBORO HMA INC
(*Suby of* HMA) ★
1499 Fair Rd, Statesboro, GA 30458-1683
Tel (912) 486-1000 *Founded/Ownrshp* 1937, 1995
Sales 210.0MM *EMP* 1[E]
SIC 8062 Hospital, medical school affiliated with residency
CEO: Bob Bigley
**Pr:* Dawn Cartee
**Pr:* Brooks A Keel
**COO:* Leanne Binkley
CFO: Chris Hilton
CFO: Eric Smith
CFO: David Williamson
**CFO:* Joanna Zimmerman
Nrsg Dir: Mary Anderson

D-U-N-S 07-450-3657
■ STATESVILLE HMA LLC
DAVIS REGIONAL MEDICAL CENTER
(*Suby of* HMA) ★
218 Old Mocksville Rd, Statesville, NC 28625-1930
Tel (704) 873-0281 *Founded/Ownrshp* 2008
Sales 64.9MM *EMP* 1,055
SIC 8051 8063 8062 Skilled nursing care facilities; Psychiatric hospitals; General medical & surgical hospitals
CEO: Andy Davis
Dir IT: Joe Peters
Surgeon: Martin J Carignan

D-U-N-S 18-413-6570 IMP/EXP
STATIC CONTROL COMPONENTS INC
(*Suby of* APEX MICROELECTRONICS CO., LTD.)
3010 Lee Ave, Sanford, NC 27332-6210
Tel (919) 774-3808 *Founded/Ownrshp* 2015
Sales 541.4MM[E] *EMP* 1,200
SIC 3629 Static elimination equipment, industrial
Pr: William K Swartz
VP: Juan C Bonell
VP: Elaine Holub
VP: Rob Leonard
VP: Michael L Swartz
VP: Michael Swartz
**Prin:* Edwin H Swartz
Snr Sftwr: Randy Nelson
Snr Ntwrk: Michael Fulcher
Software D: John Safrit
Sftwr Eng: David Barber

D-U-N-S 07-941-9028
STATIC CONTROL IC-DISC INC
3010 Lee Ave, Sanford, NC 27332-6210
Tel (919) 774-3808 *Founded/Ownrshp* 1987
Sales 20.4MM[E] *EMP* 1,000
SIC 7389
VP: William London

D-U-N-S 01-661-3254
STATION CASINOS INC
(*Suby of* STATION CASINOS LLC) ★
4949 N Rancho Dr, Las Vegas, NV 89130-3505
Tel (702) 658-4900 *Founded/Ownrshp* 2000
Sales 26.4MM[E] *EMP* 1,000
SIC 7011 Casino hotel
Pr: Lorengo Fertitta
**VP:* Terry Downey
IT Man: Chuck Kessen

D-U-N-S 08-111-5479
STATION CASINOS INC
1505 S Pavilion Center Dr, Las Vegas, NV 89135-1403
Tel (702) 495-3000 *Founded/Ownrshp* 2011
Sales NA *EMP* 12,224
SIC 8741 7993 7011

D-U-N-S 96-855-6931
STATION CASINOS LLC
(*Suby of* STATION VOTECO LLC) ★
1505 S Pavilion Center Dr, Las Vegas, NV 89135-1403
Tel (702) 495-3000 *Founded/Ownrshp* 2011
Sales 1.3MMM *EMP* 11,600
SIC 7011 Casino hotel
CEO: Frank J Fertitta III
Pr: Stephen L Cavallaro
CFO: Marc J Falcone
Ex VP: Richard J Haskins
Ex VP: Scott M Nielson
VP: Scott Kreiger

D-U-N-S 07-851-4397
STATION VOTECO LLC
1505 S Pavilion Center Dr, Las Vegas, NV 89135-1403
Tel (702) 495-3000 *Founded/Ownrshp* 2010
Sales 1.3MMM[E] *EMP* 12,000[E]
SIC 7011 Casino hotel
Pr: Frank J Fertitta III

D-U-N-S 96-941-8052
STATOIL EXPLORATION CO
BRIGHAM EXPLORATION COMPANY
(*Suby of* STATOIL USA PROPERTIES INC) ★
6300 Bridge Point Pkwy, Austin, TX 78730-5073
Tel (512) 427-3300 *Founded/Ownrshp* 1997
Sales 236.2MM[E] *EMP* 89[E]
SIC 1311 Crude petroleum & natural gas
Prin: Harold D Carter
**CFO:* Eugene B Shepherd Jr
**Ex VP:* David T Brigham
Ex VP: Shepherd Eugene
**Ex VP:* A Lance Langford
**Ex VP:* Jeffery E Larson
**Prin:* Stephen C Hurley
**Prin:* Stephen P Reynolds
**Prin:* Hobart A Smith
**Prin:* Scott W Tinker PHD

D-U-N-S 01-685-1219 IMP
STATOIL MARKETING & TRADING (US) INC
(*Suby of* STATOIL US HOLDINGS INC) ★
120 Long Ridge Rd 3eo1, Stamford, CT 06902-1839
Tel (203) 978-6900 *Founded/Ownrshp* 1997
Sales 6.9MMM *EMP* 85[E]
Accts Kpmg Llp Stamford Connecticu
SIC 5172 Petroleum products
Pr: Jan Rune Schopp
CFO: Trygved Falck
**VP:* Gary Aucoin
VP: Geir Bjornstad
VP: Jens Okland
**VP:* Martin Pastore
VP: Andrew Winkle
Counsel: Meagan Keiser

D-U-N-S 13-007-3534
STATOIL NATURAL GAS LLC
(*Suby of* STATOIL ASA)
120 Long Ridge Rd, Stamford, CT 06902-1839
Tel (203) 978-6900 *Founded/Ownrshp* 2003
Sales 3.5MMM *EMP* 15
Accts Kpmg Llp Stamford Connecticu
SIC 4924 Natural gas distribution
CFO: Bjorn R Eide
CFO: Gary A Turiano
VP: Geir Bjornstad
VP: Einar M Jensen
VP: David E Jones
VP: Martin J Pastore
CIO: Nina U Tronstad

D-U-N-S 18-625-6103 IMP
STATOIL US HOLDINGS INC
(*Suby of* STATOIL PETROLEUM AS)
120 Long Ridge Rd, Stamford, CT 06902-1839
Tel (203) 978-6900 *Founded/Ownrshp* 1987
Sales 7.1MMM[E] *EMP* 904
SIC 5172 1382 Crude oil; Fuel oil; Oil & gas exploration services
Pr: Helge Haugane
VP: Martin Pastore

D-U-N-S 07-983-1316
STATOIL USA PROPERTIES INC
(*Suby of* STATOIL US HOLDINGS INC) ★
2103 Citywest Blvd # 800, Houston, TX 77042-2833
Tel (713) 918-8200 *Founded/Ownrshp* 2008
Sales 237.2MM[E] *EMP* 277[E]
SIC 1382 Oil & gas exploration services
Pr: Bent Pedersen

STATUS LEATHER
See CORINTHIAN INC

STAUFFER GLOVE & SAFETY
See STAUFFER MANUFACTURING CO

D-U-N-S 00-233-6204 IMP
STAUFFER MANUFACTURING CO (PA)
STAUFFER GLOVE & SAFETY
361 E 6th St, Red Hill, PA 18076-1118
Tel (215) 679-4446 *Founded/Ownrshp* 1955
Sales 83.3MM[E] *EMP* 160
SIC 5085 5199

D-U-N-S 00-196-6472 IMP/EXP
STAVIS SEAFOODS INC (MA)
212 Northern Ave Ste 305, Boston, MA 02210-2088
Tel (617) 482-6349 *Founded/Ownrshp* 1929
Sales 203.5MM[E] *EMP* 120
Accts Gray Gray & Gray Llp Westwo
SIC 5146 Seafoods
Pr: Richard Stavis
Pr: Robert Landy
Treas: Mary Fleming
VP: Stuart Altman
DP Exec: Abbe Moore
QA Dir: Jeremy Okwuosa
Dir IT: Robert Galloni
Dir IT: David Nole
VP Mktg: Ruth Levy
Mktg Mgr: Mike Lynch

D-U-N-S 07-923-0934
STAVROS CENTER FOR INDEPENDENT LIVING INC
210 Old Farm Rd, Amherst, MA 01002-2704
Tel (413) 256-0473 *Founded/Ownrshp* 1974
Sales 183.1MM *EMP* 100
Accts Lester Halpern & Company Pc
SIC 8322 Self-help organization
Pr: Glenn Hartmann
CFO: Seren Derin
**Treas:* Donna M Bliznak
Treas: Bill McCarthy
**VP:* Nancy Bazanchuk
VP: Angelina Ramirez
**Ex Dir:* Jim Kruidenier

D-U-N-S 88-428-6691
STCHARLES TRUCKING INC
FIVE STAR LOGISTICS
650 N Raddant Rd, Batavia, IL 60510-4207
Tel (630) 584-4285 *Founded/Ownrshp* 1990
Sales 110.0MM *EMP* 50

SIC 4214 Local trucking with storage
Pr: Caroline McNaloy
**Pr:* Albert Cianci

D-U-N-S 05-750-5109
STEAD MOTORS INC
STEAD PONTIAC GMC
1800 N Main St, Walnut Creek, CA 94596-4107
Tel (925) 937-5060 *Founded/Ownrshp* 1993
Sales 157.6MM^E *EMP* 605
SIC 5511 Automobiles, new & used; Pickups, new & used; Vans, new & used
Pr: Michael Stead
**VP:* Sid Savarani
Exec: Sue Romano
Genl Mgr: Ernie Campora

STEAD PONTIAC GMC
See STEAD MOTORS INC

D-U-N-S 96-212-6780
STEADFAST INCOME REIT INC
18100 Von Karman Ave # 500, Irvine, CA 92612-0196
Tel (949) 852-0700 *Founded/Ownrshp* 2009
Sales 209.3MM *EMP* 31^E
Accts Ernst & Young Llp Irvine Cal
SIC 6798 Real estate investment trusts
CEO: Rodney F Emery
**Pr:* Phillip Meserve
**COO:* Ana Marie Del Rio
**CFO:* Dinesh K Davar
CFO: Dinesh Davar
**Ex VP:* Christopher M Hilbert
VP: Michael Ebenhoch
VP: Tim McCabe
VP: Jake Wallace
VP: Daniel Williams
VP: David Willkomm
VP: Joshua Wyatt
Exec: Preston Corman

D-U-N-S 11-266-0402
■ **STEAK N SHAKE INC**
STEAK N SHAKE OPERATIONS, INC.
(*Suby of* BIGLARI HOLDINGS INC) ★
36 S Pennsylvania St # 500, Indianapolis, IN 46204-3630
Tel (317) 633-4100 *Founded/Ownrshp* 1984
Sales 591.0MM^E *EMP* 16,000
Accts Ernst & Young Llp
SIC 5812 6794 Restaurant, family: chain; Franchises, selling or licensing
Pr: Sardar Biglari
Ch Bd: Alan B Gilman
Pr: Peter Dunn
COO: William Hall
CFO: Tom Murray
Sr VP: Jim Flaniken
Sr VP: Scott Norrick
Sr VP: Gary T Reinwald
VP: Michael Burk
VP: William Hart
VP: Michael Loftis
VP: Scott Palmer
VP: Jim Valentino
VP: Doug Willard
Board of Directors: S Sue Aramian

STEAK N SHAKE OPERATIONS, INC.
See STEAK N SHAKE INC

D-U-N-S 94-677-2464
STEAM GENERATING TEAM LLC
SGT
7207 Ibm Dr 3a, Charlotte, NC 28262-4307
Tel (704) 805-2810 *Founded/Ownrshp* 1996
Sales 108.6MM^E *EMP* 2,000
SIC 1796 Power generating equipment installation
**Pr:* Rich Kalman
**CFO:* Rich Stewart
**VP:* Steve Sills

STEAMSHIP AUTHORITY, THE
See WOODS HOLE MARTHAS VINEYARD AND NANTUCKET STEAMSHIP AUTHORITY

D-U-N-S 82-815-4133
STEARNS BANK NATIONAL ASSOCIATION
(*Suby of* STEARNS FINANCIAL SERVICES, INC.)
4191 2nd St S, Saint Cloud, MN 56301-3761
Tel (320) 253-6607 *Founded/Ownrshp* 2003
ales NA *EMP* 199^E
C 6021 National commercial banks
Norman C Skalicky
FO: Matt Geist
**Treas:* Robert S Steuck
Ofcr: Roforth Christopher
Ofcr: Jeremy Goltz
Ofcr: Julianne Hartung
Ex VP: Michael Worthington
Sr VP: Steve Domine
Sr VP: Steve Domini
Sr VP: Jan Hanson
Sr VP: Amy Johnson
Sr VP: Barbara Jones
Sr VP: Diane Nistch
Sr VP: Amber Ventura
VP: Jeff Anderson
VP: Catherine Bonner
VP: Bill Brindley
VP: Mike Giasone
VP: Tom Hosier
VP: Jack Postregna
VP: Steve Schiffler

D-U-N-S 05-224-2385
STEARNS CONRAD AND SCHMIDT CONSULTING ENGINEERS INC
SCS ENGINEERS
3900 Kilroy Arprt Way # 100, Long Beach, CA 90806-6816
Tel (562) 426-9544 *Founded/Ownrshp* 1970
Sales 157.6MM *EMP* 771
SIC 8711 1541 8748

D-U-N-S 62-429-7891
STEARNS LENDING LLC
555 Anton Blvd Ste 300, Costa Mesa, CA 92626-7667
Tel (714) 513-7777 *Founded/Ownrshp* 1984
Sales NA *EMP* 1,500
SIC 6162 Mortgage bankers & correspondents
CEO: Brian S Hale
**Pr:* Katherine Le
**COO:* James Hecht
**CFO:* Gary B Fabian
Ex VP: Tom Hunt
Ex VP: Kathleen L Vaughan
Sr VP: John F Cady
Sr VP: Greg Davis
VP: Oscar Laud
VP: Aaron Samples
**CIO:* Thomas W Neary

D-U-N-S 00-224-0984 IMP/EXP
STEBBINS ENGINEERING AND MANUFACTURING CO (NY)
363 Eastern Blvd, Watertown, NY 13601-3194
Tel (315) 782-3000 *Founded/Ownrshp* 1884, 1980
Sales 208.4MM^E *EMP* 1,168
SIC 1799 3443

D-U-N-S 02-467-5258
STEBBINS ENTERPRISES INC (NH)
PRO CON CONSTRUCTION
1359 Hooksett Rd, Hooksett, NH 03106-1809
Tel (603) 623-8811 *Founded/Ownrshp* 1977
Sales 84.5MM^E *EMP* 132^E
SIC 1542 1541 Commercial & office building, new construction; Commercial & office buildings, renovation & repair; Industrial buildings, new construction; Renovation, remodeling & repairs: industrial buildings
CEO: Mark R Stebbins
CFO: Bruce Desmarias

D-U-N-S 61-464-6719 IMP
■ **STEC INC**
(*Suby of* WESTERN DIGITAL CORP) ★
3001 Daimler St, Santa Ana, CA 92705-5812
Tel (415) 222-9996 *Founded/Ownrshp* 2013
Sales 131.0MM^E *EMP* 954
SIC 3572 3674 3577 Computer storage devices; Semiconductors & related devices; Computer peripheral equipment
Pr: Stephen D Milligan
Pr: Faheem Hayat
Pr: Jalal Sadr
Pr: Mahdi Zaidan
Sr VP: Michael Burnie
VP: Debbie Friedman
VP: DOT Hill
VP: Vaughn Miller
VP: Andy Mills
VP: Mark Rochlin
VP: Ken Samel
Exec: Davide Villa
Dir Surg: Mehran Ramezani

STEEL AMERICA
See SHIP COLONNAS YARD INC

D-U-N-S 00-717-2703 IMP/EXP
STEEL AND PIPE SUPPLY CO INC (KS)
VEBATRUST
555 Poyntz Ave Ste 122, Manhattan, KS 66502-0126
Tel (800) 521-2345 *Founded/Ownrshp* 1933
Sales 846.6MM *EMP* 625
Accts Bkd Kansas City Mo
SIC 5051 Metals service centers & offices
Ch Bd: Dennis Mullin
**Pr:* Matthew Crocker
**CFO:* Tia Schmidt
**Ex VP:* Connie Casper
**Sr VP:* Dirk Daveline
**VP:* Jack Crocker
Dir IT: Matthew Paul
Sfty Mgr: Clyde Teeter
Plnt Mgr: Ed Rowe
Board of Directors: Andy Becker, Joann Goldstein

D-U-N-S 09-106-1234 IMP/EXP
STEEL AND PIPES INC
Road 1rio, Caguas, PR 00725
Tel (787) 747-9415 *Founded/Ownrshp* 1979
Sales 102.5MM^E *EMP* 155
Accts Fpv & Galindez San Juan Puer
SIC 5051 3446 3317 5085 Steel; Ornamental metalwork; Steel pipe & tubes; Valves & fittings
CEO: Filepe V Cos
**Pr:* Filepe V Figueroa
CFO: Iliana Bouet
CFO: Nancy Lopez
VP: Alberto Vidal
Sls Mgr: Carlos Roman

STEEL AND WIRE
See MNP CORP

STEEL CITY TRUCK & AUTO
See GAS CITY LTD

D-U-N-S 60-743-6107 IMP
■ **STEEL DYNAMICS COLUMBUS LLC**
(*Suby of* SDI) ★
1945 Airport Rd, Columbus, MS 39701-9526
Tel (662) 245-4200 *Founded/Ownrshp* 2014
Sales 314.9MM^E *EMP* 790^E
SIC 3325 Rolling mill rolls, cast steel
Genl Mgr: Madhu Ranade
Netwrk Eng: William Ware

D-U-N-S 80-820-2725 IMP/EXP
▲ **STEEL DYNAMICS INC**
SDI
7575 W Jefferson Blvd, Fort Wayne, IN 46804-4131
Tel (260) 969-3500 *Founded/Ownrshp* 1993
Sales 7.5MMM *EMP* 7,780^E
Tkr Sym STLD *Exch* NGS
SIC 3312 3316 7389 Blast furnaces & steel mills; Plate, sheet & strip, except coated products; Structural & rail mill products; Bar, rod & wire products; Cold finishing of steel shapes; Scrap steel cutting
Pr: Mark D Millett
CFO: Theresa E Wagler
Treas: Rick Poinsatte
Ex VP: Russell B Rinn
Ex VP: Richard P Teets Jr
Sr VP: Christopher A Graham
VP: David Bednarz
VP: Joe Crawford
VP: Bob Francis
VP: Robert E Francis
VP: Ricky Gillenwater
VP: Thomas Hartman
VP: Alex Hoffman
VP: Robert A Simon
VP: Richard T Teets
VP: Theresa Waglr
VP: Kent Weber
Board of Directors: John C Bates, Keith E Busse, Frank D Byrne, Traci M Dolan, Paul B Edgerley, Jurgen Kolb, James C Marcuccilli, Bradley S Seaman, Gabriel L Shaheen

STEEL DYNAMICS ROANOKE BAR DIV
See ROANOKE ELECTRIC STEEL CORP

D-U-N-S 03-335-8581 IMP
■ **STEEL EXCEL INC**
(*Suby of* SPH GROUP HOLDINGS LLC) ★
1133 Westchester Ave N-222, White Plains, NY 10604-3516
Tel (914) 461-1300 *Founded/Ownrshp* 2011
Sales 132.6MM *EMP* 763^E
Accts Bdo Usa Llp New York New Yor
Tkr Sym SXCL *Exch* OTO
SIC 1389 7353 7032 Oil & gas wells: building, repairing & dismantling; Oil field equipment, rental or leasing; Sporting & recreational camps
CEO: Jack L Howard
**Ch Bd:* Warren G Lichtenstein
CFO: James F McCabe Jr
Board of Directors: John Mutch, John J Quicke, Gary W Ullman, Robert J Valentine

STEEL FAB
See SAMUEL STRAPPING SYSTEMS INC

D-U-N-S 04-090-3366 IMP/EXP
STEEL FABRICATORS LLC
721 Ne 44th St, Oakland Park, FL 33334-3150
Tel (954) 772-0440 *Founded/Ownrshp* 1962
Sales 118.5MM^E *EMP* 203
SIC 5051 Iron & steel (ferrous) products
Pr: Kurt Langsenkamp
COO: Tom Petrilla
**VP:* Sidney Blaauw
VP: Michael Jorgensen
VP: Mike Russell
Ql Cn Mgr: Gordon Jensen

D-U-N-S 05-189-1356 EXP
STEEL KING INDUSTRIES INC (WI)
2700 Chamber St, Stevens Point, WI 54481-4899
Tel (715) 341-3120 *Founded/Ownrshp* 1970, 1985
Sales 105.0MM^E *EMP* 300
Accts Wipfli Llp Wausau Wisconsin
SIC 3441 3537 3412 2542 Fabricated structural metal; Industrial trucks & tractors; Metal barrels, drums & pails; Partitions & fixtures, except wood
Pr: Jay Anderson
**CFO:* Dan Ladd
**Ch:* Robert White
**VP:* Timothy Tessmer
**VP:* Glenn Thiede
Plnt Mgr: Kim Hoppenrath
Plnt Mgr: Steve Krueger
Natl Sales: Kevin Curry
Mktg Dir: Donald Heemstra
Mktg Mgr: Kelly Kubisiak
Sls Mgr: Mike Curry

STEEL OF WEST VIRGINIA
See SWVA INC

D-U-N-S 17-546-0690 IMP/EXP
■ **STEEL OF WEST VIRGINIA INC**
(*Suby of* STEEL DYNAMICS ROANOKE BAR DIV) ★
17th St & 2nd Ave, Huntington, WV 25703
Tel (304) 696-8200 *Founded/Ownrshp* 1982
Sales 341.4MM *EMP* 75^E
SIC 3441 Fabricated structural metal
Pr: Timothy R Duke
**VP:* John O'Connor
Dir IT: Nancy Wallace
Sls Mgr: Jean Simmons

D-U-N-S 17-195-0025
▲ **STEEL PARTNERS HOLDINGS LP**
SPLP
590 Madison Ave Rm 3202, New York, NY 10022-8536
Tel (212) 520-2300 *Founded/Ownrshp* 1990
Sales 998.0MM *EMP* 3,548^E
Tkr Sym SPLP *Exch* NYS
SIC 3479 3497 1381 6141 Etching & engraving; Copper foil; Gold foil or leaf; Nickel foil; Silver foil or leaf; Drilling oil & gas wells; Consumer finance companies
Ch: Warren G Lichtenstein
Pr: Jack L Howard
CFO: Douglas B Woodworth

D-U-N-S 00-313-5154 IMP
STEEL PARTNERS II LP
590 Madison Ave Rm 3202, New York, NY 10022-8536
Tel (212) 758-3232 *Founded/Ownrshp* 1993
Sales 286.4MM^E *EMP* 2,693
SIC 5191 2874 Insecticides; Phosphatic fertilizers
Prin: Warren Lichtenstein
VP: Jack Howard
Mng Dir: John McNamara

STEEL SALES REALTY
See AMERICAN STEEL AND ALUMINUM CORP

D-U-N-S 04-686-4401
STEEL SERVICE CORP
2260 Flowood Dr, Jackson, MS 39232-9086
Tel (601) 939-9222 *Founded/Ownrshp* 1969
Sales 92.5MM^E *EMP* 150
Accts Carr Riggs & Ingram Llc Rid
SIC 3441 1791 3496 3443 Fabricated structural metal; Structural steel erection; Miscellaneous fabricated wire products; Fabricated plate work (boiler shop)
Pr: Lawrence A Cox
Ex VP: James Simonson
**VP:* Stewart C Heard
VP Mktg: Roger Ferril

D-U-N-S 05-682-6910 IMP/EXP
STEEL TECHNOLOGIES LLC
(*Suby of* NUMIT LLC) ★
700 N Hurstbourne Pkwy, Louisville, KY 40222-5393
Tel (502) 245-2110 *Founded/Ownrshp* 2010
Sales 408.0MM^E *EMP* 1,013
SIC 3312 3316 Sheet or strip, steel, hot-rolled; Cold-rolled strip or wire
Pr: Michael J Carroll
COO: Robert Mooney
COO: Stuart N Ray
**Ex VP:* Rick P Furber
VP: Curtis Chase
VP: L Curt Chase
VP: Richard A Payton
VP: James C Walters Jr
Genl Mgr: Tamera Anderson
Genl Mgr: Tom Woods
Snr Sftwr: Scott Bishop

D-U-N-S 00-544-1381 IMP/EXP
STEEL WAREHOUSE CO LLC (IN)
STEEL WAREHOUSE OF SOUTH BEND
2722 Tucker Dr, South Bend, IN 46619-4292
Tel (574) 236-5100 *Founded/Ownrshp* 1946, 1967
Sales 459.4MM^E *EMP* 1,700
SIC 5051

STEEL WAREHOUSE OF SOUTH BEND
See STEEL WAREHOUSE CO LLC

D-U-N-S 07-385-7559 IMP
STEEL WAREHOUSE OF WISCONSIN INC
(*Suby of* STEEL WAREHOUSE OF SOUTH BEND) ★
535 W Forest Hill Ave, Oak Creek, WI 53154-2950
Tel (414) 764-4800 *Founded/Ownrshp* 1973
Sales 89.3MM^E *EMP* 187^E
SIC 5051 Steel
CEO: David Lerman
**Pr:* James Lerman
**VP:* Donald Lerman
**VP:* Gerald Lerman
**VP:* Marc Lerman
Off Mgr: Colleen Collins
Opers Mgr: Randy Gross

D-U-N-S 00-601-6547 IMP/EXP
▲ **STEELCASE INC**
901 44th St Se, Grand Rapids, MI 49508-7594
Tel (616) 247-2710 *Founded/Ownrshp* 1912
Sales 3.0MMM *EMP* 11,000
Accts Deloitte & Touche Llp Grand R
Tkr Sym SCS *Exch* NYS
SIC 2522 2521 3648 8748 Office furniture, except wood; Chairs, office: padded or plain, except wood; Desks, office: except wood; Cabinets, office: except wood; Wood office furniture; Chairs, office: padded, upholstered or plain: wood; Desks, office: wood; Cabinets, office: wood; Lighting equipment; Business consulting
Pr: James P Keane
**Ch Bd:* Robert C Pew III
Pr: Ulrich H E Gwinner
CFO: David C Sylvester
Ofcr: Lizbeth S O'Shaughnessy
Sr VP: Guillaume M Alvarez
Sr VP: Eddy F Schmitt
VP: Sara E Armbruster
VP: Donna Flynn
VP: Robert G Krestakos
VP: Terrence J Lenhardt
VP: James N Ludwig
VP: Gale Moutrey
VP: Allan W Smith Jr
VP: Pamela Woodward
Board of Directors: Lawrence J Blanford, William P Crawford, Connie K Duckworth, R David Hoover, David W Joos, Cathy D Ross, Peter M Wege II, P Craig Welch Jr, Kate Pew Wolters

STEELE CORP SEC ADVISORY SVCS
See STEELE INTERNATIONAL INC

D-U-N-S 94-693-7000
STEELE INTERNATIONAL INC
STEELE CORP SEC ADVISORY SVCS
1 Sansome St Ste 3500, San Francisco, CA 94104-4436
Tel (415) 781-4300 *Founded/Ownrshp* 1994
Sales 41.9MM^E *EMP* 1,031
SIC 7381 8742 8748 Detective & armored car services; Management consulting services; Agricultural consultant
CEO: Kenneth Kurtz
Ex Dir: Richard W Ilmot
Rgnl Mgr: Murray Rouse

D-U-N-S 02-448-9502
STEELFAB INC
8623 Old Dowd Rd, Charlotte, NC 28214-8022
Tel (704) 394-5376 *Founded/Ownrshp* 1955
Sales 445.0MM *EMP* 900
SIC 3441 3449

D-U-N-S 83-169-9314
STEELRIVER INFRASTRUCTURE FUND NORTH AMERICA LP
(*Suby of* STEELRIVER INFRASTRUCTURE PARTNERS LP) ★
1 Letterman Dr Ste 500, San Francisco, CA 94129-1496
Tel (415) 848-5448 *Founded/Ownrshp* 2009
Sales 917.6MM^E *EMP* 1,300
SIC 4924 Natural gas distribution
Pt: Chris Kinney
Pt: John Anderson
Pt: Dennis Mahoney

D-U-N-S 83-169-9173
STEELRIVER INFRASTRUCTURE PARTNERS LP
1 Letterman Dr, San Francisco, CA 94129-1494
Tel (415) 512-1515 *Founded/Ownrshp* 2009
Sales 146.3MM^E *EMP* 1,300

SIC 6719 Investment holding companies, except banks
Pt: Christopher P Kinney
Pt: John Anderson
Pt: Dennis Mahoney

D-U-N-S 06-076-2432 IMP/EXP
STEELSCAPE LLC
(*Suby of* BLUESCOPE STEEL NORTH AMERICA CORP) ★
222 W Kalama River Rd, Kalama, WA 98625-9420
Tel (360) 673-8200 *Founded/Ownrshp* 1991, 2009
Sales 184.3MM^E *EMP* 500
SIC 3479 Aluminum coating of metal products
Pr: Adam Newman
Pr: John Cross
CFO: Jim Tener
VP: Don Ammons
VP: Michael Antonucci
VP: Scott Cooley
VP: Gemma Curci
VP: Dj Schmidt
VP: Mike Wire
CIO: Justin Powell
CTO: Jason Hannula

D-U-N-S 17-525-1248 IMP
STEELSUMMIT HOLDINGS INC
(*Suby of* SUMITOMO CORP OF AMERICAS) ★
1718 Jp Hennessy Dr, La Vergne, TN 37086-3525
Tel (615) 641-8600 *Founded/Ownrshp* 2006
Sales 119.6MM^E *EMP* 175
SIC 5051 Steel
Pr: Katsuya Inubushi
**COO:* Todd Rollins
**CFO:* Edmond Luz
**Ex VP:* Takahiro Saito
Sr VP: Dennis Grottola
VP: Rob Hanks
VP: Koji Hata
VP: Haruhiko Yoshida
Dir IT: Eddie Clay
Dir IT: Roman Kiszenia
Sls Mgr: Pat Alley

D-U-N-S 06-635-7740
STEELWAVE INC
4000 E 3rd Ave Ste 600, Foster City, CA 94404-4828
Tel (650) 571-2200 *Founded/Ownrshp* 2004
Sales 219.0MM^E *EMP* 1,200
SIC 6552 8741 6531 Land subdividers & developers, commercial; Land subdividers & developers, residential; Financial management for business; Real estate agents & managers
CEO: Barry S Diraimondo
**Pr:* C Preston Butcher

D-U-N-S 07-914-8646
STEELWAVE LLC
4000 E 3rd Ave Ste 500, Foster City, CA 94404-4824
Tel (650) 571-2200 *Founded/Ownrshp* 2003
Sales 49.4MM^E *EMP* 1,200
SIC 6552 8741 6531 Land subdividers & developers, commercial; Financial management for business; Real estate agents & managers
Pr: Michael Navarro
Sr VP: Stacy McClaughry
Mng Dir: Seth Hiromura
Mng Dir: Edward Nazaradeh

STEEV WEST FOURTH
See DR JAYS INC

D-U-N-S 02-911-9013
STEFANINI INC
(*Suby of* STEFANINI CONSULTORIA E ASSESSORIA EM INFORMATICA S/A)
27335 W 11 Mile Rd, Southfield, MI 48033-2231
Tel (248) 357-2866 *Founded/Ownrshp* 2010
Sales 300.2MM^E *EMP* 1,600^E
SIC 7379
CEO: Antonio Moreira
Pr: Dennis J Kelly
**CFO:* Sally A Brandtneris
Sr VP: Christoph Neut
VP: Robert Ardrey
VP: Robert Gumber
**VP:* Heidi K Hagle
VP: Ernst Voegtle
Dir Bus: Chris Schmidt
Prgrm Mgr: Colleen Gaura-Leksutin
Brnch Mgr: Bryon Brown

D-U-N-S 02-756-1984 IMP
STEIN DISTRIBUTING INC
C. STEIN DISTRIBUTING
(*Suby of* IDAHO DISTRIBUTING) ★
5408 Ne 88th St Ste B101, Vancouver, WA 98665-0990
Tel (360) 693-8251 *Founded/Ownrshp* 2001
Sales 89.7MM^E *EMP* 160
Accts Ford Black & Co Pc Portla
SIC 5181 5182 Beer & other fermented malt liquors; Wine
Pr: Craig Stein
CFO: Rob Schnieder
Sls Mgr: Dennis McAuliff

D-U-N-S 08-047-4331 IMP/EXP
STEIN FIBERS LTD
4 Computer Dr W Ste 200, Albany, NY 12205-1630
Tel (518) 489-5700 *Founded/Ownrshp* 1976
Sales 266.9MM *EMP* 186
Accts Teal Becker & Chiaramonte Cp
SIC 2824 Polyester fibers
Ch Bd: Sidney J Stein III
**Pr:* Peter J Spitalny
CFO: Allen Greenberg
**CFO:* Allen Greenburg
VP: David Knight
CTO: Andrew Swartz

D-U-N-S 04-201-1999 IMP
STEIN GARDEN CENTERS INC
JAVIC WHOLESALE DIVISION
5400 S 27th St, Milwaukee, WI 53221-3726
Tel (414) 761-5400 *Founded/Ownrshp* 1968
Sales 147.9MM^E *EMP* 570
SIC 5261 5992 Nurseries & garden centers; Nursery stock, seeds & bulbs; Lawn & garden equipment; Plants, potted; Flowers, fresh
Ch: Jack H Stein
**Pr:* Mark Birmingham
COO: Ed Malleck
**COO:* Werner Sperzel
**Sec:* Joan Stein
**Prin:* Ed Malek
**Prin:* David Stein
Genl Mgr: Rudy Zeilhofer
Dir IT: David Haas

D-U-N-S 06-605-5997 IMP
STEIN INC
1929 E Royalton Rd Ste C, Cleveland, OH 44147-2868
Tel (440) 526-9301 *Founded/Ownrshp* 1973
Sales 92.6MM^E *EMP* 300
SIC 3399 3312 5084 Iron ore recovery from open hearth slag; Blast furnaces & steel mills; Industrial machinery & equipment
CEO: Donald Ries
**CFO:* David Holvey
VP: Joe Russo
**Prin:* Marc Glasgow

D-U-N-S 00-506-4493 IMP
■ **STEIN MART BUYING CORP** (FL)
(*Suby of* STEIN MART INC) ★
1200 Riverplace Blvd # 1000, Jacksonville, FL 32207-1809
Tel (904) 346-1500 *Founded/Ownrshp* 1997
Sales 160.1MM^E *EMP* 250
SIC 5199 Variety store merchandise
CEO: Michael D Fisher
Ch Bd: Jay Stein
VP: Clayton Robertson

D-U-N-S 00-704-1346 IMP
▲ **STEIN MART INC**
1200 Riverplace Blvd # 1000, Jacksonville, FL 32207-1809
Tel (904) 346-1500 *Founded/Ownrshp* 1908
Sales 1.3MMM *EMP* 11,000
Accts Kpmg Llp Jacksonville Florid
Tkr Sym SMRT *Exch* NGS
SIC 5311 5651 Department stores; Family clothing stores
Pr: D Hunt Hawkins
**Ch Bd:* Jay Stein
CFO: Gregory W Kleffner
**V Ch Bd:* John H Williams Jr
Ex VP: Stein Mart
Ex VP: Gary L Pierce
Sr VP: Sharon Hart
VP: Michael Bennett
VP: Jim Casey
VP: Jane Dever
VP: Steven Horowitz
VP: Glori Katz
VP: Kelly Keene
VP: Kathryn L Orr
VP: Jennifer Wellington
Creative D: Laurie Thompson-Price
Board of Directors: Irwin Cohen, Lisa Galanti, Mitchell W Legler, Richard L Sisisky, Burton M Tansky

STEINER DOORS
See A G M DECO INC

D-U-N-S 00-798-0907
STEINER ELECTRIC CO (IL)
GIGAAGE
1250 Touhy Ave, Elk Grove Village, IL 60007-4985
Tel (847) 228-0400 *Founded/Ownrshp* 1923, 1916
Sales 222.0MM *EMP* 480
Accts Crowe Horwath Llp Oak Brook
SIC 5065 5063 Electronic parts & equipment; Electrical apparatus & equipment
Pr: Richard Kerman
Pr: Kris Cervantes
CFO: Edward Carroll
CFO: Bernie Dost
VP: Kevin Feeney
VP: Richard Hamer
VP: Jeff Izenstark
VP: David Keasler
VP: Mike Kirouac
Genl Mgr: Bret Bevers
Genl Mgr: Jeff Izenspark

D-U-N-S 95-811-2062 IMP/EXP
STEINWAY AND SONS
(*Suby of* STEINWAY MUSICAL INSTRUMENTS INC) ★
1 Steinway Pl, Long Island City, NY 11105-1033
Tel (718) 721-2600 *Founded/Ownrshp* 1853
Sales 96.6MM^E *EMP* 500^E
SIC 3931 5736 Pianos, all types: vertical, grand, spinet, player, etc.; Pianos
Ch Bd: Michael Sweeney
Pr: Kyle R Kirkland
Pr: Ronald Losby
Treas: Dennis Hanson
Ofcr: Elizabeth Olson
Ex VP: Darren Marshall
Ex VP: Dana D Messina
Sr VP: Amy Nenner
VP: John Disalvo
VP: Olaf Gube
VP: Paul Hopper

STEINWAY HALL
See STEINWAY INC

D-U-N-S 05-858-1554 IMP
STEINWAY INC
STEINWAY HALL
(*Suby of* STEINWAY PIANO CO INC) ★
1 Steinway Pl, Long Island City, NY 11105-1033
Tel (718) 721-2600 *Founded/Ownrshp* 1997
Sales 115.0MM^E *EMP* 625
SIC 3931 5736 Pianos, all types: vertical, grand, spinet, player, etc.; Pianos
CEO: Ronald Losby
Ex VP: Kyle R Kirkland

D-U-N-S 95-802-0737 IMP/EXP
STEINWAY MUSICAL INSTRUMENTS INC
(*Suby of* PIANISSIMO HOLDINGS CORP)
1133 Ave Of The Am Fl 33, New York, NY 10036
Tel (781) 894-9770 *Founded/Ownrshp* 2013
Sales 269.6MM^E *EMP* 1,698^E
SIC 3931 Musical instruments; Pianos, all types: vertical, grand, spinet, player, etc.; String instruments & parts; Woodwind instruments & parts
Pr: Michael T Sweeney
Pr: Ron Losby
Pr: John Stoner Jr
**Treas:* Dennis M Hanson
**VP:* Donna M Lucente

D-U-N-S 96-382-3315
STEINWAY PIANO CO INC
(*Suby of* SELMER PARIS) ★
600 Industrial Pkwy, Elkhart, IN 46516-5414
Tel (574) 522-1675 *Founded/Ownrshp* 1997
Sales 115.0MM^E *EMP* 1,000
SIC 3931 Pianos, all types: vertical, grand, spinet, player, etc.
Pr: John Stoner Jr
Ex VP: Messina Dana
VP: Drew Chuppe
VP: Mark Neal
Opers Mgr: Karen Stephan

D-U-N-S 00-284-7499
STEINY AND CO INC (CA)
221 N Ardmore Ave, Los Angeles, CA 90004-4503
Tel (626) 962-1055 *Founded/Ownrshp* 1956
Sales 91.6MM^E *EMP* 300
SIC 1731 General electrical contractor; Safety & security specialization
CEO: Susan Steiny
**Ch Bd:* John O Steiny
**CFO:* Vincent Mauch
Off Mgr: J Serrano

D-U-N-S 01-754-7530
STELLA ORTON HOME CARE AGENCY INC
3155 Amboy Rd Ste 1, Staten Island, NY 10306-2799
Tel (718) 987-4300 *Founded/Ownrshp* 1982
Sales 37.1MM *EMP* 1,200
Accts Rolando A Blancocpa Pllc Bald
SIC 8082 Home health care services
Ch: Edward Rabowski
**CFO:* Denise Blanchard
**Ex Dir:* Levester Burnley

D-U-N-S 60-592-9814
STELLA-JONES CORP
(*Suby of* STELLA-JONES US HOLDING CORP) ★
2 Gateway Ctr Ste 1000, Pittsburgh, PA 15222
Tel (412) 894-2846 *Founded/Ownrshp* 2005
Sales 149.6MM^E *EMP* 550
SIC 2491 2421 3531 Wood preserving; Railroad ties, sawed; Railway track equipment
Pr: Brian McManus
**VP:* Douglas Fox

D-U-N-S 96-814-0959 EXP
STELLA-JONES CORP
(*Suby of* STELLA-JONES INC)
603 Stanwix St Ste 1000, Pittsburgh, PA 15222-1423
Tel (412) 325-0202 *Founded/Ownrshp* 2005
Sales 198.0MM^E *EMP* 620
SIC 2491 Wood preserving; Railroad cross bridges & switch ties, treated wood
Pr: Brian McManus
**CFO:* Eric Vachon
**Treas:* Remi Godin
**Sr VP:* Doug Fox
**VP:* Marla Eichenbaum
**VP:* George Labelle

D-U-N-S 00-500-7364 EXP
STELLA-JONES US HOLDING CORP
(*Suby of* STELLA-JONES INC)
603 Stanwix St, Pittsburgh, PA 15222-1425
Tel (304) 372-2211 *Founded/Ownrshp* 1955
Sales 149.6MM^E *EMP* 650
Accts Arnett & Foster Pllc Cha
SIC 2491 Wood preserving
CEO: Brian McManus
**Sr VP:* Eric Vachon
**VP:* Marla Eichenbaum
**VP:* Gordon Murray

D-U-N-S 80-169-4290
STELLAR COMPANIES INC
STELLAR GROUP, THE
2900 Hartley Rd, Jacksonville, FL 32257-8221
Tel (904) 899-9393 *Founded/Ownrshp* 1992
Sales 336.1MM *EMP* 600
Accts Rsm Us Llp Jacksonville Flor
SIC 1542 8711 1541 Design & erection, combined: non-residential; Engineering services; Food products manufacturing or packing plant construction
CEO: Ronald H Foster Jr
**Pr:* Michael S Santarone
**CFO:* Scott V Witt

STELLAR GROUP, THE
See STELLAR COMPANIES INC

D-U-N-S 06-320-2597
STELLAR MANAGEMENT GROUP INC
412 Georgia Ave Ste 300, Chattanooga, TN 37403-1853
Tel (423) 265-7090 *Founded/Ownrshp* 1994
Sales 169.8MM^E *EMP* 1,986
SIC 5064 Garbage disposals
Pr: Bob Bullard

D-U-N-S 01-070-9053
STELLAR MICROELECTRONICS INC
(*Suby of* NEOTECH) ★
28454 Livingston Ave, Valencia, CA 91355-4172
Tel (661) 775-3500 *Founded/Ownrshp* 2016
Sales 165.9MM^E *EMP* 239
SIC 5065 Semiconductor devices
Pr: Sudesh Arora
Ql Cn Mgr: Rick Thompson

D-U-N-S 00-895-5544
■ **STELLAR ONE BANK**
(*Suby of* UNION BANKSHARES CORP) ★
102 S Main St, Culpeper, VA 22701-3065
Tel (540) 382-4951 *Founded/Ownrshp* 2002
Sales NA *EMP* 124
SIC 6021 National commercial banks
Pr: O R Barham
Sr VP: George Pulliam
**VP:* Jeffery Farrar
VP: Rhonda Long

D-U-N-S 01-474-9290
STELLARONE CORP
590 Peter Jefferson Pkwy, Charlottesville, VA 22911-4628
Tel (434) 964-2211 *Founded/Ownrshp* 1996
Sales NA *EMP* 759^E
SIC 6022

STEMC
See SOUTHWEST TENNESSEE ELECTRIC MEMBERSHIP CORP

D-U-N-S 00-732-8149 IMP/EXP
■ **STEMCO LP**
(*Suby of* ENPRO INDUSTRIES INC) ★
300 Industrial Dr, Longview, TX 75602-4720
Tel (903) 232-3500 *Founded/Ownrshp* 1953
Sales 180.3MM^E *EMP* 467
SIC 3714 Motor vehicle parts & accessories
Pr: Jon Cox
CFO: Daniel Grgurich
VP: Ignacio Jaimes
VP: Carlos Masters
VP: Bob Montgomery
VP: Jim Reis
Plnt Mgr: Tom Jones
Sls Mgr: Alejandro Ayala
Sls Mgr: Manny Cordoviz
Sales Asso: Beth Black
Sales Asso: Gayann Nash

STEMCO MOTOR WHEEL
See STEMCO PRODUCTS INC

D-U-N-S 61-472-7712 EXP
■ **STEMCO PRODUCTS INC**
STEMCO MOTOR WHEEL
(*Suby of* STEMCO LP) ★
37770 Amrhein Rd, Livonia, MI 48150-1014
Tel (734) 416-8911 *Founded/Ownrshp* 2012
Sales 110.9MM^E *EMP* 467
SIC 3714 3465 Brake drums, motor vehicle; Hub caps, automobile: stamped metal
CEO: W Ed Meador
**CFO:* Wendy Cox
**VP:* John Haapala

D-U-N-S 79-141-4100 IMP
STEMCOR SPECIAL STEELS LLC
(*Suby of* MOORGATE INDUSTRIES LIMITED)
5847 San Felipe St # 2400, Houston, TX 77057-3163
Tel (281) 252-3625 *Founded/Ownrshp* 2006
Sales 186.5MM^E *EMP* 401
SIC 5051 Steel
Pr: Tom Turnipseede
Opers Mgr: Jt Munger

D-U-N-S 36-111-3988 IMP/EXP
STEMCOR USA INC
(*Suby of* MOORGATE INDUSTRIES LIMITED)
2 Park Ave Rm 1600, New York, NY 10016-5700
Tel (212) 563-0262 *Founded/Ownrshp* 1988
Sales 97.4MM^E *EMP* 55
Accts Deloitte Llp London United K
SIC 5051 8711 Metals service centers & offices; Engineering services
CEO: Steven M Graf
**CEO:* Julian Verden
**CFO:* Michael Broom
**Ch:* John Soden
**VP:* Laurie Barilla
**VP:* Richard Edmonds
**VP:* Christopher Williams

D-U-N-S 05-380-7392 IMP/EXP
STEMILT GROWERS LLC
3135 Warehouse Rd, Wenatchee, WA 98801-9193
Tel (509) 663-1451 *Founded/Ownrshp* 1964
Sales 745.4MM^E *EMP* 1,600
SIC 0723 Fruit (fresh) packing services
Pr: West A Mathison
CFO: David Millheisler
Treas: Kyle Mathison
Treas: Julie Orendor
VP: David Mathison
VP: Thomas K Mathison
Exec: Larry Nennott
Genl Mgr: Hans Greve
Genl Mgr: Dave Mathison
Dir IT: Rodney Dye
IT Man: Sean Akers

D-U-N-S 87-269-3176
STENCO CONSTRUCTION CO LLC
12741 Farmington Rd, Livonia, MI 48150-1624
Tel (734) 427-8843 *Founded/Ownrshp* 1998
Sales 84.5MM *EMP* 20
Accts Yeo & Yeo Pc Ann Arbor Mi
SIC 1541 Industrial buildings & warehouses

D-U-N-S 96-914-5346
STENO EMPLOYMENT SERVICES INC
8560 Vineyard Ave Ste 208, Rancho Cucamonga, CA 91730-4394
Tel (909) 476-1404 *Founded/Ownrshp* 2009
Sales 46.5MM^E *EMP* 2,000
SIC 7363 Employee leasing service
CEO: Jaime Silguero
**Pr:* Ahmad Jackson

STENS POWER EQUIPMENT PARTS
See ARIENS SPECIALTY BRANDS LLC

STEP 2
See STEP2 CO LLC

D-U-N-S 11-904-3276
STEP UP FOR STUDENTS INC
FLORIDA TAX CREDIT SCHOLARSHIP
4655 Salisbury Rd Ste 400, Jacksonville, FL 32256-0958
Tel (877) 735-7837 *Founded/Ownrshp* 2000
Sales 457.8MM *EMP* 17E
Accts Mcgladrey Llp Melbourne Fl
SIC 8299 Educational services
Ch Bd: John Kirtley
**CFO:* Kim Dyson
VP: Glen Gilzean

D-U-N-S 09-536-1564
STEP-BY-STEP INC
744 Kidder St Frnt, Wilkes Barre, PA 18702-7018
Tel (570) 829-3477 *Founded/Ownrshp* 1977
Sales 58.4MM *EMP* 1,000
Accts Matlowski Corporation Pc Wilk
SIC 8322 8361 Individual & family services; Rehabilitation center, residential: health care incidental
Pr: James Bobeck
**COO:* Michael Bermatovich
**CFO:* Michael Kasenchak
**VP:* Edith Hennedaul
VP: Denise Holton

D-U-N-S 62-488-0779 IMP/EXP
STEP2 CO LLC
STEP 2
(*Suby of* BACKYARD DISCOVERY) ★
10010 Aurora Hudson Rd, Streetsboro, OH 44241-1619
Tel (866) 429-5200 *Founded/Ownrshp* 2016
Sales 198.3MM *EMP* 900
SIC 3089 3944 3423 Molding primary plastic; Games, toys & children's vehicles; Hand & edge tools
CEO: Christopher P Quinn
Ex VP: Lysa Liemer
Ex VP: Wayne Stock
VP: Dotti Foltz
VP: Brian McDonald
IT Man: Tony Gallo
Sfty Mgr: Margaret Smerglia
Opers Mgr: Sara Rector
Prd Mgr: Jason Witkosky
Corp Couns: Holly Ohlrich

D-U-N-S 00-513-0182 IMP/EXP
▲ STEPAN CO
22 W Frontage Rd, Northfield, IL 60093-3470
Tel (847) 446-7500 *Founded/Ownrshp* 1932
Sales 1.7MMM *EMP* 2,073
Accts Deloitte & Touche Llp Chicago
Tkr Sym SCL *Exch* NYS
SIC 2843 2821 2087 2865 Surface active agents; Sulfonated oils, fats or greases; Emulsifiers, except food & pharmaceutical; Polyurethane resins; Phthalic anhydride resins; Extracts, flavoring; Cyclic organic intermediates
Ch Bd: F Quinn Stepan
CFO: Scott D Beamer
VP: Scott R Behrens
VP: James Butterwick
VP: Jennifer A Hale
VP: John Hall
VP: Scott C Mason
VP: Arthur W Mergner
VP: Deb Stefaniak
VP: Debra A Stefaniak
Exec: Richard Adams
Board of Directors: Michael R Boyce, Randall S Dearth, Joaquin Delgado, Gregory E Lawton, Jan Stern Reed, Edward J Wehmer

D-U-N-S 07-389-4727
STEPHEN F AUSTIN STATE UNIVERSITY
S F A
1936 North St, Nacogdoches, TX 75965-3940
Tel (936) 468-3401 *Founded/Ownrshp* 1923
Sales 152.6MME *EMP* 2,914
SIC 8221 University
Pr: Dr Baker Pattillo
VP: Tammya Adams
VP: Danny Gallant
VP: Valerie Griffith
VP: Becky Smith
VP: Amanda Suter
VP: Steven Westbrook
Exec: Kim Baggett
Ex Dir: Monique Cossich
Dir IT: Paul Davis
VP Opers: Betty Ford

D-U-N-S 03-743-5026
STEPHEN F AUSTIN STATE UNIVERSITY FOUNDATION INC
Vista At Alumni Dr 303, Nacogdoches, TX 75962-0001
Tel (936) 468-5406 *Founded/Ownrshp* 1970
Sales 1.5MME *EMP* 2,000
SIC 8221 University
Pr: Baker Pattillo
**Prin:* Jill Spill

D-U-N-S 00-150-3010 IMP/EXP
STEPHEN GOULD CORP (NJ)
35 S Jefferson Rd, Whippany, NJ 07981-1043
Tel (973) 428-1500 *Founded/Ownrshp* 1939
Sales 594.7MME *EMP* 325
SIC 2631 2759 Container, packaging & boxboard; Labels & seals: printing
CEO: Michael Golden
**Pr:* John Golden
**Pr:* Justin Golden
**Pr:* Peter Van Slyke
**CFO:* Anthony Lupo
**VP:* Dale Golden
IT Man: Denise Cumpek
IT Man: John Nogrady
QC Dir: Praveen Gupta
Mktg Dir: Robert Rosenbaum
Mktg Dir: Andy Wiener

D-U-N-S 79-761-1464
STEPHEN L LAFRANCE HOLDINGS INC
3017 N Midland Dr, Pine Bluff, AR 71603-4828
Tel (870) 535-5171 *Founded/Ownrshp* 1997
Sales 199.5MME *EMP* 3,000
SIC 5912 6794 Drug stores; Franchises, selling or licensing
Pr: Stephen L Lafrance Sr
**Pr:* Mark A Wagner
**VP:* John A Mann
VP: John Trainer

D-U-N-S 04-356-2370 IMP
■ STEPHEN L LAFRANCE PHARMACY INC (AR)
USA DRUG
(*Suby of* WALGREENS) ★
3017 N Midland Dr, Pine Bluff, AR 71603-4828
Tel (870) 535-5171 *Founded/Ownrshp* 1968, 2012
Sales 274.7MME *EMP* 1,500
SIC 5122 5912 Cosmetics, perfumes & hair products; Drug stores & proprietary stores
Pr: Mark A Wagner
CFO: Richard McNaulty
**Treas:* Jason Dubinsky
Sr Cor Off: John T Namir
**VP:* John A Mann

D-U-N-S 83-290-9035
STEPHENS CAPITAL PARTNERS LLC
111 Center St Ste 200, Little Rock, AR 72201-4425
Tel (800) 643-9691 *Founded/Ownrshp* 2006
Sales 134.6MME *EMP* 700E
SIC 6211 Investment bankers
VP: David Phillips

D-U-N-S 00-195-0898
STEPHENS INC
(*Suby of* SI HOLDINGS INC) ★
111 Center St Ste 200, Little Rock, AR 72201-4425
Tel (501) 377-2000 *Founded/Ownrshp* 1933
Sales 184.2MM *EMP* 475
Accts Deloitte & Touche Llp Parsip
SIC 6211 Investment bankers; Bond dealers & brokers
Pr: Warren A Stephens
Pr: Jason Majors
COO: Curtis F Bradbury
Treas: Kathy Bryant
Treas: C Ray Gash
Chf Cred: David Prince
Chf Cred: Phil Shellabarger
Ofcr: Michael Nolte
Ex VP: Jon E M Jacoby
Sr VP: George J Sousoulas
VP: Anthony T Allio
VP: Shae Belford
VP: Nick Bellmann
VP: Bo Bittle
VP: Bo Brister
VP: Abigail Buchanan
VP: Becky Burgess
VP: Kevin R Burns
VP: Sarah Campbell
VP: Ed Carter
VP: Mark Castle

D-U-N-S 07-188-2633
STEPHENS INSTITUTE
ACADEMY OF ART UNIVERSITY
79 New Montgomery St, San Francisco, CA 94105-3410
Tel (415) 274-2200 *Founded/Ownrshp* 1964
Sales 105.5MME *EMP* 2,000E
SIC 8299 8221 Art school, except commercial; University
Pr: Elisa Stephens
**Ch:* Richard A Stephens
Ex VP: Melissa Marshall
VP: Kate Griffeath
VP: Jonathan Ward
Exec: Monica Amitin
Assoc Dir: Michael Robertson
Assoc Dir: Jeremy Stout
Ex Dir: Joyce Gomez
Cmptr Lab: Jack Tiranasar
Web Dev: Oliver Nguyen

D-U-N-S 18-296-0807 IMP/EXP
STEPHENS LLC
111 Center St Ste 200, Little Rock, AR 72201-4425
Tel (501) 377-2000 *Founded/Ownrshp* 1933
Sales 126.2MME *EMP* 1,000E
SIC 6719 Investment holding companies, except banks
Ch Bd: Jack T Stephens
**Pr:* Warren A Stephens
**COO:* Curt Bradbury
**Treas:* Kathy Bryant
**Treas:* C Ray Gash
Ex VP: James Simpson
Ex VP: William L Tedford Jr
VP: Chad Crank
**Exec:* Jon E M Jacoby
Mng Dir: N R Nelson Jr
IT Man: Kevin M Wilcox

D-U-N-S 05-196-0805
STEPHENS MEDIA LLC (NV)
LAS VEGAS REVIEW-JOURNAL
1111 W Bonanza Rd, Las Vegas, NV 89106-3545
Tel (702) 383-0211 *Founded/Ownrshp* 2015
Sales NA *EMP* 2,100
SIC 2711

D-U-N-S 04-811-2429 IMP/EXP
STEPHENS PIPE & STEEL LLC
(*Suby of* HOUCHENS INDUSTRIES INC) ★
2224 E Highway 619, Russell Springs, KY 42642-7928
Tel (270) 866-3331 *Founded/Ownrshp* 2008
Sales 305.9MM *EMP* 1,000E
Accts Bkd Llp Bowling Green Kentu
SIC 5051 3315 Pipe & tubing, steel; Steel; Chain link fencing
Pr: Terry L Stephens
VP: Ray Mann Jr
Genl Mgr: Ted Eysenbach
IT Man: Treva Cowell
Sls Mgr: David Gaskin
Sales Asso: Frank Roberge

D-U-N-S 03-297-7217
STEPHENSON WHOLESALE CO INC
INDIAN NATION WHOLESALE
230 S 22nd Ave, Durant, OK 74701-5646
Tel (580) 920-0125 *Founded/Ownrshp* 1953
Sales 316.0MM *EMP* 305
Accts Bdo Usa Llp Dallas Texas
SIC 5194 5145 5143 5142 5141 5113 Tobacco & tobacco products; Cigarettes; Candy; Dairy products, except dried or canned; Packaged frozen goods; Groceries, general line; Industrial & personal service paper
CEO: Tammy Cross
**Pr:* Corey Cooper
CFO: Jerry Wheatley
**Sec:* Gregory Cross
VP: Becky Spellman
Sls Dir: Carter Adair

D-U-N-S 06-486-0364
STEPTOE & JOHNSON LLP
MICHAEL KAIL
1330 Connecticut Ave Nw, Washington, DC 20036-1704
Tel (202) 429-3000 *Founded/Ownrshp* 1912
Sales 101.9MME *EMP* 575
SIC 8111

D-U-N-S 36-359-6297 IMP
▲ STERICYCLE INC
28161 N Keith Dr, Lake Forest, IL 60045-4528
Tel (847) 367-5910 *Founded/Ownrshp* 1989
Sales 2.9MMM *EMP* 25,672
Tkr Sym SRCL *Exch* NGS
SIC 4953 Medical waste disposal
Pr: Charles A Alutto
**Ch Bd:* Mark C Miller
**COO:* Brent Arnold
**CFO:* Daniel V Ginnetti
Ofcr: Brenda R Frank
**Ex VP:* Michael J Collins
Ex VP: John P Schetz

D-U-N-S 96-268-0984
STERIGENICS HOLDINGS LLC
(*Suby of* STERIGENICS INTERNATIONAL LLC) ★
3 Parkway N Ste 100n, Deerfield, IL 60015-2560
Tel (847) 607-6060 *Founded/Ownrshp* 2011
Sales 178.8MME *EMP* 1,200
SIC 6719 Investment holding companies, except banks

D-U-N-S 07-983-2075
STERIGENICS INTERNATIONAL LLC
2015 Spring Rd Ste 650, Oak Brook, IL 60523-3909
Tel (630) 928-1700 *Founded/Ownrshp* 2004
Sales 553.4MME *EMP* 1,200
SIC 7389 Product sterilization service
Genl Mgr: Peter Baker

D-U-N-S 09-849-9569 IMP
STERIGENICS US LLC
STERIPRO LABORATORIES
(*Suby of* STERIGENICS INTERNATIONAL LLC) ★
3 Parkway N Ste 100n, Deerfield, IL 60015-2560
Tel (847) 607-6060 *Founded/Ownrshp* 1997
Sales 298.8MME *EMP* 1,200
SIC 7389 Product sterilization service
Ch: Michael Mulhern
**CEO:* Michael J Mulhern
Treas: Greg Fisher
Exec: Valerie Balding
Plnt Mgr: Chuck Freegon
Ql Cn Mgr: Rebecca Campbell

D-U-N-S 00-113-3057 IMP/EXP
STERILITE CORP (MA)
30 Scales Ln, Townsend, MA 01469-1010
Tel (978) 597-1000 *Founded/Ownrshp* 1939
Sales 236.3MME *EMP* 1,800
SIC 3089 4226

D-U-N-S 17-589-9459 IMP/EXP
■ STERILMED INC
(*Suby of* ETHICON ENDO-SURGERY INC) ★
5010 Cheshire Pkwy N # 2, Plymouth, MN 55446-4101
Tel (888) 541-0078 *Founded/Ownrshp* 2011
Sales 231.1MME *EMP* 600
SIC 5047 Medical equipment & supplies; Medical laboratory equipment; Diagnostic equipment, medical
CEO: Michael W Gustafson
**CFO:* Chuck Karpinske
**Treas:* Noel Fairbanks
VP: Tom Schlick
Genl Mgr: Uri Yaron
IT Man: Rick Haskins
Ql Cn Mgr: Keith Miller
Natl Sales: Steve Melin
Mktg Dir: Keith Hoof

STERIPRO LABORATORIES
See STERIGENICS US LLC

D-U-N-S 17-736-0039 IMP/EXP
STERIS CORP
(*Suby of* STERIS PLC)
5960 Heisley Rd, Mentor, OH 44060-1834
Tel (440) 354-2600 *Founded/Ownrshp* 2015
Sales 1.8MMM *EMP* 7,600
SIC 3841 3842 3845 Surgical & medical instruments; Diagnostic apparatus, medical; Sterilizers, hospital & surgical; Endoscopic equipment, electromedical
Pr: Walter M Rosebrough Jr
Pr: Robert E Moss
**CFO:* Michael J Tokich
**Chf Cred:* Kathie Bardwell
Ex VP: Greg Meunier
Sr VP: David Johnson
Sr VP: Sudhir K Pahwa
VP: Dan Carestio
VP: Kevan Fight
VP: John Fowler
VP: Ronald Galovich
VP: Pete Gergely
VP: Trey Howard
VP: Brian Kaufman
VP: Dennis Kovit
VP: Gerard Reis
VP: Lewis Schwartz
VP: Lara Stark
VP: Dave Wartluft
VP: Adam Zangerle
VP: John Zangerle

D-U-N-S 78-812-9153
STERIS ISOMEDIX OPERATIONS INC
(*Suby of* STERIS CORP) ★
5960 Heisley Rd, Mentor, OH 44060-1834
Tel (440) 354-2600 *Founded/Ownrshp* 1997
Sales 52.2MME *EMP* 1,000E
SIC 8734 Industrial sterilization service
Pr: Robert E Moss
Treas: Karen L Burton
VP: Michael J Tokich

D-U-N-S 18-173-9178 IMP
STERITECH GROUP INC
(*Suby of* JC EHRLICH) ★
6701 Carmel Rd Ste 300, Charlotte, NC 28226-0205
Tel (704) 544-1900 *Founded/Ownrshp* 2015
Sales 107.5MME *EMP* 750
SIC 7342 8721 Exterminating & fumigating; Auditing services
CEO: Rich Ennis
**Pr:* Jim Cashman
**Pr:* Doug Sutton
**CFO:* Mike Lynch
VP: Bob Nelson
VP: Jennifer Courtney Trice
VP: Wade Whitman
VP: Paul Wilkinson
**CIO:* Raja Musunuru
Software D: Leslie Dillingham
Sls Mgr: Robert Sproule

STERLING
See GERSON CO

D-U-N-S 06-472-7621
■ STERLING & STERLING LLC
STERLINGRISK
(*Suby of* BROADSTREET PARTNERS INC) ★
135 Crossways Park Dr # 300, Woodbury, NY 11797-2005
Tel (516) 487-0300 *Founded/Ownrshp* 2016
Sales NA *EMP* 184
SIC 6411 Insurance brokers; Insurance information & consulting services; Advisory services, insurance
CEO: David Sterling
Pr: Joseph Santospirito
Pr: Howard Tollin
CFO: Joanne Krush
Chf Mktg O: Jason Walker
Ex VP: Barry Wolf
Sr VP: Connie Chiara
Sr VP: Doreen Dicicco
Sr VP: Steve Jasinski
Sr VP: Marc Kravitz
Sr VP: Eli Mishanie
Sr VP: Michael O'Donnell
V Ch: AVI Cohen
VP: Mark Dweck
VP: Pamela Fitzgerald
VP: David Fried
VP: Richard Lippin
VP: Meghan McDonough
VP: Gina Murphy
VP: Maryalice Nazaretian
VP: Dennis Sturtz

D-U-N-S 03-585-6082
▲ STERLING BANCORP
400 Rella Blvd, Montebello, NY 10901-4241
Tel (845) 369-8040 *Founded/Ownrshp* 2003
Sales NA *EMP* 1,089E
Tkr Sym STL *Exch* NYS
SIC 6021 National commercial banks
Pr: Jack L Kopnisky
**Ch Bd:* Louis J Cappelli
COO: Rodney C Whitwell
CFO: Luis Massiani
Ex VP: Michael E Finn
Exec: James R Peoples
Board of Directors: Richard O'toole, Robert Abrams, Burt Steinberg, John P Cahill, Craig S Thompson, James F Deutsch, William E Whiston, Fernando Ferrer, William F Helmer, Thomas G Kahn, James J Landy, Robert W Lazar, John C Millman

D-U-N-S 04-318-5123 IMP/EXP
STERLING BANCORP
650 5th Ave Ste 2406, New York, NY 10019-6108
Tel (212) 757-3300 *Founded/Ownrshp* 1966
Sales NA *EMP* 553E
SIC 6021

D-U-N-S 04-867-9013
■ STERLING BANCSHARES INC
(*Suby of* COMERICA INC) ★
2950 North Loop W # 1200, Houston, TX 77092-8843
Tel (713) 466-8300 *Founded/Ownrshp* 2011
Sales NA *EMP* 1,012E
SIC 6022 State commercial banks
Pr: J Downey Bridgwater
V Ch: Max W Ells
CEO: John A Rossitto
CFO: Bob E Bailey
**CFO:* Zach L Wasson
Chf Cred: Daryl D Bohls
Bd of Dir: G E Powell
**Ofcr:* Travis L Jaggers
**Ex VP:* Deborah A Dinsmore
**Ex VP:* James W Goolsby Jr

D-U-N-S 06-963-4103
■ STERLING BANK
(*Suby of* STERLING BANCSHARES INC) ★
2550 North Loop W Ste 600, Houston, TX 77092-8912
Tel (713) 466-8300 *Founded/Ownrshp* 1981
Sales NA *EMP* 630
SIC 6022 State commercial banks
Pr: J Downey Bridgewater
**Ch Bd:* George Martinez
CEO: Lane Allen
CEO: Jeff Vincent

*CFO: Eugene S Putnam
*Chf Cred: Bob S Smith
*Ex VP: Deborah Dinsmore
*Ex VP: Travis L Jaggers
Ex VP: Pamela H Lovett
*Ex VP: Sonny B Lyles
*Ex VP: Michelle Mahfouz
*Ex VP: Glenn Rust
*Sr VP: Jim Goolsby
*Sr VP: Bambi L Mc Cullough
*Sr VP: C Wallis McMath Jr
*Sr VP: Philip Montgomery
Sr VP: Jeff Strasner
VP: Cody Kiser
Board of Directors: Edward Bardegett

D-U-N-S 06-484-5159
STERLING BOILER AND MECHANICAL INC
1420 Kimber Ln, Evansville, IN 47715-4025
Tel (812) 479-5447 Founded/Ownrshp 1982
Sales 155.7MM[E] EMP 800[E]
Accts Harding Shymanski & Company
SIC 1711 3443 Mechanical contractor; Fabricated plate work (boiler shop)
Pr: Daniel G Felker
*VP: Butch Bradley

STERLING CAPITAL PARTNERS
See STERLING PARTNERS LLC

D-U-N-S 93-770-4302
STERLING COMMERCE LLC
4600 Lakehurst Ct, Dublin, OH 43016-2248
Tel (614) 798-2192 Founded/Ownrshp 2010
Sales 150.1MM[E] EMP 2,500
SIC 7372

D-U-N-S 93-883-6541
STERLING COMPUTERS CORP
600 Stevens Port Dr, Dakota Dunes, SD 57049-5149
Tel (605) 242-4000 Founded/Ownrshp 1996
Sales 329.4MM EMP 150
SIC 7373 Office computer automation systems integration; Value-added resellers, computer systems; Local area network (LAN) systems integrator
CEO: Jean Marie Moore
*Pr: Brad Moore
*CFO: Jennifer Deitloff
*VP: Darrell Moore

D-U-N-S 78-365-0328
▲ STERLING CONSTRUCTION CO INC
1800 Hughes Landing Blvd # 250, The Woodlands, TX 77380-3688
Tel (281) 214-0800 Founded/Ownrshp 1955
Sales 623.6MM EMP 1,565
Tkr Sym STRL Exch NGS
SIC 1611 1622 1623 Highway & street construction; Bridge, tunnel & elevated highway; Water, sewer & utility lines
CEO: Paul J Varello
*Ch Bd: Milton L Scott
COO: Con L Wadsworth
CFO: Ronald A Ballschmiede
Sr VP: Roger M Barzun
Board of Directors: Marian M Davenport, Maarten D Hemsley, Charles R Patton, Richard O Schaum

D-U-N-S 82-811-9201
STERLING CONSTRUCTION MANAGEMENT LLC
3158 Baron Ln Unit E, Rifle, CO 81650-7400
Tel (307) 362-7906 Founded/Ownrshp 2004
Sales 170.0MM EMP 350
SIC 1623 Pipeline construction
CFO: Pat Simpson

D-U-N-S 61-227-2109
STERLING ENTERTAINMENT ENTERPRISES LLC
SPORTSNET NEW YORK
75 Rockefeller Plz Fl 29, New York, NY 10019-6930
Tel (212) 485-4400 Founded/Ownrshp 2004
Sales 85.6MM[E] EMP 250[E]
SIC 4833 Television broadcasting stations
Prin: Steve Raab
Ofcr: Brian Erdlen
Sr VP: David Newman
Dir IT: Gil Santana
Prd Mgr: Erin Farrar
Sls&Mrk Ex: Maria D Paris
Mktg Mgr: Carole Witten

D-U-N-S 79-637-4155
STERLING FINANCIAL CORP
111 N Wall St, Spokane, WA 99201-0609
Tel (509) 358-8097 Founded/Ownrshp 1992
Sales NA EMP 2,532[E]
SIC 6036

D-U-N-S 62-267-4208 IMP/EXP
STERLING FLUID SYSTEMS (USA) LLC
PEERLESS PUMP COMPANY
(Suby of GRUNDFOS HOLDING AG)
2005 Dr Mrtn Lthr Kng Jr, Indianapolis, IN 46202-1165
Tel (317) 925-9661 Founded/Ownrshp 2012
Sales 163.5MM[E] EMP 400
SIC 3561 Pumps & pumping equipment
Pr: Dean Douglas
VP: Jim Longshore
Genl Mgr: Tim Ballengee
Genl Mgr: Scott Patterson
Genl Mgr: Anders Thorsell
CTO: Jim Fleming
Mfg Mgr: George Pickett
Mktg Mgr: Elizabeth Condakes
Mktg Mgr: Clarissa Riddle

D-U-N-S 82-635-0373
STERLING GROUP INC
3010 Santa Fe Ct, Missoula, MT 59808-1730
Tel (406) 251-5788 Founded/Ownrshp 1986
Sales NA EMP 1,118
SIC 8741

D-U-N-S 78-518-0774
STERLING GROUP L P
CLAYTON, DUBILIER & RICE
9 Greenway Plz Ste 2400, Houston, TX 77046-0897
Tel (713) 877-8257 Founded/Ownrshp 1987
Sales 447.2MM[E] EMP 1,475
SIC 6799 Investors
Pt: Frank J Hevrdejs
Pt: Gregory L Elliott
Pt: C Kevin Garland
Pt: John D Hawkins
Pt: Hunter Nelson
Pt: William C Oehmig
Pt: Gary Rosenthal
Pt: Kent Wallace

D-U-N-S 82-954-7855
STERLING GROUP PARTNERS II LP
CD&R ROADHOUSE HOLDINGS
(Suby of CLAYTON DUBILIER & RICE) ★
3890 W Northwest Hwy # 400, Dallas, TX 75220-8108
Tel (214) 956-5100 Founded/Ownrshp 2004
Sales 38.5MM[E] EMP 1,000
SIC 5211 Roofing material
Genl Pt: Vin Perella

D-U-N-S 62-342-5258
STERLING GROUP PHYSICIAN SERVICES LLC
STERLING HEALTHCARE
1000 Park Forty Plz # 500, Durham, NC 27713-5249
Tel (919) 383-0355 Founded/Ownrshp 1977
Sales 830.4MM[E] EMP 1,956
SIC 8741 8742 Hospital management; Hospital & health services consultant
Pr: Eugene Dauchert
Pr: Dana Fortin
CFO: Philip B Arnold
CFO: Stan Haynes
CFO: Gary Jensen
CFO: Brenda Lazel
Ofcr: Mary Haynes
Ofcr: Sarah C Herzog
*Ex VP: G Scott Dillon
Sr VP: Donna Campbell
Sr VP: James M Douthitt
Sr VP: Linda Ellis
Sr VP: David Long
Sr VP: David Mc Mc Fadden
Sr VP: David McFadden
VP: Chuck Gavazzi
VP: Shanna Howe
VP: Michael Pinell
VP: Dianne Steele
VP: Anna Webb

STERLING HEALTHCARE
See STERLING GROUP PHYSICIAN SERVICES LLC

D-U-N-S 02-037-3234
STERLING HOSPITALITY INC
HOUSTON HOTEL
2950 Reedy Creek Blvd, Kissimmee, FL 34747-1714
Tel (407) 997-3481 Founded/Ownrshp 2000
Sales 22.9MM[E] EMP 1,300
SIC 8741 8721 Hotel or motel management; Accounting, auditing & bookkeeping
Pr: Larry Bernick
*VP: Randy Butkus
VP: David Origlio
*VP: Jim Sorenson

STERLING, INC.
See STERLING INC

D-U-N-S 00-607-4173 IMP/EXP
STERLING INC
BALL & JEWELL
(Suby of ACS GROUP) ★
2900 S 160th St, New Berlin, WI 53151-3606
Tel (414) 354-0970 Founded/Ownrshp 1917
Sales 161.6MM[E] EMP 805
SIC 3823 3542 3559 Industrial process control instruments; Presses: hydraulic & pneumatic, mechanical & manual; Plastics working machinery; Robots, molding & forming plastics
Pr: Tom Breslin
*Treas: Bob Wozniak

D-U-N-S 01-749-2349
STERLING INC
STERLING, INC.
(Suby of SIGNET GROUP LIMITED)
375 Ghent Rd, Fairlawn, OH 44333-4600
Tel (216) 867-1230 Founded/Ownrshp 1932
Sales 195.1MM[E] EMP 1,500
SIC 5944 Jewelry stores
Ch Bd: Terry Burman
*CEO: Mark Light
*Ex VP: Bill Montalto
*Sr VP: Ed Hrabek
*Sr VP: Terry Klein
Sr VP: Mario Weiss
VP: Robert Glaser
VP: Joan M Holstein
Genl Mgr: Ronald Evans

D-U-N-S 04-005-9586
STERLING INFOSYSTEMS INC
STERLINGBACKCHECK
1 State St Fl Plaza24, New York, NY 10004-1561
Tel (800) 899-2272 Founded/Ownrshp 1982
Sales 852.4MM[E] EMP 3,700
SIC 7375 7381 Data base information retrieval; Detective services
CEO: William Greenblatt
*Pr: Dave Dinesen
*Pr: Clare Hart
*Pr: Rchus Seldon
*Pr: Richard Seldon
*COO: Alla Schay
*CFO: Daniel P Obrien
Bd of Dir: Michael Lotito
*Chf Mktg O: Julia Mair
Ofcr: Antonia Banewicz
Ofcr: John Mallios
*Ex VP: Sean Cunningham
*Ex VP: Bob Maguire
Ex VP: Herb Siegel

*Sr VP: Shannon Buggy
*Sr VP: Rolus Lessus
*Sr VP: Shvvas Procey
*Sr VP: Vikas Vig
Sr VP: Lance Zacker
VP: David Ehrenfried
VP: Joy Henry

D-U-N-S 06-201-9328 IMP/EXP
STERLING JEWELERS INC (OH)
JARED THE GALLERIA OF JEWELRY
(Suby of SIGNET GROUP LIMITED)
375 Ghent Rd, Fairlawn, OH 44333-4600
Tel (330) 668-5000 Founded/Ownrshp 1953, 1990
Sales 4.5MMM[E] EMP 9,900
SIC 3423 Jewelers' hand tools
Ch Bd: Terry Burman
*Pr: Mark Light
CFO: Robert Trabucco
*Ex VP: Bill Montalto
Ex VP: William Montalto
*Sr VP: Ed Hrabek
*Sr VP: Terence J Klein
Sr VP: Mario Weiss
VP: Simon Cashman
VP: Gary Ciolli
VP: Dave Clunk
VP: Rick Davis
VP: Lynn Dennison
VP: Dave Everton
VP: Cathy Fischer
*VP: George Frankovich
VP: Robert Glaser
VP: Lori Glass
*VP: James Grant
VP: Ed Hrabak
VP: Robert Knapp

D-U-N-S 13-958-9878
■ STERLING LIFE INSURANCE CO
(Suby of MUNICH HEALTH NORTH AMERICA INC) ★
2219 Rimland Dr Ste 100, Bellingham, WA 98226-8660
Tel (360) 647-9080 Founded/Ownrshp 1958
Sales NA EMP 465[E]
SIC 6411 Insurance agents, brokers & service
Pr: Michael A Muchnicki
Pr: Gerald Reilly
CFO: David Goltz
VP: Mr Todd Tippets

D-U-N-S 02-497-2770 IMP/EXP
STERLING LUMBER CO
501 E 151st St, Phoenix, IL 60426-2402
Tel (708) 388-2223 Founded/Ownrshp 1973
Sales 107.1MM[E] EMP 150[E]
SIC 5031 7389 2448 Lumber: rough, dressed & finished; Log & lumber broker; Pallets, wood; Skids, wood
Pr: Carter Sterling
*CEO: John Sterling
COO: Mike O'Connell
*Treas: Cooper Sterling
*VP: Carson Sterling
Genl Mgr: Brad Zenner
Manager: Jay Bailey

STERLING MED STAFFING GROUP
See STERLING MEDICAL CORP

D-U-N-S 13-753-9750
STERLING MEDICAL CORP
STERLING MED STAFFING GROUP
411 Oak St, Cincinnati, OH 45219-2504
Tel (513) 984-1800 Founded/Ownrshp 1989
Sales 3.7MM EMP 1,200[E]
Accts Clark Schaefer Hackett & Co C
SIC 8741 Management services; Administrative management
CEO: Richard Blatt
*Pr: Edwin Blatt
*VP: Brandon Blatt
Dir Bus: John Robinson
IT Man: Barb Nelson
IT Man: Jan Taylor
Site Mgr: Deborah Aldridge
Site Mgr: Renee Seiler
Pgrm Dir: Doug Dennis

D-U-N-S 00-699-0782 IMP/EXP
STERLING NATIONAL BANK
650 5th Ave Fl 4, New York, NY 10019-6108
Tel (212) 757-3300 Founded/Ownrshp 1929
Sales NA EMP 333
SIC 6021

D-U-N-S 07-542-2725 IMP
■ STERLING NATIONAL BANK
PROVIDENT BANK
(Suby of STERLING BANCORP) ★
400 Rella Blvd Fl 3, Montebello, NY 10901-4241
Tel (845) 369-8040 Founded/Ownrshp 1888
Sales NA EMP 499
SIC 6035 Federal savings banks
Ch Bd: William F Helmer
Pr: Thomas X Geisel
Pr: Rick Jones
*Pr: Jim Peoples
*COO: Rodney Whitwell
Chf Cred: Wayne Miller
Sr VP: Nicole Bonica
Sr VP: Suzanne Copeland
Sr VP: Louis J De Luca
*Sr VP: Joe Giamartino
Sr VP: Ben Hirsh
Sr VP: Thomas Kokinias
Sr VP: Gabriel Safdie
Sr VP: Jeffery Wall
VP: Carl Capuano
VP: Rita Champ
VP: Prakash Chonkar
VP: David Dix
VP: James Florian
VP: Robert Foster
VP: Joseph Marcella

STERLING PACIFIC MEAT COMPANY
See INTERSTATE MEAT & PROVISION

D-U-N-S 00-431-2450 IMP
STERLING PAPER CO (OH)
(Suby of ROSEMARK PAPER INC) ★
1845 Progress Ave, Columbus, OH 43207-1726
Tel (614) 443-0303 Founded/Ownrshp 1937
Sales 128.9MM[E] EMP 98
SIC 5111 5199 Printing paper; Packaging materials
Pr: Robert Rosenfeld
Mktg Mgr: Rebecca Garfin

D-U-N-S 04-242-7547
STERLING PARK HEALTH CARE CENTER
(Suby of TEALWOOD CARE CENTERS) ★
142 1st St N, Waite Park, MN 56387-1273
Tel (320) 252-9595 Founded/Ownrshp 2000
Sales 21.3MM[E] EMP 1,300
SIC 8051 Skilled nursing care facilities

D-U-N-S 12-648-3762
STERLING PARTNERS LLC
STERLING CAPITAL PARTNERS
650 S Exeter St Ste 1000, Baltimore, MD 21202-4209
Tel (443) 703-1700 Founded/Ownrshp 1985
Sales 98.6MM[E] EMP 340
SIC 6211 Investment firm, general brokerage
Mng Dir: R A Macksey Jr

D-U-N-S 87-805-1127 IMP/EXP
STERLING PRODUCTS INC
ACS GROUP
(Suby of ACS GROUP) ★
1100 E Woodfield Rd # 550, Schaumburg, IL 60173-5135
Tel (847) 273-7700 Founded/Ownrshp 1979
Sales 165.6MM[E] EMP 805
SIC 3559 3823 3542 Plastics working machinery; Industrial process control instruments; Presses: hydraulic & pneumatic, mechanical & manual
Pr: James E Holbrook
Sr Cor Off: Jim Cook
Sr Cor Off: Barbara Otoole
Sr Cor Off: Randy Smith
VP: Larry Bowman
VP: Kevin Chudyk
IT Man: Bill Hofmann

D-U-N-S 00-159-4225 IMP/EXP
■ STERLING PUBLISHING CO INC
(Suby of BARNES & NOBLE INC) ★
1166 Avenue Of The Flr 17, New York, NY 10036
Tel (212) 532-7160 Founded/Ownrshp 1949, 2003
Sales 240.4MM[E] EMP 250
SIC 5192 2731 Books; Books: publishing only
Ch Bd: Mitchell S Klipper
VP: Denise Allen
*VP: James Benjamin
VP: Marilyn Kretzer
VP: Mary McAveney
*VP: Charles Nurnberg
Exec: Kerri Cuocci
Exec: Shannon Gallagher
CIO: Dionis Almonte
IT Man: Cardenas Cesar
VP Opers: Kim Brown

D-U-N-S 10-335-6739
STERLING SAVINGS BANK
FIRST INDEPENDENT BANK
111 N Wall St, Spokane, WA 99201-0696
Tel (509) 624-4121 Founded/Ownrshp 1981
Sales NA EMP 1,656
SIC 6036 6162 6035 6141 6153

STERLING STEEL 0530
See STERLING STEEL CO LLC

D-U-N-S 10-674-0561 IMP
■ STERLING STEEL CO LLC
STERLING STEEL 0530
(Suby of LEGGETT & PLATT INC) ★
101 Avenue K, Sterling, IL 61081-3229
Tel (815) 548-7000 Founded/Ownrshp 2002
Sales 126.4MM[E] EMP 260
SIC 3312 Rods, iron & steel: made in steel mills
Genl Mgr: Andy Moore
Sfty Dirs: Tobin Kirk
Sfty Mgr: Coldy Snyder
Opers Mgr: Kevin Mullen

STERLINGBACKCHECK
See STERLING INFOSYSTEMS INC

STERLINGRISK
See STERLING & STERLING LLC

D-U-N-S 04-858-9394 IMP
STERMAN MASSER INC
2 Fearnot Rd, Sacramento, PA 17968-9528
Tel (570) 682-3709 Founded/Ownrshp 1754
Sales 101.3MM EMP 124
SIC 0134 2099

STERNE AGEE
See AGEE STERNE GROUP INC

D-U-N-S 07-208-5509
■ STERNE AGEE & LEACH INC
(Suby of STERNE AGEE) ★
800 Shades Creek Pkwy, Birmingham, AL 35209-4532
Tel (205) 226-3397 Founded/Ownrshp 1916
Sales 205.1MM[E] EMP 1,100
SIC 6211 Investment firm, general brokerage
CEO: James F Dixon III
Mng Pt: Keith Storms
Pr: Walter S Robertson III
Ofcr: Lee Chambliss
Ofcr: Patrick Dogan
Ofcr: Mandy Poe
Sr VP: Andrew Chambless
Sr VP: Neil Kennedy
Sr VP: Rishi Parekh
Sr VP: Eric Saar
Sr VP: Russell Sugg
Sr VP: Tip Tipton
VP: William D Burke
VP: Gerhard Erdelji
VP: William Moore
VP: Mike Serio

D-U-N-S 03-057-6359 IMP/EXP
■ STERNO PRODUCTS LLC
STERNOCANDLELAMP
(*Suby of* STERNOCANDLELAMP HOLDINGS INC) ★
1880 Compton Ave Ste 101, Corona, CA 92881-2780
Tel (951) 682-9600 *Founded/Ownrshp* 2014
Sales 120.3MM[E] *EMP* 300
SIC 3641 3645 3589 3634 2899 Electric lamps; Table lamps; Food warming equipment, commercial; Chafing dishes, electric; Chemical preparations
CEO: Don Hinshaw
CFO: Steve Pellegrini
VP: Dennis Dyck
VP: Mike Pacharis
VP: Scott Rylko
IT Man: Brett Witzel
VP Sls: Lane Murlin
Mktg Dir: Shane Peck

STERNOCANDLELAMP
See STERNO PRODUCTS LLC

D-U-N-S 07-960-0254
■ STERNOCANDLELAMP HOLDINGS INC
(*Suby of* COMPASS DIVERSIFIED HOLDINGS) ★
61 Wilton Rd Ste 2, Westport, CT 06880-3121
Tel (203) 221-1703 *Founded/Ownrshp* 2014
Sales 951.2MM[E] *EMP* 3,516[E]
SIC 6211 Investment firm, general brokerage
Pr: Patrick A Maciariello
Ch Bd: C Sean Day
CFO: Ryan J Faulkingham

D-U-N-S 80-912-8499 IMP
STERNSCHNUPPE LLC
3325 W Sunset Rd Ste E, Las Vegas, NV 89118-3906
Tel (702) 458-6797 *Founded/Ownrshp* 1993
Sales 121.0MM[E] *EMP* 892
SIC 3612 Ballasts for lighting fixtures

STETSON HATS
See RHE HATCO INC

D-U-N-S 04-709-0428
STETSON UNIVERSITY INC
421 N Woodland Blvd, Deland, FL 32723-8300
Tel (386) 822-7000 *Founded/Ownrshp* 1883
Sales 124.1MM *EMP* 1,033
Accts Mcgladrey Llp Orlando Florid
SIC 8221 University
Pr: Laurel Barrie
Assoc VP: Albert T Allen
VP: Joel Bauman
VP: Allisyn Bernard
VP: Bruce Chong
VP: Shelly Cornish
VP: Darby Dickerson
VP: Zeyna Flutie
VP: Nicholas Fuller
VP: Greg Garfinkel
VP: Will Giberson
VP: Audrey Glenski
VP: Anna Goldstein
**VP:* Frank R Huth
VP: Robert Huth
VP: Kristelle Ibarreta
VP: Carol Julian
VP: Caden Krawchuk
VP: C Macan
VP: Joy McGuirl-Hadley
VP: Michael Mekdeci

D-U-N-S 07-621-1846
STEUBEN FOODS INC
15504 Liberty Ave, Jamaica, NY 11433-1000
Tel (718) 291-3333 *Founded/Ownrshp* 1981
Sales 114.1MM[E] *EMP* 325
SIC 2032 2026 Puddings, except meat: packaged in cans, jars, etc.; Yogurt; Milk drinks, flavored
Prin: Jeffrey Sokal
Pr: Len Carruthers
**Pr:* Kenneth Schlossberg
VP: Bruce Budinoff
**VP:* David Cantor
Ql Cn Mgr: Steve Crescente

STEVE MADDEN
See STEVEN MADDEN LTD

D-U-N-S 18-054-1864 IMP/EXP
STEVE SELVIN ASSOCIATES INC
NEW WORLD SALES
207 Union St, Hackensack, NJ 07601-4225
Tel (201) 488-3332 *Founded/Ownrshp* 1978
Sales 119.2MM[E] *EMP* 51
SIC 5136 5137 Men's & boys' clothing; Women's & children's clothing
CEO: Steve Selvin
Off Mgr: Chris Saakow

D-U-N-S 12-143-5960 IMP/EXP
STEVE SILVER CO
1000 Fm 548, Forney, TX 75126-6458
Tel (972) 564-2601 *Founded/Ownrshp* 1983
Sales 100.0MM *EMP* 250
SIC 5021 Household furniture; Tables, occasional; Dining room furniture
Ch Bd: Norman Preskitt
Pr: Steve Silver
VP: Dejun Wang
Prin: Jeff Lankford
IT Man: Scott Garza
Sfty Dirs: Kay Sloan
VP Mktg: Valeri Mallett
Mktg Dir: Boyd Barnhardt
Sls Mgr: Rocco Monaco

STEVECO
See GRAPEMAN FARMS LP

D-U-N-S 05-841-4020 IMP/EXP
STEVEN ENGINEERING INC
230 Ryan Way, South San Francisco, CA 94080-6370
Tel (650) 588-9200 *Founded/Ownrshp* 1975
Sales 146.2MM[E] *EMP* 110
SIC 5085 Industrial supplies
CEO: Bonnie A Walter
**Pr:* Kenneth D Walter
**Ex VP:* Bryan J Wolfgram
Ex VP: Bryan J Wolfgram
**VP:* Paul E Burk III
Tech Mgr: Thomas J Fletcher
VP Mktg: Paul Burke III
Mktg Mgr: Mark Miyaji
Sls Mgr: Chad R Walte
Sls Mgr: Chad Walter
Sales Asso: Marcus Detry

D-U-N-S 14-982-8159
STEVEN LAVERTY
BEVERLY HOSPITAL
85 Herrick St, Beverly, MA 01915-1790
Tel (978) 927-7880 *Founded/Ownrshp* 2004
Sales 327.0MM *EMP* 8
SIC 8062 General medical & surgical hospitals
Pr: Steven Laverty
CFO: Joe Porcello
Doctor: David Koh MD

D-U-N-S 78-585-1056 IMP/EXP
▲ STEVEN MADDEN LTD
STEVE MADDEN
5216 Barnett Ave, Long Island City, NY 11104-1018
Tel (718) 446-1800 *Founded/Ownrshp* 1990
Sales 1.4MMM *EMP* 3,578
Tkr Sym SHOO *Exch* NGS
SIC 3143 3144 3149 5632 Men's footwear, except athletic; Women's footwear, except athletic; Children's footwear, except athletic; Handbags; Apparel accessories
Ch Bd: Edward R Rosenfeld
**Pr:* Amelia Newton Varela
COO: Awadhesh Sinha
CFO: Arvind Dharia
Chf Mktg O: Karla Frieders
Ex VP: Michele Bergerac
Ex VP: Richard Zech
VP: Claudio Bruxel
VP: Peter Chang
VP: Jaime Levy
VP: Cynthia Mora
VP: Antonella Paradiso
VP: Wendy Steinberg
Board of Directors: Rose Peabody Lynch, Peter Migliorni, Richard P Randall, Ravi Sachdev, Thomas H Schwartz, Robert Smith

D-U-N-S 14-169-0474
■ STEVEN MARK SERVICE MERCHANDISERS INC
(*Suby of* CVS HEALTH CORP) ★
1 Cvs Dr, Woonsocket, RI 02895-6146
Tel (401) 765-1500 *Founded/Ownrshp* 1987
Sales 18.3MM[E] *EMP* 1,441[E]
SIC 7389 Personal service agents, brokers & bureaus
Pr: Thomas Ryan

D-U-N-S 06-058-9709
STEVEN P KIM DPM
4761 Hoen Ave, Santa Rosa, CA 95405-7862
Tel (707) 545-0570 *Founded/Ownrshp* 2010
Sales 544.0MM *EMP* 3
SIC 8043 Offices & clinics of podiatrists
Prin: Steven Kim

D-U-N-S 83-879-6241 EXP
STEVEN-ROBERT ORIGINALS LLC
CLASSIC BAKERY PRODUCTS
2780 Tower Rd, Aurora, CO 80011-3501
Tel (303) 375-9925 *Founded/Ownrshp* 1995
Sales 110.0MM[E] *EMP* 800
SIC 2053 2024 2099 Frozen bakery products, except bread; Dairy based frozen desserts; Desserts, ready-to-mix
CEO: Steven Fabos
**Pr:* Brian McGuire
CFO: Leslie Surber
**VP:* Charles Kosmont

D-U-N-S 06-700-4580
STEVENS AVIATION INC
600 Delaware St, Greenville, SC 29605-5495
Tel (864) 678-6000 *Founded/Ownrshp* 1989
Sales 117.6MM[E] *EMP* 505
SIC 4522 4581 5088 5599 Air transportation, nonscheduled; Aircraft cleaning & janitorial service; Aircraft engines & engine parts; Aircraft equipment & supplies; Aircraft, self-propelled
Pr: Glenn Brown
VP: Larry Baker
**VP:* Neil McGrail
**VP:* Jim Williams
**VP:* Paul Witt
**Ex Dir:* John Rigby
Rgnl Mgr: Flip Cuthbertson
Rgnl Mgr: Herb Cutherbertson
IT Man: Kevin Hewitt
Sls Mgr: Jamie Smith
Sls Mgr: Phil Stearns

D-U-N-S 00-643-4708
STEVENS CONSTRUCTION CORP (WI)
2 Buttonwood Ct, Madison, WI 53718-2156
Tel (608) 222-5100 *Founded/Ownrshp* 1952, 2009
Sales 103.1MM *EMP* 35[E]
Accts Baker Tilly Virchow Krause Ll
SIC 1522 1542 Hotel/motel, new construction; Multi-family dwellings, new construction; Commercial & office building, new construction; Hospital construction; School building construction
CEO: Mark A Rudnicki
**Pr:* Geoffrey Vine
**VP:* Glenn Hofer
**VP:* Brian Wagner
MIS Dir: Gerald L Henrich
Sfty Dirs: Duane Reith
Snr PM: Roman Symberski

STEVENS CREEK VOLKSWAGEN
See CORBRO LLC

D-U-N-S 05-039-2307
STEVENS ENGINEERS & CONSTRUCTORS INC (OH)
7850 Freeway Cir Ste 100, Cleveland, OH 44130-6317
Tel (440) 234-7888 *Founded/Ownrshp* 1929, 1970
Sales 104.4MM *EMP* 270
Accts Cohen & Company Ltd Cleveland
SIC 1541 1711 8711 Industrial buildings, new construction; Renovation, remodeling & repairs: industrial buildings; Mechanical contractor; Construction & civil engineering
CEO: Thomas Snyder
**Pr:* John Murray
**Treas:* Vicki Anderson
**VP:* Rich Suranski
**Prin:* Vince Gravelle
IT Man: David Ehrenberger
Mtls Mgr: Curt Survance

D-U-N-S 00-627-4476 IMP/EXP
STEVENS INDUSTRIES INC
STEVENS TOT-MATE
704 W Main St, Teutopolis, IL 62467-1212
Tel (217) 540-3100 *Founded/Ownrshp* 1967, 1998
Sales 108.8MM[E] *EMP* 500[E]
Accts Bkd Llp Decatur Il
SIC 2531 2679 2511 Public building & related furniture; Wallboard, decorated: made from purchased material; Juvenile furniture: wood
Pr: Tom Wegman
CFO: Jim Buhmerkempe
**Sec:* James Buhnerkempe
VP: Randy Thoele
Sfty Mgr: Ryan Lee
Ql Cn Mgr: John Elder
Mktg Dir: Bob Lueken
Manager: Ron Ohnesorge
Sls Mgr: Patrick Gibbons
Sls Mgr: Tim Wente

D-U-N-S 06-427-1570
STEVENS INSTITUTE OF TECHNOLOGY (INC)
1 Castle Point Ter, Hoboken, NJ 07030-5906
Tel (201) 216-5000 *Founded/Ownrshp* 1870
Sales 266.7MM *EMP* 500
Accts Lb Grant Thornton Llp Hoboken
SIC 8221 College, except junior
Pr: Nariman Farvardin
Pr: Dawn Dasilva
Pr: Steven Smith
Pr: Mary Wheeler
CFO: Stephano Falconi
CFO: Randy L Greene
Trst: Marty Valerio
VP: David Dodd
VP: Malcolm R Kahn
VP: Robert Maffia
VP: Joseph Mitola
VP: Mary Rediger
VP: Edward Stukane
Exec: Henry P Dobbelaar
Exec: Jan Klein
Exec: Keith Sheppard
Assoc Dir: Deborah Berkley
Assoc Dir: Tony Blazini
Assoc Dir: Elizabeth Gill
Assoc Dir: Sharen Glennon
Assoc Dir: Robert Lechich

D-U-N-S 61-412-5938
STEVENS POINT AREA PUBLIC SCHOOL DISTRICT
1900 Polk St, Stevens Point, WI 54481-5875
Tel (715) 345-5444 *Founded/Ownrshp* 1862
Sales 86.5MM *EMP* 1,000
Accts Schenck Sc Green Gay Wiscon
SIC 8211 Public elementary & secondary schools
**Prin:* David Lockett
Pr Dir: Sarah Odonnell
HC Dir: Sarah Tatton

D-U-N-S 07-982-2176
■ STEVENS POINT DISTRIBUTION CENTER LLC
(*Suby of* SUPERVALU HOLDINGS INC) ★
2828 Wayne St, Stevens Point, WI 54481-4169
Tel (952) 828-4000 *Founded/Ownrshp* 2015
Sales 69.2MM[E] *EMP* 5,006[E]
SIC 5411 Grocery stores
Pr: Karla C Robertson
Treas: Devon J Hart
VP: Bruce H Besanko
**VP:* David W Johnson
**VP:* Stuart D McFarland
VP: Kimberly J Myrdahl
VP: Doyle J Troyer

STEVENS TOT-MATE
See STEVENS INDUSTRIES INC

D-U-N-S 04-904-2237
STEVENS TRANSPORT INC
9757 Military Pkwy, Dallas, TX 75227-4805
Tel (972) 216-9000 *Founded/Ownrshp* 1969
Sales 668.7MM *EMP* 2,100
Accts Saddock & Co Pllc Dallas T
SIC 4213 Trucking, except local
Ch: Steven L Aaron
**Pr:* Clay Aaron
Ex VP: Mike Richey
**Ex VP:* Mike Ritchey
**Sr VP:* Todd Aaron
VP: Cathy Kaiser
**VP:* Bob H Nelson
VP: William Tallent
Exec: John Brandt
Creative D: Matt Blake
Off Mgr: Cindy Boesz

D-U-N-S 06-490-2315
STEVENSON UNIVERSITY INC
1525 Greenspring Vly Rd, Stevenson, MD 21153-0641
Tel (410) 486-7000 *Founded/Ownrshp* 1947
Sales 141.4MM *EMP* 550
Accts Kpmg Llp Baltimore Md
SIC 8221 College, except junior
Pr: Kevin Manning
Pr: Sherry Bithell
CFO: Tim Campbell
**Treas:* Thomas F Brady
**V Ch Bd:* Henry D Felton IV
VP: Steve Close
VP: Steven W Close
VP: Claire E Moore
Assoc Dir: Paul Cantabene
Off Mgr: Deborah Blake
CIO: Steve Engorn

D-U-N-S 00-810-9845 IMP
STEVES & SONS INC
203 Humble Ave, San Antonio, TX 78225-1317
Tel (210) 924-5111 *Founded/Ownrshp* 1958
Sales 116.0MM[E] *EMP* 800
SIC 2431

D-U-N-S 62-129-1731
STEVINSON AUTOMOTIVE INC
1726 Cole Blvd Ste 300, Golden, CO 80401-3214
Tel (303) 232-2006 *Founded/Ownrshp* 1989
Sales 130.4MM[E] *EMP* 450
SIC 5511 New & used car dealers
Pr: Kent Stevinson
Exec: Kevin Starbuck
Sls Mgr: Mike Myers
Sales Asso: Ezzedin Fitouri

STEW LEONARD'S
See WINE LABELS LLC

D-U-N-S 01-877-6450 IMP
STEW LEONARDS HOLDINGS LLC
G & L DISTRIBUTORS
100 Westport Ave, Norwalk, CT 06851-3915
Tel (203) 847-9088 *Founded/Ownrshp* 1993
Sales 238.0MM[E] *EMP* 1,242
SIC 5411 Supermarkets, hypermarket

STEWARD HEALTH CARE
See STEWARD ST ELIZABETHS MEDICAL CENTER OF BOSTON INC

D-U-N-S 14-411-9476
STEWARD HEALTH CARE SYSTEM LLC
CARITAS CHRISTI HEALTH CARE
500 Boylston St, Boston, MA 02116-3740
Tel (617) 419-4700 *Founded/Ownrshp* 1985
Sales 1.4MMM[E] *EMP* 26,000
SIC 8082 Home health care services
Ex VP: Joseph Maher
Ex VP: Mark Rich
VP: Ryan Boxill
VP: Timothy Crowley
VP: Maria Gray
VP: John Jurczyk
VP: Harvey Kowaloff
VP: Davor Kvaternik
VP: Rhonda Miller
VP: Karen Murray
VP: Koji Nishimura
VP: Daniel Oniel
VP: Paul Quinn
VP: Kim Wedge
VP: Neville Zar
VP Bus Dev: Michael Bushell

D-U-N-S 06-285-0132
STEWARD HOME CARE INC
500 Boylston St, Boston, MA 02116-3740
Tel (781) 551-5600 *Founded/Ownrshp* 2012
Sales 99.4MM[E] *EMP* 17,000
SIC 8082 Home health care services
CEO: Ralph De La Torre
**Pr:* Michael G Callum MD
**Pr:* Joshua Putter
**CFO:* Mark Rich

D-U-N-S 96-542-3614
STEWARD NORWOOD HOSPITAL INC
NORWOOD HOSPITAL, A CARITAS FA
800 Washington St Ste 1, Norwood, MA 02062-3487
Tel (781) 769-4000 *Founded/Ownrshp* 2010
Sales 168.3MM *EMP* 99
SIC 8062 General medical & surgical hospitals
Pr: Emily Holliman
**Pr:* Margaret Hanson
**CFO:* Mark S Johnson
**VP:* Mary T Kinneman
**VP:* Matthew H Lowry
Dir Rx: Nancy Huff
Adm Dir: John Gale

D-U-N-S 96-542-2061
STEWARD ST ANNES HOSPITAL CORP
SAINT ANNE'S HOSPITAL
795 Middle St, Fall River, MA 02721-1733
Tel (508) 674-5741 *Founded/Ownrshp* 2010
Sales 229.2MM *EMP* 99[E]
SIC 8062 General medical & surgical hospitals
Pr: Craig Jesiolowski Fache
**Treas:* Stephen Farber
Dir Sec: Sheila L Wallace

D-U-N-S 96-542-4703
STEWARD ST ELIZABETHS MEDICAL CENTER OF BOSTON INC
STEWARD HEALTH CARE
736 Cambridge St, Boston, MA 02135-2907
Tel (617) 789-3000 *Founded/Ownrshp* 2010
Sales 325.5MM *EMP* 99
SIC 8062 General medical & surgical hospitals
Pr: Roger Mitty
Chf Rad: Jeffrey Mendel
CFO: Joseph Ionnoni
CFO: Joseph Lannoni
Trst: Denis Dowdle
Trst: James Dunn
Trst: G Hamilton
Trst: Philip Haughey
Trst: Robert Kcintyre
Trst: George Tully
Top Exec: Marvin J Lopez
Assoc VP: Eric Stastny
VP: Patti Embry-Tautenhan
VP: Lorain Oconner
VP: Cathy Oconnor
VP: Nancy Van Zant
Dir OR: Alan McGoldrick
Dir Inf Cn: James Mackinnon

D-U-N-S 94-380-3072 EXP
STEWART & STEVENSON CAPITAL CORP
(*Suby of* STEWART & STEVENSON LLC) ★
601 W 38th St, Houston, TX 77018-6403
Tel (713) 868-7700 *Founded/Ownrshp* 2009
Sales 1.2MMM *EMP* 100

Accts Ernst & Young Llp Houston Te
SIC 5084 5013 5078 5082 3711 3537 Engines & transportation equipment; Engines & parts, diesel; Engines, gasoline; Materials handling machinery; Automotive supplies & parts; Refrigeration units, motor vehicles; General construction machinery & equipment; Road construction equipment; Forestry equipment; Military motor vehicle assembly; Truck trailers, used in plants, docks, terminals, etc.
Pr: Michael L Grimes
Sls Mgr: Tom Loomis

D-U-N-S 05-698-1962 IMP/EXP
STEWART & STEVENSON FDDA LLC
FLORIDA DETROIT DIESEL-ALLISON
(*Suby of* STEWART & STEVENSON LLC) ★
5040 University Blvd W, Jacksonville, FL 32216-5990
Tel (904) 737-7330 *Founded/Ownrshp* 2013
Sales 163.8MM^E *EMP* 700
SIC 5084 7699 Industrial machinery & equipment; Engines & parts, diesel; Industrial machinery & equipment repair
CEO: John Merrifield
**Pr:* Sergio Jimenez
**CFO:* William Murray
**Ex VP:* Don Mann
VP: Donald Mann
IT Man: Colette Lundy
Manager: Charlie Simon
Mktg Mgr: Kerry Kline
Sls Mgr: Tracy Collins

D-U-N-S 61-639-2671 IMP/EXP
STEWART & STEVENSON LLC
1000 La St Ste 5900, Houston, TX 77002
Tel (713) 751-2600 *Founded/Ownrshp* 2006
Sales 2.8MMM^E *EMP* 3,600
SIC 5084 5082 3533 7353 Industrial machinery & equipment; Oil field equipment; Oil & gas field machinery; Oil & gas drilling rigs & equipment; Oil equipment rental services
CEO: John B Simmons
Pr: John Merrifield
COO: Darrell Richey
CFO: Jack L Pieper
VP: Kelly Lamont
VP: Pat McPhee
VP: William L Moll
Brnch Mgr: Mike Dobbs
Brnch Mgr: Dan Durham
Brnch Mgr: Jack Werner
Genl Mgr: Jared Shannon
Board of Directors: Nina Ansary, Frank C Carlucci, James W Crystal, Robert L Hargrave, John D Macomber, Anthony G Petrello, J Robinson West

D-U-N-S 61-668-4598 IMP/EXP
STEWART & STEVENSON POWER PRODUCTS LLC
(*Suby of* STEWART & STEVENSON LLC) ★
1000 La St Ste 5900, Houston, TX 77002
Tel (713) 751-2600 *Founded/Ownrshp* 2005
Sales 1.2MMM^E *EMP* 2,300^E
SIC 1389 5084 5082 3533 7353 Construction, repair & dismantling services; Bailing, cleaning, swabbing & treating of wells; Gas field services; Oil field services; Industrial machinery & equipment; Oil field equipment; Oil & gas field machinery; Oil & gas drilling rigs & equipment; Oil equipment rental services
Pr: Bob Hargrave

D-U-N-S 80-744-8139
STEWART BUILDERS INC
KEYSTONE CONCRETE PLACEMENT
16575 Village Dr, Jersey Village, TX 77040-1124
Tel (713) 983-8002 *Founded/Ownrshp* 1991
Sales 319.5MM *EMP* 1,400
SIC 1771 Concrete work
Pr: Donald G Stewart
**Sec:* Mark Stewart
**VP:* Scott Anderson
VP: Rodney Horn
**VP:* Bradley Stewart
VP: Craig Stewart
**VP:* Donald C Stewart
Genl Mgr: Johnny Bethke
Dir IT: Jeff Rogers
Sfty Mgr: Kim Allen
Sfty Mgr: Chris Reid

D-U-N-S 05-501-6943
■ STEWART ENTERPRISES INC
(*Suby of* SCI) ★
1333 S Clearview Pkwy, New Orleans, LA 70121-1014
Tel (504) 729-1400 *Founded/Ownrshp* 1970
Sales 305.8MM^E *EMP* 4,800
SIC 7261 5087 Funeral service & crematories; Cemetery & funeral directors' equipment & supplies; Funeral directors' equipment & supplies
Pr: Curtis G Briggs
Pr: Randall L Stricklin
**CEO:* Thomas M Kitchen
**Treas:* Lewis J Derbes Jr
Treas: Anna J Schumacher
Treas: Lori Trahan
**Ex VP:* Lawrence Hawkins
**Ex VP:* Kenneth Myers Jr
**Sr VP:* Martin De Laureal
Sr VP: Michael H Miller
VP: Martin R Laur Al
**VP:* Kent Alphonso
VP: Kent J Alphonso
**VP:* Christine Hunsaker
VP: Raymond Jeandron
**VP:* Angela M Lacour
**VP:* Larry Merington
VP: Philip P Monti
VP: Gerald G Robinson
**VP:* Philip Sprick
**VP:* G Kenneth Stephens Jr

D-U-N-S 05-363-0323
▲ STEWART INFORMATION SERVICES CORP
1980 Post Oak Blvd, Houston, TX 77056-3899
Tel (713) 625-8100 *Founded/Ownrshp* 1893
Sales NA *EMP* 6,900
Tkr Sym STC *Exch* NYS
SIC 6361 8742 7389 Title insurance; Real estate consultant; Financial services
CEO: Matthew W Morris
**Ch Bd:* Thomas G Apel
Pr: Patrick H Beall
Pr: Steven M Lessack
COO: Timothy Okrie
CFO: J Allen Berryman
Treas: Stephen Abdella
V Ch Bd: Malcolm S Morris
V Ch Bd: Stewart Morris Jr
Bd of Dir: Judy Heath
VP: Bobbie Adams
VP: Frank Alvstad
VP: Hector F Barraza
VP: Patti Bonner
VP: Anne-Marie Cianfichi
VP: Thomas E Dunn
VP: Diane Fox
VP: Kay Gregory
VP: Jason Harrison
VP: Borgia Houser
VP: Jose Menendez
Board of Directors: Arnaud Ajdler, James Chadwick, Glenn C Christenson, Robert L Clarke, Frank Keating, Laurie C Moore, Clifford Press

D-U-N-S 09-151-8423
STEWART RICHEY CONSTRUCTION INC
WEST SIDE MASONRY
(*Suby of* HOUCHENS INDUSTRIES INC) ★
2137 Glen Lily Rd, Bowling Green, KY 42101-9479
Tel (270) 842-5184 *Founded/Ownrshp* 2000
Sales 157.3MM^E *EMP* 340
SIC 1542 1521 1541 Commercial & office building, new construction; Commercial & office buildings, renovation & repair; General remodeling, single-family houses; New construction, single-family houses; Industrial buildings & warehouses
CEO: James Stewart
**Pr:* Rodney Rodgers
**CFO:* William Garrison
Chf Mktg O: Molly Druen
**VP:* Robby Grimes
VP: John Hendrick
VP: Mike Murugesan
VP: Marv Strode
VP: Steve Tyson
Exec: Robin Amonett
Genl Mgr: John Baird

D-U-N-S 07-391-5118
■ STEWART TITLE CO
(*Suby of* STEWART TITLE GUARANTY CO) ★
1980 Post Oak Blvd Ste 80, Houston, TX 77056-3899
Tel (713) 625-8100 *Founded/Ownrshp* 1910
Sales NA *EMP* 4,837
SIC 6361 7389 8713 8742 6541 Title insurance; Mapmaking or drafting, including aerial; Surveying services; Business planning & organizing services; Title & trust companies
Pr: Matt Morris
Div Pres: Jennifer Greenwood
Div Pres: Mike Pryor
Div Pres: Kim Risi
Ofcr: Dawn Anderson
Ofcr: Tom Blount
Ofcr: Wil Campos
Ofcr: Deborah Crangle-Brisch
Ofcr: Heather Lindstrom
Ofcr: Yadir Najera
Ofcr: Douglas Polley
Ofcr: Benedict Sander
Ofcr: Gina Voshel
Ofcr: Lyndsay Williams
Ofcr: Crissy Wilson
Ex VP: E A Smith
Sr VP: Ted Jones
VP: Dana Duncan
VP: Peter Johndrow
VP: Maritza Quezada
VP: Stephen C Reid

D-U-N-S 05-248-8210
■ STEWART TITLE GUARANTY CO
(*Suby of* STEWART INFORMATION SERVICES CORP) ★
1980 Post Oak Blvd Ste 61, Houston, TX 77056-3899
Tel (713) 625-8100 *Founded/Ownrshp* 1908
Sales NA *EMP* 5,600
SIC 6361 6541 Real estate title insurance; Title abstract offices
CEO: Matthew Morris
Treas: Ken Anderson Jr
Div Pres: James Bennett
Ex VP: Mark Edward Winter
Sr VP: Allen Berryman
Sr VP: James Lanzetta
Sr VP: Allan Wasserman
VP: Jim Czapiga
VP: Michael F Frederick
VP: Mark Johnson
VP: Christopher Lawrence
VP: Benedict Sander
VP: Tony Sandoval
VP: Mistie Smith

D-U-N-S 61-874-0773
■ STEWART TITLE INSURANCE CO
(*Suby of* STEWART TITLE GUARANTY CO) ★
300 E 42nd St Fl 10, New York, NY 10017-5947
Tel (212) 922-0050 *Founded/Ownrshp* 1987
Sales NA *EMP* 406
SIC 6361 Title insurance
Pr: John F Welling
**Ch Bd:* Michael Skalka
**CFO:* Julie A Curlen
**Treas:* Max Crisp
Sr VP: Barry Balonek
Opers Mgr: Henry Ruhlandt

D-U-N-S 60-616-9571
■ STEWART TITLE NORTH TEXAS INC
(*Suby of* STEWART TITLE INSURANCE CO) ★
15950 Dallas Pkwy Ste 100, Dallas, TX 75248-6628
Tel (972) 386-9898 *Founded/Ownrshp* 1987
Sales NA *EMP* 161
SIC 6361 6541

D-U-N-S 07-293-1926
■ STEWART TITLE OF CALIFORNIA INC
(*Suby of* STEWART TITLE CO) ★
525 N Brand Blvd Ste 100, Glendale, CA 91203-3992
Tel (818) 291-9145 *Founded/Ownrshp* 1996
Sales NA *EMP* 600
SIC 6361 Guarantee of titles
Pr: Steve Vivanco
Treas: Gregg Unrath
Div Pres: Steven Rosansky
VP: Brian Glaze
VP: Sandra Kuhlman
VP: Marie Sturgel
Exec: Vera Oomens
MIS Dir: Linda Salcido

D-U-N-S 13-431-7713
STEWARTS CONCRETE & BOBCAT
8771 S Desoto Dr, Mohave Valley, AZ 86440-9353
Tel (928) 788-4453 *Founded/Ownrshp* 2003
Sales 185.8MM *EMP* 20
SIC 1771 Concrete work
Owner: Josh Stewart

D-U-N-S 00-207-6511 IMP
STEWARTS SHOPS CORP (NY)
2907 State Route 9, Ballston Spa, NY 12020-4201
Tel (518) 581-1201 *Founded/Ownrshp* 1926
Sales 1.6MMM *EMP* 3,800
Accts Saxbst Llp Albany New York
SIC 5411 Convenience stores, chain
Pr: Gary C Dake
**Ch:* William P Dake
**Treas:* Michael Cocca
Top Exec: Zachary Demars
Ex VP: Richard Donn
VP: Dave Caruso
VP: Susan Dake
**VP:* Nancy Trimbur
Dist Mgr: Bob Barhydt
Dist Mgr: Dan Daley
Dist Mgr: Nick Grande

D-U-N-S 78-041-4652 IMP
STG INC
11091 Sunset Hills Rd # 200, Reston, VA 20190-5378
Tel (703) 691-2480 *Founded/Ownrshp* 1986
Sales 209.7MM *EMP* 1,250
SIC 4813 Telephone communication, except radio
Ch Bd: Simon S Lee
Pr: Paul Fernandes
COO: John J Barrass
CFO: Charles Cosgrove
Treas: Keith Lynch
Sr VP: Glenn W Davis
Sr VP: Bill Perlowitz
Sr VP: Robert L Phoebus
Sr VP: James Scampavia
VP: Tilak Agerwala
VP: Tony Giovanini
VP: Chris Girolamo
VP: Gene Kelly
VP: Tamera Rush
VP: Robert Sunich
VP: Leah Fendley Tarbell
VP: Lee Wilson
Dir Bus: Duncan Sutton
Comm Man: Michelle Dempsey

D-U-N-S 17-957-0403
STG INTERNATIONAL INC
STGI
99 Canal Center Plz # 500, Alexandria, VA 22314-5504
Tel (571) 970-3729 *Founded/Ownrshp* 1997
Sales 98.4MM^E *EMP* 1,800
SIC 7361 Employment agencies
Pr: Michelle S Lee
**COO:* Jeff Bell
**VP:* Marcia Euwema
**VP:* Laurie Hughes
VP: Vishwa Kyasaram
Prgrm Mgr: Ken Murphy
Prgrm Mgr: Ian Nuzzo
Prgrm Mgr: Michele Stein
Prgrm Mgr: Marne Valeros
IT Man: Kent Taylor

STGI
See STG INTERNATIONAL INC

STI GROUP
See SOUTHEAST TEXAS INDUSTRIES INC

D-U-N-S 00-609-6408
STI HOLDINGS INC
STOUGHTON
416 S Academy St, Stoughton, WI 53589-2657
Tel (608) 873-2500 *Founded/Ownrshp* 1961
Sales 296.4MM^E *EMP* 1,000
SIC 6719 Personal holding companies, except banks
Pr: Donald D Wahlin
**Treas:* Mike Fontaine
VP: Cliff Strelow
DP Exec: Lauren Swenson
IT Man: Dave Nowak

D-U-N-S 00-206-3378
STIEFEL LABORATORIES INC
(*Suby of* GLAXOSMITHKLINE SL HOLDINGS, INC.)
20 Tw Alexander Dr, Durham, NC 27709-0294
Tel (888) 784-3335 *Founded/Ownrshp* 1944, 2008
Sales 238.3MM^E *EMP* 2,000
SIC 5122 2834 Pharmaceuticals; Pharmaceutical preparations
Ch Bd: Charles W Stiefel
**Pr:* William D Humphries
Pr: Simon Jose
**CFO:* Michael T Cornelius
**Ofcr:* Gavin Corcoran
**VP:* Kristen Belmonte Slaoui
Genl Mgr: Jose De Guevara
CIO: Alexander Barkas
Dir IT: John Mnares
IT Man: Maria Cabal
Sales Exec: Evelyn Chan

D-U-N-S 10-656-5955
▲ STIFEL FINANCIAL CORP
501 N Broadway, Saint Louis, MO 63102-2188
Tel (314) 342-2000 *Founded/Ownrshp* 1890
Sales 2.3MMM *EMP* 7,100^E
Tkr Sym SF *Exch* NYS
SIC 6211 6719 Brokers, security; Investment holding companies, except banks
Ch Bd: Ronald J Kruszewski
**Ch Bd:* Richard J Himelfarb
**Ch Bd:* Ben A Plotkin
**Ch Bd:* Thomas W Weisel
**Pr:* James M Zemlyak
Sr VP: Mark P Fisher
Sr VP: James M Marischen
**Sr VP:* Thomas B Michaud
Sr VP: David M Minnick
Sr VP: David D Sliney
Board of Directors: James M Oates, Bruce A Beda, Kelvin R Westbrook, Kathleen Brown, Michael J Zimmerman, Michael B Brown, John P Dubinsky, Robert E Grady, Frederick O Hanser, Maura A Markus, Thomas P Mulroy, Victor J Nesi

D-U-N-S 00-632-6938
■ STIFEL NICOLAUS & CO INC
(*Suby of* STIFEL FINANCIAL CORP) ★
501 N Broadway, Saint Louis, MO 63102-2188
Tel (314) 342-2000 *Founded/Ownrshp* 1900
Sales 735.1MM^E *EMP* 1,495
SIC 6211 Investment firm, general brokerage
Sr VP: David D Sliney
**Ch Bd:* Ronald J Kruszewski
Pr: Katy Watchha
**CFO:* James M Zemlyak
CFO: Jim Zemolyak
**Ex VP:* Victor Nesi
Sr VP: John F Lee
**VP:* Michael F Imhoff
VP: Brandon Kanitz
**VP:* Thomas R Kendrick IV
VP: J J Schlafly III
**VP:* Hugo J Warns III Cfa

D-U-N-S 06-599-7181 IMP/EXP
STIHL INC
(*Suby of* STIHL INTERNATIONAL GMBH)
536 Viking Dr, Virginia Beach, VA 23452-7391
Tel (757) 486-9100 *Founded/Ownrshp* 1987
Sales 389.2MM^E *EMP* 2,113
SIC 3546 3398

STILES CONSTRUCTION
See STILES CORP

D-U-N-S 05-376-5699
STILES CORP
STILES CONSTRUCTION
301 E Las Olas Blvd, Fort Lauderdale, FL 33301-2295
Tel (954) 627-9150 *Founded/Ownrshp* 1970
Sales 218.9MM *EMP* 284
Accts Templeton & Company Llp Fort
SIC 1542 1541 Commercial & office building, new construction; Industrial buildings, new construction
CEO: Terry W Stiles
**Pr:* Douglas P Eagon
**COO:* Stephen R Palmer
CFO: Lourdes Vidal
Sr VP: Jeff McDonough
VP: George Bou
VP: Tim Fiske
VP: Ryan Karlin
VP: David Lee
VP: John Preston
VP: Rachel Sardenga
VP Bus Dev: Russ Biffis
Exec: Joe Darnaby
Exec: Terry Hardmon

D-U-N-S 07-928-2612 IMP
STILES MACHINERY INC
(*Suby of* HOMAG GROUP AG)
3965 44th St Se, Grand Rapids, MI 49512-3982
Tel (616) 698-7500 *Founded/Ownrshp* 2014
Sales 118.5MM^E *EMP* 252
SIC 5084 Woodworking machinery; Plastic products machinery; Metalworking machinery; Packaging machinery & equipment
Pr: Christian Vollmers
Pr: John L Casto
Pr: David K Rothwell
COO: Robert Paulson
CFO: Andreas Muehlbauer
Ex VP: Russ Suor
VP: Gene Newburg
VP: William B Pitt
VP: Robert Slater
VP: Russ Sour
VP: Ed Zachow

STILLWATER AREA SCHOOL DST
See INDEPENDENT SCHOOL DISTRICT 834

STILLWATER INSURANCE GROUP
See STILLWATER INSURANCE SERVICES INC

D-U-N-S 07-847-5029
STILLWATER INSURANCE SERVICES INC (CA)
STILLWATER INSURANCE GROUP
4905 Belfort Rd Ste 110, Jacksonville, FL 32256-6007
Tel (904) 997-7336 *Founded/Ownrshp* 2002
Sales NA *EMP* 135
SIC 6331 Property damage insurance
Pr: Mark O Davey
VP: Michael W Whatley

D-U-N-S 07-122-6989
STILLWATER MEDICAL CENTER AUTHORITY
1323 W 6th Ave, Stillwater, OK 74074-4399
Tel (405) 372-1480 *Founded/Ownrshp* 1910
Sales 153.4MM *EMP* 1,100
SIC 8062 General medical & surgical hospitals
Pr: Jerry Moeller
CFO: Karen Hendren
Chf Mktg O: Todd Green
Dir Rx: William Arrington
CTO: Lisa Eckles
Dir IT: Roy Lavicky
IT Man: Chris Barj
IT Man: Chip Latham
Orthpdst: B H Jameson

Anesthlgy: Terry Baartman
Doctor: R J Daniels

D-U-N-S 07-857-9504
STILLWATER MEDICAL GROUP
(*Suby of* GROUP HEALTH PLAN, INC)
927 Churchill St W, Stillwater, MN 55082-6605
Tel (952) 883-6048 *Founded/Ownrshp* 1995
Sales 30.3MM^E *EMP* 4,059^E
SIC 8011 Offices & clinics of medical doctors
CEO: Jeff Robertson

D-U-N-S 07-910-4173
STILLWATER MEDICAL PHYSICIAN CLNIC
1815 W 6th Ave, Stillwater, OK 74074-4202
Tel (405) 743-7300 *Founded/Ownrshp* 2013
Sales 13.6MM^E *EMP* 1,075
SIC 8011 Primary care medical clinic
Pr: Steven Taylor

D-U-N-S 00-719-6033
STILLWATER MILLING CO LLC (OK)
512 E 6th Ave, Stillwater, OK 74074-3600
Tel (405) 372-2766 *Founded/Ownrshp* 1891, 1937
Sales 100.7MM *EMP* 169
Accts Mcguire & Company Pc Cpas
SIC 2048 5999 Livestock feeds; Feed & farm supply
Pr: David F Fairbanks
Treas: David Airbanks
Ex VP: Eugene P Reding
VP: Pamela Gill
IT Man: Rob Fisher
IT Man: James Teri
Sfty Mgr: Roland Wallace
Sales Exec: Sydnee Donaho
Sls Mgr: David Smith

D-U-N-S 10-657-2233 IMP
▲ STILLWATER MINING CO
26 W Dry Creek Cir, Littleton, CO 80120-8063
Tel (406) 373-8700 *Founded/Ownrshp* 1992
Sales 726.3MM *EMP* 1,439^E
Tkr Sym SWC *Exch* NYS
SIC 1099 Palladium group ores mining; Platinum group ores mining
Pr: Michael J McMullen
**Ch Bd:* Brian Schweitzer
CFO: Christopher M Bateman
Bd of Dir: Michael McGuire
Ex VP: Greg Struble
VP: Dee L Bray
VP: Bruce E Gilbert
VP: Kristen K Koss
VP: Gregory K Roset
VP: Kevin G Shiell
VP: Dave A Shuck
VP: Terrell I Ackerman
VP: Brent R Wadman
VP: Gina Wilson
Board of Directors: George M Bee, Patrice E Merrin, Lawrence Peter O'hagen, Michael S Parrett, Gary A Sugar

STILLWATER NAT BNK & TR CO
See BANK SNB

D-U-N-S 00-904-8604 IMP
STIMSON LUMBER CO
520 Sw Yamhill St Ste 700, Portland, OR 97204-1330
Tel (503) 222-1676 *Founded/Ownrshp* 1953
Sales 246.2MM^E *EMP* 749
SIC 2421 2493 2411 Lumber: rough, sawed or planed; Hardboard, tempered; Logging camps & contractors
**CFO:* Bill Peressini
CFO: William Peressini
**Treas:* Samantha Christensen
Exec: Coral Hanssen
**VP Mfg:* Jeff Webber

D-U-N-S 04-254-7471
STINE LLC
STINE LUMBER CO
2950 Ruth St, Sulphur, LA 70665-8042
Tel (337) 527-0121 *Founded/Ownrshp* 1945
Sales 147.8MM^E *EMP* 600
Accts Mcelroy Quirk & Burch Pc Cp
SIC 5211 Lumber & other building materials
**CFO:* Tim Stine
VP: Kevin Kosco
VP: Bill Kurtz
VP: Alexander Sandy
**VP:* Gary Stine
Store Mgr: Donald Bricker
CIO: Robert Spears
**VP Mktg:* David Stine
Sls Dir: Christine Hinson
Sales Asso: Dan Dicharry
Sales Asso: Josh Stine

STINE LUMBER CO
See STINE LLC

D-U-N-S 19-596-2139 EXP
■ STINGER WELLHEAD PROTECTION INC
(*Suby of* OIL STATES INTERNATIONAL INC) ★
4301 Will Rogers Pkwy # 600, Oklahoma City, OK 73108-1835
Tel (405) 702-6575 *Founded/Ownrshp* 2005
Sales 104.2MM^E *EMP* 340
SIC 1389 Oil field services
Pr: Bob McGuire
CFO: Alex Tang
**Sec:* Alfred Neustaedter
VP: Cindy B Taylor

D-U-N-S 07-867-3088 IMP
STINGRAY ENERGY SERVICES
STINGRAY PRESSURE PUMPING
42739 National Rd, Belmont, OH 43718-9669
Tel (405) 648-4177 *Founded/Ownrshp* 2012
Sales 142.6MM^E *EMP* 264^E
SIC 1389 Gas field services
VP: Jack Tarver

STINGRAY PRESSURE PUMPING
See STINGRAY ENERGY SERVICES

D-U-N-S 04-978-4069
STINKER STORES INC
3184 W Elder St, Boise, ID 83705-4709
Tel (208) 375-0942 *Founded/Ownrshp* 2002
Sales 273.1MM *EMP* 500
Accts Eidebailly Llp Boise Id
SIC 5541 Filling stations, gasoline
Pr: Charley Jones
**CFO:* Lou Albecoa
**VP:* Shawn Davis

D-U-N-S 01-065-4507
STINSON LEONARD STREET LLP
1201 Walnut St Ste 2900, Kansas City, MO 64106-2178
Tel (816) 842-8600 *Founded/Ownrshp* 1995
Sales 194.7MM^E *EMP* 985
SIC 8111 General practice law office
Prin: Mark D Hinderks
V Ch: Sharon Stolte
**COO:* Terry E Brummer
**CFO:* Doug Doerfler
Trst: Robert Ginn
VP: Neil Shortlidge
**Prin:* Lowell V Stortz
Genl Couns: Allen Blair
Genl Couns: Howard Kaplan
Genl Couns: Kent Stallard
Corp Couns: Jonathan Gottlieb

D-U-N-S 08-013-4731
STION CORP
6321 San Ignacio Ave, San Jose, CA 95119-1202
Tel (408) 284-7200 *Founded/Ownrshp* 2013
Sales 104.5MM^E *EMP* 250
SIC 3674 Semiconductors & related devices
CEO: Chet Farris
CFO: Daniel Teo
VP: Jeff Cheng
VP: Garrett Hickey
CTO: Gregory Page
Dir IT: Sanjeev Gupta
VP Mfg: Louis Golato
Mktg Mgr: Seth Stulgis
Snr Mgr: Graeme Kling

D-U-N-S 01-931-7416
STIS INC
SOUTHEAST TEXAS INDUS SVCS
3127 Texas Ave, Bridge City, TX 77611-4919
Tel (409) 697-3350 *Founded/Ownrshp* 2001
Sales 112.7MM^E *EMP* 400
SIC 1541 Industrial buildings & warehouses
Pr: Paul Spence
**VP:* Richard Purkey
Div Mgr: Robin McGlothlin

D-U-N-S 00-771-7424 IMP/EXP
STM INDUSTRIES INC (NC)
SHURTECH BRANDS
1985 Tate Blvd Se Ste 2, Hickory, NC 28602-1433
Tel (828) 322-2700 *Founded/Ownrshp* 1996
Sales 617.3MM^E *EMP* 1,125
Accts Mcgladrey & Pullen Llp Charlo
SIC 2672 Tape, pressure sensitive: made from purchased materials
CEO: Stephen Sufford
**Pr:* James B Shuford
**CFO:* Don Pomeroy
Board of Directors: Dorothy B Shuford, Stephen P Shuford

D-U-N-S 82-847-3384
STMICROELECTRONICS (NORTH AMERICA) HOLDING INC
(*Suby of* STMICROELECTRONICS N.V.)
1310 Electronics Dr, Carrollton, TX 75006-7005
Tel (972) 466-6000 *Founded/Ownrshp* 2003
Sales 372.0MM^E *EMP* 4,182^E
SIC 3674 Semiconductors & related devices; Memories, solid state; Microprocessors
VP: Bob Banks
**VP:* Lawrence Ercoline
VP: Lisa K Jorgenson
VP: Dan Merchant
VP: Kim Peters
CTO: Charlie Loh
IT Man: Paul Schultz

D-U-N-S 06-517-4484 IMP
STMICROELECTRONICS INC
(*Suby of* STMICROELECTRONICS (NORTH AMERICA) HOLDING INC) ★
750 Canyon Dr Ste 300, Coppell, TX 75019-4009
Tel (972) 466-6000 *Founded/Ownrshp* 1972
Sales 372.0MM^E *EMP* 4,182
SIC 3674

D-U-N-S 87-421-9926
STOCK BUILDING SUPPLY HOLDINGS LLC
8020 Arco Corp Dr Ste 400, Raleigh, NC 27617
Tel (919) 431-1000 *Founded/Ownrshp* 2009
Sales NA *EMP* 2,557
SIC 5211 2431 5031 5713 5251

D-U-N-S 83-123-1258
■ STOCK BUILDING SUPPLY WEST LLC
(*Suby of* BMC EAST LLC) ★
1133 W 9000 S, West Jordan, UT 84088-9033
Tel (801) 561-9000 *Founded/Ownrshp* 2009
Sales 58.4MM^E *EMP* 1,400
SIC 5031 5211 2439 Lumber, plywood & millwork; Lumber & other building materials; Structural wood members

D-U-N-S 36-194-2212
▲ STOCK YARDS BANCORP INC
1040 E Main St, Louisville, KY 40206-1856
Tel (502) 582-2571 *Founded/Ownrshp* 1988
Sales NA *EMP* 519
Accts Kpmg Llp Louisville Kentucky
Tkr Sym SYBT *Exch* NGS
SIC 6022 State commercial banks; State trust companies accepting deposits, commercial
Ch Bd: David P Heintzman
Pr: Cherie Cambron
**Pr:* James A Hillebrand
Pr: Marcia Sweat
CFO: Nancy B Davis
Ofcr: William M Dishman
Ofcr: Philip S Poindexter
Trst Ofcr: Erin Arnold
Trst Ofcr: Josh Shapiro
Ex VP: Michael J Croce
Ex VP: Clay Stinnett
Ex VP: T Clay Stinnett
Ex VP: Kathy Thompson
Sr VP: Sheila A Stoke
VP: Dan Bachman
VP: Tracy Biddix
VP: Jimmy Evans
VP: Melinda Golde
VP: Brian Hall
VP: Laura Haynes
VP: Ryan Keener

D-U-N-S 00-694-5703 IMP/EXP
■ STOCK YARDS BANK & TRUST CO INC (KY)
(*Suby of* STOCK YARDS BANCORP INC) ★
1040 E Main St, Louisville, KY 40206-1888
Tel (502) 625-1790 *Founded/Ownrshp* 1904
Sales NA *EMP* 415
SIC 6022 State trust companies accepting deposits, commercial
Ch Bd: David H Brooks
**Pr:* James A Hillebrand
COO: Charlene Nay
**CFO:* Nancy B Davis
Ofcr: Randy Childress
Ex VP: Bill Dishman
**Ex VP:* Phillip S Smith
**Ex VP:* Kathy C Thompson
VP: Greg Berting
VP: James Brown
VP: Shannon Budnick
VP: Amy Cory
VP: Aprel G Doherty
VP: Nancy Flowers
VP: Patrick Gamble
VP: Avery Hudspeth
VP: Jeane Kehl
VP: Lynn Land
VP: Pam Nalley
VP: Michelle Shipley
VP: Janice Siewertsen
Board of Directors: Stephen M Priebe

D-U-N-S 15-255-8482
■ STOCKBRIDGE & SHERWOOD TELEPHONE CO LLC
TDS
(*Suby of* TDS TELECOMMUNICATIONS CORP) ★
N287 Military Rd, Sherwood, WI 54169-9603
Tel (920) 989-1501 *Founded/Ownrshp* 1969
Sales 853.0MM *EMP* 99
SIC 4813 Telephone communication, except radio
**Genl Mgr:* Michael Van Denelsem

D-U-N-S 06-177-7799
STOCKBRIDGE/SBE HOLDINGS LLC
5900 Wilshire Blvd # 3100, Los Angeles, CA 90036-5013
Tel (323) 655-8000 *Founded/Ownrshp* 2007
Sales 61.0MM^E *EMP* 3,000
SIC 7011 Hotels; Casino hotel
CEO: Sam Nazarian

STOCKCAP
See SINCLAIR & RUSH INC

STOCKMAN BANK
See STOCKMAN FINANCIAL CORP

D-U-N-S 00-647-2575
STOCKMAN BANK OF MONTANA (MT)
(*Suby of* STOCKMAN BANK) ★
700 Main St, Miles City, MT 59301-3122
Tel (406) 234-8420 *Founded/Ownrshp* 1981
Sales NA *EMP* 200
SIC 6022 State commercial banks
Pr: Stanley A Markuson
Bd of Dir: Terry Lee
Bd of Dir: Darrin Maas
Ofcr: Katie Davis
Ofcr: Karen Hugg
Ofcr: Debby Lester
Ofcr: Anita Muri
Sr VP: Donna Ronning
VP: Jerry Anderson
VP: Dennis Bakken
VP: Brian Cooley
VP: Alan Holom
VP: Linda Wiedeman

D-U-N-S 00-671-9249
STOCKMAN FINANCIAL CORP
STOCKMAN BANK
700 Main St, Miles City, MT 59301-3122
Tel (406) 234-8420 *Founded/Ownrshp* 1980
Sales NA *EMP* 200
SIC 6022 State commercial banks
Pr: Robert C Lucas
Sec: Lloyd Sohl
Ofcr: Kelly Katz
Ofcr: Katie Lawler
Ofcr: Wade Whiteman
Sr VP: Bill Bickle
Sr VP: Faye Warren
Counsel: David Dennis
Board of Directors: Mary M Singleton

D-U-N-S 07-698-0960
STOCKMENS LIVESTOCK MARKET INC
1200 E Highway 50, Yankton, SD 57078-4132
Tel (402) 640-8420 *Founded/Ownrshp* 1962
Sales 104.0MM *EMP* 40
SIC 5154 Auctioning livestock
Pr: Gail F Sohler

D-U-N-S 80-377-5048
STOCKTON COGEN (I) INC
7201 Hamilton Blvd, Allentown, PA 18195-9642
Tel (610) 481-4911 *Founded/Ownrshp* 2014
Sales 519.0MM *EMP* 8^E
SIC 4911 Electric services
Pr: David J Taylor
**CEO:* John Paul Jones

STOCKTON STEEL DIVISION
See HERRICK CORP

D-U-N-S 08-384-6378
STOCKTON UNIFIED SCHOOL DISTRICT (CA)
SUSD
701 N Madison St, Stockton, CA 95202-1634
Tel (209) 933-7000 *Founded/Ownrshp* 1852
Sales 156.6MM^E *EMP* 3,000
SIC 8211 Public elementary & secondary schools
**Pr:* Sara L Cazares
**VP:* Gloria Allen
Dir Sec: Marcus Donlin
HC Dir: Maryjo Cowan

D-U-N-S 11-983-9082
STOCKTON UNIVERSITY
101 Vera King Farris Dr, Galloway, NJ 08205-9441
Tel (609) 652-1776 *Founded/Ownrshp* 1971
Sales 156.0MM *EMP* 1,360^E
Accts Grant Thornton Llp New York
SIC 8221 College, except junior
Pr: Harvey Kesselman
Treas: Denise Green
Ofcr: Claudine Keenan
VP: Thomasa Gonzalez
VP: Toni Hilsin
Exec: Brian Jackson
Assoc Dir: Glenn Brown
Assoc Dir: Paula Dollarhide
Art Dir: Henry Kuiken
Snr Mgr: Scott Huston

D-U-N-S 05-597-4109
STOEL RIVES LLP
760 Sw 9th Ave Ste 3000, Portland, OR 97205-2587
Tel (503) 224-3380 *Founded/Ownrshp* 1942
Sales 124.7MM^E *EMP* 864
SIC 8111 General practice law office
Prin: E Walter Van Valkenburg
**Pt:* Bradley F Tellam
**Pt:* Robert D Van Brocklin
Mng Pt: Virginia Pedreira
**Ch Bd:* Henry H Hewitt
**Ch Bd:* William H Holmes
**Ch Bd:* Ron Lone
**Ch Bd:* Steven T Lovett
**Ch Bd:* Per A Ramfjord
**Ch Bd:* Joan Snyder

D-U-N-S 00-705-6245 IMP/EXP
STOLLE MACHINERY CO LLC (CA)
6949 S Potomac St, Centennial, CO 80112-4036
Tel (303) 708-9044 *Founded/Ownrshp* 2003
Sales 256.6MM^E *EMP* 520
SIC 3542 Metal container making machines: cans, etc.
**CFO:* Denise Stasiak
Treas: Pat Passeck

D-U-N-S 04-845-0683 IMP/EXP
STOLLER INTERNATIONAL INC
9090 Katy Fwy Ste 400, Houston, TX 77024-1696
Tel (713) 461-1493 *Founded/Ownrshp* 1987
Sales 144.8MM^E *EMP* 250^E
SIC 5191 2879 Fertilizer & fertilizer materials; Agricultural chemicals
Ch Bd: Jerry Stoller
VP: Albert Liptay

D-U-N-S 07-526-5629
■ STOLLER NEWPORT NEWS NUCLEAR INC
(*Suby of* HUNTINGTON INGALLS INDUSTRIES INC) ★
105 Technology Dr Ste 190, Broomfield, CO 80021-3432
Tel (303) 546-4300 *Founded/Ownrshp* 2014
Sales 122.2MM^E *EMP* 650
SIC 8744 Facilities support services;
Pr: Nicholas Lombardo
**COO:* Curt Hull Sr
**VP:* Gerald Boyd
**VP:* Sharon Brady
**VP:* Darin Dobbins
**VP:* Douglas Gail
**VP:* Donald George
VP: Curt Hall
**VP:* Thomas Johnston
**VP:* Joseph Legare
**VP:* Frazier Lockhart
**VP:* Barbara Mazurowski
**VP:* Jeff Neff
**VP:* Eric Olson
**VP:* Carolyn Pittman

D-U-N-S 04-857-5229 IMP/EXP
STOLLER USA INC
(*Suby of* STOLLER INTERNATIONAL INC) ★
9090 Katy Fwy Ste 400, Houston, TX 77024-1696
Tel (713) 461-1493 *Founded/Ownrshp* 1978
Sales 144.8MM^E *EMP* 250
Accts Eepb Pc Houston Tx
SIC 5191 8731 Fertilizer & fertilizer materials; Agricultural research
Ch Bd: Jerry H Stoller
**VP:* Guillermo De La Borda
**VP:* Dr Albert Liptay
VP: Joe Rice

STOLT PARCEL TANKERS DIV
See STOLT-NIELSEN TRANSPORTATION GROUP LTD

D-U-N-S 00-583-6044 IMP/EXP
STOLT-NIELSEN TRANSPORTATION GROUP LTD
STOLT PARCEL TANKERS DIV
800 Connecticut Ave 4e, Norwalk, CT 06854-1631
Tel (203) 299-3600 *Founded/Ownrshp* 1974
Sales 103.4MM^E *EMP* 4,500
SIC 4499 4213

D-U-N-S 04-470-7883 IMP/EXP
STOLT-NIELSEN USA INC
(*Suby of* STOLT-NIELSEN LIMITED)
15635 Jacintoport Blvd, Houston, TX 77015-6534
Tel (203) 299-3600 *Founded/Ownrshp* 1989
Sales 209.4MM[E] *EMP* 1,192
SIC 4731 Brokers, shipping; Agents, shipping
CEO: Otto Fritzner
**CFO:* Jan Engelhardtsen
**Treas:* Howard Merkle
VP: Greg Johnson
Ex Dir: Mark Martecchini

D-U-N-S 00-321-8484 IMP/EXP
■ **STONCOR GROUP INC**
STONHARD
(*Suby of* REPUBLIC POWDERED METALS INC) ★
1000 E Park Ave, Maple Shade, NJ 08052-1200
Tel (800) 257-7953 *Founded/Ownrshp* 1993
Sales 469.0MM[E] *EMP* 1,730
SIC 2851 Coating, air curing
CEO: David Reif
Pr: Michael Jewell
CFO: Mark Mc Gonigle
CFO: Mark McGonigle
CFO: Frank Sullivan
**Ex VP:* Margaret R Fynan
VP: Peggy Fynan
VP: Rick Neill
VP: Paul Patti
VP: Fred Pfaff
Area Mgr: Thomas Blair

D-U-N-S 36-443-9372
STONE & WEBSTER OVERSEAS GROUP INC
45 Milk St Bsmt, Boston, MA 02109-5102
Tel (617) 778-7500 *Founded/Ownrshp* 2000
Sales 36.4MM[E] *EMP* 1,670
SIC 8742 8711 Management consulting services; Industrial engineers
Pr: James P Carroll

D-U-N-S 07-987-9381
STONE CANYON INDUSTRIES LLC
1250 4th St, Santa Monica, CA 90401-1366
Tel (310) 570-4869 *Founded/Ownrshp* 2014
Sales 956.6MM[E] *EMP* 2,708[E]
SIC 6282 Investment advice; Investment advisory service
CEO: James H Fordyce
Pr: Michael Neumann
CEO: Adam Cohn
VP: Sascha Kaeser
VP: Shawn Malleck

D-U-N-S 80-666-6459
▲ **STONE ENERGY CORP**
625 E Kaliste Saloom Rd # 201, Lafayette, LA 70508-2540
Tel (337) 237-0410 *Founded/Ownrshp* 1993
Sales 544.6MM *EMP* 310[E]
Accts Ernst & Young Llp New Orleans
Tkr Sym SGY *Exch* NYS
SIC 1311 1382 Crude petroleum & natural gas; Crude petroleum production; Natural gas production; Oil & gas exploration services
Ch Bd: David H Welch
CFO: Kenneth H Beer
Sr VP: Lisa S Jaubert
Sr VP: John J Leonard
Sr VP: E J Louviere
Sr VP: Keith A Seilhan
Sr VP: Richard L Toothman Jr
Sr VP: Florence M Ziegler
VP: Thomas L Messonnier
Dir Risk M: Heather Lecky
Brnch Mgr: Andrew L Gates
Board of Directors: Bobbie J Duplantis, Peter D Kinnear, David T Lawrence, Robert S Murley, Richard A Pattarozzi, Donald E Powell, Kay G Priestly, Phyllis M Taylor, George R Christmas

STONE ENTERTAINMENT
See VOLCOM LLC

D-U-N-S 93-284-1633 IMP
STONE PLASTICS AND MANUFACTURING INC
8245 Riley St Ste 100, Zeeland, MI 49464-8568
Tel (616) 748-9740 *Founded/Ownrshp* 1999
Sales 101.9MM[E] *EMP* 120
SIC 5162 3089 Plastics products; Injection molding of plastics
Pr: Mark J Mason

D-U-N-S 92-698-9765
STONE POINT CAPITAL LLC
20 Horseneck Ln Ste 1, Greenwich, CT 06830-6300
Tel (203) 862-2900 *Founded/Ownrshp* 2005
Sales 2.0MM[E] *EMP* 2,035
SIC 6726 Management investment funds, closed-end
CEO: Charles A Davis
**Bd of Dir:* Stephen Friedman
VP: Emanuel Citron
VP: Jarryd Levine
VP: Twana Payne
VP: Eric Rosenzweig
VP: Monica Vitoria
Prin: Mary Kazemi
Mng Dir: Philip Moyles
Dir IT: Ivan Flores

D-U-N-S 19-531-7409 IMP/EXP
STONE SOURCE LLC
215 Park Ave S Fl 7, New York, NY 10003-1603
Tel (212) 979-6400 *Founded/Ownrshp* 2006
Sales 87.5MM[E] *EMP* 135
SIC 5032 Marble building stone; Granite building stone
CFO: Fred Adler

D-U-N-S 00-839-8661 EXP
■ **STONE SOUTHWEST INC**
(*Suby of* WESTROCK RKT CO) ★
150 N Michigan Ave, Chicago, IL 60601-7553
Tel (312) 346-6600 *Founded/Ownrshp* 2012
Sales 153.7MM[E] *EMP* 3,400
SIC 2631 2611 2621 2435 2436 2421 Linerboard; Container, packaging & boxboard; Pulp produced from wood base; Newsprint paper; Plywood, hardwood or hardwood faced; Panels, softwood plywood; Veneer stock, softwood; Lumber: rough, sawed or planed
Ch Bd: Roger W Stone
Treas: Michael B Wheeler
VP: Arnold F Brookstone
VP: Alan Stone

STONEBRIDGE COMPANIES
See STONEBRIDGE REALTY ADVISORS INC

D-U-N-S 00-854-7598 IMP
STONEBRIDGE INDUSTRIES INC
MAYCO PLASTICS
(*Suby of* K C P) ★
42400 Merrill Rd, Sterling Heights, MI 48314-3238
Tel (586) 323-0348 *Founded/Ownrshp* 1996
Sales 85.9MM[E] *EMP* 624[E]
SIC 3496 3462 3451 Miscellaneous fabricated wire products; Iron & steel forgings; Screw machine products
Pr: Ed Wright
**COO:* Robert Roberts
**CFO:* Mark Blaufuss

D-U-N-S 80-856-4462
STONEBRIDGE REALTY ADVISORS INC
STONEBRIDGE COMPANIES
9100 E Panorama Dr # 300, Englewood, CO 80112-3404
Tel (303) 785-3100 *Founded/Ownrshp* 1991
Sales 147.8MM[E] *EMP* 3,000
SIC 7011 Hotels & motels
Pr: Navin Dimond
Pr: Nasim Mansurov
Pr: Scott McChesney
Pr: Chris Stein
**CFO:* David Womack
**VP:* Rita Dimond
VP: Sandra Esparza
VP: Matt Friend
VP: Randy Santulli
VP: Peter Underwood
Genl Mgr: Laura Brooks

D-U-N-S 17-219-8678
▲ **STONEGATE BANK**
400 N Federal Hwy, Pompano Beach, FL 33062-4312
Tel (954) 315-5500 *Founded/Ownrshp* 2004
Sales NA *EMP* 275
Tkr Sym SGBK *Exch* NGS
SIC 6022 State commercial banks
Pr: David Seleski
**COO:* Steve Cameron
**CFO:* Sharon Jones
Sr Cor Off: Jerry Oliver
**Chf Cred:* Staci Bluestein
**Ofcr:* Steve Sanzone
Ex VP: Joseph Bamond
**Ex VP:* Kris Barnhart
**Ex VP:* Wade Faircloth
**Ex VP:* Erin Knight
**Ex VP:* Pablo Veintimilla
**Sr VP:* Robert McCracken
Sr VP: Brad Severson
VP: Kathy Castellano
VP: Jerry Grace
VP: Mark L Huard
VP: Heather Keir
VP: Erin D Knight
VP: Karen Korabek
VP: Jennifer Olson
VP: Josh Schiffrin

D-U-N-S 19-719-3209
▲ **STONEGATE MORTGAGE CORP**
9190 Priority Way West Dr, Indianapolis, IN 46240-6426
Tel (317) 663-5100 *Founded/Ownrshp* 1976
Sales NA *EMP* 927[E]
Tkr Sym SGM *Exch* NYS
SIC 6162 Mortgage bankers & correspondents
Pr: James V Smith
**Ch Bd:* Richard A Kraemer
COO: Pam Starr
Ofcr: Clark Jennings
Ofcr: Carrie Preston
Ex VP: David Dill
VP: Efe Aghimien
CIO: R Douglas Gilmore
Prd Mgr: Kevin Smith
Genl Couns: David E Kress
Board of Directors: Kevin B Bhatt, James G Brown, Sam Levinson, Richard A Mirro, J Scott Mumphrey

D-U-N-S 07-571-1440
STONEHILL COLLEGE INC
320 Washington St, North Easton, MA 02357-0001
Tel (508) 565-1000 *Founded/Ownrshp* 1948
Sales 139.7MM *EMP* 642
Accts Pricewaterhousecoopers Llp Bo
SIC 8221 College, except junior
Pr: Mark T Cregan
**Treas:* Edward Casieri
**Ex VP:* Rev Robert J Kruse
VP: James Lies
**VP:* Jennifer Mathews
**Prin:* Fr John Denning
Off Admin: Nicole Miller
Genl Couns: Thomas V Flynn
Counsel: Amee Synnott
Snr Mgr: Taylor Steimle

D-U-N-S 07-912-4987
STONEMOR GP LLC
3600 Horizon Blvd Ste 100, Feasterville Trevose, PA 19053-4965
Tel (215) 826-2947 *Founded/Ownrshp* 2004
Sales 42.4MM[E] *EMP* 3,380
SIC 6553 Cemeteries, real estate operation
Ch Bd: Lawrence Miller

D-U-N-S 05-948-2682
▲ **STONEMOR PARTNERS LP**
3600 Horizon Blvd Ste 100, Trevose, PA 19053-4965
Tel (215) 826-2800 *Founded/Ownrshp* 1999
Sales 305.6MM *EMP* 3,444
Tkr Sym STON *Exch* NYS
SIC 6553 7261 Cemeteries, real estate operation; Funeral service & crematories
Ch Bd: Lawrence Miller
Genl Pt: Stonemor GP LLC
CFO: Sean P McGrath
VP: Anthony Ciccone
VP: Vaughn Giwa
VP: Patti Kone
VP Admn: Frank Milles
Rgnl Mgr: Ted Dirkman
Rgnl Mgr: Kevin Mueller
Genl Mgr: Mark Heintzelman
Off Admin: Laura Wood

D-U-N-S 78-051-4696
STONEPATH GROUP INC
STONEPATH LOGISTICS
2200 Alaskan Way Ste 200, Seattle, WA 98121-3602
Tel (206) 336-5400 *Founded/Ownrshp* 1999
Sales 410.2MM *EMP* 508
SIC 4731 Freight transportation arrangement
CEO: Martin Muller-Rmheld
**Ch Bd:* Dennis M Pelino
Sr VP: Robert F Manner

STONEPATH LOGISTICS
See STONEPATH GROUP INC

D-U-N-S 96-803-7536 IMP
■ **STONERIDGE ELECTRONICS INC**
STONERIDGE ELECTRONICS NA
(*Suby of* STONERIDGE INC) ★
21 Butterfield Trail Blvd A, El Paso, TX 79906-5269
Tel (915) 593-2011 *Founded/Ownrshp* 1965
Sales 84.0MM *EMP* 1,000[E]
SIC 3679 3714 Electronic circuits; Motor vehicle electrical equipment
Pr: John C Corey
COO: Laura Lujan
**VP:* Thomas A Beaver
**VP:* Kevin B Kramer
**VP:* Michael D Sloan
**VP:* George E Strickler
Sls&Mrk Ex: Rob Semko

STONERIDGE ELECTRONICS NA
See STONERIDGE ELECTRONICS INC

D-U-N-S 60-628-0873 IMP/EXP
▲ **STONERIDGE INC**
39675 Mackenzie Dr # 400, Novi, MI 48377-1607
Tel (330) 856-2443 *Founded/Ownrshp* 1965
Sales 644.8MM *EMP* 4,100
Tkr Sym SRI *Exch* NYS
SIC 3714 3679 3625 Motor vehicle electrical equipment; Instrument board assemblies, motor vehicle; Harness assemblies for electronic use: wire or cable; Electronic switches; Actuators, industrial
Pr: Jonathan B Degaynor
**Ch Bd:* William M Lasky
Pr: Thomas A Beaver
Pr: Peter Kruk
Pr: Sergio De Cerqueira Leite
Pr: Michael D Sloan
CFO: Robert R Krakowiak
Ofcr: Alisa A Nagle
Ex VP: George E Strickler
VP: Richard P Adante
VP: Anthony L Moore

D-U-N-S 02-633-4564
STONERIVER INC
(*Suby of* PROGRESSIVE ENTERPRISES HOLDINGS INC) ★
250 N Sunny Slope Rd # 110, Brookfield, WI 53005-4811
Tel (262) 207-2101 *Founded/Ownrshp* 2007
Sales 135.5MM[E] *EMP* 2,200
SIC 7371 Computer software development
CEO: Kenneth L Dowd Jr
**VP:* Kristine Blommel
**VP:* David Clark

D-U-N-S 18-040-6100
STONERIVER INC
(*Suby of* STONE POINT CAPITAL LLC) ★
222 3rd Ave Se Ste 405, Cedar Rapids, IA 52401-1542
Tel (319) 378-5773 *Founded/Ownrshp* 2007
Sales 96.4MM[E] *EMP* 2,035
SIC 7371 Computer software development
CEO: Gary Anderson
**Pr:* Anthony Perdichezzi
**CFO:* Stewart Gerson
**CFO:* Costa John
**Sr VP:* Tom Chesbrough
VP: Jim Woodward

D-U-N-S 87-815-1083 IMP/EXP
STONEWALL KITCHEN LLC
2 Stonewall Ln, York, ME 03909-1665
Tel (207) 351-2713 *Founded/Ownrshp* 1991
Sales 112.3MM[E] *EMP* 400
SIC 2033 2035 2032 5149 5064 Jams, jellies & preserves: packaged in cans, jars, etc.; Pickled fruits & vegetables; Seasonings & sauces, except tomato & dry; Canned specialties; Spices & seasonings; Electrical appliances, television & radio
Pr: Jonathan King
**COO:* Lori King
VP: Natalie King
**VP:* James Stott
Exec: Eric Rousseau
Dir Lab: Judi Delaney-Shirley
QA Dir: Tammy Sawyer
Dir IT: Wilder Jason
IT Man: Bill Bosach
Netwrk Eng: Kelly Blanchard
Mfg Dir: Thomas Cassidy

STONEWAY CONSTRUCTION SUPPLY
See GARY MERLINO CONSTRUCTION CO INC

D-U-N-S 06-716-8245
STONEWAY ELECTRIC SUPPLY CO (WA)
402 N Perry St, Spokane, WA 99202-2921
Tel (509) 535-2933 *Founded/Ownrshp* 1974, 1980
Sales 114.9MM[E] *EMP* 265
SIC 5063

D-U-N-S 06-713-5855
STONEWAY ELECTRIC SUPPLY CO OF SPOKANE (INC)
1212 E Front Ave, Spokane, WA 99202-2148
Tel (509) 535-2933 *Founded/Ownrshp* 1980
Sales 132.0MM *EMP* 50
Accts Mcdirmid Mikkelsen & Secrest
SIC 5063 Electrical apparatus & equipment
Pr: Cliston Kelly
**CFO:* Ralph Jones

D-U-N-S 00-151-1174
STONEWOOD HOLDINGS LLC (FL)
PEACH VALLEY RESTAURANT GROUP
780 W Granada Blvd # 100, Ormond Beach, FL 32174-2300
Tel (386) 760-2282 *Founded/Ownrshp* 2000
Sales 54.1MM[E] *EMP* 1,200
SIC 5812 Grills (eating places)
CFO: Mark Peterson
Genl Mgr: Matthew Sgroi

STONHARD
See STONCOR GROUP INC

D-U-N-S 15-674-8928
STONY BROOK UNIVERSITY
(*Suby of* SUNY ADMINISTRATION) ★
100 Nicolls Rd, Stony Brook, NY 11794-0001
Tel (631) 632-6000 *Founded/Ownrshp* 2005
Sales 651.6MM[E] *EMP* 3,782[E]
SIC 8221 9411 University; Administration of educational programs;
Pr: Samuel L Stanley Jr
CFO: Glenn J Klein
Bd of Dir: Christopher Lee
VP: Andrew Narus
Exec: Kathleen Green
Assoc Dir: Lisa Chichura
Assoc Dir: Raymond Dawson
Assoc Dir: Andrea Lipack
Assoc Dir: Ivan Lowe
Genl Mgr: Chris Garofalo
Nurse Mgr: Jane Collins

D-U-N-S 60-471-1861 IMP
STOP & SHOP SUPERMARKET CO
GIANT OF LANDOVER
(*Suby of* STOP & SHOP SUPERMARKET CO LLC) ★
1385 Hancock St, Quincy, MA 02169-5103
Tel (717) 960-1700 *Founded/Ownrshp* 1914
Sales 4.0MMM[E] *EMP* 62,000
SIC 5411 Supermarkets, chain
Pr: Marc E Smith
Dir Vol: Jesse Dixon
Pr: Brian W Hotarek
Pr: Peter M Phillipes
COO: Dick Boer
Treas: Richard J Picariello
Ex VP: Dean Cohagan
Sr VP: Robert Manson
Sr VP: Joseph D Mc Glinchey
Sr VP: Rick Picariello
VP: Andrea Astrachan
VP: Gail Goolkasian
VP: Jihad Rizkallah
VP: Chris Williams

D-U-N-S 18-891-0863 IMP/EXP
STOP & SHOP SUPERMARKET CO LLC
(*Suby of* AFS) ★
1385 Hancock St, Quincy, MA 02169-5103
Tel (800) 767-7772 *Founded/Ownrshp* 1989
Sales 13.6MMM[E] *EMP* 169,835
SIC 5411 Supermarkets, chain; Supermarkets, 55,000-65,000 square feet (superstore)
Ex VP: Paula Labian
Ex VP: Mark E Smith
Ex VP: Donald Sussman
Sr VP: Richard A Baird
Sr VP: Brian W Hotarek
Sr VP: Robert A Manson
VP: Joel Boone
VP: Bill Brophy
VP: Tim Mahoney
VP: Kathy Phillips
VP: Kristina Rota
VP: Steve Rowell
Dir Rx: Sandra Narine
Dir Rx: Anand Patel
Board of Directors: F I Ahlqvist, P P J Butzelaar, A M Meurs, E S Moerk, J L M Sliepenbeek, C H Van Der Hoeven, P J Van Dun, R Zwartendijk

D-U-N-S 09-844-2858
■ **STOP IN FOOD STORES INC**
(*Suby of* FUEL OILS) ★
3000 Ogden Rd, Roanoke, VA 24018-8857
Tel (540) 772-4900 *Founded/Ownrshp* 1979
Sales 229.6MM[E] *EMP* 700
SIC 5411 Convenience stores
Pr: Ron Hare
VP: Roy E Foutz III
**VP:* John Newton

STOP N GO
See NATIONAL CONVENIENCE STORES INC

STOP N GO FOODS
See S-N-GO STORES INC

STORAGE USA
See EXTRA SPACE MANAGEMENT INC

STORE 24
See TEDESCHI FOOD SHOPS INC

D-U-N-S 03-139-7880
STORE CAPITAL CORP
8501 E Prnceaz Dr Ste 190, Scottsdale, AZ 85255
Tel (480) 256-1100 *Founded/Ownrshp* 2011
Sales 284.7MM *EMP* 60
Accts Ernst & Young Llp Phoenix A
Tkr Sym STOR *Exch* NYS
SIC 6798 Real estate investment trusts
Pr: Christopher H Volk
**Ch Bd:* Morton H Fleischer
CFO: Catherine Long
Chf Cred: Michael T Bennett
Ex VP: Brad Bennett

Ex VP: Christopher K Burbach
Ex VP: Mary Fedewa
Ex VP: Michael J Zieg
Sr VP: Julie Dimond
VP: Craig Barnett
VP: Elizabeth Burm
Exec: Jackie Stiouis
Board of Directors: Joseph M Donovan, Mary Fedewa, William F Hipp, Einar A Seadler, Mark N Sklar, Quentin P Smith Jr

STOREROOM-ON-SITE
See SYNOVOS INC

D-U-N-S 08-762-4425 IMP
STORK UNITED CORP
3201 Rotary Dr, Charlotte, NC 28269-4493
Tel (704) 598-7171 *Founded/Ownrshp* 2013
Sales 135.5MM^E *EMP* 713
SIC 5084 3552 3556

STORMONT VAIL HEALTH
See STORMONT-VAIL HEALTHCARE INC

D-U-N-S 06-795-7423 IMP
STORMONT-VAIL HEALTHCARE INC
STORMONT VAIL HEALTH
1500 Sw 10th Ave, Topeka, KS 66604-1301
Tel (785) 354-6000 *Founded/Ownrshp* 1984
Sales 582.2MM *EMP* 4,500
Accts Rsm Us Llp Davenport Iowa
SIC 8062 General medical & surgical hospitals
CEO: Randall Peterson
**CFO:* Kevin Han
**Sr VP:* Kent P D
**VP:* Bernard Becker
**VP:* David Cuningham
**VP:* Tracy O'Rourke
**VP:* Carol Perry
**VP:* Janet Stanek
VP: Robert Worthington
**VP:* Deb Yocum
Dir OR: Craig Koppen
Dir Risk M: Jim Kilmartin
Dir Lab: Diane Burton
Dir Rx: Doug Pederson

D-U-N-S 09-149-3940 IMP
STOROPACK INC
FOAM PAC MATERIALS COMPANY
(*Suby of* STOROPACK DEUTSCHLAND GMBH + CO. KG)
4758 Devitt Dr, West Chester, OH 45246-1106
Tel (513) 874-0314 *Founded/Ownrshp* 1978
Sales 110.0MM *EMP* 323
SIC 5199 3086 2671 Packaging materials; Packaging & shipping materials, foamed plastic; Packaging paper & plastics film, coated & laminated
Ch Bd: Hans Reichenecker
**Pr:* Daniel Wachter
**CFO:* Gregg Battaglia
**VP:* Thomas G Eckel
**VP:* Joe Lagrasta
**VP:* Lester Whisnant
IT Man: Brian Patel
Mtls Mgr: Randy Gabbard
Plnt Mgr: Jim Henshaw
Plnt Mgr: Zach Zamira
Prd Mgr: Casey Pierson

D-U-N-S 06-520-1626
STORY CONSTRUCTION CO
300 S Bell Ave, Ames, IA 50010-7707
Tel (515) 232-4358 *Founded/Ownrshp* 1972
Sales 86.1MM *EMP* 125
Accts Rsm Us Llp Des Moines Iowa
SIC 1542 1629 Commercial & office building, new construction; Institutional building construction; School building construction; Hospital construction; Waste water & sewage treatment plant construction
Pr: Michael A Espeset
**Pr:* Mike Espeset
COO: Patrick Geary
**CFO:* Steve C Tenney
Sr VP: Larry Sperlich
**VP:* Tenney Steven C
Genl Mgr: Erin Kurth
Off Mgr: Lisa Camp
Sfty Mgr: Joe Hewitt

D-U-N-S 06-409-0715 IMP
STOUFFER CORP
(*Suby of* TSC HOLDINGS INC) ★
30003 Bainbridge Rd, Solon, OH 44139-2205
Tel (440) 349-5757 *Founded/Ownrshp* 2011
Sales 1.5MMM^E *EMP* 8,620
SIC 2038 Dinners, frozen & packaged; Soups, frozen
Prin: Peter Knox
VP: George Sell
CIO: Mark Brown
MIS Dir: Joe Kardamis

STOUGHTON
See STI HOLDINGS INC

D-U-N-S 79-542-7165 IMP
STOUGHTON TRAILERS LLC
(*Suby of* STOUGHTON) ★
416 S Academy St, Stoughton, WI 53589-2684
Tel (608) 873-2500 *Founded/Ownrshp* 2002
Sales 123.2MM^E *EMP* 224^E
SIC 3715 Truck trailers
Sls Dir: Greg Moc

STOWE MOUNTAIN RESORT
See MT MANSFIELD CO INC

D-U-N-S 61-465-3652
STOWERS INSTITUTE FOR MEDICAL RESEARCH
1000 E 50th St, Kansas City, MO 64110-2262
Tel (816) 926-4000 *Founded/Ownrshp* 2008
Sales 179.5MM *EMP* 335
Accts Pricewaterhousecoopers Llp Wa
SIC 8733 Medical research
Ch Bd: Richard Brown
**Pr:* David Chao
**VP:* Abby Freeman

D-U-N-S 83-060-0438
STOWERS RESOURCE MANAGEMENT INC
1000 E 50th St, Kansas City, MO 64110-2262
Tel (816) 926-4000 *Founded/Ownrshp* 2009
Sales 107.3MM *EMP* 3
Accts Kpms Llp Columbus Oh
SIC 8741 Management services
Prin: J Scott Pettet

D-U-N-S 01-460-6839 IMP
STP NUCLEAR OPERATING CO
SOUTH TXAS PRJ ELC GNRTING STN
8 Miles W Wdsworth Fm 521, Wadsworth, TX 77483
Tel (361) 972-3611 *Founded/Ownrshp* 1997
Sales 500.0MM *EMP* 1,350
SIC 4911
Pr: Dennis Koehl
Treas: Ronald G Hyde
**Sr VP:* Tim Powell
VP: Robert Rysner
VP: Kathleen Tremblay
Genl Mgr: Tim Bowman
CIO: Phillip Sullivan
CTO: Christopher Meemken
Dir IT: Waco W Bankston
Snr PM: Dean Owens
Snr Mgr: Brenda Verbeck

D-U-N-S 01-637-2468
STRACK AND VAN TIL SUPER MARKET INC
(*Suby of* CENTRELLA FOODS) ★
9632 Cline Ave, Highland, IN 46322-3094
Tel (219) 924-6932 *Founded/Ownrshp* 1930, 1959
Sales 299.0MM^E *EMP* 2,300
Accts Mcgladrey & Pullen Llp Chicag
SIC 5411 8741 4226 Supermarkets, independent; Management services; Special warehousing & storage
Pr: David Wilkinson
**CFO:* Keith Bruxvoort
**VP:* Joe Kolavo
**VP:* Rex Mudge
**VP:* Andrew Raab
**VP:* Jeff Strack
**VP:* Robert Wasiuta
VP Opers: Andy Raab

D-U-N-S 60-507-7734
STRAND ENERGY CO
515 S Flower St Ste 4800, Los Angeles, CA 90071-2241
Tel (213) 225-5900 *Founded/Ownrshp* 1988
Sales 398.4MM^E *EMP* 380
SIC 1311 Crude petroleum & natural gas production
CEO: Halbert S Washburn
**Pr:* Randall Breitenbach

D-U-N-S 05-573-4807
■ **STRANDED OIL RESOURCES CORP**
SORC
(*Suby of* ALLEGHANY CAPITAL CORP) ★
110 N Rubey Dr Unit 120, Golden, CO 80403-3219
Tel (512) 279-7870 *Founded/Ownrshp* 2011
Sales 28.6MM^E *EMP* 1,265^E
SIC 8742 Business planning & organizing services
CEO: Mark See
Prin: Sheila Griffith

STRATA COMMUNICATIONS
See STRATA INC

D-U-N-S 00-892-5794
STRATA CORP
1600 N 48th St, Grand Forks, ND 58203-1101
Tel (701) 775-4205 *Founded/Ownrshp* 1962
Sales 175.9MM^E *EMP* 225
SIC 1611 3273 1442 5032 Highway & street construction; Ready-mixed concrete; Construction sand mining; Gravel mining; Masons' materials
CEO: James Bradshaw
**VP:* Judith A Bradshaw

D-U-N-S 06-336-0374
STRATA INC
STRATA COMMUNICATIONS
3501 Everett Ave, Everett, WA 98201-3816
Tel (425) 259-6016 *Founded/Ownrshp* 1988
Sales 108.5MM^E *EMP* 1,555
SIC 1799 Antenna installation
Pr: Denise Lorenz

D-U-N-S 85-911-9695
STRATACACHE INC
STRATACACHE PRODUCTS
2 Emmet St Ste 200, Dayton, OH 45405-4958
Tel (937) 224-0485 *Founded/Ownrshp* 1990
Sales 111.0MM *EMP* 295
SIC 5734 4822 Software, business & non-game; Nonvocal message communications
CEO: Chris Riegel
**CFO:* Kevin McGree
Sr VP: Ken Boyle
**Sr VP:* Russell Young
VP: Yogesh Chopra
**VP:* John Rau
Ex Dir: Marc Castejon
IT Man: Melissa Higgins
VP Sls: Paul Rinaldi
Sls Mgr: Stephanie Hardy

STRATACACHE PRODUCTS
See STRATACACHE INC

D-U-N-S 82-925-2209 IMP/EXP
STRATAS FOODS LLC
7130 Goodlett Frm Pkwy # 200, Cordova, TN 38016-4992
Tel (888) 404-1004 *Founded/Ownrshp* 2008
Sales 787.3MM^E *EMP* 544^E
SIC 2079 Edible fats & oils
CEO: Tedd Kruse
Pr: Gary Harmon
CFO: Steven Zehr
VP: Fred Baine
VP: Deborah Murdock
Genl Mgr: Michael Vanfleet
VP Mfg: Kevin Swanson

D-U-N-S 78-794-6300 IMP
STRATASYS DIRECT INC
STRATASYS DIRECT MANUFACTURING
(*Suby of* SEURAT HOLDINGS INC) ★
28309 Avenue Crocker, Valencia, CA 91355-1251
Tel (661) 295-4400 *Founded/Ownrshp* 2015
Sales 95.4MM^E *EMP* 338
SIC 3089 Plastic processing; Casting of plastic
CEO: Joseph Allison
**CFO:* Peter Keller
**CFO:* Tom Smolders
Sr VP: Jeff Lemker
VP: Kent Firestone
VP: Tom Vorgitch
Snr Sftwr: Jeff Hilmo
Snr Sftwr: Luis Vasconez
Sftwr Eng: Terry Downing
Sftwr Eng: Jacob Ferrell
Opers Mgr: Tim Carroll

STRATASYS DIRECT MANUFACTURING
See STRATASYS DIRECT INC

D-U-N-S 61-346-5806 IMP
STRATASYS INC
MOJO
(*Suby of* SEURAT HOLDINGS INC) ★
7665 Commerce Way, Eden Prairie, MN 55344-2001
Tel (800) 801-6491 *Founded/Ownrshp* 2012
Sales 212.6MM^E *EMP* 339^E
SIC 3577 Computer peripheral equipment
CEO: David Reis
Pr: S Scott Crump
COO: Thomas W Stenoien
CFO: Robert F Gallagher
CFO: Erez Simha
Ofcr: Tim Bohling
Ofcr: Joshu Claman
Ex VP: Lawrence M Doerr
Ex VP: Hanoch Magid
Ex VP: Dan Yalon
VP: Patrick Carey
Exec: Jesse Roitenberg
Board of Directors: Ralph E Crump, Edward J Fierko, John J McEleney, Clifford H Schwieter, Gregory L Wilson

D-U-N-S 80-010-9154
STRATEGIC EQUIPMENT AND SUPPLY CORP
TRIMARK STRATEGIC
(*Suby of* TRIMARK UNITED EAST) ★
1461 S Belt Line Rd # 100, Coppell, TX 75019-4938
Tel (469) 240-7200 *Founded/Ownrshp* 2004
Sales 202.9MM^E *EMP* 410
SIC 5046 Cooking equipment, commercial
Pr: Marty Monnat
**CFO:* Bill White
Ex VP: Rich Schuttenhelm
Dir IT: Brad Herndon

D-U-N-S 03-470-6721
STRATEGIC EQUIPMENT LLC
(*Suby of* TRIMARK UNITED EAST) ★
1461 S Belt Line Rd # 100, Coppell, TX 75019-4938
Tel (469) 240-7200 *Founded/Ownrshp* 2013
Sales 323.0MM *EMP* 550
SIC 5046 Commercial cooking & food service equipment
Pr: Marty Monnat
**CFO:* Karen McCain
VP: Strategic Bates
Dir IT: Brad Herndon

D-U-N-S 60-765-2740
STRATEGIC HOTELS & RESORTS INC
200 W Madison St Ste 1700, Chicago, IL 60606-3538
Tel (312) 658-5000 *Founded/Ownrshp* 2004
Sales 1.0MMM *EMP* 35^E
SIC 6798

D-U-N-S 13-253-5258 IMP/EXP
STRATEGIC INDUSTRIES LLC
26 Main St Ste 200, Chatham, NJ 07928-2425
Tel (732) 512-0195 *Founded/Ownrshp* 2000
Sales NA *EMP* 2,550
SIC 3724 3499 3451 3083 3111

D-U-N-S 62-295-3230 IMP
STRATEGIC MATERIALS INC
WESTERN STRATEGIC MATERIALS
(*Suby of* WILLIS STEIN & PARTNERS MANAGEMENT III LLC) ★
16365 Park Ten Pl Ste 200, Houston, TX 77084-5062
Tel (281) 647-2700 *Founded/Ownrshp* 2005
Sales 150.9MM^E *EMP* 600
SIC 4953 Recycling, waste materials
Pr: Denis Suggs
COO: Tom Burns
**CFO:* Michael Ramirez
**Ex VP:* Curtis Bucey
**Sr VP:* Laurie Borg
**Sr VP:* Matt Keresman
**Sr VP:* Jimmy Rayford
VP: Richard Abramowitz
**VP:* David Cabello
**VP:* Allan Goertz
Opers Mgr: Gozde Capar
Board of Directors: Emil Fajersson, Matt Schafer, Denis Suggs, John Willis

D-U-N-S 92-634-6529 IMP/EXP
STRATEGIC PARTNERS INC
CHEROKEE UNIFORM
9800 De Soto Ave, Chatsworth, CA 91311-4411
Tel (818) 671-2100 *Founded/Ownrshp* 2012
Sales 156.3MM^E *EMP* 557
SIC 3143 3144 5139 2339 2389 2329 Men's footwear, except athletic; Women's footwear, except athletic; Shoes; Women's & misses' outerwear; Uniforms & vestments; Sweaters & sweater jackets: men's & boys'
CEO: Michael Singer
**CFO:* Robert Pierpoint
Mktg Dir: Mark Buckston

D-U-N-S 82-521-1501
STRATEGIC PRODUCTS AND SERVICES LLC
STRATEGIC PRODUCTS AND SVCS
300 Littleton Rd Ste 200, Parsippany, NJ 07054-4841
Tel (973) 540-0600 *Founded/Ownrshp* 1984
Sales 300.0MM *EMP* 800
SIC 5999

STRATEGIC PRODUCTS AND SVCS
See STRATEGIC PRODUCTS AND SERVICES LLC

D-U-N-S 62-695-7674
STRATEGIC RESOURCES INC
7927 Jones Branch Dr 600w, Mc Lean, VA 22102-3329
Tel (703) 749-3040 *Founded/Ownrshp* 1988
Sales 98.0MM^E *EMP* 1,000
Accts Goodman & Company
SIC 8742 8748 7373 Management consulting services; Business consulting; Computer systems analysis & design
Pr: Rose McElrath Slade
**VP:* Mark Patterson
Off Mgr: Lena Akeredolu

D-U-N-S 18-992-0692
STRATEGIC RESTAURANTS ACQUISITION CO LLC
3000 Executive Pkwy, San Ramon, CA 94583-4255
Tel (925) 328-3300 *Founded/Ownrshp* 2004
Sales 255.7MM^E *EMP* 7,000
SIC 5812 Fast-food restaurant, chain
VP: Tammy Johns
Dir Risk M: Mike Dupuis
Dist Mgr: Greg Long
Dist Mgr: Don Zimmerman
Dir IT: David Knutson
VP Opers: Mahendra Modha

D-U-N-S 16-961-4547
STRATEGIC SECURITY CORP
4 Higbie Dr, Smithtown, NY 11787-3440
Tel (212) 509-0547 *Founded/Ownrshp* 2002
Sales 1.5MM^E *EMP* 1,500
SIC 7381 Protective services, guard; Security guard service
Mng Dir: Joseph C Sordi
**CEO:* Christie Demonte

D-U-N-S 15-140-5271
STRATEGIC STAFFING SOLUTIONS LC
645 Griswold St Ste 2900, Detroit, MI 48226-4206
Tel (888) 738-3261 *Founded/Ownrshp* 1990
Sales 188.0MM^E *EMP* 1,500
SIC 8742 Personnel management consultant
Pr: Cynthia Pasky
CFO: Ed Amanimo
**CFO:* Paul Huxley
CFO: Edward Mannino
Bd of Dir: Thomas Costello
VP: Allen Coleman
VP: Jeff Nelson
Ex Dir: Kenneth Rohrs
Prgrm Mgr: Matt Hoerauf
Brnch Mgr: Renande Lainee
Brnch Mgr: Jerry Poenitske

D-U-N-S 96-403-5765
STRATEGIC STORAGE TRUST INC
SMARTSTOP SELF STORAGE
111 Corporate Dr Ste 120, Ladera Ranch, CA 92694-1199
Tel (949) 429-6600 *Founded/Ownrshp* 2007
Sales 98.2MM *EMP* 15^E
SIC 6798 Real estate investment trusts
Pr: H Michael Schwartz
**CFO:* Michael S McClure
Ex VP: Paula Mathews
Dist Mgr: Maria D Avellana
Dist Mgr: Simon Chan
Dist Mgr: Amy Sylvester
**CIO:* Wayne Johnson

STRATFORD BOARD OF EDUCATION
See STRATFORD SCHOOL DISTRICT

D-U-N-S 18-386-1301
STRATFORD SCHOOL DISTRICT
STRATFORD BOARD OF EDUCATION
1000 E Broadway, Stratford, CT 06615-5911
Tel (203) 381-2012 *Founded/Ownrshp* 1639
Sales NA *EMP* 1,343
SIC 9411
**COO:* Clarence Zachery
Schl Brd P: Andrea Veilleux
Teacher Pr: Margaret Lasek

STRATHAM MEMORIAL SCHOOL
See EXETER SCHOOL DISTRICT

D-U-N-S 14-814-6236
STRATIX CORP
4920 Avalon Ridge Pkwy, Peachtree Corners, GA 30071-1572
Tel (770) 326-7580 *Founded/Ownrshp* 2016
Sales 131.6MM^E *EMP* 160^E
SIC 4812

D-U-N-S 12-623-1638
STRATOS INC
SERVICEMASTER BY STRATOS
66 N Main St, Memphis, TN 38103-2134
Tel (901) 683-0064 *Founded/Ownrshp* 2009
Sales 29.5MM^E *EMP* 1,069
SIC 7349 Building maintenance services
Pr: Stacy McCall
**VP:* Jim Black
**VP:* Meredith Black
**VP:* Chris McCall

STRATOSPHERE CASINO HT & TWR
See STRATOSPHERE GAMING LLC

D-U-N-S 04-035-0444
STRATOSPHERE GAMING LLC
STRATOSPHERE CASINO HT & TWR
(*Suby of* AMERICAN CASINO & ENTRMT PRPTS) ★
2000 Las Vegas Blvd S, Las Vegas, NV 89104-2597
Tel (702) 380-7777 *Founded/Ownrshp* 1994

Sales 72.0MM[E] *EMP* 2,100
SIC 7011 Hotels & motels
**VP:* Matthew Mascali
CTO: Matt Morgan

D-U-N-S 80-452-2324
STRATOSPHERE LLC
AMERICAN CASINO & ENTRMT PRPTS
(*Suby of* AMERICAN CASINO & ENTERTAINMENT PROPERTIES LLC) ★
2000 Las Vegas Blvd S, Las Vegas, NV 89104-2597
Tel (702) 380-7777 *Founded/Ownrshp* 1993
Sales 144.2MM[E] *EMP* 2,150[E]
SIC 7011 7999 Casino hotel; Tourist attractions, amusement park concessions & rides; Amusement ride
Prin: Frank Riolo
VP: Kim Davis
VP: Steve Mann
Exec: Richard Giffen
Mktg Dir: Todd Ford

D-U-N-S 82-970-0330
STRATOSPHERE QUALITY LLC
12024 Exit 5 Pkwy, Fishers, IN 46037-7940
Tel (317) 578-1455 *Founded/Ownrshp* 2009
Sales 102.0MM *EMP* 2,000[E]
SIC 7389 Inspection & testing services
CEO: Tom Gray
COO: Craig Palmer
**CFO:* Olga Chaikouskaya
**Sr VP:* Kyle Coffinger
**VP:* Charlie Ungetheim
Opers Mgr: Faisal Ali
Opers Mgr: Kevin Cox
Opers Mgr: Mike Gleim
Opers Mgr: Jim Harris
Opers Mgr: Scott Richie
Opers Mgr: Nick Roberts

D-U-N-S 87-916-8029
▲ STRATTEC SECURITY CORP
3333 W Good Hope Rd, Milwaukee, WI 53209-2043
Tel (414) 247-3333 *Founded/Ownrshp* 1994
Sales 401.4MM *EMP* 3,420
Tkr Sym STRT *Exch* NGM
SIC 3714 3364 3429 Motor vehicle parts & accessories; Zinc & zinc-base alloy die-castings; Manufactured hardware (general)
Pr: Frank J Krejci
CFO: Patrick J Hansen
VP: Rolando J Guillot
VP: Dennis A Kazmierski
VP: Richard P Messina
VP: Brian J Reetz
VP: Guillermo Villa
Prgrm Mgr: Joe Baaki
Prgrm Mgr: Thomas Majeski
Prgrm Mgr: Paul Waller
Admn Mgr: Mark Smith
Board of Directors: Thomas W Florsheim, Michael J Koss, Harold M Stratton II, David R Zimmer

D-U-N-S 00-787-0637
■ STRATTON CORP
STRATTON MOUNTAIN RESORT
(*Suby of* STRATTON SKI CORPORATION)
5 Village Lodge Rd, South Londonderry, VT 05155-9600
Tel (802) 297-2200 *Founded/Ownrshp* 1960
Sales 69.2MM[E] *EMP* 1,500[E]
SIC 7011 7992 1531 6512 5941 Ski lodge; Public golf courses; Condominium developers; Property operation, retail establishment; Sporting goods & bicycle shops
Ch Bd: Joe S Houssian
**Ch Bd:* Hugh R Smythe
**Pr:* Sky Foulks
**Treas:* Gary L Raymond
**VP:* John E Currie
VP: Myra Foster
**VP:* Laura Mullen
Off Mgr: Kristen Simonetti

D-U-N-S 00-742-8550
STRATTON EQUITY COOPERATIVE CO
98 Colorado Ave, Stratton, CO 80836-1166
Tel (719) 348-5326 *Founded/Ownrshp* 1915
Sales 120.5MM *EMP* 111
SIC 5153 5191 5171 5541

D-U-N-S 19-701-5217
STRATTON MOUNTAIN COUNTRY CLUB
(*Suby of* STRATTON MOUNTAIN RESORT) ★
Stratton Mtn Access Rd, South Londonderry, VT 05155
Tel (802) 297-1005 *Founded/Ownrshp* 1964
Sales 288.0M *EMP* 1,293[E]
SIC 7997 Country club, membership
Pr: James Tierney
**Treas:* Robert Minners

STRATTON MOUNTAIN RESORT
See STRATTON CORP

STRATUS TECHNOLOGIES GROUP SA
See STRATUS TECHNOLOGIES INC

D-U-N-S 06-109-6306 IMP/EXP
STRATUS TECHNOLOGIES INC
STRATUS TECHNOLOGIES GROUP SA
5 Mill Main Pl Ste 500, Maynard, MA 01754
Tel (978) 461-7000 *Founded/Ownrshp* 2014
Sales 297.6MM[E] *EMP* 972
SIC 7372 Prepackaged software
Pr: David C Laurello
**CFO:* Christina Clohecy
Bd of Dir: Kevin C Nickelberry
**Chf Mktg O:* Nigel Dessau
VP: Susan W Bailey
VP: Susan Bailey
VP: Susan Deeney
VP: Michael Ellis
VP: Peter Flynn
VP: David Harrington
VP: Karyn Lantier
VP: Christopher P Moore
VP: Tony Murphy
**VP:* Fred Prifty
VP: Frederick S Prifty
VP: James Robichaud
VP: Eric-Jan Schmidt
VP: Tim Wegner

D-U-N-S 07-954-9010
STRAUB CLINIC & HOSPITAL
(*Suby of* HAWAII PACIFIC HEALTH) ★
888 S King St, Honolulu, HI 96813-3097
Tel (808) 522-4000 *Founded/Ownrshp* 2001
Sales 413.7MM *EMP* 2,000
SIC 8011 8062

D-U-N-S 02-884-0775 IMP
STRAUB DISTRIBUTING CO LTD
4633 E La Palma Ave, Anaheim, CA 92807-1909
Tel (714) 779-4000 *Founded/Ownrshp* 1948
Sales 142.2MM[E] *EMP* 280
SIC 5181 Beer & other fermented malt liquors
Genl Pt: Michael L Cooper
Pt: Robert K Adams
Pt: Don Beightol
VP: John Durazo
VP: Rickey Kim
Manager: Terrie Trimmer
Manager: Mike Phillips

D-U-N-S 05-657-4890
STRAUB INTERNATIONAL INC (KS)
ROTH EQUIPMENT
214 Sw 40 Ave, Great Bend, KS 67530-9354
Tel (620) 792-5256 *Founded/Ownrshp* 1971, 1972
Sales 93.0MM *EMP* 145
Accts Adams Brown Beran & Ball Chtd
SIC 5083 5531 Agricultural machinery & equipment; Truck equipment & parts
CEO: Larry Straub
**Pr:* Ronald Straub
**CFO:* Kathy Straub
VP: Randy Veatch
Off Mgr: Jewel Davis
Store Mgr: Marlin Bartel
Sales Exec: Doug Barrett

D-U-N-S 60-768-9643
STRAUMANN USA LLC
(*Suby of* STRAUMANN HOLDING AG)
60 Minuteman Rd, Andover, MA 01810-1008
Tel (978) 747-2500 *Founded/Ownrshp* 1989
Sales 125.5MM[E] *EMP* 200
SIC 5047 Dental equipment & supplies
Ex VP: Andy Molnar
**Pr:* Jim Frontero
Sr VP: Gerhard Bauer
VP: Douglas Fogg
Exec: George Koskinas
Exec: Dionne Schneider
**Prin:* Thomas Dressendrfer
**Prin:* Andreas L Meier
**Prin:* Beat Spalinger
Genl Mgr: Angela Young
Dir IT: Peter Muszka

STRAUSS DISCOUNT AUTO
See R & S PARTS AND SERVICE INC

D-U-N-S 01-355-2229
STRAUSS PAPER CO INC
10 Slater St, Port Chester, NY 10573-4997
Tel (914) 937-0004 *Founded/Ownrshp* 1960
Sales 90.1MM[E] *EMP* 99
Accts O Connor Davies Munns & Dobbin
SIC 5113 Industrial & personal service paper
Dept Mgr: Mike Csanko
Sales Exec: Robert Tamilio
Sls Dir: Patrick Moody
Sales Asso: Angelo Coviello
Sales Asso: Shirley Vivar

D-U-N-S 18-115-3347
STRAW HAT COOPERATIVE CORP
STRAW HAT PIZZA
18 Crow Canyon Ct Ste 150, San Ramon, CA 94583-1740
Tel (925) 837-3400 *Founded/Ownrshp* 1987
Sales 19.1MM[E] *EMP* 1,000
SIC 5812 Pizzeria, chain
Pr: Joshua Richman

STRAW HAT PIZZA
See STRAW HAT COOPERATIVE CORP

D-U-N-S 01-398-5580
▲ STRAYER EDUCATION INC (MD)
2303 Dulles Station Blvd, Herndon, VA 20171-6353
Tel (703) 561-1600 *Founded/Ownrshp* 1892
Sales 434.4MM *EMP* 1,401[E]
Tkr Sym STRA *Exch* NGS
SIC 8221 Colleges universities & professional schools; College, except junior
CEO: Karl McDonnell
**Ch Bd:* Robert S Silberman
Pr: Brian W Jones
COO: Rosemary J Rose
CFO: Daniel W Jackson
Sr VP: Kelly J Bozarth
Opers Mgr: Randi S Reich
Board of Directors: Charlotte F Beason, William E Brock, John T Casteen III, Robert R Grusky, Todd A Milano, G Thomas Waite III, J David Wargo

STRAYER UNIV - CNCNNATI CAMPUS
See STRAYER UNIVERSITY INC

D-U-N-S 96-443-1766
STRAYER UNIVERSITY INC
STRAYER UNIV - CNCNNATI CAMPUS
2303 Dulles Station Blvd # 100, Herndon, VA 20171-6354
Tel (703) 561-1710 *Founded/Ownrshp* 2008
Sales 446.0MM[E] *EMP* 20[E]
SIC 8221

STREAM ENERGY
See STREAM GAS & ELECTRIC LTD

D-U-N-S 15-900-8395
STREAM GAS & ELECTRIC LTD
STREAM ENERGY
1950 N Stemmons Fwy F, Dallas, TX 75207-3134
Tel (214) 800-4400 *Founded/Ownrshp* 2004
Sales 406.0MM[E] *EMP* 499
SIC 4911 Electric services
CEO: Mr Mark Schiro
COO: John Littlejohn
Dir Soc: Kimberly Girard
Ex Dir: Ernest Franklin
CIO: Chris Hayden
QA Dir: Patricia Simpson
Dir IT: George Nemer
Software D: Catherine Kenny
Software D: Eric McCormick
Software D: Uma Murala
Ql Cn Mgr: Gaston Garza

D-U-N-S 80-862-8502
■ STREAM GLOBAL SERVICES INC
(*Suby of* SGS HOLDINGS, INC.)
3285 Northwood Cir # 120, Eagan, MN 55121-4206
Tel (651) 288-2979 *Founded/Ownrshp* 2014
Sales 702.9MM[E] *EMP* 37,000
SIC 7389 Telemarketing services
CEO: Kathryn V Marinello
COO: Brian Delaney
CFO: Michael Henricks
Ex VP: Robert Dechant
Ex VP: Gregory Hopkins
Sr VP: Laurie Dunn
Sr VP: Ruth Obrien
VP: Rick Pusag
Exec: Jessica Mollet
Prgrm Mgr: Arnel Galinato
Rgnl Mgr: Linda Killam
Board of Directors: Barry K Allen, Alfredo I Ayala, G Drew Conway, Matthew Cwiertnia, Paul G Joubert, David B Kaplan, Peter D Maquera, R Davis Noell, Nathan Walton

D-U-N-S 88-321-9149
■ STREAM INTERNATIONAL INC
(*Suby of* STREAM GLOBAL SERVICES INC) ★
3010 Waterview Pkwy, Richardson, TX 75080-1400
Tel (469) 624-5000 *Founded/Ownrshp* 1982
Sales 342.0MM[E] *EMP* 14,000[E]
SIC 8744 Facilities support services
Pr: Toni Portman
**Pr:* Katryn V Marinello
CFO: Tom Andrews
**CFO:* Tom Andrus
**CFO:* Michael Henricks
**Treas:* Russell Birk
**Treas:* Leo Vannoni
Sr VP: Laurie Dunn
**VP:* Gregory G Hopkins
VP: Jose Miranda
VP: Julie M Schoenfeld
VP: Bawa J Singh

D-U-N-S 07-146-3046 IMP/EXP
STREAMLIGHT INC
30 Eagleville Rd Ste 1, Eagleville, PA 19403-1422
Tel (610) 631-0600 *Founded/Ownrshp* 1973
Sales 101.1MM *EMP* 270
SIC 3648 Flashlights
Pr: Raymond Sharrah
COO: Kevin Burger
**CFO:* George C Collier III
CFO: George Collier
Genl Mgr: Courtney Phillips
Plnt Mgr: Brian Troxel
S&M/VP: Brian Correia
Mktg Dir: Mary Giangiulio
Mktg Dir: Loring Grove
Sls Dir: Eric Pike
Manager: Brian Osborn

D-U-N-S 60-977-9947 EXP
■ STREATER LLC
STREATER STORE FIXTURES
(*Suby of* THORCO INDUSTRIES) ★
411 S 1st Ave, Albert Lea, MN 56007-1779
Tel (800) 527-4197 *Founded/Ownrshp* 2000
Sales 172.7MM[E] *EMP* 700
SIC 2542 2541 Fixtures, store: except wood; Fixtures: display, office or store: except wood; Store fixtures, wood; Display fixtures, wood

STREATER STORE FIXTURES
See STREATER LLC

STREET & SMITH SPORTS GROUP
See AMERICAN CITY BUSINESS JOURNALS INC

STREETSBORO OPERATIONS
See FACIL NORTH AMERICA INC

STREICHER MOBILE FUELING
See SMF ENERGY CORP

D-U-N-S 19-607-2367 EXP
STREMICKS HERITAGE FOODS LLC
4002 Westminster Ave, Santa Ana, CA 92703-1310
Tel (714) 775-5000 *Founded/Ownrshp* 1990
Sales 502.6MM[E] *EMP* 430
SIC 2026 Fluid milk; Cream, sour; Cottage cheese; Yogurt
CFO: Mike Malone
VP: Rob Ball
VP: Jin Jo
VP: Jason Jones
VP: Ken Miller
VP: Jerry Moran
VP: Kerry Roberts
CTO: Tonya Rosenbloom
CTO: Lou Stremick
Opers Mgr: Mallissa Pikul
Plnt Mgr: Andy Holm

D-U-N-S 10-690-0157
STRESS CARE/BRIDGES
GRANDVIEW HOSPITAL
405 W Grand Ave, Dayton, OH 45405-7538
Tel (937) 723-3200 *Founded/Ownrshp* 2000
Sales 324.4MM *EMP* 4
SIC 8069 Drug addiction rehabilitation hospital
Prin: Peggy Mann
Obsttrcn: Leslie Kern
Phys Thrpy: Donna Baker

D-U-N-S 87-890-2139
STRESS CON INDUSTRIES INC
50500 Design Ln, Shelby Township, MI 48315-3124
Tel (586) 731-1628 *Founded/Ownrshp* 1991
Sales 114.9MM[E] *EMP* 500
SIC 3272 Precast terrazo or concrete products
Pr: Dennis Declerk
Off Mgr: Dennis Declerke
Opers Mgr: Tom Grzeskowiak
Ql Cn Mgr: Brian Curtis

D-U-N-S 06-211-5050 IMP
STRESS ENGINEERING SERVICES INC
MOHR ENGINEERING DIVISION
13800 Westfair East Dr, Houston, TX 77041-1101
Tel (281) 955-2900 *Founded/Ownrshp* 1972
Sales 153.8MM[E] *EMP* 195
Accts Grant Thornton Llp Houston T
SIC 8711 Consulting engineer
Pr: Joe R Fowler
**Treas:* Helen Chan
**Sr VP:* W Thomas Asbill
**VP:* Clint Haynes
**VP:* J Randy Long
**VP:* John R Long
VP: Randy Long
**VP:* Charles A Miller
**VP:* Jack E Miller
**VP:* Jack Miller
**VP:* Ronald D Young
Dir Lab: Lane Wilson
Board of Directors: Claudio Allevato, Kenneth Bhalla, Stewart A Fox, Christopher Matice

D-U-N-S 00-820-2285
STRIBLING EQUIPMENT LLC
JOHN DEERE AUTHORIZED DEALER
(*Suby of* G S & L ENTERPRISES INC) ★
408 Highway 49 S, Richland, MS 39218-8403
Tel (601) 939-1000 *Founded/Ownrshp* 1983
Sales 105.6MM[E] *EMP* 350
SIC 5082 7353 General construction machinery & equipment; Heavy construction equipment rental
Pr: Gerald Swanson
**CEO:* Selby A Ireland
Treas: William B Bearth III

D-U-N-S 00-249-3732 IMP
STRICK CORP
225 Lincoln Hwy, Fairless Hills, PA 19030-1103
Tel (215) 949-3600 *Founded/Ownrshp* 1936
Sales 84.4MM[E] *EMP* 380
SIC 3715 2426 3713 3537 Truck trailers; Trailer bodies; Truck trailer chassis; Demountable cargo containers; Flooring, hardwood; Truck & bus bodies; Industrial trucks & tractors
Ch Bd: Frank Katz
**CFO:* John Badey
Top Exec: Mary B Caldwell
**VP:* Joseph Puchino
**VP:* George Schmidt
IT Man: Kristen Gemberling
VP Opers: Steve Burns

STRIDE RITE BOOTERY
See STRIDE RITE CHILDRENS GROUP LLC

D-U-N-S 05-598-7135 IMP
■ STRIDE RITE CHILDRENS GROUP LLC
STRIDE RITE BOOTERY
(*Suby of* STRIDE RITE CORP) ★
500 Totten Pond Rd Ste 1, Waltham, MA 02451-1924
Tel (617) 824-6000 *Founded/Ownrshp* 2009
Sales 126.0MM[E] *EMP* 800
SIC 5139 5661 Footwear; Children's shoes
VP: John J Nannicelli
**CFO:* Frank Caruso
Treas: Gordon W Johnson Jr
Sr VP: Matt Feiner
CIO: Sahal Laher

D-U-N-S 00-101-7078 IMP/EXP
■ STRIDE RITE CORP (MA)
(*Suby of* WOLVERINE WORLD WIDE INC) ★
500 Totten Pond Rd Ste 1, Waltham, MA 02451-1924
Tel (617) 824-6000 *Founded/Ownrshp* 1919, 2013
Sales 931.0MM[E] *EMP* 3,100
SIC 5139 5661 3149 Footwear, athletic; Shoes; Shoe stores; Children's shoes; Footwear, athletic; Children's footwear, except athletic
Pr: Blake W Krueger
Pr: Rick Blackshaw
**Pr:* Gregg Ribatt
**CFO:* Frank A Caruso
**Sr VP:* Yusef Akyuz
Sr VP: Tom Morgan
VP: Lee Baxter
VP: Christopher Langway
VP Mktg: Kiran Smith
Board of Directors: Daniel Boggan, Judith Hofer, John McGovern, D Olivet, Matthew Rubel, Robert Wheeler

D-U-N-S 14-599-6430
STRIKE LLC
PICKETT SYSTEMS
1800 Hughes Landing Blvd # 500, The Woodlands, TX 77380-1684
Tel (713) 389-2400 *Founded/Ownrshp* 2003
Sales 745.3MM *EMP* 1,000
Accts Uhy Llp Cpas Houston Tx
SIC 1623 Oil & gas line & compressor station construction
VP: Cole Pate
Genl Mgr: Charlie Brown

D-U-N-S 80-806-8295
■ STRIPES LLC
(*Suby of* SUSSER HOLDINGS LLC) ★
4433 Baldwin Blvd 9911, Corpus Christi, TX 78408-2707
Tel (361) 884-2463 *Founded/Ownrshp* 2007
Sales 49.6MM[E] *EMP* 2,030[E]
SIC 5812 Eating places
Pr: Steven C Desutter

COO: Rocky Dewbre
CFO: Mary Sullivan

D-U-N-S 88-323-8438
■ **STRIPES LLC**
CIRCLE K
(Suby of SUSSER HOLDINGS CORP) ★
4525 Ayers St, Corpus Christi, TX 78415-1401
Tel (361) 225-0129 Founded/Ownrshp 1995
Sales 121.4MM^E EMP 750
SIC 5411 Convenience stores, chain
CEO: Sam L Susser
VP: Cal McIntosh
VP: Richard Sebastian

D-U-N-S 83-234-3722
STRIVECTIN OPERATING CO INC
(Suby of STRIVECTIN HOLDINGS, LLC)
601 W 26th St Rm 1505, New York, NY 10001-1138
Tel (212) 220-3400 Founded/Ownrshp 2009
Sales 100.0MM EMP 80
SIC 8743 Sales promotion
COO: Cori Aleardi
*CEO: Joan Malloy
*CFO: Brad Schnieider
Chf Mktg O: Amanda Baldwin
VP: Robert Yates
Rgnl Mgr: Kayla Hester

D-U-N-S 00-303-6548
STROEHMANN BAKERIES LC
255 Business Center Dr # 200, Horsham, PA 19044-3424
Tel (215) 672-8010 Founded/Ownrshp 1924
Sales 124.8MM^E EMP 3,500^E
SIC 2051 5461

D-U-N-S 12-070-3459 IMP
STRONGHAVEN INC
ADVANCE DESIGN & PACKAGING
(Suby of HOOD PACKAGING CORP) ★
2727 Paces Ferry Rd Se 1-1850, Atlanta, GA 30339-6173
Tel (678) 235-2713 Founded/Ownrshp 2014
Sales 225.5MM^E EMP 450
SIC 2653 Boxes, corrugated: made from purchased materials
Pr: Douglas A Johnston
*CFO: Lawrence Samples
VP: Pete Mullen
Genl Mgr: Karen Kirkman
Sls Dir: Steve Duncan

D-U-N-S 18-067-2420
STRONGHOLD ENGINEERING INC
2000 Market St, Riverside, CA 92501-1769
Tel (951) 684-9303 Founded/Ownrshp 1991
Sales 120.3MM^E EMP 250
Accts Gallina Llp Sacramento Calif
SIC 1611 General contractor, highway & street construction
Pr: Beverly A Bailey
*Mng Pt: Scott Bailey
CFO: Cheryl Parris
Off Mgr: Ashley Powell
Genl Couns: Dan Rasmussen

D-U-N-S 05-865-9210 IMP/EXP
STRONGWELL CORP
400 Commonwealth Ave, Bristol, VA 24201-3800
Tel (276) 645-8000 Founded/Ownrshp 1993
Sales 107.0MM^E EMP 500
SIC 3089 Awnings, fiberglass & plastic combination
CEO: G David Oakley Jr
*COO: A Keith Liskey
*Treas: John E Delaney Jr
Bd of Dir: Ann Tickle
Mng Dir: Spike Tickle
QA Dir: Gloria I Wadle
Opers Mgr: Dennis Martin
Mktg Mgr: Barry Myers
Manager: Bill Faust
Sls Mgr: Tom Carlson
Sls Mgr: Gene Smith

D-U-N-S 04-543-3455
STROOCK & STROOCK & LAVAN LLP
180 Maiden Ln Fl 17, New York, NY 10038-4982
Tel (212) 806-5400 Founded/Ownrshp 1876
Sales 98.0MM^E EMP 520^E
SIC 8111

STROUHAL TIRE CENTER
See STROUHAL TIRE RECAPPING PLANT LTD

D-U-N-S 04-112-6681
STROUHAL TIRE RECAPPING PLANT LTD
STROUHAL TIRE CENTER
8206 Hwy 59, Hungerford, TX 77448
Tel (979) 532-1579 Founded/Ownrshp 1967
Sales 192.9MM^E EMP 160
SIC 5014 Tire & tube repair materials
CEO: Don Strouhal
*Pr: Nancy Macha
*Treas: Ann Strouhal
*VP: Don Strouhal Jr

D-U-N-S 01-761-5464
STROZ FRIEDBERG LLC
32 Avenue Of The Americas # 1, New York, NY 10013-2473
Tel (212) 981-6540 Founded/Ownrshp 2000
Sales 130.8MM^E EMP 308
SIC 7379 Computer related consulting services
CEO: Michael Patsalos-Fox
Ofcr: David Crampton
VP: Christine Gabitass
VP: Nicole Acton Jones
VP: Steve Kim
VP: Melissa Kriz
VP: Matt Levy
VP: Michael Panico
VP: Jeffrey Rabkin
VP: Keith Slotter
VP: Rachel Womack

STRS OHIO
See STATE TEACHERS RETIREMENT SYSTEM OF OHIO

D-U-N-S 08-234-7287 IMP/EXP
STRUCTURAL GROUP INC
10150 Old Columbia Rd, Columbia, MD 21046-1274
Tel (410) 850-7000 Founded/Ownrshp 1976
Sales 352.0MM^E EMP 1,690
SIC 1771 Concrete repair
CEO: Peter Emmons
Treas: Dan Fangio
Sr VP: Scott Greenhaus
Prgrm Mgr: Patrick McGuire
Sftwr Eng: Manuel Chavez
Sftwr Eng: Alain Licona
Mfg Mgr: Shane Taylor

D-U-N-S 10-210-0518
STRUCTURAL INTEGRITY ASSOCIATES INC
5215 Hellyer Ave Ste 210, San Jose, CA 95138-1079
Tel (408) 978-8200 Founded/Ownrshp 2002
Sales 90.7MM^E EMP 260
SIC 8711 Consulting engineer
CEO: Laney H Bisbee
Ch: Ricard A Mattson
Treas: David Stager
VP: Nathaniel G Cofie
VP: Matthew C Dowling
VP: Christine King
VP: Ian Perrin
IT Man: Cindy Metzger
Netwrk Mgr: Todd Zimmerman

D-U-N-S 00-811-9414 IMP
■ **STRUCTURAL METALS INC** (TX)
CMC STEEL TEXAS
(Suby of COMMERCIAL METALS CO) ★
1 Steel Mill Dr, Seguin, TX 78155-7510
Tel (830) 372-8200 Founded/Ownrshp 2014
Sales 228.8MM^E EMP 885
SIC 3312 3441 3462 Blast furnaces & steel mills; Bars & bar shapes, steel, hot-rolled; Structural shapes & pilings, steel; Forgings, iron & steel; Fabricated structural metal; Iron & steel forgings
CEO: Joseph Alvarado
Pr: Tracy Porter
Treas: Carey Dubois
VP: Mike Holcomb
VP: Russell Rinn
Brnch Mgr: Martin Swayze
Plnt Mgr: Phillip Feidenberger
VP Sls: Hugh Ghormley

D-U-N-S 60-198-2775 IMP
STRUCTURAL PRESERVATION SYSTEMS LLC
(Suby of STRUCTURAL GROUP INC) ★
10150 Old Columbia Rd, Columbia, MD 21046-1274
Tel (410) 850-7000 Founded/Ownrshp 2004
Sales 166.3MM EMP 897
Accts Mcgladrey Llp Baltimore Mar
SIC 1771 Concrete repair
Snr PM: Vivika Ross

D-U-N-S 61-178-6328
STRUCTURAL STEEL HOLDING INC
6210 Saint Louis St, Meridian, MS 39307-7209
Tel (601) 483-5381 Founded/Ownrshp 1988
Sales 84.0MM^E EMP 300
SIC 3441 3443 4213 Fabricated structural metal; Fabricated plate work (boiler shop); Trucking, except local
Pr: Tommy E Dulaney
*Sec: Donna Reid
*Ex VP: James T Dean Jr
Sls Mgr: Randy Blass

D-U-N-S 04-111-7412 IMP
STRUCTURAL TECHNOLOGIES LLC
V S L
(Suby of STRUCTURAL GROUP INC) ★
10150 Old Columbia Rd, Columbia, MD 21046-1274
Tel (410) 850-7000 Founded/Ownrshp 1998
Sales 89.3MM^E EMP 179
SIC 1622 8711 Bridge construction; Construction & civil engineering
Brnch Mgr: Yosbany Ballate
Div Mgr: Gregory Hunsicker
Dir IT: Jason Kasch
Mfg Mgr: Shane Taylor

D-U-N-S 05-668-8781 IMP
STRUCTURE TONE INC
330 W 34th St Fl 11, New York, NY 10001-2406
Tel (212) 481-6100 Founded/Ownrshp 1971
Sales 931.6MM^E EMP 1,796
Accts Grassi & Co Cpas Pc New Yor
SIC 8741 Administrative management; Circuit management for motion picture theaters; Construction management
Ch Bd: James K Donaghy
Pr: Anthony M Carvette
CEO: Robert W Mullen
CFO: Brett Phillips
V Ch Bd: Brian M Donaghy
Ex VP: Marc Leed
VP: Rebecca Leonardis
VP: Stephen Neeson
Dir Bus: John Clark
Prin: Richard Ryan
Off Mgr: Sheri Pelletier

D-U-N-S 80-134-1488
STRUCTURED COMMUNICATION SYSTEMS INC
12901 Se 97th Ave Ste 400, Clackamas, OR 97015-7907
Tel (503) 513-9979 Founded/Ownrshp 1995
Sales 86.7MM EMP 122
SIC 7373 5045 Computer systems analysis & design; Systems integration services; Computers, peripherals & software
Pr: Ronald L Fowler
VP: Andrew G Edgar
VP: Chris Tenes
Snr Ntwrk: Brian Patten
Netwrk Eng: Ed Brimmer
Netwrk Eng: Calvin Kirkendall
Sales Exec: Brian Oleary

Sls Mgr: Bill Ketrenos
Sales Asso: Brian Fowler

D-U-N-S 10-827-7633 EXP
STRUEVER BROS ECCLES & ROUSE INC
2400 Boston St Ste 404, Baltimore, MD 21224-4787
Tel (443) 573-4000 Founded/Ownrshp 1983
Sales 91.0MM^E EMP 300
SIC 1542 1522 Commercial & office building contractors; Residential construction
Pr: Carl W Struever
*CFO: John R Kovax
*Treas: Charles Eccles

D-U-N-S 00-537-3089
▲ **STRYKER CORP** (MI)
2825 Airview Blvd, Portage, MI 49002-1802
Tel (269) 385-2600 Founded/Ownrshp 1941
Sales 9.9MMM EMP 29,500
Tkr Sym SYK Exch NYS
SIC 3841 3842 2599 Surgical instruments & apparatus; Saws, surgical; Bone drills; Suction therapy apparatus; Implants, surgical; Hospital beds
Ch Bd: Kevin A Lobo
Pr: Lonny J Carpenter
Pr: Mark A Philip
Pr: Timothy J Scannell
CFO: Glenn Boehnlein
*CFO: William R Jellison
VP: Yin C Becker
*VP: William E Berry Jr
VP: William Berry
VP: Tina Fleming
VP: Art Hartman
VP: Matt Moreau
VP: Charlie O'Brien
VP: Thomas Pontius
VP: Alisandra Rizzolo
VP: Bernd Robioneck
*VP: Bijoy S N Sagar
VP: Bijoy Sagar
VP: Melinda Slaughter
VP: Meg Smith
VP: Elizabeth A Staub

STRYKER ORTHOPAEDICS
See HOWMEDICA OSTEONICS CORP

D-U-N-S 36-380-7249 IMP
■ **STRYKER PUERTO RICO LIMITED**
(Suby of STRYKER CORP) ★
Hwy 3 Km 131 2 Las Guasim, Arroyo, PR 00714
Tel (787) 839-7688 Founded/Ownrshp 1988
Sales 185.3MM^E EMP 850
SIC 3841 Surgical & medical instruments
Pr: Ronald A Elenbaas
*Treas: Chris Hommerich
*VP: Pito Garcia
Sls Mgr: Emily Folan
Board of Directors: Carlos Rivera

D-U-N-S 02-019-8912 IMP
■ **STRYKER SUSTAINABILITY SOLUTIONS INC**
(Suby of STRYKER CORP) ★
1810 W Drake Dr Ste 101, Tempe, AZ 85283-4327
Tel (888) 888-3433 Founded/Ownrshp 2009
Sales 264.0MM^E EMP 900^E
SIC 5084 5047 7699 3842 3841 Recycling machinery & equipment; Medical & hospital equipment; Surgical instrument repair; Surgical appliances & supplies; Surgical & medical instruments
Pr: Brian White
*COO: Rick Ferreira
*CFO: Tim Einwechter
VP: Chris Dible
VP: Tina Fleming
VP: Eric Varty
Dist Mgr: Marcella McNamee
Dist Mgr: Joseph Pascuzzi
Dist Mgr: Jeff Shupe
QA Dir: Chris Sugg
Dir IT: Kara Reyes

STS
See CAMEO GLOBAL INC

D-U-N-S 09-369-2296 IMP
STS OPERATING INC
SUNSOURCE
2301 W Windsor Ct, Addison, IL 60101-1460
Tel (630) 317-2700 Founded/Ownrshp 2011
Sales 1.1MMM^E EMP 1,000
SIC 5084 Industrial machinery & equipment
Pr: Justin Jacobi
*CFO: Chuck Freeman
Sr Cor Off: Charles Freman
Ex VP: Philip Baker
Brnch Mgr: Bill Meyers
Dist Mgr: Greg Obenchain
Genl Mgr: Patti Gallardo
Sls Mgr: Tim Crouch
Sls Mgr: Maria Gajda
Sls Mgr: Brent Meyer
Sls Mgr: Burt Smith

STS TIRE & AUTO SERVICE CTRS
See SOMERSET TIRE SERVICE INC

STSOLUTIONS
See SALEM TOOLS INC

STUART ANDERSON'S BLACK ANGUS
See AMERICAN RESTAURANT GROUP INC

D-U-N-S 04-252-4759 EXP
STUART BUILDING PRODUCTS LLC
1341 Nw 15th St, Pompano Beach, FL 33069-1728
Tel (954) 971-7264 Founded/Ownrshp 2011
Sales 117.3MM^E EMP 43^E
SIC 5032 Concrete building products

D-U-N-S 00-696-4324 IMP
STUART C IRBY CO (MS)
IRBY ELECTRICAL DISTRIBUTORS
(Suby of SONEPAR USA) ★
815 Irby Dr, Jackson, MS 39201-5806
Tel (601) 960-7346 Founded/Ownrshp 1926, 2005
Sales 804.6MM^E EMP 900

SIC 5063 Electrical apparatus & equipment; Electrical fittings & construction materials; Transformers & transmission equipment; Lighting fixtures
Pr: Michael Wigton
*CFO: John Honigfort
*Treas: Andy Waring
Ex VP: Bob Croft
*Prin: David Gabriel
Genl Mgr: Tracy Johnson
Info Man: John Mitchell
VP Opers: Mike Richardson
VP Opers: Brad Slocum
Opers Mgr: Bary Burns
Opers Mgr: Josh Law
Board of Directors: Rich Antonaros, John Honigfort, Mike Leech, Joe Lenoir, Jack May, Brad Slocum

D-U-N-S 94-727-5251 IMP
STUART WEITZMAN INC
STUART WEITZMAN SHOE STORE
50 W 57th St Fl 10, New York, NY 10019-3914
Tel (212) 582-9500 Founded/Ownrshp 1992
Sales 84.8MM^E EMP 180^E
SIC 5661 Footwear, athletic
Pr: Stuart Weitzman
VP: Susan McDaniel

D-U-N-S 07-937-4193
STUART WEITZMAN RETAIL STORES LLC
(Suby of STUART WEITZMAN SHOE STORE) ★
625 Madison Ave Frnt 3, New York, NY 10022-1801
Tel (212) 582-6388 Founded/Ownrshp 2005
Sales 84.8MM EMP 180
SIC 7389 3171 5999 Shoe designers; Women's handbags & purses; Alarm & safety equipment stores
CEO: Wayne Kulkin

STUART WEITZMAN SHOE STORE
See STUART WEITZMAN INC

D-U-N-S 85-910-8982
■ **STUBHUB INC**
STUBHUB.COM
(Suby of EBAY INC) ★
199 Fremont St Fl 4, San Francisco, CA 94105-6634
Tel (415) 222-8400 Founded/Ownrshp 2000
Sales 87.4MM^E EMP 350^E
SIC 7374 7999 7922 Data processing & preparation; Ticket sales office for sporting events, contract; Ticket agency, theatrical
Pr: Chris Tsakalakis
*COO: Noah Goldberg
*CFO: Ajay Gopal
*Chf Mktg O: Jennifer Betka
*VP: Raji Arasu
Off Admin: Marlain Harrison
Snr Ntwrk: Mark Stradling
CTO: Srini Venakatesan
QC Dir: Satish Nair
Mktg Mgr: Bridget Burton
Mktg Mgr: Geoff Lester
Board of Directors: Frank Biondi

STUBHUB.COM
See STUBHUB INC

D-U-N-S 09-709-5079
STUDENT LOAN FINANCE CORP
124 S 1st St, Aberdeen, SD 57401-4107
Tel (605) 622-4400 Founded/Ownrshp 1978
Sales NA EMP 180
SIC 6141 Personal credit institutions
Pr: Norgrin Sanderson
*Ch Bd: Larry O'Toole
COO: Rod Dobberpuhl
*CFO: Larry Buckmeier
VP: Deb Dahme
VP: John Heier
VP: Susie Miller
VP: Reid Moehn
VP Opers: Spencer Aberle

D-U-N-S 00-960-6281
STUDENT TRANSPORTATION OF AMERICA INC
3349 Hwy 138, Wall Township, NJ 07719-9671
Tel (732) 280-4200 Founded/Ownrshp 1997
Sales 2.1MMM^E EMP 14,006
SIC 4151 School buses
CEO: Denis Gallagher
*COO: Patrick Vaughan
COO: Patrick R Vaughan
*CFO: Patrick J Walker
VP: John Dimaiolo
VP: Gregg Peterson
Exec: Regina Wilson
Comm Dir: Doug Coupe
*CTO: Keith Engelbert
CTO: Sam Wells
IT Man: John Sorrentino
Board of Directors: Barbara Basney

D-U-N-S 83-210-5865
STUDIO 3 PARTNERS LLC
EPIX
1515 Broadway Rm 43, New York, NY 10036-8901
Tel (212) 846-4004 Founded/Ownrshp 2008
Sales 339.6MM EMP 2
Accts Pricewaterhousecoopers Llp N
SIC 4841 Cable & other pay television services
CEO: Mark Greenberg
*CFO: Keith Eckert
Ex VP: Jocelyn Diaz
VP: Shane Brennan
VP: Marc Rosenberg
VP: Ben Tappan
Creative D: Jason Bylan
Prd Mgr: Nina Burnett
Assoc Ed: Jasmine Colon

STUDIO PRINT GROUP
See OFFSET PAPERBACK MFRS INC

D-U-N-S 05-064-7361 IMP/EXP
STULLER INC (LA)
302 Rue Louis Xiv, Lafayette, LA 70508-5735
Tel (337) 262-7700 Founded/Ownrshp 1970
Sales 580.1MM^E EMP 1,600

SIC 5094 3911 Jewelry & precious stones; Jewel settings & mountings, precious metal
CEO: Matthew G Stuller
**Pr:* George Daniel Clark
COO: Yvonne Dauphine
**CFO:* Linus J Cortez III
**VP:* Jennifer East
Ex Dir: Ashley Brown
Ex Dir: Jim Hebert
Ex Dir: Belit Myers
Ex Dir: Katie Smith
DP Dir: Scott Melkild
QA Dir: Julie Trahan

D-U-N-S 02-028-4514 IMP/EXP
STULZ AIR TECHNOLOGY SYSTEM INC
STULZ-ATS
(*Suby of* STULZ-ATS) ★
1572 Tilco Dr, Frederick, MD 21704-6659
Tel (301) 620-2033 *Founded/Ownrshp* 2001
Sales 118.3MM^E *EMP* 400
SIC 3585 Refrigeration & heating equipment
Pr: Joerg Desler
**CFO:* Thorsten Weiss
**VP:* Brian Hatmaker
VP: Kim Hendrickson
VP: Albert Stulz
Exec: Kevin Cole
IT Man: Betty Kunz
IT Man: Steve Sites
Opers Mgr: Pam Northup
S&M/VP: Matt Miller
Mktg Mgr: Anne Shubert

D-U-N-S 07-876-0761 IMP/EXP
STULZ INVESTMENT CORP OF AMERICA
STULZ-ATS
(*Suby of* STULZ HOLDING GMBH)
1572 Tilco Dr, Frederick, MD 21704-6659
Tel (301) 620-2033 *Founded/Ownrshp* 2006
Sales 106.4MM^E *EMP* 792
SIC 3822 Auto controls regulating residntl & coml environmt & applncs
Pr: Jurgen Stulz
**Treas:* Holger Ramcke
**VP:* Albert Stulz
VP Prd: Joerg Desler

STULZ-ATS
See STULZ AIR TECHNOLOGY SYSTEM INC

STULZ-ATS
See STULZ INVESTMENT CORP OF AMERICA

D-U-N-S 04-105-0022 IMP
STUMP PRINTING CO INC
STUMP'S
101 Carroll Rd, South Whitley, IN 46787-1139
Tel (260) 723-5171 *Founded/Ownrshp* 1991
Sales 104.9MM^E *EMP* 185
SIC 5199 2679 5961 2759 Novelties, paper; Novelties, paper: made from purchased material; Catalog sales; Commercial printing
CEO: N Shepard Moyle
**CFO:* Jeanice Croy
**Ex VP:* Wendy Moyle
VP: Katie Burns
VP: Ervin Glass
Sales Exec: Keith Bansemer

STUMP'S
See STUMP PRINTING CO INC

STUPP BRIDGE COMPANY
See STUPP BROS INC

D-U-N-S 00-629-9853
STUPP BROS INC (MO)
STUPP BRIDGE COMPANY
3800 Weber Rd, Saint Louis, MO 63125-1160
Tel (314) 638-5000 *Founded/Ownrshp* 1856
Sales 413.3MM^E *EMP* 931
Accts Uhy Llp St Louis Missouri
SIC 3441 3317 6022 Fabricated structural metal; Steel pipe & tubes; State commercial banks
Pr: John P Stupp Jr
**Pr:* Ed Scram
**CFO:* Samuel W Duggan II
**Ex VP:* R Philip Stupp Jr
**Sr VP:* John Clark
VP: Richard Inserra
VP: E P Stupp
**VP:* Robert Turner
Board of Directors: Ronald T Barnes, Samuel W Duggan II, Kenneth J Kubacki, Edward L Scram, John P Stupp Jr, R Philip Stupp Jr, Thomas L Turner

D-U-N-S 07-570-5475
STURDY MEMORIAL HOSPITAL INC (MA)
211 Park St, Attleboro, MA 02703-3137
Tel (508) 222-5200 *Founded/Ownrshp* 1910, 1982
Sales 163.9MM *EMP* 1,300
Accts Grant Thornton Llp Westboroug
SIC 8062 8011 General medical & surgical hospitals; Medical centers
Pr: Bruce Auerbach MD
**Treas:* Joseph F X Casey

D-U-N-S 02-906-8707
STURDY OIL CO
MORENO PETROLEUM
1511 Abbott St, Salinas, CA 93901-4599
Tel (831) 422-8801 *Founded/Ownrshp* 1930
Sales 114.1MM *EMP* 85
SIC 5172 5541 Gasoline; Fuel oil; Filling stations, gasoline
CEO: Jonathon P Fanoe
**CFO:* Neil Fanoe Jr
**Sec:* Keith Schwehr

STURGEON & SON
See STURGEON SERVICES INTERNATIONAL INC

D-U-N-S 00-477-6787
■ **STURGEON ELECTRIC CO INC**
(*Suby of* MYR GROUP INC) ★
12150 E 112th Ave, Henderson, CO 80640-9116
Tel (303) 227-6990 *Founded/Ownrshp* 1999
Sales 343.2MM^E *EMP* 1,250
SIC 1731 1623 General electrical contractor; Electric power line construction
Pr: William A Koertner
**Pr:* Richard S Swartz Jr
**COO:* Rick S Swartz
Treas: Norberto Cruz
Treas: Gregory Wolf
**Sr VP:* Tod Cooper
**Sr VP:* William H Green
Sr VP: Mark Romano
**VP:* Gerald B Engen
VP: John Fluss
VP: Michael Sievert

D-U-N-S 80-419-5142
STURGEON SERVICES INTERNATIONAL INC
STURGEON & SON
3511 Gilmore Ave, Bakersfield, CA 93308-6205
Tel (661) 322-4408 *Founded/Ownrshp* 1972
Sales 189.9MM^E *EMP* 450
SIC 6719 Personal holding companies, except banks
Pr: Paul H Sturgeon
**Ch Bd:* Oliver Sturgeon
COO: Christopher Rodman
**CFO:* Joe D'Angelo
**VP:* Gina Blankenship
Genl Mgr: John Powell

D-U-N-S 00-175-0975
STURGIS MOLDED PRODUCTS CO
SMP
70343 Clark Rd, Sturgis, MI 49091-9755
Tel (269) 651-9381 *Founded/Ownrshp* 1966
Sales 84.3MM^E *EMP* 200
SIC 3089 3544 Injection molding of plastics; Special dies, tools, jigs & fixtures
Pr: Mark D Weishaar
**CFO:* Herbert A Keeler
Sr VP: Bud Clark
**VP:* Chris Emery
**VP:* Paul G Feaman
**VP:* Jason Harloff
**VP:* Kelly L Presta

D-U-N-S 02-487-6885
STURM FINANCIAL GROUP INC
3033 E 1st Ave Ste 300, Denver, CO 80206-5619
Tel (303) 394-5023 *Founded/Ownrshp* 1999
Sales 193.9MM^E *EMP* 135
SIC 6282 Investment advisory service
Pr: Donald Sturm
CFO: Susan Sturm
VP: Steve Griego
Dept Mgr: Grant Slovek

D-U-N-S 00-794-6478 IMP/EXP
■ **STURM FOODS INC** (WI)
(*Suby of* TREEHOUSE FOODS INC) ★
215 Center St, Manawa, WI 54949-9277
Tel (920) 596-2511 *Founded/Ownrshp* 1905, 2010
Sales 380.6MM^E *EMP* 700
SIC 5149

D-U-N-S 00-116-2569 IMP
▲ **STURM RUGER & CO INC**
1 Lacey Pl, Southport, CT 06890-1207
Tel (203) 259-7843 *Founded/Ownrshp* 1949
Sales 551.0MM *EMP* 1,920^E
Accts Rsm Us Llp Stamford Connecti
Tkr Sym RGR *Exch* NYS
SIC 3484 3324 Pistols or pistol parts, 30 mm. & below; Revolvers or revolver parts, 30 mm. & below; Rifles or rifle parts, 30 mm. & below; Shotguns or shotgun parts, 30 mm. & below; Commercial investment castings, ferrous
CEO: Michael O Fifer
V Ch: John A Cosentino Jr
**Pr:* Christopher J Killoy
CFO: Thomas A Dineen
VP: Mark T Lang
VP: Steve Maynard
VP: Kevin B Reid Sr
VP: Thomas P Sullivan
Ex Dir: Jeffrey Barger
Plnt Mgr: Richard David
Ql Cn Mgr: Trent Diebel
Board of Directors: John A Cosentino Jr, Sandra S Froman, C Michael Jacobi, Terrence O'connor, Ronald C Whitaker, Phillip C Widman

D-U-N-S 00-948-2530
STUSSER ELECTRIC CO
(*Suby of* C E D) ★
660 S Andover St, Seattle, WA 98108-5235
Tel (206) 623-1501 *Founded/Ownrshp* 1993
Sales 101.2MM^E *EMP* 150
SIC 5063 Electrical apparatus & equipment
Ch Bd: Keith W Colburn
**Pr:* Antonio Monis Jr
VP: Phil Davis
**VP:* Stanley S Graham
**VP:* Ronald D Heronemus
**VP:* Bernard E Lyons
**Prin:* Patrick Donahue
Genl Mgr: Stan Stoffel
Sls&Mrk Ex: John Lezon

STV ARCHITECTS DIV
See STV ARCHITECTS INC

D-U-N-S 00-250-4678
STV ARCHITECTS INC (PA)
STV ARCHITECTS DIV
(*Suby of* STV) ★
205 W Welsh Dr, Douglassville, PA 19518-8713
Tel (610) 385-8200 *Founded/Ownrshp* 1946, 1967
Sales 70.7MM^E *EMP* 1,200
SIC 8711 Consulting engineer
Pr: D M Servedio
COO: Matthew Smith
**CFO:* Peter Knipe
Sr VP: Milo E Riverso
VP: John A Agro
VP: Robert Darlington
VP: Sandra Gitlin
VP: Robert E Griffith
**VP:* M Haratunian
VP: Timothy Mason
VP: Donald J Mauer
Exec: John Agro
Exec: Terry Hall
Exec: Doreen Lutcavage

D-U-N-S 78-420-0201
STV CONSTRUCTION INC
(*Suby of* STV INC) ★
205 W Welsh Dr, Douglassville, PA 19518-8713
Tel (610) 385-8200 *Founded/Ownrshp* 2000
Sales 121.1MM *EMP* 278
SIC 8741 Construction management
Pr: Milo Riverso
**CFO:* Peter Knipe
**Ch:* Dominick M Servedio
**Sr VP:* Steve Pressler

D-U-N-S 04-452-0146
STV GROUP INC
STV
205 W Welsh Dr, Douglassville, PA 19518-8713
Tel (610) 385-8200 *Founded/Ownrshp* 1967
Sales 294.3MM^E *EMP* 1,700^E
SIC 8712 8711 Architectural services; Engineering services
Pr: Milo E Riverso
**Ch Bd:* Dominick M Servedio
V Ch: Ted Kleiner
COO: Maher Z Labib
**COO:* Michael Della Rocca
**CFO:* Thomas Butcher
CFO: Jon Pedersen
CFO: Whitney A Sanders
Ex VP: Majid Hedayati
Ex VP: Maher Labib
Ex VP: William Matts
**Ex VP:* Steve Pressler
Sr VP: John Agro
Sr VP: Thomas A Anderson
Sr VP: Wagih S Andraos
Sr VP: Martin F Boyle
Sr VP: Anthony J Corteal Jr
Sr VP: Anthony G Cracchiolo
Sr VP: Anthony Cracchiolo
Sr VP: Brian Flaherty
Sr VP: Margarita D Gagliardi
Board of Directors: Michael Garz

D-U-N-S 04-835-7735
STV INC
(*Suby of* STV) ★
225 Park Ave S Fl 5, New York, NY 10003-1604
Tel (212) 529-2722 *Founded/Ownrshp* 1932
Sales 165.1MM^E *EMP* 1,533^E
SIC 8711 8712 8741 Engineering services; Architectural engineering; Architectural engineering; Construction management
CEO: Milo E Riverso
COO: Michael S Della Rocca
**CFO:* Thomas W Butcher
Ofcr: Brittany Griffis
**Ex VP:* William F Matts
Ex VP: Jon Miller
Ex VP: Jonathan Miller
**Ex VP:* Steve J Pressler
Sr VP: Robert Davidson
**Sr VP:* Gary Doven
**Sr VP:* Michael D Garz
Sr VP: David Ziskind
VP: Charles B Belser
VP: Ken Bossung
VP: Pe M Hedayati
VP: Nadine Roper
**VP:* Linda Rosenberg
VP: Will I Flores
VP: Samuel S Yu
Exec: Gus Maimis
Dir Bus: Jennifer Murphy

D-U-N-S 01-985-7138
STX WIRELESS OPERATIONS LLC
CRICKET STX
5887 Copley Dr, San Diego, CA 92111-7906
Tel (858) 882-6000 *Founded/Ownrshp* 2010
Sales 414.8MM^E *EMP* 4,000
SIC 4812 Cellular telephone services
Pr: Douglas Hutcheson
**CFO:* Jerry Elliot

D-U-N-S 04-524-6659
STYLE CREST ENTERPRISES INC
2450 Enterprise St, Fremont, OH 43420-8553
Tel (419) 355-8586 *Founded/Ownrshp* 1970
Sales 148.6MM^E *EMP* 525^E
SIC 3089 5075 Plastic hardware & building products; Awnings, fiberglass & plastic combination; Siding, plastic; Warm air heating & air conditioning
CEO: Thomas L Kern
**Pr:* Henry Valle
**CFO:* Tyrone G Frantz
**Sec:* Phillip Burton
**Ex VP:* Bryan T Kern
VP Sls: Mike Kern
Mktg Mgr: Jeff Gwinnup
Sls Mgr: Theresa Sholl
Board of Directors: George A Gray

D-U-N-S 17-862-2403 IMP/EXP
STYLE CREST INC
(*Suby of* STYLE CREST ENTERPRISES INC) ★
2450 Enterprise St, Fremont, OH 43420-8553
Tel (419) 332-7369 *Founded/Ownrshp* 1996
Sales 141.1MM^E *EMP* 500^E
SIC 3089 5075 Siding, plastic; Warm air heating & air conditioning
CEO: Thomas Kern
**Pr:* Henry Valle
**CFO:* Tyrone G Frantz
**Sec:* Phillip Burton
**Ex VP:* William Goad
**Ex VP:* Bryan T Kern
**Ex VP:* Michael J Kern
**Ex VP:* James Miller
Exec: Trudy Nellessen
Exec: Pamella Weller
Dir Bus: Don Mulligan

STYLE NETWORK
See E ENTERTAINMENT TELEVISION INC

D-U-N-S 04-256-1266 EXP
STYLE-VIEW PRODUCTS INC
ALUMA CRAFT PRODUCTS
1800 N Bayshore Dr # 4001, Miami, FL 33132-3234
Tel (305) 634-9688 *Founded/Ownrshp* 1964
Sales 223.1MM^E *EMP* 2,800
SIC 3442 3444 3443 3354 Storm doors or windows, metal; Awnings, sheet metal; Canopies, sheet metal; Fabricated plate work (boiler shop); Aluminum extruded products
Pr: Mark A Caplan
**VP:* Albert M Caplan

D-U-N-S 79-337-2509 IMP
STYLES FOR LESS INC
1205 N Miller St Ste 120, Anaheim, CA 92806-1933
Tel (714) 400-2525 *Founded/Ownrshp* 1992
Sales 122.2MM^E *EMP* 900
Accts White Nelson Diehl Evans Llp
SIC 5621 Women's clothing stores
CEO: Michael P Deangelo
**Pr:* Douglas Pereira
CFO: Augie Dangelo
**CFO:* Augie Deangelo II
CFO: Robert Hipp
CFO: David Tinkham
VP: Robert Torz
Rgnl Mgr: Dena Mahaffey
Brnch Mgr: Jeanette Jost
Dist Mgr: Tammy Sanchez
Genl Mgr: Melanie Gonzales

SU
See SYRACUSE UNIVERSITY

D-U-N-S 06-606-6325 IMP/EXP
SUAREZ CORP INDUSTRIES
SCI
7800 Whipple Ave Nw, North Canton, OH 44720-6928
Tel (330) 494-5504 *Founded/Ownrshp* 1973
Sales 173.8MM^E *EMP* 700
SIC 5961 5944

D-U-N-S 03-087-7908
SUASIN CANCER CARE INC
RADIATION THERAPY AT QUEENS ME
1301 Punchbowl St, Honolulu, HI 96813-2402
Tel (512) 583-0205 *Founded/Ownrshp* 2012
Sales 1.0MMM *EMP* 4^E
Accts Ernst & Young Us Llp San Dieg
SIC 8011 Radiologist
Prin: Winlove B Suasin

SUB OF KENDERD
See ROSEWOOD HEALTH CARE CENTER

D-U-N-S 07-844-0797 IMP/EXP
SUB-ZERO GROUP INC (WI)
4717 Hammersley Rd, Madison, WI 53711-2708
Tel (608) 271-2233 *Founded/Ownrshp* 2006
Sales 308.5MM^E *EMP* 800^E
SIC 3632 Refrigerators, mechanical & absorption: household
Pr: James Bakke
**CFO:* Edward Murphy
VP: Charles Verri
**VP Sls:* Steven Dunlap

D-U-N-S 00-611-2254 IMP
SUB-ZERO INC
(*Suby of* SUB-ZERO GROUP INC) ★
4717 Hammersley Rd, Madison, WI 53711-2708
Tel (608) 271-2233 *Founded/Ownrshp* 1945
Sales 308.5MM^E *EMP* 800
SIC 3632 Refrigerators, mechanical & absorption: household; Freezers, home & farm
CEO: Jim Bakke
**Pr:* James J Bakke
COO: Scott La Sleur
**CFO:* Edward Murphy
VP: Brent Clever
VP: Jim Crow
VP: Mike Grimm
VP: Ed Murphy
VP: Steve Zimmerschied
Exec: Garth Blackburn
Genl Mgr: Dave Burgette
Board of Directors: Helen Bakke, Robert Frame, Henrik Moe, George A Nelson, Thomas Pyle, Thomas Ragatz, Jay Smith, Allen Wilkins

D-U-N-S 05-327-6648 IMP/EXP
SUBARU OF AMERICA INC
(*Suby of* FUJI HEAVY INDUSTRIES LTD.)
2235 Rte 70 W, Cherry Hill, NJ 08002-3380
Tel (856) 488-8500 *Founded/Ownrshp* 1990
Sales 561.0MM^E *EMP* 700
SIC 5012 5013 7515 8732 Automobiles; Automotive supplies & parts; Passenger car leasing; Market analysis, business & economic research
CEO: Tomomi Nakamura
**Pr:* Thomas Doll
CFO: R Curtis Allen
Treas: Isao Kobayashi
Chf Mktg O: Alan Bethke
Sr VP: Jeff Walters
VP: Mamoru Aida
VP: R Allen
VP: Robert Dougherty
VP: Tomohiko Ikeda
VP: Hideki Ishido
VP: Ichiro Kudo
VP: Pamela Steckroat
Exec: Jerry Vanwechel
Board of Directors: Yasuo Koskai

D-U-N-S 18-600-3646 IMP/EXP
SUBARU OF INDIANA AUTOMOTIVE INC
(*Suby of* FUJI HEAVY INDUSTRIES LTD.)
5500 State Road 38 E, Lafayette, IN 47905-9405
Tel (765) 449-1111 *Founded/Ownrshp* 2003
Sales 644.1MM^E *EMP* 2,300
SIC 3711 Automobile assembly, including specialty automobiles
CEO: Masahiro Kasai
**CFO:* T Nishizawa
Sr Cor Off: Yuji Ito
Sr Cor Off: Masahid Sugimoto
Ofcr: Connie Sniff

Ex VP: Naosumi Horie
Ex VP: Kenji Udagawa
VP: Scott Brand
VP: David Rausch
VP: Yutaka Shimoyachi
**Prin:* Hiroyuki Oikawa

D-U-N-S 13-695-7425 IMP/EXP
SUBSEA 7 (US) LLC
(*Suby of* SUBSEA 7 HOLDING INC)
10787 Clay Rd, Houston, TX 77041-5597
Tel (281) 966-7600 *Founded/Ownrshp* 2002
Sales 84.1MM^E *EMP* 160
SIC 1629 3731 Marine construction; Offshore supply boats, building & repairing
CEO: Jean Cahuzac
**Pr:* Ian Cobban
**COO:* John Evans
**CFO:* Ricardo Rosa
**Ex VP:* Steve Wisely
**VP:* Mark Webster
Genl Mgr: Garry Williams

D-U-N-S 96-961-4408
SUBSIDIARIES OF INSTITUTE FOR TRANSFUSION MEDICINE
5 Parkway Ctr, Pittsburgh, PA 15220-3608
Tel (412) 209-7300 *Founded/Ownrshp* 2011
Sales 196.5MM *EMP* 3^E
Accts Deloitte Tax Llp Pittsburgh
SIC 8733 Noncommercial research organizations

SUBURBAN COLLECTION
See SUBURBAN MOTORS CO INC

D-U-N-S 79-300-4532
SUBURBAN CONTRACT CLEANING INC
SUBURBAN INTEGRATED
65 Bay State Dr Ste 4, Braintree, MA 02184-5244
Tel (781) 356-4400 *Founded/Ownrshp* 1992
Sales 44.2MM^E *EMP* 1,100
SIC 7349 Janitorial service, contract basis
Pr: Glenn A Pratt
**CEO:* Tom McGovern
**Ex VP:* Chris Pratt
Exec: Linda Mazzola
Telecom Ex: Paul Martin

D-U-N-S 82-745-7719
SUBURBAN HOSPITAL HEALTHCARE SYSTEM INC
(*Suby of* JOHNS HOPKINS HEALTH SYS CORP) ★
8600 Old Georgetown Rd, Bethesda, MD 20814-1422
Tel (301) 896-3100 *Founded/Ownrshp* 2012
Sales 5.2MM *EMP* 2,000
SIC 8062 General medical & surgical hospitals
Pr: Brian Gragnolati
**COO:* Jacky Schultz
CIO: Joseph Addison

D-U-N-S 07-479-9867
SUBURBAN HOSPITAL INC
(*Suby of* JOHNS HOPKINS HEALTH SYS CORP) ★
8600 Old Georgetown Rd, Bethesda, MD 20814-1497
Tel (301) 896-3100 *Founded/Ownrshp* 1986
Sales 284.8MM *EMP* 1,550
SIC 8062 Hospital, affiliated with AMA residency
Pr: Gene E Green
**Pr:* Brian A Gragnolati
Ofcr: Paul Radecki
Sr VP: Leslie Webber
VP: Joseph Linstrom
Pathlgst: Kay K Liang

SUBURBAN INTEGRATED
See SUBURBAN CONTRACT CLEANING INC

D-U-N-S 10-619-2057 IMP
SUBURBAN MANUFACTURING CO
(*Suby of* R V PRODUCTS DIV) ★
676 Broadway St, Dayton, TN 37321-1122
Tel (423) 775-2131 *Founded/Ownrshp* 1989
Sales 109.2MM^E *EMP* 513
SIC 3585 Air conditioning units, complete: domestic or industrial; Air conditioning, motor vehicle; Furnaces, warm air: electric
CEO: Peter Thompson
**VP:* Jerry Bonacorsi
**VP:* Roger Panoz
**VP:* Jane Wilkey
Mktg Dir: Mike Leach
Mktg Mgr: Chase Marshall

D-U-N-S 10-155-2941
SUBURBAN MOBILITY AUTHORITY FOR REGIONAL TRANSPORATION
SMART
535 Griswold St Ste 600, Detroit, MI 48226-3691
Tel (313) 223-2100 *Founded/Ownrshp* 1967
Sales 116.8MM^E *EMP* 1,040
Accts Plante & Moran Pllc Southfiel
SIC 4111 Bus line operations
CEO: Dan Dirks
CEO: Tony Toth
**Genl Mgr:* John C Hertel

D-U-N-S 01-675-7320 IMP
SUBURBAN MOTORS CO INC
SUBURBAN COLLECTION
1810 Maplelawn Dr, Troy, MI 48084-4616
Tel (248) 643-0070 *Founded/Ownrshp* 1978
Sales 90.2MM^E *EMP* 230
SIC 5511 Automobiles, new & used
Pr: David T Fischer
**CFO:* Tim Leroy
VP: John Jansen
Genl Mgr: David Butler
Off Mgr: Teresa Brown
CTO: Dan Doran
Mktg Mgr: Mark Ribick
Sls Mgr: Marc Sturm
Sales Asso: Aaron Davidson
Sales Asso: Tom Gaynor
Sales Asso: James Hunter

D-U-N-S 00-545-2958 IMP
SUBURBAN PLASTICS CO (IL)
340 Renner Dr, Elgin, IL 60123-6999
Tel (847) 741-4900 *Founded/Ownrshp* 1946
Sales 86.3MM^E *EMP* 500
SIC 3089 Injection molding of plastics
Pr: Stuart Baxter
Treas: Anna Miller
**VP:* Jeremy Baxter
MIS Mgr: Dennis McElroy
Opers Mgr: David Mayo
Plnt Mgr: Keith Kazmer
Plnt Mgr: N Olofson

D-U-N-S 14-078-4443
■ **SUBURBAN PROPANE LP**
(*Suby of* HOMETOWN HEARTH & GRILL) ★
240 State Route 10, Whippany, NJ 07981-2105
Tel (973) 887-5300 *Founded/Ownrshp* 2003
Sales 344.1MM^E *EMP* 2,300
SIC 5983 Fuel oil dealers
CEO: Mark Alexander

D-U-N-S 93-924-1584 IMP
▲ **SUBURBAN PROPANE PARTNERS LP**
240 Route 10 W, Whippany, NJ 07981-2105
Tel (973) 887-5300 *Founded/Ownrshp* 1928
Sales 1.0MMM *EMP* 3,646
Tkr Sym SPH *Exch* NYS
SIC 5984 5172 4939 1711 Liquefied petroleum gas dealers; Liquefied petroleum gas, delivered to customers' premises; Propane gas, bottled; Gases, liquefied petroleum (propane); Combination utilities; Heating & air conditioning contractors
Pr: Michael A Stivala
**Ch Bd:* Harold R Logan Jr
CFO: Michael A Kuglin
Sr VP: Paul Abel
Sr VP: Steven C Boyd
Sr VP: Neil E Scanlon
VP: Jeffrey S Jolly
VP: Kim Zellers
VP Bus: Mark Anton
Mng Dir: Art Tate
Off Mgr: Velvet Anderson
Board of Directors: Lawrence C Caldwell, Matthew J Chanin, John D Collins, John Hoyt Stookey, Jane Swift

SUBWAY
See SPEEDY STOP FOOD STORES LLC

SUBWAY
See MORRIS HOLDINGS INC

SUBWAY
See ROTTINGHAUS CO INC

D-U-N-S 00-287-9844
▲ **SUCAMPO PHARMACEUTICALS INC**
805 King Farm Blvd # 550, Rockville, MD 20850-6542
Tel (301) 961-3400 *Founded/Ownrshp* 1996
Sales 153.1MM *EMP* 159^E
Accts Ernst & Young Llp Mclean Vir
Tkr Sym SCMP *Exch* NGM
SIC 2834 Pharmaceutical preparations
Ch Bd: Peter Greenleaf
CFO: Andrew Smith
Ofcr: Thomas J Knapp
Ofcr: Peter Lichtlen
Ex VP: Max Donley
Ex VP: Brad E Fackler
Sr VP: Steven Caff
VP: Taryn Beridon
VP: Steven Caffe
VP: Takashi Sekida
VP: Silvia Taylor
Board of Directors: Paul Edick, Daniel P Getman, John J Johnson, Barbara A Munder, Maureen E O'connell, Robert J Spiegel, Timothy P Walbert

D-U-N-S 83-018-6487
SUCCESS ACADEMY CHARTER SCHOOLS INC
95 Pine St Fl 6, New York, NY 10005-3917
Tel (646) 597-4641 *Founded/Ownrshp* 2006
Sales 42.4MM *EMP* 1,300
Accts Fruchter Rosen & Co Pc New Yo
SIC 8741 Administrative management; Financial management for business
CEO: Eva Moskowitz
**CFO:* Dennis McIntosh
**VP:* Noel Leeson
Assoc Dir: Lee Qiu
Pr Mgr: Alexis Cox

SUCCESS FACTORS
See SUCCESSFACTORS INC

D-U-N-S 02-250-5021
SUCCESS FOODS MANAGEMENT GROUP LLC
TORCHY'S TACOS
4501 Springdale Rd, Austin, TX 78723-6031
Tel (512) 441-8900 *Founded/Ownrshp* 2007
Sales 82.2MM^E *EMP* 1,000^E
SIC 8741 5812 Business management; Eating places
Genl Mgr: Sam Kretschmer

D-U-N-S 80-915-9460
SUCCESSFACTORS INC
SUCCESS FACTORS
(*Suby of* SAP AMERICA INC) ★
1 Tower Pl Fl 11, South San Francisco, CA 94080-1828
Tel (800) 845-0395 *Founded/Ownrshp* 2012
Sales 75.3MM^E *EMP* 1,047^E
SIC 7371 Computer software development
Pr: Price Shawn
Pr: Mike Ettling
COO: Matt Leone
CFO: Klein Christian
CFO: Bruce C Felt
CFO: Christian Klein
CFO: Christiane Ohlgart
Ofcr: Victoria Bernholz
Ofcr: Jimmy Chaplin
Sr VP: Graham R Younger
VP: Peter Baskin
VP: Heida Biddle
VP: Steven Dyer
VP: Mercedes Ellison
VP: Robin Farwell
VP: Philip Haine
VP: William Harmer
VP: Peter Howes
VP: Pete Jacoby
VP: Matti Karell
VP: Tom Leire

D-U-N-S 11-279-2015
SUCDEN AMERICAS CORP
(*Suby of* SUCRES ET DENREES)
701 Brickell Ave Ste 1200, Miami, FL 33131-2820
Tel (305) 374-4440 *Founded/Ownrshp* 1997
Sales 1.2MMM *EMP* 26^E
SIC 6221 Commodity traders, contracts
Pr: Thierry Songeur
**CFO:* Nicolas Sotile

D-U-N-S 07-951-2058 IMP/EXP
SUCRO CAN SOURCING LLC
2990 Ponce De Leon Blvd # 401, Coral Gables, FL 33134-6803
Tel (305) 901-5222 *Founded/Ownrshp* 2014
Sales 100.0MM *EMP* 8^E
SIC 5159 5149 Sugar, raw; Sugar, refined
CEO: Jonathan Taylor
**CFO:* Patrick Orlando

D-U-N-S 00-637-5414 IMP/EXP
SUD-CHEMIE INC
(*Suby of* CLARIANT CORP) ★
1600 W Hill St, Louisville, KY 40210-1750
Tel (502) 634-7361 *Founded/Ownrshp* 1974, 2011
Sales 127.0MM^E *EMP* 700
SIC 2819 Catalysts, chemical
**Ch Bd:* Von Au
**Pr:* George Buehler
**Pr:* Martin Doyle
**CEO:* John Ray
**CFO:* Bernd Holzhauer
Genl Mgr: Juergn Kammer
Genl Mgr: Albert Zhao
QA Dir: Christopher Luckett
QA Dir: Eric Weston
IT Man: Stefan Richter
IT Man: Michael Uber

SUDBURY FARMS
See ROCHE BROS SUPERMARKETS INC

D-U-N-S 13-931-5873 IMP/EXP
SUDDATH COMPANIES
815 S Main St Ste 400, Jacksonville, FL 32207-8187
Tel (904) 390-7100 *Founded/Ownrshp* 1978
Sales 456.3MM *EMP* 2,350
SIC 4214 4731

SUDDATH RELOCATION SYSTEMS
See SUDDATH VAN LINES INC

D-U-N-S 00-985-8051
SUDDATH VAN LINES INC (IL)
SUDDATH RELOCATION SYSTEMS
(*Suby of* SUDDATH COMPANIES) ★
815 S Main St Ste 400, Jacksonville, FL 32207-8157
Tel (904) 390-7100 *Founded/Ownrshp* 1919, 1978
Sales 530.0MM *EMP* 2,100
Accts Conner Hubbard & Company Llc
SIC 4213 4731 4214 Household goods transport; Freight forwarding; Household goods moving & storage, local
CEO: Michael Brannigan
**CFO:* James G Barnett
VP: Nick Christian
**VP:* Paul Gleason
**VP:* Juanita Hall
**VP:* Elizabeth E Spradley
MIS Mgr: Kevin Hastings
VP Opers: Russell O'Dell
Sfty Mgr: Jeff Osburn
Psych: Leslie McComb

SUDDENLINK COMMUNICATIONS
See CEQUEL COMMUNICATIONS HOLDINGS LLC

SUDDENLINK COMMUNICATIONS
See UNIVERSAL CABLE HOLDINGS INC

SUDDENLINK COMMUNICATIONS
See CEQUEL COMMUNICATIONS LLC

D-U-N-S 00-697-5023
SUEZ ENVIRONNEMENT
(*Suby of* SUEZ GROUPE)
461 From Rd Ste 400, Paramus, NJ 07652-3526
Tel (201) 767-9300 *Founded/Ownrshp* 2000
Sales 1.4MMM^E *EMP* 2,000
SIC 4941 Water supply
CEO: Bertrand Camus
**COO:* Robert J Iacullo
CFO: Xavier Castro
**CFO:* Philippe Dartienne
**Ch:* Anthony Coscia
**Treas:* Michael Algranati
Ex VP: Patrick Cairo
**Sr VP:* Robert Gerber
**Sr VP:* Rich Henning
**Sr VP:* Marie Waugh
VP: Tim Blagsvedt

D-U-N-S 12-255-6046
SUEZ NORTH AMERICA INC
UNITED WATER DELAWARE
(*Suby of* DEGREMONT)
2000 First State Blvd, Wilmington, DE 19804-3569
Tel (302) 633-5670 *Founded/Ownrshp* 2003
Sales 428.7MM^E *EMP* 1,400
SIC 4941 3569 3589 Water supply; Generators: steam, liquid oxygen or nitrogen; Water treatment equipment, industrial
Pr: Axel Vayssiere
**Treas:* Michael Algranati
VP: Joseph Boyle
**Genl Mgr:* Susan Skomorucha
Snr Mgr: Wayne Marti

D-U-N-S 06-313-6592 IMP
SUEZ TREATMENT SOLUTIONS INC
(*Suby of* SUEZ GROUPE)
461 From Rd Ste 400, Paramus, NJ 07652-3526
Tel (804) 756-7600 *Founded/Ownrshp* 2009
Sales 140.9MM^E *EMP* 326
SIC 3589 Sewage & water treatment equipment
Ch Bd: Maximilien Pellegrini
**Ch Bd:* Vernon D Lucy
**Treas:* Robert W Winslow
**Sr VP:* Paul G Davia
**VP:* Albert A Pristera
Board of Directors: Patrice Keime, Barry Windsor

D-U-N-S 08-024-5444
SUEZ WATER INC
(*Suby of* SUEZ GROUPE)
461 From Rd Ste 400, Paramus, NJ 07652-3526
Tel (201) 767-9300 *Founded/Ownrshp* 2002
Sales 102.5MM^E *EMP* 2,000^E
SIC 6719 4941 4952 Public utility holding companies; Water supply; Sewerage systems
Pr: Eric Gernath

D-U-N-S 10-138-3016
SUEZ WATER NEW JERSEY INC
UNITED WATER NEW JERSEY INC.
(*Suby of* SUEZ ENVIRONNEMENT) ★
461 From Rd Ste 400, Paramus, NJ 07652-3526
Tel (201) 767-9300 *Founded/Ownrshp* 1983
Sales 325.1MM^E *EMP* 400
Accts Ernst & Young Llp Stamford
SIC 4941 Water supply
CEO: Tony Harding
Pr: Robert Iacullo
CFO: Edward Imparato
Treas: Michael Algranati
VP: James Glozzy
Plnt Mgr: Peter Kania
Sls Mgr: Sandra Chandler

D-U-N-S 78-779-9832
SUFFOLK CITY OF PUBLIC SCHOOLS
100 N Main St Ste 1, Suffolk, VA 23434-4529
Tel (757) 925-6754 *Founded/Ownrshp* 1646
Sales 78.7MM^E *EMP* 2,000
SIC 8211 Public elementary & secondary schools
VP: James Green
VP: Lisa Milburn
IT Man: Hilda Harmon

D-U-N-S 10-790-4625
SUFFOLK CONSTRUCTION CO INC
65 Allerton St, Boston, MA 02119-2923
Tel (617) 445-3500 *Founded/Ownrshp* 1982
Sales 2.6MMM *EMP* 1,150
SIC 1542 Commercial & office building contractors
CEO: John F Fish
Pr: Andrew Ball
**CFO:* Michael Azarela
**Treas:* Mike Lindblom
Chf Mktg O: Kimberly Steimle
Ex VP: Marc Crisafulli
Ex VP: Jeffrey Gouveia
Ex VP: Chris Mayer
Ex VP: Stephen Skinner
Ex VP: Peter Welsh
Ex VP: Christopher Woods
VP: Dan Antonellis
VP: Corren Collura
VP: Susan Gray
VP: Chris Kennedy
VP: Angus Leary
VP: Kevin McDonough
VP: Nicole Mills
VP: Vin Murphy
VP: Andrew Potts
VP: Wendy Venoit

D-U-N-S 06-801-7615
SUFFOLK COUNTY COMMUNITY COLLEGE
(*Suby of* SUNY ADMINISTRATION) ★
533 College Rd, Selden, NY 11784-2899
Tel (631) 451-4110 *Founded/Ownrshp* 1957
Sales 43.6MM^E *EMP* 1,000
SIC 8222 9411 Community college; Administration of educational programs;
Pr: Shaun L McKay
**Pr:* Shirley Robinson Tippins
Assoc VP: Maria Delongoria
**Ex VP:* George Gatta
**VP:* James Camniss
**VP:* Charles Stein
**VP:* Michael Weissberg
Assoc Dir: Christopher Blake
Off Mgr: Sandra O'Hara
Dir IT: Douglas Kahn
Dir IT: Gary Ording

D-U-N-S 06-801-9181
SUFFOLK COUNTY WATER AUTHORITY INC
4060 Sunrise Hwy, Oakdale, NY 11769-1005
Tel (631) 563-0255 *Founded/Ownrshp* 1951
Sales 373.0MM^E *EMP* 570
SIC 4941 Water supply
CEO: Jeffrey W Szabo
**CEO:* Joseph M Pokorny Pe
CEO: Carmen Miller
**CFO:* Douglas Celiberti
Bd of Dir: Jane Devine
Ofcr: Jolanta Rechul
VP: Jane Devin
Ex Dir: John Pavacic
Snr Mgr: Janice E Tinsley
Snr Mgr: Eric White

D-U-N-S 07-657-7709
SUFFOLK UNIVERSITY
120 Tremont St, Boston, MA 02108-4910
Tel (617) 573-8000 *Founded/Ownrshp* 1906
Sales 235.0MM *EMP* 800
Accts Kpmg Llp Boston Ma
SIC 8221 8244 University; Business college or school
Pr: James McCarthy
Treas: Barbara Moore
**VP:* Francis Flannery
VP: Greg Gatlin
VP: John Nucci
VP: Colm Renehan
Assoc Dir: Brett Kinney
Assoc Dir: Michele Rapp
Assoc Dir: Lisa Vigliotta
Chf Nrs Of: Lauren Williams
Off Admin: Usha Chanbrasekhar

D-U-N-S 07-988-0011
SUFFOLK UNIVERSITY
8 Ashburton Pl, Boston, MA 02108-2770
Tel (617) 573-8000 *Founded/Ownrshp* 2015
Sales 322.3MM *EMP* 6[E]
Accts Kpmg Llp Boston Ma
SIC 8221 Colleges universities & professional schools

D-U-N-S 14-332-7232
SUFFOLK/KRAFT CONSTRUCTION CO LLC
65 Allerton St, Boston, MA 02119-2901
Tel (617) 445-3500 *Founded/Ownrshp* 2003
Sales 732.0M[E] *EMP* 1,500
SIC 1542 Nonresidential construction

D-U-N-S 14-156-8209 IMP/EXP
SUGAR AMERICANE REFINING LLC
AMCANE SUGAR
21010 Trolley Indus Dr, Taylor, MI 48180-1841
Tel (313) 299-1300 *Founded/Ownrshp* 2003
Sales 84.8MM[E] *EMP* 4[E]
SIC 2062 Cane sugar refining

D-U-N-S 07-229-4916 IMP
SUGAR C&H CO INC
(*Suby of* DOMINO SUGAR) ★
830 Loring Ave, Crockett, CA 94525-1104
Tel (510) 787-2121 *Founded/Ownrshp* 2005
Sales 111.5MM[E] *EMP* 550
SIC 2062 Cane sugar refining; Refined cane sugar from purchased raw sugar or syrup; Granulated cane sugar from purchased raw sugar or syrup; Powdered cane sugar from purchased raw sugar or syrup
CEO: Antonio L Contreras
**Pr:* Luis J Fernandez
**CFO:* Gregory H Smith
**Treas:* Gregory A Maitner
**Co-Pr:* Antonio Contreras
**VP:* Armando A Tabernilla
Opers Mgr: Eva Maes
Secur Mgr: Steve Shimel

D-U-N-S 00-444-4998 IMP
SUGAR CANE GROWERS COOPERATIVE OF FLORIDA
GLADES SUGAR HOUSE
1500 W Sugar House Rd, Belle Glade, FL 33430-5400
Tel (561) 996-5556 *Founded/Ownrshp* 1960
Sales 100.6MM *EMP* 500
SIC 2061 Raw cane sugar
Pr: Antonio L Contreras
**Ch Bd:* John L Hundley
**CFO:* Brian R Lohmann
Sr VP: C David Goodlett
**VP:* Jose F Alvarez
**VP:* William Kramer
VP: Barbara Miedema
Cmptr Lab: Aubrey Trotman
IT Man: Carlos Marin
VP Mktg: Matthew B Hoffman
Board of Directors: Paul R Orsenigo, Fritz C Stein

D-U-N-S 00-431-0561 IMP/EXP
SUGAR CREEK PACKING CO (OH)
2101 Kenskill Ave, Wshngtn CT Hs, OH 43160-9404
Tel (740) 335-7440 *Founded/Ownrshp* 1966
Sales 698.3MM[E] *EMP* 1,750
SIC 2013 2011 Bacon, side & sliced: from purchased meat; Meat packing plants
CEO: John Richardson
**COO:* Michael Richardson
**CFO:* Thomas J Bollinger
**VP:* Rob Howe
CIO: Edward Rodden
IT Man: Kim Morris
IT Man: Kimberly Morris
IT Man: Scott Vandevanter
Netwrk Eng: Wesley Dawes
Opers Mgr: Jim Savage
Plnt Mgr: Darren Kleinsorge

D-U-N-S 11-292-3172 EXP
SUGAR FOODS CORP
950 3rd Ave Fl 21, New York, NY 10022-2786
Tel (212) 753-6900 *Founded/Ownrshp* 1961
Sales 351.3MM[E] *EMP* 750
SIC 2869 2023 2099 2068 7389 Sweeteners, synthetic; Cream substitutes; Sugar; Seasonings & spices; Packaged combination products: pasta, rice & potato; Bread crumbs, not made in bakeries; Salted & roasted nuts & seeds; Packaging & labeling services
Pr: Marty Wilson
**Ch Bd:* Donald G Tober
**Pr:* Stephen Odell
**CFO:* Jack Vivinetto
**VP:* Myron Stein
Opers Mgr: Brian Thomson

D-U-N-S 83-431-0950
SUGAR MOUNTAIN CAPITAL LLC
PASTA & CO
801 Blanchard St Ste 300, Seattle, WA 98121-2874
Tel (206) 322-1644 *Founded/Ownrshp* 1999
Sales 94.8MM[E] *EMP* 231[E]
SIC 5142 Frozen fish, meat & poultry
Exec: Darren McNally
Genl Mgr: Nina Simutis
Site Mgr: Kurt B Dammeier

D-U-N-S 02-531-9526
■ **SUGAR STEEL CORP**
(*Suby of* RELIANCE STEEL & ALUMINUM CO) ★
2521 State St Ste 1, Chicago Heights, IL 60411-4300
Tel (708) 757-9500 *Founded/Ownrshp* 1966
Sales 284.9MM[E] *EMP* 150[E]
SIC 5051 Structural shapes, iron or steel
Pr: Robert Sugar
Dir IT: Kevin Statz
Sls Mgr: Tim Cleary
Sls Mgr: Skeet Luther
Sls Mgr: Pat O'Brien

SUGARLOAF CREATIONS
See NATIONAL ENTERTAINMENT NETWORK LLC

D-U-N-S 80-645-1431 IMP/EXP
■ **SUGARTOWN WORLDWIDE LLC**
LILLY PULITZER
(*Suby of* OXFORD INDUSTRIES INC) ★
800 3rd Ave, King of Prussia, PA 19406-1412
Tel (610) 878-5550 *Founded/Ownrshp* 2010
Sales 147.8MM[E] *EMP* 400
SIC 2339 2361 5136 5611 Sportswear, women's; Girls' & children's dresses, blouses & shirts; Sportswear, men's & boys'; Clothing, sportswear, men's & boys'
CEO: Scott A Beaumont
**Pr:* James B Bradbeer Jr
Ofcr: Keary McNew
VP: Susan Hill
Comm Man: Eleni Tavantzis
Sales Asso: Julienne Irwin
Snr Mgr: Eleni McCready
Snr Mgr: Alison Merchant
Board of Directors: Kate Kenny

D-U-N-S 00-923-0814
SUISAN CO
333 Kilauea Ave Ste 202, Hilo, HI 96720-3013
Tel (808) 935-8511 *Founded/Ownrshp* 1941
Sales 131.5MM[E] *EMP* 170
SIC 5142 5146 Packaged frozen goods; Fish, fresh
CEO: Glenn T Hashimoto
**Pr:* Rex Yoshio Matsuno
**Ex VP:* Glen Hashimoto
**VP:* Kyle S Kawano
**VP:* Toshio Maeda

D-U-N-S 02-338-4225 IMP
SUIT-KOTE CORP
1911 Lorings Crossing Rd, Cortland, NY 13045-9775
Tel (607) 753-1100 *Founded/Ownrshp* 1931
Sales 278.7MM[E] *EMP* 700
SIC 2951 1611 Asphalt & asphaltic paving mixtures (not from refineries); Highway & street paving contractor
Pr: Frank H Suits Jr
**CFO:* James Ehle
**VP:* Scott Harris
**VP:* Dan Quinlan
**VP:* Steve Rebman
**VP:* Paul Suits
Rgnl Mgr: Steve Sanfilippo
Cmptr Lab: Jacob Eggleston

SUITE TECHNOLOGY
See IBAHN CORP

D-U-N-S 09-008-5531 IMP/EXP
SUIZA DAIRY CORP
(*Suby of* GLORIA S.A.)
131 De Diego Ave, San Juan, PR 00921
Tel (787) 792-7300 *Founded/Ownrshp* 1935, 2002
Sales 195.2MM *EMP* 800
Accts Deloitte & Touche Llp San Jua
SIC 2026 2037 Fluid milk; Fruit juices
Prin: Francisco Perez

D-U-N-S 80-639-3620
■ **SUIZA DAIRY GROUP LLC**
(*Suby of* DEAN HOLDING CO) ★
2515 Mckinney Ave # 1200, Dallas, TX 75201-1908
Tel (214) 303-3400 *Founded/Ownrshp* 2006
Sales 136.3MM[E] *EMP* 299[E]
SIC 0241 Dairy farms
CEO: Gregg L Engles

SUJA JUICE
See SUJA LIFE LLC

D-U-N-S 07-917-5283
SUJA LIFE LLC
SUJA JUICE
8380 Camino Santa Fe, San Diego, CA 92121-2657
Tel (855) 879-7852 *Founded/Ownrshp* 2012
Sales 148.9MM[E] *EMP* 205
SIC 5149 Fruit peel
CEO: Jeffrey Church
**Pr:* James Brennan
Opers Mgr: Heather Baker

D-U-N-S 00-530-6022
SUKUP MANUFACTURING CO (IA)
1555 255th St, Sheffield, IA 50475-7711
Tel (641) 892-4222 *Founded/Ownrshp* 1963
Sales 188.3MM[E] *EMP* 530
SIC 3523 Farm machinery & equipment; Driers (farm): grain, hay & seed; Planting machines, agricultural
Ch Bd: Eugene G Sukup
**Pr:* Charles E Sukup
**VP:* Steven E Sukup
Sfty Dirs: Brett Nelson
Ql Cn Mgr: Ben Furleigh

D-U-N-S 00-554-5835 IMP/EXP
SULLAIR LLC (IN)
(*Suby of* ACCUDYNE INDUSTRIES LLC) ★
3700 E Michigan Blvd, Michigan City, IN 46360-6527
Tel (219) 879-5451 *Founded/Ownrshp* 2006, 2013
Sales 191.1MM[E] *EMP* 550[E]
SIC 3569 3563 Filters, general line: industrial; Air & gas compressors including vacuum pumps
CEO: Scott Nelson
VP: David Booth
VP: Robert Lauson
VP Bus Dev: Raymond Klingler
Trfc Mgr: Sue Hannon
Mktg Dir: David Andrews

D-U-N-S 07-771-4780
SULLIVAN & CROMWELL LLP
125 Broad St Fl 35, New York, NY 10004-2498
Tel (212) 558-4000 *Founded/Ownrshp* 1879
Sales 370.6MM[E] *EMP* 1,931
SIC 8111 General practice attorney, lawyer
Ch: H Rodgin Cohen
Pt: Izumi Akai
Pt: Robert Chu
Pt: John Evangelekos
Pt: Wolfgang Feuring
Pt: Keiji Hatano
Pt: Waldo D Jones Jr
Pt: Robert A Sacks
Pt: Joseph Shenker
Pt: William D Torchiana
Pt: Marc R Trevino
Pt: Chun WEI
Mng Pt: Garth W Bray
Mng Pt: Richard H Klapper
Mng Pt: Daryl A Libow
Mng Pt: Robert M Schlein
CFO: Robert Howard
Treas: Pauline Webster
Ofcr: Norma J Arnold
Ofcr: Whitney Chatterjee

D-U-N-S 83-098-1205
SULLIVAN & MCLAUGHLIN COMPANIES INC
SULLIVAN MCLAUGHLIN COMPANIES
74 Lawley St, Boston, MA 02122-3608
Tel (617) 474-0500 *Founded/Ownrshp* 1969
Sales 90.6MM[E] *EMP* 440
SIC 1731 Electrical work
CEO: Dennis Miller
**Pr:* Hugh McLaughlin
COO: Larry Richmond
**CFO:* Joseph Gates
**Ex VP:* John Rudicus
Genl Mgr: Shawn Greenwood
IT Man: Paul Rix
Opers Mgr: Will Bissonnette

D-U-N-S 08-407-4228
SULLIVAN COUNTY
100 North St, Monticello, NY 12701-1163
Tel (845) 794-3000 *Founded/Ownrshp* 1830
Sales NA *EMP* 1,213
SIC 9111 County supervisors' & executives' offices
Ch: Jonathan Rouis
CFO: Robert Vandusen
Ex Dir: Laura Quigley

SULLIVAN COUNTY HIGHWAY DEPT
See COUNTY OF SULLIVAN

D-U-N-S 07-979-8731
SULLIVAN COUNTY SCHOOLS
154 Blountville Byp, Blountville, TN 37617-4575
Tel (423) 354-1000 *Founded/Ownrshp* 2015
Sales 46.1MM[E] *EMP* 1,261[E]
SIC 8211 Public elementary & secondary schools
Dir Sec: Karen Nave
MIS Dir: Nicole Wolfe
Teacher Pr: Wendel Smith
HC Dir: Carly Crowder
HC Dir: Shanan Smith

D-U-N-S 87-984-6723
SULLIVAN GJ & ASSOCIATES INC
SULLIVAN GROUP, THE
800 W 6th St Ste 1800, Los Angeles, CA 90017-2701
Tel (213) 626-1000 *Founded/Ownrshp* 1980
Sales NA *EMP* 325
SIC 6411 Insurance brokers
Pr: Gerald J Sullivan
CFO: Paul Cunningham
VP: Paul Bubnis
VP: Hank Haldeman
Off Mgr: Amy Baldukas
Off Mgr: Margaret Philpotts
CIO: Lee Willson

SULLIVAN GROUP, THE
See SULLIVAN GJ & ASSOCIATES INC

D-U-N-S 79-704-4989
SULLIVAN GROUP
37 W Fairmont Ave # 100, Savannah, GA 31406-3456
Tel (912) 352-3800 *Founded/Ownrshp* 1991
Sales 98.4MM[E] *EMP* 3,000
SIC 7361 Employment agencies
Pr: Martin Sullivan
**VP:* Kim Dawson

D-U-N-S 06-945-2600
SULLIVAN INTERNATIONAL GROUP INC (CA)
2750 Womble Rd Ste 100, San Diego, CA 92106-6114
Tel (619) 260-1432 *Founded/Ownrshp* 1998
Sales 102.6MM[E] *EMP* 132
SIC 4959

D-U-N-S 10-115-5539
SULLIVAN INVESTMENT CO INC
SULLIVAN TIRE CO
41 Accord Park Dr, Norwell, MA 02061-1614
Tel (781) 982-1550 *Founded/Ownrshp* 1979
Sales 264.1MM *EMP* 950
Accts O Connor & Drew Pc Braintr
SIC 5531 7534 Automotive tires; Rebuilding & retreading tires
CEO: Robert D Sullivan
**CFO:* Joseph M Zaccheo
**Treas:* Paul J Sullivan

SULLIVAN MCLAUGHLIN COMPANIES
See SULLIVAN & MCLAUGHLIN COMPANIES INC

SULLIVAN TIRE CO
See SULLIVAN INVESTMENT CO INC

D-U-N-S 01-959-6386
SULLIVAN TIRE CO INC
(*Suby of* SULLIVAN TIRE CO) ★
41 Accord Park Dr, Norwell, MA 02061-1614
Tel (781) 982-1550 *Founded/Ownrshp* 1955
Sales 218.0MM[E] *EMP* 800
SIC 5531 7538 5014 Automotive tires; General automotive repair shops; Automobile tires & tubes
Pr: Robert D Sullivan
**Pr:* John E Donovan Jr
**CFO:* Joseph M Zaccheo
**Treas:* Paul J Sullivan
VP Mktg: Paul Sullivan

SULLIVAN'S FOODS
See J B SULLIVAN INC

D-U-N-S 05-501-3283
SULLY-MILLER CONTRACTING CO INC
BLUE DIAMOND MATERIALS
(*Suby of* SULLY-MILLER HOLDING CORPORATION)
135 Sstate College Ste 400, Brea, CA 92821
Tel (714) 578-9600 *Founded/Ownrshp* 1997
Sales 128.1MM[E] *EMP* 343
SIC 1611 Highway & street construction
Pr: Dave Martinez
**CFO:* Tim Orchard
**VP:* Scott Bottomley
**VP:* Russ Caruso
**VP:* Mike Edwards
**VP:* Mitchell P Vigna
CIO: Marcella Wilson
VP Opers: Bill Boyd
Sls Mgr: Mike Acosta
Snr PM: Gary Downey
Board of Directors: Georges Ausseil, Dominique Leveille

SULPHUR SPRINGS CULTURED SPC
See SAPUTO DAIRY FOODS USA LLC

D-U-N-S 06-326-1721
SULPHUR SPRINGS VALLEY ELECTRIC COOPERATIVE INC CHARITABLE
311 E Wilcox Dr, Sierra Vista, AZ 85635-2527
Tel (520) 384-2221 *Founded/Ownrshp* 2000
Sales 86.6MM[E] *EMP* 215
SIC 4911 1731 1623 Distribution, electric power; Generation, electric power; Transmission, electric power; Electric power systems contractors; Communication line & transmission tower construction
CEO: Creden W Huber
**Pr:* Kathy Thatcher
**CFO:* Kirby Chapman
Sls Mgr: Jim Gross

D-U-N-S 00-136-1203 IMP
SULTANA DISTRIBUTION SERVICES INC (NY)
600 Food Center Dr, Bronx, NY 10474-7037
Tel (718) 842-4674 *Founded/Ownrshp* 1957, 1995
Sales 157.1MM[E] *EMP* 85[E]
SIC 5145 5149 Confectionery; Groceries & related products
**CFO:* Christine Magnatta
Assoc VP: Nancy Becker
**VP:* Clifford Bauer
VP: Esta Belkin
Opers Mgr: David Marusiak
Mktg Dir: Jaclyn Gold

D-U-N-S 15-402-4111 IMP/EXP
SULZER PUMPS (US) INC
(*Suby of* SULZER US HOLDING INC) ★
1255 Enclave Pkwy 300, Houston, TX 77077-1846
Tel (281) 934-6014 *Founded/Ownrshp* 1988
Sales 367.5MM[E] *EMP* 908
SIC 3594 Pumps, hydraulic power transfer
CEO: Cesar Montenegro
Pr: Mauricio Bannwart
Pr: Janis Gzik
VP: Fernando Bermudez
VP: Jack Feinstein
VP: Roy Horner
VP: Kevin Oconnell
VP: Roger Peck
VP: Paul Robinson
Rgnl Mgr: Aaron Johnson
Genl Mgr: Jacques De Salis

D-U-N-S 10-765-4261 IMP/EXP
SULZER TURBO SERVICES HOUSTON INC
(*Suby of* SULZER US HOLDING INC) ★
11518 Old La Porte Rd, La Porte, TX 77571-9516
Tel (713) 567-2700 *Founded/Ownrshp* 1985
Sales 156.6MM[E] *EMP* 330
SIC 3569 Centrifuges, industrial
Pr: Darayus Pardivala
**VP:* Michael Curran
**VP:* Scott Fahey
VP: Barney McLaughlin
CIO: Louis Fleissner
Board of Directors: Derek Alexander, Billy Coleman

D-U-N-S 09-075-5984 IMP/EXP
SULZER US HOLDING INC
(*Suby of* SULZER AG)
2277 Plaza Dr Ste 600, Sugar Land, TX 77479-6608
Tel (832) 886-2299 *Founded/Ownrshp* 1997
Sales 1.0MMM *EMP* 2,867
SIC 7699 3594

SUMCO PHOENIX
See SUMCO SOUTHWEST CORP

D-U-N-S 12-341-4794 IMP
SUMCO PHOENIX CORP
(*Suby of* SUMCO CORPORATION)
19801 N Tatum Blvd, Phoenix, AZ 85050-4201
Tel (480) 473-6000 *Founded/Ownrshp* 1989
Sales 414.0MM[E] *EMP* 600
SIC 3674 Semiconductors & related devices
CEO: Jiro Ryuta
Pr: Toshiro Tanaka
Ex VP: Gregory Kasianchuk
**VP:* Robert Koehler
**VP:* Jun Kudo
**VP:* Jim Swantko
**VP:* Greg Zeoli
Exec: Jim Ellick
Exec: Mike Hargraves
Exec: Georgene Jander
Genl Mgr: Barb Black

D-U-N-S 92-944-4941 IMP
SUMCO SOUTHWEST CORP
SUMCO PHOENIX
(*Suby of* SUMCO PHOENIX CORP) ★
19801 N Tatum Blvd, Phoenix, AZ 85050-4201
Tel (480) 473-6000 *Founded/Ownrshp* 1995
Sales 87.4MM[E] *EMP* 362
SIC 3674 Silicon wafers, chemically doped
Pr: Shigetoshi Shibuya
**Treas:* Kenneth Manicki
**VP:* Mark Dobbins
Board of Directors: Mark Dobbins, Nicholas Stroud

D-U-N-S 61-496-2298 IMP
SUMCO USA SALES CORP
CINCINNATI DIV
2099 Gateway Pl Ste 400, San Jose, CA 95110-1017
Tel (408) 352-3880 *Founded/Ownrshp* 2002
Sales 76.1MM^E *EMP* 1,300
SIC 3674

SUMIQUIP
See LINDER INDUSTRIAL MACHINERY CO

D-U-N-S 78-471-7618
SUMITOMO BAKELITE NORTH AMERICA INC
SBHPP
(*Suby of* SUMITOMO BAKELITE COMPANY LIMITED)
46820 Magellan Dr Ste C, Novi, MI 48377-2454
Tel (248) 313-7000 *Founded/Ownrshp* 2000
Sales 93.0MM^E *EMP* 360
SIC 2821 Molding compounds, plastics
CEO: Shintaro Ishiwata

D-U-N-S 00-892-1025 IMP/EXP
SUMITOMO CORP OF AMERICAS
(*Suby of* SUMITOMO CORPORATION)
300 Madison Ave, New York, NY 10017-6232
Tel (212) 207-0700 *Founded/Ownrshp* 1952
Sales 5.3MMM^E *EMP* 14,143
SIC 5051 5172 5084 5063 5141

SUMITOMO DRIVE TECHNOLOGIES
See SUMITOMO MACHINERY CORP OF AMERICA

D-U-N-S 09-718-4022 IMP
SUMITOMO ELECTRIC CARBIDE INC
(*Suby of* SUMITOMO ELECTRIC HARDMETAL CORP.)
1001 E Business Center Dr, Mount Prospect, IL 60056-6080
Tel (847) 635-0044 *Founded/Ownrshp* 1979
Sales 89.4MM^E *EMP* 350
SIC 5084 Machine tools & accessories
Pr: Yasuhisa Hashimoto
**Treas:* Takahiro Kimura
Treas: Takeshi Suzuki
VP: Mitsuhiro Goto
Opers Mgr: Carlos Villalobos
Mktg Dir: Paul Ratzki
Mktg Mgr: Masatoshi Maeda
Manager: Todd Schneider
Sls Mgr: Kevin Schaefer

D-U-N-S 17-563-8741 IMP
SUMITOMO ELECTRIC WIRING SYSTEMS INC
SEWS
(*Suby of* SUMITOMO ELECTRIC INDUSTRIES, LTD.)
1018 Ashley St, Bowling Green, KY 42103-2499
Tel (270) 782-7397 *Founded/Ownrshp* 1986
Sales 1.6MMM^E *EMP* 6,000
SIC 3714 5063 3694 Automotive wiring harness sets; Wire & cable; Engine electrical equipment
Ch Bd: Makoto Tani
**Pr:* Toru Kuwahara
VP: Sal Giacopelli
Exec: Duane Harrison
**Prin:* Takashi Kawakatsu
Prgrm Mgr: Jeremy Bates
Prgrm Mgr: Keith Boone
Prgrm Mgr: Jack Collins
Prgrm Mgr: Andrew King
Brnch Mgr: John King
Genl Mgr: Ken Woosley

D-U-N-S 88-388-1336
SUMITOMO FORESTRY AMERICA INC
CCX
(*Suby of* SUMITOMO FORESTRY CO., LTD.)
1110 112th Ave Ne Ste 202, Bellevue, WA 98004-4571
Tel (425) 454-2355 *Founded/Ownrshp* 1997
Sales 384.1MM^E *EMP* 250^E
SIC 8741 5099 Construction management; Timber products, rough
Pr: Thomas Andrew Hanchin
VP: David Videon
Prin: Eita Muto

D-U-N-S 00-299-4507 IMP
SUMITOMO MACHINERY CORP OF AMERICA (DE)
SUMITOMO DRIVE TECHNOLOGIES
(*Suby of* SUMITOMO HEAVY INDUSTRIES, LTD.)
4200 Holland Blvd, Chesapeake, VA 23323-1529
Tel (757) 485-3355 *Founded/Ownrshp* 1966
Sales 160.4MM^E *EMP* 300
SIC 5063 3568 Power transmission equipment, electric; Power transmission equipment; Drives, chains & sprockets
**Pr:* Ronald J Smith
**CFO:* Masato Sugimori
**Sr VP:* Masao Hirota
VP: Antonio Monteiro
**VP:* James Travers
Exec: Christy Vindeola
Netwrk Mgr: Paul Degroff
Opers Mgr: Erik Sundt
Plnt Mgr: Mike Wozniel
**VP Sls:* Matthew Roberson
Mktg Dir: Steve Leins

D-U-N-S 04-241-4420 IMP
SUMITOMO METAL MINING AMERICA INC
(*Suby of* SUMITOMO METAL MINING CO., LTD.)
701 5th Ave Ste 2150, Seattle, WA 98104-7004
Tel (206) 405-2800 *Founded/Ownrshp* 1998
Sales 133.9MM^E *EMP* 5
SIC 1081 Metal mining services
Pr: Norifumi Ushirone
**Pr:* Ryoichi Suvuki
**VP:* Takashi Kuriyama
**VP:* Ryota Sekine
**VP:* Katsuya Tanaka

D-U-N-S 09-807-5141 IMP
SUMITOMO METAL MINING POGO LLC
POGO MINES
(*Suby of* SUMITOMO METAL MINING AMERICA INC) ★
50 Mile Pogo Mile Rd, Delta Junction, AK 99737
Tel (907) 895-2740 *Founded/Ownrshp* 2009
Sales 133.2MM^E *EMP* 131^E
SIC 1041 Gold ores mining
Genl Mgr: Chris Kennedy
**Genl Mgr:* Larry Davy
Genl Mgr: Robert Jacko
Off Mgr: Barbara Brice

D-U-N-S 07-968-2974
SUMITOMO MITSUI FINANCE AND LEASING CO LTD
(*Suby of* SUMITOMO MITSUI BANKING CORPORATION)
277 Park Ave Fl 15, New York, NY 10172-3003
Tel (212) 224-4000 *Founded/Ownrshp* 2013
Sales 270.0MM^E *EMP* 30
SIC 7389 Financial services
Pr: Yoshinori Kawamura
**VP:* Erik Gibbons
**Genl Mgr:* S Ide

D-U-N-S 78-842-3812
SUMITOMO MITSUI TRUST BANK (USA) INC
(*Suby of* SUMITOMO MITSUI TRUST BANK, LIMITED)
111 River St, Hoboken, NJ 07030-5773
Tel (201) 595-8900 *Founded/Ownrshp* 1987
Sales NA *EMP* 156
SIC 6021 National trust companies with deposits, commercial
Pr: Ryo Azumane
Bd of Dir: Hidehiko Asai
Bd of Dir: Kuniyuki Shudo
**Ex VP:* Richard Macarthur
Sr VP: Sandeep Aggarwal
Sr VP: Bill Austin
**Sr VP:* William Austin
Sr VP: George Bartell
**Sr VP:* Robert Bielunas
Sr VP: Nagaoka Naotsune
**Sr VP:* Lazzaro Stoia
VP: James Hartin
VP: Yukihiro Iwasaki
VP: Henry Ortiz

D-U-N-S 02-824-4598 IMP/EXP
SUMITOMO RUBBER NORTH AMERICA INC
FALKEN TIRE CORPORATION
(*Suby of* SUMITOMO RUBBER INDUSTRIES, LTD.)
8656 Haven Ave, Rancho Cucamonga, CA 91730-9103
Tel (909) 466-1116 *Founded/Ownrshp* 2006
Sales 108.0MM^E *EMP* 126
SIC 5014 Tires & tubes; Automobile tires & tubes; Truck tires & tubes
CEO: Richard Smallwood
VP: Peter Buck
VP: Fumikazu Yamashita
Ex Dir: Rick Brennan
QA Dir: Sam Choo
Tech Mgr: Jim Johnson
Mktg Mgr: Nick Fousekis
Sales Asso: Rindy Mendez
Snr Mgr: Mark Richter
Snr Mgr: James Yim

D-U-N-S 11-832-7162 IMP/EXP
SUMITOMO RUBBER USA LLC
GOODYEAR
(*Suby of* SUMITOMO RUBBER INDUSTRIES, LTD.)
80 State St, Tonawanda, NY 14150-4030
Tel (716) 879-8200 *Founded/Ownrshp* 1999
Sales 419.5MM^E *EMP* 1,153
SIC 5531 Automotive tires
CEO: Kenji Onga
**Treas:* Mary Kasprzak
**VP:* Donald M Delaney
**VP:* Kevin A Olifiers
**VP:* Ryan Waldron
IT Man: Jeffrey Jensen
Plnt Mgr: Tim Frossell

D-U-N-S 02-062-8384
SUMMA BARBERTON CITIZENS HOSPITAL
SUMMACARE INSURANCE COMPANY
(*Suby of* SUMMACARE INSURANCE CO) ★
155 5th St Ne, Barberton, OH 44203-3332
Tel (330) 615-3000 *Founded/Ownrshp* 2007
Sales 179.2MM *EMP* 1,100
SIC 8062 General medical & surgical hospitals
CEO: James Pope
Ofcr: Chuck Jose
VP: Mark Matthews
Surgeon: Thomas Wehmann
Doctor: Kenneth Berkovitz
Doctor: Glenn Black
Doctor: Andrea Cerone
Doctor: Elizabeth Connelly
Doctor: Chris Cook
Doctor: James Eley
Doctor: Jon Elias

D-U-N-S 07-690-2923
SUMMA HEALTH SYSTEM
SUMMACARE INSURANCE COMPANY
95 Arch St Ste G50, Akron, OH 44304-1477
Tel (330) 375-3000 *Founded/Ownrshp* 1926
Sales 1.1MMM^E *EMP* 7,406
Accts Ernst & Young Us Llp Indianap
SIC 8062 General medical & surgical hospitals
Pr: Thomas J Strauss
Chf Rad: Daniel Finelli
Dir Recs: Dianna Earnest
**Ch Bd:* Charles Isroff
Pr: Marty Hauser
**COO:* Valerie Gibson
COO: Steven P Schmidt
COO: Claude Vicente
COO: Claude Vincenti
CFO: Brian Derrick
CFO: Mike Manfull
CFO: Thomas P O'Neill
CFO: Tom Oneill
**CFO:* C Michael Rutherford
CFO: Michael Rutherford
Treas: Susan Savene
Ofcr: Lanie Ward
Sr VP: Gregory Kall
Sr VP: Jason Niehaus
Sr VP: Erik Steele
Sr VP: Ben Sutton

D-U-N-S 13-110-4085 IMP/EXP
SUMMA HOLDINGS INC
8223 Brecksville Rd # 100, Cleveland, OH 44141-1361
Tel (440) 838-4700 *Founded/Ownrshp* 1983
Sales 594.4MM^E *EMP* 1,604
SIC 2542 3462 3569 7359 3728 Lockers (not refrigerated): except wood; Cabinets: show, display or storage: except wood; Shelving, office & store: except wood; Gears, forged steel; Lubricating systems, centralized; Equipment rental & leasing; Aircraft assemblies, subassemblies & parts
Ch Bd: James Benenson Jr
CFO: John E Cvetic
**Co-Pr:* Clement C Benenson
**Co-Pr:* James Benenson III

D-U-N-S 12-252-0245
SUMMA INSURANCE CO INC
SUMMACARE
(*Suby of* SUMMACARE INSURANCE CO) ★
10 N Main St, Akron, OH 44308-1958
Tel (800) 996-8411 *Founded/Ownrshp* 1995
Sales NA *EMP* 540
SIC 6321 6311 Health insurance carriers; Life insurance
Pr: Martin P Hauser
V Ch: Charles R Vignos
**CEO:* Claude Vincenti
**VP:* Annette M Ruby

SUMMACARE
See SUMMA INSURANCE CO INC

SUMMACARE INSURANCE COMPANY
See SUMMA HEALTH SYSTEM

SUMMACARE INSURANCE COMPANY
See SUMMA BARBERTON CITIZENS HOSPITAL

SUMMER CREST APARTMENTS
See PLAZA MANOR PRESERVATION LP

D-U-N-S 12-359-8984
▲ SUMMER INFANT INC
1275 Park East Dr, Woonsocket, RI 02895-6185
Tel (401) 671-6550 *Founded/Ownrshp* 1985
Sales 205.8MM *EMP* 197
Tkr Sym SUMR *Exch* NAS
SIC 2514 2399 3842 3261 Juvenile furniture, household: metal; Infant carriers; Personal safety equipment; Bathroom accessories/fittings, vitreous china or earthenware
Pr: Mark Messner
CFO: William E Mote Jr
QA Dir: Kathleen Carlson
QA Dir: Martin D Rivera
Sls Mgr: Sarah Matteau
Board of Directors: Evelyn Dan, Martin Fogelman, Robin Marino, Alan Mustacchie, Robert Stebenne, Stephen J Zelkowicz

SUMMERFEST
See MILWAUKEE WORLD FESTIVAL INC

SUMMERLIN HOSPITAL
See UHS SUMMERLIN RECEIVING

D-U-N-S 17-618-3523
■ SUMMERLIN HOSPITAL MEDICAL CENTER LLC
(*Suby of* UNIVERSAL HEALTH SERVICES INC) ★
657 N Town Center Dr, Las Vegas, NV 89144-6367
Tel (702) 233-7000 *Founded/Ownrshp* 1997
Sales 101.1MM^E *EMP* 600
SIC 8062 8011 General medical & surgical hospitals; Offices & clinics of medical doctors
CEO: Robert Freymuller
Dir Recs: Peggy Cruse
**COO:* Claude Wise
**CFO:* Bonny Sorensen
Dir Lab: Lydia Coleman
Dir Lab: Phyllis T Lilly
Chf Nrs Of: Linda Lopes
Ansthlgy: Selwyn A Kidney
Doctor: Cathy Aja
HC Dir: Lori Briggs

D-U-N-S 00-881-2273
SUMMERS-TAYLOR INC
300 W Elk Ave, Elizabethton, TN 37643-2614
Tel (423) 543-3181 *Founded/Ownrshp* 1948
Sales 160.8MM^E *EMP* 400
SIC 1611 1794 3273

D-U-N-S 08-021-1909
SUMMERTIME HOLDING CORP
1301 Solana Blvd Ste 2100, Westlake, TX 76262-1675
Tel (817) 961-2100 *Founded/Ownrshp* 2015
Sales 234.9MM^E *EMP* 5,442^E
SIC 6719 7371 Investment holding companies, except banks; Custom computer programming services
CEO: Tony Aquila

D-U-N-S 07-842-5419
■ SUMMERVILLE AT HAZEL CREEK LLC
HAZEL CREEK ASSISTED LIVING
(*Suby of* BROOKDALE SENIOR LIVING) ★
6125 Hazel Ave, Orangevale, CA 95662-4558
Tel (916) 988-7901 *Founded/Ownrshp* 2006
Sales 20.0MM^E *EMP* 3,130^E
SIC 8361 Home for the aged
Owner: Lonnie Irvine

D-U-N-S 80-746-2882
SUMMERWOOD CORP
KFC
14 Balligomingo Rd, Conshohocken, PA 19428-2725
Tel (610) 260-1500 *Founded/Ownrshp* 1994
Sales 47.3MM^E *EMP* 1,600
SIC 5812 Fast-food restaurant, chain
CEO: Robert Eaton
Pr: Terry Brown-Walker
**Pr:* John Marsella Jr
**Sec:* Celeste Nasuti
Exec: David Demarco
**Prin:* James Nasuti
Sys Admin: Terry Brown Walker
VP Opers: Bret Baevsky
VP Opers: Jim Fullam

SUMMIT
See MORTEX PRODUCTS INC

D-U-N-S 84-473-2941
SUMMIT CONSOLIDATION GROUP INC
10497 Town Cntry Way 3, Houston, TX 77024-1117
Tel (713) 554-2244 *Founded/Ownrshp* 1997
Sales 32.7MM^E *EMP* 1,040
Accts R E Bassie & Co Pc Houston
SIC 7373 7371 4813 Computer integrated systems design; Custom computer programming services;
Ch Bd: Walter D Davis III
**CFO:* Lamont J Waddell
**Prin:* Joel Flowers

D-U-N-S 08-751-4121
■ SUMMIT CONSULTING LLC
(*Suby of* GREAT AMERICAN HOLDING INC) ★
2310 Commerce Point Dr, Lakeland, FL 33801-6880
Tel (863) 665-6060 *Founded/Ownrshp* 2014
Sales NA *EMP* 750
SIC 6331 6411 Fire, marine & casualty insurance; Insurance information & consulting services
Pr: Carol P Sipe
CFO: David Conaway
VP: Mike Arnold
VP: John D Hanselman
VP: Gary J Ostrow
VP: James Wood
Comm Man: Tracy Lungmus
Dir IT: Kelly Stone
Netwrk Mgr: Meryl Crews
VP Mktg: Daniel King

D-U-N-S 82-639-2008
SUMMIT CONTRACTING GROUP INC
1000 Rverside Ave Ste 800, Jacksonville, FL 32204
Tel (904) 268-5515 *Founded/Ownrshp* 2007
Sales 101.9MM *EMP* 45
Accts Barley Mcnamara & Wild Jacks
SIC 1522 Apartment building construction
Pr: Michael Mark Padgett
**CEO:* Nicole Padgett
CFO: Richard J Longo
CFO: Katherine May
**VP:* Bernie Cornelius

D-U-N-S 05-606-5121
SUMMIT CREDIT UNION
2424 Rimrock Rd, Madison, WI 53713-2701
Tel (608) 244-2400 *Founded/Ownrshp* 1935
Sales NA *EMP* 140
SIC 6062 State credit unions, not federally chartered
Ex Dir: Kim Sponem
**CFO:* Keith Peterson

SUMMIT DISTRIBUTING
See SLBS MANAGEMENT INC

D-U-N-S 08-527-5170 IMP/EXP
SUMMIT ELECTRIC SUPPLY CO INC
2900 Stanford Dr Ne, Albuquerque, NM 87107-1814
Tel (505) 346-2900 *Founded/Ownrshp* 1977
Sales 426.9MM *EMP* 650
Accts Redw Llc Albuquerque New Mex
SIC 5063 Electrical supplies
Pr: Victor R Jury Jr
**Pr:* Paul Jeffries
CFO: Valerie Knight
**Sr VP:* Joe Chesky
VP: Jennifer Baca
VP: Scott Cogan
VP: Mike Custred
VP: Dan Ferrari
VP: Gary Leader
VP: David Wascom
Creative D: Kevin Glasgow
Board of Directors: Joe Chesky, Jan Jury-Efurd, David L Meredith, Scott Meredith

D-U-N-S 05-912-6701
SUMMIT FIRE PROTECTION CO
SUMMIT MECHANICAL
575 Minnehaha Ave W, Saint Paul, MN 55103-1573
Tel (651) 288-0777 *Founded/Ownrshp* 1999
Sales 157.5MM^E *EMP* 450
SIC 1711 Fire sprinkler system installation
CEO: John J Evrard
Pr: Dean Howard
**Pr:* Quintin Rubald
Div Mgr: Brett Carley
Div Mgr: Chris Leaver
IT Man: Matt Praught
Opers Mgr: Stacy Reese

D-U-N-S 55-692-8216
SUMMIT GROUP INC
HAMPTON INN
2701 S Minn Ave Ste 6, Sioux Falls, SD 57105-4746
Tel (512) 538-2300 *Founded/Ownrshp* 1998
Sales 66.0MM^E *EMP* 1,600
SIC 7011 Hotels & motels
Pr: Kerry W Boekelheide
**COO:* Dan Hampton
Sr VP: Kristina Anderson
Genl Mgr: Nancy Gasperetti
Genl Mgr: Robert Rose
Sls Mgr: Anglea Haynie

D-U-N-S 15-213-8228
SUMMIT HEALTH
112 N 7th St, Chambersburg, PA 17201-1720
Tel (717) 267-3000 *Founded/Ownrshp* 1985
Sales 480.5MM *EMP* 2,968
Accts Smith Elliott Kearns & Company
SIC 8099 Childbirth preparation clinic
Pr: Norman P Epstein
Pr: Michele Zeigler
COO: John Massimilla

*CFO: Patrick O'Donnell
CFO: Patrick Odonnell
Treas: Rodger Savage
Ofcr: Mary Rine
Ex VP: Katherine E Cashdollar
VP: Carol Cryer
VP: Sherri Stahl
Exec: Kendra Neiderer
Dir Rx: Dave Grant

D-U-N-S 06-935-7067
SUMMIT HEALTH CARE REGIONAL MEDICAL CENTER
2200 E Show Low Lake Rd, Show Low, AZ 85901-7800
Tel (928) 537-6338 Founded/Ownrshp 2011
Sales 155.8MM EMP 50
SIC 8062 General medical & surgical hospitals
Prin: Edgar J Pringle
CTO: Stevie Burnside
VP Opers: Doug Gilchrist
QC Dir: Carolyn Jacobs

D-U-N-S 10-120-0017
■ **SUMMIT HEALTH INC**
(Suby of QUEST DIAGNOSTICS INC) ★
27175 Haggerty Rd, Novi, MI 48377-3626
Tel (248) 799-8303 Founded/Ownrshp 2014
Sales 181.5MM^E EMP 12,000
SIC 8099 8741 Health screening service; Management services
Pr: Richard Penington
*COO: Doug Finch
VP: Sandra Drake
Prgrm Mgr: Seth Ruben
Opers Mgr: Edward Wheeler
Natl Sales: Deb Martinez
Doctor: Rebecca L Pound

SUMMIT HEALTHCARE
See SUMMIT MEDICAL PLAZA LLC

D-U-N-S 08-446-2118
SUMMIT HEALTHCARE ASSOCIATION
2200 E Show Low Lake Rd, Show Low, AZ 85901-7831
Tel (928) 537-4375 Founded/Ownrshp 1976
Sales 140.8MM EMP 700^E
Accts Schmidt Westergard & Company P
SIC 8621 Professional membership organizations
Ch: John Corder
Chf Path: Larry Shaw
*Treas: Becky Thompson
Chf Mktg O: Angie Kolling
Ofcr: Marian Howe
Chf Nrs Of: Thia Ebert
CIO: Aaron Young
IT Man: Paul Wade
Mtls Mgr: David Hughes
Mtls Mgr: Paul Wang
Mktg Dir: Terry Lapointe
Board of Directors: Neal Thompson

D-U-N-S 06-495-2508
SUMMIT HOLDING ONE CORP
10330 Old Columbia Rd, Columbia, MD 21046-2133
Tel (410) 312-6000 Founded/Ownrshp 2005
Sales 130.4MM^E EMP 777^E
SIC 6719 Investment holding companies, except banks

SUMMIT HOLDINGS
See ROBERTS TRUCK CENTER HOLDING CO LLC

D-U-N-S 96-802-8238
■ **SUMMIT HOTEL OP LP**
(Suby of SUMMIT HOTEL PROPERTIES INC) ★
12600 Hill Country Blvd, Austin, TX 78738-6723
Tel (512) 538-2300 Founded/Ownrshp 2010
Sales 134.2MM EMP 65^E
SIC 7011
CEO: Daniel P Hansen
CFO: Stuart Becker

D-U-N-S 96-554-0474
▲ **SUMMIT HOTEL PROPERTIES INC**
12600 Hill Country Blvd, Austin, TX 78738-6723
Tel (512) 538-2300 Founded/Ownrshp 2010
Sales 463.4MM EMP 40^E
Tkr Sym INN Exch NYS
SIC 6798 Real estate investment trusts
Pr: Daniel P Hansen
*Ch Bd: Thomas W Storey
COO: Craig J Aniszewski
CFO: Greg A Dowell
Ex VP: Christopher R Eng
VP: Paul Ruiz
Board of Directors: Bjorn R L Hanson, Jeffrey W Jones, Kenneth J Kay

D-U-N-S 07-936-3809
SUMMIT MATERIALS CORPS I INC
(Suby of SUMMIT MATERIALS LLC) ★
1550 Wynkoop St Fl 3, Denver, CO 80202-1383
Tel (303) 893-0012 Founded/Ownrshp 2011
Sales 121.8MM^E EMP 355^E
SIC 1542 1611 Nonresidential construction; Highway & street paving contractor
Ch Bd: Thomas Hill
*CFO: Brian Harris

D-U-N-S 07-936-3794
SUMMIT MATERIALS HOLDINGS II LLC
(Suby of SUMMIT MATERIALS LLC) ★
1550 Wynkoop St Fl 3, Denver, CO 80202-1383
Tel (303) 893-0012 Founded/Ownrshp 2010
Sales 90.9MM^E EMP 265^E
SIC 1542 1611 Nonresidential construction; Highway & street paving contractor

D-U-N-S 07-978-8130
SUMMIT MATERIALS HOLDINGS LLC
(Suby of SUMMIT MATERIALS HOLDINGS LP) ★
1550 Wynkoop St Fl 3, Denver, CO 80202-1383
Tel (303) 893-0012 Founded/Ownrshp 2011
Sales 1.4MMM^E EMP 3,990^E
SIC 1542 1611 Nonresidential construction; Highway & street paving contractor
Pr: Thomas W Hill
Ch Bd: Howard L Lance

D-U-N-S 07-978-7470
SUMMIT MATERIALS HOLDINGS LP
1550 Wynkoop St Fl 3, Denver, CO 80202-1383
Tel (303) 893-0012 Founded/Ownrshp 2013
Sales 1.4MMM^E EMP 3,990^E
SIC 1542 1611 Nonresidential construction; Highway & street paving contractor
Pr: Thomas W Hill
Ch Bd: Howard L Lance

D-U-N-S 07-974-9066
▲ **SUMMIT MATERIALS INC**
1550 Wynkoop St Fl 3, Denver, CO 80202-1383
Tel (303) 893-0012 Founded/Ownrshp 2009
Sales 1.4MMM EMP 4,300^E
Tkr Sym SUM Exch NYS
SIC 1422 1622 1795 Cement rock, crushed & broken-quarrying; Bridge, tunnel & elevated highway; Wrecking & demolition work
Pr: Thomas W Hill
*Ch Bd: Howard L Lance
COO: Douglas C Rauh
CFO: Brian J Harris
Ofcr: Kevin A Gill
Ex VP: Thomas A Beck
Ex VP: Michael J Brady
Ex VP: M Shane Evans
Ex VP: Damian J Murphy

D-U-N-S 07-978-8615
SUMMIT MATERIALS INTERMEDIATE HOLDINGS LLC
(Suby of SUMMIT MATERIALS HOLDINGS LLC) ★
1550 Wynkoop St Fl 3, Denver, CO 80202-1383
Tel (303) 893-0012 Founded/Ownrshp 2011
Sales 1.4MMM^E EMP 3,990^E
SIC 1542 1611 Nonresidential construction; Highway & street paving contractor
Pr: Thomas W Hill
Ch Bd: Howard L Lance

D-U-N-S 02-583-5321
SUMMIT MATERIALS LLC
(Suby of SUMMIT MATERIALS INTERMEDIATE HOLDINGS LLC) ★
1550 Wynkoop St Fl 3, Denver, CO 80202-1383
Tel (303) 893-0012 Founded/Ownrshp 2008
Sales 1.4MMM EMP 3,990
SIC 1542 1611 Nonresidential construction; Highway & street paving contractor
Pr: Thomas W Hill
*Ch Bd: Howard L Lance
CFO: Brian J Harris
CFO: Clint Pulley
Genl Mgr: Angela Dziubek

SUMMIT MECHANICAL
See SUMMIT FIRE PROTECTION CO

SUMMIT MEDICAL CENTER
See HCA HEALTH SERVICES OF TENNESSEE INC

D-U-N-S 07-395-0446
SUMMIT MEDICAL CENTER
SURGERY CTR OF ALTA BATES SUMM
(Suby of ALTA BATES SUMMIT MEDICAL CTR) ★
350 Hawthorne Ave, Oakland, CA 94609-3100
Tel (510) 655-4000 Founded/Ownrshp 1955
Sales 321.5MM EMP 2,200
SIC 8062 8221 5947

D-U-N-S 07-836-9323
SUMMIT MEDICAL GROUP INC
ST. ELIZABETH PHYSICIANS
334 Thomas More Pkwy, Crestview Hills, KY 41017-3464
Tel (859) 344-3737 Founded/Ownrshp 1995
Sales 228.4MM EMP 50
SIC 8011 General & family practice, physician/surgeon
Pr: Glenn Loomis

D-U-N-S 07-932-5403
SUMMIT MEDICAL GROUP PA
1 Diamond Hill Rd, Berkeley Heights, NJ 07922-2104
Tel (908) 277-8880 Founded/Ownrshp 1999
Sales 119.5MM^E EMP 662
SIC 8099 8011 Medical services organization; Childbirth preparation clinic; Offices & clinics of medical doctors
Ch: Charles J Wittmann Jr
*CEO: Jeffrey Le Benger
*COO: Karen M Graham
*Prin: Olympia Lang
*Ex Dir: Andrew Mintz
Genl Mgr: Tammy Pesterfield
Surgeon: John Cunningham
Doctor: Fred Aueron
Doctor: David Bullek
Doctor: Susan Cantor
Doctor: Charles Gelber

D-U-N-S 83-050-8227
SUMMIT MEDICAL PLAZA LLC
SUMMIT HEALTHCARE
2200 E Show Low Lake Rd, Show Low, AZ 85901-7831
Tel (928) 537-4375 Founded/Ownrshp 2007
Sales 136.6MM EMP 8
SIC 8361 Rehabilitation center, residential: health care incidental
Pr: John Corder
CIO: Tom Sallis

D-U-N-S 07-860-3350
▲ **SUMMIT MIDSTREAM PARTNERS LP**
1790 Hughes, The Woodlands, TX 77380
Tel (832) 413-4770 Founded/Ownrshp 2009
Sales 371.3MM EMP 294^E
Tkr Sym SMLP Exch NYS
SIC 4922 Natural gas transmission
Pr: Steven J Newby
Genl Pt: Summit Midstream GP
CFO: Matthew S Harrison

D-U-N-S 00-109-1842 IMP/EXP
SUMMIT PACKAGING SYSTEMS INC
SPS
400 Gay St, Manchester, NH 03103-6817
Tel (603) 669-5410 Founded/Ownrshp 1975
Sales 149.2MM^E EMP 510
SIC 3499 3089 Aerosol valves, metal; Caps, plastic
Pr: Gordon C Gilroy
*CFO: Michael Conway
*Treas: Scott N Gilroy

D-U-N-S 78-331-3856
SUMMIT PARTNERS LP
222 Berkeley St Fl 18, Boston, MA 02116-3755
Tel (617) 824-1000 Founded/Ownrshp 1999
Sales 287.0MM^E EMP 1,806
SIC 6799 Venture capital companies
Genl Pt: Thomas Jennings
Genl Pt: Sotiris Lyritzis
Prin: Peter Connolly
Prin: Greg Goldfarb
Prin: Christian Strain
Mng Dir: Bruce R Evans

D-U-N-S 78-470-2578
SUMMIT PLACE LIVING CENTER LLC
807 Se Main St, Simpsonville, SC 29681-7150
Tel (864) 963-6069 Founded/Ownrshp 2006
Sales 906.5MM EMP 99
SIC 8051 Skilled nursing care facilities

D-U-N-S 05-969-7201 IMP
SUMMIT POLYMERS INC
SUMMIT-MEXICO
6715 S Sprinkle Rd, Portage, MI 49002-9707
Tel (269) 324-9330 Founded/Ownrshp 1972
Sales 231.7MM^E EMP 2,000
SIC 3089 Injection molding of plastics
Pr: James Haas
*CFO: John Meyer
*VP: Gregory Goodman
Exec: Janet Westra
Prgrm Mgr: Paul Bassett
Prgrm Mgr: Steve Boyea
Prgrm Mgr: Garry Ellison
Prgrm Mgr: Brian Hirst
Prgrm Mgr: Daniel Marshall
Prgrm Mgr: Mark Roodbeen
Prgrm Mgr: Todd Rozankovich

D-U-N-S 79-428-8014
SUMMIT REALTY GROUP INC
177 Riverside Ave Ste F, Newport Beach, CA 92663-4080
Tel (619) 987-1630 Founded/Ownrshp 2007
Sales 100.0MM EMP 25^E
SIC 8742 Business consultant
Pr: Cynthia A Manno
*CFO: John Frederick Manno
Sales Asso: Zack Cummins

D-U-N-S 10-765-2075
SUMMIT SECURITY SERVICES INC
390 Rxr Plz Lobbyl, Uniondale, NY 11556-0390
Tel (516) 240-2400 Founded/Ownrshp 1976
Sales 121.2MM^E EMP 3,025
SIC 7381 Protective services, guard; Security guard service
Pr: Richard N Auletta
CFO: Brendon McDonald
*Ch: Nicholas Auletta
Ofcr: Ramon Raymond
Ofcr: Ralph Scarborough
VP: Joseph Biondo
VP: Daniel Sepulveda
Dir IT: Arnie Rind
VP Opers: Robert Tracy
Sls Dir: Christopher Byrne
Sls Dir: Tony Triolo

D-U-N-S 79-181-4114
SUMMIT SERVICES GROUP INC
3220 Tillman Dr Ste 300, Bensalem, PA 19020-2028
Tel (215) 639-4274 Founded/Ownrshp 1991
Sales 5.9MM^E EMP 1,500
SIC 7213 7349 Linen supply; Building maintenance services
Pr: Joseph Cuzzupoli
*CFO: Larry Freni
*VP: John Bullock

D-U-N-S 01-910-9162
SUMMIT SLICKLINE INC
20701 County Road 50, La Salle, CO 80645-4417
Tel (970) 397-1808 Founded/Ownrshp 2014
Sales 1.3MMM EMP 6
SIC 1389 7389 Cleaning wells;
Pr: Frederick J Chandler
*Treas: Jeremiah Bullard

SUMMIT STATIONERS
See CARLTON CARDS RETAIL INC

SUMMIT TRUCK GROUP
See ROBERTS TRUCK CENTER OF OKLAHOMA LLC

SUMMIT-MEXICO
See SUMMIT POLYMERS INC

D-U-N-S 07-259-0508
SUMMIT-REED CITY INC
1315 S Mission Rd, Mount Pleasant, MI 48858-5613
Tel (989) 772-2028 Founded/Ownrshp 1993
Sales 84.1MM^E EMP 48
SIC 1311

D-U-N-S 07-881-2462
SUMMITMEDIA LLC
2700 Corporate Dr Ste 115, Birmingham, AL 35242-2735
Tel (205) 322-2987 Founded/Ownrshp 2012
Sales 90.3MM^E EMP 310
SIC 4832 Radio broadcasting stations
Ch: Carl Parmer

D-U-N-S 06-909-5990
SUMNER COUNTY BOARD OF EDUCATION
695 E Main St, Gallatin, TN 37066-2472
Tel (615) 451-5200 Founded/Ownrshp 1801
Sales 154.8MM^E EMP 4,000
SIC 8211 Public elementary & secondary schools; High school, junior or senior; Public vocational/technical school
Ex Dir: Benny Bills
Bd of Dir: Angela Alexander
Bd of Dir: Tim Brewer
Bd of Dir: Brian Cook
Bd of Dir: Ben Harris
Bd of Dir: Rob Wheeler
Bd of Dir: Ted W Wise
*Prin: Ken Henderson
Adm Dir: Larry Riggsbee
MIS Dir: Annie Cobb
Cmptr Lab: Cindy Thurman

D-U-N-S 07-846-5268
SUMNER COUNTY SCHOOL DISTRICT
695 E Main St, Gallatin, TN 37066-2472
Tel (615) 451-5200 Founded/Ownrshp 2012
Sales 6.1MM^E EMP 3,370^E
SIC 8211 Elementary & secondary schools
Bd of Dir: Phyllis Graves
Dir IT: Bob Wall
Pr Dir: Jeremy Johnson
Teacher Pr: Shawn Curtis

D-U-N-S 12-174-9501
SUMNER GROUP INC
COPYING CONCEPTS
6717 Waldemar Ave, Saint Louis, MO 63139-3533
Tel (314) 633-8000 Founded/Ownrshp 1984
Sales 108.2MM^E EMP 495
SIC 5044 7699 5112 Office equipment; Duplicating machines; Photocopy machines; Photocopy machine repair; Office supplies
Ch Bd: Steven P Sumner
*Pr: Kevin Laury
*Sec: Fred G Weaver
*Ex VP: Edmund C Sumner

SUMNER REGIONAL MEDICAL CENTER
See SRHS BANKRUPTCY INC

SUMTER BUILDERS
See SUMTER UTILITIES INC

D-U-N-S 00-797-5345
SUMTER ELECTRIC COOPERATIVE INC (FL)
SECO
330 S Us 301, Sumterville, FL 33585-4903
Tel (352) 237-4107 Founded/Ownrshp 1938
Sales 365.1MM EMP 390
Accts Purvis Gray & Company Llp Tal
SIC 4911 Distribution, electric power
Pr: Ray F Vick
*Pr: Wilson G Sheppard
*CEO: James P Duncan
*Sec: Robert G Gentry
*Sec: Robin R Henion
Chf Mktg O: Diane Steed
Ofcr: Gabriel Sanchez
VP: Kathryn Gloria
*VP: Jerry D Hatfield
VP: Jerry Hatfield
VP: Gregg Morrell

D-U-N-S 18-564-7567
SUMTER SCHOOL DISTRICT
1345 Wilson Hall Rd, Sumter, SC 29150-1890
Tel (803) 469-6900 Founded/Ownrshp 1952
Sales 147.1MM^E EMP 3,000
Accts Harper Poston & Moree Pa Ge
SIC 8211 Public elementary & secondary schools
Adm Dir: Gloria Brailsford
Dir Sec: Robin Mixon
IT Man: Angela Ramsey
Pr Dir: Mary Sheridan
HC Dir: Lashonda McElveen

D-U-N-S 00-792-0234
■ **SUMTER UTILITIES INC**
SUMTER BUILDERS
(Suby of QUANTA SERVICES INC) ★
1151 N Pike W, Sumter, SC 29153-1954
Tel (803) 469-8585 Founded/Ownrshp 1935, 1974
Sales 253.4MM^E EMP 820
SIC 1623 Electric power line construction
Pr: Derek O' Bradovich
Div VP: Brad Beck
DP Exec: Fowler Ryan

D-U-N-S 14-518-3328
SUMTOTAL SYSTEMS LLC
(Suby of SKILLSOFT CORP) ★
2850 Nw 43rd St Ste 150, Gainesville, FL 32606-6966
Tel (352) 264-2800 Founded/Ownrshp 2014
Sales 275.3MM^E EMP 1,009^E
SIC 7371 Computer software development; Computer software development & applications
CEO: Hardeep Gulati
*COO: Philip Bookman
*CFO: Jeff Laborde
Ofcr: Beau Monday
Sr VP: James Federico
Sr VP: Kanani Harnish
Sr VP: Murray Laidley
VP: Scott Andriano
VP: Brad Crain
VP: Shawn Dean
VP: Friedmar Jochum
VP: Amber Lloyd
VP: Christophe Marre
VP: Mark Pumper
VP: John Shrader
VP: Marcus Wasdin
VP: Kristie Willix

SUN & SKI SPORTS
See RETAIL CONCEPTS INC

D-U-N-S 60-712-1506 IMP
SUN AND SANDS ENTERPRISES LLC
PRIME TIME INTERNATIONAL
86705 Avenue 54 Ste A, Coachella, CA 92236-3814
Tel (760) 399-4278 Founded/Ownrshp 1986
Sales 123.9MM EMP 100
Accts Osborne Rincon La Quinta Ca
SIC 0161 Lettuce farm; Snap bean farm (bush & pole); Cantaloupe farm; Watermelon farm

Sales Exec: Jim Auchard
**Sales Exec:* Chuck Hodges

D-U-N-S 15-092-3894
▲ SUN BANCORP INC
350 Fellowship Rd Ste 101, Mount Laurel, NJ 08054-1201
Tel (856) 691-7700 *Founded/Ownrshp* 1985
Sales NA *EMP* 395E
Tkr Sym SNBC *Exch* NGS
SIC 6029 Commercial banks
Pr: Thomas M Obrien
Ch Bd: Sidney R Brown
Pr: Thomas M O'Brien
CFO: Thomas R Brugger
Ex VP: Nicos Katsoulis
Ex VP: Patricia M Schaubeck
Board of Directors: Jeffrey S Brown, Anthony R Coscia, F Clay Creasey Jr, Peter Galetto Jr, Eli Kramer, William J Marino, Wilbur L Ross Jr, Keith Stock, Grace C Torres

D-U-N-S 08-407-7256
SUN BASKET INC
1170 Olinder Ct, San Jose, CA 95122-2619
Tel (408) 669-4418 *Founded/Ownrshp* 2012
Sales 100.0MM *EMP* 435
SIC 2099 Ready-to-eat meals, salads & sandwiches
CEO: Adam Zbar

SUN BELLE IMPORTS
See SUN BELLE INC

D-U-N-S 00-995-4735 IMP
SUN BELLE INC
SUN BELLE IMPORTS
3810 Rose St, Schiller Park, IL 60176-2122
Tel (708) 343-4545 *Founded/Ownrshp* 1986
Sales 116.3MME *EMP* 100E
SIC 5149 Natural & organic foods
Pr: Janice Honigberg
VP: John A Hedges

D-U-N-S 17-517-7849 IMP
SUN BELLE INC
3810 Rose St, Schiller Park, IL 60176-2122
Tel (708) 343-4545 *Founded/Ownrshp* 1986
Sales 213.0MM *EMP* 145
SIC 5148 Fresh fruits & vegetables
Pr: Janice Honigberg
**VP:* John Hedges
Genl Mgr: Al Lemke
QA Dir: Steve Geever
Tech Mgr: Miguel Ahumada
Opers Mgr: Jose Garcia
Opers Mgr: Saldarriaga Santiago

D-U-N-S 06-875-0228
SUN CAPITAL PARTNERS INC
5200 Town Center Cir # 600, Boca Raton, FL 33486-1015
Tel (561) 962-3400 *Founded/Ownrshp* 1995
Sales 17.5MMME *EMP* 76,615
SIC 6799 2672 2671 5812 5411 5311 Investors; Coated paper, except photographic, carbon or abrasive; Packaging paper & plastics film, coated & laminated; Eating places; Grocery stores; Department stores; Department stores, discount; Department stores, non-discount
CEO: Marc Leder
Treas: Jane Marlow
Sr VP: Todd Buchman
VP: Michael J McConvery
Mng Dir: Richard Brown
Admn Mgr: Lizabeth Murphy

D-U-N-S 14-463-8558 IMP/EXP
SUN CHEMICAL CORP
SUN CHEMICAL INKS DIVISION GPI
(*Suby of* DIC CORPORATION)
35 Waterview Blvd Ste 100, Parsippany, NJ 07054-1285
Tel (973) 404-6000 *Founded/Ownrshp* 2009
Sales 2.5MMME *EMP* 8,000
SIC 2893 2865 Printing ink; Color pigments, organic
Pr: Rudi Lenz
**CFO:* Gerry Brady
CFO: Fairchild Dornier
**Chf Mktg O:* Felipe Meliado
**Ofcr:* John L McKeown
VP: Jeffrey Berger
VP: Martin Cellerier
VP: Eric Finkelman
VP: Penny Holland
VP: Brian Leen
VP: Robert Lorenz
VP: Jeffrey Shaw
VP: Ed Toliopolous
VP: Biagio N Vignolo
VP: Chris Weighill
Dir Lab: Kelly Walker
Comm Man: Sherry James
Board of Directors: Kazuo Kudo, Kazuo Sugie

SUN CHEMICAL INKS DIVISION GPI
See SUN CHEMICAL CORP

SUN CITY PRODUCE COMPANY
See SUN COMMODITIES INC

SUN COAST
See RECORD TOWN INC

D-U-N-S 00-959-3393 IMP/EXP
SUN COAST MERCHANDISE CORP
6315 Bandini Blvd, Commerce, CA 90040-3115
Tel (323) 720-9700 *Founded/Ownrshp* 1943
Sales 109.1MME *EMP* 250
SIC 5099 Brass goods
Pr: Kumar C Bhavnani
Ofcr: Walter Rubin
**VP:* Dilip Bhavnani
CIO: Vinay Arora
IT Man: Mukhtar Ahmed
Sales Exec: Aroon Bhavnani

D-U-N-S 15-406-7896
SUN COAST RESOURCES INC
6405 Cavalcade St Bldg 1, Houston, TX 77026-4315
Tel (713) 844-9600 *Founded/Ownrshp* 1985
Sales 1.3MMME *EMP* 1,649E
SIC 5172 2992 5084 1389 Petroleum brokers; Lubricating oils & greases; Oil well machinery, equipment & supplies; Oil field services
Pr: Kathy E Lehne
Sec: Lisa L Smith
VP: Samantha Aycock
VP: Tom Bittenbender
Dir IT: Bryan Frazier
Opers Mgr: Larry Bothmann

D-U-N-S 01-207-3990 IMP/EXP
SUN COMMODITIES INC
SUN CITY PRODUCE COMPANY
2230 Sw 2nd St, Pompano Beach, FL 33069-3121
Tel (954) 972-8383 *Founded/Ownrshp* 1998
Sales 121.9MME *EMP* 140
SIC 5148 Fresh fruits & vegetables
Pr: Gregg Leslie
**Sec:* Orland R Bethel
**VP:* Gary R Bethel

D-U-N-S 17-520-8784
▲ SUN COMMUNITIES INC
27777 Franklin Rd Ste 200, Southfield, MI 48034-8205
Tel (248) 208-2500 *Founded/Ownrshp* 1975
Sales 674.7MM *EMP* 1,790E
Tkr Sym SUI *Exch* NYS
SIC 6798 2451 Real estate investment trusts; Mobile homes
Ch Bd: Gary A Shiffman
Pr: John B McLaren
CFO: Karen J Dearing
Ex VP: Jonathan M Colman
VP: Chelsey Bannister
VP: Jim Hoekstra
VP: Tom Obranovic
VP: Brian Schroeder
Mktg Mgr: Ian Frank
Sales Asso: Patrick Otten
Board of Directors: Stephanie W Bergeron, Brian M Hermelin, Ronald A Klein, Ronald L Piasecki, Arthur A Weiss

SUN COUNTRY AIRLINES
See MN AIRLINES LLC

D-U-N-S 07-837-9978
■ SUN EDISON
(*Suby of* SUNEDISON INC) ★
501 Pearl Dr, Saint Peters, MO 63376-1071
Tel (636) 474-5000 *Founded/Ownrshp* 1959
Sales 574.1MME *EMP* 1,600E
SIC 3674 Semiconductors & related devices
Pr: Ahmad R Chatila
CFO: Jeffrey L Hall
Ex VP: Jose Coria
Ex VP: Hari Immadi
Sr VP: Dean Eoff
VP: Matt Rohm
VP: Sally Townsley
Dir Bus: Yong Liu
Genl Mgr: Andrea Orzan
Snr Sftwr: Ranjan Banerji
Snr Ntwrk: Alex Jentillucci

D-U-N-S 02-425-8361
SUN GORDMANS LLC
1926 S 67th St, Omaha, NE 68106-2800
Tel (402) 691-4000 *Founded/Ownrshp* 2008
Sales 335.2MME *EMP* 5,500E
SIC 5651 Family clothing stores
CEO: Jeffrey Gordman
**Prin:* Daniel Ron

D-U-N-S 08-011-9561
▲ SUN GORDMANS LP
5200 Town Center Cir # 600, Boca Raton, FL 33486-1015
Tel (561) 394-0550 *Founded/Ownrshp* 2008
Sales 657.8MME *EMP* 5,500E
SIC 5651 5963 Family clothing stores; Home related products, direct sales

SUN GRAPHIX/DIV
See GEIGER BROS

D-U-N-S 78-727-7854 IMP/EXP
SUN GRO HORTICULTURE DISTRIBUTION INC
SUNSHINE
770 Silver St, Agawam, MA 01001-2907
Tel (413) 786-4343 *Founded/Ownrshp* 2002
Sales 524.6MME *EMP* 1,001
SIC 1499 2875 Peat grinding; Peat mining; Fertilizers, mixing only
Pr: John Hill
COO: Chris Bednar
**COO:* Hris Bednar
Treas: Jack Cunningham
**Treas:* Andrew Soward

D-U-N-S 04-373-3369
SUN HEALTH CORP
WALTER O BOSWELL MEMORIAL HOSP
(*Suby of* BANNER RESEARCH INSTITUTE) ★
14719 W Grand Ave Ste 113, Surprise, AZ 85374-7203
Tel (623) 876-5350 *Founded/Ownrshp* 1981
Sales 163.0MME *EMP* 2,584
SIC 8062 8051 8082 7361 8733 6531 General medical & surgical hospitals; Skilled nursing care facilities; Home health care services; Nurses' registry; Medical research; Real estate agents & managers
CEO: Ronald D Guziak
**Ch Bd:* Paul A Hofstad
**V Ch Bd:* Morey J Jensen
Ofcr: Bonnie Olsen
**VP:* Ron Austerlade
**VP:* Penny Cowden
Sls Dir: Jackie Lusson

D-U-N-S 80-743-2380 IMP
■ SUN HEALTHCARE GROUP INC
(*Suby of* GENESIS HEALTHCARE CORP) ★
18831 Von Karman Ave # 400, Irvine, CA 92612-1533
Tel (949) 255-7100 *Founded/Ownrshp* 2012
Sales 484.1MME *EMP* 28,697
SIC 8011 8322 Medical insurance plan; Referral service for personal & social problems
CEO: George V Hager
Pr: Melissa Craig
Ofcr: Tracy Chiara
Ofcr: Linda Wiesemann
Sr VP: Richard J Spinello
**VP:* Richard Edwards
VP: Sharon Warren
Mng Dir: Charles McQueary
Mng Dir: John Nickoll
Dir IT: Steve Lyon
IT Man: Howard Skow
Board of Directors: Gregory S Anderson, Tony M Astorga, Christian K Bement, Michael J Foster, Barbara B Kennelly, Milton J Walters

D-U-N-S 83-006-0773
SUN HOLDINGS INC
ARBY'S
3318 Forest Ln Ste 300, Dallas, TX 75234-7774
Tel (972) 620-2287 *Founded/Ownrshp* 2006
Sales 51.7MME *EMP* 1,713E
SIC 5812 Fast-food restaurant, chain
CEO: Guillermo Perales
Mktg Dir: Lulu Perales
Genl Couns: Michael Mahan
Corp Couns: Lauren Glesby

D-U-N-S 05-259-9727
▲ SUN HYDRAULICS CORP (FL)
1500 W University Pkwy, Sarasota, FL 34243-2290
Tel (941) 362-1200 *Founded/Ownrshp* 1970
Sales 200.7MM *EMP* 862E
Tkr Sym SNHY *Exch* NGS
SIC 3492 Fluid power valves & hose fittings; Control valves, fluid power: hydraulic & pneumatic
Pr: Wolfgang H Dangel
**Ch Bd:* Philippe Lemaitre
CFO: Tricia L Fulton
Ofcr: Mark B Bokorney
Ofcr: Steven Hancox
Ofcr: Tim A Twitty
Board of Directors: Marc Bertoneche, Doug Britt, Allen J Carlson, David W Grzelak, Christine L Koski, Alexander Schuetz, David N Wormley

D-U-N-S 17-358-8393
SUN LIFE ASSURANCE CO OF CANADA (US)
(*Suby of* DELAWARE LIFE HOLDINGS LLC) ★
1 Sun Life Park, Wellesley, MA 02481-5615
Tel (781) 237-6030 *Founded/Ownrshp* 2013
Sales NA *EMP* 3
SIC 6311 6282 Life insurance; Life insurance carriers; Investment advisory service
Pr: Wes Thompson
Treas: Lyman B Thompson
**Sr VP:* Scott Davis
**Sr VP:* Bob Klein
**Sr VP:* Terry Mullen
VP: Bruce Gordon
VP: Arthur R McMurrich
VP: Michael Moran
VP: Robert P Vrolyk

D-U-N-S 85-935-6008
SUN LIFE FINANCIAL (US) SERVICES CO INC
(*Suby of* SUN LIFE ASSURANCE CO OF CANADA (US)) ★
1 Sun Life Executive Park, Wellesley, MA 02481
Tel (781) 237-6030 *Founded/Ownrshp* 1988
Sales NA *EMP* 162E
SIC 6311 Life insurance
Ch Bd: John D McNeil
**Pr:* James McNulty
**Pr:* Westley V Thompson
**CEO:* Dean Connors
**CFO:* Larry R Madge
CFO: Dale Pounder
**Treas:* L Brock Thompson
Ofcr: Joanna M Stanton
Ex VP: Mark Woodford
Sr VP: Andrew Darfoor
**Sr VP:* Scott M Davis
Sr VP: Scott Davis
Sr VP: Keith Gubbay
**Sr VP:* David J Healy
**Sr VP:* David D Horn
**Sr VP:* Kenneth A McCullum
**Sr VP:* Terrence J Mullen
**Sr VP:* Michael E Shunney
Sr VP: Michael Shunney
**VP:* Claude Accum
**VP:* H Roy Bentley

D-U-N-S 14-317-5888
SUN LIFE OF CANADA (US) HOLDINGS INC
(*Suby of* SUN LIFE ASSURANCE COMPANY OF CANADA)
1 Sun Life Park, Wellesley, MA 02481-5615
Tel (781) 237-6030 *Founded/Ownrshp* 1997
Sales NA *EMP* 2,591
SIC 6311 Life insurance
Pr: Robert C Salipante
**CFO:* Gary Corsi

D-U-N-S 13-782-1984 IMP/EXP
SUN MACKIE LLC
5200 Town Center Cir # 470, Boca Raton, FL 33486-1015
Tel (561) 394-0550 *Founded/Ownrshp* 2002
Sales 170.5MME *EMP* 1,437
SIC 3651 Household audio & video equipment; Audio electronic systems; Loudspeakers, electrodynamic or magnetic; Music distribution apparatus
CEO: Marc J Leder
**CEO:* Rodger R Krouse
**VP:* Scott W Edwards
**VP:* Thomas S King
**VP:* Case Kuehn
**VP:* Chris Metz
**VP:* Clarence E Terry

SUN MART PUMP N SAVE STATIONS
See SUN PACIFIC ENERGY INC

SUN MICROSYSTEMS
See ORACLE AMERICA INC

D-U-N-S 11-627-2717 IMP
■ SUN NATIONAL BANK
(*Suby of* SUN BANCORP INC) ★
226 W Landis Ave Ste 1, Vineland, NJ 08360-8142
Tel (800) 786-9066 *Founded/Ownrshp* 1985
Sales NA *EMP* 125E
SIC 6021 National commercial banks
Pr: Thomas X Geisel
**Ch Bd:* Bernard A Brown
Pr: Richard Wagner
**COO:* Jack R Allison IV
COO: Dorothy Antrim
**CFO:* Thomas R Brugger
CFO: Dan A Chil
**CFO:* Dan A Chila
**CFO:* Robert B Crowl
**Chf Cred:* Imran Riaz
**Ofcr:* Brad Fouss
**Ofcr:* Nicos Katsoulis
**Ofcr:* Anthony Morris
Assoc VP: Bob Preidt
**Ex VP:* Albert J Celini
**Ex VP:* Derek W Chauvette
**Ex VP:* Michele Estep
**Ex VP:* James S Killough
**Ex VP:* Robert F Mack
**Ex VP:* Bart Speziali
Sr VP: Anthony W Lamarca
Board of Directors: Keith Stock

SUN OPTA FD INGREDIENTS GROUP
See SUNOPTA INGREDIENTS INC

D-U-N-S 02-733-2832 IMP
SUN PACIFIC ENERGY INC
SUN MART PUMP N SAVE STATIONS
501 W Canal Dr, Kennewick, WA 99336-3815
Tel (509) 586-1135 *Founded/Ownrshp* 1981
Sales 83.0MME *EMP* 255
SIC 5172 5541 5411 Petroleum products; Filling stations, gasoline; Convenience stores, independent
Pr: Craig Eerkes

D-U-N-S 18-052-7665
SUN PACIFIC FARMING COOPERATIVE INC
ALLIED FARMING COMPANY
1250 E Myer Ave, Exeter, CA 93221-9345
Tel (559) 592-7121 *Founded/Ownrshp* 1973
Sales 122.8MME *EMP* 600
SIC 0762 Citrus grove management & maintenance services
Pr: Berne H Evans III
**Sec:* Bob Reniers
Ofcr: Jeanne Wilkerson
Ofcr: Jeannie Wilkinson

D-U-N-S 18-620-5170 IMP
SUN PACIFIC MARKETING COOPERATIVE INC
1095 E Green St, Pasadena, CA 91106-2503
Tel (213) 612-9957 *Founded/Ownrshp* 1998
Sales 538.5MME *EMP* 1,600
SIC 5148 Fresh fruits & vegetables
CEO: Berne H Evans III
**Pr:* Bob Dipiazza
**CFO:* Adam Smith
**Treas:* Robert Reniers
**VP:* Barney Evans
VP: Norman Evans

SUN PACIFIC PACKERS
See EXETER PACKERS INC

SUN PHARMACEUTICAL INDUSTRIES
See TARO PHARMACEUTICALS USA INC

D-U-N-S 14-697-4886 IMP
SUN PHARMACEUTICAL INDUSTRIES INC
(*Suby of* SUN PHARMACEUTICAL INDUSTRIES LIMITED)
270 Prospect Plains Rd, Cranbury, NJ 08512-3605
Tel (609) 495-2800 *Founded/Ownrshp* 1984
Sales 565.7MM *EMP* 535
Accts Rehmann Robson Llc Troy Mi
SIC 2834 Pharmaceutical preparations
CEO: Subramanian Kalyanasundaram
**CFO:* Mukul Rathi
**Sr VP:* Robert Kurkiewicz
VP: Rakesh Mehta
Ex Dir: Jitendra Doshi
Ex Dir: Jeffrey Yuan
Genl Mgr: Sunil Singh
CTO: Amit Shah
Board of Directors: F Folsom Bell, Timothy S Manney, Eddie R Munson, Sudhir V Valia

D-U-N-S 07-093-1480 IMP/EXP
SUN PRODUCTS CORP
(*Suby of* HENKEL CONSUMER GOODS INC) ★
60 Danbury Rd, Wilton, CT 06897-4406
Tel (203) 254-6700 *Founded/Ownrshp* 2016
Sales 1.4MMME *EMP* 48E
SIC 2841 Detergents, synthetic organic or inorganic alkaline; Dishwashing compounds
Pr: Jeffrey P Ansell
Pr: Scott Almquist
COO: Al Drewes
Treas: Joldy Macedonio
Chf Mktg O: Ed Vlacich
Ofcr: Gretchen Crist
Ofcr: Brian Del Buono
Ofcr: Blair P Hawley
Sr VP: Lora Vanvelsor
VP: Noel Allen
VP: Jim Duncan
VP: John Langford
VP: Sam P Perrone

D-U-N-S 14-266-7836
SUN SUITES INTERESTS LLLP
4770 S Atlanta Rd Se, Atlanta, GA 30339-1557
Tel (404) 350-9990 *Founded/Ownrshp* 1997
Sales 239.3MME *EMP* 3,550
SIC 6719 Investment holding companies, except banks

D-U-N-S 05-595-4457
■ **SUNTRUST BANKS OF FLORIDA INC**
(*Suby of* SUNTRUST BANKS INC) ★
200 S Orange Ave, Orlando, FL 32801-3410
Tel (407) 237-4141 *Founded/Ownrshp* 1985
Sales NA *EMP* 7,900
SIC 6021 6022 National commercial banks; State commercial banks
Ch Bd: Theodore J Hoepner
Ex VP: Jimmy O Williams
Ex VP: Julie Wolf
Sr VP: Cathleen Nash
VP: Philip Brenner
VP: Mike Karney
VP: Paul C Schreiber
VP: Lorraine Waters

D-U-N-S 14-076-9154
SUN VALLEY CO
(*Suby of* GRAND AMERICA HOTEL) ★
1 Sun Valley Rd, Sun Valley, ID 83353
Tel (208) 622-4111 *Founded/Ownrshp* 1977
Sales 152.9MM[E] *EMP* 2,000
SIC 7011 7996 Ski lodge; Resort hotel; Theme park, amusement
CEO: Bruce Fery
* *Pr:* Russ Matthews
* *VP:* Tim Silva
Sales Exec: Mark Thoreson
Sales Exec: Bert Witsil
Counsel: Scott Mayeda

D-U-N-S 78-581-3205 IMP
SUN VALLEY GROUP INC
3160 Upper Bay Rd, Arcata, CA 95521-9690
Tel (707) 822-2885 *Founded/Ownrshp* 1991
Sales 124.6MM[E] *EMP* 400
SIC 0181 Flowers: grown under cover (e.g. greenhouse production); Flowers grown in field nurseries; Bulbs, growing of
Pr: Leendert De Vries
Exec: David Aronovici
Rgnl Mgr: Debbie Hartman
Snr Sftwr: Roxanne McGuire
Sls Mgr: Doug Dobecki

D-U-N-S 04-137-8514 IMP
SUN WHOLESALE SUPPLY INC
SUNCOAST CHEMICALS
(*Suby of* PORPOISE POOL & PATIO INC) ★
6385 150th Ave N, Clearwater, FL 33760-2399
Tel (727) 524-3299 *Founded/Ownrshp* 1981
Sales 255.9MM[E] *EMP* 200
SIC 5169 5021 5023 5091 Swimming pool & spa chemicals; Outdoor & lawn furniture; Fireplace equipment & accessories; Hot tubs
Ch: Fred A Thomas
* *Pr:* John Thomas
* *COO:* Jim Eisch

D-U-N-S 95-790-0939 IMP/EXP
SUN WORLD INTERNATIONAL INC
16351 Driver Rd, Bakersfield, CA 93308-9733
Tel (661) 392-5000 *Founded/Ownrshp* 1976
Sales 428.6MM[E] *EMP* 2,500
SIC 0723 0172 0174 0175 0179 0161 Vegetable crops market preparation services; Vegetable packing services; Grapes; Citrus fruits; Deciduous tree fruits; Date orchard; Mango grove; Melon farms; Pepper farm, sweet & hot (vegetables)
Ch Bd: Keith Brackpool
* *CEO:* Timothy J Shaheen
Sales Exec: Gordon Robertson

D-U-N-S 00-923-4378 IMP/EXP
SUN-MAID GROWERS OF CALIFORNIA
13525 S Bethel Ave, Kingsburg, CA 93631-9232
Tel (559) 897-6235 *Founded/Ownrshp* 1923
Sales 382.9MM *EMP* 800
Accts Kpmg Llp Sacramento Californ
SIC 5149 Groceries & related products
Pr: Barry F Kriebel
CFO: Braden Bender
Sr VP: Richard Paumen
VP: Kayhan Hazrati
VP: Tomo Naito
VP: John Slinkard
Exec: Jeffrey Bortolussi
Dir Rx: Giulio Bernardi
CIO: Andy Schmidt
IT Man: Dan Scrivner
Tech Mgr: Tim Bernhardson
Board of Directors: David Peters, Mitch Bagdasarian, Paul Toste, Jeffrey P Bortolussi, V Chm, Ed Coelho, Russel A Efird, Robert D Epperson, Darren D Hoff, Jeffrey W Jue, Steve Kister, Jon E Marthedal

D-U-N-S 00-413-7949 IMP
■ **SUN-SENTINEL CO INC** (DE)
NEWS & SUN SENTINEL COMPANY
(*Suby of* TRONC INC) ★
500 E Broward Blvd # 800, Fort Lauderdale, FL 33394-3018
Tel (954) 356-4000 *Founded/Ownrshp* 1925, 2014
Sales 208.1MM[E] *EMP* 900
SIC 2711 Newspapers, publishing & printing
Ch: Douglas Lyons
V Ch: Cindy Bibliowicz
* *Pr:* Howard Greenberg
COO: Scott Smith
* *Ch:* Robyn Motley
* *Sr VP:* John McKeon
VP: Bob Christie
* *VP:* Michael Labonia
Genl Mgr: Tom Davidson
Dir IT: Linda Hart
QI Cn Mgr: Slade Wentworth

D-U-N-S 19-356-9993
SUN-TIMES MEDIA GROUP INC
(*Suby of* SUN-TIMES MEDIA HOLDINGS LLC) ★
350 N Orleans St Fl 10, Chicago, IL 60654-1700
Tel (312) 321-2299 *Founded/Ownrshp* 2009
Sales 302.9MM[E] *EMP* 2,322[E]
SIC 2711 Newspapers, publishing & printing
CEO: Tim Knight
Pr: Jerry J Strader
* *Pr:* Blair Richard Surkamer
CEO: Jeremy Deedes
* *CFO:* Thomas L Kram
Bd of Dir: Paul T Anderson
Bd of Dir: Frank Buxton
Bd of Dir: Andrew Davis
Bd of Dir: Robert Falls
Bd of Dir: Ann Filmer
Bd of Dir: Jim Fitzpatrick
Bd of Dir: Frank Galati
Bd of Dir: Jean Gottlieb
Bd of Dir: Tanya R Townsend
Bd of Dir: Wendell Tucker
Bd of Dir: James Zahn
Sr VP: David C Martin
* *Sr VP:* Barbara Swanson
VP: Jim Dyer
VP: Paul B Healy
VP: John J Martin
Board of Directors: Michael E Katzenstein, Robert B Poile, Graham W Savage, Robert A Schmitz

D-U-N-S 83-268-2632
SUN-TIMES MEDIA HOLDINGS LLC
(*Suby of* WRAPPORTS LLC) ★
350 N Orleans St Fl 10, Chicago, IL 60654-1700
Tel (312) 321-2299 *Founded/Ownrshp* 2011
Sales 304.8MM[E] *EMP* 2,330[E]
SIC 2711 Newspapers, publishing & printing
CEO: Timothy P Knight
* *Pr:* Bradley Phillip Bell
* *CEO:* Rodney O'Neal
* *Ch:* John A Canning
* *Ch:* Michael W Ferro

D-U-N-S 12-943-9212
■ **SUNAMERICA ANNUITY AND LIFE ASSURANCE CO**
(*Suby of* SUNAMERICA LIFE INSURANCE CO) ★
1 Sun America Ctr, Los Angeles, CA 90067-6100
Tel (310) 772-6000 *Founded/Ownrshp* 1986
Sales NA *EMP* 347[E]
SIC 6311 Life insurance funds, savings bank
CEO: Jay Wintrob
Mng Pt: Keith Honig
Pr: Janna Greer
CFO: David J Dietz
CFO: N Scott Gillis
Treas: Michael J Campbell
Sr VP: James Belardi
Sr VP: Marc H Gamsin
Sr VP: Marc Gamsin
Sr VP: Robert J Scheinerman
VP: Rodney Haviland
VP: Monica Suryapranata
Exec: Jeffrey Auld

D-U-N-S 00-690-2142
■ **SUNAMERICA INC**
(*Suby of* AIG) ★
1 Sun America Ctr Fl 38, Los Angeles, CA 90067-6101
Tel (310) 772-6000 *Founded/Ownrshp* 1957
Sales NA *EMP* 2,500
SIC 6091 6311 6211 6282 6411 6371 Nondeposit trust facilities; Life insurance carriers; Mutual funds, selling by independent salesperson; Brokers, security; Dealers, security; Manager of mutual funds, contract or fee basis; Pension & retirement plan consultants; Pension, health & welfare funds
Ch: Eli Broad
Pr: Rodney Haviland
CEO: Jay S Wintrob
COO: Howard Heitner
Ex VP: James R Belardi
Ex VP: Jana Waring Greer
Ex VP: Stewart Polakov
Sr VP: Michael J Akers
Sr VP: Mary L Cavanaugh
Sr VP: Randall W Epright
Sr VP: N Scott Gillis
Sr VP: Leslie Hunnicutt
Sr VP: Todd M McGrath
Sr VP: Scott H Richland
VP: Gavin Friedman
VP: George L Holdridge
VP: Jonathan Woodland
Board of Directors: William F Aldinger III, David O Maxwell, Barry Munitz, Lester Pollack, Carl E Reichardt, Sanford C Sigoloff, Harold M Williams, Karen Hastie Williams

D-U-N-S 09-337-7570
■ **SUNAMERICA INVESTMENTS INC**
(*Suby of* SUNAMERICA INC) ★
1 Sun America Ctr Fl 37, Los Angeles, CA 90067-6103
Tel (310) 772-6000 *Founded/Ownrshp* 1978
Sales 2.0MMM *EMP* 190
SIC 8741 6211 6282 7311 Administrative management; Financial management for business; Security brokers & dealers; Investment advisory service; Advertising agencies
Pr: Eli Broad

D-U-N-S 00-695-0505
■ **SUNAMERICA LIFE INSURANCE CO**
(*Suby of* SAFG RETIREMENT SERVICES INC) ★
1 Sun America Ctr Fl 36, Los Angeles, CA 90067-6104
Tel (310) 772-6000 *Founded/Ownrshp* 1890, 1999
Sales NA *EMP* 609[E]
SIC 6311

D-U-N-S 61-898-4272
■ **SUNBEAM AMERICAS HOLDINGS LLC**
(*Suby of* SUNBEAM OUTDOOR PRODUCTS) ★
2381 Nw Executive Ctr Dr, Boca Raton, FL 33431-8560
Tel (561) 912-4100 *Founded/Ownrshp* 1990
Sales 612.1M *EMP* 6,000
SIC 3631 2514 3421 3634 3829 3841 Barbecues, grills & braziers (outdoor cooking); Metal lawn & garden furniture; Lawn furniture: metal; Scissors, shears, clippers, snips & similar tools; Shears, hand; Clippers, fingernail & toenail; Electric housewares & fans; Hair dryers, electric; Blenders, electric; Food mixers, electric: household; Thermometers & temperature sensors; Temperature sensors, except industrial process & aircraft; Thermometers, liquid-in-glass & bimetal type; Geophysical & meteorological testing equipment; Blood pressure apparatus
Ch Bd: Jerry W Levin
Dir IT: Rich Johnson

D-U-N-S 07-952-0866
SUNBEAM GP LLC
(*Suby of* AMSURG CORP) ★
1 Maritime Plz, San Francisco, CA 94111-3404
Tel (615) 665-1283 *Founded/Ownrshp* 2007
Sales 118.0MM[E] *EMP* 3,000[E]
SIC 6719 Investment holding companies, except banks
CEO: Christopher A Holden

SUNBEAM OUTDOOR PRODUCTS
See AMERICAN HOUSEHOLD INC

D-U-N-S 00-131-5134 IMP
■ **SUNBEAM PRODUCTS INC** (DE)
(*Suby of* NEWELL BRANDS) ★
2381 Nw Executive Ctr Dr, Boca Raton, FL 33431-8560
Tel (561) 912-4100 *Founded/Ownrshp* 1981, 2005
Sales 3.0MMM[E] *EMP* 6,000
SIC 3631 3634 Barbecues, grills & braziers (outdoor cooking); Electric housewares & fans; Hair dryers, electric; Blenders, electric; Food mixers, electric: household
Pr: Andrew C Hill
Pr: Deborah Macdonald
VP: Debra Bruce
* *VP:* John Capps
VP: Carlos Coroalles
VP: James Junker
VP: Kyle Kaiser
VP: Patricia Madueno
VP: Stanley Ng
VP: Alejandro Pena
Prgrm Mgr: David Owens

D-U-N-S 00-377-5418 IMP
SUNBEAM TELEVISION CORP
WSVN MIAMI
1401 79th Street Cswy, North Bay Village, FL 33141-4104
Tel (305) 751-6692 *Founded/Ownrshp* 1953
Sales 180.8MM[E] *EMP* 556
SIC 4833 6512 Television broadcasting stations; Commercial & industrial building operation
Pr: Edmund N Ansin
* *CFO:* Roger Metcalf
Ex VP: Chris Wayland
* *VP:* Andrew L Ansin
* *VP:* Robert Leider
Mktg Dir: Ross Kramer

D-U-N-S 00-469-5370 IMP
SUNBELT BEVERAGE CO LLC
BREAKTHRU BEVERAGE GROUP
60 E 42nd St Ste 1915, New York, NY 10165-1904
Tel (212) 699-7000 *Founded/Ownrshp* 1997
Sales 2.3MMM[E] *EMP* 7,500
SIC 5182 Bottling wines & liquors
CEO: Charles Merinoff
COO: Greg Baird
CFO: Gene D Luciana
Ch: Raymond R Herrman Jr
Ch: Ray Herrmann
Ex VP: Ann Giambusso
Ex VP: Gene Luciano
VP: Gerald Baxter
VP: Arlyn B Miller
VP: Daniel Stuart
Opers Mgr: Bob Grear

SUNBELT PLASTIC EXTRUSIONS
See SOUTHERN IMPERIAL INC

D-U-N-S 10-177-6490 IMP/EXP
SUNBELT RENTALS INC
(*Suby of* ASHTEAD HOLDINGS LLC) ★
2341 Deerfield Dr, Fort Mill, SC 29715-8298
Tel (803) 578-5811 *Founded/Ownrshp* 1990
Sales 3.3MMM[E] *EMP* 8,261
SIC 7359 7353 Equipment rental & leasing; Tool rental; Oil equipment rental services
CEO: Brendan Horgan
COO: Tim Stommel
Ex VP: Kurt Kenkel
Sr VP: Kirby Miner
Sr VP: John Washburn
Dir Bus: Leo Peixoto
Brnch Mgr: Scott Sabo
Genl Mgr: Bradley Horner
Genl Mgr: Ed Ramirez
CTO: Donald Wood
DP Exec: Bryan Foust

D-U-N-S 07-925-4410
SUNBELT RENTALS INDUSTRIAL SERVICES LLC
(*Suby of* SUNBELT RENTALS INC) ★
2341 Deerfield Dr, Fort Mill, SC 29715-8298
Tel (803) 578-5811 *Founded/Ownrshp* 2013
Sales 79.5MM[E] *EMP* 1,000
SIC 7359 Equipment rental & leasing
CEO: Brendan Horgan

D-U-N-S 79-060-8215 IMP/EXP
SUNBELT SUPPLY CO INC
(*Suby of* SHALE-INLAND) ★
3750 Hwy 225, Pasadena, TX 77503
Tel (713) 672-2222 *Founded/Ownrshp* 2012
Sales 221.8MM[E] *EMP* 174[E]
SIC 5085 Industrial tools
Pr: Brent W Scheps
* *VP:* Larry A Feld
Sls Mgr: Danny Holt
Sales Asso: Matt Baker

D-U-N-S 08-000-2522
■ **SUNBRIDGE CARE ENTERPRISES WEST LLC**
KINGSBURG CENTER
(*Suby of* GENESIS HEALTHCARE LLC) ★
1101 Stroud Ave, Kingsburg, CA 93631-1016
Tel (559) 897-5881 *Founded/Ownrshp* 1981
Sales 6.5MM[E] *EMP* 3,597[E]
SIC 8051 Skilled nursing care facilities

SUNBRIDGE CARE REHABILITATION
See SUNBRIDGE HEALTHCARE LLC

SUNBRIDGE CARE REHABILITATION
See SUNBRIDGE RETIREMENT CARE ASSOCIATES INC

D-U-N-S 19-875-0242
■ **SUNBRIDGE HEALTHCARE LLC**
SUNBRIDGE CARE REHABILITATION
(*Suby of* SUN HEALTHCARE GROUP INC) ★
101 Sun Ave Ne, Albuquerque, NM 87109-4373
Tel (505) 821-3355 *Founded/Ownrshp* 1993
Sales 265.1MM[E] *EMP* 15,000
SIC 8052 8051 Intermediate care facilities; Skilled nursing care facilities
Pr: William Mathies
* *CEO:* George V Hager Jr
CFO: Walter Boston
* *CFO:* Jerry Roles
CFO: Ernest Schofield
* *Ex VP:* Paul D Bach
* *VP:* Logan Sexton

D-U-N-S 60-375-2999
■ **SUNBRIDGE RETIREMENT CARE ASSOCIATES INC**
SUNBRIDGE CARE REHABILITATION
(*Suby of* SUNBRIDGE CARE REHABILITATION) ★
101 Sun Ave Ne, Albuquerque, NM 87109-4373
Tel (505) 821-3355 *Founded/Ownrshp* 1998
Sales 18.1MM[E] *EMP* 2,200
SIC 6513 3842 Retirement hotel operation; Surgical appliances & supplies
Prin: William A Mathies
* *Treas:* Craig Hayes

D-U-N-S 00-407-5271
SUNBURST HOSPITALITY CORP
10750 Columbia Pike # 300, Silver Spring, MD 20901-4448
Tel (301) 592-3800 *Founded/Ownrshp* 1965
Sales 218.8MM[E] *EMP* 1,500[E]
SIC 8741 7011 Hotel or motel management; Hotels & motels; Motel, franchised; Hotel, franchised
Pr: Kevin Hanley
Ch Bd: Charles Ledsinger
CFO: Joseph P Smith
Ex VP: Pamela M Williams
VP: Russ Carlson
VP: Jim Maccutcheon
VP: Rob Marshall
VP: Thomas Mirgon
VP: Douglas Verner
VP: Pam Williams
Exec: Teresa Whitehead

D-U-N-S 11-084-3567
SUNBURY GENERATION LP
2384 N Old Trl, Selinsgrove, PA 17870-8067
Tel (570) 884-1200 *Founded/Ownrshp* 2006
Sales 96.5MM[E] *EMP* 115
SIC 4911 Electric services
CFO: Neil Hedrick
* *Pt:* Jim Martin
CFO: Jeff Specht
VP: Edward Griegel

D-U-N-S 15-178-6464 IMP/EXP
SUNCAST CORP
701 N Kirk Rd, Batavia, IL 60510-1433
Tel (630) 879-2050 *Founded/Ownrshp* 1984
Sales 267.4MM[E] *EMP* 800
SIC 2519 3052 3432 Lawn furniture, except wood, metal, stone or concrete; Garden furniture, except wood, metal, stone or concrete; Rubber hose; Lawn hose nozzles & sprinklers
Pr: Thomas A Tisbo
Ex VP: Michael Hamilton
Ex VP: Tracy Nugent
Ex VP: Tracy Scruggs
VP: Bob Lehr
* *VP:* Dean Mitchell
VP: Steve Whitehead
* *Prin:* Carl Smucker
Genl Mgr: Bill Sullivan
MIS Dir: Edward Booth
Sftwr Eng: Bradley Lippoldt

D-U-N-S 01-607-3972
SUNCOAST CARING COMMUNITY INC
5771 Roosevelt Blvd, Clearwater, FL 33760-3407
Tel (727) 586-4432 *Founded/Ownrshp* 2008
Sales 89.2MM[E] *EMP* 1,400
Accts Crowe Horwath Llp Chicago Il
SIC 6719 Personal holding companies, except banks
Pr: Rafael Sciullo
CFO: Anne Hochsprung
Prin: Michael Gaines

SUNCOAST CHEMICALS
See SUN WHOLESALE SUPPLY INC

D-U-N-S 08-137-5206
SUNCOAST CREDIT UNION
6801 E Hillsborough Ave, Tampa, FL 33610-4110
Tel (800) 999-5887 *Founded/Ownrshp* 1934
Sales NA *EMP* 1,000
Accts Hutto & Carver Pa Pensacola
SIC 6062 6061 State credit unions; Federal credit unions
Pr: Kevin Johnson
Ch Bd: Earl W Whitlock
V Ch: Patricia K Marsh
Treas: Linda Dunmire
Sr Ex VP: Linda Darling
Sr VP: Melva McKay Bass
Sr VP: Susan C Johnson
Sr VP: Julie A Renderos
VP: Darlene Helms
VP: Stephen Johnson
VP: Nancy Osterman
VP: Nancy Ostermann

SUNCOAST HOSPICE
See HOSPICE OF FLORIDA SUNCOAST

D-U-N-S 07-014-1577 IMP/EXP
SUNCOAST POST-TENSION LTD
(*Suby of* HAYWARD BAKER INC) ★
509 N Sam Houston Pkwy E # 300, Houston, TX 77060-4130
Tel (281) 445-8886 *Founded/Ownrshp* 2007
Sales 163.6MM^E *EMP* 500
SIC 3315 3316 3496 3449 Cable, steel: insulated or armored; Cold finishing of steel shapes; Miscellaneous fabricated wire products; Miscellaneous metalwork
CEO: William Larkin
Genl Pt: Keller HB One
Ltd Pt: Keller HB Two
CFO: Arnold Wasser
VP: Jim Blaisdell
**VP:* Robert Brown
**VP:* Larry Stadler
**Prin:* Peter Davis
Genl Mgr: Hank Cronin
Genl Mgr: Bill Manson
Dir IT: Sharon Flood

SUNCOAST ROOFER'S SUPPLY
See SRS DISTRIBUTION INC

D-U-N-S 06-916-2202
SUNCOAST TECHNICAL COLLEGE
ADULT & CMNTY ENRICHMENT ACE
4748 Beneva Rd, Sarasota, FL 34233-1756
Tel (941) 361-6590 *Founded/Ownrshp* 1967
Sales 233.9MM^E *EMP* 150^E
SIC 8249 Trade school

D-U-N-S 61-733-9031
▲ SUNCOKE ENERGY INC
1011 Warrenville Rd # 600, Lisle, IL 60532-0903
Tel (630) 824-1000 *Founded/Ownrshp* 2010
Sales 1.3MMM *EMP* 1,125^E
Tkr Sym SXC *Exch* NYS
SIC 3312 1241 Blast furnaces & steel mills; Coal mining services
Ch Bd: Frederick A Henderson
CFO: Fay West
Chf Cred: Katherine T Gates
Sr VP: P Michael Hardesty
Sr VP: Gary P Yeaw
VP: Allison S Lausas
VP: Jonathan S Lock
VP: Mark Newman
Board of Directors: Andrew D Africk, Alvin Bledsoe, Robert J Darnall, Peter B Hamilton, Robert A Peiser, John W Rowe, James E Sweetman

D-U-N-S 07-857-9672
■ SUNCOKE ENERGY PARTNERS LP
(*Suby of* SUN COAL & COKE LLC)
1011 Warrenville Rd # 600, Lisle, IL 60532-0903
Tel (630) 824-1000 *Founded/Ownrshp* 2012
Sales 838.5MM *EMP* 606^E
Tkr Sym SXCP *Exch* NYS
SIC 3312 Blast furnaces & steel mills; Coke oven products (chemical recovery); Coal gas derived from chemical recovery coke ovens
Ch Bd: Frederick A Henderson
Genl Pt: Suncoke E LLC
CFO: Fay West

D-U-N-S 01-624-0652
■ SUNCOM WIRELESS HOLDINGS INC
(*Suby of* T-MOBILE USA INC) ★
12920 Se 38th St, Bellevue, WA 98006-1350
Tel (425) 378-4000 *Founded/Ownrshp* 2008
Sales 103.4MM^E *EMP* 1,924
SIC 4812 Cellular telephone services; Paging services; Radio pager (beeper) communication services
Ch Bd: Michael E Kalogris
CFO: Eric Haskell
**Treas:* Daniel E Hopkins
**Ex VP:* William A Robinson
IT Man: Laura M Shawporter

D-U-N-S 13-517-8007 IMP
SUNCOR ENERGY (USA) INC
(*Suby of* SUNCOR ENERGY INC)
717 17th St Ste 2900, Denver, CO 80202-3324
Tel (303) 793-8000 *Founded/Ownrshp* 1997
Sales 304.5MM^E *EMP* 500
SIC 2911 Petroleum refining
Pr: Jay W Thornton
**Treas:* Marlowe Allison
VP: Lynn Allan
Natl Sales: Chuck Stevens

D-U-N-S 80-555-6409
■ SUNCREST HEALTHCARE INC
(*Suby of* ALMOST FAMILY INC) ★
9510 Ormsby Station Rd # 300, Louisville, KY 40223-5016
Tel (615) 627-9267 *Founded/Ownrshp* 2013
Sales 39.6MM^E *EMP* 1,340^E
SIC 8082 Home health care services
CEO: John W Dant III
**Pr:* Scott Mahosky
**COO:* Rexanne Domico
**CFO:* Don Borchert
**CFO:* Gary W Rasmussen
**Ex VP:* Brenda Dunn
**Ex VP:* John Kiehl
**VP:* Kari Byrne
Exec: Vicky Freed
Off Mgr: Angela Saturley

SUNDAY STAR LEDGER
See NEWARK MORNING LEDGER CO

SUNDOWN NATURALS
See REXALL SUNDOWN INC

D-U-N-S 08-256-2299 IMP/EXP
SUNDOWNER TRAILERS INC (OK)
9805 Ok Highway 48 S, Coleman, OK 73432-1215
Tel (580) 937-4255 *Founded/Ownrshp* 1981
Sales 181.7MM^E *EMP* 500
SIC 3715 Trailers or vans for transporting horses
Pr: Larry Shipman
**VP:* John Shipman
**Prin:* Gary Shipman
CTO: Jeremy Currie

IT Man: Bub Sampson
IT Man: Justin Walker
Plnt Mgr: Kent Hall
Manager: Tim Barron

D-U-N-S 07-335-4982
SUNDT COMPANIES INC
2015 W River Rd Ste 101, Tucson, AZ 85704-1676
Tel (520) 750-4600 *Founded/Ownrshp* 1998
Sales 934.1MM *EMP* 1,500
Accts Mayer Hoffman & Mccann
SIC 1542 1771 1611 Nonresidential construction; Concrete work; Highway & street construction
Ch Bd: J Douglas Pruitt
**Pr:* David S Crawdford
**CEO:* Raymond C Bargull
**COO:* Eric Hedlund
**COO:* Mike Hoover
**CFO:* Kevin M Burnett
**Sr VP:* Ronald Stuff
VP: Carol Peabody

D-U-N-S 09-803-8607
SUNDT CONSTRUCTION INC
(*Suby of* SUNDT COMPANIES INC) ★
2620 S 55th St, Tempe, AZ 85282-1903
Tel (480) 293-3000 *Founded/Ownrshp* 1890
Sales 823.6MM *EMP* 1,000
Accts Mayer Hoffman & Mccann
SIC 1542 1611 1629 1541 8741 Commercial & office building, new construction; Specialized public building contractors; General contractor, highway & street construction; Airport runway construction; Earthmoving contractor; Dam construction; Land preparation construction; Mine loading & discharging station construction; Industrial buildings, new construction; Construction management
Ch Bd: J Douglas Pruitt
**Pr:* David S Crawford
Pr: Cade Rowly
**COO:* Eric Hedlund
**COO:* Mike Hoover
**CFO:* Kevin M Burnett
**Sr VP:* Ronald Stuff
VP: Travis McCarthy
VP: Barbara Terry
VP: Brady Terry
Info Man: Todd Barker

D-U-N-S 95-664-0395 IMP/EXP
SUNDYNE LLC
(*Suby of* ACCUDYNE INDUSTRIES LLC) ★
14845 W 64th Ave, Arvada, CO 80007-7523
Tel (303) 425-0800 *Founded/Ownrshp* 2013
Sales 145.4MM^E *EMP* 325^E
SIC 3563 3561 Air & gas compressors; Industrial pumps & parts
Pr: Jeff Wiemelt
Ofcr: Bony Wilcox
VP: Tammy Stevens
Admn Mgr: Gary Dickes

D-U-N-S 36-183-4617
▲ SUNEDISON INC
13736 Rverport Dr Ste 180, Maryland Heights, MO 63043
Tel (314) 770-7300 *Founded/Ownrshp* 1984
Sales 2.4MMM *EMP* 7,260
Tkr Sym SUNEQ *Exch* OTC
SIC 3674 Semiconductors & related devices; Photovoltaic devices, solid state; Silicon wafers, chemically doped
CEO: John S Dubel
**Ch Bd:* Emmanuel T Hernandez
Pr: David A Ranhoff
Pr: Carlos Domenech Zornoza
CFO: Philip J Gund
Ofcr: Matthew E Herzberg
Ex VP: Paul Gaynor
Sr VP: Stephen O'Rourke
Sr VP: Martin H Truong
VP: Nagendra Cherukupalli
VP: Jim McNeill
Board of Directors: Antonio R Alvarez, Clayton C Daley Jr, Claire Gogel, Georganne C Proctor, James B Williams, Randy H Zwirn

D-U-N-S 07-965-9218
SUNEDISON INTERNATIONAL INC
501 Pearl Dr, Saint Peters, MO 63376-1071
Tel (636) 474-5000 *Founded/Ownrshp* 1997
Sales 118.0MM^E *EMP* 624^E
SIC 3559 Semiconductor manufacturing machinery

D-U-N-S 82-790-4991
SUNEDISON INTERNATIONAL LLC
13736 Rverport Dr Ste 180, Maryland Heights, MO 63043
Tel (443) 909-7200 *Founded/Ownrshp* 2009
Sales 119.5MM^E *EMP* 278^E
SIC 4911 Electric services

D-U-N-S 17-472-5494 IMP/EXP
■ SUNEDISON LLC
(*Suby of* SUNEDISON INC) ★
600 Clipper Dr, Belmont, CA 94002-4119
Tel (650) 453-5600 *Founded/Ownrshp* 2009
Sales 150.5MM^E *EMP* 250
SIC 4911 Electric services
Sr VP: Jubran Whalan
VP: Martha Duggan
VP: Len Jornlin
Genl Mgr: Liborio Nanni
Sls&Mrk Ex: Greg Ashley
Sls Dir: Tim Osullivan
Manager: Russ Wright
Manager: Sam Youneszadeh

D-U-N-S 02-500-3009 IMP
SUNENERGY1 LLC
192 Raceway Dr, Mooresville, NC 28117-6509
Tel (704) 662-0375 *Founded/Ownrshp* 2010
Sales 100.0MM *EMP* 200
SIC 1711 Solar energy contractor
Pr: Kenny Habul
**COO:* Bradley Fite
**VP:* Kim Habul

**VP:* Joel Sossaman
**Genl Mgr:* Wally Coble

D-U-N-S 80-127-2621
SUNFLOWER ELECTRIC HOLDINGS INC
301 W 13th St, Hays, KS 67601-3087
Tel (785) 628-2845 *Founded/Ownrshp* 1957
Sales 125.3MM^E *EMP* 215
SIC 4911 Generation, electric power; Transmission, electric power
VP Admn: James E Hanks Sr
**CFO:* Sidney J Severson
**Treas:* Jayne Clarke

D-U-N-S 05-475-3611
SUNFLOWER ELECTRIC POWER CORP (KS)
(*Suby of* SUNFLOWER ELECTRIC HOLDINGS INC) ★
301 W 13th St, Hays, KS 67601-3087
Tel (785) 628-2845 *Founded/Ownrshp* 1957
Sales 137.9MM^E *EMP* 215
Accts Kpmg Llp Kansas City Missour
SIC 4911 Generation, electric power; Transmission, electric power
Pr: Stuart Lowry
**Pr:* Jana Horsfall
**CFO:* H Davis Rooney
**Sr VP:* Kyle Nelson
VP: Bill Branch
Exec: Tom Zerfas
Snr Mgr: Tom Hestermann

SUNFLOWER FOOD STORE
See SOUTHEAST FOODS INC

D-U-N-S 00-715-7597 IMP
SUNFLOWER MANUFACTURING CO INC
AGCO
3154 Hallie Trl, Beloit, KS 67420-3175
Tel (785) 738-2261 *Founded/Ownrshp* 1945, 2002
Sales 88.2MM^E *EMP* 257
SIC 3523 Farm machinery & equipment; Plows, agricultural: disc, moldboard, chisel, listers, etc.
Pr: Gerald Meier
**VP:* Ronald E Harris
DP Exec: Mark Palen
Mtls Mgr: Jim Wiles
Ql Cn Mgr: Greg Girard
Mktg Mgr: Bruce Cooper
Mktg Mgr: Tom Draper
Sales Asso: Jeri Schlaefli

SUNGARD
See FIS FINANCIAL SYSTEMS LLC

SUNGARD
See FIS SYSTEMS INTERNATIONAL INC

SUNGARD
See FIS EPROCESS INTELLIGENCE LLC

SUNGARD
See FIS SG LLC

D-U-N-S 08-476-4836
SUNGARD AVAILABILITY SERVICES LP (PA)
680 E Swedesford Rd, Wayne, PA 19087-1605
Tel (484) 582-2000 *Founded/Ownrshp* 2000, 2014
Sales 1.0MMM^E *EMP* 2,300
SIC 7374 Computer processing services
CEO: Andrew A Stern
COO: Nick Magliato
**CFO:* Susan Lynch
**CFO:* Bob Singer
**CFO:* Robert Singer
**Ex VP:* John Cerciello
**Ex VP:* Andy Dzerovych
**Ex VP:* Jack Dziak
Ex VP: Jack J Dziak Jr
Ex VP: Keith Tilley
Exec: Bob Husbands
Exec: Michael Kouhi
Exec: Bob Kramlich
Exec: Mike Kuta
Board of Directors: Randy J Hendricks

D-U-N-S 05-098-0168
■ SUNGARD BUSINESS SYSTEMS LLC
(*Suby of* FIS DATA SYSTEMS INC) ★
680 E Swedesford Rd, Wayne, PA 19087-1605
Tel (484) 582-2000 *Founded/Ownrshp* 2005
Sales 112.9MM^E *EMP* 400
SIC 7374 5734 Data processing service; Software, business & non-game
CEO: Russ Fradin
**Pr:* Bill Byerly
VP: David Kennedy
**VP:* Richard N Matthews
VP: Bob Rushing
DP Exec: Cindy Nicholson
Board of Directors: Andy Bronstein, Lawrence A Gross, Michael J Ruane

D-U-N-S 79-917-3377
■ SUNGARD CAPITAL CORP II
(*Suby of* SUNGARD) ★
680 E Swedesford Rd, Wayne, PA 19087-1605
Tel (484) 582-2000 *Founded/Ownrshp* 2005
Sales 2.8MMM *EMP* 13,000^E
SIC 7372 7374 Prepackaged software; Data processing & preparation
Pr: Russell P Fradin
**Ch Bd:* Glenn H Hutchins
CFO: Charles J Neral
Ofcr: Patricia K Cassidy
VP: Christopher Breakiron

D-U-N-S 07-951-8209
■ SUNGARD HOLDCO LLC
(*Suby of* SUNGARD HOLDING CORP) ★
680 E Swedesford Rd, Wayne, PA 19087-1605
Tel (484) 582-2000 *Founded/Ownrshp* 2005
Sales 2.8MMM^E *EMP* 12,230^E
SIC 7372 7374 Prepackaged software; Data processing & preparation
Pr: Russell P Fradin

D-U-N-S 07-951-8006
■ SUNGARD HOLDING CORP
(*Suby of* SUNGARD CAPITAL CORP II) ★
680 E Swedesford Rd, Wayne, PA 19087-1605
Tel (888) 332-2564 *Founded/Ownrshp* 2005
Sales 2.8MMM^E *EMP* 13,000^E
SIC 7372 7374 Prepackaged software; Data processing & preparation
Pr: Russell P Fradin
**CFO:* Marianne Brown
**VP:* Regina Brab
**Prin:* Chris Breakiron

D-U-N-S 10-181-9662
■ SUNGARD PUBLIC SECTOR INC
(*Suby of* FIS DATA SYSTEMS INC) ★
1000 Business Center Dr, Lake Mary, FL 32746-5585
Tel (407) 304-3235 *Founded/Ownrshp* 2003
Sales 251.9MM^E *EMP* 750
SIC 5045 Computer software
Pr: Gilbert O Santos
**Pr:* Michael J Borman
CFO: David Gratham
CFO: Bruce E Langston
**Ex VP:* Chris Coleman
**Ex VP:* Ronald E Goodrow
VP: Phillip C Gulliford
VP: C J Slattery
Admn Mgr: Linda Hickman
CIO: Almy Charles
Software D: Ferdie Balagot

D-U-N-S 86-127-8377
SUNGEVITY INC
66 Franklin St Ste 310, Oakland, CA 94607-3734
Tel (510) 496-5500 *Founded/Ownrshp* 2006
Sales 92.1MM^E *EMP* 266
SIC 1711 8713 Solar energy contractor; Surveying services
Pr: Danny Kennedy
CEO: Amanda Duisman
COO: David Dunlap
CFO: Drew Hamer
CFO: Ken Schwarz
Chf Mktg O: Gagan Sandhu
Ofcr: Sloane Morgan
Sr VP: Liz Ludwig
Sr VP: Elizabeth K Rushforth
Sr VP: Shawn Yerkes
VP: David Parker
VP: Ariel Tseitlin
Board of Directors: Charles Finnie

D-U-N-S 07-866-7307
SUNGLASS HUT TRADING LLC
(*Suby of* LUXOTTICA GROUP) ★
4000 Luxottica Pl, Mason, OH 45040-8114
Tel (513) 765-4001 *Founded/Ownrshp* 2008
Sales 568.8MM^E *EMP* 5,428^E
SIC 5995 Optical goods stores

D-U-N-S 03-342-7027
SUNGROW HORTICULTURE CANADA INC
770 Silver St, Agawam, MA 01001-2907
Tel (800) 732-8667 *Founded/Ownrshp* 1930
Sales 127.5MM^E *EMP* 45
SIC 0782 Lawn & garden services
Pr: Mitch Weaver
COO: Chris Bednar
VP: Michael Evans
Manager: Ben Bonds
Sls Mgr: Wayne Bagwell
Sls Mgr: Jennifer Barnes
Sls Mgr: Mark Dommer
Sls Mgr: Doris Williams
Sls Mgr: Donna Wright
Snr Mgr: Rick Lopez

D-U-N-S 78-267-7744 IMP/EXP
SUNHAM HOME FASHIONS LLC
136 Madison Ave Fl 16, New York, NY 10016-6711
Tel (212) 695-1218 *Founded/Ownrshp* 2000
Sales 200.0MM^E *EMP* 150
SIC 2392 Blankets, comforters & beddings
CEO: Howard Yung
Pr: Jane Bognacki
COO: Arthur Coubanou
CFO: Courbanou Arthur
CFO: Arthur Courbanou
VP: Gregory Chletsos
Off Mgr: Emily Ross
Off Admin: Lauren Green
Opers Mgr: Simpi Singh
Natl Sales: Jodell Proctor
Sls Dir: Coryn Caroselli

D-U-N-S 80-126-0030 IMP/EXP
SUNIVA INC
(*Suby of* SHUNFENG INTERNATIONAL CLEAN ENERGY LIMITED)
5765 Peachtree Indus Blvd, Norcross, GA 30092-3502
Tel (404) 477-2700 *Founded/Ownrshp* 2016
Sales 158.0MM^E *EMP* 315^E
SIC 3674 3433 Solar cells; Solar heaters & collectors
CTO: Ajeet Rohatgi
**Pr:* Alex Zhu
**Ex VP:* Matt Card
**Ex VP:* Marc Rogovin
Sr VP: Gregory Mihalik
VP: Bruce Mc Pherson
VP: Daniel Meier
VP: Dan Meyier
VP Mktg: J Bryan Ashley
VP Sls: Bryan Ashley
Board of Directors: Francisco Sanchez

D-U-N-S 00-823-7018 IMP/EXP
SUNKIST GROWERS INC (CA)
27770 N Entertainment Dr # 120, Valencia, CA 91355-1093
Tel (818) 986-4800 *Founded/Ownrshp* 1893
Sales 1.1MMM *EMP* 500
SIC 5148 2033 2037 2899 6794 5046 Fruits, fresh; Fruit juices: packaged in cans, jars, etc.; Fruit juice concentrates, frozen; Lemon oil (edible); Orange oil; Grapefruit oil; Copyright buying & licensing; Display equipment, except refrigerated
Pr: Russell Hanlin II
COO: Jim Padden

*CFO: Richard G French
*Sr VP: Michael Wootton
*VP: Russell L Hanlin II
VP: Ted R Leaman
*VP: John Mc Guigan
VP: Michael Wooton
CTO: Matthew Melhuish
CTO: David Pott
Opers Mgr: Dean Troxell

D-U-N-S 06-954-1100
SUNLAND CONSTRUCTION INC
2532 Aymond St, Eunice, LA 70535-6843
Tel (337) 546-0241 Founded/Ownrshp 1974
Sales 1.1MMM^E EMP 2,200
SIC 1623 Oil & gas pipeline construction; Water main construction
Pr: Craig V Meier
*Ch Bd: John E Soileau
*Pr: Mark O'Roke
*Treas: Michael Brown
*Treas: Mark Gandy
VP: Craig Meier
*VP: Richard Renfro
VP: Bill W Strickland
Area Mgr: Benjamin Hughes
Genl Mgr: David Clavier
Sfty Dirs: Ron Oakley

SUNLAND SHUTTERS
See TA CHEN INTERNATIONAL INC

D-U-N-S 07-357-7595 IMP
SUNLAND TRADING INC
21 Locust Ave Ste 1a, New Canaan, CT 06840-4735
Tel (203) 966-4166 Founded/Ownrshp 2002
Sales 90.0MM EMP 4
SIC 5149 Honey
Pr: Nicholas J Sargeantson
Exec: Edith Bley-Fuhrmann

D-U-N-S 96-041-2906 IMP
SUNLIGHT SUPPLY INC
NATIONAL GARDEN WHOLESALE
5408 Ne 88th St Ste A101, Vancouver, WA 98665-0990
Tel (360) 883-8846 Founded/Ownrshp 2000
Sales 112.3MM^E EMP 225
SIC 3524 5191 Lawn & garden equipment; Garden supplies
Pr: Craig Ryan Hargreaves
VP: Marty Becker
*VP: Kim Hargreaves
*VP: Kne Hunter
*VP: Rob Williams
Mng Dir: Mike Sinclair
Web Dev: Eric Gerrard
Trfc Mgr: Jesse Gonzales
*VP Sls: Doug Hargreaves
Mktg Dir: Yvette Wade
Sls Mgr: Michelle White

D-U-N-S 07-988-1302
■ **SUNLIGHT US CO INC**
(Suby of GIBRALTAR INDUSTRIES INC) ★
3556 Lake Shore Rd # 100, Buffalo, NY 14219-1445
Tel (716) 826-6500 Founded/Ownrshp 2015
Sales 90.5MM^E EMP 100^E
SIC 3499 3316 3441 3398 Strapping, metal; Cold finishing of steel shapes; Fabricated structural metal; Metal heat treating
Pr: Frank Heard
CFO: Kenneth W Smith
Treas: Timothy F Murphy
Sr VP: Paul M Murray

D-U-N-S 00-424-3127
▲ **SUNLINK HEALTH SYSTEMS INC**
900 Cir 75 Pkwy Se # 650, Atlanta, GA 30339-3946
Tel (770) 933-7000 Founded/Ownrshp 2001
Sales 63.4MM EMP 1,851^E
Accts Cherry Bekaert Llp Atlanta G
Tkr Sym SSY Exch ASE
SIC 8062 8051 5912 General medical & surgical hospitals; Skilled nursing care facilities; Drug stores & proprietary stores
Pr: Robert M Thornton Jr
CFO: Mark J Stockslager
Board of Directors: Steven J Baileys, Karen B Brenner, Gene E Burleson, C Michael Ford, Christopher H B Mills, Howard E Turner

D-U-N-S 01-281-2561
■ **SUNLINK HEALTHCARE CORP** (GA)
(Suby of SUNLINK HEALTH SYSTEMS INC) ★
900 Circle 75 Pkwy Se # 13, Atlanta, GA 30339-3035
Tel (770) 850-1109 Founded/Ownrshp 2000
Sales 151.2MM^E EMP 1,000
SIC 8051 8062 Skilled nursing care facilities; General medical & surgical hospitals
Ch Bd: Robert M Thornton Jr
CFO: Pete Morris
CFO: Debbie Self
*CFO: Mark J Stockslager
Ofcr: Tammy Bruce
Ofcr: Anne Challis
Ofcr: Rob Followell
VP: Yvonne Creech
VP: Vickie Demers
*VP: Jack M Spurr
Opers Mgr: Harrison Makundi

SUNMART TRAVEL CENTERS & CONV
See PETROLEUM WHOLESALE LP

SUNNEN ABRASIVES & LUBRICANTS
See SUNNEN PRODUCTS CO

D-U-N-S 00-629-1348 IMP/EXP
SUNNEN PRODUCTS CO
SUNNEN ABRASIVES & LUBRICANTS
7910 Manchester Rd, Saint Louis, MO 63143-2793
Tel (314) 781-2100 Founded/Ownrshp 1927
Sales 168.4MM^E EMP 683
SIC 3549 3541 Metalworking machinery; Honing & lapping machines
Pr: Christ Miltenberger
*Pr: Matt Kreider
*Pr: Chris Miltenberger
*COO: Michael Haughey
Brnch Mgr: Chip Smith
IT Man: Tom Nuetzel
Opers Mgr: Mark Bergjans
Manager: Joey Callan
Manager: Bob Dolder
Manager: Rick Saindon
Snr Mgr: Than Huynh

D-U-N-S 09-830-7663 EXP
SUNNILAND CORP
1735 State Road 419, Longwood, FL 32750-3781
Tel (407) 322-2421 Founded/Ownrshp 1982
Sales 160.0MM^E EMP 249
SIC 5033 5191 Roofing, asphalt & sheet metal; Fertilizer & fertilizer materials
Pr: Tom Moore
*CFO: John Cahill
*Treas: Richard T Frank
Genl Mgr: Lee Moore
Opers Mgr: Aaron Leslie
Plnt Mgr: John Callaghan
Natl Sales: Tony Owen
Manager: Tricia Starkey
Sls Mgr: Adrian Quinones
Sales Asso: Jody McDonald
Sales Asso: Cheryl Williams

D-U-N-S 00-407-4688 IMP/EXP
SUNNY DELIGHT BEVERAGE CO
(Suby of BRYNWOOD PARTNERS VII LP) ★
10300 Alliance Rd Ste 500, Blue Ash, OH 45242-4767
Tel (513) 483-3300 Founded/Ownrshp 2016
Sales 343.1MM^E EMP 400
SIC 2086 Fruit drinks (less than 100% juice): packaged in cans, etc.
Pr: Tim Voelkerding
CFO: Brian Grote
Sr VP: Ellen Iobst
VP: Eric Meyer
Area Mgr: Jeremy Weatherford
VP Mfg: Dan Sileo
Opers Mgr: Randall Kirk
Opers Mgr: Patrick Temple
Ql Cn Mgr: Jo Kohus
Natl Sales: Joseph Jankowski
Mktg Mgr: Natalia Gomez

D-U-N-S 78-737-9010 IMP/EXP
SUNNYGEM LLC
500 N F St, Wasco, CA 93280-1435
Tel (661) 758-0491 Founded/Ownrshp 2005
Sales 83.4MM EMP 300
Accts Baker Peterson & Franklin Cpa
SIC 2033 3556 Fruit juices: fresh; Juice extractors, fruit & vegetable: commercial type

SUNNYSIDE ADULT DAY CARE
See SUNNYSIDE HOME CARE PROJECT INC

SUNNYSIDE FARMS
See SSI-TURLOCK DAIRY DIVISION

D-U-N-S 17-516-6313
SUNNYSIDE HOME CARE PROJECT INC
SUNNYSIDE ADULT DAY CARE
4331 39th St Ste A, Sunnyside, NY 11104-4343
Tel (718) 784-6173 Founded/Ownrshp 1975
Sales 23.2MM EMP 2,000
SIC 8361 8322 Geriatric residential care; Geriatric social service
Ex Dir: Judy Zangwill
Bd of Dir: Sanket J Bulsara

D-U-N-S 07-444-6816
SUNNYSIDE UNIFIED SCHOOL DISTRICT 12
2238 E Ginter Rd, Tucson, AZ 85706-5806
Tel (520) 545-2024 Founded/Ownrshp 1921
Sales 88.5MM^E EMP 1,700
Accts Heinfeld Meech & Co Pc Tuc
SIC 8211 Public elementary school; Public junior high school; Public senior high school
Treas: Kathy Laird
VP: Kathy Dong
Ex Dir: Steve Holmes
Dir Sec: Genie Favela
Sfty Dirs: Sixto Molina
Schl Brd P: Daniel Hernandez
Psych: George Meisch
Psych: Julia Ramos-Grenier
Psych: Belinda Stevens

SUNNYVALE SEAFOOD
See S C S INC

SUNOCO
See ATLANTIC PETROLEUM CORP

D-U-N-S 05-715-2217 IMP
■ **SUNOCO INC**
(Suby of ENERGY TRANSFER PARTNERS LP) ★
3801 West Chester Pike, Newtown Square, PA 19073-2320
Tel (215) 977-3000 Founded/Ownrshp 2012
Sales 2.8MMM^E EMP 2,046
SIC 5541 2911 2869 2865 5171 5052 Filling stations, gasoline; Petroleum refining; Industrial organic chemicals; Acetone, synthetic; Phenol, alkylated & cumene; Petroleum terminals; Coal & coke
Pr: Brian P Macdonald
Treas: Stephen H Clark
Treas: Kowal N Katria
Treas: Charmian Uy
Ofcr: Ann C Mul
*Ofcr: Dennis Zeleny
Ex VP: Thomas Luka
*Sr VP: Stacy L Fox
Sr VP: Deborah Fretz
Sr VP: Frederick A Henderson
Sr VP: Vincent J Kelley
*Sr VP: Robert W Owens
VP: Cynthia A Archer

D-U-N-S 00-134-4985 IMP/EXP
■ **SUNOCO INC (R&M)** (PA)
(Suby of SUNOCO INC) ★
3801 West Chester Pike, Newtown Square, PA 19073-2320
Tel (215) 977-3000 Founded/Ownrshp 1971
Sales 1.0MMM^E EMP 2,046
SIC 5541 2869 2911 5411 Filling stations, gasoline; Ethylene glycols; Petroleum refining; Convenience stores, chain
Ch Bd: John G Drosdick
*Pr: John D Pickering
*Treas: Daniel I Platt
*Treas: Charmian Uy
*Sr VP: Deborah M Fretz
VP: Karl F Fails
VP: Jack Foltz
*VP: Brian P Macdonald
*VP: James F Wagner
Mktg Dir: Fred McConnell

D-U-N-S 06-471-7981
▲ **SUNOCO LOGISTICS PARTNERS LP**
3807 West Chester Pike, Newtown Square, PA 19073-2304
Tel (866) 248-4344 Founded/Ownrshp 2001
Sales 10.4MMM EMP 2,500^E
Tkr Sym SXL Exch NYS
SIC 4612 4613 5171 5172 Crude petroleum pipelines; Refined petroleum pipelines; Petroleum bulk stations & terminals; Crude oil
Pr: Michael J Hennigan
Genl Pt: Sunoco P LLC
CFO: Peter J Gvazdauskas
CFO: Martin Salinas
Sr VP: Kathleen Shea-Ballay
Exec: Meghan Zaffarese
Sfty Dirs: Rahn Monreal
Opers Supe: Troy Clayton
Opers Supe: John Foltz
Pr Mgr: Joe McGinn

D-U-N-S 07-851-9681
▲ **SUNOCO LP**
8020 Park Ln Ste 200, Dallas, TX 75231-6055
Tel (214) 981-0700 Founded/Ownrshp 2012
Sales 16.9MMM EMP 11,850
Tkr Sym SUN Exch NYS
SIC 5172 6519 5541 Petroleum products; Engine fuels & oils; Real property lessors; Filling stations, gasoline
Pr: Robert W Owens
Genl Pt: Sunoco GP LLC
Ch Bd: Matthew S Ramsey
VP: Wes Scott

D-U-N-S 07-994-2391
■ **SUNOCO PARTNERS LLC**
(Suby of ENERGY TRANSFER PARTNERS LP) ★
3807 West Chester Pike, Newtown Square, PA 19073-2304
Tel (866) 248-4344 Founded/Ownrshp 2001
Sales 22.9MM^E EMP 2,250
SIC 4612 Crude petroleum pipelines
Pr: Michael J Hennigan
*Ch Bd: Marshall S McCrea III
*CFO: Martin Salinas Jr
Ofcr: Meghan Zaffarese
Sr VP: Kathleen Shea-Ballay
Board of Directors: Steven R Anderson, Scott A Angelle, Basil Leon Bray, Thomas P Mason, Jamie Welch

D-U-N-S 80-699-3577 IMP/EXP
SUNOPTA FOODS INC
(Suby of SUNOPTA INC)
7301 Ohms Ln Ste 600, Edina, MN 55439-2343
Tel (952) 820-2518 Founded/Ownrshp 2004
Sales 748.2MM^E EMP 902^E
SIC 5149 Natural & organic foods
CEO: Steve Bromley
V Ch: Alan Murray
VP: Mark Taggets
Dir IT: Dave Bastida
Plnt Mgr: Scott Gordon
Prd Mgr: Doug Fenske

D-U-N-S 62-798-9700 IMP/EXP
SUNOPTA INGREDIENTS INC
SUN OPTA FD INGREDIENTS GROUP
7301 Ohms Ln Ste 600, Edina, MN 55439-2343
Tel (831) 685-6506 Founded/Ownrshp 2004
Sales 123.9MM^E EMP 136
SIC 5159

D-U-N-S 13-166-1746 IMP
SUNOVION PHARMACEUTICALS INC
SUNOVION RESPIRATORY DEV
(Suby of DAINIPPON SUMITOMO PHARMA AMERICA HOLDINGS INC) ★
84 Waterford Dr, Marlborough, MA 01752-7010
Tel (508) 481-6700 Founded/Ownrshp 2012
Sales 645.0MM^E EMP 2,400
SIC 2834 Pharmaceutical preparations
V Ch: Hiroshi Nomura
Pr: Nobuhiko Tamura
CFO: Jolene Varney
Ex VP: Hiroyuki Baba
Ex VP: Robert Gregorio
Ex VP: Thomas Large
Ex VP: Antony Loebel
Ex VP: Albert Parker
Sr VP: Matthew Dambrosio
VP: Robin Cruz
VP: Chris Gish
VP: John Guarino
VP: Tony Magnetti
VP: Lee Murray
VP: Bill Yelle
Assoc Dir: Nasiba Abdul-Karim
Assoc Dir: Alkesh Amin
Assoc Dir: Mamta Arora
Assoc Dir: Roman Battle
Assoc Dir: Hali Black
Assoc Dir: Ruby Burke

SUNOVION RESPIRATORY DEV
See SUNOVION PHARMACEUTICALS INC

SUNPHARMA
See RANBAXY PHARMACEUTICALS INC

D-U-N-S 18-386-9593 IMP
■ **SUNPOWER CORP**
(Suby of TOTAL ENERGIES NOUVELLES ACTIVIT)
77 Rio Robles, San Jose, CA 95134-1859
Tel (408) 240-5500 Founded/Ownrshp 2011
Sales 1.5MMM EMP 8,309
Tkr Sym SPWR Exch NGS
SIC 3674 3679 Solar cells; Photoelectric cells, solid state (electronic eye); Power supplies, all types: static
Ch Bd: Thomas H Werner
Pr: Howard J Wenger
COO: Marty T Neese
CFO: Charles D Boynton
Ex VP: Lisa Bodensteiner
Ex VP: Jorg Heinemann
Ex VP: Douglas J Richards
Sr VP: Eric Branderiz
VP: Scott Fraass
VP: Bill Kelly
VP: Michaele Laforge
VP: Diana MA
VP: Jim Parker
VP: Ashok Tiwari
Board of Directors: Arnaud Chaperon, Bernard Clement, Humbert De Wendel, Denis Giorno, Daniel Laure, Catherine A Lesjak, Thomas R McDaniel, Patrick Wood III

D-U-N-S 05-293-4841
■ **SUNQUEST INFORMATION SYSTEMS INC** (PA)
(Suby of ROPER TECHNOLOGIES INC) ★
250 S Williams Blvd, Tucson, AZ 85711-4472
Tel (520) 570-2000 Founded/Ownrshp 1979, 2012
Sales 137.0MM^E EMP 700^E
SIC 7373 7371 Computer systems analysis & design; Custom computer programming services
Pr: Richard Atkin
*Pr: Matt Hawkins
CFO: Nina M Detruk
*CFO: Kathy Jehle
*Sr VP: Lisa Conley
Sr VP: Joseph Stumpt
VP: Derek S Eckelman
VP: Manish Muzumdar
VP: David M Post
*Prin: Bhaskar AV
Snr Sftwr: Roger Boesiger

SUNRIDGE FARMS
See FALCON TRADING CO

D-U-N-S 05-675-6802
SUNRISE AG SERVICE CO
104 S 1st St, Easton, IL 62633-9301
Tel (309) 562-7296 Founded/Ownrshp 1986
Sales 96.9MM^E EMP 54
SIC 5191 5171 5541 Farm supplies; Petroleum bulk stations; Gasoline service stations
Pr: Larry Garlisch
*Pr: Charles Taylor
*Sec: Ron Kuhlmann
*VP: Don Friend
*VP: Rudy Schilling
Opers Mgr: Jason Harrison
Plnt Mgr: Todd Livengood
Plnt Mgr: Mike Willing
Mktg Mgr: Mike Beck

D-U-N-S 83-171-4451
SUNRISE BRANDS LLC
801 S Figueroa St # 2500, Los Angeles, CA 90017-5504
Tel (323) 780-8250 Founded/Ownrshp 1995
Sales 92.4MM^E EMP 270^E
SIC 2339 2331 2335 2337 Jeans: women's, misses' & juniors'; Slacks: women's, misses' & juniors'; Shorts (outerwear): women's, misses' & juniors'; Jackets, untailored: women's, misses' & juniors'; Women's & misses' blouses & shirts; T-shirts & tops, women's: made from purchased materials; Shirts, women's & juniors': made from purchased materials; Women's, juniors' & misses' dresses; Skirts, separate: women's, misses' & juniors'
CEO: Gerard Guez
V Ch: Todd Kay
COO: Don Waldman
*COO: Donald Waldman
*CFO: Peter Akaragian
Chf Mktg O: Jackie Swerz
VP: Karen Wasserman
Off Mgr: Lisa Kan
CIO: Yves Guez
IT Man: Maria Fajardo

SUNRISE CHILDREN'S HOSPITAL
See SUNRISE HOSPITAL AND MEDICAL CENTER LLC

D-U-N-S 19-828-0500
SUNRISE COAL LLC
1183 E Canvasback Dr, Terre Haute, IN 47802-5304
Tel (812) 299-2800 Founded/Ownrshp 2002
Sales 114.1MM^E EMP 154
SIC 1222 Bituminous coal-underground mining
Pr: Brent K Bilsland
*CFO: Lawrence Martin
*VP: Ronald E Laswell

D-U-N-S 06-383-3230
SUNRISE COMMUNITY INC
9040 Sw 72nd St, Miami, FL 33173-3432
Tel (305) 275-3365 Founded/Ownrshp 1969
Sales 58.7MM EMP 4,000
Accts Moore Stephens Lovelace Pa
SIC 8052 8331 8322 Home for the mentally retarded, with health care; Job training & vocational rehabilitation services; Individual & family services
Pr: Leslie W Leech Jr
*Treas: James G Weeks
VP: Zach Wray
CTO: Scarleth Lopez

D-U-N-S 13-109-8139
■ **SUNRISE CONNECTICUT AVENUE ASSISTED LIVING LLC**
MARRIOTT
(Suby of BRIGHTON GARDENS) ★
5111 Connecticut Ave Nw, Washington, DC 20008-2004
Tel (202) 966-8020 Founded/Ownrshp 2003
Sales 30.3MM^E EMP 3,000
SIC 6513 Retirement hotel operation
Pr: Paul E Johnson Jr
*Treas: Terrance P Morrow

Board of Directors: J W Marriott Jr

D-U-N-S 13-959-0178
SUNRISE ELECTRIC SUPPLY INC
UTILITY MANAGEMENT AND SUPPLY
130 S Addison Rd, Addison, IL 60101-3865
Tel (630) 543-1111 *Founded/Ownrshp* 1986
Sales 133.3MM^E *EMP* 80
SIC 5063 5211 Electrical supplies; Electrical construction materials
Pr: Roy K Landgren
**CFO:* Bob Doherty
Sales Asso: Terry Presslak

D-U-N-S 94-892-5847
SUNRISE FARMS INC
2060 White Ave, Harris, IA 51345-7549
Tel (712) 735-6010 *Founded/Ownrshp* 1995
Sales 100.0MM *EMP* 200
SIC 0252 Chicken eggs
Pr: Philip O Sonstegard
**CFO:* Max Barnett

SUNRISE GROUP, THE
See PHINEAS CORP

D-U-N-S 17-509-2063 IMP/EXP
SUNRISE GROWERS INC
SUNRISE GROWERS-FROZSUN FOODS
(*Suby of* SUNOPTA INC)
701 W Kimberly Ave # 210, Placentia, CA 92870-6354
Tel (714) 630-2170 *Founded/Ownrshp* 2015
Sales 351.3MM^E *EMP* 350
SIC 5148 2037 Fruits; Frozen fruits & vegetables
Pr: Edward Haft
**CFO:* Joe McCarthy
VP: Erwin Hettervik
Genl Mgr: Maria Gonzalez
Genl Mgr: Dave Yvanovich

SUNRISE GROWERS-FROZSUN FOODS
See SUNRISE GROWERS INC

SUNRISE HEALTHCARE CENTER
See SUNRISE OAKS NURSING CENTER

D-U-N-S 02-015-6535
■ SUNRISE HOSPITAL AND MEDICAL CENTER LLC
SUNRISE CHILDREN'S HOSPITAL
(*Suby of* HOSPITAL COPORATION OF AMERICA) ★
3186 S Maryland Pkwy, Las Vegas, NV 89109-2306
Tel (702) 731-8080 *Founded/Ownrshp* 1993
Sales 305.1MM^E *EMP* 2,500^E
SIC 8062 Hospital, affiliated with AMA residency
CEO: Todd Sklanberg
Dir Risk M: Lucille Compton
Dir Lab: Gina Vokits
Dir Rx: Gazala Khan
Chf Nrs Of: Michael Bainger
Chf Nrs Of: Michael Bassinger
Sls&Mrk Ex: Saneep Lalit
Doctor: Candy Jensen

D-U-N-S 01-966-6098 IMP/EXP
SUNRISE MEDICAL HHG INC
SUNRISE MEDICAL HM HEALTHCARE
(*Suby of* SUNRISE MEDICAL NORTH AMERICAN) ★
7477 Dry Creek Pkwy, Niwot, CO 80503-8021
Tel (303) 218-4600 *Founded/Ownrshp* 1986
Sales 262.6MM^E *EMP* 1,850
SIC 3842 3844 Wheelchairs; X-ray apparatus & tubes
CEO: Thomas Rossnagel
**Pr:* Alan Panzer
**Ch:* Michael Cannizzano
VP: Partha Biswas
VP: Pete Coburn
VP: Mark Hostak
VP: Larry Price
VP: David Sherlin
IT Man: Jeff Dickman
Sls Dir: Jake McCullough

SUNRISE MEDICAL HM HEALTHCARE
See SUNRISE MEDICAL HHG INC

D-U-N-S 09-805-5820 IMP/EXP
SUNRISE MEDICAL HOLDINGS INC
(*Suby of* VSM INVESTORS LLC) ★
7477 Dry Creek Pkwy, Niwot, CO 80503-8021
Tel (303) 218-4600 *Founded/Ownrshp* 2000
Sales 299.9MM^E *EMP* 1,850
SIC 3842 Wheelchairs; Respirators
**CEO:* Michael N Cannizzaro
Sr VP: Roxane Cromwell
VP: Betty Johnson
VP: Dean Levesque
VP: Sony Stewart
CIO: Geoff Cooper
Dir IT: Jose Camacho
Mtls Mgr: Abraham Baez

SUNRISE MEDICAL NORTH AMERICAN
See VCP MOBILITY INC

SUNRISE MOUNTAIN VIEW HOSPITAL
See MOUNTAINVIEW HOSPITAL INC

D-U-N-S 04-790-5646
SUNRISE OAKS NURSING CENTER
SUNRISE HEALTHCARE CENTER
600 Sunrise Ave, Roseville, CA 95661-4110
Tel (916) 782-3131 *Founded/Ownrshp* 2001
Sales 547.7MM *EMP* 16^E
SIC 8051 Skilled nursing care facilities
Prin: Dixie Kneisler

SUNRISE RTRMENT HM COMMUNITIES
See SUNRISE SENIOR LIVING MANAGEMENT INC

D-U-N-S 92-616-2173
■ SUNRISE SENIOR LIVING LLC
BRIGHTON GARDENS
(*Suby of* BREWER HOLDCO INC) ★
7902 Westpark Dr, Mc Lean, VA 22102-4202
Tel (703) 273-7500 *Founded/Ownrshp* 1994
Sales 1.7MMM^E *EMP* 31,600
SIC 6513 Retirement hotel operation
CEO: Mark S Ordan
V Ch: D W Faeer
**COO:* Chris Winkle
CFO: Edward Burnett
**CFO:* Marc Richards
Ofcr: Farinaz Tehran
Sr VP: Gregg Colon
Sr VP: Laure Duhot
**Sr VP:* Jeff Fischer
Sr VP: Jeffrey M Jasnoff
Sr VP: Ronald Jeanneault
Sr VP: Nancy King
Sr VP: Philip Kroskin
Sr VP: Felipe Mestre
Sr VP: Uma Singh
VP: Jim May
VP: Paul Milstein
VP: Rick Werber
VP: Tom Zigray
Comm Man: Beth Johnson

D-U-N-S 05-320-0945
■ SUNRISE SENIOR LIVING MANAGEMENT INC (VA)
SUNRISE RTRMENT HM COMMUNITIES
(*Suby of* BRIGHTON GARDENS) ★
7902 Westpark Dr, Mc Lean, VA 22102-4202
Tel (703) 273-7500 *Founded/Ownrshp* 1981, 1994
Sales 115.8MM^E *EMP* 3,500
SIC 8361 8741 8052 Geriatric residential care; Management services; Intermediate care facilities
Ch Bd: Paul Klaassen
Pr: Felipe Mestre
CEO: Mark Ordan
CFO: Marc Richards
Ex VP: B C Swinton
Ex VP: Tiffany L Tomasso
Sr VP: Carol Tucker
VP: Rita Altman
VP: Teresa Klaassen
VP: Meghan Lublin
VP: David Painter
VP: Daniel Schwartz
VP: Nancy Voisin

SUNRISE TOYOTA SCION
See NYLSI INC

SUNROAD ENTERPRISES
See SUNROAD HOLDING CORP

D-U-N-S 87-830-0011
SUNROAD HOLDING CORP
SUNROAD ENTERPRISES
4445 Estgate Mall Ste 400, San Diego, CA 92121
Tel (858) 362-8500 *Founded/Ownrshp* 1991
Sales 113.7MM^E *EMP* 359
SIC 6719 Investment holding companies, except banks
CEO: Uri Feldman
Pr: Michael Dow
**Pr:* Aaron Feldman
**VP:* Rick Tronboll
VP: Rick Vann

D-U-N-S 07-825-8193
SUNROC BUILDING MATERIALS INC
(*Suby of* CLYDE COMPANIES INC) ★
520 S 800 W, Lindon, UT 84042-1684
Tel (801) 802-6952 *Founded/Ownrshp* 2009
Sales 90.4MM^E *EMP* 540
SIC 5031 Lumber, plywood & millwork; Building materials, exterior
Pt: David Abbott
**Pr:* Jeremy Hafen
Genl Mgr: Michael Levie

D-U-N-S 00-909-5209
SUNROC CORP (UT)
(*Suby of* CLYDE COMPANIES INC) ★
3657 S River Rd, St George, UT 84790-6212
Tel (435) 634-2200 *Founded/Ownrshp* 1938, 1999
Sales 387.9MM^E *EMP* 800
SIC 5031 3273 5032 3271 1442 Lumber, plywood & millwork; Ready-mixed concrete; Brick, stone & related material; Concrete block & brick; Construction sand & gravel
Pr: Rhys Weaver
**Treas:* Don McGee
**VP:* Dave Cook
**VP:* Russell Leslie
VP: Mark Wimmer

D-U-N-S 00-722-9300
SUNROCK GROUP HOLDINGS CORP
200 Horizon Dr Ste 100, Raleigh, NC 27615-4947
Tel (919) 747-6400 *Founded/Ownrshp* 2004
Sales 168.5MM^E *EMP* 150
SIC 1429 3273 2951 1411 Trap rock, crushed & broken-quarrying; Ready-mixed concrete; Asphalt paving mixtures & blocks; Dimension stone
Ch Bd: Bryan M Pfohl
**CFO:* Gregg W Bowler
**Ex VP:* Elisabeth A Pfohl Sasser
**VP:* Katherine M Pfohl
**VP:* John A Tankard III

D-U-N-S 82-863-0660
▲ SUNRUN INC
595 Market St Fl 29, San Francisco, CA 94105-2842
Tel (415) 580-6900 *Founded/Ownrshp* 2007
Sales 304.6MM *EMP* 3,395
Tkr Sym RUN *Exch* NGS
SIC 3674 Solar cells
CEO: Lynn Jurich
Sr Pt: Samantha Ames
**Ch Bd:* Edward Fenster
**COO:* Paul Winnowski
**CFO:* Bob Komin
VP: Jason Cavaliere
VP: Antonio Cintra
VP: Bryan Miller
VP: Gary Wayne
VP: Matthew Woods
Dir Bus: Ryan Work

D-U-N-S 04-251-0763 IMP
■ SUNRUN INSTALLATION SERVICES INC
(*Suby of* SUNRUN INC) ★
775 Fiero Ln Ste 200, San Luis Obispo, CA 93401-7904
Tel (805) 528-9705 *Founded/Ownrshp* 1997
Sales 91.9MM^E *EMP* 2,171^E
Accts Kpmg San Franscisco Ca
SIC 1731 Electric power systems contractors
CEO: Helen Wallace
CFO: Tom Digiovanni
CFO: Gary Morris
**CFO:* David Termondt
Sr VP: Dan Alcombright
Sr VP: Alan Russo
Dir Bus: Chris Fennimore
**Prin:* Paul Detering
Manager: Mike Gallagher
Sls Mgr: Michael Lind
Sls Mgr: Ryan Park

D-U-N-S 07-936-4371
■ SUNRUN SOUTH LLC
(*Suby of* SUNRUN INC) ★
595 Market St Fl 29, San Francisco, CA 94105-2842
Tel (415) 580-6900 *Founded/Ownrshp* 2014
Sales 120.1MM^E *EMP* 932^E
SIC 5074 Heating equipment & panels, solar
CEO: Lynn Jurich
**Pr:* Tom Holland
**Ch:* Edward Fenster
Sls Mgr: Todd Maki

D-U-N-S 02-553-3704
SUNSET FOOD MART INC
SUNSET FOODS
777 Central Ave Ste 2, Highland Park, IL 60035-3246
Tel (847) 234-8380 *Founded/Ownrshp* 1937
Sales 175.4MM^E *EMP* 900
SIC 5411 5921 Grocery stores, independent; Supermarkets; Liquor stores
CEO: John E Cortesi
**Treas:* Ronald Cizzon
**VP:* Richard Cortesi

SUNSET FOODS
See SUNSET FOOD MART INC

D-U-N-S 78-514-5843
SUNSET PARK HEALTH COUNCIL INC
NYU LUTHERAN FAMILY HEALTH CEN
150 55th St Ste 1, Brooklyn, NY 11220-2508
Tel (718) 630-7000 *Founded/Ownrshp* 1975
Sales 114.6MM *EMP* 99
Accts Deloitte Tax Llp Jericho Ny
SIC 8099 Physical examination service, insurance
Pr: Larry K McReynolds

D-U-N-S 96-104-3338
SUNSET STATION HOTEL AND CASINO
SONOMA CELLAR STEAKHOUSE
(*Suby of* STATION CASINOS LLC) ★
1301 W Sunset Rd, Henderson, NV 89014-6607
Tel (702) 547-7777 *Founded/Ownrshp* 1997
Sales 39.7MM^E *EMP* 1,800
SIC 7011 5962 7389 Casino hotel; Food vending machines; Beverage vending machines; Cigarettes vending machines; Telephone services
Ch Bd: Frank J Fertitta III
CFO: Joanie Scrivner
**Ex VP:* Steven Cacallaro
**Genl Mgr:* Pat Kerns
Sls Dir: Lauren Davis

SUNSHINE
See SUN GRO HORTICULTURE DISTRIBUTION INC

D-U-N-S 05-162-7321
SUNSHINE BOUQUET CO
3 Chris Ct Ste A, Dayton, NJ 08810-1543
Tel (732) 274-2900 *Founded/Ownrshp* 1991
Sales 161.6MM *EMP* 200
SIC 5193 3999 Flowers, fresh; Flowers, artificial & preserved
Pr: John Simko
**CFO:* Andrew Johnston
MIS Dir: Mike Dawson
Opers Mgr: Martin Chavez
Mktg Mgr: Victor Monzon
Sales Asso: Dale May

D-U-N-S 03-272-2852
SUNSHINE CLEANING SYSTEMS INC
3445 Ne 12th Ter, Oakland Park, FL 33334-4577
Tel (954) 772-0884 *Founded/Ownrshp* 1981
Sales 46.4MM^E *EMP* 1,110
SIC 7349 Janitorial service, contract basis; Window cleaning
Pr: Larry Calufetti
**Treas:* Laura Coenen
**VP:* Doran C Rose
**VP Admn:* Roger Diel
Brnch Mgr: David Wodehouse

D-U-N-S 03-928-7958
SUNSHINE HOUSE INC
12 Interchange Blvd, Greenville, SC 29607-5700
Tel (864) 990-1820 *Founded/Ownrshp* 1975
Sales 120.8MM^E *EMP* 2,600
SIC 8351 Child day care services; Preschool center
Pr: Wes Wooten
**Prin:* Barbara Hill

D-U-N-S 00-400-9981 IMP/EXP
SUNSHINE MILLS INC
500 6th St Sw, Red Bay, AL 35582-4084
Tel (256) 356-9541 *Founded/Ownrshp* 1988, 1960
Sales 211.0MM^E *EMP* 1,000
SIC 2047 2048 5149

D-U-N-S 04-865-9338 IMP/EXP
SUNSHINE RAISIN CORP (CA)
NATIONAL RAISIN COMPANY
626 S 5th St, Fowler, CA 93625-9745
Tel (559) 834-5981 *Founded/Ownrshp* 1968
Sales 149.9MM^E *EMP* 450
SIC 2064 0723 Candy & other confectionery products; Crop preparation services for market
Pr: Linda Kay Abdulian
CFO: Clint Weiler
Dir IT: Vincent Saul
Natl Sales: David Joseph
Sls Mgr: Joe Wengerd

D-U-N-S 03-245-9547
SUNSHINE RESTAURANT MERGER SUB LLC
IHOP
13650 Nw 8th St Ste 103, Sunrise, FL 33325-6239
Tel (305) 931-5454 *Founded/Ownrshp* 2007
Sales 79.6MM^E *EMP* 1,600
SIC 5812 Restaurant, family: chain
**Pr:* Bob Leonard
**CFO:* Moiese Lakhani
**VP:* Martin Freedman
VP: Bill Gowanloch

D-U-N-S 07-844-4677
SUNSHINE STATE DAIRY FARMS LLC (FL)
(*Suby of* SOUTHEAST MILK INC) ★
3304 Sydney Rd, Plant City, FL 33566-1181
Tel (813) 754-1847 *Founded/Ownrshp* 2005
Sales 99.1MM^E *EMP* 100
SIC 5143 2048 Milk; Livestock feeds

SUNSOURCE
See STS OPERATING INC

SUNSOUTH ADVERTISING
See POWERSOUTH ENERGY COOPERATIVE

D-U-N-S 78-295-4882
SUNSOUTH LLC
4100 Hartford Hwy, Dothan, AL 36305-4900
Tel (334) 678-7861 *Founded/Ownrshp* 2006
Sales 264.3MM *EMP* 318
Accts Mcclintock Nelson & Associate
SIC 5083 Farm & garden machinery
IT Man: Kim Winslett

D-U-N-S 02-506-6358 IMP/EXP
SUNSTAR AMERICAS INC
(*Suby of* SUNSTAR INC.)
301 E Central Rd, Schaumburg, IL 60195-1901
Tel (773) 777-4000 *Founded/Ownrshp* 1923, 1988
Sales 159.1MM^E *EMP* 470
SIC 3843 Dental equipment & supplies
Pr: Daniel Descary
Pr: Leoncio Gonzalez
**CFO:* Richard McMahon
**Ex VP:* Hiroki Nakanishi
**Ex VP:* Eduardo Vargas
VP: Yoshihiro Kaneda
VP: Mike Mercurio
Dir Soc: Laurene Calabrese
Mktg Dir: Jim Doyle
Mktg Mgr: Jessica Barry
Mktg Mgr: Evelina Leece

D-U-N-S 05-689-9339
SUNSTATE EQUIPMENT CO LLC
(*Suby of* SUMIQUIP) ★
5552 E Washington St, Phoenix, AZ 85034-2134
Tel (602) 275-2398 *Founded/Ownrshp* 2013
Sales 233.1MM^E *EMP* 1,000
SIC 7359 7353 Industrial truck rental; Heavy construction equipment rental
Ch Bd: Michael L Watts
**Pr:* Christopher Watts
**CEO:* Benno Jurgemeyer
**CFO:* Garth Price
Exec: Mary Peterson
Genl Mgr: Jeremy Banks
IT Man: Cheryl McAllister
IT Man: Dan Nabrotzky
Info Man: Steve Sharkey
Opers Mgr: Jeff Vanmarter
Sales Exec: Scott Jones

D-U-N-S 02-969-1727
SUNSTATES SECURITY LLC
7011 Albert Pick Rd Ste B, Greensboro, NC 27409-9532
Tel (336) 664-6944 *Founded/Ownrshp* 1998
Sales 953.3M^E *EMP* 1,450
SIC 7381 Security guard service
CEO: Kathryn Burrell
**COO:* Denis J Kelly

D-U-N-S 60-119-1393 IMP
▲ SUNSTONE HOTEL INVESTORS INC
120 Vantis Dr Ste 350, Aliso Viejo, CA 92656-2686
Tel (949) 330-4000 *Founded/Ownrshp* 1984
Sales 1.2MMM *EMP* 50^E
Tkr Sym SHO *Exch* NYS
SIC 6798 Real estate investment trusts
Pr: John V Arabia
**Ch Bd:* Douglas M Pasquale
COO: Marc A Hoffman
CFO: Bryan A Giglia
Ex VP: Robert C Springer
Sr VP: David Klein
Board of Directors: W Blake Baird, Andrew Batinovich, Z Jamie Behar, Thomas A Lewis, Keith M Locker, Murray J McCabe, Keith P Russell

D-U-N-S 92-896-9773
SUNSTONE HOTEL PROPERTIES INC
HAMPTON INN
(*Suby of* HAMPTON INN) ★
120 Vantis Dr Ste 350, Aliso Viejo, CA 92656-2686
Tel (949) 330-4000 *Founded/Ownrshp* 2004
Sales 97.5MM^E *EMP* 2,000
SIC 7011 Hotels & motels
Pr: Arthur Buser
Ex VP: John Elston
Ex VP: Evan Studer
VP: Kenneth Biehl
VP: Olivier Kolpin

D-U-N-S 00-912-1716 IMP/EXP
SUNSWEET GROWERS INC (CA)
901 N Walton Ave, Yuba City, CA 95993-9370
Tel (530) 674-5010 *Founded/Ownrshp* 1917
Sales 301.7MM *EMP* 700
Accts Moss & Moss Adams Llp Stockto
SIC 2034 2037 2086 Dried & dehydrated fruits; Fruit juices; Fruit drinks (less than 100% juice): packaged in cans, etc.
Pr: Dane Lance
**CEO:* Ana Klein
**Ch:* Gary Thiara
**VP:* Sharon Braun

VP: Brad Schuler
VP: Robert Shuler
**VP:* Harold Upton
**VP:* Melvin Ward
Brnch Mgr: John Sarvis
Off Mgr: Lori Garofalo
Dir IT: John Bierly

D-U-N-S 07-882-1533
SUNTECK HOLDINGS LLC
(*Suby of* COMVEST GROUP) ★
6413 Congress Ave Ste 260, Boca Raton, FL 33487-2854
Tel (561) 988-9456 *Founded/Ownrshp* 2013
Sales 433.4MM^E *EMP* 364
SIC 4731 6719 Transportation agents & brokers; Investment holding companies, except banks
Ch Bd: Harry Wachtel
**Pr:* Michael P Williams
**CFO:* William Wunderlich

D-U-N-S 09-889-6756
SUNTECK INC
(*Suby of* SUNTECK HOLDINGS LLC) ★
6413 Congress Ave Ste 260, Boca Raton, FL 33487-2854
Tel (561) 988-9456 *Founded/Ownrshp* 2013
Sales 433.4MM^E *EMP* 363^E
SIC 4731 Transportation agents & brokers
CEO: Ken Forster
CFO: John Jacobi

D-U-N-S 96-967-7590
SUNTECK TRANSPORT CO INC
(*Suby of* SUNTECK TRANSPORT GROUP INC) ★
6413 Congress Ave Ste 260, Boca Raton, FL 33487-2854
Tel (561) 988-9456 *Founded/Ownrshp* 1997
Sales 395.8MM *EMP* 100
SIC 8741 4731 Management services; Freight transportation arrangement
CEO: Ken Forster
**CFO:* John Jacobi

D-U-N-S 07-832-6644
SUNTECK TRANSPORT GROUP INC
(*Suby of* SUNTECK INC) ★
6413 Congress Ave Ste 260, Boca Raton, FL 33487-2854
Tel (561) 988-9456 *Founded/Ownrshp* 2011
Sales 395.8MM^E *EMP* 107
SIC 4731 Freight transportation arrangement
CEO: Ken Forster
CFO: John Jacobi

D-U-N-S 11-487-4014 IMP/EXP
SUNTERRACE CASUAL FURNITURE INC
US LEISURE
(*Suby of* JARDIN NETHERLANDS B.V.)
2369 Chrles Rper Jnas Hwy, Stanley, NC 28164-2246
Tel (704) 263-1967 *Founded/Ownrshp* 1996
Sales 141.2MM^E *EMP* 500
Accts Kost Forer Gabbay & Kasierer
SIC 2519 Fiberglass & plastic furniture
Pr: Thom Lombardo
**Genl Mgr:* Stacey Byers

D-U-N-S 06-773-7031 IMP/EXP
SUNTORY INTERNATIONAL CORP (CA)
(*Suby of* SUNTORY SPIRITS LIMITED)
600 3rd Ave Fl 21, New York, NY 10016-1916
Tel (212) 891-6600 *Founded/Ownrshp* 1967
Sales 147.8MM *EMP* 2,199
Accts Pricewaterhousecoopers Llp Ne
SIC 5149 2084 2086 5499 5812 Mineral or spring water bottling; Soft drinks; Wines, brandy & brandy spirits; Wines; Bottled & canned soft drinks; Soft drinks: packaged in cans, bottles, etc.; Health & dietetic food stores; Water: distilled mineral or spring; Ethnic food restaurants; American restaurant; Japanese restaurant
Pr: Tsuyoshi Nishizaki
**CFO:* Tsutomu Santoki
**Treas:* Yoshito Shihara
**Ex VP:* Yoshihiko Kunimoto

D-U-N-S 01-740-5171 IMP/EXP
SUNTREE LLC (AZ)
4502 W Monterosa St, Phoenix, AZ 85031-2300
Tel (480) 719-6900 *Founded/Ownrshp* 1997
Sales 1.2MMM^E *EMP* 75
SIC 2068 Nuts: dried, dehydrated, salted or roasted
**CFO:* Michael Horwitz
QA Dir: Paul Aldama
QA Dir: Lucia Thomas
VP Opers: Tom D'Ambrosio

D-U-N-S 08-023-1142
SUNTREE SNACK FOODS LLC
4502 W Monterosa St, Phoenix, AZ 85031-2300
Tel (480) 719-6900 *Founded/Ownrshp* 2015
Sales 180.0MM^E *EMP* 75
SIC 2068 Salted & roasted nuts & seeds
Pr: Brian Huff
**CFO:* Michael Horwitz

D-U-N-S 95-918-8426
SUNTREE-OXFORD ASSOCIATES LIMITED DIVIDEND HOUSING ASSOCIATION
1100 Sunview Dr, Saint Johns, MI 48879-2281
Tel (989) 224-8910 *Founded/Ownrshp* 1999
Sales 29.6MM^E *EMP* 3,900
SIC 6513 Apartment building operators
Pt: Leeann Morein

D-U-N-S 03-839-7741
■ **SUNTRUST BANK**
(*Suby of* SUNTRUST BANKS INC) ★
303 Peachtree St Ne Fl 30, Atlanta, GA 30308-3208
Tel (877) 782-0175 *Founded/Ownrshp* 1985
Sales NA *EMP* 2,990
SIC 6021 National commercial banks
CEO: William H Rogers
**Pr:* James M Wells III
CFO: Mark A Chancy
**CFO:* Aleem Gillani
Treas: Jerome T Lienhard
Ofcr: Masoud K Hosseini
Assoc VP: Deborah Barnhart
Ex VP: Teresa A Laskey
Sr VP: Jeffrey Bay
Sr VP: Tom Cassey
**Sr VP:* Karen Clark
Sr VP: Patricia Levy
Sr VP: Ken Solis
VP: Jason Beam
VP: Janet Brady
VP: Eric Coss
VP: Paul Field
VP: Anna Grant
VP: Arvo Kasari
VP: Radha Krishnan
VP: Laura Martin

D-U-N-S 14-443-7795
▲ **SUNTRUST BANKS INC**
303 Peachtree St Ne, Atlanta, GA 30308-3201
Tel (800) 786-8787 *Founded/Ownrshp* 1984
Sales NA *EMP* 24,043^E
Tkr Sym STI *Exch* NYS
SIC 6021 6022 6211 6091 6282 National commercial banks; State commercial banks; Investment firm, general brokerage; Investment bankers; Brokers, security; Nondeposit trust facilities; Investment advisory service; Manager of mutual funds, contract or fee basis
Ch Bd: William H Rogers Jr
Pr: Marc Bearden
Pr: Dev Bhandary
Pr: Frank Bornemann
Pr: Jeffrey Charron
Pr: Robert Crow
Pr: David Demus
Pr: Tarek Dernaika
Pr: Teresa Devault
Pr: Debra Doernberg
Pr: Nomie Dube
Pr: Judy Everett
Pr: Sharon Freeman
Pr: Charlotte Harper
Pr: Joann Johnson
Pr: Syed Saleem
Pr: Milton Sepulveda
Pr: Imran Shaukat
Pr: Dorinda C Smith
Pr: Laura Spencer
Pr: Eric Sukkert
Board of Directors: Dallas S Clement, Paul R Garcia, M Douglas Ivester, Kyle Prechtl Legg, Donna S Morea, David M Ratcliffe, Frank P Scruggs Jr, Bruce L Tanner, Thomas R Watjen

D-U-N-S 05-343-4494
■ **SUNTRUST COMMUNITY DEVELOPMENT CORP**
(*Suby of* SUNTRUST BANK) ★
201 4th Ave N Ste 1700, Nashville, TN 37219-2008
Tel (615) 748-4000 *Founded/Ownrshp* 2000
Sales NA *EMP* 1,135^E
SIC 6021 National commercial banks
Ch Bd: Robert E McNeilly
Ofcr: Jeanne Kinney
Ofcr: David Wellborn
Ex VP: Jackie Braiden
Ex VP: Margaret Callihan
Ex VP: John Clay
Ex VP: Walter Hale
Ex VP: David Thibodeau
Grp VP: Bonnie J Lloyd
Sr VP: Tom Van Etten
VP: Nancy Boring
VP: Jack Bradley
VP: William Callaway
VP: Kenneth Lee
VP: Denise Shaw

D-U-N-S 00-190-1503
■ **SUNTRUST EQUITY FUNDING LLC**
(*Suby of* SUNTRUST BANKS INC) ★
25 Park Pl Ne Lbby 2, Atlanta, GA 30303-2918
Tel (404) 477-6818 *Founded/Ownrshp* 1891
Sales NA *EMP* 3,000^E
SIC 6021 National commercial banks
Ch Bd: Roberts Long
CFO: Thomas E Fullilove
Ch: G Prendergast
Treas: Michael Martin
**Treas:* John W Spiegel
Bd of Dir: Mary Bullock
Bd of Dir: William Chace
Bd of Dir: Gaylord Coan
Bd of Dir: Larry Gellerstedt
Bd of Dir: John Glover
Bd of Dir: William Johnson
Bd of Dir: Dennis Love
Bd of Dir: Joseph Rogers
Ofcr: Jocelyn S Miller
Ofcr: Tanya Pavlin
Assoc VP: Emily Goolsby
Ex VP: P Walczuk
Ex VP: Howard Williams
Grp VP: Gerard Adams
Grp VP: Andrew S McGhee
Grp VP: Ann Williams

D-U-N-S 07-475-9655
■ **SUNTRUST MORTGAGE INC**
(*Suby of* SUNTRUST BANK) ★
901 Semmes Ave, Richmond, VA 23224-2270
Tel (804) 291-0740 *Founded/Ownrshp* 1998
Sales NA *EMP* 838
SIC 6162

D-U-N-S 94-541-2484
SUNWEST RESTAURANT CONCEPTS INC
BLACK BEAR DINER
6360 E Thomas Rd Ste 100, Scottsdale, AZ 85251-7054
Tel (480) 659-1000 *Founded/Ownrshp* 1997
Sales 31.5MM^E *EMP* 1,025
SIC 5812 Restaurant, family: chain
CEO: David Doty
Pr: Robin Yoshimura
Sec: Edward Doty

SUNY ADMINISTRATION
See HUDSON VALLEY COMMUNITY COLLEGE

SUNY ADMINISTRATION
See STATE UNIVERSITY OF NEW YORK

D-U-N-S 61-269-7342
SUNY COLLEGE AT CORTLAND
(*Suby of* SUNY ADMINISTRATION) ★
38 Cheney Hall, Cortland, NY 13045-2452
Tel (607) 753-2011 *Founded/Ownrshp* 2006
Sales 6.0MMM *EMP* 750^E
Accts Kpmg Llp Albany New York
SIC 8221 9411 Colleges universities & professional schools; Administration of educational programs;
Pr: Erik J Bitterbaum
VP: Kerry Mincher

D-U-N-S 06-365-1921
SUNY COLLEGE AT FREDONIA
(*Suby of* SUNY ADMINISTRATION) ★
280 Central Ave, Fredonia, NY 14063-1127
Tel (716) 673-3111 *Founded/Ownrshp* 2013
Sales 51.0MM^E *EMP* 1,518
SIC 8221 9411 Colleges universities & professional schools; Administration of educational programs;
Prin: Donald A Mac Phee
Assoc VP: Kevin Kearns

D-U-N-S 01-744-5581
SUNY COLLEGE AT ONEONTA
(*Suby of* SUNY ADMINISTRATION) ★
108 Ravine Pkwy, Oneonta, NY 13820-2685
Tel (607) 436-3500 *Founded/Ownrshp* 2003
Sales 468.1M *EMP* 1,000^E
SIC 8221 9411 Colleges universities & professional schools; Administration of educational programs;
Prin: Alan Donovan
**Pr:* Nancy Kleniewski
Pr: Katherine Milavec
Ofcr: Tim Hayes
Ofcr: Andrew Stammel
Ofcr: Denise Straut
Assoc VP: Lisa Wenck
VP: Paul Adamo
VP: Franklin Chambers
VP: Thomas M Rathbone
Comm Dir: Hal Legg
Mng Ofcr: Terrence Mitchell

D-U-N-S 19-308-5537
SUNY COLLEGE AT OSWEGO
(*Suby of* SUNY ADMINISTRATION) ★
702 Culkin Hall, Oswego, NY 13126-3525
Tel (315) 312-2222 *Founded/Ownrshp* 1968
Sales 65.2MM^E *EMP* 1,200^E
SIC 8221 9411 Colleges universities & professional schools; Administration of educational programs;
Pr: Debra F Stanelley
**VP:* Nickolus Lyons
Assoc Dir: Michael Pisa

D-U-N-S 02-152-7197
SUNY DOWNSTATE MEDICAL CENTER
(*Suby of* SUNY ADMINISTRATION) ★
450 Clarkson Ave, Brooklyn, NY 11203-2012
Tel (718) 270-1000 *Founded/Ownrshp* 2006
Sales 342.0MM^E *EMP* 2,700^E
SIC 8221 9411 Colleges universities & professional schools; Administration of educational programs;
Pr: John Williams
Chf Rad: Salvatore Sclafani
Pr: John Larosa
Pr: Donald Minick
Pr: David Pappalardo
Pr: Tony Selvadurai
Chf Mktg O: Jeffrey Borer
VP: Konstantin Astafurov
VP: Joann Bradley
VP: Olipriya Das
VP: Hendrina Goeloe-Alston
VP: Ralph Rossi
VP: Patricia Winston
Dir Teleco: Loretta Lavasseur
Assoc Dir: Jeffrey Lee
Assoc Dir: Dilip Nath
Dir Rad: James Shanahan
Dir Rx: Nicholas Galeota

D-U-N-S 09-034-7241
SUNY UNIVERSITY AT BUFFALO
OFFICE OF THE PRESIDENT
(*Suby of* SUNY ADMINISTRATION) ★
501 Capen Hall, Buffalo, NY 14260-1600
Tel (716) 645-2901 *Founded/Ownrshp* 2006, 1846
Sales 430.3MM^E *EMP* 6,651^E
Accts Kpmg Llp Buffalo Ny
SIC 8221 9411 Colleges universities & professional schools; Administration of educational programs;
Pr: Satish K Tripathi
VP: Alexander Cartwright
VP: Jorge V Jos
Assoc Dir: Irene H Moyer
**Prin:* John Simpson
Ex Dir: Douglas Usiak
DP Exec: Barbara Dobbins
IT Man: Russ Miller
Netwrk Mgr: Timothy Matie
Doctor: David Hojnacki

D-U-N-S 02-986-5743
SUNY UPSTATE MEDICAL UNIVERSITY
750 E Adams St Ste Wh, Syracuse, NY 13210-1834
Tel (315) 464-5540 *Founded/Ownrshp* 2001
Sales 837.7M^E *EMP* 9,000
SIC 8011 Pathologist
Pr: Dr Danielle Laraque
**Pr:* Dr Danielle Laraque-Arena
Assoc VP: Robert Quinn
Dir Lab: Bob Quinn
Dir Rx: Steven Ciullo
Dir Rx: Kelly Jacobs
Genl Mgr: Cheri Clarry
IT Man: Jim Dwyer
IT Man: DOT Ryan
Doctor: Deborah J Mann
Doctor: Evis Petrela

SUOMINEN NONWOVEN
See WINDSOR LOCKS NONWOVENS INC

D-U-N-S 07-831-1654 IMP
SUOMINEN US HOLDING INC
(*Suby of* SUOMINEN OYJ)
3 Chirnside Rd, Windsor Locks, CT 06096-1142
Tel (860) 654-8331 *Founded/Ownrshp* 2011
Sales 212.3MM^E *EMP* 278^E
SIC 2297 Nonwoven fabrics

SUP-RX-PHARMACY
See PIGGLY WIGGLY CENTRAL INC

SUPER 8 MOTEL
See SUPER 8 WORLDWIDE INC

D-U-N-S 06-285-6141
■ **SUPER 8 WORLDWIDE INC**
SUPER 8 MOTEL
(*Suby of* WYNDHAM WORLDWIDE CORP) ★
22 Sylvan Way Fl 3, Parsippany, NJ 07054-3801
Tel (850) 973-3331 *Founded/Ownrshp* 1993
Sales 1.4MMM^E *EMP* 24,000
SIC 6794 Copyright buying & licensing; Franchises, selling or licensing; Patent buying, licensing, leasing; Performance rights, publishing & licensing
Pr: Franz S Hanning
Treas: Robert Lowen

D-U-N-S 05-980-4666
SUPER A FOODS INC
7200 Dominion Cir, Commerce, CA 90040-3647
Tel (323) 869-0600 *Founded/Ownrshp* 1973
Sales 93.5MM^E *EMP* 600
SIC 5411 Grocery stores, independent
Ch Bd: Louis A Amen
**CEO:* James Amen
**VP:* Joud Tedmori
Exec: Jo A Timony

D-U-N-S 94-803-2438 IMP
SUPER CENTER CONCEPTS INC
SUPERIOR GROCERS
15510 Carmenita Rd, Santa Fe Springs, CA 90670-5610
Tel (562) 345-9000 *Founded/Ownrshp* 1997
Sales 937.5MM^E *EMP* 4,200
SIC 5411 Grocery stores, chain
CEO: Mimi R Song
**COO:* Phil Lawrence
CFO: William Cote
Ex VP: Marie Song
**VP:* Joe Cooney
VP: Michael Jukam
VP: Eddie Whalen
Dist Mgr: Chris Gonzalez
Genl Mgr: Sebastian Rodriguez

D-U-N-S 83-965-5545
SUPER D DRUGS ACQUISITION CO
USA DRUG
(*Suby of* STEPHEN L LAFRANCE HOLDINGS INC) ★
2100 Brookwood Dr, Little Rock, AR 72202-1734
Tel (501) 296-3300 *Founded/Ownrshp* 1997
Sales 149.2MM^E *EMP* 1,500
SIC 5912 Drug stores & proprietary stores
CEO: Joe Courtright
COO: Linda Walls
**VP:* Mike Kerr
VP: Jason Lafrance
Nurse Mgr: Chandra G Johnson

SUPER D PHANTOM DISTRIBUTION
See C D LISTENING BAR INC

D-U-N-S 80-910-2239
▲ **SUPER MICRO COMPUTER INC**
980 Rock Ave, San Jose, CA 95131-1615
Tel (408) 503-8000 *Founded/Ownrshp* 1993
Sales 2.2MMM *EMP* 2,247
Tkr Sym SMCI *Exch* NGS
SIC 3571 3572 7372 Electronic computers; Computer storage devices; Prepackaged software
Ch Bd: Charles Liang
CFO: Howard Hideshima
**Treas:* Chiu-Chu Liu Liang
Sr VP: Phidias Chou
**Sr VP:* Yih-Shyan Liaw
VP: Todd Warner
Sls Mgr: Derek Tong
Sls Mgr: Anhquan Vu
Board of Directors: Laura Black, Michael S McAndrews, Sherman Tuan

SUPER PANTRY
See TRI STAR MARKETING INC

D-U-N-S 19-628-7762
SUPER PETROLEUM INC
25 Braintree Hill Park # 409, Braintree, MA 02184-8718
Tel (781) 356-1960 *Founded/Ownrshp* 1996
Sales 119.9MM^E *EMP* 414^E
SIC 5541 Gasoline service stations
Pr: Muftah M Bugazia

SUPER STRUE VALUE
See MASS MARKETING INC

SUPER SAVER
See VARIETY WHOLESALERS INC

D-U-N-S 96-732-8837
SUPER SERVICE HOLDINGS LLC
6000 Clay Ave Sw, Grand Rapids, MI 49548-5785
Tel (616) 530-8551 *Founded/Ownrshp* 2009
Sales 211.4MM^E *EMP* 1,425
SIC 4213 Trucking, except local
Pr: Dan Strong
**CFO:* Larry Carrier

D-U-N-S 96-553-1937
SUPER SERVICE LLC
(*Suby of* SUPER SERVICE HOLDINGS LLC) ★
6000 Clay Ave Sw, Grand Rapids, MI 49548-5785
Tel (616) 530-8558 *Founded/Ownrshp* 2009
Sales 204.1MM *EMP* 1,300
SIC 4213 Trucking, except local
Pr: Dan Strong
**CFO:* Larry Carrier
Dir Risk M: Bruce Tourison

IT Man: Bob Maggard
Manager: Scott Anderson

SUPER SHOE STORES
See MACRO RETAILING LLC

D-U-N-S 00-654-9141 IMP
SUPER STEEL LLC (WI)
7900 W Tower Ave, Milwaukee, WI 53223-3253
Tel (414) 362-9114 *Founded/Ownrshp* 1966, 2010
Sales 85.2MM^{E} *EMP* 250
SIC 3443 3444 3441 3446 Fabricated plate work (boiler shop); Sheet metalwork; Fabricated structural metal; Architectural metalwork
Pr: Dirk Smith
Ch Bd: Paul Luber
CFO: Brad Nennig
QA Dir: Rico White
QC Dir: Dan Klumpyan
Sls Dir: Jason Gaare
Sales Asso: Heather McArthur
Board of Directors: James Forbes, Steve Graff, Dennis Kuester, Paul Luber, John Maciver

D-U-N-S 62-159-6345 IMP/EXP
SUPER STORE INDUSTRIES
2800 W March Ln Ste 210, Stockton, CA 95219-8200
Tel (209) 473-8100 *Founded/Ownrshp* 1990
Sales 155.7MM^{E} *EMP* 774
SIC 2026 2024 5149 5142

D-U-N-S 79-634-2371 IMP/EXP
SUPERTALENT TECHNOLOGY CORP
2077 N Capitol Ave, San Jose, CA 95132-1009
Tel (408) 957-8133 *Founded/Ownrshp* 1991
Sales 118.1MM^{E} *EMP* 670
SIC 5045 Computers, peripherals & software
Pr: Abraham MA
VP: Robbie Chikhani
Genl Mgr: Jonathan Yu
Sls Mgr: Carmen Aviles
Sls Mgr: Richard Garber
Sls Mgr: Jeffrey Vassallo
Genl Couns: Mark Musto

D-U-N-S 60-694-5947 IMP
SUPERBAG USA CORP
9291 Baythorne Dr, Houston, TX 77041-7742
Tel (713) 462-1173 *Founded/Ownrshp* 1989
Sales 120.0MM^{E} *EMP* 275^{E}
SIC 2673 5411 Plastic bags: made from purchased materials; Grocery stores
Pr: Simon Bazbaz
VP: Laura Ledbetter
IT Man: Michael Crass

D-U-N-S 04-000-2180
■ **SUPERCUTS INC**
(*Suby of* REGIS CORP) ★
7201 Metro Blvd, Minneapolis, MN 55439-2131
Tel (952) 947-7777 *Founded/Ownrshp* 1996
Sales 86.6MM^{E} *EMP* 6,000
SIC 7231 Unisex hair salons
CEO: Dan Hanrahan
**Pr:* Mark Kartaric
**CFO:* Paul Plate

SUPERGRAPHICS
See GM NAMEPLATE INC

SUPERINTENDENT OF DOCUMENTS
See US GOVERNMENT PUBLISHING OFFICE

D-U-N-S 96-370-5616
SUPERIOR BANK
4350 W Cypress St Ste 102, Tampa, FL 33607-4181
Tel (813) 350-6728 *Founded/Ownrshp* 2010
Sales NA *EMP* 6^{E}
SIC 6021 National commercial banks
Prin: Jenna Sivewright

D-U-N-S 62-384-8889 IMP
SUPERIOR BEVERAGE GROUP LTD
31031 Diamond Pkwy, Solon, OH 44139-5463
Tel (440) 703-4580 *Founded/Ownrshp* 2003
Sales 85.8MM^{E} *EMP* 208^{E}
SIC 5149 5499 Beverages, except coffee & tea; Beverage stores
Pt: Mike Caffrey
**Pt:* John W Fleming
Area Mgr: Tom Hennes
Area Mgr: Doug Miller
CIO: Al Vignolini
IT Man: Tim Peck
Sls Mgr: Jerry Fahrlander

D-U-N-S 05-317-9610
SUPERIOR BULK LOGISTICS INC
CARRYTRANSIT
711 Jorie Blvd Ste 101n, Oak Brook, IL 60523-2285
Tel (630) 573-2555 *Founded/Ownrshp* 1986
Sales 518.8MM^{E} *EMP* 1,160
SIC 4213 Heavy hauling; Liquid petroleum transport, non-local
CEO: Len Fletcher
**Ch Bd:* Richard T Lewis
**Pr:* William J O'Donnell
COO: William Odonell
**Treas:* Timothy McCann
VP: Ron Bowman
**VP:* William R Lavery

D-U-N-S 79-297-8876 IMP
SUPERIOR COMMUNICATIONS INC
PUREGEAR
5027 Irwindale Ave # 900, Baldwin Park, CA 91706-2187
Tel (626) 388-2573 *Founded/Ownrshp* 1991
Sales 854.6MM *EMP* 273
SIC 5065 Communication equipment
Ch Bd: Solomon Chen
**Pr:* Jeffrey Banks
Pr: James Chen
**CFO:* Keith Kam
Ofcr: Keith Kamchief
Ex VP: Lee Batson
**VP:* Robert Chen
VP: Victor Wang
Prgrm Mgr: Donna McLellan

Genl Mgr: Roxana Cao
CTO: Mark Veals

SUPERIOR COMPONENTS DIV
See SUPERIOR INDUSTRIES INC

D-U-N-S 10-218-8281
SUPERIOR CONSOLIDATED INDUSTRIES INC
SC2
801 Sw Jefferson Ave, Peoria, IL 61605-3918
Tel (309) 677-5980 *Founded/Ownrshp* 1988
Sales 125.0MM^{E} *EMP* 1,500
SIC 7389 1721 Packaging & labeling services; Industrial painting
Pr: Kevin M McGinty
**Ch:* Paul R Killinger
**Sec:* L Douglas Coartney
VP: Steve Baumann
Sfty Dirs: Kevin Laughlin
Sfty Dirs: Linda Rife

D-U-N-S 00-484-4981
SUPERIOR CONSTRUCTION CO INC
1455 Louis Sullivan Dr, Portage, IN 46368-6437
Tel (219) 886-3728 *Founded/Ownrshp* 1940, 1959
Sales 90.0MM *EMP* 450
Accts Crowe Horwath Llp Oak Brook
SIC 1541 1629 1622 Industrial buildings, new construction; Waste water & sewage treatment plant construction; Oil refinery construction; Bridge construction; Highway construction, elevated
Ch: John L Largura
**Pr:* Daniel J Sopczak
CFO: Raymond Nelson
**Ex VP:* Richard Ayers
**VP:* Thomas Adam
**VP:* Stephen Cuson
VP: Theodore Cuson
VP: Rodney Vittetoe

D-U-N-S 83-035-6619
SUPERIOR CONSTRUCTION CO SOUTHEAST LLC
7072 Business Park Blvd N, Jacksonville, FL 32256-2749
Tel (904) 292-4240 *Founded/Ownrshp* 1938
Sales 117.4MM^{E} *EMP* 302^{E}
SIC 1611 General contractor, highway & street construction
Pr: Richard J Ayers
**Sec:* Nicholas E Largura
**Ex VP:* Peter G Kelley
**VP:* Curtis E Long
**VP:* Bobby Naik
Exec: Maggie Leneri

D-U-N-S 13-518-3999
SUPERIOR COURT OF CALIFORNIA
247 W 3rd St, San Bernardino, CA 92415-0300
Tel (909) 708-8678 *Founded/Ownrshp* 1998
Sales NA *EMP* 1,000
SIC 9211
**CEO:* Christina M Volkers
**CFO:* Pam Nay

D-U-N-S 00-608-8249 IMP
SUPERIOR DIE SET CORP (WI)
900 W Drexel Ave, Oak Creek, WI 53154-1935
Tel (414) 764-4900 *Founded/Ownrshp* 1923
Sales 133.6MM^{E} *EMP* 400
SIC 3544 3443 3599 Special dies, tools, jigs & fixtures; Fabricated plate work (boiler shop); Machine & other job shop work
CEO: Casimir H Janiszewski
**Pr:* Frank Janiszewski
CFO: Lynette Ellman
**CFO:* Lynette Ellman-Grass
**VP:* William L Fitzwater
Exec: Joe Kucharski

D-U-N-S 03-433-2135
SUPERIOR ELECTRICAL MECHANICAL & PLUMBING INC
8613 Helms Ave, Rancho Cucamonga, CA 91730-4521
Tel (909) 357-9400 *Founded/Ownrshp* 2005
Sales 87.5MM^{E} *EMP* 291
SIC 1731 1711 General electrical contractor; Mechanical contractor
CEO: David A Stone Jr
**Pr:* Walt Schobel
**CFO:* Pam Metzer

SUPERIOR ENERGY SERVICES
See WARRIOR ENERGY SERVICES CORP

D-U-N-S 93-363-2952 IMP/EXP
▲ **SUPERIOR ENERGY SERVICES INC**
1001 La St Ste 2900, Houston, TX 77002
Tel (713) 654-2200 *Founded/Ownrshp* 1991
Sales 2.7MMM *EMP* 8,300
Tkr Sym SPN *Exch* NYS
SIC 1389 3533 7353 Servicing oil & gas wells; Well plugging & abandoning, oil & gas; Oil & gas field machinery; Oil field equipment, rental or leasing
Pr: David D Dunlap
**Ch Bd:* Terence E Hall
CFO: Robert S Taylor
Ex VP: Westervelt T Ballard Jr
Ex VP: Westy Ballard
Ex VP: James A Holleman
Ex VP: William B Masters
Ex VP: Gregory L Miller
Ex VP: Danny R Young
VP: Larry Davis
VP: Jeff Dismuke
VP: David Hart
VP: James Spexarth
VP: John Stude
Exec: A Patrick Bernard
Board of Directors: Harold J Bouillion, James M Funk, Peter D Kinnear, Michael McShane, W Matt Ralls

D-U-N-S 00-278-1490 IMP
■ **SUPERIOR ENERGY SERVICES LLC**
(*Suby of* SESI LLC) ★
5801 Highway 90 E, Broussard, LA 70518-5914
Tel (337) 714-4545 *Founded/Ownrshp* 1998
Sales 747.4MM^{E} *EMP* 1,200^{E}
SIC 1389 7353 Well plugging & abandoning, oil & gas; Oil field services; Oil field equipment, rental or leasing
CEO: David Dunlap
**Ch Bd:* Terence E Hall
CFO: Robert Taylor
VP: Jeff Dubois

SUPERIOR ESSEX
See ESSEX GROUP INC

D-U-N-S 14-675-7500 IMP
SUPERIOR ESSEX HOLDING CORP
(*Suby of* SUPERIOR ESSEX INC) ★
150 Interstate N Pkwy, Atlanta, GA 30339-2154
Tel (770) 657-6000 *Founded/Ownrshp* 2003
Sales 150.5MM^{E} *EMP* 1,400
SIC 3357 Nonferrous wiredrawing & insulating
CEO: Justin F Deedy
**CFO:* David S Aldridge
Counsel: Barbara L Backford

D-U-N-S 13-105-1851 IMP
SUPERIOR ESSEX INC
(*Suby of* LS CABLE & SYSTEM LTD.)
6120 Powers Ferry Rd # 150, Atlanta, GA 30339-2999
Tel (770) 657-6000 *Founded/Ownrshp* 1999
Sales 1.5MMM^{E} *EMP* 4,500
SIC 3357 Communication wire
Pr: Stephen M Carter
**CEO:* Justin F Deedy Jr
**CFO:* David S Aldridge
Bd of Dir: H Jack
Ex VP: Patrick Jack
Ex VP: J David Reed
**Sr VP:* Debrah Baker-Oliver
**Sr VP:* Tracye C Gilleland
**Sr VP:* Debbie Baker Oliver
**Sr VP:* Mary Love Sullenberger
VP: Ed Cronin

D-U-N-S 15-337-0077 IMP
SUPERIOR ESSEX INTERNATIONAL LP
(*Suby of* SUPERIOR ESSEX INC) ★
6120 Powers Ferry Rd # 150, Atlanta, GA 30339-2999
Tel (770) 657-6000 *Founded/Ownrshp* 1998
Sales 314.4MM^{E} *EMP* 1,400
SIC 3357 Communication wire
CEO: Brian Kim
CFO: Augustine Shim
Sr VP: Debbie Baker-Oliver
Sr VP: Matt Odonnell
Sr VP: Mary Love Sullenberger
VP: Terry Richards
VP: Bill Zellar

SUPERIOR FARMS
See TRANSHUMANCE HOLDING CO INC

D-U-N-S 11-259-3702 IMP/EXP
SUPERIOR FIBERS INC
SMARTPAC
1333 Corporate Dr Ste 350, Irving, TX 75038-2554
Tel (972) 600-9953 *Founded/Ownrshp* 1984
Sales 123.3MM^{E} *EMP* 774
SIC 3677 3569

SUPERIOR FOODS COMPANIES, THE
See SUPERIOR FOODS INC

D-U-N-S 15-160-9377 IMP/EXP
SUPERIOR FOODS INC
SUPERIOR FOODS COMPANIES, THE
275 Westgate Dr, Watsonville, CA 95076-2470
Tel (831) 728-3691 *Founded/Ownrshp* 1983
Sales 132.5MM^{E} *EMP* 100
SIC 5142 Fruits, frozen; Vegetables, frozen; Fruit juices, frozen
Ch Bd: David E Moore
**Pr:* Mateo Lettunich
**CEO:* R Neil Happee
COO: Neil Happee
**CFO:* H Monroe Howser III
CFO: Monroe Howser
Genl Mgr: Nick Pengelly
QA Dir: Stephanie Fry
Opers Mgr: Grayson Moore
S&M/VP: John Amador

D-U-N-S 00-512-0001 IMP/EXP
SUPERIOR GRAPHITE CO
10 S Riverside Plz # 1470, Chicago, IL 60606-3838
Tel (312) 559-2999 *Founded/Ownrshp* 1917
Sales 93.8MM^{E} *EMP* 300
Accts Rsm Us Llp Chicago Illinois
SIC 3295 Graphite, natural: ground, pulverized, refined or blended
Pr: Edward O Carney
CFO: Elena Zaydlin
**Ch:* Peter R Carney
**Sr VP:* Ron G Pawelko
VP: Andy Rill
Genl Mgr: Mark Wanta
Genl Mgr: Pinggui Wu
IT Man: Eric Olsen
Mktg Dir: Gerard Hand
Mktg Dir: Dennis Shannon
Sls Mgr: Barry Ringstrom

SUPERIOR GROCERS
See SUPER CENTER CONCEPTS INC

D-U-N-S 06-236-2496 IMP
SUPERIOR GROUP INC
100 Front St Ste 525, Conshohocken, PA 19428-2887
Tel (610) 397-2040 *Founded/Ownrshp* 1981
Sales 237.1MM^{E} *EMP* 2,000
SIC 5051 3357 3317 3491 3469 7389 Tubing, metal; Nonferrous wiredrawing & insulating; Tubing, mechanical or hypodermic sizes: cold drawn stainless; Industrial valves; Metal stampings; Packaging & labeling services
Ch: William G Warden III
Pr: Peter G Gould
CEO: William G Warden IV
Treas: John Morrash
VP: Beth Hucker
VP: John M Morrash

D-U-N-S 05-709-8501 IMP/EXP
SUPERIOR INDUSTRIES INC
SUPERIOR COMPONENTS DIV
315 State Highway 28, Morris, MN 56267-4699
Tel (320) 589-2406 *Founded/Ownrshp* 2013
Sales 178.7MM^{E} *EMP* 1,600
SIC 3535 Conveyors & conveying equipment
CEO: Micah Zeltwanger
**Pr:* Jarrod Felton
**CFO:* Tom Zosel
VP: Stanley Wulf
Genl Mgr: Jason Adams
Genl Mgr: Michael Monaghan
IT Man: Russ Koehl
Software D: Gabe Grimley
Sftwr Eng: David Ruprecht
Ql Cn Mgr: Rob Jergenson
Mktg Dir: Mary Erholtz

D-U-N-S 05-080-9177 IMP
▲ **SUPERIOR INDUSTRIES INTERNATIONAL INC**
26600 Telg Rd Ste 400, Southfield, MI 48033
Tel (248) 352-7300 *Founded/Ownrshp* 1957
Sales 727.9MM *EMP* 3,050
Tkr Sym SUP *Exch* NYS
SIC 3714 Motor vehicle wheels & parts
Pr: Donald J Stebbins
**Ch Bd:* Margaret S Dano
CFO: Kerry A Shiba
Sr VP: Parveen Kakar
Sr VP: Lawrence R Oliver
Sr VP: James F Sistek
VP: Scot S Bowie
Board of Directors: Michael R Bruynesteyn, Jack A Hockema, Paul J Humphries, James S McElya, Timothy C McQuay, Ellen Richstone, Francisco S Uranga

D-U-N-S 09-933-4971 EXP
SUPERIOR LUBRICANTS CO INC
S L
32 Ward Rd, North Tonawanda, NY 14120-2494
Tel (716) 693-8412 *Founded/Ownrshp* 1979
Sales 86.1MM^{E} *EMP* 88
Accts Freed Maxick & Battaglia Cpas
SIC 5172 5013 Lubricating oils & greases; Automotive supplies
Pr: Michael Anczok
Pr: Steve Lazzara
**CFO:* Dale Steinwald
**VP:* Harold G Anderson
**VP:* Claude H Roth

D-U-N-S 00-505-1081 IMP/EXP
SUPERIOR METAL PRODUCTS INC (OH)
AMERICAN TRIM
1005 W Grand Ave, Lima, OH 45801-3400
Tel (419) 228-1145 *Founded/Ownrshp* 1958
Sales 460.0MM^{E} *EMP* 1,500
SIC 3469 3429 Metal stampings; Porcelain enameled products & utensils; Ornamental metal stampings; Manufactured hardware (general)
CEO: Leo Hawk
**Pr:* Richard Pfeifer
**CEO:* Jeffrey A Hawk
**Treas:* Dana Morgan
Brnch Mgr: Mike Staddon
Netwrk Eng: Shad McGrath
Plnt Mgr: Gary Fosnaugh
Ql Cn Mgr: Melissa Dean

D-U-N-S 03-999-4975 IMP
SUPERIOR OIL CO INC
SUPERIOR SOLVENTS AND CHEM
1402 N Capitol Ave # 100, Indianapolis, IN 46202-2375
Tel (317) 781-4400 *Founded/Ownrshp* 1972
Sales 221.1MM *EMP* 287
SIC 5169 5162 Chemicals & allied products; Plastics materials
CEO: Robert W Andersen
**Pr:* Kurt A Hettinga
**VP:* Shane Cline
VP: Scott Cox
**VP:* Thomas Fleming
VP: Cox Scott
**VP:* Bryan Teed
Exec: Jay Baker
Genl Mgr: Steve McIlwain
Genl Mgr: Tom Meisel
Genl Mgr: John Nelson

D-U-N-S 87-935-7358
SUPERIOR PETROLEUM CO
SUPERIOR SUNOCO & CARWASH
8199 Mcknight Rd, Pittsburgh, PA 15237-5749
Tel (412) 364-2200 *Founded/Ownrshp* 1994
Sales 230.7MM *EMP* 250
SIC 7542 Carwashes
Pr: Milo C Ritton
**VP:* Kathryn Kellogg
**VP:* Thomas O Madden

D-U-N-S 00-917-4293 IMP
SUPERIOR PLUS CONSTRUCTION PRODUCTS CORP
WINROC-SPI
(*Suby of* SUPERIOR PLUS LP)
1650 Manheim Pike Ste 202, Lancaster, PA 17601-3088
Tel (717) 569-3900 *Founded/Ownrshp* 2009
Sales 500.0MM *EMP* 722
SIC 5039 5033 Ceiling systems & products; Roofing, siding & insulation; Insulation materials
Pr: Mike Farrell
CFO: Benjamin G Dicarlo
Sr VP: Daniel D Bofinger
Sr VP: Charles F Schattgen
VP: Dan Bofinger
VP: Michael Conner
VP: Michael Feehrey
VP: Ray Horan
VP: Richard J Mitchell
Dist Mgr: Rich Cleminson
Genl Mgr: Sammy Kosh

D-U-N-S 01-341-0444 IMP/EXP
SUPERIOR PLUS ENERGY SERVICES INC
GRIFFITH ENERGY
(*Suby of* SUPERIOR PLUS CORP)
1870 Winton Rd S Ste 200, Rochester, NY 14618-3960
Tel (585) 328-3930 *Founded/Ownrshp* 1922
Sales 579.3MM^E *EMP* 530
SIC 5171 5983 Petroleum terminals; Petroleum bulk stations; Fuel oil dealers
Ch Bd: Keith Wrisley
**Ch:* Greg L McCamus
**VP:* Monte Bambrough
VP: Julien Houle
**VP:* Janice Jones
**VP:* Inder Minhas

D-U-N-S 06-614-2225
■ **SUPERIOR POOL PRODUCTS LLC**
(*Suby of* SOUTH CENTRAL POOL) ★
4900 E Landon Dr, Anaheim, CA 92807-1980
Tel (714) 693-8035 *Founded/Ownrshp* 2000
Sales 146.5MM^E *EMP* 760
SIC 5091 Swimming pools, equipment & supplies
Pr: David Chess
**Genl Mgr:* Bill Cook
**Genl Mgr:* Scott Frantz
**Genl Mgr:* Don White

D-U-N-S 00-136-0494 IMP
SUPERIOR PRINTING INK CO INC (NY)
100 North St, Teterboro, NJ 07608-1202
Tel (201) 478-5600 *Founded/Ownrshp* 1918
Sales 112.7MM^E *EMP* 450
SIC 2893 2851 Printing ink; Gravure ink; Varnishes
Pr: Jeffrey Simons
Pr: Richard Killian
CFO: Harold Reuben
CFO: Harold Rubin
VP: Torres Angel
Plnt Mgr: Kirk Knoch
Plnt Mgr: Chris Vignola

D-U-N-S 05-132-1487
SUPERIOR PRODUCTS DISTRIBUTORS INC
S P D I
1403 Meriden Waterbury Rd, Milldale, CT 06467
Tel (860) 621-3621 *Founded/Ownrshp* 1967
Sales 95.1MM^E *EMP* 150
SIC 5074 5032 5082 7353 Pipes & fittings, plastic; Concrete building products; Contractors' materials; Heavy construction equipment rental
Pr: Ralph Crispino Jr
**VP:* Dennis Crispino
Sales Exec: Kris Bates

D-U-N-S 36-061-5066
SUPERIOR READY MIX CONCRETE LP
SOUTHLAND READY MIX CONCRETE
1508 Mission Rd, Escondido, CA 92029-1194
Tel (760) 745-0556 *Founded/Ownrshp* 1989
Sales 204.1MM^E *EMP* 700
SIC 3273 1611 5032 Ready-mixed concrete; Surfacing & paving; Gravel; Sand, construction
Pt: Donald Lee
Dir IT: Luke Faber
Mtls Mgr: Chuck Martin
Sfty Mgr: Danny Ritzer

D-U-N-S 36-109-8192
■ **SUPERIOR SILICA SANDS LLC**
(*Suby of* EMERGE ENERGY SERVICES LP) ★
6000 Western Pl Ste 465, Fort Worth, TX 76107-4687
Tel (817) 841-8070 *Founded/Ownrshp* 2015
Sales 243.2MM^E *EMP* 230
SIC 1429 Sandstone, crushed & broken-quarrying
**CEO:* Rick Shearer
**COO:* Jim Walker
**CFO:* Paul Manigrasso
Info Man: Duane Wilke
Sfty Mgr: Chase Bachman
Sls Dir: Ken Meu
Sls Dir: Ken Neu

SUPERIOR SOLVENTS AND CHEM
See SUPERIOR OIL CO INC

SUPERIOR SUNOCO & CARWASH
See SUPERIOR PETROLEUM CO

SUPERIOR SUPPLY & STEEL
See SENTRY SUPPLY INC

D-U-N-S 02-778-4883
SUPERIOR TIRE SERVICE INC
4230 27th Ct Se, Salem, OR 97302-1184
Tel (503) 585-1955 *Founded/Ownrshp* 1956
Sales 115.1MM^E *EMP* 150
SIC 5014 7534 3011 Automobile tires & tubes; Tire recapping; Automobile tires, pneumatic
Pr: Ryan Timothy
**Ch Bd:* James W Ryan
**Pr:* James Rowe
CFO: Derek Malsam
**CFO:* Robert Potter

D-U-N-S 15-050-2136
SUPERIOR TRAILER SALES CO
501 Us Highway 80 E, Mesquite, TX 75182-9263
Tel (972) 226-3893 *Founded/Ownrshp* 1988
Sales 98.0MM *EMP* 95
SIC 5511 Trucks, tractors & trailers: new & used
CEO: Frank L Deel III
**Pr:* Benton Reynolds
**Treas:* Joe Allen
**VP:* Jerry Dumont
Sales Exec: Steve Bailey

D-U-N-S 00-235-3407 IMP
■ **SUPERIOR TUBE CO INC** (PA)
(*Suby of* AMETEK SENSOR TECHNOLOGY BUS) ★
3900 Germantown Pike, Collegeville, PA 19426-3112
Tel (610) 489-5200 *Founded/Ownrshp* 1934, 2015
Sales 97.4MM^E *EMP* 250
SIC 3317 3498 Steel pipe & tubes; Fabricated pipe & fittings
Pr: Robert Henry
**Treas:* John M Morrash
Genl Mgr: Wade Burcehll
Genl Mgr: Kevin Heaphy
Dir IT: Daniel Koch
Opers Mgr: Ben Huber
Natl Sales: Rahul Gujar
Sls Mgr: Erik Latranyi

D-U-N-S 00-203-6507 IMP/EXP
▲ **SUPERIOR UNIFORM GROUP INC** (FL)
10055 Seminole Blvd, Seminole, FL 33772-2539
Tel (727) 397-9611 *Founded/Ownrshp* 1920
Sales 210.3MM *EMP* 1,278^E
Accts Mayer Hoffman Mccann Pc Cle
Tkr Sym SGC *Exch* NGM
SIC 2389 3999 7389 Uniforms & vestments; Identification badges & insignia; Telemarketing services
CEO: Michael Benstock
**Ch Bd:* Sidney Kirschner
**Pr:* Alan D Schwartz
COO: Andrew D Demott Jr
Ex VP: Peter Benstock
VP: Jordan M Alpert
VP: Scott Delin
VP: Dominic Leide
VP: Charles Sheppard
Sls Dir: Errol Pegler
Mktg Mgr: Amy Henry
Board of Directors: Robin M Hensley, Paul V Mellini, Todd E Siegel

SUPERIOR WOOD TREATING
See MANKE LUMBER CO INC

D-U-N-S 02-703-5021
SUPERIOR WORKFORCE SOLUTIONS INC
250 International Dr, Williamsville, NY 14221-5700
Tel (716) 631-8310 *Founded/Ownrshp* 1965
Sales 141.9MM^E *EMP* 3,000
SIC 7363

SUPERIOR'S BRAND MEATS
See FRESH MARK INC

D-U-N-S 05-996-1466
SUPERMARKET MANAGEMENT INC
TOPS MARKET
460 Niagara St Ste 1, Buffalo, NY 14201-1898
Tel (716) 853-5787 *Founded/Ownrshp* 1971
Sales 90.9MM^E *EMP* 1,073
SIC 5411 Supermarkets, independent
Pr: Philip A Perna
**Ch Bd:* Frank J Perna
**Treas:* Paul F Perna
**VP:* Robert J Bavisotto

D-U-N-S 16-196-4283
■ **SUPERMARKET OPERATORS OF AMERICA INC**
(*Suby of* SUPERVALU INC) ★
11840 Valley View Rd, Eden Prairie, MN 55344-3643
Tel (952) 828-4000 *Founded/Ownrshp* 1987
Sales 2.9MMM^E *EMP* 18,000
SIC 5411 4225 Supermarkets; General warehousing & storage
CEO: Jeffrey Noddle
**Pr:* Pamela Knous
**Treas:* Sherry Smith
**VP:* David Boehnen
**VP:* Francis O'Kefe
Dir Sec: Dan Cermak

D-U-N-S 78-791-1986
SUPERMEDIA INC
VERIZON DIRECTORIES DISPOSITION
(*Suby of* DEX MEDIA INC) ★
2200 W Airfield Dr, Dfw Airport, TX 75261-4008
Tel (972) 453-7000 *Founded/Ownrshp* 1994
Sales 411.8MM^E *EMP* 3,200
SIC 2741 Telephone & other directory publishing
Pr: Joseph A Walsh
Pr: Eric D Chandler
Pr: Briggs Ferguson
Pr: W Scott Hanle
Pr: Sandra L Henjum
CFO: Genevieve Dailey
CFO: Samuel D Jones
Ex VP: Frank P Gatto
Ex VP: Steven Nord
Ex VP: Debra M Ryan
Ex VP: Cody Wilbanks
Sr VP: Michael Pawlowski
VP: Dane Beck
VP: Dave Landry
Exec: Barbara Kemp

D-U-N-S 00-516-2227 IMP
SUPERMEDIA LLC
VERIZON
(*Suby of* DEX MEDIA INC) ★
2200 W Airfield Dr, Dfw Airport, TX 75261-4008
Tel (972) 453-7000 *Founded/Ownrshp* 2009
Sales 203.6MM^E *EMP* 600
SIC 2741 6719 Directories, telephone: publishing only, not printed on site; Investment holding companies, except banks
Pr: Gerard Corcoran
Pr: Frank Gatto
CFO: Samuel D Jones
VP: Lester K W Chu
VP: Joe Garza
VP: David R Landry
VP: Patrick Marshall
VP: John J McDonald
**VP:* William Mundy
VP: Brian Ritenour
VP: Sandra L Roach
VP: David N Schoenberger

D-U-N-S 03-063-6305
SUPERMERCADO LA HACIENDA INC
224 S Larkin Ave, Joliet, IL 60436-1248
Tel (815) 724-0200 *Founded/Ownrshp* 2014
Sales 300.0MM *EMP* 1
SIC 5411 Grocery stores
Pr: Al Shaiash

SUPERMERCADOS MR SPECIAL
See MR SPECIAL SUPERMARKETS INC

D-U-N-S 36-306-6452
SUPERNUS PHARMACEUTICALS INC
1550 E Gude Dr, Rockville, MD 20850-1339
Tel (301) 838-2500 *Founded/Ownrshp* 2005
Sales 144.4MM *EMP* 344
Tkr Sym SUPN *Exch* NGM
SIC 2834 Pharmaceutical preparations
Pr: Jack A Khattar
**Ch Bd:* Charles W Newhall III
CFO: Gregory S Patrick
Chf Mktg O: Stefan K F Schwabe
Sr VP: Padmanabh P Bhatt
Sr VP: Victor Vaughn
VP: Jones Bryan
Genl Mgr: Michelle Morgan
Sls Mgr: Drew Kain
Sales Asso: Rebecca Ortman
Board of Directors: Georges Gemayel, Frederick M Hudson, William A Nuerge, John M Siebert

D-U-N-S 11-622-2886
SUPERPUMPER INC
(*Suby of* SPF ENERGY INC) ★
100 27th St Ne, Minot, ND 58703-5164
Tel (701) 852-0061 *Founded/Ownrshp* 1996
Sales 118.6MM *EMP* 230
SIC 5541 5411 Filling stations, gasoline; Convenience stores, independent
Pr: Jeff Farstad
**Treas:* Bruce Hest
**VP:* Dennis Krueger
Genl Mgr: Kris Wolla
Opers Mgr: Mark Nordgaard

D-U-N-S 10-802-9737
SUPERSHUTTLE INTERNATIONAL INC
(*Suby of* TRANSDEV NORTH AMERICA INC) ★
14500 N Northsight Blvd # 329, Scottsdale, AZ 85260-3641
Tel (480) 609-3000 *Founded/Ownrshp* 1985
Sales 295.9MM^E *EMP* 1,360
SIC 4111 Local & suburban transit
CEO: R Brian Wier
COO: Kristi Carter
**Treas:* Terrence Oates
VP: Chris Lynn
VP: Michael Stinson
Exec: Thomas Lavoy

D-U-N-S 02-366-1726
SUPERTEL HOSPITALITY MANAGEMENT INC
(*Suby of* CONDOR HOSPITALITY TRUST, INC.)
1800 W Pswalk Ave Ste 200, Norfolk, NE 68701
Tel (402) 371-2520 *Founded/Ownrshp* 2001
Sales 111.6MM *EMP* 963
SIC 7011 Hotels & motels
Pr: Kelly A Walters
CFO: Donavon A Heimes
VP: Dave Walter
Exec: Kevin Taylor
Board of Directors: Steve H Borgmann, Joseph Caggiano, Allen L Dayton, Patrick J Jung, Loren Steele, George R Whittemore, Jeffrey M Zwerdling

D-U-N-S 00-696-5214
■ **SUPERVALU HOLDINGS INC**
(*Suby of* SUPERMARKET OPERATORS OF AMERICA INC) ★
11840 Valley View Rd, Eden Prairie, MN 55344-3643
Tel (952) 828-4000 *Founded/Ownrshp* 1992
Sales 2.9MMM^E *EMP* 16,000
SIC 5411 Supermarkets
CEO: Jeffrey Noddle
**Pr:* Leon Bergmann
**CEO:* Craig R Herkert
**Treas:* Kim M Erickson
**Ex VP:* Michael Moore
Sr VP: Sherry M Smith
**VP:* John Breedlove
**VP:* Gregory C Heying

D-U-N-S 00-696-1411 IMP
▲ **SUPERVALU INC**
11840 Valley View Rd, Eden Prairie, MN 55344-3643
Tel (952) 828-4000 *Founded/Ownrshp* 1871
Sales 17.5MMM *EMP* 38,000
Accts Kpmg Llp Minneapolis Minnes
Tkr Sym SVU *Exch* NYS
SIC 5411 5141 Grocery stores; Groceries, general line
Pr: Mark Gross
**Ch Bd:* Gerald L Storch
COO: Bruce H Besanko
Bd of Dir: Bernie Grutsch
Ex VP: Randy Burdick
Ex VP: Robert Butler
Ex VP: Tim Holt
Ex VP: Michael Moore
Ex VP: Karla C Robertson
Ex VP: James Weidenheimer
Sr VP: Susan S Grafton
VP: Shannon Anglin
VP: Rick Collison
VP: Mark Gossett
VP: Jim Jacobsen
VP: Terry Mahoney
VP: Tom Sargent
VP: Shirl Stoeing
VP: Larry Tobias
VP: Tom Yeager
Board of Directors: Wayne C Sales, Donald R Chappel, Irwin S Cohen, Francesca Ruiz De Luzuriag, Philip L Francis, Eric G Johnson, Mathew M Pendo, Matthew E Rubel, Frank A Savage, Mary A Winston

D-U-N-S 79-085-6108
■ **SUPERVALU TRANSPORTATION INC**
(*Suby of* SUPERVALU INC) ★
11840 Valley View Rd, Eden Prairie, MN 55344-3691
Tel (952) 828-4000 *Founded/Ownrshp* 1991
Sales 91.1MM^E *EMP* 2,300
SIC 4213 Contract haulers
CEO: Jeff Noddle
**Ch Bd:* Michael W Wright
COO: Jim Stringfellow
Treas: David A Cairns
VP: Monica Abrams
VP: Laurence L Anderson
VP: Charles D Dugan
VP: Burt Fealing
VP: William C Hunt
VP: Reuben Johnson
VP: Ronald T Mendes
VP: David Oliver
VP: Yolanda M Scharton
VP: Todd Sheldon
VP: Nancy Superchi
VP: Doyle J Troyer

SUPPLEMENTAL HEALTH CARE
See SHC SERVICES INC

D-U-N-S 04-375-3669
SUPPLIES DISTRIBUTORS INC
505 Millenium Dr, Allen, TX 75013-2774
Tel (972) 881-2900 *Founded/Ownrshp* 2001
Sales 326.3MM^E *EMP* 220^E
SIC 5045 5112 Computers, peripherals & software; Stationery & office supplies
Pr: Joseph Farrell
**Ex VP:* Thomas Madden
**VP:* Gibson Dawson

D-U-N-S 93-151-8302
SUPPLIES NETWORK INC
(*Suby of* D M I) ★
5 Research Park Dr, Saint Charles, MO 63304-5685
Tel (636) 300-4001 *Founded/Ownrshp* 1991
Sales 101.4MM^E *EMP* 104
SIC 5112 Stationery & office supplies
CEO: Sean Fleming
**Pr:* Greg Welchans
CFO: David B Gresham
Treas: Jack Easterling
**Sr VP:* Doug Johnson
**Sr VP:* Barney Kister
**VP:* David Concors
VP: Gloria Lewis
Dir Bus: David Reinkemeyer
Manager: Tim Cichacki
Sls Mgr: Tim Gramlich

SUPPLY CHAIN INTEGRATOR
See WORLD CLASS INDUSTRIES INC

SUPPLY FORCE
See SUPPLYFORCE.COM LLC

D-U-N-S 19-466-5279 IMP
SUPPLY NETWORK INC
VIKING SUPPLY NET
(*Suby of* VIKING CORP) ★
210 N Industrial Park Rd, Hastings, MI 49058
Tel (269) 945-9501 *Founded/Ownrshp* 1988
Sales 106.6MM^E *EMP* 170
SIC 5087 Sprinkler systems
Pr: Kevin Ortyl
**Ch Bd:* Thomas T Groos
CFO: Janice A Oshinski
Genl Mgr: Harv Hughey
Mktg Mgr: Jeff Norton
Sls Mgr: Perry Adams

D-U-N-S 00-255-4632
SUPPLY NEW ENGLAND INC
KITCHEN AND BATH GALLERY
123 East St, Attleboro, MA 02703-3953
Tel (508) 222-5555 *Founded/Ownrshp* 2000
Sales 94.5MM^E *EMP* 131
Accts O Brien Riley & Ryan Pc Brain
SIC 5074 Plumbing & hydronic heating supplies
CEO: Jason Reardon
**Pr:* James W Reardon
**Treas:* Russell G Wilde
MIS Mgr: Arthur Fowle

D-U-N-S 15-528-6847
SUPPLY SOURCE DYNAMICS INC
311 E Vickery Blvd, Fort Worth, TX 76104-1352
Tel (817) 336-0451 *Founded/Ownrshp* 1917
Sales 600.0MM *EMP* 950
SIC 5074 Plumbing & hydronic heating supplies
CEO: Scott Sangalli
**Pr:* Darrell Hawkins
**Sec:* Charles Allen

D-U-N-S 00-698-7218 IMP/EXP
■ **SUPPLY TECHNOLOGIES LLC**
I L S
(*Suby of* PARK-OHIO HOLDINGS CORP) ★
6065 Parkland Blvd Ste 1, Cleveland, OH 44124-6145
Tel (440) 947-2100 *Founded/Ownrshp* 1998
Sales 40.2MM^E *EMP* 1,500
SIC 5085 3452 3469 Fasteners, industrial: nuts, bolts, screws, etc.; Bolts, nuts, rivets & washers; Screws, metal; Nuts, metal; Stamping metal for the trade
Pr: Michael L Justice
CFO: John Ehrzanowski
VP: Brad Hudson
VP: James Smetham
VP: Seth Swanner
Admn Mgr: David Trippy
QA Dir: Nicole Driscoll
Sftwr Eng: Komlavi Ekouevi
Opers Mgr: Tom Blevins
Opers Mgr: Mike Nixon
Opers Mgr: Jim Rabb
Board of Directors: Edward F Crawford

SUPPLY WORKS
See INTERLINE BRANDS INC

D-U-N-S 11-605-7019 IMP
SUPPLYCORE INC
303 N Main St Ste 800, Rockford, IL 61101-1050
Tel (815) 997-1624 *Founded/Ownrshp* 1987
Sales 106.4MM^E *EMP* 185
SIC 5072 5085 Hardware; Industrial supplies
CEO: Peter Provenzano
CFO: Chris Albert
VP: Richard Alpaugh
**VP:* Steve Cotone
VP: Tet Hadavas
VP: Nate Johnson
VP: Matt Marshall
VP: Mike Paul
**VP:* Patrick Voller

VP: Pat Wilson
VP Bus Dev: John Mayles
Exec: Mike Koerner

D-U-N-S 12-568-1473
SUPPLYFORCE.COM LLC
SUPPLY FORCE
700 American Ave Ste 300, King of Prussia, PA 19406-4031
Tel (866) 776-8289 *Founded/Ownrshp* 1981
Sales 154.1MM^E *EMP* 126
SIC 5085 Industrial supplies
CFO: Michael Hill
**CEO:* John Burke
**Ex VP:* John Ludlam
VP: Jim Besikof
VP: Rick Thurston
VP: Bobby Wade
IT Man: Tom Nykanen

D-U-N-S 02-874-5227
SUPPLYONE HOLDINGS CO INC
11 Campus Blvd, Newtown Square, PA 19073-3247
Tel (484) 582-5005 *Founded/Ownrshp* 1998
Sales 514.7MM^E *EMP* 800^E
SIC 2653 5113 Corrugated & solid fiber boxes; Industrial & personal service paper
Pr: William T Leith
**CFO:* Jack Keeney
VP Opers: Don Cullen
VP Sls: Jim Burgener
Mktg Dir: Kim Griffin
Sls Dir: Joe Salvemini

D-U-N-S 10-001-6216 IMP
SUPPLYONE INC
(*Suby of* SUPPLYONE HOLDINGS CO INC) ★
11 Campus Blvd Ste 150, Newtown Square, PA 19073-3246
Tel (484) 582-1004 *Founded/Ownrshp* 1998
Sales 386.9MM^E *EMP* 775
SIC 5113 Industrial & personal service paper
Pr: William Leith
CFO: Jeff Billman
CFO: Gary Ferns
**Treas:* William Laughlin
VP: John Caruso
VP: Jim Dolehide
VP: Jamey Nolan
Genl Mgr: Margaret McCambridge
Genl Mgr: Frank Thomas
IT Man: Bill Lee
IT Man: Jeff McConnell

D-U-N-S 06-266-5659
SUPPORT AVIATION LLC
(*Suby of* AVIATION EQUIPMENT SUPPORT INC)
208 W Highland St, Altamonte Springs, FL 32714-2511
Tel (407) 731-4118 *Founded/Ownrshp* 2012
Sales 170.6MM *EMP* 200
Accts Robert K Gainer-Bellaire Gai
SIC 4581 Airports, flying fields & services
CEO: Nicholas Yodice
VP: Nagecimia O'Shoula
Board of Directors: Karen George, Robert George, Gregory Laughlin

SUPPORT CENTER
See NOB HILL GENERAL STORE INC

D-U-N-S 61-517-7735
SUPPORT SOLUTIONS OF MID-SOUTH LLC
5909 Shelby Oaks Dr # 100, Memphis, TN 38134-7317
Tel (901) 383-9193 *Founded/Ownrshp* 2005
Sales 47.5MM^E *EMP* 1,000^E
SIC 8361 Home for the mentally handicapped
CFO: Jeff Durbin
**Prin:* Randall Tracy
Ex Dir: Kathleen Lafevor

D-U-N-S 04-783-8342
▲ SUPPORT.COM INC
900 Chesapeake Dr Fl 2, Redwood City, CA 94063-4727
Tel (650) 556-9440 *Founded/Ownrshp* 1997
Sales 77.3MM *EMP* 1,695
Tkr Sym SPRT *Exch* NGS
SIC 7374 7372 Data processing & preparation; Business oriented computer software
CEO: Rick Bloom
**Ch Bd:* Joshua E Schechter
COO: Roop Lakkaraju
VP: Chris Koverman
IT Man: Riju Kalarickal
Mktg Mgr: Ritu Singh
Board of Directors: Brian J Kelley, Bradley L Radoff, Eric Singer, Tim Stanley

SUPPOSITORIA LABORATORY
See PERRIGO NEW YORK INC

D-U-N-S 03-153-3060 IMP
SUPREME BEVERAGE CO INC
3217 Messer Airport Hwy, Birmingham, AL 35222-1259
Tel (205) 251-8010 *Founded/Ownrshp* 1945
Sales 143.3MM^E *EMP* 178
SIC 5181 Beer & other fermented malt liquors
Pr: Charles Schilleci
**Treas:* J B Schilleci Jr
Genl Mgr: Barry Clough
Opers Mgr: Jimmy Stewart

D-U-N-S 06-470-2988 IMP/EXP
■ SUPREME CORP
(*Suby of* SUPREME INDUSTRIES INC) ★
2581 Kercher Rd, Goshen, IN 46528-7556
Tel (574) 642-4888 *Founded/Ownrshp* 1984
Sales 298.3MM^E *EMP* 1,500
Accts Crowe Chizek And Company Llp
SIC 3713 3792 3585 Truck bodies (motor vehicles); Bus bodies (motor vehicles); Van bodies; Travel trailers & campers; Refrigeration & heating equipment
Pr: Robert W Wilson
**Ch Bd:* Herbert M Gardner
**V Ch:* Omer G Kropf
**CFO:* Jeff Mowery
**VP:* William J Barrett
Genl Mgr: Christopher Allison
Genl Mgr: Steve O'Dell
Genl Mgr: Steve Odell
Genl Mgr: Mike Oium
Genl Mgr: Al Schroeder
Genl Mgr: Barry Smith

SUPREME COURT
See ALABAMA UNIFIED JUDICIAL SYSTEM

SUPREME COURT CLERK OFFICE
See JUDICIARY COURTS OF STATE OF ARKANSAS

D-U-N-S 36-175-9210
SUPREME COURT OF COMMONWEALTH OF PUERTO RICO
SUPREME COURT OF THE COMMWL PR
(*Suby of* COMMONWEALTH OF PUERTO RICO) ★
286 Munoz Rivera Ave We Western, San Juan, PR 00919
Tel (787) 641-6600 *Founded/Ownrshp* 1952
Sales NA *EMP* 5,000
SIC 9211 Courts; Federal courts; Local courts; State courts

SUPREME COURT OF THE COMMWL PR
See SUPREME COURT OF COMMONWEALTH OF PUERTO RICO

D-U-N-S 36-070-8705
SUPREME COURT OF STATE OF DELAWARE
(*Suby of* STATE OF DELAWARE)
55 The Grn, Dover, DE 19901-3611
Tel (302) 739-4155 *Founded/Ownrshp* 1776
Sales NA *EMP* 1,483
SIC 9211 State courts;
Prin: Myron T Steel

D-U-N-S 36-070-8374
SUPREME COURT OF STATE OF TENNESSEE
(*Suby of* STATE OF TENNESSEE) ★
511 Union St Ste 600, Nashville, TN 37219-1768
Tel (615) 253-2868 *Founded/Ownrshp* 1796
Sales NA *EMP* 2,150
SIC 9211 State courts
Comm Dir: Michele Wojciechowski
Genl Mgr: Sue A Olson
Genl Mgr: Sharon Putnam
Dir IT: Joel Kestner
IT Man: Pam Hancock

SUPREME COURT OF TEXAS
See JUDICIARY COURTS OF STATE OF TEXAS

D-U-N-S 16-190-6136
■ SUPREME COURT UNITED STATES
(*Suby of* U S GOVERNMENT) ★
1 1st St Ne, Washington, DC 20543-0001
Tel (202) 479-3000 *Founded/Ownrshp* 1790
Sales NA *EMP* 11,634
SIC 9211 Federal courts; ;
Snr Mgr: Jeffrey P Minear

D-U-N-S 80-754-8953
SUPREME ENTERPRISES INC
204 N Ector Dr, Euless, TX 76039-3542
Tel (817) 267-6090 *Founded/Ownrshp* 1991
Sales 71.9MM^E *EMP* 14,000
SIC 7363 Employee leasing service; Temporary help service
Pr: David Williams
**Treas:* Mike Wilkens
**VP:* Pat Fry
**VP:* Angie Gillum
**VP:* Perry Gillum

SUPREME FAN/INDUSTRIAL AIR
See LAU INDUSTRIES INC

D-U-N-S 07-139-1007 IMP/EXP
▲ SUPREME INDUSTRIES INC
2581 Kercher Rd, Goshen, IN 46528-7556
Tel (574) 642-3070 *Founded/Ownrshp* 1974
Sales 278.4MM *EMP* 1,400^E
Tkr Sym STS *Exch* ASE
SIC 3537 3713 3799 Industrial trucks & tractors; Truck & bus bodies; Stake, platform truck bodies; Trailers & trailer equipment
Pr: Mark D Weber
**Ch Bd:* Herbert M Gardner
CFO: Matthew W Long
**Ex VP:* William J Barrett
VP: Roman Jach
VP: Michael L Oium
Sls Mgr: Ken Marks
Board of Directors: Peter D Barrett, Edward L Flynn, Arthur J Gajarsa, Thomas B Hogan Jr, Michael L Klofas, Mark C Neilson, Wayne A Whitener

D-U-N-S 00-409-6780 IMP/EXP
■ SUPREME INTERNATIONAL LLC
(*Suby of* PERRY ELLIS INTERNATIONAL INC) ★
3000 Nw 107th Ave, Doral, FL 33172-2133
Tel (305) 592-2830 *Founded/Ownrshp* 2002
Sales 412.2MM^E *EMP* 1,174
SIC 2325 Men's & boys' trousers & slacks; Shorts (outerwear): men's, youths' & boys'; Jeans: men's, youths' & boys'
Pr: Steve Harriman
Pr: William V Roberti
COO: Bill Johnsen
Ex VP: Raymond Camano
Sr VP: Steven S Barr
Sr VP: Frank D Keeney
Sr VP: Ronald G Threadgill
VP: Todd Feste
VP: Terri Gonzalez
VP: Dennis Lappen
VP Sls: Dennis Kraus

SUPREME LENDING
See EVERETT FINANCIAL INC

D-U-N-S 07-231-0501 IMP
SUPREME LOBSTER AND SEAFOOD CO
SUPREME LOBSTER COMPANY
220 E North Ave, Villa Park, IL 60181-1207
Tel (630) 834-3474 *Founded/Ownrshp* 1974
Sales 158.6MM^E *EMP* 150
SIC 5146 Seafoods
Pr: Dominic P Stramaglia
Off Mgr: Judy Bianchi
Mktg Dir: Moses Trejo

SUPREME LOBSTER COMPANY
See SUPREME LOBSTER AND SEAFOOD CO

D-U-N-S 00-131-6132 IMP/EXP
SUPREME OIL CO INC
ADMIRATION FOODS
(*Suby of* STRATAS FOODS LLC) ★
66 Grand Ave Ste 201, Englewood, NJ 07631-6500
Tel (201) 408-0800 *Founded/Ownrshp* 1978, 2016
Sales 644.2MM^E *EMP* 450
SIC 5149 2079 Condiments; Edible fats & oils
Pr: Michael Leffler
COO: Nicole Acrish
CFO: John Matsen
Ofcr: Michael Kurland
Dir Bus: Scott Goldsberry
Manager: Arlene Hernandez

D-U-N-S 07-664-8609 IMP/EXP
SUR LA TABLE INC
(*Suby of* INVESTCORP INTERNATIONAL INC) ★
6100 4th Ave S Ste 500, Seattle, WA 98108-3219
Tel (206) 613-6000 *Founded/Ownrshp* 1994
Sales 175.0MM^E *EMP* 429
SIC 5719 Kitchenware
Pr: Jonathan Schwefel
**Pr:* Diane Neal
**CFO:* Debbie Brownfield
**Co-Ch Bd:* Kathy Tierney
**Treas:* Sherri Baker
VP: Nathan Carson
VP: Mark Comstock
VP: Brian Costello
VP: Kevin Ertell
VP: Jeff Gottlieb
**VP:* Kelly Kennedy
VP: Will Schoentrup
**VP:* Karin Seeger
Exec: David Pressley

SURA
See SOUTHEASTERN UNIVERSITIES RESEARCH ASSOCIATION INC

D-U-N-S 07-049-6575
SURDNA FOUNDATION INC
330 Madison Ave Fl 30, New York, NY 10017-5016
Tel (212) 557-0010 *Founded/Ownrshp* 1917
Sales 162.4MM *EMP* 12
SIC 6732 8742 Charitable trust management; Management consulting services
Pr: Phillip Henderson
**Pr:* Ed Skaloot
**Ch:* Elizabeth Kelly
**Treas:* Frederick Moon III
Comm Dir: George Soule
Pgrm Dir: Shawn Escoffery

D-U-N-S 18-467-2272 IMP
SURE FIT INC
(*Suby of* FOCUS FOOD SERVICES) ★
8000 Quarry Rd Ste C, Alburtis, PA 18011-9599
Tel (610) 264-7300 *Founded/Ownrshp* 1914
Sales 88.0MM *EMP* 94
SIC 5023 Slip covers (furniture); Pillowcases; Draperies
CEO: Marc Navarre
Pr: George De Sotle
CEO: Marc Navarre
CFO: John Nucero
Dir IT: Michael Herman

D-U-N-S 09-773-0972
SURE WINNER FOODS INC
SW FOODS
2 Lehner Rd, Saco, ME 04072-1836
Tel (207) 282-1258 *Founded/Ownrshp* 1979
Sales 169.2MM^E *EMP* 85
SIC 5143 4226 2024 Ice cream & ices; Special warehousing & storage; Ice cream & frozen desserts
Pr: Mark Irving
Ex VP: Keith Benot
VP: Robert Irving
Area Mgr: Jason Brooks
Area Mgr: Jason Carr
Area Mgr: Matt Corser
Area Mgr: Greg Martin
Opers Mgr: John Wright

D-U-N-S 09-757-5849 IMP/EXP
SUREFIRE LLC
18300 Mount Baldy Cir, Fountain Valley, CA 92708-6122
Tel (714) 545-9444 *Founded/Ownrshp* 2000
Sales 170.6MM^E *EMP* 490
SIC 3648 3842 3484 Lighting equipment; Flashlights; Ear plugs; Guns (firearms) or gun parts, 30 mm. & below
Pr: John W Matthews
**CFO:* Sean Vo
VP: Diane Chow
Dir IT: Jennifer Curley
IT Man: Don Forbes
Mfg Mgr: Gustav Bonse
Sales Asso: Kathleen Spear

D-U-N-S 13-068-3670
■ SUREPAYROLL INC
BUSINESS ONLINE PAYROLL
(*Suby of* PAYCHEX INC) ★
2350 Ravine Way Ste 100, Glenview, IL 60025-7621
Tel (847) 676-8420 *Founded/Ownrshp* 2011
Sales 100.0MM *EMP* 300
SIC 8721 Payroll accounting service
Pr: Michael Alter
**Sr VP:* Rick Gunther
**VP:* Steve Kania
**Genl Mgr:* Andrew Roe
Snr Sftwr: Gheorghe Milas
**CTO:* Michael Fineberg
QI Cn Mgr: Jun Yang
Natl Sales: Cindy Falzone
**VP Mktg:* Scott Brandt
Mktg Mgr: Patrick Gavin
Sales Asso: Matthew Hudson

D-U-N-S 60-516-5943 IMP/EXP
SURESOURCE LLC
BUILT NY
20 Constitution Blvd S, Shelton, CT 06484-4302
Tel (203) 922-7500 *Founded/Ownrshp* 1989
Sales 151.7MM^E *EMP* 150
SIC 5045 Computer software
CEO: Reuben Hendelo
COO: Aaron Turner
**CFO:* Peter Kopcha
IT Man: Jake Bogey

SURETY ABSTRACT SERVICES
See SURETY TITLE CO LLC

D-U-N-S 93-372-1946
SURETY TITLE CO LLC
SURETY ABSTRACT SERVICES
11 Eves Dr Ste 150, Marlton, NJ 08053-3114
Tel (856) 988-8900 *Founded/Ownrshp* 1992
Sales NA *EMP* 175
SIC 6361 6541 Title insurance; Title & trust companies
Pr: Brian Klaus
**CFO:* John J De Santis
CFO: John De De Santis
Ofcr: Lynn Peterson
Ofcr: Donald Spencer
Ex VP: John J Desantis Jr
**VP:* Keith Langan
**VP:* Michael Ryan
VP Sls: Jonathan Quinn
Sls Mgr: Christopher Mooney

SUREWAY
See FOOD GIANT SUPERMARKETS INC

D-U-N-S 01-526-1936 IMP
■ SUREWEST COMMUNICATIONS
(*Suby of* CONSOLIDATED COMMUNICATIONS HOLDINGS INC) ★
211 Lincoln St, Roseville, CA 95678-2614
Tel (916) 786-6141 *Founded/Ownrshp* 2012
Sales 353.2MM^E *EMP* 812
SIC 4813 4812 Telephone communication, except radio; Local telephone communications; Long distance telephone communications; Cellular telephone services
CEO: Steven C Oldham
Pr: Jennifer Wilson
**COO:* C Robert Udell Jr
**CFO:* Steven L Childers
Sr VP: Fred Arcuri
**Sr VP:* Steven J Shirar
Ex Dir: Haavard Sterri
**CIO:* Christopher A Young
Sfty Mgr: Mike Doyle

D-U-N-S 14-715-8133
■ SUREWEST FINANCIAL CORP
(*Suby of* CNA SURETY CORP) ★
101 S Phillips Ave, Sioux Falls, SD 57104-6735
Tel (605) 336-0850 *Founded/Ownrshp* 1997
Sales NA *EMP* 747
SIC 6351 Fidelity or surety bonding
Pr: Steven T Pate
**Pr:* Mark Vonnahme

D-U-N-S 78-012-6538
SURGE RESOURCES INC
920 Candia Rd, Manchester, NH 03109-5201
Tel (603) 623-0007 *Founded/Ownrshp* 1994
Sales 74.7MM^E *EMP* 2,000
SIC 8742 7361 7363 Human resource consulting services; Placement agencies; Employee leasing service
Pr: Kevin Attar
**Treas:* George Attar

D-U-N-S 96-808-8158
SURGERY CENTER HOLDINGS INC
SURGERY PARTNERS
1450 Brickell Ave Fl 31, Miami, FL 33131-3460
Tel (813) 514-9571 *Founded/Ownrshp* 2011
Sales 548.9MM *EMP* 6,610
SIC 6799 Investors
CEO: Michael Doyle

D-U-N-S 07-395-7789
SURGERY CENTER OF ALTA BATES SUMMIT MEDICAL CENTER LLC
ALTA BATES SUMMIT MEDICAL CTR
(*Suby of* SUTTER C H S) ★
2450 Ashby Ave, Berkeley, CA 94705-2067
Tel (510) 204-4444 *Founded/Ownrshp* 1936
Sales 421.2MM^E *EMP* 4,300
SIC 8062 General medical & surgical hospitals
Pr: Warren Kirk
**CFO:* Robert Petrina
Ofcr: Steve Austin
Assoc Dir: William Green
Assoc Dir: Adam Husney
Adm/Dir: Natilee Newton
Genl Mgr: Myesha Kirk
IT Man: Keith Cooley
Obsttrcn: Stephen Smith
Opthamlgy: Rose S Kiprov
Opthamlgy: James E Langham

D-U-N-S 04-686-2541
SURGERY CENTER TORRANCE L P (CA)
AMSURG
(*Suby of* AMSURG CORP) ★
23560 Crenshaw Blvd # 104, Torrance, CA 90505-5233
Tel (310) 784-5880 *Founded/Ownrshp* 2001, 2012
Sales 29.3MM^E *EMP* 1,613^E
SIC 8011 Ambulatory surgical center
Pt: Nick Silvino MD
Pt: Ripu Arora MD
Pt: Marc Colman MD
Pt: Steve Dinsmore MD
Pt: Neiman Low MD
Pt: John Maher MD
Pt: Al Marrone MD
Pt: Daryl Rheuark MD
Pt: Arnie Serkin MD

Pt: Jerry Unatin MD
Pt: Vincent Valdez MD
Pt: Steven Wan MD
Pt: Barry Wolstan MD
Board of Directors:

SURGERY CTR OF ALTA BATES SUMM
See SUMMIT MEDICAL CENTER

SURGERY PARTNERS
See SYMBION INC

SURGERY PARTNERS
See SURGERY CENTER HOLDINGS INC

D-U-N-S 08-000-5830
■ SURGERY PARTNERS INC
(*Suby of* HIG SURGERY CENTERS LLC) ★
40 Burton Hills Blvd # 500, Nashville, TN 37215-6186
Tel (615) 234-5900 *Founded/Ownrshp* 2004
Sales 959.8MM *EMP* 5,100[E]
Tkr Sym SGRY *Exch* NGS
SIC 8062 3851 General medical & surgical hospitals; Ophthalmic goods
CEO: Michael T Doyle
Pt: John Crysel
**Ch Bd:* Christopher Laitala
CFO: Teresa F Sparks
Sr VP: Jennifer B Baldock
Sr VP: Dennis Dean
VP: Matt Musso
Board of Directors: Teresa Deluca, Adam Feinstein, Matthew I Lozow, Brent Turner

D-U-N-S 02-426-2934
▲ SURGICAL CARE AFFILIATES INC
510 Lake Cook Rd Ste 400, Deerfield, IL 60015-4971
Tel (847) 236-0921 *Founded/Ownrshp* 2007
Sales 1.0MMM *EMP* 5,248[E]
Tkr Sym SCAI *Exch* NGS
SIC 8093 Specialty outpatient clinics
Ch Bd: Andrew Hayek
COO: Michael A Rucker
CFO: Tom W F De Weerdt
Ex VP: Joseph T Clark
Ex VP: Richard L Sharff Jr
Snr Mgr: Chase Jones

D-U-N-S 80-010-0583
■ SURGICAL CARE AFFILIATES LLC
(*Suby of* SURGICAL CARE AFFILIATES INC) ★
569 Brookwood Vlg Ste 901, Birmingham, AL 35209-4513
Tel (205) 545-2572 *Founded/Ownrshp* 2007
Sales 766.2MM[E] *EMP* 5,000[E]
SIC 8741 Hospital management
CEO: Andrew Hayek
**COO:* Joseph Clark
CFO: Debbie Holt
**Bd of Dir:* Todd B Sisitsky
**Ex VP:* Pete Clemens
Ex VP: Michael A Rucker
Ex VP: Rich Scharff
Ex VP: Chip Wann
**Sr VP:* Gerry Biala
Sr VP: Shannon Blakeley
**Sr VP:* Goran Dragolovic
Sr VP: Randy Mink
VP: Suzanne Rogers
Exec: Joe Arruda
Board of Directors: Thomas C Geiser, Curtis Lane, Leonard D Schaeffer, Todd D Sisitsky

D-U-N-S 03-814-0786
SURGICAL STAFF INC
120 Saint Matthews Ave, San Mateo, CA 94401-2807
Tel (650) 558-3999 *Founded/Ownrshp* 1984
Sales 30.7MM[E] *EMP* 1,200
SIC 7363 Temporary help service
Pr: Beverly Foster
**Sr VP:* Nancy Russell

D-U-N-S 10-005-9088
SURRY COUNTY SCHOOL DISTRICT
209 N Crutchfield St, Dobson, NC 27017-8805
Tel (336) 386-8211 *Founded/Ownrshp* 1917
Sales 52.3MM[E] *EMP* 1,079
SIC 8211 Public elementary & secondary schools; Public elementary school; Public junior high school; Public senior high school
MIS Dir: David Brown
Dir IT: Kristi Manuel

SURVEY SAMPLING INTERNATIONAL
See OPINIONOLOGY LLC

D-U-N-S 09-976-2676
SURVEY SAMPLING INTERNATIONAL LLC
S S I
6 Research Dr Ste 200, Shelton, CT 06484-6228
Tel (203) 225-6191 *Founded/Ownrshp* 1977
Sales 186.4MM[E] *EMP* 1,300[E]
SIC 8732 Market analysis or research; Survey service: marketing, location, etc.
CEO: Chris Fanning
**Pr:* Calista Corley
**Pr:* Andrew Moffatt
**Pr:* Jeff Welch
**Chf Mktg O:* Chris Clarke
Sr VP: Jim Daxner
VP: Tom Johnson
VP: Harry Kelley
CIO: Troy Lauritzen
Dir IT: Gerald Cap
Sftwr Eng: Mark Conklin

D-U-N-S 86-720-3556
SURVEYING AND MAPPING LLC
S A M
4801 Sw Pkwy Ste 100, Austin, TX 78735-8903
Tel (512) 447-0575 *Founded/Ownrshp* 1994
Sales 109.7MM[E] *EMP* 680
Accts Weaver And Tidwell Llp Aus
SIC 8713 Surveying services
Pr: Samir G Hanna
**CFO:* Rick Cabrera
**VP:* Coleman Cunningham
**VP:* Michael R Hatcher
IT Man: Shannon Brooks
IT Man: Brian Faure

D-U-N-S 14-783-8197 IMP/EXP
SURYA CARPET INC
SURYA RUGS
(*Suby of* SURYA CARPET PRIVATE LIMITED)
1 Surya Dr, White, GA 30184
Tel (706) 625-4823 *Founded/Ownrshp* 1986
Sales 97.7MM[E] *EMP* 200
Accts Morehouse Group Pc Dalton
SIC 5023 2273 Carpets; Decorative home furnishings & supplies; Carpets & rugs
CEO: Surya M Tiwari
**CFO:* Cesar Guerra

SURYA RUGS
See SURYA CARPET INC

D-U-N-S 07-868-7131
SUS - MENTAL HEALTH PROGRAMS INC (NY)
305 7th Ave Fl 7, New York, NY 10001-6008
Tel (212) 633-6900 *Founded/Ownrshp* 1980
Sales 100.0MM *EMP* 1,000
SIC 8699 Charitable organization
CEO: Donna Colonna
CFO: Mike Whelan

D-U-N-S 87-862-7207
■ SUSA PARTNERSHIP LP
(*Suby of* EXTRA SPACE STORAGE INC) ★
175 Toyota Plz, Memphis, TN 38103-5601
Tel (901) 252-2000 *Founded/Ownrshp* 2005
Sales 90.5MM[E] *EMP* 1,700
SIC 4225 Warehousing, self-storage
Prin: Diane Cooper

SUSAN G KMEN FOR CURE AFFLATES
See SUSAN G KOMEN BREAST CANCER FOUNDATION INC

D-U-N-S 17-777-5822
SUSAN G KOMEN BREAST CANCER FOUNDATION INC
SUSAN G KMEN FOR CURE AFFLATES
5005 Lbj Fwy Ste 250, Dallas, TX 75244-6125
Tel (972) 855-1600 *Founded/Ownrshp* 1982
Sales 118.3MM *EMP* 260
Accts Lb Ernst & Young Us Llp Fort
SIC 8699 8069 8011 8099 Charitable organization; Cancer hospital; Internal medicine practitioners; Blood related health services
Pr: Judith A Salerno
Ch Bd: Alexine Clement Jackson
Ch Bd: Dr Lasalle B Lessall
Pr: Martina Hone
Pr: Elizabeth Thompson
CFO: Bob Green
CFO: Gail Marcus
Chf Mktg O: Katrina McGhee
Ex VP: Patrice Tosi
VP: Carol Corcoran
VP: Eric Montgomery
VP: Miguel Perez
VP: Kimberly Simpson
VP: Carrie Walsh

D-U-N-S 01-731-4699
SUSAN THOMPSON BUFFETT FOUNDATION
222 Kiewit Plz, Omaha, NE 68131
Tel (402) 943-1300 *Founded/Ownrshp* 2009
Sales 246.2MM *EMP* 3
SIC 8641 Civic social & fraternal associations
Prin: Carol Loomis

SUSD
See STOCKTON UNIFIED SCHOOL DISTRICT

D-U-N-S 10-167-0610
SUSQUEHANNA BANCSHARES INC
26 N Cedar St, Lititz, PA 17543-1514
Tel (717) 626-4721 *Founded/Ownrshp* 1982
Sales NA *EMP* 3,395[E]
SIC 6021

D-U-N-S 00-791-2298 IMP
■ SUSQUEHANNA BANK
(*Suby of* BB&T CORP) ★
9 E Main St, Lititz, PA 17543-1926
Tel (717) 627-1778 *Founded/Ownrshp* 1800
Sales NA *EMP* 1,559
SIC 6022 State trust companies accepting deposits, commercial
Ch Bd: Andrew Samuel
**Pr:* William J Reuter
**CFO:* Mark Czrkel
**Treas:* Samuel G Reel Jr
**Chf Cred:* Christopher D Holt
VP: Charles Flick
Board of Directors: Jeffrey F Lehman, Robert E Poole Jr

D-U-N-S 60-689-6892
■ SUSQUEHANNA COMMERCIAL FINANCE INC
(*Suby of* BB&T) ★
2 Country View Rd Ste 300, Malvern, PA 19355-1420
Tel (610) 705-4999 *Founded/Ownrshp* 2004
Sales 353.7MM[E] *EMP* 68
SIC 8741 Financial management for business
CEO: Kenneth Collins
**Pr:* Robert Boyer
**CFO:* Brian Pickett
**Ex VP:* Christine Brown
**Ex VP:* Jeffrey Nicholas
VP: Angela Thomas

SUSQUEHANNA HEALTH
See SUSQUEHANNA PHYSICIAN SERVICES

SUSQUEHANNA HEALTH SYSTEM
See SUSQUEHANNA VENTURES INC

D-U-N-S 87-843-5825
SUSQUEHANNA HEALTH SYSTEM
700 High St, Williamsport, PA 17701-3100
Tel (570) 321-1000 *Founded/Ownrshp* 1993
Sales 465.9MM[E] *EMP* 3,500
Accts Bkd Llp Springfield Mo
SIC 8741 Hospital management
Ch Bd: Richard W Dewald
**Pr:* Steven Johnson
CFO: Ronald Gilbert
**CFO:* Charles Santangelo
**V Ch Bd:* Sister Joanne Bednar
Ofcr: Thomas O'Connell
VP: Sherry Watts
Adm Dir: Charles Martin
Off Mgr: Toni Hiller
CTO: Matthew McLaughlin
VP Opers: Rita Spangler

D-U-N-S 94-815-2590
SUSQUEHANNA INTERNATIONAL GROUP LLP
SIG
401 E City Ave Ste 220, Bala Cynwyd, PA 19004-1117
Tel (610) 617-2600 *Founded/Ownrshp* 2001
Sales 1.0MMM[E] *EMP* 1,600
SIC 6211 Security brokers & dealers
CFO: Brian Sullivan
Chf Cred: John Henry
Ofcr: Jerry O'Connell
Ofcr: Jerry Oconnell
Ex VP: Roger Sullivan
Exec: Lauren Hof
Dir Risk M: Bob Farrell
Assoc Dir: James Fitzgibbons
Assoc Dir: Alan Goldberg
Assoc Dir: Todd Silverberg
Assoc Dir: Todd Simkin

D-U-N-S 00-300-3431 IMP/EXP
SUSQUEHANNA PFALTZGRAFF CO INC (DE)
140 E Market St, York, PA 17401-1219
Tel (717) 848-5500 *Founded/Ownrshp* 1941
Sales 300.0MM[E] *EMP* 1,900
SIC 4832 4841 6512 Radio broadcasting stations; Cable television services; Nonresidential building operators
Pr: William H Simpson
CFO: John L Finlayson
Ch: Louis J Appell Jr
Treas: George N Appell
VP: Craig W Bremer
VP: Peter P Brubaker
VP: Marsha M Everton
VP: Jack R Kay
VP: David Kennedy
**VP:* Helen Appell Norton
Board of Directors: Charles Abbott, Louis J Appell III, Helen N Coon, Robert Pokelwaldt

D-U-N-S 10-966-7246
SUSQUEHANNA PHYSICIAN SERVICES
SUSQUEHANNA HEALTH
1100 Grampian Blvd, Williamsport, PA 17701-1909
Tel (570) 320-7444 *Founded/Ownrshp* 1987
Sales 91.0MM *EMP* 3,000
Accts Bkd Llp Springfield Mo
SIC 8011 Physicians' office, including specialists
Pr: Stephen Johnson
CFO: Candy Bliss
**CFO:* Charles Santangelo
Dir Rad: Craig Osborn
Adm Dir: Brian Fache
Doctor: Guy Bantleman
Nrsg Dir: Deborah Fontaine
Board of Directors: Jenny

D-U-N-S 36-226-8849
SUSQUEHANNA VENTURES INC
SUSQUEHANNA HEALTH SYSTEM
(*Suby of* SUSQUEHANNA HEALTH SYSTEM) ★
1100 Grampian Blvd, Williamsport, PA 17701-1909
Tel (570) 326-8718 *Founded/Ownrshp* 2015
Sales 87.4MM *EMP* 1
SIC 8062 General medical & surgical hospitals
CEO: Steven P Johnson
**Treas:* Al Clapps
Surgeon: Renee L Quarterman

D-U-N-S 08-215-7041
■ SUSSER CO LTD
(*Suby of* STRIPES LLC) ★
4545 Ayers St, Corpus Christi, TX 78415
Tel (361) 883-6321 *Founded/Ownrshp* 1966
Sales 49.6MM[E] *EMP* 2,000
SIC 6531 Real estate brokers & agents
Pt: Jerry L Susser
Pt: Rocky Dewbre
Pt: Sam J Susser

D-U-N-S 78-563-4549 IMP
■ SUSSER HOLDINGS CORP
(*Suby of* SUNOCO LP) ★
4525 Ayers St, Corpus Christi, TX 78415-1401
Tel (361) 884-2463 *Founded/Ownrshp* 2015
Sales 540.7MM[E] *EMP* 1,954[E]
SIC 5411 5541 5172 Convenience stores, chain; Gasoline service stations; Petroleum products
Pr: Sam L Susser
Pr: David Wishard
**CFO:* Mary E Sullivan
**Ex VP:* E V Bonner Jr
**Ex VP:* Steven C Desutter
**Ex VP:* Rocky B Dewbre
VP: Gail Workman
VP Bus Dev: Cal McIntosh
Area Mgr: Manuel Barrera
Area Mgr: Jesse Chavez
Area Mgr: Thelma Delgado

D-U-N-S 80-002-4437
■ SUSSER HOLDINGS LLC
(*Suby of* SUNOCO LP) ★
4433 Baldwin Blvd, Corpus Christi, TX 78408-2707
Tel (361) 693-3698 *Founded/Ownrshp* 1997
Sales 103.5MM[E] *EMP* 2,035[E]
SIC 5411 Grocery stores
Prin: Sam Susser
VP: Patrick Albro
VP: Sandra Brimhall
VP: Otis Peaks
VP: Eduardo Pereda
VP: Lee Rahmberg
Div Mgr: Mario Mungia

Mktg Mgr: Helen Gignac
Sls Mgr: Rusty Johnson

D-U-N-S 02-664-4682
■ SUSSER PETROLEUM CORP
RUSCHE DISTRIBUTING
(*Suby of* CIRCLE K) ★
555 E Airtex Dr, Houston, TX 77073-6099
Tel (832) 234-3746 *Founded/Ownrshp* 1999
Sales 95.5MM[E] *EMP* 35
SIC 5172 7389 Petroleum products; Lubricating oils & greases; Service station supplies, petroleum; Credit card service
Ch Bd: Sam L Susser
**Pr:* Rocky Dewbre
**CFO:* Mary Sullivan

D-U-N-S 07-858-0773
■ SUSSER PETROLEUM OPERATING CO LLC
(*Suby of* SUNOCO LP) ★
555 E Airtex Dr, Houston, TX 77073-6099
Tel (832) 234-3600 *Founded/Ownrshp* 2012
Sales 122.5MM[E] *EMP* 519[E]
SIC 5172 Petroleum products
CEO: Sam L Susser
**Pr:* Rocky Dewbre
**Ex VP:* E V Bonner Jr
**Sr VP:* Gail Workman
**VP:* Lees Phelps

D-U-N-S 07-880-6570
■ SUSSER PETROLEUM PROPERTY CO LLC
(*Suby of* SUNOCO LP) ★
555 E Airtex Dr, Houston, TX 77073-6099
Tel (832) 234-3600 *Founded/Ownrshp* 2012
Sales 247.5MM[E] *EMP* 500[E]
SIC 5172 6519 Engine fuels & oils; Real property lessors
Pr: Robert Owens

D-U-N-S 83-314-2420 IMP
SUSSEX IM INC
SUSSEX INJECTION MOLDING
N65w24770 Main St, Sussex, WI 53089-2651
Tel (262) 246-8022 *Founded/Ownrshp* 2009
Sales 88.2MM[E] *EMP* 210
SIC 3089 Injection molded finished plastic products
Pr: Keith Everson
Pr: Pat Kinjerski
**CFO:* Dvaid Guagliardo
VP: Philip Salzman
IT Man: Joanna Rosen
VP Sls: Edward Fabiszak

SUSSEX INJECTION MOLDING
See SUSSEX IM INC

D-U-N-S 15-421-6550
SUSSEX INSURANCE CO
(*Suby of* ENSTAR GROUP LIMITED)
221 Dawson Rd, Columbia, SC 29223-1704
Tel (803) 735-0672 *Founded/Ownrshp* 2015
Sales NA *EMP* 300
SIC 6331 Fire, marine & casualty insurance
CEO: Paul Brockman
COO: Harvey Galloway
Treas: Robert A Leichtle
Ofcr: Greg Anderson
VP: Nick Bhatt
VP: Jeri Boysia
VP: J Gardham
Dir IT: Cheryl Rudell
Mktg Mgr: Paul Povey

D-U-N-S 07-484-6312
SUTHERLAND ASBILL & BRENNAN LLP
700 6th St Nw Ste 700, Washington, DC 20001-3980
Tel (202) 383-0100 *Founded/Ownrshp* 1924
Sales 130.1MM[E] *EMP* 900
SIC 8111 Antitrust & trade regulation law; Securities law; Environmental law; Administrative & government law
Mng Pt: Mark D Wasserman
Pt: Dennis L Allen
Pt: Bruce M Bettigole
Pt: Thomas E Bisset
Pt: Michele Borens
Pt: Thomas R Bundy III
Pt: Michael C Castellon
Pt: David M Cayce
Pt: Rachel Giesber Clingman
Pt: Joseph M Depew
Pt: James R Dwyer
Pt: Jeffrey H Mace
Pt: John J Mahon
Pt: Neb Minnear
Pt: Joh H Mobley II
Pt: Mary E Monahan
Pt: Robert J Neis
Pt: John S Pruitt
Pt: M Kristan Rizzolo
Pt: Steven L Roberts
Pt: Brian L Rubin

D-U-N-S 07-869-3218
SUTHERLAND ASSET MANAGEMENT CORP
2 Bridge Ave Ste 322, Red Bank, NJ 07701-4603
Tel (732) 978-7518 *Founded/Ownrshp* 2014
Sales NA *EMP* 4[E]
SIC 6162 Mortgage bankers & correspondents
CEO: Thomas Capasse
Pr: Jack Ross
CFO: Frederick C Herbst
CIO: Thomas Buttacavoli

D-U-N-S 17-329-3085
SUTHERLAND GLOBAL SERVICES INC
1160 Pittsford Victor Rd A, Pittsford, NY 14534-3825
Tel (585) 586-5757 *Founded/Ownrshp* 1986
Sales 2.0MMM[E] *EMP* 13,215
SIC 8742 Banking & finance consultant
CEO: Dilip R Vellodi
Pr: David Holdridge
Pr: Stephen P Lynch
Pr: Vinayak K Pendyala
Pr: Michael Shannon

*COO: Ashok Jain
*CFO: Micheal Bartusek
CFO: T R Sanhanakishnan
Treas: Joe R Kawulok
*Chf Cred: Kam Shenai
Assoc VP: Deepak Nair
Sr VP: G Bala
*Sr VP: Bharat Chadda
Sr VP: Marwan Chouha
Sr VP: Ronald Knight
*Sr VP: Daniel Lang
Sr VP: Muthu Narayanan
VP: John Abou
VP: Paul Balcerzak
VP: Alan Barnes
VP: Barbara Barnes

D-U-N-S 03-371-6101
SUTHERLANDS FOODSERVICE INC
16 Forest Pkwy Bldg K, Forest Park, GA 30297-2015
Tel (404) 366-8550 Founded/Ownrshp 1947
Sales 123.6MM^E EMP 201
SIC 5144 5148 5147 5143 5141 Poultry products; Eggs; Fruits, fresh; Vegetables, fresh; Meats, fresh; Dairy products, except dried or canned; Groceries, general line
Pr: James E Sutherland Jr
*CFO: Bonnie Sutherland Wilson

SUTHERLANDS LUMBER COMPANY
See CIMARRON LUMBER AND SUPPLY CO

D-U-N-S 07-188-2724
SUTTER BAY HOSPITALS
CALIFORNIA PACIFIC MEDICAL CTR
(Suby of SUTTER C H S) ★
633 Folsom St Fl 5, San Francisco, CA 94107-3623
Tel (415) 600-6000 Founded/Ownrshp 1885
Sales 1.5MMM EMP 3,597
Accts Ernst & Young Us Llp San Dieg
SIC 8062 8733 General medical & surgical hospitals; Research institute
Pr: Martin Brotman MD
*CEO: Warren Browner
Bd of Dir: Steven Cummings
Bd of Dir: John F Forbes
Bd of Dir: Judy Garber
Bd of Dir: Susan E Hankinson
Bd of Dir: Joyce Hansen
Bd of Dir: Marston Nauman
Bd of Dir: Dave Razavi
Assoc Dir: Sara Swenson
Surgeon: Sachinandan Banerjee

SUTTER C H S
See SUTTER SOLANO MEDICAL CENTER INC

SUTTER C H S
See SUTTER HEALTH

D-U-N-S 06-887-7372
SUTTER CENTRAL VALLEY HOSPITALS (CA)
MEMORIAL MEDICAL CENTER
(Suby of SUTTER C H S) ★
1700 Coffee Rd, Modesto, CA 95355-2803
Tel (209) 526-4500 Founded/Ownrshp 1947, 2009
Sales 392.7MM^E EMP 4,000
Accts Ernst & Young Llp Roseville
SIC 8062 General medical & surgical hospitals
CEO: James Conforti
*Ch Bd: Todd Smith
V Ch: Tom V Groningen
*CEO: David P Benn
*CEO: Sutter Pat Fry
*COO: Steve Mitchell
*CFO: Eric Dalton
Treas: Nadder Mirsepassi
Bd of Dir: Charles Suntra
Exec: Beth McKinsey
Dir Rad: Mark Munden
Dir Rad: Della Tiwater
Board of Directors: James H Barnick, Tom V Groningen, Robert Keizer, James D Mayol, Terry Sweeney, Della Tiwater, Joan Watson

D-U-N-S 78-218-6977
SUTTER CONNECT LLC
SUTTER PHYSICIAN SERVICES
(Suby of SUTTER C H S) ★
10470 Old Placrvl Rd # 100, Sacramento, CA 95827-2539
Tel (916) 854-6600 Founded/Ownrshp 1989
Sales 35.9MM^E EMP 1,800
SIC 8742 8741 8721 Hospital & health services consultant; Management information systems consultant; Management services; Accounting, auditing & bookkeeping
CEO: Charles V Wirth
Dir IT: Robert Raymond
Doctor: Betsy Carrabello

D-U-N-S 93-764-4909
SUTTER EAST BAY MEDFNDTN
3687 Mt Diablo Blvd # 200, Lafayette, CA 94549-3746
Tel (510) 204-6622 Founded/Ownrshp 2009
Sales 113.3MM EMP 3
Accts Ernst & Young Us Llp Rosevill
SIC 8641 Civic social & fraternal associations
Prin: Len Alison

D-U-N-S 02-769-3305
SUTTER GOULD MEDICAL FOUNDATION
1700 Mchenry Ave Ste 60b, Modesto, CA 95350-4333
Tel (209) 526-4500 Founded/Ownrshp 2005
Sales 305.0MM EMP 4
Accts Ernst & Young Us Llp Rosevill
SIC 8011 Offices & clinics of medical doctors
Prin: John Kelly Nations

SUTTER HEALTH
See SUTTERCARE CORP

SUTTER HEALTH
See SUTTER MEDICAL FOUNDATION

D-U-N-S 12-181-6615
SUTTER HEALTH
SUTTER C H S
2200 River Plaza Dr, Sacramento, CA 95833-4134
Tel (916) 733-8800 Founded/Ownrshp 1981
Sales 11.0MMM EMP 48,000
SIC 8062 8051 8011 6513 General medical & surgical hospitals; Skilled nursing care facilities; Offices & clinics of medical doctors; Retirement hotel operation
Pr: Patrick Fry
Chf Rad: Richard Porzio
COO: Randy Ross
CFO: William Anderson
CFO: Siri Nelson
CFO: Robert D Reed
Ofcr: Wilma Acosta
Ofcr: John B Fache
Ofcr: Gordon Hunt MD
Sr VP: Gordon C Hunt Jr
Sr VP: Gary F Loveridge
Sr VP: Jonathan Manis
VP: Jodi Davis
Exec: Arlene Cullum
Exec: Theodora Owens
Exec: Darrel Schmucker
Dir Risk M: Mary Christensen
Dir Lab: Chris Flaherty
Dir Lab: Jennifer Schiffgens
Comm Dir: Jill Antonides PH
Dir Rx: Jeannette Hanni
Board of Directors: Theodore Ted Saenger, Geraldine R Brinton, Elizabeth Vilardo MD, Mary Brown, Sharon Y Woo, Gary L Depolo, Don Wreden MD, Alexander Gonzalez, Jim Gray Chb, David H Jeppson, Richard M Levy Phd, Todd Murray, Andrew Pansini

D-U-N-S 07-154-3870 IMP
SUTTER HEALTH SACRAMENTO SIERRA REGION
SUTTER MEMORIAL HOSPITAL
(Suby of SUTTER C H S) ★
2200 River Plaza Dr, Sacramento, CA 95833-4134
Tel (916) 733-8800 Founded/Ownrshp 1935
Sales 1.8MMM EMP 4,000
Accts Ernst & Young Us Llp San Dieg
SIC 8062 8063 8052 General medical & surgical hospitals; Psychiatric hospitals; Intermediate care facilities
CEO: Patrick E Fry
Pr: Darling Lones
Obsttrcn: Jeffrey Stern

D-U-N-S 00-919-5280 IMP/EXP
SUTTER HOME WINERY INC
TRINCHERO FAMILY ESTATES
100 Saint Helena Hwy S, Saint Helena, CA 94574-2204
Tel (707) 963-3104 Founded/Ownrshp 1948
Sales 199.6MM^E EMP 625
Accts Brotemarkle Davis & Co Llp St
SIC 2084 0172 Wines; Grapes
CEO: Roger J Trinchero
V Ch: Roger Trinchero
*CEO: Louis Trinchero
Sr VP: Peter Larson
VP: Glenn Andrade
VP: Dave Derby
VP: Tom Fantham
*VP: Anthony R Torres
CTO: Dave Sneed
VP Opers: Bob Torres
Ql Cn Mgr: Mara Walls

SUTTER MEDICAL CTR SANTA ROSA
See SUTTER SANTA ROSA REGIONAL HOSPITAL

D-U-N-S 79-298-4957
SUTTER MEDICAL FOUNDATION
SUTTER HEALTH
2700 Gateway Oaks Dr, Sacramento, CA 95833-4337
Tel (916) 887-7122 Founded/Ownrshp 1992
Sales 128.4MM^E EMP 700
Accts Ernst & Young Llp Roseville
SIC 8741 Hospital management; Nursing & personal care facility management
CEO: Tom Blinn
COO: Gary Zufelt
Prgrm Mgr: Michon Henderson
IT Man: Kelly Danna
Surgeon: Eric London

SUTTER MEMORIAL HOSPITAL
See SUTTER HEALTH SACRAMENTO SIERRA REGION

SUTTER PHYSICIAN SERVICES
See SUTTER CONNECT LLC

D-U-N-S 10-178-1388
SUTTER ROSEVILLE MEDICAL CENTER
1 Medical Plaza Dr, Roseville, CA 95661-3037
Tel (916) 781-1000 Founded/Ownrshp 1950
Sales 558.2MM EMP 1,700
SIC 8062 General medical & surgical hospitals
CEO: Patrick Brady
Dir IT: Bob Smith
Plas Surg: Eric C Gage

D-U-N-S 07-611-2713
SUTTER ROSEVILLE MEDICAL CENTER FOUNDATION
1 Medical Plaza Dr, Roseville, CA 95661-3037
Tel (916) 781-1000 Founded/Ownrshp 1950
Sales 2.6MM EMP 2,000
Accts Ernst & Young Llp Roseville
SIC 8062 General medical & surgical hospitals
Pr: Patricia Marquez

D-U-N-S 09-398-8079
SUTTER SANTA ROSA REGIONAL HOSPITAL
SUTTER MEDICAL CTR SANTA ROSA
(Suby of SUTTER C H S) ★
30 Mark West Springs Rd, Santa Rosa, CA 95403-1436
Tel (707) 576-4000 Founded/Ownrshp 1921
Sales 213.2MM EMP 122
SIC 8062 General medical & surgical hospitals
Pr: Sarah Krevans
*Pr: Barbara Eichhorn
*Treas: Ann Marie Luffler
*VP: Shirley Flournoy
Dir Inf Cn: Erin Buchanan
Dir Soc: Beth Krumbien
Off Mgr: Susan Baldwin
CIO: Charlie Kennedy
IT Man: Shaun Ralston
Netwrk Eng: Jim Collins
Obsttrcn: Frank J Miraglia

D-U-N-S 07-168-7859
SUTTER SOLANO MEDICAL CENTER INC
SUTTER C H S
(Suby of SUTTER C H S) ★
300 Hospital Dr, Vallejo, CA 94589-2594
Tel (707) 554-4444 Founded/Ownrshp 1952
Sales 124.2MM EMP 560
SIC 8062 General medical & surgical hospitals
*CFO: Brett Moore
Dir IT: Jim Barringham

D-U-N-S 04-000-5068
SUTTER VISITING NURSE ASSOCIATION & HOSPICE
VNAHNC
(Suby of SUTTER C H S) ★
1900 Powell St Ste 300, Emeryville, CA 94608-1815
Tel (866) 652-9178 Founded/Ownrshp 2000
Sales 171.0MM EMP 1,000
Accts Ernst & Young Llp Roseville
SIC 8082 Visiting nurse service
CEO: Marcia Reissig
*COO: Maryellen Rota
CFO: Greg Davis
*CFO: Gregg Davis
Dir Rx: Frank Wong
Psych: Richard Jamil

D-U-N-S 15-215-1585 IMP
SUTTERCARE CORP
SUTTER HEALTH
(Suby of SUTTER C H S) ★
2200 River Plaza Dr, Sacramento, CA 95833-4134
Tel (916) 733-8800 Founded/Ownrshp 1985
Sales 1.5MMM EMP 3,300
SIC 8051 8062 Skilled nursing care facilities; General medical & surgical hospitals
CEO: Van Johnson
*CFO: Robert Reed
Sr Cor Off: Jackie Bright
Bd of Dir: Andrew Pansini
Ofcr: Judy Li
Sr VP: Gordon C Hunt
Exec: Thomas Ream
Dir Lab: Chris Flaherty
Snr Ntwrk: Shawn Fuller
Snr Ntwrk: Bill Pinkerton
Snr Ntwrk: Kyle Tooker

D-U-N-S 11-789-6100
SUTTON FORD INC
LINCOLN MERCURY
21315 Central Ave, Matteson, IL 60443-2893
Tel (708) 720-8000 Founded/Ownrshp 1989
Sales 106.2MM^E EMP 82
SIC 5511 Automobiles, new & used
Pr: Nathaniel K Sutton
*Sec: Sue Sthafroth
Mktg Mgr: Kristina Sutton
Sls Mgr: Marcus Ware
Sales Asso: Andre Green

D-U-N-S 07-911-0444
SUTTON HOLDING CORP (TX)
2330 Interstate 30, Mesquite, TX 75150-2720
Tel (972) 755-8200 Founded/Ownrshp 2013
Sales 101.9MM^E EMP 61
SIC 7377 Computer rental & leasing; Computer hardware rental or leasing, except finance leasing; Computer peripheral equipment rental & leasing
Pr: Gary Sutton
*CFO: David Rieck

SUZANO GROUP
See SUZANO PULP AND PAPER AMERICA INC

D-U-N-S 60-913-6742 IMP/EXP
SUZANO PULP AND PAPER AMERICA INC
SUZANO GROUP
(Suby of SUZANO PAPEL E CELULOSE S/A.)
800 Corporate Dr Ste 320, Fort Lauderdale, FL 33334-3618
Tel (954) 772-7716 Founded/Ownrshp 1988
Sales 369.6MM EMP 19
Accts Barnes Small & Mcgee Cpas Bo
SIC 5111 Printing paper
Prin: Fernando Silveira
*Pr: David Feffer
*VP: Daniel Feffer

D-U-N-S 36-080-2784 IMP
SUZLON WIND ENERGY CORP
(Suby of SUZLON ENERGY LIMITED)
8750 W Bryn Mawr Ave # 900, Chicago, IL 60631-3655
Tel (773) 328-5073 Founded/Ownrshp 2001
Sales 85.3MM^E EMP 350^E
SIC 3511 Turbines & turbine generator sets
CEO: Duncan Koerbel
COO: Rahul Limje
COO: Pete Schmidt
VP: Manoj Bakshi
VP: Todd Karasek
*VP: Claudia Mann
VP: Chintan Shah
*VP: Joseph Siprut
VP: Johan Swarts
Exec: Paresh Abchung
Exec: Archana Holkar
Exec: Rashi Kapoor
Exec: Jigar Kavaiya
Exec: Parveen Naik
Dir Bus: David Capparelli
Board of Directors: Frans Fisscher

SUZUKI GALLERY
See GALLERY AUTOMOTIVE GROUP LLC

D-U-N-S 07-881-0169 IMP/EXP
SUZUKI MOTOR OF AMERICA INC
SUZUKI USA
(Suby of SUZUKI MOTOR CORPORATION)
3251 E Imperial Hwy, Brea, CA 92821-6795
Tel (714) 996-7040 Founded/Ownrshp 2012
Sales 122.0MM^E EMP 350
SIC 3751 3519 3799 Motorcycles & related parts; Outboard motors; Recreational vehicles
Pr: Takeshi Hayasaki
Trst: Robert Alsip
*Ex VP: Takuya Sato
VP: Art Hashima
VP: Ed Sedeno
Assoc Dir: Mark Eastman
Assoc Dir: Tom Hosner
Snr Sftwr: Jun Lin
CIO: Terrence Hu
Opers Mgr: Scott Marker
Opers Mgr: Claudia Romo

SUZUKI USA
See SUZUKI MOTOR OF AMERICA INC

D-U-N-S 80-473-2048 IMP
SV PROBE INC
(Suby of SV PROBE PTE. LTD.)
9185 S Farmer Ave Ste 105, Tempe, AZ 85284-2912
Tel (480) 635-4700 Founded/Ownrshp 2006
Sales 105.7MM^E EMP 703
SIC 3825 Test equipment for electronic & electrical circuits
Pr: Kevin Kurtz
*VP: Karen Lynch
IT Man: Mylinh Ho
Manager: Robert Stampahar
Sales Asso: Wanda Sherman

D-U-N-S 10-277-8255
▲ SVB FINANCIAL GROUP
3003 Tasman Dr, Santa Clara, CA 95054-1191
Tel (408) 654-7400 Founded/Ownrshp 1999
Sales NA EMP 1,914^E
Tkr Sym SIVB Exch NGS
SIC 6022 State commercial banks
Pr: Greg W Becker
*Ch Bd: Roger F Dunbar
Pr: Philip C Cox
Pr: Alice Daluz
COO: Bruce E Wallace
COO: Bruce Wallace
CFO: Michael R Descheneaux
Treas: Michelle McKay
Chf Cred: Marc C Cadieux
Bd of Dir: Eric Benhamou
Chf Mktg O: Michelle A Draper
Ofcr: Andy Enroth
Ofcr: Suanne Mingrone
VP: Dan Aguilar
VP: Thomas Armstrong
VP: Reisa Babic
VP: Tim Barnes
VP: Alex Barry
VP: Brian Bell
VP: James Caron
VP: Don Chandler
Board of Directors: Eric A Benhamou, David M Clapper, Joel P Friedman, C Richard Kramlich, Jeffrey N Maggioncalda, Mary John Miller, Kate D Mitchell, John F Robinson

SVEC
See SEQUACHEE VALLEY ELECTRIC CO-OPERATIVE INC

D-U-N-S 00-915-2539
SVENHARDS SWEDISH BAKERY (CA)
701 Industrial Dr, Exeter, CA 93221-2102
Tel (831) 623-4375 Founded/Ownrshp 1949, 1959
Sales 95.8MM^E EMP 300
Accts Rina Accountancy Corp Walnut
SIC 2051 Bagels, fresh or frozen
CEO: Ronny D Svenhard
*Pr: Michelle Svenhard Barnett
*COO: David C Kunkel
*VP: Borje Svenhard
Genl Mgr: Vicki Nagle
CIO: Kerry Kurisu
QA Dir: Ai Scaramelli
Sales Asso: Chad Svenhard

D-U-N-S 15-710-0913 IMP/EXP
SVM MINERALS HOLDINGS INC
(Suby of KARNAVATI HOLDINGS INC) ★
9401 Indian Creek Pkwy, Overland Park, KS 66210-2007
Tel (913) 344-9500 Founded/Ownrshp 2008
Sales 554.2MM^E EMP 648
SIC 1479 Salt & sulfur mining
Pr: John Tancredi

D-U-N-S 06-547-4178
■ SVO MANAGEMENT INC
(Suby of STARWOOD VACATION SERVICES INC) ★
9002 San Marco Ct, Orlando, FL 32819-8600
Tel (407) 239-3100 Founded/Ownrshp 1991
Sales 39.9MM^E EMP 1,060^E
SIC 6531 Real estate managers
Pr: Joel Pope
*Pr: Matthew Avril

SW BARRICK & SONS
See LAUREL SAND & GRAVEL INC

SW FOODS
See SURE WINNER FOODS INC

D-U-N-S 12-547-9332 IMP
SW GROUP LLC
SHOPPERS WORLD
9 E 40th St Fl Mezz, New York, NY 10016-0402
Tel (646) 688-2608 Founded/Ownrshp 1999
Sales 224.9MM^E EMP 1,400^E
SIC 5311 Department stores

D-U-N-S 96-501-7358
SW MERGER ACQUISITION CORP
245 Park Ave, New York, NY 10167-0002
Tel (212) 648-2355 Founded/Ownrshp 2010
Sales 602.3MM^E EMP 1,225^E
SIC 4941 4952 Water supply; Sewerage systems
Prin: Andrew F Walters

D-U-N-S 96-742-0329
SW RETAIL GROUP LLC
(*Suby of* SHOPPERS WORLD) ★
9 E 40th St Fl Mezz, New York, NY 10016-0402
Tel (646) 688-2608 *Founded/Ownrshp* 2009
Sales 75.8MM^E *EMP* 1,000
SIC 5311 Department stores

D-U-N-S 00-797-6215
SW WASHINGTON HOSPITAL INC
REBOUND PHYSICAL THERAPY
400 Ne Mother Joseph Pl, Vancouver, WA 98664-3200
Tel (360) 514-2000 *Founded/Ownrshp* 2001
Sales 120.7MM^E *EMP* 3,400^E
SIC 8062 General medical & surgical hospitals
Pr: Joseph Kortum
**CFO:* David Willie
**VP:* Cheri Meyer Hofer
**Prin:* Renate Atkins
**Prin:* Gil Rodriguez
Surgeon: Jeffrey A Sunshine

D-U-N-S 00-418-5906 IMP/EXP
SWAGELOK CO
29500 Solon Rd, Solon, OH 44139-3474
Tel (440) 248-4600 *Founded/Ownrshp* 1947
Sales 1.1MMM^E *EMP* 3,000
SIC 3494 3491 3599 Pipe fittings; Pressure valves & regulators, industrial; Machine shop, jobbing & repair
Pr: Arthur F Anton
CFO: James Cavoli
CFO: Frank Roddy
Treas: Joseph Gambatese
Treas: Diane Mekker
Ex VP: Frank J Roddy
VP: Sylvie A Bon
VP: Wil Christensen
VP: Nick Ezzone
VP: Joel Hanish
VP: James Hanson
VP: Matthew Loiccolo
VP: Matt Lopiccolo
VP: Matthew P Lopiccolo
VP: Ken Malec
VP: Kay Miller
VP: Michael F Neff
VP: David E O'Connor
VP: Timothy Rosengarten
VP: Paul Wright
Exec: Bill Menz
Board of Directors: William N West

D-U-N-S 08-477-1158
SWAN EMPLOYER SERVICES
1306 E 74th Ave Ste 200, Anchorage, AK 99518-3212
Tel (907) 344-7926 *Founded/Ownrshp* 1998
Sales 34.9MM^E *EMP* 1,420
SIC 7363 8721 Employee leasing service; Accounting, auditing & bookkeeping
Pr: John Swan
COO: Annamae Bryan

D-U-N-S 00-633-1094 IMP/EXP
SWAN SURFACES LLC
SWANSTONE
515 Olive St Ste 900, Saint Louis, MO 63101-1835
Tel (314) 231-8148 *Founded/Ownrshp* 1964
Sales 102.4MM^E *EMP* 290
SIC 2541 5722 3431 Counter & sink tops; Kitchens, complete (sinks, cabinets, etc.); Bathroom fixtures, including sinks
CEO: Steve Anderson
**CFO:* David King
**Treas:* Dan Zittel
**VP:* Massoud Salessi
IT Man: Brian Kinzel
Mktg Mgr: Leah Dugan

D-U-N-S 02-825-3300 IMP
SWANER HARDWOOD CO INC
5 W Magnolia Blvd, Burbank, CA 91502-1776
Tel (818) 953-5350 *Founded/Ownrshp* 1968
Sales 83.0MM *EMP* 220
SIC 2435 5031 Hardwood veneer & plywood; Lumber: rough, dressed & finished; Plywood
CEO: Keith M Swaner
**Pr:* Gary Swaner
**Treas:* Stephen Haag
Dir IT: Richard Seston

D-U-N-S 13-435-1498 IMP
SWANK AUDIO VISUALS LLC
639 Gravois Bluffs Blvd E, Fenton, MO 63026-7737
Tel (636) 680-9000 *Founded/Ownrshp* 1937
Sales NA *EMP* 1,005
SIC 7359

SWANK CNSTR & DEVOES BLDRS SVC
See SWANK ENTERPRISES

D-U-N-S 04-521-5795
SWANK ENTERPRISES
SWANK CNSTR & DEVOES BLDRS SVC
615 Pondera Ave, Valier, MT 59486
Tel (406) 279-3241 *Founded/Ownrshp* 1946
Sales 126.1MM *EMP* 100
SIC 1542 5211

D-U-N-S 14-968-1541 IMP
SWANN COMMUNICATIONS USA INC
12636 Clark St, Santa Fe Springs, CA 90670-3950
Tel (562) 777-2551 *Founded/Ownrshp* 2000
Sales 120.0MM *EMP* 87
SIC 5045 7382 Computers, peripherals & software; Security systems services
Pr: Keith Oldridge
**Ch:* Jeffrey Lew
**VP:* Guy Pithie
Opers Mgr: Alex Peralta
Natl Sales: Sandy Scott

D-U-N-S 00-902-3474
SWANSON GROUP INC (OR)
2695 Glendale Valley Rd, Glendale, OR 97442-9715
Tel (541) 832-1121 *Founded/Ownrshp* 1951
Sales 232.8MM^E *EMP* 650^E
SIC 2421 2436 4522 Lumber: rough, sawed or planed; Softwood veneer & plywood; Helicopter carriers, nonscheduled
Pr: Steve Swanson
COO: Arthur Swanson
**COO:* Chuck Wert
**CFO:* Rick Bernheisel
VP: Jim Dudley
**VP:* Tim Hennessey

D-U-N-S 12-545-2081
SWANSON GROUP MFG LLC
(*Suby of* SWANSON GROUP INC) ★
2695 Glendale Valley Rd, Glendale, OR 97442-9715
Tel (541) 832-1121 *Founded/Ownrshp* 2001
Sales 97.2MM^E *EMP* 341^E
SIC 2435 Plywood, hardwood or hardwood faced; Veneer stock, hardwood
CEO: Steven D Swanson
**COO:* Chuck Wert
CFO: Rick Bernheisel
**VP:* Chris Swanson

D-U-N-S 06-478-0083 IMP
SWANSON HEALTH PRODUCTS INC
4075 40th Ave S, Fargo, ND 58104-3912
Tel (701) 356-2700 *Founded/Ownrshp* 2016
Sales 91.1MM^E *EMP* 350
SIC 5499 2834 Vitamin food stores; Pharmaceutical preparations
CEO: Katie Doyle
**Pr:* Rick Rayl
**CFO:* Doug Anderson
Bd of Dir: Jan Hanson
Mng Dir: Leon Schalkwyk
IT Man: Jennifer Kelley
IT Man: Jeremy Skogen
Web Dev: Ben Armstrong
Web Dev: Todd Carlson
Opers Mgr: John Rogstad
Opers Mgr: Scott Trana

D-U-N-S 00-436-2513 IMP
SWANSON INDUSTRIES INC (WV)
(*Suby of* AEA INVESTORS LP) ★
2608 Smithtown Rd, Morgantown, WV 26508-2494
Tel (304) 292-0021 *Founded/Ownrshp* 2000, 2012
Sales 132.1MM^E *EMP* 600
SIC 3593 3471 7629 5084

SWANSTONE
See SWAN SURFACES LLC

D-U-N-S 18-794-9904 IMP
SWAROVSKI NORTH AMERICA LIMITED
SIGNITY AMERICAS
(*Suby of* SWAROVSKI US HOLDING LIMITED) ★
1 Kenney Dr, Cranston, RI 02920-4403
Tel (401) 463-6400 *Founded/Ownrshp* 1955
Sales 235.5MM^E *EMP* 850
SIC 3961 5023 3231 Costume jewelry; Glassware; Products of purchased glass
Pr: Daniel Cohen
VP: Douglas Brown
VP: Stephen Kahler
**VP:* John Simms
**VP:* Stephan Toljan
Store Mgr: Lexie Toledo
Software D: Sharon Bettencourt
Mktg Mgr: Audrey Witt
Snr Mgr: Raymond O'Connor
Snr Mgr: Mark Olivo

D-U-N-S 60-576-1089
SWAROVSKI US HOLDING LIMITED
(*Suby of* D. SWAROVSKI KG)
1 Kenney Dr, Cranston, RI 02920-4403
Tel (401) 463-6400 *Founded/Ownrshp* 1955
Sales 270.5MM^E *EMP* 1,000
SIC 3961 3231 5048 5099 Costume jewelry; Novelties, glass: fruit, foliage, flowers, animals, etc.; Ophthalmic goods; Crystal goods
Pr: Daniel Cohen
**CFO:* Douglas Brown

D-U-N-S 07-375-5381
SWARTHMORE COLLEGE
500 College Ave Ste 2, Swarthmore, PA 19081-1390
Tel (610) 328-8000 *Founded/Ownrshp* 1864
Sales 139.1MM *EMP* 700
Accts Pricewaterhousecoopers Llp Ph
SIC 8221 College, except junior
Pr: Rebecca Chop
Ofcr: George Darbes
VP: Greg Brown
VP: Lois Falzone
VP: C S Hain
VP: Dan West
Comm Dir: Nancy Nicely
Ex Dir: Joy Charlton
Off Admin: Sonia Begonia

D-U-N-S 10-328-6126 IMP/EXP
SWATCH GROUP U S INC
SWATCH WATCH DIVISION
(*Suby of* THE SWATCH GROUP AG)
1200 Harbor Blvd Fl 7, Weehawken, NJ 07086-6728
Tel (201) 271-1400 *Founded/Ownrshp* 1978
Sales 362.7MM^E *EMP* 700
SIC 5063 3625 5094 3873 Electrical apparatus & equipment; Timing devices, electronic; Watches & parts; Timers for industrial use, clockwork mechanism only
Ch Bd: Hanspeter Rentsch
**Pr:* Nick Hayek
Pr: Bob Moore
**Sr VP:* Joseph A Mella
Sr VP: Patrick Roney
VP: Joseph Panetta
Dir Soc: Kiwan Anderson
Genl Mgr: Jean-Marc Bories
Genl Mgr: Steve Cohen
CIO: Carlegera Polizzi
MIS Dir: Stephen Bolcar

SWATCH WATCH DIVISION
See SWATCH GROUP U S INC

SWBC
See SOUTHWEST BUSINESS CORP

SWC, AQC
See SEA WORLD LLC

SWCA ENVIRONMENTAL CONSULTANTS
See SWCA INC

D-U-N-S 11-914-9730
SWCA INC
SWCA ENVIRONMENTAL CONSULTANTS
3033 N Central Ave # 145, Phoenix, AZ 85012-2808
Tel (602) 274-3831 *Founded/Ownrshp* 1984
Sales 159.7MM^E *EMP* 723
SIC 8748 8711 8731 8733 Environmental consultant; Engineering services; Commercial physical research; Noncommercial research organizations
Ch: Robert K Wilson
**CEO:* John R Thomas
**CFO:* Denis Henry
**VP:* Becky Montgomery
Dir Bus: Eileen Fagan
Brnch Mgr: Christi Haswell
Off Admin: Kimberly Proa
Mktg Mgr: Michelle Weigman
Genl Couns: Andrienne Tremblay
Snr PM: Jim Dawson
Snr PM: Jon Kehmeier
Board of Directors: Scott Slessman

SWD SEAGRAVE
See SEAGRAVE FIRE APPARATUS LLC

D-U-N-S 08-172-9899 IMP
SWEDA CO LLC
17411 E Valley Blvd, City of Industry, CA 91744-5159
Tel (626) 357-9999 *Founded/Ownrshp* 2007
Sales 149.9MM^E *EMP* 200
SIC 5094 5044 Watches & parts; Clocks; Calcvlators, electronic
CEO: Jim Hagan
**VP:* Kellie Claudio
**VP:* Scott Pearson
VP: Cindy Qin

D-U-N-S 06-847-7181
SWEDISH COVENANT HOSPITAL
5145 N California Ave, Chicago, IL 60625-3687
Tel (773) 878-8200 *Founded/Ownrshp* 1986
Sales 259.4MM *EMP* 1,800
SIC 8062 8059

D-U-N-S 04-017-0516 IMP
SWEDISH EDMONDS (WA)
21601 76th Ave W, Edmonds, WA 98026-7507
Tel (425) 640-4000 *Founded/Ownrshp* 1962
Sales 222.8MM *EMP* 1,400
SIC 8062 General medical & surgical hospitals
Pr: John Koster
**Pr:* Rodney Hochman
COO: Lane Savitch
**CFO:* Gary Wangsmo
**Treas:* Todd Hofheins
**Treas:* Sharon Pearl
VP: Kent Hargrave
VP: Jack Kirkman
Dir Rad: Judy Lynch
Dir Rad: Maurice Santillanes
Genl Mgr: David Hulse

D-U-N-S 07-926-4420
SWEDISH HEALTH SERVICES
SWEDISH MED CENTER/FIRST HL
(*Suby of* PROVIDENCE HEALTH & SERVICES) ★
747 Broadway, Seattle, WA 98122-4379
Tel (206) 386-6000 *Founded/Ownrshp* 2012
Sales 1.2MMM *EMP* 10,000
SIC 8011 Medical centers
CEO: Anthony Armada
VP: Don Theophilus
VP: John Vassall
VP: Nancy Wood
Dir Rad: Steven Dofelmier
Dir Rx: Randall Gerth
Prin: Lily K Jung
Ex Dir: Kit Massengale
Nurse Mgr: Wendy Connors
Nurse Mgr: Catherine Davis
CTO: Janice Newell
Board of Directors: James Scroggs

D-U-N-S 14-430-4151 IMP
SWEDISH MATCH NORTH AMERICA LLC
(*Suby of* SWEDISH MATCH AB)
1021 E Cary St Ste 1600, Richmond, VA 23219-4000
Tel (804) 787-5100 *Founded/Ownrshp* 1996
Sales 561.0MM *EMP* 1,100
SIC 2131 5199 Chewing tobacco; Smoking tobacco; Snuff; Lighters, cigarette & cigar
Pr: Lars Dahlgren
**Pr:* Richard Flaherty
**CFO:* Thomas Hayes
**Ch:* Conny Karlsson
Bd of Dir: Kenneth Ek
Bd of Dir: Tuve Johanesson
Bd of Dir: Eva Larsson
Ofcr: Anna Lekander
Ex VP: David Danziger
Sr VP: Nick Simeonidis
VP: Henrik Brehmer
VP: Thomas Hammargren
VP: Nina Hanses
VP: Magnus Heimburg
VP: Graham Jones
**VP:* Stephen Newsome
VP: Roine Nygren
**VP:* Gerard J Roerty Jr
VP: Ulf Svensson

SWEDISH MED CENTER/FIRST HL
See SWEDISH HEALTH SERVICES

D-U-N-S 07-133-1875
SWEDISH PHYSICIANS DIVISION
600 University St # 1200, Seattle, WA 98101-1176
Tel (206) 320-2700 *Founded/Ownrshp* 1999
Sales 38.3MM^E *EMP* 1,500
Accts Deloitte & Touch Llp
SIC 8011 8741 Offices & clinics of medical doctors; Management services
Ex Dir: Warren Fine

D-U-N-S 11-604-6426
SWEDISHAMERICAN HEALTH SYSTEM CORP
(*Suby of* UW HOSPITAL) ★
1401 E State St, Rockford, IL 61104-2315
Tel (815) 968-4400 *Founded/Ownrshp* 2015
Sales 34.7MM *EMP* 2,011
Accts Mcgladrey Llp Chicago Il
SIC 8743 6512 8742 8099 8082 8062 Promotion service; Commercial & industrial building operation; Business consultant; Medical services organization; Home health care services; General medical & surgical hospitals
CEO: Bill Gorski
Treas: Donald L Haring
VP: David Rydell
Exec: Lynn Jennings
Nurse Mgr: Patti Loveland
Nurse Mgr: Sally Luecke
Off Admin: Sarah Swain
Pathlgst: Sara Fleming
Podiatrist: John Nielsen
Doctor: Scott Bailey
Doctor: Harvey Einhorn

D-U-N-S 07-457-3932
SWEDISHAMERICAN HOSPITAL
(*Suby of* SWEDISHAMERICAN HEALTH SYSTEM CORP) ★
1401 E State St, Rockford, IL 61104-2315
Tel (815) 968-4400 *Founded/Ownrshp* 1911
Sales 159.4M^E *EMP* 1,599
SIC 8062 General medical & surgical hospitals
CEO: Bill Gorski
**CFO:* Don Haring
**Ex VP:* John R Mecklenburg
VP: Ann Gantzer
**VP:* Michael F Richter
Off Mgr: Jason E Roth
VP Opers: Jedediah L Cantrell
Mktg Dir: Brian Reck
Mktg Mgr: Dennis Eccles
Sls Mgr: Kathy Anderson
Doctor: Catherine Gentz

D-U-N-S 00-533-7399 EXP
SWEEPSTER ATTACHMENTS LLC
HARLEY ATTACHMENTS
(*Suby of* PALADIN ATTACHMENTS) ★
2800 Zeeb Rd, Dexter, MI 48130-2204
Tel (734) 996-9116 *Founded/Ownrshp* 2005
Sales 228.8MM^E *EMP* 1,300
SIC 3589 3991 Dirt sweeping units, industrial; Brooms; Street sweeping brooms, hand or machine; Brushes, household or industrial
Tech Mgr: Jason Swiontek
Plnt Mgr: Gene Granowicz
Plnt Mgr: Michael Rosebrough
Sls Mgr: Kathy Grau

D-U-N-S 08-245-9509 IMP
SWEET CANDY LLC
SWEET FACTORY
929 W Barkley Ave, Orange, CA 92868-1208
Tel (877) 817-9338 *Founded/Ownrshp* 2002
Sales 206.6MM^E *EMP* 2,000
SIC 5441 Candy, nut & confectionery stores
**CEO:* David Kim

SWEET FACTORY
See SWEET CANDY LLC

D-U-N-S 07-909-8213
SWEET FROG LLC
SWEETFROG
10800 Midlothian Tpke # 300, North Chesterfield, VA 23235-4725
Tel (804) 893-3151 *Founded/Ownrshp* 2011
Sales 28.8MM^E *EMP* 1,200^E
SIC 5812 6794 Frozen yogurt stand; Franchises, selling or licensing

D-U-N-S 14-256-1112 IMP/EXP
SWEET PEOPLE APPAREL INC
MISS ME
4715 S Alameda St, Vernon, CA 90058-2014
Tel (323) 235-7300 *Founded/Ownrshp* 2003
Sales 116.5MM *EMP* 135
Accts Moss Adams Llp Los Angeles
SIC 5137 Women's & children's clothing
CEO: Eric S Choi
**CFO:* Soohan Kim
VP: Young Cho
**VP:* Stella Y Choi
Genl Couns: Lilly Kim

D-U-N-S 00-913-9676 IMP/EXP
SWEET STREET DESSERTS INC
722 Hiesters Ln, Reading, PA 19605-3095
Tel (610) 929-0616 *Founded/Ownrshp* 1982
Sales 148.7MM^E *EMP* 700
SIC 2053 Frozen bakery products, except bread
Pr: Sandy L Solmon
**CFO:* Anthony Digirolamo
Chf Mktg O: Chris White
**VP:* Doug Messinger
Genl Mgr: Brendan Jones
Dir IT: Jim Hartman
Tech Mgr: Don Kostival
Prd Mgr: Marianne Good
VP Sls: Rick Kirkpatrick
Mktg Mgr: Robin Drenzer
Mktg Mgr: George Frangakis

SWEETFROG
See SWEET FROG LLC

D-U-N-S 08-182-7545
SWEETWATER COUNTY SCHOOL DISTRICT 1
3550 Foothill Blvd, Rock Springs, WY 82901-4851
Tel (307) 352-3400 *Founded/Ownrshp* 1920
Sales 110.7MM *EMP* 1,050
Accts Lovelett Skogen & Associates
SIC 8211 Public elementary & secondary schools
Genl Mgr: Gayle Kendall
Teacher Pr: Megan Mentzel

SWEETWATER MUSIC TECH DIRECT
See SWEETWATER SOUND INC

D-U-N-S 11-821-4535 IMP/EXP
SWEETWATER SOUND INC
SWEETWATER MUSIC TECH DIRECT
5501 Us Highway 30 W, Fort Wayne, IN 46818-8998
Tel (260) 432-8176 *Founded/Ownrshp* 1997
Sales 98.4MM^E *EMP* 500
SIC 7389 5736 5999 Recording studio, noncommercial records; Musical instrument stores; Audio-visual equipment & supplies
Pr: Chuck Surack
VP: Javier Bayouth
VP: Greg Clark
VP: Troy Hartman
VP: Phil Rich
VP: Mike Ross
Exec: Brian Randol
IT Man: Joe McNeely
IT Man: Ryan Sloan
Software D: Joe Lester
Netwrk Eng: Kevin Loughin

D-U-N-S 07-873-3029
SWEETWATER UNION HIGH SCHOOL DISTRICT
1130 Fifth Ave, Chula Vista, CA 91911-2812
Tel (619) 691-5500 *Founded/Ownrshp* 1997
Sales 205.5MM^E *EMP* 3,521
Accts Christywhite Accountancy Corpo
SIC 8211 Public elementary & secondary schools
CFO: Blenka Lemus
Bd of Dir: Paula Hall
Bd of Dir: Frank Tarantino
Ofcr: Kevin Pike
VP: Nicholas Segura
VP: Arturo Solis
Prgrm Mgr: Mabelle Glithero
Area Supr: Leisa Gonzales
Area Supr: Bruce Hicks
Genl Mgr: Karen Michel
Off Admin: Laura Arteaga

D-U-N-S 05-253-5239 IMP/EXP
SWEETWORKS INC
NIAGARA CHOCOLATES
3500 Genesee St, Buffalo, NY 14225-5015
Tel (716) 634-4545 *Founded/Ownrshp* 1998
Sales 142.1MM^E *EMP* 500^E
SIC 2066 2067 2064 Chocolate; Chewing gum; Candy & other confectionery products; Chocolate candy, except solid chocolate; Lollipops & other hard candy
CEO: Philip Terranova
IT Man: Todd Fisher
Mfg Mgr: Drew Keller
Plnt Mgr: Sara Kelly
Prd Mgr: Jeffrey Geiger
Prd Mgr: Rosaline Williams
Mktg Dir: Kathy Bassininski
Manager: Greg Steinacker
Sls Mgr: Julie Davidson
Sls Mgr: Jason Lagomarsino

SWELL SOFTWARE
See NXP USA INC

SWENSON, BARRY BUILDER
See GREEN VALLEY CORP

D-U-N-S 10-900-3467 IMP
SWEPI LP
SHELL
(*Suby of* SHELL ENERGY RESOURCES INC) ★
200 N Dairy Ashford Rd, Houston, TX 77079-1101
Tel (713) 241-6161 *Founded/Ownrshp* 1983
Sales 791.6MM^E *EMP* 175
SIC 1311 1382 5169 Crude petroleum production; Natural gas production; Oil & gas exploration services; Carbon dioxide
Pr: Raoul Restucci
**Pt:* R A Lane
**Pt:* Steve J Paul
**Pt:* J K Pritts
**Pt:* E J Voiland
Dir IT: Dennis Windsor
IT Man: Kent Kaufmann
IT Man: John Kievit
Tech Mgr: Gaurdie Banister

SWETT & CRAWFORD GROUP, THE
See SWETT & CRAWFORD OF GEORGIA INC

D-U-N-S 02-278-2985
SWETT & CRAWFORD GROUP INC
(*Suby of* ED BROKING GROUP LIMITED)
7230 Mcginnis Ferry Rd # 300, Suwanee, GA 30024-1283
Tel (404) 240-5200 *Founded/Ownrshp* 2008
Sales NA *EMP* 1,051^E
SIC 6411 Insurance agents & brokers
CEO: J Neal Abernathy
COO: Michael S Sadler
COO: Steve Sadler
**CFO:* Michael Bavely
Chf Mktg O: Mason Power
Ofcr: Terri T Snell
Ex VP: Peter Dumas
**Ex VP:* Emma Garner
Ex VP: Robert J Greenebaum Jr
Ex VP: Edward A Magliaro
Ex VP: Richard J Martin
**Ex VP:* Terri T Snell
Ex VP: Jason White
VP: Mike Baeurle
VP: Nancy Batten
VP: Jim Bishop
VP: Ron Boudreaux
VP: Jeff Coles
VP: Tom Gerlach
VP: Robert Hegarty
VP: Melissa Judd

D-U-N-S 00-959-3419
SWETT & CRAWFORD OF GEORGIA INC
SWETT & CRAWFORD GROUP, THE
(*Suby of* SWETT & CRAWFORD GROUP INC) ★
3350 Riverwood Pkwy Se # 1100, Atlanta, GA 30339-3335
Tel (404) 240-5200 *Founded/Ownrshp* 1915, 2013
Sales NA *EMP* 245^E
SIC 6411 Insurance brokers
Pr: Neal Abernathy
**Ch Bd:* Dave Hartoch
COO: Michael S Sadler
Ex VP: Robert J Greenebaum Jr
Ex VP: Edward A Magliaro
Ex VP: Richard J Martin
Ex VP: Terri T Snell
Ex VP: Terri Snell
Ex VP: Margaret Zechlin
Sr VP: Sandra Hevaghan
**Sr VP:* Terri Snell
VP: Michael Bavely
VP: Eric Bell
VP: Catherine Butschek
VP: Kyle Chapman
VP: Ron Levitt
VP: Jennifer Pinto

SWF, DCO, AQF
See SEA WORLD OF FLORIDA LLC

D-U-N-S 02-536-9521
SWH MIMIS CAFE LLC (CA)
(*Suby of* LE DUFF AMERICA INC) ★
12201 Merit Dr Ste 900, Dallas, TX 75251-3139
Tel (866) 926-6636 *Founded/Ownrshp* 1978, 2013
Sales 119.5MM^E *EMP* 2,412
SIC 5812 American restaurant
COO: Daniel R Dillon
**Pr:* Mark A Mears
**CFO:* Edward T Bartholemy
VP Opers: Mike Foster
VP Opers: John Shackelford

SWIFF-TRAIN COMPANY
See AMERICAN STEEL INC

D-U-N-S 00-894-6089 IMP/EXP
SWIFF-TRAIN CO LLC
EARTHWERKS
(*Suby of* SWIFF-TRAIN CO) ★
2500 Agnes St, Corpus Christi, TX 78405-1618
Tel (361) 883-1706 *Founded/Ownrshp* 1941
Sales 85.0MM^E *EMP* 117
SIC 5023 Floor coverings
Pt: La Train
Pt: Don Evans
Pt: Jeffrey Train
Pt: Kenneth Train

D-U-N-S 07-152-1967
SWIFT COMMUNICATIONS INC
NEVADA COUNTY PUBLISHING CO
580 Mallory Way, Carson City, NV 89701-5360
Tel (775) 850-7676 *Founded/Ownrshp* 1977
Sales 138.0MM^E *EMP* 650
SIC 2711

D-U-N-S 03-815-8502
SWIFT DENIM SERVICES INC
(*Suby of* GALEY & LORD LLC) ★
5 Concourse Pkwy Ste 2, Atlanta, GA 30328-5350
Tel (770) 901-6300 *Founded/Ownrshp* 1996
Sales 69.8MM^E *EMP* 1,000
SIC 2211 Twills, drills, denims & other ribbed fabrics: cotton
Pt: Lynn Tilton

D-U-N-S 00-182-4127
SWIFT ELECTRICAL SUPPLY CO
100 Hollister Rd Unit C1, Teterboro, NJ 07608-1139
Tel (201) 462-0900 *Founded/Ownrshp* 1943
Sales 108.7MM^E *EMP* 70
SIC 5063 Electrical apparatus & equipment
Pr: August A Sodora Jr
**CFO:* Irwin Turk
**Treas:* Christopher Sodora
IT Man: Keith Garrett

D-U-N-S 02-147-1529
▲ SWIFT ENERGY CO
17001 Northchase Dr # 100, Houston, TX 77060-6098
Tel (281) 874-2700 *Founded/Ownrshp* 1979
Sales 244.7MM *EMP* 228^E
Tkr Sym SFYWQ *Exch* OTO
SIC 1311 Crude petroleum & natural gas; Crude petroleum & natural gas production
CEO: Robert J Banks
Ch Bd: Marcus C Rowland
CFO: Alton D Heckaman Jr
Sr VP: Steven L Tomberlin
VP: Michael Coffield
VP: Bruce Vincent
Software D: Ron Danley
Board of Directors: Michael Duginski, Gabriel Ellisor, David Geenberg, Peter Kirchof, Charles Wampler

D-U-N-S 61-536-9753
SWIFT ENERGY OPERATING LLC
17001 Northchase Dr # 100, Houston, TX 77060-6098
Tel (281) 874-2700 *Founded/Ownrshp* 2005
Sales 376.3MM^E *EMP* 220^E
SIC 1311 Crude petroleum production; Natural gas production
Treas: Adrian D Shelley
VP: Joseph A Amico
VP: Tara L Seaman

SWIFT HOG BUYERS
See SWIFT PORK CO

D-U-N-S 15-643-4581 IMP
SWIFT LEASING CO INC
2200 S 75th Ave, Phoenix, AZ 85043-7410
Tel (602) 269-9700 *Founded/Ownrshp* 1985
Sales 53.4MM^E *EMP* 1,200^E
SIC 7513 Truck leasing, without drivers
Ch Bd: Jerry Moyes
**Pr:* Richard Stocking
**Ex VP:* Ginnie Henkels
**Ex VP:* Kenneth C Runnels
**Ex VP:* Mark Young
**VP:* Mike Ruchensky

D-U-N-S 10-741-2025
SWIFT LOGISTICS CO INC
2200 S 75th Ave, Phoenix, AZ 85043-7410
Tel (602) 269-9700 *Founded/Ownrshp* 1994
Sales 4.3MMM^E *EMP* 3,000
SIC 8742 Transportation consultant
CEO: Jerry Moyes
**Pr:* Jerry C Moyes
**CFO:* Ginnie Henkels
CFO: Gary Inzer
**Ex VP:* Kenneth C Runnels
**Ex VP:* Rodney Sartor
**Genl Mgr:* Sherry Bartch

D-U-N-S 60-583-5185 IMP/EXP
SWIFT PORK CO
SWIFT HOG BUYERS
(*Suby of* JBS USA LLC) ★
1770 Promontory Cir, Greeley, CO 80634-9039
Tel (970) 506-8000 *Founded/Ownrshp* 1996
Sales 1.0MMM^E *EMP* 5,900
SIC 5154 Hogs
**CEO:* Bill Lovette
Treas: Taya Buranakitpaiboon
Snr Mgr: Brandon Addington

D-U-N-S 61-295-5799
▲ SWIFT TRANSPORTATION CO
2200 S 75th Ave, Phoenix, AZ 85043-7410
Tel (602) 269-9700 *Founded/Ownrshp* 1966
Sales 4.2MMM *EMP* 21,000^E
Tkr Sym SWFT *Exch* NYS
SIC 4213 4231 Trucking, except local; Contract haulers; Trucking terminal facilities
CEO: Jerry Moyes
**Ch Bd:* Richard H Dozer
Pr: Richard Stocking
Pr: Steven Van Kirk
CFO: Virginia Henkels
Treas: Shawntela Martinez
Ex VP: Mickey R Dragash
Ex VP: Ginnie Henkels
Ex VP: Rebecca Ranninger
Ex VP: Kenneth C Runnels
VP: John Arnold
VP: Jason Bates
VP: Michael Ruchensky
VP: Amanda Smith
VP: Gregory Smith
Board of Directors: Glenn Brown, Jose A Cardenas, William F Riley III, David Vander Ploeg

D-U-N-S 07-243-3154
SWIFT TRANSPORTATION CO INC
2200 S 75th Ave, Phoenix, AZ 85043-7410
Tel (602) 269-9700 *Founded/Ownrshp* 1990
Sales NA *EMP* 13,000
SIC 4213 4225

D-U-N-S 01-661-5445
SWIFTY OIL LLC
1515 W Tipton St, Seymour, IN 47274-2205
Tel (812) 522-1640 *Founded/Ownrshp* 1963
Sales 200.1MM^E *EMP* 800
SIC 5541 5411 Gasoline service stations; Convenience stores, independent
Pr: William Klinger
**Ch:* Donald W Myers Sr
**Ex VP:* Gordon Bayes
**VP:* Kathy Covey

D-U-N-S 01-084-0049 IMP/EXP
SWIGER COIL SYSTEMS LTD
4677 Manufacturing Ave, Cleveland, OH 44135-2673
Tel (216) 362-7500 *Founded/Ownrshp* 2010
Sales 88.4MM^E *EMP* 190
SIC 3621 3677 Electric motor & generator parts; Coils, for electric motors or generators; Electronic coils, transformers & other inductors
VP: Dennis Sabol

D-U-N-S 00-946-0791 IMP
SWINERTON BUILDERS
SWINERTON MGT & CONSULTING
(*Suby of* SWINERTON INC) ★
260 Townsend St, San Francisco, CA 94107-1719
Tel (415) 421-2980 *Founded/Ownrshp* 1963
Sales 2.8MMM *EMP* 900
Accts Gallina Llp Walnut Creek Cal
SIC 1541 1522 1542 Industrial buildings, new construction; Steel building construction; Hotel/motel, new construction; Commercial & office building, new construction; Commercial & office buildings, renovation & repair; Specialized public building contractors
Ch Bd: Jeffrey C Hoopes
Pr: John T Capener
Pr: Gary J Rafferty
CFO: Randall Brinkhoff
CFO: Linda G Schowalter
Ofcr: Bret Long
Ex VP: Frank Foellmer
Ex VP: Eric Foster
Sr VP: Donald D Adair
Sr VP: Dave Higgins
VP: Kerry M Atkinson
VP: Leonard J Bischel
VP: David C Callis
VP: Scott V Conrad
VP: George S Ehara
VP: James E Farrell
VP: Jeffrey S Gee
VP: Kimberly D Grant
VP: David B Green
VP: David H Grubb Jr
VP: Ray A Haj

D-U-N-S 84-975-4288 IMP
SWINERTON INC
260 Townsend St, San Francisco, CA 94107-1719
Tel (415) 421-2980 *Founded/Ownrshp* 1963
Sales 2.8MMM *EMP* 900
Accts Gallina Llp Walnut Creek Cal
SIC 1542 1541 6531 1522 Nonresidential construction; Industrial buildings & warehouses; Real estate managers; Residential construction
CEO: Jeffrey C Hoopes
**Pr:* Gary J Rafferty
**CFO:* Linda G Showalter
Ofcr: Randall Brinkhoff
**Ex VP:* Frank Foellmer
**Ex VP:* Eric M Foster
**Sr VP:* Donald D Adair
**Sr VP:* John T Capener
**VP:* Charlene M Atkinson
VP: Kerry Atkinson
VP: Gretchen Baker
VP: Daniel Beyer
VP: Jeffrey S Gee
VP: Ray Haj
VP: Paul E Holmes
VP: Glenna Kelly
**VP:* Charles R Moore
**VP:* Sheri Ann Murphy
VP: Sheri Murphy
**VP:* Wade Oberman
**VP:* Bradley K Peterson

SWINERTON MGT & CONSULTING
See SWINERTON BUILDERS

D-U-N-S 03-124-8826
SWIRE PACIFIC HOLDINGS INC
COCA-COLA
(*Suby of* SWIRE PACIFIC LIMITED)
12634 S 265 W Bldg A, Draper, UT 84020-7931
Tel (801) 816-5300 *Founded/Ownrshp* 1978
Sales 470.1MM *EMP* 1,800
SIC 2086 Bottled & canned soft drinks
CEO: Jack Pelo
COO: Steve Quercia
**CFO:* James Sloan
**Sr VP:* Jeff Edwards
**VP:* Joyce W Hawkins
**VP:* Paul Lukanowski
Area Mgr: Shawn Stehle
Div Mgr: Bryan Brewer
Netwrk Mgr: Spencer Kartchner
Sales Exec: Brett Ellis
Sales Exec: Jeff Judd

D-U-N-S 96-568-7663
SWISHER HYGIENE INC
4725 Piedmont Row Dr # 400, Charlotte, NC 28210-4281
Tel (704) 364-7707 *Founded/Ownrshp* 1994
Sales 193.7MM *EMP* 1,200^E
Accts Grant Thornton Llp Columbia
SIC 5169 Specialty cleaning & sanitation preparations
Ch Bd: Richard L Handley
**Pr:* William M Pierce
COO: Blake W Thompson
CFO: William T Nanovsky
Board of Directors: Joseph Burke, William D Pruitt, David Prussky

D-U-N-S 00-406-2766 IMP/EXP
SWISHER INTERNATIONAL GROUP INC
(*Suby of* HAY ISLAND HOLDING CORP) ★
20 Thorndal Cir, Darien, CT 06820-5421
Tel (203) 656-8000 *Founded/Ownrshp* 1999
Sales 874.5MM^E *EMP* 1,600
SIC 5194 Tobacco & tobacco products
Pr: Peter J Ghiloni
**COO:* William T Ziegler
VP: Ralph Corasanti
VP: Lee Creasman
VP Mktg: Jackie Ziegler

D-U-N-S 08-003-8515
SWISHER INTERNATIONAL INC
20 Thorndal Cir, Darien, CT 06820-5421
Tel (203) 656-8000 *Founded/Ownrshp* 1966
Sales 68.1MM^E *EMP* 10,001
SIC 5194 Tobacco & tobacco products
Ch: William T Ziegler
Pr: Peter J Ghiloni
CFO: Howard L Romanow
VP: Ralph P Corasaniti
Sls Mgr: Tami Brown

D-U-N-S 05-418-5715
SWISS POST SOLUTIONS INC
(*Suby of* DIE SCHWEIZERISCHE POST AG)
10 E 40th St Fl 9, New York, NY 10016-0201
Tel (212) 204-0900 *Founded/Ownrshp* 2006
Sales 161.0MM^E *EMP* 1,600^E
SIC 8744 Facilities support services
CEO: Dan Moscatiello
CFO: Baiju Coilparampil
CFO: Matthieu Martin
Ofcr: Russ Cusick
Ofcr: Mike Mannix
Assoc VP: Paula Vayas
Ex VP: Karen Cumming
Sr VP: Heidi Cohen
VP: John Chestnut
VP: Joe Mackin

D-U-N-S 82-910-4582
SWISS POST US HOLDINGS INC
10 E 40th St Fl 9, New York, NY 10016-0201
Tel (212) 204-0900 *Founded/Ownrshp* 2005
Sales 81.0MM *EMP* 1,600^E
SIC 6719 Investment holding companies, except banks
CEO: Dan Moscatiello
CFO: Baiju Coilparampil
Prin: Mitchell D Weiner

D-U-N-S 94-918-0525
SWISS RE AMERICA HOLDING CORP
(*Suby of* SCHWEIZERISCHE RUCKVERSICHERUNGS-GESELLSCHAFT AG)
5200 Metcalf Ave, Overland Park, KS 66202-1265
Tel (913) 676-5200 *Founded/Ownrshp* 1973
Sales NA *EMP* 7,000
SIC 6331 6311 Property damage insurance; Fire, marine & casualty insurance: stock; Life reinsurance
CEO: Michel M Lis
**Ch Bd:* Walter B Kielholz
**Pr:* Ronald R Pressman
COO: Agostino Galvagni
**COO:* Thomas Wellauer
CFO: Alejandra Ancarani

*CFO: Marc A Meiches
*CFO: George Quinn
Sr VP: Steve Andrzejewski
Sr VP: Susan Dowdall
Sr VP: Bill Fellows
Sr VP: Kyle Lew
Sr VP: Josephine Link
Sr VP: Jose Ordinaslewis
Sr VP: Alexandra Pizzinini
Sr VP: John Prange
Sr VP: Maria Stolfi
VP: Pamela Carr
VP: Charles Connors
VP: Marianne Cumming
VP: Chethan Giri

D-U-N-S 00-696-5602
SWISS RE SOLUTIONS HOLDING CORP
(Suby of SCHWEIZERISCHE RUCKVERSICHERUNGS-GESELLSCHAFT AG)
5200 Metcalf Ave, Overland Park, KS 66202-1265
Tel (913) 676-5200 Founded/Ownrshp 1914, 2007
Sales NA EMP 4,000
SIC 6331 Fire, marine & casualty insurance & carriers
CFO: Marc Allen Meiches
Pr: Dan Eudy
Treas: Dorsey Lewis
Ofcr: Ken Brock
Ex VP: Hoyt H Wood Jr
*Sr VP: John M Connelly
Sr VP: Howard T Johnson
Sr VP: Joseph Wolf Levin
Sr VP: Mark Leonard Ricciardelli
*Sr VP: Nicholas Spaeth
VP: Jim Kirby
Board of Directors: Bernhard Christofink, Jorgen K Jensen, Annette K Sadolin, Robin Peppe Sterneck, John E Tiller Jr, Terry Lee Younghanz

SWISS REINSURANCE AMERICA
See SR CORPORATE SOLUTIONS AMERICA HOLDING CORP

D-U-N-S 00-698-8471
SWISS REINSURANCE AMERICA CORP
(Suby of SWISS REINSURANCE AMERICA) ★
175 King St, Armonk, NY 10504-1613
Tel (914) 828-8000 Founded/Ownrshp 1940
Sales NA EMP 1,651
SIC 6331 Property damage insurance
Pr: Donnell William
Ch Bd: Pierre Ozendo
Pr: Patrick Mailloux
CFO: George Quinn
Treas: Daniel G Gibson
Sr VP: Michael Graziano
Sr VP: Kathryn Hyland
Sr VP: Diane Link
Sr VP: Anthony Mormino
Sr VP: Nicolas Romanque
Sr VP: Stefanie Stratos
Sr VP: Edouard H Vieux Jr
Sr VP: Matthias Weber
VP: Martin Bages
VP: Ashish Bamba
VP: Rakhee Chopra
VP: Michael Cochran
VP: Richard Daillak
VP: Sam Gonzalez
VP: Harini Kannan
VP: Cynthia Landry

D-U-N-S 07-945-6811
SWISS REINSURANCE AMERICA CORP
(Suby of SWISS RE AMERICA HOLDING CORP) ★
5200 Metcalf Ave, Overland Park, KS 66202-1265
Tel (913) 676-5200 Founded/Ownrshp 2014
Sales NA EMP 986ᴱ
SIC 6311 Life reinsurance
Pr: Patrick Mailloux
VP: Chuck Manning
VP: Christopher R Ritter
VP: Nicole Yarbrough
Netwrk Mgr: Milan Makani

SWISS TECH PRODUCTS
See INTERDESIGN INC

D-U-N-S 00-526-7323 EXP
SWISS VALLEY FARMS COOPERATIVE
247 Research Pkwy, Davenport, IA 52806-7342
Tel (563) 468-6600 Founded/Ownrshp 1930, 1958
Sales 591.8MMᴱ EMP 750
SIC 5143 2022 5191 2023 Milk & cream, fluid; Cheese, natural & processed; Fertilizer & fertilizer materials; Dried milk; Powdered whey; Lactose, edible (milk sugar)
CEO: Don Boelens
*Pr: Gerald Bratland
*Pr: J Gordon Toyne
*Treas: Thomas Newburg
*VP: Randy Schaefer

SWISSLOG HLTHCARE SOLUTIONS NA
See TRANSLOGIC CORP

SWISSOTEL HOTELS AND RESORTS
See SWISSOTEL MANAGEMENT CORP

D-U-N-S 96-556-3083
SWISSOTEL MANAGEMENT CORP
SWISSOTEL HOTELS AND RESORTS
(Suby of SWISSOTEL MANAGEMENT GMBH)
323 E Wacker Dr, Chicago, IL 60601-5282
Tel (312) 565-0565 Founded/Ownrshp 1996
Sales 46.2MMᴱ EMP 1,500
SIC 7011 Hotels
Pr: Andreas Meinhold
Pr: Hannelore Uhl
Sr VP: Jack Breisacher
*VP: Brunner Niederer
Exec: Daniel McGee
Comm Man: Jacqueline Boyd
Genl Mgr: Tim Herman
Genl Mgr: Michael Koltes

D-U-N-S 02-945-5115
SWISSPORT CARGO SERVICES LP (CA)
(Suby of SWISSPORT USA INC) ★
23723 Air Frt Ln Bldg 5, Dulles, VA 20166
Tel (703) 742-4300 Founded/Ownrshp 1982, 1996
Sales 52.6MMᴱ EMP 1,726ᴱ
SIC 4581

D-U-N-S 04-706-2435
SWISSPORT CORP
45025 Aviation Dr Ste 350, Dulles, VA 20166-7526
Tel (703) 742-4300 Founded/Ownrshp 1971
Sales NA EMP 10,000
SIC 7363

D-U-N-S 11-620-1062 EXP
SWISSPORT FUELING INC
45025 Aviation Dr Ste 350, Dulles, VA 20166-7526
Tel (703) 742-4338 Founded/Ownrshp 1995
Sales 182.1MMᴱ EMP 570
SIC 5172 Aircraft fueling services
Pr: Stanley Livingston
Treas: Patrick Donahoe
Treas: Lindy Milner
*Treas: Dany Nasr
*Ex VP: Joseph Phelan
VP: Joseph Bonnevier
*VP: Mark Norris
VP: Joseph B Swissport
Exec: Erich Bodenmann
Exec: Earl L Estrella

D-U-N-S 15-203-1071
SWISSPORT USA INC
(Suby of SWISSPORT INTERNATIONAL AG)
151 Northpoint Dr, Houston, TX 77060-3207
Tel (281) 443-7687 Founded/Ownrshp 2003
Sales 366.2MMᴱ EMP 6,500
SIC 4581 Airports, flying fields & services
CEO: Abderaman El-Aoufir
*Pr: Mathew Ellingson
*COO: Tommy Watt
*CFO: Robert Hamm
*Ex VP: Matt Ellingson

D-U-N-S 78-769-5121
SWISSPORT USA INC
45025 Aviation Dr Ste 350, Dulles, VA 20166-7526
Tel (703) 742-4300 Founded/Ownrshp 1971
Sales 822.4MMᴱ EMP 4,900
SIC 4581 Airports, flying fields & services
CEO: Joseph J Phelan
VP: Sean M Klinge
VP: Greg Reeves
VP: Nicosia Smith
VP: Robin Ward
Genl Mgr: Chris Holden
Dir IT: David Hislop
IT Man: Jessica Melendez
Opers Mgr: Tony Notaro
S&M/VP: Antonio Alvarez
Sls Dir: Tom Stevenson

D-U-N-S 60-990-0373 IMP
SWITCH LTD
7135 S Decatur Blvd, Las Vegas, NV 89118-4376
Tel (702) 444-4000 Founded/Ownrshp 2003
Sales 172.6MMᴱ EMP 340ᴱ
SIC 4899 Data communication services
CEO: Rob Roy
*CFO: Thomas Morton
*Ex VP: Brian Boles
Ex VP: Terri Borden
*Ex VP: Jim Devane
*Ex VP: Lesley McVay
Ex VP: Kristi Overgaard
*Ex VP: Missy Young

D-U-N-S 92-985-7563
SWLHS INC
1701 Oak Park Blvd, Lake Charles, LA 70601-8911
Tel (337) 494-3204 Founded/Ownrshp 1994
Sales 262.8MMᴱ EMP 1,501ᴱ
SIC 5912 Drug stores
Pr: Larry Graham
*VP: Tim Coffey
*VP: David Usher
*VP: Charles Whitson

SWM INTL
See SCHWEITZER-MAUDUIT INTERNATIONAL INC

D-U-N-S 07-955-6230
■ **SWN DRILLING CO**
(Suby of SOUTHWESTERN ENERGY CO INC) ★
2350 N Sam Hous, Houston, TX 77032
Tel (281) 618-4700 Founded/Ownrshp 2014
Sales 3.7MMᴱ EMP 1,313ᴱ
SIC 1311 Crude petroleum & natural gas production

SWS ENVIRONMENTAL SERVICES
See PROGRESSIVE ENVIRONMENTAL SERVICES INC

D-U-N-S 10-669-4193 IMP
SWS ENVIRONMENTAL SERVICES
BEACHSIDE SERVICES
(Suby of SWS ENVIRONMENTAL SERVICES) ★
1619 Moylan Rd, Panama City Beach, FL 32407-4073
Tel (850) 234-8428 Founded/Ownrshp 1990
Sales 146.9MMᴱ EMP 544
SIC 1794 Excavation work
CEO: Eric Zimmer
*Ch Bd: Jim Weber Jr
*Pr: Eugene Cookson
CFO: Jeff Sweren
Sr VP: Bucky Thompson
VP: Val Garner
VP: Jim Nardozzi
VP Opers: Harry Marsh
VP Mktg: Jamie Michael
Corp Couns: Brian Cross

D-U-N-S 78-364-3216
SWS GROUP INC
1201 Elm St Ste 3500, Dallas, TX 75270-2108
Tel (214) 859-1800 Founded/Ownrshp 1972
Sales 311.2MM EMP 892ᴱ
SIC 6211 6029

D-U-N-S 02-630-0483 IMP
SWS RE-DISTRIBUTION CO INC
S W S
1440 Lemay Dr Ste 104, Carrollton, TX 75007-4965
Tel (214) 483-1076 Founded/Ownrshp 1959
Sales 86.3MMᴱ EMP 45
SIC 5087 Janitors' supplies
CEO: Camille Fournier
*Pr: Bobby Cheney
Off Mgr: Deirdre Brennan
Sales Exec: Dave Fournier

D-U-N-S 94-981-7642 IMP
SWSNY INC
345 Underhill Blvd, Syosset, NY 11791-3425
Tel (516) 921-9005 Founded/Ownrshp 2004
Sales 92.6MMᴱ EMP 300
SIC 5182 Wine
CEO: Harvey Chaplin

SWT STOCKTON
See SOUTHWEST TRADERS INC

D-U-N-S 05-602-7402 IMP
■ **SWVA INC**
STEEL OF WEST VIRGINIA
(Suby of STEEL OF WEST VIRGINIA INC) ★
17th St & Second Ave, Huntington, WV 25703
Tel (304) 696-8200 Founded/Ownrshp 1982
Sales 307.6MM EMP 9
SIC 3441 3312 Fabricated structural metal; Billets, steel
Pr: Timothy R Duke
CFO: Dexter Childers

D-U-N-S 00-922-1318
SYAR INDUSTRIES INC
VALLEJO BUILDING MATERIALS
2301 Napa Vallejo Hwy, NAPA, CA 94558-6242
Tel (707) 252-8711 Founded/Ownrshp 1938
Sales 91.1MMᴱ EMP 300ᴱ
SIC 5032 2951 0762 7992 5932

D-U-N-S 87-853-2741
SYBASE 365 INC
4511 Singer Ct Ste 300, Chantilly, VA 20151-1743
Tel (925) 236-5000 Founded/Ownrshp 2013
Sales 94.7MMᴱ EMP 7,500
SIC 3577 Computer peripheral equipment
Pr: Marty Beard

D-U-N-S 13-156-3215
SYBASE INC
(Suby of SAP AMERICA INC) ★
1 Sybase Dr, Dublin, CA 94568-7986
Tel (925) 236-5000 Founded/Ownrshp 2010
Sales 274.9MMᴱ EMP 3,819
SIC 7372 Prepackaged software
Pr: John S Chen
Pr: Pramod Iyengar
COO: Lynne Rosen
*CFO: Jeffrey G Ross
*Chf Mktg O: Raj Nathan
Ex VP: George Hoppa
Ex VP: Peter Lemme
Ex VP: Brad McInroy
Ex VP: Ronald Ouellet
Ex VP: Thomas Volk
Sr VP: Eric Miles
*VP: Daniel R Carl
VP: Hanes Carter
VP: Laurie Keating
VP: Mark A Pine
VP: Terry Stepien

D-U-N-S 03-774-1840
SYBRA LLC
ARBY'S
(Suby of ARBYS RESTAURANT GROUP INC) ★
1155 Perimeter Ctr # 1100, Atlanta, GA 30338-5463
Tel (678) 514-4100 Founded/Ownrshp 2002
Sales 116.8MMᴱ EMP 4,323
SIC 5812 Fast-food restaurant, chain

D-U-N-S 80-972-2689 IMP/EXP
■ **SYBRON DENTAL SPECIALTIES INC**
ANALYTIC ENDODONTICS
(Suby of DANAHER CORP) ★
1717 W Collins Ave, Orange, CA 92867-5422
Tel (714) 516-7400 Founded/Ownrshp 2006
Sales 749.5MMᴱ EMP 4,117
SIC 3843 2834 Dental laboratory equipment; Orthodontic appliances; Pharmaceutical preparations
CEO: Dan Even
Pr: Steven Semmelmayer
CEO: Henricus A M Van Duijnhoven
Ex VP: Daniel Even
VP: Jason Davis
VP: Mark C Yorba
Rgnl Mgr: Todd Di Pretoro
Dir IT: Robert Winter
IT Man: JC Chung
IT Man: Paul Ham
IT Man: Trish Tazelaar

SYBRON ENDO
See ORMCO CORP

D-U-N-S 05-133-3180
SYCAMORE PARTNERS LLC
9 W 57th St Ste 3100, New York, NY 10019-2701
Tel (212) 796-8500 Founded/Ownrshp 1996
Sales 6.0MM EMP 24,353
SIC 6552 Land subdividers & developers, commercial

D-U-N-S 96-973-6342
SYCAMORE PARTNERS MANAGEMENT LP
9 W 57th St Ste 3100, New York, NY 10019-2701
Tel (212) 796-8500 Founded/Ownrshp 2011
Sales 7.9MMMᴱ EMP 44,501ᴱ
SIC 6211 Investment firm, general brokerage

D-U-N-S 10-916-1752
SYCUAN BAND OF KUMEYAAY NATION
SYCUAN INSURANCE SERVICES
3007 Dehesa Rd, El Cajon, CA 92019-2806
Tel (619) 445-6002 Founded/Ownrshp 1983
Sales NA EMP 2,000
SIC 9131 Indian reservation
Ch Bd: Daniel Tucker
*V Ch Bd: Joe Sandoval

D-U-N-S 10-243-0647
SYCUAN CASINO
SYCUAN RESORT AND CASINO
5459 Casino Way, El Cajon, CA 92019
Tel (619) 445-6002 Founded/Ownrshp 1983
Sales 79.2MMᴱ EMP 2,000
SIC 7999 7997 Gambling establishment; Membership sports & recreation clubs
Genl Mgr: Sheila Howe
Treas: Lashunna Davidson
Sr VP: Javier Murillo
Ex Dir: Mitch Bradley
Dir Sec: Juan Baca
Genl Mgr: Jim Muse
Dir IT: Patrick Tinklenberg
IT Man: Ricky Andaya
Manager: Rebecca Barr
Sls Mgr: Ashley Sapp
Art Dir: Chris Vance

SYCUAN INSURANCE SERVICES
See SYCUAN BAND OF KUMEYAAY NATION

SYCUAN RESORT AND CASINO
See SYCUAN CASINO

SYDNEY AT THE RADISSON
See GREENLEAF HOSPITALITY GROUP INC

D-U-N-S 78-472-6390 IMP
■ **SYGMA NETWORK INC**
(Suby of SYSCO CORP) ★
5550 Blazer Pkwy Ste 300, Dublin, OH 43017-3478
Tel (614) 734-2500 Founded/Ownrshp 1988
Sales 3.0MMMᴱ EMP 3,500
SIC 5149 Groceries & related products
CEO: Thomas Russell
Pr: Steven Deasey
Ch: Joseph A Sugar
Ex VP: Robert O Emmett
Ex VP: Grady Metoyer
VP: Jimmy Abrego
VP: William Bolzenius
VP: Craig Cunningham
VP: Bob Gerlach
VP: Robert Gerluch
VP: Bob Johnson
VP: Kirk Krajewski
VP: Thomas P Kurz
VP: James Lafoe
VP: John W Lewis
VP: Colleen Moote
VP: David Myers
VP: Mark Peterson
VP: John Rivers
VP: Terri Shamblin
VP: Gary Toth

D-U-N-S 96-194-9703
■ **SYKES ACQUISITION LLC**
(Suby of SYKES ENTERPRISES INC) ★
400 N Ashley Dr, Tampa, FL 33602-4300
Tel (813) 274-1000 Founded/Ownrshp 2010
Sales 302.0MMᴱ EMP 18,100
SIC 7379 Computer related maintenance services

D-U-N-S 04-175-9564
▲ **SYKES ENTERPRISES INC**
400 N Ashley Dr Ste 2800, Tampa, FL 33602-4327
Tel (813) 274-1000 Founded/Ownrshp 1977
Sales 1.2MMM EMP 54,550ᴱ
Tkr Sym SYKE Exch NGS
SIC 7379 7389 Computer related consulting services; Telephone services
Pr: Charles E Sykes
*Ch Bd: James S Macleod
CFO: John Chapman
Ex VP: Andrew J Blanchard
Ex VP: James T Holder
Ex VP: Jenna R Nelson
Ex VP: David L Pearson
VP: William N Rocktoff
VP: Lance Zingale
Ex Dir: Jim Gully
Telecom Ex: Donna Cunningham
Board of Directors: Vanessa C L Chang, Michael P Delong, Carlos E Evans, Lorraine L Lutton, James S Macleod, William J Meurer, William D Muir Jr, Paul L Whiting

SYLVAN
See SNYDER ASSOCIATED COMPANIES INC

D-U-N-S 07-843-4690
SYLVAN FM HOLDING LLC
1001 State St, Perth Amboy, NJ 08861-2001
Tel (732) 826-7474 Founded/Ownrshp 2008
Sales 121.3MMᴱ EMP 524ᴱ
SIC 1711 Mechanical contractor
Pr: Robert H Metz

SYLVAN LEARNING CENTERS
See EDUCATE INC

D-U-N-S 01-468-8212
SYLVAN UNION SCHOOL DISTRICT
605 Sylvan Ave, Modesto, CA 95350-1599
Tel (209) 574-5000 Founded/Ownrshp 1946
Sales 96.2MM EMP 760
Accts Vavrinek Trine Day & Co Ll
SIC 8211 Public elementary & secondary schools
*Pr: Chad Brown
Bd of Dir: David Collins
Dir IT: Denise Castro
IT Man: Rick Harms
IT Man: Doug Souza
Psych: Christina Saul
HC Dir: Hedi Reyes

D-U-N-S 04-950-4855
SYLVANIA CITY SCHOOL DISTRICT
SYLVANIA SCHOOLS
4747 N Hlland Sylvania Rd, Sylvania, OH 43560
Tel (419) 824-8500 Founded/Ownrshp 1900
Sales 93.5MM EMP 930

Accts Julian & Grube Inc Westervi
SIC 8211 Public elementary & secondary schools
**CFO:* Laura K Sauber
Treas: Robin Robinson
Treas: Arlene Wilson
Bd of Dir: Stephen Rothschild
Dir IT: Sheryl O'Shea
Pr Dir: Bethany Cooper
Teacher Pr: Keith Limes
Psych: Maria Arite

D-U-N-S 10-151-0543
SYLVANIA FRANCISCAN HEALTH
1715 Indian Wood Cir # 200, Maumee, OH 43537-4055
Tel (419) 882-8373 *Founded/Ownrshp* 1983
Sales 12.5MM *EMP* 4,800E
SIC 8062 8741 General medical & surgical hospitals; Management services
Pr: James Pope
**Pr:* John W O'Connell
**Treas:* William Waters
Trst: Mary A Grzeskowiak
Trst: Mary J Mike
Sr VP: Robert B Tracz

D-U-N-S 05-070-5532
SYLVANIA LIGHTING SERVICES CORP
(*Suby of* OSRAM SYLVANIA INC) ★
200 Ballardvale St, Wilmington, MA 01887-1074
Tel (978) 570-3000 *Founded/Ownrshp* 1969, 2010
Sales 218.7MME *EMP* 2,600E
SIC 7349 Lighting maintenance service
Pr: Jes Hansen
CFO: Jean Paul Michel
**Treas:* Timothy J Lesch
**Treas:* William Mahoney
**Treas:* Jesko D Von Stechow
VP: Geoffrey Hunt
VP: James Scott
Exec: Tom Ciskoski
Exec: Kimberly Russell
**Prin:* Charles A L'Ecuyer
Brnch Mgr: Brian Martin

SYLVANIA SCHOOLS
See SYLVANIA CITY SCHOOL DISTRICT

D-U-N-S 05-098-4202
SYLVEST FARMS INC
3500 West Blvd, Montgomery, AL 36108-4536
Tel (334) 281-0400 *Founded/Ownrshp* 1988
Sales 69.4MME *EMP* 1,300
SIC 0251 2015 Broiling chickens, raising of; Poultry, slaughtered & dressed
Pr: Dean E Falk
**Ex VP:* Lyman L Campbell
**Ex VP:* Richard Taylor

D-U-N-S 06-469-6941 IMP
▲ SYMANTEC CORP
350 Ellis St, Mountain View, CA 94043-2202
Tel (650) 527-8000 *Founded/Ownrshp* 1982
Sales 3.6MMM *EMP* 11,000
Accts Kpmg Llp Santa Clara Califor
Tkr Sym SYMC *Exch* NGS
SIC 7372 7379 Prepackaged software; Application computer software; Utility computer software; Business oriented computer software; Computer related consulting services
CEO: Greg Clark
Ch Bd: Daniel H Schulman
Pr: Michael Fey
Pr: Mark S Garfield
Pr: Ajei S Gopal
CFO: Thomas J Seifert
CFO: Thomas Seifert
Ex VP: Scott C Taylor
Sr VP: Roxane Divol
Sr VP: Stephen Trilling
VP: Ken Schneider
Board of Directors: Frank E Dangeard, Kenneth Y Hao, Geraldine B Laybourne, David L Mahoney, Robert S Miller, Anita M Sands, V Paul Unruh, Suzanne M Vautrinot

D-U-N-S 80-676-7625
SYMBION HOLDINGS CORP
(*Suby of* SURGERY PARTNERS) ★
40 Burton Hills Blvd # 500, Nashville, TN 37215-6199
Tel (615) 234-5900 *Founded/Ownrshp* 2014
Sales 401.0MME *EMP* 3,305
SIC 8011 8093 8062 Ambulatory surgical center; Specialty outpatient clinics; General medical & surgical hospitals
CEO: Michael Doyle
**CFO:* Teresa F Sparks
**Chf Cred:* Jennifer Baldock

D-U-N-S 08-070-7503
SYMBION INC
SURGERY PARTNERS
(*Suby of* SYMBION HOLDINGS CORP) ★
40 Burton Hills Blvd # 500, Nashville, TN 37215-6199
Tel (615) 234-5900 *Founded/Ownrshp* 1996, 2007
Sales 390.4MME *EMP* 2,100
SIC 8011 8093 8062 Ambulatory surgical center; Specialty outpatient clinics; General medical & surgical hospitals
Ch Bd: Richard E Francis Jr
**Pr:* Clifford G Adlerz
**CFO:* Teresa F Sparks
Sr VP: Kenneth C Mitchell
VP: Elizabeth Campbell
VP: Michelle Jones
VP: Matt Petty
VP: Trent Webb
VP: David G Williamson
Exec: Andrea Linn
Dir IT: Joseph Vesneski

SYMBOL MATTRESS
See EASTERN SLEEP PRODUCTS CO

SYMBOL TECHNOLOGIES DELAWARE
See SYMBOL TECHNOLOGIES LLC

D-U-N-S 06-597-3067 IMP/EXP
■ SYMBOL TECHNOLOGIES LLC
SYMBOL TECHNOLOGIES DELAWARE
(*Suby of* ZEBRA TECHNOLOGIES CORP) ★
1 Zebra Plz, Holtsville, NY 11742-1300
Tel (631) 737-6851 *Founded/Ownrshp* 2014
Sales 2.0MMME *EMP* 4,500
SIC 4812 Cellular telephone services
CEO: Edward Fitzpatrick
**CFO:* Timothy T Yates
**Treas:* Cary Schmiedel
VP: James M Conboy
**Prin:* Paul Kiernen
Sftwr Eng: Tony Russo

D-U-N-S 60-219-8785
■ SYMCOR INC
(*Suby of* XEROX CORP) ★
3399 Peachtree Rd Ne # 850, Atlanta, GA 30326-2810
Tel (404) 504-0100 *Founded/Ownrshp* 2011
Sales 56.2MME *EMP* 2,000
SIC 7374 Data processing service
CEO: Edd Killroy
Sr VP: Roger Leitner
**Sr VP:* Mike Thomas
**VP:* Graham Bailey
**VP:* Michelle Bullock
VP: Nancy Laidman
VP: Hugh McCullough
VP: Mike Nolin
VP: Tim Relke
**CIO:* Tom Cronin
**CIO:* Dennis Maloney

SYMETRA FINANCIAL
See SYMETRA LIFE INSURANCE CO

D-U-N-S 16-455-8830
SYMETRA FINANCIAL CORP
(*Suby of* SUMITOMO LIFE INSURANCE COMPANY)
777 108th Ave Ne Ste 1200, Bellevue, WA 98004-5135
Tel (425) 256-8000 *Founded/Ownrshp* 2016
Sales NA *EMP* 1,230E
SIC 6311 6411 Life insurance; Pension & retirement plan consultants
Pr: Thomas M Marra
Pr: Dennis Brewer
Pr: Phil Calderone
Pr: Darlene Chandler
Pr: Greg Faux
Pr: Michael Murphy
Pr: Dawn Reyes
Pr: Liz Wilbur
CFO: Margaret A Meister
Treas: Nicholas Mocciolo
Ex VP: Jonathan E Curley
Ex VP: Terry Festervand
Ex VP: Dan Guilbert
Ex VP: Roger Harbin
Ex VP: Mark E Hunt
Sr VP: David S Goldstein
Sr VP: Christine A Katzmar Holmes
Sr VP: Evan S Moskovit
VP: Eric Baldwin
VP: Thomas Bittner
VP: Lynda Brown
Board of Directors: Peter S Burgess, David T Foy, Lois W Grady, Sander M Levy, Robert R Lusardi

D-U-N-S 00-794-2790
SYMETRA LIFE INSURANCE CO
SYMETRA FINANCIAL
(*Suby of* SYMETRA FINANCIAL CORP) ★
777 108th Ave Ne Ste 1200, Bellevue, WA 98004-5135
Tel (877) 796-3872 *Founded/Ownrshp* 1957
Sales NA *EMP* 1,100
SIC 6311 6324 6411 Life insurance; Hospital & medical service plans; Insurance agents, brokers & service
CEO: Thomas Marra
Pr: Rey Castro
COO: Paul Mistretta
Assoc VP: Jasyn Sadler
Ex VP: Jonathan E Curley
Ex VP: Michael Fry
Ex VP: Richard Lavoice
Sr VP: Joel C Kneisley
Sr VP: George McKinnon
Sr VP: Michael Roscoe
VP: Jeremy Alyea
VP: Philip Calderone
VP: Jeff Farmer
VP: Gregory Faux
VP: Brent Martonik
VP: Harry Monti
VP: Curt Olson
VP: Michael Polonsky
VP: John Richter

D-U-N-S 96-018-9041 IMP
SYMMETRY MEDICAL INC
(*Suby of* TECOMET INC) ★
3724 N State Road 15, Warsaw, IN 46582-7000
Tel (574) 268-2252 *Founded/Ownrshp* 2014
Sales 399.9MME *EMP* 500
SIC 3841 3842 Surgical & medical instruments; Orthopedic appliances
CEO: William Dow
Pr: Robert S Rutledge
CFO: John Connollyn
Sr VP: Andrew J Miclot
VP: David J Golde
QA Dir: Mike Parrish
IT Man: Mark Morgans
IT Man: Ray Sherwood
IT Man: Jason Trammel
Mtls Mgr: Randy Woodcock
Plnt Mgr: Max Elder

D-U-N-S 07-964-1356
SYMMETRY SURGICAL INC
(*Suby of* ROUNDTABLE HEALTHCARE PARTNERS LP) ★
3034 Owen Dr, Antioch, TN 37013-2413
Tel (615) 883-9090 *Founded/Ownrshp* 2014, 2016
Sales 84.5MM *EMP* 1E
SIC 5047 Surgical equipment & supplies
Pr: Thomas J Sullivan
VP: Hedy Hashemi

VP Sls: Keith Sweeney
Mktg Mgr: Lindsay Spinner

D-U-N-S 07-929-3778
SYMPHONY TALENT LLC
45 Rockefeller Plz # 659, New York, NY 10111-0100
Tel (212) 999-9000 *Founded/Ownrshp* 2007
Sales 134.6MME *EMP* 300
Accts Deloitte & Touche Llp
SIC 7372 7361 Business oriented computer software; Employment agencies
CEO: Roopesh Nair
**CFO:* Barak Ben-Gal
**Ch:* Romesh Wadhwani
Sr VP: Sal Apuzzio
Sr VP: Samantha Loveland
Sr VP: Gayleen Robinson
VP: Ben Camacho

D-U-N-S 15-871-0835
SYMPHONY TECHNOLOGY GROUP LLC
2475 Hanover St, Palo Alto, CA 94304-1114
Tel (650) 935-9500 *Founded/Ownrshp* 2001
Sales 898.0MME *EMP* 5,665
SIC 8748 6719 Business consulting; Investment holding companies, except banks
CEO: Romesh Wadhwani
Ex VP: John Fors

D-U-N-S 93-326-0887
SYMQUEST GROUP INC
(*Suby of* MINOLTA BUSINESS SYSTEMS) ★
30 Community Dr Ste 5, South Burlington, VT 05403-6834
Tel (802) 658-9890 *Founded/Ownrshp* 2015
Sales 89.4MME *EMP* 186
SIC 5044 8243 Office equipment; Copying equipment; Software training, computer
Pr: Lawrence Sudbay
**VP:* Nicole M Carignan
Netwrk Mgr: Darrin Lamothe
Netwrk Eng: Joshua Goldberg
Netwrk Eng: Kyle Smith
Netwrk Eng: Joe Wager
Opers Mgr: Jo Joy
Sls Dir: James A Edgerton
Sls Mgr: Dayle Goad
Snr Mgr: Ted Eames

D-U-N-S 01-161-4286 IMP/EXP
SYMRISE INC (NJ)
(*Suby of* SYMRISE AG)
300 North St, Teterboro, NJ 07608-1204
Tel (201) 462-5559 *Founded/Ownrshp* 1956, 1994
Sales 315.2MME *EMP* 720
SIC 2869 Perfume materials, synthetic; Flavors or flavoring materials, synthetic
CEO: Achim Daub
Pr: Mike Cavender
**CEO:* Dr Heinz-Jurgen Bertram
**CFO:* Bernd Hirsch
**CFO:* Klaus-Peter Steinhof
Top Exec: Sandra Corneau
VP: Patricia Bilodeau
VP: Jasmine Chong
VP: Patricia Cuneo
VP: Renee Defranco
VP: Fred Kritzer
VP: Torsten Kulke
VP: Emmanuel Laroche
VP: Keith McDermott
VP: Norbert Richter
VP: Isabelle Vacheret
VP: Usha Vijay
VP: James Zitelli
Exec: Terry Mahon
Dir Bus: Carol McBride

D-U-N-S 01-226-7324 IMP
SYMS CORP (NJ)
1 Syms Way, Secaucus, NJ 07094-9400
Tel (201) 902-9600 *Founded/Ownrshp* 1983
Sales 445.1MM *EMP* 26E
SIC 5651 5661

D-U-N-S 12-543-4808
▲ SYNACOR INC
40 La Riviere Dr Ste 300, Buffalo, NY 14202-4306
Tel (716) 853-1362 *Founded/Ownrshp* 1998
Sales 110.2MM *EMP* 387E
Tkr Sym SYNC *Exch* NGM
SIC 7371 7374 Custom computer programming services; Custom computer programming services; Data processing service
Pr: Himesh Bhise
**Ch Bd:* Jordan Levy
Pr: George G Chamoun
CFO: William J Stuart
CFO: William Stuart
Sr VP: Timothy Schermerhorn
VP: Ron Bernstein
VP: Michael Bishara
VP: Molly Chvala
VP: Meredith Roth
VP: Anand Subramanian
Board of Directors: Gary L Ginsberg, Andrew Kau, Michael J Montgomery, Scott Murphy

D-U-N-S 80-205-3256 IMP
SYNAGRO TECHNOLOGIES INC
RPM MARKETING
(*Suby of* EQT PARTNERS AB)
435 Williams Ct Ste 100, Baltimore, MD 21220-2888
Tel (800) 370-0035 *Founded/Ownrshp* 2013
Sales 593.9MME *EMP* 874
SIC 4953 Refuse systems
CEO: Stephen W Cole
**Pr:* D Eric Zimmer
**COO:* Mark B McCormick
**CFO:* Chris Dunkerley
CFO: Chris M Dunkerley
VP: Chibby Alloway
VP: Pamela K Racey
VP: Pete Sarin
Genl Mgr: Kathleen Wright
CIO: David Hilmer
Tech Mgr: Kari Saganski

D-U-N-S 00-334-9065 IMP
▲ SYNALLOY CORP
4510 Cox Rd Ste 201, Glen Allen, VA 23060-3394
Tel (864) 585-3605 *Founded/Ownrshp* 1945
Sales 175.4MM *EMP* 411E
Tkr Sym SYNL *Exch* NGM
SIC 3317 3443 2865 2899 2869 Steel pipe & tubes; Process vessels, industrial: metal plate; Color pigments, organic; Chemical preparations; Industrial organic chemicals
Pr: Craig C Bram
**Ch Bd:* Murray H Wright
Pr: J Greg Gibson
Pr: J Kyle Pennington
CFO: Dennis M Loughran
Ex VP: John Tidlow
Genl Mgr: Greg Gibson
Board of Directors: Anthony A Callander, Susan S Gayner, Henry L Guy, Amy J Michtich, James W Terry Jr, Vincent W White

D-U-N-S 15-510-5794
▲ SYNAPTICS INC
1251 Mckay Dr, San Jose, CA 95131-1709
Tel (408) 904-1100 *Founded/Ownrshp* 1986
Sales 1.6MMM *EMP* 1,789E
Tkr Sym SYNA *Exch* NGS
SIC 3577 7372 Computer peripheral equipment; Application computer software
Pr: Richard A Bergman
**Ch Bd:* Francis F Lee
CFO: Wajid Ali
Sr VP: Kevin D Barber
Sr VP: Scott Deutsch
Sr VP: John McFarland
Sr VP: Bret C Sewell
Sr VP: Huibert Verhoeven
Sr VP: Alex Wong
VP: Kathleen Bayless
VP: Kin Cheung
VP: Ritu Favre
VP: Patrick Worfolk
Board of Directors: Jeffrey D Buchanan, Nelson C Chan, Keith B Geeslin, Russell J Knittel, Richard L Sanquini, James L Whims

D-U-N-S 61-637-9520
▲ SYNCHRONOSS TECHNOLOGIES INC
200 Crossing Blvd Fl 8, Bridgewater, NJ 08807-2861
Tel (866) 620-3940 *Founded/Ownrshp* 2000
Sales 578.8MM *EMP* 1,895E
Tkr Sym SNCR *Exch* NGS
SIC 7371 4813 Custom computer programming services; Computer software development & applications;
Ch Bd: Stephen G Waldis
Pr: Robert Garcia
CFO: Karen L Rosenberger
Chf Mktg O: Omar T Llez
Ex VP: David Berry
Ex VP: Patrick J Doran
Ex VP: George Navarro
Ex VP: Chris Putnam
Ex VP: Daniel Rizer
Ex VP: Joel Silverman
Sr VP: Daniel H Ives
VP: Jim Hasemann
VP: Chuck Machlin
Board of Directors: William J Cadogan, Charles E Hoffman, Thomas J Hopkins, James M McCormick, Donnie M Moore

D-U-N-S 15-921-4522
■ SYNCHRONY BANK
(*Suby of* SYNCHRONY FINANCIAL) ★
170 W Election Rd Ste 125, Draper, UT 84020-6425
Tel (801) 619-4760 *Founded/Ownrshp* 2013
Sales NA *EMP* 6,700
SIC 6035 Federal savings banks
Prin: Kurt Grossheim
**Pr:* Mark Wolters
**Ch:* Thomas L Gray Jr
VP: Jim McConville
Mktg Dir: Gail R Giffen

D-U-N-S 07-933-2033
▲ SYNCHRONY FINANCIAL
777 Long Ridge Rd, Stamford, CT 06902-1247
Tel (203) 585-2400 *Founded/Ownrshp* 2013
Sales NA *EMP* 12,000
Tkr Sym SYF *Exch* NYS
SIC 6021 7389 National commercial banks; Financial services
Pr: Margaret M Keane
CEO: David Fasoli
CEO: Glenn P Marino
CEO: Thomas M Quindlen
CFO: Brian D Doubles
Treas: Eric Duenwald
Ex VP: Henry F Greig
Ex VP: Jonathan S Mothner
Sr VP: David P Melito
Sr VP: Todd Rodden
VP: Bart Schaller

D-U-N-S 05-060-3849
SYNCORA GUARANTEE INC
(*Suby of* SYNCORA HOLDINGS LTD.)
135 W 50th St Fl 20, New York, NY 10020-1201
Tel (212) 478-3400 *Founded/Ownrshp* 1999
Sales NA *EMP* 116
SIC 6399 Deposit insurance
CEO: Susan Comparato
**COO:* Frederick B Hnat
Bd of Dir: Brian M O Hara
Bd of Dir: Frederick Hnat
**Sr VP:* Michael Corbally
**Sr VP:* Drew D Hoffman
VP: Andrea Bierman
Exec: Bonnie Gray
Mng Dir: Thomas Gove
Genl Couns: Ravind Karamsingh

D-U-N-S 08-329-4632
SYNCREON AMERICA INC
(*Suby of* SYNCREON TECHNOLOGY (UK) LTD)
2851 High Meadow Cir, Auburn Hills, MI 48326-2792
Tel (248) 377-4700 *Founded/Ownrshp* 2014
Sales 118.0MME *EMP* 300

SIC 4731 Freight transportation arrangement
CEO: Brian Enright
CIO: Julian Mordaunt
Dir IT: Niall O Mahony
Plnt Mgr: Marvin Belinoski

D-U-N-S 82-812-6255
SYNCREON HOLDINGS INC
2851 High Meadow Cir # 250, Auburn Hills, MI 48326-2791
Tel (248) 377-4700 *Founded/Ownrshp* 1993
Sales 393.2MM[E] *EMP* 4,500[E]
SIC 3559 Automotive related machinery
CEO: Brian Enright
COO: Steve Faulkner
COO: David Minns
**COO:* John Semplonius
**CFO:* Carine Van Landschoot
Ex VP: Annette Cyr
VP: Ken Bohane
VP: Brian McCarey
**VP:* Kenneth Pocius
VP: Hans Vandermeulen
VP: Donna Zeiter

D-U-N-S 60-242-6608
SYNCREON TECHNOLOGY (USA) LLC
NAL.SYNCREON
1200 N Greenbriar Dr, Addison, IL 60101-1049
Tel (630) 261-3100 *Founded/Ownrshp* 2009
Sales 118.5MM[E] *EMP* 620
SIC 7389 4222 Personal service agents, brokers & bureaus; Warehousing, cold storage or refrigerated
Pr: Douglas E Witt
**CEO:* Brian Enright
**CFO:* Anthony Pellegrino
CFO: Anthony Pelligrino
Dir Bus: Dan Bombrys

D-U-N-S 00-537-8518 IMP
SYNCRO CORP (MI)
1030 Sundown Dr Nw, Arab, AL 35016-2000
Tel (256) 586-6045 *Founded/Ownrshp* 1938
Sales 86.0MM[E] *EMP* 225
SIC 3714 3625 3694 3823 3643 Motor vehicle brake systems & parts; Brakes, electromagnetic; Alternators, automotive; Ignition apparatus, internal combustion engines; Industrial instrmnts msrmnt display/control process variable; Current-carrying wiring devices
Pr: Edwin Childress
**Sec:* Christopher Andreae
**VP:* Bruce Biggard
**VP:* Larry Fleming
**VP:* Jerry Hart
MIS Dir: Rick Purdom
Sls&Mrk Ex: Fleming Larry
Sls Mgr: Larry Sleming
Board of Directors: Robert Anderson, Wayne Andreae Jr, Hugh M Archer, Richard F Eberline, John Iseman, Benjamin W Jayne

D-U-N-S 07-270-0198
SYNCSORT INC
50 Tice Blvd Ste 250, Woodcliff Lake, NJ 07677-7730
Tel (877) 700-0970 *Founded/Ownrshp* 1968
Sales 98.8MM[E] *EMP* 220[E]
SIC 7371 Computer software development; Computer software systems analysis & design, custom
CEO: Josh Rogers
**COO:* Krish Venkataraman
CFO: Bob Bies
**Chf Mktg O:* Gary Survis
VP: Bryan Ashley
Prgrm Mgr: Dennis Meyers
Off Admin: Solange Teiletche
Snr Sftwr: Eugene Baskayan
Dir IT: John Trchala
IT Man: Octavius A Viera
Software D: Ujjwal Wadhawan

D-U-N-S 06-509-5507
SYNDEX CORP
6950 Neuhaus St, Houston, TX 77061-4607
Tel (713) 923-1057 *Founded/Ownrshp* 1910
Sales 239.6MM[E] *EMP* 560
SIC 5148 Fruits, fresh; Vegetables, fresh
Ch Bd: Cary Hoffman
**VP:* Jerry Farrell
**VP:* Mark Steakley
**Genl Mgr:* G D Farrell Sr

D-U-N-S 00-605-4217 IMP/EXP
SYNDICATE SALES INC
2025 N Wabash Ave, Kokomo, IN 46901-2063
Tel (765) 457-7277 *Founded/Ownrshp* 1955
Sales 106.6MM[E] *EMP* 410
SIC 3089 Injection molding of plastics
Ch Bd: Delmar Demaree Jr
**Pr:* David M Hendrickson
CFO: Linda Utter
**VP:* Laura D Shinall
Natl Sales: Robin Dils
Manager: Ken Anderson

D-U-N-S 16-855-6426
SYNECHRON INC
SYNECHRON TECHNOLOGIES
(*Suby of* SYNECHRON TECHNOLOGIES PRIVATE LIMITED)
1 Corporate Pl S Ste 200, Piscataway, NJ 08854-6116
Tel (732) 562-0088 *Founded/Ownrshp* 2005
Sales 135.1MM[E] *EMP* 4,227
SIC 8748 Business consulting
CEO: Faisal Husain
CFO: Zia Bhutta
Bd of Dir: Kevin Carney
Chf Mktg O: George Ravich
Snr Sftwr: Anupama Bhat
IT Man: Anuj Kapoor
Tech Mgr: Manoj Bhoyar
Tech Mgr: Amol Kad
Sftwr Eng: Vishal Kumar

SYNECHRON TECHNOLOGIES
See SYNECHRON INC

D-U-N-S 61-921-5502
SYNERGON HEALTH SYSTEM INC
520 S Maple Ave, Oak Park, IL 60304-1022
Tel (708) 660-6661 *Founded/Ownrshp* 1990
Sales 1.4MM *EMP* 1,500
SIC 8062 8051 8082 General medical & surgical hospitals; Skilled nursing care facilities; Home health care services
Pr: Bruce Elegant
**Pr:* Leonard J Muller
**CFO:* Gay Vincent

SYNERGY ENERGY HOLDINGS
See BELL SUPPLY CO LLC

D-U-N-S 07-888-5917
SYNERGY ENERGY HOLDINGS LLC
114 E Foreline St, Gainesville, TX 76240-3320
Tel (940) 612-0417 *Founded/Ownrshp* 2013
Sales 257.3MM[E] *EMP* 276[E]
SIC 5084 Industrial machinery & equipment
CEO: Kelly Stanley
**Ch Bd:* Ayman Naguib

D-U-N-S 55-651-6185
SYNERGY HEALTH NORTH AMERICA INC
(*Suby of* SYNERGY HEALTH LIMITED)
401 E Jackson St Ste 3100, Tampa, FL 33602-5228
Tel (813) 891-9550 *Founded/Ownrshp* 1991
Sales 476.0MM[E] *EMP* 799[E]
SIC 5047 7213 Surgical equipment & supplies; Linen supply
CEO: Richard Steeves
CFO: Mark R Faris
CFO: Wallace D Ruiz
Sr Cor Off: John Simmons
Ex VP: J T Boosales
Sr VP: William J Braun
Sr VP: David J McGuire
VP: John Hornbeck
VP: Curtis Martell
VP: Glen Thesselwade
VP: Robert C Wolf
Exec: Barbara Ridge
Board of Directors: James T Boosales, James M Emanuel, Charles W Federico, Michael D Israel, Charles T Orsatti, Wayne R Peterson

SYNERGY HEALTH OF ST JOSEPH'S
See SAINT JOSEPHS COMMUNITY HOSPITAL

D-U-N-S 00-456-4131
SYNERGY RESOURCES CORP
1625 Broadway Ste 300, Denver, CO 80202-4739
Tel (720) 616-4300 *Founded/Ownrshp* 2005
Sales 112.3MM[E] *EMP* 62
Tkr Sym SYRG *Exch* ASE
SIC 1381 Drilling oil & gas wells
Ch Bd: Lynn A Peterson
COO: Michael Eberhard
COO: Michael J Eberhard
COO: Craig D Rasmuson
COO: Nick Spence
COO: Nick A Spence
CFO: James P Henderson
VP: Matthew Miller
Exec: Tom Birmingham
Board of Directors: Jack Aydin, Daniel E Kelly, Raymond E McElhaney, Rick A Wilber

D-U-N-S 14-336-0910
SYNERGY SERVICES INC
(*Suby of* TALENTWAVE) ★
4601 Dtc Blvd Ste 650, Denver, CO 80237-2549
Tel (303) 468-2070 *Founded/Ownrshp* 2015
Sales NA *EMP* 3,000
Accts Anton Collins Mitchell Llp De
SIC 7371 Computer software systems analysis & design, custom
CEO: Tim Miller
**Pr:* Scott Zirbel
**Ex VP:* Gary Cornick
Sr VP: Kimball Norup
Sr VP: Mark Young
VP: Julie Tran
**CTO:* David Whipple
Dir IT: Jason Clark

D-U-N-S 01-072-7241
SYNERGY SOLUTIONS INC
3141 N 3rd Ave Ste C100, Phoenix, AZ 85013-4355
Tel (602) 296-1600 *Founded/Ownrshp* 1999
Sales 49.8MM[E] *EMP* 1,200
SIC 7389 Telemarketing services
Pr: Lori Fentem
**Ch Bd:* Steve Moak
**COO:* Corey Conklin
Dir IT: Jody Halsey

D-U-N-S 07-882-4041
SYNERGY55 INC
85 W Algonquin Rd Ste 600, Arlington Heights, IL 60005-4421
Tel (847) 437-0200 *Founded/Ownrshp* 1998
Sales 514.7MM[E] *EMP* 372[E]
SIC 8741 Management services
CEO: Steve Dehmlow

SYNERON CANDELA
See CANDELA CORP

SYNERON CANDELA
See SYNERON INC

D-U-N-S 80-102-3644
SYNERON INC
SYNERON CANDELA
(*Suby of* SYNERON MEDICAL LTD)
3 Goodyear Ste A, Irvine, CA 92618-2050
Tel (949) 716-6670 *Founded/Ownrshp* 2000
Sales 109.4MM[E] *EMP* 413[E]
SIC 3845 Laser systems & equipment, medical
Ch Bd: Shimon Eckhouse
**Pr:* Doron Gerstel
**CEO:* Shimon Eckhouse
**CFO:* Asaf Alperovitz
**CFO:* Fabian Tenenbaum
**VP:* Leslie Rigali
**VP:* Dr Opher Shapira
Manager: Elisa M Jozwiak

Sls Mgr: Ashley Jachetta
Sls Mgr: Jason Peters

D-U-N-S 00-799-4572 EXP
SYNGENTA CORP
(*Suby of* SYNGENTA AG)
3411 Silverside Rd # 100, Wilmington, DE 19810-4811
Tel (302) 425-2000 *Founded/Ownrshp* 2000
Sales 1.5MMM[E] *EMP* 5,134
SIC 2879 5191 8741 Agricultural chemicals; Seeds: field, garden & flower; Management services
VP: Jason Fogden
**Treas:* Henry P Graef
Treas: Joe Virion
Top Exec: Bette Newsome
Comm Man: Pam Molitor
Genl Mgr: Paul Luxton
CIO: Davor Pisk
Tech Mgr: Mark Kitt
VP Opers: Pat Crump
Sfty Mgr: Claudia Gonzalez
Mktg Mgr: Susan Keefer

D-U-N-S 96-661-6633 IMP/EXP
SYNGENTA CROP PROTECTION LLC
GOLDSMITH SEEDS
(*Suby of* SYNGENTA AG)
410 S Swing Rd, Greensboro, NC 27409-2012
Tel (336) 632-6000 *Founded/Ownrshp* 2000
Sales 2.0MMM[E] *EMP* 5,000
SIC 0721 Crop protecting services
Pr: Valdemir Fisher
**Treas:* Henry P Graef
VP: Jan Rowe-Caps
Genl Mgr: Charles Catalano
CIO: Wayne McCray
Mktg Dir: Kim Dawson
Mktg Mgr: Susan Morris
Pathlgst: Michael Agnew
Corp Couns: Warren Boerger

D-U-N-S 00-696-2427 IMP/EXP
SYNGENTA SEEDS INC
(*Suby of* SYNGENTA CORP) ★
11055 Wayzata Blvd, Hopkins, MN 55305-1526
Tel (612) 656-8600 *Founded/Ownrshp* 1884
Sales 504.6MM[E] *EMP* 2,060
SIC 2074 2075 2076 5191 Cottonseed oil mills; Soybean oil mills; Vegetable oil mills; Seeds: field, garden & flower
CEO: David Morgan
VP: Karen Park Gallivan

D-U-N-S 61-036-5814
SYNICO STAFFING LLC
3033 Excelsior Blvd # 495, Minneapolis, MN 55416-5227
Tel (612) 926-6000 *Founded/Ownrshp* 2006
Sales 40.5MM[E] *EMP* 1,200
SIC 7363 Temporary help service

D-U-N-S 17-072-0598
SYNIVERSE HOLDINGS INC
(*Suby of* BUCCANEER HOLDINGS LLC) ★
8125 Highwoods Palm Way, Tampa, FL 33647-1776
Tel (813) 637-5000 *Founded/Ownrshp* 2014
Sales 861.4MM *EMP* 2,538[E]
SIC 4812 3663 Radio telephone communication; Radio & TV communications equipment
Pr: Stephen Gray
CFO: Bob Reich
Chf Mktg O: Mary Clark
VP: Laura Binion
VP: Martin A Picciano
CTO: Chris Rivera

D-U-N-S 78-281-9155 IMP
SYNIVERSE TECHNOLOGIES LLC
(*Suby of* SYNIVERSE HOLDINGS INC) ★
8125 Highwoods Palm Way, Tampa, FL 33647-1776
Tel (813) 637-5000 *Founded/Ownrshp* 1989
Sales 558.8MM[E] *EMP* 1,289
SIC 4812 3663 Cellular telephone services; Mobile communication equipment
CEO: Stephen C Gray
Pr: Mahesh Prasad
COO: Alfred De Cardenas
Bd of Dir: Bob Marino
Ex VP: Alfredo De Cardenas
Ex VP: Lori Gonnu
Sr VP: Patrick George
VP: Jody Clermont
VP: Paul Corrao
VP: James L Huseby
VP: Giorgio Miano
Board of Directors: Julius Genachowski, Dan Mead

D-U-N-S 05-599-1053 IMP
▲ **SYNNEX CORP**
44201 Nobel Dr, Fremont, CA 94538-3178
Tel (510) 656-3333 *Founded/Ownrshp* 1980
Sales 13.3MMM *EMP* 72,500
Tkr Sym SNX *Exch* NYS
SIC 5734 Computer & software stores
Pr: Kevin Murai
Pt: Michael R Thomson
V Ch: Calvin Currie
Pr: Peter Larocque
COO: Dennis Polk
CFO: Marshall Witt
Bd of Dir: Andrea Zulberti
Sr VP: Peter Coleman
Sr VP: Peter J Coleman
Sr VP: Harry W Edwards
Sr VP: Gary Gulmon
Sr VP: Simon Leung
Sr VP: William P Sheldon
Sr VP: Robert L Stegner
Sr VP: Fred Towns
Sr VP: Tj Trojan
VP: Doug Bone
VP: David Dennis
VP: Jane Fogarty
VP: Mike Gazdic
VP: Steve Ichinaga
Board of Directors: Fred A Breidenbach, Matthew F C Miau, Gregory L Quesnel, Dwight A Steffensen, Thomas Wurster, Duane Zitzner, Andrea Zulberti

D-U-N-S 16-149-9579
▲ **SYNOPSYS INC**
690 E Middlefield Rd, Mountain View, CA 94043-4033
Tel (650) 584-5000 *Founded/Ownrshp* 1986
Sales 2.4MMM *EMP* 10,284
Tkr Sym SNPS *Exch* NGS
SIC 7371 Computer software development
Ch Bd: Aart J De Geus
**Pr:* CHI-Foon Chan
**CFO:* Brian M Beattie
**CFO:* Trac Pham
Treas: Geoffrey E Sloma
Bd of Dir: Kevin Harer
Ex VP: Antun Domic
Ex VP: Manoj Gandhi
Ex VP: Thomas Gardner
Ex VP: Joachim Kunkel
**Ex VP:* Joseph W Logan
Sr VP: David P Burow
Sr VP: Dierdre Hanford
Sr VP: Ernst W Hirt
Sr VP: Howard Ko
Sr VP: Andreas Kuehlmann
Sr VP: Jack J Warecki
VP: Sunil Ashtaputre
VP: George Bayz
VP: Prakash Bhalerao
VP: Kevin Brelsford
Board of Directors: Alfred F Castino, Janice D Chaffin, Bruce R Chizen, Deborah A Coleman, John G Schwarz, Roy Vallee, Steven C Walske

D-U-N-S 88-325-7057
SYNOPTEK INC
19520 Jamboree Rd Ste 110, Irvine, CA 92612-2429
Tel (949) 241-8600 *Founded/Ownrshp* 2015
Sales 87.7MM[E] *EMP* 475
SIC 7379 Computer related consulting services
CEO: Tim Britt
VP: Mike Bank
VP: Tim Becker
VP: Eric Condorniz
**VP:* Jonathan Dippert
**VP:* Miles Feinberg
VP: Carl Jenkins
**VP:* Matt McGraw
VP: Todd Richey
Software D: Richard Clements
Mktg Dir: Michael Brinks

SYNOVA
See ALTIMETRIK CORP

D-U-N-S 96-818-6411
SYNOVOS INC
STOREROOM-ON-SITE
100 Matsonford Rd Ste 400, Radnor, PA 19087-4589
Tel (610) 293-5940 *Founded/Ownrshp* 1996
Sales 408.4MM[E] *EMP* 330
SIC 5085 8741 Industrial supplies; Management services
Pr: Carlos Tellez
**CFO:* Albert Thorp
**Ch:* Larry Newhart
**Treas:* Lawrence E Newhart
Sr VP: Bob Depaolo
**Sr VP:* Robert Depaolo
**Sr VP:* Michael V Weinberg
**VP:* Marilyn Dawes
VP: George Krauter
VP: Michael Weinberg
VP: Read Wellington
VP: Scott West

SYNOVUS
See BANK OF NORTH GEORGIA

D-U-N-S 00-692-5754
■ **SYNOVUS BANK** (GA)
CB&T
(*Suby of* SYNOVUS FINANCIAL CORP) ★
1148 Broadway, Columbus, GA 31901-2429
Tel (706) 649-4900 *Founded/Ownrshp* 1988, 1972
Sales NA *EMP* 4,452[E]
SIC 6022 State commercial banks
Ch Bd: James D Yancey
Pr: Stephen A Milton
CEO: Kessel D Stelling Jr
CFO: Thomas J Prescott
Ex VP: D Wayne Akins Jr
Ex VP: R Dallis Copeland Jr
Ex VP: Jon Dodds
Ex VP: Timothy Farmer
Ex VP: Allen J Gula Jr
Ex VP: Samuel F Hatcher
Sr VP: Brick F Luke
Sr VP: Randy Lunsford
VP: Mitchell Watkins

D-U-N-S 07-586-4314
▲ **SYNOVUS FINANCIAL CORP**
1111 Bay Ave Ste 500, Columbus, GA 31901-5269
Tel (706) 649-2311 *Founded/Ownrshp* 1972
Sales NA *EMP* 4,452[E]
Tkr Sym SNV *Exch* NYS
SIC 6021 6022 7389 National commercial banks; State commercial banks; Financial services
Ch Bd: Kessel D Stelling
Pr: Vicki Kimbro-Moore
Pr: J Barton Singleton
COO: Allen J Gula Jr
CFO: Kevin Blair
CFO: Kevin S Blair
Chf Cred: Kevin J Howard
Ofcr: D Wayne Akins Jr
Ofcr: Mark G Holladay
Ex VP: Roy Dallis Copeland Jr
Ex VP: Amy Hudock
Ex VP: Allan E Kamensky
Ex VP: Curtis J Perry
VP: Amy Dial
VP: Robert Persons

D-U-N-S 93-879-2819
■ **SYNOVUS TRUST CO NA**
(*Suby of* SYNOVUS FINANCIAL CORP) ★
1148 Broadway, Columbus, GA 31901-2429
Tel (706) 649-2311 *Founded/Ownrshp* 1995
Sales 320.7MM *EMP* 159
SIC 6733 6282 Trusts; Investment advice

Pr: George Flowers
Sr VP: Mark J Brown
Dir IT: Jon Smith

SYNTEC CONSULTING
See ADVANTEDGE BUSINESS GROUP LLC

D-U-N-S 18-350-8548 IMP
SYNTEC INDUSTRIES LLC
438 Lavender Dr Nw, Rome, GA 30165-2262
Tel (706) 235-1158 *Founded/Ownrshp* 2001
Sales 150.0MM *EMP* 500
SIC 2273 5023 Carpets & rugs; Floor coverings
Pr: Bill Watters
**COO:* J Tom Watters Jr
CFO: Burton B Weil
VP: Colin Dunn
**VP:* Joe Watters
Mfg Dir: Wayne Brown
Sales Exec: Bill Waters
Natl Sales: Michael Huffman

SYNTEL
See CCL LABEL INC

D-U-N-S 10-844-4944
▲ SYNTEL INC
525 E Big Beaver Rd # 300, Troy, MI 48083-1367
Tel (248) 619-2800 *Founded/Ownrshp* 1980
Sales 968.6MM *EMP* 24,537^E
Tkr Sym SYNT *Exch* NGS
SIC 7371 7372 8748 Custom computer programming services; Prepackaged software; Systems analysis & engineering consulting services
Pr: Rakesh Khanna
**Ch Bd:* Bharat Desai
**Ch Bd:* Prashant Ranade
CFO: Anil Agrawal
Ofcr: Daniel M Moore
**VP:* Neerja Sethi
Board of Directors: Thomas Doeke, Rajesh Mashruwala, Vinod Sahney, Rex E Schlaybaugh Jr

D-U-N-S 02-414-0787
SYNTERACTHCR CORP
(*Suby of* SYNTERACTHCR HOLDINGS CORP) ★
5759 Fleet St Ste 100, Carlsbad, CA 92008-4710
Tel (760) 268-8200 *Founded/Ownrshp* 2008
Sales 83.2MM^E *EMP* 670
SIC 8731 Commercial physical research
CEO: Wendel Barr
Pr: Stewart Bieler
CFO: Keith Kelson
Sr VP: Matthew Smith
VP: Martine Dehlinger-Kremer
VP: Glenn Dodds
VP: Etienne Drouet
VP: Dieter Seitz-Tutter
Exec: Francisco Harrison
Assoc Dir: Jennifer Gearhart
Assoc Dir: Dan Haight
Assoc Dir: Alissa Ruelle
Assoc Dir: Dean Schulenberg
Assoc Dir: Shyla Vanreenen
Dir Bus: Jennifer Jackson

D-U-N-S 00-345-0011
SYNTERACTHCR HOLDINGS CORP
5759 Fleet St Ste 100, Carlsbad, CA 92008-4710
Tel (760) 268-8200 *Founded/Ownrshp* 2008, 2016
Sales 83.2MM^E *EMP* 680
SIC 8731 Commercial physical research
CEO: Wendel Barr
CFO: Keith Kelson
Ofcr: Stewart Bieler

D-U-N-S 83-541-8229
SYNTERACTHCR INC
(*Suby of* SYNTERACTHCR CORP) ★
5759 Fleet St Ste 100, Carlsbad, CA 92008-4710
Tel (760) 268-8200 *Founded/Ownrshp* 1995
Sales 83.2MM^E *EMP* 670
SIC 8731 Commercial physical research
CEO: Wendel Barr
**Pr:* Ellen Morgan
**CFO:* Keith Kelson
**Chf Mktg O:* Richard Paul
**Ex VP:* Russ Holmes
Sr VP: Rod M Saponjic
Sr VP: Matthew P Smith
VP: Raymond Pollum
VP: Dieter Seitz-Tutter
Exec: Mary Clegg
Exec: Brooke Cobbs
Exec: Michelle Conroy
Exec: Jenna Daly
Exec: Philip Doren
Exec: Patrick Gallagher
Exec: Scott Iwasaki
Exec: Jennifer Jackson
Exec: Monique Ortega
Exec: Justin Scarfeo
Assoc Dir: Mary K Romero
Dir Bus: Megan O'Keefe

D-U-N-S 06-989-2289 IMP
SYNTHES (USA) LP (DE)
1302 Wrights Ln E, West Chester, PA 19380-3417
Tel (610) 719-5000 *Founded/Ownrshp* 1988
Sales 393.1MM^E *EMP* 3,500^E
SIC 3842 3841

D-U-N-S 13-595-9661 IMP
■ SYNTHES INC
(*Suby of* SYNTHES USA) ★
1302 Wrights Ln E, West Chester, PA 19380-3417
Tel (610) 647-9700 *Founded/Ownrshp* 2012
Sales 1.4MM^E *EMP* 7,003
SIC 3841 3842 6719 Surgical & medical instruments; Surgical appliances & supplies; Implants, surgical; Investment holding companies, except banks
Pr: Michel Orsinger
**CFO:* Robert Donohue
**Chf Cred:* Jeffrey Miller
**Ex VP:* Mark Pannenberg
**Sr VP:* Kurt Birchler
VP: Tim Davis
VP: Steve Dixon
VP: Lynn Malinoski
**VP:* Mike Stevens
VP: William Thiele
**VP:* Jon Verbiest
Dir Bus: Jim Hearn

SYNTHES USA
See DEPUY SYNTHES INC

D-U-N-S 07-939-1174
SYNTRON MATERIAL HANDLING LLC
2730 Highway 145, Saltillo, MS 38866-6814
Tel (662) 869-5711 *Founded/Ownrshp* 2014
Sales 144.3MM^E *EMP* 350^E
SIC 3532 Mining machinery
CEO: Tony Kurtz
Manager: Gina Wren

D-U-N-S 80-557-5110 IMP
▲ SYNUTRA INTERNATIONAL INC
2275 Res Blvd Ste 500, Rockville, MD 20850
Tel (301) 840-3888 *Founded/Ownrshp* 2004
Sales 365.0MM *EMP* 2,700^E
Tkr Sym SYUT *Exch* NGS
SIC 2023 Dietary supplements, dairy & non-dairy based; Powdered baby formula; Powdered milk
Ch Bd: Liang Zhang
Pr: Weiguo Zhang
CFO: Ning Cai
VP Prd: Xisen Mu
Sls Mgr: Jason Li

D-U-N-S 96-413-9047
SYOSSET CENTRAL SCHOOL DISTRICT
99 Pell Ln, Syosset, NY 11791-2902
Tel (516) 364-5600 *Founded/Ownrshp* 2010
Sales 27.7M *EMP* 1,500^E
Accts Koestner And Associates Llc S
SIC 8211 Public elementary & secondary schools
MIS Dir: Wing Lau
Teacher Pr: Jeanette Perrotta

D-U-N-S 00-959-4495 IMP
■ SYPRIS DATA SYSTEMS INC
(*Suby of* SYPRIS SOLUTIONS INC) ★
160 Via Verde, San Dimas, CA 91773-3901
Tel (909) 962-9400 *Founded/Ownrshp* 1997
Sales 287.4MM^E *EMP* 1,454
SIC 3572 3651 Computer tape drives & components; Tape recorders: cassette, cartridge or reel: household use
Pr: Darrell Robertson

D-U-N-S 55-549-1489 IMP
■ SYPRIS ELECTRONICS LLC
(*Suby of* SYPRIS SOLUTIONS INC) ★
10421 Univ Ctr Dr Ste 100, Tampa, FL 33612-6403
Tel (813) 972-6000 *Founded/Ownrshp* 1989
Sales 84.0MM^E *EMP* 425^E
SIC 3672 3679 Printed circuit boards; Electronic circuits
Ch Bd: Jeffrey T Gill
**Ch Bd:* Robert E Gill
**VP:* James M Long
VP: Robert G Marrah
IT Man: Glenn Schmidt
Software D: Howard Williams
VP Opers: Edmund Stuczynski
Sls Mgr: Jay Civitillo

D-U-N-S 14-847-9967
▲ SYPRIS SOLUTIONS INC
101 Bullitt Ln Ste 450, Louisville, KY 40222-5474
Tel (502) 329-2000 *Founded/Ownrshp* 1998
Sales 145.3MM *EMP* 735^E
Tkr Sym SYPR *Exch* NGM
SIC 3672 3679 3812 3674 3462 Printed circuit boards; Electronic circuits; Detection apparatus: electronic/magnetic field, light/heat; Semiconductors & related devices; Iron & steel forgings
Pr: Jeffrey T Gill
**Ch Bd:* Robert E Gill
CFO: Anthony C Allen
VP: Richard L Davis
VP: John R McGeeney
VP: John McGeeney
VP: John J Walsh
VP: John Walsh
IT Man: Glenn Schmidt
Mtls Mgr: Cliff Shepherd
Board of Directors: John F Brinkley, Gary L Convis, William G Ferko, R Scott Gill, William L Healey, Robert F Lentz, Sidney R Petersen, Robert Sroka

D-U-N-S 11-596-0189 IMP/EXP
■ SYPRIS TECHNOLOGIES INC
(*Suby of* SYPRIS SOLUTIONS INC) ★
2820 W Broadway, Louisville, KY 40211-1219
Tel (502) 774-6011 *Founded/Ownrshp* 1926
Sales 166.0MM^E *EMP* 840
SIC 3462 Iron & steel forgings; Automotive forgings, ferrous: crankshaft, engine, axle, etc.
Pr: Paul Larochelle
**CFO:* Jon Shellhaas
**Prin:* Jeffery T Gill

D-U-N-S 02-364-8566
SYRACUSE CITY SCHOOL DISTRICT
725 Harrison St, Syracuse, NY 13210-2395
Tel (315) 435-4499 *Founded/Ownrshp* 2010
Sales 197.4MM^E *EMP* 4,350^E
SIC 8211 Public elementary & secondary schools
CFO: Suzanne Slack
Bd of Dir: Monique C Wright-Williams
Dir: Michael C Schmidt
MIS Dir: Mary Killenbec
Schl Brd P: Kim Rohadfox-Ceaser

D-U-N-S 00-225-7350 IMP
SYRACUSE UNIVERSITY
SU
900 S Crouse Ave Ste 620, Syracuse, NY 13244-0001
Tel (315) 443-1870 *Founded/Ownrshp* 1870
Sales 513.5MM^E *EMP* 4,350
Accts Kpmg Llp Syracuse Ny
SIC 8221 University
**Pr:* Nancy Cantor
**Pr:* Dr Melvin A Eggers
Pr: Lavonda Reed
**Pr:* Eric Spina
Treas: Scott Kemp
**Treas:* William F Patrick
**Treas:* David Smith
**Treas:* Barbara Wells
Assoc VP: Sarah Scalese
VP: Sherburne B Abbott
VP: Kal Alston
VP: Rebecca R Kantrowitz
VP: Patrick Kelly
VP: Emanuel Mirabal
VP: Elizabeth O'Rourke
VP: Vanessa Salman
VP: Jeff Saltz
VP: Ryan Williams
Exec: Douglas Frank
Exec: Jeffrey Turner

D-U-N-S 83-221-8700 IMP
SYS-CON LLC
4444 Park Blvd, Montgomery, AL 36116-1634
Tel (334) 281-1520 *Founded/Ownrshp* 2002
Sales 150.0MM *EMP* 90
SIC 1541 Factory construction

SYSCA
See SH GROUP INC

D-U-N-S 03-150-6202
■ SYSCO ALBANY LLC
(*Suby of* SYSCO CORP) ★
1 Liebich Ln, Halfmoon, NY 12065-1421
Tel (518) 877-3200 *Founded/Ownrshp* 2012
Sales 267.6MM^E *EMP* 550^E
SIC 5149 5963 Canned goods: fruit, vegetables, seafood, meats, etc.; Food services, direct sales
CEO: Raymond Schiffer
VP: Wilfred Cartier
Dir IT: Ray Schiffer
VP Mktg: Bill Fleming
Mktg Dir: Christine Lorusso
Sls Mgr: Tom Teal

D-U-N-S 14-758-0989 IMP
■ SYSCO ASIAN FOODS INC
(*Suby of* SYSCO CORP) ★
1300 L Orient St, Saint Paul, MN 55117-3995
Tel (651) 558-2400 *Founded/Ownrshp* 2002
Sales 133.3MM^E *EMP* 332
SIC 5149 Groceries & related products
Pr: Kevin A Berg
**Pr:* Frank Hamel
COO: Tom Hietpas
Treas: Kirk G Drummond
Ex VP: Bradley P Dusto
VP: Darrell Clem
**VP:* Paul Hamel
Genl Mgr: Mike Neira
Telecom Ex: Dan Diamond
CIO: Scott Reynolds
CTO: Thomas Kesteloot

D-U-N-S 61-733-4172
■ SYSCO ATLANTA LLC
(*Suby of* SYSCO CORP) ★
2225 Riverdale Rd, College Park, GA 30337-5121
Tel (404) 765-9900 *Founded/Ownrshp* 1999
Sales 513.4MM^E *EMP* 680
SIC 5141 Groceries, general line
Pr: Gordon L Graham
**CFO:* Kirk W Vogeley
**Ex VP:* Joseph P Piazza
Ex VP: Joseph M Piazza
MIS Dir: Leroy McCreary
IT Man: Yolanda Longino
IT Man: Patrick Rodgers
Opers Mgr: Thom Etty
Mktg Mgr: Tim Duncan
Doctor: Lisa Waring

D-U-N-S 79-692-3449 IMP
■ SYSCO BALTIMORE LLC
(*Suby of* SYSCO CORP) ★
8000 Dorsey Run Rd, Jessup, MD 20794-9482
Tel (410) 799-7000 *Founded/Ownrshp* 1988
Sales 409.6MM^E *EMP* 700
SIC 5142 5149 5087 Packaged frozen goods; Canned goods: fruit, vegetables, seafood, meats, etc.; Restaurant supplies
Pr: Keith D Shapiro
CFO: Robert E Dlandstra
Bd of Dir: Rich Triolo
Ex VP: Steven Higgs
**Sr VP:* Don Tarwater
VP: Frank J Bowman
VP: James W Furlong
VP: Robert Jones
VP: Toni Watson
Prgrm Mgr: Brenda Williams
Genl Mgr: Steve Bergman

D-U-N-S 06-351-8054
■ SYSCO BARABOO LLC
(*Suby of* SYSCO CORP) ★
910 South Blvd, Baraboo, WI 53913-2723
Tel (800) 733-8217 *Founded/Ownrshp* 1970
Sales 207.7MM^E *EMP* 610
SIC 5141 5142 5046 5148 Groceries, general line; Fruits, frozen; Vegetables, frozen; Poultry, frozen: packaged; Restaurant equipment & supplies; Fresh fruits & vegetables
Pr: Robert A Jauch
Genl Pt: Terry Fedkenheuer
Ex VP: Bill Day
Ex VP: Robert Jauch
Sr VP: Chuck Staes
VP: Richard Abbey
VP: Gary Cullen
**VP:* June Lee
VP: Mark Palmer
Dir IT: Don Wilson
VP Opers: Ron Shanks

D-U-N-S 15-779-6251 IMP
■ SYSCO BOSTON LLC
(*Suby of* SYSCO CORP) ★
99 Spring St, Plympton, MA 02367-1701
Tel (781) 422-2300 *Founded/Ownrshp* 2002
Sales 471.7MM^E *EMP* 840^E
SIC 5149 Groceries & related products
Pr: Charles Fraser
VP: Leonard Horgan
VP: Leonard Horgan
VP: Joel Schafferman
VP: Mary Schumacher
Exec: Julia Gannon
Exec: Kimberly Letendre
Genl Mgr: Matthew Myers
CIO: Carol Chavers
CIO: Dave Kenney
Dir IT: Mark Dankert

D-U-N-S 03-561-2345
■ SYSCO CENTRAL ALABAMA INC
(*Suby of* SYSCO CORP) ★
1000 Sysco Dr, Calera, AL 35040-4992
Tel (205) 668-0001 *Founded/Ownrshp* 1996
Sales 171.2MM^E *EMP* 403
SIC 5149 5147 5142 5144 5143 Groceries & related products; Meats & meat products; Packaged frozen goods; Poultry & poultry products; Dairy products, except dried or canned
Ch Bd: Manny Fernandez
**Pr:* Tom Ben
**CEO:* Bill Delaney
CFO: Erica Herbert
**Ex VP:* Wallace Ralph
Ex VP: Ralph Wallace
**Sr VP:* Brian Beach
**Sr VP:* Greg Bertrand
**Sr VP:* Scott Charlton
**VP:* Bill Day
VP: Doug Vertein
Dir Risk M: Brian Metzler

D-U-N-S 79-912-6172
■ SYSCO CENTRAL FLORIDA INC
(*Suby of* SYSCO CORP) ★
200 W Story Rd, Ocoee, FL 34761-3004
Tel (407) 877-8500 *Founded/Ownrshp* 1989
Sales 208.8MM^E *EMP* 500
SIC 5149 Groceries & related products
Pr: Hank Varnell
**CFO:* Richard Matthews
VP: James M Danahy
VP: Bill Williams
Genl Mgr: Wendell Thompson
IT Man: Loida Garcia
VP Opers: Jerry Lamitie
VP Mktg: Clay Bloxom
VP Mktg: Brian Gunther
Mktg Dir: Barry Leff
Mktg Dir: Chris Swanson
Board of Directors: Louis Carlin

D-U-N-S 01-789-2373
■ SYSCO CENTRAL OHIO INC
(*Suby of* SYSCO CORP) ★
2400 Harrison Rd, Columbus, OH 43204-3508
Tel (614) 272-0658 *Founded/Ownrshp* 2002
Sales 90.5MM^E *EMP* 300
SIC 5141 5142 Groceries, general line; Packaged frozen goods
Pr: Debra Hamernick
CFO: Thomas Harkless
CFO: Chris Kreidler
Sr Cor Off: Lynn Zullo
Sr VP: Michael Haunert
VP: Charlie Anderson
VP: Mark Eggett
VP: Neil Peffer
Dir IT: William Jones
VP Opers: Rick Evans

D-U-N-S 09-957-2992
■ SYSCO CENTRAL TEXAS INC
(*Suby of* SYSCO CORP) ★
1260 Schwab Rd, New Braunfels, TX 78132-5155
Tel (830) 730-1000 *Founded/Ownrshp* 1991
Sales 221.8MM^E *EMP* 800
SIC 5141 Groceries, general line
Pr: Stephen D Higgs
**Sr VP:* Michael A Fuller
**VP:* Russell T Libby
**VP:* Gary M Walker
IT Man: Rebecca Dresch
VP Opers: Rudy Villanueva
VP Mktg: Terry Brooks
Sls Mgr: Bill Olivier

D-U-N-S 80-655-0604
■ SYSCO CHICAGO INC
(*Suby of* SYSCO CORP) ★
250 Wieboldt Dr, Des Plaines, IL 60016-3100
Tel (847) 699-5400 *Founded/Ownrshp* 1989
Sales 221.8MM^E *EMP* 670
SIC 5149 5142 Canned goods: fruit, vegetables, seafood, meats, etc.; Packaged frozen goods
Pr: Bill Delaney
**Ch Bd:* Manny Fernandez
CFO: Doug Boadway
CFO: Joel Grade
CFO: Michele Graves
**Treas:* Dianne Sanders
Ex VP: Donna Becker
**Ex VP:* Bill Day
**Ex VP:* Twila Day
**Sr VP:* Brian Beach
VP: Greg Bertrand
VP: Michael Furlong
VP: Bill Omara
VP: Charles Staes

D-U-N-S 12-236-0972
■ SYSCO CINCINNATI LLC
(*Suby of* SYSCO CORP) ★
10510 Evendale Dr, Cincinnati, OH 45241-2516
Tel (513) 563-6300 *Founded/Ownrshp* 2002
Sales 218.5MM^E *EMP* 483
SIC 5144 5149 5143 5113 Poultry & poultry products; Groceries & related products; Dairy products, except dried or canned; Industrial & personal service paper
Pr: Joseph P Calabrese
Pr: Dwuan Hamond
Ex Dir: Bill Puff
Rgnl Mgr: Jim Norris
Dir IT: Leia Aquino
Dir IT: Scott Bowling

Dir IT: Edward Poorbaugh
Dir IT: David Siemsen
IT Man: Mike Seamon
S&M/VP: Bill Cartier

D-U-N-S 08-456-7457
■ SYSCO COLUMBIA LLC
(*Suby of* SYSCO CORP) ★
131 Sysco Ct, Columbia, SC 29209-5143
Tel (803) 239-4000 *Founded/Ownrshp* 2001
Sales 221.8MM^E *EMP* 440
SIC 5141 5046 5142 5147 5148 Groceries, general line; Restaurant equipment & supplies; Packaged frozen goods; Meats, fresh; Fresh fruits & vegetables
CEO: Michael K Brawner
VP: Jesse Gonzales
Exec: Kevin Graef
Dir Risk M: Pete Garcia
Dir Risk M: Joseph Murry
Dir IT: Charles Denham
**Dir IT:* Bruce Matthews
Dir IT: Terry Plourde
Dir IT: Luis Solis
IT Man: Trevor Gibison
IT Man: Trevor Gibson

D-U-N-S 82-824-7457
■ SYSCO CONNECTICUT LLC
(*Suby of* SYSCO CORP) ★
100 Inwood Rd, Rocky Hill, CT 06067-3422
Tel (860) 571-5600 *Founded/Ownrshp* 2002
Sales 86.3MM^E *EMP* 136^E
SIC 5149 5142 Groceries & related products; Packaged frozen goods
CFO: Kristen Cutler
CFO: Kristin Kotler
VP: Alan Faneuf
VP: Walter Gill
VP: Jack Weaver
Exec: Maryann Rafferty
Genl Mgr: Craig Albert
Dir IT: Steve Pirok
Dir IT: Ayer Stephen
Dir IT: Roselyn Tubay
IT Man: Bill Hargrove

D-U-N-S 05-109-9661
▲ SYSCO CORP
1390 Enclave Pkwy, Houston, TX 77077-2099
Tel (281) 584-1390 *Founded/Ownrshp* 1970
Sales 50.3MMM *EMP* 51,900^E
Accts Ernst & Young Llp Houston Te
Tkr Sym SYY *Exch* NYS
SIC 5149 5142 5143 5144 5148 5137 Groceries & related products; Dried or canned foods; Beverages, except coffee & tea; Packaged frozen goods; Frozen fish, meat & poultry; Frozen vegetables & fruit products; Dairy products, except dried or canned; Poultry & poultry products; Fresh fruits & vegetables; Children's goods
CEO: William J Delaney
**Ch Bd:* Jackie M Ward
Pr: Thomas L Bene
CFO: Joel T Grade
Ex VP: Russell T Libby
Ex VP: Wayne R Shurts
Board of Directors: Nelson Peltz, Daniel J Brutto, Edward D Shirley, John M Cassaday, Richard G Tilghman, Judith B Craven, Joshua D Frank, Larry C Glasscock, Jonathan Golden, Joseph A Hafner Jr, Bradley M Halverson, Nancy S Newcomb

D-U-N-S 05-882-2289 IMP
■ SYSCO DETROIT LLC
(*Suby of* SYSCO CORP) ★
41600 Van Born Rd, Canton, MI 48188-2746
Tel (734) 397-7990 *Founded/Ownrshp* 1999
Sales 193.2MM^E *EMP* 700
SIC 5087 Restaurant supplies
CEO: Bill Delaney
Ex VP: Larry J Accardi
Ex VP: Thomas Barnes
**Ex VP:* Tom Ben
Ex VP: Kenneth J Carrig
Ex VP: Michael Green
Ex VP: John K Stubblefield
**Sr VP:* Brian Beach
Sr VP: James C Graham
Sr VP: James E Lankford
Sr VP: Andrew L Malcolm
Sr VP: Stephen F Smith
VP: Ted Behen
VP: Robert G Culak
VP: Gary W Cullen
VP: Mary B Moehring
VP: Brian M Sturgeon
VP: Robert C Thurber
VP: Thomas G Wason
VP: Craig G Watson

D-U-N-S 05-394-5259 EXP
■ SYSCO EASTERN MARYLAND LLC
LANKFORD - SYSCO FOOD SERVICES
(*Suby of* SYSCO CORP) ★
33239 Costen Rd, Pocomoke City, MD 21851-3909
Tel (410) 677-5555 *Founded/Ownrshp* 1964
Sales 230.4MM^E *EMP* 700
SIC 5141 Groceries, general line
Pr: Fred Lankford
**Pr:* Mike Gershenfeld
**Treas:* Diane Sanders
Ex VP: Dacia Lucas
**Ex VP:* William Tubb
**VP:* William D Byrd
VP: Kevin Hughes
CIO: Danny Byrd
CIO: Twila M Day

D-U-N-S 05-176-3969
■ SYSCO GRAND RAPIDS LLC
(*Suby of* SYSCO CORP) ★
3700 Sysco Ct Se, Grand Rapids, MI 49512-2043
Tel (616) 956-0700 *Founded/Ownrshp* 2000
Sales 3.4MMM^E *EMP* 47,800
SIC 5141 5087 Groceries, general line; Restaurant supplies
VP: Robert Yeager
CFO: Dwuan Hammond
VP: Brent Zomerlei

Sls&Mrk Ex: Laura Phars
VP Merchng: Randy Ruiter
Merch Mgr: Jim Hoekstra

D-U-N-S 03-720-4617 IMP
■ SYSCO GUEST SUPPLY LLC
GUEST SUPPLY SERVICES
(*Suby of* SYSCO CORP) ★
4301 Us Highway 1 Ste 300, Monmouth Junction, NJ 08852-1973
Tel (609) 514-9696 *Founded/Ownrshp* 2005
Sales 1.2MMM^E *EMP* 1,127
SIC 5122 2844 5131 5139 7011 8741 Toilet soap; Druggists' sundries; Shampoos, rinses, conditioners: hair; Toilet preparations; Mouthwashes; Sewing accessories; Hair accessories; Shoe accessories; Hotels; Casino hotel; Hotel or motel management
CEO: Clifford W Stanley
Ofcr: Yokaira Tejada
VP: R Bibe
VP: Susan Craig
VP: Tom David
VP: Craig Setter
VP: Dave M Shattuck
VP: Dave Shattuck
VP: Teri Unsworth
VP: Paul Xenis
Exec: Shirl Bingel

D-U-N-S 00-317-6880 IMP
■ SYSCO HAMPTON ROADS INC
(*Suby of* SYSCO CORP) ★
7000 Harbour View Blvd, Suffolk, VA 23435-2756
Tel (757) 399-2451 *Founded/Ownrshp* 1953, 1999
Sales 195.1MM^E *EMP* 490
SIC 5141 5147 5148 Groceries, general line; Lard; Fresh fruits & vegetables
Pr: John Hall
**Ch Bd:* Frederick Lanford
**CFO:* Michael S Larock
**Sr VP:* John Ehehalt
**Sr VP:* Steven C Houfek
VP: David Petray
Dir Risk M: Lauren Hayes
Genl Mgr: Kathy Sprague
Sales Exec: Horton Robby
Mktg Dir: Angie Isenhour

D-U-N-S 07-876-9604
■ SYSCO HOLDINGS LLC
(*Suby of* SYSCO CORP) ★
1390 Enclave Pkwy, Houston, TX 77077-2025
Tel (281) 584-1728 *Founded/Ownrshp* 2010
Sales 115.9MM^E *EMP* 1,550
SIC 5141 5142 5143 5144 5145 5146 Groceries, general line; Packaged frozen goods; Dairy products, except dried or canned; Poultry & poultry products; Confectionery; Fish & seafoods
Pr: Russell T Libby

D-U-N-S 79-912-6420
■ SYSCO INDIANAPOLIS LLC
(*Suby of* SYSCO CORP) ★
4000 W 62nd St, Indianapolis, IN 46268-2518
Tel (317) 291-2020 *Founded/Ownrshp* 1988
Sales 141.6MM^E *EMP* 300
SIC 5149 5046 5411 Groceries & related products; Commercial cooking & food service equipment; Grocery stores
Pr: Steve Neely
Manager: Roger Cain
Sales Asso: Terry Watts

D-U-N-S 80-920-1411 EXP
■ SYSCO INTERNATIONAL FOOD GROUP INC
(*Suby of* SYSCO CORP) ★
2401 Police Center Dr, Plant City, FL 33566-7139
Tel (813) 707-6161 *Founded/Ownrshp* 2004
Sales 323.0MM *EMP* 180^E
SIC 5144 5149 Poultry & poultry products; Groceries & related products
Pr: Lisa Aunspaugh
CFO: Chris Zarreke
VP: Henry Jimenez
Exec: Rob Ogilbee
Exec: Terry Reynoso
Genl Mgr: Tim Duncan
VP Sls: Mark Spengler

D-U-N-S 80-516-6964
■ SYSCO IOWA INC
(*Suby of* SYSCO CORP) ★
1 Sysco Dr, Ankeny, IA 50021-3911
Tel (515) 289-5300 *Founded/Ownrshp* 1988
Sales 95.0MM^E *EMP* 283
SIC 5149 5147 5142 5144 5113 5143 Dried or canned foods; Canned goods: fruit, vegetables, seafood, meats, etc.; Meats, fresh; Packaged frozen goods; Meat, frozen: packaged; Dinners, frozen; Poultry: live, dressed or frozen (unpackaged); Industrial & personal service paper; Disposable plates, cups, napkins & eating utensils; Dairy products, except dried or canned
Pr: Jolly Henry P
**Pr:* Suzanne Spack
**Treas:* Kathy Oates Gish
**Treas:* Libby T Russell
VP: Ron Dillon
Genl Mgr: Wayne Baumhover
Genl Mgr: Kim Hermanson
VP Mktg: Corey Brown

D-U-N-S 82-534-6534
■ SYSCO JACKSON LLC
(*Suby of* SYSCO CORP) ★
4400 Milwaukee St, Jackson, MS 39209-2636
Tel (601) 354-1701 *Founded/Ownrshp* 2002
Sales 116.1MM^E *EMP* 133^E
SIC 5142 Packaged frozen goods
Pr: Mark Scheamacchia
IT Man: George Futris
Mktg Dir: Brian Carlew
Sls Mgr: Fred Ferguson

D-U-N-S 79-912-6271 IMP/EXP
■ SYSCO JACKSONVILLE INC
(*Suby of* SYSCO CORP) ★
1501 Lewis Industrial Dr, Jacksonville, FL 32254-1697
Tel (904) 781-5070 *Founded/Ownrshp* 1992
Sales 132.6MM^E *EMP* 325
SIC 5149 5147 5144 5963 Groceries & related products; Meats & meat products; Poultry & poultry products; Food service, coffee-cart
Pr: Rick Rawald
Ex VP: Roy Hockenbrocht
**VP:* Thomas P Kurz
Genl Mgr: Gregory Lee
IT Man: Chris Albury
VP Sls: Don Wilson
Sls Mgr: David Litaker

D-U-N-S 00-696-6030
■ SYSCO KANSAS CITY INC (MO)
(*Suby of* SYSCO CORP) ★
1915 E Kansas City Rd, Olathe, KS 66061-5858
Tel (913) 829-5555 *Founded/Ownrshp* 1924, 1975
Sales 312.4MM^E *EMP* 750
SIC 5149 5141 Groceries & related products; Groceries, general line
Pr: Bill Delaney
**CFO:* Mark Daubert
**CFO:* David Knecht
**Ch:* Manny Fernandez
**Ex VP:* Troy Vesp
VP: Patricia Chase
**VP:* Terri Couture
**VP:* Doug Kramer
Exec: Linda Jacobson
Exec: Mary Johnson
CTO: Ron Groen

D-U-N-S 78-532-7743 IMP/EXP
■ SYSCO LOS ANGELES INC
(*Suby of* SYSCO CORP) ★
20701 Currier Rd, Walnut, CA 91789-2904
Tel (909) 595-9595 *Founded/Ownrshp* 1988
Sales 221.8MM^E *EMP* 1,000
SIC 5141 5084 Groceries, general line; Food industry machinery
CEO: Daniel S Haag
**Ex VP:* Sal Adelberg
Ex VP: Saul Adelsberg
**Sr VP:* John KAO
VP: Dana Anderson
VP: Mary Brumbaugh
VP: Andy Moreno
VP: Joseph Peccoralo
VP: Angela Phillips
Exec: Brunson Achiu
Admn Mgr: Betty Lawrence

D-U-N-S 00-799-2787
■ SYSCO LOUISVILLE INC (DE)
(*Suby of* SYSCO CORP) ★
7705 National Tpke, Louisville, KY 40214-4803
Tel (502) 367-6131 *Founded/Ownrshp* 1901
Sales 168.7MM^E *EMP* 400^E
SIC 5141 Groceries, general line
Pr: Steve Hocker
**CFO:* Lisa Bowling
Treas: William J Delaney III
**VP:* Barbara Green
VP: Steven Hocker
Software D: Jim Martel

D-U-N-S 00-385-5640 IMP
■ SYSCO METRO NEW YORK LLC
(*Suby of* SYSCO CORP) ★
20 Theodore Conrad Dr, Jersey City, NJ 07305-4614
Tel (201) 451-0997 *Founded/Ownrshp* 1922
Sales 270.4MM^E *EMP* 530
SIC 5141 5144 5142 5147 5087 Groceries, general line; Poultry products; Eggs; Packaged frozen goods; Meats & meat products; Restaurant supplies
Pr: Phillip Lahm
**Pr:* Mike Scanlon
**Ex VP:* Frank S Recine
**VP:* Karen Casey
**VP:* Dean Nichols
IT Man: David Pearson
Opers Mgr: Bobby Heims
S&M/VP: Linda Oshea
S&M/VP: Frank Recine

D-U-N-S 19-144-6525
■ SYSCO MINNESOTA INC
(*Suby of* SYSCO CORP) ★
2400 County Road J, Saint Paul, MN 55112-4507
Tel (763) 785-9000 *Founded/Ownrshp* 2007
Sales 170.7MM^E *EMP* 480
SIC 5141 5812 5813 Groceries, general line; Eating places; Drinking places
Pr: Timothy K Hogan
CFO: William J Delaney
**CFO:* Scott Sterling
Ex VP: Debbie Hammermick
VP: Ferris Kelly
VP: Nancy Pickel
Exec: Noah Barton
Exec: Scott McGuire
Telecom Ex: Laurie Santos
Dir IT: Scott Kerfoot
Sfty Mgr: Peter Leppi

D-U-N-S 82-507-2960
■ SYSCO MONTANA INC
(*Suby of* SYSCO CORP) ★
1509 Monad Rd, Billings, MT 59101-3229
Tel (406) 247-1100 *Founded/Ownrshp* 1988
Sales 177.8MM^E *EMP* 450
SIC 5149 5142 5141 Groceries & related products; Packaged frozen goods; Groceries, general line
Pr: Patrick H Burton
Ex VP: William Zink
VP: Steve Bodden
Dir IT: Eric Brubaker
IT Man: Jerry Ross
IT Man: Diana Stein
IT Man: Bin Yang
VP Opers: Bob Taylor
Opers Mgr: Keith Caswell
Sls&Mrk Ex: Chuck Verbeck
VP Sls: Michael Morrison

D-U-N-S 05-915-8634
■ SYSCO NASHVILLE LLC
ROBERT ORR SYSCO
(*Suby of* SYSCO CORP) ★
1 Hermitage Plz, Nashville, TN 37209-1002
Tel (615) 350-7100 *Founded/Ownrshp* 1972
Sales 223.9MM^E *EMP* 600
SIC 5142 5149 Frozen vegetables & fruit products; Frozen fish, meat & poultry; Cooking oils & shortenings; Pet foods
CEO: Nicholas Taras
CFO: John Gentile
Ex VP: William J Delaney III
VP: Rennie Askew
VP: Bar Ivy
VP: Jim Kennedy
VP: Craig Watson
Dir IT: Jim Gentry
Dir IT: Larry Woodward
S&M/VP: John Howard

D-U-N-S 60-583-9377 IMP
■ SYSCO NEW MEXICO LLC
(*Suby of* SYSCO CORP) ★
601 Comanche Rd Ne, Albuquerque, NM 87107-4103
Tel (505) 761-1200 *Founded/Ownrshp* 2002
Sales 96.3MM^E *EMP* 344
SIC 5141 Groceries, general line
CEO: Bill Delaney
Ch Bd: Jackie L Ward
Pr: Tom Bene
COO: John Schwenke
Sr VP: Brian Beach
Sr VP: Greg Bertrand
VP: Frank Casner
VP: Mike Hammond
VP: David Hester
VP: Kelly Price
Dir IT: John Castro

D-U-N-S 07-955-7971
■ SYSCO NEWPORT MEAT CO
(*Suby of* SYSCO CORP) ★
16691 Hale Ave, Irvine, CA 92606-5025
Tel (949) 399-4200 *Founded/Ownrshp* 1976, 1999
Sales 167.6MM^E *EMP* 227
SIC 5147 5142 Meats, fresh; Packaged frozen goods
CEO: Timothy K Hussman
**CFO:* Denise Van Voorhis
VP: Michael Drury
VP: Chuck McDaniel
Genl Mgr: Pollyann Thomas
VP Sls: Patrick Singer

D-U-N-S 06-636-5784
■ SYSCO NORTH TEXAS
(*Suby of* SYSCO USA I INC) ★
800 Trinity Dr, Lewisville, TX 75056-5297
Tel (469) 384-6000 *Founded/Ownrshp* 1970
Sales 600.9MM^E *EMP* 685
SIC 5141 Groceries, general line
Pr: Hank Warnel
**CFO:* Carlos Reyes
CFO: Scott Sterling
VP: Don Connell
VP: Margie McAllister
IT Man: Thomas Huffhines
IT Man: Ben Porras
Sls Dir: Brian Weale
Mktg Mgr: Lindsay Insinga

D-U-N-S 01-966-1466
■ SYSCO NORTHERN NEW ENGLAND INC
(*Suby of* SYSCO CORP) ★
55 Thomas Dr, Westbrook, ME 04092-3825
Tel (207) 871-0700 *Founded/Ownrshp* 1975
Sales 250.0MM^E *EMP* 400
SIC 5141 5147 5148 5142 Groceries, general line; Meats & meat products; Fresh fruits & vegetables; Packaged frozen goods
CEO: Gregory E Otterbein
**Pr:* Ralph Freije
**CFO:* John Rodrigue
VP: Tom Mannett
**VP:* Dain Thomason
Exec: Ken Newsome
**Prin:* Rob Huether
Genl Mgr: Brian Turner
VP Opers: Rick Jordan
**VP Sls:* William Clark
S&M/VP: Doug Voter

D-U-N-S 00-791-4435 IMP
■ SYSCO PHILADELPHIA LLC
(*Suby of* SYSCO CORP) ★
600 Packer Ave, Philadelphia, PA 19148-5304
Tel (215) 218-1348 *Founded/Ownrshp* 1922
Sales 315.7MM^E *EMP* 500
SIC 5149 Groceries & related products
Pr: William G Tubb
COO: Fredrick Casinelli
CFO: William Mastrosimone
Sr VP: Scott W Barrows
VP: Rajasekhar Gummadapu
VP: Michael Vargason
VP: Ira Wilson
VP Opers: James Froant
Sfty Mgr: Charles Kern
Opers Mgr: Samuel Fowler Jr
Sales Exec: Steven Kane

D-U-N-S 01-494-7360 IMP
■ SYSCO PITTSBURGH LLC
(*Suby of* SYSCO CORP) ★
1 Whitney Dr, Harmony, PA 16037
Tel (724) 452-2100 *Founded/Ownrshp* 1986
Sales 118.5MM^E *EMP* 300
SIC 5142 5149 5148 5023 5113 5046 Meat, frozen: packaged; Groceries & related products; Fresh fruits & vegetables; Kitchenware; Towels, paper; Napkins, paper; Paper & products, wrapping or coarse; Commercial cooking & food service equipment
Pr: Bill Delaney
Ch Bd: Manny Fernandez
Sr VP: Brian Beach
Sr VP: Greg Bertrand
Sr VP: Bob Davis
IT Man: David Bednar

D-U-N-S 82-507-7134
■ **SYSCO PORTLAND INC**
(Suby of SYSCO CORP) ★
26250 Sw Parkway Ctr Dr, Wilsonville, OR 97070-9606
Tel (503) 682-8700 Founded/Ownrshp 1988
Sales 275.7MM^E EMP 500
SIC 5141 5046 Groceries, general line; Restaurant equipment & supplies
Pr: John Nolan
*CFO: Greg Wolfe
VP: Trisha Ferris
*VP: John Ristler
VP: Scott Sonnemaker
VP: Gregory Wolfe
Exec: Mike Nguyen
Genl Mgr: Amy Barnes
CIO: Rob Wolters
VP Opers: Van Hooper
Sls&Mrk Ex: Bobbie McDonald

D-U-N-S 07-905-1723 EXP
■ **SYSCO SACRAMENTO INC** (DE)
(Suby of SYSCO CORP) ★
7062 Pacific Ave, Pleasant Grove, CA 95668-9731
Tel (916) 275-2714 Founded/Ownrshp 2000
Sales 221.8MM^E EMP 393
SIC 5141 5142 Groceries, general line; Packaged frozen goods
Ch Bd: Jackie L Ward
*Pr: Bill Delaney
Pr: Delmer Schnuelle
*Ex VP: Tom Bene
Ex VP: Delmar Schnelly
*Sr VP: Brian Beach
*Sr VP: Greg Bertrand
Sr VP: Joe Brodie
Sr VP: Mark Tuttle
VP: Jim Gentry
VP: Gloria Tzintzun
Exec: Robert Smith
Dir Bus: Dave Riccio

D-U-N-S 04-035-6060 IMP/EXP
■ **SYSCO SAN DIEGO INC**
(Suby of SYSCO CORP) ★
12180 Kirkham Rd, Poway, CA 92064-6879
Tel (858) 513-7300 Founded/Ownrshp 1996
Sales 221.8MM^E EMP 370
SIC 5141 5142 5147 5148 5084 Groceries, general line; Packaged frozen goods; Meats & meat products; Fresh fruits & vegetables; Food industry machinery
CEO: Kevin Mangan
Pr: Howard Poole
*VP: Debra Morey
IT Man: Jeff Orton
Mktg Dir: Brian Hughes
Sls Mgr: Summer Duggins

D-U-N-S 05-304-6025 EXP
■ **SYSCO SAN FRANCISCO INC**
(Suby of SYSCO CORP) ★
5900 Stewart Ave, Fremont, CA 94538-3134
Tel (510) 226-3000 Founded/Ownrshp 1939
Sales 434.8MM^E EMP 650
SIC 5141 5147 5142 Groceries, general line; Meats, fresh; Packaged frozen goods
Pr: James Ehlers
*VP: Bruce Luong
VP: Randy Timmer
MIS Dir: Mark Jones
Sys/Mgr: David Wong
Oper/Dir: Eugine Kendig
Sls&Mrk Ex: Scott Yelle
VP Sls: Don Chen

D-U-N-S 83-556-8965 EXP
■ **SYSCO SEATTLE INC**
(Suby of SYSCO CORP) ★
22820 54th Ave S, Kent, WA 98032-4898
Tel (206) 622-2261 Founded/Ownrshp 1988
Sales 294.9MM^E EMP 650
SIC 5142 5141 Packaged frozen goods; Groceries, general line
Prin: Bill Delaney
Treas: Douglas R Madison
VP: Ken Christie
VP: Kris Rubino
Brnch Mgr: Lori Laney
Genl Mgr: Tim Tauscheck
Dir IT: Sean Padgen
VP Opers: Corey Hess
Opers Mgr: Tom Fox
VP Mktg: Goeff Lieberman
VP Merchng: Kevin Sloan

D-U-N-S 19-484-5012 IMP/EXP
■ **SYSCO SOUTH FLORIDA INC**
(Suby of SYSCO CORP) ★
12500 Nw 112th Ave, Medley, FL 33178-1055
Tel (305) 651-5421 Founded/Ownrshp 1969
Sales 221.8MM^E EMP 600
SIC 5149 5147 5142 5113 5143 5144 Dried or canned foods; Meats, fresh; Packaged frozen goods; Disposable plates, cups, napkins & eating utensils; Dairy products, except dried or canned; Poultry & poultry products
Pr: Thomas C Crytser
Pr: Emery Smith
*CFO: Paula Kramer
Sr Cor Off: Tim Brown
VP: Claude Boisson
*VP: Barbara B Green
*VP: Thomas P Kurz
Exec: Thomas Clark
VP Admn: La G D Riker
CIO: Rob Wolters
CTO: Nancy Merryman

D-U-N-S 12-294-8750 IMP/EXP
■ **SYSCO SOUTHEAST FLORIDA LLC**
(Suby of SYSCO CORP) ★
1999 Dr M Lthr Kng Jr Bld Martin, Riviera Beach, FL 33404
Tel (561) 842-1999 Founded/Ownrshp 1999
Sales 187.4MM^E EMP 440
SIC 5149 Groceries & related products
Pr: Glenn Boies
CFO: Steven Seale
Dir IT: Robert Boucher
Opers Mgr: Jim Lissy
VP Mktg: Billy Gunst
Sls Mgr: John Adams

D-U-N-S 16-846-6451
■ **SYSCO SPOKANE INC**
(Suby of SYSCO CORP) ★
300 N Baugh Way, Post Falls, ID 83854-5224
Tel (208) 777-9511 Founded/Ownrshp 2004
Sales 94.6MM^E EMP 200
SIC 5046 5141 Restaurant equipment & supplies; Groceries, general line
Pr: Layton Rosencrance
*CFO: Greg Wolfe
*Ch: Scott Sonnemaker
*Treas: Mike Nguyen
Sr VP: Thomas Shaeffer

D-U-N-S 82-507-2820
■ **SYSCO ST LOUIS LLC**
(Suby of SYSCO CORP) ★
3850 Mueller Rd, Saint Charles, MO 63301-8042
Tel (636) 940-9230 Founded/Ownrshp 1970
Sales 155.8MM^E EMP 285
SIC 5141 5149 5146 5143 5142 Groceries, general line; Groceries & related products; Fish & seafoods; Dairy products, except dried or canned; Packaged frozen goods
CEO: Bill Delaney
*Ch Bd: Jackie L Ward
*Sr VP: Brian Beach
*Sr VP: Greg Bertrand
*VP: Tom Ben
Genl Mgr: Tom Potzman
IT Man: Dave Marstall
VP Opers: Rick Evans
Opers Mgr: Allen Scarff
Mktg Dir: John Pumphrey
Sls Mgr: Mark Boxdorfer

D-U-N-S 11-235-9922
■ **SYSCO SYRACUSE LLC**
(Suby of SYSCO CORP) ★
2508 Warners Rd, Warners, NY 13164-9707
Tel (315) 672-7000 Founded/Ownrshp 1970
Sales 177.4MM^E EMP 520
SIC 5141 Groceries, general line
Pr: Chuck Fraser
CFO: Robert S Laurie Jr
VP: Linda Oshea
Exec: Regina Lagattuta
Genl Mgr: Michele Williams
IT Man: Tom Neave
VP Sls: Phillip Campolo
VP Sls: Linda O'Shea

D-U-N-S 96-817-1160 IMP
■ **SYSCO USA I INC**
(Suby of SYSCO CORP) ★
1390 Enclave Pkwy, Houston, TX 77077-2025
Tel (281) 584-1390 Founded/Ownrshp 2010
Sales 600.9MM^E EMP 690
SIC 5141 5142 5143 5144 5145 5146 Groceries, general line; Packaged frozen goods; Dairy products, except dried or canned; Poultry & poultry products; Confectionery; Fish & seafoods
Pr: Michael W Green
CFO: Stephen P Harris
*VP: G Mitchell Elmer

D-U-N-S 07-881-7720
■ **SYSCO USA II LLC**
(Suby of SYSCO CORP) ★
1390 Enclave Pkwy, Houston, TX 77077-2025
Tel (281) 584-1390 Founded/Ownrshp 2010
Sales 134.9MM^E EMP 324^E
SIC 5141 5143 5144 5145 5146 Groceries, general line; Dairy products, except dried or canned; Poultry & poultry products; Confectionery; Fish & seafoods
Pr: Bill Delaney
*Ch Bd: Jackie L Ward
*Pr: Tom Bene
*Pr: Mike Green
*VP: Brian Beach

D-U-N-S 02-376-3451
■ **SYSCO VIRGINIA LLC**
(Suby of SYSCO CORP) ★
5081 S Valley Pike, Rockingham, VA 22801-3932
Tel (540) 434-0761 Founded/Ownrshp 1970
Sales 170.0MM^E EMP 400
SIC 5149 5142 5113 5148 5147 5143 Dried or canned foods; Beverages, except coffee & tea; Soft drinks; Packaged frozen goods; Napkins, paper; Eating utensils, disposable plastic; Fruits, fresh; Vegetables, fresh; Meats, fresh; Dairy products, except dried or canned
Pr: Dave Kraft
*CFO: Scott Blackshaw
VP Bus Dev: Dominick Launi
Genl Mgr: Sarah Amos
Genl Mgr: Mary Long
DP Dir: Scott King
DP Dir: Helen Link

D-U-N-S 92-932-3939 IMP
■ **SYSCO WEST COAST FLORIDA INC**
(Suby of SYSCO CORP) ★
3000 69th St E, Palmetto, FL 34221-8440
Tel (941) 721-1450 Founded/Ownrshp 1995
Sales 225.7MM^E EMP 600^E
SIC 5149 5141 Canned goods: fruit, vegetables, seafood, meats, etc.; Dried or canned foods; Groceries, general line
Pr: Larry L Koelsch
*Pr: Ned Solomon
*CFO: Matthew C Lange
Ex VP: Timothy L Duncan
Ex VP: Timothy Duncan
Ex VP: Mike Green
*VP: Michael Johnson
Genl Mgr: Hunter Lankford
Genl Mgr: Jason Wallen
IT Man: Joe Thiel
VP Mktg: Mike Birnbam

D-U-N-S 02-679-6367
■ **SYSCO WEST TEXAS INC**
(Suby of SYSCO CORP) ★
714 2nd Pl, Lubbock, TX 79401-1502
Tel (806) 747-2678 Founded/Ownrshp 2000
Sales 102.5MM^E EMP 200
SIC 5146 5147 Fish & seafoods; Meats & meat products
Pr: Michael Davis
*Treas: Kathy Oates Gish
*VP: Thomas P Kurz
*VP: Russell T Libby
VP: Fred Steck
*VP: Billy Watson
Mktg Mgr: Greg Sield

D-U-N-S 07-874-0500
■ **SYSCO WESTERN MINNESOTA INC**
APPERT'S FOODSERVICE
(Suby of SYSCO CORP) ★
900 Highway 10 S, Saint Cloud, MN 56304-1824
Tel (320) 251-3200 Founded/Ownrshp 2012
Sales 125.8MM^E EMP 300
SIC 5141 5142 5143 5144 5145 5146 Groceries, general line; Packaged frozen goods; Dairy products, except dried or canned; Poultry & poultry products; Confectionery; Fish & seafoods
CEO: Michael G Pilkington
Genl Mgr: Ray Meyer
VP Opers: Tim Devins
VP Mktg: Brian Preusser
Manager: Jerry Cheney
Doctor: Kathy Kirchner

D-U-N-S 00-496-2155
SYSKA HENNESSY GROUP INC (NY)
(Suby of SYSCA) ★
1515 Broadway Fl 14, New York, NY 10036-5709
Tel (212) 921-2300 Founded/Ownrshp 1933, 2005
Sales 100.4MM^E EMP 500
SIC 8711 Consulting engineer
Ch Bd: Cyrus Izzo
CFO: Robert Discone
VP: Mark Etheridge
VP: Robert Geremia
VP: Jerry Hartford
VP: Daniel H Nall
VP: Victor Steffen
Genl Couns: Benyacar Michelle

D-U-N-S 02-186-0424 IMP
SYSMEX AMERICA INC
(Suby of SYSMEX CORPORATION)
577 Aptakisic Rd, Lincolnshire, IL 60069-4325
Tel (847) 996-4500 Founded/Ownrshp 1974
Sales 303.0MM^E EMP 700
SIC 5047 3841 Instruments, surgical & medical; Medical instruments & equipment, blood & bone work
Pr: John Kershaw
CFO: Jeffrey Black
CFO: Alex Garini
Ex VP: Robert Degnan
Ex VP: Andre Ezers
VP: David Arms
VP: Rebecca Ballenger
VP: Peter Benzinger
VP: David Boyer
VP: Robert E Degnan
VP: Bearet Edgarton
VP: Brad Kaiser
VP: Cailin Kolk
VP: Travis Lossing
VP: Jim Mueller
VP: Craig Nekali
VP: Rey Recinto
VP: Greg Reinwald
VP: Stanley Rolon
VP: Peter E Shearstone
VP: Vaughn Smith

D-U-N-S 18-326-3169
SYSPRO IMPACT SOFTWARE INC
959 S Coast Dr Ste 100, Costa Mesa, CA 92626-1786
Tel (714) 437-1000 Founded/Ownrshp 1991
Sales 107.1MM^E EMP 200
SIC 5045 7372 7371 Computer software; Prepackaged software; Custom computer programming services
CEO: Brian Stein
*Pr: Joey Benadretti
Netwrk Mgr: Jeff Arbuckle
Pr Mgr: Stan Goodrich
Mktg Mgr: Odete Passingham
Sls Mgr: Mike Davies

D-U-N-S 00-980-5326
SYSTEM ELECTRIC CO
704 Central Pkwy E # 1200, Plano, TX 75074-5537
Tel (972) 422-2665 Founded/Ownrshp 2013
Sales 102.0MM^E EMP 500
Accts Maryanov Madsen Gordon & Campb
SIC 1731 General electrical contractor
Pr: Jim Gomes
*CFO: Josh Edwards
*Treas: John Gomes
*Ex VP: Michael Gomes
VP: Rudy Moreno

D-U-N-S 08-555-7056
■ **SYSTEM ENERGY RESOURCES INC**
(Suby of ENTERGY CORP) ★
1340 Echelon Pkwy Ste 100, Jackson, MS 39213-8210
Tel (601) 368-5000 Founded/Ownrshp 1974
Sales 632.4MM EMP 4
Accts Deloitte & Touche Llp New Or
SIC 4911 Generation, electric power
Ch Bd: Theodore H Bunting Jr
*CFO: Andrew S Marsh
Ex VP: Marcus V Brown
Sr VP: Alyson M Mount

D-U-N-S 80-587-6856
SYSTEM ONE HOLDINGS LLC
12 Federal St Ste 205, Pittsburgh, PA 15212-5753
Tel (412) 995-1900 Founded/Ownrshp 2007
Sales 306.2MM^E EMP 2,745
SIC 7361 Employment agencies
CEO: Troy Gregory
Pr: Kevin Goss
*COO: Greg Lignelli
*CFO: Dan Moran
*Ex VP: Tim Bosse
*Ex VP: Mark Fenske
Dir IT: Dana Leone
Dir IT: Dana Murphy
Sfty Dirs: Pamela S Kincaid
Opers Mgr: David Book
Opers Mgr: John Brenner

D-U-N-S 04-036-5652
SYSTEM PARKING INC
(Suby of PARKING SERVICE INC) ★
180 N La Salle St # 1700, Chicago, IL 60601-2501
Tel (312) 819-5050 Founded/Ownrshp 1994
Sales 44.1MM^E EMP 1,200
SIC 7521 Parking garage; Parking lots
Pr: Thomas P Phillips
*Sec: John Phillips
*VP: Dennis Quinn

D-U-N-S 01-069-2338 IMP/EXP
SYSTEM SENSOR LTD
3825 Ohio Ave, Saint Charles, IL 60174-5465
Tel (630) 377-6674 Founded/Ownrshp 1984
Sales 299.1MM^E EMP 2,000
SIC 3669

D-U-N-S 07-339-8414
SYSTEM SOFTWARE ASSOCIATES INC DEL
SSA
500 W Madison St Ste 1600, Chicago, IL 60661-4555
Tel (312) 258-6000 Founded/Ownrshp 1985
Sales 40.8MM^E EMP 1,500^E
SIC 7372 7373 Application computer software; Business oriented computer software; Computer-aided engineering (CAE) systems service
Ch Bd: Robert R Carpenter
Dir IT: Walter Pecile

D-U-N-S 79-933-1392
SYSTEM STUDIES & SIMULATION INC
S3
615 Discovery Dr Nw, Huntsville, AL 35806-2801
Tel (256) 539-1700 Founded/Ownrshp 1992
Sales 84.5MM^E EMP 448
SIC 3761 7379 8711 Guided missiles & space vehicles; Computer related maintenance services; Engineering services
CEO: Jan Smith
*Pr: Tom Houser
*CFO: Suzanne Ryan
CFO: Srinivas Srini
Ofcr: Gerald Burton
Ofcr: Frank Millerd
Ofcr: Robert Simpson
Sr VP: John Briggs
*Sr VP: Bob Johnson
*Sr VP: Mike Moody
Prgrm Mgr: Curtis Ballard

SYSTEM TWT TRANSPORTATION
See TRANS-SYSTEM INC

SYSTEMAX
See SYX DISTRIBUTION INC

D-U-N-S 88-447-5039
▲ **SYSTEMAX INC**
11 Harbor Park Dr, Port Washington, NY 11050-4656
Tel (516) 608-7000 Founded/Ownrshp 1949
Sales 1.8MMM EMP 3,300
Tkr Sym SYX Exch NYS
SIC 5961 5046 Catalog & mail-order houses; Computers & peripheral equipment, mail order; Commercial equipment; Shelving, commercial & industrial; Lockers, not refrigerated
Pr: Lawrence Reinhold
Ch Bd: Richard Leeds
Pr: John Marrah
CEO: Perminder Dale
CFO: Steven Goldschein
V Ch Bd: Bruce Leeds
Chf Mktg O: Shawn Lamb
Ex VP: Rajesh Seth
Ex VP: Adam W Shaffer
Ex VP: Richard Wallet
Sr VP: Eric Lerner
VP: Thomas Axmacher
VP: Leslie Biggs
VP: Erika Pap
VP: Ben White
Board of Directors: Stacy Dick, Marie Adler-Kravecas, Robert Rosenthal

SYSTEMAX RETAIL SALES
See TIGERDIRECT INC

D-U-N-S 96-272-3722
SYSTEMS & SERVICES TECHNOLOGIES INC
SST
(Suby of EXPERT GLOBAL SOLUTIONS INC) ★
4315 Pickett Rd, Saint Joseph, MO 64503-1600
Tel (800) 392-8308 Founded/Ownrshp 2002
Sales 47.3MM^E EMP 1,200
SIC 7374 Data processing & preparation
Pr: John J Chappell
IT Man: Dennis Peterson
Sales Exec: Rick Moffett

D-U-N-S 00-626-5466 IMP
SYSTEMS DRS SUSTAINMENT INC
DRS TECHNOLOGIES
(Suby of DRS TECHNOLOGIES INC) ★
201 Evans Ln, Saint Louis, MO 63121-1126
Tel (314) 553-4000 Founded/Ownrshp 1940, 2006
Sales 351.3MM^E EMP 1,100
SIC 3715 3537 3812 3829 3769 Semitrailers for missile transportation; Aircraft loading hoists; Radar systems & equipment; Measuring & controlling devices; Guided missile & space vehicle parts & auxiliary equipment
Pr: Daniel A Rodriquez
VP: Mattia Cavanna
VP: Shane Hegarty
*VP: Steven J Landmenin

Prin: Richard A Schneider
Snr Sftwr: Matthew Blevins
Dir IT: Angala Boyd
Dir IT: Natalie Hegarty
IT Man: John Luecking
Board of Directors: Robert F Mehmel, Mark S Newman

D-U-N-S 12-656-4801
SYSTEMS ELECTRO COATING LLC
253 Old Jackson Rd, Madison, MS 39110-9485
Tel (601) 407-2340 *Founded/Ownrshp* 2001
Sales 106.7MM *EMP* 60
Accts Horne Llp Ridgeland Mississi
SIC 3479 Coating of metals & formed products
COO: James M Cguffie

SYSTEMS GROUP, THE
See SYSTEMS PLANT SERVICES INC

D-U-N-S 78-304-4597
■ SYSTEMS MADE SIMPLE INC
(*Suby of* LEIDOS HOLDINGS INC) ★
149 Northern Concourse # 1, Syracuse, NY 13212-6000
Tel (315) 455-3200 *Founded/Ownrshp* 2016
Sales 335.1MM *EMP* 430^E
SIC 7371 8742 Computer software systems analysis & design, custom; Computer software development; Hospital & health services consultant
Pr: Albert M Nardslico
* *COO:* Ronald S Fishbeck
* *CFO:* Christopher Roberts
* *Chf Mktg O:* Viet Nguyen
* *Ex VP:* Robert Sheahan
VP: Charles De Sanno
VP: Gina Gallagher
VP Admn: Paul Stevens
* *CIO:* Ezra H Oyer
VP Opers: Matthew Wilson

D-U-N-S 11-335-4021
SYSTEMS PLANT SERVICES INC
SYSTEMS GROUP, THE
214 N Wa Ave Ste 700, El Dorado, AR 71730-5659
Tel (870) 862-1315 *Founded/Ownrshp* 2014
Sales 195.8MM^E *EMP* 450
SIC 1629 Industrial plant construction
* *Pr:* Lee Morgan
* *COO:* Michael S Hays
* *VP:* George Maguire
CTO: Jonathan Taylor

D-U-N-S 02-773-9028 IMP/EXP
SYSTEMS SERVICES OF AMERICA INC
SSA PHOENIX
(*Suby of* SERVICES GROUP OF AMERICA INC) ★
1640 S 39th Ave, Phoenix, AZ 85009-6114
Tel (480) 927-4700 *Founded/Ownrshp* 2001
Sales 536.1MM^E *EMP* 450
SIC 5147 5113 5142 5149 5143 Meats, fresh; Meats, cured or smoked; Disposable plates, cups, napkins & eating utensils; Boxes & containers; Packaged frozen goods; Groceries & related products; Dairy products, except dried or canned
Pr: Timothy Holland
* *VP:* Brad Parker
* *VP:* Steve Twist
Natl Sales: Elizabeth Blascruz

D-U-N-S 80-298-6695 IMP
SYSTEX PRODUCTS CORP
(*Suby of* SHIMIZU INDUSTRY CO.,LTD.)
300 Buckner Rd, Battle Creek, MI 49037-5602
Tel (269) 964-8800 *Founded/Ownrshp* 1992
Sales 84.1MM *EMP* 217^E
Accts Plante & Moran Pllc Portage
SIC 3089 Injection molded finished plastic products
Ch Bd: Tamotsu Inoue
* *Pr:* Naohisa Miyashita
* *Treas:* Makoto Saito
Snr Mgr: Jason Bailey
Snr Mgr: Jennifer Gatu
Board of Directors: Tamotsu Inoue

D-U-N-S 09-806-0754
■ SYTEX GROUP INC
(*Suby of* LEIDOS HOLDINGS INC) ★
700 N Frederick Ave, Gaithersburg, MD 20879-3328
Tel (301) 240-7000 *Founded/Ownrshp* 2016
Sales 1.0MM^E *EMP* 2,410
SIC 4813 Telephone communication, except radio
Pr: Sydney Martin
Treas: Sharon Martin
VP: Terrell Jones
VP: Terry Jones
VP: Richard Neal
Opers Mgr: Susan McCrea

D-U-N-S 36-205-1203
■ SYTEX INC
(*Suby of* LEIDOS HOLDINGS INC) ★
700 N Frederick Ave, Gaithersburg, MD 20879-3328
Tel (301) 240-7000 *Founded/Ownrshp* 2016
Sales 74.0MM^E *EMP* 1,210
SIC 4813 Telephone communication, except radio
Pr: Sydney Martin
* *Treas:* Sharon Martin
Sr VP: Kevin B Soder
VP: Andrew R D'Angelo
VP: Ralph A Palmieri

D-U-N-S 14-838-7611 IMP
■ SYX DISTRIBUTION INC
SYSTEMAX
(*Suby of* SYSTEMAX INC) ★
175 Ambassador Dr, Naperville, IL 60540-4084
Tel (516) 608-7000 *Founded/Ownrshp* 2004
Sales 71.8MM^E *EMP* 1,255
SIC 5734 Computer & software stores
Pr: Richard Leeds
* *Ex VP:* Larry Reinhold
* *Prin:* Robert Leeds
* *Prin:* Carl Siorention

T

D-U-N-S 02-747-6647 IMP
T & A SUPPLY CO INC
6821 S 216th St Bldg A, Kent, WA 98032-2440
Tel (206) 282-3770 *Founded/Ownrshp* 1957
Sales 120.0MM *EMP* 179
SIC 1771 5023 1752 2431 Flooring contractor; Floor coverings; Carpets; Floor cushion & padding; Resilient floor coverings: tile or sheet; Wood floor installation & refinishing; Doors & door parts & trim, wood
Pr: Owen E Strecker Jr
* *VP:* Mark Strecker
Prin: Greg Szalay
Brnch Mgr: Gary Cooper
Sfty Mgr: Nikki Cross
Mktg Dir: Steve Urlacher
Sls Dir: Ed Benz
Sls Dir: Danny Camp
Mktg Mgr: Holiday Van
Sales Asso: Gary Heintz
Sales Asso: Lynn Yoneyama

T & C VILLAGE MARKETS
See TOWN & COUNTRY FOOD STORES INC

D-U-N-S 61-488-8357
T & D SOLUTIONS LLC
6411 Masonic Dr, Alexandria, LA 71301-2320
Tel (318) 442-8138 *Founded/Ownrshp* 2012
Sales 276.3MM^E *EMP* 550^E
SIC 1623 Water, sewer & utility lines
VP: Scott Shoulders
Dist Mgr: Hugh Sutton

D-U-N-S 07-991-3308
T & J FOODS LLC
(*Suby of* TAIYANG INTERNATIONAL (HOLDINGS) GROUP LIMITED)
233 S Wacker Dr Ste 8325, Chicago, IL 60606-6505
Tel (312) 357-5137 *Founded/Ownrshp* 2013
Sales 250.0MM *EMP* 20
SIC 5147 Meats & meat products

D-U-N-S 06-509-2314 IMP
T & L DISTRIBUTING (TX)
7350 Langfield Rd, Houston, TX 77092-1450
Tel (713) 461-7802 *Founded/Ownrshp* 1958, 1972
Sales 91.8MM *EMP* 131
Accts John T Jones & Company Pllc
SIC 5023 Floor coverings
Pr: Jeff Thomas
Sr VP: Bob Eady
VP: Veronica Martinez
Genl Mgr: Laura Klink
Sls Dir: Brian Peyton
Sls Mgr: Scott Carson
Sls Mgr: Doug Gonzales

D-U-N-S 11-158-1588
T & T REPROGRAPHICS INC
PR2 BLUEPRINT
5100 Newport Dr Ste 1, Rolling Meadows, IL 60008-3825
Tel (847) 398-5855 *Founded/Ownrshp* 2008
Sales 600.0MM *EMP* 4
SIC 7334 Blueprinting service
Pr: Takshal Mehta

D-U-N-S 83-608-2354
T & T STAFF MANAGEMENT INC
511 Executive Center Blvd, El Paso, TX 79902-1018
Tel (915) 771-0393 *Founded/Ownrshp* 1994
Sales 116.8MM *EMP* 6,600
Accts Lauterbach Borschow & Company
SIC 7361 Employment agencies
Pr: Thad A Steele Jr
VP: Dennis Healy
* *VP:* Aaron Montoya
* *VP:* Kathryn G Steele

D-U-N-S 04-947-2236
T & W OF KNOXVILLE INC
LEXUS OF KNOXVILLE
10315 Parkside Dr, Knoxville, TN 37922-1947
Tel (865) 218-3300 *Founded/Ownrshp* 1982
Sales 87.5MM^E *EMP* 267
SIC 5511 7538 5531 Automobiles, new & used; General automotive repair shops; Automotive & home supply stores
Pr: Terry Taylor
* *VP:* Doug White
* *Genl Mgr:* Andy White
* *Off Mgr:* Sharon Fields
Dir IT: Jonathan Bentley
Sls Mgr: Kevin Fox
Sls Mgr: Dwayne Griffith
Sls Mgr: Logan Waggoner
Sales Asso: John Fox
Sales Asso: Paige Hughes
Sales Asso: Phil Rains

D-U-N-S 15-688-3753 IMP
T & W TIRE LLC
25 N Council Rd, Oklahoma City, OK 73127-4931
Tel (405) 787-6711 *Founded/Ownrshp* 1987
Sales 135.8MM^E *EMP* 300
SIC 5531 Automotive tires
Genl Pt: Charles Wilson
Mng Pt: Kane Russel
Mng Pt: Steven Theissen
Pr: CD Wilson
Exec: Darrin Newfield
Genl Mgr: Gregg Stigall
Genl Mgr: Ryan Woodard
IT Man: Fred Berry
Sales Asso: Tony Elliott

D-U-N-S 09-884-5019 IMP/EXP
T - H MARINE SUPPLIES INC
200 Finney Dr Sw, Huntsville, AL 35824-2205
Tel (256) 772-0164 *Founded/Ownrshp* 1994
Sales 200.0MM *EMP* 52
SIC 5551 3999 3429 Marine supplies & equipment; Atomizers, toiletry; Aircraft & marine hardware, inc. pulleys & similar items
Pr: Jeff Huntley
* *VP:* Bill Huntley
* *Genl Mgr:* Jeffrey Huntley Jr
* *Off Mgr:* Bonnie Davidson
Plnt Mgr: Kevin Campbell
Prd Mgr: Melonie Tolbert
Sls Mgr: Bill Applegate
Sls Mgr: Luke Dunkin

T A C
See ACCESSORY CORP

D-U-N-S 82-487-3137
■ T A HOLDINGS CORP
TA TRAVEL CENTERS OF AMERICA
(*Suby of* TRAVELCENTERS OF AMERICA INC) ★
24601 Center Ridge Rd # 200, Cleveland, OH 44145-5677
Tel (440) 808-9100 *Founded/Ownrshp* 1993
Sales 71.8MM^E *EMP* 4,500
Accts Price Waterhouse Llp Pittsbur
SIC 5541 Truck stops
Pr: Edwin P Kuhn
CFO: James W George
VP: Tim Doane
VP: Michael H Hinderliter

T A S
See TURBINE AIR SYSTEMS LTD

D-U-N-S 05-950-6063
T A SOLBERG CO INC
TRIG'S FOOD & DRUG
420 Oneida St, Minocqua, WI 54548
Tel (715) 356-7711 *Founded/Ownrshp* 1974
Sales 195.2MM^E *EMP* 1,000
SIC 5541 Filling stations, gasoline
Ch Bd: Trygve Solberg
* *Pr:* Lee A Guenther
* *VP:* Tula Solberg

D-U-N-S 02-412-4661
▲ T AIR INC
AIRT
3524 Airport Rd, Maiden, NC 28650-9056
Tel (828) 464-8741 *Founded/Ownrshp* 1980
Sales 148.2MM *EMP* 618
Tkr Sym AIRT *Exch* NAS
SIC 4512 3728 7699 Air cargo carrier, scheduled; Aircraft parts & equipment; Aircraft flight instrument repair
Ch Bd: Nicholas J Swenson
CFO: Candice L Otey
Board of Directors: Seth G Barkett, William R Foudray, Gary S Kohler, Andrew L Osborne, John A Reeves, Andrew J Stumpf

D-U-N-S 04-132-3023
T B PENICK & SONS INC
15435 Innovation Dr # 100, San Diego, CA 92128-3443
Tel (858) 558-1800 *Founded/Ownrshp* 1984
Sales 139.2MM *EMP* 455^E
Accts Akt Llp San Diego California
SIC 1541 1542 Industrial buildings & warehouses; Nonresidential construction
CEO: Marc E Penick
Pr: Frank Klemaske
Pr: Timothy Penick
CFO: John Boyd
Ex VP: Byron Klemaske
VP: Jamie Awford
VP: Victor Klemaske
Exec: Jason Avila
Exec: Melissa Holmes
Exec: Judy Vilont
Sls Mgr: Clarissa Campbell

T C E COMMUNICATIONS
See TRI-CITY ELECTRIC CO OF IOWA

T C P
See TENNENBAUM CAPITAL PARTNERS LLC

T C U
See TEXAS CHRISTIAN UNIVERSITY INC

T C V S
See TERUMO CARDIOVASCULAR SYSTEMS CORP

D-U-N-S 18-756-0904
T D BANKNORTH INSURANCE GROUP
(*Suby of* TD BANKNORTH MASSACHUSETTS) ★
75 John Roberts Rd Bldg C, South Portland, ME 04106-6964
Tel (207) 239-3500 *Founded/Ownrshp* 2001
Sales NA *EMP* 500
SIC 6411 Insurance agents, brokers & service
Pr: Joseph Fico
CFO: Deborah S Coffrin
CFO: Rick Doane
Treas: James Kilbride

T D I
See TRANSPORT DRIVERS INC

T D R
See TURLOCK DAIRY & REFRIGERATION INC

D-U-N-S 00-721-7102
T D WILLIAMSON INC (OK)
6120 S Yale Ave Ste 1700, Tulsa, OK 74136-4235
Tel (918) 493-9494 *Founded/Ownrshp* 1920
Sales 539.5MM *EMP* 1,425
SIC 7389 Pipeline & power line inspection service
Ch Bd: Stephen Williamson
* *Pr:* Robert D McGrew
Chf Mktg O: Robert Bockmeulen
Sr VP: D Bruce Binkley
* *Sr VP:* Bruce A Thames
* *VP:* Mike Benjamin
VP: Jon D Major
VP: David R Miller
VP: Paul Poppell
Genl Mgr: Dan Haykal
Netwrk Eng: Cameron Hadley
Board of Directors: Thomas G Brennan, Robert M Howe, Jack E Short, C Ian Sym-Smith, A B Steen, Wayne E Swearingen, Stephen D Williamson

D-U-N-S 09-755-8274
T E C WELL SERVICE INC
851 W Harrison Rd, Longview, TX 75604-5208
Tel (903) 759-0082 *Founded/Ownrshp* 2011
Sales 128.0MM^E *EMP* 140
SIC 1389 Servicing oil & gas wells
* *Sec:* Grace Shore
Div Mgr: Terry Baker
Div Mgr: Dee Johns

T E M A
See TOYOTA MOTOR ENGINEERING & MANUFACTURING NORTH AMERICA INC

D-U-N-S 05-068-2020 IMP
T F LOUDERBACK INC
BAY AREA BEVERAGE
700 National Ct, Richmond, CA 94804-2008
Tel (510) 965-6120 *Founded/Ownrshp* 1969
Sales 98.1MM^E *EMP* 102^E
SIC 5181 5149 2037 2033 Beer & other fermented malt liquors; Beverages, except coffee & tea; Juices; Frozen fruits & vegetables; Canned fruits & specialties
Pr: Tj Louderback
* *Pr:* Thomas F Louderback
* *CFO:* Ciaran Byrne
* *CFO:* Tom Echaniz
* *CFO:* David Hendrickson
* *VP:* Mike Woolf
Dist Mgr: Tom Roberts
Div Mgr: Chris Reed
Snr Ntwrk: Ryan Smith
Opers Mgr: Tom Senadenos
Sls Mgr: Anthony Avizenis

T GEN
See TRANSLATIONAL GENOMICS RESEARCH INSTITUTE

D-U-N-S 11-150-2688
T H ONE INC
TANG GROUP
3773 Howard Hughes Pkwy 350n, Las Vegas, NV 89169-0949
Tel (702) 734-3700 *Founded/Ownrshp* 1996
Sales 96.5MM *EMP* 5
SIC 6719 Personal holding companies, except banks
Pr: Cyrus Tang
* *Treas:* Walter Hauk

T I D
See TURLOCK IRRIGATION DISTRICT

D-U-N-S 04-159-5060
T J SAMPSON COMMUNITY HOSPITAL
TJ REGIONAL HEALTH
1301 N Rise St, Glasgow, KY 42141
Tel (270) 651-1305 *Founded/Ownrshp* 2011
Sales 1.9MM^E *EMP* 1,300
SIC 8062 General medical & surgical hospitals
CEO: Bud Wethington

D-U-N-S 09-816-4239
T K STANLEY INC
6739 Highway 184, Waynesboro, MS 39367-9201
Tel (601) 735-2855 *Founded/Ownrshp* 1979
Sales 705.6MM^E *EMP* 700
SIC 1389 Oil & gas wells: building, repairing & dismantling
Pr: Steve Farrar
* *Sec:* Woody Farrar
Sfty Mgr: Ralph Smith
Sales Exec: Paul Hood

D-U-N-S 18-951-6065
T L C CO INC
TLC PLUMBING & UTILITY
5000 Edith Blvd Ne, Albuquerque, NM 87107-4125
Tel (505) 761-9696 *Founded/Ownrshp* 1987
Sales 95.4MM^E *EMP* 307
SIC 1711 Plumbing, heating, air-conditioning contractors
Pr: Dale L Armstrong
* *VP:* Ronald P Burnett
Exec: Burr Dickinson
Genl Mgr: Paul Layer
Genl Mgr: Tom McConnell
Mtls Mgr: Randy Cox
Mktg Dir: Mindy Gonzales
Sls Mgr: Bryan Huskisson

D-U-N-S 02-847-6414 IMP
T M COBB CO
HALEY BROS
500 Palmyrita Ave, Riverside, CA 92507-1196
Tel (951) 248-2400 *Founded/Ownrshp* 1947
Sales 98.9MM^E *EMP* 360
SIC 2431 3442 Door frames, wood; Window & door frames
Pr: Jeffrey Cobb
* *VP:* Thomas J Cobb
VP: Dave Elliott-Presley
IT Man: Bill Moore

T M D
See TOLEDO MOLDING & DIE INC

T M M
See TOKIO MARINE AMERICA

T. M. P.
See TMP WORLDWIDE ADVERTISING & COMMUNICATIONS LLC

T N G
See TNG GP

D-U-N-S 11-335-1803
■ T N P ENTERPRISES INC
(*Suby of* PNM RESOURCES INC) ★
4100 Intl Plaza Ste 900, Fort Worth, TX 76109-4839
Tel (817) 731-0099 *Founded/Ownrshp* 2005
Sales 345.3MM^E *EMP* 700
SIC 4911 Generation, electric power; Transmission, electric power; Distribution, electric power
Pr: W Douglas Hobbs
COO: Mike Bray
Ch: Jeffry E Sterba
VP: Michael D Blanchard

VP: David Harkness
VP: Terry R Horn
IT Man: Vincent Quijano

T. O. HAASTIRE 501
See TO HAASTIRE CO INC

T P G
See TEXAS ENERGY FUTURE HOLDINGS LIMITED PARTNERSHIP

T P I
See ISG INFORMATION SERVICES GROUP AMERICAS INC

T R A
See TRAD NORTH AMERICA INC

T R B
See TORY BURCH LLC

T R I . E O
See TRI-ED DISTRIBUTION INC

D-U-N-S 80-100-6347
T RTOPPERS INC
320 Fairchild Ave, Pueblo, CO 81001-4818
Tel (719) 948-4902 *Founded/Ownrshp* 1991
Sales 134.7MM *EMP* 43
Accts Shirts & Motz Boise Idaho
SIC 2066 Chocolate & cocoa products
Pr: Tim Rode
Pr: Robert Schwartz
**CFO:* Bob Rode
**VP:* Greg Rode
Ql Cn Mgr: Majid Khodabakhsh
Sales Exec: Myra Consonero

D-U-N-S 00-498-7608
■T ROWE PRICE ASSOCIATES INC
(*Suby of* T ROWE PRICE GROUP INC) ★
100 E Pratt St, Baltimore, MD 21202-1009
Tel (410) 345-2000 *Founded/Ownrshp* 1979
Sales 1.0MMM[E] *EMP* 4,100[E]
SIC 6799 Investors
CEO: James Kennedy
**Pr:* Christopher Alderson
**Ch:* Brian Rogers
Bd of Dir: D Garrett
VP: MarkT Edwards
VP: Philip Garcia
VP: John Gilner
VP: Douglas Harrison
VP: James Riepe
VP: Charles P Smith

D-U-N-S 04-567-3662
▲T ROWE PRICE GROUP INC
100 E Pratt St, Baltimore, MD 21202-1009
Tel (410) 345-2000 *Founded/Ownrshp* 1937
Sales 4.2MMM *EMP* 5,999[E]
Accts Kpmg Llp Baltimore Maryland
Tkr Sym TROW *Exch* NGS
SIC 6282 Investment advisory service
Pr: William J Stromberg
Ch Bd: Brian C Rogers
Pr: Laura Burd
Pr: Ronnie Kurlander
Pr: Adam Rickel
Pr: Jaideep Shanbhag
Pr: Stephen Zettlemoyer
CFO: Kenneth V Moreland
V Ch Bd: Edward C Bernard
VP: Christopher D Alderson
VP: Frank Alonso
VP: Steve Booth
VP: Adam Brown
VP: Brian Burns
VP: Renee Christoff
VP: Josephine Colon
VP: Tina Cragg
VP: Femi Dada
VP: Kim Dedominicis
VP: Paul Deluca
VP: Jean Dunn
Board of Directors: Dwight S Taylor, Mark S Bartlett, Anne Marie Whittemore, Mary K Bush, Sandra S Wijnberg, H Lawrence Culp Jr, Alan D Wilson, Donald B Hebb Jr, Freeman A Hrabowski III, James A C Kennedy, Robert F Maclellan, Olympia J Snowe, Alfred Sommer

T S A
See TRANSPORTATION SECURITY ADMINISTRATION

T S C
See TEXAS STERLING CONSTRUCTION CO

T S I
See TRANSPORTATION SERVICES INC

T T S
See THRU TUBING SOLUTIONS INC

T U H
See TEMPLE UNIVERSITY HOSPITAL INC

T W C
See TWC WISE COMPUTER INC

T W G
See TULSA WINCH INC

D-U-N-S 15-691-1620
T W M INDUSTRIES
CARL'S JR.
899 Cherry Ave, San Bruno, CA 94066-2949
Tel (650) 583-6491 *Founded/Ownrshp* 1984
Sales 27.9MM[E] *EMP* 1,000
SIC 5812 Fast-food restaurant, chain
Pt: Be Wierdsma
Pt: Gene Ciufo
Pt: Stella Thompson
Pt: Tom Thompson

D-U-N-S 11-593-1552
TY LIN INTERNATIONAL
(*Suby of* TY LIN INTERNATIONAL GROUP) ★
345 California St Fl 23, San Francisco, CA 94104-2646
Tel (415) 291-3700 *Founded/Ownrshp* 1964
Sales 128.3MM[E] *EMP* 737
SIC 8711 Consulting engineer
Pr: Alvaro J Piedrahita
**CFO:* Robert A Peterson
**Ch:* Man Chung Tang
**Ofcr:* Veronica Fennie
Assoc VP: Maribel Castillo
Assoc VP: Michael Fitzpatrick
Sr VP: Juan Murillo
**VP:* Allison Bagby
VP: Darin Bryant
VP: Dean Collins
VP: Ronald L Freeland
VP: Sorin Garber
VP: Dennis Jang
VP: Marwan Nader
VP: Elizabeth M Wiecha

D-U-N-S 17-220-8287
T&N ASPHALT SERVICES INC
3643 S 700 W Ste C, South Salt Lake, UT 84119-4181
Tel (801) 266-1626 *Founded/Ownrshp* 2004
Sales 111.3MM *EMP* 5
SIC 1611 Surfacing & paving; Driveway, parking lot & blacktop contractors; Pavement marking contractor
Pr: Nick Howell
**VP:* Margie Howell

D-U-N-S 61-677-2042 IMP
■T-3 ENERGY SERVICES INC
(*Suby of* ROBBINS & MYERS INC) ★
140 Cypress Station Dr # 225, Houston, TX 77090-1686
Tel (713) 944-5950 *Founded/Ownrshp* 2011
Sales 85.0MM[E] *EMP* 628
SIC 5211 3491 7699 Energy conservation products; Pressure valves & regulators, industrial; Industrial equipment services
VP: Connie A Bailey
Opers Mgr: Art Narcisi
Opers Mgr: Don Weldon
Plnt Mgr: Scott Gooding
VP Sls: Allan C Bruns

D-U-N-S 00-728-8087 IMP/EXP
T-L IRRIGATION CO
151 E Hwy 6 And Ab Rd, Hastings, NE 68901
Tel (402) 462-4128 *Founded/Ownrshp* 1955
Sales 91.3MM[E] *EMP* 300
SIC 3523 3561 3479 7359 Fertilizing, spraying, dusting & irrigation machinery; Pumps, domestic: water or sump; Galvanizing of iron, steel or end-formed products; Equipment rental & leasing
Pr: Leroy W Thom
**Ex VP:* James Thom
**VP:* David Thom
Store Mgr: Ben Wood
Sfty Dirs: Chris Thom
Natl Sales: Clark Bauer
Natl Sales: Jim Kostal
Mktg Mgr: Ryan Webber
Sls Mgr: Houston Hennigh

T-MICHAEL INTERNATIONAL
See STARCREST PRODUCTS OF CALIFORNIA INC

D-U-N-S 14-537-3945
■T-MOBILE US INC
(*Suby of* DEUTSCHE TELEKOM AG)
12920 Se 38th St, Bellevue, WA 98006-7305
Tel (425) 378-4000 *Founded/Ownrshp* 2013
Sales 32.0MMM *EMP* 50,000[E]
Accts Pricewaterhousecoopers Llp Se
Tkr Sym TMUS *Exch* NGS
SIC 4813 Telephone communication, except radio; Wire telephone
Pr: John J Legere
**Ch Bd:* Timotheus Hottges
COO: Steve Shiflet
COO: G Michael Sievert
CFO: J Braxton Carter
Ex VP: David R Carey
Ex VP: Jon A Freier
Ex VP: Unmukt Gadkari
Ex VP: Gary A King
Ex VP: David A Miller
Ex VP: Raymond Perrenet
Ex VP: Neville R Ray
Sr VP: Herbert Graves
VP: Simon O Agyemang
VP: Ian Blomeen
VP: James Brody
VP: Brian Brueckman
VP: Laura Buckland
VP: Catherine Captain
VP: Savinay Dangi
VP: Shelley Davis
Board of Directors: W Michael Barnes, Thomas Dannenfeldt, Lawrence H Guffey, Bruno Jacobfeuerborn, Raphael Kubler, Thorsten Langheim, Teresa A Taylor, Kelvin R Westbrook

D-U-N-S 06-852-8376 IMP
■T-MOBILE USA INC
(*Suby of* T-MOBILE US INC) ★
12920 Se 38th St, Bellevue, WA 98006-7305
Tel (425) 378-4000 *Founded/Ownrshp* 1999, 2013
Sales 20.7MMM[E] *EMP* 34,518[E]
SIC 4812 4899 Radio telephone communication; Data communication services
Pr: Robert Dotson
Mng Pt: Ronald Lum
Pr: Betty Jones
**Pr:* John Legere
Pr: AMI L Silverman
COO: Robert Stevens
**CFO:* Michael Morgan
Chf Mktg O: Cole Brodman
**Chf Mktg O:* Denny Marie Post
**Chf Mktg O:* Michael Sievert
**Ex VP:* David Carey
Ex VP: Juin-Jet Hwang
Ex VP: Drew Kelton
Sr VP: John Birrer
Sr VP: Christian Rigamonti
Sr VP: Andrew Sherrard
VP: Tim Adams
**VP:* James Alling
**VP:* Braxton Carter
VP: John Diefenbach
VP: Larry Dolot

D-U-N-S 17-986-8708
■T-SYSTEMS NORTH AMERICA INC
(*Suby of* T-SYSTEMS INTERNATIONAL GMBH)
1901 Butterfield Rd # 700, Downers Grove, IL 60515-5403
Tel (630) 493-6100 *Founded/Ownrshp* 1997
Sales 420.0MM *EMP* 730
Accts Ernst & Young Llp Chicago Il
SIC 7379 8748 Computer related consulting services; Telecommunications consultant
Mng Dir: Paul Warrenfelt
V Ch: Wolfgang Heinz
CFO: Bertus Cilliers
CFO: Johannes Cilliers
Sr Ex VP: Guido Kerkhoff
Sr VP: Arrie Revelinghuys
VP: Bill Daly
VP: Anthony Dambrosi
VP: Tom Galgano
VP: Goetz Huttel
VP: Sergio Perez
VP: Volker Reible
VP: Anthony Roma
VP: Thomas Salva
VP: Jurgen Schulze
VP: Frank Westermann
Exec: Anne Pistono
Dir Surg: John Sarkis
Board of Directors: David McDougall

D-U-N-S 07-966-8704
T2 COMPUTING INC (NY)
119 W 23rd St Ste 206, New York, NY 10011-2427
Tel (212) 220-9600 *Founded/Ownrshp* 2014, 2016
Sales 85.0MM *EMP* 120[E]
SIC 7373 7379 Value-added resellers, computer systems; Computer related consulting services
CEO: Jerry Gepner
**VP:* Ian Ash
**VP:* Alex Church

D-U-N-S 06-327-4208 IMP
■T2 MEDICAL INC
(*Suby of* CORAM CVS/SPCLTY INFUSION SVCS) ★
555 17th St Ste 1500, Denver, CO 80202-3900
Tel (303) 672-8631 *Founded/Ownrshp* 2005
Sales 60.4MM[E] *EMP* 1,500
SIC 8082 Home health care services
Pr: Robert Allen
**VP:* Michael Dell

T3 TIRE CENTERS
See TIRE CENTERS LLC

TA
See TA ASSOCIATES

D-U-N-S 07-536-0321
TA ASSOCIATES
TA
200 Clarendon St Ste 5600, Boston, MA 02116-5043
Tel (617) 574-6700 *Founded/Ownrshp* 1968
Sales 259.5MM[E] *EMP* 330
SIC 6799 Venture capital companies
CEO: Elizabeth De Saint-Aignan
Pr: Jerry Rawls
COO: Jeffrey C Hadden
Sr VP: Jeffrey A Del Papa
Sr VP: Ethan K Liebermann
Sr VP: J Morgan Seigler
VP: Mark H Carter
VP: Lisa M Harris
VP: Lisa Harris
VP: Pamela Bliss Harris
VP: Pamela Harris
VP: Clara M Jackson
VP: Lovisa Lander
VP: Emily C McGinty
VP: Jonathan Meeks
VP: Benedikt Prinz
VP: Roberto E Ramirez
VP: Morgan Seigler
VP: Aditya Sharma
VP: Amara Suebsaeng
VP: Tad Yanagi
Board of Directors: Jennifer McAuliffe Mulloy

D-U-N-S 78-666-0071
TA ASSOCIATES MANAGEMENT LP
200 Clarendon St Fl 56, Boston, MA 02116-5021
Tel (617) 574-6700 *Founded/Ownrshp* 1993
Sales 1.8MMM[E] *EMP* 602
SIC 6799 Venture capital companies
Ch Bd: Brian J Conway
VP: Max Cancre
VP: John Dicola
VP: Clara Jackson
VP: Michael Libert
VP: Diana Martz
VP: Alex Melamud
VP: Lee Mooney
VP: Amara Suebsaeng
VP: Sarah Wang
Dir IT: Damon Khouri

D-U-N-S 07-797-4897 IMP/EXP
TA CHEN INTERNATIONAL INC
SUNLAND SHUTTERS
(*Suby of* TA CHEN STAINLESS PIPE CO., LTD.)
5855 Obispo Ave, Long Beach, CA 90805-3715
Tel (562) 808-8000 *Founded/Ownrshp* 1989
Sales 1.1MMM *EMP* 500
Accts Chen & Fan Accountancy Corpora
SIC 3452 5051 Bolts, nuts, rivets & washers; Steel
CEO: Johnny Hsieh
**CFO:* Lucy Kuo
**VP:* James Chang
VP: Dean Crumrie
**VP:* John Hellighausen
VP: John Hellinghausen
IT Man: Ronald Leblanc
Natl Sales: Michael Gatzonis
Sls&Mrk Ex: Richard Ripley
VP Sls: Michelle Chesnutt

D-U-N-S 80-895-1248
TA DELAWARE INC
TOWER INTERNATIONAL
17672 N Laure Park Dr Ste, Novi, MI 48377
Tel (248) 675-6000 *Founded/Ownrshp* 1993
Sales 228.8MM[E] *EMP* 11,000
SIC 3469 Metal stampings
Pr: Mark Malcom
**COO:* Michael Rajkovic
COO: Mike Rajkovic
**Ex VP:* James Gouin
Sr VP: Paul Radkoski
Ex Dir: Derek Fiebig
Opers Mgr: Cathy Branum

D-U-N-S 61-525-7847 IMP
■TA INSTRUMENTS - WATERS LLC
(*Suby of* WATERS TECHNOLOGIES CORP) ★
159 Lukens Dr, New Castle, DE 19720-2795
Tel (302) 777-0712 *Founded/Ownrshp* 1996
Sales 90.4MM[E] *EMP* 500
SIC 3826 Instruments measuring thermal properties
CFO: Randy Mercner
CTO: Rob Woehr
IT Man: Susan Carruth
Info Man: Susan Bookout
Software D: Stephen Eshelman
Software D: Anthony Okocha
Mktg Mgr: David Bohnsack
Sls Mgr: Mike Golinar
Sls Mgr: Bob Milliken
Sls Mgr: Daniel Roedolf
Sls Mgr: Pete Shickel

D-U-N-S 00-699-6615
TA LOVING CO
400 Patetown Rd, Goldsboro, NC 27530-8132
Tel (919) 734-8400 *Founded/Ownrshp* 1937
Sales 162.0MM[E] *EMP* 320
SIC 1541 1542 1623

D-U-N-S 82-469-9946
■TA OPERATING LLC
PETRO STOPPING CENTER
(*Suby of* QUAKER STEAK & LUBE) ★
24601 Center Ridge Rd # 200, Westlake, OH 44145-5677
Tel (440) 808-9100 *Founded/Ownrshp* 1993
Sales 4.0MMM[E] *EMP* 10,000
SIC 5541 7538 5812 5411 6794 Filling stations, gasoline; Truck stops; General truck repair; Eating places; Fast food restaurants & stands; Convenience stores; Franchises, selling or licensing
CEO: Thomas O Brien
**Ex VP:* ARA Bagdasarian
**Ex VP:* Andrew J Rebholz
**Ex VP:* Barry Richards

D-U-N-S 15-118-9578
TA SERVICES INC
(*Suby of* PS LOGISTICS LLC) ★
241 Regency Pkwy, Mansfield, TX 76063-5090
Tel (800) 626-2185 *Founded/Ownrshp* 1986
Sales 91.1MM[E] *EMP* 330
SIC 4731 4213 Brokers, shipping; Agents, shipping; Trucking, except local
Pr: Scott Schell
**CFO:* Charles Dismuke
VP: Jackie Askelson
VP: Ken Cromwell
Genl Mgr: Cheryl Ross
Opers Mgr: Norma Venezia
Sales Exec: Joann Porritt
VP Sls: Tom Webster

TA TRAVEL CENTERS OF AMERICA
See T A HOLDINGS CORP

TABAN CO
See ISHAN INTERNATIONAL INC

D-U-N-S 07-189-0305 EXP
TABC INC
(*Suby of* T E M A) ★
6375 N Paramount Blvd, Long Beach, CA 90805-3301
Tel (562) 984-3305 *Founded/Ownrshp* 1974
Sales 115.7MM[E] *EMP* 800[E]
SIC 3714 3713 3469 Motor vehicle parts & accessories; Truck beds; Metal stampings
CEO: Michael Bafan
**Treas:* Yoshiaki Nishino
VP: Donald Haller
Dir IT: Todd Hernandez

D-U-N-S 18-758-3141 IMP
TABLE MOUNTAIN CASINO
8184 Table Mountain Rd, Friant, CA 93626
Tel (559) 822-2485 *Founded/Ownrshp* 1987
Sales 49.9MM[E] *EMP* 1,000
SIC 7999 Gambling establishment
Sr VP: Frances Dandy
COO: Ted Thay
Exec: Ricardo Nunez
Dir IT: Paul Barlow
Sls Mgr: Andres Rico

D-U-N-S 60-386-5093
▲TABLEAU SOFTWARE INC
837 N 34th St Ste 200, Seattle, WA 98103-8965
Tel (206) 633-3400 *Founded/Ownrshp* 2003
Sales 653.5MM *EMP* 3,008[E]
Tkr Sym DATA *Exch* NYS
SIC 7372 Prepackaged software; Business oriented computer software
Ch Bd: Christian Chabot
CFO: Thomas Walker
Chf Mktg O: Elissa Fink
Ex VP: Keenan M Conder
Ex VP: Jay Peir
Ex VP: Kelly Wright
VP: Keenan Conder
VP: Dan Jewett
VP: Scott Jones
VP: Lynn Smith
VP: Dave Story
Board of Directors: Forest Baskett, Billy Bosworth, Patrick Hanrahan, Elliott Jurgensen Jr, John McAdam, Brooke Seawell

TABOR AND MC COURTE
See ATLANTA HILL RESTAURANT CORP

TAC
See TRUMAN ARNOLD COMPANIES

D-U-N-S 06-010-2965 IMP/EXP
TAC INC
(*Suby of* SCHNEIDER ELECTRIC BUILDINGS AMERICAS INC) ★
1 High St, Andover, MA 01810-3527
Tel (978) 470-0555 *Founded/Ownrshp* 2004
Sales 121.1MM[E] *EMP* 2,400
SIC 3822 Building services monitoring controls, automatic
CEO: Arne Frank
CFO: David Sharp

D-U-N-S 78-563-5376 IMP/EXP
TAC MANUFACTURING INC
(*Suby of* TRAM INC) ★
4111 County Farm Rd, Jackson, MI 49201-9065
Tel (517) 789-7000 *Founded/Ownrshp* 1991
Sales 109.7MM[E] *EMP* 600
SIC 3714 3625 Motor vehicle parts & accessories; Relays & industrial controls
Pr: Hiro Ysui
* *Pr:* Kiyoshi Sasaki
* *VP:* Y Hirai
QC Dir: Chip Wood

D-U-N-S 60-896-2650
TACALA INC
TACO BELL
4268 Cahaba Heights Ct, Vestavia, AL 35243-5711
Tel (205) 985-9626 *Founded/Ownrshp* 1989
Sales 93.7MM[E] *EMP* 3,000
SIC 5812

D-U-N-S 09-400-4228 IMP
TACALA LLC
TACO BELL
3750 Corporate Woods Dr, Vestavia, AL 35242-2207
Tel (205) 443-9600 *Founded/Ownrshp* 2012
Sales 95.4MM[E] *EMP* 2,318
SIC 5812 Fast-food restaurant, chain
VP: John Figert

D-U-N-S 79-986-6116
TACALA NORTH INC
TACO BELL
4268 Cahaba Heights Ct, Vestavia, AL 35243-5711
Tel (205) 985-2364 *Founded/Ownrshp* 1996
Sales 38.0MM *EMP* 2,800
SIC 5812 Fast-food restaurant, chain
CEO: Richard D Reese

D-U-N-S 61-648-6879
TACHI PALACE HOTEL & CASINO
17225 Jersey Ave, Lemoore, CA 93245-9760
Tel (559) 924-7751 *Founded/Ownrshp* 2006
Sales 59.5MM[E] *EMP* 1,500
SIC 7011 Casino hotel
Owner: Tachi Yokut
CFO: Richard Laudale
CFO: Jim Snead

D-U-N-S 17-830-7153 IMP
TACHI-S ENGINEERING USA INC
(*Suby of* TACHI-S CO.,LTD.)
23227 Commerce Dr, Farmington Hills, MI 48335-2705
Tel (248) 478-5050 *Founded/Ownrshp* 1986
Sales 155.8MM[E] *EMP* 930
SIC 2531 8711 Seats, automobile; Designing: ship, boat, machine & product
Pr: Hiroyuki Miki
Prgrm Mgr: Akemi Sullivan
Ql Cn Mgr: Rita Bridge
Snr Mgr: Frank Sakmar

TACO BELL
See CHARTER FOODS INC

TACO BELL
See OCAT INC

TACO BELL
See LAS-CAL CORP

TACO BELL
See AUSTIN TACALA CORP

TACO BELL
See DOLAN FOSTER ENTERPRISES LLC

TACO BELL
See NORDIC CORP

TACO BELL
See TWINS INTERNATIONAL INC

TACO BELL
See TACALA LLC

TACO BELL
See SOUTHERN MULTIFOODS INC

TACO BELL
See ES-O-EN CORP

TACO BELL
See R L C ENTERPRISES INC

TACO BELL
See B & G FOOD ENTERPRISES OF TEXAS LLC

TACO BELL
See B & G FOOD ENTERPRISES INC

TACO BELL
See R&L FOODS INC

TACO BELL
See BELL AMERICAN GROUP LLC

TACO BELL
See BURGERBUSTERS INC

TACO BELL
See TACALA INC

TACO BELL
See BORDER FOODS INC

TACO BELL
See RESTAURANT SYSTEMS INC

TACO BELL
See TACALA NORTH INC

TACO BELL
See PACIFIC BELLS LLC

D-U-N-S 00-965-7149 IMP
■ **TACO BELL CORP** (CA)
(*Suby of* YUM BRANDS INC) ★
1 Glen Bell Way, Irvine, CA 92618-3344
Tel (949) 863-4500 *Founded/Ownrshp* 1962, 1997
Sales 3.6MMM[E] *EMP* 175,000
SIC 5812 6794 Fast-food restaurant, chain; Franchises, selling or licensing
CEO: Brian Niccol
* *Pr:* Emil Brolick
* *Chf Mktg O:* Bob Fulmer
Chf Mktg O: David Ovens
VP: Anna Hoo
Brnch Mgr: Keisha Achurra
Brnch Mgr: Mindy Bebault
Brnch Mgr: Tammie Blackburn
Brnch Mgr: Sandra Brathall
Brnch Mgr: Sergio Chavez
Brnch Mgr: Ted Daniels
Board of Directors: Robert D Walter, Michael J Cavanagh, Mirian M Graddick-Weir, David W Dorman, Massimo Ferragamo, Bonnie G Hill, Jonathan S Linen, Thomas C Nelson, David C Novak, Thomas M Ryan, Sam Su

D-U-N-S 78-384-6426
TACO BUENO RESTAURANTS LP
1605 Lbj Fwy Ste 800, Farmers Branch, TX 75234-6099
Tel (800) 440-0778 *Founded/Ownrshp* 1967
Sales 155.8MM[E] *EMP* 3,710[E]
SIC 5812 6794 Eating places; Caterers; Franchises, selling or licensing
CEO: Mike Roper
COO: David Allen
Treas: Steven Abney
Chf Mktg O: Jeff Carl
VP: Darek Hys
VP: Kevin Lewis
VP: Jeff Seeberger
VP: Tom Veale
Dist Mgr: Mark Williams
Genl Mgr: Patrice Walker
VP Opers: Alan Wyse

D-U-N-S 00-119-7011 IMP/EXP
TACO INC (NY)
1160 Cranston St, Cranston, RI 02920-7300
Tel (401) 942-8000 *Founded/Ownrshp* 1920
Sales 165.9MM[E] *EMP* 500
SIC 3433 3561 3443 3822 Heating equipment, except electric; Pumps & pumping equipment; Heat exchangers: coolers (after, inter), condensers, etc.; Auto controls regulating residntl & coml environmt & applncs
Pr: John H White Jr
Pr: Richard Pasquini
* *Pr:* Wil Vandewiel
* *Treas:* Glenn Graham
* *Sr VP:* Kyle Adamonis
Sr VP: Chris Integlia
* *Sr VP:* Thomas Lawrence
Sr VP: Stephan Pearson
VP: Nelson Laurance
MIS Dir: David McElreath
QA Dir: Gary Williams

D-U-N-S 60-667-0511
TACOTICO INC
505 S Broadway Ave # 205, Wichita, KS 67202-3900
Tel (316) 683-6621 *Founded/Ownrshp* 1987
Sales 68.8MM[E] *EMP* 1,000
SIC 6794 Franchises, selling or licensing
Ch Bd: R Gene Smith
* *Pr:* Kevin Ravin
* *CEO:* George Baker

D-U-N-S 04-182-6798
TACOMA COMMUNITY COLLEGE
6501 S 19th St Bldg 14, Tacoma, WA 98466-6100
Tel (253) 566-5058 *Founded/Ownrshp* 1965
Sales 57.0MM *EMP* 1,922
SIC 8222 8351 Community college; Child day care services
Pr: Shiela K Ruhland
* *Prin:* Pamela J Transue
CTO: Marie Freyre
Psych: Craig Cowden

D-U-N-S 07-926-3042
TACOMA PUBLIC SCHOOLS
TACOMA SCHOOL DISTRICT 10
601 S 8th St, Tacoma, WA 98405-4614
Tel (253) 571-1000 *Founded/Ownrshp* 1915
Sales 143.2MM[E] *EMP* 3,700
SIC 8211 Public senior high school; Public junior high school; Public elementary school
* *Pr:* Debbie Winskill
VP: Scott Heinze
* *VP:* Kurt Miller
Dir Sec: Miguel Villanermosa
MIS Dir: Michael Farmer
MIS Dir: Shaun Taylor
Sfty Dirs: Miguel Villahermosa
Pr Dir: Dan Voelpel
Psych: Cynthia Endicott
Psych: Jean Lubken
Psych: Anneliese Nobles

TACOMA SCHOOL DISTRICT 10
See TACOMA PUBLIC SCHOOLS

TACOMAC SPORTS GRILL
See TM RESTAURANT GROUP LLC

TACONIC
See TONOGA INC

D-U-N-S 04-172-2133 IMP
TACONIC BIOSCIENCES INC
SAS SUPPLY
1 Hudson City Ctr, Hudson, NY 12534-2354
Tel (609) 860-0806 *Founded/Ownrshp* 1952
Sales 256.0MM[E] *EMP* 720
Accts Pricewaterhousecoopers Llp Al
SIC 0279 Laboratory animal farm
CEO: Robert J Rosenthal
Pr: David T Hansen
Pr: Todd F Little
Sr VP: Patrick Laverty
Sr VP: Michael Mullen
VP: Manfred Huschka
VP: David Lester
IT Man: Phillipe Heffley
VP Mktg: Nancy Sandy
Sls Mgr: Steve Rashbaum
Snr Mgr: Meggan Keith

D-U-N-S 03-110-2627 IMP/EXP
TACONY CORP
1760 Gilsinn Ln, Fenton, MO 63026-2044
Tel (636) 349-3000 *Founded/Ownrshp* 1946
Sales 175.9MM[E] *EMP* 625
Accts Bkd Llp St Louis Missouri
SIC 3634 Electric housewares & fans
CEO: Kristin Humes
Pr: Bill Hinderer
Ch: Kenneth J Tacony
Ex VP: William H Hinderer
Sr VP: Steve J Jeffery
Sr VP: John Kaido
Dir IT: Jim Rich

D-U-N-S 02-408-0579
TAD PGS INC
ADECCO GOVERNMENT SOLUTIONS
(*Suby of* ADECCO TECHNICAL) ★
1001 3rd Ave W Ste 460, Bradenton, FL 34205-7841
Tel (941) 746-4434 *Founded/Ownrshp* 1997
Sales 80.0MM *EMP* 1,600
SIC 7363 Temporary help service
CEO: Tom Lash
* *CFO:* Wendy Harkins
Ofcr: Tiffany Hanson
* *VP:* Tom Brewer
* *VP:* Gina Harvey

TAESL
See TEXAS AERO ENGINE SERVICES LLC

TAG
See ANSWER GROUP INC

D-U-N-S 60-259-6298
TAG HOLDINGS INC
(*Suby of* SOUTH CHINA (JERSEY) HOLDINGS LTD)
6901 Riverport Dr Ste B, Louisville, KY 40258-2852
Tel (214) 469-3300 *Founded/Ownrshp* 1988
Sales 150.0MM[E] *EMP* 200
SIC 2321 2339 2369 Men's & boys' dress shirts; Sport shirts, men's & boys': from purchased materials; Women's & misses' outerwear; Girls' & children's outerwear
Pr: Donald Young
* *Pr:* Walter Bearden
* *Pr:* Norman Goldberg
Ex VP: John Liu
VP: Butch Troutt

TAG TRUCK CENTER
See TAG TRUCK ENTERPRISES LLC

D-U-N-S 80-340-4974
TAG TRUCK ENTERPRISES LLC
TAG TRUCK CENTER
1650 E Brooks Rd, Memphis, TN 38116-1926
Tel (901) 345-5633 *Founded/Ownrshp* 2007
Sales 190.5MM *EMP* 250
Accts Dixon Hughes Goodman Llp Memp
SIC 5511 Trucks, tractors & trailers: new & used
VP: Laura Craft
VP: Doug Mick
Brnch Mgr: Tiffany Gooch
Genl Mgr: Jason Stewart

D-U-N-S 15-770-1350 IMP/EXP
TAGHLEEF INDUSTRIES INC
AET FILMS
(*Suby of* TAGHLEEF INDUSTRIES (L L C))
500 Creek View Rd Ste 301, Newark, DE 19711-8549
Tel (302) 326-5500 *Founded/Ownrshp* 2012
Sales 330.9MM[E] *EMP* 825
SIC 3081 Polypropylene film & sheet
CEO: Detlef Schuhmann
* *COO:* Wolfgang Meyer
COO: Van Wiese
CFO: Brian P Crescenzo
* *Ch:* Rashed Al Ghurair
IT Man: Mike Sherrill
QC Dir: Albert Shen
Mktg Mgr: Paul Marquard

TAHER FOOD SERVICES
See TAHER INC

D-U-N-S 10-224-4142
TAHER INC
TAHER FOOD SERVICES
5570 Smetana Dr, Minnetonka, MN 55343-9022
Tel (952) 945-0505 *Founded/Ownrshp* 1981
Sales 95.9MM[E] *EMP* 2,900
SIC 5812 Contract food services
Pr: Bruce Taher
VP: Deb Renneke
Creative D: Shawn Eiken
Comm Dir: Sylvia Evenson
Mng Dir: M Alam

TAHLEQUAH CITY HOSPITAL
See TAHLEQUAH MEDICAL GROUP LLC

D-U-N-S 07-240-5442
TAHLEQUAH HOSPITAL AUTHORITY
NORTHEASTERN HEALTH SYSTEM
1400 E Downing St, Tahlequah, OK 74464-3324
Tel (918) 456-0641 *Founded/Ownrshp* 1988
Sales 93.5MM *EMP* 450[E]
SIC 8062 General medical & surgical hospitals
CEO: Brian Woodliff
* *COO:* David Mc Clain
* *CFO:* Julie Newman
Dir IT: Erin Pack

D-U-N-S 83-241-7187
TAHLEQUAH MEDICAL GROUP LLC
TAHLEQUAH CITY HOSPITAL
1400 E Downing St, Tahlequah, OK 74464-3324
Tel (918) 456-0641 *Founded/Ownrshp* 2009
Sales 83.2MM *EMP* 99
SIC 8011 8062 Offices & clinics of medical doctors; General medical & surgical hospitals
Dir IT: Aaron Pack

D-U-N-S 04-599-6246
TAHOE FOREST HOSPITAL DISTRICT
10121 Pine Ave, Truckee, CA 96161-4856
Tel (530) 587-6011 *Founded/Ownrshp* 1952
Sales 108.3MM *EMP* 600
Accts Matson & Iso Chico Californi
SIC 8062 General medical & surgical hospitals
CEO: Robert Schapper
Chf Rad: Tad Laird
* *CFO:* Crystal Betts
Ofcr: Gail Betz
Off Mgr: Linda Freitas
CIO: Jake Dorst
CTO: Margaret Holmes
IT Man: Maureen Blankenship
IT Man: Greg Szabo
Mktg Dir: Paige Thomason
Mktg Mgr: Terry Smith

D-U-N-S 02-399-3284
▲ **TAHOE RESOURCES INC**
5310 Kietzke Ln Ste 200, Reno, NV 89511-2044
Tel (775) 825-8574 *Founded/Ownrshp* 2009
Sales 519.7MM *EMP* 2,055
Tkr Sym TAHO *Exch* NYS
SIC 1021 1041 1044 1031 1311 Copper ores; Gold ores; Silver ores; Lead & zinc ores; Crude petroleum & natural gas; Natural gas production
Ch Bd: C Kevin McArthur
Pr: Ronald W Clayton
CFO: Mark Sadler
VP: Edie Hofmeister
Exec: Brian Brodsky

TAIHEIYO CEMENT USA, INC.
See TAIHEIYO CEMENT USA INC

D-U-N-S 17-541-8052 IMP/EXP
TAIHEIYO CEMENT USA INC
TAIHEIYO CEMENT USA, INC.
(*Suby of* TAIHEIYO CEMENT CORPORATION)
2025 E Fincl Way Ste 200, Glendora, CA 91741
Tel (626) 852-6200 *Founded/Ownrshp* 1986
Sales 121.6MM[E] *EMP* 1,000
SIC 3241 3273 Portland cement; Ready-mixed concrete
Pr: Noboru Kasai
Treas: Masashi Inoue
* *Treas:* Yukio Tsuda
VP: Rick Patton
Exec: Bill Paritt
Genl Mgr: Michael Smith
IT Man: Tom Catledge

D-U-N-S 08-014-2523 IMP/EXP
▲ **TAILORED BRANDS INC**
6380 Rogerdale Rd, Houston, TX 77072-1624
Tel (281) 776-7000 *Founded/Ownrshp* 2015
Sales 3.5MMM[E] *EMP* 26,100[E]
Tkr Sym TLRD *Exch* NYS
SIC 5611 5621 5632 5661 5699 Men's & boys' clothing stores; Clothing accessories: men's & boys'; Suits, men's; Tie shops; Women's clothing stores; Apparel accessories; Women's shoes; Uniforms & work clothing
CEO: Douglas S Ewert
V Ch: David H Edwab
COO: Bruce K Thorn
CFO: Jon W Kimmins
Chf Mktg O: Mary Beth Blake
Ex VP: Mark Neutze
Ex VP: Hyon Park
Ex VP: A Alexander Rhodes
Ex VP: William C Silveira
Ex VP: Carole L Souvenir
Ex VP: Matt Stringer
Sr VP: Brian T Vaclavik
VP: Julie Macmedan

TAILWIND CAPITAL
See TAILWIND MANAGEMENT LP

D-U-N-S 19-386-7913
TAILWIND MANAGEMENT LP
TAILWIND CAPITAL
485 Lexington Ave Rm 2300, New York, NY 10017-2622
Tel (212) 271-3800 *Founded/Ownrshp* 2005
Sales 256.7MM[E] *EMP* 272
SIC 6799 Investors
Mng Pt: Lawrence Sorrell
Pt: David S Bauman
Pt: Jeffrey M Calhoun
Pt: Mark Epstein
Pt: James Hoch
Pt: Douglas Karp
Pt: Frank V Sica
Mng Dir: Adam Stuhlberger

D-U-N-S 83-201-6773
TAILWIND TECHNOLOGIES INC
1 Propeller Pl, Piqua, OH 45356-2655
Tel (937) 778-4200 *Founded/Ownrshp* 1988
Sales 200.0MM *EMP* 800[E]
SIC 3356 Titanium
Pr: James W Brown III
* *CFO:* Matthew L Jesch
Sr VP: Mike Piscatella
* *Prin:* Joseph W Brown
* *Prin:* Michael J Piscatella

TAIWAN SEMICDTR MFG CO LTD
See TSMC DEVELOPMENT INC

D-U-N-S 04-361-4601 IMP/EXP
TAKASAGO INTERNATIONAL CORP (USA)
(*Suby of* TAKASAGO INTERNATIONAL CORPORATION)
4 Volvo Dr, Rockleigh, NJ 07647-2508
Tel (201) 767-9001 *Founded/Ownrshp* 1968

Sales 133.3MM[E] *EMP* 350
SIC 2844 Concentrates, perfume
Ch Bd: Sean G Traynor
**CEO:* Ritaro Igaki
**CFO:* Joseph Wesolowski
**Ex VP:* Haruo Nakanishi
**Ex VP:* Yoshiaki Suda
**Sr VP:* Brian Buck
**Sr VP:* Masayuki Mita
VP: Alfredo A Asuncion
VP: Fred Guerra
VP: Raymond Honey[II]
VP: Frederic Jacques
VP: Hidenori Kumobayashi
**VP:* Hiroyuki Matsumoto
VP: Takashi Matsuo
VP: Dulce Paredes
VP: Hiroki Take
VP: Gary Titus
**VP:* Kazuhiko Tokoro
Exec: Lisette U Masur

TAKATA
See TK HOLDINGS INC

TAKE
See NAVITAS INC

D-U-N-S 94-583-7425
TAKE CARE EMPLOYER SOLUTIONS LLC
(*Suby of* PREMISE HEALTH HOLDING CORP) ★
5500 Maryland Way Ste 200, Brentwood, TN 37027-4973
Tel (615) 665-9500 *Founded/Ownrshp* 2004
Sales NA *EMP* 1,000
SIC 6324 Hospital & medical service plans
Pr: Dickson Thayer
**Pr:* Haywood D Cochrane Jr
**CFO:* Shannon Wolcott
**VP:* April Lannom

D-U-N-S 82-968-1063
▲TAKE-TWO INTERACTIVE SOFTWARE INC
622 Broadway Fl 6, New York, NY 10012-2600
Tel (646) 536-2842 *Founded/Ownrshp* 1993
Sales 1.4MMM *EMP* 2,933[E]
Accts Ernst & Young Llp New York N
Tkr Sym TTWO *Exch* NGS
SIC 7371 7372 Computer software development; Home entertainment computer software
Ch Bd: Strauss Zelnick
Pr: Karl Slatoff
CFO: Lainie Goldstein
Bd of Dir: Michael Malone
Ex VP: Daniel Emerson
Ex VP: Daniel P Emerson
Off Admin: Fernando Corrales
Sls Dir: Bob Blau
Board of Directors: Robert A Bowman, Michael Dornemann, Jay J Moses, Michael Sheresky, Susan Tolson

D-U-N-S 80-526-2532 IMP
TAKEDA AMERICA HOLDINGS INC
767 3rd Ave, New York, NY 10017-2023
Tel (212) 421-6954 *Founded/Ownrshp* 1993
Sales 2.0MMM[E] *EMP* 4,115
SIC 5122 5169 2819

D-U-N-S 80-033-3093
TAKEDA DEVELOPMENT CENTER AMERICAS INC
(*Suby of* TAKEDA PHARMACEUTICALS USA INC) ★
1 Takeda Pkwy, Deerfield, IL 60015-5713
Tel (224) 554-6500 *Founded/Ownrshp* 2003
Sales 84.4MM[E] *EMP* 549
SIC 2834 Pharmaceutical preparations
Ch: Nancy Joseph-Ridge
**Pr:* Stuart Dollow
Treas: John Campbell
VP: Qais Mekki
Assoc Dir: James Morley
Assoc Dir: Suzanne Myatt
Prgrm Mgr: Kari Palbicke
Prgrm Mgr: Shannon Zimmerman
QA Dir: Jenipher Dalton
Dir IT: George Pappas
Info Man: Ladonna Randle
Board of Directors: Nancy Siepman

D-U-N-S 03-999-7266
TAKEDA PHARMACEUTICALS AMERICA INC
(*Suby of* TAKEDA PHARMACEUTICALS USA INC) ★
1 Takeda Pkwy, Deerfield, IL 60015-5713
Tel (224) 554-6500 *Founded/Ownrshp* 2000
Sales 211.3MM[E] *EMP* 2,137
SIC 2834 Pharmaceutical preparations
Pr: Douglas Cole
Treas: Helen Pring

D-U-N-S 04-187-7817 IMP
TAKEDA PHARMACEUTICALS USA INC
(*Suby of* TAKEDA PHARMACEUTICAL COMPANY LIMITED)
1 Takeda Pkwy, Deerfield, IL 60015-5713
Tel (224) 554-6500 *Founded/Ownrshp* 1999
Sales 1.6MMM[E] *EMP* 2,695
SIC 2834 Pharmaceutical preparations
Pr: Helen Pring
Pr: Mary-Jo Dempson
Pr: Ramona Sequeira
CFO: Brendan Gilboy
Ofcr: Jeanine Jiganti
Sr VP: Ken Greisman
Sr VP: Andrew Hull
VP: Richard Daly
VP: David Recker
VP: Curtis Rhine
VP: Robert Weiland
VP Bus: Nick Manusos
Assoc Dir: Jeffrey Gudmundson
Assoc Dir: Monique Morehead
Assoc Dir: Gregory Murawski
Assoc Dir: Tina Posey

D-U-N-S 09-778-8574 IMP/EXP
TAKEUCHI MFG (US) LTD
(*Suby of* TAKEUCHI MFG. CO., LTD.)
519 Bonnie Valentine Way, Pendergrass, GA 30567-4233
Tel (706) 693-3600 *Founded/Ownrshp* 1963
Sales 339.3MM *EMP* 62
Accts Deloitte & Touche Llp
SIC 5082 Road construction & maintenance machinery
Pr: Clay M Eubanks
**CFO:* Renee Paulk
**VP:* Jeff Stewart

D-U-N-S 04-263-0900 IMP/EXP
TAKKT AMERICA HOLDING INC
770 S 70th St, Milwaukee, WI 53214-3109
Tel (414) 443-1700 *Founded/Ownrshp* 2013
Sales 274.9MM[E] *EMP* 1,000
SIC 5084 Industrial machinery & equipment
CEO: Felix Zimmermann
**Treas:* Daniel Paruzynski

D-U-N-S 11-261-0204 IMP
TAKUMI STAMPING INC
(*Suby of* PACIFIC INDUSTRIAL CO., LTD.)
8585 Seward Rd, Fairfield, OH 45011-8652
Tel (513) 642-0081 *Founded/Ownrshp* 2001
Sales 97.5MM[E] *EMP* 300
SIC 3469 Stamping metal for the trade
Pr: Ken Naruse

D-U-N-S 04-682-3050 IMP/EXP
TAL INTERNATIONAL CONTAINER CORP
(*Suby of* TAL INTERNATIONAL GROUP INC) ★
100 Manhattanville Rd # 13, Purchase, NY 10577-2134
Tel (914) 251-9000 *Founded/Ownrshp* 2004
Sales 372.0MM[E] *EMP* 172
SIC 7359 Equipment rental & leasing
Pr: Brian M Sondey
CFO: Chand Khan
Sr VP: Fred Baptista
Sr VP: John Burns
Sr VP: Adrian Dunner
VP: Serkan Badoglu
VP: Michael Broadhurst
VP: Jeffrey Casucci
VP: Aaron Cox
VP: Michelle Gallagher
VP: Antonio Hung
VP: Michael Limoncelli
VP: Marc Pearlin
VP: John Pearson
VP: Bernd Schackier
VP: Mark Tranchita
VP: Kevin Valentine
VP: Belisario Zapata
Exec: Edward Mann
Exec: Ronald Petrunoff
Board of Directors: Malcolm P Baker, Bruce Berkowitz, A Richard Caputo Jr, Brian J Higgins, John J Jordan II, Frederic H Lindeberg, David W Zalaznick, Douglas J Zych

D-U-N-S 17-786-1353
TAL INTERNATIONAL GROUP INC
(*Suby of* TRITON INTERNATIONAL LIMITED)
100 Manhattanville Rd # 13, Purchase, NY 10577-2134
Tel (914) 251-9000 *Founded/Ownrshp* 2016
Sales 650.4MM *EMP* 342
SIC 7359 5085 4412 Equipment rental & leasing; Shipping container leasing; Bins & containers, storage; Deep sea foreign transportation of freight
Pr: Brian M Sondey
CFO: John Burns
Genl Mgr: Sean Morris
CIO: Annemarie Gaspari
IT Man: Robby Looymans
IT Man: Takaki Tetsuomi
Netwrk Eng: Charles Khury
Opers Supe: Keith K Wong
Opers Mgr: Richard Cornwall
Mktg Dir: Edward Tang

D-U-N-S 07-590-7175 IMP
TALARIA CO LLC
HINCKLEY COMPANY, THE
1 Lil Hrbr Landing Prt, Portsmouth, RI 02871
Tel (401) 683-7100 *Founded/Ownrshp* 1999
Sales 203.9MM[E] *EMP* 740
SIC 3732 Boat building & repairing
COO: Jim McManus
CFO: Ellen Kinley
**CFO:* Jeanette Smith
Genl Mgr: Brian Donnelly
Genl Mgr: Bob Hood
DP Exec: Peter Bratsos
Opers Mgr: Patrick Carroll
Sls Dir: Eric Champlin

D-U-N-S 15-052-0344 IMP
TALARIS INC
(*Suby of* GLORY GLOBAL SOLUTIONS (HOLDINGS) LIMITED)
3333 Warrenville Rd # 310, Lisle, IL 60532-9831
Tel (630) 577-1000 *Founded/Ownrshp* 2008
Sales 221.3MM[E] *EMP* 1,700
SIC 3578 3499 Banking machines; Safes & vaults, metal; Safe deposit boxes or chests, metal
Pr: Joseph P Patten
Mng Dir: Christof Domeisen
VP Sls: Joe Rossa
Mktg Dir: Paul Adams

TALBOT SCHOOL OF THEOLOGY
See BIOLA UNIVERSITY INC

D-U-N-S 01-939-7892 IMP/EXP
TALBOTS INC
(*Suby of* TLB HOLDINGS LLC) ★
1 Talbots Dr Ste 1, Hingham, MA 02043-1583
Tel (781) 749-7600 *Founded/Ownrshp* 1947, 2012
Sales 1.3MMM[E] *EMP* 8,737[E]
SIC 5621 5137 5632 5641 Women's clothing stores; Women's & children's clothing; Women's accessory & specialty stores; Apparel accessories; Children's wear
Pr: Lizanne Kindler
CFO: Edward L Larsen
CFO: Mary Lynn Phillips

**Chf Mktg O:* Lori Wagner
**Ex VP:* Benedetta I Casamento
Ex VP: Benedetta Casamento
**Ex VP:* Gregory I Poole
Ex VP: Philip H Kowalczyk
**Ex VP:* Richard T O'Connell Jr
**Sr VP:* Vickie Costa
Sr VP: Paul V Kastner
**Sr VP:* John Kovac
Sr VP: Julie Lorigan
Sr VP: Avra Myers
**Sr VP:* Lisa Pisano
Sr VP: Stuart Stolper
**Sr VP:* Patrick Walsh
Sr VP: Sue Walsh
VP: Sandra Boxell
VP: Alan Boyce
VP: Peter Delahunt
Board of Directors: Michael Weiss

D-U-N-S 07-621-1911
TALCO PLASTICS INC
1000 W Rincon St, Corona, CA 92880-9228
Tel (951) 531-2000 *Founded/Ownrshp* 1986
Sales 100.5MM[E] *EMP* 150
SIC 4953 2821 Recycling, waste materials; Plastics materials & resins
Ch: John L Shedd Sr
**Pr:* John L Shedd Jr
**VP:* William O'Grady
**VP:* Ron Petty
**VP:* Bob Shedd
Plnt Mgr: Paul Morris

TALCOTT GARDENS APTS
See TALCOTT GARDENS LIMITED PARTNERSHIP

D-U-N-S 96-738-3212
TALCOTT GARDENS LIMITED PARTNERSHIP
TALCOTT GARDENS APTS
135 West St, New Britain, CT 06051-1407
Tel (860) 229-9554 *Founded/Ownrshp* 2011
Sales 31.6MM[E] *EMP* 1,828
SIC 6513 Apartment building operators

D-U-N-S 78-700-2661
TALECRIS PLASMA RESOURCES INC
(*Suby of* GRIFOLS SHARED SERVICES NORTH AMERICA INC) ★
79 Tw Alexander Dr 4101, Durham, NC 27709-0152
Tel (817) 921-1886 *Founded/Ownrshp* 2011
Sales 45.1MM[E] *EMP* 1,000
SIC 8099
CEO: Gregory Rich
CFO: Max Debrouwer
**Ex VP:* Shinji Wada
**VP:* David Bell

D-U-N-S 07-970-7054
▲TALEN ENERGY CORP
835 Hamilton St Ste 150, Allentown, PA 18101-2400
Tel (888) 211-6011 *Founded/Ownrshp* 2016
Sales 4.4MMM *EMP* 4,981
Tkr Sym TLN *Exch* NYS
SIC 4911 Electric services; Distribution, electric power; Generation, electric power; Transmission, electric power
Pr: Paul A Farr
CFO: Jeremy R McGuire
Chf Cred: Clarence J Hopf Jr
Ofcr: Timothy S Rausch
Ofcr: James E Schinski
VP: Paul M Breme
VP: Jeffrey Helsel
Prgrm Mgr: Marc Davis

D-U-N-S 04-741-4524
■TALEN ENERGY MARKETING LLC
(*Suby of* TALEN ENERGY SUPPLY LLC) ★
835 Hamilton St Ste 150, Allentown, PA 18101-2400
Tel (610) 774-5151 *Founded/Ownrshp* 2008
Sales 549.9MM[E] *EMP* 2,182[E]
SIC 4911 ;
Pr: Robert D Gabbard
**Treas:* Mark F Wilten
Sr VP: Gene Alessandrini
**VP:* Gene L Alessandrini
VP: John Cotter
IT Man: Ron Kosman
IT Man: Tracy Taylor
Counsel: Paul Russell

D-U-N-S 01-522-1703
■TALEN ENERGY SERVICES GROUP LLC
(*Suby of* TALEN ENERGY MARKETING LLC) ★
2 N 9th St, Allentown, PA 18101-1139
Tel (610) 774-4005 *Founded/Ownrshp* 2011
Sales 192.4M[E] *EMP* 1,302[E]
SIC 4911 Distribution, electric power
Pr: Rick L Klingensmith
Treas: James E Abel

D-U-N-S 01-526-2459
TALEN ENERGY SERVICES HOLDINGS LLC
835 Hamilton St, Allentown, PA 18101-2426
Tel (610) 774-5151 *Founded/Ownrshp* 2000
Sales 526.3MM[E] *EMP* 1,900
SIC 4911 1711 3625

D-U-N-S 79-545-1475
■TALEN ENERGY SERVICES NORTHEAST INC
PPL ENERGY SERVICES NORTHEAST
(*Suby of* TALEN ENERGY SUPPLY LLC) ★
50 Inwood Rd Ste 3, Rocky Hill, CT 06067-3439
Tel (860) 513-1036 *Founded/Ownrshp* 1999
Sales 118.5MM[E] *EMP* 300
SIC 1711 1629 Plumbing, heating, air-conditioning contractors; Waste water & sewage treatment plant construction
VP: Louis V Coppi
VP: Thomas W Kibel
VP: Kenneth E Podolak

D-U-N-S 06-655-2626
■TALEN ENERGY SUPPLY LLC
(*Suby of* TALEN ENERGY CORP) ★
835 Hamilton St Ste 150, Allentown, PA 18101-2400
Tel (888) 211-6011 *Founded/Ownrshp* 2000
Sales 4.4MMM *EMP* 4,981[E]
SIC 4911 Electric services; Generation, electric power; Transmission, electric power
Pr: Paul A Farr
**CFO:* Jeremy R McGuire
Board of Directors: Paul M Breme, Clarence J Hopf

D-U-N-S 14-495-6252
■TALEN GENERATION LLC
(*Suby of* TALEN ENERGY SUPPLY LLC) ★
835 Hamilton St Ste 150, Allentown, PA 18101-2400
Tel (610) 774-6418 *Founded/Ownrshp* 1999
Sales 448.6MM[E] *EMP* 525
SIC 4911 Distribution, electric power
Pr: David G Decampli

D-U-N-S 04-638-8935
■TALEN MONTANA LLC
(*Suby of* TALEN GENERATION LLC) ★
303 N 28th St Ste 400, Billings, MT 59101-1255
Tel (406) 237-6900 *Founded/Ownrshp* 1999
Sales 351.5MM *EMP* 500
SIC 4911 Distribution, electric power
Pr: James H Miller
COO: Mike Interline
**COO:* Bradley E Spencer

D-U-N-S 60-765-4589
■TALENS MARINE & FUEL LLC
(*Suby of* MARTIN MIDSTREAM PARTNERS LP) ★
1707 Evangeline Hwy, Jennings, LA 70546-3923
Tel (800) 256-3835 *Founded/Ownrshp* 2013
Sales 285.8MM[E] *EMP* 225
SIC 5172 7389 Petroleum products; Packaging & labeling services

D-U-N-S 07-993-5970
TALENTNET INC
2219 Sawdust Rd Ste 603, Spring, TX 77380-2577
Tel (844) 825-3686 *Founded/Ownrshp* 2014
Sales 165.0MM *EMP* 25
SIC 7361 Executive placement
Pr: Amber O Prothero
**VP:* Justin Lumby

TALENTWAVE
See IC COMPLIANCE LLC

D-U-N-S 11-960-1990
■TALEO CORP
(*Suby of* ORACLE CORP) ★
4140 Dublin Blvd Ste 400, Dublin, CA 94568-7757
Tel (925) 452-3000 *Founded/Ownrshp* 2012
Sales 93.0MM[E] *EMP* 1,164
SIC 7372 Prepackaged software; Business oriented computer software
Pr: Dorian Daley
**CFO:* Eric Ball
Ofcr: Martin Dubois
**Ex VP:* Guy Gauvin
**Ex VP:* Neil Hudspith
Ex VP: Zachary Stitz
**Sr VP:* Jason Blessing
VP: Bill Barlow
VP: Susan Chenoweth
VP: Didi Derrico
VP: Debbie Shotwell
Dir Bus: Steven Goforth

TALG
See SOUTHEAST FROZEN FOODS CO LP

TALISMA
See CAMPUS MANAGEMENT CORP

D-U-N-S 12-654-8440
TALISMAN ENERGY USA INC
(*Suby of* REPSOL OIL & GAS CANADA INC)
2445 Tech Forest Blvd # 1200, Spring, TX 77381-5261
Tel (281) 210-2100 *Founded/Ownrshp* 2004
Sales 104.9MM[E] *EMP* 67
SIC 1311 Natural gas production
Pr: James F O'Driscoll
Board of Directors: James W Buckee, April Crane, Philip D Dolan, M D McDonald, M J Sheppard, Scott Tompkins

D-U-N-S 07-286-4056 IMP
TALK AMERICA HOLDINGS INC
(*Suby of* CAVALIER TELEPHONE MID-ATLANTIC LLC) ★
2134 W Laburnum Ave, Richmond, VA 23227-4342
Tel (804) 422-4100 *Founded/Ownrshp* 2006
Sales 92.6MM[E] *EMP* 1,200
SIC 4813 Local & long distance telephone communications
Pr: Edward Meyercord
**Pr:* Edward B Meyercord III
**CFO:* David Zahka
**Treas:* Thomas Walsh
**Ex VP:* Jeffrey Earhart
**Ex VP:* Aloysius T Lawn IV
**CIO:* Timothy W Leonard

TALK2US
See MP DIRECT INC

D-U-N-S 60-814-0281
TALKAMERICA INC
NETWORK SERVICES
(*Suby of* TALK AMERICA HOLDINGS INC) ★
12020 Sunrise Valley Dr # 250, Reston, VA 20191-3440
Tel (703) 391-7518 *Founded/Ownrshp* 1995
Sales 62.9MM[E] *EMP* 1,100
SIC 4813 Long distance telephone communications
Ch Bd: Gabriel Battista
**Pr:* Edward B Meyercord III
**CFO:* David G Zahka
Sr VP: Mark Wayne

TALL CEDARS MOBILE COURT
See KING COUNTY HOUSING AUTHORITY

D-U-N-S 96-428-5795
TALLTREE FOODS HOLDINGS INC
BLUE RIBBON
400 Hamilton Ave Ste 230, Palo Alto, CA 94301-1834
Tel (650) 264-7750 *Founded/Ownrshp* 2013
Sales 147.2MM^E *EMP* 501^E
SIC 2013 Sausages from purchased meat
CEO: Tim Bruer

D-U-N-S 04-066-2926
TALLADEGA COUNTY BOARD OF EDUCATION
106 South St W Ste A, Talladega, AL 35160-2459
Tel (256) 362-1401 *Founded/Ownrshp* 1899
Sales 85.7M *EMP* 1,022
SIC 8211 Public elementary & secondary schools
CFO: Avery Lorenzo Embry

D-U-N-S 07-324-5193
TALLAHASSEE CITY OF (INC)
300 S Adams St, Tallahassee, FL 32301-1731
Tel (850) 891-8441 *Founded/Ownrshp* 1825
Sales NA *EMP* 2,633
Accts Carr Riggs & Ingram Llc Tall
SIC 9111 City & town managers' offices;
**Treas:* Gary Herndon
IT Man: Mary Guertin

D-U-N-S 61-385-5956
■TALLAHASSEE MEDICAL CENTER INC
COLUMBIA TLLAHASSEE CMNTY HOSP
(*Suby of* HOSPITAL COPORATION OF AMERICA) ★
2626 Capital Medical Blvd, Tallahassee, FL 32308-4402
Tel (850) 325-5000 *Founded/Ownrshp* 1994
Sales 155.2MM *EMP* 1,000
SIC 8062 General medical & surgical hospitals
CEO: Bud Wethington
**Pr:* Samuel N Hazen
Chf Mktg O: Howard Clark
**Sr VP:* David G Anderson
**Sr VP:* Donald W Stinnett
**VP:* Natalie H Cline
**VP:* John M Franck II
Dir Risk M: Linda Deeb
Sfty Mgr: Ralph Waccary
Pr Dir: Ellen Cole
Orthpdst: Craig Butler

D-U-N-S 07-919-8594
TALLAHASSEE MEMORIAL HEALTHCARE INC
TALLAHASSEE MEMORIAL HOSPITAL
1300 Miccosukee Rd, Tallahassee, FL 32308-5054
Tel (850) 431-1155 *Founded/Ownrshp* 1948
Sales 589.5MM *EMP* 6,430
SIC 8062 General medical & surgical hospitals
Pr: G Mark O'Bryant
CFO: Bill Giudice
**CFO:* William Giudice
**Treas:* Harold A Brock Jr
Treas: Frederick Carroll
**Sec:* Tom Noel
Ofcr: Andrea Eklund
Ofcr: Mahmood Haq
VP: Jason Moore
Off Mgr: Lynn Jackson
Nurse Mgr: Leeann Barfield

TALLAHASSEE MEMORIAL HOSPITAL
See TALLAHASSEE MEMORIAL HEALTHCARE INC

TALLEY & ASSOCIATES
See TALLEY INC

D-U-N-S 04-643-7422 IMP/EXP
TALLEY INC
TALLEY & ASSOCIATES
12976 Sandoval St, Santa Fe Springs, CA 90670-4061
Tel (562) 906-8000 *Founded/Ownrshp* 1983
Sales 143.2MM^E *EMP* 175
SIC 5065 Communication equipment; Amateur radio communications equipment
CEO: John R Talley
**Pr:* Mark D Talley
**CFO:* George R Hulbert
**Ex VP:* Elizabeth J Talley
**VP:* Patrick Slynn
**VP:* Jeffrey R Talley
VP: Scott Wenk

D-U-N-S 01-253-3606
TALLGRASS COMMODITIES LLC (KS)
420 Lincoln St, Wamego, KS 66547-1632
Tel (855) 494-8484 *Founded/Ownrshp* 2007
Sales 109.2MM *EMP* 20
SIC 0119 Feeder grains
Pr: Chad Villwok

D-U-N-S 07-877-5873
TALLGRASS DEVELOPMENT LP
4200 W 115th St Ste 350, Leawood, KS 66211-2733
Tel (513) 941-0500 *Founded/Ownrshp* 2012
Sales 371.0MM^E *EMP* 66^E
SIC 4922 Pipelines, natural gas
Prin: Jacob Soliday

D-U-N-S 07-974-2113
TALLGRASS ENERGY GP LP
4200 W 115th St Ste 350, Leawood, KS 66211-2733
Tel (913) 928-6060 *Founded/Ownrshp* 2015
Sales 536.2MM *EMP* 6
Accts Pricewaterhousecoopers Llp De
Tkr Sym TEGP *Exch* NYS
SIC 4922 Natural gas transmission
Pr: David G Dehaemers Jr
CFO: Gary J Brauchle

TALLGRASS ENERGY PARTNERS
See TALLGRASS OPERATIONS LLC

D-U-N-S 07-852-8479 IMP/EXP
▲TALLGRASS ENERGY PARTNERS LP
4200 W 115th St Ste 350, Leawood, KS 66211-2733
Tel (913) 928-6060 *Founded/Ownrshp* 2013
Sales 536.2MM *EMP* 6^E
Tkr Sym TEP *Exch* NYS
SIC 4922 4923 Natural gas transmission; Pipelines, natural gas; Storage, natural gas; Gas transmission & distribution
Pr: David G Dehaemers Jr
Genl Pt: Tallgrass Mlp GP
COO: William R Moler
CFO: Gary J Brauchle

D-U-N-S 07-958-2699
TALLGRASS OPERATIONS LLC (CO)
TALLGRASS ENERGY PARTNERS
(*Suby of* TALLGRASS DEVELOPMENT LP) ★
4200 W 115th St Ste 350, Leawood, KS 66211-2733
Tel (913) 928-6060 *Founded/Ownrshp* 2008
Sales 371.0MM *EMP* 450^E
SIC 4922 Pipelines, natural gas
CEO: David Dehaemers
**Prin:* Mitch Meyer

D-U-N-S 82-716-7904
TALMER BANK AND TRUST
2301 W Big Beaver Rd # 525, Troy, MI 48084-3320
Tel (248) 649-2301 *Founded/Ownrshp* 2009
Sales NA *EMP* 547^E
SIC 6022

D-U-N-S 14-751-7044
■TALON THERAPEUTICS INC
(*Suby of* SPECTRUM PHARMACEUTICALS INC) ★
157 Technology Dr, Irvine, CA 92618-2402
Tel (949) 788-6700 *Founded/Ownrshp* 2013
Sales 186.0MM *EMP* 241
SIC 2834 8731 Pharmaceutical preparations; Commercial physical research
CEO: Joseph W Turgeon

D-U-N-S 07-874-9669
TALOS PRODUCTION LLC
1600 Smith St, Houston, TX 77002-7362
Tel (713) 328-3000 *Founded/Ownrshp* 2013
Sales 408.4MM^E *EMP* 181^E
SIC 1382 Geophysical exploration, oil & gas field
Pr: Timothy S Duncan
**Ex VP:* John L Harrison
**Ex VP:* Stephen E Heitzman
**Ex VP:* William S Moss III
**Ex VP:* John A Parker
**Prin:* John Harrison

D-U-N-S 00-880-3918
TALQUIN ELECTRIC COOPERATIVE INC (FL)
1640 W Jefferson St, Quincy, FL 32351-2134
Tel (850) 627-7651 *Founded/Ownrshp* 1940
Sales 123.7MM *EMP* 180
Accts Purvis Gray & Company Llp Tal
SIC 4931 Electric & other services combined
Pr: Mal Green
COO: Gary Stallons
**CFO:* Eugene Kanikovsky
Bd of Dir: Bobby Strickland
**VP:* Carrie L Durden
VP: Joe Hayden
VP: Amos Sumner
Genl Mgr: Sean Alderman
Genl Mgr: Tracy Bensle
Genl Mgr: Gary Stallon
Off Mgr: Mike Greene

D-U-N-S 05-920-8835
■TALX CORP
EQUIFAX WORKFORCE SOLUTIONS
(*Suby of* EQUIFAX INC) ★
11432 Lackland Rd, Saint Louis, MO 63146-3516
Tel (314) 214-7000 *Founded/Ownrshp* 2007
Sales 255.7MM^E *EMP* 1,889
SIC 7373 7379 7389

D-U-N-S 06-508-3917 IMP/EXP
TAM INTERNATIONAL INC
4620 Southerland Rd, Houston, TX 77092-3020
Tel (713) 462-7617 *Founded/Ownrshp* 1973
Sales 109.6MM^E *EMP* 350
SIC 3533 Oil & gas field machinery
Ch Bd: Lawrence Sanford
**Pr:* Bently Sanford
**CFO:* Gene Morris
VP Sls: John Crooks

TAMA PAPERBOARD
See CARAUSTAR INDUSTRIES INC

D-U-N-S 00-202-8751 IMP
■TAMBRANDS SALES CORP
TAMPAX
(*Suby of* P&G) ★
1 Procter And Gamble Plz, Cincinnati, OH 45202-3315
Tel (513) 983-1100 *Founded/Ownrshp* 1936, 1997
Sales 169.0MM^E *EMP* 1,900
SIC 2676 Tampons, sanitary: made from purchased paper
Pr: Wolfgang C Berndt
VP: R T Blanchard
VP: T A Garrett
VP: Mark D Ketchum
VP: T A Moore
VP: Erik G Nelson
VP: G R Perkinson
VP: Michael J Power
VP: R C Rogge
VP: Shaw F Skillings
VP: Thomas Soper

TAMC
See AROOSTOOK MEDICAL CENTER INC

D-U-N-S 07-410-2906 IMP/EXP
TAMCO INC
TAMCO STEEL
(*Suby of* GERDAU LONG STEEL NORTH AMER) ★
12459 Arrow Rte, Rancho Cucamonga, CA 91739-9607
Tel (909) 899-0660 *Founded/Ownrshp* 2010
Sales 138.9MM^E *EMP* 350
SIC 3449 Bars, concrete reinforcing: fabricated steel
Pr: Jack D Stutz
Ex VP: L McDermott
**VP:* Carl Krepper
**VP:* A Brad Wilkins
VP: Matthew Yeatman
Opers Mgr: Mark Mossey

TAMCO STEEL
See TAMCO INC

D-U-N-S 06-114-8268
TAMERON AUTOMOTIVE GROUP INC
TAMERON HONDA
1675 Montgomery Hwy, Birmingham, AL 35216-4998
Tel (205) 396-3108 *Founded/Ownrshp* 1972
Sales 104.6MM *EMP* 170
Accts Henderson Hutcherson & Mccullo
SIC 5511 5013 Automobiles, new & used; Automotive supplies & parts
CEO: Tom Acheson
**Pr:* Daniel W Braden
**Sec:* A John Lucas

TAMERON HONDA
See TAMERON AUTOMOTIVE GROUP INC

D-U-N-S 07-870-5227
■TAMINCO CORP
(*Suby of* EASTMAN CHEMICAL CO) ★
200 S Wilcox Dr, Kingsport, TN 37660-5147
Tel (423) 229-2000 *Founded/Ownrshp* 2003, 2014
Sales 129.6MM^E *EMP* 851^E
SIC 2869 Amines, acids, salts, esters
Pr: David A Golden

D-U-N-S 78-665-7424 IMP/EXP
■TAMINCO US LLC
(*Suby of* EASTMAN CHEMICAL CO) ★
7540 Windsor Dr Ste 411, Allentown, PA 18195-1019
Tel (610) 366-6730 *Founded/Ownrshp* 2014
Sales 126.9MM^E *EMP* 200^E
SIC 2869 5169 Amines, acids, salts, esters: Chemicals, industrial & heavy
CEO: Laurent Lenoir
**Pr:* Geoff Ingham
**CFO:* Kurt Decat
**Ch:* Pol Vanderhaeghen
**Ex VP:* Johan De Saeghar
Ex VP: Edward Yocum
**VP:* Jean M Denis
**VP:* Guy Wouters
Opers Mgr: Joseph Szulczewski
Opers Mgr: Jim Yanora

D-U-N-S 00-713-9876 IMP
TAMKO BUILDING PRODUCTS INC
220 W 4th St, Joplin, MO 64801-2504
Tel (417) 624-6644 *Founded/Ownrshp* 1941
Sales 402.6MM^E *EMP* 1,867
SIC 2952

D-U-N-S 00-443-5996 IMP/EXP
TAMPA ARMATURE WORKS INC (FL)
TAW
6312 S 78th St, Riverview, FL 33578-8835
Tel (813) 621-5661 *Founded/Ownrshp* 1921
Sales 154.4MM *EMP* 650
Accts Warren Averett Llc Tampa Fl
SIC 5063 3613 3621 Motors, electric; Switchgear & switchboard apparatus; Motors & generators
Pr: James A Turner III
**Treas:* Michael Macinnes
Off Mgr: Victoria Lopez
Off Mgr: Nancy Spencer
Plnt Mgr: Michael Boyce
Plnt Mgr: Mike Castin
Plnt Mgr: Mark Grimley
Prd Mgr: David Adams
Sls Dir: Regis McCafferty

D-U-N-S 04-608-5056 IMP/EXP
TAMPA BAY FISHERIES INC
KITCHEN'S SEAFOOD
3060 Gallagher Rd, Dover, FL 33527-4728
Tel (813) 752-8883 *Founded/Ownrshp* 1991
Sales 115.1MM^E *EMP* 450
SIC 2092 Seafoods, fresh: prepared
Pr: Robert Jr Paterson
VP: Chris Newman
**VP:* Tom Tao
**Prin:* Mark Marsh
IT Man: Michelle Wardlaw
Sls Mgr: Neal Gonzalez

TAMPA BAY LIGHTNING, THE
See LIGHTNING HOCKEY LP

D-U-N-S 87-802-0853
TAMPA BAY SPORTS ENTERTAINMENT LLC
490 1st Ave S, Saint Petersburg, FL 33701-4204
Tel (727) 893-8111 *Founded/Ownrshp* 2010
Sales 174.2MM^E *EMP* 1,300^E
SIC 2711 Newspapers
Ch: Jeff Vinik
CFO: Jana Jones
Ofcr: Garron Von Gunten
VP: Stephen Foster
CIO: Beth Sholer
Dir IT: Reitberger Fred
Opers Mgr: John Silverstein
Sls Mgr: Monica Boyer
Snr Mgr: Alex Leary
Assoc Ed: Martin Dyckman

D-U-N-S 08-136-7112
TAMPA BAY WATER A REGIONAL WATER SUPPLY AUTHORITY
2575 Enterprise Rd, Clearwater, FL 33763-1102
Tel (727) 796-2355 *Founded/Ownrshp* 1974
Sales 153.5MM *EMP* 132
Accts Ernst & Young Llp
SIC 4941 Water supply
Ch: Susan Latvala
**COO:* Charles Carden
Exec: Jon Kennedy
Exec: Krista Simon
Comm Man: Michelle Rapp
**Prin:* Chuck Carden
Dept Mgr: Robert McConnell
**Genl Mgr:* Gerald Seeber
IT Man: Dave Detwiler
Snr Mgr: Roberta Kety
Snr Mgr: Ron Parker

TAMPA COMMONS
See TIME CUSTOMER SERVICE INC

D-U-N-S 00-692-4286 IMP/EXP
TAMPA ELECTRIC CO (FL)
(*Suby of* TECO ENERGY INC) ★
702 N Franklin St, Tampa, FL 33602-4429
Tel (813) 228-1111 *Founded/Ownrshp* 1899
Sales 2.4MMM *EMP* 2,385
SIC 4911 4924 Generation, electric power; Transmission, electric power; Distribution, electric power; Natural gas distribution
CEO: John B Ramil
**Ch Bd:* Sherrill W Hudson
Pr: Gordon L Gillette
CFO: Sandra W Callahan
Ofcr: Charles A Attal III
VP: Gina Chung
VP: Thomas Hernandez
CIO: Karen Mincey
QA Dir: Rhonda Kelly
IT Man: Maru Martinez
Info Man: Jody Barnes
Board of Directors: James L Ferman Jr, Evelyn V Follit, Joseph P Lacher, Loretta A Penn, Tom L Rankin, William D Rockford, Paul L Whiting

TAMPA GENERAL HEALTHCARE
See FLORIDA HEALTH SCIENCES CENTER INC

D-U-N-S 03-590-6279
TAMPA GENERAL HOSPITAL
1 Tampa General Cir, Tampa, FL 33606-3571
Tel (813) 844-4527 *Founded/Ownrshp* 2011
Sales 1.0MMM *EMP* 5^E
SIC 8062 General medical & surgical hospitals
Prin: Bridget Jude Pugh

TAMPA HONDALAND
See DUVAL MOTOR CO INC

D-U-N-S 08-068-5647 IMP
TAMPA MAID FOODS LLC
(*Suby of* WATKINS ASSOCIATED INDUSTRIES INC) ★
1600 Kathleen Rd, Lakeland, FL 33805-3435
Tel (863) 687-4411 *Founded/Ownrshp* 1974
Sales 105.0MM^E *EMP* 350
SIC 2092 Fresh or frozen packaged fish
Pr: Dave Pearce
**Ch Bd:* George Watkins
Treas: George Ready
**Sec:* Eric S Wahlen
**VP:* Lori Phillips
**VP:* Mario L Pullara
Genl Mgr: Michael Rhoads
QA Dir: Carl Tamborello
IT Man: Kevin Alves
VP Mfg: Kevin Stallworth
Sfty Dirs: Gary Clark

D-U-N-S 07-873-2755
TAMPA MEDIA GROUP INC
TAMPA TRIBUNE, THE
202 S Parker St, Tampa, FL 33606-2308
Tel (813) 259-7711 *Founded/Ownrshp* 2012
Sales 120.1MM^E *EMP* 600
SIC 2711 Newspapers, publishing & printing
Prin: Robert Loring
**Prin:* Gary Alcock

D-U-N-S 08-083-5556
TAMPA METROPOLITAN AREA YOUNG MENS CHRISTIAN ASSOCIATION INC
110 E Oak Ave, Tampa, FL 33602-2210
Tel (813) 224-9622 *Founded/Ownrshp* 1908
Sales 37.6MM *EMP* 1,650
Accts Cbiz Mhm Llc Clearwater Fl
SIC 8641 Civic associations; Youth organizations; Social associations
Pr: Thomas Looby
**CFO:* Todd Bray
CFO: Lynette McKown
**Treas:* Doug Arthur
Bd of Dir: Rony Braswell
Bd of Dir: Philip J Cole III
Bd of Dir: Sherry Cornett
Bd of Dir: Sharon Dicks
Bd of Dir: Scott Doster
Bd of Dir: Scott Garlick
Bd of Dir: Richard Hopkins
Bd of Dir: Robert Kantor
Bd of Dir: Sheila Mayeski
Bd of Dir: Steve Niernan
Bd of Dir: Robert Norton
Bd of Dir: Reginald Pope
Bd of Dir: Ronnie Preusch
Bd of Dir: Pete Radeka
Bd of Dir: Rhett Rollyson
Bd of Dir: Sean Stewart
Bd of Dir: Steven Tombrink

D-U-N-S 19-717-0137
TAMPA PIPELINE CORP
5802 Hartford St, Tampa, FL 33619-9616
Tel (813) 623-2431 *Founded/Ownrshp* 1986
Sales 76.2MM^E *EMP* 2,500
SIC 4613 Refined petroleum pipelines
Pr: Robert L Rose

TAMPA TRIBUNE, THE
See TAMPA MEDIA GROUP INC

TAMPAX
See TAMBRANDS SALES CORP

D-U-N-S 84-561-9142
TAMU COMMERCE
P.O. Box 3011 (75429-3011)
Tel (903) 886-5060 *Founded/Ownrshp* 2009
Sales 13.0MM^E *EMP* 1,300
SIC 8611 Business associations
Pr: Dan Jones

D-U-N-S 10-287-2603
TANADGUSIX CORP
TDX
615 E 82nd Ave Ste 200, Anchorage, AK 99518-3159
Tel (907) 278-2312 *Founded/Ownrshp* 1973
Sales 139.5MM *EMP* 294
SIC 1796 7011 7359 Installing building equipment; Hotels; Equipment rental & leasing
CEO: Ron P Philemonoff
**Pr:* Jason Bourdukofsky Sr
CFO: Doug Koprowski

TANANA CHIEFS CONFERENCE
See DENA NENA HENASH

D-U-N-S 78-896-9652
TANANA CHIEFS CONFERENCE
122 1st Ave Ste 600, Fairbanks, AK 99701-4899
Tel (907) 452-8251 *Founded/Ownrshp* 1915
Sales 123.5MM *EMP* 2ᴱ
SIC 8699 Athletic organizations
Prin: Donald Honea Sr
Prin: Trimble Gilbert
Prin: Jerry Isaac
Prin: Carl Jerue
Prin: Pat McCarty

D-U-N-S 09-786-0956
TANDBERG TELEVISION INC
4500 River Green Pkwy, Duluth, GA 30096-8312
Tel (678) 812-6300 *Founded/Ownrshp* 2001
Sales 134.0MMᴱ *EMP* 400ᴱ
SIC 4841

TANDEM GLOBAL LOGISTICS
See C H POWELL CO

D-U-N-S 00-959-8884
TANDEM HEALTH CARE OF CHESWICK INC
CONSULATE HEALTH CARE CHESWICK
(*Suby of* CONSULATE HEALTH CARE LLC) ★
3876 Saxonburg Blvd, Cheswick, PA 15024-2228
Tel (412) 767-4998 *Founded/Ownrshp* 1998
Sales 423.5MMᴱ *EMP* 100ᴱ
SIC 8051 Skilled nursing care facilities
Ch Bd: Lawrence Deering
**Pr:* Joseph Conte
Doctor: Missy Oglesby

D-U-N-S 18-920-7087
TANDEM HEALTHCARE OF WEST PALM BEACH INC
(*Suby of* EDGEWOOD MANOR OF WESTERVILLE) ★
1626 Davis Rd, West Palm Beach, FL 33406-5640
Tel (561) 439-8897 *Founded/Ownrshp* 1997
Sales 15.8MMᴱ *EMP* 3,980ᴱ
SIC 8059 8051 Nursing home, except skilled & intermediate care facility; Skilled nursing care facilities
Pr: Marty B Clark
Sls&Mrk Ex: Susan Watchet

D-U-N-S 01-563-0668 IMP/EXP
TANDUS CENTIVA INC
(*Suby of* TARKETT DELAWARE) ★
311 Smith Industrial Blvd, Dalton, GA 30721-8661
Tel (706) 259-9711 *Founded/Ownrshp* 2012
Sales 490.7MMᴱ *EMP* 1,579
SIC 2273 Carpets & rugs
Pr: Glen A Hussmann
**CFO:* Leonard F Ferro
**Sr VP:* J Bradley Cummings
Sr VP: James Harley
**Sr VP:* Rusty Joyce
**Sr VP:* Dan Mayfield
VP: Don Chupik
**VP:* Mausi McDaniel
VP: Jim Sandy
VP Mfg: Jim Harley
Opers Mgr: David Wilkinson

TANDUS FLOORING
See TANDUS GROUP INC

D-U-N-S 15-983-4613
TANDUS GROUP INC
TANDUS FLOORING
311 Smith Industrial Blvd, Dalton, GA 30721-8661
Tel (706) 259-9711 *Founded/Ownrshp* 1996
Sales 301.5MMᴱ *EMP* 1,623ᴱ
SIC 2273 Carpets, textile fiber
CEO: Glenn Hussman
Pr: Sandy Butler
**Pr:* Roger Ray
CFO: Jeff Goldbird
Ofcr: Tressia Watkins
**Sr VP:* Lee Schilling
**VP:* Stephen Martin Burns
**VP:* Len Ferro
**VP:* James T Harley
Plnt Mgr: David Haynes
Prd Mgr: Chad Morrow

D-U-N-S 61-327-4133 IMP
▲TANDY BRANDS ACCESSORIES INC
ROLFS
501 N College St, Waxahachie, TX 75165-3361
Tel (214) 519-5200 *Founded/Ownrshp* 1990
Sales 114.0MM *EMP* 399ᴱ
Tkr Sym TBAC *Exch* OTO
SIC 3172 5961 Personal leather goods;
Ch Bd: Roger R Hemminghaus
Pr: Jane Batts
Pr: Randy Lockard
CFO: Chuck Talley
Ex VP: Alexandra All
Ex VP: Robert J McCarten
VP: Kristin Sperlin
Board of Directors: Lisbeth R McNabb, William D Summitt

D-U-N-S 03-993-7917 IMP/EXP
▲TANDY LEATHER FACTORY INC
1900 Se Loop 820, Fort Worth, TX 76140-1003
Tel (817) 872-3200 *Founded/Ownrshp* 1980
Sales 84.1MM *EMP* 584ᴱ
Tkr Sym TLF *Exch* NGM
SIC 5948 5199 3111 Leather goods, except luggage & shoes; Leather, leather goods & furs; Accessory products, leather; Lace leather

CEO: Shannon L Greene
**Ch Bd:* Joseph R Mannes
**Pr:* Mark Angus
CFO: Shannon Greene
Sls&Mrk Ex: Jim Kovach
Board of Directors: Jefferson Gramm, T Field Lange, L Edward Martin III, James Pappas

TANG GROUP
See T H ONE INC

D-U-N-S 09-922-4859
▲TANGER FACTORY OUTLET CENTERS INC
3200 Northline Ave # 360, Greensboro, NC 27408-7616
Tel (336) 292-3010 *Founded/Ownrshp* 1993
Sales 439.3MM *EMP* 625
Tkr Sym SKT *Exch* NYS
SIC 6798 Real estate investment trusts
Pr: Steven B Tanger
Ch Bd: William G Benton
COO: Thomas E McDonough
CFO: Frank C Marchisello Jr
CFO: James F Williams
Treas: Carrie Geldner
Treas: Virginia R Summerell
Ofcr: Carrie A Geldner
Ex VP: Chad D Perry
Sr VP: Manuel O Jessup
Sr VP: Lisa J Morrison
Sr VP: Charles A Worsham
VP: Rick Farrar
Board of Directors: Bridget M Ryan-Berman, Jeffrey B Citrin, David B Henry, Thomas J Reddin, Thomas E Robinson, Allan L Schuman

D-U-N-S 01-796-2148
■TANGER PROPERTIES LIMITED PARTNERSHIP (NC)
(*Suby of* TANGER FACTORY OUTLET CENTERS INC) ★
3200 Northline Ave # 360, Greensboro, NC 27408-7616
Tel (336) 292-3010 *Founded/Ownrshp* 1993
Sales 439.3MM *EMP* 614
Accts Pricewaterhousecoopers Llp Ch
SIC 6798 Real estate investment trusts
Ch Bd: Steven B Tanger
CFO: Frank C Marchisello Jr
Sr VP: Carrie A Warren
VP: Kevin M Dillon
VP: Lisa J Morrison

D-U-N-S 11-428-1090
TANGIPAHOA PARISH SCHOOL BOARD INC
59656 Puleston Rd, Amite, LA 70422-5616
Tel (985) 748-2433 *Founded/Ownrshp* 1877
Sales 188.0MM *EMP* 2,500
Accts Carr Riggs & Ingram Llc Met
SIC 8211 School board
Pr: Brett Duncan
**CFO:* Bret Schnadelbach
Prin: Danette Ragusa
Board of Directors: Chris Cohea- Board Preside

D-U-N-S 07-960-8293
TANGIPAHOA PARISH SCHOOL SYSTEM
59656 Puleston Rd, Amite, LA 70422-5616
Tel (985) 748-2416 *Founded/Ownrshp* 2014
Sales 198.1MM *EMP* 2,353ᴱ
Accts Laporte Apac Covington La
SIC 8211 Public elementary & secondary schools
Off Admin: Monica Echols
Off Admin: Cynthia Jenkins
Cmptr Lab: Catherine Donnow
IT Man: Carol Edwards
Teacher Pr: Ron Genco
Psych: Terri Brignac
Doctor: Tammy Campo
HC Dir: Jennifer Carona
HC Dir: Verna Thompson

TANGLEWOOD
See BOSTON SYMPHONY ORCHESTRA INC

D-U-N-S 78-329-6387
TANGO TRANSPORT LLC
2933 Belclaire Dr, Frisco, TX 75034-5969
Tel (318) 683-6700 *Founded/Ownrshp* 1991
Sales 239.6MMᴱ *EMP* 925
SIC 4213

D-U-N-S 13-514-6673
▲TANGOE INC
35 Executive Blvd, Orange, CT 06477-3621
Tel (203) 859-9300 *Founded/Ownrshp* 2000
Sales 212.4MM *EMP* 2,339
Tkr Sym TNGO *Exch* NGS
SIC 7372 Application computer software
Acting CEO: James Foy
CFO: Jay Zager
Ch: Gerald Kokos
Chf Mktg O: Sidra Berman
Ofcr: Manuel N Sousa
Sr VP: Eric J Wansong
VP: Melanie Baran
VP: Ryan Burke
VP: Stan Cherak
VP: Andy Cohen
VP: Gerry Denza
VP: John Dretler
VP: Matt Evans
VP: Don Farias
VP: Mike Fuhrmeister
VP: Matt Kane
VP: Thomas Kreisig
VP: Jaan Leemet
VP: Ken Lienemann
VP: Garrett Long
VP: Ian Lovatt
Board of Directors: David M Coit, Gary P Golding, Ronald W Kaiser, Jackie R Kimzey, Gerald G Kokos, Richard S Pontin, Noah J Walley

D-U-N-S 06-476-5654 IMP/EXP
TANIMURA & ANTLE FRESH FOODS INC
1 Harris Rd, Salinas, CA 93908-8608
Tel (831) 455-2950 *Founded/Ownrshp* 1988
Sales 569.3MMᴱ *EMP* 2,500
SIC 0161 0182 0723 2099 Lettuce farm; Celery farm; Cauliflower farm; Food crops grown under cover; Vegetable packing services; Food preparations
Pr: Rick Antle
**COO:* Ken Silveira
**CFO:* Vic Feuerstein
CFO: Vic Goochey
**Ex VP:* Mike Antle
**Ex VP:* Gary Tanimura
**VP:* Steve Bassi
**VP:* Tom Casas
**VP:* Robert Nielsen
**VP:* Carmen Ponce
Sales Exec: Jason Grolnick

TANK & TUMMY STORES
See PUGH OIL CO INC

D-U-N-S 55-741-0201 IMP/EXP
TANK CONNECTION LLC
3609 N 16th St, Parsons, KS 67357-3401
Tel (620) 423-0251 *Founded/Ownrshp* 2003
Sales 125.9MMᴱ *EMP* 125
SIC 5084 3443 Industrial machinery & equipment; Tanks, storage; Industrial vessels, tanks & containers
Genl Mgr: Glenda Reynolds
Manager: John Haight
Manager: David Mann
Manager: Paul Martin
Manager: Marty Millis

D-U-N-S 79-347-5232
TANKERSLEY FOOD SERVICE LLC
3203 Industrial Park Rd # 303, Van Buren, AR 72956-6109
Tel (479) 471-6800 *Founded/Ownrshp* 2005
Sales 137.1MMᴱ *EMP* 200ᴱ
SIC 5142 Packaged frozen goods
VP: Thomas Moon
VP Sls: Rick Daughtary

D-U-N-S 15-731-2737
TANKSTAR USA INC
ROGER'S CARTAGE
611 S 28th St, Milwaukee, WI 53215-1201
Tel (414) 671-3039 *Founded/Ownrshp* 1986
Sales 302.5MMᴱ *EMP* 1,500
SIC 4213

D-U-N-S 03-902-6802 IMP/EXP
TANNER INDUSTRIES INC
NATIONAL AMMONIA DIV
735 Davisville Rd Ste 3, Southampton, PA 18966-3277
Tel (215) 322-1238 *Founded/Ownrshp* 1890
Sales 158.5MMᴱ *EMP* 130
SIC 5169 Ammonia
Ch Bd: Raymond C Tanner
**Pr:* Stephen B Tanner
Treas: Eric Hindawi
**Sec:* Eric R Hindawi
**VP:* Greg W Tanner
Sfty Mgr: John Post
Sfty Mgr: Harold Siver
Sales Exec: Lisa Conway
Manager: Bryan Stolee
Board of Directors: Donna Tanner

D-U-N-S 06-918-9066
TANNER MEDICAL CENTER INC (GA)
TANNER MEDICAL CTR CARROLLTON
705 Dixie St, Carrollton, GA 30117-3818
Tel (770) 836-9666 *Founded/Ownrshp* 1949
Sales 223.9MM *EMP* 1,600
SIC 8062

TANNER MEDICAL CTR CARROLLTON
See TANNER MEDICAL CENTER INC

D-U-N-S 62-258-1908
TAOS MOUNTAIN LLC
121 Daggett Dr, San Jose, CA 95134-2110
Tel (408) 324-2800 *Founded/Ownrshp* 1996
Sales 118.8MMᴱ *EMP* 550
SIC 7379 Computer related consulting services
CEO: Ricardo Urrutia
Pr: Katherine Brown
COO: Jeff Lucchesi
CFO: Mary Hale
VP: Carrina Cappadona
VP: Michele Marshall
VP: Ryan Munson
VP: Patricia Palumbo
VP: Trish Palumbo
VP: Patty Shrum
Exec: Chris Browne
Exec: Brenna Obrien
Exec: Ben Polson
Board of Directors: Robert Clark, Mark Deblois, Jared Paquette

D-U-N-S 95-956-6626
TAP OPERATING CO LLC
400 W Artesia Blvd, Compton, CA 90220-5501
Tel (310) 900-5500 *Founded/Ownrshp* 2008
Sales 87.2MMᴱ *EMP* 1,200
SIC 5013 Truck parts & accessories

D-U-N-S 04-732-8521 IMP
TAP PHARMACEUTICAL PRODUCTS INC
675 N Field Dr, Lake Forest, IL 60045-4832
Tel (847) 582-2000 *Founded/Ownrshp* 2008
Sales 275.3MMᴱ *EMP* 3,118
SIC 5122

D-U-N-S 96-459-9422 IMP/EXP
TAP WORLDWIDE LLC
4 WHEEL PARTS PERFORMANCE CTRS
400 W Artesia Blvd, Compton, CA 90220-5501
Tel (310) 900-5500 *Founded/Ownrshp* 2009
Sales 775.8MMᴱ *EMP* 1,200ᴱ
SIC 5013 Motor vehicle supplies & new parts
Pr: Greg Adler
COO: Rich Botello
**COO:* Tim Mongi

**CFO:* Mark Lane
Comm Dir: Eric Couts
Rgnl Mgr: Dennis Dady
Dir IT: Greg Gardiner
IT Man: Mike Ahmad
Opers Mgr: Greg Bolton
Sls Dir: David Rittenhouse
Sls Mgr: Eileen Duran

TAPCO
See TRAFFIC AND PARKING CONTROL CO INC

D-U-N-S 12-442-9937
■TAPCO UNDERWRITERS INC
(*Suby of* CRC INSURANCE SERVICES INC) ★
3060 S Church St, Burlington, NC 27215-5153
Tel (336) 584-8892 *Founded/Ownrshp* 2008
Sales NA *EMP* 175
Accts Stout Stuart Mcgowen & King Ll
SIC 6411 Insurance agents, brokers & service
Pr: Tapley O Johnson III
Treas: Floyd L Ingold Jr
**Ex VP:* J D Henderson
**Ex VP:* Bill Pinson
VP: Virginia Clancy
**VP:* Buster Ingold Jr
Mng Dir: Todd Coleman
MIS Dir: Douglas Crumpton
Sls Mgr: Ellen McBride

D-U-N-S 14-240-5724 IMP/EXP
TAPCOENPRO LLC
(*Suby of* DOWNSTREAM AGGREGATOR, LLC)
16315 Market St, Channelview, TX 77530-4427
Tel (281) 247-8100 *Founded/Ownrshp* 2015
Sales 89.6MMᴱ *EMP* 100ᴱ
SIC 3491 Industrial valves
Pr: Ruben Lah
CFO: John Furka
Genl Mgr: Joe Dittola
Genl Mgr: John Gamuz
Genl Mgr: Elango Narendran

TAPIA BROTHERS CO
See TAPIA ENTERPRISES INC

D-U-N-S 13-050-0994 IMP
TAPIA ENTERPRISES INC
TAPIA BROTHERS CO
6067 District Blvd, Maywood, CA 90270-3560
Tel (323) 560-7415 *Founded/Ownrshp* 1985
Sales 269.0MMᴱ *EMP* 225
SIC 5141 Groceries, general line
CEO: Raul Tapia
**Treas:* Francisco Tapia

D-U-N-S 93-050-9609
TAPPET BROTHERS ASSOCIATES
DEWEY CHEETHAM & HOWE
5 John F Kennedy St # 304, Cambridge, MA 02138-4916
Tel (617) 876-6632 *Founded/Ownrshp* 1988
Sales 9.4MMᴱ *EMP* 1,800
SIC 7922 Radio producers
Pt: Thomas Magliozzi
Pt: Doug Berman
Pt: Ray Magliozzi

TAPS
See TRIDENT INSURANCE SERVICES LLC

D-U-N-S 12-168-8873
TAR HEEL CAPITAL CORP NO 2
WENDY'S
166 Southgate Dr Ste 10, Boone, NC 28607-2905
Tel (828) 264-4221 *Founded/Ownrshp* 1977
Sales 36.2MMᴱ *EMP* 1,000
SIC 5812 Fast-food restaurant, chain
CEO: Jim Furman Jr
**Pr:* Tad Dolbier
CFO: Heath Betchley
**CFO:* Melissa Collins
**Sec:* Richard Furman
**VP:* Robert Frist
VP Opers: Bob Gasbarro

D-U-N-S 11-506-2994
TARBELL FINANCIAL CORP
1403 N Tustin Ave Ste 380, Santa Ana, CA 92705-8691
Tel (714) 972-0988 *Founded/Ownrshp* 1982
Sales NA *EMP* 1,300
SIC 6163 6531 6099 Mortgage brokers arranging for loans, using money of others; Real estate brokers & agents; Escrow institutions other than real estate
CEO: Donald Tarbell
**Pr:* Tina Jimov
**COO:* Jin Lee
**CFO:* Ronald Tarbell

TARBELL REALTORS
See F M TARBELL CO

D-U-N-S 84-376-2449
TARBORO NURSING CARE
911 Western Blvd, Tarboro, NC 27886-4016
Tel (252) 823-2041 *Founded/Ownrshp* 2000
Sales 722.3MM *EMP* 125
SIC 8051 Skilled nursing care facilities
Owner: Steve Powell

D-U-N-S 78-951-4200
■TARGA ENERGY LP
ATLAS ENERGY, L.P.
(*Suby of* TARGA RESOURCES CORP) ★
1000 Commerce Dr Ste 400, Pittsburgh, PA 15275-1033
Tel (412) 489-0006 *Founded/Ownrshp* 2015
Sales 19.6MMᴱ *EMP* 1,074ᴱ
SIC 1311 4922 Crude petroleum & natural gas; Natural gas transmission
Pr: Edward E Cohen
Genl Pt: Atlas Energy GP
CFO: Sean P McGrath
CFO: Matthew J Meloy

D-U-N-S 07-874-0629
■TARGA PIPELINE MID-CONTINENT HOLDINGS LLC
(*Suby of* ATLAS PIPELINE OPER PARTNR LP) ★
110 W 7th St Ste 2300, Tulsa, OK 74119-1017
Tel (918) 574-3500 *Founded/Ownrshp* 2015
Sales 331.0MM[E] *EMP* 366[E]
SIC 4922 Natural gas transmission

D-U-N-S 12-427-8057
■TARGA PIPELINE MID-CONTINENT LLC
ATLAS PIPELINE
(*Suby of* TARGA PIPELINE MID-CONTINENT HOLDINGS LLC) ★
110 W 7th St Ste 2300, Tulsa, OK 74119-1017
Tel (918) 574-3500 *Founded/Ownrshp* 2015
Sales 329.0MM[E] *EMP* 336[E]
SIC 1389 Processing service, gas
Pr: Eugene N Dubay
Pr: Daniel C Herz
**COO:* Patrick McDonie
CFO: David Hall
**CFO:* Robert Karlovich III
CFO: Robert W Karlovich
VP: Todd Bazata
VP: Mike Coon
VP: Greg Dibold
Area Mgr: Wayne Bennett

D-U-N-S 80-650-9381
■TARGA PIPELINE OPERATING PARTNERSHIP LP
ATLAS PIPELINE OPER PARTNR LP
(*Suby of* TARGA PIPELINE PARTNERS LP) ★
1845 Walnut St, Philadelphia, PA 19103-4708
Tel (412) 489-0006 *Founded/Ownrshp* 1999
Sales 331.0MM[E] *EMP* 371[E]
SIC 1311 Crude petroleum & natural gas production
CEO: Edward Cohen
CFO: Sean McGrath

D-U-N-S 08-539-8530 IMP
■TARGA PIPELINE PARTNERS LP
(*Suby of* TARGA RESOURCES PARTNERS LP) ★
1000 Commerce Dr Ste 400, Pittsburgh, PA 15275-1033
Tel (877) 950-7473 *Founded/Ownrshp* 2015
Sales 383.9MM[E] *EMP* 450[E]
SIC 4922 Natural gas transmission; Pipelines, natural gas
Pr: Eugene N Dubay
CFO: Eric T Kalamaras
Ex VP: Bill May
VP: Brian J Begley
VP: Tom Williams

TARGA RESOURCES
See TRI RESOURCES INC

D-U-N-S 82-738-9847
▲TARGA RESOURCES CORP
1000 La St Ste 4300, Houston, TX 77002
Tel (713) 584-1000 *Founded/Ownrshp* 2005
Sales 6.6MMM *EMP* 1,870[E]
Tkr Sym TRGP *Exch* NYS
SIC 4922 4924 Natural gas transmission; Pipelines, natural gas; Storage, natural gas; Natural gas distribution
CEO: Joe Bob Perkins
**Ch Bd:* James W Whalen
**V Ch:* Michael A Heim
Pr: Jeffrey J McParland
CFO: Matthew J Meloy
CFO: Mattthew J Meloy
Ofcr: John R Sparger
Ex VP: Paul W Chung
Ex VP: Patrick J McDonie
Ex VP: Dan C Middlebrooks
Ex VP: D Scott Pryor
Ex VP: Clark White
VP: Linda Troeh
Board of Directors: Charles R Crisp, Robert B Evans, Laura C Fulton, Rene R Joyce, Chris Tong

D-U-N-S 82-739-0266
■TARGA RESOURCES LLC
(*Suby of* TARGA RESOURCES) ★
1000 Louisiana St # 4300, Houston, TX 77002-5036
Tel (713) 873-1000 *Founded/Ownrshp* 2003
Sales 138.1MM[E] *EMP* 217[E]
SIC 1389 6799 Servicing oil & gas wells; Investors
CEO: Joe Bob Perkins
**Pr:* Michael A Heim
**CFO:* Matthew J Meloy
**Ex VP:* Roy E Johnson
VP Mktg: Hunter Battle

D-U-N-S 78-433-9918
■TARGA RESOURCES PARTNERS LP
(*Suby of* TARGA RESOURCES CORP) ★
1000 Louisiana St # 4300, Houston, TX 77002-5036
Tel (713) 584-1000 *Founded/Ownrshp* 2016
Sales 6.6MMM *EMP* 1,870[E]
SIC 4922 4924 5172 Natural gas transmission; Natural gas distribution; Gases, liquefied petroleum (propane)
CEO: Joe Bob Perkins
Genl Pt: Targa Resources GP LLC
CFO: Matthew J Meloy
Ex VP: Michael A Heim
VP: Stacy Duke
Area Mgr: Greg Stephenson
IT Man: Jeffrey J McParland
Counsel: David Honeycutt
Snr Mgr: Arturo Herr

D-U-N-S 06-462-2124
■TARGET CAPITAL CORP
TARGET FINANCIAL SERVICES
(*Suby of* TARGET CORP) ★
1000 Nicollet Mall, Minneapolis, MN 55403-2542
Tel (612) 304-6073 *Founded/Ownrshp* 1994
Sales 149.4MM[E] *EMP* 800[E]
SIC 6282 Investment advice
CEO: Brian C Cornell
**Pr:* Terry Scully
Exec: Zhi Zhong

TARGET CENTER
See AEG MANAGEMENT TWN LLC

D-U-N-S 00-696-1700 IMP/EXP
▲TARGET CORP (MN)
1000 Nicollet Mall, Minneapolis, MN 55403-2542
Tel (612) 304-6073 *Founded/Ownrshp* 1902
Sales 73.7MMM *EMP* 341,000
Accts Ernst & Young Llp Minneapolis
Tkr Sym TGT *Exch* NYS
SIC 5311 5411 Department stores; Grocery stores
Ch Bd: Brian C Cornell
V Ch: Mollie McCarty
COO: John J Mulligan
CFO: Catherine R Smith
Treas: Morgan Thomas
Chf Mktg O: Mark Tritton
Ofcr: Janna Adair-Potts
Ofcr: Jason Goldberger
Ofcr: Don H Liu
Ex VP: Patricia Adams
Ex VP: Trish Adams
Ex VP: Casey L Carl
Ex VP: Melinda Hanson
Ex VP: Jeff Jones
Ex VP: Jodeen Kozlak
Ex VP: Stephanie A Lundquist
Ex VP: Michael E McNamara
Ex VP: Jacqueline Hourigan Rice
Ex VP: Mark J Tritton
Sr VP: Timothy R Baer
Sr VP: Ben Cook
Board of Directors: Anne M Mulcahy, Roxanne S Austin, Kenneth L Salazar, Douglas M Baker Jr, Calvin Darden, Henrique De Castro, Robert L Edwards, Melanie L Healey, Donald R Knauss, Monica C Lozano, Mary E Minnick

TARGET FINANCIAL SERVICES
See TARGET CAPITAL CORP

TARGET ROCK
See CURTISS-WRIGHT FLOW CONTROL CORP

D-U-N-S 00-192-0065
■TARGET SOURCING SERVICES CORP
AMC
(*Suby of* TARGET CORP) ★
500 Fashion 7th Ave Fl 5a, New York, NY 10018
Tel (800) 440-0680 *Founded/Ownrshp* 1916, 2012
Sales 62.6MM[E] *EMP* 2,000
SIC 7389 Purchasing service
Pr: Stacia Anderson
VP: Barbara Dugan
**VP:* Theodore Taylor

D-U-N-S 96-275-4128 IMP
■TARGET STORES INC
(*Suby of* TARGET CORP) ★
1000 Nicollet Mall, Minneapolis, MN 55403-2542
Tel (612) 304-6073 *Founded/Ownrshp* 1962
Sales 22.7MMM[E] *EMP* 341,000[E]
SIC 5411 5311 5461 Supermarkets; Department stores, discount; Bakeries
CEO: Brian C Cornell
**Pr:* Terri Simard
VP: Pam Johnson

D-U-N-S 04-816-2981 IMP/EXP
TARGUS INTERNATIONAL LLC
1211 N Miller St, Anaheim, CA 92806-1933
Tel (714) 765-5555 *Founded/Ownrshp* 2016
Sales 400.0MM *EMP* 400
SIC 5199 Bags, baskets & cases
CEO: Mikel Williams
**Pr:* Bill Oppenlander
**CFO:* Victor C Streufert
Sr VP: Theresa Hope-Reese
Sr VP: Robert Shortt
VP: James Demanett
VP: Allen H Gharapetian

TARKETT DELAWARE
See TARKETT INC

D-U-N-S 05-431-8142 IMP
TARKETT INC
TARKETT DELAWARE
(*Suby of* TARKETT INC)
16910 Munn Rd, Chagrin Falls, OH 44023-5411
Tel (800) 899-8916 *Founded/Ownrshp* 1981, 1994
Sales 676.6MM[E] *EMP* 2,379
SIC 3069 Flooring, rubber: tile or sheet
CEO: Jeff Buttitta
**Pr:* Jack Lee
**Sec:* Peter De Bonis
Chf Mktg O: Jonathan Klinger
VP: Debbie McLaughlin
Tech Mgr: Brad Marler
Software D: Hollis Barden
Sls Mgr: Joe Bongiorno

D-U-N-S 02-916-3741
TARKETT USA INC
JOHNSONITE
(*Suby of* TARKETT)
30000 Aurora Rd, Solon, OH 44139-2728
Tel (440) 543-8916 *Founded/Ownrshp* 1996
Sales 373.1MM[E] *EMP* 1,500
SIC 3253 Ceramic wall & floor tile
Pr: Jeff Fenwick
**CFO:* Nicolas Carre
CFO: Christopher Webb
Exec: Carmen Pastore

D-U-N-S 07-316-1697
TARLETON STATE UNIVERSITY
TEXAS A & M UNIVERSITY
(*Suby of* TEXAS A & M UNIVERSITY) ★
1333 W Washington St, Stephenville, TX 76401-4168
Tel (254) 968-9107 *Founded/Ownrshp* 1899
Sales 114.9MM *EMP* 822[E]
SIC 8221 University
Pr: F Dominic Dottavio
Pr: Susie Fagan
Assoc VP: Jim Cook
Assoc VP: Joe Strandridge
Assoc Dir: Van Evans
Ex Dir: Robert Hooper
Tech Mgr: Johnny Feagan

D-U-N-S 11-296-8839
TARMAC MID-ATLANTIC INC
(*Suby of* TITAN AMERICA LLC) ★
1151 Azalea Garden Rd, Norfolk, VA 23502-5601
Tel (757) 858-6500 *Founded/Ownrshp* 1991
Sales 80.4MM[E] *EMP* 1,062
SIC 3273 1442 3272 3271 Ready-mixed concrete; Construction sand & gravel; Concrete products; Pipe, concrete or lined with concrete; Blocks, concrete or cinder: standard
Pr: John D Carr
VP: Terry G Aldridge
VP: Bruce A Smith
Mktg Mgr: Larry Summers
Board of Directors: Anthony Hopkins

D-U-N-S 17-376-2329 IMP
TARO PHARMACEUTICALS USA INC
SUN PHARMACEUTICAL INDUSTRIES
(*Suby of* TARO PHARMACEUTICAL INDUSTRIES LTD.)
3 Skyline Dr Ste 120, Hawthorne, NY 10532-2131
Tel (914) 345-9000 *Founded/Ownrshp* 1965
Sales 169.5MM[E] *EMP* 325
SIC 5122 Pharmaceuticals
CEO: James Kedrowski
**Ch Bd:* Barry Levitt
VP: William Coote
VP: Michael Kalb
VP: Rakesh Mehta
VP: Samuel Rubinstein
Assoc Dir: Senajda Celaj
Ex Dir: Ralph Bohrer
Tech Mgr: Kristine Semetsis
Info Man: Peter Zurlo
VP Mfg: Joseph Schlosser

D-U-N-S 07-321-6871
TARPON SPRINGS HOSPITAL FOUNDATION INC
FLORIDA HOSPITAL NORTH PINELLA
1395 S Pinellas Ave, Tarpon Springs, FL 34689-3790
Tel (727) 942-5000 *Founded/Ownrshp* 1947
Sales 96.6MM *EMP* 1,600
SIC 8062 General medical & surgical hospitals
Pr: Steve Maclauchlan

D-U-N-S 07-313-9040
TARRANT COUNTY COLLEGE DISTRICT
1500 Houston St, Fort Worth, TX 76102-6524
Tel (817) 515-5220 *Founded/Ownrshp* 1965
Sales 322.3MM[E] *EMP* 3,050
SIC 5942 8221 College book stores; Colleges universities & professional schools
Ex Dir: Erma Johnson Hadley
**Pr:* Louise Appleman
**Pr:* Bill Coppola
**Pr:* Tahita Fulkerson
**Pr:* Allen Goben
**Pr:* Peter Jordan
**Pr:* Elva C Leblanc
Bd of Dir: Michael Cinatl
Ofcr: Klothe Mary
VP: Tunson Carrie
VP: Michael Devlin
**VP:* Mark McClendon
**VP:* Nina Petty
VP: Magdalena Teja
**VP:* Kristin Vandergriff

D-U-N-S 06-836-8901
TARRANT COUNTY HOSPITAL DISTRICT (TX)
JOHN PETER SMITH HOSPITAL
1500 S Main St, Fort Worth, TX 76104-4917
Tel (817) 921-3431 *Founded/Ownrshp* 1913
Sales 557.6MM *EMP* 3,000
SIC 8062 General medical & surgical hospitals
CEO: Robert Earley
**Pr:* David M Cecero
**COO:* Bill Whitman
**CFO:* Randy Rogers
CFO: Allan Townsend
Ex VP: Gary Floyd
Sr VP: Nikki Sumpter
VP: Scott Rule
Dir Lab: Conrado Sampang
Adm Dir: Kathleen Whelen
MIS Dir: Jim Roberts

D-U-N-S 06-836-5220
TARRANT COUNTY TEXAS (INC) (TX)
100 E Weatherford St, Fort Worth, TX 76196-0206
Tel (817) 884-1111 *Founded/Ownrshp* 1849
Sales NA *EMP* 3,945
Accts Kpmg Llp Dallas Tx
SIC 9111 Executive offices;
**CFO:* B Glen Whitley
Off Mgr: Tina Valdez
Dir IT: Jessica Buchert
IT Man: Rodney Crockett
Netwrk Eng: Vernon Leonard
Psych: Peggy McCray

D-U-N-S 60-206-4222 IMP
TARSADIA HOTELS
620 Newport Center Dr # 1400, Newport Beach, CA 92660-8025
Tel (949) 610-8000 *Founded/Ownrshp* 1976
Sales 67.4MM[E] *EMP* 1,500
SIC 7011

TARTAN TEXTILE SERVICES
See TTS INC

D-U-N-S 04-116-6372 IMP
TARTER GATE CO LLC
10739 S Us 127, Dunnville, KY 42528-6037
Tel (435) 744-0770 *Founded/Ownrshp* 1966
Sales 133.0MM[E] *EMP* 600
SIC 3446 0219 Fences, gates, posts & flagpoles; General livestock

D-U-N-S 00-636-9516 IMP/EXP
TARTER GATE WOOD PRODUCTS INC (KY)
10739 S Us 127, Dunnville, KY 42528-6037
Tel (606) 787-2081 *Founded/Ownrshp* 1945, 1980
Sales 123.9MM[E] *EMP* 600[E]
SIC 3446 2448 2499 2426 2421 Architectural metalwork; Pallets, wood; Fencing, docks & other outdoor wood structural products; Hardwood dimension & flooring mills; Sawmills & planing mills, general
Pr: Donald R Tarter
**Sec:* Vivian K Tarter
**VP:* Travis Cox
**VP:* David A Tarter

TAS
See TAS CONSTRUCTION INC

D-U-N-S 04-306-4901
■TAS COMMERCIAL CONCRETE CONSTRUCTION LLC
(*Suby of* ORION GROUP HOLDINGS INC) ★
19319 Oil Center Blvd, Houston, TX 77073-3354
Tel (281) 230-7500 *Founded/Ownrshp* 1980
Sales 149.7MM[E] *EMP* 1,500
SIC 1771 Concrete work
Treas: Robert Bacon
**VP:* Eddie Sanders
Sfty Dirs: Grace Fox

D-U-N-S 13-170-8740
TAS COMMERCIAL CONCRETE LLC
(*Suby of* SCULLY SERVICES LLC) ★
19319 Oil Center Blvd, Houston, TX 77073-3354
Tel (281) 230-7500 *Founded/Ownrshp* 2002
Sales 97.8MM[E] *EMP* 781[E]
SIC 8711 Construction & civil engineering
Pt: Mark Scully
Exec: Grace Fox

D-U-N-S 10-684-3956
TAS CONSTRUCTION INC
TAS
19319 Oil Center Blvd, Houston, TX 77073-3354
Tel (281) 230-7500 *Founded/Ownrshp* 1980
Sales 102.6MM[E] *EMP* 1,150
Accts Houston Texas
SIC 1771 Concrete work; Foundation & footing contractor; Concrete pumping
Pr: Mark T Scully
**Treas:* Robert Bacon

D-U-N-S 80-902-5799
TAS HOLDING INC
TIMCO
623 Radar Rd, Greensboro, NC 27410-6221
Tel (336) 668-4410 *Founded/Ownrshp* 2006
Sales 91.1MM[E] *EMP* 3,400
SIC 4581 5088 Airports, flying fields & services; Airport control tower operation, except government; Fixed base operator; Aircraft & space vehicle supplies & parts
CEO: Kevin Carter
**Pr:* Rick Salanitri

D-U-N-S 87-802-3050
TAS-CGSMC INC
CUSHING CAMPUS
235 N Pearl St, Brockton, MA 02301-1794
Tel (508) 427-3000 *Founded/Ownrshp* 1993
Sales NA *EMP* 1,100
SIC 8062

D-U-N-S 19-601-5648
TAS-CHFH
HOLY FAMILY HOSPITAL & MED CTR
(*Suby of* CARITAS CHRISTI HEALTH CARE) ★
70 East St, Methuen, MA 01844-4597
Tel (978) 687-0156 *Founded/Ownrshp* 1984
Sales 108.3MM[E] *EMP* 1,700
Accts Feeley & Driscoll Pc Boston
SIC 8062 General medical & surgical hospitals
Ch Bd: Peter Gori
**Pr:* Thomas Sager
COO: Martha McDrury
Ex VP: Joseph Maher Jr
Dir Lab: Donald G Ross
Dir Rad: Katherine Miller
Dir Sec: Jim Deroche
Doctor: Dhirendra Pathak

D-U-N-S 07-171-7250
TAS-CNH INC
CARITAS NORWOOD HOSPITAL
(*Suby of* CARITAS CHRISTI HEALTH CARE) ★
800 Washington St Ste 1, Norwood, MA 02062-3487
Tel (781) 769-4000 *Founded/Ownrshp* 1997
Sales 127.7MM[E] *EMP* 1,800
Accts Feeley & Driscoll Pc Boston
SIC 8062 General medical & surgical hospitals
Pr: John B Chessare
Dir Recs: Melanie Altruda
COO: Willian Flemimg
**Sr VP:* Robert Guyon
VP: William Fleming
VP: Diana Franchitto
VP: Mary A Glynn
Dir Lab: Patricia Watson
MIS Dir: Lynn Bowen
Pathlgst: Lori Adcock
Surgeon: Adam M Glasgow

D-U-N-S 07-379-7292
TAS-CSEMCB INC
CARITAS MEDICAL GROUP
(*Suby of* CARITAS CHRISTI HEALTH CARE) ★
736 Cambridge St, Boston, MA 02135-2907
Tel (617) 789-3149 *Founded/Ownrshp* 1872
Sales 164.1MM[E] *EMP* 2,365
SIC 8062 General medical & surgical hospitals
Pr: Christopher O Connor
Dir Recs: Kathleen Forde
**CEO:* J Bryan Hehir
COO: Ellie Bergeron
**CFO:* William Sullivan
VP: Lynn Bowen
VP: David Chicoine
VP: Mark Tarlton
Dir Case M: Cheryl Warren
Dir Rx: Patricia Masters
Off Mgr: Joanne Goyco

D-U-N-S 07-381-5987
TAS-CVRHS INC
70 East St, Methuen, MA 01844-4597
Tel (978) 687-0151 *Founded/Ownrshp* 1984
Sales 23.6MM[E] *EMP* 1,500
SIC 8062 General medical & surgical hospitals
Ch Bd: John E Fenton Jr
**Pr:* Tom Sager

D-U-N-S 07-572-8170
TAS-SAHC INC
ST ANNE'S HOSPITAL
795 Middle St, Fall River, MA 02721-1733
Tel (508) 674-5600 *Founded/Ownrshp* 1985
Sales 102.1MM[E] *EMP* 1,250
SIC 8062 8011 General medical & surgical hospitals; Oncologist
Pr: Craig Jesiolowski
**Ch Bd:* Vimala Vadakuntadan
**Pr:* Michael Bushell
**VP:* Carole A Billington
Exec: Christin Hale
Dir Rad: Joan Sousa
Chf Nrs Of: Carole Billington
Pr Mgr: Karen Champagne

TASC
See ENGILITY CORP

D-U-N-S 12-722-8377
TASCO AUTO COLOR CORP
(*Suby of* TWF HOLDING CORPORATION)
10323 Veterans Mem Dr, Houston, TX 77038-1727
Tel (281) 999-3761 *Founded/Ownrshp* 2008
Sales 87.1MM[E] *EMP* 200
SIC 5198 5013 5231 5531 Paints, varnishes & supplies; Automotive supplies & parts; Body repair or paint shop supplies, automotive; Paint; Automotive parts
Prin: Thomas W Ferguson
Treas: Wesley Thompson
VP: Lee Martinez
Store Mgr: Wayne Dysinger
Telecom Ex: David Abrahams

D-U-N-S 83-217-6382 IMP
▲TASER INTERNATIONAL INC
17800 N 85th St, Scottsdale, AZ 85255-6311
Tel (480) 991-0797 *Founded/Ownrshp* 1993
Sales 197.8MM *EMP* 549[E]
Tkr Sym TASR *Exch* NGS
SIC 3489 Ordnance & accessories
CEO: Patrick W Smith
**Ch Bd:* Michael Garnreiter
Pr: Luke S Larson
CFO: Daniel M Behrend
Ex VP: Joshua M Isner
Genl Mgr: Marcus W L Womack
Genl Couns: Douglas E Klint
Board of Directors: John S Caldwell, Richard H Carmona, Mark W Kroll, Judy Martz, Matthew R McBrady, Bret Taylor

D-U-N-S 02-633-5183
TASKUS INC
3233 Donald, Santa Monica, CA 90405
Tel (888) 400-8275 *Founded/Ownrshp* 2008
Sales 854.9M[E] *EMP* 5,000
SIC 7374 Data processing service
CEO: Bryce Maddock
Pr: Jaspar Weir
CFO: Balaji Sekar
Sr VP: Lital Gilad-Shaoulian
Dir Surg: Michael Epsenhart
Off Mgr: Martin Ayala
Off Mgr: Karina Riffo
CIO: Christopher McLaughlin-Brooks
IT Man: Sonny Narcelles
Opers Mgr: King Leung
Opers Mgr: Matthew Mink

D-U-N-S 02-408-8858 EXP
TASMAN INDUSTRIES INC (KY)
TASMAN LEATHER
930 Geiger St, Louisville, KY 40206-1616
Tel (502) 785-7477 *Founded/Ownrshp* 1947
Sales 85.4MM[E] *EMP* 330
SIC 3111 5159 Leather tanning & finishing; Hides
Pr: Norman Tasman
**VP:* David Ernstberger

TASMAN LEATHER
See TASMAN INDUSTRIES INC

D-U-N-S 00-226-6369 IMP
■TASTY BAKING CO (PA)
TASTY KAKE
(*Suby of* FLOWERS FOODS INC) ★
4300 S 26th St, Philadelphia, PA 19112-1608
Tel (215) 221-8500 *Founded/Ownrshp* 1914, 2011
Sales 220.8MM[E] *EMP* 637
SIC 2051 2052 Cakes, pies & pastries; Cakes, bakery: except frozen; Pies, bakery: except frozen; Doughnuts, except frozen; Bakery products, dry; Cookies; Pretzels
Pr: Charles P Pizzi
**Treas:* Eugene P Malinowski
Treas: John M Pettine
**Ex VP:* Robert V Brown
Sr VP: David Marberger
VP: Hugo Fernandes
VP: Lisa Hanssen
VP: Thomas Junod
**VP:* Paul D Ridder
Sls&Mrk Ex: Robin Caterson
VP Sls: Christopher Rahey

TASTY KAKE
See TASTY BAKING CO

D-U-N-S 05-432-8054
TATA AMERICA INTERNATIONAL CORP (NY)
TCS AMERICA
(*Suby of* TATA CONSULTANCY SERVICES LIMITED)
101 Park Ave Rm 2603, New York, NY 10178-2604
Tel (212) 557-8038 *Founded/Ownrshp* 1975, 2005
Sales 755.2MM *EMP* 1,700
Accts Deloitte Haskins & Sells Llp
SIC 7379 Computer related consulting services
CEO: Cyrus Mistry
CFO: S Mahalingam
Bd of Dir: Bharat Wakhlu
Ex VP: Gabriel Rozman
Sr VP: V Ramakrishnan
VP: Kaushik Chatterjee
VP: Alan Hughes
VP: John Lenzen
VP: Raman Venkatraman
Exec: Sanjay Singh
Comm Dir: Michael McCabe
Dir Bus: Ron Jankowski
Dir Bus: Divya Suvarna
Mng Ofcr: Dharmesh Gandhi
Board of Directors: Cyrus Mistry

D-U-N-S 16-805-4737 IMP/EXP
TATA CHEMICALS NORTH AMERICA INC
TCNA
(*Suby of* TATA CHEMICALS LIMITED)
100 Enterprise Dr Ste 701, Rockaway, NJ 07866-2176
Tel (973) 599-5500 *Founded/Ownrshp* 2008
Sales 223.9MM[E] *EMP* 736
SIC 2812 Soda ash, sodium carbonate (anhydrous)
CEO: J Martin Keighley
Top Exec: Pearl Mascarenhas
**VP:* Ron Achter
**VP:* Scott Ellis
VP: Bo Pennington
Genl Mgr: Sunil Deshpande
Genl Mgr: Chris Douville
S&M/VP: Christopher Douville
Snr Mgr: Tata Sons

D-U-N-S 14-734-6063
TATA COMMUNICATIONS (AMERICA) INC
TELEGLOBE VSNL INTERNATIONAL
(*Suby of* TATA COMMUNICATIONS LIMITED)
2355 Dulles Corner Blvd # 700, Herndon, VA 20171-6154
Tel (703) 657-8400 *Founded/Ownrshp* 2012
Sales 485.6MMM *EMP* 100[E]
Accts T R Chadha & Co Llp Lower Par
SIC 4813
CEO: Vinod Kumar
**Pr:* Anthony Bartolo
**COO:* John Hayduk
**CFO:* Pratibha K Advani
**CFO:* Sanjay Baweja
Treas: Jose Tertraulti
**Ex VP:* John R Freeman
**Ex VP:* David M Ryan
Sr VP: Jean-Pierre Gratton
Sr VP: Christian Michaud
VP: Mike Galvin
VP: Jim Hamrick
VP: Rogena Harris
VP: Avanish Pande
Exec: Atul Kumar
Exec: Dominic Marsan
Exec: Allison Ponturo
Exec: Joe Romanow
Exec: Hui Shen

D-U-N-S 00-715-4458
TATA COMMUNICATIONS (US) INC
(*Suby of* TATA CONSULTANCY SERVICES LIMITED)
90 Matawan Rd Ste 300, Matawan, NJ 07747-2653
Tel (732) 888-6700 *Founded/Ownrshp* 1997, 2006
Sales 107.2MM[E] *EMP* 285
SIC 4813
Prin: Liam Strong
Ch Bd: Thomas Evslin
Pr: Gerald Liam Strong
COO: Eric G Weiss
VP: Eleanor Carrara
VP: Shashi Kaligotla
VP: M MA
VP: Dominic Tetu
VP: Theodore M Weitz
Exec: Bablo Amonkar
Exec: Abhishek Mishra
Exec: Prashant Nagaje
Exec: Hemant Ninawe
Exec: Ankush Pawar
Exec: Atit Sheth
Assoc Dir: Eduardo Lobato
Assoc Dir: Gaurav Tambar
Board of Directors: Liam Strong

D-U-N-S 60-299-0012
TATA TECHNOLOGIES INC
(*Suby of* TATA TECHNOLOGIES LIMITED)
41050 W 11 Mile Rd, Novi, MI 48375-1902
Tel (248) 426-1482 *Founded/Ownrshp* 1997
Sales 280.1MM[E] *EMP* 890
SIC 8711 Engineering services
CEO: Warren Harris
Pr: Biswadip Shome
**Pr:* Samir Yajnik
**CEO:* Patrick McGoldrick
**CFO:* Samrat Gupta
Assoc VP: Wishwas Julka
Ex VP: Ron Bienkowski
Sr VP: Sushaiv Wadekar
VP: Harry Hanson
Exec: Pradeep Charan
Exec: Pallavi Kulkarni

TATE & LYLE CITRIC ACID
See TATE & LYLE INGREDIENTS AMERICAS LLC

D-U-N-S 12-232-0559 IMP/EXP
TATE & LYLE INGREDIENTS AMERICAS LLC
TATE & LYLE CITRIC ACID
(*Suby of* TATE & LYLE PUBLIC LIMITED COMPANY)
2200 E Eldorado St, Decatur, IL 62521-1578
Tel (217) 423-4411 *Founded/Ownrshp* 1988
Sales 852.3MM[E] *EMP* 2,098
SIC 2046 Wet corn milling
CEO: John Schnake
**CEO:* Javed Ahmed
**CFO:* Nick Hampton
Treas: Ralph Tizora
Ex VP: Rob Gibber
Ex VP: Rob Luijten
VP: Rick Becker
VP: Dan Curry
VP: Robert Hough
VP: Robert Peterson
VP: Vincent Pinneri
VP: Lawrence Pociask
VP: Rand Roslak
VP: Robert V Schaneffelt
VP: Doug Varvil
Board of Directors: Rene Baugnee, Pierre Callebaut V Chb, Paul S Lewis, Pat Mohen, Larry G Pillard, Robert M Powers, Neil M Shaw, H Saxson Tate

D-U-N-S 87-661-5097
TATEM BROWN FAMILY PRACTICE
GAMBLE, JAMES MD
2225 E Evesham Rd Ste 101, Voorhees, NJ 08043-1557
Tel (856) 795-7075 *Founded/Ownrshp* 1984
Sales 266.3MM *EMP* 100
SIC 8011 General & family practice, physician/surgeon

D-U-N-S 10-335-7398
TATITLEK CORP
561 E 36th Ave, Anchorage, AK 99503-4137
Tel (907) 278-4000 *Founded/Ownrshp* 1973
Sales 130.0MM *EMP* 45
SIC 0811 6552 7361 Tree farm; Subdividers & developers; Employment agencies
Ch: Lloyd Allen
**Pr:* Roy Totemoff
**Treas:* Sheri Buretta
**VP:* Ken Vlasoff

D-U-N-S 05-867-1538
TATUM DEVELOPMENT CORP
11 Parkway Blvd, Hattiesburg, MS 39401-8893
Tel (601) 544-6043 *Founded/Ownrshp* 1981
Sales 788.3MM[E] *EMP* 660
SIC 5141 5084 4924 3443 Groceries, general line; Welding machinery & equipment; Natural gas distribution; Vessels, process or storage (from boiler shops): metal plate
Pr: Robert O Tatum
**Sec:* Frederick E Tatum
**VP:* John M Tatum Jr
Off Mgr: Debbie Ingram

D-U-N-S 00-810-7922 IMP/EXP
TAUBER OIL CO
55 Waugh Dr Ste 700, Houston, TX 77007-5837
Tel (713) 869-8700 *Founded/Ownrshp* 1953
Sales 2.2MMM *EMP* 135
Accts Mohle Adams Houston Texas
SIC 1311 Crude petroleum & natural gas
Pr: Richard E Tauber
COO: Dack Franks
**Ex VP:* David W Tauber
VP: Ollivier Giampietri
**VP:* Stephen E Hamlin
VP: John Happ
VP: David Kayle
VP: Brad Kerby
VP: Connie Kubiak
VP: Saul Laurel
VP: Ed Naspinski
VP: Wakefield Papa
VP: Mauricio Ruiz
VP: John Wakefield
Exec: Elizabeth Meredith
Dir Risk M: Alan Barto

D-U-N-S 79-817-8885
▲TAUBMAN CENTERS INC
200 E Long Lake Rd # 300, Bloomfield Hills, MI 48304-2324
Tel (248) 258-6800 *Founded/Ownrshp* 1973
Sales 557.1MM *EMP* 615[E]
Tkr Sym TCO *Exch* NYS
SIC 6798 Real estate investment trusts
Ch Bd: Robert S Taubman
Pr: Rene Tremblay
**COO:* William S Taubman
CFO: Simon J Leopold
Ex VP: David S Joseph II
Ex VP: Stephen J Kieras
VP: Maureen Fill
VP: David A Wolff
Board of Directors: Graham T Allison, Jerome A Chazen, Craig M Hatkoff, Peter Karmanos Jr, Ronald W Tysoe, Myron E Ullman III

D-U-N-S 96-140-3847
TAUNTON INC
TAUNTON PRESS
63 S Main St, Newtown, CT 06470-2355
Tel (203) 426-8171 *Founded/Ownrshp* 1995
Sales 85.3MM[E] *EMP* 844
SIC 2721 2731 7812 5963 Magazines: publishing only, not printed on site; Books: publishing only; Video tape production; Direct sales, telemarketing
CEO: Daniel R McCarthy
**Ch Bd:* Andrea Roman
**Pr:* Timothy Rahr
Dir IT: Jay Hartley

D-U-N-S 04-661-6033
TAUNTON MUNICIPAL LIGHTING PLANT
CITY OF TAUNTON
33 Weir St, Taunton, MA 02780-3931
Tel (508) 824-5844 *Founded/Ownrshp* 1882, 1897
Sales 97.2MM[E] *EMP* 165
SIC 4911 Generation, electric power
Ch: Joseph Martin
Chf Mktg O: Mike Horrigan
Genl Mgr: Joseph Balin
HC Dir: Jeanine Flaherty
Snr Mgr: Al Santos

TAUNTON PRESS
See TAUNTON INC

D-U-N-S 13-806-1937
TAVANT TECHNOLOGIES INC
3965 Freedom Cir Ste 750, Santa Clara, CA 95054-1285
Tel (408) 519-5400 *Founded/Ownrshp* 2000
Sales 35.0MM[E] *EMP* 1,000[E]
Accts Berger Lewis San Jose Ca
SIC 7371 Custom computer programming services; Computer software development; Computer software systems analysis & design, custom
CEO: Sarvesh Mahesh
**CFO:* Venkata Devana
Ofcr: Krishnan Pp
**Sr VP:* Hassan Rashid
Exec: Shannon Lane
**Prin:* Jerome Marr
**Prin:* Rajiv Ranjan
**CTO:* Manish Arya
QA Dir: Deepak Kumar
VP Sls: Raj Nair
Sls Dir: Tarun Kapoor

D-U-N-S 11-293-8956
TAVISTOCK RESTAURANT GROUP
PAPA RAZZI
35 Braintree Hill Park # 1107, Braintree, MA 02184-8703
Tel (781) 817-4400 *Founded/Ownrshp* 2011
Sales 108.6MM[E] *EMP* 3,200
SIC 5812 Italian restaurant; American restaurant
Ch Bd: Charles F Sarkis
**Pr:* Bryan Lockwood
**CFO:* Richard P Dalton
**Treas:* Robert J Ciampa
VP Opers: Ann M Lagrotteria

D-U-N-S 14-154-4820
TAVISTOCK RESTAURANTS LLC
CALIFORNIA CAFE
(*Suby of* T R RESTAURANTS HOLDING LTD)
2024 N Woodlawn St # 417, Wichita, KS 67208-1879
Tel (510) 594-4262 *Founded/Ownrshp* 2003
Sales 72.1MM[E] *EMP* 1,590
SIC 5812 Cafe
CEO: John T Bettin
COO: Aniel Chopra
IT Man: Randal White

TAVO VASQUEZ DISTRIBUTING
See MARIBEL RESENDIZ

TAW
See TAMPA ARMATURE WORKS INC

D-U-N-S 07-836-0632 EXP
TAWA SERVICES INC
6281 Regio Ave Fl 2, Buena Park, CA 90620-1023
Tel (714) 521-8899 *Founded/Ownrshp* 2012
Sales 197.0MM[E] *EMP* 270
SIC 5149 5411 Groceries & related products; Grocery stores
CEO: Jonson Chen
**CEO:* Young You

D-U-N-S 13-959-4857 IMP
TAWA SUPERMARKET INC
99 RANCH MARKET
6281 Regio Ave, Buena Park, CA 90620-1023
Tel (714) 521-8899 *Founded/Ownrshp* 1984
Sales 234.1MM[E] *EMP* 1,300
SIC 5411 Supermarkets, independent
CEO: Chang Hua K Chen
COO: Yong You
CFO: Alice Chen
Top Exec: Raymond MA
Ex VP: Daniel Au
VP: Peter Tran
IT Man: Sridhar Nannuru
Mktg Dir: Henry Sun
Counsel: Iris Leong
Board of Directors: Allen Lee

TAX ASSISTANCE GROUP
See TAX DEFENSE NETWORK LLC

D-U-N-S 88-354-7838
TAX COMMISSION UTAH STATE
(*Suby of* EXECUTIVE OFFICE OF STATE OF UTAH) ★
210 N 1950 W, Salt Lake City, UT 84134-9000
Tel (801) 297-2200 *Founded/Ownrshp* 1995
Sales NA *EMP* 1,038
SIC 9311 Taxation department, government;
Ch: John Valentine
Ofcr: Jeff Johnson
Ofcr: Jennifer Stansfield
Prgrm Mgr: Mike Godfrey

D-U-N-S 87-659-2598
TAX DEFENSE NETWORK LLC
TAX ASSISTANCE GROUP
9000 Southside Blvd # 11000, Jacksonville, FL 32256-6768
Tel (904) 421-4410 *Founded/Ownrshp* 1997
Sales 85.0MM *EMP* 250
SIC 7299 Personal financial services; Debt counseling or adjustment service, individuals
Pr: Joseph Valinho
VP: Frank Valinhho
Sls Dir: Brad Blankley

TAX OFFICE
See FAYETTE COUNTY PUBLIC SCHOOLS

D-U-N-S 80-678-0722
TAXATION AND FINANCE DEPARTMENT NEW YORK STATE
(*Suby of* EXECUTIVE OFFICE OF STATE OF NEW YORK) ★
W A Harriman Campus Bldg, Albany, NY 12227-0001
Tel (518) 457-2244 *Founded/Ownrshp* 1788
Sales NA *EMP* 25,644
SIC 9311 Taxation department, government;
Treas: Eric Mostert

D-U-N-S 78-394-3694
TAXI HOLDINGS CORP
(*Suby of* WELLSPRING DISTRIBUTION INC) ★
390 Park Ave, New York, NY 10022-4608
Tel (212) 318-9800 *Founded/Ownrshp* 2008
Sales 160.9MM[E] *EMP* 7,940[E]
SIC 5812 6794 Drive-in restaurant; Franchises, selling or licensing

D-U-N-S 18-275-5038 IMP
TAYLOR & FRANCIS GROUP LLC
(*Suby of* INFORMA GROUP PLC)
6000 Broken Sound Pkwy Nw # 300, Boca Raton, FL 33487-5704
Tel (800) 634-7064 *Founded/Ownrshp* 2004
Sales 107.0MM[E] *EMP* 500

SIC 2721 2731 Periodicals: publishing only; Trade journals: publishing only, not printed on site; Books: publishing only; Textbooks: publishing only, not printed on site
Pr: Roger Graham Horton
Ex VP: Kevin Bradley
Ex VP: Timothy Emmett Dages
VP: Marc Levine
IT Man: Dan Maher
VP Mktg: Stacey Mironov
Mktg Mgr: David Grubbs

D-U-N-S 00-267-3226
TAYLOR CAPITAL GROUP INC
9550 W Higgins Rd, Rosemont, IL 60018-4906
Tel (847) 653-7978 *Founded/Ownrshp* 1996
Sales NA *EMP* 938ᴱ
SIC 6022

TAYLOR COMMUNICATIONS
See STANDARD REGISTER INC

D-U-N-S 00-617-5806
TAYLOR CORP
1725 Roe Crest Dr, North Mankato, MN 56003-1807
Tel (507) 625-2828 *Founded/Ownrshp* 1974
Sales 5.1MMMᴱ *EMP* 12,190
SIC 8742 2752 2677 2759 Management consulting services; Commercial printing, lithographic; Envelopes; Commercial printing
CEO: Deb Taylor
**CFO:* Tom Johnson
CFO: Curtis Mohr
CFO: Kim Walters
**Ch:* Glen A Taylor
Bd of Dir: David Wachowiak
**Chf Mktg O:* Steven Singer
Ex VP: John Mattes
Ex VP: Larry Wagner
VP: Renee Belina
VP: Lewis Dennis
VP: Al Hughes
VP: Glenn Kidd
VP: Jason Moreau

TAYLOR EXTENDED CARE
See CARTERET COUNTY GENERAL HOSPITAL CORP

D-U-N-S 55-583-3672
TAYLOR FARMS CALIFORNIA INC
(*Suby of* TAYLOR FRESH FOODS INC) ★
150 Main St Ste 500, Salinas, CA 93901-3462
Tel (831) 754-0471 *Founded/Ownrshp* 1995
Sales 295.3MMᴱ *EMP* 1,400
SIC 0723 Vegetable crops market preparation services
Owner: Bruce Taylor
**Pr:* Alec Leach
**CFO:* Thomas Bryan
Dir Bus: Ed St Clair
IT Man: Bryan Bockman
VP Opers: Jerrett Stoffel
Sls Mgr: Chris Downs
Snr Mgr: Paul Mulrooney

D-U-N-S 93-830-8103 IMP
TAYLOR FARMS FLORIDA INC
(*Suby of* TAYLOR FRESH FOODS INC) ★
7492 Chancellor Dr, Orlando, FL 32809-6242
Tel (407) 515-8436 *Founded/Ownrshp* 1996
Sales 156.0MMᴱ *EMP* 480
SIC 3523 Grading, cleaning, sorting machines, fruit, grain, vegetable
Ch Bd: Bruce Taylor
**Pr:* Tim Unick
**CFO:* Tom Bryan
**Prin:* Alec Leach

D-U-N-S 06-548-5943
TAYLOR FARMS MARYLAND INC
(*Suby of* TAYLOR FRESH FOODS INC) ★
9055 Junction Dr, Annapolis Junction, MD 20701-1107
Tel (301) 617-2942 *Founded/Ownrshp* 2000
Sales 150.0MM *EMP* 500ᴱ
SIC 5431 0723 Fruit & vegetable markets; Vegetable crops market preparation services
Genl Mgr: Michael George
Manager: Scott Casciano

D-U-N-S 12-376-0758
TAYLOR FARMS TEXAS INC
(*Suby of* TAYLOR FRESH FOODS INC) ★
1001 N Cockrell Hill Rd, Dallas, TX 75211-1318
Tel (214) 421-1947 *Founded/Ownrshp* 1995
Sales 221.8MMᴱ *EMP* 1,304
SIC 5149 Health foods
CEO: Bruce Taylor
**Pr:* James Hyatt
**CFO:* Thomas Bryan
Sfty Dirs: Thalia Vasquez

D-U-N-S 87-852-1277 IMP
TAYLOR FRESH FOODS INC
150 Main St Ste 400, Salinas, CA 93901-3442
Tel (831) 676-9023 *Founded/Ownrshp* 1995
Sales 3.0MMM *EMP* 3,500
SIC 0723 Vegetable crops market preparation services
CEO: Bruce Taylor
VP: Glen Fry
Genl Mgr: Alan Applonie
Ql Cn Mgr: Greg McLucas
Ql Cn Mgr: Heather Pask-Atkins
Snr PM: Ashley Boozer

D-U-N-S 84-741-2293 IMP/EXP
TAYLOR GROUP INC
650 N Church Ave, Louisville, MS 39339-2033
Tel (662) 773-3421 *Founded/Ownrshp* 1991
Sales 508.4MMᴱ *EMP* 1,000
SIC 7699 5999 Industrial equipment services; Engine & motor equipment & supplies
Pr: W A Taylor III
**VP:* Jimmy G Ramsey
**VP:* Robert D Taylor

TAYLOR GUITARS
See TAYLOR-LISTUG INC

D-U-N-S 09-774-9360
TAYLOR HOLDINGS INC
(*Suby of* TAYLOR GROUP INC) ★
650 N Church Ave, Louisville, MS 39339-2033
Tel (662) 773-3421 *Founded/Ownrshp* 1973
Sales 153.0MMᴱ *EMP* 1,000
SIC 5051 Steel
Pr: William A Taylor Jr
**Treas:* Pete Reynolds
**VP:* Jimmy Ramsey
**VP:* Robert Davis Taylor

D-U-N-S 84-767-6053
TAYLOR HOSPITAL
(*Suby of* CROZER-KEYSTONE HEALTH SYSTEM) ★
175 E Chester Pike, Ridley Park, PA 19078-2284
Tel (610) 595-6000 *Founded/Ownrshp* 1900
Sales 96.9MMᴱ *EMP* 1,000
SIC 8062 General medical & surgical hospitals
CEO: Joan Richards
**Pr:* Diane Miller
Off Mgr: Jim Cape
Off Mgr: Kathy Gillan
Doctor: Armando Mendez
Doctor: Gregory Tadduni
Nrsg Dir: Christine Mendez
Pharmcst: Josh Patel
Pharmcst: Doreen Yeung

D-U-N-S 00-339-8294 IMP/EXP
TAYLOR MACHINE WORKS INC
(*Suby of* TAYLOR GROUP INC) ★
650 N Church Ave, Louisville, MS 39339-2033
Tel (662) 773-3421 *Founded/Ownrshp* 1927
Sales 313.7MMᴱ *EMP* 810
SIC 3537 Forklift trucks
Pr: William A Taylor III
**Treas:* Pete Reynolds
**VP:* Richard P Ballard
Mng Dir: John Paschal
Ql Cn Mgr: Tommy McKinley
Sls Mgr: Donald Woodruff Jr
Board of Directors: Edith T Paschal, John C Ryan, Mitzie Taylor

D-U-N-S 00-206-3634 IMP/EXP
TAYLOR MADE GROUP HOLDINGS INC
NELSON A TAYLOR CO
66 Kingsboro Ave, Gloversville, NY 12078-3415
Tel (518) 725-0681 *Founded/Ownrshp* 1908
Sales 200.2MMᴱ *EMP* 1,300
SIC 3429

D-U-N-S 96-275-9408
TAYLOR MADE GROUP LLC
(*Suby of* NELSON A TAYLOR CO) ★
66 Kingsboro Ave, Gloversville, NY 12078-3415
Tel (518) 725-0681 *Founded/Ownrshp* 2009
Sales 135.9MMᴱ *EMP* 890ᴱ
SIC 3429 3231 Marine hardware; Windshields, glass: made from purchased glass
Mktg Mgr: Mike Oathout

D-U-N-S 04-328-5675
TAYLOR MCCORMICK INC (PA)
2001 Market St Fl 10, Philadelphia, PA 19103-7066
Tel (215) 592-4200 *Founded/Ownrshp* 1946, 1989
Sales 84.3MMᴱ *EMP* 400
SIC 8711 Consulting engineer
Pr: Thomas A Caramanico
**CFO:* D J Freedman
**Ex VP:* James C Wiggins
**VP:* John D Kahil
IT Man: Elisa Greene
VP Mktg: Gary Bellotti

D-U-N-S 07-870-3254
▲TAYLOR MORRISON HOME CORP
4900 N Scottsdale Rd # 2000, Scottsdale, AZ 85251-7656
Tel (480) 840-8100 *Founded/Ownrshp* 2012
Sales 2.9MMM *EMP* 1,600ᴱ
Tkr Sym TMHC *Exch* NYS
SIC 1521 New construction, single-family houses
Pr: Sheryl D Palmer
**Ch Bd:* Timothy R Eller
**Pr:* Sheryl Palmer
CFO: C David Cone
Ofcr: Graham Hughes
Ex VP: Erik Heuser
Ex VP: Alan E Laing
VP: Bob Witte
Sales Asso: Maribel Leon
Sales Asso: Brenda McCallion
Sales Asso: Brian Nelson
Board of Directors: John Brady, Kelvin Davis, James Henry, Joe S Houssian, Jason Keller, Peter Lane, Anne L Mariucci, David Merritt, James Sholem

D-U-N-S 13-714-0427
■TAYLOR MORRISON INC
TAYLOR WOODROW HOMES
(*Suby of* TAYLOR MORRISON HOME CORP) ★
4900 N Scottsdale Rd # 2000, Scottsdale, AZ 85251-7656
Tel (480) 840-8100 *Founded/Ownrshp* 2008
Sales 138.0MMᴱ *EMP* 167ᴱ
SIC 1521 New construction, single-family houses
Pr: Sheryl Palmer
**Ch Bd:* Tim Eller
Pr: Brad Carr
Pr: Steve Wethor
CFO: Ed Barnes
CFO: David Cone
Treas: Calvin Boyd
Ex VP: Robert Witte
VP: C David Cone
VP: Patty Crane
VP: Kathleen R Owen
Exec: Cristina Iaboni
Board of Directors: Peter Lane

TAYLOR PROPANE GAS
See GIBSON ENERGY MARKETING LLC

D-U-N-S 00-732-4627 IMP
TAYLOR PUBLISHING CO
(*Suby of* AAC) ★
1550 W Mockingbird Ln, Dallas, TX 75235-5007
Tel (214) 819-8321 *Founded/Ownrshp* 1938, 2000
Sales 289.5MMᴱ *EMP* 1,439
SIC 2731 2732 Books: publishing & printing; Books: printing & binding
Pr: Donald J Percenti
CFO: Steve Bower
**CFO:* Richard Russell
Sr Cor Off: Craig Van Pelt
Sr VP: Mike Parker
**VP:* W Gregg Smart
Sftwr Eng: Payam Shabaneh
Opers Mgr: Chris Wells
VP Sls: Michael Parker
Mktg Dir: Mike Cobb
Sls Mgr: Corey Mundwiler

TAYLOR ROOFING CO
See D C TAYLOR CO

D-U-N-S 07-841-4331
TAYLOR SCHOOL DISTRICT (MI)
23033 Northline Rd, Taylor, MI 48180-4625
Tel (734) 374-1200 *Founded/Ownrshp* 1920
Sales 78.7MMᴱ *EMP* 1,308
Accts Abraham & Gaffney Pc Roche
SIC 8211 Public elementary & secondary schools
Sfty Dirs: Michelle Marshall

TAYLOR WOODROW HOMES
See TAYLOR MORRISON INC

D-U-N-S 07-336-1545 IMP
TAYLOR-LISTUG INC
TAYLOR GUITARS
1980 Gillespie Way, El Cajon, CA 92020-1096
Tel (619) 258-6957 *Founded/Ownrshp* 1974
Sales 109.0MM *EMP* 920ᴱ
SIC 3931 Guitars & parts, electric & nonelectric
CEO: Kurt Listug
**Pr:* Robert Taylor
VP: Richard Berry
VP: Keith Brawley
VP: Ed Granero
VP: Kur Lisug
VP: Brian Swerdfeger
VP: Chris Wellons
VP: Barbara Wight
Dir IT: Ted Corral
Plnt Mgr: Sergio Villanueva

D-U-N-S 13-720-7622
TAYLOR-SMART LLC
2207 N Center St, Bonham, TX 75418-2112
Tel (903) 583-7481 *Founded/Ownrshp* 2000
Sales 168.4MMᴱ *EMP* 550ᴱ
Accts Fox Byrd & Company Pc Dal
SIC 5171 Petroleum bulk stations & terminals

D-U-N-S 80-865-4417 IMP/EXP
TAYLOR-WHARTON INTERNATIONAL LLC
TWI
5600 Rowland Rd Ste 170, Minnetonka, MN 55343-4419
Tel (717) 763-5060 *Founded/Ownrshp* 2007
Sales 501.5MMᴱ *EMP* 1,662
SIC 3443 3491 Tanks, lined: metal plate; Tanks, standard or custom fabricated: metal plate; Vessels, process or storage (from boiler shops): metal plate; Gas valves & parts, industrial
CEO: Bill Corbin
**Pr:* Amato Spagnoletti
Pr: Len York
**CEO:* Eric Rottier
**COO:* Roland Wright
**CFO:* Jim Hoppel
Treas: Denise Macivor
**VP:* Maggie Debner
**VP:* Suzanne Rosenthal
**VP:* Joseph Sorce

TAYLOR-WHARTON-CRYOGENICS
See TW CRYOGENICS LLC

D-U-N-S 09-727-9541 IMP/EXP
TAYLORMADE GOLF CO INC
(*Suby of* ADIDAS NORTH AMERICA INC) ★
5545 Fermi Ct, Carlsbad, CA 92008-7324
Tel (877) 860-8624 *Founded/Ownrshp* 1979
Sales 274.8MMᴱ *EMP* 800
SIC 3949 Shafts, golf club
Pr: Mark King
CEO: Ben Sharpe
CFO: Melissa Claassen
Ex VP: John Kawaja
Ex VP: Sean Toulon
Sr VP: Bill Reimus
VP: Howard Allrad
VP: David Bradley
VP: Dave Brownie
VP: Tom Collard
VP: John Gonsalves
VP: Eric G Laborde
VP: Blake McHenry
VP: Jan Strickland
Creative D: Jesus Cobian

D-U-N-S 07-680-5449
TAZEWELL COUNTY BOARD OF EDUCATION
209 W Fincastle Tpke, Tazewell, VA 24651-1062
Tel (276) 988-5511 *Founded/Ownrshp* 1805
Sales 42.0MMᴱ *EMP* 1,100
SIC 8211 School board
Ch Bd: David Woodard

D-U-N-S 06-252-6673
TBA INSURANCE GROUP LIMITED PARTNERSHIP
STATE NATIONAL COMPANIES
1900 L Don Dodson Dr, Bedford, TX 76021-8222
Tel (817) 265-2000 *Founded/Ownrshp* 1973
Sales NA *EMP* 400
SIC 6331 6163 Fire, marine & casualty insurance; Loan brokers
Pt: Lonnie Ledbetter
**Pt:* Terry Ledbetter
Pr: Charlie Miller
Pr: Bill Nemecek
Ex VP: David Cleff
VP: David Crawford
VP: Don West
Exec: Matthew Freeman

D-U-N-S 15-078-4648 IMP/EXP
TBC CORP
(*Suby of* SUMITOMO CORP OF AMERICAS) ★
4300 Tbc Way, Palm Beach Gardens, FL 33410-4281
Tel (561) 227-0955 *Founded/Ownrshp* 2005
Sales 3.3MMMᴱ *EMP* 9,400
SIC 5014 Tire & tube repair materials
Ch Bd: Lawrence C Day
**Pr:* J Glen Gravatt
COO: Michael Gould
COO: Kevin A Kormondy
**CFO:* Timothy J Miller
Ex VP: John Kairys
Sr VP: Markus Hockenson
**Sr VP:* Terry L Trantina
Sr VP: Brant Wilson
VP: Bob Crostarosa
VP: Mike Feliton
VP: James Fleming
VP: Ron Gooch
VP: Bryan Hoppe
VP: Greg Ingram
VP: Marty Krcelic
VP: Brian Leporin
VP: Dino Medina
VP: Cpsm Ortega
VP: Richard Purol
VP: James Rowe

D-U-N-S 06-360-6172 IMP/EXP
TBC RETAIL GROUP INC
(*Suby of* BIG O TIRES) ★
4280 Prof Ctr Dr Ste 400, Palm Beach Gardens, FL 33410
Tel (561) 383-3000 *Founded/Ownrshp* 2001
Sales 232.9MMᴱ *EMP* 1,880
SIC 7538 5531 7534 General automotive repair shops; Automotive tires; Tire retreading & repair shops
CEO: Erik R Olsen
**Pr:* N William Ihnken
VP: Loren Jacobs
Exec: Sandra Sallman
Brnch Mgr: Roxanne Williamson
CIO: Peter Wellman
IT Man: Valerie Meglis

D-U-N-S 94-743-5595
TBC SHARED SERVICES INC
BIG O TIRES
(*Suby of* TBC CORP) ★
742 S Main St, Sebastopol, CA 95472-4275
Tel (707) 829-9864 *Founded/Ownrshp* 1992
Sales 292.6MMᴱ *EMP* 2,170ᴱ
SIC 5531 7534 Automotive tires; Tire retreading & repair shops
Pr: Timothy J Miller
**Sec:* Terry Trantina
Dir: Frank Setteducate
Genl Mgr: Ben Hammond
Genl Mgr: Nick Jones
Store Mgr: Mark Simon

TBEI
See TRUCK BODIES & EQUIPMENT INTERNATIONAL INC

D-U-N-S 13-110-2183
TBHC DELIVERS LLC
2967 Sidco Dr, Nashville, TN 37204-3709
Tel (800) 235-3798 *Founded/Ownrshp* 1999
Sales 100.0MM *EMP* 105
SIC 5149 Pizza supplies
Pr: Britt Hunt
**CFO:* Mitch Walker
Dist Mgr: Orville Hess
Dist Mgr: Greg Price

D-U-N-S 06-820-6119
■TBWA CHIAT/DAY INC
(*Suby of* E GRAPHICS) ★
488 Madison Ave Fl 7, New York, NY 10022-5727
Tel (212) 804-1000 *Founded/Ownrshp* 1973, 1995
Sales 73.7MMᴱ *EMP* 1,000
SIC 7311 8743 Advertising agencies; Sales promotion
Pr: Robert Harwood-Matthews
CFO: Jonathan Ramsden
Chf Cred: Stephen Butler
Ofcr: AVI Karshmer
**Ofcr:* Aki Spicer
**Ofcr:* Evan Weissbrot
Sr VP: Morgan McAlenney
Exec: Tasha Dean
Exec: Hashi Meltzer
Exec: Brett Pfeiffer
Dir: Jennifer Costello
Dir: Julie Maciver
Dir: Scott Stanner
Creative D: Walt Connelly
Creative D: Mariota Essery
Creative D: Liz Levy
Creative D: Jason Locey
Creative D: Chris Ribeiro
Creative D: Harris Wilkinson
Mng Ofcr: Doug Melville

D-U-N-S 85-848-5295
■TBWA WORLDWIDE INC
E GRAPHICS
(*Suby of* OMNICOM GROUP INC) ★
488 Madison Ave, New York, NY 10022-5702
Tel (212) 804-1000 *Founded/Ownrshp* 1995
Sales 149.0MM *EMP* 1,290
SIC 7311 Advertising agencies
Pr: Troy Ruhanen
**Ch Bd:* Tom Carroll
**Pr:* Keith Smith
Pr: Perry Valkenburg
Pr: James Vincent
Pr: Gary Wenzel
**COO:* Emmanuel Andre

**CFO:* James Fenton
CFO: Erwan Guillou
**Ch:* Lee Clow
**Ch:* Jean-Marie Dru
Dir: Scott Macmaster

TC AXIAL DIV
See TWIN CITY FAN COMPANIES LTD

D-U-N-S 83-036-9799
TC GLOBAL INC
TULLY'S COFFEE
2003 Western Ave Ste 660, Seattle, WA 98121-2177
Tel (206) 233-2070 *Founded/Ownrshp* 1992
Sales 92.6MM^E *EMP* 670^E
SIC 2095 5149 Roasted coffee; Coffee roasting (except by wholesale grocers); Coffee, green or roasted
Pr: Scott M Pearson
CFO: Catherine M Campbell
VP: Kirk Heinrich
VP: Brian Helm
VP Opers: Dana Pratt
VP Sls: Robert Martin
Board of Directors: Scott I Anderson, Janet L Hendrickson, Gregory A Hubert, Stephen B Loeb

D-U-N-S 61-506-4669 EXP
TC HEARTLAND LLC
HEARTLAND FOOD PRODUCTS GROUP
14300 Clay Terrace Blvd, Carmel, IN 46032-3629
Tel (317) 566-9750 *Founded/Ownrshp* 2004
Sales 188.3MM^E *EMP* 475^E
SIC 2099 Sorghum syrups: for sweetening
CEO: Teodor Gelov
Dir IT: Jeff Mack

D-U-N-S 00-524-8992 IMP/EXP
TC INDUSTRIES INC (IL)
MILL PRODUCTS DIVISION
(*Suby of* TERRA COTTA HOLDINGS CO) ★
3703 S Il Route 31, Crystal Lake, IL 60012-1412
Tel (815) 459-2401 *Founded/Ownrshp* 1881, 1948
Sales 179.7MM *EMP* 514^E
Accts Plante & Moran Pllc
SIC 3499 3398 Machine bases, metal; Metal heat treating
Pr: George A Perry IV
**Ch Bd:* Thomas Z Hayward Jr
Ofcr: Bill Weber
VP: Fred Ballstaedt
VP: Wayne Gritzmacher
Exec: Adriana Henao
Genl Mgr: Bob Berry
Genl Mgr: Tom Carter
CTO: John Nelson
MIS Mgr: Robert Kamin
Opers Mgr: Bill Hudachek

D-U-N-S 78-479-2694
▲TC PIPELINES LP
700 Louisiana St Ste 700, Houston, TX 77002-2873
Tel (877) 290-2772 *Founded/Ownrshp* 1998
Sales 441.0MM *EMP* 7^E
Tkr Sym TCP *Exch* NYS
SIC 4922 Natural gas transmission; Pipelines, natural gas
Pr: Brandon M Anderson
Genl Pt: Tc Pipelines GP
Ch Bd: Karl Johannson
CFO: Nathaniel A Brown
Treas: William C Morris
VP: Terry C Ofremchuk
VP: Janine M Watson

D-U-N-S 06-581-9703
TCA TOLEDO LLC
3611 N Kedzie Ave Fl 2, Chicago, IL 60618-4513
Tel (773) 463-1234 *Founded/Ownrshp* 2001
Sales 61.2MM *EMP* 2,000
SIC 7991 Health club
Prin: Frank Beresh

TCB
See THOMA CRESSEY BRAVO INC

TCC
See TECHNICAL CHEMICAL CO

TCC
See TISHMAN CONSTRUCTION CORP

TCC MATERIALS
See TWIN CITY CONCRETE PRODUCTS CO INC

TCDRS
See TEXAS COUNTY AND DISTRICT RETIREMENT SYSTEM

TCEC
See TRI-COUNTY ELECTRIC COOPERATIVE INC

TCF BANK
See TCF NATIONAL BANK

D-U-N-S 16-196-3707
▲TCF FINANCIAL CORP
200 Lake St E, Wayzata, MN 55391-1693
Tel (952) 745-2760 *Founded/Ownrshp* 1987
Sales NA *EMP* 6,755^E
Tkr Sym TCB *Exch* NYS
SIC 6021 National commercial banks
Pr: Craig R Dahl
**Ch Bd:* William A Cooper
**COO:* Thomas F Jasper
CFO: Brian W Maass
Chf Cred: Mark A Bagley
Ofcr: James M Costa
Ex VP: Brad Adams
Ex VP: Thomas J Butterfield
Ex VP: William S Henak
Sr VP: Susan D Bode
Sr VP: Joseph T Green
Sr VP: Tamara K Schuette
Sr VP: Barbara E Shaw
VP: Lou Burman
VP: Donald Hawkins
Board of Directors: Julie H Sullivan, Peter Bell, Barry N Winslow, William F Bieber, Richard A Zona, Theodore J Bigos, Karen L Grandstrand, George G Johnson, Richard H King, Vance K Opperman, James M Ramstad, Roger J Sit

D-U-N-S 00-621-5131
■TCF NATIONAL BANK
TCF BANK
(*Suby of* TCF FINANCIAL CORP) ★
1405 Xenium Ln N Ste 180, Minneapolis, MN 55441-4406
Tel (612) 661-8450 *Founded/Ownrshp* 1987
Sales NA *EMP* 6,992
SIC 6021 6159 National commercial banks; Machinery & equipment finance leasing
CEO: William A Cooper
Pr: Gary Peterson
**Pr:* Robert Scott
**CFO:* Neil W Brown
Ofcr: Jane Atwood
Ex VP: Bob Brueggeman
**Ex VP:* Sara L Evers
**Ex VP:* Tom Finnegan
**Ex VP:* Mark Jeter
**Ex VP:* Gregory J Pulles
Sr VP: Zafar Farooq
Sr VP: Syd Libsack
VP: Brett Olivo
VP: John Sams
VP: Chris Taylor
VP: Jeff Vint
VP: Terry Waagmeester
Board of Directors: Justin Horstman

D-U-N-S 80-844-6996
■TCFS HOLDINGS INC
(*Suby of* SUNOCO LP) ★
3515 S Bryant Blvd, San Angelo, TX 76903-9309
Tel (325) 655-0676 *Founded/Ownrshp* 1999
Sales 51.6MM^E *EMP* 1,951
SIC 5411 Convenience stores, chain
Pr: Sam L Susser
**CFO:* Mary E Sullivan
**Ex VP:* E V Bonner Jr
Exec: Kathy Maberry
Ex Dir: Patty Rush

TCH
See ELECTRONIC FUNDS SOURCE LLC

D-U-N-S 10-732-9687
TCH PEDIATRIC ASSOCIATES INC
8080 N Stadium Dr Ste 200, Houston, TX 77054-1877
Tel (832) 824-6626 *Founded/Ownrshp* 1994
Sales 142.8MM *EMP* 13^E
SIC 8011 Pediatrician
Ch Bd: Ralph D Feigin
**Pr:* Ayse O McCraken
**CFO:* Paul Heardon
**VP:* Martin I Lorin

TCI
See TRANSCONTINENTAL REALTY INVESTORS INC

D-U-N-S 19-717-6167 IMP
■TCI INC
TCI POWDER COATINGS
(*Suby of* REPUBLIC POWDERED METALS INC) ★
734 Dixon Dr, Ellaville, GA 31806-3414
Tel (229) 937-5411 *Founded/Ownrshp* 1996
Sales 90.0MM^E *EMP* 250
SIC 2851 Coating, air curing
Pr: Doug Greene
CFO: Jerry Cook
VP: Jack Slade
Snr Mgr: Steve Jones

TCI POWDER COATINGS
See TCI INC

TCM
See COMPUTER MERCHANT LTD

TCM
See TRANSITIONAL CARE MANAGEMENT LLC

D-U-N-S 80-554-2649
TCML BUSINESS TRUST
95 Longwater Cir, Norwell, MA 02061-1635
Tel (781) 878-1070 *Founded/Ownrshp* 1999
Sales 127.3MM *EMP* 2
Accts Jameson & Company Pc Lexin
SIC 8611 Business associations
Prin: John R Danieli

TCNA
See TATA CHEMICALS NORTH AMERICA INC

D-U-N-S 79-690-5607
TCOMT INC
111 N Market St Ste 670, San Jose, CA 95113-1112
Tel (408) 351-3340 *Founded/Ownrshp* 2006
Sales 90.0MM *EMP* 89
SIC 3663 Mobile communication equipment
Pr: Clifford Rhee
**Ch:* Michael Luther
**VP:* Vito Picicci

TCP
See TECHNICAL CONSUMER PRODUCTS INC

D-U-N-S 96-829-5498
TCP CAPITAL CORP
2951 28th St Ste 1000, Santa Monica, CA 90405-2993
Tel (310) 566-1000 *Founded/Ownrshp* 2006
Sales 146.8MM *EMP* 4
Accts Ernst & Young Llp Los Angeles
Tkr Sym TCPC *Exch* NGS
SIC 6799 Investors
Ch Bd: Howard M Levkowitz
**Pr:* Rajneesh Vig
CFO: Paul L Davis
Ofcr: Elizabeth Greenwood

D-U-N-S 06-161-2271 IMP/EXP
TCP GLOBAL CORP
AUTOBODY DEPOT
6695 Rasha St, San Diego, CA 92121-2240
Tel (858) 909-2110 *Founded/Ownrshp* 1979
Sales 127.2MM^E *EMP* 67
SIC 5198 5231 Paints; Paint
Pr: Dean A Faucett
**VP:* Rick Faucett

Store Mgr: Matt Herring
Prd Mgr: Kevin Gofstein

TCS AMERICA
See TATA AMERICA INTERNATIONAL CORP

TCSG
See TECHNICAL COLLEGE SYSTEM OF GEORGIA FOUNDATION INC

D-U-N-S 02-989-8843
TCSI-TRANSLAND INC
TRANSLAND BROKERAGE
1601 W Old Route 66, Strafford, MO 65757-7415
Tel (417) 864-5710 *Founded/Ownrshp* 1982
Sales 91.1MM^E *EMP* 285
SIC 4213 Trucking, except local
CEO: Mark Walker
**Pr:* Michael Walker
**CFO:* Tanny Campbell
**VP:* Scott Chastain
VP: Jerry Vanarsdall
Exec: Jeannie Farmer
**Prin:* Glendon Walker
VP Sls: Joe Magee

D-U-N-S 07-995-1580
TCT MOBILE (US) INC
ALCATEL ONE TOUCH
(*Suby of* TCL COMMUNICATION TECHNOLOGY HOLDINGS LIMITED)
25 Edelman Ste 200, Irvine, CA 92618-4359
Tel (949) 892-2990 *Founded/Ownrshp* 2016
Sales 656.0MM *EMP* 200
SIC 5999 5065 Mobile telephones & equipment; Mobile telephone equipment
Genl Mgr: Steve Cistulli
Tech Mgr: Zaki Mashood

D-U-N-S 61-972-0105
■TCW GROUP INC
TRUST COMPANY OF THE WEST
(*Suby of* CARLYLE GROUP L P) ★
865 S Figueroa St # 2100, Los Angeles, CA 90017-2543
Tel (213) 244-0000 *Founded/Ownrshp* 2013
Sales NA *EMP* 515
SIC 6022 6282 6211 State trust companies accepting deposits, commercial; Investment advisory service; Security brokers & dealers
CEO: Marc I Stern
**Pr:* David B Lippman
**CFO:* Richard Villa
**Ex VP:* Meredith S Jackson
**Sr VP:* David Asarnow
Sr VP: Dipo Ashiru
Sr VP: Heather Conforto Beatty
Sr VP: Jonathan W Botts
**Sr VP:* Kevin Finch
Sr VP: Brian C Ford
Sr VP: Frank Gioia
**Sr VP:* Melinda Newman
Sr VP: Jeff Nuruki
**Sr VP:* Drew Sweeney
Sr VP: Michael Wright

D-U-N-S 05-916-0507
TCW INC
22 Stanley St, Nashville, TN 37210-2133
Tel (615) 255-1122 *Founded/Ownrshp* 2003
Sales 85.5MM *EMP* 625
SIC 4731 4225 Freight consolidation; General warehousing
CEO: Scott George
**Pr:* David W Manning
**CFO:* Alan Witt
VP: Tim Smith
Brnch Mgr: Teresa Brooks
Sfty Dirs: Ronnie Holland
Opers Mgr: Nathan Herron

D-U-N-S 09-339-4096 EXP
■TD AMERITRADE CLEARING INC
AMERIVEST
(*Suby of* TD AMERITRADE HOLDING CORP) ★
200 S 108th Ave, Omaha, NE 68154-2631
Tel (402) 331-2744 *Founded/Ownrshp* 1981
Sales 996.0MM^E *EMP* 3,882
SIC 6211 Security brokers & dealers
**Ch Bd:* John Joe Ricketts
Pr: Chris Armstrong
**Pr:* Felix B Davidson
**COO:* Randy McDonald
**CFO:* William J Gerber
**Treas:* James A Powell
**VP:* Mike Brennan
**VP:* Jim Masters
CIO: John Kileen
VP Sls: Christopher Powers
Sls Mgr: Art Davis

D-U-N-S 15-065-1875
▲TD AMERITRADE HOLDING CORP
200 S 108th Ave, Omaha, NE 68154-2631
Tel (402) 331-7856 *Founded/Ownrshp* 1971
Sales 3.3MMM *EMP* 5,690
Accts Ernst & Young Llp Chicago Il
Tkr Sym AMTD *Exch* NGS
SIC 6211 Security brokers & dealers
CEO: Fredric J Tomczyk
**Ch Bd:* Joseph H Moglia
**Pr:* Tim Hockey
Pr: Kenneth I Feldman
CFO: Stephen J Boyle
Treas: Denise Karkos
Chf Mktg O: Anne L Nelson
Ofcr: T Christian Armstrong
Ofcr: Mike Brennan
Ofcr: Lisa Henoch
Ofcr: David Kimm
Ofcr: Gerald Kroger
Ofcr: Colleague Waycaster
Ex VP: Karen Ganzlin
Ex VP: Ellen L S Koplow
Ex VP: John Letteri
Ex VP: John Mullin
Ex VP: Steven Quirk
Sr VP: Jerry Bartlett
VP: Gary Ausman
VP: Jessica Bednarovsky

Board of Directors: Lorenzo A Bettino, V Ann Hailey, Brian Levitt, Karen E Maidment, Irene R Miller, Mark L Mitchell, Wilbur J Prezzano, Todd M Ricketts, Allan R Tessler

D-U-N-S 09-612-0811
■TD AMERITRADE INC
WATERHOUSE SECURITIES
(*Suby of* AMERIVEST) ★
1005 N Ameritrade Pl, Bellevue, NE 68005-4245
Tel (402) 970-7000 *Founded/Ownrshp* 1978
Sales 538.6MM^E *EMP* 1,850
SIC 6211 Security brokers & dealers; Dealers, security
Ch Bd: J Thomas Bradley Jr
**Pr:* John B Bunch
**Pr:* Kevin Sterns
COO: John Bell
COO: Thomas Nally
**V Ch Bd:* Diane Walker
Ex VP: Ellen Koplow
**Ex VP:* Richard H Neiman
VP: Anand Upadhye
Brnch Mgr: Margaret Czyz
Opers Mgr: Lori Kilstrom

D-U-N-S 04-179-4504
TD AUTO FINANCE LLC
(*Suby of* TD BANK US HOLDING CO) ★
27777 Inkster Rd, Farmington Hills, MI 48334-5326
Tel (248) 427-6800 *Founded/Ownrshp* 2011
Sales NA *EMP* 2,300
SIC 6153 5511 Financing of dealers by motor vehicle manufacturers organ.; Direct working capital financing; Mercantile financing; New & used car dealers
CEO: Thomas F Gilman
COO: Gino Cozza
**CFO:* Leland Wilson
VP: Shawn Crabtree
VP: Jan Forhan
VP: Marsha Greco
VP: Scott McClenaghan
VP: J Rgen Rochert
VP: Jeff Wassel
VP: Malik Wooden
Exec: Charles Bass
**Dir Risk M:* Darcy Walker

D-U-N-S 00-694-9424
TD BANK NA
TD BANKNORTH MASSACHUSETTS
(*Suby of* TD BANK US HOLDING CO) ★
1701 Marlton Pike E # 200, Cherry Hill, NJ 08003-2335
Tel (856) 751-2739 *Founded/Ownrshp* 1869, 1988
Sales NA *EMP* 6,200
SIC 6021 National commercial banks
Pr: Mike Pedersen
Pr: Kati Amarantes
Pr: Debra Decato
Pr: Robert G Hoak
Pr: Nick Milnthorpe
Pr: Collin Proctor
Pr: Denise Smith
Pr: Brenda Woods
**CFO:* Manjit Singh
Ofcr: Ajai Bambawale
Ofcr: Mary Huff
Ofcr: Benjamin Jenkins
Ofcr: Janene McMullen
Ofcr: Edward P Schreiber
Ex VP: Greg Braca
Ex VP: Paul Clark
Ex VP: Fred Graziano
Ex VP: Ellen Patterson
Ex VP: Edward B Pollock
Ex VP: Michael Rhodes
Ex VP: Greg Smith
Board of Directors: William E Bennett, P Kevin Condron, Stanley E Grayson, Dana S Levenson, Alan N Macgibbon, Thomas J Mullin, Wilbur Prezzano, Peter G Vigue

D-U-N-S 19-712-3789
TD BANK US HOLDING CO
(*Suby of* TORONTO-DOMINION BANK, THE)
2 Portland Sq, Portland, ME 04101-4088
Tel (207) 761-8500 *Founded/Ownrshp* 2005
Sales NA *EMP* 23,622
SIC 6022 State commercial banks
Ch Bd: Brian M Levitt
Pr: Jesus Diaz
**Pr:* Bharat B Masrani
Treas: Sandy McAlonie
Ex VP: Mark Lawler
Ex VP: Carol Mitchell
Ex VP: Webb Steven
Sr VP: Scassa Cristina
Sr VP: McEvoy James
Sr VP: Christina McGuinness
Sr VP: Keith Nisbet
Sr VP: Edelstein Richard
VP: Patrick B Blalock
VP: David Chau
VP: Stephen Elia
VP: Rakesh Kumar
VP: Robert Lorenson
VP: Christine Wrobel

TD BANKNORTH GARDEN
See DELAWARE NORTH COMPANIES INC - BOSTON

D-U-N-S 02-494-8775
TD BANKNORTH LEASING CORP
(*Suby of* TD BANK US HOLDING CO) ★
70 Gray Rd, Falmouth, ME 04105-2299
Tel (207) 317-4616 *Founded/Ownrshp* 1983
Sales NA *EMP* 1,000
SIC 6712 Bank holding companies
Pr: Toby Cook
VP: Wendy Coburn
VP: Lisa Gruner
VP: Stephen Richardson
VP: Christine Wrobel
Netwrk Mgr: James Huiere
Mktg Dir: Andrew Nicolai

TD BANKNORTH MASSACHUSETTS
See TD BANK NA

D-U-N-S 80-021-9748
TD BANKNORTH NATIONAL ASSOCIATION
(*Suby of* TD BANK US HOLDING CO) ★
1000 Macarthur Blvd, Mahwah, NJ 07430-2035
Tel (201) 236-2680 *Founded/Ownrshp* 2014
Sales NA *EMP* 5,022[E]
SIC 6029 Commercial banks
Prin: Lissette Fernandez
VP: Michael Sullo

D-U-N-S 13-979-4973
TD EQUIPMENT FINANCE INC
(*Suby of* TD BANKNORTH MASSACHUSETTS) ★
1006 Astoria Blvd, Cherry Hill, NJ 08003-2311
Tel (856) 470-5741 *Founded/Ownrshp* 2004
Sales NA *EMP* 46
SIC 6021 National commercial banks
Pr: Anthony R Sasso

D-U-N-S 06-628-7368 IMP
TD FOOD GROUP INC
THEODAVIES FOOD SERVICE GROUP
828 Fort Street Mall # 130, Honolulu, HI 96813-4332
Tel (808) 566-3200 *Founded/Ownrshp* 2013
Sales 62.3MM[E] *EMP* 2,251
SIC 5812 6794 Pizzeria, chain; Franchises, selling or licensing
Pr: Henry M Katsuda
Treas: Janis Lawton
**VP:* Kevin Kurihara

D-U-N-S 11-281-7130
TD SERVICES INC
TDINDUSTRIES
13850 Diplomat Dr, Dallas, TX 75234-8812
Tel (972) 888-9500 *Founded/Ownrshp* 1947
Sales 91.0MM[E] *EMP* 800
SIC 8711 Energy conservation engineering
Pr: Harrel McDowell
CFO: Mike Patrick

D-U-N-S 19-504-9085 IMP
■**TDG OPERATIONS LLC**
MASLAND CARPETS & RUGS
(*Suby of* DIXIE GROUP INC) ★
716 Bill Myles Dr, Saraland, AL 36571-3302
Tel (251) 675-9080 *Founded/Ownrshp* 1988
Sales 278.2MM[E] *EMP* 1,200[E]
SIC 2273 Carpets & rugs
CEO: Daniel K Frierson
Pr: Paul Breland
Pr: Tom Martin
Exec: John Underwood
Dept Mgr: Jim Jernigan
Tech Mgr: Paul Spurling
VP Opers: David Hobbs
VP Mktg: Steve Cocozza
VP Sls: Brett Bennet
VP Sls: Ted O'Hanlan
Sls Dir: Donald Dolan

TDINDUSTRIES
See TD SERVICES INC

D-U-N-S 00-736-8780
TDINDUSTRIES INC
13850 Diplomat Dr, Dallas, TX 75234-8812
Tel (972) 888-9500 *Founded/Ownrshp* 1946
Sales 563.9MM[E] *EMP* 1,600
SIC 1711 Plumbing, heating, air-conditioning contractors
Ch: Jack Lowe
**Pr:* L B Houston Jr
**Pr:* Michael J Kotubey
**CEO:* Harold F Macdowell
**CFO:* Michael J Fitzpatrick
Ex VP: Bill Parten
**Ex VP:* Maureen Underwood
Ex VP: Robert G Wilken
**Sr VP:* Jason Cinek
Sr VP: Ed White
Sr VP: David J Youden
VP: George Athens
VP: Tasos Banos
VP: Jim Biven
**VP:* Phil Claybrooke
VP: Steven Garza
VP: Randee Herrin
**VP:* Rod Johannsen
VP: Timothy S McNew
VP: Nikki Morgan
Dir Soc: Scott Burrows

D-U-N-S 09-946-8720 IMP/EXP
TDK USA CORP
(*Suby of* TDK CORPORATION)
455 Rxr Plz, Uniondale, NY 11556-3811
Tel (516) 535-2600 *Founded/Ownrshp* 1981
Sales 286.0MM[E] *EMP* 1,200
SIC 3679 8741 Recording & playback apparatus, including phonograph; Administrative management; Financial management for business
Ch Bd: Francis J Sweeney Jr
VP: Tom Kossmann
VP: Susan Sparks

D-U-N-S 05-131-1371 IMP
TDK-LAMBDA AMERICAS INC
TDK-LMBDA AMRICAS HIGH PWR DIV
(*Suby of* TDK-LAMBDA CORPORATION)
405 Essex Rd, Tinton Falls, NJ 07753-7701
Tel (732) 922-9300 *Founded/Ownrshp* 2005
Sales 110.1MM[E] *EMP* 317
SIC 3629 Power conversion units, a.c. to d.c.: static-electric
Ch Bd: Frank Sweeney
**Pr:* Pascal Chauffson
Dir IT: Bob Finn
VP Opers: Wayne Morrison
Sls&Mrk Ex: Gail Kadi

TDK-LMBDA AMRICAS HIGH PWR DIV
See TDK-LAMBDA AMERICAS INC

TDS
See MCDANIEL TELEPHONE CO

TDS
See UNION TELEPHONE CO

TDS
See NORWAY TELEPHONE CO INC

TDS
See RIVERSIDE TELECOM LLC

TDS
See MOSINEE TELEPHONE CO LLC

TDS
See WILLISTON TELEPHONE CO

TDS
See TIPTON TELEPHONE CO INC

TDS
See EASTCOAST TELECOM OF WISCONSIN LLC

TDS
See SOUTHEAST TELEPHONE CO OF WISCONSIN LLC

TDS
See DEPOSIT TELEPHONE CO INC

TDS
See POTLATCH TELEPHONE CO

TDS
See CAMDEN TELEPHONE CO INC

TDS
See ISLAND TELEPHONE CO

TDS
See BLACK EARTH TELEPHONE CO LLC

TDS
See TEXAS DISPOSAL SYSTEMS INC

TDS
See MERCHANTS AND FARMERS TELEPHONE CO

TDS
See DICKEYVILLE TELEPHONE LLC

TDS
See STOCKBRIDGE & SHERWOOD TELEPHONE CO LLC

TDS
See SALEM TELEPHONE CO

TDS
See WYANDOTTE TELEPHONE CO

TDS
See NEW CASTLE TELEPHONE CO

TDS
See VERNON TELEPHONE CO INC

TDS
See MID-AMERICA TELEPHONE INC

TDS
See HOLLIS TELEPHONE CO INC

D-U-N-S 83-307-4409
■**TDS LONG DISTANCE CORP**
(*Suby of* TDS TELECOMMUNICATIONS CORP) ★
525 Junction Rd Ste 6000, Madison, WI 53717-2153
Tel (608) 831-1000 *Founded/Ownrshp* 2000
Sales 298.4MM[E] *EMP* 2,700
SIC 4813 Telephone communication, except radio
Pr: David Wittwer

TDS TELECOMMUNICATIONS
See MID-STATE TELEPHONE CO

TDS TELECOMMUNICATIONS
See TRI-COUNTY TELEPHONE CO INC

D-U-N-S 55-622-4459
■**TDS TELECOMMUNICATIONS CORP**
(*Suby of* TELEPHONE AND DATA SYSTEMS INC) ★
525 Junction Rd Ste 1000, Madison, WI 53717-2152
Tel (608) 664-4000 *Founded/Ownrshp* 1988
Sales 947.0MM *EMP* 3,300
SIC 4813

TDT
See TRANS DIGITAL TECHNOLOGIES LIMITED LIABILITY CO

TDX
See TANADGUSIX CORP

D-U-N-S 18-485-1793
■**TDY HOLDINGS LLC**
(*Suby of* ATI OPERATING HOLDINGS LLC) ★
1403 Foulk Rd Ste 200, Wilmington, DE 19803-2788
Tel (302) 254-4172 *Founded/Ownrshp* 2013
Sales 1.0MMM[E] *EMP* 3,541[E]
SIC 3462 Iron & steel forgings
Prin: Ken Kubacki

D-U-N-S 00-957-8113 IMP/EXP
■**TDY INDUSTRIES LLC**
ATI SPECIALTY MATERIALS
(*Suby of* TDY HOLDINGS LLC) ★
1000 Six Ppg Pl, Pittsburgh, PA 15222
Tel (412) 394-2896 *Founded/Ownrshp* 2013
Sales 1.0MMM[E] *EMP* 4,107
SIC 3356 3312 3316 3339 3369 Zirconium; Titanium; Nickel; Blast furnaces & steel mills; Cold finishing of steel shapes; Primary nonferrous metals; Nonferrous foundries
CEO: Richard J Harshman
**Pr:* L Patrick Hassey
Pr: Robert S Wetherbee
**Ex VP:* Richard Harshman
**Ex VP:* Dale G Reid
Sr VP: Kevin Kramer
VP: Bradley Forsythe
**VP:* Danny L Greenfield

TE CONNECTIVITY
See TYCO ELECTRONICS CORP

TE CONNECTIVITY
See COMMSCOPE CONNECTIVITY SOLUTIONS LLC

TE CONNECTIVITY
See MEASUREMENT SPECIALTIES INC

D-U-N-S 07-959-4418
TE CONNECTIVITY INC
(*Suby of* TE CONNECTIVITY LTD.)
607 14th St Nw Ste 250, Washington, DC 20005-2072
Tel (202) 471-3400 *Founded/Ownrshp* 2012
Sales 23.5MMM[E] *EMP* 90,000
SIC 3678 3643 Electronic connectors; Current-carrying wiring devices; Connectors & terminals for electrical devices
Pr: Harold Barksdale

D-U-N-S 07-954-1762
TE CONNECTIVITY MOG INC
(*Suby of* TE CONNECTIVITY LTD.)
501 Oakside Ave, Redwood City, CA 94063-3800
Tel (650) 361-5292 *Founded/Ownrshp* 2014
Sales 574.6MM[E] *EMP* 11,000[E]
SIC 3229 Fiber optics strands
Genl Mgr: Craig Newell

D-U-N-S 07-950-4600
TE CONNECTIVITY SEACON PHOENIX INC
(*Suby of* TE CONNECTIVITY MOG INC) ★
15 Gray Ln Ste 108, Ashaway, RI 02804-1210
Tel (401) 637-4952 *Founded/Ownrshp* 2014
Sales 222.8MM[E] *EMP* 5,014[E]
SIC 3229 Fiber optics strands
Genl Mgr: Craig Newell

D-U-N-S 78-744-1138
TE PRODUCTS PIPELINE CO LIMITED PARTNERSHIP
1100 La St Ste 1600, Houston, TX 77002
Tel (713) 381-3636 *Founded/Ownrshp* 1990
Sales NA *EMP* 1,000
SIC 4613 4922

D-U-N-S 62-140-4383
TEACH FOR AMERICA INC
25 Broadway Fl 12, New York, NY 10004-1056
Tel (212) 279-2080 *Founded/Ownrshp* 1989
Sales 331.1MM *EMP* 250
Accts Oconnor Davies Llp Harrison
SIC 7361 Teachers' agency
Ch Bd: Wendy Kopp
**CEO:* Elisa Villanueva Beard
**CFO:* Josh Grigg
Treas: Kate Baker
**Treas:* Stephen Mandel
Ex VP: Susan Asiyanbi
Sr VP: Greg Wendt
VP: Stephanie Audette
VP: Peter Gluck
VP: Raegen Miller
Exec: Zach Neumeyer
Exec: Robert Scully
Exec: Lori Vetters

D-U-N-S 07-105-0983 IMP
TEACHERS COLLEGE COLUMBIA UNIVERSITY
525 W 120th St, New York, NY 10027-6605
Tel (212) 678-3000 *Founded/Ownrshp* 1886
Sales 228.3MM *EMP* 1,200
SIC 8221

D-U-N-S 06-596-0205
TEACHERS FEDERAL CREDIT UNION
TFCU
100 Hauppauge, Hauppauge, NY 11788
Tel (631) 698-7000 *Founded/Ownrshp* 1952
Sales NA *EMP* 650
SIC 6061 Federal credit unions
Pr: Robert G Allen
CFO: C J Meyers
CFO: Chris J Meyers
Ex VP: Tom Fallon
Ex VP: Thomas A Filon
Ex VP: Steven Goldstein
VP: Fred Schaefer

D-U-N-S 12-371-9820
TEACHERS HEALTH TRUST
2950 E Rochelle Ave, Las Vegas, NV 89121-5399
Tel (702) 866-6133 *Founded/Ownrshp* 2002
Sales 156.6MM *EMP* 25
Accts Kafoury Armstrong & Co Reno
SIC 6733 Trusts
Prin: Peter Albert

TEACHERS INSRN & ANNUITY ASSOC
See ASSET CHURCHILL MANAGEMENT LLC

D-U-N-S 00-172-4962
TEACHERS INSURANCE AND ANNUITY ASSOCIATION OF AMERICA
730 3rd Ave Ste 2a, New York, NY 10017-3207
Tel (212) 490-9000 *Founded/Ownrshp* 1918, 2002
Sales NA *EMP* 2,082
SIC 6311 Life insurance
Pr: Roger W Ferguson Jr
Pr: Dermot J Obrien
CEO: Scott C Evans
**COO:* Ronald R Pressman
**CFO:* Georganne C Proctor
**CFO:* Virginia M Wilson
**Treas:* Gary Chinery
Bd of Dir: Edward Hundert
Bd of Dir: Sidney Ribeau
**Chf Mktg O:* Janice Innis-Thompson
Ofcr: Brandon Becker
**Ofcr:* Bertram L Scott
Ex VP: Canan Abayhan
Ex VP: Maliz Beams
Ex VP: Bob Benoit
**Ex VP:* I Steven Goldstein
Ex VP: Elsa Hetherington
Ex VP: Ira J Hoch
**Ex VP:* George W Madison
**Ex VP:* Elizabeth A Monrad
**Ex VP:* J Keith Morgan

D-U-N-S 07-183-8812
TEACHERS INSURANCE AND ANNUITY ASSOCIATION-COLLEGE RETIREMENT EQUITIES FUND
TIAA-CREF
730 3rd Ave Ste 2a, New York, NY 10017-3213
Tel (212) 490-9000 *Founded/Ownrshp* 1918
Sales NA *EMP* 7,515
SIC 6311 Life insurance
Pr: Roger W Ferguson Jr
Pr: Robert Leary
Chf Inves: Susan Tannehill
Ofcr: Richard Biegen
Ofcr: Larry Chadwick
Ofcr: Robert Cillis
**Ex VP:* Stephen Gruppo
**Ex VP:* Jeff Hickling
**Ex VP:* Rahul Merchant
**Ex VP:* Keith Morgan
**VP:* Kathie Andrade
**VP:* Scott Blandford
**VP:* Brian Bohaty
**VP:* Doug Chittenden
VP: Meredith Kornreich
VP: Nick Miles
**VP:* Marjorie Pierre-Merrit

D-U-N-S 10-219-9189
■**TEACHERS INSURANCE CO INC**
(*Suby of* HORACE MANN EDUCATORS CORP) ★
1 Horace Mann Plz, Springfield, IL 62715-0001
Tel (217) 789-2500 *Founded/Ownrshp* 1989
Sales NA *EMP* 200
SIC 6311 Life insurance
CFO: Peter H Heckman
CFO: Peter H Eckman
VP: Amie Irving

D-U-N-S 16-851-4669
TEACHERS RETIREMENT FUND
DULUTH TEACHRS RTMNT FUND ASSN
625 E Central Entrance, Duluth, MN 55811-5500
Tel (218) 722-2894 *Founded/Ownrshp* 1910
Sales 99.5MM *EMP* 5
Accts Wipfli Llp Duluth Mn
SIC 8631 Employees' association
Ex Dir: Jay Stoffel
Ex Dir: Michael Stoffel

D-U-N-S 80-764-8639
TEACHERS RETIREMENT SYSTEM OF STATE OF ILLINOIS
(*Suby of* STATE OF ILLINOIS) ★
2815 W Washington St # 200, Springfield, IL 62702-7412
Tel (217) 753-0370 *Founded/Ownrshp* 1939
Sales NA *EMP* 175
SIC 6371 9199 Pension, health & welfare funds;
Chf Inves: Stan Rupnik
Ofcr: Kenneth Musick
Off Mgr: Tammy Green
Sys Mgr: Charlotte Morgan

TEALWOOD CARE CENTERS
See SENIOR TEALWOOD LIVING

D-U-N-S 03-927-5685
TEAM BENEFITS CORP
(*Suby of* TEAM SERVICES) ★
901 W Alameda Ave 100, Burbank, CA 91506-2801
Tel (818) 558-3261 *Founded/Ownrshp* 2011
Sales 589.0MM[E] *EMP* 42
SIC 8721 Payroll accounting service
Pr: Gerald K Schwartz
**COO:* Mark R Sullivan
**VP:* Brenda Schwartz

D-U-N-S 06-222-4515
TEAM BIONDI LLC
248 Easton Tpke, Lake Ariel, PA 18436-4792
Tel (570) 503-7087 *Founded/Ownrshp* 2008
Sales 400.0MM *EMP* 28
SIC 3537 Trucks, tractors, loaders, carriers & similar equipment

D-U-N-S 03-927-1395
TEAM COMPANIES INC
TEAM SERVICES
901 W Alameda Ave Ste 100, Burbank, CA 91506-2801
Tel (818) 558-3261 *Founded/Ownrshp* 2001
Sales 1.3MMM *EMP* 160
SIC 8721 Payroll accounting service
Pr: Gerald K Schwartz
**CFO:* An De Vooght
**Ex VP:* Justin Kramer
VP: Lori Tedds
Comm Man: Carol Davies
Off Mgr: Candy Converse
VP Prd: Carl Zucker
VP Mktg: Mark Egmon
Board of Directors: Justin Kramer, Geoffrey Matus, Elliott Pollack, Gerald K Schwartz, Ken Zignorski

D-U-N-S 61-018-5290 IMP/EXP
TEAM EXPRESS DISTRIBUTING LLC
SOFTBALL.COM
5750 Northwest Pkwy # 100, San Antonio, TX 78249-3374
Tel (210) 525-9161 *Founded/Ownrshp* 2013
Sales 85.0MM[E] *EMP* 275[E]
SIC 5941 5091 Baseball equipment; Sporting & recreation goods
**Pr:* Michael Marney
**CEO:* Mark Marney
**CFO:* Mark Andersen
Manager: Jeremy Fisher

D-U-N-S 06-623-5222
TEAM FOCUS INSURANCE GROUP LLC
1300 Sawgrs Corp Pkwy # 300, Sunrise, FL 33323-2824
Tel (954) 331-4800 *Founded/Ownrshp* 2000
Sales 92.0MM[E] *EMP* 375
SIC 6719 6411 Personal holding companies, except banks; Insurance agents, brokers & service; Insurance information & consulting services
Ch Bd: Douglas Bullington
**Pr:* Kevin Tromer

*COO: Michael Steinman
*CFO: James Blake
*Sr VP: William Brauer
*Sr VP: Laura Decespedes
*VP: Luis Valdes

TEAM FORD LINCOLN
See TEAM FORD LLC

D-U-N-S 17-424-7622
TEAM FORD LLC
TEAM FORD LINCOLN
5445 Drexel Rd, Las Vegas, NV 89130-1605
Tel (702) 395-5100 Founded/Ownrshp 2000
Sales 109.6MM EMP 150
SIC 5511 Automobiles, new & used
Genl Mgr: Claude Chiles
Genl Mgr: Al McDonald
Sls Mgr: Bill Jenkins
Sls Mgr: Adam Zito

D-U-N-S 14-383-6547
▲TEAM HEALTH HOLDINGS INC
TEAMHEALTH
265 Brookview Centre Way, Knoxville, TN 37919-4049
Tel (865) 693-1000 Founded/Ownrshp 1979
Sales 3.6MMM EMP 18,800E
Tkr Sym TMH Exch NYS
SIC 7363 8741 Medical help service; Hospital management; Nursing & personal care facility management
Pr: Leif Murphy
Ch Bd: H Lynn Massingale
COO: Oliver V Rogers
CFO: David P Jones
Chf Mktg O: Miles S Snowden
Ex VP: Steven E Clifton
Ex VP: Steven Clifton
Sr VP: Heidi Allen
Board of Directors: James L Bierman, Edwin M Crawford, Glenn A Davenport, Patrick E Fry, Mary R Grealy, Vicky B Gregg, Neil M Kurtz, Scott Ostfeld, Kenneth H Paulus

D-U-N-S 87-925-8895
■TEAM HEALTH INC
TEAMHEALTH
(Suby of TEAMHEALTH) ★
265 Brookview Centre Way, Knoxville, TN 37919-4049
Tel (865) 693-1000 Founded/Ownrshp 2005
Sales 95.9MME EMP 562
SIC 8099 Physical examination & testing services
CEO: Oliver Rogers
*Ch Bd: Lynn Massingale
Pr: Laureen Callan
Pr: Stacy Goldsholl
Pr: Michelle Maddox
Pr: Betty Moon
*Pr: Michael D Snow
*CEO: Greg Roth
COO: Barbara Blevins
*COO: Michael Hatcher
COO: Oliver Rogers
*CFO: Joe Carman
*CFO: David P Jones
CFO: Terrie Stevens
CFO: Tony Vetrano
Treas: Jack McAllister
Bd of Dir: Nicholas W Alexos
Bd of Dir: Glenn A Davenport
Bd of Dir: Earl P Holland
Bd of Dir: Dana O'Brien
Bd of Dir: Kenneth W O'Keefe

D-U-N-S 07-417-4145
▲TEAM INC
13131 Dar Ashford Ste 600, Sugar Land, TX 77478
Tel (281) 331-6154 Founded/Ownrshp 1973
Sales 842.0MM EMP 5,900E
Tkr Sym TISI Exch NYS
SIC 7389 7699 Pipeline & power line inspection service; Boiler & heating repair services; Industrial equipment services
Pr: Ted W Owen
*Ch Bd: Philip J Hawk
Pr: Jeffrey L Ott
Pr: Declan Rushe
Pr: Arthur F Victorson
*CFO: Greg L Boane
Genl Mgr: Ted Vidimos
Dir IT: Shawn McMillin
Mktg Dir: Jason Box
Board of Directors: Jeffery G Davis, Vincent D Foster, Sylvia J Kerrigan, Emmett J Lescroart, Michael A Lucas, Louis A Waters

D-U-N-S 06-963-1851
■TEAM INDUSTRIAL SERVICES INC
(Suby of TEAM INC) ★
200 Hermann Dr, Alvin, TX 77511-5596
Tel (281) 388-5525 Founded/Ownrshp 1985
Sales 127.2MME EMP 2,400
SIC 8748 8711 7699 Environmental consultant; Engineering services; Consulting engineer; Industrial equipment services; Valve repair, industrial
Ch Bd: Philip J Hawk
*Ex VP: Pete W Wallace
*Sr VP: Andre C Bouchard
Sr VP: Butch Bouchard
*Sr VP: John P Kearns
VP: James Campbell
*VP: Ted W Owen
*VP: David Palmore Sr
VP: Keith Tucker
*VP: Art Victorson Sr
Exec: Andre Bouchard

D-U-N-S 16-192-3206 IMP
TEAM INDUSTRIES BAGLEY-AUDUBON INC
(Suby of TEAM INDUSTRIES INC) ★
105 Park Ave Nw, Bagley, MN 56621-9558
Tel (218) 694-3550 Founded/Ownrshp 1993
Sales 203.3MM EMP 581
Accts Peffer & Wallace Ltd Cambridg
SIC 3599 8711 3714 Machine shop, jobbing & repair; Engineering services; Transmissions, motor vehicle
Pr: David Ricke

D-U-N-S 86-726-4434 IMP
TEAM INDUSTRIES INC
105 Park Ave Nw, Bagley, MN 56621-9558
Tel (218) 694-3550 Founded/Ownrshp 1993
Sales 321.0MME EMP 1,100
Accts Peffer & Wallace Ltd Cambri
SIC 3599 8711 3714 Machine shop, jobbing & repair; Engineering services; Axles, motor vehicle
Pr: David Ricke
*CFO: Steve Kast
*Ex VP: Michael Matthews
*Sr VP: Robert Skawski
Genl Mgr: Dave Osterman
IT Man: Chris Rendall
Mtls Mgr: Gustafson Gail

D-U-N-S 86-757-9901
TEAM MARKETING ALLIANCE LLC
307 W Cole St, Moundridge, KS 67107-7533
Tel (620) 345-3560 Founded/Ownrshp 2000
Sales 334.2MM EMP 17
Accts Lindburg Vogel Pierce Faris Ce
SIC 5153 Grain elevators
Prin: Ted Schultz

TEAM ONE
See TEAM-ONE EMPLOYMENT SPECIALISTS LLC

D-U-N-S 15-567-8076
TEAM REAL ESTATE INC
BROKERAGE SOUTHWEST
601 Broadway St, Rock Springs, WY 82901-6347
Tel (307) 362-1275 Founded/Ownrshp 1999
Sales 100.0MM EMP 17
SIC 6531 Real estate agents & managers
Pr: Maggie Riley
Sales Asso: Kelly Palmer
Sales Asso: Shauna Rood

TEAM SERVICES
See TEAM COMPANIES INC

D-U-N-S 19-233-9703 IMP/EXP
TEAM TECHNOLOGIES INC
TNI
5949 Commerce Blvd, Morristown, TN 37814-8209
Tel (423) 587-2199 Founded/Ownrshp 2012
Sales 185.9MME EMP 760
SIC 2844 5122 5719 3991 Denture cleaners; Toothpastes or powders, dentifrices; Toothbrushes, except electric; Brushes; Brooms & brushes; Brushes, except paint & varnish
Pr: Marshall White
IT Man: David Gurley
Plnt Mgr: Bob Walton
Ql Cn Mgr: Maggie Costigan
Mktg Dir: Gene Danico

D-U-N-S 13-710-8630 IMP
TEAM TEN LLC
AMERICAN EAGLE PAPER MILLS
1600 Pennsylvania Ave, Tyrone, PA 16686-1758
Tel (814) 684-1610 Founded/Ownrshp 2002
Sales 93.5MME EMP 270
SIC 2621 Paper mills; Uncoated paper
Pr: Michael P Grimm
*COO: Scott Igoe
CTO: Jeffrey Yothers
Tech Mgr: Tim Berkhouse
Tech Mgr: Tim Miller
Opers Mgr: Tom Benoit
Ql Cn Mgr: Ron Jones
VP Sls: Richard Koch

TEAM TIRES PLUS
See MORGAN TIRE & AUTO LLC

TEAM TIRES PLUS
See BRIDGESTONE RETAIL OPERATIONS LLC

TEAM TREX
See TREX CORP INC

D-U-N-S 19-735-3303
TEAM WASHINGTON INC
DOMINO'S PIZZA
8381 Old Courthouse Rd # 100, Vienna, VA 22182-3818
Tel (703) 734-7080 Founded/Ownrshp 1983
Sales 50.0MM EMP 1,650
SIC 5812 Pizzeria, chain
Pr: Mary L Carraway
*Treas: Thomas H Anderson
Ex Dir: Brendan Bunn

D-U-N-S 00-946-8773
TEAM-ONE EMPLOYMENT SPECIALISTS LLC
TEAM ONE
2999 Overland Ave Ste 212, Los Angeles, CA 90064-4243
Tel (310) 481-4482 Founded/Ownrshp 2001
Sales 35.0MM EMP 5,000
SIC 7361 Employment agencies
CFO: Daniel Cox
Genl Mgr: Raymond Barajas

D-U-N-S 60-285-5017
TEAM-ONE STAFFING SERVICES INC
TEAMONE EMPLOYMENT SPECIALIST
10801 National Blvd # 104, Los Angeles, CA 90064-4140
Tel (310) 481-4480 Founded/Ownrshp 1988
Sales 44.8MME EMP 5,290
Accts Hillas & Nocera Cpa S Woodlan
SIC 7361 Employment agencies
Pr: Frank Moran
Assoc Ed: Kara Kieffer

D-U-N-S 07-878-7237
TEAMDETROIT LLC
(Suby of W P P) ★
550 Town Center Dr, Dearborn, MI 48126-2751
Tel (313) 615-2000 Founded/Ownrshp 2006, 2014
Sales 98.4MME EMP 1,251E
SIC 7311 Advertising agencies
CEO: Satish Korde
Mng Pt: Jan Starr
*Pr: David Murphy
*Chf Cred: Toby Barlow
Ex VP: Betsy Lazar
Ex VP: Linda Taylor
Sr VP: Traci Armstrong
Sr VP: Bob Doppel
Sr VP: John Gray
Sr VP: Michelle Gross
Sr VP: Lisbeth Keast
Sr VP: Daryl Laflamme
Sr VP: Kristen Schweitzer
Sr VP: Stephanie Stevenson
VP: Sarah Fraser
VP: Dan Hogan
VP: Marla Laurain
VP: Denise Moczydlowsky
VP: Uma Pishati
VP: Delisha Upshaw
Assoc Dir: Sefi Grossman

TEAMHEALTH
See TEAM HEALTH HOLDINGS INC

TEAMHEALTH
See TEAM HEALTH INC

TEAMONE EMPLOYMENT SPECIALIST
See TEAM-ONE STAFFING SERVICES INC

D-U-N-S 01-991-9187
TEAMSTER BENEFIT TRUST
39420 Liberty St Ste 260, Fremont, CA 94538-2297
Tel (510) 796-4676 Founded/Ownrshp 2001
Sales 268.5MM EMP 3
Accts Lindquist Llp San Ramon Ca
SIC 8631 6411 Labor unions & similar labor organizations; Insurance agents, brokers & service
Pr: Fred Lipman

TEAMSTERS CARE
See TEAMSTERS UNION 25 HEALTH SERVICES & INSURANCE PLAN

D-U-N-S 96-676-6086
TEAMSTERS HEALTH AND WELFARE FUND OF PHILADELPHIA AND VICINITY
6981 N Park Dr Ste 400, Pennsauken, NJ 08109-4207
Tel (856) 382-2400 Founded/Ownrshp 2011
Sales 107.5MM EMP 21E
SIC 8631 Labor unions & similar labor organizations

D-U-N-S 80-702-3580
TEAMSTERS NEW YORK STATE CONFERENCE
151 Northern Concourse # 1, Syracuse, NY 13212-4050
Tel (315) 455-9790 Founded/Ownrshp 2007
Sales 205.2MM EMP 2E
SIC 6722 Management investment, open-end

D-U-N-S 10-115-8715
TEAMSTERS UNION 25 HEALTH SERVICES & INSURANCE PLAN
TEAMSTERS CARE
16 Sever St, Boston, MA 02129-1305
Tel (617) 241-9220 Founded/Ownrshp 1965
Sales NA EMP 73
Accts Michael J Maher Cpa Waltham
SIC 6371 Union welfare, benefit & health funds
Ex Dir: Carol Blanchard
Dir IT: Christopher Walsh

D-U-N-S 00-917-4830 EXP
TEASDALE FOODS INC
901 Packers St, Atwater, CA 95301-4614
Tel (209) 358-5616 Founded/Ownrshp 1998
Sales 195.3MME EMP 693E
SIC 2034 2032 Dehydrated fruits, vegetables, soups; Beans, baked without meat: packaged in cans, jars, etc.; Chili with or without meat: packaged in cans, jars, etc.; Mexican foods: packaged in cans, jars, etc.
CEO: Chris Kiser
*CFO: Russell Kenerly
Opers Mgr: Veronica Gomez
Mktg Mgr: Dick Renna

D-U-N-S 10-380-2570 IMP
■TEAVANA CORP
(Suby of TEAVANA HOLDINGS INC) ★
3630 Peachtree Rd Ne # 1480, Atlanta, GA 30326-1552
Tel (404) 495-0760 Founded/Ownrshp 2001
Sales 218.7MME EMP 1,819E
SIC 5499 Tea
CEO: Andrew Mack
*CFO: Dan Glennon
*CFO: Ricahrd Lautch
Area Mgr: Leila Gerwig
Area Mgr: Henry Gomez
Area Mgr: Shemiah Laskey
Dist Mgr: Kim Horback
Dir IT: Mark Mospan
IT Man: Justin Dang
Opers Mgr: Courtney Franklin

D-U-N-S 93-953-7671
■TEAVANA HOLDINGS INC
(Suby of STARBUCKS CORP) ★
3393 Peachtree Rd Ne # 317, Atlanta, GA 30326-1162
Tel (404) 995-8200 Founded/Ownrshp 2012
Sales 234.6MME EMP 2,652E
SIC 5499 Tea
CEO: Andrew T Mack
*CFO: Daniel P Glennon
*Ex VP: Peter M Luckhurst
*VP: David V Christopherson
*VP: Juergen W Link
VP Mktg: John Aylward

D-U-N-S 08-746-2883 IMP
TEC EQUIPMENT INC
PORTLAND MACK TRUCKS
750 Ne Columbia Blvd, Portland, OR 97211-1406
Tel (503) 285-7667 Founded/Ownrshp 1973
Sales 247.9MME EMP 484
SIC 5511 7538 7549 Automobiles, new & used; General truck repair; Trailer maintenance
Pr: David A Thompson
CFO: Greg Schuttenhelm
VP Admn: Gerald Reimer
Brnch Mgr: Casey Jones
DP Exec: Linda Homen
Sls&Mrk Ex: Kami Cady
Mktg Dir: Drew Blevins
Sls Mgr: Adam Vanderbee

D-U-N-S 19-064-4435 IMP
TECAN US GROUP INC
(Suby of TECAN GROUP AG)
9401 Globe Center Dr # 140, Morrisville, NC 27560-6211
Tel (919) 361-5200 Founded/Ownrshp 2006
Sales 105.0MME EMP 160
SIC 5047 3841 Medical equipment & supplies; Surgical & medical instruments
CEO: David Martyr
*CFO: Rudolf Eugster
*CFO: Ray Szafranski Jr
*Ex VP: Martin Brusdeilins
Exec: Kevin Moore
QA Dir: Taunya Alexander
QA Dir: Melody Humbles
Opers Mgr: Eugene Tunney
Ql Cn Mgr: Richard Lloyd
Ql Cn Mgr: Laura Popa
VP Sls: Peter Siesel

D-U-N-S 04-167-0399
TECH AGRICULTURAL INC
125 Front St, Buttonwillow, CA 93206
Tel (661) 323-1001 Founded/Ownrshp 1963
Sales 90.7MME EMP 75
SIC 5191 Fertilizer & fertilizer materials; Insecticides
Pr: Donald Houchin
*Sec: Steve Houchin
*VP: Wallace Houchin

D-U-N-S 08-194-0553 IMP/EXP
▲TECH DATA CORP
5350 Tech Data Dr, Clearwater, FL 33760-3122
Tel (727) 539-7429 Founded/Ownrshp 1974
Sales 26.3MMM EMP 9,000
Tkr Sym TECD Exch NGS
SIC 5045 Computers, peripherals & software; Computer peripheral equipment; Printers, computer; Terminals, computer
CEO: Robert M Dutkowsky
*Ch Bd: Steven A Raymund
Pr: Ken Lamneck
Pr: Joseph H Quaglia
Pr: Yuda Saydun
COO: Richard T Hume
CFO: Charles V Dannewitz
Ex VP: John Tonnison
Sr VP: Darryl Branch
Sr VP: Timothy J Curran
Sr VP: Brian Davis
Sr VP: Charles E Franklin
Sr VP: Henrick Funch
Sr VP: Andy Gass
Sr VP: Elio Levy
Sr VP: Rod Millar
Sr VP: Sherri P Nadeau
Sr VP: Robert G O'Malley
Sr VP: Joe Quaglia
Sr VP: Jeffrey L Taylor
Sr VP: Lisa Thibodeau
Board of Directors: Charles E Adair, Harry J Harczak Jr, Bridgette Heller, Kathleen Misunas, Thomas I Morgan, Patrick G Sayer

D-U-N-S 82-739-2072
■TECH DATA LATIN AMERICA INC
(Suby of TECH DATA CORP) ★
2200 Nw 112th Ave, Miami, FL 33172-1823
Tel (305) 593-5000 Founded/Ownrshp 1993
Sales 700.0MM EMP 500
SIC 5045 Computers, peripherals & software
CEO: Robert M Dutkowsky
*CFO: Charles V Dannewitz
*CFO: Jeffery P Howells
*Sr VP: Joseph B Trepani
*Sr VP: David R Vetter
*VP: Luis Olivera

D-U-N-S 96-396-6783 EXP
■TECH DATA PRODUCT MANAGEMENT INC
(Suby of TECH DATA CORP) ★
5350 Tech Data Dr, Clearwater, FL 33760-3122
Tel (727) 539-7429 Founded/Ownrshp 1996
Sales 179.7MME EMP 490
SIC 5045 Computers, peripherals & software; Computer peripheral equipment; Printers, computer; Terminals, computer
CEO: Robert M Dutkowsky
*Ex VP: Jeffery P Howells
*Ex VP: John Tonnison
*Sr VP: Charles V Dannewitz
*Sr VP: Joseph B Trepani
VP: Robert Hribernik
IT Man: Frank Bolanger
IT Man: April Hatton
IT Man: Kellie McKnight
Sls Dir: Toby McDuffie

TECH DEPOT
See 4 SURE.COM INC

D-U-N-S 04-301-4059 IMP
■TECH GROUP INC
(Suby of WEST PHARMACEUTICAL SERVICES INC) ★
14677 N 74th St, Scottsdale, AZ 85260-2486
Tel (480) 281-4500 Founded/Ownrshp 1967, 2005
Sales 228.8MME EMP 2,100
SIC 3089 Injection molding of plastics; Plastic containers, except foam; Caps, plastic
CEO: Don Morel
CFO: Thomas A Niemiec
VP: Michael McLaughlin
Exec: Larry Mucciarelli
Exec: James Tenney
Prin: Steven K Uhlmann
IT Man: Jeffrey McGuire
Sftwr Eng: Ivvy Baker
Mtls Mgr: John Sherman
Ql Cn Mgr: Cindy Crawford

TECH INTERNATIONAL
See TECHNICAL RUBBER CO INC

D-U-N-S 14-745-4495 IMP
TECH L ENTERPRISES INC
7701 Forsyth Blvd Ste 600, Saint Louis, MO 63105-1875
Tel (314) 727-5550 Founded/Ownrshp 2004
Sales 83.3MM[E] EMP 726
SIC 5063 Lighting fixtures
CEO: Sam Fox

D-U-N-S 14-499-7384 IMP
TECH LIGHTING LLC
ENCOMPASS LIGHTING GROUP
(Suby of TECH L ENTERPRISES INC) ★
7400 Linder Ave, Skokie, IL 60077-3219
Tel (847) 410-4400 Founded/Ownrshp 2004
Sales 83.3MM[E] EMP 400
SIC 5063

D-U-N-S 07-051-4505
TECH USA INC (MD)
8334 Veterans Hwy, Millersville, MD 21108-2524
Tel (410) 584-9003 Founded/Ownrshp 1998
Sales 145.8MM[E] EMP 1,750
SIC 8742 Management consulting services
CEO: Thomas B Howell
Mng Pt: Evangeline A Cantonjos
Ofcr: Brett Barnett
VP: Clay W Gallegos
*VP: Grover C Outland
Dir Bus: Alana Com
IT Man: Katie Bell

D-U-N-S 04-171-0609
TECH-ETCH INC
45 Aldrin Rd, Plymouth, MA 02360-4886
Tel (508) 747-0300 Founded/Ownrshp 1964
Sales 85.5MM[E] EMP 450
SIC 3469 3672 3479 Metal stampings; Printed circuit boards; Etching & engraving
Pr: George E Keeler
*Treas: Kevin J Feeney
Treas: John Rogers
*VP: Richard P Balonis
*VP: Kiernan P Kearney
*VP: Roy B Whittaker
Genl Mgr: Bruce McAllister
MIS Dir: Karen K Bitterman
IT Man: Robert Emmert
IT Man: Paul W Hachey
VP Opers: Roy Whitaker

D-U-N-S 14-454-3659 IMP
TECHKO INC
27301 Calle De La Rosa, San Juan Capistrano, CA 92675-1875
Tel (949) 486-0678 Founded/Ownrshp 1982
Sales 88.9MM[E] EMP 1,000
SIC 3699 3589 Security devices; Shredders, industrial & commercial
CEO: Joseph Y Ko
*VP: Rosemary Borne
Mktg Dir: Richard Montalban

D-U-N-S 13-941-2134 IMP/EXP
TECHMER PM INC
18420 S Laurel Park Rd, Compton, CA 90220-6015
Tel (310) 632-9211 Founded/Ownrshp 1997
Sales 139.6MM[E] EMP 500
SIC 2821 Plastics materials & resins
Pr: John R Manuck

D-U-N-S 14-847-4216 IMP/EXP
TECHMER PM LLC
1 Quality Cir, Clinton, TN 37716-4017
Tel (865) 457-6700 Founded/Ownrshp 2003
Sales 228.1MM EMP 585
SIC 2821 Plastics materials & resins
CFO: Paul Dinunzio
VP: Bill Horn
VP: Ken Jacobson
VP Admn: Brian West
Genl Mgr: Craig Brunnett
Info Man: Greg Brock
Netwrk Eng: Vikas Patel
Opers Mgr: Ron Lawson
Ql Cn Mgr: Bhushan Deshpande
Ql Cn Mgr: Angela Thornhill
Sales Exec: Jack U Murphy

D-U-N-S 07-840-0385
■**TECHNETICS GROUP LLC** (NC)
(Suby of GARLOCK BEARINGS) ★
5605 Carnegie Blvd # 500, Charlotte, NC 28209-4642
Tel (704) 731-1500 Founded/Ownrshp 2011
Sales 168.4MM[E] EMP 777
SIC 3053 3351 Gaskets & sealing devices; Copper rolling & drawing

D-U-N-S 04-225-6222 IMP
■**TECHNI-TOOL INC** (PA)
(Suby of WW GRAINGER INC) ★
1547 N Trooper Rd, Worcester, PA 19490
Tel (610) 941-2400 Founded/Ownrshp 1960, 2012
Sales 125.6MM[E] EMP 180
SIC 5085 Electric tools
Pr: Paul H Weiss
*VP: Bill Kushner
*VP: Michael T Ryan
*VP: Stuart Weiss
Mktg Dir: Kevin McNamee

D-U-N-S 00-120-0252 IMP/EXP
TECHNIC INC (RI)
47 Molter St, Cranston, RI 02910-1011
Tel (401) 781-6100 Founded/Ownrshp 1944, 1965
Sales 125.9MM[E] EMP 425
SIC 2899 3559 Metal treating compounds; Electroplating machinery & equipment
Pr: Hrant Shoushanian
*CFO: Scott Carlisle
*Ex VP: Alfred M Weisberg
VP: Steve Schaefer
VP: Rob Schetty
*VP: David Weisberg
Dir Lab: Justin Lloyd
CTO: Dominick Pisarro
MIS Dir: Carl Koerner

Dir IT: Chris Sicard
IT Man: Rick Retzer

D-U-N-S 06-515-3249
TECHNICAL AID CORP
ADVANTAGE TECHNICAL RESOURCES
(Suby of ADVANTAGE STAFFING) ★
220 Norwood Park S Ste 2, Norwood, MA 02062-4690
Tel (781) 251-8000 Founded/Ownrshp 2005
Sales 91.1MM[E] EMP 2,421[E]
SIC 7363

TECHNICAL AUTO PARTS
See MUSASHI AUTO PARTS MICHIGAN INC

D-U-N-S 00-731-7399 IMP/EXP
TECHNICAL CHEMICAL CO
TCC
3327 Pipeline Rd, Cleburne, TX 76033-7749
Tel (817) 645-6088 Founded/Ownrshp 1961
Sales 150.0MM EMP 312
SIC 2992

D-U-N-S 60-471-9088
TECHNICAL COLLEGE SYSTEM OF GEORGIA FOUNDATION INC
TCSG
(Suby of EXECUTIVE OFFICE OF STATE OF GEORGIA) ★
1800 Century Pl Ne # 550, Atlanta, GA 30345-4308
Tel (404) 679-1600 Founded/Ownrshp 1984
Sales 807.5MM[E] EMP 14,500
SIC 8211 9199 Secondary school;
V Ch: Ben I Copeland Sr
*CFO: Cannon Carr Jr
Ofcr: Gary Blunt
Board of Directors: Brad Sims

D-U-N-S 80-590-1535 IMP/EXP
TECHNICAL CONSUMER PRODUCTS INC
TCP
325 Campus Dr, Aurora, OH 44202-6662
Tel (800) 324-1496 Founded/Ownrshp 2001
Sales 210.1MM[E] EMP 292
SIC 5063 Lighting fittings & accessories
CEO: Kaj Den Daas
*Pr: Solomon Yan
*CFO: Brian Catlett
Sr VP: Bill Tortora
Sales Asso: Daniel Manijak
Snr Mgr: Sharon Gallagher

D-U-N-S 93-907-2443
TECHNICAL INDUSTRIES INC
336 Pinewoods Rd, Torrington, CT 06790-2350
Tel (860) 489-2160 Founded/Ownrshp 1994
Sales 95.4MM[E] EMP 364[E]
SIC 3089 Injection molding of plastics
Pr: Susan O Parent
VP: R Dale Smith

D-U-N-S 00-429-3569 IMP/EXP
TECHNICAL RUBBER CO INC
TECH INTERNATIONAL
200 E Coshocton St, Johnstown, OH 43031-1083
Tel (740) 967-9015 Founded/Ownrshp 2001
Sales 112.6MM[E] EMP 550
SIC 3011 5014 2891 Tire sundries or tire repair materials, rubber; Tire & tube repair materials; Sealing compounds, synthetic rubber or plastic
CEO: Micheal Chambers
Pr: Barry Gant
*Pr: Dan Layne
*COO: Robert Overs
*CFO: Kim Hansen
Ex VP: Bob Overs
*Sr VP: Gary Armstrong
Exec: Tammy Harmon
IT Man: Roger Blocher
*Sfty Dirs: Jeff Sellers
Natl Sales: Tim Bevier

D-U-N-S 61-494-0922
■**TECHNICAL STAFFING RESOURCES LLC**
(Suby of KBR INC) ★
10 Inverness Center Pkwy, Birmingham, AL 35242-4889
Tel (205) 437-7100 Founded/Ownrshp 2008
Sales 162.1MM[E] EMP 700
SIC 8711 7363 Engineering services; Help supply services
CFO: Jim Daniels

D-U-N-S 06-171-8060
TECHNICAL TRAINING INC
TTI-GLOBAL
3903 W Hamlin Rd, Rochester Hills, MI 48309-3233
Tel (248) 853-5550 Founded/Ownrshp 1976
Sales 141.6MM[E] EMP 1,800
SIC 8742 8999 Training & development consultant; Technical manual preparation
Pr: Lori Blaker
*CFO: Christine Santos
Prgrm Mgr: Bill Tradewell
IT Man: Adam Kennedy
IT Man: Bryan Tomczyk
Sales Exec: Shirley Brzezinski
Sls Dir: Stefan Baier
Mktg Mgr: Kevin Dever

TECHNICAL USA
See TOUSA INC

D-U-N-S 02-932-2612
TECHNICAL YOUTH LLC
BROOKSOURCE
8365 Keystone Xing # 104, Indianapolis, IN 46240-2685
Tel (317) 475-0079 Founded/Ownrshp 2000
Sales NA EMP 1,099
SIC 7379 Computer related consulting services
CEO: Ryan Hasbrook
*CFO: Jeff Weiser
Dir Bus: Michael Haas

TECHNICOLOR ENTERTAINMENT SVCS
See TECHNICOLOR THOMSON GROUP INC

D-U-N-S 08-007-5790
TECHNICOLOR HOME ENTERTAINMENT
437 New Sanford Rd, La Vergne, TN 37086-4184
Tel (615) 372-9258 Founded/Ownrshp 2015
Sales 61.6M[E] EMP 1,300
SIC 3652 Pre-recorded records & tapes
CEO: Lanny Raimondo
Pr: Orlando F Raimondo
CFO: Patricia Dave

D-U-N-S 78-448-1582 IMP/EXP
TECHNICOLOR HOME ENTERTAINMENT SERVICES INC
TECHNICOLOR VIDEO SERVICES
(Suby of TECHNICOLOR USA INC) ★
3233 Mission Oaks Blvd, Camarillo, CA 93012-5097
Tel (805) 445-1122 Founded/Ownrshp 2006
Sales 343.0MM[E] EMP 3,100
SIC 7819 Video tape or disk reproduction
CEO: Lanny Raimondo
*Pr: Orlando F Raimondo
*CFO: Patricia Dave
VP: Elaine Singleton

D-U-N-S 00-693-2842 IMP/EXP
TECHNICOLOR THOMSON GROUP INC
TECHNICOLOR ENTERTAINMENT SVCS
(Suby of TECHNICOLOR)
2233 N Ontario St Ste 300, Burbank, CA 91504-4500
Tel (818) 260-3600 Founded/Ownrshp 2001
Sales 118.7MM[E] EMP 2,030[E]
SIC 7819 7384

D-U-N-S 00-693-2305 IMP/EXP
TECHNICOLOR USA INC
(Suby of TECHNICOLOR)
4 Research Way, Princeton, NJ 08540-6618
Tel (317) 587-3000 Founded/Ownrshp 1987
Sales 1.4MMM[E] EMP 10,286
SIC 3651 3861 3661

TECHNICOLOR VIDEO SERVICE
See TECHNICOLOR VIDEOCASSETTE OF MICHIGAN INC

TECHNICOLOR VIDEO SERVICES
See TECHNICOLOR HOME ENTERTAINMENT SERVICES INC

D-U-N-S 78-448-1657 IMP
TECHNICOLOR VIDEOCASSETTE OF MICHIGAN INC
TECHNICOLOR VIDEO SERVICE
(Suby of TECHNICOLOR ENTERTAINMENT SVCS) ★
3233 Mission Oaks Blvd, Camarillo, CA 93012-5138
Tel (805) 445-1122 Founded/Ownrshp 1987
Sales 43.5MM[E] EMP 2,000
SIC 7819 Video tape or disk reproduction
Pr: Lanni Ormonvo

D-U-N-S 03-809-3050 IMP/EXP
TECHNICOTE INC
222 Mound Ave, Miamisburg, OH 45342-2996
Tel (800) 358-4448 Founded/Ownrshp 1980
Sales 84.6MM[E] EMP 207
SIC 2672 Adhesive papers, labels or tapes: from purchased material; Labels (unprinted), gummed: made from purchased materials
Pr: Doug O'Connell
COO: Sue Scudder
*Prin: Dorothy L Chapman
*Prin: Peggy Curtiss
*Prin: Michael A Ogline
Genl Mgr: Doug Oconnell
Dir IT: Michael Hardwick
Dir IT: Guido Wernicke
IT Man: George Corbett
Plnt Mgr: Carl Gilbert
Plnt Mgr: Scott Givens

D-U-N-S 96-820-1371
TECHNIFY MOTOR (USA) INC
(Suby of AVIC INTERNATIONAL HOLDING CORPORATION)
2039 S Broad St, Mobile, AL 36615-1286
Tel (251) 438-3411 Founded/Ownrshp 2010
Sales 114.0MM[E] EMP 425[E]
SIC 5088 Transportation equipment & supplies
Pr: Guangquan Wu

TECHNIKS INDUSTRIES
See TECHNIKS LLC

D-U-N-S 96-638-7672 IMP/EXP
TECHNIKS LLC
TECHNIKS INDUSTRIES
(Suby of AUDAX GROUP LP) ★
9930 E 56th St, Indianapolis, IN 46236-2810
Tel (317) 803-8000 Founded/Ownrshp 1996
Sales 149.1MM[E] EMP 802
SIC 5084 5049 Industrial machinery & equipment; Precision tools
CEO: Greg Webb
*COO: Mark Lesher
VP Sls: Michael Eniex
Manager: Chris Deal

D-U-N-S 10-348-4309 EXP
TECHNIMARK LLC
180 Commerce Pl, Asheboro, NC 27203-0515
Tel (336) 498-4171 Founded/Ownrshp 2007
Sales 1.0MMM[E] EMP 2,000
SIC 3089 5199 Injection molding of plastics; Packaging materials
Pr: Brad Wellington
VP: Carlos Dias
VP: Kris Peavy
VP: Kevin Sharma
QA Dir: Nancy Brenner
Tech Mgr: Rick Cauwels
Mtls Mgr: Karen Routh
Sfty Mgr: Tom Younger
Plnt Mgr: Gary Bean
Prd Mgr: Royce Young
Ql Cn Mgr: Bradley Berry

D-U-N-S 79-912-1855
TECHNIMARK REYNOSA LLC
(Suby of TECHNIMARK LLC) ★
180 Commerce Pl, Asheboro, NC 27203-0515
Tel (336) 498-4171 Founded/Ownrshp 2007
Sales 241.1MM[E] EMP 1,400
SIC 3089 Injection molding of plastics
Treas: Maria Kemp

D-U-N-S 01-965-9834 IMP/EXP
TECHNIP STONE & WEBSTER PROCESS TECHNOLOGY INC
(Suby of TECHNIP USA HOLDINGS INC) ★
11740 Katy Fwy Ste 100, Houston, TX 77079-1254
Tel (281) 870-1111 Founded/Ownrshp 2012
Sales 189.3MM[E] EMP 1,400[E]
SIC 8711 Chemical engineering
Pr: Stan Knez
Pr: Vincent Ledoux
*COO: Wim Vanderflier
CFO: Philippe Dorlencourt
*Treas: Paul Gullo
Sr VP: Jim O'Sullivan
VP: Todd Cartwright
VP: Gary Dellesky
*VP: Samuel K Robison
VP: Brent Schier
Ex Dir: Bob Braun

D-U-N-S 80-076-3369
TECHNIP USA HOLDINGS INC
(Suby of TECHNIP OFFSHORE INTERNATIONAL)
11740 Katy Fwy Ste 100, Houston, TX 77079-1254
Tel (281) 870-1111 Founded/Ownrshp 1992
Sales 643.9MM[E] EMP 4,346[E]
SIC 8711 Engineering services
Pr: Deanna Goodwin
Pr: David Dickson
Sr VP: Syed F Mohammad
IT Man: Chris Handwerk
IT Man: Omar Subotic
Board of Directors: Bernard Di Tullio, Patrick Picard, Julian Waldron

D-U-N-S 60-963-1098 IMP/EXP
TECHNIP USA INC
(Suby of TECHNIP USA HOLDINGS INC) ★
11740 Katy Fwy Ste 100, Houston, TX 77079-1254
Tel (281) 870-1111 Founded/Ownrshp 1992
Sales 415.9MM[E] EMP 1,200[E]
SIC 8711 8741 Engineering services; Construction management
Ch: Thierry Pilenko
Pr: Deanna Goodwin
COO: Ada Mejia
CFO: Philippe Dorlencourt
CFO: Julian Waldron
Ex VP: Philippe Barril
Sr VP: Dave Dickson
Sr VP: Nello Uccelletti
VP: Christophe Belorgeot
VP: Will Davie
VP: Jim Ermon
VP: Patrick Pouillot
VP: Cindy Viktorin
VP: Robert Wilkins
Board of Directors: Bernard Di Tullio, John Harrison, Julian Waldron

D-U-N-S 00-610-2438 IMP
TECHNIPLAS LLC
DICKTEN MASCH PLASTICS
N44w33341 Wtrtwn Plnk Rd, Nashotah, WI 53058-9707
Tel (262) 369-5555 Founded/Ownrshp 2010
Sales 191.6MM[E] EMP 300
SIC 3089 3544 Plastic processing; Injection molded finished plastic products; Special dies, tools, jigs & fixtures
Genl Mgr: Tom Sloane
Dir IT: Darwin Gaster
IT Man: Kristina Hokanson
IT Man: Larry Mosher
Mtls Mgr: Matt Dickinson
Plnt Mgr: Brad Anderson
Ql Cn Mgr: David Keene

D-U-N-S 78-213-8028 IMP
TECHNISAND INC
SANTROL
(Suby of FAIRMOUNT MINERALS) ★
11833 Ravenna Rd, Chardon, OH 44024-7006
Tel (440) 285-3132 Founded/Ownrshp 1991
Sales 106.4MM[E] EMP 118
SIC 1442 Sand mining
Pr: Jenniffer Deckard

D-U-N-S 19-668-1746
TECHNISOURCE INC
PROVALI
2050 Spectrum Blvd, Fort Lauderdale, FL 33309-3008
Tel (954) 308-7600 Founded/Ownrshp 2007
Sales NA EMP 1,626
SIC 7363 5045 7361

D-U-N-S 06-617-4533
TECHNO COATINGS INC (CA)
TECHNO WEST
1391 S Allec St, Anaheim, CA 92805-6304
Tel (714) 635-1130 Founded/Ownrshp 1974
Sales 109.2MM[E] EMP 350
SIC 1542 1629 1721 1799

TECHNO WEST
See TECHNO COATINGS INC

TECHNOLOGENT
See THOMAS GALLAWAY CORP

TECHNOLOGIES INC ARLINGTON VA
See DRS ICAS LLC

TECHNOLOGY
See BOULDER VALLEY SCHOOL DISTRICT RE-2

TECHNOLOGY INTEGRATION GROUP
See PC SPECIALISTS INC

D-U-N-S 03-526-1049 IMP/EXP
TECHNOLOGY RESEARCH LLC
TRC
(*Suby of* SOUTHWIRE COLEMAN) ★
4525 140th Ave N Ste 900, Clearwater, FL 33762-3864
Tel (727) 535-0572 *Founded/Ownrshp* 2011
Sales 112.5MM^E *EMP* 529
SIC 3613 Control panels, electric; Distribution boards, electric
CEO: G Gary Yetman
**Pr:* J Kurt Hennelly
**CFO:* J G Cochran
**CFO:* Robert D Woltil
**Sec:* Richard N Burger
**VP:* J Bradley Freeman
**VP:* Douglas B Tilghman
Ex Dir: John Simmons
Opers Mgr: Robert Vantassel
Mktg Mgr: Erica Ortiz

D-U-N-S 05-388-5604
TECHNOLOGY SERVICE CORP
TSC
962 Wayne Ave, Silver Spring, MD 20910-4433
Tel (301) 576-2300 *Founded/Ownrshp* 1966
Sales 135.7MM^E *EMP* 404
SIC 8711 Electrical or electronic engineering
Pr: Michael Syracuse

D-U-N-S 07-981-8405 IMP/EXP
TECHNOLOGY SUPPLIER LLC
81 Hobart St, Hackensack, NJ 07601-3912
Tel (201) 500-8050 *Founded/Ownrshp* 2012
Sales 100.0MM *EMP* 63
SIC 7389 Advertising, promotional & trade show services
Pr: Alex Blaker

D-U-N-S 03-982-7290
TECHNOLOGY TRANSFER INC
R.S.A.
16969 N Texas Ave Ste 400, Webster, TX 77598-4085
Tel (281) 488-7961 *Founded/Ownrshp* 1997
Sales 94.2MM^E *EMP* 40^E
SIC 7361 7379 Employment agencies; Data processing consultant
Pr: George Black
**COO:* Stephen Sweeney
**VP:* Jani Clemons
**VP:* Sally Culley
**VP:* Richard O Gross
**VP:* Jason Kuhn

D-U-N-S 15-090-1411
TECHNOSOFT CORP
28411 Northwestern Hwy # 640, Southfield, MI 48034-5507
Tel (248) 603-2600 *Founded/Ownrshp* 1996
Sales 120.0MM *EMP* 3,500
SIC 7379 Computer related consulting services
CEO: Radhakrishnan Gurusamy
**COO:* Rajiv Marwah
**Ex VP:* Mandar Kulkarni
**Ex VP:* Genga Rama Moorthy
**VP:* Srinivas Kamath
VP: Shanta Santaprakash
VP: Bruce Stopka
Snr Sftwr: Rajasekar Thangaraj
Dir IT: Luard Mandija
IT Man: Badari Prasad
Opers Mgr: Prabhu Mohan

D-U-N-S 17-521-3065
TECHNOTRIM INC
(*Suby of* ADIENT US LLC) ★
49200 Halyard Dr, Plymouth, MI 48170-2481
Tel (734) 254-6600 *Founded/Ownrshp* 2016
Sales 493.2MM *EMP* 1,500
SIC 2399 Seat covers, automobile
Pr: Kiyoo Kubota
Treas: Robert J Becker

TECHSTYLE FASHION GROUP
See TECHSTYLE INC

D-U-N-S 05-275-8501 IMP/EXP
TECHSTYLE INC
TECHSTYLE FASHION GROUP
800 Apollo St, El Segundo, CA 90245-4701
Tel (310) 683-0940 *Founded/Ownrshp* 2009
Sales 140.5MM^E *EMP* 378^E
SIC 5961 5661 5632 5651 Catalog & mail-order houses; Catalog sales; Jewelry, mail order; Women's shoes; Handbags; Jeans stores
CEO: Adam Goldenberg
**Pr:* Kimora Lee Simmons
CFO: Heidi Crane
**Co-CEO:* Don Ressler
Ex VP: Matt Fojut
Sr VP: Lauren Uppington
VP: Traci Milholend
Off Mgr: Aurore Connor
Snr Sftwr: Chris Rankin
IT Man: Ruben Mejia
Mktg Mgr: Ryan Heller
Board of Directors: Mark Leschly

D-U-N-S 10-769-7042
▲TECHTARGET INC
275 Grove St Ste 1-150, Auburndale, MA 02466-2274
Tel (617) 431-9200 *Founded/Ownrshp* 1999
Sales 111.8MM *EMP* 696^E
Tkr Sym TTGT *Exch* NGM
SIC 7375 Information retrieval services; On-line data base information retrieval
CEO: Mike Cotoia
**Ch Bd:* Gregory Strakosch
Pr: Kevin Beam
CFO: Janice O'Reilly
Sr VP: Bill Crowley
VP: Ken Male
VP: Brian McGovern
Ex Dir: Don Hawk
Sftwr Eng: Bob Hennessey
Sftwr Eng: Bori Konstantinov
Sftwr Eng: Matthew Parmenter
Board of Directors: Robert D Burke, Leonard P Forman, Bruce Levenson, Roger M Marino

D-U-N-S 14-596-3141 IMP
TECHTRONIC INDUSTRIES NORTH AMERICA INC
TTI
(*Suby of* TECHTRONIC INDUSTRIES COMPANY LIMITED)
303 Intrntl Cir Ste 490, Hunt Valley, MD 21030-1444
Tel (443) 391-1541 *Founded/Ownrshp* 2003
Sales 1.8MMM^E *EMP* 2,075
SIC 5083 5251 Lawn machinery & equipment; Tools, power
CEO: Joseph Galli Jr
Pr: Dyann Kostello
CFO: Kenneth Faith
Sr VP: Norm Macdonald
**VP:* David Levush
Creative D: Wade Franks
Genl Mgr: Carlos Escobedo
QA Dir: Jess Abell
Prd Mgr: Vicki Myers
VP Sls: Matt Winter
Mktg Dir: Michelle Painter

TECHTRONIC INDUSTRIES PWR EQP
See ONE WORLD TECHNOLOGIES INC

D-U-N-S 96-037-6916
TECHWELL SURVEYS CORP
610 W 83rd St, Odessa, TX 79764-1912
Tel (432) 362-3711 *Founded/Ownrshp* 2007
Sales 100.0MM *EMP* 3
SIC 4911 7389 Electric services;

D-U-N-S 00-906-2316 IMP
TECK AMERICAN INC
(*Suby of* TECK RESOURCES LIMITED)
501 N Riverpoint Blvd # 300, Spokane, WA 99202-1659
Tel (509) 747-6111 *Founded/Ownrshp* 2008
Sales 499.9MM^E *EMP* 910
SIC 1081 Exploration, metal mining
Ch Bd: Norman B Keevil
**Pr:* Mayank M Ashar
**Pr:* Donald R Lindsay
**Treas:* H C Chu
**Ex VP:* Takashi Kuriyama
**Sr VP:* Dale E Andres
**Sr VP:* Andrew Golding
**Sr VP:* D H Horswill
**VP:* M E Agg
**VP:* F S Daley
**VP:* C B Diluzio
**VP:* D W Godlewski
VP: Greg Waller

D-U-N-S 60-590-3772
TECMA GROUP L L C
TECMA GROUP OF COMPANIES
2000 Wyoming Ave Ste A, El Paso, TX 79903-3830
Tel (915) 534-4252 *Founded/Ownrshp* 1986
Sales 77.7MM^E *EMP* 2,008^E
SIC 7389 Brokers' services
Pr: K Alan Russell
**Ex VP:* Toby M Spoon
VP: Rodger Lovrenich
VP Opers: Jose Grajeda

TECMA GROUP OF COMPANIES
See TECMA GROUP L L C

D-U-N-S 62-611-2502
TECNICO CORP
(*Suby of* A M H) ★
831 Industrial Ave, Chesapeake, VA 23324-2614
Tel (757) 545-4013 *Founded/Ownrshp* 2008
Sales 96.4MM^E *EMP* 450
SIC 3446 3443 3441 3444 3731 Architectural metalwork; Shipbuilding & repairing; Fabricated plate work (boiler shop); Sheet metalwork; Fabricated structural metal
Pr: Raymond G Wittersheim
**Sr VP:* Mark L Oakley
**VP:* Richard C Freeman
**VP:* Larry E Torrech

D-U-N-S 18-657-6013 EXP
TECO DIVERSIFIED INC
(*Suby of* TECO ENERGY INC) ★
702 N Franklin St, Tampa, FL 33602-4429
Tel (813) 228-4111 *Founded/Ownrshp* 1987
Sales 168.1MM^E *EMP* 2,282
SIC 1221 Bituminous coal & lignite-surface mining
Pr: Steve Winistorfer
**CFO:* Gordan L Gillette

D-U-N-S 04-829-5869 IMP/EXP
TECO ENERGY INC (FL)
(*Suby of* EMERA INCORPORATED)
702 N Franklin St, Tampa, FL 33602-4429
Tel (813) 228-1111 *Founded/Ownrshp* 1981, 2016
Sales 2.7MMM *EMP* 4,400^E
SIC 4911 4924 4424 1221 1222 Electric services; Distribution, electric power; Generation, electric power; Transmission, electric power; Natural gas distribution; Intercoastal transportation, freight; Bituminous coal surface mining; Coal preparation plant, bituminous or lignite; Unit train loading facility, bituminous or lignite; Bituminous coal-underground mining
Pr: John B Ramil
Pr: Charles R Black
Pr: William N Cantrell
Pr: Sal Litrico
Pr: Richard E Ludwig
Pr: J J Shackleford
CFO: Sandra W Callahan
Ofcr: Mark Kane
Sr VP: Charles A Attal III
Sr VP: Phil L Barringer
Sr VP: Gregory W Blunden
Sr VP: Richard Lehfeldt
VP: Spence Autry
VP: Dee Brown
VP: Wraye Grimard
VP: Keith Gruetzmacher
VP: Thomas L Hernandez
VP: Karen Mincey
VP: Bruce Narzissenfeld
VP: David Nicholson
VP: Brad Register

D-U-N-S 92-682-9417 EXP
TECO HOLDINGS USA INC
(*Suby of* TECO ELECTRIC & MACHINERY CO., LTD.)
5100 N Interstate 35, Round Rock, TX 78681-2421
Tel (512) 255-4141 *Founded/Ownrshp* 1995
Sales 355.5MM *EMP* 380
Accts Pricewaterhousecoopers Llp Ta
SIC 3621 Motors & generators
Pr: H C Meng
CFO: Hank Chang

TECO PEOPLES GAS SYSTEM
See PEOPLES GAS

D-U-N-S 78-625-0225 IMP
TECO-WESTINGHOUSE MOTOR CO
(*Suby of* TECO HOLDINGS USA INC) ★
5100 N Interstate 35 A, Round Rock, TX 78681-2461
Tel (512) 218-7448 *Founded/Ownrshp* 1987
Sales 213.9MM^E *EMP* 353
SIC 3621 Motors, electric
Pr: Vincent Tang
**CFO:* Emily KAO
**Treas:* I-Hsin KAO
VP: Bill Miller
Exec: Josie Hernandez
Plng Mgr: Cary Dilloway
CIO: Blane Alsworth
Sls Mgr: Robert Richards

D-U-N-S 07-410-8176
TECOLOTE RESEARCH INC
420 S Fairview Ave # 201, Goleta, CA 93117-3627
Tel (805) 571-6366 *Founded/Ownrshp* 1973
Sales 91.7MM^E *EMP* 583
SIC 8742 8731 Management consulting services; Commercial physical research
Pr: James Y Takayesu
**Ofcr:* Karen H McKernan
Exec: Nancy Colombo
Snr Sftwr: Gary Kearney
CTO: Mike Dalessandro
Dir IT: Kelly Border
Tech Mgr: Aileen Donohue
Tech Mgr: Lisa Espelien
Tech Mgr: Jennifer Kirchhoffer
Tech Mgr: Brian Rutt
Sales Exec: Linda Williamson
Board of Directors: Brad Frederic, William Jago, Arthur Kluge, Karen McKernan, James Takayesu

D-U-N-S 11-056-6259
TECOMET INC
115 Eames St, Wilmington, MA 01887-3380
Tel (978) 642-2400 *Founded/Ownrshp* 2013
Sales 963.6MM^E *EMP* 2,661
SIC 3841 3444 Diagnostic apparatus, medical; Surgical instruments & apparatus; Medical instruments & equipment, blood & bone work; Sheet metalwork
CEO: William Dow
CFO: John Connolly
Prgrm Mgr: Chris Thompson
Genl Mgr: Joseph Buturlia
IT Man: Donna Baker
IT Man: Allan Chin
Sfty Dirs: Jimmy Montanaro
Opers Mgr: Alexander Curry
Prd Mgr: Erik Paquette
Ql Cn Mgr: Richard Hoftiezer
Ql Cn Mgr: Mike Virusso

D-U-N-S 12-583-7471
TECTA AMERICA CORP
9450 Bryn Mawr Ave, Rosemont, IL 60018-5248
Tel (847) 581-3888 *Founded/Ownrshp* 2013
Sales 779.4MM^E *EMP* 3,000
SIC 1761 Roofing, siding & sheet metal work
CEO: Mark Santacrose
**COO:* Mark Gaulin
VP: Mike Arduino
VP: Robert Farrell
VP: Mike Kliber
VP: Richard Lewis
VP: Daryl Maronic
VP: Jim Stark
VP: Paul Stubitsch
Genl Mgr: Jeremy Dicken
Off Mgr: Kelly Ryan

D-U-N-S 82-900-2729
TECTA HOLDING INC
6450 Brayn Mawr Ste 500, Rosemont, IL 60018
Tel (847) 581-3888 *Founded/Ownrshp* 2008
Sales 80.4MM^E *EMP* 4,000
SIC 1761 Roofing contractor
Pr: Paul Stubitsch
CFO: Eileen Kanerick

D-U-N-S 00-504-9440 IMP/EXP
TECUMSEH PRODUCTS CO
(*Suby of* MA INDUSTRIAL JV LLC) ★
5683 Hines Dr, Ann Arbor, MI 48108-7901
Tel (734) 585-9500 *Founded/Ownrshp* 1930, 2015
Sales 724.4MM *EMP* 5,800
SIC 3585 3679 Parts for heating, cooling & refrigerating equipment; Compressors for refrigeration & air conditioning equipment; Condensers, refrigeration; Hermetic seals for electronic equipment
Pr: Harold M Karp
Pr: Ronald E Pratt
Pr: Eric L Stolzenberg
**CFO:* Janice E Stipp
**Ex VP:* Jerry L Mosingo
Ex VP: Jerry Mosingo
IT Man: Emery Goniea
Board of Directors: Stephanie H Boyse, Mitchell I Quain, Robert E Rossiter, Terence C Seikel, Douglas M Suliman Jr

TECXTAR
See MGS GROUP NORTH AMERICA INC

D-U-N-S 86-132-7146
TED RUSSELL FORD INC
8551 Kingston Pike, Knoxville, TN 37919-5300
Tel (865) 693-7611 *Founded/Ownrshp* 1986
Sales 92.5MM^E *EMP* 230
SIC 5511 5521 5531 Automobiles, new & used; Used car dealers; Automotive parts
Pr: Ted Russell
**Sec:* Bart Lashley
**VP:* Drama Russell
VP: Howard Varnedoe
Sales Asso: Alonzo Keener

D-U-N-S 04-706-2740
TEDESCHI FOOD SHOPS INC
STORE 24
(*Suby of* 7-ELEVEN INC) ★
14 Howard St, Rockland, MA 02370-1929
Tel (781) 878-8210 *Founded/Ownrshp* 1967
Sales NA *EMP* 1,500
SIC 5411 Convenience stores, chain
Pr: Peter D Tedeschi
**CFO:* Richard Jasper
**Treas:* Robert L Tedeschi Jr
Sr VP: Alan Reaerton
**VP:* Raymond L Tedeschi

D-U-N-S 05-872-3706
TEDS MONTANA GRILL INC
133 Luckie St Nw Ste 200, Atlanta, GA 30303-2036
Tel (404) 521-9796 *Founded/Ownrshp* 2001
Sales 65.6MM^E *EMP* 1,831^E
SIC 5812 Grills (eating places)
CEO: George W McKerrow
**CFO:* Danielle Clark
**CFO:* Kristi Nyhof
VP: Jeff Darby
Dir IT: William Benz
Site Mgr: Jacob Haskell
Site Mgr: Monica Korycinski
Site Mgr: Jason Salisbury

TEEGARDEN, DAVID K M D
See TRINITY MOTHER FRANCIS HEALTH SYSTEM

TEES
See TEXAS A&M ENGINEERING EXPERIMENT STATION

D-U-N-S 15-286-0925
TEG STAFFING INC
(*Suby of* EASTRIDGE ADM STAFFING) ★
2604 El Camino Real Ste B, Carlsbad, CA 92008-1205
Tel (619) 584-3444 *Founded/Ownrshp* 2003
Sales 18.2MM^E *EMP* 1,600
SIC 7363 Temporary help service
Pr: Nanci Porter

D-U-N-S 00-220-5698 EXP
▲TEGNA INC
7950 Jones Branch Dr, Mc Lean, VA 22102-3302
Tel (703) 854-7000 *Founded/Ownrshp* 1906
Sales 3.0MMM *EMP* 10,020^E
Accts Ernst & Young Llp Mclean Vir
Tkr Sym TGNA *Exch* NYS
SIC 2711 4813 4841 4833 Newspapers, publishing & printing; ; Cable television services; Television broadcasting stations
Pr: Gracia C Martore
Ch Bd: Marjorie Magner
Pr: Larry Audas
Pr: Donald W Bailey
Pr: Maria Barrs
Pr: John C Deushane
Pr: Robert Granfeldt
Pr: Pamela Henson
Pr: Larry Kramer
Pr: Walt Lafferty
Pr: Eric Land
Pr: Karen Lincoln
Pr: Dave Lougee
Pr: John F Maher
Pr: Mary Murcko
Pr: Edward S Power
Pr: Jason Taylor
Pr: Melinda Vonderahe
Pr: Gary L Watson
Pr: Larry Whitaker
Pr: John A Williams
Board of Directors: Jennifer Dulski, Howard D Elias, Lidia Fonseca, Jill Greenthal, Scott K McCune, Susan Ness, Bruce P Nolop, Neal Shapiro

D-U-N-S 18-433-8940
TEGP INC
(*Suby of* EASTRIDGE ADM STAFFING) ★
2375 Northside Dr Ste 360, San Diego, CA 92108-2713
Tel (619) 584-3408 *Founded/Ownrshp* 2005
Sales 28.9MM^E *EMP* 1,500
SIC 7363 Temporary help service
Pr: Michael Santos

D-U-N-S 82-981-0154
TEGRA MEDICAL LLC
9 Forge Pkwy, Franklin, MA 02038-3135
Tel (508) 541-4200 *Founded/Ownrshp* 2007
Sales 86.5MM^E *EMP* 295
SIC 3841 Surgical & medical instruments
CEO: J Mark King
**Pr:* Bob Roche
**CEO:* Robert Pietrafesa
**CFO:* Bill Fisher
**CFO:* Joe Kajano
**VP:* Tom Burns
**VP:* Walter Gacek
**VP:* Deborah L Harnois
**VP:* Bob Miller
**VP:* Mike Treleaven
Genl Mgr: Kevin Carroll

D-U-N-S 00-298-6404
■TEGRANT ALLOYD BRANDS INC
SONOCO ALLOYD
(*Suby of* SONOCO PROTECTIVE SOLUTION) ★
1401 Pleasant St, Dekalb, IL 60115-2663
Tel (815) 756-8451 *Founded/Ownrshp* 1961, 2007
Sales 101.6MM^E *EMP* 560
SIC 3089 3565 Blister or bubble formed packaging, plastic; Trays, plastic; Packaging machinery
Pr: Ron Leach
**Sr VP:* James L Price
Telecom Ex: Jan Waldauer
Dir IT: Rod Engstrom
IT Man: Tom Woolaway
Plnt Mgr: Vince Manalio

D-U-N-S 79-657-0435 EXP
■TEGRANT CORP
SONOCO PROTECTIVE SOLUTION
(*Suby of* SONOCO PRODUCTS CO) ★
1401 Pleasant St, Dekalb, IL 60115-2663
Tel (815) 756-8451 *Founded/Ownrshp* 2007
Sales 775.2MM^E *EMP* 3,370
SIC 2671 Plastic film, coated or laminated for packaging
Pr: Ron Leach
**Prin:* Vicki Arthur
Sfty Mgr: Jim Ingallino
VP Sls: Tom Gordon
Mktg Mgr: Rachel D Coltin

D-U-N-S 79-648-0874
■TEGRANT HOLDING CORP
(*Suby of* SONOCO PRODUCTS CO) ★
1401 Pleasant St, Dekalb, IL 60115-2663
Tel (815) 756-8451 *Founded/Ownrshp* 2013
Sales 140.1MM^E *EMP* 3,370
SIC 3089 3565 Blister or bubble formed packaging, plastic; Packing & wrapping machinery
Pr: Ronald G Leach
**Sec:* Jay Hereford

TEICHERT CONSTRUCTION
See A TEICHERT & SON INC

D-U-N-S 00-691-1135 IMP
TEICHERT INC
3500 American River Dr, Sacramento, CA 95864-5802
Tel (916) 484-3011 *Founded/Ownrshp* 1887
Sales 793.9MM^E *EMP* 1,800^E
SIC 3273 5032 1611 1442 1521 5039 Ready-mixed concrete; Brick, stone & related material; Highway & street construction; Construction sand & gravel; Single-family housing construction; Air ducts, sheet metal
Pr: Judson T Riggs
**Ch Bd:* Louis V Riggs
**CFO:* Narendra M Pathipati
CFO: Pat Pathipati
VP: Robin Creger
VP: F Crosthwaite
VP: Deon Good
VP: Steve Mitchell
VP: Richard Pixton
Exec: Donna Modellas
Exec: Carol Stanger
Board of Directors: Melita M Teichert, Bruce F Allen, Michael A Ziegler, George L Cook, Thomas J Hammer Jr, George M Hughes, Martha H Marsh, Judson T Riggs, Louis V Riggs, James W Taylor, Frederick A Teichert

D-U-N-S 00-809-4026 IMP
TEIJIN ARAMID USA INC
(*Suby of* TEIJIN HOLDINGS USA INC) ★
801 Blacklawn Rd Sw Ste F, Conyers, GA 30012-5187
Tel (770) 929-0781 *Founded/Ownrshp* 2000
Sales 175.0MM *EMP* 20
SIC 5131 Piece goods & notions
Pr: George Perkins

D-U-N-S 12-159-4100 IMP
TEIJIN HOLDINGS USA INC
(*Suby of* TEIJIN LIMITED)
600 Lexington Ave Fl 27, New York, NY 10022-7680
Tel (212) 308-8744 *Founded/Ownrshp* 2000
Sales 295.1MM^E *EMP* 1,200
SIC 5131 Piece goods & notions
Ch Bd: Giichi Monta

D-U-N-S 96-086-3483
TEIJIN PHARMA USA LLC
(*Suby of* TEIJIN HOLDINGS USA INC) ★
773 San Marin Dr Ste 2230, Novato, CA 94945-1366
Tel (415) 893-1518 *Founded/Ownrshp* 2008
Sales 101.3MM^E *EMP* 1,013^E
SIC 5131 Piece goods & notions
Off Mgr: Martha Schneider

D-U-N-S 61-496-5911 EXP
TEJAS TUBULAR PRODUCTS INC
8799 North Loop E Ste 300, Houston, TX 77029-1242
Tel (281) 822-3400 *Founded/Ownrshp* 2011
Sales 306.0MM^E *EMP* 600^E
SIC 3317 3498 Steel pipe & tubes; Tube fabricating (contract bending & shaping); Couplings, pipe: fabricated from purchased pipe
Pr: Maximo A Tejeda
CFO: Bobby Bell
CFO: Bill Murphy
IT Man: Ricardo Martinez
Ql Cn Mgr: Srihari Vasudevan
Sales Exec: Larry Palmer
Snr Mgr: Patricia Flores

D-U-N-S 96-883-2381
TEJAS TUBULAR PRODUCTS INC
8526 Green River Dr, Houston, TX 77028-2835
Tel (281) 822-3400 *Founded/Ownrshp* 1990
Sales 300.0MM *EMP* 700
SIC 5051

D-U-N-S 80-462-8899
TEKAKWITHA LIVING CENTER INC
RAINBOW DAYCARE
622 Veterans Ave, Sisseton, SD 57262-1418
Tel (605) 698-7693 *Founded/Ownrshp* 1991
Sales 351.1MM *EMP* 17
SIC 8351 Child day care services

D-U-N-S 09-944-9076
TEKELEC GLOBAL INC
5200 Paramount Pkwy, Morrisville, NC 27560-8499
Tel (919) 460-5500 *Founded/Ownrshp* 2013
Sales NA *EMP* 1,291
SIC 3661 3825 7371

D-U-N-S 00-991-6094 IMP
TEKFOR INC
TEKFOR USA
(*Suby of* NEUMAYER TEKFOR HOLDING GMBH)
3690 Long Rd, Wooster, OH 44691-7962
Tel (330) 202-7420 *Founded/Ownrshp* 2001
Sales 85.3MM^E *EMP* 265
SIC 3462 Automotive forgings, ferrous: crankshaft, engine, axle, etc.
Pr: Kevin Weldi
Prgrm Mgr: Andrew Hemming
Ql Cn Mgr: Robin Martin

TEKFOR USA
See TEKFOR INC

D-U-N-S 09-949-1235
TEKMARK GLOBAL SOLUTIONS LLC
100 Metroplex Dr Ste 102, Edison, NJ 08817-2684
Tel (732) 572-5400 *Founded/Ownrshp* 1979
Sales 127.2MM^E *EMP* 900
SIC 7379 7371 7363 Computer related consulting services; Custom computer programming services; Temporary help service
Pr: John Giunta
CFO: Charles K Miller
CFO: Chuck Miller
VP: Dave Donohue
VP: Stephen Haran
VP: Leonard Semon
VP: Kenneth Smyth
Dir Rx: Barrett Robb
Dir Rx: Robert Scarcelle
Dir Bus: Greg Giunta
IT Man: Jacqueline Lavignera

D-U-N-S 60-617-3839 IMP
TEKNETIX INC
2501 Garfield Ave, Parkersburg, WV 26101-1916
Tel (304) 489-3600 *Founded/Ownrshp* 1989
Sales 92.0MM^E *EMP* 200
SIC 3672 7371 Printed circuit boards; Computer software systems analysis & design, custom
Pr: Joseph Florence
Pr: Burt Thurman
**VP:* John W Florence
Prgrm Mgr: Debbie Steele

D-U-N-S 04-202-3333 IMP/EXP
TEKNI-PLEX INC
TEKNIPLEX CO
460 E Swedesford Rd # 3000, Wayne, PA 19087-1835
Tel (484) 690-1520 *Founded/Ownrshp* 1994, 2013
Sales 1.1MMM^E *EMP* 2,500
SIC 2679 3462 3052 2672 Egg cartons, molded pulp: made from purchased material; Pump & compressor forgings, ferrous; Garden hose, plastic; Cloth lined paper: made from purchased paper; Coated paper, except photographic, carbon or abrasive; Glazed paper, except photographic, carbon or abrasive
Pr: Paul J Young
Pr: Paul Rosowski
**CFO:* Robert M Larney
**Treas:* Art Richards
Sr VP: Miguel A Nistal
Sr VP: Norman Patterson
Sr VP: Luc Vercruyssen
VP: Rochelle G Krombolz
VP: Amy Nolan
VP: Lance Novotny
VP: Jeff Rishel

D-U-N-S 14-044-5680 IMP/EXP
TEKNI-PLEX MANAGEMENT LLC
260 N Denton Tap Rd, Coppell, TX 75019-2142
Tel (972) 304-5077 *Founded/Ownrshp* 1994
Sales 138.2MM^E *EMP* 3,300
SIC 3089 2631 2656 Trays, plastic; Blister or bubble formed packaging, plastic; Coated paperboard; Sanitary food containers
VP: Phil Bourgeois

D-U-N-S 19-476-0385
TEKNION LLC
(*Suby of* TEKNION CORPORATION)
350 Fellowship Rd Ste 100, Mount Laurel, NJ 08054-1201
Tel (856) 552-5750 *Founded/Ownrshp* 1996
Sales 164.3MM^E *EMP* 200
SIC 5021 Office & public building furniture
Pr: Mark Dodick
VP: Gina Chapman
VP: Scott Deugo
VP: Bill McKeown
VP: Joe Rende
VP: Roger Schlick
Exec: Leslie Thompson
Mng Dir: Barry Bielawski
Dist Mgr: Edward Devine
Dist Mgr: Nicolle Schneider
Genl Mgr: Myron Heppner

TEKNIPLEX CO
See TEKNI-PLEX INC

TEKNOR APEX BROWNSVILLE
See TEKNOR APEX TENNESSEE CO

D-U-N-S 04-536-7968 IMP/EXP
TEKNOR APEX CO
505 Central Ave, Pawtucket, RI 02861-1900
Tel (401) 725-8000 *Founded/Ownrshp* 1924
Sales 1.0MMM^E *EMP* 2,500
Accts Piccirelli Gilstein & Company
SIC 3087 3069 3052 2869 3081 2821 Custom compound purchased resins; Custom compounding of rubber materials; Mats or matting, rubber; Garden hose, rubber; Plasticizers, organic: cyclic & acyclic; Plastic film & sheet; Thermoplastic materials
Ch Bd: Jonathan D Fain
**Pr:* William J Murray
**CFO:* James Morrison
Treas: David Fox
VP: Bill Murray
VP: Craig White
Off Mgr: Anja Goemans
CIO: Ray Rockefeller
Dir IT: Al Loureiro
Telecom Mg: Gail Richardson
Tech Mgr: Maryellen Cox

D-U-N-S 05-487-6834 IMP
TEKNOR APEX TENNESSEE CO
TEKNOR APEX BROWNSVILLE
(*Suby of* TEKNOR APEX CO) ★
751 N Dupree Ave, Brownsville, TN 38012-1708
Tel (731) 772-4842 *Founded/Ownrshp* 1971
Sales 85.4MM^E *EMP* 700^E
SIC 3052 Rubber & plastics hose & beltings
CEO: Jonathan D Fain
Sls Mgr: Gary Tapkas

TEKPARTNERS
See P2P STAFFING CORP

D-U-N-S 78-117-9668
TEKSERVE CORP
SMART MACHINES
119 W 23rd St Frnt 1, New York, NY 10011-2427
Tel (212) 929-3645 *Founded/Ownrshp* 1987
Sales 110.0MM *EMP* 120^E
SIC 7378 5734

TEKSYSTEMS GLOBAL SVC
See TEKSYSTEMS INC

D-U-N-S 96-576-2909
TEKSYSTEMS INC
TEKSYSTEMS GLOBAL SVC
(*Suby of* ALLEGIS GROUP INC) ★
7437 Race Rd, Hanover, MD 21076-1112
Tel (410) 540-7700 *Founded/Ownrshp* 1997
Sales 3.6MMM *EMP* 2,900
Accts Pricewaterhousecoopers Llp Ba
SIC 7379 7376 7373 Computer related consulting services; Computer facilities management; Computer integrated systems design
Pr: Jay Alvather
VP: Tim Cerny
VP: Chris Russell
Dir Rx: Chris Silman
Dir Rx: Jaime Studebaker
Ex Dir: Eric Staebell
Mng Dir: Adam I Ferencz
Brnch Mgr: Dave Roberts
Snr Sftwr: Chris Benedict
Snr Sftwr: Venkatesh Joejode
Snr Sftwr: Arun Mathew

TEKTRONIX COMMUNICATIONS
See TEKTRONIX TEXAS LLC

D-U-N-S 00-902-0231 IMP
■TEKTRONIX INC (OR)
(*Suby of* FORTIVE CORP) ★
14150 Sw Karl Braun Dr, Beaverton, OR 97005-2381
Tel (800) 833-9200 *Founded/Ownrshp* 1946, 2016
Sales 1.3MMM^E *EMP* 5,028
SIC 3825

D-U-N-S 00-428-4170
■TEKTRONIX SERVICE SOLUTIONS INC
(*Suby of* TEKTRONIX INC) ★
6120 Hanging Moss Rd, Orlando, FL 32807-3701
Tel (407) 678-6900 *Founded/Ownrshp* 1944, 2001
Sales 106.9MM^E *EMP* 822
SIC 3812 3674 8734 7699 Detection apparatus: electronic/magnetic field, light/heat; Semiconductors & related devices; Testing laboratories; Professional instrument repair services
Pr: Robert S Lutz
**CFO:* Ingrid West
**Treas:* Frank T McFaden
**VP:* Laurence S Smith

D-U-N-S 36-060-4920
■TEKTRONIX TEXAS LLC
TEKTRONIX COMMUNICATIONS
(*Suby of* POTOMAC HOLDING LLC) ★
2200 Penn Ave Nw Ste 800w, Washington, DC 20037-1731
Tel (202) 828-0850 *Founded/Ownrshp* 2015
Sales 114.5MM^E *EMP* 483
SIC 7372 Prepackaged software
Pr: Richard Kenedi
CFO: Lorrie Mathers
VP: Samir Marwaha
VP: Ken Pecot
VP: Manuel Stopnicki
Software D: Randi Neuberger

D-U-N-S 04-446-2475
■TEL-DRUG INC
CIGNA TEL-DRUG
(*Suby of* CIGNA) ★
4901 N 4th Ave, Sioux Falls, SD 57104-0444
Tel (605) 809-8166 *Founded/Ownrshp* 1993
Sales 71.8MM^E *EMP* 26,608^E
SIC 5912 5961 Drug stores; Pharmaceuticals, mail order
Pr: Eric S Elliott
**CEO:* David Cordani
Pharmcst: Frankie Chen
Pharmcst: Grant Stahl
Pharmcst: Dominic Wieneke

D-U-N-S 10-395-4350
TELAID INDUSTRIES INC
13 W Main St, Niantic, CT 06357-2335
Tel (860) 739-4461 *Founded/Ownrshp* 1981
Sales 85.0MM^E *EMP* 180
SIC 7373 Local area network (LAN) systems integrator; Office computer automation systems integration
Ch Bd: Thomas Patsiga
**Pr:* Scott Patsiga
**CEO:* William J Patsiga
**COO:* Christopher T Patsiga
VP: Michael Korcuba
IT Man: Jessica Jones
IT Man: Grant Murray
IT Man: Ryan Todd

D-U-N-S 18-640-0065 IMP
TELAMON CORP
1000 E 116th St, Carmel, IN 46032-3416
Tel (317) 818-6888 *Founded/Ownrshp* 1980
Sales 612.0MM^E *EMP* 650
Accts Bkd Llp Indianapolis Indian
SIC 4813 8711 3357 ; Data telephone communications; Engineering services; Communication wire
CEO: Stanley Chen
Pr: Keith Gallant
Pr: Robert Kuhlmann
Pr: Randall P Muench
CFO: Larry Rodiman
Ch: Albert M Chen
Sr VP: Shawn Skeel
VP: Cathy White
VP Bus: Fred Huang
Exec: Leonard Strickland
Ex Dir: Lurys Fuhrman

TELAMON INTERNATIONAL
See TELAMON TECHNOLOGIES CORP

D-U-N-S 08-502-0683 IMP/EXP
TELAMON TECHNOLOGIES CORP
TELAMON INTERNATIONAL
(*Suby of* TELAMON CORP) ★
1000 E 116th St, Carmel, IN 46032-3416
Tel (317) 818-6888 *Founded/Ownrshp* 1982
Sales 607.5MM^E *EMP* 585
SIC 3661 Telephones & telephone apparatus
Pr: Albert Chen
**Pr:* Michael Shen
**CFO:* John Ludwig
CFO: Larry Rodeman
Dir IT: Jeffrey Wu

D-U-N-S 18-750-2059
TELAPEX INC
1018 Highland Pkwy # 500, Ridgeland, MS 39157-2089
Tel (601) 355-1522 *Founded/Ownrshp* 1959
Sales 334.9MM^E *EMP* 461^E
SIC 4812 4813 Cellular telephone services; Telephone communication, except radio
CEO: Carson Hughes
**Pr:* James H Creekmore
**Pr:* Wesley Goings
Sr VP: Chuck McBride
**VP:* Wade Creekmore Jr
**VP:* Sidney C Crews
**VP:* L Brooks Derryberry
**VP:* Carol A Grigsby
**VP:* Helen Simmons

D-U-N-S 14-812-6378 IMP
TELCO INTERCONTINENTAL CORP
9812 Whithorn Dr, Houston, TX 77095-5001
Tel (281) 500-8270 *Founded/Ownrshp* 1985
Sales 19.0MMM *EMP* 24
SIC 5063 5065 3575 Electronic wire & cable; Telephone equipment; Cathode ray tube (CRT), computer terminal
Pr: Frank C Liang
**VP:* MEI-Yun Liang
Opers Mgr: Sue Yu
Sls Mgr: J Campbell

D-U-N-S 13-543-0275
TELCOBUY.COM LLC
(*Suby of* WORLD WIDE TECHNOLOGY HOLDING CO INC) ★
60 Weldon Pkwy, Maryland Heights, MO 63043-3202
Tel (314) 569-7000 *Founded/Ownrshp* 2002
Sales 246.4MM^E *EMP* 320
SIC 5065 Electronic parts & equipment
CEO: James Kavanaugh
**Pr:* Mark J Catalano
**CFO:* Thomas W Strunk
VP: Mark Franke
**VP:* John Miller
Prgrm Mgr: Mark A Yaeger
Dir IT: Greg Palumbo
**VP Mfg:* Kurt Grimminger
Sls Mgr: Tammy Merz
Sls Mgr: Lindsey Pfeiffer
Sls Mgr: Claire M Shenberg

D-U-N-S 16-508-6484
■TELCOM CONSTRUCTION INC
(*Suby of* DYCOM INDUSTRIES INC) ★
2218 200th St E, Clearwater, MN 55320-1636
Tel (320) 558-9485 *Founded/Ownrshp* 2015
Sales 146.3MM^E *EMP* 460
SIC 1623 Telephone & communication line construction
Pr: Mark Muller
Sr VP: David Rantasha
VP: Steve Brings
VP: Mike Gillette

D-U-N-S 10-864-9864
TELCORDIA TECHNOLOGIES INC
ICONECTIV
(*Suby of* TELEFON AB LM ERICSSON)
444 Hoes Ln, Piscataway, NJ 08854-4104
Tel (732) 699-6800 *Founded/Ownrshp* 2011
Sales 158.2MM^E *EMP* 300^E
SIC 7371 7373 8742 Computer software development; Systems engineering, computer related; Training & development consultant
CEO: Richard Jacowleff
**CFO:* Jerry Fechter
**Ex VP:* Tara O'Neil Diaz
**Ex VP:* Chris Drake
**Ex VP:* Magnus Mandersson
**Sr VP:* Per Borgklint
**Sr VP:* Anthony Cresti
VP: Brian Moore
**VP:* David Wilson
Dir Bus: Denise Eslinger
Ex Dir: Anita Amin

D-U-N-S 05-165-4861
TELE-MEDIA CORP
320 W College Ave, Pleasant Gap, PA 16823-7425
Tel (814) 359-3481 *Founded/Ownrshp* 1985
Sales 178.9MM^E *EMP* 1,200
SIC 4841 Cable television services
CEO: Robert Tudek
CFO: Robert Stemler
Sr VP: Tony Swain
VP: Frank Vicente
Opers Mgr: Lesley Strouse

D-U-N-S 07-654-7363
TELECARE CORP
1080 Marina Village Pkwy # 100, Alameda, CA 94501-1078
Tel (510) 337-7950 Founded/Ownrshp 1965
Sales 138.9MM^E EMP 2,050^E
Accts Pricewaterhousecoopers San Fr
SIC 8063 8011 Psychiatric hospitals; Health maintenance organization
Pr: Anne L Baker
CFO: Marshall Langfeld
Sr VP: Anita Barnas
Sr VP: Faith Richie
Sr VP: Faithe Richie
Sr VP: Steve Wilson
VP: Stacey Calhoun
VP: Carol Caputo
VP: Pat Doyle
VP: Ross Peterson
Exec: Sam Gould
Comm Dir: Shea McGuier
Board of Directors: David J Kears

D-U-N-S 08-761-1323
■TELECHECK SERVICES INC
(Suby of FIRST DATA CORP) ★
5251 Westheimr Rd B100, Houston, TX 77056-5499
Tel (713) 331-7600 Founded/Ownrshp 1992
Sales 81.2MM^E EMP 2,200
SIC 7389 7374 6153 Check validation service; Credit card service; Data processing service; Credit card services, central agency collection
Pr: Jeff Baer
CFO: Harold Winfield
Sr VP: Hodges Marshall
Sr VP: Randy Rutledge
Sr VP: Thomas Strachan
Sr VP: Randy Templeton
Sr VP: Fritz Weitzel
VP: Jean Espinal
VP: Laura Hughes
VP: Kerry Sellen
QA Dir: Antoine Bui

D-U-N-S 03-820-8120 IMP
TELECOM ITALIA SPARKLE OF NORTH AMERICA INC
(Suby of TELECOM ITALIA SPARKLE SPA)
622 3rd Ave Fl 38, New York, NY 10017-6729
Tel (212) 310-9000 Founded/Ownrshp 2003
Sales 214.6MM EMP 23
Accts Pricewaterhousecoopers Spa
SIC 4813 Telephone communications broker; Data telephone communications; Voice telephone communications
Ch Bd: Riccardo Delleanic
*Ch Bd: Elisabetta Ripa
CFO: Joseph Rubino
VP: Luciano Piovano
VP: Claudio Rullent

D-U-N-S 19-697-0503
■TELECOMMUNICATION SYSTEMS INC
(Suby of COMTECH TELECOMMUNICATIONS CORP) ★
275 West St, Annapolis, MD 21401-3400
Tel (410) 263-7616 Founded/Ownrshp 2016
Sales 359.8MM EMP 1,115
SIC 7373 4899 Computer integrated systems design; Systems integration services; Systems engineering, computer related; Data communication services
Pr: Maurice B Tose
COO: Richard A Young
CFO: Thomas M Brandt Jr
Chf Mktg O: Timothy J Lorello
Sr VP: Jay F Whitehurst
VP: Charles Burns
VP: Tim Cochran
VP: Mark Longstaff
VP: Brian McNealy
VP: Jude Panetta
VP: Roger Seaton
Dir Lab: Ricky Chan

D-U-N-S 14-221-6147
TELECOMMUNICATIONS MANAGEMENT LLC
NEW WAVE COMMUNICATION
1 Montgomery Plz Fl 4, Sikeston, MO 63801-3006
Tel (573) 481-2420 Founded/Ownrshp 2002
Sales 160.0MM EMP 620
SIC 4899 Communication signal enhancement network system
Pr: Phillip Spencer
*CFO: Rod Siemers
VP: Tom Gleason
Genl Mgr: Greg Lathun
Netwrk Mgr: Galen Kruger
Tech Mgr: Tracy Goodwin

D-U-N-S 09-056-5672 EXP
TELECOMUNICACIONES DE PUERTO RICO INC
TELPRI
(Suby of TENEDORA TELPRI, S.A. DE C.V.)
1515 Ave Fd Roosevelt 14 Flr 14, San Juan, PR 00920
Tel (787) 782-8282 Founded/Ownrshp 1914, 2007
Sales 1.4MMM^E EMP 4,900
SIC 4813 Local telephone communications
CEO: Christina Lambert
*Pr: Enrique Ortiz De Montellano
*Treas: Ana Betancourt
VP: Manuel E Hern Ndez

D-U-N-S 06-274-1368 IMP
TELECT INC
22245 E Appleway Blvd Ste, Liberty Lake, WA 99019
Tel (509) 926-6000 Founded/Ownrshp 1982
Sales 150.3MM^E EMP 810
SIC 3661 Telephones & telephone apparatus; Switching equipment, telephone
Pr: Wayne Williams
CFO: Stan Hilbert
*Ch: Bill Williams
*VP: Walt Takisaki
Sls Dir: Russ Evans
Sls Dir: Rob Jackson

D-U-N-S 11-363-3189
■TELEDYNE BROWN ENGINEERING INC
(Suby of TELEDYNE DGO) ★
300 Sparkman Dr Nw, Huntsville, AL 35805-1994
Tel (256) 726-1000 Founded/Ownrshp 1999
Sales 233.4MM^E EMP 800^E
SIC 8731 Energy research
Ch Bd: Robert Mehrabian
*Pr: Rex D Geveden
*Pr: Jan Hess
VP: Mike Gilchrist
VP: Mark J Gradkowski
VP: Jane Hess
VP: Paul Munafo
VP: Bob Palik
VP: John L Regner
Dir Soc: Doug Dixon
VP Admn: Charles Grainger

TELEDYNE DGO
See TELEDYNE TECHNOLOGIES INC

TELEDYNE IMAGING SENSORS
See TELEDYNE SCIENTIFIC & IMAGING LLC

D-U-N-S 12-101-6427 IMP
■TELEDYNE INSTRUMENTS INC
CETAC TECHNOLOGIES
(Suby of TELEDYNE DGO) ★
16830 Chestnut St, City of Industry, CA 91748-1017
Tel (626) 961-9221 Founded/Ownrshp 2001
Sales 338.7MM^E EMP 2,131
SIC 3829 3823 Measuring & controlling devices; Flow instruments, industrial process type
Ch Bd: Robert Mehrabian
*CFO: Dale Schnittzer
*Treas: Steve Blackwood

D-U-N-S 00-727-4194
■TELEDYNE ISCO INC
(Suby of TELEDYNE DGO) ★
4700 Superior St, Lincoln, NE 68504-1328
Tel (402) 464-0231 Founded/Ownrshp 1959
Sales 86.9MM^E EMP 390
SIC 3823 3826 Water quality monitoring & control systems; Liquid chromatographic instruments
VP: Dave Kennedy
Mng Dir: Scott Blakley
IT Man: Michael Adams
IT Man: Mary Hiatt
IT Man: Chris Olson
IT Man: Tanya Sims
Sftwr Eng: Jason Armstrong
Mfg Dir: Richard Grundman
Mktg Mgr: William Soulliere

D-U-N-S 04-176-7765
■TELEDYNE ISOTOPES (INC)
(Suby of TELEDYNE BROWN ENGINEERING INC) ★
300 Sparkman Dr Nw, Huntsville, AL 35805-1912
Tel (256) 726-1000 Founded/Ownrshp 2000
Sales 40.1MM^E EMP 1,000
SIC 8734 Testing laboratories; Radiation laboratories
Pr: James Link
*CFO: Janice L Hess
*VP: Jan Hess
*VP: Marty Runkle
Opers Mgr: Holcomb Sandy
Board of Directors: Hudson B Drake, Douglas J Grant, James McGovern

D-U-N-S 00-163-6950 IMP
■TELEDYNE LECROY INC
(Suby of TELEDYNE DGO) ★
700 Chestnut Ridge Rd, Chestnut Ridge, NY 10977-6435
Tel (845) 425-2000 Founded/Ownrshp 1964, 2012
Sales 187.0MM^E EMP 544
SIC 3825 3829 Oscillographs & oscilloscopes; Measuring & controlling devices
Ch Bd: Thomas H Reslewic
*CFO: Sean B O'Connor
Ofcr: Sean Connor
VP: Scott R Bausback
VP: Luis B Boza
VP: Conrad Fernandes
VP: Kevin Fitzgerald
*VP: David C Graef
VP: Rene Haas
*VP: Corey L Hirsch PHD
VP: Joe Mendolia
VP: James Mueller
VP: Hitesh Patel
*VP: Roberto Petrillo
Board of Directors: Robert E Anderson, Walter O Lecroy Jr, Norman R Robertson, William G Scheerer, Allyn C Woodward Jr

TELEDYNE MICROWAVE SOLUTIONS
See TELEDYNE WIRELESS LLC

D-U-N-S 61-174-5860 IMP
■TELEDYNE ODI INC
OCEAN DESIGN
(Suby of CETAC TECHNOLOGIES) ★
1026 N Williamson Blvd, Daytona Beach, FL 32114-7113
Tel (386) 236-0780 Founded/Ownrshp 1999
Sales 91.6MM^E EMP 250
SIC 3678 Electronic connectors
Pr: Michael Read
Pr: Roger White
Sr VP: Ken Nagengast
VP Bus Dev: Shadi Awwad
Dir IT: Conley Moore
IT Man: Michael Gilmore
Opers Mgr: Ron Woody

D-U-N-S 96-795-3613
■TELEDYNE SCIENTIFIC & IMAGING LLC
TELEDYNE IMAGING SENSORS
(Suby of TELEDYNE DGO) ★
1049 Camino Dos Rios, Thousand Oaks, CA 91360-2362
Tel (805) 373-4545 Founded/Ownrshp 2006
Sales 104.9MM^E EMP 475
SIC 8731 8732 8733 Commercial physical research; Commercial nonphysical research; Noncommercial research organizations
Pr: Jagmohan Bajaj
Ofcr: Tucker Grant
*Sr VP: Lisa Porter
VP: Bertrand Bovard
VP: Louis Kilmer
Off Mgr: Denise W Hinton
IT Man: Jay Johnston
Opers Mgr: Edward Merlo
Prd Mgr: Joseph Hosack
Sls&Mrk Ex: Paula Ross
Sls Dir: Ron Latreille

D-U-N-S 11-235-8432
▲TELEDYNE TECHNOLOGIES INC
TELEDYNE DGO
1049 Camino Dos Rios, Thousand Oaks, CA 91360-2362
Tel (805) 373-4545 Founded/Ownrshp 1960
Sales 2.3MMM EMP 9,200
Tkr Sym TDY Exch NYS
SIC 3679 3761 3519 3724 3812 3674 Electronic circuits; Guided missiles & space vehicles; Internal combustion engines; Gasoline engines; Engines, diesel & semi-diesel or dual-fuel; Aircraft engines & engine parts; Research & development on aircraft engines & parts; Aircraft control systems, electronic; Navigational systems & instruments; Semiconductors & related devices
Ch Bd: Robert Mehrabian
Pr: Edwin Roks
COO: Aldo Pichelli
Treas: Stephen F Blackwood
Ofcr: George C Bobb III
Sr VP: Melanie S Cibik
VP: Carl Adams
VP: Cynthia Y Belak
VP: Kelly Briley
VP: Chris Gorman
VP: Jennifer Kuo
VP: Michael Rudy
Dir Risk M: Tina Cameron
Board of Directors: Roxanne S Austin, Charles Crocker, Kenneth C Dahlberg, Simon M Lorne, Robert A Malone, Paul D Miller, Jane C Sherburne, Michael T Smith, Wesley W Von Schack

D-U-N-S 14-229-6073 IMP
■TELEDYNE WIRELESS LLC
TELEDYNE MICROWAVE SOLUTIONS
(Suby of TELEDYNE DGO) ★
1274 Terra Bella Ave, Mountain View, CA 94043-1820
Tel (650) 691-9800 Founded/Ownrshp 2003
Sales 104.0MM EMP 567
SIC 3679 Microwave components
Pr: Michael Ryan
IT Man: Dana Fogle
Mfg Mgr: Val Terry
Prd Mgr: Ken Nolan

TELEFLEX
See ARROW INTERNATIONAL INC

D-U-N-S 00-234-8191 IMP
▲TELEFLEX INC
550 E Swedesford Rd # 400, Wayne, PA 19087-1607
Tel (610) 225-6800 Founded/Ownrshp 1943
Sales 1.8MMM EMP 12,200^E
Accts Pricewaterhousecoopers Llp Ph
Tkr Sym TFX Exch NYS
SIC 3841 3842 Surgical & medical instruments; Surgical appliances & supplies
Ch Bd: Benson F Smith
Pr: Clifford Hollis
COO: Liam J Kelly
COO: Liam Kelly
CFO: Thomas E Powell
Sr VP: Thomas A Kennedy
VP: Timothy F Duffy
VP: Cameron B Hicks
VP: Jackie Hollenbach
VP: Louis T Horvath
VP: James J Leyden
VP: Michael Muhlberger
Exec: Donna Earley
Exec: Stephanie Snyder
Board of Directors: George Babich Jr, Patricia C Barron, William R Cook, Candace H Duncan, W Kim Foster, Jeffrey A Graves, Stephen K Klasko, Stuart A Randle

TELEFLEX MARINE
See SIERRA INTERNATIONAL INC

D-U-N-S 36-346-2024 IMP/EXP
■TELEFLEX MEDICAL INC
(Suby of TELEFLEX INC) ★
3015 Carrington Mill Blvd, Morrisville, NC 27560-5437
Tel (919) 544-8000 Founded/Ownrshp 1994
Sales 416.7MM^E EMP 1,939^E
SIC 3842 Surgical appliances & supplies
Pr: Benson Smith
*CEO: George Babich Jr
COO: Sam Goldstein
CFO: Thomas E Powell
Treas: Jake Elguicze
*Treas: C Jeffrey Jacobs
*VP: Gregg W Winter
Prgrm Mgr: Rob C Caron
Dir IT: Randy Defilippis
IT Man: Raj Cirigiri
Mktg Mgr: Sarah C Cumming

TELEFLORA
See WONDERFUL CO LLC

D-U-N-S 12-717-4295
TELEFONICA USA
(Suby of TELEFONICA DATACORP SA)
1111 Brickell Ave # 1000, Miami, FL 33131-3122
Tel (305) 925-5300 Founded/Ownrshp 2000
Sales 91.9MM^E EMP 200
SIC 7375 7374 4813 Information retrieval services; On-line data base information retrieval; Data processing service; Optical scanning data service;
Prin: Angel Barrio Ruiz
CFO: Victor Navarro
Treas: Rafael Arranz
Treas: Marcelo Prieto
VP: Felipe Cucalon
Mng Dir: Juan Mosquera
Dir IT: Laura Aquiar
Dir IT: Rafael Graulau
Netwrk Eng: Gilberto Chez
Mktg Dir: Raul Fraile
Sls Dir: Alberto Warnken

D-U-N-S 07-927-5746
TELEFONICA USA INC
1111 Brickell Ave # 1000, Miami, FL 33131-3122
Tel (305) 925-5298 Founded/Ownrshp 1999
Sales 95.0MM EMP 40
SIC 5065 4813 Mobile telephone equipment; Modems, computer; Telephone cable service, land or submarine
*CFO: Francisco Briceno

TELEGLOBE VSNL INTERNATIONAL
See TATA COMMUNICATIONS (AMERICA) INC

D-U-N-S 06-082-6646 IMP
■TELEMUNDO COMMUNICATIONS GROUP INC
(Suby of NBC UNIVERSAL LLC) ★
2290 W 8th Ave, Hialeah, FL 33010-2017
Tel (305) 884-8200 Founded/Ownrshp 2000
Sales 13.2MM^E EMP 1,017
SIC 4833 7313 Television broadcasting stations; Radio, television, publisher representatives
CEO: Javier Maynulet
*Pr: James McNamara
COO: Jacqueline Hern Ndez
*COO: Alan J Sokol
*CFO: Lynn A Calpeter
CFO: Andre Fern Ndez
VP: Karina Etchison
VP: Susan Solano
Genl Mgr: Diana Mogoll N
VP Sls: Xavier Aristimuno
Sls Mgr: Ana Pinos

D-U-N-S 62-204-8150
▲TELENAV INC
4655 Great America Pkwy, Santa Clara, CA 95054-1233
Tel (408) 245-3800 Founded/Ownrshp 1999
Sales 183.3MM EMP 579^E
Tkr Sym TNAV Exch NGS
SIC 3812 Search & navigation equipment; Navigational systems & instruments
Ch Bd: HP Jin
CFO: Michael Strambi
VP: Rohan Chandran
VP Mktg: Dariusz Paczuski
Board of Directors: Samuel Chen, Douglas Miller, Richard Todaro, Ken Xie, Joseph M Zaelit

D-U-N-S 60-107-8272 IMP
TELENETWORK PARTNERS LTD
350 Barnes Dr, San Marcos, TX 78666-6176
Tel (512) 707-3100 Founded/Ownrshp 1993
Sales 147.0MM^E EMP 768
SIC 4813
Owner: Anthony Herrera
COO: Dion Miller
VP: Roger Martin
VP: Nick Riley
Exec: Carly Brooks
QA Dir: Rachel Hamby
QA Dir: Cynthia Ortega
IT Man: David Reyes
Opers Mgr: Lawrence Drinkard
Opers Mgr: Jenna Goldberg
Opers Mgr: Dan Stapleton

TELEPACIFIC COMMUNICATIONS
See US TELEPACIFIC CORP

D-U-N-S 03-010-4140
TELEPACIFIC COMMUNICATIONS
(Suby of US TELEPACIFIC HOLDINGS CORP) ★
515 S Flower St Fl 36, Los Angeles, CA 90071-2221
Tel (213) 213-3000 Founded/Ownrshp 2006
Sales 163.1MM^E EMP 918^E
SIC 4813 Telephone communication, except radio;
CEO: Richard A Jalkut
Pr: James E Ferguson
CFO: Timothy J Medina
Ofcr: Russell A Shipley
Sr VP: Ken Bisnoff
Sr VP: Roger A Pachuta
Sr VP: Steven A Reimer
VP: Anthony J Marion Jr
VP: Michele D Sadwick
Exec: Michelle Cheverton-Lett
Genl Mgr: Mike Karageorge

TELEPERFORMANCE
See TPUSA - FHCS INC

TELEPERFORMANCE USA
See TPUSA INC

D-U-N-S 05-057-5695
▲TELEPHONE AND DATA SYSTEMS INC
30 N La Salle St Ste 4000, Chicago, IL 60602-2587
Tel (312) 630-1900 Founded/Ownrshp 1968
Sales 5.1MMM EMP 10,400^E
Tkr Sym TDS Exch NYS
SIC 4812 4813 Cellular telephone services; ; Local & long distance telephone communications; Local telephone communications
Pr: Leroy T Carlson Jr
*Ch Bd: Walter C D Carlson
CFO: Douglas D Shuma
Treas: Peter L Sereda
Sr VP: Jane W McCahon
Sr VP: Kurt B Thaus
Sr VP: Scott H Williamson
VP: Vicki Bernards
VP: John Toomey
VP: Theodore E Wiessing
Mktg Mgr: Laura Luallen
Board of Directors: David A Wittwer, Letitia G Carlson, George W Off, Prudence E Carlson, Walter C D Carlson, Clarence A Davis, Kenneth R Meyers, Christopher D O'leary, Mitchell H Saranow, Gary L

Sugarman, Herbert S Wander

D-U-N-S 08-150-9218 IMP
■TELEPHONICS CORP
(*Suby of* GRIFFON CORP) ★
815 Broadhollow Rd, Farmingdale, NY 11735-3937
Tel (631) 755-7000 *Founded/Ownrshp* 1968
Sales 348.2MM^E *EMP* 1,087
SIC 3669 3661 3679 3812 3663 Intercommunication systems, electric; Telephone & telegraph apparatus; Electronic circuits; Radar systems & equipment; Air traffic control systems & equipment, electronic; Radio & TV communications equipment
Pr: Joseph Battaglia
* *CFO:* Dominick Nocera
Ofcr: Rich Hines
VP: Joseph M Beck
VP: Joseph Beck
VP: Hector Colon
VP: Gary Fortmeyer
VP: Richard Frazita
VP: John Geary
* *VP:* Kevin McSweeney
VP: James Pitts
VP: Ed Schiefer
VP: Anthony Stewart
Exec: Regina McCormick

D-U-N-S 12-251-8335
■TELEPORT COMMUNICATIONS GROUP INC (DEL CORP)
(*Suby of* AMERICAN TELEPHONE AND TELG) ★
429 Ridge Rd, Dayton, NJ 08810-1323
Tel (732) 392-2000 *Founded/Ownrshp* 1998
Sales 110.9MM^E *EMP* 1,500^E
SIC 4813 Telephone communication, except radio
Pr: Robert Annunziata

D-U-N-S 86-803-8840
TELERIK INC
(*Suby of* TELERIK AD)
201 Jones Rd Ste 200, Waltham, MA 02451-1609
Tel (888) 365-2779 *Founded/Ownrshp* 2006
Sales 106.0MM^E *EMP* 550^E
SIC 5045 Computers, peripherals & software
CEO: Vassil Terziev
CEO: Svetozar Georgiev
Treas: Dimitre Taslakov
Ex VP: Derek Langone
VP: Todd Anglin
VP: Chris Sells
VP: Simeon Stoychev
Prin: Hristo Kosev
Software D: Elena Peneva
Software D: Alexander Valchev
Sls Dir: Brandon Strange

D-U-N-S 03-943-4147
■TELERX MARKETING INC
(*Suby of* MERCK SHARP & DOHME CORP) ★
723 Dresher Rd, Horsham, PA 19044-2299
Tel (215) 347-5700 *Founded/Ownrshp* 1995
Sales 191.1MM *EMP* 1,750
SIC 7389 8742 Telemarketing services; Marketing consulting services
Pr: Linda Schellenger
* *CFO:* Mark Fehnel
Ex VP: Ron Able
* *Sr VP:* Paula Applebach
* *Sr VP:* Linda Comp
Sr VP: Diana Helfistine
* *Sr VP:* Frank Pettinato
VP: Kevin Connolly
VP: Dale Conwell
VP: Kathleen Demarco
VP: Deanna Desmet
VP: Keith Heilner
VP: Diana Helfinstine
VP: Micki Mikula
VP: Horacio Rodriguez
VP Bus Dev: Sam Diliberto
VP Bus Dev: Keith Jeppson
VP Bus Dev: David Morrell

TELESCAPE
See TRUCONNECT COMMUNICATIONS INC

D-U-N-S 10-113-7586
■TELESECTOR RESOURCES GROUP INC
VERIZON
(*Suby of* VERIZON COMMUNICATIONS INC) ★
140 West St, New York, NY 10007-2141
Tel (212) 395-1000 *Founded/Ownrshp* 1984
Sales 160.1MM^E *EMP* 6,400
SIC 8742 Management consulting services
Ch Bd: Lowell C McAdam
* *Ch Bd:* Marc C Reed
* *Pr:* Ivan G Seidenberg
* *Treas:* Richard Russell
* *VP:* George A Barletta
* *VP:* Brian R Lane
* *VP:* Casimir S Skrzypczak
IT Man: Wadood Syed
Netwrk Mgr: Karen Collins
Netwrk Eng: Andrew Geneux

D-U-N-S 92-634-8103
▲TELETECH HOLDINGS INC
9197 S Peoria St, Englewood, CO 80112-5833
Tel (303) 397-8100 *Founded/Ownrshp* 1982
Sales 1.2MMM *EMP* 46,000^E
Tkr Sym TTEC *Exch* NGS
SIC 7389 Telemarketing services; Telephone solicitation service
Ch Bd: Kenneth D Tuchman
V Ch: James E Barlett
Ofcr: Michael Wellman
Ex VP: Martin F Deghetto
Ex VP: Martin Deghetto
Ex VP: Charles Gallacher
Ex VP: Keith Gallacher
Ex VP: Judi A Hand
Ex VP: Robert N Jimenez
Ex VP: Regina M Paolillo
Sr VP: Michael Jossi
Sr VP: Margaret B McLean
VP: George Anderson
VP: Marc Arseneau
VP: Chris Bowe
VP: Karen Breen
VP: Chris Burton
VP: Sean Carithers
VP: Darla Combs
VP: Chris Condon
VP: Jill Davies
Board of Directors: Tracy L Bahl, Gregory A Conley, Robert N Frerichs, Marc L Holtzman

D-U-N-S 05-907-7177
■TELETECH SERVICES CORP
(*Suby of* TELETECH HOLDINGS INC) ★
9197 S Peoria St, Englewood, CO 80112-5833
Tel (303) 397-8100 *Founded/Ownrshp* 1982
Sales 334.3MM^E *EMP* 4,450
SIC 7389 Telemarketing services
CEO: Kenneth Tuchman
Pr: Joe Schlosser
Pr: Daniel Woods
* *CFO:* Regina Paolillo
CFO: John Troka
Treas: Ginger Hestetler
Ex VP: Joe Bellini
Ex VP: Richard Bledsoe
* *Ex VP:* Martin Deghetto
* *Ex VP:* Keith Gallacher
Sr VP: Charles Koskovich
Sr VP: Chris Macdonald
Sr VP: Sandra Smith
VP: Chris Condon
VP: Milos Djokovic
VP: Greg Flaherty
VP: Robert Merkel
VP: Garrett Mullins

D-U-N-S 11-138-3290 IMP
■TELETRAC INC
FLEET MANGEMENT SOLUTIONS
(*Suby of* FORTIVE CORP) ★
7391 Lincoln Way, Garden Grove, CA 92841-1428
Tel (714) 897-0877 *Founded/Ownrshp* 2016
Sales 195.5MM^E *EMP* 350^E
SIC 4899 Data communication services
Pr: Tj Chung
* *COO:* Tim Van Cleve
Snr Sftwr: Hoang Pham
Sales Asso: Norm Bergstrom
Genl Couns: Mark Schwarz

TELETRONICS/PMP
See DCX-CHOL ENTERPRISES INC

D-U-N-S 80-755-4274
■TELEVISION FOOD NETWORK GP
SCRIPPS NETWORK
(*Suby of* SCRIPPS NETWORKS INTERACTIVE INC) ★
75 9th Ave, New York, NY 10011-7006
Tel (212) 366-0509 *Founded/Ownrshp* 1993
Sales 90.6MM^E *EMP* 159
SIC 4841 Cable television services
Pt: Judy Girad
Sr Cor Off: Jacques Torres
Sr VP: Eileen Opatut
VP: David Griffith
VP: Bill Kossman
Dir Soc: Tyler Florence
Sls&Mrk Ex: Lynn Brindell
Sls&Mrk Ex: Carie Welsch
Mktg Mgr: Erica Villalba

D-U-N-S 00-896-0585
TELEVISION WISCONSIN INC
MORGAN MURPHY MEDIA
(*Suby of* EVENING TELEGRAM CO) ★
7025 Raymond Rd, Madison, WI 53719-5053
Tel (608) 271-4321 *Founded/Ownrshp* 1945
Sales 139.8MM^E *EMP* 600
SIC 4833 Television broadcasting stations
Pr: Elizabeth Murphy Burns
COO: Brian R Burns
* *Treas:* John B Murphy
VP: Neal Oberg
* *VP:* David Sanks
Genl Mgr: Tom Keeler
Sales Exec: Tim McCaffrey

D-U-N-S 16-737-9150 IMP/EXP
TELEX COMMUNICATIONS HOLDINGS INC
(*Suby of* AUTOMOTIVE GROUP) ★
12000 Portland Ave, Burnsville, MN 55337-1522
Tel (877) 863-4166 *Founded/Ownrshp* 2006
Sales 163.0MM^E *EMP* 1,800
SIC 3663 3669 3679 Radio & TV communications equipment; Antennas, transmitting & communications; Studio equipment, radio & television broadcasting; Receiver-transmitter units (transceiver); Visual communication systems; Headphones, radio
Pr: Raymond V Malpocher
Pr: Tom Kulikowski
Pr: Mathias Von Heydenkampf
CFO: Greg Richter
Ofcr: Laura Papenhagen
VP: Kathy Curran
VP: Ralph K Strader
Board of Directors: Keith W Abell, Brian P Friedman, Patrick J Haltoran, Stuart B Katz, Edgar S Woolard Jr

D-U-N-S 79-060-2767
TELGIAN CORP
10230 S 50th Pl, Phoenix, AZ 85044-5209
Tel (480) 753-5444 *Founded/Ownrshp* 1991
Sales 87.1MM^E *EMP* 240
SIC 1711 8711 1731 8748 Fire sprinkler system installation; Fire protection engineering; Fire detection & burglar alarm systems specialization; Systems analysis & engineering consulting services
CEO: James Tomes
* *CFO:* Brian Ballard
* *Ch:* Russell Leavitt
Div Pres: Alan Gargano
Bd of Dir: Jerry Childers
Bd of Dir: William Thomas
Ex VP: Bob Caputo
Ex VP: John Fannin III
Ex VP: Jason Hand
Ex VP: Bill Holden
* *VP:* Ralph E Bless Jr
VP: Dave Cameron
* *VP:* John Campbell
* *VP:* John Estok
* *VP:* Steve Goyette
* *VP:* Juan Olivari
* *VP:* Tom Parrish
VP: Steven R Smith
* *VP:* Patrick Tesche
* *VP:* Thomas C Wright
VP: Thomas Wright

TELL CITY CONCRETE SUPPLY
See MULZER CRUSHED STONE INC

TELLABS
See CORIANT INTERNATIONAL INC

D-U-N-S 07-441-0333
TELLABS INC
(*Suby of* MARLIN EQUITY PARTNERS LLC) ★
1415 W Diehl Rd, Naperville, IL 60563-9950
Tel (630) 798-8800 *Founded/Ownrshp* 2013
Sales 637.3MM^E *EMP* 2,525
SIC 3661 1731 Telephones & telephone apparatus; Multiplex equipment, telephone & telegraph; Communications specialization
Pr: Daniel P Kelly
* *CFO:* Lawrence A Rieger
CFO: Andrew B Szafran
* *Ex VP:* John M Brots
Ex VP: Kenneth G Craft
Ex VP: Thomas J Gruenwald
Ex VP: Roger J Heinz
Ex VP: Rizwan Khan
Ex VP: Victoria L Perrault
Ex VP: Vikram R Saksena
* *Ex VP:* James M Sheehan
Sr VP: John C Kohler
VP: Rafael Alvarez
* *VP:* Kyle Matthews
* *VP:* Michael Miles
VP: Gregory Nulty

D-U-N-S 09-927-6359
TELLEPSEN BUILDERS LP
(*Suby of* TELLEPSEN CORP) ★
777 Benmar Dr Ste 400, Houston, TX 77060-3607
Tel (281) 447-8100 *Founded/Ownrshp* 2012
Sales 110.6MM^E *EMP* 300
SIC 1542 Commercial & office building contractors
CEO: Howard T Tellepsen Jr
* *COO:* Steve C Peterson
COO: Steve Peterson
* *CFO:* Charles W Sommer
Snr PM: Eric Pearson

D-U-N-S 07-839-8325
TELLEPSEN CORP (TX)
777 Benmar Dr Ste 400, Houston, TX 77060-3607
Tel (281) 447-8100 *Founded/Ownrshp* 1977
Sales 187.5MM^E *EMP* 375^E
SIC 1521 Single-family housing construction
CEO: Howard T Tellepsen Jr
* *Pr:* Tadd Tellepsen
CFO: Warren Prihoda
* *CFO:* Charles W Sommer
Ex VP: William Peel
* *VP:* Steve C Peterson
Dir IT: Lee Nugent
Sfty Dirs: Fortino Aguilera
Sfty Dirs: Benedicto Cansino
Sfty Dirs: Darrick Hammons
Sfty Dirs: Erick Martinez

D-U-N-S 78-742-6428
TELLUS OPERATING GROUP LLC
602 Crescent Pl Ste 100, Ridgeland, MS 39157-8676
Tel (601) 898-7444 *Founded/Ownrshp* 1998
Sales 92.8MM^E *EMP* 60
SIC 1311 Crude petroleum production
CFO: Tom Wofford
VP: Sheila Dykes

D-U-N-S 01-524-8714 EXP
■TELOGIS INC
(*Suby of* VERIZON TELEMATICS INC) ★
20 Enterprise Ste 100, Aliso Viejo, CA 92656-7104
Tel (949) 389-5500 *Founded/Ownrshp* 2001, 2016
Sales 89.0MM *EMP* 374
SIC 7374 Data processing & preparation
CTO: Ralph Mason
* *Pr:* Jason Koch
* *Pr:* A Newth Morris IV
* *Ex VP:* Susan Heystee
Sr VP: Chris Belden
* *CTO:* Ted Serentelos

D-U-N-S 05-628-0621 IMP
▲TELOS CORP (MD)
19886 Ashburn Rd, Ashburn, VA 20147-2358
Tel (703) 724-3800 *Founded/Ownrshp* 1997
Sales 120.6MM *EMP* 521^E
Tkr Sym TLSRP *Exch* OTO
SIC 7373 Systems integration services
Ch Bd: John B Wood
COO: Edward L Williams
CFO: Michele Nakazawa
CFO: Michelle Nakazawa
Treas: Tom Ferrara
Bd of Dir: Lloyd Jones
Ofcr: Rinaldi Pisani
Ofcr: Richard P Tracy
Ex VP: Michael P Flaherty
Ex VP: Robert J Marino
Ex VP: Emmett Wood
Ex VP: Jefferson V Wright
Sr VP: Brendan D Malloy
Sr VP: Alvin F Whitehead
VP: Hugh Barrett
VP: Polly Downey
VP: Steve Kelly
VP: Francis Masters
VP: James C Morehouse
VP: Kyle Scott
Exec: Tom Eltringham
Board of Directors: Bernard C Bailey, David Borland, Seth W Hamot, Bruce R Harris, Charles S Mahan Jr, John W Maluda, Robert J Marino, Andrew R Siegel, Jerry O Tuttle

TELPRI
See TELECOMUNICACIONES DE PUERTO RICO INC

D-U-N-S 62-393-5111 IMP/EXP
TELQUEST INTERNATIONAL CORP
AMERICAN TELEPHONE HEADQARTERS
26 Commerce Rd Ste B, Fairfield, NJ 07004-1606
Tel (973) 808-4588 *Founded/Ownrshp* 1984
Sales 90.9MM^E *EMP* 150
SIC 5065 Telephone equipment
Pr: Alfred Adel

D-U-N-S 19-726-4625 IMP/EXP
■TELSMITH INC
(*Suby of* ASTEC INDUSTRIES INC) ★
10910 N Industrial Dr, Mequon, WI 53092-4331
Tel (262) 242-6600 *Founded/Ownrshp* 1990
Sales 100.0MM *EMP* 275
SIC 3531 3532 Construction machinery; Crushing, pulverizing & screening equipment
Pr: Richard Patek
* *Pr:* Matt Haven

D-U-N-S 82-494-2697 IMP
TELSTAR NORTH AMERICA INC
(*Suby of* AZBIL TELSTAR SL.)
1504 Grundy Ln, Bristol, PA 19007-1521
Tel (215) 826-0770 *Founded/Ownrshp* 2006
Sales 116.4MM^E *EMP* 900
SIC 3565 Packaging machinery
Pr: Paul Stewart
* *Genl Mgr:* Paul Valerio
Sls Mgr: John T Connor

D-U-N-S 12-202-3757
TELVENT DTN LLC
SCHNEIDER ELECTRIC
(*Suby of* SCHNEIDER ELECTRIC SE)
9110 W Dodge Rd Ste 100, Omaha, NE 68114-3334
Tel (402) 390-2328 *Founded/Ownrshp* 2011
Sales 144.2MM^E *EMP* 691
SIC 7375 Remote data base information retrieval
Pr: John Leiferman
COO: Joseph Urzendowski
Ex VP: Laurent Vernerey
VP: Barry Mosbrucker
Snr Ntwrk: Jamie Sobczyk
QA Dir: Ann Lutz
Web Dev: Darryl Cunningham
Sftwr Eng: Mary Vanderveen
Sls Dir: James Dean
Sls Dir: Mike Karloff
Mktg Mgr: Troy Gibson

D-U-N-S 13-194-5156
TELVENT USA LLC
(*Suby of* SCHNEIDER ELECTRIC HOLDINGS INC) ★
1415 S Roselle Rd, Palatine, IL 60067-7337
Tel (717) 944-5460 *Founded/Ownrshp* 2011
Sales 111.2MM^E *EMP* 750
SIC 7379 8748 Computer related consulting services; Systems engineering consultant, ex. computer or professional
Pr: John Leiferman

D-U-N-S 03-079-4726
TELVISTA INC
1605 Lyndon B Johnson Fwy, Dallas, TX 75234-6802
Tel (972) 919-7800 *Founded/Ownrshp* 2001
Sales 582.6MM^E *EMP* 2,000
SIC 4813 Telephone/video communications
Pr: Higinio Sanchez
* *COO:* David Arellano
VP: Kimberly Keaton
* *VP:* Ruben Rosas
VP: Cindi Wiebold
VP Bus Dev: Jim Horan
Dir Soc: Janett Israel
* *CIO:* Alvaro Holguin
QA Dir: Agapito Soto
IT Man: Randal Johnson
IT Man: Carlos Lopez
Board of Directors: Annette Baker

D-U-N-S 11-351-1716 IMP
■TELX LLC
(*Suby of* DIGITAL REALTY TRUST INC) ★
1 State St Fl 21, New York, NY 10004-1561
Tel (212) 480-9049 *Founded/Ownrshp* 2015
Sales 165.0MM^E *EMP* 309
SIC 4899 Data communication services
CEO: Willaim Stein
* *COO:* Jarrett Appleby
* *CFO:* Andrew Power
Sr VP: Michael C Devito
* *Sr VP:* Joshua Mills
* *Sr VP:* Matt Miszewski
* *Sr VP:* John Stewart
* *Sr VP:* Michael Terlizzi
Off Mgr: Lisa Robinson
* *CIO:* Scott Peterson
Opers Mgr: Kawika Kaholokula

D-U-N-S 04-112-7879 IMP
■TELXON CORP
(*Suby of* SYMBOL TECHNOLOGIES DELAWARE) ★
1 Zebra Plz, Holtsville, NY 11742-1300
Tel (631) 738-2400 *Founded/Ownrshp* 2000
Sales 63.0MM^E *EMP* 1,549
SIC 3571 7373 3663 Personal computers (microcomputers); Systems integration services; Radio & TV communications equipment
Ch Bd: John W Paxton
Pr: Kenneth A Cassady
CFO: Woody M McGee
VP: David H Briggs
VP: Laurel Meissner
Board of Directors: Richard J Bogomolny, John H Cribb, J James Gallagher, R D Garwood, Robert A Goodman, Dennis Lehr, Raj Reddy

TEM-PRESS DIVISION
See LECO CORP

TEMCO
See CHS COOPERATIVES

TEMCO FACILITY SERVICES
See TEMCO SERVICE INDUSTRIES INC

D-U-N-S 80-887-7708
■TEMCO LLC
(*Suby of* CHS INC) ★
5500 Cnex Dr Mail Stn 370 Mail Station, Inver Grove Heights, MN 55077
Tel (651) 355-6471 *Founded/Ownrshp* 2002
Sales 3.3MMM *EMP* 75
SIC 5153 Soybeans; Wheat; Corn

D-U-N-S 04-615-6980
TEMCO SERVICE INDUSTRIES INC
TEMCO FACILITY SERVICES
417 5th Ave Fl 9, New York, NY 10016-2204
Tel (212) 889-6353 *Founded/Ownrshp* 1968
Sales 414.6MM^E *EMP* 10,000
SIC 7349 7342 6289 Building maintenance, except repairs; Janitorial service, contract basis; Exterminating & fumigating; Termite control; Security custodians
CEO: Henrik Thomassian
COO: Vince Dalsass
**COO:* Rene Jacobsen
**Ch:* Herman J Hellman
**Ex VP:* Joerg Joergensen
**Sr VP:* Joseph J Bailey
**Sr VP:* Mark Hellman
**Sr VP:* Thomas Lawless
**Sr VP:* Keith Pahira

D-U-N-S 03-144-0171
■TEMECULA VALLEY HOSPITAL INC
(*Suby of* UNIVERSAL HEALTH SERVICES INC) ★
31700 Temecula Pkwy, Temecula, CA 92592-5896
Tel (951) 331-2200 *Founded/Ownrshp* 2012
Sales 116.0MM *EMP* 1^E
SIC 8062 General medical & surgical hospitals
CEO: Marvin Pember
**CFO:* Barry Thornfinnson
**Ofcr:* Neil Colica
Dir Lab: Linda Patterson
**Prin:* Marcia Jackson
HC Dir: Kirsten Gaston

D-U-N-S 03-973-3639
TEMECULA VALLEY UNIFIED SCHOOL DISTRICT
31350 Rancho Vista Rd, Temecula, CA 92592-6200
Tel (951) 676-2661 *Founded/Ownrshp* 1909
Sales 208.5MM^E *EMP* 2,866
Accts Vavrinek Trine Day & Co Ll
SIC 8211 Public elementary & secondary schools
Bd of Dir: Kristi Rutz-Robbins
Ofcr: Evelyn Spoon
Genl Mgr: Karen Coppess
Pr Dir: Laura Boss
Psych: John Kroncke

TEMIC AUTOMOTIVE NORTH AMERICA
See CONTINENTAL AUTOMOTIVE SYSTEMS INC

D-U-N-S 00-962-3398 IMP
TEMP-CONTROL MECHANICAL CORP
ROLOK PRODUCTS
4800 N Channel Ave, Portland, OR 97217-7616
Tel (503) 285-9851 *Founded/Ownrshp* 1953
Sales 98.8MM^E *EMP* 250
SIC 1711 3444 1731 Warm air heating & air conditioning contractor; Ventilation & duct work contractor; Refrigeration contractor; Plumbing contractors; Sheet metalwork; Electrical work
Pr: James F Culbertson J
**Ch:* James F Culbertson Jr
**VP:* Ken Phillips
Exec: Jeffrey Neal
QA Dir: Tony Barsotti
IT Man: Josh Pickett
Opers Supe: Lora Skjoldager

TEMPCO
See AS HOLDINGS INC

D-U-N-S 05-945-7820 IMP/EXP
TEMPCO ELECTRIC HEATER CORP
607 N Central Ave, Wood Dale, IL 60191-1452
Tel (630) 350-2252 *Founded/Ownrshp* 1972
Sales 83.9MM^E *EMP* 340
SIC 3567 3369 3829 Heating units & devices, industrial: electric; Castings, except die-castings, precision; Thermocouples
Pr: Fermin Adames
CFO: Terry Biltz
Sr VP: Richard Sachs
Genl Mgr: John Byrnes
MIS Dir: Dave Cattapan
IT Man: Kevin Mann
VP Opers: William Kilberry
Prd Mgr: Tom Hittie
Sls Mgr: Michael Mallon
Board of Directors: Fermin Adames Jr Secretar

D-U-N-S 10-000-2104
TEMPE ELEMENTARY SCHOOL DISTRICT
3205 S Rural Rd, Tempe, AZ 85282-3853
Tel (480) 730-7359 *Founded/Ownrshp* 1900
Sales 97.1MM^E *EMP* 1,800
Accts Larson Allen Llp Mesa Arizon
SIC 8211 Public elementary school
Dir Sec: Erin Antavaros
Off Mgr: Dawn Hatfield
MIS Dir: Cyndie Denton
Dir IT: Sandy Reinhardt
Pr Dir: Wendy Reeck
Pr Dir: Christine Trujillo
Teacher Pr: Mike Minghine
HC Dir: Denise Allen

D-U-N-S 02-165-9099 IMP
TEMPE UNION HIGH SCHOOL DISTRICT 213 (INC)
500 W Guadalupe Rd, Tempe, AZ 85283-3599
Tel (480) 839-0292 *Founded/Ownrshp* 1912
Sales 66.9MM^E *EMP* 1,100
Accts Heinfeld Meech & Co Pc P
SIC 8211 Public senior high school
COO: Jan Moreci
**CFO:* Diane Meulemans
Bd of Dir: Moses Sanchez
Bd of Dir: Brandon Schmoll
VP: Deeanne McClenahan
Exec: Deborah Flakes
Exec: Dave Newton
IT Man: Kit Townsend
Netwrk Eng: Shaun Zielonka
Schl Brd P: Michele Helm
Teacher Pr: Kevin Mendivil

D-U-N-S 00-516-2441 IMP
TEMPEL STEEL CO (IL)
5500 N Wolcott Ave, Chicago, IL 60640-1020
Tel (773) 250-8000 *Founded/Ownrshp* 1945
Sales 713.5MM^E *EMP* 1,900
SIC 3469 3313 3316 3398 5051 Stamping metal for the trade; Electrometallurgical products; Cold finishing of steel shapes; Metal heat treating; Metals service centers & offices
CEO: Gary Wagner
COO: Robert Potter
COO: David Silvestri
CFO: Maggie Garbacz
**CFO:* D Joseph Ridyard
**Ch:* Christopher Stephan
Treas: Jeff Bloxdorf
VP: Robert Nichols
Admn Mgr: Jim Ray
Genl Mgr: Richard Buff
Off Admin: Kathleen Caminiti

D-U-N-S 00-798-1004
TEMPERATURE EQUIPMENT CORP
BRYANT MUNGO
(*Suby of* LEXINGTON CORPORATE ENTERPRISES INC) ★
17725 Volbrecht Rd Ste 1, Lansing, IL 60438-4539
Tel (708) 418-0900 *Founded/Ownrshp* 1955, 2005
Sales 113.5MM^E *EMP* 200
SIC 5075 Warm air heating & air conditioning
CEO: Skip Mungo
CFO: Lon Miller
Treas: David Yanow
VP: Francis Donovan
VP: Denis Marino
VP: Jim Ottoman
VP: Timothy Scott
VP: Mike Smid
Brnch Mgr: Bob Johnson
Genl Mgr: Louise O'Connor
Opers Mgr: Ronald Jakowitsch

D-U-N-S 05-291-0197
TEMPLE INDEPENDENT SCHOOL DISTRICT
200 N 23rd St, Temple, TX 76504-2486
Tel (254) 215-7513 *Founded/Ownrshp* 1883
Sales 86.6MM^E *EMP* 1,300
Accts Lott Vernon & Company Pc
SIC 8211 8299 Elementary & secondary schools; Airline training
Pr: Steve Wright
Genl Mgr: Larry Placencia
Pr Dir: Matthew Leblanc
Teacher Pr: David McCauley
Psych: Lauren Pruitt
Psych: Jan Vinci

D-U-N-S 96-939-5396
TEMPLE PHYSICIANS INC
3509 N Broad St, Philadelphia, PA 19140-4105
Tel (215) 926-9050 *Founded/Ownrshp* 2011
Sales 87.8MM *EMP* 1
SIC 8661 Temples
Prin: Larry Kasier

D-U-N-S 96-388-8917
TEMPLE UNIVERSITY HEALTH SYSTEM FOUNDATION
3509 N Broad St Fl 9, Philadelphia, PA 19140-4105
Tel (215) 707-2000 *Founded/Ownrshp* 2016
Sales 115.9MM *EMP* 14^E
SIC 8211 8221 Academy; University
Pr: Dr Larry Kaiser

D-U-N-S 01-596-1118
TEMPLE UNIVERSITY HEALTH SYSTEM INC
2450 W Hunting Park Ave, Philadelphia, PA 19129-1302
Tel (215) 926-9050 *Founded/Ownrshp* 1995
Sales 713.2MM^E *EMP* 7,573
Accts Deloitte & Touche Llp Philade
SIC 8741 Hospital management
Ch Bd: Jane Scaccetti
**Pr:* Larry Kaiser
**CFO:* Robert H Lux
**Treas:* Edward A Chabalowski
**Ex VP:* Howard R Grant
Board of Directors: Larry Kaiser

D-U-N-S 83-154-1185
TEMPLE UNIVERSITY HOSPITAL INC
T U H
(*Suby of* TEMPLE UNIVERSITY-OF COMMONWEALTH SYSTEM OF HIGHER EDUCATION) ★
3401 N Broad St, Philadelphia, PA 19140-5189
Tel (215) 707-2000 *Founded/Ownrshp* 1995
Sales 206.1MM^E *EMP* 5,000
SIC 8062 General medical & surgical hospitals
Pr: John Kastainis
COO: Dale Schlegel
Treas: Gerald P Oetzel
VP: Jane Scaccetti
Dir Sec: William Bergman
Surgeon: Joseph Thoder
Obsttrcn: Stacey L Jeronis
Doctor: Gilbert Siu

D-U-N-S 05-712-3192 IMP
TEMPLE UNIVERSITY-OF COMMONWEALTH SYSTEM OF HIGHER EDUCATION
1801 N Broad St, Philadelphia, PA 19122-6003
Tel (215) 204-1380 *Founded/Ownrshp* 1884
Sales 2.7MMM *EMP* 9,061
Accts Deloitte & Touche Llp Philade
SIC 8221 University
Pr: Neil D Theobald
VP: Laurel Harrish
VP: Kenneth Lawrence
Assoc Dir: Anne Bayless
Assoc Dir: Trisha Noel
Assoc Dir: Michael Tarantino
Dir Bus: David J Alpers
**Prin:* Ann Weaver Hart
Ex Dir: Raymond Destephanis
Ex Dir: Naji Khoury
Info Man: Barbara Dolhansky

D-U-N-S 00-606-1204
TEMPLETON COAL CO INC
GLAS-COL DIV
701 Wabash Ave Ste 501, Terre Haute, IN 47807-3293
Tel (812) 232-7037 *Founded/Ownrshp* 1920
Sales 173.0MM^E *EMP* 750
Accts Bkd Llp
SIC 5074 3567 3961 5049 3089 Plumbing fittings & supplies; Heating equipment (hydronic); Heating units & devices, industrial: electric; Rosaries & small religious articles, except precious metal; Religious supplies; Injection molded finished plastic products
CEO: Thomas E Templeton
Treas: Tom Thomas
Sec: Tomas Thomas

D-U-N-S 60-459-6932
■TEMPLETON INTERNATIONAL INC
(*Suby of* FRANKLIN TEMPLETON INVESTMENTS) ★
300 Se 2nd St Ste 600, Fort Lauderdale, FL 33301-1950
Tel (954) 527-7500 *Founded/Ownrshp* 1992
Sales 129.6MM^E *EMP* 1,346
SIC 6282 Investment counselors
Pr: Charles E Johnson
**Treas:* Martin Flanagan
Assoc VP: Eduardo Diaz
**VP:* Kenneth Lewis

D-U-N-S 80-123-0913
■TEMPLETON WORLDWIDE INC
FRANKLIN TEMPLETON INVESTMENTS
(*Suby of* FRANKLIN RESOURCES INC) ★
500 E Broward Blvd # 900, Fort Lauderdale, FL 33394-3000
Tel (954) 527-7500 *Founded/Ownrshp* 1992
Sales 761.4MM^E *EMP* 2,646
SIC 6211 6282 8742 8748 Dealers, security; Mutual funds, selling by independent salesperson; Investment counselors; Management information systems consultant; Business consulting
Sr VP: Gregory E Mc Gowan
V Ch: Rupert H Johnson Jr
**COO:* Martin L Flanagan
Sr VP: Gordon Wright
VP: Jan Marshall
IT Man: Susmita Pattnaik
Sls&Mrk Ex: Huishan Chen

TEMPO INTERNATIONAL
See ELIAS BEN INDUSTRIES CORP

TEMPORARY STAFFING
See DEPAUL INDUSTRIES

TEMPORARY STAFFING SERVICES
See MEADOR STAFFING SERVICES INC

TEMPSTAR STAFFING
See JMM SERVICES INC

D-U-N-S 05-741-6963 IMP
■TEMPUR PRODUCTION USA LLC
(*Suby of* TEMPUR WORLD LLC) ★
203 Tempur Pedic Dr # 102, Duffield, VA 24244-5321
Tel (276) 431-7150 *Founded/Ownrshp* 2000
Sales 114.2MM^E *EMP* 300^E
SIC 2515 Mattresses & foundations
Pr: Robert Trussell Jr
**Pr:* Tom Bryant
CFO: Wayne Fields
**Sec:* William H Poche
**VP:* Lars Hansen

D-U-N-S 13-753-2797 IMP/EXP
▲TEMPUR SEALY INTERNATIONAL INC
1000 Tempur Way, Lexington, KY 40511-1386
Tel (800) 878-8889 *Founded/Ownrshp* 2002
Sales 3.1MMM *EMP* 7,200^E
Tkr Sym TPX *Exch* NYS
SIC 2515 2392 Mattresses & foundations; Mattresses, containing felt, foam rubber, urethane, etc.; Pillows, bed: made from purchased materials
Ch Bd: Scott L Thompson
V Ch: Robert Trussell
Pr: Richard Anderson
Pr: David Montgomery
CFO: Barry Hytinen
CFO: Barry A Hytinen
Treas: Bill Poche
Chf Mktg O: Jay Spenchian
Ex VP: Lou Jones
Sr VP: Bhaskar RAO
VP: Pete Barr
VP: Carmen Dabiero
VP: Jim O'Donnell
VP: Shailesh Patel
VP: Brent Pfister
VP: Bruce Rintoul
Board of Directors: Evelyn S Dilsaver, John A Heil, Jon L Luther, Richard W Neu, Robert B Trussell Jr

D-U-N-S 02-060-3010 IMP/EXP
■TEMPUR WORLD LLC
(*Suby of* TEMPUR SEALY INTERNATIONAL INC) ★
1713 Jaggie Fox Way, Lexington, KY 40511-2512
Tel (859) 259-4838 *Founded/Ownrshp* 2000, 2002
Sales 115.0MM^E *EMP* 1,000
SIC 2515 Mattresses & bedsprings
Pr: Robert Trussell
**CFO:* Dale Williams
**Ex VP:* H Thomas Bryant
**Ex VP:* David Montgomery
**Sr VP:* David C Fogg
**VP:* Jeffrey B Johnson

D-U-N-S 78-734-7434 IMP/EXP
■TEMPUR-PEDIC NORTH AMERICA LLC
(*Suby of* TEMPUR SEALY INTERNATIONAL INC) ★
1000 Tempur Way, Lexington, KY 40511-1386
Tel (888) 811-5053 *Founded/Ownrshp* 2001
Sales 252.1MM^E *EMP* 200
SIC 5021 Beds & bedding
CFO: Dale Williams
Mktg Mgr: Sarah Hajjar

D-U-N-S 09-524-0136 IMP
TEMPUS INC
1201 New York Ave Nw # 300, Washington, DC 20005-3999
Tel (800) 834-2497 *Founded/Ownrshp* 2010
Sales NA *EMP* 75
SIC 6099 Foreign currency exchange
CEO: Juan Pablo Carriedo
**Ofcr:* Andrew Woelflein
Sr VP: Greg Salvaggio
**CTO:* Glenn Kerr
**Genl Couns:* Jamie W Ang
Board of Directors: Juan Pablo Carriedo Hector

D-U-N-S 01-438-5210
TEMPUS RESORTS INTERNATIONAL LTD
7345 Greenbriar Pkwy, Orlando, FL 32819-8935
Tel (407) 363-1717 *Founded/Ownrshp* 1997
Sales 36.8MM^E *EMP* 1,200
Accts Alison Walls By Fax On August
SIC 7011 6531 Resort hotel; Time-sharing real estate sales, leasing & rentals
Pr: Roger Farwell
Sr Cor Off: John Borresen
Ofcr: Andrew Marcus
Exec: Joni Regan
IT Man: Mark Keck

D-U-N-S 82-587-1440
TEN ENTHUSIAST NETWORK LLC
(*Suby of* SOURCE INTERLINK COMPANIES INC) ★
831 S Douglas St Ste 100, El Segundo, CA 90245-4956
Tel (310) 531-9900 *Founded/Ownrshp* 1991
Sales 174.6MM^E *EMP* 440
SIC 5192 Books, periodicals & newspapers
CEO: Scott P Dickey
Ch Bd: Peter H Englehart
Pr: Chris Argentieri
CFO: Bill Sutman
Chf Mktg O: Jonathan Anastas
Chf Mktg O: Brad Gerber
Ex VP: John B Bode
Ex VP: Stephanie S Justice

D-U-N-S 83-295-1672
■TEN NETWORK HOLDING INC
(*Suby of* ADULT SWIM GAMES) ★
1 Cnn Ctr Nw, Atlanta, GA 30303-2762
Tel (404) 827-1700 *Founded/Ownrshp* 2007
Sales 86.2MM^E *EMP* 1,000^E
SIC 4833 Television broadcasting stations
CEO: Mark H Lazarus

D-U-N-S 82-804-0738
TEN-X LLC
AUCTION.COM
1 Mauchly, Irvine, CA 92618-2305
Tel (949) 859-2777 *Founded/Ownrshp* 2008
Sales 156.8MM^E *EMP* 300^E
SIC 6531 Real estate agents & managers
CEO: Monte J M Koch
Pr: Sarah Andrews
**Pr:* Keith McLane
Pr: Deborah Sullivan
**CEO:* Jeffrey Frieden
**COO:* Jim Corum
**COO:* Daniel Culler
**CFO:* Bruce Felt
**CFO:* Aman Kothari
CFO: Tim Morse
Chf Mktg O: Maurren Waters
**Ex VP:* Michael Callahan
**Ex VP:* Chris Chamberlain
**Ex VP:* Mindy Heppberger
**Ex VP:* Joseph Joffrion
**Ex VP:* Rick Sharga
**Ex VP:* Gordon Smith
Sr VP: Trent Ferris
Sr VP: Patrick McClain
**Sr VP:* Eva Tapia
Sr VP: Paul Weiskopf

TENA
See SCA AMERICAS INC

D-U-N-S 13-184-7225
TENABLE NETWORK SECURITY INC
7021 Columbia Gateway Dr # 200, Columbia, MD 21046-2967
Tel (410) 872-0555 *Founded/Ownrshp* 2002
Sales 161.8MM^E *EMP* 625^E
SIC 7372 7371 Prepackaged software; Computer software development & applications
CEO: Ron Gula
Pr: Jack Huffard
CFO: Steve Vintz
Ofcr: Dave Cole
Sr VP: Mike Kirby
VP: Matt Alderman
VP: Corey Bodzin
VP: Jonathan Brody
VP: Ann Burns
VP: Andrew Gabor
VP: Cynthia Gula
VP: Gary Jackson
VP: Todd Kisaberth
VP: David Korba
VP: John Liccione
VP: John Lyons
VP: Sean Molloy
VP: Gal Nir
VP: Brad Pollard
Dir Risk M: Renaud Deraison
Board of Directors: Michael D Capellas, Ron Gula, John C Huffard Jr

D-U-N-S 62-318-3845
TENABLE PROTECTIVE SERVICES INC
2423 Payne Ave, Cleveland, OH 44114-4428
Tel (216) 361-0002 *Founded/Ownrshp* 1986
Sales 85.3MM^E *EMP* 3,256
Accts Mellon & Beder Inc Clevelan
SIC 7381 Security guard service; Private investigator
CEO: Peter Miragliotta
**Pr:* Francis Crish
**CFO:* Carl Wagner
Admn Mgr: Mindy Velez

D-U-N-S 10-866-5142 IMP
TENACIOUS HOLDINGS INC
ERGODYNE
1021 Bandana Blvd E # 220, Saint Paul, MN 55108-5130
Tel (651) 642-9889 *Founded/Ownrshp* 2006
Sales 105.7MM^E *EMP* 250
SIC 5099 Safety equipment & supplies
CEO: Thomas F Votel
**CFO:* Leon R Hoffmann
**Sr VP:* Mark B Lindstrom
**VP:* Sue Horvath
Oper/Mgr: Gregg Schrab

TENARIS
See MAVERICK TUBE CORP

D-U-N-S 13-112-1766 IMP
TENARIS GLOBAL SERVICES (USA) CORP
(*Suby of* TENARIS SA)
2200 West Loop S Ste 800, Houston, TX 77027-3532
Tel (713) 767-4400 *Founded/Ownrshp* 1984
Sales 1.1MMM^E *EMP* 4,649
SIC 3317 Steel pipe & tubes
Pr: Brad Lowe
COO: Barbara Crosby
CFO: Nancy Hernandez
**CFO:* Chris North
Treas: Andrew Ricks
Genl Mgr: Mauricio Lacouture
Dir IT: Gabriel Belforti
Dir IT: Blair Bissett
Dir IT: Eduardo Garzon
Dir IT: Luis German
Dir IT: Ernesto Valdivia
Board of Directors: Umberto Bochhini

TENARIS HYDRIL
See HYDRIL CO

D-U-N-S 07-868-5995
TENASKA BROWNSVILLE PARTNERS LLC
14302 Fnb Pkwy, Omaha, NE 68154-4446
Tel (402) 691-9500 *Founded/Ownrshp* 1987, 2012
Sales 133.1MM^E *EMP* 500
SIC 4911 Generation, electric power

D-U-N-S 17-013-5292
TENASKA CAPITAL MANAGEMENT LLC
(*Suby of* TENASKA INC) ★
14302 Fnb Pkwy, Omaha, NE 68154-4446
Tel (402) 691-9571 *Founded/Ownrshp* 2003
Sales 270.6MM^E *EMP* 10^E
SIC 8742 Management consulting services
VP: Randy Cullison
VP: Erin Harms
VP: Silke Jasinski
Mng Dir: Grant Davis
Mng Dir: Chris Leitner

D-U-N-S 19-738-7603
TENASKA ENERGY INC
(*Suby of* TENASKA INC) ★
14302 Fnb Pkwy, Omaha, NE 68154-4446
Tel (402) 691-9500 *Founded/Ownrshp* 1999
Sales 312.9MM^E *EMP* 300^E
SIC 4911 4924 4939 8742 Electric services; ; Combination utilities; Marketing consulting services
Ch Bd: Howard L Hawks
**CFO:* Jerry K Crouse
**Ex VP:* Michael C Lebens
VP: Jeremy Carpenter
VP: Jim H Ric
VP: Kevin Smith
Exec: Sara Frink
Dir Risk M: Michael Noonan
Mng Dir: John Gilbreath
CTO: Keith Emery
Dir IT: Paul Swoap

D-U-N-S 02-168-0330
TENASKA FRONTIER PARTNERS LTD (TX)
14302 Fnb Pkwy, Omaha, NE 68154-4446
Tel (402) 691-9500 *Founded/Ownrshp* 1998, 2006
Sales 219.1MM *EMP* 28
Accts Kpmg Llp Omaha Ne
SIC 4911 Generation, electric power
Ch Bd: Howard Hawks
CFO: Jerry Crouse
Ex VP: Thomas Hendricks
Ex VP: Michael Lawler
Ex VP: Ronald Quinn
VP: Lori Bruck
VP: Terry Cameron
VP: Terry Clarke
VP: William Horton
VP: David Kirkwood
VP: Timothy Kudron
VP: Douglas Lauver
VP: Michael Meyer
VP: William Simpson
VP: Ronald Tanner
VP: Martin Titus
VP: Gregory Van Dyke
VP: Mark Whitt

D-U-N-S 17-440-1190
TENASKA INC
14302 Fnb Pkwy, Omaha, NE 68154-4446
Tel (402) 691-9500 *Founded/Ownrshp* 1986
Sales 748.6MM^E *EMP* 688^E
SIC 4924 4911 4939 8742 Natural gas distribution; Electric services; Combination utilities; Management consulting services
Pr: Howard L Hawks
**Pr:* Darrell W Bevelhymer
**Pr:* David G Fiorelli
**CEO:* Jerry K Crouse
**CEO:* Paul G Smith
**CFO:* Gregory A Van Dyke
**Treas:* Michael F Lawler
**Ofcr:* Ronald N Quinn
**Ex VP:* Thomas E Hendricks
**Ex VP:* Michael C Lebens
Ex VP: David N Schettler
Ex VP: Mark J Whitt
VP: Tom A Boyd
VP: Lori A Bruck
VP: Mark Foreman
VP: Timothy Kudron
VP: Marc L Petersen
VP: Daniel G Ramaekers

D-U-N-S 62-424-0628
TENASKA MARKETING VENTURES
14302 Fnb Pkwy, Omaha, NE 68154-4446
Tel (402) 758-6100 *Founded/Ownrshp* 1990
Sales 113.5MM *EMP* 91
SIC 4924 Natural gas distribution
Ch: Howard L Hawks
Pr: Fred R Hunzeker
Sr VP: Lori A Bruck
Sr VP: Terry K Cameron
VP: Terry Clarke
VP: Mark A McQuade
VP: Mike Metzler
VP: John Obermiller
VP: David N Schettler
VP: Martin E Titus
Mktg Mgr: Matt Martindale

D-U-N-S 07-968-8773
TENASKA PENNSYLVANIA PARTNERS LLC
14302 Fnb Pkwy, Omaha, NE 68154-4446
Tel (402) 691-9581 *Founded/Ownrshp* 2009
Sales 148.5MM^E *EMP* 450
SIC 4911 Distribution, electric power
Pr: Jerry Crouse
**VP:* Tim Kudron

D-U-N-S 08-543-7028 IMP
TENCARVA MACHINERY CO LLC
SOUTHERN SALES COMPANY
(*Suby of* TENCARVA HOLDINGS I, INC)
1115 Pleasant Ridge Rd, Greensboro, NC 27409-9529
Tel (336) 665-1435 *Founded/Ownrshp* 1978
Sales 209.4MM *EMP* 360
Accts Dmj & Co Pllc Greensboro N
SIC 5084 Industrial machinery & equipment
Pr: Edwin W Pearce III
Sec: Mike Penni
**Sec:* Eddie Rhyne
**VP:* Bill Allen
**VP:* Ed Guffee
**VP:* Robert Hudson
**VP:* Harold S Muse Jr
**VP:* Steve Newsome
**VP:* Harry S Taylor III
**VP:* Donald A Wirth
Genl Mgr: Susan Ingram

TENCATE NICOLON
See NICOLON CORP

TENCATE PROTECTIVE FABRICS
See SOUTHERN MILLS INC

D-U-N-S 60-712-4583
TENDERCARE (MICHIGAN) INC
111 W Michigan St, Milwaukee, WI 53203-2903
Tel (800) 395-5000 *Founded/Ownrshp* 1989
Sales 74.3MM^E *EMP* 3,100
Accts Rehmann Robson Cheboygan Mi
SIC 8051 Skilled nursing care facilities
Ch Bd: Louis B Lukenda
Pr: Timothy Lukenda
Treas: Sherry Brooks

TENET
See DES PERES HOSPITAL INC

TENET
See AMISUB OF CALIFORNIA INC

D-U-N-S 07-602-3704 EXP
■**TENET GOOD SAMARITAN HOSPITAL INC**
GOOD SAMARITAN MEDICAL CENTER
(*Suby of* TENET HEALTHCARE CORP) ★
1309 N Flagler Dr, West Palm Beach, FL 33401-3406
Tel (561) 655-5511 *Founded/Ownrshp* 2001
Sales 4.6M *EMP* 1,200
Accts Diane Glenn Stuart Fl
SIC 8062 General medical & surgical hospitals
CEO: Mark Nosacka
Chf Rad: Ross Lieberfarb
COO: Steven Burghart
CFO: Oscar Fernandez
Dir Lab: Debbie Perini
Dir Bus: Yvonne Odette
VP Mktg: Denise Rigopoulos
Doctor: George Guzewicz

D-U-N-S 02-811-8065
■**TENET HEALTH SYSTEM SPALDING INC**
(*Suby of* TENET HEALTHCARE CORP) ★
601 S 8th St, Griffin, GA 30224-4213
Tel (770) 228-2721 *Founded/Ownrshp* 1996
Sales 117.9MM *EMP* 772
SIC 8062 General medical & surgical hospitals
CEO: John Quinn
COO: Donna Costanza
COO: John Grah Fache
COO: Yolanda Grady
COO: Rebecca Logan
VP: Mark Corcoran
VP: Michael Hongola
Exec: Jim Ledet
Dir Case M: Terri Donati
Dir Lab: Mike Brown
Dir Lab: Vera Foster
Dir Lab: Amita Patel
Dir Rad: William Vazquez
Dir Rx: Dennis Simmons

D-U-N-S 06-511-0041
TENET HEALTH SYSTEMS NORRIS INC
KENNETH NORRIS CANCER HOSPITAL
1441 Eastlake Ave, Los Angeles, CA 90089-0112
Tel (323) 865-3000 *Founded/Ownrshp* 1982
Sales 179.2MM *EMP* 352
SIC 8069 Cancer hospital
CEO: Scott Evans
CFO: Robert Abeles
**CFO:* Strawn Steele
Dir Rad: William Oehlenschlager
Sfty Mgr: Pedro Ayala
Pathlgst: Petrus C Duyne
Surgeon: Vincent Rowe
Surgeon: Peter Vukasin
Nrsg Dir: Ellen Whalen
HC Dir: Mike Fong
Board of Directors: Stephen Sample, James Zumberge

D-U-N-S 05-386-6661
▲**TENET HEALTHCARE CORP**
1445 Ross Ave Ste 1400, Dallas, TX 75202-2703
Tel (469) 893-2200 *Founded/Ownrshp* 1969
Sales 18.7MMM *EMP* 134,630^E
Tkr Sym THC *Exch* NYS
SIC 8062 8069 8741 8063 8082 8011 General medical & surgical hospitals; Specialty hospitals, except psychiatric; Hospital management; Psychiatric hospitals; Home health care services; Health maintenance organization
Ch Bd: Trevor Fetter
Pr: J Eric Evans
Pr: John Widdel
CFO: Daniel J Cancelmi
Treas: Tyler Murphy
Ofcr: Melanie Roberts
Ofcr: Alma Terrazas
Sr VP: Audrey T Andrews
Sr VP: Kyle Burtnett
Sr VP: Clint Hailey
VP: Paul Castanon
VP: Lane Cooley
VP: Stephen Diaz
VP: Bill Durham
VP: Mary Garrido
VP: Sue Monaco
VP: Stephen M Mooney
VP: Bill Morrison
VP: Mark Peacock
VP: Douglas Rabe
VP: Michael Rice
Board of Directors: Tammy Romo, John P Byrnes, Randolph C Simpson, Brenda J Gaines, James A Unruh, Karen M Garrison, Peter M Wilver, Freda C Lewis-Hall, Edward Kangas, J Robert Kerrey, Richard R Pettingill, Matthew J Ripperger, Ronald A Rittenmeyer

D-U-N-S 87-724-6207
■**TENET HEALTHCARE FOUNDATION**
(*Suby of* TENET HEALTHSYSTEM MEDICAL INC) ★
1445 Ross Ave Ste 1400, Dallas, TX 75202-2703
Tel (469) 893-2000 *Founded/Ownrshp* 1997
Sales 155.4MM^E *EMP* 2,746
SIC 8049 Occupational therapist
Pr: Trevor Fetter
**Pr:* Britt T Reynolds
COO: Ricky Johnston
**CFO:* Daniel J Cancelmi
Sls&Mrk Ex: Mary Villarreal
Counsel: Richard Freddo

TENET HEALTHSYSTEM DESERT INC
See DESERT REGIONAL MEDICAL CENTER INC

D-U-N-S 79-984-6386
■**TENET HEALTHSYSTEM HAHNEMANN LLC**
HAHNEMANN UNIVERSITY HOSPITAL
(*Suby of* TENET HEALTHSYSTEM MEDICAL INC) ★
230 N Broad St, Philadelphia, PA 19102-1121
Tel (215) 762-7000 *Founded/Ownrshp* 1998
Sales 205.4MM^E *EMP* 2,200
SIC 8062 General medical & surgical hospitals
CEO: Mike Halter
**COO:* James Burke
**CFO:* Brian Reilly
Pathlgst: Prabha Patel
Surgeon: Jessica M Babcock
Surgeon: Alexander Crean
Surgeon: Ryan A Gruner
Surgeon: Majda Hadziahmetovic
Surgeon: Christopher R Hoffman
Surgeon: Amrit S Khalsa
Surgeon: Julie Mani

D-U-N-S 06-549-7059
■**TENET HEALTHSYSTEM HOSPITALS INC**
(*Suby of* TENET HEALTHCARE CORP) ★
13737 Noel Rd Ste 100, Dallas, TX 75240-2019
Tel (469) 893-2000 *Founded/Ownrshp* 1968
Sales 392.5MM^E *EMP* 5,000
SIC 8062 General medical & surgical hospitals
CEO: Britt Reynolds
**Pr:* Barry P Schochet
**Treas:* Pamela M Farrington
VP: George Amrom
VP: David Bordofske
VP: Kat Ruffin
Dir Rx: Jennifer Mitchell
Adm Dir: Jami Osterlund

D-U-N-S 00-968-6395
■**TENET HEALTHSYSTEM MEDICAL INC**
(*Suby of* TENET HEALTHCARE CORP) ★
1445 Ross Ave Ste 1400, Dallas, TX 75202-2703
Tel (469) 893-2000 *Founded/Ownrshp* 1995
Sales 1.8MMM^E *EMP* 27,400
SIC 8062 8063 6512 General medical & surgical hospitals; Psychiatric hospitals; Commercial & industrial building operation
**Treas:* Stephen Farber
VP: Tricia Johnson
**VP:* Leonard Rosenfeld

D-U-N-S 14-652-2750
■**TENET HEALTHSYSTEM ST CHRISTOPHERS HOSPITAL FOR CHILDREN LLC**
(*Suby of* TENET HEALTHCARE CORP) ★
160 E Erie Ave, Philadelphia, PA 19134-1011
Tel (215) 427-5000 *Founded/Ownrshp* 1875
Sales 114.5MM^E *EMP* 2,850
SIC 8069 Children's hospital
CEO: Carolyn Jackson
Treas: Charles Morrison
Pathlgst: Christos D Katsetos
Doctor: Amy Levin
Doctor: Anna Oriordan
Snr Mgr: Daniel Schidlow

D-U-N-S 07-131-0106 IMP
■**TENET HIALEAH HEALTHSYSTEM INC**
HIALEAH HOSPITAL
(*Suby of* TENET HEALTHCARE CORP) ★
651 E 25th St, Hialeah, FL 33013-3814
Tel (305) 693-6100 *Founded/Ownrshp* 1996
Sales 124.2MM *EMP* 800
SIC 8062 General medical & surgical hospitals
CEO: Ralph A Aleman
**CEO:* Ronald Bireman
**CFO:* Art West
**Treas:* Tyler Murphy
Off Mgr: Margie Portuondo
Nurse Mgr: Susan Chediak
Dir QC: Jesusa Alfonso
Mtls Dir: Marie Canady
Doctor: Felipe Caballero

D-U-N-S 05-886-9215
■**TENET HOSPITALS LIMITED** (TX)
HOSPITALS PRVIDENCE MEM CAMPUS
(*Suby of* TENET HEALTHCARE CORP) ★
2001 N Oregon St, El Paso, TX 79902-3320
Tel (915) 577-6011 *Founded/Ownrshp* 1906, 1995
Sales 575.6MM^E *EMP* 5,301
SIC 8062 General medical & surgical hospitals
Mng Pt: Sally Deitch
**Pt:* John Harris
COO: Preston Simmons
Exec: Juan Murillo
Dir Risk M: Leslie Bates
Sys Mgr: Anthony Dorsch
Pathlgst: Harry Wilson

D-U-N-S 96-675-9388
TENEX CAPITAL MANAGEMENT LP
60 E 42nd St Rm 5230, New York, NY 10165-0009
Tel (212) 457-1138 *Founded/Ownrshp* 2009
Sales 466.0MM^E *EMP* 1,955
SIC 6722 Management investment, open-end
CEO: Michael Green
CFO: Chad Spooner
Sr VP: Ben Kramer
VP: Sandi Tevelow
VP: Gabriel Wood
Mng Dir: Varun Bedi
Mng Dir: J P Bretl
Mng Dir: Joe Cottone
Mng Dir: Scott Galletti

TENIX DATAGATE
See TENIX HOLDINGS INC

D-U-N-S 13-705-8074
TENIX HOLDINGS INC
TENIX DATAGATE
925 Tommy Munro Dr Ste J, Biloxi, MS 39532-2134
Tel (228) 594-6800 *Founded/Ownrshp* 2002
Sales 40.6MM^E *EMP* 3,269
SIC 8748 Business consulting
Prin: Carlo Salteri
**CFO:* Ken Sheridan
**Prin:* Paul Salteri
**Ex Dir:* Robert Salteri

D-U-N-S 00-624-7126 IMP/EXP
▲**TENNANT CO** (MN)
701 Lilac Dr N, Minneapolis, MN 55422-4687
Tel (763) 540-1200 *Founded/Ownrshp* 1870
Sales 811.8MM *EMP* 3,202
Tkr Sym TNC *Exch* NYS
SIC 3589 3635 Commercial cleaning equipment; Dirt sweeping units, industrial; Floor washing & polishing machines, commercial; Carpet shampooer
Pr: H Chris Killingstad
CFO: Thomas Paulson
Ex VP: Sam Beloate
Sr VP: David W Huml
Sr VP: Carol E McKnight
Sr VP: Jeffrey C Moorefield
Sr VP: Michael W Schaefer
Sr VP: Heidi M Wilson
Sr VP: Richard H Zay
VP: Tom Paulson
Ex Dir: James Weston
Board of Directors: William F Austen, Carol S Eicher, Donal L Mulligan, Stephen G Shank, Steven A Sonnenberg, David S Wichmann, David Windley

D-U-N-S 00-503-6900 IMP/EXP
■**TENNECO AUTOMOTIVE OPERATING CO INC**
(*Suby of* TENNECO INC) ★
500 N Field Dr, Lake Forest, IL 60045-2595
Tel (847) 482-5000 *Founded/Ownrshp* 1917
Sales 4.6MMM^E *EMP* 15,150
SIC 3714 3699 Shock absorbers, motor vehicle; Electrical equipment & supplies
CEO: Gregg Sherrill
**CFO:* Kenneth R Trammell
**Treas:* John E Kunz
**Ex VP:* James B Harrington
Ex Dir: Robin Kuhn
IT Man: Shane Richter
Opers Mgr: Tony Melo
Sls Dir: Dave Peace

D-U-N-S 18-144-2526 IMP/EXP
▲**TENNECO INC**
500 N Field Dr, Lake Forest, IL 60045-2595
Tel (847) 482-5000 *Founded/Ownrshp* 1996
Sales 8.2MMM *EMP* 30,000

Tkr Sym TEN *Exch* NYS
SIC 3714 Motor vehicle parts & accessories; Motor vehicle engines & parts; Shock absorbers, motor vehicle
Ch Bd: Gregg M Sherrill
**COO:* Brian J Kesseler
CFO: Kenneth R Trammell
Ex VP: Timothy E Jackson
Ex VP: Richard Sloan
Ex VP: Neal A Yanos
Sr VP: Peng Guo
Sr VP: James D Harrington
Sr VP: Henry Hummel
Sr VP: Enrique Orta
Sr VP: Joseph A Pomaranski
VP: Peter Acker
VP: Glenn Drodge
VP: Alex Gelbcke
VP: Jack Hall
VP: Edward Hang
VP: James Harrington
VP: Jeff Koviak
VP: John E Kunz
VP: Donald R Miller
VP: Jen Molnar
Board of Directors: Thomas C Freyman, Dennis J Letham, James S Metcalf, Roger B Porter, David B Price Jr, Paul T Stecko, Jane L Warner, Roger J Wood

D-U-N-S 15-873-6616
TENNENBAUM CAPITAL PARTNERS LLC
T C P
2951 28th St Ste 1000, Santa Monica, CA 90405-2993
Tel (310) 396-5451 *Founded/Ownrshp* 1999
Sales 146.7MM^E *EMP* 82^E
SIC 6726 Management investment funds, closed-end
Mng Pt: Mark Holdsworth
Board of Directors: Gary Lembo

TENNESEE LEE COMPANY
See LEE CO

TENNESSEE ALLOYS COMPANY
See CORE METALS GROUP LLC

D-U-N-S 87-813-5631
TENNESSEE BOARD OF REGENTS
1 Bridgestone Park, Nashville, TN 37214-2428
Tel (615) 366-4400 *Founded/Ownrshp* 1972
Sales 645.7MM^E *EMP* 32,400
SIC 8211 Public elementary & secondary schools
Dir Recs: Sharon Bowen
Dir Recs: Jan Roark
Ex Dir: Alignment Nashville
Ex Dir: Shelia Owens
Ex Dir: TN Tomorrow
Opers Mgr: Jon Calisi
HC Dir: Tim Amyx
HC Dir: Amy Deaton
HC Dir: David Ogden
Genl Couns: Rich Haglund
Counsel: Heather Stewart

D-U-N-S 87-829-8090
TENNESSEE DEPARTMENT OF CHILDRENS SERVICES
(*Suby of* EXECUTIVE OFFICE OF STATE OF TENNESSEE) ★
Cordell Hull Bldg 7th Fl, Nashville, TN 37243-0001
Tel (615) 741-9699 *Founded/Ownrshp* 1996
Sales 61.7MM^E *EMP* 3,000
SIC 8322 9441 Child related social services;
**Prin:* Bonnie Honirch
**Prin:* Steve Hornsby
**Prin:* Thomas Riche

D-U-N-S 87-901-5311
TENNESSEE DEPARTMENT OF CORRECTION
(*Suby of* EXECUTIVE OFFICE OF STATE OF TENNESSEE) ★
320 6th Ave N Fl 6, Nashville, TN 37243-1400
Tel (615) 741-1000 *Founded/Ownrshp* 1871
Sales NA *EMP* 2,600
SIC 9223 House of correction, government;
Genl Mgr: Anna Sparks

D-U-N-S 87-901-6251
TENNESSEE DEPARTMENT OF EDUCATION
(*Suby of* EXECUTIVE OFFICE OF STATE OF TENNESSEE) ★
710 James Robertson Pkwy, Nashville, TN 37243-1219
Tel (615) 741-5158 *Founded/Ownrshp* 1923
Sales NA *EMP* 1,300
SIC 9411 State education department;

D-U-N-S 87-835-5437
TENNESSEE DEPARTMENT OF ENVIRONMENT AND CONSERVATION
(*Suby of* EXECUTIVE OFFICE OF STATE OF TENNESSEE) ★
312 Rosa L Parks Ave, Nashville, TN 37243-1102
Tel (615) 532-0109 *Founded/Ownrshp* 1905
Sales NA *EMP* 3,200
SIC 9511 Environmental agencies;

D-U-N-S 87-855-6299
TENNESSEE DEPARTMENT OF HUMAN SERVICES
(*Suby of* EXECUTIVE OFFICE OF STATE OF TENNESSEE) ★
400 Deaderick St Fl 15, Nashville, TN 37243-1403
Tel (615) 313-4700 *Founded/Ownrshp* 1827
Sales NA *EMP* 4,150
SIC 9441 Administration of social & manpower programs;
**CFO:* Rick Brown
Ofcr: Nika Anderson
Prgrm Mgr: Kristina Giard
Prgrm Mgr: Karen Guinn
Prgrm Mgr: Robert Locey
Genl Mgr: Zenola Diggs
Genl Mgr: Winfield Shiers
Web Dev: Gina Julian
Counsel: Barbara Broersma
Counsel: Kelly Young
Snr Mgr: Michael Patton

D-U-N-S 87-855-6919
TENNESSEE DEPARTMENT OF LABOR AND WORKFORCE DEVELOPMENT
DIVISION OF LABOR STANDARDS
(*Suby of* EXECUTIVE OFFICE OF STATE OF TENNESSEE) ★
220 French Landing Dr, Nashville, TN 37243-1002
Tel (615) 741-3002 *Founded/Ownrshp* 1923
Sales NA *EMP* 2,001
SIC 9651 Labor regulatory agency;
IT Man: Chris Risher

D-U-N-S 87-889-0425
TENNESSEE DEPARTMENT OF MENTAL HEALTH & SUBSTANCE ABUSE SERVICES
TENNESSEE DEPT MENTAL HLTH
(*Suby of* EXECUTIVE OFFICE OF STATE OF TENNESSEE) ★
500 Deaderick St, Nashville, TN 37243-0001
Tel (615) 770-0464 *Founded/Ownrshp* 1953
Sales NA *EMP* 2,000
SIC 9431
CFO: Martin Robert
Genl Couns: Jane Young

D-U-N-S 87-829-7415
TENNESSEE DEPARTMENT OF SAFETY
HIGHWAY PARTOL
(*Suby of* EXECUTIVE OFFICE OF STATE OF TENNESSEE) ★
1150 Foster Ave Fl 2, Nashville, TN 37243-4400
Tel (615) 251-5166 *Founded/Ownrshp* 1919
Sales NA *EMP* 1,900
SIC 9229 Public safety bureau, government;
IT Man: Tim Hancock

D-U-N-S 87-829-7712
TENNESSEE DEPARTMENT OF TRANSPORTATION
(*Suby of* EXECUTIVE OFFICE OF STATE OF TENNESSEE) ★
505 Deaderick St Ste 700, Nashville, TN 37243-1402
Tel (615) 741-2848 *Founded/Ownrshp* 1915
Sales NA *EMP* 4,867^E
SIC 9621 Regulation, administration of transportation;
Treas: Jeff Nicholson
CIO: Joe Kirk
Dir IT: Keith Cunha
Pr Dir: Lyndsay Botts

TENNESSEE DEPT MENTAL HLTH
See TENNESSEE DEPARTMENT OF MENTAL HEALTH & SUBSTANCE ABUSE SERVICES

D-U-N-S 17-263-6268
TENNESSEE DEPT OF HEALTH
DIVISION OF FISCAL SERVICES
(*Suby of* EXECUTIVE OFFICE OF STATE OF TENNESSEE) ★
710 James Robertson Pkwy, Nashville, TN 37243-1219
Tel (615) 741-3111 *Founded/Ownrshp* 1877
Sales NA *EMP* 4,200
SIC 9431 Administration of public health programs;
VP: Paul G Smith Jr
VP: Charles W White Sr
MIS Dir: Jim Hayes
Ql Cn Mgr: Karen Thomas
Doctor: James Montag Jr

D-U-N-S 00-572-0347 IMP
TENNESSEE DTR INC
(*Suby of* DTR INDUSTRIES INC) ★
199 Pottertown Rd, Midway, TN 37809-3213
Tel (423) 422-4454 *Founded/Ownrshp* 1996, 2013
Sales 158.9MM^E *EMP* 750^E
SIC 3069 3052 Medical sundries, rubber; Automobile hose, rubber
Ch: Shigehiro Okada
**Pr:* Tsu Matsui
QA Dir: Mark Norris
VP Mfg: Webster Booze
VP Mfg: Randy Rumbley
Ql Cn Mgr: Danny Lambert

TENNESSEE ELECTRIC COOP ASSN
See APPALACHIAN ELECTRIC COOPERATIVE

D-U-N-S 96-813-8156
TENNESSEE ENERGY ACQUISITION CORP
1808 Ashland City Rd A, Clarksville, TN 37043-6440
Tel (931) 920-3499 *Founded/Ownrshp* 1996
Sales 262.6MM *EMP* 5
Accts Jackson Thornton & Co Pc Mo
SIC 4924 Natural gas distribution
Pr: Mark McCutchen
**Treas:* Rhonda Wall

D-U-N-S 00-403-6430 IMP/EXP
TENNESSEE FARMERS COOPERATIVE INC (TN)
AG FINANCE SOLUTIONS
180 Old Nashville Hwy, La Vergne, TN 37086-2813
Tel (615) 793-8011 *Founded/Ownrshp* 1945
Sales 750.0MM *EMP* 500
SIC 5191 5013 5014 5172 5122 2048 Farm supplies; Fertilizers & agricultural chemicals; Animal feeds; Automotive supplies & parts; Automotive batteries; Tires & tubes; Automobile tires & tubes; Petroleum products; Diesel fuel; Gasoline; Animal medicines; Prepared feeds
CEO: Bart Krisle
**CFO:* Shannon Huff
VP Mktg: Allen Sparkman

D-U-N-S 00-792-1018
TENNESSEE FARMERS MUTUAL INSURANCE CO (TN)
PROPERTY AND CASUALTY INSUR CO
147 Bear Creek Pike, Columbia, TN 38401-2266
Tel (877) 876-2222 *Founded/Ownrshp* 1952, 1948
Sales NA *EMP* 870
SIC 6331 Automobile insurance; Property damage insurance; Fire, marine & casualty insurance & carriers
CEO: Matthew Scoggins
**Pr:* Lacy Upchurch
**Treas:* Wayne Harris
Assoc Dir: Melissa Bratton

D-U-N-S 00-193-9164 IMP
■TENNESSEE GAS PIPELINE
(*Suby of* KINDER MORGAN) ★
569 Brookwood Vlg Ste 749, Birmingham, AL 35209-4508
Tel (205) 325-3513 *Founded/Ownrshp* 1940
Sales 621.5MM^E *EMP* 1,300
SIC 4922 Pipelines, natural gas
Ch Bd: Richard D Kinder
**Ch Bd:* John Somerhalder II
**Pr:* Stephen Beasley
IT Man: Robert Yaffe
Board of Directors: William A Wise

D-U-N-S 87-829-6789
TENNESSEE MILITARY DEPARTMENT
TENNESSEE NATIONAL GUARD
(*Suby of* EXECUTIVE OFFICE OF STATE OF TENNESSEE) ★
3041 Sidco Dr Ste 401, Nashville, TN 37204-4505
Tel (615) 313-3001 *Founded/Ownrshp* 1796
Sales NA *EMP* 1,300
SIC 9711 Air Force
Ch: Tommy Hodge
Genl Mgr: Barry Collins
Genl Mgr: Robin Sweet
Genl Couns: Fred Denson

TENNESSEE NATIONAL GUARD
See TENNESSEE MILITARY DEPARTMENT

D-U-N-S 01-297-2282
■TENNESSEE SOUTHERN REGIONAL HEALTH
(*Suby of* HISTORIC LIFEPOINT HOSPITALS INC) ★
185 Hospital Rd, Winchester, TN 37398-2404
Tel (931) 967-8200 *Founded/Ownrshp* 1998
Sales 206.1MM^E *EMP* 9,300
SIC 8062 General medical & surgical hospitals
Dir Rad: Tommy Kimbrough
QA Dir: Maryanne Carusso
Pathlgst: Marica Garica
Doctor: Barry Cortis
Nrsg Dir: Denise Hambrick
Nrsg Dir: Phyllis Matasits

TENNESSEE STAMPINGS PORTLAND
See NORTH AMERICAN STAMPING GROUP LLC

D-U-N-S 10-881-4179
TENNESSEE STATE UNIVERSITY
(*Suby of* UNIVERSITY AND COMMUNITY COLLEGE SYSTEM TENNESSEE STATE) ★
3500 John A Merritt Blvd, Nashville, TN 37209-1561
Tel (615) 963-5000 *Founded/Ownrshp* 1970
Sales 107.9MM *EMP* 1,234
SIC 8221 University
Pr: Dr Glenda Baskin Glover
**Pr:* Melvin N Johnson
Ex VP: Robert Hampton
**VP:* Cynthia Brooks
VP: Thad Davenport

D-U-N-S 60-709-2186 IMP
TENNESSEE TBDN CO
1410 Us Highway 70 Byp, Jackson, TN 38301-5074
Tel (731) 421-4800 *Founded/Ownrshp* 2001
Sales 145.9MM^E *EMP* 410
SIC 3714 Motor vehicle parts & accessories; Oil strainers, motor vehicle
Pt: Tokuji Yamauchi
Pt: Max Aoyama
Exec: Jill Austin
Cmptr Lab: Rick Cole
Dir IT: Rusty Perry
Prd Mgr: Chad Hardin
Snr Mgr: Shane Holmes

D-U-N-S 87-864-8153
TENNESSEE TECHNOLOGICAL UNIVERSITY
1 William L Jones Dr, Cookeville, TN 38505-0001
Tel (931) 372-3101 *Founded/Ownrshp* 1915
Sales 174.5MM^E *EMP* 1,096
SIC 8221 University
Pr: Philip Oldham
Treas: Jon Jonakin
VP: Cheryl Montgomery
VP: Katherine Osburn
**VP:* Danny Rose
**VP:* Claire Stinson
**VP:* Jeff Young
Dir Lab: Paul Tsai
Ex Dir: Josephine McQuail
Prgrm Mgr: Betty Vaudt
Telecom Mg: Charlie Ferrill

D-U-N-S 00-188-3032
■TENNESSEE VALLEY AUTHORITY
(*Suby of* EXECUTIVE OFFICE OF UNITED STATES GOVERNMENT) ★
400 W Summit Hill Dr, Knoxville, TN 37902-1419
Tel (865) 632-2101 *Founded/Ownrshp* 1933
Sales 10.6MMM *EMP* 10,918
Tkr Sym TVC *Exch* NYS
SIC 4911 9631 Generation, electric power; Distribution, electric power; Regulation, administration of utilities;
Pr: William D Johnson
**Ch Bd:* Joe H Ritch
COO: Charles G Pardee
CFO: John M Thomas III
Bd of Dir: Robert Campbell
Bd of Dir: William Jenkins
Ofcr: Joseph P Grimes Jr
Ofcr: Van M Wardlaw
Ex VP: Sherry A Quirk
Sr VP: Katherine J Black
Sr VP: Janet J Brewer
Sr VP: Ricardo G Perez
Sr VP: Michael D Skaggs
Sr VP: Jay Stowe
Sr VP: Jay C Stowe
VP: John M Hoskins
VP: Jimmy Johnson
VP: Tom D Kilgore
VP: Ron Owens
VP: David Schavey
VP: Jeffery Swanson
Board of Directors: Marilyn A Brown, V Lynn Evans, Richard C Howorth, Virginia T Lodge, C Peter Mahurin, Eric M Satz, Ronald A Walter

D-U-N-S 01-272-5821
TENNESSEE WEST HEALTHCARE INC (TN)
HEALTH PARTNERS
620 Skyline Dr, Jackson, TN 38301-3923
Tel (731) 541-5000 *Founded/Ownrshp* 1994
Sales 388.2MM^E *EMP* 5,000
SIC 8062 General medical & surgical hospitals
Ch: Greg Milam
VP: Marty Fordham
Opers Mgr: Jerry Anthony
Pharmcst: Nancy Tucker

D-U-N-S 13-100-2078 IMP
TENNESSEE ZANINI INC
(*Suby of* ZANINI AUTO GRUP SA)
840 Industrial Dr, Winchester, TN 37398-1246
Tel (931) 967-8544 *Founded/Ownrshp* 2003
Sales 86.1MM^E *EMP* 220
SIC 5013 Automotive supplies & parts; Automotive supplies
Pr: Edward Torras
Ql Cn Mgr: Danny Carson

D-U-N-S 01-273-3564
TENNIER INDUSTRIES INC
755 Nw 17th Ave Ste 106, Delray Beach, FL 33445-2522
Tel (561) 999-9710 *Founded/Ownrshp* 1980
Sales 101.0MM^E *EMP* 700
SIC 2311 Military uniforms, men's & youths': purchased materials
CEO: Howard Thier
**CFO:* Steven W Eisen

D-U-N-S 06-859-6782
TENNIS CORP OF AMERICA
MIDTOWN ATHLETIC CLUBS
3611 N Kedzie Ave Fl 2, Chicago, IL 60618-4513
Tel (773) 463-1234 *Founded/Ownrshp* 1969
Sales 132.1MM^E *EMP* 2,200
SIC 7991 Health club
Pr: Steven Schwartz
**Ch Bd:* Alan G Schwartz
**CFO:* Frank Nusko
Exec: Susan Morris

TENNOVA HEALTHCARE
See MERCY HEALTH PARTNERS INC

TENNOVA HEALTHCARE-CLEVELAND
See CLEVELAND TENNESSEE HOSPITAL CO LLC

D-U-N-S 00-403-5853 IMP/EXP
TENNSCO CORP (TN)
PLANT 5
201 Tennsco Dr, Dickson, TN 37055-3014
Tel (615) 446-8000 *Founded/Ownrshp* 1962
Sales 99.3MM^E *EMP* 525
SIC 2542

D-U-N-S 85-848-9578 IMP/EXP
TENOWO INC
(*Suby of* TENOWO GMBH)
1968 Kawai Rd, Lincolnton, NC 28092-5916
Tel (704) 732-3525 *Founded/Ownrshp* 2013
Sales 14.1MM^E *EMP* 1,500
SIC 2297

D-U-N-S 10-962-8490 IMP/EXP
TENSAR CORP GEORGIA
2500 Northwinds Pkwy # 50, Alpharetta, GA 30009-2243
Tel (770) 344-2090 *Founded/Ownrshp* 1988
Sales 138.2MM^E *EMP* 500^E
SIC 3089 8711

D-U-N-S 78-317-2588
TENSAR INTERNATIONAL CORP
2500 Northwinds Pkwy # 500, Alpharetta, GA 30009-2243
Tel (770) 344-2090 *Founded/Ownrshp* 1988
Sales 100.5MM^E *EMP* 300
SIC 8711 3089 Civil engineering; Plastic hardware & building products
CEO: Robert F Briggs
**Pr:* Mike Lawrence
**CFO:* David Morris
Rgnl Mgr: Kevin McIlvaine
Genl Mgr: Jerry White
Mktg Dir: Jim Penman

D-U-N-S 00-714-3654 IMP
TENSION ENVELOPE CORP (NY)
819 E 19th St, Kansas City, MO 64108-1781
Tel (816) 471-3800 *Founded/Ownrshp* 1886
Sales 9.1MM^E *EMP* 1,253
SIC 2677 Envelopes
Ch Bd: Bert Berkley
**Pr:* William S Berkley
**CEO:* Bill Berkley
**Treas:* Dick Berkley
**Sec:* Richard Berkley
**V Ch Bd:* Walter L Hiersteiner
**VP:* Gary Surbaugh
Plnt Mgr: Bob Bellafronto
Sls Dir: Mike Coash

D-U-N-S 15-480-9222 IMP
■TENSOLITE LLC
CARLISLE INTERCONNECT TECH
(*Suby of* CARLISLE SYNTEC SYSTEMS (DIV)) ★
100 Tensolite Dr, Saint Augustine, FL 32092-0590
Tel (904) 829-5600 *Founded/Ownrshp* 1960
Sales 188.5MM^E *EMP* 1,000
SIC 3357 3643 3679 Nonferrous wiredrawing & insulating; Electric connectors; Harness assemblies for electronic use: wire or cable
Pr: John E Berlin
CFO: Amelia Murillo
VP: Amelia Murello

CTO: Richard Alder
Ql Cn Mgr: Shawn Jutte

D-U-N-S 00-304-5205
TEOCAL TRANSPORT INC (CA)
2101 Carden St, San Leandro, CA 94577-2245
Tel (510) 569-3485 *Founded/Ownrshp* 1990
Sales 424.1MM *EMP* 35
SIC 4214 Local trucking with storage
CEO: Rafael Aguirre

D-U-N-S 11-994-8255
TEOCO CORP
12150 Monu Dr Ste 400, Fairfax, VA 22033
Tel (703) 322-9200 *Founded/Ownrshp* 1994
Sales 204.4MM^E *EMP* 605^E
SIC 7379 Computer related consulting services
CEO: Atul Jain
V Ch: Philip Giuntini
**Pr:* Philip M Giuntini
**CFO:* AVI Goldstein
**Ex VP:* Hemant Minocha
**Ex VP:* Eitan Naor
VP: Yossi Arviv
VP: Jim Browning
VP: Roman Cybyk
VP: Thomas Kins
VP: Andrew Miceli
VP: Kurkjian Michael
VP: Chuck Privitera
VP: Orlando Pulido
VP: Rob Roy
VP: Shouvik Roy
VP: Tal Sharon
VP: Carlos Varela

D-U-N-S 85-915-4911
TEPA LLC
5045 List Dr, Colorado Springs, CO 80919-3321
Tel (719) 596-8114 *Founded/Ownrshp* 2007
Sales 83.6MM^E *EMP* 157^E
SIC 5039 Metal buildings
CEO: Ken Harris
COO: Matt Metcalf

D-U-N-S 78-176-8122
■**TEPPCO PARTNERS LP**
(*Suby of* ENTERPRISE PRODUCTS PARTNERS LP) ★
1100 Louisiana St # 1600, Houston, TX 77002-5227
Tel (713) 381-3636 *Founded/Ownrshp* 2009
Sales 1.0MMM^E *EMP* 2,400
SIC 4925 5171 Gas production and/or distribution; Liquefied petroleum gas, distribution through mains; Petroleum bulk stations & terminals
Pr: Alex Pourbaix
Pt: John N Goodpasture
Pt: Tracy E Ohmart
Pt: Patricia A Totten

D-U-N-S 80-199-0768
▲**TERADATA CORP**
10000 Innovation Dr, Miamisburg, OH 45342-4927
Tel (866) 548-8348 *Founded/Ownrshp* 1979
Sales 2.5MMM *EMP* 11,300^E
Accts Pricewaterhousecoopers Llp A
Tkr Sym TDC *Exch* NYS
SIC 3571 3572 7372 7371 Electronic computers; Mainframe computers; Minicomputers; Personal computers (microcomputers); Computer storage devices; Disk drives, computer; Prepackaged software; Application computer software; Software programming applications
CEO: Victor L Lund
Ch Bd: James M Ringler
COO: Robert Fair
COO: Robert E Fair Jr
CFO: Stephen Scheppmann
Ofcr: Saundra Davis
Ex VP: Dan Harrington
Ex VP: Daniel Harrington
VP: Justin Borgman
VP: Michael Brown
VP: Elizabeth Corley
VP: Bob Ellison
VP: Keith Henry
VP: Laura Jividen
VP: Tricia H Lane
VP: Tom Russell
VP: John Tulley
Exec: Walter Fierro
Board of Directors: Lisa R Bacus, Nancy E Cooper, Cary T Fu, Michael P Gianoni, David E Kepler, Victor L Lund, John G Schwarz, William S Stavropoulos

D-U-N-S 80-708-7528
■**TERADATA OPERATIONS INC**
(*Suby of* TERADATA CORP) ★
10000 Innovation Dr, Miamisburg, OH 45342-4927
Tel (937) 242-4030 *Founded/Ownrshp* 2007
Sales 442.9MM^E *EMP* 1,815
SIC 3571 Electronic computers
Pr: John Emanuel
Ofcr: Samuel Schwartz

D-U-N-S 00-101-7490 IMP
▲**TERADYNE INC** (MA)
600 Riverpark Dr, North Reading, MA 01864-2634
Tel (978) 370-2700 *Founded/Ownrshp* 1960
Sales 1.6MMM *EMP* 4,100^E
Tkr Sym TER *Exch* NYS
SIC 3825 3643 3674 Semiconductor test equipment; Test equipment for electronic & electrical circuits; Connectors & terminals for electrical devices; Semiconductors & related devices
Pr: Mark E Jagiela
**Ch Bd:* Roy A Vallee
CFO: Gregory R Beecher
Treas: Stuart Osattin
Ex VP: Matt Matthew
VP: Andy Blanchard
VP: Michael Bradley
VP: John Casey
VP: Charles J Gray
VP: Charlie Gray
VP: Mike Malone
VP: Brad Robbins
VP: Gregory Smith
VP: Scott Therrien
VP: Joseph Wrinn
Board of Directors: Michael A Bradley, Daniel W Christman, Edwin J Gillis, Timothy E Guertin, Mercedes Johnson, Paul J Tufano

D-U-N-S 86-132-0349
TERAMAR STAFFING INC
1075 N 51st Ave Ste 102, Phoenix, AZ 85043-5563
Tel (602) 288-0500 *Founded/Ownrshp* 2005
Sales 22.1MM^E *EMP* 1,500
SIC 7363 Labor resource services
CEO: Joseph Skrzymowski
**VP:* Scott Prast

D-U-N-S 04-303-7837 IMP
TERENCE CARDINAL COOKE HEALTH CARE CENTER
ARCHCARE
1249 5th Ave, New York, NY 10029-4413
Tel (212) 360-1000 *Founded/Ownrshp* 1979
Sales 103.4MM *EMP* 1,400
SIC 8051 Skilled nursing care facilities
Pr: James Introne
**Ch:* Roger Imperial II
Sls Mgr: Mary Ryan-Maher
Pharmcst: Sheepon Alam
HC Dir: Mary Wagner

D-U-N-S 02-257-4552
▲**TEREX CORP**
200 Nyala Farms Rd Ste 2, Westport, CT 06880-6261
Tel (203) 222-7170 *Founded/Ownrshp* 1983
Sales 6.5MMM *EMP* 20,400
Tkr Sym TEX *Exch* NYS
SIC 3531 3537 Construction machinery; Cranes; Aerial work platforms: hydraulic/elec. truck/carrier mounted; Scrapers (construction machinery); Industrial trucks & tractors; Lift trucks, industrial: fork, platform, straddle, etc.; Stackers, power (industrial truck stackers); Straddle carriers, mobile
Pr: John L Garrison Jr
**Ch Bd:* David A Sachs
Pr: Eric A Nielsen
Pr: Hyeryun Lee Park
CFO: Kevin P Bradley
Sr VP: Kevin A Barr
Sr VP: Eric I Cohen
Sr VP: Doug Friesen
Sr VP: Brian J Henry
VP: James Barr
VP: Gilberto Carvalho
VP: Amy George
VP: Joe George
VP: Owen Jervis
VP: Wayne Norris
VP: Peter Rall
VP: Tom Sparks
VP: Angel Tian

D-U-N-S 04-938-0942 IMP/EXP
■**TEREX MHPS CORP**
TEREX USA
(*Suby of* TEREX MHPS GMBH)
106 12th St Se, Waverly, IA 50677-4200
Tel (877) 794-5284 *Founded/Ownrshp* 2002
Sales 97.0MM^E *EMP* 425
Accts Grant Thornton Llp Cleveland
SIC 3536 Cranes, industrial plant; Hoists
Pr: John Paxton
**CFO:* Bernhard Barth
**VP:* Bill Jepson

TEREX ROADBUILDING
See CMI TEREX CORP

TEREX USA
See TEREX MHPS CORP

D-U-N-S 05-792-0605 IMP/EXP
■**TEREX USA LLC**
CEDARAPIDS
(*Suby of* TEREX CORP) ★
200 Nyala Farms Rd, Westport, CT 06880-6265
Tel (203) 222-7170 *Founded/Ownrshp* 1999
Sales 243.8MM^E *EMP* 870
SIC 3532 Crushing, pulverizing & screening equipment
Genl Mgr: Greg Meng
Genl Mgr: Lowell Puls

D-U-N-S 00-625-0484 EXP
■**TEREX UTILITIES INC**
(*Suby of* TEREX CORP) ★
500 Oakwood Rd, Watertown, SD 57201-4166
Tel (605) 882-4000 *Founded/Ownrshp* 1945
Sales 141.0MM^E *EMP* 450
SIC 3531 3537 Construction machinery; Industrial trucks & tractors
Pr: Patrick Carol
CFO: Bill McNichols
Dir IT: Alok Maheshwari

D-U-N-S 06-710-5429 IMP/EXP
TERLATO WINE GROUP LTD
LOCAL WINE TOURS
900 Armour Dr, Lake Bluff, IL 60044-1926
Tel (847) 604-8900 *Founded/Ownrshp* 1981
Sales 210.1MM^E *EMP* 370
SIC 5182 2084 8743 Wine; Wines; Promotion service
Ch Bd: Anthony J Terlato
**Pr:* William A Terlato
Sr VP: John Scribner
VP: Liz Barrett
VP: Doug Fletcher
VP: Bryan Glancy
Exec: Kelly Goodman
Dist Mgr: Brian Horvath
Off Mgr: Judy Vaughn
IT Man: Shane Fischer
IT Man: Mike Kalfas

TERMFINDER.COM
See EFINANCIAL LLC

TERMINAL 1 MANAGEMENT
See TERMINAL ONE GROUP ASSOCIATION LP

D-U-N-S 01-166-9996
TERMINAL ONE GROUP ASSOCIATION LP
TERMINAL 1 MANAGEMENT
Jfk International Airport, Jamaica, NY 11430
Tel (718) 751-1700 *Founded/Ownrshp* 1994
Sales 136.2MM *EMP* 17
Accts Mcgladrey Llp New York Ny
SIC 4581 Airport terminal services
Ex Dir: Edward J Paquette
Pt: Korean Air
Pt: Japan Airlines
Pt: Air France
CEO: Peter Baschnonga
COO: Hyung Ho Lee
CFO: Saburo Tanisaka

D-U-N-S 15-724-1688
■**TERMINIX INTERNATIONAL CO LIMITED PARTNERSHIP**
(*Suby of* SERVICEMASTER CONSUMER SERVICES LIMITED PARTNERSHIP) ★
860 Ridge Lake Blvd, Memphis, TN 38120-9434
Tel (901) 766-1400 *Founded/Ownrshp* 1986
Sales 654.5MM^E *EMP* 7,104
SIC 7342 7389 Pest control services; Termite control; Air pollution measuring service
Pr: Tom Brackett
CFO: Mark W Peterson
Treas: Lawrence L Mariano III
VP: Phil Barber
VP: Sherry R Brooks
VP: Norman Goldenberg
VP: Stephen R Good
VP: James McMahon
Brnch Mgr: Scott Ballard
Brnch Mgr: Drew Lenear
Brnch Mgr: J Walker

D-U-N-S 93-334-2388
■**TERMINIX INTERNATIONAL INC**
(*Suby of* SERVICEMASTER CONSUMER SERVICES LIMITED PARTNERSHIP) ★
860 Ridge Lake Blvd # 101, Memphis, TN 38120-9424
Tel (901) 766-1100 *Founded/Ownrshp* 1986
Sales 53.4MM^E *EMP* 1,043
SIC 7342 Pest control services
Pr: Chuck Fallon
**Pr:* Don Karnes
Pr: Larry Pruitt
**CFO:* Ted Schulz
**Sec:* Catherine Brush
Ex VP: Steven C Preston
**VP:* Tom Courtney
Brnch Mgr: Neil Baugh
Brnch Mgr: Hadi Bishir
Brnch Mgr: Tom Burkhart
Brnch Mgr: Rhonda Castillo

D-U-N-S 03-607-5240
TERMINIX SERVICE INC
3618 Fernandina Rd, Columbia, SC 29210-5221
Tel (803) 772-1783 *Founded/Ownrshp* 1947
Sales 138.9MM^E *EMP* 1,125
Accts Elliott Davis Decosimo Llc C
SIC 7342 Pest control services
Ch Bd: Marion A Lex Knox Jr
**Pr:* Scott Fortson
**V Ch Bd:* Thomas N Fortson Jr
**VP:* Rion Cobb
**VP:* Susan M Douglas
**VP:* Trevor Knox
MIS Dir: John Dorn
Dir IT: Jay Harper

D-U-N-S 02-562-9387
TERRA COTTA HOLDINGS CO
3703 S Il Route 31, Crystal Lake, IL 60012-1412
Tel (815) 459-2400 *Founded/Ownrshp* 1977
Sales 179.8MM^E *EMP* 524
Accts Plante & Moran Pllc
SIC 3499 3398 6531 Machine bases, metal; Metal heat treating; Real estate agents & managers
Ch Bd: Thomas Hayward Jr
**Pr:* Robert Berry
**CFO:* Frank Celmer
**CFO:* John Nelson
**V Ch Bd:* George Berry III
**Ex VP:* George Berry IV

D-U-N-S 07-989-4968
TERRA ENERGY PARTNERS LLC
4828 Loop Central Dr # 900, Houston, TX 77081-2212
Tel (281) 936-0355 *Founded/Ownrshp* 2015
Sales 150.1MM^E *EMP* 204^E
SIC 5172 Fuel oil; Petroleum brokers; Gases
CEO: Michael Land
**COO:* Keith Brown

D-U-N-S 13-359-0526
TERRA HOLDINGS LLC
770 Lexington Ave Rm 301, New York, NY 10065-8193
Tel (212) 508-7200 *Founded/Ownrshp* 1995
Sales 111.9MM^E *EMP* 1,500^E
SIC 6531 Real estate agent, residential
Sr VP: Hunter Frick
CIO: James Cahill

D-U-N-S 10-112-3578 IMP
■**TERRA INDUSTRIES INC**
(*Suby of* CF INDUSTRIES INC) ★
600 4th St Terra Ctr, Sioux City, IA 51102
Tel (712) 943-5501 *Founded/Ownrshp* 2010
Sales 306.4MM^E *EMP* 938
SIC 2873 Nitrogenous fertilizers; Ammonia & ammonium salts; Fertilizers: natural (organic), except compost
Pr: Michael L Bennett
CFO: Daniel D Greenwell
Sr VP: Joseph D Giesler
Sr VP: Douglas M Stone
VP: Edward J Dillon
VP: John W Huey
VP: Kenny Schmitz
VP: Paul Thompson
Dir IT: Tammy Stokes
VP Mfg: Richard S Sanders Jr
Counsel: Karl Baranowski

D-U-N-S 61-300-8424
TERRA MILLENNIUM CORP
1060 Hensley St, Richmond, CA 94801-2117
Tel (510) 233-2500 *Founded/Ownrshp* 2002
Sales 390.3MM^E *EMP* 750^E
Accts Armanino Llp San Ramon Calif
SIC 1741 8711 Refractory or acid brick masonry; Engineering services
Pr: Mark C Stutzman
**CFO:* Michael P Elam
CFO: Michael Eram
**Sr VP:* David W Miller
**Sr VP:* Gary A Stewart
**VP Sls:* Craig P Jackson

D-U-N-S 14-994-9547 IMP
▲**TERRA NITROGEN CO LP**
4 Parkway N Ste 400, Deerfield, IL 60015-2542
Tel (847) 405-2400 *Founded/Ownrshp* 1991
Sales 581.7MM *EMP* 299
Tkr Sym TNH *Exch* NYS
SIC 2873 Nitrogen solutions (fertilizer)
Pr: W Anthony Will
CFO: Dennis P Kelleher

D-U-N-S 94-865-9842
■**TERRA RENEWAL SERVICES INC**
(*Suby of* DARLING INGREDIENTS INC) ★
201 S Denver Ave Ste B, Russellville, AR 72801-5019
Tel (479) 498-0500 *Founded/Ownrshp* 2013
Sales 338.4MM^E *EMP* 500
SIC 4953 4212 Sludge disposal sites; Liquid haulage, local
Pr: Andrew M McNeill
**VP:* Mike Brooks
**VP:* George Langis
**VP:* Todd Mathes

D-U-N-S 80-919-0148
TERRA-GEN POWER LLC
1095 Avenue Of The Americ, New York, NY 10036-6797
Tel (646) 829-3900 *Founded/Ownrshp* 2008
Sales 103.6MM^E *EMP* 90^E
SIC 4911 Generation, electric power
CEO: James R Pagano
Pr: Timothy Prenger
COO: Kenneth P Hoffman
COO: Daniel Pease
CFO: John O'Connor
Sr VP: Steve Doyon
Sr VP: Frank Peacock
VP: Joseph Greco
Mng Dir: Jeff Cast
Sfty Mgr: Lisa Harding

D-U-N-S 61-356-9961
TERRACON CONSULTANTS INC
18001 W 106th St Ste 300, Olathe, KS 66061-6447
Tel (913) 599-6886 *Founded/Ownrshp* 2000
Sales 531.4MM *EMP* 3,747
Accts Bkd Llp Kansas City Mo
SIC 8742 8711 8748 8741 Industry specialist consultants; Engineering services; Testing services; Administrative management
Pr: David Gaboury
CFO: Roger R Herting
Treas: Donald J Vrana
Ex VP: Dan Israel
Sr VP: C Harold Cobb
Sr VP: Michael Covert
Sr VP: Robert Pavlicek
Admn Mgr: Elaine Motisi
Dept Mgr: Andy Ruocco
Off Mgr: Ryan Roy
Off Mgr: Frank Whitman

D-U-N-S 07-941-7891
■**TERRAFORM POWER INC**
(*Suby of* SUNEDISON INC) ★
7550 Wisconsin Ave Fl 9, Bethesda, MD 20814-3559
Tel (240) 762-7700 *Founded/Ownrshp* 2014
Sales 469.5MM *EMP* 2^E
Tkr Sym TERP *Exch* NGS
SIC 4911 Electric services; Distribution, electric power; Generation, electric power; Transmission, electric power
Ch Bd: Peter Blackmore
Sr VP: Sebastian Deschler
Sr VP: Yana Kravtsova

D-U-N-S 07-981-7723
TERRANE METALS CORP
(*Suby of* THOMPSON CREEK METALS CO USA) ★
26 W Dry Creek Cir # 810, Littleton, CO 80120-8063
Tel (303) 761-8801 *Founded/Ownrshp* 2015
Sales 10.8MM^E *EMP* 1,000
SIC 1081 Metal mining services
Owner: Jacques Perron

TERRANEA RESORT
See LONG POINT DEVELOPMENT LLC

TERRE HAUTE FIRST NATIONAL BANK
See FIRST FINANCIAL BANK NA

TERREBONNE GENERAL MEDICAL CTR
See HOSPITAL SERVICE DISTRICT NO 1

D-U-N-S 07-507-7511
TERREBONNE PARISH CONSOLIDATED GOVERNMENT
8026 Main St Ste 300, Houma, LA 70360-3407
Tel (985) 873-6454 *Founded/Ownrshp* 1834
Sales NA *EMP* 1,013
Accts Bourgeois Bennett Llc Houma
SIC 9111 Executive offices;
Pr: Michel Claudet
**CFO:* Jamie Elfert
CFO: Kandace Mauldin
Off Mgr: Gayle Vaughn
IT Man: Ben Smith
Opers Supe: James Guidry

D-U-N-S 02-926-9685
TERREBONNE PARISH SCHOOL BOARD INC
201 Stadium Dr, Houma, LA 70360-2732
Tel (985) 876-7400 *Founded/Ownrshp* 1884

Sales 187.9MM *EMP* 2,650
Accts Lanaux & Felger Houma Louisi
SIC 8211 School board
Pr: Roger Dale Dehart
Dir Sec: Nason Authement
Dir IT: Ramona Brunet
IT Man: Dale Legendre
Schl Brd P: Roosevelt Thomas
Teacher Pr: Debra Yarbrough
HC Dir: Alton Johnson

D-U-N-S 07-980-2895
TERREBONNE PARISH SCHOOLS
201 Stadium Dr, Houma, LA 70360-2732
Tel (985) 876-7400 *Founded/Ownrshp* 2015
Sales 187.4MM *EMP* 2,650ᴱ
Accts Lanaux & Felger Houma Louisi
SIC 8211 Public elementary & secondary schools

D-U-N-S 88-429-0610 IMP
■TERREMARK WORLDWIDE INC
(*Suby of* VERIZON COMMUNICATIONS INC) ★
2 S Biscayne Blvd # 2800, Miami, FL 33131-1802
Tel (305) 961-3200 *Founded/Ownrshp* 2011
Sales 259.3MMᴱ *EMP* 712
SIC 4813 8742 Telephone communication, except radio; Marketing consulting services
Pr: David J Small
Pr: Agustin Abalo
Pr: Herman Oggel
**COO:* Nelson Fonseca
Sr VP: Barry Field
Sr VP: Sandra Gonzalezlevy
VP: Michael Alexiou
VP: Derrick Cardenas
**VP:* Christopher Drumgoole
VP: Howard Grodin
VP: Ed Guevara
**VP:* Paul L Mattiola
VP: Jessica Portela
VP: Mario Santana
VP: Josh Snowhorn
VP: Annie Williams
Exec: Vincent Fernandez
Dir Surg: Eddy Espaillat
Assoc Dir: Daniel Chavez

D-U-N-S 83-284-5023
TERRENO REALTY CORP
101 Montgomery St Ste 200, San Francisco, CA 94104-4124
Tel (415) 655-4580 *Founded/Ownrshp* 2009
Sales 95.9MM *EMP* 18
Accts Ernst & Young Llp San Francis
Tkr Sym TRNO *Exch* NYS
SIC 6798 Real estate investment trusts
Ch Bd: W Blake Baird
**Pr:* Michael A Coke
CFO: Jaime J Cannon
VP: John Meyer
VP: Gregory N Spencer
VP: Lori J Stone

D-U-N-S 03-494-5626
TERRIBLE HERBST INC
5195 Las Vegas Blvd S, Las Vegas, NV 89119-3209
Tel (702) 597-6296 *Founded/Ownrshp* 1959
Sales 124.8MMᴱ *EMP* 300
SIC 5541 Filling stations, gasoline
Pr: Jerry E Herbst
**Sec:* Maryanna Herbst
**VP:* Ed Herbst
VP: Tim Herbst
Exec: Adriana Robar
IT Man: David Wideman

D-U-N-S 19-962-7431
TERRY ENERGY INC
TERRY PETROLEUM CO
(*Suby of* JEFFERSON ENERGY I LP) ★
3104 Edloe St Ste 205, Houston, TX 77027-6022
Tel (713) 552-0002 *Founded/Ownrshp* 1985
Sales 98.5MM *EMP* 4
SIC 1389 Oil field services
Pr: Ed Cotham
**Ch:* Howard Terry
Treas: Chase Johnson
**VP:* Robert Carter Overton III
**VP:* Robert Parker
VP: Christian Wallace

D-U-N-S 08-712-2110
TERRY FOUNDATION
600 Jefferson St Ste 1600, Houston, TX 77002-7328
Tel (713) 552-0002 *Founded/Ownrshp* 2001
Sales 98.5MM *EMP* 3ᴱ
SIC 8641 Civic social & fraternal associations
Prin: Edward Cotham

TERRY PETROLEUM CO
See TERRY ENERGY INC

D-U-N-S 06-331-2961 EXP
TERRY TAYLOR FORD CO
GARY YEOMANS FORD
1420 N Tomoka Farms Rd, Daytona Beach, FL 32124-7606
Tel (386) 274-6700 *Founded/Ownrshp* 1982
Sales 104.1MMᴱ *EMP* 290
SIC 5511 7532 Automobiles, new & used; Body shop, automotive
Pr: Terry Taylor
**VP:* Gary Yeomans
**Prin:* Stephen Terry
IT Man: John Lacy
Sls Mgr: Steve Ferreira
Sales Asso: Paul Opezzo

D-U-N-S 06-603-4588 IMP
TERRYS TIRE TOWN INC
(*Suby of* AMERICAN TIRE DISTRIBUTORS INC) ★
12200 Herbert Wayne Ct, Huntersville, NC 28078-6335
Tel (330) 821-5022 *Founded/Ownrshp* 1978
Sales 146.3MMᴱ *EMP* 225
SIC 5014 5531 Automobile tires & tubes; Truck tires & tubes; Automotive tires
Pr: Jason Yaudes

D-U-N-S 00-797-8117
TERTELING HOLDING CO INC
SLORA COMPANY
3858 N Garden Center Way, Boise, ID 83703-5008
Tel (208) 342-0018 *Founded/Ownrshp* 1979
Sales 247.3MMᴱ *EMP* 725
SIC 5082 Excavating machinery & equipment
Pr: J L Terteling
**Ex VP:* Flinda Terteling
VP: George Mackie

D-U-N-S 06-321-2377 IMP
TERUMO AMERICAS HOLDING INC
(*Suby of* TERUMO CORPORATION)
2101 Cottontail Ln, Somerset, NJ 08873-5115
Tel (732) 302-4900 *Founded/Ownrshp* 1972
Sales 522.2MMᴱ *EMP* 1,137
SIC 3841 Surgical & medical instruments; Needles, suture; Catheters
CEO: Yutaro Shintaku
**CFO:* John Pinto
**VP:* Hiroshi Matsumura
VP: Judy Pearlman
Genl Mgr: Robert Oneill
Plnt Mgr: Lalor Dave
Sls Mgr: Colleen Ebert
Snr Mgr: Tony Meo

D-U-N-S 83-306-5050 IMP
TERUMO BCT HOLDING CORP
(*Suby of* TERUMO CORPORATION)
10811 W Collins Ave, Lakewood, CO 80215-4440
Tel (303) 232-6800 *Founded/Ownrshp* 2011
Sales 566.2MMᴱ *EMP* 2,300ᴱ
SIC 3841 6719 Surgical & medical instruments; Blood transfusion equipment; Investment holding companies, except banks
CEO: David Perez
**CEO:* Ronald Devore
**CFO:* Rusty Spinney
Treas: Tim Strong
**Sr VP:* Teresa Ayers
**Sr VP:* Bob Cole
**Sr VP:* Tom Jordan
**Sr VP:* Stacey Jo Kirkland
**Sr VP:* Scott Larson
**Sr VP:* Craig Rinehardt
CIO: Scot Moir

D-U-N-S 80-167-9200
TERUMO BCT INC
ACPN
(*Suby of* TERUMO BCT HOLDING CORP) ★
10811 W Collins Ave, Lakewood, CO 80215-4440
Tel (303) 232-6800 *Founded/Ownrshp* 1990
Sales 420.6MMᴱ *EMP* 2,000ᴱ
SIC 8733 3842 3845 5047 7352 7699 Noncommercial research organizations; Surgical appliances & supplies; Electromedical equipment; Medical & hospital equipment; Medical equipment rental; Professional instrument repair services
Pr: David Perez
**CFO:* Russell Spinney
Treas: Bryan Potthoff
Ex VP: Antoinette Gawin
**VP:* Chris Fletcher
VP: Lisa Hayes
VP: Bob Jewell
**VP:* Stacey Jo Kirkland
**VP:* Scott Larson
Genl Mgr: Rob Hempelman
Snr Sftwr: Jimi Dodge

D-U-N-S 17-765-5466 IMP
TERUMO CARDIOVASCULAR SYSTEMS CORP
T C V S
(*Suby of* TERUMO AMERICAS HOLDING INC) ★
6200 Jackson Rd, Ann Arbor, MI 48103-9586
Tel (734) 663-4145 *Founded/Ownrshp* 1999
Sales 221.5MM *EMP* 700
SIC 3845 3841 Electromedical equipment; Surgical & medical instruments; Needles, suture; Catheters
Pr: Mark Sutter
VP: Gael Tisack
Prgrm Mgr: Stacey Allen
Genl Mgr: Micheal Buscemi
Plng Mgr: Kathy Wetzel
Snr Sftwr: Richard Eneberg
QA Dir: Jason Gutsch
Plnt Mgr: Don Smith
Ql Cn Mgr: Adam Rada
VP Mktg: Sharon Ryan
Mktg Dir: Lyne C Keller

D-U-N-S 00-398-5090
TERUYA BROS LIMITED (HI)
ROYAL STAMP CO
1276 Young St Ste B, Honolulu, HI 96814-1867
Tel (808) 591-8946 *Founded/Ownrshp* 1947
Sales 61.6MMᴱ *EMP* 1,150
SIC 5411 Supermarkets, chain; Convenience stores, chain
Ch Bd: Raymond Teruya

D-U-N-S 08-775-5492 EXP
TERVIS TUMBLER CO
201 Triple Diamond Blvd, North Venice, FL 34275-3634
Tel (941) 966-2114 *Founded/Ownrshp* 1968
Sales 144.6MMᴱ *EMP* 300
SIC 3089 Cups, plastic, except foam
Ch: Norbert Donnelly
Pr: Dorothy Lierman
CEO: John P Redmond Jr
COO: Mark Lawson
VP: Britt Irwin
VP: Danene Jaffe
VP: Luis Lopez
VP: Joan Rubendall
Exec: Marueen Altmann
Store Mgr: Michelle Kromer
DP Dir: Rick Drass

D-U-N-S 00-687-9067
■TERVITA LLC
MOBLEY OILFIELD SERVICES
(*Suby of* REPUBLIC SERVICES OF FLORIDA LIMITED PARTNERSHIP) ★
10613 W Sam Huston Pkwy N, Houston, TX 77064-4657
Tel (832) 399-4500 *Founded/Ownrshp* 2015
Sales 229.3MMᴱ *EMP* 522
SIC 1389 Oil field services
Pr: John Gibson Jr
**Treas:* Richard Brimble
**VP:* Greg Ford
**Prin:* David Werklund
Off Mgr: Marsha Smith
Dir IT: John Lassen

D-U-N-S 07-991-2997
▲TESCO CORP
11330 Clay Rd Ste 350, Houston, TX 77041-5588
Tel (713) 359-7000 *Founded/Ownrshp* 1993
Sales 542.9MM *EMP* 2,050ᴱ
Tkr Sym TESO *Exch* NGS
SIC 3533 Oil & gas drilling rigs & equipment; Oil field machinery & equipment
Pr: Fernando R Assing
COO: John Gatlin
CFO: Christopher L Boone
Sr VP: Dean Ferris
VP: Chuck Matula
VP: Randy Nemeth
VP: Thomas B Sloan Jr
VP: Darko Ulakovic
VP: Susan Zeletz
Exec: Dave Warner
Dir Bus: Jason Scott
Board of Directors: John P Dielwart, Fred J Dyment, Gary L Kott, R Vance Milligan, Doug Ramsay, Rose Robeson, Michael W Sutherlin

D-U-N-S 87-888-3164
■TESCO CORP (US)
TESCO DRILLING TECH U S A
(*Suby of* TESCO CORP) ★
11330 Clay Rd Ste 350, Houston, TX 77041-5588
Tel (713) 359-7000 *Founded/Ownrshp* 1981
Sales 279.7MM *EMP* 279
SIC 7353 5082 1389 1381 Oil field equipment, rental or leasing; Oil field equipment; Oil field services; Drilling oil & gas wells
Pr: Fernando R Assing
CFO: Christopher L Boone
CFO: Robert L Kayl
VP: Nigel Lakey
VP: Dan Withoff
Exec: Keith Bullen
Dir Bus: Mark George
Genl Mgr: Suqwinder Bassi
Genl Mgr: Barry Beibrbach
Genl Mgr: Andrew Davis
Off Mgr: Kim Dietrich

TESCO DRILLING TECH U S A
See TESCO CORP (US)

D-U-N-S 00-625-0880
■TESCOM CORP (MN)
EMERSON PROCESS MANAGEMENT
(*Suby of* EMERSON ELECTRIC CO) ★
12616 Industrial Blvd Nw, Elk River, MN 55330-2491
Tel (763) 441-6330 *Founded/Ownrshp* 1917
Sales 92.0MM *EMP* 190ᴱ
SIC 3491 3625 3494 Automatic regulating & control valves; Relays & industrial controls; Valves & pipe fittings
VP: Susan Hughes
**CFO:* Jim Tomczak
Bd of Dir: Ofer Albeck
VP: Elaine Jindra
Ex Dir: Itai Dor
Genl Mgr: Mark Cramer
Genl Mgr: Theresa Johnson
Genl Mgr: Linsey Wallace
QA Dir: Rebecca Petersen
IT Man: Lynda Years
Mktg Mgr: Steve Horner

TESD
See TREDYFFRIN-EASTTOWN SCHOOL DISTRICT (INC)

D-U-N-S 14-828-4255 IMP
▲TESLA MOTORS INC
3500 Deer Creek Rd, Palo Alto, CA 94304-1317
Tel (650) 681-5000 *Founded/Ownrshp* 2003
Sales 4.0MMMM *EMP* 28,331
Tkr Sym TSLA *Exch* NGS
SIC 3711 3714 Motor vehicles & car bodies; Cars, electric, assembly of; Motor vehicle parts & accessories
Ch Bd: Elon Musk
Pr: Jon McNeill
CFO: Jason Wheeler
VP: Eric Branderiz
VP: Doug Field
VP: Greg Reichow
VP: Susan Repo
VP: Nancy Yan
CTO: Jeffrey B Straubel
Ql Cn Mgr: Justin Song
Mktg Mgr: SEI Liu
Board of Directors: Brad W Buss, Robyn M Denholm, Ira Ehrenpreis, Antonio J Gracias, Stephen T Jurvetson

D-U-N-S 07-651-6090
■TESORO COMPANIES INC
(*Suby of* TESORO CORP) ★
19100 Ridgewood Pkwy, San Antonio, TX 78259-1834
Tel (210) 626-7390 *Founded/Ownrshp* 1985
Sales 110.9MMᴱ *EMP* 220ᴱ
SIC 8741 Administrative management
Pr: Bruce Smith
Assoc VP: Alan Gustin
Sr VP: Warren Anderson
VP: Jeff Bauer
**VP:* Don Beere
VP: Tracy D Jackson
VP: Curtis Jeffords
VP: Joe Ran
VP: Daniel Riley
VP: John Sherburne
VP: Brian Sullivan
VP: Karen Vazquez
Exec: Earl Borths
Dir Rx: Sandra Perry

D-U-N-S 00-813-3480 IMP/EXP
▲TESORO CORP
19100 Ridgewood Pkwy, San Antonio, TX 78259-1834
Tel (210) 626-6000 *Founded/Ownrshp* 1939
Sales 28.7MMMM *EMP* 6,000ᴱ
Accts Ernst & Young Llp San Antonio
Tkr Sym TSO *Exch* NYS
SIC 2911 1311 5983 5984 Petroleum refining; Gasoline; Jet fuels; Diesel fuels; Crude petroleum & natural gas; Crude petroleum production; Natural gas production; Fuel oil dealers; Liquefied petroleum gas dealers
Ch Bd: Gregory J Goff
CFO: Steven M Sterin
Treas: Brad S Lakhia
Ex VP: Keith M Casey
Ex VP: Charles S Parrish
Ex VP: Kim K Rucker
Ex VP: Cynthia J Warner
Sr VP: Michael J Morrison
Sr VP: Daryl R Schofield
VP: Tracy D Jackson
Board of Directors: Rodney F Chase, Edward G Galante, Robert W Goldman, David Lilley, Mary Pat McCarthy, Jimmy W Nokes, Susan Tomasky, Michael E Wiley, Patrick Y Yang

D-U-N-S 96-804-2452
▲TESORO LOGISTICS LP
19100 Ridgewood Pkwy, San Antonio, TX 78259-1834
Tel (210) 626-6000 *Founded/Ownrshp* 2010
Sales 1.1MMMM *EMP* 853ᴱ
Accts Ernst & Young Llp San Antonio
Tkr Sym TLLP *Exch* NYS
SIC 1311 4612 Crude petroleum & natural gas; Crude petroleum production; Crude petroleum pipelines
CEO: Gregory J Goff
Genl Pt: Tesoro Logistics GP
Pr: Phillip M Anderson

D-U-N-S 07-932-9878
■TESORO LOGISTICS OPERATIONS LLC
(*Suby of* TESORO LOGISTICS LP) ★
19100 Ridgewood Pkwy, San Antonio, TX 78259-1834
Tel (210) 626-4280 *Founded/Ownrshp* 2014
Sales 167.2MMᴱ *EMP* 321ᴱ
SIC 4922 Pipelines, natural gas
Pr: Phillip M Anderson
**Treas:* Brad S Lakhia
**VP:* Joseph J Bookout
**Prin:* D Jeffrey Haffner

D-U-N-S 02-975-9037 IMP
■TESORO REFINING & MARKETING CO LLC
(*Suby of* TESORO CORP) ★
19100 Ridgewood Pkwy, San Antonio, TX 78259-1834
Tel (210) 828-8484 *Founded/Ownrshp* 1979
Sales 949.1MMᴱ *EMP* 2,200
SIC 2911 5541 Petroleum refining; Gasoline service stations
Pr: Gregory J Goff
Ex VP: Keith Casey
Ex VP: Charles S Parrish
Ex VP: Steven Sterin
Ex VP: Cynthia Warner
VP: Daniel S Cameron
VP: Chad J Falgout
VP: David L Foster
VP: Arlen O Glenewinkel
Mktg Dir: Don Reese

TESSCO
See POWER LINE INFRASTRUCTURE SERVICES INC

D-U-N-S 12-432-4455
TESSCO ENERGY SERVICES INC
(*Suby of* PLH GROUP INC) ★
1031 Andrews Hwy Ste 450, Midland, TX 79701-3805
Tel (432) 563-0071 *Founded/Ownrshp* 2000
Sales 110.0MM *EMP* 814
SIC 4911 Electric services
CEO: Mark Crowson
**Pr:* Ron Moose
**CFO:* Ken Dodgen

D-U-N-S 08-421-5677 IMP
■TESSCO INC
(*Suby of* TESSCO TECHNOLOGIES INC) ★
11126 Mccormick Rd, Hunt Valley, MD 21031-4302
Tel (410) 229-1000 *Founded/Ownrshp* 1994
Sales 540.1MMᴱ *EMP* 800
SIC 5065 Communication equipment
Ch Bd: Robert B Barnhill Jr
**VP:* Jay G Baitler
VP: Mary B Smith
Exec: Paul Tobis
Sales Asso: Kelly Thomas
Snr Mgr: Jeremy Lippenholz

D-U-N-S 02-263-4265 IMP/EXP
▲TESSCO TECHNOLOGIES INC
11126 Mccormick Rd, Hunt Valley, MD 21031-4302
Tel (410) 229-1000 *Founded/Ownrshp* 1982
Sales 530.6MM *EMP* 786
Tkr Sym TESS *Exch* NGM
SIC 5065 Telephone & telegraphic equipment; Mobile telephone equipment; Communication equipment; Electronic parts
CEO: Murray Wright
Ch Bd: Robert B Barnhill Jr
CFO: Aric Spitulnik
Treas: Cynthia King
Sr VP: Craig A Oldham
Sr VP: Pete Peterson
Sr VP: Douglas A Rein
Sr VP: Steven K Tom
VP: Mike Gross

Dir Bus: Matt Bavosa
Dir Bus: Amber Darda
Board of Directors: Jay G Baitler, John D Beletic, Dennis J Shaughnessy, Morton F Zifferer Jr

D-U-N-S 08-047-6742
▲TESSERA HOLDING CORP
3025 Orchard Pkwy, San Jose, CA 95134-2017
Tel (408) 321-6000 *Founded/Ownrshp* 2016
Sales 411.5MM^E *EMP* 748
SIC 3674 Semiconductors & related devices
Pr: Jon Kirchner

D-U-N-S 13-648-2275 IMP
■TESSERA TECHNOLOGIES INC
(*Suby of* TESSERA HOLDING CORP) ★
3025 Orchard Pkwy, San Jose, CA 95134-2017
Tel (408) 321-6000 *Founded/Ownrshp* 2016
Sales 273.3MM *EMP* 264^E
Tkr Sym TSRA *Exch* NGS
SIC 6794 3674 Patent owners & lessors; Patent buying, licensing, leasing; Integrated circuits, semiconductor networks, etc.; Memories, solid state
CEO: Tom Lacey
Pr: Jon E Kirchner
CFO: Robert Andersen
Chf Mktg O: Peter Van Deventer
Ofcr: Kevin Doohan
Ofcr: Kris M Graves
Genl Mgr: Petronel Bigioi
CTO: Steve Teig

D-U-N-S 07-160-2312 IMP/EXP
TESSY PLASTICS CORP
700 Visions Dr, Skaneateles, NY 13152-6475
Tel (315) 689-3924 *Founded/Ownrshp* 1973
Sales 190.1MM^E *EMP* 600
SIC 3089 3549 Injection molding of plastics; Assembly machines, including robotic
**CFO:* Ed Pietruniak
**Treas:* Ken Beck
VP: Matthew Biernacki
Exec: Nils Hammerich
Prgrm Mgr: Dave Snyder
Genl Mgr: Joseph Raffa
Plnt Mgr: Barry Carson
Mktg Dir: Mark Halstead
Pgrm Dir: John Werner

D-U-N-S 09-894-5389 IMP/EXP
TEST-RITE PRODUCTS CORP
(*Suby of* TEST-RITE INTERNATIONAL (U.S.) CO., LTD.)
1900 Burgundy Pl, Ontario, CA 91761-2317
Tel (909) 605-9899 *Founded/Ownrshp* 2011
Sales 141.1MM *EMP* 120
Accts Chen & Fan Accountancy Corpora
SIC 5023 Home furnishings
Pr: Chester Lee
**Treas:* Christina MA
Ex VP: Melvin Shiraki

D-U-N-S 78-580-8569
TESTA PRODUCE INC
4555 S Racine Ave, Chicago, IL 60609-3371
Tel (312) 226-3237 *Founded/Ownrshp* 1991
Sales 137.1MM^E *EMP* 122
SIC 5148 5812 Vegetables, fresh; Eating places
Pr: Peter Testa
**CFO:* Len Moskowitz
Ex VP: Len Maskowitz
**VP:* Dominick Testa

D-U-N-S 17-364-6071
TESTAMERICA ENVIRONMENTAL SERVICES LLC
(*Suby of* HIG CAPITAL MANAGEMENT INC) ★
4101 Shuffel St Nw, North Canton, OH 44720-6900
Tel (330) 497-9396 *Founded/Ownrshp* 2002
Sales 469.0MM^E *EMP* 3,015
SIC 8734 Water testing laboratory
CEO: James Hyman
**CFO:* Ben Erwin

D-U-N-S 09-125-4896
TESTAMERICA HOLDINGS INC
(*Suby of* TESTAMERICA ENVIRONMENTAL SERVICES LLC) ★
4101 Shuffel St Nw, North Canton, OH 44720-6900
Tel (330) 497-9396 *Founded/Ownrshp* 2002, 2006
Sales 436.5MM^E *EMP* 2,531
SIC 8734 Testing laboratories
CEO: Rachel Brydon Jannetta
**CFO:* Stuart Stoller

D-U-N-S 03-804-0759
TESTAMERICA LABORATORIES INC
(*Suby of* TESTAMERICA HOLDINGS INC) ★
4101 Shuffel St Nw, North Canton, OH 44720-6900
Tel (800) 456-9396 *Founded/Ownrshp* 2008
Sales 411.6MM^E *EMP* 2,273
SIC 8734 Soil analysis; Water testing laboratory
CEO: Rachel Brydon Jannetta
**CFO:* Stuart Stoller
Genl Mgr: Chris Oprandi
Off Mgr: Rebecca Garcia

D-U-N-S 06-236-6851
TETCO INC (TX)
1100 Ne Loop 410 Ste 900, San Antonio, TX 78209-1574
Tel (210) 821-5900 *Founded/Ownrshp* 1982, 2001
Sales 1.1MMM^E *EMP* 3,500
SIC 4213 5411 1611 5193 Liquid petroleum transport, non-local; Convenience stores; Highway & street paving contractor; Nursery stock
Pr: Javier Trevino
**Ch Bd:* Tom E Turner Jr
**CFO:* Don Bowden
**CFO:* Patrick Furlong
**VP:* Jon R Turner
**Prin:* Gerry O Telle
VP Admn: Kyle Donovan
Off Mgr: Carol Center

D-U-N-S 01-332-1430 IMP
TETERS FLORAL PRODUCTS INC
SAGE AND COMPANY
1425 S Lillian Ave, Bolivar, MO 65613-2316
Tel (800) 333-7178 *Founded/Ownrshp* 1957
Sales 235.2MM^E *EMP* 400
SIC 5193 Artificial flowers
CEO: John Silvestri
Pr: Jennifer Behme
CFO: Jack Casper
Ex VP: Beth Cohney
Ex VP: Nick Kong
VP: Jones Elliott
Dir IT: Harvey Lackey
Prd Mgr: Brenda Ross
Sales Exec: Beth Kohne
Mktg Dir: Kelly Baker

D-U-N-S 01-752-0803
TETON BUILDINGS LLC
2701 Magnet St, Houston, TX 77054-4509
Tel (713) 351-6300 *Founded/Ownrshp* 2013
Sales 123.5MM^E *EMP* 325
SIC 1542 Commercial & office building contractors
CEO: Greg Borysko

D-U-N-S 07-295-6642
TETON COUNTY HOSPITAL DISTRICT
ST JOHNS HOSPITAL & NURSING HM
625 E Broadway Ave, Jackson, WY 83001-8642
Tel (307) 733-3636 *Founded/Ownrshp* 1957
Sales 95.9MM *EMP* 450
SIC 8062 8052 8051 General medical & surgical hospitals; Intermediate care facilities; Skilled nursing care facilities
Ch Bd: Michael Tennican
**V Ch:* Barbara Herz
**CEO:* Lou Hochheiser
**COO:* Gary Trauner
**CFO:* John Krenm
**Treas:* C Scott Gibson
**Ofcr:* Lynn Campbell
Ofcr: Stuart Smith
Ofcr: Marty Trott
Exec: Michele Nevarez
Dir Rad: Michelle Pask
Dir Rx: Ken Jarman

D-U-N-S 84-988-7260 IMP
■TETRA APPLIED TECHNOLOGIES INC
(*Suby of* TETRA TECHNOLOGIES INC) ★
24955 Interstate 45, Spring, TX 77380-3055
Tel (281) 367-1983 *Founded/Ownrshp* 1988
Sales 119.8MM^E *EMP* 234
SIC 1389 Well plugging & abandoning, oil & gas
Pr: Richard D Dodson
**Treas:* Bruce A Cobb
**VP:* Paul D Coombs
**VP:* Geoffrey M Hertel

D-U-N-S 92-605-8553
TETRA FINANCIAL GROUP LLC
6995 S Union Park Ctr # 400, Cottonwood Heights, UT 84047-6088
Tel (801) 748-2200 *Founded/Ownrshp* 2002
Sales NA *EMP* 45
SIC 6153 Working capital financing
CFO: David Lamb

TETRA PAK CPS
See TETRA PAK INC

D-U-N-S 08-271-4692 IMP/EXP
TETRA PAK INC
TETRA PAK CPS
(*Suby of* TETRA PAK US HOLDINGS INC) ★
3300 Airport Rd, Denton, TX 76207-2199
Tel (940) 565-8800 *Founded/Ownrshp* 1984
Sales 383.4MM^E *EMP* 1,039
SIC 2671 3565 5084 Paper coated or laminated for packaging; Packaging machinery; Hydraulic systems equipment & supplies
Pr: Michael Zacka
**CFO:* Rubin Loppez
Top Exec: Mark Meyer
VP: John Felzan
**VP:* Brian Kennel
VP: Steve Nichols
Sfty Dirs: Chris Gorman
Plnt Mgr: David Hammons

D-U-N-S 60-923-6997 IMP/EXP
TETRA PAK MATERIALS LP
(*Suby of* TETRA PAK CPS) ★
101 Corporate Woods Pkwy, Vernon Hills, IL 60061-3109
Tel (847) 955-6000 *Founded/Ownrshp* 1951
Sales 159.3MM^E *EMP* 556^E
SIC 2671 Paper coated or laminated for packaging
Pr: Uno Kjellberg

D-U-N-S 96-737-3564 IMP/EXP
TETRA PAK US HOLDINGS INC
(*Suby of* TETRA LAVAL INTERNATIONAL SA)
101 Corporate Woods Pkwy, Vernon Hills, IL 60061-3109
Tel (940) 565-8800 *Founded/Ownrshp* 1951
Sales 383.4MM^E *EMP* 1,481
SIC 2656 Food containers (liquid tight), including milk cartons
CEO: Dennis Jonsson
**Pr:* Ruben Lopez
COO: Ken Eno
VP: Brian Kennell
VP: Ed Klein
Exec: Harshad Kulkarni
Exec: Flavio Lopes
Comm Man: Anna Droben
CTO: Hattie West
IT Man: Audra Baggett
Tech Mgr: Carl L Lins

D-U-N-S 12-897-4271
■TETRA TECH EC INC
(*Suby of* TETRA TECH INC) ★
6 Century Dr Ste 3, Parsippany, NJ 07054-4611
Tel (973) 630-8000 *Founded/Ownrshp* 2003
Sales 134.5MM^E *EMP* 1,057
SIC 8748 Business consulting
Ch Bd: Frank C Gross
**COO:* John De Feis
**COO:* Donald I Rogers
Ex VP: John De Feis Jr
**Ex VP:* Jonathan Weiss
**Sr VP:* Larry Brown
**VP:* James Leonard
Comm Man: Penny Dimler

D-U-N-S 13-934-1978
■TETRA TECH EMC INC
(*Suby of* TETRA TECH INC) ★
100 Camino Ruiz, Camarillo, CA 93012-6700
Tel (805) 484-9082 *Founded/Ownrshp* 2003
Sales 208.2MM^E *EMP* 13,000
SIC 8711 7371 Consulting engineer; Computer software development & applications
Pr: Dan L Batrack
**Pr:* Patrick D Haun
**VP:* James E Bailey Jr
**VP:* Ven M Burdick
**VP:* Frank C Gross
**VP:* Douglas G Smith

D-U-N-S 04-522-4250
▲TETRA TECH INC
3475 E Foothill Blvd, Pasadena, CA 91107-6024
Tel (626) 351-4664 *Founded/Ownrshp* 1966
Sales 2.5MMM *EMP* 13,000
Tkr Sym TTEK *Exch* NGS
SIC 8711 Engineering services; Civil engineering; Consulting engineer
Ch Bd: Dan L Batrack
Pr: Frank Gross
CFO: Steven M Burdick
Ex VP: Ronald J Chu
Sr VP: Brian N Carter
Sr VP: Craig L Christensen
Sr VP: Bob Ozibko
Sr VP: Janis B Salin
Board of Directors: Hugh M Grant, Patrick C Haden, J Christopher Lewis, Joanne M Maguire, Kimberly E Ritrievi, J Kenneth Thompson, Richard H Truly, Kirsten M Volpi

D-U-N-S 02-444-3327 IMP/EXP
▲TETRA TECHNOLOGIES INC
24955 Interstate 45, The Woodlands, TX 77380-3055
Tel (281) 367-1983 *Founded/Ownrshp* 1981
Sales 1.1MMM *EMP* 3,000
Accts Ernst & Young Llp Houston Te
Tkr Sym TTI *Exch* NYS
SIC 2819 1389 Brine; Calcium chloride & hypochlorite; Oil & gas wells: building, repairing & dismantling; Well plugging & abandoning, oil & gas; Testing, measuring, surveying & analysis services
Ch Bd: William D Sullivan
Pr: Stuart M Brightman
COO: Joseph Elkhoury
CFO: Elijio V Serrano
Ex VP: Stuart M Brightan
Sr VP: Gary C Hanna
Sr VP: Peter J Pintar
Sr VP: Matthew J Sanderson
Sr VP: Bass C Wallace Jr
VP: Joseph Meyer
Ql Cn Mgr: Patrick Hage

TEVA
See BARR LABORATORIES INC

D-U-N-S 00-990-6397
TEVA NEUROSCIENCE INC
(*Suby of* TEVA PHARMACEUTICAL INDUSTRIES LIMITED)
11100 Nall Ave, Leawood, KS 66211-1205
Tel (913) 777-3000 *Founded/Ownrshp* 1999
Sales 86.6MM^E *EMP* 450^E
SIC 2834 Drugs acting on the central nervous system & sense organs
Pr: Larry R Downey
Exec: Brent Ballow
Exec: Tanya Crusco
Exec: Wendy Goodman
Exec: Kym Graef
Exec: Andy Tenaglia
Sls Mgr: Todd Gasper

TEVA NORTH AMERICA
See TEVA PHARMACEUTICALS USA INC

D-U-N-S 79-436-2533 IMP
TEVA PARENTERAL MEDICINES INC
(*Suby of* TEVA NORTH AMERICA) ★
19 Hughes, Irvine, CA 92618-1902
Tel (949) 455-4700 *Founded/Ownrshp* 2005
Sales 225.1MM^E *EMP* 830
SIC 2834 Pills, pharmaceutical
Ch Bd: Phillip Frost
**CEO:* Karin Shanahan
**V Ch Bd:* Amir Elstein
**Sr VP:* Nir Baron
**VP:* Iris Beck-Codner
**Prin:* David Dreyer
Genl Mgr: Jeffery Herdfeld

D-U-N-S 00-162-7975 IMP/EXP
TEVA PHARMACEUTICALS USA INC
TEVA NORTH AMERICA
(*Suby of* TEVA PHARMACEUTICAL INDUSTRIES LIMITED)
1090 Horsham Rd, North Wales, PA 19454-1505
Tel (215) 591-3000 *Founded/Ownrshp* 1985, 1996
Sales 1.1MMM^E *EMP* 1,025
SIC 2834 2833 5122 Pharmaceutical preparations; Penicillin preparations; Drugs acting on the respiratory system; Drugs acting on the cardiovascular system, except diagnostic; Medicinals & botanicals; Penicillin: bulk, uncompounded; Antibiotics; Pharmaceuticals
Pr: Sigurdur Olafsson
**Treas:* Vito Mairone
Ex VP: Edward Hogan
Ex VP: Mark Salyer
VP: Debra Barrett
VP: Mark Campbell
VP: Maureen Cavanaugh
VP: Dan Driscoll
VP: Karen Gotting-Smith
**VP:* Deborah Griffin
VP: Denisa Hurtukova
VP: Chaim Hurvitz
VP: Lynda Johnson
VP: Frederick J Killion
VP: Rivka Kreitman
VP: Allen Marko
VP: Nicholas Maselli
VP: Ildiko Mehes
VP: Shosh Neumann
VP: Bill Northington
VP: Spyros Papapetropoulos

D-U-N-S 36-070-1192
TEX ROBBINS TRANSPORTATION LLC
1100 Northway Dr, Fort Worth, TX 76131-1425
Tel (817) 306-1000 *Founded/Ownrshp* 2004
Sales 177.0MM *EMP* 456
Accts Davis Kinard & Co Pc Abilene
SIC 4213 Trucking, except local
Pr: Kevin Jordan
CFO: Kristi Cheek

TEX SOL
See HEATH CONSULTANTS INC

D-U-N-S 60-917-0030
TEX-LA ELECTRIC COOPERATIVE OF TEXAS INC
2905 Westward Dr, Nacogdoches, TX 75964-1231
Tel (936) 560-9532 *Founded/Ownrshp* 1980
Sales 129.0MM *EMP* 7
SIC 4911 Distribution, electric power

TEXACO
See E & C ENTERPRISES INC

D-U-N-S 13-111-4662 IMP
■TEXACO EXPLORATION AND PRODUCTION INC
(*Suby of* TEXACO INC) ★
1500 Louisiana St, Houston, TX 77002-7308
Tel (800) 962-1223 *Founded/Ownrshp* 1982
Sales 913.7MM^E *EMP* 7,000
SIC 5541 5511 1321 Filling stations, gasoline; Automobiles, new & used; Natural gas liquids
Pr: Clarence P Cazalot Jr
Top Exec: Gordon Marshall
Sr VP: Pankaj Pithwa
VP: Melody Meyer
Genl Mgr: Mike Rodriguez

D-U-N-S 00-134-5164 IMP
■TEXACO INC
(*Suby of* CHEVRON CORP) ★
6001 Bollinger Canyon Rd, San Ramon, CA 94583-2324
Tel (925) 842-1000 *Founded/Ownrshp* 1902
Sales 1.9MMM^E *EMP* 19,011
SIC 5541 5511 1321 4612 4613 4412 Filling stations, gasoline; Automobiles, new & used; Natural gas liquids production; Crude petroleum pipelines; Refined petroleum pipelines; Deep sea foreign transportation of freight
Ch Bd: David O'Reilly
**CEO:* Kari H Endries
Ex VP: Patricia Woertz
Sr VP: William K Tell
VP: Darald Callahan
VP: James Link
VP: William Tell
VP: Glen Tilton
VP: William Wicker
Genl Mgr: Allen J Krowe

TEXACOTE
See TEXTILE RUBBER AND CHEMICAL CO INC

D-U-N-S 07-859-2789 IMP/EXP
TEXAS A & M RESEARCH FOUNDATION INC (TX)
400 Harvey Mtchl Pkwy 3, College Station, TX 77845-4375
Tel (979) 845-8600 *Founded/Ownrshp* 1944
Sales 105.5MM *EMP* 483
Accts Ingram Wallis & Co Pc Br
SIC 8741 Administrative management
Pr: Leo J Paterra
**CFO:* Linda Woodman
VP: Steve Garrett

TEXAS A & M UNIVERSITY
See TEXAS A&M UNIVERSITY SYSTEM

TEXAS A & M UNIVERSITY
See TEXAS A&M UNIVERSITY-COMMERCE

TEXAS A & M UNIVERSITY
See TARLETON STATE UNIVERSITY

TEXAS A & M UNIVERSITY
See TEXAS A&M UNIVERSITY-CORPUS CHRISTI

TEXAS A & M UNIVERSITY
See TEXAS A&M AGRILIFE EXTENSION SERVICE

TEXAS A & M UNIVERSITY
See TEXAS A&M AGRILIFE RESEARCH

D-U-N-S 62-785-2775 IMP
TEXAS A & M UNIVERSITY
(*Suby of* TEXAS A & M UNIVERSITY) ★
301 Tarrow St Fl 6, College Station, TX 77840-7896
Tel (979) 862-3003 *Founded/Ownrshp* 1993
Sales 975.4MM *EMP* 8,159
SIC 8221

D-U-N-S 06-944-7381
TEXAS A & M UNIVERSITY KINGSVILLE
(*Suby of* TEXAS A & M UNIVERSITY) ★
700 University Blvd, Kingsville, TX 78363-8202
Tel (361) 593-3344 *Founded/Ownrshp* 1917
Sales 95.8MM *EMP* 935
SIC 8221 University
Pr: Steven Tallant
**VP:* Rex Gandy
**VP:* Randy Hughes
Assoc Dir: Patricia Adams
Assoc Dir: Romana Cantu
Assoc Dir: Maria Ortiz

Assoc Dir: William P Saenz
Assoc Dir: Gina Smith
Adm Dir: Rebecca Trant
Ex Dir: Leon Bazar
Off Mgr: Melissa Guajardo
Board of Directors: Rebecca Davis

D-U-N-S 78-156-8837
TEXAS A&M AGRILIFE EXTENSION SERVICE
TEXAS A & M UNIVERSITY
(*Suby of* TEXAS A & M UNIVERSITY) ★
2147 Tamu, College Station, TX 77843-0001
Tel (979) 458-4383 *Founded/Ownrshp* 1915
Sales 40.3MM *EMP* 5,000
SIC 8731 8221 Agricultural research; University
CFO: Donna Alexander

D-U-N-S 84-720-5713
TEXAS A&M AGRILIFE RESEARCH
TEXAS A & M UNIVERSITY
(*Suby of* TEXAS A & M UNIVERSITY) ★
2147 Tamu, College Station, TX 77843-0001
Tel (979) 458-4383 *Founded/Ownrshp* 1892
Sales 112.0MM *EMP* 1,800
SIC 8731 8221 Agricultural research; University
CFO: Debra Cummings
**Genl Mgr:* Loree Lewis
Genl Mgr: Tribbie Sandner

D-U-N-S 84-720-5572
TEXAS A&M ENGINEERING EXPERIMENT STATION
TEES
7607 Eastmark Dr Ste 101, College Station, TX 77840-4027
Tel (979) 458-7643 *Founded/Ownrshp* 1993
Sales 104.3MM *EMP* 1,500
SIC 8711 Engineering services
**CFO:* John Crawford

D-U-N-S 84-720-7891
TEXAS A&M ENGINEERING EXTENSION SERVICE
(*Suby of* TEXAS A & M UNIVERSITY) ★
301 Tarrow St, College Station, TX 77840-7896
Tel (979) 845-7641 *Founded/Ownrshp* 1919
Sales 82.8MM *EMP* 1,500
SIC 8331 8711 8748 8111 Job training & vocational rehabilitation services; Fire protection engineering; Safety training service; Legal services
CFO: Arturo Alonzo Jr
Assoc Dir: Mike Wisby
Admn Mgr: Norma Cintu

D-U-N-S 62-735-0929
TEXAS A&M FOUNDATION
401 George Bush Dr, College Station, TX 77840-2811
Tel (979) 845-8161 *Founded/Ownrshp* 1953
Sales 160.1MM *EMP* 95^E
Accts Bkd Llp Houston Tx
SIC 6732 8399 Educational trust management; Fund raising organization, non-fee basis
Pr: Dr Eddie J Davis
**CFO:* Doyle Thompson
Sr VP: Tina Evans
**Sr VP:* James J Palincsar
**Sr VP:* John R Stropp
VP: Janet Handley
VP: Glenn Pittsford
MIS Dir: Chris Speier
IT Man: Judith Lewis
Info Man: Steve Catlin

D-U-N-S 96-545-9584
TEXAS A&M HEALTH SCIENCE CENTER
TEXAS A&M HEALTH SCIENCE CTR
(*Suby of* TEXAS A & M UNIVERSITY) ★
200 Technology Way, College Station, TX 77845-3424
Tel (979) 436-9200 *Founded/Ownrshp* 2000
Sales 136.7MM *EMP* 50^E
SIC 8299 8221 Educational services; Colleges universities & professional schools
Pr: Nancy Dickey
VP: David Cantrell
Comm Dir: Katherine Hancock
Prgrm Mgr: Marisa Galimbertti
Mktg Dir: Sloane Williams

TEXAS A&M HEALTH SCIENCE CTR
See TEXAS A&M HEALTH SCIENCE CENTER

D-U-N-S 04-291-5991 IMP
TEXAS A&M UNIVERSITY SYSTEM
TEXAS A & M UNIVERSITY
301 Tarrow St Fl 3, College Station, TX 77840-7896
Tel (979) 458-6100 *Founded/Ownrshp* 1876
Sales 31.8MM *EMP* 22,000
SIC 8221 8731 8742 8011 University; Agricultural research; Transportation consultant; Clinic, operated by physicians
**Pr:* R Bowen Loftin
**Pr:* Michael Young
**CFO:* Barry Nelson
**CFO:* K Sue Redman
**Chf Mktg O:* Steven B Moore
Sr VP: Sue K Redman
VP: Pierce E Cantrell
VP: David Carlson
**VP:* Dr Rihard E Ewing
VP: Linda Fitzpatrick
VP: Tito Guerrero
**VP:* Michael G O'Quinn
**VP:* Dave Parrott
VP: Ahmad Sawas
**VP:* Charles A Sippial Sr
VP: Charles A Sippil
**VP:* Dr Jerry R Strawser
**VP:* Dr Robert L Walker
Exec: Richard Colley
Assoc Dir: Janie Alcala
Comm Man: Terri Parker

D-U-N-S 07-313-1419
TEXAS A&M UNIVERSITY-COMMERCE
TEXAS A & M UNIVERSITY
(*Suby of* TEXAS A & M UNIVERSITY) ★
2600 W Neal St, Commerce, TX 75428-4311
Tel (903) 886-5041 *Founded/Ownrshp* 1889
Sales 104.5MM *EMP* 1,200
SIC 8221 University
Pr: Dan Jones
VP: Mary Hendrix
Creative D: Paul Bryan
CTO: Deborah Davies
CTO: Jaime Harper

D-U-N-S 09-510-0152
TEXAS A&M UNIVERSITY-CORPUS CHRISTI
TEXAS A & M UNIVERSITY
(*Suby of* TEXAS A & M UNIVERSITY) ★
6300 Ocean Dr Unit 5756, Corpus Christi, TX 78412-5756
Tel (361) 825-5700 *Founded/Ownrshp* 1947, 1971
Sales 111.9MM *EMP* 1,401
SIC 8221 University
Pr: Flavius Killebrew
Top Exec: Brittany Smalley
Assoc VP: Dr David Billeaux
Assoc VP: Claudia L McDonald
Ex VP: Jody H Nelsen
VP: Trent Hill
VP: Louis Katz
VP: Thomas Rosales
Dir Teleco: Keith Franger
Dir Bus: Ian Gallett
Ex Dir: Anne Baker

D-U-N-S 02-731-3761
TEXAS AERO ENGINE SERVICES LLC
TAESL
(*Suby of* ROLLS-ROYCE NORTH AMERICA INC) ★
2100 Eagle Pkwy, Fort Worth, TX 76177-2301
Tel (817) 224-0711 *Founded/Ownrshp* 1998
Sales 488.4MM^E *EMP* 700
SIC 7538

D-U-N-S 09-408-2856
TEXAS AIR SYSTEMS INC
6029 Campus Circle Dr W # 100, Irving, TX 75063-2768
Tel (972) 570-4700 *Founded/Ownrshp* 1977
Sales 150.2MM^E *EMP* 120
SIC 5075 1711 Warm air heating & air conditioning; Plumbing, heating, air-conditioning contractors
Pr: Daniel M Ruehs
**Ex VP:* Tom Cooksey

D-U-N-S 96-160-0751
TEXAS AIRSYSTEMS LLC
6029 Campus Circle Dr W, Irving, TX 75063-2767
Tel (210) 499-0004 *Founded/Ownrshp* 2007
Sales 109.1MM^E *EMP* 307^E
SIC 3563 Air & gas compressors; Vacuum pumps, except laboratory
CEO: Gerald P Braun
VP: Cooksey D Thomas
Genl Mgr: Bruce Colborne

D-U-N-S 62-102-0940
TEXAS AMERICAN RESOURCES CO
401 Congress Ave Ste 1600, Austin, TX 78701-3755
Tel (512) 480-8700 *Founded/Ownrshp* 1990
Sales 223.6MM^E *EMP* 45
SIC 1311 1382

D-U-N-S 08-356-0193
TEXAS AMERICAN TITLE CO
2000 Bering Dr Ste 900, Houston, TX 77057-3779
Tel (713) 988-9999 *Founded/Ownrshp* 2007
Sales NA *EMP* 225
SIC 6361 8111 Title insurance; Legal services
Ch Bd: Herb L Williams
**CFO:* Brian Ahlquist
**Sr VP:* Pamela Roberson
Brnch Mgr: Michael Allen
Brnch Mgr: Denham Lisa

D-U-N-S 03-777-0575 IMP
TEXAS AROMATICS LP
3555 Timmons Ln Ste 700, Houston, TX 77027-6450
Tel (713) 520-2900 *Founded/Ownrshp* 1980
Sales 531.6MM *EMP* 17
Accts Weaver And Tidwell Llp Ho
SIC 5172 Petroleum products
Pt: Melbern G Glasscock
Treas: Staci Vol
Ex VP: Jeffrey Bell
VP: Trenton L Kelley
VP Sls: Ed Echols

D-U-N-S 00-895-1014
TEXAS BANK & TRUST CO
(*Suby of* LONGVIEW DELAWARE CORPORATION)
300 E Whaley St, Longview, TX 75601-6417
Tel (903) 237-5500 *Founded/Ownrshp* 1958
Sales NA *EMP* 300
SIC 6022 State commercial banks
Pr: Rogers Pope Jr
Ofcr: Jeanie Anderson
Ofcr: Peggy L Coyne
Ex VP: Randall Andrews
Ex VP: Shane Best
Ex VP: Roy Eon
Sr VP: Larry Day
Sr VP: Connie Milligan
Sr VP: Beverly Rose
Sr VP: James Sheridan
Sr VP: Lori Sirman
Sr VP: Yanika Valentine
Sr VP: Mark Walling
Sr VP: David Wilson
VP: Jeff Cheavens
VP: Sherry Gibbon
VP: Crystal Hardy
VP: Chan Turner
Exec: Buffy Dyess

TEXAS BOOKMAN, THE
See HALF PRICE BOOKS RECORDS MAGAZINES INC

D-U-N-S 05-999-7663
▲TEXAS CAPITAL BANCSHARES INC
2000 Mckinney Ave Ste 700, Dallas, TX 75201-1985
Tel (214) 932-6600 *Founded/Ownrshp* 1998
Sales NA *EMP* 1,329^E
Tkr Sym TCBI *Exch* NGS
SIC 6022 State commercial banks
Pr: C Keith Cargill
**Ch Bd:* Larry L Helm
**COO:* Peter B Bartholow
VP: Raul Cantu
Dir Risk M: John D Hudgens
Board of Directors: James H Browning, Preston M Geren III, Charles S Hyle, Steven P Rosenberg, Robert W Stallings, Dale W Tremblay, Ian J Turpin, Patricia A Watson

D-U-N-S 05-476-5222
■TEXAS CAPITAL BANK NATIONAL ASSOCIATION
TEXAS CAPITAL BANK-DALLAS
(*Suby of* TEXAS CAPITAL BANCSHARES INC) ★
2000 Mckinney Ave Ste 700, Dallas, TX 75201-1985
Tel (214) 932-6600 *Founded/Ownrshp* 1997, 1998
Sales NA *EMP* 507
SIC 6021 National commercial banks
CEO: Keith Cargill
**Ch Bd:* Joseph M Grant
Pr: Vince Ackerson
**Pr:* Russell Hartsfield
**Pr:* George Jones Jr
**CEO:* C Keith Cargill
**COO:* Peter Bartholow
COO: Karen Goettl
**COO:* Jim White
**CFO:* Julie Anderson
CFO: Peter B Artholow
CFO: Peter Barthelow
**Ex VP:* David L Cargill
**Ex VP:* David Folz
Ex VP: Tricia Linderman
Ex VP: Tim Loudermilk
Ex VP: Cara McDaniel
**Ex VP:* Robert A McDaniel
Ex VP: Benjamin A Rathjen
Sr VP: Lo Andrews
Sr VP: Judy Blanton

TEXAS CAPITAL BANK-DALLAS
See TEXAS CAPITAL BANK NATIONAL ASSOCIATION

D-U-N-S 01-318-1469
TEXAS CES INC
3333 Ih 35 N Bldg F, Gainesville, TX 76240
Tel (940) 668-5100 *Founded/Ownrshp* 2006
Sales 1.3MMM^E *EMP* 2,500
SIC 1389 Servicing oil & gas wells
Pr: Jeff Kaufmann
**VP:* William B Masters
**VP:* Brian K Moore
**VP:* Robert S Taylor
**Prin:* Ken Harrison

D-U-N-S 05-453-3448
TEXAS CHILDRENS HEALTH PLAN INC (TX)
(*Suby of* TEXAS CHILDRENS HOSPITAL) ★
1919 S Braeswood Blvd, Houston, TX 77030-4444
Tel (832) 824-2939 *Founded/Ownrshp* 1995
Sales NA *EMP* 70
Accts Crowe Horwath Llp Chicago Il
SIC 6324 Health maintenance organization (HMO), insurance only
Pr: Chris Born

D-U-N-S 07-461-5394
TEXAS CHILDRENS HOSPITAL
6621 Fannin St, Houston, TX 77030-2399
Tel (832) 824-1000 *Founded/Ownrshp* 1947
Sales 1.5MMM *EMP* 6,000
SIC 8011 8062 Offices & clinics of medical doctors; General medical & surgical hospitals
Pr: Mark Wallace
Pr: Lori Williams
CFO: David Bowersox
CFO: Benjamin Melson
VP: May Joe Andre
VP: Claire M Bassett
VP: Peter Dawson
VP: Lance Lightfoot
VP: John Scales
VP: Douglas Spade
Dir Rx: Brady S Moffett
Dir Bus: Howar Hilten

D-U-N-S 00-696-8707
TEXAS CHILDRENS HOSPITAL FOUNDATION (TX)
6621 Fannin St Ste 210, Houston, TX 77030-2358
Tel (832) 824-6230 *Founded/Ownrshp* 2005
Sales 127.2MM *EMP* 50
SIC 8011 Physicians' office, including specialists

D-U-N-S 96-661-2561
TEXAS CHILDRENS PHYSICIAN GROUP INC
6621 Fannin St, Houston, TX 77030-2358
Tel (832) 824-2982 *Founded/Ownrshp* 2011
Sales 304.4MM *EMP* 4
Accts Ernst & Young Us Llp Houston
SIC 8011 General & family practice, physician/surgeon

D-U-N-S 04-380-7882
TEXAS CHRISTIAN UNIVERSITY INC
T C U
2800 S University Dr, Fort Worth, TX 76129-0001
Tel (817) 257-7000 *Founded/Ownrshp* 1869
Sales 637.5MM *EMP* 3,400
Accts Pricewaterhousecoopers Llc Fo
SIC 8221 University
Chf Inves: Michael Garrison
Chf Inves: James Hille
Sr VP: David E Dmondson
VP: Julie Brandenburg
VP: Gillian Hogan
VP: Jake Neal
VP: Leah Reynolds

VP: Hillary Shepheard
Mng Dir: Kerry Cornelius
DP Exec: Maria Vega
Dir IT: David Edmondson

D-U-N-S 19-007-5143
TEXAS CITY OF FRISCO
6101 Frisco Square Blvd # 1000, Frisco, TX 75034-3239
Tel (972) 335-5555 *Founded/Ownrshp* 1902
Sales NA *EMP* 1,000
Accts Crowe Horwath Llp Dallas Tex
SIC 9111 Executive offices; City & town managers' offices
V Ch: Jim Wilson
Ofcr: Glynda Covington
Ofcr: Radd Rotello
Ofcr: Amy Smithart
Ofcr: Seth Yates
Snr Mgr: Greg Ward

D-U-N-S 55-567-2513
TEXAS CLOTHING HOLDING CORP
11511 Luna Rd, Dallas, TX 75234-6022
Tel (214) 956-4494 *Founded/Ownrshp* 2012
Sales 631.6MM^E *EMP* 3,205^E
SIC 2325 2311 2321 5611 Men's & boys' trousers & slacks; Slacks, dress: men's, youths' & boys'; Jeans: men's, youths' & boys'; Shorts (outerwear): men's, youths' & boys'; Tailored suits & formal jackets; Men's & boys' furnishings; Men's & boys' clothing stores

D-U-N-S 10-224-7793
TEXAS COMPETITIVE ELECTRIC HOLDINGS CO LLC
TXU ENERGY
(*Suby of* ENERGY FUTURE COMPETITIVE HOLDINGS CO LLC) ★
1601 Bryan St Ste 510, Dallas, TX 75201-3483
Tel (214) 812-4600 *Founded/Ownrshp* 2001
Sales 1.2MMM^E *EMP* 2,000^E
SIC 4911 4922 Electric services; Natural gas transmission
CEO: Jim Burke
**Ch Bd:* John F Young
**COO:* Scott A Hudson
CFO: Dan Farrell
**CFO:* Paul M Keglevic
Ex VP: David Campbell
**Sr VP:* David Faranetta
**VP:* Gabe Castro
**VP:* Cecily Small Gooch
**VP:* Floyd Nickerson
**VP:* Don Smith

D-U-N-S 06-237-9086
TEXAS COUNTY AND DISTRICT RETIREMENT SYSTEM
TCDRS
901 S Mopac, Austin, TX 78746
Tel (512) 328-8889 *Founded/Ownrshp* 1967
Sales 994.4MM *EMP* 108
Accts Kpmg Llp Austin Tx
SIC 6733 Trusts, except educational, religious, charity: management
Ex Dir: Gene Glass
CIO: Stephen Kell

D-U-N-S 02-649-8881 IMP
TEXAS CRUSHED STONE CO INC (TX)
5300 S Interstate 35, Georgetown, TX 78626-7764
Tel (512) 255-4405 *Founded/Ownrshp* 1947
Sales 91.7MM^E *EMP* 140
SIC 1422 2951 1442 Crushed & broken limestone; Asphalt paving mixtures & blocks; Construction sand & gravel
Pr: W B Snead
Sls Mgr: David Johnson
Board of Directors: W H Campbell, H T Cox, Clint Fraser, Lee Fulks, Jay C Sloan

D-U-N-S 04-656-3099 IMP
TEXAS DE BRAZIL (ADDISON) CORP
2952 N Stemmons Fwy, Dallas, TX 75247-6114
Tel (214) 615-2184 *Founded/Ownrshp* 1999
Sales 90.5MM^E *EMP* 1,500
SIC 5812 Ethnic food restaurants
CEO: Salah Izzedin
**Pr:* Leila Izzedin
**VP:* Salim Asrawi
Dir Soc: Marcia Avona
Dir Soc: Josh McCormick
Dir Soc: Anthony Quiles
Genl Mgr: Miguel Urbina
Snr Mgr: Leonardo Pierret

D-U-N-S 80-739-1529
TEXAS DEPARTMENT OF AGING AND DISABILITY SERVICES
(*Suby of* HEALTH AND HUMAN SERVICES COMMISSION TEXAS) ★
701 W 51st St, Austin, TX 78751-2312
Tel (512) 438-3011 *Founded/Ownrshp* 1965
Sales NA *EMP* 13,774^E
SIC 9441 Income maintenance programs;
COO: Lawrence Parker
**COO:* Tom Phillips
**CFO:* James Jenkins
Prgrm Mgr: Lena Brown-Owens
Prgrm Mgr: Mark Dermit
Prgrm Mgr: Nicole Matthews
Snr Ntwrk: Susan Hutchinson
QA Dir: Stacie Flenoy
IT Man: Alfonso Matamoros
Opers Mgr: Lisa Laney
Pr Mgr: Cecilia Cavuto

D-U-N-S 14-904-8006
TEXAS DEPARTMENT OF ASSISTIVE AND REHABILITATIVE SERVICES
(*Suby of* HEALTH AND HUMAN SERVICES COMMISSION TEXAS) ★
4900 N Lamar Blvd, Austin, TX 78751-2316
Tel (512) 424-4601 *Founded/Ownrshp* 2004
Sales NA *EMP* 3,000

SIC 9441 Administration of social & manpower programs;
Comm Man: Cassie L Fisher
Genl Mgr: Michael Hooks

D-U-N-S 07-338-9926
TEXAS DEPARTMENT OF CRIMINAL JUSTICE
(Suby of EXECUTIVE OFFICE OF STATE OF TEXAS) ★
861 Interstate 45 N 227b, Huntsville, TX 77320-1143
Tel (936) 295-6371 Founded/Ownrshp 1989
Sales NA EMP 42,000
SIC 9223 9229 Prison, government; ; Criminal justice statistics center, government;
Ex Dir: Brad Livingston
Exec: Robert Hurst
*Prin: Bryan Collier
*Ex Dir: Art Moseley
Dir IT: Michael Bell

D-U-N-S 80-678-1936
TEXAS DEPARTMENT OF INSURANCE
(Suby of EXECUTIVE OFFICE OF STATE OF TEXAS) ★
333 Guadalupe St Ste 2, Austin, TX 78701-3942
Tel (512) 463-6169 Founded/Ownrshp 1998
Sales NA EMP 900
SIC 6411 9651 Insurance agents, brokers & service; Insurance commission, government
CFO: Sandra Smith

D-U-N-S 80-678-0664
TEXAS DEPARTMENT OF MILITARY
(Suby of EXECUTIVE OFFICE OF STATE OF TEXAS) ★
2200 W 35th St Bldg 11, Austin, TX 78703-1222
Tel (512) 782-5001 Founded/Ownrshp 1845
Sales NA EMP 1,334
SIC 9711 National security;
Ex Dir: Maj Gen John Nichols
*Ex Dir: Major General John Nichols
Board of Directors: Duane Waddill

D-U-N-S 80-678-2272
TEXAS DEPARTMENT OF PUBLIC SAFETY
(Suby of EXECUTIVE OFFICE OF STATE OF TEXAS) ★
5805 N Lamar Blvd, Austin, TX 78752-4431
Tel (512) 424-2000 Founded/Ownrshp 2009
Sales NA EMP 3,916
SIC 9229 9221 Public order & safety statistics centers; ; Police protection;
Ofcr: Esther Corwin
Ofcr: Nathanael Haddox
Ofcr: Tim Hoffman
Ofcr: Jim Kelley
Ofcr: John Nelson
Ofcr: Fernando Perez
Ofcr: David Solis
Genl Mgr: Steve McCraw
Genl Couns: Duncan R Fox
Counsel: Janette Ansolabehere
Counsel: Elizabeth Goins

D-U-N-S 80-739-1511
TEXAS DEPARTMENT OF STATE HEALTH SERVICES
DSHS
(Suby of HEALTH AND HUMAN SERVICES COMMISSION TEXAS) ★
1100 W 49th St, Austin, TX 78756-3101
Tel (512) 776-6946 Founded/Ownrshp 1901
Sales NA EMP 11,900
SIC 9431 Administration of public health programs;
*CFO: Machelle Pharr
*CFO: Bill Wheeler
Ofcr: Dennis Dannels
Ofcr: Carrie Williams
Exec: Jerry Bradshaw
Off Mgr: Debbie Blount
Telecom Mg: Cynthia Galvan
Telecom Mg: Tracy Lisenby
Info Man: Javier Gonzalez
Prd Mgr: Carol Jackson
Snr PM: Sandy Crow

D-U-N-S 80-678-2553
TEXAS DEPARTMENT OF TRANSPORTATION
(Suby of EXECUTIVE OFFICE OF STATE OF TEXAS) ★
150 E Riverside Dr, Austin, TX 78704-1202
Tel (512) 463-8588 Founded/Ownrshp 1991
Sales NA EMP 14,720
SIC 9621 Regulation, administration of transportation;
Ex Dir: James M Bass
CFO: Brian Ragland
Ofcr: Lauren Garduno Pe
Ofcr: Dee Porter
VP: Alanna Humphries
VP: Graig Miser
Exec: Michael Peters
*Ex Dir: Marc D Williams
Brnch Mgr: Madjid Benchouia
Brnch Mgr: Eric Gleason
Brnch Mgr: Darryl Zercher

D-U-N-S 80-873-0360
TEXAS DEPT OF FAMILY AND PROTECTIVE SERVICES
(Suby of HEALTH AND HUMAN SERVICES COMMISSION TEXAS) ★
701 W 51st St, Austin, TX 78751-2312
Tel (512) 438-3240 Founded/Ownrshp 1993
Sales NA EMP 6,000
SIC 9441 Administration of social & manpower programs;
Dir IT: Beng Kuan
Netwrk Mgr: Sherly Scott
Tech Mgr: Gary Baker
Web Dev: Darren Dube

D-U-N-S 09-290-1214
TEXAS DISPOSAL SYSTEMS INC
TDS
12200 Carl Rd, Creedmoor, TX 78610-2184
Tel (512) 421-1300 Founded/Ownrshp 1977
Sales 389.0MM^E EMP 527
SIC 4953 Garbage: collecting, destroying & processing
CEO: Bobby Gregory
*Pr: Eddie Dick
*CFO: Tom Mistler
*VP: Jim Gregory
Genl Mgr: Lisa Oney

D-U-N-S 01-080-7279
TEXAS DOW EMPLOYEES CREDIT UNION
1001 Fm 2004 Rd, Lake Jackson, TX 77566-4012
Tel (979) 297-1154 Founded/Ownrshp 1954
Sales NA EMP 703
SIC 6062 State credit unions
CEO: Steph Sherrodd
Pr: Calvin Howell
*Pr: Ed Speed
*Ch: Marcus Stephenson
Treas: Peggy Miltenberger
*Treas: Ed Zingleman
Ofcr: Ronnie Mindiola
Ofcr: Cindy Rowe
*VP: Janice Arizmendi
VP: Matthew Diaz
VP: Gary Lanier
VP: Robert Lockett
*VP: Ron Miles
*VP: Paul Perdue
VP: Milton Stevens
VP: Bonnie Tucker
VP: Andrew Wayman
*VP: Lance Wortham

D-U-N-S 00-793-2908 IMP
■TEXAS EASTERN TRANSMISSION LP
(Suby of SPECTRA ENERGY CORP) ★
5400 Westheimer Ct, Houston, TX 77056-5353
Tel (713) 627-5400 Founded/Ownrshp 1947, 2007
Sales 946.0MM^E EMP 700
Accts Deloitte & Touche Llp Housto
SIC 4922 Pipelines, natural gas; Storage, natural gas
Pt: Martha B Wyrsch

D-U-N-S 00-792-4178
TEXAS ELECTRIC COOPERATIVES INC
1122 Colorado St Ste 2400, Austin, TX 78701-2167
Tel (512) 454-0311 Founded/Ownrshp 1940
Sales 200.0MM EMP 200
SIC 2491 3612 8621 Poles & pole crossarms, treated wood; Power & distribution transformers; Professional membership organizations
Pr: Mike Williams
CFO: Elizabeth Montoya CPA
Mfg Dir: Carlton Penney
Prd Mgr: Dacia Rivers
Sls Dir: Martin Bevins
Art Dir: Andy Doughty

D-U-N-S 80-808-4607
TEXAS ENERGY FUTURE HOLDINGS LIMITED PARTNERSHIP
TPG
301 Commerce St Ste 3300, Fort Worth, TX 76102-4133
Tel (817) 871-4000 Founded/Ownrshp 2007
Sales 17.3MMM^E EMP 15,750
SIC 4911 6211 Electric services; Generation, electric power; Transmission, electric power; Distribution, electric power; Investment firm, general brokerage
Pt: Karl Peterson
Pr: David Bonderman
CFO: John Viola
Chf Inves: Jonathan Coslet
Ofcr: David Reintjes
VP: David Brooks
VP: Daniel Frydman
VP: Paul D Hackwell
VP: Robert Kostow
VP: Elly Thio
VP: Gaurav Trehan
VP: David Trujillo
Exec: Carl Pascarella
Assoc Dir: Jackson Hildebrand
Assoc Dir: Vishal Shah

D-U-N-S 96-777-9570
TEXAS ENERGY SERVICES LP
4932 N Us Hwy 281, Alice, TX 78332
Tel (361) 664-5020 Founded/Ownrshp 2003
Sales 351.7MM^E EMP 415
SIC 1389 Oil field services
Genl Pt: John Crisp
Genl Pt: Charles C Forbes

D-U-N-S 08-215-6241 IMP
TEXAS ENTERPRISES INC
ALLIED SALES COMPANY
5005 E 7th St, Austin, TX 78702-5022
Tel (512) 385-2167 Founded/Ownrshp 1953
Sales 250.0MM EMP 205
SIC 5172 Lubricating oils & greases
Pr: F Ford Smith Jr
*CFO: Cody Douglas
*Treas: Allen Smith
VP: Melvin Williams

D-U-N-S 05-233-5788
■TEXAS EZPAWN MANAGEMENT INC
(Suby of EZCORP INC) ★
1901 Capital Pkwy, Austin, TX 78746-7613
Tel (512) 314-3400 Founded/Ownrshp 1993
Sales 91.8MM^E EMP 1,815^E
SIC 8741 Management services
Pr: Barry William Guest
*VP: Nanci Tucker
*VP: Thomas H Welch Jr

D-U-N-S 62-537-9813
TEXAS FARM BUREAU MUTUAL INSURANCE CO
FARM BUREAU INSURANCE
7420 Fish Pond Rd, Waco, TX 76710-1010
Tel (254) 772-3030 Founded/Ownrshp 1998
Sales NA EMP 550
SIC 6411 Insurance agents, brokers & service
Ex Dir: Vernie R Glasson
*Pr: Kenneth Dierschke
*Pr: Mike F Gerik
*Treas: Ron Lawson
Ex VP: Mike Gerik
*VP: Paul Ehlert
Sls&Mrk Ex: Bo Wilborn
Genl Couns: John Stephens
Board of Directors: Darren Callaway

D-U-N-S 83-629-3290
TEXAS GAMBLING HALL & HOTEL INC
(Suby of STATION CASINOS LLC) ★
2101 Texas Star Ln, North Las Vegas, NV 89032-3562
Tel (702) 631-1000 Founded/Ownrshp 1995
Sales 12.0MM^E EMP 1,300
SIC 7011 7999 5812 Casino hotel; Gambling establishment; Eating places
Pr: Frank J Fertitta III

D-U-N-S 82-618-6780
■TEXAS GAS SERVICE CO
(Suby of ONE GAS INC) ★
5602 E Grimes St, Harlingen, TX 78550-1818
Tel (956) 444-3900 Founded/Ownrshp 2008
Sales 57.6MM^E EMP 2,255^E
SIC 1311 Natural gas production

D-U-N-S 11-597-2101 IMP/EXP
■TEXAS GAS TRANSMISSION LLC
(Suby of BOARDWALK PIPELINES LP) ★
610 W 2nd St, Owensboro, KY 42301-0739
Tel (270) 926-8686 Founded/Ownrshp 2003
Sales 94.0MM^E EMP 604^E
SIC 4922 Pipelines, natural gas
CFO: Jamie L Buski
VP: James R Hendrix
VP: David Moseley
VP Opers: Jack Ralph

TEXAS GAS TRANSPORT
See NATURAL GAS SUPPLY LLC

D-U-N-S 18-561-5924
■TEXAS GENCO HOLDINGS INC
(Suby of NRG ENERGY INC) ★
12301 Kurland Dr, Houston, TX 77034-4812
Tel (281) 897-2610 Founded/Ownrshp 2001
Sales 407.4M^E EMP 1,564
SIC 4911 Electric services
Ch Bd: Jack Fusco

D-U-N-S 05-342-8611
TEXAS GUARANTEED STUDENT LOAN CORP
TGSLC
301 Sundance Pkwy, Round Rock, TX 78681-8004
Tel (512) 219-5700 Founded/Ownrshp 1980
Sales NA EMP 600
Accts Kpmg Llp Oklahoma City Ok
SIC 6111 Student Loan Marketing Association
Pr: Sue McMillin
Pr: Cal Abbott
Pr: Jim Zimmerman
VP: Kim Alexander
*VP: Lloyd Dodge Sr
VP: Dianne Ivy
VP: Andy Levy
VP: Carol Lindsey
VP: Deanne Varner
Dir Soc: Judy Cunningham
Snr Ntwrk: Javier Garcia

D-U-N-S 02-539-0164
TEXAS HEALTH ARLINGTON MEMORIAL HOSPITAL (TX)
(Suby of TEXAS HEALTH RESOURCES) ★
800 W Randol Mill Rd, Arlington, TX 76012-2504
Tel (682) 236-6695 Founded/Ownrshp 2009
Sales 252.9MM EMP 1,600
SIC 8062 General medical & surgical hospitals
Pr: Blake Kretz
*Pr: Kirk King
*VP: Donna Bertram
*VP: Bradford Davis

D-U-N-S 06-423-4636
TEXAS HEALTH HARRIS METHODIST HOSPITAL FORT WORTH
HARRIS MEDICAL LABORATORY
(Suby of TEXAS HEALTH RESOURCES) ★
1301 Pennsylvania Ave, Fort Worth, TX 76104-2122
Tel (817) 250-2000 Founded/Ownrshp 1999
Sales 713.2MM EMP 3,500
SIC 8062 General medical & surgical hospitals
Pr: Lillie Biggins
Chf Rad: William Reese
COO: Jeff Reecer
Bd of Dir: Bonita Hairston
Bd of Dir: Mitchel Kruger
Bd of Dir: Danny Mitchell
Bd of Dir: Scott Simms
*Ofcr: Joseph Prosser
Dir Rx: Randy Ball
Chf Nrs Of: Sharon Dingman
*Chf Nrs Of: Elaine Nelson

D-U-N-S 07-838-8055 IMP
TEXAS HEALTH PRESBYTERIAN HOSPITAL DALLAS
(Suby of ALECTO HEALTHCARE SERVICES LLC) ★
8200 Walnut Hill Ln, Dallas, TX 75231-4426
Tel (214) 345-6789 Founded/Ownrshp 1966
Sales 539.1MM^E EMP 3,200
SIC 8062 Hospital, affiliated with AMA residency
Pr: James Berg
*CFO: Bryan Craft
Ofcr: Aurora Esteves
Ofcr: Sherry Petrillo
Ex VP: Johnathan Scholl
VP: David Jackson
VP: Jim Logsdon
Dir Risk M: Jennifer Rainer
Chf Nrs Of: James D Edmonson
CIO: Edward Marx
Mktg Dir: Deena McAllister

D-U-N-S 01-971-6773
TEXAS HEALTH RESOURCES
612 E Lamar Blvd Ste 400, Arlington, TX 76011-4125
Tel (682) 236-7900 Founded/Ownrshp 1997
Sales 718.3MM EMP 21,277^E
SIC 8062 General medical & surgical hospitals
CEO: Barclay Berdan
Chf Rad: Glen Wilbert
*Pr: Charles W Boes
*CFO: Ronald R Long
Ofcr: June Gerson
Sr Ex VP: Stephen Hanson
*Ex VP: Harold Berenzweig
*Ex VP: Jeffrey L Canose
Ex VP: Mary A Garza
Ex VP: Mark Lester
Sr VP: Edward W Marx
VP: Luanne Armstrong
VP: Scott Auzenne
VP: James Berg
VP: Charles Boes
VP: Nommo Z Combs
VP: Tom Dennis
VP: Cynda Grimes
VP: Robert S Hewes
VP: Ken Kramer
VP: Jennifer Lee

D-U-N-S 16-892-2610
TEXAS HEART HOSPITAL OF SOUTHWEST LLP
BHCS
(Suby of BHCS) ★
1100 Allied Dr, Plano, TX 75093-5348
Tel (469) 241-8900 Founded/Ownrshp 2004
Sales 261.1MM EMP 139
SIC 8062 General medical & surgical hospitals
Pt: Mark Valentine
*Pt: Gary Brock
*VP: Morgan Brad

D-U-N-S 03-009-6314
TEXAS HEART INSTITUTE
2450 Holcombe Blvd # 341, Houston, TX 77021-2039
Tel (832) 828-1000 Founded/Ownrshp 2012
Sales 736.7MM EMP 2
SIC 8099 Health & allied services
Prin: Chris Born

D-U-N-S 07-314-4958
TEXAS HLTH HRS MTHDT HSPTL HEB
EDWARDS CANCER CENTER
(Suby of TEXAS HEALTH RESOURCES) ★
1615 Hospital Pkwy, Bedford, TX 76022-5934
Tel (817) 848-4000 Founded/Ownrshp 1997
Sales 258.8MM EMP 1,094
SIC 8062 8063 8069 General medical & surgical hospitals; Psychiatric hospitals; Drug addiction rehabilitation hospital
Pr: Fred N Ekery
Chf Rad: Eric Davis
Ofcr: Gail Shepperd
VP: Susann Land
Dir Lab: Sharon Harris
Off Mgr: Glenda Spivey
CIO: Kurt Crawford
Mktg Dir: Anna Riehm
Obsttrcn: Mark Messing
Doctor: Janice K Tomberlin MD

D-U-N-S 07-418-6743
TEXAS HOME HEALTH OF AMERICA LP
1455 Auto Center Dr # 200, Ontario, CA 91761-2239
Tel (972) 201-3800 Founded/Ownrshp 2005
Sales 98.6MM^E EMP 12,000
SIC 8049 Nurses, registered & practical
Pt: Steve Abshire
Pt: Judy Bishop
Pt: Mark Lamp
Pt: Duff Whitaker
CFO: Randy Kurtz
Ex Dir: Breta Galler
Ex Dir: Sharon Hoyng
Sales Exec: Earlynn Chesser

D-U-N-S 04-558-9579 IMP
TEXAS HYDRAULICS INC
PRECISE HARD CHROME
3410 Range Rd, Temple, TX 76504-1237
Tel (254) 778-4701 Founded/Ownrshp 2016
Sales 191.6MM^E EMP 1,000
SIC 3593 3443 Fluid power cylinders, hydraulic or pneumatic; Industrial vessels, tanks & containers
CEO: Michael G Clute
*Pr: Pascal A Gerard
*CFO: L C Gordon Jr
*VP: David Boothby
*Prin: Martin Gonzalez
*Prin: Karl Keip
Sfty Mgr: Dawn Wyatt
Manager: Bruno Hagstrom

D-U-N-S 04-108-3403 IMP
■TEXAS INDUSTRIES INC
TXI
(Suby of MARTIN MARIETTA MATERIALS INC) ★
1503 Lyndon B Johnson Fwy # 400, Dallas, TX 75234-6007
Tel (972) 647-6700 Founded/Ownrshp 2014
Sales 941.7MM^E EMP 2,040^E
SIC 3241 3299 3281 3273 Masonry cement; Sand lime products; Gravel painting; Limestone, cut & shaped; Ready-mixed concrete
Pr: C Howard Nye
*CFO: Anne H Lloyd
VP: Barry M Bone
VP: Phillip Gaynor
VP: James McCraw
Div Mgr: Barrett Reese
Genl Mgr: Vince Tate
Genl Mgr: Tom Zais
Sfty Mgr: Jess Gandy
Plnt Mgr: Gary Allen
Plnt Mgr: Kevin Deatley

D-U-N-S 00-732-1904 IMP/EXP
▲TEXAS INSTRUMENTS INC
12500 Ti Blvd, Dallas, TX 75243-0592
Tel (214) 479-3773 Founded/Ownrshp 1930
Sales 13.0MMM EMP 29,977
Accts Ernst & Young Llp Dallas Tex
Tkr Sym TXN Exch NGS

SIC 3674 3613 3822 3578 Microprocessors; Microcircuits, integrated (semiconductor); Computer logic modules; Memories, solid state; Power circuit breakers; Thermostats & other environmental sensors; Calculators & adding machines
CEO: Richard K Templeton
CFO: Kevin P March
Ex VP: Brian T Crutcher
Sr VP: Stephen A Anderson
Sr VP: Cynthia Hoff Trochu
Sr VP: Bing Xie
VP: Niels Anderskouv
VP: Paul J Fego
VP: Markus Perger
VP: Tom Springmeier
VP: Tim G Williams
Dir Soc: Michelle Raab
Board of Directors: Wayne R Sanders, Ralph W Babb Jr, Ruth J Simmons, Mark A Blinn, Christine Todd Whitman, Daniel A Carp, Janet F Clark, Carrie S Cox, Jean M Hobby, Ronald Kirk, Pamela H Patsley, Robert E Sanchez

TEXAS JASMINE WHOLESALE
See INDUS ENTERPRISES INC

D-U-N-S 02-168-1432 IMP
TEXAS KENWORTH CO
MHC KENWORTH
(*Suby of* MURPHY-HOFFMAN CO) ★
4040 Irving Blvd, Dallas, TX 75247-5886
Tel (214) 920-7300 *Founded/Ownrshp* 1975
Sales 89.3MM^E *EMP* 250
SIC 5012 5013 7513 7538 Trucks, commercial; Truck tractors; Automotive supplies & parts; Trailer parts & accessories; Truck leasing, without drivers; Truck rental, without drivers; Truck engine repair, except industrial
Pr: Tim Murphy
Genl Mgr: Steve Ellington
Sls Mgr: Bob Bowden

TEXAS LAND & CATTLE CO
See C C TEXAS INC

D-U-N-S 80-655-4171
TEXAS LANDFILL MANAGEMENT LLC
(*Suby of* TDS) ★
12200 Carl Rd, Creedmoor, TX 78610-2184
Tel (512) 421-1300 *Founded/Ownrshp* 2000
Sales 189.3MM^E *EMP* 300
SIC 4953 Refuse systems
CEO: Bob Gregory

D-U-N-S 00-793-7873
TEXAS LIFE INSURANCE CO
(*Suby of* WILTON REASSURANCE CO) ★
900 Washington Ave # 400, Waco, TX 76701-1283
Tel (254) 752-6521 *Founded/Ownrshp* 1901
Sales NA *EMP* 140
SIC 6311 Legal reserve life insurance
Pr: Steven P Cates
Ofcr: Doug Dixon
**VP:* Paul Anderson
VP: Ted Bianchi
**VP:* Carroll Fadal
VP: Francis George
**VP:* George Miller
**VP:* Larry Owens
**VP:* Steve Worley
Assoc Dir: Bill Richter
Assoc Dir: Dalila Richter

D-U-N-S 03-731-1172
TEXAS MEDICAL LIABILITY TRUST
MEDICAL MAL PRACTICE
901 S Mo Pac Expy V500, Austin, TX 78746-5942
Tel (512) 425-5800 *Founded/Ownrshp* 1978
Sales NA *EMP* 165^E
SIC 6321 Accident & health insurance
CEO: Bobby Ray Fields
Pr: Mike Mullen
**CFO:* C Ray Dernel
CFO: Pamela Hoernis
Sr VP: Jill McLain
VP: Debbie Giese
VP: Vincent Kasch
VP: Treg Russell
Dir Risk M: Stacy Patterson
Dir Bus: Patrick Ellis
Rgnl Mgr: Brian Dittmar

D-U-N-S 07-137-4052
TEXAS MUNICIPAL POWER AGENCY
TMPA
12824 Fm 244 Rd, Anderson, TX 77830-5642
Tel (936) 873-2013 *Founded/Ownrshp* 1976
Sales 121.7MM^E *EMP* 137
SIC 4911 Generation, electric power
Genl Mgr: Gary T Parsons
Ofcr: Mandy Schaefer
Sfty Mgr: Timothy D Sanfor
Plnt Mgr: Craig York

D-U-N-S 78-508-0037
TEXAS MUTUAL INSURANCE CO
6210 E Hwy 290, Austin, TX 78723-1098
Tel (512) 322-3800 *Founded/Ownrshp* 1991
Sales NA *EMP* 790
SIC 6331 Workers' compensation insurance
Bd of Dir: Bob Barnes
Sr VP: Terry Frakes
Sr VP: Gloria Lara
Sr VP: Steve Math
VP: Mike Barron
VP: Lynette Caldwell
VP: Kim Haugaard
VP: Curtis Johnson Jr
VP: Randy Johnson
VP: Jeff Lentz
VP: Jo Norton
Exec: Cindy Smith
Board of Directors: Linda Foster, Bernie Francis, Eric Oliver

TEXAS ORTHOPEDIC HOSPITAL
See ORTHOPEDIC HOSPITAL LTD

TEXAS PACIFIC GROUP
See TPG CAPITAL MANAGEMENT LP

D-U-N-S 10-264-7005 IMP/EXP
TEXAS PETROCHEMICALS LP
(*Suby of* TPC GROUP LLC) ★
8600 Park Place Blvd, Houston, TX 77017-2599
Tel (713) 477-9211 *Founded/Ownrshp* 1973
Sales 137.7MM^E *EMP* 283
SIC 2869 Butadiene (industrial organic chemical)
Pr: Charles W Shaver
**CFO:* Robert R Whitlow
Sr VP: Luis Batiz
Sr VP: Michael White
IT Man: Anthony Passwater
Opers Mgr: Haskell Berry
S&M/VP: Ron Wolliver

D-U-N-S 61-901-0770
TEXAS PETROLEUM INVESTMENT CO INC
5850 San Felipe St # 250, Houston, TX 77057-8007
Tel (713) 789-9225 *Founded/Ownrshp* 1989
Sales 1.6MMM^E *EMP* 160^E
SIC 1382

D-U-N-S 00-895-0321 IMP/EXP
TEXAS PIPE AND SUPPLY CO LTD
INSTALLOY
2330 Holmes Rd, Houston, TX 77051-1098
Tel (713) 799-9235 *Founded/Ownrshp* 1918
Sales 564.4MM^E *EMP* 500
Accts Harper & Pearson Company Pc
SIC 5051 Pipe & tubing, steel
Ch Bd: Jerry R Rubenstein
**Pt:* Maury Rubenstein
**Pr:* Keith Rubenstein
**CFO:* Carl Lenz
Treas: Rusty Rubenstein
Sr VP: James R Dunn
VP: Bo Rubenstein
IT Man: Tim Barth
IT Man: Clint Kohler
IT Man: Bob Meyer
Manager: Lorenzo Villarreal

D-U-N-S 00-894-9182 IMP
TEXAS PLYWOOD AND LUMBER CO INC
1001 E Avenue K, Grand Prairie, TX 75050-2638
Tel (972) 262-1331 *Founded/Ownrshp* 1953
Sales 89.7MM^E *EMP* 131
SIC 5031 2431 Lumber: rough, dressed & finished; Plywood; Millwork; Molding, all materials; Doors, wood
Pr: Geoffrey M Yates
Pr: Bill Farmer
COO: Jim Coleman
Opers Mgr: Chris Jacobs

D-U-N-S 14-466-3213
TEXAS REGIONAL DELAWARE INC
TEXAS STATE BANK
(*Suby of* TEXAS REGIONAL BANCSHARES, INC.)
3900 N 10th St Fl 11, McAllen, TX 78501-1993
Tel (956) 631-5400 *Founded/Ownrshp* 1997
Sales NA *EMP* 1,500
SIC 6022 6541 State commercial banks; Title search companies
CEO: Glen Roney
**CFO:* R T Pigott Jr
Ex VP: Rod Pittman
**VP:* Susan Dietz
VP: Linda L Faulconer
VP: Arden Hills
VP: Nicole Spoor
**Exec:* Paul S Moxley
Mktg Dir: Ann Hoelscher

D-U-N-S 07-613-8416
■TEXAS ROADHOUSE HOLDINGS LLC
(*Suby of* TEXAS ROADHOUSE INC) ★
6040 Dutchmans Ln Ste 400, Louisville, KY 40205-3358
Tel (502) 426-9984 *Founded/Ownrshp* 1997
Sales 421.9MM^E *EMP* 9,700
SIC 5812 6794 Steak restaurant; Patent owners & lessors

D-U-N-S 14-822-8351
▲TEXAS ROADHOUSE INC
6040 Dutchmans Ln Ste 200, Louisville, KY 40205-3305
Tel (502) 426-9984 *Founded/Ownrshp* 1993
Sales 1.8MMM *EMP* 47,900^E
Tkr Sym TXRH *Exch* NGS
SIC 5812 6794 Restaurant, family: chain; Franchises, selling or licensing
Ch Bd: W Kent Taylor
Mng Pt: Paul Ashton
Pr: Scott M Colosi
Chf Mktg O: S Chris Jacobsen
Pr Dir: Mary Palmer
Board of Directors: Gregory N Moore, James F Parker, James R Ramsey, Kathleen M Widmer, James R Zarley

D-U-N-S 06-896-8734
TEXAS SCOTTISH RITE HOSPITAL FOR CHILDREN
SCOTTISH HOSPITAL FOR CHILDREN
2222 Welborn St, Dallas, TX 75219-3924
Tel (214) 559-5000 *Founded/Ownrshp* 1921
Sales 185.7MM *EMP* 850^E
Accts Ernst & Young Llp Dallas Tx
SIC 8069 Children's hospital
Ch Bd: Lyndon L Olson Jr
**Pr:* J C Montgomery Jr
**Pr:* Robert Walker
**Treas:* J M Willson Jr
**V Ch Bd:* Harold D Carter
**V Ch Bd:* Lee Drain
Chf Mktg O: Mark Murphey
Ofcr: Jacqueline Baer
Ofcr: Elayne Esterline
Ofcr: Manny Mendoza
Ofcr: Terry Murphy
**VP:* M Douglas Adkins
**VP:* Fred E Allen
VP: Mark Bateman
**VP:* Stephanie Brigger
**VP:* Daniel H Chapman
**VP:* Graham H Childress
VP: Donald Corben-Smith
**VP:* Lori Dalton
**VP:* Vester T Hughes Jr
**VP:* Kristina L Keever-Smith

D-U-N-S 07-954-8564
TEXAS SCOTTISH RITE HOSPITAL FOR CRIPPLED CHILDREN
2222 Welborn St, Dallas, TX 75219-3924
Tel (214) 559-5000 *Founded/Ownrshp* 1921
Sales 648.0MM *EMP* 800
SIC 8069 Orthopedic hospital
Pr: Robert L Walker

D-U-N-S 05-029-8975
TEXAS SOUTHERN UNIVERSITY
TSU
3100 Cleburne St, Houston, TX 77004-4598
Tel (713) 313-7011 *Founded/Ownrshp* 1947
Sales 105.8MM *EMP* 1,000^E
Accts Whitley Penn Houston Texas
SIC 8221 University
Pr: John M Rudley
Ofcr: Lames Junior
Ofcr: Ivory Scott
Ex VP: James Douglas
Sr VP: Charlene Evans
Sr VP: Gayla B Thomas
VP: Lynn Rodriguez
VP: William Saunders
VP: Kimberly Williams
VP: Bruce Wilson
Comm Dir: Charlotte Washington

D-U-N-S 82-585-2478
TEXAS STAFFING SERVICES INC
TRENDSETTER STAFFING
3000 Richmond Ave Ste 120, Houston, TX 77098-3188
Tel (713) 522-4800 *Founded/Ownrshp* 1993
Sales 86.2MM^E *EMP* 60
Accts Steven E Weil & Co Cpas Pc
SIC 7363 Employee leasing service
Pr: Charles Joekel
**COO:* Pat Tammaro
**Ex VP:* Bruce Gear
**VP:* Linda Robertson

D-U-N-S 13-661-0172 IMP
TEXAS STAR NUT AND FOOD CO INC
NATURES EAT
206 Market Ave, Boerne, TX 78006-3003
Tel (830) 249-8300 *Founded/Ownrshp* 2001
Sales 105.1MM^E *EMP* 70
SIC 5145 2068 Nuts, salted or roasted; Nuts: dried, dehydrated, salted or roasted
Pr: John C Taylor Jr
CFO: Susan Facile
Off Mgr: Barbara Walker
Ql Cn Mgr: Kelly Carver

TEXAS STATE BANK
See TEXAS REGIONAL DELAWARE INC

D-U-N-S 06-898-6645
TEXAS STATE TECHNICAL COLLEGE
TSTC SYSTEM
3801 Campus Dr Bldg 3210, Waco, TX 76705-1696
Tel (254) 799-3611 *Founded/Ownrshp* 1965
Sales 148.8MM *EMP* 1,474
SIC 8221 8222 Colleges universities & professional schools; Technical institute
**Pr:* Elton E Stuckly Jr
Assoc VP: Javier De Leon
Assoc VP: Cindy Reily
**Ex VP:* Rob Wolaver
VP: Kevin Dorton
**VP:* Paul Woodfin
Ex Dir: Lynda Y Lopez
Store Mgr: Greg Guercio
Dir IT: Patrick Davison
Dir IT: Richard Martin
IT Man: David Kofnovec

D-U-N-S 10-140-5814
TEXAS STATE UNIVERSITY SYSTEM
208 E 10th St Ste 600, Austin, TX 78701-2407
Tel (512) 463-1808 *Founded/Ownrshp* 1911
Sales 6.2MM *EMP* 3,196
SIC 8221 University
Ofcr: Linda Camarillo
Pr Dir: Mike Wintemute
Genl Couns: Diane Corley
Genl Couns: Nelly Herrera

D-U-N-S 07-460-2368
TEXAS STATE UNIVERSITY-SAN MARCOS
ASSOCIATE VP OF RESEARCH
(*Suby of* TEXAS STATE UNIVERSITY SYSTEM) ★
601 University Dr, San Marcos, TX 78666-4684
Tel (512) 245-2111 *Founded/Ownrshp* 1899
Sales 436.7MM *EMP* 3,156
SIC 8221 University
Pr: Denise Trauth
Pr: Valerie R Van Vlack
Treas: Terrance Ondreyka
Treas: Valarie Van Vlack
VP: Juan M Guerra Jr
VP: Carl E Laky
VP: Nancy Nusbaum
VP: Rebecca Prince
VP: Joanne Smith
VP: Carl Van Wyatt
**Prin:* Bill Covington

D-U-N-S 01-766-4611
TEXAS STATION GAMBLING HALL & HOTEL INC
SAN LORENZO ITALIAN RESTAURANT
(*Suby of* STATION CASINOS LLC) ★
2101 Texas Star Ln, North Las Vegas, NV 89032-3562
Tel (702) 631-1000 *Founded/Ownrshp* 1995
Sales 14.7MM^E *EMP* 1,300
SIC 7011 7993 Casino hotel; Slot machines; Gambling machines, coin-operated
Pr: Frank Fertitta III
**COO:* William Warner
**CFO:* Glenn Christenson
**VP:* Lorenzo Fertitta

D-U-N-S 01-048-4673 IMP/EXP
TEXAS STEEL CONVERSION INC
3101 Holmes Rd, Houston, TX 77051-1199
Tel (713) 733-6013 *Founded/Ownrshp* 1976
Sales 100.7MM^E *EMP* 450
SIC 3498 Fabricated pipe & fittings
**Pr:* Brian Binau
CFO: Bob Hall
Sr VP: Roland Wilson
VP: Alfred Cox
VP: Frank Serna

D-U-N-S 03-758-6273 IMP
■TEXAS STEEL PROCESSING INC
TEXAS STEEL'S
(*Suby of* JOSEPH T RYERSON & SON INC) ★
5480 Windfern Rd, Houston, TX 77041-7512
Tel (281) 822-3200 *Founded/Ownrshp* 2010
Sales 85.8MM *EMP* 125
SIC 5051 Black plate, iron or steel
CFO: Jack Southern
**Treas:* Robert J Joubran
**VP:* Stephen T Zollo

TEXAS STEEL'S
See TEXAS STEEL PROCESSING INC

D-U-N-S 08-495-8933
■TEXAS STERLING CONSTRUCTION CO
T S C
(*Suby of* STERLING CONSTRUCTION CO INC) ★
20810 Fernbush Dr, Houston, TX 77073-3599
Tel (281) 821-9091 *Founded/Ownrshp* 1955
Sales 209.0MM *EMP* 1,143
Accts Grant Thornton Llp Houston T
SIC 1611 1623 Concrete construction: roads, highways, sidewalks, etc.; Water main construction
Pr: Peter J Holland
**CFO:* James Allen Jr
Treas: Karen Stempinski
**Ex VP:* Terry D Williamson
**VP:* William G Garrison
**VP:* Joseph P Harper Jr
**VP:* William B Mitchell

D-U-N-S 60-998-0727
TEXAS TECH UNIVERSITY HEALTH SCIENCES CENTER
TTUHSC
(*Suby of* TEXAS TECH UNIVERSITY SYSTEM) ★
4004 82nd St C, Lubbock, TX 79423-2065
Tel (806) 743-1842 *Founded/Ownrshp* 1969
Sales 367.7MM^E *EMP* 5,017
SIC 8221 University
Pr: Tedd Mitchell
**Ex VP:* Elmo M Cavin Jr
VP: Glen Provost
Exec: Zoe Metcalf
Assoc Dir: Suzanna Cisneros

D-U-N-S 04-136-7053
TEXAS TECH UNIVERSITY SYSTEM
2500 Broadway, Lubbock, TX 79409
Tel (806) 742-2011 *Founded/Ownrshp* 1923
Sales 692.3MM^E *EMP* 6,635
SIC 8221 University
Pr: David Schmidt
CFO: Kyle Clark
Bd of Dir: Bob McComb
Assoc VP: Brent Ross
Ex VP: Sergey Nikishin
VP: Mallory Allred
VP: Sriya Das
VP: Mary Diaz
VP: Clara Garcia
VP: Juan Sanchez Munoz
Assoc Dir: Jon M Bernal
Assoc Dir: Paul Blake
Assoc Dir: Daniel Burns
Assoc Dir: Don Davis
Assoc Dir: Ken Gassiot
Assoc Dir: Zane Reif
Assoc Dir: Kathryn R Suchy

TEXAS TRUCK CENTERS OF HOUSTON
See INTERNATIONAL TRUCKS OF HOUSTON LLC

D-U-N-S 05-188-9731
TEXAS UNITED CORP (TX)
4800 San Felipe St, Houston, TX 77056-3908
Tel (713) 877-1793 *Founded/Ownrshp* 1970
Sales 376.6MM^E *EMP* 378
SIC 1479 2819 4619 2899 3299 7353 Amblygonite mining; Sodium & potassium compounds, exc. bleaches, alkalies, alum.; Brine; Slurry pipeline operation; Salt; Ceramic fiber; Heavy construction equipment rental
Ch Bd: Iris P Webre
**Pr:* R W Sneed
**CEO:* Wayne Sneed
**Treas:* Stacey Owens
**Sr VP:* Cathy Gillis
VP: Scott Whitelaw

TEXAS WASATCH GROUP
See TEXAS WASATCH INSURANCE SERVICES LP

D-U-N-S 15-292-6320
TEXAS WASATCH INSURANCE SERVICES LP
TEXAS WASATCH GROUP
100 E Royal Ln Ste 320, Irving, TX 75039-4223
Tel (214) 838-5500 *Founded/Ownrshp* 2003
Sales NA *EMP* 138^E
SIC 6411 6799 Insurance agents, brokers & service; Investors
Ch Bd: Mark Jones
**V Ch:* Robyn Jones
**COO:* Michael Colby
Mng Dir: Matthew Colby
Off Mgr: Stracy McShurley
Sls Dir: Gary Delavan

D-U-N-S 07-315-7844
TEXAS WESLEYAN UNIVERSITY (TX)
1204 Nicole St Apt 1603, Fort Worth, TX 76120-4144
Tel (817) 531-4444 *Founded/Ownrshp* 1890

Sales 103.3MM *EMP* 480
Accts Lb Bkd Llp Fort Worth Tx
SIC 8221 University
Pr: Harold Jeffcoat
CFO: Carolyn Hiebert
Trst: Martin Frost
Trst: Frank Turrella
Assoc VP: Steve Roberts
VP: Pati Alexander
VP: Chadd Bridwell
VP: Caren Handleman
**VP:* Dave Voskuil
Exec: Krista H Bailey
Ex Dir: Chris Cohen

D-U-N-S 01-398-7421
TEXAS WESTERN MANAGEMENT PARTNERS LP
13747 Montfort Dr Ste 115, Dallas, TX 75240-4493
Tel (469) 385-6248 *Founded/Ownrshp* 2008
Sales 66.6MM^E *EMP* 1,800^E
SIC 7011 Hotels
Mng Pt: Gene Carter
Sr VP: William Bagwell
VP Sls: Sarah Williams
Mktg Mgr: Sunny Brewer

D-U-N-S 60-552-0345
TEXAS WINGS INC
HOOTERS
1815 The Exchange Se, Atlanta, GA 30339-2027
Tel (770) 799-2241 *Founded/Ownrshp* 1989
Sales 54.9MM^E *EMP* 2,500
SIC 5812 American restaurant
Pr: Kelly Hall
**Ex VP:* Scott Wilkinson

D-U-N-S 06-897-9848
TEXAS WOMANS UNIVERSITY FOUNDATION
304 Administration Dr, Denton, TX 76204
Tel (940) 898-3525 *Founded/Ownrshp* 1901
Sales 160.3MM^E *EMP* 1,200
SIC 8221 University
Ch: Nancy Millichamp
**Pr:* Ann Stuart
**Treas:* Brenda Floyd
Bd of Dir: William Bussman
Assoc VP: Gary Ray
VP: Elizabeth Snapp
Genl Mgr: Don Stauldint
Sfty Dirs: Vicki Byrd
Pgrm Dir: Rob Maurer

D-U-N-S 02-320-3306
TEXAS-HEALTH-PHYSICIANS-GROUP
THPG
(*Suby of* TEXAS HEALTH RESOURCES) ★
9229 Lbj Fwy Ste 250, Dallas, TX 75243-4403
Tel (214) 860-6300 *Founded/Ownrshp* 1995
Sales 427.2MM *EMP* 8^E
SIC 8099 Medical services organization
Pr: Shawn Parsley

D-U-N-S 00-792-9441
■**TEXAS-NEW MEXICO POWER CO** (TX)
TNMP
(*Suby of* T N P ENTERPRISES INC) ★
577 N Garden Ridge Blvd, Lewisville, TX 75067-2691
Tel (972) 420-4189 *Founded/Ownrshp* 1925, 1963
Sales 287.9MM *EMP* 351^E
SIC 4911 Generation, electric power; Transmission, electric power; Distribution, electric power
CEO: Patricia K Collawn
VP: John Edwards
VP: Thomas G Sategna
CIO: Georgia Chambers
Board of Directors: Ron N Darnell, Charles N Eldred, Ron E Talbot, Neal Walker

D-U-N-S 00-361-5528
TEXICAN INDUSTRIAL ENERGY MARKETING LLC
1 Allen Ctr Ste 1150, Houston, TX 77002
Tel (713) 650-6579 *Founded/Ownrshp* 1999
Sales 265.0MM *EMP* 7
SIC 4924
CEO: Robert Blevins
**Pr:* Paul Hyland
**CFO:* Alan Griffin

D-U-N-S 15-722-0096
TEXICAN NATURAL GAS CO
1 Allen Ctr 1 Allen Center, Houston, TX 77002
Tel (713) 650-6579 *Founded/Ownrshp* 1985
Sales 289.0MM^E *EMP* 15
Accts Warren Averett Kimbrough & M
SIC 4923 Gas transmission & distribution
Pr: Robert Blevins
**CFO:* A Alan Griffin
VP: Skip Redd
VP: Jeff Zarr

D-U-N-S 06-423-8017
TEXLAND PETROLEUM LP
777 Main St Ste 3200, Fort Worth, TX 76102-5344
Tel (817) 336-2751 *Founded/Ownrshp* 1973
Sales 373.0MM^E *EMP* 70^E
SIC 1311 1382

D-U-N-S 96-956-1141
TEXOMA HEALTHCARE SYSTEM
1000 Memorial Dr, Denison, TX 75020-2035
Tel (903) 416-4000 *Founded/Ownrshp* 1997
Sales 50.8MM^E *EMP* 1,200
Accts Pricewaterhousecoopers Llp
SIC 8062 8059 General medical & surgical hospitals; Personal care home, with health care
Pr: Arthur L Hoenberger
**CFO:* Bobby Pruiett
**Ex VP:* Harry Kirshman

D-U-N-S 60-246-8969 EXP
TEXON DISTRIBUTING LP
11757 Katy Fwy Ste 1400, Houston, TX 77079-1725
Tel (281) 531-8400 *Founded/Ownrshp* 1997
Sales 185.9MM^E *EMP* 100
SIC 5172 Petroleum products

CEO: Terry Looper
COO: Ronnie Andrews
CFO: Leonard Russo
Treas: Lou Torczynski
Sr VP: Mark Johnson
Sr VP: Reid E Smith
VP: Tom Burns
VP: Cyndi Smink
VP: Gary Wawak
VP: Robert Willette
Genl Mgr: Kent Nettleingham

D-U-N-S 02-593-0678
TEXOR PETROLEUM CO INC
3340 Harlem Ave, Riverside, IL 60546-2126
Tel (708) 447-1999 *Founded/Ownrshp* 1974
Sales 207.2MM^E *EMP* 104
SIC 5172 5541 Gasoline; Filling stations, gasoline
CEO: Thomas E Gleitsman
**Pr:* Anthony E Speiser
**Ex VP:* Michael Lins
**Sr VP:* Barry Trilla
**VP:* William McCloskey
Genl Mgr: Bill McCloskey
Store Mgr: Jerri Blanton
Store Mgr: Scot Gray
VP Mktg: William Shireman

D-U-N-S 12-159-8379
TEXPAR ENERGY LLC
(*Suby of* PETROENERGY LLC) ★
920 10th Ave N, Onalaska, WI 54650-2166
Tel (800) 323-7350 *Founded/Ownrshp* 2005
Sales 176.2MM^E *EMP* 83
SIC 5171 4925 5172 Petroleum bulk stations & terminals; Mixed natural & manufactured gas, distribution; Diesel fuel
Pr: Scott P Mathy
VP: Bob Ploetz
Genl Mgr: Leon Glenn

D-U-N-S 00-102-3621 IMP/EXP
TEXTILE RUBBER AND CHEMICAL CO INC (GA)
TEXACOTE
1300-1350 Tiarco Dr Sw, Dalton, GA 30721
Tel (706) 277-1300 *Founded/Ownrshp* 1956
Sales 355.6MM^E *EMP* 450
SIC 5169 2821 Synthetic rubber; Elastomers, nonvulcanizable (plastics)
CEO: Frederick H Howalt III
CFO: Christopher Horton
**CFO:* J Christopher Horton

D-U-N-S 18-054-8729 IMP/EXP
TEXTILES FROM EUROPE INC
VICTORIA CLASSICS
5901 W Side Ave Fl 6, North Bergen, NJ 07047-6451
Tel (212) 213-1828 *Founded/Ownrshp* 1987
Sales 86.6MM^E *EMP* 190^E
SIC 5131 Knit fabrics; Textiles, woven
**Ch Bd:* Haskel Cohen
**Pr:* Toby Cohen
**COO:* Marcelo Slutzky
**Ex VP:* Albert Sasson
**VP:* Lisa Brier

TEXTRON AVIATION
See CESSNA AIRCRAFT CO

TEXTRON AVIATION
See BEECHCRAFT CORP

D-U-N-S 07-988-0866
■**TEXTRON AVIATION INC** (KS)
(*Suby of* TEXTRON INC) ★
1 Cessna Blvd, Wichita, KS 67215-1400
Tel (316) 517-6000 *Founded/Ownrshp* 2014
Sales 4.5MMM^E *EMP* 20,424^E
SIC 4581 Airports, flying fields & services
Pr: Scott Ernest
Sr VP: Kriya Shortt
VP: Ron Draper
VP: Marcelo Moreira
VP: David Nolte
VP: Jessica Pruss
VP: Brian Rohloff
Prgrm Mgr: Christopher Kidd
Area Mgr: Mike Van Hart
Genl Mgr: Tony Balestracci
Dir IT: Krista Taylor

TEXTRON DEFENSE SYSTEMS
See TEXTRON SYSTEMS CORP

D-U-N-S 00-133-8979 IMP/EXP
▲**TEXTRON INC**
40 Westminster St, Providence, RI 02903-2525
Tel (401) 421-2800 *Founded/Ownrshp* 1923
Sales 13.4MMM *EMP* 35,000^E
Tkr Sym TXT *Exch* NYS
SIC 3721 3724 3728 3799 3829 3546 Aircraft; Airplanes, fixed or rotary wing; Helicopters; Aircraft engines & engine parts; Aircraft parts & equipment; Recreational vehicles; Golf carts, powered; Aircraft & motor vehicle measurement equipment; Power-driven handtools
Ch Bd: Scott C Donnelly
COO: Frederick M Strader
CFO: Frank T Connor
Chf Cred: E Robert Lupone
Ex VP: Cheryl H Johnson
Sr VP: R Siisi Adu-Gyamfi
Sr VP: Kevin J Cosgriff
Sr VP: Robert Hotaling
Sr VP: John King
VP: Mark S Bamford
VP: Jim Dolan
VP: Stewart Holmes
VP: Lou King
VP: Paul McGartoll
VP: Paul Rerick
VP: Jeff Rose
VP: Diane K Schwarz
VP: Jeff Spielvogel
Board of Directors: James L Ziemer, Kathleen M Bader, Maria T Zuber, R Kerry Clark, James T Conway, Ivor J Evans, Lawrence K Fish, Paul E Gagne, Dain M Hancock, Lord Powell, Lloyd G Trotter

D-U-N-S 00-136-7903 IMP/EXP
■**TEXTRON LYCOMING CORP**
(*Suby of* TEXTRON INC) ★
40 Westminster St, Providence, RI 02903-2525
Tel (401) 421-2800 *Founded/Ownrshp* 1985
Sales 188.7MM^E *EMP* 862
SIC 3728 3724 Aircraft parts & equipment; Wing assemblies & parts, aircraft; Aircraft engines & engine parts
Ch Bd: James F Hardymon
**CEO:* Scott C Donnelly
**COO:* Lewis B Campbell
**Ex VP:* Thomas P Hollowell
**Ex VP:* William F Wayland
**VP:* Frank T Connor
**VP:* Adele Suddes
**VP:* Douglas R Wilburne

TEXTRON SYSTEMS
See AAI CORP

D-U-N-S 12-413-1124 IMP
■**TEXTRON SYSTEMS CORP**
TEXTRON DEFENSE SYSTEMS
(*Suby of* TEXTRON LYCOMING CORP) ★
201 Lowell St, Wilmington, MA 01887-4113
Tel (978) 657-5111 *Founded/Ownrshp* 1966
Sales 146.7MM^E *EMP* 710
SIC 3483 5088 Ammunition components; Transportation equipment & supplies
Pr: Ellen Lord
**COO:* Jack Cronin
CFO: Robert Sullivan
**Treas:* Mary F Lovejoy
Ex VP: Jim Dolan
Sr VP: Kevin J Cosgriff
Sr VP: Stuart Grief
Sr VP: Dan Hanlon
Sr VP: Robert Powers
VP: John Cancellara
**VP:* Julie Duffy
**VP:* Dana L Goldberg
**VP:* Paul Mc Gartoll
VP: Brian Sinkiewicz
VP: Tom Walmsley
Exec: Dottie Crisa
Dir Surg: Dennis Racine

D-U-N-S 19-591-6403
■**TEXTURA CORP**
(*Suby of* ORACLE CORP) ★
1405 Lake Cook Rd, Deerfield, IL 60015-5213
Tel (866) 839-8872 *Founded/Ownrshp* 2016
Sales 86.7MM *EMP* 580
SIC 7372 Prepackaged software
Pr: Patrick Allin
**CFO:* Jillian Sheehan
**Ex VP:* Michael Antis
**Ex VP:* Linda Debruin
**Ex VP:* David Kelly
VP: Nikki Mehta
VP: Andy Nissenberg
Mktg Mgr: Kate Hubbard
Counsel: Heidi Gluck

TEXTUS GROUP
See MOMENTUM TEXTILES LLC

D-U-N-S 96-692-9957 IMP
TEYMA USA & ABENER ENGINEERING AND CONSTRUCTION SERVICES PARTNERSHIP
ABENGOA SOLAR
(*Suby of* ABENGOA SA)
57750 S Painted Rock Rd, Phoenix, AZ 85012
Tel (303) 928-8500 *Founded/Ownrshp* 2010
Sales 85.3MM^E *EMP* 120
Accts Pricewatehousecoopers Llp Den
SIC 3433 Solar heaters & collectors
CEO: Leonardo Maccio

D-U-N-S 02-057-2398 IMP/EXP
TEYS (USA) INC
770 N Halsted St Ste 202, Chicago, IL 60642-6930
Tel (312) 492-7163 *Founded/Ownrshp* 2000, 2006
Sales 350.3MM *EMP* 9
Accts Bansley And Kiener Llp Chica
SIC 2011 Beef products from beef slaughtered on site
Ch Bd: Allan Teys
**Pr:* Michael Forrest
**CEO:* Brad Teys

D-U-N-S 79-900-9410
TF COURIER INC
(*Suby of* TFI HOLDINGS USA INC) ★
5429 Lyndon B Johnson Fwy, Dallas, TX 75240-2607
Tel (214) 560-9000 *Founded/Ownrshp* 2011
Sales 228.6MM^E *EMP* 800
SIC 4513 4215 8741 Air courier services; Courier services, except by air; Management services
Pr: Scott Leveridge
Ofcr: Beverly Santiago
VP: David Fenty
**VP:* Richard Gray
**VP:* Gilbert Jones
VP: Andrew Pardue
VP: Richard Pople
VP: Jim Witmer
Mgt/VP: Andy Argento
Brnch Mgr: David Kardos
Opers Supe: Cesar Lopez

D-U-N-S 93-324-1382
TF FINAL MILE LLC
DYNAMEX OR HAZEN FINAL MILE
(*Suby of* TF COURIER INC) ★
5429 Lbj Fwy Ste 900, Dallas, TX 75240-2664
Tel (214) 560-9000 *Founded/Ownrshp* 2015
Sales 160.9MM^E *EMP* 700
SIC 4215 4513 Courier services, except by air; Air courier services
Pr: James Welch

D-U-N-S 16-194-9011
TF INTER-HOLDINGS INC
17141 State Road 4, Goshen, IN 46528-6674
Tel (574) 533-0302 *Founded/Ownrshp* 1948

Sales 168.7MM^E *EMP* 270
SIC 5147 4213 5144 Meats & meat products; Refrigerated products transport; Poultry products
Pr: Paris-Ball Miller
**CFO:* Neal Yoder

TFC CANOPY
See CENTURION INDUSTRIES INC

TFCU
See TEACHERS FEDERAL CREDIT UNION

D-U-N-S 02-037-4146 EXP
TFE LOGISTICS GROUP INC
(*Suby of* IMSCO) ★
3633 Wheeler Rd Ste 350, Augusta, GA 30909-6545
Tel (706) 855-1014 *Founded/Ownrshp* 1975
Sales 224.1MM^E *EMP* 1,500
SIC 1541 Industrial buildings & warehouses
Pr: Nancy C Hall
**Pr:* David W Bowles
**CFO:* Robert Prugar
**Treas:* Tammy A Bridgers
IT Man: Frank Deroller

D-U-N-S 07-831-8401
TFI HOLDINGS USA INC
(*Suby of* TRANSFORCE INC)
5429 L B Johnson Fwy 10 Ste 1000, Dallas, TX 75240
Tel (877) 396-2639 *Founded/Ownrshp* 2011
Sales 231.4MM^E *EMP* 815^E
SIC 4215 8741 4513 Courier services, except by air; Management services; Air courier services
Pr: Alain Bedard

D-U-N-S 00-321-9615 IMP
TFI WIND DOWN INC
THOMASVILLE FURNITURE
1925 Eastchester Dr, High Point, NC 27265-1404
Tel (336) 472-4000 *Founded/Ownrshp* 1996, 2013
Sales 933.5MM^E *EMP* 4,320
SIC 2511 2512 Dining room furniture: wood; Wood bedroom furniture; Living room furniture: upholstered on wood frames
Pr: Ira Glazer
Pr: Al Moscatell
Ofcr: Jim Adams
Sfty Mgr: Richard Moseley
Plnt Mgr: Rick Stanco
Sales Exec: Jane Campbell
Sls Mgr: John Lynch

D-U-N-S 05-575-3372
TFORCE ENERGY SERVICES INC
SPECIALIZED CRANE & RIGGING CO
(*Suby of* TRANSFORCE INC)
3800 E 42nd St Ste 417, Odessa, TX 79762-5928
Tel (303) 770-6511 *Founded/Ownrshp* 2011
Sales 106.0MM^E *EMP* 800
SIC 4213 Automobiles, transport & delivery
**VP:* Jared Clark
**VP:* Scott Collins
**VP:* Malcolm Gordon

D-U-N-S 83-138-0113
TFP INTERNATIONAL INC
TRADE FINANCE SOLUTIONS
(*Suby of* TRADE FINANCE SOLUTIONS INC) ★
20807 Biscayne Blvd # 203, Aventura, FL 33180-1410
Tel (786) 279-2900 *Founded/Ownrshp* 2015
Sales 100.0MM^E *EMP* 40^E
SIC 7389 Financial services
Pr: J Stephen McDonald
CFO: Cris Neely
Sr VP: Peter Nunes

D-U-N-S 79-879-4926
■**TFS FINANCIAL CORP**
(*Suby of* THIRD FEDERAL SAVINGS) ★
7007 Broadway Ave, Cleveland, OH 44105-1441
Tel (216) 441-6000 *Founded/Ownrshp* 1997
Sales NA *EMP* 4
Tkr Sym TFSL *Exch* NGS
SIC 6035 Savings institutions, federally chartered; Federal savings & loan associations
Ch Bd: Marc A Stefanski
COO: Paul J Huml
COO: Paul Huml
CFO: David S Huffman
VP: Jim French
**VP:* Meredith S Weil
VP Mktg: Marc Stesanski

D-U-N-S 07-997-5746
TFS NEWCO LLC
7-ELEVEN
(*Suby of* 7-ELEVEN INC) ★
14 Howard St, Rockland, MA 02370-1929
Tel (781) 878-8210 *Founded/Ownrshp* 2015
Sales 92.8MM^E *EMP* 1,500^E
SIC 5411 Convenience stores
Pr: Joseph M Depinto
Ex VP: Robert Tedeschi
VP: Glenn Leger
Div Mgr: Barbara Greenwood
Genl Mgr: Ibrahim Abboud
Genl Mgr: Jeff Mettler
Genl Mgr: Mike Sullivan
Store Mgr: Michael Moen
CIO: Pamela Legendre

D-U-N-S 07-962-9228
TFS RT INC
TRADE FINANCE SOLUTIONS
(*Suby of* TRADE FINANCE SOLUTIONS) ★
20807 Biscayne Blvd # 203, Aventura, FL 33180-1410
Tel (416) 240-8404 *Founded/Ownrshp* 2013
Sales NA *EMP* 40
SIC 6082 Foreign trade & international banking institutions
Pr: Steve McDonald
**CFO:* Chris Neely

D-U-N-S 03-174-1502 IMP
TG AUTOMOTIVE SEALING KENTUCKY LLC (KY)
(*Suby of* TOYODA GOSEI CO., LTD.)
501 Frank Yost Ln, Hopkinsville, KY 42240-6817
Tel (270) 475-1400 *Founded/Ownrshp* 2001, 1949

Sales 94.4MM[E] *EMP* 564
SIC 3465 Automotive stampings

D-U-N-S 10-996-9373 IMP
TG FLUID SYSTEMS USA CORP
TG NORTH AMERICA
(*Suby of* TOYODA GOSEI CO., LTD.)
100 Brighton Interior Dr, Brighton, MI 48116-7469
Tel (810) 220-6161 *Founded/Ownrshp* 1995
Sales 85.0MM *EMP* 350
SIC 3082 3089 Unsupported plastics profile shapes; Plastic processing
Pr: Bryan Soddrill

D-U-N-S 16-137-2248 IMP/EXP
TG MISSOURI CORP
(*Suby of* TOYODA GOSEI NORTH AMERICA CORP) ★
2200 Plattin Rd, Perryville, MO 63775-3300
Tel (573) 547-1041 *Founded/Ownrshp* 1986
Sales 226.0MM[E] *EMP* 1,677[E]
SIC 5531 Automotive parts
Pr: Tadashi Arashima
Mtls Mgr: Gary Ward
Plnt Mgr: Tony Wade

TG NORTH AMERICA
See TG FLUID SYSTEMS USA CORP

TGG
See THOMAS G GALLAGHER INC

TGI FRIDAY'S
See BISTATE BISTRO ASSOCIATES LP

TGI FRIDAY'S
See BISTRO MANAGEMENT INC

TGI FRIDAY'S
See CARLSON RESTAURANTS INC

TGI FRIDAY'S
See BRIAD RESTAURANT GROUP LLC

D-U-N-S 05-636-1140
TGI FRIDAYS INC
(*Suby of* SENTINEL CAPITAL PARTNERS LLC) ★
19111 Dallas Pkwy, Dallas, TX 75287-3199
Tel (972) 662-5400 *Founded/Ownrshp* 2014
Sales 616.4MM[E] *EMP* 5,000
SIC 5812 6794 Restaurant, family: chain; Franchises, selling or licensing
Pr: Nick Shepherd
Pr: Edgar Guevara
Pr: Connie Klein
Pr: Lee Sanders
Pr: Ian Saunders
Ex VP: Ricky Richardson
Sr VP: John Gilbert
Sr VP: Suzanne Hanna
Sr VP: Tom Kurrikoff
VP: Jean Baudrand
VP: Craig Cunningham
VP: Carl Robie
VP: Cindy Syracuse

TGS
See TRANS-GLOBAL SOLUTIONS INC

D-U-N-S 55-667-4927 IMP/EXP
TGS-NOPEC GEOPHYSICAL CO
(*Suby of* ACECA NORGE AS)
10451 Clay Rd, Houston, TX 77041-8753
Tel (713) 860-2100 *Founded/Ownrshp* 1998
Sales 264.0MM[E] *EMP* 346
SIC 1382 Oil & gas exploration services
CEO: Hnery H Hamilton
**Ch Bd:* David W Worthington
**Pr:* Pierre Benichou
**CFO:* Arne Helland
**VP:* J Kimberly Abdallah
VP: Pete Bennion
**VP:* Mark H Winchell
**CTO:* David Hicks
IT Man: Mike Jeffers
IT Man: Tony Katz
Info Man: Irena Musielewicz
Board of Directors: Kathleen Arthur, Nils B Gulnes, Elisabeth Harstad, Steven E Lambert, Colette Lewiner

TGSLC
See TEXAS GUARANTEED STUDENT LOAN CORP

D-U-N-S 10-692-3329 IMP
TH FOODS INC
(*Suby of* M I C) ★
2134 Harlem Rd, Loves Park, IL 61111-2752
Tel (800) 896-2396 *Founded/Ownrshp* 1984
Sales 96.5MM[E] *EMP* 300
SIC 2052 Crackers, dry
Pr: Terry Jessen
**Ch Bd:* Mark Tanabe
**VP:* Jeff Baldwin
QA Dir: Jeffrey Coticchio
IT Man: Jeff Lisitza
Opers Mgr: Scott Chehak
Sls Mgr: Dani Amman
Sls Mgr: Donna Duwe

D-U-N-S 07-430-5277 IMP
TH PLASTICS INC
106 E Main St, Mendon, MI 49072-9650
Tel (269) 496-8495 *Founded/Ownrshp* 1974
Sales 100.9MM[E] *EMP* 340
SIC 3089 Injection molded finished plastic products
CEO: Patrick J Haas
**Pr:* Chris Haas
**CFO:* Dan Day
**VP:* Michael McCaw
**VP:* Elizabeth Mitchell
**VP:* Scott Mitchell
IT Man: Samuel Newton
Prd Mgr: Jason Jones
Ql Cn Mgr: Christopher Salyer
Ql Cn Mgr: Teresa Thomas

D-U-N-S 11-872-2339 IMP/EXP
THAI SUMMIT AMERICA CORP
OGIHARA AMERICA COR
(*Suby of* OGIHARA CORPORATION)
1480 Mcpherson Park Dr, Howell, MI 48843-1936
Tel (517) 548-4900 *Founded/Ownrshp* 1985
Sales 241.5MM[E] *EMP* 854
SIC 3465 Body parts, automobile: stamped metal
Pr: Chumpol Rangson
VP: Lowell Blackbourn
VP: Woody Iddhibhakdibongse
VP: Hideo Soneoka

D-U-N-S 16-729-1785 EXP
THAI UNION INTERNATIONAL INC
(*Suby of* THAI UNION GROUP PUBLIC COMPANY LIMITED)
9330 Scranton Rd Ste 500, San Diego, CA 92121-7706
Tel (858) 558-9662 *Founded/Ownrshp* 1996
Sales 86.2MM[E] *EMP* 70[E]
SIC 2091 Tuna fish: packaged in cans, jars, etc.; Salmon: packaged in cans, jars, etc.

D-U-N-S 00-325-3788
THALES DEFENSE & SECURITY INC
(*Suby of* THALES)
22605 Gateway Center Dr, Clarksburg, MD 20871-2001
Tel (240) 864-7000 *Founded/Ownrshp* 1964, 2001
Sales 132.0MM[E] *EMP* 400[E]
SIC 3663 Receivers, radio communications
Pr: Mike Sheehan
CFO: Chris Hamilton
**CFO:* Brian Miller
CFO: Wilson Smith
Ofcr: Robert Hall
VP: Stacey Bostock
VP: Glen Parker
Prgrm Mgr: Jeffrey Detwiler
Genl Mgr: Marc Darmon
CIO: Jose Aleman
QA Dir: Jacqui Ottey

D-U-N-S 00-179-3692
THALES INC
(*Suby of* THALES USA INC) ★
2733 Crystal Dr Ste 1200, Arlington, VA 22202-3585
Tel (703) 838-9685 *Founded/Ownrshp* 1958, 2001
Sales 70.3MM[E] *EMP* 1,200
SIC 8742 Industry specialist consultants
Pr: Allan Cameron
**CEO:* Lawrence Cavaiola
Chf Mktg O: Pierre Schaeffer
**VP:* Pierre-Edouard Arbel
VP: Guy Blanguermon
VP: Paul-Andre Bloch
**VP:* Howard M Diamond
Pgrm Dir: Paul Brown
Snr Mgr: Raj Ramasamy

D-U-N-S 08-895-6800 IMP
THALES USA INC
(*Suby of* THALES)
2733 Crystal Dr, Arlington, VA 22202-3584
Tel (703) 413-6029 *Founded/Ownrshp* 1976
Sales 4.4MMM[E] *EMP* 68,000
SIC 5065 3699 3679 3841 8711 7371 Electronic parts; Electronic tubes: receiving & transmitting or industrial; Flight simulators (training aids), electronic; Electronic circuits; Surgical & medical instruments; Engineering services; Computer software development & applications
CEO: Allan Cameron
VP: Veronique Silverman
Board of Directors: Francois Chabannes, Marcel De Picciotto, Bernard Jaudeau, Louis Le Portz, Daniel Rapenne, Jacques Vannier, Denis Verret

D-U-N-S 85-903-2091 IMP
■THALES-RAYTHEON SYSTEMS CO LLC
(*Suby of* RAYTHEON CO) ★
1801 Hughes Dr, Fullerton, CA 92833-2200
Tel (714) 446-3118 *Founded/Ownrshp* 2001
Sales 334.5MM[E] *EMP* 750
SIC 5065 Security control equipment & systems
VP: Matt Pothecary
Prgrm Mgr: Steven Bruce
Genl Mgr: Robert Musulas
Snr Ntwrk: Andre Bullock

D-U-N-S 07-792-9776
THALHIMER INC MORTON G
11100 W Broad St, Glen Allen, VA 23060-5813
Tel (804) 648-5881 *Founded/Ownrshp* 1991
Sales 133.7MM[E] *EMP* 250
SIC 1542 6531 6799 6513 6512 Commercial & office building contractors; Real estate brokers & agents; Real estate investors, except property operators; Apartment building operators; Nonresidential building operators
CEO: Paul F Silver
Treas: David Dustin
**Treas:* Edmond Pittman
**Ex VP:* Jeffrey S Bisger
**Ex VP:* Evan M Magrill
**Ex VP:* C Lee Warfield III
Ex VP: Lee Warfield III
Ex VP: Lee C Warfield
**Sr VP:* Steve Brincefield
Sr VP: Jeff Cooke
Sr VP: John Coppedge
**Sr VP:* Mark Douglas
**Sr VP:* David R Dustin Jr
**Sr VP:* Gary Hooper
Sr VP: George Stuckey
Sr VP: John Tison
Sr VP: Rob Wright
VP: Meredith Dickerson
VP: Mark Erickson
**VP:* Edward Kimple
VP: Norman Moon Jr

D-U-N-S 00-980-3016
THALLE CONSTRUCTION CO INC
900 Nc Highway 86 N, Hillsborough, NC 27278-8226
Tel (919) 245-1490 *Founded/Ownrshp* 1947
Sales 123.7MM[E] *EMP* 175
SIC 1611 1622 1623 1629 Highway & street construction; Bridge, tunnel & elevated highway; Water, sewer & utility lines; Dam construction
CEO: Peter K Tully
**COO:* Steve Kohler
**Ex VP:* Lawrence Fantozzi

THANKS
See O C TANNER CO

THANKS
See O C TANNER RECOGNITION CO

D-U-N-S 06-969-6649 IMP
■THARCO CONTAINER INC
(*Suby of* THARCO HOLDINGS INC) ★
2222 Grant Ave, San Lorenzo, CA 94580-1804
Tel (510) 276-8600 *Founded/Ownrshp* 1952
Sales 227.6MM[E] *EMP* 1,000
SIC 2653 Corrugated & solid fiber boxes
CEO: Bruce A Garner
**Pr:* Oscar B Fears
**CFO:* Marvin Press
Ofcr: Dale Flom
VP: Dan Lancaster
Prd Mgr: Brian Johnson
Manager: Dan Beers

D-U-N-S 03-942-1495 IMP
■THARCO HOLDINGS INC
(*Suby of* BOISE INC) ★
2222 Grant Ave, San Lorenzo, CA 94580-1804
Tel (303) 373-1860 *Founded/Ownrshp* 1999
Sales 227.6MM[E] *EMP* 1,001
SIC 2653 3086 2675 Corrugated & solid fiber boxes; Plastics foam products; Die-cut paper & board
CEO: Oscar B Fears
**CFO:* Jason Bowman
Genl Mgr: Tom Pulley
Off Mgr: Debbie Rose

D-U-N-S 09-546-4848 IMP
THARPE CO INC
ENGAGE2EXCEL
(*Suby of* THARPEROBBINS CO INC) ★
149 Crawford Rd, Statesville, NC 28625-8546
Tel (704) 872-5231 *Founded/Ownrshp* 2001
Sales 143.0MM[E] *EMP* 215[E]
SIC 5199 Gifts & novelties
Ch Bd: John S Tharpe
Pr: G Brett Tharpe
CFO: Joel A Kepley
Sr VP: Christopher Cheney
Sr VP: Anthony Luciano
VP: R Reid Gibson

D-U-N-S 96-889-8093
THARPEROBBINS CO INC
(*Suby of* GRIDIRON TRADING MANAGEMENT CO LLC) ★
149 Crawford Rd, Statesville, NC 28625-8546
Tel (704) 872-5231 *Founded/Ownrshp* 2010
Sales 149.4MM[E] *EMP* 260[E]
Accts Mcgladrey Llp Charlotte Nort
SIC 3911 Pins (jewelry), precious metal
CEO: Brett Tharpe
**COO:* John Bradley
**CFO:* Joel Kepley
Treas: Derek Killian
**Sr VP:* Anthony Luciano Jr
**Sr VP:* Susan Tolle
VP: Christopher Ludwig
CIO: Neal Cao
Sls Dir: Brenton Spry

D-U-N-S 07-972-5036
THATCHER GROUP INC
1905 W Fortune Rd, Salt Lake City, UT 84104-3724
Tel (801) 972-4587 *Founded/Ownrshp* 2000
Sales 100.5MM[E] *EMP* 525
SIC 2819 Industrial inorganic chemicals
Pr: Craig N Thatcher

THAT'S PICKLICIOUS
See MOUNT OLIVE PICKLE CO INC

D-U-N-S 86-912-2143
THAYER CAPITAL PARTNERS LP
1455 Penn Ave Nw Ste 350, Washington, DC 20004-1012
Tel (202) 371-0150 *Founded/Ownrshp* 1992
Sales 228.7MM[E] *EMP* 3,080[E]
SIC 6211 Security brokers & dealers
Pt: Fred Malek
Pt: Ivor J Evans
Pt: Jim Forese
CFO: Lisa Winthers
VP: John Comly
Brnch Mgr: Kasia Swierczek
Mktg Dir: Richard Linville

D-U-N-S 17-504-2209 IMP/EXP
THAYER DISTRIBUTION
333 Swedesboro Ave, Gibbstown, NJ 08027-1220
Tel (800) 999-4271 *Founded/Ownrshp* 1978
Sales 192.8MM *EMP* 100
Accts Gold Gerstein Group Llc Voorh
SIC 5145 Candy
Ch Bd: Juan Gallicchio
**Pr:* Diego Gallicchio
**CFO:* Jim Owens
**Sec:* Marina Dunn
VP: Diego Gallicchio

THAYER LODGING GROUP
See HOTEL ACQUISITION CO LLC

D-U-N-S 83-675-8672
THAYER LODGING GROUP INC
(*Suby of* BROOKFIELD ASSET MANAGEMENT INC)
1997 Annapolis Exchange P, Annapolis, MD 21401-3294
Tel (410) 268-0515 *Founded/Ownrshp* 2014
Sales 272.2MM[E] *EMP* 1,500[E]
SIC 6799 6726 Investors; Investment offices
CEO: Leland C Pillsbury
**Pr:* Bruce Wiles
**CEO:* Leland Pillsbury
VP: Angela Chen
VP: Kim Gauthier
VP: Chris King
VP: Steven M Neiman
VP Inf Sys: Mike Uwe

D-U-N-S 15-764-3383
THAYER-BLUM FUNDING III LLC
1455 Penn Ave Nw Ste 350, Washington, DC 20004-1028
Tel (202) 371-0150 *Founded/Ownrshp* 2002
Sales 76.3MM[E] *EMP* 1,717
SIC 6722 3672 3577 Management investment, open-end; Printed circuit boards; Computer peripheral equipment

THC
See WEST BOCA MEDICAL CENTER INC

D-U-N-S 04-471-5998
■THD AT-HOME SERVICES INC
(*Suby of* HOME DEPOT) ★
2690 Cumberland Pkwy Se # 300, Atlanta, GA 30339-3913
Tel (770) 779-1423 *Founded/Ownrshp* 1997
Sales 83.4MM[E] *EMP* 825
SIC 8741 Construction management
CFO: Scott Schnell
**COO:* Michael Esposito
Treas: Carol B Tome
VP: Joseph J Deangelo
**Prin:* Barry Figaretto

THEATER MERCHANDISING
See BOSTON CULINARY GROUP INC

D-U-N-S 02-448-5893 IMP
THEATRES COBB III LLC (AL)
COBB THEATRES
2000b Southbridge Pkwy # 100, Birmingham, AL 35209-7723
Tel (205) 802-7766 *Founded/Ownrshp* 2000
Sales 104.5MM[E] *EMP* 1,500
SIC 7832 Motion picture theaters, except drive-in
Pr: Robert M Cobb
COO: Jeremy P Welman
CFO: Ricky Thomas
VP: Loretta Thomas
Exec: Isaac Stewart
Ex Dir: Guy Austin
Dir IT: Steve Bankston
Dir IT: Fred Dobbs

THEDA CLARK MEDICAL CENTER
See THEDA CLARK MEMORIAL HOSPITAL (INC)

D-U-N-S 07-385-6189
THEDA CLARK MEMORIAL HOSPITAL (INC)
THEDA CLARK MEDICAL CENTER
130 2nd St, Neenah, WI 54956-2883
Tel (920) 729-3100 *Founded/Ownrshp* 1909
Sales 183.7MM *EMP* 1,200
SIC 8062 General medical & surgical hospitals
CEO: Dean Gruner
**COO:* Matthew Furlan
**Sr VP:* Kim Barnas

D-U-N-S 18-130-7307
THEDACARE INC
122 E College Ave Ste 2a, Appleton, WI 54911-5741
Tel (920) 735-5560 *Founded/Ownrshp* 1984
Sales 809.6MM *EMP* 7,000
Accts Wipfli Llp Milwaukee Wiscons
SIC 8062 General medical & surgical hospitals
CEO: Dean Gruner
**Ch Bd:* John Davis
COO: Matt Furlan
COO: Laura Reed
CFO: Patrick Erlandson
**CFO:* Tim Olson
**V Ch Bd:* Terry Timm
Trst: Kathleen Qualheim
Trst: Mark Scott
Trst: Jon M Stellmacher
Trst: Philip Vogt
Sr VP: Kathryn Correia
Sr VP: Jeff Hunter
Sr VP: William Mann
**VP:* Jim Matheson

D-U-N-S 06-689-6937
THEDACARE MEDICAL CENTER - BERLIN INC
(*Suby of* THEDACARE INC) ★
225 Memorial Dr, Berlin, WI 54923-1243
Tel (920) 361-1313 *Founded/Ownrshp* 1910
Sales 87.4MM *EMP* 495
Accts Wipfli Llp Green Bay Wi
SIC 8062 8051 8011 General medical & surgical hospitals; Skilled nursing care facilities; Offices & clinics of medical doctors
CEO: John Feeney
**CFO:* Tim Olson
VP: Dan Hodgkins
VP: Eleanore Wilson
Chf Nrs Of: Jamie O'Malley
Prin: Anthony Racki MD
Nurse Mgr: Tina Burch
Psych: Georgeanne Chier
Psych: Joel Cler
Pgrm Dir: H Knight
Snr Mgr: Tim Dickerson

D-U-N-S 08-727-2001
THEISENS INC (IA)
6201 Chavenelle Rd, Dubuque, IA 52002-9692
Tel (563) 556-4738 *Founded/Ownrshp* 1927
Sales 102.7MM[E] *EMP* 275
SIC 5531 5999 5699 5261 Automotive & home supply stores; Farm equipment & supplies; Work clothing; Nurseries & garden centers
Pr: Leo A Theisen
**Treas:* Christopher Theisen

THEODAVIES FOOD SERVICE GROUP
See TD FOOD GROUP INC

THEODORE TUNICK INSURANCE
See MARSHALL & STERLING ENTERPRISES INC

D-U-N-S 15-432-4859
THEOREM CLINICAL RESEARCH INC
1016 W 9th Ave Ste 300, King of Prussia, PA 19406-1221
Tel (484) 679-2400 *Founded/Ownrshp* 2011
Sales NA *EMP* 1,200

SIC 8731 8071 2834

D-U-N-S 78-118-4239
THERACARE OF NEWYORK INC
116 W 32nd St Fl 8, NewYork, NY 10001-3214
Tel (212) 564-2350 Founded/Ownrshp 1991
Sales 74.4MM^E EMP 2,300
SIC 8093 7361 Specialty outpatient clinics; Placement agencies
Ch Bd: John Calderon
COO: Hank Hubbard
*CFO: Laurel Locastro

D-U-N-S 11-437-9522
THERAGENICS CORP
(Suby of JUNIPER HOLDINGS, INC.)
5203 Bristol Indus Way, Buford, GA 30518-1799
Tel (770) 271-0233 Founded/Ownrshp 2013
Sales 154.4MM^E EMP 534^E
SIC 2834 3842 Druggists' preparations (pharmaceuticals); Surgical appliances & supplies
Ch Bd: M Christine Jacobs
*CFO: Francis J Tarallo
Ex VP: Eric Meyers
*Ex VP: C Russell Small
*Ex VP: Bruce W Smith
Opers Mgr: Andre Stallings

D-U-N-S 15-838-8061 IMP/EXP
■ **THERAPAK LLC**
(Suby of VWR CORP) ★
651 Wharton Dr, Claremont, CA 91711-4819
Tel (909) 267-2000 Founded/Ownrshp 2016
Sales 249.1MM^E EMP 492
SIC 5047 Medical equipment & supplies; Diagnostic equipment, medical
Pr: Todd Gates
CFO: Arbie Harootoonian
VP: Frank Brandauer
VP: Randy Hawk
Natl Sales: Barry Johnston
Sales Asso: Kevin Champion

THERM PACIFIC
See HKF INC

D-U-N-S 00-415-9869 IMP
■ **THERM-O-DISC INC** (OH)
(Suby of EECO INC) ★
1320 S Main St, Mansfield, OH 44907-5500
Tel (419) 525-8500 Founded/Ownrshp 1945, 1968
Sales 512.1MM^E EMP 4,000
SIC 3822 3823 Built-in thermostats, filled system & bimetal types; Industrial instrmnts msrmnt display/control process variable
CEO: Charles C G
VP: Scott Klonowski
*VP: Martin Leslie
VP: Steve Motter
Exec: Susan Henley
Genl Mgr: Keith Kuipers
Dir IT: Rick Gerich
Opers Mgr: Bryan Pugh
Plnt Mgr: Matt Grist
Ql Cn Mgr: Jeffrey A Mueck
S&M/VP: Dan Johnston

D-U-N-S 05-563-6856 IMP
THERMA CORP
1601 Las Plumas Ave, San Jose, CA 95133-1613
Tel (408) 347-3400 Founded/Ownrshp 1971
Sales 228.8MM^E EMP 1,200
SIC 3444 3448 Sheet metalwork; Prefabricated metal components
CEO: Joseph Parisi
*CFO: Nicki Parisi
Brnch Mgr: Larry Ginn
IT Man: Larry Narachi
Snr PM: Mike Miller

D-U-N-S 09-217-3731 IMP
■ **THERMA-TRU CORP**
(Suby of FORTUNE BRANDS HOME & SECURITY INC) ★
1750 Indian Wood Cir # 100, Maumee, OH 43537-4079
Tel (419) 891-7400 Founded/Ownrshp 2011
Sales 528.6MM^E EMP 2,000
SIC 3442 Metal doors
Pr: Brett Finley
*CFO: David Haddix
VP: Manny Francione
VP: Jeff Glosser
VP: Kessler Jeff
VP: Carol M Summersgill
Area Mgr: Clair Moore
Dist Mgr: Patrick Pelham
DP Exec: Ben Lane
Dir IT: John Clarke
Mktg Mgr: Verena Sharp

D-U-N-S 18-316-4706 IMP/EXP
THERMAL CERAMICS INC
MORGAN ADVANCED MATERIALS
(Suby of MORGANITE INDUSTRIES INC) ★
2102 Old Savannah Rd, Augusta, GA 30906-2197
Tel (706) 796-4200 Founded/Ownrshp 1988
Sales 200.0MM EMP 600
SIC 3299 3255 5085 3296 3264 3053 Ceramic fiber; Brick, clay refractory; Castable refractories, clay; Refractory material; Mineral wool; Porcelain electrical supplies; Gaskets, packing & sealing devices
CEO: John Stang
*Ch Bd: Jim McRickard
*VP: Dell Hadden
Dir IT: Jerry Rockefeller
Plnt Mgr: Brad Fogle
Mktg Mgr: Tom Rebernak
Sls Mgr: George Alvarez
Sls Mgr: Tom Viverito

D-U-N-S 05-228-4759 IMP/EXP
THERMAL ENGINEERING INTERNATIONAL (USA) INC
BABCOCK POWER
(Suby of BABCOCK POWER INC) ★
10375 Slusher Dr, Santa Fe Springs, CA 90670-3748
Tel (323) 726-0641 Founded/Ownrshp 1919, 2002
Sales 89.3MM EMP 250
Accts Deloitte & Touche Llp Hartofr
SIC 3443 8711 Air coolers, metal plate; Condensers, steam; Heat exchangers: coolers (after, inter), condensers, etc.; Economizers (boilers); Professional engineer
CEO: Xavier A Dorai
Pr: Brian Antonini
Pr: William Farris
Pr: Andrew Finizio
Pr: Abraham L Yarden
COO: Joseph A Nitzken
*CFO: Christine Porsch
*Sr VP: Armond Davidian
*Sr VP: Kenneth Murakoshi
Sr VP: Kenneth D Murakoshi
*Sr VP: Clement Tam
Sr VP: Clement W Tam
*VP: Anthony Brandano
VP: Anthony A Brandano
*VP: Jan Marte Contreras
*VP: William J Ferguson Jr
*VP: Michael Goodwin
*VP: Geoffrey Greenberg
VP: Geoffrey B Greenberg
*VP: Micahel D Leclair
*VP: Scott Leeman
Board of Directors: Xavier Dorai, William J Ferguson Jr, Michael D Leclair, Dale S Miller

THERMAL SOLUTIONS
See TSI GROUP INC

D-U-N-S 07-841-5541 IMP
THERMAL SOLUTIONS MANUFACTURING INC
15 Century Blvd Ste 102, Nashville, TN 37214-3692
Tel (615) 806-7907 Founded/Ownrshp 2012
Sales 102.7MM^E EMP 142^E
SIC 3714 Radiators & radiator shells & cores, motor vehicle
CEO: George Scherff
CFO: Glenn Hollis
Brnch Mgr: Robin Mendel
Genl Mgr: Perry Breningstall

D-U-N-S 04-606-7922 IMP
■ **THERMAL STRUCTURES INC**
(Suby of HEICO AEROSPACE HOLDINGS CORP) ★
2362 Railroad St, Corona, CA 92880-5421
Tel (951) 736-9911 Founded/Ownrshp 1999
Sales 95.2MM^E EMP 330
SIC 3724 Aircraft engines & engine parts
Pr: Vaughn Barnes
VP: Gavin Lemon
MIS Dir: Rocky Branum
Dir IT: Jeff Smith
Mfg Dir: John Velker
Ql Cn Mgr: David B Herrmann
Ql Cn Mgr: Shawn Johnston
Sls Mgr: Monica Allphin

D-U-N-S 87-628-8932 IMP/EXP
THERMASYS GROUP HOLDING CO
2776 Gunter Park Dr E, Montgomery, AL 36109-1415
Tel (334) 244-9240 Founded/Ownrshp 2005
Sales 103.4MM^E EMP 924
SIC 3714 3443

D-U-N-S 13-838-8090
■ **THERMO ELECTRON NORTH AMERICA LLC**
(Suby of THERMO FISHER SCIENTIFIC WEST PALM HOLDINGS LLC) ★
770 Northpoint Pkwy # 100, West Palm Beach, FL 33407-1901
Tel (561) 688-8700 Founded/Ownrshp 2014
Sales 85.7MM^E EMP 600^E
SIC 3826 Analytical instruments
Sr VP: Seth H Hoogasian
*VP: Kenneth J Apicerno
Off Mgr: Angela Ardy

D-U-N-S 01-570-3833 IMP
■ **THERMO FINNIGAN LLC**
(Suby of THERMO FISHER SCIENTIFIC INC) ★
355 River Oaks Pkwy, San Jose, CA 95134-1908
Tel (408) 965-6000 Founded/Ownrshp 2001
Sales 103.9MM^E EMP 600
SIC 3826 Analytical instruments
Off Mgr: Shana Gray
Sftwr Eng: Andrew McKewan

D-U-N-S 17-075-5479 IMP
■ **THERMO FISHER SCIENTIFIC (ASHVILLE) LLC**
(Suby of THERMO FISHER SCIENTIFIC INC) ★
28 Schenck Pkwy Ste 400, Asheville, NC 28803-5088
Tel (828) 658-2711 Founded/Ownrshp 2006
Sales 243.7MM^E EMP 867
SIC 3585 3826 3821 3829 Refrigeration & heating equipment; Analytical instruments; Laboratory apparatus & furniture; Measuring & controlling devices
Pr: Bill McMahon

D-U-N-S 00-140-8673 IMP/EXP
▲ **THERMO FISHER SCIENTIFIC INC**
168 3rd Ave, Waltham, MA 02451-7551
Tel (781) 622-1000 Founded/Ownrshp 1956
Sales 16.9MMM EMP 55,060
Accts Pricewaterhousecoopers Llp Bo
Tkr Sym TMO Exch NYS
SIC 3826 3845 3823 3629 Analytical instruments; Environmental testing equipment; Analytical optical instruments; Gas testing apparatus; Electromedical equipment; Electromedical apparatus; Electrotherapeutic apparatus; Industrial instrmnts msrmnt display/control process variable; Industrial process measurement equipment; Electronic generation equipment
Ch Bd: Jim P Manzi
Pr: Marc N Casper
Treas: Henry Singh
Assoc VP: Angela Peters
Ex VP: Michael Belford
Ex VP: Lori A Daniels
Ex VP: Mark P Stevenson
Ex VP: Peter M Wilver
Sr VP: Joseph C Beery
Sr VP: Seth H Hoogasian
Sr VP: Thomas W Loewald
VP: Ken Apicerno
VP: Karen Blum
VP: Peter Brennan
VP: Randy Carter
VP: Larry Cook
VP: Richard Dirocco
VP: Gary Galluzzi
VP: Peter Granick
VP: Peter E Hornstra
VP: Mark Ibison

D-U-N-S 08-038-9029
■ **THERMO FISHER SCIENTIFIC WEST PALM HOLDINGS LLC**
(Suby of THERMO FISHER SCIENTIFIC INC) ★
168 3rd Ave, Waltham, MA 02451-7551
Tel (781) 622-1000 Founded/Ownrshp 2014
Sales 85.7MM^E EMP 600
SIC 3826 Analytical instruments

D-U-N-S 11-099-2547
■ **THERMO FLUIDS INC**
NUVERRA
(Suby of HECKMANN ENVIRONMENTAL SERVICES, INC.)
8925 E Pima Center Pkwy # 105, Scottsdale, AZ 85258-4409
Tel (480) 270-5702 Founded/Ownrshp 2015
Sales 175.6MM^E EMP 293^E
SIC 5093 Oil, waste
COO: Ted Sinclair
Chf Mktg O: Todd J Bogart
Genl Mgr: Eric Spencer
IT Man: Todd Bogart
Natl Sales: Barbara Contreras

THERMO FSHER SCNTFIC RMEL PDTS
See REMEL INC

D-U-N-S 00-432-0693 IMP/EXP
THERMO KING CORP
PHOENIX GLOBAL DISTRIBUTION
(Suby of INGERSOLL-RAND CO) ★
314 W 90th St, Minneapolis, MN 55420-3693
Tel (952) 887-2200 Founded/Ownrshp 1997
Sales 663.0MM^E EMP 2,929
SIC 3585 Refrigeration equipment, complete; Air conditioning, motor vehicle; Air conditioning units, complete: domestic or industrial
CEO: Richard Pittard
Pr: Raymond Pittard
VP: David Deane
Genl Mgr: Bob Van Horn
Sftwr Eng: Phillip Abbott
Mtls Mgr: Diana Soto-Marengo
Sales Exec: Bill Pascoe
Mktg Mgr: Michael Schlough
Sls Mgr: Tim Edwards

D-U-N-S 10-574-1730 IMP
THERMO KING DE PUERTO RICO INC
(Suby of INGERSOLL-RAND CO) ★
517 Zona Industrial, Arecibo, PR 00612-3072
Tel (787) 878-1690 Founded/Ownrshp 1997
Sales 154.4MM^E EMP 880
Accts Pricewaterhousecoopers Llp Sa
SIC 3585 Refrigeration & heating equipment
Plnt Mgr: Blanca Velez

D-U-N-S 94-796-5695
■ **THERMO OPTEK CORP**
(Suby of THERMO FISHER SCIENTIFIC INC) ★
27 Forge Pkwy, Franklin, MA 02038-3135
Tel (508) 553-5100 Founded/Ownrshp 2000
Sales 75.7MM^E EMP 1,150
SIC 3823

D-U-N-S 96-774-6293
▲ **THERMON GROUP HOLDINGS INC**
100 Thermon Dr, San Marcos, TX 78666-5947
Tel (512) 396-5801 Founded/Ownrshp 1954
Sales 281.9MM EMP 1,021^E
Tkr Sym THR Exch NYS
SIC 8711 Industrial engineers
Pr: Bruce A Thames
*Ch Bd: Charles A Sorrentino
CFO: Jay C Peterson
Sr VP: Rene Van Der Salm

D-U-N-S 96-974-3926
■ **THERMON HEAT TRACING SERVICES INC**
(Suby of THERMON GROUP HOLDINGS INC) ★
100 Thermon Dr, San Marcos, TX 78666-5947
Tel (512) 396-5801 Founded/Ownrshp 1982
Sales 278.0MM EMP 150^E
SIC 8711 Industrial engineers
Pr: Rodney Bi Bingham
*Treas: Ryan Dennison

D-U-N-S 96-735-7604
■ **THERMON HOLDING CORP**
(Suby of THERMON GROUP HOLDINGS INC) ★
100 Thermon Dr, San Marcos, TX 78666-5947
Tel (512) 396-5801 Founded/Ownrshp 2011
Sales 270.5MM EMP 0^E
SIC 6719 Holding companies
Pr: Rodney Bingham

D-U-N-S 11-255-4498
■ **THERMON INDUSTRIES INC**
(Suby of THERMON GROUP HOLDINGS INC) ★
100 Thermon Dr, San Marcos, TX 78666-5947
Tel (512) 396-5801 Founded/Ownrshp 1983
Sales 88.4MM^E EMP 500
SIC 3643 Current-carrying wiring devices
CEO: Rodney Dingham
*Pr: Mark Burdick
*CFO: David Ralph
*VP: George P Alexender
*VP: Roy Barth
VP: Richard Hageman
Comm Dir: Linda Dietert
Manager: Jeff Stein

D-U-N-S 05-264-7757 IMP/EXP
■ **THERMON MANUFACTURING CO INC**
(Suby of THERMON GROUP HOLDINGS INC) ★
100 Thermon Dr, San Marcos, TX 78666-5947
Tel (512) 396-5801 Founded/Ownrshp 1971
Sales 98.1MM^E EMP 250
Accts Ernst & Young Llp Austin Te
SIC 3643 3612 Current-carrying wiring devices; Power transformers, electric
Pr: Rodney L Bingham
Ch Bd: Jacob Johanson
*CFO: Jay C Peterson
CFO: Fred Schulte
*Treas: Ryan Dennison
Ex VP: Bruce Thames
*Sr VP: George Alexander
Sr VP: Rodney Bigham
*Sr VP: Rene Der Salm
*VP: Soy Barth
VP: Rich Huelett
Comm Dir: Linda Dietert

D-U-N-S 94-549-2296
■ **THERMOQUEST CORP**
(Suby of THERMO FISHER SCIENTIFIC INC) ★
355 River Oaks Pkwy, San Jose, CA 95134-1908
Tel (408) 965-6000 Founded/Ownrshp 1995
Sales 431.8MM EMP 1,215
SIC 3826 3823

THERMOTRON INDUSTRIES
See VENTUREDYNE LTD

D-U-N-S 80-859-6303 EXP
THERMOTRON INDUSTRIES INC
(Suby of THERMOTRON INDUSTRIES) ★
291 Kollen Park Dr, Holland, MI 49423-3487
Tel (616) 392-1491 Founded/Ownrshp 1962
Sales 108.1MM^E EMP 680
SIC 3569 Testing chambers for altitude, temperature, ordnance, power
Prin: Brian Nahey
Pr: Ron Lampen
Software D: Caleb Billman
VP Mfg: Mike Teravest
Plnt Mgr: Frank Amatangelo
Mktg Mgr: Mark Pyk
Manager: Chris Scholten
Sls Mgr: Will Dion
Sls Mgr: Bradley A Grande
Sls Mgr: Steve Lain
Sls Mgr: Jacob Wiechertjes

D-U-N-S 00-218-9322 IMP/EXP
THERMWELL PRODUCTS CO INC (NJ)
FROST KING
420 State Rt 17, Mahwah, NJ 07430-2135
Tel (201) 684-4400 Founded/Ownrshp 1910
Sales 217.4MM^E EMP 700
SIC 3442 Moldings & trim, except automobile: metal; Weather strip, metal
Pr: David B Gerstein
Pr: Tim Popiela
*CFO: Mark Heitlinger
*Ex VP: Vincent Giarratana
*VP: Mel B Gerstein
VP: Sternerg Robert
*VP Mfg: Chris Riccio

D-U-N-S 05-333-4892 IMP/EXP
THETFORD CORP
(Suby of DKM LTD) ★
7101 Jackson Rd, Ann Arbor, MI 48103-9506
Tel (734) 769-6000 Founded/Ownrshp 1988
Sales 103.7MM^E EMP 400
SIC 3632 3089 2842 2621 3431 2899 Refrigerators, mechanical & absorption: household; Toilets, portable chemical: plastic; Sanitation preparations; Sanitary tissue paper; Metal sanitary ware; Chemical preparations
CFO: Stephane Cordeille
*Pr: Kevin Phillips
*CFO: Peter Struijs
*VP: Barry Eckel

THETRADEDESK
See TRADE DESK INC

D-U-N-S 00-144-1146 IMP/EXP
THG CORP
SORENSEN SYSTEMS
70 Bearfoot Rd, Northborough, MA 01532-1514
Tel (508) 393-7660 Founded/Ownrshp 1933
Sales 86.6MM^E EMP 145
SIC 5085 5084 3569 3728 3625 3494 Industrial supplies; Hose, belting & packing; Tanks, pressurized; Rubber goods, mechanical; Hydraulic systems equipment & supplies; Compressors, except air conditioning; Lubricating equipment; Aircraft parts & equipment; Relays & industrial controls; Valves & pipe fittings
Pr: Carey D Rhoten
*CFO: Jay Hannon
VP: Thelma Desrosiers
VP: Bill Rodny
Genl Mgr: Lisa Charmchi
QC Dir: Jerry Lamothe
Plnt Mgr: Jon Mitton
Sales Exec: Preston Sturdevant
Sales Asso: Tracy Law

D-U-N-S 08-391-3913 EXP
THIBIANT INTERNATIONAL INC
(Suby of CORPORATION DEVELOPPEMENT KNOWLTON INC)
20320 Prairie St, Chatsworth, CA 91311-6026
Tel (818) 709-1345 Founded/Ownrshp 2016
Sales 132.2MM^E EMP 450
SIC 2844 Cosmetic preparations
CEO: Patrick Thibiant

THIBODAUX REGIONAL MEDICAL CTR
See HOSPITAL SERVICE DISTRICT 3 LAFOURCHE PARISH

D-U-N-S 12-119-3403
THIELE TECHNOLOGIES INC
HUDSON- SHARP MACHINE COMPANY
(*Suby of* BARRY-WEHMILLER COMPANIES INC) ★
315 27th Ave Ne, Minneapolis, MN 55418-2715
Tel (612) 782-1200 *Founded/Ownrshp* 1995
Sales 132.0MM^E *EMP* 423
SIC 3565 Packaging machinery; Carton packing machines; Bag opening, filling & closing machines
Pr: Laurence P Smith
CFO: James W Lawson
Treas: Michael D Zaccarello
VP: Gregory L Coonrod
VP: David M Gianini
VP: Dean Grell
VP: Bob Odom
Exec: Donna Taylor
IT Man: Ken Block
Site Mgr: Erna Maxwell
Prd Mgr: Bill Corrigan

D-U-N-S 06-230-5479 IMP
THIELSCH ENGINEERING INC
195 Frances Ave, Cranston, RI 02910-2211
Tel (401) 785-0241 *Founded/Ownrshp* 1984
Sales 83.8MM^E *EMP* 150^E
SIC 5084 5043 5172 5085 Welding machinery & equipment; Photographic equipment & supplies; Gases, liquefied petroleum (propane); Industrial supplies
Pr: Thomas E Lent
**Pr:* ARA Nalbandian
**CEO:* Vincent Graziano
Ofcr: Mike Pernini
**VP:* Peter Kennefick
VP: Laurel Stoddard
Comm Man: Celeste Langlois
IT Man: Dan Caluori
IT Man: Peter Ferreira
Opers Mgr: Michael Elias
Sls Mgr: Steve Wilmes

THILMANY PAPERS
See EXPERA SPECIALTY SOLUTIONS LLC

D-U-N-S 19-635-8543
THINGS REMEMBERED INC
5500 Avion Park Dr, Highland Heights, OH 44143-1992
Tel (440) 473-2000 *Founded/Ownrshp* 2012
Sales 950.2MM^E *EMP* 4,000
SIC 7389 5947 Engraving service; Gift shop
Ch Bd: Lisa Gavales
**Pr:* Michael Anthony
**Sr VP:* Tony Chivari
**Sr VP:* Mark I Lilien
**Sr VP:* Linda Postell
VP: Adam Boucher
VP: Jill Brincko
**VP:* Amy Myers
VP: Thomas Quayle
Dist Mgr: David Myers
Off Mgr: Dwayne Freed

THINK FAST TOYS.COM
See AVALANCHE STRATEGIES LLC

D-U-N-S 07-474-3845
THINK TOGETHER
2101 E 4th St Ste 200b, Santa Ana, CA 92705-3822
Tel (714) 543-3807 *Founded/Ownrshp* 1997
Sales 47.1MM *EMP* 2,500
Accts Stephens Reidinger & Beller Lp
SIC 8299 Tutoring school
CEO: Randy Barth
**CFO:* Mike Frobenius
**Ch:* Eric Boden
Exec: Jennifer Matsuda
**Prin:* Ken Geisick
Prgrm Mgr: Ismael Candelas
Genl Mgr: Adriana Kingston
Genl Mgr: Fernando Reyes
CTO: Natalia Flores
IT Man: Bill Miller
Snr Mgr: Brenda Alvarez

D-U-N-S 18-861-7179 IMP/EXP
THIRD COAST PACKAGING INC
THIRD COAST TERMINALS
1871 Mykawa Rd, Pearland, TX 77581-3207
Tel (281) 412-0275 *Founded/Ownrshp* 2002
Sales 88.2MM^E *EMP* 40
SIC 5172 4783 2899 Naptha; Packing goods for shipping; Chemical preparations
Pr: Jim Clawson Jr
**VP:* Grif Carnes
**VP:* Larry Rysavy

THIRD COAST TERMINALS
See THIRD COAST PACKAGING INC

D-U-N-S 01-564-6859
▲THIRD FEDERAL SAVINGS
103 Foulk Rd Ste 101, Wilmington, DE 19803-3742
Tel (302) 661-2009 *Founded/Ownrshp* 2000
Sales NA *EMP* 1,111
SIC 6035 Savings institutions, federally chartered
Ch Bd: Marc Stefanski
**CFO:* Stephen Fowle
Opers Mgr: Marianne Piterans

D-U-N-S 00-445-4138
■THIRD FEDERAL SAVINGS AND LOAN ASSOCIATION OF CLEVELAND
(*Suby of* THIRD FEDERAL SAVINGS) ★
7007 Broadway Ave, Cleveland, OH 44105-1490
Tel (800) 844-7333 *Founded/Ownrshp* 1938
Sales NA *EMP* 1,000
SIC 6035 Federal savings & loan associations
Ch Bd: Marc A Stefanski
**COO:* Bernard Kobak
**COO:* John P Ringenbach
**CFO:* David Huffman
Ofcr: Judith Z Adam
Ofcr: Susan Jaworski
Exec: Crystal Robinson
Dir Risk M: Bryon Callahan
Dir Risk M: Terry Paulett
Rgnl Mgr: Calvin Kennedy
Brnch Mgr: Linda Cooley

D-U-N-S 15-288-6821
THIRD POINT LLC
390 Park Ave Fl 18, New York, NY 10022-4608
Tel (212) 715-3880 *Founded/Ownrshp* 1995
Sales 340.0MM *EMP* 70
SIC 6799 Investors
CEO: Daniel S Loeb
Mng Pt: Robert Schwartz
**COO:* Joshua L Targoff
CFO: Mendy Haas
**CFO:* Richard Haas
Ofcr: James Gallagher
Ofcr: William Song
Mng Dir: Elissa Doyle
Mng Dir: Justin Rimel
CTO: Scott Zionic
IT Man: Andrew Doran

D-U-N-S 00-393-3595 IMP
THIRTEEN PRODUCTIONS LLC
(*Suby of* WNET) ★
825 8th Ave Fl 14, New York, NY 10019-7435
Tel (212) 560-2000 *Founded/Ownrshp* 1962
Sales 105.2MM^E *EMP* 100^E
SIC 4833 Television broadcasting stations
Pr: Neil Shapiro
**CFO:* Robert Clauser
**VP:* Kennneth Devine
**VP:* Joshua C Nathan
VP: Charlene Shapiro

D-U-N-S 18-639-6342
THIRTY-ONE GIFTS LLC
3425 Morse Xing, Columbus, OH 43219-6014
Tel (614) 414-4300 *Founded/Ownrshp* 2005
Sales 217.1MM^E *EMP* 1,818^E
SIC 5947 Gift shop
CEO: Cynthia M Monroe
Dir Soc: Aimee Kain
Dir Soc: Clara Valentino
Ex Dir: Lou Fratturo
Ex Dir: Phil Jarvis
Ex Dir: Anna Schuler
Dir IT: Don Grevenow
Info Man: Annie Kerregan
Netwrk Eng: Roy Kidder
VP Mktg: Denaze Springer
Sls Dir: Patricia Macer

THIS
See TURTLE & HUGHES INC

D-U-N-S 96-222-9170
▲THL CREDIT INC
100 Federal St Fl 31, Boston, MA 02110-1883
Tel (800) 450-4424 *Founded/Ownrshp* 2010
Sales 94.2MM *EMP* 6^E
Accts Pricewaterhousecoopers Llp B
Tkr Sym TCRD *Exch* NGS
SIC 6726 Management investment funds, closed-end
CIO: Christopher J Flynn
**Ch Bd:* Nancy Hawthorne
Pr: W Hunter Stropp
COO: Terrence W Olson
Co-CEO: Sam W Tillinghast

D-U-N-S 60-521-8064 IMP
THL-NORTEK INVESTORS LLC
100 Federal St Ste 3100, Boston, MA 02110-1847
Tel (617) 227-1050 *Founded/Ownrshp* 2004
Sales 357.5MM^E *EMP* 10,000
SIC 3585 3444 3634 2431 Refrigeration & heating equipment; Sheet metalwork; Electric housewares & fans; Millwork
Mng Dir: Margaret Covell
Mng Dir: Ganesh RAO
Mng Dir: Kent Weldon

D-U-N-S 03-496-6671
THOLL FENCE INC
800 Glendale Ave, Sparks, NV 89431-5720
Tel (775) 358-8680 *Founded/Ownrshp* 1959
Sales 190.8MM^E *EMP* 3,673
SIC 1799

D-U-N-S 82-466-7906
THOMA BRAVO LLC
300 N La Salle Dr # 4350, Chicago, IL 60654-3415
Tel (312) 254-3300 *Founded/Ownrshp* 2014
Sales 1.6MMM^E *EMP* 2,420^E
SIC 6799 Investors
Mng Pt: Carl D Thoma
**Pt:* Seth Boro
**Pt:* Orlando Bravo
**Pt:* Scott Crabill
**Pt:* Lee M Mitchell
**Pt:* Holden Spaht
VP: Mike Hoffmann
VP: Arvindh Kumar
VP: A J Rohde
VP: Robert Sayle
VP: Peter Stefanski

D-U-N-S 01-381-4889
THOMA CRESSEY BRAVO INC
TCB
300 N La Salle Dr # 4350, Chicago, IL 60654-3415
Tel (312) 254-3300 *Founded/Ownrshp* 1998
Sales 616.2MM^E *EMP* 3,905
SIC 6799 8711 6311 6321 6531 7373 Venture capital companies; Engineering services; Life insurance; Accident & health insurance; Real estate agents & managers; Turnkey vendors, computer systems
Pr: Carl D Thoma
**CFO:* Katie Brennan
VP: Wayne Carpenter
**VP:* Bryan Cressey
VP: Peter Ehrich
VP: Lee M Mitchel
**VP:* Lee N Mitchell
Prin: David Mayer
Prin: D C Osborn
Prin: D J Plessinger
Prin: Jeanne Plessinger

D-U-N-S 00-215-4433 IMP/EXP
THOMAS & BETTS CORP (TN)
(*Suby of* ABB LTD)
8155 T&B Blvd, Memphis, TN 38125
Tel (901) 252-5000 *Founded/Ownrshp* 1996
Sales 3.3MMM^E *EMP* 9,400
SIC 3643 3312 3567 Electric connectors; Structural shapes & pilings, steel; Heating units & devices, industrial: electric
Pr: Charles L Treadway
Sr VP: David L Alyea
Sr VP: Juan J Cruz
Sr VP: Peggy Gann
VP: Stanley T Locke
VP: Connie C Muscarella
VP: J N Raies
VP: Franklin Sullivan
Exec: Raymond Spence
Prin: Ed Antar
Genl Mgr: Bane Todorovic
Board of Directors: Jeananne K Hauswald, Dean Jernigan, Ronald B Kalich Sr, Kenneth R Masterson, Rufus H Rivers, Kevin L Roberg, David D Stevens

D-U-N-S 55-667-5346
THOMAS & BETTS INTERNATIONAL INC
(*Suby of* THOMAS & BETTS CORP) ★
8155 T And B Blvd, Memphis, TN 38125-8888
Tel (901) 682-7766 *Founded/Ownrshp* 1967
Sales 228.8MM^E *EMP* 5,000
SIC 3699 3678 Electrical equipment & supplies; Electronic connectors
CEO: Dominic J Pileggi

D-U-N-S 04-811-1827 IMP
THOMAS & BETTS POWER SOLUTIONS LLC
J T PACKARD
(*Suby of* THOMAS & BETTS CORP) ★
5900 Eastport Blvd Bldg 5, Richmond, VA 23231-4459
Tel (804) 236-3300 *Founded/Ownrshp* 2007
Sales 110.0MM *EMP* 190
SIC 3629 Power conversion units, a.c. to d.c.: static-electric
Pr: Christian M Tecca
CFO: David Watkins
VP: Laura Brocklehurt
VP: James McGarvey
**Genl Mgr:* Pedro Mendieta
Dir IT: Hitesh Thakkar
Dir IT: Rich Wozniak
Software D: Joey Cornelius

D-U-N-S 19-143-6625
THOMAS AND KING INC
APPLEBEE'S
249 E Main St Ste 101, Lexington, KY 40507-1330
Tel (859) 254-2180 *Founded/Ownrshp* 1987
Sales 127.8MM^E *EMP* 5,000
SIC 5812

D-U-N-S 62-321-8468
THOMAS AND KING OF ARIZONA INC
APPLEBEE'S
249 E Main St Ste 101, Lexington, KY 40507-1330
Tel (859) 254-2180 *Founded/Ownrshp* 1990
Sales 52.0MM^E *EMP* 4,000
SIC 5812 5813 Italian restaurant; Bar (drinking places)
Pr: Michael Scanlon
VP: Cynthia Clark

D-U-N-S 02-100-3801
■THOMAS BLACK CORP
(*Suby of* SAFETY INSURANCE GROUP INC) ★
20 Custom House St # 400, Boston, MA 02110-3555
Tel (617) 951-0600 *Founded/Ownrshp* 2001
Sales NA *EMP* 512
SIC 6411 Insurance agents; Property & casualty insurance agent
Ch Bd: David Brussard
**Treas:* Bill Begley

D-U-N-S 00-323-3970
THOMAS BUILT BUSES INC
THOMAS BUSES
(*Suby of* DAIMLER TRUCKS NORTH AMERICA LLC) ★
1408 Courtesy Rd, High Point, NC 27260-7248
Tel (336) 889-4871 *Founded/Ownrshp* 1916
Sales 183.7MM^E *EMP* 1,769
SIC 3711 3713

THOMAS BUSES
See THOMAS BUILT BUSES INC

D-U-N-S 18-712-0233
THOMAS CONCRETE INDUSTRIES INC
(*Suby of* THOMAS CONCRETE GROUP AB)
2500 Cumberland Pkwy Se # 200, Atlanta, GA 30339-3922
Tel (770) 431-3300 *Founded/Ownrshp* 1985
Sales 199.8MM^E *EMP* 995
SIC 3273 5032 Ready-mixed concrete; Concrete & cinder block
Ch Bd: Karl Stenstrom
**Pr:* Jan Meijer
**CEO:* Johnny Senter
**CFO:* Barbara Evans
**CFO:* Bo E Nilsson
**VP:* Bill Davis
VP: Scott Senter
IT Man: Fredrik H Ekehaell
Plnt Mgr: Tracy Parker

D-U-N-S 08-543-2938
THOMAS CONCRETE OF GEORGIA INC
(*Suby of* THOMAS CONCRETE INDUSTRIES INC) ★
2500 Cumbrld Pkwy Se 20 Ste 200, Atlanta, GA 30339
Tel (770) 969-8545 *Founded/Ownrshp* 1977
Sales 141.2MM^E *EMP* 750
SIC 3273 Ready-mixed concrete
CEO: Johnny Senter
COO: Bradley Smith
Brnch Mgr: Jeremy Cochran
CTO: John Cook
Dir IT: Donald Blair
Tech Mgr: Justin Lazenby
Sls Mgr: Scott Mayer

THOMAS CUISINE MANAGEMENT
See THOMAS MANAGEMENT CORP

D-U-N-S 13-757-4898
THOMAS FIVE LTD
WENDY'S
5131 Post Rd Ste 203, Dublin, OH 43017-1197
Tel (614) 764-9495 *Founded/Ownrshp* 2014
Sales 31.1MM^E *EMP* 1,000
SIC 5812 Fast-food restaurant, chain
Mng Pt: Wendy Morse
**Pt:* Pamela Farber
**Pt:* Lorie Seitz
**Pt:* Molly Thomas

THOMAS FOODS INTERNATIONAL
See FOODCOMM INTERNATIONAL

D-U-N-S 00-142-0611 IMP
THOMAS G GALLAGHER INC (MA)
TGG
109 Smith Pl, Cambridge, MA 02138-1063
Tel (617) 661-7000 *Founded/Ownrshp* 1940, 1979
Sales 106.4MM *EMP* 120
Accts Feeley & Driscoll Pc
SIC 1711 Plumbing, heating, air-conditioning contractors
Pr: Brian T Potter
CFO: Kevin Turner
**VP:* Tom Devine
**VP:* Shawn Guertin
**VP:* Kevin J Potter
Off Mgr: Sara Cunningham

D-U-N-S 13-109-0735
THOMAS GALLAWAY CORP
TECHNOLOGENT
100 Spectrum Center Dr # 700, Irvine, CA 92618-4962
Tel (949) 716-9500 *Founded/Ownrshp* 2002
Sales 119.5MM^E *EMP* 154
SIC 7371 5045 Custom computer programming services; Computers & accessories, personal & home entertainment
CEO: Lezlie L Gallaway
**Pr:* Tom Gallaway
CFO: Peter Frankovsky
**Ex VP:* Marco Mohajer
**VP:* Jim Bevis
VP: Tom King
**VP:* Mike McLaughlin
VP: Brian Raposo
VP: Rod Wright
Prac Mgr: Mark Huff
Prgrm Mgr: Keith Vincent
Board of Directors: Jim Bevis

D-U-N-S 96-359-6726
THOMAS H LEE ADVISORS II LP
100 Federal St, Boston, MA 02110-1802
Tel (617) 227-1050 *Founded/Ownrshp* 1988
Sales 3.3MMM^E *EMP* 12,502^E
SIC 6282 Investment advice
Pr: Anthony J Dinovi
Mng Pt: Steve Ezzes
Sr VP: Stephanie S Stamatos
VP: Julia E C Brau
VP: Hobard A Cook
VP: Hobart A Cook
VP: Tyler D Griffith
VP: Douglas Haber
VP: Joined Thomas H Lee
Prin: Julia B Donnelly
Prin: Scott M Sperling

D-U-N-S 79-153-6902
THOMAS HEALTH SYSTEM INC
ST. FRANCIS HOSPITAL OF CHARLE
4605 Maccorkle Ave Sw, South Charleston, WV 25309-1311
Tel (304) 347-6500 *Founded/Ownrshp* 2006
Sales 279.1MM *EMP* 1,900^E
Accts Arnett Carbis Toothman Llp Ch
SIC 8741 Hospital management; Business management
Pr: Stephen Dexter
CFO: Renee Cross
Ex VP: Jeff Murphy
VP: Rebecca Brannon
VP: Brian Lilly
Dir Bus: Sara Cloer
CIO: Jane Harless
Doctor: John Burdette
Doctor: William Jeffery MD
Genl Couns: Aaron Alexander
Board of Directors: Thomas Heywood

D-U-N-S 13-167-2169
THOMAS HJ MEMORIAL HOSPITAL INC
4605 Maccorkle Ave Sw, South Charleston, WV 25309-1311
Tel (304) 766-3697 *Founded/Ownrshp* 1989
Sales 22.3MM^E *EMP* 1,200
SIC 8062 General medical & surgical hospitals
Pr: Steven Dexter
COO: Daniel Lauffer Fache
Pharmcst: Teresa Blundell

THOMAS HOSPITAL
See GULF HEALTH HOSPITALS INC

D-U-N-S 00-380-5272
THOMAS J DYER CO (OH)
5240 Lester Rd, Cincinnati, OH 45213-2522
Tel (513) 321-8100 *Founded/Ownrshp* 1908
Sales 94.6MM^E *EMP* 279
SIC 1711 Plumbing contractors; Ventilation & duct work contractor; Warm air heating & air conditioning contractor
CEO: Thomas D Grote Sr
COO: Joe Mirlisena

D-U-N-S 00-137-8892 IMP/EXP
THOMAS J LIPTON INC
UNILEVER FOODS CHILL
75 Merritt Blvd, Trumbull, CT 06611-5435
Tel (206) 381-3500 *Founded/Ownrshp* 2006
Sales 18.5M^E *EMP* 2,200
SIC 2099 2034 2035 2033 2098 2024

D-U-N-S 96-833-7696
THOMAS JEFFERSON NATIONAL ACCELERATOR FACILITY
JEFFERSON LAB
12000 Jefferson Ave # 12, Newport News, VA 23606-4468
Tel (757) 269-7100 *Founded/Ownrshp* 2011
Sales 138.7MM *EMP* 700
SIC 8731 Energy research
Prin: Hugh Montgomery
Bd of Dir: Wally Melnitchouk
VP: Carlos Salgado
Exec: Adrian Durant
Assoc Dir: Andrew Hutton
Assoc Dir: Christoph Leemann
DP Exec: Mike Staron
DP Exec: Kelly Tremblay
Dir IT: Chip Watson
Sftwr Eng: David Sheppard
Netwrk Eng: Brent Morris

D-U-N-S 05-328-4659
THOMAS JEFFERSON UNIVERSITY (PA)
JEFFERSON MEDICAL COLLEGE
1020 Walnut St Ste 1, Philadelphia, PA 19107-5567
Tel (215) 955-6000 *Founded/Ownrshp* 1824, 2016
Sales 776.8MM *EMP* 10,000
Accts Pricewaterhousecoopers Llp P
SIC 8062 8221 Hospital, professional nursing school; Hospital, medical school affiliation; Colleges universities & professional schools
CEO: Stephen K Klasko
**Pr:* Richard C Gozon
**Treas:* Alfred Salvato
Trst: Nancy Czarnecki
Trst: Edward Driscoll
Trst: Brian G Harrison
Trst: Frank Slattery
Trst: James Stratton
**VP:* Richard J Schmid
CIO: Doug Herrick
CIO: John Hoffler

D-U-N-S 96-053-5045 IMP
THOMAS JEFFERSON UNIVERSITY HOSPITALS INC
111 S 11th St, Philadelphia, PA 19107-4824
Tel (215) 955-5806 *Founded/Ownrshp* 1996
Sales 1.4MMM *EMP* 4,701
Accts Pricewaterhousecoopers Llp Ph
SIC 8062 General medical & surgical hospitals
Pr: David P McQuaid
**COO:* Alan Brechbill
COO: Richard Webster
CFO: George Rizzutl
Trst: Ira Brind
**Sr VP:* Neil Lubarsky
Sr VP: Geno Merli
VP: Susan Kunkel
VP: Stacey Meadows
VP: Patrice Miller
VP: Andrew Nathans
Exec: Mary Grant
Dir Lab: Rex B Conn
Dir Rx: Claudine El-Beyrouty

D-U-N-S 18-154-9916
THOMAS MANAGEMENT CORP
THOMAS CUISINE MANAGEMENT
700 E Franklin Rd, Meridian, ID 83642-7992
Tel (208) 884-5766 *Founded/Ownrshp* 1986
Sales 107.9MM^E *EMP* 525^E
SIC 5963 Food services, direct sales
Pr: Mark Kadell
**COO:* Greg Turpen
Treas: Matt Thomas
**VP:* Aaron Coleman
Exec: Seth E Bostick
Dist Mgr: Gregg Anderson
Dist Mgr: Kathleen Haggerty
Dist Mgr: Bill Vonbargen
Mktg Dir: Kriste Sumpter
Sls Mgr: Hal Hersley

D-U-N-S 03-984-6068
THOMAS PETROLEUM LLC
(*Suby of* PILOT THOMAS LOGISTICS) ★
9701 Us Highway 59 N, Victoria, TX 77905-5567
Tel (361) 582-5100 *Founded/Ownrshp* 1980
Sales 101.7MM^E *EMP* 406^E
SIC 5171 4225

THOMAS PRODUCTS DIVISION
See GARDNER DENVER THOMAS INC

D-U-N-S 03-624-6283 IMP
THOMAS PROPERTIES GROUP INC
515 S Flower St Ste 600, Los Angeles, CA 90071-2241
Tel (213) 613-1900 *Founded/Ownrshp* 2004
Sales 90.6MM *EMP* 141^E
SIC 6531

D-U-N-S 00-128-8414
THOMAS PUBLISHING CO LLC (NY)
5 Penn Plz Fl 9, New York, NY 10001-1860
Tel (212) 695-0500 *Founded/Ownrshp* 1898
Sales 246.7MM^E *EMP* 900
SIC 2741 2721 7374 7331 Directories: publishing only, not printed on site; Catalogs: publishing only, not printed on site; Trade journals: publishing only, not printed on site; Data processing service; Direct mail advertising services
Pr: Tom Holst Knudsen
Ch Bd: Jos E Andrade
Ex Dir: Stephen Buckley
Snr Ntwrk: Derek Leuridan
CTO: Hans Wald
Dir IT: John Blevins
IT Man: Kunal Choudhary
IT Man: Scott Emerich
IT Man: Walter K Koopalethes
Software D: Goutam Rajput
Software D: Michael Sadek

D-U-N-S 06-883-8042
THOMAS RONALD HALL OD
HALL VISION CLINIC
3610 Pruetts Chapel Rd, Paragould, AR 72450-6148
Tel (870) 236-8500 *Founded/Ownrshp* 2011
Sales 250.0MM *EMP* 2
SIC 8011 Offices & clinics of medical doctors
Owner: Thomas Ronald Hall

D-U-N-S 78-736-1476
THOMAS SAINT MIDTOWN HOSPITAL
SETON LODGE
(*Suby of* SETON LODGE) ★
2000 Church St, Nashville, TN 37236-4400
Tel (615) 284-5555 *Founded/Ownrshp* 2001
Sales 407.8MM *EMP* 4,500
SIC 8062 8011 General medical & surgical hospitals; Offices & clinics of medical doctors
CEO: Bernie Sherry
Dir Recs: Shonda Cannon
**Pr:* Tom Beeman
**CFO:* Renee Kessler
**CFO:* Ken Venuto
**VP:* Richard Glenn
Chf Nrs Of: Kathie Hirsch
Off Mgr: Cheryl Fassler
Off Mgr: Marla King
Off Mgr: Jessica Martineau
Dir QC: Missy Sanford

THOMAS SCIENTIFIC
See ARTHUR H THOMAS CO

THOMASVILLE FURNITURE
See TFI WIND DOWN INC

THOMASVILLE FURNITURE
See HERITAGE HOME GROUP LLC

THOMPSON & ELM
See CCC ASSOCIATES CO

D-U-N-S 07-485-6204
THOMPSON & KNIGHT LLP
1 Arts Plz 1722, Dallas, TX 75201
Tel (214) 969-1700 *Founded/Ownrshp* 1999
Sales 104.9MM^E *EMP* 750
SIC 8111 General practice attorney, lawyer
Mng Pt: Emily A Parker
Sr Pt: Amy Curtis
Sr Pt: Holt J Foster
Sr Pt: Herbert J Hammond
Sr Pt: Mark Weibel
Pt: Ted M Benn
Pt: Mark M Sloan
Pr: Armando Cavanha
COO: Diane Scheffler
CFO: Tom Laughlin
Treas: Timothy McCormick
Ofcr: Becky S Jackson
Ofcr: Nicole Olajuwon
Ofcr: Rita I Howdeshell
Board of Directors: Timothy R McCormick, Dallas Parker

D-U-N-S 02-035-4833
THOMPSON COBURN LLP
505 N 7th St Ste 2700, Saint Louis, MO 63101-1693
Tel (314) 552-6000 *Founded/Ownrshp* 1929
Sales 143.5MM^E *EMP* 650
SIC 8111 General practice law office
Pt: Steven E Garlock
Pt: Clifford Godiner
Pt: Paul Griesemer
Pt: Richard Jaudes
Pt: Lewis R Mills
Pt: Thomas J Minogue
Pt: Michael J Morris
Pt: Jon M Moyers
Pt: Carl J Pesce
Pt: Brendan Ryan
Pt: Timothy Sarsfield
Pt: Steven C Schwendemann
Pt: Julie T Woessner
VP: James Fogle
Exec: Theresa Brandstatter

D-U-N-S 15-421-5818 IMP
THOMPSON CONSTRUCTION GROUP INC
THOMPSON TURNER CONSTRUCTION
100 N Main St, Sumter, SC 29150-4948
Tel (803) 773-8005 *Founded/Ownrshp* 1986
Sales 282.5MM *EMP* 120
SIC 7349 1711 1721 1541 Cleaning service, industrial or commercial; Mechanical contractor; Exterior commercial painting contractor; Interior commercial painting contractor; Industrial buildings & warehouses
Pr: Greg A Thompson
**CFO:* Curtis Hutto
CFO: Diane Schultz
VP: Barry Falin
VP: Ron Going
VP: Bob Landers
**VP:* Marco G Lardi
VP: Rick Lotts
**VP:* Lewis E Thompson
**VP:* Harold Turner

D-U-N-S 08-041-0562
THOMPSON CREEK METALS CO INC
26 W Dry Creek Cir, Littleton, CO 80120-8063
Tel (303) 761-8801 *Founded/Ownrshp* 2000
Sales 494.1MM *EMP* 700
Tkr Sym TCPTF *Exch* OTO
SIC 1021 1041 1044 1061 Copper ores; Gold ores; Silver ores; Ferroalloy ores, except vanadium
Pr: Jacques Perron
**Ch Bd:* Timothy J Haddon
CFO: Pamela L Saxton
Chf Cred: Mark A Wilson
Board of Directors: Denis C Arsenault, Carol T Banducci, Kevin Drover, James L Freer, James P Geyer, Anne E Giardini

D-U-N-S 83-304-8304 IMP
THOMPSON CREEK METALS CO USA
26 W Dry Creek Cir, Littleton, CO 80120-8063
Tel (303) 761-8801 *Founded/Ownrshp* 1998
Sales 494.1MM *EMP* 1,000
Accts Kpmg Llp Denver Colorado
SIC 1061 Molybdenum ores mining
Pr: Jacques Perron
**Ch Bd:* Kevin Loughrey
**CFO:* Pamela L Saxton
**VP:* Robert Dorfler
VP: Bruce R Wright
Genl Mgr: Larry D Clark
Sls Mgr: Jeff Allison
Snr Mgr: Emad Agha

D-U-N-S 80-939-9165 IMP/EXP
THOMPSON CREEK MINING CO
(*Suby of* THOMPSON CREEK METALS CO USA) ★
26 W Dry Creek Cir # 810, Littleton, CO 80120-8063
Tel (303) 783-6413 *Founded/Ownrshp* 1993
Sales 101.0MM^E *EMP* 1,000
SIC 2899 1061 Anti-glare material; Molybdenum ores mining
CEO: Kevin Loughrey
**Pr:* Jacques Perron
**CFO:* Pamela L Saxton
**Ex VP:* Mark Wilson

D-U-N-S 07-925-8785
THOMPSON CREEK MINING LTD
(*Suby of* THOMPSON CREEK MINING CO) ★
26 W Dry Creek Cir # 810, Littleton, CO 80120-8063
Tel (303) 761-8801 *Founded/Ownrshp* 1997
Sales 11.7MM^E *EMP* 1,000
SIC 1061 2899 2819 Molybdenum ores mining; Chemical preparations; Industrial inorganic chemicals
CEO: Kevin Loughrey
CFO: Pamela L Saxton
Ex VP: Mark Wilson

D-U-N-S 08-233-9268
THOMPSON HINE LLP
127 Public Sq, Cleveland, OH 44114-1217
Tel (216) 566-5500 *Founded/Ownrshp* 1898
Sales 123.7MM^E *EMP* 814
SIC 8111 General practice law office
Pt: Michael L Hardy
Genl Pt: Timothy Coughlin
Pt: James B Aronoff
Pt: April M Boise
Pt: Richard A De Palma
Pt: Ludo M Deklerck
Pt: Charles L Freed
Pt: Laura Hauser
Pt: Dave Huprich
Pt: JC Miller
Pt: Craig Morterhous
Pt: Matthew Nicely
Pt: Marci P Schmerler
Pt: Patricia M Smitson
Pt: George J Walsh
Mng Pt: David J Hooker
Mng Pt: Deborah Read
COO: Frank A Lamanna
CFO: Michael Goldberg
CFO: Michael E Goldbrg
CFO: Steve Mauro

D-U-N-S 09-496-7424 EXP
THOMPSON HOSPITALITY CORP
OBI SUSHI
1741 Bus Ctr Dr Ste 200, Reston, VA 20190
Tel (703) 757-5500 *Founded/Ownrshp* 1998
Sales 109.0MM *EMP* 3,000
SIC 5812 Restaurant, family: chain
Pr: Warren M Thompson
**COO:* Maurice Jenoure
**CFO:* Ali Azima
**Sr VP:* Shawn O'Quinn
**Sr VP:* Benita Thompson-Byas
VP: Carl Levin

D-U-N-S 07-422-0372
THOMPSON HOSPITALITY SERVICES LLC
(*Suby of* OBI SUSHI) ★
1741 Bus Ctr Dr Ste 200, Reston, VA 20190
Tel (703) 757-5560 *Founded/Ownrshp* 1997
Sales 79.4MM *EMP* 1,000
SIC 5812 Contract food services
Ch: Warren W Thompson
COO: Maurice Jenoure
CFO: Ali Azima

THOMPSON J CLEO
See THOMPSON PETROLEUM CORP

D-U-N-S 16-093-6175 EXP
THOMPSON MACHINERY COMMERCE CORP
CATERPILLAR AUTHORIZED DEALER
1245 Bridgestone Pkwy, La Vergne, TN 37086-3510
Tel (615) 256-2424 *Founded/Ownrshp* 1980
Sales 245.9MM^E *EMP* 520
SIC 5082 7353 Construction & mining machinery; Earth moving equipment, rental or leasing
Pr: Dewitt C Thompson
**CFO:* James B Ezzell
**Treas:* Mike White
**VP:* John Thompson
VP: Myra Wray
Exec: Tom Kilbane
Exec: Donny Virden
IT Man: Johnny Taylor
MIS Mgr: Jj Lay
Sls Mgr: Jim Simmons

D-U-N-S 00-965-2355 IMP/EXP
THOMPSON OLDE INC
3250 Camino Del Sol, Oxnard, CA 93030-8998
Tel (800) 827-1565 *Founded/Ownrshp* 1944
Sales 88.2MM^E *EMP* 150
SIC 5023 2631 5149 Kitchenware; Container, packaging & boxboard; Spices & seasonings
CEO: Jeffrey M Shumway
**CFO:* Scott Ash
VP: Dale Deberry
Sfty Mgr: Doug McKenzie
Natl Sales: Roy R Amsrud

D-U-N-S 05-217-6294
THOMPSON PETROLEUM CORP (TX)
THOMPSON J CLEO
325 N Saint Paul St # 4300, Dallas, TX 75201-3801
Tel (214) 953-1177 *Founded/Ownrshp* 1978
Sales 92.9MM^E *EMP* 90
SIC 1311 Crude petroleum production; Natural gas production
VP: Linda Thompson Gordon
**Pr:* James Cleo Thompson Jr
**Treas:* Cliff T Milford
**VP:* Frank Peterman
**VP:* Christine Thompson
**VP:* Jean C Thompson

D-U-N-S 08-037-4234
THOMPSON SCHOOL DISTRICT R2J (CO)
800 S Taft Ave, Loveland, CO 80537-6347
Tel (970) 613-5000 *Founded/Ownrshp* 1868
Sales 151.6MM *EMP* 2,113
Accts Swanhorst & Company Llc Green
SIC 8211 Public elementary school; Public junior high school; Public senior high school
**CFO:* Steve Towne
Exec: Melissa Adams
Exec: Michael Hausmann
IT Man: Nancy Douglas
IT Man: Sherry Shay
Sftwr Eng: Gaurav Pal
Teacher Pr: Bill Siebers
Psych: Pamela Knipscheer

D-U-N-S 06-935-1997 IMP/EXP
THOMPSON STEEL CO INC (MA)
ARROW THOMPSON METALS
120 Royall St Ste 2, Canton, MA 02021-1096
Tel (781) 828-8800 *Founded/Ownrshp* 1923, 1974
Sales 104.4MM^E *EMP* 250
SIC 5051 3316 Steel; Strip steel, cold-rolled: from purchased hot-rolled
CEO: Mary Ryan
Pr: Edward Ryan
CFO: Mary L Ryan
Treas: Frederick Conway
Plnt Mgr: Douglas Fisk
VP Sls: Donald Troendly

D-U-N-S 88-375-6082 EXP
THOMPSON THRIFT CONSTRUCTION INC
THOMPSON THRIFT DEVELOPMENT
901 Wabash Ave Ste 300, Terre Haute, IN 47807-3233
Tel (812) 235-5959 *Founded/Ownrshp* 1994
Sales 118.4MM^E *EMP* 105
SIC 1542 6531 Commercial & office building, new construction; Real estate agents & managers
Pr: John Thompson
**CFO:* Cindy Gordon
CFO: Sindy Gordon
Sr VP: Jose Kreutz
Sr VP: Henry Stadler
VP: John Andres
**VP:* Jerry Ennis
VP: Julie Galloway
**VP:* Paul Thrift
Dir Bus: Roy Dressler
CTO: Henry Standler

THOMPSON THRIFT DEVELOPMENT
See THOMPSON THRIFT CONSTRUCTION INC

D-U-N-S 00-890-0542 IMP/EXP
THOMPSON TRACTOR CO INC
CATERPILLAR AUTHORIZED DEALER
2258 Pinson Valley Pkwy, Birmingham, AL 35217-2009
Tel (334) 215-5000 *Founded/Ownrshp* 1957
Sales 613.3MM^E *EMP* 1,500
SIC 5082 5084 5085 General construction machinery & equipment; Mining machinery & equipment, except petroleum; Logging equipment & supplies; Industrial machinery & equipment; Industrial supplies
Ch Bd: Michael D Thompson
**Treas:* Paul Tombrello
**Ex VP:* Michael G Rooney
VP: Bob Bacon
VP: Kenny Bishop
**VP:* Guy S Clifton
**VP:* Thomas H McGough
Brnch Mgr: Jared Pennington
Genl Mgr: Brian Hamilton
Netwrk Mgr: Bobby Morris
Mtls Mgr: Richard Lindley

D-U-N-S 04-352-1512
THOMPSON TRUCK & TRAILER INC
HAWKEYE INTERNATIONAL TRUCKS
2740 6th St Sw, Cedar Rapids, IA 52404-4002
Tel (319) 364-2491 *Founded/Ownrshp* 1998
Sales 107.5MM^E *EMP* 364
SIC 5012 Trucks, commercial
Pr: Dennis Thompson
COO: Travis Thompson
**Sec:* Sharon Lovtinsky
Exec: David Duwe
Genl Mgr: Jeff Young
Off Mgr: Kathy Hougland
Store Mgr: John Hunt
Dir IT: Dan Abbott
Dir IT: Jason Bleadorn
Sfty Dirs: Carl Bright

THOMPSON TURNER CONSTRUCTION
See THOMPSON CONSTRUCTION GROUP INC

THOMSON FINANCIAL
See THOMSON REUTERS (MARKETS) LLC

D-U-N-S 94-577-3950 IMP
THOMSON PLASTICS INC
130 Quality Dr, Thomson, GA 30824-8021
Tel (706) 828-7508 *Founded/Ownrshp* 1996
Sales 114.6MM^E *EMP* 400^E
SIC 3949 3089 Sporting & athletic goods; Plastic containers, except foam; Injection molding of plastics
CEO: Bruce A Landino
**Pr:* Rick Kibbey
**Pr:* Jeff Miller
**CFO:* Charles Irminger
**VP:* Harvey Bright
Plnt Mgr: Genu Rebottaro
Ql Cn Mgr: Mike Lamb

THOMSON REUTERS
See REUTERS AMERICA LLC

D-U-N-S 07-939-8738
THOMSON REUTERS (GRC) INC
2711 Centerville Rd # 400, Wilmington, DE 19808-1660
Tel (212) 227-7357 *Founded/Ownrshp* 2012

Section I

Businesses Alphabetically

Sales 11.7MM^E EMP 3,000
SIC 7291 8111 8721 8733 8741 Tax return preparation services; Legal services; Accounting services, except auditing; Research institute; Scientific research agency; Management services
Prin: Thomson Reuters

D-U-N-S 00-615-8414 IMP
■THOMSON REUTERS (LEGAL) INC (MN)
(Suby of THOMSON FINANCIAL) ★
610 Opperman Dr, Eagan, MN 55123-1340
Tel (651) 687-7000 Founded/Ownrshp 1876
Sales 4.7MMM^E EMP 16,000
SIC 2731 Books: publishing & printing; Textbooks: publishing & printing
CEO: Michael Suchsland
*Pr: Brian H Hall
COO: Vincent Caraher
*CFO: Paul Fischer
VP: Bernadette Johnston
VP: Kevin Ritchey
VP: Stephen Rubley
Exec: Tristi Wilson
Snr Sftwr: Matthew Dimich
Snr Sftwr: Janusz Gryczman
Snr Sftwr: Jeff Hall

D-U-N-S 00-220-8221
■THOMSON REUTERS (MARKETS) LLC
THOMSON FINANCIAL
(Suby of THOMSON COMPANY INC, THE)
3 Times Sq Lbby Mailroom, New York, NY 10036-6564
Tel (646) 223-4000 Founded/Ownrshp 2011
Sales 5.0MMM^E EMP 16,000
SIC 7375 Information retrieval services
VP: Miftah Khan
VP: Richard Peterson
Exec: Peter Shea
Mng Dir: David Gandy

D-U-N-S 16-910-8482
THOMSON REUTERS (SCIENTIFIC) INC
ISI RESEARCHSOFT
(Suby of ONEX CORPORATION)
1500 Spring Garden St # 400, Philadelphia, PA 19130-4127
Tel (215) 386-0100 Founded/Ownrshp 2016
Sales 77.1MM^E EMP 4,200
SIC 8731 Commercial physical research
Pr: Vincent Caraher
Treas: Mike Eastwood
VP: Sari Dweck

D-U-N-S 00-232-0455
■THOMSON REUTERS (SCIENTIFIC) LLC
ENDNOTE
(Suby of THOMSON COMPANY INC, THE)
1500 Spring Garden St # 400, Philadelphia, PA 19130-4127
Tel (215) 386-0100 Founded/Ownrshp 1992
Sales 98.5MM^E EMP 800
SIC 2741 7372 Miscellaneous publishing; Prepackaged software
Pr: Christopher Kibarian
CEO: James C Smith
Ex VP: Stephane Bello

D-U-N-S 11-721-1693
■THOMSON REUTERS (TAX & ACCOUNTING) INC
ACCOUNTANTS MEDIA GROUP
(Suby of THOMSON REUTERS US LLC) ★
2395 Midway Rd, Carrollton, TX 75006-2521
Tel (800) 431-9025 Founded/Ownrshp 1969
Sales 340.3MM^E EMP 1,500
SIC 2721 7371 Periodicals: publishing only; Computer software development
CEO: James C Smith
*Pr: Roy Martin
*Pr: Brian Pecarrelli
*CFO: Stephane Bello
*Treas: Robert Bahash
*VP: Sari Dwek
VP: Daniel Napoli
Prin: Lori Sheehy

D-U-N-S 12-624-6532
■THOMSON REUTERS APPLICATIONS INC
(Suby of WEST A THOMSON REUTERS BUS) ★
610 Opperman Dr, Eagan, MN 55123-1340
Tel (651) 687-7000 Founded/Ownrshp 2002
Sales 98.4MM^E EMP 3,941^E
SIC 7374 Data processing & preparation
CEO: Peter Warwick
*Pr: Brian Hall

D-U-N-S 09-075-8129 IMP
■THOMSON REUTERS CORP
(Suby of WOODBRIDGE COMPANY LIMITED, THE)
3 Times Sq Lbby Mailroom, New York, NY 10036-6564
Tel (646) 223-4000 Founded/Ownrshp 1977
Sales 12.2MMM EMP 52,000
Tkr Sym TRI Exch NYS
SIC 2741 8111 7372 7383 Miscellaneous publishing; Legal services; Prepackaged software; News syndicates
Pr: James C Smith
*Ch Bd: David Thomson
Pr: Vin Caraher
Pr: David W Craig
Pr: Gonzalo Lissarrague
Pr: Susan Taylor Martin
Pr: Brian Peccarelli
CFO: Stephane Bello
Ofcr: Gus Carlson
Ofcr: Mark Schlageter
Ex VP: Rick King
Ex VP: Neil Masterson
Ex VP: Brian Scanlon
Ex VP: Deirdre Stanley
Ex VP: Diedre Stanley
VP: Benjamin Goodband
Board of Directors: Peter J Thomson, Sheila C Bair, David W Binet, Mary Cirillo, W Edmund Clark, Michael E Daniels, P Thomas Jenkins, Ken Olisa, Vance K Opperman, Barry Salzberg

D-U-N-S 87-275-2626
■THOMSON REUTERS US LLC
(Suby of THOMSON REUTERS CORP) ★
1 Station Pl Ste 6, Stamford, CT 06902-6893
Tel (203) 539-8000 Founded/Ownrshp 1996
Sales 364.2MM^E EMP 2,500^E
SIC 2711 Newspapers, publishing & printing
CEO: Dick Harington
Sr VP: Pam Kushmerick
Sr VP: Charles Siegel
Sr VP: Carl Urbania
*VP: Edward Friedland
VP: Martin Jones
VP: Kristen McCarthy
VP: Parks Morris
VP: Anna Patruno

D-U-N-S 18-481-5496
THOR EQUITIES LLC
THOR PROPERTIES
25 W 39th St Fl 11, New York, NY 10018-4074
Tel (212) 529-5055 Founded/Ownrshp 2001
Sales 283.5MM^E EMP 850^E
SIC 6531 6211 6282 Real estate brokers & agents; Real estate managers; Investment bankers; Investment advisory service
Pr: Joseph Jack Sitt
VP: Adam Rappaport

D-U-N-S 03-820-4913 IMP/EXP
▲THOR INDUSTRIES INC
601 E Beardsley Ave, Elkhart, IN 46514-3305
Tel (574) 970-7460 Founded/Ownrshp 1980
Sales 4.5MMM EMP 10,450^E
Tkr Sym THO Exch NYS
SIC 3799 3711 Recreational vehicles; Buses, all types, assembly of
Pr: Robert W Martin
*Ch Bd: Peter B Orthwein
Pr: CAM Boyer
CFO: Colleen A Zuhl
Ex VP: Aram Koltookian
Sr VP: Todd Woelfer
VP: Kenneth D Julian
VP: John Rhymer
Board of Directors: Andrew E Graves, Wilson R Jones, J Allen Kosowsky, Alan Siegel, Jan H Suwinski, James L Ziemer

D-U-N-S 61-466-3722
■THOR MOTOR COACH INC
(Suby of THOR INDUSTRIES INC) ★
520 County Road 15, Elkhart, IN 46516-9552
Tel (574) 266-1111 Founded/Ownrshp 1990
Sales 164.4MM^E EMP 275
SIC 3716 3792 Motor homes; Recreational van conversion (self-propelled), factory basis; Travel trailers & campers
Pr: Jeff Kime
Natl Sales: Adam Gudger

D-U-N-S 04-901-0077
THOR PALMER HOUSE HOTEL LLC
PALMER HOUSE HILTON
(Suby of THOR PROPERTIES) ★
17 E Monroe St Lbby 10, Chicago, IL 60603-5620
Tel (312) 726-7500 Founded/Ownrshp 2005
Sales 126.4MM EMP 850
SIC 7011 Hotels & motels
Genl Mgr: Dean Lane
Mng Dir: Daniel Chan
Sls Mgr: Tiffany Wu

THOR PROPERTIES
See THOR EQUITIES LLC

D-U-N-S 07-015-6955 IMP
■THORATEC CORP
(Suby of ST JUDE MEDICAL INC) ★
6035 Stoneridge Dr, Pleasanton, CA 94588-3270
Tel (925) 847-8600 Founded/Ownrshp 2015
Sales 477.5MM EMP 1,030
SIC 3845 3841 Electromedical equipment; Surgical & medical instruments; Diagnostic apparatus, medical
Pr: D Keith Grossman
*CFO: Taylor C Harris
VP: Robin Bostic
VP: Lauren Hernandez
VP: Donald Middlebrook
VP: Laxmi Perii
VP: Gil Rivas
Exec: Julie Piona
Dir Lab: Judy Benenato
Sftwr Eng: Thomas Palmer
Sfty Dirs: Michael Magnano

THORCO INDUSTRIES
See LA DARLING CO LLC

D-U-N-S 79-587-0534 IMP
■THORCO INDUSTRIES LLC
(Suby of THORCO INDUSTRIES) ★
1401 Highway 49b, Paragould, AR 72450-3139
Tel (417) 682-3375 Founded/Ownrshp 1983
Sales 121.1MM^E EMP 400
SIC 5063 Electronic wire & cable
Exec: Tom Day

D-U-N-S 19-395-3726 IMP
THORLABS INC
56 Sparta Ave, Newton, NJ 07860-2402
Tel (973) 579-7227 Founded/Ownrshp 1986
Sales 217.1MM^E EMP 704
SIC 3826 Analytical optical instruments
Pr: Alex Cable
COO: Carmine Lencsak
CFO: Robert Regimbal
Genl Mgr: David Beatson
Genl Mgr: Peter Heim
Snr Sftwr: Trey Taylor
IT Man: Shashi Muir
Tech Mgr: Carl Lin
Sls Dir: Enrique Chang
Mktg Mgr: Anjul Davis

D-U-N-S 83-565-4690
THORNBURG INVESTMENT MANAGEMENT
THORNBURG INVESTMENT MGT
2300 N Ridgetop Rd, Santa Fe, NM 87506-8361
Tel (505) 984-0200 Founded/Ownrshp 1984
Sales 114.1MM^E EMP 250
SIC 6211 Underwriters, security
CEO: Brian Mickman
*Sec: Carolyn Dobbs
Ofcr: Annette Alire
Ofcr: Kay Condiss
Ofcr: Stephen Velie
Ex VP: Michael Doorley
*VP: Brian J McMahon
Exec: Stephanie Gonzales
Comm Dir: Rebecca Carrier
*Prin: Dawn Fisher
Mng Dir: Chris Elsmark

THORNBURG INVESTMENT MGT
See THORNBURG INVESTMENT MANAGEMENT

D-U-N-S 06-251-2397
THORNTON TOMASETTI INC (NY)
51 Madison Ave Fl 19, New York, NY 10010-1692
Tel (917) 661-7800 Founded/Ownrshp 1956, 1971
Sales 286.0MM^E EMP 1,200
SIC 8711 8712

THORNTONS FLEETWORKS
See THORNTONS INC

D-U-N-S 05-427-4758
THORNTONS INC
THORNTONS FLEETWORKS
10101 Linn Station Rd # 200, Louisville, KY 40223-3848
Tel (502) 425-8022 Founded/Ownrshp 1952
Sales 414.5MM^E EMP 2,500
SIC 5461 5411 Bakeries; Convenience stores
Pr: Matthew A Thornton
Pr: Jason Doyle
COO: Graham Baughman
*COO: Tony Harris
*CFO: Christopher Kamer
*Ex VP: Brenda Stackhouse
*VP: David Bridgers
VP: Gary Maynard
Rgnl Mgr: Scott Bell
Genl Mgr: Nicholas Barber
Genl Mgr: Patricia Berens

D-U-N-S 02-270-9278
THORTON TOWNSHIP HIGH SCHOOL DISTRICT 205
15001 Broadway Ave, Harvey, IL 60426-2272
Tel (708) 225-4036 Founded/Ownrshp 1985
Sales 122.9MM EMP 10
SIC 8211 Secondary school

D-U-N-S 61-059-2917 IMP
THORWORKS INDUSTRIES INC
SEALMASTER
2520 Campbell St, Sandusky, OH 44870-5309
Tel (419) 626-4375 Founded/Ownrshp 1990
Sales 90.0MM^E EMP 175
Accts Miller Mcdonald Inc Cpas Berni
SIC 2851 3531 2952 2951 2891 2816 Paints & paint additives; Construction machinery; Asphalt felts & coatings; Asphalt paving mixtures & blocks; Adhesives & sealants; Inorganic pigments
Pr: David Thorson
*CFO: Chris Nielsen

D-U-N-S 00-324-2781 IMP
THOS SOMERVILLE CO
16155 Trade Zone Ave, Upper Marlboro, MD 20774-8733
Tel (301) 390-9575 Founded/Ownrshp 1951
Sales 518.9MM^E EMP 400
SIC 5074 5075 Plumbing fittings & supplies; Warm air heating equipment & supplies; Air conditioning & ventilation equipment & supplies
CEO: Patrick J McGowan
*VP: Daniel Kelly
*VP: Bruce Livingston
*VP: Pete Misiewicz
*VP: Douglas Riley
*VP: Scott Weir
*Prin: Thos Somerville
Off Mgr: Cindy Phipps
Sales Asso: Scott Fraley
Sales Asso: Linda Kates
Sales Asso: Derek Miller

D-U-N-S 80-770-8490
THOUGHTWORKS INC
200 E Randolph St # 2500, Chicago, IL 60601-6501
Tel (312) 373-1000 Founded/Ownrshp 1993
Sales 282.8MM^E EMP 1,700
SIC 8741 Management services
Ch: Neville Roy Singham
*Pr: Guo Xiao
*CFO: Erin Cummins
*CFO: Dan Goodwin
Ofcr: Matthew Simons
VP: Gary Degregorio
*VP: Bruce Ferguson
Mng Dir: Ronaldo Ferraz
Mng Dir: Craig Gorsline
Mng Dir: Xiao Guo
Mng Dir: Nick Hines

THPG
See TEXAS-HEALTH-PHYSICIANS-GROUP

D-U-N-S 61-572-7450
THQ INC
THQ SAN DIEGO
21900 Burbank Blvd # 100, Woodland Hills, CA 91367-7922
Tel (818) 591-1310 Founded/Ownrshp 1997
Sales 112.7MM^E EMP 1,088^E
SIC 7372

THQ SAN DIEGO
See THQ INC

D-U-N-S 07-875-8878
THR PROPERTY MANAGEMENT LP
1201 Elm St Ste 1600, Dallas, TX 75270-2038
Tel (214) 965-6053 Founded/Ownrshp 2012
Sales 49.3MM^E EMP 1,400
SIC 6531 Real estate agents & managers
CEO: Walt Smith
COO: Marysusan Wanich
CFO: Pal Ottesen

D-U-N-S 06-995-6225 IMP/EXP
THRALL ENTERPRISES INC
180 N Stetson Ave, Chicago, IL 60601-6794
Tel (312) 621-8200 Founded/Ownrshp 1972
Sales 140.5MM^E EMP 500
SIC 2893 Printing ink
Ch Bd: Jeffrey J Thrall
Treas: Nancy G Haller
*VP: James R Thrall
*VP: Marilynn Thrall

THRASHERS TOOLS AND TOYS
See DENISE THRASHER

D-U-N-S 07-520-9858
THREE CITIES RESEARCH INC
(Suby of QUILVEST PRIVATE EQUITY LTD)
37 W 20th St Ste 908, New York, NY 10011-3715
Tel (212) 838-9660 Founded/Ownrshp 1991
Sales 200.8MM^E EMP 2,351
SIC 6282 Investment advisory service
VP: J William Uhrig
*Pr: Willem De Vogel
Mng Dir: Christopher Erickson

THREE PICKWICK PLAZA
See GENERAL ATLANTIC LLC

D-U-N-S 07-180-7895
THREE RIVERS COMMUNITY HOSPITAL AND HEALTH CENTER
(Suby of ASANTE HEALTH SYSTEM) ★
500 Sw Ramsey Ave, Grants Pass, OR 97527-5554
Tel (541) 472-7000 Founded/Ownrshp 1996
Sales 127.7MM EMP 650
SIC 8062 General medical & surgical hospitals
Pr: Roy Vinyard

D-U-N-S 08-833-7423
THREE RIVERS CORP
3069 E Vantage Point Dr, Midland, MI 48642-7830
Tel (989) 631-9726 Founded/Ownrshp 1976
Sales 126.5MM^E EMP 300
Accts Andrews Hooper Pavlik Plc Mid
SIC 1542 1541 Commercial & office building, new construction; Industrial buildings, new construction
Pr: Dan Kozakiewicz
*COO: Randy Sherman
*Sr VP: Kevin Gay
*Sr VP: Clifford J Pelton
VP: Ted High
*VP: Mike Mallek
Exec: Elaine Sobieray
Off Admin: Peggy Yost

D-U-N-S 10-096-3334
THREE RIVERS HOLDINGS INC
300 Oxford Dr, Monroeville, PA 15146-2361
Tel (412) 858-4000 Founded/Ownrshp 1999
Sales 15.7MM^E EMP 1,200
SIC 8011 Health maintenance organization
Pr: Warren Carmichael
*Sec: William Lawson Jr

D-U-N-S 15-634-1323
THREE RIVERS PARK DISTRICT
3000 Xenium Ln N, Plymouth, MN 55441-2661
Tel (763) 559-9000 Founded/Ownrshp 1957
Sales 65.6MM EMP 2,430
Accts Redpath And Company Ltd St
SIC 7999 Recreation services
Pr: Judith Anderson
*CFO: Howard Koolick
*Sec: Carol Schreiber
*VP: Marilynn Corcoran

THREE RIVERS UROLOGY - UPMC
See UPMC HEALTH SYSTEM

D-U-N-S 11-121-5559
THREE SAINTS BAY LLC
(Suby of OLD HARBOR NATIVE CORP) ★
10440 Balls Ford Rd, Manassas, VA 20109-2501
Tel (703) 365-0450 Founded/Ownrshp 2002
Sales 121.1MM^E EMP 150
SIC 8742 Business consultant
Pr: Jeffrey Babos
CFO: Larry Mosher
Ofcr: Beverly Buswell
Genl Mgr: Melanie Rotz

D-U-N-S 60-357-4880
THREE SPRINGS INC
1131 Eagletree Ln Sw, Huntsville, AL 35801-6491
Tel (256) 880-3339 Founded/Ownrshp 1985
Sales 25.5MM^E EMP 1,032
Accts Barfield Murphy Shank & Smit
SIC 8322 8093 Child related social services; Mental health clinic, outpatient
Pr: R Gary Saliba
*Treas: Steve Koslow

D-U-N-S 10-005-7348
THREE VILLAGE CENTRAL SCHOOL DISTRICT
100 Suffolk Ave, Stony Brook, NY 11790-1821
Tel (631) 730-4000 Founded/Ownrshp 1967
Sales 100.5MM^E EMP 1,298
Accts Rs Abrams & Co Llp Ronkon
SIC 8211 Public elementary & secondary schools
Prin: Lori Biro

THREE Z PRINTING
See THREE-Z PRINTING CO

D-U-N-S 00-796-3408
THREE-WAY CHEVROLET CO
4501 Wible Rd, Bakersfield, CA 93313-2639
Tel (661) 847-6400 Founded/Ownrshp 1977

Sales 137.3MM *EMP* 190
SIC 5511 5531 7515 7538 7532

D-U-N-S 08-691-8950
THREE-Z PRINTING CO
THREE Z PRINTING
902 W Main St, Teutopolis, IL 62467-1329
Tel (217) 857-3153 *Founded/Ownrshp* 1977
Sales 150.8MM^E *EMP* 450
SIC 2752 Commercial printing, offset
Pr: Dan Zerrusen
* *Treas:* Lorraine Zerrusen
* *VP:* Bill Zerrusen
VP: Bill Zerrusenis
CTO: Peggy Probst

THREESIXTY GROUP
See MERCHSOURCE LLC

THRESHER ARTISAN WHEAT
See AGSPRING IDAHO LLC

D-U-N-S 02-119-2216 IMP/EXP
THRESHOLD ENTERPRISES LTD
VANGUARD MARKETING
23 Janis Way, Scotts Valley, CA 95066-3546
Tel (831) 438-6851 *Founded/Ownrshp* 1978
Sales 148.1MM^E *EMP* 500^E
SIC 2833 Vitamins, natural or synthetic: bulk, uncompounded
CEO: Ira L Goldberg
CFO: Gary Swartzman
IT Man: Charlie Knowler
QC Dir: Phil Garner
Ql Cn Mgr: Eric Dudas
VP Mktg: Todd Williams
Mktg Dir: Brian Cayton
Mktg Mgr: Maribel Rodolfo
Sales Asso: Michael Preston
Snr Mgr: Linette Quist

THRIFT TOWN
See NORQUIST SALVAGE CORP INC

THRIFTY CAR RENTAL
See THRIFTY RENT-A-CAR SYSTEM INC

D-U-N-S 04-724-6400
THRIFTY DRUG STORES INC
THRIFTY WHITE DRUG
6055 Nathan Ln N Ste 200, Plymouth, MN 55442-1675
Tel (763) 513-4300 *Founded/Ownrshp* 1966
Sales 388.8MM^E *EMP* 1,700
SIC 5912 Drug stores
Pr: Robert J Narveson
Pr: Jeffrey Lindoo
* *CFO:* Mark Basco
Dir IT: Matt Ode

THRIFTY ICE CREAM
See BON SUISSE INC

D-U-N-S 12-718-8618
■THRIFTY INC
(*Suby of* DOLLAR THRIFTY AUTOMOTIVE GROUP INC) ★
5310 E 31st St Ste 100, Tulsa, OK 74135-5009
Tel (918) 665-3930 *Founded/Ownrshp* 1999
Sales 176.5MM^E *EMP* 2,500
SIC 6794 7515 7514 7513 Franchises, selling or licensing; Passenger car leasing; Rent-a-car service; Truck leasing, without drivers; Truck rental, without drivers
Sr Cor Off: Chuck Barbo
VP: Craig Floyd
Admn Mgr: Cherie Claussen
Admn Mgr: Carol Macneil
Admn Mgr: Brian Michael
Admn Mgr: Carla Ulschak

D-U-N-S 00-723-1434
■THRIFTY RENT-A-CAR SYSTEM INC
THRIFTY CAR RENTAL
(*Suby of* THRIFTY INC) ★
14501 Hertz Quail Spgs, Oklahoma City, OK 73134-2628
Tel (918) 665-3930 *Founded/Ownrshp* 1950
Sales 88.7MM^E *EMP* 1,900
SIC 7515 7514 7513 Passenger car leasing; Rent-a-car service; Truck leasing, without drivers; Truck rental, without drivers
Pr: R Scott Anderson
VP: Dave Cumberland
VP: Randy Holder
Brnch Mgr: Steven Woodruff
DP Exec: Rick Morris
Sales Exec: Al Bryant
Sls Mgr: Steven Degeorge

THRIFTY WHITE DRUG
See THRIFTY DRUG STORES INC

THRILLIST.COM
See MMETRO.COM LLC

THRIVE LIFE
See SHELF RELIANCE LLC

D-U-N-S 00-614-4166 IMP
THRIVENT FINANCIAL FOR LUTHERANS FOUNDATION
625 4th Ave S, Minneapolis, MN 55415-1665
Tel (920) 734-5721 *Founded/Ownrshp* 1978
Sales NA *EMP* 5,800
SIC 6311 6321 8742 6411 6211 Fraternal life insurance organizations; Fraternal accident & health insurance organizations; Management consulting services; Insurance agents, brokers & service; Security brokers & dealers
CEO: Bruce J Nicholson
* *Pr:* Bradford L Hewitt
CFO: Randall L Boushek
* *Treas:* Randy Boushek
* *Chf Inves:* Russell W Swansen
* *Ex VP:* Pamela J Moret
Ex VP: Jon Stellmacher
* *Sr VP:* David Anderson
Sr VP: Jennifer Martin
Sr VP: Fred Ohlde
* *Sr VP:* Teresa J Rasmussen
VP: Kurt Bester
VP: Bruce Fear
VP: Barb Foote
VP: Earl Johnston
VP: Gwen Kuhrt
VP: Tim Schmidt
VP: Steve Wendt
Dir Soc: Joette Zembal
Creative D: Gene Smaciarz
Comm Man: Eileen Chanen
Board of Directors: Albert K W Siu, Addie J Butler, Adrian M Tocklin, Robert H Hoffman, Thomas R Zehnder, James M Hushagen, Richard C Kessler, Richard C Lundell, John P McDaniel, Paul W Middeke, Paul D Schrage, Kurt M Senske

THRIVERX
See BIORX LLC

D-U-N-S 04-153-7171
■THRU TUBING SOLUTIONS INC
T T S
(*Suby of* RPC INC) ★
11515 S Portland Ave, Oklahoma City, OK 73170-9707
Tel (405) 692-1900 *Founded/Ownrshp* 2006
Sales 134.4MM^E *EMP* 200^E
SIC 1389 Oil field services
Pr: Andy Ferguson

D-U-N-S 13-761-9284 IMP/EXP
THRUSTMASTER OF TEXAS INC
6900 Thrustmaster Dr, Houston, TX 77041-2682
Tel (713) 937-6295 *Founded/Ownrshp* 1985
Sales 96.8MM^E *EMP* 275
Accts Mohle Adams Houston Texas
SIC 3531 Construction machinery; Marine related equipment
Pr: Joe Bekker
* *CFO:* Greg Ault
* *VP:* Xiaohong Dou
Mtls Mgr: Bob Cook

D-U-N-S 00-242-9355 IMP
THRUWAY AUTHORITY OF NEW YORK STATE
200 Southern Blvd, Albany, NY 12209-2018
Tel (518) 436-2700 *Founded/Ownrshp* 1950
Sales 306.5MM^E *EMP* 2,840^E
Accts Toski & Co Cpas Pc Willi
SIC 4785 4499 Toll road operation; Canal operation
Ex Dir: Thomas Madison
* *CFO:* John Bryan
Ofcr: Denis Britvan
* *Ex Dir:* Bill Finch
* *Ex Dir:* Michael R Fleischer
Ex Dir: Claire Murphy
Genl Mgr: Keith Fragomeni
Dir IT: Robert Reilly
IT Man: Maryellen McCormack
IT Man: Mildred Selby
Software D: Carlo Crisafulli

D-U-N-S 79-028-6905
THULE HOLDING INC
(*Suby of* THULE HOLDING AB)
42 Silvermine Rd, Seymour, CT 06483-3928
Tel (203) 881-9600 *Founded/Ownrshp* 2004
Sales 111.1MM^E *EMP* 1,088^E
SIC 3792 3714 Travel trailers & campers; Tops, motor vehicle
Pr: Fred Clark
* *VP:* Moreen Parente
Dir IT: Mary Dostal
Dir IT: Lary Jinesky
VP Opers: Patrick Monahan

D-U-N-S 61-437-5178 IMP/EXP
THULE INC
(*Suby of* THULE HOLDING INC) ★
42 Silvermine Rd, Seymour, CT 06483-3928
Tel (203) 881-9600 *Founded/Ownrshp* 1992
Sales 101.0MM^E *EMP* 400
SIC 3714 5021 Tops, motor vehicle; Racks
Pr: Fred Clark
* *Pr:* Bruce Bossidy
Pr: Jay Caron
VP: Patrick Monahan
VP: Maureen Murphy-Parente
* *VP:* Fred Wyckoff
VP: Tripp Wyckoff
Exec: Vin Bove
Mng Dir: Greg Baktis
Telecom Ex: Rosanne Martinez
CIO: Mary Dostal

D-U-N-S 00-891-2529
THUMANN INC
THUMANNS
670 Dell Rd Ste 1, Carlstadt, NJ 07072-2292
Tel (201) 935-3636 *Founded/Ownrshp* 1949
Sales 85.4MM *EMP* 205
Accts Peter Gill Cpa Llc Hawthorn
SIC 2013 Sausages from purchased meat; Cured meats from purchased meat
Pr: Robert S Burke
* *VP:* Robert Burke Jr

THUMANNS
See THUMANN INC

D-U-N-S 08-370-5707
■THUNDER BASIN COAL CO LLC
BLACK THUNDER MINE
(*Suby of* ARCH COAL INC) ★
5669 Hwy 450, Wright, WY 82732
Tel (307) 939-1300 *Founded/Ownrshp* 1976, 1997
Sales 113.0MM *EMP* 530
SIC 1221 Surface mining, bituminous

D-U-N-S 92-680-8940
THUNDER BASIN CORP
(*Suby of* AMERICAN MANUFACTURING CORP) ★
103 Foulk Rd Ste 151, Wilmington, DE 19803-3742
Tel (610) 962-3770 *Founded/Ownrshp* 1991
Sales 100.2MM^E *EMP* 1,617
SIC 3566 2298 Gears, power transmission, except automotive; Speed changers (power transmission equipment), except auto; Drives, high speed industrial, except hydrostatic; Rope, except asbestos & wire; Twine
Ch Bd: Russell C Ball III
* *CFO:* Tim Dwyer

D-U-N-S 00-885-8701
THUNDERBIRD RESOURCES EQUITY INC (OK)
9400 Broadway Ext Ste 600, Oklahoma City, OK 73114-7423
Tel (405) 600-0711 *Founded/Ownrshp* 1998
Sales 98.6MM^E *EMP* 112^E
SIC 1311 Crude petroleum & natural gas production
CEO: David Baggett
* *Pr:* Michael J Rohleder
* *CFO:* James A Merrill
Bd of Dir: Ken L Kenworthy
* *Ex VP:* Gary D Jackson
* *Ex VP:* Harry C Stahel Jr
VP: Gary Jackson
Opers Mgr: Deborah Downs
VP Mktg: Keith Leffel
Mktg Mgr: David Donnell
Mktg Mgr: Jarred Witt

D-U-N-S 02-768-3242
THUNDERBIRD SHERMS MARKET INC
SHERM'S FOOD 4 LESS
730 S Grape St, Medford, OR 97501-3628
Tel (541) 857-0850 *Founded/Ownrshp* 1967
Sales 189.7MM^E *EMP* 650
SIC 5411 Grocery stores, independent
Pr: Sherm Olsrud
* *VP:* Steve Olsrud
Genl Mgr: Wayne Wiedeman
Off Mgr: Stacy Whidaker

D-U-N-S 80-988-7164
THUNDERCAT TECHNOLOGY LLC
1925 Isaac Newton Sq E # 180, Reston, VA 20190-5030
Tel (703) 674-0216 *Founded/Ownrshp* 2007
Sales 387.4MM *EMP* 44
Accts Gaffey Deane Talley Plc Resto
SIC 5045 Computers, peripherals & software
CEO: Thomas Deierlein

D-U-N-S 01-884-6204
THURSTON FOODS INC
30 Thurston Dr, Wallingford, CT 06492-2448
Tel (203) 265-1525 *Founded/Ownrshp* 1947
Sales 213.3MM^E *EMP* 170
SIC 5141 5147 5142 5113 Groceries, general line; Meats & meat products; Packaged frozen goods; Industrial & personal service paper
Pr: William D Thurston Jr
* *CFO:* Peter L Malone
CFO: Peter L Maone
* *Treas:* Douglas J Thurston Jr
Sls Mgr: Jeff Noccioli

D-U-N-S 07-666-1222
THURSTON NORTH PUBLIC SCHOOLS
305 College St Ne, Lacey, WA 98516-5390
Tel (360) 412-4400 *Founded/Ownrshp* 1954
Sales 151.7MM *EMP* 1,400
Accts Brian Sonntag Cgfm
SIC 8211 Public elementary school; Public junior high school; Public senior high school
Treas: Mary Nairn
Ofcr: Linda L Gallivan
Ex Dir: Teena Barnes
IT Man: Courtney Schrieve
Teacher Pr: Joseph Brem Gartner
HC Dir: Karie Remy-Anderson

THYMES
See BURNS CONSULTING INC

THYSSENKRUMP
See UHDE CORP OF AMERICA

D-U-N-S 83-110-5986 IMP/EXP
THYSSENKRUPP AUTOMOTIVE SALES & TECHNICAL CENTER INC
(*Suby of* THYSSENKRUPP NORTH AMERICA INC) ★
3155 W Big Beaver Rd # 260, Troy, MI 48084-3002
Tel (248) 530-2902 *Founded/Ownrshp* 1998
Sales 128.2MM^E *EMP* 450
SIC 5013 3714 Motor vehicle supplies & new parts; Motor vehicle parts & accessories
Pr: Craig Shetler
Sr VP: Frank Ehrenberg
VP: David Buhl
Dir Bus: Carl Mero
Mng Dir: Klaus Heinekamp
Prgrm Mgr: Martin Sulecki
Brnch Mgr: Jeffrey Garden
IT Man: Frank Brady
IT Man: Harold Hoffman
VP Sls: Scott Day

THYSSENKRUPP AUTOMOTVE SALES &
See THYSSENKRUPP CRANKSHAFT CO LLC

D-U-N-S 78-156-7078 IMP/EXP
THYSSENKRUPP CRANKSHAFT CO LLC
THYSSENKRUPP AUTOMOTVE SALES &
(*Suby of* THYSSENKRUPP AUTOMOTIVE SALES & TECHNICAL CENTER INC) ★
1000 Lynch Rd, Danville, IL 61834-5811
Tel (217) 431-0060 *Founded/Ownrshp* 1999
Sales 122.6MM^E *EMP* 450
SIC 3714 3462 Universal joints, motor vehicle; Automotive & internal combustion engine forgings
Dir IT: Bernd Huelsebusch

D-U-N-S 01-956-3621
THYSSENKRUPP ELEVATOR AMERICAS CORP
(*Suby of* THYSSENKRUPP NORTH AMERICA INC) ★
11605 Haynes Bridge Rd, Alpharetta, GA 30009-8669
Tel (678) 319-3240 *Founded/Ownrshp* 1999
Sales 1.8MMM^E *EMP* 9,200
SIC 7699 3534 1796 Elevators: inspection, service & repair; Elevators & equipment; Elevator installation & conversion
CEO: W Barry Pletch
* *Pr:* Richard T Hussey
* *CFO:* James Harrison
* *Ex VP:* Stuart Prior
* *VP:* Eric Scrudders
* *VP:* Scott J Silitsky
* *VP:* David Turnage
Off Mgr: Denise Larson
Dir IT: Guenter Sube
Software D: Richard Ford
Opers Mgr: Scott Seabeck

D-U-N-S 13-044-1751 IMP/EXP
THYSSENKRUPP ELEVATOR CORP
(*Suby of* THYSSENKRUPP ELEVATOR AMERICAS CORP) ★
11605 Haynes Bridge Rd # 650, Alpharetta, GA 30009-8669
Tel (678) 319-3240 *Founded/Ownrshp* 1999
Sales 1.8MMM^E *EMP* 8,000
SIC 3534 1796 7699 Elevators & equipment; Elevator installation & conversion; Elevators: inspection, service & repair
CEO: Rich Hussey
* *Pr:* Barry Pletch
* *CFO:* James Harrison
* *CFO:* Steve Wedge
* *Treas:* Bruce Fisher
Treas: Scott Silitsky
Ofcr: David Turnage
* *VP:* Gerald Gearhard

D-U-N-S 17-138-1168 IMP/EXP
THYSSENKRUPP ELEVATOR MANUFACTURING INC
(*Suby of* THYSSENKRUPP ELEVATOR CORP) ★
9280 Crestwyn Hills Dr, Memphis, TN 38125-8508
Tel (901) 261-1800 *Founded/Ownrshp* 2008
Sales 87.7MM^E *EMP* 200
SIC 3534 Elevators & equipment
Pr: Lon Ainsley
Pr: Gregg Garner
* *Treas:* Richard T Hussey
* *VP:* Frank Dancy
VP: Peter Engwer
Software D: William Rodgers
Mktg Mgr: Julie McKenzie

THYSSENKRUPP HEARN
See THYSSENKRUPP INDUSTRIAL SERVICES NA INC

D-U-N-S 00-742-4018
THYSSENKRUPP INDUSTRIAL SERVICES NA INC
THYSSENKRUPP HEARN
(*Suby of* THYSSENKRUPP RAW MATERIALS USA) ★
22355 W 11 Mile Rd, Southfield, MI 48033-4735
Tel (248) 233-5600 *Founded/Ownrshp* 2000
Sales 167.5MM^E *EMP* 650
SIC 4225 4731 General warehousing; Freight transportation arrangement
CEO: Christian Dohr
* *Pr:* Brian Diephuis
* *CFO:* Norbert Goetz
* *VP:* Sam Baioff
Exec: Connie Barnes
IT Man: Linda Tennant
Sls Mgr: Robert Bognar
Sls Mgr: Steven Brandt
Sls Mgr: Christopher Lang
Sls Mgr: Kyle Wohler
Sales Asso: Shawn Lehmann

D-U-N-S 00-887-4356 IMP/EXP
THYSSENKRUPP MATERIALS NA INC (MI)
THYSSENKRUPP RAW MATERIALS USA
(*Suby of* THYSSENKRUPP AG)
22355 W 11 Mile Rd, Southfield, MI 48033-4735
Tel (248) 233-5600 *Founded/Ownrshp* 1931
Sales 2.5MMM *EMP* 2,800
SIC 5051 5162 3444 8741 Metals service centers & offices; Aluminum bars, rods, ingots, sheets, pipes, plates, etc.; Plastics sheets & rods; Sheet metalwork; Management services
Pr: Christian Dohr
Recvr: Joseph Alvey
* *CFO:* Norbert Goertz
* *Ch:* Joachim Limberg
* *Treas:* Annette Skiba
Ex VP: Richard Greaves
VP: James Baber
VP: Jeff Fischer
VP: Scot Marlin
Brnch Mgr: Scott Gibler
Brnch Mgr: Todd Ziedonis

D-U-N-S 10-919-2724
THYSSENKRUPP NORTH AMERICA INC
(*Suby of* THYSSENKRUPP AG)
111 W Jackson Blvd # 2400, Chicago, IL 60604-4154
Tel (312) 525-2800 *Founded/Ownrshp* 1982
Sales 13.6MMM^E *EMP* 25,000
SIC 6719 3714 Investment holding companies, except banks; Axles, motor vehicle
CEO: Torsten Gessner
* *Ch:* Heinrich Hiesinger
Ofcr: Gerald Gearhard
Ofcr: Michael Paik
VP: Tom Bradsley
VP: Gerald McHenry
Exec: Brenda Baszkowski
* *Prin:* Derrick Richter
Brnch Mgr: Blaine Coupal
Brnch Mgr: John Henderson
Brnch Mgr: Craig Roy

D-U-N-S 77-994-1397 IMP/EXP
THYSSENKRUPP PRESTA DANVILLE LLC
(*Suby of* THYSSENKRUPP NORTH AMERICA INC) ★
75 Walz Crk, Danville, IL 61834-9373
Tel (217) 444-5500 *Founded/Ownrshp* 1991
Sales 111.5MM^E *EMP* 300
SIC 3714 Camshafts, motor vehicle
Pr: Carlos Dias

D-U-N-S 14-376-0838 IMP/EXP
THYSSENKRUPP PRESTA NORTH AMERICA LLC
(*Suby of* THYSSENKRUPP NORTH AMERICA INC) ★
1597 E Industrial Dr, Terre Haute, IN 47802-9265
Tel (812) 299-5000 *Founded/Ownrshp* 2016
Sales 250.0MM *EMP* 450
SIC 5013 Automotive supplies & parts
CEO: Richard Hirschmann
**COO:* Yashar Kazemi
Ofcr: Liwei Liu
Exec: Peter Allaart
Sfty Mgr: Dustin Bishop
Ql Cn Mgr: James Ramp

THYSSENKRUPP RAW MATERIALS USA
See THYSSENKRUPP MATERIALS NA INC

TI
See TREASURE ISLAND LLC

D-U-N-S 61-793-7651
TI AUTOMOTIVE INC
WALL GROW
1272 Doris Rd Ste 100, Auburn Hills, MI 48326-2617
Tel (248) 276-4721 *Founded/Ownrshp* 1987
Sales 1.0MMM^E *EMP* 2,587^E
SIC 5013 7538 Automotive supplies & parts; General automotive repair shops
Pr: William Kozyra
Pr: Drew Sheffield
**CFO:* Tim Knutson
**Ofcr:* Domenico Milicia
VP: Steve Beckman
**VP:* Hans Dieltjens
VP: Rodney Morris
**VP:* David Murrell
VP: Jan Svec
**VP:* Steve Taylor
Mng Dir: Mike Wildfong

D-U-N-S 07-926-8782 EXP
TI AUTOMOTIVE LLC
(*Suby of* TI AUTOMOTIVE USA HOLDINGS LIMITED)
2020 Taylor Rd, Auburn Hills, MI 48326-1771
Tel (248) 494-5000 *Founded/Ownrshp* 2001
Sales 732.2MM^E *EMP* 2,588^E
SIC 3317 3312 3599 3052 3714 3585 Tubes, seamless steel; Tubing, mechanical or hypodermic sizes: cold drawn stainless; Tubes, steel & iron; Amusement park equipment; Plastic hose; Filters: oil, fuel & air, motor vehicle; Fuel systems & parts, motor vehicle; Air conditioning equipment, complete

D-U-N-S 96-743-9949
TI EMPLOYEES HEALTH BENEFIT TRUST
7839 Churchill Way, Dallas, TX 75251-1901
Tel (972) 995-3333 *Founded/Ownrshp* 2011
Sales NA *EMP* 2^E
Accts Ernst & Young Us Llp Indian
SIC 6351 Surety insurance

D-U-N-S 00-535-5656 IMP
TI GROUP AUTOMOTIVE SYSTEMS LLC
(*Suby of* TI AUTOMOTIVE LLC) ★
2020 Taylor Rd, Auburn Hills, MI 48326-1771
Tel (248) 296-8000 *Founded/Ownrshp* 1922, 2008
Sales 732.2MM^E *EMP* 2,588
SIC 3317 3312 3599 3052 3714 3585 Tubes, seamless steel; Tubing, mechanical or hypodermic sizes: cold drawn stainless; Tubes, steel & iron; Hose, flexible metallic; Plastic hose; Fuel systems & parts, motor vehicle; Filters: oil, fuel & air, motor vehicle; Refrigeration & heating equipment
CEO: William Kozyra
Pr: Bill Laule
**CFO:* Tim Knutson
Ofcr: Jim Kropp
**Ex VP:* Hans Dieltjens
**Ex VP:* David Murrell
**Ex VP:* Phil Stephenson
Mng Dir: Brian Hildebrand

TI WIRE
See TREE ISLAND WIRE (USA) INC

D-U-N-S 07-983-3628
TIAA CREF INVESTMENT MANAGEMENT LLC
TIAA-CREF
(*Suby of* TEACHERS INSURANCE AND ANNUITY ASSOCIATION OF AMERICA) ★
8500 Andrew Carnegie Blvd, Charlotte, NC 28262-8500
Tel (704) 595-1000 *Founded/Ownrshp* 1997
Sales 250.7MM^E *EMP* 86^E
SIC 6726 6722 Investment offices; Management investment, open-end
Sr VP: David Edwards
Ofcr: Darrian Hopkins
Sr VP: Elizabeth Palmer
VP: Jim Walker
Dir Risk M: Donna Dernar
Mng Dir: John Gay
Mng Dir: James Gouin
Mng Dir: Nichol Merritt
CIO: Annabelle Bexiga
Telecom Mg: Vernon Frost
IT Man: Sunil Amin

D-U-N-S 96-785-2562
TIAA REAL ESTATE ACCOUNT
730 3rd Ave, New York, NY 10017-3206
Tel (212) 490-9000 *Founded/Ownrshp* 2011
Sales 683.9MM *EMP* 2^E
SIC 6531 Real estate agents & managers

TIAA-CREF
See TEACHERS INSURANCE AND ANNUITY ASSOCIATION-COLLEGE RETIREMENT EQUITIES FUND

TIAA-CREF
See TIAA CREF INVESTMENT MANAGEMENT LLC

D-U-N-S 82-693-2522
TIAA-CREF INDIVIDUAL & INSTITUTIONAL SERVICES LLC
(*Suby of* TEACHERS INSURANCE AND ANNUITY ASSOCIATION OF AMERICA) ★
730 3rd Ave Ste 2a, New York, NY 10017-3213
Tel (212) 490-9000 *Founded/Ownrshp* 2004
Sales 474.6MM^E *EMP* 1,019
SIC 6211 Security brokers & dealers
CEO: Roger W Ferguson Jr
CFO: Tom Lynch
Treas: Gary Chinery
Ex VP: Kathie Andrade
Ex VP: Ronald Pressman

TIAA-CREF INDVL&INSTL SVS
See TIAA-CREF TRUST CO FSB

D-U-N-S 12-374-8480
TIAA-CREF TRUST CO FSB
TIAA-CREF INDVL&INSTL SVS
(*Suby of* TIAA-CREF INDIVIDUAL & INSTITUTIONAL SERVICES LLC) ★
1 Metropolitan Sq, Saint Louis, MO 63102-2723
Tel (314) 588-9738 *Founded/Ownrshp* 1998
Sales 137.7MM *EMP* 232
SIC 7389 6282 Financial services; Investment advice
Pr: Robert Mason
**Treas:* Kay Love
Trst Ofcr: Margaret Noll
VP: Ladd Doyt
VP: Timothy Prosser

D-U-N-S 79-157-8359
TIANJIN POOL & SPA CORP
POOLINE PRODUCTS
2701-2711 Garfield Ave, Commerce, CA 90040
Tel (626) 571-1885 *Founded/Ownrshp* 2005
Sales 3.0MMM^E *EMP* 9
SIC 5169 5091 Swimming pool & spa chemicals; Swimming pools, equipment & supplies
CEO: Shouzhe Wang
Sys Admin: Frank Sahagun

D-U-N-S 05-661-8325
TIB - INDEPENDENT BANKERSBANK
INDEPENDENT BANKERSBANK THE
(*Suby of* INDEPENDENT BANKERS FINANCIAL CORP) ★
11701 Luna Rd, Farmers Branch, TX 75234-6026
Tel (972) 650-6000 *Founded/Ownrshp* 1981
Sales NA *EMP* 350
SIC 6022 State commercial banks
Pr: Gayle M Earls
Pr: Si Tarighi
**CEO:* Michael G O Rourke
Ofcr: Tony Mueller
**Ex VP:* Patricia F Blackshear
Ex VP: Patricia Blackshear
Ex VP: Kevin R Drew
Ex VP: Patrick Gray
**Ex VP:* T Patrick Gray
**Ex VP:* David A Linaburg
Ex VP: David Linaburg
Sr VP: Eric Allen
Sr VP: Don Briscoe
Sr VP: Don Gearhart
Sr VP: James Hudson
Sr VP: Maggi Metheany
Sr VP: Chuck Phelan
Sr VP: Barry Renfroe
Sr VP: David Temple
Sr VP: Greg Todd
VP: Terri Bacot

D-U-N-S 00-342-6892
■TIB FINANCIAL CORP
(*Suby of* CAPITAL BANK FINANCIAL CORP) ★
599 Tamiami Trl N Ste 101, Naples, FL 34102-5624
Tel (239) 263-3344 *Founded/Ownrshp* 1996, 2010
Sales NA *EMP* 1,389^E
SIC 6022 State commercial banks
Ch Bd: R Eugene Taylor
**CFO:* Christopher G Marshall
**Ex VP:* R Bruce Singletary
Ex VP: Millard J Younkers
Sr VP: Clay W Cone
VP: Eric Gerhart
VP: Kathi Zanella

TIBA CONSULTING
See TIBA LLC

D-U-N-S 83-964-1185
TIBA LLC
TIBA CONSULTING
(*Suby of* TIBA MANAGEMENTBERATUNG GMBH)
29600 Southfield Rd 200, Southfield, MI 48076-2039
Tel (248) 633-6067 *Founded/Ownrshp* 2009
Sales 90.0MM^E *EMP* 4
SIC 8742 Management consulting services
Owner: Till H Balser

D-U-N-S 79-953-4789
TIBCO SOFTWARE INC
3303 Hillview Ave, Palo Alto, CA 94304-1279
Tel (650) 846-1000 *Founded/Ownrshp* 2014
Sales 1.2MMM^E *EMP* 4,000^E
SIC 7371 7373 Custom computer programming services; Systems integration services
CEO: Murray Rhode
CFO: Thomas Berquist
Ofcr: William Hughes
**Ex VP:* Bill Hughes
Ex VP: Tom Laffey
**Ex VP:* Matt Quinn
Ex VP: Rajnish Verma
Sr VP: Frank Bergandi
VP: Paul Asmar
VP: Craig Byar
VP: Cynthia Fields
VP: Steven Hoffman
VP: Ian Hunter
VP: Jeffery McLellan
VP: David Rosen
VP: Vivek RAO
VP: Rafael C Toscano
Exec: Sandy Seril
Dir Soc: John Davis

D-U-N-S 12-140-0170
TIC - INDUSTRIAL CO WYOMING INC
(*Suby of* TIC - THE INDUSTRIAL COMPANY)
1474 Willer Dr, Casper, WY 82604-1896
Tel (307) 235-9958 *Founded/Ownrshp* 1992
Sales 152.1MM^E *EMP* 1,700
Accts Grant Thornton Llp Denver C
SIC 1629 Industrial plant construction
Pr: Dean Brister
VP: Donald Brust
VP: R W Mc Kenzie

D-U-N-S 15-178-4485 IMP
TIC HOLDINGS INC
(*Suby of* KIEWIT CORP) ★
9780 Pyramid Ct Ste 100, Englewood, CO 80112-6078
Tel (970) 879-2561 *Founded/Ownrshp* 2008
Sales 1.9MMM^E *EMP* 5,500^E
SIC 1541 1629 1623 1542 Industrial buildings, new construction; Marine construction; Oil & gas pipeline construction; Commercial & office building contractors
Ch Bd: Ronald W Mc Kenzie
**COO:* John C Paul
**CFO:* Jim Kissane
**Ex VP:* Terry J Carlsgaard
**Ex VP:* Leroy Meador
VP: Bruce Hinde
VP: Victor Lazar
Dir IT: John Harris
Dir IT: Kent Morrison

D-U-N-S 16-558-7341
TICC CAPITAL CORP
8 Sound Shore Dr Ste 255, Greenwich, CT 06830-7272
Tel (203) 983-5275 *Founded/Ownrshp* 2003
Sales 87.4MM *EMP* 3
Accts Pricewaterhousecoopers Llp N
Tkr Sym TICC *Exch* NGS
SIC 6726 Management investment funds, closed-end
CEO: Jonathan H Cohen
Pr: Saul B Rosenthal
CFO: Patrick F Conroy
CFO: Patrick Conroy
Sr VP: Hari Srinivasan
VP: Sunil Abraham
Mng Dir: Branko Krmpotic

D-U-N-S 08-066-8262
TICKETMASTER CORP
7060 Hollywood Blvd Ste 2, Los Angeles, CA 90028-6030
Tel (323) 769-4600 *Founded/Ownrshp* 1988
Sales NA *EMP* 4,390
SIC 7999 7922

D-U-N-S 93-396-7515
■TICKETMASTER ENTERTAINMENT LLC
(*Suby of* LIVE NATION ENTERTAINMENT INC) ★
8800 W Sunset Blvd, West Hollywood, CA 90069-2105
Tel (800) 653-8000 *Founded/Ownrshp* 2010
Sales 73.1MM^E *EMP* 4,390
SIC 7922 Ticket agency, theatrical; Agent or manager for entertainers
CEO: Ron Bension
Snr Sftwr: Tejal Gandhi
Snr Ntwrk: Nikolai Tsankov
Dir IT: Alan Waldman
Mktg Dir: Jenna Corday

D-U-N-S 62-331-3129
TICKETMASTER GROUP INC
3701 Wilshire Blvd Fl 9, Los Angeles, CA 90010-2804
Tel (800) 745-3000 *Founded/Ownrshp* 1993
Sales NA *EMP* 4,390^E
SIC 7999

D-U-N-S 05-821-8763
TICKETMOB LLC
(*Suby of* CVENT INC) ★
11833 Mississippi Ave, Los Angeles, CA 90025-6134
Tel (800) 927-0939 *Founded/Ownrshp* 2013
Sales 26.9MM^E *EMP* 1,145^E
SIC 8741 Management services
CEO: Scot Richardson
**CTO:* Nasi Peretz

D-U-N-S 01-142-9607 IMP/EXP
■TICONA POLYMERS INC
(*Suby of* KEP AMERICAS) ★
222 Las Colinas Blvd W 900n, Irving, TX 75039-5421
Tel (972) 443-4000 *Founded/Ownrshp* 1998
Sales 124.7MM^E *EMP* 880
SIC 3087

D-U-N-S 05-282-5689
■TICOR TITLE CO OF CALIFORNIA
(*Suby of* TICOR TITLE INSURANCE CO INC) ★
1500 Quail St Ste 300, Newport Beach, CA 92660-2754
Tel (714) 289-7100 *Founded/Ownrshp* 2003
Sales NA *EMP* 790
SIC 6361 Title insurance
Pr: Rick Bashore

D-U-N-S 07-410-3003
■TICOR TITLE INSURANCE CO INC
(*Suby of* CHICAGO TITLE AND TRUST CO) ★
131 N El Molino Ave, Pasadena, CA 91101-1873
Tel (616) 302-3121 *Founded/Ownrshp* 1965
Sales NA *EMP* 917^E
SIC 6361 Real estate title insurance
Ch Bd: John Rau
**CFO:* Gust Totlis
**Treas:* Peter Leemputte
**Ex VP:* Paul T Sands Jr
**VP:* Bryan Willis
MIS Dir: Todd Freeman

TIDELANDS GEORGETOWN MEM HOSP
See GEORGETOWN MEMORIAL HOSPITAL

D-U-N-S 94-791-0691
TIDES CENTER
The Prsdio 1014 Trney Ave, San Francisco, CA 94129
Tel (415) 561-6400 *Founded/Ownrshp* 1994
Sales 95.5MM *EMP* 600
Accts Fontanello Duffield & Otake Lp
SIC 8399 Community development groups
CEO: Kriss Deiglmeier
**CFO:* Judith Hill
**Prin:* Gary Schwartz

D-U-N-S 03-812-5951
TIDES FOUNDATION
Presidio Bldg 1014, San Francisco, CA 94129
Tel (415) 561-6400 *Founded/Ownrshp* 1976
Sales 114.0MM *EMP* 27
Accts Fontanello Duffield & Otake
SIC 8399 Community development groups; Social change association
Pr: Drummond Pike
**Ex Dir:* Brain Byrnes

TIDEWATER CREDIT SERVICES
See TIDEWATER FINANCE CO

D-U-N-S 82-562-2913
TIDEWATER FINANCE CO
TIDEWATER CREDIT SERVICES
6520 Indian River Rd, Virginia Beach, VA 23464-3439
Tel (757) 579-6444 *Founded/Ownrshp* 1992
Sales NA *EMP* 200
SIC 6141 Installment sales finance, other than banks
Pr: Arthur B Sandler
COO: Billy Fuller
**VP:* Nathan D Benson
**VP:* William C Fuller Jr

D-U-N-S 00-197-2496 IMP/EXP
▲TIDEWATER INC
601 Poydras St Ste 1500, New Orleans, LA 70130-6061
Tel (504) 568-1010 *Founded/Ownrshp* 1956
Sales 979.0MM *EMP* 6,550^E
Accts Deloitte & Touche Llp New Or
Tkr Sym TDW *Exch* NYS
SIC 4424 4493 4492 Intercoastal transportation, freight; Boat yards, storage & incidental repair; Towing & tugboat service
Pr: Jeffrey M Platt
**Ch Bd:* Richard A Pattarozzi
COO: Jeffrey A Gorski
CFO: Quinn P Fanning
Ex VP: Joseph M Bennett
Ex VP: Bruce D Lundstrom
Area Mgr: Frank Gibone
Area Mgr: Bryan Hupp
Genl Couns: James C Wilbert
Board of Directors: M Jay Allison, James C Day, Richard T Du Moulin, Morris E Foster, J Wayne Leonard, Richard D Paterson, Robert L Potter, Cindy B Taylor, Jack E Thompson

D-U-N-S 18-472-4540
TIDEWELL HOSPICE INC
5955 Rand Blvd, Sarasota, FL 34238-5160
Tel (941) 552-7500 *Founded/Ownrshp* 1979
Sales 95.3MM *EMP* 800
Accts Kerkering Barberio & Co Saras
SIC 8082 Home health care services
CEO: Gerard Radford
Dir Vol: Lynne Corrigan
COO: Mary Poe
**CFO:* Saida Brunouhamd
**Treas:* Thomas E Combs
Ex VP: Joelle Angsten
Ex VP: David Lafferty
Ex VP: Stephen Leedy
Ex VP: Neville Sarkari
VP: Irene Henderson
**VP:* Michael R Uselton

D-U-N-S 06-351-9193 IMP/EXP
TIDI PRODUCTS LLC
570 Enterprise Dr, Neenah, WI 54956-4865
Tel (920) 751-4300 *Founded/Ownrshp* 2015
Sales 139.0MM^E *EMP* 250^E
SIC 3843 3841 5047 Dental equipment & supplies; Surgical & medical instruments; Medical equipment & supplies
Pr: Kevin McNamara
**CFO:* Frank Macknica
VP: Todd Swanson
Genl Mgr: Laurie Kimball
QC Dir: Dion Brandt
Sls Mgr: Brad Binder

D-U-N-S 05-304-1752
TIDYMANS LLC
(*Suby of* COUNTY MARKET) ★
10020 E Knox Ave Ste 500, Spokane Valley, WA 99206-5097
Tel (509) 928-7480 *Founded/Ownrshp* 1965, 1986
Sales 72.2MM^E *EMP* 1,066
SIC 5411 Supermarkets, chain

D-U-N-S 03-738-1022
TIDYMANS MANAGEMENT SERVICES INC
COUNTY MARKET
10020 E Knox Ave Ste 500, Spokane Valley, WA 99206-5097
Tel (509) 928-7480 *Founded/Ownrshp* 1998
Sales 118.8MM^E *EMP* 2,500^E
Accts Bdo Seidman Llp Spokane Was
SIC 5411 Supermarkets, chain
Pr: Michael Davis
**CFO:* Karla Wright Hayden
**VP:* Jerry Streeter

TIEM PARTS CENTER
See TOYOTA INDUSTRIAL EQUIPMENT MFG INC

TIENDAS SINDICALES
See SPFM LP

D-U-N-S 79-681-5483
TIER REIT INC
5950 Sherry Ln Ste 700, Dallas, TX 75225-6562
Tel (972) 483-2400 *Founded/Ownrshp* 2002
Sales 282.3MM *EMP* 55^E
Accts Deloitte & Touche Llp Dallas
SIC 6798 Real estate investment trusts
Pr: Scott W Fordham
**Ch Bd:* Richard I Gilchrist
CFO: Dallas E Lucas

Ex VP: William J Reister
Sr VP: Telisa Webb Schelin
Board of Directors: Robert S Aisner, Charles G Dannis, Thomas M Herzog, M Jason Mattox, Steven W Partridge, G Ronald Witten

D-U-N-S 08-947-6097
TIERNEY BROTHERS INC
PROJECTOR POINT.COM
1771 Energy Park Dr, Saint Paul, MN 55108-2720
Tel (612) 331-5500 *Founded/Ownrshp* 1978
Sales 150.3MM[E] *EMP* 100[E]
SIC 5049 5043 3651 Engineers' equipment & supplies; Motion picture equipment; Household audio & video equipment
CEO: James Tierney
**Ch Bd:* Tom Tierney
**COO:* Susan Nelson

D-U-N-S 55-606-5022
TIERPOINT LLC
(*Suby of* CEQUEL DATA CENTERS LP) ★
520 Maryville Centre Dr # 300, Saint Louis, MO 63141-5820
Tel (314) 594-1300 *Founded/Ownrshp* 2012
Sales 160.4MM[E] *EMP* 350[E]
SIC 7374 Computer graphics service
CEO: Jerald L Kent
COO: Thomas P McMillin
CFO: Mary Meduski
Ex VP: Wendy Knudsen
Sr VP: Pete Abel
Sr VP: Jim Fox
Sr VP: Keith Markley
VP: David Foster

D-U-N-S 04-963-5462
TIERPOINT SPOKANE ONE & TWO LLC
(*Suby of* TIERPOINT LLC) ★
520 Maryville Centre Dr, Saint Louis, MO 63141-5820
Tel (314) 315-9372 *Founded/Ownrshp* 2012
Sales 100.0MM *EMP* 130
SIC 6719 Investment holding companies, except banks
CEO: Jerald L Kent
**Pr:* Paul Estes
**Pr:* Thomas P McMillin
**Pr:* Mary Meduski
**CFO:* Andy Stewart
Ex VP: Wendy Knudsen
**Sr VP:* Jim Fox
Genl Mgr: Jeremy Pope

D-U-N-S 06-931-1546 IMP/EXP
TIETEX INTERNATIONAL LTD (SC)
TIETEX TECHNICAL
3010 N Blackstock Rd, Spartanburg, SC 29301-5500
Tel (864) 574-0500 *Founded/Ownrshp* 1972
Sales 206.3MM[E] *EMP* 1,209
SIC 2297 2258 2221

TIETEX TECHNICAL
See TIETEX INTERNATIONAL LTD

D-U-N-S 00-121-1473 IMP
▲TIFFANY & CO
200 5th Ave Bsmt 2, New York, NY 10010-3307
Tel (212) 755-8000 *Founded/Ownrshp* 1837
Sales 4.1MMM *EMP* 12,200[E]
Accts Pricewaterhousecoopers Llp Ne
Tkr Sym TIF *Exch* NYS
SIC 5944 5094 5719 5943 5999 5961 Jewelry stores; Clocks; Watches; Silverware; Precious stones & metals; Jewelry; Watches & parts; Silverware or plated ware; China; Glassware; Pictures, wall; Stationery stores; Writing supplies; Perfumes & colognes; Toiletries, cosmetics & perfumes; Catalog sales; Jewelry, mail order; Cosmetics & perfumes, mail order; Gift items, mail order
CEO: Frederic Cumenal
**Ch Bd:* Michael J Kowalski
Pr: Richard Moore
CFO: Ralph Nicoletti
Treas: Michael Connolly
Ofcr: Caroline D Naggiar
Ex VP: Jill Beraud
Ex VP: Beth Owen-Canavan
Sr VP: Jean-Marc Bellaiche
Sr VP: Pamela H Cloud
Sr VP: Jennifer S De Winter
Sr VP: Philippe Galti
Sr VP: Philippe Galtie
Sr VP: Leigh M Harlan
Sr VP: Andrew W Hart
Sr VP: Jon M King
Sr VP: John S Petterson
VP: Celeste Aarons-Jenkins
VP: Judy Baldissard
VP: Raffaella Banchero
VP: Thomas E Barric
Board of Directors: Rose Marie Bravo, Gary E Costley, Lawrence K Fish, Abby F Kohnstamm, Charles K Marquis, Peter W May, William A Shutzer, Robert S Singer

D-U-N-S 06-114-3954 EXP
TIFFIN MOTOR HOMES INC
105 2nd St Nw, Red Bay, AL 35582-3859
Tel (256) 356-8661 *Founded/Ownrshp* 1972
Sales 168.7MM[E] *EMP* 545[E]
SIC 3716 Motor homes
Pr: Robert A Tiffin Jr
**Sec:* Tim Tiffin
**VP:* David S Tiffin
**Prin:* Bob Tiffin
Plnt Mgr: Tem Massey

D-U-N-S 08-218-1108
TIFT COUNTY BOARD OF EDUCATION
207 Ridge Ave N, Tifton, GA 31794-4323
Tel (229) 387-2400 *Founded/Ownrshp* 1930
Sales 68.5MM[E] *EMP* 1,032
SIC 8211 School board
Ch Bd: Kim Rutland

D-U-N-S 96-864-9579
TIFT COUNTY HOSPITAL AUTHORITY
901 18th St E, Tifton, GA 31794-3648
Tel (229) 382-7120 *Founded/Ownrshp* 2011
Sales 292.3MM *EMP* 32[E]
Accts Draffin & Tucker Llp Cpas A
SIC 8062 General medical & surgical hospitals
Prin: Gina Bennett

D-U-N-S 07-979-9686
TIFT COUNTY SCHOOLS
207 Ridge Ave N, Tifton, GA 31794-4323
Tel (229) 387-2400 *Founded/Ownrshp* 2015
Sales 12.5MM[E] *EMP* 1,137[E]
SIC 8211 Public elementary & secondary schools
HC Dir: Gina Cox

D-U-N-S 06-759-6031
TIFT REGIONAL MEDICAL CENTER (GA)
901 18th St E, Tifton, GA 31794-3648
Tel (229) 382-7120 *Founded/Ownrshp* 1965
Sales 1.0MM *EMP* 1,400
Accts Allen Pritchet Tifton Ga
SIC 8062 General medical & surgical hospitals
CEO: William T Richardson
**COO:* Chris Dorman
**CFO:* Dennis Crum
**Sr VP:* William Guest
VP: Andrew Flemer
**VP:* Carol Smith
Dir Lab: Ginny Paulk
Dir Rad: Kelly Douglas
Dir Rad: Raymond C Evans
Dir Rad: Wayne Stewart
Mtls Mgr: Roger Waldron

D-U-N-S 11-853-4783
TIFT REGIONAL MEDICAL CENTER
901 18th St E, Tifton, GA 31794-3648
Tel (229) 382-7120 *Founded/Ownrshp* 1982
Sales 288.5MM *EMP* 1,825[E]
SIC 8062 General medical & surgical hospitals
Pr: William Richardson
COO: Chris Dorman
VP: Dennis Crum
VP: Carol Smith
Dir Rx: Emily Schramm
Adm Dir: Cindy Mitchell
Prac Mgr: Malinda Hilton
Admn Mgr: Connie Wilcox
CIO: Guy McAllister
Telecom Mg: Wade Brewer
IT Man: Tonia Waldrop

D-U-N-S 80-373-4326
TIG HOLDINGS INC
TIG SPECIALTY INSUR SOLUTIONS
(*Suby of* FAIRFAX FINANCIAL HOLDINGS LIMITED)
250 Commercial St # 5000, Manchester, NH 03101-1116
Tel (603) 656-2200 *Founded/Ownrshp* 2000
Sales NA *EMP* 1,538
SIC 6331 Property damage insurance; Fire, marine & casualty insurance: stock; Automobile insurance
CFO: Richard F Corver

D-U-N-S 00-958-6140
TIG INSURANCE CO
(*Suby of* TIG INSURANCE GROUP) ★
250 Commercial St # 5000, Manchester, NH 03101-1116
Tel (603) 656-2200 *Founded/Ownrshp* 1987
Sales NA *EMP* 800
SIC 6331 Fire, marine & casualty insurance; Property damage insurance
Pr: Richard Scott Donovan
**Treas:* Michael John Sluka

D-U-N-S 60-757-8689
TIG INSURANCE GROUP
(*Suby of* TIG SPECIALTY INSUR SOLUTIONS) ★
250 Commercial St # 5000, Manchester, NH 03101-1116
Tel (603) 656-2200 *Founded/Ownrshp* 1993
Sales NA *EMP* 800
SIC 6331 Property damage insurance; Fire, marine & casualty insurance & carriers
Ch Bd: Jon W Rotenstreich
**Pr:* Don D Hutson
**CEO:* Nick Bently

TIG SPECIALTY INSUR SOLUTIONS
See TIG HOLDINGS INC

D-U-N-S 05-020-8271
TIGARD-TUALATIN SCHOOL DISTRICT
WASHINGTON COUNTY SCHL DST 23J
6960 Sw Sandburg St, Tigard, OR 97223-8039
Tel (503) 431-4000 *Founded/Ownrshp* 1969
Sales 154.7MM *EMP* 1,400
Accts Pauly Rogers And Co Pc Tig
SIC 8211 Public combined elementary & secondary school
COO: Robert Koehler
**CFO:* David Moore
Ofcr: Scott Baker
Assoc Dir: Carol Kinch
Pr Dir: Susan Stark-Haydon
Teacher Pr: Wanda Hennelly
HC Dir: Joyce Woods

TIGER FUEL COMPANY
See GREENBRIER INC

TIGER TANKS OFFSHORE RENTAL
See OFFSHORE RENTAL LTD

D-U-N-S 14-411-4055 IMP/EXP
■TIGERDIRECT INC
SYSTEMAX RETAIL SALES
(*Suby of* PCM INC) ★
7795 W Flagler St Ste 35, Miami, FL 33144-2367
Tel (305) 415-2200 *Founded/Ownrshp* 2015
Sales 177.1MM[E] *EMP* 475
SIC 5961 5734 Computer software, mail order; Computers & peripheral equipment, mail order; Computer & software stores
Ch: Richard Leeds
CEO: Gilbert J Fiorentino
COO: Larry Mondry
CFO: Mike Bryk
Treas: Lawrence P Reinhold
Ex VP: John A Ollet
VP: Joseph Dunne
VP: Mark A Pacetti
VP: Mark A Pcetti
VP: Charles Steinberg
Dir Bus: Sammy Saloum

D-U-N-S 09-177-0933 IMP
TIGERFLEX CORP
(*Suby of* TIGERS POLYMER CORPORATION)
801 Estes Ave, Elk Grove Village, IL 60007-4903
Tel (847) 439-1766 *Founded/Ownrshp* 1978
Sales 208.9MM[E] *EMP* 1,120
SIC 3052 Plastic hose
Pr: Hitoya Kodama

D-U-N-S 18-054-8497 IMP
TIGERPOLY MANUFACTURING INC
(*Suby of* TIGERS POLYMER CORPORATION)
6231 Enterprise Pkwy, Grove City, OH 43123-9271
Tel (614) 871-0045 *Founded/Ownrshp* 1987
Sales 104.5MM[E] *EMP* 350
SIC 3089 3714 3621 3061 Blow molded finished plastic products; Motor vehicle parts & accessories; Motors & generators; Mechanical rubber goods
Pr: Seiji Shiga
**Prin:* Michael S Crane
**Prin:* Yasuhiko Tomita
QC Dir: Tom Kallis

D-U-N-S 08-008-2738 IMP/EXP
TIGERS (USA) GLOBAL LOGISTICS INC
KAMINO INTERNATIONAL TRANSPORT
(*Suby of* TIGERS (HK) CO. LIMITED)
25 Northwest Point Blvd # 1025, Elk Grove Village, IL 60007-1056
Tel (516) 825-4774 *Founded/Ownrshp* 1991
Sales 99.9MM[E] *EMP* 175
SIC 4731 4581 4522 4512 Foreign freight forwarding; Airports, flying fields & services; Air transportation, nonscheduled; Air transportation, scheduled
Pr: Sebastian Tschackert
**Ch Bd:* Robert Snelson
**CFO:* James McGregor

D-U-N-S 07-990-6045
TIGERS GLOBAL LOGISTICS INC
20024 85th Ave S, Kent, WA 98031-1278
Tel (253) 246-4184 *Founded/Ownrshp* 2015
Sales 102.8M[E] *EMP* 2,011
SIC 4789 Pipeline terminal facilities, independently operated

D-U-N-S 62-107-2573
■TIGRENT ENTERPRISES INC
(*Suby of* TIGRENT INC) ★
1612 Cape Coral Pkwy E, Cape Coral, FL 33904-9618
Tel (239) 542-0643 *Founded/Ownrshp* 2005
Sales 115.0MM *EMP* 100
SIC 8249 Business training services
CFO: Anne M Donoho

D-U-N-S 04-793-7748 IMP
▲TIGRENT INC
1612 Cape Coral Pkwy E, Cape Coral, FL 33904-9618
Tel (239) 542-0643 *Founded/Ownrshp* 1992
Sales 210.2MM[E] *EMP* 375[E]
Accts Ehrhardt Keefe Steiner & Hottm
Tkr Sym TIGE *Exch* OTO
SIC 8249 Business training services
CEO: Anthony C Humpage
**CEO:* Bret Charlesworth
**CFO:* Anne M Donoho
**CFO:* Charles F Kuehne
Bd of Dir: Steven Barre
Ofcr: James May
Exec: Cindy Prout
Board of Directors: Steven C Barre, Jason Hammerman, Murray A Indick, Marc Scholvinck

D-U-N-S 02-354-8787
TILCON CONNECTICUT INC
(*Suby of* TILCON INC) ★
642 Black Rock Ave, New Britain, CT 06052-1037
Tel (860) 224-6010 *Founded/Ownrshp* 1981
Sales 127.7MM[E] *EMP* 300
SIC 5032 1611 3273 2951 Sand, construction; Highway & street paving contractor; Ready-mixed concrete; Asphalt paving mixtures & blocks
Pr: Carmine Abate

D-U-N-S 02-366-5045
TILCON INC
(*Suby of* OLDCASTLE INC) ★
301 Hartford Ave, Newington, CT 06111-1503
Tel (860) 223-3651 *Founded/Ownrshp* 1996
Sales 451.5MM[E] *EMP* 800
SIC 1611 5032 3273 2951 Highway & street paving contractor; Sand, construction; Gravel; Stone, crushed or broken; Ready-mixed concrete; Asphalt paving mixtures & blocks
Pr: Joseph Abate
**Ch Bd:* Angelo Tomasso Jr
**Pr:* Joseph A Abate
**CFO:* Anthony P Germano
**Treas:* Richard Foster
**Sr VP:* James Ryan
**VP:* Michael Carbone
**VP:* Richard D Johnson
**VP:* Mike Mogensen
**Exec:* Peter M Lohne
Dir IT: Jared Smith

D-U-N-S 00-779-4316 IMP
TILCON NEW YORK INC
TOTOWA ASPHALT
(*Suby of* TILCON INC) ★
162 Old Mill Rd, West Nyack, NY 10994-1406
Tel (845) 358-4500 *Founded/Ownrshp* 1964, 1981
Sales 323.5MM[E] *EMP* 276
SIC 1429 Trap rock, crushed & broken-quarrying; Dolomitic marble, crushed & broken-quarrying
Ch Bd: Christopher J Madden
**Pr:* John Cooney Jr
VP: Sean Osullivan
Plnt Mgr: Jeff Russell

D-U-N-S 08-322-6233
TILDEN MINING CO LC
1100 Superior Ave E, Cleveland, OH 44114-2530
Tel (216) 694-5278 *Founded/Ownrshp* 1988
Sales 421.9MM[E] *EMP* 1,400
SIC 1011 Iron ore mining; Iron ore pelletizing; Iron ore beneficiating

D-U-N-S 07-853-7775 EXP
▲TILE SHOP HOLDINGS INC
14000 Carlson Pkwy, Plymouth, MN 55441-5300
Tel (763) 852-2988 *Founded/Ownrshp* 2010
Sales 292.9MM *EMP* 1,410
Tkr Sym TTS *Exch* NGS
SIC 5211 5961 2891 Tile, ceramic; Masonry materials & supplies; Catalog & mail-order houses; Adhesives & sealants
Pr: Chris R Homeister
**Ch Bd:* Peter H Kamin
CFO: Kirk L Geadelmann
Sr VP: Joseph Kinder
Sr VP: Carl Randazzo
Board of Directors: Christopher T Cook, Peter J Jacullo III, Todd Krasnow, Philip B Livingston, Robert A Rucker

D-U-N-S 13-062-8969 IMP/EXP
TILE SHOP INC
14000 Carlson Pkwy, Plymouth, MN 55441-5300
Tel (763) 541-9720 *Founded/Ownrshp* 1984
Sales 257.1MM *EMP* 250
Accts Ernst & Young Llp Minneapolis
SIC 5713 5023 Floor tile; Resilient floor coverings: tile or sheet
CEO: Robert A Rucker
COO: Chris Homeister
Brnch Mgr: Crista Koch
Genl Mgr: Amir Khakbaz
Store Mgr: James Collison
Store Mgr: Christopher Delaney
Store Mgr: Steve Gilerman
Store Mgr: Krista Green
Store Mgr: Michael Kubik
Store Mgr: Julia May
Store Mgr: Brian Sorensen

TILLAMOOK CHEESE
See TILLAMOOK COUNTY CREAMERY ASSOCIATION

D-U-N-S 03-080-2045
TILLAMOOK COUNTRY SMOKER INC
8250 Warren Ave, Bay City, OR 97107
Tel (503) 377-2222 *Founded/Ownrshp* 1975
Sales 159.6MM[E] *EMP* 330
SIC 5147 Meats, cured or smoked
Pr: A Crawford Smith
**Treas:* Peggy Lehman
**VP:* Gryce Smith
Off Mgr: Kari K Tally
Plnt Mgr: Dick Crosley
Sls Dir: Mark Rempel

D-U-N-S 00-790-9278 IMP
TILLAMOOK COUNTY CREAMERY ASSOCIATION (OR)
TILLAMOOK CHEESE
4185 Highway 101 N, Tillamook, OR 97141-7770
Tel (503) 842-4481 *Founded/Ownrshp* 1909
Sales 182.5MM[E] *EMP* 550
SIC 2022 2024 2021 Natural cheese; Ice cream & frozen desserts; Creamery butter
Pr: Patrick Criteser
Ch Bd: George Allen
**Pr:* James McMullen
**CEO:* Harold Strunk
**CFO:* Herbert Dorn
V Ch Bd: Don Josi
VP: William Tennant Jr
Mktg Mgr: Mike Franklin

D-U-N-S 06-362-3474
TILLER CORP
BARTON SAND & GRAVEL
7200 Hemlock Ln N Ste 200, Maple Grove, MN 55369-5590
Tel (763) 424-5400 *Founded/Ownrshp* 1953
Sales 337.2MM[E] *EMP* 225
SIC 1442 2951 Construction sand & gravel; Paving mixtures
CEO: Chad B Sauer
**Ex VP:* Gaylen Ghylin
VP: Steve Sauer
Genl Mgr: Dale Blum
Dir IT: Gene Schaff
Opers Mgr: Todd Laubis
Sls Mgr: Joe Winkel

TILLY'S
See WORLD OF JEANS & TOPS

D-U-N-S 78-943-3252
▲TILLYS INC
10 Whatney, Irvine, CA 92618-2807
Tel (949) 609-5599 *Founded/Ownrshp* 1982
Sales 550.9MM *EMP* 4,900[E]
Tkr Sym TLYS *Exch* NYS
SIC 5651 5661 Family clothing stores; Shoe stores
Pr: Edmond Thomas
**Ch Bd:* Hezy Shaked
CFO: Michael L Henry
Chf Mktg O: Debbie Anker-Morris
Ofcr: Jon Kubo
VP: Shelly Bueno
VP: Christina Campbell
VP: Barb Krol
VP: Carolyn S McNamara
VP: Efren Medellin
Rgnl Mgr: Laura Schmied
Board of Directors: Doug Collier, Seth Johnson, Janet Kerr, Bernard Zeichner

D-U-N-S 10-426-6700
TIM HORTONS USA INC
MAIDSTONE COFFEE
(*Suby of* TDL GROUP CORP, THE)
5505 Blue Lagoon Dr, Miami, FL 33126-2029
Tel (888) 376-4835 *Founded/Ownrshp* 1995
Sales 92.4MM[E] *EMP* 170

SIC 6794 5812 Franchises, selling or licensing; Coffee shop; Fast-food restaurant, chain
CEO: Marc Caira
**Ch Bd:* Paul D House
**COO:* David F Clanachan
**CFO:* Cynthia J Devine
**Ex VP:* Mike Meilleur
VP: Larry Mench

D-U-N-S 62-104-8227
TIM ICENHOWER OIL AND GAS INC
5916 Industrial Drive Ext, Bossier City, LA 71112-2623
Tel (318) 752-2293 *Founded/Ownrshp* 1994
Sales 197.0MM^E *EMP* 380^E
SIC 1382 Oil & gas exploration services
**CFO:* Patrick Caraway

TIMBER PRODUCTS COMPANY
See TIMBER PRODUCTS CO LIMITED PARTNERSHIP

D-U-N-S 19-052-4512 IMP/EXP
TIMBER PRODUCTS CO LIMITED PARTNERSHIP
TIMBER PRODUCTS COMPANY
305 S 4th St, Springfield, OR 97477-5404
Tel (541) 747-4577 *Founded/Ownrshp* 1967
Sales 397.5MM *EMP* 1,100
SIC 2436 2435 5031 2493 Plywood, softwood; Veneer stock, softwood; Plywood, hardwood or hardwood faced; Lumber: rough, dressed & finished; Particleboard products
CEO: J H Gonyea II
COO: Joe Gonyea III
CFO: Allan W Emrick
CFO: Erik Vos
Ex VP: Arno Pelkonen
VP: David Gonyea
Mng Dir: Alexander Gibson
Rgnl Mgr: Josh Ketsdever
VP Mfg: Larry Brockmann
Sfty Mgr: David Hanson
Plnt Mgr: Dave Pope

D-U-N-S 05-097-0946
TIMBER PRODUCTS INSPECTION INC
(*Suby of* WRD INC) ★
1641 Sigman Rd Nw, Conyers, GA 30012-3465
Tel (770) 922-8000 *Founded/Ownrshp* 1987
Sales 109.8MM^E *EMP* 83
SIC 0851 8734

D-U-N-S 06-413-5676
TIMBERLAKE & DICKSON INC
CENTURY SALES AND SERVICE
3520 W Miller Rd Ste 110, Garland, TX 75041-6098
Tel (214) 349-2320 *Founded/Ownrshp* 1965
Sales 1.0MMM *EMP* 17
SIC 5075 Warm air heating equipment & supplies; Air conditioning & ventilation equipment & supplies
Pr: Preston W Dickson
Genl Mgr: Linda Nelson

D-U-N-S 05-294-3669
TIMBERLAKE & HITE CO INC (SC)
209 Flintlake Rd, Columbia, SC 29223-7834
Tel (803) 276-0510 *Founded/Ownrshp* 1897
Sales 120.0MM^E *EMP* 475
SIC 5141 Groceries, general line
Pr: David R Clark
**Sec:* P Thomas Perkins
Bd of Dir: R Guy
VP: Jere Loggins
Genl Mgr: Karen Anderson
Genl Mgr: Chuck Walters
Mktg Dir: Chris Davenport

TIMBERLAKE CNSTR CO OKLA
See TIMBERLAKE CONSTRUCTION CO INC

D-U-N-S 03-061-7179
TIMBERLAKE CONSTRUCTION CO INC
TIMBERLAKE CNSTR CO OKLA
7613 N Classen Blvd, Oklahoma City, OK 73116-7088
Tel (405) 840-2521 *Founded/Ownrshp* 1976
Sales 96.3MM^E *EMP* 54
Accts Luton & Co Pllc Cpas Oklah
SIC 1542 1541 Commercial & office building, new construction; Industrial buildings, new construction
Pr: David B Timberlake
**Pr:* Bryan Timberlake
**Sr VP:* John W Cox
**Sr VP:* Robert Renshaw
Sfty Dirs: Jordan Adkisson
Sfty Dirs: Casey Louge
Board of Directors: Bryan Timberlake

D-U-N-S 06-675-4250 IMP/EXP
TIMBERLAND LLC
200 Domain Dr, Stratham, NH 03885-2575
Tel (603) 772-9500 *Founded/Ownrshp* 2011
Sales NA *EMP* 7,500
SIC 3143 3144 2386 2329 2321 2325

D-U-N-S 08-033-4922
TIMBERLANE REGIONAL SAU
SCHOOL ADMINISTRATIVE UNIT
30 Greenough Rd, Plaistow, NH 03865-2724
Tel (603) 382-6119 *Founded/Ownrshp* 2016
Sales 51.6MM^E *EMP* 1,097
SIC 8211 Public elementary & secondary schools
Ex Dir: Debra Armfield

TIMCO
See TAS HOLDING INC

TIMCO AVIATION SERVICES
See TRIAD INTERNATIONAL MAINTENANCE CORP

D-U-N-S 60-578-4081 IMP/EXP
TIMCO AVIATION SERVICES INC
HAECO AMERICAS
(*Suby of* HAECO USA HOLDINGS INC) ★
623 Radar Rd, Greensboro, NC 27410-6221
Tel (336) 668-4410 *Founded/Ownrshp* 2014
Sales 768.6MM^E *EMP* 3,400
SIC 4581 5088 Aircraft servicing & repairing; Transportation equipment & supplies
CEO: Richard Kendall
Pr: Mark Peterman
Pr: Jim Sokol
CFO: Lee Fox
Ex VP: Elizabeth Mehaffey
VP: Sam Ahad
VP: Samuel Ahad
VP: Mike Anderson
VP: Barrett Hanley
VP: Jose Pevida
VP: Steve Richards
VP: Margaret Stancil

D-U-N-S 01-180-9597
TIMCO INC
PLANET HONDA
2285 Us Highway 22 W, Union, NJ 07083-8404
Tel (908) 964-1600 *Founded/Ownrshp* 1996
Sales 93.1MM^E *EMP* 200
SIC 5511 Automobiles, new & used
Pr: Tim Ciasulli
Dir IT: Patrick Knieriem

D-U-N-S 05-784-7444
TIMCO SERVICES INC
1724 E Milton Ave, Lafayette, LA 70508-7973
Tel (337) 233-5185 *Founded/Ownrshp* 1976
Sales 113.1MM^E *EMP* 100
SIC 1389 Running, cutting & pulling casings, tubes & rods
Pr: Mark Guidry
**Pr:* W N Pressley
**VP:* Mike Maraist

D-U-N-S 60-343-0976
■**TIME CUSTOMER SERVICE INC**
TAMPA COMMONS
(*Suby of* TIME INC) ★
1 N Dale Mabry Hwy # 150, Tampa, FL 33609-2700
Tel (813) 878-6427 *Founded/Ownrshp* 1986
Sales 102.3MM^E *EMP* 1,600
SIC 7389 7374 Subscription fulfillment services: magazine, newspaper, etc.; Data processing service
Pr: Timothy Adams
**VP:* Bob Becksted
**VP:* Andrew A Bragg
**VP:* Barry Elliott
Sls&Mrk Ex: Dakari Gibbon

D-U-N-S 12-581-1117 IMP/EXP
▲**TIME INC**
225 Liberty St Ste C2, New York, NY 10281-1049
Tel (212) 522-1212 *Founded/Ownrshp* 1922
Sales 3.1MMM *EMP* 7,200
Tkr Sym TIME *Exch* NYS
SIC 2721 Magazines: publishing only, not printed on site
Pr: Rich Battista
Pr: Richard Battista
Pr: Peter Katsafanas
Pr: Jennifer Wong
COO: Jen Wong
CFO: Jeffrey J Bairstow
Ofcr: Gregory Giangrande
Ofcr: Norman Pearlstine
Ex VP: Lynne Biggar
Ex VP: Colin Bodell
Ex VP: Leslie Dukker Doty
Ex VP: Mark P Ford
Ex VP: Lawrence A Jacobs
Ex VP: Erik Moreno
Ex VP: Evelyn Webster
Sr VP: Andy Bush
Sr VP: Kurt RAO
VP: Matt Fanelli
VP: Robert Ferreira
VP: Manish Gupta
VP: Judith Hammerman
Board of Directors: Michael P Zeisser, David A Bell, John M Fahey Jr, Manuel A Fernandez, Dennis J Fitzsimons, Betsy D Holden, Kay Koplovitz, J Randall Macdonald, Ronald S Rolfe, Howard Stringer

D-U-N-S 17-683-6133
■**TIME INSURANCE CO**
ASSURANT HEALTH
(*Suby of* ASSURANT INC) ★
501 W Michigan St, Milwaukee, WI 53203-2706
Tel (414) 271-3011 *Founded/Ownrshp* 1982
Sales NA *EMP* 29^E
SIC 6321 Health insurance carriers
Pr: Adam Lamnin
COO: Rajeev Bal
Treas: Kevin Michaels
Chf Mktg O: Steve Deraleau
Ofcr: Katie Porter
Ofcr: Louise Solaperto
Sr VP: Mike Kellen
Sr VP: Jennifer Kopps-Wagner
**Sr VP:* Scott Krienke
Sr VP: Howard Miller
VP: David Andrews
VP: David Barney
VP: Mark Berquist
VP: Rob Guilbert
VP: Kay Kerlin
VP: Hiram Machado
VP: Norbert Monfort
VP: Bill Nelson
VP: Brian Wegner
VP: Brian Wolf
Dir Soc: Denise Garczynski

TIME WARNER
See SPECTRUM MANAGEMENT HOLDING CO LLC

TIME WARNER CABLE
See TIME WARNER INC

D-U-N-S 79-078-4474
■**TIME WARNER CABLE ENTERPRISES LLC**
(*Suby of* TIME WARNER) ★
400 Atlantic St Ste 6, Stamford, CT 06901-3533
Tel (877) 495-9201 *Founded/Ownrshp* 1992
Sales 1.2MMM^E *EMP* 16,000
SIC 7812 4841 Motion picture production & distribution; Cable television services
Ch Bd: Richard D Parsons
COO: Joan H Gillman
COO: Dinesh C Jain
COO: John Keib
COO: Philip G Meeks
CFO: Michael Kelly
**CFO:* Wayne H Pace
CFO: Matthew Siegel
**V Ch Bd:* Kenneth Novack
Ofcr: Melinda C Witmer
**Ex VP:* Paul T Cappuccio
Ex VP: Ellen M East
Ex VP: Hamid R Heidary
Ex VP: Gail G Mackinnon
Ex VP: Peter C Stern
Sr VP: William F Osbourne Jr

D-U-N-S 78-680-4828
■**TIME WARNER CABLE SAN ANTONIO LP**
(*Suby of* TIME WARNER) ★
1900 Blue Crest Ln, San Antonio, TX 78247-4315
Tel (703) 713-9342 *Founded/Ownrshp* 2009
Sales 800.0MM *EMP* 5,000
SIC 4841 Cable television services
**Pr:* John Owen
COO: Greg Stahl
COO: Steve Sullivan
**CFO:* William Osbourne
Exec: Mike Lozano
Brnch Mgr: Tiffany Vela
Genl Mgr: Phil Jackson
Opers Supe: Stephen Knox
Sales Exec: James Copeland
Sales Exec: Ronald Nance
Mktg Dir: Deborah A Solis

D-U-N-S 05-429-5717
TIME WARNER ENTERTAINMENT ADVANCE NEWHOUSE PARTNERSHIP
7010 Airport Rd, El Paso, TX 79906-4941
Tel (512) 288-5440 *Founded/Ownrshp* 2012
Sales NA *EMP* 1,298
SIC 4841

D-U-N-S 83-635-1197
■**TIME WARNER ENTERTAINMENT-ADVANCE/NEWHOUSE PARTNERSHIP**
(*Suby of* TIME WARNER CABLE ENTERPRISES LLC) ★
400 Atlantic St Ste 6, Stamford, CT 06901-3533
Tel (212) 364-8200 *Founded/Ownrshp* 1995
Sales 233.3MM^E *EMP* 1,298
SIC 4841 Cable television services
VP: David McLaughlin
Counsel: Robert Kane
Snr Mgr: John Bergman
Snr Mgr: Joe Paisley

D-U-N-S 07-918-0179
TIME WARNER INC
TIME WARNER CABLE
6005 Fair Lakes Rd, East Syracuse, NY 13057-4250
Tel (315) 234-1000 *Founded/Ownrshp* 2013
Sales 194.6MM^E *EMP* 245^E
SIC 5063 Wire & cable
VP: Carrie Bocian
VP: Susan Weinstein
Snr Ntwrk: Darren Kara
Netwrk Eng: Orlando Gravely
Opers Mgr: Elena Bambekova
Counsel: Carolyn Desai
Snr Mgr: Judy Jenacaro

D-U-N-S 79-952-7630 IMP/EXP
▲**TIME WARNER INC**
1 Time Warner Ctr Bsmt B, New York, NY 10019-6010
Tel (212) 484-8000 *Founded/Ownrshp* 2001
Sales 28.1MMM *EMP* 24,800
Tkr Sym TWX *Exch* NYS
SIC 4841 7812 2731 2721 Cable & other pay television services; Cable television services; Subscription television services; Motion picture & video production; Motion picture production & distribution; Television film production; Video tape production; Book publishing; Magazines: publishing only, not printed on site
Ch Bd: Jeffrey L Bewkes
Pr: Mark Darcy
COO: Greg D'Alba
COO: John D Maatta
CFO: Howard M Averill
CFO: Edward A Romano
Chf Mktg O: Kristen O'Hara
Ofcr: Karen Magee
Ofcr: Kristen Ohara
Ofcr: Jack Wakshlag
Ex VP: David Baldwin
Ex VP: Carolyn Blackwood
Ex VP: Paul T Cappuccio
Ex VP: Steven C Davidson
Ex VP: Michael Gabriel
Ex VP: Gary Ginsberg
Ex VP: Kenneth Lerer
Ex VP: Courteney Monroe
Ex VP: John A Rogovin
Ex VP: Olivia Smashum
Ex VP: Mayo S Stuntz Jr
Board of Directors: Deborah C Wright, James L Barksdale, William P Barr, Stephen F Bollenbach, Robert C Clark, Mathias Dopfner, Jessica P Einhorn, Carlos M Gutierrez, Fred Hassan, Paul D Wachter

D-U-N-S 02-046-4892
TIMEC ACQUISITIONS INC
(*Suby of* BROADSPECTRUM PTY LTD)
155 Corporate Pl, Vallejo, CA 94590-6968
Tel (707) 642-2222 *Founded/Ownrshp* 2004
Sales 162.2MM^E *EMP* 1,050
SIC 1629 Industrial plant construction; Chemical plant & refinery construction
Pr: Pat McMahon
**COO:* Gary Green
**CFO:* Dennis Turnipseed
VP: Dennis Truet

D-U-N-S 05-388-2049
TIMEC COMPANIES INC
(*Suby of* TIMEC ACQUISITIONS INC) ★
155 Corporate Pl, Vallejo, CA 94590-6968
Tel (707) 642-2222 *Founded/Ownrshp* 1998
Sales 162.2MM^E *EMP* 1,000
SIC 1629 1799 Industrial plant construction; Chemical plant & refinery construction; Oil refinery construction; Welding on site
Pr: Dennis Turnipseed
Genl Couns: Brent Babow

TIMES COMMUNICATIONS CO
See SEATTLE TIMES CO

D-U-N-S 08-334-2253 IMP/EXP
■**TIMES FIBER COMMUNICATIONS INC**
(*Suby of* AMPHENOL CORP) ★
358 Hall Ave, Wallingford, CT 06492-3574
Tel (203) 265-8500 *Founded/Ownrshp* 1992
Sales 168.4MM^E *EMP* 700
SIC 3357 Coaxial cable, nonferrous
Pr: R Adam Norwitt
Pr: Martin Loeffler
**Ex VP:* Diana G Reardon
IT Exec: Craig Southard

TIMES HERALD
See ALAMEDA NEWSPAPERS INC

TIMES NEWS, THE
See PENCOR SERVICES INC

D-U-N-S 00-610-3691
TIMES PRINTING LLC
(*Suby of* KAPPA MEDIA GROUP INC) ★
100 Industrial Dr, Random Lake, WI 53075-1693
Tel (920) 994-4396 *Founded/Ownrshp* 2016
Sales 140.4MM^E *EMP* 300
SIC 2752 Commercial printing, offset
CEO: Nick Karabots
Pr: John R Scholler
Treas: Jean Vetter
VP: Donald Baumann
VP: James Scholler
Genl Mgr: Rick Bortolotti
Plnt Mgr: Randy Lobe
Sls Mgr: Shawn Scholler
Counsel: John Herbers

D-U-N-S 00-409-0312 IMP/EXP
TIMES PUBLISHING CO (FL)
490 1st Ave S, Saint Petersburg, FL 33701-4223
Tel (727) 893-8111 *Founded/Ownrshp* 1884, 1904
Sales 747.2MM^E *EMP* 3,190
SIC 2711 2721 Newspapers, publishing & printing; Magazines: publishing & printing; Periodicals: publishing & printing
Ch Bd: Paul Tash
CFO: R M Caoll
**CFO:* Jana Jones
CFO: Mike Sholar
**VP:* Corty Andrew P
Exec: Sherrie Newmister
Comm Dir: Jounice Nealy
Rgnl Mgr: Rob Jennings
Brnch Mgr: Bill Coats
IT Man: John Buchenhorst
Info Man: Dick Murdock
Board of Directors: Sebastian Dortch

TIMES SUPER MARKET
See QSI INC

TIMES-NEWS, THE
See LEE PUBLICATIONS INC

TIMET
See TITANIUM METALS CORP

TIMEWISE FOOD STORES
See LANDMARK INDUSTRIES HOLDINGS LTD

D-U-N-S 00-116-5208 IMP
TIMEX GROUP USA INC
(*Suby of* TIMEX GROUP B.V.)
555 Christian Rd, Middlebury, CT 06762-3206
Tel (203) 346-5000 *Founded/Ownrshp* 1857
Sales 387.1MM^E *EMP* 2,000
SIC 3873 Watches & parts, except crystals & jewels
CEO: Paolo Marai
Treas: Amir Rosenthal
Sr VP: Robert Butler
Sr VP: Greg Miller
VP: W John Dryfe
VP: Thomas Essery
VP: Louis M Galie
VP: Donna Kelsey
VP: Peter Kohlsaat
VP: Frank A Sherer
Snr Sftwr: Michael Cardin

TIMKEN AEROSPACE
See TIMKEN US LLC

D-U-N-S 00-446-5100 IMP/EXP
▲**TIMKEN CO** (OH)
4500 Mount Pleasant St Nw, North Canton, OH 44720-5450
Tel (234) 262-3000 *Founded/Ownrshp* 1899
Sales 2.8MMM *EMP* 14,000
Tkr Sym TKR *Exch* NYS
SIC 3562 Ball & roller bearings; Roller bearings & parts
Pr: Richard G Kyle
Pr: Christopher A Coughlin
CFO: Philip D Fracassa
Treas: Bailey Ballantine
Ex VP: William R Burkhart
Sr VP: Michael J Hill
Sr VP: J Ted Mihaila
Sr VP: Daniel E Muller
VP: Mike Connors
VP: Sheila Cowles
VP: Rory Lubic
VP: Nancy Noeske
VP: Sandra L Rapp
VP: Brian Ruel
VP: Dennis Wasielewski
Exec: Chris McGriff
Board of Directors: Jacqueline F Woods, Maria A Crowe, John A Luke Jr, Christopher L Mapes, James F Palmer, Joseph W Ralston, John P Reilly, Frank C Sullivan, John M Timken Jr, Ward J Timken Jr

D-U-N-S 04-166-0445 IMP/EXP
■TIMKEN CORP
(Suby of TIMKEN AEROSPACE) ★
4500 Mount Pleasant St Nw, North Canton, OH 44720-5450
Tel (330) 471-3378 Founded/Ownrshp 1998
Sales 191.7MM^E EMP 720
SIC 5085 5051 Bearings, bushings, wheels & gears; Aluminum bars, rods, ingots, sheets, pipes, plates, etc.
CEO: Richard G Kyle
*Ex VP: William R Burkhart
*Ex VP: Christopher A Coughlin
*VP: Ronald J Myers
IT Man: Mihai Grigorescu

D-U-N-S 00-480-1577
■TIMKEN MOTOR & CRANE SERVICES LLC
WAZEE A TIMKEN BRAND
(Suby of TIMKEN CO) ★
4850 Moline St, Denver, CO 80239-2624
Tel (303) 623-8658 Founded/Ownrshp 2013
Sales 106.9MM^E EMP 200
Accts Bauerle And Company Pc Den
SIC 5063 1731 7694 3613 3536 Motors, electric; General electrical contractor; Electric motor repair; Switchgear & switchboard apparatus; Cranes, industrial plant
Pr: Richard G Kyle
VP: Jonathan Glessner
*Genl Mgr: Evette Beal
*Genl Mgr: Karen Imrie
Prd Mgr: Carl McClure

D-U-N-S 08-009-7156
■TIMKEN SMO LLC
CARLISLE BELTS
(Suby of TIMKEN CO) ★
2601 W Battlefield St, Springfield, MO 65807-4009
Tel (866) 773-2926 Founded/Ownrshp 2013
Sales 106.7MM^E EMP 391^E
SIC 3451 3714 Screw machine products; Air conditioner parts, motor vehicle
Pr: Maria A Crowe
Dir Soc: Ken Appell

TIMKEN SUPER PRECISION
See MPB CORP

D-U-N-S 00-114-8717 IMP
■TIMKEN US LLC
TIMKEN AEROSPACE
(Suby of TIMKEN CO) ★
336 Mechanic St, Lebanon, NH 03766-2614
Tel (603) 443-5217 Founded/Ownrshp 1866
Sales 1.0MMM^E EMP 9,800
SIC 3562 Ball bearings & parts
CEO: James W Griffith
*Pr: Mike Arnold
*Pr: Jacqueline Dado
*Pr: Richard G Kyle
*CFO: Philip D Fracassa
*Ex VP: William R Burkhart
*Ex VP: Christopher A Coughlin
*VP: Richard M Boyer
VP: G R Kelleher
Area Mgr: Jackie Driscoll
Snr Mgr: David Cadwell

D-U-N-S 07-923-6657
▲TIMKENSTEEL CORP
1835 Dueber Ave Sw, Canton, OH 44706-2728
Tel (330) 471-7000 Founded/Ownrshp 1899
Sales 1.1MMM EMP 2,600^E
Accts Ernst & Young Llp Cleveland
Tkr Sym TMST Exch NYS
SIC 3312 Blast furnaces & steel mills
Ch Bd: Ward J Timken Jr
CFO: Christopher J Holding
Ex VP: William P Bryan
Ex VP: Frank A Dipiero
Ex VP: Robert N Keeler
Ex VP: Thomas D Moline
Ex VP: Donald L Walker
VP: Tina M Beskid
VP: Karen Hannum
Exec: Brian Heid
Prgrm Mgr: Jack Bouer
Board of Directors: Joseph A Carrabba, Phillip R Cox, Diane C Creel, Terry L Dunlap, Randall H Edwards, Donald T Misheff, John P Reilly, Ronald A Rice, Randall A Wotring

D-U-N-S 04-996-8738
TIMMONS GROUP INC
1001 Boulders Pkwy # 300, North Chesterfield, VA 23225-5522
Tel (804) 200-6500 Founded/Ownrshp 1953
Sales 84.5MM^E EMP 440
SIC 8711 8713 Civil engineering; Surveying services
Pr: Brian F Bortell
*Treas: Vince Doherty
Top Exec: Kirsten Timmons
*VP: Tim Davey
VP: Andrew Gould
Prin: Stephen D Hostetler
Admn Mgr: Junie West
Snr Sftwr: George Simpson
Snr Sftwr: Norman Staggs
Snr PM: Michael Patey

D-U-N-S 00-334-9326
■TIMPANOGOS REGIONAL HOSPITAL (UT)
COLUMBIA HCA
(Suby of HOSPITAL COPORATION OF AMERICA) ★
750 W 800 N, Orem, UT 84057-3660
Tel (801) 714-6000 Founded/Ownrshp 1998, 2001
Sales 104.8MM EMP 500
SIC 8062 General medical & surgical hospitals
Dir Rad: Amy Dalton
DP Dir: Rick Nelson
Dir QC: Paula Strasburg
Dir IT: Richard Nielson
Software D: David Haskell
Doctor: Ron Barlow
Pharmcst: Stacey Kearns
Pharmcst: Alissa White
HC Dir: Michele Hansen

D-U-N-S 02-014-5786
TIMPANOGOS REGIONAL HOSPITAL
750 W 800 N, Orem, UT 84057-3660
Tel (801) 714-6000 Founded/Ownrshp 2009
Sales 102.0MM EMP 25^E
SIC 8062 General medical & surgical hospitals

D-U-N-S 01-493-8426
TIMS AIRBRUSH LLC
10490 Vaughn Way, Commerce City, CO 80022-9497
Tel (303) 944-9497 Founded/Ownrshp 2012
Sales 800.0MM EMP 1
SIC 8999 7389 Art related services; Hand painting, textile

D-U-N-S 10-281-3136
TIMS BUICK HYUNDAI SUBARU & GMC INC
TIM'S PONTIAC
1006 Comm Dr, Prescott, AZ 86305
Tel (877) 838-6541 Founded/Ownrshp 1983
Sales 85.2MM^E EMP 186
SIC 5511 Automobiles, new & used
Pr: Timothy J Coury
*Sec: Diane L Korte
*VP: Sheila M Coury
VP: Robby Hinshaw

TIM'S PONTIAC
See TIMS BUICK HYUNDAI SUBARU & GMC INC

D-U-N-S 07-952-3385
TIN LIZZYS CONSOLIDATED LLC
2030 Powers Ferry Rd Se, Atlanta, GA 30339-2823
Tel (678) 681-9503 Founded/Ownrshp 2014
Sales 85.6MM^E EMP 672
SIC 6719 Personal holding companies, except banks
CEO: Tory Bartlett
CFO: Antonio Johnson

D-U-N-S 10-792-3567 IMP/EXP
TINDALL CORP
3076 N Blackstock Rd, Spartanburg, SC 29301-5566
Tel (864) 576-3230 Founded/Ownrshp 1963
Sales 151.0MM^E EMP 750
SIC 3272

D-U-N-S 03-471-0061 IMP
TINDELLS INC
TINDELLS LUMBER & BLDG MTLS
7751 Norris Fwy, Knoxville, TN 37938-4226
Tel (865) 922-7751 Founded/Ownrshp 1907
Sales 143.7MM^E EMP 361
SIC 5031 5211 2439 Lumber, plywood & millwork; Building materials, exterior; Building materials, interior; Lumber: rough, dressed & finished; Lumber & other building materials; Structural wood members
Ch: Carl Tindel
*Pr: Johan Van Tilburg
*CFO: Roger L Bates
Brnch Mgr: Michael Day
Sales Exec: Richard Tindell

TINDELLS LUMBER & BLDG MTLS
See TINDELLS INC

D-U-N-S 00-202-2721 IMP/EXP
TINGUE BROWN & CO
535 N Midland Ave, Saddle Brook, NJ 07663-5521
Tel (201) 796-4490 Founded/Ownrshp 1902
Sales 90.6MM^E EMP 315
SIC 5087 3089 2394

D-U-N-S 55-677-6941
TINICUM CAPITAL PARTNERS II LP
800 3rd Ave Fl 40, New York, NY 10022-7603
Tel (212) 446-9300 Founded/Ownrshp 2004
Sales 446.0MM^E EMP 1,700^E
SIC 6211 3429 3621 Security brokers & dealers; Metal fasteners; Motors, electric
Pt: Eric Ruttenberg

D-U-N-S 07-428-1684
TINKER FEDERAL CREDIT UNION
4140 W I 40 Service Rd, Oklahoma City, OK 73108-2066
Tel (405) 732-0324 Founded/Ownrshp 1946
Sales NA EMP 550
SIC 6061 Federal credit unions
Pr: Michael D Kloiber
*Ex VP: Billie Houston
*Sr VP: Lisa Leeper
*Sr VP: Donna Olsen
*Sr VP: Brenda Peddycoart
Sr VP: Susan J Rogers
Sr VP: Matt Stratton
VP: Jay Foote
VP: Justin Hightower
VP: Loretta Ross
VP: Margaret Scallorn
VP: Alan Schaefer
VP: Doug Warren
VP: Grant Woldun
VP: Patrick Yager

D-U-N-S 60-290-9702
TINKER FEDERAL CREDIT UNION
(Suby of TINKER FEDERAL CREDIT UNION) ★
5101 W 6th Ave, Stillwater, OK 74074-6967
Tel (405) 707-7440 Founded/Ownrshp 2005
Sales NA EMP 1
SIC 6062 State credit unions
Prin: Michael Kloiber

TIO JANS MRGRITAS MEXICAN REST
See MARGARITAS MANAGEMENT GROUP INC

D-U-N-S 00-232-2543 IMP/EXP
TIOGA PIPE INC (PA)
2450 Wheatsheaf Ln, Philadelphia, PA 19137-1028
Tel (215) 831-0700 Founded/Ownrshp 1945
Sales 152.4MM^E EMP 20^E
SIC 5051 Pipe & tubing, steel
Pr: Andrew Keiser
*Treas: Bennett W Keiser
*VP: David Keiser
Genl Mgr: Steve Bujnowski
Genl Mgr: Gregory Johnson
Genl Mgr: Craig Stiffler
QA Dir: Lisa Smith
Sls Dir: Joe McNelis

D-U-N-S 03-379-5584
TIP TOP POULTRY INC
327 Wallace Rd, Marietta, GA 30062-3573
Tel (770) 973-8070 Founded/Ownrshp 1958
Sales 278.0MM EMP 1,500
SIC 2015 Poultry, processed: fresh; Poultry, processed: frozen; Chicken, processed: cooked
Ch: Robin A Burruss
*Pr: Brad Respess
*CFO: Charlie Singleton
*Sec: David C Austin
*VP: Chester A Austin
*VP: Brian Tucker
Sfty Mgr: Todd Jones

TIPP DISTRIBUTOR
See JARRITOS INC

D-U-N-S 36-155-9016 IMP
TIPP DISTRIBUTORS INC
NOVAMEX
(Suby of TIPP DISTRIBUTOR) ★
500 W Overland Ave # 300, El Paso, TX 79901-1085
Tel (915) 594-1618 Founded/Ownrshp 1999
Sales 113.6MM^E EMP 126
Accts Mancera Sc
SIC 5149 Specialty food items; Soft drinks
CEO: Fernandez I Luis
*Pr: Ramon Carrasco
*Ex VP: Sandford Gross
*VP: Thomas B De Leon
*VP: Hill A Francisco
Rgnl Mgr: Maria Reyes

D-U-N-S 07-598-4559
TIPPECANOE SCHOOL CORP
21 Elston Rd, Lafayette, IN 47909-2899
Tel (765) 474-2481 Founded/Ownrshp 1962
Sales 110.0MM EMP 1,800
SIC 8211 Public elementary school; Public junior high school; Public senior high school
Pr: Jim Slaven
*Pr: Randy Bond
*CFO: Kimberly J Fox
CIO: Mike Watson
HC Dir: Cynthia Mason
Board of Directors: Thomas Schmidt, Lori Shorforth, Martina Thompson, Mike Watson

D-U-N-S 07-967-4217
TIPPMANN CONSTRUCTION LLC (IN)
9009 Coldwater Rd Ste 300, Fort Wayne, IN 46825-2072
Tel (260) 490-3000 Founded/Ownrshp 2008
Sales 134.0MM EMP 39
SIC 1541 1796 Warehouse construction; Installing building equipment
Pr: Dale Budzon

D-U-N-S 18-106-3538
TIPPMANN PROPERTIES INC
9009 Coldwater Rd Ste 300, Fort Wayne, IN 46825-2072
Tel (260) 490-3000 Founded/Ownrshp 1982
Sales 116.5MM^E EMP 539
SIC 8741 Management services
Pr: John Tippman Sr
*Pr: Charles Tippmann
*Pr: John Tippmann Jr
Treas: Jeff Hastings
Sr VP: Brad Hastings
Sr VP: Steven Tippmann
VP: Jason Branstetter
VP: Joseph Greco
VP: Ron Kozicki
Brnch Mgr: Matt Helbling
Genl Mgr: Brian Ehrsam

D-U-N-S 18-418-7409
TIPTON COUNTY SCHOOL DISTRICT INC
TIPTON COUNTY SCHOOLS
1580 Highway 51 S, Covington, TN 38019-3221
Tel (901) 476-7148 Founded/Ownrshp 1961
Sales 60.3MM^E EMP 1,700
SIC 8211 Public elementary & secondary schools
MIS Dir: Leaanne McCammon
*Opers Supe: Rickey Fayne
Teacher Pr: Mary Haywood
Psych: Lisa Bradford
HC Dir: Sherrie Yarbro

TIPTON COUNTY SCHOOLS
See TIPTON COUNTY SCHOOL DISTRICT INC

D-U-N-S 00-779-3045
■TIPTON TELEPHONE CO INC
TDS
(Suby of TDS TELECOMMUNICATIONS CORP) ★
117 E Washington St, Tipton, IN 46072-1750
Tel (765) 675-4185 Founded/Ownrshp 1895, 1954
Sales 853.0MM EMP 2,700
SIC 4813 Local & long distance telephone communications
Pr: Dave Witter
*Pr: Joe F Watson
*Sec: Ben Hobbs
*VP: Norman Martz
*Genl Mgr: Howard E Pottenger
Board of Directors: Nancy E Urmston

D-U-N-S 80-671-4833
▲TIPTREE FINANCIAL INC
780 3rd Ave Fl 21, New York, NY 10017-2167
Tel (212) 446-1400 Founded/Ownrshp 2007
Sales NA EMP 929^E
Tkr Sym TIPT Exch NAS
SIC 6162 6282 6311 6798 Mortgage bankers & correspondents; Investment advice; Life insurance; Real estate investment trusts
CEO: Jonathan Ilany
Ch Bd: Michael G Barnes
COO: Julia Wyatt
CFO: Sandra Bell
Bd of Dir: Richard Price
Ofcr: Timothy Schott
VP: Neil C Rifkind
Off Mgr: Elizabeth Sztyk
Board of Directors: Lesley Goldwasser, John E Mack, Richard A Price, Bradley E Smith

D-U-N-S 07-915-7516
■TIPTREE OPERATING CO LLC
CARE INVESTMENT TRUST
(Suby of TIPTREE FINANCIAL INC) ★
780 3rd Ave Rm 2103, New York, NY 10017-2167
Tel (212) 446-1410 Founded/Ownrshp 2012
Sales 347.8MM^E EMP 497^E
SIC 8082 Home health care services
CEO: Salvatore V Riso Jr
Prin: Michael G Barnes
Prin: Geoffrey N Kauffman

D-U-N-S 14-422-3609 IMP
TIRE CENTERS LLC
T3 TIRE CENTERS
(Suby of MICHELIN NORTH AMERICA INC) ★
310 Inglesby Pkwy, Duncan, SC 29334-9173
Tel (864) 329-2700 Founded/Ownrshp 1999
Sales 1.3MMM^E EMP 2,600
SIC 5014 5531 7534 Tires & tubes; Automobile tires & tubes; Truck tires & tubes; Automotive tires; Rebuilding & retreading tires
Pr: Guy Pekle
CFO: Norman King
CFO: Frank Skorvewski
VP: Jim Borkey
VP: Greg Kerce
VP: Nate Kirian
VP: Chuck McFadden
Exec: Carole Roos
Genl Mgr: Matt Boemia
Genl Mgr: Steve Comarata
Dir IT: Melanie Cox

D-U-N-S 02-233-3434 IMP
TIRE FACTORY INC
(FORMALY: NORTHWEST TIRE FACTORY LLC)
6102 N Marine Dr, Portland, OR 97203-6481
Tel (503) 283-6494 Founded/Ownrshp 1999
Sales 83.3MM^E EMP 51^E
SIC 5014 Automobile tires & tubes
CEO: Walter Lybeck
*CEO: Walter Lybek
Off Mgr: Jan Warren
Mktg Mgr: Larry Birtcher

D-U-N-S 08-370-2019
TIRE GUYS INC
TIRE-RAMA
1401 Industrial Ave, Billings, MT 59101-3128
Tel (406) 245-4006 Founded/Ownrshp 1994
Sales 90.0MM EMP 450
SIC 5531

TIRE RACK, THE
See TIRE RACK INC

D-U-N-S 06-471-5410 IMP/EXP
TIRE RACK INC
TIRE RACK, THE
7101 Vorden Pkwy, South Bend, IN 46628-8422
Tel (888) 541-1777 Founded/Ownrshp 1973
Sales 1.2MMM^E EMP 600
SIC 5014 3714 Automobile tires & tubes; Motor vehicle wheels & parts
Pr: Michael A Joines
CFO: Joe IAMS
*Ch: Thomas F Veldman
Ofcr: Dan Dixon
VP: Matthew E Dmonds
*VP: Matthew E Edmonds
*VP: Mark P Veldman
Exec: Stacey Toth
Off Mgr: Cathy Shreve
CIO: Jean Roberson
Dir IT: John Rastetter

TIRE WHOLESALE WAREHOUSE
See BRIDGESTONE AMERICAS TIRE OPERATIONS LLC

TIRE-RAMA
See TIRE GUYS INC

D-U-N-S 11-237-2052 IMP
TIRECO INC
500 W 190th St Ste 100, Gardena, CA 90248-4270
Tel (310) 767-7990 Founded/Ownrshp 1972
Sales 146.0MM^E EMP 200
SIC 5014 5013 5051 Tires, used; Wheels, motor vehicle; Tubing, metal
Pr: Chris Holbert
CFO: John Chen
Sftwr Eng: Yayoi Christiansen
S&M/VP: Victor LI
Sls Dir: Rick Papelian
Sls Dir: Rick Papelion
Sls Dir: Ken Thornton
Sls Mgr: Ivan Zepeda

D-U-N-S 05-773-8494
■TISHMAN CONSTRUCTION CORP
TCC
(Suby of AECOM TECHNICAL SERVICES INC) ★
100 Park Ave Fl 5, New York, NY 10017-5502
Tel (212) 708-6800 Founded/Ownrshp 2010
Sales 243.3MM^E EMP 850
SIC 8741 1611 Construction management; General contractor, highway & street construction
Ch Bd: Daniel Tishman
*Pr: Jay Badame
*Pr: John Livingston
*Pr: Peter Marchetto
*CEO: Daniel McQuade
*CFO: Paul W Praylo
*Treas: Larry Schwarzwalder
*Ex VP: Edward Cettina
*Ex VP: Jeffrey Dodd
*Ex VP: Thomas A Erickson
*Ex VP: John Krush
*Ex VP: James McLean
*Ex VP: Vincent Piscopo
*Sr VP: Judy Herman

**Sr VP:* James Raved
VP: Christopher Phillips

D-U-N-S 08-042-2306 IMP
■TISHMAN REALTY & CONSTRUCTION CO INC
(*Suby of* AECOM) ★
100 Park Ave Fl 5, New York, NY 10017-5502
Tel (212) 708-6800 *Founded/Ownrshp* 1999
Sales 208.1MM^E *EMP* 1,100
SIC 8741 6552 Construction management; Subdividers & developers
Pr: Daniel R Tishman
CFO: Obaid Khan
Treas: Larry Schwartzwalder
Ex VP: Eugene Benjamin
Ex VP: Robert Blackman
Ex VP: Charles C Cocotas
Ex VP: Paul Diamond
Ex VP: Daniel P McQuade
Ex VP: Joseph B Ryan
Sr VP: Richard Kielar
Sr VP: Daniel Spiegel
VP: Jennifer Espina
VP: Zeke Faham
VP: Sonja Glatzhofer
VP: Dennis Mahoney
VP: James Raved

D-U-N-S 61-524-2013
TISHMAN SPEYER PROPERTIES LP
45 Rockefeller Plz Conc1, New York, NY 10111-0229
Tel (212) 715-0300 *Founded/Ownrshp* 1984
Sales 15.3MM^E *EMP* 1,510^E
SIC 6531 6552 Real estate managers; Land subdividers & developers, commercial
Mng Pt: Jerry I Speyer
Pt: David Augarten
Pt: Rob Speyer
CFO: Revathy Ashok
VP: Sean Schaefer
Exec: Greg Coverdale
Exec: Donna Maimin
Exec: Elaine Philis
Ex Dir: Nadine Peyser
Mng Dir: Eric Adler
Mng Dir: Luiz Ceotto

D-U-N-S 19-075-7732 IMP/EXP
TITAN AMERICA LLC
(*Suby of* TITAN CEMENT CO. S.A.)
1151 Azalea Garden Rd, Norfolk, VA 23502-5601
Tel (757) 858-6500 *Founded/Ownrshp* 1980
Sales 397.6MM^E *EMP* 2,109
SIC 3241 3273 3271 4213

D-U-N-S 09-538-1687 IMP
TITAN CONTRACTING & LEASING CO INC
(*Suby of* HORN INTERMEDIATE HOLDINGS, INC.)
2205 Ragu Dr, Owensboro, KY 42303-1437
Tel (270) 683-6564 *Founded/Ownrshp* 1978
Sales 135.1MM^E *EMP* 250
SIC 1711 Mechanical contractor
Pr: Michael E Horn
**CFO:* Michael Lampert
**Sec:* Judy Hood
VP: Ron Woodward
Genl Mgr: Bill Stone
Genl Mgr: William Stone
Dir IT: Steven Hunter
Sfty Dirs: Jerry Maggard

D-U-N-S 15-096-8142 IMP/EXP
TITAN FLORIDA LLC
1151 Azalea Garden Rd, Norfolk, VA 23502-5601
Tel (757) 858-2095 *Founded/Ownrshp* 2001
Sales 180.4MM^E *EMP* 774
SIC 3273 Ready-mixed concrete

D-U-N-S 12-907-6035
TITAN GLOBAL HOLDINGS INC
17760 Preston Rd, Dallas, TX 75252-5663
Tel (214) 751-7777 *Founded/Ownrshp* 2002
Sales 418.3MM *EMP* 24
SIC 5172 4813 Petroleum products; Telephone communications broker
Pr: Bryan Chance
Pr: Kurt Jensen
COO: Radu Achiriloaie
CFO: Daniel Guimond
CFO: R Scott Hensell
Chf Cred: Douglas Ballman
Ex VP: Michael F D'Onofrio
Ex VP: Michael Kadlec
Sr VP: Ernestine Clark
Sr VP: Debra Manis
VP: Mike Berg
VP: Sammy M Jibrin
VP: Stephen Saul Kennedy
Dir Risk M: Frank Orlando

D-U-N-S 62-673-2999
TITAN HOLDINGS INC
(*Suby of* MICRON HOLDINGS INC) ★
4436 Broadmoor Ave Se, Kentwood, MI 49512-5305
Tel (616) 698-0707 *Founded/Ownrshp* 2004
Sales 0.6 *EMP* 2,612
SIC 3714 Motor vehicle parts & accessories
Pr: John C Kennedy
**COO:* John R Buchan
COO: Eduardo Renner De Castilho
COO: Jonathan B Degaynor
**CFO:* Warren A Veltman
**VP:* Thomas K O'Mara

D-U-N-S 01-643-5559 IMP/EXP
■TITAN II INC
(*Suby of* HUNTINGTON INGALLS INDUSTRIES INC) ★
4101 Washington Ave, Newport News, VA 23607-2734
Tel (757) 380-2000 *Founded/Ownrshp* 1939
Sales 6.9MMM^E *EMP* 37,000^E
Accts Deloitte & Touche Llp Los Ang
SIC 3728 3761 7373 3721 4581 3812 Aircraft parts & equipment; Guided missiles, complete; Guided missiles & space vehicles, research & development; Computer integrated systems design; Airplanes, fixed or rotary wing; Research & development on aircraft by the manufacturer; Aircraft servicing & repairing; Search & detection systems & instruments; Radar systems & equipment; Defense systems & equipment; Warfare counter-measure equipment
CEO: Mike Petters
COO: Michael Williams
**CFO:* James F Palmer
**Treas:* Mark Rabinowitz
Sr VP: Christopher T Jones
Sr VP: James M Myers
VP: Samuel Abbate
VP: Patrick M Antkowiak
**VP:* Jerri Fuller Dickseski
VP: Nimish Doshi
VP: Steven L Enewold
VP: W Dennis Gallimore
**VP:* Bruce N Hawthorne
VP: Cheryl L Janey
VP: Mark W Kenny
VP: Amy King
VP: Bob Klein
**VP:* Alexis C Livanos
**VP:* Jennifer C McGarey
VP: Bernard P McVey Jr
VP: Patricia A Newby
Board of Directors: Kevin W Sharer, Lewis W Coleman, Thomas B Fargo, Victor H Fazio, Donald E Felsinger, Stephen E Frank, Bruce S Gordon, Madeleine Kleiner, Karl J Krapek, Richard B Myers

D-U-N-S 10-319-8883 IMP/EXP
▲TITAN INTERNATIONAL INC
2701 Spruce St, Quincy, IL 62301-3473
Tel (217) 228-6011 *Founded/Ownrshp* 1890
Sales 1.3MMM *EMP* 6,000^E
Tkr Sym TWI *Exch* NYS
SIC 3312 3714 3011 Blast furnaces & steel mills; Wheels, motor vehicle; Wheel rims, motor vehicle; Motor vehicle brake systems & parts; Differentials & parts, motor vehicle; Agricultural tires, pneumatic; Pneumatic tires, all types
Ch Bd: Maurice M Taylor Jr
Pr: Paul G Reitz
CFO: James M Froisland
CIO: Jebora Brockk
Manager: Terry Nagel
Board of Directors: Richard M Cashin Jr, Gary L Cowger, Albert J Febbo, Peter B McNitt, Mark H Rachesky, Anthony L Soave

D-U-N-S 03-747-0606 EXP
▲TITAN MACHINERY INC
644 E Beaton Dr, West Fargo, ND 58078-2648
Tel (701) 356-0130 *Founded/Ownrshp* 1980
Sales 1.3MMM *EMP* 2,547
Accts Deloitte & Touche Llp Minneap
Tkr Sym TITN *Exch* NGS
SIC 5251 5082 Hardware; Road construction & maintenance machinery; Road construction equipment; Logging & forestry machinery & equipment; Mining machinery & equipment, except petroleum
Ch Bd: David Meyer
CFO: Mark Kalvoda
Genl Mgr: Thomas Bethel
Store Mgr: Steve Barger
Store Mgr: Mario Garcia
Store Mgr: Troy Gillespie
Store Mgr: Larry Luther
Store Mgr: Helio Oliveira
Store Mgr: Dale Spartz
CIO: Kevin Harrison
IT Man: Mike Hall

TITAN OIL ANALYSIS LABORATORY
See SIEGEL OIL CO

D-U-N-S 07-841-0448
TITAN PRIVATE HOLDINGS I LLC
5200 Paramount Pkwy, Morrisville, NC 27560-8499
Tel (919) 460-5500 *Founded/Ownrshp* 2011
Sales 49.8MM^E *EMP* 1,291
SIC 3661 3825 7371 Telephone & telegraph apparatus; Test equipment for electronic & electrical circuits; Computer software development & applications
Pr: Ronald J De Lange

D-U-N-S 14-891-4307
■TITAN PROPANE LLC
HERITAGE PROPANE
(*Suby of* AMERIGAS PARTNERS LP) ★
460 N Gulph Rd Ste 100, King of Prussia, PA 19406-2815
Tel (610) 337-7000 *Founded/Ownrshp* 2004
Sales 201.1MM^E *EMP* 1,600^E
SIC 5984 5172 Liquefied petroleum gas dealers; Petroleum products
**COO:* Paul Grady
**CFO:* Dave Riggan
Treas: Len H York
IT Man: Thomas Flak
IT Man: Chris Willis
Mktg Mgr: Joe Sorce
Genl Couns: Stephen Zamansky

D-U-N-S 86-831-7066 IMP/EXP
■TITAN TIRE CORP
(*Suby of* TITAN INTERNATIONAL INC) ★
2345 E Market St, Des Moines, IA 50317-7597
Tel (515) 265-9200 *Founded/Ownrshp* 1992
Sales 375.3MM^E *EMP* 1,450
SIC 3011 Automobile tires, pneumatic; Truck or bus tires, pneumatic; Agricultural tires, pneumatic
Pr: Steven M Briggs
**Pr:* Bill Campbell
**Treas:* Kent Hackamack
VP: Raymond W Evans
Ql Cn Mgr: Enes Rizvic
S&M/VP: Jeff Vasichek

D-U-N-S 05-402-0693 IMP/EXP
■TITAN WHEEL CORP OF ILLINOIS
(*Suby of* TITAN INTERNATIONAL INC) ★
2701 Spruce St, Quincy, IL 62301-3477
Tel (217) 228-6023 *Founded/Ownrshp* 1997
Sales 187.8MM^E *EMP* 900
SIC 3499 Wheels: wheelbarrow, stroller, etc.: disc, stamped metal
Pr: P David Salen
**CFO:* Kent Hackamack
Sales Asso: Tina Stock

D-U-N-S 92-616-7164 IMP
TITANIUM INDUSTRIES INC
18 Green Pond Rd Ste 1, Rockaway, NJ 07866-2054
Tel (973) 983-1185 *Founded/Ownrshp* 2001
Sales 123.3MM^E *EMP* 116
SIC 5051 3542 3462 Iron & steel (ferrous) products; Metal deposit forming machines; Flange, valve & pipe fitting forgings, ferrous
Pr: Brett S Paddock
**CFO:* Robert M Barba
**CFO:* Joseph Ferment
**VP:* Greg Himstead
**VP:* Dan Williams
Mng Dir: Vasanth Kini
Mng Dir: Craig Simpson
Genl Mgr: Debby Hazen
Sls Mgr: Cindy Lee
Sales Asso: Carole Boswell
Sales Asso: Bob Wermeling

D-U-N-S 04-182-9318 IMP/EXP
■TITANIUM METALS CORP
TIMET
(*Suby of* PCC) ★
224 Valley Creek Blvd # 200, Exton, PA 19341-2300
Tel (610) 968-1300 *Founded/Ownrshp* 2013
Sales 748.8MM^E *EMP* 2,750
SIC 3356 Titanium; Titanium & titanium alloy bars, sheets, strip, etc.
CFO: James W Brown
V Ch: Steven L Watson
Pr: Joan Clark
COO: Robert E Musgraves
Treas: J A Spendiff
Treas: John Wrba
Ex VP: Robert D Graham
Ex VP: Christian L Onhard
VP: H C Graves
VP: Kelly D Luttmer
VP: Andrew B Nace
VP: Scott E Sullivan

D-U-N-S 82-755-6452 IMP
TITANX ENGINE COOLING INC
(*Suby of* TITANX ENGINE COOLING AB)
2258 Allen Street Ext, Jamestown, NY 14701-2330
Tel (716) 665-7129 *Founded/Ownrshp* 2007
Sales 155.9MM^E *EMP* 320
SIC 3714 Air conditioner parts, motor vehicle
CEO: Stefan Nordstrm
Pr: Matthew Moore
CFO: Cedric Huslin
VP: Ulf Hellgesson
VP: Mats Hman
VP: Bruno Jouannet
VP: Jonas Nilsson
VP: Mikael Persson
Ql Cn Mgr: Eric Johnson

TITEFLEX AEROSPACE
See SMITHS TUBULAR SYSTEMS-LACONIA INC

D-U-N-S 08-745-0490 IMP
TITEFLEX CORP (CT)
(*Suby of* SMITHS GROUP PLC)
603 Hendee St, Springfield, MA 01104-3034
Tel (413) 271-8170 *Founded/Ownrshp* 1978, 2001
Sales 147.9MM^E *EMP* 630
SIC 3052 3599 Plastic hose; Hose, flexible metallic
Pr: William T Smith
**Pr:* Robert Burns
**Treas:* John S Maggi
VP: Joseph Abbruzzi
**VP:* Kevin Hoben
VP: Carmin Lattell
Genl Mgr: Steven Bonnell
MIS Mgr: Kathe Turner
Sales Asso: Teri Bacon

D-U-N-S 07-767-4661
TITLE GUARANTY OF HAWAII INC
235 Queen St Fl 2nd, Honolulu, HI 96813-4685
Tel (808) 533-6261 *Founded/Ownrshp* 1960
Sales NA *EMP* 225^E
SIC 6361 Real estate title insurance
Pr: Michael A Pietsch
**CFO:* Lois Kawano
Ofcr: Elizabeth Andrade
Ofcr: Lynne Nakamura
**Sr VP:* David Pietsch Jr
Brnch Mgr: Brandon J Choi
Brnch Mgr: Alan S Chun
Brnch Mgr: Ketura Demattos
Brnch Mgr: Janet Lum
Brnch Mgr: Carol Mendes
Brnch Mgr: Joel Navarro

D-U-N-S 79-073-1454
■TITLE RESOURCE GROUP LLC
TRG
(*Suby of* REALOGY SERVICES GROUP LLC) ★
3001 Leadenhall Rd, Mount Laurel, NJ 08054-4609
Tel (856) 914-8500 *Founded/Ownrshp* 1999
Sales 1.8MMM^E *EMP* 2,315
SIC 6541 6211 Title abstract offices; Mortgages, buying & selling
Pr: Donald Casey
**Sr VP:* Michael Gozdan
**Sr VP:* Walter Mullen
**Sr VP:* Thomas N Rispoli Jr
**Sr VP:* Nehal Trivedi
VP: Thomas Duffy
VP: Don Evans
VP: Jeffrey Gueiss
VP: Neil Gulley
VP: Harry Yazbek
VP: Brenda Yurick

D-U-N-S 78-582-5886
■TITLE RESOURCES GUARANTY CO
(*Suby of* TRG) ★
8111 L B Johnson Fwy 12 Ste 1200, Dallas, TX 75251
Tel (972) 644-6500 *Founded/Ownrshp* 2006
Sales NA *EMP* 20
SIC 6361 Title insurance
Pr: J Scott McCall
VP: Annette Aviles
VP: Michael Dullea
VP: John Gilbert
VP: Clayton Greenberg
VP: Gretchen Valentine
Prd Mgr: Leslie Gross
Genl Couns: Wade Thunhorst
Counsel: Sarah Kaseforth

D-U-N-S 61-339-8911
TITLE SOURCE INC
NATIONAL TITLE SOURCE
662 Woodward Ave, Detroit, MI 48226-3433
Tel (888) 848-5355 *Founded/Ownrshp* 1997
Sales 141.7MM^E *EMP* 350
SIC 6541 Title abstract offices
Pr: Jeff Eisenshtadt
**COO:* Brian Hughes
Ofcr: Barbara Jackson
Assoc VP: Aaron Weller
Sr VP: David Budziszewski
VP: Tom Horton
VP: Gopi Jayaraman
VP: Deborah Lawrence-Auten
VP: Steve Nadolski
**VP:* Colleen Ramsey
VP: Carlie Smith
VP: Janet M Voisine

D-U-N-S 00-823-8385
■TITLE365 CO (CA)
(*Suby of* EXPERIENCE 1 INC) ★
5000 Birch St Ste 300, Newport Beach, CA 92660-2147
Tel (877) 365-9365 *Founded/Ownrshp* 2009
Sales 325.2MM^E *EMP* 350^E
SIC 6541 Title & trust companies
CEO: Michael J Tafoya
**Pr:* Vickie Crestani
**Pr:* Peter Derbonne
Pr: Joseph Kleist
**Sr VP:* Peter Bowman
Sr VP: Ed Christie
Sr VP: Sharon Grannis
Sr VP: Jeremy Harmon
**Sr VP:* Shaun Morey
**Sr VP:* Peter Richter
VP: Thomas C Bolduc
VP: Candy Jackson
VP: Tasha Manzano

D-U-N-S 83-036-4209
TITLEMAX OF TEXAS INC
(*Suby of* TMX FINANCE LLC) ★
15 Bull St Ste 200, Savannah, GA 31401-2686
Tel (912) 525-2675 *Founded/Ownrshp* 2009
Sales NA *EMP* 813^E
SIC 6141 Automobile & consumer finance companies
CEO: Tracy Young

D-U-N-S 00-188-3086
TITLEONE EXCHANGE CO (ID)
1101 W River St Ste 201, Boise, ID 83702-7068
Tel (208) 424-8511 *Founded/Ownrshp* 2000
Sales 90.0MM^E *EMP* 275
SIC 6541 Title & trust companies
Pr: Mark Pidd
VP: Doug Brigham

D-U-N-S 05-232-2315
■TITLEVEST AGENCY OF NEW YORK INC
(*Suby of* FIRST AMERICAN TITLE INSURANCE CO) ★
44 Wall St Fl 10, New York, NY 10005-2415
Tel (212) 757-5800 *Founded/Ownrshp* 2015
Sales NA *EMP* 105
SIC 6361 Title insurance
Pr: Brian Tormey
**CFO:* James Leslie
Ofcr: David Ransom
Sr VP: Jacqueline Gold
VP: David Baron
Mng Dir: Mitchell Birner
Mng Dir: Robert Buzard
Mng Dir: Maria Fogliano
Mng Dir: Christine Gagliardi
Mng Dir: James Melnichok
Sales Exec: Christie Edwards

D-U-N-S 08-038-4739
▲TIVO CORP
2 Circle Way, San Carlos, CA 94070
Tel (408) 562-8400 *Founded/Ownrshp* 2016
Sales 1.0MMM^E *EMP* 2,661^E
Tkr Sym TIVO *Exch* NGS
SIC 7374 7929 Computer graphics service; Entertainment service
Pr: Thomas Carson
CFO: Peter Halt
Ex VP: Samir Armaly
Ex VP: Bill Corry
Ex VP: Sean Matthews
Ex VP: Pamela Sergeeff
Ex VP: Pete Thompson

D-U-N-S 96-989-0904
■TIVO SOLUTIONS INC
(*Suby of* TIVO CORP) ★
2160 Gold St, Alviso, CA 95002-3700
Tel (408) 519-9100 *Founded/Ownrshp* 2016
Sales 489.6MM *EMP* 46^E
SIC 7371 Computer software development & applications
Pr: Thomas Carson
COO: Pete Thompson
CFO: Peter Halt
Ofcr: Dustin Finer
Ex VP: Samir Armaly
Ex VP: Bill Corry
Ex VP: Pamela Sergeeff
Sr VP: Naveen Chopra

VP: Teri Bommarito
VP: Shannon Lynch
Prgrm Mgr: Anthony Gonzales

D-U-N-S 00-808-5607 IMP/EXP
■TIW CORP
(*Suby of* DRIL-QUIP INC) ★
12300 Main St, Houston, TX 77035-6206
Tel (713) 729-2110 *Founded/Ownrshp* 2016
Sales 87.6MM *EMP* 350
Accts Hein & Associates Llp Houston
SIC 3533 Oil field machinery & equipment; Gas field machinery & equipment
Pr: Stephen R Pearce
CFO: Carl C Washington
Ex VP: Britt O Braddick
VP: Ray Hyatt
Board of Directors: Gary M Pearce, Louis M Pearce III

T.J. MAXX
See TJX COMPANIES INC

T.J. MAXX
See MARMAXX OPERATING CORP

TJ REGIONAL HEALTH
See T J SAMPSON COMMUNITY HOSPITAL

D-U-N-S 05-682-7454
TJ SAMSON COMMUNITY HOSPITAL
1301 N Race St, Glasgow, KY 42141-3483
Tel (270) 651-4444 *Founded/Ownrshp* 1926
Sales 151.8MM *EMP* 1,012
SIC 8062 General medical & surgical hospitals
Pr: Henry Royse
CFO: Roy Spencer
**Treas:* Follis Crow
**VP:* Dan Foutch
Exec: Brittany Vincent
Dir Inf Cn: Shea Wilson
Genl Mgr: Marilyn Sink
Doctor: Anupama Kaul
Cert Phar: Jamie Bennett
Cert Phar: Larry Davidson
Cert Phar: Kim McCoy

D-U-N-S 00-695-5215
▲TJX COMPANIES INC
T.J. MAXX
770 Cochituate Rd Ste 1, Framingham, MA 01701-4698
Tel (508) 390-1000 *Founded/Ownrshp* 1919
Sales 30.9MMM *EMP* 216,000
Accts Pricewaterhousecoopers Llp Bo
Tkr Sym TJX *Exch* NYS
SIC 5311 5651 5719 Department stores, discount; Family clothing stores; Beddings & linens
Pr: Ernie Herrman
Owner: Bradford Dunn
**Ch Bd:* Carol Meyrowitz
Pr: Sandi Anderson
Pr: David Averill
Pr: Jennifer Brady
Pr: Joan Brassil
Pr: Cindy Buffi
Pr: Mary Clark
Pr: Mike Farrell
Pr: Katie Fink
Pr: Jacqui Hebden
Pr: Frederick L Mullen
Pr: Lauren Mullin
Pr: Rose Riggieri
Pr: Kevin Taparausky
Pr: Joe Walsh
CFO: Scott Goldenberg
Ofcr: Emma Jackson
Ex VP: Louis Luciano
Sr VP: Peter Benjamin
Board of Directors: Jose B Alvarez, Alan M Bennett, David T Ching, Michael F Hines, Amy B Lane, John F O'brien, William H Swanson

D-U-N-S 03-660-5194 IMP
TK HOLDINGS INC
(*Suby of* TKJ CORPORATION)
4611 Wiseman Blvd, San Antonio, TX 78251-4202
Tel (210) 509-0762 *Founded/Ownrshp* 1989
Sales 256.8MM^E *EMP* 1,200
SIC 2399 Seat belts, automobile & aircraft; Seat covers, automobile
CEO: Yoshiyasu Kikuchi
**Pr:* Robert Fisher
**VP:* Teresa Clark
Dir IT: Thomas Kelly
Ql Cn Mgr: Mauricio Ramon

D-U-N-S 18-560-5854 IMP/EXP
TK HOLDINGS INC
TAKATA
(*Suby of* TAKATA CORPORATION)
2500 Takata Dr, Auburn Hills, MI 48326-2634
Tel (248) 373-8040 *Founded/Ownrshp* 1989
Sales 6.7MMM^E *EMP* 16,900
SIC 2221 2399 2396 3714 Automotive fabrics, manmade fiber; Seat belts, automobile & aircraft; Seat covers, automobile; Automotive trimmings, fabric; Motor vehicle parts & accessories
CEO: Shigehisa Takada
Pr: Juichiro Takada
Sr VP: Al Bernat
VP: Alby Berman
VP: Kirk Morris
Genl Mgr: Bruce D Angiolillo
QA Dir: Laurie Wayne
IT Man: Mike Gartland
Ql Cn Mgr: Andres Gangemi
VP Sls: Kevin Kennedy
Sls Dir: Jack Vaughn

D-U-N-S 80-671-9931 IMP
TK HOLDINGS INC
104 E 9th St, Douglas, AZ 85607-2151
Tel (520) 805-4000 *Founded/Ownrshp* 2006
Sales 14.6MM^E *EMP* 1,000
SIC 7549 Automotive maintenance services
Genl Mgr: Ramon Rieera

TKA FABCO
See MARTINREA AUTOMOTIVE-STRUCTURES (USA) INC

D-U-N-S 08-140-9658
TL WALLACE CONSTRUCTION INC
4025 Highway 35 N, Columbia, MS 39429-8763
Tel (601) 736-4525 *Founded/Ownrshp* 2012
Sales 131.8MM^E *EMP* 298
Accts Nicholson & Company Pllc Hatt
SIC 1611 4212 8322 Highway & street construction; Garbage collection & transport, no disposal; Emergency shelters
CEO: Thomas L Wallace
**Pr:* Harry Morgan
**Treas:* Janet Price
VP: Billy J Clark
**VP:* Jimmy Kendrick
**VP:* Joey Reagan
**VP:* James Mike Wallace
Exec: Bill Hasbrook
Off Mgr: Teah Thornhill

D-U-N-S 17-802-5016
TLB HOLDINGS LLC
9 W 57th St, New York, NY 10019-2701
Tel (212) 796-8555 *Founded/Ownrshp* 2012
Sales 1.3MMM^E *EMP* 8,900^E
SIC 5961 5661 5632 5641 5621 Catalog sales; Women's apparel, mail order; Clothing, mail order (except women's); Women's shoes; Apparel accessories; Children's wear; Women's clothing stores; Women's sportswear; Dress shops

TLC
See MVP GROUP INTERNATIONAL INC

D-U-N-S 07-401-2550
TLC HEALTH NETWORK (NY)
TRI CNTY CHEM DPNDENCY PROGRAM
845 Route 5 And 20, Irving, NY 14081-9706
Tel (716) 951-7000 *Founded/Ownrshp* 1937, 2000
Sales 24.1MM^E *EMP* 1,225
SIC 8062 8069 Hospital, medical school affiliated with nursing & residency; Substance abuse hospitals
CEO: John Galati
CFO: Dave Crone
Prin: Jonathan Lawrence
Nurse Mgr: Laura J Norwood
IT Man: Ron Blount
Sls Mgr: Sharon A Rinehart
Doctor: Bonnie Nobles
Pharmcst: Chuck Spicola

D-U-N-S 92-845-0915
TLC MANAGEMENT INC
1800 N Wabash Rd Ste 300, Marion, IN 46952-1300
Tel (765) 671-2282 *Founded/Ownrshp* 1991
Sales 126.9MM^E *EMP* 2,000
SIC 8741 Nursing & personal care facility management
Pr: Gary L Ott
**Sec:* Dwight A Ott
VP: Chris Cook
**VP:* Lawrence W Maxwell
Dir Bus: Paul Riccio

TLC NURSING CENTER
See DHS OF BLUNT COUNTY LLC

TLC PLUMBING & UTILITY
See T L C CO INC

D-U-N-S 12-511-6876
TLC VISION (USA) CORP
LASIK
(*Suby of* TLC VISION CORPORATION)
16305 Swingley Ridge Rd # 300, Chesterfield, MO 63017-1777
Tel (636) 534-2300 *Founded/Ownrshp* 2003
Sales 100.1MM^E *EMP* 1,230
SIC 8011 Ophthalmologist
CEO: Charles Bono
**COO:* James B Tiffany
**CFO:* William J McManus
**Treas:* Jane Frazier
**Ex VP:* Jimmy Feinstein
**VP:* Tony Bowar
**VP:* Ellen-Jo Plass
VP: Beth Rogers
**Prin:* George Neal
Board of Directors: James Rogers

D-U-N-S 05-634-5309 IMP/EXP
TLD AMERICA CORP
TLD GROUP
(*Suby of* ALVEST (USA) INC) ★
812 Bloomfield Ave, Windsor, CT 06095-2340
Tel (860) 602-3400 *Founded/Ownrshp* 1991
Sales 98.5MM^E *EMP* 45^E
SIC 5088 3728 7629 Aircraft & parts; Aircraft equipment & supplies; Aircraft parts & equipment; Aircraft electrical equipment repair
Pr: Mark L Garlasco
**Ch Bd:* Jean Marie Falconis
VP: Mark Blalock
Genl Mgr: Richard Bacha
**Off Mgr:* Frank Gustafson
Dir IT: Gary Edbrooke
Plnt Mgr: Fadi Anbouba

TLD GROUP
See TLD AMERICA CORP

TLG
See LARSON GROUP

TM CELL
See TM WIRELESS COMMUNICATION SERVICES INC

D-U-N-S 18-065-1825
TM RESTAURANT GROUP LLC
TACOMAC SPORTS GRILL
6220 Shiloh Rd Ste 100, Alpharetta, GA 30005-8347
Tel (678) 679-1210 *Founded/Ownrshp* 2012
Sales 71.8MM^E *EMP* 2,500
SIC 5812 Eating places
CEO: Bob Campbell
**COO:* Susie Addo
**CFO:* Cyrus Commissariat

D-U-N-S 96-229-7045 IMP
TM WIRELESS COMMUNICATION SERVICES INC
TM CELL
10205 Nw 19th St Ste 101, Doral, FL 33172-2535
Tel (305) 421-9938 *Founded/Ownrshp* 2004
Sales 132.5MM *EMP* 55
SIC 5065 Mobile telephone equipment
Pr: Frank Cheng
VP: Charles Cheng
VP: Mario Ego-Aguirre
Opers Mgr: Thomas Stone
VP Sls: Raul Carrillo

TMA
See TRANSAXLE MANUFACTURING OF AMERICA CORP

D-U-N-S 00-428-3040 IMP/EXP
■TMARZETTI CO (OH)
INN MAID PRODUCTS
(*Suby of* LANCASTER COLONY CORP) ★
1105 Schrock Rd Fl 3, Columbus, OH 43229-1146
Tel (614) 846-2232 *Founded/Ownrshp* 1927, 1931
Sales 485.0MM^E *EMP* 1,706
SIC 2035 2098 Dressings, salad: raw & cooked (except dry mixes); Noodles (e.g. egg, plain & water), dry
Pr: David Ciesinski
Treas: John Boylan
VP: Ernie Grindstaff
VP: Jeff Harris
VP: Bob Holtcamp
VP: Tom Kellett
VP: Watts Patterson
VP: Tim Tate
VP: Mark Wilder
VP: Charlotte Wines
CIO: Kevin Moran

D-U-N-S 13-941-2308
TMC HEALTHCARE
TUCSON MEDICAL CENTER
5301 E Grant Rd, Tucson, AZ 85712-2805
Tel (520) 327-5461 *Founded/Ownrshp* 1992
Sales 5.9MM *EMP* 2,885
SIC 8051 8062 Skilled nursing care facilities; General medical & surgical hospitals
Pr: Judith F Rich
CFO: Steve Bush
Chf Mktg O: Jason Krupp MD
Sr VP: David Ressler
Dir Sec: Bill Fleming
MIS Dir: Cathy Travers
Dir IT: Frimmel Celaya
Dir IT: Linda Walker
Doctor: Timothy Marshall
Pharmcst: Anna Mitchell

TMC TRANSPORTATION
See ANNETT HOLDINGS INC

D-U-N-S 14-783-6167 IMP/EXP
TMCI HOLDINGS INC
B MANISCHEWITZ COMPANY
80 Avenue K, Newark, NJ 07105-3803
Tel (201) 553-1100 *Founded/Ownrshp* 1986
Sales 636.3MM^E *EMP* 2,500
SIC 5122 5023 5072 5112 5049 5199 Medicine cabinet sundries; Druggists' sundries; Cosmetics; Home furnishings; Hardware; Stationery; School supplies; Pet supplies; General merchandise, non-durable
CEO: Mark Weinsten
**Ch Bd:* Richard A Bernstein
**Pr:* Bruce W Glickstein
CFO: Brian Duffy
**Treas:* Hal B Weiss
**V Ch Bd:* Lewis J Korman
**Sr VP:* Ira A Gomberg
Mktg Dir: David Most

D-U-N-S 00-821-9763 IMP
TMEIC CORP
TMEIC-GE
(*Suby of* TOSHIBA MITSUBISHI-ELECTRIC INDUSTRIAL SYSTEMS CORPORATION)
1325 Electric Rd, Salem, VA 24153
Tel (540) 283-2000 *Founded/Ownrshp* 2000
Sales 134.3MM^E *EMP* 374
SIC 8711 Engineering services
CEO: Dale Guidry
CFO: Aj Graham
**Ex VP:* Shigeru Taniguchi
Opers Mgr: John Maia
Mktg Mgr: Paul Blaiklock
Manager: Richard Warriner
Sls Mgr: Derrick Parker
Sls Mgr: Donn Samsa

TMEIC-GE
See TMEIC CORP

D-U-N-S 03-062-5060
TMG HEALTH INC
(*Suby of* BLUE CROSS AND BLUE SHIELD) ★
100 Four Falls Corporate, Conshohocken, PA 19428-2950
Tel (610) 878-9111 *Founded/Ownrshp* 2008
Sales NA *EMP* 1,450
SIC 6321 Health insurance carriers
Pr: Susan Molina
COO: Charles Wayland
CFO: James Watson
CFO: James H Watson
Ofcr: Valerie Cerra
Ofcr: Patricia Savitsky
Sr VP: Doug Albro
Sr VP: William Pierce Jr
Sr VP: Trish Savitsky
Sr VP: Michael Walsh
VP: Teig Boyle
VP: Lee Coffman
VP: Kathy Dufour
VP: Tmg Health
VP: James Kolata
VP: Deanna Forte Lahey
VP: Michael McGarrigle
VP: John Sanders

D-U-N-S 62-499-1522
TMH PHYSICIAN ORGANIZATION
6565 Fannin St Ste D200, Houston, TX 77030-2703
Tel (713) 441-4182 *Founded/Ownrshp* 2004
Sales 360.5MM *EMP* 14^E
SIC 8071 Neurological laboratory
CEO: John Lyle
**Treas:* Mike Giblin
**Treas:* Edward L Tyrrell

D-U-N-S 93-339-1005
TMI HOSPITALITY LP
COMFORT INN
4850 32nd Ave S, Fargo, ND 58104-7812
Tel (701) 235-1060 *Founded/Ownrshp* 1993
Sales 250.8MM^E *EMP* 4,000
SIC 7011

TMK IPSCO
See IPSCO TUBULARS INC

D-U-N-S 07-883-2668
TMK IPSCO INC
10120 Houston Oaks Dr, Houston, TX 77064-3514
Tel (281) 949-1023 *Founded/Ownrshp* 2013
Sales 413.6MM^E *EMP* 1,180^E
SIC 1389 Pipe testing, oil field service
CEO: Piotr Galitzine
COO: Joel Mastervich
CFO: Evgeny Makarov
**Sr VP:* Scott Barnes
**VP:* Prasenjit Adhikari
**VP:* Ryan Chadwick
VP: Peter Smith
Genl Mgr: Bert Wingrove

TMK-IPSCO
See IPSCO KOPPEL TUBULARS LLC

D-U-N-S 11-075-1414
TML MULTISTATE INTERGOVERNMENTAL EMPLOYEE BENEFITS POOL
TMLIEBP
1821 Rutherford Ln 300, Austin, TX 78754-5197
Tel (512) 719-6500 *Founded/Ownrshp* 2000
Sales 125.7MM *EMP* 148
Accts Grant Thornton Llp Houston T
SIC 8611 Business associations
Ex Dir: Susan Smith
CIO: Andy Rainosek

TMLIEBP
See TML MULTISTATE INTERGOVERNMENTAL EMPLOYEE BENEFITS POOL

D-U-N-S 78-532-9884
TMP WORLDWIDE ADVERTISING & COMMUNICATIONS LLC
T. M. P.
125 Broad St Fl 10, New York, NY 10004-2705
Tel (646) 613-2000 *Founded/Ownrshp* 2006
Sales 114.1MM^E *EMP* 560
SIC 7311 Advertising agencies
Pr: Michelle Abbey
Mng Pt: Jan Geurts
Pr: Eric Douglas
**CFO:* Tom Fitzsimmons
CFO: Chris Power
Ex VP: Steve Pogorzelski
VP: Lesley Decanio
VP: Brian Di Bartolomeo
VP: Amy Eckert
VP: Lori Erickson
VP: Tammy Garmey
VP: Joe Howell
VP: Stacey McLeod
VP: Todd Pierce
VP: Thea Randall
VP: Valerie Roush
VP: Diego Sanson
VP: Timothy Spillane
VP: Vince Vitti
Creative D: Yvette Milne
Comm Dir: Christopher Bosworth

TMPA
See TEXAS MUNICIPAL POWER AGENCY

TMR
See TRADEMARK METALS RECYCLING LLC

TMS INTERNATIONAL CORPORATION
See TMS INTERNATIONAL HOLDING CORP

D-U-N-S 96-333-1280
TMS INTERNATIONAL CORP
12 Monongahela Ave, Glassport, PA 15045-1315
Tel (412) 678-6141 *Founded/Ownrshp* 2007
Sales 200.8MM^E *EMP* 1,200^E
SIC 3312 4731 3399 7359 4213 Blast furnaces & steel mills; Railroad freight agency; Iron, powdered; Equipment rental & leasing; Trucking, except local
Pr: Raymond S Kalouche
Ch Bd: Joseph Curtin
CFO: Daniel E Rosati
Ex VP: Leon Z Heller
Ex VP: Thomas E Lippard
Ex VP: William R Miller
Sr VP: Hank Wilson
VP: Bob Huseman
VP: Jim Penney
Genl Mgr: Pascal Martin

D-U-N-S 61-439-4299
TMS INTERNATIONAL HOLDING CORP
TMS INTERNATIONAL CORPORATION
(*Suby of* TMS INTERNATIONAL CORP) ★
12 Monongahela Ave, Glassport, PA 15045-1315
Tel (412) 678-6141 *Founded/Ownrshp* 1987
Sales 200.8MM^E *EMP* 1,200
SIC 3312 4731 3399 7359 4213 Blast furnaces & steel mills; Railroad freight agency; Iron, powdered; Equipment rental & leasing; Trucking, except local
Pr: Raymond Kalouche
**Pr:* J David Aronson
CFO: Dan Rosati
Bd of Dir: Colin Osborne
Ex VP: Thomas Lippard
**Ex VP:* Daniel E Rosati
Sr VP: David Aronson

*Sr VP: Jonathan M Fingeret
Sr VP: William Miller
Sr VP: Daniel Rosati
VP: Simon Golding
VP: Joseph Jung
VP: Tom Lippard
VP: Tim Lynch
VP: Tom Montagino
VP: Hideyuki Nishizawa
VP: Rich Pegher
VP: Kirk Peters
VP: Kevin Rudman
VP: Robert Subasic
VP: Hank Wilson

D-U-N-S 00-450-0419 IMP/EXP
TMS INTERNATIONAL LLC
OLYMPIC MILL SERVICES DIVISION
(Suby of TMS INTERNATIONAL CORP) ★
12 Monongahela Ave, Glassport, PA 15045-1315
Tel (412) 678-6141 Founded/Ownrshp 1987
Sales 173.8MM[E] EMP 426
SIC 3312 4731 3399 7359 4213 Blast furnaces & steel mills; Railroad freight agency; Iron, powdered; Equipment rental & leasing; Trucking, except local
CEO: Raymond Kalouche
*COO: J David Aronson
COO: Jim Fiore
CFO: Dan Rosati
*CFO: Daniel E Rosati
VP: Kelly Boyer
Mng Dir: Detlef Mu Ller
Dist Mgr: John Turner
Genl Mgr: Dai Moriya
Off Mgr: Tim Frankenfield
MIS Dir: Michael McGraw

D-U-N-S 80-800-4170
TMST INC
125 Lincoln Ave Ste 100, Santa Fe, NM 87501-2052
Tel (505) 989-1900 Founded/Ownrshp 1993
Sales 153.5MM[E] EMP 671
SIC 6531 6798 Real estate agent, commercial; Mortgage investment trusts
Pr: Anne-Drue Anderson
Ex VP: Daniel Bissonnette
VP: Sandra Stocker

D-U-N-S 15-134-4413
■TMW SYSTEMS INC
(Suby of TRIMBLE INC) ★
6085 Parkland Blvd, Mayfield Heights, OH 44124-4184
Tel (216) 831-6606 Founded/Ownrshp 1986
Sales 116.5MM[E] EMP 340
SIC 7372 Business oriented computer software
Pr: David Wangler
*COO: Rod Strata
Bd of Dir: Clayton Slade
Ex VP: Timothy Leonard
*Ex VP: David Mook
*Ex VP: Jeffrey Ritter
*Ex VP: Scott Vanselous
*Sr VP: Michael August
*Sr VP: Randall Burrell
*Sr VP: David Schildmeyer
VP: Renaldo Adler
VP: Mike August
VP: Gene Elkins
*VP: Mike Kositzky
VP: Kathi Laughman
*VP: David McKinney
VP: Dave Schildmeyer
VP: Corey Staheli
VP: James Stevenson
*VP: Ray West

D-U-N-S 07-915-9741
TMX FINANCE HOLDINGS INC
15 Bull St Ste 200, Savannah, GA 31401-2686
Tel (912) 525-2675 Founded/Ownrshp 2012
Sales 982.2MM[E] EMP 5,800[E]
SIC 6719 Investment holding companies, except banks
CEO: Tracy Young

D-U-N-S 00-570-8597
TMX FINANCE LLC (GA)
(Suby of TMX FINANCE HOLDINGS INC) ★
15 Bull St Ste 200, Savannah, GA 31401-2686
Tel (912) 525-2675 Founded/Ownrshp 2003
Sales NA EMP 5,383
Accts Mcgladrey Llp Raleigh North
SIC 6141 Automobile & consumer finance companies
CEO: Tracy Young
Pr: Rich Stacy
Sr VP: Otto W Bielss III
Sr VP: Douglas W Marohn
Dist Mgr: Josh Henderson
Dir IT: Julie Feldman
IT Man: Jeremy Cate

D-U-N-S 88-386-1254
TNC (US) HOLDINGS INC
(Suby of VNU INTERNATIONAL B.V.)
770 Broadway Fl 8, New York, NY 10003-9575
Tel (646) 654-5500 Founded/Ownrshp 1977
Sales 3.2MMM[E] EMP 34,730
SIC 8732 2721 2732 2741 Business research service; Periodicals: publishing only; Magazines: publishing only, not printed on site; Books: printing & binding; Directories: publishing only, not printed on site
Ch Bd: David Calhoun
Pr: Mitch Barns
Pr: Bruce Dennler
Pr: Greg Farrar
*CFO: Brian J West
Sr Cor Off: Robin Gaster
Sr Cor Off: Chris Perkett
Ofcr: Andrew Cawood
*Ofcr: Earl H Doppelt
*Ofcr: Mary Liz Finn
*Ofcr: Susan Whiting
*Ex VP: Thomas A Mastrelli
*Sr VP: David Berger
Sr VP: Linda McCutcheon
Sr VP: Brian Zueg
VP: Jason Bubenicek
VP: Salwa Fertitta
*VP: Lisa Longo
*VP: Fred Steinmann
Exec: Paul Morgan
Creative D: Emily Chang

D-U-N-S 00-712-1841 IMP
TNEMEC CO INC (MO)
CHEMPROBE COATING SYSTEMS
6800 Corporate Dr, Kansas City, MO 64120-1372
Tel (816) 483-3400 Founded/Ownrshp 1919
Sales 120.5MM EMP 265
Accts Rsm Us Llp
SIC 2851 Coating, air curing; Lacquers, varnishes, enamels & other coatings
CEO: Peter Cortelyou
*CFO: Steven Eiserer
*Ex VP: Albert C Bean IV
Sls Dir: Vaughn O'Dea

D-U-N-S 05-201-6500
TNG GP
T N G
1955 Lake Park Dr Se # 400, Smyrna, GA 30080-8858
Tel (770) 863-9000 Founded/Ownrshp 2012
Sales 1.0MMM EMP 2,000[E]
SIC 5192 Magazines
Pr: David Parry
VP: Jeff Cowan
Genl Mgr: Leeroy Perkins
Genl Mgr: Dale Poor
IT Man: Diana Cullingham
VP Sls: Kerry Cook

D-U-N-S 15-528-3302 IMP
TNG WORLDWIDE INC
INDUSTRY SOURCE, THE
29683 Wk Smith Dr Stet, New Hudson, MI 48165
Tel (248) 347-7700 Founded/Ownrshp 1985
Sales 87.2MM[E] EMP 250[E]
Accts Plante & Moran Pllc Southfie
SIC 5099 5087 Tanning salon equipment & supplies; Beauty parlor equipment & supplies
CEO: Larry Gaynor
*CFO: Dawn Kuhn
*VP: Teresa Gaynor
*VP: Edmond Verbeke
VP Mktg: Mark Losey

TNI
See TEAM TECHNOLOGIES INC

TNMP
See TEXAS-NEW MEXICO POWER CO

D-U-N-S 13-940-4763
TNS INC
(Suby of TRIDENT PRIVATE HOLDINGS I LLC) ★
10740 Parkridge Blvd # 100, Reston, VA 20191-5422
Tel (703) 453-8300 Founded/Ownrshp 2013
Sales 479.5MM[E] EMP 1,303[E]
SIC 4813 7374 Data telephone communications; Data processing service
CEO: Henry H Graham Jr
*Pr: Michael Q Keegan
*CFO: Dennis L Randolph Jr
Ex VP: John J McDonnell
*Ex VP: James T McLaughlin
Sr VP: Robert Tr Hin
VP: Patrick Bobst
VP: John Owens

TNS MEDIA INTELLIGENCE
See KANTAR MEDIA INTELLIGENCES INC

D-U-N-S 13-041-6530
TNT CRANE & RIGGING INC
925 S Loop W, Houston, TX 77054-4606
Tel (713) 644-6113 Founded/Ownrshp 2013
Sales 216.7MM[E] EMP 1,123
SIC 7353 1611

TNT EXPRESS
See TNT USA INC

TNT FIREWORKS
See AMERICAN PROMOTIONAL EVENTS INC

D-U-N-S 03-438-7894 IMP/EXP
■TNT USA INC
TNT EXPRESS
(Suby of TNT EXPRESS WORLDWIDE B.V.)
68 S Service Rd Ste 340, Melville, NY 11747-2358
Tel (631) 712-6700 Founded/Ownrshp 1994
Sales 139.5MM[E] EMP 625
SIC 4513 Air courier services
Pr: Matthew J McDonough
*CFO: Stephen Ernst
*VP: Mary Conway Laponte
*VP: Robert Van Zeyl
Genl Mgr: Lee-Ann Colyn

D-U-N-S 03-506-7057 IMP
TO HAAS TIRE CO INC
T. O. HAAS TIRE 501
(Suby of AMERICAN TIRE DISTRIBUTORS INC) ★
1415 W Commerce Way, Lincoln, NE 68521-3650
Tel (402) 434-3434 Founded/Ownrshp 2000
Sales 97.1MM[E] EMP 303
SIC 5014 5531 7539 Automobile tires & tubes; Automotive tires; Automotive repair shops
CEO: T O Haas
*Pr: Randall Haas
*VP: Rick Haas
Store Mgr: Mick Lile
Mktg Mgr: Fred Knight
Sls Mgr: Paul Faughn
Sales Asso: Gai Labudda

D-U-N-S 00-697-9400 IMP
TOA (USA) LLC (IN)
2000 Pleiades Dr, Mooresville, IN 46158-7144
Tel (317) 834-0522 Founded/Ownrshp 2000
Sales 214.2MM[E] EMP 292
SIC 3714 Air brakes, motor vehicle
CEO: Shinichi Iizuka
*Pr: Junichiro Kondo
Ex VP: Shozo Suzuki
Ex Dir: Don Stock
VP Mfg: Tim Clayton

D-U-N-S 03-503-7688
TOBA INC
2621 W Us Highway 30, Grand Island, NE 68803-5230
Tel (308) 389-5987 Founded/Ownrshp 1995
Sales 277.7MM[E] EMP 330
SIC 5148 5194 5145 5141 Fresh fruits & vegetables; Cigarettes; Confectionery; Groceries, general line
Pr: Tony Wald
CFO: Jack Schiefelbein
*Treas: Robert H Wald
VP: Kendra Kuehl
*Exec: Ray Absher

D-U-N-S 96-229-6760
TOBACCO ROOT MOUNTAINS CARE CENTER
TRMCC
326 Madison St, Sheridan, MT 59749-9636
Tel (406) 842-5418 Founded/Ownrshp 1964
Sales 395.5MM EMP 55
SIC 8051 Skilled nursing care facilities
Nrsg Dir: Connie Cox

TOBEY HOSPITAL
See SOUTHCOAST HOSPITALS GROUP INC

D-U-N-S 07-972-1507
TODAI FRANCHISING LLC
19481 San Jose Ave, Rowland Heights, CA 91748-1435
Tel (909) 869-7727 Founded/Ownrshp 1997
Sales 67.3MM[E] EMP 1,100
SIC 6794 Franchises, selling or licensing
CEO: Hans Kim

TODAYS OFFICE PROFESSIONALS
See SFN PROFESSIONAL SERVICES LLC

TODCO
See OFFSHORE DRILLING CO

D-U-N-S 00-291-8691 EXP
TODCO
2000 W Sam Houston Pkwy S # 800, Houston, TX 77042-3630
Tel (713) 278-6000 Founded/Ownrshp 1997
Sales 316.1MM[E] EMP 3,030
SIC 1381 Drilling oil & gas wells
Pr: Jan Rask
*Ch Bd: Thomas N Amonett
VP: Bryce H Dickinson
VP: Michael P Donaldson
VP: Claus E Fyling
VP: Lloyd M Pellegrin
Board of Directors: Suzanne V Baer, R Don Cash, Thomas M Hamilton, Thomas R Hix, Robert L Zorich

TODD & SARGENT
See SARGENT GROUP INC

D-U-N-S 00-782-0004
TODD & SARGENT INC
(Suby of TODD & SARGENT) ★
2905 Se 5th St, Ames, IA 50010-9761
Tel (515) 232-0442 Founded/Ownrshp 1994
Sales 150.0MM EMP 150
SIC 1541 1542 Warehouse construction; Industrial buildings, new construction; Food products manufacturing or packing plant construction; Nonresidential construction
Ch Bd: Lee M Sargent
*Pr: William H Bokhoven
*CFO: Jerry Murphy
*Treas: Dan Sargent
*Ex VP: Jon Sargent
*VP: Bill Bokhoven
*VP: Art Jenison
*VP: Clint Steele
IT Man: James Holston

D-U-N-S 04-249-6328
TODD HLAVATY MD
RADIATION THERAPY
601 W Leota St, North Platte, NE 69101-6525
Tel (308) 535-7405 Founded/Ownrshp 1998
Sales 161.5MM EMP 11
SIC 8011 Oncologist
CFO: Krystal Claymore
Ofcr: Beth Nozicka
Dir Lab: Laura Ryan
Chf Nrs Of: Tadd Greenfield
Ansthlgy: Forrest S Ragland
Dir Health: Stan Johnson

D-U-N-S 05-948-7397 EXP
TOGO PACKING CO INC
2125 Rochester Rd, Montgomery, IL 60538-1066
Tel (800) 575-3365 Founded/Ownrshp 1974
Sales 95.0MM[E] EMP 500
SIC 2011 Meat packing plants
Pr: Rafael Caballero Jr
IT Man: George Gastelum
VP Opers: Antonio Caballero
Prd Mgr: Tony Caballero
VP Sls: Dennis Keene

D-U-N-S 80-742-5694
TOHONO OODHAM GAMING ENTERPRISE
DESERT DIAMND CASINOS & ENTRMT
1100 W Pima Mine Rd, Green Valley, AZ 85614
Tel (520) 342-3000 Founded/Ownrshp 1993
Sales 90.3MM[E] EMP 1,450
SIC 7999 7011 Gambling establishment; Casino hotel
CEO: Scott Sirois
COO: Libby Francisco
CFO: Michael Morgan
Dir Sec: David Nay
Sfty Dirs: Michelle Abril

D-U-N-S 06-328-7130
TOHONO OODHAM NATION
Hc 86, Sells, AZ 85634
Tel (520) 383-6540 Founded/Ownrshp 1937
Sales NA EMP 1,500
SIC 9131

TOKAI RIKA GROUP
See TRMI INC

D-U-N-S 03-822-1198
TOKIO MARINE AMERICA
T M M
(Suby of TOKIO MARINE & NICHIDO FIRE INSURANCE CO., LTD.)
230 Park Ave Fl 2, New York, NY 10169-0499
Tel (212) 297-6600 Founded/Ownrshp 1976
Sales NA EMP 350
SIC 6411 Insurance agents, brokers & service
Ch: Koki Umeda
*Pr: Hiroshi Hasegawa
*CFO: Lawrence Moloney
CFO: Dawn Thomas
*Genl Couns: Steven Goldstein

TOKIO MARINE HCC
See HOUSTON CASUALTY CO

TOKIO MARINE HCC
See HCC INSURANCE HOLDINGS INC

D-U-N-S 00-995-2728
TOKIO MARINE SPECIALTY INSURANCE CO
1 Bala Plz Ste 100, Bala Cynwyd, PA 19004-1401
Tel (610) 206-7822 Founded/Ownrshp 2012
Sales NA EMP 18[E]
SIC 6411 Insurance agents, brokers & service
VP: Ted Nienburg
Sr VP: Scott Bayer
*VP: Susan Doering
*VP: Biju Joy
VP: Ed Kocur
*VP: Jon Peeples
Snr Mgr: Tuan Nguyen

D-U-N-S 05-224-5628
TOKYO ELECTRON AMERICA INC
(Suby of TOKYO ELECTRON US HOLDINGS INC) ★
2400 Grove Blvd, Austin, TX 78741-6500
Tel (512) 424-1000 Founded/Ownrshp 2009
Sales 322.7MM[E] EMP 1,000
SIC 3559 8711 Semiconductor manufacturing machinery; Engineering services
Ch Bd: Tetsuo Tsuneishi
*Pr: Larry Smith
*CEO: Barry Mayer
VP: Scott Sechovec
CIO: Russ Finney
DP Exec: Gloria Holstine
Tech Mgr: Paul Schleicher
Mktg Mgr: Nathan Baxter

D-U-N-S 19-298-6177 IMP
TOKYO ELECTRON US HOLDINGS INC
(Suby of TOKYO ELECTRON LIMITED)
2400 Grove Blvd, Austin, TX 78741-6500
Tel (512) 424-1000 Founded/Ownrshp 2005
Sales 315.2MM[E] EMP 1,200
SIC 3674 Semiconductors & related devices
Pr: Tetsuro Higashi
Sr VP: Barry Mayer
VP: Yukio Saeki
*VP: Scott Sechovec
VP: Bobby Shirai
Dir IT: Noel Russell
Software D: Paul Benson
Sftwr Eng: Kazuko Ishibashi
Opers Mgr: Joe Day

TOLEDO CITY SCHOOL DISTRICT
See TOLEDO PUBLIC SCHOOLS

D-U-N-S 10-984-5321 IMP
TOLEDO CLINIC INC
4235 Secor Rd, Toledo, OH 43623-4299
Tel (419) 473-3561 Founded/Ownrshp 1962
Sales 122.3MM[E] EMP 1,000
SIC 8011 Physicians' office, including specialists
Pr: Ian S Elliot
CFO: Charles Kopitke
*Sec: Timothy Husted
*VP: Wiliam Sternfeld
Dir Lab: Delite McKee
*Prin: E L Doermann
*Prin: Edward G Seybold
Ex Dir: Rick Gray
Off Mgr: Gwyn Hart
Off Mgr: Deb Hulles
Off Mgr: Gina Smith

D-U-N-S 00-790-4626
■TOLEDO EDISON CO
(Suby of FIRSTENERGY CORP) ★
76 S Main St Bsmt, Akron, OH 44308-1817
Tel (800) 447-3333 Founded/Ownrshp 1901
Sales 476.9MM EMP 390[E]
SIC 4911 Distribution, electric power; Transmission, electric power
CEO: Anthony J Alexander
Pr: C E Jones
*CFO: Mark T Clark
Treas: J F Pearson
Ex VP: L L Vespoli
VP: Harvey L Wagner
Prin: Jasmine Witherspoon
Board of Directors: Anthony J Alexander

D-U-N-S 05-416-9354
TOLEDO HOSPITAL
PROMEDICA TOLEDO HOSPITAL
(Suby of PROMEDICA HEALTH SYSTEMS INC) ★
2142 N Cove Blvd, Toledo, OH 43606-3896
Tel (419) 291-4000 Founded/Ownrshp 1876
Sales 745.4MM EMP 5,586
SIC 8011 8062 Offices & clinics of medical doctors; Hospital, professional nursing school with AMA residency
CEO: Alan Brass
*Pr: Barbara Steele
*Pr: Kevin Webb
*CFO: Cathy Hanley
Assoc Dir: Cindy Dusik
Software D: Mark Woek
Ansthlgy: Howard A Black
Ansthlgy: WEI S Jueng

D-U-N-S 60-915-8415 IMP
TOLEDO MOLDING & DIE INC
T M D
1429 Coining Dr, Toledo, OH 43612-2932
Tel (419) 470-3950 *Founded/Ownrshp* 2011
Sales 390.1MM[E] *EMP* 1,025
SIC 3089 3544 Injection molded finished plastic products; Special dies, tools, jigs & fixtures
Pr: Don Harbaugh
**CFO:* Bill Hylan
**CFO:* Jacob Master
**VP:* Joni Schmidt
Prgrm Mgr: Jeffrey Cohen
Prgrm Mgr: Arron Krott
Genl Mgr: David Spotts
CTO: Mary McCoy
DP Dir: John White
MIS Mgr: Tony Nader
Software D: Mike Snyir

D-U-N-S 05-417-0295
TOLEDO PUBLIC SCHOOLS
TOLEDO CITY SCHOOL DISTRICT
1609 N Summit St, Toledo, OH 43604-1806
Tel (419) 729-8200 *Founded/Ownrshp* 1837
Sales 193.8MM[E] *EMP* 3,600
Accts Mary Taylor Cpa Toledo Oh
SIC 8211 Public elementary & secondary schools; Public combined elementary & secondary school; Public adult education school; Public vocational/technical school
Pr: Bob Vasquez
**Ch Bd:* Cecelia Adams
Bd of Dir: Jack Ford
**Bd of Dir:* Lisa Sobecki
**VP:* Chris Varwig
Comm Dir: Patricia Mazur
**Prin:* Polly Taylor-Gerken
MIS Dir: Chad Henderly
IT Man: Dave Falzone
Opers Mgr: Steve Kosinski
Psych: Stephanie Dillabaugh

D-U-N-S 96-613-7320
■**TOLEDO REFINING CO LLC**
(*Suby of* PBF HOLDING CO LLC) ★
1819 Woodville Rd, Oregon, OH 43616-3159
Tel (419) 698-6600 *Founded/Ownrshp* 2010
Sales 222.4MM[E] *EMP* 430[E]
SIC 1629 Oil refinery construction
CEO: Tom Nimbley
**Pr:* Michael D Gayda
**Sr VP:* Jeffrey Dill
**Sr VP:* Matthew C Lucey
**VP:* Paul Davis

D-U-N-S 01-627-3344
TOLEDO SCHOOL DISTRICT 237
130 N 5th St, Toledo, WA 98591
Tel (360) 864-6325 *Founded/Ownrshp* 1947
Sales 461.2MM *EMP* 115
SIC 8211 Public junior high school; Public senior high school
Dir Sec: Tom Martin
Genl Mgr: Kaie Opsahl

D-U-N-S 06-182-8521
▲**TOLL BROTHERS INC**
250 Gibraltar Rd, Horsham, PA 19044-9869
Tel (215) 938-8000 *Founded/Ownrshp* 1967
Sales 4.1MMM *EMP* 3,900
Accts Ernst & Young Llp Philadelphi
Tkr Sym TOL *Exch* NYS
SIC 1521 1522 Single-family housing construction; New construction, single-family houses; Townhouse construction; Residential construction; Apartment building construction
Ch Bd: Robert I Toll
Pr: Richard T Hartman
CEO: Douglas C Yearley Jr
CFO: Martin P Connor
V Ch Bd: Bruce E Toll
Div VP: John Tolbert
Div VP: Daniel Wright
Sr VP: John McDonald
VP: Evan Ernest
VP: Tim Gibbon
VP: William Gilligan
VP: Michael Grubb
VP: Tom Hendricks
VP: Terry Hodge
VP: Michael Klouda
VP: Bill Meyers
VP: Charles Templeton
VP: Gregg Ziegler
Board of Directors: Edward G Boehne, Richard J Braemer, Christine N Garvey, Carl B Marbach, John A McLean, Stephen A Novick, Paul E Shapiro

D-U-N-S 82-994-1280
TOLL GLOBAL FORWARDING (AMERICAS) INC
(*Suby of* TOLL HOLDINGS LIMITED)
800 Federal Blvd Ste 3, Carteret, NJ 07008-1098
Tel (732) 750-9000 *Founded/Ownrshp* 2010
Sales 130.8MM[E] *EMP* 800[E]
SIC 4789 4731 Cargo loading & unloading services; Freight forwarding
CEO: Myles O'Brien
**Pr:* Bob O'Neill
**CFO:* Robert Agresti
**Treas:* Joe Cangelosi
Ofcr: Joseph Desaye
**VP:* Robert Wu

D-U-N-S 12-153-3603
TOLL GLOBAL FORWARDING SCS (USA) INC
FMI
(*Suby of* TOLL HOLDINGS LIMITED)
800 Federal Blvd Ste 2, Carteret, NJ 07008-1098
Tel (732) 750-9000 *Founded/Ownrshp* 2008
Sales 100.0MM *EMP* 400
SIC 4731 8741 Freight transportation arrangement; Management services
CEO: Mick Fountain
**Pr:* Joseph Desaye
COO: Cynthia Paul
**CFO:* Dan Ludwig
CFO: Joanna Scott
CFO: Paul L Shahbazian
VP: Gary Pedersen

D-U-N-S 83-202-1674
TOLMAR HOLDING INC
701 Centre Ave, Fort Collins, CO 80526-1843
Tel (970) 212-4500 *Founded/Ownrshp* 2009
Sales 146.5MM[E] *EMP* 581[E]
SIC 2834 Pharmaceutical preparations; Vitamin, nutrient & hematinic preparations for human use
CEO: Michael R Duncan
VP: J Steven Garrett
VP: Michelle Mantas
**VP:* David Speights

D-U-N-S 79-115-6578 IMP
TOLMAR INC
(*Suby of* TOLMAR HOLDING INC) ★
701 Centre Ave, Fort Collins, CO 80526-1843
Tel (970) 212-4500 *Founded/Ownrshp* 2006
Sales 95.1MM[E] *EMP* 388[E]
SIC 2834 Pharmaceutical preparations
CEO: Michael R Duncan
**VP:* David Speights

D-U-N-S 07-886-8654
TOLT SOLUTIONS INC
(*Suby of* POMEROY GROUP HOLDINGS INC) ★
3550 Rutherford Rd, Taylors, SC 29687-2142
Tel (864) 322-4200 *Founded/Ownrshp* 2015
Sales 235.9MM[E] *EMP* 735
SIC 8748 7379 7374 7373 Systems analysis & engineering consulting services; Computer related consulting services; Data processing service; Systems engineering, computer related; Office computer automation systems integration
CEO: Keith Bradley
**Pr:* John Gularson
**CFO:* Michael McClellan
Sr VP: Paul Civils
Sr VP: Tim Gallegos
Board of Directors: Keith Bradley, James Pade

D-U-N-S 05-311-3254
TOM BUSH VOLKSWAGEN INC
BUSH, TOM BMW
(*Suby of* BUSH INDUSTRIES CORP) ★
9850 Atlantic Blvd, Jacksonville, FL 32225-6536
Tel (904) 725-0911 *Founded/Ownrshp* 1970
Sales 141.4MM[E] *EMP* 211
SIC 5511 Automobiles, new & used
CEO: John P Bush
**Pr:* Thomas M Bush
**COO:* Telis Assimenios
CFO: Bernie Keefe
**VP:* Thomas M Bush III
Genl Mgr: Rob Davidson
IT Man: Lisa Fagin
Sales Exec: Marcelo Sackel
Mktg Dir: Steve Aten
Sales Asso: Barbara Beasley
Sales Asso: Matthew Moore

D-U-N-S 11-861-2394
TOM CHEI TORAH INSTITUTE
1372 47th St, Brooklyn, NY 11219-2611
Tel (718) 438-3061 *Founded/Ownrshp* 1988
Sales 122.0MM *EMP* 3[E]
SIC 8733 Research institute

TOM DUFFY COMPANY DIVISION
See B R FUNSTEN & CO

D-U-N-S 87-690-3147 EXP
TOM GRADDY ENTERPRISES INC
VAN GUARD TRUCK CENTER ATLANTA
3348 Peachtree Rd Ne, Atlanta, GA 30326-1067
Tel (404) 363-8390 *Founded/Ownrshp* 1994
Sales 194.8MM[E] *EMP* 439[E]
SIC 5531 5511 7538 5012 Automotive parts; Automobiles, new & used; General truck repair; Automobiles & other motor vehicles
Pr: Thomas Ewing
**CFO:* Nathan Rawlins
Ex VP: John Thomas
VP: Ronald Kline
Sales Asso: Buford Plumley
Sales Asso: Tim Yacovone

D-U-N-S 06-373-6367 IMP
TOM JAMES CO
TOM JAMES RETAIL DIVISION
263 Seaboard Ln, Franklin, TN 37067-4877
Tel (615) 771-6633 *Founded/Ownrshp* 1967
Sales 317.5MM *EMP* 2,600
Accts Crosslin & Associates Pc N
SIC 2311 2325 2323 2321 5611 Suits, men's & boys': made from purchased materials; Men's & boys' trousers & slacks; Men's & boys' neckwear; Men's & boys' furnishings; Men's & boys' clothing stores
CEO: Sergio Casalena
Sr Pt: Sarah Staggs
**Pr:* Joe Blair
**Pr:* Todd Browne
Pr: Steve Gray
COO: Craig Forrest
**CFO:* James P Williams
Treas: Phil Williams
VP: Steve Adelsberg
VP: Missy Barker
VP: Deepak Chhatwal
VP: David Christopher
VP: Les Heisterberg
Exec: Teresa Blanquel
Exec: Kelly Bourne
Exec: Zachary Frank
Exec: Dan Hook
Exec: Tom James
Exec: Hank Lee
Exec: Emmanuel Orhuozee
Exec: Steven Steffel
Board of Directors: Spencer Hays

TOM JAMES RETAIL DIVISION
See TOM JAMES CO

D-U-N-S 06-855-0375 IMP
TOM LANGE CO INC
755 Apple Orchard Rd, Springfield, IL 62703-5914
Tel (217) 786-3300 *Founded/Ownrshp* 1962
Sales 441.3MM *EMP* 110
Accts Kerber Eck & Braeckel Llp S
SIC 5148 Fruits, fresh
CEO: Phil Gumpert
**Pr:* Greg Reinauer
**Sec:* Hugh Seelbach
**Sr VP:* Jimmy Griswold
**Sr VP:* Bruce Rubin
VP: Jim Griswold
**VP:* Michael Smith

D-U-N-S 03-238-7250 EXP
TOM NEHL TRUCK CO
417 Edgewood Ave S, Jacksonville, FL 32254-3727
Tel (904) 389-3653 *Founded/Ownrshp* 1958
Sales 107.5MM[E] *EMP* 206
SIC 5511 5531 7538 Automobiles, new & used; Truck equipment & parts; General truck repair
Pr: Steve Bacalis
VP: Brian Backenstose
**VP:* Wanda Cotter
**VP:* Pat Mauldin
**VP:* Chuck Sowers

TOM SEPTIC CONSTRUCTION
See DON CHAPIN CO INC

TOM THUMB
See JUNIOR FOOD STORES OF WEST FLORIDA INC

D-U-N-S 00-792-5985
TOM THUMB FOOD & DRUGS INC (DE)
RANDALL'S
(*Suby of* RANDALLS FOOD MARKETS INC) ★
3663 Briarpark Dr, Houston, TX 77042-5205
Tel (713) 268-3500 *Founded/Ownrshp* 1953
Sales 976.2MM[E] *EMP* 13,368
SIC 5411 5912 5499 6512 6552 Supermarkets, chain; Drug stores; Gourmet food stores; Commercial & industrial building operation; Shopping center, property operation only; Land subdividers & developers, commercial
Pr: Jack W Evans Jr
**CFO:* Bob L Gowens
Site Mgr: Peggy Walker

D-U-N-S 07-888-4001
TOMAHAWK ACQUISITION LLC
(*Suby of* VISTA EQUITY PARTNERS LLC) ★
150 California St Fl 19, San Francisco, CA 94111-4550
Tel (415) 765-6500 *Founded/Ownrshp* 2013
Sales 50.5MM[E] *EMP* 1,609
SIC 6726 7371 Investment offices; Computer software development

D-U-N-S 08-220-4520 IMP
TOMARCO CONTRACTOR SPECIALTIES INC
TOMARCO FASTENING SYSTEMS
14848 Northam St, La Mirada, CA 90638-5747
Tel (714) 523-1771 *Founded/Ownrshp* 1977
Sales 96.9MM[E] *EMP* 95
Accts Erich Josephs Cpa Long Beach
SIC 5072 Hand tools; Power handtools; Builders' hardware
CEO: William Thompson
**Pr:* Keith Watkins
COO: Dave Lewis
Rgnl Mgr: Nick Ciminello
Rgnl Mgr: Larry Hook
IT Man: Antony Murguia
Sales Exec: Steve Aguilar
Mktg Mgr: Andrea Mayes
Sls Mgr: John Malatacca

TOMARCO FASTENING SYSTEMS
See TOMARCO CONTRACTOR SPECIALTIES INC

D-U-N-S 79-900-6747
TOMATOES EXTRAORDINAIRE INC
SPECIALTY PRODUCE
1929 Hancock St Ste 150, San Diego, CA 92110-2062
Tel (619) 295-3172 *Founded/Ownrshp* 1992
Sales 88.4MM[E] *EMP* 150
SIC 5149 Specialty food items
Pr: Robert Harrington
**VP:* Richard Harrington

TOMBALL FOREST
See FOREST TOMBALL PRODUCTS INC

D-U-N-S 07-013-4325
TOMBALL HOSPITAL AUTHORITY
TOMBALL REGIONAL MEDICAL CTR
605 Holderrieth Blvd, Tomball, TX 77375-6445
Tel (281) 351-1623 *Founded/Ownrshp* 1974
Sales 155.7MM[E] *EMP* 1,450
SIC 8062

D-U-N-S 06-071-3641
TOMBALL INDEPENDENT SCHOOL DISTRICT
310 S Cherry St, Tomball, TX 77375-6668
Tel (281) 357-3100 *Founded/Ownrshp* 1924
Sales 142.6MM *EMP* 1,450
Accts Hereford Lynch Sellars & Kir
SIC 8211 Public elementary school; Public junior high school; Public senior high school
**Pr:* John E McStravick
**CFO:* James Ross
Bd of Dir: Andrew Easton
Bd of Dir: Sam Gregson
Bd of Dir: Mark Lewandowski
Bd of Dir: Pam Norsworthy
Trst: Michael Pratt
Dir Risk M: Rich Vela
IT Man: Tina Deleon
IT Man: Diane Tiewell

TOMBALL REGIONAL MEDICAL CTR
See TOMBALL HOSPITAL AUTHORITY

TOMBALL REGIONAL MEDICAL CTR
See TOMBALL TEXAS HOSPITAL CO LLC

D-U-N-S 96-637-3727
TOMBALL TEXAS HOSPITAL CO LLC
TOMBALL REGIONAL MEDICAL CTR
605 Holderrieth Blvd, Tomball, TX 77375-6445
Tel (281) 401-7500 *Founded/Ownrshp* 2011
Sales 57.9MM *EMP* 3,000[E]
Accts Lio Ellen Hh Stutts Cpa To
SIC 8062 General medical & surgical hospitals
CEO: Tom Jackson
CFO: Richard Ervin
Ex VP: John Kelley
VP: Renee Ford
Snr Mgr: Sharla Lear

TOMCO SEED
See MCGREGOR CO

D-U-N-S 00-169-0288 IMP/EXP
TOMEN AMERICA INC
(*Suby of* TOYOTA TSUSHO CORPORATION)
805 3rd Ave Fl 16, New York, NY 10022-7513
Tel (212) 355-3600 *Founded/Ownrshp* 2006
Sales 1.4MMM[E] *EMP* 1,500
SIC 5153 5169 5031 5131 2261 Grains; Chemicals & allied products; Lumber: rough, dressed & finished; Plywood; Textiles, woven; Finishing plants, cotton
Ch Bd: Atsushi Mizuno
**Pr:* Nobuyuki Minowa
**CFO:* Hiroshi Tominaga
**Sr VP:* John Maraia
Genl Mgr: Matt Yamaguchi

TOMMIE VAUGHN FORD
See TOMMIE VAUGHN MOTORS INC

D-U-N-S 02-666-3732
TOMMIE VAUGHN MOTORS INC
TOMMIE VAUGHN FORD
1201 N Shepherd Dr, Houston, TX 77008-6532
Tel (713) 869-4661 *Founded/Ownrshp* 1955
Sales 88.0MM[E] *EMP* 225
SIC 5511 Automobiles, new & used; Pickups, new & used; Vans, new & used
Pr: James J Janke
**Pr:* Tommie Vaughn
**Sec:* Joe Blair
**VP:* Jean V Janke
**VP:* Jim Janke
Store Mgr: Chris Bull
Web Dev: Michael Getz
Sls Mgr: Wally Delarosa
Sls Mgr: Richard Moreno
Sales Asso: Christina Creel

D-U-N-S 18-368-7206
■**TOMMY BAHAMA GROUP INC**
(*Suby of* OXFORD INDUSTRIES INC) ★
400 Fairview Ave N # 488, Seattle, WA 98109-5371
Tel (206) 622-8688 *Founded/Ownrshp* 2003
Sales 481.2MM[E] *EMP* 1,500
SIC 7389 5651 5136 5137 Apparel designers, commercial; Unisex clothing stores; Men's & boys' clothing; Women's & children's clothing
CEO: Terry R Pillow
**Pr:* Thomas Chubb III
**COO:* Doug Wood
**CFO:* Ken Kong
Sr VP: Stephen Cirona
**VP:* Thomas E Campbell
**VP:* Lucio Dalla Gasperina
**VP:* K Grassmyer
**VP:* Don Kerkes
**VP:* Anne Shoemaker
Creative D: Tom Prowell

D-U-N-S 78-055-2667 IMP
■**TOMMY HILFIGER USA INC**
DSK INDUSTRIES
(*Suby of* TOMMY HILFIGER CORPORATION)
601 W 26th St Rm 500, New York, NY 10001-1142
Tel (212) 840-8888 *Founded/Ownrshp* 1994
Sales 392.5MM[E] *EMP* 4,000
SIC 5611 5632 5641 5136 5137 5139 Clothing, sportswear, men's & boys'; Women's accessory & specialty stores; Children's wear; Men's & boys' clothing; Women's & children's outerwear; Handbags; Footwear
CEO: Emanuel Chirico
**CEO:* Fred Gehring
**COO:* George Carrara
Ch: Tommy Hilfiger
**Chf Mktg O:* Avery Baker
Ex VP: Jeannine D'Onofrio
Sr VP: Hethre Faust
VP: Craig Burchfield
VP: Brigitte Danielmeyer
VP: Zach Eichman
VP: Caroline Foley
VP: John Freedman
VP: Suzanne Fuller
VP: Lisa Gange
VP: Khatija Ghasletwala
VP: John Grippo
VP: Bobby Hough
VP: Chris Love
VP: Gregory Palazzo
VP: Michael Pietrunti
VP: Pj Reynolds

D-U-N-S 04-153-2073 IMP
■**TOMOTHERAPY INC** (WI)
(*Suby of* ACCURAY INC) ★
1240 Deming Way, Madison, WI 53717-1954
Tel (608) 824-2800 *Founded/Ownrshp* 1997, 2011
Sales 90.8MM[E] *EMP* 600
SIC 3829 Medical diagnostic systems, nuclear
CEO: Fred Robertson
COO: Steve Books
**COO:* Steven Brooks
CFO: Stephen C Hathaway
**CFO:* Thomas E Powell
**Chf Cred:* Rafael L Vaello
Sr VP: John Maclennan
VP: Kenneth D Buroker
VP: Delwin T Coufal
**VP:* Brenda S Furlow
VP: Alison Johnson
VP: Gustavo Olivera

VP: Robert Zahn
Exec: Nicole Olthafer

D-U-N-S 00-561-8319
▲TOMPKINS FINANCIAL CORP (NY)
The Cmns, Ithaca, NY 14851
Tel (607) 273-3210 *Founded/Ownrshp* 1995
Sales NA *EMP* 1,038E
Accts Kpmg Llp Rochester New York
Tkr Sym TMP *Exch* ASE
SIC 6022 State commercial banks
Pr: Stephen S Romaine
**Ch Bd:* Thomas R Rochon
Pr: Brian A Howard
COO: Francis M Fetsko
**V Ch Bd:* James W Fulmer
Ofcr: Deborah Hoover
Ofcr: Gerald J Klein Jr
Ex VP: David S Boyce
Ex VP: Alyssa H Fontaine
Ex VP: Scott L Gruber
Ex VP: Gregory J Hartz
Ex VP: John M McKenna
Ex VP: Susan M Valenti
Sr VP: Bonita N Lindberg
VP: Paula Barron
VP: Glenn Cobb
VP: Kimberly Dove
VP: John Poli
VP: Scott Pronti
VP: Bill Steinmetz
VP: Tracy Vanderzee
Board of Directors: Alfred J Weber, John E Alexander, Craig Yunker, Paul J Battaglia, Daniel J Fessenden, Carl E Haynes, Susan A Henry, Patricia A Johnson, Frank C Milewski, Sandra A Parker, Michael H Spain

D-U-N-S 04-420-6428
■TOMPKINS TRUST CO
(*Suby of* TOMPKINS FINANCIAL CORP) ★
110 N Tioga St, Ithaca, NY 14850-4320
Tel (607) 257-1909 *Founded/Ownrshp* 1995
Sales 103.5MM *EMP* 1E
SIC 6733 Trusts
Ch Bd: James Byrnes
Sr VP: Gregory Hartz
VP: David Boyce
VP: James Frey
VP: Greg May
**Prin:* Steven Garner
CIO: Rick Page

D-U-N-S 87-909-5214 IMP
TOMRA OF NORTH AMERICA (INC)
(*Suby of* TOMRA SYSTEMS ASA)
1 Corporate Dr Ste 710, Shelton, CT 06484-6243
Tel (203) 447-8800 *Founded/Ownrshp* 1986
Sales 350.7MME *EMP* 1,100
SIC 5046 Vending machines, coin-operated
Prin: Stefan Ranstrand
**Treas:* Gregory Kelly
Sr VP: Debbie Hall
Sales Exec: Paula Chiungos

D-U-N-S 80-092-4938
TOMS RIVER REGIONAL SCHOOLS
1144 Hooper Ave Ste 304, Toms River, NJ 08753-8361
Tel (732) 505-5500 *Founded/Ownrshp* 1954
Sales 30.0M *EMP* 1,933E
SIC 8211 8741 Public elementary & secondary schools; Management services
Brnch Mgr: Christopher Tofanicchio
Dir IT: Leonard Niebo
IT Man: Elizabeth McCarthy
IT Man: Nancy Tomecko
VP Sls: Barbara Britske

D-U-N-S 04-326-3557
TOMS SIERRA CO INC
SIERRA ENERGY
1020 Winding Creek Rd, Roseville, CA 95678-7041
Tel (916) 218-1600 *Founded/Ownrshp* 1959
Sales 98.3MME *EMP* 204
SIC 5541 Filling stations, gasoline
Pr: Brad Barnett
Ex VP: Torgny Nilsson
VP Opers: Laura Carroll

D-U-N-S 09-609-9064 IMP/EXP
TOMS TRUCK CENTER INC
12221 Monarch St, Garden Grove, CA 92841-2906
Tel (714) 835-5070 *Founded/Ownrshp* 1974
Sales 92.8MME *EMP* 194
SIC 5511 5012 7538 Trucks, tractors & trailers: new & used; Trucks, commercial; Truck engine repair, except industrial
CEO: Kevin C Heidler
**Pr:* George P Heidler Jr
VP: Ken Fetters

D-U-N-S 05-220-5718 IMP/EXP
TOMY CORP
(*Suby of* TOMY COMPANY,LTD.)
2021 9th St Se, Dyersville, IA 52040-2316
Tel (563) 875-2000 *Founded/Ownrshp* 1998
Sales 91.9MME *EMP* 840
SIC 5092 Toys & hobby goods & supplies
CEO: Gregory J Kilrea
**Pr:* Kaz Sugiyama
**COO:* Mark Shinohara

D-U-N-S 07-868-0460
TOMY HOLDINGS INC
(*Suby of* TOMY COMPANY,LTD.)
2015 Spring Rd Ste 400, Oak Brook, IL 60523-1865
Tel (630) 573-7200 *Founded/Ownrshp* 2012
Sales 118.5MME *EMP* 775E
SIC 5092 5945 Toys & hobby goods & supplies; Toys & games
CEO: Gregory J Kilrea
**COO:* Masayuki Nagatake
**CFO:* Peter A Nicholson
**Ex VP:* Helena Lo
VP Sls: Rod Voss
Mktg Dir: Sarah Moen

D-U-N-S 06-518-3758 IMP/EXP
TOMY INTERNATIONAL INC
(*Suby of* TOMY HOLDINGS INC) ★
2021 9th St Se, Dyersville, IA 52040-2384
Tel (563) 875-2000 *Founded/Ownrshp* 1987
Sales 118.5MME *EMP* 478
SIC 5092 Toys & games; Toys
CEO: Harold Meij
COO: Masayuki Nagatake
Sr VP: Doris Koopmann
VP: Karen Knepper
VP: Kim Neville
Sls Mgr: Robert Agnew

D-U-N-S 02-213-5586 IMP
TONE BROTHERS INC
TONE'S SPICES
(*Suby of* A C H RETAIL PRODUCTS) ★
2301 Se Tones Dr, Ankeny, IA 50021-8790
Tel (515) 965-2711 *Founded/Ownrshp* 2004
Sales 87.0MME *EMP* 490
SIC 2087 2099 Extracts, flavoring; Spices, including grinding
CEO: Charles Martin
**Pr:* Daniel Antonelli
**CFO:* Jeffrey Atkins
Exec: Jay Cruise
Software D: Monica Andrade
Mktg Mgr: Steve Gordon

TONERCYCLE
See INKCYCLE INC

TONE'S SPICES
See TONE BROTHERS INC

D-U-N-S 17-896-3091
TONKA BAY EQUITY PARTNERS LLC
301 Carlson Pkwy Ste 325, Hopkins, MN 55305-5410
Tel (952) 345-2030 *Founded/Ownrshp* 2004
Sales 106.3MME *EMP* 524
SIC 6799 Investors

D-U-N-S 00-796-6367
TONN AND BLANK CONSTRUCTION LLC (IN)
(*Suby of* SAINT JAMES HOSPITAL) ★
1623 Greenwood Ave, Michigan City, IN 46360-5525
Tel (219) 879-7321 *Founded/Ownrshp* 1922
Sales 91.4MME *EMP* 228
SIC 1542 Nonresidential construction
CEO: Jon Gilmore
**VP:* Larry Ballah
**VP:* Joe Coar
**VP:* Scott Wells
IT Man: Steve Eckiss
Ql Cn Mgr: Jeff Chapman
Sls&Mrk Ex: Gene Smith
Snr PM: Brien Delich
Snr PM: David Dyer

D-U-N-S 00-208-2550 IMP
TONOGA INC
TACONIC
136 Coon Brook Rd, Petersburg, NY 12138-4303
Tel (518) 658-3202 *Founded/Ownrshp* 1961, 1974
Sales 139.6MME *EMP* 500
SIC 2295 3629 Resin or plastic coated fabrics; Electronic generation equipment
Ch: Andrew G Russell
**CFO:* Larry Carroll
**Ex VP:* Lawrence Carroll
**VP:* Sharon Goodermote
**VP:* Manfred Huschka
**VP:* Scott Schulz
Snr Sftwr: Moonray Schepart
Sfty Mgr: Chris Headly
Ql Cn Mgr: CJ Brownellwilkins
Sls Mgr: Suzanne Seymour

D-U-N-S 79-021-7264
TONTINE CAPITAL PARTNERS LIMITED PARTNERSHIP
55 Railroad Ave Ste 103, Greenwich, CT 06830-6378
Tel (203) 769-2000 *Founded/Ownrshp* 2007
Sales 52.5MME *EMP* 2,800
SIC 7389 Financial services
Pr: Brian Nisbet

D-U-N-S 00-616-0642
TONY DOWNS FOODS CO (MN)
DOWNS FOOD GROUP
54934 210th Ln, Mankato, MN 56001-2100
Tel (507) 375-3111 *Founded/Ownrshp* 1948
Sales 94.1MME *EMP* 350
SIC 2015 2099 Chicken, processed: frozen; Chicken, processed: canned; Food preparations
CEO: Richard Downs
**Pr:* Mike Downs
**VP:* Greg Cook
**VP:* Mitch Forstie
Dir IT: Byron Bruce
Dir IT: Eric Henderson

D-U-N-S 79-882-0189
TONY GULLO MOTORS I LP
GULLO TOYOTA CONROE
500 Interstate 45 S, Conroe, TX 77304-2625
Tel (936) 539-9191 *Founded/Ownrshp* 1993
Sales 100.7MM *EMP* 130
SIC 7549 5511 5531 Automobiles, new & used; Pickups, new & used; Vans, new & used; Automotive parts
Genl Pt: Anthony Gullo
Pt: Rowan Collins
Pt: Corky Gullo
Pt: Tony Gullo

TONY ROMA'S
See SLAYMAKER GROUP INC

TONY ROMA'S
See ROMACORP INC

D-U-N-S 02-903-2513 IMP
■TONYS FINE FOODS
(*Suby of* UNITED NATURAL FOODS INC) ★
3575 Reed Ave, West Sacramento, CA 95605-1628
Tel (916) 374-4000 *Founded/Ownrshp* 1934
Sales 626.3MME *EMP* 555
SIC 5147 5143 5149 Meats, cured or smoked; Cheese; Groceries & related products
CEO: Scott Berger
**Pr:* Karl Berger
Div Mgr: Nancy Espinoza
Opers Mgr: David Apling
Sls Dir: Greg Spivey
Pr Mgr: Jennifer Gonzales

TOOELE BOARD OF EDUCATION
See TOOELE COUNTY SCHOOL DISTRICT

D-U-N-S 08-932-1798
TOOELE COUNTY SCHOOL DISTRICT
TOOELE BOARD OF EDUCATION
92 Lodestone Way, Tooele, UT 84074-8050
Tel (435) 833-1900 *Founded/Ownrshp* 2010
Sales 82.8M *EMP* 1,400
Accts Squire & Company Pc Orem Ut
SIC 8211 Public elementary school; Public junior high school; Public senior high school
**Pr:* Scott Bryan
Bd of Dir: Kathy Taylor
**VP:* Carol Jensen
IT Man: Jim Langston
Teacher Pr: Terry Christenson

D-U-N-S 06-884-7615
TOOH DINEH INDUSTRIES INC
(*Suby of* DINEH CO-OPERATIVES, INC)
Leupp School Rd Bldg 4, Leupp, AZ 86035
Tel (928) 686-6477 *Founded/Ownrshp* 1982
Sales 1.4MMM *EMP* 164
SIC 3679 3672 Electronic circuits; Printed circuit boards
Pr: Alex Riggs Sr
**Treas:* Jon D Colvin

D-U-N-S 60-623-1033
TOOJAYS MANAGEMENT LLC
TOOJAY'S ORIGINAL GOURMET DELI
3654 Georgia Ave, West Palm Beach, FL 33405-2121
Tel (561) 659-9011 *Founded/Ownrshp* 1983
Sales 180.4MME *EMP* 1,600
Accts Grant Thornton Llp Fort Laude
SIC 8741 Restaurant management
Ch: Jay Trungale
Pr: Alan Knuckles
**Pr:* Alan Nuckles
CFO: Heather Holmstrom
**Ex VP:* Neal Chianese
**VP:* Jay A Brown
**VP:* Annie Catz
**VP:* Dennis Snuszka
Area Supr: Richard Jabara
Genl Mgr: Shaun Gibson
Dir IT: Dave Diamond

TOOJAY'S ORIGINAL GOURMET DELI
See TOOJAYS MANAGEMENT LLC

TOOL CRIB OF THE NORTH
See ACME ELECTRIC MOTOR INC

D-U-N-S 62-436-2575
TOOLOW INC
4273 Reids Way, Berkeley, CA 94704
Tel (408) 694-2361 *Founded/Ownrshp* 2015
Sales 20.0MMM *EMP* 2
SIC 7379

D-U-N-S 08-021-5647
TOOT N TOTUM FOOD STORES LLC
1201 S Taylor St, Amarillo, TX 79101-4313
Tel (806) 373-4351 *Founded/Ownrshp* 2007
Sales 250.0MM *EMP* 800
SIC 5411 5541 Grocery stores, independent; Gasoline service stations
Pr: Greg Mitchell
VP: David Johnson

D-U-N-S 02-598-4287
TOOT N TOTUM FOOD STORES LP
1201 S Taylor St, Amarillo, TX 79101-4313
Tel (806) 373-4351 *Founded/Ownrshp* 1999
Sales 165.0MME *EMP* 530
SIC 5541 5411

D-U-N-S 55-687-0483
■TOOTSIE ROLL CO INC
(*Suby of* TOOTSIE ROLL INDUSTRIES LLC) ★
7401 S Cicero Ave, Chicago, IL 60629-5885
Tel (773) 838-3400 *Founded/Ownrshp* 1979
Sales 132.2MME *EMP* 1,000
SIC 2064 Candy & other confectionery products
Pr: Ellen R Gordon
**Treas:* Barry Bowen

D-U-N-S 00-128-9495 IMP/EXP
▲TOOTSIE ROLL INDUSTRIES INC
7401 S Cicero Ave, Chicago, IL 60629-5885
Tel (773) 838-3400 *Founded/Ownrshp* 1896
Sales 540.1MM *EMP* 2,000
Tkr Sym TR *Exch* NYS
SIC 2064 Candy & other confectionery products
Ch Bd: Ellen R Gordon
CFO: G Howard Ember Jr
Treas: Barry P Bowen
VP: Peter Lebron
VP: John P Majors
Plnt Mgr: Stephen Green
Trfc Mgr: Tim Hackett
VP Mktg: Thomas E Corr
Mktg Mgr: Zel Peterson
Board of Directors: Lana Jane Lewis-Brent, Paula M Wardynski

D-U-N-S 96-980-3175
■TOOTSIE ROLL INDUSTRIES LLC
(*Suby of* TOOTSIE ROLL INDUSTRIES INC) ★
7401 S Cicero Ave, Chicago, IL 60629-5885
Tel (773) 245-4202 *Founded/Ownrshp* 2005
Sales 182.4MME *EMP* 1,265
SIC 2064 Candy & other confectionery products
Pr: Ellen Gordon
**CFO:* G Howard Ember
**Treas:* Barry Bowen

D-U-N-S 02-570-8009
TOP AG COOPERATIVE INC
702 S Elevator St, Okawville, IL 62271
Tel (618) 243-5293 *Founded/Ownrshp* 2005
Sales 107.1MM *EMP* 75
Accts Bergan Kdv Ltd Cedar Rapids
SIC 5153 5191 Grains; Farm supplies
Pr: Brian Kunz
**Sec:* Steve Meentemeyer
**VP:* Jeff Rennegarbe
Genl Mgr: Ribin Venn
Board of Directors: Kim Graul, Steve Lintker, Jeff Rennegarbe, Mike Vonbokel

D-U-N-S 02-565-7263
TOP FLIGHT GRAIN MONTICELLO CO
420 W Marion St, Monticello, IL 61856-1832
Tel (217) 762-2163 *Founded/Ownrshp* 1903
Sales 210.0MM *EMP* 60
SIC 5153 5191 4221 Grain elevators; Fertilizer & fertilizer materials; Farm product warehousing & storage
Genl Mgr: Scott Docherty
Brnch Mgr: Russel Wright
**Genl Mgr:* Richard Thomas

TOP FOOD & DRUGS
See HAGGEN INC

D-U-N-S 80-705-5053
TOP GOLF USA INC
(*Suby of* GOLF ENTERTAINMENT INTERNATIONAL LIMITED)
8750 N Cntl Expy Ste 1200, Dallas, TX 75231
Tel (214) 377-5053 *Founded/Ownrshp* 2003
Sales 162.8MME *EMP* 2,200
SIC 7999 5812 5941 Miniature golf course operation; Eating places; Golf goods & equipment
Ch: Erik Anderson
**CEO:* Joseph M Vrankin
**VP:* Randy Starr
Dir Soc: Geoff Lane
**Prin:* Luz Smith
Opers Mgr: Beth Seidensticker
Mktg Mgr: Michael Angelides
Mktg Mgr: Ashley Harkness
Mktg Mgr: Charlotte Payne
Sls Mgr: Brandi Brumback
Sls Mgr: Jessica Flom

D-U-N-S 17-433-0001
TOP RX LLC
2950 Brother Blvd Ste 102, Bartlett, TN 38133-3968
Tel (800) 542-8677 *Founded/Ownrshp* 2011
Sales 95.4MME *EMP* 155
SIC 5122 Pharmaceuticals
Pr: Scott Franklin
CFO: Elaine Nutt
**VP:* Norma Elaine McNutt
IT Man: Ralph Smith
Sls Dir: Jonathan Keith

D-U-N-S 07-975-5168
TOP SHOP LLC (IA)
5515 Council St Ne, Cedar Rapids, IA 52402-2021
Tel (319) 393-1041 *Founded/Ownrshp* 2015
Sales 1.2MMM *EMP* 7
SIC 2541 Counter & sink tops
Pr: Jeffrey Palmer

D-U-N-S 13-767-7592 IMP
■TOP-FLITE GOLF CO
(*Suby of* CALLAWAY GOLF CO) ★
425 Meadow St, Chicopee, MA 01013-2201
Tel (413) 536-1200 *Founded/Ownrshp* 2003
Sales 84.8MME *EMP* 1,400
SIC 5941 Sporting goods & bicycle shops
Pr: Jame Craigie
**Pr:* Robert Penicka
VP: Ed Several
Mktg Mgr: Jared Zimmerman
Sls Mgr: Joe Kennedy

D-U-N-S 09-999-8940
TOPA EQUITIES LTD
TOPA RISK MANAGEMENT SERVICES
1800 Ave Of The Ste 1400, Los Angeles, CA 90067
Tel (310) 203-9199 *Founded/Ownrshp* 1962
Sales NA *EMP* 2,000
SIC 6163 5181 7538 Loan brokers; Beer & other fermented malt liquors; General truck repair
CEO: Marion Anderson
**Ch Bd:* John E Anderson
VP: Darren Bell
VP: Anne Mehrtens
VP: Jj O'Brien
VP: Robin N Platt
VP: Christine Thompson
**Prin:* Robert R Hollman

TOPA RISK MANAGEMENT SERVICES
See TOPA EQUITIES LTD

D-U-N-S 92-762-1730 EXP
TOPAC USA INC
TOSHIBA BUSINESS SOLUTIONS
(*Suby of* TOSHIBA AMERICA BUSINESS SOLUTIONS INC) ★
9740 Irvine Blvd, Irvine, CA 92618-1608
Tel (949) 462-6000 *Founded/Ownrshp* 2005
Sales 123.5MME *EMP* 840E
SIC 5044 Office equipment
CEO: Rick Taylor
Pr: Fred C Berger
Pr: Mark Downing
VP: Dimitrios Soursos
VP: Wayne Wilkinson
Dir IT: Bill Macfarlane
VP Opers: Jim Hawkins
Sls Mgr: Pete Kaczmarek
Board of Directors: Dennis Eversole, Brian Merriman

D-U-N-S 07-980-2132
▲TOPBUILD CORP
260 Jimmy Ann Dr, Daytona Beach, FL 32114-1318
Tel (386) 304-2200 *Founded/Ownrshp* 1929
Sales 1.6MMM *EMP* 8,000E
Tkr Sym BLD *Exch* NYS

SIC 1742 1761 1751 5033 Insulation, buildings; Gutter & downspout contractor; Garage door, installation or erection; Insulation materials
CEO: Gerald Volas
Pt: Mark R Moore
Ch Bd: Alec C Covington
Pr: Robert M Buck
CFO: John S Peterson
Ofcr: Robin L Reininger
VP: Michelle A Friel
Board of Directors: Dennis W Archer, Carl T Camden, Joseph S Cantie, Mark A Petrarca, Margaret M Whelan

D-U-N-S 09-678-8047 EXP
■TOPBUILD SERVICES GROUP CORP (FL)
(*Suby of* TOPBUILD CORP) ★
260 Jimmy Ann Dr, Daytona Beach, FL 32114-1318
Tel (386) 304-2200 *Founded/Ownrshp* 1974, 2015
Sales 2.5MMM^E *EMP* 4,772
SIC 1742 Insulation, buildings
CEO: Robert Buck
**Ex VP:* James Hazelwood

D-U-N-S 07-294-3876 IMP/EXP
TOPCO ASSOCIATES LLC
(*Suby of* TOPCO HOLDINGS INC (COOPERATIVE)) ★
150 Northwest Point Blvd # 6, Elk Grove Village, IL 60007-1015
Tel (847) 676-3030 *Founded/Ownrshp* 2001
Sales 1.1MMM^E *EMP* 450
SIC 5141 Groceries, general line
CEO: Randall J Skoda
**Treas:* Kyle Der
**Ex VP:* Paul Matthews
**Sr VP:* Andrew J Broccolo
**Sr VP:* James E Goers
**Sr VP:* Shawn Greenwald
**Sr VP:* Ian Grossman
**Sr VP:* Christopher T Hooks
VP: Thomas Frey
VP: Christophe Hooks
VP: Brian Josephs
VP: Linda Severin
VP: Laird Snelgrove

D-U-N-S 00-693-5977 IMP/EXP
TOPCO HOLDINGS INC (COOPERATIVE)
150 Northwest Point Blvd, Elk Grove Village, IL 60007-1015
Tel (847) 676-3030 *Founded/Ownrshp* 1944
Sales 13.1MMM *EMP* 514^E
SIC 5141 8699 Groceries, general line; Food co-operative
Pr: Randall J Skoda
Treas: Kyle Der
Sr VP: Kenneth H Guy
Sr VP: Daniel F Mazur
Sr VP: Michael F Ricciardi
Sr VP: E Russ Wolfe
Comm Dir: Danell O'Neill
QA Dir: Sarah Greenwald
Genl Couns: Andrew Broccolo

D-U-N-S 14-003-7305 IMP
TOPCON AMERICA CORP
(*Suby of* TOPCON CORPORATION)
111 Bauer Dr, Oakland, NJ 07436-3123
Tel (201) 599-5117 *Founded/Ownrshp* 2001
Sales 249.3MM^E *EMP* 1,400
SIC 3845 Laser systems & equipment, medical
Pr: David Mudrick
Sr VP: Albert Zahalka
Mktg Mgr: Donald Winfield

D-U-N-S 05-354-7238 IMP
TOPCON MEDICAL SYSTEMS INC
(*Suby of* TOPCON AMERICA CORP) ★
111 Bauer Dr, Oakland, NJ 07436-3123
Tel (201) 599-5100 *Founded/Ownrshp* 1970
Sales 74.1MM *EMP* 1,000
SIC 3841 3826 3827 3829 3851 5049 Surgical & medical instruments; Analytical instruments; Optical instruments & apparatus; Surveying instruments & accessories; Ophthalmic goods; Scientific instruments; Engineers' equipment & supplies; Optical goods; Surveyors' instruments
Pr: Shigehiro Ogino
**Pr:* David Mudrick
**VP:* Alena Acosta
Manager: Justin A Jones

D-U-N-S 80-983-9707 IMP/EXP
TOPCON POSITIONING SYSTEMS INC
(*Suby of* TOPCON AMERICA CORP) ★
7400 National Dr, Livermore, CA 94550-7340
Tel (925) 245-8300 *Founded/Ownrshp* 1993
Sales 108.3MM^E *EMP* 300
SIC 3829 3625 3823 3699 8713 1794 Surveying instruments & accessories; Relays & industrial controls; Industrial instrmnts msrmnt display/control process variable; Electrical equipment & supplies; Surveying services; Excavation work
Pr: Raymond O'Connor
COO: David Mudrick
CFO: Jim Paetz
Ex VP: M Yamazaki
Sr VP: John Beaver
Sr VP: Mark S Bittner
Sr VP: Joe Brabec
Sr VP: Eduardo Falcon
Sr VP: David Vaughn
VP: James Orsino
VP: Ray Vallejo
Dir Bus: Mauricio Jaimes

TOPEKA FAMILY PRACTICE
See ST FRANCIS HEALTH CENTER INC

TOPEKA METAL SPECIALTIES
See LB STEEL LLC

TOPEKA PUBLIC SCHOOLS
See TOPEKA UNIFIED SCHOOL DISTRICT 501

D-U-N-S 09-674-7183
TOPEKA UNIFIED SCHOOL DISTRICT 501
TOPEKA PUBLIC SCHOOLS
624 Sw 24th St, Topeka, KS 66611-1208
Tel (785) 295-3000 *Founded/Ownrshp* 1854, 1900
Sales 169.8MM *EMP* 2,500
Accts Berberich Trahan & Co Pa To
SIC 8211 Public elementary & secondary schools
CFO: Michael Jones
Treas: Mary Heald
Bd of Dir: Judi Botros
Bd of Dir: Miki Brown
Bd of Dir: Cheryl Tuckwin
Bd of Dir: Suzanne Williams
Trst: Kenneth Butler
VP: Lisa Potts
VP: Katrina Taggart
VP: Sharon Tolin
VP: Rhonda Tomlinson

D-U-N-S 06-617-2278
TOPGOLF INTERNATIONAL INC
8750 N Cntl Expy Ste 1200, Dallas, TX 75231
Tel (214) 377-0615 *Founded/Ownrshp* 2008
Sales 1.1MMM^E *EMP* 3,524
SIC 3949 Driving ranges, golf, electronic
CEO: Ken May
Sls Dir: Tiffany Holton
Mktg Mgr: Ligia Bermudez
Mktg Mgr: Marissa Olberding
Sls Mgr: Sherae Bell
Sls Mgr: Jordan Dyck
Sls Mgr: Lindsey Elliott
Sls Mgr: Lauren R Grubb
Sls Mgr: Natalie Samb
Sls Mgr: Jacilyn Tucker

TOPICZ
See NOVELART MANUFACTURING CO

D-U-N-S 19-636-8211 IMP
TOPPAN PHOTOMASKS INC
(*Suby of* TOPPAN PRINTING CO., LTD.)
131 E Old Settlers Blvd, Round Rock, TX 78664-2211
Tel (512) 310-6500 *Founded/Ownrshp* 2005
Sales 290.7MM^E *EMP* 1,660
SIC 3559 Semiconductor manufacturing machinery
Pr: Michael Hadsell
COO: James Northup
**CFO:* Barry F Pomeroy
**Ex VP:* James W Boeckman
Ex VP: Jim Boeckman
Ex VP: Paul Chipman
**Ex VP:* Dr Franklin Kalk
Ex VP: Kenneth Rygler
VP: Bud Caverly
VP: Greg Easley
VP: Park Kw
VP: John Lynn
VP: Larry McKinley
VP: Adrian Phillips
VP: Marshall Turner
VP: Stephen A Wilson
VP: Steve Wilson
Exec: Tonya Hindes
Dir Bus: Kent Ibsen

D-U-N-S 18-283-1651 IMP/EXP
TOPPS CO INC
(*Suby of* JOE TORNANTE-MDP HOLDING LLC) ★
1 Whitehall St Fl 4, New York, NY 10004-3612
Tel (212) 376-0300 *Founded/Ownrshp* 2007
Sales 354.0MM^E *EMP* 422
SIC 5145 5092 5112 2064 Confectionery; Candy; Chewing gum; Toys & games; Playing cards; Social stationery & greeting cards; Albums, scrapbooks & binders; Candy & other confectionery products; Lollipops & other hard candy
Pr: Michael Brandstaedter
**CFO:* Joseph Del Toro
Bd of Dir: James N Perry
VP: Dan Carus
VP: Michael Dombroski
VP: Ira Freidman
VP: Mike Gardner
VP: Joe Kellachan
VP: David Leiner
VP: Jeff Mickeal
VP: Tom Mozeleski
Creative D: John Williams
Board of Directors: Steven Chiang

D-U-N-S 12-678-5257 IMP
TOPRE AMERICA CORP
(*Suby of* TOPRE CORPORATION)
1580 County Rd Ste 222, Cullman, AL 35057
Tel (256) 735-2600 *Founded/Ownrshp* 2002
Sales 122.7MM^E *EMP* 235^E
SIC 2396 Automotive & apparel trimmings
Pr: Shinichiro Uchigasaki
**VP:* Ktawag Kongo
Exec: Carl English

TOPS FRIENDLY MARKETS
See TOPS MARKETS LLC

D-U-N-S 07-963-2082
TOPS HOLDING II CORP
6363 Main St, Williamsville, NY 14221-5855
Tel (716) 635-5000 *Founded/Ownrshp* 1962
Sales 2.5MMM *EMP* 31,100
SIC 5411 Grocery stores
Ch Bd: Frank Curci
**COO:* Kevin Darrington
CFO: David Langless
**Ex VP:* Jack Barrett
Ex VP: Kevin R Darrington
**Sr VP:* Lynne Burgess
Sr VP: Ron Ferri
**Sr VP:* John Persons
VP: Mike Metz

D-U-N-S 96-714-6866
TOPS HOLDING LLC
(*Suby of* TOPS HOLDING II CORP) ★
6363 Main St, Williamsville, NY 14221-5855
Tel (716) 635-5000 *Founded/Ownrshp* 2007
Sales 2.7MMM^E *EMP* 16,000^E
SIC 5411 Grocery stores; Supermarkets, chain; Supermarkets, hypermarket; Supermarkets
Pr: Frank Curci
**Ch Bd:* Gary Matthews
COO: Kevin Darrington
CFO: William R Mills
Sr VP: Jack Barrett
Sr VP: Lynne Burgess
Sr VP: John Persons

TOPS MARKET
See SUPERMARKET MANAGEMENT INC

D-U-N-S 00-697-6773
TOPS MARKETS LLC
TOPS FRIENDLY MARKETS
(*Suby of* TOPS HOLDING LLC) ★
6363 Main St, Williamsville, NY 14221-5855
Tel (716) 635-5000 *Founded/Ownrshp* 2005, 2007
Sales 2.7MMM^E *EMP* 16,000
SIC 5411 5141 5147 5148 5122 5912 Supermarkets, chain; Convenience stores; Groceries, general line; Meats & meat products; Fruits, fresh; Vegetables, fresh; Drugs, proprietaries & sundries; Drug stores & proprietary stores
Prin: Frank Curci
CFO: Kevin Darrington
Ex VP: Amy Parker
Sr VP: Jack Barrett
VP: Brian Huckle
Exec: Karen Butler
Exec: Larry Scott
Dir Bus: Nicky Walsh
Store Mgr: Mike Schreiner
Snr Mgr: William Costa

D-U-N-S 05-328-5009
TOPS PT LLC
(*Suby of* TOPS FRIENDLY MARKETS) ★
6363 Main St, Williamsville, NY 14221-5855
Tel (716) 635-5000 *Founded/Ownrshp* 2010
Sales 303.8MM^E *EMP* 6,002
SIC 5411 Supermarkets
Sr VP: Jack Barrett

D-U-N-S 00-911-7524 IMP/EXP
■TOPS SLT INC
(*Suby of* RR DONNELLEY) ★
225 Broadhollow Rd # 300, Melville, NY 11747-4822
Tel (631) 675-5700 *Founded/Ownrshp* 2014
Sales 51.7M^E *EMP* 2,260
SIC 2675

D-U-N-S 05-238-8147 IMP
TOPSON DOWNS OF CALIFORNIA INC
3840 Watseka Ave, Culver City, CA 90232-2633
Tel (310) 558-0300 *Founded/Ownrshp* 1971
Sales 351.6MM^E *EMP* 330
Accts Kaufman & Kabani Los Angeles
SIC 5137 Women's & children's clothing
Pr: John Poyer
**CFO:* Kristopher Scott
IT Man: Alex Perez

D-U-N-S 14-779-8987 IMP
TOPY AMERICA INC
(*Suby of* TOPY INDUSTRIES,LIMITED)
980 Chenault Rd, Frankfort, KY 40601-8835
Tel (502) 783-1250 *Founded/Ownrshp* 2008
Sales 99.9MM^E *EMP* 567^E
SIC 3714 Wheels, motor vehicle
Pr: Terry Kurihara
**Pr:* Kenichi Nagai
Treas: Yukinori Ayata
**Treas:* Masayuki Yamaguchi
VP: Makoto Mizoguchi
Genl Mgr: Samuel Amburgey
CIO: Jon Lash
QA Dir: Keith English
QC Dir: Richard Cremeans
Plnt Mgr: Sam Ambrugey

D-U-N-S 80-983-1308 IMP/EXP
TORAY COMPOSITES (AMERICA) INC
(*Suby of* TORAY HOLDING (USA) INC) ★
19002 50th Ave E, Tacoma, WA 98446-3752
Tel (253) 846-1777 *Founded/Ownrshp* 1992
Sales 228.8MM^E *EMP* 550
SIC 3624 Carbon & graphite products
Pr: Dennis Frett
**Ch Bd:* Yasuo Suga
**Treas:* Chikako Takeoka
**Ex VP:* T Odagiri
**VP:* Tim Kirk
Genl Mgr: Jeff Cross
DP Exec: Jamie Sergeant
Dir IT: Junichi Fujikawa
Dir IT: Masao Katsurauma
Dir IT: Akihiro Nikkaku
Dir IT: Chiaki Tanaka

D-U-N-S 06-258-1660 IMP/EXP
TORAY HOLDING (USA) INC
(*Suby of* TORAY INDUSTRIES,INC.)
461 5th Ave Fl 9, New York, NY 10017-7730
Tel (212) 697-8150 *Founded/Ownrshp* 1997
Sales 601.3MM^E *EMP* 1,200
SIC 2821 Plastics materials & resins
Pr: Akihiro Nikkaku
**Prin:* Yasuke Orito

D-U-N-S 06-230-8150 IMP/EXP
TORAY PLASTICS (AMERICA) INC
(*Suby of* TORAY HOLDING (USA) INC) ★
50 Belver Ave, North Kingstown, RI 02852-7520
Tel (401) 667-2426 *Founded/Ownrshp* 1985
Sales 255.0MM^E *EMP* 705
SIC 3081

D-U-N-S 04-869-0127
TORCH ENERGY ADVISORS INC
1331 Lamar St Ste 1450, Houston, TX 77010-3122
Tel (713) 650-1246 *Founded/Ownrshp* 1996
Sales 597.2MM^E *EMP* 99^E
SIC 1311 1382 8741 8742

D-U-N-S 12-251-5708
TORCH TECHNOLOGIES INC
4035 Chris Dr Sw Ste C, Huntsville, AL 35802-4192
Tel (256) 319-6000 *Founded/Ownrshp* 2002
Sales 85.7MM^E *EMP* 385^E
Accts Anglin Reichmann Snellgrove &
SIC 8711 Engineering services
Pr: William Roark
**CFO:* Sue Clark
CFO: James Moule
**VP:* John Watson
IT Man: Bill Roark
Snr Mgr: Timothy Palmer
Board of Directors: B Joseph Alexander, Larry Capps, Gary Connor, Clark Monk Jr, William Roark, Matthew Rogers

TORCHLIGHT DEBT OPPORTUNITY
See TORCHLIGHT INVESTORS LLC

D-U-N-S 12-251-2650
TORCHLIGHT INVESTORS LLC
TORCHLIGHT DEBT OPPORTUNITY
475 5th Ave Fl 10, New York, NY 10017-6293
Tel (212) 883-2800 *Founded/Ownrshp* 2011
Sales 83.6MM^E *EMP* 60^E
SIC 6722 6282 Management investment, open-end; Investment advice
CEO: Daniel Simon Heflin
**COO:* Trevor Rozowsky
**CFO:* Robert Del Monaco
**CFO:* Patrick J Tully Jr
Sr VP: Timothy Zietara
VP: Mike Butz
VP: Darrell Hunnicutt
VP: Gianluca Montalti
VP: Steven Nordyke
VP: Dean Rostovosky
Mng Dir: Kenneth D Campbell

D-U-N-S 04-563-1009
▲TORCHMARK CORP
3700 S Stonebridge Dr, McKinney, TX 75070-5934
Tel (972) 569-4000 *Founded/Ownrshp* 1979
Sales NA *EMP* 3,115^E
Tkr Sym TMK *Exch* NYS
SIC 6321 6311 Health insurance carriers; Reinsurance carriers, accident & health; Life insurance carriers; Life reinsurance
Ch Bd: Gary L Coleman
**Ch Bd:* Larry M Hutchison
Pr: Steven J Dichiaro
Pr: Steven K Greer
Pr: Bill E Leavell
Pr: Kenneth J Matson
CEO: Roger C Smith
CFO: Frank M Svoboda
Chf Inves: W Michael Pressley
Ofcr: Vern D Herbel
Ex VP: Domenico Bertini
Ex VP: J Matthew Darden
Ex VP: Ben W Lutek
Ex VP: James E McPartland
Ex VP: R Brian Mitchell
VP: Arvelia Bowie
VP: Michael C Majors
VP: Carol A McCoy
Board of Directors: Paul J Zucconi, Charles E Adair, Marilyn A Alexander, David L Boren, Jane M Buchan, Robert W Ingram, Steven P Johnson, Lloyd W Newton, Darren M Rebelez, Lamar C Smith

TORCHY'S TACOS
See SUCCESS FOODS MANAGEMENT GROUP LLC

D-U-N-S 01-184-7571
TORCON INC (NJ)
328 Newman Springs Rd # 5, Red Bank, NJ 07701-5685
Tel (732) 704-9800 *Founded/Ownrshp* 1965
Sales 211.1MM^E *EMP* 275
SIC 1542 Commercial & office building, new construction
Co-Pr: Benedict Torcivia Jr
**CFO:* Philip Fischer
**Co-Pr:* Joseph Torcivia
**Sr VP:* Richard A Estrin
**Sr VP:* Frank Fossella
VP: Michael Armento
Genl Mgr: Dan McDermott

D-U-N-S 06-285-1332
TORGERSON PROPERTIES INC
103 15th Ave Nw Ste 200, Willmar, MN 56201-2195
Tel (320) 235-7207 *Founded/Ownrshp* 1972
Sales 91.2MM^E *EMP* 1,500
SIC 7011 5812 5813 Hotels & motels; Restaurant, family: chain; Cocktail lounge
CEO: Tom Torgerson
VP: Kathy Aamot
**Prin:* Sheryl Walton
Genl Mgr: Holly Crompton

D-U-N-S 83-948-9143 IMP
TORIN INC
4355 E Brickell St, Ontario, CA 91761-3700
Tel (909) 390-8588 *Founded/Ownrshp* 1993
Sales 99.2MM *EMP* 32
Accts Raymond Chao Alhambra Califo
SIC 5084 Industrial machinery & equipment
CEO: Jun Ji

D-U-N-S 02-861-3719 IMP
TORN & GLASSER INC
1622 E Olympic Blvd, Los Angeles, CA 90021-1922
Tel (213) 593-1332 *Founded/Ownrshp* 1941
Sales 144.6MM^E *EMP* 155
SIC 5149 5153 5145 5191 Fruits, dried; Spices & seasonings; Rice, unpolished; Beans, dry: bulk; Nuts, salted or roasted; Seeds: field, garden & flower
CEO: Robert Glasser
**VP:* Greg Glasser
IT Man: Rick Bode

D-U-N-S 00-647-7400 IMP/EXP
▲TORO CO
8111 Lyndale Ave S, Bloomington, MN 55420-1136
Tel (952) 888-8801 *Founded/Ownrshp* 1914
Sales 2.3MMM *EMP* 6,874^E
Tkr Sym TTC *Exch* NYS

SIC 3523 3524 3494 3645 Fertilizing, spraying, dusting & irrigation machinery; Turf equipment, commercial; Grounds mowing equipment; Greens mowing equipment; Lawn & garden equipment; Lawn & garden tractors & equipment; Lawn & garden mowers & accessories; Sprinkler systems, field; Garden, patio, walkway & yard lighting fixtures: electric
Ch Bd: Michael J Hoffman
**Pr:* Richard Olson
**CFO:* Renee J Peterson
VP: Judy Altmaier
VP: William E Brown Jr
**VP:* Timothy P Dordell
VP: Michael Edmiston
**VP:* Blake M Grams
VP: Blake Grams
**VP:* Thomas J Larson
VP: Darren L Redetzke
VP: Kim Wellman

TORO EMPLOYEES FEDERAL CR UN
See TORO LLC

D-U-N-S 14-595-0817 IMP/EXP
■TORO LLC
TORO EMPLOYEES FEDERAL CR UN
(*Suby of* TORO CO) ★
8111 Lyndale Ave S, Minneapolis, MN 55420-1136
Tel (952) 887-8041 *Founded/Ownrshp* 1999
Sales 167.1MM[E] *EMP* 369[E]
SIC 3524 5083 Lawn & garden mowers & accessories; Lawn & garden machinery & equipment
Pr: Betty Daun
COO: Tom Lamoureux
CFO: Steve Wolfe
Genl Mgr: Mark B Stinson
VP Opers: Sandra J Meurlot
Opers Mgr: Pete Chromczak
Opers Mgr: Vern Kermeen
Plnt Mgr: Micheal Frank
Ql Cn Mgr: Rick Montes
Secur Mgr: Orlin Lewis
VP Mktg: Warren Daun

D-U-N-S 03-811-9186 IMP
■TORO MANUFACTURING CORP
(*Suby of* TORO CO) ★
8111 Lyndale Ave S, Minneapolis, MN 55420-1136
Tel (952) 888-8801 *Founded/Ownrshp* 1998
Sales 91.6MM[E] *EMP* 1,000
SIC 3084 Plastics pipe

D-U-N-S 01-896-6542
TORQUED-UP ENERGY SERVICES INC
110 N College Ave # 1000, Tyler, TX 75702-7240
Tel (903) 363-0300 *Founded/Ownrshp* 2007
Sales 361.6MM[E] *EMP* 263[E]
SIC 1381

D-U-N-S 61-228-1527
TORRANCE HEALTH ASSOCIATION INC
PHYSICIAN OFFICE SUPPORT SVCS
23550 Hawthorne Blvd, Torrance, CA 90505-4731
Tel (310) 325-9110 *Founded/Ownrshp* 1985
Sales 554.5MM *EMP* 3,500
Accts Ernst & Young Llp Los Angeles
SIC 8062 General medical & surgical hospitals
CEO: Craig Leach
**CFO:* Doug Klebe
**Sr VP:* Peggy Berwald
**Sr VP:* Sally Eberhard
**Sr VP:* John McNamara
**VP:* Bill Larson
**VP:* Bernadette Reid
Genl Mgr: Kyle Campbell

D-U-N-S 07-227-4426
TORRANCE MEMORIAL MEDICAL CENTER
PHYSICIAN OFFICE SUPPORT SERVI
(*Suby of* PHYSICIAN OFFICE SUPPORT SVCS) ★
3330 Lomita Blvd, Torrance, CA 90505-5002
Tel (310) 325-9110 *Founded/Ownrshp* 1985
Sales 454.0MM *EMP* 3,500
SIC 8062 Hospital, affiliated with AMA residency
Pr: Craig Leach
COO: Craig Leach
Treas: Dennis Fitzgerald
Sr VP: Peggy Berwald
Sr VP: John McNamara
VP: Peggy Burwald
VP: Linda Dobie
VP: Robin Hill
VP: Doug Klebe
VP: Barb Lequire
VP: Bernadette Reid
VP: Mike Thomas
Dir Rx: Steve Thompson

D-U-N-S 08-377-6997
TORRANCE UNIFIED SCHOOL DISTRICT
2335 Plaza Del Amo, Torrance, CA 90501-3420
Tel (310) 972-6500 *Founded/Ownrshp* 1947
Sales 124.8MM[E] *EMP* 1,806
SIC 8211 Public elementary & secondary schools
CEO: Michael Wermers
Genl Mgr: Ron Lau
MIS Dir: Gil Mara
Schl Brd P: Dawn Lee
Psych: Rosalind Myatt
Psych: Sallie Reeves

D-U-N-S 02-954-6173
TORRANCE VAN & STORAGE CO
S & M MOVING SYSTEMS
12128 Burke St, Santa Fe Springs, CA 90670-2678
Tel (562) 567-2100 *Founded/Ownrshp* 1918
Sales 88.6MM[E] *EMP* 400
SIC 4214 4213 Local trucking with storage; Trucking, except local
Pr: Steven Todare
COO: Anthony Locatelli
CFO: Michael D'Oliveira
**VP:* Martin Stadler
Genl Mgr: Dennis Allsopp
IT Man: Dennis Bruce
IT Man: Michael Doliveira

D-U-N-S 79-003-3935
TORRENT PHARMA INC
(*Suby of* TORRENT PHARMACEUTICALS LIMITED)
150 Allen Rd Ste 102, Basking Ridge, NJ 07920-3856
Tel (269) 544-2299 *Founded/Ownrshp* 2004
Sales 122.0MM *EMP* 22
SIC 2834 Pharmaceutical preparations
CEO: Sanjay Gupta
**Pr:* Kamesh Venugopal
**VP:* Dawn Chitty

TORRESDALE CAMPUS
See ARIA HEALTH

TORRID
See HOT TOPIC INC

D-U-N-S 07-959-8567
TORRID LLC
18305 San Jose Ave, City of Industry, CA 91748-1237
Tel (626) 839-4681 *Founded/Ownrshp* 2013
Sales 372.8MM[E] *EMP* 5,000[E]
SIC 5621 Women's clothing stores; Women's specialty clothing stores
**CEO:* Lisa Harper
Treas: Brenda Morris
Sls Mgr: Brandi Carey

D-U-N-S 19-119-4195 IMP
TORY BURCH LLC
T R B
11 W 19th St Fl 7, New York, NY 10011-4277
Tel (212) 683-2323 *Founded/Ownrshp* 2003
Sales 344.4MM[E] *EMP* 2,500
SIC 5621 Women's clothing stores
VP: Cheryl Larobardier
VP: Kim McLaren
VP: Robert P Page
CTO: John Douglas
Opers Mgr: Tyson Hilscher
VP Sls: Dina Burton

D-U-N-S 02-218-8359
TOSA FOUNDATION
3130 Alpine Rd, Portola Vally, CA 94028-7549
Tel (650) 851-6922 *Founded/Ownrshp* 2010
Sales 92.6MM *EMP* 3[E]
SIC 8641 Civic social & fraternal associations
Prin: John P Morgridge

D-U-N-S 07-980-2715
TOSCA SERVICES LLC
303 Peachtree Center Ave, Atlanta, GA 30303-1279
Tel (920) 569-5335 *Founded/Ownrshp* 2015
Sales 100.0MM[E] *EMP* 400
SIC 7359 5144 Shipping container leasing; Eggs
CEO: Jere E Dhein
**CFO:* Eric Frank
**CFO:* Scott Smith
**VP:* Dave Rodgers
**VP:* Michael Wasson

D-U-N-S 08-995-1177 IMP/EXP
TOSHIBA AMERICA BUSINESS SOLUTIONS INC (CA)
(*Suby of* TOSHIBA TEC CORPORATION)
9740 Irvine Blvd, Irvine, CA 92618-1608
Tel (949) 462-6000 *Founded/Ownrshp* 1999, 2007
Sales 1.7MMM[E] *EMP* 3,259
SIC 5044 Copying equipment
Ch Bd: Masahiro Yamada
Pr: Matt Barnes
**Pr:* Mark Mathews
Pr: Hiroyuki Watanabe
**CFO:* Desmond Allen
CFO: Michael Torcaso
VP: Michael Math
VP: R Tungate
VP: Susan Wilson
Genl Mgr: Michael Mathy
CIO: Yoshihiro Okada

D-U-N-S 60-645-6119 IMP
TOSHIBA AMERICA ELECTRONIC COMPONENTS INC
(*Suby of* TOSHIBA AMERICA INC) ★
9740 Irvine Blvd Ste D700, Irvine, CA 92618-1697
Tel (949) 462-7700 *Founded/Ownrshp* 1998
Sales 512.2MM[E] *EMP* 2,300
SIC 3651 3631 3674 3679 5065 5064 Television receiving sets; Video cassette recorders/players & accessories; Microwave ovens, including portable: household; Semiconductors & related devices; Electronic circuits; Electronic parts & equipment; Video cassette recorders & accessories; High fidelity equipment
CEO: Hideya Yamaguchi
**Pr:* Hitoshi Otsuka
**Ex VP:* Ichiro Hirata
VP: Sean Collins
**VP:* Farhad Mafie
VP: Bill Nutini
VP: Hank Roberts
**VP:* Richard Tobias
Dir Bus: Thomas Cornell
Dir Bus: Rakesh Sethi
Dir IT: Wayne Liem

D-U-N-S 07-977-2481
TOSHIBA AMERICA ENERGY SYSTEMS CORP
(*Suby of* TOSHIBA AMERICA INC) ★
3545 Whitehall Park Dr # 500, Charlotte, NC 28273-4180
Tel (704) 548-7777 *Founded/Ownrshp* 2014
Sales 99.2MM[E] *EMP* 520[E]
SIC 3674 Semiconductors & related devices
CEO: Ali Azad
Sr VP: Michael Culbreth
VP: Hirokazu Egawa
VP: Ted Pichalski
IT Man: Sheila Lacks
Sales Exec: Ceil Marnell
Sls Mgr: Mike Gehring

D-U-N-S 06-499-3082 IMP/EXP
TOSHIBA AMERICA INC
(*Suby of* TOSHIBA CORPORATION)
1251 Ave Of Ameri Ste 4100, New York, NY 10020
Tel (212) 596-0600 *Founded/Ownrshp* 1965
Sales 2.0MMM[E] *EMP* 8,000
SIC 3651 3631 5064 5075 3571 3661 Television receiving sets; Video cassette recorders/players & accessories; Microwave ovens, including portable: household; Video cassette recorders & accessories; High fidelity equipment; Compressors, air conditioning; Personal computers (microcomputers); Multiplex equipment, telephone & telegraph
CEO: Hideo Ito
**Ch Bd:* Takeshi Okatomi
**Pr:* Hiromitsu Igarashi
**Pr:* Hisashi Izumi
**Pr:* Toru Uchiike
**CFO:* Takamasa Ikawa
**Ch:* Fukakushi Masahiko
**Treas:* Katsufumi Nomura
**Sr VP:* John Anderson
**Sr VP:* Tsuyoshi Kimura
VP: Peter Noonan
VP: Cindy O'Donnell
VP: Nader RAD

D-U-N-S 19-409-6525 IMP/EXP
TOSHIBA AMERICA INFORMATION SYSTEMS INC
(*Suby of* TOSHIBA AMERICA INC) ★
1251 Ave Of The Ste 4110, New York, NY 10020
Tel (949) 583-3000 *Founded/Ownrshp* 1989
Sales 302.7MM[E] *EMP* 750[E]
SIC 3571 3577 3572 3661 5045 Electronic computers; Computer peripheral equipment; Disk drives, computer; Telephones & telephone apparatus; Facsimile equipment; Computers, peripherals & software
CEO: Mark Simons
**VP:* Ted Flati
CIO: Stephen Young
Sls&Mrk Ex: Siva Peruvemba
Sls Dir: Timothy Boyle

D-U-N-S 36-235-2106 IMP/EXP
TOSHIBA AMERICA MEDICAL SYSTEMS INC
TOSHIBA MEDICAL SYSTEMS
(*Suby of* TOSHIBA AMERICA INC) ★
2441 Michelle Dr, Tustin, CA 92780-7047
Tel (714) 730-5000 *Founded/Ownrshp* 1989
Sales 8.5MM[E] *EMP* 1,090
SIC 5047 X-ray machines & tubes; Medical equipment & supplies
CEO: Shuzo Yamamoto
Mng Pt: Carol-Davis Grossman
CEO: Donald Fowler
CFO: John Patterson
Sr VP: Peter N S Annand
VP: Karen Barack-Lapoint
VP: Calum G Cunningham
VP: Lawrence Dentice
VP: Scott Goodwin
VP: Dennis Kennelly
VP: Robert Kreps
VP: Naoshi Obara
VP: Nader RAD
VP: John Serovich
VP: Eric Weisner
Exec: Joshua Emperado
Dir Rx: Steve Metildi
Dir Bus: Michael Brigham

D-U-N-S 60-943-4758 IMP
TOSHIBA AMERICA MRI INC
(*Suby of* TOSHIBA AMERICA INC) ★
280 Utah Ave Ste 200, South San Francisco, CA 94080-6883
Tel (650) 737-6686 *Founded/Ownrshp* 1989
Sales 132.6MM[E] *EMP* 190
SIC 3845 8731 Magnetic resonance imaging device, nuclear; Commercial physical research
CEO: Fredric J Friedberg
**Pr:* John Stringer
**VP:* Lisa Cortes
**VP:* M Hasegawa
**VP:* M Katsurada
Board of Directors: M Hasegawa, M Katsurada

D-U-N-S 02-094-7117 IMP
TOSHIBA AMERICA NUCLEAR ENERGY CORP
(*Suby of* TOSHIBA AMERICA INC) ★
3545 Whitehall Park Dr # 500, Charlotte, NC 28273-4180
Tel (704) 548-7777 *Founded/Ownrshp* 2009
Sales 228.1MM[E] *EMP* 1,202[E]
SIC 3443 5211 Plate work for the nuclear industry; Energy conservation products
Pr: Akio Shioiri
VP: Hitoshi Yabuta

TOSHIBA BUSINESS SOLUTIONS
See TOPAC USA INC

D-U-N-S 96-835-5045
TOSHIBA BUSINESS SOLUTIONS (USA) INC
(*Suby of* TOSHIBA AMERICA BUSINESS SOLUTIONS INC) ★
9740 Irvine Blvd, Irvine, CA 92618-1608
Tel (949) 462-6000 *Founded/Ownrshp* 1994
Sales 72.8MM[E] *EMP* 2,167[E]
SIC 7629 5044 5999 Business machine repair, electric; Office equipment; Business machines & equipment
CEO: Mark Mathews

D-U-N-S 07-851-6618
TOSHIBA GLOBAL COMMERCE SOLUTIONS INC
(*Suby of* TOSHIBA GLOBAL COMMERCE SOLUTION HOLDINGS CORPORATION)
3901 S Miami Blvd, Durham, NC 27703-9135
Tel (984) 444-7153 *Founded/Ownrshp* 2012
Sales 472.3MM[E] *EMP* 804[E]
SIC 8742 7375 Retail trade consultant; Information retrieval services
Pr: Scott Maccabe
**Ch Bd:* Masato Yamamoto
**CFO:* Sam Craig
**Treas:* Willis Lumpkin
**Sr VP:* Kenneth Hammer
Sr VP: Stephen K Markham
**VP:* John Gaydac
Sftwr Eng: Leonid Derbinsky
Sls Dir: Paul Kennedy

D-U-N-S 04-165-6000 IMP/EXP
TOSHIBA INTERNATIONAL CORP
(*Suby of* TOSHIBA AMERICA INC) ★
13131 W Little York Rd, Houston, TX 77041-5807
Tel (713) 466-0277 *Founded/Ownrshp* 1967
Sales 530.2MM[E] *EMP* 1,700
SIC 3621 5084 5063 3613 3594 3572 Motors & generators; Generators & sets, electric; Engines & transportation equipment; Generators; Switchgear & switchboard apparatus; Fluid power pumps & motors; Computer storage devices
CEO: Masaaki Osumi
Pr: Tatsuo Doko
CFO: Herbert Marchand
CFO: Ken Sheaffer
Ch: Atsutoshi Nishida
Sr VP: Michael Avera
Sr VP: Mike Ayers
Sr VP: Hiroshi Kasagi
VP: Margaret McKay
Plnt Mgr: Don Robinson
Secur Mgr: Chris Garinger

TOSHIBA MEDICAL SYSTEMS
See TOSHIBA AMERICA MEDICAL SYSTEMS INC

D-U-N-S 78-693-3221
TOSHIBA NUCLEAR ENERGY HOLDINGS (US) INC
(*Suby of* TOSHIBA CORPORATION)
1251 Ave Of Amrcs 400 Ste 4100, New York, NY 10020
Tel (212) 596-0600 *Founded/Ownrshp* 2006
Sales 3.9MMM[E] *EMP* 12,805
SIC 8711 3829 3823 2819 Electrical or electronic engineering; Measuring & controlling devices; Industrial instrmnts msrmnt display/control process variable; Industrial inorganic chemicals
Pr: Masao Niwano

D-U-N-S 61-492-4314 IMP
TOSOH AMERICA INC
(*Suby of* TOSOH CORPORATION)
3600 Gantz Rd, Grove City, OH 43123-1895
Tel (614) 539-8622 *Founded/Ownrshp* 1989
Sales 262.7MM[E] *EMP* 800
SIC 5169 3564 5047 5052 Industrial chemicals; Blowers & fans; Diagnostic equipment, medical; Coal & other minerals & ores
Pr: Jan Top

D-U-N-S 17-225-5296
TOTAL AIRPORT SERVICES INC
34406 N 27th Dr Ste 140, Phoenix, AZ 85085-6079
Tel (623) 215-9941 *Founded/Ownrshp* 2004
Sales 144.0MM[E] *EMP* 900
SIC 4581 Airports, flying fields & services
CEO: Jack Evans
**CEO:* William J Evans Jr
**COO:* Gerald Kolasch
**CFO:* Scott Offerdahl
**Sr VP:* Denny L Eichenbaum
**VP:* Harry Hoge
**VP:* Daniel Malinowski

D-U-N-S 00-568-2575 IMP/EXP
TOTAL AMERICAN SERVICES INC
100 Town Square Pl # 401, Jersey City, NJ 07310-2778
Tel (206) 626-3500 *Founded/Ownrshp* 1999
Sales 188.2MM[E] *EMP* 2,386[E]
SIC 2911 4612 5541 2895 Petroleum refining; Crude petroleum pipelines; Gasoline service stations; Carbon black
Pr: Ronald W Haddock

TOTAL BEAUTY SOURCE, THE
See WORMSER CORP

TOTAL COMFORT OF WISCONSIN
See TOTAL MECHANICAL INC

D-U-N-S 79-651-2510
■TOTAL DELAWARE INC
(*Suby of* TOTAL HOLDINGS USA INC) ★
1201 La St Ste 1800, Houston, TX 77002
Tel (713) 483-5000 *Founded/Ownrshp* 2001
Sales 184.8MM[E] *EMP* 2,872[E]
SIC 1311 1382 Crude petroleum & natural gas; Oil & gas exploration services
Pr: Jean-Pierre Seeuws
IT Man: Pierre Mesnard
VP Opers: Vincent Saubestre
Opers Mgr: Bill Hall

TOTAL ELECTRONICS
See CAL-COMP USA (INDIANA) INC

D-U-N-S 13-328-3049
TOTAL EMED INC
SPHERIS
(*Suby of* SP WIND DOWN INC) ★
9009 Carothers Pkwy # 303, Franklin, TN 37067-1704
Tel (615) 261-1500 *Founded/Ownrshp* 2000
Sales 44.9MM[E] *EMP* 3,549
SIC 7338 Secretarial & court reporting
CEO: Steve Simpson
**CFO:* Tony James
VP: John Rhome
Netwrk Eng: Clifton Teate
VP Opers: Chris Cummings

D-U-N-S 83-312-0210
TOTAL EQUIPMENT AND SERVICE
(*Suby of* C J SPECIALTY RENTAL TOOLS) ★
4801 Glen Rose Hwy, Granbury, TX 76048-6214
Tel (817) 573-3550 *Founded/Ownrshp* 2011
Sales 185.3MM[E] *EMP* 102[E]
SIC 3533 Oil & gas drilling rigs & equipment

Pr: Barry Beadle

D-U-N-S 08-041-1277
■TOTAL FILTRATION SERVICES INC
(*Suby of* CLARCOR INC) ★
2071 Congressional Dr, Saint Louis, MO 63146-4103
Tel (314) 202-3635 *Founded/Ownrshp* 2011
Sales 241.2MM^E *EMP* 1,000
SIC 7699 Filter cleaning
Pr: Jeff Orlando

D-U-N-S 07-638-6168
TOTAL HEALTH CARE INC
3011 W Grand Blvd # 1600, Detroit, MI 48202-3000
Tel (313) 871-2000 *Founded/Ownrshp* 1973
Sales 272.3MM *EMP* 100
Accts Plante & Moran Pllc Auburn Hi
SIC 8011 Health maintenance organization
Prin: Hamann

D-U-N-S 03-781-0702 IMP/EXP
■TOTAL HOLDINGS USA INC
(*Suby of* TOTAL SA)
1201 La St Ste 1800, Houston, TX 77002
Tel (713) 483-5000 *Founded/Ownrshp* 1981
Sales 17.4MMM^E *EMP* 13,000
SIC 1382 1311 Oil & gas exploration services; Crude petroleum & natural gas
CEO: Agnes D'Oliveira
VP: Belly Campbell
VP: Herve Chagnoux
VP: Robert Kilpatrick
VP: Jonathan Marsh
VP: Carolyn Sanders
Genl Mgr: Mark Recht
IT Man: Yves-Andres Andres
IT Man: Elisa Campbell
IT Man: Darin Cross
IT Man: Kathleen McGovern

TOTAL LOGISTICS
See BENORE LOGISTIC SYSTEMS INC

D-U-N-S 62-307-7435 EXP
■TOTAL LOGISTICS ONLINE LLC
RYDER
(*Suby of* RYDER INTEGRATED LOGISTICS INC) ★
10717 Adams St Ste 200, Holland, MI 49423-9079
Tel (800) 333-5599 *Founded/Ownrshp* 2011
Sales 140.5MM^E *EMP* 2,071
SIC 7513 Truck rental & leasing, no drivers
Pr: Peter Westermann
Pr: Tim Alderink
Pr: Marc Kennedy
Pr: Renee Vick
CFO: Rachel Lillie
MIS Dir: Debbie Stegmier
Dir IT: Matt Kavanaugh
Sfty Dirs: Steve Alberda
Opers Mgr: Michael McSpadden
Opers Mgr: Michele Vandenbrand

D-U-N-S 62-049-0631
TOTAL LONGTERM CARE INC
INNOVAGE
(*Suby of* TOTAL COMMUNITY OPTIONS, INC.)
8950 E Lowry Blvd, Denver, CO 80230-7030
Tel (303) 832-1001 *Founded/Ownrshp* 1989
Sales 173.0MM *EMP* 580
Accts Bkd Llp Colorado Springs Co
SIC 8322 8082 Geriatric social service; Home health care services
Ch: Lee Anneberg
**Pr:* Maureen Hewitt
**COO:* Gina Deblassie
**CFO:* John D Irons
**CFO:* Angela Oakley
**Treas:* Den Dickey
VP: Cindy Hogan
Dir IT: Ken Melvin

D-U-N-S 04-347-9070
TOTAL MECHANICAL INC (WI)
TOTAL COMFORT OF WISCONSIN
W234n2830 Paul Rd, Pewaukee, WI 53072-5731
Tel (262) 523-2510 *Founded/Ownrshp* 1968
Sales 103.8MM^E *EMP* 300
SIC 1711 1791 3823 Mechanical contractor; Ventilation & duct work contractor; Warm air heating & air conditioning contractor; Structural steel erection; Temperature instruments: industrial process type
Pr: Dennis Braun
**Ex VP:* Timothy Braun
VP: Dennis Anderson
VP: Kirk Westfahl
Div Mgr: Thomas Jacobi P E

D-U-N-S 11-894-7568
■TOTAL MIXER TECHNOLOGIES LLC
(*Suby of* OSHKOSH CORP) ★
2307 Oregon St, Oshkosh, WI 54902-7062
Tel (920) 235-9150 *Founded/Ownrshp* 2002
Sales 427.4MM^E *EMP* 2,575^E
SIC 3531 Mixers, concrete

D-U-N-S 00-733-6290 IMP/EXP
■TOTAL PETROCHEMICALS & REFINING USA INC
TOTAL PORT ARTHUR REFINERY
(*Suby of* TOTAL HOLDINGS USA INC) ★
1201 La St Ste 1800, Houston, TX 77002
Tel (713) 483-5000 *Founded/Ownrshp* 1958
Sales 763.0MM^E *EMP* 1,550
SIC 2911 2899 2869 Petroleum refining; Gasoline; Jet fuels; Kerosene; Chemical preparations; Fuels
CEO: Geoffroy Petit
CFO: Bertrand De La Noue
**CFO:* Bertrand De La Nue
**VP:* Isabelle Kieffer
Dir IT: Mike Ivey
IT Man: Pascal Barberon
IT Man: Jean-Benoit Collet
IT Man: Mark Czerwiec
Netwrk Eng: Cedric Chosson
Opers Mgr: Gary Guilhas
Mktg Mgr: Michael Stefano
Board of Directors: Francois Cornelis

TOTAL PETROLEUM
See SOUTHWEST GEORGIA OIL CO INC

TOTAL PLASTICS INTERNATIONAL
See TOTAL PLASTICS RESOURCES LLC

D-U-N-S 08-886-7643 IMP/EXP
TOTAL PLASTICS RESOURCES LLC
TOTAL PLASTICS INTERNATIONAL
2810 N Burdick St Ste A, Kalamazoo, MI 49004-3637
Tel (269) 344-0009 *Founded/Ownrshp* 2016
Sales 135.0MM *EMP* 375
SIC 3083 5162 Thermoplastic laminates: rods, tubes, plates & sheet; Plastics sheets & rods
Pr: Thomas Garrett
Brnch Mgr: Teresa Rowe
IT Man: Dana E Freedman

TOTAL PORT ARTHUR REFINERY
See TOTAL PETROCHEMICALS & REFINING USA INC

D-U-N-S 79-145-9410
TOTAL QUALITY LOGISTICS LLC
TQL
(*Suby of* KGBO HOLDINGS INC) ★
4289 Ivy Pointe Blvd, Cincinnati, OH 45245-0002
Tel (513) 831-2600 *Founded/Ownrshp* 1997
Sales 2.2MMM *EMP* 2,150^E
Accts Barnes Denning & Co Ltd C
SIC 4731 Truck transportation brokers
CEO: Kenneth G Oaks
**Pr:* Kerry Bryne
CFO: Mike Zins
Ex VP: Kerry Byrne
Exec: Justin Ackerman
Exec: David Bennett
Exec: Scott Briggs
Exec: Stephanie Burke
Exec: Ryan Carter
Exec: Jeremy Chalk
Exec: Evan Davies
Exec: Drew Duddey
Exec: Dennis Ferguson
Exec: Lauren Gillette
Exec: Jason Hillman
Exec: Brian Hinton
Exec: David Hooper
Exec: Jeff Jones
Exec: John Leininger
Exec: Nicholas Liening
Exec: Dave Lindsay

D-U-N-S 03-971-1569
■TOTAL RENAL CARE INC
(*Suby of* DAVITA INC) ★
2000 16th St, Denver, CO 80202-5117
Tel (253) 280-9501 *Founded/Ownrshp* 1979
Sales 155.5MM^E *EMP* 2,100^E
SIC 8092 Kidney dialysis centers
CEO: Dennis L Kogod
**Pr:* George B Dehuff III
VP: Linda Alcorta
Dir Rx: Maricela Lara-Nevarez

D-U-N-S 07-831-3391
TOTAL RENAL CARE INC
PALOS PARK DIALYSIS
13155 S La Grange Rd, Orland Park, IL 60462-1162
Tel (800) 424-6589 *Founded/Ownrshp* 1979
Sales 73.9M^E *EMP* 10,000
SIC 8092 Kidney dialysis centers
Pr: Jim Hilger

D-U-N-S 02-288-7354
TOTAL RESOURCE AUCTIONS INC
TRA AUCTIONS
(*Suby of* COX AUTOMOTIVE INC) ★
6205 Pachtree Dunwoody Rd, Atlanta, GA 30328-4524
Tel (678) 645-0000 *Founded/Ownrshp* 2008
Sales 136.6MM^E *EMP* 1,250^E
SIC 5012 Automobile auction
Pr: Sandy Schwartz
**VP:* Doug Depaolo

D-U-N-S 15-322-4766
TOTAL SAFETY US INC
H2WR / EHS SERVICES
11111 Wilcrest Green Dr # 375, Houston, TX 77042-4855
Tel (713) 353-7100 *Founded/Ownrshp* 2003
Sales 688.2MM^E *EMP* 1,560
SIC 8748 5084 7699 Business consulting; Safety equipment; Medical equipment repair, non-electric
CEO: Troy W Thacker
**Pr:* David E Fanta
Pr: Clive Mitchell
COO: Steve Brown
**COO:* Paul Tyree
**CFO:* Clinton W Roeder
Treas: Gary Wright
Sr VP: Darrell Whitley
Dist Mgr: Bill Schmucker
Genl Mgr: Jeremy Dean
CIO: Darren Flynt

D-U-N-S 01-008-7780
TOTAL SERVICE SUPPLY LP
513 Vortex Dr, New Iberia, LA 70560-9821
Tel (337) 365-5954 *Founded/Ownrshp* 2002
Sales 97.5MM^E *EMP* 150^E
SIC 5085 Industrial supplies
Pr: Gary Rider
Genl Pt: Tssgp LLC
Pr: Rashid Shamsie

D-U-N-S 09-987-2926 IMP
TOTAL SOURCE MANUFACTURING
TOTAL SOURCE MANUFACTURING CO
1445 Engineer St, Vista, CA 92081-8846
Tel (760) 598-2146 *Founded/Ownrshp* 1998
Sales 146.6MM^E *EMP* 1,800
SIC 3821 Laboratory equipment: fume hoods, distillation racks, etc.
Pr: Stacy Camp
Pr: Saied Sardarian

TOTAL SOURCE MANUFACTURING CO
See TOTAL SOURCE MANUFACTURING

D-U-N-S 09-476-4057 IMP
TOTAL SWEETENERS INC
BATORY FOODS
1700 E Higgins Rd Ste 300, Des Plaines, IL 60018-3800
Tel (847) 299-1999 *Founded/Ownrshp* 1979
Sales 396.7MM^E *EMP* 200
SIC 5149 Groceries & related products
Pr: Ronald Friedman
Treas: Alan Kessler
**Prin:* Abel Friedman
Genl Mgr: Liisa Holcomb
IT Man: Jessy Cook
IT Man: Jessy Myles
Plnt Mgr: Rick Theodore

D-U-N-S 10-199-1222
▲TOTAL SYSTEM SERVICES INC
TSYS
1 Tsys Way, Columbus, GA 31901-4222
Tel (706) 644-6081 *Founded/Ownrshp* 1982
Sales 2.7MMM *EMP* 10,500
Tkr Sym TSS *Exch* NYS
SIC 7374 Data processing service
Ch Bd: M Troy Woods
**Pr:* Pamela A Joseph
Pr: Chip Torbert
CFO: Paul M Todd
Chf Cred: William A Pruett
Sr Ex VP: Kenneth Tye
Ex VP: Karim Ahmad
Ex VP: Allen Pettis
Ex VP: Bill Pruette
Ex VP: Marty Wood
VP: Troy Alvarez
VP: Stewart Bacon
VP: Jennifer Leroy
VP: Bill Pruett
VP: Stephen Schultz
Exec: G Sanders Griffith III
Exec: Anthony W Hodge
Exec: Patricia A Watson
Exec: David E Wood
Assoc Dir: Jennifer Googe
Assoc Dir: Robert Murphy
Board of Directors: Richard W Ussery, James H Blanchard, James D Yancey, Kriss Cloninger III, Walter W Driver Jr, Sidney E Harris, William M Isaac, Mason H Lampton, Connie D McDaniel, Philip W Tomlinson, John T Turner

D-U-N-S 62-755-3258
TOTAL TRANSPORTATION OF MISSISSIPPI LLC
(*Suby of* TRANSPORTATION INVESTMENTS INC.)
125 Riverview Dr, Richland, MS 39218-4401
Tel (601) 936-2104 *Founded/Ownrshp* 2006
Sales 86.8MM^E *EMP* 575
SIC 4213 Trucking, except local
Pr: John D Stomps
COO: John Stomps
**Treas:* Ray M Harlin
**VP:* Max L Fuller
Exec: Nancy Sistrunk
Opers Mgr: Trai Swaney
Sales Exec: Jolly Mayfield
Board of Directors: Lisa Pate

TOTAL WINE AND MORE
See RETAIL SERVICES & SYSTEMS INC

D-U-N-S 11-273-7127
TOTAL-WESTERN INC
(*Suby of* BRAGG CRANE & RIGGING) ★
8049 Somerset Blvd, Paramount, CA 90723-4396
Tel (562) 220-1450 *Founded/Ownrshp* 1987
Sales 102.7MM^E *EMP* 250
SIC 1389 Oil field services; Construction, repair & dismantling services; Excavating slush pits & cellars; Grading oil & gas well foundations
CEO: Paul F Conrad
**CFO:* Mary A Pool
VP: Leonard Crespo
**VP:* Earl Grebing
VP: John Young
Rgnl Mgr: John Jopling
VP Opers: Steve Johnson

D-U-N-S 06-693-5727
TOTALBANK
(*Suby of* WIZINK BANK SA.)
100 Se 2nd St, Miami, FL 33131-2100
Tel (305) 982-3310 *Founded/Ownrshp* 1996
Sales NA *EMP* 254
SIC 6022 6163 State commercial banks; Loan brokers
CEO: William J Heffernan
**Ch Bd:* Adrienne Arsht
**Pr:* Luis De La Aguilera
**COO:* Lyan Fernandez
**CFO:* Alberto Manrara
**CFO:* Jose Marina
Sr Cor Off: Alberto Manara
Ofcr: John Galendez
Ofcr: Jonanht Inguanzo
**Ex VP:* Jorge N Carvallo
Ex VP: Lydia Fernandez
Ex VP: Francisco Nieto
Ex VP: Jay Pelham
Sr VP: Juan Babani
Sr VP: Rosse Barrantes
Sr VP: Angelica Delaportilla
**Sr VP:* Carla Garcia
Sr VP: Richard Hudson
Sr VP: Maritza Jaime
Sr VP: Mary Macnamara
Sr VP: Ivan Montesimos

D-U-N-S 02-151-4211 IMP/EXP
TOTALL METAL RECYCLING INC (IL)
2700 Missouri Ave, Granite City, IL 62040-2029
Tel (618) 877-0585 *Founded/Ownrshp* 1993, 2002
Sales 119.7MM^E *EMP* 105
SIC 5093 Scrap & waste materials
Pr: Toben Suarez
**CFO:* Larry Present
Dir IT: Kip Pabst
IT Man: Anita Hurst
Sfty Dirs: Jeremy Zottarelle

Manager: Neil Hines
Plnt Mgr: Lance Paszkiewicz

D-U-N-S 80-807-0689
TOTE INC
(*Suby of* SALTCHUK RESOURCES INC) ★
14 Nassau St Ste 3, Princeton, NJ 08542-4533
Tel (609) 454-3651 *Founded/Ownrshp* 2002
Sales 120.2MM^E *EMP* 650^E
SIC 4731 Freight transportation arrangement
CEO: Anthony Chiarello
**CFO:* Hugh Simpson
**Ex VP:* Peter Keller
**Sr VP:* Michael Holt
**Sr VP:* Kevin Kendrick
VP: Frank Peake
VP: John S Tirpak

D-U-N-S 10-178-6507 IMP/EXP
TOTER LLC
(*Suby of* WASTEQUIP LLC) ★
841 Meacham Rd, Statesville, NC 28677-2983
Tel (800) 424-0422 *Founded/Ownrshp* 2007
Sales 113.4MM^E *EMP* 150
SIC 3089 3536 3469 3412 2821 Garbage containers, plastic; Hoists; Metal stampings; Metal barrels, drums & pails; Plastics materials & resins
Pr: John Scott
**CFO:* Steve Svetik
Sales Asso: Linda Lassiter
Snr Mgr: Kellie Clark

D-U-N-S 00-926-8470 IMP
TOTES ISOTONER HOLDINGS CORP (DE)
9655 International Blvd, West Chester, OH 45246-4861
Tel (513) 682-8200 *Founded/Ownrshp* 1994
Sales 118.6MM^E *EMP* 1,400
SIC 2381 3151 2211 3021 5699 Gloves, woven or knit: made from purchased materials; Leather gloves & mittens; Umbrella cloth, cotton; Rubber & plastics footwear; Umbrellas; Stockings: men's, women's & children's; Raincoats; Leather garments
CEO: Daniel S Rajczak
**CFO:* Donna Deye
**VP:* Joshua Beckenstein
**Prin:* Doug Baker

D-U-N-S 96-525-1986 IMP
TOTO USA HOLDINGS INC
(*Suby of* TOTO LTD.)
1155 Southern Rd, Morrow, GA 30260-2917
Tel (770) 960-8531 *Founded/Ownrshp* 1996
Sales 122.6MM^E *EMP* 500
SIC 3088 3431 3261 Bathroom fixtures, plastic; Metal sanitary ware; Vitreous plumbing fixtures
CEO: Daijiro Nogata
**Pr:* Toshio Kitano
**CFO:* James Brandon
CFO: Miles Casaday

TOTOWA ASPHALT
See TILCON NEW YORK INC

D-U-N-S 36-105-4369
TOTOWA PEDIATRICS
400 W Blackwell St, Dover, NJ 07801-2525
Tel (973) 989-3645 *Founded/Ownrshp* 2005
Sales 307.6MM *EMP* 3
SIC 8011 Pediatrician
Prin: Maribel Martinez

TOTSA
See ATLANTIC TRADING & MARKETING INC

D-U-N-S 12-840-1333 IMP/EXP
TOUCH INTERNATIONAL INC
2222 W Rundberg Ln # 200, Austin, TX 78758-5469
Tel (512) 832-8292 *Founded/Ownrshp* 2002
Sales 99.3MM^E *EMP* 450
SIC 3575 3577 Computer terminals; Computer peripheral equipment
Pr: Michael Woolstrum
CFO: Steve Stiles
VP: Heather McLaren
**CTO:* Gary Barrett

D-U-N-S 17-013-0975
TOUCHMARK LIVING CENTERS INC
5150 Sw Griffith Dr, Beaverton, OR 97005-3069
Tel (503) 646-5186 *Founded/Ownrshp* 1980
Sales 97.2MM^E *EMP* 1,097
SIC 8051 Skilled nursing care facilities
CEO: Werner G Nistler Jr
**Pr:* Thomas J Moe
Ex VP: Thomas Biel
Ex VP: Bernie Neil
**Sr VP:* William V Belanger
Sr VP: Richard Wessell
VP: Marge Coalman
VP: Steve Ferrarini
VP: Tucker Fife
**VP:* Steve W Nistler
VP: Thomas Spelman

TOUCHPOINT
See PUBLICIS HEALTHCARE SOLUTIONS INC

D-U-N-S 00-791-0243 IMP/EXP
TOUCHPOINT INC (PA)
210 N Brinton Lake Rd, Concordville, PA 19331
Tel (610) 459-4000 *Founded/Ownrshp* 1899
Sales 601.9MM^E *EMP* 2,800
SIC 6512 3452 Commercial & industrial building operation; Nuts, metal; Bolts, metal; Screws, metal
Pr: Brian M Mc Neill
**VP:* Raymond Canzanese
**VP:* Michael Mc Philmy
Ql Cn Mgr: Chuck Zimmer

TOUCHPOINT PRINT SOLUTIONS
See ONETOUCHPOINT CORP

D-U-N-S 94-821-3061 IMP
■TOUCHSENSOR TECHNOLOGIES LLC
(*Suby of* METHODE ELECTRONICS INC) ★
203 N Gables Blvd, Wheaton, IL 60187-4818
Tel (630) 221-9000 *Founded/Ownrshp* 1997
Sales 166.0MM^E *EMP* 300

SIC 5065 3674 Electronic parts & equipment; Modules, solid state
CEO: Thomas Schreiber
CFO: Robert Arazmas

D-U-N-S 96-611-2539
TOUCHSTONE COMMUNITIES INC
250 W Nottingham Dr # 200, San Antonio, TX 78209-1896
Tel (210) 828-5686 *Founded/Ownrshp* 2005
Sales 110.8MM^E *EMP* 2,500^E
SIC 8741 Nursing & personal care facility management
CEO: Stan Studer Jr
**Pr:* Carl Fellbaum
COO: Lynda Jennings
**COO:* Kai Mayne
**COO:* Greg Moore
COO: Britta Strickland
**CFO:* Lynnea Castillo
VP: Ann Chirhart
**VP:* Sandra Klein
**VP:* Sam Planta
VP: Bryon Sehlke
Board of Directors: Carl Fellbaum, Stan Studer Jr

D-U-N-S 16-957-7603
■TOUCHSTONE WIRELESS REPAIR AND LOGISTICS LP
INGRAM MICRO MOBILITY
(*Suby of* INGRAM MICRO INC) ★
501 Airtech Pkwy, Plainfield, IN 46168-7408
Tel (317) 707-2355 *Founded/Ownrshp* 1979
Sales 459.1MM^E *EMP* 1,800^E
SIC 4812 5065 Cellular telephone services; Electronic parts & equipment
Pr: Bashar Nejdawi
Dir Surg: Greg Roberts
Dir Surg: Ron Wacker
Genl Mgr: Luis Natal
Sales Asso: Aaron Brigham

D-U-N-S 92-669-2716
TOURICO HOLIDAYS INC
(*Suby of* TRAVEL HOLDINGS INC) ★
220 E Central Pkwy # 4000, Altamonte Springs, FL 32701-3400
Tel (407) 667-8700 *Founded/Ownrshp* 1994
Sales 1.0MMM *EMP* 150
SIC 4724 Travel agencies
CEO: Uri Argov
COO: Asi Ginio
CFO: Michael McIntyre
Treas: Francesca Johnson
Chf Mktg O: Ron Neuman
Ofcr: Wendy Friedberg
Ex VP: Gadi Bober
Ex VP: Stephen Skidgel
Sr VP: Neil Emerson
VP: Steve Caron
VP: Tammy James
VP: Amir Kalmar
VP: Phillip Lee
VP: Dominik Riber

D-U-N-S 92-721-2191
TOURISM ARTS AND HERITAGE CABINET
(*Suby of* EXECUTIVE OFFICE OF COMMONWEALTH OF KENTUCKY) ★
500 Mero St Fl 24, Frankfort, KY 40601-1987
Tel (502) 564-4270 *Founded/Ownrshp* 1983
Sales NA *EMP* 2,341
SIC 9512 Recreational program administration, government;
Ex Dir: Robin Brewer
Ex Dir: Tim Pollard
Brnch Mgr: Eric Monhollon
Brnch Mgr: Liz Rodgers
Genl Couns: William R Dexter
Genl Couns: Ladonna Koebel

D-U-N-S 07-525-6305
TOURO COLLEGE
500 7th Ave Fl 5, New York, NY 10018-0821
Tel (646) 565-6000 *Founded/Ownrshp* 1970
Sales 334.1MM *EMP* 4,600
Accts Kpmg Llp New York Ny
SIC 8221 College, except junior
Pr: Alan Kadish
**Pr:* Mel Ness
CEO: Bernard J Luskin
**Sr VP:* Alan Schoor
VP: Danny Choy
VP: Mark Epelbaum
VP: Robert Goldschmidt
VP: Yitzchok Goldson
VP: Matthew Karr
VP: Henry Rubin
Assoc Dir: Emil Euaparadorn

D-U-N-S 07-507-4971
TOURO INFIRMARY
1401 Foucher St, New Orleans, LA 70115-3593
Tel (504) 897-7011 *Founded/Ownrshp* 1852
Sales 273.6MM *EMP* 1,424
SIC 8062 General medical & surgical hospitals
Pr: James Montgomery
COO: Sue Pitosis
CFO: Cynthia Polt
Sr VP: Suzane Haggard
VP: Christine Albert
VP: Dale Mertens
Exec: Lance Franklin
Dir Soc: Robert Hoerner
Dir: Greg Barker
Ex Dir: Barbara Adcock
Off Mgr: Robert Gardner

D-U-N-S 11-848-4500 IMP
TOUSA INC
TECHNICAL USA
4000 Hollywood Blvd # 555, Hollywood, FL 33021-6853
Tel (954) 364-4000 *Founded/Ownrshp* 2002
Sales NA *EMP* 1,461
SIC 1521 1522 6162 6541

D-U-N-S 62-065-9037
TOWBIN AUTOMOTIVE ENTERPRISES INC
TOWBIN INFINITI
5550 W Sahara Ave, Las Vegas, NV 89146-3329
Tel (702) 253-7000 *Founded/Ownrshp* 1990
Sales 113.5MM^E *EMP* 456
SIC 5511 7514 Automobiles, new & used; Rent-a-car service
Ch Bd: Daniel L Towbin
**VP:* Carolynn Towbin
Sls Mgr: Jake Vance

TOWBIN INFINITI
See TOWBIN AUTOMOTIVE ENTERPRISES INC

D-U-N-S 80-587-5932
■TOWER AUTOMOTIVE HOLDINGS USA LLC
TOWER INTERNATIONAL
(*Suby of* TOWER INTERNATIONAL INC) ★
17672 N Laurel Park Dr 400e, Livonia, MI 48152-3984
Tel (248) 675-6000 *Founded/Ownrshp* 2007
Sales 594.8MM^E *EMP* 2,257^E
SIC 3465 Automotive stampings
Treas: Amy Durand

D-U-N-S 80-560-9224 IMP
■TOWER AUTOMOTIVE OPERATIONS USA I LLC
(*Suby of* TOWER INTERNATIONAL) ★
17672 N Laurel Park Dr 400e, Livonia, MI 48152-3984
Tel (248) 675-6000 *Founded/Ownrshp* 2007
Sales 512.5MM^E *EMP* 2,257
SIC 3465 Automotive stampings
Pr: Dev B Kapadia
**Treas:* Jeffrey L Lomasky
Sr Cor Off: Gyula Meleghy
**VP:* Seth Gardner

D-U-N-S 79-552-4750
TOWER ENERGY GROUP
1983 W 190th St Ste 100, Torrance, CA 90504-6240
Tel (310) 538-8000 *Founded/Ownrshp* 1989
Sales 395.3MM^E *EMP* 492^E
SIC 5172 Gasoline
Prin: John Rogers
Sr VP: John Hendrick
VP: Tom Haug
**VP:* Twanna Rogers
Software D: Mina Sardari

TOWER F C U
See TOWER FEDERAL CREDIT UNION

D-U-N-S 07-492-2873
TOWER FEDERAL CREDIT UNION
TOWER F C U
7901 Sandy Spring Rd # 102, Laurel, MD 20707-3589
Tel (301) 490-6926 *Founded/Ownrshp* 1953
Sales NA *EMP* 490
SIC 6163 6061 Loan brokers; Federal credit unions
Ch Bd: George Cumberledge
**Pr:* Martin Breland
CFO: Allen Bach
**Treas:* Charles Nossick
Ofcr: Toni Jones
Ofcr: Nichele Torres
Sr VP: Richard Brake
VP: Rhonda Scp
VP: Barry Stricklin
VP: Jenny Vipperman
CTO: Allen W Bach

D-U-N-S 96-878-6996
TOWER GROUP INC
(*Suby of* TOWER GROUP INTERNATIONAL LTD)
800 Plaza Two 8, Jersey City, NJ 07311-1104
Tel (212) 655-2000 *Founded/Ownrshp* 1996
Sales NA *EMP* 1,417^E
SIC 6411 Property & casualty insurance agent
CEO: William W Fox
CFO: William E Hitselberger
**Ch:* Jan R Van Gorder
Ofcr: Micjael Leschack
Ex VP: Sunil Agarwal
**Ex VP:* Bill Hitselberger
Ex VP: Gary S Maier
Sr VP: Salvatore V Abano
**Sr VP:* William F Dove
Sr VP: Stephen L Kibbehouse
**Sr VP:* Scott T Melnik
**Sr VP:* Elliot S Orol
Sr VP: Christian K Pechmann
Sr VP: Laurie Ranegar
Sr VP: Bruce W Sanderson
Sr VP: Catherine M Wragg
VP: Andrew Colannino
VP: George J Daddario Jr
VP: Theresa Delproire
VP: James Roberts
VP: Norma Rodriguez

D-U-N-S 03-938-8038
TOWER HILL INSURANCE GROUP INC
7201 Nw 11th Pl, Gainesville, FL 32605-3150
Tel (352) 332-8800 *Founded/Ownrshp* 1972
Sales NA *EMP* 400
SIC 6331 7371 Fire, marine & casualty insurance; Computer software development
CEO: Charles Willimason
**Ch Bd:* William J Shively
**CEO:* Charles Williamson
**COO:* Donald C Matz Jr
Bd of Dir: Karen McCleave
Sr VP: Lane Bussey
Sr VP: Kimberly Iriarte
Sr VP: Laura Marin
VP: Timothy Burns
VP: Kathleen Derum
VP: Robert Dilauro
VP: Tom Jasick
Dir Soc: Donna Shively

D-U-N-S 62-188-5821
TOWER INSURANCE CO OF NEW YORK
(*Suby of* TOWER GROUP INC) ★
120 Broadway Ste 31, New York, NY 10271-3100
Tel (212) 655-2000 *Founded/Ownrshp* 1996
Sales NA *EMP* 500^E
SIC 6411 Property & casualty insurance agent
Pr: Michael H Lee
**Treas:* Frank Colalucci
VP: Brian Finkelstein
Dir IT: Lindy Caciopo

TOWER INTERNATIONAL
See TOWER AUTOMOTIVE HOLDINGS USA LLC

TOWER INTERNATIONAL
See TA DELAWARE INC

D-U-N-S 80-626-0134 IMP
▲TOWER INTERNATIONAL INC
17672 N Laurel Park Dr, Livonia, MI 48152-3984
Tel (248) 675-6000 *Founded/Ownrshp* 1993
Sales 1.9MMM *EMP* 8,300
Tkr Sym TOWR *Exch* NYS
SIC 3465 3441 Automotive stampings; Body parts, automobile: stamped metal; Fabricated structural metal
Pr: Mark Malcolm
**Ch Bd:* Nicholas D Chabraja
Pr: James Bernard
Pr: James C Gouin
Pr: Par Malmhagen
COO: Michael Rajkovic
CFO: James Gouin
CFO: Phil Pfefferle
Sr VP: William Cook
Sr VP: Jeffrey L Kersten
VP: Mary Brown
VP: Dave Bushi
VP: Jim Firlit
VP: Doug Wagner
Board of Directors: Alison Davis-Blake, Thomas K Brown, James Chapman, Frank E English Jr

D-U-N-S 79-548-7714
TOWER US HOLDINGS INC
JAZZ TECHNOLOGIES, INC.
(*Suby of* TOWER SEMICONDUCTOR LTD)
4321 Jamboree Rd, Newport Beach, CA 92660-3007
Tel (949) 435-8000 *Founded/Ownrshp* 2008
Sales 221.4MM *EMP* 805
SIC 3674 Wafers (semiconductor devices)
CEO: Marco Racanelli
CFO: Ronit Vardi
CTO: Steve Wozniak
Mktg Dir: Corey Fukushima

D-U-N-S 19-430-9386
TOWERBROOK CAPITAL PARTNERS LP
65 E 55th St Fl 27, New York, NY 10022-3362
Tel (212) 699-2200 *Founded/Ownrshp* 2005
Sales 1.9MMM^E *EMP* 3,200
SIC 6282 Investment advice
CEO: Neal Moszkowski
**Genl Pt:* Ramez Susu
COO: Filippo Cardini
**CFO:* Jennifer Ternoey Glassman
Mng Dir: Jonathan Bilzin
Mng Dir: Robin Esterson
Mng Dir: Winston Ginsberg
Mng Dir: Christoph Lueneburger
Mng Dir: Karim Saddi
Off Mgr: Elsie Ramos

TOWERJAZZ
See JAZZ SEMICONDUCTOR INC

TOWERS WATSON & CO.
See WTW DELAWARE HOLDINGS LLC

D-U-N-S 00-361-2327
TOWERS WATSON DELAWARE HOLDINGS INC
(*Suby of* TOWERS WATSON & CO) ★
335 Madison Ave Fl 20, New York, NY 10017-4633
Tel (212) 309-3400 *Founded/Ownrshp* 1958
Sales 664.8MM^E *EMP* 7,700^E
SIC 8742 8999 Compensation & benefits planning consultant; Human resource consulting services; Actuarial consultant
Ch Bd: John J Haley
**CFO:* Roger F Millay
Top Exec: Eric Speer
**VP:* Walter W Bardenwerper
**VP:* Carl A Hess
VP: Mary Tavarozzi
**VP:* Gene H Wickes
Exec: Gail McKee
Mng Dir: Jack Gibson
Mng Dir: Stephen Lowe
Mng Dir: Laura Sejen

D-U-N-S 00-326-1047
TOWERS WATSON DELAWARE INC
(*Suby of* TOWERS WATSON & CO) ★
901 N Glebe Rd, Arlington, VA 22203-1853
Tel (703) 258-8000 *Founded/Ownrshp* 2010
Sales 192.5MM^E *EMP* 3,500^E
SIC 8742 Management consulting services
Pr: John J Haley
VP: Paul Platten

D-U-N-S 04-225-8319 IMP
TOWERS WATSON PENNSYLVANIA INC
(*Suby of* TOWERS WATSON & CO) ★
263 Tresser Blvd Ste 700, Stamford, CT 06901-3226
Tel (203) 326-5400 *Founded/Ownrshp* 2010
Sales 450.7MM^E *EMP* 5,300^E
SIC 8742 7371 Management consulting services; Human resource consulting services; Compensation & benefits planning consultant; Transportation consultant; Computer software systems analysis & design, custom
Ch Bd: Mark V Mactas
**CFO:* Robert G Hogan
CFO: Mark Wilson
**Treas:* William Apostolides
Ex VP: Leo Magrath
Ex VP: John P Woods
Sr VP: Michael Brownsell
Sr VP: Lois Massa
Sr VP: Adrienne Reid
**Sr VP:* Eric M Simpson
Sr VP: John Smithson
Sr VP: Spencer Woodbury
**VP:* Walter Bardenwerper
VP: Nick Dipietra
VP: Keith Dobrolinsky
VP: Shaun Flynn
VP: Chris Moresco
VP: Michael L Waterman
VP: Sharon Wunderlich

D-U-N-S 04-571-3856
TOWLIFT INC
1395 Valley Belt Rd, Brooklyn Heights, OH 44131-1474
Tel (216) 749-6800 *Founded/Ownrshp* 2000
Sales 113.8MM^E *EMP* 300
SIC 5084 7699 7359 Materials handling machinery; Industrial machine parts; Industrial machinery & equipment repair; Industrial truck repair; Equipment rental & leasing
Pr: David H Cannon
**VP:* David Bongorno
VP: Len Tober
Genl Mgr: Robert Kwieciak
Plnt Mgr: Jim Vacha
Sls&Mrk Ex: Marlene Hallack
Sls Mgr: Steve Horne
Sls Mgr: Todd Kozlowski

D-U-N-S 02-700-0983 IMP
■TOWN & COUNTRY FOOD STORES INC
T & C VILLAGE MARKETS
(*Suby of* SUNOCO LP) ★
3515 S Bryant Blvd, San Angelo, TX 76903-9309
Tel (325) 655-0676 *Founded/Ownrshp* 1965
Sales 221.5MM^E *EMP* 1,950
SIC 5411 Convenience stores, chain
Ex VP: E V Bonner
**Pr:* Alvin New
**Sr VP:* Devin Bates
Dir IT: Casey Gay

D-U-N-S 02-449-1268
■TOWN & COUNTRY FORD INC
(*Suby of* SONIC AUTOMOTIVE INC) ★
5401 E Independence Blvd, Charlotte, NC 28212-0504
Tel (704) 536-5600 *Founded/Ownrshp* 1967
Sales 137.0MM *EMP* 245
SIC 5511 7538 7532 5521 Automobiles, new & used; Trucks, tractors & trailers: new & used; General automotive repair shops; Body shop, trucks; Used car dealers
VP: William Sullivan
Mktg Dir: Bruton Smith

D-U-N-S 02-725-7906
TOWN & COUNTRY MARKETS INC
SHORELINE CENTRAL MARKET
130 5th Ave S Ste 126, Edmonds, WA 98020-3652
Tel (360) 598-7300 *Founded/Ownrshp* 1985
Sales 147.8MM^E *EMP* 850
SIC 5411 Grocery stores, independent
Pr: William Weymer
**Pr:* Bill Weyner
**Treas:* Larry Nakata
**VP:* Susan Allen
**VP:* Ronald Nakata
**VP:* Nakata Ronald Tadeshi
Store Dir: Tom Hall

TOWN & COUNTRY SUPER MARKET 1
See TOWN AND COUNTRY SUPER MARKET INC

TOWN & COUNTRY SUPERMARKET
See TOWN AND COUNTRY GROCERS OF FREDERICKTOWN MISSOURI INC

TOWN AND COUNTRY
See ATLAS HOTELS INC

D-U-N-S 12-654-5388
TOWN AND COUNTRY CO-OP INC
BILL'S AUTO SERVICE
813 Clark Ave, Ashland, OH 44805-1967
Tel (419) 281-2153 *Founded/Ownrshp* 2003
Sales 109.2MM^E *EMP* 200
SIC 5541 5261 5999 Gasoline service stations; Fertilizer; Farm equipment & supplies; Feed & farm supply
CEO: Al Holdren
**Pr:* Charles Holdren
**COO:* Jean Bratton
**CFO:* Brian Amstuz
VP: Gary Besancon
VP: Bill Rohrbaugh
Brnch Mgr: Dave Plank
Site Mgr: Bob Mole
Opers Mgr: John Runion
Plnt Mgr: Jason Bruner

D-U-N-S 06-856-4855
TOWN AND COUNTRY GROCERS OF FREDERICKTOWN MISSOURI INC (MO)
TOWN & COUNTRY SUPERMARKET
208 Lincoln Dr, Fredericktown, MO 63645-8518
Tel (573) 783-6477 *Founded/Ownrshp* 1971
Sales 242.5MM^E *EMP* 1,600
SIC 5411 Supermarkets, independent
CEO: Bob Hufford
**Pr:* Linda Hufford Kemp
**VP:* Wayne Gott
Pharmcst: Debbie Brown

D-U-N-S 03-111-6957
TOWN AND COUNTRY SUPER MARKET INC
TOWN & COUNTRY SUPER MARKET 1
1104 E Highway 32, Salem, MO 65560-2818
Tel (573) 729-2325 *Founded/Ownrshp* 1962
Sales 88.7MM^E *EMP* 800
SIC 5411 Supermarkets, independent
Pr: Wayne Gott
**Sec:* Betty Gott
VP: Joe Polizzi

D-U-N-S 03-526-4654
TOWN AND COUNTRY SUPPLY ASSOCIATION
CENEX
18 8th Ave, Laurel, MT 59044-2943
Tel (406) 628-6314 *Founded/Ownrshp* 1997
Sales 99.3MM *EMP* 124
Accts Moss Adams Llp Yakima Washi

SIC 5984 5191 5411 5999 Liquefied petroleum gas dealers; Fertilizers & agricultural chemicals; Convenience stores; Farm equipment & supplies
Pr: Robert Williams
**CEO:* Wes Burley
**Sec:* Jeff Michaels
**VP:* Tom Mohr
Genl Mgr: Wesley Burley

D-U-N-S 01-860-7788 IMP/EXP
TOWN FAIR TIRE CENTERS INC (CT)
460 Coe Ave, East Haven, CT 06512-3800
Tel (203) 467-8600 *Founded/Ownrshp* 1961
Sales 304.8MM^E *EMP* 600
Accts Samet & Company Pc Chestnut H
SIC 5531 5014 5013 Automotive tires; Automotive parts; Batteries, automotive & truck; Automobile tires & tubes; Automotive batteries
Pr: Neil Mellen
**Ex VP:* Michael Mellen
VP: Mike Barbaro
Store Mgr: Troy Zillich
CTO: Paul Montagna
Sfty Mgr: Mark Avitable

TOWN HALL
See TOWN OF WEYMOUTH

D-U-N-S 06-698-8619
TOWN OF AGAWAM
CITY O AGAWAM
36 Main St, Agawam, MA 01001-1837
Tel (413) 786-0400 *Founded/Ownrshp* 1855
Sales NA *EMP* 1,200
SIC 9111 Mayors' offices
V Ch: George Bitzas
**Treas:* Laurel Placzek
Bd of Dir: Pauline Berthiume
Ofcr: Brian Strong
VP: Robert Rossi
Dir IT: Jeffrey Hulbert

TOWN OF ANDOVER
See ANDOVER PUBLIC SCHOOLS

D-U-N-S 07-661-7729
TOWN OF ANDOVER
36 Bartlet St, Andover, MA 01810-3882
Tel (978) 623-8225 *Founded/Ownrshp* 1646
Sales NA *EMP* 1,100
Accts Powers & Sullivan Llc Wakefie
SIC 9111 City & town managers' offices
IT Man: Adrian Dominguez
HC Dir: Evertt Penny Jr

D-U-N-S 07-380-2126
TOWN OF ARLINGTON
730 Massachusetts Ave, Arlington, MA 02476-4908
Tel (781) 316-3000 *Founded/Ownrshp* 1807
Sales NA *EMP* 1,663
Accts Powers & Sullivan Llc Wakefi
SIC 9111 City & town managers' offices;
Ofcr: Natasha Wayden
Exec: Joan Roman
Psych: Joslyn Capone

D-U-N-S 07-953-0747
TOWN OF BARNSTABLE
230 South St, Hyannis, MA 02601-3935
Tel (508) 862-4661 *Founded/Ownrshp* 1639
Sales NA *EMP* 1,250
Accts Powers & Sullivan Llc Wakefi
SIC 9111 Executive offices, state & local
**Pr:* Frederick Chirigotis
**Treas:* Debra Blanchette
Ofcr: David Anthony

D-U-N-S 07-380-2712
TOWN OF BILLERICA
365 Boston Rd Ste 207, Billerica, MA 01821-1882
Tel (978) 671-0928 *Founded/Ownrshp* 1655
Sales NA *EMP* 1,000
Accts Powers & Sullivan Llc Wakefi
SIC 9111 City & town managers' offices;
**Treas:* John Clark

D-U-N-S 06-801-6187
TOWN OF BROOKHAVEN
1 Independence Hl Frnt, Farmingville, NY 11738-2150
Tel (631) 451-6680 *Founded/Ownrshp* 1686
Sales NA *EMP* 1,311
Accts Toski & Co Pc Williamsvil
SIC 9111 Mayors' offices
Bd of Dir: Daniel Sicilian
Ofcr: Louis Sansevero
VP: Catherine Moreo
Snr Mgr: Lisa Keys

D-U-N-S 07-555-0921
TOWN OF CARY
316 N Academy St, Cary, NC 27513-4500
Tel (919) 469-4048 *Founded/Ownrshp* 1871
Sales NA *EMP* 1,152
Accts Cherry Bekaert Llp Raleigh N
SIC 9111 City & town managers' offices;
Ofcr: Ryan Blackburn
Exec: Khalil Nasir
IT Man: Mike Mull
Netwrk Mgr: Greg Powers
Opers Mgr: Susan Morey
Sls&Mrk Ex: Deanna Boone
Snr Mgr: Kent Pack

D-U-N-S 08-033-4121
TOWN OF CHEEKTOWAGA
3301 Broadway St, Cheektowaga, NY 14227-1088
Tel (716) 686-3400 *Founded/Ownrshp* 1870
Sales NA *EMP* 1,100
Accts Drescher & Malecki Llp Cheekt
SIC 9111 City & town managers' offices;
Ofcr: Alice Magierski
Ofcr: Scott Thrun
Pr Dir: Carla Kosmerl
Snr Mgr: Tim White

D-U-N-S 08-157-5375
TOWN OF CHELMSFORD
50 Billerica Rd, Chelmsford, MA 01824-3102
Tel (978) 250-5201 *Founded/Ownrshp* 1655
Sales NA *EMP* 1,235
Accts Powers & Sullivan Llc Wakefi
SIC 9111 City & town managers' offices;
**Treas:* John Sousa

D-U-N-S 04-009-7875
TOWN OF DARTMOUTH
400 Slocum Rd, North Dartmouth, MA 02747-3234
Tel (508) 910-1800 *Founded/Ownrshp* 1664
Sales NA *EMP* 1,316
Accts Melanson Heath & Company Pc
SIC 9111
**Treas:* Gregory W Barnes

D-U-N-S 00-707-0824
TOWN OF EDMESTON (NY)
607965 6th W St, Edmeston, NY 13335
Tel (607) 965-9823 *Founded/Ownrshp* 1867
Sales NA *EMP* 2,009^E
SIC 9111

D-U-N-S 07-538-8801
TOWN OF FAIRFIELD
725 Old Post Rd, Fairfield, CT 06824-6684
Tel (203) 256-3000 *Founded/Ownrshp* 1639
Sales NA *EMP* 1,266
Accts Cohnreznick Llp Hartford Con
SIC 9121 Legislative bodies, state & local;
Snr Mgr: Jennifer Carpenter

D-U-N-S 07-952-7685
TOWN OF FRAMINGHAM
EDGELL GROVE CEMETERY
150 Concord St, Framingham, MA 01702-8325
Tel (508) 532-5400 *Founded/Ownrshp* 1700
Sales NA *EMP* 4,000
Accts Melanson Heath & Company Pc A
SIC 9111 City & town managers' offices;
**CFO:* Rob Addleson
CFO: Mary Kelley
**Treas:* Steven Price
Ofcr: Mike McCarthy
**Prin:* Robert Haltin
MIS Dir: Carly P Melo
Netwrk Mgr: Jamie Schiavone
Snr Mgr: Steven Trask

D-U-N-S 02-100-0195
TOWN OF FRANKLIN
355 E Central St Ste 1, Franklin, MA 02038-2041
Tel (508) 528-7900 *Founded/Ownrshp* 1778
Sales NA *EMP* 1,200
SIC 9111

D-U-N-S 03-843-4924
TOWN OF GILBERT
50 E Civic Center Dr, Gilbert, AZ 85296-3463
Tel (480) 503-6000 *Founded/Ownrshp* 1920
Sales NA *EMP* 1,330
Accts Heinfeld Meech & Co Pc T
SIC 9111 Executive offices, state & local;
Sfty Dirs: Jessica Koberna
Plnt Mgr: Gene Schmidt

D-U-N-S 07-943-8809
TOWN OF GILBERT ARIZONA
50 E Civic Center Dr, Gilbert, AZ 85296-3463
Tel (480) 503-6400 *Founded/Ownrshp* 2014
Sales NA *EMP* 1,200
SIC 9111 Executive offices

D-U-N-S 07-211-9589
TOWN OF GREENWICH
101 Field Point Rd Ste 1, Greenwich, CT 06830-6488
Tel (203) 622-7700 *Founded/Ownrshp* 1640
Sales NA *EMP* 2,200
Accts Mcgladrey Llp New Haven Conn
SIC 9111 City & town managers' offices;
Prin: Peter Tesei
Ofcr: Peter Mynarski
Exec: Ann Stone
Ex Dir: Betty Link
Dir IT: Thomas Klein
IT Man: Roland Gieger
Sales Exec: Rick Massi
Ansthlgy: David B Ernstein

D-U-N-S 06-803-5872
TOWN OF HEMPSTEAD
1 Washington St, Hempstead, NY 11550-4921
Tel (516) 489-5000 *Founded/Ownrshp* 1644
Sales NA *EMP* 2,052
SIC 9111 City & town managers' offices;

D-U-N-S 06-804-3256
TOWN OF HUNTINGTON
HUNTINGTON TOWN HALL
100 Main St, Huntington, NY 11743-6904
Tel (631) 351-3177 *Founded/Ownrshp* 1653
Sales NA *EMP* 1,177
Accts Israeloff Trattner & Co Pc
SIC 9111 City & town managers' offices;
Exec: Don McKay
Ex Dir: Joan Cergol

D-U-N-S 07-659-2716
TOWN OF LEXINGTON
1625 Massachusetts Ave, Lexington, MA 02420-3801
Tel (781) 862-0500 *Founded/Ownrshp* 1642
Sales NA *EMP* 2,200
Accts Melanson Heath Andover Ma
SIC 9111 City & town managers' offices;
Ofcr: Michael Sowle
Off Mgr: Kathy Severance
Dir IT: Dorinda Goodman

D-U-N-S 13-008-3173
TOWN OF LORRAINE
HIGHWAY DEPARTMENT
20876 County Route 189, Lorraine, NY 13659-3190
Tel (315) 232-4676 *Founded/Ownrshp* 1998
Sales 105.2MM *EMP* 9
SIC 9111 City & town managers' offices
Ex Dir: Vince Moore

D-U-N-S 06-009-5072
TOWN OF MARSHFIELD
870 Moraine St, Marshfield, MA 02050-3490
Tel (781) 834-5552 *Founded/Ownrshp* 1640
Sales NA *EMP* 1,000
SIC 9121 Town council;
Treas: Nancy Holt
**Ch Bd:* Patricia Epstein
Ofcr: Debbie Sullivan

D-U-N-S 08-003-2634
TOWN OF NATICK
13 E Central St Ste 1, Natick, MA 01760-4627
Tel (508) 647-6410 *Founded/Ownrshp* 1781
Sales NA *EMP* 1,800
Accts Cliftonlarsonallen Llp Bosto
SIC 9111 City & town managers' offices;
Treas: Robert Palmer
Genl Mgr: Elizabeth Kelley
Genl Mgr: Jeffrey Towne

D-U-N-S 07-661-8867
TOWN OF NEEDHAM
1471 Highland Ave, Needham, MA 02492-2605
Tel (781) 455-7500 *Founded/Ownrshp* 1711
Sales NA *EMP* 1,500
Accts Melanson Heath Andover Ma
SIC 9111 City & town managers' offices;
**Treas:* Evelyn M Poness
Ex Dir: Jamie B Gutner
MIS Dir: Roger Macdonald

D-U-N-S 08-480-3881
TOWN OF NORTH ATTLEBOROUGH
43 S Washington St, North Attleboro, MA 02760-1642
Tel (508) 699-0100 *Founded/Ownrshp* 1887
Sales NA *EMP* 1,000
SIC 9121 City council;
**Treas:* Diana Afanza
Treas: William Moffitt
Ofcr: Rick Weidman
Dir IT: Keith Mueller
Snr Mgr: Michael Brousseau

D-U-N-S 08-421-1572
TOWN OF NORWOOD (MA)
566 Washington St, Norwood, MA 02062-2298
Tel (781) 762-1240 *Founded/Ownrshp* 1872
Sales NA *EMP* 1,035
Accts Melanson Heath Andover Ma
SIC 9121 Congress
Genl Mgr: John J Carroll
**Treas:* Cheryl Golden
**Treas:* Robert J Marsh
**Treas:* Robert McGuire
Ofcr: Martin F Baker
Ofcr: Michael Benedetti
Ofcr: Paul A Bishop
Ofcr: Peter Borroni
Ofcr: Clifford Brown
Ofcr: Sheila Condrin
Ofcr: Claire O Connell
Ofcr: Anthony Copponi
Ofcr: Arthur Doolan
Ofcr: Ann Fleming
Ofcr: Ellen Flynn
Ofcr: Gregory Gamel
Ofcr: Jerilyn Glassman
Ofcr: Kevin Grasso
Ofcr: Donna Gronroos
Ofcr: Robert Harkins
Ofcr: Daniel Kehoe

TOWN OF OCEAN CITY
See MAYOR AND CITY COUNCIL OF OCEAN CITY

D-U-N-S 07-236-9622
TOWN OF OYSTER BAY
54 Audrey Ave, Oyster Bay, NY 11771-1593
Tel (516) 624-6498 *Founded/Ownrshp* 1653
Sales NA *EMP* 1,200
Accts Cullen & Danowski Llp Port J
SIC 9199 General government administration

D-U-N-S 08-157-5672
TOWN OF RANDOLPH
41 S Main St, Randolph, MA 02368-4839
Tel (781) 961-0911 *Founded/Ownrshp* 1793
Sales NA *EMP* 1,716
SIC 9121 Town council;
Off Mgr: Joanne Coffman

D-U-N-S 07-660-4826
TOWN OF SCITUATE
600 Chief Just Cshng Hghy, Scituate, MA 02066-3229
Tel (781) 545-8700 *Founded/Ownrshp* 1730
Sales NA *EMP* 1,000
SIC 9121 City council;
Ch: Shawn Harris

D-U-N-S 07-213-4414
TOWN OF STRATFORD
MAYOR
2725 Main St, Stratford, CT 06615-5818
Tel (203) 385-4001 *Founded/Ownrshp* 1639
Sales NA *EMP* 1,322
Accts Mcgladrey Llp New Haven Con
SIC 9111 City & town managers' offices;
**Treas:* Marie Craig
Bd of Dir: Brian Budd
Mktg Dir: Susan Collier
Mktg Dir: Patricia Naylor

D-U-N-S 07-061-9382
TOWN OF SUDBURY
322 Concord Rd, Sudbury, MA 01776-1800
Tel (978) 443-8891 *Founded/Ownrshp* 1639
Sales NA *EMP* 1,099
Accts Sullivan Rogers & Company Ll
SIC 9111 City & town managers' offices;
Ch: Lawrence O Brien

D-U-N-S 07-213-1147
TOWN OF TRUMBULL
5866 Main St, Trumbull, CT 06611-3113
Tel (203) 452-5080 *Founded/Ownrshp* 1797
Sales NA *EMP* 1,161
Accts Blum Shapiro & Company Pc
SIC 9111 City & town managers' offices;
**Treas:* Bruce Stern

D-U-N-S 08-130-1244
TOWN OF VERNON
14 Park Pl, Vernon, CT 06066-3291
Tel (860) 870-3690 *Founded/Ownrshp* 1808
Sales NA *EMP* 1,000^E
Accts Cohn Reznick Llp Hartford C
SIC 9111 City & town managers' offices;
Dir IT: Robert Sigan

D-U-N-S 07-536-3937
TOWN OF WALPOLE
135 School St, Walpole, MA 02081-2837
Tel (508) 660-7289 *Founded/Ownrshp* 1724
Sales NA *EMP* 1,000
Accts Roselli Clark & Associates W
SIC 9111 Mayors' offices
**Ch:* Eric A Kraus
Sfty Mgr: Warren Goodman

D-U-N-S 07-835-2463
TOWN OF WALPOLE
RECREATION DEPARTMENT
135 School St, Walpole, MA 02081-2837
Tel (508) 660-7353 *Founded/Ownrshp* 2012
Sales 84.4MM *EMP* 3
SIC 7999 Recreation services

D-U-N-S 07-661-7935
TOWN OF WELLESLEY
525 Washington St, Wellesley, MA 02482-5918
Tel (781) 431-1019 *Founded/Ownrshp* 1881
Sales NA *EMP* 1,300
Accts Powers & Sullivan Llc Wakefi
SIC 9111 City & town managers' offices;
Treas: Marc Waldman
Ofcr: Brian Shore
**Ex Dir:* Hans Larsen

D-U-N-S 80-785-5098
TOWN OF WEST HARTFORD
50 S Main St Ste 2, West Hartford, CT 06107-2431
Tel (860) 561-7500 *Founded/Ownrshp* 1919
Sales NA *EMP* 2,659
Accts Blum Shapiro & Company Pc W
SIC 9111
Ofcr: Helen Lee
Dir IT: Jared Morin
Snr Mgr: Ted Goerner
Snr Mgr: Nancy Salvatore

D-U-N-S 07-661-8610
TOWN OF WESTFORD
55 Main St, Westford, MA 01886-2597
Tel (978) 692-5500 *Founded/Ownrshp* 1729
Sales NA *EMP* 1,000
Accts Melanson Heath Andover Ma
SIC 9111 City & town managers' offices;
**Treas:* Christine Collins
**Treas:* Suzanne Marchand

D-U-N-S 08-004-9018
TOWN OF WESTON
11 Townhouse Rd, Weston, MA 02493-2000
Tel (781) 786-5070 *Founded/Ownrshp* 1712
Sales NA *EMP* 1,030
SIC 9111 Mayors' offices
**Prin:* Donna S Vanderclock
Off Admin: Anne Bennett

D-U-N-S 07-212-5248
TOWN OF WESTPORT
110 Myrtle Ave, Westport, CT 06880-3514
Tel (203) 226-8311 *Founded/Ownrshp* 1710
Sales NA *EMP* 1,850
Accts Mcgladrey Llp New Haven Conn
SIC 9111 City & town managers' offices;
VP: Sharon Silver
IT Man: Dwight Caines
Pr Dir: Joyce Losen

D-U-N-S 03-354-7688
TOWN OF WESTWOOD
580 High St, Westwood, MA 02090-1607
Tel (781) 326-6450 *Founded/Ownrshp* 1897
Sales NA *EMP* 1,000
Accts Power & Sullivan Llc Wakefie
SIC 9111 City & town managers' offices;
Treas: James J Gavin

D-U-N-S 07-660-7274
TOWN OF WEYMOUTH
TOWN HALL
75 Middle St, Weymouth, MA 02189-1359
Tel (781) 335-2000 *Founded/Ownrshp* 1635
Sales NA *EMP* 1,173
SIC 9111 City & town managers' offices
CFO: William McKinney
Ofcr: Thomas Anderson
Ofcr: Scott Harrington
Ofcr: George Pontes
Opers Mgr: Al Cowing

D-U-N-S 04-370-9070
TOWN PUMP INC
LUCKY LIL'S
600 S Main St, Butte, MT 59701-2549
Tel (406) 497-6700 *Founded/Ownrshp* 1953
Sales 599.4MM^E *EMP* 1,800
SIC 5541 5411 7993 6512 5812 Filling stations, gasoline; Convenience stores, independent; Gambling establishments operating coin-operated machines; Property operation, retail establishment; Restaurant, family: independent
Pr: Thomas Kenneally Sr
**Sec:* Mary Kenneally
**VP:* Daniel Kenneally
Dist Mgr: Scott Arensmeyer
Dir IT: Ric Tamietti
Opers Mgr: Julie Corbin
Sls Mgr: Brian Miller

D-U-N-S 96-845-5845
TOWN RESIDENTIAL LLC
33 Irving Pl Frnt 1, New York, NY 10003-2332
Tel (212) 557-6500 *Founded/Ownrshp* 2010
Sales 128.3MM^E *EMP* 293^E

SIC 6531 Real estate agents & managers
CEO: Andrew S Heiberger

D-U-N-S 60-475-6200
▲TOWN SPORTS INTERNATIONAL HOLDINGS INC
5 Penn Plz Fl 4, New York, NY 10001-1843
Tel (212) 246-6700 *Founded/Ownrshp* 1973
Sales 424.3MM *EMP* 7,500^E
Tkr Sym CLUB *Exch* NGM
SIC 7991 7997 Physical fitness facilities; Physical fitness clubs with training equipment; Exercise facilities; Membership sports & recreation clubs
Ch Bd: Patrick Walsh
COO: Gregory Bartoli
CFO: Carolyn Spatafora
Chf Mktg O: Michelle Ryan
Sr VP: Nitin Ajmera
Dir Rx: Anthony Messina
Dir IT: Todd Gordon
Board of Directors: Martin J Annese, Jason M Fish, Thomas J Galligan III, L Spencer Wells

D-U-N-S 07-280-7639 IMP
■TOWN SPORTS INTERNATIONAL INC
NEW YORK SPORTS CLUB
(*Suby of* TOWN SPORTS INTERNATIONAL HOLDINGS INC) ★
5 Penn Plz Fl 4, New York, NY 10001-1843
Tel (212) 246-6700 *Founded/Ownrshp* 1996
Sales 236.4MM^E *EMP* 7,800
Accts Pricewaterhousecoopers Llp Ne
SIC 7997 7991 Racquetball club, membership; Tennis club, membership; Health club
Ch Bd: Mark Smith
**Pr:* Robert Giardina
**COO:* Martin Annese
Genl Mgr: William Alves
Genl Mgr: Nick Distelbrink
Genl Mgr: John Gibbs
Dir IT: Long Dang
Dir IT: Todd Gordon
IT Man: Alexander Alimanestianu
Sls Dir: Adam Rubin
Sls Dir: Mike Santiago

D-U-N-S 94-332-4848
TOWNE HOLDINGS INC
(*Suby of* CHARTERHOUSE EQUITY PARTNERS) ★
24805 Us Highway 20, South Bend, IN 46628-5911
Tel (574) 233-3183 *Founded/Ownrshp* 2005
Sales 388.2M^E *EMP* 1,456
SIC 4213 Trucking, except local
Pr: Tom Downey
**CFO:* Joe Duely
Ex VP: Lina D Cesare
**Ex VP:* Nelson Gentiletti
**Sr VP:* Robert Attaia
**VP:* Jean Belisle
**VP:* Bernard Bussieres
**VP:* Joseph Dooley
**VP:* Michel Lemay
**VP:* Louise Piche
Genl Mgr: Olivier Kervella

D-U-N-S 60-948-4928
TOWNE PARK LLC
1 Park Pl Ste 200, Annapolis, MD 21401-3581
Tel (410) 267-6111 *Founded/Ownrshp* 1988
Sales 487.6MM^E *EMP* 8,000^E
SIC 7521 4119 Automobile parking; Local passenger transportation
CEO: Jerry South
**Pr:* Dave Nichols
**COO:* Rick Sorrells
**CFO:* Mark Norwicz
**Ex VP:* Matt Cahill
Ex VP: Frank Pikus
VP: Chris Carsten
VP: David Ryan
Area Mgr: Sergio Amezcua
Area Mgr: George Juarez
Area Mgr: Alex Pizarro

D-U-N-S 05-276-9655 IMP
▲TOWNEBANK (VA)
6001 Harbour View Blvd, Suffolk, VA 23435-2767
Tel (757) 638-6700 *Founded/Ownrshp* 1998
Sales NA *EMP* 1,009
Accts Dixon Hughes Goodman Llp Norf
Tkr Sym TOWN *Exch* NGS
SIC 6022 State commercial banks
Pr: J Morgan Davis
V Ch: Thomas C Broyles
V Ch: John W Failes
V Ch: Ernest F Hardee
CEO: Jacqueline B Amato
CEO: G Robert Aston Jr
COO: William B Littreal
CFO: Clyde E McFarland Jr
Bd of Dir: R V Owens
Ofcr: Philip M Rudisill
Ex VP: Kevin Fly
Ex VP: Tommy Rueger
Sr VP: David Patterson
VP: John Fruit
VP: Mark Hubbard
VP: Holly Monaco

D-U-N-S 07-986-3223
■TOWNS END STUDIOS LLC
(*Suby of* ZYNGA INC) ★
699 8th St, San Francisco, CA 94103-4901
Tel (415) 802-7936 *Founded/Ownrshp* 2015
Sales 8.1MM^E *EMP* 1,000
SIC 7371 Computer software development & applications

D-U-N-S 01-654-5519
TOWNSEND CORP
KELLY ELECTRIC
1015 W Jackson St, Muncie, IN 47305-1556
Tel (765) 468-3007 *Founded/Ownrshp* 2001
Sales 342.6MM^E *EMP* 2,000
SIC 0783 Tree trimming services for public utility lines
CEO: Gary V Townsend
**Pr:* Phillip E Chambers
**Pr:* Royce A Shewman
CFO: Michael McClure
CFO: Michelle Molin
**Treas:* Mark Kimbrough
**Treas:* J Michael McClure
**VP:* Ray Swarington
**Prin:* David Trittipo
Off Mgr: Christina Stanley
Mktg Dir: John Roselle

TOWNSEND ENERGY
See TOWNSEND OIL CORP

D-U-N-S 01-282-1971
TOWNSEND OIL CORP
TOWNSEND ENERGY
(*Suby of* GRIFFITH ENERGY) ★
64 Main St, Le Roy, NY 14482-1493
Tel (585) 768-8188 *Founded/Ownrshp* 1978
Sales 121.6MM *EMP* 60
Accts Robinson & Gordon Cpas Pc
SIC 5171 5983 Petroleum bulk stations; Fuel oil dealers
Pr: Kevin P Brady
Ofcr: Amanda Logsdon

TOWNSENDS
See OMTRON USA LLC

D-U-N-S 06-745-4512
TOWNSHIP HIGH SCHOOL DISTRICT 211 FOUNDATION
1750 S Roselle Rd Ste 100, Palatine, IL 60067-7302
Tel (708) 359-3300 *Founded/Ownrshp* 1875
Sales 304.9MM *EMP* 1,909
Accts Baker Tilly Virchow Krause
SIC 8211 Public senior high school
IT Man: Sheldon Luo
MIS Mgr: Paul Goilisch
Netwrk Eng: Chris Shin
Pr Dir: Thomas Petersen
Teacher Pr: Eric Wenckowski
Psych: Suzanne Adamski
Psych: Ashley August
Psych: Caryn Bova
Psych: Ashley Curtin
Psych: Ashley Hill
Psych: Jessica Kruer

D-U-N-S 06-747-1755
TOWNSHIP HIGH SCHOOL DISTRICT 214
2121 S Goebbert Rd, Arlington Heights, IL 60005-4205
Tel (847) 718-7600 *Founded/Ownrshp* 1922
Sales 306.6MM *EMP* 1,550
Accts Baker Tilly Virchow Krause Ll
SIC 8211 Public senior high school
Pr: Alva Kreutcer
VP: Mark Hineman
**VP:* Dan Petro
Exec: Julie Laskowski
Exec: Sarah Pick
**Prin:* William J Dussling
IT Man: Herbert Mueller
Pr Dir: Patrick Mogge

D-U-N-S 82-900-0314
▲TOWNSQUARE MEDIA INC
240 Greenwich Ave, Greenwich, CT 06830-6597
Tel (203) 861-0900 *Founded/Ownrshp* 2010
Sales 441.2MM *EMP* 2,900
Tkr Sym TSQ *Exch* NYS
SIC 4832 Radio broadcasting stations
Ch Bd: Steven Price
CFO: Stuart Rosenstein
Ex VP: Erik Hellum
Ex VP: Michael Josephs
Ex VP: Christopher Kitchen
Ex VP: Dhruv Prasad
Ex VP: Scott Schatz
Ex VP: Mark Stewart
Ex VP: Bill Wilson
Ex VP: Claire Yenicay
VP: Aarona Jordan
VP: Johnny Lathrop
VP: Christine Sieks
VP: Rob Williams

D-U-N-S 14-337-2741
TOWSON UNIVERSITY
(*Suby of* UNIVERSITY MD AT BALTIMORE) ★
8000 York Rd, Baltimore, MD 21252-0002
Tel (410) 704-2000 *Founded/Ownrshp* 2006
Sales 209.3MM^E *EMP* 2,500^E
SIC 8221 Colleges universities & professional schools
Pr: Robert Caret
CFO: James P Sheehan
Ex VP: Roger Hayden
VP: Bill Leimback
Assoc Dir: Tia Freiburger
Assoc Dir: Mary A Hewitt
Assoc Dir: Marie Lilly
Ex Dir: Sergei Zverev
IT Man: Mark Profili
Netwrk Eng: Nate F Morehead
Pr Dir: Peter Schlehr

D-U-N-S 78-373-8743 IMP/EXP
TOYO INK INTERNATIONAL CORP
(*Suby of* TOYO INK SC HOLDINGS CO., LTD.)
1225 N Michael Dr, Wood Dale, IL 60191-1019
Tel (866) 969-8696 *Founded/Ownrshp* 1989
Sales 99.8MM^E *EMP* 200
SIC 2893 5112 Printing ink; Writing ink
Pr: Fusao Ito
**CFO:* John Higgins
**Treas:* Jane Krasmer

D-U-N-S 15-674-9520 IMP
TOYO TIRE HOLDINGS OF AMERICAS INC
(*Suby of* TOYO TIRE & RUBBER CO.,LTD.)
5900 Katella Ave Ste 200a, Cypress, CA 90630-5019
Tel (562) 431-6502 *Founded/Ownrshp* 1988
Sales 238.3MM^E *EMP* 800
SIC 3011 Automobile inner tubes
CEO: Tomoshige Mizutani

D-U-N-S 16-852-6411 IMP
TOYO TIRE NORTH AMERICA MANUFACTURING INC
(*Suby of* TOYO TIRE HOLDINGS OF AMERICAS INC) ★
3660 Highway 411 Ne, White, GA 30184-2427
Tel (678) 721-7200 *Founded/Ownrshp* 2004
Sales 205.9MM^E *EMP* 800
SIC 3011 Automobile inner tubes
CEO: Don Bunn
CFO: Noriyuki Dan
CFO: Allan Huggins

D-U-N-S 07-880-9058
TOYODA GOSEI BROWNSVILLE TEXAS LLC (TX)
(*Suby of* TOYODA GOSEI NORTH AMERICA CORP) ★
107 Joaquin Cavazos Rd, Los Indios, TX 78567
Tel (956) 290-8802 *Founded/Ownrshp* 2012
Sales 200.0MM *EMP* 18
SIC 3711 Automobile bodies, passenger car, not including engine, etc.
**Pr:* Ritoshi Hizutari
**Ch:* Toru Koyama
Genl Mgr: David Garcia

D-U-N-S 11-388-3891 IMP/EXP
TOYODA GOSEI NORTH AMERICA CORP
(*Suby of* TOYODA GOSEI CO., LTD.)
1400 Stephenson Hwy, Troy, MI 48083-1189
Tel (248) 280-2100 *Founded/Ownrshp* 1999
Sales 913.1MM *EMP* 5,292
SIC 3069 3089 Weather strip, sponge rubber; Automotive parts, plastic
Pr: Hiromi Ikehata
Sr Cor Off: Tokio Horigome
**VP:* John Baylis
**VP:* Joseph Mannino
**VP:* Kani Masayasu
**VP:* Masato Takeda
Opers Mgr: Jay Turnage
VP Sls: Tetsuya Takahashi

TOYOTA BOSHOKU AMERICA
See TOYOTA BOSHOKU KENTUCKY LLC

D-U-N-S 10-204-5767 IMP
TOYOTA BOSHOKU AMERICA INC
(*Suby of* TOYOTA BOSHOKU CORPORATION)
1360 Dolwick Rd Ste 125, Erlanger, KY 41018-3159
Tel (859) 817-4000 *Founded/Ownrshp* 2006
Sales 2.7MMM *EMP* 948
SIC 3711 5013 Automobile assembly, including specialty automobiles; Automotive trim
CEO: Yoshihiro Ito
**Ex VP:* Norimichi Adachi
**Ex VP:* Ikuo Mochizuki
**Ex VP:* Shinichi Yamaguchi
VP: Ted Schafer
Exec: Peggy Phillips
CTO: Lynelle Coomes
Prd Mgr: Mike Ledford

D-U-N-S 87-789-9695 IMP
TOYOTA BOSHOKU ILLINOIS LLC
A T S
(*Suby of* TOYOTA BOSHOKU AMERICA INC) ★
100 Trim Masters Dr, Lawrenceville, IL 62439-9501
Tel (618) 943-5300 *Founded/Ownrshp* 2008
Sales 122.6MM^E *EMP* 470
SIC 3714 Motor vehicle parts & accessories
CEO: Akira Furusawa
Pr: Shuhei Toyoda
COO: Shigetoshi Miyoshi
Genl Mgr: Barry Derousse
Genl Mgr: Stephanie Stitt

D-U-N-S 03-766-3597 IMP
TOYOTA BOSHOKU KENTUCKY LLC
TOYOTA BOSHOKU AMERICA
(*Suby of* TOYOTA BOSHOKU AMERICA INC) ★
1051 Withrow Ct, Bardstown, KY 40004-2605
Tel (502) 349-6000 *Founded/Ownrshp* 2003
Sales 85.1MM^E *EMP* 332^E
SIC 5511 Automobiles, new & used
Prin: Shinji Kano
**Prin:* Kenji Akase
**Prin:* Toshiyuki Kawasakoi
**Prin:* Shigetoshi Miyoshi
**Prin:* Teruo Suzuki
Genl Mgr: Stephanie Stitt
IT Man: Greg Hopper

TOYOTA CENTER
See FHA/RALEIGH INC

D-U-N-S 03-308-6104
TOYOTA FINANCIAL SERVICES INTERNATIONAL CORP
TOYOTA FNCL SVCS AMERICAS CORP
(*Suby of* TOYOTA FINANCIAL SERVICES CORPORATION)
19001 S Western Ave, Torrance, CA 90501-1106
Tel (310) 618-4000 *Founded/Ownrshp* 2000
Sales 9.4MMM^E *EMP* 3,305^E
SIC 5511 Automobiles, new & used
CEO: Takuo Sasaki
V Ch: Mike Colbus
**Pr:* Jim Lentz
VP: Mike Bafan
Software D: MAI Nguyen

TOYOTA FNCL SVCS AMERICAS CORP
See TOYOTA FINANCIAL SERVICES INTERNATIONAL CORP

D-U-N-S 60-978-2594 IMP
TOYOTA INDUSTRIAL EQUIPMENT MFG INC
TIEM PARTS CENTER
(*Suby of* TOYOTA INDUSTRIES NORTH AMERICA INC) ★
5555 Inwood Dr, Columbus, IN 47201-9755
Tel (812) 342-0060 *Founded/Ownrshp* 1988
Sales 180.8MM^E *EMP* 850^E
SIC 3537 Forklift trucks
Pr: Yoshimitsu Ogihara
COO: Susumu Toyoda
**Ex VP:* Koyu Suzuki
**VP:* Marv Johnson
**VP:* Bruce Nolting
VP: Mike Prebeck
VP: Steve Pride
QI Cn Mgr: Doug Campbell

D-U-N-S 07-849-9785 IMP
TOYOTA INDUSTRIES COMPRESSOR PARTS AMERICA CO
(*Suby of* TOYOTA INDUSTRIES NORTH AMERICA INC) ★
500 Valentine Indus Pkwy, Pendergrass, GA 30567-4238
Tel (706) 693-7200 *Founded/Ownrshp* 2012
Sales 107.1MM^E *EMP* 318
SIC 5075 Automotive air conditioners
CEO: Katsunori Kawai
**Pr:* Haruhiko Kimata
**CFO:* Hiroyuki Nomura

D-U-N-S 13-589-3746 IMP/EXP
TOYOTA INDUSTRIES NORTH AMERICA INC
(*Suby of* TOYOTA INDUSTRIES CORPORATION)
3030 Barker Dr, Columbus, IN 47201-9611
Tel (812) 341-3810 *Founded/Ownrshp* 2002
Sales 1.5MMM^E *EMP* 855^E
SIC 3585 5084 Air conditioning, motor vehicle; Lift trucks & parts
Pr: Yoshimitsu Ogihara
Plnt Mgr: Marty Brown

TOYOTA LIFT OF HOUSTON
See CARRUTH-DOGGETT INC

D-U-N-S 03-174-8770 IMP
TOYOTA MATERIAL HANDLING USA INC
(*Suby of* TOYOTA INDUSTRIES NORTH AMERICA INC) ★
5559 Inwood Dr, Columbus, IN 47201-9755
Tel (800) 381-5879 *Founded/Ownrshp* 2001
Sales 1.1MMM *EMP* 200
SIC 5084 Lift trucks & parts
Pr: Jeff Rufener
**Ch:* Brett Wood
**Treas:* Hitoshi Matsuoka
VP: Alan Cseresznyak
Mktg Mgr: Luis Chaves

TOYOTA MATERIAL HDLG NTHRN CAL
See RJMS CORP

D-U-N-S 12-202-8798 IMP/EXP
TOYOTA MOTOR CREDIT CORP
(*Suby of* TOYOTA FNCL SVCS AMERICAS CORP) ★
19001 S Western Ave, Torrance, CA 90501-1106
Tel (310) 468-1310 *Founded/Ownrshp* 1983
Sales NA *EMP* 3,251
SIC 6141 Personal credit institutions; Automobile & consumer finance companies; Automobile loans, including insurance; Financing: automobiles, furniture, etc., not a deposit bank
Pr: Michael Groff
**CFO:* Chris Ballinger
**Treas:* Toshiaki Kawai
Sr VP: David Pulliccioni
Tech Mgr: Marvin Le
Sftwr Eng: Eddie Blandon
Board of Directors: James E Lentz III, Kazuo Ohara, Yasuhiro Yomoda

D-U-N-S 96-165-9588 EXP
TOYOTA MOTOR ENGINEERING & MANUFACTURING NORTH AMERICA INC
T E M A
(*Suby of* TOYOTA MOTOR NORTH AMERICA INC) ★
25 Atlantic Ave, Erlanger, KY 41018-3188
Tel (469) 292-1074 *Founded/Ownrshp* 2006
Sales 1.8MMM^E *EMP* 6,500
SIC 3711 3713 8741 Motor vehicles & car bodies; Truck & bus bodies; Management services
CEO: Osamu Nagata
CFO: Charles Brown
Treas: Kozuo Nishieda
Ex VP: Steve St Angelo
Ex VP: Ray Tanguay
Sr VP: D Cuneo
Sr VP: Kiyoshi Furuta
Sr VP: Sam Heltman
VP: James Bolte
VP: Pete Gritton
Genl Mgr: Gus Camacho
Board of Directors: Y Ishizaka, H Okuda, A Takahashi

TOYOTA MOTOR ENGINEERING MANUF
See BODINE ALUMINUM INC

D-U-N-S 03-665-3202 IMP/EXP
TOYOTA MOTOR MANUFACTURING INDIANA INC
TOYOTA MTR ENGRG & MFG N AMER
(*Suby of* T E M A) ★
4000 S Tulip Tree Dr, Princeton, IN 47670-2300
Tel (812) 387-2000 *Founded/Ownrshp* 1996
Sales 757.9MM^E *EMP* 4,300^E
SIC 3711 Truck & tractor truck assembly
Ch Bd: Seizo Okamoto
**Pr:* Norm Bafunno
**Sec:* Tsutomu Kobayashi

D-U-N-S 16-195-5380 IMP/EXP
TOYOTA MOTOR MANUFACTURING KENTUCKY INC
(*Suby of* T E M A) ★
1001 Cherry Blossom Way, Georgetown, KY 40324-9598
Tel (502) 868-2000 *Founded/Ownrshp* 1988
Sales 71.8MM^E *EMP* 6,500
SIC 5511 Automobiles, new & used
Pr: Wilbert W James Jr
**Pr:* Mike Daprile
**Pr:* Pete Gritton
**Treas:* Takashi Asai
**Treas:* Takasuki Haruki
**Treas:* Toshihiko Ubukata
Sr VP: Heltman Sam
Sr VP: Koichi Sugihara

***VP:** Matt Amezawa
***VP:** Dan Antis
VP: Dian Ogilvie
***VP:** Steven St Angelo
Board of Directors: T Minoura, H Okuda, A Takahoshi

D-U-N-S 17-011-4776 EXP
TOYOTA MOTOR MANUFACTURING TEXAS INC
(*Suby of* T E M A) ★
1 Lone Star Pass, San Antonio, TX 78264-3638
Tel (210) 263-4000 *Founded/Ownrshp* 2003
Sales 71.8MM^E *EMP* 2,295
SIC 5511 Automobiles, new & used
Pr: Jose Manuel Da Rosa
Treas: Nosukazu Takano
**Treas:* Masanao Watanabe
Bd of Dir: Casey Harmon
**VP:* Kirk Kohler
VP: Otto Samponga
VP Admn: Luis D Garza
Genl Mgr: Dan Antis
Genl Mgr: Dave Martin

D-U-N-S 00-428-6394 IMP/EXP
TOYOTA MOTOR MANUFACTURING WEST VIRGINIA INC (WV)
TOYOTA MTR ENGRG & MFG N AMER
(*Suby of* T E M A) ★
1 Sugar Maple Ln, Buffalo, WV 25033-9430
Tel (304) 937-7000 *Founded/Ownrshp* 1996
Sales 228.8MM^E *EMP* 550
SIC 3714 3519 Rebuilding engines & transmissions, factory basis; Internal combustion engines
Pr: Millie Marshall
VP: Sandra Maynard
**Prin:* Yoji Suzuki

D-U-N-S 96-355-0769 IMP/EXP
TOYOTA MOTOR NORTH AMERICA INC
(*Suby of* TOYOTA MOTOR CORPORATION)
601 Lexington Ave Fl 49, New York, NY 10022-4636
Tel (212) 751-3053 *Founded/Ownrshp* 2006
Sales 2.0MMM^E *EMP* 8,950
SIC 5511 5012 3711 Automobiles, new & used; Automobiles; Motor vehicles & car bodies
CEO: Yukitoshi Funo
**Pr:* Shigeru Hayakawa
Ofcr: Julie A Hamp
Sr VP: Dian D Ogilvie
Sr VP: Sumio Ohtsuji
**Sr VP:* Ray Tanguay
VP: Patricia Pineda
VP: Patricia Salas Pineda
VP Admn: Barbara Jones
CIO: Barbra Cooper
Board of Directors: S Toyoda

D-U-N-S 00-959-5505 IMP/EXP
TOYOTA MOTOR SALES USA INC
SCION
(*Suby of* TOYOTA MOTOR NORTH AMERICA INC) ★
19001 S Western Ave, Torrance, CA 90501-1106
Tel (310) 468-4000 *Founded/Ownrshp* 1957
Sales NA *EMP* 8,900
SIC 6159 5012 3711 Automobile finance leasing; Commercial vehicles; Motor vehicles & car bodies
Ch: Yoshimi Inaba
**Pr:* Kazuo Ohara
COO: Patrick Moore
**CFO:* Tracey Doi
CFO: Tracey C Doi
Treas: Katsuyuki Kusakawa
Ofcr: Masato Yamanami
Ex VP: Sean Nozaki
Grp VP: Chris Hostetter
Grp VP: Randy Pflughaupt
Sr VP: Bob Carter
Sr VP: Robert S Carter
Sr VP: Donald Esmond
Sr VP: Donald V Esmond
VP: Ernest J Bastien
VP: Jon Bucci
VP: Dave Camden
VP: George Christoff
VP: James H Colon
VP: Jim Colon
VP: Barbara Cooper

TOYOTA MTR ENGRG & MFG N AMER
See TOYOTA MOTOR MANUFACTURING WEST VIRGINIA INC

TOYOTA MTR ENGRG & MFG N AMER
See TOYOTA MOTOR MANUFACTURING INDIANA INC

TOYOTA OF CLERMONT
See CLERMONT MOTOR SALES LLC

TOYOTA OF EL CAJON
See K MOTORS INC

TOYOTA OF ESCONDIDO
See GARRICK MOTORS INC

TOYOTA OF HOLLYWOOD
See TRIANGLE AUTO CENTER INC

D-U-N-S 03-464-6353
TOYOTA RESEARCH INSTITUTE INC
TRI
(*Suby of* TOYOTA MOTOR CORPORATION)
1 Kendall Sq Bldg 100, Cambridge, MA 02139-1562
Tel (857) 285-6160 *Founded/Ownrshp* 2015
Sales 200.0MM *EMP* 120
SIC 8733 Research institute
CEO: Dr Gill Pratt
**COO:* Dr Eric Krotkov
**CTO:* Dr James Kuffner

D-U-N-S 12-722-8927
TOYOTA TECHNOLOGICAL INSTITUTE AT CHICAGO
6045 S Kenwood Ave, Chicago, IL 60637-2803
Tel (773) 834-2500 *Founded/Ownrshp* 2001
Sales 92.7MM *EMP* 25
Accts Plante & Moran Pllc Chicago
SIC 8221 Colleges universities & professional schools

Ch Bd: Tatsuro Toyoda
Treas: Masashi Hisamoto

D-U-N-S 00-179-0468 IMP/EXP
TOYOTA TSUSHO AMERICA INC (NY)
(*Suby of* TOYOTA TSUSHO CORPORATION)
805 3rd Ave Fl 17, New York, NY 10022-7550
Tel (212) 355-3600 *Founded/Ownrshp* 1961
Sales 1.1MMM^E *EMP* 1,100
SIC 5051 5013 4225 6331 5153 Steel; Ferrous metals; Nonferrous metal sheets, bars, rods, etc.; Automotive supplies; General warehousing & storage; Fire, marine & casualty insurance; Grain & field beans
Pr: Akihiro Sago
Treas: Kazumasa Miyazaki
Ex VP: Yoshiki Miura
Sr VP: Arthur Harrison
Sr VP: Futoshi Horisaki
Sr VP: Michael Lavender
Sr VP: Thomas Neyens
Sr VP: George Pierce
VP: Steve Tames
Natl Sales: Frank Zarcone
Board of Directors: Jun Karube

TOYOTA-WILDE AUTOMOTIVE GROUP
See WILDE OF WEST ALLIS INC

D-U-N-S 96-850-7152 IMP
TOYOTETSU AMERICA INC
TTNA
(*Suby of* TOYODA IRON WORKS CO.,LTD.)
100 Pin Oak Dr, Somerset, KY 42503-7600
Tel (606) 274-9005 *Founded/Ownrshp* 1995
Sales 213.0MM^E *EMP* 755
SIC 3465 3714 3429 Automotive stampings; Motor vehicle parts & accessories; Manufactured hardware (general)
Pr: Jiro Iwase
Ofcr: Doug Carter
**VP:* Hiroshi Hattori
**VP:* Herbert Krase
VP: Lee Voight
Genl Mgr: Mark Redmond
Off Mgr: Brinda Hurt
QA Dir: Jarritt Sharpe
QA Dir: David Tallent
Sales Asso: Laura Brock

D-U-N-S 00-698-5808 IMP/EXP
TOYS "R" US INC
1 Geoffrey Way, Wayne, NJ 07470-2066
Tel (973) 617-3500 *Founded/Ownrshp* 1948
Sales 11.8MMM *EMP* 62,000
SIC 5945 5734 5999 5735 5641 5941 Toys & games; Children's toys & games, except dolls; Dolls & accessories; Games (chess, backgammon & other durable games); Software, computer games; Personal computers; Swimming pools, above ground; Records; Children's wear; Infants' wear; Sporting goods & bicycle shops; Bicycle & bicycle parts
Ch Bd: David A Brandon
V Ch: Timothy Grace
Pr: Wolfgang Link
Pr: Monika M Merz
Pr: Melanie Teed-Murch
CFO: Michael J Short
Ch: Kevin Macnab
Chf Mktg O: Richard Barry
Ex VP: David J Schwartz
Ex VP: Patrick J Venezia
Ex VP: Amy Von Walter
Sr VP: Richard A Lennox
Sr VP: Debbie Lentz
Sr VP: Reg McLay
VP: Desire Alexander
VP: Frederick Apfel
VP: John Gregory
VP: Troy Rice
VP: Kevin Sayers
VP: Jamie Uitdenhowen
VP: Robert Zarra
Board of Directors: Joshua Bekenstein, Richard Goodman, Matthew S Levin, Joseph Macnow, Paul E Raether, Wendy Silverstein, Nathaniel H Taylor

D-U-N-S 96-487-4684
TOYS "R" US PROPERTY CO II LLC
(*Suby of* TOYS "R" US INC) ★
1 Geoffrey Way, Wayne, NJ 07470-2066
Tel (973) 617-3500 *Founded/Ownrshp* 2010
Sales 118.4MM *EMP* 4^E
SIC 6512 Nonresidential building operators
CEO: Antonio Urcelay

D-U-N-S 78-425-5692 IMP/EXP
TOYS "R" US-DELAWARE INC
BABIES "R" US
(*Suby of* TOYS "R" US INC) ★
1 Geoffrey Way, Wayne, NJ 07470-2066
Tel (973) 617-3500 *Founded/Ownrshp* 2003
Sales 4.6MMM^E *EMP* 57,900
SIC 5945 5999 5641 Toys & games; Infant furnishings & equipment; Children's & infants' wear stores
CEO: David A Brandon
**CFO:* Michael Short
**Ex VP:* Richard Barry
Genl Mgr: Howard Guren
Board of Directors: Michael M Calbert, Michael D Fascitelli

D-U-N-S 78-641-3302
TP MECHANICAL CONTRACTORS INC
1500 Kemper Meadow Dr, Cincinnati, OH 45240-1638
Tel (513) 851-8881 *Founded/Ownrshp* 1999
Sales 278.3MM^E *EMP* 525
SIC 6552 Subdividers & developers
Pr: Scott Teepe Sr
Mng Pt: Robert J Mauntel
**Pr:* Bill Riddle
**VP:* Jason Ralstin
Exec: Sarah IPSA
Dir IT: Randy Blakeslee
Dir IT: John Pennell
Sys Mgr: Tim Parrett
Opers Mgr: David Nagel
Snr Mgr: Brian Kuhlman
Snr Mgr: Tim Sargent

D-U-N-S 01-598-9784 IMP
TP-LINK USA CORP
145 S State College Blvd # 400, Brea, CA 92821-5818
Tel (626) 333-0234 *Founded/Ownrshp* 2008
Sales 104.6MM *EMP* 110^E
SIC 5045 Computer peripheral equipment
CEO: Zheng Wu
**VP:* Andy Chen
VP: David LI
Exec: Marianne Huang
Off Mgr: Amie Wu
Mktg Dir: Dana Knight

D-U-N-S 17-356-7996 IMP/EXP
TPC GROUP INC
1 Allen Ctr Ste 1000, Houston, TX 77002
Tel (713) 627-7474 *Founded/Ownrshp* 2012
Sales 2.4MMM^E *EMP* 525
SIC 2869 Industrial organic chemicals; Butadiene (industrial organic chemical)
Pr: Michael T McDonnell
**Pr:* Ed Dineen
**CFO:* Miguel A Desdin
Treas: Kim Craig
**Sr VP:* Eugene R Allspach
Sr VP: Charles W Graham
VP: Sandra Davis
VP: Allen Eschette
VP: Charles Graham
VP: Shelly Heuser
VP: Ann Levy
VP: Andrew Miller
VP: Courtney Ruth
**VP:* Rishi A Varma
**VP:* Roger Wollenberg

D-U-N-S 36-142-5395 IMP
TPC GROUP LLC
(*Suby of* TPC GROUP INC) ★
1 Allen Center 500, Houston, TX 77002
Tel (713) 477-9211 *Founded/Ownrshp* 2004
Sales 2.4MMM^E *EMP* 463
SIC 2869 Butadiene (industrial organic chemical)
Pr: Michael T McDonnell
Sr VP: Luis Bitaz
Sr VP: Russ Crockett
Exec: Donna Smelser
Mfg Dir: Rudy McCamish

TPG
See PORTLAND GROUP INC

TPG ADVISORS II
See TPG ASIA ADVISORS II INC

D-U-N-S 03-939-6143 IMP
TPG ASIA ADVISORS II INC
TPG ADVISORS II
301 Commerce St Ste 3300, Fort Worth, TX 76102-4133
Tel (817) 871-4000 *Founded/Ownrshp* 1993
Sales 228.8MM^E *EMP* 11,000
SIC 3674 Semiconductors & related devices
Pr: David Bonderman

D-U-N-S 87-654-2077
TPG CAPITAL MANAGEMENT LP
TEXAS PACIFIC GROUP
301 Commerce St Ste 3300, Fort Worth, TX 76102-4133
Tel (817) 871-4000 *Founded/Ownrshp* 1992
Sales 6.2MMM^E *EMP* 9,093
SIC 6726 3674 6799 3993 6719 Investment offices; Silicon wafers, chemically doped; Venture capital companies; Signs & advertising specialties; Investment holding companies, except banks
Mng Pt: David Bonderman
Pt: James G Coulter
Pt: Vivek Paul
Pt: Ganendran Sarvananthan
Mng Pt: Ben Gray
COO: Jerome C Vascellaro
CFO: Jim O'Brien
CFO: John E Viola
VP: Cindy Black
VP: Jennifer Dixon
VP: Sid Khotkar
VP: Peter McGoohan
VP: Tetsuro Onitsuka
VP: Tanguy Serra
VP: David A Spuri
VP: Spencer Stenmark
Dir Soc: Marti Templeton

TPG CREATIVE CAPITAL
See ACCELERATE HOLDINGS CORP

TPG GROWTH
See TPG PARTNERS III LP

D-U-N-S 00-346-7981
TPG HOLDINGS LLC
(*Suby of* BELFOR PROPERTY RESTORATION) ★
719 Griswold St Ste 2100, Detroit, MI 48226-3360
Tel (313) 496-3500 *Founded/Ownrshp* 2011
Sales 36.8MM^E *EMP* 1,350
SIC 7349 Janitorial service, contract basis
Prin: Sheldon Yellen

D-U-N-S 11-082-9793
TPG PARTNERS III LP
TPG GROWTH
(*Suby of* TEXAS PACIFIC GROUP) ★
345 California St # 3300, San Francisco, CA 94104-2606
Tel (415) 743-1500 *Founded/Ownrshp* 1999
Sales 947.6MM^E *EMP* 1,740
SIC 1311 1389 4922 5082 Crude petroleum production; Natural gas production; Oil field services; Natural gas transmission; Oil field equipment
Mng Pt: William E McGlashan
Pt: David Bonderman
Pt: James G Coulter
Pt: William S Price
Mng Pt: Richard Schifter
CFO: Jeff Ekberg
VP: Mark Braganza
VP: Tanguy Serra
Mng Dir: David Ibnale

Mng Dir: Bryan Taylor
Mng Dir: Jim Williams

D-U-N-S 08-626-6215
TPG PARTNERS LP
301 Commerce St Ste 3300, Fort Worth, TX 76102-4133
Tel (817) 871-4000 *Founded/Ownrshp* 1985
Sales 389.1MM^E *EMP* 2,091^E
SIC 6722 Management investment, open-end
Pt: James G Coulter
Genl Pt: Tpg Genpar LP
VP Opers: Jerome C Vascellaro

D-U-N-S 07-833-0042
TPG SPECIALTY LENDING INC
301 Commerce St Ste 3300, Fort Worth, TX 76102-4133
Tel (817) 871-4000 *Founded/Ownrshp* 2010
Sales 173.4MM *EMP* 5
Accts Kpmg Llp San Francisco Ca
Tkr Sym TSLX *Exch* NYS
SIC 6726 Investment offices
Ch Bd: Joshua Easterly
COO: Robert Ollwerther
CFO: Alan Kirshenbaum
Treas: Steven Pluss
**Co-CEO:* Michael E Fishman
Chf Cred: Jennifer Mello
VP: Robert Kostow
VP: Phillip Warren

D-U-N-S 13-160-3743 IMP
TPH ACQUISITION LLLP
PARTS HOUSE, THE
10321 Fortune Pkwy, Jacksonville, FL 32256-3680
Tel (904) 731-3034 *Founded/Ownrshp* 2002
Sales 135.5MM^E *EMP* 300
SIC 5013 Automotive supplies
Pr: David Honig
**COO:* David Miller
**VP:* Brian Mendelson
IT Man: Brian Hashman

D-U-N-S 00-119-4661
▲TPI COMPOSITES INC
8501 N Scottsdale Rd # 280, Scottsdale, AZ 85253-2759
Tel (480) 305-8910 *Founded/Ownrshp* 1968
Sales 585.8MM *EMP* 6,000
Tkr Sym TPIC *Exch* NGM
SIC 3728 Blades, aircraft propeller: metal or wood
Pr: Steven C Lockard
**Ch Bd:* Paul G Giovacchini
COO: Mark R McFeely
CFO: William E Siwek
**Ofcr:* Wayne G Monie
Ex VP: Thomas J Castle
Ex VP: Lars Moller
VP: Ramesh Gopalakrishnan
Mtls Mgr: Leo Allen
QI Cn Mgr: Jaime Manon
QI Cn Mgr: Mike Paulson
Board of Directors: Stephen B Bransfield, Michael L Derosa, Philip J Deutch, Scott N Humber, Daniel G Weiss

D-U-N-S 00-337-4097 IMP/EXP
TPI CORP
114 Roscoe Fitz Rd, Johnson City, TN 37615-3436
Tel (800) 682-3398 *Founded/Ownrshp* 1949
Sales 137.0MM^E *EMP* 550
SIC 3567 3564 Heating units & devices, industrial: electric; Ventilating fans: industrial or commercial
CEO: Robert E Henry Jr
Pt: Thomas Young
Sr VP: Dan Berry
VP: Roger Perkins
VP: Martha Preston
CIO: Indy Banerjee
CIO: Tom Lang
Mtls Mgr: Jack Miller
Sls Mgr: Alessandro La Bella
Board of Directors: Robert T Dennis, Robert E Henry Sr

D-U-N-S 87-954-6658 IMP
■TPI IOWA LLC
(*Suby of* TPI COMPOSITES INC) ★
2300 N 33rd E, Newton, IA 50208-8261
Tel (641) 791-3500 *Founded/Ownrshp* 2007
Sales 215.8MM^E *EMP* 500
SIC 3083 Laminated plastics plate & sheet
CEO: Steven Lockard
**COO:* Wayne G Monie
COO: Wayne Monie
CFO: John Goldsberry

D-U-N-S 00-535-8130
■TPI PETROLEUM INC
VICKERS PETROLEUM DIVISION
(*Suby of* ONE INTERNATIONAL CENTER) ★
6000 N Loop 1604 W, San Antonio, TX 78249-1100
Tel (210) 592-2000 *Founded/Ownrshp* 1937, 1970
Sales 177.8MM^E *EMP* 2,090
SIC 2911 5541 4612 4212 4213

D-U-N-S 17-257-8775
TPP ACQUISITION INC
PICTURE PEOPLE, THE
1155 Kas Dr Ste 180, Richardson, TX 75081-1970
Tel (972) 265-7600 *Founded/Ownrshp* 2005
Sales 127.2MM^E *EMP* 3,800
SIC 7221 Photographic studios, portrait
Pr: Charlie M Masson
CFO: Tom Jewell
**CFO:* Jerry Kollar
**CFO:* Mary Knight Tyler
VP: Jeff Belloti
**Brnch Mgr:* Michael McDiffett
Tech Mgr: Fernando Duarte
Sales Asso: Sara Goolsby

D-U-N-S 17-097-0169
TPS PARKING MANAGEMENT LLC
PARKING SPOT, THE
200 W Monroe St Ste 1500, Chicago, IL 60606-5114
Tel (312) 781-9396 *Founded/Ownrshp* 2011
Sales 101.7MM^E *EMP* 700

SIC 7521 Automobile parking
CEO: Kevin J Shrier
**Sr VP:* Tim Holic
**Sr VP:* Todd Johnson
**Sr VP:* Mary Ruberry
**Sr VP:* Mark P Wildman

D-U-N-S 01-619-7282
TPUSA - FHCS INC
TELEPERFORMANCE
(*Suby of* TELEPERFORMANCE USA) ★
215 N Marengo Ave Ste 160, Pasadena, CA 91101-1524
Tel (213) 873-5100 *Founded/Ownrshp* 2014
Sales 480.9MM^E *EMP* 4,576^E
SIC 7376 7373 Computer facilities management; Systems integration services
Pr: Jeff Balagna
**Treas:* Dean Duncan

D-U-N-S 04-647-5013
TPUSA INC
TELEPERFORMANCE USA
(*Suby of* TELEPERFORMANCE SE)
6510 S Millrock Dr # 150, Holladay, UT 84121-4027
Tel (801) 257-5800 *Founded/Ownrshp* 1993
Sales 1.2MMM^E *EMP* 12,000
SIC 7389 Telemarketing services
CEO: Dominick Dato
**Pr:* Jeff Balagna
Pr: Sheila Curr
Pr: Jeff Koehler
COO: Stephanie Wilson
**CFO:* Brad Hansen
Ex VP: Michael Anderson
Ex VP: Dan Kramer
Ex VP: Mark Pfeiffer
Sr VP: Evan Davis
Sr VP: Blair Frankenberg
Sr VP: Tom Gebhart
Sr VP: Roger Nunn
VP: Matthew Bowman
VP: Jeffrey Hest
VP: Brad Lindemann
VP: Gary L McInnis
**VP:* Brent Welch
VP: Mark Wiley
VP: Jeremy Young

D-U-N-S 05-970-8356
TPUSA INC
1991 S 4650 W, Salt Lake City, UT 84104-4701
Tel (801) 257-5800 *Founded/Ownrshp* 1995
Sales 4.0MMM *EMP* 100
SIC 7389 Telemarketing services
CEO: Dominick Dato
**Pr:* Jeff Balagna
**CFO:* Brad Hansen
**VP:* Brent Welch

TQL
See TOTAL QUALITY LOGISTICS LLC

D-U-N-S 17-990-5393
TR BRYANT ASSOCIATES INC
377 Hoes Ln, Piscataway, NJ 08854-4138
Tel (732) 981-0440 *Founded/Ownrshp* 1983
Sales 19.8MM^E *EMP* 1,500
Accts Sax Macy Fromm & Co Pc Clif
SIC 7363 7361 Temporary help service; Executive placement
CEO: Jean Bryant
**Pr:* Kathy Warren
**VP:* Thomas R Bryant

D-U-N-S 04-549-6986
■**TR MANUFACTURING LLC**
(*Suby of* CORNING INC) ★
45757 Northport Loop W, Fremont, CA 94538-6460
Tel (510) 657-3850 *Founded/Ownrshp* 2015
Sales 120.0MM *EMP* 254
SIC 3699 Electrical equipment & supplies; Extension cords
Pr: Dom Tran
**COO:* Jack Cho
Prgrm Mgr: Scott Cho
Prgrm Mgr: Hung Tran

TRA AUCTIONS
See TOTAL RESOURCE AUCTIONS INC

D-U-N-S 07-911-4659
TRAC INTERMODAL LLC
750 College Rd E, Princeton, NJ 08540-6646
Tel (609) 452-8900 *Founded/Ownrshp* 2012
Sales 102.0MM^E *EMP* 672^E
SIC 7359 3715 5012 Equipment rental & leasing; Truck trailers; Trailers for passenger vehicles
CEO: Keith E Lovetro
**COO:* Val T Noel
**CFO:* Chris Annese
Treas: Blake Morris
**Ex VP:* Gregg Carpene
Sr VP: Mark Michaels
VP: Inbal Arie
VP: James Bowe
VP: Rich Hediger
VP: Richard Mazur
**VP:* Kevin Snyder
VP: Todd Steiner

D-U-N-S 04-462-9020
TRAC-WORK INC (TX)
3801 N I 45, Ennis, TX 75119-0977
Tel (972) 875-6565 *Founded/Ownrshp* 1968
Sales 149.8MM^E *EMP* 300
SIC 1629

D-U-N-S 18-891-8163 IMP
TRACE DIE CAST INC
140 Graham Ave, Bowling Green, KY 42101-9180
Tel (270) 781-0049 *Founded/Ownrshp* 1987
Sales 112.5MM^E *EMP* 475
SIC 3363 Aluminum die-castings
CEO: Lowell M Guthrie
**Pr:* Chris Guthrie

D-U-N-S 12-132-4573
TRACE3 INC
7565 Irvine Center Dr # 200, Irvine, CA 92618-4919
Tel (949) 333-1801 *Founded/Ownrshp* 2001
Sales 132.3MM^E *EMP* 300
SIC 8742 Sales (including sales management) consultant
CEO: Hayes Drumwright
**CEO:* Tyler Beecher
Chf Mktg O: Paul Wiederkehr
Sr VP: Paul Markel
**VP:* Terri Cooper
VP: Tony Olzak
VP: Tim Pivnicny
VP: Kristin Struttmann
Mktg Dir: Todd Gallina
Sales Asso: Dori Nutter
Sales Asso: Greg Patterson

D-U-N-S 15-035-1815
TRACER CONSTRUCTION LLC
(*Suby of* FLOW CONTROL US HOLDING CORP) ★
7433 Harwin Dr, Houston, TX 77036-2007
Tel (713) 868-5500 *Founded/Ownrshp* 2000
Sales 93.9MM^E *EMP* 528
SIC 1731 Electrical work
Pr: Alok Maskara
Pr: David A Dunbar
Treas: Michael G Meyer
VP: Angela D Lageson
VP: David B Megna
VP: Christophe Pattyn
VP: Rashmi Raj
VP: Gustavo A Saldarriaga
IT Man: Mark Wasserman

D-U-N-S 05-350-5314
TRACER INDUSTRIES INC
(*Suby of* FLOW CONTROL US HOLDING CORP) ★
7433 Harwin Dr, Houston, TX 77036-2007
Tel (713) 868-5500 *Founded/Ownrshp* 2000
Sales 201.5MM^E *EMP* 4,000
SIC 1711 1731 Plumbing, heating, air-conditioning contractors; Electrical work
Pr: David Megna
**CFO:* Jeff Megna
VP: John S Jenkins Jr
**VP:* James Redmond
Mktg Dir: Rudy Johnston

D-U-N-S 01-077-7084 IMP/EXP
TRACEY ROAD EQUIPMENT INC
6803 Manlius Center Rd, East Syracuse, NY 13057-3904
Tel (315) 437-1471 *Founded/Ownrshp* 1976
Sales 87.3MM^E *EMP* 200
SIC 5082 5012 7353 7699 5013 Road construction equipment; Commercial vehicles; Trucks, commercial; Heavy construction equipment rental; Construction equipment repair; Truck parts & accessories
Pr: Gerald W Tracey
**COO:* Christopher Polomino
**VP:* Joel Chesley
**VP:* Debbie Tracey

D-U-N-S 94-678-3222 IMP/EXP
TRACFONE WIRELESS INC
(*Suby of* AMX USA HOLDING, S.A. DE C.V.)
9700 Nw 112th Ave, Medley, FL 33178-1353
Tel (305) 640-2000 *Founded/Ownrshp* 2010
Sales 360.0MM^E *EMP* 734^E
SIC 4813 4812 Telephone communications broker; Cellular telephone services
Pr: Joe Mirto
Pr: Francisco Zerpa
Ex VP: John Collier
Ex VP: Stephen Ritter
Ex VP: Richard Salzman
VP: Robert Buznego
VP: Cesar Cruz
VP: Johnathan Drissel
VP: Steven Emmett
VP: Jesus Fernandez
VP: Jill Garcia
VP: Nathan Landrau
VP: David Lawing
VP: Juan Peraza
VP: Richard Smallman
VP: Tom Tang
VP: Lucien Tenn
VP: Raymundo Varela
VP: Israel Velez
VP: Ralph Wasner
VP: Ian Woods

D-U-N-S 15-422-3077 IMP/EXP
TRACKER MARINE LLC
(*Suby of* BASS PRO SHOPS) ★
2500 E Kearney St, Springfield, MO 65898-0001
Tel (417) 873-5900 *Founded/Ownrshp* 1978
Sales 324.1MM^E *EMP* 2,500
SIC 3732

D-U-N-S 01-750-9360 EXP
■**TRACO DELAWARE INC**
(*Suby of* ARCONIC EUROPE SARL)
71 Progress Ave, Cranberry Township, PA 16066-3596
Tel (724) 776-7000 *Founded/Ownrshp* 1994, 2010
Sales 201.6MM^E *EMP* 1,600^E
SIC 3442 3211 3444 3448 3354 7992 Storm doors or windows, metal; Skylight glass; Insulating glass, sealed units; Skylights, sheet metal; Greenhouses: prefabricated metal; Aluminum extruded products; Public golf courses
CEO: Robert P Randall
**CFO:* Fran Stephen
**VP:* John Kalakos
**VP:* Brett Randall
Sls&Mrk Ex: Dave Forrest

D-U-N-S 18-387-3280
TRACO PRODUCTION SERVICES INC
425 Griffin Rd, Youngsville, LA 70592-5517
Tel (337) 857-6000 *Founded/Ownrshp* 1987
Sales 123.1MM^E *EMP* 137
SIC 5082 1389 Oil field equipment; Oil & gas wells: building, repairing & dismantling
Pr: Tommy R Allen
**Pr:* Troy D Collins

**Sec:* Gaynell Allen
**Sr VP:* Kendall R Allen
**VP:* Elton Broussard
Opers Mgr: Troy Romero

D-U-N-S 79-709-2603 IMP
TRACTOR & EQUIPMENT CO
CATERPILLAR AUTHORIZED DEALER
(*Suby of* HARNISH GROUP INC) ★
17035 W Valley Hwy, Tukwila, WA 98188-5519
Tel (425) 251-9800 *Founded/Ownrshp* 1929
Sales 141.4MM^E *EMP* 400
SIC 5082 Construction & mining machinery
Pr: John J Harnish
**VP:* Richard Bellin
**VP:* Troy Hickey
VP: Jagi Nichols
Sls Mgr: Toby Lester

D-U-N-S 00-796-0503 IMP/EXP
TRACTOR & EQUIPMENT CO INC (AL)
5336 Airport Hwy, Birmingham, AL 35212-1599
Tel (205) 591-2131 *Founded/Ownrshp* 1943, 2008
Sales 209.8MM^E *EMP* 450
SIC 5082 Construction & mining machinery
Pr: Dan Stracener
**CFO:* Jamie Steele
**Ex VP:* Steve Day
VP: Gerald Carroll
VP: Larry Watkins
Assoc Dir: Christopher M Howard
Brnch Mgr: Mack Brice
Brnch Mgr: Frank Dabbs
Brnch Mgr: Kevin Reid
IT Man: Buddy Averett
IT Man: Joseph Minor

D-U-N-S 00-693-2917 IMP
▲**TRACTOR SUPPLY CO**
5401 Virginia Way, Brentwood, TN 37027-7536
Tel (615) 440-4000 *Founded/Ownrshp* 1938
Sales 6.2MMM *EMP* 12,000
Accts Ernst & Young Llp Nashville
Tkr Sym TSCO *Exch* NGS
SIC 5999 5261 5251 5531 5699 Farm equipment & supplies; Feed & farm supply; Nurseries & garden centers; Lawnmowers & tractors; Garden tractors & tillers; Fertilizer; Tools; Pumps & pumping equipment; Truck equipment & parts; Work clothing
Pr: Gregory A Sandfort
**Ch Bd:* Cynthia T Jamison
CFO: Anthony F Crudele
Chf Mktg O: Steve Barbarick
Sr VP: Robert D Mills
Sr VP: Benjamin F Parrish Jr
Board of Directors: Johnston C Adams, Peter D Bewley, Keith R Halbert, Ram Krishnan, George Mackenzie, Edna K Morris, Mark J Weikel

D-U-N-S 07-989-5654
■**TRACTOR SUPPLY CO OF TEXAS LP** (TX)
(*Suby of* TRACTOR SUPPLY CO) ★
5401 Virginia Way, Brentwood, TN 37027-7536
Tel (877) 718-6750 *Founded/Ownrshp* 2001
Sales 5.7MMM^E *EMP* 12,000^E
SIC 5084 5999 Tractors, industrial; Farm equipment & supplies
CEO: Gregory A Sandfort
Ex VP: Steve K Barbarick
Ex VP: Anthony F Crudele
Ex VP: Lee J Downing
Sr VP: Chad M Frazell

TRACY & RYDER
See PARK WEST COMPANIES INC

D-U-N-S 80-642-5026 IMP
TRACY INDUSTRIES INC
GENUINE PARTS DISTRIBUTORS
3737 Capitol Ave, City of Industry, CA 90601-1732
Tel (562) 692-9034 *Founded/Ownrshp* 1946
Sales 142.0MM *EMP* 216
SIC 3519 7538
CEO: Timothy Engvall
**VP:* Erma Jean Tracy
Dir IT: Lisa Schumacher

D-U-N-S 07-188-7301
TRACY UNIFIED SCHOOL DISTRICT
1875 W Lowell Ave, Tracy, CA 95376-2262
Tel (209) 830-3200 *Founded/Ownrshp* 1912
Sales 94.7MM^E *EMP* 1,500
SIC 8211 Public elementary & secondary schools; High school, junior or senior
COO: Jay Fishburn
VP: Kelly Lewis
Prgrm Mgr: Julie Stocking
Off Mgr: Sue Edmiston
CIO: Cheryl Reszka
Schl Brd P: Ted Guzman
HC Dir: Cindy Edminston

D-U-N-S 61-437-4791 IMP/EXP
TRAD NORTH AMERICA INC
TRA
(*Suby of* T.RAD CO., LTD.)
750 Frank Yost Ln, Hopkinsville, KY 42240-6820
Tel (270) 885-9116 *Founded/Ownrshp* 1993
Sales 137.0MM^E *EMP* 495
SIC 3433 Radiators, except electric
Pr: Tatsuya Kikuyama
Dir Lab: Larry Duke
Genl Mgr: Phil Dunn
Genl Mgr: Monty Guier
QA Dir: Audra Lacy
IT Man: Roy Staley
Opers Mgr: Toshio Sato
Sls Mgr: Rick Fujimura

D-U-N-S 02-506-1787
▲**TRADE DESK INC**
THETRADEDESK
42 N Chestnut St, Ventura, CA 93001-2662
Tel (805) 585-3434 *Founded/Ownrshp* 2010
Sales 113.8MM *EMP* 387^E
Tkr Sym TTD *Exch* NGM
SIC 7311 Advertising agencies
CEO: Jeff Green
**Pr:* Jeff T Green

**COO:* Robert D Perdue
CFO: Paul E Ross
Chf Cred: Brian J Stempeck
Dir Bus: Matt Mitchell
CTO: David R Pickles
Mktg Mgr: Parisa Ebrahimi
Board of Directors: Roger Ehrenberg, Kathryn E Falberg, Thomas Falk, Eric B Paley, Juan N Villalonga, David B Wells

TRADE FINANCE SOLUTIONS
See TFS RT INC

TRADE FINANCE SOLUTIONS
See TFP INTERNATIONAL INC

D-U-N-S 82-518-2673
TRADE FINANCE SOLUTIONS INC
20807 Biscayne Blvd # 203, Aventura, FL 33180-1410
Tel (786) 279-2900 *Founded/Ownrshp* 1999
Sales 100.0MM^E *EMP* 40
SIC 7389 Financial services
Pr: Steve McDonald

TRADE STYLE FAMILY FARE SPRMKT
See FAMILY FARE INC

D-U-N-S 96-620-8204
TRADEBE ENVIRONMENTAL SERVICES LLC
(*Suby of* TRADEBE GP) ★
1433 E 83rd Ave Ste 200, Merrillville, IN 46410-6307
Tel (800) 388-7242 *Founded/Ownrshp* 1986
Sales 262.1MM^E *EMP* 742
SIC 4953 7699 1389 Hazardous waste collection & disposal; Recycling, waste materials; Ship boiler & tank cleaning & repair, contractors; Industrial equipment cleaning; Lease tanks, oil field: erecting, cleaning & repairing
CEO: Victor De Villalonga
**COO:* Sergio Nusimovich Kolodny
CFO: Mike Ferraro
Ex VP: Glynda Harrington
VP: Terry Healy
Genl Mgr: Bob Obrien
Dir IT: Jordan Denney
Opers Mgr: Joe Festa
Natl Sales: Jennifer Logan

D-U-N-S 02-022-1619
TRADEBE GP
(*Suby of* TRADEBE ENVIRONMENTAL SERVICES SL)
4343 Kennedy Ave, East Chicago, IN 46312-2723
Tel (800) 388-7242 *Founded/Ownrshp* 2008
Sales 262.6MM^E *EMP* 742
Accts Mcgladrey & Pullen Llp Chica
SIC 4953 7699 1389 Hazardous waste collection & disposal; Recycling, waste materials; Ship boiler & tank cleaning & repair, contractors; Industrial equipment cleaning; Lease tanks, oil field: erecting, cleaning & repairing
Prin: Victor C De Villalonga
Prin: Victor Creixell De Villalonga

TRADEBE TRANSPORTATION
See TRADEBE TREATMENT AND RECYCLING NORTHEAST LLC

D-U-N-S 85-938-5254 IMP/EXP
TRADEBE TREATMENT AND RECYCLING LLC
(*Suby of* TRADEBE ENVIRONMENTAL SERVICES LLC) ★
4343 Kennedy Ave, East Chicago, IN 46312-2723
Tel (219) 397-3951 *Founded/Ownrshp* 2008
Sales 89.9MM^E *EMP* 320
SIC 4953 Hazardous waste collection & disposal
Prin: Robert O'Brien
**Prin:* Sergio Nusimovich Kolodny
IT Man: Daniel Snyder
Plnt Mgr: David Linder

D-U-N-S 15-413-3672
TRADEBE TREATMENT AND RECYCLING NORTHEAST LLC
TRADEBE TRANSPORTATION
47 Gracey Ave, Meriden, CT 06451-2284
Tel (203) 238-8102 *Founded/Ownrshp* 1982
Sales 242.3MM^E *EMP* 350
SIC 4953 1442 4212

D-U-N-S 00-886-9398 IMP
TRADEHOME SHOE STORES INC (MN)
TRADEHOME SHOES
8300 97th St S, Cottage Grove, MN 55016-4341
Tel (651) 459-8600 *Founded/Ownrshp* 1921, 1999
Sales 104.7MM^E *EMP* 975^E
SIC 5661 Shoe stores; Footwear, athletic
CEO: Patrick Teal
CFO: Stacy Robjent
**VP:* John Munn
**VP:* Bob Wasvick
**VP:* Steve Welter
**VP:* Brian Wilkinson
Mktg Dir: Lorne Streiff

TRADEHOME SHOES
See TRADEHOME SHOE STORES INC

D-U-N-S 01-216-6810 IMP/EXP
■**TRADEMARK METALS RECYCLING LLC**
TMR
(*Suby of* DAVID J JOSEPH CO) ★
The Lincoln Center 5401 W, Tampa, FL 33609
Tel (813) 226-0088 *Founded/Ownrshp* 1998
Sales 105.2MM^E *EMP* 400
SIC 5093 1081 Metal scrap & waste materials; Nonferrous metals scrap; Metal mining services
Pr: Brad Ford
**VP:* Greg Oelrich
**VP:* Brian Phillippi
Genl Mgr: Carl Coghlan
Genl Mgr: Ron Lehan
Genl Mgr: Tyrone McCloud
Genl Mgr: Phil Speigel
Genl Mgr: Phil Spiegel
CTO: Ronald Christenson
Sfty Mgr: Argelio Chappotin
Sfty Mgr: Terry McWhorter

TRADER JOE FONTANA WAREHOUSE
See WORLD CLASS DISTRIBUTION INC

D-U-N-S 00-622-6666 IMP/EXP
TRADER JOES CO (CA)
TRADER JOE'S MARKETS
(*Suby of* T.A.C.T. HOLDING, INC.)
800 S Shamrock Ave, Monrovia, CA 91016-6346
Tel (626) 599-3700 *Founded/Ownrshp* 1958, 2008
Sales 1.3MMM^E *EMP* 5,500
SIC 5411 5921

TRADER JOE'S MARKETS
See TRADER JOES CO

TRADESMAN TRUCK ACCESSORIES
See LUND INTERNATIONAL HOLDING CO

D-U-N-S 80-529-6753
TRADESMEN INTERNATIONAL LLC
9760 Shepard Rd, Macedonia, OH 44056-1124
Tel (440) 349-3432 *Founded/Ownrshp* 1990
Sales 98.0MM^E *EMP* 326
SIC 7361 Labor contractors (employment agency)
Pr: Joseph O Wesley
Pr: George Brophy
**COO:* Stephen Bowker Sr
**CFO:* John Marko
**Sr VP:* Mike Christiansen
VP: Bill Klausman
**VP:* Ron Rowen
VP: Sandra Welker
Genl Mgr: Ryan Allen
Genl Mgr: Mark Chilelli
Genl Mgr: Scott Crim

D-U-N-S 83-325-1184
TRADESOURCE INC
205 Hallene Rd Unit 211, Warwick, RI 02886-2452
Tel (401) 384-6148 *Founded/Ownrshp* 1995
Sales 47.5MM^E *EMP* 1,200
SIC 7361 1751 1711 1731 1742 1721 Employment agencies; Carpentry work; Heating & air conditioning contractors; Mechanical contractor; Plumbing contractors; Electrical work; Acoustical & ceiling work; Painting & paper hanging
CEO: Jim Ferry
**CFO:* Gordon Sigman
**Ch:* Richard Kaskel
**VP:* Steve Blank
**VP:* Tres Huber

D-U-N-S 00-718-3481
TRADESTATION GROUP INC
8050 Sw 10th St Ste 4000, Plantation, FL 33324-3290
Tel (954) 652-7000 *Founded/Ownrshp* 2011
Sales 217.3MM^E *EMP* 510^E
SIC 6211 Security brokers & dealers
CEO: Salomon Sredni
**COO:* John R Roberts
**CFO:* Edward Codispoti
Ofcr: Richard Libertucci
VP: Keith Black
VP: T Keith Black
**VP:* William P Cahill
Exec: Loren Lopez
Brnch Mgr: Adam Cohn
Snr Sftwr: Manideep Bora
Snr Sftwr: Mike Elledge

D-U-N-S 15-995-1060
■TRADEWEB MARKETS LLC
(*Suby of* THOMSON FINANCIAL) ★
1177 Avenues Of The Am, New York, NY 10036
Tel (646) 430-6000 *Founded/Ownrshp* 1998
Sales 276.0MM^E *EMP* 850
SIC 6211 Bond dealers & brokers
CEO: Lee Olesky
Pr: Richard Greco
**Pr:* Billy Hult
Pr: Taisiya Kapatsinskaya
Pr: Harish Korada
Pr: Marguerite White
**CFO:* Robert Warshaw
Ofcr: Michael Webb
VP: Frank Aldridge
VP: Vanessa Bonora
VP: Andrew Chu
VP: McCous Fevrier
VP: Paul Garavente
VP: Jonathan Herbert
VP: Jim Leary
VP: Arnaud Malfoy
VP: Satish Sundri
VP: Juan Vargas

D-U-N-S 80-857-8301
■TRADEWINDS HEATING & AIR CONDITIONING
(*Suby of* NICOR ENERGY SERVICES CO) ★
2019 Corporate Ln Ste 159, Naperville, IL 60563-9748
Tel (630) 718-2700 *Founded/Ownrshp* 2007
Sales 170.6M^E *EMP* 1,439^E
SIC 1711 Plumbing, heating, air-conditioning contractors
Prin: Dale Larkin

D-U-N-S 08-028-0594
TRADING CORP
5516 Scott View Ln, Lakeland, FL 33813-3064
Tel (754) 900-7666 *Founded/Ownrshp* 2016
Sales 800.0MM *EMP* 40
SIC 5045 5961 Computers, peripherals & software; Catalog & mail-order houses
Pr: Victor Franco

D-U-N-S 95-763-9925 IMP
TRADING TECHNOLOGIES INTERNATIONAL INC
222 S Riverside Plz # 1000, Chicago, IL 60606-5902
Tel (312) 476-1000 *Founded/Ownrshp* 1994
Sales 150.4MM^E *EMP* 500
SIC 7371 Computer software development
CEO: Rick Lane
Ch Bd: Harris Brumfield
COO: Chris Maurer
CFO: Evangelos Gialouris
Chf Mktg O: Brian Mehta
Ex VP: Steve Borsand
Ex VP: Doug Duquette
Ex VP: Roger Mills
Ex VP: Russ Rausch
VP: Parker Boveroux
VP: Katie Burgoon
VP: Joan Ebersole
VP: Chuck Horvat
VP: Bharat Mittal
VP: Richard Prybell

D-U-N-S 19-326-9131
TRADITION (NORTH AMERICA) INC
(*Suby of* TRADITION SERVICE HOLDING SA)
255 Greenwich St Fl 4, New York, NY 10007-5506
Tel (212) 791-4500 *Founded/Ownrshp* 1978
Sales 203.4MM^E *EMP* 912
SIC 6211 Security brokers & dealers
Pr: Emil Assentato
**Treas:* Judy Ricciardi
Ofcr: Eric Earnhardt
Ofcr: Jessica Sorial
Ofcr: Karen Tarlow
Ex VP: Jim Jacoby
Sr VP: Matthew Poiset
Sr VP: George Zeolla
VP: John Chirico
VP: Gregg Deutsch
VP: John Gangi
VP: Glenn Haberfield
VP: Bob Vitale

D-U-N-S 80-971-4272
TRADITIONAL BAKERY INC
SAINT LOUIS BREAD CO
2040 W Vista St, Springfield, MO 65807-5921
Tel (417) 889-8282 *Founded/Ownrshp* 1992
Sales 1.9MM *EMP* 1,600^E
SIC 5461 5812

D-U-N-S 78-497-3443 IMP
TRAEGER PELLET GRILLS LLC
1215 E Wilmington Ave # 200, Salt Lake City, UT 84106-4280
Tel (855) 382-2560 *Founded/Ownrshp* 2013
Sales 89.1MM^E *EMP* 325
SIC 3631 Barbecues, grills & braziers (outdoor cooking)
CEO: Jeremy Andrus

D-U-N-S 02-344-3864 IMP
TRAFFIC AND PARKING CONTROL CO INC
TAPCO
5100 W Brown Deer Rd, Milwaukee, WI 53223-2322
Tel (262) 814-7000 *Founded/Ownrshp* 1957
Sales 168.2MM^E *EMP* 150
SIC 5063 3444 3646 Signaling equipment, electrical; Service entrance equipment, electrical; Sheet metal specialties, not stamped; Ornamental lighting fixtures, commercial
Pr: John Kugel
**COO:* Jason Kugel
**CFO:* Eric Stangel
**CFO:* Vicki Wachtl
**Ex VP:* Andy Bergholz
VP: Kristine Awe
**VP:* Andrew Bergholz
Div Mgr: Mark Henke
CIO: Shaun Johnson
Opers Mgr: Diane Schulz
Mktg Dir: Robert Christiansen

D-U-N-S 94-268-8565 IMP
TRAFFIC MANAGEMENT INC
2435 Lemon Ave, Signal Hill, CA 90755-3462
Tel (562) 595-4278 *Founded/Ownrshp* 1992
Sales 117.9MM^E *EMP* 649
SIC 7389 8741 Flagging service (traffic control); Business management
CEO: Christopher H Spano
**COO:* Jonathan Spano
Area Mgr: Vincent Nathan
Sales Exec: Sandra Clawson
VP Sls: William Kearney
VP Sls: Michael Sprouse

D-U-N-S 96-973-7654
TRAFFIC TECH HOLDING CORP
(*Suby of* TRAFFIC TECH INC)
180 N Michigan Ave # 700, Chicago, IL 60601-7487
Tel (514) 343-0044 *Founded/Ownrshp* 2005
Sales 116.0MM^E *EMP* 566^E
SIC 4731 Truck transportation brokers
CEO: Brian Arnott

D-U-N-S 08-817-6466
TRAFFIC TECH INC
(*Suby of* TRAFFIC TECH HOLDING CORP) ★
910 Hale Pl Ste 100, Chula Vista, CA 91914-3598
Tel (514) 343-0044 *Founded/Ownrshp* 1997
Sales 110.8MM^E *EMP* 500
SIC 4731 Brokers, shipping; Domestic freight forwarding; Foreign freight forwarding
CEO: Brian Arnott
VP: Murray Bannerman
VP: Andrea Martens
Counsel: Amanda Bell

D-U-N-S 07-956-2841
TRAFIGURA CORPUS CHRISTI HOLDINGS INC
(*Suby of* TRAFIGURA AG)
7002 Marvin L Berry Rd, Corpus Christi, TX 78409-2818
Tel (361) 884-4000 *Founded/Ownrshp* 2013
Sales NA *EMP* 1,270
SIC 6719 Investment holding companies, except banks

D-U-N-S 07-958-3119
■TRAFIGURA TERMINALS LLC
CORPUS CHRISTI SHIP CHANNEL
(*Suby of* BUCKEYE TEXAS PARTNERS LLC) ★
1401 Mckinney St Ste 1375, Houston, TX 77010-4034
Tel (832) 203-6400 *Founded/Ownrshp* 2011
Sales 34.7MM^E *EMP* 1,270
SIC 4491 Docks, piers & terminals
Pr: Jeff Kopp
**Sec:* Ernie Kohnke

D-U-N-S 82-777-6522
TRAFIGURA TRADING LLC
(*Suby of* TRAFIGURA BEHEER B.V.)
1401 Mckinney St Ste 1500, Houston, TX 77010-4042
Tel (832) 203-6400 *Founded/Ownrshp* 2015
Sales 155.1MM^E *EMP* 150^E
SIC 6799 Commodity contract trading companies
Pr: Joseph H Rosenfield
**CFO:* Rodney Malcolm

D-U-N-S 09-115-5614 IMP/EXP
TRAFON GROUP INC
PACKERS PROVISION
Mercado Cntl 1229 Crr 28 St Mercado Centr, San Juan, PR 00920
Tel (787) 783-0011 *Founded/Ownrshp* 2014
Sales 140.0MM^E *EMP* 220^E
SIC 5142 Frozen vegetables & fruit products; Fruits, frozen
Pr: Carlos Trapaga
Ch Bd: Roberto Trapaga
Ex VP: Javier Pietrantoni
VP: Leyda Fresse

D-U-N-S 06-865-5018 IMP/EXP
TRAIL KING INDUSTRIES INC
(*Suby of* CC INDUSTRIES) ★
300 E Norway Ave, Mitchell, SD 57301-4777
Tel (605) 996-2562 *Founded/Ownrshp* 2010
Sales 158.8MM^E *EMP* 556
SIC 3715 3713 Truck trailers; Dump truck bodies
Pr: Carol P Lowe
VP: Joseph Kolb
VP: Bruce D Yakley
Sfty Dirs: Beth Reich
Plnt Mgr: Jerry Thomsen
Sls Mgr: Bill Soll

D-U-N-S 10-001-1480
TRAILBLAZER HEALTH ENTERPRISES LLC
(*Suby of* BLUE CROSS BLUE SHIELD OF SOUTH CAROLINA) ★
8330 L B Johnson Fwy 10 Ste 100, Dallas, TX 75243
Tel (469) 372-2000 *Founded/Ownrshp* 1998
Sales NA *EMP* 1,800
SIC 6324 Hospital & medical service plans
Pr: Gil R Glover
Treas: Michael J Mizeur
Brnch Mgr: Bob Mays
Board of Directors: Brian M Rubin

D-U-N-S 82-818-0955
TRAILBLAZER HEALTH ENTERPRISES LLC
(*Suby of* TRAILBLAZER HEALTH ENTERPRISES LLC) ★
I-20 At Alpine Road, Columbia, SC 29219-0001
Tel (803) 788-4138 *Founded/Ownrshp* 2008
Sales NA *EMP* 750^E
SIC 6324 Hospital & medical service plans
VP: George Johnson

D-U-N-S 88-474-7523
TRAILER COUNTRY INC
5326 Land O Lakes Blvd, Land O Lakes, FL 34639-3411
Tel (813) 929-0700 *Founded/Ownrshp* 2008
Sales 330.0MM *EMP* 9
SIC 5599 Utility trailers
Pr: Jennifer Amerson

TRAILER FLEET SERVICES
See TRANSPORT INTERNATIONAL POOL INC

TRAILER JOCKEY
See CAPACITY OF TEXAS INC

TRAIL'S END POPCORN COMPANY
See WEAVER POPCORN CO INC

D-U-N-S 17-520-4494 IMP
TRAM INC
(*Suby of* TOKAI RIKA CO., LTD.)
47200 Port St, Plymouth, MI 48170-6082
Tel (734) 254-8500 *Founded/Ownrshp* 1986
Sales 286.2MM^E *EMP* 672
Accts Deloitte & Touche Llp Detroit
SIC 3714 3643 Motor vehicle electrical equipment; Current-carrying wiring devices
CEO: Masayuki Morita
Ch Bd: Yoshihei Iida
Pr: Yutaka Yamauchi
Treas: Koji Umeda
VP: Koichi Kihira
VP: Rich Peavler
Prgrm Mgr: John Gray
IT Man: Jim Owens
Ql Cn Mgr: Elta Ewing
Snr Mgr: Gustav Svensson
Board of Directors: D Wilton

D-U-N-S 82-469-6355
■TRAMMELL CROW CENTRAL TEXAS LTD
(*Suby of* TRAMMELL CROW CO) ★
2001 Ross Ave Ste 325, Dallas, TX 75201-8005
Tel (214) 267-0400 *Founded/Ownrshp* 1998
Sales 180.4MM^E *EMP* 1,800
SIC 6799 6552 6512 Real estate investors, except property operators; Land subdividers & developers, commercial; Nonresidential building operators
CEO: William Concannon

D-U-N-S 96-363-7822
■TRAMMELL CROW CO
(*Suby of* CB RICHARD ELLIS REAL ESTATE SERVICES LLC) ★
2100 Mckinney Ave Ste 900, Dallas, TX 75201-6907
Tel (214) 863-3000 *Founded/Ownrshp* 2006
Sales 290.6MM^E *EMP* 6,000
SIC 6512 Nonresidential building operators; Commercial & industrial building operation
CEO: Danny Queenan
V Ch: Erwin Graves
**COO:* Michael S Duffy
**CFO:* Derek R McClain
Chf Inves: James Rgroch
Chf Inves: Matthew Skhourie
Ofcr: Brent Burgess
Ofcr: Steven Lilly
**Ex VP:* John F Bell
Ex VP: Rich Branning
**Ex VP:* Arlin E Gaffner
Ex VP: Steve Levere
Ex VP: James P Quinn
Sr VP: Robert Brandon
Sr VP: Davis Griffin
Sr VP: Mark McDermott
Sr VP: James Murray-Coleman
Sr VP: Matt Riecken
VP: Jim Andersen
VP: John Balestra
VP: Joel Behrens

D-U-N-S 78-325-6100
TRAMMELL CROW RESIDENTIAL CO
TRAMMELL CROW RESIDENTIAL SVCS
3819 Maple Ave, Dallas, TX 75219-3913
Tel (214) 922-8400 *Founded/Ownrshp* 1986
Sales 67.9MM^E *EMP* 1,795
SIC 6513 6512 6531 Apartment building operators; Nonresidential building operators; Real estate agents & managers
CEO: Kenneth Valach
**Pr:* Sam Boykin
**Pr:* Tony Ditteaux
**CFO:* Cliff Breining
**CFO:* Timothy Hogan
Assoc VP: Carter W Hopkins
Sr VP: Karsten Peterson
VP: Jason Bentley
VP: Jack Marquardt
VP: Todd Murphy
Mng Dir: Tom Dichiara

TRAMMELL CROW RESIDENTIAL SVCS
See TRAMMELL CROW RESIDENTIAL CO

D-U-N-S 04-190-9466 IMP/EXP
TRAMMO INC
1 Rockefeller Plz Fl 9, New York, NY 10020-2078
Tel (212) 223-3200 *Founded/Ownrshp* 1965
Sales 8.9MMM *EMP* 461
Accts Deloitte & Touche Llp
SIC 5191 5172 5169 Fertilizer & fertilizer materials; Petroleum products; Gases, liquefied petroleum (propane); Chemicals & allied products
Pr: Henk Van Dalfsen
COO: Edward G Weiner
Treas: James H Benfield
Ex VP: Fred M Lowenfels
Ex VP: Fred Lowenfels
Sr VP: Louis Epstein
Sr VP: Robert Lovett
Sr VP: Oliver K Stanton
VP: Todd Matthes
VP: Bernard Rock
Snr Mgr: Scott Chu

D-U-N-S 15-474-9543 IMP/EXP
TRAMONTINA USA INC
(*Suby of* TRAMONTINA S/A. CUTELARIA)
12955 W Airport Blvd, Sugar Land, TX 77478-6119
Tel (281) 340-8400 *Founded/Ownrshp* 1986
Sales 94.7MM^E *EMP* 59
SIC 5046 5072 5085 Cooking equipment, commercial; Cutlery; Hand tools; Tools
CEO: Clovis Tramontina
**Pr:* Antonio J Galafassi
Pr: Mars Mashburn
**Treas:* Eduardo Scomazzon
**VP:* Luiz R Sganderlla
Sales Exec: Sam Schwartzberg
VP Sls: Tony Pecoraro

D-U-N-S 07-027-2299 EXP
TRANE CO
TRANE COOLING & HEATING SYSTEM
(*Suby of* TRANE US INC) ★
3600 Pammel Creek Rd, La Crosse, WI 54601-7599
Tel (608) 787-2000 *Founded/Ownrshp* 1971
Sales 742.3MM^E *EMP* 2,620^E
SIC 3585 Refrigeration & heating equipment
Pr: David S Regnery
CFO: Doron Grofman
Treas: Janet M Pfeffer
Treas: Robert Smolen
DP Exec: Marleen Haas
IT Man: Terry Baier
Software D: Bob Lyden
Mktg Mgr: John Suzukida

TRANE COOLING & HEATING SYSTEM
See TRANE CO

D-U-N-S 19-144-4587 IMP
TRANE INC
(*Suby of* INGERSOLL-RAND US TRANE HOLDINGS CORP) ★
1 Centennial Ave Ste 101, Piscataway, NJ 08854-3921
Tel (732) 652-7100 *Founded/Ownrshp* 2008
Sales 9.0MMM^E *EMP* 29,000^E
SIC 3585 Refrigeration & heating equipment
Pr: David Regnery
**Ch Bd:* Michael W Lamach
CFO: John Hodson
VP: Tamatha Nagle
Area Mgr: Forrest Grahmann
Area Mgr: Randy Jones
Admn Mgr: Joseph Esposito
Brnch Mgr: Barry Elsasser
Dir IT: Kevin Reeves
IT Man: Shaun Smith
Sfty Dirs: Billy Shepherd

D-U-N-S 00-134-4621 IMP/EXP
TRANE US INC
(*Suby of* TRANE INC) ★
1 Centennial Ave Ste 101, Piscataway, NJ 08854-3921
Tel (732) 652-7100 *Founded/Ownrshp* 1885, 2008
Sales 8.0MMM^E *EMP* 29,000
SIC 3585 Refrigeration & heating equipment; Air conditioning units, complete: domestic or industrial; Counters & counter display cases, refrigerated
Pr: Michael W Lamach
**Pr:* David S Regnery
Admn Mgr: Christopher Comperchio
Dir IT: David Gerber
Snr Mgr: Angie Gensler

D-U-N-S 04-058-4810
TRANS ALTA
913 Big Hanaford Rd, Centralia, WA 98531-9101
Tel (360) 736-9901 *Founded/Ownrshp* 1999
Sales 1.8MMM^E *EMP* 800
SIC 4911 Generation, electric power
Pr: Linda Chambers

D-U-N-S 17-996-4747
TRANS DIGITAL TECHNOLOGIES LIMITED LIABILITY CO
TDT
1255 23rd St Nw Ste 100, Washington, DC 20037-1208
Tel (571) 730-7029 *Founded/Ownrshp* 2014
Sales 110.0MM^E *EMP* 1,600
SIC 7373 Systems engineering, computer related
CEO: Robert Eckel
Pr: Sen Kenneth Scheflen
Sr VP: James Albers
VP: David Stallings
Prin: Diane Grochmal
Counsel: Charles Taylor

D-U-N-S 04-487-2369 IMP
TRANS HEALTHCARE INC
930 Ridgebrook Rd, Sparks, MD 21152-9481
Tel (410) 773-1000 *Founded/Ownrshp* 1995
Sales NA *EMP* 30,000
SIC 8011 8051

D-U-N-S 07-960-8259
TRANS OCEAN LTD
4 Greenway Plz Ste 100, Houston, TX 77046-0403
Tel (713) 232-7500 *Founded/Ownrshp* 2014
Sales 126.8MM^E *EMP* 6^E
SIC 1381 Drilling oil & gas wells
Pr: Jeremy D Thigpen
COO: John Stobart
CFO: Mark Mey
Dir Risk M: Keith Avery

D-U-N-S 10-320-1489
TRANS STATES AIRLINES INC
U S AIRWAYS EXPRESS
11495 Navaid Rd 340, Bridgeton, MO 63044-2302
Tel (314) 222-4300 *Founded/Ownrshp* 1982
Sales 196.8MM^E *EMP* 1,000
SIC 4512 Air passenger carrier, scheduled
Ch Bd: Hulas Kanodia
**CEO:* Richard A Leach
**COO:* Fred Oxley
Ofcr: Joshua Dixon
Ofcr: Michael Wilchcombe
**Sr VP:* Gerry Wigmore
**VP:* Al Blosse
**VP:* David Hayes
Exec: Eileen Plante
Rgnl Mgr: Carl Caiani
CTO: Scott Short

D-U-N-S 10-339-6610 IMP/EXP
TRANS WESTERN POLYMERS INC
7539 Las Positas Rd, Livermore, CA 94551-8202
Tel (925) 449-7800 *Founded/Ownrshp* 1983
Sales 149.5MM^E *EMP* 400
SIC 2673 5023 3089 Plastic bags: made from purchased materials; Kitchen tools & utensils; Tableware, plastic
Ch Bd: Joon B Bai
**Pr:* Stephen Bai
COO: Ron Richardson
**VP:* Matthew Kim
Sales Exec: Joe Lagana

D-U-N-S 05-937-1823
▲TRANS WORLD ENTERTAINMENT CORP
38 Corporate Cir, Albany, NY 12203-5197
Tel (518) 452-1242 *Founded/Ownrshp* 1972
Sales 334.6MM *EMP* 3,000
Tkr Sym TWMC *Exch* NGM
SIC 5735 5731 5734 7841 5961 Record & prerecorded tape stores; Audio tapes, prerecorded; Compact discs; Records; Video tapes, blank; Tape recorders & players; Software, computer games; Video tape rental; Video disk/tape rental to the general public; Record &/or tape (music or video) club, mail order
CEO: Michael Feurer
Ch Bd: Robert J Higgins
CFO: John Anderson
Chf Mktg O: Scott Hoffman
Ex VP: Bruce J Eisenberg
VP: Bruce Long
Dist Mgr: Michael Barker
Board of Directors: Martin Hanaka, Robert E Marks, Joseph G Morone, Michael Nahl, W Michael Reickert, Michael B Solow

D-U-N-S 00-397-2080
TRANS WORLD RADIO
TWR
300 Gregson Dr, Cary, NC 27511-6444
Tel (919) 460-9597 *Founded/Ownrshp* 1952
Sales 99.1MM^E *EMP* 500^E
Accts Capin Crouse Llp Atlanta Geo
SIC 4832 Radio broadcasting stations
Ch: Thomas J Lowell
**CFO:* Steve Hippe
Treas: Bert Stokes
VP: John Roessner
Software D: Ryan Seal

D-U-N-S 02-147-7294
TRANS-GLOBAL SOLUTIONS INC
TGS
11811 East Fwy Ste 630, Houston, TX 77029-1952
Tel (713) 453-0341 *Founded/Ownrshp* 1978
Sales 182.2MM^E *EMP* 580
Accts Doeren Mayhew Houston Texas
SIC 4491 4013 4789 Marine cargo handling; Railroad switching; Railroad maintenance & repair services
Ch Bd: Nita Scott
**Pr:* Richard R Scott
**CFO:* Daniel J Orsini
Sfty Dirs: Robert B Tomb

TRANS-MOUNTAIN EQUIPMENT
See JD ABRAMS LP

D-U-N-S 14-441-3325 IMP/EXP
TRANS-OCEAN PRODUCTS INC
(*Suby of* MARUHA CAPITAL INVESTMENT INC) ★
350 W Orchard Dr, Bellingham, WA 98225-1769
Tel (360) 671-6886 *Founded/Ownrshp* 1985
Sales 90.0MM^E *EMP* 200
SIC 2091

D-U-N-S 03-960-5980
TRANS-PAK INC
520 Marburg Way, San Jose, CA 95133-1619
Tel (408) 254-0500 *Founded/Ownrshp* 1969
Sales 84.1MM^E *EMP* 261
SIC 7389 Packaging & labeling services
Ch: Arlene Inch
**Pr:* Bob Lally
**CEO:* Bert Inch
**COO:* Ray Horner
**CFO:* Chris Lee
Sr VP: Keith Wolf
**Sr VP:* Keith Wolfe
VP: Mark Wordekemper
Exec: Carmen Dasilva
Mng Dir: Rene Corona
IT Man: Nicolas Del Real

D-U-N-S 05-354-0386
■TRANS-PORTE INC
US FOODS OF ILLINOIS
(*Suby of* US FOODS INC) ★
9399 W Higgins Rd, Rosemont, IL 60018-6900
Tel (847) 720-8000 *Founded/Ownrshp* 1990
Sales NA *EMP* 25,000
SIC 5812 Contract food services
Pr: Bob Aiken
**Pr:* John Lederer
**COO:* Stuart Schuette
CFO: Bob Fishbune
**CFO:* Fareed Khan
**Ex VP:* David B Eberhardt
Ex VP: Raymond Roberts
**Sr VP:* Jorge Hernandez
Sr VP: Debra Lawson
VP: David Bermingham
**VP:* Dan Cakora
VP: Jerry Kalteux
VP: Tom Moses
**VP:* Juliette Pryor
VP: Peggy Schreiber
**VP:* David Schreibman
Board of Directors: Robert Aiken Jr, David B Eberhardt, Allan Swanson

D-U-N-S 17-821-2874
TRANS-RESOURCES INC
17780 Collins Ave, Sunny Isles Beach, FL 33160-2827
Tel (305) 933-8301 *Founded/Ownrshp* 2009
Sales 117.6MM^E *EMP* 736
Accts Pricewater House Coopers Llp
SIC 2873 2819 2879 Nitrogen solutions (fertilizer); Industrial inorganic chemicals; Potasssium nitrate & sulfate; Fungicides, herbicides
Exec: Mark Hirsh

D-U-N-S 80-816-2598
TRANS-SYSTEM INC
SYSTEM TWT TRANSPORTATION
7405 S Hayford Rd, Cheney, WA 99004-9633
Tel (509) 623-4001 *Founded/Ownrshp* 1972
Sales 236.8MM *EMP* 650
Accts Eidebailly Llp Spokane Washi
SIC 4213 4731 Trucking, except local; Building materials transport; Refrigerated products transport; Freight transportation arrangement
Ch Bd: James C Williams
COO: Dennis J Williams
CFO: Deanna Adams
**CFO:* Gary R King
**Treas:* Ted Rehwald
**Ex VP:* Dale J Peterson
Dir IT: Pat Soran

D-U-N-S 18-856-9396 EXP
TRANS-WEST INC
TRANSWEST TRUCK TRAILER RV
20770 Interstate 76, Brighton, CO 80603-4000
Tel (303) 289-3161 *Founded/Ownrshp* 1990
Sales 205.3MM^E *EMP* 350
SIC 5511 5012 Automobiles, new & used; Trucks, noncommercial; Trucks, commercial
Pr: George Eidsness
**Treas:* Barbara Eidsness
**VP:* Mark Stenseth
Area Mgr: Gene Deych
IT Man: John Durkin

D-U-N-S 62-386-2562
TRANSACTION NETWORK SERVICES INC
POINT OF SERVICES DIV
(*Suby of* TNS INC) ★
10740 Parkridge Blvd # 100, Reston, VA 20191-5422
Tel (703) 453-8300 *Founded/Ownrshp* 2001
Sales 233.8MM^E *EMP* 716
SIC 4813 7389 7374 Data telephone communications; Credit card service; Data processing & preparation
Pr: Michael Keegan
Pr: David Kaemmer
Pr: Bryan Warburton
CFO: Mike Keegan
**Treas:* Dennis Randolph
Ofcr: Alex Nuttall
**Ex VP:* Mark Cole
**Ex VP:* Alan Schwartz
Sr VP: John Banfield
Sr VP: Jim Foster
Sr VP: Clayton Liabraaten
Sr VP: Francis McDonagh
**Sr VP:* David Neal
VP: Franz Bader
**VP:* Craig Conway
**VP:* Raymond Low
VP: David Oconnor
VP: Edward Robles
VP: William G Scheible
Dir Bus: John Owens

D-U-N-S 61-045-4261 IMP
TRANSALTA CENTRALIA GENERATION LLC
TRANSALTA USA
(*Suby of* TRANSALTA CORPORATION)
913 Big Hanaford Rd, Centralia, WA 98531-9101
Tel (360) 330-8130 *Founded/Ownrshp* 1999
Sales 2.5MMM^E *EMP* 800
SIC 4911
Pr: Dawn Farrell
**CFO:* Donald Tremblay
**Ex VP:* Wayne Collins
**Ex VP:* Cynthia Johnston
**Ex VP:* Rob Schaefer
Opers Supe: Mark Richardson
Plnt Mgr: Bill Grant

TRANSALTA USA
See TRANSALTA CENTRALIA GENERATION LLC

D-U-N-S 18-059-4079
TRANSAM TRUCKING INC
15910 S Us 169 Hwy, Olathe, KS 66062-3800
Tel (913) 782-5300 *Founded/Ownrshp* 1987
Sales 123.8MM^E *EMP* 825
SIC 4213 Trucking, except local; Refrigerated products transport
Pr: Russ McElliott
VP: Rod Crum
VP: Perry Sibenaller
IT Man: Ben Stine
Sls Dir: Dennis Goodeyon
Sls Mgr: Ann Miller

D-U-N-S 78-656-6075
TRANSAMERICA ADVISORS LIFE INSURANCE CO
(*Suby of* AEGON USA LLC) ★
4333 Edgewood Rd Ne, Cedar Rapids, IA 52499-3830
Tel (800) 346-3677 *Founded/Ownrshp* 2007
Sales NA *EMP* 5
Accts Pricewaterhousecoopers Llp C
SIC 6311 Life insurance
Pr: Blake S Bostwick
**CFO:* Eric J Martin
**Sr VP:* Marc Cahn
**VP:* John T Mallett
VP: Alison Ryan
Comm Man: Deb Harrison
Comm Man: Patty Parr
Snr Mgr: Jen Campbell
Snr Mgr: Tricia Henderson

TRANSAMERICA AFFINITY SERVICES
See AEGON DIRECT MARKETING SERVICES INC

TRANSAMERICA AGENCY NETWORK
See TRANSAMERICA PREMIER LIFE INSURANCE CO

D-U-N-S 00-691-3313
TRANSAMERICA CORP
(*Suby of* AEGON USA, INC.)
4333 Edgewood Rd Ne, Cedar Rapids, IA 52499-3830
Tel (319) 398-8511 *Founded/Ownrshp* 1906
Sales NA *EMP* 6,500
SIC 6311 Life insurance
Pr: Patrick S Baird
Pr: Aimee Tesoro
Treas: M C Fowler
Ofcr: Bas Verhagen
Sr VP: Gregory Tucker
Sr VP: Craig Vermie
VP: David Feltman
VP: Alan Fletcher
VP: Jennifer High
VP: Thomas Nordstrom
VP: Larry N Norman
VP: Amy Powell
VP: Lindsay Schumacher
VP: Bill Swartz
Comm Man: Renee Preslar

D-U-N-S 00-690-8446
TRANSAMERICA FINANCE CORP (DE)
(*Suby of* TRANSAMERICA CORP) ★
600 Montgomery St Fl 16, San Francisco, CA 94111-2718
Tel (415) 983-4000 *Founded/Ownrshp* 1931, 1990
Sales NA *EMP* 1,369^E
SIC 6311 Life insurance
Ch Bd: Robert A Watson
**Pr:* James L Schoedinger
CFO: Ed Elubb
**Treas:* Robert R McDuff
**Chf Cred:* Keith Mason
**Sr VP:* Thomas G Bastian
**Sr VP:* Phillip Rice
**VP:* Stephen H Foltz
**VP:* Austin D Kim
**VP:* John J Mohr
**VP:* Mary L Rottman

D-U-N-S 19-867-6855
TRANSAMERICA FINANCIAL LIFE INSURANCE CO
(*Suby of* AEGON USA, INC.)
440 Mamaroneck Ave, Harrison, NY 10528-2418
Tel (319) 355-8511 *Founded/Ownrshp* 2005
Sales NA *EMP* 50
SIC 6311 Life insurance
Pr: Peter Gregory Kunkel

D-U-N-S 07-226-8642
TRANSAMERICA INSURANCE CORP
(*Suby of* TRANSAMERICA CORP) ★
4333 Edgewood Rd Ne, Cedar Rapids, IA 52499-0001
Tel (319) 355-4883 *Founded/Ownrshp* 1969
Sales NA *EMP* 3,766
SIC 6321

D-U-N-S 06-668-0430
TRANSAMERICA LIFE INSURANCE CO (IA)
(*Suby of* AEGON USA, INC.)
4333 Edgewood Rd Ne, Cedar Rapids, IA 52499-0002
Tel (319) 398-8511 *Founded/Ownrshp* 1971, 1999
Sales NA *EMP* 386
SIC 6371 6311 Pension, health & welfare funds; Life insurance
Pr: Larry Norman
**Pr:* Brenda K Clancy
**Treas:* C Michiel Van Katwijk
**Treas:* Karen R Wright
Chf Mktg O: Lisa Woodard
Chf Inves: Tom Wald
Ex VP: Mike Harkins
Sr VP: Craig D Vermie
VP: David Blankenship
VP: Jon Fortune
VP: Scott Hedgepeth
VP: Nancy Johnston
VP: Kathleen Modzelewski
VP: Lindsay Schumacher
VP: Mark Stueven
Comm Man: Deb Harrison

D-U-N-S 00-690-8347
TRANSAMERICA OCCIDENTAL LIFE INSURANCE CO
(*Suby of* TRANSAMERICA SERVICE CO INC) ★
1150 S Olive St Fl 23, Los Angeles, CA 90015-2477
Tel (213) 742-2111 *Founded/Ownrshp* 1906
Sales NA *EMP* 3,700
SIC 6311 6371 6321 6324 6799 Life insurance carriers; Life reinsurance; Pension funds; Health insurance carriers; Accident insurance carriers; Reinsurance carriers, accident & health; Group hospitalization plans; Investors
Pr: Ronald Wagley
Pr: Christopher Castro
CFO: Joseph Gilmour
Sr VP: Laura Scully
VP: Julie Quinlan
Dir IT: Amy Wagner
Pr Mgr: Nicole Lorey
Manager: Derek Oneill

D-U-N-S 00-695-0281
TRANSAMERICA PREMIER LIFE INSURANCE CO (IA)
TRANSAMERICA AGENCY NETWORK
(*Suby of* AEGON USA, INC.)
4333 Edgewood Rd Ne, Cedar Rapids, IA 52499-0002
Tel (319) 355-8511 *Founded/Ownrshp* 1858, 1991
Sales NA *EMP* 4,000
SIC 6311 6321 Life insurance carriers; Accident insurance carriers
Pr: Brenda K Clancy
**Treas:* C Michiel Van Katwijk
**VP:* H Stacey Boyer
Dist Mgr: Perry Guidry

D-U-N-S 84-849-8671
TRANSAMERICA SERVICE CO INC
(*Suby of* TRANSAMERICA CORP) ★
1150 S Olive St, Los Angeles, CA 90015-2211
Tel (213) 742-2111 *Founded/Ownrshp* 2015
Sales NA *EMP* 3,708
SIC 6311 Life insurance
Prin: Ronald Wagley
VP: Nicki Bair
VP: Roy Chongkit
CTO: Virginia Wilson
IT Man: Andrew Deguia
Mktg Mgr: Shawn Kennedy
Counsel: Deborah Alexander

D-U-N-S 04-933-1481 IMP/EXP
■TRANSAMERICAN DISSOLUTION CO LLC
FOUR WHEEL PARTS WHOLESALERS
(*Suby of* BEAR STEARNS COMPANIES LLC) ★
400 W Artesia Blvd, Compton, CA 90220-5501
Tel (310) 900-5500 *Founded/Ownrshp* 2005
Sales 1.0MMM^E *EMP* 2,000
SIC 5531 5013 Automotive parts; Automotive supplies & parts
CFO: Tim Mongi
IT Man: Mike Ahmad
IT Man: Gerg Gardner
Mktg Dir: Rob Forman
Sls Mgr: Jay Barnett

D-U-N-S 61-254-8636
■TRANSATLANTIC HOLDINGS INC
(*Suby of* ALLEGHANY CORP) ★
80 Pine St Fl 9, New York, NY 10005-1797
Tel (212) 365-2200 *Founded/Ownrshp* 2012
Sales NA *EMP* 630
SIC 6331 Fire, marine & casualty insurance
CEO: Robert F Orlich
Pr: Paul Bailey
**Pr:* Paul A Bonny
Pr: Matthew Brown
Pr: Victor Delgado
**Pr:* Michael C Sapnar
**Pr:* Javier E Vijil
**CFO:* Steven S Skalicky
Bd of Dir: Stephen Bradley
**Ex VP:* Gary A Schwartz
VP: John Byrne
VP: Kasing Chung
VP: Robert Heaton
VP: Richard Henderson
VP: Matthew Mahoney
VP: Paul F McKeon
VP: Julian Spence
VP: Darlene Tom
VP: Robert Wagner
Exec: Frances Gibson
Exec: Edward Kelley
Board of Directors: Stephen P Bradley, Ian H Chippendale, John G Foos, John L McCarthy, Richard S Press

D-U-N-S 96-617-6146
▲TRANSATLANTIC PETROLEUM LTD
16803 Dallas Pkwy, Addison, TX 75001-5212
Tel (214) 220-4323 *Founded/Ownrshp* 1985
Sales 85.0MM *EMP* 619
Tkr Sym TAT *Exch* ASE
SIC 1311 Crude petroleum & natural gas
Ch Bd: N Malone Mitchell III
Pr: Todd C Dutton
COO: Mustafa Yavuz
CFO: Hilda Kouvelis
VP: Chad D Burkhardt
VP: Harold Muncy

D-U-N-S 00-699-1376
■TRANSATLANTIC REINSURANCE CO
(*Suby of* TRANSATLANTIC HOLDINGS INC) ★
1 Liberty Plz Fl 17, New York, NY 10006-1407
Tel (212) 365-2200 *Founded/Ownrshp* 1952
Sales NA *EMP* 500
SIC 6331 Reciprocal interinsurance exchanges: fire, marine, casualty
Pr: Robert F Orlich
Owner: Maria Taveras
**Ch Bd:* Bob Orlich
Pr: Elise McKenzie
Pr: Victor Mora
Pr: Javier E Vijil
CFO: Steven S Skalicky
**Ofcr:* Julian Spence
Assoc VP: Jose De Tomas
Ex VP: Robert M Baldrey
Ex VP: Paul A Bonny
Ex VP: Paul F McKeon
Ex VP: Geoffrey N Peach
Ex VP: Michael Sapnar
Ex VP: Gary A Schwartz
Ex VP: Nicholas Tzaneteas
Sr VP: Kenneth Apsel
Sr VP: Eugene Fisher
Sr VP: Glenn E Gardner
Sr VP: Andrew Gaudencio
Sr VP: David J Kalainoff
Board of Directors: Kenneth Brandt, Julian Spence

D-U-N-S 09-562-0709 IMP
TRANSAXLE MANUFACTURING OF AMERICA CORP
TMA
240 Waterford Park Dr, Rock Hill, SC 29730-8099
Tel (803) 329-8900 *Founded/Ownrshp* 2001
Sales 100.0MM^E *EMP* 148
SIC 3714 Motor vehicle parts & accessories
Pr: Toshiyuki Hasegawa
**Pr:* Steven Pehowski
**Treas:* Paul Watson

TRANSCANADA KEYSTONE PIPELINE
See NORTHERN BORDER PIPELINE CO

D-U-N-S 86-744-6627
TRANSCARE CORP
(*Suby of* PATRIARCH PARTNERS LLC) ★
1 Metrotech Ctr Fl 20, Brooklyn, NY 11201-3949
Tel (718) 251-4600 *Founded/Ownrshp* 1993
Sales 2.6MM^E *EMP* 2,000
SIC 4119 Ambulance service
Pr: David A White
**CFO:* Patrick Seiler
**Ex VP:* James O'Conner
VP: Don Cardone
Comm Man: Paul Borine
**Prin:* Eli Levy
CTO: John Foerst
IT Man: David Sanders
Trfc Dir: Kevin Badlu
Trfc Dir: Tony Peixoto
Opers Mgr: Matt Larrabee

D-U-N-S 83-567-6354
TRANSCARE NEW YORK INC
(*Suby of* TRANSCARE CORP) ★
3305 Jerusalem Ave # 201, Wantagh, NY 11793-2028
Tel (718) 763-8888 *Founded/Ownrshp* 1994
Sales 684.1M^E *EMP* 1,100
SIC 4119 Ambulance service
Pr: David A White
**CFO:* Patrick Seiler

D-U-N-S 03-792-5926
TRANSCARGOBG INC
812 Oregon Trl, Roselle, IL 60172-1309
Tel (847) 980-3779 *Founded/Ownrshp* 2011
Sales 95.0MM *EMP* 2
SIC 4212 Local trucking, without storage

D-U-N-S 00-246-4964 IMP/EXP
▲TRANSCAT INC
35 Vantage Point Dr, Rochester, NY 14624-1175
Tel (585) 352-7777 *Founded/Ownrshp* 1964
Sales 122.1MM *EMP* 548^E
Tkr Sym TRNS *Exch* NGM
SIC 5049 7699 Scientific & engineering equipment & supplies; Scientific equipment repair service
Pr: Lee D Rudow
**Ch Bd:* Charles P Hadeed
CFO: Michael J Tschiderer
CFO: John J Zimmer
VP: Robert A Flack
VP: Jay Kumar
VP: Rainer Stellrecht
VP: Scott Sutter
VP: Michael J Tschiderer
VP: Jay F Woychick
VP: Jay Woychieck
Board of Directors: Richard J Harrison, Gary J Haseley, Paul D Moore, Angela J Panzarella, Alan H Resnick, Carl E Sassano, John T Smith

TRANSCEND SERVICES, INC.
See NUANCE TRANSCRIPTION SERVICES INC

D-U-N-S 00-175-1841 IMP/EXP
TRANSCENDIA INC
9201 Belmont Ave, Franklin Park, IL 60131-2842
Tel (847) 678-1800 *Founded/Ownrshp* 2013
Sales 334.4MM^E *EMP* 774
SIC 3081 5162 Plastic film & sheet; Plastics products
Pr: Andy J Brewer
**CFO:* Claudio Colacino
CFO: Anthony Powell
Sr VP: William Smith
VP: Mark Baumann
VP: Greg Carlin
VP: Evan Everett
VP: Brian Franks
VP: David Kim
VP: Richard Locke
VP: Melissa Rust
Exec: Julie Stertzbach
Dir Rx: Theresa Vanna
Board of Directors: Stewart Dadies, Mike Silverman, Brett Snyder, Mark Stevens, Rob Weiss

D-U-N-S 07-836-6351
TRANSCENTRA INC
(*Suby of* SOURCEHOV LLC) ★
4855 Peachtree Industrial, Berkeley Lake, GA 30092-3013
Tel (678) 728-2500 *Founded/Ownrshp* 2016
Sales 417.8MM^E *EMP* 1,400
SIC 7373 Systems software development services
CEO: Lynn Boggs
Pr: Kevin Lee
CFO: David O'Leary
Ex VP: Todd Shiver
VP: Brian Duke
Exec: Brittany Gottlich
Dir Bus: James Larriva
Dir Bus: Rob Macmahon
Software D: William McDonald
Opers Supe: Anthony Cucurullo
Opers Supe: Tollie Giddings

D-U-N-S 00-523-3580
TRANSCO INC
200 N La Salle St # 1550, Chicago, IL 60601-1034
Tel (312) 896-8527 *Founded/Ownrshp* 1986
Sales 109.8MM *EMP* 600
SIC 4789 3743 3296 1742

D-U-N-S 02-302-2556
■TRANSCO INC
(*Suby of* MCLANE CO INC) ★
4747 Mclane Pkwy, Temple, TX 76504-4854
Tel (254) 771-7500 *Founded/Ownrshp* 1994
Sales 60.1MM^E *EMP* 3,500
SIC 4213 Trucking, except local
Pr: William G Rosier
**Pr:* Mike Youngblood
**Treas:* Kevin J Koch

D-U-N-S 15-631-8768
TRANSCO LINES INC
60 Transco Park Dr, Russellville, AR 72802-2141
Tel (479) 967-5700 *Founded/Ownrshp* 1973
Sales 128.7MM^E *EMP* 350
SIC 4213 Trucking, except local; Refrigerated products transport
Pr: Terry A Wallace
**VP:* Timothy D Harrell
Genl Mgr: Michael Barr
VP Opers: Bradley Heisterkamp
Sfty Dirs: Alan Massey

D-U-N-S 00-793-3021
TRANSCONTINENTAL GAS PIPE LINE CO LLC
(*Suby of* WILLIAMS PARTNERS OPERATING LLC) ★
2800 Post Oak Blvd, Houston, TX 77056-6100
Tel (713) 215-2000 *Founded/Ownrshp* 1948, 1995
Sales 1.5MMM *EMP* 4^E
Accts Ernst & Young Llp Houston Te
SIC 4922 Natural gas transmission; Storage, natural gas
CEO: Rory L Miller
Sr VP: Phillip D Wright
VP: Richard D Rodekohr

D-U-N-S 16-086-3403
▲TRANSCONTINENTAL REALTY INVESTORS INC
TCI
1603 Lbj Fwy Ste 800, Dallas, TX 75234-6061
Tel (469) 522-4200 *Founded/Ownrshp* 1984
Sales 102.2MM *EMP* 4^E
Accts Farmer Fuqua & Huff Pc Rich
Tkr Sym TCI *Exch* NYS
SIC 6798 Real estate investment trusts; Mortgage investment trusts
Pr: Daniel J Moos
**Ch Bd:* Henry Butler
CFO: Steven Abney
CFO: Gene S Bertcher
Ex VP: Louis J Corna

TRANSCOR ASTRA GROUP
See ASTRA OIL CO LLC

D-U-N-S 10-258-0508
■TRANSCORE HOLDINGS INC
(*Suby of* ROPER TECHNOLOGIES INC) ★
3721 Tecport Dr, Harrisburg, PA 17111-1200
Tel (717) 561-5812 *Founded/Ownrshp* 2004
Sales 408.2MM^E *EMP* 1,943
SIC 7373 Computer integrated systems design; Systems integration services; Value-added resellers, computer systems
Pr: John Simler
**Ex VP:* Kelly Gravelle
VP: Bob Ball
VP: Jane Lyndon
VP: Ronald Rahn
VP: Ken Sherman
VP: Shane Smith
VP: Jonathan Thornton
Prgrm Mgr: Victor Foreman
Dir IT: Deborah A Taylor
Opers Mgr: Jenell Tripp

D-U-N-S 15-074-2583
■TRANSCORE LP
(*Suby of* TRANSCORE HOLDINGS INC) ★
3721 Tecport Dr Ste 102, Harrisburg, PA 17111-1200
Tel (615) 988-8960 *Founded/Ownrshp* 2007
Sales 408.2MM^E *EMP* 927
SIC 1731 Electrical work
Pr: Tracy Marks
Pr: John Simler
Ex VP: Tim Bickmore
Sr VP: Michael Schultz
VP: Joseph Grabias
VP: Tim Schock
Prgrm Mgr: Bill Chambers
Dir IT: Fergus Caldicott
Dir IT: Sander Lindor
IT Man: Dan Barde
IT Man: Mark Ginsburg

D-U-N-S 11-873-5914
TRANSDEV NORTH AMERICA INC
720 E Bttrfeld Rd Ste 300, Lombard, IL 60148
Tel (630) 571-7070 *Founded/Ownrshp* 1998
Sales 2.8MMM^E *EMP* 16,470
SIC 4111 4131 4173 Local & suburban transit; Commuter bus operation; Bus line operations; Intercity bus line; Bus terminal & service facilities
CEO: Mark Joseph
COO: Don Saunders
**COO:* Kenneth Westbrook
**CFO:* Jan Horstmann
Ex VP: Alan Moldawer
Sr VP: Ron Hartman
**Sr VP:* Bill McCloud
VP: Andrew Dybel
**VP:* Alan B Moldawer
**VP:* Kevin Oom
**VP:* Ruth L Otte
VP: Richard J Palmieri
Exec: Wim Kurver
Board of Directors: Xavier Girre, Pierre Francois Riolacci

D-U-N-S 83-161-7829
TRANSDEV ON DEMAND INC
(*Suby of* TRANSDEV NORTH AMERICA INC) ★
14500 N Northsight Blvd, Scottsdale, AZ 85260-3658
Tel (480) 609-3000 *Founded/Ownrshp* 2008
Sales 212.7MM^E *EMP* 5,025
SIC 4111 Local & suburban transit
CEO: Bill George
**Pr:* Dave Bird
**VP:* Judy Robertson

D-U-N-S 00-280-6123
TRANSDEV SERVICES INC
(*Suby of* TRANSDEV NORTH AMERICA INC) ★
720 E Bttrfeld Rd Ste 300, Lombard, IL 60148
Tel (630) 571-7070 *Founded/Ownrshp* 1909, 2001
Sales 1.4MMM^E *EMP* 10,000
SIC 4119 4121 Local passenger transportation; Taxicabs
CEO: Mark Joseph
**COO:* Mike Murray
**CFO:* Jan Horstmann
**Ex VP:* Alan B Moldawer
Sr VP: Anita Skotnicki
**VP:* Ronald J Hartman
Dir Risk M: Nancy Leeson
IT Man: Richard Jenkins
Board of Directors: Jan Horstmann, Mark Joseph, Alan Moldawer

D-U-N-S 13-547-2285
▲TRANSDIGM GROUP INC
1301 E 9th St Ste 3000, Cleveland, OH 44114-1871
Tel (216) 706-2960 *Founded/Ownrshp* 1993
Sales 3.1MMM *EMP* 8,200^E
Accts Ernst & Young Llp Cleveland
Tkr Sym TDG *Exch* NYS
SIC 3728 5088 Aircraft parts & equipment; Aircraft equipment & supplies
Ch Bd: W Nicholas Howley
COO: Robert S Henderson
COO: Kevin Stein
COO: Kevin M Stein
CFO: Terrance M Paradie
Sr Ex VP: Gregory Rufus
Ex VP: Bernt G Iversen II
Ex VP: Roger V Jones
Ex VP: John Leary
Ex VP: Peter Palmer
Ex VP: Joel Reiss
Ex VP: Albert Rodriguez
Ex VP: James Skulina
Ex VP: Jorge Valladares III
Board of Directors: William Dries, Mervin Dunn, Michael Graff, Sean P Hennessy, Raymond F Laubenthal, Douglas W Peacock, Robert J Small, John Staer

D-U-N-S 80-878-4326
■TRANSDIGM INC
AEROCONTROLEX
(*Suby of* TRANSDIGM GROUP INC) ★
4223 Monticello Blvd, Cleveland, OH 44121-2814
Tel (216) 706-2939 *Founded/Ownrshp* 2012
Sales 768.0MM^E *EMP* 1,150
SIC 5088 3563 3625 3492 3691 3491 Aircraft equipment & supplies; Air & gas compressors; Relays & industrial controls; Fluid power valves & hose fittings; Alkaline cell storage batteries; Batteries, rechargeable; Lead acid batteries (storage batteries); Nickel cadmium storage batteries; Industrial valves
Ch Bd: W Nicholas Howley
**Pr:* Raymond Laubenthal
**CFO:* Gregory Rufus
**Ex VP:* Robert Henderson
**Ex VP:* Albert Rodriguez

D-U-N-S 04-765-5584 EXP
TRANSERVICE LEASE CORP
5 Dakota Dr, New Hyde Park, NY 11042-1107
Tel (800) 645-8018 *Founded/Ownrshp* 1985
Sales 77.6MM^E *EMP* 1,100
SIC 7699 7539 4212 7353 Industrial truck repair; Trailer repair; Truck rental with drivers; Heavy construction equipment rental
Pr: Dennis M Schneider
**CFO:* Eric R Sklar
**Ch:* Edward J Flannigan
**Ex VP:* William G Doherty
**Ex VP:* Joseph N Evangelist
Ex VP: Dennis Schneider
VP: Anthony Fetta
VP: Wolfgang Marschhauser
MIS Dir: Michael Kwock
Mktg Dir: Marie Jansen

D-U-N-S 96-644-7260
TRANSERVICE LOGISTICS INC
5 Dakota Dr Ste 209, New Hyde Park, NY 11042-1109
Tel (800) 645-8018 *Founded/Ownrshp* 1995
Sales 154.3MM^E *EMP* 600
SIC 4212 Truck rental with drivers
Ch: Edward J Flannigan
**Pr:* Dennis M Schneider
**CFO:* Eric R Sklar
**Ex VP:* Joseph N Evangelist
VP: Terry Lutz
Opers Mgr: Michael Femminello
Opers Mgr: Brandon Mack
Sls Dir: Marty Bohan

TRANSFIELD SERVICES
See BROADSPECTRUM DOWNSTREAM SERVICES INC

D-U-N-S 92-627-6296
TRANSFIRST INC
1393 Veterans Hwy 307s, Hauppauge, NY 11788-3070
Tel (631) 840-6900 *Founded/Ownrshp* 2014
Sales 113.2MM^E *EMP* 1,000
SIC 7389 Financial services
Pr: John Shlonsky
**COO:* Steve Cadden
**CFO:* Nancy Disman
Ofcr: Richard Busichio
**Ofcr:* Paulette Sasso
**Sr VP:* John Kirkpatrick
Sr VP: Brian McCutcheon
**Sr VP:* Andrew Rueff
**Sr VP:* Mark W Travis
Sr VP: Jo Wilson
Ex Dir: Joseph Salem

D-U-N-S 01-371-2026
TRANSFIRST LLC
(*Suby of* TRANSFIRST INC) ★
12202 Airport Way Ste 100, Broomfield, CO 80021-2596
Tel (800) 654-9256 *Founded/Ownrshp* 2000
Sales 98.4MM^E *EMP* 1,000
SIC 7374 Data processing & preparation
CEO: Thomas Rouse
Assoc VP: Dawn Price
Assoc VP: Natalie Worley
VP: Brent Barg
VP: Hodges Marshall
VP: Joan E Ryan
VP: Jessica Thrasher
Exec: Kris Burns
Prgrm Mgr: Michael Cravatt
IT Man: Jaland Worley
Software D: Chris Farrow

D-U-N-S 78-216-8033
TRANSFORCE INC
5520 Cherokee Ave Ste 200, Alexandria, VA 22312-2319
Tel (703) 838-5580 *Founded/Ownrshp* 2015
Sales 134.2MM^E *EMP* 1,180
SIC 7363 Help supply services; Labor resource services; Employee leasing service; Temporary help service
Pr: David W Broome
Pr: Shannon Bolan
**Pr:* David Broome
**CFO:* Howard Fowlur
Sr VP: Dan Costello
VP: Robert Abbot
VP: Robert Abbott
VP: Curtis Carr
VP: John Creager
VP: Deborah Johson
VP: Tom Olsen
VP: Lisa Poore
VP: Michael Taylor

D-U-N-S 18-748-2018
TRANSFREIGHT LLC
(*Suby of* PENSKE LOGISTICS LLC) ★
3940 Olympic Blvd Ste 500, Erlanger, KY 41018-3190
Tel (859) 372-5930 *Founded/Ownrshp* 2015
Sales 197.6MM^E *EMP* 1,700
SIC 4213 8742 Automobiles, transport & delivery; Transportation consultant
CEO: Martin J Miller
**COO:* Steve Beverly
**CFO:* Jeffrey Lucas
VP: David Noon
Genl Mgr: Matt Davison
Genl Mgr: Larry Przybylski
Dir IT: Jim Mullem
Opers Mgr: Colin Mowbray
Snr Mgr: Matt Clapper

D-U-N-S 82-477-2847 IMP/EXP
TRANSHUMANCE HOLDING CO INC
SUPERIOR FARMS
2530 River Plaza Dr # 200, Sacramento, CA 95833-3675
Tel (530) 758-3091 *Founded/Ownrshp* 1997
Sales 180.7MM *EMP* 400
SIC 5421 5142 Food & freezer plans, meat; Meat, frozen: packaged
Pr: Rick Stott
Pr: David Waggoner
CFO: Jeff Evanson
Exec: Rebecca Adkins
Genl Mgr: James Teitscheid
CIO: Mike McCormick
Mktg Dir: Gary Pfeiffer
Mktg Mgr: Angela Gentry

D-U-N-S 00-216-3178 IMP
TRANSISTOR DEVICES INC
ASTRODYNE TDI
36 Newburgh Rd, Hackettstown, NJ 07840-3904
Tel (908) 850-1595 *Founded/Ownrshp* 1951, 1961
Sales 341.4MM^E *EMP* 1,977
SIC 3612 3625 3672 3812 3829 Power transformers, electric; Switches, electric power; Printed circuit boards; Search & navigation equipment; Measuring & controlling devices
Pr: James M Feely
**Ch Bd:* Joshua Hauser
**COO:* Robert Smolinski
COO: Chris Viola
**CFO:* J Christopher Viola
**VP:* Bill Gray
**CTO:* Garry Mulcahy
Dir IT: John Schmidt
Mktg Dir: Ron Hamaoui
Sls Dir: Simo Yu
Mktg Mgr: Louis Squeo

D-U-N-S 07-781-5512
TRANSIT EMPLOYEE HEALTH & WELFARE PLAN
2701 Whitney Pl Ste B, Forestville, MD 20747-3457
Tel (301) 568-2294 *Founded/Ownrshp* 1954
Sales 149.4MM *EMP* 4
SIC 8099 Medical services organization

D-U-N-S 00-806-8454 IMP/EXP
TRANSIT MIX CONCRETE & MATERIALS CO
TRINITY AGGREGATE DISTRIBUTION
850 Pine St, Beaumont, TX 77701-1851
Tel (409) 835-4934 *Founded/Ownrshp* 1991
Sales NA *EMP* 1,835
SIC 3273

D-U-N-S 96-678-4423
TRANSITION CAPITAL PARTNERS LP
2100 Mckinney Ave # 1501, Dallas, TX 75201-2119
Tel (214) 978-3800 *Founded/Ownrshp* 1995
Sales 117.3MM^E *EMP* 1,507
SIC 6799 Venture capital companies
CFO: Matthias Lietsch
Off Mgr: Stacye Wolfe

D-U-N-S 10-837-1571
TRANSITIONAL CARE MANAGEMENT LLC
TCM
3333 Warrenville Rd # 200, Lisle, IL 60532-1999
Tel (847) 720-8700 *Founded/Ownrshp* 1999
Sales 31.6MM^E *EMP* 1,000
SIC 8051 Skilled nursing care facilities
**Pr:* Beth Benoudiz
**Pr:* Denise Norman
**COO:* Mike Filippo
**VP:* Liana Allison

D-U-N-S 80-912-9778
TRANSITIONAL HEALTH PARTNERS
NORMAL LIFE OF SHERIDAN
400 Perimeter Ctr Ter Ne, Atlanta, GA 30346-1227
Tel (770) 698-9040 *Founded/Ownrshp* 1993
Sales 36.3MM^E *EMP* 4,000
SIC 8051 Convalescent home with continuous nursing care
Pt: J Stephen Eaton

TRANSITIONS LENSES
See TRANSITIONS OPTICAL INC

D-U-N-S 61-900-3106 IMP
TRANSITIONS OPTICAL INC
TRANSITIONS LENSES
(*Suby of* ESSILOR INTERNATIONAL)
9251 Belcher Rd N, Pinellas Park, FL 33782-4201
Tel (727) 545-0400 *Founded/Ownrshp* 2014
Sales 129.4MM^E *EMP* 500
SIC 3229 3851 Ophthalmic glass, except flat; Lenses, ophthalmic
Pr: Paddy McDermott
VP: Hillie Stanley
Dir Soc: Mary Katsougrakis
Genl Mgr: Jost Alves
Mfg Mgr: Christopher Rauscher
Ql Cn Mgr: James Kieffer
Mktg Mgr: Michael Coppes
Mktg Mgr: Vanessa Johns
Mktg Mgr: Dana Reid
Mktg Mgr: Isabelle Tremblay
Counsel: Gretchen Walsh

TRANSLAND BROKERAGE
See TCSI-TRANSLAND INC

D-U-N-S 11-806-9611
TRANSLATIONAL GENOMICS RESEARCH INSTITUTE
T GEN
445 N 5th St, Phoenix, AZ 85004-2157
Tel (602) 343-8400 *Founded/Ownrshp* 2002
Sales 84.2MM *EMP* 150^E
Accts Ernst & Young Us Llp Phoenix
SIC 8731 Commercial physical research
Pr: Jeffrey M Trent
**Pr:* Michael Bassoff
**COO:* Tess Burleson
**COO:* Richard Love
CFO: Liz Montemayor
**Treas:* Cindy Parseghian
**Ex VP:* Daniel D Von Hoff
VP: Jim Harris
VP: Cassandra Lucas
VP: Timothy McDaniel
VP: Galen Perry
**VP:* Janine Tilli

D-U-N-S 80-486-1578
TRANSLATIONAL ONCOLOGY RESEARCH INTERNATIONAL INC
1033 Gayley Ave Ste 207, Los Angeles, CA 90024-3426
Tel (310) 824-1919 *Founded/Ownrshp* 2003
Sales 7.4MM *EMP* 1,900
Accts Daniel B Gamiao Ea Inc Arcad
SIC 8011 8732 8742 Oncologist; Market analysis or research; Marketing consulting services
CFO: James Muff

D-U-N-S 10-255-2015 IMP
TRANSLOGIC CORP
SWISSLOG HLTHCARE SOLUTIONS NA
(*Suby of* SWISSLOG HOLDING AG)
10825 E 47th Ave, Denver, CO 80239-2913
Tel (303) 371-7770 *Founded/Ownrshp* 1999
Sales 133.0MM *EMP* 340
Accts Kpmg Llp Montreal Canada
SIC 3535 Pneumatic tube conveyor systems; Robotic conveyors
Ch: Hans Ziegler
Treas: Daniel G King
Treas: John F Williams
Top Exec: Ian Channing
Ex VP: Robert Rasmussen
VP: Mike Hoganson
VP: Dennis McWherter
VP: Scott Palmerville
Sls&Mrk Ex: Emma Rawlinson
VP Sls: Anthony Pugliese

D-U-N-S 00-994-5417
TRANSLOGIX LLC
(*Suby of* A W C) ★
2001 E 122nd St, Chicago, IL 60633-2336
Tel (773) 646-8300 *Founded/Ownrshp* 2007
Sales 55.9MM^E *EMP* 1,000
SIC 4731 Freight forwarding

D-U-N-S 12-279-3458 IMP
TRANSMONTAIGNE LLC
(*Suby of* ARCLIGHT CAPITAL PARTNERS LLC) ★
1670 Broadway Ste 3100, Denver, CO 80202-4815
Tel (303) 626-8200 *Founded/Ownrshp* 2014
Sales 519.4MM^E *EMP* 600
SIC 5172 Crude oil
CEO: Charles Dunlap
**Treas:* Frederick W Boutin
**Ex VP:* Michael A Hammell
Ex VP: Chee Ooi
Sr VP: Brian Couch
Sr VP: Deborah A Davis
VP: Brian Cannon
VP: Ron Majors
Off Mgr: Cathy Lujan
Dir IT: Raj Shah
Software D: Redding Bacon

D-U-N-S 19-428-7327
▲TRANSMONTAIGNE PARTNERS LP
1670 Broadway Ste 3100, Denver, CO 80202-4815
Tel (303) 626-8200 *Founded/Ownrshp* 2005
Sales 152.5MM *EMP* 450
Tkr Sym TLP *Exch* NYS
SIC 4612 5171 Crude petroleum pipelines; Petroleum terminals
CEO: Frederick W Boutin
Genl Pt: Transmontaigne GP LLC
Pr: Gregory J Pound

D-U-N-S 08-662-6678
TRANSMONTAIGNE PRODUCT SERVICES LLC
(*Suby of* TRANSMONTAIGNE LLC) ★
1670 Broadway Ste 3100, Denver, CO 80202-4815
Tel (303) 626-8200 *Founded/Ownrshp* 1998
Sales 111.9MM^E *EMP* 700
SIC 4789 Pipeline terminal facilities, independently operated
Pr: Randall J Larson
**Treas:* Fredreick W Boutin
Bd of Dir: D D Shaffer
Sr VP: Deborah Davis

TRANSOCEAN
See GLOBAL MARINE INC

D-U-N-S 00-793-2288 IMP/EXP
TRANSOCEAN INC
(*Suby of* TRANSOCEAN LTD.)
4 Greenway Plz Ste 700, Houston, TX 77046-0406
Tel (713) 232-7500 *Founded/Ownrshp* 1953
Sales 6.8MMM^E *EMP* 21,100
Accts Ernst & Young Llp Houston T
SIC 1381 Drilling oil & gas wells
Pr: Steven Newman
COO: John Stobart
Ex VP: Rob Saltiel
Ex VP: Ihab Toma
VP: Alan A Broussard
VP: Dennis R Long
VP: Adrian Rose
Board of Directors: Steven Newman, W Richard Anderson, Kristian Siem, Thomas W Cason, Robert M Sprague, Richard L George, Ian C Strachan, Victor E Grijalva, J Michael Talbert, Tan Ek Kia, John L Whitmire, Steve Lucas, Jon A Marshall, Martin B McNamara, Edward R Muller

D-U-N-S 01-155-3176
TRANSOM CAPITAL GROUP LLC
10990 Wilshire Blvd # 440, Los Angeles, CA 90024-3950
Tel (424) 293-2818 *Founded/Ownrshp* 2007
Sales 115.0MM^E *EMP* 646^E
SIC 6799 Investors
Mng Dir: Russell Roenick

TRANSPARTS OF CHICAGO
See DACCO INC

TRANSPERFECT GLOBAL
See TRANSPERFECT TRANSLATIONS INTERNATIONAL INC

D-U-N-S 96-827-3115
TRANSPERFECT GLOBAL INC
3 Park Ave Fl 39, New York, NY 10016-5934
Tel (212) 689-5555 *Founded/Ownrshp* 2007
Sales 471.0MM *EMP* 3,500
SIC 7389 7371 8748 Translation services; Computer software development & applications; Business consulting
CEO: Elizabeth Elting
**CEO:* Phil Shawe
**COO:* Roy B Trujillo
VP: Ryan Simper
IT Man: Brian Kulawiak

D-U-N-S 80-578-4337
TRANSPERFECT TRANSLATIONS INTERNATIONAL INC
TRANSPERFECT GLOBAL
(*Suby of* TRANSPERFECT GLOBAL INC) ★
3 Park Ave Fl 39, New York, NY 10016-5934
Tel (212) 689-5555 *Founded/Ownrshp* 1992
Sales 470.0MM^E *EMP* 3,500
SIC 7389 8748 8111 Translation services; Business consulting; Legal services
CEO: Elizabeth Elting
**CEO:* Phil Shawe
COO: Roy B Trujillo
**Sr VP:* Brooke Christian
Sr VP: Jin Lee
Sr VP: Kevin Obarski
VP: Michael Edwards
VP: Jessica Eker
VP: Jordan Ellington
VP: Matt Hauser
VP: Mark Peeler
VP: Michael Sank
VP Bus Dev: Jennifer Peters
Exec: Heather Bosley
Exec: Suzanne Fish
Exec: Najat Messaoud
Dir Bus: Glenn Banton
Dir Bus: Amanda George
Dir Bus: Alejandro Gonzalez
Dir Bus: Andrew Green
Dir Bus: Marco Marino

TRANSPLACE INTERNATIONAL
See CI (TRANSPLACE) HOLDINGS LLC

D-U-N-S 14-939-9300 IMP/EXP
TRANSPLACE TEXAS LP
3010 Gaylord Pkwy Ste 200, Frisco, TX 75034-8679
Tel (972) 731-4500 *Founded/Ownrshp* 2001
Sales 619.8MM^E *EMP* 1,000
SIC 4731 Freight transportation arrangement
CEO: Thomas K Sanderson
Pr: George Abernathy
Pr: Brooks Bentz
Pr: John Kelly
CFO: Tony Cossentino
Ofcr: Adrianne Court
Ofcr: Matt Dean
Ex VP: Vincent Biddlecombe
Ex VP: Steven Crowther
Ex VP: Frank McGuigan
VP: Mona Cayard
VP: Kim Crawford

D-U-N-S 94-140-8614
TRANSPLANT SERVICES DALLAS
(*Suby of* BHCS) ★
3410 Worth St Ste 950, Dallas, TX 75246-2064
Tel (214) 820-2050 *Founded/Ownrshp* 2011
Sales 10.9MM^E *EMP* 1,285^E
SIC 8999 Artists & artists' studios
Bd of Dir: Jerry Barker Jr

TRANSPLANT SOCIETY
See AUXILIO MUTUO HOSPITAL

TRANSPORT AMERICA
See TRANSPORT CORP OF AMERICA INC

D-U-N-S 01-719-7450
TRANSPORT CORP OF AMERICA INC (MN)
TRANSPORT AMERICA
(*Suby of* GESTION TFORCE INC.)
1715 Yankee Doodle Rd # 100, Eagan, MN 55121-1793
Tel (651) 686-2500 *Founded/Ownrshp* 1980, 2014
Sales 375.0MM *EMP* 855^E
SIC 4213 Contract haulers; Refrigerated products transport
Pr: Keith R Klein
**CFO:* Dan Patnode
Sr VP: Craig Coyan
VP: Christopher R Licht
VP: Kelly Polk
VP: Gaurav Thamman
VP: Sue West
Dir IT: Tom Benusa
Info Man: Dale Anderson
VP Opers: Scott D Hunt
Sls Dir: Jim Locke

D-U-N-S 05-693-6248
TRANSPORT DRIVERS INC
T D I
3540 Seven Bridges Dr # 300, Woodridge, IL 60517-1668
Tel (630) 766-2721 *Founded/Ownrshp* 1988
Sales 69.1MM^E *EMP* 1,500
SIC 7363 Truck driver services
Pr: Ronald P Formento
**CFO:* John Urman
VP: Donald Scheisser
Exec: Frank Villalobos
Brnch Mgr: Mike Bales
Brnch Mgr: Katy Clement
Brnch Mgr: Scott Gayheart
Brnch Mgr: David Goldzweig
Brnch Mgr: Candis Markus
Brnch Mgr: Nicole Perez
Brnch Mgr: Robert Taylor

TRANSPORT FINANCE
See KENWORTH SALES CO

D-U-N-S 04-962-4679
TRANSPORT INTERNATIONAL POOL INC
TRAILER FLEET SERVICES
(*Suby of* HNA HOLDINGS GROUP CO., LTD.)
530 E Swedesford Rd, Wayne, PA 19087-1603
Tel (484) 254-0100 *Founded/Ownrshp* 1957
Sales 713.9MM^E *EMP* 2,433
SIC 5511 7519 Trucks, tractors & trailers: new & used; Trailer rental; Mobile home rental, except on site
Pr: Joseph J Artuso
CEO: Felicia Carnaroli
CFO: Richard Wilson
**Treas:* Michael Killoren
**VP:* Joseph Zambrano

D-U-N-S 09-875-9418
TRANSPORT INTERNATIONAL POOL INC
GE MODULAR SPC/TRLR FLT SVCS
(*Suby of* TRAILER FLEET SERVICES) ★
530 E Swedesford Rd, Wayne, PA 19087-1603
Tel (484) 254-0100 *Founded/Ownrshp* 1987
Sales 48.2MM^E *EMP* 2,000
SIC 7519 7513 5511 5211 Trailer rental; Truck rental & leasing, no drivers; Trucks, tractors & trailers: new & used; Prefabricated buildings
Pr: Marty Thomas
**Treas:* Michael Killoren
VP: Chris Buda
**VP:* Glenn Johnson
VP: Tom Loane
VP: Dean Rogers
**VP:* Joseph Zambrano
Dir IT: Suzanne Wetherinston
MIS Mgr: Ellen Hawkins
Snr Mgr: Sunil Bijlani

D-U-N-S 03-002-7361
TRANSPORT LEASING CO LLP
TRANSYSTEMS SERVICES
1901 Benefis Ct, Great Falls, MT 59405-4373
Tel (406) 727-7500 *Founded/Ownrshp* 2001
Sales 107.9MM *EMP* 300
SIC 7513 Truck rental, without drivers
Genl Pt: Patrick W Rice
**Pt:* Scott Lind
**Pt:* Daniel Rice
**Pt:* M Kathleen Rice
**Pt:* Peter C Rice
**Pt:* Rosemary A Waters
VP: Ann Powers

D-U-N-S 00-298-4276
TRANSPORT SERVICE CO (IL)
(*Suby of* KENAN ADVANTAGE GROUP INC) ★
2001 Spring Rd Ste 400, Oak Brook, IL 60523-1903
Tel (630) 472-5900 *Founded/Ownrshp* 1946
Sales 85.1MM^E *EMP* 650
SIC 4213 4731

D-U-N-S 83-073-2306
TRANSPORTATION 100 LLC
12404 Park Central Dr 300s, Dallas, TX 75251-1800
Tel (972) 228-7300 *Founded/Ownrshp* 2008
Sales NA *EMP* 2,810
SIC 4213 4731

D-U-N-S 96-580-6677
TRANSPORTATION AMERICA INC
2766 Nw 62nd St, Miami, FL 33147-7662
Tel (305) 308-8110 *Founded/Ownrshp* 2001
Sales 67.2MM^E *EMP* 1,162^E
SIC 4212 Local trucking, without storage
CEO: Raymond Gonzalez
**VP:* Rene Gonzalez

D-U-N-S 92-732-8732
TRANSPORTATION CABINET KENTUCKY
(*Suby of* EXECUTIVE OFFICE OF COMMONWEALTH OF KENTUCKY) ★
200 Mero St, Frankfort, KY 40601-1920
Tel (502) 564-3020 *Founded/Ownrshp* 1837
Sales NA *EMP* 2,500
SIC 9621 Regulation, administration of transportation;
**Ex Dir:* Liz Charlotte
Admn Mgr: Wilma Rice
Brnch Mgr: Tom Wright
IT Man: Cheryl Cole
Netwrk Eng: Dan Mauer

TRANSPORTATION COMMISSION
See MISSISSIPPI DEPARTMENT OF TRANSPORTATION

TRANSPORTATION CONCEPTS
See PARKING CONCEPTS INC

D-U-N-S 19-248-7965
TRANSPORTATION DIST COMMISION OF HAMPTON ROADS
HAMPTON ROADS TRANSIT
3400 Victoria Blvd, Hampton, VA 23661-1509
Tel (757) 222-6000 *Founded/Ownrshp* 1975
Sales 72.8MM^E *EMP* 1,000^E
SIC 4111 Bus line operations
Pr: William E Harrell
Pr: Sibyl Pappas
**CFO:* Brandon Singleton
Exec: Kimberly Ackerman
Plng Mgr: Antoinette White
QA Dir: Tony Ferguson
IT Man: Ty Dennis

D-U-N-S 10-273-5151 IMP/EXP
TRANSPORTATION INSIGHT LLC
CUSTOM SHIPPING SOLUTIONS
310 Main Avenue Way Se, Hickory, NC 28602-3513
Tel (828) 485-5000 *Founded/Ownrshp* 1999
Sales 689.0MM *EMP* 200
SIC 8742 Transportation consultant
Pr: Chris Baltz
**Ch Bd:* Paul Thompson
**COO:* Laura Easley
**CFO:* Reynolds Faulkner
CFO: Reynolds C Faulkner
VP: Jim Taylor
Sls Mgr: Christie Buckland

D-U-N-S 00-693-2933
■TRANSPORTATION INSURANCE CO (IL)
TRANSPORTATION INSURANCE CO INC.
(*Suby of* CNA INSURANCE) ★
333 S Wabash Ave, Chicago, IL 60604-4107
Tel (312) 822-5000 *Founded/Ownrshp* 1938, 2008
Sales NA *EMP* 6,000
SIC 6411 Insurance agents, brokers & service
**Pr:* Philip L Engel
COO: Bernard Hengesbaugh
Treas: Lew Nathan
**Sr VP:* Donald M Lowry
VP: D B Schaeffer
CIO: Patricia A Cusick
CTO: Curtis Carpenter
VP Sls: Rick Bonesteel

TRANSPORTATION INSURANCE CO INC.
See TRANSPORTATION INSURANCE CO

D-U-N-S 11-274-6297
■TRANSPORTATION SECURITY ADMINISTRATION
TSA
(*Suby of* EXECUTVE OFC OF US GOVT) ★
601 S 12th St, Arlington, VA 20598-0100
Tel (877) 872-7990 *Founded/Ownrshp* 2001
Sales NA *EMP* 50,000^E
SIC 9621 Regulation, administration of transportation;
**Prin:* Melvin Carraway
**Prin:* Kenneth Fletcher
**Prin:* Thomas McDaniels

D-U-N-S 09-965-6621
TRANSPORTATION SERVICES INC
TSI
18165 Telegraph Rd, Romulus, MI 48174-9620
Tel (734) 282-4444 *Founded/Ownrshp* 1979
Sales 92.5MM[E] *EMP* 400
SIC 4213 Trucking, except local
**CFO:* Michael Zavislak
Trfc Dir: Tony Ciccone
Sls Mgr: John Lawrence

TRANSPORTATION SYSTEMS GLOBA
See ALSTOM SIGNALING OPERATION LLC

D-U-N-S 80-910-2148 IMP
TRANSPORTATION TECHNOLOGIES INDUSTRIES INC
(*Suby of* ACCURIDE CORP) ★
7140 Office Cir, Evansville, IN 47715-8235
Tel (812) 962-5000 *Founded/Ownrshp* 2005
Sales 347.1MM[E] *EMP* 2,400
Accts Deloitte & Touche Llp
SIC 2531 3714 3321 4741 3471 Vehicle furniture; Motor vehicle wheels & parts; Motor vehicle brake systems & parts; Brake drums, motor vehicle; Ductile iron castings; Rental of railroad cars; Electroplating of metals or formed products
Pr: Terrence Keating
Sr VP: Anthony A Donatelli
VP: Kenneth M Tallering

D-U-N-S 01-083-7789
TRANSPORTATION UNLIMITED INC (OH)
3740 Carnegie Ave Ste 101, Cleveland, OH 44115-2756
Tel (216) 426-0088 *Founded/Ownrshp* 1974
Sales 52.8MM[E] *EMP* 8,000
SIC 7363 4213 4212 Truck driver services; Trucking, except local; Local trucking, without storage
Pr: Samuel Lucarelli
**Sec:* Jason Lucarelli
**VP:* Michael Panzarelli
Dir IT: Dan Folino

TRANSPRTTION CORRIDOR AGENCIES
See SAN JOAQUIN HILLS TRANSPORTATION CORRIDOR AGENCY

D-U-N-S 78-406-5810
TRANSTAR HOLDING CO
(*Suby of* FRIEDMAN FLEISCHER & LOWE CAPITAL PARTNERS III, L.P.)
5900 Landerbrook Dr Bsmt, Cleveland, OH 44124-4085
Tel (440) 684-1400 *Founded/Ownrshp* 2005
Sales 111.6MM *EMP* 2,300
SIC 3444 3281 2952 Metal roofing & roof drainage equipment; Cut stone & stone products; Asphalt felts & coatings
Ch: Frank N Linsalata
**Pr:* Monte Ahuja
**CFO:* Jeffrey R Marshall
**VP:* Mark A Kirk
**VP:* Stephen B Perry

D-U-N-S 36-258-7362
■**TRANSTAR INC**
(*Suby of* UNITED STATES STEEL CORP) ★
1200 Penn Ave Ste 300, Pittsburgh, PA 15222-4219
Tel (412) 433-4644 *Founded/Ownrshp* 2001
Sales 108.1MM[E] *EMP* 1,469
SIC 4449 4731

D-U-N-S 07-689-6174 IMP/EXP
TRANSTAR INDUSTRIES INC
NICKELS PERFORMANCE
(*Suby of* LINSALATA CORP) ★
7350 Young Dr, Cleveland, OH 44146-5390
Tel (440) 232-5100 *Founded/Ownrshp* 2005
Sales 724.7MM[E] *EMP* 2,300
SIC 5013

D-U-N-S 10-877-1259
TRANSTECK INC
FREIGHTLINER OF BRIDGEPORT
4303 Lewis Rd, Harrisburg, PA 17111-2539
Tel (717) 564-6151 *Founded/Ownrshp* 1999
Sales 118.9MM[E] *EMP* 475
SIC 5511 New & used car dealers
CEO: Neal Hufford
**CFO:* Randy Wirth

D-U-N-S 07-857-8196
▲**TRANSUNION**
555 W Adams St Fl 1, Chicago, IL 60661-3614
Tel (312) 985-2000 *Founded/Ownrshp* 2012
Sales 1.5MMM *EMP* 4,200[E]
Tkr Sym TRU *Exch* NYS
SIC 7323 Credit reporting services; Credit bureau & agency
Ch Bd: Leo F Mullin
Pr: James M Peck
COO: David Emery
CFO: Samuel A Hamood
Ex VP: John W Blenke
Ex VP: Christopher A Cartwright
Ex VP: John T Danaher
Ex VP: Gerald M McCarthy Jr
Ex VP: David M Neenan
VP: Michael Gaughan
VP: Michael Patterson
VP: Jeff Reynolds

TRANSUNION CORP.
See TRANSUNION INTERMEDIATE HOLDINGS INC

D-U-N-S 96-707-0103
■**TRANSUNION INTERACTIVE INC**
TRUECREDIT.COM
(*Suby of* TRANSUNION CORP) ★
555 W Adams St, Chicago, IL 60661-3719
Tel (805) 782-8282 *Founded/Ownrshp* 2013
Sales 170.0MM *EMP* 60[E]
SIC 7323 Credit reporting services
CEO: Jim Peck
**Pr:* John Danaher
**Ch:* Kurt Locher
**VP:* David McCrary
Off Mgr: Shamina Lewis
Mktg Mgr: Elena Laramie
Snr Mgr: Ramdas Kenjale

D-U-N-S 19-838-0938
■**TRANSUNION INTERMEDIATE HOLDINGS INC**
TRANSUNION CORP.
(*Suby of* TRANSUNION) ★
555 W Adams St Fl 2, Chicago, IL 60661-5753
Tel (312) 258-1717 *Founded/Ownrshp* 2012
Sales 882.3MM[E] *EMP* 3,700[E]
Accts Ernst & Young Llp Chicago I
SIC 7323 Credit bureau & agency
Ch: Penny Pritzker
Pr: Chris Cartwright
Pr: Jim Peck
Pr: Lawrence Tsong
CFO: S Allen Hamood
Ofcr: Barry Botruff
Ex VP: Kelley Buchanan
Ex VP: Michael P Kiyosaki
Ex VP: Mary Krupka
Ex VP: Mark McElroy
VP: Jim Bohnsack
VP: Bob Callaci
VP: Paul Fritz
VP: Thomas Higgins
VP: Sarah Kilburg
VP: Cathy Madden
VP: Michael D Oconnell
VP: Michael Snitman
VP: Tony Terrazas
Comm Dir: Cliff Oneal

D-U-N-S 09-530-0208
■**TRANSUNION LLC**
(*Suby of* TRANSUNION CORP) ★
555 W Adams St Fl 1, Chicago, IL 60661-3614
Tel (312) 985-2000 *Founded/Ownrshp* 2005
Sales 666.8MM[E] *EMP* 3,400
SIC 8741 Financial management for business
CEO: Jim Peck
**Pr:* Harry Gambill
**COO:* David M Emery
**CFO:* Samuel Allen Hamood
CFO: William Holbrook
CFO: Scott E Schubrt
**V Ch Bd:* Robert A Pritzker
Ex VP: Paul Janis
**Ex VP:* Steve Sassaman
Ex VP: Jan Temple
VP: Gary Friedlander
**VP:* John Gbur
VP: Jeffrey Hellinga
VP: Michael Jones
VP: Ather Mahmood
VP: Daniel Toth
Exec: Justin Naples
Comm Dir: David Eastman

TRANSWEST TRUCK TRAILER RV
See TRANS-WEST INC

D-U-N-S 02-081-8886
TRANSWESTERN COMMERCIAL SERVICES LLC
1900 West Loop S Ste 1300, Houston, TX 77027-3218
Tel (713) 270-7000 *Founded/Ownrshp* 1998
Sales 232.7MM[E] *EMP* 1,420
SIC 6512 Commercial & industrial building operation
Ch: Robert Duncan
Pr: Chip Clarke
**Pr:* Larry Heard
Pr: Kevin Roberts
**COO:* Mark Doran
**CFO:* Steve Harding
Ex VP: Ronald E Davis Jr
Ex VP: H Larson
Ex VP: Ty Puckett
Sr VP: Lisa Johnston
Sr VP: Gregory Schott
Sr VP: Brian Watts
VP: Tim Bennett
VP: Alex S Bryant
VP: David Clarkson
VP: Randy Cone
VP: Kenady Davis
VP: Laurie Findley
VP: Edward Fish
VP: Joe Friedman
VP: Tod A Harrison

D-U-N-S 00-793-3047
■**TRANSWESTERN PIPELINE CO LLC** (DE)
(*Suby of* ENERGY TRANSFER PARTNERS LP) ★
711 Louisiana St Ste 900, Houston, TX 77002-2831
Tel (281) 714-2000 *Founded/Ownrshp* 1957, 2006
Sales 690.7MM[E] *EMP* 1,100
Accts Grant Thornton Llp Houston T
SIC 4922 Pipelines, natural gas
CEO: Kelcy Warren
Pr: Marshall S McCrea III
CFO: Martin Salinas

D-U-N-S 80-509-7169
TRANSWESTERN PUBLISHING CO LLC
(*Suby of* HIBU INC) ★
8344 Clairemont Mesa Blvd, San Diego, CA 92111-1307
Tel (858) 467-2800 *Founded/Ownrshp* 1997
Sales 98.5MM[E] *EMP* 1,869
SIC 2741

D-U-N-S 87-319-6158
TRANSWOOD CARRIERS INC
2565 Saint Marys Ave, Omaha, NE 68105-1668
Tel (402) 346-8092 *Founded/Ownrshp* 1994
Sales 150.0MM *EMP* 450
SIC 4213 4212 7513 Trucking, except local; Local trucking, without storage; Truck rental & leasing, no drivers
Pr: Brian K Wood
**VP:* Stan Meier
VP: William Sawim
**VP:* Bill Sawin

D-U-N-S 10-759-5233
TRANSWOOD INC
(*Suby of* TRANSWOOD CARRIERS INC) ★
2565 Saint Marys Ave, Omaha, NE 68105-1668
Tel (402) 346-8092 *Founded/Ownrshp* 1994
Sales 89.4MM[E] *EMP* 300
SIC 4212 4213 Local trucking, without storage; Trucking, except local
Pr: Brian K Wood
**VP:* Stan Meier
**VP:* Bill Sawin
CIO: Roger Funkhouser
Dir IT: Patrick Oneill
Dir IT: Dick Stuart

D-U-N-S 07-935-1563
■**TRANSWORKS OF INDIANA INC**
(*Suby of* NORFOLK SOUTHERN RAILWAY CO) ★
9910 Dupont Circle Dr E, Fort Wayne, IN 46825-1617
Tel (260) 487-4400 *Founded/Ownrshp* 2014
Sales 20.7MM[E] *EMP* 1,281[E]
SIC 4011 Railroads, line-haul operating
Pr: Tim Minnich

D-U-N-S 06-303-5471
TRANSWORLD SYSTEMS INC
(*Suby of* PLATINUM EQUITY LLC) ★
500 Virginia Dr Ste 514, Fort Washington, PA 19034-2707
Tel (703) 757-0977 *Founded/Ownrshp* 2014
Sales 108.3MM[E] *EMP* 700
SIC 7322 Collection agency, except real estate
CEO: Joseph Laughlin
**Sr VP:* Bernard P Zeng
VP: Charles Baumler
**VP:* Jim Kirby
Rgnl Mgr: David Kirk
Dist Mgr: Michael Taylor
**VP Sls:* Stephen Dobie
**Mktg Dir:* John Yanny
Manager: Mark Wilson

D-U-N-S 80-865-8392
TRANSWORLD WORLDWIDE INC
(*Suby of* TRANSOCEAN INC) ★
4 Greenway Plz Ste 700, Houston, TX 77046-0406
Tel (713) 232-7500 *Founded/Ownrshp* 2007
Sales 47.2MM[E] *EMP* 5,962
SIC 1381 1311 Drilling oil & gas wells; Crude petroleum & natural gas production
Pr: Robert L Long

D-U-N-S 04-510-2084
TRANSYSTEMS CORP
TS
2400 Pershing Rd Ste 400, Kansas City, MO 64108-2526
Tel (816) 329-8700 *Founded/Ownrshp* 1966
Sales 144.2MM *EMP* 1,000
Accts Kpmg Llp Kansas City Mo
SIC 8711 Consulting engineer
Ch Bd: Brian G Larson
**COO:* Paul Malir
**CFO:* Julie Frigon
CFO: Angela E Murphy
Ex VP: Grace Dysico
**Ex VP:* Rick Morsches
VP: Danny Davis
VP: Thomas Munson
VP: Wesley R Weir
Admn Mgr: Donna Weston
**CIO:* Kanon Cozad

D-U-N-S 03-002-7304
TRANSYSTEMS LLC
1901 Benefis Ct, Great Falls, MT 59405-4373
Tel (406) 727-7500 *Founded/Ownrshp* 1998, 1942
Sales 97.9MM *EMP* 277
SIC 4212 Local trucking, without storage; Farm to market haulage, local; Coal haulage, local
**Pr:* Scott Lind
**VP:* Daniel Rice

TRANSYSTEMS SERVICES
See TRANSPORT LEASING CO LLP

D-U-N-S 00-790-0020 IMP/EXP
TRANZONIC COMPANIES
CCP INDUSTRIES
26301 Curtiss Wright Pkwy # 200, Richmond Heights, OH 44143-1454
Tel (216) 535-4300 *Founded/Ownrshp* 1946
Sales 360.2MM[E] *EMP* 1,109
SIC 2676 2211 2326 2842 2273 2262 Sanitary paper products; Napkins, sanitary: made from purchased paper; Tampons, sanitary: made from purchased paper; Diapers, paper (disposable): made from purchased paper; Scrub cloths; Work garments, except raincoats: waterproof; Sanitation preparations, disinfectants & deodorants; Industrial plant disinfectants or deodorants; Mats & matting; Napping: manmade fiber & silk broadwoven fabrics
CEO: Thomas Friedl
**CFO:* Patrick Fitzmaurice
VP: Greg Decapio
Area Mgr: Paul Sullivan
Dist Mgr: Scott Ruderman
Genl Mgr: Chauck Acker
Genl Mgr: Tom Sriedl
Dir IT: Matthew McCormick
Opers Mgr: SIS Ballom

D-U-N-S 00-256-0522
TRAP ROCK INDUSTRIES INC (NJ)
460 River Rd, Kingston, NJ 08528
Tel (609) 924-0300 *Founded/Ownrshp* 1860
Sales 200.9MM[E] *EMP* 600
SIC 3273 3272 1429 1611 Ready-mixed concrete; Concrete products; Trap rock, crushed & broken-quarrying; Highway & street paving contractor
Pr: Joseph M Stavola
**VP:* Wayne Byard
**VP:* Michael Crowley
Sls Dir: Tim Tolin
Sls Mgr: Mike Conti
Board of Directors: Joseph M Stavola

D-U-N-S 00-153-3082 IMP
■**TRAULSEN & CO INC**
(*Suby of* ILLINOIS TOOL WORKS INC) ★
4401 Blue Mound Rd, Fort Worth, TX 76106-1928
Tel (817) 625-9671 *Founded/Ownrshp* 1939, 1998
Sales 132.0MM[E] *EMP* 350
SIC 3585 Refrigeration & heating equipment
Pr: Stewart Hudnut
VP: Cliff Hill

D-U-N-S 18-108-1498
TRAV CORP
WESTWOOD COLLEGE OF TECHNOLOGY
10249 Church Ranch Way # 200, Broomfield, CO 80021-5489
Tel (303) 426-7000 *Founded/Ownrshp* 1986
Sales 285.0MM *EMP* 2,753
SIC 4724 Travel agencies
Pr: Kirk T Riedinger
**VP:* James Z Turner
Netwrk Mgr: Leo Caire

D-U-N-S 04-556-8359
TRAVEL AND TRANSPORT INC
2120 S 72nd St Ste 120, Omaha, NE 68124-6310
Tel (402) 399-4500 *Founded/Ownrshp* 1984
Sales 103.4MM[E] *EMP* 1,300
Accts Lutz & Company Pc Omaha N
SIC 4724 Tourist agency arranging transport, lodging & car rental
CEO: Kevin O'Malley
**CEO:* Bill Tech
**COO:* Tim Fleming
**Ex VP:* Michael P Kubasik
Ex VP: Kevin Omalley
**Sr VP:* Nancy J Miller
VP: Candy Ellertson
VP: Josh Weiss
**VP:* Joshua Weiss
VP: James Winterscheid
Exec: Monica M Colligan

D-U-N-S 15-084-7309
■**TRAVEL GUARD GROUP INC**
(*Suby of* AIG) ★
3300 Business Park Dr, Stevens Point, WI 54482-8851
Tel (715) 345-0505 *Founded/Ownrshp* 1985
Sales NA *EMP* 312
SIC 6411 Insurance brokers
Pr: John Noel
Pr: Dave McHone
Pr: Bonnie Raschka
**CFO:* James Koziol
Chf Mktg O: Bob Gallagher
Assoc VP: Bruce Hart
Sr VP: James Page
VP: Brent Bland
VP: Rick Ensign
VP: Tom Nohelty
**VP:* Thomas Zavadsky
Exec: Connie Janowski

D-U-N-S 19-424-1365
TRAVEL HOLDINGS INC
(*Suby of* TRAVEL HOLDINGS PARENT CORPORATION)
220 E Central Pkwy # 4010, Altamonte Springs, FL 32701-3417
Tel (407) 215-7465 *Founded/Ownrshp* 1985
Sales 1.0MMM[E] *EMP* 600
Accts Marcum Llp Miami Fl
SIC 4724 Travel agencies
CEO: Uri Argov
**COO:* Asi Ginio
CFO: Robert Fischer
**CFO:* Michael McIntyre
CFO: Robert Stockwell
Treas: Francesca Johnson
Ofcr: Wendy Friedberg
Ex VP: Ofir Cohen
Ex VP: Tammy James
Ex VP: Amir Kalmar
Ex VP: Steve Skidgel
Ex VP: Doron Zohar
VP: Paul Kitching

D-U-N-S 09-857-7828
TRAVEL INC
4355 River Green Pkwy, Duluth, GA 30096-2572
Tel (770) 291-4100 *Founded/Ownrshp* 1979
Sales 532.9MM *EMP* 256
SIC 4724

D-U-N-S 82-535-6285
TRAVEL LEADERS GROUP LLC
3033 Campus Dr Ste W320, Plymouth, MN 55441-2747
Tel (763) 744-3700 *Founded/Ownrshp* 2008
Sales 201.0MM[E] *EMP* 975[E]
SIC 4724 Travel agencies
Pr: Ninan Chacko
**Ch:* Michael Batt
VP: JD O'Hara
Board of Directors: Barry Liben

D-U-N-S 12-424-7326
TRAVEL NURSE ACROSS AMERICA LLC
5020 Northshore Dr Ste 2, North Little Rock, AR 72118-5330
Tel (501) 663-5288 *Founded/Ownrshp* 2004
Sales 180.0MM *EMP* 900
SIC 7361 Employment agencies
**COO:* Steve Murray
VP Sls: Gary Jones

TRAVEL PORTAL
See TRAVELPORT INC

D-U-N-S 02-092-7880 IMP
TRAVEL TAGS INC (MN)
XTREME GRAPHICS
(*Suby of* TAYLOR CORP) ★
5842 Carmen Ave, Inver Grove Heights, MN 55076-4413
Tel (651) 450-1201 *Founded/Ownrshp* 1973, 2006
Sales 103.8MM[E] *EMP* 379

SIC 2396 3999 2752 Printing & embossing on plastics fabric articles; Identification tags, except paper; Commercial printing, lithographic
CEO: Barb Cederberg
**Pr:* Al Rausch
Bd of Dir: Carl Rodriguez
VP: Bill Cahill
VP: Timothy Lebens
VP: Chris Shimek
VP: John Tomczyk
Off Mgr: Sharon R Dick
QA Dir: Todd Ethen
IT Man: Tony Hoffman
VP Opers: Ken Dishno

D-U-N-S 80-775-8594
■TRAVELCENTERS OF AMERICA INC
(*Suby of* QUAKER STEAK & LUBE) ★
24601 Center Ridge Rd # 200, Westlake, OH 44145-5634
Tel (440) 808-9100 *Founded/Ownrshp* 2000
Sales 1.8MMM[E] *EMP* 10,000
SIC 5541 7538 5812 5411 Filling stations, gasoline; Truck stops; General truck repair; Eating places; Fast food restaurants & stands; Convenience stores
Ch: Edwin P Kuhn
Ch Bd: Timothy Doane
CFO: John R Hoadley
Ex VP: Michael J Lombardi
Ex VP: Andrew J Rebholz
Ex VP: Barry A Richards
Ex VP: Mark R Young
Sr VP: Michael H Hinderliter
VP: William Bartkus
VP: Steven C Lee
Brnch Mgr: Mike Strzok
Board of Directors: Robert Branson, Michael Greene, Steven Gruber, Louis Mischianti, Chris Patterson, Rowan Taylor

D-U-N-S 79-100-1857
▲TRAVELCENTERS OF AMERICA LLC
QUAKER STEAK & LUBE
24601 Center Ridge Rd # 200, Westlake, OH 44145-5634
Tel (440) 808-9100 *Founded/Ownrshp* 1992
Sales 5.8MMM *EMP* 24,250
Accts Rsm Us Llp Cleveland Ohio
Tkr Sym TA *Exch* NGS
SIC 5541 5812 7538 Gasoline service stations; Truck stops; American restaurant; Coffee shop; General truck repair
Pr: Thomas M O'Brien
CFO: Andrew J Rebholz
Ex VP: Michael J Lombardi
Ex VP: Barry A Richards
Ex VP: Mark R Young
Sr VP: Rodney Bresnahan
Sr VP: Skip McGary
Sr VP: William E Myers II
Sr VP: John Ponczoch
Sr VP: Peter P Ward
VP: Randy Graham
VP: William Myers
Board of Directors: Barbara D Gilmore, Lisa Harris Jones, Arthur G Koumantzelis, Joseph L Morea, Barry M Portnoy

D-U-N-S 01-071-5774
■TRAVELERS CASUALTY AND SURETY CO
TRAVELERS INSURANCE
(*Suby of* TRI STATE BUSINESS SYSTEMS INC) ★
1 Tower Sq 8ms, Hartford, CT 06183-0001
Tel (860) 277-0111 *Founded/Ownrshp* 2004
Sales NA *EMP* 88
SIC 6411 6351 Insurance agents, brokers & service; Surety insurance
Ch Bd: Brian William Maclean
CFO: Jay Steven Benet
Sr VP: Diane D Bengston
VP: Michael Doody
Exec: William Patrick Hannon
Genl Couns: Kenneth Franklin Spence III

D-U-N-S 01-298-9195
■TRAVELERS CASUALTY AND SURETY CO OF AMERICA
TRAVELERS INSURANCE
(*Suby of* TRAVELERS INSURANCE) ★
1 Tower Sq 2ms, Hartford, CT 06183-0001
Tel (860) 277-0111 *Founded/Ownrshp* 1964
Sales NA *EMP* 33[E]
SIC 6411 6351 Insurance agents, brokers & service; Surety insurance
Pr: Jay S Fishman
CFO: Jay Benet
Ch: Robert I Lipp
Ex VP: James Francis Cerone
Ex VP: Charles Joseph Clarke
Ex VP: Ronald Edward Foley Jr
Ex VP: James David Gibbs
Ex VP: Joseph Patrick Kiernan
Ex VP: Glenn David Lammey
Ex VP: Robert Paul Restrepo Jr
Ex VP: Alan Mark Silberstein
Sr VP: Paul Augustine Healy
Sr VP: Peter Norris Higgins
Sr VP: Christine Barbara Mead
Sr VP: James Michael Michener
Sr VP: Charles Timothy Morris
Sr VP: Richard Ford Morrison
Sr VP: Richard William Palczynski
Sr VP: David Alan Tyson
Sr VP: Forrest Denney Voss
Sr VP: Walter Douglas Willett

D-U-N-S 85-866-7058
■TRAVELERS CASUALTY CO OF CONNECTICUT
ONE TOWER SQUARE 8MS
(*Suby of* ONE TOWER SQUARE 8MS) ★
1 Tower Sq, Hartford, CT 06183-0001
Tel (860) 277-0111 *Founded/Ownrshp* 1990
Sales NA *EMP* 5
SIC 6331 6351 6321 Fire, marine & casualty insurance; Surety insurance; Accident & health insurance
CEO: Charles Clarke
**CFO:* J Steven Benet

D-U-N-S 01-046-5768
■TRAVELERS CASUALTY INSURANCE CO OF AMERICA
TRAVELERS INSURANCE
(*Suby of* TRAVELERS INSURANCE) ★
1 Tower Sq, Hartford, CT 06183-0001
Tel (860) 277-0111 *Founded/Ownrshp* 1996
Sales NA *EMP* 1[E]
SIC 6411 Insurance agents, brokers & service
Pr: Robert Irving Lipp
**V Ch:* Jay S Fishman
**CFO:* William Patrick Hannon
**Treas:* Henry Joseph Ziber
**Ex VP:* James F Cerone
**Ex VP:* Charles J Clarke
**Ex VP:* Ronald E Foley Jr
**Ex VP:* James D Gibbs
**Ex VP:* Joseph Patrick Kirnan
**Ex VP:* Glenn D Lammey
**Ex VP:* Robert P Restrepo Jr
**Ex VP:* Alan M Silberstein
**VP:* James M Michener

D-U-N-S 01-298-6878
■TRAVELERS COMMERCIAL CASUALTY CO
TRAVELERS INSURANCE
(*Suby of* TRAVELERS INSURANCE) ★
1 Tower Sq, Hartford, CT 06183-0001
Tel (860) 277-0111 *Founded/Ownrshp* 1981, 1996
Sales NA *EMP* 10[E]
SIC 6351 6331 Liability insurance; Fire, marine & casualty insurance
Ch Bd: Robert Irving Lipp
**V Ch:* Charles Joseph Clarke
**V Ch:* Jay S Fishman
**CFO:* William Patrick Hannon
**Ex VP:* Ronald Edward Foley Jr
**Ex VP:* James David Gibbs
**Ex VP:* Joseph Patrick Kiernan
**Ex VP:* Glenn David Lammey
**Ex VP:* Alan Mark Silberstein
**Sr VP:* James Michael Michener
VP: Laura Horan

D-U-N-S 01-176-3088
■TRAVELERS COMMERCIAL INSURANCE CO
TRAVELERS INSURANCE
(*Suby of* TRAVELERS INSURANCE) ★
1 Tower Sq, Hartford, CT 06183-0001
Tel (860) 548-9948 *Founded/Ownrshp* 1990
Sales NA *EMP* 25
SIC 6411 Insurance agents, brokers & service
Ch Bd: Robert Irving Lipp
**CFO:* William Patrick Hannon
**Sr VP:* James Michael Michener
VP: Alvito Vaz

D-U-N-S 03-996-7024
TRAVELERS COMPANIES FOUNDATION INC
1 Tower Sq, Hartford, CT 06183-0001
Tel (800) 842-5075 *Founded/Ownrshp* 2010
Sales NA *EMP* 1,371[E]
SIC 6321 Accident insurance carriers
Prin: Maureen Bass
Sr VP: Salvatore Desimone
VP: Ralph Blanchard
VP: Bryan Bonadies
VP: Charlie Coon
VP: Robert Jenkins
VP: Kim Kennedy
VP: John Miletti
VP: Cheryl Morgan
VP: Glenn Reese
VP: Mark Ruegg
VP: Sarah Russell

D-U-N-S 00-696-3540
▲TRAVELERS COMPANIES INC
485 Lexington Ave, New York, NY 10017-2630
Tel (917) 778-6000 *Founded/Ownrshp* 1853
Sales NA *EMP* 30,900[E]
Accts Kpmg Llp New York New York
Tkr Sym TRV *Exch* NYS
SIC 6331 6351 6321 Fire, marine & casualty insurance & carriers; Automobile insurance; Workers' compensation insurance; Property damage insurance; Surety insurance; Surety insurance bonding; Liability insurance; Accident & health insurance
CEO: Alan D Schnitzer
**Ch Bd:* Jay S Fishman
V Ch: Brigid Murphy
Pr: Brian W Maclean
Pr: Paul Munson
Pr: Greg Toczydlowski
CFO: Jay S Benet
Treas: Jim Strupp
Bd of Dir: Alexis Cruz
Ofcr: Robert Dahl
Ofcr: Bruce R Jones
Ex VP: Robert C Brody
Ex VP: Lisa Caputo
Ex VP: Lisa M Caputo
Ex VP: Bill Cunningham
Ex VP: Gail Deangelis
Ex VP: Fred R Donner
Ex VP: Marlyss J Gage
Ex VP: William H Heyman
Ex VP: Patrick J Kinney
Ex VP: Madelyn Lankton
Board of Directors: Donald J Shepard, Alan L Beller, Laurie J Thomsen, John H Dasburg, Janet M Dolan, Kenneth M Duberstein, Patricia L Higgins, Thomas R Hodgson, William J Kane, Cleve L Killingsworth Jr, Philip T Ruegger III

D-U-N-S 17-615-7410
■TRAVELERS HOME AND MARINE INSURANCE CO
TRAVELERS INSURANCE
(*Suby of* TRAVELERS INSURANCE) ★
1 Tower Sq 2ms, Hartford, CT 06183-0001
Tel (860) 548-9948 *Founded/Ownrshp* 2005
Sales 53.9MM *EMP* 6,000
SIC 4724 Travel agencies
Ch Bd: Charles J Clarke
**Pr:* Douglas G Elliot
Ofcr: Christopher Williams
Sls Mgr: Denise Sailor
Board of Directors: Jay Benet, Charles Clarke

D-U-N-S 00-691-7405
■TRAVELERS INDEMNITY CO (CT)
TRAVELERS INSURANCE
(*Suby of* TRI STATE BUSINESS SYSTEMS INC) ★
1 Tower Sq, Hartford, CT 06183-0001
Tel (860) 277-0111 *Founded/Ownrshp* 1903, 1996
Sales NA *EMP* 20,000
SIC 6411 6331 Insurance agents, brokers & service; Fire, marine & casualty insurance
Pr: Jay S Fishman
V Ch: Jay S Fihman
**CFO:* Jay Benet
Ex VP: Ronald E Foly
Ex VP: James D Gibbs
Ex VP: Joseph P Kiernan
Ex VP: Glenn D Lammey
VP: Ralph Blanchard
VP: Walter Cieslak
VP: Brian Clancy
VP: Michael J Doody
VP: James Harris

D-U-N-S 05-982-9945
■TRAVELERS INDEMNITY CO OF AMERICA INC
TRAVELERS INSURANCE
(*Suby of* TRAVELERS INSURANCE) ★
1 Tower Sq, Hartford, CT 06183-0001
Tel (860) 277-0111 *Founded/Ownrshp* 1966
Sales NA *EMP* 4
SIC 6411 6531 Insurance agents, brokers & service; Real estate agents & managers
Pr: Charles Clark

D-U-N-S 05-982-9820
■TRAVELERS INDEMNITY CO OF CONNECTICUT
TRAVELERS INSURANCE
(*Suby of* TRAVELERS INSURANCE) ★
1 Tower Sq, Hartford, CT 06183-0001
Tel (860) 548-9948 *Founded/Ownrshp* 1966
Sales NA *EMP* 3
SIC 6411 6331 Insurance agents, brokers & service; Fire, marine & casualty insurance
Ch Bd: Robert Irving Lipp

TRAVELERS INSURANCE
See CHARTER OAK FIRE INSURANCE CO

TRAVELERS INSURANCE
See PHOENIX INSURANCE CO

TRAVELERS INSURANCE
See TRAVELERS INDEMNITY CO

TRAVELERS INSURANCE
See UNITED PACIFIC INSURANCE CO

TRAVELERS INSURANCE
See TRAVELERS CASUALTY AND SURETY CO

TRAVELERS INSURANCE
See TRAVELERS COMMERCIAL INSURANCE CO

TRAVELERS INSURANCE
See TRAVELERS CASUALTY AND SURETY CO OF AMERICA

TRAVELERS INSURANCE
See TRAVELERS CASUALTY INSURANCE CO OF AMERICA

TRAVELERS INSURANCE
See TRAVELERS PERSONAL SECURITY INSURANCE CO

TRAVELERS INSURANCE
See TRAVELERS COMMERCIAL CASUALTY CO

TRAVELERS INSURANCE
See TRAVELERS INDEMNITY CO OF CONNECTICUT

TRAVELERS INSURANCE
See TRAVELERS INDEMNITY CO OF AMERICA INC

TRAVELERS INSURANCE
See TRAVELERS HOME AND MARINE INSURANCE CO

TRAVELERS INSURANCE
See FARMINGTON CASUALTY CO

D-U-N-S 96-396-8735
TRAVELERS INSURANCE COMPANIES
385 Washington St, Saint Paul, MN 55102-1309
Tel (651) 310-7911 *Founded/Ownrshp* 2010
Sales NA *EMP* 3,719[E]
SIC 6411 Insurance agents, brokers & service
Ofcr: Michelle Meschke
Sr VP: Wade Overgaard
VP: Loren Danielson
VP: Brian Depaulis
VP: Shari Diamond
VP: Suzanne Drehmel
VP: Elliott Flies
VP: Denis Guenthner
VP: Diane Hayes
VP: Christine Kalla
VP: Rick Kessler
VP: Joseph Lamott
VP: Larry Mills
VP: Jennifer Palo
VP: Wendy Skjerven
VP: Steve W Sullivan
VP: Beverly Turner
VP: Russell Vance
VP: Kathryn Walker
Exec: Dawn Higgins
Dir Bus: Kevin Field

D-U-N-S 01-129-6378
■TRAVELERS PERSONAL SECURITY INSURANCE CO
TRAVELERS INSURANCE
(*Suby of* STANDARD FIRE INSURANCE CO) ★
1 Tower Sq, Hartford, CT 06183-0001
Tel (860) 277-0111 *Founded/Ownrshp* 1990
Sales NA *EMP* 1,671[E]
SIC 6411 Insurance agents, brokers & service
Pr: Jay Stephen Fishman
**CFO:* William Patrick Hannon
**Sr VP:* James Michael Michener

D-U-N-S 93-393-1263
■TRAVELERS PROPERTY CASUALTY CORP
ONE TOWER SQUARE 8MS
(*Suby of* TRAVELERS COMPANIES INC) ★
1 Tower Sq 8ms, Hartford, CT 06183-0001
Tel (860) 277-0111 *Founded/Ownrshp* 1979
Sales NA *EMP* 30,500[E]
SIC 6411 Insurance agents, brokers & service
Ch Bd: Brian W Maclean
Pr: Lisa Caputo
**CFO:* Jay S Benet
**Treas:* Maria Olivo
**Ex VP:* Andy F Bessette
**Ex VP:* John P Clifford Jr
Ex VP: Laura Horan
**Sr VP:* James C Adams
Sr VP: George A Ryn
Sr VP: Janet R Stain
VP: Keith F Anderson
VP: Scott Belden
VP: Ralph Blanchard
VP: Jon Gice
VP: Russell Johnson

D-U-N-S 83-728-0197
TRAVELEX CURRENCY SERVICES INC
(*Suby of* TRAVELEX LIMITED)
122 E 42nd St Rm 2800, New York, NY 10168-2897
Tel (212) 363-6206 *Founded/Ownrshp* 1983
Sales NA *EMP* 239
SIC 6099 Foreign currency exchange
Ch: Jon Dario
**Pr:* Tracy Hamnock
**CEO:* Peter Jackson
COO: Rod McMorran
**CFO:* Richard Guest
CFO: John Martin
**Treas:* Clive Kahn
Brnch Mgr: George Farges
Genl Mgr: Martin Shoestock
Off Admin: Anthony Horne
CTO: Nick Jones

D-U-N-S 80-664-2158
■TRAVELOCITY.COM LP
(*Suby of* SABRE CORP) ★
5400 L B Johnson Fwy 50 Ste 500, Dallas, TX 75240
Tel (682) 605-1000 *Founded/Ownrshp* 2015
Sales 116.0MM[E] *EMP* 2,500
SIC 4724 Tourist agency arranging transport, lodging & car rental
Pr: Roshan Mendis
Mng Pt: Terrel Jones
CFO: John Mills
Chf Mktg O: Victoria Treyger
Ofcr: Transient C Taylor
Sr VP: Johnathan Perkel
VP: Bryan Estep
VP: Ginny Mahl
CTO: Dave Matthews
Dir IT: Tony N Sergio
IT Man: Kelly Winkler
Board of Directors: Kathy Misnuas

D-U-N-S 02-028-0793
TRAVELPORT INC
TRAVEL PORTAL
(*Suby of* TRAVELPORT LIMITED) ★
6 Campus Dr Ste 1, Parsippany, NJ 07054-4406
Tel (770) 563-7400 *Founded/Ownrshp* 2013
Sales 342.4MM[E] *EMP* 1,585[E]
SIC 4724 Travel agencies
Pr: Jeff Clarke
CFO: Bernard Bot
CFO: Philip Emery
CFO: Daryl E Raiford
**Chf Mktg O:* Jon Hall
**Ex VP:* Eric J Bock
**Ex VP:* Terence P Conley
Ex VP: Terence Conley
Ex VP: Kurt Ekert
Ex VP: Jo-Anne Kruse
Ex VP: Matt Minetola
Ex VP: Stephen Shurrock
Sr VP: Dirk J Vande Beek
VP: Paul A Hesser
VP: Linda Long
Exec: Aurelia Berry

D-U-N-S 07-923-9077
TRAVELPORT LIMITED
(*Suby of* TRAVELPORT)
300 Galleria Pkwy Se, Atlanta, GA 30339-3153
Tel (770) 563-7400 *Founded/Ownrshp* 1971
Sales 1.6MMM[E] *EMP* 3,500[E]
SIC 4724 Travel agencies
Pr: Gordon A Wilson
CFO: Philip Emery
Ex VP: Eric J Bock
Ex VP: Kurt Ekert
Ex VP: Mark Ryan
VP: Tracie Carillo
VP: Jimmy McCullough
Dir Bus: Monique Cansdell
Dir Bus: Monique Jensen
Comm Man: Gerhard Meyer
Prgrm Mgr: Joe Todd
Board of Directors: Gavin R Baiera, Gregory Blank Mand Scott M

D-U-N-S 15-984-7458
TRAVELPORT LLC
(*Suby of* TRAVEL PORTAL) ★
6 Campus Dr Ste 1, Parsippany, NJ 07054-4406
Tel (770) 563-7400 *Founded/Ownrshp* 2001
Sales 162.7MM[E] *EMP* 1,400

SIC 7375 Information retrieval services
Pr: Sam E Galeotos
**Ch Bd:* Samuel Katz
COO: Mark Huntley
CFO: Mike Rescoe
Ex VP: David Grizzle
**Ex VP:* Janie Kaung
Ex VP: Gerald Lampaert
**Ex VP:* Dan Neuburger
**Ex VP:* Gordon Wilson
**Sr VP:* Kenneth Esterow
Sr VP: Kevin Monaco
VP: Marcus Allen
VP: Mark Gibaldi
VP: Derek Sharp
Exec: William Griffith

D-U-N-S 61-484-2896
TRAVELPORT LP
(*Suby of* TRAVEL PORTAL) ★
300 Galleria Pkwy Se, Atlanta, GA 30339-3153
Tel (770) 563-7400 *Founded/Ownrshp* 2007
Sales 179.3MM^E^ *EMP* 1,460
SIC 7374 Data processing & preparation
Sr VP: Susan J Powers
Sr VP: Simon Gray
VP: Ken Klein
VP: Rabih Saab
Dir Bus: Hilton Montr
Rgnl Mgr: Arijit Munshi
Genl Mgr: Mark Fallon
Off Admin: Shawn Tapley
CIO: Jason Note
Opers Mgr: Pete Lundgren
Sales Exec: Roberta Evans

D-U-N-S 11-221-0286
▲TRAVELZOO INC
590 Madison Ave Rm 3700, New York, NY 10022-8528
Tel (212) 484-4900 *Founded/Ownrshp* 1998
Sales 141.7MM *EMP* 473^E^
Tkr Sym TZOO *Exch* NGS
SIC 7313 7373 Electronic media advertising representatives; Computer integrated systems design
Ch Bd: Christopher Loughlin
**Ch Bd:* Holger Bartel
CFO: Glen Ceremony
**CTO:* Ralph Bartel
Sls Mgr: Zach Alpert
Sls Mgr: Bryan Garber
Board of Directors: Michael Karg, Donovan Neale-May, Mary Reilly, Beatrice Tarka, Caroline Tsay

D-U-N-S 08-036-5349
TRAVERSE CITY AREA PUBLIC SCHOOLS
412 Webster St, Traverse City, MI 49686-2650
Tel (231) 933-1700 *Founded/Ownrshp* 1938
Sales 113.2MM *EMP* 1,825
Accts Maner Costerisan Pc Lansing
SIC 8211 Public elementary & secondary schools; Public junior high school; Public senior high school
**CFO:* Paul Soma
Dir Sec: Rod Lowes
IT Man: Todd Neibauer
Pr Dir: Albert Dimas

D-U-N-S 04-002-0794
TRAVIS CREDIT UNION
1 Travis Way, Vacaville, CA 95687-3276
Tel (707) 449-4000 *Founded/Ownrshp* 1951
Sales NA *EMP* 500
Accts Turner Warren Hwang & Conrad
SIC 6061 Federal credit unions
CEO: Patsy Vanouwerkerk
Brnch Mgr: Stacey Meyers
Brnch Mgr: Steve Vlach
IT Man: Tracy Kelly

D-U-N-S 00-906-8578 IMP
TRAVIS PATTERN & FOUNDRY INC
1413 E Hawthorne Rd, Spokane, WA 99218-3100
Tel (509) 466-1798 *Founded/Ownrshp* 1971
Sales 120.6MM^E^ *EMP* 500
SIC 3523 3369 3313 3321 3625 Irrigation equipment, self-propelled; Castings, except die-castings, precision; Alloys, additive, except copper: not made in blast furnaces; Gray & ductile iron foundries; Switches, electronic applications
Pr: Travis Garske
**VP:* Scott Chaffin
**VP:* Daniel Garske

D-U-N-S 09-937-2567
TRAX INTERNATIONAL CORP
8337 W Sunset Rd Ste 250, Las Vegas, NV 89113-2211
Tel (702) 216-4455 *Founded/Ownrshp* 1979
Sales 220.1MM *EMP* 500
Accts Cherry Bekaert Llp Tysons Cor
SIC 7373 8711 7376 8742 8744 Computer integrated systems design; Engineering services; Computer facilities management; Management consulting services; Facilities support services
CEO: F Craig Wilson
**CFO:* Pamela Hormell
**Sr VP:* John Fargason
**Sr VP:* Charles Garcia
**Sr VP:* Gregory Warner
**VP:* Susan Bigbee
**VP:* William Sample

D-U-N-S 78-367-3023
TRAXYS NORTH AMERICA LLC
(*Suby of* TRAXYS SARL)
825 3rd Ave Fl 9, New York, NY 10022-9522
Tel (212) 918-8000 *Founded/Ownrshp* 2006
Sales NA *EMP* 300
SIC 6111 7389 Federal & federally sponsored credit agencies; Advertising, promotional & trade show services
**CFO:* Todd Hermanson
**Ch:* Alan K Docter
Sr VP: Daniel Katz
**VP:* Bernard De Busscher
VP: Mike Reid
Exec: Tony Voltolina
Dir Bus: Michael Hochschild
Mng Dir: Peter Hochschild
Mng Dir: Erez Ichilov
Mng Dir: Daniel Marx
Genl Mgr: Marc Bosschaerts

D-U-N-S 07-283-1969 IMP
TRAY-PAK CORP
Tuckerton Rd And, Reading, PA 19605
Tel (888) 926-1777 *Founded/Ownrshp* 1975
Sales 123.6MM^E^ *EMP* 300
SIC 3089 Trays, plastic
Pr: Scott Myers
CFO: Jeff Patterson
Dir IT: Ed Gunderson
Sfty Mgr: Dave Rothenberger
VP Sls: Kevin E Gramley

D-U-N-S 00-693-7023 IMP
TRAYLOR BROS INC
835 N Congress Ave, Evansville, IN 47715-2484
Tel (812) 477-1542 *Founded/Ownrshp* 1946
Sales 320.0MM *EMP* 412
Accts Bkd Llp Evansville Indiana
SIC 1622 Bridge construction
CEO: Christopher Traylor
**VP:* Donald C Bartow
**VP:* Cornelius J Meagher
**VP:* George Williamson
Dir Risk M: Eric Friend
**Prin:* Michael Traylor
Admn Mgr: Jenny Reising
Div Mgr: Carl Johnson
QA Dir: Bryan Casey
Sfty Mgr: Steve Stier

TRC
See TECHNOLOGY RESEARCH LLC

D-U-N-S 05-418-3884
▲TRC COMPANIES INC
650 Suffolk St, Lowell, MA 01854-3642
Tel (978) 970-5600 *Founded/Ownrshp* 1969
Sales 465.1MM *EMP* 3,700^E^
Accts Deloitte & Touche Llp Boston
Tkr Sym TRR *Exch* NYS
SIC 7363 8734 7382 8748 Engineering help service; Pollution testing; Security systems services; Environmental consultant
Ch Bd: Christopher P Vincze
CFO: Thomas W Bennet Jr
Ofcr: Jim Stephenson
Sr VP: John W Cowdery
Sr VP: Martin H Dodd
Sr VP: James Mayer
VP: Robert Callender
VP: Mark Lorentzen
VP: Jeff Wiese
Exec: Lauren O'Donnell
Prgrm Mgr: Marc Theobald
Board of Directors: John A Carrig, F Thomas Casey, Stephen M Duff, Richard H Grogan, Stephanie C Hildebrandt, Kathleen M Shanahan, Dennis E Welch

D-U-N-S 06-551-6288
■TRC ENVIRONMENTAL CORP (CT)
(*Suby of* TRC COMPANIES INC) ★
21 Griffin Rd N Ste 1, Windsor, CT 06095-1590
Tel (860) 289-8631 *Founded/Ownrshp* 1970, 1971
Sales 190.8MM^E^ *EMP* 600
SIC 8748 8711 Environmental consultant; Engineering services
CEO: Christopher Vincze
**Pr:* Robert Petersen
**Treas:* Thomas W Bennet
**Sr VP:* Glenn E Harkness
**Sr VP:* Gale F Hoffnagle
**VP:* Steven D Macneil
**VP:* Carl Paschetag

D-U-N-S 83-328-7464
TRC GROUP INC
3721 Douglas Blvd Ste 375, Roseville, CA 95661-4255
Tel (916) 784-7745 *Founded/Ownrshp* 2009
Sales 350.2MM^E^ *EMP* 3,000^E^
SIC 5153 Grain & field beans
Pr: Jay Kapila
**CFO:* Xavier Verspierren
**VP:* Amilcar Ybarra

D-U-N-S 86-794-8572
■TREASURE CHEST CASINO LLC
(*Suby of* BOYD GAMING CORP) ★
5050 Williams Blvd, Kenner, LA 70065-1400
Tel (504) 443-8000 *Founded/Ownrshp* 1997
Sales 35.8MM^E^ *EMP* 1,200
SIC 7999 Gambling establishment
Off Mgr: Alice Boudreaux
MIS Dir: Greg Wax
Mktg Mgr: Bobby Thornton

D-U-N-S 02-533-0853
TREASURE ISLAND FOODS INC
3460 N Broadway St, Chicago, IL 60657-2599
Tel (773) 327-3880 *Founded/Ownrshp* 1961
Sales 105.6MM^E^ *EMP* 500
SIC 5411 5921 Supermarkets, chain; Liquor stores
Pr: Christ Kamberos
**Pr:* Maria Kamberos

D-U-N-S 07-574-4289
TREASURE ISLAND LLC
TI
(*Suby of* RUFFIN ACQUISITION LLC) ★
3300 Las Vegas Blvd S, Las Vegas, NV 89109-8916
Tel (702) 894-7111 *Founded/Ownrshp* 1991
Sales 315.0MM^E^ *EMP* 3,000
SIC 7011 7231

D-U-N-S 10-866-9987
TREASURE ISLAND RESORT AND CASINO
MIN
(*Suby of* PRAIRIE ISLAND INDIAN COMMUNITY) ★
5734 Sturgeon Lake Rd, Welch, MN 55089-9647
Tel (651) 388-6300 *Founded/Ownrshp* 1984
Sales 57.0MM^E^ *EMP* 1,500
SIC 7999 7011 5812 Bingo hall; Game parlor; Hotels; Eating places
CEO: Michael Heavner
**Genl Mgr:* Eddie Lynn
Dir IT: Doug Kranig
IT Man: Dawn Casey
IT Man: Gary Sturm
IT Man: Cindy Taube
Secur Mgr: Clint Pitonak

TREASURES OFFICE
See COUNTY OF BUTTE

D-U-N-S 05-325-1302 IMP
TREASURY WINE ESTATES AMERICAS CO
(*Suby of* TREASURY WINE ESTATES LIMITED)
555 Gateway Dr, NAPA, CA 94558-6291
Tel (707) 259-4500 *Founded/Ownrshp* 1973
Sales 389.9MM^E^ *EMP* 1,300
SIC 2084 Wines
CEO: Michael Clarke
**Pr:* Robert Foye
**Pr:* Bob Spooner
**CFO:* Noel Meehan
Ofcr: Paul Conroy
**Ofcr:* Francesca Schuler
VP: Rachel Ashley
VP: Michael Cerio
**VP:* Martin Foster
VP: Bruce Herman
**VP:* Walter Klenz
VP: Jeff Marek
Exec: Stephen Fox

TREAT AMERICA FOOD SERVICES
See MYRON GREEN CORP

D-U-N-S 01-386-1009
TREAT AMERICA MANAGEMENT CO LLC (KS)
TREAT OF AMERICA
8500 Shawnee Mission Pkwy # 100, Merriam, KS 66202-2960
Tel (913) 268-5800 *Founded/Ownrshp* 2006
Sales 249.0MM^E^ *EMP* 1,400^E^
SIC 5963 Food services, direct sales
VP: Kay Phr
VP: William Pellien
Exec: Greg Cook
Genl Mgr: Christopher Snyder
Genl Mgr: Rich Spicl
CTO: Mark Madden
Opers Mgr: John D Warner
Mktg Mgr: Michael Kricsfeld MBA
Manager: John Shene
Sls Mgr: Dave Lamaster

TREAT OF AMERICA
See TREAT AMERICA MANAGEMENT CO LLC

D-U-N-S 04-667-0634
▲TRECORA RESOURCES
1650 Highway 6 Ste 190, Sugar Land, TX 77478-4926
Tel (409) 385-8300 *Founded/Ownrshp* 1967
Sales 241.9MM *EMP* 296^E^
Tkr Sym TREC *Exch* NYS
SIC 2911 Petroleum refining
Pr: Simon Upfill-Brown
**Ch Bd:* Nicholas N Carter
Pr: Peter Loggenberg
CFO: Sami Ahmad
Treas: Connie Cook
VP: Ronald Franklin

D-U-N-S 55-546-3785 IMP/EXP
▲TREDEGAR CORP
1100 Boulders Pkwy # 200, North Chesterfield, VA 23225-4064
Tel (804) 330-1000 *Founded/Ownrshp* 1988
Sales 876.0MM *EMP* 2,800
Tkr Sym TG *Exch* NYS
SIC 3081 2671 3083 3354 Plastic film & sheet; Plastic film, coated or laminated for packaging; Laminated plastics plate & sheet; Aluminum extruded products
Pr: John D Gottwald
**Ch Bd:* William M Gottwald
CFO: D Andrew Edwards
VP: Michael W Giancaspro
Plnt Mgr: Steven Hunt
Board of Directors: George C Freeman III, George A Newbill, Kenneth R Newsome, Gregory A Pratt, Thomas G Snead Jr, Carl E Tack III

D-U-N-S 62-445-3754 IMP/EXP
■TREDEGAR FILM PRODUCTS CORP
(*Suby of* TREDEGAR CORP) ★
1100 Boulders Pkwy # 200, North Chesterfield, VA 23225-4064
Tel (804) 330-1000 *Founded/Ownrshp* 2000
Sales 279.1MM^E^ *EMP* 1,200^E^
SIC 3081 Unsupported plastics film & sheet
Pr: Mary Jane Hellyar
VP: Brent King
Sls&Mrk Ex: Jim Cree

D-U-N-S 04-899-5187 IMP
TREDIT TIRE & WHEEL CO INC
(*Suby of* CHESTNUT HOLDINGS INC) ★
3305 Charlotte Ave, Elkhart, IN 46517-1194
Tel (574) 293-0581 *Founded/Ownrshp* 1995
Sales 148.9MM^E^ *EMP* 150
SIC 5014 5013 Tires & tubes; Wheels, motor vehicle
CEO: Terrence J O'Rourke
**Ch Bd:* James McCready
**Pr:* Ron Pike
VP: Timothy Ball
**VP:* Jennifer D Sailor
IT Man: Josh Hostetler
Sfty Mgr: Mark Longcor
Opers Mgr: Robert Fox

D-U-N-S 07-373-6811
TREDYFFRIN-EASTTOWN SCHOOL DISTRICT (INC)
TESD
940 W Valley Rd Ste 1700, Wayne, PA 19087-1856
Tel (610) 240-1900 *Founded/Ownrshp* 1908
Sales 112.7MM *EMP* 1,000
SIC 8211 Public elementary & secondary schools; Public junior high school; Public senior high school
VP: Genevieve Matz
IT Man: Steve Stork

D-U-N-S 79-706-5245 IMP
TREE ISLAND WIRE (USA) INC
TI WIRE
(*Suby of* TREE ISLAND INDUSTRIES LTD)
3880 Valley Blvd, Walnut, CA 91789-1515
Tel (909) 594-7511 *Founded/Ownrshp* 1983
Sales 108.9MM^E^ *EMP* 600
SIC 3315 Wire, steel: insulated or armored
Ch Bd: Amar S Doman
**CEO:* Dale R Maclean
**CFO:* Nancy Davies
VP: Dale McLean
**VP:* Stephen Ogden
VP: Kurt Sidell
Exec: Bruce Yost
Sls&Mrk Ex: Sandy Patterson

D-U-N-S 00-926-8319 IMP/EXP
TREE TOP INC (WA)
220 E 2nd Ave, Selah, WA 98942-1408
Tel (509) 697-7251 *Founded/Ownrshp* 1960
Sales 399.9MM *EMP* 1,100
SIC 2033 2034 2037 Fruit juices: packaged in cans, jars, etc.; Fruits, dried or dehydrated, except freeze-dried; Frozen fruits & vegetables
Pr: Keith Gomes
**CFO:* Dwaine Brown
Treas: Scott Taylor
**Sr VP:* Lindsay Buckner
**Sr VP:* Dan Hagerty
**Sr VP:* Tom Hurson
**VP:* Nancy Buck
**VP:* Cris Hales
VP: Doug Webster
Genl Mgr: Debi Garrison
Software D: David Eisenheim

D-U-N-S 36-062-4857
▲TREEHOUSE FOODS INC
2021 Spring Rd Ste 600, Oak Brook, IL 60523-1860
Tel (708) 483-1300 *Founded/Ownrshp* 2005
Sales 3.2MMM *EMP* 5,880^E^
Tkr Sym THS *Exch* NYS
SIC 2035 2023 2032 2033 2087 Pickles, sauces & salad dressings; Cream substitutes; Puddings, except meat: packaged in cans, jars, etc.; Soups & broths: canned, jarred, etc.; Jams, jellies & preserves: packaged in cans, jars, etc.; Powders, drink
Ch Bd: Sam K Reed
Pr: Dennis F Riordan
Ex VP: Thomas E O'Neill
Ex VP: Harry J Walsh
Ex VP: Harry Walsh
Sr VP: Rachel R Bishop
Sr VP: Erik Kahler
VP: Jo Osborn
Comm Dir: Nicole Curtin
Prd Mgr: Joshua Link
Board of Directors: George V Bayly, Diana S Ferguson, Linda K Massma, Dennis F O'brien, Frank J O'-connell, Ann M Sardini, Gary D Smith, David B Vermylen

D-U-N-S 82-640-9369 IMP/EXP
■TREEHOUSE PRIVATE BRANDS INC
(*Suby of* TREEHOUSE FOODS INC) ★
800 Market St, Saint Louis, MO 63101-2506
Tel (314) 877-7300 *Founded/Ownrshp* 2016
Sales 3.2MMM^E^ *EMP* 5,880
SIC 2043 2052 2068 2035 Cereal breakfast foods; Crackers, dry; Cookies; Nuts: dried, dehydrated, salted or roasted; Dressings, salad: raw & cooked (except dry mixes); Seasonings & sauces, except tomato & dry
CEO: Sean Connoly
Pr: Walt George
Pr: Ronald D Wilkinson
CFO: Scott Monette
Treas: Scott E Messel
Treas: Den Sescleifer
VP: Gregory A Billhartz
VP: Charles G Huber
Dir IT: Paul Garcia
Dir IT: Don Rowe
Opers Mgr: John Brodie

D-U-N-S 02-666-1116
TREES INC
(*Suby of* UTILITY VEGETATION SERVICES INC) ★
650 N Sam Houston Pkwy E, Houston, TX 77060-5906
Tel (281) 447-1327 *Founded/Ownrshp* 1999
Sales 67.5MM^E^ *EMP* 1,000
SIC 0783 0782 Tree trimming services for public utility lines; Pruning services, ornamental tree; Surgery services, ornamental tree; Lawn & garden services
Pr: David Fleishaner
VP: George Leszkowicz
**VP:* William Mills

D-U-N-S 08-922-7391 IMP
TREES N TRENDS INC
JEWELRY AND HANDBANG WAREHOUSE
3229 Benton Rd, Paducah, KY 42003-0346
Tel (270) 443-5100 *Founded/Ownrshp* 1992
Sales 93.8MM^E^ *EMP* 425
SIC 5999 3999 5947 5193 Artificial flowers; Artificial trees & flowers; Hair clippers for human use, hand & electric; Artcraft & carvings; Gift baskets; Florists' supplies; Planters & flower pots
Pr: Joe L Wallace
**CFO:* Bruce A Wilcox
**Sec:* Cynthia L Wallace
**VP:* Joseph David Bailey
**VP:* Bryant C Uthoff

D-U-N-S 06-708-4293
TREFZ CORP
MCDONALD'S
10 Middle St Ste 1701, Bridgeport, CT 06604-4292
Tel (203) 367-3621 *Founded/Ownrshp* 1964
Sales 61.2MM^E^ *EMP* 1,500
SIC 5812 6531 8721 Fast-food restaurant, chain; Real estate agents & managers; Billing & bookkeeping service
Pr: Ernest C Trefz
**CFO:* Robert J Hull Jr
**Treas:* Christian J Trefz

D-U-N-S 02-046-5852 IMP/EXP
TREK BICYCLE CORP
801 W Madison St, Waterloo, WI 53594-1379
Tel (920) 478-2191 *Founded/Ownrshp* 1976
Sales 238.7MM^E *EMP* 1,189
SIC 5941 3429 Sporting goods & bicycle shops; Bicycle racks, automotive
CEO: John Burke
Pr: Steve Malchow
VP: Robert Burns
VP: John Shanks
VP: Joseph Siefkes
Snr Sftwr: Jason Dove
CTO: Connie LI
MIS Dir: Jeff R Stang
Mfg Mgr: Sheldon Benzine
Mfg Mgr: Tony Smook
Natl Sales: Paul Moran

D-U-N-S 60-341-1117 IMP
TRELLEBORG AUTOMOTIVE USA INC
(*Suby of* VIBRACOUSTIC GMBH)
400 Aylworth Ave, South Haven, MI 49090-1707
Tel (269) 637-2116 *Founded/Ownrshp* 2014
Sales 299.2MM^E *EMP* 900
SIC 3061 3625 Automotive rubber goods (mechanical); Noise control equipment
Pr: Mark Brooks
**Sr VP:* Patrik Romberg
VP: Joe Gervais
Mng Dir: Simon Wilson
IT Man: Massimiliano Ferrazzi
Prd Mgr: Thomas Ahlstrm
Mktg Mgr: Wade Singler
Manager: Ty Molter
Sls Mgr: Carol Corbisello

D-U-N-S 00-151-9503 IMP
TRELLEBORG COATED SYSTEMS US INC
(*Suby of* TRELLEBORG CORP) ★
715 Railroad Ave, Rutherfordton, NC 28139-2207
Tel (864) 576-1210 *Founded/Ownrshp* 1937
Sales 281.5MM^E *EMP* 978
SIC 2295 2221 2394 2396 2211 Coated fabrics, not rubberized; Manmade & synthetic broadwoven fabrics; Tarpaulins, fabric: made from purchased materials; Automotive & apparel trimmings; Laundry fabrics, cotton
Ch: Sren Mellstig
**Pr:* Kieth Dye
**CFO:* Danny Hall
Ql Cn Mgr: Alan Marshall
Mktg Mgr: Ben Petereson

D-U-N-S 19-871-9429 IMP
TRELLEBORG CORP
(*Suby of* TRELLEBORG AB)
200 Veterans Blvd Ste 3, South Haven, MI 49090-8663
Tel (269) 639-9891 *Founded/Ownrshp* 1988
Sales 831.0MM^E *EMP* 2,381
SIC 3341 1021 1044 1031 4226 1041 Secondary precious metals; Copper ore mining & preparation; Silver ores mining; Zinc ores mining; Liquid storage; Gold ores mining
Pr: Torgney Astrom
**CFO:* Joe Jervais
**VP:* Richard Hodgson
VP: Alan McBride
Dir Bus: Johan Frithiof
Mng Dir: John Bennett
Corp Couns: Hakan Jonsson
Snr Mgr: Bonnie Everetts

D-U-N-S 16-082-5733 IMP/EXP
TRELLEBORG OFFSHORE US INC
(*Suby of* TRELLEBORG CORP) ★
1902 Rankin Rd, Houston, TX 77073-5110
Tel (281) 774-2600 *Founded/Ownrshp* 2006
Sales 108.3MM^E *EMP* 400
SIC 3533 Oil field machinery & equipment
Pr: Mark Engus
VP: Jerolyn Jones
Dir IT: Dave Nash

D-U-N-S 00-833-6182 IMP
TRELLEBORG SEALING SOLUTIONS US INC
BUSAKSHAMBAN
(*Suby of* TRELLEBORG CORP) ★
2531 Bremer Rd, Fort Wayne, IN 46803-3014
Tel (260) 749-9631 *Founded/Ownrshp* 2004
Sales 403.6MM^E *EMP* 1,510
SIC 3089 Plastic processing; Bearings, plastic
Pr: Tim Callison
Pr: Peter Hahn
Pr: Linda Muroski
**VP:* Kevin Alofs
**VP:* Per Danielsson
**VP:* Henning Jensen
QC Dir: Frank Williams

D-U-N-S 07-972-5658
TREMAYNE ANTONIO WILLIAMS GLOBAL ESTATE ENTRUST TRUST
INTERNTNAL WRLDWIDE INVSTMENTS
12955 Walsingham Rd # 197, Largo, FL 33774-3538
Tel (727) 218-0199 *Founded/Ownrshp* 2014
Sales 100.0MM *EMP* 1
SIC 6733 Private estate, personal investment & vacation fund trusts
Pr: Treymayne Williams

D-U-N-S 00-418-8702 IMP/EXP
■TREMCO INC
(*Suby of* RPM INTERNATIONAL INC) ★
3735 Green Rd, Beachwood, OH 44122-5730
Tel (216) 292-5000 *Founded/Ownrshp* 1997
Sales 508.2MM^E *EMP* 1,406
SIC 2891 2952 1761 1752 2851 2842 Sealants; Caulking compounds; Adhesives; Epoxy adhesives; Roofing materials; Coating compounds, tar; Asphalt saturated board; Roofing contractor; Floor laying & floor work; Paints & allied products; Specialty cleaning, polishes & sanitation goods
CEO: Jeffrey L Korach
**Pr:* Randall J Korach
**CFO:* Mike Drumm
**Div Pres:* Chuck Houk
**Div Pres:* Deryl Kratzer
**Div Pres:* Moorman Scott
Ofcr: Brian Stack
VP: Lynn Armbruster
VP: Mary Curry
VP: Kimberly Orr
VP: Ken Recko
Exec: Jamie Gill
Exec: Marianne Hadaway
Exec: Eric Horstman

D-U-N-S 62-015-6521 IMP
TREMONT GROUP INC
GROWERS AG
201 East St, Woodland, CA 95776-3523
Tel (530) 662-5442 *Founded/Ownrshp* 1990
Sales 172.7MM^E *EMP* 120
SIC 5191 Fertilizers & agricultural chemicals
Pr: Johnny Council
**Pr:* Leslie Lyman
CFO: Larry Chellemi
Sfty Dirs: Calvin Taylor
Snr Mgr: Julie Newton

D-U-N-S 15-163-5146
▲TREMOR VIDEO INC
1501 Broadway Fl 8, New York, NY 10036-5601
Tel (646) 723-5300 *Founded/Ownrshp* 2005
Sales 173.8MM *EMP* 335^E
Tkr Sym TRMR *Exch* NYS
SIC 7311 Advertising agencies
Pr: William Day
**Ch Bd:* Paul Caine
CFO: John S Rego
Chf Mktg O: Jennifer Catto
Sr VP: John Walsh
VP: Aaron Saltz
VP: Calvin Wong
Snr Sftwr: Richard Spring
Board of Directors: Rachel Lam, Warren Lee, James Rossman, Robert Schechter, Michael Todd

TRENCH-IT
See INTREN INC

D-U-N-S 15-373-6871 IMP
TREND OFFSET PRINTING SERVICES INC
3701 Catalina St, Los Alamitos, CA 90720-2402
Tel (562) 598-2446 *Founded/Ownrshp* 1986
Sales 305.0MM^E *EMP* 1,200
Accts Deloitte & Touche Llp Los Ang
SIC 2752 Commercial printing, offset
Ch Bd: Anthony Jacob Lienau
**Pr:* Jim Davis
**CEO:* Todd Nelson
**COO:* Munir Ahmed
**COO:* Steve Furlong
**CFO:* Adam Lienau
Treas: Kevin Edgecombe
VP: Randy Ginsberg
VP: Mark Leese
Exec: Tom Underwood
IT Man: Lewis Story

D-U-N-S 01-881-0551
TREND PERSONNEL SERVICES INC (TX)
2701 Sunset Ridge Dr, Rockwall, TX 75032-0005
Tel (214) 553-5505 *Founded/Ownrshp* 1997
Sales 55.2MM^E *EMP* 5,800
SIC 7361 Employment agencies
Pr: Daniel W Bobst
**Pr:* Dan Bobst

D-U-N-S 12-869-5330 IMP
TREND TECHNOLOGIES LLC
(*Suby of* TTL HOLDINGS LLC) ★
4626 Eucalyptus Ave, Chino, CA 91710-9215
Tel (909) 597-7861 *Founded/Ownrshp* 2002
Sales 111.7MM^E *EMP* 450
SIC 3444 3469 3499 Metal housings, enclosures, casings & other containers; Electronic enclosures, stamped or pressed metal; Aquarium accessories, metal
Dir IT: Ron Begin
VP Mfg: Brian Dickstein
Ql Cn Mgr: Dave Vickers
Pgrm Dir: Paul Anderson
Pgrm Dir: Carlos Flores
Pgrm Dir: Tuan Tran
Board of Directors: Jim Hill, Leo Lawless, Paul Walsh

TRENDSETTER STAFFING
See TEXAS STAFFING SERVICES INC

D-U-N-S 79-110-6651
TRENT SEVERN ENVIRONMENTAL SERVICES INC
(*Suby of* SEVERN TRENT (DEL) INC) ★
2002 W Grand Pkwy N, Katy, TX 77449-1963
Tel (281) 578-4200 *Founded/Ownrshp* 1983
Sales 253.4MM^E *EMP* 1,400
SIC 8741 3589

D-U-N-S 96-402-6236
TRENTON PUBLIC SCHOOL DISTRICT
108 N Clinton Ave, Trenton, NJ 08609-1014
Tel (609) 656-4900 *Founded/Ownrshp* 2010
Sales 83.1MM^E *EMP* 2,096^E
SIC 8211 Public elementary & secondary schools
VP: Alexander Brown
Dir Sec: Wilfred Ortiz
Software D: Michael Iapalucci
Software D: Nola Occhipinti
Software D: Sheryl Reid
Software D: Troy Soto
Pr Dir: Perry Lattiboudere
Schl Brd P: Diane Campbell
Schl Brd P: Patricia Daley

TRESCO LIGHTING
See REV-A-SHELF CO LLC

D-U-N-S 05-506-6112
TRESIERRAS BROTHERS CORP
TRESIERRAS MARKET 3
618 San Fernando Rd, San Fernando, CA 91340-3405
Tel (818) 365-8859 *Founded/Ownrshp* 1974
Sales 87.0MM^E *EMP* 380
SIC 5411 5461 Grocery stores; Bakeries
Pr: Richard Tresierras
Genl Mgr: Felipe Rodriguez

TRESIERRAS MARKET 3
See TRESIERRAS BROTHERS CORP

D-U-N-S 92-976-5303
TREVCON CONSTRUCTION CO INC
30 Church St, Liberty Corner, NJ 07938
Tel (908) 580-0200 *Founded/Ownrshp* 1998
Sales 134.8MM *EMP* 75
Accts Cohnreznick Llp Eatontown Ne
SIC 1629 1623 Dams, waterways, docks & other marine construction; Sewer line construction; Water main construction
Pr: Ronald A Treveloni Jr
**Treas:* Catherine Treveloni
VP: John E Eckart

TREVDAN BUILDING SUPPLY
See TREVDAN INC

D-U-N-S 04-878-0225 IMP
TREVDAN INC
TREVDAN BUILDING SUPPLY
1031 Pottstown Pike, Chester Springs, PA 19425-3512
Tel (610) 458-9860 *Founded/Ownrshp* 1980
Sales 94.8MM^E *EMP* 123
SIC 5031 Lumber, plywood & millwork
Pr: Lawrence J Kanavy
Genl Mgr: Tom Allridge

D-U-N-S 01-529-5231 IMP/EXP
TREVI ICOS CORP
(*Suby of* TREVI SPA)
38 3rd Ave, Charlestown, MA 02129-4502
Tel (617) 241-4800 *Founded/Ownrshp* 1997
Sales 83.6MM *EMP* 120
Accts Darmody Merlino & Co Llp B
SIC 1629 1622 Dam construction; Bridge construction; Tunnel construction; Highway construction, elevated
Ch: Ricardo Petrocelli
Pr: Stefano Valagussa
CFO: Franco Filippi
Co-Ch Bd: Stefano Trevisani
Treas: Daniele Forti
VP: Mario Mauro

TREX
See GREATER OMAHA PACKING CO INC

D-U-N-S 03-306-1750 IMP/EXP
▲TREX CO INC
160 Exeter Dr, Winchester, VA 22603-8614
Tel (540) 542-6300 *Founded/Ownrshp* 1996
Sales 440.8MM *EMP* 700
Tkr Sym TREX *Exch* NYS
SIC 2421 Outdoor wood structural products
Pr: James E Cline
**Ch Bd:* Ronald W Kaplan
CFO: Bryan H Fairbanks
Sr VP: William R Gupp
VP: Jay T Scripter
IT Man: Ryan Levan
IT Man: Kathleen M Ryman
VP Mktg: Adam D Zambanini
VP Sls: Christopher P Gerhard
Board of Directors: Michael F Golden, Jay M Gratz, Frank H Merlotti Jr, Richard E Posey, Patricia B Robinson, Gerald Volas

D-U-N-S 84-027-8308 EXP
TREX CORP INC
TEAM TREX
(*Suby of* TREX) ★
851 Burlway Rd Ste 400, Burlingame, CA 94010-1713
Tel (650) 342-7333 *Founded/Ownrshp* 1996
Sales 100.0MM *EMP* 7
SIC 5147 Meat brokers
Pr: Mark Melnick

TRG
See TITLE RESOURCE GROUP LLC

D-U-N-S 18-162-7451
TRG CUSTOMER SOLUTIONS INC
IBEX GLOBAL
(*Suby of* IBEX GLOBAL SOLUTIONS PLC)
1700 Penn Ave Nw Ste 560, Washington, DC 20006-4725
Tel (202) 289-9898 *Founded/Ownrshp* 2004
Sales 118.5MM^E *EMP* 8,000
SIC 7389 Telemarketing services
CEO: Bob Dechant
**CFO:* Karl Gabel
**Ch:* Nadeem Elahi
Ofcr: Paulette Thompson
Ex VP: Julie Casteel
MIS Dir: Bill Jolish

D-U-N-S 13-234-4875
TRG HOLDINGS LLC
RESOURCE GROUP, THE
(*Suby of* TRG PAKISTAN LIMITED)
1700 Penn Ave Nw Ste 560, Washington, DC 20006-4725
Tel (202) 289-9898 *Founded/Ownrshp* 2003
Sales 114.7MM^E *EMP* 4,000
SIC 7323 Commercial (mercantile) credit reporting bureau
VP Bus Dev: Jeff Symon
CTO: Roberto Singson
VP Sls: Dennis Finnerman
Mktg Mgr: Lindsay Foster
Sls Mgr: Andrey Abramov

D-U-N-S 82-966-5491
TRG WIND DOWN LLC
201 Hancock Blvd, Reading, PA 19611
Tel (610) 775-3301 *Founded/Ownrshp* 2005
Sales 279.8MM^E *EMP* 700
SIC 3713 3792 3469 5531 7532

TRI
See TOYOTA RESEARCH INSTITUTE INC

D-U-N-S 00-439-6610 IMP
■TRI CITY ALUMINUM CO (PA)
(*Suby of* TRACO DELAWARE INC) ★
71 Progress Ave, Cranberry Township, PA 16066-3511
Tel (724) 799-8917 *Founded/Ownrshp* 1943
Sales 175.5MM^E *EMP* 1,566
SIC 3442 3354 7992 Storm doors or windows, metal; Aluminum extruded products; Public golf courses
Pr: Robert Randall
COO: John Kalakos
Treas: Fran Stephen

D-U-N-S 07-963-6458
TRI CITY FOODS OF ILLINOIS INC
BURGER KING
1400 Opus Pl Ste 900, Downers Grove, IL 60515-5762
Tel (630) 598-3300 *Founded/Ownrshp* 2014
Sales 70.1MM^E *EMP* 2,452^E
SIC 5812 Fast-food restaurant, chain
CEO: Todd Bartmess
**CFO:* Joel Aaseby

TRI CNTY CHEM DPNDENCY PROGRAM
See TLC HEALTH NETWORK

D-U-N-S 07-612-3447
■TRI COUNTIES BANK
(*Suby of* TRICO BANCSHARES) ★
63 Constitution Dr, Chico, CA 95973-4937
Tel (530) 898-0300 *Founded/Ownrshp* 1981
Sales NA *EMP* 624
SIC 6029 6163 Commercial banks; Loan brokers
Ch Bd: William J Casey
**Ch Bd:* Alex A Vereschagin Jr
**Pr:* Richard P Smith
**COO:* John S Fleshood
**COO:* Robert Steveson
**CFO:* Thomas Reddish
Treas: Dan Padden
**V Ch Bd:* Michael W Koehnen
Ofcr: Janet Aytes
**Ofcr:* Craig Carney
Ofcr: Judy Hess
Ex VP: Daniel Bailey
**Ex VP:* Richard O'Sullivan
Ex VP: Richard Osullivan
Ex VP: Richard Sullivan
Ex VP: Carol Ward
**Sr VP:* Bruce Barnett
Sr VP: George Barstow
**Sr VP:* Glenn C Hunter
Sr VP: Glenn Hunter
VP: David Allumbaugh

D-U-N-S 00-792-1539
TRI COUNTY ELECTRIC MEMBERSHIP CORP (TN)
TRI-COUNTY ELECTRIC
405 College St, Lafayette, TN 37083-1729
Tel (615) 666-2111 *Founded/Ownrshp* 1936
Sales 116.1MM *EMP* 147
SIC 4911 Distribution, electric power
Ex VP: Paul Thompson
**Prin:* T P Thompson
Opers Mgr: Jerry Wilmore
Mktg Mgr: Tammy Dixon

D-U-N-S 07-989-6935
▲TRI POINTE GROUP INC
19540 Jamboree Rd Ste 300, Irvine, CA 92612-8452
Tel (949) 438-1400 *Founded/Ownrshp* 2009
Sales 2.4MMM *EMP* 961^E
Tkr Sym TPH *Exch* NYS
SIC 1531 Speculative builder, single-family houses
CEO: Douglas F Bauer
**Ch Bd:* Barry S Sternlicht
Pr: Thomas J Mitchell
CFO: Michael D Grubbs
VP: Bradley W Blank
VP: Glenn J Keeler
VP: Kevin Wilson
VP Mktg: Linda H Mamet

D-U-N-S 83-073-7859
■TRI POINTE HOMES INC
(*Suby of* TRI POINTE GROUP INC) ★
19520 Jamboree Rd Ste 300, Irvine, CA 92612-2429
Tel (949) 438-1400 *Founded/Ownrshp* 2009
Sales 1.7MMM *EMP* 961^E
SIC 1531 Speculative builder, single-family houses
CEO: Douglas F Bauer
**Ch Bd:* Barry S Sternlicht
Pr: Thomas J Mitchell
CFO: Michael D Grubbs
Div Pres: Tom Grable
VP: Bradley W Blank
VP: Glenn Keeler
Sls Dir: Tom Gable
Board of Directors: Lawrence B Burrows, Daniel S Fulton, Kristin F Gannon, Steven J Gilbert, Christopher D Graham, Constance B Moore, Thomas B Rogers

D-U-N-S 13-873-5688 IMP/EXP
■TRI RESOURCES INC
TARGA RESOURCES
(*Suby of* TARGA RESOURCES CORP) ★
1000 Louisiana St # 4300, Houston, TX 77002-5005
Tel (713) 584-1000 *Founded/Ownrshp* 2005
Sales 153.3MM^E *EMP* 1,050
SIC 1321 1381 1382 Natural gas liquids; Liquefied petroleum gases (natural) production; Natural gas liquids production; Natural gasoline production; Drilling oil & gas wells; Oil & gas exploration services
CEO: Rene R Joyce
V Ch: Dennis Plato
Pr: Joe Bob Perkins
Pr: James W Whalen
CFO: Jeffrey J McParland
Ex VP: Paul W Chung
Exec: Jeffrey McParland
Area Mgr: Bryan Crismon
Plnt Mgr: Laurie Stiles

D-U-N-S 06-586-1879
TRI STAR ENERGY LLC
1740 Ed Temple Blvd, Nashville, TN 37208-1850
Tel (615) 313-3600 *Founded/Ownrshp* 2000
Sales 749.4MM *EMP* 500E
Accts Lattimore Black Morgaan & Ca
SIC 5331 5172 Variety stores; Gasoline
CFO: Jeff Williams
Treas: Donald Critchton
VP: John Jewell
VP: Mohamed Makky
Dist Mgr: Josh Bacon
Dist Mgr: Kelley Bishop
Dist Mgr: Larry Farina
Dist Mgr: Tim Forsythe
Dist Mgr: Steve Glidewell
Sls Mgr: Terry Messmer
Sls Mgr: Mike Reed

D-U-N-S 02-588-5401
TRI STAR MARKETING INC
SUPER PANTRY
2211 W Bradley Ave, Champaign, IL 61821-1827
Tel (217) 367-8386 *Founded/Ownrshp* 1975
Sales 134.0MME *EMP* 500
SIC 5541 5411 5172

D-U-N-S 04-156-3891
■TRI STATE BUSINESS SYSTEMS INC
(*Suby of* ONE TOWER SQUARE 8MS) ★
1 Tower Sq, Hartford, CT 06183-0001
Tel (860) 277-0111 *Founded/Ownrshp* 2002
Sales NA *EMP* 21,000
SIC 6311 6321 Life insurance carriers; Accident & health insurance carriers
CEO: Jay Fishnan
**COO:* Brian Clain
**CFO:* Jay S Benet
**Ch:* Charles Clarke
**Treas:* Doug Russell

D-U-N-S 08-479-5236
TRI STATE JOINT FUND
25 Research Dr, Milford, CT 06460-8516
Tel (203) 876-3100 *Founded/Ownrshp* 1966
Sales NA *EMP* 20
SIC 6371 Union trust funds

TRI STATE MACK
See TRI-STATE TRUCK CENTER INC

D-U-N-S 00-417-8182 IMP/EXP
TRI VANTAGE LLC (NC)
(*Suby of* GLENRAVEN.COM) ★
1831 N Park Ave, Burlington, NC 27217-1137
Tel (800) 786-1876 *Founded/Ownrshp* 1876
Sales 122.3MME *EMP* 235
SIC 5199 5088 5099 5091 2394 Canvas products; Fabrics, yarns & knit goods; Marine supplies; Signs, except electric; Camping equipment & supplies; Awnings, fabric: made from purchased materials

D-U-N-S 00-922-7701
TRI VENTURES INC
AQUENT
711 Boylston St, Boston, MA 02116-2616
Tel (617) 535-5000 *Founded/Ownrshp* 2001
Sales 397.2MME *EMP* 5,700
SIC 7363 Chauffeur service
Pr: Ann Webster
VP: Larry Bartlett
VP: Jeff Garner
VP: Steven Kapner
**VP:* Deb McCusker
VP: Paul Petersen
VP: John C Pustell
VP: Thomas Reynolds
VP: Robin Simonsen
**Prin:* John Chuang
Mng Dir: Barry Baxter

D-U-N-S 06-388-2757
TRI-BORO CONSTRUCTION SUPPLIES INC
465 E Locust St, Dallastown, PA 17313-1901
Tel (717) 246-3095 *Founded/Ownrshp* 1974
Sales 90.9MME *EMP* 105
SIC 5082 3496 5251 Masonry equipment & supplies; Concrete reinforcing mesh & wire; Tools, hand
Pr: Glenn C Rexroth
**VP:* Glenn C Rexroth Jr
Sales Exec: Gary Price

D-U-N-S 00-280-1330
TRI-CITY ELECTRIC CO OF IOWA
T C E COMMUNICATIONS
6225 N Brady St, Davenport, IA 52806-0002
Tel (563) 322-7181 *Founded/Ownrshp* 1927
Sales 155.2MM *EMP* 350
SIC 1731 General electrical contractor
CEO: Daniel F Palmer
**Pr:* Douglas Palmer
**CFO:* Kirby L Zam
**VP:* Larry Devolder
Snr Sftwr: David Timmer

D-U-N-S 13-078-1912
TRI-CITY ELECTRICAL CONTRACTORS INC
SOUTH ATL TRI-CITY ELEC CONTRS
430 West Dr, Altamonte Springs, FL 32714-3378
Tel (407) 788-3500 *Founded/Ownrshp* 2002
Sales 141.0MM *EMP* 504
Accts Vestal & Wiler Orlando Flori
SIC 1731 Electric power systems contractors
Pr: Jack A Olmstead
**CFO:* Michael A Germana
CFO: Cheryl A Lulli
VP: Jon Belcher
**VP:* Rance Borderick
CIO: Ronald Milton
CTO: Allan Rubenstein
Snr PM: Dana Bermedez

D-U-N-S 07-872-8862
TRI-CITY HOSPITAL DISTRICT INC
TRI-CITY MEDICAL CENTER
4002 Vista Way, Oceanside, CA 92056-4506
Tel (760) 724-8411 *Founded/Ownrshp* 1957
Sales 321.8MM *EMP* 2,121
SIC 8062 General medical & surgical hospitals
Ch: Larry Schallock
Chf Rad: Stephen Schmitter
**CEO:* Casey Fatch
**CFO:* Robert Wardwell
CFO: Alex Yu
**Treas:* Rosemarie V Reno
VP: Joseph Gilmore
VP: Joe Kasper
VP: Daniel Martinez
VP Bus Dev: Chris Bass
Exec: Heather Manley
Dir Risk M: Kevin McQueen
Dir Lab: Charlie Szentesi

TRI-CITY MEDICAL CENTER
See TRI-CITY HOSPITAL DISTRICT INC

D-U-N-S 60-973-4900 IMP
TRI-COASTAL DESIGN GROUP INC
40 Harry Shupe Blvd, Wharton, NJ 07885-1646
Tel (973) 560-0300 *Founded/Ownrshp* 1990
Sales 148.0MME *EMP* 200
SIC 5137 5199 Women's & children's accessories; Gifts & novelties
Pr: Marvin Stutz
CFO: Ronald Fiore
**Treas:* Michael Mastrangelo
Sr Cor Off: Daniel Zar
Ex VP: Jamshid Zar
MIS Dir: Peter Massung
VP Sls: Korosh Zar

D-U-N-S 05-446-3120
TRI-CON INC
EXPRESS MART
7076 W Port Arthur Rd, Beaumont, TX 77705-0224
Tel (409) 835-2237 *Founded/Ownrshp* 1964
Sales 168.4MM *EMP* 150
Accts Theobald Demahy & Co Pc Be
SIC 5541 5172 5411 Gasoline service stations; Petroleum products; Convenience stores
CEO: Samir E Sarkis
**Pr:* Elias Sarkis
**VP:* Imad Sarkis
Dist Mgr: Brandon Perry
Opers Mgr: Ron Nicklas

D-U-N-S 08-006-8380
TRI-COUNTIES ASSOCIATION FOR DEVELOPMENTALLY DISABLED INC
TRI-COUNTIES REGIONAL CENTER
520 E Montecito St, Santa Barbara, CA 93103-3278
Tel (805) 962-7881 *Founded/Ownrshp* 1968
Sales 229.2MM *EMP* 240
Accts Windes Inc Long Beach Ca
SIC 8322 Association for the handicapped
Pr: Bob Cobbs
**Ex Dir:* Omar Noorzad

TRI-COUNTIES REGIONAL CENTER
See TRI-COUNTIES ASSOCIATION FOR DEVELOPMENTALLY DISABLED INC

D-U-N-S 18-912-8986
■TRI-COUNTY BANK
(*Suby of* AMERIS BANCORP) ★
350 E Wade St, Trenton, FL 32693-3271
Tel (352) 463-1547 *Founded/Ownrshp* 2001
Sales NA *EMP* 20
SIC 6022 State commercial banks
Pr: John H Ferguson
**VP:* Sandy Hilliard

TRI-COUNTY ELECTRIC
See TRI COUNTY ELECTRIC MEMBERSHIP CORP

D-U-N-S 00-725-4881
TRI-COUNTY ELECTRIC COOPERATIVE INC
TCEC
995 Mile 46 Rd, Hooker, OK 73945
Tel (580) 652-2418 *Founded/Ownrshp* 1945, 1986
Sales 98.5MM *EMP* 52
Accts Bkd Llp Tulsa Ok
SIC 4911 Distribution, electric power
CEO: Jack Perkins
IT Man: Joel Gerber

D-U-N-S 00-894-5123
TRI-COUNTY ELECTRIC COOPERATIVE INC
600 Northwest Pkwy, Azle, TX 76020-2998
Tel (817) 444-3201 *Founded/Ownrshp* 1939
Sales 85.0MME *EMP* 136
SIC 4911

D-U-N-S 02-035-1789
TRI-COUNTY GROUP XV INC
PYRAMID GROUP
1912 Independence St, Cape Girardeau, MO 63703-5823
Tel (573) 339-1864 *Founded/Ownrshp* 2016
Sales 29.7MME *EMP* 1,400
SIC 8082 Home health care services
Pr: Steven C Bradford
**COO:* Cale Bradford
**CFO:* Richard G Lewis
Ex VP: S Kling
**Prin:* Howard Wood

D-U-N-S 00-790-9096 IMP
TRI-COUNTY METROPOLITAN TRANSPORTATION DISTRICT OF OREGON
TRI-MET
1800 Sw 1st Ave Ste 300, Portland, OR 97201-5354
Tel (503) 238-7433 *Founded/Ownrshp* 1969
Sales 205.5MME *EMP* 2,429
Accts Moss-Adams Llp Portland Oreg
SIC 4111 Bus line operations; Trolley operation; Commuter rail passenger operation
VP: Dave Bolender
Exec: Roberta Altstadt
Ex Dir: Bernie Bottomly
Ex Dir: Brian Playfair
Ex Dir: Randy Stedman
Genl Mgr: Ron Imondi
Genl Mgr: A J Oconnor
Genl Mgr: Lester Spitler
Snr Sftwr: Mike Gilligan
Dir IT: Tim McHugh
IT Man: Kelly Rogstad

D-U-N-S 83-806-2995
TRI-COUNTY TELEPHONE CO INC
TDS TELECOMMUNICATIONS
525 Junction Rd, Madison, WI 53717-2152
Tel (608) 661-3114 *Founded/Ownrshp* 2009
Sales 950.0M *EMP* 2,700
SIC 4813 Local & long distance telephone communications
Pr: David Wittwer
Tech Mgr: Marty Corso
Software D: Kenya Little
Software D: Brian Stephan
Mktg Mgr: Brian Buchanan

D-U-N-S 19-140-8400 IMP/EXP
TRI-DIM FILTER CORP
93 Industrial Dr, Louisa, VA 23093-4126
Tel (540) 967-2600 *Founded/Ownrshp* 1989
Sales 128.5MM *EMP* 400
Accts Becher Della Torre Gitto & Com
SIC 3564 Filters, air: furnaces, air conditioning equipment, etc.
CEO: John C Stanley
**Pr:* Darren L Hernandez
**Chf Mktg O:* William L Lofiego
**Ofcr:* Mark E King
Mfg Mgr: William Holly
Manager: Jenn Wurslin
Sls Mgr: Jeffrey Atkinson
Sls Mgr: Gregory Fassler
Sls Mgr: Mike Shepperd

D-U-N-S 88-378-6071 IMP
TRI-ED DISTRIBUTION INC
T R I. E O
(*Suby of* TRI-ED/NORTHERN VIDEO) ★
135 Crossways Park Dr # 101, Woodbury, NY 11797-2005
Tel (516) 941-2800 *Founded/Ownrshp* 2010
Sales 250.9MME *EMP* 309
SIC 5065 Security control equipment & systems
CEO: Theodore Dosch
**Pr:* Pat Comunale
**CFO:* Mike Bitonti
**Prin:* Roxanna M Lake
Brnch Mgr: Frank Arcuri
Brnch Mgr: Allen Brown
MIS Dir: John Petersen
Mktg Mgr: Lynette Baranowski
Sales Asso: Eddie Alas
Sales Asso: Fawn Denton
Sales Asso: Jon Moreland

TRI-ED/NORTHERN VIDEO
See NORTHERN VIDEO SYSTEMS INC

TRI-ED/NORTHERN VIDEO
See TRI-NORTHERN SECURITY DISTRIBUTION INC

D-U-N-S 03-179-6907
TRI-ENERGY COOPERATIVE
CENEX
219 N 20th St, Bismarck, ND 58501-4736
Tel (701) 223-8707 *Founded/Ownrshp* 1934
Sales 108.8MM *EMP* 130
SIC 5812 5541 5251 Drive-in restaurant; Ice cream stands or dairy bars; Snow cone stand; Filling stations, gasoline; Builders' hardware
CEO: Cy Fix
**Pr:* Dan Belohlavek
**Sec:* Kevin Scmidt

D-U-N-S 02-258-7976
TRI-GAS & OIL CO INC
3941 Federalsburg Hwy, Federalsburg, MD 21632-2620
Tel (410) 754-2000 *Founded/Ownrshp* 1963
Sales 98.2MM *EMP* 119
Accts Tgm Group Llc Salisbury Mary
SIC 5172 5984 4731 Petroleum products; Propane gas, bottled; Freight forwarding
Pr: Keith A McMahan
**COO:* L Nash McMahan
Treas: Douglas Mahan
**Ex VP:* Earl Slacum
Ex Dir: Doris Keene

D-U-N-S 07-989-5394
TRI-ISOTRYLINE LLC (WA)
2187 Newcastle Ave # 101, Cardiff By The Sea, CA 92007-1848
Tel (909) 626-4855 *Founded/Ownrshp* 2015
Sales 85.0MME *EMP* 17
SIC 5169 Industrial chemicals
Pr: Jason Scott
CEO: David A Bruck
CFO: Ron Dunmyer
VP Sls: Kevin Dostal

D-U-N-S 07-873-0916
TRI-LAKES PETROLEUM CO LLC
943 E State Highway 76, Branson, MO 65616-8466
Tel (417) 334-3940 *Founded/Ownrshp* 2012
Sales 100.0MM *EMP* 18
SIC 5172 Petroleum products

D-U-N-S 18-654-0431 EXP
TRI-MEATS INC
17 W 662 Butterfi, Oakbrook Terrace, IL 60181
Tel (630) 705-2800 *Founded/Ownrshp* 1986
Sales 119.7MM *EMP* 18
SIC 5147 Meats & meat products
CEO: Richard D Smurawski
**VP:* Rick Smurawski
Genl Mgr: Bo Blackburn

TRI-MET
See TRI-COUNTY METROPOLITAN TRANSPORTATION DISTRICT OF OREGON

D-U-N-S 01-485-9466
TRI-NORTH BUILDERS INC (WI)
2625 Research Park Dr, Fitchburg, WI 53711-4908
Tel (608) 271-8717 *Founded/Ownrshp* 1981
Sales 125.0MME *EMP* 130
Accts Brent Drews Cpa S Middleton
SIC 1541 1542 1521 Renovation, remodeling & repairs: industrial buildings; Commercial & office buildings, renovation & repair; Commercial & office building, new construction; New construction, single-family houses
CEO: Thomas Thayer
**VP:* Chad Ferguson
**VP:* Carl Hardy
**VP:* Jerry Roach
**VP:* Joel Stancer
**VP:* Robert H Thayer II
**Prin:* Donald F Thayer
Sales Exec: Steve Bachofen
Mktg Dir: Robert Thayer

D-U-N-S 96-325-5273
TRI-NORTHERN SECURITY DISTRIBUTION INC
TRI-ED/NORTHERN VIDEO
135 Crossways Park Dr # 101, Woodbury, NY 11797-2008
Tel (516) 941-2800 *Founded/Ownrshp* 2012
Sales 365.0MME *EMP* 560
SIC 5065 Security control equipment & systems
CEO: Steve Roth
**Pr:* Mark Haney
**COO:* Pat Comunale
**Ex VP:* Paul Haney
**Sr VP:* Brian James
**Sr VP:* James Rothstein
Brnch Mgr: Dan Murphy
**VP Mktg:* Paul Swan

D-U-N-S 04-094-9869 IMP/EXP
■TRI-STAR ELECTRONICS INTERNATIONAL INC
CARLISLE INTERCONNECT
(*Suby of* CARLISLE COMPANIES INC) ★
2201 Rosecrans Ave, El Segundo, CA 90245-4910
Tel (310) 536-0444 *Founded/Ownrshp* 2005
Sales 85.2MME *EMP* 435
SIC 3643 Current-carrying wiring devices; Connectors, electric cord
Pr: John Berlin
**VP:* Amelia Murillo
VP: Bob Wimer
Dir IT: Ben Damon
IT Man: Sheila Adame

D-U-N-S 13-760-8766
TRI-STARR MANAGEMENT SERVICES INC
LEGACY SUPPLY CHAIN SERVICES
1941 Citrona Dr, Fernandina Beach, FL 32034-4414
Tel (909) 321-0507 *Founded/Ownrshp* 1991
Sales 152.7MME *EMP* 1,100
SIC 8741 Management services
CEO: Ron Cain
Ex VP: Thomas Rouen Jr
VP: John St Pierre
VP Opers: Jim Nugent

TRI-STATE EMPLOYER SERVICES
See TRI-STATE EMPLOYMENT SERVICE INC

D-U-N-S 80-109-3915
TRI-STATE EMPLOYMENT SERVICE INC
TRI-STATE EMPLOYER SERVICES
160 Broadway Fl 15, New York, NY 10038-4203
Tel (212) 346-7960 *Founded/Ownrshp* 1993
Sales 173.6MME *EMP* 3,500
SIC 7361 Employment agencies
CEO: Robert Cassera
Ex VP: John P Messina Sr
VP: Joe Carnato
VP: Anthony Cassera
VP: Thom Tokash
Dir IT: Joseph Basanta
VP Sls: Mike Fonseca

D-U-N-S 04-176-1404
TRI-STATE ENVELOPE CORP
20th Market St, Ashland, PA 17921
Tel (570) 875-0433 *Founded/Ownrshp* 1966
Sales 156.5MME *EMP* 450
SIC 2677 Envelopes
Pr: John Swensen
CFO: Anthony Aulenti
Treas: Joel W Orgler
VP: Frank De Carlo
VP: Bob Earls

D-U-N-S 96-394-8658 IMP
TRI-STATE FOREST PRODUCTS INC
2105 Sheridan Ave, Springfield, OH 45505-2419
Tel (937) 323-6325 *Founded/Ownrshp* 1999
Sales 93.7MME *EMP* 77
SIC 5031 Lumber, plywood & millwork
CEO: Tom Latham
COO: Becky Siderits
**CFO:* Tom Berghouse
**VP:* Rob Latham
Brnch Mgr: James Hausbeck
Brnch Mgr: Troy Jeffery
Brnch Mgr: Doug Smith
Tech Mgr: Dan Miller
Opers Mgr: Lloyd Glydewell
Mktg Dir: Lance Sanders
Manager: Dwayne Wilson

D-U-N-S 09-712-7724
TRI-STATE GARDEN SUPPLY INC
GARDENSCAPE
And Sandy Pt Rd Rr 38, Eau Claire, PA 16030
Tel (724) 867-1711 *Founded/Ownrshp* 1962
Sales 158.2MME *EMP* 300E
SIC 5191 Farm supplies; Fertilizer & fertilizer materials
Ch: David E Kasmoch
**Treas:* Edna Mae Kasmoch

D-U-N-S 04-263-4378 IMP
TRI-STATE GENERATION AND TRANSMISSION ASSOCIATION INC
1100 W 116th Ave, Westminster, CO 80234-2814
Tel (303) 452-6111 *Founded/Ownrshp* 1952
Sales 1.1MMME *EMP* 1,500
SIC 4911

D-U-N-S 19-671-5312
TRI-STATE MOTOR TRANSIT CO INC
8141 E 7th St, Joplin, MO 64801-9283
Tel (800) 234-8768 Founded/Ownrshp 1998
Sales 56.5MM[E] EMP 1,135
SIC 4213 4731 Trucking, except local; Brokers, shipping
Ch Bd: Ed Mc Cormick

D-U-N-S 06-685-2419
TRI-STATE PETROLEUM CORP
2627 Vance Ave, Wheeling, WV 26003-7239
Tel (304) 277-3232 Founded/Ownrshp 1974
Sales 200.0MM EMP 300
SIC 5171 Petroleum bulk stations
CEO: Colleen McGlinn
*COO: Edward J Coyne II
*CFO: Erin C Merrick

D-U-N-S 01-629-5164
TRI-STATE REFRACTORIES CORP
(Suby of SKANSKA US CIVIL MIDWEST INC) ★
1127 E Virginia St, Evansville, IN 47711-5724
Tel (812) 425-3466 Founded/Ownrshp 1955, 2012
Sales 44.6MM[E] EMP 2,390[E]
SIC 1741 5085 Refractory or acid brick masonry; Chimney construction & maintenance; Refractory material
Pr: Jerry Wells
*Sec: John M Luckett
*VP: Alan W Braun
*VP: Nelson Freeman

D-U-N-S 03-479-9726
TRI-STATE TRUCK CENTER INC
TRI STATE MACK
494 E Eh Crump Blvd, Memphis, TN 38126-4620
Tel (901) 947-5000 Founded/Ownrshp 1945
Sales 163.8MM[E] EMP 335
SIC 5511 7513 5012 Trucks, tractors & trailers: new & used; Truck leasing, without drivers; Trucks, commercial
CEO: Rod Maddox
*Pr: James D Maddox
*CFO: Jason McAlister
Sr Cor Off: Fontaine Maddox
VP: David Ellis
*VP: Jason Maddox
VP: Earl Triplett
Sales Exec: Steve Bajurny
Sales Asso: Joe Coletta

D-U-N-S 00-170-6167 IMP/EXP
TRI-UNION FROZEN PRODUCTS INC
CHICKEN OF SEA FROZEN FOODS
(Suby of THAI UNION GROUP PUBLIC COMPANY LIMITED)
222 N Sepulveda Blvd # 155, El Segundo, CA 90245-5648
Tel (516) 740-4100 Founded/Ownrshp 1968
Sales 98.3MM[E] EMP 75
SIC 5146 Seafoods
Pr: Bryan Rosenberg
*Ex VP: Paul McCarthy
*VP: Brendon Beck
VP: John Boyle
VP: Carlos Faria
Dir Surg: Grace Bischoff
IT Man: Mary J Casrto

D-U-N-S 17-202-2154 IMP/EXP
TRI-UNION SEAFOODS LLC
CHICKEN OF SEA INTERNATIONAL
(Suby of THAI UNION INTERNATIONAL INC) ★
9330 Scranton Rd Ste 500, San Diego, CA 92121-7706
Tel (858) 558-9662 Founded/Ownrshp 1996
Sales 86.2MM[E] EMP 70
SIC 5146 2091 Fish & seafoods; Tuna fish: packaged in cans, jars, etc.; Salmon: packaged in cans, jars, etc.
Pr: Shue Wing Chan
COO: Jim Davit
*COO: David E Roszmann
*Sr VP: Jim Cox
*Sr VP: Christie Fleming
VP: Kevin Bixler
*VP: Ignatius Dharma
VP: Dennis Hixson
Software D: Richard Hylton
S&M/VP: Brenden Beck

D-U-N-S 00-790-2331 IMP
TRI-W GROUP INC
MILITARY SPEC PACKAGING
835 Goodale Blvd, Columbus, OH 43212-3824
Tel (614) 228-5000 Founded/Ownrshp 1916
Sales 313.0MM[E] EMP 1,241
SIC 3694 7538 7537

D-U-N-S 00-240-9787 IMP
TRI-WEST LTD
12005 Pike St, Santa Fe Springs, CA 90670-6100
Tel (562) 692-9166 Founded/Ownrshp 1981
Sales 182.6MM EMP 250
Accts Kmj Corbin & Company Llp Cost
SIC 5023 Floor coverings; Resilient floor coverings: tile or sheet; Wood flooring
Pt: Allen Gage
CFO: Jim Johnston
*CFO: Randy Sims
Exec: Bob Taylor
IT Man: Naser Long
IT Man: Jackson Uyeda
*VP Opers: John Lubinxki
Board of Directors: Don Heimark

D-U-N-S 00-669-1427
TRI-WIRE ENGINEERING SOLUTIONS INC
890 East St, Tewksbury, MA 01876-1452
Tel (978) 640-6899 Founded/Ownrshp 1995
Sales 130.1MM[E] EMP 800
SIC 1623 8748 Telephone & communication line construction; Telecommunications consultant
CEO: John Wade
*Pr: John R Wade III
*COO: John Marsh
*VP: Lori Boisvert
*VP: Arnold Greene
*VP: Tina McAuliffe
Exec: Tina Auliffe
Opers Mgr: Marc Severino

D-U-N-S 12-675-6217 IMP
TRIAD CATALOG CO LLC
SOFT SURROUNDINGS
1100 N Lindbergh Blvd, Saint Louis, MO 63132-2914
Tel (314) 812-5200 Founded/Ownrshp 1999
Sales 106.4MM[E] EMP 340[E]
SIC 5961 Women's apparel, mail order; Furniture & furnishings, mail order
CEO: Thomas Wicher
Pr: Ann Hjemboe
Netwrk Eng: Chris Candrl
Opers Supe: Christy McKey
Opers Supe: Jessica Meier-Hanks
Opers Mgr: Jim Manno
Prd Mgr: Rosemary Sturm

D-U-N-S 62-380-1417
TRIAD DIGITAL MEDIA LLC
100 Carillon Pkwy Ste 100, Saint Petersburg, FL 33716-1208
Tel (727) 231-5041 Founded/Ownrshp 2004
Sales 98.4MM[E] EMP 400
SIC 7311 Advertising agencies
CEO: Roger Berdusco
Pr: Nicole Bond
Pr: David Haase
Pr: Sherry Smith
CFO: Tom Baumlin
Ex VP: Jill Orr
Sr VP: David Blinn
Sr VP: Misty Brown
Sr VP: Wendy Larrison
Sr VP: Joe Reichl
Sr VP: Ana Toro
VP: Peter Bavaro
VP: Sean Cheyney
Dir Risk M: Brian Quinn

D-U-N-S 07-920-0856
TRIAD E&C HOLDINGS LLC
(Suby of NEWTRON GROUP L L C) ★
8183 W El Cajon Dr, Baton Rouge, LA 70815-8035
Tel (225) 927-8921 Founded/Ownrshp 2013
Sales 306.1MM EMP 1,300
Accts Hannis T Bourgeois Llp Baton
SIC 1731 Electrical work; Fiber optic cable installation

D-U-N-S 06-504-6146
TRIAD ELECTRIC & CONTROLS INC
(Suby of TRIAD E&C HOLDINGS LLC) ★
2288 N Airway Dr, Baton Rouge, LA 70815-8132
Tel (225) 923-0604 Founded/Ownrshp 1982
Sales 286.8MM EMP 1,200
Accts Hannis T Bourgeois Llp Baton
SIC 1731 Electrical work
Pr: Brian Bordelon
VP: Danny Campbell
VP: Eric Coco
VP: Kenneth Lester
VP: Wes Mincin

D-U-N-S 62-694-0506
■TRIAD FINANCIAL CORP
(Suby of DRIVE FINANCIAL SERVICES) ★
8585 N Stemmons Fwy, Dallas, TX 75247-3836
Tel (817) 521-8127 Founded/Ownrshp 2009
Sales 32.2MM[E] EMP 1,150
SIC 7389 Financial services
Pr: Daniel Leonard
Ofcr: Jonathan Fox
*Sr VP: Scott A France
*Sr VP: Mark A Kelly
VP: Michael Anderson
VP: Rush Blevins
*VP: Jeffrey O Butcher
VP: Bob Gill
VP: Mary Haller
*VP: Randall L Hatley Sr
*VP: Regina N Krug
*VP: Raymond C Scott
VP: Shelia Shelton
VP: Jackie Trask
VP: Brent West
Dir Bus: Nigel Fisher

D-U-N-S 08-543-9313
TRIAD GROUP INC
623 W Main St, Yadkinville, NC 27055-7804
Tel (336) 679-8852 Founded/Ownrshp 1976
Sales 678.0MM[E] EMP 1,220
SIC 8051 5047 7374 Skilled nursing care facilities; Medical equipment & supplies; Data processing service
Pr: Nolan G Brown

D-U-N-S 80-879-4424
▲TRIAD GUARANTY INC
1900 Crestwood Blvd, Irondale, AL 35210-2051
Tel (205) 951-4012 Founded/Ownrshp 1993
Sales NA EMP 201[E]
Tkr Sym TGICQ Exch OTO
SIC 6351 Mortgage guarantee insurance
Ch Bd: William T Ratliff III
Pr: Gregory J McKenzie
VP: Georgia Copeland
VP: Kymme F Hoyle
VP: Pamela T Morrison
VP: Ken Nash
VP: Madeline Oler
VP: Greg Williams
Exec: Kathleen Balaschak
Exec: Jim Suetholz
Exec: Slutzker Taggart

D-U-N-S 18-950-2441
TRIAD INTERNATIONAL MAINTENANCE CORP
TIMCO AVIATION SERVICES
(Suby of HAECO AMERICAS) ★
623 Radar Rd, Greensboro, NC 27410-6221
Tel (336) 668-4410 Founded/Ownrshp 1989
Sales 84.6MM[E] EMP 706[E]
SIC 4581 Aircraft servicing & repairing
CEO: Richard Kendall
*Pr: Mark Peterman
*Pr: Jim Sokol
*CFO: Lee Fox

D-U-N-S 79-896-2135 IMP/EXP
TRIAD ISOTOPES INC
4205 Vineland Rd Ste L1, Orlando, FL 32811-6628
Tel (407) 872-8455 Founded/Ownrshp 2006
Sales 159.7MM[E] EMP 1,000
SIC 5912 Drug stores & proprietary stores
Pr: Dom Meffe
CFO: Linda Anderson
CFO: Mel Lazin
Ofcr: Hoang T Nguyen
VP: Maureen Brockman
VP: Vanerka Deborah
*VP: William McCormick
VP: Joan Schuckenbrock
Dir Rx: Sean Murphy
Genl Mgr: James Wilkinson
IT Man: David Johnson

D-U-N-S 10-789-6292
TRIAD MEDICAL SERVICES INC
(Suby of TRIAD GROUP INC) ★
623 W Main St, Yadkinville, NC 27055-7804
Tel (336) 679-8852 Founded/Ownrshp 1976
Sales 638.2MM[E] EMP 683
SIC 8082 Home health care services
Pr: Nolan G Brown
*VP: Gene Doss
*VP: James G Swaim

TRIAD METALS INTERNATIONAL
See METAL TRADERS INC

D-U-N-S 07-546-7464
■TRIAD OF ALABAMA LLC
FLOWERS HOSPITAL
(Suby of COMMUNITY HEALTH SYSTEMS INC) ★
4370 W Main St, Dothan, AL 36305-1056
Tel (334) 793-5000 Founded/Ownrshp 2001
Sales 204.1MM EMP 1,878[E]
SIC 8062 8082 General medical & surgical hospitals; Home health care services
Pr: Keith Granger
CFO: Mike Hallford
VP: Dan Cumbie
VP: Barry Moss
Dir Case M: Rachel Donelli
Dir Rad: Michael N Dowig
Comm Man: Missy Wright
Dir IT: Alexander Dan
Dir IT: Erik Marsh
Dir IT: Patti Pellhem
VP Opers: Alta Beegle

D-U-N-S 87-959-8837
TRIAGE CONSULTING GROUP
221 Main St Ste 1100, San Francisco, CA 94105-1949
Tel (415) 512-9400 Founded/Ownrshp 1994
Sales 98.0MM EMP 503
SIC 8742 8748 Hospital & health services consultant; Business consulting
Pr: Brian Neece
CFO: James Hebert
*Treas: Damon Lewis
VP: Tracy Packingham
VP: Shauna Stewart
Prgrm Mgr: Melissa Sorenson
Off Mgr: Kim Mc Lemore
Off Admin: Kim McLemore
Snr Mgr: April Buescher
Snr Mgr: Shauna Garrison
Snr Mgr: Katy Hanson
Board of Directors: Sean Alavi, Brian Neece

D-U-N-S 00-495-1513
TRIANGLE ASSOCIATES INC (MI)
3769 3 Mile Rd Nw, Grand Rapids, MI 49534-1233
Tel (616) 453-3950 Founded/Ownrshp 1963
Sales 86.3MM EMP 150
Accts Rehmann Robson Llc Grand Rapi
SIC 1542 1541 Commercial & office building, new construction; Institutional building construction; Industrial buildings, new construction
CEO: Craig Datema
*Ch Bd: Craig S Datema
Pr: Jim Conner
*Pr: Mitch Watt
*CEO: Michael A Rodrigues
CFO: Anita Rathbun
*Ex VP: James L Huyser
*Ex VP: Jim Huyser
*Sr VP: Paul Lemley
*Sr VP: Jeffrey Scott
*VP: Jeff Scott

D-U-N-S 10-896-7993 EXP
TRIANGLE AUTO CENTER INC
TOYOTA OF HOLLYWOOD
1841 N State Road 7, Hollywood, FL 33021-4510
Tel (855) 398-2449 Founded/Ownrshp 1965
Sales 102.7MM[E] EMP 265
SIC 5511 7532 Automobiles, new & used; Exterior repair services
Pr: Craig M Zinn
*VP: Anthony D Stampone
Dir IT: Simon Chong
IT Man: Simon Chung
IT Man: Israel Washington
Sales Exec: Scott Cooper

D-U-N-S 79-139-7818
▲TRIANGLE CAPITAL CORP
3700 Glenwood Ave Ste 530, Raleigh, NC 27612-5539
Tel (919) 719-4770 Founded/Ownrshp 2006
Sales 121.2MM EMP 26[E]
Accts Ernst & Young Llp Raleigh No
Tkr Sym TCAP Exch NYS
SIC 7389 Financial services
Pr: E Ashton Poole
*Ch Bd: Garland S Tucker III
*COO: Cary B Nordan
*CFO: Steven C Lilly
*Chf Cred: Jeffrey A Dombcik
VP: James Burke
VP: Thomas Moses

D-U-N-S 00-332-3185 IMP/EXP
TRIANGLE CHEMICAL CO
206 Lower Elm St, Macon, GA 31206-1087
Tel (478) 743-1548 Founded/Ownrshp 1947
Sales 162.0MM[E] EMP 95
SIC 5191 Fertilizers & agricultural chemicals; Herbicides; Insecticides
Ch Bd: Wycliff R Griffin
V Ch: Spencer Black
*CEO: Eugene M Maddux
*CFO: Henry B Puckett
*Treas: Dick Maddux
*VP: Tom B Thomson
Area Mgr: Chason Peck
IT Man: Kevin Bassett

D-U-N-S 08-008-1292 IMP
TRIANGLE DISTRIBUTING CO
HEIMARK DISTRIBUTING
12065 Pike St, Santa Fe Springs, CA 90670-2964
Tel (562) 699-3424 Founded/Ownrshp 1957
Sales 86.8MM[E] EMP 270
Accts Kmj Corbin & Company Llp Cost
SIC 5181 Beer & other fermented malt liquors
Ch Bd: Donald Heimark
*Pr: Peter H Heimark
*Sec: Mike Crow

D-U-N-S 10-175-1006
TRIANGLE GRADING & PAVING INC
1521 Huffman Mill Rd, Burlington, NC 27215-8815
Tel (336) 584-1745 Founded/Ownrshp 1984
Sales 115.9MM[E] EMP 250
SIC 1611 1794 Grading; Highway & street paving contractor; Excavation work
Pr: Ronnie Kirkpatrick Sr
Pr: Ronald G Kirkpatick Sr
VP: Gray Kirkpatrick
VP: R G Kirkpatrick Jr
Mtls Mgr: Hank Kirkpatrick

TRIANGLE LABEL
See G R B INC

D-U-N-S 01-786-7484
▲TRIANGLE PETROLEUM CORP
1200 17th St Ste 2500, Denver, CO 80202-5837
Tel (303) 260-7125 Founded/Ownrshp 2003
Sales 358.1MM EMP 385[E]
Tkr Sym TPLM Exch ASE
SIC 1311 1382 Crude petroleum & natural gas; Oil & gas exploration services
Pr: Jonathan Samuels
*Ch Bd: Peter Hill
CEO: R Curt Dacar
COO: Dominic Spencer
CFO: Mike Grijalva
Off Mgr: Dana Biagioni
Software D: Jay Ockers
Opers Mgr: Tony Hale
Prd Mgr: John Zellitti
Mktg Dir: Colby Drechsel
Board of Directors: Roy Aneed, Gus Halas, Randal Matkaluk

D-U-N-S 08-041-2078
TRIANGLE PRIVATE HOLDINGS I LLC
601 Lexington Ave Fl 59, New York, NY 10022-4611
Tel (212) 231-0095 Founded/Ownrshp 2016
Sales 91.5MM[E] EMP 3,451[E]
SIC 6719 Investment holding companies, except banks

D-U-N-S 80-340-3815
TRIANGLE SERVICES INC
MAINTECH ACQUISITION
10 5th St Ste 200, Valley Stream, NY 11581-1263
Tel (516) 561-1700 Founded/Ownrshp 1960
Sales 226.6MM[E] EMP 3,100
SIC 7349 4581 1799 7382

TRIANGLE SYSTEMS
See IDX CORP

D-U-N-S 15-136-4825
TRIANON INDUSTRIES CORP
24331 Sherwood, Center Line, MI 48015-1060
Tel (586) 759-2200 Founded/Ownrshp 1986
Sales 16.2M[E] EMP 3,141
Accts Arthur Andersen Llp Detroit
SIC 3465 3544 Automotive stampings; Special dies & tools; Jigs & fixtures
Pr: Francis Barge
*CFO: Jean-Claude Garolla
Board of Directors: Michael Delaney, David Howe, John Wurster

D-U-N-S 00-165-6995
TRIANZ (CA)
(Suby of TRIANZ HOLDINGS PRIVATE LIMITED)
3979 Freedom Cir Ste 210, Santa Clara, CA 95054-1248
Tel (408) 387-5800 Founded/Ownrshp 2000
Sales 88.1MM[E] EMP 618
SIC 7379
Pr: Srikanth Manchala
*CFO: Anusuya Chaman
*CFO: Ganesh Venkataraman
*VP: Keshav Gupta
VP: Vivek Gupta
VP: Ira Horowitz
VP: Sanil Kumar
VP: Joanne Mack
*VP: Santhosh S Nagaraj
*VP: Sanjay Shitole
*VP: Sunder Tirumala
Exec: Upendra Kondoju

D-U-N-S 36-154-6380
■TRIARC ACQUISITION LLC
(Suby of WENDYS CO) ★
1155 Perimeter Ctr, Atlanta, GA 30338-5463
Tel (678) 514-4101 Founded/Ownrshp 2000
Sales 251.6MM[E] EMP 27,930[E]
SIC 5812 Fast-food restaurant, chain
CEO: Roland C Smith

D-U-N-S 00-201-1924
TRIBTOTAL MEDIA INC (PA)
PENNYSAVER
503 Martin Street D L C, Pittsburgh, PA 15212
Tel (412) 321-6460 *Founded/Ownrshp* 2003
Sales 202.6MM^E *EMP* 1,100
SIC 5994 Newsstand
Pr: Jennifer L Bertetto
**Pr:* Ralph Martin
COO: Jennifer Bertetto
**Treas:* Raymond A Hartung
**VP:* Edward Harrell

D-U-N-S 05-503-4800
TRIBAL CASINO GAMING ENTERPRISES
HARRAH'S CHEROKEE
777 Casino Dr, Cherokee, NC 28719-9761
Tel (877) 811-0777 *Founded/Ownrshp* 2015
Sales 318.8MM^E *EMP* 3,700
SIC 7011 Casino hotel
Genl Mgr: Brooks Robinson
Exec: Rich Elkovich
Exec: Michael Marshall
**Prin:* Jerry Egelus
Off Admin: Sherri Booth
Mktg Mgr: Jill Parker

TRIBAL EMPLOYMENT RIGHTS OFF
See CONFEDERATED TRIBES OF COLVILLE RESERVATION

TRIBAL GOVERNMENT
See ST CROIX CHIPPEWA INDIANS OF WISCONSIN

TRIBAL GOVERNMENT
See CITIZEN POTAWATOMI NATION

D-U-N-S 16-666-5245
TRIBALCO LLC
4915 Saint Elmo Ave # 501, Bethesda, MD 20814-6084
Tel (301) 652-8450 *Founded/Ownrshp* 2004
Sales 111.4MM^E *EMP* 105
SIC 8748 Telecommunications consultant
Pr: Kevin Moss
**COO:* Andrew Stern
Ofcr: Jeremy Catrone
VP Sls: Joseph Castro
Mktg Dir: Larry Opack

D-U-N-S 17-503-6461 IMP
TRIBE MEDITERRANEAN FOODS INC
(*Suby of* OSEM INVESTMENTS LTD.)
100 Myles Standish Blvd # 1, Taunton, MA 02780-7340
Tel (774) 961-0000 *Founded/Ownrshp* 2008
Sales 129.4MM^E *EMP* 120
SIC 5141 Groceries, general line
Pr: Adam Carr
**CFO:* Charles S Webster
CFO: Scott Webster
Treas: Amichai Ben

D-U-N-S 00-131-6272 IMP/EXP
TRIBORO QUILT MANUFACTURING CORP
172 S Broadway Ste 100, White Plains, NY 10605-1885
Tel (914) 428-7551 *Founded/Ownrshp* 1933
Sales 105.0MM *EMP* 77
SIC 5023 5999 Blankets; Pillowcases; Pet supplies
Ch Bd: Joel Kaplan
COO: Walter Zurkovsky
VP: Jaclyn Buttacavoli
VP: Josh Jordan
**VP:* Alvin Kaplan
Genl Mgr: Dennis Amendola
CTO: Kathleen Kelly
Ql Cn Mgr: Chuck Wells

D-U-N-S 07-524-3139
TRIBOROUGH BRIDGE & TUNNEL AUTHORITY
(*Suby of* M T A) ★
Robert Moses Bldg Randal, New York, NY 10035
Tel (212) 360-3000 *Founded/Ownrshp* 1933
Sales 70.7MM^E *EMP* 1,500
SIC 4785 Toll bridge operation; Tunnel operation, vehicular
Pr: Michael C Ascher

D-U-N-S 83-002-4423
TRIBRIDGE HOLDINGS LLC
4830 W Kennedy Blvd # 890, Tampa, FL 33609-2593
Tel (813) 287-8887 *Founded/Ownrshp* 2008
Sales 103.6MM^E *EMP* 650
SIC 6719 Investment holding companies, except banks
IT Man: John Schloemann

D-U-N-S 01-628-1073
■ **TRIBUNE BROADCASTING CO LLC**
TRIBUNE CABLE
(*Suby of* TRIBUNE MEDIA CO) ★
435 N Michigan Ave Fl 2, Chicago, IL 60611-4024
Tel (312) 222-3333 *Founded/Ownrshp* 1980
Sales 502.7MM^E *EMP* 1,594
SIC 4833 4832 Television broadcasting stations; Radio broadcasting stations
Pr: Nils E Larsen
**Pr:* John Reardon
**CEO:* Peter Liguori
**COO:* Jerry Kersting
**CFO:* Gerald Agema
**Ch:* Nils Larsen
Ex VP: Brian Dollenmayer
Sr VP: Steve Charlier
Sr VP: Steve Farber
Sr VP: Bart Feder
Sr VP: Vince Giannini
Sr VP: Hank Hundemer
VP: James T Aitken
**VP:* Ira Glodstone
VP: Scott Heath
VP: Kristin Long
VP: Ashley Messina
VP: Michael Page
VP: Paul Perozeni
VP: Chris Topf
**VP:* John Vitanovec

TRIBUNE CABLE
See TRIBUNE BROADCASTING CO LLC

D-U-N-S 05-260-3206
TRIBUNE CO
202 S Parker St, Tampa, FL 33606-2308
Tel (813) 259-7711 *Founded/Ownrshp* 2012
Sales NA *EMP* 1,200
SIC 2711

D-U-N-S 05-300-8020
■ **TRIBUNE INTERACTIVE INC** (DE)
(*Suby of* TRONC INC) ★
435 N Michigan Ave Fl 2, Chicago, IL 60611-4024
Tel (312) 222-3232 *Founded/Ownrshp* 1996, 2014
Sales 83.2MM^E *EMP* 360
SIC 4813 ;
Pr: Chandler Bigelow
**COO:* Jeff Kapugi
**CFO:* Erica Thornton
Ex VP: Mike Glickenhaus
Sr VP: Julie Anderson
Sr VP: Dana Hayes
Sr VP: Kim Johnson
VP: Ellen Glassberg
**Genl Mgr:* Brigid Kenney

D-U-N-S 00-516-1542
▲ **TRIBUNE MEDIA CO**
435 N Michigan Ave Fl 2, Chicago, IL 60611-4024
Tel (212) 210-2786 *Founded/Ownrshp* 1847
Sales 2.0MMM *EMP* 8,000
Tkr Sym TRCO *Exch* NYS
SIC 4833 4832 7922 7941 Television broadcasting stations; Radio broadcasting stations; Television program, including commercial producers; Baseball club, professional & semi-professional
Pr: Peter Liguori
**Ch Bd:* Bruce A Karsh
CEO: Tony Hunter
CEO: Nils Larsen
CEO: John Reardon
CFO: Chandler Bigelow
Treas: Brad Moore
Ofcr: Peter Hernon
Ex VP: Steven Berns
Ex VP: Brian Dollenmayer
Ex VP: Carolyn Gilbert
Ex VP: John Hendricks
Ex VP: Melanie Hughes
Ex VP: Edward P Lazarus
Ex VP: Julio Marenghi
Ex VP: William Nagel
Ex VP: Edwin Ong
Sr VP: Harry Amsden
Sr VP: Sean Compton
Sr VP: David P Eldersveld
Sr VP: Richard Graziano
Board of Directors: Craig A Jacobson, Peter M Kern, Michael Kreger, Ross Levinsohn, Peter E Murphy, Laura R Walker

D-U-N-S 79-432-9896
■ **TRIBUNE PUBLISHING CO LLC**
(*Suby of* TRONC INC) ★
435 N Michigan Ave Fl 2, Chicago, IL 60611-4024
Tel (312) 222-9100 *Founded/Ownrshp* 1991
Sales 1.6MMM^E *EMP* 7,100
SIC 2711 Newspapers
Pr: Jack Fuller
**Ch Bd:* Eddy Hartenstein
**COO:* Kathy Thomson
**Treas:* David Granat
**Ex VP:* John Bode
**Ex VP:* Robert Gremillion
**Ex VP:* Julie Xanders
Sr VP: Mark Campbell
Sr VP: Dan Hickey
**Sr VP:* Matthew Hutchison
**Sr VP:* Bob Thomas
VP: Kathy Beiriger
VP: Vincent Casanova
**VP:* Darko Dejanovic
**VP:* Phil Doherty
**VP:* James O'Dell
VP: Alex Rotonen
**VP:* Howard Tyner
**VP:* David Underhill
VP: Edward Wolf

D-U-N-S 00-434-4438
TRIBUNE REVIEW PUBLISHING CO
DAILY COURIER
503 Marti St D L Clark B, Pittsburgh, PA 15212
Tel (724) 834-1151 *Founded/Ownrshp* 1970
Sales 108.4MM^E *EMP* 1,200
SIC 2711

D-U-N-S 80-823-8484 IMP
TRIBUTE ENERGY INC
2100 West Loop S Ste 1220, Houston, TX 77027-3599
Tel (281) 768-5300 *Founded/Ownrshp* 2007
Sales 118.6MM *EMP* 12
Accts Doerenmayhew Houston Texas
SIC 5169 3295 2821 Chemicals & allied products; Clay for petroleum refining, chemically processed; Elastomers, nonvulcanizable (plastics)
Pr: James Rew
CFO: Cesar Purgato
Genl Mgr: Eduardo Contreiras
Opers Mgr: Julia Rew

D-U-N-S 61-907-5752 EXP
TRICAN WELL SERVICE LP
5825 N Sam Houston Pkwy W # 600, Houston, TX 77086-1551
Tel (281) 716-9152 *Founded/Ownrshp* 2015
Sales 252.7MM^E *EMP* 501
SIC 2911 1481 1389

TRICARE MANAGEMENT ACTIVITY
See DEFENSE HEALTH AGENCY

D-U-N-S 10-755-0733
▲ **TRICO BANCSHARES**
63 Constitution Dr, Chico, CA 95973-4937
Tel (530) 898-0300 *Founded/Ownrshp* 1981
Sales NA *EMP* 1,009^E
Accts Crowe Horwath Llp Sacramento
Tkr Sym TCBK *Exch* NGS
SIC 6022 State commercial banks
Ch Bd: William J Casey
**Pr:* Richard P Smith
COO: John S Fleshood
COO: Carol A Ward
CFO: Thomas J Reddish
**V Ch Bd:* Michael W Koehnen
Ofcr: Craig B Carney
Ofcr: Glenn C Hunter
Ex VP: Dan Bailey
Ex VP: Daniel K Bailey
Ex VP: Michael J Cushman
Ex VP: Richard B O'Sullivan
VP: Kay Armstrong
VP: Bret Funde
VP: Raymond Rios
Exec: Susan Shepherd

D-U-N-S 00-279-3602
TRICO ELECTRIC COOPERATIVE INC (AZ)
8600 W Tangerine Rd, Marana, AZ 85658-8973
Tel (520) 744-2944 *Founded/Ownrshp* 1945
Sales 92.5MM *EMP* 132
Accts Bkd Llp Tulsa Ok
SIC 4911 Distribution, electric power
CEO: Vincent Nitido
**Pr:* George P Davies
**Treas:* L Nick Buckelew
**VP:* Charles B Despain

D-U-N-S 92-728-9405
TRICO MARINE SERVICES INC
3200 Southwest Fwy # 2950, Houston, TX 77027-7579
Tel (888) 369-8929 *Founded/Ownrshp* 1993
Sales 64.6MM^E *EMP* 1,780^E
SIC 4412 Deep sea foreign transportation of freight
Pr: Suzanne Kean
VP: Charles Tizzard

D-U-N-S 00-210-7399 IMP/EXP
TRICO PRODUCTS CORP
(*Suby of* CROWNE GROUP LLC) ★
3255 W Hamlin Rd, Rochester Hills, MI 48309-3231
Tel (248) 371-1700 *Founded/Ownrshp* 2014
Sales 300.0MM^E *EMP* 343
SIC 3714 3069 3082 8734 8731 Motor vehicle parts & accessories; Windshield wiper systems, motor vehicle; Wipers, windshield, motor vehicle; Tubing, rubber; Tubes, unsupported plastic; Testing laboratories; Commercial physical research
CEO: James Wiggins
Ql Cn Mgr: Gustavo Benavides

D-U-N-S 17-408-0838 IMP/EXP
TRICO TECHNOLOGIES CORP
(*Suby of* TRICO PRODUCTS CORP) ★
1995 Billy Mitchell Blvd, Brownsville, TX 78521-5697
Tel (956) 544-2722 *Founded/Ownrshp* 1986
Sales 300.0MM *EMP* 343
SIC 3714 Motor vehicle parts & accessories; Windshield wiper systems, motor vehicle
Pr: Greg Flake
**Pr:* David Cummings
Sfty Dirs: Pete Lopez

D-U-N-S 94-570-6612 IMP/EXP
TRICON ENERGY INC
777 Post Oak Blvd Ste 550, Houston, TX 77056-3315
Tel (713) 963-0066 *Founded/Ownrshp* 1996
Sales 185.1MM^E *EMP* 320^E
SIC 6719 Investment holding companies, except banks
Pr: Ignacio Torras
CFO: Brian Morris
Ofcr: Brad Lockwood
VP: Bryan Elwood

TRICON ENERGY, LTD.
See TRICON INTERNATIONAL LTD

D-U-N-S 02-314-0093
TRICON INTERNATIONAL LTD (TX)
TRICON ENERGY, LTD.
777 Post Oak Blvd Ste 550, Houston, TX 77056-3315
Tel (713) 963-0066 *Founded/Ownrshp* 1997
Sales 1.7MMM^E *EMP* 355
SIC 5169 7389 4789 Chemicals & allied products; Financial services; Cargo loading & unloading services
Pr: Ignacio Torras
Genl Pt: Tricon Energy
Pt: Amit Bansal
Pt: Bryan Elwood
Pt: Daniel Green
Pt: Serra Kucukoglu
Pt: Brad Lockwood
Pt: Shi WEI Min
Pt: Sanjay Moolgi
Pt: Brian Morris
Off Mgr: Michelle Davila

D-U-N-S 03-856-5867
TRICOR AMERICA INC
717 Airport Blvd, South San Francisco, CA 94080-1815
Tel (650) 877-3650 *Founded/Ownrshp* 2000
Sales 114.1MM^E *EMP* 750
SIC 4513 Air courier services
CEO: Chee Bor Louie
CFO: Scott Tanaka
**VP:* Garrett Louie
Dir IT: Sean Clark

D-U-N-S 00-145-6961 IMP
■ **TRICOR DIRECT INC**
SETON IDENTIFICATION PRODUCTS
(*Suby of* BRADY CORP) ★
20 Thompson Rd, Branford, CT 06405-2842
Tel (203) 488-8059 *Founded/Ownrshp* 1981
Sales 134.5MM^E *EMP* 647
SIC 3479 Name plates: engraved, etched, etc.
Genl Mgr: Pascale Deman
**Treas:* Aaron J Pearce
**VP:* Kathleen Johnson
Genl Mgr: Hans-Jergen Gudmundsson

TRICOR PACIFIC CAPITAL PARTNER
See BFG SUPPLY CO LLC

D-U-N-S 80-767-9019
TRICOR PACIFIC CAPITAL PARTNERS (FUND IV) US LP
(*Suby of* TRICOR PACIFIC CAPITAL INC)
1 Westminster Pl Ste 100n, Lake Forest, IL 60045-1885
Tel (847) 295-4410 *Founded/Ownrshp* 2007
Sales 208.5MM^E *EMP* 250^E
SIC 6211 Security brokers & dealers
Pt: Bradley S Seaman
Pt: Scott A Daum
Pt: Jonathan O Dries
Pt: John Kobza
Pt: Nicholas A Peters
Pt: Jack L Westerman

D-U-N-S 00-650-3791 IMP/EXP
TRICORBRAUN INC
(*Suby of* CHS CAPITAL) ★
6 Cityplace Dr Ste 100, Saint Louis, MO 63141-7157
Tel (314) 569-3633 *Founded/Ownrshp* 2006
Sales 576.1MM^E *EMP* 500
SIC 5085 Glass bottles; Plastic bottles; Commercial containers
CEO: Keith Strope
**Ch Bd:* Kenneth Kranzberg
COO: George Dempsey
COO: Susan Hale
**CFO:* Chuck Pfister
CFO: Neil Tinzberg
CFO: Neil Tzinberg
Bd of Dir: Sterling Anthony
Ofcr: Neil Tinberg
Ex VP: George Eempsey
Ex VP: Craig Sawicki
VP: Dan Dunwibbie
VP: Dave Kettler
VP: Douglas Kliska
VP: George M Schoen
VP: William Stultz

D-U-N-S 07-341-9194
TRICORE REFERENCE LABORATORIES
1001 Woodward Pl Ne, Albuquerque, NM 87102-2705
Tel (505) 938-8999 *Founded/Ownrshp* 1998
Sales 50.8MM *EMP* 1,051
Accts Cliftonlarsonallen Albuquerqu
SIC 8071 Medical laboratories
CEO: Khosrow Shotorbani
COO: Leonard A Poikey
COO: Toby Simon
CFO: Dorothy Ennis
**CFO:* Renee Ennis
VP: Jason Leonard
Exec: Stella Saindon
Dir Lab: Clare Davis
CIO: William Baker
CIO: Michael H Knellinger
IT Man: David Hall

D-U-N-S 01-893-8903
TRIDEC AQUISITION CO INC
800 Federal Blvd, Carteret, NJ 07008-1098
Tel (732) 750-9000 *Founded/Ownrshp* 2008
Sales 93.9MM^E *EMP* 600^E
SIC 6719 Investment holding companies, except banks
Ch Bd: Greg Desaye
**Pr:* Robert Agresti
**CEO:* Bob O'Neill
**COO:* Joe Desaye
Sec: Neil Devine

TRIDENT HEALTH
See TRIDENT MEDICAL CENTER LLC

D-U-N-S 03-302-8395
TRIDENT INSURANCE SERVICES LLC
TAPS
(*Suby of* ARGO GROUP INTERNATIONAL HOLDINGS, LTD.)
175 E Houston St Ste 1300, San Antonio, TX 78205-2265
Tel (210) 342-8808 *Founded/Ownrshp* 2004
Sales NA *EMP* 167
SIC 6411 Insurance agents, brokers & service
VP: Craig Comeaux

D-U-N-S 07-744-1517
■ **TRIDENT MEDICAL CENTER LLC**
TRIDENT HEALTH
(*Suby of* HOSPITAL COPORATION OF AMERICA) ★
9330 Medical Plaza Dr, Charleston, SC 29406-9104
Tel (843) 797-7000 *Founded/Ownrshp* 1994
Sales 203.1MM^E *EMP* 2,000
SIC 8062 8011 General medical & surgical hospitals; Offices & clinics of medical doctors
Dir Vol: Stephanie Parker
Dir Sec: Michael Shirey
MIS Dir: Paul Annastas
Dir IT: Paul Parker
VP Opers: Karl Leistikow
Mktg Dir: Bob Behanian
Nutrtnst: Nicole Greenway
Pharmcst: Marlea Wellein
Phys Thrpy: Larry Lowell
HC Dir: Angela Brady
HC Dir: Donna Daws

D-U-N-S 18-105-9304
TRIDENT MICROSYSTEMS INC
1170 Kifer Rd, Sunnyvale, CA 94086-5303
Tel (408) 962-5000 *Founded/Ownrshp* 1987
Sales 557.2MM *EMP* 1,522^E
SIC 3674

D-U-N-S 07-875-8795
TRIDENT PRIVATE HOLDINGS I LLC
601 Lexington Ave 59th Fl, New York, NY 10022-4611
Tel (212) 231-0095 *Founded/Ownrshp* 2012
Sales 479.5MM^E *EMP* 1,303^E
SIC 4813 7374 Data telephone communications; Data processing service

D-U-N-S 06-336-2370 IMP/EXP
TRIDENT SEAFOODS CORP
5303 Shilshole Ave Nw, Seattle, WA 98107-4000
Tel (206) 783-3818 *Founded/Ownrshp* 1972
Sales 2.6MMM^E *EMP* 9,000

SIC 2092 5146 5091 0912 Seafoods, frozen: prepared; Crabmeat, frozen; Fish, frozen: prepared; Seafoods; Fishing equipment & supplies; Finfish
CEO: Charles Bundrant
Pr: Gerald Dowd
Pr: Paul Padgett
CFO: Phil Bishop
Treas: Thomas J Moore
Ex VP: Edd Perry
VP: Brian Alley
VP: Jill Bundrant
VP: Joseph L Bundrant
VP: Bart Eaton
VP: John Garner
VP: Allen Kimball
VP: Kassie Sumida
VP: Bob Woodard
Board of Directors: Douglas Bart Eaton, Peter J Kuttel, Steve Okerlund, Edd A Perry

D-U-N-S 09-374-7475 IMP
TRIDENT STEEL CORP
12825 Flushing Meadows Dr # 110, Saint Louis, MO 63131-1837
Tel (314) 822-0500 *Founded/Ownrshp* 1978
Sales 228.6MM[E] *EMP* 22
SIC 5051 Pipe & tubing, steel
Pr: Kevin Beckmann
**VP:* Matthew Beckmann
**VP:* Hope Snow
**VP Sls:* David Leahy

D-U-N-S 96-832-5113
TRIDENT USA HEALTH SERVICES LLC
930 Ridgebrook Rd Fl 3, Sparks, MD 21152-9481
Tel (800) 786-8015 *Founded/Ownrshp* 2008
Sales 106.8MM[E] *EMP* 676
SIC 8734 X-ray inspection service, industrial

D-U-N-S 96-534-9256
TRIEST AG GROUP INC
1101 Industrial Blvd, Greenville, NC 27834-9089
Tel (252) 758-4263 *Founded/Ownrshp* 2010
Sales 89.0MM *EMP* 190[E]
SIC 8748 Business consulting
Pr: Dean Storkan
**CFO:* John Williams
**VP:* Victor Lilley

D-U-N-S 80-785-4427 IMP/EXP
TRIGEM ENTERPRISES INC
FINETEC COMPUTER
2075 Zanker Rd, San Jose, CA 95131-2107
Tel (408) 943-9193 *Founded/Ownrshp* 1992
Sales 98.8MM *EMP* 35
SIC 5734 Computer peripheral equipment
CEO: James Zhi Fang Shen
Genl Mgr: John Shen
Sls Dir: Maria Panno
Mktg Mgr: Esther Swen
Sls Mgr: Megan Walton

D-U-N-S 83-047-9668 IMP
TRIGEN LABORATORIES LLC
(*Suby of* AVISTA CAPITAL HOLDINGS LP) ★
400 Crossing Blvd, Bridgewater, NJ 08807-2863
Tel (732) 721-0070 *Founded/Ownrshp* 2013
Sales 143.0MM[E] *EMP* 2,258[E]
SIC 2834 Pharmaceutical preparations
Pr: Dave Purdy
**COO:* JD Schaub
**CFO:* Doug Subers
**Treas:* Steve Squashic
**VP:* Kevin Hudy

TRIG'S FOOD & DRUG
See T A SOLBERG CO INC

D-U-N-S 07-349-6007
TRIGYN TECHNOLOGIES INC
(*Suby of* TRIGYN TECHNOLOGIES LIMITED)
100 Metroplex Dr Ste 101, Edison, NJ 08817-2684
Tel (732) 777-0050 *Founded/Ownrshp* 1999
Sales 74.8MM *EMP* 1,250
SIC 7371 7379 Computer software development;
Pr: Homiyar Panday
**Ch:* R Ganapathi
**VP:* Thomas Gordon
IT Man: Sew Jordan
VP Sls: Milind Anhyankar
Board of Directors: R Ganapathi

TRIHEALTH HOSPITAL
See BETHESDA HOSPITAL INC

TRIHEALTH HOSPITAL
See BETHESDA INC

D-U-N-S 16-165-5985
TRIHEALTH INC
(*Suby of* CHI) ★
619 Oak St, Cincinnati, OH 45206-1613
Tel (513) 569-6111 *Founded/Ownrshp* 1994
Sales 184.0MM *EMP* 13,000
Accts Bkd Llp Cincinnati Oh
SIC 8741 Hospital management
Pr: John Prout
Ex VP: Will Groneman
**Ex VP:* William Groneman
**Ex VP:* Claus Vonzychlin
**Sr VP:* Robert Halonen
VP: David Dornheggen
VP: Dennis Kolb
VP: Brian Krause
VP: Welling Richard
VP: Newman Stefanie
VP: John Sunde
VP: Tim Walter
Exec: Holly Stegeman
Dir Risk M: Larry Johnstal
Dir Lab: Karen Henderson

D-U-N-S 96-583-3887
TRIHEALTH PHYSICIAN INSTITUTE
619 Oak St, Cincinnati, OH 45206-1613
Tel (513) 569-5126 *Founded/Ownrshp* 1983
Sales 90.8MM *EMP* 4
Accts Deloitte Tax Llp Cincinnati
SIC 8011 General & family practice, physician/surgeon

Prin: Alec J Fisher

D-U-N-S 03-898-7145
TRILLIANT FOOD AND NUTRITION LLC
NEW MEXICO COFFEE COMPANY
1101 Moasis Dr, Little Chute, WI 54140-1296
Tel (920) 788-1252 *Founded/Ownrshp* 2003
Sales 221.8MM[E] *EMP* 450
SIC 5149 2099 2095 Coffee, green or roasted; Tea; Food preparations; Roasted coffee
CEO: Mike Upchurch

TRILLIUM ENVIRONMENTAL SVCS
See POCH STAFFING INC

D-U-N-S 03-887-1747
TRILLIUM FARM HOLDINGS LLC
TRILLIUM FARMS
10513 Croton Rd, Johnstown, OH 43031-9105
Tel (740) 893-7200 *Founded/Ownrshp* 2011
Sales 182.7MM[E] *EMP* 450[E]
SIC 5499 Eggs & poultry
CEO: Jim Dean
**COO:* Douglas Mack
**Prin:* Doug Taylor

TRILLIUM FARMS
See TRILLIUM FARM HOLDINGS LLC

D-U-N-S 06-513-5295
■TRILLIUM SOFTWARE INC
(*Suby of* HARTE HANKS INC) ★
17 New England Executive, Burlington, MA 01803-5223
Tel (978) 901-0000 *Founded/Ownrshp* 1979
Sales 120.8MM[E] *EMP* 408
SIC 7374 Data processing service
Ch Bd: John Sweeney
**CEO:* Philip Galati
CFO: Sid Hoffman
**Treas:* Federico Ortiz
**Ex VP:* Michael A Hutnyan
Sr VP: Randall L Bean
Sr VP: Clinton Cove
**Sr VP:* Len Dubois
Sr VP: Spencer Joyner
**Sr VP:* Bernard Lecuyer
**Sr VP:* Kevin W McCarthy
VP: Robert Driscoll
VP: Eric Ecker
VP: Harriet Heyman
VP: Richard Hockhauser
VP: Ralph Holt
VP: Michelle Mogielnicki
VP: Sylvio Ramos
Dir Bus: Steven Sparrow

D-U-N-S 96-261-4991
TRILOGY FULFILLMENT LLC
(*Suby of* GOLDEN GATE CAPITAL) ★
6600 Alum Creek Dr, Groveport, OH 43125-9420
Tel (614) 491-0553 *Founded/Ownrshp* 2010
Sales 79.7MM[E] *EMP* 5,045[E]
SIC 8742 Distribution channels consultant

D-U-N-S 05-908-6178
TRILOGY REHAB SERVICES LLC
HEALTH CTR AT HRRISON MEM HOSP
2701 Chestnut Station Ct, Louisville, KY 40299-6395
Tel (800) 335-1060 *Founded/Ownrshp* 1998
Sales 155.0MM[E] *EMP* 4,000
SIC 8059 1542 8741 8051 Rest home, with health care; Hospital construction; Management services; Skilled nursing care facilities
COO: Daniel Livy
CFO: Steven Van
Div VP: Steve Robison
VP: Jay Trumbo
Dir Bus: Karl Moore
Ex Dir: Andra Bladen
Ex Dir: Jessica Crafton
Ex Dir: Eileen Heffelmire
Ex Dir: Cindi Lents
Ex Dir: Manu Mooker
Ex Dir: Mike Wray

D-U-N-S 18-876-1142
TRILOK INDUSTRIES INC
670 Village Trce Ne, Marietta, GA 30067-4096
Tel (678) 325-2960 *Founded/Ownrshp* 1987
Sales 89.6MM[E] *EMP* 450
SIC 1799 1742

D-U-N-S 18-332-8707
TRIM MASTERS INC
1360 Dolwick Rd Ste 125, Erlanger, KY 41018-3159
Tel (859) 887-6000 *Founded/Ownrshp* 1987
Sales 118.2MM[E] *EMP* 1,794
Accts Pricewaterhousecoopers Llp
SIC 2531 Seats, automobile
Pr: Kenji Akase
Treas: Phillip D Ashcraft
VP: Beth Rae

D-U-N-S 07-967-2759 IMP
■TRIM SYSTEMS OPERATING CORP
CVG TRIM SYSTEMS
(*Suby of* CVG) ★
7800 Walton Pkwy, New Albany, OH 43054-8233
Tel (614) 289-5360 *Founded/Ownrshp* 2004
Sales 129.9MM[E] *EMP* 1,200
SIC 3714 Motor vehicle parts & accessories
Pr: Gerald L Armstrong

D-U-N-S 92-886-8801
TRIM-RITE FOOD CORP INC
801 Commerce Pkwy, Carpentersville, IL 60110-1721
Tel (847) 649-3400 *Founded/Ownrshp* 2013
Sales 196.6MM[E] *EMP* 200
SIC 5147 Prepared pork products from purchased pork; Ham, boiled: from purchased meat; Ham, boneless: from purchased meat; Pork, cured: from purchased meat
Pr: James Jendruczek
**CFO:* David Piotrowski
**VP:* Michael Lookingland
**VP Sls:* David Bulgarelli

D-U-N-S 00-680-6632
TRIMAC ACTIVE INC
(*Suby of* TRIMAC TRANSPORTATION SERVICES INC)
15333 John F Kennedy Blvd # 800, Houston, TX 77032-2351
Tel (281) 985-0000 *Founded/Ownrshp* 1942
Sales 433.1MM[E] *EMP* 1,700
SIC 4213

D-U-N-S 12-120-9378
TRIMAC TRANSPORTATION INC
(*Suby of* TRIMAC ACTIVE INC) ★
15333 John F Kenn Blvd, Houston, TX 77032
Tel (281) 985-0000 *Founded/Ownrshp* 1988
Sales 96.4MM[E] *EMP* 716
SIC 4789 Cabs, horse drawn: for hire
Ch Bd: Jeffery J McCaig
**Pr:* Tom Connard
**CFO:* Craig Bourgeois
**VP:* Jim D'Alessio
**VP:* William Marchbank

D-U-N-S 13-039-2348 IMP/EXP
TRIMACO LLC
2300 Gateway Centre Blvd # 200, Morrisville, NC 27560-9669
Tel (919) 674-3476 *Founded/Ownrshp* 2002
Sales 103.5MM[E] *EMP* 255
SIC 2851 2621 2672 2679 2394 Paints & allied products; Poster & art papers; Masking tape: made from purchased materials; Building paper, laminated: made from purchased material; Canvas & related products
VP: Maria P Costello

D-U-N-S 11-204-3943
TRIMARAN FUND MANAGEMENT LLC
1325 Ave Of The Flr 34, New York, NY 10019
Tel (212) 616-3700 *Founded/Ownrshp* 2005
Sales 275.2MM[E] *EMP* 2,450[E]
SIC 6211 Investment firm, general brokerage
Mng Pt: Dean Kehler
Mng Dir: Andrea Kellett
VP Sls: Ben Hill

D-U-N-S 78-532-5643
TRIMARAN POLLO PARTNERS LLC
3333 Michelson Dr, Irvine, CA 92612-0625
Tel (949) 399-2000 *Founded/Ownrshp* 2005
Sales 37.3MM[E] *EMP* 4,460
SIC 5812 Fast-food restaurant, chain
CEO: Stephen E Carley

TRIMARK ADAMS-BURCH
See ADAMS-BURCH LLC

D-U-N-S 02-521-9023
TRIMARK MARLINN INC (IL)
6100 W 73rd St Ste 1, Chicago, IL 60638-6107
Tel (708) 496-1700 *Founded/Ownrshp* 1946, 1978
Sales 100.1MM[E] *EMP* 106
SIC 5046 Restaurant equipment & supplies
Pr: Michael Siegel

TRIMARK RW SMITH
See R W SMITH & CO

TRIMARK SS KEMP
See S S KEMP & CO

TRIMARK STRATEGIC
See STRATEGIC EQUIPMENT AND SUPPLY CORP

TRIMARK UNITED EAST
See TRIMARK USA LLC

D-U-N-S 01-859-1339 IMP
TRIMARK UNITED EAST INC
(*Suby of* TRIMARK UNITED EAST) ★
505 Collins St, Attleboro, MA 02703-8039
Tel (508) 399-6000 *Founded/Ownrshp* 1998
Sales 121.4MM[E] *EMP* 170[E]
SIC 5046 5021 5113 5087 Commercial cooking & food service equipment; Cooking equipment, commercial; Restaurant furniture; Cups, disposable plastic & paper; Dishes, disposable plastic & paper; Napkins, paper; Bags, paper & disposable plastic; Janitors' supplies
Pr: Jerald Hyman

D-U-N-S 55-637-4549 IMP/EXP
TRIMARK USA LLC
TRIMARK UNITED EAST
(*Suby of* WARBURG PINCUS LLC) ★
505 Collins St, Attleboro, MA 02703-8039
Tel (508) 399-2400 *Founded/Ownrshp* 1998
Sales 1.0MMM[E] *EMP* 950
SIC 5021 5023 Bar furniture; Dining room furniture; Restaurant furniture; Kitchenware; Glassware; Kitchen tools & utensils
**CFO:* Jeff Gonzalez

D-U-N-S 17-559-1072 IMP/EXP
▲TRIMAS CORP
39400 Woodward Ave # 130, Bloomfield Hills, MI 48304-5151
Tel (248) 631-5450 *Founded/Ownrshp* 1986
Sales 1.5MMM *EMP* 7,000
Tkr Sym TRS *Exch* NGS
SIC 3799 3714 3443 2672 3452 3545 Trailer hitches; Motor vehicle parts & accessories; Trailer hitches, motor vehicle; Fabricated plate work (boiler shop); Drums, knockout (reflux, etc.): metal plate; Cylinders, pressure: metal plate; Tape, pressure sensitive: made from purchased materials; Bolts, nuts, rivets & washers; Bolts, metal; Screws, metal; Machine tool accessories; Drills (machine tool accessories); Milling cutters
Pr: Thomas A Amanto
**Ch Bd:* Samuel Valenti III
Pr: Tom Aepelbacher
Pr: Lynn Brooks
Pr: David Pritchett
Pr: Marc A Roberts
Pr: John Schaefer
CFO: Robert J Zalupski
CFO: Mark Zeffiro
Bd of Dir: Eugene Miller

Sr VP: Joshua A Sherbin
Comm Man: Sherry Lauderback
Board of Directors: Marshall A Cohen, Richard M Gabrys, Nancy S Gougarty, Eugene A Miller, Herbert K Parker, Nick L Stanage, Daniel P Tredwell

D-U-N-S 09-498-2386
▲TRIMBLE INC
935 Stewart Dr, Sunnyvale, CA 94085-3913
Tel (408) 481-8000 *Founded/Ownrshp* 1978
Sales 2.2MMM *EMP* 8,451
Tkr Sym TRMB *Exch* NGS
SIC 3812 3829 Navigational systems & instruments; Measuring & controlling devices
Pr: Steven W Berglund
**Ch Bd:* Ulf J Johansson
**CFO:* Robert G Painter
**V Ch Bd:* Nickolas W Vande Steeg
Sr VP: Darryl R Matthews
Sr VP: Sachin J Sankpal
VP: Joe Denniston
VP: Bryn A Fosburgh
VP: Christopher W Gibson
VP: Mark Harrington
**VP:* James A Kirkland
VP: J Rgen D Kliem
VP: Jurgen D Kliem
VP: Leah Lambertson
VP: James A Veneziano
Board of Directors: Borje Ekholm, Merit E Janow, Ronald S Nersesian, Mark S Peek

D-U-N-S 10-241-0094
TRIMEDX INDIA LLC
(*Suby of* ASCENSION HEALTH) ★
5451 Lakeview Pkwy S Dr, Indianapolis, IN 46268-4115
Tel (877) 874-6339 *Founded/Ownrshp* 1998
Sales 115.3MM[E] *EMP* 500[E]
SIC 7699 Life saving & survival equipment, non-medical: repair; Medical equipment repair, non-electric
CEO: Greg Ranger
**CFO:* Jim Fanelli
VP: Dale Hockel
Exec: Kelly Stillman
Dir Bus: Carol Sysak
Dir IT: Robert Cadick
Dir IT: Jim Morris
Site Mgr: Josh Treviao
Mktg Dir: Jennefer Pursifull

D-U-N-S 18-066-6356
TRIMEGA PURCHASING ASSOCIATION
5600 N River Rd Ste 700, Rosemont, IL 60018-5165
Tel (847) 699-3330 *Founded/Ownrshp* 1995
Sales 189.4MM *EMP* 27
SIC 7389 Purchasing service
Pr: Charlie Cleary
**Pr:* Mike Maggio
**Ch:* Foss Jones
**Ex VP:* Greg Fish
**Ex VP:* Grady Taylor
**VP:* Michael Morris
**VP:* Gene Rigitano
Mktg Mgr: Allison Little

D-U-N-S 19-515-5122
TRIMONT REAL ESTATE ADVISORS INC
3424 Peachtree Rd Ne # 2200, Atlanta, GA 30326-1156
Tel (404) 420-5600 *Founded/Ownrshp* 2015
Sales 129.7MM[E] *EMP* 400
SIC 6531 Real estate listing services
CEO: Brian Ward
COO: Michael Wimberly
**CFO:* Yean Lee
Sr VP: Jeffrey L Arpin
Sr VP: Henry Cobb
Sr VP: Eric Lind
VP: Bob Anderson
VP: Ron Bowell
VP: Robert Brasfield
VP: Jonathan Childs
VP: Christopher Cummings
VP: Sam Kaplan
VP: Scott Monroe
Exec: Kim Alexander
Exec: John Schwartz

TRINCHERO FAMILY ESTATES
See SUTTER HOME WINERY INC

D-U-N-S 60-654-1415
▲TRINET GROUP INC
1100 San Leandro Blvd # 300, San Leandro, CA 94577-1599
Tel (510) 352-5000 *Founded/Ownrshp* 1988
Sales 2.6MMM *EMP* 2,500
Tkr Sym TNET *Exch* NYS
SIC 7361 8721 Employment agencies; Accounting, auditing & bookkeeping
Pr: Burton M Goldfield
**Ch Bd:* H Raymond Bingham
CFO: William Porter
Sr VP: Edward Griese
Sr VP: John Turner
VP: John Cataldo
VP: Christopher Davis
VP: Pravin Kumar
VP: Sterling Mace
VP Bus Dev: Timothy Frazier
Exec: Linda Dater
Board of Directors: Martin Babinec, Paul Chamberlain, Katherine August-Dewilde, Kenneth Goldman, David C Hodgson, John H Kispert, Wayne B Lowell

TRINI MOTH FRAN HOSP AND CLIN
See CHRISTUS TRINITY MOTHER FRANCES HEALTH SYSTEM

TRINI MOTHE FRANC HOSPI
See TRINITY MOTHER FRANCES HEALTH SYSTEM FOUNDATION

TRINIDAD BENHAM
See TRINIDAD/BENHAM CORP

TRINIDAD BENHAM
See TRINIDAD/BENHAM HOLDING CO

D-U-N-S 00-691-6092 IMP/EXP
TRINIDAD/BENHAM CORP
TRINIDAD BENHAM
(*Suby of* TRINIDAD BENHAM) ★
3650 S Yosemite St # 300, Denver, CO 80237-1838
Tel (303) 220-1400 *Founded/Ownrshp* 1917
Sales 578.2MM[E] *EMP* 720
SIC 5149 5153 2034 2099 Pasta & rice; Dried or canned foods; Field beans; Dehydrated fruits, vegetables, soups; Food preparations
CEO: Carl C Hartman
**Pr:* Linda L Wamsley
COO: Larry Kubo
**CFO:* Gary Peters
Treas: Keith Love
VP: Jason Knudson
VP: Su Wright
Dir Bus: John Adam
IT Man: Tim Hagan
Software D: Beaver John
Opers Mgr: Brian Draves

D-U-N-S 09-191-2097 IMP/EXP
TRINIDAD/BENHAM HOLDING CO
TRINIDAD BENHAM
3650 S Yosemite St # 300, Denver, CO 80237-1838
Tel (303) 220-1400 *Founded/Ownrshp* 1978
Sales 578.2MM[E] *EMP* 720

SIC 5153 5149 Field beans; Pasta & rice
CEO: Carl Hartman
**Pr:* Linda Walmsley
**Sec:* Gary Peters

D-U-N-S 06-579-3267 IMP
TRINITAS REGIONAL MEDICAL CENTER
225 Williamson St, Elizabeth, NJ 07202-3625
Tel (908) 351-0714 *Founded/Ownrshp* 1905
Sales 365.1MM[E] *EMP* 2,700
SIC 8062 General medical & surgical hospitals
Pr: Gary Huran
CFO: Dennis Hemmingway
Ofcr: Grant Knaggs
VP: Mary Corrigan
VP: Bernadett Countryman
Dir Rx: Sharon Greasheimer
Dir IT: David Eicher
IT Man: Francis Montemayor
Info Man: Rose Peterson
Sfty Dirs: Joann Blount
Ansthlgy: Teimouraz V Vassilidze
Board of Directors: Ernest Federici

TRINITY AGGREGATE DISTRIBUTION
See TRANSIT MIX CONCRETE & MATERIALS CO

D-U-N-S 96-832-9354
TRINITY BAY CITY HOLDINGS LLC
AUTOMTIVE TRNSCTION SVCS GROUP
712 Waltham Ct, El Paso, TX 79922-2128
Tel (915) 877-1700 *Founded/Ownrshp* 2010
Sales 100.0MM *EMP* 10
SIC 5511 New & used car dealers

D-U-N-S 15-733-7551 IMP
TRINITY BIOTECH INC
CLARK LABORATORIES
(*Suby of* TRINITY BIOTECH PUBLIC LIMITED COMPANY)
2823 Girts Rd, Jamestown, NY 14701-9666
Tel (800) 325-3424 *Founded/Ownrshp* 1994
Sales 142.0MM[E] *EMP* 390
SIC 5047 Medical equipment & supplies
CEO: Ronan O Caoimh
CFO: Kevin Tansley
Genl Mgr: Joseph Vacante

TRINITY BROADCASTING NETWORK
See TRINITY CHRISTIAN CENTER OF SANTA ANA INC

D-U-N-S 06-446-2674 IMP
TRINITY CHRISTIAN CENTER OF SANTA ANA INC
TRINITY BROADCASTING NETWORK
2442 Michelle Dr, Tustin, CA 92780-7015
Tel (714) 665-3619 *Founded/Ownrshp* 1973
Sales 141.2MM *EMP* 350
Accts Goodrich Baron Goodyear Long
SIC 4833 7922 Television broadcasting stations; Television program, including commercial producers
**Pr:* Paul F Crouch
Treas: John Casoria
Treas: Margie Tuccillo
Bd of Dir: Colby May
VP: Terry Hickey
VP: Bob Higley
Exec: Randall Riley
Dept Mgr: Amor Steffon
Genl Mgr: Linda Cook
CTO: Marvin Vosper
Site Mgr: Alayna S Watson

D-U-N-S 06-925-9950
TRINITY COLLEGE
300 Summit St Ste 1, Hartford, CT 06106-3186
Tel (860) 297-2000 *Founded/Ownrshp* 1823
Sales 191.4MM *EMP* 2,062
SIC 8221

D-U-N-S 06-898-5480
TRINITY CONSULTANTS INC
12700 Park Central Dr # 2100, Dallas, TX 75251-1546
Tel (972) 661-8100 *Founded/Ownrshp* 1974, 2015
Sales 99.0MM[E] *EMP* 275
SIC 8748 Environmental consultant
Pr: Jay Hofmann
**CFO:* Dave Larsen
Admn Mgr: Aaron Aundrey

D-U-N-S 96-963-0321
TRINITY CONTINUING CARE SERVICES - INDIANA INC
17410 College Pkwy # 200, Livonia, MI 48152-2369
Tel (734) 542-8300 *Founded/Ownrshp* 2011
Sales 131.6MM *EMP* 15[E]
SIC 8051 Convalescent home with continuous nursing care

Pr: Kenneth Robbins

D-U-N-S 07-103-2007
TRINITY EPISCOPAL SCHOOL CORP
TRINITY SCHOOL
139 W 91st St, New York, NY 10024-1326
Tel (212) 873-1650 *Founded/Ownrshp* 1709
Sales 83.7MM *EMP* 200
Accts Eisneramper Llp New York Ny
SIC 8211 Private elementary & secondary schools; Secondary school
Prin: Suellayn H Scull
**Pr:* Andrew Brownstein
Assoc Dir: Lisa Bianchi

TRINITY ESC
See TRNLWB LLC

D-U-N-S 07-176-2694
TRINITY HEALTH
TRINITY HOSPITAL
1 Burdick Expy W, Minot, ND 58701-4406
Tel (701) 857-5260 *Founded/Ownrshp* 1922
Sales 430.7MM *EMP* 2,600
Accts Clifton Larson Allen Llp Minn
SIC 8011 8051 8062 Primary care medical clinic; Convalescent home with continuous nursing care; General medical & surgical hospitals
CEO: John M Kutch
Pr: Karen Haroutunian
**CFO:* Dennis Empey
**Ch:* Patrick Holien
VP: Trent Chastain
VP: Antoinette Green
VP: Tauana McDonald
VP: Mark Rossman
**VP:* Randy Schwan
**VP:* Paul Simonson
**VP:* Thomas Warsocki

D-U-N-S 06-097-6008
TRINITY HEALTH CORP
CATHOLIC HEALTH EAST
20555 Victor Pkwy, Livonia, MI 48152-7031
Tel (734) 343-1000 *Founded/Ownrshp* 1978
Sales 1.0MMM *EMP* 51,100
SIC 8741 8062 Hospital management; Nursing & personal care facility management; General medical & surgical hospitals
Pr: Richard J Gilfillan
**CEO:* Judith M Persichilli
COO: Becky Lund
CFO: Benjamin R Carter
CFO: Sandy Cohan
Treas: James W Bosscher
**Treas:* Benjamin Carter
**Chf Mktg O:* Donald Bignotti
**Chf Inves:* James Bosscher
Ofcr: Amy Gendron
Ofcr: Camille Orso
Ex VP: Debra A Canales
Ex VP: John Capasso
Ex VP: Clayton Fitzhugh
Ex VP: Dan Hale
Ex VP: Sally E Jeffcoat
Ex VP: Mark I Froimson
**Ex VP:* Paul G Neumann
Ex VP: Jodie O'Connell
Ex VP: Barbara A Walters
**Sr VP:* Paul F Conlon

D-U-N-S 94-340-6371
TRINITY HEALTH SYSTEM
TRINITY MEDICAL CENTER EAST
(*Suby of* TRINITY MEDICAL CENTER EAST) ★
380 Summit Ave, Steubenville, OH 43952-2667
Tel (740) 283-7000 *Founded/Ownrshp* 1995
Sales 5.0MM[E] *EMP* 1,640
Accts Plante & Moran Pllc Cleveland
SIC 8062 8011 General medical & surgical hospitals; Hospital, AMA approved residency; Offices & clinics of medical doctors
CEO: Fred Brower
COO: Sue Thompson
**CFO:* Elizabeth Allen
VP: Joann Mulrooney
Ex Dir: Joseph Edmiston
Genl Mgr: Jorja Schofield
CIO: Barbara Kornbau
IT Man: Brian Fancett

D-U-N-S 12-624-5682
TRINITY HEALTH-MICHIGAN
ST. JOSEPH MERCY POTU HURON
(*Suby of* CATHOLIC HEALTH EAST) ★
20555 Victor Pkwy, Livonia, MI 48152-7031
Tel (810) 985-1500 *Founded/Ownrshp* 1976
Sales 2.4MMM *EMP* 700[E]
SIC 8062 General medical & surgical hospitals
CEO: Rebekah Smith
**CFO:* Mike Gusho

TRINITY HOSPITAL
See ADVOCATE HEALTH AND HOSPITALS CORP

TRINITY HOSPITAL
See TRINITY HEALTH

D-U-N-S 01-745-6182
TRINITY HOSPITAL HOLDING CO
TRINITY MEDICAL CENTER EAST
380 Summit Ave, Steubenville, OH 43952-2667
Tel (740) 264-8000 *Founded/Ownrshp* 1997
Sales 231.4MM *EMP* 1,640
Accts Ernst & Young Llp Pittsburgh
SIC 8062 8741 General medical & surgical hospitals; Management services
Ch Bd: Clyde Metzger MD
**Pr:* Fred B Bower
VP: Melissa Buksa

D-U-N-S 00-732-4254 IMP/EXP
▲TRINITY INDUSTRIES INC
2525 N Stemmons Fwy, Dallas, TX 75207-2400
Tel (214) 631-4420 *Founded/Ownrshp* 1933
Sales 6.3MMM *EMP* 22,030
Tkr Sym TRN *Exch* NYS
SIC 3743 3731 3531 3444 3441 3443 Freight cars & equipment; Tank freight cars & car equipment; Barges, building & repairing; Offshore supply boats, building & repairing; Crew boats, building & repairing; Fishing vessels, large: building & repairing; Concrete plants; Guard rails, highway: sheet metal; Fabricated structural metal; Building components, structural steel; Fabricated structural metal for bridges; Industrial vessels, tanks & containers
Ch Bd: Timothy R Wallace
Pr: William A McWhirter
CFO: James E Perry
Treas: Neil Shoop
Ofcr: Melendy E Lovett
Ofcr: S Theis Rice
Ex VP: Jeff N Raasch
Sr VP: Richard G Brown
Sr VP: D S Menzies
Sr VP: Tim Schitter
VP: Madhuri Andrews
VP: Rich Bacsi
VP: Scott Beasley
VP: Jack Cunningham
VP: Tom Dalrymple
VP: Tammy Gilbert
VP: Terry Goodwin
VP: Ginny Gray
VP: John Guarino
VP: Mary E Henderson
VP: Dale Hill
Board of Directors: John L Adams, Rhys J Best, David W Biegler, Antonio Carrillo, Ronald J Gafford, Adrian Lajous, Charles W Matthews, Douglas L Rock

D-U-N-S 03-971-3896
■TRINITY INDUSTRIES LEASING CO
(*Suby of* TRINITY INDUSTRIES INC) ★
2525 N Stemmons Fwy, Dallas, TX 75207-2400
Tel (800) 227-8844 *Founded/Ownrshp* 1979
Sales 110.8MM[E] *EMP* 62
SIC 4741 4499 Rental of railroad cars; Marine salvaging & surveying services
CEO: Timothy R Wallace
**Pr:* Stephen Menzies
**CIO:* Jesse V Crews

D-U-N-S 18-770-1941
TRINITY LOGISTICS INC
50 Fallon Ave, Seaford, DE 19973-1578
Tel (302) 253-3900 *Founded/Ownrshp* 1979
Sales 156.8MM[E] *EMP* 300
SIC 4731 Truck transportation brokers
Pr: Jeffrey Banning
**CFO:* Doug Potvin
Sr VP: Billy Banning
**Sr VP:* William Banning
**VP:* Darrel Banning
VP: Ralph Massey
VP: Brandy McMullen
VP: Sarah Ruffcorn
Genl Mgr: Douglas Heilesen
Genl Mgr: John Nelson
Sftwr Eng: Steve Robison

D-U-N-S 09-352-8768
TRINITY MATERIALS INC
401 N Interstate Hwy 45, Ferris, TX 75125-1800
Tel (972) 544-5900 *Founded/Ownrshp* 1993
Sales 89.2MM[E] *EMP* 184
SIC 3273 Ready-mixed concrete
Pr: Carl Campbell
**Treas:* Gail M Peck
**Treas:* James E Perry
**Sr VP:* S Theis Rice

TRINITY MEDICAL CENTER
See AFFINITY HOSPITAL LLC

TRINITY MEDICAL CENTER
See TRINITY REGIONAL HEALTH SYSTEM

D-U-N-S 07-561-2895
TRINITY MEDICAL CENTER
TRINITY ROCK ISLAND
(*Suby of* TRINITY MEDICAL CENTER) ★
2701 17th St, Rock Island, IL 61201-5393
Tel (309) 779-5000 *Founded/Ownrshp* 1992
Sales 281.2MM *EMP* 2,184
SIC 8062 General medical & surgical hospitals
CEO: Richard Seidler
Pr: Cheri Bustos
**CFO:* Gregory Pagliuzza
CFO: Kevin Vermeer
VP: Jeff Stolze

D-U-N-S 14-189-5883
TRINITY MEDICAL CENTER
TRINITY MEDICAL CTR AT TER PK
(*Suby of* TRINITY MEDICAL CENTER) ★
4500 Utica Ridge Rd, Bettendorf, IA 52722-1626
Tel (563) 742-2000 *Founded/Ownrshp* 2004
Sales 72.9MM *EMP* 2,600
SIC 8062 General medical & surgical hospitals
CEO: Andrea Coleman
Exec: Michael Patterson
Nrsg Dir: Becky Johnson

TRINITY MEDICAL CENTER EAST
See TRINITY HOSPITAL HOLDING CO

TRINITY MEDICAL CENTER EAST
See TRINITY HEALTH SYSTEM

D-U-N-S 06-875-9307
TRINITY MEDICAL CENTER WEST
4000 Johnson Rd, Steubenville, OH 43952-2364
Tel (740) 264-8000 *Founded/Ownrshp* 1913
Sales 61.5MM[E] *EMP* 1,800
Accts Ernst & Young Llp Pittsburgh
SIC 8062 General medical & surgical hospitals
Pr: Fred B Brower
Dir Rad: Frank Hamilton
Dir Sec: Dave Nicholson
IT Man: Dean M Lucarelli
Opers Mgr: Margaret Franklin

TRINITY MEDICAL CTR AT TER PK
See TRINITY MEDICAL CENTER

D-U-N-S 07-954-1575
■TRINITY MEYER UTILITY STRUCTURES LLC
(*Suby of* TRINITY INDUSTRIES INC) ★
2525 N Stemmons Fwy, Dallas, TX 75207-2401
Tel (901) 566-6500 *Founded/Ownrshp* 2014
Sales 121.9MM[E] *EMP* 476[E]
SIC 1623 Communication line & transmission tower construction; Transmitting tower (telecommunication) construction
CEO: Timothy R Wallace
**CFO:* James E Perry

D-U-N-S 07-047-2381
TRINITY MOTHER FRANCES HEALTH SYSTEM FOUNDATION
TRINI MOTHE FRANC HOSPI
800 E Dawson St, Tyler, TX 75701-2036
Tel (903) 531-5057 *Founded/Ownrshp* 1984
Sales 711.6MM *EMP* 3,551[E]
Accts Bkd Llp Dallas Tx
SIC 8062 General medical & surgical hospitals
Pr: J Lindsey Bradley
**Pr:* Randall V Childress
**COO:* Steven Keuer
**COO:* Ray Thompson
**CFO:* William Bellenfant
CFO: Joyce Hester
**Co-Pr:* David Teegarden
Ofcr: Jim Murray
Sr VP: Laura Owen
VP: Jeff Pearson
VP: Lee Portwood

D-U-N-S 02-733-7567
TRINITY MOTHER FRANCIS HEALTH SYSTEM
TEEGARDEN, DAVID K M D
910 E Houston St Ste 550, Tyler, TX 75702-8366
Tel (903) 526-2644 *Founded/Ownrshp* 1978
Sales 96.3MM *EMP* 40[E]
SIC 8011 Internal medicine, physician/surgeon
Prin: David Teegarden MD

D-U-N-S 19-916-1886 IMP
TRINITY PACKAGING CORP
357 Main St, Armonk, NY 10504-1808
Tel (914) 273-4111 *Founded/Ownrshp* 1917
Sales 164.0MM[E] *EMP* 525
SIC 2673 2679 Plastic bags: made from purchased materials; Paper products, converted
CEO: John H Freund
**Pr:* Peter Freund
CFO: Mark Rohte
**CFO:* Bob Rotolo
QA Dir: Jacob Schreiber
Plnt Mgr: Tim Shiley

D-U-N-S 07-910-1329 IMP
TRINITY PLASTICS INC
(*Suby of* IBS) ★
9 Peach Tree Hill Rd, Livingston, NJ 07039-5702
Tel (973) 994-8018 *Founded/Ownrshp* 2013
Sales 111.9MM[E] *EMP* 500[E]
SIC 2673 3081 Bags: plastic, laminated & coated; Unsupported plastics film & sheet
Pr: Joe Chen

D-U-N-S 11-280-7768
■TRINITY RAIL GROUP LLC
(*Suby of* TRINITY INDUSTRIES INC) ★
2525 N Stemmons Fwy, Dallas, TX 75207-2401
Tel (214) 631-4420 *Founded/Ownrshp* 2001
Sales 92.2MM[E] *EMP* 270
SIC 3743 Locomotives & parts; Sleeping cars, railroad
CEO: Timothy R Wallace
COO: Tony Andrukaitis
Sr VP: George Creighton
Sr VP: Scott G Merrifield
VP: Clay Howard
VP: Helmut Hvizdalek
**VP:* Gail Peck
VP: Mark H Van Cleave
Ex Dir: David McGuire
Dir IT: Larry Harmeyer
IT Man: Steve Bell

D-U-N-S 78-494-2914
TRINITY REGIONAL HEALTH SYSTEM
TRINITY MEDICAL CENTER
2701 17th St, Rock Island, IL 61201-5351
Tel (309) 779-5000 *Founded/Ownrshp* 1984
Sales 2.3MM *EMP* 2,700
SIC 8062 8741 General medical & surgical hospitals; Management services
CEO: Rick Seidler
**Pr:* William B Leaver
CFO: Kevin Vermeer
Genl Mgr: Tom Neuberger
MIS Dir: Tony Drews
Dir IT: Shawn Wyant
Sls&Mrk Ex: Cheri Bustos
Opthamlgy: Eric Bligard
Opthamlgy: Michael J Howcroft
Opthamlgy: Raz D Penmatcha
Opthamlgy: Eileen M Wayne

D-U-N-S 08-726-1103
TRINITY REGIONAL MEDICAL CENTER (IA)
802 Kenyon Rd Ste 1, Fort Dodge, IA 50501-5740
Tel (515) 574-6800 *Founded/Ownrshp* 1908, 1987
Sales 97.5MM *EMP* 855
SIC 8062 8093 General medical & surgical hospitals; Hospital, AMA approved residency; Rehabilitation center, outpatient treatment
CEO: Sue Thompson
**Pr:* John C Taets
**Treas:* Thomas Schnurr
**Sec:* Rhonda M Chambers
Off Mgr: Jody Estergaard
IT Man: Shannon McQuillen

TRINITY ROCK ISLAND
See TRINITY MEDICAL CENTER

TRINITY SCHOOL
See TRINITY EPISCOPAL SCHOOL CORP

D-U-N-S 16-106-7186
TRINITY SENIOR LIVING COMMUNITIES
MERCY CONTINUING CARE
17410 College Pkwy # 200, Livonia, MI 48152-2369
Tel (734) 542-8300 *Founded/Ownrshp* 1986
Sales 59.0MM^E *EMP* 1,800
SIC 8361 Home for the aged
CEO: Ken Robibns
**CFO:* Steve Gosik
MIS Dir: Joe Niester

D-U-N-S 62-180-4913
TRINITY SERVICES GROUP INC
477 Commerce Blvd, Oldsmar, FL 34677-2809
Tel (813) 854-4264 *Founded/Ownrshp* 2013
Sales 456.0MM^E *EMP* 2,800
SIC 8744 Facilities support services
Pr: Larry G Vaughn
**COO:* Peter Hess
**Prin:* John Varnado
Genl Couns: Steve Hould

D-U-N-S 06-747-8248
TRINITY SERVICES INC
301 Veterans Pkwy, New Lenox, IL 60451-2899
Tel (815) 485-6197 *Founded/Ownrshp* 1950
Sales 52.6MM *EMP* 1,075
Accts Jwm Inc Arlington Heights Il
SIC 8211 8322 School for the retarded; Individual & family services
CEO: Arthur Dykstra
**CFO:* Michael Sieling
Genl Mgr: Mary Grove
IT Man: Ray Carmody
IT Man: Cheryl Lipinski
IT Man: Sally Ritchey
Board of Directors: Scott Creech, Bob Libman, Barbara McGoldrick, Ken Stromsland, Rolf Troha

TRINITY SNIOR LVING CMMUNITIES
See SANCTUARY AT HOLY CROSS

D-U-N-S 00-792-8468
■**TRINITY UNIVERSAL INSURANCE CO**
(*Suby of* KEMPER CORP) ★
12790 Merit Dr Ste 400, Dallas, TX 75251-1256
Tel (312) 661-4930 *Founded/Ownrshp* 1990
Sales NA *EMP* 2,000^E
SIC 6331 Automobile insurance; Property damage insurance; Fire, marine & casualty insurance & carriers
Pr: Jack Lubner
**Treas:* Richard Roeske
**VP:* Steve Holl
**VP:* Clark H Roberts
IT Man: Paula McNair
VP Mktg: Kevin McNamara

D-U-N-S 00-813-3456
TRINITY UNIVERSITY
1 Trinity Pl, San Antonio, TX 78212-7200
Tel (210) 999-7011 *Founded/Ownrshp* 1869
Sales 128.8MM *EMP* 700
Accts Grant Thornton Llp Dallas Tx
SIC 8221 University
Pr: Dennis Wahlburg
**Pr:* John R Brazil
Pr: Sharon Jones
Pr: Amy New
**CEO:* Richard Radke
**Sec:* Mary Mickus
Trst: James Dicke
Assoc VP: Duane Coltharp
VP: Michael Bacon
VP: Chris Ellertson
VP: James Fabiaschi
VP: Michael R Fishe
VP: Gary Logan
**VP:* Craig McCoy
**VP:* Marc Raney
VP: David Tuttle
**VP:* Dr Charles B White
Dir Rx: Jerry Ferguson

D-U-N-S 00-984-4564
TRINITY VALLEY ELECTRIC COOPERATIVE INC (TX)
TVEC
1800 E State Highway 243, Kaufman, TX 75142-4114
Tel (972) 932-2214 *Founded/Ownrshp* 1977
Sales 146.9MM *EMP* 153
SIC 4911 Distribution, electric power
CEO: Jerry B Boze
**COO:* Thomas Watson
**CFO:* Frank Skube
Dir IT: Greg Starek
IT Man: Jerry Woolston

TRINITY VALLEY FOODS
See IRVING BRAKEBUSH INC

D-U-N-S 83-316-7310 IMP/EXP
TRINSEO LLC
(*Suby of* TRINSEO SA)
1000 Chesterbrook Blvd # 300, Berwyn, PA 19312-1084
Tel (610) 240-3200 *Founded/Ownrshp* 2009
Sales 831.7MM^E *EMP* 2,100
SIC 2821 Plastics materials & resins
CEO: Christopher D Pappas
**COO:* Martin Pugh
**CFO:* John A Feenan
**Ex VP:* Angelo Chaclas
**Ex VP:* Marilyn Horner
Sr VP: Tim Stedman
Sr VP: Hayati Yarkadas
**VP:* Jeff Denton
**VP:* Catherine Maxey
CIO: Richard Fabrizio
Board of Directors: Philip R Martens, Ruth Springham

D-U-N-S 02-227-4328
TRIOAK FOODS INC
103 W Railroad St, Oakville, IA 52646-4735
Tel (319) 766-2230 *Founded/Ownrshp* 1951
Sales 285.2MM *EMP* 120
SIC 0213 5153

D-U-N-S 07-836-5437
■**TRIPADVISOR INC**
(*Suby of* LIBERTY TRIPADVISOR HOLDINGS INC) ★
400 1st Ave, Needham, MA 02494-2815
Tel (781) 800-5000 *Founded/Ownrshp* 2000
Sales 1.4MMM *EMP* 3,008^E
Tkr Sym TRIP *Exch* NGS
SIC 4724 7374 Travel agencies; Data processing & preparation; Data processing service
Pr: Stephen Kaufer
**Ch Bd:* Gregory B Maffei
Pr: Dermot M Halpin
CEO: Barrie Seidenberg
CFO: Ernst Teunissen
Sr VP: Seth J Kalvert

D-U-N-S 00-190-4387
■**TRIPADVISOR LLC** (MA)
(*Suby of* TRIPADVISOR INC) ★
400 1st Ave, Needham, MA 02494-2815
Tel (781) 800-5000 *Founded/Ownrshp* 2000
Sales 95.2MM^E *EMP* 211^E
SIC 7374 Computer graphics service
Genl Pt: Fred Pratt
Pr: Dermot Halpin
CFO: Julie MB Bradley
Sr VP: Andy Gelfond
Sr VP: Robin Ingle
VP: Julio Bruno
VP: Marc Caltabiano
VP: Desiree Fish
VP: Todd McClain
VP: Brian Schmidt
VP: Nicholas Shanny
Dir Bus: Maud Larpent
Dir Bus: Lisa Promise

D-U-N-S 00-983-1280
TRIPIFOODS INC (NY)
1427 William St, Buffalo, NY 14206-1807
Tel (716) 853-7400 *Founded/Ownrshp* 1917, 1911
Sales 197.4MM^E *EMP* 260
Accts Freed Maxick & Battaglia Cpa
SIC 5141 5194 5145 5143 5142 5122 Groceries, general line; Cigarettes; Candy; Dairy products, except dried or canned; Packaged frozen goods; Cosmetics, perfumes & hair products; Toiletries
**Sr VP:* Joseph C Tripi
**VP:* Thaddeus Cwudzinski
**VP:* Michael Duser
**VP:* Robert N Wolski
Dir IT: Nick Macchioni
IT Man: Dominick Macchioni
VP Sls: Joseph Tripi

D-U-N-S 17-382-3147 IMP/EXP
TRIPLE "B" CORP
CHARLIE'S PRODUCE
4103 2nd Ave S, Seattle, WA 98134-2305
Tel (206) 625-1412 *Founded/Ownrshp* 1986
Sales 511.2MM^E *EMP* 1,062
SIC 5148 Fruits, fresh
CEO: Charlie Billow
**Pr:* Ray Bowen
CFO: Craig Tin
Genl Mgr: Oliver Evans
Genl Mgr: Jeremy Smith
CIO: Jason Warden
MIS Mgr: David WEI
Opers Mgr: Christine Marr
Opers Mgr: Joe Troje
Sls Mgr: Jim McDonald
Sls Mgr: Roy Murdock
Board of Directors: Terry Bagley, Jane Van Dorn, Robert Viggers, Gary Young

D-U-N-S 01-615-5389
TRIPLE "R" TRAFFIC CONTROL & BARRICADE RENTAL "LLC
509 Scott Ave Ste 106, Woodland Park, CO 80863-3201
Tel (720) 641-8099 *Founded/Ownrshp* 1997
Sales 135.0MM *EMP* 50
SIC 7389 Flagging service (traffic control)

D-U-N-S 09-029-1030
■**TRIPLE - S SALUD INC**
(*Suby of* TRIPLE-S MANAGEMENT CORP) ★
1441 Ave Fd Roosevelt, San Juan, PR 00920-2717
Tel (787) 749-4949 *Founded/Ownrshp* 1959, 1999
Sales NA *EMP* 1,200
Accts Kpmg Llp San Juan Pr
SIC 6321 Health insurance carriers
Pr: Socorro Rivas
**Ch Bd:* Fernando Isern MD
**Treas:* Vicente Leon
Ofcr: Angel Tirado
VP: Sara Lopez
VP: Fernando Rivera
**VP:* Wilmer Rodriguez MD
VP: Cesar Rubert

D-U-N-S 08-929-5406 IMP
TRIPLE -T FOODS INC
1601 W Mckay St, Frontenac, KS 66763-8136
Tel (620) 231-7779 *Founded/Ownrshp* 1976
Sales 150.0MM *EMP* 200
SIC 2047 Dog & cat food
Pr: Kurt Terlip
**VP:* Chris Terlip
Genl Mgr: Joe Kadi

TRIPLE A
See CALIFORNIA STATE AUTOMOBILE ASSOCIATION INTER-INSURANCE BUREAU

D-U-N-S 87-264-2913
TRIPLE A SUPPLIES INC
PROCUREMENT SYSTEMS SERVICES
50 Jeanne Dr, Newburgh, NY 12550-1701
Tel (845) 566-4200 *Founded/Ownrshp* 1992
Sales 93.7MM^E *EMP* 100
SIC 5169 Specialty cleaning & sanitation preparations
Ch Bd: Susan St Pierre
**Pr:* Aaron Weiss
Genl Mgr: Sam Baum
Mktg Mgr: Oliver Spiecker
Sales Asso: Joel Fried

D-U-N-S 13-812-9692
TRIPLE CANOPY INC
(*Suby of* CONSTELLIS HOLDINGS LLC) ★
12018 Sunrise Valley Dr # 140, Reston, VA 20191-3444
Tel (703) 673-5000 *Founded/Ownrshp* 2014
Sales 86.9MM^E *EMP* 606^E
SIC 7381 8748 Security guard service; Safety training service
CEO: Ignacio Balderas
**Pr:* Gregory Mulligan
COO: Arthur Christy
**COO:* Nils Sorenson
CFO: Tom Magnani
CFO: Karen Sanchez
Sr Cor Off: Susan Lynch
Ofcr: David Cassidy
Ofcr: Kerry Miller
Ofcr: William Polk
Sr VP: Alan C Ptak
VP: Jarrett Dahl
VP: Alan Donohue
VP: Patrick A Garvey
VP: Jeff Johnson
VP: Juliet Simpson
VP: Bruce Smith
VP Bus Dev: Bev Daly
VP Bus Dev: Matthew Fay
VP Bus Dev: Gerald Goss
Exec: Ryan Dombrowski

TRIPLE INDUSTRIAL
See TRIPLE S INDUSTRIAL CORP

D-U-N-S 82-675-7478
TRIPLE POINT TECHNOLOGY INC
(*Suby of* ION INVESTMENT GROUP LIMITED)
57 Greens Farms Rd, Westport, CT 06880-6140
Tel (203) 291-7979 *Founded/Ownrshp* 1996
Sales 128.3MM^E *EMP* 890
SIC 7371 Computer software systems analysis & design, custom
Pr: Peter Armstrong
**CFO:* Oni Chuckwu
**Treas:* Paul D'Amico
VP: Wah C Chu
VP: Karan Renjen
VP: Ashwin Save
VP: Simon Woods
Dir Sec: Howie Adams
Prac Mgr: Mark James
Off Mgr: Karen Blackburn
Snr Sftwr: Craig Smith

D-U-N-S 60-712-4153
TRIPLE S INDUSTRIAL CORP
TRIPLE INDUSTRIAL
860 W Chance Rd, Lumberton, TX 77657-7112
Tel (409) 755-4077 *Founded/Ownrshp* 1989
Sales 101.4MM^E *EMP* 600
SIC 1799 1791 Exterior cleaning, including sandblasting; Structural steel erection
Pr: R L Simmons Jr
**Sec:* Patricia Simmons

D-U-N-S 01-254-5794
TRIPLE S TIRE CO INC
405 S 9th St, Elwood, IN 46036-2362
Tel (765) 552-5765 *Founded/Ownrshp* 1982
Sales 150.4MM *EMP* 39
SIC 5014 5531

D-U-N-S 61-913-0123
TRIPLE T TRANSPORT INC
704 Radio Dr, Lewis Center, OH 43035-7112
Tel (740) 657-3244 *Founded/Ownrshp* 2011
Sales 116.9MM *EMP* 61
SIC 4731 Transportation agents & brokers
Pr: Darin Puppel
**CFO:* Wade Amelung
**VP:* Terry McKenzie
**VP:* David Santisi

D-U-N-S 07-873-2862
TRIPLE-I HOLDINGS LLC
7400 Fullerton Rd Ste 210, Springfield, VA 22153-2830
Tel (703) 635-7088 *Founded/Ownrshp* 2012
Sales 149.3MM^E *EMP* 574^E
SIC 7379 6719 Computer related consulting services; Investment holding companies, except banks
CEO: Steven Ikirt

D-U-N-S 96-336-0545
■**TRIPLE-S ADVANTAGE INC**
AMERICAN HEALTH MEDICARE
(*Suby of* TRIPLE - S SALUD INC) ★
1 Calle 1 Fl 3, Guaynabo, PR 00968-1704
Tel (787) 620-1919 *Founded/Ownrshp* 2011
Sales NA *EMP* 71^E
SIC 6321 Health insurance carriers
Pr: Madeline Hernandez
**COO:* Marita Vasquez
**Chf Mktg O:* Ivonne Vega Perez
**VP:* Ken Wiens

D-U-N-S 07-454-3120
▲**TRIPLE-S MANAGEMENT CORP**
1441 Ave Fd Roosevelt, San Juan, PR 00920-2717
Tel (787) 749-4949 *Founded/Ownrshp* 1959
Sales NA *EMP* 3,257^E
Tkr Sym GTS *Exch* NYS
SIC 6324 6311 6321 Hospital & medical service plans; Life insurance; Benevolent insurance associations; Life insurance funds, savings bank; Accident & health insurance
Ch Bd: Luis A Clavell-Rodriguez
CFO: Juan J Roman-Jimenez
Chf Mktg O: Jose E Novoa-Loyola
VP: Carlos L Rodriguez-Ramos
CIO: Juan J Diaz-Gotia
Board of Directors: Jorge L Fuentes-Benejam, David H Chafey Jr, Miguel Figueroa-Collazo, Joseph A Frick, Roberto Santa Maria-Ros, Antonio F Faria-Soto

D-U-N-S 02-666-1413 IMP/EXP
TRIPLE-S STEEL HOLDINGS INC
6000 Jensen Dr, Houston, TX 77026-1113
Tel (713) 697-7105 *Founded/Ownrshp* 1978
Sales 800.0MM *EMP* 1,100
SIC 5051 6719 Steel; Investment holding companies, except banks
CEO: Gary Wayne Stein
CFO: Walter Fowlkes
Sec: Shirley Stein
Exec: Torre Lodolce
Telecom Ex: Matt Wray
Opers Mgr: Ryan Crochet
Opers Mgr: Tim Roach

D-U-N-S 00-864-4820 IMP/EXP
TRIPLE-S STEEL SUPPLY LLC
(*Suby of* TRIPLE-S STEEL HOLDINGS INC) ★
6000 Jensen Dr, Houston, TX 77026-1113
Tel (713) 354-4100 *Founded/Ownrshp* 1985
Sales 186.7MM^E *EMP* 379
SIC 5051 Steel decking
CEO: Gary Stein
VP Sls: Paul Pierantozzi

TRIPP LITE
See TRIPPE MANUFACTURING CO

D-U-N-S 00-509-4099 IMP/EXP
TRIPPE MANUFACTURING CO
TRIPP LITE
1111 W 35th St Fl 12, Chicago, IL 60609-1404
Tel (773) 869-1111 *Founded/Ownrshp* 1930
Sales 168.7MM^E *EMP* 500
Accts Deloitte & Touche Llp Chicago
SIC 3577 Computer peripheral equipment
CEO: Elbert Howell
**Pr:* Glen Haeflinger
**CFO:* Charles Lang
Sr Cor Off: Daniel Sanchez
Rgnl Mgr: Jeff Novak
Snr Sftwr: Stuart Marks
QA Dir: Daniel Howard
QA Dir: Aldo Kestler
Dir IT: Keith Anderson
Tech Mgr: Venkatapathi Boyalla
Sftwr Eng: Joyce Norris

TRIPPS
See BATTLEGROUND RESTAURANT GROUP INC

D-U-N-S 05-913-6577
■**TRIPWIRE INC**
(*Suby of* BELDEN INC) ★
101 Sw Main St Ste 1500, Portland, OR 97204-3243
Tel (503) 276-7500 *Founded/Ownrshp* 2015
Sales 98.3MM^E *EMP* 350
SIC 7371 Custom computer programming services
Pr: James B Johnson
**CFO:* Kelly Lang
VP: Dave Dickison
VP: Neil Harvey
VP: Mitchell Jukanovich
VP: John Kelly
VP: Rod Murchison
VP: Jack Sebbag
Snr Sftwr: Josh Hegg
**CTO:* Dwayne Melancon
IT Man: Mark Ramsey

D-U-N-S 78-907-2431
■**TRIQUINT SALES & DESIGN INC**
(*Suby of* QORVO US INC) ★
2300 Ne Brookwood Pkwy, Hillsboro, OR 97124-5300
Tel (503) 615-9000 *Founded/Ownrshp* 2009
Sales 64.6MM^E *EMP* 1,484
SIC 3825 Semiconductor test equipment
Pr: Ralph Quinsey

D-U-N-S 94-747-2119
TRIS PHARMA INC
2033 Rte 130 Ste D, Monmouth Junction, NJ 08852
Tel (732) 940-2800 *Founded/Ownrshp* 2000
Sales 84.6MM^E *EMP* 350
SIC 8731 Commercial physical research
VP: Norma Cappetti
Pr: Gerry Cocuzza
Pr: Janet Penner
COO: Patricia Donohue
**Ofcr:* Sharon Clarke
VP: Peter Ciano
**VP:* Dominick Dipaolo
**VP:* Cheryl Patnick
VP: Cheryl Patrick
VP: Gwen Washington
**VP:* Amanda Wohlleber
Dir Lab: Zhisong Liu
Assoc Dir: Archana Sharma

D-U-N-S 93-110-8468 IMP
TRISH MCEVOY LTD
430 Commerce Blvd, Carlstadt, NJ 07072-3013
Tel (201) 559-9234 *Founded/Ownrshp* 1981
Sales 98.5MM^E *EMP* 100
SIC 5122 Cosmetics; Perfumes
Ch Bd: Trish Mc Evoy
Mktg Mgr: Jaclyn Shor

THE TRISTAFF GROUP
See GARICH INC

TRISTAR HEALTH SYSTEMS
See HCA HEALTH SERVICES OF TEXAS INC

D-U-N-S 11-716-1229
TRISTAR INSURANCE GROUP INC
TRISTART RISK MANAGEMENT
100 Oceangate Ste 700, Long Beach, CA 90802-4368
Tel (562) 495-6600 *Founded/Ownrshp* 1982
Sales NA *EMP* 1,650
SIC 6331 8741 Workers' compensation insurance; Management services
Pr: Thomas J Veale
**CFO:* Denise J Cotter
**Sr VP:* Joseph McLaughlin
VP: Pamela Guiles
VP: Mary Ann Lubeskie
VP: Richard D Thibault
Brnch Mgr: Christian Tuell
CIO: Craig Evans
Dir IT: Dan Hamersley

TRISTAR SOUTHERN HILLS MED CTR
See HCA HEALTH SERVICES OF TENNESSEE INC

TRISTART RISK MANAGEMENT
See TRISTAR INSURANCE GROUP INC

D-U-N-S 79-099-9531
■TRISTATE CAPITAL BANK
(*Suby of* TRISTATE CAPITAL HOLDINGS INC) ★
301 Grant St Ste 2700, Pittsburgh, PA 15219-6414
Tel (412) 304-0304 *Founded/Ownrshp* 2006
Sales NA *EMP* 30
SIC 6029 Commercial banks
Ch Bd: James F Getz
**Pr:* Brian Fetterolf
**Pr:* William Schenk
**CFO:* Mark L Sullivan
Sr VP: Jan Bone
Sr VP: Robert Gambitsky
Sr VP: Thomas Joseph
Sr VP: Trent Meteer
Sr VP: Colleen Pietrusinski
Sr VP: Debbie Rodgers
Sr VP: Albert C Snyder
VP: Debra Flinner
VP: Mary Roos

D-U-N-S 82-602-1961
▲TRISTATE CAPITAL HOLDINGS INC
301 Grant St Ste 2700, Pittsburgh, PA 15219-6414
Tel (412) 304-0304 *Founded/Ownrshp* 2007
Sales NA *EMP* 192
Tkr Sym TSC *Exch* NGS
SIC 6022 State commercial banks; State trust companies accepting deposits, commercial
Ch Bd: James F Getz
**CFO:* Mark L Sullivan
**V Ch Bd:* A William Schenck III
VP: Michael Blasko
VP: John Buglione
VP: David Hurtuk
Board of Directors: David L Bonvenuto, Anthony J Buzzelli, Helen Hanna Casey, E H Dewhurst, James J Dolan, James E Minnick, Richard B Seidel, John B Yasinsky, Richard A Zappala

D-U-N-S 80-957-1029
TRISTRATA INC
NEOSTRATA
307 College Rd E, Princeton, NJ 08540-6608
Tel (609) 520-0715 *Founded/Ownrshp* 1993
Sales 128.1MM[E] *EMP* 85
SIC 5122 Cosmetics
Pr: Dr Eugene J Van Scott
**VP:* Dr Ruey J Yu
**Prin:* Richard Wildnauer

D-U-N-S 14-267-2737
TRISUN HEALTHCARE LLC
1703 W 5th St, Austin, TX 78703-4893
Tel (512) 634-4900 *Founded/Ownrshp* 2002
Sales 36.9MM[E] *EMP* 1,114[E]
SIC 8051 Skilled nursing care facilities
**Pr:* Steve Wood
**CEO:* Lew Little Jr
**COO:* James Hardee
VP: Debbie Weems
HC Dir: Lorena Hampton

D-U-N-S 01-588-0115
TRITEC BUILDING CO INC
45 Research Way Ste 100, East Setauket, NY 11733-6401
Tel (631) 751-0300 *Founded/Ownrshp* 1986
Sales 100.0MM *EMP* 48
SIC 6552 8742 Subdividers & developers; Construction project management consultant
Ch Bd: James L Coughlan
**COO:* Robert Loscalzo
**VP:* Kenneth Abrami
**VP:* Robert E Kent
**Prin:* Daniel P Coughlan
**Prin:* Martin A Depasquale
VP Opers: Ken Abrami

D-U-N-S 14-739-2013
TRITECH SOFTWARE SYSTEMS
9477 Waples St Ste 100, San Diego, CA 92121-2934
Tel (858) 799-7000 *Founded/Ownrshp* 2014
Sales 138.5MM[E] *EMP* 532
SIC 7371

D-U-N-S 79-903-6665
TRITON MEDIA GROUP LLC
15303 Ventura Blvd # 1500, Sherman Oaks, CA 91403-3137
Tel (323) 290-6900 *Founded/Ownrshp* 2006
Sales 380.6MM[E] *EMP* 1,500
SIC 4832 Radio broadcasting stations, music format
CEO: Nathaniel Parker Hudnut
**Ch Bd:* Sean Moriarty
Pr: Patrick Reynolds
Ex VP: Dominick Milano
VP: Francis Champoux

TRITON WATER
See ALAMANCE FOODS INC

D-U-N-S 13-472-3217
■TRIUMPH ACTUATION SYSTEMS - VALENCIA INC
(*Suby of* TRIUMPH GROUP INC) ★
28150 Harrison Pkwy, Valencia, CA 91355-4109
Tel (661) 295-1015 *Founded/Ownrshp* 2001
Sales 93.9MM[E] *EMP* 250
SIC 3823 Industrial instrmnts msrmnt display/control process variable
Pr: Lea Black
**Pr:* Bill Boyd
**VP:* Charles Haen
Mtls Mgr: Dave Hatfield
Mfg Mgr: Pat Barry

D-U-N-S 78-994-7608
■TRIUMPH AEROSPACE SYSTEMS GROUP INC
(*Suby of* TRIUMPH GROUP INC) ★
899 Cassatt Rd Ste 210, Berwyn, PA 19312-1190
Tel (610) 251-1000 *Founded/Ownrshp* 2004
Sales 211.9MM[E] *EMP* 982[E]
SIC 3728 Aircraft assemblies, subassemblies & parts
Prin: Richard C III

D-U-N-S 07-966-1027
■TRIUMPH AEROSTRUCTURES - TULSA LLC
(*Suby of* TRIUMPH GROUP INC) ★
3330 N Mingo Rd, Tulsa, OK 74116-1211
Tel (615) 361-2061 *Founded/Ownrshp* 2014
Sales 88.2MM[E] *EMP* 800
SIC 3728 3999 Aircraft parts & equipment; Aircraft body & wing assemblies & parts; Atomizers, toiletry
Pr: Steve Blackwell

D-U-N-S 80-740-8054 IMP
■TRIUMPH AEROSTRUCTURES LLC
(*Suby of* TRIUMPH GROUP INC) ★
300 Austin Blvd, Red Oak, TX 75154-4608
Tel (972) 515-8276 *Founded/Ownrshp* 2010
Sales 1.6MMM[E] *EMP* 5,990
SIC 3721 3728 3812 3769 Aircraft; Aircraft parts & equipment; Search & navigation equipment; Guided missile & space vehicle parts & auxiliary equipment
Ch: Richard C III
**Pr:* Jeffry D Frisby
**CFO:* Keith B Howe
**CFO:* M David Kornblatt
**VP:* Stephen A Davis
**VP:* Kevin P McGlinchey
**VP:* John B Wright II
Genl Mgr: Clay Crawford
Genl Mgr: Scott Dibler
Genl Mgr: Robert Harvey
Genl Mgr: Scott Mispagel

D-U-N-S 15-556-9312 IMP
TRIUMPH APPAREL CORP
530 Fashion Ave Ste M1, New York, NY 10018-4878
Tel (212) 302-2606 *Founded/Ownrshp* 1982
Sales 87.7MM[E] *EMP* 475
SIC 2331 Women's & misses' blouses & shirts
Pr: Carol Hockman
**CFO:* John A Sarto
VP: Philip Davis
**Prin:* Donald Schupak

D-U-N-S 05-370-3239
▲TRIUMPH BANCORP INC
12700 Park Central Dr # 1700, Dallas, TX 75251-1500
Tel (214) 365-6930 *Founded/Ownrshp* 2010
Sales NA *EMP* 501[E]
Tkr Sym TBK *Exch* NGS
SIC 6022 State commercial banks
Pr: Aaron P Graft
**Ch Bd:* Carlos M Sepulveda Jr
CFO: R Bryce Fowler
Ex VP: Raymond W Sperring III
Sr VP: Adam D Nelson
VP: Gail Lehmann

D-U-N-S 12-642-9021
■TRIUMPH COMPOSITE SYSTEMS INC
(*Suby of* TRIUMPH GROUP INC) ★
1514 S Flint Rd, Spokane, WA 99224-9447
Tel (509) 623-8536 *Founded/Ownrshp* 2003
Sales 125.9MM[E] *EMP* 463
SIC 3724 3728 Aircraft engines & engine parts; Aircraft landing assemblies & brakes
Pr: Patrick Jones
**CFO:* John Bartholdson
**Prin:* Chuck Ruchert
**Prin:* Kathleen Sharp
Prgrm Mgr: Gary Baird
Genl Mgr: Richard Augsburger
Genl Mgr: Bea Marr
QC Dir: Ron Brown
Sfty Mgr: Brenda Ellerbrook

D-U-N-S 07-879-2471
■TRIUMPH ENGINE CONTROL SYSTEMS LLC
GOODRICH
(*Suby of* TRIUMPH GROUP INC) ★
1 Charter Oak Blvd, West Hartford, CT 06110-1328
Tel (860) 236-0651 *Founded/Ownrshp* 2013
Sales 178.7MM[E] *EMP* 560
SIC 3728 3724 3812 Aircraft body & wing assemblies & parts; Aircraft engines & engine parts; Aircraft control instruments
VP: Alec Searle
Dir IT: Art Jaffe
IT Man: Amy Mitchell
Snr Mgr: Joseph Borrelli

D-U-N-S 13-838-4891 IMP
TRIUMPH FOODS LLC
5302 Stockyards Expy, Saint Joseph, MO 64504-3616
Tel (816) 396-2700 *Founded/Ownrshp* 2003
Sales 228.8MM[E] *EMP* 2,800
SIC 2011 Pork products from pork slaughtered on site

D-U-N-S 82-819-4758 IMP/EXP
■TRIUMPH GEAR SYSTEMS INC
TRIUMPH GEAR SYSTEMS- PARK CY
(*Suby of* TRIUMPH GROUP INC) ★
6125 Silver Creek Dr, Park City, UT 84098-6242
Tel (435) 649-1900 *Founded/Ownrshp* 2004
Sales 86.0MM[E] *EMP* 243
SIC 3593 3728 3812 Fluid power actuators, hydraulic or pneumatic; Gears, aircraft power transmission; Search & navigation equipment
Pr: Dan Hennen
**CFO:* Teressa Zimmermann
Genl Mgr: Cathy Anderton
Genl Mgr: Pat Coward
Sfty Mgr: Kendall Thaxton
Counsel: John Wright
Pgrm Dir: Ron Bray

TRIUMPH GEAR SYSTEMS- PARK CY
See TRIUMPH GEAR SYSTEMS INC

TRIUMPH GROUP
See TRIUMPH INSULATION SYSTEMS LLC

D-U-N-S 80-763-6451 IMP/EXP
▲TRIUMPH GROUP INC
899 Cassatt Rd Ste 210, Berwyn, PA 19312-1190
Tel (610) 251-1000 *Founded/Ownrshp* 1993
Sales 3.8MMM *EMP* 14,602
Accts Ernst & Young Llp Philadelphi
Tkr Sym TGI *Exch* NYS
SIC 3728 3724 3812 Aircraft body & wing assemblies & parts; Aircraft engines & engine parts; Aircraft control instruments
Pr: Daniel J Crowley
Ch Bd: Ralph E Eberhart
CFO: James F McCabe Jr
CFO: Jeffrey L McRae
Ex VP: Michael Abram
Ex VP: Thomas Holtzhum
Ex VP: Thomas Holzthum
Ex VP: Rick Rozenjack
Ex VP: Marylou Thomas
Sr VP: Richard Lovely
Sr VP: John B Wright II
VP: Thomas A Quigley III
VP: Doug Riley
Board of Directors: Paul Bourgon, John G Drosdick, Richard C Gozon, Dawne S Hickton, Richard C III, William L Mansfield, Adam J Palmer, Joseph M Silvestri, George Simpson

D-U-N-S 78-647-8714
■TRIUMPH HEALTHCARE HOLDINGS INC
(*Suby of* REHABCARE HOSPITAL HOLDINGS LLC) ★
7333 North Fwy Ste 500, Houston, TX 77076-1322
Tel (713) 699-8879 *Founded/Ownrshp* 2009
Sales NA *EMP* 3,700
SIC 6324 Hospital & medical service plans
VP: William Hardaway
**Sr VP:* Lawrence A Humphrey
**VP:* Lance Carlson
**VP:* Robert N Helms
**VP:* Kevin Williams
Dir Risk M: Linda Bowman

D-U-N-S 14-139-9027
■TRIUMPH HOSPITAL BAYTOWN
PHARMACY DEPARTMENT
(*Suby of* TRIUMPH HEALTHCARE HOLDINGS INC) ★
1700 James Bowie Dr, Baytown, TX 77520-3302
Tel (281) 420-7800 *Founded/Ownrshp* 2003
Sales 28.0MM[E] *EMP* 1,000
SIC 8062 General medical & surgical hospitals
Prin: Reba Dade
Dir Recs: Marsha Cherubin

D-U-N-S 83-016-5077 IMP
■TRIUMPH INSULATION SYSTEMS LLC
TRIUMPH GROUP
(*Suby of* TRIUMPH AEROSPACE SYSTEMS GROUP INC) ★
2925 S Roosevelt St 2, Tempe, AZ 85282-2012
Tel (949) 250-4999 *Founded/Ownrshp* 2009
Sales 185.3MM[E] *EMP* 900
SIC 3728 Aircraft parts & equipment
VP: Scott Holland
**CFO:* Jeffry L McRae
**VP:* R Jamed Cudd
**VP:* Robin Derogatis
**VP:* John B Wright II
Genl Mgr: Rick Molus
IT Man: Terry Mealy
IT Man: Jean White
VP Sls: Jeff Tomei

D-U-N-S 08-017-5346
TRIUMPH STRUCTURES - EAST TEXAS
899 Cassatt Rd Ste 210, Berwyn, PA 19312-1190
Tel (610) 251-1000 *Founded/Ownrshp* 2016
Sales 23.0MM[E] *EMP* 1,001
SIC 3324 Aerospace investment castings, ferrous

D-U-N-S 00-838-2806 IMP/EXP
■TRIUMPH STRUCTURES-LOS ANGELES INC
(*Suby of* TRIUMPH GROUP INC) ★
17055 Gale Ave, City of Industry, CA 91745-1808
Tel (626) 965-1642 *Founded/Ownrshp* 1937
Sales 92.6MM[E] *EMP* 364
SIC 3599 Machine & other job shop work
Pr: Lanny Shirk
CEO: Jeffrey D Frisby
Genl Mgr: Pete Perry
Genl Mgr: Greg Valenzuela
IT Man: Randy Balagtas
IT Man: Brad Rees

D-U-N-S 19-634-9492
TRIUMVIRATE ENVIRONMENTAL INC
200 Innerbelt Rd 4, Somerville, MA 02143-4402
Tel (617) 623-0109 *Founded/Ownrshp* 1988
Sales 116.8MM[E] *EMP* 368
SIC 4212 Hazardous waste transport
Pr: John McQuillan
**COO:* Doug Youngen
**CFO:* William Lyons
Ofcr: Ron Souza
**VP:* Thomas Aicardi
**VP:* Timothy Mooney
Exec: Peg Marcus
Mng Dir: Kevin Brayton
Prgrm Mgr: Benjamin Mallard
Prgrm Mgr: Travis Nierendorf
Genl Mgr: Tom Goss

D-U-N-S 07-998-7763
TRIVERGENT HEALTH ALLIANCE MSO LLC (MD)
1800 Dual Hwy Ste 304, Hagerstown, MD 21740-6651
Tel (301) 790-9130 *Founded/Ownrshp* 2014
Sales 76.7MM[E] *EMP* 1,250
SIC 8742 Hospital & health services consultant
CEO: Raymond Grahe

D-U-N-S 80-043-5880
TRIVEST FUND III LP
550 S Dixie Hwy Ste 300, Coral Gables, FL 33146-2701
Tel (305) 858-2200 *Founded/Ownrshp* 2000
Sales 133.7MM[E] *EMP* 42
SIC 6799 5712 Commodity investors; Office furniture
Mng Pt: Troy Templeton
Pt: Jamie E Elias

D-U-N-S 15-181-0868 IMP/EXP
TRIVIDIA HEALTH INC
NIPRO DIAGNOSTICS
(*Suby of* SINOCARE INC.)
2400 Nw 55th Ct, Fort Lauderdale, FL 33309-2672
Tel (800) 342-7226 *Founded/Ownrshp* 2016
Sales 200.0MM *EMP* 550[E]
SIC 5113 Industrial & personal service paper
Pr: Scott Verner
**CFO:* Dean Sorrentino
Sr VP: Gregg Johnson
VP: Daniel Falter
Dir: Jonathan Ovitt
Mng Dir: Christopher Avery
CIO: Mark Rousseau
Software D: Bill Daniels
VP Sls: Michael Patterson
Mktg Mgr: Stacey Del Santo
Manager: Lisa Gagliardi

D-U-N-S 94-558-0587
TRIWEST HEALTHCARE ALLIANCE CORP
15810 N 28th Ave, Phoenix, AZ 85053-4021
Tel (602) 564-2000 *Founded/Ownrshp* 1995
Sales 98.4MM[E] *EMP* 1,700
SIC 8741 8062 Hospital management; General medical & surgical hospitals
Pr: David J McIntyre Jr
CFO: Elizabeth Dodd
Sr VP: Bob Kaplan
VP: David Brooks
VP: Don Brown
VP: Alice Demarais
VP: Kathy Fliehler
**VP:* Larry Haggerty
**VP:* Willie Inazu
VP: Andrumada King
VP: Harold McCracken
VP: Scott Montplaisir
VP: Rick Nash

TRIZAC PROPERTIES
See TRZ HOLDINGS II INC

D-U-N-S 61-188-5567
■TRIZETTO CORP
(*Suby of* COGNIZANT TECHNOLOGY SOLUTIONS CORP) ★
9655 Maroon Cir, Englewood, CO 80112-5914
Tel (303) 495-7000 *Founded/Ownrshp* 2014
Sales 609.5MM[E] *EMP* 2,000
SIC 7373 8742 Computer integrated systems design; Hospital & health services consultant
CEO: Jude Dieterman
Pr: Jeb Evans
Pr: Max Marquez
Pr: Lynne Minto
Pr: Scott Moeller
**Pr:* Rob Scavo
Pr: Mark Turner
Pr: Robert Yengle
**CFO:* Douglas E Barnett
Treas: Michael Sunderland
Assoc VP: Christopher Heller
Assoc VP: Jason Strong
**Ex VP:* Pierre Samec
**Ex VP:* Dan Spirek
Sr VP: Sherwood Chapman
Sr VP: John G Jordan
Sr VP: Diane Marra
Sr VP: Thomas Rekart
Sr VP: Jim Wade
VP: Tricia Bailey
VP: Bill Bakken

D-U-N-S 80-815-3105
TRL INC
TRUCK CENTERS OF ARKANSAS
11700 Valentine Rd, North Little Rock, AR 72117-9312
Tel (501) 955-3200 *Founded/Ownrshp* 2007
Sales 96.4MM[E] *EMP* 180
SIC 5012 Automobiles & other motor vehicles
Pr: Todd Havens
**COO:* Rick Vassar
Opers Mgr: Robbie Robinson
VP Sls: Scott Manchester

TRMCC
See TOBACCO ROOT MOUNTAINS CARE CENTER

D-U-N-S 04-963-6116 IMP
TRMI INC
TOKAI RIKA GROUP
(*Suby of* TRAM INC) ★
100 Hill Brady Rd, Battle Creek, MI 49037-7301
Tel (269) 966-0800 *Founded/Ownrshp* 1997
Sales 161.0MM[E] *EMP* 550
SIC 3714 3643 Motor vehicle electrical equipment; Electric switches
Pr: Ken Noguchi
IT Man: Vernon Grandberry

D-U-N-S 07-986-8304
TRNLWB LLC
TRINITY ESC
1112 E Cpeland Rd Ste 500, Arlington, TX 76011
Tel (800) 581-3117 *Founded/Ownrshp* 2013
Sales 12.4MM[E] *EMP* 10,000
SIC 3271 Concrete block & brick
Pr: Carl Campbell
**VP:* Steven Rowe

TROCO OIL COMPANY
See ROYAL MFG CO LP

D-U-N-S 00-827-4375 IMP/EXP
TROJAN BATTERY CO LLC
12380 Clark St, Santa Fe Springs, CA 90670-3804
Tel (800) 423-6569 *Founded/Ownrshp* 1925
Sales 215.8MM[E] *EMP* 600
SIC 3691 3692 Lead acid batteries (storage batteries); Primary batteries, dry & wet
Pr: Jeff Elder
**COO:* John Beering
**CFO:* Edward Dunlap

*Ex VP: Dave Godber
*Sr VP: Mike Everett
*Sr VP: Bryan Godber
*Sr VP: Elke Hisdchman
*Sr VP: Mat Segal
*Sr VP: Bill Shaffer
VP: Robert Gibson
VP: Yvonne Schroeder

D-U-N-S 07-948-7647
▲TRONC INC
435 N Michigan Ave, Chicago, IL 60611-4066
Tel (312) 222-9100 Founded/Ownrshp 2013
Sales 1.6MMM EMP 7,165^E
Tkr Sym TRNC Exch NGM
SIC 2711 Newspapers; Newspapers, publishing & printing
CEO: Justin C Dearborn
*Ch Bd: Michael W Ferro Jr
Pr: Tony W Hunter
Pr: Timothy E Ryan
CFO: Terry Jimenez
Ex VP: Julie K Xanders
Board of Directors: Carol Crenshaw, David Dreier, Philip G Franklin, Eddy W Hartenstein, Richard A Recka, Donald Tang

D-U-N-S 07-978-3799
TRONOX ALKALI CORP
(Suby of TRONOX US HOLDINGS INC) ★
1735 Market St, Philadelphia, PA 19103-7501
Tel (215) 299-6904 Founded/Ownrshp 2014
Sales 252.8MM^E EMP 1,000
SIC 2812 Sodium bicarbonate; Caustic soda, sodium hydroxide; Soda ash, sodium carbonate (anhydrous)
CEO: Tom Casey
*Pr: Edward T Flynn
*CFO: Terry J Harding
*Treas: John Merturi
*VP: Frederick A V On Ahrens
*VP: Aaron Reichl
*VP Mktg: Sanjay Gandhi
*VP Mktg: Jeffrey Rasmussen
Board of Directors: Katherine Harper, Richard Muglia

D-U-N-S 11-340-4719 IMP/EXP
TRONOX ALKALI WYOMING CORP
(Suby of TRONOX ALKALI CORP) ★
580 Westvaco Rd, Green River, WY 82935
Tel (307) 875-2580 Founded/Ownrshp 2015
Sales 246.3MM^E EMP 1,000
SIC 2812 Soda ash, sodium carbonate (anhydrous)
Pr: Edward T Flynn
*CFO: Terry J Harding
Treas: Thomas C Deas
*VP: Frederick A V On Ahrens
*VP: Aaron Reichl
IT Man: Dee Murphy
*VP Mktg: Sanjay Gandhi
*VP Mktg: Jeffrey Rasmussen
Snr PM: Daniel Moulden
Board of Directors: Katherine Harper, Richard Muglia

D-U-N-S 00-828-6114 IMP/EXP
TRONOX INC
(Suby of TRONOX US HOLDINGS INC) ★
1 Stamford Plz, Stamford, CT 06901-3271
Tel (203) 705-3800 Founded/Ownrshp 2005
Sales 429.3MM^E EMP 925
SIC 2819 2421 Industrial inorganic chemicals; Sodium compounds or salts, inorg., ex. refined sod. chloride; Manganese dioxide powder, synthetic; Ammonium chloride, hydroxide & molybdate; Railroad ties, sawed
Ch Bd: Thomas Casey
*CFO: Daniel Greenwell
*Ex VP: John D Romano
VP: Robert Y Brown
*VP: Michael J Foster
VP: Debbie Schramm
Board of Directors: Robert M Gervis, Andrew P Hines, Wayne A Hinman, Ilan Kaufthal, Jeffry N Quinn

D-U-N-S 14-443-1913 IMP
TRONOX LLC
TRONOX OKLAHOMA
(Suby of TRONOX US HOLDINGS INC) ★
1 Kerr Mcgee Rd, Savannah, GA 31404-1068
Tel (912) 652-1000 Founded/Ownrshp 2000
Sales 131.0MM^E EMP 718
SIC 2816 2819 5198 Titanium dioxide, anatase or rutile (pigments); Sulfuric acid, oleum; Colors & pigments
CFO: Robert Wohleber
Treas: Mike Rauh
Sr VP: W Peter Woodward
VP: Greg Pilcher

D-U-N-S 61-894-6409 IMP/EXP
TRONOX LLC
(Suby of TRONOX WORLDWIDE LLC) ★
3301 Nw 150th St, Oklahoma City, OK 73134-2009
Tel (405) 775-5000 Founded/Ownrshp 1997
Sales 228.8MM^E EMP 2,000
SIC 2819 2816 Inorganic acids, except nitric & phosphoric; Titanium dioxide, anatase or rutile (pigments)
CEO: Tom Casey
*Pr: Trevor Arran
VP: Debbie Schramm

TRONOX OKLAHOMA
See TRONOX LLC

D-U-N-S 14-700-5453 IMP/EXP
TRONOX US HOLDINGS INC
(Suby of TRONOX LIMITED)
3301 Nw 150th St, Oklahoma City, OK 73134-2009
Tel (405) 775-5000 Founded/Ownrshp 2012
Sales 813.1MM^E EMP 3,600^E
SIC 2816 2819 5198 Titanium dioxide, anatase or rutile (pigments); Sulfuric acid, oleum; Colors & pigments
CEO: Tom Casey
*CFO: Katherine C Harper
*CFO: Robert Wohleber
*Treas: Mike Rauh
*Sr VP: Trevor Arran
*Sr VP: Michael J Foster
*Sr VP: Greg Pilcher
*Sr VP: John D Romano
*Sr VP: W Peter Woodward

D-U-N-S 13-524-8586 EXP
TRONOX WORLDWIDE LLC
(Suby of TRONOX INC) ★
3301 Nw 150th St, Oklahoma City, OK 73134-2009
Tel (405) 775-5000 Founded/Ownrshp 2002
Sales 228.8MM^E EMP 2,015^E
SIC 2819 2816 Inorganic acids, except nitric & phosphoric; White pigments; Titanium dioxide, anatase or rutile (pigments)

D-U-N-S 96-558-1515
TROON GOLF LLC
15044 N Scottsdale Rd # 300, Scottsdale, AZ 85254-8131
Tel (480) 606-1000 Founded/Ownrshp 1996
Sales 262.9MM^E EMP 1,500
SIC 8741 6552 Management services; Subdividers & developers
CEO: Dana Garmany
*Ex VP: John Easterbrook
Ex VP: John W Easterbrook
*Ex VP: Ruth Engle
*Ex VP: Jay McGrath
*Ex VP: Tim Schantz
Ex VP: Timothy Schantz
Sr VP: Mike Ryan
*Sr VP: Ryan Walls
VP: Cindy Daughhette
VP: Charlene Gallob
VP: Jeff Hansen
VP: Jim McLaughlin
VP: Chris Terjesen
VP: Scott Van Newkirk
VP: Cary Westmark
Exec: John Farley
Exec: John Greene
Exec: Danny Woodbridge

TROOP K
See STATE POLICE NEW YORK

TROPIC FLEET SERVICES
See TROPIC OIL CO

D-U-N-S 03-257-0111 IMP/EXP
TROPIC OIL CO
TROPIC FLEET SERVICES
9970 Nw 89th Ct, Medley, FL 33178-1478
Tel (305) 888-4611 Founded/Ownrshp 1952
Sales 147.1MM^E EMP 62
Accts Gravier Llp Coral Gables Fl
SIC 5172 Fuel oil; Lubricating oils & greases
CEO: George E Levasser
*Pr: Stephen J Gorey
*CFO: Marlin Evenson
CFO: Evenson Marlin
VP: David Gurney
*VP: Joseph P Rodriguez
Sls Mgr: Roger Mackintosh

D-U-N-S 06-361-5660 EXP
TROPIC SUPPLY INC
JOHNSON CONTRLS AUTHORIZED DLR
151 Ne 179th St, Miami, FL 33162-1087
Tel (305) 652-7717 Founded/Ownrshp 1973
Sales 109.4MM^E EMP 200
SIC 5078 5075 Refrigeration equipment & supplies; Air conditioning & ventilation equipment & supplies
CEO: Charles F Del Vecchio Sr
*Pr: Charles F Del Vecchio Jr
*Prin: Chuck Del Vecchio
Sls Mgr: Todd Nolte

D-U-N-S 06-786-8646 IMP
TROPICAL CHEESE INDUSTRIES INC
452 Fayette St, Perth Amboy, NJ 08861-3805
Tel (732) 442-4898 Founded/Ownrshp 1983
Sales 104.8MM^E EMP 320
SIC 2022 5143 Cheese, natural & processed; Cheese
Pr: Rafael Mendez
*CFO: Michelle Stornell
VP: Alex Lopez
Genl Mgr: Sonal Patel
IT Man: Peadro Mandez
IT Man: Pedro Mendez
Sfty Mgr: Leo Rojas
Plnt Mgr: John Santana
Prd Mgr: Roberto Encarnacion
Manager: Nelson Ardila
Sls Mgr: Henry Panitz

D-U-N-S 08-507-6115 IMP/EXP
TROPICAL NUT & FRUIT CO
1100 Continental Blvd, Charlotte, NC 28273-6380
Tel (704) 588-0400 Founded/Ownrshp 1977
Sales 101.6MM^E EMP 160
SIC 5149 5145 2099 2068 Specialty food items; Nuts, salted or roasted; Food preparations; Salted & roasted nuts & seeds
Pr: John R Bauer
*Ch Bd: Carolyn Y Bennett
Pr: Todd Amato
*Pr: John Bauer
Treas: Jerry York
*Sec: Betty Lee York
*VP: Angela Bauer
*VP: Michael R P York
Dir IT: Gil Dango
IT Man: Kathy Groover
Sales Exec: Rich Edenfield

D-U-N-S 00-581-7721
TROPICAL SHIPPING USA LLC (FL)
(Suby of SALTCHUK RESOURCES INC) ★
501 Avenue P, Riviera Beach, FL 33404-7240
Tel (561) 863-5737 Founded/Ownrshp 1954, 2014
Sales 287.8MM^E EMP 1,100
SIC 4412 4789 Deep sea foreign transportation of freight; Cargo loading & unloading services
Pr: Rick Murrell
Genl Mgr: Davika Puran
IT Man: Jennifer Wade
Sales Exec: Kim Martin
Sls&Mrk Ex: Matty Appice

D-U-N-S 96-479-1763
■TROPICANA ATLANTIC CITY CORP
TROPICANA CASINO & RESORT
(Suby of TROPICANA ENTERTAINMENT INC) ★
2831 Boardwalk, Atlantic City, NJ 08401-6390
Tel (609) 340-4000 Founded/Ownrshp 2015
Sales 85.9MM^E EMP 2,800
SIC 7011 Hotels & motels
Prin: Tony Rodio Radio
*Pr: Mark Giannantonio
*VP: Christina Broome
Ex Dir: Meg Lewis
Snr Mgr: Bill Poulton

TROPICANA CASINO & RESORT
See TROPICANA ATLANTIC CITY CORP

TROPICANA CASINO AND RESORT
See TROPICANA ENTERTAINMENT INC

D-U-N-S 79-039-4212
TROPICANA ENTERTAINMENT HOLDINGS LLC
3930 Howard Hughes Pkwy, Las Vegas, NV 89169-0943
Tel (702) 589-3900 Founded/Ownrshp 2006
Sales 159.6MM^E EMP 9,802
SIC 7011 Casino hotel

D-U-N-S 03-275-8526
TROPICANA ENTERTAINMENT INC (NJ)
TROPICANA CASINO AND RESORT
(Suby of RAMADA NEW JERSEY HOLDINGS CORP) ★
2831 Brighton Ave, Atlantic City, NJ 08401
Tel (609) 340-4000 Founded/Ownrshp 1978, 1989
Sales 222.3MM^E EMP 4,000
SIC 7011 Casino hotel
CEO: Dennis Gomes
*Pr: Pam Popielarski
VP: Stephen E Heise
Dir Sec: Ron Pisko
MIS Dir: Don Kneifel
Tech Mgr: Chip Alton
Sales Exec: Maureen Kern

D-U-N-S 83-320-0251
■TROPICANA ENTERTAINMENT INC
(Suby of ICAHN ENTERPRISES HOLDINGS LP) ★
8345 W Sunset Rd Ste 300, Las Vegas, NV 89113-2177
Tel (702) 589-3900 Founded/Ownrshp 2009
Sales 811.4MM EMP 7,100^E
Tkr Sym TPCA Exch OTO
SIC 7011 7999 Casino hotel; Gambling machines, operation; Gambling establishment
Pr: Anthony P Rodio
*Ch Bd: Carl C Icahn
CFO: Theresa Glebocki
Sr VP: William C Murtha
VP: Chuck Barry
VP: Chris Benak
CIO: Joe Long
Board of Directors: Daniel A Cassella, Keith Cozza, Hunter C Gary, William A Leidesdorf, Daniel H Scott

D-U-N-S 79-039-4253
TROPICANA ENTERTAINMENT INTERMEDIATE HOLDINGS LLC
(Suby of TROPICANA ENTERTAINMENT HOLDINGS LLC) ★
740 Centre View Blvd, Crestview Hills, KY 41017-5434
Tel (859) 578-1100 Founded/Ownrshp 2006
Sales 48.2MM^E EMP 9,802
SIC 7011 Casino hotel
CFO: Richard Fitzpatrick

D-U-N-S 80-789-3073
TROPICANA ENTERTAINMENT LLC
(Suby of TROPICANA ENTERTAINMENT INTERMEDIATE HOLDINGS LLC) ★
740 Centre View Blvd, Crestview Hills, KY 41017-5434
Tel (859) 669-1500 Founded/Ownrshp 2007
Sales 136.2M^E EMP 9,800^E
SIC 7929

D-U-N-S 83-065-6331
TROPICANA ENTERTAINMENT LLC
(Suby of TROPICANA ENTERTAINMENT HOLDINGS LLC) ★
3930 Howard Hughes Pkwy # 400, Las Vegas, NV 89169-0947
Tel (702) 589-3900 Founded/Ownrshp 2006
Sales 100.9MM^E EMP 9,832^E
SIC 7011 Casino hotel
VP: David Zamarin
VP: Joe Long
Ex Dir: Genet Carlson
Ex Dir: Lisa Dennis

D-U-N-S 62-791-9392
TROPICANA EXPRESS INC
RAMADA INN
(Suby of COLUMBIA SUSSEX CORP) ★
2121 S Casino Dr, Laughlin, NV 89029-1519
Tel (702) 299-0306 Founded/Ownrshp 2009
Sales 57.5MM^E EMP 1,400
SIC 7011 Hotels & motels
Pr: Paul Rubeli
*VP: John Lind
Exec: Max Fellner
Ex Dir: Tim Blessing
Sls Mgr: Erica Moreno

D-U-N-S 96-259-3021
■TROPICANA LAS VEGAS INC
(Suby of PENN NATIONAL GAMING INC) ★
3801 Las Vegas Blvd S, Las Vegas, NV 89109-4325
Tel (702) 739-2222 Founded/Ownrshp 2015
Sales 83.4MM^E EMP 1,400
SIC 7011 Hotels & motels
Pr: Alejandro Yemenidjian
CFO: Jason Goudie
VP: George Haldeman
VP: Arik Knowles
VP: Donna Marcou-Stafford
Exec: Mark Bryan
VP Mktg: Joe Messina
Sls Dir: Lynda Richardson
Sls Mgr: Chris Chapman
Sls Mgr: Yolanda Villanueva

D-U-N-S 00-410-0665 IMP
■TROPICANA PRODUCTS INC (DE)
(Suby of PEPSICO INC) ★
1275 26th Ave E, Bradenton, FL 34208-3918
Tel (941) 747-4461 Founded/Ownrshp 1947, 1998
Sales 961.2MM^E EMP 3,500
SIC 2033 2037 2086 2048 Fruit juices: fresh; Fruit juice concentrates, frozen; Fruit drinks (less than 100% juice): packaged in cans, etc.; Citrus seed meal, prepared as animal feed
Pr: Greg Shearson
CFO: John Dieter
*CFO: John Riley
Sr VP: Roger Berdusco
*Sr VP: Clay Small
*VP: Melinda Brown
Genl Mgr: Emad Marwan
CIO: Al Fitguerou
IT Man: Cindy Palmer
Plnt Mgr: Paul Carr
Prd Mgr: Mark Feldman

D-U-N-S 07-936-3285
■TROPICANA ST LOUIS LLC
(Suby of TROPICANA ENTERTAINMENT INC) ★
3930 Howard Hughes Pkwy # 4, Las Vegas, NV 89169-0943
Tel (702) 589-3900 Founded/Ownrshp 2013
Sales 78.8M^E EMP 6,700
SIC 7011 Casino hotel
Ch Bd: Carl C Icahn

D-U-N-S 00-409-5832 IMP/EXP
TROPITONE FURNITURE CO INC (FL)
(Suby of WINSTON FURNITURE CO ALA) ★
5 Marconi, Irvine, CA 92618-2594
Tel (949) 595-2000 Founded/Ownrshp 1954
Sales 124.2MM^E EMP 600
SIC 2514 2522 Garden furniture, metal; Camp furniture: metal; Office furniture, except wood
VP: Randy Danielson
Pr: Richard Rivera
Ex VP: Mark Gorr
Genl Mgr: Rebecca Cotogno
Opers Mgr: Louis Frasche
Sls&Mrk Ex: Tanya Stevens
Snr Mgr: Demetrius Linebarger

D-U-N-S 03-497-6449
TROTTER INC
TROTTER LUMBER
300 Railway, Arcadia, NE 68815
Tel (308) 789-6200 Founded/Ownrshp 1962
Sales 109.5MM^E EMP 100
SIC 5191 5153 5172 Fertilizers & agricultural chemicals; Grains; Petroleum products
Pr: James Trotter
*CFO: Trina Trotter
*Sec: Virginia Trotter
*Prin: Jess Trotter

TROTTER LUMBER
See TROTTER INC

D-U-N-S 03-133-1473
TROUP COUNTY BOARD OF EDUCATION
TROUP COUNTY SCHOOL SYSTEM
100 N Davis Rd Ste C, Lagrange, GA 30241-1620
Tel (706) 812-7900 Founded/Ownrshp 1872
Sales 75.3MM^E EMP 1,800
SIC 8211

TROUP COUNTY SCHOOL SYSTEM
See TROUP COUNTY BOARD OF EDUCATION

D-U-N-S 07-997-3589
TROUP COUNTY SCHOOL SYSTEM
100 N Davis Rd, Lagrange, GA 30241-1620
Tel (706) 812-7900 Founded/Ownrshp 1872
Sales 37.5MM^E EMP 1,800
SIC 8211 Public elementary & secondary schools
Pr Dir: Yolanda Stephen
Teacher Pr: Sequita Freeman

D-U-N-S 00-794-2204 IMP/EXP
TROUT-BLUE CHELAN-MAGI INC (WA)
CHELAN FRUIT COOPERATIVE
8 Howser Rd, Chelan, WA 98816-9590
Tel (509) 682-2591 Founded/Ownrshp 1921
Sales 169.6MM EMP 675
SIC 0723 0175 4222 Fruit (fresh) packing services; Fruit sorting services; Deciduous tree fruits; Warehousing, cold storage or refrigerated
CEO: Reggie Collins
*CFO: Todd Kammers
Off Mgr: Tom Riggan
Board of Directors: Keith Carenmter

D-U-N-S 01-011-0278
TROUTMAN SANDERS LLP
600 Peachtree St Ne # 5200, Atlanta, GA 30308-2216
Tel (404) 885-3000 Founded/Ownrshp 1897
Sales 323.4MM^E EMP 1,400
SIC 8111

D-U-N-S 84-748-1053
TROUTMAN SANDERS LLP POLITICAL ACTION COMMITTEE INC
600 Peachtree St Ne Ste 5, Atlanta, GA 30308-2219
Tel (404) 885-3000 Founded/Ownrshp 1995
Sales 2.1MM^E EMP 1,000
SIC 8651 Political action committee
CEO: Kevin C Greene
*CFO: Dewitt R Rogers

D-U-N-S 08-509-7702
TROVER CLINIC FOUNDATION
TROVER FOUNDATION
200 Clinic Dr, Madisonville, KY 42431-1665
Tel (270) 825-7200 Founded/Ownrshp 1956
Sales 184.1MM EMP 6^E
SIC 8093 Family planning clinic
Prin: M E Clancy
*Ch: Robert Groves

TROVER FOUNDATION
See TROVER CLINIC FOUNDATION

TROVER HEALTH SYSTEM
See BAPTIST HEALTH MADISONVILLE INC

D-U-N-S 60-614-7502
TROVER SOLUTIONS INC
9390 Bunsen Pkwy, Louisville, KY 40220-3789
Tel (502) 214-1340 *Founded/Ownrshp* 2007
Sales NA *EMP* 725
SIC 6411 7322 Insurance agents, brokers & service; Adjustment & collection services
Pr: Robert Bader
**CFO:* Glan French
CFO: Stephen Zaniboni
Ex VP: Robert G Bader Jr
**Ex VP:* Gary Liter
Ex VP: Debra M Murphy
**Ex VP:* Douglas R Sharps
VP: Sharon Callahan
VP: Jason Cooper
**VP:* Daniel Gibson
VP: Cheri Hall
VP: Dwayne Hart
VP: Matthew Smith

D-U-N-S 05-397-7120 IMP
TROVERCO INC
LANDSHIRE SANDWICHES
727 N 1st St, Saint Louis, MO 63102-2501
Tel (800) 468-3354 *Founded/Ownrshp* 1961
Sales 158.5MM^E^ *EMP* 435
SIC 2099 5149 Sandwiches, assembled & packaged: for wholesale market; Coffee, green or roasted
CEO: Joseph E Trover Jr
Pr: Dale J Musick
Rgnl Mgr: Jim Anderson
Rgnl Mgr: Kevin McAlester
Dist Mgr: Bill Riner
Plnt Mgr: Bud Fuhrman
Mktg Dir: Matt Piskulic

D-U-N-S 07-355-3331
TROXELL COMMUNICATIONS INC
TXL DISTRIBUTION
(*Suby of* TXL HOLDING CORP) ★
4675 E Cotton Center Blvd # 155, Phoenix, AZ 85040-2998
Tel (602) 437-7240 *Founded/Ownrshp* 1983
Sales 222.3MM^E^ *EMP* 180^E^
SIC 5064 Television sets; High fidelity equipment; Tape players & recorders
CEO: Michael Ruprich
**Ch Bd:* Johnathan Cozzi
**CEO:* Mike Ruprich
VP: Baron Carlson
**VP:* Geron Meeks
**VP:* Craig Schramm
Board of Directors: Baron Carlson, Johnathan Cozzi, Gregory Harper, Michael Ruprich, Alan Wilkinson

D-U-N-S 00-214-4517 IMP/EXP
TROY CHEMICAL CORP INC
(*Suby of* TROY CORP) ★
1 Avenue L, Newark, NJ 07105-3895
Tel (973) 443-4200 *Founded/Ownrshp* 1952, 1991
Sales 199.7MM^E^ *EMP* 234
SIC 5169 Industrial chemicals
CEO: Daryl D Smith
**Pr:* William B Smith
Treas: Kroum Penev
Bd of Dir: Jean Gerardo
**VP:* Ismael Colon
**VP:* David E Faherty
**VP:* Alexander Geraro
**VP:* Bob Okin
**VP:* Kroum Tenev
Genl Mgr: Sam Eskandar
Genl Mgr: Chris Smith

TROY CITY SCHOOLS
See ENLARGED CITY SCHOOL DISTRICT OF TROY

D-U-N-S 00-843-3534
TROY CONSTRUCTION LLC (TX)
8521 Mchard Rd, Houston, TX 77053-4826
Tel (281) 437-8214 *Founded/Ownrshp* 1950, 2000
Sales 295.9MM^E^ *EMP* 550^E^
SIC 1623 8711 Oil & gas pipeline construction; Building construction consultant
CEO: David D Owner
**Pr:* Alan Owens
**CFO:* Dan O'Hare
CFO: Dan Oahare
**Treas:* Kathy Kusmich
**VP:* Jerry Blasdel
**VP:* Glenn Crawford
VP: Bernie Drane
**VP:* Mike Jameson
VP: Mike Jamison
**VP:* John Lohman

D-U-N-S 79-120-0959 IMP/EXP
TROY CORP
8 Vreeland Rd, Florham Park, NJ 07932-1501
Tel (973) 443-4200 *Founded/Ownrshp* 1991
Sales 204.6MM^E^ *EMP* 361
SIC 2869 Industrial organic chemicals
Pr: Daryl D Smith
COO: Richard Rotherham
CFO: Rick Bowen
CFO: Theresa Oree
Treas: Kroum Penev
**VP:* Ismael Colon
**VP:* David E Faherty
**VP:* Alexander M Gerardo
VP: Bob Okin
**VP:* Donald A Shaw
VP: W Smith
Exec: Aysel Calkap

D-U-N-S 05-305-7022 IMP
■**TROY DESIGN & MANUFACTURING CO**
(*Suby of* FORD MOTOR CO) ★
12675 Berwyn, Redford, MI 48239-2748
Tel (313) 592-2300 *Founded/Ownrshp* 1981
Sales 151.0MM^E^ *EMP* 500
SIC 3465 Automotive stampings
Pr: John L Lowery
Prgrm Mgr: Jerry Schwartz
Genl Mgr: Tim Sallade
QA Dir: Steve Misch
IT Man: Lee Murray
VP Opers: Ned Oliver
QC Dir: John Boehm
Snr Mgr: Paul Abbey

D-U-N-S 07-938-9517
TROY R-III SCHOOL DISTRICT
951 W College St, Troy, MO 63379-1112
Tel (636) 462-6098 *Founded/Ownrshp* 2014
Sales 18.7MM^E^ *EMP* 1,093^E^
SIC 8211 Elementary & secondary schools
Prin: Mark S Penny

D-U-N-S 06-883-4795
TROY SCHOOL DISTRICT
475 First St, Troy, MI 48098
Tel (248) 823-4000 *Founded/Ownrshp* 1950
Sales 160.6MM *EMP* 1,100
Accts Yeo & Yeo Pc Saginaw Mi
SIC 8211 Public elementary & secondary schools
Pr: Nancy Philippart
**Trst:* Wendy Underwood
**VP:* Ida Edmunds
**VP:* Todd Miletti
Dir IT: Andrew Moore
IT Man: Renelle Tolan
Pr Dir: Kerry Birmingham
Teacher Pr: Dave Pass
Psych: Lisa Piejak
Psych: Deborah Sheldon

D-U-N-S 07-209-0939
TROY UNIVERSITY
600 University Ave, Troy, AL 36082-0001
Tel (334) 670-3179 *Founded/Ownrshp* 1887
Sales 201.3MM^E^ *EMP* 3,000
SIC 8221 University
Opers Mgr: Kyle Gassiott
Board of Directors: Tara Donaldson, Judy Fulmer, Leigh Ann Paramore

D-U-N-S 01-635-0761
TROYER FOODS INC
(*Suby of* TF INTER-HOLDINGS INC) ★
17141 State Road 4, Goshen, IN 46528-6674
Tel (574) 533-0302 *Founded/Ownrshp* 1948, 1996
Sales 158.7MM^E^ *EMP* 260
SIC 5147 5144 5141 5146 Meats & meat products; Poultry & poultry products; Groceries, general line; Seafoods
Pr: Paris Ball-Miller
**CEO:* Rebecca Ball-Miller
**CFO:* Neal Yoder
Ex VP: Dick Armington
VP: Paul Stoops
Store Mgr: Lisa Solina-Hampton
Dir IT: Daniel Sark
IT Man: Jeff Slabaugh
VP Opers: Tony Swihart
Mfg Dir: Bill Bernath
Mfg Dir: Don Bingham

D-U-N-S 07-836-8070
TRP ACQUISITION CORP
ROOM PLACE, THE
1000 N Rohlwing Rd Ste 46, Lombard, IL 60148-1187
Tel (630) 261-2380 *Founded/Ownrshp* 1996
Sales 157.8MM^E^ *EMP* 580^E^
SIC 2512 Living room furniture: upholstered on wood frames
CEO: Joe Connolly

D-U-N-S 82-572-7803
TRT DEVELOPMENT CO - CCB
(*Suby of* OMNI HOTELS) ★
4001 Maple Ave Ste 600, Dallas, TX 75219-3241
Tel (800) 809-6664 *Founded/Ownrshp* 1990
Sales 311.6MM^E^ *EMP* 2,340
SIC 7011 Hotels & motels
Pr: Robert B Rowling
CFO: Terry Philen

D-U-N-S 61-759-7919
TRT HOLDINGS INC
OMNI HOTELS
4001 Maple Ave Ste 600, Dallas, TX 75219-3241
Tel (214) 283-8500 *Founded/Ownrshp* 1989
Sales 1.4MMM^E^ *EMP* 12,000
SIC 7011 7991 1382 Hotels; Physical fitness facilities; Physical fitness clubs with training equipment; Exercise facilities; Aerobic dance & exercise classes; Oil & gas exploration services
Ch Bd: Robert B Rowling
**Pr:* James D Caldwell
**Pr:* Dave Schnabel
**CFO:* Terrance Philen
**Sr VP:* David G Adams
**Sr VP:* Mike Garcia
VP: Jennifer Galloway
VP: Lesli Reynolds
VP: Jeff Smith
VP: Garrett Swaldi
Off Admin: Angelica Vazquez

D-U-N-S 78-126-1235
TRT HOTEL CO LLC
(*Suby of* TRT DEVELOPMENT CO - CCB) ★
420 Decker Dr, Irving, TX 75062-3952
Tel (972) 730-6664 *Founded/Ownrshp* 2007
Sales 65.6MM^E^ *EMP* 1,740
SIC 7011 Hotels
CEO: Jim Caldwell
Sr Cor Off: Michael Deitemeyer
Sr VP: Terrell T Philen Jr
Sr VP: Michael Smith
Sr VP: Tom Vautz

D-U-N-S 00-101-9389
TRU CORP
TRU-CONNECTOR
(*Suby of* KINGS ELECTRONICS) ★
245 Lynnfield St, Peabody, MA 01960-5049
Tel (978) 532-0775 *Founded/Ownrshp* 2014
Sales 201.9MM^E^ *EMP* 1,270
SIC 3643 3678 Connectors & terminals for electrical devices; Electronic connectors
Pr: Timothy S O'Neil
**Treas:* Suzanne Perakis
VP: Anthony Martinello
Mng Dir: Stephen Eccles
Info Man: Jeffrey Wallace
Ql Cn Mgr: Paul Oberlander

TRU-CONNECTOR
See TRU CORP

D-U-N-S 10-762-6152 IMP
TRU-SPEC METALS INC
3075 N Oak Grove Ave, Waukegan, IL 60087-1817
Tel (847) 360-8400 *Founded/Ownrshp* 1984
Sales 14.0MMM *EMP* 9
SIC 5051

D-U-N-S 01-633-6790
▲**TRUCEPT INC** (NV)
500 La Terraza Blvd, Escondido, CA 92025-3875
Tel (866) 961-5763 *Founded/Ownrshp* 1995
Sales 27.7MM *EMP* 7,000
Tkr Sym TREP *Exch* OTO
SIC 8721 8748 8742 Payroll accounting service; Employee programs administration; Compensation & benefits planning consultant
Pr: Brian Bonar

D-U-N-S 19-397-1264 IMP
TRUCK ACCESSORIES GROUP LLC
LEER
(*Suby of* J B POINDEXTER & CO INC) ★
28858 Ventura Dr, Elkhart, IN 46517-8832
Tel (574) 522-5337 *Founded/Ownrshp* 1994
Sales 247.0MM^E^ *EMP* 1,100
SIC 3713 Truck tops
CEO: John B Poindexter
VP: Ray Fundora
IT Man: Chris Handerson
Mktg Dir: Mike Sanford

D-U-N-S 78-061-3654
TRUCK BODIES & EQUIPMENT INTERNATIONAL INC
TBEI
52182 Ember Rd, Lake Crystal, MN 56055-2388
Tel (507) 726-2728 *Founded/Ownrshp* 2006
Sales 226.0MM^E^ *EMP* 892
SIC 3713 4953 Truck & bus bodies; Dumps, operation of
Pr: Bob Fines
**Pr:* Robert Fines
**COO:* Eric Blackwell
**CFO:* Dave Strehl
**VP:* Tina Albright
**VP:* Jerry Frost
Genl Mgr: Joe Paulsen
IT Man: Kurt Weinberg
S&M/VP: Henry Bell
Mktg Mgr: Nikki Kyle
Sls Mgr: Sandy Elkins

D-U-N-S 05-261-2272 IMP
TRUCK CENTERS INC
2280 Formosa Rd, Troy, IL 62294-3170
Tel (618) 667-3454 *Founded/Ownrshp* 1970
Sales 203.1MM^E^ *EMP* 392
SIC 5531 5511 7538 5012 4522 7699

TRUCK CENTERS OF ARKANSAS
See TRL INC

TRUCK CITY FORD
See LEIF JOHNSON FORD INC

D-U-N-S 19-723-0415 EXP
TRUCK COMPONENTS INC
(*Suby of* TRANSPORTATION TECHNOLOGIES INDUSTRIES INC) ★
8819 N Brooks St, Tampa, FL 33604-1809
Tel (813) 933-1166 *Founded/Ownrshp* 2005
Sales 306.3MM^E^ *EMP* 1,010^E^
SIC 5013 Truck parts & accessories
Pr: John Messina

D-U-N-S 18-003-6238
TRUCK COUNTRY OF INDIANA INC
FREIGHTLINER TRUCKS
(*Suby of* MCCOY GROUP INC) ★
1851 W Thompson Rd, Indianapolis, IN 46217-9353
Tel (317) 788-1533 *Founded/Ownrshp* 2014
Sales 273.9MM^E^ *EMP* 700
SIC 5511 5531 7538 7539

D-U-N-S 06-325-4452
TRUCK COUNTRY OF IOWA INC
FREIGHTLINER
(*Suby of* MCCOY GROUP INC) ★
2099 Southpark Ct Ste 2, Dubuque, IA 52003-8095
Tel (563) 556-3773 *Founded/Ownrshp* 2011
Sales 130.1MM^E^ *EMP* 457
SIC 5012 5531 7538 Trucks, commercial; Automotive & home supply stores; General automotive repair shops
Pr: Michael R McCoy
**CFO:* Bill Arnold
**VP:* John R Mc Coy
VP Opers: John R McCoy
Mktg Dir: Ann Miller

D-U-N-S 10-672-3976
TRUCK COUNTRY OF WISCONSIN INC
(*Suby of* MCCOY GROUP INC) ★
4195 Anderson Rd, Deforest, WI 53532-2906
Tel (608) 249-1090 *Founded/Ownrshp* 2011
Sales 112.6MM^E^ *EMP* 400
SIC 5012 7538 Trucks, commercial; General truck repair
Pr: John R McCoy
**VP:* Michael McCoy

D-U-N-S 00-314-0530 EXP
TRUCK ENTERPRISES INC (VA)
3440 S Main St, Harrisonburg, VA 22801-9758
Tel (540) 564-6900 *Founded/Ownrshp* 1961
Sales 148.8MM^E^ *EMP* 350
SIC 5511 5531 7538 7539 Trucks, tractors & trailers: new & used; Truck equipment & parts; General truck repair; Trailer repair
CEO: James E Hartman
Chf Mktg O: Edgar Miller
Ofcr: Frances Jordan
VP: Joe Bryson
VP: Dave Marshall
**VP:* Edward F Rose Jr
IT Man: Kara Eppard
Mktg Mgr: Kyle Coleman

D-U-N-S 08-006-2804
TRUCK HERO INC
5400 S State Rd, Ann Arbor, MI 48108-9754
Tel (734) 677-0444 *Founded/Ownrshp* 2015
Sales 95.4MM^E^ *EMP* 101^E^
SIC 3714 Pickup truck bed liners
CEO: William Reminder
Ex VP: Sean Marks
**Genl Couns:* Marla Zwas

TRUCK PARTS SPECIALIST
See NATIONAL TRUCK PARTS OF MIDWEST INC

D-U-N-S 00-959-5331
TRUCK UNDERWRITERS ASSOCIATION
(*Suby of* FARMERS INSURANCE) ★
4680 Wilshire Blvd, Los Angeles, CA 90010-3807
Tel (323) 932-3200 *Founded/Ownrshp* 1935
Sales 81.5MM^E^ *EMP* 2,845
SIC 8621 Professional membership organizations
Pr: Leonard H Gelfand
**VP:* Gerald Faulwell
**VP:* Martin Feinstein
**VP:* Jason Katz
**VP:* John Lynch

D-U-N-S 00-211-5343 IMP/EXP
TRUCK-LITE CO INC
SIGNAL STAT PRODUCT LINE
(*Suby of* PENSKE CO LLC) ★
310 E Elmwood Ave, Falconer, NY 14733-1421
Tel (716) 665-6214 *Founded/Ownrshp* 1955
Sales 185.3MM^E^ *EMP* 1,300
Accts Deloitte & Touche Llp
SIC 3648 3647 Lighting equipment; Vehicular lighting equipment
Pr: Brian Kupchella
CFO: Scott Fink
CFO: Germaine R Shanahan
Sr VP: Timothy Walker
VP: John Cecco
VP: Robert Ives
VP: Martin Schroeder
VP: B Van Riper
Rgnl Mgr: Rick Nex
Rgnl Mgr: Mike Verret
Genl Mgr: Roger Elmer

D-U-N-S 96-870-9142 IMP/EXP
TRUCK-LITE CO LLC
310 E Elmwood Ave, Falconer, NY 14733-1421
Tel (716) 665-6214 *Founded/Ownrshp* 2015
Sales 500.0MM *EMP* 1,000^E^
SIC 3647 Vehicular lighting equipment
Pr: Brian Kupchella
**COO:* Jeff Church
**CIO:* Donald Alexander

D-U-N-S 07-940-7365
TRUCKPRO HOLDING CORP
1610 Century Center Pkwy, Memphis, TN 38134-8957
Tel (901) 252-4200 *Founded/Ownrshp* 2006
Sales 1.3MMM^E^ *EMP* 2,600^E^
SIC 5531 7539 Truck equipment & parts; Brake repair, automotive
CEO: Steven J Riordan
**CFO:* Steve Martin
**Treas:* Sharon Carter

D-U-N-S 03-476-9273 IMP/EXP
TRUCKPRO LLC
(*Suby of* TRUCKPRO HOLDING CORP) ★
1610 Century Center Pkwy, Memphis, TN 38134-8957
Tel (901) 252-4200 *Founded/Ownrshp* 2001
Sales 1.3MMM^E^ *EMP* 2,600
SIC 5531 7539 Truck equipment & parts; Brake repair, automotive
CEO: Steven J Riordan
**CFO:* Steve Martin
**Treas:* Sharon Carter
VP: Russell Etters
Genl Mgr: Marsha Wise
Sls Mgr: Dale Hargis

D-U-N-S 87-654-4909
TRUCO ENTERPRISES LP
ON THE BORDER PRODUCTS
2727 Realty Dr Ste 134, Carrollton, TX 75006-5422
Tel (972) 869-4600 *Founded/Ownrshp* 2014
Sales 136.0MM *EMP* 50
SIC 5145 Snack foods
Genl Pt: David Silver III
Pr: Jeff Partridge
CFO: Nicki Wolpmann
VP: Leslie Concors
Off Admin: Jennifer Zavala
QA Dir: Eudaldo Shealy
Opers Mgr: Ryan Randall
Opers Mgr: Tom Riley
VP Sls: Amir Zahedi

D-U-N-S 07-633-5665
TRUCONNECT COMMUNICATIONS INC
TELESCAPE
10440 N Cntl Expy Ste 700, Dallas, TX 75231
Tel (877) 771-7736 *Founded/Ownrshp* 2001
Sales 206.5MM^E^ *EMP* 675
SIC 4813 Telephone communication, except radio
CEO: Mathew Johnson
Pr: Robert A Yap
Sr VP: Juan Carlos Davila
VP: Mike Nobles
Creative D: Laural Carr
Snr Mgr: Jeanette Gonzalez

TRUE COMPANIES
See TRUE OIL LLC

TRUE FORM
See MAIDENFORM INC

D-U-N-S 07-978-7124
TRUE HEALTH DIAGNOSTICS LLC
6170 Research Rd Ste 211, Frisco, TX 75033-3504
Tel (844) 341-1491 *Founded/Ownrshp* 2014
Sales 314.0MM^E *EMP* 197^E
SIC 8011 8069 Diabetes specialist, physician/surgeon; Chronic disease hospital
CEO: Chris Grottenthaler
**COO:* Mohit Khan
**COO:* Gary L Smith
**CFO:* Christian Richards
**Ofcr:* Kenneth Johnson
**Sr VP:* Carol Nellis
Sr VP: Blake Whitaker

D-U-N-S 13-007-9663
TRUE LEAF FARMS LLC
1275 San Justo Rd, San Juan Bautista, CA 95045-9733
Tel (831) 623-4667 *Founded/Ownrshp* 2002
Sales 138.1MM^E *EMP* 500
SIC 2034 Vegetables, dried or dehydrated (except freeze-dried)
Plnt Mgr: Jared Gill

D-U-N-S 00-629-9135 IMP/EXP
TRUE MANUFACTURING CO INC (MO)
2001 E Terra Ln, O Fallon, MO 63366-4434
Tel (636) 240-2400 *Founded/Ownrshp* 1945, 1955
Sales 215.3MM^E *EMP* 500
SIC 3585 Refrigeration equipment, complete
Pr: Steven L Trulaske
VP: John Mulry
**Prin:* Steve Trulaske
Dept Mgr: Eddie Powell
Web Dev: Gina Passante
Ql Cn Mgr: Ryan Doolin
VP Mktg: Steve Alexander
Sls Dir: Viktor Eklund
Manager: Jonathan Bagni
Manager: Jim Barry
Sls Mgr: Lee Elliott

D-U-N-S 00-543-7769
■TRUE NORTH COMMUNICATIONS INC
(*Suby of* INTERPUBLIC GROUP OF COMPANIES INC) ★
1114 Ave Of The Americas, New York, NY 10036-7703
Tel (212) 704-1200 *Founded/Ownrshp* 2001
Sales 257.5MM^E *EMP* 12,060
SIC 7311 Advertising agencies
CEO: Michael I Roth
**Ch Bd:* David A Bell
Ex VP: Ramesh Rajan
VP: Shelina Dinani
**VP:* Frank Mergenthaler
Dir IT: Susan Hinch
Snr Mgr: Guy Beach

D-U-N-S 08-015-3141
TRUE NORTH ENERGY LLC
10346 Brecksville Rd, Brecksville, OH 44141-3338
Tel (877) 245-9336 *Founded/Ownrshp* 1999
Sales 276.5MM^E *EMP* 1,000
SIC 5541 5172 Gasoline service stations; Gasoline; Engine fuels & oils; Service station supplies, petroleum
Pr: Mark E Lyden
**CFO:* John W Guzdanski
VP: Mary B Lyden
**VP:* Keith A McIntyre
Dist Mgr: John Belak
Dist Mgr: Jaime Martinez
Dist Mgr: Joe Sahdala
Dist Mgr: Greg Wood
Genl Mgr: Tom Gimmartino
Genl Mgr: Donna Heinz
Genl Mgr: Ben Sunderlin

D-U-N-S 00-387-4146
TRUE OIL LLC
TRUE COMPANIES
455 N Poplar St, Casper, WY 82601-1783
Tel (307) 237-9301 *Founded/Ownrshp* 1953
Sales 179.7MM^E *EMP* 139
SIC 1311 Crude petroleum production; Natural gas production
CFO: Dwain Park
Treas: Ken White
IT Man: Jayson Broughton
Netwrk Mgr: Kathie Meinzer
Software D: Deb Klug

TRUE PALS
See WESTERN FAMILY FOODS INC

D-U-N-S 14-115-3978 IMP
TRUE RELIGION APPAREL INC
TRUE RELIGION BRAND JEANS
(*Suby of* TOWERBROOK CAPITAL PARTNERS LP) ★
1888 Rosecrans Ave # 1000, Manhattan Beach, CA 90266-3795
Tel (323) 266-3072 *Founded/Ownrshp* 2013
Sales 1.1MMM^E *EMP* 3,086
SIC 2369 2325 2339 Girls' & children's outerwear; Jeans: girls', children's & infants'; Men's & boys' trousers & slacks; Jeans: men's, youths' & boys'; Women's & misses' outerwear; Jeans: women's, misses' & juniors'
CEO: John Ermatinger
**Pr:* Lynne Koplin
COO: Darryl Rosenberg
COO: Daryl Rosenburg
**CFO:* Eric Bauer
**CFO:* Peter F Collins
**Sr VP:* David Chiovetti
Sr VP: Rosella Giuliani
**Sr VP:* Kelly Gvildys
Store Mgr: Brett Vick
CIO: Jennifer Terrill
Board of Directors: John Anderson, Marcello Bottoli, Joseph Coulombe, G Louis Graziadio III, Robert L Harris II, Seth R Johnson, Mark S Maron

TRUE RELIGION BRAND JEANS
See TRUE RELIGION APPAREL INC

TRUE RELIGION BRAND JEANS
See GURU DENIM INC

D-U-N-S 07-872-0443 IMP/EXP
TRUE TEMPER SPORTS INC (DE)
PROJECT X
8275 Tournament Dr # 200, Memphis, TN 38125-8881
Tel (901) 746-2000 *Founded/Ownrshp* 1930, 2009
Sales 196.5MM^E *EMP* 692
SIC 5091 3949 Golf equipment; Shafts, golf club
Pr: Scott C Hennessy
**CFO:* Jason A Jenne
Sr VP: Fred H Geyer
**VP:* Graeme Horwood
VP: Graeme Lawson
Dir IT: Steven Gilbert
QC Dir: Eddie Naritomi
Ql Cn Mgr: Wayne Howell
Sls&Mrk Ex: William R Beatty
S&M/VP: Raeford Lucas
Mktg Mgr: Chad Hall

D-U-N-S 00-109-4309 IMP
TRUE TEXTILES INC
(*Suby of* DUVALTEX INC)
5300 Corprte Grv Dr Se, Grand Rapids, MI 49512-5514
Tel (616) 301-7540 *Founded/Ownrshp* 2016
Sales 130.6MM^E *EMP* 500^E
SIC 2221 Manmade & synthetic broadwoven fabrics
CEO: Tom Olive
CFO: Marc Pescosolido
CIO: Rick Cowan
Sys Mgr: Donna Absher
Mktg Mgr: Gregg Vanderkooi

TRUE VALUE
See L AND M SUPPLY INC

D-U-N-S 00-692-9681 EXP
TRUE VALUE CO
8600 W Bryn Mawr Ave 100s, Chicago, IL 60631-3505
Tel (773) 695-5000 *Founded/Ownrshp* 1953
Sales 1.4MMM^E *EMP* 3,000
Accts Mcgladrey Llp Schaumburg Ill
SIC 5072 2851 3991 Hardware; Paints & paint additives; Paint & varnish brushes
Pr: John Hartmann
**Ch Bd:* Brent Burger
COO: Bill Caprel
**COO:* Abhinav Shukla
**CFO:* Deborah O' Connor
CFO: David A Shadduck
Treas: Michael Brixey
Treas: Barbara Wagner
**Chf Mktg O:* Heath Ashenfelter
Ofcr: Ken Goodgame
**Sr VP:* Cathy Anderson
**Sr VP:* Leslie A Weber
VP: Rick Brown
VP: Barbara Byrum
VP: Thomas De Nault
**VP:* Rosalee Hermens
**VP:* Fred L Kirst
VP: Eric Lane
VP: Ken Lanis
Exec: Nora Polley
Dir Bus: Andrew Balzer
Board of Directors: Cheryl Bachelder, Richard E George Jr, Michael S Glode, Thomas S Hanemann, Kenneth A Niefeld, David Y Schwartz, Brian M Webb, Charles W Welch, Larry Zigerelli

D-U-N-S 13-170-5246 IMP
TRUE WORLD FOODS NEW YORK LLC
SHINSHU
(*Suby of* TRUE WORLD GROUP) ★
32-34 Papetti Plz, Elizabeth, NJ 07206-1432
Tel (908) 351-9090 *Founded/Ownrshp* 1993
Sales 116.7MM^E *EMP* 300
SIC 5146 Fish, fresh; Fish, frozen, unpackaged; Seafoods

TRUE WORLD GROUP
See TRUE WORLD HOLDINGS LLC

D-U-N-S 09-949-2217 IMP/EXP
TRUE WORLD HOLDINGS LLC
TRUE WORLD GROUP
(*Suby of* ONE UP ENTERPRISES INC) ★
24 Link Dr, Rockleigh, NJ 07647-2504
Tel (201) 750-0024 *Founded/Ownrshp* 1976
Sales 366.6MM^E *EMP* 1,461
SIC 5146 Fish & seafoods

D-U-N-S 14-440-6014
▲TRUEBLUE INC
1015 A St, Tacoma, WA 98402-5122
Tel (253) 383-9101 *Founded/Ownrshp* 1989
Sales 2.7MMM *EMP* 5,500^E
Tkr Sym TBI *Exch* NYS
SIC 7363 Help supply services; Temporary help service
CEO: Steven C Cooper
**Ch Bd:* Joseph P Sambataro Jr
Pr: Patrick Beharelle
Pr: Wayne W Larkin
CFO: Derrek L Gafford
Ofcr: Randall Rothschiller
Ex VP: James E Defebaugh
Ex VP: Jonathan D Means
Ex VP: Taryn R Owen
Sr VP: John Demarest
VP: Robert Breen
VP: Diana Hice
VP: Joanna Monroe
VP: Gerald Renoe
Exec: Scott Nickerson
Dir Risk M: Stacy Shields
Comm Dir: Devin Smith
Board of Directors: Colleen B Brown, William C Goings, Kim Harris Jones, Stephen M Robb, Jeffrey B Sakaguchi, Bonnie W Soodik, William W Steele

D-U-N-S 60-280-3244
▲TRUECAR INC
120 Broadway Ste 200, Santa Monica, CA 90401-2385
Tel (800) 200-2000 *Founded/Ownrshp* 2005
Sales 259.8MM *EMP* 574
Tkr Sym TRUE *Exch* NGS
SIC 5012 7299 Automobiles & other motor vehicles; Automotive brokers; Information services, consumer
Pr: Chip Perry
Sr Pt: Adri Lewis
Sr Pt: Chris Shaw
Pt: Jason Nierman
Pt: Dave Pributsky
Pt: David Pributsky
CFO: Michael Guthrie
Ofcr: John Stephenson
Ex VP: Bernie Brenner
Ex VP: Larry Dominique
Ex VP: Neeraj Gunsagar
Ex VP: Mark Miller
Ex VP: Jim Nguyen
Ex VP: Brian Skutta
Ex VP: Tom Taira
Sr VP: Tommy McClung
Sr VP: Jim Menard
VP: Jim Berger
VP: Jeff Bolke
VP: David Giffin
VP: Bill Lepler
Board of Directors: Todd Bradley, Robert Buce, Christopher Claus, Steven Dietz, Thomas Gibson, John Krafcik

TRUECREDIT.COM
See TRANSUNION INTERACTIVE INC

D-U-N-S 15-047-7677
TRUENET COMMUNICATIONS CORP
(*Suby of* FUJITSU NETWORK COMMUNICATIONS INC) ★
7666 Blanding Blvd, Jacksonville, FL 32244-5112
Tel (904) 777-9052 *Founded/Ownrshp* 2016
Sales 110.4MM^E *EMP* 300
SIC 4899 Data communication services
Pr: Tom Prestwood
**CFO:* Laura Carden
**Ex VP:* Mark Lampke
VP: Charles Owens
Brnch Mgr: Drackett Bruce

D-U-N-S 03-792-1111
TRUENORTH COMPANIES LC
500 1st St Se, Cedar Rapids, IA 52401-2002
Tel (319) 364-5193 *Founded/Ownrshp* 2000
Sales NA *EMP* 190
SIC 6411 Insurance agents
Pt: Larry Bergdale
**Pt:* Loren Coppock
**Pt:* Duane Smith
Mng Pt: Russ Nieland
Mng Pt: Charlie Weber
Mng Pt: Kevin Welu
Pr: Bert Mayo
Ofcr: Mark Gray
Ex VP: Max Smith
Exec: Vicki Voellinger
Mng Dir: Bryan Taylor

D-U-N-S 00-614-8613 IMP
TRUENORTH STEEL INC
702 13th Ave E, West Fargo, ND 58078-3304
Tel (701) 373-7781 *Founded/Ownrshp* 1943
Sales 193.3MM^E *EMP* 500^E
SIC 3443 3444 3441 Tanks, standard or custom fabricated: metal plate; Sheet metalwork; Fabricated structural metal
CEO: Ole Rommesmo Jr
**Pr:* Dan Kadrmas
CFO: Mark Kuznia
CFO: Lisa Reich
**VP:* Lisa Right
**VP:* Bryan Zingraf
Area Mgr: Tom Prill
Brnch Mgr: Bob Sieve
IT Man: Krysia Devous
Sfty Dirs: Rod Schober
Prd Mgr: Ken Renowski

TRUFLO
See PHILLIPS & TEMRO INDUSTRIES INC

D-U-N-S 12-323-0679 IMP
TRUFOOD MFG INC
610 Alpha Dr, Pittsburgh, PA 15238-2802
Tel (412) 963-2330 *Founded/Ownrshp* 2002
Sales 90.4MM^E *EMP* 160
SIC 2066 2064 Chocolate; Candy & other confectionery products; Breakfast bars
Pr: Peter S Tsudis
**VP:* George S Tsudis

D-U-N-S 08-025-3894
TRUGREEN HOLDING CORP
1790 Kirby Pkwy Ste 300, Memphis, TN 38138-7411
Tel (901) 251-4002 *Founded/Ownrshp* 2013
Sales 3.5MMM^E *EMP* 15,573^E
SIC 0782 6719 Lawn care services; Personal holding companies, except banks
CEO: David Alexander

D-U-N-S 62-268-1351
TRUGREEN LIMITED PARTNERSHIP
BAREFOOT
(*Suby of* TRUGREEN HOLDING CORP) ★
1790 Kirby Pkwy Forum Ii Ste 300 Forum Ii, Memphis, TN 38138
Tel (901) 681-1800 *Founded/Ownrshp* 2014
Sales 4.0MMM^E *EMP* 16,000
SIC 0782 Lawn care services
CEO: David Alexander
COO: Jim Gimeson
VP: Martin Click
VP: Tim Ehrhart
VP: Robert V Gruben
VP: Jamey Jones
Brnch Mgr: Frank Musto
Genl Mgr: Jared Kuhnhenn
Genl Mgr: Steve Marini
Genl Mgr: Joel McKay
Genl Mgr: Tina Morgan

D-U-N-S 06-342-9765 IMP
TRUITT BROS INC
1105 Front St Ne, Salem, OR 97301-1034
Tel (503) 365-2837 *Founded/Ownrshp* 1972
Sales 86.5MM^E *EMP* 400^E
SIC 3556 Dehydrating equipment, food processing
VP: David J Truitt
**CFO:* Alan Wynn
Manager: Kathy Rowland

D-U-N-S 15-782-4731 IMP/EXP
TRUJILLO & SONS INC
3325 Nw 62nd St, Miami, FL 33147-7533
Tel (305) 633-6482 *Founded/Ownrshp* 1996
Sales 106.5MM^E *EMP* 100
Accts Garcia & Garcia Pa Miami
SIC 5141 Groceries, general line
VP: Don Gertzman
Genl Mgr: Julio Diaz
IT Man: Ileana Trujillo

TRULAND GROUP
See TRULAND SYSTEMS CORP

D-U-N-S 36-380-6795
TRULAND SYSTEMS CORP
TRULAND GROUP
1900 Oracle Way Ste 700, Reston, VA 20190-4733
Tel (703) 464-3000 *Founded/Ownrshp* 1977
Sales NA *EMP* 1,315
SIC 1731

D-U-N-S 80-214-9893
■TRULIA INC
(*Suby of* ZILLOW GROUP INC) ★
535 Mission St Fl 7, San Francisco, CA 94105-3223
Tel (415) 648-4358 *Founded/Ownrshp* 2014
Sales 251.9MM *EMP* 1,036
Accts Deloitte & Touche Llp San Jos
SIC 7374 Data processing & preparation
CEO: Peter Flint
Pr: Lloyd Frink
COO: Paul Levine
CFO: Prashant Aggarwal
VP: Larry Illg
Snr Sftwr: Joshua Johnson
Snr Sftwr: Laurence Skegg
CTO: Daniele Farnedi
Web Dev: Vincent Lum
Software D: Louis Eisenberg
Sftwr Eng: Pradip Marsonia

D-U-N-S 96-216-0722 EXP
TRULITE GLASS & ALUMINUM SOLUTIONS LLC
403 Westpark Ct Ste 201, Peachtree City, GA 30269-3577
Tel (678) 593-9200 *Founded/Ownrshp* 2010
Sales 3.0MMM^E *EMP* 7,020
SIC 3354 3449 Aluminum extruded products; Miscellaneous metalwork
CTO: Claire Murphy

D-U-N-S 04-930-9172 IMP
TRULY NOLEN OF AMERICA INC
TRULY NOLEN PEST CONTROL
3636 E Speedway Blvd, Tucson, AZ 85716-4018
Tel (800) 528-3442 *Founded/Ownrshp* 1955
Sales 115.6MM *EMP* 1,000
SIC 7342

TRULY NOLEN PEST CONTROL
See TRULY NOLEN OF AMERICA INC

D-U-N-S 02-713-9807
TRUMAN ARNOLD COMPANIES
TAC
701 S Robison Rd, Texarkana, TX 75501-6747
Tel (903) 794-3835 *Founded/Ownrshp* 2012
Sales 1.6MMM *EMP* 550
SIC 5172 4581 Gasoline; Diesel fuel; Airport hangar rental
Pr: Greg Arnold
**CFO:* Steve McMillen
VP: Michael Davis
VP: Steve Peterson
VP: Benny Walsh
Genl Mgr: Jerry C Black
Genl Mgr: Scott Field
Mktg Dir: David Edwards
Mktg Mgr: Derrick Maynard
Manager: Shirley Allen
Manager: Rob Case
Board of Directors: James Day, Steve McMillen

D-U-N-S 07-306-7407
TRUMAN MEDICAL CENTER INC
2301 Holmes St, Kansas City, MO 64108-2677
Tel (816) 404-1000 *Founded/Ownrshp* 1962
Sales 418.6MM *EMP* 3,000
Accts Bkd Llp Kansas City Mo
SIC 8062 General medical & surgical hospitals
Pr: John F Bluford
COO: Marsha L Morgan
COO: Linda Turner
CFO: Allen Johnson
Ofcr: Marcia Johnson
Sr VP: Mitzi Cardenas
VP: Marcos Deleon
VP: Lynda Donegan
VP: Dmeter Dragovich
VP: Cici Rojas
VP: Barbara Zubeck
Dir Rad: Carole Jones
Dir Rx: Denny G Fuate
Dir Rx: Erin Pender
Board of Directors: Dennis O'leary

D-U-N-S 00-893-9043
TRUMBULL CORP (PA)
225 N Shore Dr, Pittsburgh, PA 15212-5860
Tel (412) 807-2000 *Founded/Ownrshp* 1955
Sales 198.2MM^E *EMP* 400
SIC 1611 Highway & street construction
CEO: Clifford R Rowe Jr
**Pr:* George E Mezey
**Treas:* Dominic Coccagna
**Ex VP:* Stephen M Clark
**Ex VP:* John P Maffeo Jr
**VP:* Joseph J Franceschini
Exec: Victoria Jamison
Sfty Mgr: Joe F Sranceschini

TRUMBULL COUNTY AUDITOR'S OFFI
See COUNTY OF TRUMBULL

D-U-N-S 00-397-9358 IMP
TRUMBULL INDUSTRIES INC (OH)
400 Dietz Rd Ne, Warren, OH 44483-2749
Tel (330) 393-6624 *Founded/Ownrshp* 1922, 1945
Sales 102.6MM^E *EMP* 275
SIC 5074 5085 5064

D-U-N-S 07-674-6148
TRUMBULL MEMORIAL HOSPITAL (OH)
1350 E Market St, Warren, OH 44483-6628
Tel (330) 841-9011 *Founded/Ownrshp* 1984
Sales 134.5MM *EMP* 2,000
SIC 8062 8049 General medical & surgical hospitals; Physical therapist
Pr: Walter J Pishkur
**Pr:* Kristopher Hoce
**COO:* Jeff Rexroad
COO: Kevin Speigel
CFO: Marla Lisbon
**VP:* Henry Seybold
**Prin:* R A Cobb Et Al
**Prin:* Charles Fillins
**Prin:* William Wallace
Ex Dir: Melanie Vlad
Pathlgst: Robert C Bennett

D-U-N-S 84-804-4954
TRUMBULL MEMORIAL HOSPITAL FOUNDATION
MAHONING VLY HMTOLOGY ONCOLOGY
1350 E Market St, Warren, OH 44483-6608
Tel (330) 841-9376 *Founded/Ownrshp* 1890
Sales 725.3M *EMP* 3,000
SIC 8011 Hematologist
CFO: Henry Sebold
**Pr:* Charles Johns

D-U-N-S 94-677-3306
TRUMP ENTERTAINMENT RESORTS INC
1000 Boardwalk, Atlantic City, NJ 08401-7415
Tel (609) 449-5534 *Founded/Ownrshp* 1995
Sales 473.3MM *EMP* 3,700
SIC 7011 7999 Casino hotel; Gambling & lottery services
CEO: Robert F Griffin
**CFO:* David R Hughes
VP: Michael Mellon
Opers Mgr: Mark Juliano

TRUMP INTERNATIONAL HT & TWR
See TRUMP ORGANIZATION INC

D-U-N-S 07-295-9232
TRUMP ORGANIZATION INC
TRUMP INTERNATIONAL HT & TWR
725 5th Ave Bsmt A, New York, NY 10022-2516
Tel (212) 832-2000 *Founded/Ownrshp* 1981
Sales 54.5MM^E *EMP* 4,000
SIC 6531 7922 6794 Real estate brokers & agents; Real estate managers; Entertainment promotion; Franchises, selling or licensing
Ch: Donald J Trump
Ex VP: Russell Flicker
**Ex VP:* Donald J Trump Jr
**Ex VP:* Eric Trump
**Ex VP:* Ivanka Trump
VP: Ron Lieberman
VP: Larry Masciocchi
Exec: Evan Sheridan
Dir Sec: Keith Schiller
Genl Mgr: Margaret Caronia
MIS Dir: Joe Petruzzi

D-U-N-S 19-713-9140
TRUMP TAJ MAHAL ASSOCIATES LLC
TRUMP TAJ MAHAL CASINO RESORT
1000 Boardwalk, Atlantic City, NJ 08401-7415
Tel (609) 345-4045 *Founded/Ownrshp* 2005
Sales 107.3MM^E *EMP* 6,200
SIC 7011 Casino hotel
CFO: David Hughes
Off Mgr: Cindi Lepine

TRUMP TAJ MAHAL CASINO RESORT
See TRUMP TAJ MAHAL ASSOCIATES LLC

D-U-N-S 80-159-6792
TRUMP TAJ MAHAL REALTY CORP
1000 Boardwalk, Atlantic City, NJ 08401-7415
Tel (609) 449-1000 *Founded/Ownrshp* 1988
Sales 36.1MM^E *EMP* 2,000
SIC 6512 Nonresidential building operators
Ch: Donald Trump

D-U-N-S 04-918-4039 IMP/EXP
TRUMPF INC
(*Suby of* TRUMPF INTERNATIONAL BETEILIGUNGS-GMBH)
111 Hyde Rd, Farmington, CT 06032-2851
Tel (860) 255-6000 *Founded/Ownrshp* 1969
Sales 196.2MM^E *EMP* 640^E
SIC 3542 3423 3546 Sheet metalworking machines; Hand & edge tools; Power-driven handtools
Pr: Peter Hoecklin
Mng Pt: Mathias Kammuller
**Ch Bd:* Nicola Leibinger-Kammuller
V Ch: Peter Leibinger
**Sr VP:* John Burke Doar
VP: Robert Castonguay
**VP:* Stuart Douglas Devnew
VP: Kevin Domingue
VP: Mariella Kuon
Mng Dir: Jorge Areyzaga
Mng Dir: Soumitra Joshi

D-U-N-S 00-793-3062 IMP
■**TRUNKLINE GAS CO LLC**
(*Suby of* SOUTHERN UNION GAS) ★
5051 Westheimr Rd # 1428, Houston, TX 77056-5720
Tel (713) 989-2193 *Founded/Ownrshp* 1947
Sales 377.1MM^E *EMP* 600
Accts Pricewaterhousecoopers Llp Ho
SIC 4922 Pipelines, natural gas
Sr VP: Michael T Langston
Sr VP: Jeryl L Mohn
Sr VP: Gary P Smith
VP: Cynthia C Albert
VP: Jack Boatman
VP: Richard Craig
VP: Drew Fossum
VP: Bradley Holmes
VP: Gary W Lefelar
VP: Michael D Vanhemert

D-U-N-S 07-947-7906
TRUPANION INC
6100 4th Ave S Ste 200, Seattle, WA 98108-3234
Tel (855) 727-9079 *Founded/Ownrshp* 2000
Sales NA *EMP* 439
Tkr Sym TRUP *Exch* NGM
SIC 6324 8011 Hospital & medical service plans; Medical insurance plan
Pr: Darryl Rawlings
**Ch Bd:* Murray Low
COO: Ian Moffat
CFO: Tricia Plouf
Chf Mktg O: Margaret Tooth
Genl Mgr: Lisa Marcotte
QA Dir: Steve Warshaw
Sftwr Eng: Oleksii Boiko
Board of Directors: Chad Cohen, Michael Doak, Robin Ferracone, Dan Levitan, H Hays Lindsley, Glenn Novotny, Howard Rubin

D-U-N-S 96-442-3185
TRUPOINTE COOPERATIVE INC
215 Looney Rd, Piqua, OH 45356-4147
Tel (937) 575-6780 *Founded/Ownrshp* 2010
Sales 1.3MMM^E *EMP* 450
SIC 5153 5191

D-U-N-S 79-952-4835
TRUSSWAY HOLDINGS INC
9411 Alcorn St, Houston, TX 77093-6753
Tel (713) 691-6900 *Founded/Ownrshp* 1995
Sales 269.8MM^E *EMP* 1,500
SIC 2439 Trusses, except roof: laminated lumber
Pr: Bill Adams
Mktg Dir: Michael Estes

D-U-N-S 96-370-6788
TRUSSWAY INDUSTRIES INC
(*Suby of* TRUSSWAY HOLDINGS INC) ★
9411 Alcorn St, Houston, TX 77093-6753
Tel (713) 691-6900 *Founded/Ownrshp* 1999
Sales 250.1MM^E *EMP* 1,543^E
SIC 2439 Trusses, except roof: laminated lumber
CEO: Jeff Smith

D-U-N-S 93-853-5671
TRUSSWAY MANUFACTURING INC
(*Suby of* TRUSSWAY INDUSTRIES INC) ★
9411 Alcorn St, Houston, TX 77093-6753
Tel (719) 322-9662 *Founded/Ownrshp* 2010
Sales 203.1MM^E *EMP* 700
SIC 2439 5031 Trusses, wooden roof; Structural assemblies, prefabricated: wood
CEO: Jim Thomas
**Pr:* Steve Stewart
CFO: John Gray
**CFO:* Kendall Hoyd
VP: Michael Estes
**VP:* Tony Harris
VP: David Pogue
Off Mgr: Ingrid Brown
Off Mgr: Karen Coats
Site Mgr: Daryl Matzelle
Site Mgr: Rob Sjoholm

TRUST COMPANY OF THE WEST
See TCW GROUP INC

D-U-N-S 07-723-8772
■**TRUST CO OF WEST**
(*Suby of* TRUST CO OF WEST) ★
865 S Figueroa St # 1800, Los Angeles, CA 90017-2543
Tel (213) 244-0000 *Founded/Ownrshp* 1971
Sales 100.2MM^E *EMP* 515
SIC 6211 Bond dealers & brokers
Pr: David Lippman
**Ch Bd:* Robert A Day
CFO: Bill Sonneborn
**CFO:* Richard M Villa
**V Ch Bd:* Ernest O Ellison
**V Ch Bd:* Thomas E Larkin
**Ex VP:* Alvin R Albe Jr
**Ex VP:* Mark I Stern
Ex VP: Michael Olson
Sr VP: Frank Gioia
Sr VP: Javier Segovia
Sr VP: Patricia A Wachtell
**VP:* Joseph Mburschinger
VP: Adam Coppersmith
VP: Patrick Dennis
**VP:* David Sdevito
**VP:* Mark Wgibello
VP: Jesal Mehta
VP: Michael Utley
Exec: Steven Shamaly

TRUST EMPLOYEE ADM & MGT
See RISK MANAGEMENT STRATEGIES INC

TRUST FOR GOVERNORS ISLAND, TH
See GOVERNORS ISLAND CORP

D-U-N-S 11-889-9090
TRUSTAFF MANAGEMENT INC
TRUSTAFF TRAVEL NURSES
4675 Cornell Rd, Blue Ash, OH 45241-2461
Tel (513) 272-3999 *Founded/Ownrshp* 2002
Sales 305.7MM *EMP* 2,000
SIC 8741 Personnel management
CEO: Brent Loring
**COO:* Pam Oliver
**VP:* Doug Dean
VP: Michelle Filipkowski
VP: Larry Hoelscher
**VP:* Sean Loring
Exec: Andrew Gehler
Exec: Clint Martz
Exec: Walt Reep
Exec: Ben Sanchez
Exec: Scott Whissel
Dir Bus: Jason Stockton

TRUSTAFF TRAVEL NURSES
See TRUSTAFF MANAGEMENT INC

D-U-N-S 79-104-2497
■**TRUSTCO BANK**
(*Suby of* TRUSTCO BANK CORP NY) ★
1 Sarnowski Dr, Schenectady, NY 12302-3503
Tel (518) 344-7510 *Founded/Ownrshp* 2007
Sales NA *EMP* 801^E
SIC 6022 State commercial banks
Prin: Robert Cormick

D-U-N-S 09-968-5729
▲**TRUSTCO BANK CORP NY**
5 Sarnowski Dr, Glenville, NY 12302-3503
Tel (518) 377-3311 *Founded/Ownrshp* 1981
Sales NA *EMP* 787^E
Tkr Sym TRST *Exch* NGS
SIC 6022 State commercial banks; State trust companies accepting deposits, commercial
Pr: Robert J McCormick
**Ch Bd:* Anthony J Marinello
COO: Robert T Cushing
CFO: Michael M Ozimek
Treas: Eric W Schreck
Ex VP: Robert M Leonard
Ex VP: Scot R Salvador

D-U-N-S 00-132-5935 IMP/EXP
TRUSTED MEDIA BRANDS INC
READER'S DIGEST
(*Suby of* RITTLEWOOD HOLDING CO) ★
750 3rd Ave Fl 3, New York, NY 10017-2723
Tel (914) 238-1000 *Founded/Ownrshp* 1922, 2014
Sales 1.6MMM^E *EMP* 4,300
SIC 2721 2731 5961 2741 Magazines: publishing only, not printed on site; Books: publishing only; Books, mail order (except book clubs); Record &/or tape (music or video) club, mail order; Miscellaneous publishing
Pr: Bonnie Kintzer
**Ch Bd:* Randall Curran
**COO:* Howard Halligan
**COO:* Brian Kennedy
**CFO:* Dean Durbin
**Chf Mktg O:* Alec Casey
Chf Mktg O: Leslie Dukker-Doty
**Ofcr:* Catherine M Cassidy
**Ofcr:* Vincent Errico
Ofcr: Bruce Kelley
**Ofcr:* Richard Sutton
**Sr VP:* Phyllis Gebhardt
Sr VP: Joann Murray
Sr VP: Brad Thomas
VP: William Adler
VP: Kirsten Marchioli
**VP:* Mark Sirota
**VP:* Elizabeth Vaccariello

D-U-N-S 13-582-9161
■**TRUSTEE PROGRAM UNITED STATES**
(*Suby of* UNITED STATES DEPARTMENT OF JUSTICE) ★
20 Massachusetts, Washington, DC 20530-0001
Tel (202) 307-1399 *Founded/Ownrshp* 2009
Sales NA *EMP* 1,106
SIC 9222 United States attorneys' offices;
Prin: Santal Manos

TRUSTEES OF AMHERST COLLEGE
See EMILY DICKINSON MUSEUM

D-U-N-S 06-698-5367
TRUSTEES OF AMHERST COLLEGE
103 Converse Hl, Amherst, MA 01002
Tel (413) 542-2000 *Founded/Ownrshp* 1821
Sales 216.8MM *EMP* 667
SIC 8221

D-U-N-S 04-589-6339
TRUSTEES OF BOSTON COLLEGE
140 Commonwealth Ave, Chestnut Hill, MA 02467-3800
Tel (617) 552-8000 *Founded/Ownrshp* 1863
Sales 733.0MM *EMP* 2,493^E
Accts Pricewaterhousecoopers Llp Bo
SIC 8221 College, except junior
Pr: William P Leahy Sj
Pr: Kelli Armstrong
Treas: John D Burke
**Treas:* Peter C McKenzie
Assoc VP: Avner Ash
VP: Alicia Angeles
VP: Mark Ben
VP: Michael Bourque
VP: Christian Brand
VP: Mary Corcoran
VP: Donna Cullinan
VP: Martin Dugal
VP: John Feudo
VP: Michael Forcier
VP: Thomas Keady
VP: Jan Larson
VP: Patricia McCormack
VP: James McIntyre
VP: Madeleine G Moore
VP: Marian G Moore
VP: Pat Ryan

D-U-N-S 04-943-5266
TRUSTEES OF BOSTON UNIVERSITY
1 Silber Way, Boston, MA 02215-1703
Tel (617) 353-9550 *Founded/Ownrshp* 1839
Sales 1.1MMM^E *EMP* 10,400
SIC 8221

D-U-N-S 07-534-9506
TRUSTEES OF CLARK UNIVERSITY
950 Main St, Worcester, MA 01610-1400
Tel (508) 793-7711 *Founded/Ownrshp* 1887
Sales 111.3MM *EMP* 600
Accts Grant Thornton Llp Boston Ma
SIC 8221 University
Pr: David P Angel
**Treas:* James Collins
Ofcr: Laurie Cormier
Ofcr: Michelle Smith
VP: C A McGadney
VP: Jason Morrow
Assoc Dir: Jonathan Burton
Off Admin: Jeanne McNeil
Dir IT: Pete Wason
Netwrk Mgr: Michael Cole
Opers Mgr: Mike Moran

D-U-N-S 01-062-8170
TRUSTEES OF COLORADO SCHOOL OF MINES
1500 Illinois St, Golden, CO 80401-1887
Tel (303) 273-3000 *Founded/Ownrshp* 1874
Sales 153.2MM^E *EMP* 1,000
Accts Bkd Llp Denver Co
SIC 8221 University
Pr: Anne Stark Walker
V Ch: Pam Blome
VP: Vy Duong
VP: Macy Kiel
VP: Debra Lasich
VP: Arthur Sacks
**VP:* Bill Scoggins
VP: Bruce Trudgill PHD
VP: Kirsten Volpi
**Prin:* Michelle Merz-Hutchinson
**Prin:* Susan Potter

D-U-N-S 04-917-9401 IMP
TRUSTEES OF COLUMBIA UNIVERSITY IN CITY OF NEW YORK
116th And Bdwy Way, New York, NY 10027
Tel (212) 854-9970 *Founded/Ownrshp* 1754
Sales 3.8MMM *EMP* 13,200
Accts Pricewaterhousecoopers Llp N
SIC 8221 8062 University; General medical & surgical hospitals; Hospital, medical school affiliated with residency
Pr: Lee C Bollinger
Pr: Susan K Feagin
Pr: Susan Glancy
Ofcr: Marsha L Wagner
Sr Inv Off: Roger Vincent
Assoc VP: Michelle Brown-Nevers
Assoc VP: Joseph Mannino
Assoc VP: Ellen S Smith
**Sr Ex VP:* Robert Kasdin
Ex VP: Nicholas B Dirks
Ex VP: Lee Goldman
Ex VP: Maxine Griffith
Ex VP: Joseph A Ienuso
Ex VP: G Michael Purdy
Ex VP: Jeffrey F Scott
Ex VP: David M Stone
**Ex VP:* Anne Sulivan
VP: Nicholas Dirks
VP: Kenneth Prewitt
VP: Luca Trevisan
Exec: David Hoeve

D-U-N-S 62-188-9815
TRUSTEES OF COLUMBIA UNIVERSITY IN CITY OF NEW YORK
HEALTH SCIENCES DIVISION
630 W 168th St Fl 4, New York, NY 10032-3725
Tel (212) 305-2862 *Founded/Ownrshp* 2015
Sales 370.9MM^E *EMP* 7,000^E
SIC 8221 8733 8062 University; Research institute; General medical & surgical hospitals

D-U-N-S 04-102-7822 IMP
TRUSTEES OF DARTMOUTH COLLEGE
20 Lebanon St, Hanover, NH 03755-3564
Tel (603) 646-1110 *Founded/Ownrshp* 1769
Sales 876.2MM *EMP* 5,000
Accts Pricewaterhousecoopers Llp B
SIC 8221 College, except junior
Pr: Philip J Hanlon
V Ch: John J Donahoe
Trst: Leon D Black
Trst: Christine B Bucklin
Trst: Denise M Dupre
Trst: Jose W Fernandez
Trst: William W Helman
Trst: Jeffrey R Immelt
Trst: Pamela J Joyner
Trst: John Lynch
Trst: Stephen F Mandel
Trst: Albert G Mulley
Trst: Sherri C Oberg
Trst: John A Rich
Trst: Peter M Robinson
Trst: Thurman J Rodgers
Trst: Stephen F Smith
Trst: Diana L Taylor
Chf Inves: David Ru
Assoc Dir: Jim Barr
Assoc Dir: Allison Hawke

D-U-N-S 07-105-9042
TRUSTEES OF DAVIDSON COLLEGE
209 Ridge Rd, Davidson, NC 28035
Tel (704) 894-2000 *Founded/Ownrshp* 1837
Sales 107.4MM^E *EMP* 800
Accts Kpmg Llp Greensboro Nc
SIC 8221 College, except junior
Pr: Carol Quillen
VP: Edward A Kania
Dir Rx: Mary Jones
Ex Dir: Garlene Davis
CIO: Raechelle Clemmons

D-U-N-S 06-697-3587
TRUSTEES OF DEERFIELD ACADEMY
7 Boyden Ln, Deerfield, MA 01342-5002
Tel (413) 772-0241 *Founded/Ownrshp* 1797
Sales 121.1MM *EMP* 337
Accts Blum Shapiro & Company Pc We
SIC 8211 Preparatory school
Prin: Margarita Curtis
**CFO:* Joe Manori
Psych: Elizabeth Bishop

D-U-N-S 05-241-6294
TRUSTEES OF ESTATE OF BERNICE PAUAHI BISHOP
KAMEHAMEHA SCHOOLS
567 S King St Ste 200, Honolulu, HI 96813-3079
Tel (808) 523-6200 *Founded/Ownrshp* 1884
Sales 915.0MM *EMP* 1,500
Accts Pricewaterhousecoopers Llp Wa

SIC 8211 Catholic combined elementary & secondary school
CEO: Dee Jay Mailer
**CFO:* Michael Loo
**Ch:* Robert K U Kihune
**Trst:* J Douglas Ing
**Trst:* Diane J Plotts
**Trst:* Nainoa Thompson
VP: Christopher Pating
VP: Colleen Wong
VP: Ryan Yamamoto
Snr Ntwrk: Ryan Okutani
IT Man: Jesse Eurich

D-U-N-S 06-276-3016
TRUSTEES OF GRINNELL COLLEGE (IA)
KDIC FM RADIO
733 Broad St, Grinnell, IA 50112-2227
Tel (641) 269-3500 *Founded/Ownrshp* 1846
Sales 104.6MM *EMP* 535
Accts Cliftonlarsonallen Llp Minne
SIC 8221 College, except junior
Pr: Raynard S Kington
VP: Joe Bagnoli
VP: Gwenna Ihrie
VP: Jim Reische
Assoc Dir: Jonathan Edwards
Assoc Dir: Gretchen Zimmermann
Comm Dir: Jim Powers
Mtls Mgr: Roger Bauman
Mtls Mgr: Ron Cooper
Pgrm Dir: Katie Simmons

D-U-N-S 96-488-3248
TRUSTEES OF HAMLINE UNIVERSITY OF MINNESOTA
1536 Hewitt Ave Ms-Ai775, Saint Paul, MN 55104-1205
Tel (651) 523-2800 *Founded/Ownrshp* 2010
Sales 123.3MM *EMP* 41
SIC 8221 Colleges universities & professional schools
Ch: Rodney Jordan
Trst: Laura Chin

D-U-N-S 06-698-1226
TRUSTEES OF HAMPSHIRE COLLEGE
893 West St, Amherst, MA 01002-3372
Tel (413) 549-4600 *Founded/Ownrshp* 1965
Sales 92.3MM *EMP* 548
Accts Kpmg Llp Boston Ma
SIC 8221 College, except junior
Pr: Jonathan Lash
Pr: Abby Ferguson
Pr: Joanna Olin
VP: Mark K Spiro
Dir Lab: Naya Gabriel
Ex Dir: Sharon Shaloo
IT Man: Barbara Aldrich
IT Man: Adam Stoffolano
Netwrk Eng: Josiah Erikson
Mktg Dir: Agudelo Hart
Mktg Dir: Michael Medeiros

D-U-N-S 00-604-6700 IMP
TRUSTEES OF INDIANA UNIVERSITY
509 E 3rd St, Bloomington, IN 47401-3654
Tel (812) 855-0516 *Founded/Ownrshp* 1820
Sales 2.2MMM *EMP* 16,000
SIC 8221 University
Pr: Michael A McRobbie
Pr: Linda Hunt
CFO: Maryfrances McCourt
CFO: Neil Theobald
Ofcr: Diana Borecky
Ex VP: John S Applegate
Ex VP: Charles R Bantz
Ex VP: Peter Bogdanovich
Ex VP: Eric Bruder
Ex VP: Mitch Ennis
Ex VP: Duane Schau
VP: Frances Adjorlolo
VP: David K Ayers
VP: Elliott R Barkan
VP: Stew Cobine
VP: Cory Cochran
VP: Dennis Cromwell
VP: Christine Fitzpatrick
VP: Julie Head
VP: Stephen Keucher
VP: Garrett Lance
Board of Directors: William R Cast MD, Philip N Eskew Jr, Stephen L Ferguson, Jack M Gill, Arthur D King, Thomas E Reilly Jr, Patrick A Shoulders, Sue H Talbot

TRUSTEES OF LAWRENCEVILLE SCHO
See LAWRENCEVILLE SCHOOL

D-U-N-S 07-758-3813
TRUSTEES OF MEASE HOSPITAL INC
MEASE HEALTH CARE
(*Suby of* BAYCARE EDUCATION SERVICES) ★
601 Main St, Dunedin, FL 34698-5848
Tel (727) 733-1111 *Founded/Ownrshp* 1938
Sales 430.9MM *EMP* 2,000
Accts Ernst & Young Us Llp Atlanta
SIC 8062 General medical & surgical hospitals
CEO: Philip K Beauchamp
**Pr:* James Pfieffer
COO: Lou Galdieri
**CFO:* Carl Tremone
Dir Rad: Peggy McBrayer
Doctor: Richard G Lacamera MD

D-U-N-S 06-698-5714 EXP
TRUSTEES OF MOUNT HOLYOKE COLLEGE
50 College St, South Hadley, MA 01075-1448
Tel (413) 538-2000 *Founded/Ownrshp* 1836
Sales 204.7MM *EMP* 1,000^E^
SIC 8221 Colleges & universities
Pr: Lynn Pasquerella
**Treas:* Janice Albino
Trst: Margaret L Woff
VP: Dawn Blyda
VP: Kassandra Jolley
VP: Michelle Leclerc
VP: Sonya Stephens
Dir Risk M: Elizabeth Carmichael
Dir Lab: Marc Boucher
Assoc Dir: John Fortini
Assoc Dir: Cindy Legare
Assoc Dir: Kevin McCaffrey

D-U-N-S 61-364-5985
TRUSTEES OF PHILLIPS ACADEMY
ANDOVER ACADEMY
180 Main St, Andover, MA 01810-4166
Tel (978) 749-4000 *Founded/Ownrshp* 1778
Sales 90.6MM *EMP* 600
Accts Mayer Hoffman Mccann Pc Bos
SIC 8211 8412 Academy; Museum
COO: Stephen Carter
Ofcr: Kassie Archambault
Ofcr: Sharyn Bahn
Ofcr: Wendy Cogswell
Ofcr: Roger Cowley
Top Exec: Peter Merrill
Assoc Dir: Nancy Alpert
Assoc Dir: Sallie L Batchelor
Assoc Dir: Lauren Cote
Assoc Dir: Michael Fennell
Assoc Dir: Leislie Godo-Solo
Assoc Dir: Jennifer Savino
Assoc Dir: Stephen Silversides

D-U-N-S 00-248-4665 IMP/EXP
TRUSTEES OF PRINCETON UNIVERSITY
1 Nassau Hall, Princeton, NJ 08544-2001
Tel (609) 258-3000 *Founded/Ownrshp* 1746
Sales 1.6MMM *EMP* 6,000^E^
Accts Pricewaterhousecoopers Llp Ne
SIC 8221 University
Pr: Christopher L Eisgruber
**Treas:* Carolyn Ainslie
Treas: Carolyn N Ainslie
**Ex VP:* Treby Williams
VP: Jay Dominick
Assoc Dir: Diana Altegoer
Assoc Dir: Edward Freeland
Assoc Dir: Anthony E Novembre
Assoc Dir: Beth Perrino
Assoc Dir: Katherine Stellato
Assoc Dir: Catherine B Weber
Comm Man: Mikeo Brenda
Comm Man: Donald Kanka

D-U-N-S 04-219-6998
TRUSTEES OF ROANOKE COLLEGE (VA)
221 College Ln, Salem, VA 24153-3747
Tel (540) 375-2500 *Founded/Ownrshp* 1842
Sales 107.6MM *EMP* 400^E^
SIC 8221 7929 College, except junior; Entertainers & entertainment groups
Pr: Sabine O'Hara
**Pr:* Michael C Maxey
**Ch:* Morris Cregger Jr
**Treas:* Mark P Nottsinger
VP: Judi Nelson
VP: George Zubrod
Exec: Edward Phillips
Assoc Dir: Anita Webster
Ex Dir: Jack Williams
Off Mgr: Sandra Jackson
Telecom Mg: Carolyn T Rail

D-U-N-S 06-698-9427
TRUSTEES OF SMITH COLLEGE
10 Elm St College Hall, Northampton, MA 01063-0001
Tel (413) 585-2550 *Founded/Ownrshp* 1871
Sales 406.7MM *EMP* 1,300
Accts Kpmg Llp Hartford Ct
SIC 8221 Colleges universities & professional schools
Pr: Kathleen McCartney
Treas: Lora Olson
Bd of Dir: Wayne Smith
Ofcr: Mary E Irwin
**VP:* Ruth Constantine
VP: David Deswert
VP: Karin George
VP: Ronald Smith
VP: Ileana Streinu
Dir Teleco: Sharon A Moore
Assoc Dir: Jason T Bauer-Clapp
Assoc Dir: Cheryl A Dellecese
Assoc Dir: Michael Ireland
Assoc Dir: Karl Kowitz

D-U-N-S 07-175-0079
TRUSTEES OF ST JOSEPHS COLLEGE
SJC
278 Whites Bridge Rd, Standish, ME 04084-5236
Tel (207) 892-6766 *Founded/Ownrshp* 1912
Sales 56.1MM *EMP* 1,000
Accts Mayer Hoffman Mccann Pc Bos
SIC 8221 College, except junior
Pr: Dr James Dlugos
**CFO:* Yvonne Berry
**VP:* Joanne Bean
**VP:* Michael Pardales
**VP:* Sr Kathleen Sullivan
Assoc Dir: Loni English

D-U-N-S 07-313-4835
TRUSTEES OF TUFTS COLLEGE
TUFTS UNIVERSITY
169 Holland St Ste 318, Somerville, MA 02144-2401
Tel (617) 628-5000 *Founded/Ownrshp* 1852
Sales 965.7MM *EMP* 4,100
Accts Pricewaterhousecoopers Llp Bo
SIC 8221 2791 2752 University; Typesetting; Commercial printing, lithographic
Pr: Anthony Monaco
**Ch Bd:* Nathan Gantcher
V Ch: Peter R Dolan
CFO: Thompson William
**Ch:* James A Stern
Treas: Darleen F Karp
**Treas:* Thomas S Mc Gurty
Trst: Alfred I Tauber
Trst: Thomas M Alperin
Trst: Robert R Bendetson
Trst: Claire M Davis
Trst: Jeannie H Diefenderfer
Trst: Daniel J Doherty
Trst: Laurie A Gabriel
Trst: Steven M Galbraith
Trst: Steven A Goldstein
Trst: Joanne S Gowa
Trst: Varney J Hintlian
Trst: Deborah R Jospin
Trst: Brian H Kavoogian
Trst: Jeffrey B Kindler

D-U-N-S 05-937-5584
TRUSTEES OF UNION COLLEGE IN TOWN OF SCHENECTADY IN STATE OF NEW YORK
807 Union St, Schenectady, NY 12308-3256
Tel (518) 388-6630 *Founded/Ownrshp* 1795
Sales 178.3MM *EMP* 870^E^
Accts Lb Grant Thornton Llp New Yor
SIC 8221 College, except junior
Pr: Stephen C Ainlay
CIO: Borkowski Ellen

D-U-N-S 04-225-0712 IMP/EXP
TRUSTEES OF UNIVERSITY OF PENNSYLVANIA
CLINICAL PRACTICES OFT
3451 Walnut St, Philadelphia, PA 19104-6205
Tel (215) 898-6301 *Founded/Ownrshp* 1753
Sales 8.7MMM^E^ *EMP* 20,433
Accts Pricewaterhousecoopers Llc Ph
SIC 8221 9411 University; Administration of educational programs
Pr: Amy Gutmann
V Ch: Jon Huntsman
**COO:* Robert Martin
Ofcr: Linda Yoder
Ex VP: Sanjeev Khanna
**Ex VP:* Dr Arthur Rubenstein
Sr VP: Wendy S White
VP: Robin H Beck
**VP:* Craig R Carnaroli
VP: John J Heuer
VP: Anne Papageorge
VP: John H Zeller
Assoc Dir: Thierry Chauche
Assoc Dir: Jamie Grant
Assoc Dir: Claire Klieger
Assoc Dir: Rosanne Lurie
Assoc Dir: Wendy McGeehan
Assoc Dir: Erin McGowan
Assoc Dir: James Pardonek
Assoc Dir: Todd Rothman

D-U-N-S 06-860-5054
TRUSTEES OF WHEATON COLLEGE
HONEY ROCK CAMP
501 College Ave, Wheaton, IL 60187-5501
Tel (630) 752-5000 *Founded/Ownrshp* 1861
Sales 179.5MM *EMP* 820
Accts Crowe Horwath Llp Chicago Il
SIC 8221 College, except junior
Pr: Philip G Ryken
Treas: David E Johnston
**VP:* Dr Paul Chelsen
**VP:* Dr Mark Dillon
**VP:* Dr Dale Kemp
VP: Fabien Laugier
Off Admin: Sarah Thom
Opers Mgr: Janelle Kwee
Pr Dir: Latonya Taylor

D-U-N-S 95-709-5404
TRUSTHOUSE SERVICES GROUP INC
(*Suby of* ELIOR)
4135 Southstream Blvd # 250, Charlotte, NC 28217-4514
Tel (704) 424-1071 *Founded/Ownrshp* 2013
Sales 102.7MM^E^ *EMP* 2,957
SIC 5812 Contract food services
CEO: Michael Bailey
CFO: Patrick Putnam
**CFO:* Hugh F Totman
Ofcr: Anne-Isabelle Gros
**Ex VP:* Chris Ciatto
**VP:* Deborah M Devere
**VP:* James M Everett
**VP:* Dan Kubanet

TRUSTMARK COMPANIES
See TRUSTMARK LIFE INSURANCE CO

TRUSTMARK COMPANIES
See TRUSTMARK INSURANCE CO (MUTUAL)

TRUSTMARK COMPANIES
See TRUSTMARK MUTUAL HOLDING CO

D-U-N-S 07-791-1360 IMP
▲TRUSTMARK CORP
248 E Capitol St Ste 704, Jackson, MS 39201-2508
Tel (601) 208-5111 *Founded/Ownrshp* 1968
Sales NA *EMP* 2,941^E^
Tkr Sym TRMK *Exch* NGS
SIC 6021 National commercial banks
Pr: Gerard R Host
**Ch Bd:* Daniel A Grafton
CFO: Louis E Greer
VP: Walt James
VP: Mike Oconnell
Brnch Mgr: Penny Sorrell
Opers Mgr: Richard G Hickson
Sls Mgr: Jay Wheatley
Board of Directors: Adolphus B Baker, Tracy T Conerly, Toni D Cooley, John M McCullouch, Harris V Morrissette, Richard H Puckett, R Michael Summerford, Leroy G Walker Jr, William G Yates III

D-U-N-S 06-439-7581
TRUSTMARK INSURANCE CO (MUTUAL)
TRUSTMARK COMPANIES
(*Suby of* TRUSTMARK COMPANIES) ★
400 N Field Dr, Lake Forest, IL 60045-4809
Tel (847) 283-4145 *Founded/Ownrshp* 1913
Sales NA *EMP* 4,100
SIC 6321 6311 Health insurance carriers; Accident insurance carriers; Life insurance carriers
Ch Bd: Donald M Peterson
**Ch Bd:* J Grover Thomas Jr
**CEO:* Dave McDonough
**CFO:* J Brinke Marcuccilli
**Treas:* Richard D Batten
**Ex VP:* Chris Martin
**Ex VP:* Mark Schmidt
Sr VP: John Anderson
**Sr VP:* Jim Derleth
Sr VP: M Ray Haase
**Sr VP:* Ebby Khazaeli
Sr VP: Kate Martin
Sr VP: Barbara Wurfel
VP: Catherine Bresler
VP: David J Flores
VP: Lisa Haag
VP: Daniel Hanke
VP: Jeff McLeroy
VP: Stephen Penny
VP: Joe Pray
VP: Wendy Warren
Board of Directors: Frederick Blackmon, Woodruff A Burt, Peter Drake, Robert B Duncan, Leonard P Judy, Maribeth S Rahe, David Weick, Peter D Ziegler

D-U-N-S 06-048-0688
TRUSTMARK LIFE INSURANCE CO
TRUSTMARK COMPANIES
(*Suby of* TRUSTMARK COMPANIES) ★
400 N Field Dr, Lake Forest, IL 60045-2581
Tel (847) 615-1500 *Founded/Ownrshp* 1985
Sales NA *EMP* 3
SIC 6321 Accident & health insurance
Ch Bd: Donald Peterson
**Pr:* Grover Thomas
VP: Frank G Gramm

D-U-N-S 79-657-9659
TRUSTMARK MUTUAL HOLDING CO
TRUSTMARK COMPANIES
400 N Field Dr, Lake Forest, IL 60045-4809
Tel (847) 615-1500 *Founded/Ownrshp* 2004
Sales 531.8MM^E^ *EMP* 7,872
SIC 7991 8099 Physical fitness facilities; Health screening service
Ch: J Grover Thomas
Pr: Scott Bartlett
Pr: Doug Reilly
**Ofcr:* Jim Coleman
Ofcr: Ron Watt
Sr VP: Kate Martin
**Sr VP:* Dennis L Schoff
**Sr VP:* Dan Simpson
VP: John Anderson
VP: Nancy Eckrich
VP: Marisue Fasick
VP: Phil Goss
VP: Donna Heiser
VP: Deborah O'Connor
VP: Rich Olejniczak
VP: Dennis Richling
VP: Debbie Rutledge
Assoc Dir: Traci Chistopher
Dir Rx: Dave Punke
Board of Directors: Kevin Slawin

D-U-N-S 07-195-2345
■TRUSTMARK NATIONAL BANK
(*Suby of* TRUSTMARK CORP) ★
248 E Capitol St Ste 704, Jackson, MS 39201-2582
Tel (601) 208-5111 *Founded/Ownrshp* 1968
Sales NA *EMP* 254
SIC 6021 National commercial banks
Ch: Richard G Hickson
**Ch Bd:* Daniel A Grafton
**Treas:* Louis E Greer
Ofcr: Chris Barnes
Ofcr: Michael Belmes
Ofcr: Marcia Walker
Trst Ofcr: Stephen Samson
Ex VP: Zach Wasson
Sr VP: Mitch Bleske
Sr VP: John E Bonar
Sr VP: Cindy Brown
Sr VP: Donald Cioban
Sr VP: Tod Etheredge
Sr VP: Ella J Putnam
Sr VP: Christopher Styga
VP: Cathy Baldwin
VP: Bobbie Celano
VP: Barry Collier
VP: Chris Conken
VP: Cathy Duncan
VP: Katie Ferrell
Board of Directors: Kenneth W Williams, Reuben V Anderson, William G Yates Jr, Adolphus B Baker, William C Deviney Jr, C Gerald Garnett, Richard Hickson, David H Hoster, John M McCullouch, Richard Puckett, R Michael Summerford

D-U-N-S 12-891-6397
TRUSTWAVE CORP
AMBIRONTRUSTWAVE
(*Suby of* SINGAPORE TELECOM USA INC.)
70 W Madison St Ste 1050, Chicago, IL 60602-4281
Tel (312) 873-7500 *Founded/Ownrshp* 2000
Sales 118.7MM^E^ *EMP* 40^E^
SIC 7299 7373 Information services, consumer; Systems integration services
CEO: Robert McCullen
Pr: Jason Skaria
COO: Andrew Bokor
**COO:* Rick Miller
**CFO:* William G Barker
**CFO:* Kevin Kilraine
Chf Mktg O: Leo J Cole
Ex VP: Dave Feringa
**Ex VP:* James Kunkel
**Sr VP:* Michael Bartlett
Sr VP: John Chiochetti
Sr VP: Michael Petitti
Sr VP: Jim Ritchings
Sr VP: Chris Schueler
**Sr VP:* Phil J Smith
Sr VP: Charles Spallitta
VP: Michael Cerick
VP: Larry French
VP: Karen Lindgren
VP: Cas Purdy
VP: Niren Shah

D-U-N-S 16-947-6889
TRUSTWAVE HOLDINGS INC
(*Suby of* AMBIRONTRUSTWAVE) ★
70 W Madison St Ste 1050, Chicago, IL 60602-4281
Tel (312) 750-0950 *Founded/Ownrshp* 2005
Sales 115.7MM^E^ *EMP* 40
SIC 7373 7372 Systems integration services; Prepackaged software
CEO: Robert J McCullen

CFO: Mark Iserloth
Ex VP: Andrew Bokor
VP: Steven Mallia
VP: Marc Shinbrood
VP: Brian Trevey
Mkt Mgr: Kelly Shelton

D-U-N-S 96-822-0314
■TRUTEAM LLC
(*Suby of* TOPBUILD SERVICES GROUP CORP) ★
260 Jimmy Ann Dr, Daytona Beach, FL 32114-1318
Tel (386) 304-2200 *Founded/Ownrshp* 2003
Sales 492.5MM[E] *EMP* 6,112[E]
SIC 1742 1761 1751 1521 Insulation, buildings; Gutter & downspout contractor; Garage door, installation or erection; General remodeling, single-family houses
Pr: Robert M Buck
* *Treas:* George Sellew
* *Ex VP:* John S Peterson
Sr VP: Larry Laseter
* *VP:* David Cushen
Prgrm Mgr: Stephanie Borba
Rgnl Mgr: Jeff Curtin
Dist Mgr: Logan Plunkett
Div Mgr: Matt Hashagen
Div Mgr: Jeff Salmon
Div Mgr: Andrew Short

D-U-N-S 80-957-1201 IMP/EXP
TRUTH HARDWARE CORP
(*Suby of* TYMAN PLC)
700 W Bridge St, Owatonna, MN 55060-2775
Tel (507) 451-5620 *Founded/Ownrshp* 1979
Sales 158.9MM[E] *EMP* 900
SIC 2431 3442 3429 Windows & window parts & trim, wood; Metal doors, sash & trim; Manufactured hardware (general)
Pr: Jeffrey Graby
CFO: Patti Siegfried
Exec: Rachel White

TRUVEN HEALTH ANALYTICS
See TRUVEN HOLDING CORP

D-U-N-S 03-683-8092
■TRUVEN HEALTH ANALYTICS INC (DE)
(*Suby of* TRUVEN HEALTH ANALYTICS) ★
100 Phoenix Dr, Ann Arbor, MI 48108-2635
Tel (734) 913-3000 *Founded/Ownrshp* 2008, 2012
Sales 53.1MM[E] *EMP* 2,100
SIC 8742 Hospital & health services consultant
Pr: Mike Boswood
Pr: Drew Cable
* *COO:* Roy Martin
* *COO:* Jon Newpol
* *CFO:* Phil Buckingham
* *Ofcr:* Anita Mahon
Sr VP: August Calhoun
Sr VP: Bob Kelley
VP: Ron Goetzel
VP: Rahul Joglekar
VP: Charly Kurian
VP: Mason Russell

D-U-N-S 11-026-5902
■TRUVEN HOLDING CORP
TRUVEN HEALTH ANALYTICS
(*Suby of* IBM) ★
100 Phoenix Dr Ste 100, Ann Arbor, MI 48108-2600
Tel (734) 913-3000 *Founded/Ownrshp* 2012
Sales 549.6MM[E] *EMP* 2,110[E]
Accts Pricewaterhousecoopers Llp Ne
SIC 8742 Hospital & health services consultant
Pr: Mike Boswood
* *COO:* Roy Martin
* *Ex VP:* Phil Buckingham
* *Ex VP:* Jon Newpol
* *Genl Couns:* Andra Heller

D-U-N-S 11-204-4248 IMP
TRW AUTOMOTIVE INC
(*Suby of* ZF TRW AUTOMOTIVE HOLDINGS CORP) ★
12025 Tech Center Dr, Livonia, MI 48150-2122
Tel (734) 266-2600 *Founded/Ownrshp* 2003
Sales 16.2MMM[E] *EMP* 57,499
Accts Ernst & Young Llp Troy Michi
SIC 3714 Connecting rods, motor vehicle engine; Steering mechanisms, motor vehicle; Brake drums, motor vehicle; Hydraulic fluid power pumps for auto steering mechanism
Pr: John C Plant
* *Ex VP:* Steven Lunn
* *VP:* Aly A Badawy
* *VP:* Joseph Cantie
* *VP:* Peter J Lake
* *VP:* Josef Pickenhahn
Prgrm Mgr: Jeff Massey
Board of Directors: William Lawrence, Paul H O'neill, Philip Odeen, Robert H Swan, Howard Knicely Kathleen We

D-U-N-S 12-375-2912 IMP/EXP
TRW AUTOMOTIVE US LLC
(*Suby of* ZF TRW AUTOMOTIVE HOLDINGS CORP) ★
12001 Tech Center Dr, Livonia, MI 48150-2122
Tel (734) 855-2600 *Founded/Ownrshp* 2002
Sales 971.7MM[E] *EMP* 4,507
SIC 3679 3469 3089 Electronic switches; Metal stampings; Plastic processing
CEO: John C Plant
* *Ex VP:* Joseph S Cantie
* *Ex VP:* Steven Lunn

D-U-N-S 60-936-2421 IMP
TRW VEHICLE SAFETY SYSTEMS INC
(*Suby of* ZF TRW AUTOMOTIVE HOLDINGS CORP) ★
4505 26 Mile Rd, Washington, MI 48094-2600
Tel (734) 855-2600 *Founded/Ownrshp* 2003
Sales 1.4MMM[E] *EMP* 9,500
SIC 3714 Motor vehicle parts & accessories
Pr: James F Smith
CFO: Joseph S Cantie
Ex VP: Peter Holdmann
Ex VP: Peter J Lake
Ex VP: Neil E Marchuk
Ex VP: Mark Stewart
Sftwr Eng: Alexander Schemmel
VP Opers: Steven Lunn

D-U-N-S 02-816-8876
TRYKO PARTNERS LLC
575 Route 70 Fl 2, Brick, NJ 08723-4042
Tel (732) 961-9991 *Founded/Ownrshp* 1989
Sales 131.5MM[E] *EMP* 250[E]
SIC 6531 8051 Real estate managers; Skilled nursing care facilities
CEO: Yitzchok Rokowsky
* *Pr:* Yonah Kohn
* *VP:* Hirsch Chinn
* *VP:* Mark Gold
* *VP:* Jack Nusbaum

D-U-N-S 08-776-3491
TRZ HOLDINGS II INC
TRIZAC PROPERTIES
(*Suby of* BROOKFIELD ASSET MANAGEMENT INC)
3 World Financial Ctr, New York, NY 10281-1013
Tel (212) 693-8150 *Founded/Ownrshp* 2006
Sales 86.7MM[E] *EMP* 356[E]
SIC 6798 Real estate investment trusts
Pr: Dennis Friedrich
* *CFO:* Craig J Laurie
Dir Sec: Byron McDaniel

TS
See TRANSYSTEMS CORP

D-U-N-S 07-880-1572
TS TECH AMERICAS INC (OH)
(*Suby of* TS TECH CO., LTD.)
8458 E Broad St, Reynoldsburg, OH 43068-9749
Tel (614) 575-4100 *Founded/Ownrshp* 2013
Sales 1.1MMM[E] *EMP* 6,186
SIC 5099 Child restraint seats, automotive
Pr: Minoru Maeda
Sr VP: Takayuki Maegawa
VP: Kazuhisa Saito
Snr Mgr: Hideaki Takagi

D-U-N-S 88-352-6634 IMP
TS TECH USA CORP
(*Suby of* TS TECH AMERICAS INC) ★
8400 E Broad St, Reynoldsburg, OH 43068-9749
Tel (614) 577-1088 *Founded/Ownrshp* 2013
Sales 113.5MM[E] *EMP* 400[E]
SIC 3714 Motor vehicle body components & frame
Pr: Kazuhiso Saito
* *VP:* Rudy Claming
* *VP:* Hideo Mizusawa
Genl Mgr: Kazumi Morioka
Dir IT: Frank Kotsonis
Info Man: Wendell Long

D-U-N-S 16-125-8363 IMP
TS TRIM INDUSTRIES INC
(*Suby of* TS TECH AMERICAS INC) ★
6380 Canal St, Canal Winchester, OH 43110-9640
Tel (614) 837-4114 *Founded/Ownrshp* 2013
Sales 92.4MM[E] *EMP* 435
SIC 5013 3465 3714 3083

TSA LUGGAGE LOCKS
See SAFE SKIES LLC

D-U-N-S 17-539-1242 IMP/EXP
TSA STORES INC
SPORTS AUTHORITY
(*Suby of* SPORTS AUTHORITY INC) ★
1050 W Hampden Ave, Englewood, CO 80110-2118
Tel (303) 200-5050 *Founded/Ownrshp* 2003
Sales 1.1MMM[E] *EMP* 9,010
SIC 5941 4832 Sporting goods & bicycle shops; Sports
Ch Bd: Martin E Hanaka
Exec: Nesa E Hassanein

D-U-N-S 83-459-6822
TSB NUCLEAR ENERGY USA GROUP INC
(*Suby of* TOSHIBA NUCLEAR ENERGY HOLDINGS (US) INC) ★
1000 Westinghouse Dr, Cranberry Township, PA 16066-5228
Tel (412) 374-4111 *Founded/Ownrshp* 1996
Sales 3.9MMM[E] *EMP* 12,804
SIC 3823 3559 Nuclear reactor controls; Nuclear reactor control rod & drive mechanism
Pr: Richard Gabbianelli
* *Treas:* Michael F Wilson
* *VP:* F R Coates

TSC
See TECHNOLOGY SERVICE CORP

D-U-N-S 14-749-0031
TSC HOLDINGS INC
(*Suby of* NESTLE HOLDINGS INC) ★
800 N Brand Blvd, Glendale, CA 91203-1245
Tel (818) 549-6000 *Founded/Ownrshp* 1985
Sales 1.5MMM[E] *EMP* 8,625
SIC 2038 Frozen specialties
Ch Bd: Joe Weller
* *Treas:* Manfred R Lehmann
* *Sr VP:* Kristin Adrian

D-U-N-S 00-303-1924 IMP
TSC OFFSHORE CORP (TX)
7611 Railhead Ln, Houston, TX 77086-3255
Tel (832) 456-3900 *Founded/Ownrshp* 1990
Sales 230.2MM[E] *EMP* 1,300
SIC 3533 Oil & gas drilling rigs & equipment
CEO: Robert A Sliva
* *Pr:* Robert S Shinfield
* *Sr VP:* Robert J Ream
* *VP:* Scott Fullerton
* *VP:* William R Lewis
* *CTO:* Dr Sun Yuanhui

D-U-N-S 03-057-0433
TSG RESOURCES INC
339 E Maple St Ste 110, North Canton, OH 44720-2593
Tel (330) 498-8107 *Founded/Ownrshp* 1972
Sales 2.3MM[E] *EMP* 5,500
SIC 8742 Business planning & organizing services
CEO: Dennis Conley

D-U-N-S 62-054-0729
TSG SKI & GOLF LLC
HERITAGE APPAREL
565 Mountain Village Blvd, Telluride, CO 81435-9521
Tel (970) 728-6900 *Founded/Ownrshp* 2003
Sales 33.8MM[E] *EMP* 1,000
SIC 7997 Membership sports & recreation clubs
IT Man: Benjamin Whyting
Mktg Mgr: Bill Kight

D-U-N-S 79-637-5868
■TSI GROUP INC
THERMAL SOLUTIONS
(*Suby of* B/E AEROSPACE INC) ★
94 Tide Mill Rd, Hampton, NH 03842-2705
Tel (603) 964-0296 *Founded/Ownrshp* 2010
Sales 97.3MM[E] *EMP* 778
SIC 3599 3398 3443 3444 Machine & other job shop work; Machine shop, jobbing & repair; Brazing (hardening) of metal; Fabricated plate work (boiler shop); Housings, pressure; Heat exchangers, plate type; Sheet metalwork
CEO: Gregory R Tucker
Pr: E J Mondor
Pr: Kevin Rowan
* *CFO:* David K Helms
* *Ex VP:* Dale Jessick
Comm Man: Kristy Sugg

D-U-N-S 05-593-5928 IMP/EXP
TSI HOLDING CO
999 Exectve Pkwy Dr # 202, Saint Louis, MO 63141-6336
Tel (314) 628-6000 *Founded/Ownrshp* 1980
Sales 154.9MM[E] *EMP* 1,125
SIC 5094 5051 Jewelry & precious stones; Pipe & tubing, steel
Pr: John C Hauck
* *CFO:* Annette M Eckerle
* *Ex VP:* Craig Iammarino

D-U-N-S 00-625-3124 IMP
TSI INC (MN)
(*Suby of* CHURCHILL COMPANIES) ★
500 Cardigan Rd, Saint Paul, MN 55126-3996
Tel (651) 483-0900 *Founded/Ownrshp* 1961
Sales 274.3MM[E] *EMP* 850
SIC 3579 3829 3823 3845 3825 Time clocks & time recording devices; Measuring & controlling devices; Industrial instrmnts msrmnt display/control process variable; Electromedical equipment; Instruments to measure electricity
CEO: John J Fauth
Pr: Tom Kennedy
Treas: Robert F Gallagher
Sr Cor Off: Victor Cornellier
Ofcr: Jerry Bark
Sr VP: Lowell D Nystrom
VP: Gary Davis
VP: Tom Jacobson
VP: Joylynn Jarvis
VP: Neil Marchuk
VP: Rich Remiarz
VP: Greg Wheatley

D-U-N-S 13-920-0542
TSK OF AMERICA INC
(*Suby of* HI-LEX CORPORATION)
5200 Wayne Rd, Battle Creek, MI 49037-7392
Tel (269) 968-0781 *Founded/Ownrshp* 2003
Sales 214.4MM[E] *EMP* 617[E]
SIC 3357 Automotive wire & cable, except ignition sets: nonferrous

D-U-N-S 15-342-1623
TSL LTD
5217 Monroe St Ste A1, Toledo, OH 43623-4604
Tel (419) 843-3200 *Founded/Ownrshp* 1986
Sales 35.0MM[E] *EMP* 2,500
SIC 7363 Truck driver services
Pr: Donald J Finnegan

D-U-N-S 82-876-0061 IMP
TSMC DEVELOPMENT INC
TAIWAN SEMICDTR MFG CO LTD
(*Suby of* TSMC PARTNERS LTD.)
5509 Nw Parker St, Camas, WA 98607-8557
Tel (360) 817-3000 *Founded/Ownrshp* 1996
Sales 169.2MM[E] *EMP* 1,172[E]
SIC 3674 Semiconductor circuit networks
Prin: Kc Shu
COO: Steve TSO
VP: Kc Hsu
Mng Dir: Sue Metzger
Genl Mgr: Chris Gomez
CIO: Eric Chou
CIO: Gene Toler
CTO: Steve Hill
Dir IT: Rick Wright
IT Man: Kingbird Lin
IT Man: Phillip Yu

TSS MEDICAL
See TSS TECHNOLOGIES INC

D-U-N-S 01-768-9373 IMP
TSS TECHNOLOGIES INC
TSS MEDICAL
8800 Global Way, West Chester, OH 45069-7070
Tel (513) 772-7000 *Founded/Ownrshp* 1975
Sales 123.5MM[E] *EMP* 400
SIC 3599 8711 Machine shop, jobbing & repair; Mechanical engineering
Pr: Brent Nichols
Chf Mktg O: Bruce Bacon
* *VP:* Charles B Nichols Jr
* *VP:* Scott Nichols
Assoc Dir: Joe Haupt
* *Prin:* Leila B Nichols
* *Prin:* Charles P Taft
* *Prin:* Ruth Zimmerman
Mng Dir: Kriss Cloninger
Manager: Steve Nesmith
Ql Cn Mgr: Edwin Davish
Board of Directors: Leila B Nichols

D-U-N-S 01-987-2461 IMP
TST NA TRIM LLC (TX)
(*Suby of* TS TECH AMERICAS INC) ★
401 E Olmos Ave, Hidalgo, TX 78557
Tel (956) 843-3500 *Founded/Ownrshp* 2010
Sales 228.8MM[E] *EMP* 3,000
SIC 3465 Automotive stampings
Pr: Kazuhisa Saito
* *Treas:* Yasuo Kibe

TSTC SYSTEM
See TEXAS STATE TECHNICAL COLLEGE

TSTIMPRESO
See IMPRESO INC

TSU
See TEXAS SOUTHERN UNIVERSITY

D-U-N-S 61-031-8987
TSVC INC
18001 W 106th St Ste 300, Olathe, KS 66061-6447
Tel (913) 599-6886 *Founded/Ownrshp* 2006
Sales 98.4MM[E] *EMP* 3,680
SIC 7389 Inspection & testing services
CEO: David Gaboury

TSYS
See TOTAL SYSTEM SERVICES INC

TT ELECTRONICS
See BI TECHNOLOGIES CORP

D-U-N-S 61-035-7670
TT OF LAKE NORMAN LLC
LAKE NRMAN CHRYSLER JEEP DODGE
20700 Torrence Chapel Rd, Cornelius, NC 28031-6318
Tel (704) 896-3800 *Founded/Ownrshp* 2008
Sales 90.0MM *EMP* 140
SIC 5511 New & used car dealers
Exec: Stephanie Lang
Off Admin: Jennifer Patterson
DP Exec: Lois Stapleton
Sls Mgr: Bill Gibson
Sales Asso: Willie Brown
Sales Asso: Sam Dewitt
Sales Asso: Ed Lucas

D-U-N-S 80-711-4819
TTEC-TESORO JOINT VENTURE
5250 Challedon Dr, Virginia Beach, VA 23462-6304
Tel (770) 825-7100 *Founded/Ownrshp* 2007
Sales 100.0MM *EMP* 99
SIC 1542 Commercial & office building contractors
Prin: Don Rogers
Prin: Leonard F Jones

TTI
See TECHTRONIC INDUSTRIES NORTH AMERICA INC

TTI FLOOR CARE NORTH AMERICA
See ROYAL APPLIANCE MFG CO

D-U-N-S 79-682-5292 IMP
TTI FLOOR CARE NORTH AMERICA INC
ROYAL APPLIANCE MANUFACTURING
(*Suby of* TTI FLOOR CARE NORTH AMERICA) ★
7005 Cochran Rd, Solon, OH 44139-4303
Tel (440) 996-2000 *Founded/Ownrshp* 2007
Sales 287.8MM[E] *EMP* 550
SIC 5072 3825 Power tools & accessories; Power measuring equipment, electrical
Pr: Chris Gurreri
CFO: Bill Brown
CFO: Matt Shene
VP: Paul Bagwell
VP: Stacy E Cordier
VP: Chris Fisher
Admn Mgr: Jeri Clark
Dist Mgr: Joe Jardine
Dir IT: Michael Ferris
IT Man: Chris Bailey
IT Man: Catherine Mattson

TTI FLOORCARE
See HOOVER INC

D-U-N-S 05-742-1000 IMP/EXP
■TTI INC
(*Suby of* BERKSHIRE HATHAWAY INC) ★
2441 Northeast Pkwy, Fort Worth, TX 76106-1816
Tel (817) 740-9000 *Founded/Ownrshp* 2007
Sales 2.8MMM[E] *EMP* 5,076
SIC 5065 Electronic parts; Resistors, electronic; Capacitors, electronic; Connectors, electronic
CEO: Paul Andrews Jr
* *Pr:* Mike Morton
Pr: Dave Ryder
* *CFO:* Nick M Kypreos
CFO: Scott Slack
Bd of Dir: Jim Milacek
VP: Don Akery
VP: Jim Antall
VP: Don Freeman
VP: Keenan Jeworski
VP: Laurie Kane
VP: Michael Knight
VP: Nick Kypreos
VP: Lew Lafornara
VP: David Minter
VP: Jim Pasquale
VP: Melanie Pizzey
VP: Thomas Rolle
VP: John Sandy
VP: Joe Venturella

TTI-GLOBAL
See TECHNICAL TRAINING INC

D-U-N-S 17-240-3870
TTL HOLDINGS LLC
(*Suby of* EEP HOLDINGS LLC) ★
4626 Eucalyptus Ave, Chino, CA 91710-9215
Tel (909) 597-7861 *Founded/Ownrshp* 2002
Sales 111.7MM[E] *EMP* 1,400[E]
SIC 3089 3544 Molding primary plastic; Special dies, tools, jigs & fixtures

D-U-N-S 61-528-2696
■TTM ADVANCED CIRCUITS INC
(*Suby of* TTM TECHNOLOGIES INC) ★
234 Cashman Dr, Chippewa Falls, WI 54729-3543
Tel (715) 720-5000 *Founded/Ownrshp* 2003
Sales 85.0MM[E] *EMP* 1,200
SIC 3672 3674 Printed circuit boards; Modules, solid state
CEO: David Cote
Pr: Thomas T Edman
Ex VP: Canice T K Chung
Ex VP: Douglas L Soder
Sr VP: Dale Knecht
Sr VP: Shawn Powers
CTO: Larry Kittelberger

D-U-N-S 78-508-9553 IMP
■TTM PRINTED CIRCUIT GROUP INC
(*Suby of* TTM TECHNOLOGIES INC) ★
2630 S Harbor Blvd, Santa Ana, CA 92704-5829
Tel (714) 327-3000 *Founded/Ownrshp* 2006
Sales 106.3MM[E] *EMP* 1,500[E]
SIC 3672 Printed circuit boards
Pr: Thomas T Edman
**CFO:* Steve Richards
Ex VP: Douglas L Soder

D-U-N-S 09-228-0015 IMP
▲TTM TECHNOLOGIES INC
1665 Scenic Ave Ste 250, Costa Mesa, CA 92626-1455
Tel (714) 327-3000 *Founded/Ownrshp* 1978
Sales 2.1MMM *EMP* 29,570
Tkr Sym TTMI *Exch* NGS
SIC 3672 Printed circuit boards
Pr: Thomas T Edman
**Ch Bd:* Robert E Klatell
COO: Brian Barber
CFO: Todd B Schull
Ex VP: Chung Tai Keung Canice
Ex VP: D Soder
Ex VP: Douglas L Soder
VP: Tom Clapprood
VP: Julie Insley
VP: Dale Knecht
VP: Raj Kumar
VP: Jacqueline Ling
VP: Brittany Soto
VP: Clay Zha
Dir Bus: Ingrid Albrecht
Board of Directors: Kenton K Alder, James K Bass, Philip G Franklin, Ronald W Iverson, John G Mayer, Dov S Zakheim

TTNA
See TOYOTETSU AMERICA INC

D-U-N-S 01-718-4578
TTS INC
TARTAN TEXTILE SERVICES
333 N Sam Houston Pkwy E, Houston, TX 77060-2414
Tel (281) 716-2000 *Founded/Ownrshp* 1998
Sales 22.8MM[E] *EMP* 3,000
SIC 7213 Linen supply
Pr: Carol Tate Forrester
**Sec:* Robert Forrester
**Sls Mgr:* Jon Schott

D-U-N-S 61-520-7094
TTS LLC
11000 Frisco St Ste 100, Frisco, TX 75033-2033
Tel (214) 778-0800 *Founded/Ownrshp* 2005
Sales 98.4MM[E] *EMP* 95[E]
SIC 4214 Local trucking with storage
CEO: Andy Cole
**COO:* Jeffrey Vielhaber
**CFO:* Dennis Farnsworth
**Sr VP:* Jeffrey R Brashares
**VP:* Robert Ebinger
VP: Jeff Holm

D-U-N-S 01-266-9771
TTU HSC RESEARCH & GRADUATE SCHOOL
HEALTH SCIENCES CENTER
3601 4th St Rm 2b106, Lubbock, TX 79430-0002
Tel (806) 743-2556 *Founded/Ownrshp* 1970
Sales 21.5MM[E] *EMP* 2,000
SIC 8221 Colleges & universities
VP: Barbara Pence
**Pr:* M R Wilson MD

TTUHSC
See TEXAS TECH UNIVERSITY HEALTH SCIENCES CENTER

D-U-N-S 18-556-9600 IMP/EXP
▲TTWF LP
2801 Post Oak Blvd, Houston, TX 77056-6136
Tel (713) 960-9111 *Founded/Ownrshp* 2004
Sales 4.4MMM[E] *EMP* 17,405
SIC 2821 2869 2865 Polyethylene resins; Vinyl resins; Olefins; Styrene
CEO: Albert Chao
Pt: James Chao
CFO: M Steven Bender
VP: Andrew Kenner
Prin: George J Mangieri
Prin: Stephen Wallace

D-U-N-S 00-791-5010 IMP
TTX CO
101 N Wacker Dr, Chicago, IL 60606-1784
Tel (312) 853-3223 *Founded/Ownrshp* 1955
Sales 555.7MM[E] *EMP* 1,685
SIC 4741

TUALITY COMMUNITY HOSPITAL
See TUALITY HOSPITAL INC

TUALITY HEALTH PLACE
See TUALITY HEALTHCARE

TUALITY HEALTHCARE
See TUALITY HOME HEALTH INC

D-U-N-S 05-707-3538 IMP
TUALITY HEALTHCARE
TUALITY HEALTH PLACE
335 Se 8th Ave, Hillsboro, OR 97123-4246
Tel (503) 681-1111 *Founded/Ownrshp* 1984
Sales 143.7MM[E] *EMP* 1,300
Accts Fordham Goodfellow Llp Hillsb
SIC 8062 General medical & surgical hospitals
Pr: Manuel Berman
COO: Chris Senz
CFO: Tim Fleischmann
Exec: Cheryl Gebhart
Telecom Ex: Sam Parker
Snr Ntwrk: Rowell Andal
IT Man: Kim Lierman
Mtls Mgr: Kevin Madison
Ansthlgy: Nathan J Hildebrant
Doctor: Ian Freeman
Doctor: Natalie Ku MD

D-U-N-S 10-796-9818
TUALITY HEALTHCARE FOUNDATION INC
(*Suby of* TUALITY HEALTH PLACE) ★
335 Se 8th Ave, Hillsboro, OR 97123-4246
Tel (503) 681-1850 *Founded/Ownrshp* 1983
Sales 18.3MM[E] *EMP* 1,200
SIC 8082 7374 6512 5999 7359 Home health care services; Data processing service; Nonresidential building operators; Medical apparatus & supplies; Equipment rental & leasing
Pr: Richard V Stenson

D-U-N-S 93-949-5131
TUALITY HOME HEALTH INC
TUALITY HEALTHCARE
1809 Maple St, Forest Grove, OR 97116-1939
Tel (503) 357-2737 *Founded/Ownrshp* 1983
Sales 182.2MM *EMP* 20
SIC 8082 Home health care services
**Pr:* John Colletti
Dir Lab: Cyndi Christy
Doctor: Daniel Jarman-Miller

D-U-N-S 00-282-8015
TUALITY HOSPITAL INC
TUALITY COMMUNITY HOSPITAL
335 Se 8th Ave, Hillsboro, OR 97123-4246
Tel (503) 681-1111 *Founded/Ownrshp* 2000
Sales 155.7MM *EMP* 10
SIC 8062 General medical & surgical hospitals
CEO: Richard Stenson
Chf Rad: Laurence Hornick
CEO: Dick Stenson
CIO: Sonney Sapra
Mktg Dir: Gerry Ewing
Nrsg Dir: Eunice Rech
Pharmcst: Julie Turner
HC Dir: Lisa Bettencourt

D-U-N-S 14-558-6934
TUBA CITY REGIONAL HEALTHCARE CORP
167 N Main St, Tuba City, AZ 86045
Tel (928) 283-2501 *Founded/Ownrshp* 2002
Sales 144.3MM *EMP* 800[E]
Accts Redw Llc Phoenix Az
SIC 8062 General medical & surgical hospitals
Pr: Christopher Curley
**Treas:* Kimberlee Williams
**VP:* Tincer Nez Sr
Exec: Ltcdr T Sharp
Dir Lab: Atlanta Begay
Dir Rx: James Young
Dir Sec: Thomas Yazzie
IT Man: Theresa White
Web Dev: Vernon Davis
Software D: Katie Magee
Plnt Mgr: Terry Crank

D-U-N-S 00-152-1897 IMP/EXP
TUBE LIGHT CO INC
300 E Park St, Moonachie, NJ 07074-1188
Tel (201) 641-6660 *Founded/Ownrshp* 1928
Sales 110.2MM[E] *EMP* 180
SIC 5046 5085 Signs, electrical; Ink, printers'
Pr: Leon H Jaffe
**VP:* Edwin McCarter
Exec: Howard Kaplan
Board of Directors: Leon H Jaffe, Edwin McCarter, Sharon J Schwartz

D-U-N-S 00-603-7196 IMP
TUBE PROCESSING CORP
AEROFAB
604 E Legrande Ave, Indianapolis, IN 46203-3907
Tel (317) 787-1321 *Founded/Ownrshp* 1939
Sales 103.3MM[E] *EMP* 475
SIC 3498 3356 3469 7692 3444 3728 Fabricated pipe & fittings; Tube fabricating (contract bending & shaping); Nickel & nickel alloy pipe, plates, sheets, etc.; Machine parts, stamped or pressed metal; Brazing; Sheet metalwork; Aircraft parts & equipment
Pr: George J Seybert
**VP:* Steven R Dreyer
Genl Mgr: Dean Mantha
IT Man: Prem Devarak
Ql Cn Mgr: Mark McDaniel
Board of Directors: Kathryn Jacobsen

D-U-N-S 95-618-8770
▲TUBEMOGUL INC
1250 53rd St Ste 2, Emeryville, CA 94608-2965
Tel (510) 653-0126 *Founded/Ownrshp* 2007
Sales 180.7MM *EMP* 577[E]
Tkr Sym TUBE *Exch* NGS
SIC 7372 Prepackaged software
Pr: Brett Wilson
COO: Rob Gatto
CFO: Ron Will
Chf Mktg O: Keith Eadie
Ofcr: Paul Joachim
VP: Soren Abildgaard
VP: Tim Cull
VP: Nan Guo
VP: John Henderson
VP: Alok Kothari
VP: Taylor Schreiner
Board of Directors: Russell Fradin, Jack Lazar, Paul Levine, David Toth

TUBOSCOPE
See VARCO LP

D-U-N-S 82-476-1964 IMP
TUBOSCOPE INC
NOV
2919 Holmes Rd, Houston, TX 77051-1025
Tel (713) 799-5100 *Founded/Ownrshp* 2008
Sales 99.3MM[E] *EMP* 200[E]
SIC 1381 Drilling oil & gas wells
Pr: Isaac Joseph
**VP:* Clay C Williams

D-U-N-S 04-160-8265 IMP/EXP
TUBULAR MACHINED PRODUCTS
90 Campbell Acres Rd, Cleveland, TX 77328-8553
Tel (713) 504-8932 *Founded/Ownrshp* 2011
Sales 150.0MM *EMP* 235
SIC 5051 3492 7389 Tubing, metal; Hose & tube couplings, hydraulic/pneumatic;
Owner: David L Reeves Jr

D-U-N-S 06-368-1431
TUBULAR PRODUCTS CO
(*Suby of* SAMUEL, SON & CO., LIMITED)
1400 Red Hollow Rd, Birmingham, AL 35215-2962
Tel (205) 856-1300 *Founded/Ownrshp* 2008
Sales 137.9MM[E] *EMP* 250
SIC 3317 Tubes, seamless steel; Tubing, mechanical or hypodermic sizes: cold drawn stainless
Pr: Charlie Brown
Opers Mgr: Craig Armstrong

D-U-N-S 83-063-6804
TUBULAR RAIL INC
5000 Milwee St Apt 43, Houston, TX 77092-6630
Tel (713) 834-7905 *Founded/Ownrshp* 2007
Sales 100.0MM *EMP* 3
SIC 4731 Transportation agents & brokers
Pr: Robert C Pulliam

D-U-N-S 79-186-2840
TUBULAR SERVICES LLC
(*Suby of* D D G INC) ★
1010 Mccarty St, Houston, TX 77029-2493
Tel (713) 675-6212 *Founded/Ownrshp* 1978
Sales 226.7MM[E] *EMP* 350
SIC 1389 Running, cutting & pulling casings, tubes & rods
Telecom Ex: Rick Hickman
**VP:* Bob Sherrill
Genl Mgr: James Stalsby
Off Mgr: Elvira Junco
Off Mgr: Tina Silvey
IT Man: Matt Sanders
Ql Cn Mgr: Wendell Hill
Mktg Dir: Ed Summers

D-U-N-S 00-633-1995 IMP/EXP
■TUBULAR STEEL INC (MO)
(*Suby of* RELIANCE STEEL & ALUMINUM CO) ★
1031 Executive Parkway Dr, Saint Louis, MO 63141-6339
Tel (314) 851-9200 *Founded/Ownrshp* 1976, 2016
Sales 150.0MM *EMP* 227
SIC 5051

D-U-N-S 02-445-7610
TUCANOS DEVELOPMENT LLC
12345 W Alameda Pkwy, Lakewood, CO 80228-2800
Tel (303) 237-1340 *Founded/Ownrshp* 2008
Sales 158.3MM[E] *EMP* 900
SIC 6799 Investors
CEO: Steve Oldham
**CFO:* Joe Heeb

D-U-N-S 82-524-7364 IMP/EXP
TUCKER ENERGY SERVICES INC
TUCKER TECHNOLOGIES
(*Suby of* TUCKER ENERGY SERVICES LTD)
411 N Sam Houston Pkwy E # 300, Houston, TX 77060-3555
Tel (281) 442-9095 *Founded/Ownrshp* 1993
Sales 107.1MM[E] *EMP* 150
SIC 1389 3533 Oil consultants; Well logging equipment
Pr: Wayne Tucker
CFO: Paul Emery
**CFO:* Jameel Muradali
**VP:* Sean Tucker
**Prin:* Christopher Tucker
Div Mgr: Nestor Silva
Tech Mgr: Shane Persad
Opers Supe: Mikhail Barcellos
Opers Supe: David Hennings
Opers Mgr: Wayne Cokes

TUCKER ROCKY DISTRIBUTING
See ED TUCKER DISTRIBUTOR INC

TUCKER TECHNOLOGIES
See TUCKER ENERGY SERVICES INC

D-U-N-S 00-690-2704 IMP
TUCSON ELECTRIC POWER CO INC (AZ)
(*Suby of* UNS ENERGY CORP) ★
88 E Broadway Blvd, Tucson, AZ 85701-1720
Tel (520) 571-4000 *Founded/Ownrshp* 1963
Sales 1.3MMM *EMP* 1,398[E]
SIC 4911 Generation, electric power; Transmission, electric power; Distribution, electric power
Pr: David G Hutchens
V Ch: Renee Marruffo
**CFO:* Kevin P Larson
Treas: Kentton C Grant
VP: Timothy Davis
VP: Philip Dion III
VP: Thomas Hansen
VP: Todd C Hixon
VP: Karen G Kissinger
VP: Karen Kissinger
VP: Mark Mansfield
VP: Frank P Marino
VP: Thomas McKenna
VP: Martin Rodriguez
Comm Dir: Art McDonald
Comm Dir: Joe Salkowski
Comm Man: Joseph Barrios
Board of Directors: Philip J Dion

D-U-N-S 82-487-8086
TUCSON HOTELS LP
JOHN Q HAMMONS HOTELS
2711 Centerville Rd # 400, Wilmington, DE 19808-1660
Tel (678) 830-2438 *Founded/Ownrshp* 1989
Sales 593.0MM *EMP* 5,800
SIC 7011 Hotels & motels
VP: Chris Pawelko
**Pt:* Ron Brown
**Pt:* Jonathan Eilian

TUCSON MEDICAL CENTER
See TMC HEALTHCARE

D-U-N-S 00-690-2712
TUCSON MEDICAL CENTER (AZ)
5301 E Grant Rd, Tucson, AZ 85712-2874
Tel (520) 327-5461 *Founded/Ownrshp* 1920
Sales 449.2MM *EMP* 3,000
SIC 8062 8051 6513 8741 Hospital, AMA approved residency; Skilled nursing care facilities; Retirement hotel operation; Management services
Pr: Judith F Rich
COO: Lynn Mergen
CFO: Walter Yokobosky Jr
Ofcr: Richard Rodriguez
VP: Peggy Bernhardt
**VP:* Linda Wojtowicz
Exec: David Griffis
Exec: Katy Nance
Exec: Peter Pylutki
Exec: Deborah Turner
Ansthlgy: Jorge Favela

TUCSON PAYROLL DEPT
See CITY OF TUCSON

D-U-N-S 07-245-7609
TUCSON UNIFIED SCHOOL DISTRICT
1010 E 10th St, Tucson, AZ 85719-5813
Tel (520) 225-6000 *Founded/Ownrshp* 2000
Sales 429.3MM[E] *EMP* 9,000
Accts Heinfeld Meech & Co Pc Tuc
SIC 8211 Public elementary & secondary schools
COO: Rudy Flores
Exec: Anna Maiden
Ex Dir: Shirley Kiser
Ex Dir: Lynn Webster
Dir Sec: Ray Cashen
Off Mgr: Celina Altamirano
Off Mgr: Leigh Anne
Off Mgr: Norma Gallegos
Off Mgr: Ramona Lopez
Off Mgr: Julie Lujan
Off Mgr: Shirley Miller

D-U-N-S 11-601-4119
TUDOR INVESTMENT CORP
1275 King St, Greenwich, CT 06831-2936
Tel (203) 863-6700 *Founded/Ownrshp* 1980
Sales 784.4MM *EMP* 291
Accts Ernst & Young Llp New York N
SIC 6282 Investment advice; Manager of mutual funds, contract or fee basis
Ch Bd: Paul T Jones II
**CEO:* Mark Dalton JD
**CFO:* John Torell
Ofcr: Brooke Bernstein
VP: Mohamed Alam
VP: Alberto Antonini
VP: Andrew Bound
VP: Tim Bryden
VP: Victor Calaba
VP: Ryan Gage
VP: Michael Glennan
VP: Joseph Intagliata
VP: Anson Lee
VP: Surbhi Mehta
VP: Miriam Roiter
VP: Brandon Sica
VP: Paul Vdovets
VP: Amit Wadhwa
Board of Directors: Alberto Borrero, Rich Carlin, Bill Flaherty, Israel Pearson, Jocelyn Rose, Angel Ubide

D-U-N-S 06-637-8175 IMP
▲TUESDAY MORNING CORP
6250 Lbj Fwy, Dallas, TX 75240-6354
Tel (972) 387-3562 *Founded/Ownrshp* 1974
Sales 956.4MM *EMP* 9,067
Accts Ernst & Young Llp Dallas Te
Tkr Sym TUES *Exch* NGS
SIC 5947 5719 5944 5948 5945 5712 Gift shop; Housewares; Bath accessories; Linens; Silverware; Luggage, except footlockers & trunks; Toys & games; Furniture stores
CEO: Steven R Becker
**Ch Bd:* Terry L Burman
Pr: Melissa Phillips
CFO: Stacie R Shirley
Ex VP: Phillip D Hixon
Sr VP: Meredith Bjorck
VP: Karen Goodman
VP: Duane Huesers
VP: Kelly J Munsch
VP: Tom Sangalli
VP: Paul Schleef
Board of Directors: Frank M Hamlin, William Montalto, Sherry M Smith, Jimmie L Wade, Richard S Willis

D-U-N-S 80-274-8723 IMP/EXP
■TUESDAY MORNING INC
(*Suby of* TUESDAY MORNING CORP) ★
6250 Lbj Fwy, Dallas, TX 75240-6354
Tel (972) 387-3562 *Founded/Ownrshp* 1975
Sales 166.4MM[E] *EMP* 500
SIC 5311 2392 5719

D-U-N-S 07-933-5285
TUFCO HOLDINGS LLC
(*Suby of* GRIFFIN HOLDINGS LLC) ★
3161 S Ridge Rd, Green Bay, WI 54304-5626
Tel (920) 336-0054 *Founded/Ownrshp* 2014
Sales 99.2MM[E] *EMP* 325[E]
SIC 2679 Paper products, converted
Prin: Lou Lecalsey

D-U-N-S 07-986-2872
TUFCO LP
(*Suby of* TUFCO TECHNOLOGIES INC) ★
3161 S Ridge Rd, Green Bay, WI 54304-5626
Tel (920) 336-0054 *Founded/Ownrshp* 2014
Sales 95.0MM *EMP* 325
SIC 5122 5112 2676 Toiletries; Sales & receipt books; Sanitary paper products
Pr: Larry Grabowy
**Ch Bd:* Robert J Simon
**CFO:* Michael B Wheeler

D-U-N-S 80-354-5649 IMP
TUFCO TECHNOLOGIES INC
(*Suby of* TUFCO HOLDINGS LLC) ★
3161 S Ridge Rd, Green Bay, WI 54304-5626
Tel (920) 336-0054 *Founded/Ownrshp* 1974
Sales 99.2MM *EMP* 325
SIC 2679 Paper products, converted
Pr: Larry Grabowy
CFO: Michael B Wheeler
Sr VP: Michele M Corrigan
Sr VP: James F Robinson
Area Mgr: Johnny Buff
Area Mgr: Julie Oneill
IT Man: Michael Anderson
IT Man: Dave Greasler
Manager: Pat Tilkens
Sls Mgr: Courtney Wood

D-U-N-S 11-751-4943 IMP
TUFF SHED INC
1777 S Harrison St # 600, Denver, CO 80210-3931
Tel (303) 753-8833 *Founded/Ownrshp* 1981
Sales 221.9MM^E *EMP* 715
SIC 2452

D-U-N-S 60-689-1737 IMP/EXP
TUFF TORQ CORP
(*Suby of* KANZAKI KOKYUKOKI MFG. CO.,LTD.)
5943 Commerce Blvd, Morristown, TN 37814-1051
Tel (423) 585-2000 *Founded/Ownrshp* 1989
Sales 185.9MM^E *EMP* 513
SIC 3679 3524 Electronic loads & power supplies; Lawn & garden mowers & accessories
Pr: Shigenori Sakikawa
Sr VP: Lyons Hamblen
**VP:* Robert Bobo
**Prin:* Naoki Yamakaji
Software D: Josh Graham
Sfty Dirs: Mike Haag
Ql Cn Mgr: Jeff Caudill
Ql Cn Mgr: Bryan Stiles
Sls Mgr: Scott Wilmoth

D-U-N-S 03-274-8233 IMP/EXP
TUFFYS PET FOODS INC
(*Suby of* KLN ENTERPRISES INC) ★
245 1st Ave N, Perham, MN 56573-1821
Tel (218) 346-7500 *Founded/Ownrshp* 1947
Sales 120.9MM^E *EMP* 500
SIC 2047 Dog & cat food
CEO: Kenneth Nelson

TUFLINE
See XOMOX CORP

D-U-N-S 00-332-8994 IMP
TUFTCO CORP
TUFTING MACHINE DIVISION
2318 S Holtzclaw Ave, Chattanooga, TN 37408-2308
Tel (423) 648-3869 *Founded/Ownrshp* 1960, 1985
Sales 83.4MM^E *EMP* 275
SIC 3552 Creels, textile machinery
CEO: Jack L Frost
**Pr:* Steve L Frost
**CFO:* J Michael Minter
**Ex VP:* Mike Minter
**VP:* Thomas M Bishop
**VP:* Bill Fowler
**VP:* Steve Martin
Plnt Mgr: Bob Creswell

TUFTING MACHINE DIVISION
See TUFTCO CORP

D-U-N-S 17-055-8746
TUFTS ASSOCIATED HEALTH PLANS INC
TUFTS ASSOCIATED HMO
705 Mount Auburn St, Watertown, MA 02472-1508
Tel (617) 972-9400 *Founded/Ownrshp* 1987
Sales NA *EMP* 2,700
SIC 6324 Hospital & medical service plans; Health maintenance organization (HMO), insurance only
Pr: James Roosevelt Jr
Pr: Hayat Assaf
**Pr:* Steven A Tolman
COO: Thomas A Croswell
CFO: Umesh Kurpad
Treas: Daniel Tukey
Ofcr: Ben Lasher
**Ex VP:* George A Russell Jr
**Sr VP:* Patty Blake
Sr VP: Tracey Carter
Sr VP: Brian P Pagliaro
Sr VP: Marc Spooner
Sr VP: Tricia Trebino
VP: Patricia Blake
VP: Kenneth Bowden
VP: Lydia Greene
VP: Joseph Imbimbo
VP: Richard Ng
VP: Christina Severin
VP: Patti E Tautenhan

TUFTS ASSOCIATED HMO
See TUFTS ASSOCIATED HEALTH PLANS INC

D-U-N-S 78-326-5499
TUFTS MEDICAL CENTER INC
(*Suby of* BOSTON FLOATING HOSPITAL) ★
800 Washington St, Boston, MA 02111-1552
Tel (617) 636-5000 *Founded/Ownrshp* 1983
Sales 595.7MM *EMP* 3,800
SIC 8062 7371 8742 8741 General medical & surgical hospitals; Computer software development; Business consultant; Hospital & health services consultant; Hospital management; Nursing & personal care facility management
CEO: Michael Wagner
**Ch Bd:* Malcolm L Sherman
**Pr:* Deeb Salem
CFO: Robert Beauchamp
**Chf Mktg O:* Saul N Weingart
Ofcr: Scott Neely
VP: Susan Blanchard
VP: Brooke Hynes
Dir OR: Laurie Lovejoy
Dir Lab: Jim Roger
Dir Rx: Russel Roberts

D-U-N-S 07-953-2263
TUFTS MEDICAL CENTER PARENT INC
BOSTON FLOATING HOSPITAL
800 Washington St, Boston, MA 02111-1552
Tel (617) 636-5000 *Founded/Ownrshp* 1964
Sales 595.7MM^E *EMP* 3,800
Accts Cbiz Tofias Boston Ma
SIC 8062 7371 Hospital, medical school affiliation; Computer software development
Ch: Tom Hollister
**Pr:* Eric Beyer
**CEO:* Ellen Zane
**Ch:* Joseph Campanelli
**Ch:* John Rockart
**Ch:* Matthew Stone
**Treas:* C Okay Agba
VP: Susan Blanchard
Dir Lab: Stephen P Naber
Off Mgr: Lisa Young
Pgrm Dir: Charlie Cassidy

TUFTS UNIVERSITY
See TRUSTEES OF TUFTS COLLEGE

D-U-N-S 06-449-5559
■ **TUG MANUFACTURING CORP**
S & STAGS
(*Suby of* TEXTRON INC) ★
2652 S Main St Nw, Kennesaw, GA 30144-3520
Tel (770) 422-7230 *Founded/Ownrshp* 2014
Sales 102.9MM^E *EMP* 250^E
SIC 3537 Trucks, tractors, loaders, carriers & similar equipment; Tractors, used in plants, docks, terminals, etc.: industrial
Pr: Stefan Vereecke
Pr: Don L Chapman
Pr: John Keating
Sec: Carol Ouzts
VP: John Barclay

D-U-N-S 11-400-0396 IMP/EXP
■ **TUG TECHNOLOGIES CORP**
(*Suby of* S & STAGS) ★
1995 Duncan Dr Nw, Kennesaw, GA 30144-3511
Tel (770) 422-7230 *Founded/Ownrshp* 2014
Sales 102.9MM^E *EMP* 250
SIC 3537 Trucks, tractors, loaders, carriers & similar equipment
CEO: Stefaan Vereecke
CFO: Michael Klaes
VP: Nigel Aubrey
Rgnl Mgr: Uwe Dannhauer
Off Mgr: Karen Taz
VP Sls: Brad Compton

D-U-N-S 79-651-8285
TULALIP RESORT CASINO
10200 Quil Ceda Blvd, Quil Ceda Village, WA 98271-9163
Tel (360) 716-6000 *Founded/Ownrshp* 2007
Sales 110.2MM^E *EMP* 2,500
SIC 7011 Casino hotel
Prin: Ken Kettler
Ofcr: Aneda Rodersfield
Ex VP: Theresa Jira
Exec: Marci Fryberg
Dir Soc: Annie Bartolome
**Prin:* Ron Foff
Genl Mgr: Ron Foss
Dir IT: Patti Comack
Dir IT: Terry Reeves
IT Man: Shawn Williamson
Sales Exec: Donna A Cappa

D-U-N-S 04-018-2198
TULALIP TRIBES OF WASHINGTON
2832 116th St Ne, Tulalip, WA 98271-9491
Tel (360) 716-4000 *Founded/Ownrshp* 1940
Sales 329.9MM^E *EMP* 1,200
SIC 4841 Cable television services
Genl Mgr: Sheryl Fryberg
Ofcr: Stacey Parks
Ofcr: Ginny Ramos
Ex Dir: Ray Fryberg
Ex Dir: Dana Posey
IT Man: Stephen Doherty

TULANE MEDICAL CENTER
See UNIVERSITY HEALTHCARE SYSTEM LC

TULANE UNIVERSITY
See ADMINISTRATORS OF TULANE EDUCATIONAL FUND

D-U-N-S 03-547-4712
TULANE UNIVERSITY HOSPITAL AND CLINIC
ORTHOPEDIC DEPARTMENT
1415 Tulane Ave Fl 4, New Orleans, LA 70112-2600
Tel (504) 988-3516 *Founded/Ownrshp* 2001
Sales 318.9MM *EMP* 3
SIC 8011 Orthopedic physician
Prin: James Bennett MD
CIO: Sue Rachuig
Doctor: Robert Ascuitto
Doctor: Carlos Ramirez

TULARE HOME CARE
See TULARE LOCAL HEALTH CARE DISTRICT

D-U-N-S 07-878-0699
TULARE LOCAL HEALTH CARE DISTRICT
TULARE HOME CARE
869 N Cherry St, Tulare, CA 93274-2207
Tel (559) 685-3462 *Founded/Ownrshp* 1951
Sales 88.0MM^E *EMP* 700
SIC 8062 General medical & surgical hospitals
CEO: Shawn Bolouki
**Pr:* Sherrie Bell
**CFO:* Fred Capozello
VP: Steven Debuskey
Mktg Dir: Sherri Bakke

D-U-N-S 07-846-3278
TULIP US HOLDINGS INC
ORCHID ORTHOPEDIC SOLUTIONS
1489 Cedar St, Holt, MI 48842-1875
Tel (517) 694-2300 *Founded/Ownrshp* 2011
Sales 290.0MM *EMP* 1,720
SIC 3842 Orthopedic appliances
CEO: Michael E Miller
Pr: Jerome Jurkiewicz

D-U-N-S 07-350-2093 IMP
TULLAHOMA INDUSTRIES LLC
401 Nw Atlantic St, Tullahoma, TN 37388-3503
Tel (931) 455-1314 *Founded/Ownrshp* 1999
Sales 123.2MM^E *EMP* 350
SIC 2311 2339 2326 Men's & boys' suits & coats; Women's & misses' outerwear; Men's & boys' work clothing
CEO: Richard Davenport
**COO:* Dale Brewer

D-U-N-S 80-790-4958
TULLETT PREBON AMERICAS CORP
(*Suby of* TULLETT PREBON PLC)
199 Water St Fl 17, New York, NY 10038-3539
Tel (212) 208-2000 *Founded/Ownrshp* 2003
Sales 115.6MM^E *EMP* 600
SIC 6211 7373 Brokers, security; Systems software development services; Computer systems analysis & design
CEO: John Abularrage
**Pr:* Mark Perkins
COO: Joseph Gregory
**COO:* Louis Scotto
**CFO:* William C Holub
**Ch:* Marcus Bolton
Ofcr: Darren Brooks
Ex VP: Thomas Yaeger
Sr VP: Michael Allen
VP: Mary Mohamed
VP: Kevin Olsen
VP: Judith Stazyk

D-U-N-S 61-508-3169 IMP
TULLY CONSTRUCTION CO INC
12750 Northern Blvd, Flushing, NY 11368-1520
Tel (718) 446-7000 *Founded/Ownrshp* 1978
Sales 158.5MM^E *EMP* 450
SIC 1611 Highway & street construction; Surfacing & paving; Concrete construction: roads, highways, sidewalks, etc.; Grading
Pr: Peter K Tully
CFO: Rick Macchiarulo
**Treas:* James M Tully
VP: Kenneth Tully Jr
**VP:* Thomas E Tully

TULLY'S COFFEE
See TC GLOBAL INC

D-U-N-S 06-454-4422
TULSA COMMUNITY COLLEGE FOUNDATION
6111 E Skelly Dr Ste 200, Tulsa, OK 74135-6198
Tel (918) 595-7000 *Founded/Ownrshp* 1970
Sales 3.4MM *EMP* 2,802
Accts Crowe Horwath Llp Dallas Tx
SIC 8222 Community college
Pr: Thomas K McKeon
**CFO:* Gary Crooms
**CFO:* Mark McMullen
**CFO:* Jeff Nevins
**Ch:* Ronald S Looney
Ofcr: Wayne Drewry
**Ex VP:* John Kontogianes

D-U-N-S 12-571-6808
TULSA COMMUNITY FOUNDATION
7030 S Yale Ave Ste 600, Tulsa, OK 74136-5749
Tel (918) 494-8823 *Founded/Ownrshp* 1998
Sales 139.2MM *EMP* 3
Accts Hogantaylor Llp Tulsa Ok
SIC 8733 Noncommercial research organizations

TULSA PUBLIC SCHOOLS
See INDEPENDENT SCHOOL DISTRICT 1 OF TULSA COUNTY

D-U-N-S 15-351-4567 IMP
■ **TULSA WINCH INC**
T W G
(*Suby of* DE-STA-CO) ★
11135 S James Ave, Jenks, OK 74037-1731
Tel (918) 298-8300 *Founded/Ownrshp* 1997
Sales 130.9MM^E *EMP* 150
SIC 5084 3566 3531 Winches; Speed changers, drives & gears; Winches
Pr: Steve Oden
**VP:* Mark E Blohm
Sftwr Eng: John Hassell
Mfg Mgr: David N Whiedden
Plnt Mgr: Paul Rinehart

TULSA WORLD
See BH MEDIA GROUP HOLDINGS INC

TUMAC COMMODITIES
See TUMAC LUMBER CO INC

D-U-N-S 00-941-8997 IMP
TUMAC LUMBER CO INC
TUMAC COMMODITIES
805 Sw Broadway Ste 1500, Portland, OR 97205-3325
Tel (503) 721-7696 *Founded/Ownrshp* 1959
Sales 320.0MM *EMP* 100
SIC 5031 5159 Lumber: rough, dressed & finished; Particleboard; Cotton merchants & products
CEO: Bradley McMurchie
**Pr:* Tim Gustavson
**COO:* Timothy J Leipzig
**CFO:* Jim Adcock

D-U-N-S 09-327-3910
TUMBLEWEED INC
TUMBLEWEED RESTAURANT
2301 River Rd Ste 200, Louisville, KY 40206-1093
Tel (502) 893-0323 *Founded/Ownrshp* 1978
Sales 108.7MM^E *EMP* 2,500
SIC 5812 Mexican restaurant; Restaurant, family: independent
Pr: Matt Higgins
**CFO:* Glennon F Mattingly
Genl Couns: Gregory A Compton

TUMBLEWEED RESTAURANT
See TUMBLEWEED INC

D-U-N-S 07-839-9397
TUMI HOLDINGS INC
(*Suby of* SAMSONITE INTERNATIONAL S.A.)
1001 Durham Ave Ste 1b, South Plainfield, NJ 07080-2300
Tel (908) 756-4400 *Founded/Ownrshp* 2016
Sales 547.6MM *EMP* 1,484^E
SIC 3161 3172 5948 Traveling bags; Clothing & apparel carrying cases; Satchels; Card cases; Wallets; Luggage & leather goods stores
Pr: Jerome S Griffith
CFO: Michael J Mardy
Ex VP: Peter L Gray
Sr VP: Steven M Hurwitz

D-U-N-S 07-514-6829 IMP/EXP
TUMI INC
(*Suby of* TUMI HOLDINGS INC) ★
1001 Durham Ave Ste 1b, South Plainfield, NJ 07080-2300
Tel (908) 756-4400 *Founded/Ownrshp* 2012
Sales 430.5MM^E *EMP* 963
SIC 5199 5948 3161

D-U-N-S 80-266-1173 EXP
TUNDRA RESTAURANT SUPPLY INC
(*Suby of* DIVERSIFIED FOODSERVICE SUPPLY INC) ★
3825 Walnut St Unit E, Boulder, CO 80301-2566
Tel (303) 440-4142 *Founded/Ownrshp* 2010
Sales 250.0MM *EMP* 230
SIC 5046 5074 Restaurant equipment & supplies; Plumbing & hydronic heating supplies
Pr: Wayne Lajoie
**VP:* Jeff Day
VP: Jeff Katz
**VP:* Michael Lewis
CIO: Tim Schell
IT Man: Susan Tempero
Opers Mgr: Kirk Dietz
Sales Asso: Alyse Brown

D-U-N-S 08-043-9234
TUNDRA SPECIALTIES INC
2845 29th St Unit E, Boulder, CO 80301-1228
Tel (888) 388-6372 *Founded/Ownrshp* 2015
Sales 250.0MM *EMP* 125
SIC 5087 Restaurant supplies
CEO: Mike Cate
**Pr:* Wayne Lajoie
**CFO:* Ken Gridan

D-U-N-S 18-253-0386
TUNGLAND CORP
4747 N 7th St Ste 300, Phoenix, AZ 85014-3656
Tel (602) 224-5052 *Founded/Ownrshp* 1983
Sales 44.4MM^E *EMP* 2,310
SIC 6513 Apartment building operators
Pr: Robert Tungland
CFO: Tom Peressini
**VP:* Leslie Tungland

D-U-N-S 82-573-5152 IMP
■ **TUNICA ROADHOUSE CORP**
(*Suby of* CAESARS ENTERTAINMENT CORP) ★
13615 Old Highway 61 N, Robinsonville, MS 38664-9739
Tel (662) 363-4900 *Founded/Ownrshp* 2005
Sales 14.6MM^E *EMP* 1,100
SIC 7999 7011 5813 5812 Gambling establishment; Hotels & motels; Drinking places; Eating places
Pr: John Kapioltas
**Treas:* Mike D Cryan
**VP:* James P Smith
Genl Mgr: Doug Pattison
Dir IT: Tim Boccaleri

D-U-N-S 80-780-6463
TUNICA-BILOXI GAMING AUTHORITY
PARAGON CASINO RESORT
711 Paragon Pl, Marksville, LA 71351-6002
Tel (318) 253-1946 *Founded/Ownrshp* 2007
Sales 79.6MM^E *EMP* 1,400
SIC 7011 7999 5999 Casino hotel; Gambling establishment; Spas & hot tubs
Pr: Pat Minchey
Bd of Dir: Marc Becker
VP: Billy Hendrix

D-U-N-S 00-969-0926
TUNICA-BILOXI TRIBAL ECONOMIC DEVELOPMENT CORP
PARAGON CASINO RESORT
164 Yuroni Rd, Marksville, LA 71351-3096
Tel (318) 253-9767 *Founded/Ownrshp* 1974
Sales 114.9MM^E *EMP* 2,500^E
SIC 5812 Fast-food restaurant, chain
CFO: Jackie Bonnette
**Ch:* Earl Barbry
**Ex VP:* Michael J Frawley
VP Mktg: Nancy Herrington

TUNKHANNOCK MANOR
See UMH NY CORP

D-U-N-S 02-483-2700
TUNNEL HILL PARTNERS LP
390 N Broadway Ste 220, Jericho, NY 11753-2110
Tel (516) 806-6232 *Founded/Ownrshp* 2008
Sales 89.2MM^E *EMP* 102^E
SIC 4953 Refuse systems
**Pr:* William F Rinaldi
CFO: Kevin McEnery
VP: Joseph Rutigliano

TUOMEY HEALTHCARE SYSTEM
See PALMETTO HEALTH TUOMEY

D-U-N-S 82-907-3217
TUOMEY MEDICAL PROFESSIONALS
129 N Washington St, Sumter, SC 29150-4949
Tel (803) 774-9000 *Founded/Ownrshp* 1994
Sales 206.2MM *EMP* 8[E]
SIC 8011 Offices & clinics of medical doctors
Prin: Paul Johnson

D-U-N-S 09-379-6993
TUPELO PUBLIC SCHOOL DISTRICT
72 S Green St, Tupelo, MS 38804-4756
Tel (662) 841-8850 *Founded/Ownrshp* 1918
Sales 55.3MM[E] *EMP* 1,200
Accts Je Vance & Company Pa Cpas
SIC 8211 Public elementary & secondary schools
**Pr:* Rob Hudson
VP: Amy Heyer
**VP:* Kenneth Wheeler
Exec: Kay Bishop
IT Man: Holly Kulp
**Schl Brd P:* Eddie Prather
Psych: Karen Givhan
Pharmcst: Anna Taylor

D-U-N-S 94-356-1720 IMP
▲TUPPERWARE BRANDS CORP
14901 S Orange Blossom Tr, Orlando, FL 32837-6600
Tel (407) 826-5050 *Founded/Ownrshp* 1996
Sales 2.2MMM *EMP* 13,000[E]
Tkr Sym TUP *Exch* NYS
SIC 3089 2844 Kitchenware, plastic; Toilet preparations; Toilet preparations
Ch Bd: E V Goings
Pr: Allen Dando
Pr: Asha Gupta
Pr: Lucy Orlando
Pr: Patricia A Stitzel
CFO: Michael S Poteshman
Treas: Edward Davis
Ofcr: Lillian D Garcia
Ofcr: Georg H Jaggy
Ex VP: William J Wright
Sr VP: Nicholas K Poucher
VP: Luciano G Rangel
VP: Bob Wagner
Exec: Teresa Burchfield
Board of Directors: Joyce M Roche, Catherine A Bertini, M Anne Szostak, Susan M Cameron, Kriss Cloninger III, Meg Crofton, Antonio Monteiro De Castro, Angel R Martinez, Robert J Murray, David R Parker, Richard T Riley

D-U-N-S 80-823-9800 IMP
■TUPPERWARE US INC
(*Suby of* DART INDUSTRIES INC) ★
14901 S Ornge Blossom Trl, Orlando, FL 32837-6600
Tel (407) 826-5050 *Founded/Ownrshp* 1989
Sales 154.4MM[E] *EMP* 711[E]
SIC 3089 Jars, plastic
CEO: Thomas M Roehlk
**Ch Bd:* Ev Goings
Pr: Pablo Munoz
Pr: Joyce Pace
**CFO:* Micheal Poteshman
**Treas:* Dave Davis
Sr VP: David T Halversen
VP: Christian Skr Der
VP: Jos Timmerman
Genl Mgr: Don Frazier
Dir IT: Deepak Kaushik

D-U-N-S 60-354-9361
TUR-PAK FOODS INC
KUSTOM PAK
6201 Macarthur St, Sioux City, IA 51111-1313
Tel (712) 258-9354 *Founded/Ownrshp* 1989
Sales 93.5MM[E] *EMP* 200
SIC 5147 Meats & meat products
Pr: Leroy Zachow
**VP:* Stan Sherman Jr
Board of Directors: Marc I Sherman, Stanley D Sherman

D-U-N-S 07-699-6354 IMP/EXP
TURBANA CORP (FL)
FYFFES NORTH AMERICA INC.
(*Suby of* C I UNION DE BANANEROS DE URABA S A UNIBAN)
999 Ponce De Leon Blvd # 900, Coral Gables, FL 33134-3078
Tel (305) 445-1542 *Founded/Ownrshp* 1970
Sales 179.3MM *EMP* 31
Accts Rms Us Llp Miami Florida
SIC 5148 Fresh fruits & vegetables
CEO: Juan David Alarcon
CFO: Luis Brito
VP: Ricardo Echeverri
VP: Herbert Garritt
Sls Mgr: Scott Dimartini

D-U-N-S 09-248-8696 IMP/EXP
TURBINE AIR SYSTEMS LTD
T A S
6110 Cullen Blvd, Houston, TX 77021-3316
Tel (713) 877-8700 *Founded/Ownrshp* 1998
Sales 101.1MM[E] *EMP* 120
SIC 3585 Refrigeration equipment, complete
CEO: Tom Pierson
**Pr:* Mike Brady
**Pr:* Craig M Hurlbert
**CFO:* John Lilley
**Ex VP:* Gary Hilberg
**VP:* Doug Backlund
VP: Brian Kariker
**Prin:* Dana Pierson
IT Man: Brian George
Opers Mgr: Adolfo Aguilera

D-U-N-S 18-140-0193
TURBINE ENGINE COMPONENTS TECHNOLOGIES - UTICA CORP
(*Suby of* U C A HOLDINGS INC) ★
2 Halsey Rd, Whitesboro, NY 13492-3401
Tel (315) 768-8070 *Founded/Ownrshp* 1895
Sales 212.8MM[E] *EMP* 1,300
SIC 3724 3511 3429 3842 3769 Aircraft engines & engine parts; Turbines & turbine generator sets & parts; Clamps, couplings, nozzles & other metal hose fittings; Surgical appliances & supplies; Guided missile & space vehicle parts & auxiliary equipment
Pr: Rob Cohen
VP Bus Dev: Tom Moorefield
Plnt Mgr: Mike Finley
Ql Cn Mgr: Marc Paglialonga

D-U-N-S 15-737-3457 IMP
TURBINE ENGINE COMPONENTS TECHNOLOGIES CORP
(*Suby of* U C A HOLDINGS INC) ★
1211 Old Albany Rd, Thomasville, GA 31792-3552
Tel (229) 228-2600 *Founded/Ownrshp* 2001
Sales 237.9MM[E] *EMP* 1,300
SIC 3463 3724 3714 3469 Engine or turbine forgings, nonferrous; Aircraft engines & engine parts; Motor vehicle parts & accessories; Metal stampings
Pr: Robert Cohen
CFO: Jill Martha
**CFO:* Bernard Stanek
CFO: Bernard W Stanek
Bd of Dir: William Coquillette
Ofcr: Keith Wortman
VP: Frederick Butler
VP: Deedee Sadler
VP: Colin Strain
VP: Stephen Wurst
Prgrm Mgr: Joseph Menke

D-U-N-S 07-871-8161
TURBO RESTAURANT LLC
ARBY'S
(*Suby of* ARBYS) ★
7750 N Macarthur Blvd 1, Irving, TX 75063-7514
Tel (972) 620-2287 *Founded/Ownrshp* 2012
Sales 16.1MM[E] *EMP* 1,008[E]
SIC 5812 Fast-food restaurant, chain

D-U-N-S 18-573-4746 IMP
TURBOCAM INC
TURBOCAM INTERNATIONAL
607 Calef Hwy, Barrington, NH 03825-7237
Tel (603) 749-6066 *Founded/Ownrshp* 1985
Sales 95.1MM[E] *EMP* 240[E]
SIC 3599 Machine & other job shop work
Pr: Marian Noronha
CFO: D Dougles Patteson
**CFO:* Doug Patteson
**VP:* John Bressoud
**VP:* Robert Bujeaud
Exec: Bill Cole
Exec: Rob Taylor
Genl Mgr: Keith Lin
Genl Mgr: Ken Mazzochi
Mktg Mgr: Dave Pincince
Sls Mgr: Mike Blackburn

TURBOCAM INTERNATIONAL
See TURBOCAM INC

D-U-N-S 05-693-3906 IMP
TURBOCOMBUSTOR TECHNOLOGY INC
PARADIGM PRECISION
(*Suby of* PARADIGM ORILLIA TECHNOLOGY INC)
3651 Se Commerce Ave, Stuart, FL 34997-4981
Tel (772) 287-7770 *Founded/Ownrshp* 1972
Sales 132.2MM[E] *EMP* 472
SIC 3724 3728 3444 Engine mount parts, aircraft; Aircraft parts & equipment; Sheet metalwork
Pr: Greg Bennett
**CFO:* Diane Lockhart
IT Man: Vijay Khosla

D-U-N-S 08-112-1212 IMP
TURCK INC
3000 Campus Dr, Plymouth, MN 55441-2656
Tel (763) 553-9224 *Founded/Ownrshp* 1987
Sales 123.5MM[E] *EMP* 500
SIC 3625 Switches, electronic applications
CEO: David Lagerstrom
Pr: Guido Frohnhaus
Pr: Giuido Fronhaus
CFO: Robert Diem
CFO: Dave Lagerstrom
VP: Murray Death
Prgrm Mgr: Jack Schreiber
Admn Mgr: Helda Eekhoff
IT Man: Jesse Hill
VP Opers: Albert Kirsch
Mktg Dir: Brad Larson

D-U-N-S 09-746-8110
TURELK INC
3700 Santa Fe Ave Ste 200, Long Beach, CA 90810-2169
Tel (310) 835-3736 *Founded/Ownrshp* 1978
Sales 110.0MM *EMP* 110
SIC 1542 Commercial & office building contractors
CEO: Michael G Turi
**Pr:* Michael R Paselk
**VP:* Fred Capper
VP: Earl Lund
VP: Marcos Ramirez
Dir IT: Anees Elbruki
VP Mktg: Toni Scarpinato
Snr PM: Mike Matejcek

D-U-N-S 55-701-4094 EXP
TURF CARE SUPPLY CORP
(*Suby of* PLATINUM EQUITY LLC) ★
50 Pearl Rd Ste 200, Brunswick, OH 44212-5703
Tel (877) 220-1014 *Founded/Ownrshp* 1974
Sales 169.6MM[E] *EMP* 435[E]
SIC 2873 Nitrogenous fertilizers
Pr: William Milowitz
Pr: Mark Clark
Pr: Turfcare Supply
**COO:* Mark Mangan
**COO:* Frank Vetter
**CFO:* Jeffrey Bailey
**CFO:* Richard C Nihei
VP: Mark Austin
VP: Nick Costello
VP: Brian Shannon
Plnt Mgr: Brian Menu

TURFGRASS
See RESIDEX LLC

D-U-N-S 07-935-6892
TURFIX LLC
2228 Mount Curve Ave, Saint Joseph, MI 49085-2024
Tel (888) 495-3195 *Founded/Ownrshp* 2005
Sales 750.0MM *EMP* 6
SIC 0782 Turf installation services, except artificial

D-U-N-S 01-398-8043 IMP
■TURKEY HILL LP
(*Suby of* GERBES SPRMKT / KING SOOPERS) ★
2601 River Rd, Conestoga, PA 17516-9327
Tel (717) 872-5461 *Founded/Ownrshp* 1931, 1985
Sales 188.5MM[E] *EMP* 800
SIC 2026 2024 Milk processing (pasteurizing, homogenizing, bottling); Ice cream, bulk
Treas: Kathy Reinholds
Pt: John Cox
Treas: James Arnold
IT Man: Ian Cox
Sfty Mgr: Jeffrey Groff
Plnt Mgr: Larry Ibach
Plnt Mgr: Lerry Ipach
Plnt Mgr: Larry Ipod
Mktg Mgr: Melissa Mattilio

D-U-N-S 16-813-3515
TURKEY VALLEY FARMS LLC
112 S 6th St, Marshall, MN 56258-3063
Tel (507) 337-3100 *Founded/Ownrshp* 2008
Sales 148.3MM *EMP* 450
Accts Cliftonlarsonallen Llp Austin
SIC 2015 Turkey processing & slaughtering
Pr: Richard Huisinga
**CFO:* Beth Wosmek
**Ex VP:* Richard A Peterson
**VP:* Keith Burger
VP: Willis Cooan
Plnt Mgr: Joe Como
Board of Directors: Keith Burger, Blake Holden, Theodore Huisinga, Timothy Johnson, Rayburn Norling, Richard Peterson, Pete Rothfork

D-U-N-S 19-600-0657
TURKISH AIRLINES INC
(*Suby of* TURK HAVA YOLLARI ANONIM ORTAKLIGI)
350 5th Ave Ste 7510, New York, NY 10118-7591
Tel (800) 874-8875 *Founded/Ownrshp* 1988
Sales 505.9MM[E] *EMP* 10,239
SIC 4512 Air passenger carrier, scheduled
Admn Mgr: Maietta Mancuso
Mktg Mgr: Philip Westernoff

D-U-N-S 09-798-8877
TURLOCK DAIRY & REFRIGERATION INC
T D R
1819 S Walnut Rd, Turlock, CA 95380-9219
Tel (209) 667-6455 *Founded/Ownrshp* 1972
Sales 95.9MM[E] *EMP* 100
SIC 5083 7699 1542 Dairy machinery & equipment; Industrial equipment services; Nonresidential construction
CEO: Mathew Anthony Bruno
**Pr:* Tony Bruno

D-U-N-S 04-600-4933
TURLOCK IRRIGATION DISTRICT
T I D
333 E Canal Dr, Turlock, CA 95380-3946
Tel (209) 883-8222 *Founded/Ownrshp* 1887
Sales 296.7MM[E] *EMP* 412
Accts Pricewaterhousecoopers Llp Sa
SIC 4911 4971 Generation, electric power; Distribution, electric power; Impounding reservoir, irrigation; Water distribution or supply systems for irrigation
Pr: Ron Macedo
**VP:* Joe Alamo
VP: Alison Bryson
VP: Robert Santos
VP: Kate Schulenberg
**Prin:* Larry Gilbertson
**Prin:* Brian Lafollette
**Prin:* Joseph E Malaski
Dir IT: Diana Brink
IT Man: Jeff Hanson
IT Man: Jeff Leal

D-U-N-S 07-689-7862 IMP
TURN 5 INC
AMERICANMUSCLE.COM
7 Lee Blvd, Malvern, PA 19355-1234
Tel (610) 251-2397 *Founded/Ownrshp* 2000
Sales 84.3MM[E] *EMP* 145
SIC 5531 Automotive accessories
Pr: Christopher R Francy
**Pr:* Stephen C Voudouris
**VP:* Andrew Voudouris
Mktg Mgr: Paul Corey

D-U-N-S 06-825-0216 IMP
TURN ON PRODUCTS INC
ALMOST FAMOUS CLOTHING
270 W 38th St Rm 1200, New York, NY 10018-1573
Tel (212) 764-2121 *Founded/Ownrshp* 1974
Sales 170.0MM[E] *EMP* 95
Accts Mayer Hoffman Mccann Cpas New
SIC 2339 2331 Sportswear, women's; Women's & misses' blouses & shirts
Pr: Peter Kossoy
**CFO:* Marc Wasserman
**VP:* Robert Regina

D-U-N-S 15-575-2652
TURNBERRY ASSOCIATES
19501 Biscayne Blvd # 3400, Miami, FL 33180-2375
Tel (305) 937-6262 *Founded/Ownrshp* 1954
Sales 107.8MM[E] *EMP* 1,300
SIC 6512 6552 Commercial & industrial building operation; Subdividers & developers
Pr: Michael Talbert
**Genl Pt:* Eugene Kessler
**Pt:* Philip Goldfarb
**Pt:* Bernard Redlich
**Pt:* Donald Soffer Sr
CFO: Patrick Powers
**Treas:* William P Shook
Ofcr: Marsha Bourjolly
VP: Bud Hall
VP: Willie Ivory
VP: Yoo M Pak
**VP:* John A Ritz
VP: Joseph Szymaszek
Dir Risk M: Melissa Levin

D-U-N-S 00-331-9068 IMP/EXP
■TURNER BROADCASTING SYSTEM INC (GA)
ADULT SWIM GAMES
(*Suby of* HISTORIC TW INC) ★
1 Cnn Ctr Nw 14sw, Atlanta, GA 30303-2762
Tel (404) 575-7250 *Founded/Ownrshp* 1965, 1996
Sales 2.1MMM[E] *EMP* 6,940
SIC 7822 4833 4841 7812 Motion picture distribution; Television broadcasting stations; Cable television services; Motion picture production
CEO: John Martin
**V Ch:* Terence F McGuirk
**Pr:* Andrew T Heller
**Pr:* Stan Kasten
**Pr:* Mark Lazarus
**Pr:* David R Levy
**Pr:* David Levy
Pr: Paul Miller
**Pr:* Louise Sams
**Pr:* Jim Walton
Pr: Gerhard Zeiler
**COO:* Greg D'Alba
COO: Libby Hendrix
**CFO:* Pascal Desroches
CFO: Jim Guward
**Ofcr:* Jack Wakshlag
**Ex VP:* Garth Ancier
**Ex VP:* Jim McCaffrey
**Ex VP:* Victoria W Miller
**Ex VP:* Kelly Regal
**Ex VP:* Scott Teissler
Board of Directors: Phil Kent

D-U-N-S 00-699-1525 IMP
TURNER CONSTRUCTION CO INC (OH)
(*Suby of* TURNER CORP) ★
375 Hudson St Fl 6, New York, NY 10014-3667
Tel (212) 229-6000 *Founded/Ownrshp* 1902, 1984
Sales 10.4MMM *EMP* 5,000
Accts Deloitte & Touche Llp Dallas
SIC 1542 1541 1522 8741 8742 Nonresidential construction; Commercial & office building, new construction; Institutional building construction; Specialized public building contractors; Industrial buildings, new construction; Factory construction; Hotel/motel, new construction; Construction management; Management consulting services; Construction project management consultant
Pr: Peter J Davoren
Ch Bd: Joseph King
COO: John Diciurcio
CFO: Karen Gould
Ex VP: Nicholas Billotti
Ex VP: Pasquale A Difilippo
Sr VP: Michael J Kuntz
VP: Rory C Dejohn
Sfty Mgr: Robert Sahagun
Sfty Mgr: Kristine Wunder
Ql Cn Mgr: Richard Corey

D-U-N-S 10-327-3827 IMP
TURNER CORP
(*Suby of* HOCHTIEF USA INC) ★
375 Hudson St Rm 700, New York, NY 10014-3667
Tel (212) 229-6000 *Founded/Ownrshp* 1999
Sales 10.5MMM *EMP* 5,000
Accts Deloitte & Touche Llp Dallas
SIC 1542 1541 1522 8742 Nonresidential construction; Commercial & office building, new construction; Institutional building construction; Specialized public building contractors; Industrial buildings & warehouses; Industrial buildings, new construction; Factory construction; Hotel/motel, new construction; Condominium construction; Construction project management consultant
Ch Bd: Peter J Davoren
CFO: Karen Gould
Ex VP: John A Diciurcio
Ex VP: Richard P Homan
Sr VP: Thomas B Gerlach Jr
Sr VP: Edward McNeill
VP: Don Oshiro
Dir IT: Robert Knight
IT Man: Caryn Conlin
Sfty Mgr: Elijah Aidelogie
Sfty Mgr: Wayne Baruch

TURNER DAIRIES
See TURNER HOLDINGS LLC

D-U-N-S 04-370-1440
TURNER GAS CO INC
2825 W 500 S, Salt Lake City, UT 84104-4407
Tel (801) 973-6886 *Founded/Ownrshp* 1991
Sales 149.3MM[E] *EMP* 190
Accts Bierwolf Morrill & Nilson Pll
SIC 5172 4213 Gases, liquefied petroleum (propane); Trucking, except local
Pr: James Turner
**Treas:* Michael Turner
Opers Mgr: Matt Schroeder

D-U-N-S 80-660-6760
TURNER HOLDINGS LLC
TURNER DAIRIES
(*Suby of* PRAIRIE FARMS DAIRY INC) ★
2040 Madison Ave, Memphis, TN 38104-2747
Tel (901) 726-5684 *Founded/Ownrshp* 2006
Sales 162.6MM[E] *EMP* 530
SIC 2026 Milk processing (pasteurizing, homogenizing, bottling)
Plnt Mgr: Charles Nutter

D-U-N-S 96-856-2079
TURNER INDUSTRIAL MAINTENANCE LLC
(*Suby of* TURNER INDUSTRIES GROUP LLC) ★
8687 United Plaza Blvd, Baton Rouge, LA 70809-7009
Tel (225) 922-5050 *Founded/Ownrshp* 2004
Sales 23.4MM[E] *EMP* 1,200

SIC 7349 Building & office cleaning services
**CEO:* Roland M Toups
**VP:* Dwight Braud

D-U-N-S 00-977-2062 IMP/EXP
TURNER INDUSTRIES GROUP LLC
8687 United Plaza Blvd, Baton Rouge, LA 70809-7009
Tel (225) 922-5050 *Founded/Ownrshp* 2001
Sales 1.2MMM^E *EMP* 10,000
SIC 7359 7699 Equipment rental & leasing; Industrial machinery & equipment repair
CEO: Roland M Toups
V Ch: Thomas H Turner
Pr: Gary Jones
CFO: Lester J Griffon Jr
Sr VP: John Golasheskysaid
Sr VP: Stephen M Toups
VP: John Adams
VP: Ronnie Breaux
VP: Tim Drake
Area Mgr: Ronnie Hemphill
Admn Mgr: Connie M Paxton

D-U-N-S 96-856-2145
TURNER INDUSTRIES OF CALIFORNIA
(*Suby of* TURNER INDUSTRIES GROUP LLC) ★
8687 United Plaza Blvd, Baton Rouge, LA 70809-7009
Tel (225) 922-5050 *Founded/Ownrshp* 2011
Sales 9.6MM^E *EMP* 1,084^E
SIC 1541 Industrial buildings & warehouses
Opers Mgr: Michael A Welborn

D-U-N-S 08-400-2237
TURNER INTERNATIONAL INDUSTRIES INC
(*Suby of* TURNER CORP) ★
375 Hudson St Fl 6, New York, NY 10014-7462
Tel (212) 229-6000 *Founded/Ownrshp* 1984
Sales 6.0MMM *EMP* 226
SIC 8741 8712 1542 Administrative management; Architectural services; Nonresidential construction
Pr: Abrar Sheriff
**Ch Bd:* Ralph WA Johnson
**CEO:* Peter Davoren
**COO:* John Diciurcio
**Treas:* Donald Sleeman
**Ex VP:* Richard Homan
**Sr VP:* Rory Dejohn
**VP:* Joseph V Vumbacco

D-U-N-S 16-654-2626 IMP
TURNER SPECIALTY SERVICES LLC
(*Suby of* TURNER INDUSTRIES GROUP LLC) ★
8687 United Plaza Blvd, Baton Rouge, LA 70809-7009
Tel (225) 922-5050 *Founded/Ownrshp* 2001
Sales 98.5MM^E *EMP* 500
SIC 1541 7699 Industrial buildings & warehouses; Industrial equipment services
Ch: Roland M Toups
Treas: L J Griffon
VP: B F Files
VP: A L Lambert
VP: D R McAll
VP: D L McCollister

D-U-N-S 00-690-1177
TURNER SUPPLY CO (AL)
DO IT BEST
250 N Royal St, Mobile, AL 36602-4080
Tel (205) 252-6000 *Founded/Ownrshp* 1905
Sales 153.7MM^E *EMP* 150
SIC 5085 5251 Industrial supplies; Rubber goods, mechanical; Hardware
Ch Bd: Howard Schramm
**Pr:* Howard M Schramm III
**CFO:* Michael Clarke
VP: Jim Johnson
VP: Bruce M Reagan
**VP:* Bruce Regan
**VP:* Tommy Thompson
VP: Steve Williams
Assoc Dir: Gabriel Morales
Dir Bus: David Wilson
Brnch Mgr: Joe Foster

D-U-N-S 14-625-5950
▲TURNING POINT BRANDS INC
5201 Interchange Way, Louisville, KY 40229-2184
Tel (502) 778-4421 *Founded/Ownrshp* 1988
Sales 197.2MM *EMP* 231
Accts Rsm Us Llp Greensboro North
Tkr Sym TPB *Exch* NYS
SIC 2131 Chewing & smoking tobacco
CEO: Lawrence S Wexler
**Ch Bd:* Thomas F Helms Jr
CFO: Mark A Stegeman
Sr VP: James W Dobbins
Sr VP: James M Murray

TURNING STONE CASINO
See ONEIDA INDIAN NATION

D-U-N-S 05-121-8316
TURNING TECHNOLOGIES LLC
255 W Federal St, Youngstown, OH 44503-1207
Tel (330) 746-3015 *Founded/Ownrshp* 2002
Sales 180.1MM^E *EMP* 670^E
SIC 7372 Business oriented computer software; Educational computer software
CEO: Mike Broderick
**Pr:* Dave Kauer
**Ofcr:* Dr Tina Rooks
**VP:* Sheila Hura
VP: Meghan Odonnell
**VP:* Kevin Owens
VP: Dan Rinn
QA Dir: Matthew Ward
Dir IT: Randy Horton
IT Man: Sonel Friedman
Web Dev: Michael Zimmerman

D-U-N-S 00-302-7349
TURNPIKE COMMISSION PA (PA)
PTC
700 S Eisenhower Blvd, Middletown, PA 17057-5529
Tel (717) 939-9551 *Founded/Ownrshp* 1937
Sales NA *EMP* 2,200
SIC 9621 Regulation, administration of transportation

CEO: Mark P Compton
COO: Gary Hentz
COO: Craig R Shuey
CFO: Blair J Fishburn
CFO: Nikolaus Grieshaber
VP: Robert Schlegel
Genl Mgr: Perry Culver
Genl Mgr: Darla Kelchner
Snr Ntwrk: Stephen Durborow
Snr Ntwrk: Camilla Harle
Opers Mgr: Brian Ranck

D-U-N-S 00-171-3437 IMP/EXP
TURTLE & HUGHES INC
THIS
1900 Lower Rd, Linden, NJ 07036-6586
Tel (732) 574-3600 *Founded/Ownrshp* 1923
Sales 590.9MM *EMP* 900
Accts Eisneramper Llp
SIC 5063 5085 Electrical apparatus & equipment; Industrial supplies
Ch Bd: Jayne Millard
**Pr:* Mike Devoney
**Pr:* Richard Reffler
**COO:* Kevin Doyle
**CFO:* Christopher Rausch
**Ex VP:* Frank W Millard
VP: Luis Valls
Exec: Joe Ross
Comm Dir: Julie Wyckoff
Brnch Mgr: Alan Schlecter
Genl Mgr: Chris Mauro
Board of Directors: Fred Desanti, Donald Difrancesco, Bruce Merrifield, Jayne Millard, Anthony Sartor, Kathleen Shanahan, Kathryn Swintek

D-U-N-S 96-333-2502 IMP
▲TURTLE BEACH CORP
12220 Scripps Summit Dr # 100, San Diego, CA 92131-3698
Tel (914) 345-2255 *Founded/Ownrshp* 2010
Sales 162.7MM *EMP* 221^E
Tkr Sym HEAR *Exch* NGM
SIC 3679 Parametric amplifiers
Pr: Juergen Stark
**Ch Bd:* Ronald Doornink
CFO: John T Hanson
Sr VP: Rodney Schutt
VP: Arnie Grever
Board of Directors: Laureen Debuono, Kenneth A Fox, William E Keitel, Andrew Wolfe

TURTLE CREEK CASINO
See GRAND TRAVERSE BAND LLC

TURTLE WAX CARWASH & CAR APPEA
See TURTLE WAX INC

D-U-N-S 00-513-8771 IMP/EXP
TURTLE WAX INC (IL)
TURTLE WAX CARWASH & CAR APPEA
2250 W Pinehurst Blvd # 150, Addison, IL 60101-6103
Tel (630) 455-3700 *Founded/Ownrshp* 1944
Sales 301.6MM^E *EMP* 900
SIC 2842 Specialty cleaning, polishes & sanitation goods; Automobile polish; Shoe polish or cleaner; Metal polish
CEO: Denis John Healy Jr
**Pr:* Denis J Healy Sr
**VP:* Thomas Kelly
VP: Barry Ruche
Genl Mgr: Henry Richter
Dir IT: Dawn Ikeda
Sls Mgr: Tony Turner
Counsel: Richard Capalby

D-U-N-S 10-797-6425
TUSCALOOSA CITY BOARD OF EDUCATION
1210 21st Ave, Tuscaloosa, AL 35401-2934
Tel (205) 759-3700 *Founded/Ownrshp* 1930
Sales 78.4MM^E *EMP* 1,350
Accts Ronald L Jones
SIC 8211 School board
Ch: Lee Garrison

D-U-N-S 07-979-8734
TUSCALOOSA CITY SCHOOLS
1210 21st Ave, Tuscaloosa, AL 35401-2934
Tel (205) 759-3560 *Founded/Ownrshp* 2015
Sales 59.7MM^E *EMP* 1,557^E
SIC 8211 Public elementary & secondary schools
Pr Dir: Lesley Bruinton
Teacher Pr: Deron Cameron
HC Dir: Sharon Dickerson

D-U-N-S 10-064-1935
TUSCALOOSA COUNTY BOARD OF EDUCATION
1118 Greensboro Ave, Tuscaloosa, AL 35401-2825
Tel (205) 758-0411 *Founded/Ownrshp* 1875
Sales 91.2MM^E *EMP* 2,016
SIC 8211 School board
Pr: Gary Mims
**Pr:* Mark Nelson
CFO: Patrick Conner

D-U-N-S 00-314-7352 IMP/EXP
TUSCARORA YARNS INC
8760 Franklin St E, Mount Pleasant, NC 28124-8788
Tel (704) 436-6527 *Founded/Ownrshp* 1899
Sales 93.1MM^E *EMP* 305
SIC 2281 Knitting yarn, spun; Weaving yarn, spun
Ch: Martin B Foil Jr
**CEO:* David Roberts
VP: Dee Harris
VP: Adrian Hernandez
VP: Ervin Johnson
**VP:* Andy Long
**VP:* Joe McLester
Dir IT: Ronnie Wilson
Board of Directors: Frank H Dunn Jr, Carolyn V Foil, Dame Hamby, Leslie Hodnett, David Meek, Robert B Taylor Jr,, Bud W Willis III

D-U-N-S 12-821-4178
TUSKEGEE UNIVERSITY
1200 W Montgomery Rd, Tuskegee Institute, AL 36088-1909
Tel (334) 727-8011 *Founded/Ownrshp* 1881
Sales 173.2MM^E *EMP* 1,047
SIC 8221 University
Pr: Brian Johnson
Pr: Matthew Jenkins
Pr: Benjamin F Payton
CFO: Leslie Porter
Ex VP: Walter Hill
VP: Barbara Williams
Assoc Dir: Conrad Bonsi
Off Admin: Patterson Sonettra
CIO: Fred Judkins
IT Man: Don Fuhr
Psych: James Hall

D-U-N-S 10-064-4939
TUSTIN UNIFIED SCHOOL DISTRICT
300 S C St, Tustin, CA 92780-3633
Tel (714) 730-7515 *Founded/Ownrshp* 1971
Sales 95.7MM^E *EMP* 1,465
Accts Nigro Nigro & White Murrieta
SIC 8211 Public elementary & secondary schools
**CFO:* Anthony Soria
Treas: Dena Vela
Bd of Dir: Jonathan Abelove
Off Mgr: Raquel Pineira
Dir IT: Carol Cutti
Dir IT: Jeremy Powell
Pr Dir: Mark Eliot
Teacher Pr: Chuck Lewis
Instr Medi: Theresa Walsh
HC Dir: Sean Diaz

D-U-N-S 14-478-0566 IMP/EXP
TUTCO INC
(*Suby of* SMITHS GROUP INTERNATIONAL HOLDINGS LIMITED)
500 Gould Dr, Cookeville, TN 38506-4154
Tel (931) 432-4141 *Founded/Ownrshp* 1994
Sales 90.0MM *EMP* 578
SIC 3634 Heating units, for electric appliances
Pr: William T Smith
COO: Bret Holmes
**Treas:* Beth Dalton
VP: Keith Howard
**VP:* Patrick D McCaffrey
Exec: Dan Riggsbee
Dir IT: Dan Riggsbee
IT Man: Dan Rigsby
Plnt Mgr: Rick Lineberry

D-U-N-S 00-514-3946 IMP/EXP
TUTHILL CORP
8500 S Madison St, Burr Ridge, IL 60527-6284
Tel (630) 382-4900 *Founded/Ownrshp* 1927
Sales 341.8MM^E *EMP* 670
Accts Mcgladrey & Pullen
SIC 3561 3586 3524 Pumps & pumping equipment; Gasoline pumps, measuring or dispensing; Blowers & vacuums, lawn
Ch: James G Tuthill Jr
Pr: Mark Hampshire
**CEO:* Thomas M Carmazzi
**Treas:* David Groeber
VP: Jim Ahlborn
VP: Mark Almeida
VP: Keith Barker
**VP:* Anthony Belmonte
VP: Tony Belmonte
VP: David Schardt
Exec: Dave Neave
Int Pr: Ray Mueller

D-U-N-S 06-049-5298
TUTHILL CORP
BLUE MOUNTAIN SKI AREA
1660 Blue Mountain Dr, Palmerton, PA 18071
Tel (610) 826-7700 *Founded/Ownrshp* 1974
Sales 47.8MM^E *EMP* 1,200
SIC 7011 Ski lodge
Pr: Barbara T Green
**Treas:* Diane Tuthill
**VP:* Bruce Ebert
**VP:* Mike Mulcahy
IT Man: Ron Keck
Board of Directors: Abraham Nemitz

D-U-N-S 13-860-1229
TUTLE & TUTLE TRUCKING INC
3672 W Highway 67, Cleburne, TX 76033-8523
Tel (817) 556-2131 *Founded/Ownrshp* 2002
Sales 154.5MM^E *EMP* 800^E
SIC 4212 Local trucking, without storage
Pr: Tommy P Tutle
**VP:* Gary D Tutle
Comm Dir: Brian Gannon

D-U-N-S 00-901-1222
■TUTOR PERINI BUILDING CORP
(*Suby of* TUTOR PERINI CORP) ★
5055 E Washington St # 210, Phoenix, AZ 85034-2036
Tel (602) 256-6777 *Founded/Ownrshp* 1914, 1974
Sales 352.4MM *EMP* 250
Accts Deloitte & Touche Llp Los An
SIC 1541 1542 8741 Industrial buildings, new construction; Commercial & office building, new construction; Specialized public building contractors; Construction management
Pr: Craig W Shaw
**Treas:* William B Sparks
**Ex VP:* Robert Band
Ex VP: Travis Burton
Ex VP: Michael McLean
Ex VP: Peter Sukalo
Sr VP: Daniel Hoisman
Sr VP: Kevin J Woods
**VP:* Shelton Grantham
**VP:* Robert P Marano II
**VP:* Richard J Rizzo

D-U-N-S 00-695-4432 IMP/EXP
▲TUTOR PERINI CORP (MA)
15901 Olden St, Sylmar, CA 91342-1051
Tel (818) 362-8391 *Founded/Ownrshp* 1894
Sales 4.9MMM *EMP* 10,626
Tkr Sym TPC *Exch* NYS
SIC 1542 8741 1611 1791 8711 Commercial & office building contractors; Construction management; Concrete construction: roads, highways, sidewalks, etc.; Structural steel erection; Concrete reinforcement, placing of; Construction & civil engineering
Ch Bd: Ronald N Tutor
**Pr:* James A Frost
CFO: Gary G Smalley
**V Ch Bd:* Michael R Klein
Ex VP: Michael Kershaw
Ex VP: Craig W Shaw
Sr VP: Michael E Ciskey
Sr VP: Leonard K Kaae
VP: Travis Burton
VP: David Randall
VP: Mark Robison
VP Bus Dev: Buschmeyer Stephen
Dir Bus: Joseph McKenna
Board of Directors: Marilyn A Alexander, Peter Arkley, Sidney J Feltenstein, Robert C Lieber, Raymond R Oneglia, Dale A Reiss, Donald D Snyder

D-U-N-S 02-776-6401
TUTOR PERINI CORP
15901 Olden St, Sylmar, CA 91342-1051
Tel (818) 362-8391 *Founded/Ownrshp* 1918
Sales 158.5MM^E *EMP* 7,733
SIC 1542 1611 1622 Specialized public building contractors; Commercial & office building contractors; Highway & street construction; Bridge, tunnel & elevated highway
Ch Bd: Ronald N Tutor
**Pr:* Robert Band
CFO: Michael J Kershaw
Treas: William B Sparks
Ex VP: James Frost
Board of Directors: Marilyn A Alexander, Peter Arkley, Michael R Klein, Robert L Miller, Raymond R Oneglia, Donald D Snyder

TUTOR TIME CHILD CA
See TUTOR TIME LEARNING CENTERS LLC

D-U-N-S 18-291-6499
TUTOR TIME LEARNING CENTERS LLC
TUTOR TIME CHILD CA
(*Suby of* LEARNING CARE GROUP INC) ★
21333 Haggerty Rd Ste 300, Novi, MI 48375-5537
Tel (248) 697-9000 *Founded/Ownrshp* 2002
Sales 132.2MM *EMP* 2,519^E
SIC 8351 Child day care services

D-U-N-S 08-593-5690 IMP/EXP
■TUTOR-SALIBA CORP
(*Suby of* TUTOR PERINI CORP) ★
15901 Olden St, Sylmar, CA 91342-1051
Tel (818) 362-8391 *Founded/Ownrshp* 2008
Sales 30.0MM *EMP* 1,200
Accts Deloitte & Touche Llp Los An
SIC 1542 1629 7353 1799 6552 Commercial & office building, new construction; Subway construction; Cranes & aerial lift equipment, rental or leasing; Rigging & scaffolding; Subdividers & developers
CEO: Ronald N Tutor
**COO:* Jack Frost
**CFO:* William B Sparks
Ex VP: Naseeb Saliba
**Sr VP:* John D Barrett
**Sr VP:* David L Randall

TUTTLE-CLICK AUTOMOTIVE GROUP
See TUTTLE-CLICK INC

D-U-N-S 14-790-8826
TUTTLE-CLICK INC
TUTTLE-CLICK AUTOMOTIVE GROUP
41 Auto Center Dr, Irvine, CA 92618-2803
Tel (949) 472-7400 *Founded/Ownrshp* 1985
Sales 157.6MM^E *EMP* 350
SIC 5511 Automobiles, new & used
CEO: Christopher Cotter
**VP:* James H Click
Exec: David Dickason
**Prin:* Bob Tuttle
Sls Mgr: Kristin Taylor

D-U-N-S 36-295-0388
TUV SUD AMERICA INC
(*Suby of* TUV SUD AG)
10 Centennial Dr Fl 2a, Peabody, MA 01960-7900
Tel (978) 573-2500 *Founded/Ownrshp* 2004
Sales 120.2MM^E *EMP* 690
SIC 8734 Product testing laboratories
CEO: Jim Marsh
**Pr:* Ian Nicol
**CFO:* Christoph Weimer
**VP:* Gary Minks
**VP:* Vince Williams
**Prin:* Karsten Xander

D-U-N-S 04-676-7612 IMP
TUXEDO JUNCTION INC
120 Earhart Dr, Williamsville, NY 14221-7078
Tel (716) 633-2400 *Founded/Ownrshp* 1969
Sales 84.7MM^E *EMP* 200
SIC 5136 5699 7299 Men's & boys' clothing; Formal wear; Clothing rental services; Dress suit rental; Tuxedo rental
Ch: Barry M Snyder
Pr: Calvin Cleveland
Sr VP: Joe Terranova
Mktg Dir: Nancy Macdonald

D-U-N-S 82-918-0657
TV GUIDE MAGAZINE LLC
(*Suby of* NATIONAL TELEVISION BOOK CO) ★
50 Rockefeller Plz Fl 14, New York, NY 10020-1617
Tel (212) 852-7500 *Founded/Ownrshp* 2015
Sales 121.9MM^E *EMP* 235
SIC 2721 Magazines: publishing & printing
CEO: David J Fishman
**CFO:* Michell Lindquist
CFO: Vincent Ohanyan
Creative D: Rose Fiorentino

D-U-N-S 61-620-8729
TVAR SOLUTIONS LLC
1320 Old Chain Bridge Rd # 445, Mc Lean, VA 22101-3956
Tel (703) 635-3900 Founded/Ownrshp 2006
Sales 90.8MM EMP 21
SIC 5045 7379 3571 Computers, peripherals & software; Computer related maintenance services; Electronic computers
CEO: David Saunders
VP: Jose Castro
VP: Chris Thoureen
Exec: Laleh Alemzadeh
Genl Mgr: Adam Fagan
Ql Cn Mgr: Jessica Jenkins
VP Sls: Glenn Zimmerman
Mktg Mgr: Lauren Baird
Mktg Mgr: Lauren Trexler
Sales Asso: Christopher Clifton

D-U-N-S 13-778-1097 IMP
■TVC COMMUNICATIONS LLC
(Suby of WESCO DISTRIBUTION INC) ★
800 Airport Rd, Annville, PA 17003-9002
Tel (717) 838-3790 Founded/Ownrshp 2004
Sales 148.5MM[E] EMP 334
SIC 3663 2298 Radio & TV communications equipment; Cable, fiber
CEO: James R Manari
Pr: Steve Quinn
Sr VP: Ken Olsen
VP: Matt Hartman
VP: John Witmer
Opers Mgr: Enrique Cortes
Trfc Mgr: Dulcie Adams
Sls&Mrk Ex: Brian Bairstow
Sls&Mrk Ex: D'Arcy McGoldrick
Mktg Mgr: Stephanie Beck
Mktg Mgr: Dave Hofstetter

D-U-N-S 36-154-6740 IMP
TVCI HOLDING INC
VOLLRATH
(Suby of WINDWAY CAPITAL CORP) ★
1236 N 18th St, Sheboygan, WI 53081-3201
Tel (920) 457-4851 Founded/Ownrshp 1988
Sales 161.7MM[E] EMP 800
SIC 3914 3365 3089 Silverware & plated ware; Aluminum foundries; Tableware, plastic
Pr: Terry J Kohler
*VP: John Mc Clary Jr

TVEC
See TRINITY VALLEY ELECTRIC COOPERATIVE INC

D-U-N-S 05-409-2457 IMP/EXP
TVH PARTS CO
16355 S Lone Elm Rd, Olathe, KS 66062-9238
Tel (913) 829-1000 Founded/Ownrshp 1972
Sales 186.9MM[E] EMP 341
SIC 5084 Lift trucks & parts
Pr: Patrick McLaughlin
*VP: Frank Carter
*Prin: Els Thermote
*Prin: Dirk Von Holt
Genl Mgr: David Wood
Mtls Mgr: Cory McKernan
Sales Exec: Ryan Walker
Advt Dir: Darrell Loomis

D-U-N-S 11-896-0673 IMP
TVI INC
VALUE VILLAGE
(Suby of VALUE VILLAGE STORES) ★
11400 Se 6th St Ste 220, Bellevue, WA 98004-6452
Tel (425) 462-1515 Founded/Ownrshp 1954
Sales 686.0MM[E] EMP 20,000
SIC 5932 5251 5311 5331 Used merchandise stores; Hardware; Department stores; Variety stores
Pr: Kenneth Wayne Alterman
*Pr: Rodney J Van Leeuwen
*CEO: Thomas Ellison
Treas: Doug Dempster
VP: Don Gorskil

D-U-N-S 80-108-1915 IMP/EXP
TW CRYOGENICS LLC
TAYLOR-WHARTON-CRYOGENICS
(Suby of TWI) ★
4075 Hamilton Blvd, Theodore, AL 36582-8575
Tel (251) 443-8680 Founded/Ownrshp 2007
Sales 91.0MM[E] EMP 480[E]
SIC 3443 Cryogenic tanks, for liquids & gases
CEO: Robert E Gadomski
COO: Roland Wright
VP: Hoyt Fitzsimmons
Plnt Mgr: Verde McGrew

D-U-N-S 00-791-6570 IMP/EXP
TW METALS INC (PA)
(Suby of ONEAL INDUSTRIES INC) ★
760 Constitution Dr # 204, Exton, PA 19341-1149
Tel (610) 458-1300 Founded/Ownrshp 1907, 2005
Sales 425.0MM EMP 773
SIC 1761 Sheet metalwork
Pr: Jack H Elrod
*CFO: Kirk E Moore
*VP: Barry Ronsheimer
*VP: Bill Schmid
Mktg Mgr: Tavio Sorrentino
Sls Mgr: Dan Carducci
Sales Asso: Sue Peters

TW TELECOM, LLC
See LEVEL 3 TELECOM LLC

D-U-N-S 11-932-2845
■TW TELECOM MANAGEMENT CO LLC
(Suby of TW TELECOM LLC) ★
2342 Technology Dr, O Fallon, MO 63368-7200
Tel (636) 625-7000 Founded/Ownrshp 2006
Sales 79.3MM[E] EMP 1,300
SIC 4813 Telephone communication, except radio
Pr: Paul Pierron
Ch Bd: James F Lynch
Pr: Michael P Miller
CFO: J Glenn Custar
Ex VP: Randall P Muench
Sr VP: James C Falvey
Sr VP: Ines Lebow
VP: Daran Churovich
VP: Steve Patterson
VP: Greg Truitt
Exec: Wilson Haney
Exec: Julia Heckathorn
Exec: Patti Hypes
Exec: Eddie Kane
Exec: Brian McArthur
Exec: Avery Sharp
Exec: Steve Stonestreet
Exec: Brad Strauss

D-U-N-S 18-535-7709
■TW TELECOM OF COLORADO LLC
(Suby of TW TELECOM LLC) ★
10475 Park Meadows Dr, Littleton, CO 80124-5433
Tel (636) 625-7000 Founded/Ownrshp 2006
Sales 257.4MM[E] EMP 1,300
SIC 4812 4813 Cellular telephone services; Telephone communication, except radio
CEO: Larissa L Herda
*Ch Bd: James F Lynch
*Pr: John T Blount
*CFO: Dan Lensgraf
*Sr VP: Lawrence P Beilenson
*Sr VP: Ines Lebow
*Sr VP: Michael A Rouleau
*Sr VP: Harold W Teets
VP: John Efutich
VP: Harold Teets
IT Man: Mike Stahl

D-U-N-S 01-599-1842
■TWA AIRLINES LLC
(Suby of AMERICAN AIRLINES INC) ★
4333 Amon Carter Blvd, Fort Worth, TX 76155-2605
Tel (817) 963-1234 Founded/Ownrshp 2001
Sales 161.5MM[E] EMP 17,625
SIC 4512 4522 4581 Air passenger carrier, scheduled; Air cargo carrier, scheduled; Flying charter service; Airport terminal services; Aircraft maintenance & repair services; Aircraft storage at airports
Pr: William F Compton
COO: Stan Henderson
Sr VP: Kathleen A Soled

D-U-N-S 78-915-3079 IMP
■TWB CO LLC
(Suby of WORTHINGTON INDUSTRIES INC) ★
1600 Nadeau Rd, Monroe, MI 48162-9317
Tel (734) 289-6400 Founded/Ownrshp 2008
Sales 270.0MM[E] EMP 430
SIC 3465 Automotive stampings
Pr: Ivan Meltzer
Prin: Ryan Kane
IT Man: Deron Smith
Sfty Mgr: Mike Pekan

D-U-N-S 60-940-8505 IMP/EXP
TWC WISE COMPUTER INC
TWC
3515 Nw 114th Ave, Doral, FL 33178-1848
Tel (305) 594-5725 Founded/Ownrshp 1989
Sales 90.0MM EMP 30
SIC 5045 Computers & accessories, personal & home entertainment
Pr: Luigi Boria
*VP: Graciela Boria
*Genl Mgr: Ernesto Bernal

TWCC
See WEATHER CHANNEL INC

D-U-N-S 83-124-9599
■TWCC HOLDING CORP
WEATHER CHANNEL, THE
(Suby of IBM) ★
300 Interstate N Pkwy Se, Atlanta, GA 30339-2403
Tel (770) 226-0000 Founded/Ownrshp 1932
Sales 304.6MM[E] EMP 700
SIC 4833 4813 7812 8999 Television broadcasting stations; ; Video production; Weather related services
CEO: Michael Kelly
*CEO: David W Kenny
*CFO: Jeroen Peter Johan Kuipers
Sr VP: David Shipps
Sr VP: Jeremy Steinberg
Sr VP: Indira Venkat
VP: Freddy Flaxman
VP: Chris Huff
VP: Zarrilli Michael
VP: Piper Walker
VP: Pau Walsh
VP: Landon Williams
Exec: George Callard
Exec: Mark Gildersleeve

D-U-N-S 16-118-5269
TWD & ASSOCIATES INC
1751 Pinnacle Dr Ste 900, Mc Lean, VA 22102-4008
Tel (703) 820-9777 Founded/Ownrshp 2003
Sales 93.5MM[E] EMP 275
SIC 7371

TWECO-ARCAIR
See VICTOR TECHNOLOGIES INTERNATIONAL INC

D-U-N-S 00-537-6249 IMP
■TWEDDLE GROUP INC (MI)
(Suby of NUANCE COMMUNICATIONS INC) ★
24700 Maplehurst Dr, Clinton Township, MI 48036-1336
Tel (586) 307-3700 Founded/Ownrshp 1954, 2013
Sales 169.7MM[E] EMP 650
SIC 2732 2791 2752 2759 2741 7371 Book printing; Photocomposition, for the printing trade; Typesetting, computer controlled; Commercial printing, lithographic; Commercial printing; Technical manual & paper publishing; Computer software development & applications
Pr: Paul Wilbur
Pr: Joe O'Deven
CFO: Daniel Titus
Ex VP: Atul Kishore
VP: Geral Chapman
VP: Laura Klimaski
VP: Brian Suszek
Prgrm Mgr: Jonathan Madill
CIO: Ty Beltramo
CIO: Gerry Chapman
Dir IT: Eric Gordin

D-U-N-S 00-233-8804 IMP/EXP
TWEED GREENE & CO INC (PA)
2075 Detwiler Rd, Kulpsville, PA 19443
Tel (215) 256-9521 Founded/Ownrshp 1903
Sales 343.4MM[E] EMP 1,007
SIC 3053 Gaskets & sealing devices
CEO: Felix Paino
*Pr: Michael Delfiner
*CFO: Kevin J Lukiewski
*Treas: William Maher
VP: Michael Brewer
CIO: Dave Hogan

D-U-N-S 96-575-8188 IMP
■TWEEN BRANDS INC
JUSTICE BRANDS
(Suby of ASCENA RETAIL GROUP INC) ★
8323 Walton Pkwy, New Albany, OH 43054-9522
Tel (614) 775-3500 Founded/Ownrshp 2009
Sales 1.7MMM[E] EMP 12,200
SIC 5641 Children's wear
Pr: Brian E Lynch
Pr: Sally A Boyer
Pr: Scott M Bracale
COO: William E May
*CFO: Jason Judd
Treas: Richard Marinzel
*Ex VP: Lece Lohr
Ex VP: Lece F Lohr
Sr VP: Gregory Henchel
Sr VP: Ronald Robinson
VP: Elaine Bruck
VP: Karen Etzkorn
VP: Peter Krier
VP: Susan Meeder
VP: Douglas J Probst
VP: Jon Thompson
Exec: Brian Rogers

D-U-N-S 60-979-1046 IMP
■TWEEN BRANDS SERVICE CO
(Suby of JUSTICE BRANDS) ★
8323 Walton Pkwy, New Albany, OH 43054-9522
Tel (614) 775-3500 Founded/Ownrshp 2002
Sales 131.0MM[E] EMP 1[E]
SIC 5137 Women's & children's clothing
CEO: Michael W Rayden
*CFO: Rolando Deaguiar
Ex VP: Alan J Hochman
Ex VP: Lece Lohr
Ex VP: Ronnie Robinson
*Sr VP: Karen S Etzkorn
Sr VP: Jenny Hoffman
Sr VP: Chris Kaighn
Sr VP: Michael Keane
Dir Surg: Suzanne Stoddard

D-U-N-S 09-681-8547
TWEET-GAROT MECHANICAL INC
2545 Larsen Rd, Green Bay, WI 54303-4840
Tel (920) 498-0400 Founded/Ownrshp 1968
Sales 91.4MM[E] EMP 350
SIC 1711 3444 Mechanical contractor; Sheet metalwork
CEO: Timothy J Howald
VP: Michael Sturdivant
VP: Ray Wihtbroe

D-U-N-S 03-815-0694 IMP
TWEEZERMAN INTERNATIONAL LLC
(Suby of ZWILLING J. A. HENCKELS AG)
2 Tri Harbor Ct, Port Washington, NY 11050-4617
Tel (516) 676-7772 Founded/Ownrshp 1975
Sales 88.6MM[E] EMP 175
SIC 5087 Beauty parlor equipment & supplies
Pr: Juergen Bosse
Mktg Dir: Christine Pasculio

D-U-N-S 00-699-1533 IMP/EXP
■TWENTIETH CENTURY FOX FILM CORP
FOX FILMS ENTERTAINMENT
(Suby of FOX FILMED ENTERTAINMENT) ★
10201 W Pico Blvd, Los Angeles, CA 90064-2606
Tel (310) 369-1000 Founded/Ownrshp 1915
Sales 403.5MM[E] EMP 2,000
SIC 7812 Motion picture production & distribution; Video tape production; Motion picture production & distribution, television; Television film production
Ch Bd: K Rupert Murdoch
V Ch: Robert Harper
CFO: Dean Hallett
Sr Cor Off: Chase Carey
Sr Cor Off: Jon Eelbarrio
Sr VP: Robert Gottlieb
Sr VP: Steven Melnick
VP: Kate Corsmeier
*VP: Florence Grace
VP: Steve Harrington
VP: Paul Hoffman
VP: Larry Jones
VP: Dean Norris
Assoc Dir: Nagaraju Mantena

D-U-N-S 61-503-8775
■TWENTIETH CENTURY FOX HOME ENTERTAINMENT LLC
(Suby of FOX FILMS ENTERTAINMENT) ★
10201 W Pico Blvd, Los Angeles, CA 90064-2651
Tel (310) 369-1000 Founded/Ownrshp 2005
Sales 312.3MM[E] EMP 1,500
SIC 4833 Television broadcasting stations
CFO: Dean Hallett
Ex VP: Vincent Marcais
Sr VP: Joanne Burns
Sr VP: Yoni Cohen
Sr VP: James Finn
VP: Jodi Chisarick
VP: Gary Hall
VP: Eileen Ige
VP: John Koscheka
VP: Patrick Moran
VP: Eileen O'Neill
VP: Marci Proietto
VP: Janet Savage

D-U-N-S 07-885-6350
TWENTIETH SUPPORT COMMAND
2400 21st St Bush Rver Rd, Aberdeen Proving Gro, MD 21010
Tel (410) 436-0330 Founded/Ownrshp 2013
Sales NA EMP 5,000
SIC 9711 Air Force

TWENTY ONE HUNDRED PRODUCTIONS
See INTERVARSITY CHRISTIAN FELLOWSHIP/USA

D-U-N-S 17-577-8443 IMP/EXP
▲TWENTY-FIRST CENTURY FOX INC
1211 Ave Of The Americas, New York, NY 10036-8701
Tel (212) 852-7000 Founded/Ownrshp 1979
Sales 27.3MMM EMP 20,500
Tkr Sym FOX Exch NGS
SIC 4833 4841 Television broadcasting stations; Cable & other pay television services
CEO: James R Murdoch
*Ch Bd: K Rupert Murdoch
*Ch Bd: Lachlan K Murdoch
*V Ch: Chase Carey
CFO: John P Nallen
Ex VP: Janet Nova
Ex VP: Michael Regan
Ex VP: Chip Smith
Sr VP: Lou Ermilio
Sr VP: Julie Henderson
Sr VP: Latha Maripuri
VP: Karolina Cuprys
VP: Michael Florin
VP: Brian Turchin
VP: Nilesh Zaveri
Exec: Gerson A Zweifach
Board of Directors: Delphine Arnault, James W Brewer, David R Devoe, Roderick I Eddington, Jacques Nasser, Robert S Silberman, Jeffrey W Ubben

D-U-N-S 10-256-0588
TWENTYMILE COAL LLC
(Suby of PEABODY ENERGY CORP) ★
29515 Routt County Rd 2 # 27, Oak Creek, CO 80467
Tel (970) 879-3800 Founded/Ownrshp 2004
Sales 258.3MM[E] EMP 350
SIC 1222 Underground mining, subbituminous
*Pr: James F Roberts
Plnt Mgr: Mike Ludlow

D-U-N-S 06-373-7142
TWFRIERSON CONTRACTOR INC
DESIGN SYSTEMS BUILDERS
2971 Kraft Dr, Nashville, TN 37204-3618
Tel (615) 367-2434 Founded/Ownrshp 1958
Sales 129.9MM EMP 145
SIC 1541 1542

D-U-N-S 83-045-4067
TWG HOLDINGS INC
(Suby of WARRANTY GROUP INC) ★
175 W Jackson Blvd Fl 11, Chicago, IL 60604-2709
Tel (312) 356-3000 Founded/Ownrshp 2006
Sales NA EMP 2,300[E]
SIC 6399 8721 6411 Warranty insurance, automobile; Accounting, auditing & bookkeeping; Insurance agents, brokers & service
Prin: Thomas W Warsop III

D-U-N-S 55-690-7822
TWG WARRANTY GROUP INC
(Suby of TWG HOLDINGS INC) ★
175 W Jackson Blvd Fl 11, Chicago, IL 60604-2709
Tel (312) 356-3000 Founded/Ownrshp 2006
Sales NA EMP 1,850
SIC 6399 8721 6411 Warranty insurance, automobile; Accounting, auditing & bookkeeping; Insurance agents, brokers & service
CEO: David L Cole
*Pr: Michael Frosch
*CFO: David I Vickers
*Treas: Kevin P Diamond
*Ex VP: John H Serafin
*Sr VP: John Curtis
*Sr VP: Barbara Goff
*Sr VP: Anthony M Jackovich
*Sr VP: Robert P Mancuso
*VP: Jeanne Jurasek
*VP: Brian Ollech

TWI
See TAYLOR-WHARTON INTERNATIONAL LLC

D-U-N-S 00-937-0111
▲TWILIO INC
645 Harrison St Fl 3, San Francisco, CA 94107-3624
Tel (415) 390-2337 Founded/Ownrshp 2008
Sales 166.9MM EMP 567[E]
Tkr Sym TWLO Exch NYS
SIC 7372 4812 Prepackaged software; Business oriented computer software; Cellular telephone services
Ch Bd: Jeff Lawson
COO: Roy Ng
CFO: Lee Kirkpatrick
VP: Robert Van Brewster
VP: Robert Vanbrewster
Genl Mgr: Michael Bratsafolis
IT Man: John Campos
Sftwr Eng: Chandra Kuchi
Sls Mgr: Pamela Morrow
Genl Couns: Karyn Smith
Board of Directors: Richard Dalzell, Byron Deeter, Elena Donio, James McGeever, Scott Raney, Erika Rottenberg

D-U-N-S 55-593-1302
TWIN CITY BAGEL INC
NATIONAL CHOICE BAKERY
130 Hardman Ave S, South Saint Paul, MN 55075-2453
Tel (651) 554-0200 Founded/Ownrshp 1991
Sales 95.4MM[E] EMP 360
SIC 2051 Bagels, fresh or frozen
Pr: Shimon Harosh
*VP: Micheal Rouache
Prd Mgr: Oscar Zambrano

D-U-N-S 02-048-8284
TWIN CITY CONCRETE PRODUCTS CO INC
TCC MATERIALS
2025 Centre Pointe Blvd # 300, Mendota Heights, MN 55120-1221
Tel (651) 688-9116 Founded/Ownrshp 1953
Sales 134.5MM^E EMP 360
SIC 5032 3273 3255 1442 Concrete mixtures; Ready-mixed concrete; Construction sand & gravel
CEO: Hammon T Becken
Pr: Troy Enge
Pr: Michael Fritz
Prin: Claude Anderson
Prin: Thor Becken
Prin: Art Gillen
Plnt Mgr: Dave Ethier
Plnt Mgr: John Thompson
Plnt Mgr: Scott Wheeler

D-U-N-S 06-654-1194 IMP
TWIN CITY FAN COMPANIES LTD
TC AXIAL DIV
5959 Trenton Ln N, Minneapolis, MN 55442-3238
Tel (763) 551-7500 Founded/Ownrshp 1973
Sales 487.6MM^E EMP 900
SIC 3564 5084 Blowers & fans; Industrial machinery & equipment
Ch Bd: Charles L Barry
*Pr: Michael Barry
COO: Mark Hansen
CFO: Julie Dale
*V Ch Bd: Zika Srejovic
Chf Mktg O: Tim Clifford
Ex VP: Brad Jacobson
VP: Robert L Bennett
*VP: James Herrboldt
VP: Jim Schick
*VP: Rob Sink
VP: Jess Talley

D-U-N-S 00-593-0458
■**TWIN CITY FIRE INSURANCE CO**
(Suby of HARTFORD FIRE INSURANCE CO (INC)) ★
1 Hartford Plz, Hartford, CT 06115-1702
Tel (860) 547-5000 Founded/Ownrshp 1910
Sales NA EMP 2,500
SIC 6331 Property damage insurance
Ch Bd: Neal Steven
*CFO: David Michel Johnson
Sr VP: David Bradley

D-U-N-S 00-925-2347 IMP/EXP
TWIN CITY FOODS INC (WA)
10120 269th Pl Nw, Stanwood, WA 98292-4736
Tel (206) 515-2400 Founded/Ownrshp 1945
Sales 189.9MM^E EMP 800
Accts Williams & Nulle Mount Vernon
SIC 2037 Vegetables, quick frozen & cold pack, excl. potato products
Pr: Roger O Lervick
*Pr: John Lervick
*CFO: Virgil Roehl
VP: Charlie Hiatt
*VP: Mark Lervick
VP: Adena Ray
Exec: Kim Price
IT Man: Miller Dave
VP Opers: Mick Lovgreen

D-U-N-S 00-609-0997 IMP/EXP
▲**TWIN DISC INC**
1328 Racine St, Racine, WI 53403-1700
Tel (262) 638-4000 Founded/Ownrshp 1918
Sales 166.2MM EMP 921^E
Accts Pricewaterhousecoopers Llp Mi
Tkr Sym TWIN Exch NGS
SIC 3568 3566 3714 Power transmission equipment; Clutches, except vehicular; Couplings, shaft: rigid, flexible, universal joint, etc.; Joints, swivel & universal, except aircraft & automotive; Speed changers, drives & gears; Torque converters, except automotive; Reduction gears & gear units for turbines, except automotive; Motor vehicle parts & accessories; Power transmission equipment, motor vehicle; Clutches, motor vehicle; Universal joints, motor vehicle
Pr: John H Batten
*Ch Bd: David B Rayburn
COO: Malcolm F Moore
CFO: Jeffrey S Knutson
VP: Dean J Bratel
VP: Michael B Gee
VP Admn: Fred Timm
Genl Mgr: Barbara Barker
Board of Directors: Michael Doar, Janet P Giesselman, David W Johnson, Michael C Smiley, Harold M Stratton II, David R Zimmer

D-U-N-S 96-517-7889
TWIN EAGLE RESOURCE MANAGEMENT LLC
8847 W Sam Houston Pkwy N, Houston, TX 77040-5369
Tel (713) 341-7332 Founded/Ownrshp 2010
Sales 440.7MM^E EMP 400
Accts Grant Thornton Llp Houston
SIC 4911 4924 5983 Electric services; Natural gas distribution; Fuel oil dealers
Ch: Charles L Watson
*Pr: Griff Jones
*COO: Danny J REA
*CFO: Rob Doty
*Ex VP: Jimmy Thomas
Sr VP: Nathan Crowell
Sr VP: Nir Grossman
Sr VP: Tom W Wolf
VP: Andy Blanchard
VP: Michael Clinchard
VP: Antoinette Firestack
VP: Troy Kelly
*VP: Larry Leverettc
VP: Doug Taylor

D-U-N-S 10-001-5353
TWIN FALLS SCHOOL DISTRICT 411
201 Main Ave W, Twin Falls, ID 83301-6103
Tel (208) 733-0134 Founded/Ownrshp 1908
Sales 75.0MM EMP 1,100
Accts Dennis R Brown Cpa Twin Falls
SIC 8211 Public elementary & secondary schools
Pr Dir: Eva Craner

D-U-N-S 08-130-9312
TWIN MAPLES NURSING HOME (OH)
31054 State Route 93, Mc Arthur, OH 45651-8925
Tel (740) 596-5955 Founded/Ownrshp 1974
Sales 260.4MM EMP 45
SIC 8051 8052 Skilled nursing care facilities; Intermediate care facilities
Pr: Virginia Ratliff
*Sec: Fred Ratliff
*VP: Crystal Ratliff
Sales Exec: Tonya Kennedy

D-U-N-S 00-957-9330 IMP
TWIN MED LLC
11333 Greenstone Ave, Santa Fe Springs, CA 90670-4618
Tel (323) 582-9900 Founded/Ownrshp 1997
Sales 418.2MM^E EMP 500
SIC 5047 Medical equipment & supplies
CEO: Kerry Weems
CFO: David Klarner
Ch: Steve Rechnitz
VP: Carlos Gonzales
VP: Johnny Lin
VP: Werner Nischt
VP: Shlomo Rechnitz
VP: Matt Weenig
VP: Chris Wyler
Opers Mgr: Richard Mason
Mktg Dir: David Blonder
Board of Directors: Jonathan M Goldstein, Jennifer M Mulloy

TWIN RIVER CASINO
See UTGR INC

TWIN RIVER FOODS
See TWIN RIVERS GROUP INC

D-U-N-S 92-987-6829 EXP
TWIN RIVERS FOODS INC
(Suby of TWIN RIVER FOODS) ★
1 E Colt Square Dr, Fayetteville, AR 72703-2884
Tel (479) 444-8898 Founded/Ownrshp 1995
Sales 323.3MM^E EMP 1,600
SIC 2015 Poultry slaughtering & processing
CEO: Matt Duffy
*VP: Maynard Anderson
*VP: Doug Tyler

D-U-N-S 17-640-6445 IMP/EXP
TWIN RIVERS GROUP INC
TWIN RIVER FOODS
1 E Colt Square Dr, Fayetteville, AR 72703-2884
Tel (479) 444-8898 Founded/Ownrshp 1997
Sales 323.3MM^E EMP 1,600
SIC 5142 Packaged frozen goods
VP: Maynard Anderson
*Owner: Matthew Duffy
CFO: Jody Edwards
*VP: Michael Bennish
*VP: Dan Henderson
IT Man: Rhonda Forguson

D-U-N-S 96-188-7374
TWIN RIVERS PAPER CO CORP
82 Bridge Ave, Madawaska, ME 04756-1229
Tel (207) 523-2350 Founded/Ownrshp 2010
Sales 182.7MM^E EMP 667
SIC 2621 Paper mills
CEO: Timothy Lowe
*Pr: Ken Winterhalter
*COO: John Reichert
*CFO: Wayne Gosse
CFO: Wayne Johnson
*VP: Jean-Pierre Grenon
VP: Johnson Wayne
Genl Mgr: Paul McKinley
Dir IT: Mike Breau
IT Man: Patrick Dufour
VP Opers: Mike Reider

D-U-N-S 96-188-7515 IMP/EXP
TWIN RIVERS PAPER CO LLC
82 Bridge Ave, Madawaska, ME 04756-1229
Tel (207) 728-3321 Founded/Ownrshp 2010
Sales 176.6MM^E EMP 667^E
SIC 2621 Paper mills
Pt: Timothy Lowe
Pt: Jeffrey C Dutton
Pt: Wayne Gosse
Pt: Jean-Pierre Grenon
Pt: Ken Winterhalter
CEO: Robert Snyder
Ch: Tim Lowe
Genl Mgr: Gary Curtis
VP Opers: Brian Sass
Sfty Mgr: Robert Pelletier
VP Sls: Tony Rigelman

D-U-N-S 80-729-0189
TWIN RIVERS UNIFIED SCHOOL DISTRICT
5115 Dudley Blvd, McClellan, CA 95652-1024
Tel (916) 566-1600 Founded/Ownrshp 2008
Sales 323.8MM EMP 3,300
Accts Gilbert Associates Inc Sacr
SIC 8211 School board
Prin: Kirk Williams
Pr Dir: Zenobia Gerald
Instr Medi: Debbie Hanlon
HC Dir: Bonita Mallory
Board of Directors: Bob Bastian, Linda Fowler, Janis Green, Cortez Quinn, Michelle Rivas, Roger Westrup

D-U-N-S 07-528-8126
TWIN TIER MANAGEMENT CORP
GUTHRIE ENTERPRISES
(Suby of GUTHRIE CLINIC) ★
Guthrie Sq, Sayre, PA 18840
Tel (570) 888-6666 Founded/Ownrshp 1982
Sales 49.6MM^E EMP 2,500^E
SIC 8741 5912 Hospital management; Drug stores
Pr: Mary Mannix
*Sec: Michele Sisto

D-U-N-S 04-367-6464 IMP/EXP
TWIN-STAR INTERNATIONAL INC
CLASSIC FLAME
1690 S Congress Ave # 210, Delray Beach, FL 33445-6330
Tel (561) 665-8084 Founded/Ownrshp 1999
Sales 204.8MM EMP 42
SIC 5719 Fireplaces & wood burning stoves
Co-Pr: Marc Sculler
*Co-Pr: Pete Harper
*Ex VP: Andy Bandremer

D-U-N-S 09-948-9379 IMP
TWININGS NORTH AMERICA INC
(Suby of R.TWINING AND COMPANY LIMITED)
777 Passaic Ave Ste 230, Clifton, NJ 07012-1884
Tel (973) 591-0600 Founded/Ownrshp 1980
Sales 113.7MM EMP 60
SIC 2099

D-U-N-S 16-855-1997
TWINLAB CORP
(Suby of IDEASPHERE) ★
2255 Glades Rd Ste 342w, Boca Raton, FL 33431-7379
Tel (212) 651-8500 Founded/Ownrshp 2003
Sales 95.7MM^E EMP 400^E
SIC 2099 2834 2731 2721 2833 Tea blending; Vitamin preparations; Books: publishing only; Statistical reports (periodicals): publishing only; Medicinals & botanicals
CEO: Naomi Whittel
*Ofcr: Richard Neuwirth
Ex VP: Kate Pastor
VP: Steve Heacock
VP: Ann M Stephens

D-U-N-S 03-245-8874
TWINLAB HOLDINGS INC
IDEASPHERE
3133 Orchard Vista Dr Se, Grand Rapids, MI 49546-7033
Tel (616) 464-5000 Founded/Ownrshp 1968
Sales 165.0MM^E EMP 500
SIC 2833 2834 5149 2721 Medicinals & botanicals; Pharmaceutical preparations; Groceries & related products; Periodicals
CEO: David V Andel
*Pr: Mark Fox
*CFO: Steven R Heacock
*V Ch Bd: Bill Nicholson
*V Ch Bd: Anthony Robbins
VP: Henry Choi
VP: Ray Jaglowski
Assoc Dir: Lou Martilotta

D-U-N-S 05-431-0466
TWINS INTERNATIONAL INC
TACO BELL
2275 Half Day Rd Ste 300, Bannockburn, IL 60015-1232
Tel (847) 374-1200 Founded/Ownrshp 1999
Sales 66.4MM^E EMP 3,000
SIC 5812 Fast-food restaurant, chain
CEO: John Kallergis
*Pr: Nick Kallergis

D-U-N-S 00-467-9305
▲**TWITTER INC**
1355 Market St Ste 900, San Francisco, CA 94103-1337
Tel (415) 222-9670 Founded/Ownrshp 2006
Sales 2.2MMM EMP 3,905
Tkr Sym TWTR Exch NYS
SIC 7375 On-line data base information retrieval
CEO: Jack Dorsey
*Ch Bd: Omid Kordestani
COO: Adam Bain
CFO: Anthony Noto
VP: Morgan Field
Snr Sftwr: Michael Anderson
Snr Sftwr: Nicholas Gorski
Snr Sftwr: John Woodell
CTO: Adam Messinger
Sftwr Eng: Yiting Bian
Sftwr Eng: Jordan Bull
Board of Directors: Peter Fenton, Martha Lane Fox, Hugh Johnston, Debra L Lee, David Rosenblatt, Marjorie Scardino, bret Tay, Eva Williams

TWO DEGREES
See SLALOM LLC

D-U-N-S 00-307-6650
TWO FARMS INC (MD)
ROYAL FARMS
3611 Roland Ave, Baltimore, MD 21211-2408
Tel (410) 889-0200 Founded/Ownrshp 1959, 1964
Sales 196.3MM^E EMP 1,000
SIC 5411

D-U-N-S 11-334-5487
TWO GUYS SERVICE LLC
45662 Terminal Dr, Dulles, VA 20166-4340
Tel (703) 481-0222 Founded/Ownrshp 2001
Sales 33.2MM^E EMP 1,000
SIC 7349 1541 Janitorial service, contract basis; Renovation, remodeling & repairs: industrial buildings
VP Opers: Robert Baldwin

D-U-N-S 83-256-1976
▲**TWO HARBORS INVESTMENT CORP**
590 Madison Ave Fl 3600, New York, NY 10022-8531
Tel (612) 629-2500 Founded/Ownrshp 2009
Sales 769.9MM EMP 4^E
Accts Ernst & Young Llp Minneapolis
Tkr Sym TWO Exch NYS
SIC 6798 Real estate investment trusts
Pr: Thomas E Siering
*Ch Bd: Brian C Taylor
CFO: Brad Farrell
*CIO: William Roth

D-U-N-S 14-242-3404 IMP/EXP
TWO RIVERS TERMINAL LLC
(Suby of LAND VIEW INC) ★
3300c N Glade Rd, Pasco, WA 99301-9389
Tel (509) 547-7776 Founded/Ownrshp 2003
Sales 86.1MM^E EMP 65^E
SIC 5191 5999 Fertilizers & agricultural chemicals; Farm equipment & supplies
Genl Mgr: Jeff Campbell
IT Man: Nate Eichner

D-U-N-S 05-630-7960 IMP/EXP
TWOS CO INC (NY)
PASSPORT COLLECTION'S
500 Saw Mill River Rd, Elmsford, NY 10523-1027
Tel (914) 664-2277 Founded/Ownrshp 1968
Sales 94.9MM^E EMP 225
SIC 5199 5023 5094 Gifts & novelties; Decorative home furnishings & supplies; Jewelry
Ch: Roberta Gottlieb
Pr: Thomas Gottlieb
Chf Mktg O: Tom Zimmerman
VP: Harvey Matlick
Ex Dir: Alejandro F Caceres
Mng Dir: Mark Bennett
Mng Dir: Annegret Boylan
Mng Dir: Pamela Lingenfelser
Mng Dir: Chris Olson
IT Man: Lawrence Gray
IT Man: Tom Price

D-U-N-S 04-142-1306
TWOTON INC
BURGER KING
1743 Rohrerstown Rd, Lancaster, PA 17601-2319
Tel (717) 569-5791 Founded/Ownrshp 1966
Sales 275.0M^E EMP 1,500
SIC 5812
Pr: Gerald Mitchell
*Treas: Rita Zimmerman

TWR
See TRANS WORLD RADIO

TXI
See TEXAS INDUSTRIES INC

D-U-N-S 95-790-0194 IMP
■**TXI OPERATIONS LP**
(Suby of TXI) ★
1341 W Mockingbird Ln 700w, Dallas, TX 75247-6913
Tel (972) 647-6700 Founded/Ownrshp 1996
Sales 173.5MM^E EMP 500
SIC 3273 3271 3272 1442 Ready-mixed concrete; Blocks, concrete or cinder: standard; Brick, concrete; Pipe, concrete or lined with concrete; Sand mining; Gravel mining
CEO: Mel G Brekhus
Pr: Robert D Rogers
CFO: Richard M Fowler
VP: Frederick G Anderson
VP: James R Mc Craw
VP: Robert C Moore
Sls Mgr: Barbara Schmidt

TXL DISTRIBUTION
See TROXELL COMMUNICATIONS INC

D-U-N-S 07-881-3643
TXL HOLDING CORP
4675 E Cotton Center Blvd, Phoenix, AZ 85040-4809
Tel (602) 437-7240 Founded/Ownrshp 2008
Sales 222.3MM^E EMP 250
SIC 5064 Television sets
Ch Bd: Johnathan Cozzi
*Pr: Alan Wilkinson
*Treas: Steven Decillis III
Board of Directors: Baron Carlson, Johnathan Cozzi, Gregory Harper, Michael Ruprich, Alan Wilkinson

TXU
See LUMINANT MINING CO LLC

TXU ENERGY
See TEXAS COMPETITIVE ELECTRIC HOLDINGS CO LLC

D-U-N-S 00-792-8344
TXU ENERGY INDUSTRIES CO (TX)
(Suby of ENERGY FUTURE HOLDINGS CORP) ★
1601 Bryan St Ste 34-068, Dallas, TX 75201-3411
Tel (214) 812-4600 Founded/Ownrshp 1945, 1997
Sales 882.8MM^E EMP 5,000
SIC 4911 Generation, electric power; Transmission, electric power; Distribution, electric power
CEO: Michael J McNally
*Ch Bd: Erle Nye
*Treas: Kirk R Oliver
Ofcr: Scott Peters
Sr Ex VP: Cynthia Rogers
VP: Don Drane
VP: Donna Ready
VP: Jack Redding
VP: Allen V Smith
Netwrk Eng: Stanley Burchell

D-U-N-S 17-333-7028
TXU ENERGY RETAIL CO LLC
(Suby of ENERGY FUTURE HOLDINGS CORP) ★
1601 Bryan St, Dallas, TX 75201-3411
Tel (214) 812-4449 Founded/Ownrshp 1996
Sales 302.2MM^E EMP 350
SIC 4911 Electric services
CEO: James A Burke
*COO: Scott A Hudson
*Sr VP: David Faranetta
*VP: Gabe Castro
*VP: Cecily Small Gooch

D-U-N-S 09-055-2246 IMP
TXU ENERGY SERVICES CO LLC
(Suby of ENERGY FUTURE HOLDINGS CORP) ★
1601 Bryan St, Dallas, TX 75201-3411
Tel (214) 812-4600 Founded/Ownrshp 2001
Sales 514.8MM^E EMP 2,000
SIC 3679 Transducers, electrical
Genl Mgr: Brian N Dickie
DP Dir: Mark Weidner
Sales Exec: Pat Degroote

D-U-N-S 06-825-7695
TXU TRANSITION BOND CO L L C
(Suby of ONCOR ELECTRIC DELIVERY CO LLC) ★
1601 Bryan St, Dallas, TX 75201-3411
Tel (214) 814-4600 Founded/Ownrshp 2002

Sales 150.7MM^E *EMP* 450
SIC 4911 Electric services
Prin: Dan Farrell

D-U-N-S 84-714-5161
TXU UNITED KINGDOM HOLDINGS CO
(*Suby of* ENERGY FUTURE HOLDINGS CORP) ★
1601 Bryan St, Dallas, TX 75201-3411
Tel (214) 812-4600 *Founded/Ownrshp* 1998
Sales 4.3MMM^E *EMP* 5,500
SIC 4911 Electric services
Ch Bd: Erle Nye
**Treas:* Kirk R Oliver
**V Ch Bd:* H Jarrell Gibbs

D-U-N-S 15-176-0451 IMP/EXP
TY INC
280 Chestnut Ave, Westmont, IL 60559-1139
Tel (630) 920-1515 *Founded/Ownrshp* 1986
Sales 90.1MM^E *EMP* 300
SIC 5092

D-U-N-S 05-461-1041
TY LIN INTERNATIONAL GROUP
345 California St Fl 23, San Francisco, CA 94104-2646
Tel (415) 291-3700 *Founded/Ownrshp* 1989
Sales 153.6MM^E *EMP* 2,100
Accts Ernst & Young Llp San Franci
SIC 8711 Consulting engineer
Pr: Robert A Peterson

TY VALVE
See LOCKWOOD INTERNATIONAL INC

D-U-N-S 03-730-5646
■TYBRIN CORP
(*Suby of* JACOBS ENGINEERING GROUP INC) ★
1030 Titan Ct, Fort Walton Beach, FL 32547-6638
Tel (850) 337-2500 *Founded/Ownrshp* 2009
Sales 101.3MM^E *EMP* 1,250
SIC 7371

TYCO
See SENSORMATIC INTERNATIONAL INC

TYCO ELECTONIC
See PRECISION INTERCONNECT LLC

D-U-N-S 02-114-5741
TYCO ELECTRONICS BLANKET
100 Amp Dr, Harrisburg, PA 17106
Tel (717) 810-2598 *Founded/Ownrshp* 2013
Sales 107.7MM^E *EMP* 87^E
SIC 5023 Blankets
**Prin:* Chad Morgan

D-U-N-S 00-301-2549 IMP/EXP
TYCO ELECTRONICS CORP (PA)
TE CONNECTIVITY
(*Suby of* TE CONNECTIVITY INC) ★
1050 Westlakes Dr, Berwyn, PA 19312-2400
Tel (717) 986-7275 *Founded/Ownrshp* 1941, 2014
Sales 23.5MMM^E *EMP* 90,000
SIC 3678 3643 Electronic connectors; Current-carrying wiring devices; Connectors & terminals for electrical devices
Ch: Tom Lynch
COO: Joe Donahue
Treas: Mario Calastri
Ex VP: John Jenkins
Ex VP: Robert Scott
Ex VP: Robert N Shaddock
Sr VP: Minoru Okamoto
VP: Luke Whitebread
Prin: James Otoole
Prin: Christine Voelz-Dexter
Rgnl Mgr: Shawn Murray

D-U-N-S 04-146-3456 IMP
TYCO ELECTRONICS INTEGRATED CABLE SYSTEMS LLC
(*Suby of* TE CONNECTIVITY) ★
100 Piscataqua Dr, Newington, NH 03801-8002
Tel (603) 436-6100 *Founded/Ownrshp* 2007
Sales 165.5MM^E *EMP* 275
SIC 3357 Fiber optic cable (insulated)
Genl Mgr: Jonathan J Dufour
MIS Dir: Joe Stokel
Mktg Mgr: Robert L Suydam
Mktg Mgr: Janet Wade

D-U-N-S 00-232-4452 IMP
TYCO ELECTRONICS SUBSEA COMMUNICATIONS LLC
(*Suby of* TE CONNECTIVITY) ★
250 Industrial Way W, Eatontown, NJ 07724-2296
Tel (732) 578-7000 *Founded/Ownrshp* 1997
Sales 219.0MM^E *EMP* 1,178
SIC 3661 5063 7373 1731 8999 Telephone & telegraph apparatus; Insulators, electrical; Computer systems analysis & design; Communications specialization; Communication services
Pr: Aaron Stucki
CFO: David Van Rossum
**VP:* Chris Carobene
**VP:* Thomas M Lynch
Dir Surg: Renae Leary
Mng Dir: Ekaterina Golovchenko
Genl Mgr: Jonathan Dufour
**VP Sls:* Michael Rieger
Mktg Dir: Courtney McDaniel
Snr Mgr: Michael Lindstedt

D-U-N-S 00-807-0682 IMP
TYCO ENGINEERED PRODUCTS & SERVICES
(*Suby of* TYCO INTERNATIONAL MANAGEMENT CO LLC) ★
9600 W Gulf Bank Rd, Houston, TX 77040-3112
Tel (609) 720-4200 *Founded/Ownrshp* 1997
Sales 322.4MM^E *EMP* 4,276
SIC 3491 3625 3621 Industrial valves; Automatic regulating & control valves; Actuators, industrial; Motors & generators
Pr: Robert Mead
**Treas:* Barbara Miller
**VP:* John J Guarnieri

D-U-N-S 07-163-0842 EXP
TYCO FIRE PRODUCTS LP
TYCO FIRE PROTECTION PRODUCTS
(*Suby of* TYCO INTERNATIONAL MANAGEMENT CO LLC) ★
1400 Pennbrook Pkwy, Lansdale, PA 19446-3840
Tel (215) 362-0700 *Founded/Ownrshp* 1984, 1999
Sales 421.9MM^E *EMP* 1,335
SIC 3569 3494 3321 5085 Sprinkler systems, fire: automatic; Valves & pipe fittings; Sprinkler systems, field; Water pipe, cast iron; Valves & fittings
Pt: Colleen Repplier
Pt: Robert Roche
Pt: Ryan K Stafford
Sr Cor Off: Montgomery Smith
Bd of Dir: John Corcoran
VP: Patsy Castro
VP: Rick Dotterer
VP: Steve Grisko
VP: Paul Janusz
VP: Dennis Kennedy
VP: Rohan Pal
VP: William J Smith
VP: Jay Thomas
Dir Risk M: Thomas McDonald
Dir Risk M: Carolyn Wilks

D-U-N-S 14-039-5760 IMP
TYCO FIRE PRODUCTS LP
(*Suby of* TYCO INTERNATIONAL MANAGEMENT CO LLC) ★
8902 N Interstate 27, Lubbock, TX 79403-6713
Tel (806) 472-2400 *Founded/Ownrshp* 2000
Sales 148.4MM^E *EMP* 567
SIC 3569 Filters; Sprinkler systems, fire: automatic
Pr: Len Schiavone
Off Mgr: Scott Going
IT Man: Carl Tipton
Prd Mgr: Jerry Forsythe

TYCO FIRE PROTECTION PRODUCTS
See TYCO FIRE PRODUCTS LP

D-U-N-S 19-657-8736
TYCO INTEGRATED SECURITY LLC
(*Suby of* TYCO INTERNATIONAL MANAGEMENT CO LLC) ★
4700 Exchange Ct Ste 300, Boca Raton, FL 33431-4450
Tel (561) 226-8201 *Founded/Ownrshp* 2012
Sales 3.2MMM^E *EMP* 20,020
SIC 7382 7381 1731 Security systems services; Guard services; Electrical work
Pr: Mark Vandover
Pr: Pam Runkel
COO: John Kock
CFO: David Benjamin
CFO: Mick Lopez
VP: Teresa Maia
**VP:* Tony McGraw
Exec: Shaunte Scott
Area Mgr: Robert Watson
Brnch Mgr: Ben Brookheart
Dist Mgr: Michael Vito

D-U-N-S 00-102-3472 EXP
TYCO INTERNATIONAL MANAGEMENT CO LLC
(*Suby of* JOHNSON CONTROLS INC) ★
9 Roszel Rd Ste 2, Princeton, NJ 08540-6205
Tel (609) 720-4200 *Founded/Ownrshp* 1962, 2016
Sales 12.9MMM^E *EMP* 39,000
SIC 3999 1711 1731 3669 3491 Fire extinguishers, portable; Fire sprinkler system installation; Safety & security specialization; Fire detection & burglar alarm systems specialization; Fire detection systems, electric; Smoke detectors; Fire alarm apparatus, electric; Industrial valves; Automatic regulating & control valves
CEO: George R Oliver
Pr: Edward D Breen
Pr: Paul Fitzhenry
COO: Bob Vanourek
CFO: Frank Sklarsky
Ofcr: John E Evard
Ex VP: Dar Arif
Ex VP: Judith A Reinsdorf
Ex VP: Robert Scott
Sr VP: Carol Anthony Davidson
Sr VP: Carol John
Sr VP: Shelley Stewart
VP: Tony D'Onofrio
VP: B Doherty
VP: Lisa Geller
VP: Terry L Hall
VP: Alfred J Lechner
VP: Jacquie Marshall
VP: Bob O'Connell
VP: Dan Powell
VP: Mike Ryan

D-U-N-S 14-492-2077 IMP
TYCO SIMPLEXGRINNELL
GRINNELL FIRE PRTCTION SYSTEMS
1501 Nw 51st St, Boca Raton, FL 33431-4438
Tel (561) 988-3658 *Founded/Ownrshp* 1986
Sales 954.1MM^E *EMP* 19,000
SIC 3569 3491 Sprinkler systems, fire: automatic; Automatic regulating & control valves; Fire hydrant valves; Water works valves; Gas valves & parts, industrial
CEO: John F Fort
Ex VP: Jerry Boggess
Ex VP: Robert Mead
Exec: Fares Khalidi
Dist Mgr: Dana Manners

D-U-N-S 83-220-5900
TYCOM LIMITED
(*Suby of* TYCO INTERNATIONAL MANAGEMENT CO LLC) ★
10 Park Ave, Morristown, NJ 07960-4700
Tel (973) 753-3040 *Founded/Ownrshp* 1997
Sales 90.9MM^E *EMP* 1,250
SIC 3643 1623 Current-carrying wiring devices; Cable laying construction
Pr: Neil R Garvey
CFO: David Van Rossam
VP: Robert Paski

Dir IT: Pete Sereguso
Snr Mgr: Michael Lindstedt

D-U-N-S 82-834-4056
TYDE GROUP WORLDWIDE LLC
(*Suby of* SUN CAPITAL PARTNERS INC) ★
5700 Crooks Rd Ste 207, Troy, MI 48098-2809
Tel (248) 879-7656 *Founded/Ownrshp* 2007
Sales 126.8MM^E *EMP* 2,088^E
SIC 3592 Carburetors
Prin: Steven Dow

D-U-N-S 19-466-4926 IMP/EXP
TYDEN GROUP HOLDINGS CORP
(*Suby of* CRIMSON INVESTMENTS) ★
409 Hoosier Dr, Angola, IN 46703-9335
Tel (740) 420-6777 *Founded/Ownrshp* 2005
Sales 344.8MM^E *EMP* 1,286^E
SIC 3953 2891 Figures (marking devices), metal; Sealants
CEO: Steve Oneil
**CFO:* Bruce Heinemann

TYDENBROOKS
See EJ BROOKS CO

D-U-N-S 08-018-0760
TYLER BLUFF WIND PROJECT LLC
(*Suby of* EDF RENEWABLE ENERGY INC) ★
15445 Innovation Dr, San Diego, CA 92128-3432
Tel (888) 903-6926 *Founded/Ownrshp* 2013
Sales 85.5MM^E *EMP* 827
SIC 4911 Electric services
Pr: Tristan Grimbert
Treas: Kara Vongphakdy
Ex VP: Larry Barr
Ex VP: Robert Miller
Ex VP: Ryan Pfaff

TYLER CREEK GOLF CLB CMPGROUND
See SAND PRODUCTS CORP

D-U-N-S 07-984-3447
TYLER INDEPENDENT SCHOOL DISTRICT
1319 Earl Campbell Pkwy, Tyler, TX 75701-9697
Tel (903) 262-1000 *Founded/Ownrshp* 1955
Sales 188.8MM *EMP* 2,500
Accts Prothro Wilhelmi And Company
SIC 8211 Public elementary & secondary schools
Pr: Michelle Carr
**Pr:* Orenthia Mason
**CFO:* Tosha Bjork
Bd of Dir: Gina Orr
Ofcr: Martha Miller
**VP:* Andy Bergfeld
Exec: Artimese Lawrence
DP Exec: Katie Lasseter
IT Man: Marla Barron
IT Man: John Orbaugh
Prd Mgr: Gregory McRae

TYLER PIPE COMPANY
See MCWANE INC

D-U-N-S 04-108-9293
▲TYLER TECHNOLOGIES INC
5101 Tennyson Pkwy, Plano, TX 75024-3525
Tel (972) 713-3700 *Founded/Ownrshp* 1998
Sales 591.0MM *EMP* 3,586^E
Tkr Sym TYL *Exch* NYS
SIC 7372 Prepackaged software
Pr: John S Marr Jr
**Ch Bd:* John M Yeaman
COO: Bret Dixon
CFO: Brian K Miller
Ex VP: Bruce Borcher
Ex VP: H Lynn Moore Jr
Ex VP: H Moore
**Ex VP:* Dustin R Womble
VP: Sean Craig
VP: David Grossman
VP: Ryan Hountz
VP: Siobhan Kerley
VP: Mary Lavik
VP: Lynn Moore
VP: W Michael Smith
VP: Kelly Sprong
VP: Ted Thien
VP: Stefan Werdegar
Comm Man: Cindy Haley
Board of Directors: Donald R Brattain, Glenn A Carter, Brenda A Cline, J Luther King Jr, Larry D Leinweber, Daniel M Pope

D-U-N-S 06-240-2356
TYNDALE ENTERPRISES INVESTMENT CORP
22341 Sw 66th Ave # 1205, Boca Raton, FL 33428-5953
Tel (561) 239-5273 *Founded/Ownrshp* 2012
Sales 320.0MM *EMP* 2
SIC 5137 Lingerie
Pr: Edson Tomasin

D-U-N-S 15-380-8613
TYONEK NATIVE CORP
1689 C St Ste 219, Anchorage, AK 99501-5131
Tel (907) 272-0707 *Founded/Ownrshp* 1973
Sales 178.9MM^E *EMP* 204
SIC 6552 Subdividers & developers
CEO: Tom Harris
**Ch Bd:* Elizabeth J Standifer
**Pr:* Michaelene Stephan
**Pr:* Seraphim Stephan Sr
**CFO:* Steve Taylor
**Treas:* Jaison Standifer
**VP:* Donald P Girvan
**VP:* McCord Emil J
**VP:* Emil J McCord

D-U-N-S 11-599-4923
■TYSON BREEDERS INC
(*Suby of* TYSON FOODS INC) ★
2200 W Don Tyson Pkwy, Springdale, AR 72762-6901
Tel (479) 290-4000 *Founded/Ownrshp* 1989
Sales 21.0MM^E *EMP* 2,000
SIC 0254 Poultry hatcheries
Ch: Don Tyson
VP: Devin Cole
**VP:* John H Tyson

VP Sls: Dave Madissoany
Sls Mgr: Gary Harris

D-U-N-S 05-706-1806 EXP
■TYSON CHICKEN INC
(*Suby of* TYSON FOODS INC) ★
2200 W Don Tyson Pkwy, Springdale, AR 72762-6901
Tel (479) 290-4000 *Founded/Ownrshp* 1998
Sales 243.6MM^E *EMP* 7,800
SIC 0252 0253 0254 0251 2015 2013 Chicken eggs; Turkey egg farm; Turkey farm; Poultry hatcheries; Broiling chickens, raising of; Frying chickens, raising of; Roasting chickens, raising of; Chicken slaughtering & processing; Turkey processing & slaughtering; Luncheon meat, poultry; Prepared beef products from purchased beef
Pr: Donnie Smith
CEO: John H Tyson
CFO: Steven Hankins
Treas: Dennis Leatherby
Ofcr: Greg Lee
VP: Rodney Pless
VP: Davis L Van Bebber
Prin: Don Tyson

D-U-N-S 04-630-5124
■TYSON FARMS OF TEXAS INC
(*Suby of* TYSON FOODS INC) ★
1019 Shelbyville St, Center, TX 75935-3741
Tel (936) 598-2474 *Founded/Ownrshp* 1952
Sales 174.2MM^E *EMP* 1,100
SIC 2015 Chicken, processed: fresh; Poultry, slaughtered & dressed
Pr: John H Tyson
**Pr:* Leland E Tollett
**Ex VP:* Gerald Johnston
VP: Beth Smith
**VP:* Barbara Tyson
Exec: Jerry Powell
Dir IT: Jeff Brock
Sfty Mgr: David Coonce

D-U-N-S 00-690-3702 IMP/EXP
▲TYSON FOODS INC
2200 W Don Tyson Pkwy, Springdale, AR 72762-6901
Tel (479) 290-4000 *Founded/Ownrshp* 1935
Sales 41.3MMM *EMP* 113,000
Accts Pricewaterhousecoopers Llp F
Tkr Sym TSN *Exch* NYS
SIC 2011 2015 2032 2096 2048 Meat packing plants; Beef products from beef slaughtered on site; Pork products from pork slaughtered on site; Chicken slaughtering & processing; Ethnic foods: canned, jarred, etc.; Tortillas: packaged in cans, jars etc.; Potato chips & similar snacks; Tortilla chips; Feeds from meat & from meat & vegetable meals
CEO: Donnie Smith
Ch Bd: John Tyson
Pr: Bernie Adcock
Pr: Larry Alsip
Pr: Andrew P Callahan
Pr: Thomas P Hayes
Pr: Tom Hayes
Pr: Donnie King
Pr: Stephen Stouffer
Pr: Todd Walker
Pr: Noel White
CFO: Dennis Leatherby
CFO: Jeanette Nida
Treas: Michelle Brown
Ofcr: Sally Grimes
Ofcr: Mary Oleksiuk
Ex VP: Howell P Carper
Ex VP: Mary A Oleksiuk
Ex VP: Mike Roetzel
Ex VP: David L Van Bebber
Sr VP: Curt T Calaway
Board of Directors: Mike Beebe, Mikel A Durham, Kevin M McNamara, Cheryl S Miller, Brad T Sauer, Jeffrey K Schomburger, Robert Thurber, Barbara A Tyson

D-U-N-S 00-729-6056 IMP/EXP
■TYSON FRESH MEATS INC
(*Suby of* TYSON FOODS INC) ★
800 Stevens Port Dr, Dakota Dunes, SD 57049-5005
Tel (605) 235-2061 *Founded/Ownrshp* 2001
Sales 6.6MMM^E *EMP* 41,000
SIC 2011 Boxed beef from meat slaughtered on site; Pork products from pork slaughtered on site
Pr: Steve Stoffer
**Pr:* Richard Bond
**Ex VP:* Chris Daniel
Sr VP: Roel Andriessen
**Sr VP:* Noel White
**VP:* Bernard Leonard
**VP:* Charles F Mostek
**VP:* Todd Neff
VP: Todd Nogelmeier
Dir Lab: Bruce George
Prgrm Mgr: Adam Pfeifer

D-U-N-S 09-012-5555 IMP/EXP
TZ ACQUISITION CORP
26301 Curtiss Wright Pkwy, Richmond Heights, OH 44143-4413
Tel (216) 535-4300 *Founded/Ownrshp* 1997
Sales 89.5MM^E *EMP* 1,100
SIC 2676 2211 2326 2842 2262 Sanitary paper products; Napkins, sanitary: made from purchased paper; Tampons, sanitary: made from purchased paper; Diapers, paper (disposable): made from purchased paper; Scrub cloths; Work garments, except raincoats: waterproof; Sanitation preparations, disinfectants & deodorants; Industrial plant disinfectants or deodorants; Napping: manmade fiber & silk broadwoven fabrics
Pr: Kenneth Vuylsteke
CFO: Christopher T Cira
**CFO:* Thomas S Friedl

D-U-N-S 82-788-7006
TZ HOLDINGS LP
567 San Nicolas Dr # 120, Newport Beach, CA 92660-6513
Tel (949) 719-2200 *Founded/Ownrshp* 2008
Sales 58.0MM^E *EMP* 2,000
SIC 7372 Prepackaged software

Prin: Regina Paolillo

D-U-N-S 07-281-5020
TZELL TRAVEL LLC
(*Suby of* TRAVEL LEADERS GROUP LLC) ★
119 W 40th St Fl 14, New York, NY 10018-2514
Tel (212) 944-2121 *Founded/Ownrshp* 1975
Sales 100.0MM^E *EMP* 975
SIC 4724 Travel agencies
Sr VP: Jerry Behrens
**CFO:* Willie Lynch
Bd of Dir: Dan Cadiz
Bd of Dir: Marie Mazzei
**Sr VP:* Cindy Schlansky
VP: Lisa Benzakein
**VP:* Scott Booth
VP: Christopher J Griffin
Admn Mgr: Jeannie Fernandez
Off Mgr: Dawn Garrett
Dir IT: Edward Schiffino

U

U A B
See UNIVERSITY OF ALABAMA AT BIRMINGHAM

U A M S MEDICAL CENTER
See UAMS EYE CENTER

U A W
See INTERNATIONAL UNION UNITED AUTOMOBILE AEROSPACE AND AGRICULTURAL IMPLEMENT WORKERS OF AM

U B
See UNIVERSITY OF BRIDGEPORT

D-U-N-S 06-141-7270
U B FOUNDATION ACTIVITIES INC (NY)
UNIVERSITY OF BUFFALO FOUNDATI
101 Center For Tommorrow, Buffalo, NY 14260-7400
Tel (716) 645-3013 *Founded/Ownrshp* 1992
Sales 85.9MM *EMP* 30^E
Accts Kpmg Llp Boston Ma
SIC 6732 Educational trust management
Ch Bd: Francis M Letro
**Treas:* Robert E Denning
**Ex Dir:* Edward Schneider

D-U-N-S 09-805-7115
U B O C INSURANCE INC
(*Suby of* MUFG UNION BANK NA) ★
445 S Figueroa St, Los Angeles, CA 90071-1602
Tel (213) 236-7700 *Founded/Ownrshp* 1983
Sales NA *EMP* 154^E
SIC 6411 Insurance agents
Pr: Dale L Jansen

U B S
See UBS BANK USA

U B S
See UBS SECURITIES LLC

D-U-N-S 88-366-0078
U C A HOLDINGS INC
1 W Pack Sq Ste 305, Asheville, NC 28801-3419
Tel (828) 210-8120 *Founded/Ownrshp* 1976
Sales 274.3MM^E *EMP* 1,300^E
SIC 6719 Investment holding companies, except banks
CEO: Kenneth E Glass
VP: David Nolletti

U C F
See UNIVERSITY OF CENTRAL FLORIDA BOARD OF TRUSTEES

U C M
See USIBELLI COAL MINE INC

D-U-N-S 96-314-1978
U C SAN DIEGO FOUNDATION
UC SAN DIEGO
9500 Gilman Dr, La Jolla, CA 92093-5004
Tel (858) 534-1032 *Founded/Ownrshp* 2010
Sales 86.3MM *EMP* 43^E
Accts Mark Boyer Cpa La Jolla Ca
SIC 8699 Charitable organization
Pr: Steve Gamer
**CFO:* Marlene D Shaver
Ofcr: Lisa Meredith
**VP:* Kathy Drucquer Duff
Mktg Dir: Joleen Schultz

U D C
See UNIVERSITY OF DISTRICT OF COLUMBIA

U D F
See UNITED DAIRY FARMERS INC

U D T
See UNITED DATA TECHNOLOGIES INC

U E C
See UNITED ENERGY CORP

U F C PENSION TRUST FUND
See SOUTHERN CAL UNITED FOOD & COMMERCIAL WORKERS UNIONS & FOOD EMPLOYERS PENSION TRUST FUND

D-U-N-S 80-081-7715
U F I TRANSPORTATION LLC
(*Suby of* COMFORT FURNITURE) ★
60063 Puckett Dr, Amory, MS 38821-9602
Tel (662) 257-1811 *Founded/Ownrshp* 2005
Sales 110.4MM^E *EMP* 220^E
SIC 5021 Furniture
VP: Jim Packett

U L A
See UNITED LAUNCH ALLIANCE LLC

U M B BANK
See UMB BANK NATIONAL ASSOCIATION

U N D
See UNIVERSITY OF NORTH DAKOTA

U N H
See UNIVERSITY SYSTEM OF NEW HAMPSHIRE

U N I
See UNIVERSITY OF NORTHERN IOWA

D-U-N-S 19-557-4736
■ **U O P EQUITEC SERVICES INC**
(*Suby of* UNIVERSAL OIL PRODUCTS COMPANY)
25 E Algonquin Rd, Des Plaines, IL 60016-6100
Tel (847) 391-2000 *Founded/Ownrshp* 1989
Sales 148.7MM^E *EMP* 2,000
SIC 3533 Oil & gas field machinery
Pr: Carlos Guimaraes
**Pr:* Graeme Donald
**Treas:* George Davidson
IT Man: Shouvik Dutta
IT Man: Steven Philoon
Info Man: Michael Koo

D-U-N-S 85-849-1533 IMP
U P M C HORIZON
SHENANGO VALLEY MEDICAL CENTER
(*Suby of* UPMC HEALTH BENEFITS) ★
110 N Main St, Greenville, PA 16125-1726
Tel (724) 588-2100 *Founded/Ownrshp* 1998
Sales 164.8MM^E *EMP* 1,000
SIC 8062 General medical & surgical hospitals
CEO: Joseph D Simko
Chf Path: Lina Perry
VP: Chris Kolic
**Prin:* Don Awrey
Off Mgr: Mark Kuntz
Doctor: Veeraiah Perni

D-U-N-S 07-217-2661
U P M C SHADYSIDE
(*Suby of* UPMC HEALTH BENEFITS) ★
5230 Centre Ave, Pittsburgh, PA 15232-1304
Tel (412) 623-2121 *Founded/Ownrshp* 1982
Sales 351.3MM^E *EMP* 2,131
SIC 8062 General medical & surgical hospitals
Pr: Henry A Mordoh
Dir Risk M: Rick Kidwell
CIO: Maureen Potts
Board of Directors: G Nicholas Beckwith III, Thomas J Hilliard, John P McComb Jr, W Duff McCrady

U P S
See FRITZ COMPANIES INC

U P S
See UPS SUPPLY CHAIN SOLUTIONS INC

U P S
See UPS FUEL SERVICES INC

U R T
See UNITED ROAD TOWING INC

U S A
See UNITED STRUCTURES OF AMERICA INC

U S AIRWAYS EXPRESS
See TRANS STATES AIRLINES INC

U S ARCHITECTURAL LIGHTING
See US POLE CO INC

D-U-N-S 12-660-7824
■ **U S ARMY CORPS OF ENGINEERS**
(*Suby of* UNITED STATES DEPARTMENT OF THE ARMY) ★
441 G Street Nw, Washington, DC 20314-0001
Tel (804) 435-9362 *Founded/Ownrshp* 1779
Sales NA *EMP* 37,550
SIC 9711 Army
Brnch Mgr: Thomas Roche
CIO: Todd Duncan
CIO: Carl Hilton
CTO: Wilbert Berrios
IT Man: Carole Bell
IT Man: Dan Eng
IT Man: John McMaster
IT Man: Andrew Miller
Netwrk Mgr: George Moncrief
Sys Mgr: Sam Han
Info Man: Robin German

U S C
See ULLIMAN SCHUTTE CONSTRUCTION LLC

U S C
See UNIVERSITY OF SOUTHERN CALIFORNIA

D-U-N-S 02-791-5235
U S C EDUCATIONAL FOUNDATION
1600 Hampton St Ste 814, Columbia, SC 29208-3403
Tel (803) 777-1466 *Founded/Ownrshp* 1956
Sales 85.4MM *EMP* 10
SIC 8221 University
Pr: Andrew Sorenson
**Prin:* Jerome Odom

U S D A
See UNITED STATES DEPARTMENT OF AGRICULTURE

D-U-N-S 00-890-7313
U S ENGINEERING CO (MO)
3433 Roanoke Rd, Kansas City, MO 64111-3778
Tel (816) 753-6969 *Founded/Ownrshp* 1893, 1997
Sales 246.3MM^E *EMP* 800
Accts Bkd Llp Kansas City Mo
SIC 1711 Mechanical contractor; Plumbing contractors; Warm air heating & air conditioning contractor; Refrigeration contractor
CEO: Henry T Nottberg
**Pr:* Tim L Moormeier
CFO: Tyler Nottberg
**CFO:* Brendan Rittle

U S EQUITY PARTNERS
See WASSERSTEIN & CO LP

U S GOVERNMENT
See GOVERNMENT OF UNITED STATES

U S HEALTH AND LIFE
See US HEALTH HOLDINGS LTD

D-U-N-S 10-198-6156 IMP/EXP
U S HOLDINGS INC
EAGLE MANUFACTURING GROUP
3200 W 84th St, Hialeah, FL 33018-4908
Tel (305) 885-0301 *Founded/Ownrshp* 1937
Sales 168.1MM^E *EMP* 610
SIC 3321 3543 Gray iron castings; Foundry pattern-making
Pr: Alex Debogory Jr
**COO:* Alex L Bogory
COO: Ronn Page
**CFO:* David Brunswick
**Treas:* Alex S Debogory
Ex VP: Paula Cavache
**VP:* David H Brunswick
**VP:* Jamie Rubin
CIO: David Miller
Dir IT: Usha Krishna
IT Man: Ralf Torres

U S I
See UNIFIED SOLUTIONS INC

U S I
See USI SERVICES GROUP INC

U S M
See US MOTIVATION INC

D-U-N-S 00-652-5794 IMP
U S MANUFACTURING CORP
28201 Van Dyke Ave, Warren, MI 48093-2713
Tel (586) 467-1600 *Founded/Ownrshp* 2014
Sales 378.5MM^E *EMP* 800^E
SIC 3714 3462 3356 Motor vehicle parts & accessories; Axle housings & shafts, motor vehicle; Differentials & parts, motor vehicle; Steering mechanisms, motor vehicle; Iron & steel forgings; Nonferrous rolling & drawing
Pr: Brian A Simon
CFO: John R Dallacqua
CFO: Mark Roll
Ex VP: Joseph A Simon
VP: Jeff Johnson
VP: Adel Khanfar
Area Supr: James Brzezinski
Area Supr: Karl Ritter
Area Supr: Monica Smith
Plnt Mgr: Don Ross
Ql Cn Mgr: Syed Hasan

U S O
See UNITED SERVICE ORGANIZATIONS INC

D-U-N-S 12-653-6929
■ **U S OFFICE OF PERSONNEL MANAGEMENT**
O P M
(*Suby of* EXECUTIVE OFFICE OF UNITED STATES GOVERNMENT) ★
1900 E St Nw Ste 7f14, Washington, DC 20415-0001
Tel (202) 606-1800 *Founded/Ownrshp* 1979
Sales NA *EMP* 3,700
Accts Kpmg Llp Washington Dc
SIC 9199 Personnel agency, government;
Pr: James Thieme
**CFO:* Mark Reger
**CFO:* Keith Willingham
Ofcr: Lucy Antone
Ofcr: Jeanne Friedrich
Ofcr: Gregory Kellner
Dir IT: Vivian Mackey
IT Man: Paul Burke
IT Man: Mary Price
IT Man: Susan Stepanski
Sftwr Eng: Art Hallock

U S ONCOLOGY
See PHYSICIAN RELIANCE NETWORK INC

U S P A
See FIRST COMMAND FINANCIAL PLANNING INC

U S R A
See UNIVERSITIES SPACE RESEARCH ASSOCIATION

D-U-N-S 01-426-9781
U S RESTAURANTS INC
1780 Swede Rd, Blue Bell, PA 19422-3522
Tel (610) 277-4200 *Founded/Ownrshp* 1981
Sales 47.8MM^E *EMP* 1,500
SIC 5812 Fast-food restaurant, chain
Pr: Steven M Lewis
**CFO:* Michael J Kadelski
**Sec:* Vernon W Hill
**VP:* Henry White
**VP:* Gregory R Winans

U S S I
See UNITED STATES STEEL INTERNATIONAL INC

D-U-N-S 00-893-6841 IMP
■ **U S SILICA CO**
(*Suby of* US SILICA HOLDINGS INC) ★
8490 Progress Dr Ste 300, Frederick, MD 21701-4996
Tel (301) 682-0600 *Founded/Ownrshp* 1968
Sales 544.8MM^E *EMP* 844
SIC 1446 1455 1459 Silica sand mining; Kaolin mining; Aplite mining
Pr: Bryan Shinn
**CFO:* Donald Merril
**Treas:* Michael L Thompson
Treas: Michael Thompson
**VP:* John Blanchard
VP: John P Blanchard
**VP:* Bradford Casper
VP: Bradford B Casper
**VP:* David Murry
**VP:* Jason Tedrow
**VP:* Don Weinheimer
**VP:* Michael Winkler
**VP:* Adam Yoxtheimer

D-U-N-S 00-663-1720
U S TECH SOLUTIONS INC
10 Exchange Pl Ste 1820, Jersey City, NJ 07302-4934
Tel (201) 524-9600 *Founded/Ownrshp* 2000
Sales 120.0MM *EMP* 2,200^E
SIC 7379 7372 Computer related consulting services; Prepackaged software

CEO: Manoj Agarwal
Pr: Adam Klaucke
**CFO:* Jack Balakristnan
VP: Digant Vashi
Exec: Roshni Kukreja
Dir Bus: Samantha Enos
Snr Mgr: Nandini Kondagari

D-U-N-S 00-633-6572 IMP
U S TOOL GRINDING INC (MO)
U.S. TOOL GROUP
2000 Progress Dr, Farmington, MO 63640-9158
Tel (573) 431-3856 *Founded/Ownrshp* 1958
Sales 349.0MM *EMP* 700
Accts Uhy Llp St Louis Missouri
SIC 3541 3545 Machine tools, metal cutting type; Machine tool accessories
Pr: Bruce Williams
**VP:* Mike Baugh
**VP:* Jim Galati
**VP:* Brent Williams
Prgrm Mgr: Clyde Archer
Prgrm Mgr: Jim Brown
Off Admin: Kris Helbey
QA Dir: Ken Campanelli
IT Man: Mark Heflin
IT Man: Sherre Long
Site Mgr: Mercedes Bertagna

D-U-N-S 02-987-4526 IMP
U S TOY CO INC
CONSTRUCTIVE PLAYTHINGS
13201 Arrington Rd, Grandview, MO 64030-2886
Tel (816) 761-5900 *Founded/Ownrshp* 1954
Sales 84.9MM^E *EMP* 250
SIC 5049 5092 5945

D-U-N-S 11-365-3245 IMP/EXP
U S WEATHERFORD L P
WEATHERFORD ARTIFICIAL LIFTS
(*Suby of* WEATHERFORD WORLDWIDE HOLDINGS GMBH)
2000 Saint James Pl, Houston, TX 77056-4123
Tel (713) 693-4000 *Founded/Ownrshp* 1995
Sales 4.0MMM^E *EMP* 15,000
SIC 3498 3533 Fabricated pipe & fittings; Oil & gas field machinery; Oil field machinery & equipment
CEO: B Duroc-Danner
**VP:* James M Hudgins
IT Man: Bradley Lee

D-U-N-S 15-191-5949 IMP
U S XPRESS INC
XPRESS NETWORK SOLUTIONS
(*Suby of* US XPRESS ENTERPRISES INC) ★
4080 Jenkins Rd, Chattanooga, TN 37421-1174
Tel (866) 266-7270 *Founded/Ownrshp* 1985
Sales 969.4MM^E *EMP* 8,600
SIC 4213 Trucking, except local
Pr: Max L Fuller
Treas: Ray M Harlin
Ex VP: Eric Fuller
Ex VP: Lisa Pate
VP: Corey Bonner
VP: Jeff Seibenhener
Prgrm Mgr: Jeff Eidson
Tech Mgr: Keith Bailey
Software D: Ken Killian
Netwrk Eng: Jeremy Keys
Snr Mgr: Billy Stone

U S Z
See VOTORANTIM METAIS NORTH AMERICA INC

U T A
See UTAH TRANSIT AUTHORITY (UTA)

U T I INSURANCE
See UNITED TEACHER ASSOCIATES INC

U V U
See UTAH VALLEY UNIVERSITY

D-U-N-S 02-332-8446
U W PROVISION CO INC
2315 Pleasant View Rd, Middleton, WI 53562-5524
Tel (608) 836-7421 *Founded/Ownrshp* 1961
Sales 94.2MM^E *EMP* 100
SIC 5147 Meats, fresh
Pr: Steve Kalscheur
**VP:* Ronald Krantz
Sales Exec: Dean Johnson
Board of Directors: Steven Kalscheur, Ronald Krantz

D-U-N-S 80-934-8555
U-GAS INC
895 Bolger Ct, Fenton, MO 63026-2017
Tel (636) 343-9770 *Founded/Ownrshp* 1978
Sales 123.0MM^E *EMP* 306^E
SIC 5541 Gasoline service stations
Pr: Paul Taylor
CFO: Margaret Amend
Chf Mktg O: Bradford R Goette
VP: Perry Cheatham
VP Opers: Colleen Lynn

D-U-N-S 19-473-0412
■ **U-HAUL CO OF CALIFORNIA**
(*Suby of* U-HAUL INTERNATIONAL INC) ★
44511 S Grimmer Blvd, Fremont, CA 94538-6309
Tel (800) 528-0463 *Founded/Ownrshp* 1971
Sales 53.6MM^E *EMP* 1,200
SIC 7513 7519 4226 Truck rental & leasing, no drivers; Trailer rental; Special warehousing & storage
Pr: Dave Adams

D-U-N-S 00-473-5952
■ **U-HAUL CO OF DISTRICT OF COLUMBIA INC**
(*Suby of* U-HAUL INTERNATIONAL INC) ★
2727 N Central Ave, Phoenix, AZ 85004-1158
Tel (602) 263-6011 *Founded/Ownrshp* 2000
Sales 10.9MM^E *EMP* 1,400
SIC 7513 Truck rental & leasing, no drivers
CEO: Joe Shoen
Off Mgr: Della Cox

D-U-N-S 13-368-3750
■ U-HAUL CO OF MAINE INC
(*Suby of* AMERCO) ★
1325 Airmotive Way # 100, Reno, NV 89502-3201
Tel (775) 688-6300 *Founded/Ownrshp* 2003
Sales 93.8MM^E^ *EMP* 5,033^E^
SIC 7513 Truck rental & leasing, no drivers
Prin: Anita Owens
Ex VP: Ron Frank
VP Sls: Toby Bridgeman

D-U-N-S 04-237-0775 IMP/EXP
■ U-HAUL INTERNATIONAL INC
(*Suby of* AMERCO) ★
2727 N Central Ave, Phoenix, AZ 85004-1158
Tel (602) 263-6011 *Founded/Ownrshp* 1951
Sales 1.9MMM^E^ *EMP* 13,750
Accts Bdo Seidman
SIC 7513 7519 7359 5531 4226 8741 Truck rental & leasing, no drivers; Trailer rental; Equipment rental & leasing; Tool rental; Lawn & garden equipment rental; Automotive accessories; Household goods, warehousing; Business management
CEO: Edward Joe Shoen
Pr: Garner Carey
Pr: Angie Dewinter
COO: Frank Lister
CFO: Amy Elletson
CFO: Gary Kern
CFO: Robert T Peerson
**CFO:* Robert T Peterson
**Ex VP:* John C Taylor
VP: Cleo Crimmins
VP: Christopher Johnson
VP: Henry P P Kelly
VP: Renee Royer
VP: Bob Wesson
Exec: Kevin Kiley

U-PAK
See GO-MART INC

U-PUMP-IT
See PEERLESS TYRE CO

UA
See UNITED ARTISTS THEATRE CO

D-U-N-S 96-398-6133
UA (UNITED ASSOCIATION) LOCAL 13 OF JOURNEY MAN AND A PREMISES OF PLUMBING
1850 Mount Read Blvd, Rochester, NY 14615-3703
Tel (585) 338-2360 *Founded/Ownrshp* 1890
Sales 200.2M *EMP* 1,100
Accts Bonadio & Co Llp Pittsford
SIC 8631 Collective bargaining unit
Brnch Mgr: William Kurtv
**Pr:* Bruce Bowes
**Treas:* Brandon Tumia
**VP:* John Carpenter
**Prin:* Terry Moore

D-U-N-S 07-765-1511
UAB MEDICAL WEST
995 9th Ave Sw, Bessemer, AL 35022-4527
Tel (205) 481-7000 *Founded/Ownrshp* 1973
Sales 111.7MM *EMP* 729
SIC 8062 General medical & surgical hospitals
CEO: Don Lilly
Chf Path: Steven Osheal
**CFO:* Jim Thornton
**Treas:* Dan Eagar
Sr VP: Keith Pennington
Sr VP: Brandon Slocum
Dir Risk M: Charlene Jordan
Dir Rx: Russell Patterson
Dir Pat Ac: Angie Jacks
QA Dir: Linda Coogan
Dir IT: Bob Duckworth

UAIC
See UNITED AUTOMOBILE INSURANCE GROUP INC

UAMPS
See UTAH ASSOCIATED MUNICIPAL POWER SYSTEMS

UAMS
See UNIVERSITY OF ARKANSAS FOR MEDICAL SCIENCES

D-U-N-S 84-181-4775
UAMS EYE CENTER
U A M S MEDICAL CENTER
921 Ne 13th St, Oklahoma City, OK 73104-5007
Tel (405) 456-1000 *Founded/Ownrshp* 1993
Sales 43.2MM^E^ *EMP* 10,000
SIC 8011 Ophthalmologist
Dir Rad: Robert Fincher

D-U-N-S 16-339-6596
UANT VENTURES LLP
612 E Lamar Blvd Ste 700, Arlington, TX 76011-4128
Tel (817) 543-4905 *Founded/Ownrshp* 2004
Sales 77.3MM^E^ *EMP* 1,551^E^
SIC 6719 Investment holding companies, except banks
Pr: Mike Redd

UAPB
See UNIVERSITY OF ARKANSAS AT PINE BLUFF

D-U-N-S 83-753-3561
UAW PUBLIC RELATIONS
INTERNATIONAL UNION UAW
8000 E Jefferson Ave, Detroit, MI 48214-3963
Tel (313) 926-5291 *Founded/Ownrshp* 2002
Sales 171.6MM *EMP* 18
SIC 8743 Public relations & publicity
Owner: Ron Gettlefinger

D-U-N-S 01-266-5378 IMP
UB DISTRIBUTORS LLC
UNION BEER DISTRIBUTORS
1213 Grand St, Brooklyn, NY 11211-1800
Tel (718) 497-2407 *Founded/Ownrshp* 1996
Sales 101.8MM^E^ *EMP* 200
SIC 5181 Beer & ale
Pr: Christopher Sheehan
Treas: Doug Macdonald
Exec: Jeff Annis
Exec: Conor Giard

UBC
See UNITED BIOSOURCE LLC

D-U-N-S 01-389-5459
UBER TECHNOLOGIES INC
UBERCAB
(*Suby of* UBER INTERNATIONAL B.V.)
1455 Market St Fl 4, San Francisco, CA 94103-1355
Tel (415) 986-2715 *Founded/Ownrshp* 2010
Sales 927.2MM^E^ *EMP* 895
SIC 7372 Application computer software
CEO: Travis Kalanick
Ch: Margaret E Walsh

UBERCAB
See UBER TECHNOLOGIES INC

D-U-N-S 80-454-0094 IMP
UBI LIQUIDATING CORP
MARIANNE'S
300 Nixon Ln, Edison, NJ 08837-3831
Tel (201) 319-9093 *Founded/Ownrshp* 2003
Sales 317.6MM^E^ *EMP* 2,700
SIC 5621 5641 5651 5137 5632 Women's clothing stores; Children's & infants' wear stores; Family clothing stores; Women's & children's clothing; Women's accessory & specialty stores
Pr: Celia Clancy
**Pr:* Steve Newman
CFO: Gina Fernandez
CFO: Scott Hurd
**Treas:* Michael Abate
**Ex VP:* David Brown
Ex VP: Diane J Combes
VP: Gary Bashur
VP: John Coniglio
VP: Julie Daly
VP: Karen Harriston
VP: Luis Malave
VP: Ronald Race
VP: Mary Stokum
Board of Directors: Robert Grayson

D-U-N-S 78-070-6953
▲ UBIQUITI NETWORKS INC
2580 Orchard Pkwy, San Jose, CA 95131-1033
Tel (408) 942-3085 *Founded/Ownrshp* 2005
Sales 666.4MM *EMP* 537^E^
Accts Pricewaterhousecoopers Llp Sa
Tkr Sym UBNT *Exch* NGS
SIC 7373 Local area network (LAN) systems integrator
Ch Bd: Robert J Pera
VP: Anne Fazioli
VP: Benjamin Moore
CTO: John Sanford
Sftwr Eng: Sun Luke
Board of Directors: Michael E Hurlston, Ronald A Sege, Rafael Torres

D-U-N-S 05-322-7567
UBM INC
(*Suby of* UBM PLC)
2 Penn Plz, New York, NY 10121-0101
Tel (212) 600-3000 *Founded/Ownrshp* 1999
Sales 228.8MM^E^ *EMP* 3,500
SIC 2721 2711 8732 2741 Periodicals; Newspapers; Commercial nonphysical research; Business research service; Business service newsletters: publishing & printing
CEO: David Levin
Ex VP: Nikki Milne
Sr VP: Stacey Lisowski
**Sr VP:* Patrick Nohilly
Sr VP: Steve Resnick
Sr VP: Angela Scalpello
VP: Margaret Chamberlain
VP: Stephen Corrick
VP: Robyn Duda
VP: Amy Erdman
Dir Soc: Christine Montoya
Creative D: Jasveer Mehay

D-U-N-S 06-592-6420
UBM LLC
UBM TECH
(*Suby of* UBM PLC)
2 Penn Plz Fl 15, New York, NY 10121-1700
Tel (516) 562-5085 *Founded/Ownrshp* 2013
Sales 610.8MM^E^ *EMP* 1,567
SIC 2721 2711 7319 7389 Periodicals: publishing only; Newspapers; Media buying service; Decoration service for special events
CEO: Robert Faletra
Pr: Steve Johnston
Treas: Sandra Cipriano
Chf Inves: Alexander Fleiss
Ex VP: Kelley Damore
Ex VP: Marco Pardi
Sr VP: Suzan Kalim
Sr VP: Lisa Mackenzie
Sr VP: Beth Rivera
Sr VP: Gnosoulla Tsioupra-Lewis
VP: Gwen Deutsch
VP: Brian Gillooly
VP: Matthew Q Reber
VP: Michael Russak
Exec: John Soat
Dir Soc: Sara McGinness
Creative D: Lisa Katz
Board of Directors: Patrick Nohilly

UBM TECH
See UBM LLC

UBS AG
See UBS FINANCIAL SERVICES INC

UBS AG
See UBS SECURITIES LLC

UBS AG LONDON RENCH
See UBS ENERGY LLC

D-U-N-S 60-541-6072
UBS ASSET MANAGEMENT (AMERICAS) INC
(*Suby of* UBS AG)
1 N Wacker Dr Ste 3700, Chicago, IL 60606-2859
Tel (312) 525-4111 *Founded/Ownrshp* 1998
Sales 101.2MM^E^ *EMP* 600
SIC 6211 Investment firm, general brokerage
Pr: Robert J McCann
COO: Richard Dale
Sr VP: Robert Loupee
IT Man: Andrew Giordano

D-U-N-S 13-140-0132
UBS BANK USA
U B S
(*Suby of* U B S) ★
299 S Main St Ste 2275, Salt Lake City, UT 84111-2370
Tel (801) 532-2741 *Founded/Ownrshp* 2002
Sales NA *EMP* 15
SIC 6021 National commercial banks
CEO: Ellen Brawaikley
V Ch: Allen G Braithwaite III
COO: George Coburn
Sr VP: Christopher R Soutas

D-U-N-S 78-147-2964
UBS ENERGY LLC
UBS AG LONDON RENCH
(*Suby of* UBS AG)
677 Washington Blvd, Stamford, CT 06901-3707
Tel (203) 719-3000 *Founded/Ownrshp* 2001
Sales 149.5MM^E^ *EMP* 1,000
SIC 6211 6799 Brokers, security; Dealers, security; Investors

D-U-N-S 00-695-3004
UBS FINANCIAL SERVICES INC
UBS IB
(*Suby of* UBS AG) ★
1285 Ave Of The Americas, New York, NY 10019-6096
Tel (212) 713-2000 *Founded/Ownrshp* 1880
Sales 7.2MMM^E^ *EMP* 15,505
SIC 6211 6282 Brokers, security; Investment advisory service
CEO: Sergio P Ermotti
**Pr:* Mark B Sutton
COO: Stewart Brenner
COO: Dan Cochran
**CFO:* Robert J Chersi
**CFO:* Regina A Dolan
Chf Mktg O: John Hannasch
Chf Inves: John Shane
Ofcr: John Dalby
Ofcr: Paula Polito
**Ex VP:* Theodore Levine
**Ex VP:* James D Price
**Sr VP:* Anthony Divalerio
**Sr VP:* Dianne O'Donnell
VP: Noel Becker
VP: Pearl Bruce
VP: Hillary Cullen
**VP:* Christopher Dimuria
VP: Jose Garcia
**VP:* Georgia Hanford
**VP:* Daniel Hauschild

D-U-N-S 02-120-2701
UBS FINANCIAL SERVICES INC
UBS AG
(*Suby of* UBS AG) ★
499 Washington Blvd, Jersey City, NJ 07310-1995
Tel (201) 318-5900 *Founded/Ownrshp* 2010
Sales 154.7MM^E^ *EMP* 2,410^E^
SIC 6211 Security brokers & dealers
Ch: Axel A Weber
Assoc Dir: Mark Burke
Mng Dir: Douglas Rennie

UBS IB
See UBS FINANCIAL SERVICES INC

D-U-N-S 83-016-9012
UBS REAL ESTATE SECURITIES INC
(*Suby of* UBS IB) ★
1285 Av Of Amrc Fl Sconc1, New York, NY 10019
Tel (212) 713-2000 *Founded/Ownrshp* 1978
Sales 119.8MM^E^ *EMP* 24^E^
SIC 6211 Brokers, security
Prin: Frank Byrne

D-U-N-S 06-493-0894
UBS SECURITIES LLC
UBS AG
(*Suby of* UBS AG)
677 Washington Blvd, Stamford, CT 06901-3707
Tel (203) 719-3000 *Founded/Ownrshp* 2000
Sales 7.3MMM^E^ *EMP* 21,000
SIC 6211 6221 6289 6311 6091 6282 Security brokers & dealers; Brokers, security; Dealers, security; Stock option dealers; Commodity brokers, contracts; Commodity dealers, contracts; Futures brokers & dealers, commodity; Exchange clearinghouses, security; Life insurance carriers; Nondeposit trust facilities; Investment advisory service
Pr: John P Costas
CFO: John Dalby
**CFO:* Robert B Mills
Chf Inves: Reid Campbell
Ofcr: Jim Cai
Ofcr: Dianne Francis
Ofcr: Orly Shacham
Sr VP: Ryan A McClellan
Sr VP: M K Penwell
Sr VP: Richard Stone
VP: Bill Fitzpatrick
VP: Kyle Hublitz
VP: Brendan M Reidy
VP: Steven Westerman
Assoc Dir: Joel Geller
Assoc Dir: Kevin Pluff
Assoc Dir: Brooke Zelesnick

D-U-N-S 78-715-7874
UBS SECURITIES LLC
U B S
(*Suby of* UBS AG)
677 Washington Blvd, Stamford, CT 06901-3707
Tel (203) 719-3000 *Founded/Ownrshp* 1996
Sales 1.1MMM^E^ *EMP* 4,300
SIC 6211 6282 Brokers, security; Investment counselors
CFO: Daniel McLsaac
Assoc Dir: Michael Mirsky
Ex Dir: Eric Beltz
Ex Dir: Michael Gerardi

UC
See UNITED CENTRAL INDUSTRIAL SUPPLY CO LLC

D-U-N-S 88-386-4597
UC HEALTH LLC
3200 Burnet Ave, Cincinnati, OH 45229-3019
Tel (513) 585-6000 *Founded/Ownrshp* 1995
Sales 1.0MMM^E^ *EMP* 10,000
Accts Deloitte Tax Llp Cincinnati
SIC 8741 Management services; Hospital management
CEO: James Kingsbury
COO: Nancy Barone
COO: Tom Daskalakis
COO: Peter N Gilbert
CFO: Matt Nealon
CFO: Karen Shadowens
Ofcr: Jennifer Jackson
VP: Patrick Baker
VP: Jay Brown
VP: Mark Carey
VP: Anthony Condia
VP: Tony Condia
VP: John Deledda
VP: William Dirkes
VP: Charity Fannin
VP: Gary Harris
VP: Gayla Harvey
VP: John Renner
VP: Ron Rohlfing
VP: Andrea Stewart
VP: Stephen Strakowski

D-U-N-S 07-950-0772
UC HOLDINGS INC
300 Galleria Officentre, Southfield, MI 48034-4700
Tel (248) 728-8642 *Founded/Ownrshp* 2005
Sales 1.3MMM *EMP* 4,000
SIC 3465 3714 Body parts, automobile: stamped metal; Motor vehicle engines & parts
CEO: Mark Allan
**CEO:* Douglas Delgrosso

UC RUSAL MKTG & MGT LTD CYPRUS
See RUSAL AMERICA CORP

UC SAN DIEGO
See U C SAN DIEGO FOUNDATION

UCAR CARBON
See GRAFTECH INTERNATIONAL HOLDINGS INC

D-U-N-S 80-820-9878
UCARE MINNESOTA
500 Stinson Blvd, Minneapolis, MN 55413-2615
Tel (612) 676-6500 *Founded/Ownrshp* 1987
Sales NA *EMP* 550
SIC 6324 Health maintenance organization (HMO), insurance only
Pr: Nancy Feldman
**CFO:* Beth Monsrud
CFO: Elizabeth Monsrud
**Chf Mktg O:* Russel J Kuzel
Ofcr: Linda Pellett
**Sr VP:* Laurie Dean
**Sr VP:* Thomas Mahowald
**Sr VP:* Mark Traynor
**Sr VP:* Ghita Worcester
Exec: Margaret Beauchem
Comm Man: Deanne Probst

D-U-N-S 17-427-1379 EXP
UCB CHEMICALS CORP
2000 Lake Park Dr Se, Smyrna, GA 30080-7611
Tel (770) 434-6188 *Founded/Ownrshp* 2011
Sales 84.9MM^E^ *EMP* 430
SIC 5169 5191 5162 Synthetic rubber; Chemicals, agricultural; Resins
Pr: Larry Golen
CFO: Jack McNeese
**Treas:* Chris Finnley
**VP:* B Bayer
**VP:* M O'Brien
Pdt Mgr: Edwin Jenkins
Snr Mgr: Diane Vandeputte

D-U-N-S 03-748-0084 IMP
UCB INC
(*Suby of* UCB SA)
1950 Lake Park Dr Se, Smyrna, GA 30080-7648
Tel (770) 970-7500 *Founded/Ownrshp* 1987
Sales 313.5MM^E^ *EMP* 460
SIC 5122 8731 8732 Pharmaceuticals; Commercial physical research; Commercial nonphysical research
CEO: Jeffrey Wren
**Pr:* Greg Duncan
**Pr:* Fabrice Egros
**CFO:* Thiyagaraja Ravindran
**Treas:* Scott Philip Gee
VP: Stephanie Clerk
VP: Clive Davis
VP: Todd Edwards
**VP:* Doug Hooper
VP: Bruce Lavin
VP: Victor Sloan
**VP:* Denelle Waynick
Assoc Dir: Sascha Ahrweiler
Assoc Dir: Olivier Corin
Assoc Dir: Debbi Denison
Assoc Dir: Christina Lake
Assoc Dir: William Mandarino
Assoc Dir: Simon Sheard
Assoc Dir: David Wilson
Assoc Dir: Raymond Wysmierski

D-U-N-S 95-985-5599
UCC HOLDINGS CORP
2100 Norman Dr, Waukegan, IL 60085-6752
Tel (847) 473-5900 *Founded/Ownrshp* 2008
Sales 144.6MM[E] *EMP* 400[E]
SIC 3443 8711 Fabricated plate work (boiler shop); Designing: ship, boat, machine & product
Pr: Andrew Warrington

UCC TOTALHOME
See DIRECTBUY INC

UCCI
See UNITED CONCORDIA LIFE AND HEALTH INSURANCE CO

UCCI
See UNITED CONCORDIA COMPANIES INC

D-U-N-S 07-359-5436
■ **UCF HOTEL VENTURE**
LOEWS HTELS AT UNVRSAL ORLANDO
(*Suby of* LOEWS HOTELS & RESORTS) ★
6800 Lakewood Plaza Dr, Orlando, FL 32819-5580
Tel (407) 503-9000 *Founded/Ownrshp* 1998
Sales 69.9MM[E] *EMP* 1,000
SIC 7011 5813 5812 Hotels & motels; Drinking places; Eating places
CFO: Tina Samson
Pt: Universal Rank Hotel
Pt: Loews Hotel Orlando
Dir Risk M: Steve Walsh
Dir IT: Rob Conti
Netwrk Mgr: Luis Diaz
Netwrk Mgr: Paul Williams

D-U-N-S 62-444-9968 IMP
UCHICAGO ARGONNE LLC
ARGONNE NATIONAL LABORATORY
5801 S Ellis Ave Ste 601, Chicago, IL 60637-5418
Tel (773) 702-9476 *Founded/Ownrshp* 2016
Sales 507.0MM *EMP* 3,201[E]
SIC 8733 Noncommercial research organizations
Ch Bd: Robert J Zimmer
**Pr:* Peter B Littlewood
**CEO:* Donald H Levy
**COO:* Paul K Kearns
CFO: Stephen H Southworth
Ofcr: Doug Lenhart
VP: Donald Walko
CIO: Charles E Catlett
CTO: Ruiying Wu
Dir IT: Donna Keto
Dir IT: Rick Stevens

D-U-N-S 02-077-4709 IMP
UCHIYAMA MANUFACTURING AMERICA LLC
(*Suby of* UCHIYAMA MANUFACTURING CORP.)
494 Arrington Bridge Rd, Goldsboro, NC 27530-8538
Tel (919) 731-2364 *Founded/Ownrshp* 1999
Sales 118.5MM[E] *EMP* 300
SIC 5085 3714 3053 Gaskets; Seals, industrial; Motor vehicle parts & accessories
CEO: Taizo Uchiyama
**Pr:* Masatomo Sueki
**Sec:* Linda Jennings
VP: Akihiko Kishida

UCI
See UNITED COMPONENTS LLC

D-U-N-S 96-487-0831
UCI ACQUISITION HOLDINGS (NO 1) CORP
(*Suby of* UCI HOLDINGS LIMITED)
14601 Highway 41 N, Evansville, IN 47725-9357
Tel (812) 867-4156 *Founded/Ownrshp* 2010
Sales 438.6MM[E] *EMP* 3,900[E]
SIC 3714 Motor vehicle parts & accessories
CEO: Bruce Zorich
CFO: Ricardo Alvergue

D-U-N-S 07-888-1603
UCI HOLDINGS LLC
2727 Geesling Rd, Denton, TX 76208-1408
Tel (940) 243-7676 *Founded/Ownrshp* 2006
Sales 228.8MM *EMP* 1,060
SIC 3357 Communication wire
CEO: Andy Blanchard

D-U-N-S 80-832-9952 IMP
UCI INTERNATIONAL INC
UCI-FRAM AUTOBRANDS
(*Suby of* UCI ACQUISITION HOLDINGS (NO 1) CORP) ★
1900 W Field Ct, Lake Forest, IL 60045-4828
Tel (812) 867-4156 *Founded/Ownrshp* 2011
Sales 438.6MM[E] *EMP* 3,850[E]
SIC 3714 Motor vehicle parts & accessories
CEO: Bruce Zorich
**CFO:* Mark Blaufuss
VP: Joe Doolan
VP: Daniel Johnston
**VP:* Keith A Zar
CIO: Mark Wikingstad
**VP Sls:* Curtis Draper

D-U-N-S 11-812-8776
UCI MEDICAL AFFILIATES INC
DOCTORS CARE
1818 Henderson St, Columbia, SC 29201-2619
Tel (803) 782-4278 *Founded/Ownrshp* 1981
Sales 60.6MM[E] *EMP* 1,070[E]
SIC 8093 8741 Specialty outpatient clinics; Administrative management
Pr: Michael Stout MD
**CFO:* Joseph A Boyle
**CFO:* Ryan Foster
CFO: Jerry F Wells
Bd of Dir: Fatimah O Ndiaye
Ofcr: John Denton
VP: Nancy Wilkes
Mng Dir: John Saunders
Off Mgr: Mary Hudson
IT Man: Jonathan Johnson
Doctor: Lindsay Baumann

UCI-FRAM AUTOBRANDS
See UCI INTERNATIONAL INC

UCI-FRAM AUTOBRANDS
See FRAM GROUP OPERATIONS LLC

UCLA
See UNIVERSITY OF CALIFORNIA LOS ANGELES

UCLA BOOKSTORE
See ASSOCIATED STUDENTS UCLA

D-U-N-S 07-293-0829
UCLA FOUNDATION
10920 Wilshire Blvd # 200, Los Angeles, CA 90024-6502
Tel (310) 794-3193 *Founded/Ownrshp* 1945
Sales 351.6MM *EMP* 317
Accts Pricewaterhousecoopers Llp Lo
SIC 6732 Educational trust management
Ex Dir: Peter Hayashida
**Treas:* Neal Axelrod
VP: Denise Sloan
VP: Dennis Slon

D-U-N-S 00-406-4819
UCLA HEALTH SYSTEM AUXILIARY
10920 Wilshire Blvd # 1700, Los Angeles, CA 90024-6502
Tel (310) 794-0500 *Founded/Ownrshp* 1981
Sales 206.1MM[E] *EMP* 17,000
SIC 8082 Home health care services
Pr: David T Feinberg
**Ex VP:* Patricia Kapur
**Ex Dir:* Patty Cuen

UCN
See INCONTACT INC

UCONN
See UNIVERSITY OF CONNECTICUT

D-U-N-S 07-888-8049
■ **UCP INC**
(*Suby of* PICO HOLDINGS INC) ★
99 Almaden Blvd Ste 400, San Jose, CA 95113-1604
Tel (408) 207-9499 *Founded/Ownrshp* 2004, 2008
Sales 278.7MM *EMP* 187[E]
Tkr Sym UCP *Exch* NYS
SIC 1521 1531 6552 Single-family housing construction; New construction, single-family houses; Operative builders; Land subdividers & developers, residential
Pr: Dustin L Bogue
**Ch Bd:* Michael C Cortney
CFO: James M Pirrello

UCSF BENIOFF CHLD HOSP OAKLAND
See CHILDRENS HOSPITAL & RESEARCH CENTER AT OAKLAND

UCT
See ULTRA CLEAN HOLDINGS INC

UCT
See ULTRA CLEAN TECHNOLOGY SYSTEMS AND SERVICE INC

D-U-N-S 07-184-5101
UDELHOVEN OILFIELD SYSTEMS SERVICES INC
(*Suby of* HARDING HOLDINGS INC) ★
184 E 53rd Ave, Anchorage, AK 99518-1222
Tel (907) 344-1577 *Founded/Ownrshp* 1970
Sales 148.7MM *EMP* 150
SIC 1541 1542 8711 Industrial buildings, new construction; Commercial & office building, new construction; Engineering services
Pr: James Udelhoven
CFO: Cathy Duxbury
**VP:* Barbara Udelhoven
CIO: Tom Carrell

UDFC
See UNIVERSAL DISPLAY AND FIXTURE CO

UDM
See UNIVERSITY OF DETROIT MERCY

D-U-N-S 06-602-5859
▲ **UDR INC**
1745 Shea Center Dr # 200, Highlands Ranch, CO 80129-1540
Tel (720) 283-6120 *Founded/Ownrshp* 1972
Sales 894.6MM *EMP* 1,611
Tkr Sym UDR *Exch* NYS
SIC 6798 Real estate investment trusts
Pr: Thomas W Toomey
**Ch Bd:* James D Klingbeil
COO: Jerry A Davis
CFO: Shawn G Johnston
Treas: William T O'Sheilds
**V Ch Bd:* Lynne B Sagalyn
Sr VP: Martha R Calin
VP: Teresa Barker
VP: Matthew Cozad
VP: C Davis
VP: Richard Giannotti
VP: Thomas Herzog
VP: Milton Scott
VP: Cindy Shepardson
VP: Douglas Walker
Exec: Warren L Troupe
Dir Risk M: Kay Jones
Board of Directors: Katherine A Cattanach, Robert P Freeman, Jon A Grove, Mary Ann King, Clint D McDonnough, Robert A McNamara, Mark R Patterson

D-U-N-S 00-359-5415 IMP/EXP
■ **UE MANUFACTURING LLC**
(*Suby of* UNITED HOLDINGS LLC) ★
10000 Nw 2nd St, Oklahoma City, OK 73127-7149
Tel (405) 947-3321 *Founded/Ownrshp* 2001, 1994
Sales 225.9MM[E] *EMP* 76
SIC 5084 Oil well machinery, equipment & supplies
Pr: Bill Moore
VP Sls: Ronnie Stover

UFCW
See UNITED FOOD AND COMMERCIAL WORKERS INTERNATIONAL UNION

D-U-N-S 96-457-7204
UFCW AND EMPLOYERS AZ H AND W TRUST
2400 W Dunlap Ave Ste 250, Phoenix, AZ 85021-2946
Tel (602) 249-3582 *Founded/Ownrshp* 2010
Sales 137.1MM *EMP* 3
Accts Miller Kaplan Arase & Co L
SIC 8631 Labor unions & similar labor organizations

D-U-N-S 86-082-8693
UFCW LOCAL 152 HEALTH & WELFARE FUND
27 Roland Ave Ste 100, Mount Laurel, NJ 08054-1038
Tel (856) 793-2500 *Founded/Ownrshp* 2007
Sales 107.5MM *EMP* 13[E]
Accts Bond Beebe Pc Bethesda Md
SIC 8099 Health & allied services
Prin: Frank Vaccaro

D-U-N-S 96-280-7918
UFCW NATIONAL HEALTH AND WELFARE FUND
66 Grand Ave Ste A, Englewood, NJ 07631-6500
Tel (201) 569-8802 *Founded/Ownrshp* 2010
Sales NA *EMP* 3
Accts Novak Francella Llc Bala Cynw
SIC 6371 Pension, health & welfare funds
Prin: Maurice Hodos

UFG
See UNITED FIRE & CASUALTY CO

D-U-N-S 36-428-4489
UFP GRANDVIEW LLC
UNIVERSAL FOREST PRODUCTS
1000 S 3rd St, Grandview, TX 76050-2339
Tel (817) 866-3306 *Founded/Ownrshp* 1978
Sales 104.9MM[E] *EMP* 567
SIC 5031 2439 Lumber: rough, dressed & finished; Structural wood members
Ch Bd: William G Currie
**Pr:* Patrick M Webster
**CEO:* Matthew J Missad
**CFO:* Michael R Cole
Genl Mgr: Scott Songer

D-U-N-S 00-322-2874
■ **UFP MID-ATLANTIC LLC**
UNIVERSAL FOREST PRODUCTS
(*Suby of* UNIVERSAL FOREST PRODUCTS INC) ★
5631 S Nc Highway 62, Burlington, NC 27215-9025
Tel (336) 226-9356 *Founded/Ownrshp* 1956, 1998
Sales 121.2MM[E] *EMP* 780
SIC 2439 Trusses, wooden roof; Trusses, except roof: laminated lumber
CEO: Matthew J Missad
Treas: Tamara Dryden
VP: Donald James
VP: Jennifer Meyer
Genl Mgr: Jeff Kinyo
Genl Mgr: Steve White
CTO: Tom Beaty

D-U-N-S 00-104-2100 EXP
▲ **UFP TECHNOLOGIES INC**
100 Hale St, Newburyport, MA 01950-3504
Tel (978) 352-2200 *Founded/Ownrshp* 1963
Sales 138.8MM *EMP* 722
Tkr Sym UFPT *Exch* NAS
SIC 3086 Packaging & shipping materials, foamed plastic; Padding, foamed plastic
Ch Bd: R Jeffrey Bailly
CFO: Ronald J Lataille
Sr VP: Mitchell C Rock
Sr VP: William David Smith
VP: Daniel J Shaw Jr
VP: Daniel Shaw
MIS Dir: Bruce Wright
Prd Mgr: Glenn Kallery
Sls Mgr: William Glade
Board of Directors: Daniel C Croteau, Kenneth L Gestal, Marc Kozin, Thomas Oberdorf, Robert W Pierce Jr, Lucia Luce Quinn, David K Stevenson

D-U-N-S 07-847-5890
■ **UFP WARRENS LLC**
(*Suby of* UNIVERSAL FOREST PRODUCTS INC) ★
County Rd 0 610 Rr St, Warrens, WI 54666
Tel (608) 378-4904 *Founded/Ownrshp* 2010
Sales 3.0MMM *EMP* 57
SIC 5031 Lumber, plywood & millwork
VP: Scott Bravata
**Prin:* Bob Lees
Genl Mgr: Rick Dorman

D-U-N-S 07-847-5885
UFP WOODBURN LLC
UNIVERSAL FOREST PRODUCTS
2895 Progress Way, Woodburn, OR 97071-9783
Tel (503) 226-6240 *Founded/Ownrshp* 2013
Sales 221.8MM[E] *EMP* 4,800
SIC 5031 Lumber, plywood & millwork
Brnch Mgr: Eric Miller
**Brnch Mgr:* Steve Koehn

UFS MSSC
See UNIVERSITY OF SOUTH FLORIDA MEDICAL SERVICES SUPPORT CORP

D-U-N-S 96-858-8298 IMP
UFX HOLDING I CORP
(*Suby of* AEA INVESTORS LP) ★
55 E 52nd St Fl 35, New York, NY 10055-0110
Tel (212) 644-5900 *Founded/Ownrshp* 2006
Sales 56.0MM[E] *EMP* 1,121
SIC 3299 Ceramic fiber
Prin: Vincent MAI

D-U-N-S 78-782-2456
UFX HOLDING II CORP
(*Suby of* UFX HOLDING I CORP) ★
55 E 52nd St Fl 35, New York, NY 10055-0110
Tel (212) 644-5900 *Founded/Ownrshp* 2003
Sales 56.0MM[E] *EMP* 1,121
SIC 3299 Ceramic fiber
Prin: Vincent MAI

D-U-N-S 05-511-0791
UG2 LLC
1 International Pl # 1402, Boston, MA 02110-2618
Tel (617) 279-8100 *Founded/Ownrshp* 2012
Sales 37.8MM[E] *EMP* 1,700[E]
SIC 7349 Building & office cleaning services

UGA RESEARCH FOUNDATION
See UNIVERSITY OF GEORGIA RESEARCH FOUNDATION INC

D-U-N-S 00-791-2967
■ **UGI CENTRAL PENN GAS INC** (PA)
(*Suby of* UGI UTILITIES INC) ★
2 N 9th St, Allentown, PA 18101-1139
Tel (610) 796-3499 *Founded/Ownrshp* 1944, 2008
Sales 156.4MM[E] *EMP* 457
SIC 4924 Natural gas distribution
CEO: Michael E Bray
**Pr:* John F Sipics
Treas: James E Abel
VP: John V Preston

D-U-N-S 00-791-5069
▲ **UGI CORP** (PA)
460 N Gulph Rd Ste 100, King of Prussia, PA 19406-2815
Tel (610) 337-1000 *Founded/Ownrshp* 1991
Sales 5.6MMM *EMP* 8,500
Accts Ernst & Young Llp Philadelphi
Tkr Sym UGI *Exch* NYS
SIC 4932 Gas & other services combined
Pr: John L Walsh
Pr: Roger Perreault
CFO: Kirk R Oliver
Treas: Robert Knauss
VP: Davinder S Athwal
VP: Jim Budd
VP: Monica M Gaudiosi
VP: Carole Hagy
VP: Bradley C Hall
VP: Marie-Dominique Ortiz-Landazab
VP: David Pataki
VP: Steve Quagliana
Exec: Cynthia A Martello
Board of Directors: M Shawan Bort, Richard W Gochnauer, Lon R Greenberg, Frank S Hermance, Ernest E Jones, Anne Pol, Marvin O Schlanger, James B Stallings Jr, Roger B Vincent

UGI ENERGY LINK
See UGI ENERGY SERVICES LLC

D-U-N-S 88-350-4581
■ **UGI ENERGY SERVICES LLC**
UGI ENERGY LINK
(*Suby of* UGI ENTERPRISES INC) ★
1 Meridian Blvd Ste 2c01, Reading, PA 19610-3230
Tel (484) 663-5824 *Founded/Ownrshp* 1995
Sales 142.7MM[E] *EMP* 200
SIC 4924 Natural gas distribution
Pr: Bradley Hall
Pr: Matt Dutzman
**Treas:* Hugh J Gallagher
**Treas:* Robert W Krick
VP: Alisa E Harris
**VP:* Angela K Rodriguez
Info Man: Linda Yarchuk
Manager: Mike Trymbiski
Board of Directors: Lon R Greenberg, Bradley C Hall, Anthony Mendecino

D-U-N-S 88-336-7518
■ **UGI ENTERPRISES INC**
(*Suby of* UGI CORP) ★
460 N Gulph Rd, Valley Forge, PA 19482
Tel (610) 337-1000 *Founded/Ownrshp* 1994
Sales 159.2MM[E] *EMP* 233
SIC 5172 Gases, liquefied petroleum (propane)
CEO: John L Walsh
**Ch Bd:* Lon R Greenberg
**Pr:* Bradley C Hall
**Treas:* Robert W Krick
**Treas:* Daniel Platt
VP: Stewart L Cohen
VP: Angela K Rodriguez
VP Opers: Amy Hunt

D-U-N-S 07-940-9443
UGI EUROPE INC
460 N Gulph Rd, King of Prussia, PA 19406-2815
Tel (610) 337-1000 *Founded/Ownrshp* 2001
Sales 8.2MMM *EMP* 12,800[E]
SIC 1321 Cycle condensate production (natural gas)
Pr: John Walsh

D-U-N-S 79-937-6595
■ **UGI UTILITIES INC**
(*Suby of* UGI CORP) ★
2525 N 12th St Ste 360, Reading, PA 19605-2771
Tel (610) 796-3400 *Founded/Ownrshp* 1925
Sales 768.4MM *EMP* 1,520
SIC 4939 Combination utilities
Pr: Robert F Beard
**Ch Bd:* Lon R Greenberg
CFO: Kirk R Oliver
**V Ch Bd:* John L Walsh
Sr VP: Vicki O Ebner
VP: Hans Bell
Board of Directors: M Shawn Bort, Richard W Gochnauer, Frank S Hermance, Ernest E Jones, Anne Pol, Marvin O Schlanger, James B Stallings Jr, Roger B Vincent

UGMA
See UTTAM GALVA NORTH AMERICA INC

D-U-N-S 17-342-5760 IMP
UGN INC
(*Suby of* AUTONEUM HOLDING AG)
18410 Crossing Dr Ste C, Tinley Park, IL 60487-6209
Tel (773) 437-2400 *Founded/Ownrshp* 1986
Sales 397.9MM[E] *EMP* 1,250
SIC 3714 Motor vehicle parts & accessories
Pr: Peter Anthony
**COO:* Randy Khalaf
**VP:* Darrell Cook
**VP:* Esther Jones
**VP:* Nicolas Leclercq

*VP: Ron Myotte
VP: Ronald Myotte
VP: Kenta Shinohara
Exec: Ralph Pollaro
Prgrm Mgr: Mike Gattone
Software D: Roderick Carlson

D-U-N-S 79-077-4637
■ UGS CAPITAL CORP
(Suby of SIEMENS INDUSTRY INC) ★
5800 Gran Pkwy Ste 600, Plano, TX 75024
Tel (972) 987-3000 Founded/Ownrshp 2004
Sales 160.2MM[E] EMP 7,200
SIC 7372

D-U-N-S 79-920-0977
■ UHC OF CALIFORNIA
PACIFICARE OF CALIFORNIA
(Suby of PACIFICARE HEALTH SYSTEMS LLC) ★
5995 Plaza Dr, Cypress, CA 90630-5028
Tel (714) 952-1121 Founded/Ownrshp 2000
Sales NA EMP 3,000
SIC 6324 8732 Health maintenance organization (HMO), insurance only; Commercial nonphysical research
Prin: Brad A Bowlus
*Treas: Michael Montevideo
Mng Dir: Terry Hartshorn
Mng Dir: Dominic Ng
Rgnl Mgr: Phyllis Graham
Brnch Mgr: Lisa Espinosa
Software D: Gobinath Eswaran
Sls Dir: Steve Flemmer

D-U-N-S 82-883-4916
UHDE CORP OF AMERICA
THYSSENKRUMP
1370 Wash Pike Ste 510, Bridgeville, PA 15017-2862
Tel (412) 257-8277 Founded/Ownrshp 1997
Sales 569.0MM EMP 100[E]
SIC 8711 7299

UHEALTH
See JACKSON MEMORIAL HOSPITAL

UHH
See UNITE HERE HEALTH

UHHS-GEAUGA REGIONAL HOSPITAL
See UNIVERSITY HOSPITALS GEAUGA MEDICAL CENTER

UHS
See UNITED HEALTH SERVICES INC

D-U-N-S 80-257-7218
UHS HOLDCO INC
383 Madison Ave Fl 40, New York, NY 10179-0001
Tel (212) 272-2000 Founded/Ownrshp 2007
Sales 448.6MM[E] EMP 2,489[E]
SIC 7352 5047 Medical equipment rental; Medical & hospital equipment
Ch Bd: Gary D Blackford
Prin: Bret D Bowerman
Prin: John D Howard
Prin: Robert Juneja

D-U-N-S 02-162-7513
UHS INC
6308 8th Ave, Kenosha, WI 53143-5031
Tel (262) 656-2273 Founded/Ownrshp 1998
Sales 4.6MM EMP 1,600[E]
Accts Wipfli Llp Milwaukee Wi
SIC 8062 General medical & surgical hospitals
Pr: Richard O Schmitt Jr

D-U-N-S 60-989-5735
■ UHS OF DELAWARE INC
(Suby of UNIVERSAL HEALTH SERVICES INC) ★
367 S Gulph Rd, King of Prussia, PA 19406-3121
Tel (610) 768-3300 Founded/Ownrshp 1985
Sales 172.0MM[E] EMP 800
SIC 8062 General medical & surgical hospitals
CEO: Alan B Miller
*Pr: Marc Miller
*Treas: Cheryl Ramagano
*VP: Steve Filton
*VP: Debra Osteen
Netwrk Eng: Tom Leary

D-U-N-S 01-055-9383
■ UHS OF PEACHFORD LP
(Suby of UNIVERSAL HEALTH SERVICES INC) ★
2151 Peachford Rd, Atlanta, GA 30338-6534
Tel (770) 455-3200 Founded/Ownrshp 1964, 2000
Sales 59.9MM EMP 66,575
SIC 8011 Psychiatric clinic
CEO: Matt Crouch
*COO: Reese Daniel
Dir Risk M: Sharon Stackhouse
Dir Rx: Rebecca Pirouz
Pharmcst: Mark Morganstern

D-U-N-S 61-736-3973
UHS OFTEXOMA INC
5016 S Us Highway 75, Denison, TX 75020-4584
Tel (903) 416-4000 Founded/Ownrshp 1965
Sales 257.0MM EMP 1,300
SIC 8062 General medical & surgical hospitals
CEO: Ron Seal
*Pr: Arthru L Hoenberger
Pr: Patrick McGrael
COO: Justin Kendrick
CFO: Gerard Hebert
Bd of Dir: Theresa Dickson
*VP: Minnie Burkhardt
*VP: Harry Kirshman
*VP: Bobby Pruett
*Prin: Mike Mayes
Surgeon: Ikram Kureshi

D-U-N-S 05-468-3593
UHS PHYSICIANS LLC
2100 Stantonsburg Rd, Greenville, NC 27834-2818
Tel (252) 847-6809 Founded/Ownrshp 2010
Sales 96.2MM EMP 13[E]
SIC 8211 High school, junior or senior
IT Man: Ed McFall

D-U-N-S 05-081-9115
UHS SUMMERLIN RECEIVING
SUMMERLIN HOSPITAL
657 N Town Center Dr, Las Vegas, NV 89144-6367
Tel (702) 233-7000 Founded/Ownrshp 2010
Sales 335.6MM EMP 20[E]
SIC 8211 High school, junior or senior
CEO: Luke Les

D-U-N-S 10-313-9853 IMP
■ UHS-CORONA INC
CORONA REGIONAL MED CTR HOSP
(Suby of UNIVERSAL HEALTH SERVICES INC) ★
800 S Main St, Corona, CA 92882-3420
Tel (951) 737-4343 Founded/Ownrshp 1978
Sales 169.5MM EMP 1,100
SIC 8062 General medical & surgical hospitals
CEO: Marvin Pember
*Pr: Alan B Miller
*CEO: Ken Rivers
CFO: Nancy Jangaon
Chf Nrs Of: Norene Bowers
*Prin: Kevan Metcalf
CIO: Jeanie Bruce
IT Man: Jimmy Tran
Surgeon: Kathy Bowersox-Miess
Ansthlgy: Mahesh S De Silva
HC Dir: Amal Numan

UHS-PRUITT
See PRUITT CORP

D-U-N-S 06-097-0568
UHY ADVISORS INC
30 S Wacker Dr Ste 1330, Chicago, IL 60606-7404
Tel (312) 578-9600 Founded/Ownrshp 1998
Sales 103.9MM[E] EMP 1,091
SIC 8721 Certified public accountant
Ch Bd: Robert C Basten
Pr: James B McGuire
Pr: Joseph Rude
CEO: Richard Kotlow
COO: Rick David
CFO: Bill White
CFO: William White
Treas: Dennis Bikun
V Ch Bd: Rick Stein
Bd of Dir: Bernard Fay
VP: Jeremy Robin
Dir Bus: Jeffrey Seeney

UI
See UNITED ILLUMINATING CO

D-U-N-S 83-135-3003
UI ACQUISITION HOLDING CO
33 Broome Corporate Pkwy, Conklin, NY 13748-1510
Tel (607) 779-7522 Founded/Ownrshp 2006
Sales 145.4MM[E] EMP 1,020
SIC 3559 Electronic component making machinery
Pr: Jean-Luc Pelissier
*VP: Keith O'Leary

D-U-N-S 79-540-8868
UI HOLDING CO
(Suby of UI ACQUISITION HOLDING CO) ★
33 Broome Corporate Pkwy, Conklin, NY 13748-1510
Tel (607) 779-7522 Founded/Ownrshp 2006
Sales 145.4MM[E] EMP 1,018
SIC 3559 Electronic component making machinery
Pr: Jeroen Schmits
*CFO: Patrick J Gillard
VP: Koen A Gieskes

D-U-N-S 80-426-8113 IMP
■ UIL HOLDINGS CORP
(Suby of AVANGRID INC) ★
52 Farm View Dr, New Gloucester, ME 04260-5100
Tel (203) 499-2000 Founded/Ownrshp 2015
Sales 1.6MMM EMP 1,902[E]
SIC 4931 4924 Electric & other services combined; Natural gas distribution
Pr: Ignacio Estella
CFO: Pablo Canales
Board of Directors: Thelma R Albright, Arnold L Chase, Betsy Henley-Cohn, John L Lahey, Daniel J Miglio, William F Murdy, William B Plummer, Donald R Shassian

D-U-N-S 06-981-1537
UINTAH BASIN MEDICAL CENTER
250 W 300 N, Roosevelt, UT 84066-2336
Tel (435) 725-2008 Founded/Ownrshp 1944
Sales 83.8MM EMP 680
Accts Aycock Miles & Assoc Cpas Roo
SIC 8062 8082 7352 8092 8361 General medical & surgical hospitals; Home health care services; Medical equipment rental; Kidney dialysis centers; Rehabilitation center, residential: health care incidental
CEO: Bradley Lebaron
CFO: Brent Hayles
VP: Brad Jenkins
VP: Preston Marx
Dir Rx: Lonnie Anderson
Off Mgr: Chris Killian
QA Dir: Brianna Martinez
Netwrk Mgr: Brian McCormack
Software D: Vicci Betts
VP Opers: Jonathan Rhee
Opers Mgr: Robert Grosland

D-U-N-S 02-931-4783
UK HEALTHCARE GOODSAMARITAN HOSPITAL
310 S Limestone, Lexington, KY 40508-3008
Tel (859) 226-7000 Founded/Ownrshp 1888
Sales 91.4MM[E] EMP 632
SIC 8062 8011 General medical & surgical hospitals; Offices & clinics of medical doctors
CEO: Frank Birne
*COO: Mark Armstrong
*Ex VP: Dr Michael Karpf

D-U-N-S 06-470-2638
UKAS BIG SAVER FOODS INC
4260 Charter St, Vernon, CA 90058-2520
Tel (323) 582-7222 Founded/Ownrshp 1977
Sales 133.1MM[E] EMP 600
SIC 5411 Grocery stores, independent

CEO: Uka Solanki
*VP: Nalini Solanki
Genl Mgr: Martha Rodriguez
VP Opers: Jose Huerta

D-U-N-S 07-467-6867
UKIAH ADVENTIST HOSPITAL
UKIAH VALLEY MEDICAL CENTER
275 Hospital Dr, Ukiah, CA 95482-4531
Tel (707) 463-7346 Founded/Ownrshp 1956
Sales 148.0MM EMP 653
Accts Ernst & Young Llp Roseville
SIC 8062 General medical & surgical hospitals
Pr: Terry Burns
CFO: Rod Granger
Bd of Dir: Jeremy Mann
VP: Beverly Schmunk
Dir Lab: Bob Machafferty
Dir Rad: Steve Daugherty
Chf Nrs Of: Gerry Chaney
Netwrk Eng: Debra McEntee
Mtls Dir: Kathy Smith
Sls&Mrk Ex: Gerald McNaughten
Orthpdst: Brian M Cable

UKIAH VALLEY MEDICAL CENTER
See UKIAH ADVENTIST HOSPITAL

D-U-N-S 07-925-3902
UKPEAGVIK INUPIAT CORP
1250 Agvik St, Barrow, AK 99723
Tel (907) 852-4460 Founded/Ownrshp 1973
Sales 812.6MM[E] EMP 1,750
Accts Kpmg Llp Anchorage Ak
SIC 1542 6512 6331 1389 4449 Commercial & office building contractors; Commercial & industrial building operation; Property damage insurance; Oil field services; Canal & intracoastal freight transportation
Pr: Anthony Edwardsen
*Sr Pt: Gerrie L Heureux
CFO: Walt George
*Ch: Price Brower
*Treas: Mary Jane Lang
*Sr VP: David Klopp
*VP: Herman L Ahsoak
*VP: David Maasak Leavitt Jr
Genl Mgr: Jack Laasch
Ql Cn Mgr: Jason Shade
Board of Directors: Charles D N Brower

UKROP'S PHARMACY
See UKROPS SUPER MARKETS INC

D-U-N-S 06-601-7302
UKROPS SUPER MARKETS INC
UKROP'S PHARMACY
2001 Maywill St Ste 100, Richmond, VA 23230-3236
Tel (804) 304-3000 Founded/Ownrshp 1937
Sales 69.5M EMP 5,600
SIC 5411

UL
See UNDERWRITERS LABORATORIES INC

UL EHS SUSTAINABILITY
See PUREWORKS INC

D-U-N-S 07-835-1534
UL LLC
(Suby of UL) ★
333 Pfingsten Rd, Northbrook, IL 60062-2002
Tel (847) 272-8800 Founded/Ownrshp 1997
Sales 676.6MM[E] EMP 5,800
SIC 8734 Product testing laboratory, safety or performance
Pr: Keith E Williams
Sr VP: Traci Simonsen
VP: Steve Hewson
Dir Lab: John Divelbiss
Dir Bus: Maggie Diaz
Prgrm Mgr: Matt Erkert
Prgrm Mgr: Paulette Swan
Genl Mgr: Doug Grillaert
Genl Mgr: William Riley
Genl Mgr: Simin Zhou
IT Man: Richard Frankel

D-U-N-S 06-707-4336 IMP/EXP
ULBRICH OF ILLINOIS INC
(Suby of ULBRICH SPECIALTY STRIP MIL) ★
12340 S Laramie Ave, Alsip, IL 60803-3292
Tel (708) 489-9500 Founded/Ownrshp 1970
Sales 107.1MM[E] EMP 80[E]
SIC 5051 Steel
CEO: Frederick C Ulbrich III
*Pr: Gregg Boucher
*COO: John C Cei
*Prin: Steve Pertchi
Admn Mgr: AMI Faymonville
*Genl Mgr: Raymond Sistino
QA Dir: Ron Kleinschmidt
Plnt Mgr: Mike Wolf
Manager: Leonard Kowalski
Sls Mgr: Mike Alstrits
Sales Asso: Robert Bauske

ULBRICH SPECIALTY STRIP MIL
See ULBRICH STAINLESS STEELS & SPECIAL METALS INC

D-U-N-S 00-116-2171 IMP
ULBRICH STAINLESS STEELS & SPECIAL METALS INC (CT)
ULBRICH SPECIALTY STRIP MIL
153 Washington Ave, North Haven, CT 06473-1710
Tel (203) 239-4481 Founded/Ownrshp 1924
Sales 232.2MM[E] EMP 623
SIC 3316 3356 5051 3341 3312 Strip steel, cold-rolled: from purchased hot-rolled; Nickel & nickel alloy: rolling, drawing or extruding; Titanium & titanium alloy: rolling, drawing or extruding; Strip, metal; Secondary nonferrous metals; Blast furnaces & steel mills
CEO: Frederick C Ulbrich III
*COO: John J Cei
COO: Chris Ulbrich
Exec: Alice Stengel

Dir IT: Michael March
Mtls Mgr: Neil Connolly
Mfg Mgr: Mike Marzik
Mfg Mgr: Joe Zehnder
Plnt Mgr: Arnie Muniz
Ql Cn Mgr: James Wierzbinski
Manager: Nicholas Wahl

D-U-N-S 03-961-2668 IMP/EXP
ULINE INC
12575 Uline Dr, Pleasant Prairie, WI 53158-3686
Tel (262) 612-4200 Founded/Ownrshp 1980
Sales 3.3MMM[E] EMP 2,800
SIC 5113 Shipping supplies; Corrugated & solid fiber boxes
*Pr: Elizabeth Uihlein
*CEO: Richard E Uihlein
*CFO: Frank Unick
VP: Cindy Giesen
VP: Dawn McClary
*VP: Stephen Uihlein
Exec: Theresa Whitehead
IT Man: Joe Greca
Sys Mgr: Roy Cox
Web Dev: Ryan Palmquist
Web Dev: Susan Ratajczyk
Board of Directors: Duke Vice President, Liz President, Brian Vp, Steve Vice President, Freddy Corporate Planner

D-U-N-S 60-504-2357
ULLICO INC
1625 I St Nw Fl 5, Washington, DC 20006-4014
Tel (202) 682-0900 Founded/Ownrshp 1927
Sales NA EMP 325
Accts Ernst & Young Llp Washington
SIC 6311 6321 Life insurance; Accident & health insurance
Ch Bd: Joseph Hunt
Pr: John Hoffen
Pr: Christine Mullen
*Pr: Edward M Smith
*CEO: Mark Singleton
COO: Cathy Humphrey
*CFO: David J Barra
CFO: Damon Gasque
Acting Pr: Joseph R Linehan
VP: Craig Arneson
VP: Kelly Ellston
VP: Joseph Linehan
VP: Jeremiah O'Connor
VP: Rick Silas

D-U-N-S 01-824-7820
ULLIMAN SCHUTTE CONSTRUCTION LLC (OH)
U S C
9111 Springboro Pike, Miamisburg, OH 45342-4420
Tel (937) 247-0375 Founded/Ownrshp 1998
Sales 185.3MM[E] EMP 300
SIC 1629 Waste water & sewage treatment plant construction
Exec: Allen McCullough
Genl Mgr: John Coffin
Genl Mgr: Matthew Ulliman
Off Mgr: Jean Brooks
Sfty Dirs: Brian Danik
Site Mgr: Travis Brubaker
Snr PM: Nicholas Hedrick

D-U-N-S 60-816-8597 IMP
▲ ULTA SALON COSMETICS & FRAGRANCE INC
1000 Remington Blvd # 120, Bolingbrook, IL 60440-5114
Tel (630) 410-4800 Founded/Ownrshp 1990
Sales 3.9MMM EMP 26,500
Accts Ernst & Young Llp Chicagoill
Tkr Sym ULTA Exch NGS
SIC 5999 5632 5961 Cosmetics; Perfumes & colognes; Hair care products; Women's accessory & specialty stores; Catalog & mail-order houses
CEO: Mary N Dillon
*Ch Bd: Charles J Philippin
CFO: Scott M Settersten
Ofcr: Jeffrey J Childs
Ofcr: David C Kimbell
VP: Jeff McGowan
CIO: Diane Randolph
Board of Directors: Michelle L Collins, Robert F Diromualdo, Dennis K Eck, Catherine A Halligan, Charles Heilbronn, Michael R Macdonald, George Mrkonic, Lorna E Nagler, Vanessa A Wittman

D-U-N-S 61-872-4491 IMP
■ ULTERRA DRILLING TECHNOLOGIES LP
(Suby of AMERICAN SECURITIES LLC) ★
420 Throckmorton St # 1110, Fort Worth, TX 76102-3728
Tel (817) 293-7555 Founded/Ownrshp 2016
Sales 140.0MM EMP 323
SIC 5084 3533 Drilling equipment, excluding bits; Bits, oil & gas field tools: rock
Pr: John Clunan
CFO: Maria Mejia
Bd of Dir: Bob Iversen
VP: Rocky Frazier
Exec: Dewayne Glasgow
Area Mgr: Jon Schmidt
Dist Mgr: Danny Delmas
Dist Mgr: Mitch Dunham
Dist Mgr: David Stark
VP Sls: Mike Crawford
Sls Mgr: Deuce Whitaker

D-U-N-S 07-925-6245
ULTIMA HOSPITALITY LLC
(Suby of WATERTON RESIDENTIAL) ★
30 S Wacker Dr Ste 3600, Chicago, IL 60606-7462
Tel (312) 948-4500 Founded/Ownrshp 2009
Sales 35.9MM[E] EMP 1,071[E]
SIC 8741 Hotel or motel management
Pr: Marc Swerdlow
COO: Mark Zettl
Sr VP: Diane Fox

D-U-N-S 62-599-7614
▲ ULTIMATE SOFTWARE GROUP INC
2000 Ultimate Way, Weston, FL 33326-3643
Tel (800) 432-1729 *Founded/Ownrshp* 1996
Sales 618.0MM *EMP* 2,880[E]
Tkr Sym ULTI *Exch* NGS
SIC 7372 Business oriented computer software
Ch Bd: Scott Scherr
**V Ch:* Marc D Scherr
COO: James Alu
CFO: Mitchell K Dauerman
Ofcr: William Hicks
Sr VP: Jon Harris
Sr VP: Jody Kaminsky
Sr VP: Robert Manne
Sr VP: Vivian Maza
Sr VP: Adam Rogers
VP: Donald Causey
VP: Paul Gonzalez
VP: Martin Hartshorne
VP: Terry L Hudak
VP: Brenda Jennings
VP: Pam Keefe
VP: John Machado
VP: Lee McDermott
VP: Pat Pickren
VP: Stephen Reid
VP: Michael Schaberl
Board of Directors: James A Fitzpatrick Jr, Alois T Leiter, Leroy A Vander Putten, Rick A Wilber, Robert A Yanover

ULTIMATE STAFFING SERVICES
See ROTH STAFFING COMPANIES LP

D-U-N-S 14-219-7065
▲ ULTRA CLEAN HOLDINGS INC
UCT
26462 Corporate Ave, Hayward, CA 94545-3914
Tel (510) 576-4400 *Founded/Ownrshp* 2002
Sales 469.1MM *EMP* 1,817
Tkr Sym UCTT *Exch* NGS
SIC 3674 Semiconductors & related devices
CEO: James P Scholhamer
**Ch Bd:* Clarence L Granger
CFO: Sheri Brumm
Sr VP: Mark G Bingaman
Sr VP: Deborah Hayward
Sr VP: Michael Henderson
Sr VP: Lavi A Lev
Sr VP: Bruce Wier
VP: Joshua Kramer
Snr Mgr: Lynda Scherrer

D-U-N-S 78-718-3680 IMP
■ ULTRA CLEAN TECHNOLOGY SYSTEMS AND SERVICE INC
UCT
(*Suby of* UCT) ★
26462 Corporate Ave, Hayward, CA 94545-3914
Tel (510) 576-4400 *Founded/Ownrshp* 1991
Sales 113.3MM[E] *EMP* 320
SIC 3823 Industrial instrmnts msrmnt display/control process variable
CEO: Jim Skullhammer
**Pr:* Leonard Mezhvinsky
**CFO:* Casey Eichler
CFO: Phil Kagel
**Sr VP:* Deborah Hayward
**Sr VP:* Lavi Lev
**Sr VP:* Bruce Wier
Mtls Dir: Mark Engelhardt
S&M/Dir: Gary Kihara
Sls Mgr: Joyce Zhang

ULTRA DIAMOND & GOLD OUTLET
See ULTRA STORES INC

ULTRA ELECTRONICS
See UNDERSEA SENSOR SYSTEMS INC

D-U-N-S 06-080-2720 IMP/EXP
ULTRA ELECTRONICS AIRPORT SYSTEMS INC (GA)
(*Suby of* ULTRA ELECTRONICS HOLDINGS PLC)
107 Church Hill Rd Ste G2, Sandy Hook, CT 06482-1194
Tel (203) 270-3696 *Founded/Ownrshp* 2001
Sales 302.9MM *EMP* 1,677
SIC 3625 Electric controls & control accessories, industrial
CEO: Graeme Stacey
**CFO:* David Loose

D-U-N-S 09-377-6685 IMP
ULTRA ELECTRONICS DEFENSE INC
(*Suby of* ULTRA ELECTRONICS AIRPORT SYSTEMS INC) ★
4101 Smith School Rd, Austin, TX 78744-3206
Tel (512) 327-6795 *Founded/Ownrshp* 1997
Sales 272.7MM[E] *EMP* 1,037
SIC 3812 3825 Search & navigation equipment; Instruments to measure electricity
CFO: Phyllis Youngdahl
Snr Mgr: Mary Woo

ULTRA ELECTRONICS HERLEY
See HERLEY INDUSTRIES INC

ULTRA ELECTRONICS HERLEY
See HERLEY-CTI INC

D-U-N-S 10-987-3901
ULTRA PETROLEUM CORP
400 N Sam Houston Pkwy E # 1200, Houston, TX 77060-3548
Tel (281) 876-0120 *Founded/Ownrshp* 1979
Sales 839.1MM *EMP* 167[E]
SIC 1311 Crude petroleum & natural gas
Ch Bd: Michael D Watford
CFO: Garland R Shaw
Sr VP: C Bradley Johnson
VP: Mike Patterson
VP: Kent Rogers
VP: Garrett B Smith
VP: Mark Smith
Exec: Theresa Brandon
Exec: Julie Danvers
QA Dir: Jennifer Butterworth
Prd Mgr: Dan Bulfer

Board of Directors: Roger A Brown, W Charles Helton, Michael J Keeffe, Stephen J McDaniel

D-U-N-S 78-213-6147 IMP
ULTRA STORES INC
ULTRA DIAMOND & GOLD OUTLET
122 S Michigan Ave # 800, Chicago, IL 60603-6118
Tel (312) 922-3800 *Founded/Ownrshp* 2012
Sales NA *EMP* 1,035
SIC 5944

D-U-N-S 18-890-6606 IMP
ULTRA TRADING INTERNATIONAL LTD
2875 Ne 191st St Ste 201, Aventura, FL 33180-2830
Tel (305) 466-4443 *Founded/Ownrshp* 1986
Sales 120.0MM[E] *EMP* 11
SIC 5141 Food brokers
Ch Bd: Moshe Schwartz
VP: Sam Schwartz
Sls Mgr: Greg Davis

D-U-N-S 01-336-9913 IMP/EXP
ULTRADENT PRODUCTS INC (UT)
505 W 10200 S, South Jordan, UT 84095-3800
Tel (801) 572-4200 *Founded/Ownrshp* 1978
Sales 213.8MM[E] *EMP* 1,000[E]
SIC 3843 Dental equipment & supplies
Pr: Dirk S Jeffs
COO: Scott Wellwood
CFO: Daniel McKasson
MIS Dir: Erwin Fischer
Mktg Mgr: Sean Kennedy

D-U-N-S 18-610-4014
■ ULTRAMAR DIAMOND SHAMROCK INC
ONE INTERNATIONAL CENTER
(*Suby of* DIAMOND SHAMROCK REFINING AND MARKETING CO) ★
6000 N Loop 1604 W, San Antonio, TX 78249-1100
Tel (210) 627-2003 *Founded/Ownrshp* 1991
Sales 177.8MM[E] *EMP* 2,290
SIC 6512 Commercial & industrial building operation
Ch: Roger Hemminghaus
**Pr:* Jean Gaulin
**Treas:* Steven A Blank
**Ex VP:* Timothy J Fretthold
**VP:* Curtis Anastasio

D-U-N-S 00-917-4921
■ ULTRAMAR INC
(*Suby of* VALERO ENERGY CORP) ★
1 Valero Way, San Antonio, TX 78249-1616
Tel (210) 345-2000 *Founded/Ownrshp* 2002
Sales 295.7MM[E] *EMP* 2,000
SIC 2911 5172 5541 Petroleum refining; Gasoline; Lubricating oils & greases; Service station supplies, petroleum; Filling stations, gasoline; Truck stops
CEO: William R Klesse
**Ex VP:* Kimberly S Bowers
**Sr VP:* Jay D Browning
**Sr VP:* Anthony D Jones
**VP:* Cheryl L Thomas

D-U-N-S 15-347-2084 IMP/EXP
ULTRAPAK LTD
STARPAK
9690 W Wingfoot Rd, Houston, TX 77041-9037
Tel (713) 329-9183 *Founded/Ownrshp* 2003
Sales 141.4MM[E] *EMP* 288
SIC 5162 Plastics materials
Pr: Isaac Bazbaz
Snr Mgr: Laura Cardosa

ULTRATECH
See VOLM COMPANIES INC

D-U-N-S 80-205-1722
▲ ULTRATECH INC
3050 Zanker Rd, San Jose, CA 95134-2126
Tel (408) 321-8835 *Founded/Ownrshp* 1979
Sales 149.1MM *EMP* 312[E]
Tkr Sym UTEK *Exch* NGS
SIC 3559 Semiconductor manufacturing machinery
Ch Bd: Arthur W Zafiropoulo
CFO: Bruce R Wright
VP: Dave Ghosh
Sftwr Eng: Sergey Vartanov
Sls Mgr: Belinda Kause
Snr Mgr: Kevin Riddell
Board of Directors: Ronald Black, Michael Child, Beatriz V Infante, Dennis R Raney, Henri Richard

D-U-N-S 08-136-8391
ULYSSES CAREMARK HOLDING CORP
44 S Broadway Fl 12f, White Plains, NY 10601-4411
Tel (914) 934-5200 *Founded/Ownrshp* 2011
Sales NA *EMP* 400[E]
SIC 6311 6321 Life insurance; Accident & health insurance carriers
CEO: Larry J Merlo
**Pr:* John Wardle
Treas: James McAleer
Ofcr: Steve Black
VP: Jeff Fihe
VP: Patrick Kittell
**VP:* Robert A Waegelein
Exec: Kirk Clove
Genl Mgr: Marks Felice
VP Sls: Barb Hnatko

D-U-N-S 07-145-0027
UM HOLDING CO (DE)
56 N Haddon Ave Ste 300, Haddonfield, NJ 08033-2438
Tel (856) 354-2200 *Founded/Ownrshp* 1972
Sales 234.0MM *EMP* 1,321
SIC 8099 Physical examination & testing services
Ch Bd: John Aglialoro
**Pr:* Joan Carter
**CFO:* Arthur Hicks
VP: Deborah Mc Keever

UM NY
See UNIVERSAL MCCANN WORLDWIDE INC

D-U-N-S 96-403-6409
▲ UMAMI SUSTAINABLE SEAFOOD INC
1230 Columbia St Ste 440, San Diego, CA 92101-8517
Tel (619) 544-9177 *Founded/Ownrshp* 2014
Sales 97.4MM *EMP* 515
Tkr Sym UMAM *Exch* OTO
SIC 5146 0912 Fish & seafoods; Finfish
CEO: Timothy Fitzpatrick
**Ch Bd:* James White
CFO: Mimi Moreno-Campoy
Off Mgr: Aida Aleman

D-U-N-S 04-434-8642
UMASS MEMORIAL COMMUNITY HOSPITALS INC
119 Belmont St, Worcester, MA 01605-2903
Tel (508) 334-1000 *Founded/Ownrshp* 1995
Sales 286.1MM *EMP* 10,000
Accts Pricewaterhousecoopers Llp B
SIC 8062 General medical & surgical hospitals
CEO: Eric Dickson
**Pr:* John O'Brien
VP: Jay Brady
VP: Dana Swenson
VP: Allison Wollen
CIO: George Brenckla
IT Man: Scott Lgos
Obsttrcn: Petra H Belady
Genl Couns: Joseph Fournier
Genl Couns: Muriel Fraker

D-U-N-S 11-070-9771
UMASS MEMORIAL COMMUNITY MEDICAL GROUP INC
POKOLY, THOS B
121 Lincoln St, Worcester, MA 01605-2429
Tel (508) 757-7745 *Founded/Ownrshp* 1965
Sales 468.1MM *EMP* 3
Accts Pricewaterhousecoopers Llp B
SIC 8011 Obstetrician; Gynecologist; Fertility specialist, physician
Prin: Thomas Pokoly MD

D-U-N-S 94-984-0581
UMASS MEMORIAL HEALTH CARE INC
365 Plantation St Ste 300, Worcester, MA 01605-2397
Tel (508) 754-6026 *Founded/Ownrshp* 1997
Sales 2.0MMM[E] *EMP* 10,000
SIC 8011 Offices & clinics of medical doctors
Pr: Peter H Levine
Chf Rad: Joseph T Ferrucci
CFO: Therese Day
**CFO:* Todd Keating
CFO: Michele Streeter
Sr VP: Nancy R Kruger
Sr VP: Cheryl Lapriore
Sr VP: Dana Swenson
VP: CAM Bienvenue
Dir Lab: Amanda Jenkins
Off Mgr: Jane Hearn

D-U-N-S 96-968-7123
UMASS MEMORIAL HEALTH CARE INC AND AFFILIATES GROUP RETURN
306 Belmont St 120, Worcester, MA 01604-1004
Tel (508) 334-5106 *Founded/Ownrshp* 2011
Sales 2.6MMM[E] *EMP* 500
Accts Feeley & Driscoll Pc Boston
SIC 8748 Business consulting
Prin: Bob Feldmann
CEO: Dr Eric Dickson
CFO: Sergio Melgar
Sr VP: Barbara Fisher

D-U-N-S 10-547-2869 IMP
UMASS MEMORIAL MEDICAL CENTER INC
55 Lake Ave N, Worcester, MA 01655-0002
Tel (508) 334-1000 *Founded/Ownrshp* 2002
Sales 1.3MMM *EMP* 1[E]
SIC 8062 General medical & surgical hospitals
CEO: Eric Dickson
**Pr:* John G O Brien
CFO: Todd Keating
Top Exec: John Keaney Jr
VP: Bryan Cheshire
Dir Rad: Kathy Green
Dir Rx: Elizabeth Radigan
Dir Rx: Maichi Tran
Off Mgr: Mary Brandimarte
Off Mgr: Cindy French
Off Mgr: Marianne Girard

D-U-N-S 13-790-7726
■ UMASS MEMORIAL MEDICAL CENTER INC
(*Suby of* QUEST DIAGNOSTICS INC) ★
119 Belmont St, Worcester, MA 01605-2903
Tel (508) 334-1000 *Founded/Ownrshp* 2013
Sales 1.5MMM *EMP* 300[E]
Accts Pricewaterhousecooper Llp Bos
SIC 8062 Hospital, medical school affiliation
CEO: John Obrien
Pr: Willis Chandler
**Pr:* Eric Dickson M D
**Treas:* Todd Keating
**Ex VP:* Wendy Waring
**Sr VP:* Gary Lapidas
Sr VP: Dana Swenson
Exec: Elizabeth Cox
Assoc Dir: Christine Runyan
Dir Rad: Susan A Afonso
Dir Rad: Dennis D Coughlin
Dir Rad: Paul Lofrumento
Dir Rx: Dennis Brown

D-U-N-S 04-126-8376
UMATILLA ELECTRIC COOPERATIVE
750 W Elm Ave, Hermiston, OR 97838-1282
Tel (541) 567-6414 *Founded/Ownrshp* 1937
Sales 87.2MM *EMP* 165
SIC 4911 Distribution, electric power
CEO: Steven Eldrige
Genl Mgr: Kevin Ince
Genl Mgr: Will McClintock
Opers Mgr: Steve Ferraro

UMB BANK
See UMB FINANCIAL CORP

D-U-N-S 00-696-5487
■ UMB BANK NATIONAL ASSOCIATION
U M B BANK
(*Suby of* UMB BANK) ★
1010 Grand Blvd Fl 3, Kansas City, MO 64106-2220
Tel (816) 842-2222 *Founded/Ownrshp* 1913
Sales NA *EMP* 2,000[E]
SIC 6021 National commercial banks
Pr: Michael D Hagedorn
**Ch Bd:* Mariner Kemper
**Pr:* Peter J Desilva
**Pr:* James Sangster
**CFO:* Micheal Hagajon
CFO: Joe Scherer
**V Ch Bd:* Peter Desilva
**Chf Inves:* Kc Mathews
**Ex VP:* Joseph J Gazzoli
**Ex VP:* Dennis Rilinger
Ex VP: Kirk Vaughan
Sr VP: Katherine Hunter
Sr VP: Jan Leonard
Sr VP: Tom Mathis
VP: Mark Chilton
VP: Ben Hoffman
VP: Drue Thomas
VP: Marty Trepp

D-U-N-S 05-544-4384
▲ UMB FINANCIAL CORP
UMB BANK
1010 Grand Blvd, Kansas City, MO 64106-2202
Tel (816) 860-7930 *Founded/Ownrshp* 1967
Sales NA *EMP* 3,498[E]
Tkr Sym UMBF *Exch* NGS
SIC 6021 National commercial banks
Ch Bd: J Mariner Kemper
Ch Bd: Craig Anderson
Ch Bd: W Thomas Chulick
V Ch: John R Bightman
Pr: James Davis
**Pr:* Peter J Desilva
Pr: Shannon Eigenberger
Pr: Nicholas Estes
Pr: Cullin Faison
Pr: Josh Fink
Pr: Mike Groff
Pr: Erika Miller
Pr: Bob Page
Pr: Jeffrey Peterson
Pr: Brian Raish
Pr: Michael Rattenne
Pr: Sean Renfro
Pr: Edin Salkic
Pr: Brenna Staples
Pr: Chad Treacy
Pr: Jeremy Veath
Board of Directors: Kris A Robbins, Warner L Baxter, Thomas D Sanders, Robin C Beery, L Joshua Sosland, David R Bradley Jr, Paul Uhlmann III, Nancy K Buese, Leroy J Williams, Terrence P Dunn, Thomas J Wood III, Kevin C Gallagher, Greg M Graves, Alexander C Kemper, Tim Murphy

UMDNJ
See UNIVERSITY OF MEDICINE AND DENTISTRY OF NJ (INC)

UMES
See UNIVERSITY OF MARYLAND EASTERN SHORE

D-U-N-S 07-085-3387
UMH NY CORP
TUNKHANNOCK MANOR
10 Acre Pl, Binghamton, NY 13904-2715
Tel (607) 775-6400 *Founded/Ownrshp* 1958
Sales 11.0MM *EMP* 1,200
Accts Baker Tilly Virchow Krause Llp
SIC 8059 8051 8741 Rest home, with health care; Skilled nursing care facilities; Management services
Pr: Brian Picchini
MIS Mgr: Joyce Clegg

D-U-N-S 87-738-3752 IMP/EXP
UMICORE USA INC
(*Suby of* UMICORE SA)
3600 Glenwood Ave Ste 250, Raleigh, NC 27612-4945
Tel (919) 874-7171 *Founded/Ownrshp* 1993
Sales 113.2MM[E] *EMP* 650
SIC 5052 5051 5093 5169 3339 Metallic ores; Nonferrous metal sheets, bars, rods, etc.; Metal scrap & waste materials; Industrial chemicals; Cobalt refining (primary)
Pr: Ravila Gupta
**Pr:* Marc Van Sande
**Treas:* Jacques Dandoy
**Treas:* Karen McHarg
**Ex VP:* Mark Caffarey
**Ex VP:* Richard Laird
Genl Mgr: Yves Simons
Genl Mgr: Rene Wiskemann
Dir IT: Chuck Poznich
Opers Mgr: Hans Vercammen

UMMC
See UNIVERSITY OF MARYLAND MIDTOWN HEALTH INC

UMMS
See CIVISTA MEDICAL CENTER INC

UMMS
See UNIVERSITY OF MARYLAND REHABILITATION INSTITUTE OF SOUTHERN MARYLAND

UMMS
See UNIVERSITY OF MARYLAND MEDICAL SYSTEM CORP

UMPHYSICIANS
See UNIVERSITY OF MINNESOTA PHYSICIANS

D-U-N-S 03-631-8723
■ UMPQUA BANK
(*Suby of* UMPQUA HOLDINGS CORP) ★
445 Se Main St, Roseburg, OR 97470-4900
Tel (541) 440-3961 *Founded/Ownrshp* 1953
Sales NA *EMP* 1,530
SIC 6021 National commercial banks
Pr: William Haden

Pr: Cort O'Haver
CEO: Raymond Davis
CFO: Daniel Sullivan
Chf Cred: Brad Copeland
Ex VP: Steve May
Ex VP: Tory Nixon
Ex VP: Sonny Sonnenstein
Sr VP: Donna Huntsman
VP: Sandy Hunt
Board of Directors: Peggy Fowler, Luis Machuca, Hilliard Terry

D-U-N-S 11-721-4911
▲ UMPQUA HOLDINGS CORP
1 Sw Columbia St Ste 1200, Portland, OR 97258-2013
Tel (503) 727-4100 *Founded/Ownrshp* 1999
Sales NA *EMP* 4,491E
Tkr Sym UMPQ *Exch* NGS
SIC 6035 6022 Savings institutions, federally chartered; State commercial banks
Pr: Raymond P Davis
Pr: Cort L O'Haver
Pr: J Gregory Seibly
CFO: Ronald L Farnsworth
Treas: Neal T McLaughlin
Ex VP: Gary F Neal
Ex VP: Cort Oahaver
Ex VP: Andrew H Ognall
Board of Directors: Bryan L Timm, Luanne Calvert, Peggy Y Fowler, Stephen M Gambee, James S Greene, Luis F Machuca, Maria M Pope, John F Schultz, Susan F Stevens, Hilliard C Terry III

D-U-N-S 02-709-4882
■ UMR INC
(*Suby of* UNITED HEALTHCARE SERVICES INC) ★
11 Scott St, Wausau, WI 54403-4875
Tel (800) 826-9781 *Founded/Ownrshp* 2000
Sales NA *EMP* 4,000E
SIC 6324 8748 Dental insurance; Group hospitalization plans; Employee programs administration
CEO: Jay M Anliker
CFO: Bruce Czech

UMSI
See UNIMET METAL SUPPLY INC

UMUC
See UNIVERSITY OF MARYLAND UNIVERSITY COLLEGE ALUMNI ASSOCIATION INC

D-U-N-S 00-337-4477 IMP/EXP
UNAKA CO INC (TN)
1500 Industrial Rd, Greeneville, TN 37745-3541
Tel (423) 639-1171 *Founded/Ownrshp* 1950, 1996
Sales 167.8MME *EMP* 600
SIC 2099 3469 2514 2253 4226 Ready-to-eat meals, salads & sandwiches; Metal stampings; Chairs, household: metal; Tables, household: metal; T-shirts & tops, knit; Special warehousing & storage
CEO: Robert Austin Jr
COO: Buddy Yonz
**Treas:* L A Yonz
VP: Gordon Newman
Dir IT: Keith Lloyd
Dir IT: Raymond Spears
IT Man: Steve Wallin
Mktg Dir: Kevin Moore
Sls Dir: Robert Leifert
Sls Mgr: Dawn Whitle

D-U-N-S 06-158-6140 IMP/EXP
■ UNARCO INDUSTRIES LLC
(*Suby of* THORCO INDUSTRIES LLC) ★
400 Se 15th St, Wagoner, OK 74467-7900
Tel (918) 485-9531 *Founded/Ownrshp* 1999
Sales 91.8MME *EMP* 400E
SIC 3496 Woven wire products
Pr: Kenneth Bush
Pr: Marshall Lock
Pr: Woody Smith
**CFO:* Robert Musslewhite
CIO: Rodney Fisk
VP Sls: Richard Wilconson
Mktg Mgr: Greg Dallen

D-U-N-S 83-629-6509 IMP/EXP
UNARCO MATERIAL HANDLING INC
(*Suby of* RENCO GROUP INC) ★
701 16th Ave E, Springfield, TN 37172-3305
Tel (615) 384-3531 *Founded/Ownrshp* 1995
Sales 165.0MM *EMP* 785
SIC 5084 2542 Industrial machinery & equipment; Racks, merchandise display or storage: except wood
CEO: Gary Slater
**VP:* Linda Liscara
**VP:* Paul Neal
Prgrm Mgr: Anthony Wheelus
Plnt Mgr: Randy Roberts
Trfc Mgr: Tom Burwinkel
Natl Sales: Chad Barlow
Natl Sales: Brian Meyer
VP Mktg: Linda Lascara

D-U-N-S 00-751-2825
UNBOUND
1 Elmwood Ave, Kansas City, KS 66103-2118
Tel (913) 384-6500 *Founded/Ownrshp* 1981
Sales 120.9MM *EMP* 160
Accts Bkd Llp Kansas City Mo
SIC 8399 Fund raising organization, non-fee basis
Pr: Scott Wasserman
IT Man: Neveda Wayland
Pr Dir: Elizabeth Alex

UNC HOSPITALS
See UNIVERSITY OF NORTH CAROLINA HOSPITALS

UNC-G
See UNIVERSITY OF NORTH CAROLINA AT GREENSBORO INVESTMENT FUND INC

UNCA
See UNIVERSITY OF NORTH CAROLINA AT ASHEVILLE

UNCFU
See UNITED NATIONS FEDERAL CREDIT UNION

D-U-N-S 80-019-8595
UNCN HOLDINGS INC
320 Park Ave Ste 2500, New York, NY 10022-6815
Tel (212) 893-9500 *Founded/Ownrshp* 2007
Sales 29.9MME *EMP* 7,150
SIC 8011 Ambulatory surgical center
Pr: D Scott Mackesy
Bd of Dir: Patrick Welsh
**VP:* Michael Donovan
VP: Jonathan M Rather

D-U-N-S 11-157-8985 IMP/EXP
▲ UNDER ARMOUR INC
1020 Hull St Ste 300, Baltimore, MD 21230-5358
Tel (410) 454-6428 *Founded/Ownrshp* 1996
Sales 3.9MMM *EMP* 13,400E
Tkr Sym UA *Exch* NYS
SIC 2329 2353 2339 3021 Men's & boys' sportswear & athletic clothing; Hats, caps & millinery; Women's & misses' outerwear; Rubber & plastics footwear
Ch Bd: Kevin A Plank
Pr: Jason Larose
CFO: Lawrence P Molloy
Ofcr: Kerry D Chandler
Ofcr: Kip Fulks
Ofcr: Michael Lee
Ex VP: James H Hardy Jr
Ex VP: Carolyn Johnson
Ex VP: Lisa Struble
VP: Chris Bate
VP: Kevin Eskridge
VP: Randy Harward
VP: Monica Mirro
Dir Soc: Trisha Joyce
Board of Directors: Byron K Adams Jr, George W Bodenheimer, Douglas E Coltharp, Anthony W Deering, Karen W Katz, Alvin Bernard Krongard, William R McDermott, Eric T Olson, Harvey L Sanders

UNDERCARE
See INTER-CITY TIRE & AUTO CENTER INC

UNDERGROUND ATTITUDE
See SHOE SENSATION INC

D-U-N-S 04-618-5794 IMP/EXP
UNDERSEA SENSOR SYSTEMS INC
ULTRA ELECTRONICS
(*Suby of* ULTRA ELECTRONICS HOLDINGS PLC)
4868 E Park 30 Dr, Columbia City, IN 46725-8861
Tel (260) 244-3500 *Founded/Ownrshp* 1998
Sales 91.9MME *EMP* 438E
SIC 3812 Nautical instruments; Navigational systems & instruments; Search & detection systems & instruments
Pr: Joseph Peters
VP: Douglas Randol
Prgrm Mgr: Sue Drohan
Genl Mgr: David Jost
CIO: Jay Dearmond
IT Man: Rodney Shull
Ql Cn Mgr: Kelly Turner
Sls Dir: Tim Barnes

D-U-N-S 04-158-2297
UNDERWOOD FRUIT AND WAREHOUSE CO LLC
401 N 1st Ave, Yakima, WA 98902-2125
Tel (509) 457-6177 *Founded/Ownrshp* 1948
Sales 205.7MME *EMP* 650
SIC 5149 2033 Canned goods: fruit, vegetables, seafood, meats, etc.; Fruits & fruit products in cans, jars, etc.
Ch: John M Bloxom Jr
**Pr:* Don Gibson

D-U-N-S 07-705-9152
UNDERWOOD MEMORIAL HOSPITAL INC
509 N Broad St, Woodbury, NJ 08096-1617
Tel (856) 845-0100 *Founded/Ownrshp* 1966
Sales 130.5MME *EMP* 1,700
Accts Pricewaterhousecoopers Llp Ph
SIC 8062 General medical & surgical hospitals
Pr: Maryann Sullivan
COO: Eileen Cardile
Sr VP: James Brant
**VP:* Kurt W Kaulback
VP: Kurt Kaulback
VP: Paul Lambrecht
Dir Risk M: Jane Brook
Dir Rad: Maureen Sacchetti
Ex Dir: Barbara Mihatov
Ex Dir: Bill Morrison
CIO: Bob Mizia

D-U-N-S 00-693-2990 IMP
UNDERWRITERS LABORATORIES INC
UL
333 Pfingsten Rd, Northbrook, IL 60062-2096
Tel (847) 272-8800 *Founded/Ownrshp* 1936
Sales 1.7MMME *EMP* 10,846
Accts Pricewaterhousecoopers Llp Ph
SIC 8734 Product testing laboratory, safety or performance; Water testing laboratory
Pr: Keith E Williams
**Pr:* Sara A Greenstein
**Pr:* Sajeev Jesudas
Pr: Benjamin J Miller
Pr: Gitte Schjotz
**COO:* Charles D Abounader
COO: Bob Levine
CFO: Michael Saltzman
**Ch:* Tom Chapin
**Ch:* Doug Grillaert
**Ch:* Steve Hewson
**Ch:* Bob Jamieson
**Ch:* Don Talka
Trst: Dominic Ho
Trst: Tadakatsu Sano
Ofcr: Terry Brady
**Sr VP:* Christian Anschuetz
**Sr VP:* Ben Miller
**Sr VP:* Hiroshi Yamaki
VP: C Also
VP: Patrick W Boyle

D-U-N-S 04-042-3188
UNDERWRITERS SAFETY AND CLAIMS INC
(*Suby of* CHURCHILL INSURANCE ASSOCIATES INC) ★
1700 Eastpoint Pkwy, Louisville, KY 40223-4140
Tel (502) 244-1343 *Founded/Ownrshp* 1954
Sales NA *EMP* 300
SIC 6411 Insurance agents
Pr: Bruce W Ferguson
Treas: James K Johnson
**Ex VP:* Scott C Ferguson
Ex VP: Stuart J Ferguson
**Ex VP:* Jack D Stewart
VP: Gary G Gilmour
VP: Robert L Haner
VP: Gary A Mongilutz
VP: Eugene Reis
Dir Bus: Justin Newton
Board of Directors: Robert Reeves

UNDP
See UNITED NATIONS DEVELOPMENT PROGRAMME

UNFI
See UNITED NATURAL FOODS WEST INC

UNFI SPECIALTY DIST SERICES
See MILLBROOK DISTRIBUTION SERVICES INC

D-U-N-S 00-883-4855
UNGER CONSTRUCTION CO
910 X St, Sacramento, CA 95818-2128
Tel (916) 325-5500 *Founded/Ownrshp* 1974
Sales 91.0MM *EMP* 120
SIC 1542 1541

D-U-N-S 06-458-9112 IMP
UNGER FABRIK LLC
1515 E 15th St, Los Angeles, CA 90021-2711
Tel (213) 222-1010 *Founded/Ownrshp* 1998
Sales 100.0MME *EMP* 197
Accts Moss Adams Llp Los Angeles C
SIC 2339 Women's & misses' athletic clothing & sportswear
CEO: Richard Sneider
CEO: Arthur Gordon

UNGERER & COMPANY
See UNGERER INDUSTRIES INC

D-U-N-S 96-375-2782
UNGERER & CO INC
(*Suby of* UNGERER & CO) ★
4 Bridgewater Ln, Lincoln Park, NJ 07035-1491
Tel (973) 628-0600 *Founded/Ownrshp* 1981
Sales 100.0MME *EMP* 290
SIC 0119 Oil grains
CEO: Kenneth G Voorhees Jr
CFO: Richard Dambres Jr
VP: John Olsen

D-U-N-S 00-155-1423 IMP/EXP
UNGERER INDUSTRIES INC
UNGERER & COMPANY
4 Bridgewater Ln, Lincoln Park, NJ 07035-1491
Tel (973) 628-0600 *Founded/Ownrshp* 1893
Sales 110.6MME *EMP* 400
SIC 2899 2844 2087

D-U-N-S 07-070-1958
UNI CARE
233 S Wacker Dr, Chicago, IL 60606-7147
Tel (312) 234-7000 *Founded/Ownrshp* 1993
Sales 41.6MME *EMP* 1,600
SIC 8011 Health maintenance organization
Pr: David Fields
Genl Mgr: Kelly Dee
Sls&Mrk Ex: John Cole

D-U-N-S 07-879-1028
UNI-CHARTERING USA LLC (TX)
CHEMICAL OR VEGOIL TRANSPORTAT
840 Gessner Rd Ste 210, Houston, TX 77024-4154
Tel (281) 833-7271 *Founded/Ownrshp* 2011
Sales 183.9MM *EMP* 5
SIC 4491 Marine cargo handling
Mng Dir: Franz Ekmann
Mng Dir: Hans Thorsen

D-U-N-S 03-767-5279 EXP
UNI-MARTS LLC
STATE GAS & OIL DIVISION
1155 Benner Pike 100, State College, PA 16801-7322
Tel (814) 234-6000 *Founded/Ownrshp* 2004
Sales 286.7MME *EMP* 2,450
SIC 5411 5541 5993 6794 5172 Convenience stores, chain; Filling stations, gasoline; Cigarette store; Franchises, selling or licensing; Gasoline

D-U-N-S 78-435-1319 IMP
UNI-SELECT USA INC
AUTO PLUS
1155 Roberts Blvd Nw # 175, Kennesaw, GA 30144-3666
Tel (770) 701-5000 *Founded/Ownrshp* 2002
Sales 1.0MMME *EMP* 3,400
SIC 5013

D-U-N-S 15-735-2634
UNIBAR SERVICES INC
ACCU-READ SERVICES
4325 Concourse Dr, Ann Arbor, MI 48108-9688
Tel (734) 769-2600 *Founded/Ownrshp* 1985
Sales NA *EMP* 1,200
SIC 1623

D-U-N-S 18-155-8040 IMP
UNICAL AVIATION INC
680 S Lemon Ave, City of Industry, CA 91789-2934
Tel (626) 813-1901 *Founded/Ownrshp* 1990
Sales 206.8MME *EMP* 200
SIC 5088 Aircraft & parts
Pr: Han Tan
CFO: Mercy Tan
Treas: Mercy Tjiptorahardjo
Ex VP: Florence Sy

VP: Eddie Chen
VP: Andrew Ko
VP: John Lee
Mng Dir: Rochelle Racela
QC Dir: Grace Patricia
Sales Exec: Edward Chiao
Sales Exec: Denise Limoseputro

D-U-N-S 07-688-8382
■ UNICARE LIFE & HEALTH INSURANCE CO
(*Suby of* ANTHEM INC) ★
5151 Camino Ruiz Ste A, Camarillo, CA 93012-8648
Tel (888) 742-2505 *Founded/Ownrshp* 2004
Sales NA *EMP* 1,800
SIC 6411 6324 Insurance agents, brokers & service; Group hospitalization plans
Pr: David W Fields
**CFO:* David C Colby
Sales Exec: Mark Goswein

D-U-N-S 02-410-4341 IMP
UNICARRIERS AMERICAS CORP (IL)
NISSAN FORKLIFT
(*Suby of* UNICARRIERS CORPORATION.)
240 N Prospect St, Marengo, IL 60152-3235
Tel (800) 871-5438 *Founded/Ownrshp* 1966, 2013
Sales 118.2MME *EMP* 340E
SIC 3537 3519 5084 Lift trucks, industrial: fork, platform, straddle, etc.; Gasoline engines; Lift trucks & parts; Engines, gasoline
Pr: James J Radous III
**CFO:* Tom Prusinski
**VP:* Steve Cianci
**VP:* Dan Domberg
Genl Mgr: Derek Robson
Sls&Mrk Ex: Joyce Kasmer
Sales Asso: Kathy Insko
Snr Mgr: Dixie Jirak

UNICEL
See RURAL CELLULAR CORP

D-U-N-S 18-705-9332 EXP
UNICITY INTERNATIONAL INC
1201 N 800 E, Orem, UT 84097-2742
Tel (801) 226-2600 *Founded/Ownrshp* 2006
Sales 144.8MME *EMP* 500
SIC 5149 Groceries & related products
Ch: Curt Hedges
**Pr:* Brent Morrill
**CEO:* Stewart Hughes
COO: Dan Hughes
Ex VP: Christopher Kim
VP: Kathan Blair
Off Mgr: Yolanda Lacey
QA Dir: Cory Baker
Dir IT: Daniel Zaldivar
Software D: David Weinerman
Opers Mgr: Steven Newsome

D-U-N-S 60-341-1570 IMP
UNICOM ENGINEERING INC
NEI
(*Suby of* UNICOM GLOBAL INC) ★
25 Dan Rd, Canton, MA 02021-2817
Tel (781) 332-1000 *Founded/Ownrshp* 2012
Sales 275.0MM *EMP* 264E
SIC 3572 7372 Computer storage devices; Business oriented computer software
Pr: Corry Hong
CFO: Dave Wheeler
Treas: Cheryl Smith
Treas: Lawrence Yelsey
Sr VP: Richard P Graber
VP: Ray Corey
VP: Lois Farkas
VP: Johnathan Gauthier
VP: Richard Graber
VP: Ken Groh
VP: William Oconnell
VP: Ray Pineau
VP: Peter Sebilian
VP: John Willing

UNICOM GLOBAL
See UNICOM SYSTEMS INC

D-U-N-S 07-857-0513
UNICOM GLOBAL INC
15535 San Fernando Mssion, Mission Hills, CA 91345-1343
Tel (818) 838-0606 *Founded/Ownrshp* 1981
Sales 275.0MME *EMP* 270
SIC 8732 6552 7389 7371 Merger, acquisition & reorganization research; Subdividers & developers; Financial services; Computer software development & applications
Pr: Corry S Hong
**VP:* Russ Guzzo
Dir Bus: Martin Webley
Opers Mgr: Andrew Hong

D-U-N-S 10-793-9357 IMP
UNICOM GOVERNMENT INC
(*Suby of* UNICOM GLOBAL) ★
15010 Conference Center D, Chantilly, VA 20151-3854
Tel (703) 502-2000 *Founded/Ownrshp* 1986
Sales 324.8MME *EMP* 160E
SIC 5045 Computers; Computer peripheral equipment; Computer software
Pr: Corry S Hong
VP: Peter Whitefeild
Dir Bus: David Shaeffer
Mng Dir: Christopher Lee
Prgrm Mgr: Danielle Bare
Prgrm Mgr: Maggie Thompson
Genl Mgr: Blanche Kochenthal
CTO: Daniel Kent
QA Dir: Anthony Best
IT Man: Pam Green
IT Man: Joe Hackett
Board of Directors: Christine Hong, Corry Hong

D-U-N-S 16-139-5389 IMP/EXP
UNICOM SYSTEMS INC
UNICOM GLOBAL
1143 Summit Dr, Beverly Hills, CA 90210-2252
Tel (818) 838-0606 *Founded/Ownrshp* 1995

Sales 346.6MM^E *EMP* 700
SIC 7371 Computer software development & applications
Pr: Corry S Hong
CFO: Neil Watt
VP: Eugene Smith
Genl Mgr: Patti Bowman
Mktg Dir: Paul Kim
Genl Couns: Gerard R Kilroy

UNICOR
See FEDERAL PRISON INDUSTRIES INC

UNICORR GROUP
See CONNECTICUT CONTAINER CORP

D-U-N-S 15-994-1962
UNIDEN HOLDING INC
(*Suby of* UNIDEN HOLDINGS CORPORATION)
4700 Amon Carter Blvd, Fort Worth, TX 76155-2207
Tel (817) 858-3300 *Founded/Ownrshp* 1997
Sales 90.5MM^E *EMP* 210
SIC 5063 5065

D-U-N-S 02-696-4044
UNIDINE CORP
1000 Washington St # 510, Boston, MA 02118-5006
Tel (617) 467-3700 *Founded/Ownrshp* 2001
Sales 129.2MM^E *EMP* 967^E
SIC 8741 Restaurant management
Pr: Richard Schenkel
* *CFO:* David Silva
* *Sr VP:* Larry Abrams
VP: Tim Bouchard
* *VP:* Charles P Kelsey
* *VP:* Timothy Lamson
VP: Ellen Lowre
* *VP:* Holly Molinaro
VP: Karen O'Neil
VP: Adam Pickus
VP: Chris Stainton
Exec: Jay Cedrone
Exec: Fred Duggan
Exec: Joe Engle
Exec: Dave Grein
Exec: David Guinane
Exec: James E Wedderburn
Dir Bus: James Hunter
Dir Bus: Correna Lukas

D-U-N-S 05-554-5925 IMP/EXP
▲ UNIFI INC (NY)
7201 W Friendly Ave, Greensboro, NC 27410-6237
Tel (336) 294-4410 *Founded/Ownrshp* 1969
Sales 643.6MM *EMP* 2,500
Accts Kpmg Llp Greensboro North C
Tkr Sym UFI *Exch* NYS
SIC 2281 2282 2221 Nylon yarn, spinning of staple; Polyester yarn, spun: made from purchased staple; Polyester filament yarn: throwing, twisting, winding, etc.; Textured yarn; Spandex broadwoven fabrics
Pr: Thomas H Caudle Jr
CFO: Sean D Goodman
Board of Directors: William J Armfield IV, Robert J Bishop, Paul R Charron, Archibald Cox Jr, William L Jasper, James M Kilts, Kenneth G Langone, James D Mead, Suzanne M Present

D-U-N-S 62-400-7071 IMP/EXP
■ UNIFI MANUFACTURING INC
(*Suby of* UNIFI INC) ★
7201 W Friendly Ave, Greensboro, NC 27410-6237
Tel (336) 294-4410 *Founded/Ownrshp* 1996
Sales 599.0MM^E *EMP* 2,396
SIC 2281 Nylon yarn, spinning of staple; Polyester yarn, spun: made from purchased staple
CEO: William L Jasper
* *Pr:* R Roger Berrier Jr
* *CFO:* Sean D Goodman
* *VP:* Thomas H Caudle Jr

D-U-N-S 03-766-4401 IMP
■ UNIFIED BRANDS INC
(*Suby of* DOVER RFRGN & FD EQP INC) ★
2016 Gees Mill Rd Ne, Conyers, GA 30013-1301
Tel (601) 372-3903 *Founded/Ownrshp* 2005
Sales 118.5MM^E *EMP* 625
SIC 3469 Metal stampings
Pr: William Strenglis
* *CFO:* Micheal Moody
Treas: Calvin McDonald
Sr VP: Lynn Bay
CTO: Carol Lee
VP Sls: Jeff Hessel

D-U-N-S 13-259-3505 IMP
UNIFIED COMMUNICATIONS INTERNATIONAL LLC
AFFINITY
1921 Nw 82nd Ave, Doral, FL 33126-1011
Tel (305) 677-7888 *Founded/Ownrshp* 2000
Sales 88.8MM^E *EMP* 70^E
SIC 5065

D-U-N-S 36-070-8531
UNIFIED COURT SYSTEM OF NEW YORK STATE
APPELLATE SUPREME COURT
(*Suby of* STATE OF NEW YORK) ★
20 Eagle St, Albany, NY 12207-1009
Tel (518) 455-7700 *Founded/Ownrshp* 1788
Sales NA *EMP* 13,100
SIC 9211 State courts;
Ofcr: Leigh Freeman

D-U-N-S 78-281-6698
UNIFIED GOVERNMENT OF ATHENS-CLARKE COUNTY
301 College Ave Ste 300, Athens, GA 30601-2715
Tel (706) 613-3010 *Founded/Ownrshp* 1991
Sales NA *EMP* 1,400
Accts Mauldin & Jenkins Llc Atlant
SIC 9111
Ofcr: Greg Dickson
Ofcr: Kim Johnson
Ofcr: Lesley Moore
Ofcr: George Pope
Sr VP: Richard White
Genl Mgr: Eric Blair
Off Admin: Elizabeth McLean
IT Man: Steve Davis
IT Man: Barry Fuller
Snr Mgr: Jacqueline Elder

D-U-N-S 03-069-3592
UNIFIED GOVERNMENT OF WYANDOTTE COUNTY
WYANDOTTE CNTY/KNSAS CTY, UNFD
701 N 7th St, Kansas City, KS 66101-3035
Tel (913) 573-5000 *Founded/Ownrshp* 1997
Sales NA *EMP* 2,100
Accts Allen Gibbs & Houlik Lc W
SIC 9111 Executive offices;
Sls Mgr: Mary Barnes
Corp Couns: Harold T Walker

D-U-N-S 00-690-6804 IMP/EXP
UNIFIED GROCERS INC (CA)
5200 Sheila St, Commerce, CA 90040-3906
Tel (323) 264-5200 *Founded/Ownrshp* 1922
Sales 3.7MMM *EMP* 2,807
SIC 5141 6331 Groceries, general line; Fire, marine & casualty insurance; Workers' compensation insurance
Pr: Robert M Ling Jr
CFO: Christine Neal
Ex VP: Randy Delgado
Sr VP: Leon G Bergmann
Sr VP: Blake W Larson
Sr VP: Randall G Scoville
VP: Joe Falvey
VP: Gary S Herman
Ex Dir: Mike Anthony
Ex Dir: Mike O'Donnell
Store Mgr: Jan Tiel
Board of Directors: Jay T McCormack, Bradley A Alford, G Robert McDougall, Louis A Amen, John Najjar, John Berberian, Gregory A Saar, Oscar Gonzalez, Thomas S Sayles, Richard E Goodspeed, Mimi R Song, Paul Kapioski, Michael S Trask, Mark Kidd, Kenneth Ray Tucker, John D Lang, Richard L Wright, Roger M Laverty

D-U-N-S 80-435-5931
UNIFIED MANAGEMENT CORP
1 E Wacker Dr Ste 3504, Chicago, IL 60601-1474
Tel (312) 828-9480 *Founded/Ownrshp* 1992
Sales 306.5MM *EMP* 30
Accts Poulos & Bayer Chicago Il
SIC 7363

D-U-N-S 04-306-3221
UNIFIED SCHOOL DISTRICT 259
WICHITA PUBLIC SCHOOLS
201 N Water St, Wichita, KS 67202-1292
Tel (316) 973-4000 *Founded/Ownrshp* 1871
Sales 626.5MM *EMP* 5,406
Accts Allen Gibbs & Houlik Lc Wic
SIC 8211 8249 8331 Public elementary & secondary schools; High school, junior or senior; Vocational schools; Job training & vocational rehabilitation services
* *CFO:* Jim Freeman
* *CFO:* Linda Jones
VP: Wichita Boe
Ex Dir: Jim Means
Ex Dir: Steven Shook
Dir Sec: Terri Moses
CIO: Cathy Barbieri
Dir IT: Jennifer Sinclair
IT Man: Christopher Murphy
Netwrk Mgr: Toby Taylor
Schl Brd P: Shiral Login

D-U-N-S 02-685-2376
UNIFIED SCHOOL DISTRICT 383 (KS)
BOARD OF EDUCATION
2031 Poyntz Ave, Manhattan, KS 66502-3868
Tel (785) 587-2000 *Founded/Ownrshp* 1858
Sales 111.6MM *EMP* 1,300
SIC 8211 8249 Public elementary & secondary schools; Elementary school; High school, junior or senior; Vocational schools

D-U-N-S 61-277-1477 IMP
UNIFIED SOLUTIONS INC
U S I
9801 80th Ave, Pleasant Prairie, WI 53158-2221
Tel (262) 942-5200 *Founded/Ownrshp* 1989
Sales 84.8MM^E *EMP* 250
SIC 4783 Packing goods for shipping
Pr: James Lipowski
* *VP:* Janet M Barootian
Netwrk Eng: Jim McCarthy

D-U-N-S 01-972-3535 IMP
▲ UNIFIRST CORP
68 Jonspin Rd, Wilmington, MA 01887-1086
Tel (978) 658-8888 *Founded/Ownrshp* 1936
Sales 1.4MMM *EMP* 12,700
Tkr Sym UNF *Exch* NYS
SIC 7218 2326 Industrial clothing launderers; Industrial uniform supply; Work clothing supply; Men's & boys' work clothing
Ch Bd: Ronald D Croatti
* *CFO:* Steven S Sintros
* *Treas:* Cynthia Croatti
* *Sr VP:* Michael A Croatti
* *Sr VP:* David A Difillippo
* *Sr VP:* David M Katz
Brnch Mgr: Nick Colarelli
Brnch Mgr: Todd Davis
Brnch Mgr: Jeremy Dinneen
Brnch Mgr: Adam Dufresne
Brnch Mgr: Saul Rodriguez

D-U-N-S 96-610-6817
UNIFRAX HOLDING CO
(*Suby of* UFX HOLDING II CORP) ★
55 E 52nd St Fl 35, New York, NY 10055-0110
Tel (212) 644-5900 *Founded/Ownrshp* 2006
Sales 56.0MM^E *EMP* 1,121
SIC 3299 Ceramic fiber
Prin: Vincent MAI
Mng Dir: Joseph D Carrabino
Mng Dir: Martin C Eltrich
Mng Dir: Daniel H Klebes

D-U-N-S 96-646-8779 IMP/EXP
■ UNIFRAX I LLC
(*Suby of* AMERICAN SECURITIES LLC) ★
600 Riverwalk Pkwy Ste 120, Tonawanda, NY 14150
Tel (716) 768-6500 *Founded/Ownrshp* 1986
Sales 437.3MM^E *EMP* 1,121
SIC 3299 Ceramic fiber
Pr: David E Brooks
CFO: John Dandolph
Sr VP: Kevin J Gorman
VP: Kevin O'Gorman
Exec: Melissa Widener
CIO: Shelly Bush
Snr Mgr: Jeffrey Champagne

D-U-N-S 00-623-4678
UNIFY FINANCIAL FEDERAL CREDIT UNION
1899 Western Way Ste 100, Torrance, CA 90501-1146
Tel (310) 536-5000 *Founded/Ownrshp* 1958
Sales NA *EMP* 280
SIC 6061 Federal credit unions
Prin: Gordon M Howe
* *CEO:* Gordon M Howe
COO: Gordon Howe
VP: Scott Johnson
VP: Jonathan Oliver
Brnch Mgr: Stephen Kewley
Brnch Mgr: Christie Ponce
Brnch Mgr: Bill Welch
Brnch Mgr: Tiffany West
Snr Ntwrk: Jimmy Cordova
IT Man: Diana McNack

D-U-N-S 06-272-5577
UNIGARD INC
(*Suby of* WINTERTHUR U S HOLDINGS INC) ★
2125 158th Ct Ne, Bellevue, WA 98008-2126
Tel (425) 641-4321 *Founded/Ownrshp* 1980, 1993
Sales NA *EMP* 525
SIC 6321 6331 Accident insurance carriers; Fire, marine & casualty insurance & carriers; Property damage insurance
CEO: Peter Christen
* *Ch Bd:* Lawrence P O'Connor
* *CFO:* Dale E Abbrederis
* *VP:* Arnie Chatterton
VP: John Dunlop
* *VP:* Sean McGourty

D-U-N-S 06-167-0428
UNIGARD INSURANCE CO
UNIGARD INSURANCE GROUP
(*Suby of* UNIGARD INC) ★
15800 Northup Way, Bellevue, WA 98008-2537
Tel (425) 641-4321 *Founded/Ownrshp* 1993
Sales NA *EMP* 400
SIC 6331 Fire, marine & casualty insurance & carriers; Property damage insurance
Ch Bd: Peter Christen
Ex VP: Richard Boone
VP: Arne Chatterton
VP: Paul Neuss

UNIGARD INSURANCE GROUP
See UNIGARD INSURANCE CO

D-U-N-S 07-821-3550
UNIGARD PACIFIC INSURANCE CO
QBE
(*Suby of* WINTERTHUR U S HOLDINGS INC) ★
15800 Northup Way, Bellevue, WA 98008-2537
Tel (425) 644-5236 *Founded/Ownrshp* 2007
Sales NA *EMP* 500
SIC 6331 6411 Property damage insurance; Fire, marine & casualty insurance: mutual; Automobile insurance; Insurance agents, brokers & service
Pr: Peter Christen
CFO: Dale Abbrederis
* *Treas:* Le Ann Weese
VP: Chris Alberghini
CIO: Pat Hearn

D-U-N-S 55-693-3166 IMP
UNIGEN CORP
45388 Warm Springs Blvd, Fremont, CA 94539-6102
Tel (510) 668-2088 *Founded/Ownrshp* 1991
Sales 216.4MM^E *EMP* 750
SIC 3674 3572

UNIGRO
See L & L NURSERY SUPPLY INC

D-U-N-S 00-696-5180 IMP/EXP
UNIGROUP INC (MO)
1 Premier Dr, Fenton, MO 63026-2989
Tel (636) 305-5000 *Founded/Ownrshp* 1942
Sales 426.4MM^E *EMP* 902
SIC 4213 7513 5087 Household goods transport; Truck rental & leasing, no drivers; Moving equipment & supplies
Prin: H Daniel McCollister
* *Pr:* James G Powers
COO: Anthony M Decanti
COO: James R Petzel
* *CFO:* L Brent Stottlemyre
* *Treas:* Richard K Smith Jr
Ofcr: Jan Robey Alonzo
Ofcr: Stephan E Burkhardt
Ofcr: Casey P Ellis
Sr VP: Patrick G Baehler
Sr VP: Rupert O Morley
VP: Jeremy C Beglin
VP: David G Motherwell
Board of Directors: Katherine Holman, Gerald P Stadler, James A Alexander, Darrell Horne, Larry Stanley, Rick Anderson, Mark K Johnson, Barry Vaughn, Tom Andrsen, Steve Komorous, Quinn Bell, Michael Marchese, David Corragin, Chuck Mattes, Bruce Dusenberry, H Daniel Mc Collister, Robert Eckhardt, William B Meyer, David Harrelson, John J Planes, Steven A Herman, David Sabada

D-U-N-S 10-256-0083
■ UNILAB CORP
QUEST DIAGNOSTICS
(*Suby of* QUEST DIAGNOSTICS INC) ★
8401 Fallbrook Ave, West Hills, CA 91304-3226
Tel (818) 737-6000 *Founded/Ownrshp* 2003
Sales 388.4MM^E *EMP* 37,000
SIC 8071 Testing laboratories
CEO: Surya Mohapatra
VP: Delbert Fisher
VP: Michael Hughes
VP: Ed Norris
Exec: Christopher Hoagland
Exec: Jim Kearney
* *Mng Dir:* Robert Moverley
Dept Mgr: Lin Husted
QA Dir: Michael A Warner
Dir IT: Clyde Allen
Mtls Mgr: Mark Vento

D-U-N-S 04-361-4007 IMP/EXP
UNILEVER BESTFOODS NORTH AMERICA
(*Suby of* UNILEVER UNITED STATES INC) ★
800 Sylvan Ave, Englewood Cliffs, NJ 07632-3201
Tel (201) 894-4000 *Founded/Ownrshp* 2002
Sales 533.3MM^E *EMP* 1,604
SIC 2046 2034 2035 2098 2099 2051 Wet corn milling; Dextrose; High fructose corn syrup (HFCS); Glucose; Soup mixes; Mayonnaise; Macaroni products (e.g. alphabets, rings & shells), dry; Noodles (e.g. egg, plain & water), dry; Peanut butter; Cakes, bakery: except frozen; Pastries, e.g. danish: except frozen; Bagels, fresh or frozen; Bread, all types (white, wheat, rye, etc): fresh or frozen
Pr: Charles R Shoemate
CFO: Robert Gluck
CFO: Neil Vorchheimer
Sr VP: Neil Vorchherimer
VP: Tim Crowell
VP: Steve Heaslip
VP: Stanislav Hofman
VP: Tim Ransome
Exec: Gale Griffin
Software D: Mary Kobolakis
Software D: Mary Sonkin

UNILEVER FOODS CHILL
See THOMAS J LIPTON INC

UNILEVER FOODS DRY
See CONOPCO INC

D-U-N-S 08-004-9524
UNILEVER MANUFACTURING (US) INC
(*Suby of* UNILEVER FOODS DRY) ★
800 Sylvan Ave, Englewood Cliffs, NJ 07632-3201
Tel (800) 298-5018 *Founded/Ownrshp* 2011
Sales 208.6MM^E *EMP* 1,800
SIC 2844 2099 Toilet preparations; Seasonings: dry mixes
CEO: Howard B Bernick

D-U-N-S 09-432-0132 IMP
UNILEVER UNITED STATES INC (DE)
(*Suby of* UNILEVER PLC)
700 Sylvan Ave, Englewood Cliffs, NJ 07632-3113
Tel (201) 894-4000 *Founded/Ownrshp* 1977
Sales 6.0MMM^E *EMP* 13,000
SIC 2035 2086 2024 2038 2844 2841 Pickles, sauces & salad dressings; Dressings, salad: raw & cooked (except dry mixes); Mayonnaise; Spreads, sandwich: salad dressing base; Bottled & canned soft drinks; Ice cream & frozen desserts; Frozen specialties; Toilet preparations; Toothpastes or powders, dentifrices; Hair preparations, including shampoos; Cosmetic preparations; Detergents, synthetic organic or inorganic alkaline; Dishwashing compounds; Soap: granulated, liquid, cake, flaked or chip
Pr: Michael B Polk
Ex VP: Eugenio Minvielle
* *Sr VP:* John Bird
Sr VP: Amanda Sourry
VP: Philip Cohen
VP: Kevin George
VP: Kevin B George
VP: Lisa Klauser
VP: Bill Knees
VP: Daan Thorn-Leeson
VP: Todd Tillemans

D-U-N-S 04-017-9827 IMP/EXP
■ UNILIN FLOORING NC LLC
(*Suby of* MOHAWK INDUSTRIES INC) ★
550 Cloniger Dr, Thomasville, NC 27360-4960
Tel (336) 313-4000 *Founded/Ownrshp* 2004
Sales 222.6MM^E *EMP* 850
SIC 2421 2426 Flooring (dressed lumber), softwood; Hardwood dimension & flooring mills
* *VP:* Barbara M Goetz
CTO: Marc Seijn
VP Sls: Ken Peden

UNIMAC GRAPHICS
See UNION GRAPHICS INC

D-U-N-S 80-558-3143
UNIMARK LLC
(*Suby of* CONTINUUM ENERGY SERVICES LLC) ★
3540 S Boulevard Ste 205, Edmond, OK 73013-5543
Tel (405) 285-8670 *Founded/Ownrshp* 2008
Sales 284.5MM *EMP* 16
Accts Grant Thornton Llp Tulsa Ok
SIC 4924 Natural gas distribution

D-U-N-S 07-841-6933
UNIMAVEN INC
74 Green St, Hackensack, NJ 07601-4004
Tel (201) 500-8050 *Founded/Ownrshp* 2011
Sales 150.0MM *EMP* 51
SIC 4225 General warehousing & storage
Pr: Alex Blaker

D-U-N-S 19-872-0666 IMP
UNIMET METAL SUPPLY INC
UMSI
150 Lackawanna Ave, Parsippany, NJ 07054-1057
Tel (973) 673-5700 *Founded/Ownrshp* 1989
Sales 121.5MM^E *EMP* 175^E

SIC 3324 Aerospace investment castings, ferrous
Pr: Robert Flynn
CFO: Dennis Flynn
VP: Louis Nordt
Prin: Moore Jphillip

D-U-N-S 05-154-4757 IMP/EXP
UNIMIN CORP
(*Suby of* SCR - SIBELCO NV)
258 Elm St, New Canaan, CT 06840-5300
Tel (203) 966-8880 *Founded/Ownrshp* 1970
Sales 3.4MMM^E *EMP* 3,400
SIC 1446 1499 1422 1459 4011 1442 Silica mining; Quartz crystal (pure) mining; Dolomite, crushed & broken-quarrying; Nepheline syenite quarrying; Steam railroads; Construction sand & gravel
Ch: Kevin F Crawford
Pr: Luke C Anderson
CFO: Luke Anderson
Treas: William E Whamond
Treas: Douglas M Zove
Ex VP: Thomas M Kilroy Jr
Sr VP: H Frederick Barnard III
VP: Joseph C Shapiro
Plnt Mgr: Larry Coger
Plnt Mgr: Glenn Robertson

D-U-N-S 18-566-8431
UNION BANK
UNION BANK AND TRUST
(*Suby of* OLNEY BANCSHARES OF TEXAS INC)
4921 N May Ave, Oklahoma City, OK 73112-6041
Tel (405) 949-7200 *Founded/Ownrshp* 2007
Sales NA *EMP* 78
SIC 6022 State trust companies accepting deposits, commercial
Pr: E Wilson Roberts
**V Ch Bd:* Kenneth A Skopec
**Sr VP:* Larry Allen
**Sr VP:* Ron Moreland
Sr VP: Jean M Sharp
VP: Robert Heffron

UNION BANK AND TRUST
See UNION BANK

D-U-N-S 03-634-7128
UNION BANK AND TRUST CO
3643 S 48th St, Lincoln, NE 68506-4390
Tel (402) 488-0941 *Founded/Ownrshp* 2005
Sales NA *EMP* 800
SIC 6111 6029 6162 6021 6035 6022 Student Loan Marketing Association; Commercial banks; Mortgage bankers & correspondents; National commercial banks; Federal savings banks; State commercial banks
Ch Bd: Jay L Dunlap
**Pr:* Angie Muhliesen
**CEO:* Ross W Wilcox
CFO: Greig Payne
**Sr VP:* Alan Fosler
**Sr VP:* Keith May
Sr VP: L G Searcey
VP: Stephanie Dinger
VP: Debbie Lentz
VP: Tom Weinandt
Opers Mgr: Brent Smith

UNION BANK CAL FOUNDATION
See UNION BANK FOUNDATION

D-U-N-S 06-778-9487
UNION BANK FOUNDATION
UNION BANK CAL FOUNDATION
(*Suby of* MUFG UNION BANK NA) ★
445 S Figueroa St Ste 710, Los Angeles, CA 90071-1615
Tel (213) 236-5000 *Founded/Ownrshp* 2005
Sales NA *EMP* 4,200
SIC 6022 State commercial banks
Pr: Masashi Oka
**Ch Bd:* John F Harrigan
**Ex VP:* W H Wofford
Sr VP: Hitesh Mehta
**VP:* David Anderson

D-U-N-S 80-973-6882
UNION BANK OF CALIFORNIA
(*Suby of* MUFG AMERICAS HOLDINGS CORP) ★
445 S Figueroa St Ste 710, Los Angeles, CA 90071-1615
Tel (213) 236-6444 *Founded/Ownrshp* 2008
Sales NA *EMP* 2,521^E
SIC 6022 State commercial banks
Prin: John Harrigan
Pr: Jesus Serrano
Ofcr: Jose Dizon
Ofcr: Richard Faulkner
Ofcr: Gerald Ford
Ofcr: Runa Kargupta
Ofcr: Brenda Lopez
Ofcr: Roslyn Sherrill
Ofcr: Pascal Uttinger
Sr VP: Robert Leeper
Sr VP: Robert Olson
Sr VP: Kevin Zitar
VP: Emilia Barton
VP: Phreda Devereaux
VP: Albert Frausto
VP: Caroline Guttman
VP: Adam Hofberg
VP: Fanny Lee
VP: Kenji Ogawa
VP: Carol Shahdousti

D-U-N-S 80-762-8656
▲ UNION BANKSHARES CORP
1051 E Cary St Ste 1200, Richmond, VA 23219-4044
Tel (804) 633-5031 *Founded/Ownrshp* 1991
Sales NA *EMP* 1,471^E
Accts Ernst & Young Llp Richmond
Tkr Sym UBSH *Exch* NGS
SIC 6022 State commercial banks
Pr: G William Beale
**Ch Bd:* Raymond D Smoot Jr
CFO: Robert M Gorman
Ofcr: Loreen A Lagatta
Ex VP: Elizabeth M Bentley
Ex VP: David G Bilko
Ex VP: M Dean Brown
Ex VP: Jeffrey W Farrar
Ex VP: D Anthony Peay
VP: Randy Burcham
VP: Greg Gruner
VP: Scott Jenkins
VP: Kathleen Mack
VP: Jeff Mead
Board of Directors: Alan W Myers, L Bradford Armstrong, Thomas P Rohman, John C Asbury, Linda V Schreiner, Glen C Combs, Raymond L Slaughter, Beverley E Dalton, Charles W Steger, Gregory L Fisher, Ronald L Tillett, Daniel I Hansen, Keith L Wampler, Jan S Hoover, Patrick J McCann, W Tayloe Murphy Jr

UNION BEER DISTRIBUTORS
See UB DISTRIBUTORS LLC

UNION BUILDING MAINTENANCE
See UNISERVE FACILITIES SERVICES CORP

D-U-N-S 00-128-9008
■ UNION CARBIDE CORP (NY)
(*Suby of* DOW CHEMICAL CO) ★
1254 Enclave Pkwy, Houston, TX 77077-2564
Tel (281) 966-2727 *Founded/Ownrshp* 1917, 2001
Sales 5.8MMM *EMP* 5,000^E
SIC 2869 2821 Industrial organic chemicals; Ethylene oxide; Ethylene glycols; Alcohols, industrial: denatured (non-beverage); Thermosetting materials; Thermoplastic materials
Pr: Richard A Wells
CFO: Ignacio Molina

D-U-N-S 00-699-9890
UNION CENTRAL LIFE INSURANCE CO
(*Suby of* AMERITAS HOLDING CO) ★
1876 Waycross Rd, Cincinnati, OH 45240-2899
Tel (866) 696-7478 *Founded/Ownrshp* 1867
Sales NA *EMP* 1,200
SIC 6311 6321 Mutual association life insurance; Mutual accident & health associations; Accident associations, mutual
CEO: Joann Martin
Treas: Connie Grosser
Treas: Holly Hughes
Bd of Dir: Linda Depew
**Ex VP:* David F Westerbeck
**Sr VP:* Dale Donald Johnson
VP: Kurt Allen
**VP:* Christopher T Lutz
VP: Raymond Picone
VP: Daniel Shick
VP: Erik Simmons
VP: Rick Stiens
VP: Steven Valerius
VP: Robert Verbryke
VP: Douglas Waters
VP: Paul Wesling
VP: Rich Wiedenbeck

D-U-N-S 09-238-1615
UNION CITY CITY OF INC
5047 Union St, Union City, GA 30291-1455
Tel (770) 964-2288 *Founded/Ownrshp* 1908
Sales NA *EMP* 1,157
Accts Mauldin & Jenkins Llc Macon
SIC 9111 9221 City & town managers' offices; ; Municipal police;
Exec: Dennis Moore

D-U-N-S 10-005-9138
UNION COUNTY BOARD OF EDUCATION
UNION COUNTY PUBLIC SCHOOLS
400 N Church St, Monroe, NC 28112-4804
Tel (704) 296-9898 *Founded/Ownrshp* 1884
Sales 324.4MMM *EMP* 5,427
Accts Anderson Smith & Wike Pllc We
SIC 8211 Public elementary & secondary schools

UNION COUNTY HOSPITAL
See COMMUNITY UNITED METHODIST HOSPITAL INC

UNION COUNTY PUBLIC SCHOOLS
See UNION COUNTY BOARD OF EDUCATION

D-U-N-S 00-468-9767
UNION COUNTY PUBLIC SCHOOLS
400 N Church St, Monroe, NC 28112-4804
Tel (704) 296-9898 *Founded/Ownrshp* 2010
Sales 140.8MM^E *EMP* 3,642^E
SIC 8211 Public elementary & secondary schools
Dir Sec: Jarrod McCraw
Info Man: Leann Moore
Pr Dir: Tahira Stalberte
Teacher Pr: Lillian Rorie

D-U-N-S 02-407-4887
UNION DRILLING INC
952 Echo Ln Ste 460, Houston, TX 77024-2816
Tel (817) 735-8793 *Founded/Ownrshp* 2012
Sales NA *EMP* 1,300^E
SIC 1381

D-U-N-S 00-696-8655 IMP
■ UNION ELECTRIC CO
AMEREN MISSOURI
(*Suby of* AMEREN CORP) ★
1901 Chouteau Ave, Saint Louis, MO 63103-3003
Tel (314) 621-3222 *Founded/Ownrshp* 1922
Sales 3.6MMM *EMP* 3,924^E
Accts Pricewaterhousecoopers Llp St
SIC 4931 Electric & other services combined;
Ch Bd: Michael L Moehn
**CFO:* Martin J Lyons Jr
**Sr VP:* Daniel F Cole
**Sr VP:* Fadi M Diya
**Sr VP:* Gregory L Nelson
Sr VP: Bruce A Steinke

D-U-N-S 16-171-4774
■ UNION ELECTRIC DEVELOPMENT CORP
(*Suby of* AMEREN CORP) ★
1901 Chouteau Ave, Saint Louis, MO 63103-3003
Tel (618) 234-3523 *Founded/Ownrshp* 2008
Sales 566.1M *EMP* 3,200
SIC 4911 4924 Generation, electric power; ;
CEO: Charles W Mueller
VP: Charles Bremer
VP: Gregory L Nelson
VP: Ronald C Zdellar

D-U-N-S 00-699-7084
UNION ELECTRIC MEMBERSHIP CORP
UNION POWER COOPERATIVE
1525 N Rocky River Rd, Monroe, NC 28110-7958
Tel (704) 220-1408 *Founded/Ownrshp* 1939
Sales 139.4MM *EMP* 121
Accts Adams Jenkins Cheatham Pc Mid
SIC 4911 Distribution, electric power
CEO: Gregory Andress
**Ch Bd:* B L Starnes
**V Ch:* Lee Roy Kirk Jr
**CFO:* Theresa Conyers
**Treas:* Jan Haigler
Opers Mgr: Lonnie Kirkley

D-U-N-S 00-432-0701 IMP/EXP
■ UNION ELECTRIC STEEL CORP
(*Suby of* AMPCO-PITTSBURGH CORP) ★
726 Bell Ave, Carnegie, PA 15106-1137
Tel (412) 429-7655 *Founded/Ownrshp* 1984
Sales 100.0MM *EMP* 380
SIC 3325 3398 3312 Rolling mill rolls, cast steel; Metal heat treating; Blast furnaces & steel mills
CEO: James G Park
**Pr:* Rodney L Scagline
**CEO:* Robert G Carothers
VP: Amy McCormick
**VP:* Virginia Oberleitner
**VP:* George A Ott
VP: William Shollito
**VP:* Edward J Siddons
**VP:* Jason B Sychterz
**VP:* Charles L Thompson
VP Bus Dev: Vincent Ricciardi

UNION FINANCIAL SERVICES
See NELNET STUDENT LOAN CORP-1

D-U-N-S 02-784-8886
UNION GRAPHICS INC
UNIMAC GRAPHICS
350 Michele Pl, Carlstadt, NJ 07072-2304
Tel (201) 372-1000 *Founded/Ownrshp* 1979
Sales 124.2MM^E *EMP* 355^E
SIC 6719 Investment holding companies, except banks
CEO: George Amann
CFO: Jim Sandham
VP: Charles Amann
VP: Michael Anzalone
VP: Thomas D'Andrea
VP: Michael Didonna
Exec: Leo Scullion
Genl Mgr: Nancy Disano
Web Dev: Dominic Gratale
VP Prd: George Luthcke
Mfg Dir: Butch McNulty

D-U-N-S 04-073-8627
UNION HOSPITAL
99 Beauvoir Ave, Summit, NJ 07901-3533
Tel (973) 740-0607 *Founded/Ownrshp* 1993
Sales 15.7MM^E *EMP* 1,163
SIC 8062 General medical & surgical hospitals
Ex Dir: Katherine Koyne
**CFO:* Thomas Soprano

D-U-N-S 07-452-9819
UNION HOSPITAL ASSOCIATION
659 Boulevard St, Dover, OH 44622-2077
Tel (330) 343-3311 *Founded/Ownrshp* 1906
Sales 109.7MM *EMP* 1,000^E
SIC 8062 8011 General medical & surgical hospitals; Offices & clinics of medical doctors
CEO: William W Harding
Chf Path: David Brown
Pr: Cathy Corbett
**Pr:* Bruece James
Ofcr: Susan Ladrach
VP: Diana Boyd
VP: Robert J Craig
Dir: Carey Gardner
Dir Rad: Karen Pace
Dir Rad: Kyle Wallick
Dir Rx: Pam Swarny

D-U-N-S 07-207-5252
UNION HOSPITAL INC
1606 N 7th St, Terre Haute, IN 47804-2780
Tel (812) 238-7000 *Founded/Ownrshp* 1895
Sales 384.9MM *EMP* 1,960
SIC 8062 General medical & surgical hospitals
CEO: Steven M Holman
Chf Rad: Rasik B Ganatra
Chf Rad: Lingan Sidda
COO: Jack Hill
COO: Steve Reed
CFO: Wayne R Hutson
CFO: Wayne Hutson
Treas: Don Scott
Bd of Dir: Dave Doerr
Bd of Dir: Steven McDonald
Ofcr: Lori Moon
VP: John Bolinger
VP: Robert Craig
VP: Yevette Cress
VP: Kym Frank
VP: Wayne R Hutson
VP: Kym Pfrank
VP: Jody Stoldt
VP: Sally A Zuel
Dir Lab: Mary L Albert
Dir Lab: Marylou Alberts

D-U-N-S 94-738-1612
UNION HOSPITAL OF CECIL COUNTY HEALTH SERVICES INC
(*Suby of* UNION HOSPITAL OF CECIL COUNTY INC) ★
106 Bow St, Elkton, MD 21921-5544
Tel (410) 392-7009 *Founded/Ownrshp* 1930
Sales NA *EMP* 1,200
Accts Pricewaterhousecoopers Llp Ba
SIC 6324 8062 Hospital & medical service plans; General medical & surgical hospitals
Pr: Kenneth Lewis MD
CIO: Rick Edwards
Info Man: Mike Thompson

D-U-N-S 84-938-7188
UNION HOSPITAL OF CECIL COUNTY INC
106 Bow St, Elkton, MD 21921-5544
Tel (410) 620-3753 *Founded/Ownrshp* 1903
Sales 156.6MM *EMP* 2,203
SIC 8062 General medical & surgical hospitals
Pr: Kenneth Lewis MD
**COO:* David Gipson
Sr VP: Laurie Beyer
**VP:* Mary Lynn Devlin
Dir QC: Amanda McMullen
Pathlgst: Richard Szumel
Ansthlgy: Mark Mancuso

D-U-N-S 00-699-1574
UNION LABOR LIFE INSURANCE CO (MD)
(*Suby of* ULLICO INC) ★
8403 Colesville Rd # 1000, Silver Spring, MD 20910-6331
Tel (202) 682-0900 *Founded/Ownrshp* 1927
Sales NA *EMP* 325
SIC 6311 6321 6324 6371 Life insurance carriers; Accident insurance carriers; Health insurance carriers; Group hospitalization plans; Pensions
Ch Bd: Terrence O'Sullivan
CFO: Dave Barra
CFO: Mark Singleton

D-U-N-S 07-827-9007
UNION MEMORIAL HOSPITAL
MEDSTAR UNION MEMORIAL HOSP
(*Suby of* MEDSTAR HEALTH VNA) ★
201 E University Pkwy, Baltimore, MD 21218-2891
Tel (410) 554-2865 *Founded/Ownrshp* 1854
Sales 413.7MM *EMP* 2,400
SIC 8062 General medical & surgical hospitals; Hospital, professional nursing school with AMA residency
Pr: Bradley S Chambers
Chf Mktg O: Richard Heitmiller
VP: Michael C Cather
Pathlgst: Arthar McTighe
Pathlgst: Monica Yocum
Obsttrcn: Nathan Berger
Dir Health: Dina Smoker

D-U-N-S 07-105-7871
UNION MEMORIAL REGIONAL MEDICAL CENTER INC
CAROLINAS MEDICAL CENTER UNION
600 Hospital Dr, Monroe, NC 28112-6000
Tel (980) 993-3100 *Founded/Ownrshp* 1968
Sales 74.2MM^E *EMP* 1,301
SIC 8062 8011 General medical & surgical hospitals; Offices & clinics of medical doctors
Pr: Michael Lutes
COO: Phyllis Wingate-Jones
CFO: Greg Gombar
VP: Alan Taylor
Exec: Elizabeth Faulk
Exec: Jean Goldner
Mktg Dir: Corinne Weber
Pathlgst: Joyce Mills

D-U-N-S 00-694-6578
■ UNION NATIONAL LIFE INSURANCE CO
(*Suby of* UNITED INSURANCE CO OF AMERICA) ★
12115 Lackland Rd, Saint Louis, MO 63146-4025
Tel (877) 710-5081 *Founded/Ownrshp* 1926
Sales NA *EMP* 750
SIC 6311 Assessment life insurance agents
Pr: Jerry W Hester
**Treas:* Paul Hillman
**VP:* James A Marquette

D-U-N-S 04-834-1283 IMP/EXP
▲ UNION PACIFIC CORP
1400 Douglas St, Omaha, NE 68179-1001
Tel (402) 544-5000 *Founded/Ownrshp* 1969
Sales 21.8MMM *EMP* 47,457
Accts Deloitte & Touche Llp Omaha
Tkr Sym UNP *Exch* NYS
SIC 4011 Railroads, line-haul operating
Ch Bd: Lance M Fritz
Pr: Robert N Belt
Pr: Ashok Fichadia
Pr: Sam Hughes
CFO: Robert M Knight Jr
Treas: Mary Sanders Jones
Ofcr: Diane K Duren
Ofcr: Rhonda S Ferguson
Ex VP: Eric L Butler
Ex VP: Cameron A Scott
Sr VP: D Lynn Kelley
Sr VP: Scott D Moore
Sr VP: Lynden L Tennison
VP: Paul Borseth
VP: Linda Brandl
VP: Scott Clark
VP: Brenda Mainwaring
VP: Joseph E O'Connor Jr
VP: Patrick J O'Malley
VP: Michael A Rock
VP: Todd M Rynaski
Board of Directors: Jose H Villarreal, Andrew H Card Jr, David B Dillon, Judith Richards Hope, Charles C Krulak, Jane H Lute, Michael R McCarthy, Michael W McConnell, Thomas F McLarty III, Steven R Rogel

D-U-N-S 00-699-1590 IMP/EXP
■ UNION PACIFIC RAILROAD CO INC
(*Suby of* UNION PACIFIC CORP) ★
1400 Douglas St, Omaha, NE 68179-0002
Tel (402) 544-5000 *Founded/Ownrshp* 1897, 2011
Sales 7.3MMM^E *EMP* 40,000
Accts Deloitte & Touche Llp Omaha
SIC 4011 Railroads, line-haul operating
Pr: L M Fritz
Pr: Bill Behrendt
Pr: Paul Borseth
Pr: Patricia Carnie
Pr: Mark Davis
Pr: Ashok Fichadia
**Pr:* Lance M Fritz
Pr: Michelle Gerhardt
Pr: David Giandinoto

Pr: Matthew Gloeb
Pr: Lee Grimes
Pr: John J Hovanec
Pr: Shane Keller
Pr: Ed Kemp
Pr: Karen Krabbe
Pr: Donna Kush
Pr: Tony Love
Pr: Brian McGavock
Pr: Bradley Moore
Pr: Michael Newcomb
Pr: Rick Rivera
Board of Directors: Andrew H Card Jr, Thomas J Donohue, Archie W Dunham, Judith Richards Hope, Charles C Krulak, Michael W McConnell, Thomas F McLarty III, Steven R Rogel

D-U-N-S 02-093-7074
UNION PACIFIC RAILROAD EMPLOYES HEALTH SYSTEMS (UT)
1040 N 2200 W Ste 200, Salt Lake City, UT 84116-2929
Tel (801) 595-4300 *Founded/Ownrshp* 1947
Sales NA *EMP* 100
Accts 5500tax Group Inc Riverside
SIC 6371 Pension, health & welfare funds
Pr: Dell Butterfield
**VP:* Kevin J Potts

D-U-N-S 07-975-2153
UNION PARTNERS I LLC
1400 16th St Ste 250, Oak Brook, IL 60523-8802
Tel (630) 822-7000 *Founded/Ownrshp* 2014
Sales 106.4MM[E] *EMP* 70
SIC 8741 7389 Management services; Metal cutting services
**VP:* Christopher Walter

UNION POWER COOPERATIVE
See UNION ELECTRIC MEMBERSHIP CORP

D-U-N-S 03-188-9425
UNION REGIONAL MEDICAL CENTER
600 Hospital Dr, Monroe, NC 28112-6000
Tel (704) 283-3100 *Founded/Ownrshp* 2010
Sales 169.3MM *EMP* 17[E]
SIC 8011 Medical centers

D-U-N-S 06-002-5129
UNION SAVINGS BANK (CT)
226 Main St, Danbury, CT 06810-6697
Tel (203) 830-4200 *Founded/Ownrshp* 1866
Sales NA *EMP* 353
SIC 6036 Savings institutions, not federally chartered
CEO: Francis G Dattalo
Pr: Charles Frosch
COO: Jay C Lent
CFO: Paul Bruce
Ofcr: Stacy Ashby
Ofcr: Coral Ozerhoski
Ofcr: Jill Tuz
Ex VP: Lynne A Beardsley
Ex VP: David A Birkins
Ex VP: Frederick Judd
Sr VP: Pat Carlson
Sr VP: Margaret Condon
Sr VP: Mary Pat Cottrell
Sr VP: Belinda Ireland
Sr VP: Gary E Lemme
Sr VP: Brian McGuigan
Sr VP: Jim Rusiecki
Sr VP: Georgina Sherman
VP: Susan Anderson
VP: Joseph Brancato
VP: Awilda Caisse

D-U-N-S 07-286-5694
UNION SAVINGS BANK
8534 E Kemper Rd Fl 1, Cincinnati, OH 45249-3701
Tel (513) 489-1955 *Founded/Ownrshp* 1904
Sales NA *EMP* 1[E]
SIC 6036 Savings & loan associations, not federally chartered
Pr: Harry G Yeaggy
**CFO:* Robert Bogenschutz
Bd of Dir: Ione Potter
Ofcr: Todd Green
Ofcr: Betsy Marks
Sr VP: Brenda Bingaman
Sr VP: Brett Boston
Sr VP: Jeanne Wade
VP: Darryl Akers
VP: Jonathan Deshler
VP: David Egts
VP: Scott Senete
Dir Bus: Larry Mohr

UNION SCHOOL DISTRICT
See INDEPENDENT SCHOOL DISTRICT 9 TULSA COUNTY OK

D-U-N-S 00-696-3615
■ **UNION SECURITY INSURANCE CO**
(*Suby of* INTERFINANCIAL INC) ★
6941 Vista Dr, West Des Moines, IA 50266-9309
Tel (651) 361-4000 *Founded/Ownrshp* 2004
Sales NA *EMP* 1,737
SIC 6321 6324 Accident & health insurance; Hospital & medical service plans
Pr: John S Roberts
**CFO:* Stacia N Almquist
VP: Nancy L Panzer-Howe

D-U-N-S 61-545-3602
■ **UNION STANDARD INSURANCE GROUP LLC**
(*Suby of* BERKLEY REGIONAL INSURANCE CO) ★
222 Las Colinas Blvd W # 1300, Irving, TX 75039-2027
Tel (972) 719-2400 *Founded/Ownrshp* 1982
Sales NA *EMP* 240
SIC 6331 Fire, marine & casualty insurance
Pr: Keith Mitchell
CFO: John Gray
**Ch:* Craig W Sparks
VP: Tom Cawley
**VP:* Gregory R Perkins
Brnch Mgr: Bill Emerick

D-U-N-S 13-785-8861
UNION STREET MORTGAGE
4403 N Beltwood Pkwy, Dallas, TX 75244-3216
Tel (866) 499-3411 *Founded/Ownrshp* 2002
Sales NA *EMP* 20
SIC 6162 Mortgage bankers & correspondents
Pt: Mike Harrell
Pt: Ron Blake
Off Mgr: Elva Dellossantos
Opers Mgr: Tina Poisson

UNION SUPPLY COMPANY
See UNION SUPPLY GROUP INC

D-U-N-S 78-254-4092 IMP
UNION SUPPLY GROUP INC
UNION SUPPLY COMPANY
2301 E Pacifica Pl, Rancho Dominguez, CA 90220-6210
Tel (310) 603-8899 *Founded/Ownrshp* 1991
Sales 117.3MM *EMP* 325
SIC 5141 5139 5136 Groceries, general line; Footwear; Men's & boys' clothing
CEO: Tom Thomas
**COO:* Guy Steele
CFO: Scott Schaldenbrand
**Ex VP:* Lyndel Hay
**VP:* Dave Cardona
**VP:* Alison Maker
Prgrm Mgr: Ashley Lear
**CTO:* Doyle Schaefers
Dir IT: Terry Hauser
Dir IT: Billy Navidad
IT Man: Chris Peck

D-U-N-S 00-516-1112 IMP/EXP
■ **UNION TANK CAR CO**
(*Suby of* MARMON HOLDINGS INC) ★
175 W Jackson Blvd # 2100, Chicago, IL 60604-2683
Tel (312) 431-3111 *Founded/Ownrshp* 1980
Sales 2.0MMM[E] *EMP* 6,176
SIC 3743 4741 4789 5051 Train cars & equipment, freight or passenger; Railroad car rebuilding; Rental of railroad cars; Railroad car repair; Metals service centers & offices
Pr: Kenneth P Fischl
**CFO:* Mark J Garrette
**VP:* Robert K Lorch
IT Man: Jackson Jones
Board of Directors: Frank S Ptak

D-U-N-S 00-378-9203
■ **UNION TELEPHONE CO**
TDS
(*Suby of* TELEPHONE AND DATA SYSTEMS INC) ★
7 Central St, Farmington, NH 03835-3745
Tel (603) 859-3700 *Founded/Ownrshp* 1903
Sales 50.8MM[E] *EMP* 2,700
SIC 4813 Telephone communication, except radio
Pr: David Wittwer

D-U-N-S 00-942-7030
UNION TELEPHONE CO
UNION WIRELESS
850 N Hwy 414, Mountain View, WY 82939
Tel (307) 782-6131 *Founded/Ownrshp* 1914
Sales 103.6MM[E] *EMP* 300
Accts Moss-Adams Llp Spokane Washi
SIC 4813 4812 Data telephone communications; Telephone cable service, land or submarine; ; Cellular telephone services
CEO: John G Woody
**Pr:* Howard D Woody
**CFO:* James Woody
**VP:* John Woody
Dir IT: Renee Buzarde
Sfty Dirs: Fred Schillreff
Sls Dir: Casey Lamoreaux

D-U-N-S 11-055-5005 IMP/EXP
■ **UNION UNDERWEAR CO INC**
FRUIT OF THE LOOM
(*Suby of* UNION UNDERWEARR) ★
1 Fruit Of The Loom Dr, Bowling Green, KY 42103-7932
Tel (270) 781-6400 *Founded/Ownrshp* 2002
Sales 2.2MMM[E] *EMP* 1,000
SIC 8661 Baptist Church
Ch: John B Holland
**Pr:* Richard D Medlin
**CFO:* G William Newton
Ex VP: Richard D Melin
**Sr VP:* David T Whitaker
VP: Leslie T Dooley
**VP:* T Leslie Dooley
VP: John Ray
**VP:* Ed Weldon

UNION UNDERWEARR
See FRUIT OF LOOM INC

D-U-N-S 07-354-4116
UNION UNIVERSITY
1050 Union University Dr, Jackson, TN 38305-3697
Tel (731) 668-1818 *Founded/Ownrshp* 1823
Sales 95.6MM *EMP* 455
SIC 8221 University
Pr: Samuel W Oliver
Assoc VP: James Avery
**VP:* Gary Carter
VP: Robert Simpson
Assoc Dir: Esperanza Gonzalez
IT Man: Deana Peoples

UNION WIRELESS
See UNION TELEPHONE CO

UNIONBAY SPORTSWEAR
See SEATTLE PACIFIC INDUSTRIES INC

D-U-N-S 02-114-4530
UNIONDALE UNION FREE SCHOOL DISTRICT
933 Goodrich St, Uniondale, NY 11553-2400
Tel (516) 560-8957 *Founded/Ownrshp* 1906
Sales 161.0MM *EMP* 1,300
SIC 8211 Public elementary & secondary schools
**Pr:* Emerson Mott
**Treas:* Clerance Little
**VP:* James Sharp
HC Dir: Sylvia Kallich

D-U-N-S 94-594-9225 EXP
UNIPEC AMERICA INC
(*Suby of* CHINA INTERNATIONAL UNITED PETROLEUM & CHEMICALS CO., LTD.)
410 Park Ave Ste 610, New York, NY 10022-4407
Tel (212) 759-5085 *Founded/Ownrshp* 2010
Sales 1.5MMM *EMP* 26
Accts Pricewaterhousecoopers Llp
SIC 5172 Petroleum products
Pr: Lei Chen
**Treas:* Qingquan Xie
**VP:* Xinghong Liu

D-U-N-S 07-958-4436
UNIPRES ALABAMA INC
990 Duncan Farms Rd, Steele, AL 35987-1756
Tel (256) 538-1974 *Founded/Ownrshp* 2014
Sales 100.0MM *EMP* 250
SIC 3465

D-U-N-S 16-093-5581 IMP
UNIPRES USA INC
(*Suby of* UNIPRES CORPORATION)
201 Kirby Dr, Portland, TN 37148-2006
Tel (615) 325-7311 *Founded/Ownrshp* 1987
Sales 210.6MM[E] *EMP* 380
SIC 3465 Body parts, automobile: stamped metal
Pr: M Nakazato
VP: Kazuaki Ueno
Prgrm Mgr: Doug Mitchell
Area Mgr: Shane Craddock
Area Mgr: Steve Hammond
QI Cn Mgr: Aaron Leininger
QI Cn Mgr: Robert Letourneau

D-U-N-S 18-408-0018
UNIPRO FOODSERVICE INC
2500 Cumbrld Pkwy Se 60 Ste 600, Atlanta, GA 30339
Tel (770) 952-0871 *Founded/Ownrshp* 1958
Sales 1.2MMM *EMP* 140
Accts Ha&W Llp Atlanta Georgia
SIC 5147 5141 5146 5142 Meats & meat products; Groceries, general line; Fish & seafoods; Packaged frozen goods
COO: Bob Stewart
Div VP: Tom Stewart
Ex VP: Don Gilligan
Sr VP: Robert Komar
VP: Tom Brockman
VP: Gary Butler
VP: Jack Carlson
VP: Joe Clark
VP: Harris Couch
VP: Stan Crais
VP: Mark Dawson
VP: Edward Delaney
VP: Dave Devlin
VP: Patty Duffey
VP: Keith Durnell
VP: Terry Fisher
VP: Gail Hollis
VP: Keith Jeanis
VP: Judy McDaniel
VP: Martin Miller
VP: Tom Morin

D-U-N-S 04-058-4963
▲ **UNIQUE FABRICATING INC**
800 Standard Pkwy, Auburn Hills, MI 48326-1415
Tel (248) 853-2333 *Founded/Ownrshp* 1975
Sales 143.3MM *EMP* 734
Tkr Sym UFAB *Exch* ASE
SIC 3053 3086 3296 2671 Gaskets, all materials; Plastics foam products; Mineral wool; Packaging paper & plastics film, coated & laminated
Prin: John Weinhardt
**Ch Bd:* Richard L Baum Jr
Pr: Murray Vrooman
CFO: Thomas Tekiele
CFO: Tekiele Tom
Info Man: Keith Oconnor
Board of Directors: William Cooke, Paul Frascoia, James Illikman, Kim North, Donn J Viola

UNIQUE HR
See UNIQUE STAFF LEASING I LTD

D-U-N-S 00-226-5502 IMP/EXP
UNIQUE INDUSTRIES INC (PA)
4750 League Island Blvd, Philadelphia, PA 19112-1222
Tel (215) 336-4300 *Founded/Ownrshp* 1961
Sales 164.2MM[E] *EMP* 800
SIC 2679

D-U-N-S 78-449-7125
UNIQUE PREMIUM METALS INC
3250 Ocean Park Blvd # 350, Santa Monica, CA 90405-3208
Tel (213) 622-9995 *Founded/Ownrshp* 1991
Sales 100.0MM *EMP* 6
SIC 5094 Precious metals
Pr: Nelson Colton

D-U-N-S 96-788-0340
UNIQUE RISK AND ADMINISTRATIVE SERVICES (US) INC
(*Suby of* G BRADFORD CO INC) ★
4646 Corona Dr Ste 105, Corpus Christi, TX 78411-4383
Tel (361) 852-6392 *Founded/Ownrshp* 2002
Sales 13.2MM[E] *EMP* 1,675[E]
SIC 7363 Employee leasing service
Prin: Lindsay Henry

D-U-N-S 03-965-6686
UNIQUE STAFF LEASING I LTD
UNIQUE HR
(*Suby of* BRADFORD HOLDING CO INC) ★
4646 Corona Dr Ste 105, Corpus Christi, TX 78411-4383
Tel (361) 852-6392 *Founded/Ownrshp* 2000
Sales 47.4MM *EMP* 3,400
Accts Tranbarger And Company Llp Co
SIC 7363 Employee leasing service
CEO: Garry Bradford
Ex VP: Rebecca Bradford
VP Mktg: Greg Maisel

D-U-N-S 96-773-9280
UNIQUE STAFF LEASING III LTD
(*Suby of* BRADFORD HOLDING CO INC) ★
4646 Corona Dr Ste 105, Corpus Christi, TX 78411-4383
Tel (361) 852-6392 *Founded/Ownrshp* 2003
Sales 76.1MM *EMP* 3,400
Accts Tranbarger And Company Llp Co
SIC 7363 Help supply services
CEO: Garry Bradford
Ex VP: Rebecca Bradford
VP Mktg: Greg Maisel

D-U-N-S 79-605-4604
UNIQUE VENTURES GROUP LLC
231 Chestnut St Ste 302, Meadville, PA 16335-3457
Tel (814) 337-6300 *Founded/Ownrshp* 2006
Sales 5.0MM[E] *EMP* 1,140
SIC 5812 Fast food restaurants & stands
Prin: Marc Teaberry

D-U-N-S 00-872-5434
▲ **UNIROYAL GLOBAL ENGINEERED PRODUCTS INC**
1800 2nd St Ste 970, Sarasota, FL 34236-5992
Tel (941) 906-8580 *Founded/Ownrshp* 1998
Sales 99.7MM *EMP* 415[E]
Accts Frazier & Deeter Llc Tampa
Tkr Sym UNIR *Exch* OTO
SIC 2824 2396 Vinyl fibers; Automotive trimmings, fabric
CEO: Edmund C King
**Ch Bd:* Howard R Curd
Exec: Elizabeth Henson

D-U-N-S 03-086-9390
UNISERVE FACILITIES SERVICES CORP
UNION BUILDING MAINTENANCE
2363 S Atlantic Blvd, Commerce, CA 90040-1256
Tel (213) 533-1000 *Founded/Ownrshp* 1966
Sales 8.5MM *EMP* 1,150
SIC 7349 Janitorial service, contract basis
Ch Bd: Sam M Hwang
COO: Anthony Santana
Mktg Dir: Eugene Hwang

D-U-N-S 36-402-4828
■ **UNISON INDUSTRIES LLC**
(*Suby of* GE ENGINE SERVICES LLC) ★
7575 Baymeadows Way, Jacksonville, FL 32256-7525
Tel (904) 739-4000 *Founded/Ownrshp* 2002
Sales 434.7MM[E] *EMP* 1,330
SIC 3694 Ignition apparatus & distributors
Pr: Michael Grunza
CFO: Patricia Hord
**Treas:* Jamere Jackson
VP: Bill Bussa
**VP:* Barbara A Cameron
VP: Joe Sedlock
Genl Mgr: Joe Howington
Genl Mgr: Hari Joshi
MIS Dir: William Hilinski
IT Man: Mark McWaters
MIS Mgr: Chris Gould

D-U-N-S 13-590-2539
UNISOURCE ENERGY SERVICES INC
88 E Broadway Blvd, Tucson, AZ 85701-1720
Tel (520) 571-4000 *Founded/Ownrshp* 2003
Sales 277.5MM[E] *EMP* 359
SIC 4911 4923 Distribution, electric power; Generation, electric power; Transmission, electric power; Gas transmission & distribution
Pr: James S Pignatelli
**COO:* Dennis R Nelson
**CFO:* Kevin P Larson
**Ex VP:* David G Hutchens
**VP:* Karen G Kissinger
**VP:* Gary A Smith

D-U-N-S 08-012-6591
UNISTAFF PRO INC
344 E Irving Park Rd, Roselle, IL 60172-2007
Tel (708) 450-1600 *Founded/Ownrshp* 2009
Sales 26.0MM *EMP* 1,500
SIC 7361 Employment agencies
Pr: Fiorella Auriemma
VP: Frank Auriemma

D-U-N-S 55-591-4050 IMP
UNISTAN INC
5500 United Dr Se, Smyrna, GA 30082-4755
Tel (678) 305-2080 *Founded/Ownrshp* 1988
Sales 339.7MM[E] *EMP* 700
SIC 5182 5181 Bottling wines & liquors; Beer & other fermented malt liquors
CEO: Douglas J Hertz
**CFO:* Mark Popowski
Mktg Mgr: Chris Brown

UNISTRESS
See PETRICCA INDUSTRIES INC

D-U-N-S 14-424-3425 IMP
■ **UNISTRUT INTERNATIONAL CORP**
(*Suby of* ATKORE INTERNATIONAL INC) ★
16100 Lathrop Ave, Harvey, IL 60426-6021
Tel (800) 882-5543 *Founded/Ownrshp* 1923
Sales 131.5MM[E] *EMP* 550
SIC 3441 1791 3446 3448 3496 3429 Fabricated structural metal; Structural steel erection; Partitions & supports/studs, including accoustical systems; Trusses & framing: prefabricated metal; Cable, uninsulated wire: made from purchased wire; Manufactured hardware (general)
Pr: John P Williamson
Treas: James A Mallak
VP: Karl J Schmidt
Prin: Nelda J Connors
IT Man: Kathy Gross

UNISTRUT-COLUMBUS
See LOEB ELECTRIC CO

D-U-N-S 00-535-8932
▲ UNISYS CORP
801 Lakeview Dr Ste 100, Blue Bell, PA 19422-1961
Tel (215) 986-4011 *Founded/Ownrshp* 1873
Sales 3.0MMM *EMP* 23,000
Accts Kpmg Llp Philadelphia Penns
Tkr Sym UIS *Exch* NYS
SIC 7373 7378 7379 3571 3572 Systems integration services; Computer & data processing equipment repair/maintenance; Computer peripheral equipment repair & maintenance; Computer related consulting services; Minicomputers; Personal computers (microcomputers); Computer storage devices
Pr: Peter A Altabef
Pt: Venkatapathi Puvvada
**Ch Bd:* Paul E Weaver
CFO: Janet Brutschea Haugen
CFO: Inder M Singh
Treas: Scott A Battersby
Chf Mktg O: Ann Sung Ruckstuhl
Sr VP: Tarek El-Sadany
Sr VP: Gerald P Kenney
Sr VP: David A Loeser
VP: Peter Chen
VP: Michael Morrison
VP: Tom Patterson
VP: Michael M Thomson
Board of Directors: Jared L Cohon, Alison Davis, Nathaniel A Davis, Denise K Fletcher, Philippe Germond, Leslie F Kenne, Lee D Roberts

D-U-N-S 15-352-3840
▲ UNIT CORP
8200 S Unit Dr, Tulsa, OK 74132-5300
Tel (918) 493-7700 *Founded/Ownrshp* 1963
Sales 854.2MM *EMP* 1,179
Tkr Sym UNT *Exch* NYS
SIC 1381 1382 1311 Drilling oil & gas wells; Oil & gas exploration services; Crude petroleum production; Natural gas production
Pr: Larry D Pinkston
**Ch Bd:* John G Nikkel
CFO: David T Merrill
Sr VP: Mark E Schell
VP: Mark Colclasure
VP: Rick Heck
Exec: Brad Guidry
Exec: Lavita Hill
Genl Mgr: Daniel Scott
CTO: Michael Sellers
IT Man: Don Jones
Board of Directors: J Michael Adcock, Gary R Christopher, Steven B Hildebrand, Carla S Mashinski, William B Morgan, Larry C Payne, G Bailey Peyton IV, Robert J Sullivan Jr

D-U-N-S 86-951-4109
■ UNIT DRILLING CO
(*Suby of* UNIT CORP) ★
8200 S Unit Dr, Tulsa, OK 74132-5300
Tel (918) 493-7700 *Founded/Ownrshp* 1963
Sales 150.7MM^E *EMP* 351
SIC 1381 Redrilling oil & gas wells
**Pr:* Larry Pinkston
**CFO:* David Merrill
**VP:* Mark Schell

D-U-N-S 18-900-3973
■ UNIT PETROLEUM CO
(*Suby of* UNIT CORP) ★
8200 S Unit Dr, Tulsa, OK 74132-5300
Tel (918) 493-7700 *Founded/Ownrshp* 1984
Sales 132.6MM^E *EMP* 110
SIC 1311 Crude petroleum production; Natural gas production
Ch Bd: John G Nikkel
**Pr:* Larry D Pinkston
**CFO:* David T Merrill
**Sr VP:* Mark E Shell
Genl Mgr: Mark E Schell

D-U-N-S 80-116-8675
UNITE HERE HEALTH
UHH
711 N Commons Dr, Aurora, IL 60504-4197
Tel (630) 236-5100 *Founded/Ownrshp* 2011
Sales NA *EMP* 300
Accts Macneil Accounting & Consultin
SIC 6371 Pension, health & welfare funds
CEO: Matthew Walker
**Pr:* Kathy Silver
**COO:* Dolores Michael
**CFO:* John Johnson
Ofcr: Phyllis Haag
Dir IT: Steve Nauman

D-U-N-S 14-463-3203 IMP
UNITED ACQUISITION CORP
(*Suby of* RED APPLE GROUP INC) ★
802 N West St, Wilmington, DE 19801-1526
Tel (302) 651-9856 *Founded/Ownrshp* 1985
Sales 2.0MMM^E *EMP* 4,625
SIC 2911 5541 2951 Petroleum refining; Filling stations, gasoline; Asphalt paving mixtures & blocks
Ch Bd: John A Catsimatidis
**VP:* Ralph G Schwab
**VP:* Myron Turfitt

D-U-N-S 07-883-6988
UNITED AGENCIES INC (CA)
KEMPER INSURANCE
301 E Colo Blvd Ste 200, Pasadena, CA 91101
Tel (626) 564-2670 *Founded/Ownrshp* 1962
Sales NA *EMP* 132
SIC 6411 Insurance agents; Insurance brokers
Ch Bd: Thomas Hays
**Pr:* Gary Conkey
CFO: Karen Bader
**VP:* Robert W Bader
VP: Jeff Chan
VP: Lynn Mobley
**VP:* J O Youngfleish III
Exec: Joyce Ash
Dept Mgr: Jeff Ramirez
Off Mgr: Tom Farr
Off Mgr: Janice Hing

D-U-N-S 80-769-6567
UNITED AGRICULTURAL ASSOCIATION EMP WELFARE BENE PLTR
54 Corporate Park, Irvine, CA 92606-5105
Tel (949) 975-1424 *Founded/Ownrshp* 2007
Sales 89.5MM *EMP* 2^E
Accts United Agricultural Employee W
SIC 8699 Membership organizations
Prin: Kirti Mutatkar

D-U-N-S 06-794-6210
UNITED AGRICULTURAL COOPERATIVE INC
911 S Wharton St, El Campo, TX 77437-6125
Tel (979) 543-6284 *Founded/Ownrshp* 1982
Sales 96.0MM *EMP* 75
Accts D Williams & Co Pc Lubbo
SIC 5251 0724 5083 4221 5153 Hardware; Cotton ginning; Agricultural machinery; Cotton compresses & warehouses; Grains
Pr: Anthony Kresta
**Pr:* Daniel Javranovic
**Genl Mgr:* Jimmy N Roppolo

UNITED AIRFREIGHT SERVICES
See CJ KOREA EXPRESS USA CORP

D-U-N-S 09-944-7401
■ UNITED AIRLINES INC
(*Suby of* UNITED CONTINENTAL HOLDINGS INC) ★
233 S Wacker Dr Ste 430, Chicago, IL 60606-6462
Tel (872) 825-4000 *Founded/Ownrshp* 2010
Sales 37.8MMM *EMP* 84,000
SIC 4512 4513 4729 Air passenger carrier, scheduled; Air cargo carrier, scheduled; Air courier services; Airline ticket offices
CEO: Oscar Munoz
Pr: Scott Kirby
COO: Gregory L Hart
COO: Clarence D McLean
COO: Thomas F Otoole
CFO: John D Rainey
V Ch Bd: James E Compton
Ofcr: David McKneely
Ofcr: Douglas Scheuffele
Ofcr: Laurice Williams
Ex VP: Gustav Akerblom
Ex VP: Jeffrey T Foland
Ex VP: Keith Halbert
Ex VP: Brett J Hart
Ex VP: Ben Hirst
Ex VP: Linda Jojo
Sr VP: Rebecca Cox
Sr VP: Mark Erwin
Sr VP: William Meehan
Sr VP: Thomas Otoole
VP: J Grizzle

D-U-N-S 00-116-9929 IMP/EXP
UNITED ALUMINUM CORP
100 United Dr, North Haven, CT 06473-3295
Tel (203) 575-9771 *Founded/Ownrshp* 1891
Sales 95.5MM^E *EMP* 150
SIC 3353 Coils, sheet aluminum
Pr: John S Lapides
CTO: Ken Tracz
Sls Dir: Robert Pendleton
Sls Mgr: Ronald Fasano
Sls Mgr: Ratko Pejovic
Sls Mgr: Carmen Schaffer

D-U-N-S 10-677-8715 IMP/EXP
UNITED AMERICAN ACQUISITION CORP
EASY GARDENER
3022 Franklin Ave, Waco, TX 76710-7352
Tel (859) 987-5389 *Founded/Ownrshp* 1994
Sales 86.0MM *EMP* 31^E
SIC 2211 0782 3423 2875 Canvas & other heavy coarse fabrics: cotton; Lawn & garden services; Hand & edge tools; Fertilizers, mixing only
Pr: David Jackson
**CEO:* Karen Bettege
IT Man: Tricia Anderson
Info Man: Lee Fahlenkamp
VP Mfg: Andrew Loberger
VP Opers: Sheila Jones
VP Sls: Paul Logue

D-U-N-S 07-313-1047
■ UNITED AMERICAN INSURANCE CO
(*Suby of* TORCHMARK CORP) ★
3700 S Stonebridge Dr, McKinney, TX 75070-5934
Tel (800) 331-2512 *Founded/Ownrshp* 1981
Sales NA *EMP* 676
SIC 6321 6311 Accident insurance carriers; Health insurance carriers; Life insurance carriers
CEO: Vern D Herbel
**Ch Bd:* Andrew W King
**Ch Bd:* Mark S Mc Andrew
**Pr:* Rosemary Montgomery
**Ex VP:* Larry D Strong
**Sr VP:* Charles Mankamyer
**Sr VP:* Rosemary J Montgomery
**VP:* Jon Adams
**VP:* Jeff Alexander
**VP:* Jon Erbe
**VP:* Michael Gaisbauer
**VP:* Keith Ryan
**VP:* Bill Smallwood

D-U-N-S 19-464-8317
■ UNITED ARTISTS THEATRE CIRCUIT INC
(*Suby of* UA) ★
7132 Regal Ln, Knoxville, TN 37918-5803
Tel (865) 922-1123 *Founded/Ownrshp* 2002
Sales 180.6MM *EMP* 1,329^E
SIC 7832

D-U-N-S 79-377-0306
■ UNITED ARTISTS THEATRE CO
UA
(*Suby of* REGAL ENTERTAINMENT HOLDINGS INC) ★
9110 E Nichols Ave # 200, Centennial, CO 80112-3405
Tel (303) 792-3600 *Founded/Ownrshp* 2002
Sales 180.6MM^E *EMP* 4,095
SIC 7832 Motion picture theaters, except drive-in
Ch Bd: Michael L Campbell
CFO: David Giesler
Ex VP: Ray Nutt

D-U-N-S 02-734-0747
UNITED ASSOCIATION
3 Park Pl Ste 300, Annapolis, MD 21401-3722
Tel (410) 269-2000 *Founded/Ownrshp* 2009
Sales 97.3MM *EMP* 3^E
SIC 8641 Civic social & fraternal associations
Prin: William Height
Trst: William Hite

UNITED ASSOCIATION OF JAPPI
See UNITED ASSOCIATION OF JOURNEYMEN & APPRENTICES OF PLUMBING & PIPEFITTERS

D-U-N-S 07-266-2448
UNITED ASSOCIATION OF JOURNEYMEN & APPRENTICES OF PLUMBING & PIPEFITTERS
UNITED ASSOCIATION OF JAPPI
3 Park Pl, Annapolis, MD 21401-3687
Tel (410) 269-2000 *Founded/Ownrshp* 1889
Sales 108.2MM *EMP* 150
Accts Salter & Company Llc Bethesda
SIC 8631 Labor union
Pr: William Height
Treas: Patrick Perno
Opers Supe: Gerard Catucci

D-U-N-S 93-326-7924
UNITED AUBURN INDIAN COMMUNITY
10720 Indian Hill Rd, Auburn, CA 95603-9403
Tel (530) 883-2390 *Founded/Ownrshp* 1995
Sales NA *EMP* 2,020^E
SIC 9131 Indian reservation;
CEO: Jessica Tavares
VP: Kevin Thorstenson

D-U-N-S 11-290-6826
UNITED AUTOMOBILE INSURANCE GROUP INC
UAIC
3909 Ne 163rd St Ste 308, Miami, FL 33160-4126
Tel (305) 940-5022 *Founded/Ownrshp* 1998
Sales NA *EMP* 900^E
SIC 6411 Insurance agents, brokers & service
Pr: Richard P Parrillo Sr
Dir IT: Abraham Estevez

D-U-N-S 09-869-4870
■ UNITED BANK
(*Suby of* UNITED BANKSHARES INC) ★
2071 Chain Bridge Rd, Vienna, VA 22182-2664
Tel (703) 442-7118 *Founded/Ownrshp* 1998
Sales NA *EMP* 479
SIC 6022 State commercial banks
Pr: James J Consagra Jr
**Ch Bd:* Lawrence K Doll
Ofcr: Robert Lauta
Assoc VP: Wanda Coles
Sr VP: Scot Harlow
**VP:* Anne Pearce
VP: Mohamed Rahaman
VP: William Thompson
Genl Mgr: Jonathan Tite

D-U-N-S 18-688-8319
UNITED BANK
5350 Lee Hwy Ste 2, Arlington, VA 22207-1696
Tel (703) 534-1382 *Founded/Ownrshp* 2014
Sales NA *EMP* 123
SIC 6021 National commercial banks
CEO: James Consagra
Opers Mgr: Arleen Smith

D-U-N-S 19-296-8084
▲ UNITED BANK
45 Glastonbury Blvd # 200, Glastonbury, CT 06033-4411
Tel (860) 291-3600 *Founded/Ownrshp* 2010
Sales NA *EMP* 683^E
Accts Wolf & Company Pc Boston
Tkr Sym UBNK *Exch* NGS
SIC 6036 Savings institutions, not federally chartered; Savings & loan associations, not federally chartered; State savings banks, not federally chartered
CEO: William H W Crawford IV
**Ch Bd:* Robert A Stewart Jr
CFO: Eric R Newell
Ofcr: Barbara Parrelli
Ex VP: Daniel Flynn
Ex VP: Mark A Kucia
Ex VP: Marliese L Shaw
Sr VP: Todd Mandella
Sr VP: Tom Wolcott
VP: James Felgate
VP: Cynthia Kos
VP: Matthew Newcomb

D-U-N-S 00-691-8171
■ UNITED BANK FOUNDATION CONNECTICUT INC (CT)
ROCKVILLE BANK FOUNDATION INC
(*Suby of* UNITED BANK) ★
25 Park St, Vernon Rockville, CT 06066-3211
Tel (860) 291-3705 *Founded/Ownrshp* 1858
Sales NA *EMP* 173^E
SIC 6036 State savings banks, not federally chartered
Pr: Richard J Trachimowicz
Pr: Kristine Carlson
CEO: William H W Crawford IV
Bd of Dir: H Raymond
Ofcr: Michael Kelleher
Ofcr: Robert Landfear
Ofcr: Susan Spellacy
Ex VP: Joseph F Jeamel
Sr VP: Christopher E Buchholz
Sr VP: Gary Daigle
Sr VP: Darlene White
VP: Nancy Moon
Board of Directors: William J McGurk

D-U-N-S 00-794-5256
■ UNITED BANK INC (WV)
(*Suby of* UNITED BANKSHARES INC) ★
514 Market St, Parkersburg, WV 26101-5144
Tel (304) 424-8800 *Founded/Ownrshp* 1839, 1984
Sales NA *EMP* 700
SIC 6022 State commercial banks
Pr: Richard Adams
COO: Craige L Smith Jr
**Ex VP:* Richard Adams Jr
**Ex VP:* James Hayhurst Jr
**Ex VP:* Joe Wilson
VP: Cheryl Kemmerer
VP: Charles J Mildren
VP: Susan Morris
Div Mgr: Jane Sargent

UNITED BANKSHARES
See UNITED BROKERAGE SERVICES INC

D-U-N-S 14-730-7029
▲ UNITED BANKSHARES INC
500 Virginia St E, Charleston, WV 25301-2164
Tel (304) 424-8800 *Founded/Ownrshp* 1984
Sales NA *EMP* 1,703^E
Tkr Sym UBSI *Exch* NGS
SIC 6022 State commercial banks; State trust companies accepting deposits, commercial
Ch Bd: Richard M Adams
Pr: Keith Brill
COO: James J Consagra Jr
COO: Craige L Smith
CFO: W Mark Tatterson
Treas: Steven E Wilson
Ofcr: Larkin Wilson
Ex VP: Douglas B Ernest
Ex VP: John Neuner
Ex VP: Darren K Williams
Ex VP: Joe L Wilson
VP: Jeff Hoskins
VP: Stephen Robinson
VP: Steve Sears
VP: Connie Stone

D-U-N-S 36-110-8975 IMP/EXP
UNITED BEVERAGES OF NORTH CAROLINA LLC
105 9th St Nw, Hickory, NC 28601-6049
Tel (828) 322-1933 *Founded/Ownrshp* 2003
Sales 84.0MM *EMP* 160
Accts Rives & Associates Llp Charl
SIC 5181 Beer & ale
COO: Larry Robinson
IT Man: Janet Mitchell

D-U-N-S 14-882-9208
■ UNITED BIOSOURCE LLC
UBC
(*Suby of* EXPRESS SCRIPTS HOLDING CO) ★
920 Harvest Dr Ste 200, Blue Bell, PA 19422-1968
Tel (215) 591-2880 *Founded/Ownrshp* 2010
Sales 93.5MM^E *EMP* 1,000
SIC 8731 Biotechnical research, commercial
CEO: Ethan D Leder
**Pr:* Jeffrey L Hall
**Pr:* Brett Huselton
**Pr:* Patrick Lindsay
**CFO:* Mark P Clein
**Treas:* Peter Gaylord
Sr Cor Off: Nancy Kline
**Sr VP:* Kelly D Davis
**Sr VP:* Robert Hollamby
Sr VP: Annette Stemhagen
**VP:* Kevin G Cast
VP: Matthew Dezee
**VP:* Keith Ebling
VP: Nicole Hebbert
**VP:* Sandra R Lottes
Exec: Shubh Sethi
Assoc Dir: Anneliese Jones
Assoc Dir: Luba Nalysnyk
Dir Bus: Matthew Bush
Dir Bus: Alice Ganzar

UNITED BLOOD MANAGEMENT
See UNITED STAFFING SOLUTIONS INC

UNITED BLOOD SERVICES
See BLOOD SYSTEMS INC

D-U-N-S 00-361-9681
■ UNITED BROKERAGE SERVICES INC (WV)
UNITED BANKSHARES
(*Suby of* UNITED BANKSHARES INC) ★
514 Market St, Parkersburg, WV 26101-5144
Tel (304) 424-8781 *Founded/Ownrshp* 1997
Sales 373.9MM *EMP* 4^E
SIC 6211 Security brokers & dealers
Pr: Richard M Adams Jr
**CFO:* Cindy McGhee
Sr VP: Steve Coffman
VP: Karen Inghram
VP: Leslie Maiden
**VP:* Amy Shaver
VP: Jeannie Singer
VP: Todd Stewart
VP: Jeffrey Wade
Admn Mgr: Anna Schultheis

D-U-N-S 96-409-6593
UNITED BROTHERHOOD OF CARPENTERS AND RESILIENT FLOOR COVERERS LOCAL 2287
395 Hudson St Fl 8, New York, NY 10014-7451
Tel (212) 929-2940 *Founded/Ownrshp* 2010
Sales 521.8MM *EMP* 1,100
Accts Marshall & Moss Llp Westbury
SIC 8631 Labor unions & similar labor organizations
Pr: Kevin Fleming

UNITED BUILDING CENTERS
See LANOGA CORP

D-U-N-S 03-084-5952
UNITED CALIFORNIA DISCOUNT CORP
UNITED CALIFORNIA FACTORS
2200 E Route 66 Ste 102, Glendora, CA 91740-4674
Tel (909) 394-5400 *Founded/Ownrshp* 1976
Sales NA *EMP* 15
SIC 6153 Mercantile financing

Pr: Dave Clark
*Treas: Ken Wong
Genl Mgr: Ken Moore
Opers Supe: Amy Perez

UNITED CALIFORNIA FACTORS
See UNITED CALIFORNIA DISCOUNT CORP

D-U-N-S 61-305-0454 IMP
UNITED CELLULAR INC
1940 Enchanted Way, Grapevine, TX 76051-0965
Tel (940) 566-5735 Founded/Ownrshp 2004
Sales 145.5MM[E] EMP 264[E]
SIC 4812 Cellular telephone services
CEO: Sonny Menon
*Pr: Aziz Muscatwalla
*Treas: Shari Menon
*VP: Rafique Poonja
Off Mgr: Kathy Ali
Opers Mgr: Karim Muscatwala

D-U-N-S 84-900-3132
UNITED CENTER JOINT VENTURE
1901 W Madison St, Chicago, IL 60612-2459
Tel (312) 455-4112 Founded/Ownrshp 1994
Sales 136.2MM[E] EMP 4,999
SIC 7941 Sports field or stadium operator, promoting sports events
Pt: Jerry Reinsdorf
Pt: William Wirtz
CTO: Bob Gorman
Mktg Dir: Brooks Boyer

D-U-N-S 80-361-9238 IMP
UNITED CENTRAL BANK
4555 W Walnut St, Garland, TX 75042-5143

Tel (972) 487-1505 Founded/Ownrshp 1988
Sales NA EMP 145
SIC 6021

D-U-N-S 08-511-7554 IMP
UNITED CENTRAL INDUSTRIAL SUPPLY CO LLC
UC
(Suby of UNITED DISTRIBUTORS GROUP INC) ★
1241 Vlntr Pkwy Ste 1000, Bristol, TN 37620
Tel (423) 573-7300 Founded/Ownrshp 2012
Sales 322.5MM[E] EMP 275
SIC 5082 Mining machinery & equipment, except petroleum
CFO: Darrell Cole
*CFO: Michael Culbert
VP: Henry Looney
Brnch Mgr: Gary Bush
Brnch Mgr: WY Gillette
Brnch Mgr: Tom Pendergraft
Brnch Mgr: Joe Vendetti
Sls Mgr: Don Schmidt

D-U-N-S 07-009-4222 IMP/EXP
UNITED CEREBRAL PALSY ASSOCIATIONS OF NEW YORK STATE INC (NY)
CEREBRAL PALSY ASSOC N Y STATE
330 W 34th St Fl 15, New York, NY 10001-2406
Tel (212) 947-5770 Founded/Ownrshp 1946
Sales 112.7MM EMP 1,700
Accts Bdo Usa Llp New York Ny
SIC 8059 Personal care home, with health care
Pr: Idajean Windell
*Pr: Susan Constantino
*COO: Joseph M Pancari
*CFO: Thomas Mandelkow
*Ex VP: Duane Schielke
VP: Janis Tshena
Off Mgr: Janette Cedeno
Pgrm Dir: Kathleen McFarlin

D-U-N-S 07-523-1787
UNITED CEREBRAL PALSY OF NEW YORK CITY INC
80 Maiden Ln Fl 8, New York, NY 10038-4837
Tel (212) 683-6700 Founded/Ownrshp 1948
Sales 102.4MM EMP 1,400
Accts Baker Tilly Virchow Krause Llp
SIC 8322 Social services for the handicapped
CEO: Edward R Matthews
*Pr: Gary Geresi
*Ch: Jerome Belson
*Ex VP: James Kase
*VP: Kenneth R Auerbach
Ex Dir: R Matthews
Plnt Mgr: Linda Laul
VP Mktg: Laura Hickman
Psych: Dustin Ross

D-U-N-S 08-847-1057
UNITED CHARITIES
OWNERS OF UNITED CHARITIES BUI
633 3rd Ave Fl 10, New York, NY 10017-6701
Tel (212) 614-5393 Founded/Ownrshp 1892
Sales 125.3MM EMP 2
SIC 6512 Nonresidential building operators
Pr: Phillip Coltoff
*Treas: David R Jones

D-U-N-S 07-455-6440
UNITED CHURCH HOMES INC
CHAPEL HILL COMMUNITY
170 E Center St, Marion, OH 43302-3815
Tel (740) 382-4885 Founded/Ownrshp 1920
Sales 67.0MM EMP 1,450
SIC 8051 Skilled nursing care facilities
CEO: Rev Kenneth Daniel
*Pr: Brian S Allen
*CFO: John Stoner
Treas: William Wilkins
Sr Cor Off: Dorothy Eckert
Sr Cor Off: Mark Seckinger
Sr VP: John Renner
*VP: Edwin Allen
*VP: Vincent Dent
*VP: Timothy Hackett
VP: Laverne Joseph
*VP: Charles R Mooney
VP: Robert Weisbrodt
*VP: Pam White

D-U-N-S 09-806-7721
UNITED CO
1005 Glenway Ave, Bristol, VA 24201-3473
Tel (276) 466-3322 Founded/Ownrshp 1980
Sales 244.8MM[E] EMP 600
SIC 1382 7992 Oil & gas exploration services; Public golf courses
Ch Bd: James W Mc Glothlin
*Pr: Jeffrey Keenan
CFO: Lois A Clarke
*Ex VP: Lois Clark

D-U-N-S 18-053-3416 IMP/EXP
UNITED COAL CO LLC
SAPPHIRE COAL COMPANY
(Suby of METINVEST HOLDING, TOV)
110 Sprint Dr, Blountville, TN 37617-5455
Tel (276) 530-7411 Founded/Ownrshp 1998
Sales 932.0MM[E] EMP 1,000
SIC 1241 Coal mining services
Pr: Michael P Zervus
*VP: Jeff Bitzer
*VP: Gary B Chilcot
*VP: Kenneth R McCoy
*VP: Charles E Toppings
*VP: William B Wells Jr
Dir Sec: Michael Whisenant

D-U-N-S 09-777-8245 IMP
UNITED COMMUNICATIONS GROUP LIMITED PARTNERSHIP
9737 Washingtonian Blvd # 500, Gaithersburg, MD 20878-7337
Tel (301) 287-2700 Founded/Ownrshp 1994
Sales 194.8MM EMP 650
SIC 2721 7375 Periodicals: publishing only; Information retrieval services
CEO: Todd Foreman
*Pt: Bruce Levenson
*Pt: Edwin Peskowitz
*Pr: Nancy Becker
*CFO: Chris Dingee
*VP: Stephanie Tamburello
VP: Sean Weiss
CIO: Shalisa Mohamed

D-U-N-S 03-633-6527
■ **UNITED COMMUNITY BANK**
(Suby of UNITED COMMUNITY BANKS INC) ★
177 Highway 515 E, Blairsville, GA 30512-8579
Tel (706) 745-2151 Founded/Ownrshp 1988
Sales NA EMP 360
Accts Porter Keadle Moore Llp Atla
SIC 6022 State trust companies accepting deposits, commercial
Pr: Andrew Williams III
Pr: Lynn Harton
Pr: Tim Schools
Pr: Annmarie Wright
Chf Cred: Rob Edwards
Ex VP: Keith Brady
Ex VP: Rex S Schuette
Sr VP: Carol A Chastain
VP: William L Daniel
VP: Tim G Heard
VP: Michael Lee
Board of Directors: Kenneth L Daniels, Steven J Goldstein, Peter E Raskind, Thomas A Richlovsky

D-U-N-S 80-140-5569
UNITED COMMUNITY BANKS INC
125 Highway 515 E, Blairsville, GA 30512-8579
Tel (581) 807-3041 Founded/Ownrshp 1949
Sales NA EMP 2,000
SIC 6022 State commercial banks
CEO: Jimmy C Tallent
*CFO: Rex S Schuette

D-U-N-S 85-849-1574
▲ **UNITED COMMUNITY BANKS INC**
125 Highway 515 E, Blairsville, GA 30512-8579
Tel (706) 781-2265 Founded/Ownrshp 1988
Sales NA EMP 1,883[E]
Tkr Sym UCBI Exch NGS
SIC 6022 State commercial banks
Ch Bd: Jimmy C Tallent
*Pr: H Lynn Harton
CFO: Rex S Schuette
Chf Cred: Robert A Edwards
Chf Cred: Chris Jones
Ofcr: Kathy Duncan
Ex VP: Bradley J Miller
Sr VP: Ron Huffman
VP: Jennifer Abate
VP: Dale Boyd
VP: Bert Durand
VP: Michael Emigh
VP: Steve Feld
VP: James Magness
VP: Brad Miller
VP: Jay Roper
VP: Justin Rutledge
VP: James Stewart
VP: Will Ward
VP: Annette West
Board of Directors: Robert H Blalock, L Cathy Cox, Kenneth L Daniels, W C Nelson Jr, Thomas A Richlovsky, David C Shaver, Tim R Wallis, David H Wilkins

D-U-N-S 01-970-5800
▲ **UNITED COMMUNITY FINANCIAL CORP**
275 W Federal St, Youngstown, OH 44503-1200
Tel (330) 742-0500 Founded/Ownrshp 1998
Sales NA EMP 514
Accts Crowe Horwath Llp Cleveland
Tkr Sym UCFC Exch NGS
SIC 6036 Savings institutions, not federally chartered; Savings & loan associations, not federally chartered
Pr: Gary M Small
Pr: Sandra Beckwith
Pr: Thomas R Poe
CFO: Timothy W Esson
CFO: James Reske
Ex VP: Matthew T Garrity
Ex VP: Barbara J Radis
Sr VP: Douglas Young
VP: Anthony Dantuono
VP: Robert Steele
Board of Directors: Marty E Adams, Patrick W Bevack, Lee Burdman, Scott N Crewson, Scott D Hunter, Ellen J Tressel

D-U-N-S 13-369-1324 IMP/EXP
UNITED COMPONENTS LLC
UCI
(Suby of UCI HOLDINGS (NO.1) LIMITED)
1900 W Field Ct, Lake Forest, IL 60045-4828
Tel (812) 867-4516 Founded/Ownrshp 2011
Sales 1.2MMM[E] EMP 3,900
SIC 5013 3714 Automotive supplies & parts; Motor vehicle parts & accessories
*CFO: Mark P Blaufuss
*VP: Keith A Zar
*Prin: Ian I Fujiyama
*Prin: Paul R Lederer
*Prin: Gregory S Ledford
*Prin: Raymond A Ranelli
*Prin: John C Ritter
*Prin: David L Squier
*Prin: Martin Sumner
Board of Directors: Ian I Fujiyama, Paul R Lederer, Gregory S Ledford, Raymond A Ranelli, John C Ritter, David L Squier, Martin Sumner

D-U-N-S 86-894-1832
UNITED CONCORDIA COMPANIES INC
UCCI
(Suby of HIGHMARK BLUE CRSS-BLUE SHIELD) ★
4401 Deer Path Rd, Harrisburg, PA 17110-3983
Tel (717) 260-6800 Founded/Ownrshp 1992
Sales NA EMP 905
Accts Pricewaterhousecoopers Llp Ph
SIC 6324 Dental insurance; Health maintenance organization (HMO), insurance only
CEO: David L Holmberg
*Pr: Frederick G Merkel
*CFO: Daniel J Wright
Chf Mktg O: Sharon Muscarella
*Ofcr: James B Bramson
Ofcr: Kristie Sullenberger
Sr VP: Tom Harbold
Sr VP: Thomas Palmer
VP: Barbara Breslin
VP: Carol Sweeney
Sales Exec: Timothy Olsen

D-U-N-S 78-657-4843
UNITED CONCORDIA LIFE AND HEALTH INSURANCE CO
UCCI
(Suby of UCCI) ★
4401 Deer Path Rd, Harrisburg, PA 17110-3983
Tel (717) 260-7081 Founded/Ownrshp 1965
Sales 731.2MM EMP 1[E]
SIC 7389 Personal service agents, brokers & bureaus
CEO: Frederick Merkel
*CFO: Daniel Wright

D-U-N-S 09-438-3023
UNITED CONSTRUCTION CO
5300 Mill St, Reno, NV 89502-2320
Tel (775) 858-8090 Founded/Ownrshp 1978
Sales 90.6MM EMP 62
SIC 1541 1542

D-U-N-S 04-834-2034 IMP/EXP
▲ **UNITED CONTINENTAL HOLDINGS INC**
233 S Wacker Dr, Chicago, IL 60606-7147
Tel (872) 825-4000 Founded/Ownrshp 1968
Sales 37.8MMM EMP 84,000[E]
Accts Ernst & Young Llp Chicago Il
Tkr Sym UAL Exch NYS
SIC 4512 Air passenger carrier, scheduled; Air cargo carrier, scheduled
CEO: Oscar Munoz
Pt: Dana Sacks
*Ch Bd: Robert A Milton
Pr: Scott Dolan
Pr: J Scott Kirby
Pr: John Tague
CEO: Michael Whitaker
COO: Gregory L Hart
CFO: Andrew C Levy
Ex VP: Brett J Hart
Ex VP: Julia Haywood
Ex VP: Linda P Jojo
Sr VP: Mark R Anderson
Sr VP: Dennis Cary
Sr VP: Tony Cervone
Sr VP: James E Keenan
Sr VP: Kevin Knight
Sr VP: Douglas McKeen
Sr VP: William R Norman
Sr VP: Sandra Pineau-Boddison
Sr VP: Mark Schwab
Board of Directors: Laurence E Simmons, Carolyn Corvi, David J Vitale, Jane C Garvey, James M Whitehurst, Barnaby M Harford, Todd M Insler, Walter Isaacson, James A C Kennedy, William R Nuti, Edward M Philip, Edward L Shapiro

D-U-N-S 11-636-1994
UNITED CONTRACTORS MIDWEST INC
3151 Robbins Rd Ste A, Springfield, IL 62704-7410
Tel (217) 546-6192 Founded/Ownrshp 2001
Sales 122.9MM[E] EMP 448[E]
SIC 8742 1622 5082 Business planning & organizing services; Bridge construction; Construction & mining machinery
Pr: James P Bruner

D-U-N-S 00-507-0792 IMP/EXP
UNITED CONVEYOR CORP (IL)
CHICAGO CONVEYOR
(Suby of UCC HOLDINGS CORP) ★
2100 Norman Dr, Waukegan, IL 60085-6753
Tel (847) 473-5900 Founded/Ownrshp 1920
Sales 119.5MM[E] EMP 400
SIC 3535 Conveyors & conveying equipment
Pr: Douglas S Basler
CFO: Greg Kelley
*CFO: Mark Springer
Sr VP: Michael Kipnis
*VP: Mark Burns
VP: Mark A Burns
*VP: Daniel E Charhut
VP: William O'Donnell
Exec: Bonnie Bella
Prgrm Mgr: Gary Thompson
Dir IT: Pete Szoke

D-U-N-S 02-317-3420
UNITED COOPERATIVE
N7160 Raceway Rd, Beaver Dam, WI 53916-9315
Tel (920) 887-1756 Founded/Ownrshp 1984
Sales 579.7MM EMP 358
Accts Cliftonlarsonallen Llp Middle
SIC 5191 5171 5541 5153 5812 Fertilizer & fertilizer materials; Feed; Seeds: field, garden & flower; Petroleum bulk stations; Filling stations, gasoline; Grain elevators; Restaurant, family: chain
CEO: David Cramer
*CFO: Damian Girten
*Ch: Howard Bohl

UNITED COOPERATIVE SERVICES
See UNITED ELECTRIC COOPERATIVE SERVICES INC

D-U-N-S 94-542-0305 EXP
UNITED COPPER INDUSTRIES INC
(Suby of SOUTHWIRE CO LLC) ★
2727 Geesling Rd, Denton, TX 76208-1408
Tel (940) 243-8200 Founded/Ownrshp 2016
Sales 500.0MM EMP 300
SIC 3357 Communication wire
CEO: Jeffrey Hykin
CFO: Charlie Banham

D-U-N-S 01-765-3528
UNITED DAIRY FARMERS INC
U D F
3955 Montgomery Rd, Cincinnati, OH 45212-3798
Tel (513) 396-8700 Founded/Ownrshp 1940
Sales 591.6MM[E] EMP 3,000
SIC 5411 5143 2026 2024 5541 5451 Convenience stores, chain; Ice cream & ices; Frozen dairy desserts; Milk processing (pasteurizing, homogenizing, bottling); Ice cream & ice milk; Filling stations, gasoline; Dairy products stores
Pr: Brad Lindner
CFO: Marilyn Mitchel
*CFO: Marilyn Mitchell
IT Man: Dale Perry
VP Mktg: Mike Walker
Sls Dir: David Lindner
Sls Mgr: Mike Homan

D-U-N-S 06-563-8249
UNITED DAIRY INC (OH)
UNITED QUALITY CHEKD DAIRY
300 N 5th St, Martins Ferry, OH 43935-1647
Tel (740) 633-1451 Founded/Ownrshp 1903, 1973
Sales 193.3MM[E] EMP 650
SIC 2026 2024 Milk processing (pasteurizing, homogenizing, bottling); Ice cream, bulk
Ch: Joseph M Carson Jr
*Pr: Joseph L Carson
*Sec: George Wood
*VP: Gary Cowell
Genl Mgr: John Duty
Plnt Mgr: Jason Roscoe
*VP Mktg: James Carson

D-U-N-S 93-364-0682 EXP
UNITED DATA TECHNOLOGIES INC
U D T
8825 Nw 21st Ter, Doral, FL 33172-2421
Tel (305) 882-0435 Founded/Ownrshp 1995
Sales 110.9MM[E] EMP 120
SIC 7379 Computer related consulting services
Pr: Henry Fleches
*Pr: Gerard Amaro
*CFO: James Cline
*Chf Mktg O: Andres Campo
VP: Scott Byers
*VP: Tony Cossio
VP: Juan Hernandez
*VP: Daniel Rodriguez
*VP: Ana M Soler
Mng Dir: Justin Jimenez
Rgnl Mgr: Frank Bryant

UNITED DETECTOR TECHNOLOGY
See OSI OPTOELECTRONICS INC

D-U-N-S 83-206-2454
UNITED DEVELOPMENT FUNDING IV
1301 Municipal Way # 100, Grapevine, TX 76051-8519
Tel (214) 370-8960 Founded/Ownrshp 2009
Sales 87.8MM EMP 6[E]
SIC 6798 Real estate investment trusts

D-U-N-S 07-866-0279
UNITED DISTRIBUTORS GROUP INC
1241 Vlntr Pkwy Ste 1000, Bristol, TN 37620
Tel (423) 573-7300 Founded/Ownrshp 2006
Sales 597.5MM[E] EMP 645[E]
SIC 5082 Mining machinery & equipment, except petroleum
Pr: Darrell H Cole
*VP: Daniel D Ahuero
*VP: Benjamin B Andrews
Mktg Dir: Carl Mallory

D-U-N-S 00-797-6483 IMP
UNITED DISTRIBUTORS INC (GA)
(Suby of UNISTAN INC) ★
5500 United Dr Se, Smyrna, GA 30082-4755
Tel (678) 305-2000 Founded/Ownrshp 1952
Sales 339.7MM[E] EMP 700
SIC 5182 Liquor; Wine
Ch Bd: Douglas J Hertz
*COO: Pete Moraitakis
*CFO: Mark Popowski
VP: Chuck Guth
Genl Mgr: David Gregory
Sfty Mgr: James Shelley
Mktg Dir: Chris Brown
Sls Mgr: Brian McDaniel

D-U-N-S 96-549-9705
■ UNITED DOMINION REALTY LP
(*Suby of* UDR INC) ★
1745 Shea Center Dr # 200, Highlands Ranch, CO 80129-1540
Tel (720) 283-6120 *Founded/Ownrshp* 1995
Sales 440.4MM *EMP* 9E
SIC 6531 Real estate brokers & agents
Pr: Thomas W Toomey
CFO: David L Messenger
VP: Robert B Blanton
VP: Tracey Ceol
Dist Mgr: Heather Lovejoy
VP Mktg: Eric Waldinger
Mktg Mgr: Arm Vail

D-U-N-S 95-835-7659
■ UNITED DOMINION REALTY TRUST INC
WELLINGTON PLACE AT
(*Suby of* UDR INC) ★
4510 Cox Rd Ste 105, Glen Allen, VA 23060-6759
Tel (804) 290-4705 *Founded/Ownrshp* 1995
Sales 73.2MME *EMP* 1,363E
SIC 6798 Real estate investment trusts
Pt: Thomas W Toomey
**Pt:* Christopher D Genry
**Pt:* W Mark Wallis
Treas: Ella Neyland
Ofcr: Dave Messenger
Sr VP: Kevin W Alsh
Sr VP: Mark M Culwell
VP: Carolyn D Brown
VP: Kurt Carter
VP: Kathy O Clem
VP: Daniel C Donovan
VP: James T Flanagan
VP: Robert Landis
VP: Susan Northcutt
VP: Timothy E Stumm
VP: Katheryn Surface
VP: Robert B Tinning
VP: Kevin Walsh
Exec: Ella S Neyland

D-U-N-S 17-165-3009
UNITED EDUCATION INSTITUTE
(*Suby of* INTERNATIONAL EDUCATION CORP) ★
16485 Laguna Canyon Rd # 300, Irvine, CA 92618-3840
Tel (949) 272-7200 *Founded/Ownrshp* 1982
Sales 116.9MM *EMP* 400
SIC 8249 Vocational schools
CEO: Fartad Fateri
**CFO:* Sanjay Sardana
**Ex VP:* Ali Bayrami
**VP:* Iasu Gorfu
**VP:* Fred Keivanfar

D-U-N-S 04-646-4848
UNITED EL SEGUNDO INC
UNITED OIL
17311 S Main St, Gardena, CA 90248-3131
Tel (310) 323-3992 *Founded/Ownrshp* 1954
Sales 120.6MME *EMP* 190
SIC 5172 6531 Gasoline; Real estate leasing & rentals
Pr: Ronald Appel
**Sec:* Jeff Appel

D-U-N-S 00-801-2239
UNITED ELECTRIC CO LP (TX)
MAGIC AIRE
(*Suby of* MA ACQUISITION CO LLC) ★
501 Galveston St, Wichita Falls, TX 76301-5906
Tel (940) 397-2100 *Founded/Ownrshp* 1932, 2010
Sales 83.1MME *EMP* 250
SIC 3585 Air conditioning condensers & condensing units; Compressors for refrigeration & air conditioning equipment; Condensers, refrigeration
Pt: Ron Duncan
Sr VP: Larry Ballard
VP: Victor Moreno
VP: Dick Stearns
IT Man: Ed Stein
Netwrk Mgr: James Doolen
MIS Mgr: Keith Kruger
Sfty Mgr: Randy Crumptin
Plnt Mgr: Terry Evett
Manager: Tarry Baker
Sls Mgr: Gary Patterson

D-U-N-S 00-894-5826
UNITED ELECTRIC COOPERATIVE SERVICES INC (TX)
UNITED COOPERATIVE SERVICES
3309 N Main St, Cleburne, TX 76033-5055
Tel (817) 556-4000 *Founded/Ownrshp* 1938
Sales 201.3MM *EMP* 153
Accts Briscoe Burke & Grigsby Llp T
SIC 4911 Distribution, electric power
Pr: Ray Beavers
CFO: Lynn Godfery
**CFO:* Lynn Godfrey
CFO: William Godfrey
**Sec:* Patsy Dumas
**VP:* Larry Bays
VP: Cameron Smallwood
VP: Jared Wennermark

D-U-N-S 00-249-1512
UNITED ELECTRIC SUPPLY CO INC
10 Bellecor Dr, New Castle, DE 19720-1763
Tel (800) 322-3374 *Founded/Ownrshp* 1965
Sales 203.7MM *EMP* 343
Accts Baker Tilly Virchow Krause Llp
SIC 5063 Electrical supplies
CEO: George Vorwick
COO: Bob Crawford
**CFO:* Rich Stagliano
Treas: Jim Mulvey
VP: Sal Muzzi
Genl Mgr: Tom Reu
Dir IT: Luis Varela
Opers Mgr: Terry Walter
Mktg Dir: Connie Kappel
Sales Asso: Chuck Love

D-U-N-S 85-844-0092
UNITED ENERGY CORP
U E C
919 S 7th St Ste 405, Bismarck, ND 58504-5835
Tel (701) 255-7970 *Founded/Ownrshp* 1997
Sales 102.5MME *EMP* 125
SIC 1311 Natural gas production; Crude petroleum production
Pr: Ryan Kopseng
**CEO:* Loren Kopseng

D-U-N-S 03-715-9167
UNITED ENERGY INC
HANDEE HUGO'S
932 N Hwy 421, Clinton, NC 28328-0410
Tel (919) 785-1904 *Founded/Ownrshp* 1980
Sales 97.7MME *EMP* 366E
Accts Dixon Hughes Pllc Southern Pi
SIC 5541 5411 Filling stations, gasoline; Convenience stores, chain
Pr: Rogers H Clark
**Sec:* David K Clark
**VP:* H Manly Clark Jr

D-U-N-S 00-805-8299 IMP
■ UNITED ENGINES LLC
(*Suby of* UNITED HOLDINGS LLC) ★
5555 W Reno Ave, Oklahoma City, OK 73127-6340
Tel (800) 955-3321 *Founded/Ownrshp* 2001
Sales 144.8MME *EMP* 180
Accts Allen Gibbs & Houlik Lc Wi
SIC 5013 5084 7538 7537 Automotive supplies & parts; Engines & parts, diesel; Diesel engine repair: automotive; Automotive transmission repair shops
Pr: Bill Moore
Sls Mgr: Shawn Campbell

D-U-N-S 10-366-3084
UNITED ENVELOPE LLC
65 Railroad Ave Ste 1a, Ridgefield, NJ 07657-2130
Tel (201) 699-5800 *Founded/Ownrshp* 2009
Sales 108.7MME *EMP* 400E
SIC 2759 2677 Envelopes: printing; Envelopes
Pr: Kenneth Bernstein
VP: John Pollicino
Opers Mgr: Carlos Acosta

D-U-N-S 78-946-2442
UNITED ETHANOL LLC
1250 Chicago St, Milton, WI 53563-1844
Tel (608) 868-5900 *Founded/Ownrshp* 2003
Sales 134.1MM *EMP* 42
Accts Cliftonlarsonallen Llp Middle
SIC 2869 Ethyl alcohol, ethanol
Pr: David Cramer
CFO: Damian Girten

UNITED EXPRESS
See AIR WISCONSIN AIRLINES CORP

D-U-N-S 00-486-7743
UNITED FARM FAMILY LIFE INSURANCE CO
(*Suby of* INDIANA FARM BUREAU INC) ★
225 S East St Ste 144, Indianapolis, IN 46202-4059
Tel (317) 692-7200 *Founded/Ownrshp* 1937, 1986
Sales NA *EMP* 1,300E
SIC 6311 6411 Life insurance; Insurance agents, brokers & service
CEO: Jerry Canada
**Pr:* David Villwock
**CFO:* Joseph A Martin
**Ofcr:* Patricia Poehler
**Sr VP:* Jeffery Freeman

D-U-N-S 00-693-8005
UNITED FARM FAMILY MUTUAL INSURANCE CO
INDIANA FARM BUREAU
(*Suby of* INDIANA FARM BUREAU INC) ★
225 S East St, Indianapolis, IN 46202-4002
Tel (317) 692-7200 *Founded/Ownrshp* 1934
Sales NA *EMP* 1,200E
SIC 6331 Fire, marine & casualty insurance & carriers; Fire, marine & casualty insurance: mutual
Pr: Don Villwock
**COO:* Mark Sigler
**Ex VP:* Jerry Canada
**Sr VP:* Isabella Chism
**Sr VP:* Greg Clancy
**Sr VP:* Tom Faulconer
**Sr VP:* Lynn Brundage Jongleux
**Sr VP:* Mark Miske
**VP:* Randy Kron
VP: Keri Weaver
**Prin:* Randall C Kron

D-U-N-S 02-283-8213
UNITED FARMERS COOPERATIVE
705 E 4th St, Winthrop, MN 55396-2362
Tel (507) 237-2281 *Founded/Ownrshp* 1915
Sales 448.5MME *EMP* 269
SIC 5153 5191 5983 5083 Grains; Farm supplies; Feed; Seeds: field, garden & flower; Fertilizer & fertilizer materials; Fuel oil dealers; Farm implements
Pr: Jeff Franta
**CEO:* Jeff Nielsen
CFO: Ctp R Bauer
**CFO:* Lorie Reinarts
**Bd of Dir:* David Braun
**Prin:* Kevin Lauwagie
Dir IT: Ryan Altmann

D-U-N-S 00-798-9221 EXP
UNITED FARMERS MERCANTILE COOPERATIVE
203 W Oak St, Red Oak, IA 51566-1432
Tel (712) 623-5453 *Founded/Ownrshp* 1918
Sales 149.3MM *EMP* 106
Accts Gardiner Thomsen Pc Des Mo
SIC 5153 5191 5211 2048 Soybeans; Corn; Wheat; Oats; Feed; Fertilizer & fertilizer materials; Chemicals, agricultural; Seeds: field, garden & flower; Filling stations, gasoline; Lumber & other building materials; Prepared feeds
Pr: Kent Swanson

**CFO:* Don Davis
Genl Mgr: John Pruss

D-U-N-S 09-124-7382
UNITED FASHIONS HOLDINGS INC
UNITED FASHIONS TEXAS LIMITED
4629 Marco Dr, San Antonio, TX 78218-5420
Tel (210) 662-7140 *Founded/Ownrshp* 1994
Sales 100.7MME *EMP* 1,200E
Accts Padgett Stratemann & Co Ll
SIC 5621 5641 Ready-to-wear apparel, women's; Children's wear
Prin: Tzipora Bar-Yadin
CFO: Steven Line
VP: Greg Darnell

D-U-N-S 08-026-7453 IMP
UNITED FASHIONS OF TEXAS LLC
VOUGE
4629 Macro, San Antonio, TX 78218-5420
Tel (210) 662-7140 *Founded/Ownrshp* 1994
Sales 183.1MME *EMP* 1,500
Accts Padgett Stratermann & Co Llp
SIC 5611 5621 5651 Men's & boys' clothing stores; Women's clothing stores; Family clothing stores
Mng Pt: Tzipora Bar-Yadin
CFO: Stepehen Lane
CFO: Steven Line
CIO: Tom Ellison
Mktg Dir: Genevieve Valdes

UNITED FASHIONS TEXAS LIMITED
See UNITED FASHIONS HOLDINGS INC

D-U-N-S 08-873-1559 IMP
UNITED FEDERAL CREDIT UNION
2807 S State St, Saint Joseph, MI 49085-2454
Tel (888) 982-1400 *Founded/Ownrshp* 2006
Sales NA *EMP* 515
Accts Plante & Moran Pllc St Jose
SIC 6061 6163 Federal credit unions; Loan brokers
CEO: Terry O'Rourke
**Ch Bd:* John Steinke
**Pr:* David Weichhand
**CFO:* Mark Weber
**Treas:* Anson Lovellette
**Ex VP:* Duane Nelson
**VP:* Dorothy Baker
VP: John Blakeney
VP: Jeff Curry
VP: Greg Deusenberry
VP: Gina Harrington
VP: Brett Wier
VP: Marie Williamson
Exec: Polly Poziwilko
Board of Directors: Sherry Buck, Dennis Ciboch, Kevin Geiser, Pat Dwyer Jerry Guinane, J B Hoyt, Anson Lovellette, Tom Roth, John Steinke

D-U-N-S 07-329-8903
UNITED FEDERATION OF TEACHERS WELFARE FUND
52 Broadway Lowr, New York, NY 10004-1603
Tel (212) 539-0500 *Founded/Ownrshp* 1965
Sales NA *EMP* 60
SIC 6371 Union welfare, benefit & health funds
**Pr:* Randi Weingarten
VP: Ronald Jones

D-U-N-S 05-312-0473
UNITED FIDELITY LIFE INSURANCE CO INC
(*Suby of* IPFS CORP) ★
1055 Broadway Blvd Ste Ph, Kansas City, MO 64105-1575
Tel (816) 391-2000 *Founded/Ownrshp* 1986
Sales NA *EMP* 300E
SIC 6311 Life insurance carriers
Pr: Gary Lee Muller
**Ch Bd:* Michael Merriman
**Treas:* Mark Fallon
**VP:* Major Waldo Park Jr

D-U-N-S 55-741-1282
UNITED FINANCIAL BANCORP INC
95 Elm St, West Springfield, MA 01089-2704
Tel (413) 787-1700 *Founded/Ownrshp* 2007
Sales NA *EMP* 413E
SIC 6035

D-U-N-S 14-143-4881
■ UNITED FINANCIAL CASUALTY CO INC
(*Suby of* PROGRESSIVE INSURANCE) ★
6300 Wilson Mills Rd, Cleveland, OH 44143-2109
Tel (440) 461-5000 *Founded/Ownrshp* 2002
Sales NA *EMP* 20
SIC 6331 Fire, marine & casualty insurance
Dir Surg: Kolleda Leslie
**Dir Surg:* Leslie Kolleda

D-U-N-S 00-530-2724
■ UNITED FIRE & CASUALTY CO (IA)
UFG
(*Suby of* UNITED FIRE GROUP INC) ★
118 2nd Ave Se, Cedar Rapids, IA 52401-1253
Tel (319) 399-5700 *Founded/Ownrshp* 1946
Sales NA *EMP* 943E
Accts Ernst & Young Llp Chicago Il
SIC 6331 6311 6321 Fire, marine & casualty insurance & carriers; Life insurance carriers; Health insurance carriers
Pr: Randy A Ramlo
**CFO:* Dianne M Lyons
**Ex VP:* Michael T Wilkins
**VP:* Ray Dudonis
**VP:* Barrie W Ernst
VP: Dianne M Lyon
VP: Mildred Phillips
**VP:* Neal R Scharmer
Board of Directors: Kyle D Skogman, Christopher R Drahozal, Frank S Wilkinson Jr, Jack B Evans, Thomas W Hanley, Douglas M Hultquist, Casey D Mahon, George D Milligan, James W Noyce, Mary K Quass, John A Rife

D-U-N-S 96-930-3432
▲ UNITED FIRE GROUP INC
118 2nd Ave Se, Cedar Rapids, IA 52401-1212
Tel (319) 399-5700 *Founded/Ownrshp* 2011
Sales NA *EMP* 981E
Accts Ernst & Young Llp Des Moines
Tkr Sym UFCS *Exch* NGS
SIC 6411 6311 Insurance agents, brokers & service; Life insurance
Pr: Randy A Ramlo
**Ch Bd:* Jack B Evans
COO: Michael T Wilkins
CFO: Dawn M Jaffray
Treas: Galen Underwood
Sr VP: Fellman Seinsheimer
VP: Barrie W Ernst
VP: Sue Haupert
VP: Debbie Johnstone
VP: Douglas Penn
VP: Neal R Scharmer
Exec: Steve Watters
Board of Directors: Susan E Voss, Scott L Carlton, Brenda Kay Clancy, Christopher R Drahozal, Sarah Fisher Gardial, Casey D Mahon, George D Milligan, James W Noyce, Mary K Quass, Kyle D Skogman

D-U-N-S 06-927-7069
UNITED FOOD AND COMMERCIAL WORKERS INTERNATIONAL UNION
UFCW
1775 K St Nw, Washington, DC 20006-1502
Tel (202) 223-3111 *Founded/Ownrshp* 1888, 1979
Sales 238.0MM *EMP* 500
Accts Calibre Cpa Group Pllc Bethes
SIC 8631 Labor union
Pr: Joseph T Hansen
Treas: Esther Lopez
**Sec:* Anthony M Perrone
Ex VP: Sarah P Amos
MIS Dir: Mark Salandro
Software D: Paul Stone

D-U-N-S 96-922-7474
UNITED FOOD AND COMMERCIAL WORKERS UNIONS AND FOOD EMPLOYERS BEN FUND
6425 Katella Ave, Cypress, CA 90630-5246
Tel (714) 220-2297 *Founded/Ownrshp* 2011
Sales 575.3MM *EMP* 21E
Accts Hemming Morse Cpa S And Consul
SIC 8631 Labor union
Prin: Richard Klontz

D-U-N-S 05-024-6404
UNITED FOOD SERVICE INC
(*Suby of* SHAMROCK FOODS CO) ★
5199 Ivy St, Commerce City, CO 80022-4404
Tel (303) 289-3595 *Founded/Ownrshp* 1970
Sales 216.1MME *EMP* 500
SIC 5141 5142 5147 5148 5046 Groceries, general line; Packaged frozen goods; Meats, fresh; Fruits, fresh; Commercial cooking & food service equipment
Ch Bd: David B Hall
**Pr:* W Kent Mc Clelland
COO: Kent McClelland
Treas: Frances Clelland
**Treas:* Frances Mc Clelland
**Sec:* Norman P Mc Clelland
Genl Mgr: Pat Dunning
VP Opers: Jefferey Patterson

D-U-N-S 14-759-1689
UNITED FORMING INC
470 Riverside Pkwy, Austell, GA 30168-7803
Tel (678) 945-4224 *Founded/Ownrshp* 1984
Sales 215.0MME *EMP* 1,500
SIC 1771 Concrete work
Pr: Tom Owens
**CFO:* Kevin Swanson
**Sr VP:* George Dryden
**Sr VP:* Tim Wiser
**VP:* Rodney Adams
**VP:* John Varn
**VP:* Todd Volheim
Dist Mgr: Brian Needham
IT Man: Kevin King

UNITED FRUIT & PRODUCE
See UNITED INDUSTRIES INC

D-U-N-S 10-630-5006 IMP/EXP
UNITED FURNITURE INDUSTRIES INC
COMFORT FURNITURE
5380 Highway 145 S, Tupelo, MS 38801-0811
Tel (662) 447-4000 *Founded/Ownrshp* 1983
Sales 445.6MME *EMP* 1,200
SIC 2512 Living room furniture: upholstered on wood frames
Pr: Larry George
COO: Kim Harper
Ex VP: Jay S Quimby
VP: Rick Witt
VP Mfg: John Cox
Natl Sales: Bryan Jarvis
Natl Sales: Bob Saunders
Mktg Dir: Doug Hanby

D-U-N-S 01-980-8067 IMP
UNITED GENERAL BAKERY INC
UPPER CRUST BAKERY
3655 W Washington St, Phoenix, AZ 85009-4759
Tel (602) 255-0464 *Founded/Ownrshp* 1980
Sales 114.0MME *EMP* 400
SIC 2051 Bakery: wholesale or wholesale/retail combined
**CFO:* Frank Alexander
VP: Mary Clark
Opers Mgr: Carolyn Wasson
VP Sls: Brad Scoplitte

UNITED GROCERY OUTLET
See BARGAIN BARN INC

D-U-N-S 02-650-2851
UNITED GROUP OPERATING COMPANIES LLC (MA)
175 Campanelli Dr, Braintree, MA 02184-5206
Tel (781) 348-8000 *Founded/Ownrshp* 2007

Sales 369.0MM[E] *EMP* 650
SIC 5181 5182 Beer & other fermented malt liquors; Liquor
CEO: David J Roberts
**Pr:* Carmine A Martignetti
VP: Neal Fisher
Sls Mgr: Larry Bassett
Sls Mgr: Dan Edwards

D-U-N-S 06-743-6089
■ UNITED GUARANTY CORP
(*Suby of* AIG) ★
230 N Elm St Ste 1200, Greensboro, NC 27401-2417
Tel (336) 373-0232 *Founded/Ownrshp* 2000
Sales NA *EMP* 3,468
SIC 6351 Mortgage guarantee insurance
CEO: Donna Demaio
Pr: Elaine Beck
Pr: Rodney Collins
Pr: Melissa Colon
Pr: Della Ellis
**Pr:* Kim Garland
Pr: Gloria Goodman
Pr: Kevin Popoli
**COO:* Brian Gould
CFO: Charles Compton
CFO: Hal G Waddell
Ofcr: Thomas Parrent
Ofcr: Tom Parrent
**Sr VP:* Bill Allen
Sr VP: Margaret Avery
Sr VP: Paul Baynard
VP: Bea Bartolome
VP: Dan Blakemore
VP: Jerry Bryant
VP: Beth Catley
VP: Art Feingold

D-U-N-S 80-373-4102
■ UNITED GUARANTY INSURANCE CO
(*Suby of* UNITED GUARANTY CORP) ★
230 N Elm St Ste 1200, Greensboro, NC 27401-2417
Tel (336) 373-0232 *Founded/Ownrshp* 1992
Sales NA *EMP* 455
SIC 6351 Surety insurance
CEO: Eric Martinez
CFO: Hal G Waddell
Treas: Luther Leonard
Sr VP: Mark Amacher
Sr VP: Steve Clarke
Sr VP: Lien Tu-Chalmers
VP: Brian Bell
VP: Jim Krueger
VP: Matt Muller
VP: Liz Urquhart
VP: Jim White
Exec: Brian Smith
Dir Risk M: Tom Parrent
Board of Directors: Florence Davis, Maurice Raymond Greenberg, Edward Easton Matthews, Howard Ian Smith

D-U-N-S 07-796-3510
■ UNITED GUARANTY RESIDENTIAL INSURANCE CO
(*Suby of* UNITED GUARANTY CORP) ★
230 N Elm St, Greensboro, NC 27401-2438
Tel (336) 373-0232 *Founded/Ownrshp* 1963
Sales NA *EMP* 450
SIC 6351 Mortgage guarantee insurance
Pr: Kim Garland
**CFO:* Charles Compton
Treas: Luther G Leonard
**Sr VP:* William Allen
**VP:* William Edward Ridenour
VP Opers: Ken Parker

D-U-N-S 00-890-4575 IMP
UNITED HARDWARE DISTRIBUTING CO
5005 Nathan Ln N, Plymouth, MN 55442-3210
Tel (763) 559-1800 *Founded/Ownrshp* 1945
Sales 130.2MM[E] *EMP* 330
Accts Mcgladrey Llp Minneapolis Mi
SIC 5251 Hardware
Pr: Steven G Draeger
COO: Stan Creamer
CFO: Lenny Sweet
**Treas:* Lori Long
VP: Anthony Long
**VP:* Phil Pflepsen
**VP:* Chad Ruth
Comm Man: Brian Sonnenberg
Dir IT: Jim Guard
Dir IT: Lynn Miller
Mktg Dir: Rick Matson

D-U-N-S 06-679-8372
UNITED HEALTH SERVICES HOSPITAL INC
BINGHAMTON GENERAL HOSPITAL
(*Suby of* UHS) ★
10-42 Mitchell Ave, Binghamton, NY 13903-1617
Tel (607) 762-2200 *Founded/Ownrshp* 1984
Sales 575.7MM *EMP* 5,000
Accts Fust Charles Chambers Llp Syr
SIC 8062 Hospital, AMA approved residency
Pr: Atthew J Salanger
CFO: Kate Knapik
**Ex VP:* Rajesh Dave MD
**Sr VP:* Robert Gomulka
Dir Rx: Larry Tremel
Genl Mgr: Paula Elly
Off Mgr: Edwin Rivera
Pharmcst: Shannon Lindsey

D-U-N-S 14-450-7811
UNITED HEALTH SERVICES INC
UHS
10-42 Mitchell Ave, Binghamton, NY 13903
Tel (607) 762-3024 *Founded/Ownrshp* 1984
Sales 482.9MM *EMP* 5,190
SIC 8062 8051 General medical & surgical hospitals; Skilled nursing care facilities
Pr: Mathew Salanger
CFO: Kate Knapik
**Ex VP:* Rajesh Dave
**Sr VP:* Robert Gomulka
VP: Joe Cerra
Prgrm Mgr: Sharon Westbrook
Nurse Mgr: Sheri Renaud

Mktg Mgr: Karen Bayer
Doctor: Mary Gibson
Doctor: Yahia Lodi
Doctor: Julia Miller

UNITED HEALTHCARE
See UNITEDHEALTHCARE OF NEW ENGLAND INC

UNITED HEALTHCARE
See SIERRA HEALTH SERVICES INC

UNITED HEALTHCARE
See UNITEDHEALTHCARE OF NORTH CAROLINA INC

UNITED HEALTHCARE INSURANCE CO
See UNITEDHEALTHCARE INSURANCE CO

D-U-N-S 14-458-8738
■ UNITED HEALTHCARE OF ALABAMA INC
(*Suby of* UNITEDHEALTH GROUP INC) ★
33 Inverness Center Pkwy # 350, Birmingham, AL 35242-7649
Tel (205) 437-8500 *Founded/Ownrshp* 1989
Sales NA *EMP* 212
SIC 6324 Group hospitalization plans
Pr: David Lewis
Pr: Charles Capenter Pitts
VP: Diwakar Raman
Mktg Dir: Amy Kehoe
Board of Directors: James Gordon Carlson, David Paul Koppe, Charles Carpenter Pitts, John Aloyslus Wickens

D-U-N-S 16-960-6876
■ UNITED HEALTHCARE OF FLORIDA INC
(*Suby of* UNITED HEALTHCARE SERVICES INC) ★
495 N Keller Rd Ste 200, Maitland, FL 32751-8656
Tel (407) 659-6900 *Founded/Ownrshp* 2000
Sales NA *EMP* 1,421
SIC 6321 Health insurance carriers
Prin: David Lewis
**Pr:* Gary Schultz
CFO: Jon Schwartz
**Treas:* Alan Weiss
VP: Glenn Baker

D-U-N-S 10-694-6387
■ UNITED HEALTHCARE OF ILLINOIS INC
(*Suby of* UNITED HEALTHCARE SERVICES INC) ★
550 Warrenville Rd # 300, Lisle, IL 60532-4311
Tel (630) 725-7204 *Founded/Ownrshp* 1983
Sales NA *EMP* 1,100
SIC 6324 Health maintenance organization (HMO), insurance only
Pr: Thomas P Wiffler
COO: Michael Coe
Ch: William W McGuire
Chf Mktg O: Yasmine Winkler
Sr VP: William E Moeller
CIO: Mike Remar

D-U-N-S 16-120-6750
■ UNITED HEALTHCARE OF MIDWEST INC
(*Suby of* UNITEDHEALTH GROUP INC) ★
13655 Riverport Dr, Maryland Heights, MO 63043-4812
Tel (314) 592-7000 *Founded/Ownrshp* 1994
Sales 109.5MM[E] *EMP* 1,600
SIC 8741 6324 Management services; Health maintenance organization (HMO), insurance only
Ex VP: William W McGuire
**Treas:* David P Koppe
**Ex VP:* Jeannine M Rivet
VP: Carol Biro
VP: Carmel Colica
VP: Janice Dade
VP: Raymond Devault
VP: Tia Dillow
VP: Ellen Ewing
VP: Patrick Moeschler
VP: Darren Moquist
VP: Gary Simmons
VP: Frank Vierling
Exec: Carolyn Klucas
Assoc Dir: William Borelli
Dir Bus: Amy Grant

D-U-N-S 09-502-6860
■ UNITED HEALTHCARE OF OHIO INC
(*Suby of* UNITED HEALTHCARE SERVICES INC) ★
9200 Worthington Rd, Columbus, OH 43085
Tel (614) 410-7000 *Founded/Ownrshp* 1992
Sales NA *EMP* 525
SIC 6324 Group hospitalization plans; Health maintenance organization (HMO), insurance only
CEO: Tom Brady
**Pr:* G David Shafer
**COO:* Thomas Sullivan
VP: Mark Woessner
Dir IT: Nic Ziccardi
Mktg Mgr: James Gibbs

D-U-N-S 80-484-7093
■ UNITED HEALTHCARE OF TENNESSEE INC
(*Suby of* UNITED HEALTHCARE OF ALABAMA INC) ★
10 Cadillac Dr Ste 200, Brentwood, TN 37027-5078
Tel (615) 372-3622 *Founded/Ownrshp* 2005
Sales NA *EMP* 120
SIC 6324 Group hospitalization plans
Pr: Darlene Scott
**CFO:* Gary Baker
**Treas:* David P Koppe
**Ex VP:* Jeannine M Rivet
VP: Mark Bellman
IT Man: Eddie Cambronero
IT Man: Donald Striegel
VP Sls: Mike Kimbrell

D-U-N-S 07-177-8674
■ UNITED HEALTHCARE SERVICES INC
(*Suby of* UNITEDHEALTH GROUP INC) ★
9700 Health Care Ln, Minnetonka, MN 55343-4522
Tel (952) 936-1300 *Founded/Ownrshp* 1974
Sales NA *EMP* 33,000
SIC 6321 Accident & health insurance
Ch Bd: Aubrey Miller
**CEO:* William Arnold Munsell

COO: William Munsell
CFO: Michael Kennedy
CFO: Brian Thompson
Bd of Dir: Shawn Connolly
VP: Craig Anderson
VP: Nick Barbati
VP: Kathy Taylor
VP: Chad Walker
CIO: Rod Hamilton

UNITED HEARTLAND
See ACCIDENT FUND HOLDINGS INC

D-U-N-S 84-473-3659
UNITED HERITAGE FINANCIAL GROUP INC
UNITED HERITG MUTL LF INSUR CO
707 E United Heritage Ct, Meridian, ID 83642-8407
Tel (208) 493-6100 *Founded/Ownrshp* 2004
Sales NA *EMP* 133[E]
SIC 6311 Life insurance
Pr: Dennis Johnson
**CFO:* Todd Gill
**Ch:* Rich Hall
**Ex VP:* Jack Winderl
**Sr VP:* Deborah Sloan
**Sr VP:* Mick Ware
Web Dev: Michael Cichoski
Board of Directors: Jerome Fischer

D-U-N-S 07-300-0945
UNITED HERITAGE LIFE INSURANCE CO
UNITED HERITAGE MUTUAL LIFE IN
(*Suby of* UNITED HERITG MUTL LF INSUR CO) ★
707 E Untd Heritage Ct # 130, Meridian, ID 83642-7785
Tel (208) 475-0932 *Founded/Ownrshp* 2002
Sales NA *EMP* 110
SIC 6311 Life insurance carriers
Pr: Dennis L Johnson
CFO: Todd Gill
**Treas:* Jack Winderl
**Sr VP:* Deborah K Sloan
VP: John Bellamy
**VP:* Mick L Ware
Netwrk Mgr: Shawn Turner
Mktg Mgr: Patty Blaine

UNITED HERITAGE MUTUAL LIFE IN
See UNITED HERITAGE LIFE INSURANCE CO

UNITED HERITG MUTL LF INSUR CO
See UNITED HERITAGE FINANCIAL GROUP INC

D-U-N-S 11-072-3777
■ UNITED HOLDINGS LLC
(*Suby of* KIRBY CORP) ★
5 N Mccormick St Ste 200, Oklahoma City, OK 73127-6626
Tel (405) 947-3321 *Founded/Ownrshp* 2010
Sales 371.6MM[E] *EMP* 210
Accts Allen Gibbs & Houlik Lc Wich
SIC 5084 5013 7538 7537 3441 Engines & parts, diesel; Automotive supplies & parts; Diesel engine repair: automotive; Automotive transmission repair shops; Fabricated structural metal

D-U-N-S 07-496-1426 IMP
UNITED HOSPITAL CENTER INC
327 Medical Park Dr, Bridgeport, WV 26330-9006
Tel (681) 342-1000 *Founded/Ownrshp* 1971
Sales 293.9MM *EMP* 2,000
SIC 8062 Hospital, affiliated with AMA residency
V Ch Bd: David Alvarez
**Pr:* Bruce C Carter
**CFO:* Doug Coffman
Treas: Louis Spatare
**Treas:* Louis Stadaford
VP: Debbie Davis
VP: Geoff Marshall
Dir Rx: Dave Weekly
CIO: Ed Collins
CTO: Mary Scott
MIS Dir: Tina Williams

D-U-N-S 80-829-6966 IMP
UNITED HOSPITAL INC
RADIATION THERAPY CENTER
(*Suby of* ALLINA HOSPITALS & CLINICS) ★
333 Smith Ave N, Saint Paul, MN 55102-2344
Tel (651) 241-8000 *Founded/Ownrshp* 1971
Sales 503.6MM *EMP* 3,400
SIC 8011 Radiologist
Prin: Beth Seidl
VP: John Bien
VP: Sue Penque
Genl Mgr: Lynn Stevens
Mtls Mgr: Mary Sweeny
Sfty Mgr: Peter Grauze
Pathlgst: Linda Riley

D-U-N-S 02-046-3303
UNITED HOSPITAL SYSTEM INC
KENOSHA MEDICAL CENTER
6308 8th Ave, Kenosha, WI 53143-5031
Tel (262) 656-2011 *Founded/Ownrshp* 1910
Sales 308.3MM *EMP* 1,500
SIC 8062 General medical & surgical hospitals
Ch Bd: James A Shapiro M D
**Pr:* Richard O Schmidt Jr
**CFO:* Gary Skovronski
**Sec:* Charles Talbert
VP: Thomas Kelley
CTO: Lori Albert
Surgeon: Christopher D Stone
Anesthgy: Richard A Hawkins
Podiatrist: Antonio I Montemurro

D-U-N-S 00-691-7967 IMP
■ UNITED ILLUMINATING CO
UI
(*Suby of* UIL HOLDINGS CORP) ★
157 Church St Fl 16, New Haven, CT 06510-2103
Tel (203) 499-2000 *Founded/Ownrshp* 1899
Sales 912.3MM[E] *EMP* 920
SIC 4911 Generation, electric power; Transmission, electric power; Distribution, electric power
Pr: James P Torgerson
**Ch Bd:* Nathaniel D Woodson
**Pr:* Anthony J Vallillo
**CFO:* Richard Nicholas

Treas: Kurt Mohlman
Sr VP: Alex Deboissiere
**VP:* Steven P Favuzza
**VP:* W Marie Zanavich
Prgrm Mgr: Jennifer Parsons
Prgrm Mgr: Evan Seretan
Genl Mgr: Kevin Reed

D-U-N-S 04-870-9299
UNITED INDEPENDENT SCHOOL DISTRICT (TX)
UNITED ISD
201 Lindenwood Dr, Laredo, TX 78045-2429
Tel (956) 473-6201 *Founded/Ownrshp* 1961
Sales 444.3MM *EMP* 6,900
Accts Pattillo Brown & Hill Llp Br
SIC 8211 Public elementary & secondary schools; High school, junior or senior
Bd of Dir: Ricardo Molina
Ofcr: Jesse Perusquia
**VP:* Juan Roberto Ramirez
MIS Dir: Hector Perez
Netwrk Mgr: Cesar Tamez
Pr Dir: Rocio Moore
Board of Directors: Ricardo Molina Sr, Javier Montemayor Jr, Ramiro Veliz III

D-U-N-S 00-152-7852
■ UNITED INDUSTRIAL CORP
(*Suby of* TEXTRON INC) ★
124 Industry Ln, Hunt Valley, MD 21030-3342
Tel (410) 628-3500 *Founded/Ownrshp* 1960
Sales 59.1MM[E] *EMP* 2,316
SIC 8711 Engineering services
CEO: Richard R Erkeneff
**CFO:* James H Perry
**Treas:* Stuart F Gray
**VP:* Jonathan A Greenberg
VP: Jonathan Greenberg
Exec: P D Bocksch

D-U-N-S 06-852-7704 IMP/EXP
■ UNITED INDUSTRIES CORP
CHEMSICO
(*Suby of* SPECTRUM BRANDS HOLDINGS INC) ★
1 Rider Trl Ste 300, Earth City, MO 63045
Tel (314) 738-0375 *Founded/Ownrshp* 1973, 2005
Sales 149.2MM[E] *EMP* 500
SIC 2879 3691 Insecticides, agricultural or household; Alkaline cell storage batteries
CEO: David R Lumley
**Pr:* Andreas Rouv
**CFO:* Anthony Genito
**Ex VP:* Anthony L Genito
**Sr VP:* Nathan E Fagre
**Sr VP:* Randy Lewis
Genl Mgr: Randall Lewis

D-U-N-S 18-338-9832 IMP
UNITED INDUSTRIES INC
UNITED FRUIT & PRODUCE
55 Produce Row, Saint Louis, MO 63102-1418
Tel (314) 621-9440 *Founded/Ownrshp* 1978
Sales 165.1MM[E] *EMP* 350[E]
SIC 5148 Fruits, fresh; Vegetables, fresh
Pr: Charles O Gallagher Sr
COO: Charles Gallagher Jr
**VP:* David J Breen

D-U-N-S 00-693-3063
■ UNITED INSURANCE CO OF AMERICA
(*Suby of* KEMPER CORP) ★
12115 Lackland Rd, Saint Louis, MO 63146-4025
Tel (314) 819-4300 *Founded/Ownrshp* 1942, 1990
Sales NA *EMP* 2,600
SIC 6411 6321 6331 Insurance agents, brokers & service; Health insurance carriers; Fire, marine & casualty insurance
Pr: Donald Royster
**Treas:* Thomas Myers
**Sr VP:* Richard J Miller
**Sr VP:* Deborah L Quaglia

UNITED INTERNATIONAL
See CELLMARK INC

D-U-N-S 62-360-6014
UNITED INVESTMENT LTD
11700 Preston Rd 660-388, Dallas, TX 75230-6112
Tel (214) 632-9531 *Founded/Ownrshp* 2006
Sales 100.0MM *EMP* 19
SIC 6726 Investment offices
CEO: Kirby Gonzales

UNITED ISD
See UNITED INDEPENDENT SCHOOL DISTRICT

D-U-N-S 06-251-8071
UNITED JEWISH APPEAL-FEDERATION OF JEWISH PHILANTHROPIES OF NEW YORK CHARITABLE FUND LLC
130 E 59th St Fl 3, New York, NY 10022-1375
Tel (212) 980-1000 *Founded/Ownrshp* 1942
Sales 215.2MM *EMP* 400
Accts Kpmg Llp New York Ny
SIC 8399 Fund raising organization, non-fee basis
Pr: Jerry W Levin
**Ch Bd:* Linda Mirels
**Pr:* Alisa Robbins Doctoroff
**CEO:* Eric S Goldstein
**CEO:* John S Ruskay
CFO: Jay D Gol
**CFO:* Irvin Rosenthal
**Treas:* Roger Einiger
VP: Beatrice Vito
Exec: Dina Schechter
Assoc Dir: Alan Secter

D-U-N-S 60-130-7601 IMP
UNITED LAUNCH ALLIANCE LLC
U L A
9501 E Panorama Cir, Centennial, CO 80112-3447
Tel (720) 922-7100 *Founded/Ownrshp* 2005
Sales 1.9MMM[E] *EMP* 4,000
SIC 3761 Rockets, space & military, complete
CEO: Salvatore T Bruno
**COO:* Daniel J Collins
**CFO:* David K Lang
**CFO:* Paul Neary

Treas: Bob Lange
Ofcr: Patty Pierson
VP: Mark Bitterman
**VP:* James T Hardin Jr
**VP:* Kevin Maccary
VP: Carmine Orsini
VP: Jim Sponnick
VP: J Thomas
Exec: Howard Biegler
Exec: Melissa Sampson

D-U-N-S 06-962-0151
■ UNITED LIFE INSURANCE CO INC
(*Suby of* UFG) ★
118 2nd Ave Se, Cedar Rapids, IA 52401-1212
Tel (319) 399-5700 *Founded/Ownrshp* 1962
Sales NA *EMP* 600
SIC 6311 Life insurance carriers
Pr: John Rife
**COO:* Michael J Sheeley
**Ch:* John Scott McIntyre Jr
VP: Barrie Ernst
VP: Bruce Miller
VP: Scott Minkel
**VP:* Rickey Lee Pettyjohn

D-U-N-S 00-695-3319 IMP
UNITED LIQUORS LLC
(*Suby of* CAROLINA WINE CO) ★
500 John Hancock Rd, Taunton, MA 02780-7379
Tel (781) 348-8000 *Founded/Ownrshp* 2007
Sales 223.5MM^E *EMP* 650
SIC 5182 5181 Wine & distilled beverages; Beer & other fermented malt liquors
CEO: Caramina Martignetti
**Pr:* Mark Fisher
**CFO:* Lewis Gack
Exec: Kathleen Mansfield
MIS Dir: Alan Tainsh
Sftwr Eng: Linda Toupin
VP Opers: Ilias Potsis
Mktg Mgr: Meghan Herrick
Sales Asso: Tyler Abele
Sales Asso: Katie Ansbro
Sales Asso: Erica Babini

D-U-N-S 08-947-9067
UNITED MAILING INC
(*Suby of* IWCO DIRECT) ★
1001 Park Rd, Chanhassen, MN 55317-9235
Tel (952) 474-0961 *Founded/Ownrshp* 1977
Sales 140.0MM *EMP* 190
SIC 7331 2759 8732 Mailing service; Embossing on paper; Commercial nonphysical research
Pr: James N Andersen
**CFO:* Pete Karle
**Treas:* Dan Axelson
**Ex VP:* Thomas Wicka

D-U-N-S 06-351-3915
UNITED MARITIME GROUP LLC
U.S. UNITED OCEAN SERVICES
601 S Harbour Island Blvd, Tampa, FL 33602-5735
Tel (813) 209-4200 *Founded/Ownrshp* 2007
Sales 70.9MM^E *EMP* 1,035
SIC 4449 4424 River transportation, except on the St. Lawrence Seaway; Coastwide transportation, freight
Pr: Steven Green

UNITED MEDICAL CENTER
See NOT-FOR-PROFIT HOSPITAL CORP

UNITED MEDICAL CENTER
See NOT FOR PROFIT HOSPITAL CORP

D-U-N-S 83-379-5938
UNITED MEMORIAL MEDICAL CENTER
127 North St, Batavia, NY 14020-1631
Tel (585) 343-6030 *Founded/Ownrshp* 1900
Sales 88.8MM *EMP* 750^E
SIC 8062 8049 8011 General medical & surgical hospitals; Physical therapist; Medical centers
CEO: Mark Schoell
Chf Rad: Barry Rosenberg
Pr: Roxanne Ross
CFO: Robert Chiavetta
Bd of Dir: William Fritts
Ofcr: Diana Desautels
Sr VP: Cheryl Loverdi
VP: Mary Bowen
Dir IT: Chad Caccamise
IT Man: Steve Felix
Mtls Dir: Glen Simon

D-U-N-S 00-404-4830
UNITED METHODIST PUBLISHING HOUSE (IL)
DIMENSION FOR LIVING
2222 Rosa L Parks Blvd, Nashville, TN 37228-1306
Tel (615) 749-6000 *Founded/Ownrshp* 1789
Sales 45.9MM *EMP* 1,000
SIC 2731 5192 5942 2741 2721 Books: publishing & printing; Books, periodicals & newspapers; Book stores; Miscellaneous publishing; Periodicals
Pr: Neil M Alexander
COO: Audrey Kidd
**COO:* Larry Wallace
VP: Kossian Linda
**Ex Dir:* Jeff Barnes
**Ex Dir:* Steve Cashion
**Ex Dir:* Tamara Crabtree
**Ex Dir:* Mike Cunningham
Ex Dir: Lisa Zamora
Telecom Ex: David Bess
Opers Mgr: Jim Feuerborn

D-U-N-S 80-076-5828
UNITED NATIONAL CORP
601 S Minnesota Ave, Sioux Falls, SD 57104-4824
Tel (605) 357-3001 *Founded/Ownrshp* 1990
Sales NA *EMP* 2,900
Accts Eide Bailly Sioux Falls Sd
SIC 6021 National commercial banks
Pr: T Denny Sanford
CFO: Mike Blubaugh

D-U-N-S 07-553-6771
UNITED NATIONAL INSURANCE CO
(*Suby of* FOX PAINE & CO LLC) ★
3 Bala Plz E Ste 300, Bala Cynwyd, PA 19004-3406
Tel (610) 664-1500 *Founded/Ownrshp* 2003
Sales NA *EMP* 244
SIC 6331 Fire, marine & casualty insurance & carriers
Ch Bd: Raymond L Freudberg
Pr: Seth Freudberg
CFO: Tom McGeehan
Treas: Kevin L Tate
VP: Del Hinkle
Dir IT: Jay Karabin
Pgrm Dir: Jackie Pomales

D-U-N-S 00-170-9294 IMP/EXP
UNITED NATIONS
UNITED NATIONS SECRETARIAT
405 E 42nd St Bsmt 1, New York, NY 10017-3599
Tel (212) 963-1234 *Founded/Ownrshp* 1945
Sales NA *EMP* 14,300
SIC 9721 United Nations;
Sr Cor Off: Michael Laing
Ofcr: Assiya Akanay
Ofcr: Stephane Auvray
Ofcr: Jennifer Boggs
Ofcr: Regis Bourgault
Ofcr: Fernando Cavalcante
Ofcr: Lionel Chalopin
Ofcr: Pedro Conceicao
Ofcr: Manal Elsir
Ofcr: Andrea Kienle
Ofcr: Solveig Knudsen
Ofcr: Aristide Komze
Ofcr: Chiyuki Kozuka
Ofcr: Marcelo Lafleur
Ofcr: Michael Langelaar
Ofcr: Matti Lehtonen
Ofcr: Clement McKenzie
Ofcr: Girish Sinha
Ofcr: Aung Thu
Comm Man: Dorte L Madsen
Comm Man: Bianca Wilson

D-U-N-S 79-351-1262
UNITED NATIONS DEVELOPMENT PROGRAMME
UNDP
(*Suby of* UNITED NATIONS SECRETARIAT) ★
1 United Nations Plz Fl 3, New York, NY 10017-3515
Tel (212) 906-5000 *Founded/Ownrshp* 1966
Sales NA *EMP* 4,650
SIC 9721 United Nations;
**Pr:* He Mr Mrten Grunditz
**VP:* Rebeca Grynspan
**VP:* Mr Tarik Iziraren
**VP:* He Mr Yusra Khan

D-U-N-S 03-466-8137
UNITED NATIONS FEDERAL CREDIT UNION
UNCFU
(*Suby of* UNITED NATIONS SECRETARIAT) ★
2401 44th Rd, Long Island City, NY 11101-4605
Tel (347) 686-6000 *Founded/Ownrshp* 1947
Sales NA *EMP* 450
SIC 6061 Federal credit unions
CEO: William F Predmore
**Ch Bd:* Walter Gore
**Pr:* Michael Connery Jr
Pr: Tatayana Costa
Pr: Kumar Periasamy
COO: Lorna Colgan
Ex VP: William Predmore
**Sr VP:* James W Fenimore
VP: Prasad Balasubramaniam
VP: Debra I Costa
VP: Bill Thomas

D-U-N-S 02-817-8684
UNITED NATIONS FOUNDATION INC
UNITED NATIONS SECRETARIAT
(*Suby of* UNITED NATIONS SECRETARIAT) ★
1750 Penn Ave Nw Ste 300, Washington, DC 20006-4515
Tel (202) 887-9040 *Founded/Ownrshp* 1998
Sales 147.1MM *EMP* 102
Accts Pricewaterhousecoopers Llp Ba
SIC 8621 Professional membership organizations
CEO: Kathy Calvin
**COO:* Richard S Parnell
CFO: Walter Cortes
**CFO:* Walter Corts
Ex VP: Maureen Chalmers
**VP:* Andrew Axelrod
**VP:* Reid Detchon
Comm Dir: Amy Dielsi
Ex Dir: Patrick Madden

D-U-N-S 09-213-9802
UNITED NATIONS MINE ACTION SERVICE
1 United Nations Plz Fl 6, New York, NY 10017-3515
Tel (212) 963-3768 *Founded/Ownrshp* 1997
Sales 5.8MMM *EMP* 35
Accts Mussa Juma Assad United Repub
SIC 8699 Charitable organization
Ofcr: Kurt Chesko

D-U-N-S 62-164-1773
UNITED NATIONS POPULATION FUND
605 3rd Ave, New York, NY 10158-0180
Tel (212) 297-5000 *Founded/Ownrshp* 2004
Sales NA *EMP* 1,031
SIC 9611 Administration of general economic programs
Ex Dir: Thoraya Ahmed Obaid
IT Man: Ian Chase
IT Man: George Price
IT Man: Jim Scollins
IT Man: Lawrence Sullivan

UNITED NATIONS SECRETARIAT
See UNITED NATIONS

UNITED NATIONS SECRETARIAT
See UNITED NATIONS FOUNDATION INC

D-U-N-S 94-355-6183
▲ UNITED NATURAL FOODS INC
313 Iron Horse Way, Providence, RI 02908-5637
Tel (401) 528-8634 *Founded/Ownrshp* 1976
Sales 8.4MMM *EMP* 8,700
Tkr Sym UNFI *Exch* NGS
SIC 5149 5122 5142 Organic & diet foods; Health foods; Natural & organic foods; Cosmetics, perfumes & hair products; Vitamins & minerals; Packaged frozen goods
Pr: Steven L Spinner
**Ch Bd:* Michael S Funk
Pr: Craig H Smith
Pr: Christopher P Testa
COO: Sean F Griffin
CFO: Mark E Shamber
Chf Cred: Joseph J Traficanti
Sr VP: Eric A Dorne
Sr VP: Thomas A Dziki
Sr VP: Michael P Zechmeister
VP: Marc R Ghidotti
VP: David Megenis
VP: Rick Moller
VP: Joe Traficanti
Board of Directors: Eric P Artz, Ann Torre Bates, Denise M Clark, Gail A Graham, James P Heffernan, Peter A Roy

D-U-N-S 02-117-7381 IMP
■ UNITED NATURAL FOODS WEST INC
UNFI
(*Suby of* UNITED NATURAL FOODS INC) ★
1101 Sunset Blvd, Rocklin, CA 95765-3786
Tel (401) 528-8634 *Founded/Ownrshp* 1976
Sales 687.7MM^E *EMP* 503
SIC 5149 5141 Groceries & related products; Groceries, general line
CEO: Kurt M Luttecke
**Ch Bd:* Michael S Funk
**Pr:* Steven L Spinner
**Sr VP:* Eric A Dorne
**VP:* Sean F Griffin

D-U-N-S 07-684-2194
UNITED NEGRO COLLEGE FUND INC
COLLEGE FUND/UNCF
1805 7th St Nw Ste 100, Washington, DC 20001-3187
Tel (800) 331-2244 *Founded/Ownrshp* 1944
Sales 221.3MM *EMP* 257
SIC 8399 Fund raising organization, non-fee basis
Pr: Michael L Lomax
Top Exec: Vernon Jordan Jr
Ex VP: Sydney M Avent
Ex VP: John Donohue
VP: Therese Badon
VP: Brian Bridges
VP: Lloyd Howell Jr
VP: Paulette Jackson
VP: Maurice E Jenkins
**VP:* James H Mayo III
VP: Karl Reid
VP: Robert Rucker
VP: Richard Shropshire
VP: Cheryl Smith

D-U-N-S 00-697-0628
UNITED OF OMAHA LIFE INSURANCE CO
(*Suby of* MUTUAL OF OMAHA INSURANCE CO) ★
Mutual Of Omaha Plaza, Omaha, NE 68175-0001
Tel (402) 342-7600 *Founded/Ownrshp* 1926
Sales NA *EMP* 450
SIC 6311 6321 6324 Life insurance carriers; Health insurance carriers; Group hospitalization plans
Ch Bd: Daniel P Neary
Ex VP: Madeline Rucker
VP: Luther Lawson
VP: William Puskas
Dir Bus: Kathy Burnham
IT Man: Pat Stemmermann
Info Man: Thomas Whalen

UNITED OIL
See UNITED EL SEGUNDO INC

D-U-N-S 02-456-8149
UNITED OIL OF CAROLINAS INC
1627 Spencer Mountain Rd, Gastonia, NC 28054-9002
Tel (704) 824-3561 *Founded/Ownrshp* 1938
Sales 207.8MM *EMP* 26
Accts Butler & Stowe Gastonia Nc
SIC 5172 Petroleum products
Pr: D L Efird
**Sec:* Dick J Bedgood
**VP:* Thomas R Davis
**VP:* Tim Efird
**Prin:* Lewis Efird

D-U-N-S 05-596-3727
■ UNITED ONLINE INC
(*Suby of* B RILEY FINANCIAL INC) ★
21255 Burbank Blvd # 400, Woodland Hills, CA 91367-6610
Tel (818) 287-3000 *Founded/Ownrshp* 2016
Sales 151.1MM *EMP* 545^E
SIC 5961 7299 Mail order house; Consumer buying service
CEO: Jeff Goldstein
CFO: Edward Zinser
Ex VP: Mark Harrington
Sr VP: Shahir Fakiri
Sr VP: John Heffernan
Sr VP: Mv Krishnamurthy
VP: Karl Arambulo
Mktg Dir: Kevin Brodily
Mktg Mgr: Danny Gumport
Mktg Mgr: Deb Hanson

UNITED P & H SUPPLY
See UNITED P&H SUPPLY CO

D-U-N-S 00-643-7677 IMP/EXP
UNITED P&H SUPPLY CO
UNITED P & H SUPPLY
9947 W Carmen Ave, Milwaukee, WI 53225-2523
Tel (414) 393-6600 *Founded/Ownrshp* 1922
Sales 10.8MM *EMP* 2,000
SIC 5085 5074 3312 3463

D-U-N-S 00-794-3897
UNITED PACIFIC INSURANCE CO
TRAVELERS INSURANCE
1 Tower Sq, Hartford, CT 06183-0001
Tel (860) 277-0995 *Founded/Ownrshp* 1992
Sales NA *EMP* 1,368
SIC 6411 Insurance agents, brokers & service
CEO: Jay Fishman
**VP:* Terry Van Gilder
Netwrk Eng: Eric Miner

D-U-N-S 82-690-0081
■ UNITED PARCEL SERVICE CO
UPSCO UNITED PARCEL SERVICE CO
(*Suby of* UPS) ★
55 Glenlake Pkwy, Atlanta, GA 30328-3498
Tel (404) 828-6000 *Founded/Ownrshp* 1953
Sales 56.9MM^E *EMP* 1,194^E
SIC 4512 Air cargo carrier, scheduled
Pr: David P Abney
Area Mgr: Derek Voycey
Sls Dir: Jay Cotta

D-U-N-S 00-699-1673 IMP
UNITED PARCEL SERVICE INC
UPS
55 Glenlake Pkwy, Atlanta, GA 30328-3498
Tel (404) 828-6000 *Founded/Ownrshp* 1930
Sales NA *EMP* 75,000^E
SIC 4215

D-U-N-S 00-699-1681
▲ UNITED PARCEL SERVICE INC
UPS
55 Glenlake Pkwy, Atlanta, GA 30328-3498
Tel (404) 828-6000 *Founded/Ownrshp* 1907
Sales 58.3MMM *EMP* 444,000
Accts Deloitte & Touche Llp Atlanta
Tkr Sym UPS *Exch* NYS
SIC 4215 4513 4522 Package delivery, vehicular; Parcel delivery, vehicular; Letter delivery, private air; Package delivery, private air; Parcel delivery, private air; Flying charter service
Ch Bd: David P Abney
V Ch: John Alden
Pr: James J Barber Jr
Pr: Myron Gray
CFO: Richard N Peretz
Chf Cred: Alan Gershenhorn
Bd of Dir: Alexy Sanchez
Ofcr: Scott Childress
Ex VP: Tom Healey
Sr VP: Teresa M Finley
Sr VP: Kate Gutmann
Sr VP: Mark Wallace
VP: Costello Art
VP: Richard Behrendt
VP: Anne Bowen-Long
VP: Charles Brown
VP: Kenneth Buenker
VP: Stephanie Callaway
VP: Stephen Campbell
VP: Matthew Capozzoli
VP: Brian Carrier
Board of Directors: Kevin M Warsh, Rodney C Adkins, Michael J Burns, William R Johnson, Candace Kendle, Ann M Livermore, Rudy H P Markham, Clark T Randt Jr, John T Stankey, Carol B Tome

D-U-N-S 00-686-8772 IMP
■ UNITED PARCEL SERVICE INC (OH) (OH)
UPS
(*Suby of* UPS) ★
55 Glenlake Pkwy, Atlanta, GA 30328-3498
Tel (404) 828-6000 *Founded/Ownrshp* 1934
Sales 22.9MMM^E *EMP* 204,986
SIC 7389 Mailing & messenger services; Building scale models
CEO: D Scott Davis
**CFO:* Kurt P Kuehn
VP: Mark Kemper

UNITED PAVING
See OLDCASTLE SW GROUP INC

D-U-N-S 00-565-3464 IMP
UNITED PHOSPHORUS INC
UPI
(*Suby of* UPL LIMITED)
630 Freedom Business Ctr, King of Prussia, PA 19406-1331
Tel (610) 491-2800 *Founded/Ownrshp* 1996
Sales 114.4MM^E *EMP* 107
SIC 5191 Chemicals, agricultural
Pr: Jeffery Allison
**CFO:* Madilyn Palac
**Treas:* Shyam Kamdar

D-U-N-S 03-931-8167 IMP
UNITED PIPE & STEEL CORP
83 Turnpike Rd, Ipswich, MA 01938-1099
Tel (978) 356-9300 *Founded/Ownrshp* 1980
Sales 331.7MM^E *EMP* 122
SIC 5074 Plumbing fittings & supplies
CEO: David M Cohen
Pr: Joe Kelly
**Pr:* Greg Leidner
**CFO:* Ruben Klein
Sr VP: Michael Dfoley
VP Opers: John Renko
Sales Asso: Thomas Barker
Sales Asso: Betsy Gallop

D-U-N-S 61-471-2529 IMP/EXP
■ UNITED PIPELINE SYSTEMS USA INC
(*Suby of* INSITUFORM TECHNOLOGIES LLC) ★
135 Turner Dr, Durango, CO 81303-7971
Tel (970) 259-0354 *Founded/Ownrshp* 1991
Sales 125.0MM *EMP* 35
SIC 1623 Pipeline construction
Pr: Dorwin Hawn
Div/Sub He: Dale Kneller

D-U-N-S 09-403-7843
UNITED PIPING INC
(*Suby of* API GROUP INC) ★
4510 Airport Rd, Duluth, MN 55811-1523
Tel (218) 727-7676 *Founded/Ownrshp* 2009

Sales 112.4MM EMP 50
Accts Kpmg Llp
SIC 1623 Water, sewer & utility lines
Pr: Robert Schoneberger

D-U-N-S 00-389-8285 IMP
UNITED POWER INC A COLORADO COOPERATIVE ASSOCIATION
500 Cooperative Way, Brighton, CO 80603-8728
Tel (303) 659-0551 Founded/Ownrshp 1938
Sales 188.5MM EMP 166
Accts Decoria Maichel And Teague Ps
SIC 4911 Distribution, electric power
CEO: Ronald Asche
*Pr: Susan Petrocco
*CFO: John Parker
*Sec: Ginny Puczek
*VP: Rick Newmen
Sls&Mrk Ex: Troy Whitmore

D-U-N-S 84-319-1409
UNITED PRAIRIE COOPERATIVE
307 Main St, New Town, ND 58763-4000
Tel (701) 627-3636 Founded/Ownrshp 1929
Sales 210.0MM EMP 125
SIC 5191

D-U-N-S 07-627-5353
UNITED PRODUCERS INC
8351 N High St Ste 250, Columbus, OH 43235-1440
Tel (614) 433-2150 Founded/Ownrshp 1934
Sales 152.4MM[E] EMP 500[E]
SIC 5154 Hogs; Cattle
Pr: Mike Bumgarner
*Pr: Dennis Bolling
*CFO: Joe Werstak
Off Mgr: Loretta Baytops

UNITED PROTECTION SERVICE
See A & R SECURITY SERVICES INC

UNITED QUALITY CHEKD DAIRY
See UNITED DAIRY INC

D-U-N-S 05-003-1467 IMP/EXP
UNITED RADIO INC
BLUESTAR USA
3345 Point Pleasant Rd, Hebron, KY 41048-9711
Tel (859) 371-4423 Founded/Ownrshp 1993
Sales 178.7MM[E] EMP 84
SIC 5046 Commercial equipment
Pr: Phil Rubenstein
*CFO: Mark Fuller
*VP: Mara Charlamb
VP: Mike Jimison
Exec: Vince Alexander
Comm Dir: Lisa Haynes
Genl Mgr: Girish Parundekar
IT Man: Sean Gray
Pr Mgr: Brandy Berryhill
Sls Mgr: Ken Shaner

UNITED REFINING COMPANY
See UNITED REFINING INC

D-U-N-S 11-833-1149
UNITED REFINING CO
(Suby of UNITED REFINING CO) ★
15 Bradley St, Warren, PA 16365-3299
Tel (814) 723-1500 Founded/Ownrshp 1902
Sales 2.0MMM[E] EMP 4,207
SIC 2911 5541 5411 Petroleum refining; Oils, fuel; Asphalt or asphaltic materials, made in refineries; Gasoline service stations; Grocery stores; Convenience stores
Ch Bd: John A Catsimatidis
*Pr: Myron L Turfitt
CFO: James E Murphy
Treas: Dennis E Bee
Sr VP: Ashton L Ditka
VP: Frederick J Martin Jr
VP: John R Wagner
Board of Directors: Martin R Bring, Jacob Feinstein, Douglas Lemmonds, Andrew Maloney, Dennis Mehiel

D-U-N-S 18-785-9665
UNITED REFINING CO OF PENNSYLVANIA
(Suby of UNITED REFINING CO) ★
15 Bradley St, Warren, PA 16365-3299
Tel (814) 723-1500 Founded/Ownrshp 1902
Sales 87.6MM[E] EMP 350
SIC 5541 5411 Gasoline service stations; Truck stops; Convenience stores, chain
Ch Bd: John A Catsimatidis
*Pr: Myron L Turfitt
*CFO: James E Murphy
*Treas: Dennis E Bee Jr
*Treas: Douglas I Scalise
*Sr VP: Ashton L Ditka
VP: John Wagner

D-U-N-S 00-210-5179 IMP
UNITED REFINING INC (PA)
UNITED REFINING COMPANY
(Suby of UNITED ACQUISITION CORP) ★
15 Bradley St, Warren, PA 16365-3299
Tel (814) 723-1500 Founded/Ownrshp 1902, 1986
Sales 2.0MMM[E] EMP 4,617
SIC 2911 5541 5411 4612 Petroleum refining; Gasoline service stations; Convenience stores; Crude petroleum pipelines
Ch Bd: John A Catsimatidis
*Pr: Myron L Turfitt
*CFO: James E Murphy
*Treas: Dennis Bee
Treas: Dennis E Bee Jr
VP: Rick Curren
*VP: Ashton L Ditka
VP: Fred Martin
VP: Michael Roudybush
VP: Bob Sedon
*VP: Thomas E Skarada
Exec: Amy Gustafson
Dir: Dean Stanton

D-U-N-S 06-838-7372
UNITED REGIONAL HEALTH CARE SYSTEM INC
1600 11th St, Wichita Falls, TX 76301-4300
Tel (940) 764-3211 Founded/Ownrshp 1918
Sales 299.5MM EMP 1,950
SIC 8062 General medical & surgical hospitals
CEO: Phyliss Cowling
Ofcr: Lana Daniel
Ofcr: Fernando Tezaguic
*Sr VP: Nancy Townley
VP: Donnie Boydstun
VP: Pamela Bradshaw
*VP: Stevie Jo Brown
*VP: Rick Carpenter
*VP: Kristi Faulkner
Dir Case M: Christi Cook
Dir Lab: Gary Wells

D-U-N-S 07-785-4479
UNITED REHAB LLC
9510 Ormsby Station Rd # 101, Louisville, KY 40223-4082
Tel (502) 426-2242 Founded/Ownrshp 2005
Sales 34.2MM[E] EMP 2,200
SIC 8052 8051 8059 Intermediate care facilities; Skilled nursing care facilities; Personal care home, with health care
IT Man: Bob Dooley

D-U-N-S 00-958-6041 IMP/EXP
■ UNITED RENTALS (NORTH AMERICA) INC
(Suby of UNITED RENTALS INC) ★
100 Frist Stamford 700, Stamford, CT 06902
Tel (203) 622-3131 Founded/Ownrshp 1998
Sales 5.2MMM EMP 12,500
SIC 7353 7359 5084 Heavy construction equipment rental; Cranes & aerial lift equipment, rental or leasing; Earth moving equipment, rental or leasing; Tool rental; Industrial machinery & equipment
Pr: Michael J Kneeland
*Ch Bd: Jenne K Britell
COO: Matthew J Flannery
CFO: William B Plummer
Sr VP: Jonathan M Gottsegen
VP: Jessica T Graziano
VP: Robert Miner
Sls Mgr: David Hoffman
Board of Directors: Jose B Alvarez, Bobby J Griffin, Brian D McAuley, John S McKinney, Jason D Papastavrou, Filippo Passerini, Donald C Roof, L Keith Wimbush

D-U-N-S 17-633-3961
▲ UNITED RENTALS INC
100 1st Stamford Pl # 700, Stamford, CT 06902-9200
Tel (203) 622-3131 Founded/Ownrshp 1997
Sales 5.8MMM EMP 12,700
Accts Ernst & Young Llp Stamford C
Tkr Sym URI Exch NYS
SIC 7359 7353 Equipment rental & leasing; Tool rental; Work zone traffic equipment (flags, cones, barrels, etc.); Earth moving equipment, rental or leasing
Pr: Michael J Kneeland
COO: Matthew J Flannery
CFO: William B Plummer
Chf Mktg O: Chris Hummel
Ex VP: Kurtis Barker
Ex VP: Anthony Leopold
Sr VP: Dale A Asplund
Sr VP: Michael D Macdonald
Sr VP: Michael D Maconal
Sr VP: Steven E Nadlman
Sr VP: Craig A Pintoff
VP: Fred Bratman
VP: Gregg Christensen
VP: Loretta Foley
VP: Scott Gorton
VP: Jonathan Gottsegen
VP: Jessica T Graziano
VP: Ron Groff
VP: Randal Hajner
VP: Tom Jones
VP: Chad Matter
Board of Directors: Jose B Alvarez, Jenne K Britell, Bobby J Griffin, Brian D McAuley, John S McKinney, Jason D Papastavrou, Filippo Passerini, Donald C Roof, Keith Wimbush

D-U-N-S 19-439-0431 IMP/EXP
UNITED RETAIL GROUP INC
365 W Passaic St Ste 205, Rochelle Park, NJ 07662-3012
Tel (201) 845-0880 Founded/Ownrshp 2007
Sales NA EMP 5,500
SIC 5621

D-U-N-S 78-663-9104 IMP/EXP
UNITED RETAIL GROUP INC
365 W Passaic St Ste 12, Rochelle Park, NJ 07662-3012
Tel (201) 845-0880 Founded/Ownrshp 1989
Sales 71.8MM[E] EMP 5,000
SIC 5621 Women's clothing stores
Pr: Rafael Benaria
COO: David Holtzman
VP: Raphael Benaroya
VP Opers: David English

D-U-N-S 55-687-3664
UNITED RETIREMENT PLAN CONSULTANTS INC
545 Metro Pl S Ste 240, Dublin, OH 43017-5310
Tel (614) 923-8822 Founded/Ownrshp 2011
Sales NA EMP 300
SIC 6411 6282 Pension & retirement plan consultants; Investment advice
CEO: Lee Bachu
CFO: Christopher W Larkin
Ofcr: Russ Dempsey

UNITED RGONAL PHYSICIANS GROUP
See CARDIOVASCULAR & THORACIC SURGICAL GROUP OF WICHITA FALLS P A

D-U-N-S 00-537-5394
UNITED ROAD SERVICES INC
AUTOMOTIVE TRANSPORT TECH CTR
(Suby of CHARLESBANK CAPITAL PARTNERS LLC) ★
10701 Middlebelt Rd, Romulus, MI 48174-2714
Tel (734) 946-3232 Founded/Ownrshp 1998, 2012
Sales 371.1MM[E] EMP 1,300[E]
SIC 4213 Automobiles, transport & delivery
Ch Bd: Kathleen McCann
*Pr: Mark Anderson
*CFO: Eric Mikesell
Bd of Dir: John Becker
Ofcr: Larry Semczak
Ex VP: Andy Mell
Sr VP: Charles E Baxter
Sr VP: Dave Koster
*Sr VP: Patrick Riley
VP: Michael Martin
VP: Ed McDonnell
Dir Bus: Lou Carbonell

D-U-N-S 61-415-3323
UNITED ROAD TOWING INC
U R T
9550 Bormet Dr Ste 304, Mokena, IL 60448-8385
Tel (708) 390-2200 Founded/Ownrshp 2005
Sales 9.0MM EMP 1,200
SIC 7549 Towing services; Towing service, automotive
CEO: Gerald Corcoran
COO: Pat Fodale
*CFO: Michael Mahar
*Treas: Ruth Kozlowski
Ex VP: Robert Segura
*Sr VP: Edward Arensdorf
*Sr VP: George Bergeron
*Sr VP: Douglas Harff
*Sr VP: Thomas Tedford
Exec: Kevin Corcoran
Genl Mgr: Steve Cox

UNITED SALAD CO.
See SPADA PROPERTIES INC

D-U-N-S 02-776-1170
UNITED SALAD CO
(Suby of UNITED SALAD CO) ★
8448 Ne 33rd Dr Ste 100, Portland, OR 97211-2105
Tel (503) 288-8300 Founded/Ownrshp 1940
Sales 238.6MM[E] EMP 500
SIC 5148 0175 2033 Vegetables, fresh; Fruits, fresh; Apple orchard; Apricot orchard; Nectarine orchard; Peach orchard; Fruits: packaged in cans, jars, etc.
Pr: Ernest Spada Sr
*CFO: Teresa Spada
*VP: Ernest Spada Jr
Genl Mgr: Marie Spada
Genl Mgr: Kasandra Tracy
Sls Mgr: Steve Kenney

D-U-N-S 79-869-6951
UNITED SCAFFOLDING INC
(Suby of BROCK GROUP) ★
12021 Lakeland Park Blvd # 120, Baton Rouge, LA 70809-4200
Tel (225) 774-1480 Founded/Ownrshp 1992
Sales 53.6MM[E] EMP 1,500
SIC 1799 Fireproofing buildings
VP: Eric Chaney
CFO: Kevin Collard
*Treas: Richard Watts
Sr Cor Off: Jerry Gulotta
Sr VP: Tony Huval
Sr VP: Mike Peterson
Sr VP: Marty Stamey
Sr VP: Eddie Williams
VP: Kurt Jones
Brnch Mgr: Troy Gulotta
Brnch Mgr: Jay Kemp

D-U-N-S 03-760-1085 EXP
UNITED SCRAP METAL INC (IL)
1545 S Cicero Ave, Cicero, IL 60804-1529
Tel (708) 780-6800 Founded/Ownrshp 1979
Sales 300.0MM EMP 265
SIC 5093

D-U-N-S 01-419-4935
UNITED SEATING & MOBILITY LLC
NUMOTION
975 Hornet Dr, Hazelwood, MO 63042-2309
Tel (314) 731-7867 Founded/Ownrshp 2001
Sales 123.6MM EMP 2,032
Accts Rubinbrown Llp Saint Louis
SIC 5047 Medical equipment & supplies
Pr: Robert Gouy
Pr: Neill Rowland
*CFO: Joe Luceri
VP: Scott Austin
*Prin: Bob Gouy
Opers Mgr: Stacie Grimes

D-U-N-S 07-523-1183
UNITED SERVICE ORGANIZATIONS INC
U S O
2111 Wilson Blvd Ste 1200, Arlington, VA 22201-3052
Tel (703) 908-6400 Founded/Ownrshp 1941
Sales 130.7MM EMP 1,000
Accts Lb Grant Thornton Llp Mc Lean
SIC 8399 Council for social agency
Pr: Sloan Gibson
*CFO: Philip Parisi
Sr VP: Paul G Allvin
*Sr VP: Lisa Turner Anastasi
*Sr VP: Jack Flanagan
Sr VP: Tammy Heiser
VP: Jeremy Albritton
VP: Gena Fitzgerald
*VP: John Hanson
VP: Craig Opel
VP: Suzanne Smith
VP: John Williams

D-U-N-S 07-349-6101
UNITED SERVICES ASSOCIATION INC
11280 Aurora Ave, Des Moines, IA 50322-7905
Tel (515) 276-6763 Founded/Ownrshp 1972
Sales 101.9MM EMP 18[E]
SIC 5191 Farm supplies

CEO: Mark Morrissey
*Treas: Rob Jacobs

D-U-N-S 00-793-6941
UNITED SERVICES AUTOMOBILE ASSOCIATION (TX)
USAA
9800 Fredericksburg Rd, San Antonio, TX 78288-0001
Tel (210) 498-2211 Founded/Ownrshp 1922
Sales NA EMP 26,300
Accts Ernst & Young Llp San Antoni
SIC 6331 6311 6351 Property damage insurance; Automobile insurance; Fire, marine & casualty insurance & carriers; Life insurance carriers; Liability insurance
Pr: Josue Robles Jr
Ch Bd: John H Moellering
CFO: Joe E Harlan
Ofcr: Pam S Cipp
Ofcr: Duane G Divich
Ofcr: Nancy Hurt
Ofcr: Frank Lugo
Ofcr: Rachael Verastiqui
Assoc VP: Carl Loyd
Assoc VP: Paul Robinson
Assoc VP: Susan Stintsman
Assoc VP: Steve Zettner
Ex VP: Steven A Bennett
Ex VP: Kevin J Bergner
Ex VP: Laura Bishop
Ex VP: Elizabeth D Conklyn
Ex VP: Robert T Handren
Ex VP: Stuart Parker
Ex VP: Stephen M Speakes
Ex VP: Wendi E Strong
Ex VP: M Von Holcomb

D-U-N-S 19-332-2901
UNITED SERVICES OF AMERICA INC
AFFINECO
(Suby of AFFINECO LLC) ★
855 Main St Ste 900, Bridgeport, CT 06604-4915
Tel (203) 878-0638 Founded/Ownrshp 2002
Sales 44.1MM[E] EMP 1,500
SIC 7349 Janitorial service, contract basis
CEO: Michael Diamond
Pr: Paul Senecal
CFO: Gabor Elcsics
VP: Allan J Defilippo

D-U-N-S 04-519-8791
UNITED SHORE FINANCIAL SERVICES LLC
1414 E Maple Rd Fl 5, Troy, MI 48083-9935
Tel (248) 647-8590 Founded/Ownrshp 2012
Sales 3.7MM[E] EMP 1,800
SIC 6282 Investment advice
Prin: Mat Ishbia

D-U-N-S 13-303-6850
UNITED SITE SERVICES INC
50 Washington St 1000, Westborough, MA 01581-1013
Tel (508) 594-2655 Founded/Ownrshp 2014
Sales 718.8MM[E] EMP 1,200[E]
SIC 4953 Refuse systems
Pr: Ron Carapezzi
CFO: Ed Simoneau
Sr VP: Mark Bartholomew
Sr VP: Rich Vegter
VP: Mark Ford
VP: Mike Marrapese
*VP: Ronald Parlengas Jr
Genl Mgr: Neal Esposito
Manager: Steve Fantasia
Sales Asso: Mark Beaty

D-U-N-S 18-293-3564
UNITED SITE SERVICES OF MARYLAND INC
SOUTHERN MARYLAND SANITATION
3250 Old Washington Rd, Waldorf, MD 20602-3203
Tel (301) 396-8501 Founded/Ownrshp 2002
Sales 1,000.0M EMP 1,500
SIC 7349 Building maintenance services
Pr: Kevin Bruce

D-U-N-S 79-407-6633
UNITED SITE SERVICES OF MISSISSIPPI LLC
(Suby of UNITED SITE SERVICES INC) ★
9486 Highway 23, Belle Chasse, LA 70037-1736
Tel (866) 356-5615 Founded/Ownrshp 2007
Sales 25.2MM[E] EMP 1,500
SIC 7349 Building maintenance services

D-U-N-S 00-553-8710 IMP/EXP
UNITED SOLAR OVONIC LLC
(Suby of ENERGY CONVERSION DEVICES INC) ★
3800 Lapeer Rd, Auburn Hills, MI 48326-1734
Tel (248) 475-0100 Founded/Ownrshp 1990
Sales 124.8MM[E] EMP 1,100
SIC 3674 Semiconductors & related devices
VP: John Williams
Pr: Dr Subhendu Guha
CEO: Julian Hawkins
CFO: William C Kriss Andrews
CFO: Sanjeev Kumar
CFO: Harry Zike
Treas: Bob Dentzman
Ex VP: Joseph P Conroy
Ex VP: Jay B Knoll
VP: Jan Rosen

D-U-N-S 96-673-1606 IMP/EXP
UNITED SOURCE ONE INC
4610 Mercedes Dr Ste 110, Belcamp, MD 21017-1235
Tel (410) 278-0800 Founded/Ownrshp 2000
Sales 104.7MM[E] EMP 57
SIC 5147 5087 Meats & meat products; Restaurant supplies
Pr: Michael R Imgarten
CFO: John Quinn
Off Mgr: Kary Vanderzze
Opers Mgr: Curtis McNeal

D-U-N-S 80-204-3740
UNITED SPACE ALLIANCE LLC
LAUNCH EQUIPMENT SUPPORT SHOP
Launch Equipment Support, Kennedy Space Center, FL 32899-0001
Tel (321) 861-0733 *Founded/Ownrshp* 1996
Sales 98.4MM^E *EMP* 5,000
SIC 7389 Personal service agents, brokers & bureaus
Dir IT: Demonesha Jackson

D-U-N-S 94-494-9510
UNITED SPACE ALLIANCE LLC
3700 Bay Area Blvd # 100, Houston, TX 77058-2783
Tel (281) 212-6200 *Founded/Ownrshp* 1996
Sales 67.3MM^E *EMP* 8,000
Accts Pricewaterhousecoopers Llp Ho
SIC 8711 Aviation &/or aeronautical engineering
Pr: Scott Q Hartwig
*CEO: Daniel Brandenstein
COO: Shaw Brewster
COO: Brewster Shaw
CFO: Bill Capel
*CFO: William R Capel
*VP: Meghan Allen
*VP: Rochelle L Cooper
VP: Kim Doering
VP: Norman Gookins
VP: Scott Hartwig
VP: Craig Ove

D-U-N-S 01-748-4784
UNITED SPORTING COMPANIES INC
ELLETT BROTHERS
267 Columbia Ave, Chapin, SC 29036-8322
Tel (803) 345-3751 *Founded/Ownrshp* 2005
Sales 1.1MMM^E *EMP* 500^E
SIC 5091 Sporting & recreation goods
CEO: Brad Johnson
CIO: John McCarthy
DP Exec: Mike Eargle
Sls Mgr: Angie Barnwell

D-U-N-S 79-988-1503
UNITED STAFFING SOLUTIONS INC
UNITED BLOOD MANAGEMENT
12069 Jefferson Blvd, Culver City, CA 90230-6219
Tel (310) 305-9999 *Founded/Ownrshp* 1996
Sales 5.0MM *EMP* 1,200
SIC 7363 Help supply services
Pr: Parvez Gondal MD
*Prin: Theza Adlan
*Off Mgr: Marcia Velardo

UNITED STARS HOLDINGS
See UNITED STARS INC

D-U-N-S 11-171-8755 IMP
UNITED STARS INC
UNITED STARS HOLDINGS
1546 Henry Ave, Beloit, WI 53511-3668
Tel (608) 368-4625 *Founded/Ownrshp* 1994
Sales 0.5 *EMP* 1,210
SIC 3317 3351 3463 3613 3621 Steel pipe & tubes; Extruded shapes, copper & copper alloy; Rolled or drawn shapes: copper & copper alloy; Nonferrous forgings; Switchgear & switchgear accessories; Bus bar structures; Commutators, electric motor
CEO: Roger W West
*Pr: Richard Van Lanen
Ex VP: David M Schmitt

D-U-N-S 01-995-9949
UNITED STATES ASSOCIATION FOR UNHCR (DC)
USA FOR UNHCR
1775 K St Nw Ste 580, Washington, DC 20006-1529
Tel (855) 808-6427 *Founded/Ownrshp* 1989, 1999
Sales 16.2MM *EMP* 6,000
Accts Gelman Rosenberg & Freedman
SIC 8322 Refugee service
CEO: Anne-Marie Grey
*Ch Bd: Charles Desantis
*CFO: Yelena Bakaleva
Ofcr: Dina Jardaneh
Ofcr: Jessica Kirk-Bowman
Ofcr: Alex Mundt
Exec: Nora Sturm

D-U-N-S 00-902-9083 IMP
UNITED STATES BAKERY
FRANZ FAMILY BAKERY
315 Ne 10th Ave, Portland, OR 97232-2712
Tel (503) 232-2191 *Founded/Ownrshp* 1939
Sales 1.0MMM^E *EMP* 3,000
SIC 2051 5461 Bread, cake & related products; Bakery: wholesale or wholesale/retail combined; Doughnuts, except frozen; Pastries, e.g. danish: except frozen; Bakeries; Bread; Cookies
CEO: Murray R Albers
*Pr: Marc Albers
*CFO: Jerry Boness
VP: Todd Cornwell
VP: Kim Nisbet
VP: Barry Ware
Plnt Mgr: Bill McCarthy

D-U-N-S 06-455-4314
UNITED STATES BEEF CORP
ARBY'S
4923 E 49th St, Tulsa, OK 74135-7002
Tel (918) 665-0740 *Founded/Ownrshp* 1969
Sales 310.0MM^E *EMP* 7,000
SIC 5812 Fast-food restaurant, chain
Ch Bd: Jeffery W Davis
*Pr: Brett Pratt
*CEO: John Davis
*COO: Bo Davis
*CFO: Lori Humphrey
*Prin: Michael J Carson
*Prin: Robert L Davis
CIO: Brian Wilson
VP Opers: Al Schiltz
Mktg Dir: Kristi Weeden
Sls Mgr: Michael Beamis

D-U-N-S 11-823-9292
■ UNITED STATES CELLULAR CORP
(*Suby of* TELEPHONE AND DATA SYSTEMS INC) ★
8410 W Bryn Mawr Ave # 700, Chicago, IL 60631-3418
Tel (773) 399-8900 *Founded/Ownrshp* 1983
Sales 4.0MMM *EMP* 6,400
Tkr Sym USM *Exch* NYS
SIC 4812 4813 Cellular telephone services;
Pr: Kenneth R Meyers
*Ch Bd: Leroy T Carlson Jr
*CFO: Steven T Campbell
Ofcr: Deirdre C Drake
Ex VP: Jay M Ellison
Ex VP: Michael S Irizarry
Sr VP: Edward C Perez
Exec: Marlon Diaz
Ql Cn Mgr: Leo Voin
Mktg Mgr: Adam Coppelman
Mktg Mgr: Caroline Parisi
Board of Directors: James S Barr III, J Samuel Crowley, Walter C D Carlson, Ronald E Daly, Harry J Harczak Jr, Gregory P Josefowicz, Peter L Sereda, Cecilia D Stewart, Kurt B Thaus

D-U-N-S 07-091-3249
■ UNITED STATES COAST GUARD
USCG
(*Suby of* EXECUTVE OFC OF US GOVT) ★
2100 2nd St Sw Stop 7238, Washington, DC 20593-0005
Tel (202) 372-4411 *Founded/Ownrshp* 1790
Sales NA *EMP* 40,000
SIC 9621 Coast Guard, regulation & administration of transportation;
Ch: Robert Tapp
Pr: Jerry Davis
Ofcr: David N Bolanz
Ofcr: Gaston Brewer
Ofcr: Joey Brown
Ofcr: Samuel R Creech
Ofcr: Gene Gonzales
Ofcr: Jason W Holstead
Ofcr: Patrick McMillin
Ofcr: Patrick Pierce
Ofcr: Theresa Roberts
Ofcr: Bob Steele
Ofcr: Dale Streyle
Ofcr: Thomas Sullard
Ofcr: Lee Taylor
Ofcr: Alicia Vantran
Exec: Michael Reed

D-U-N-S 00-121-5136 IMP
UNITED STATES COLD STORAGE INC
(*Suby of* JOHN SWIRE & SONS LIMITED)
201 Laurel Rd Ste 400, Voorhees, NJ 08043-2329
Tel (856) 354-8181 *Founded/Ownrshp* 1899, 1982
Sales 458.4MM^E *EMP* 1,500
SIC 2097 4222 Block ice; Warehousing, cold storage or refrigerated
CEO: David M Harlan
*CFO: Jim Salmon
*VP: Larry Alderfer
VP: Joe Loffredo
VP: Michael Lynch
*VP: Mike Lynch
VP: Lisa Mullins
*VP: Lawrence Sokolowski
Exec: Lisa Battino
Genl Mgr: Randy Dorrell
Genl Mgr: Michael Irvin
Board of Directors: David M Harlan

D-U-N-S 00-326-0072
UNITED STATES CONFERENCE OF CATHOLIC BISHOPS (DC)
3211 4th St Ne, Washington, DC 20017-1104
Tel (202) 541-3000 *Founded/Ownrshp* 1920
Sales 243.4MM *EMP* 377
Accts Kpmg Llp Mclean Va
SIC 8661 4832 4833 Religious organizations; Radio broadcasting stations; Television broadcasting stations
Pr: Timothy Dolan
Assoc Dir: Vincent Mandile
Genl Mgr: Gregory Scott

D-U-N-S 00-195-4718 IMP/EXP
■ UNITED STATES DEPARTMENT OF AGRICULTURE (DC)
U S D A
(*Suby of* EXECUTIVE OFFICE OF UNITED STATES GOVERNMENT) ★
1400 Independence Ave Sw, Washington, DC 20250-0002
Tel (202) 720-3631 *Founded/Ownrshp* 1852
Sales NA *EMP* 104,305
SIC 9641 Regulation of agricultural marketing;
Pr: Nayyera Haq
CFO: Patricia E Haly
*CFO: Patricia E Healy
CFO: Wanda Martin
CFO: Evan J Segal
Ofcr: Christopher Lowe
Exec: Jim Caldwell
Adm Dir: Elana Cass
Adm Dir: Glen Heaton
Adm Dir: Jean Holland
Adm Dir: Linda ITOH

D-U-N-S 00-325-7920
■ UNITED STATES DEPARTMENT OF COMMERCE (DC)
US DOC
(*Suby of* EXECUTIVE OFFICE OF UNITED STATES GOVERNMENT) ★
1401 Constitution Ave Nw, Washington, DC 20230-0001
Tel (202) 482-0267 *Founded/Ownrshp* 1903
Sales NA *EMP* 50,000
SIC 9611 Administration of general economic programs;
CFO: Ellen Herbst
CFO: Scott Quehl
CFO: David M Robinson
CFO: Otto Wolf
Ofcr: Patrick McRae
Assoc Dir: Kevin Smith
Ex Dir: Kiersten Todt
Admn Mgr: Lolita Hammond
Admn Mgr: Mario Oliver
CIO: Terri Ware
Genl Couns: John J Sullivan

D-U-N-S 00-195-7737 IMP/EXP
■ UNITED STATES DEPARTMENT OF DEFENSE
(*Suby of* EXECUTIVE OFFICE OF UNITED STATES GOVERNMENT) ★
1000 Defense Pentagon # 3, Washington, DC 20301-1000
Tel (703) 692-7100 *Founded/Ownrshp* 1947
Sales NA *EMP* 1,369,022
SIC 9711 National security;
Prin: Chuck Hagel
Pt: Raj Shah
*Ch: Michael Mullen
Prin: Alan F Estevez
Prin: Mary J Miller
*Prin: John Zangardi
MIS Dir: David Lester
Genl Couns: William J Haynes
*Genl Couns: Jennifer M O'Connor

D-U-N-S 08-021-0957
UNITED STATES DEPARTMENT OF ENERGY ALBUQUERQUE OFFICE
SANDIA NATIONAL LABORATORY
1515 Eubank Blvd Se, Albuquerque, NM 87123-3453
Tel (505) 845-0011
Sales NA *EMP* 1,045^E
SIC 9611 Energy development & conservation agency, government;

D-U-N-S 08-021-0833
UNITED STATES DEPARTMENT OF ENERGY AMES OFFICE
111 Tasf Iowa State Univ, Ames, IA 50011-0001
Tel (515) 294-5643
Sales NA *EMP* 1,170^E
SIC 9611 Energy development & conservation agency, government;

D-U-N-S 08-021-0928
UNITED STATES DEPARTMENT OF ENERGY BERKELEY OFFICE
LAWRENCE BERKELEY NATIONAL LAB
1 Cyclotron Rd, Berkeley, CA 94720-8099
Tel (510) 486-4000 *Founded/Ownrshp* 2016
Sales NA *EMP* 5,000^E
SIC 9611 Energy development & conservation agency, government;
Prin: Andrew Doran
VP: Paolo Calafiura
VP: Allan Demello
VP: Jinghua Guo
VP: Howard Padmore
VP: John Taylor
Exec: Scott Classen
Exec: Vera Potapenko
Dir IT: Farhad Salmassi
Counsel: Nancy Ware
Snr Mgr: Michael Elizalde

D-U-N-S 08-021-0863
UNITED STATES DEPARTMENT OF ENERGY LIVERMORE OFFICE
LAWRENCE LIVERMORE NAT LAB
7000 East Ave, Livermore, CA 94550-9698
Tel (925) 422-1100 *Founded/Ownrshp* 2016
Sales NA *EMP* 7,000^E
SIC 9611 8731 Energy development & conservation agency, government; ; Energy research
Assoc Dir: Dona L Crawford
Assoc Dir: Bruce T Goodwin
Assoc Dir: George H Miller
IT Man: Marvin J Christensen
IT Man: Gary McCormick
IT Man: Jacqueline Peila
IT Man: Jim Sharp
IT Man: Mike Smith
IT Man: Randy Syester
Netwrk Mgr: Dawn Areson
Sys Mgr: Travis Martin

D-U-N-S 00-325-5643
■ UNITED STATES DEPARTMENT OF HEALTH & HUMAN SERVICES
(*Suby of* EXECUTIVE OFFICE OF UNITED STATES GOVERNMENT) ★
200 Independence Ave Sw, Washington, DC 20201-0004
Tel (202) 401-2281 *Founded/Ownrshp* 1980
Sales NA *EMP* 80,000
Accts Ernst & Young Llp Mclean Va
SIC 9431 Administration of public health programs;
Ch Bd: Dennis L Kasper
Ofcr: Rafael Elizalde
Ofcr: Chuck Selden
Assoc Dir: Carla G Flora
Adm Dir: Ralph A Lopez
Prgrm Mgr: Ann Abercrombie
CIO: Gary Christoph
CIO: Greg Ketcher
CTO: Susannah Fox
Web Dev: Michael McSherry
Ansthlgy: Andrew J Mannes

D-U-N-S 05-236-8391
■ UNITED STATES DEPARTMENT OF HOMELAND SECURITY
EXECUTVE OFC OF THE US GOVT
(*Suby of* EXECUTIVE OFFICE OF UNITED STATES GOVERNMENT) ★
245 Murray Ln Sw, Washington, DC 20528-1002
Tel (202) 282-8000 *Founded/Ownrshp* 2002
Sales NA *EMP* 216,000
Accts Kpmg Llp Washington Dc
SIC 9711 National security;
COO: Dallas Brown
CFO: Randall Miller
Sr Cor Off: Michael Howard
Chf Mktg O: Jeffrey W Runge
*Ofcr: Angela Bailey
Ofcr: John Kropf
Ofcr: Dean Mitchell
Exec: Rhonda Fraser
Prgrm Mgr: Howard Bonds
Genl Mgr: Asif Ali
Genl Mgr: Laura Hokenstad

D-U-N-S 00-325-4273
■ UNITED STATES DEPARTMENT OF INTERIOR
(*Suby of* EXECUTIVE OFFICE OF UNITED STATES GOVERNMENT) ★
1849 C St Nw, Washington, DC 20240-0001
Tel (202) 208-7351 *Founded/Ownrshp* 1849
Sales NA *EMP* 70,000^E
Accts Kpmg Llp Washington Dc
SIC 9512 Land, mineral & wildlife conservation;
Ofcr: Jerry Johnson
Dir Bus: Lynn McPheeters
Ex Dir: Jeffrey D Klein
Prgrm Mgr: Dennis Vasquez

D-U-N-S 00-325-7987
■ UNITED STATES DEPARTMENT OF JUSTICE
(*Suby of* EXECUTIVE OFFICE OF UNITED STATES GOVERNMENT) ★
950 Pennsylvania Ave Nw, Washington, DC 20530-0009
Tel (202) 514-2201 *Founded/Ownrshp* 1870
Sales NA *EMP* 104,220
SIC 9222 9223 United States attorneys' offices; ; Correctional institutions;
Ch: Richard S Hartunian
Exec: Robin Brown
Adm Dir: Rosa Washington
Prgrm Mgr: Brecht Donoghue
Prgrm Mgr: Ruby Qazilbash
Mktg Dir: Tuan Dinh
Genl Couns: Rafael Madan
Counsel: Rodney Patton
Snr Mgr: Craig Alexander
Snr Mgr: Letitia Grishaw
Snr Mgr: Brian Horn

D-U-N-S 00-325-5627
■ UNITED STATES DEPARTMENT OF LABOR
(*Suby of* EXECUTIVE OFFICE OF UNITED STATES GOVERNMENT) ★
200 Constitution Ave Nw, Washington, DC 20210-0001
Tel (202) 693-6002 *Founded/Ownrshp* 1913
Sales NA *EMP* 17,200
SIC 9651 Labor regulatory agency;
Ofcr: Michael Grover
Ofcr: Gail Sweeney
Exec: Michael Traweek
Dir Sec: Rick Otlowski
Admn Mgr: Theresa C James
IT Man: Bob Gregory
IT Man: Tom King
IT Man: Bill Webster
Genl Couns: Janet Dunlop
Snr Mgr: Robert Devore

D-U-N-S 88-400-8988
■ UNITED STATES DEPARTMENT OF THE AIR FORCE
(*Suby of* UNITED STATES DEPARTMENT OF DEFENSE) ★
1000 Air Force Pentagon, Washington, DC 20330-1000
Tel (703) 545-6700 *Founded/Ownrshp* 1947
Sales NA *EMP* 529,688
SIC 9711 Air Force;
CIO: Michael J Basla
CIO: Michael W Peterson
IT Man: David Aldrich
IT Man: Eddie Dunn
IT Man: Keith Gregersen
IT Man: Steve Miller
Genl Couns: Charles A Blanchard

D-U-N-S 83-554-3521
■ UNITED STATES DEPARTMENT OF THE ARMY
(*Suby of* UNITED STATES DEPARTMENT OF DEFENSE) ★
1400 Defense Pentagon, Washington, DC 20310-0001
Tel (703) 695-1717 *Founded/Ownrshp* 1775
Sales NA *EMP* 763,522
SIC 9711 Army;
Ofcr: Kathy Joe
Dir IT: Marcus Flewellen
Dir IT: James Whitt
*Genl Couns: Alissa M Starzak

D-U-N-S 88-400-6032 IMP/EXP
■ UNITED STATES DEPARTMENT OF THE NAVY
(*Suby of* UNITED STATES DEPARTMENT OF DEFENSE) ★
1200 Navy Pentagon, Washington, DC 20350-0001
Tel (703) 545-6700 *Founded/Ownrshp* 1775
Sales NA *EMP* 707,685
SIC 9711 Navy;
Chf Rad: David Phung
Ofcr: Joe R Campa
Ofcr: Kenny Hirsch
Ofcr: Edward McCue
Ofcr: Gregg Smith
Prgrm Mgr: Bill Casanova
Prgrm Mgr: Gloria Mobery
Snr Ntwrk: David McNish
*CIO: Rob Foster
CIO: Geoff Sheffer
IT Man: Edward Rounds

D-U-N-S 05-736-6221 IMP/EXP
■ UNITED STATES DEPARTMENT OF TRANSPORTATION
(*Suby of* EXECUTIVE OFFICE OF UNITED STATES GOVERNMENT) ★
1200 New Jersey Ave Se, Washington, DC 20590-0001
Tel (202) 366-4000 *Founded/Ownrshp* 1966
Sales NA *EMP* 55,000
Accts Clifton Gunderson Llp Calvert

SIC 9621
CFO: Kevin Bryan
Act CFO: Sylvia Garcia
VP: Rob Abbott
Comm Man: Robert Johnson
Adm Dir: Susan Lehman
Adm Dir: Beverly Pope
Prgrm Mgr: Janice Barnes
Prgrm Mgr: Charles Benard
Prgrm Mgr: Elizabeth Day
CIO: Terry Shelton
Dir IT: Karen Stippich

D-U-N-S 78-779-3884
■ UNITED STATES DEPT OF EDUCATION
(*Suby of* EXECUTIVE OFFICE OF UNITED STATES GOVERNMENT) ★
400 Maryland Ave Sw, Washington, DC 20202-0001
Tel (202) 245-7468 *Founded/Ownrshp* 1980
Sales NA *EMP* 4,904
SIC 9411 Administration of educational programs;
**CFO:* Thomas Skelly
Prgrm Mgr: Amalia Cuervo
Prgrm Mgr: Irene Harwarth
Prgrm Mgr: Carolyn Lampila
Prgrm Mgr: Charles Love
Prgrm Mgr: Asheley McBride
Prgrm Mgr: Diana Ohara
Brnch Mgr: Angela Baker
Genl Mgr: Lashawn Flemming
CIO: Russell Barnes
**CIO:* Jason Gray

D-U-N-S 08-768-9394
■ UNITED STATES DEPT OF ENERGY
(*Suby of* EXECUTIVE OFFICE OF UNITED STATES GOVERNMENT) ★
1000 Independence Ave Sw, Washington, DC 20585-0001
Tel (202) 586-5000 *Founded/Ownrshp* 1977
Sales NA *EMP* 14,850
SIC 9611 Energy development & conservation agency, government;
Pr: Pam Mendelson
CFO: Hai N Duog
CFO: Jayne A Fith
CFO: Thomas P Griffin
Ofcr: Michael C Kane
VP: Steven Rubin
Exec: Honora Comerford
Exec: Samantha Dickens
Exec: Mirna A Kozai
Exec: Terri Uhlmeyer
Assoc Dir: Anna Palmisano
Assoc Dir: Michael R Strayer
Assoc Dir: William J Valdez

D-U-N-S 01-207-5755
■ UNITED STATES DEPT OF ENERGY OAKRIDGE FIELD OFFICE
(*Suby of* UNITED STATES DEPT OF ENERGY) ★
200 Administration Rd Fm-73, Oak Ridge, TN 37830-8823
Tel (865) 576-0770 *Founded/Ownrshp* 2003
Sales NA *EMP* 10,390[E]
SIC 9611 Energy development & conservation agency, government;
Netwrk Mgr: Bobby Lane

D-U-N-S 13-201-9105
■ UNITED STATES DEPT OF ENERGY OHIO FIELD OFFICE
(*Suby of* UNITED STATES DEPT OF ENERGY) ★
250 E 5th St Ste 500, Cincinnati, OH 45202-4154
Tel (513) 246-0500 *Founded/Ownrshp* 2003
Sales NA *EMP* 1,292[E]
SIC 9611 Energy development & conservation agency, government;
Prin: Pete Greenwalt
Ofcr: Wendy Bauer
Ofcr: Chris Lockhart
Adm Dir: Lynette Chafin
Snr Mgr: Derrick Franklin
Snr Mgr: Michael Kaszyca

D-U-N-S 03-445-6186
■ UNITED STATES DEPT OF ENERGY RICHLAND OPERATIONS OFFICE
(*Suby of* UNITED STATES DEPT OF ENERGY) ★
825 Jadwin Ave Ste 700, Richland, WA 99352-3589
Tel (509) 376-7395 *Founded/Ownrshp* 2003
Sales NA *EMP* 5,056[E]
SIC 9611 Energy development & conservation agency, government;
Pr: Dave Brockman

D-U-N-S 92-603-8100
■ UNITED STATES DEPT OF GEOLOGICAL SURVEY
OFFICE OF THE DIRECTOR
(*Suby of* UNITED STATES DEPARTMENT OF INTERIOR) ★
12201 Sunrise Valley Dr, Reston, VA 20192-0002
Tel (703) 648-4000 *Founded/Ownrshp* 1879
Sales NA *EMP* 9,000
SIC 9511 Air, water & solid waste management;
Pr: Karen Oakley
Ofcr: Robert Leach
Ofcr: Curtis Palmer
VP: Brian Davis
Exec: Jason Siemion
Assoc Dir: David Applegate
Prin: Suzette Kimball
Software D: Walter Freeman
Sftwr Eng: Dan Swanson
Netwrk Eng: Delores James
Snr Mgr: Sherri Bredesen

D-U-N-S 04-801-1019
■ UNITED STATES DEPT OF HOUSING AND URBAN DEVELOPMENT
H U D
(*Suby of* EXECUTIVE OFFICE OF UNITED STATES GOVERNMENT) ★
451 7th St Sw Rm 5256, Washington, DC 20410-0001
Tel (202) 708-0417 *Founded/Ownrshp* 1965
Sales NA *EMP* 9,100

SIC 9531 Housing programs;
Pr: David Acevedo
Pr: Marvin Turnerjd
COO: Jim Husom
CFO: Jim Martin
Ofcr: Charles Butler
Ofcr: Therese Fretwell
VP: Peggy Nye
Adm Dir: Vivian Walton-Davis
CIO: Rafael Diaz
IT Man: George Gratheer
IT Man: James Jasinksi

D-U-N-S 04-475-8233
■ UNITED STATES DEPT OF STATE
(*Suby of* EXECUTIVE OFFICE OF UNITED STATES GOVERNMENT) ★
2201 C St Nw, Washington, DC 20520-0099
Tel (202) 632-9367 *Founded/Ownrshp* 1789
Sales NA *EMP* 19,479[E]
SIC 9721 International affairs;
Ofcr: David Benton
Ofcr: Charles R Casper Jr
Ofcr: Lauren Diekman
Ofcr: John Fogarty
Ofcr: Garrett M Gehrer
Ofcr: Jonathan Janik
Ofcr: Patrick Koucheravy
Ofcr: Maria C Melchiorre
Ofcr: Andrew Morrison
Ofcr: Wesley Scholz
Ofcr: Laura Seal
Ofcr: Aaron Sherinian
Ofcr: Amy A Simms
Ofcr: Peter Thorin
Ofcr: Elijah Waterman
Ofcr: David Wollan
Ofcr: Jeffrey A Yolangco
Ofcr: Ronald Yonashiro
Ofcr: Matthew Younger
Exec: S Abdus-Samad
Exec: April Wells

D-U-N-S 00-325-4885
■ UNITED STATES DEPT OF TREASURY
(*Suby of* EXECUTIVE OFFICE OF UNITED STATES GOVERNMENT) ★
1500 Pennsylvania Ave Nw, Washington, DC 20220-0001
Tel (202) 622-1100 *Founded/Ownrshp* 1789
Sales NA *EMP* 323,000[E]
SIC 9311 Finance, taxation & monetary policy;
CFO: Peggy Sherry
Ofcr: Nelly Johnson
Ofcr: Lukas Kohler
Assoc Dir: Dennis Oconnor
Prgrm Mgr: Michele Satchell
CIO: Jacquelyn Fletcher
Dir IT: Dave Weekley
Genl Couns: Christopher J Meade
Snr Mgr: Deborah Hayes
Snr Mgr: Gail Henderson-Green
Snr Mgr: Lester Leach

D-U-N-S 00-195-7315
■ UNITED STATES DEPT OF VETERANS AFFAIRS (DC)
(*Suby of* EXECUTIVE OFFICE OF UNITED STATES GOVERNMENT) ★
810 Vermont Ave Nw, Washington, DC 20420-0001
Tel (202) 273-5400 *Founded/Ownrshp* 1930
Sales NA *EMP* 235,000
SIC 9451 Administration of veterans' affairs;
Ofcr: Tom Allin
Ofcr: Armando De Leon
Ofcr: Katherine Devierno
Ofcr: Keith Galyon
Ofcr: Carolyn Gill
Ofcr: Judi Huffman
Ofcr: James Kirkland
Ofcr: Steve Kozick
Ofcr: Stephen Lemon
Ofcr: Carl Nielsen
Ofcr: Geralynn Nies
Ofcr: Betty Styers
Ofcr: Gerard Taylor
Ofcr: Gary Whitfield
Exec: Michael Harvey
Exec: Marie Polardino

D-U-N-S 17-715-4820 IMP/EXP
UNITED STATES ENRICHMENT CORP
USEC
6903 Rockledge Dr, Bethesda, MD 20817-1818
Tel (301) 564-3200 *Founded/Ownrshp* 1998
Sales 900.0MM[E] *EMP* 4,832
SIC 2819 2869

D-U-N-S 03-676-0262
UNITED STATES ENVIRONMENTAL SERVICES LLC
2809 E Judge Perez Dr, Meraux, LA 70075-2024
Tel (504) 279-9930 *Founded/Ownrshp* 2014
Sales 91.7MM[E] *EMP* 370
SIC 8744
CEO: Greg Johnson
COO: Rod Powell
CFO: Eric Hoffman
Ofcr: Rick Taylor
Exec: Vicki Willmon
Genl Mgr: Bob Keesee
Off Admin: Irma E Davila
Dir IT: Keith Plaisance
IT Man: Andrew Smith
Sfty Dirs: David Hamm
Opers Mgr: Chad Kalland

D-U-N-S 00-699-1715
UNITED STATES FIRE INSURANCE CO
(*Suby of* CRUM AND FORSTER INSURANCE) ★
305 Madison Ave, Morristown, NJ 07960-6117
Tel (973) 490-6600 *Founded/Ownrshp* 1824, 2000
Sales NA *EMP* 1,800
SIC 6331 Fire, marine & casualty insurance; Property damage insurance; Fire, marine & casualty insurance & carriers
CEO: Marc Adee
**COO:* Steve Mulready
**CFO:* Paul Bassaline
**Ofcr:* Al Caradonio
**Ex VP:* Gary McGeddy
**Sr VP:* Roberta Aufranc
**Sr VP:* Nicole Bennett
**Sr VP:* Robert Bennett
**Sr VP:* Mark Brown
**Sr VP:* Diana Cossetti
**Sr VP:* Steve Dresner
**Sr VP:* Don Fischer
**Sr VP:* Steve Fomchenko
**Sr VP:* Dave Ghezzi
**Sr VP:* James V Kraus
**Sr VP:* Craig Quinlty
**Sr VP:* Jack Reddy
**Sr VP:* Anthony Slimowicz
**Sr VP:* Chris Stormo

D-U-N-S 00-412-8336 EXP
UNITED STATES FOUNDRY & MANUFACTURING CORP (FL)
US FOUNDRY
(*Suby of* EAGLE MANUFACTURING GROUP) ★
8351 Nw 93rd St, Medley, FL 33166-2025
Tel (305) 885-0301 *Founded/Ownrshp* 1916, 1967
Sales 120.6MM[E] *EMP* 610
SIC 3321 3441 3322 Gray iron castings; Fabricated structural metal; Malleable iron foundries
Pr: Alex Debogory Jr
**Ch Bd:* Alex Lane De Bogory
Pr: Orlando Duran
**CFO:* David Brunswick
Chf Mktg O: Roland Aguilera
Genl Mgr: Lee Fortney
CTO: Pepe Pita
Dir IT: Brad Baggett
Sls Mgr: Teo Douchette

D-U-N-S 07-281-9816 IMP/EXP
UNITED STATES FUND FOR UNICEF
125 Maiden Ln Fl 11, New York, NY 10038-4999
Tel (800) 367-5437 *Founded/Ownrshp* 1947
Sales 500.1MM *EMP* 200
SIC 8399 Fund raising organization, non-fee basis
Pr: Caryl M Stern
**Ch Bd:* Hugh Downs
**Ch Bd:* Vince Hemmer
**Ch:* Jimmy Carter
**Ch:* Gerald R Ford
**V Ch Bd:* Gary Cohen
Ofcr: Kin Schoop
VP: Alisa Aydin
VP: Nicole Brown
VP: Hodan Hern
VP: Veronica Pollard
**VP:* Martin S Rendon
VP: Martin Rendon
Board of Directors: Daniel J Brutto

D-U-N-S 96-487-8743
UNITED STATES FUND FOR UNICEF IN KIND ASSISTANCE CORP
(*Suby of* UNITED STATES FUND FOR UNICEF) ★
125 Maiden Ln Fl 10, New York, NY 10038-4713
Tel (212) 686-5522 *Founded/Ownrshp* 2005
Sales 155.4MM *EMP* 5
SIC 8399 Advocacy group
Exec: Edward Lloyd

D-U-N-S 07-825-6609
UNITED STATES GOLF ASSOCIATION
USGA
77 Liberty Corner Rd, Far Hills, NJ 07931-2570
Tel (908) 234-2300 *Founded/Ownrshp* 1894
Sales 164.7MM *EMP* 350
Accts Bdo Usa Llp New York Ny
SIC 8699 Athletic organizations
Ex Dir: David Fay
**Pr:* Reed K Mackenzie
**Treas:* Paul Dcaruso Jr
VP: Paul D Caruso
**VP:* Walter W Driver
**VP:* Fred S Ridley
Comm Dir: Marty Parkes
Dir IT: Jessica Carroll
Dir IT: Kevin Oconnor
Web Dev: Kyle Van Saders
Opers Mgr: John Palacioz
Board of Directors: Christie Austin

D-U-N-S 00-521-2600 IMP/EXP
■ UNITED STATES GYPSUM CO INC
(*Suby of* USG CORP) ★
550 W Adams St Ste 1300, Chicago, IL 60661-3692
Tel (312) 606-4000 *Founded/Ownrshp* 1901, 1985
Sales 1.2MMM[E] *EMP* 6,772
SIC 3275 Gypsum products; Gypsum board; Gypsum plaster
Pr: James S Metcalf
Pr: Sean McGuinness
**Sr VP:* Timothy V Bixler
**Sr VP:* Dominic A Danessa
**Sr VP:* Robert B Waterhouse
VP: Joseph M Carson
VP: Kevin L Courtney
VP: Arnaud Dupuis
VP: Steven Gillhouse
VP: William J Kelley Jr
VP: Christopher J Lawson
VP: Xavier Matesanz
VP: A J Pavin
VP: Gregory D Salah
VP: Brent A Seppa
VP: Brent Seppa
VP: Thomas Snow
VP: William O White

D-U-N-S 11-263-3060 IMP
■ UNITED STATES HOLOCAUST MEMORIAL MUSEUM
(*Suby of* EXECUTIVE OFFICE OF UNITED STATES GOVERNMENT) ★
100 Roul Wallenberg Pl Sw, Washington, DC 20024-2126
Tel (202) 488-0400 *Founded/Ownrshp* 1980
Sales 163.5MM *EMP* 400
Accts Kpmg Llp Mclean Va
SIC 8412 9411 Museum;
Ch: Thomas Bernstein
**Ch Bd:* Tom Bernstein
**V Ch:* Joshua Bolten
**CEO:* Sara Bloomfield
COO: Aletta Schaap
Ofcr: Angela D Brown
Assoc Dir: Barri-Sue Black
Assoc Dir: Lisa Evans
Assoc Dir: Robert Tanen
Dir Soc: Anastasia Dieter
Prin: 55 Presidential Appointees

D-U-N-S 60-633-7673
UNITED STATES INFORMATION SYSTEMS INC
USIS
35 W Jefferson Ave, Pearl River, NY 10965-2217
Tel (845) 358-7755 *Founded/Ownrshp* 1985
Sales 115.5MM *EMP* 500
Accts Rssm And Company New City Ne
SIC 1731 Communications specialization; Voice, data & video wiring contractor
Pr: Michael Lagana
**Treas:* John Lagana
VP: Colin Clarke
**VP:* Joseph Lagana
MIS Dir: Keith Purpura
Opers Mgr: Donald Fink

D-U-N-S 00-735-1554
■ UNITED STATES LIME & MINERALS INC
(*Suby of* INBERDON ENTERPRISES LTD)
5429 Lbj Fwy Ste 230, Dallas, TX 75240-2666
Tel (972) 991-8400 *Founded/Ownrshp* 1950
Sales 130.8MM *EMP* 323[E]
Accts Grant Thornton Llp Dallas T
Tkr Sym USLM *Exch* NGM
SIC 1422 3274 6289 Crushed & broken limestone; Quicklime; Hydrated lime; Royalty owners protective associations
Pr: Timothy W Byrne
**Ch Bd:* Antoine M Doumet
CFO: M Michael Owens
**V Ch Bd:* Edward A Odishaw
VP Prd: Russell W Riggs
Plnt Mgr: Julius Harris
Plnt Mgr: Randy Maddin
VP Sls: David P Leymeister
Board of Directors: Richard W Cardin, Billy R Hughes

D-U-N-S 88-343-8459 IMP
■ UNITED STATES MARINE CORPS
MARINE CORPS INTELLIGENCE
(*Suby of* UNITED STATES DEPARTMENT OF THE NAVY) ★
Pentagon Rm 4b544, Washington, DC 20380-0001
Tel (816) 394-7628 *Founded/Ownrshp* 1775
Sales NA *EMP* 301,126[E]
SIC 9711 Marine Corps;
Prin: Michael William Hagee

D-U-N-S 04-482-4696
■ UNITED STATES MILITARY ACADEMY
WEST POINT
(*Suby of* UNITED STATES DEPARTMENT OF THE ARMY) ★
646 Swift Rd, West Point, NY 10996-1944
Tel (845) 938-2523 *Founded/Ownrshp* 1802
Sales NA *EMP* 6,727[E]
SIC 9711 Military training schools;
Ofcr: Maj Cavanaugh
Ofcr: Maj Patrick
VP: Richard Yon
Assoc Dir: Suzanne Christoff
Adm Dir: Juliza Ramirez
Off Admin: Neil Galvin
Pgrm Dir: Matthew Clark
Pgrm Dir: Thomas Lainis

D-U-N-S 93-865-0900
■ UNITED STATES MINT
(*Suby of* UNITED STATES DEPT OF TREASURY) ★
801 9th St Nw, Washington, DC 20220-0012
Tel (202) 756-6468 *Founded/Ownrshp* 1792
Sales NA *EMP* 2,200
Accts Kpmg Llp Washington Dc
SIC 9311 Finance, taxation & monetary policy;
CFO: Marty Greiner
Ofcr: Roberto Mata
CIO: Jerry Horton
Plnt Mgr: David Croft
Plnt Mgr: Mark Landry

D-U-N-S 07-523-7800
UNITED STATES OLYMPIC COMMITTEE INC
USOC
1 Olympic Plz, Colorado Springs, CO 80903
Tel (719) 632-5551 *Founded/Ownrshp* 1950
Sales 270.2MM *EMP* 400
Accts Deloitte Tax Llp Chicago Il
SIC 8699 Amateur sports promotion
CEO: Scott Blackmun
**Pr:* Peter Ueberroth
CFO: Walter Glover
**CFO:* Walter Tlover
VP: Paul George
Exec: Ruby Haddock
Exec: Diane Hilgner
Exec: Heather Jones
Exec: Brett Rogers
Assoc Dir: Richard Bittles
Assoc Dir: Keith Bryant
Assoc Dir: David McDaniel
Assoc Dir: Dianne Reynolds
Assoc Dir: Nicki Skinner
Assoc Dir: Bridget Toelle
Dir Soc: Dean Nakamura

D-U-N-S 07-092-1085
■ UNITED STATES PATENT AND TRADEMARK OFFICE
USPTO
(*Suby of* US DOC) ★
600 Dulany St Ste 1, Alexandria, VA 22314-5791
Tel (571) 272-4100 *Founded/Ownrshp* 1790
Sales NA *EMP* 9,500[E]
SIC 9651 Regulation, miscellaneous commercial sectors;
**CFO:* Anthony P Scardino

Ofcr: Robert Fawcett
Ofcr: Susan Hattan
Exec: Eboni Hughes
Exec: Sandy Phetsaenngam
Admn Mgr: Donna Chapman
Admn Mgr: Kim Lockett
Dir IT: Colleen Sheehan
IT Man: Doxie Gallon
Secur Mgr: Daniel Lindsey
Snr Mgr: Helena Payton

D-U-N-S 07-724-7059
UNITED STATES PHARMACEUTICAL GROUP LLC
(*Suby of* CONVEY HEALTH SOLUTIONS INC) ★
13621 Nw 12th St Ste 100, Sunrise, FL 33323-2846
Tel (954) 903-5000 *Founded/Ownrshp* 2001
Sales 114.9MM[E] *EMP* 530
SIC 5047 Medical equipment & supplies
CEO: Glenn M Parker
*CFO: Tim Fairbanks
Ofcr: Nicole Bailey

UNITED STATES PHARMACOPEIA
See UNITED STATES PHARMACOPOEIAL CONVENTION

D-U-N-S 07-484-5140
UNITED STATES PHARMACOPOEIAL CONVENTION
UNITED STATES PHARMACOPEIA
12601 Twinbrook Pkwy, Rockville, MD 20852-1790
Tel (301) 881-0666 *Founded/Ownrshp* 1820
Sales 276.8MM *EMP* 1,200
Accts Grant Thornton Llp Mclean Va
SIC 8731 8734 Medical research, commercial; Product testing laboratory, safety or performance
CEO: Ronald T Piervincenzi
Mng Pt: John Lowenthal
Pr: Nils Frederiks
COO: Richard Wailes
CTO: Stan Burhans
Ofcr: Susan De Mars
Ofcr: Jaap Venema
Ex VP: Praveen Tyle
Sr VP: Anthony Lakavage
Sr VP: Kelly S Willis
VP: Bruk Alemayehu
VP: Bingbing Feng
VP: Colleen Greiner
VP: Gordon Johnston
VP: Surendra K Nath
VP: Christine Stunyo
Exec: Eugenia Macarthy
Comm Man: Latifa Boyce

D-U-N-S 00-401-7851 IMP/EXP
UNITED STATES PIPE AND FOUNDRY CO LLC (AL)
(*Suby of* FORTERRA BUILDING PRODUCTS) ★
2 Chase Corporate Dr # 200, Hoover, AL 35244-3092
Tel (205) 263-8540 *Founded/Ownrshp* 1899, 2016
Sales 550.2MM[E] *EMP* 900
SIC 3321 Cast iron pipe & fittings; Pressure pipe & fittings, cast iron
Pr: William Kerfin
*CFO: Brad Overstreet
VP: Norb Gross
VP: Bob Waggoner
Dist Mgr: Jeff Davis
Genl Mgr: Chuck Smith
Genl Mgr: Ray Vuoncino
Dir IT: Bill Owen
Sfty Dirs: David Stringari
Opers Mgr: Melonie Sullivan
Plnt Mgr: Jeff Suing

D-U-N-S 00-423-4217 IMP/EXP
■ **UNITED STATES PLAYING CARD CO**
(*Suby of* NEWELL BRANDS) ★
300 Gap Way, Erlanger, KY 41018-3160
Tel (859) 815-7300 *Founded/Ownrshp* 1894
Sales 253.0MM[E] *EMP* 500
SIC 2752 5092 Playing cards, lithographed; Playing cards
Pr: Michael Slaughter
VP: Louis Eichhold
Exec: Ruth E Girvin
Ql Cn Mgr: Alex Hoffman
S&M/VP: Mike Slaughter
Mktg Mgr: Aaron Haid
Manager: Ryan Wolf

D-U-N-S 00-326-1245 IMP/EXP
UNITED STATES POSTAL SERVICE
US POST OFFICE
475 Lenfant Plz Sw # 4012, Washington, DC 20260-0004
Tel (202) 268-2000 *Founded/Ownrshp* 1776
Sales NA *EMP* 618,000[E]
SIC 4311 U.S. Postal Service
CEO: Patrick R Donahoe
COO: Megan J Brennan
CFO: Joseph Corbett
Ch: William A Campbell
Ch: Louis J Guiliano
Ch: Gary E Shapiro
Chf Mktg O: Anita J Bizzotto
Ofcr: Henry Gibson
Ofcr: Frank Scheer
Assoc VP: Jane Dyer
Ex VP: James Cochrane
Ex VP: Mary Anne Gibbons
Ex VP: Thomas Marshall
Ex VP: Kristin Seaver
VP: Richard Coughlin
VP: Vanessa Kellum
VP: Linda Kingsley
VP: Bill Mayfield
VP: Pritha Mehra
VP: Lizzie Nelson
VP: Tom Samra
Board of Directors: Carolyn Lewis Gallagher, Alan C Kessler, Katherine C Tobin

D-U-N-S 83-500-6974
■ **UNITED STATES SECRET SERVICE**
(*Suby of* EXECUTVE OFC OF US GOVT) ★
950 H St Nw, Washington, DC 20223-0001
Tel (202) 406-5708 *Founded/Ownrshp* 1905
Sales NA *EMP* 6,500[E]
SIC 9229 Law enforcement statistics center, government;
Genl Mgr: Ronald Bjornstad

D-U-N-S 04-950-1430
UNITED STATES SERVICE INDUSTRIES INC
4340 East West Hwy # 204, Bethesda, MD 20814-4467
Tel (202) 783-2030 *Founded/Ownrshp* 1912, 1969
Sales 54.5MM[E] *EMP* 1,600
SIC 7349 Building cleaning service; Janitorial service, contract basis
Pr: Tim Ruben
*Ch Bd: James Matthews
Sr VP: Joel Felrice
CTO: Andy Anzalone

D-U-N-S 07-684-3184
UNITED STATES SOCCER FEDERATION INC
US SOCCER
1801 S Prairie Ave, Chicago, IL 60616-1319
Tel (312) 808-1300 *Founded/Ownrshp* 1994
Sales 100.5MM *EMP* 92
Accts Bdo Usa Llp Chicago Illinoi
SIC 8699 Amateur sports promotion; Athletic organizations
CEO: Dan Flynn
*Pr: Sunil K Gulati
*Ex VP: Mike Edwards
Genl Mgr: Alyse Lahue

D-U-N-S 02-999-0699 IMP/EXP
▲ **UNITED STATES STEEL CORP**
600 Grant St Ste 468, Pittsburgh, PA 15219-2805
Tel (412) 433-1121 *Founded/Ownrshp* 1901
Sales 11.5MMM *EMP* 33,200[E]
Accts Pricewaterhousecoopers Llp Pi
Tkr Sym X *Exch* NYS
SIC 3312 3317 3356 Blast furnaces & steel mills; Plate, steel; Sheet or strip, steel, cold-rolled: own hot-rolled; Chemicals & other products derived from coking; Steel pipe & tubes; Tin
Pr: Mario Longhi
CFO: David B Burritt
Chf Cred: Suzanne Rich Folsom
VP: Colleen M Darragh
VP: Mark G Tabler
Board of Directors: David S Sutherland, Patricia Diaz Dennis, Patricia A Tracey, Dan O Dinges, John G Drosdick, John J Engel, Murry S Gerber, Stephen J Girsky, Paul A Mascarenas, Glenda G McNeal, Robert J Stevens

D-U-N-S 00-699-1764 EXP
■ **UNITED STATES STEEL INTERNATIONAL INC**
U S S I
(*Suby of* UNITED STATES STEEL CORP) ★
600 Grant St Ste 468, Pittsburgh, PA 15219-2805
Tel (412) 433-1121 *Founded/Ownrshp* 1898
Sales 221.8MM[E] *EMP* 2,200
SIC 5051 Steel
Pr: John P Surma
*CFO: Gretchen R Haggerty
Ex Dir: Miles Stipanovich
Genl Mgr: Stephen W Bilan

D-U-N-S 00-411-7156 IMP
UNITED STATES SUGAR CORP (FL)
111 Ponce De Leon Ave, Clewiston, FL 33440-3098
Tel (863) 983-8121 *Founded/Ownrshp* 1931
Sales 446.9MM[E] *EMP* 1,500
SIC 0133 2061 2062 2033 Sugarcane farm; Raw cane sugar; Cane sugar refining; Canned fruits & specialties
Pr: Robert H Buker Jr
*CFO: Gerard A Bernard
*Ch: William S White
*VP: Edward Almeida
VP: Dan Casper
VP: James Snively
*VP: Malcolm S Wade Jr
CIO: Carl Stringer
Sls Mgr: Angus Rimes

D-U-N-S 04-468-0650 IMP
UNITED STATES SURGICAL CORP
U.S SURGICAL
(*Suby of* COVIDIEN LP) ★
555 Long Wharf Dr Fl 4, New Haven, CT 06511-6102
Tel (203) 845-1000 *Founded/Ownrshp* 1980
Sales 206.7MM[E] *EMP* 1,419
SIC 3841 3845 3842 Surgical instruments & apparatus; Surgical stapling devices; Trocars; Electromedical apparatus; Ultrasonic scanning devices, medical; Surgical appliances & supplies
Pr: John W Kapples
*VP: Gregory Andrulonis

D-U-N-S 07-281-6168
UNITED STATES TENNIS ASSOCIATION INC
USTA
70 W Red Oak Ln Fl 1, White Plains, NY 10604-3602
Tel (914) 696-7000 *Founded/Ownrshp* 1973
Sales 242.7MM *EMP* 35[E]
SIC 8699 Athletic organizations
Ch Bd: Jon Vegusen
*Ch: Jane Brown
Bd of Dir: Joe Arias
Bd of Dir: Trevor Bain
VP: Jackie Finnigan
VP: Larry Haugness
VP: Tommy Ho
VP: Alvin Hom
VP: Bill Mountford
VP: Vinny Palmieri
VP: Stacy A Ruvo
VP: Jeff Schoch
*VP: Alan G Schwartz
Dir Soc: Jeanne Lucido
Comm Dir: Mark Winters

D-U-N-S 07-835-3927
UNITED STATES WELDING INC
600 S Santa Fe Dr, Denver, CO 80223-2403
Tel (303) 777-2475 *Founded/Ownrshp* 1928
Sales 87.0MM[E] *EMP* 125
SIC 5169 5084 5085 5047 7359 Chemicals & allied products; Welding machinery & equipment; Industrial supplies; Medical & hospital equipment; Equipment rental & leasing
Pr: Richard E Lofgren
Area Mgr: Richard Degeus
Brnch Mgr: Brian Dillon
Brnch Mgr: Dave Gulliford

D-U-N-S 96-785-2018
UNITED STEEL PAPER AND FORESTRY RUBBER MANUFACTURING ENERGY ALLIED
5 Gateway Ctr, Pittsburgh, PA 15222
Tel (412) 562-2400 *Founded/Ownrshp* 2011
Sales 489.3MM *EMP* 14[E]
Accts Schneider Downs & Co Inc Pitt
SIC 8631 Labor unions & similar labor organizations

D-U-N-S 06-872-7320
UNITED STEELWORKERS (PA)
USWA
60 Bolevard Of The Allies, Pittsburgh, PA 15222
Tel (412) 562-2400 *Founded/Ownrshp* 1942
Sales 61.5M *EMP* 1,800
SIC 8631 Trade union
Pr: Leo W Gerard
Ch Bd: Kim Nibarger
*Sec: Stan Johnson
*VP: Thomas M Conway
*VP: Jon Geenen
VP: Leon Lynch
*VP: Fred Redmond
Genl Couns: Richard J Brean

D-U-N-S 03-777-0666 IMP/EXP
UNITED STRUCTURES OF AMERICA INC
U S A
1912 Buschong St, Houston, TX 77039-1298
Tel (281) 442-8247 *Founded/Ownrshp* 1980
Sales 93.3MM[E] *EMP* 436
SIC 3448 Buildings, portable: prefabricated metal
Pr: Dain Drake
Chf Mktg O: Ron Fletcher
Ex VP: Kyle Parrish
VP: Damon Drake
VP: David Drake
Dist Mgr: Cameron Cooper
Dist Mgr: Larry Owings
Dist Mgr: Kent Smith
Snr Mgr: Larry Oxford

D-U-N-S 01-168-4748 IMP
UNITED SUBCONTRACTORS INC
(*Suby of* USI SENIOR HOLDINGS INC) ★
445 Minnesota St Ste 2500, Saint Paul, MN 55101-2139
Tel (651) 225-6300 *Founded/Ownrshp* 2004
Sales 564.6MM[E] *EMP* 1,900
SIC 1742 1796 1542 1522 Insulation, buildings; Installing building equipment; Commercial & office building contractors; Commercial & office building, new construction; Residential construction
Pr: Lw Varner Jr
*CFO: Curt Petersen
*VP: Brian Franco
*VP: Jim Tipperreiter
Dir IT: Barry Doerscher

D-U-N-S 86-870-7621
UNITED SUGARS CORP
(*Suby of* AMERICAN CRYSTAL SUGAR CO) ★
8000 W 78th St Ste 300, Minneapolis, MN 55439-2597
Tel (952) 896-0131 *Founded/Ownrshp* 1994
Sales 146.2MM[E] *EMP* 95
SIC 5149 Sugar, honey, molasses & syrups; Sugar, refined
CEO: John Doxie
Ex VP: Dirk Swart
VP: Susan Brekke
VP: Mark Gappa
VP: Steve Hines
*VP: Catherine M Maruska
VP: Raymond Smith
CIO: Randy Bakken
*VP Sls: Dirk F Swart
Mktg Mgr: Steven Hanson

D-U-N-S 00-793-7642
UNITED SUPERMARKETS LLC (TX)
(*Suby of* ALBERTSONS) ★
7830 Orlando Ave, Lubbock, TX 79423-1942
Tel (806) 791-0220 *Founded/Ownrshp* 1916, 2013
Sales 2.2MMM[E] *EMP* 10,000
Accts Robinson Burdette Martin & Ser
SIC 5411 Grocery stores, chain
CEO: Robert Taylor
*Ch Bd: Robert D Snell
*Pr: Matt Dewitt Bumstead
*CFO: Suzann Kirby
Chf Mktg O: Wes Jackson
*Ex VP: Phil Pirkle
*VP: Bradley R Beckstrom
*VP: Tony Crumpton
VP: Scott Malouf
VP: Kyle Reeves
VP: Joe Wombel
Board of Directors: Doris K Snell

D-U-N-S 02-215-4322 IMP/EXP
UNITED SUPPLIERS INC
GREENBELT TRANSPORT
224 S Bell Ave, Eldora, IA 50627
Tel (515) 509-2400 *Founded/Ownrshp* 1963
Sales 2.6MMM *EMP* 475
SIC 5191

D-U-N-S 01-395-2507
UNITED SURGICAL PARTNERS INTERNATIONAL INC
(*Suby of* USPI HOLDINGS INC) ★
15305 Dallas Pkwy # 1600, Addison, TX 75001-4637
Tel (972) 713-3500 *Founded/Ownrshp* 2007
Sales 640.8MM *EMP* 10,600
Accts Kpmg Llp Dallas Texas
SIC 8011 Ambulatory surgical center
CEO: William H Wilcox
*Ch Bd: Paul B Queally
Pr: Brett P Brodnax
CFO: Jason B Cagle
Ex VP: Philip A Spencer
Sr VP: Brett Brodnax
Sr VP: Sandra R A Karrmann
Sr VP: Angel Rodriguez
VP: David Anderson
VP: Symon Biegel
VP: Peter Blach
VP: Kristin Blewett
VP: Rich Delaby
VP: Susan Gant
VP: Mark Garvin
VP: James Jackson
VP: Marian Lowe
VP: Mark McCormick
VP: Jarod Moss
VP: Patrick Murphy
VP: Matt Pate
Board of Directors: Joel T Allison, Anthony F Ecock, John C Garrett, D Scott Mackesy, James Ken Newman, Harold L Paz, Raymond A Ranelli

D-U-N-S 14-996-8401 EXP
■ **UNITED TACONITE LLC**
UTAC
(*Suby of* CLIFFS NATURAL RESOURCES INC) ★
1100 Superior Ave E # 1500, Cleveland, OH 44114-2544
Tel (218) 744-7800 *Founded/Ownrshp* 2003
Sales 424.0MM[E] *EMP* 466
SIC 1011 Iron ore pelletizing
Treas: Ralph Dirusso
*VP: David H Gunning

D-U-N-S 04-533-6526
■ **UNITED TEACHER ASSOCIATES INC**
U T I INSURANCE
(*Suby of* GREAT AMERICAN FINANCIAL RESOURCES INC) ★
11200 Lakeline Blvd, Austin, TX 78717-6050
Tel (512) 451-2224 *Founded/Ownrshp* 1999
Sales NA *EMP* 240
SIC 6324 Hospital & medical service plans
Pr: Billy B Hill Jr

UNITED TECHNOLOGIES CARRIER
See CARRIER CORP

D-U-N-S 00-134-4142
▲ **UNITED TECHNOLOGIES CORP**
10 Farm Springs Rd, Farmington, CT 06032-2577
Tel (860) 728-7000 *Founded/Ownrshp* 1934
Sales 56.1MMM *EMP* 197,000
Accts Pricewaterhousecoopers Llp Ha
Tkr Sym UTX *Exch* NYS
SIC 3724 3585 3721 3534 3669 3699 Aircraft engines & engine parts; Research & development on aircraft engines & parts; Refrigeration & heating equipment; Aircraft; Elevators & equipment; Escalators, passenger & freight; Emergency alarms; Electrical equipment & supplies; Security devices; Security control equipment & systems
Ch Bd: Gregory J Hayes
Pr: David L Gitlin
Pr: Robert F Leduc
Pr: Robert J McDonough
CFO: Akhil Johri
Treas: David R Whitehouse
Ofcr: Elizabeth B Amato
Ex VP: Charles D Gill
Ex VP: David P Hess
Sr VP: Vince Campisi
VP: James Anderson
VP: Robert J Bailey
VP: Dave Carter
VP: Michael Savitsky
Dir Risk M: George Aliprandi
Dir Risk M: Koser Bokhari
Board of Directors: H Patrick Swygert, Lloyd J Austin III, Andre Villeneuve, John V Faraci, Christine Todd Whitman, Edward A Kangas, Ellen J Kullman, Marshall O Larsen, Harold W McGraw III, Richard B Myers, Fredric G Reynolds, Brian C Rogers

D-U-N-S 80-902-6433 IMP
■ **UNITED TECHNOLOGIES ELECTRONIC CONTROLS INC**
UT ELECTRONIC CONTROLS
(*Suby of* UNITED TECHNOLOGIES CARRIER) ★
3650 W 200 N, Huntington, IN 46750-9002
Tel (260) 359-3514 *Founded/Ownrshp* 1987
Sales 128.7MM[E] *EMP* 550
SIC 3822 Auto controls regulating residntl & coml environmt & applncs
Pr: Donald Cawley
*Treas: Joseph Gest
*VP: Ronald Bruehlman
*Prin: Kelly A Romano

D-U-N-S 09-461-9074
UNITED TEMPS INC (NV)
1550 S Ind Ave Ste 300, Chicago, IL 60605
Tel (312) 922-8558 *Founded/Ownrshp* 1985, 1999
Sales 40.0MM *EMP* 7,000
SIC 7361 Employment agencies
Pr: Richard A Simon
*CFO: David Hill
CIO: Badri Herur
Sales Exec: Harold Gordon

D-U-N-S 96-546-0025 IMP
▲ **UNITED THERAPEUTICS CORP**
1040 Spring St, Silver Spring, MD 20910-4018
Tel (301) 608-9292 *Founded/Ownrshp* 1996
Sales 1.4MMM *EMP* 750
Tkr Sym UTHR *Exch* NGS
SIC 2834 Pharmaceutical preparations
Ch Bd: Martine Rothblatt
Pr: Michael Benkowitz
CFO: James C Edgemond
CFO: James Edgemond
Ex VP: Paul A Mahon

Ex VP: David Walsh
Sr VP: Alex Sapir
VP: Bernadette Bouchet
VP: Mike Camp
VP: John Hess
VP: Marc Lorber
VP: Mike Wade
Exec: Erny Claxton
Exec: Jackie Imm
Assoc Dir: Wayne Dellamaestra
Assoc Dir: David Miller

D-U-N-S 04-377-9446
UNITED UTILITY SUPPLY COOPERATIVE INC (KY)
4515 Bishop Ln, Louisville, KY 40218-4507
Tel (502) 459-4011 *Founded/Ownrshp* 1959
Sales 101.8MM *EMP* 35
SIC 5063 Transformers, electric
Pr: Ron Sheets
* *CFO:* Tim Hargrove
VP: Philip Drexler
IT Man: Mike McHargue
VP Opers: Bill Corum
Sales Asso: Melissa Cole
Sales Asso: Joe Heyen
Sales Asso: Jeff Nelson
Sales Asso: Dick Troendly

UNITED VAN LINES
See LAWRENCE TRANSPORTATION SYSTEMS INC

UNITED VAN LINES
See ARMSTRONG TRANSFER AND STORAGE CO INC/ARMSTRONG RELOCATION CO MEMPHIS

UNITED VISION LOGISTICS
See UV LOGISTICS LLC

UNITED VISION LOGISTICS
See UV LOGISTICS ACQUISITION HOLDING CORP

UNITED WATER DELAWARE
See SUEZ NORTH AMERICA INC

UNITED WATER NEW JERSEY INC.
See SUEZ WATER NEW JERSEY INC

UNITED WATER SERVICES INC.
See N A SUEZ

D-U-N-S 04-112-2474
UNITED WAY OF GREATER HOUSTON
50 Waugh Dr, Houston, TX 77007-5813
Tel (713) 685-2300 *Founded/Ownrshp* 1951
Sales 85.3MM *EMP* 158
Accts Blazek & Vetterling Houston
SIC 8399 United Fund councils
Pr: Anna M Babin
* *VP:* Archie Dishman
Genl Mgr: Michael Stewart

D-U-N-S 07-820-1340
UNITED WAY OF KING COUNTY (WA)
720 2nd Ave, Seattle, WA 98104-1702
Tel (206) 461-3700 *Founded/Ownrshp* 1952
Sales 118.3MM *EMP* 120^E
Accts Clark Nuber Ps Bellevue Wa
SIC 8399 Fund raising organization, non-fee basis
Pr: Jon Fine
Bd of Dir: Rick Fersch
* *Ofcr:* Thomas Mitchell
* *VP:* Ashley Hulsey
* *VP:* Christine Hynes
* *VP:* Jim Yearby
Exec: Tam Jensen
Pr Mgr: Adam Bashaw

D-U-N-S 80-140-5999
UNITED WAY OF MINN AREA
404 S 8th St Ste 100, Minneapolis, MN 55404-1084
Tel (612) 340-7400 *Founded/Ownrshp* 2007
Sales 96.2MM *EMP* 3
SIC 8399 Social services
Prin: John Wilgers

D-U-N-S 96-903-7147
UNITED WELFARE FUND
13850 Queens Blvd, Briarwood, NY 11435-2642
Tel (718) 658-4848 *Founded/Ownrshp* 2011
Sales NA *EMP* 4^E
Accts Saxbst Llp New York Ny
SIC 6371 Pension, health & welfare funds
Prin: Christina Winslow

D-U-N-S 07-927-1070
UNITED WIRELESS TECHNOLOGIES INC
300 Se 5th Ave Apt 8180, Boca Raton, FL 33432-5503
Tel (561) 302-9350 *Founded/Ownrshp* 1993
Sales 182.0MM *EMP* 26
SIC 3571 3663 Electronic computers; Radio & TV communications equipment; Cellular radio telephone
Pr: Stephen B Cavayero

UNITED-ERIE DIVISION
See INTERSTATE CHEMICAL CO INC

D-U-N-S 60-545-0485
UNITEDGLOBALCOM INC
(*Suby of* LIBERTY GLOBAL INC) ★
12300 Liberty Blvd, Englewood, CO 80112-7009
Tel (303) 220-6676 *Founded/Ownrshp* 2013
Sales 55.0MM^E *EMP* 15,000
SIC 8999 4813 Communication services; Local & long distance telephone communications;
Pr: Michael T Fries
* *CFO:* Benard Dvorak
* *CFO:* Charles Hrbracken
VP: Mauricio Ramos
Mng Dir: Diederik Karsten
Dir IT: Stphane David

UNITEDHEALTH GROUP
See UNITEDHEALTHCARE OF WISCONSIN INC

D-U-N-S 11-287-1561 EXP
▲ UNITEDHEALTH GROUP INC
9900 Bren Rd E Ste 300w, Minnetonka, MN 55343-9693
Tel (952) 936-1300 *Founded/Ownrshp* 1974
Sales NA *EMP* 200,000
Tkr Sym UNH *Exch* NYS
SIC 6324 6411 6321 Health maintenance organization (HMO), insurance only; Insurance agents, brokers & service; Accident & health insurance
CEO: Stephen J Hemsley
Pr: Rossana Salvadori
Pr: Tracy Sarallo
Pr: David S Wichmann
CFO: Paul Hansen
CFO: John Rex
Treas: Rebecca Madsen
Treas: Janis Verruso
Ex VP: William Munsell
Ex VP: Eric Rangen
Ex VP: Chris Ritchie
Ex VP: Simon Stevens
Ex VP: Jeffery Verney
Ex VP: D Ellen Wilson
Sr VP: Thomas E Roos
VP: Lenys Alcoreza
VP: Tom Allenburg
VP: Christine Anderson
VP: Steven Beecy
VP: Brian Bellows
VP: Robert Benkert
Board of Directors: William C Ballard Jr, Edson Bueno, Richard T Burke, Robert J Darretta, Michele J Hooper, Rodger A Lawson, Glenn M Renwick, Kenneth I Shine, Gail R Wilensky

D-U-N-S 83-911-3115
■ UNITEDHEALTHCARE INSURANCE CO
UNITED HEALTHCARE INSURANCE CO
(*Suby of* UNITEDHEALTH GROUP INC) ★
185 Asylum St, Hartford, CT 06103-3408
Tel (860) 702-5000 *Founded/Ownrshp* 1994
Sales NA *EMP* 30,000
SIC 6311 6321 Life insurance; Accident & health insurance
Pr: Ronald B Colby
* *Pr:* Thomas E Burton
COO: Kevin J Ruth
Ex VP: John Anton
VP: Tony Nardone
VP: John Ryan
Comm Man: Kristen Lyons
CIO: Channing R Wheeler
IT Man: Jay Gamester
IT Man: Christine Gendron
IT Man: David Skovran

D-U-N-S 61-217-1546
■ UNITEDHEALTHCARE LIFE INSURANCE CO
AMERICAN MED SEC FROM PCF CARE
(*Suby of* AMERICAN MEDICAL SECURITY GROUP INC PAC) ★
3100 Ams Blvd, Green Bay, WI 54313-9700
Tel (800) 232-5432 *Founded/Ownrshp* 1997
Sales NA *EMP* 1,300
SIC 6411 6324 6311 8322 Insurance agents, brokers & service; Health maintenance organization (HMO), insurance only; Life insurance carriers; Hotline
Pr: Steve Deraleau

D-U-N-S 09-942-7155
■ UNITEDHEALTHCARE OF NEW ENGLAND INC
UNITED HEALTHCARE
(*Suby of* UNITED HEALTHCARE SERVICES INC) ★
475 Kilvert St Ste 310, Warwick, RI 02886-1360
Tel (401) 737-6900 *Founded/Ownrshp* 1992
Sales NA *EMP* 400
SIC 6324 Health maintenance organization (HMO), insurance only
Pr: Budd Fisher
Ex VP: Jeannine M Rivet
VP: Larry Cavanaugh
Exec: Scott Enos
Dir Surg: Anthony Kazlauskas
VP Sls: Eric Swain
Mktg Mgr: Jose Duchesne

D-U-N-S 15-324-0007
■ UNITEDHEALTHCARE OF NORTH CAROLINA INC
UNITED HEALTHCARE
(*Suby of* UNITEDHEALTH GROUP INC) ★
2307 W Cone Blvd Ste 200, Greensboro, NC 27408-4065
Tel (336) 540-2000 *Founded/Ownrshp* 1996
Sales NA *EMP* 346
SIC 6324 Hospital & medical service plans
Pr: Frank R Mascia
* *CFO:* Randy Giles

D-U-N-S 02-963-0498
■ UNITEDHEALTHCARE OF WASHINGTON INC
PACIFICARE
(*Suby of* PACIFICARE HEALTH PLAN ADMINISTRATORS INC) ★
1111 3rd Ave Ste 1100, Seattle, WA 98101-3207
Tel (206) 236-2500 *Founded/Ownrshp* 1994
Sales NA *EMP* 1,641^E
SIC 6324 6321 Hospital & medical service plans; Accident & health insurance
Pr: Chris Wing
* *CFO:* Don Costa
VP: Carol Kotonias - Ray
S&M/VP: Carol K Ray
Pharmcst: Cindy Christianson

D-U-N-S 10-221-5993
■ UNITEDHEALTHCARE OF WISCONSIN INC
UNITEDHEALTH GROUP
(*Suby of* UNITED HEALTHCARE SERVICES INC) ★
10701 W Research Dr, Milwaukee, WI 53226-3452
Tel (414) 443-4060 *Founded/Ownrshp* 1990
Sales NA *EMP* 365
SIC 6324 6411 6321 Hospital & medical service plans; Insurance agents, brokers & service; Accident & health insurance
CEO: Jay Fulkerson
VP: Michael Anderson
VP: Ralph Beck
VP Sls: Dustin Hinton

D-U-N-S 14-871-0858
■ UNITEDHEALTHCARE SERVICES CO OF RIVER VALLEY INC
JOHN DEERE HEALTH
(*Suby of* UNITEDHEALTH GROUP INC) ★
1300 River Dr Ste 200, Moline, IL 61265-1356
Tel (952) 936-1300 *Founded/Ownrshp* 2006
Sales NA *EMP* 900
SIC 6324 Health maintenance organization (HMO), insurance only
Pr: Richard L Bartsh MD
CFO: Carolyn Clementes
* *CFO:* James Cousins
CFO: Lloyd Wright
Ex VP: Mitchell Zamoff
VP: Michael Degeorge
VP: Luann Heinen
VP: Regis Rulisson
CIO: Jon Chapman
CTO: Kelly Abrahamson
Netwrk Eng: Jay Duitsman

D-U-N-S 09-963-1124
UNITEK GLOBAL SERVICES INC
2010 Renaissance Blvd, King of Prussia, PA 19406-2746
Tel (267) 464-1700 *Founded/Ownrshp* 1987
Sales 471.9MM *EMP* 3,200
SIC 1731 8741 8742 8711 Telephone & telephone equipment installation; Construction management; Construction project management consultant; Engineering services
CEO: John Haggerty
CFO: Andrew Herning
Sr VP: Susie C Holliday
VP: James Brennan
VP: Kathleen McCarthy
VP: Mike Williams
Sales Exec: Mark Mercer

D-U-N-S 16-906-6128
UNITEK USA LLC
(*Suby of* UNITEK GLOBAL SERVICES INC) ★
1777 Sentry Pkwy W # 302, Blue Bell, PA 19422-2227
Tel (267) 464-1700 *Founded/Ownrshp* 2004
Sales 96.7MM^E *EMP* 1,290
SIC 8742 8741 Construction project management consultant; Construction management
CEO: C Scott Hisey
* *Pr:* Peter Giacalone
* *CFO:* Ron Lejman
Dir IT: David Morris
Genl Couns: Kyle Hall

D-U-N-S 12-136-1729
▲ UNITIL CORP
6 Liberty Ln W, Hampton, NH 03842-1704
Tel (603) 772-0775 *Founded/Ownrshp* 1984
Sales 426.8MM *EMP* 500^E
Tkr Sym UTL *Exch* NYS
SIC 4911 4924 Electric services; Distribution, electric power; ; Natural gas distribution;
Ch Bd: Robert G Schoenberger
COO: Thomas P Meissner Jr
COO: Tom Meissner
CFO: Mark H Collin
Dir IT: Steven Moore

D-U-N-S 60-712-2231 EXP
UNITOR HOLDING INC
UNITOR SHIPS SERVICE
(*Suby of* WILHELMSEN SHIPS SERVICE AS)
9400 New Century Dr, Pasadena, TX 77507-1832
Tel (281) 867-2000 *Founded/Ownrshp* 1971
Sales 120.4MM^E *EMP* 1,330
SIC 5088

UNITOR SHIPS SERVICE
See UNITOR HOLDING INC

UNITRIN DATA SYSTEMS SPECIALTY
See CHARTER INDEMNITY CO

D-U-N-S 03-920-6433
■ UNITRIN DIRECT INSURANCE CO
(*Suby of* KEMPER CORP) ★
80 Blue Ravine Rd Ste 200, Folsom, CA 95630-4702
Tel (760) 603-3276 *Founded/Ownrshp* 2000
Sales NA *EMP* 575^E
SIC 6399 Warranty insurance, automobile
Pr: Scott Carter
VP: Bryan Rogers

D-U-N-S 07-590-8876
UNITRON HEARING INC
(*Suby of* PHONAK LLC) ★
14755 27th Ave N, Plymouth, MN 55447-4866
Tel (763) 744-3300 *Founded/Ownrshp* 2000
Sales 85.0MM *EMP* 240
SIC 3842 Hearing aids
Pr: Mike Dittmann
* *VP:* Jason Mayer
* *VP:* Nick Stephan
Exec: Denise Munter
Genl Mgr: Susan Mitchell
Dir IT: Susan Schmiekin
Sls&Mrk Ex: Joe Thomas
Mktg Mgr: Dan Lindhorst

D-U-N-S 01-266-5881
UNITY ELECTRIC CO INC
(*Suby of* UNITY INTERNATIONAL GROUP INC) ★
6545 Fresh Meadow Ln, Flushing, NY 11365-2088
Tel (718) 539-4300 *Founded/Ownrshp* 1977
Sales 150.0MM *EMP* 417^E
SIC 1731 Electrical work
Ch Bd: Peter Striano
Ex VP: Dominick Striano
Dir IT: Danny Lok

D-U-N-S 17-045-4730
UNITY FAMILY HEALTHCARE
ST GABRIEL'S HOSPITAL
(*Suby of* CHI) ★
815 2nd St Se, Little Falls, MN 56345-3505
Tel (320) 632-5441 *Founded/Ownrshp* 1993
Sales 83.5MM *EMP* 600
Accts Catholic Health Initiatives E
SIC 8062 General medical & surgical hospitals
Pr: Lee Boyles
* *CEO:* Chad Cooper
* *CFO:* Steve Smith
Dir Rx: Howard Kenna
* *Prin:* Carl Vaagenes
Dir IT: Bill Stevens

D-U-N-S 18-714-4019
UNITY HEALTH CARE INC
1220 12th St Se Ste 120, Washington, DC 20003-3733
Tel (202) 715-7901 *Founded/Ownrshp* 1985
Sales 95.5MM *EMP* 850
SIC 8099 Medical services organization
CEO: Vincent Keane
Treas: B Jarvis
* *Ex VP:* Ardell Butler
* *VP:* Molly Evans
VP: Angelica Journagin
CTO: Gamal El-Gamassy
Doctor: Andrea Anderson
Doctor: Aviva Zyskind
Snr Mgr: Diana Lapp

UNITY HEALTH HOSPITAL
See UNITY HOSPITAL OF ROCHESTER

D-U-N-S 15-186-7736
UNITY HEALTH PLANS INSURANCE CORP
(*Suby of* UW HOSPITAL) ★
840 Carolina St, Sauk City, WI 53583-1374
Tel (608) 643-2491 *Founded/Ownrshp* 2005
Sales NA *EMP* 200
SIC 6324 Health maintenance organization (HMO), insurance only
CEO: Terry Bolz
COO: Gail Midlowski
CFO: Jeffrey Eversoll
VP: Redovan Bursac
* *VP:* Jim Hiveley
* *VP:* Gail Midlikowski
Exec: Steve Joerger
Ex Dir: Carla Black
Dir IT: Michael Caccmise
Dir IT: Matt Dedrick
Dir IT: Matt Grant

D-U-N-S 07-969-7819 EXP
UNITY HEALTH SYSTEM
ROCHESTER REGIONAL HEALTH
89 Genesee St, Rochester, NY 14611-3201
Tel (585) 723-7000 *Founded/Ownrshp* 1971
Sales 476MM^E *EMP* 14,000
SIC 8062 General medical & surgical hospitals
CEO: Dr Eric Bieber
Chf Path: Pamrod N Carpenter
Dir Vol: Diane Lombardo
COO: Betsy McDonald
* *CFO:* Thomas Crilly
* *Treas:* Jeffery Mapstone
VP: Anita Cassano
VP: David Diercks
VP: Robert Donahue
VP: Mary Alice Keller
VP: Karen May
VP: Michael D Nazar
* *VP:* Chris Peterson
VP: Candace Smith
Dir Risk M: Chris Staertow
Dir Rx: James Rocco

D-U-N-S 96-744-1424
UNITY HEALTH SYSTEM FOUNDATION
(*Suby of* ROCHESTER REGIONAL HEALTH) ★
1555 Long Pond Rd, Rochester, NY 14626-4122
Tel (585) 723-7050 *Founded/Ownrshp* 2011
Sales 3.2MM *EMP* 2,121^E
SIC 6733 Trusts
Pr: Warren Hern

D-U-N-S 19-854-5316
UNITY HOSPITAL OF ROCHESTER
UNITY HEALTH HOSPITAL
89 Genesee St, Rochester, NY 14611-3201
Tel (585) 723-7000 *Founded/Ownrshp* 1971
Sales 435.4MM *EMP* 3,000
SIC 8062 General medical & surgical hospitals
Pr: Timothy McCormick

D-U-N-S 07-936-4841
UNITY INTERNATIONAL GROUP INC
6545 Fresh Meadow Ln, Flushing, NY 11365-2011
Tel (718) 539-4300 *Founded/Ownrshp* 2007
Sales 198.3MM^E *EMP* 664^E
SIC 1731 Electrical work
Ch Bd: Peter J Striano
Exec: Cynthia Harvey

D-U-N-S 19-220-1556
UNITY POINT HEALTH ST LUKE
NORTHWEST IOWA HOSPITAL
2720 Stone Park Blvd, Sioux City, IA 51104-3734
Tel (712) 279-3500 *Founded/Ownrshp* 1996
Sales 4.4MM *EMP* 1,500
SIC 8741 Hospital management; Nursing & personal care facility management
CEO: Peter Thoreen
* *COO:* Lynn Wold
* *CFO:* Jim Gobell
Treas: Todd Moss
* *VP:* Leah Glasgo
* *VP:* Dr Richard Hildebrand
* *VP:* Mark Thorden
Exec: Traci Statema
Nurse Mgr: Lindsay Vlaminck
Off Admin: Kay Patel
CIO: Julie Boston

UNITYPINT HLTH METHDST PROCTOR
See PROCTOR HOSPITAL

D-U-N-S 06-194-3101
UNITYPOINT AT HOME
UNITYPOINT HOSPICE
(*Suby of* UNITYPOINT HEALTH) ★
11333 Aurora Ave, Urbandale, IA 50322-7908
Tel (515) 557-3100 *Founded/Ownrshp* 1998
Sales 104.0MM *EMP* 1,200

SIC 8082 Home health care services
CEO: Alan Kaplan
**COO:* Andrew Molosky
**CFO:* Craig Flanagan
Ofcr: Marissa Smith
VP: Todd Baker
VP: Kellie Esters
VP: Mike Namanny
Ex Dir: Mary Romanco
Dir IT: James Fickbohm
Opers Supe: Brandon Rivers
Pharmcst: Tracy McVey

UNITYPOINT HEALTH
See CENTRAL IOWA HOSPITAL CORP

UNITYPOINT HEALTH
See IOWA HEALTH SYSTEM

UNITYPOINT HEALTH - METHODIST
See METHODIST MEDICAL CENTER OF ILLINOIS

UNITYPOINT HEALTH-MERITER
See MERITER HEALTH SERVICES INC

UNITYPOINT HOSPICE
See UNITYPOINT AT HOME

UNIV TENNESSEE SYSTEM OFFICE
See UNIVERSITY OF TENNESSEE

D-U-N-S 94-421-0665
UNIVANCE INC
(*Suby of* UNIVANCE CORPORATION)
3400 Corporate Dr, Winchester, KY 40391-8493
Tel (859) 737-2306 *Founded/Ownrshp* 1995
Sales 120.0MM *EMP* 250
SIC 3568 3714 5012 Power transmission equipment; Motor vehicle parts & accessories; Automobiles
Pr: Masatoshi Yamamoto
VP: Toru Onoda

D-U-N-S 09-887-7053 IMP/EXP
▲ UNIVAR INC
3075 Highland Pkwy # 200, Downers Grove, IL 60515-5560
Tel (331) 777-6000 *Founded/Ownrshp* 1924
Sales 8.9MMM *EMP* 9,200
Tkr Sym UNVR *Exch* NYS
SIC 5169 5191 8741 Industrial chemicals; Chemicals, agricultural; Industrial management
Pr: Stephen D Newlin
**Ch Bd:* William S Stavropoulos
Pr: Michael Hildebrand
Pr: David Jukes
Pr: Christopher Oversby
CFO: Carl J Lukach
Ex VP: George J Fuller
Ex VP: Stephen N Landsman
Ex VP: Manian Ramesh
Sr VP: Erik Viens
Sls Mgr: Julius Czarnecki

D-U-N-S 10-297-1785 IMP/EXP
■ UNIVAR USA INC
(*Suby of* UNIVAR INC) ★
17411 Ne Union Hill Rd, Redmond, WA 98052-3375
Tel (331) 777-6000 *Founded/Ownrshp* 1986
Sales 5.6MMM^E *EMP* 4,369
SIC 5169 5191 8741 Industrial chemicals; Chemicals, agricultural; Pesticides; Industrial management
Pr: J Erik Fyrwald
Pr: Jim Gwinn
**CFO:* Carl J Lukach
CFO: Patrick Tole
**Treas:* Kerri A Howard
Ex VP: Mark Byrne
**Ex VP:* George J Fuller
**Ex VP:* Stephen N Landsman
**VP:* Terry Arnold
**VP:* Warren T Hill
VP: Stephanie Hisle
VP: Martin Jung
VP: Brian Jurcak
**VP:* Perry T Kusakabe
VP: Craig Lawson
VP: Guy Monteil
VP: Brian Rinehart
VP: Phil Scafido
VP: Jeffrey Siegel
VP: Kendall Troutman
Comm Man: Karen Weber

D-U-N-S 17-604-6225
UNIVERA COMMUNITY HEALTH CARE
205 Park Club Ln Fl 2, Buffalo, NY 14221-5239
Tel (585) 454-1700 *Founded/Ownrshp* 1997
Sales NA *EMP* 20
SIC 6321 Health insurance carriers
Ex Dir: Robert Thompson
VP: Carrie Frank
VP: Peter Kates
Dir Rx: Steve Urbanski

D-U-N-S 78-007-8635 EXP
UNIVERSAL ACOUSTIC & EMISSION TECHNOLOGIES INC
UNIVERSAL SILENCER
1925 Us Highway 51 & 138, Stoughton, WI 53589-1911
Tel (608) 873-4272 *Founded/Ownrshp* 1959
Sales 141.4MM^E *EMP* 464
SIC 3569 3441 Filters, general line: industrial; Building components, structural steel
COO: Cary Bremigan
Pr: Steve Honerlaw
Bd of Dir: Greg Anderson
VP: Tim McElfresh
Dir IT: Carla Maloney

D-U-N-S 96-775-7282
▲ UNIVERSAL AMERICAN CORP
44 S Broadway Ste 1200, White Plains, NY 10601-4458
Tel (914) 934-5200 *Founded/Ownrshp* 2011
Sales NA *EMP* 2,993^E
Accts Deloitte & Touche Llp New Yo
Tkr Sym UAM *Exch* NYS
SIC 6311 6321 6324 Life insurance; Accident & health insurance carriers; Hospital & medical service plans
Ch Bd: Richard A Barasch
CFO: Adam C Thackery
Ofcr: Steven H Black
Ex VP: Theodore M Carpenter Jr
Ex VP: Anthony L Wolk
VP: Dinos Constantine
VP: Bill Cushman
VP: Stephanie Frank
VP: Merikay Guhring
VP: Paul Jernigan
VP: Brian Koopmans
VP: Andrea Leskes
VP: Pavan Mital
VP: David Monroe
VP: Amy Moss
VP: Tony L Wolk
Board of Directors: Sally W Crawford, Matthew W Etheridge, Mark K Gormley, Patrick J Maclaughlin

D-U-N-S 05-637-9019
UNIVERSAL AVIONICS SYSTEMS CORP
(*Suby of* SAGMA HOLDINGS ESTABLISHMENT)
3260 E Universal Way, Tucson, AZ 85756-5032
Tel (520) 295-2300 *Founded/Ownrshp* 1981
Sales 117.9MM^E *EMP* 450
SIC 3812 3829 Search & navigation equipment; Aircraft & motor vehicle measurement equipment
CEO: Paul De Herrera
**Pr:* Joachim L Naimer
**CFO:* Michael Delgado
**VP:* Dennis Ray Miller
**VP:* Dan Reida
Prgrm Mgr: George Cooley
Prgrm Mgr: Jenneca Dixon
Prgrm Mgr: Brett Neely
Snr Sftwr: S Graham
Snr Sftwr: Sean McKeon
Snr Sftwr: Ken Shavlik

UNIVERSAL BEDROOM FURNITURE
See UNIVERSAL FURNITURE LIMITED

D-U-N-S 01-711-3681
UNIVERSAL BUILDING MAINTENANCE LLC
(*Suby of* UNIVERSAL SERVICES OF AMERICA LP) ★
1551 N Tustin Ave Ste 650, Santa Ana, CA 92705-8664
Tel (714) 619-9700 *Founded/Ownrshp* 2008
Sales 72.8M^E *EMP* 5,003^E
SIC 7349 Janitorial service, contract basis
Pr: Mark Olivas
CFO: Scott Savoie

D-U-N-S 11-347-1473
UNIVERSAL CABLE HOLDINGS INC
SUDDENLINK COMMUNICATIONS
(*Suby of* SUDDENLINK COMMUNICATIONS) ★
6151 Paluxy Dr, Tyler, TX 75703-5976
Tel (330) 872-0462 *Founded/Ownrshp* 2006
Sales 120.0MM *EMP* 750^E
SIC 4841 Cable television services
Pr: Dale Bennett
**Treas:* Ashley Kimery
Ex VP: Elizabeth K Monigold
Genl Mgr: Dianne Huffstickler
IT Man: Steve Thrasher

D-U-N-S 87-859-7079 IMP
■ UNIVERSAL CITY DEVELOPMENT PARTNERS LTD
UNIVERSAL DEVELOPMENT PARTNERS
(*Suby of* NECN) ★
1000 Unversal Studios Plz, Orlando, FL 32819-7601
Tel (407) 363-8000 *Founded/Ownrshp* 2002
Sales 1.1MMM^E *EMP* 16,000^E
SIC 7996 Theme park, amusement
Pr: John R Sprouls
Pr: William A Davis
Pr: Pamela Tuscany-Warren
CFO: J L Bonnier
CFO: Trasey Satockwell
CFO: Michael J Short
CFO: Tracey L Stockwell
Treas: Charles Glass
Ex VP: Fred Lousberry
Sr VP: Ric Florell
Sr VP: Gretchen Hofmann
Sr VP: Bill McCorey
Sr VP: Michelle McKenna
Sr VP: Catherine A Roth
VP: Fred Lounsberry
Exec: David Grimm
Creative D: Todd Wineland

D-U-N-S 19-464-9257 IMP
UNIVERSAL CITY FLORIDA PARTNERS
UNIVERSAL STUDIOS FLORIDA
1000 Unversal Studios Plz, Orlando, FL 32819-7601
Tel (407) 363-8000 *Founded/Ownrshp* 1987
Sales 32.0MM^E *EMP* 5,000
SIC 7996 7819 Amusement parks; Studio property rental, motion picture
CEO: John Sprouls
Pt: Universal City Property Mgtm C

UNIVERSAL CITY NISSAN
See SAGE HOLDING CO

D-U-N-S 05-386-4948 IMP
■ UNIVERSAL CITY STUDIOS INC
UNIVERSAL STUDIOS
(*Suby of* UNIVERSAL STUDIOS INC) ★
100 Universal City Plz, Universal City, CA 91608-1085
Tel (818) 622-8477 *Founded/Ownrshp* 1965
Sales 333.7MM^E *EMP* 7,400
SIC 7812 7996 Motion picture production & distribution; Motion picture production & distribution, television; Non-theatrical motion picture production; Non-theatrical motion picture production, television; Theme park, amusement
CEO: Sid Sheinberg
**Ch Bd:* Lew R Wasserman

D-U-N-S 55-613-9116 IMP
■ UNIVERSAL CITY STUDIOS PRODUCTIONS LLLP LP
(*Suby of* VIVENDI UNIVERSAL ENTERTAINMENT LLLP) ★
100 Universal City Plz, Universal City, CA 91608-1085
Tel (818) 777-1000 *Founded/Ownrshp* 2003
Sales 43.2MM^E *EMP* 2,000^E
SIC 7812 3652 2741 5947 5944 5961 Motion picture production & distribution; Phonograph records, prerecorded; Music, sheet: publishing & printing; Gift shop; Jewelry stores; Gift items, mail order
Pr: Ron Meyer
CFO: Lynn A Calpeter
Ex VP: Maren Christensen
Ex VP: Richard Cotton
Ex VP: Rick Finkelstein
Ex VP: Patricia E Hutton
Ex VP: Kenneth L Kahrs
Ex VP: Belinda Menendez
Sr VP: Stacey Byrnes
Sr VP: Michael J Connor
Sr VP: Avy Eschenasy
Sr VP: Robert Fitzpatrick
Sr VP: J Keith Gorham
Sr VP: Elizabeth Herbst-Brady
Sr VP: James M Horowitz
Sr VP: Andrea Melville-Rickards
Sr VP: William A Sutman
Sr VP: James Watters
Sr VP: Mark A Wooster
VP: Nikki Rocco

D-U-N-S 96-152-5438
■ UNIVERSAL CITY TRAVEL PARTNERS
UNIVERSAL PRKS RSRTS VACATIONS
(*Suby of* UNIVERSAL DEVELOPMENT PARTNERS) ★
1000 Unversal Studios Plz, Orlando, FL 32819-7601
Tel (407) 363-8000 *Founded/Ownrshp* 2002
Sales 34.6MM^E *EMP* 5,030^E
SIC 7996 Amusement parks
CEO: John Sprouls
CFO: Tracey Stockwell
Sr VP: Jean L Bonnier

D-U-N-S 96-247-9445 IMP
UNIVERSAL COMMERCE LLC
COOL SURGE
3939 Everhard Rd Nw, Canton, OH 44709-4004
Tel (800) 504-8105 *Founded/Ownrshp* 2008
Sales 57.1MM^E *EMP* 1,400
SIC 5722 Air conditioning room units, self-contained
Prin: Ryan Berry
Genl Mgr: Ryan Berry

D-U-N-S 78-932-5479
UNIVERSAL COMPANIES INC
2824 N Ohio St, Wichita, KS 67219-4319
Tel (316) 832-0151 *Founded/Ownrshp* 1953
Sales 112.9MM^E *EMP* 250
SIC 5171 5541 6512 8741 6099 2992 Petroleum bulk stations; Filling stations, gasoline; Commercial & industrial building operation; Management services; Check cashing agencies; Oils & greases, blending & compounding
Pr: Michael B Maloney
**Sec:* Dennis M Maloney
Sfty Mgr: Dale Stuckey

D-U-N-S 19-843-3104
UNIVERSAL COMPUTER SYSTEMS INC
6700 Hollister St, Houston, TX 77040-5331
Tel (713) 718-1800 *Founded/Ownrshp* 1987
Sales 1.6MMM^E *EMP* 6,000
SIC 5045

D-U-N-S 05-905-7802 IMP/EXP
UNIVERSAL COOPERATIVES INC
UNIVERSAL CROP PRTCTION ALANCE
1300 Corporate Ctr Curv, Saint Paul, MN 55121-2589
Tel (651) 239-1000 *Founded/Ownrshp* 1972
Sales 94.0MM^E *EMP* 250
Accts Mcgladrey & Pullen Llp Minne
SIC 2879 5169 2298 Agricultural chemicals; Fungicides, herbicides; Chemicals & allied products; Binder & baler twine
Ch Bd: Ric Sundal
**Pr:* Terrence J Bohman
Pr: Adam Thurston
**VP:* William C Cubbage
**VP:* Dennis Gyolai
**VP:* Dale Halladay
**VP:* Jamie Larue
VP: Ken Ostrowski
**VP:* Tom Vickers
Comm Man: Nic Ramswick
**Prin:* L Bryan Morrison

D-U-N-S 00-794-1420
▲ UNIVERSAL CORP (VA)
9201 Forest Hill Ave, Richmond, VA 23235-6865
Tel (804) 359-9311 *Founded/Ownrshp* 1918
Sales 2.1MMM *EMP* 24,000
Tkr Sym UVV *Exch* NYS
SIC 5159 2141 Tobacco, leaf; Tobacco stemming & redrying; Tobacco redrying; Tobacco stemming
Ch Bd: George C Freeman III
COO: Airton L Hentschke
CFO: David C Moore
Treas: Karen Whelan
Ex VP: Theodore G Broome
Ex VP: J Huffman
VP: Robert M Peebles
VP: Preston D Wigner
Board of Directors: John B Adams Jr, Diana F Cantor, Chester A Crocker, Charles H Foster Jr, Lennart R Freeman, Thomas H Johnson, Michael T Lawton, Eddie N Moore Jr, Robert C Sledd

D-U-N-S 18-175-8749 IMP/EXP
■ UNIVERSAL CORP
(*Suby of* UNIVERSAL CORP) ★
9201 Forest Hl Ave Stony, Richmond, VA 23235
Tel (804) 359-9311 *Founded/Ownrshp* 1986
Sales 1.0MMM^E *EMP* 25,000
SIC 5194 Tobacco & tobacco products
Pr: George C Freemans III
**VP:* Keith Brewer
**VP:* Mike Ligon

UNIVERSAL CROP PRTCTION ALANCE
See UNIVERSAL COOPERATIVES INC

D-U-N-S 07-688-2666
■ UNIVERSAL DEDICATED INC
(*Suby of* UNIVERSAL LOGISTICS HOLDINGS INC) ★
12755 E 9 Mile Rd, Warren, MI 48089-2621
Tel (800) 233-9445 *Founded/Ownrshp* 2015
Sales 86.9MM^E *EMP* 969
SIC 4214 Local trucking with storage
Pr: Mike Silverwood
CFO: Don Oswald

UNIVERSAL DEVELOPMENT PARTNERS
See UNIVERSAL CITY DEVELOPMENT PARTNERS LTD

D-U-N-S 00-733-9674 IMP/EXP
UNIVERSAL DISPLAY AND FIXTURE CO
UDFC
726 E Hwy 121, Lewisville, TX 75057-4159
Tel (972) 434-8067 *Founded/Ownrshp* 1962
Sales 96.4MM^E *EMP* 500
SIC 2542 3993 Racks, merchandise display or storage: except wood; Signs & advertising specialties
Pr: F De Jesus
DP Exec: Steve Koenig
Sls Dir: Shawn Kerns

D-U-N-S 96-326-7893
▲ UNIVERSAL DISPLAY CORP
375 Phillips Blvd Ste 1, Ewing, NJ 08618-1455
Tel (609) 671-0980 *Founded/Ownrshp* 1994
Sales 191.0MM *EMP* 154^E
Tkr Sym OLED *Exch* NGS
SIC 3674 Semiconductors & related devices; Light emitting diodes
Pr: Steven V Abramson
**Ch Bd:* Sherwin I Seligsohn
**CFO:* Sidney D Rosenblatt
Sr VP: Julia J Brown
VP: Janice M Dufour
VP: Mauro Premutico
Snr Mgr: Ray Zeimet
Board of Directors: Leonard Becker, Richard C Elias, Elizabeth H Gemmill, Rosemarie B Greco, C Keith Hartley, Lawrence Lacerte

D-U-N-S 60-205-2169 IMP
▲ UNIVERSAL ELECTRONICS INC
201 Sandpointe Ave # 800, Santa Ana, CA 92707-5778
Tel (714) 918-9500 *Founded/Ownrshp* 1987
Sales 602.8MM *EMP* 2,309
Tkr Sym UEIC *Exch* NGS
SIC 3651 3625 7372 Video triggers (remote control TV devices); Relays & industrial controls; Prepackaged software
Ch Bd: Paul D Arling
COO: Louis S Hughes
CFO: Bryan M Hackworth
Ex VP: Paul J M Bennett
Ex VP: David Chong
Sr VP: Banley Chan
Sr VP: Richard A Firehammer Jr
VP: Steve Gutman
IT Man: Smitha Raj
Sls Mgr: Josh Chenault
Sls Mgr: Travis Woudstra
Board of Directors: William C Mulligan, J C Sparkman, Gregory P Stapleton, Carl E Vogel, Edward K Zinser

D-U-N-S 02-084-2275
■ UNIVERSAL ENSCO INC
UNIVERSALPEGASUS INTERNATIONAL
(*Suby of* UNIVERSALPEGASUS INTERNATIONAL INC) ★
4848 Loop Central Dr # 137, Houston, TX 77081-2355
Tel (713) 425-6000 *Founded/Ownrshp* 2008
Sales 101.3MM^E *EMP* 780^E
SIC 1389 Gas field services
CEO: Philip Luna
VP: Robert Austin
VP: Wendy Donahue
Exec: Rosina Christensen
IT Man: Mark Zuniga

D-U-N-S 04-699-1097 IMP/EXP
UNIVERSAL FIBERS INC
14401 Industrial Park Rd, Bristol, VA 24202-3705
Tel (276) 669-1161 *Founded/Ownrshp* 1999
Sales 154.9MM^E *EMP* 500
SIC 2824 2281 Organic fibers, noncellulosic; Yarn spinning mills
Pr: R Marcus Amman
CFO: Meg Collins
**CFO:* Jeffrey A Johnson
**Treas:* Bill Plaster
**VP:* Bill Goodman

UNIVERSAL FOREST PRODUCTS
See UFP MID-ATLANTIC LLC

UNIVERSAL FOREST PRODUCTS
See UFP WOODBURN LLC

UNIVERSAL FOREST PRODUCTS
See UFP GRANDVIEW LLC

D-U-N-S 01-710-4670 EXP
▲ UNIVERSAL FOREST PRODUCTS INC (MI)
2801 E Beltline Ave Ne, Grand Rapids, MI 49525-9680
Tel (616) 364-6161 *Founded/Ownrshp* 1955
Sales 2.8MMM *EMP* 7,000
Tkr Sym UFPI *Exch* NGS
SIC 2421 1796 Building & structural materials, wood; Lumber: rough, sawed or planed; Installing building equipment
CEO: Matthew J Missad
**Ch Bd:* William G Currie
Pr: Allen T Peters
Pr: Patrick M Webster
CFO: Michael R Cole
Ex VP: Patrick Benton
Ex VP: Robert D Coleman
Ex VP: C Scott Greene
Ex VP: Donald L James
Ex VP: Michael F Mordell
Ex VP: Michael Mordell
Ex VP: Jonathan West
VP: Nancy Degood
Exec: Ryan Powell

Board of Directors: John M Engler, Gary F Goode, Bruce A Merino, Mark A Murray, Thomas W Rhodes, Louis A Smith, Mary E Tuuk, Brian C Walker, Michael G Wooldridge

UNIVERSAL FURNITURE INTL
See SAMSON INVESTMENT HOLDING INC

D-U-N-S 06-382-4155 IMP
UNIVERSAL FURNITURE LIMITED
UNIVERSAL BEDROOM FURNITURE
2575 Penny Rd, High Point, NC 27265-8334
Tel (336) 822-8888 *Founded/Ownrshp* 1997
Sales 1.1MMM^E *EMP* 12,000
SIC 2511 2512 Dining room furniture: wood; Wood bedroom furniture; Upholstered household furniture
Pr: Ronald J Hoffman
**CFO:* Larry Lilan
VP: Gene Coudle
VP: Thomas H Cunningham
VP: Roger Friesen
**VP:* Catherine T McGee
VP: Kathleen Nash
MIS Dir: Jerry Word
QA Dir: Michael Lazorchick
VP Opers: John Carper
VP Sls: Kevin Miller

D-U-N-S 62-659-9658
UNIVERSAL GROUP INC
Calle 1 Lote 10 Metro Ofc St Cal, Guaynabo, PR 00968
Tel (787) 793-7202 *Founded/Ownrshp* 1986
Sales NA *EMP* 945
SIC 6411 Property & casualty insurance agent
Ch Bd: Luis M Casanas
**Pr:* Monique Miranda Merle
**CFO:* Jorge Padilla
**Ex VP:* Jorge Amadeo
**Ex VP:* Rafael Rodriguez
VP: Marisandra Amadeo
VP: Joe Ortiz
**VP:* Luis E Perez-Sanchez

D-U-N-S 09-372-5133
▲ UNIVERSAL HEALTH SERVICES INC
367 S Gulph Rd, King of Prussia, PA 19406-3121
Tel (610) 768-3300 *Founded/Ownrshp* 1979
Sales 9.0MMM *EMP* 74,600
Tkr Sym UHS *Exch* NYS
SIC 8062 8063 8093 8011 8741 General medical & surgical hospitals; Psychiatric hospitals; Specialty outpatient clinics; Ambulatory surgical center; Management services
Ch Bd: Alan B Miller
Pr: J P Christen
**Pr:* Marc D Miller
**CFO:* Steve G Filton
Treas: Martha Syms
Ex VP: Andy Belen
Ex VP: Joseph Granger
Ex VP: Beatriz Hadley
Ex VP: Kim Lederer
Ex VP: Debbie Onofrey
Ex VP: Greg Wilder
VP: Brandy Albright
VP: Melissa Alvarado
VP: James Antosy
VP: Brad Balon
VP: Charles Boyle
VP: Lorraine Castro
VP: Jerilin Cummings
VP: Chuck Debusk
VP: Will Decuyper
VP: Tasha Hoffmann
Board of Directors: Lawrence S Gibbs, John H Herrell, Robert H Hotz, Eileen C McDonnell, Anthony Pantaleoni

D-U-N-S 00-353-0745
■ UNIVERSAL HEALTH SERVICES OF RANCHO SPRINGS INC
SOUTHWEST HEALTHCARE SYSTEMS INLAND VALLEY
(*Suby of* UNIVERSAL HEALTH SERVICES INC) ★
36485 Inland Valley Dr, Wildomar, CA 92595-9681
Tel (951) 677-9712 *Founded/Ownrshp* 2000
Sales 240.3MM *EMP* 1^E
SIC 8099 8062 8011 Health screening service; General medical & surgical hospitals; Clinic, operated by physicians
CEO: Ken Rivers
Dir Rad: Cynthia Fulford

D-U-N-S 02-286-9937
UNIVERSAL HOSPITAL SERVICES INC
(*Suby of* UHS HOLDCO INC) ★
6625 W 78th St Ste 300, Minneapolis, MN 55439-2650
Tel (952) 893-3200 *Founded/Ownrshp* 2007
Sales 448.6MM *EMP* 2,489
SIC 7352 Medical equipment rental
CEO: Thomas J Leonard
Ch Bd: John L Workman
Pr: Kevin E Ketzel
CFO: James B Pekarek
Ofcr: Robert L Creviston
Sr VP: Bettyann Bird
Sr VP: Lee M Pulju
VP: Scott A Christensen
VP: Philip Zeller
Dir Bus: Dan Lucas
Board of Directors: Bret D Bowerman, David Crane, Michael C Feiner, John B Grotting, Robert Juneja, Barry P Schochet

D-U-N-S 00-222-6124 IMP/EXP
UNIVERSAL INSTRUMENTS CORP
(*Suby of* UI HOLDING CO) ★
33 Broome Corporate Pkwy, Conklin, NY 13748-1510
Tel (800) 842-9732 *Founded/Ownrshp* 1919, 2006
Sales 122.1MM^E *EMP* 545
SIC 3559 Electronic component making machinery
CEO: Jean-Luc Pelissier
**CEO:* Lynn Tilton
**CFO:* Keith O'Leary
Treas: Lisa D'Angelo

D-U-N-S 62-139-6407
▲ UNIVERSAL INSURANCE HOLDINGS INC
UVE
1110 W Coml Blvd Ste 100, Fort Lauderdale, FL 33309
Tel (954) 958-1200 *Founded/Ownrshp* 1990
Sales NA *EMP* 392^E
Tkr Sym UVE *Exch* NYS
SIC 6411 Property & casualty insurance agent
Ch Bd: Sean P Downes
**Pr:* Jon W Springer
COO: Stephen J Donaghy
CFO: Frank C Wilcox
Ofcr: Kimberly D Cooper
Board of Directors: Scott P Callahan, Darryl L Lewis, Ralph J Palmieri, Richard D Peterson, Michael A Pietrangelo, Ozzie A Schindler, Joel M Wilentz

D-U-N-S 18-963-7825
UNIVERSAL INSURANCE MANAGERS INC
101 Paramount Dr Ste 220, Sarasota, FL 34232-6044
Tel (941) 378-8851 *Founded/Ownrshp* 2003
Sales NA *EMP* 153^E
SIC 6411 Insurance agents, brokers & service
CEO: Monique Miranda Merle
**Prin:* Jorge L Padilla

D-U-N-S 02-487-2470 IMP/EXP
UNIVERSAL LIGHTING TECHNOLOGIES INC
(*Suby of* PANASONIC ECO SOLUTIONS NETWORKS CO, LTD.)
51 Century Blvd Ste 230, Nashville, TN 37214-3614
Tel (615) 316-5100 *Founded/Ownrshp* 2007
Sales 161.2MM^E *EMP* 300
SIC 3612 Fluorescent ballasts
CEO: Patrick A Sullivan
**COO:* Stuart C Horlak
**CFO:* David Riesmeyer
**Ex VP:* Joseph A Damiani
**VP:* F Luis Buentello
VP: Mark Dilling
Snr Mgr: Ranulfo Martinez

D-U-N-S 13-350-3180
▲ UNIVERSAL LOGISTICS HOLDINGS INC
12755 E 9 Mile Rd, Warren, MI 48089-2621
Tel (586) 920-0100 *Founded/Ownrshp* 2001
Sales 1.1MMM *EMP* 5,108
Tkr Sym ULH *Exch* NGS
SIC 4213 Trucking, except local
CEO: Jeff A Rogers
**Ch Bd:* Matthew T Moroun
CFO: Jude Beres
CFO: David A Crittenden
Ex VP: Ralph Castille
VP: Bill Gale
VP: Robert Sigler
VP: Mark Sokolowski
Mktg Mgr: Melissa Boussie
Sls Mgr: Jon Sturtz
Board of Directors: Frederick P Calderone, Joseph J Casaroll, Daniel J Deane, Manuel J Moroun, Michael A Regan, Daniel C Sullivan, Richard P Urban, H E Wolfe

UNIVERSAL LUBRICANTS, LLC
See CLEAN HARBORS WICHITA LLC

D-U-N-S 00-486-2959
UNIVERSAL MARITIME SERVICE CORP
(*Suby of* APM TERMINALS NORTH AMERICA INC) ★
9300 Arrowpoint Blvd, Charlotte, NC 28273-8136
Tel (704) 571-2768 *Founded/Ownrshp* 1952, 1988
Sales 89.1MM^E *EMP* 1,329^E
SIC 4491 Marine cargo handling; Marine terminals
Pr: Eric Sisco
CFO: Jeppe Jensen
CFO: Warren Sweeney
Treas: John Leopprich
**Treas:* John Loepprich
Ofcr: Ross Clarke
Ofcr: Peter Ford
Ofcr: Peder Sondergaard
Ex VP: Rich Derosa
**Sr VP:* Jack Craig
**Sr VP:* John Crowley
Sr VP: Nicholas Taro

D-U-N-S 83-234-8689
■ UNIVERSAL MCCANN WORLDWIDE INC
UM NY
(*Suby of* INTERPUBLIC GROUP OF COMPANIES INC) ★
100 W 33rd St Fl 5, New York, NY 10001-2920
Tel (212) 494-4700 *Founded/Ownrshp* 2009
Sales 98.4MM^E *EMP* 3,600
SIC 7319 Media buying service
CEO: Dary Lee
Mng Pt: Andy Corcoran
**Ch Bd:* Matt Seiler
**Pr:* Kasha Cacy
**CEO:* Jacki Kelley
**COO:* Guy Beach
CFO: Dmitry Klebanov
Chf Inves: David Cohen
Ofcr: Kristi Argyilan
Ofcr: Eileen Kiernan
Ofcr: Marc Ruxin
Ex VP: Jennifer Hohman
Ex VP: Deidre Landau
Ex VP: Scott Russell
Ex VP: Karen Stutenroth
**Sr VP:* Fiona McRobert
Sr VP: David Queamante
VP: Joe Benarroch
VP: Andrea Houston
VP: Lora Kaye
VP: Danielle Vacatello

D-U-N-S 01-956-3803
UNIVERSAL MUSIC GROUP INC (NY)
(*Suby of* VIVENDI)
2220 Colorado Ave, Santa Monica, CA 90404-3506
Tel (310) 865-4000 *Founded/Ownrshp* 1996
Sales 354.1MM^E *EMP* 1,050
SIC 7389 2741 Music recording producer; Miscellaneous publishing
Co-CEO: Lucian Grainge
COO: Max Hole
COO: Ken Robold
CFO: George Marolda
CFO: Boyd Muir
Chf Mktg O: Chris Stephenson
Ex VP: Scott Greer
Ex VP: Jeffrey Harleston
Ex VP: Joel Klaiman
Ex VP: Andrew Kronfeld
Ex VP: Tom Mackay
Ex VP: Andy McKaie
Ex VP: Cynthia Sexton
Ex VP: Will Tanous
Ex VP: Matt Voss
Sr VP: David Benjamin
Sr VP: Saheli Datta
Sr VP: Mike Donegan
Sr VP: Eddie Fernandez
Sr VP: Kim Garner
Sr VP: Kirk Harding

UNIVERSAL NISSAN
See ACTION NISSAN INC

D-U-N-S 96-152-5487
■ UNIVERSAL ORLANDO ONLINE MERCHANDISE STORE
(*Suby of* UNIVERSAL DEVELOPMENT PARTNERS) ★
1000 Unversal Studios Plz, Orlando, FL 32819-7601
Tel (407) 363-8000 *Founded/Ownrshp* 2010
Sales 1.7MM^E *EMP* 1,874^E
SIC 7996 Amusement parks
CEO: John Sprouls

D-U-N-S 17-771-1082 IMP
UNIVERSAL PACKAGING SYSTEMS INC
PAKLAB
6080 Jericho Tpke, Commack, NY 11725-2850
Tel (631) 543-2277 *Founded/Ownrshp* 1987
Sales 127.0MM^E *EMP* 1,540
SIC 2844 7389 3565 2671 Cosmetic preparations; Packaging & labeling services; Bottling machinery: filling, capping, labeling; Plastic film, coated or laminated for packaging
Ch Bd: Andrew Young III
**COO:* Alan Kristel
**CFO:* Jeffery Morlando
Ex VP: Peter Belinsky
VP: Arlette Forshage
VP: Nancy Weinmaster
IT Man: Michael Sanchez
Mfg Mgr: Cruz Hernandez
Ql Cn Mgr: Eleanor Banzuela
Ql Cn Mgr: Jean Flores
Ql Cn Mgr: Angela Raby

UNIVERSAL PERSONNEL
See UP PROFESSIONAL SOLUTIONS LLC

UNIVERSAL PLASTIC MOLD
See UPM INC

D-U-N-S 55-550-9553 IMP
UNIVERSAL POOL CO INC
GREAT ESCAPE OF ILLINOIS, THE
300 W Armory Dr, South Holland, IL 60473-2820
Tel (708) 339-6060 *Founded/Ownrshp* 1970
Sales 126.8MM^E *EMP* 200
SIC 5021 5091 Outdoor & lawn furniture; Swimming pools, equipment & supplies; Spa equipment & supplies
Pr: N Barry Poll
Sls Mgr: Mark Rush

D-U-N-S 04-666-4736 IMP
UNIVERSAL POWER GROUP INC
488 S Royal Ln, Coppell, TX 75019-3820
Tel (469) 892-1122 *Founded/Ownrshp* 1968
Sales 90.9MM *EMP* 158
SIC 5065 5063 Electronic parts; Batteries
Pr: Ian Colin Edmonds
CFO: Roger Tannery
Sr VP: Ramin Salehi
Sr VP: Julie Sansom-Reese
Sr VP: Mimi Tan
Ql Cn Mgr: Phil Golden

D-U-N-S 96-546-0905
■ UNIVERSAL PRESSURE PUMPING INC
(*Suby of* PATTERSON-UTI ENERGY INC) ★
6 Desta Dr Ste 4400, Midland, TX 79705-5540
Tel (432) 221-7000 *Founded/Ownrshp* 2010
Sales 654.9MM^E *EMP* 744
SIC 1381 Drilling oil & gas wells
CEO: William A Hendricks Jr
**CFO:* John E Vollmer III
**Sr VP:* John Carnett
Sfty Mgr: Jayme Stuteville

UNIVERSAL PRKS RSRTS VACATIONS
See UNIVERSAL CITY TRAVEL PARTNERS

D-U-N-S 07-994-0145
UNIVERSAL PROTECTION GP LLC
1551 N Tustin Ave Ste 650, Santa Ana, CA 92705-8664
Tel (714) 619-9700 *Founded/Ownrshp* 2015
Sales 897.0MM^E *EMP* 9,200^E
SIC 7381 Security guard service
Ch: Brian Cescolini
CEO: Steve Jones

D-U-N-S 07-452-4984
UNIVERSAL PROTECTION SERVICE LLC
ALLIED UNIVERSAL SECURITY SVCS
(*Suby of* UNIVERSAL PROTECTION SERVICE LP) ★
161 Washington St Ste 600, Conshohocken, PA 19428-2083
Tel (704) 334-4751 *Founded/Ownrshp* 2011
Sales 125.6MM^E *EMP* 3,500
SIC 7381 Security guard service
Ch Bd: Lawrence O'Brien Jr
**Pr:* Heather O'Brien
**Treas:* Robert Watson
**VP:* Steve Almy
**VP:* Steven Pounds
Brnch Mgr: Patrick Curran

D-U-N-S 16-862-7375
UNIVERSAL PROTECTION SERVICE LP
(*Suby of* UNIVERSAL PROTECTION GP LLC) ★
1551 N Tustin Ave Ste 650, Santa Ana, CA 92705-8664
Tel (714) 619-9700 *Founded/Ownrshp* 2009
Sales 897.0MM^E *EMP* 9,100^E
SIC 7381 Security guard service
CEO: Steve Jones
CFO: Scott Savoie
VP: Mark McCourt
Exec: Paula Malone
Dir Risk M: Tom Merlino
Dir Sec: Pat Cpp
Dir Sec: Brian Kern
Rgnl Mgr: Chuck Leader
Rgnl Mgr: Eric McGarty
Div Mgr: Ryan Belflower
Div Mgr: Ryan Okerstrom

D-U-N-S 17-894-4224
UNIVERSAL SERVICES OF AMERICA LP
1551 N Tustin Ave, Santa Ana, CA 92705-8634
Tel (714) 619-9700 *Founded/Ownrshp* 2001
Sales 2.0MMM *EMP* 50,000
SIC 7381 7349 Security guard service; Janitorial service, contract basis
CEO: Steven Jones
CEO: Toni Ippolito
Ofcr: Gregory Wereski
VP: Tony Heroff
VP: Mark McCourt
VP: Rafael Sorto
Dir Sec: Michael Bland
Dir Sec: Stephen La Rue
Dir Sec: Jose Perez
Dir Sec: Ron Rigsby
Opers Supe: Judith Hocking

UNIVERSAL SILENCER
See UNIVERSAL ACOUSTIC & EMISSION TECHNOLOGIES INC

D-U-N-S 86-133-6501 IMP
▲ UNIVERSAL STAINLESS & ALLOY PRODUCTS INC
600 Mayer St Ste 2, Bridgeville, PA 15017-2790
Tel (412) 257-7600 *Founded/Ownrshp* 1994
Sales 180.6MM *EMP* 634^E
Tkr Sym USAP *Exch* NGS
SIC 3312 Blast furnaces & steel mills; Tool & die steel; Stainless steel
Ch Bd: Dennis M Oates
CFO: Ross C Wilkin
Chf Cred: Christopher M Zimmer
Bd of Dir: David Kornblatt
Chf Mktg O: Larry J Pollock
VP: Paul A McGrath
VP: Graham McIntosh
Dir IT: Joe Abbadini
S&M/VP: Chris Zimmer
Board of Directors: Christopher L Ayers, Douglas M Dunn, M David Kornblatt

UNIVERSAL STUDIOS
See UNIVERSAL CITY STUDIOS INC

UNIVERSAL STUDIOS FLORIDA
See UNIVERSAL CITY FLORIDA PARTNERS

D-U-N-S 00-896-3415 IMP
■ UNIVERSAL STUDIOS INC
(*Suby of* NECN) ★
100 Universal City Plz, North Hollywood, CA 91608-1002
Tel (818) 777-1000 *Founded/Ownrshp* 1924, 2004
Sales 1.0MMM^E *EMP* 15,000^E
SIC 7812 3652 2741 5947 5944 5961 Motion picture production & distribution; Television film production; Phonograph records, prerecorded; Magnetic tape (audio): prerecorded; Compact laser discs, prerecorded; Music, sheet: publishing & printing; Gift shop; Novelties; Jewelry stores; Gift items, mail order; Novelty merchandise, mail order; Jewelry, mail order
Ch: Adam Fogelson
**Pr:* Ron Meyer
COO: Zach Horowitz
**CFO:* Sean Gamble
**Ch:* Donna Langley
Ex VP: Michael Moses
Sr VP: Jim Wilson
VP: Suzanne Cole
VP: Michael Daruty
VP: Evan Fong
VP: Julie Gibson
VP: James Horowitz
VP: Teresa Johnson
VP: Liz Mahaffey
VP: Bill Mandel
VP: Greg McRitchie
VP: Bob Schnieders
VP: Jamie Stevens
Exec: Johnathan Sowers
Creative D: Johnathan Murdy
Dir Bus: Noah Bergman

D-U-N-S 00-250-8133
UNIVERSAL SUPPLY CO LLC (NJ)
(*Suby of* US LBM HOLDINGS LLC) ★
582 S Egg Harbor Rd, Hammonton, NJ 08037-3341
Tel (609) 561-3000 *Founded/Ownrshp* 1965, 2010
Sales 272.0MM^E *EMP* 205
SIC 5033 5031 Roofing, asphalt & sheet metal; Siding, except wood; Lumber, plywood & millwork
Pr: Jeffrey Umosella
**CFO:* Joe Schoen
Brnch Mgr: Paul Agnese
Genl Mgr: Jim Smith
Sls Mgr: Barry Keenan
Sls Mgr: Frank Wichrowski
Sales Asso: Matt Tantillo

D-U-N-S 07-025-6664 IMP/EXP
▲ UNIVERSAL TECHNICAL INSTITUTE INC
16220 N Scottsdale Rd # 100, Scottsdale, AZ 85254-1825
Tel (623) 445-9500 *Founded/Ownrshp* 1965
Sales 347.1MM *EMP* 2,020
Tkr Sym UTI *Exch* NYS
SIC 8249 Trade school
Ch Bd: Kimberly J McWaters
Pr: Dean Michael
Pr: Eugene S Putnam Jr
Ex VP: Chad Freed
Sr VP: Jeffry B May

Sr VP: Sherrell E Smith
VP: Adrian Cordova
VP: John Gay
VP: Julian Gorman
VP: John Jenson
VP: Duane Kramer
VP: Deeann Palin
VP: Rekha Reddy-Sareen
VP: Jerry Rutter
VP: Lori Smith
VP: Rhonda Turner
Board of Directors: David A Blaszkiewicz, Alan E Cabito, Conrad A Conrad, William J Lennox Jr, Roderick R Paige, Roger S Penske, Linda J Srere, Kenneth R Trammell, John C White

D-U-N-S 83-235-3408
UNIVERSAL TRAILER CARGO GROUP
(*Suby of* UNIVERSAL TRAILER HOLDINGS CORP) ★
12800 University Dr # 300, Fort Myers, FL 33907-5332
Tel (513) 671-3880 *Founded/Ownrshp* 2009
Sales 341.7MM^E *EMP* 1,350^E
SIC 3715 Truck trailers
Pr: Kevin Page

D-U-N-S 02-164-7995 EXP
UNIVERSAL TRAILER CARGO GROUP INC
(*Suby of* UNIVERSAL TRAILER CARGO GROUP) ★
14054 C R 4, Bristol, IN 46507
Tel (574) 264-9661 *Founded/Ownrshp* 2002
Sales 263.5MM^E *EMP* 1,000
SIC 3715 Demountable cargo containers
Pr: Kevin Page
VP: Jim Brown
VP: David Lindstaedt
Genl Mgr: Roger Perlstein
Genl Mgr: Mike Story
Dir IT: Lance Dell
VP Opers: Pat Sall
Opers Mgr: Larry Gunter
VP Sls: Keith Peterson

D-U-N-S 13-782-6710 IMP
UNIVERSAL TRAILER HOLDINGS CORP
12800 University Dr # 300, Fort Myers, FL 33907-5336
Tel (513) 671-3880 *Founded/Ownrshp* 2001
Sales 615.9MM^E *EMP* 1,850
SIC 7513 Truck rental & leasing, no drivers
CEO: Terry Carlson
**CEO:* Tom Frey
**CFO:* Matt Rohwer
VP: Walter Niziolek

D-U-N-S 06-881-2072 IMP
UNIVERSAL TRIM INC
CNI/UTI
(*Suby of* NICA INC) ★
1451 E Lincoln Ave, Madison Heights, MI 48071-4136
Tel (248) 586-3300 *Founded/Ownrshp* 1982
Sales 237.9M^E *EMP* 1,173^E
SIC 3714 3199 3089 3429 Motor vehicle parts & accessories; Novelties, leather; Automotive parts, plastic; Manufactured hardware (general)
Pr: E Don Cunningham

D-U-N-S 00-254-3445
UNIVERSAL WEATHER AND AVIATION INC
UVAIR
1150 Gemini St, Houston, TX 77058-2708
Tel (713) 944-1622 *Founded/Ownrshp* 1959
Sales 335.0MM^E *EMP* 2,160
Accts Grant Thornton Co
SIC 4725 4724 Tour operators; Tours, conducted; Travel agencies
Pr: Ralph J Vasami
**Ch Bd:* Charles Gregory Evans II
**Pr:* Mark J Carmen
**COO:* Dave Diulus
COO: Dave Dulius
COO: Ralph Vasami
CFO: Kelvin R Collard
Treas: Diane Bird
Top Exec: Robin Williams
**Sr VP:* Adolfo Aragon
**Sr VP:* Bobby Butler
**Sr VP:* Jonathan Howells
Sr VP: Tim Maystrik
Sr VP: Lynda Parsons
VP: Greg Cox
VP: Carl Esposito
VP: Justine Finnett
VP: Alan Gahm
VP: Stephen Ginsberg
**VP:* Thomas Mahoney
VP: Saverio Mongelli

D-U-N-S 03-809-5758
■ UNIVERSAL WELL SERVICES INC
(*Suby of* PATTERSON-UTI ENERGY INC) ★
13549 S Mosiertown Rd, Meadville, PA 16335-8317
Tel (814) 337-1983 *Founded/Ownrshp* 2001
Sales 878.8MM^E *EMP* 1,000
SIC 1389 1382 Hydraulic fracturing wells; Oil & gas exploration services
Pr: Roger Willis
**CFO:* John E Vollmer
VP: Bill Stoner
Exec: John Stansfield
Creative D: Pat Jarrell
Netwrk Mgr: Ryan Mackowski
Software D: Ian Eccles
Opers Mgr: Everett Saunders
Opers Mgr: Berry Shelatz
Opers Mgr: Robert Snow
Sls Mgr: Jim Fontaine
Board of Directors: Bill Ruddock, Rick Thomas

D-U-N-S 83-930-5401 IMP
UNIVERSAL WILDE INC
26 Dartmouth St Ste 1, Westwood, MA 02090-2332
Tel (781) 251-2700 *Founded/Ownrshp* 2000
Sales 198.9MM^E *EMP* 560
SIC 2752 Commercial printing, lithographic
CEO: William Fitzgerald
**Pr:* John Sisson
**CFO:* Stephen Payne
**Treas:* Robert S Lieberman
Chf Mktg O: John Sison
**VP:* Jim Bailey
VP: Ed Cunningham
VP: Bob Hines
VP: Robert Joyce
Creative D: Nancy Harhut
Genl Mgr: Shawn Gill
Board of Directors: Tom Andrade, Bill Fitzgerald, Joshua Hall

UNIVERSALPEGASUS INTERNATIONAL
See UNIVERSAL ENSCO INC

D-U-N-S 07-943-2677
■ UNIVERSALPEGASUS INTERNATIONAL HOLDINGS INC
(*Suby of* HUNTINGTON INGALLS INDUSTRIES INC) ★
4848 Loop Central Dr # 600, Houston, TX 77081-2356
Tel (713) 425-6000 *Founded/Ownrshp* 2014
Sales 204.7MM^E *EMP* 1,089
SIC 7389 8711 8713 Drafting service, except temporary help; Pipeline & power line inspection service; Designing: ship, boat, machine & product; Surveying services
Pr: Philip Luna
Sr VP: Tim Brown
Sr VP: Monty Collins
Sr VP: Glenn Cormier
Sr VP: Tom Davison
Sr VP: Martin Morrison
Sr VP: Tim Zboya
VP: Michael G Queen
VP: Mark Zuniga

D-U-N-S 02-609-3666
■ UNIVERSALPEGASUS INTERNATIONAL INC (TX)
(*Suby of* HUNTINGTON INGALLS INDUSTRIES INC) ★
4848 Loop Central Dr # 600, Houston, TX 77081-2356
Tel (713) 425-6000 *Founded/Ownrshp* 1982, 2014
Sales 250.0MM *EMP* 1,400
SIC 7389 8711 8713

UNIVERSIDAD DE PUERTO RICO
See UNIVERSITY OF PUERTO RICO

D-U-N-S 09-011-2079
UNIVERSIDAD INTERAMERICANA DE PUERTO RICO INC
CENTRAL OFFICE
399 Calle Galileo, San Juan, PR 00927-4518
Tel (787) 766-1912 *Founded/Ownrshp* 1912
Sales 276.8MM *EMP* 4,306
Accts Fpv & Galindez San Juan Puer
SIC 8221 University
Pr: Manuel J Fernos
Ofcr: Ruben Pagan
**VP:* Agustin Echevarria
**VP:* Luis R Esquilin
Exec: Alicia Ayala
Software D: Bryan Atwood

D-U-N-S 96-330-8866
UNIVERSIDAD INTERAMERICANA DE PUERTO RICO INC
RECINTO DE AGUADILLA
(*Suby of* CENTRAL OFFICE) ★
Recinto De Aguadil, Aguadilla, PR 00605
Tel (787) 891-0925 *Founded/Ownrshp* 2010
Sales 240.9MM^E *EMP* 1^E
Accts Kpmg Llp San Juan Pr
SIC 8221 University
**Prin:* Luis Acevedo

UNIVERSIDAD METROPOLITANA
See SISTEMA UNIVERSITARIO ANA G MENDEZ INC

D-U-N-S 93-788-6414
UNIVERSITIES OF LOUISIANA SYSTEM
(*Suby of* LOUISIANA BOARD OF REGENTS) ★
1201 N 3rd St Ste 7300, Baton Rouge, LA 70802-5243
Tel (225) 342-6950 *Founded/Ownrshp* 1974
Sales NA *EMP* 4,500
SIC 9411 Administration of educational programs;
Pr: Randy Moffett
CFO: David C Niklas
Assoc VP: Todd Barre
VP: Edwin Litolff
Ex Dir: Kerry Davidson
**Ex Dir:* Caprice Leyoub

D-U-N-S 05-691-2900
UNIVERSITIES SPACE RESEARCH ASSOCIATION
U S R A
7178 Columbia Gateway Dr, Columbia, MD 21046-2581
Tel (410) 730-2656 *Founded/Ownrshp* 1969
Sales 112.5MM *EMP* 550
SIC 8733 Scientific research agency
Pr: Don Kniffen
**CFO:* Michele Sparrow
Ex VP: David Cummings
VP: Donald A Kniffen
**VP:* Alan Marchant
**VP:* Kevin Schmadel
VP: Kevin C Schmadel
Comm Man: Erin Senoz
Ex Dir: W D Cummings
IT Man: Mike Nassar
Opers Mgr: Debra Hallmark

D-U-N-S 15-947-0350
UNIVERSITY AND COMMUNITY COLLEGE SYSTEM TENNESSEE STATE
(*Suby of* TENNESSEE BOARD OF REGENTS) ★
1415 Murfreesboro Pike, Nashville, TN 37217-2829
Tel (615) 366-4400 *Founded/Ownrshp* 1972
Sales 381.4MM^E *EMP* 2,435
SIC 8222 Community college
**CFO:* Del Sims

D-U-N-S 11-979-8767
UNIVERSITY AT ALBANY
(*Suby of* SUNY ADMINISTRATION) ★
1400 Washington Ave, Albany, NY 12222-0100
Tel (518) 442-3300 *Founded/Ownrshp* 1844
Sales 306.0MM^E *EMP* 4,000^E
SIC 8221 9411 Colleges universities & professional schools; Administration of educational programs;
Pr: Robert J Jones
Ex VP: Deborah Read
VP: Xiaonong Zhang
Assoc Dir: Susan Herrmann
Dir IT: Michael Landin
Dir IT: Martin Manjak
IT Man: Carolyn Mayadas

D-U-N-S 07-940-5350
UNIVERSITY AT BUFFALO
501 Capen Hall, Buffalo, NY 14260-1600
Tel (716) 645-2000 *Founded/Ownrshp* 2014
Sales 126.2MM^E *EMP* 6,788^E
SIC 8221 University; Colleges & universities
Pr: Satish K Tripathi
Assoc VP: Michael Dupre
VP: Melissa Barone
VP: Sharon Chimera
VP: Ida Harris
Off Mgr: Carmella Spina
Dir IT: Christian Miller
IT Man: Russ Miller

D-U-N-S 07-999-7987
UNIVERSITY ATHLETIC ASSOCIATION INC
UNIVERSITY OF FLORIDA
157 Gale Lemerand Dr, Gainesville, FL 32611-2051
Tel (352) 375-4683 *Founded/Ownrshp* 1974
Sales 135.3MM *EMP* 350
Accts James Moore & Co Pl Gainesv
SIC 8699 Athletic organizations
CEO: Jeremy N Foley
**Ch Bd:* Bernie Machen
**Pr:* Andrew Fawbush
**Pr:* Kent Fuchs
**Treas:* Marshall M Criser III
**Treas:* Ed Poppell
**VP:* Steve Nouss
Assoc Dir: Donna S Doty
Assoc Dir: Curtis Head
IT Man: Sarah Dobson
Sls&Mrk Ex: Mike Hill

UNIVERSITY BOOK STORE
See UNIVERSITY OF TEXAS AT ARLINGTON

UNIVERSITY BOOKSTORE
See UNIVERSITY OF ARKANSAS SYSTEM

D-U-N-S 16-193-8233
UNIVERSITY CALIFORNIA BERKELEY
(*Suby of* REGENTS OF UNIVERSITY OF CALIFORNIA) ★
200 Clfrnia Hall Spc 1500, Berkeley, CA 94720-0001
Tel (510) 642-6000 *Founded/Ownrshp* 2007
Sales 659.2MM^E *EMP* 30,000^E
SIC 8221 University
CFO: Ted Huang
VP: Julia Chu
VP: Noah Ickowitz
VP: Remi Schuman
VP: Lily Zhang
Assoc Dir: Alma Valencia
Dir Soc: Danielle Lauber
Ex Dir: Jerome Engel
Ex Dir: John Huggins
Prgrm Mgr: Tom Killilea
Dept Mgr: Pamela Reynolds

UNIVERSITY CARE PLUS
See UT PHYSICIANS

UNIVERSITY CHARLESTON SC
See COLLEGE OF CHARLESTON

UNIVERSITY COLORADO HOSPITAL
See UNIVERSITY OF COLORADO HOSPITAL AUTHORITY

D-U-N-S 06-966-8291 EXP
UNIVERSITY COMMUNITY HOSPITAL INC
FLORIDA HOSPITAL TAMPA
(*Suby of* ADVENTST HLTH SYSTM SUNBELT H) ★
3100 E Fletcher Ave, Tampa, FL 33613-4613
Tel (813) 615-7887 *Founded/Ownrshp* 2010
Sales 460.4MM *EMP* 8,000
SIC 8062 General medical & surgical hospitals
VP: Michael Schultz
Dir Recs: Pamela McFadden
Ex VP: Calbin Gilebewell
Dir Lab: Kathy Naret
Dir Rad: Robert Boltuch
Dir Rad: Linwood Henry
Dir Rad: Ruth Holliday
Dir Rad: James I Okoh
Dir Rad: Frederick Laufer
Dir Rad: Richard Lynch
Dir Rad: Hugo Montes

D-U-N-S 07-833-9587 EXP
UNIVERSITY CORP FOR ATMOSPHERIC RESEARCH
NATIONAL CENTER FOR ATMOSPHERI
3090 Center Green Dr, Boulder, CO 80301-2252
Tel (303) 497-1000 *Founded/Ownrshp* 1946, 1951
Sales 212.9MM *EMP* 1,565
Accts Kpmg Llp Albuquerque Nm
SIC 8733 Scientific research agency; Educational research agency
Pr: Thomas J Bogdan
V Ch: Dennis Hartmann
Pr: Jeff Reaves
**CFO:* Kathyrn Schmoll
**CFO:* Michael Thompson
Treas: Barbara Feiner
**Treas:* Dan Wilson
Trst: Mark Abbott
Trst: Steven A Ackerman
Trst: Roberta Balstad
Trst: Rosina Rosina Bierbaum
Trst: Fred Carr
Trst: Shirley Malcom
Trst: Meg McClellan
Trst: Franklin Nutter
Trst: Steven Rutledge
Trst: Anne Thompson
Trst: Richard Truly
Trst: Don Wuebbles
VP: Beverly Broach
VP: Jack Fellows

D-U-N-S 96-631-9837
UNIVERSITY CORP FOR ATMOSPHERIC RESEARCH FOUNDATION
P.O. Box 3000 (80307-3000)
Tel (303) 497-8575 *Founded/Ownrshp* 2011
Sales 218.0MM *EMP* 5^E
Accts Deloitte Tax Llp Denver Co
SIC 8641 Civic social & fraternal associations

D-U-N-S 03-057-9213
UNIVERSITY ENTERPRISES CORP AT CSUSB
CALIF STATE UNIVERSITY
5500 University Pkwy, San Bernardino, CA 92407-2318
Tel (909) 537-5929 *Founded/Ownrshp* 1962
Sales 24.9MM *EMP* 1,100
SIC 5812 5942 8211

D-U-N-S 02-903-1796
UNIVERSITY ENTERPRISES INC
6000 J St, Sacramento, CA 95819-2605
Tel (916) 278-6672 *Founded/Ownrshp* 1951
Sales 66.6MM *EMP* 1,856
Accts Macias Gini & O Connell Llp S
SIC 8299 8741 Educational services; Management services
Ch: Alexander Gonzalez
Assoc VP: Tracy Newman
**VP:* Ming Tung Mike Lee
**Prin:* Donald Taylor
**Ex Dir:* Jim Reinhart
DP Exec: David C Hill

D-U-N-S 79-974-3013
UNIVERSITY GENERAL HEALTH SYSTEM INC
7501 Fannin St, Houston, TX 77054-1938
Tel (713) 375-7100 *Founded/Ownrshp* 2011
Sales 163.9MM *EMP* 1,113^E
SIC 8062 8059

UNIVERSITY HEALTH ASSOCIATES
See VIRGINIA WEST UNIVERSITY MEDICAL CORP

D-U-N-S 18-043-4953
UNIVERSITY HEALTH CARE INC
PASSPORT HEALTH PLAN
5100 Cmmerce Crossings Dr, Louisville, KY 40229-2128
Tel (502) 585-7900 *Founded/Ownrshp* 1997
Sales 1.3MMM *EMP* 165
Accts Mountjoy Chilton Medley Llp L
SIC 8011 6411 Health maintenance organization; Insurance agents, brokers & service
Ex Dir: Joyce Schifano
**Pr:* Larry N Cook MD
**Ch:* William B Wagner
**Treas:* Allan Tasman
**Chf Mktg O:* Jackie Simmons MD
VP: Jill Bell
VP: David M Henley
VP: Barbara G Jones
VP: Alan Krigstein
VP: Christie Spencer
**VP:* James Taylor
VP: Leslie S Zavodnick
Comm Dir: Michael Rabkin

UNIVERSITY HEALTH CONWAY
See MONROE L BRFHH L C

UNIVERSITY HEALTH GROUPS
See SHANDS JACKSONVILLE MEDICAL CENTER INC

D-U-N-S 96-784-1508
UNIVERSITY HEALTH INC
1350 Walton Way, Augusta, GA 30901-2612
Tel (706) 722-9011 *Founded/Ownrshp* 1984
Sales 445.6MM *EMP* 30
SIC 8062 General medical & surgical hospitals
CFO: David Belkoski
Mktg Dir: Rebecca Silvester
Sls Mgr: Rhea Morgan

D-U-N-S 19-477-1382
UNIVERSITY HEALTH RESOURCES INC
1350 Walton Way, Augusta, GA 30901-2612
Tel (706) 722-9011 *Founded/Ownrshp* 1984
Sales 38.6MM *EMP* 5,000
SIC 8741 Hospital management
CFO: Dave Belkoski
**COO:* James Davis

D-U-N-S 13-079-5446
UNIVERSITY HEALTH SERVICES INC
UNIVERSITY HOSPITAL
(*Suby of* UNIVERSITY HEALTH RESOURCES INC) ★
1350 Walton Way, Augusta, GA 30901-2612
Tel (706) 722-9011 *Founded/Ownrshp* 1984
Sales 427.9MM^E *EMP* 3,170
Accts University Health Services Inc
SIC 8062 General medical & surgical hospitals
Pr: James R Davis
**COO:* Jason Moore
**CFO:* Dave Belkoski
Pharmcst: Allen Hicks
Pgrm Dir: Patricia L Thomas

UNIVERSITY HEALTH SHREVEPORT
See BRFHH SHREVEPORT LLC

UNIVERSITY HEALTH SYSTEM
See BEXAR COUNTY HOSPITAL DISTRICT

D-U-N-S 00-894-7938
UNIVERSITY HEALTH SYSTEM
BEAR COUNTY HOSPITAL DISTRICT
355 Spencer Ln Ste 2, San Antonio, TX 78201-2056
Tel (210) 358-9185 *Founded/Ownrshp* 2008
Sales 150.6MM^E *EMP* 6,000
SIC 8011 6512 Medical centers; Commercial & industrial building operation
CEO: Reed Hurley

D-U-N-S 84-750-5989
UNIVERSITY HEALTH SYSTEM
ROBERT B. GREEN CAMPUS
4502 Medical Dr, San Antonio, TX 78229-4402
Tel (210) 358-4000 *Founded/Ownrshp* 1968
Sales 407.0MM *EMP* 5,000
SIC 8099 Health screening service
CEO: George B Hernandez Jr
COO: Nancy Hamstra
VP: Mary Mote
Adm Dir: Michelle Ingram
Pathlgst: Francis Sharkey
Obsttrcn: Courtney M Failor
Obsttrcn: Tiffany Remsing
Obsttrcn: Lauren M Schaub
Ansthlgy: Lee Carlisle
Ansthlgy: Cabe R Clark
Ansthlgy: Rafael Elenes

D-U-N-S 11-097-4438
UNIVERSITY HEALTH SYSTEM INC
UT MEMORIAL HOSPITAL
1924 Alcoa Hwy, Knoxville, TN 37920-1511
Tel (865) 305-9000 *Founded/Ownrshp* 1998
Sales 723.4MM *EMP* 3,200
SIC 8062 General medical & surgical hospitals
Pr: Joseph R Landsman
**COO:* David Hall
COO: W David Hall
VP: Renee Hawk
VP: Jenny James
**VP:* Susan Reed
VP: Becky Thompson
VP Bus Dev: Steven Ross
Dir Teleco: John Shearer
QA Dir: Mary Bozeman
Pathlgst: Christopher T Clark

Board of Directors: Michael Stricklandr, Bernard Bermstein, Carolyn Fairbank Biggs, Stuart Bressee, James Haslam II, James A Haslam, Joseph E Johnson, H W Sherrod Jr, Wes Stowers, Michael Strickland

D-U-N-S 86-938-4859
UNIVERSITY HEALTH SYSTEM INC
UNIVERSITY TN MEM RES CTR HOSP
(*Suby of* UT MEMORIAL HOSPITAL) ★
9000 Executive Park Dr D240, Knoxville, TN 37923-4689
Tel (865) 251-3700 *Founded/Ownrshp* 1993
Sales NA *EMP* 200
SIC 6324 8011 Hospital & medical service plans; General & family practice, physician/surgeon
Pr: C E Bilbrey
CFO: Joe Landsman
**VP:* Roger Massey

D-U-N-S 82-853-9556
UNIVERSITY HEALTH SYSTEMS OF EASTERN CAROLINA INC
VIDANT HEALTH
2100 Stantonsburg Rd, Greenville, NC 27834-2818
Tel (252) 847-4451 *Founded/Ownrshp* 1998
Sales 1.5MMM *EMP* 8,373
SIC 8062 Hospital, medical school affiliated with residency
CEO: Janet Mullaney
CFO: Lucinda Crawford
Ofcr: Janet R Mullaney
VP: Mary Sue Collier
VP: Preston N Comeaux III
CIO: Anita Hoggard
DP Dir: Beth Godard
DP Dir: Rhonda James
DP Dir: Roy Newton
QA Dir: Linda Hofler
Dir IT: Phillip Bowen

D-U-N-S 05-958-3370
UNIVERSITY HEALTHCARE ALLIANCE
7999 Gateway Blvd Ste 200, Newark, CA 94560-1197
Tel (510) 974-8281 *Founded/Ownrshp* 2010
Sales 187.4MM *EMP* 97[E]
SIC 8082 Home health care services
CEO: Bruce Harrison
**Pr:* Brian Bohman

UNIVERSITY HEALTHCARE BERKLEY
See CITY HOSPITAL INC

D-U-N-S 79-182-9604
UNIVERSITY HEALTHCARE INC
PASSPORT HEATH PLAN
5100 Cmmerce Crossings Dr, Louisville, KY 40229-2128
Tel (800) 691-5566 *Founded/Ownrshp* 2007
Sales NA *EMP* 4
Accts Mountjoy Chilton Medley Llp L
SIC 6324 Health maintenance organization (HMO), insurance only
VP: Shannon Turner
CEO: Larry Cook MD
Sls Mgr: David Henley

D-U-N-S 10-982-6214 IMP
■ **UNIVERSITY HEALTHCARE SYSTEM LC**
TULANE MEDICAL CENTER
(*Suby of* HOSPITAL COPORATION OF AMERICA) ★
1415 Tulane Ave, New Orleans, LA 70112-2600
Tel (504) 988-5263 *Founded/Ownrshp* 1994
Sales 276.2MM[E] *EMP* 3,000
SIC 8062 General medical & surgical hospitals
CEO: Robert Lynch
Exec: Susan Ingraham
Dir OR: Melissa Guidry
Dir Lab: Frances Santorelli
Off Mgr: Elaina Hardesty
Off Mgr: Erica Williams
Mktg Dir: Beth Babin
Pathlgst: Javed I Gill
Surgeon: Norman McSwain
Surgeon: Raoul P Rodriguez
Plas Surg: William S McDonald

UNIVERSITY HOSP HLTH SYS INC,
See UNIVERSITY HOSPITALS OF CLEVELAND

UNIVERSITY HOSPITAL
See STATE UNIVERSITY OF NEW YORK HEALTH SCIENCE CENTER AT SYRACUSE

UNIVERSITY HOSPITAL
See UNIVERSITY HEALTH SERVICES INC

UNIVERSITY HOSPITAL
See UNIVERSITY OF MISSOURI HEALTH CARE

D-U-N-S 11-835-0672
UNIVERSITY HOSPITAL
150 Bergen St Ste 1, Newark, NJ 07103-2406
Tel (973) 972-4300 *Founded/Ownrshp* 1975
Sales 470.3MM *EMP* 3,500
SIC 8062 General medical & surgical hospitals
CEO: James R Gonzalez
**COO:* Nancy Hamstra
**CFO:* Thomas Daly

UNIVERSITY HOSPITAL & MED CTR
See UNIVERSITY HOSPITAL LTD

UNIVERSITY HOSPITAL EAST
See OHIO STATE UNIVERSITY WEXNER MEDICAL CENTER

D-U-N-S 07-131-0437
■ **UNIVERSITY HOSPITAL LTD** (FL)
UNIVERSITY HOSPITAL & MED CTR
(*Suby of* HOSPITAL COPORATION OF AMERICA) ★
7201 N University Dr, Tamarac, FL 33321-2996
Tel (954) 721-2200 *Founded/Ownrshp* 1974
Sales 145.2MM[E] *EMP* 1,100
SIC 8062 General medical & surgical hospitals
CEO: James Cruickshank
Pr: Francine Crockett
**CFO:* Alisa Bert
VP: Paul Uhlig
Exec: Lee Chaykin
Dir Risk M: Armando Gil
Dir Lab: Lourdes Greenwood
Dir Lab: Michelle Lalicata
MIS Dir: Tom Scharff
IT Man: Hugo Smith
Pathlgst: Jason Degregorio

UNIVERSITY HOSPITAL PORTAGE MEDICAL CENTER
See ROBINSON HEALTH SYSTEM INC

D-U-N-S 06-890-4689
UNIVERSITY HOSPITALS GEAUGA MEDICAL CENTER
UHHS-GEAUGA REGIONAL HOSPITAL
(*Suby of* UNIVERSITY HOSPITALS HEALTH SYSTEM INC) ★
13207 Ravenna Rd, Chardon, OH 44024-7032
Tel (440) 285-6000 *Founded/Ownrshp* 1952
Sales 140.4MM *EMP* 613
SIC 8062 General medical & surgical hospitals
Pr: Steven Jones
Chf OB: Dichai Duangjak
**V Ch:* Robert Forino
**Treas:* John T Fitts
**Treas:* Jerry Hornick
Ofcr: Julie Novak
**VP:* Theresa Weaver
Dir Lab: Monica Lennon
Dir Rad: Maria Schmidt
Dir Bus: Donna Casey
Mktg Mgr: Tiffany Hatcher

D-U-N-S 96-836-3940
UNIVERSITY HOSPITALS HEALTH SY
11100 Euclid Ave, Cleveland, OH 44106-1716
Tel (216) 844-4663 *Founded/Ownrshp* 2011
Sales 305.1MM *EMP* 23[E]
Accts Ernst & Young Us Llp Pittsbur
SIC 8062 General medical & surgical hospitals
CEO: Thomas F Zenty III
Doctor: Richard E Grant

D-U-N-S 07-775-9405 IMP
UNIVERSITY HOSPITALS HEALTH SYSTEM INC
3605 Warrensville Ctr Rd, Shaker Heights, OH 44122-5203
Tel (216) 767-8900 *Founded/Ownrshp* 1863
Sales 2.3MMM *EMP* 30,000
Accts Ernst & Young Us Llp Pittsb
SIC 8062 8011 8741 General medical & surgical hospitals; Offices & clinics of medical doctors; Hospital management; Nursing & personal care facility management
CEO: Thomas S Zenty
**CFO:* Michael Szubski
**Treas:* Bradley Bond
**Sr VP:* Janet L Miller
VP: Elizabeth Novak

D-U-N-S 60-937-3691 IMP
UNIVERSITY HOSPITALS OF CLEVELAND
UNIVERSITY HOSP HLTH SYS INC,
(*Suby of* UNIVERSITY HOSPITALS HEALTH SYSTEM INC) ★
11100 Euclid Ave, Cleveland, OH 44106-1716
Tel (216) 844-1000 *Founded/Ownrshp* 1990
Sales 1.4MMM[E] *EMP* 25,000
SIC 8062 8069 General medical & surgical hospitals; Specialty hospitals, except psychiatric
Pr: Thomas Zenty
Chf Rad: Pablo Ros
Treas: Bradley Bond
Ofcr: Anita Russell
Top Exec: Rod Rezaee
Sr VP: Mary A Annecharico
VP: Kim Bixenstine
VP: Chenguttai Manohar
VP: Don Paulson
VP: John Wheeler
Dir Sec: Carl Meeks

UNIVERSITY LOUISVILLE HOSPITAL
See UNIVERSITY MEDICAL CENTER INC

UNIVERSITY MD AT BALTIMORE
See UNIVERSITY SYSTEM OF MARYLAND

UNIVERSITY MD ST JSEPH MED CTR
See UNIVERSITY OF MARYLAND ST JOSEPH MEDICAL CENTER LLC

D-U-N-S 04-660-2728
■ **UNIVERSITY MECHANICAL & ENGINEERING CONTRACTORS INC**
SPIRA-LOC
(*Suby of* EMCOR MECHANICAL/ELECTRICAL SERVICES (WEST) INC) ★
1168 Fesler St, El Cajon, CA 92020-1812
Tel (619) 956-2500 *Founded/Ownrshp* 1994
Sales 99.0MM[E] *EMP* 501[E]
SIC 1711 1623 8741 Mechanical contractor; Plumbing contractors; Warm air heating & air conditioning contractor; Pipeline construction; Construction management
Pr: Steve Shirley
**CFO:* Peter Novak
**Sr VP:* John Modjeski
**VP:* Steve Thompson
IT Man: Pat Vance
VP Opers: Rob Zollinger
Snr PM: Dan Hirst

UNIVERSITY MED CTR AT PRNCETON
See MEDICAL CENTER AT PRINCETON NEW JERSEY

UNIVERSITY MEDICAL CENTER
See LUBBOCK COUNTY HOSPITAL DISTRICT

UNIVERSITY MEDICAL CENTER HOSP
See LEBANON HMA LLC

D-U-N-S 78-740-2841
UNIVERSITY MEDICAL CENTER INC
UNIVERSITY LOUISVILLE HOSPITAL
530 S Jackson St, Louisville, KY 40202-1675
Tel (502) 562-3000 *Founded/Ownrshp* 1996
Sales 484.1MM *EMP* 2,000
SIC 8062 General medical & surgical hospitals
CEO: James Taylor
**Pr:* Ken Marshall
CFO: Bob Barbier
**CFO:* Robert P Barbier
CFO: Robert Barbier
**Sr VP:* Mark Pfeifer
**VP:* Mary Jane Adams
VP: Steve Amsler
VP: Stephen McGuire
Dir Lab: Karen George
Off Mgr: Laura Fry

D-U-N-S 03-670-6692
UNIVERSITY MEDICAL CENTER MANAGEMENT CORP
(*Suby of* CHILDRENS HOSPITAL) ★
2000 Canal St, New Orleans, LA 70112-3018
Tel (504) 903-3000 *Founded/Ownrshp* 2010
Sales 176.1MM *EMP* 2,000[E]
Accts Laporte Matairie La
SIC 8062 General medical & surgical hospitals
CEO: Cindy Nuesslein

D-U-N-S 06-667-7535
UNIVERSITY MEDICAL CENTER OF SOUTHERN NEVADA
1800 W Charleston Blvd, Las Vegas, NV 89102-2329
Tel (702) 383-2000 *Founded/Ownrshp* 1931
Sales 530.8MM *EMP* 3,700
SIC 8062 Hospital, medical school affiliation
Prin: Anson Van Houweling
Chf OB: Donald L Roberts
Chf Rad: Dianne Mazzu
COO: Kurt Houser
CFO: Stephanie J Merrill
CFO: George Stevens
Ofcr: Trudy Mattson
Exec: John Espinoza
Dir Lab: Lisa Gorlick
CTO: Ernie McKinley
Dir IT: Holly Kincheloe

UNIVERSITY MEDICAL CTR EL PASO
See EL PASO COUNTY HOSPITAL DISTRICT

D-U-N-S 09-359-9322
UNIVERSITY MEDICAL SERVICE ASSOCIATION INC
12901 Brc Dwns Blvd Mdc62, Tampa, FL 33612
Tel (813) 974-2124 *Founded/Ownrshp* 1973
Sales 207.6MM *EMP* 1,350
SIC 8621

UNIVERSITY MISSISSIPPI MED CTR
See UNIVERSITY NEUROSURGEONS PLLC

UNIVERSITY NTXAS HLTH SCIENCE
See UNT HEALTH SCIENCE CENTER

D-U-N-S 84-542-0090
UNIVERSITY NEUROSURGEONS PLLC
UNIVERSITY MISSISSIPPI MED CTR
2500 N State St, Jackson, MS 39216-4500
Tel (601) 984-5700 *Founded/Ownrshp* 1995
Sales 99.2MM[E] *EMP* 185
SIC 8062 General medical & surgical hospitals
Assoc Dir: Linda R Cousin
Assoc Dir: Sylvia L Greer
Ex Dir: Sara Merrick
Nurse Mgr: Wanda Deaver
Nurse Mgr: Leslie Ishee
Netwrk Eng: Jon McIntosh

UNIVERSITY NEVADA - LAS VEGAS
See BOARD OF REGENTS NEVADA SYSTEM OF HIGHER EDUCATION

D-U-N-S 04-520-7552 IMP
UNIVERSITY OF AKRON
302 Buchtel Mall, Akron, OH 44325-0002
Tel (330) 972-7111 *Founded/Ownrshp* 1870
Sales 527.3MM[E] *EMP* 5,445
Accts Plante & Moran Pllc Toledo O
SIC 8221 University
Pr: Scott Scarborough
V Ch: Ann A Brennan
Trst: Edward L Bittle
Trst: Jack Morrison Jr
Trst: Kevin O Thompson
Assoc VP: Barbara E Omalley
Sr VP: Greg Zink
VP: John E Kovatch
VP: William Kraus
VP: Angelo-Gene Monaco
VP: Denine M Rocco

D-U-N-S 03-164-8472
UNIVERSITY OF ALABAMA
ALABAMA CRMSN TIDE SFTBALL
1202 Coliseum Cir, Tuscaloosa, AL 35487-0001
Tel (205) 348-0628 *Founded/Ownrshp* 2011
Sales 382.4M[E] *EMP* 5,000
SIC 8641 Civic social & fraternal associations
Pr: Stuart Bell

D-U-N-S 06-369-0705 IMP
UNIVERSITY OF ALABAMA AT BIRMINGHAM
U A B
(*Suby of* UNIVERSITY OF ALABAMA SYSTEM) ★
701 20th St S, Birmingham, AL 35233-2031
Tel (205) 934-5493 *Founded/Ownrshp* 1936
Sales 1.3MMM *EMP* 18,765
SIC 8221 8062

D-U-N-S 04-563-2635 IMP
UNIVERSITY OF ALABAMA FOUNDATION INC
(*Suby of* UNIVERSITY OF ALABAMA SYSTEM) ★
301 Rose Adm Bldg, Tuscaloosa, AL 35487-0001
Tel (205) 348-6010 *Founded/Ownrshp* 1831
Sales 659.9MM[E] *EMP* 3,950
Accts Pricewaterhousecoopers Llp Bi
SIC 8221 University
Ex Dir: Kevin Stevens
Pr: Charles Hilburn
VP: Steven Hood
Exec: Keith Sipek
Assoc Dir: Carol Hollyhand
Cmptr Lab: Patricia E McCaffry
Dir IT: Winn Felita
Dir IT: Carolyn Russo
Mktg Mgr: Tracy Barton
Snr Mgr: Scott Montgomery

D-U-N-S 08-138-8753
UNIVERSITY OF ALABAMA HEALTH SERVICES FOUNDATION PC
KIRKLIN CLINIC
500 22nd St S Ste 100, Birmingham, AL 35233-3110
Tel (205) 731-9600 *Founded/Ownrshp* 1973
Sales 26.2MM *EMP* 3,205
Accts Pricewaterhousecoopers Llp Bi
SIC 8093 Specialty outpatient clinics
CEO: Will Ferniany
**Pr:* Dr Jim Bonner
**Pr:* Anton Bueschen
**CFO:* Michael Heckman
**Ex VP:* Patricia Pritchett
**VP:* Reed F Jones
Surgeon: James K Kirklin
Surgeon: David McGiffen
Surgeon: Richard B Morawetz
Surgeon: Albert D Pacifico
Surgeon: Mary Pharis

D-U-N-S 02-329-8859
UNIVERSITY OF ALABAMA IN HUNTSVILLE
(*Suby of* UNIVERSITY OF ALABAMA SYSTEM) ★
301 Sparkman Dr Nw, Huntsville, AL 35805-1911
Tel (256) 824-6340 *Founded/Ownrshp* 2008
Sales 140.5MM *EMP* 600
Accts Pricewaterhousecoopers Llp B
SIC 8221 Colleges universities & professional schools
Pr: Robert A Altenkirch
VP: Chih Y Loo
VP: Delois Smith
Dir Teleco: Bob Blood
Assoc Dir: Charles S Davis
Assoc Dir: Carol E Mueller
Assoc Dir: Sabrina Williams
Comm Dir: Phillip Gentry
Dir IT: Bobbijo Carter
Dir IT: Chakravarthy Deverapalli
Sftwr Eng: Feng Zhu

D-U-N-S 80-824-5794
UNIVERSITY OF ALABAMA SYSTEM
401 Queen City Ave, Tuscaloosa, AL 35401-1551
Tel (205) 348-5861 *Founded/Ownrshp* 1969
Sales 2.2MMM[E] *EMP* 25,000
Accts Pricewaterhousecoopers Llp B
SIC 5999 Hearing aids
Off Mgr: Anita Wolfe
IT Man: Kim T Bailey
IT Man: David Knight
Netwrk Eng: Lionel West
Genl Couns: Cooper Shattuck
Counsel: Helena Barkworth

D-U-N-S 83-001-9431
UNIVERSITY OF ALASKA ANCHORAGE
(*Suby of* UNIVERSITY OF ALASKA SYSTEM) ★
3211 Providence Dr, Anchorage, AK 99508-4645
Tel (907) 786-1800 *Founded/Ownrshp* 2009
Sales 180.5MM[E] *EMP* 3,500[E]
Accts Kpmg Llp Anchorage Ak
SIC 8221 University
Prin: Jeff Roe
Treas: Heather Corriere
Ofcr: Kathleen Boyle
Ofcr: Kristin Elieff
Ofcr: Marmian Grimes
Ofcr: Carin Stephens
Ofcr: Nathan Zierfuss
Assoc VP: Michelle Rizk
Exec: Beth Behner
Exec: Susan Henrichs
Exec: Jeffrey Johnston
Assoc Dir: Carol Holz
Dir: Lynne Johnson

D-U-N-S 83-001-9845
UNIVERSITY OF ALASKA FAIRBANKS
(*Suby of* UNIVERSITY OF ALASKA SYSTEM) ★
910 Yukon Dr 202, Fairbanks, AK 99775-0001
Tel (907) 474-7211 *Founded/Ownrshp* 2016
Sales 173.2MM^E *EMP* 1,955
Accts Kpmg Llp Anchorage Ak
SIC 8221 University
**Pr:* Pat Gamble
Ofcr: Cecelia Chamberlain
Ofcr: Susan Phillips
Top Exec: Rheba Dupras
Exec: Bernice M Joseph
Assoc Dir: Donna Anger
Div Mgr: Bottler Erynn
Div Mgr: Dann Toliver
Off Mgr: Margaret Kellogg
Store Mgr: Mary A Short
IT Man: Wayne Royce

D-U-N-S 04-867-9567 IMP
UNIVERSITY OF ALASKA SYSTEM
3295 College Rd, Fairbanks, AK 99709-3705
Tel (907) 450-8079 *Founded/Ownrshp* 1917
Sales 353.8MM^E *EMP* 6,629
Accts Kpmg Llp Anchorage Ak
SIC 8221 University
Prin: Patrick Gamble
Ex VP: Ashok Roy
VP: Carla Beam
Dir Risk M: Nancy Spink
Genl Mgr: Greg Petrowich
Off Admin: Janet Ballek
Genl Couns: Michael Hostina

D-U-N-S 80-634-5617 IMP
UNIVERSITY OF ARIZONA
ARIZONA BOARD OF REGENTS
(*Suby of* BRA) ★
888 N Euclid Ave Rm 510, Tucson, AZ 85719-4824
Tel (520) 626-6000 *Founded/Ownrshp* 1890
Sales 1.7MMM^E *EMP* 15,615
Accts Debra K Davenport Cpa Phoen
SIC 8221 Colleges universities & professional schools
Pr: Ann Weaver Hart
Pr: Kristen Buckles
Pr: James D Van Arsdel
CFO: Milton Castillo
**CFO:* Gregg Goldman
Top Exec: Laura Bosworth
Assoc VP: Judith A Bernas
Assoc VP: Robert Smith
Ex VP: Abed Anouti
Sr VP: Andrew C Comrie
**Sr VP:* Joe Gn Garcia
Sr VP: Jacqueline L Mok
Sr VP: Leslie P Tolbert
**Sr VP:* Melissa Vito
VP: Jennifer Barton
VP: Janet Bingham
VP: Gail Burd
VP: Styne Hill
VP: Laura T Johnson
VP: Judith Leonard
VP: Patricia Maccorquodale

D-U-N-S 02-511-7714
UNIVERSITY OF ARIZONA FOUNDATION (AZ)
1111 N Cherry Ave, Tucson, AZ 85721-0111
Tel (520) 621-5494 *Founded/Ownrshp* 1958
Sales 165.3MM *EMP* 2
Accts Ernst & Young Us Llp Phoenix
SIC 8699 Charitable organization
Pr: James Moore
Pr: Shaun Sommerer
VP: Craig Barker
VP: Lance Cavanaugh
VP: Jill Hall
Assoc Dir: Marcy Funaro
Prin: Daniel Asia
Web Dev: David Holton

D-U-N-S 07-956-8021
UNIVERSITY OF ARKANSAS AT PINE BLUFF
UAPB
(*Suby of* UNIVERSITY BOOKSTORE) ★
1200 University Dr, Pine Bluff, AR 71601-2780
Tel (870) 575-8000 *Founded/Ownrshp* 1890
Sales 107.2MM^E *EMP* 1^E
SIC 8221 Colleges universities & professional schools
Pgrm Dir: Tisha Arnold
Pgrm Dir: Verna Cottonham
Snr Mgr: Ralph Owens

D-U-N-S 60-662-5312
UNIVERSITY OF ARKANSAS FOR MEDICAL SCIENCES
UAMS
4301 W Markham St, Little Rock, AR 72205-7101
Tel (501) 686-6606 *Founded/Ownrshp* 2005
Sales 567.5MM^E *EMP* 11,000^E
SIC 8221

D-U-N-S 05-560-0001
UNIVERSITY OF ARKANSAS SYSTEM
UNIVERSITY BOOKSTORE
2404 N University Ave, Little Rock, AR 72207-3608
Tel (501) 686-2500 *Founded/Ownrshp* 1872
Sales 1.9MMM *EMP* 14,025
Accts Roger A Norman Jd Cpa Cfe
SIC 8221 University
Pr: Donald R Bobbitt
**Pr:* B Alan Sugg
VP: Dan Ferritor
**VP:* Ann Kemp
VP: Carol Kordsmeier
VP: Christina Miller
**VP:* Milo Shult
VP: Joyce Wroten
Assoc Dir: Amy Moss
Assoc Dir: Katrina Owoh
Admn Mgr: Leaundra Sanders

D-U-N-S 06-990-0579
UNIVERSITY OF ARTS
320 S Broad St, Philadelphia, PA 19102-4994
Tel (215) 717-6000 *Founded/Ownrshp* 1876
Sales 101.9MM *EMP* 650
Accts Baker Tilly Virchow Krause Llp
SIC 8221 College, except junior; University
Pr: Stephen Tarantal
Treas: Adolf Paier
Bd of Dir: Jamer Hunt
Ofcr: Daniel Sloane
**VP:* Josi Burri
**VP:* Thomas H Carnwath
**VP:* Stephen J Lightcap
Prin: Craig Johnson
Prin: James Vesey
Ex Dir: Raye Cohen
Ex Dir: Pearl Schaeffer

D-U-N-S 07-211-7633
UNIVERSITY OF BRIDGEPORT
U B
126 Park Ave, Bridgeport, CT 06604-7620
Tel (203) 576-4000 *Founded/Ownrshp* 1927
Sales 94.7MM *EMP* 611
Accts Marcum Llp New Haven Ct
SIC 8221 University
Pr: Neil A Salonen
CFO: Thomas R Oates
VP: Russ Budzilek
Comm Dir: Larry Orman
Ex Dir: David Cote
Dir IT: Susan Askew
IT Man: Arthur Dye

UNIVERSITY OF BUFFALO FOUNDATI
See U B FOUNDATION ACTIVITIES INC

D-U-N-S 82-994-6230
UNIVERSITY OF CALIFORNIA DAVIS
(*Suby of* REGENTS OF UNIVERSITY OF CALIFORNIA) ★
1 Shields Ave, Davis, CA 95616-8500
Tel (530) 752-1011 *Founded/Ownrshp* 2007
Sales 2.1MMM^E *EMP* 17,741^E
SIC 8221 9411 University; Administration of educational programs;
Ofcr: Andrew Villaruz
Exec: Mary Cummings
Exec: Leslyn Graham
Assoc Dir: Zoila Mendoza
Dir: Barbara Celli
Comm Dir: Kirsten Hertz
Admn Mgr: Cathleen Brady
Admn Mgr: Jane Ewald
DP Exec: Sunny Chow
DP Exec: Maurice Hamlet
DP Exec: Susan Heffron

D-U-N-S 10-613-4612
UNIVERSITY OF CALIFORNIA IRVINE
OFFICE OF CAMPUS COUNSEL
(*Suby of* REGENTS OF UNIVERSITY OF CALIFORNIA) ★
510 Aldrich Hall, Irvine, CA 92697-0001
Tel (949) 824-8343 *Founded/Ownrshp* 2007
Sales 1.7MMM^E *EMP* 20,000^E
Accts Pricewaterhousecoopers Llp Sa
SIC 8221 9411 University; Administration of educational programs;
VP: Morgan Sibley
Ex Dir: Diane Sagey
Genl Mgr: Shiouchuan Tsai
QA Dir: Jip Muongpruan
IT Man: Amjad Toukan
Software D: Glenn Sasano
Netwrk Eng: Heindrick Yu
Mktg Dir: Francine Matijak
Snr Mgr: Eunice Chan

D-U-N-S 79-410-6091 IMP
UNIVERSITY OF CALIFORNIA LOS ANGELES
UCLA
(*Suby of* REGENTS OF UNIVERSITY OF CALIFORNIA) ★
405 Hilgard Ave, Los Angeles, CA 90095-9000
Tel (310) 825-4321 *Founded/Ownrshp* 1869
Sales 611.1MM^E *EMP* 3,326^E
SIC 8221 9411 University; Administration of educational programs;
Pr: Carole Goldberg
Ofcr: Nancy Blumstein
VP: Daniel Kiernan
VP: Lan Ta
Assoc Dir: Jessica Chung
Assoc Dir: Karen Howard
Assoc Dir: Masai Minters
Assoc Dir: Angelina Morano
Assoc Dir: Emilie Robertson
Assoc Dir: Kathleen Tingus
Assoc Dir: Alan Toy

D-U-N-S 12-774-6837
UNIVERSITY OF CALIFORNIA RIVERSIDE ALUMNI ASSOCIATION
(*Suby of* REGENTS OF UNIVERSITY OF CALIFORNIA) ★
900 University Ave, Riverside, CA 92521-9800
Tel (951) 827-1012 *Founded/Ownrshp* 1965
Sales 288.9MM^E *EMP* 3,850^E
SIC 8221 9411 University; Administration of educational programs;
**Pr:* Mark G Yudof
Ofcr: Paul G Afroilan
Ofcr: Brandon Anderson
Ofcr: Michael Andert
Ofcr: Romanie L Arterberry
Ofcr: Robert Bailey
Ofcr: Jimmie L Bowen
Ofcr: Cindy Cerdinas
Ofcr: Amy S Ricks
Assoc Dir: Jose A Aguilar
Assoc Dir: Greg Artman

D-U-N-S 14-864-8665
UNIVERSITY OF CALIFORNIA SAN DIEGO
(*Suby of* REGENTS OF UNIVERSITY OF CALIFORNIA) ★
9500 Gilman Dr, La Jolla, CA 92093-5004
Tel (858) 534-2230 *Founded/Ownrshp* 2007
Sales 1.8MMM^E *EMP* 24,400^E
SIC 8221 9411 University; Administration of educational programs;
CEO: Marissa Sunio
Assoc VP: Seraphin Raya
VP: Sarkis Terinian
Assoc Dir: Samuel Leader
Assoc Dir: Amber Sanchez
Pharmcst: Lisa M Provencio
Snr Mgr: Elizabeth L Barrett-Connor

D-U-N-S 78-954-8547
UNIVERSITY OF CALIFORNIA SAN FRANCISCO
(*Suby of* REGENTS OF UNIVERSITY OF CALIFORNIA) ★
505 Parnassus Ave, San Francisco, CA 94143-2204
Tel (415) 476-9000 *Founded/Ownrshp* 2007
Sales 28.0MM^E *EMP* 16,202
Accts Pricewaterhousecoopers Llp S
SIC 8221 University
Bd of Dir: Patricia Arean
VP: Vien Nguyen
Ex Dir: Regis Kelly
Prgrm Mgr: Rebecca Nguyen
CIO: Leslie Yuan
IT Man: Mark Day
IT Man: Tommy Kwong
IT Man: Cindy Yoxsimer
Netwrk Mgr: Timothy S Greer
Surgeon: Saam Morshed
Obsttrcn: Larry Rand

D-U-N-S 14-518-0415
UNIVERSITY OF CALIFORNIA SAN FRANCISCO FOUNDATION
44 Montgomery St Ste 2200, San Francisco, CA 94104-4709
Tel (415) 476-6922 *Founded/Ownrshp* 1987
Sales 242.9MM *EMP* 73
SIC 8699 Charitable organization
Pr: Michael Bishop

D-U-N-S 17-990-6110
UNIVERSITY OF CALIFORNIA SANTA BARBARA
CALIFORNIA NANOSYSTEMS INST
(*Suby of* REGENTS OF UNIVERSITY OF CALIFORNIA) ★
Uc Santa Barbara Mosher A, Santa Barbara, CA 93106-0001
Tel (805) 893-8000 *Founded/Ownrshp* 2007
Sales 543.2MM^E *EMP* 8,000^E
SIC 8221 9411 University; Administration of educational programs;
Ofcr: Giulia Brofferio
Ofcr: Michael Morgan
Assoc Dir: Elise Meyer
Assoc Dir: Bruce Miller
Assoc Dir: Dan Smith
Assoc Dir: Paul Valenzuela
Prgrm Mgr: Euzetta Williams
Off Mgr: Christopher McMahon
IT Man: Ali Aghayan
Sys Mgr: Peter Duda
Info Man: Margaret O'Brien

D-U-N-S 62-693-3428
UNIVERSITY OF CALIFORNIA SANTA CRUZ
(*Suby of* REGENTS OF UNIVERSITY OF CALIFORNIA) ★
1156 High St, Santa Cruz, CA 95064-1077
Tel (831) 459-0111 *Founded/Ownrshp* 1965
Sales 340.8MM^E *EMP* 3,920^E
SIC 8221 University
Ofcr: Diane Castle
Ex VP: Bruce Darling
Ex Dir: Beth Riddle
Dept Mgr: Stephanie Casher
CTO: Omed Muzaffery
DP Exec: Bob Ridder
Dir IT: Don Korycansky
IT Man: Lisa Dequattro
IT Man: Stephen Hauskins
Ql Cn Mgr: Brian Lee
Mktg Mgr: Ronald Sudulko

D-U-N-S 00-656-2250
UNIVERSITY OF CENTRAL ARKANSAS
201 Donaghey Ave, Conway, AR 72035-5003
Tel (501) 450-5000 *Founded/Ownrshp* 1907
Sales 133.1MM^E *EMP* 1,300
Accts Roger A Norman Jd Cpa Cpe
SIC 8221 University
Pr: Tom Courtway
**CEO:* Steve Williams
Ofcr: Bradley Moore
**VP:* Jack Gillean
**VP:* Shelly Mahl
**VP:* Diane Newton
**VP:* Robert Parrent
**VP:* Jeff Pitchford
**VP:* Steve Runge
**VP:* Ronnie Williams
Assoc Dir: Nolan Brown
Dir Soc: Donna Murphy

D-U-N-S 15-080-5653 EXP
UNIVERSITY OF CENTRAL FLORIDA BOARD OF TRUSTEES
U C F
(*Suby of* BOARD GOVERNORS GENERAL OFFICE) ★
4000 Central Florida Blvd, Orlando, FL 32816-8005
Tel (407) 823-2000 *Founded/Ownrshp* 1963
Sales 706.9MM^E *EMP* 6,500
SIC 8221 Colleges universities & professional schools; University
Pr: John C Hitt
V Ch: Tom Yochum
Pr: Charles Roberts
COO: Betsy Gray
CFO: Brad Stricklin
Trst: Judy Albertson
Trst: Willie Bentley
Trst: Logan Berkowitz
Trst: Manoj Chopra
Trst: Pat Christiansen
Trst: Michael Grindstaff
Trst: Phyllis A Klock
Trst: Conrad Santiago
Trst: Al Weiss
Assoc VP: Lin Huff-Corzine
Assoc VP: David Mealor
Assoc VP: Denise L Young
VP: Temitope Awofeso
VP: Helen Donegan
VP: Taylor Ellis
VP: Alfred Harms

D-U-N-S 06-794-7556
UNIVERSITY OF CENTRAL MISSOURI
415 E Clark St 213, Warrensburg, MO 64093-2403
Tel (660) 543-4233 *Founded/Ownrshp* 1891
Sales 117.2MM *EMP* 1,368
Accts Rubinbrown Llp Overland Park
SIC 8221 University
**VP:* John Merrigan

D-U-N-S 04-940-1458
UNIVERSITY OF CENTRAL OKLAHOMA
100 N University Dr, Edmond, OK 73034-5207
Tel (405) 974-2000 *Founded/Ownrshp* 1891
Sales 172.4MM^E *EMP* 1,700^E
Accts Arledge & Associates Pc Ed
SIC 8221 University
Pr: Don Betz
Treas: Emily Herr
**VP:* John Barthell
**VP:* Don Chrusciel
VP: Kathriine Gage
**VP:* Charlie Johnson
**VP:* Myron Pope
**VP:* Cynthya Rolfe
Mktg Mgr: Teresa Metzger
Snr Mgr: Dawna Terrell

D-U-N-S 00-542-1136 IMP/EXP
UNIVERSITY OF CHICAGO
5801 S Ellis Ave Ste 1, Chicago, IL 60637-5418
Tel (773) 702-1234 *Founded/Ownrshp* 1890
Sales 3.2MMM^E *EMP* 12,120
SIC 8221 University
Pr: Robert J Zimmer
**Ch Bd:* James S Crown
Pr: Pat Ohara
CFO: Nim Chinniah
**CFO:* Donald J Reaves
Ex VP: Kenneth S Polonsky
Sr VP: Michael McGrath
VP: Daniel Adelman
VP: Cole W Camplese
VP: David Cookson
VP: Bruce Fryxell
VP: David Greene
VP: Laurence Hill
**VP:* Gregory A Jackson
VP: Gregory Jackson
VP: Dean Kreis
VP: Michael Ludwig
VP: Diana Li
VP: James G Nondorf
VP: Judith Petty
VP: Ryan Priester

D-U-N-S 80-413-2210
UNIVERSITY OF CHICAGO
INTERNATIONAL HOUSE
1414 E 59th St, Chicago, IL 60637-2916
Tel (773) 753-2270 *Founded/Ownrshp* 2008
Sales 3.0MMM *EMP* 2
SIC 7021 Dormitory, commercially operated
Pr: Robert J Zimmer

D-U-N-S 19-848-0170 IMP
UNIVERSITY OF CHICAGO MEDICAL CENTER
BERNARD MITCHELL HOSPITAL
5841 S Maryland Ave, Chicago, IL 60637-1447
Tel (773) 702-1000 *Founded/Ownrshp* 1986
Sales 1.5MMM *EMP* 5,000
Accts Pricewaterhousecoopers Llp Ch
SIC 8062 General medical & surgical hospitals
CEO: James L Maderd
Chf Rad: David Paushter
**Pr:* David Hesner
COO: Carolyn Wilson
Trst: Trisha Rooney Alden
Trst: Jeffrey S Aronin
Trst: Diane P Atwood
Trst: Benjamin D Chereskin
Trst: Carol Levy
Trst: Emily Nicklin
Trst: Kenneth J Sharigan
Trst: John A Svoboda
Trst: Marrgwen Townsend
Trst: Scott Wald
Ofcr: David Hicks
Ex VP: Kenneth Kates
VP: Mark J Chastang
VP: Jeffrey Finesilver
VP: Michael Millis
VP: Virginia M Roberts
VP: Janet T Schumaker

D-U-N-S 04-106-4767
UNIVERSITY OF CINCINNATI
2600 Clifton Ave, Cincinnati, OH 45220-2872
Tel (513) 556-6000 *Founded/Ownrshp* 1987
Sales 960.6MM^E *EMP* 14,600^E
Accts Bkd Llp Cincinnati Ohio
SIC 8221 University
Pr: Gregory H Williams
V Ch: Melissa Delbello
Chf Inves: Karl M Scheer
Assoc VP: Karen Sullivan
Ex VP: Ryan M Hays
VP: Uma R Kotagal
VP: Carol Metzger
VP: Alaa Minkara
VP: Frederick H Siff
VP: John Tew Jr
VP: Judith Trent

VP: Gregory J Vehr
Exec: Katie Pence
Assoc Dir: Gerald Bostwick
Assoc Dir: Brandi Elliott
Assoc Dir: Kathleen Scrivens

D-U-N-S 03-804-5626 IMP
UNIVERSITY OF CINCINNATI MEDICAL CENTER LLC
234 Goodman St, Cincinnati, OH 45219-2364
Tel (513) 584-1000 *Founded/Ownrshp* 1996
Sales 873.4MM *EMP* 5,000[E]
Accts Deloitte Tax Llp Cincinnati
SIC 8062 General medical & surgical hospitals
Pr: Bryan Gibler
Chf Path: David P Witte
Chf OB: Arthur T Evans II
Dir Recs: Charlesetta Mc Cray
Dir Vol: Sheila Maxwell
COO: Nancy Barone
CFO: Douglas Arvin
**Ch:* George L Strike
**Trst:* Peter D Gosmak
VP: Steve Burns
VP: Tana Casper
VP: John M Deledda
VP: Andrew Filak
Dir Teleco: Lydia Hall
Dir Inf Cn: Francine Kidd
Dir Inf Cn: Robert Wones
Dir Lab: Teresa Williams
Dir Soc: Jane Mynatt
Dir Rx: Sean Osborne

UNIVERSITY OF COLORADO DENVER
See REGENTS OF UNIVERSITY OF COLORADO

D-U-N-S 18-865-2788
UNIVERSITY OF COLORADO FOUNDATION
1800 N Grant St Ste 725, Denver, CO 80203-1114
Tel (303) 813-7935 *Founded/Ownrshp* 1967
Sales 203.9MM *EMP* 180
Accts Eks&H Lllp Denver Co
SIC 8399 Fund raising organization, non-fee basis
Pr: Jack Finlaw
Pr: Abby Benson
Ofcr: Holly Nikolich
Ofcr: Viana Rockel
**Sr VP:* Steve K Moise
VP: Maurin Anderson
VP: Geoff Barsch
**VP:* Christopher Bittman
**VP:* Curtis A Helsel
VP: Jaryd Meenach
**VP:* Dan B Palmquist
**VP:* Dennis Piper
**VP:* Kathy Rasco
VP: Will Temby
VP: Kara Vosburgh
**VP:* A Keller Young
Assoc Dir: Terry Pew

D-U-N-S 08-002-2199
UNIVERSITY OF COLORADO HEALTH
12401 E 17th Ave Ste F485, Aurora, CO 80045-2603
Tel (720) 848-1031 *Founded/Ownrshp* 2015
Sales 1.1MMM[E] *EMP* 7,593
SIC 8082 Home health care services
Genl Couns: Emily Weber
Ofcr: Christine Hogan-Newgren
VP: Michael Cancro
VP: Melissa Greer
VP: Craig Hollenbaugh
VP: Dan Rieber
IT Man: Sheila Kauffman
Ansthlgy: Tessa N Mandler
Ansthlgy: Erik J Nelson

D-U-N-S 96-913-5131
UNIVERSITY OF COLORADO HEALTH AND WELFARE TRUST
1800 N Grant St Ste 800, Denver, CO 80203-1187
Tel (303) 860-5600 *Founded/Ownrshp* 2011
Sales 154.7MM *EMP* 33[E]
SIC 6733 Trusts
Prin: David E Chadwick
Off Mgr: Jennifer Roberson

D-U-N-S 88-475-8467 IMP
UNIVERSITY OF COLORADO HOSPITAL AUTHORITY
UNIVERSITY COLORADO HOSPITAL
(*Suby of* UNIVERSITY OF COLORADO HEALTH) ★
4200 E 9th Ave, Denver, CO 80220-3706
Tel (720) 848-0000 *Founded/Ownrshp* 1989
Sales 734.0MM[E] *EMP* 4,200[E]
SIC 8062 General medical & surgical hospitals
Pr: Bruce Chroffel
COO: Tom Gronow
**COO:* John Harney
CFO: Barbara Carveth
**CFO:* Anthony Desurio
VP: Lauren Carter
VP: Steven P Ringel
VP: Carolyn Sanders
VP: Gregory V Stiegmann
VP: Suzanne Sullivan
Dir Bus: Amy Hurley

D-U-N-S 07-869-9234
UNIVERSITY OF COLORADO HOSPITALS RETIREMENT PLAN
(*Suby of* UNIVERSITY COLORADO HOSPITAL) ★
2400 S Peoria St Ste 100, Aurora, CO 80014-5417
Tel (720) 848-4011 *Founded/Ownrshp* 2012
Sales 154.7MM[E] *EMP* 218[E]
SIC 6722
Pr: John P Harney

D-U-N-S 92-757-0622
UNIVERSITY OF CONNECTICUT
UCONN
(*Suby of* GOVERNORS OFFICE STATE OF CONNECTICUT) ★
343 Mansfield Rd U-1130, Storrs, CT 06269-9000
Tel (860) 486-2000 *Founded/Ownrshp* 1881
Sales 735.8MM[E] *EMP* 4,500
Accts John C Geragosian & Robert M
SIC 8221 9199 University;
Pr: Susan Herbst
Pr: Lynn Zayachkiwsky
COO: Barry M Feldman
CFO: Paul Mc Dowell
Trst: Louise M Bailey
Trst: Michael A Bozzuto
Trst: Gerard N Burrow
Trst: Andrea Dennis-Lavigne
Trst: Peter S Drotch
Trst: Rebecca Lobo
Trst: Michael J Martinez
Trst: Mark K McQuillan
Trst: Denis J Nayden
Trst: Thomas D Ritter
Trst: Corey Schmitt
Trst: Wayne J Shepperd
Trst: Richard Treibick
Trst: Robert M Ward
Ex VP: Mun Y Choi
VP: Richard Gray
VP: Arthur Hand

D-U-N-S 07-313-4025 IMP
UNIVERSITY OF DAYTON
300 College Park Ave, Dayton, OH 45469-0002
Tel (937) 229-2919 *Founded/Ownrshp* 1850
Sales 499.8MM *EMP* 4,500
Accts Mcgladrey Llp Dayton Ohio
SIC 8221 8733 University; Noncommercial research organizations
Pr: Dr Daniel J Curran
Pr: Phillip Chick
Pr: Rob Durkle
Pr: Todd Imwalle
Pr: Jane Perrich
Pr: Cilla Shindell
Pr: Cari Wallace
Trst: Richard Davis
Trst: Lynton Scotland
VP: Theodore Kissell
Mgt/VP: Robert Johnson
Exec: Claudette Groeber
Exec: Christopher Jones
Assoc Dir: Kathleen Henderson
Assoc Dir: Shane White
Board of Directors: John Leland

D-U-N-S 05-900-7500
UNIVERSITY OF DELAWARE
220 Hullihen Hall, Newark, DE 19716-0099
Tel (302) 831-2107 *Founded/Ownrshp* 1743
Sales 908.1MM *EMP* 3,600
Accts Kpmg Llp Philadelphia Penns
SIC 8221 University
Pr: Patrick T Harker
V Ch: Robert A Fischer
Treas: Alan Brangman
**Treas:* Scott R Douglass
Treas: David E Hollowell
Chf Inves: Keith Walter
Assoc VP: Mary G Brand
VP: Jason Cash
**VP:* Jennifer Davis
**VP:* Pierre Hayward
VP: Lawrence White
Exec: Cynthia M Carroll
Exec: Jianguo Chen
Exec: Dawn B Romanczak
Exec: Devona E Williams
Assoc Dir: Carol Anderer
Assoc Dir: Victor Klemas

UNIVERSITY OF DENVER
See COLORADO SEMINARY

D-U-N-S 07-313-5402
UNIVERSITY OF DETROIT MERCY
UDM
4001 W Mcnichols Rd, Detroit, MI 48221-3038
Tel (313) 993-6000 *Founded/Ownrshp* 1871
Sales 159.0MM *EMP* 950
SIC 8221 University
Pr: Antoine M Garibaldi
Ofcr: A Raines
**VP:* Vincent Abatemarco
VP: Gregory Cascione
VP: Maria Ibarra
VP: Barbara Milbauer
**VP:* Pamela Zarkowski
Assoc Dir: Kimberly Jones
VP Admn: Steven Carignan
Off Mgr: Wendy Marshall
Off Admin: Jenifer D Young

D-U-N-S 13-746-0275 IMP
UNIVERSITY OF DISTRICT OF COLUMBIA
U D C
4200 Conn Ave Nw Ste 200, Washington, DC 20008-1122
Tel (202) 274-5000 *Founded/Ownrshp* 1851
Sales 68.6MM[E] *EMP* 1,020
Accts Kpmg Llp Washington Dc
SIC 8221 University
Pr: William Pollard
**Pr:* Allen L Sessoms
**CFO:* Ibrahim H Koroma
**Ch:* Dr Charles J Ogletree Jr
**VP:* Ken Bain
**VP:* Myrtho Blanchard
**VP:* Alan Etter
**VP:* Barbara Jumper
Exec: William Latham
Genl Mgr: Edward P Jones Jr
CIO: Mike Jacks

D-U-N-S 05-689-2565
UNIVERSITY OF FINDLAY
1000 N Main St, Findlay, OH 45840-3653
Tel (419) 422-8313 *Founded/Ownrshp* 1882
Sales 94.7MM *EMP* 800[E]
Accts Crowe Horwath Llp Columbus O
SIC 8221 University
Pr: Katherine Fell
**Ch Bd:* AR Charmes
Treas: Martin L Terry
**V Ch Bd:* Richard White
Assoc VP: Mike Volan
VP: Darin Fields
VP: Michelle M Metcalf
VP: John Mosser
**VP:* Martin Terry
Admn Mgr: Carla Dee
CTO: Helen Schneider

UNIVERSITY OF FLORIDA
See UNIVERSITY ATHLETIC ASSOCIATION INC

D-U-N-S 00-442-6771 IMP
UNIVERSITY OF FLORIDA
ENGINEERING & INDSTRL EQPMT
(*Suby of* BOARD GOVERNORS GENERAL OFFICE) ★
300 Sw 13th St, Gainesville, FL 32611-0001
Tel (352) 392-3261 *Founded/Ownrshp* 1853
Sales 1.7MMM *EMP* 5,106
Accts Sherrill F Norman Cpa Tallah
SIC 8221 University
Pr: Bernard Machen
COO: Charles E Lane
Ofcr: Susan Blair
VP: Joe Hice
**VP:* John E Poppell
Assoc Dir: Elizabeth Outler
Assoc Dir: Joseph Rojo
Assoc Dir: John Ryder
Comm Man: Richard L Bucciarei
Admn Mgr: Donna Roberts
Off Admin: Cynthia Watts-Thomas

D-U-N-S 94-513-7669
UNIVERSITY OF FLORIDA FOUNDATION INC
2012 W University Ave, Gainesville, FL 32603-1734
Tel (352) 392-1691 *Founded/Ownrshp* 1964
Sales 153.0MM *EMP* 450
SIC 8399 8641 8221 Fund raising organization, non-fee basis; Civic social & fraternal associations; Colleges universities & professional schools
Pr: Joan Ruffier
**Pr:* Jerry Davis
COO: Edward A Kelly
**VP:* Paul Robell
Assoc Dir: Jim Kerr
CIO: Robert Grillo
Dir IT: Jay Paredes
Counsel: Leslie Bram

D-U-N-S 02-171-7293
UNIVERSITY OF FLORIDA JACKSONVILLE HEALTHCARE INC
3122 New Berlin Rd, Jacksonville, FL 32226-1828
Tel (904) 244-9500 *Founded/Ownrshp* 1981
Sales 78.1MM[E] *EMP* 1,159[E]
SIC 8011 Offices & clinics of medical doctors
Ch Bd: Robert Nuss MD
**CEO:* Benrubi Guy
**CEO:* George Wilson
**CFO:* Nancy M Frashuer
Ofcr: Gary Beck
**Prin:* Guy Benrubi MD
MIS Dir: Mari B Anderson
Opers Mgr: Linda Lawson
Doctor: Carlos Arce
Doctor: Donald Conetta

D-U-N-S 96-916-0857
UNIVERSITY OF FLORIDA JACKSONVILLE PHYSICIANS INC
653 W 8th St, Jacksonville, FL 32209-6511
Tel (904) 244-9500 *Founded/Ownrshp* 1978
Sales 291.7MM *EMP* 375
Accts Pershing Yoakley & Associates
SIC 8011 Offices & clinics of medical doctors
Ch Bd: Robert Nuss
**Pr:* Guy Benrubi
**Treas:* Arshag Mooradian
**VP:* Alan Berger

D-U-N-S 07-346-0941 IMP
UNIVERSITY OF GEORGIA (GA)
(*Suby of* GEORGIA BOARD OF REGENTS) ★
424 E Broad St, Athens, GA 30602-1535
Tel (706) 542-2786 *Founded/Ownrshp* 1785
Sales 2.4MMM *EMP* 17,800
Accts Greg S Griffin Atlanta Geor
SIC 8221 University
Pr: Jere Morehead
Assoc VP: Robert E Bugbee
Sr VP: Tom S Landrum
VP: Timothy Chester
VP: Ryan Nesbit
Exec: Lagarde Aaron
Exec: Eris Adams
Exec: Evan Bates
Exec: Samantha Burke
Exec: Elizabeth Coody
Exec: Benjamin Eglinger
Exec: Lauren Espinosa
Exec: Luckett Jamia
Exec: Waronker Jeffrey
Exec: William Johnson
Exec: Hamilton Kevin
Exec: Courtney Kleeman
Exec: Caraway Kristie
Exec: Price Mara
Exec: William Mathis
Exec: Lindsey McIntyre

D-U-N-S 07-849-3765
UNIVERSITY OF GEORGIA
COMPUTER SCIENCE
(*Suby of* UNIVERSITY OF GEORGIA) ★
415 Boyds Graduate Studie, Athens, GA 30602-0001
Tel (706) 542-2911 *Founded/Ownrshp* 2012
Sales 71.8MM[E] *EMP* 1,335[E]
SIC 5734 Computer & software stores
Assoc Dir: Igor Khripunov

D-U-N-S 03-005-9034
UNIVERSITY OF GEORGIA ATHLETIC ASSOCIATION INC
1 Selig Cir B, Athens, GA 30602-1501
Tel (706) 542-1306 *Founded/Ownrshp* 1928
Sales 116.7MM *EMP* 400
Accts Ernst & Young Llp Atlanta Ga
SIC 8699 Athletic organizations
Ch Bd: Michael F Adams
CFO: Morris Collins
**Treas:* Tim Burgess

D-U-N-S 18-865-2044
UNIVERSITY OF GEORGIA FOUNDATION
394 S Milledge Ave # 100, Athens, GA 30605-5626
Tel (706) 542-6677 *Founded/Ownrshp* 1937
Sales 126.5MM *EMP* 3
SIC 8699 Charitable organization
CFO: Cindy Coyle

D-U-N-S 00-431-5578
UNIVERSITY OF GEORGIA RESEARCH FOUNDATION INC
UGA RESEARCH FOUNDATION
310 E Campus Rd 409, Athens, GA 30602-1589
Tel (706) 542-5939 *Founded/Ownrshp* 1978
Sales 170.1MM *EMP* 1
Accts Cherry Bekaert Llp Augusta G
SIC 6732 Trusts: educational, religious, etc.
Pr: Jere Morehead
**Pr:* David C Lee

D-U-N-S 06-926-4398
UNIVERSITY OF HARTFORD
HARTFORD COLLEGE FOR WOMEN
200 Bloomfield Ave, West Hartford, CT 06117-1599
Tel (860) 768-4393 *Founded/Ownrshp* 1957
Sales 181.2MM *EMP* 950
Accts Pricewaterhousecoopers Llp Ha
SIC 8221 University
Pr: Walter Harrison
Pr: Arosha Jayawickrema
Pr: Suzanne McNeil
**Treas:* Thomas J Perra
Bd of Dir: Bin Zhu
Ofcr: Daniel Peeler
Ex VP: Samrana Bertrand
Ex VP: Stillman Brown
Ex VP: Cassandra Fowlie
Ex VP: Rich Hoover
Ex VP: Randy Perez
VP: Ryan Bagdikian
VP: Parmeet Bhullar
VP: Josh Cassarino
VP: Ben Cohn
VP: Kevin Contreras
VP: Kelsey Cruikshank
VP: Ato Cudjoe
VP: Mark Diorio
VP: Sam Distefano
VP: Patrick Fayne

D-U-N-S 00-943-8664 IMP/EXP
UNIVERSITY OF HAWAII SYSTEMS
CASHIERS OFFICE
2444 Dole St, Honolulu, HI 96822-2399
Tel (808) 956-8278 *Founded/Ownrshp* 1907
Sales 1.0MMM[E] *EMP* 12,000
SIC 8221 8222 University; Community college
CEO: David McClain
**Pr:* David Lassner
COO: Mark T McNally
**CFO:* Kalbert Young
VP: Doris M Ching
VP: Risa Dickson
CIO: Dan Morrison
DP Dir: Scott Murakami

D-U-N-S 04-291-6627
UNIVERSITY OF HOUSTON SYSTEM
4302 University Dr, Houston, TX 77204-2011
Tel (713) 743-0945 *Founded/Ownrshp* 1927
Sales 605.5MM *EMP* 12,608
SIC 8221

D-U-N-S 04-154-4081 IMP
UNIVERSITY OF ILLINOIS
506 S Wright St Rm 364, Urbana, IL 61801-3649
Tel (217) 333-1000 *Founded/Ownrshp* 1867
Sales 3.8MMM *EMP* 23,660
SIC 8221

D-U-N-S 96-323-3510
UNIVERSITY OF ILLINOIS FOUNDATION
1305 W Green St, Urbana, IL 61801-2900
Tel (217) 333-0810 *Founded/Ownrshp* 2010
Sales 278.0MM *EMP* 2
Accts Deloitte Tax Llp Chicago Il
SIC 8699 Charitable organization
Prin: Sidney Micek
Telecom Ex: Carla Wright

D-U-N-S 11-984-4538
UNIVERSITY OF INCARNATE WORD
4301 Broadway St, San Antonio, TX 78209-6318
Tel (210) 829-6000 *Founded/Ownrshp* 1881
Sales 229.2MM *EMP* 690
SIC 8221

D-U-N-S 07-206-3316
UNIVERSITY OF INDIANAPOLIS
1400 E Hanna Ave, Indianapolis, IN 46227-3697
Tel (317) 788-3368 *Founded/Ownrshp* 1902
Sales 133.0MM *EMP* 740
Accts Crowe Horwath Llp Indianapoli
SIC 8221 University
Pr: Robert Manuel
Ofcr: Daniel Mulvaney
VP: Karl Knapp
VP: Chris Molloy
Assoc Dir: Minju Choi
Ex Dir: John Batey
Genl Mgr: Scott Uecker
Off Mgr: Kyleigh Gerlach
IT Man: Lisa Cook
Pr Dir: Scott Hall

D-U-N-S 06-276-1671 IMP/EXP
UNIVERSITY OF IOWA (IA)
101 Jessup Hall, Iowa City, IA 52242-0003
Tel (319) 335-3500 *Founded/Ownrshp* 1847
Sales 1.8MMM[E] *EMP* 15,600[E]
Accts David A Vaudt Cpa Des Moine
SIC 8221 University
Pr: Bruce Harreld
Pr: Jennifer Vermeer
COO: Parsons Jeff
CFO: Andrew Ives
Assoc VP: Curt A Adolphson
**Ex VP:* Barry Butler
**Sr VP:* Doug K True

VP: Trent Good
VP: Tony Maiers
VP: Todd Nelson
VP: Ryan Rodriguez
VP: Yi Shan
Exec: Stephanie Then
Assoc Dir: Catherine Koebrick
Assoc Dir: Don McLeese

UNIVERSITY OF IOWA HEALTH CARE
See UNIVERSITY OF IOWA HOSPITALS AND CLINICS

D-U-N-S 79-220-1691
UNIVERSITY OF IOWA HOSPITALS AND CLINICS
UNIVERSITY OF IOWA HEALTH CARE
200 Hawkins Dr, Iowa City, IA 52242-1009
Tel (319) 356-1616 *Founded/Ownrshp* 1898
Sales 1.1MMM^E *EMP* 7,638
Accts Kpmg Llp Des Moines Ia
SIC 8062 General medical & surgical hospitals
CEO: Kenneth P Kates
**Pr:* Sally Mason
**CEO:* Gordon Williams
**COO:* Sabi Singh
Bd of Dir: Jerold Woodhead
VP: Erin Minne
**VP:* Jean Robillard
VP: M Wilson
Dir Teleco: Patrick Duffy
Assoc Dir: Janet Roe
Dir Rad: Joong M Ahn

UNIVERSITY OF KANSAS
See KANSAS UNIVERSITY PHYSICIANS INC

D-U-N-S 00-718-0078 IMP
UNIVERSITY OF KANSAS
1450 Jayhawk Blvd Rm 225, Lawrence, KS 66045-7594
Tel (785) 864-4868 *Founded/Ownrshp* 1865
Sales 825.7MM *EMP* 12,125
SIC 8221

D-U-N-S 07-624-8616
UNIVERSITY OF KANSAS CENTER FOR RESEARCH INC
(*Suby of* UNIVERSITY OF KANSAS) ★
2385 Irving Hill Rd, Lawrence, KS 66045-7552
Tel (785) 864-3441 *Founded/Ownrshp* 1962
Sales 152.1MM *EMP* 2
Accts Chv Accounting & Consulting Se
SIC 8733 8732 8741 8731 Educational research agency; Commercial nonphysical research; Management services; Commercial physical research
Pr: Steven Warren
**Treas:* Diane Goddard

D-U-N-S 02-380-6040
UNIVERSITY OF KANSAS HOSPITAL
UNIVERSITY OF KANSAS MEDICAL C
3901 Rainbow Blvd, Kansas City, KS 66160-8500
Tel (913) 588-5000 *Founded/Ownrshp* 1998
Sales 1.3MMM *EMP* 2,750^E
SIC 8062 General medical & surgical hospitals
VP: John Jackson
**CEO:* Bob Page
VP: Terry Rusconi
Prin: Linsey Gregory
Off Mgr: Donna Barnes
CIO: Chris Hensen
Dir IT: Hossein Saiedian
Sfty Dirs: Ruth Dakotist
Plas Surg: Thomas W Larence

UNIVERSITY OF KANSAS MEDICAL C
See UNIVERSITY OF KANSAS HOSPITAL

D-U-N-S 13-121-2834
UNIVERSITY OF KANSAS MEDICAL CENTER
(*Suby of* UNIVERSITY OF KANSAS) ★
3901 Rainbow Blvd, Kansas City, KS 66160-8500
Tel (913) 588-1443 *Founded/Ownrshp* 2003
Sales 190.1MM *EMP* 30^E
SIC 8733 Noncommercial research organizations
**Prin:* Doug Girod MD
Adm Dir: Dwayne Boettcher
Ex Dir: Robert Spaniol
IT Man: Doug Elder
IT Man: Kathi Scott
Pathlgst: Eva Baughman
Pathlgst: Pratik Home
Pathlgst: Ken Howard
Pathlgst: Soumen Paul
Pathlgst: Karen Pitman
Surgeon: Samantha Alsop

D-U-N-S 96-939-0058
UNIVERSITY OF KANSAS MEDICAL CENTER RESEARCH INSTITUTE INC
3901 Rainbow Blvd, Kansas City, KS 66160-8500
Tel (913) 588-5000 *Founded/Ownrshp* 2011
Sales 109.9MM *EMP* 23
Accts Bkd Llp Kansas City Mo
SIC 8221 University

D-U-N-S 00-740-0724 IMP
UNIVERSITY OF KENTUCKY
CHEMICAL AND MATERIALS ENGRG
411 S Limestone, Lexington, KY 40508-3009
Tel (859) 257-4759 *Founded/Ownrshp* 1865
Sales 2.1MMM *EMP* 14,000
SIC 8221

D-U-N-S 07-870-4925
UNIVERSITY OF KENTUCKY
KENTUCKY RX COALITION
203 Brcknrdg Hl 168 Fnkhs, Lexington, KY 40506-0001
Tel (859) 257-9185 *Founded/Ownrshp* 2011
Sales 2.6MMM *EMP* 6
SIC 5122 Pharmaceuticals
Prin: Joey Payne

D-U-N-S 12-076-0376
UNIVERSITY OF KENTUCKY HOSPITAL AUXILIARY INC
800 Rose St, Lexington, KY 40536-7001
Tel (859) 323-5000 *Founded/Ownrshp* 1962
Sales 381.2M *EMP* 2,879
SIC 8062 General medical & surgical hospitals
Pr: Janice Boyd
**Treas:* Helen Fowler
VP: Murray B Clark
**VP:* Zavera Kanga
VP: Jay Perman
Assoc Dir: John Hoagland

D-U-N-S 11-910-8470
UNIVERSITY OF KENTUCKY RESEARCH FOUNDATION
102 Kinkead Hall, Lexington, KY 40506-0001
Tel (859) 257-4758 *Founded/Ownrshp* 1945
Sales 345.6MM *EMP* 23
SIC 8733 Research institute
Pr: Lee Todd
**Ex VP:* Wendy Baldwin
**Ex VP:* Annete Evin

D-U-N-S 07-619-2186
UNIVERSITY OF LA VERNE
1950 3rd St, La Verne, CA 91750-4401
Tel (909) 593-3511 *Founded/Ownrshp* 1891
Sales 149.5MM *EMP* 2,200
Accts Grant Thornton Llp Los Angele
SIC 8221 University
Pr: Devorah Liberman
Pr: Shannon Huggins
Pr: Jim Irwin
Treas: Avo Kechichian
Bd of Dir: Robert Neher
Bd of Dir: Richard Simpson
Trst: Lowell K Brubaker
Trst: Kenneth L Calkins
Trst: Richard H George
Trst: Benjamin C Harris
Trst: Richard A Lewis
Trst: James W Long
Trst: Stephen Martin
Trst: Mary Ann Melleby
Trst: Cecilia M Morris
Trst: Paul Moseley
Trst: Gregory G Petersen
Trst: Steven N Reenders
Trst: Valerie C Romero
Trst: Richard C Voake
Trst: Myrna L Wheeler

D-U-N-S 11-205-9584
UNIVERSITY OF LAVERNE CENTRAL CAMPUS
(*Suby of* UNIVERSITY OF LA VERNE) ★
4119 Broad St Ste 200, San Luis Obispo, CA 93401-7959
Tel (805) 788-6200 *Founded/Ownrshp* 1996
Sales 152.9MM *EMP* 6
SIC 8221 University

D-U-N-S 04-341-7377
UNIVERSITY OF LOUISIANA AT LAFAYETTE
(*Suby of* UNIVERSITIES OF LOUISIANA SYSTEM) ★
104 E University Ave, Lafayette, LA 70503-2014
Tel (337) 482-1000 *Founded/Ownrshp* 1898
Sales 742.1M *EMP* 1,942
SIC 8221 University
Pr: Dr Joseph Savoie
Bd of Dir: Lisa Lord
Ofcr: David Comeaux
Top Exec: Dana Hasselschwert
VP: Gene Fields
VP: Jerry Leblanc
VP: Bob Stewart
Assoc Dir: Mark Smith
Ex Dir: Joseph L Brown
Ex Dir: Dan Hare
Ex Dir: Eric R Holloway

D-U-N-S 05-758-8857 IMP
UNIVERSITY OF LOUISVILLE
2301 S 3rd St, Louisville, KY 40292-2001
Tel (502) 852-5555 *Founded/Ownrshp* 1798
Sales 576.1MM^E *EMP* 6,275
Accts Bkd Llp Louisville Kentucky
SIC 8221 University
Pr: James Ramsey
Pr: Terri Rutledge
Pr: R J Tomlinson
**Treas:* Larry Benz
**Treas:* Debbie Scoppechio
**Treas:* Larry W Zink
**Ex VP:* David L Dunn
Ex VP: David Dunn
Ex VP: Caitlin Durgin
VP: David Baugh
VP: Ralph Fitzpatrick
VP: Daniel Hall
**VP:* Priscilla A Hancock
**VP:* A Keith Inman
VP: Keith Inman
**VP:* Thomas R Jackson
VP: Tom Jurich
VP: Sujita Khanal
VP: Kimberly Maffet
**VP:* Larry O Owsley
VP: Larry Owsley

D-U-N-S 19-308-5339
UNIVERSITY OF MAINE AT ORONO
(*Suby of* UNIVERSITY OF MAINE SYSTEM) ★
168 College Ave, Orono, ME 04469-0001
Tel (207) 581-1865 *Founded/Ownrshp* 1968
Sales 234.9MM *EMP* 2,400
SIC 8221 University
Prin: Peter Hoff
Ex Dir: Claude Junkins
Mng Dir: Pros Bennett

D-U-N-S 07-175-0426 IMP
UNIVERSITY OF MAINE SYSTEM
16 Central St, Bangor, ME 04401-5106
Tel (207) 973-3300 *Founded/Ownrshp* 1862
Sales 453.2MM *EMP* 3,000

Accts Berry Dunn Mcneil & Parker Ll
SIC 8221 University
Pr: Claire Strickland
CFO: Alan Cyr
Bd of Dir: Peggy Hallee
VP: Evelyn Silver
Exec: Russell Rodrigue
Dir Lab: Vernon Darling
Dir Soc: Ron Beard
Rgnl Mgr: Janet Smith
Admn Mgr: Michelene Decrow
Brnch Mgr: Beth Beaudoin
IT Man: Vicky King

D-U-N-S 07-760-0591
UNIVERSITY OF MARY HARDIN-BAYLOR
900 College St, Belton, TX 76513-2599
Tel (254) 295-8642 *Founded/Ownrshp* 1845
Sales 111.6MM *EMP* 415
Accts Davis Kinard & Co Pc Belton
SIC 8221 University
Pr: Dr Randall O'Rear
**Pr:* Edward E Martin
Treas: Susan Barnes
Ofcr: Jackie Holmes
Ofcr: Gary White
Assoc VP: Susan Owens
Sr VP: Martin Edd
VP: James Ewing
**VP:* Jennifer Ramm
**VP:* Dr Steve Theodore
Dir Risk M: Larry A Pointer

D-U-N-S 16-743-4679
UNIVERSITY OF MARY WASHINGTON
(*Suby of* STATE COUNCIL OF HIGHER EDUCATION FOR VIRGINIA) ★
1301 College Ave, Fredericksburg, VA 22401-5300
Tel (540) 654-2060 *Founded/Ownrshp* 1908
Sales 68.2MM^E *EMP* 1,012
SIC 8221 7389 Colleges universities & professional schools; Professional schools; Fund raising organizations
Pr: Richard V Hurley
Ofcr: Briant Atkins
Ofcr: Jeff Perry
Ofcr: Holly Williams
**VP:* Salvatore M Meringolo
VP: Salvatore Meringolo
**VP:* Douglas N Searcy
Exec: WEI Chen
Exec: Dave Henderson
Exec: Kashef Majid
Exec: John Marsh
Assoc Dir: Patrick Heckel

D-U-N-S 14-087-0770
UNIVERSITY OF MARYLAND
UNIVERSITY OF MARYLAND OIT CSS
(*Suby of* UNIVERSITY MD AT BALTIMORE) ★
220 Arch St Fl 14, Baltimore, MD 21201-1531
Tel (410) 706-2929 *Founded/Ownrshp* 1989
Sales 448.8MM^E *EMP* 5,000
SIC 8221 8299 Colleges universities & professional schools; Educational services
Pr: Jay A Perman
Ofcr: Sarah Perez
Assoc VP: James Leoni
**VP:* Kathy Byington
VP: Maulik Patel
Assoc Dir: Jessica Hurtado
Assoc Dir: Bohyun Kim
Mng Dir: Amir Chamsaz
Mng Dir: Toby Guerin
Prgrm Mgr: Olugbenga Adewunmi
Div Mgr: Emily Goldman

D-U-N-S 06-136-4808
UNIVERSITY OF MARYLAND BALTIMORE COUNTY
(*Suby of* UNIVERSITY MD AT BALTIMORE) ★
1000 Hilltop Cir, Baltimore, MD 21250-0001
Tel (410) 455-2695 *Founded/Ownrshp* 2014
Sales 176.3MM^E *EMP* 3,854^E
SIC 8221 Colleges & universities
Pr: Freeman A Hrabowski III
Pr: Doug Pear
VP: Osman Guler
**VP:* Benjamine Lowenthal
VP: Florian Potra
Assoc Dir: Laura L Brown
Assoc Dir: Nancy L Miller

D-U-N-S 62-393-6465
UNIVERSITY OF MARYLAND COLLEGE PARK
COLLEGE PARK CAMPUS
(*Suby of* UNIVERSITY MD AT BALTIMORE) ★
Patuxent Bldg 010, College Park, MD 20742-0001
Tel (301) 405-1000 *Founded/Ownrshp* 2013
Sales 660.6MM^E *EMP* 5,074^E
SIC 8221 University
Pr: Lance W Billingsley
Ex VP: Tim O Tormoen
Exec: Nora Petty
Assoc Dir: Vincent Adams
Assoc Dir: Maria Berberabe
Adm Dir: Bill Katsereles
Ex Dir: Dolores Jackson

D-U-N-S 08-261-1302
UNIVERSITY OF MARYLAND EASTERN SHORE
UMES
(*Suby of* UNIVERSITY MD AT BALTIMORE) ★
11868 Academic Oval, Princess Anne, MD 21853-1295
Tel (410) 651-2200 *Founded/Ownrshp* 2013
Sales 61.4MM^E *EMP* 1,481^E
SIC 8221 University
Pr: Mortimer Neufville
VP: Patrick Liverpool
VP: Bernita Sims-Tucker
VP: Charles Williams
Dir IT: Philip A Taylor Jr

D-U-N-S 15-070-2553 IMP
UNIVERSITY OF MARYLAND MEDICAL SYSTEM CORP
UMMS
22 S Greene St, Baltimore, MD 21201-1544
Tel (410) 328-8667 *Founded/Ownrshp* 1984
Sales 1.4MMM *EMP* 12,000
SIC 8011 Medical centers
CEO: Robert A Chrencik
Chf Rad: Zina Novak
Dir Recs: Robin Stults
**Ch Bd:* Michael E Busch
CFO: William Cooper
**CFO:* Henry J Franey
CFO: Ginger Young
Treas: Mary Caswell
Ex VP: John W Ashworth
Ex VP: Stephen C Schimpff
**Sr VP:* Megan Arthur
**Sr VP:* Tim Babino MD
Sr VP: Allison G Brown
Sr VP: Mary Lynn Carver
Sr VP: Walter H Ettinger
Sr VP: Mark L Waerman
VP: Megan M Arthur
VP: John Ashworth
VP: Jon P Burns
VP: Joan S Hnipper
VP: Donna Jacobs
Board of Directors: Anthony Lehman MD, Leonard Stoler, Peter G Angelos, David H Nevins, Donald E Wilson MD, Robert R Bass MD, James P O'conor, David J Ramsay D M D Phil, Stephen A Burch, William M Passano Jr, Atwood Collins III, Stephen Paterakis, Lysbeth Courtney, Robert L Pevenstein, Samuel F Heffner Jr, Steven B Phillips, Richard S Hoffman, Morton B Plant, Freeman Hrabowski III Phd, Catherine E Pugh, William E Kirwan, Reverend Frank M Reid III

D-U-N-S 12-255-5691
UNIVERSITY OF MARYLAND MIDTOWN HEALTH INC
UMMC
(*Suby of* UMMS) ★
827 Linden Ave, Baltimore, MD 21201-4606
Tel (410) 225-8000 *Founded/Ownrshp* 1823
Sales 116.7M *EMP* 1,100
Accts Grant Thornton Llp Philadelph
SIC 8062 General medical & surgical hospitals
Ch Bd: Marilyn Carp
**Pr:* Brian Bailey
Chf Mktg O: Eugene Egerton
**VP:* Donald E Ray
Dir Lab: Inci Hepner
Dir Rx: Kevin Schnupp
Chf Nrs Of: Marie Vasbinder
Adm Dir: Deb Youngquist
Dir IT: Linda Hines
Sfty Dirs: Michael Plank
Doctor: George Duncan

UNIVERSITY OF MARYLAND OIT CSS
See UNIVERSITY OF MARYLAND

D-U-N-S 07-830-3476
UNIVERSITY OF MARYLAND REHABILITATION INSTITUTE OF SOUTHERN MARYLAND
UMMS
(*Suby of* UMMS) ★
2200 Kernan Dr, Gwynn Oak, MD 21207-6665
Tel (410) 448-2500 *Founded/Ownrshp* 1895
Sales 113.3MM *EMP* 490
SIC 8069

D-U-N-S 96-951-4574
UNIVERSITY OF MARYLAND SHORE REGIONAL HEALTH INC
UNIVERSITY OF MARYLAND SMCE
(*Suby of* UMMS) ★
219 S Washington St, Easton, MD 21601-2913
Tel (410) 822-1000 *Founded/Ownrshp* 1997
Sales 2.6MM^E *EMP* 1,800^E
SIC 8062 General medical & surgical hospitals
Pr: Kenneth Kozel
CFO: Joanne Hahey
Sr VP: Susan Coe
Sr VP: Robert Frank
Sr VP: William Huffner
Sr VP: Patti Willis
VP: Ruth Ann Jones
VP: Adam J Weinstein
Dir Lab: Wanda Hampton
Nurse Mgr: Debbie Burke

UNIVERSITY OF MARYLAND SMCE
See UNIVERSITY OF MARYLAND SHORE REGIONAL HEALTH INC

D-U-N-S 07-874-0930
UNIVERSITY OF MARYLAND ST JOSEPH MEDICAL CENTER LLC
UNIVERSITY MD ST JSEPH MED CTR
(*Suby of* UMMS) ★
7601 Osler Dr, Towson, MD 21204-7700
Tel (410) 337-1000 *Founded/Ownrshp* 2012
Sales 223.6MM^E *EMP* 1,950^E
SIC 8062 General medical & surgical hospitals
Ch: Francis X Kelly
**V Ch:* Edward Gilliss
**Pr:* Mohan Suntha
Ofcr: Gretchen Swimmer
**Sr VP:* Paul Nicholson
**VP:* Gail Cunningham
**VP:* Pam Jamieson
Dir Sec: Bob Wojtek

D-U-N-S 60-277-1875
UNIVERSITY OF MARYLAND UNIVERSITY COLLEGE ALUMNI ASSOCIATION INC
UMUC
(*Suby of* UNIVERSITY MD AT BALTIMORE) ★
3501 University Blvd E # 105, Adelphi, MD 20783-8054
Tel (301) 985-7122 *Founded/Ownrshp* 1990
Sales 74.2MM^E *EMP* 1,000^E

SIC 8221 Colleges universities & professional schools
Pr: Javier Miyares
CFO: Eugene Lockett
CFO: George Shoenberger
Ofcr: Denise Collier
Assoc VP: Donna Drake-Clark
Assoc VP: Lisa M Henkel
Assoc VP: Mel Medeiros
Assoc VP: George Trujillo
Sr VP: Allan J Berg
**VP:* Joseph K Adams
**VP:* Sean Chung
Dir Risk M: Donna McMahon
Assoc Dir: Laura A Beer
Assoc Dir: Michelle Reitze

D-U-N-S 07-952-0631
UNIVERSITY OF MASSACHUSETTS INC
1 Beacon St Fl 31, Boston, MA 02108-3106
Tel (617) 287-7000 *Founded/Ownrshp* 1863
Sales 1.6MMM^E *EMP* 13,196
Accts Grant Thornton Llp Boston Ma
SIC 8221 8733 8062 University; Research institute; General medical & surgical hospitals
V Ch: Henry M Thomas
**Pr:* Jack M Wilson
CEO: John Cunningham
**COO:* Michael J Green
**Treas:* Stephen W Lenhardt
Ofcr: Maryanne Steele
**Ex VP:* James Julian
Ex VP: Todd Keating
VP: Tom Chmura
**VP:* Thomas Chumura
VP: Keith Motley
Dir Risk M: Shane Conklin
Assoc Dir: Kevin Barrett
Assoc Dir: Michael Jaremchuk
Board of Directors: Philip Marquis

D-U-N-S 04-770-0711
UNIVERSITY OF MEDICINE AND DENTISTRY OF NJ (INC)
UMDNJ
(*Suby of* NEW JERSEY COMMISSION ON HIGHER EDUCATION) ★
150 Bergen St, Newark, NJ 07103-2496
Tel (973) 972-4400 *Founded/Ownrshp* 1964
Sales 1.3MMM^E *EMP* 13,000
Accts Pricewaterhousecoopers Llp N
SIC 8221 9411 University; Administration of educational programs;
Ch: Kevin M Barry MD
**Pr:* William F Owen Jr
VP: Thomas W Kenyon
VP: Sheila Mack
Ex Dir: Michael Saulich
Off Mgr: Tracey Sharp
IT Man: Nora Seay
IT Man: Jeff Steinman
Doctor: Dennis Cardone
Doctor: Natalie E Roche
Doctor: Zhong Xu

D-U-N-S 05-568-8857
UNIVERSITY OF MEMPHIS
101 Wilder Tower, Memphis, TN 38152-0001
Tel (901) 678-2111 *Founded/Ownrshp* 1912
Sales 175.4MM^E *EMP* 2,847
SIC 8221

D-U-N-S 00-414-6619
UNIVERSITY OF MIAMI
1320 S Dixie Hwy Ste 150, Coral Gables, FL 33146-2911
Tel (305) 284-5155 *Founded/Ownrshp* 1925
Sales 2.5MMM *EMP* 10,049
SIC 8221

D-U-N-S 10-255-6920 EXP
UNIVERSITY OF MIAMI MILLER SCHOOL OF MEDICINE
AB LEACH EYE HOSPITAL
900 Nw 17th St Ste 1, Miami, FL 33136-1119
Tel (305) 326-6000 *Founded/Ownrshp* 2002
Sales 128.0MM *EMP* 327^E
SIC 8069 Eye, ear, nose & throat hospital
CFO: Mark Diaz
Ofcr: Richard Parrish
Ex Dir: Marcia Beckford
Off Admin: Aja Scott
Mtls Dir: Tracy Mote
Mktg Dir: Marla Bercuson
Sls Mgr: Harry Flynn
Opthamlgy: Richard M Awdeh
Opthamlgy: Byron L AM
Opthamlgy: James T Bana
Opthamlgy: Sanjoy K Bhattacharya

D-U-N-S 87-293-8600
UNIVERSITY OF MINNESOTA DULUTH
UNIVERSITY RELATIONS AND DEV
(*Suby of* REGENTS OF UNIVERSITY OF MINNESOTA) ★
1049 University Dr, Duluth, MN 55812-3011
Tel (218) 726-8000 *Founded/Ownrshp* 1948
Sales 85.8MM^E *EMP* 1,500^E
SIC 8221 University
V Ch: Jeff Strock
VP: Kathleen O'Brien
VP: Jerry Rinehart
VP: Mary Thurn
Exec: John Finnegan
Exec: Tracy K Shaw
Assoc Dir: Bob Glunz
Comm Dir: Rhonda Zurn
Prgrm Mgr: Kimberly Borton
Mktg Dir: Sherise Morgan

D-U-N-S 15-752-3697
UNIVERSITY OF MINNESOTA PHYSICIANS
UMPHYSICIANS
720 Washington Ave Se # 200, Minneapolis, MN 55414-2924
Tel (612) 884-0600 *Founded/Ownrshp* 1985
Sales 482.1MM *EMP* 200^E
Accts Kpmg Llp Minneapolis Mn
SIC 8011 Primary care medical clinic
CEO: Bobbi Daniels
**COO:* Mary Johnson
**VP:* Barbara Gold
VP: Rodney Haas
Exec: Pam Coppa
Snr PM: Brent Krzmarzick

D-U-N-S 06-771-3560
UNIVERSITY OF MISSISSIPPI
113 Falkner, University, MS 38677-9704
Tel (662) 915-6538 *Founded/Ownrshp* 1848
Sales 401.0MM *EMP* 8,700
SIC 8221 University
Ofcr: Elizabeth Googe
Ofcr: Jason Peacock
VP: Heather Chance
Exec: Robert Bishop
Exec: Tyler Clemons
Exec: Robert Webber
Ex Dir: David Baskett
Ex Dir: Kyle Ellis
Ex Dir: Thomas Harrell
Ex Dir: Michael Johansson
Ex Dir: Michael Metcalf

D-U-N-S 92-882-4473
UNIVERSITY OF MISSISSIPPI MEDICAL CENTER RESEARCH DEVELOPMENT
BLAIR E BTSON HOSP FOR CHLDREN
2500 N State St, Jackson, MS 39216-4500
Tel (601) 984-1000 *Founded/Ownrshp* 1955
Sales 166.9MM^E *EMP* 8,000
SIC 8062 General medical & surgical hospitals
Chf Rad: Jeana Bell
Chf Rad: Timothy McCowan
**CFO:* James M Lightsey
Assoc Dir: Michelle Brown
Assoc Dir: Katie M Bryant
Dir Rx: Stacy B Conn
Ex Dir: Phillip L Grady
Ex Dir: James E Salyer
IT Man: Charlie Enicks
Tech Mgr: Ken Agbahiwe
Sls&Mrk Ex: John Herrington

D-U-N-S 19-590-0142
UNIVERSITY OF MISSOURI AT SAINT LOUIS
(*Suby of* CURATORS OF UNIVERSITY MO) ★
1 University Blvd, Saint Louis, MO 63121-4400
Tel (314) 516-5000 *Founded/Ownrshp* 2005
Sales 35.4MM^E *EMP* 1,200
SIC 8221 Colleges universities & professional schools
Prin: Thomas Goerge
**Prin:* Glen Cope
Snr Mgr: Paul Ke

D-U-N-S 80-333-4044
UNIVERSITY OF MISSOURI HEALTH CARE
UNIVERSITY HOSPITAL
1 Hospital Dr, Columbia, MO 65201-5276
Tel (573) 882-4141 *Founded/Ownrshp* 1956
Sales 125.4MM^E *EMP* 5,000^E
Accts Kpmg Llp
SIC 8062 General medical & surgical hospitals
Pr: Mitch Wasden
CFO: Robert Churchill
**CFO:* Kevin Necas
**Treas:* Ann Toellner
Off Mgr: Drayse Lanpher
CIO: George Carr
Surgeon: Erica L Ibendahl
Surgeon: Siddharth Kudav
Plas Surg: Chase D Derrick
Doctor: Michael Lambert

D-U-N-S 00-632-6904 IMP
UNIVERSITY OF MISSOURI SYSTEM
CURATORS OF THE UNIVERSITY MO
321 University Hall, Columbia, MO 65211-3020
Tel (573) 882-2712 *Founded/Ownrshp* 1839
Sales 2.2MMM *EMP* 30,282
Accts Kpmg Llp St Louis Missouri
SIC 8221 University
**Pr:* Mun Y Choi
CFO: Brian D Burnett
**Treas:* Tom Richards
Chf Inves: Thomas Richards
Assoc VP: John Gillispie
Ex VP: Henry C Foley
Sr VP: Debbie Saunders
VP: Gary K Allen
VP: Steven W Graham
VP: Jack Kennedy
**VP:* Natalie Krawitz
VP: Natalie R Krawitz
VP: Michael F Nichols
VP: Robert Schwartz
VP: Kelley Stuck
Dir: Cuba Plain
Dir: Shawn Poore
Board of Directors: David G Wasinger, Ralph Butler, Marion H Cairns, John M Carnahan III, Warren K Erdman, Bo Fraser, Judith G Haggard, Doug Russell, Cheryl D S Walker, Don Walsworth

D-U-N-S 01-037-9790 IMP
UNIVERSITY OF MONTANA
RESEARCH & SPONSORED PROGRAMS
(*Suby of* MONTANA UNIVERSITY SYSTEM) ★
32 Campus Dr Main Hall, Missoula, MT 59812-0001
Tel (406) 243-6670 *Founded/Ownrshp* 1889, 1893
Sales 160.0MM *EMP* 2,450
Accts Cindy Jorgenson Cpa Helena
SIC 8221 University
Pr: Royce C Engstrom
Mng Pt: Celine Fisher
VP: Robert A Duringer
VP: Royce C Engstrom
VP: Michael Reid
VP: Dawn Ressel
Adm Dir: Kim Anderson
Dir Sec: Jasmin York
Prgrm Mgr: Holly Kulish
CIO: Matt Riley
DP Exec: Angela Abel

D-U-N-S 62-728-4284
UNIVERSITY OF NEBRASKA FOUNDATION
1010 Lincoln Mall Ste 300, Lincoln, NE 68508-2882
Tel (402) 458-1100 *Founded/Ownrshp* 2008
Sales 342.6MM *EMP* 80
Accts Lb Kpmg Llp Omaha Ne
SIC 7389 Fund raising organizations
CEO: Brian Hastings
Sr VP: John Niemann
Area Supr: Jerome Reimer

D-U-N-S 96-390-8335
UNIVERSITY OF NEBRASKA MEDICAL CENTER
UNMC
42nd And Emile, Omaha, NE 68105
Tel (402) 559-4000 *Founded/Ownrshp* 2013
Sales 218.6MM *EMP* 1
SIC 8011 Oncologist
Prin: Harold M Maurer
**Prin:* Jennifer Larsen

D-U-N-S 02-366-3169
UNIVERSITY OF NEVADA LAS VEGAS
4505 S Maryland Pkwy, Las Vegas, NV 89154-9900
Tel (702) 895-3011 *Founded/Ownrshp* 1957
Sales 259.3MM^E *EMP* 5,000
Accts Pricewaterhousecoopers Las Ve
SIC 8221 University
Pr: Carol Harter

D-U-N-S 03-937-2227
UNIVERSITY OF NEVADA LAS VEGAS
CENTER FOR MIGRATN DEMOGRPHY
(*Suby of* NSHE) ★
4505 S Maryland Pkwy, Las Vegas, NV 89154-9900
Tel (702) 895-3354 *Founded/Ownrshp* 1957
Sales 313.8MM^E *EMP* 2,000
SIC 8221 9411 University; Administration of educational programs;
Pr: Len Jessup
Assoc Dir: Alex Herzog
Assoc Dir: Frank Lucas
Dir Soc: Barry Barto
Ex Dir: Jack Young

D-U-N-S 03-843-2469
UNIVERSITY OF NEVADA RENO
(*Suby of* NSHE) ★
1664 N Virginia St, Reno, NV 89557-0002
Tel (775) 784-1110 *Founded/Ownrshp* 1874
Sales 194.1MM^E *EMP* 1,500^E
Accts Grant Thornton Llp Reno Nv
SIC 8221 9411 University; Administration of educational programs;
Pr: John Lilley
Ofcr: Ben Owens
Ofcr: Deserie Tillman
Assoc VP: Bruce Mack
VP: John Carothers
VP: John McDonald
VP: Marsha Read
Assoc Dir: Raquel D Grafton
Assoc Dir: Amy Koeckes
Assoc Dir: Jane Long
Assoc Dir: Ronald Pardini
Dir: Stefanie Scoppettone
Creative D: Aaron Dewall

D-U-N-S 07-173-5252
UNIVERSITY OF NEW ENGLAND
11 Hills Beach Rd, Biddeford, ME 04005-9599
Tel (207) 282-3025 *Founded/Ownrshp* 1831
Sales 206.2MM *EMP* 610
Accts Cbiz Tofias Boston Ma
SIC 8221 5942 College, except junior; Book stores
Pr: Danielle N Ripich PHD
**Pr:* Sandra Featherman
Trst: Ann Butterworth
Trst: Hugo Ricci
Trst: Gerald Talbot
Trst: Tonia Tibbetts
**VP:* Ellen G Beaulieu
**VP:* Edward Bilsky
**VP:* William J Bola
**VP:* William Chance
Assoc Dir: Teresa Pierce
Dir Rx: Leslie Ochs

D-U-N-S 06-707-5382
UNIVERSITY OF NEW HAVEN INC
300 Boston Post Rd, West Haven, CT 06516-1999
Tel (203) 932-7000 *Founded/Ownrshp* 1920
Sales 258.4MM *EMP* 696
Accts Kpmg Llp Hartford Ct
SIC 8221 University
Pr: Dr Steven H Kaplan
Ofcr: Marya Neary
VP: Thomas Beebe
VP: Margaret Jablonski
VP: Bill Leete
VP: William M Leete
VP: Daniel May
VP: Jim McCoy
**VP:* George Synodi
VP: George S Synodi
**VP:* Patrick Torre
**VP:* Richard J Tuchman
Exec: Mike Monachelli
Comm Dir: Andrew Beardsley

D-U-N-S 78-412-1725
UNIVERSITY OF NEW MEXICO
REGENTS OF THE UNIVERSITY NM
1800 Roma Blvd Ne, Albuquerque, NM 87131-0001
Tel (505) 277-0732 *Founded/Ownrshp* 1899
Sales 1.3MMM *EMP* 18,362
Accts Kpmg Llp Albuquerque Nm
SIC 8221 University
Pr: Robert Frank
CEO: Wynn Goering
CFO: Anthony Masciotra
Ofcr: Bruce Cherrin
Ofcr: Nicole Dopson
Ofcr: Robert Doughty
Ex VP: Chaouki Abdallah
Ex VP: David Harris
VP: John McGraw
VP: Carlos Romero
Assoc Dir: Deborah B King
Assoc Dir: Brian Malone
Assoc Dir: Mark Reynolds

D-U-N-S 61-668-0757
UNIVERSITY OF NEW ORLEANS
(*Suby of* LOUISIANA STATE UNIVERSITY) ★
2000 Lakeshore Dr, New Orleans, LA 70122-3549
Tel (888) 514-4275 *Founded/Ownrshp* 1958
Sales 152.8MM^E *EMP* 1,500
Accts Postlethwaite & Netterville M
SIC 8221 University
Ofcr: Thomas Kitchen
Ofcr: Larry Wink
Assoc Dir: Anthony Austin
Genl Mgr: Marco Perez
Off Mgr: Jennifer Jenning
Psych: Caroline Richardson
Pgrm Dir: Ruperto Chavarri
Pgrm Dir: Walter Lane
Pgrm Dir: Irene Ziegler
Snr Mgr: Dale O'Neill

D-U-N-S 14-236-3428
UNIVERSITY OF NORTH CAROLINA
OFFICE OF THE PRESIDENT
910 Raleigh Rd, Chapel Hill, NC 27514-3916
Tel (919) 962-1000 *Founded/Ownrshp* 1999
Sales 3.9MMM^E *EMP* 46,996
Accts Koonce Wooten & Haywood Cpa
SIC 8221 Colleges universities & professional schools
Pr: Thomas W Ross
Pr: Michael Delafield
**CFO:* Charles Perusse
Sr VP: Junius J Gonzales
VP: Ray D Bose
VP: Alisa Chapman
VP: Scott Jenkins
VP: Harold Martin
VP: Matthew Rascoff
VP: Erin Schuettpelz
VP: Thomas C Shanahan
Exec: Diana Haywood
Assoc Dir: Sarah K Madison

D-U-N-S 03-051-7866
UNIVERSITY OF NORTH CAROLINA AT ASHEVILLE
UNCA
(*Suby of* OFFICE OF PRESIDENT) ★
1 University Hts, Asheville, NC 28804-3251
Tel (828) 232-5009 *Founded/Ownrshp* 1965
Sales 36.5MM *EMP* 1,260^E
Accts Beth A Wood Cpa Raleigh Nc
SIC 8221 University
Pr: Tom Ross
**CFO:* R Wayne McDevitt
CFO: William Styers
Ofcr: Jim Fox
Ofcr: Joe Jones
Ofcr: Rodger Payne
Ofcr: Tracey Rizzo
Ofcr: Alicia Shope
Ofcr: Sophia Ungert
Assoc Dir: Cheryl Alderman
Brnch Mgr: Kern A Parker

D-U-N-S 00-320-3213 IMP/EXP
UNIVERSITY OF NORTH CAROLINA AT CHAPEL HILL
CAROLINA INSTITUTE FOR DEVELO
(*Suby of* OFFICE OF PRESIDENT) ★
104 Airport Dr, Chapel Hill, NC 27599-5023
Tel (919) 962-1370 *Founded/Ownrshp* 1789
Sales 1.4MMM^E *EMP* 12,204
Accts Beth A Wood Cpa
SIC 8221 Colleges universities & professional schools
Pr: Thomas W Ross
**Ch Bd:* Michael A Steinback
CFO: Nancy Suttenfield
Ofcr: Barbara Dearry
Ofcr: Jackie Pierce
Assoc VP: Jill Hirneisen
VP: Brandon Stephenson
VP: Betty M Whichard
Exec: Larry Gallo
**Prin:* James M Barnes
**Prin:* Avery B Hall Sr

D-U-N-S 06-630-0096
UNIVERSITY OF NORTH CAROLINA AT CHARLOTTE
(*Suby of* OFFICE OF PRESIDENT) ★
9201 University City Blvd, Charlotte, NC 28223-0001
Tel (704) 687-5727 *Founded/Ownrshp* 1949
Sales 292.2MM *EMP* 3,030
Accts Beth A Wood Cpa Raleigh No
SIC 8221 University
Treas: Sarah Fox
Ofcr: Rob Covert
Ofcr: Toby A Rufty
VP: Jay Patel
Dir Risk M: Betty P Coulter
Dir Lab: John Hudak
Assoc Dir: Brian Capron
Prin: Michael G Cato
Ex Dir: Stephen Ward
CTO: Thomas Lamb
DP Exec: Marcia Kiessling

D-U-N-S 61-615-2567
UNIVERSITY OF NORTH CAROLINA AT GREENSBORO INVESTMENT FUND INC
UNC-G
(*Suby of* OFFICE OF PRESIDENT) ★
1202 Spring Garden St, Greensboro, NC 27412-5012
Tel (336) 334-5000 *Founded/Ownrshp* 1891
Sales 18.5MM *EMP* 2,400^E
Accts Beth A Wood Cpa Raleigh Nc
SIC 8221 Colleges universities & professional schools
Pr: Linda P Brady
Ofcr: Kay Canady
Ofcr: Timothy Reese
Ex VP: Scott Milman
VP: Bruce Caldwell
Exec: William Zahn

IT Man: Franklin McKee
Sfty Mgr: Chad Simmons
Art Dir: Mark Unrue

D-U-N-S 14-818-9517 IMP
UNIVERSITY OF NORTH CAROLINA HOSPITALS
UNC HOSPITALS
101 Manning Dr Bldg 2, Chapel Hill, NC 27514-4423
Tel (919) 966-5111 *Founded/Ownrshp* 1952
Sales 1.3MMM *EMP* 6,000^E
SIC 8062 Hospital, medical school affiliated with nursing & residency
Pr: Gary Park
COO: Todd Peterson
**CFO:* Chris Ellington
**Ex VP:* Brian P Goldstein
**Sr VP:* Mary Beck
Sr VP: Ben Gilbert
Sr VP: Melvin Hurston
**VP:* Amy Bragg
VP: Ray Lafrenaye
VP: Karen McCall
VP: Susan Phillips
VP: Glen Spivak
Assoc Dir: Clinton Colmenares
Assoc Dir: Ryan Miller
Assoc Dir: Melissa Rajappan
Dir Rx: Stacy Campbell-Bright

D-U-N-S 04-003-6584 EXP
UNIVERSITY OF NORTH CAROLINA WILMINGTON
(*Suby of* OFFICE OF PRESIDENT) ★
601 S College Rd, Wilmington, NC 28403-3201
Tel (910) 962-7209 *Founded/Ownrshp* 2000
Sales 96.2MM^E *EMP* 1,300
SIC 8221 Colleges universities & professional schools
Mng Pt: Joe L King III
CFO: Ronald J Core
Ex VP: Herbert McKim Jr
Exec: Thomas Simpson
Assoc Dir: Jenny Adler
Assoc Dir: Bill Atwill
Assoc Dir: Cynthia Hartmann
Assoc Dir: Jon Kapell
Dir IT: Bobby Miller
IT Man: Julie Dockens
HC Dir: James Walter

D-U-N-S 10-228-0781 IMP
UNIVERSITY OF NORTH DAKOTA
U N D
264 Centennial Dr, Grand Forks, ND 58202-6059
Tel (701) 777-2015 *Founded/Ownrshp* 1883
Sales 672.3MM *EMP* 2,756
Accts Office Of The State Auditor-Ro
SIC 8221 University
Ex Dir: Robert Kelly
Assoc VP: Lillian Elsinga
VP: Paul Lebel
VP: Steve Light
Assoc Dir: Brooke Roche
Assoc Dir: Terry Wynne
CIO: Josh Riedy
Netwrk Mgr: Terry Chan

D-U-N-S 83-696-3199 IMP
UNIVERSITY OF NORTH FLORIDA
(*Suby of* BOARD GOVERNORS GENERAL OFFICE) ★
1 U N F Dr, Jacksonville, FL 32224-2645
Tel (904) 620-1000 *Founded/Ownrshp* 1965
Sales 182.1MM^E *EMP* 1,400
SIC 8221 University
Pr: John Delaney
COO: Jerry Davis
Treas: Michael Neglia
Ofcr: Heather Strayer
Ofcr: David Zinkgraf
VP: Gerard Giordano
Dir Lab: Russel Shore
Assoc Dir: Valerie Murphy
Assoc Dir: Cameron Pucci
Assoc Dir: Kellie Woodle
Off Mgr: Barbara Dupuis

D-U-N-S 06-917-4241
UNIVERSITY OF NORTH GEORGIA
(*Suby of* GEORGIA BOARD OF REGENTS) ★
82 College Ln, Dahlonega, GA 30533
Tel (706) 864-1400 *Founded/Ownrshp* 1873
Sales 86.7MM *EMP* 700
Accts Greg S Griffin Atlanta Geor
SIC 8221 College, except junior
Pr: Dr Bonita Jacobs
Ofcr: Mike Banks
VP: Anna Brown
VP: John Clower
VP: Valerie Fambrough
VP: Brenda Finley
VP: Andy Leavitt
VP: Frank McConnell
Off Admin: Gloria Jones
Off Admin: Brenda Ricketts
CIO: Bryson Payne

D-U-N-S 11-009-1808
UNIVERSITY OF NORTH TEXAS HEALTH SCIENCE CENTER AT FORT WORTH TEXAS
3500 Camp Bowie Blvd, Fort Worth, TX 76107-2644
Tel (817) 735-2000 *Founded/Ownrshp* 1970
Sales 72.9MM^E *EMP* 1,710
SIC 8221 University
Pr: Allan Howethm
CFO: John Harman
Ex VP: Michael Hicks
Ex VP: Thomas Yorio
VP: Daniel Jensen
VP: Thomas Moorman
Exec: Courtney Umosen
Dir Soc: Shea Young
Dir Rx: C D Hooper
Ex Dir: Trisha Vanduser
CIO: Richard Harris

D-U-N-S 09-010-6191
UNIVERSITY OF NORTH TEXAS SYSTEM
GROUP
1302 Teasley Ln, Denton, TX 76205-7946
Tel (940) 565-2281 *Founded/Ownrshp* 1999
Sales 599.1MM *EMP* 10,000
SIC 8221 University

D-U-N-S 07-341-0185
UNIVERSITY OF NORTHERN COLORADO
501 20th St, Greeley, CO 80639-6900
Tel (970) 351-1890 *Founded/Ownrshp* 1889
Sales 187.0MM *EMP* 3,500^E
Accts Rubinbrown Llp Denver Co
SIC 8221 University
Pr: Kay Norton
Ofcr: William Martinez
Ofcr: Lawrence Raimer
**CIO:* Bret Naber
Dir IT: Lori A Reinsvold
Opers Mgr: James Ambrose
Mktg Dir: Randy Hash
Sls Mgr: Stacy Sharp
Psych: Justin Davis
Doctor: Heng-Yu Ku

D-U-N-S 07-313-2623 IMP
UNIVERSITY OF NORTHERN IOWA
U N I
1227 W 27th St, Cedar Falls, IA 50614-0012
Tel (319) 242-7325 *Founded/Ownrshp* 1876
Sales 152.8MM *EMP* 3,071
Accts Mary Mosiman Cpa/Warren G Je
SIC 8221 University
Pr: William Ruude
Pr: Cheryl Gaston
Ofcr: James Dally
Ofcr: Craig Skilling
**Ex VP:* Gloria Gibson
Ex VP: Jim Wohlpart
VP: Paul Andersen
VP: John Aronowitz
**VP:* William D Calhoun Jr
VP: Vicki Collum
VP: Carol Geiger
VP: Ronald Giddings
**VP:* Terry Hogan
VP: Michael Holmes
VP: Olivia Jaschen
VP: Carole Kimball
VP: Alyssa Leibfried
VP: John Stanish
VP: Virginia Thulstrup
VP: Joey Zimmerli
Assoc Dir: Kevan Forest

D-U-N-S 07-178-2403
UNIVERSITY OF NORTHWESTERN - ST PAUL
NORTHWESTERN MEDIA
3003 Snelling Ave N, Saint Paul, MN 55113-1501
Tel (651) 631-5100 *Founded/Ownrshp* 1902
Sales 94.5MM *EMP* 600
Accts Cliftonlarsonallen Llp Minne
SIC 8221 College, except junior
Pr: Alan S Cureton
**CFO:* Douglas R Schroeder
VP: Charles Aling

D-U-N-S 04-899-4727 IMP
UNIVERSITY OF NOTRE DAME DU LAC
805 Grace Hall, Notre Dame, IN 46556-6031
Tel (574) 631-6401 *Founded/Ownrshp* 1842
Sales 1.0MMM *EMP* 5,700
SIC 8221

D-U-N-S 04-686-2181
UNIVERSITY OF OKLAHOMA
UNIVERSITY OF OKLAHOMA PRESS
2800 Venture Dr, Norman, OK 73069-8216
Tel (405) 325-2000 *Founded/Ownrshp* 1890
Sales 569.9MM^E *EMP* 6,543
Accts Cole & Reed Pc Oklahoma Cit
SIC 8221 University
Pr: David L Boren
Assoc VP: Belinda Biscoe
VP: Dennis R Aebersold
VP: Catherine F Bishop
VP: Julius Hilburn
VP: Chris Kuwitzky
**Prin:* Eric H Sincoff
Off Mgr: Roberta Hovis
Sls Mgr: Diane Cannon

D-U-N-S 18-372-3519
UNIVERSITY OF OKLAHOMA FOUNDATION INC
UNIVERSITY OKLAHOMA FOUNDATION
100 W Timberdell Rd Rm 1, Norman, OK 73019-5016
Tel (405) 321-1174 *Founded/Ownrshp* 1944
Sales 132.0MM *EMP* 20
Accts Hogantaylor Llp Oklahoma City
SIC 6211 Security brokers & dealers
Pr: Ron Burton
**Treas:* Ron Winkler
**VP:* Gary Beadles

UNIVERSITY OF OKLAHOMA PRESS
See UNIVERSITY OF OKLAHOMA

D-U-N-S 04-979-3995
UNIVERSITY OF OREGON
1585 E 13th Ave, Eugene, OR 97403-1657
Tel (541) 346-1000 *Founded/Ownrshp* 1872
Sales 692.7MM *EMP* 7,971
Accts Moss Adams Llp Portland Oreg
SIC 8221 University
Int Pr: Scott Coltrane
Pr: Paul Shang
Assoc VP: Harry Battson
VP: Charles Martinez Jr
VP: Cheyney Ryan
Assoc Dir: Sheryl Eyster
Assoc Dir: Michelle Holdway
Assoc Dir: Paul Katz
Adm Dir: Miriam Bolton
Mng Dir: Paul Swangard
Genl Mgr: Charlotte Nisser

UNIVERSITY OF OREGON DEVELOPME
See UNIVERSITY OF OREGON FOUNDATION

D-U-N-S 04-762-4564
UNIVERSITY OF OREGON FOUNDATION
UNIVERSITY OF OREGON DEVELOPME
1720 E 13th Ave Ste 410, Eugene, OR 97403-2253
Tel (541) 302-0300 *Founded/Ownrshp* 1922
Sales 203.5MM *EMP* 39
Accts Moss Adams Llp Eugene Orego
SIC 8699 Charitable organization
CEO: Paul Weinhold
**COO:* Erika Funk
Bd of Dir: Dan Hollingshead
Chf Inves: Jay D Namyet
**VP:* Karl Otto
Assoc Dir: Stacy Dervin
Assoc Dir: Kirsten L Williams
CIO: Jay Namyet
Snr PM: Amin Mottahed

D-U-N-S 07-186-3260
UNIVERSITY OF PACIFIC
MCGEORGE SCHOOL OF LAW
3601 Pacific Ave, Stockton, CA 95211-0197
Tel (209) 946-2401 *Founded/Ownrshp* 1851
Sales 418.2MM *EMP* 1,500
Accts Ernst & Young Us Llp San Dieg
SIC 8221 University
Pr: Pamela Eibeck
Pr: Ron Boyd
VP: Patrick D Cavanaugh
VP: Steph Chu
VP: Elena Goldfoos
VP: M Harada
VP: Laura Merry
VP: Barrett Smith
CIO: Larry Frederick
IT Man: Mary Van Winkle
Opers Mgr: Patricia Shands

D-U-N-S 82-534-5429
UNIVERSITY OF PENNSYLVANIA
(*Suby of* CLINICAL PRACTICES OFT) ★
3451 Walnut St, Philadelphia, PA 19104-6205
Tel (215) 898-6636 *Founded/Ownrshp* 1740
Sales 6.6MMM *EMP* 70^E
Accts Pricewaterhousecoopers Llp Ph
SIC 8221 Colleges universities & professional schools
Pr: Amy Gutmann
V Ch: Michael L Tarnopol
CFO: Salvatore A Grasso
Assoc VP: Ira Harkavy
Ex VP: Joe Granda
Assoc Dir: Pamela Beatrice
Assoc Dir: Rachael Berget
Assoc Dir: Heather Calvert
Assoc Dir: Helen Cheung
Assoc Dir: Katrina Clark
Assoc Dir: Robert Forrest
Assoc Dir: Allison Grant
Assoc Dir: Patti Gregory
Assoc Dir: Katrina Harris
Assoc Dir: Bryan Haunert
Assoc Dir: Mallory Hiatt
Assoc Dir: Claire Klieger
Assoc Dir: Rosanne Lurie
Assoc Dir: Erin McGowan
Assoc Dir: Alice Nagle
Assoc Dir: Laura Peller

D-U-N-S 08-930-6492
■ **UNIVERSITY OF PHOENIX INC**
(*Suby of* APOLLO EDUCATION GROUP INC) ★
4025 S Riverpoint Pkwy, Phoenix, AZ 85040-0723
Tel (480) 966-5394 *Founded/Ownrshp* 1981
Sales 426.0MM^E *EMP* 7,200
SIC 8221 University
Ch Bd: Peter V Sperling
**Pr:* Tim Slottow
VP: Phil Lundberg
CTO: James Hoggatt
CTO: Dan Litteral
CTO: Lyn Marquis
CTO: Jeff Tice
CTO: Shannon Wilson

D-U-N-S 00-451-4360
UNIVERSITY OF PITTSBURGH
4200 5th Ave, Pittsburgh, PA 15260-0001
Tel (412) 624-4141 *Founded/Ownrshp* 1970, 1787
Sales 2.1MMM *EMP* 9,607
SIC 8221 Colleges universities & professional schools
**CEO:* Mark Nordenberg
COO: Richard J McAfee
**CFO:* Arthur Ramicone
**Treas:* Amy K Marsh
VP: Beta Keramati
VP: Ronald Linden
Assoc Dir: Nicholas Laudato
Assoc Dir: Debbie Rupert
Admn Mgr: Nancy Linderman
Off Mgr: Sherry Shrum
DP Exec: Neal Spada

D-U-N-S 14-817-7439
UNIVERSITY OF PITTSBURGH MEDICAL CENTER
UPMC HEALTH BENEFITS
600 Grant St Fl 62, Pittsburgh, PA 15219-2741
Tel (412) 647-2345 *Founded/Ownrshp* 1982
Sales 11.4MMM *EMP* 53,171
Accts Ernst & Young Llp Pittsburgh
SIC 8062 General medical & surgical hospitals
Ch: G Nicholas Beckwith
Pr: Donnell Blackwell
**Pr:* Jeffrey A Romoff
**COO:* Gregory Peaslee
CFO: Robert A Demichiei
**CFO:* Robert Be Michiei
**Chf Cred:* Janilee Johnson
Ofcr: Tom Nigra
Ex VP: Leslie C Davis
Sr VP: Steven D Shapiro
VP: Robin Romanelli
VP: Paul Wood
Dir Rad: Scott A Mirowitz
Dir Rad: James M Mountz
Dir Rad: Leland F Thaete

D-U-N-S 06-077-4846
UNIVERSITY OF PITTSBURGH PHYSICIANS
(*Suby of* UPMC HEALTH BENEFITS) ★
200 Lothrop St, Pittsburgh, PA 15213-2536
Tel (412) 647-8762 *Founded/Ownrshp* 1997
Sales 446.4MM^E *EMP* 2,708
SIC 8062 General medical & surgical hospitals
Pr: Marshall Webster
VP: Lisa Khorey
Pathlgst: Harry C Blair
Pathlgst: Cheryl Clark
Pathlgst: Anthony J Demetris
Pathlgst: Barbara Fazio
Pathlgst: Donald Kelley
Pathlgst: Michael A Nalesnik
Pathlgst: Brianne Yaege

D-U-N-S 00-941-9052
UNIVERSITY OF PORTLAND (OR)
5000 N Willamette Blvd, Portland, OR 97203-5798
Tel (503) 943-7337 *Founded/Ownrshp* 1901
Sales 143.0MM *EMP* 705^E
SIC 8221 University
VP: Eric Barger
**Pr:* E William Beauchamp
Ofcr: Jeff Rook
Netwrk Eng: Thomalton Ank
Sls&Mrk Ex: Billy McWood
Mktg Dir: John Schouten
Pgrm Dir: Mark G Epstein

D-U-N-S 09-005-1616 IMP/EXP
UNIVERSITY OF PUERTO RICO
UNIVERSIDAD DE PUERTO RICO
Jardin Botanico Sur 1187, San Juan, PR 00926
Tel (787) 250-0000 *Founded/Ownrshp* 1903
Sales 585.6MM^E *EMP* 12,000
Accts Ernst & Young Llp San Juan P
SIC 8221 University
Pr: Uroyoan Walker

D-U-N-S 07-925-7119
UNIVERSITY OF PUGET SOUND
1500 N Warner St, Tacoma, WA 98416-0005
Tel (253) 879-3100 *Founded/Ownrshp* 1903
Sales 172.9MM *EMP* 850
SIC 8221 University
Pr: Ronald R Thomas
Pr: William Morse
VP: Makenzy Bennett
VP: Maggie Mittuch
**VP:* Sherry B Mondou
Assoc Dir: Katie Barosky
Assoc Dir: Peggy Firman
CTO: Mark Cain
DP Exec: Jenny Peterson
Netwrk Mgr: Dave Hamwey
Opers Mgr: Chris Jones

D-U-N-S 07-250-5746
UNIVERSITY OF REDLANDS (CA)
1200 E Colton Ave, Redlands, CA 92374-3720
Tel (909) 793-2121 *Founded/Ownrshp* 1907
Sales 143.5MM^E *EMP* 1,017
Accts Mcgladrey Llp Cedar Rapids I
SIC 8221 University
Pr: Ralph W Kuncl
Bd of Dir: Kim Huey
Bd of Dir: Jeanne McClellan
Trst: Donald Dye
Trst: Peter Konrad
Trst: Terry Kupfer
Trst: Patrick Morris
Trst: Roger Salazar
Trst: Robert Steinbach
Trst: Ronald Troupe
VP: Philip A Glotzbch
VP: Debi Logan
VP: Kim Munkres
VP: Gabrielle Singh
VP: Ray Watts

D-U-N-S 07-570-5780
UNIVERSITY OF RHODE ISLAND
75 Lower College Rd Ste 0, Kingston, RI 02881-1966
Tel (401) 874-1000 *Founded/Ownrshp* 1892
Sales 403.1MM *EMP* 2,600
Accts O Connor & Drew Pc Braintre
SIC 8221 University
Pr: David M Dooley
VP: Mark Noll
**VP:* Gerald Sonnenfeld
**VP:* Christina Valentino
Exec: David Farmer
Assoc Dir: Michael Khalfayan
Ex Dir: Brian Chmielewski
Ex Dir: Linda Green
Ex Dir: Roosevelt Hall
CIO: Garrett Bozylinsky
QA Dir: Katherine E Bagan

D-U-N-S 05-691-5069
UNIVERSITY OF RICHMOND
28 Westhampton Way, Richmond, VA 23173-0002
Tel (804) 289-8133 *Founded/Ownrshp* 1901
Sales 264.5MM *EMP* 1,400
Accts Kpmg Llp Richmond Virginia
SIC 8221 University
Pr: Edward L Ayers
Treas: Kristina Lam
Trst: Robert L Burrus
Trst: Worth H Carter
Trst: John Davis
Trst: Robert S Jepson
Trst: Charles W Sweet
Trst: Terry H Sylvester
Trst: Douglas R Van Scoy
Trst: Sarah Walton
Trst: George W Wellde
Ofcr: R Jones
Assoc VP: Julie Solomon
VP: Mary Gardiner
VP: Jesse Kedy
VP: Laurie Melville
VP: Danielle Schweizer
VP: Carl K Sorensen

Dir Lab: Jennifer Brenzovich
Assoc Dir: Joe Testani

D-U-N-S 04-129-4109 IMP
UNIVERSITY OF ROCHESTER
601 Elmwood Ave, Rochester, NY 14642-0001
Tel (585) 275-5000 *Founded/Ownrshp* 1851
Sales 2.2MMM^E *EMP* 18,389
SIC 8221

D-U-N-S 06-446-7962 IMP/EXP
UNIVERSITY OF SAN DIEGO (CA)
5998 Alcala Park Frnt, San Diego, CA 92110-2492
Tel (619) 260-4600 *Founded/Ownrshp* 1949
Sales 453.4MM *EMP* 1,600
Accts Moss Adams Llp San Diego Cal
SIC 8221 University
Pr: Mary E Lyons
Pr: Larry Barnett
Pr: Donald Godwin
CFO: Terry Kalfayan
Bd of Dir: Teddy Wolfe
VP: Andrew T Allen
VP: Aleczander Bangert
VP: Owen Buckley
VP: Sean Essex
VP: Kevin Ganley
VP: Leslie Hennessy
VP: Phillip Juarez
VP: Kevin Karn
VP: Kirk Leopoldo
VP: Erik Molina
VP: Liz Nutting
VP: Timothy O'Malley
VP: Rommel Pinlac
VP: Weston Preising
VP: Marisa Thien
VP: Carmen Vazquez

D-U-N-S 07-877-0294 IMP
UNIVERSITY OF SAN FRANCISCO INC
USF
2130 Fulton St, San Francisco, CA 94117-1050
Tel (415) 422-5555 *Founded/Ownrshp* 1855
Sales 371.2MM *EMP* 1,200
Accts Moss Adams Llp San Francisco
SIC 8221 University
CEO: Stephen A Privett
Trst: David Agger
Trst: Richard L Bechelli
Trst: Philip L Boroughs
Trst: Francis J Butler
Trst: Gregory Chisholm
Trst: Alfred S Chuang
Trst: Arthur A Ciocca
Trst: Jeanne M Cunicelli
Trst: Ricky J Curotto
Trst: Jon D Fuller
Trst: Suzanne M Giraudo
Trst: Rose Guilbault
Trst: Martin J Jenkins
Trst: Wayne E Jerves
Trst: Oliver T Johnson
Trst: Peter K Maier
Trst: Antoinette M Malveaux
Trst: Susan G Marineau
Trst: Putra Masagung
Trst: Joan M McGrath

D-U-N-S 07-949-7681
UNIVERSITY OF SCIENCES IN PHILADELPHIA (PA)
600 S 43rd St, Philadelphia, PA 19104-4418
Tel (215) 596-8800 *Founded/Ownrshp* 1821
Sales 95.3MM *EMP* 500
Accts Kpmg Llp Philadelphia Penns
SIC 8221 Professional schools
Pr: Dr Giles Gee
**Pr:* Philip P Gerbino
**Pr:* Rod Miller
**Ch:* Marvin Samson
Trst: Samuel Barker
**Sr VP:* Joseph Trainor
Ex Dir: Richard Stefanacci
Dir Sec: Shawn Woods
CTO: Mary Kate
Dir IT: Kasia David
IT Man: Kelly Duffy

D-U-N-S 07-917-7978
UNIVERSITY OF SCRANTON
800 Linden St, Scranton, PA 18510-4501
Tel (888) 727-2686 *Founded/Ownrshp* 2003
Sales 240.2MM *EMP* 1,050
Accts Baker Tilly Virchow Krause Llp
SIC 8221 University
Pr: Kevin P Quinn S J
COO: Elaine Tweedy
Treas: Catherine King
Ofcr: Leonard Champney
VP: Christina Arbucias
VP: Harold Baillie
VP: Beth Barnett
VP: Patricia Harrington
VP: Cheryl Murphy
VP: Edward Steinmetz
VP: Gerald Zaboski
Exec: John Hopkins
Exec: Susan Trussler
Dir Teleco: Lisa Notarianni
Assoc Dir: Maryjane Rooney
Assoc Dir: Bonnie Strohl

D-U-N-S 04-293-9447
UNIVERSITY OF SOUTH (TN)
SEWANEE
735 University Ave, Sewanee, TN 37383-1000
Tel (931) 598-1000 *Founded/Ownrshp* 1858
Sales 100.3MM *EMP* 550
Accts Cherry Bekaert Llp Charlotte
SIC 8221 University
Pr: John M McCardell Jr
Treas: J Forster
Treas: Jerry Foster
**Treas:* Doug Williams
Trst: Leopoldo Alard
Trst: Neil J Alexander
Trst: Mark Andrus
Trst: Jo A Barker
Trst: Ken Baxter
Trst: Anne Bleynat
Trst: Cheryl Boutte
Trst: Lanier Brandau
Trst: Drew Broach
Trst: Joan Bryan
Trst: James Bullion
Trst: James Burchfield
Trst: Marcus Byrd
Trst: Carol Carraco
Trst: James Cate
Trst: George Clarke
Trst: Michael Curry

D-U-N-S 17-275-0234
UNIVERSITY OF SOUTH ALABAMA
307 N University Blvd # 380, Mobile, AL 36608-3074
Tel (251) 460-6101 *Founded/Ownrshp* 1963
Sales 556.5MM *EMP* 5,403
Accts Kpmg Llp Jackson Mississippi
SIC 8221 University
Pr: John W Smith
**Pr:* V Gordon Moulton
Ofcr: Paula Buerger
Ofcr: Sally Jarvis
Ofcr: Jackson Kelly
Ofcr: Jarvis Sally
Assoc VP: Michael Chambers
VP: David Blough
VP: Joseph F Busta
VP: Chris Cannon
VP: Lynne U Chronister
**VP:* Wayne Davis
Assoc Dir: Jennifer Ekman
Assoc Dir: Nix Heather

UNIVERSITY OF SOUTH ALABAMA HO
See UNIVERSITY OF SOUTH ALABAMA MEDICAL CENTER

D-U-N-S 07-947-4037
UNIVERSITY OF SOUTH ALABAMA MEDICAL CENTER
UNIVERSITY OF SOUTH ALABAMA HO
2451 Fillingim St, Mobile, AL 36617-2238
Tel (251) 471-7110 *Founded/Ownrshp* 1963
Sales 136.1MM *EMP* 2,575
SIC 8062 General medical & surgical hospitals
Pr: Mark S Williams
**CFO:* William Bush
**Treas:* Wayne Davis
Dir Rad: Maryann Hamblin
Dir Rad: Francis G Reiner
Dir Rx: Steve Bethea
Nurse Mgr: Michelle Richardson
IT Man: Suzanne Wynne
Mktg Mgr: Scott Cox
Surgeon: Goro Osawa
Obsttrcn: Dennis Robinson

D-U-N-S 04-138-7846
UNIVERSITY OF SOUTH CAROLINA
1400 Wheat St, Columbia, SC 29208-4112
Tel (803) 777-2001 *Founded/Ownrshp* 1801
Sales 839.2MM *EMP* 5,100
Accts Elliot Davis Llc Columbia S
SIC 8221 University
Pr: Harris Pastides
CFO: Rick Kelly
Trst: Arthur S Bahnmuller
Trst: James Bradley
Trst: Mark W Buyck Jr
Trst: William C Hubbard
Trst: William W Jones Jr
Trst: Toney J Lister
Trst: Mack I Whittle Jr
Trst: Darla D Moore
Trst: Michael J Mungo
Trst: James H Rex
Trst: Mark Sanford
Trst: Thomas L Stepp
Trst: Eugene P Warr Jr
Trst: Othniel H Wienges Jr
Ex VP: William T Moore
VP: Stacey Bradley
VP: William Moore
VP: Gary Snyder
**VP:* Edward Walton

D-U-N-S 92-993-0808
UNIVERSITY OF SOUTH DAKOTA
USD
(*Suby of* BOARD OF REGENTS SOUTH DAKOTA) ★
414 E Clark St, Vermillion, SD 57069-2307
Tel (605) 677-5011 *Founded/Ownrshp* 1865
Sales 98.7MM^E *EMP* 1,162
SIC 8221 9411 Colleges universities & professional schools; Administration of educational programs;
Pr: James W Abbott
**CFO:* Greg Redlin
**VP:* Dr Don Dahlin
**VP Admn:* Dr Roger Kozak
Ex Dir: Judy Struck
Software D: Chad Clites
Psych: Mary Merrigan

D-U-N-S 06-968-7242
UNIVERSITY OF SOUTH FLORIDA BOARD OF TRUSTESS
4202 E Fowler Ave, Tampa, FL 33620-8000
Tel (813) 974-2011 *Founded/Ownrshp* 1956
Sales 716.3MM^E *EMP* 16,165
Accts David W Martin Cpa Tallahass
SIC 8221 University
Pr: Judy L Genshaft
Pr: Cheryl L Byers
Pr: Jennifer Condon
Pr: Jennifer Larson
Pr: Valerie McDevitt
Pr: Tracy Muir
Pr: Judy L Polk
COO: John W Long
CFO: Clara Lugo
Bd of Dir: Danielle Dennis
Assoc VP: John Curran
Assoc VP: Phil Marty
Assoc VP: Jeff Muir
Assoc VP: Jay Wolfson
Sr VP: Charles Lockwood
Sr VP: Paul R Sanberg
VP: Christopher Duffy
VP: George W Ellis
VP: Sidney Fernandes
VP: Karen Holbrook
VP: Paula Knaus

D-U-N-S 00-432-9038
UNIVERSITY OF SOUTH FLORIDA FOUNDATION INC (FL)
3802 Spectrum Blvd # 100, Tampa, FL 33612-9212
Tel (813) 974-5095 *Founded/Ownrshp* 1980
Sales 92.1MM *EMP* 1
SIC 8699 Charitable organization
Prin: Robert P Carnahan
IT Man: Jeannine Cambensy

D-U-N-S 10-245-3078
UNIVERSITY OF SOUTH FLORIDA MEDICAL SERVICES SUPPORT CORP
UFS MSSC
12901 Brc Dwns Blvd Mdc62, Tampa, FL 33612
Tel (813) 974-2201 *Founded/Ownrshp* 1989
Sales 62.8MM *EMP* 2,500
SIC 8011 8741 Medical centers; Management services
Ex Dir: Joseph Jackson

D-U-N-S 07-293-3393 IMP/EXP
UNIVERSITY OF SOUTHERN CALIFORNIA
U S C
3720 S Flower St Fl 3, Los Angeles, CA 90007-4318
Tel (213) 740-7762 *Founded/Ownrshp* 1879
Sales 4.7MMM^E *EMP* 22,700
Accts Pricewaterhousecoopers Llp L
SIC 8221 8071 University; Medical laboratories
Pr: Steven B Sample
Pr: Lisa Howley
Pr: Lila Mauro
CFO: James M Staten
**Treas:* William Hromadka
Trst: Charles F Bolden
Trst: Ronnie Chan
Trst: M Nica C Lozano
Trst: Edward P Roski
Trst: Willis B Wood
Chf Inves: Lisa Mazzocco
Ofcr: Dominic Alpuche
Assoc VP: Theda Douglas
Ex VP: Robert Ingalls
Ex VP: George Rose
Ex VP: Stephen Schrank
**Sr VP:* Dennis Dougherty
**Sr VP:* Alan Kreditor
Sr VP: Michael Quick
VP: Anna Barbashova
VP: David Carrera

D-U-N-S 18-052-4274
UNIVERSITY OF SOUTHERN INDIANA
8600 University Blvd, Evansville, IN 47712-3590
Tel (812) 464-8600 *Founded/Ownrshp* 1965
Sales 76.2MM^E *EMP* 2,100
Accts Paul D Joyce Cpa Indianapol
SIC 8221 University
Pr: Linda Dennett
**Pr:* H Ray Hoops
Treas: Judi Kuric
**Treas:* Dr Robert Ruble
VP: Linda Bennett
VP: Cynthia S Brinker
Exec: Rohn Butterfield
Ex Dir: Richard Toeniskoetter
Genl Mgr: John Morris
Store Mgr: Carolyn L Maasberg
HC Dir: Shannon Hile

D-U-N-S 62-311-3990 IMP
UNIVERSITY OF SOUTHERN MISSISSIPPI
118 College Dr, Hattiesburg, MS 39406-0002
Tel (601) 266-1000 *Founded/Ownrshp* 1910
Sales 189.7MM *EMP* 4,500
SIC 8221 University
Pr: Shelby Thames
V Ch: Paula Smithka
**Pr:* Martha Saunders
CFO: Christi Holloway
**CFO:* Joe Morgan
Ofcr: Karen Reidenbach
Ex VP: Francis Laatsch
VP: Gordon Cannon
Assoc Dir: Kent Hegenauer
Ex Dir: Lola Norris
Ex Dir: Bob Pierce II

D-U-N-S 00-620-8664 IMP
UNIVERSITY OF ST THOMAS (MN)
2115 Summit Ave, Saint Paul, MN 55105-1096
Tel (651) 962-5000 *Founded/Ownrshp* 1885
Sales 270.1MM *EMP* 1,900
Accts Cliftonlarsonallen Llp Minnea
SIC 8221 2741 2721 College, except junior; Miscellaneous publishing; Periodicals
Pr: Dr Julie Sullivan
**Treas:* Mark Vangsgard
Trst: John Bannigan Jr
Trst: Rodney P Burwell
Trst: Burton Cohen
Trst: Gail J Dorn
Trst: Timothy P Flynn
Trst: Geoffrey C Gage
Trst: Amy R Goldman
Trst: Daniel J Haggerty
Trst: Stephen J Hemsley
Trst: Patricia Jaffray
Trst: Carol Keehan
Trst: John M Malone
Trst: Mary G Marso
Trst: Kevin McDonough
Trst: Alvin E McQuinn
Trst: Stephen P Nachtsheim
Trst: Gerald A Rauenhorst
Trst: Frank Sunberg
Trst: Kathleen J Higgins Victor

D-U-N-S 00-411-5770 IMP/EXP
UNIVERSITY OF TAMPA INC (FL)
401 W Kennedy Blvd, Tampa, FL 33606-1490
Tel (813) 253-3333 *Founded/Ownrshp* 1930
Sales 203.5MM *EMP* 525
Accts Kpmg Llp Tampa Fl
SIC 8221 University
Pr: Ronald L Vaughn
**Treas:* James L Ferman
**VP:* Richard W Ogorek
Dir Lab: Laura Henchey
Dir Lab: Mark Morris
Dir Lab: Emily Rose
Assoc Dir: Kimberly Cummings
Ex Dir: Cynthia Gandee
Ex Dir: Donna Popovich
IT Man: Vikas Jain
Doctor: Jeffrey Klepfer
Board of Directors: Jacqueline Latorella

D-U-N-S 00-338-7891
UNIVERSITY OF TENNESSEE
UNIV TENNESSEE SYSTEM OFFICE
1331 Circle Park Dr, Knoxville, TN 37916-3801
Tel (865) 974-2303 *Founded/Ownrshp* 1794
Sales 1.5MMM^E *EMP* 12,000^E
SIC 8221 University
Ch: Governor Phil Bredesen
**Pr:* Joseph A Dipietro
**Treas:* Charles M Peccolo
Trst: Spruell Driver
Trst: James A Haslam
Trst: James L Murphy
Trst: William B Stokely
Ofcr: Hiliah Corbin
**Ex VP:* David Millhorn
VP: Herb Byrd III
**VP:* Emerson H Fly
**VP:* Anthony Haynes
**VP:* Linda Hendricks
**VP:* Mary Jinks
VP: Theotis Robinson

D-U-N-S 06-423-4610
UNIVERSITY OF TEXAS AT ARLINGTON
UNIVERSITY BOOK STORE
(*Suby of* UNIVERSITY OF TEXAS SYSTEM) ★
701 S Nedderman Dr, Arlington, TX 76019-9800
Tel (817) 272-2011 *Founded/Ownrshp* 1967
Sales 328.5MM *EMP* 3,000^E
SIC 8221 8731 University; Medical research, commercial
Pr: Vistasp M Karbhari

D-U-N-S 17-023-0239 IMP/EXP
UNIVERSITY OF TEXAS AT AUSTIN
(*Suby of* UNIVERSITY OF TEXAS SYSTEM) ★
110 Inner Campus Dr G3400, Austin, TX 78712-3400
Tel (512) 471-3434 *Founded/Ownrshp* 1883
Sales 2.3MMM^E *EMP* 21,513
SIC 8221 University
Pr: William Powers Jr
Ofcr: Neil Fox
Sr VP: James L Hill
VP: Richard B Eason
**VP:* Dean Steven Leslie
Exec: Andrea Chytil
Exec: Laura Dean
Exec: Cole Holmes
Exec: Ruperto Rodriguez
Assoc Dir: Wendy Anderson
Assoc Dir: Dennis Dillon
Assoc Dir: Deanna Schexnayder

D-U-N-S 80-018-7965
UNIVERSITY OF TEXAS AT BROWNSVILLE
(*Suby of* UNIVERSITY OF TEXAS SYSTEM) ★
1 W University Blvd, Brownsville, TX 78520-4933
Tel (956) 882-8200 *Founded/Ownrshp* 1991
Sales 136.5MM^E *EMP* 1,120
SIC 8221 University

D-U-N-S 80-018-8161
UNIVERSITY OF TEXAS AT DALLAS
(*Suby of* UNIVERSITY OF TEXAS SYSTEM) ★
800 W Campbell Rd, Richardson, TX 75080-3021
Tel (972) 883-6325 *Founded/Ownrshp* 1969
Sales 164.4MM^E *EMP* 1,500
SIC 8221 University
Pr: David E Daniel
Pr: Arthur Gregg
Pr: Matthew J Grief
Assoc VP: John Walls
**Ex VP:* Bryan Wildenphal
Ex VP: Bryan H Wildenthal
**VP:* Calvin Djamison
VP: James B Gary
VP: Calvin D Jamison
Assoc Dir: Matthew C Engles
Assoc Dir: Nikki Hanegan
Assoc Dir: Tom C Kim
Assoc Dir: Wallace Martin
Assoc Dir: Lona Sandon
Assoc Dir: Hannah Stanton
Assoc Dir: Valerie Williams
Comm Man: Amanda Siegfried
Board of Directors: David E Daniel

D-U-N-S 13-205-1285
UNIVERSITY OF TEXAS AT EL PASO
(*Suby of* UNIVERSITY OF TEXAS SYSTEM) ★
500 W University Ave, El Paso, TX 79968-8900
Tel (915) 747-5000 *Founded/Ownrshp* 1914
Sales 215.2MM^E *EMP* 3,700
SIC 8221 University
Pr: Diana Natalicio
Pr: Adriana Price
VP: Catie McCorry-Andalis
Exec: Gary Hedrick
Ex Dir: Arturo Pacheco
Brnch Mgr: Miguel Sifuentesk
DP Exec: Lisa Borden
DP Exec: Jaime Casillas
DP Exec: Dawn Hearn
DP Exec: Cathey Serrano
Dir IT: Daniel Lares

D-U-N-S 80-018-9185
UNIVERSITY OF TEXAS AT SAN ANTONIO
UTSA
(*Suby of* UNIVERSITY OF TEXAS SYSTEM) ★
1 Utsa Cir, San Antonio, TX 78249-1644
Tel (210) 458-4011 *Founded/Ownrshp* 1969
Sales 327.0MM^E *EMP* 2,874
Accts Akin Doherty Klein & Feuge Pc
SIC 8221 University
Pr: Ricardo Romo
Pr: Albert Carrisalez

Ofcr: Dick Dawson
**VP:* John Frederick
**VP:* Marjie French
**VP:* Kerry Kennedy
**VP:* Jude Valdez
Dir Soc: Andrea Brown
Ex Dir: Patricia Graham
Off Mgr: Anthony Estinoza
IT Man: Lee Gildon

D-U-N-S 80-018-9235
UNIVERSITY OF TEXAS AT TYLER
UT TYLER
(*Suby of* UNIVERSITY OF TEXAS SYSTEM) ★
3900 University Blvd, Tyler, TX 75799-6600
Tel (903) 566-7000 *Founded/Ownrshp* 1980
Sales 12.6MMM *EMP* 425^E^
SIC 8221 University
Pr: Rodney H Maybry
Ch Bd: Paula Tate
CFO: Jim Ferguson
Ofcr: Sharon Brown
Ofcr: Matthew Carrillo
Ofcr: Tonya Gaddis
Admn Mgr: Katy Cline
Off Mgr: Lynn Reynolds
Netwrk Mgr: Kyle Stuart
Tech Mgr: Bob Patterson

D-U-N-S 80-077-1594
UNIVERSITY OF TEXAS HEALTH SCIENCE CENTER AT HOUSTON
UT HEALTH
(*Suby of* UNIVERSITY OF TEXAS SYSTEM) ★
7000 Fannin St Ste 700a, Houston, TX 77030-3814
Tel (713) 500-4472 *Founded/Ownrshp* 1974
Sales 560.6MM^E^ *EMP* 5,600
SIC 8221 University
Pr: Larrty R Kaiser MD
**Pr:* Giuseppe N Colasurdo
**Pr:* Kevin Dillion
**Pr:* James T Willerson
COO: Gail Mettles
Ofcr: David Jenkins
Ofcr: Christina Solis
Assoc VP: Eric Solberg
**Sr VP:* Kevin Dillon
VP: Doug Bowerman
VP: Kevin Foyle
VP: Richard McDermott
**VP:* George M Stancel
**VP:* Michael Tramonte

D-U-N-S 80-077-2162
UNIVERSITY OF TEXAS HEALTH SCIENCE CENTER AT SAN ANTONIO
UT HEALTH SAN ANTONIO
(*Suby of* UNIVERSITY OF TEXAS SYSTEM) ★
7703 Floyd Curl Dr, San Antonio, TX 78229-3901
Tel (210) 567-7000 *Founded/Ownrshp* 1985
Sales 402.4MM^E^ *EMP* 6,000
SIC 8221 University
Pr: William L Henrich
Ofcr: Elizabeth Allen
**Ex VP:* Steven A Wartman
**Sr VP:* Michael E Black
VP: Elissa Klein
Dir Lab: James Jergenson
Assoc Dir: Exing Wang
**Prin:* Mary G Delay
Prgrm Mgr: Lisa Hutcherson
DP Exec: G Henson
Dir IT: Patrick Baer

D-U-N-S 80-077-2337
UNIVERSITY OF TEXAS HEALTH SCIENCE CENTER AT TYLER
11937 Us Highway 271, Tyler, TX 75708-3154
Tel (903) 877-7777 *Founded/Ownrshp* 1947
Sales 124.1MM^E^ *EMP* 1,000^E^
SIC 8062 8221 Hospital, medical school affiliation; University
Pr: Kirk A Calhoun MD
Ofcr: Terry Whitter
VP: Angie Tippen
VP: Brigitte Tolson
Exec: Jeanette Turner
Exec: Terry Witter
Dir Risk M: Brenda Lee
Dir Lab: Janice Miller
Dir Soc: Carol Henson
Dir Rad: Ronald Jung
Dir Rad: Tim Ochran
Dir Rx: Melissa D Maeker

UNIVERSITY OF TEXAS MD ANDERSO
See REECE GREGORY MD

D-U-N-S 80-077-2139 IMP
UNIVERSITY OF TEXAS MD ANDERSON CANCER CENTER
(*Suby of* UNIVERSITY OF TEXAS SYSTEM) ★
1515 Holcombe Blvd # 207, Houston, TX 77030-4000
Tel (713) 745-4428 *Founded/Ownrshp* 1941
Sales 4.5MMM *EMP* 20,722^E^
SIC 8069

D-U-N-S 80-077-1149 IMP/EXP
UNIVERSITY OF TEXAS MEDICAL BRANCH AT GALVESTON
(*Suby of* UNIVERSITY OF TEXAS SYSTEM) ★
301 University Blvd, Galveston, TX 77555-5302
Tel (409) 772-1011 *Founded/Ownrshp* 1891
Sales 1.2MMM^E^ *EMP* 8,800
SIC 8062 General medical & surgical hospitals
Pr: David L Callender
COO: Ralph Farr
CFO: Cameron Slocum
CFO: Jason Taro
**Ex VP:* William R Elger
**Ex VP:* Danny O Jacobs
**Ex VP:* E J Pederson
**Sr VP:* Carolee Carrie King
**VP:* James F Arens MD
**VP:* George T Bryan MD
VP: Bessy Clardy
**VP:* Cary W Cooper
VP: Gregory Etzel
VP: Rex McCallum
**VP:* Richard S Moore
VP: Sharon Nguyen
**VP:* Gary E Rounding
Exec: Vince McElligott
Assoc Dir: John Donaho

UNIVERSITY OF TEXAS PAN AMERCN
See UNIVERSITY OF TEXAS RIO GRANDE VALLEY

D-U-N-S 88-383-1906
UNIVERSITY OF TEXAS RIO GRANDE VALLEY
UNIVERSITY OF TEXAS PAN AMERCN
(*Suby of* UNIVERSITY OF TEXAS SYSTEM) ★
1201 W University Dr, Edinburg, TX 78539-2909
Tel (956) 665-2110 *Founded/Ownrshp* 2011
Sales 1.2MM^E^ *EMP* 5,888
SIC 8221 University
Prin: Sarah Gonzales
Ofcr: Orlando Hinojosa

D-U-N-S 06-944-4511
UNIVERSITY OF TEXAS RIO GRANDE VALLEY FOUNDATION UTRGV FOUNDATION (TX)
UNIVERSITY OF TEXAS SYSTEM
(*Suby of* UNIVERSITY OF TEXAS SYSTEM) ★
2102 Treasure Hills Blvd, Harlingen, TX 78550-8736
Tel (956) 365-8740 *Founded/Ownrshp* 1999
Sales 315.2MM^E^ *EMP* 3,000
SIC 8221 Colleges universities & professional schools
Pr: Guy Bailey MD
**Treas:* Sara Gonzalez
Ofcr: Lydia Aleman
Ofcr: Christie Cantu
Assoc VP: Milton Howell
**Ex VP:* Martin Baylor
VP: Andreas Holzenburg
VP: Deborah Leliaert
VP: Elizabeth With
**Prin:* Havidan Rodriquez
Off Admin: Tanya Vasquez

D-U-N-S 80-077-1545
UNIVERSITY OF TEXAS SOUTHWESTERN MEDICAL CENTER
SOUTHWESTERN MEDICAL SCHOOL
(*Suby of* UNIVERSITY OF TEXAS SYSTEM) ★
5323 Harry Hines Blvd, Dallas, TX 75390-7201
Tel (214) 648-3068 *Founded/Ownrshp* 1943
Sales 1.7MMM^E^ *EMP* 12,000
SIC 8733 8011 Research institute; Medical centers
Pr: Daniel K Podolsky
Sr Cor Off: Kevin Oeffinger
**Ex VP:* Arnim E Dontes
**Ex VP:* J Gregory Fitz
Ex VP: Willis Maddrey
**Ex VP:* Bruce A Meyer
**Ex VP:* John Roan
**VP:* Cynthia K Bassel
VP: Frank Grassler
VP: Nimisha Savani
VP: Angela Wishon
Dir Lab: Qasim Ansari
Assoc Dir: M C Adamson

UNIVERSITY OF TEXAS SYSTEM
See UNIVERSITY OF TEXAS RIO GRANDE VALLEY FOUNDATION UTRGV FOUNDATION

D-U-N-S 04-200-0273 IMP/EXP
UNIVERSITY OF TEXAS SYSTEM
210 W 6th St, Austin, TX 78701-2901
Tel (512) 499-4587 *Founded/Ownrshp* 1883
Sales 24.8MMM^E^ *EMP* 81,260
SIC 8221 University
CEO: Mark A Houser
**Ch Bd:* Paul L Foster
Pr: Gilbert Loredo
**V Ch Bd:* R Steven Hicks
**V Ch Bd:* Jeffery D Hildebrand
Ofcr: Andrea Castro
Ofcr: Ana Longoria
Ofcr: Crystal Saenz
Assoc VP: Jennifer Deegan
Assoc VP: David Gabler
VP: Cherry Gonzales
VP: Tom Murillo
VP: Patricia C Ohlendorf
Exec: Carol Felkel
Exec: Pedro Reyes
Assoc Dir: Jerry Vernon
Board of Directors: Rita C Clements, Judith L Craven MD, Woody L Hunt, Cindi Taylor Krier, Tom Loeffler, Charles Miller, Patrick C Oxford, A R Tony Sanchez Jr, A W Dub Wrighter Jr

D-U-N-S 05-162-3734 IMP
UNIVERSITY OF TOLEDO
2801 W Bancroft St, Toledo, OH 43606-3390
Tel (419) 530-4636 *Founded/Ownrshp* 1872
Sales 690.2MM *EMP* 7,000
Accts Plante & Moran Pllc Toledo
SIC 8221 University
Pr: Lloyd A Jacobs
Ofcr: Rob Rieske
Assoc VP: Brenda Grant
Assoc VP: John Satkowski
Assoc VP: Jovita Williams
Ex VP: Christopher J Cooper
Ex VP: Anantharam Dadi
Sr VP: Lawrence Kelley
VP: Julianne Bonitati
VP: Jason Csehi
VP: Kevin Kucera
VP: Chelsie Lipscomb
VP: William McCreary
VP: Samuel McCrimmon
VP: Virginia Speight
VP: Kathleen Vasquez
Assoc Dir: Elias Nigem

D-U-N-S 07-242-0433 IMP
UNIVERSITY OF TULSA
800 S Tucker Dr, Tulsa, OK 74104-9700
Tel (918) 631-2000 *Founded/Ownrshp* 1894
Sales 206.1MM *EMP* 1,033
Accts Hogantaylor Llp Tulsa Ok
SIC 8221 University
Pr: Steadman Upham
Treas: Jason Avery
**Ex VP:* Kevan C Buck
Sr VP: Janis I Zink
**VP:* Kayla Acebo
**VP:* Roger N Blais
**VP:* Gerry Clancy
VP: Earl Johnson
VP: Richard P Kearns
VP: Matt Moyer
VP: Wayne A Paulison
VP: Roger W Sorochty
VP: Yolanda Taylor
Creative D: Leslie Cairns

D-U-N-S 00-909-5365 IMP
UNIVERSITY OF UTAH
201 Presidents Cir Rm 203, Salt Lake City, UT 84112-9008
Tel (801) 581-7200 *Founded/Ownrshp* 1850
Sales 3.1MMM *EMP* 18,000
Accts Office Of The Utah State Audit
SIC 8221 University
Pr: David W Pershing
Chf Inves: Jonathan Shear
VP: Richard Sperry
Assoc Dir: Karen Henriquez
Admn Mgr: Shanna Erickson
Admn Mgr: Janice K Johnson
CIO: Steve Hess
Dir IT: Chris Kidd
IT Man: Rosalie Holbrook
Info Man: Rene Enriquez
Ansthlgy: Lemoyne K Adams

UNIVERSITY OF UTAH HEALTH CARE
See UNIVERSITY OF UTAH HOSPITALS AND CLINICS

D-U-N-S 36-132-2886
UNIVERSITY OF UTAH HOSPITALS AND CLINICS
UNIVERSITY OF UTAH HEALTH CARE
50 N Medical Dr, Salt Lake City, UT 84132-0001
Tel (801) 581-2121 *Founded/Ownrshp* 1965
Sales 1.3MMM *EMP* 4,200
SIC 8062 8011 General medical & surgical hospitals; Medical centers
Pr: David Entwistle
COO: Quinn L McKenna
CFO: Gordon Crabtree
Ofcr: Joshua Grant
Ofcr: Jake Johansen
Ofcr: Jeremy Snow
VP: Christian Ries
Dir Lab: Cecelia Wright
Assoc Dir: Shane Girton
Dir Rad: Kirk Mosher
Dir Rad: William D Winter
Dir Rx: Craig C Herzog

D-U-N-S 06-681-1191
UNIVERSITY OF VERMONT & STATE AGRICULTURAL COLLEGE
85 S Prospect St, Burlington, VT 05405-1704
Tel (802) 656-3131 *Founded/Ownrshp* 1791
Sales 545.3MM *EMP* 3,710
Accts Grant Thornton Llp Boston Ma
SIC 8221 University
Pr: E Thomas Sullivan
**Treas:* Richard H Cate
Sr VP: David Rosowsky
**VP:* Jane Knodell
Exec: Meredith King
Exec: Emily Robinson
Ansthlgy: Arpita Badami
Ansthlgy: Erica L Belida
Ansthlgy: Michael C Bull
Ansthlgy: Makara Cayer
Ansthlgy: Jennifer A Danles

D-U-N-S 06-054-4954
UNIVERSITY OF VERMONT CHAMPLAIN VALLEY PHYSICIANS HOSPITAL
CVPH
(*Suby of* COMMUNITY PROVIDERS INC) ★
75 Beekman St, Plattsburgh, NY 12901-1438
Tel (518) 561-2000 *Founded/Ownrshp* 1985
Sales 308.6MM *EMP* 1,430
Accts Fust Charles Chambers Llp Syr
SIC 8062 8051 General medical & surgical hospitals; Skilled nursing care facilities
Pr: Stephens Mundy
Chf Rad: Anthony Conti
**COO:* Debra Donahue
**CFO:* Joyce Rafferty
**VP:* Michelle Lebeau
**VP:* Wouter Rietsema
VP: Bob Wollenben
Dir Case M: Debra Good
Mtls Mgr: Thomas Deyafette
Mktg Dir: Stephens Mundey
Doctor: Suzanne Elliott

D-U-N-S 06-052-5151 IMP
UNIVERSITY OF VERMONT MEDICAL CENTER INC
UNIVERSITY VERMONT MEDICAL CTR
111 Colchester Ave, Burlington, VT 05401-1473
Tel (802) 847-0000 *Founded/Ownrshp* 1994
Sales 1.1MMM *EMP* 7,000
SIC 8062 General medical & surgical hospitals
CEO: John R Brumsted
**Pr:* Eileen Whalen
**CEO:* John R Brumssted
COO: Sandra L Felis
CFO: Roger Deshaies
**CFO:* Todd Keating
Trst: Joseph Haddock
**Sr VP:* Theresa Alberghini Dipalma
Sr VP: John Evans
Sr VP: Charles Podesta
VP: Spencer Knapp
VP: Thomas Kristiansen
VP: Dawn Lebaron
VP: Charles Miceli
VP: Teresa Murphy
VP: Mitch Norotsky
VP: Betsy Sussman

D-U-N-S 01-709-1767
UNIVERSITY OF VIRGINIA
(*Suby of* RECTOR & VISITORS OF UNIVERSITY OF VIRGINIA) ★
1215 Lee St, Charlottesville, VA 22908-0816
Tel (434) 924-0000 *Founded/Ownrshp* 2011
Sales 166.9MM^E^ *EMP* 1^E^
SIC 8221 University
Pr: Lindsay H Kidd
Doctor: Dyan A Aretakis
Doctor: Curtis K Argo
Doctor: John P Barcia
Doctor: Barrett H Barnes
Doctor: Brian Belyea
Doctor: Denise E Bonds
Doctor: Virginia A Boothe
Doctor: Kenneth L Brayman
Doctor: Sue A Brown
Doctor: Ted M Burns

D-U-N-S 79-915-1159
UNIVERSITY OF VIRGINIA INVESTMENT MANAGEMENT CO
Fontain 560 Ray C Hunt Dr, Charlottesville, VA 22903
Tel (434) 924-4245 *Founded/Ownrshp* 2004
Sales 242.9MM *EMP* 2
Accts Kpmg Llp Mclean Va
SIC 6722 Management investment, open-end
CEO: Dr Lawrence E Kochard
**COO:* Kristina M Alimard

D-U-N-S 61-831-4520
UNIVERSITY OF VIRGINIA MEDICAL CENTER
(*Suby of* RECTOR & VISITORS OF UNIVERSITY OF VIRGINIA) ★
1215 Lee St, Charlottesville, VA 22908-0816
Tel (434) 924-0211 *Founded/Ownrshp* 1901
Sales 400.3MM^E^ *EMP* 4,720
SIC 8221 Colleges universities & professional schools
CEO: Pamela Sutton-Wallace
Chf Rad: Michael Dake
V Ch: Alan H Matsumoto
COO: William J Fulkerson Jr
COO: Margaret M Van Bree
COO: Margaret Vanbree
CFO: Larry L Fitzgerald
Off Mgr: Gloria Morgan
CIO: Richard Skinner
CTO: Sean Jackson
IT Man: Worthy Marti

D-U-N-S 05-724-7165
UNIVERSITY OF VIRGINIA PHYSICIANS GROUP
UVA CHILDREN'S HOSPITAL SPECIA
4105 Lewis And Clark Dr, Charlottesville, VA 22911-5801
Tel (434) 980-6110 *Founded/Ownrshp* 1979
Sales 435.2MM *EMP* 600
SIC 8721

UNIVERSITY OF WASHINGTON
See HARBORVIEW MEDICAL CENTER

D-U-N-S 04-280-3536 IMP
UNIVERSITY OF WASHINGTON INC
4311 11th Ave Ne Ste 600, Seattle, WA 98105-6369
Tel (206) 543-2100 *Founded/Ownrshp* 1861
Sales 4.2MM *EMP* 27,228
Accts Kpmg Llp Seattle Wa
SIC 8221 Colleges & universities; Service academy
Pr: Mark Emmerc
COO: Sheila Hughes
CFO: Bruce Ferguson
**Treas:* V'Ella Warren
Assoc VP: Lee Heck
VP: Randy Hodgins
VP: Constance H Kravas
VP: Sheila E Lange
VP: Paul G Ramsey
Assoc Dir: Alice Arnold
Assoc Dir: Sissy Bouchard
Assoc Dir: Linda Cook
Assoc Dir: Susan Dehoog
Assoc Dir: Katie Farver
Assoc Dir: Marcie Hinthorne
Assoc Dir: Toshiko Takenaka
Creative D: Robyn Ricks

D-U-N-S 05-300-0709
UNIVERSITY OF WEST FLORIDA
UNIVERSITY OF WEST FLORIDA BOA
(*Suby of* BOARD GOVERNORS GENERAL OFFICE) ★
11000 University Pkwy # 10, Pensacola, FL 32514-5750
Tel (850) 474-2000 *Founded/Ownrshp* 1963
Sales 103.0MM *EMP* 1,922
Accts David W Martin Cpa Tallahas
SIC 8221 University
Pr: Judy Bense
Treas: Michelle McMillan
Ofcr: Regina Bell
Ex VP: Martha Saunders
VP: Mike Dieckman
Assoc Dir: Jan Bass
Assoc Dir: Janice A Bass
Dir Soc: Shawn Henning
Off Mgr: Robin Harris
Off Mgr: Summers Karen
Off Mgr: Thornton Mari

UNIVERSITY OF WEST FLORIDA BOA
See UNIVERSITY OF WEST FLORIDA

D-U-N-S 07-594-0965
UNIVERSITY OF WEST GEORGIA
(*Suby of* GEORGIA BOARD OF REGENTS) ★
1601 Maple St, Carrollton, GA 30118-0001
Tel (678) 839-4780 *Founded/Ownrshp* 1906
Sales 108.3MM^E^ *EMP* 993
Accts Greg S Griffin-Department Of A
SIC 8221 Colleges universities & professional schools
Pr: Dr Kyle Marrero
Pr: John Head
Treas: David Boldt
Ofcr: Mardel Shumake

VP: Lindsey Armour
VP: Preston Bates
VP: Jami Bower
VP: William Gauthier
VP: Jim Gill
VP: Alexandra Gunter
VP: Nigel Hale
VP: Juanita Hicks
VP: Thomas J Hynes
VP: Scot Lingrell
VP: Ashley Small
VP: Shakira Stephens
VP: Randall Striblin
VP: Jim Sutherland
VP: Lance Thomas
VP: Logan Turner
Assoc Dir: Ketty Ballard

D-U-N-S 08-188-8471
UNIVERSITY OF WISCONSIN FOUNDATION
1848 University Ave, Madison, WI 53726-4090
Tel (608) 263-4545 *Founded/Ownrshp* 1945
Sales 480.4MM *EMP* 275
Accts Grant Thornton Llp Milwaukee
SIC 8699 Charitable organization
Pr: Michael M Knetter
Mng Pt: George F Hamel Jr
**Treas:* Bridget A Bush
Chf Inves: Julie Van Cleave
VP: Marion Brown
VP: Nancy Francisco-Welke
VP: Linda Procci
VP: Martha Taylor
Assoc Dir: Todd Hollister
Assoc Dir: Jerad Meyer
Mng Dir: Ann Lippincott
Board of Directors: Jeffrey Wiesner, Richard Antoine, Nancy Ballsrud, John Baumann, Paula Bonner, Susan Cellmer, Jerome Chazen, Paul Collins, Jeffrey Diermeier, Thomas Falk

D-U-N-S 85-921-7432 IMP
UNIVERSITY OF WISCONSIN HOSPITAL AND CLINICS AUTHORITY
(*Suby of* UNIVERSITY OF WISCONSIN SYSTEM) ★
600 Highland Ave, Madison, WI 53792-0001
Tel (608) 263-6400 *Founded/Ownrshp* 1920
Sales 1.2MMM[E] *EMP* 17,148[E]
SIC 8062 8069 General medical & surgical hospitals; Specialty hospitals, except psychiatric
CEO: Dr Jeff Grossman
**CEO:* Donna Katen Bahensky
COO: Ron Sliwiski
**CFO:* Gary Eiler
Chf Mktg O: Mary J Williams
VP: Jan Bultema
VP: Tim Gaillard
**VP:* Jeri Murphy
VP: Stephanie Volesky
Dir Teleco: Ruth Oetzman
Dir Risk M: Deb Ankowicz

D-U-N-S 83-160-7853
UNIVERSITY OF WISCONSIN HOSPITALS AND CLINICS
UW HEALTH
600 Highland Ave, Madison, WI 53792-0001
Tel (608) 263-8991 *Founded/Ownrshp* 1996
Sales 122.3MM[E] *EMP* 7,518
SIC 8062 General medical & surgical hospitals
Pr: Donna Katen Bahensky
COO: David Entwistle
**COO:* Margaret Vanbree
Surgeon: Janet Fox
Surgeon: Suzanne King
Surgeon: Stevie Marvin
Nrsg Dir: Marilyn Haynes-Brokopp
Genl Couns: Bob Miller
Genl Couns: Robert Miller

D-U-N-S 07-383-0838
UNIVERSITY OF WISCONSIN MEDICAL FOUNDATION INC
UW MEDICAL FOUNDATION
(*Suby of* UNIVERSITY OF WISCONSIN SYSTEM) ★
7974 Uw Health Ct, Middleton, WI 53562-5531
Tel (608) 821-4223 *Founded/Ownrshp* 1973
Sales 766.1MM *EMP* 3,200
Accts Mcgladrey Llp Palos Hills Il
SIC 8221 8011 2834 8299 8042 8043 University; Internal medicine, physician/surgeon; Urologist; Pediatrician; Dermatologicals; Arts & crafts schools; Offices & clinics of optometrists; Offices & clinics of podiatrists
CEO: Alan Kaplan
**Ch Bd:* Robert Golden MD
**COO:* Robert Flannery
CFO: Beverly Sears
VP: Sandy Clark
Genl Mgr: Jennifer Brown
Tech Mgr: Shane Dammen
Doctor: Kathleen R Maginot
Genl Couns: Patricia A Brdy

D-U-N-S 84-727-9689
UNIVERSITY OF WISCONSIN STEVENS POINT
CHARTWELLS UNIVERSITY OF
1015 Reserve St, Stevens Point, WI 54481-3866
Tel (715) 346-0123 *Founded/Ownrshp* 2005
Sales 22.6MM[E] *EMP* 1,000
SIC 8221 Colleges & universities
Prin: Bernie Sanders
**Prin:* Sue Konopacki
Psych: Jason Siewert
Pgrm Dir: Holly Schmies

D-U-N-S 04-118-8822
UNIVERSITY OF WISCONSIN SYSTEM
1700 Van Hise Ave, Madison, WI 53726-4044
Tel (608) 262-2321 *Founded/Ownrshp* 1849
Sales 3.4MMM *EMP* 31,992
Accts Joe Chrisman Madison Wiscons
SIC 8221 8741 University; Hospital management
Prin: Raymond Cross
Assoc VP: Stephen Kolison
**Sr VP:* Cora B Marrett
VP: Shenita Brokenburr
VP: John Diamond
**VP:* Deborah A Durcan
VP: James Henderson
**VP:* Donald J Mash
VP: Edward Meachen
VP: Hartley Murray
VP: Mark Nook
VP: Charles Pruitt
VP: James Villa
Assoc Dir: Paul Gedlinske

D-U-N-S 80-285-3403
UNIVERSITY OF WISCONSIN- SYSTEM
UNIVERSITY WISCONSIN - STOUT
(*Suby of* UNIVERSITY OF WISCONSIN SYSTEM) ★
712s Brdwy 125m Admn Bld, Menomonie, WI 54751
Tel (715) 232-2441 *Founded/Ownrshp* 1971
Sales 72.7MM[E] *EMP* 1,213
SIC 8221 University
CFO: Edward Nieskes
**Prin:* Julie Furft-Bowe
**Prin:* Diane Moen
**Prin:* Dave Williams
CIO: Joseph Brown
Psych: Ray Rivera
Pgrm Dir: URS Haltinner

D-U-N-S 17-040-3497
UNIVERSITY OF WISCONSIN-MADISON
CHANCELLOR'S OFFICE
(*Suby of* UNIVERSITY OF WISCONSIN SYSTEM) ★
500 Lincoln Dr, Madison, WI 53706-1314
Tel (608) 262-9946 *Founded/Ownrshp* 1906
Sales 434.2MM *EMP* 8,000[E]
SIC 8221 University
VP: Aliya Wilson
CIO: Bruce Maas
Dir IT: Jeanne Boston

D-U-N-S 06-969-0956
UNIVERSITY OF WYOMING
SPONSORED PROGRAMS
1000 E University Ave # 3434, Laramie, WY 82071-2001
Tel (307) 766-5766 *Founded/Ownrshp* 1989
Sales 215.9MM *EMP* 7,000
Accts Mcgee Hearne & Paiz Llp Che
SIC 8221 University
Pr: Richard C McGinity
Ofcr: Cody A Anderson
**VP:* Ben Blaylock
**VP:* Leellen Brigman
VP: Melanie Drever
**VP:* Bill Gern
VP: Jeffrey Hamerlinck
**VP:* Phillip Harris
VP: Aneesa A McDonald
VP: James Pew
Exec: Elizabeth A Hrding
Exec: Dave J Moehrke
Board of Directors: Greg Schaefer, John D Bonner, Dr Thomas Spicer, Deborah H Hammons, Hank True, Kathleen Hunt, Peter M Jorgensen, Elizabeth Kail, Ron McCue, John Patrick, Shelly Ritthaler, Walter Saunders

UNIVERSITY OKLAHOMA FOUNDATION
See UNIVERSITY OF OKLAHOMA FOUNDATION INC

D-U-N-S 07-301-9127
UNIVERSITY PATHOLOGY ASSOCIATES
50 N Medical Dr 5c124, Salt Lake City, UT 84132-0001
Tel (801) 581-5406 *Founded/Ownrshp* 2000
Sales 143.0MM *EMP* 99
SIC 8071 8011 Pathological laboratory; Pathologist
Pr: Carl Kjeldsberg
Treas: Paul Reid

D-U-N-S 61-843-8170
UNIVERSITY PHYSICIAN ASSOCIATES OF NEW JERSEY INC
30 Bergen St Ste 1, Newark, NJ 07107-3000
Tel (973) 972-5004 *Founded/Ownrshp* 1984
Sales 103.9MM *EMP* 330
SIC 8221 8011 University; Offices & clinics of medical doctors
Ex Dir: Mike Saulich

D-U-N-S 79-064-2933
UNIVERSITY PHYSICIAN GROUP
WAYNE STATE UNIVERSITY PHYSICI
540 E Cnfield St Ste 1241, Troy, MI 48083
Tel (877) 978-3627 *Founded/Ownrshp* 1999
Sales 216.5MM *EMP* 950[E]
Accts Edwards Ellis Stanley & Co Pc
SIC 8399 Health systems agency
CFO: Cynthia Sikina
**Prin:* Valerie M Parisi
**Prin:* Roberta E Sonnino

D-U-N-S 08-072-3943
UNIVERSITY PHYSICIANS & SURGEONS INC
MARSHALL MEDICAL CENTER FAMILY
1600 Med Ctr Dr Ste 1400, Huntington, WV 25701
Tel (304) 691-1630 *Founded/Ownrshp* 1976
Sales 110.8MM *EMP* 400
Accts Hess Stewart & Campbell Pllc
SIC 8011 Clinic, operated by physicians
Ex Dir: James J Schneider
**Ch Bd:* Dr Charles H Mc Kown
**CEO:* Gerry Stover
IT Man: Mike McCarthy
Board of Directors: Dr Paul Akers, Dr Daniel Cowell, Dr David Denning, Dr Robert Nerhood, Dr Ernest Walker, Dr Robert Walker, Dr Joe Werthammer

D-U-N-S 11-045-0533
UNIVERSITY PHYSICIANS HEALTH CARE
1501 N Campbell Ave, Tucson, AZ 85724-0001
Tel (520) 626-6174 *Founded/Ownrshp* 1984
Sales 417.8MM *EMP* 1
SIC 8011 General & family practice, physician/surgeon
Prin: Kathryn Reed MD
Dir Rx: Bill Francis

D-U-N-S 08-879-9176
UNIVERSITY PLAZA ASSOCIATES
UNIVERSITY SQUARE
3901 Market St Ofc B, Philadelphia, PA 19104-3115
Tel (215) 386-0351 *Founded/Ownrshp* 1976
Sales 1.3MMM *EMP* 99
SIC 6513 Apartment building operators
Pt: George Buchanan
VP: Leeann Morein
Prin: Margaret Stannard

UNIVERSITY RELATIONS AND DEV
See UNIVERSITY OF MINNESOTA DULUTH

D-U-N-S 07-264-5393
UNIVERSITY RESEARCH CO LLC
URC
7200 Wisconsin Ave # 600, Bethesda, MD 20814-4811
Tel (301) 654-8338 *Founded/Ownrshp* 1989
Sales 134.7MM *EMP* 80
Accts Rubino & Company Bethesda Ma
SIC 8742 8748 Management consulting services; Educational consultant
CFO: Richard Casciano
Ofcr: Jenna Cristiano
Ofcr: Nneka Okereke
Ofcr: Waleska Rivera
VP: Sylvia Megret
Exec: Jyotsana Ray
Assoc Dir: Robert Krusen
Assoc Dir: Aida Olkkonen
Dir Bus: Inna Sacci
Dir IT: Jonathan Rokita

D-U-N-S 11-425-8445
UNIVERSITY RESTAURANT GROUP INC
KING'S FISH HOUSE
3185 Airway Ave Ste J, Costa Mesa, CA 92626-4601
Tel (714) 432-0400 *Founded/Ownrshp* 1983
Sales 44.0MM[E] *EMP* 1,178
SIC 5812 5813 Restaurant, lunch counter; Bar (drinking places)
Pr: A Samuel King
**Ch Bd:* Jeffrey King
**CFO:* Roger Doan
Genl Mgr: Fred Velez

UNIVERSITY SQUARE
See UNIVERSITY PLAZA ASSOCIATES

D-U-N-S 00-325-6088
UNIVERSITY SYSTEM OF MARYLAND
UNIVERSITY MD AT BALTIMORE
3300 Metzerott Rd, Adelphi, MD 20783-1600
Tel (301) 445-2740 *Founded/Ownrshp* 1988
Sales 1.7MMM[E] *EMP* 28,000
Accts Sb & Company Llc Hunt Valley
SIC 8221 University
V Ch: Cole Charles
V Ch: John Dillon
V Ch: Orlan M Johnson
V Ch: Hon Kenneth
V Ch: Fatzinger Walter
CFO: Frances Hutchison
**Treas:* Gary L Attman
Treas: Patricia S Florestano
Treas: Arthur Mehlman
VP: David Makowski
VP: Ann G Wylie
Exec: Ali Rassoulpour
Assoc Dir: Lisa Marrin
Comm Man: Tanya Tuck

D-U-N-S 00-176-5866
UNIVERSITY SYSTEM OF NEW HAMPSHIRE
U N H
5 Chenell Dr Ste 301, Concord, NH 03301-8522
Tel (603) 862-1800 *Founded/Ownrshp* 1866, 1999
Sales 680.9MM *EMP* 16,000
Accts Kpmg Llp Boston Ma
SIC 8221 Colleges universities & professional schools
Treas: Carolyn Mebert
Ofcr: Katrina Boyajian
VP: Josh Goddu
VP: Susan Halloran
Comm Dir: Amy Sterndale
Ex Dir: Kathryn Cataneo
**Genl Couns:* Ron Rodgers

D-U-N-S 36-100-2129
UNIVERSITY TEXAS PHYSICIANS INF
6410 Fannin St Ste 600, Houston, TX 77030-5206
Tel (832) 325-7070 *Founded/Ownrshp* 2007
Sales 45.1MM[E] *EMP* 2,100
SIC 8011 Offices & clinics of medical doctors
Prin: Katherine Harrison

UNIVERSITY TN MEM RES CTR HOSP
See UNIVERSITY HEALTH SYSTEM INC

UNIVERSITY VERMONT MEDICAL CTR
See UNIVERSITY OF VERMONT MEDICAL CENTER INC

UNIVERSITY WASH PHYSICIANS
See ASSOCIATION OF UNIVERSITY PHYSICIANS

UNIVERSITY WISCONSIN - STOUT
See UNIVERSITY OF WISCONSIN- SYSTEM

D-U-N-S 07-841-0934
UNIVESITY OF CALIFORNIA SAN DIEGO HEALTH SYSTEM
200 W Arbor Dr 8201, San Diego, CA 92103-1911
Tel (619) 543-3713 *Founded/Ownrshp* 1868
Sales 205.7MM[E] *EMP* 5,000
SIC 8062 General medical & surgical hospitals
Prin: Tom McAsee
**CEO:* Margarita Baggett
**COO:* Duncan Campbell
**Chf Mktg O:* Angela Sciao

D-U-N-S 00-791-7347
■ UNIVEST BANK AND TRUST CO
(*Suby of* UNIVEST CORP OF PENNSYLVANIA) ★
14 N Main St, Souderton, PA 18964-1713
Tel (877) 723-5571 *Founded/Ownrshp* 1876
Sales NA *EMP* 510
SIC 6021 National commercial banks
Ch Bd: William S Aichele
**Pr:* Michael S Keim
**Pr:* K Leon Moyer
Pr: Kevin B Norris
**CFO:* Wallace H Bieler
**V Ch Bd:* Marvin A Anders
Ofcr: Kent Fuqua
**Ex VP:* Duane Brobst
**Ex VP:* Eric W Conner
Ex VP: Annette Szygiel
**Ex VP:* George D Terry
Sr VP: Barton Skurbe
VP: Rick Mack
VP: Jonathan Zeminski

D-U-N-S 02-007-6238
▲ UNIVEST CORP OF PENNSYLVANIA
14 N Main St, Souderton, PA 18964-1713
Tel (215) 721-2400 *Founded/Ownrshp* 1973
Sales NA *EMP* 717[E]
Accts Kpmg Llp Philadelphia Pennsy
Tkr Sym UVSP *Exch* NGS
SIC 6022 6282 6411 State commercial banks; Investment advice; Insurance agents, brokers & service
Pr: Jeffrey M Schweitzer
**Ch Bd:* William S Aichele
Pr: Kevin B Norris
CFO: Michael S Keim
Bd of Dir: Tom Leidy
Ex VP: Eric W Conner
VP: Kim Detwiler
VP: Timothy Hampton
Exec: Duane J Brobst
Exec: Kim Drake
Mktg Mgr: Jennifer Hammerschmidt
Board of Directors: Mark A Schlosser, Roger H Ballou, P Gregory Shelly, Todd S Benning, Michael L Turner, Douglas C Clemens, Charles Zimmerman, R Lee Delp, Margaret K Zook, William G Morral, Glenn E Moyer, K Leon Moyer, Thomas M Petro, Thomas Scannapieco

D-U-N-S 00-952-2694 IMP
UNIVISION COMMUNICATIONS INC
ROOT, THE
(*Suby of* BROADCAST MEDIA PARTNERS HOLDINGS INC) ★
605 3rd Ave Fl 12, New York, NY 10158-1299
Tel (212) 455-5200 *Founded/Ownrshp* 2007
Sales 2.4MMM[E] *EMP* 6,000
SIC 4833 Television broadcasting stations; Television translator station
CEO: Randy Falco
**Pr:* Cesar Conde
CEO: Raju Narisetti
CFO: Francisco J Lopez-Balboa
Treas: Felipe A Herrera
**Chf Mktg O:* Jessica Rodriguez
**Ofcr:* Isaac Lee
Ofcr: Tonia O'Connor
Ex VP: Marshall Cohen
Ex VP: Lee Davis
Ex VP: John W Eck
Ex VP: John Kelly
**Ex VP:* C Douglas Kranwinkle
**Ex VP:* Roberto Llamas
Ex VP: Peter H Lori
Ex VP: Jonathan D Schwartz
VP: Kath Blanco
VP: Kathleen Bohan
VP: Pier Borra
VP: Regina Breslin
VP: Neil Brooks

D-U-N-S 79-639-1014
UNIVISION HOLDINGS INC
605 3rd Ave Fl 12, New York, NY 10158-1299
Tel (212) 455-5200 *Founded/Ownrshp* 2006
Sales 2.4MMM[E] *EMP* 12,748
SIC 4833 4813 7389 Television broadcasting stations; Television translator station; ; Music recording producer
Pr: Ray Rodriguez
**CFO:* Andrew W Hobson
**Treas:* Shawn McCann
**Ex VP:* C Douglas Kranwinkle
Off Mgr: Maria Espinosa

D-U-N-S 82-469-1422
UNIVISION PRODUCTIONS
(*Suby of* ROOT) ★
9405 Nw 41st St, Doral, FL 33178-2942
Tel (305) 597-3097 *Founded/Ownrshp* 1991
Sales 228.9MM[E] *EMP* 798
SIC 4833 Television broadcasting stations
Prin: Ray Rodriguez
Pt: Sunshine Acquisition LP
VP: Emilio Aliaga
VP: Mauro Castillejos
VP: James Johannesen
VP: Ms Maria Lopez-Alvarez
VP: Ms Tonia O'Connor
VP: Nadia Pollard
Dir Soc: Neida Sandoval
Art Dir: Juliann Langere
Art Dir: Daniel Marosi

D-U-N-S 78-624-9797
UNIVISION RADIO INC
(*Suby of* ROOT) ★
2323 Bryan St Ste 1900, Dallas, TX 75201-2621
Tel (214) 758-2300 *Founded/Ownrshp* 2003
Sales 220.3MM[E] *EMP* 1,108
SIC 4832 Radio broadcasting stations
Pr: Kevin Cuddihy
**Pr:* Jose Valle
**COO:* Gary B Stone
VP: David Bernstei
VP: Laura Fisher
VP: David P Gerow
VP: JD Gonzales
VP: Jeffrey Hinson
VP: Jorge A Plasencia
VP: Marsha Sanor
VP: Eric Talbot

D-U-N-S 60-483-4234 EXP
UNIVISION TELEVISION GROUP INC
(*Suby of* ROOT) ★
500 Frank W Burr Blvd # 20, Teaneck, NJ 07666-6826
Tel (201) 287-4141 *Founded/Ownrshp* 2007
Sales 513.5MM^E *EMP* 1,136
SIC 4833 Television broadcasting stations
Pr: Joanne Lynch
CFO: George W Blank
CFO: Andrew W Bobson
**Ex VP:* Charles Stuart
VP: Matt Boxer
VP: James H Johannesen
VP: Roberto Yaez

D-U-N-S 00-700-3988
UNIVITA HEALTH HOLDINGS INC
11000 Prairie Lakes Dr # 600, Eden Prairie, MN 55344-3887
Tel (952) 516-6800 *Founded/Ownrshp* 2008
Sales 74.7MM^E *EMP* 1,338^E
SIC 8082 Home health care services
Pr: Jean Haynes
Pr: David Willcutts
COO: Bruce Baude
CFO: Jeffrey J Sjobeck
Ch: Ben Lytle
Chf Mktg O: Stephen K Holland
Ex VP: Peter Goldstein
Ex VP: Patrick Yount
Sr VP: Cindy Miller
CIO: Paul Kay
Board of Directors: Robert J Sheehy

D-U-N-S 12-349-2618
UNIVITA OF FLORIDA INC
ALL-MED SERVICES OF FLORIDA
15800 Sw 25th St, Miramar, FL 33027-4222
Tel (305) 826-0244 *Founded/Ownrshp* 2009
Sales NA *EMP* 1,000
SIC 5047 7352

D-U-N-S 96-211-7511 IMP
UNLIMITED ADVACARE INC
ADVACARE SYSTEMS
2939 N Pulaski Rd, Chicago, IL 60641-5421
Tel (773) 725-8858 *Founded/Ownrshp* 1994
Sales 109.9MM^E *EMP* 285^E
SIC 5047 Medical equipment & supplies
Pr: Larry Feldman
**CFO:* Dennis Greenberg
**VP:* Joe Frasor
**VP:* Robert Locascio

D-U-N-S 01-095-7140 IMP
UNLIMITED CARE INC (NY)
HOMECARE NURSING SERVICE
333 Westchester Ave G02, White Plains, NY 10604-2910
Tel (914) 428-4300 *Founded/Ownrshp* 1975
Sales 70.6MM^E *EMP* 2,500
SIC 8059 8011 Personal care home, with health care; Health maintenance organization
Ch: Ron Fish
**Pr:* Marcia Birnbaum
**VP:* Harriet Smith

D-U-N-S 96-632-9836
UNLIMITED DEVELOPMENT INC
285 S Farnham St, Galesburg, IL 61401-5323
Tel (309) 343-1550 *Founded/Ownrshp* 1996
Sales 100.2MM *EMP* 3
Accts Mcgladrey Llp Galesburg Il
SIC 8741 Management services
Prin: Penni Ruhl

UNMC
See UNIVERSITY OF NEBRASKA MEDICAL CENTER

D-U-N-S 07-800-1609
UNMC PHYSICIANS (NE)
BUSINESS SERVICE CENTER
988101 Nebraska Med Ctr, Omaha, NE 68198-0001
Tel (402) 559-9700 *Founded/Ownrshp* 1970, 1995
Sales 245.4MM *EMP* 1,200^E
Accts Kpmg Llp Omaha Ne
SIC 8011 Medical centers
Pr: Rod Markin MD
**CFO:* Troy Wilhelm
**Ex VP:* Cory Shaw

D-U-N-S 36-383-4784
UNO CHARTER SCHOOL NETWORK INC
209 W Jackson Blvd # 500, Chicago, IL 60606-6938
Tel (312) 637-3900 *Founded/Ownrshp* 1998
Sales 83.0MM *EMP* 10
Accts Cliftonlarsonallen Llp Oak Br
SIC 8211 Elementary & secondary schools
Prin: Andrew Alt
**Pr:* Richard L Rodriguez
Counsel: Mark Lubus

D-U-N-S 02-404-0605
UNR HOLDINGS INC
301 E Pine St, Orlando, FL 32801-2724
Tel (407) 210-6541 *Founded/Ownrshp* 2008
Sales 230.9MM *EMP* 2
SIC 6719 Holding companies
Pr: Alexey Ivanovich Kim
**VP:* Serguei Melnik
Prin: Wendy Connor

D-U-N-S 13-590-4675
UNS ELECTRIC INC
(*Suby of* UNISOURCE ENERGY SERVICES INC) ★
88 E Broadway Blvd 901, Tucson, AZ 85701-1720
Tel (928) 681-8966 *Founded/Ownrshp* 2003
Sales 94.0MM^E *EMP* 171
SIC 4911 Electric services
Pr: David G Hutchens
**VP:* Michael J Deconcini
**VP:* Philip J Dion
**VP:* Kentton C Grant

D-U-N-S 00-302-2014 IMP
UNS ENERGY CORP (AZ)
(*Suby of* FORTIS INC)
88 E Broadway Blvd, Tucson, AZ 85701-1720
Tel (520) 571-4000 *Founded/Ownrshp* 1995, 2014
Sales 1.3MMM^E *EMP* 1,979^E
SIC 4923 4911 Gas transmission & distribution; Generation, electric power; Transmission, electric power; Distribution, electric power
Pr: David G Hutchens
**CFO:* Kevin P Larson
**Chf Cred:* Karen G Kissinger
VP: Herbert Buchanan
VP: Rick Budney
VP: Jean Dirks
VP: Todd C Hixon
VP: Todd Hixon
VP: Karen G Kissiner
**VP:* Frank P Marino
VP: Peter Ruchkin
VP: Toby Voge
Exec: Cheryl Gottshall
Dir Risk M: Elizabeth Bilby
Comm Dir: Art McDonald

D-U-N-S 01-909-1037
UNT HEALTH SCIENCE CENTER
UNIVERSITY N TXAS HLTH SCIENCE
3500 Camp Bowie Blvd, Fort Worth, TX 76107-2690
Tel (817) 735-2000 *Founded/Ownrshp* 1970
Sales 48.3MM^E *EMP* 1,300^E
SIC 8031 Offices & clinics of osteopathic physicians
Pr: Michael R Williams
Bd of Dir: Yasser Salem
Ex VP: Thomas Yorio
VP: David Cistola
VP: Chirstine Kalish
Assoc Dir: Gail Herbert
Comm Man: Sally Crocker
Ex Dir: Gayanne Clemens
Ex Dir: Brian Gladue
Admn Mgr: Leonor Acevedo
Admn Mgr: Ashlee Dickerson

D-U-N-S 88-386-2203
▲ UNUM GROUP
1 Fountain Sq, Chattanooga, TN 37402-1307
Tel (423) 294-1011 *Founded/Ownrshp* 1848
Sales NA *EMP* 9,600
Tkr Sym UNM *Exch* NYS
SIC 6321 6324 6311 6371 Accident & health insurance; Accident insurance carriers; Health insurance carriers; Disability health insurance; Group hospitalization plans; Life insurance; Life insurance carriers; Pension, health & welfare funds; Pensions
Ch Bd: Thomas R Watjen
Pr: Joanne Abate
Pr: Debra Chaloux
Pr: Wendy Harlan
Pr: Charlene Jackson
Pr: Richard P McKenney
Pr: Matthew Murrell
Pr: Peter G O'Donnell
Pr: Joann Whitten
CFO: John F McGarry
Ex VP: Timothy G Arnold
Ex VP: Breege A Farrell
Ex VP: Lisa G Iglesias
Ex VP: Christopher J Jerome
Ex VP: Michael Q Simonds
Sr VP: Katherine M Miller
VP: Doug Baker
VP: Greg Breter
VP: Wes Hilliard
VP: John Leeming
VP: Nigel Moodley

D-U-N-S 07-957-0231
■ UNUM INSURANCE CO
PAUL RVERE VRBLE ANNUITY INSUR
(*Suby of* UNUM GROUP) ★
1 Mercantile St, Worcester, MA 01608-3102
Tel (508) 366-8707 *Founded/Ownrshp* 2014
Sales NA *EMP* 3^E
SIC 6311 Life insurance
Pr: Susan N Roth

D-U-N-S 04-024-9948
■ UNUM LIFE INSURANCE CO OF AMERICA
UNUMPROVIDENT
(*Suby of* UNUM GROUP) ★
2211 Congress St, Portland, ME 04122-0003
Tel (207) 575-2211 *Founded/Ownrshp* 1848
Sales NA *EMP* 3,900
SIC 6321 Accident & health insurance
Sr VP: F Dean Copeland
CFO: Robert C Greving
Treas: A M Horne
Sr Inv Off: Kim M White
**Sr VP:* Robert O Best
VP: Laura Beckmann
VP: Philip Bruen
VP: Terry Cohen
VP: Kathi Ewen
VP: John Labrie
VP: Jake Lucas
VP: Traci Melas
VP: Robert Mitchell
VP: Bob O'Brien
VP: Michael L Parker
VP: Sue Randall
VP: Susan Roth
VP: Sandra Sincero

UNUMPROVIDENT
See UNUM LIFE INSURANCE CO OF AMERICA

D-U-N-S 00-504-0654 IMP
UNVERFERTH MANUFACTURING CO INC (OH)
601 S Broad St, Kalida, OH 45853
Tel (419) 532-3121 *Founded/Ownrshp* 1948
Sales 168.3MM^E *EMP* 547
SIC 3523 Farm machinery & equipment
Pr: R Steven Unverferth
**CFO:* Dennis Kapcar
**Ch:* Richard A Unverferth
VP: Fanger Dan
**VP:* Daniel Fanger
VP: Karl Kahle
**VP:* Gladys Unverferth
Sales Asso: Brian Laudick

D-U-N-S 61-596-4780
UNVRSTY OF AR FONDTIN INC
PINE BLUFF FOUNDATION FUND
535 W Research Ctr Blvd, Fayetteville, AR 72701-6922
Tel (479) 575-5581 *Founded/Ownrshp* 1971
Sales 104.2MM *EMP* 336
Accts Hogan Taylor Llp Fayetteville
SIC 8399 Fund raising organization, non-fee basis
Ex Dir: Clay Davis
**CFO:* Dianna H Lee
CFO: Dianna Lee

D-U-N-S 19-806-1848 IMP/EXP
■ UOP LLC
HONEYWELL UOP
(*Suby of* HONEYWELL INTERNATIONAL INC) ★
25 E Algonquin Rd, Des Plaines, IL 60016-6100
Tel (847) 391-2000 *Founded/Ownrshp* 2005
Sales 3.0MMM *EMP* 4,200
SIC 2819 8711 8731 8999 3823 3479

UP ELECTRIC/WITTA SUPPLY
See STANDARD ELECTRIC CO

D-U-N-S 79-201-7402
UP PROFESSIONAL SOLUTIONS LLC
UNIVERSAL PERSONNEL
1100 Poydras St Ste 1300, New Orleans, LA 70163-1300
Tel (800) 245-8274 *Founded/Ownrshp* 1980
Sales 57.9MM^E *EMP* 1,000
SIC 7361 7363 Employment agencies; Help supply services; Temporary help service
VP: Ed Comiskey
Dir Risk M: Jane Mentz

UPI
See UNITED PHOSPHORUS INC

D-U-N-S 18-654-4250
UPLAND UNIFIED SCHOOL DISTRICT
UPLAND USD
390 N Euclid Ave Ste 100, Upland, CA 91786-4764
Tel (909) 985-1864 *Founded/Ownrshp* 1986
Sales 92.2MM *EMP* 1,040
SIC 8211 Public elementary & secondary schools
Software D: Jimi Gillespie
Software D: Monica Macauley

UPLAND USD
See UPLAND UNIFIED SCHOOL DISTRICT

D-U-N-S 03-089-1734
UPLIFT EDUCATION
UPLIFT EDUCATION-WILLIAMS PREP
1825 Market Center Blvd # 500, Dallas, TX 75207-3349
Tel (469) 621-8500 *Founded/Ownrshp* 1996
Sales 125.6MM *EMP* 1,700
Accts Evans Pingleton And Howard Pll
SIC 8211 Public senior high school; Public junior high school; Public elementary school
CFO: Stacey Lawrence
Opers Mgr: Jorge Alcala

UPLIFT EDUCATION-WILLIAMS PREP
See UPLIFT EDUCATION

UPM BLANDIN PAPER
See BLANDIN PAPER CO

D-U-N-S 00-835-3856 EXP
UPM INC
UNIVERSAL PLASTIC MOLD
13245 Los Angeles St, Baldwin Park, CA 91706-2295
Tel (626) 962-4001 *Founded/Ownrshp* 1962
Sales 89.4MM^E *EMP* 290
SIC 3544 3089 Special dies, tools, jigs & fixtures; Injection molding of plastics
CEO: Jason Dowling
**Pr:* Steve Dowling
**Ch:* Ray Dowling
**VP:* Don Ashleigh
Sls Mgr: Mike Ashleigh

D-U-N-S 12-169-2875 IMP/EXP
UPM RAFLATAC INC
(*Suby of* UPM-KYMMENE OYJ)
400 Broadpointe Dr, Mills River, NC 28759-4652
Tel (828) 651-4800 *Founded/Ownrshp* 1985
Sales 242.3MM^E *EMP* 447
SIC 2672 3083 Coated & laminated paper; Laminated plastics plate & sheet
Pr: Jussi Vanhanen
**Sr VP:* Mark Pollard
**VP:* Jan-Erik Forsstrm
Site Mgr: Jani Konkarikoski
Opers Mgr: Craig Burghardt
Sls Dir: Javier Palomares

D-U-N-S 07-216-6259 IMP
UPMC ALTOONA
(*Suby of* UPMC HEALTH BENEFITS) ★
620 Howard Ave, Altoona, PA 16601-4804
Tel (814) 889-2011 *Founded/Ownrshp* 2013
Sales 393.1MM *EMP* 2,494
SIC 8062 General medical & surgical hospitals
Pr: Jerry Murray
COO: Ronald McConnell
**CFO:* Charles R Zorger
**Sr VP:* David L Cowger
**Sr VP:* Gary R Naugle
**Sr VP:* Chris Ricken
Dir Lab: Joe Pufka
Dir: Kevin Hockenberry
Nurse Mgr: Todd Azeles
QC Dir: Sandra Kozielec
Pathlgst: Charles M Haas

D-U-N-S 07-214-9909 IMP
UPMC BRADDOCK
(*Suby of* UPMC HEALTH BENEFITS) ★
1500 5th Ave, McKeesport, PA 15132-2422
Tel (412) 636-5000 *Founded/Ownrshp* 1996
Sales 55.0MM *EMP* 1,000
SIC 8062 General medical & surgical hospitals
Ch Bd: Thomas Sterling
**COO:* Chintia Dorundo

D-U-N-S 00-914-8607
UPMC COMMUNITY PROVIDER SERVIES
(*Suby of* UPMC HEALTH BENEFITS) ★
200 Lthrpst Frbtwr 1005 Ste Forbes Tower, Pittsburgh, PA 15213
Tel (412) 647-0548 *Founded/Ownrshp* 1998, 1996
Sales 263.7MM^E *EMP* 1,600
SIC 8322 Individual & family services
Pr: Deborah Brodine

D-U-N-S 03-471-5593
UPMC EAST
2775 Mosside Blvd, Monroeville, PA 15146-2760
Tel (412) 357-3000 *Founded/Ownrshp* 2011
Sales 125.2MM *EMP* 611^E
SIC 8062 General medical & surgical hospitals
Prin: Brian J Fritz

D-U-N-S 06-875-6204
UPMC HAMOT
HAMOT MEDICAL CENTER
(*Suby of* UPMC HEALTH BENEFITS) ★
201 State St, Erie, PA 16550-0001
Tel (814) 877-6000 *Founded/Ownrshp* 1881, 2010
Sales 360.2MM *EMP* 3,159
SIC 8062 Hospital, medical school affiliated with residency
Pr: John T Malone
Pr: T Michael Simonian
**COO:* V James Fiorenzo
COO: Joseph Pepicello
**CFO:* Stephen M Danch
Chf Mktg O: Richard Long
Ofcr: Charles F Hagerty
Ofcr: Don Inderlied
Sr VP: Debbie A Burbules
Sr VP: Donald K Inderlied
Sr VP: Gary M Maras
VP: Joseph P Butler
VP: Rehka D Halligian
VP: Don Inderlide
VP: Raymond Moluski
VP: Ray Muloski
VP: Michelle M Robertson
VP: Thomas Thompson
Dir Teleco: John Emmanuel
Dir Rad: Craig A Davis

UPMC HEALTH BENEFITS
See UPMC MCKEESPORT

UPMC HEALTH BENEFITS
See MERCY UPMC

UPMC HEALTH BENEFITS
See UNIVERSITY OF PITTSBURGH MEDICAL CENTER

UPMC HEALTH BENEFITS
See UPMC NORTHWEST

D-U-N-S 83-641-0571
UPMC HEALTH PLAN INC
(*Suby of* UPMC HEALTH BENEFITS) ★
600 Grant St Fl 24, Pittsburgh, PA 15219-6609
Tel (412) 454-7642 *Founded/Ownrshp* 1999
Sales NA *EMP* 1,000^E
SIC 6321 Accident & health insurance carriers
Pr: Diane Holder
COO: Doug Azar
CFO: Paul Castillo
CFO: Robert Demichiei
Bd of Dir: Vincent Deluzio
VP: Cheryl Daniel
VP: Gordon Gebbens
VP: Sandra McAnallen
VP: Ronald Vance
Dir Rx: David Richert
Dir Rx: Matt Schonder

D-U-N-S 01-052-7392
UPMC HEALTH SYSTEM
THREE RIVERS UROLOGY - UPMC
600 Grant St, Pittsburgh, PA 15219-2702
Tel (412) 281-6646 *Founded/Ownrshp* 2009
Sales 1.0MMM^E *EMP* 62,000^E
SIC 8099 Medical services organization
CIO: Ed McCallister
Dir IT: Bill Hanna

D-U-N-S 06-685-4795
UPMC MCKEESPORT
UPMC HEALTH BENEFITS
(*Suby of* UPMC HEALTH BENEFITS) ★
1500 5th Ave, McKeesport, PA 15132-2422
Tel (412) 664-2000 *Founded/Ownrshp* 1998
Sales 133.0MM *EMP* 950
SIC 8062 General medical & surgical hospitals
Pr: Ronald H Ott
CFO: Susan Mammarrella
CTO: Rick Miller
Dir IT: James Talalai
Doctor: Arturo Castro
Doctor: Tint Lwin
Doctor: Jeffrey Oskin

D-U-N-S 79-656-7394
UPMC NORTHWEST
UPMC HEALTH BENEFITS
(*Suby of* UPMC HEALTH BENEFITS) ★
100 Fairfield Dr, Seneca, PA 16346-2130
Tel (814) 676-7600 *Founded/Ownrshp* 2001
Sales 106.2MM *EMP* 1,230^E
SIC 8741 Nursing & personal care facility management
CEO: David Patton
**CFO:* William Lucia

D-U-N-S 07-216-4395
UPMC PASSAVANT
(*Suby of* UPMC HEALTH BENEFITS) ★
9100 Babcock Blvd, Pittsburgh, PA 15237-5815
Tel (412) 367-6700 *Founded/Ownrshp* 1985
Sales 353.1MM *EMP* 1,357
SIC 8062 General medical & surgical hospitals
Pr: Teresa G Petrick

Treas: Franklin Kelley
VP: Paul Eberhart
VP: Paul Wheeler

D-U-N-S 07-497-6044
UPMC PRESBYTERIAN SHADYSIDE
(*Suby of* UPMC HEALTH BENEFITS) ★
200 Lothrop St, Pittsburgh, PA 15213-2536
Tel (412) 647-8762 *Founded/Ownrshp* 1893
Sales 1.3MMM^E *EMP* 8,200^E
Accts Ernst & Young Llp Pittsburgh
SIC 8062 General medical & surgical hospitals
Pr: John Innocenti
Mng Pt: William Pietragallo II
* *CFO:* Eileen Simmons
Ansthlgy: Erin A Sullivan

D-U-N-S 17-798-1438
UPMC ST MARGARET
(*Suby of* UPMC HEALTH BENEFITS) ★
815 Freeport Rd, Pittsburgh, PA 15215-3301
Tel (412) 784-4000 *Founded/Ownrshp* 1997
Sales 247.4MM^E *EMP* 1,501
SIC 8062 General medical & surgical hospitals
Pr: David T Martin
COO: John R Caoll
* *Ch:* Neil Y Vanhorn
VP: Gabi Daniely
* *Prin:* Darlene Rodgers
Adm Dir: Jeannie Stepano
Off Mgr: Walter Garcia
Off Mgr: Beverly Poremba
QC Dir: Marge Jacobs
Sls Dir: Philip Lassman

D-U-N-S 17-799-0652
UPMC ST MARGARET TRANSITIONAL CARE UNIT
(*Suby of* UPMC HEALTH BENEFITS) ★
815 Freeport Rd, Pittsburgh, PA 15215-3301
Tel (412) 784-4000 *Founded/Ownrshp* 1997
Sales 197.8MM^E *EMP* 1,200
Accts Internal Revenue Service
SIC 8062 General medical & surgical hospitals
Pr: Richard Sobehart
* *VP:* John Carroll
VP: Jerry Kern
* *VP:* Herman Pfeffer
* *VP:* Arthur Scully
* *VP:* Katherine Vidakovich
Dir Lab: Meredith Naples
Dir Lab: Howard E Reidbord
Pharmcst: Elaine Nigro

D-U-N-S 12-232-4999 IMP
UPONOR INC
WIRSBO COMPANY
(*Suby of* UPONOR NORTH AMERICA INC) ★
5925 148th St W, Saint Paul, MN 55124-8197
Tel (952) 891-2000 *Founded/Ownrshp* 1990
Sales 167.6MM^E *EMP* 296
SIC 3084 3567 3433 Plastics pipe; Industrial furnaces & ovens; Heating equipment, except electric
Pr: William Gray
CFO: Brad Beckman
VP: Aho Ilari
VP: Greg Lawler
VP: Brent Noonan
Mng Dir: Joe Pauly
IT Man: Scott Hellendrung
IT Man: Mark Mattei
IT Man: Darren Nicholls
Sfty Mgr: Sang Albrecht
Plnt Mgr: Rusty Callier
Board of Directors: Ake Forrsell Chb

D-U-N-S 17-125-5206
UPONOR NORTH AMERICA INC
(*Suby of* UPONOR OYJ)
5925 148th St W, Apple Valley, MN 55124-8197
Tel (952) 891-2000 *Founded/Ownrshp* 1990
Sales 167.6MM^E *EMP* 380
SIC 8742 3312 Management consulting services; Pipes & tubes
CEO: William Gray
* *Pr:* Jim Bjork
Exec: Tanya Ruszczyk
Comm Man: Karen Mellott-Foshier
Dir IT: James Quinn
Software D: Scott Kies
Mktg Mgr: Dale Stroud
Snr Mgr: Ingrid Mattsson

UPPCO
See UPPER PENINSULA POWER CO INC

D-U-N-S 03-999-5751
UPPER ALLEGHENY HEALTH SYSTEM INC
130 S Union St Ste 300, Olean, NY 14760-3676
Tel (716) 375-6975 *Founded/Ownrshp* 2009
Sales 168.9MM^E *EMP* 1,675^E
SIC 8062 General medical & surgical hospitals
CEO: Timothy J Finan
* *Sr VP:* Richard Braun
* *Sr VP:* Timothy McNamara
* *Sr VP:* William Mills
* *Sr VP:* Jason Yaworsky
VP: Gail Bagazzoli
VP: Kevin Haughney

D-U-N-S 15-535-0218
UPPER CHESAPEAKE HEALTH FOUNDATION INC
520 Upper Chesapeake 40 Ste 405, Bel Air, MD 21014
Tel (443) 643-1500 *Founded/Ownrshp* 1984
Sales 433.2M *EMP* 2,200
Accts Grant Thornton Llp Philadelph
SIC 8062 General medical & surgical hospitals
Pr: Lyle E Sheldon
Pr: Doris Walker
* *CFO:* Joseph Hoffman
Chf Mktg O: Martha Mallonee
Dir Risk M: Debbie Bittle
Adm Dir: Beverly Wehmer
Ex Dir: Vickie Bands
Off Mgr: Sherifa Clarke
Dir IT: Rick Bachman
Dir IT: Rick Casthill
Mtls Dir: Paula Fasick

D-U-N-S 07-827-8769
UPPER CHESAPEAKE MEDICAL CENTER INC
(*Suby of* UPPER CHESAPEAKE HEALTH FOUNDATION INC) ★
500 Upper Chesapeake Dr, Bel Air, MD 21014-4324
Tel (443) 643-1000 *Founded/Ownrshp* 1986
Sales 284.6MM *EMP* 850
SIC 8062 General medical & surgical hospitals
Pr: Lyle E Sheldon
Chf Rad: Noah Lightman
Chf Rad: David Smith
* *Ch Bd:* Roger E Schneider MD
* *V Ch:* Randall T Worthington
CFO: Joe Hoffman
* *Treas:* H William Acker
Sr VP: Dean Kaster
VP: Eugene Currotto
Dir Inf Cn: Colleen Clay
Dir Lab: Diane Stevens

UPPER CRUST BAKERY
See UNITED GENERAL BAKERY INC

D-U-N-S 00-484-0336
UPPER CUMBERLAND ELECTRIC MEMBERSHIP CORP (TN)
907 Main St N, Carthage, TN 37030-1002
Tel (615) 735-3208 *Founded/Ownrshp* 1938
Sales 104.7MM *EMP* 139
SIC 4911 Distribution, electric power
Pr: Morris Tyree II
COO: Donnie Brooks
* *Sec:* Joe Mullins
* *VP:* James West
* *Prin:* Mike Scudder
* *Genl Mgr:* Jimmy Gregory

D-U-N-S 07-706-3196
UPPER DARBY SCHOOL DISTRICT (INC) (PA)
4611 Bond Ave, Drexel Hill, PA 19026-4236
Tel (610) 789-7200 *Founded/Ownrshp* 1893
Sales 169.3MM *EMP* 1,450
Accts Baker Tilly Virchow Krause Ll
SIC 8211 Public elementary & secondary schools
* *Pr:* Maureen Carey
* *Treas:* Patrick Grant
* *Ex VP:* William Gaul
Dir Sec: Louis Gentile
Cmptr Lab: Ann Law
Psych: Ethan Spencer

D-U-N-S 18-705-6858 IMP/EXP
UPPER DECK CO LLC
2251 Rutherford Rd, Carlsbad, CA 92008-8815
Tel (800) 873-7332 *Founded/Ownrshp* 1988
Sales 126.5MM^E *EMP* 400
SIC 2752 5947 Souvenir cards, lithographed; Gift, novelty & souvenir shop
CEO: Richard Mc William
Pr: Jason Masherah
Ex VP: Roz Nowicki
VP: Michael Bernstein
VP: Rich Foltynewicz
Creative D: Michael Eggleston
Dir Bus: Rich Bonora
CIO: Josh Zusman
CTO: Deepak Agarwal
CTO: Frederic Prag
Dir IT: Neal Johnson

D-U-N-S 07-140-7548
UPPER MISSOURI G & T ELECTRIC CO-OPERATIVE INC
UPPER MO G & T ELC CO OPERATI
111 2nd Ave Sw, Sidney, MT 59270-4017
Tel (406) 433-4100 *Founded/Ownrshp* 1957
Sales 319.1MM *EMP* 2^E
Accts Brenner Averett & Co Pc Sidne
SIC 4911 Transmission, electric power
Pr: Roger Sorenson
* *VP:* Allen Thiessen

UPPER MO G & T ELC CO OPERATI
See UPPER MISSOURI G & T ELECTRIC CO-OPERATIVE INC

D-U-N-S 08-673-3057
UPPER PENINSULA HEALTH PLAN LLC
853 W Washington St, Marquette, MI 49855-4139
Tel (906) 225-7500 *Founded/Ownrshp* 1997
Sales NA *EMP* 88
SIC 6321 6411 Health insurance carriers; Insurance agents, brokers & service
CEO: Dennis Smith
Exec: Tanya M Jennings
Off Mgr: Barbara Payan
Netwrk Mgr: Brad Perala

D-U-N-S 00-695-9753
UPPER PENINSULA POWER CO INC
UPPCO
(*Suby of* BASALT INFRASTRUCTURE PARTNERS LLP)
1002 Harbor Hills Dr, Marquette, MI 49855-8851
Tel (906) 232-1444 *Founded/Ownrshp* 2015
Sales 162.4MM^E *EMP* 169
SIC 4911 Electric services
CEO: Barbara Siehr
* *CFO:* Nicholas Kates
VP: James Schott
* *Dir IT:* Greg Gagnon
Opers Supe: Scott Roehl
* *Genl Couns:* Stephen Serriano

UPPER VALLEY MEDICAL CENTER
See AFTER HOURS FAMILY CARE INC

D-U-N-S 62-143-7565
UPPER VALLEY MEDICAL CENTER
3130 N County Road 25a, Troy, OH 45373-1337
Tel (937) 440-4000 *Founded/Ownrshp* 1926
Sales 130.1MM *EMP* 1,800
SIC 8011 8062

D-U-N-S 93-273-1037
UPPYS CONVENIENCE STORES INC
MID-ATLNTIC CONVENIENCE STORES
1011 Boulder Springs Dr, North Chesterfield, VA 23225-4950
Tel (804) 706-4702 *Founded/Ownrshp* 2010
Sales 100.0MM^E *EMP* 550
SIC 5411 5541 Convenience stores, chain; Filling stations, gasoline
Treas: Steven M Uphoff
Sr VP: Mike Squillace
VP: Linda G Uphoff
Snr Mgr: Debbye Mahan

UPS
See UNITED PARCEL SERVICE INC (OH)

UPS
See UNITED PARCEL SERVICE INC

UPS
See UNITED PARCEL SERVICE INC

D-U-N-S 14-779-2147
■ **UPS CUSTOMHOUSE BROKERAGE INC**
(*Suby of* UPS) ★
1930 Bishop Ln Ste 200, Louisville, KY 40218-1938
Tel (502) 485-2600 *Founded/Ownrshp* 1985
Sales 60.7MM^E *EMP* 1,060
SIC 4731 Customhouse brokers
Pr: D Scott Davis
* *Treas:* Kurt P Kuehn
Exec: Christie Hughes
* *Prin:* Phil Hughes
Genl Mgr: Donald Blasi

D-U-N-S 07-860-9447
■ **UPS FREIGHT SERVICES INC**
(*Suby of* UPS) ★
1000 Semmes Ave, Richmond, VA 23224-2246
Tel (804) 231-8000 *Founded/Ownrshp* 2002
Sales 278.1MM^E *EMP* 3,000^E
SIC 4215 Courier services, except by air
Prin: Scott D Davis
Pr Mgr: Sandy Adkins

D-U-N-S 18-854-4808
■ **UPS FUEL SERVICES INC**
U P S
(*Suby of* UPS) ★
55 Glenlake Pkwy, Atlanta, GA 30328-3474
Tel (678) 339-3250 *Founded/Ownrshp* 1989
Sales 162.1MM^E *EMP* 24
SIC 5172 Engine fuels & oils
CEO: D Scott Davis
* *Pr:* Myron Gray
Pr: Daniel Gross
* *COO:* David Abney
* *CFO:* Kurt P Kuehn
* *Sr VP:* David Barnes
* *Sr VP:* John McDevitt

D-U-N-S 00-599-5071 IMP/EXP
■ **UPS GROUND FREIGHT INC**
(*Suby of* UPS) ★
1000 Semmes Ave, Richmond, VA 23224-2246
Tel (866) 372-5619 *Founded/Ownrshp* 2005
Sales 2.0MMM^E *EMP* 14,000
SIC 4213 Automobiles, transport & delivery
Ch Bd: Leo H Suggs
* *COO:* Gordon S Mackenzie
* *CFO:* Patrick D Hanley
CFO: Kurt Kuehn
Ofcr: Dale Lewis
* *Sr VP:* John W Fain
* *Sr VP:* Mark B Goodwin
VP: Paul Hoelting
* *Genl Mgr:* Arthur Morales
IT Man: Rick Jones
IT Man: Eric Webster

D-U-N-S 00-819-0683
■ **UPS LOGISTICS GROUP INC** (DE)
(*Suby of* UPS) ★
55 Glenlake Pkwy, Atlanta, GA 30328-3474
Tel (678) 746-4100 *Founded/Ownrshp* 1995
Sales 301.4MM^E *EMP* 3,200
SIC 7389 7513 4731 4513 Mailing & messenger services; Truck leasing, without drivers; Freight transportation arrangement; Air courier services
CEO: Dan Dimaggio
CFO: Doug Anderson
VP: John Haack
CIO: Jay Walsh

D-U-N-S 14-435-2911
■ **UPS STORE INC**
MAIL BOXES ETC
(*Suby of* UPS) ★
6060 Cornerstone Ct W, San Diego, CA 92121-3712
Tel (858) 455-8800 *Founded/Ownrshp* 2001
Sales 88.4MM^E *EMP* 321^E
Accts Deloitte & Touche Llp Atlanta
SIC 7389 8742 4783 Mailbox rental & related service; Printers' services: folding, collating; Packaging & labeling services; Business consultant; Packing goods for shipping
CEO: Walter T Davis
* *Pr:* Tim Davis
COO: Susan Chae
CFO: Jose Ferro
CFO: Jennifer Jonson
CFO: Harvey Saskiw
Sr Cor Off: Laureen Boykin
Sr Cor Off: Elaine Cuklanz
Sr Cor Off: Dana Delbonis
Sr Cor Off: Paul Engstenberg
Sr Cor Off: Mary-Louise Mulcahy
Sr Cor Off: Todd Parker
VP: Debra Abate
VP: Chris Adkins
VP: Jeffrey Alianiello
VP: Sean Blickle
VP: Anna Fatovic
VP: Steve Hernandez
VP: Don Higginson
VP: Ana Hung
VP: Christa Martin

D-U-N-S 61-779-3125
■ **UPS SUPPLY CHAIN SOLUTIONS GENERAL SERVICES INC**
(*Suby of* UPS) ★
55 Glenlake Pkwy, Atlanta, GA 30328-3474
Tel (404) 828-6000 *Founded/Ownrshp* 2000
Sales 300.0MM^E *EMP* 825^E
SIC 4215 Parcel delivery, vehicular
Ch: D Scott Davis
* *Treas:* Kurt Kuehn

D-U-N-S 17-946-2911 IMP/EXP
■ **UPS SUPPLY CHAIN SOLUTIONS INC**
U P S
(*Suby of* UPS) ★
12380 Morris Rd, Alpharetta, GA 30005-4177
Tel (800) 742-5727 *Founded/Ownrshp* 1988
Sales 1.3MMM^E *EMP* 11,760
SIC 8742 Administrative services consultant
Ch Bd: D Scott Davis
* *Pr:* Bob Stoffel
* *CEO:* Kurt P Kuehn
Sr VP: Paul Gettings
VP: John Boner
VP: John Haack
VP: Andy Huckbody
VP: Jeff Jones
VP: Janet Macaulay
VP: Steve McMichael
VP: Mike Panetta
VP: Dan White
VP Bus Dev: Jeff Battaglia
Exec: Dan Bryan
Assoc Dir: Randall Hanlon
Dir Bus: Ken Carlson

D-U-N-S 86-133-6584 EXP
■ **UPS WORLDWIDE LOGISTICS INC**
(*Suby of* UPS) ★
12380 Morris Rd, Alpharetta, GA 30005-4177
Tel (678) 746-4100 *Founded/Ownrshp* 2008
Sales 103.2MM^E *EMP* 1,128
SIC 7389 Mailing & messenger services
Pr: Michael Smith
Sr VP: Robert Stoffel
Prgrm Mgr: Devin Whalen
MIS Mgr: John E Donahue
VP Opers: Keith Andrey

UPSCO UNITED PARCEL SERVICE CO
See UNITED PARCEL SERVICE CO

D-U-N-S 04-725-1004 IMP
UPSHER-SMITH LABORATORIES INC
6701 Evenstad Dr N, Maple Grove, MN 55369-6026
Tel (763) 315-2000 *Founded/Ownrshp* 1970
Sales 141.2MM^E *EMP* 550
SIC 2834

D-U-N-S 00-793-0555
UPSHUR RURAL ELECTRIC COOPERATIVE CORP (TX)
URECC
1200 W Tyler St, Gilmer, TX 75644-2017
Tel (903) 843-2536 *Founded/Ownrshp* 1937
Sales 92.0MM *EMP* 90
SIC 4911 Distribution, electric power
Pr: Frankie B King
Treas: Joe Beard
* *Sec:* Joe Don Beard
* *VP:* R Cody Newman
Genl Mgr: Robert Walker
Opers Mgr: Jeff Gee

UPSON PROPANE
See WALTHALL OIL CO

D-U-N-S 07-799-0745
UPSTATE AFFILIATE ORGANIZATION
GREENVILLE HEALTH SYSTEM
701 Grove Rd, Greenville, SC 29605-4210
Tel (864) 455-7000 *Founded/Ownrshp* 1947
Sales 1.0MMM *EMP* 7,200
SIC 8069 8051 Specialty hospitals, except psychiatric; Skilled nursing care facilities
CEO: Michael C Riordan
V Ch: Harry A Chapman Jr
* *Pr:* Spence M Taylor
CFO: Susan J Bichel
* *CFO:* Terri T Newsom
Trst: Jerry E Dempsey
* *Ex VP:* Gregory J Rusnak
VP: Joe J Blake
* *VP:* Joseph J Blake Jr
* *VP:* Malcolm W Isley
VP: Rich Rogers
VP: Angelo Sinopoli
VP: Michelle Taylor Smith
VP: Tod N Tappert
VP: Suzanne K White
VP: Christopher Wright
VP: Jerry R Youkey
Exec: Michelle Villal
Dir Rad: John A Cooper

D-U-N-S 10-101-6103
UPSTATE CEREBRAL PALSY INC
1020 Mary St, Utica, NY 13501-1930
Tel (315) 724-6907 *Founded/Ownrshp* 1950
Sales 78.2MM *EMP* 1,700
Accts Bonadio & Co Llp Pittsford
SIC 8322 Association for the handicapped
Pr: Louis Tehan
Assoc VP: Patricia Carey
Assoc VP: Gordon Dunham
Sr VP: Kathleen Klosner
VP: Tara Costello
Dir Bus: Carleen Stewart
Dir Bus: Kristen Vennero
Ex Dir: Willis Tehan
QA Dir: Karen Lindsay
Dir IT: Ward Jones
Opers Mgr: Wanda Schmidt

UPSTATE HOME FOR CHILDREN & AD
See SPRINGBROOK NY INC

D-U-N-S 00-486-8055
UPSTATE NIAGARA COOPERATIVE INC (NY)
BISON PRODUCTS
25 Anderson Rd, Buffalo, NY 14225-4905
Tel (716) 892-3156 *Founded/Ownrshp* 1930
Sales 775.5MM *EMP* 700
Accts Dopkins & Company Llp Buffal
SIC 2026 Fermented & cultured milk products
CEO: Larry Webster
Pr: Daniel Wolf
COO: Brain Kornfeind
COO: Lawrence Webster
CFO: Edward Luongo
Treas: Herbert Nobles
VP: Eric Zuber
Dir Lab: Ruth Riner
Genl Mgr: Ed Porter
Genl Mgr: Doug Ricketts
CTO: Robert Russo

D-U-N-S 13-134-0304
UPSTATE UNIVERSITY MEDICAL ASSOCIATES AT SYRACUSE INC
(*Suby of* SUNY ADMINISTRATION) ★
750 E Adams St, Syracuse, NY 13210-2306
Tel (315) 464-7087 *Founded/Ownrshp* 1963
Sales 619.5MM^E^ *EMP* 8,000^E^
SIC 8221 9411 8231 Colleges universities & professional schools; ; Library services
Pr: Gregory Eastwood
**CEO:* John McCabe
**CFO:* Sturat Wright
Mtls Mgr: Brenda Rodriguez
Pathlgst: Kamal Khurana
Pharmcst: Kelly Jacobs

D-U-N-S 92-732-8075
UPWIND SOLUTIONS INC
(*Suby of* VESTAS WIND SYSTEMS A/S)
4863 Shawline St Ste A, San Diego, CA 92111-1435
Tel (866) 927-3142 *Founded/Ownrshp* 2015
Sales 84.7MM^E^ *EMP* 330
SIC 7374 4931 7373 Data processing & preparation; ; Computer systems analysis & design
Pr: Peter Wells
CFO: Mike Skelly
**VP:* Nick Gerostathos
Off Admin: Adriana Caraveo
IT Man: Kiyoshi Kanzawa
S&M/VP: Robert Bergqvist

URBAN ACTIVE
See GLOBAL FITNESS HOLDINGS LLC

D-U-N-S 07-177-8299
URBAN CONCRETE CONTRACTORS INC
24114 Blanco Rd, San Antonio, TX 78260-6615
Tel (210) 490-0090 *Founded/Ownrshp* 1974
Sales 103.9MM^E^ *EMP* 720
SIC 1771 Exterior concrete stucco contractor
CFO: Tonya Schmid

D-U-N-S 07-963-5767
▲ URBAN EDGE PROPERTIES
888 7th Ave Ste 602, New York, NY 10106-0601
Tel (212) 956-2556 *Founded/Ownrshp* 2014
Sales 322.9MM *EMP* 100^E^
Accts Deloitte & Touche Llp New Yor
Tkr Sym UE *Exch* NYS
SIC 6798 Real estate investment trusts
Ch Bd: Jeffrey S Olson
COO: Robert Minutoli
CFO: Matthew Iocco
Chf Inves: Herb Eilberg
Ex VP: Michael Zucker
VP: James Cozine
VP: Terese Furry
VP: Paul Schiffer
VP: Patricia Zafferese
VP Opers: Joseph Degiorgio
VP Opers: Bassam Mhich

URBAN HAIR AND SPA
See HAIRSTYLISTS MANAGEMENT SYSTEMS INC

D-U-N-S 07-480-3701
URBAN INSTITUTE
2100 M St Nw Fl 5, Washington, DC 20037-1207
Tel (202) 833-7200 *Founded/Ownrshp* 1968
Sales 95.1MM *EMP* 400
SIC 8733 Research institute
Pr: Sarah Rosen Wartell
CFO: Christy Visher
Trst: Robert Reischauer
Ex VP: John Rogers
Sr VP: Randall Bovbjerg
VP: William Adams
VP: Robert Berenson
VP: Deborah Hoover
VP: Kristoff Incentes
VP: Judy Johnson
VP: Nancy Lavigne
VP: Diane Levy
VP: Robert G Planansky
VP: Wayne Vroman
Dir Soc: Daphne Godfrey

URBAN LENDING SOLUTIONS
See URBAN SETTLEMENT SERVICES LLC

D-U-N-S 05-521-8412
URBAN LENDING SOLUTIONS
1001 Liberty Ave Ste 1050, Pittsburgh, PA 15222-3771
Tel (412) 325-7046 *Founded/Ownrshp* 2011
Sales NA *EMP* 1,500
SIC 6163 Mortgage brokers arranging for loans, using money of others
CEO: Charles S Sanders
CFO: Dan Chitwood
CFO: Jim Overton
Sr VP: Lydia Holzman
Exec: Shana Cooper
Software D: John Price

D-U-N-S 05-327-5483 IMP
▲ URBAN OUTFITTERS INC
5000 S Broad St, Philadelphia, PA 19112-1495
Tel (215) 454-5500 *Founded/Ownrshp* 1970
Sales 3.4MMM *EMP* 24,000
Accts Deloitte & Touche Llp Philade
Tkr Sym URBN *Exch* NGS
SIC 5621 5611 5632 5661 5719 5137 Women's clothing stores; Ready-to-wear apparel, women's; Women's sportswear; Men's & boys' clothing stores; Clothing, men's & boys': everyday, except suits & sportswear; Clothing, sportswear, men's & boys'; Clothing accessories: men's & boys'; Apparel accessories; Shoe stores; Women's shoes; Men's shoes; Housewares; Women's & children's clothing; Sportswear, women's & children's
Pr: Richard A Hayne
Pr: David W McCreight
CEO: Trish Donnelly
COO: Calvin Hollinger
CFO: Eric Artz
CFO: Francis J Conforti
**Chf Cred:* Margaret A Hayne
Creative D: Sue Otto
Dist Mgr: Angie Biggs
Dist Mgr: Joe Silva
Genl Mgr: Eleanor Riley
Board of Directors: Edward N Antonian, Scott A Belair, Harry S Cherken Jr, Elizabeth Ann Lambert, Joel S Lawson III, Robert H Strouse

D-U-N-S 07-847-6158
URBAN PENNSYLVANIA INVESTMENT MEMBER LLC
445 N Wells St Ste 200, Chicago, IL 60654-4582
Tel (312) 222-0777 *Founded/Ownrshp* 2010
Sales 162.1MM *EMP* 2
Accts Kpmg Llp Norfolk Virginia
SIC 6799 Real estate investors, except property operators

D-U-N-S 09-245-0840 IMP
URBAN SCIENCE APPLICATIONS INC
400 Renaissance Ctr # 2900, Detroit, MI 48243-1502
Tel (313) 259-9900 *Founded/Ownrshp* 1976
Sales 117.3MM^E^ *EMP* 500
SIC 8742 Marketing consulting services
Pr: James A Anderson
CFO: Richard Widgren
Ofcr: Rod Wright
VP: John Frith
VP: Paco Soler
VP: Randall Tallerico
Exec: Matt Strickroot
Mng Dir: Christine Boumansour
Mng Dir: Marco Caponera
Mng Dir: Eric Haase
Mng Dir: Ben Holmes

D-U-N-S 12-823-2894
URBAN SETTLEMENT SERVICES LLC
URBAN LENDING SOLUTIONS
11802 Ridge Pkwy Ste 200, Broomfield, CO 80021-5008
Tel (303) 996-8900 *Founded/Ownrshp* 2002
Sales 168.6MM *EMP* 2,000
SIC 6531 Real estate agents & managers
CEO: Charles Sanders
**Pr:* Mike Forgas
**CFO:* Dan Chitwood
Ex VP: Scot Rose
Sr VP: Darlene Burnham
Sr VP: Lydia Holzman
Sr VP: Rick McCoy
Sr VP: Dennis Postlewait
Sr VP: Jennifer Quinn
VP: Lisa Mackenzie

D-U-N-S 04-461-7251 EXP
URBIETA OIL INC
9701 Nw 89th Ave, Medley, FL 33178-1435
Tel (305) 884-0008 *Founded/Ownrshp* 2000
Sales 92.4MM^E^ *EMP* 30
SIC 5171 5172 Petroleum bulk stations & terminals; Gasoline
Pr: Guillermo Urbieta
**VP:* Ignacio Urbieta Jr
Sls Mgr: Henry Suarez

URC
See UNIVERSITY RESEARCH CO LLC

D-U-N-S 15-779-6368
URC LLC
PIZZERIA UNO
(*Suby of* CENTRE PARTNERS MANAGEMENT LLC) ★
100 Charles Park Rd, Boston, MA 02132-4902
Tel (617) 323-9200 *Founded/Ownrshp* 2008
Sales 39.3MM^E^ *EMP* 4,921^E^
SIC 5812 5813 6794 Pizzeria, chain; Bar (drinking places); Franchises, selling or licensing
CEO: Frank Guidara
**Pr:* Ian Baines
COO: Roger L Zingle
**CFO:* Louie Psallidas
**CFO:* Robert M Vincent
**Ex VP:* Alan M Fox

URECC
See UPSHUR RURAL ELECTRIC COOPERATIVE CORP

D-U-N-S 11-043-4136
URGENT CARE HOLDINGS INC
MED EXPRESS URGENT CARE
1751 Earl L Core Rd, Morgantown, WV 26505-5891
Tel (304) 225-2500 *Founded/Ownrshp* 2007
Sales 135.1MM^E^ *EMP* 1,000
SIC 8011 Offices & clinics of medical doctors
CEO: Frank Alderman
Pr: David Klink
Pr: John Tramontina
**COO:* Mike Geldart
**COO:* Dean Hatcher
**CFO:* Scott Leya
CFO: Jonathan Walker
**Chf Mktg O:* Robert Maha
Chf Mktg O: Julie Penn
**Chf Mktg O:* Bryan Stuchell
VP: Tim Bugin
VP: Dorothy Knight
VP: Erich Lipphardt
VP: Troy Steckler
VP: Michael Westover
Assoc Dir: Gary Derk

URGENT CARE/WALK IN SERVICE
See EAST BOSTON NEIGHBORHOOD HEALTH CENTER CORP

D-U-N-S 96-770-5893
URGENT CARES OF AMERICA HOLDINGS LLC
FASTMED URGENT CARE
(*Suby of* ABRY PARTNERS INC) ★
935 Shotwell Rd Ste 108, Clayton, NC 27520-5598
Tel (919) 550-0821 *Founded/Ownrshp* 2015
Sales 33.8MM *EMP* 1,300
Accts Grant Thornron Llp Raleigh
SIC 6719 8011 Investment holding companies, except banks; Primary care medical clinic
Pr: Kyle Bohannon
CFO: Robert Oliveri
VP: Justin Smith

URL PHARMA
See MUTUAL PHARMACEUTICAL CO INC

D-U-N-S 00-896-3787
URM STORES INC
7511 N Freya St, Spokane, WA 99217-8043
Tel (509) 467-2620 *Founded/Ownrshp* 1921
Sales 2.2MMM^E^ *EMP* 2,100
Accts Bdo Usa Llp Spokane Wa
SIC 5141 5147 Groceries, general line; Meats & meat products
Pr: Ray Sprinkle
**CFO:* Laurie Bigej
**Treas:* Brian Eldred
Ofcr: Shirley Kieviet
VP: Rich Stuber
VP: Linda Wilson
CTO: Larry Gerow
DP Dir: Craig Buhl
IT Man: Robert Burmann
Sales Asso: Mike Poffenroth

UROLOGY
See ROSWELL PARK CANCER INSTITUTE

URS
See WASHINGTON GOVERNMENT ENVIRONMENTAL SERVICES CO LLC

URS
See WASHINGTON RIVER PROTECTION SOLUTIONS LLC

D-U-N-S 07-466-0580
URS CORP
Mack Ctr Ii Mack Ctr Dr, Paramus, NJ 07652
Tel (201) 262-7000 *Founded/Ownrshp* 1970
Sales NA *EMP* 20,000
SIC 8711 8748

D-U-N-S 96-153-0545
■ URS FEDERAL SERVICES INC
URS FEDERAL SVCS INC AN AECOM
(*Suby of* AECOM GLOBAL II LLC) ★
20501 Seneca Meadows Pkwy # 300, Germantown, MD 20876-7019
Tel (301) 944-3100 *Founded/Ownrshp* 2010
Sales 1.5MMM^E^ *EMP* 17,000^E^
SIC 8711 Engineering services
Pr: Randall A Wotring
**CFO:* William M Munkacsy
Ex VP: David Swindle
**VP:* Arthur Mallamo Jr

D-U-N-S 07-912-3125
URS FEDERAL SERVICES INTERNATIONAL INC
20501 Seneca Meadows Pkwy # 300, Germantown, MD 20876-7019
Tel (301) 944-3100 *Founded/Ownrshp* 2010
Sales 98.4MM^E^ *EMP* 49,000
SIC 8711 Engineering services
Prin: Randy Wotring
Prin: Linda Raper

D-U-N-S 96-162-9529
■ URS FEDERAL SERVICES INTERNATIONAL INC
(*Suby of* URS FEDERAL SVCS INC AN AECOM) ★
1300 E 9th St Ste 500, Cleveland, OH 44114-1503
Tel (301) 944-3100 *Founded/Ownrshp* 2010
Sales 62.7MM^E^ *EMP* 5,000^E^
SIC 8711 Engineering services
Prin: Bob Snyder

D-U-N-S 07-387-1048 IMP/EXP
URS FEDERAL SUPPORT SERVICES INC
20501 Seneca Meadows Pkwy # 300, Germantown, MD 20876-7016
Tel (301) 944-3100 *Founded/Ownrshp* 2002
Sales 133.8MM^E^ *EMP* 5,100^E^
SIC 8249 4581

URS FEDERAL SVCS INC AN AECOM
See URS FEDERAL SERVICES INC

D-U-N-S 08-307-0925 IMP
URS FEDERAL TECHINCAL SERVICES INC
20501 Seneca Meadows Pkwy # 300, Germantown, MD 20876-7016
Tel (301) 944-3100 *Founded/Ownrshp* 2006
Sales 426.8MM^E^ *EMP* 4,800
SIC 8711

D-U-N-S 80-830-2116
URS GORES HOLDINGS CORP
10877 Wilshire Blvd Ste 1, Los Angeles, CA 90024-4341
Tel (310) 209-3010 *Founded/Ownrshp* 2007
Sales 72.3MM^E^ *EMP* 2,300^E^
SIC 4213 Automobiles, transport & delivery
Pr: Alex Gores

D-U-N-S 12-425-2052
■ URS GROUP INC
(*Suby of* AECOM GLOBAL II LLC) ★
300 S Grand Ave Ste 1100, Los Angeles, CA 90071-3173
Tel (213) 593-8000 *Founded/Ownrshp* 1988
Sales 4.5MMM^E^ *EMP* 27,522
SIC 8711 8712 8741 Engineering services; Consulting engineer; Architectural engineering; Construction management
CEO: Martin M Koffel
Sr VP: Hugh Blackwood
Sr VP: Andrew Kaminsky
Sr VP: Kirby Loid
Sr VP: John Schmerber
VP: John Debruin
VP: Rich Dilley
VP: Garry Horton
VP: Keith Kajiya
VP: Simon Kim
VP: Angela Lieba
VP: Ramesh Patel
VP: Jim Semple
VP: Cynthia Stinger

D-U-N-S 06-526-2573
■ URS HOLDINGS INC
(*Suby of* AECOM GLOBAL II LLC) ★
600 Montgomery St Fl 25, San Francisco, CA 94111-2727
Tel (415) 774-2700 *Founded/Ownrshp* 1991
Sales 5.4MMM^E^ *EMP* 10,500
SIC 8711 7389 6531 8249 4581 Consulting engineer; Financial services; Real estate agents & managers; Aviation school; Aircraft maintenance & repair services
CEO: Thomas W Bishop
**Ch Bd:* Martin M Koffel
Sr VP: W D Balfour
Sr VP: Dhamo S Dhamotharan
Sr VP: Robert M Gallen
Sr VP: T W Hawkes
Sr VP: Thomas Logan
VP: Robert Ray

D-U-N-S 36-127-2805
URS MIDWEST INC
AUTO TRANSPORT TECHNICAL CTR
10701 Middlebelt Rd, Romulus, MI 48174-2714
Tel (888) 278-2793 *Founded/Ownrshp* 1998
Sales 10.1MM^E^ *EMP* 1,700
SIC 4731 Truck transportation brokers
CEO: Kathleen McCann
**COO:* Mark Anderson
**CFO:* Eric Mikesell
**Sr VP:* Pat Riley
Sr VP: Patrick M Riley
VP: Charles E Baxter
VP: Bill Cole
VP: David R Larson
CIO: Matthew A Cartwright

D-U-N-S 00-506-8747 IMP/EXP
URSCHEL LABORATORIES INC (ID)
1200 Cutting Edge Dr, Chesterton, IN 46304-3554
Tel (219) 464-4811 *Founded/Ownrshp* 1910, 1938
Sales 125.6MM^E^ *EMP* 349
SIC 3556 7374 Cutting, chopping, grinding, mixing & similar machinery; Data processing service
CEO: Patrick C Urschel
**Ch Bd:* Robert R Urschel
**CFO:* Daniel Marchetti
**Ex VP:* Daniel R Urschel
VP: Mark Barlog
VP: Al Kurfman
VP: Bill Owen
Comm Dir: Dave Tipold
Mng Dir: Jack Wright
Rgnl Mgr: Steve Smock
Genl Mgr: Maria Degarmo

D-U-N-S 05-598-9321
▲ URSTADT BIDDLE PROPERTIES INC
321 Railroad Ave Ste 5, Greenwich, CT 06830-6391
Tel (203) 863-8200 *Founded/Ownrshp* 1997
Sales 115.3MM *EMP* 49^E^
Tkr Sym UBA *Exch* NYS
SIC 6798 Real estate investment trusts
CEO: Willing L Biddle
**Ch Bd:* Charles J Urstadt
COO: Stephan A Rapaglia
CFO: John T Hayes
**V Ch Bd:* Robert R Douglass
Sr VP: John Cannon
Sr VP: Linda L Lacey
Sr VP: Stephen A Rapaglia
VP: James M Aries
VP: Jeannine Iarossi
Board of Directors: Kevin J Bannon, Catherine U Biddle, Noble O Carpenter, Bryan O Colley, Richard Grellier, George H C Lawrence, Robert J Mueller

D-U-N-S 09-944-7302
US 1 INDUSTRIES INC
336 W Us Highway 30 # 201, Valparaiso, IN 46385-5345
Tel (219) 476-1300 *Founded/Ownrshp* 1981
Sales 193.3MM^E^ *EMP* 190
SIC 4213 4731 Trucking, except local; Freight transportation arrangement
Pr: Michael E Kibler
**CFO:* Harold E Antonson
Treas: Brenda Smith
Bd of Dir: William Sullivan
Dir IT: Rajesh Lakshmanamurthy
Sales Exec: Jim Anderson
Board of Directors: Brad James, Robert I Scissors, Lex Venditti, Walter Williamson

D-U-N-S 61-873-4826 IMP/EXP
US AIRCONDITIONING DISTRIBUTORS INC
U.S. AIRCONDITIONING DISTRS
16900 Chestnut St, City of Industry, CA 91748-1012
Tel (626) 854-4500 *Founded/Ownrshp* 1990
Sales 126.6MM^E^ *EMP* 370
SIC 5075 1711

U.S. AIRCONDITIONING DISTRS
See US AIRCONDITIONING DISTRIBUTORS INC

US AIRWAYS EXPRESS
See CHAUTAUQUA AIRLINES INC

US AIRWAYS EXPRESS
See PSA AIRLINES INC

US AIRWAYS EXPRESS
See PIEDMONT AIRLINES INC

D-U-N-S 06-537-7418 IMP/EXP
US AIRWAYS GROUP INC
4333 Amon Carter Blvd, Fort Worth, TX 76155-2605
Tel (480) 693-0800 *Founded/Ownrshp* 2013
Sales 3.7MMM^E *EMP* 32,138^E
SIC 4512

D-U-N-S 00-691-9229
US AIRWAYS INC
111 W Rio Salado Pkwy # 175, Tempe, AZ 85281-2882
Tel (480) 693-0800 *Founded/Ownrshp* 2013
Sales 91.1MM^E *EMP* 32,138^E
SIC 4512

D-U-N-S 09-627-5375
US ASSURE INC
8230 Nations Way, Jacksonville, FL 32256-4434
Tel (904) 398-3907 *Founded/Ownrshp* 1977
Sales NA *EMP* 400
SIC 6399 Health insurance for pets
Ch Bd: T F Petway III
**Pr:* Thomas Petway
**CEO:* Lee Ferguson
**CEO:* Ty Petway
**COO:* Ryan Schwartz
CFO: Nigel Ayers
**CFO:* Chris Emans
**VP:* Steve Bristow
VP: Cindy Willis

D-U-N-S 12-163-2137
US AUTO GROUP LIMITED
34602 Woodward Ave, Birmingham, MI 48009-0924
Tel (248) 645-5930 *Founded/Ownrshp* 1984
Sales 148.1MM^E *EMP* 400^E
SIC 5511 Automobiles, new & used
Pr: Frederick Lavery Jr
Genl Mgr: Ali Sheikh

D-U-N-S 93-326-7940
▲ US AUTO PARTS NETWORK INC
16941 Keegan Ave, Carson, CA 90746-1307
Tel (310) 735-0085 *Founded/Ownrshp* 1995
Sales 291.0MM *EMP* 1,084
Tkr Sym PRTS *Exch* NGS
SIC 5961 Automotive supplies & equipment, mail order
CEO: Shane Evangelist
**Ch Bd:* Robert J Majteles
COO: Aaron E Coleman
CFO: David Robson
CFO: Neil Watanabe
VP: David Eisler
VP: Jim Hastie
VP: Sleung Suhr
QA Dir: Noel Bautista
Advt Dir: Rob Mullner
Sales Asso: Dennis Alvarez
Board of Directors: Joshua L Berman, Jay K Greyson, Fredric W Harman, Sol Khazani, Barbara Palmer, Warren B Phelps III, Bradley E Wilson

D-U-N-S 00-621-3482
▲ US BANCORP
800 Nicollet Mall # 1500, Minneapolis, MN 55402-7014
Tel (651) 466-3000 *Founded/Ownrshp* 1929
Sales NA *EMP* 65,433
Accts Ernst & Young Llp Minneapolis
Tkr Sym USB *Exch* NYS
SIC 6021 6022 6162 6091 6159 6411 National commercial banks; State commercial banks; Mortgage bankers; Nondeposit trust facilities; Agricultural credit institutions; Equipment & vehicle finance leasing companies; Insurance brokers
Ch Bd: Richard K Davis
Pr: Troy Aipperspach
Pr: Carlos Avalos
Pr: Joseph Bailey
Pr: Susan M Bennett
Pr: Leeann Bodendorfer
Pr: Adam Bosnjak
Pr: Paul Brotherton
Pr: David Brus
Pr: Ana Carsey
Pr: Andrew Cecere
Pr: Lisa Cheadle
Pr: Grayson Dill
Pr: Emily Frankman
Pr: Mike Grundhoefer
Pr: Sandi Hampton
Pr: Pete Hansen
Pr: Cynthia Harper
Pr: Jeanna Hartzell
Pr: William Hildebrand
Pr: Jocelyn Kilpatrick
Board of Directors: David B O'maley, Douglas M Baker Jr, Craig D Schnuck, Warner L Baxter, Scott W Wine, Marc N Casper, Arthur D Collins Jr, Kimberly J Harris, Roland A Hernandez, Doreen Woo Hoo, Olivia F Kirtley, Karen S Lynch

D-U-N-S 06-653-7309
■ US BANCORP INFORMATION SERVICES INC
US BANK
(*Suby of* US BANCORP) ★
800 Nicollet Mall, Minneapolis, MN 55402-7000
Tel (651) 466-3000 *Founded/Ownrshp* 1964
Sales NA *EMP* 1,142
SIC 6411 Insurance brokers
Ch Bd: Phil Heasley
**CEO:* William L Chenevich
COO: Robert Berk
Sr VP: Gwen Boykin
Sr VP: Charles I Broadnax
Sr VP: Eve Kaplan
Sr VP: Paul Malik
Sr VP: Liana Muller
VP: Amy Dawson
VP: Jackie Gray
VP: Jeff Huber
VP: Patrick Lenertz
VP: Ben Lopez
VP: Michael Lori
VP: Ivan Mantell
VP: Coni Pasch
VP: John Paulus
VP: Gauger Stephen
VP: Ben Stodghill
Comm Man: Michael Ferraro
Comm Man: Amanda Luty

US BANK
See US BANK NATIONAL ASSOCIATION

US BANK
See US BANCORP INFORMATION SERVICES INC

D-U-N-S 06-397-2830 IMP/EXP
■ US BANK NATIONAL ASSOCIATION
US BANK
(*Suby of* US BANCORP) ★
425 Walnut St Fl 1, Cincinnati, OH 45202-3989
Tel (513) 632-4234 *Founded/Ownrshp* 1973
Sales NA *EMP* 26,089
SIC 6021 National commercial banks
Ch Bd: Richard K Davis
V Ch: Terrance R Dolan
V Ch: Richard C Hartnack
V Ch: Joseph C Hoesley
V Ch: Pamela A Joseph
V Ch: Richard B Payne Jr
Pr: Steven Bennett
Pr: Marsha Cruzan
COO: Gailyn Johnson
**CFO:* Andrew Cecere
Chf Cred: P W Parker
Ex VP: Jennie P Carlson
Ex VP: Leslie Godridge
Ex VP: Richard J Hidy
Ex VP: Howell D McCullough III
Ex VP: Lee R Mitau
Sr VP: Kathryn Albright
VP: Greg Cunningham

D-U-N-S 05-011-5844
■ US BANK NATIONAL ASSOCIATION ND
(*Suby of* US BANCORP) ★
4325 17th Ave S, Fargo, ND 58125-6200
Tel (701) 461-0346 *Founded/Ownrshp* 1998
Sales NA *EMP* 25
SIC 6021 National commercial banks
Prin: Kelley Boyum
Assoc VP: Michael Lewis

D-U-N-S 06-777-0917 IMP/EXP
US BORAX INC
(*Suby of* RIO TINTO LONDON LIMITED)
8051 E Maplewood Ave # 100, Greenwood Village, CO 80111-4714
Tel (303) 713-5000 *Founded/Ownrshp* 1989
Sales 994.3MM^E *EMP* 1,200
SIC 1474 2819 Borate compounds (natural) mining; Industrial inorganic chemicals
CEO: Dean Gehring
**COO:* Chris J Robinson
**CFO:* Jeffery R Olsen
**Chf Cred:* David A Peever
**Ofcr:* Michael J Stockman
VP: Dave Peeves
**Exec:* T Scott Griffin
Comm Dir: Deb Witmer
**CTO:* Paul J Zerella
Prd Mgr: Rick Padilla

D-U-N-S 62-404-9008
US BUILDER SERVICES LLC
272 E Deerpath Ste 308, Lake Forest, IL 60045-1947
Tel (847) 735-2066 *Founded/Ownrshp* 2006
Sales 280.0MM *EMP* 600
SIC 1742 1731 1711 Drywall; Electrical work; Plumbing contractors

D-U-N-S 01-403-1574 IMP
US CABLE OF COASTAL-TEXAS LP
28 W Grand Ave Ste 6, Montvale, NJ 07645-2194
Tel (201) 930-9000 *Founded/Ownrshp* 1997
Sales 86.2MM^E *EMP* 450
SIC 4841 Cable television services
Pt: Stephen E Myers
Pt: Michael C Anderson
Pt: James D Pearson

D-U-N-S 07-985-1277
US CHAMBER OF COMMERCE
1615 H St Nw, Washington, DC 20062-0002
Tel (202) 659-6000 *Founded/Ownrshp* 2015
Sales 206.0MM *EMP* 3^E
SIC 8611 Chamber of Commerce; Growers' associations
Pr: Tom J Donohue

D-U-N-S 93-205-0995
US COAL CORP
6301 Old Richmond Rd, Lexington, KY 40515-9730
Tel (859) 223-8820 *Founded/Ownrshp* 2006
Sales 97.7MM^E *EMP* 200
SIC 1241 Coal mining services
Pr: John A Collins
**CEO:* Robert Gabbard

US COMMODITIES
See AGMOTION INC

D-U-N-S 03-008-0449 IMP/EXP
US COMMODITIES LLC
AG MOTION SPECIALTY GRAINS
(*Suby of* US COMMODITIES) ★
730 2nd Ave S Ste 700, Minneapolis, MN 55402-2480
Tel (612) 486-3800 *Founded/Ownrshp* 2001
Sales 212.5MM^E *EMP* 77
Accts Wipfli Llp Minneapolis Mn
SIC 5191 6221 Farm supplies; Commodity contracts brokers, dealers
CFO: Bill Hren

US CONCRETE
See US CONCRETE INC

D-U-N-S 05-931-3952 EXP
▲ US CONCRETE INC
US CONCRETE
331 N Main St, Euless, TX 76039-3636
Tel (817) 835-4105 *Founded/Ownrshp* 1999
Sales 974.7MM *EMP* 2,700
Tkr Sym USCR *Exch* NAS
SIC 3273 3272 Ready-mixed concrete; Concrete products
Ch Bd: Eugene I Davis
**Pr:* William J Sandbrook
COO: Ronnie Pruitt
CFO: Joseph C Tusa Jr
Sr VP: Paul M Jolas
VP: Jeff L Davis
VP: Kevin R Kohutek
VP: Jeffrey W Roberts
Sales Exec: Randy Burson
VP Mktg: Wallace H Johnson

D-U-N-S 11-817-1628 IMP/EXP
US COTTON LLC
(*Suby of* PARKDALE MILLS INC) ★
531 Cotton Blossom Cir, Gastonia, NC 28054-5245
Tel (216) 676-6400 *Founded/Ownrshp* 2008
Sales 189.0MM^E *EMP* 500
Accts Meyners & Company Llc Albuque
SIC 2844 2241 Toilet preparations; Cotton narrow fabrics
Ch Bd: Anthony Thomas
**CEO:* John B Nims
CFO: Cecelia Meade
Treas: Steve Staley
Genl Mgr: Rolando Klein
Plnt Mgr: Bill Tyler
Manager: Gerald Spaulding

US CRITICAL
See US CRITICAL LLC

D-U-N-S 06-023-2269
US CRITICAL LLC
US CRITICAL
6 Orchard Ste 150, Lake Forest, CA 92630-8352
Tel (800) 884-8945 *Founded/Ownrshp* 2013
Sales 88.0MM^E *EMP* 65^E
SIC 3572

D-U-N-S 04-390-3322
■ US DEPARTMENT OF COMMERCE
OFFICE OF INSPECTOR GENERAL
(*Suby of* US DOC) ★
1401 Constitution Ave Nw, Washington, DC 20230-0001
Tel (202) 482-4661 *Founded/Ownrshp* 1999
Sales NA *EMP* 1,000
SIC 9611 Administration of general economic programs;
Prin: Johnnie Frazier
Ofcr: Philip Finiello
Admn Mgr: Robin Gross
Off Admin: Jennifer Bryan
Snr Mgr: Rand Ruggieri

D-U-N-S 17-537-6516
■ US DEPT OF ENERGY CHICAGO OFFICE
OFFICE SCIENCE CHICAGO OFFICE
(*Suby of* UNITED STATES DEPT OF ENERGY) ★
9800 S Cass Ave Ste 1, Lemont, IL 60439-4808
Tel (630) 252-2442 *Founded/Ownrshp* 2003
Sales NA *EMP* 3,406
SIC 9611 Energy development & conservation agency, government;
**CFO:* Thomas J Foley
Ofcr: Melinda Latimer
Ofcr: Scott Salvati
Ofcr: Deborah Weems
**Prin:* Tim Meyer
**Prin:* Cherri Schmidt
Prgrm Mgr: Anna Garcia
CIO: David Alan Frietsch
IT Man: Amir Roth

US DOC
See UNITED STATES DEPARTMENT OF COMMERCE

D-U-N-S 11-880-6587 IMP/EXP
▲ US ECOLOGY INC
251 E Front St Ste 400, Boise, ID 83702-7310
Tel (208) 331-8400 *Founded/Ownrshp* 1952
Sales 563.0MM *EMP* 1,400^E
Accts Deloitte & Touche Llp Boise
Tkr Sym ECOL *Exch* NGS
SIC 4953 Refuse systems; Acid waste, collection & disposal; Radioactive waste materials, disposal; Nonhazardous waste disposal sites
Ch Bd: Jeffrey R Feeler
CFO: Eric L Gerratt
Ex VP: Mario H Romero
Ex VP: Steven D Welling
Sr VP: Simon G Bell
Board of Directors: Joe F Colvin, Katina Dorton, Daniel Fox, Stephen A Romano, John Sahlberg

D-U-N-S 78-413-0440 IMP
US ELECTRICAL SERVICES INC
ELECTRICAL WHOLESALERS
(*Suby of* C E D) ★
701 Middle St, Middletown, CT 06457-1547
Tel (860) 522-3232 *Founded/Ownrshp* 2007
Sales 511.0MM^E *EMP* 500
SIC 5063 Electrical apparatus & equipment
Pr: Randy Eddy
**Ch:* Dean Bursch
**Treas:* Kara Haskins
Ex VP: Matthew V Procaccini
VP: Debbie Bridges
VP: Katina Mataras
VP: Mark Unkrich
Sls Dir: Lou Bongiobanni
Sales Asso: Bruce Defrehn

D-U-N-S 19-277-4347 IMP
US ENGINE VALVE CORP
(*Suby of* EATON USEV HOLDING CO INC) ★
7039 S Highway 11, Westminster, SC 29693-3998
Tel (864) 647-2061 *Founded/Ownrshp* 1988
Sales 106.0MM^E *EMP* 220
SIC 3592 Valves, engine
Pr: Robert Griffin
Exec: Mary Craft
IT Man: Christian Cook
Sfty Dirs: Clay Murphy
Plnt Mgr: Robert Dover

US EPA
See ENVIRONMENTAL PROTECTION AGENCY

D-U-N-S 87-842-3110 IMP
US EPSON INC
EPSON AMERICA
(*Suby of* SEIKO EPSON CORPORATION)
3840 Kilroy Airport Way, Long Beach, CA 90806-2452
Tel (562) 290-5678 *Founded/Ownrshp* 1993
Sales 826.1MM^E *EMP* 2,225
SIC 5045 3577 Computers, peripherals & software; Printers, computer
CEO: Seiichi Hirano
COO: Yasumasa Kitamatsu
Ex VP: Masayuki Morozumi
Sr VP: Alan Pound Sr
Mng Dir: Tadaaki Hagata
Mng Dir: Noriyuki Hama
Mng Dir: Kenji Kubota
Opers Supe: Reginald Samuels

U.S. FAMILY HEALTH PLAN
See CHRISTUS HEALTH

U.S. FARATHANE CORP
See US FARATHANE HOLDINGS CORP

D-U-N-S 05-245-2141 IMP/EXP
US FARATHANE HOLDINGS CORP
U.S. FARATHANE CORP
11650 Park Ct, Shelby Township, MI 48315-3108
Tel (248) 754-7000 *Founded/Ownrshp* 1981
Sales 876.4MM^E *EMP* 2,500
SIC 3089 Injection molding of plastics; Thermoformed finished plastic products; Casting of plastic
Pr: Andy Greenlee
Pr: Donna Amara
CFO: Rick Knappe
**Ch:* Cyril J Edwards Jr
Prgrm Mgr: Mark Avery
Prgrm Mgr: Brian Smith
Dir IT: John Lojewski

D-U-N-S 05-990-5059
US FENCE INC
BARRETTE OUTDOOR LIVING
3200 Rbert T Longway Blvd, Flint, MI 48506-4043
Tel (810) 235-0400 *Founded/Ownrshp* 2003
Sales NA *EMP* 2,500
SIC 2499

D-U-N-S 10-267-5399 IMP
US FLOORS INC
3580 Corporate Dr, Dalton, GA 30721-4900
Tel (706) 278-9491 *Founded/Ownrshp* 2016
Sales 400.0MM *EMP* 125
SIC 5713 Floor covering stores
CEO: Piet Dossche
CFO: Russell Guinn
Sec: Sabine Dosshce
Sr VP: David Lang
Rgnl Mgr: Bobby Allaway
Sls Mgr: Jay Friedland
Sls Mgr: Timothy Gofmanas
Sls Mgr: Jason McKinley
Sls Mgr: Karry Prichard
Sls Mgr: Van Turkington
Sls Mgr: Jon Wade

D-U-N-S 13-033-9232 IMP/EXP
■ US FOODS CULINARY EQUIPMENT & SUPPLIES LLC
(*Suby of* US FOODS INC) ★
5353 Nathan Ln N, Plymouth, MN 55442-1952
Tel (763) 268-1200 *Founded/Ownrshp* 1999
Sales 186.0MM^E *EMP* 240
SIC 5087 Restaurant supplies
VP: Juliette Pryor
**COO:* Stuart Schuepte
**CFO:* Ellis Swanson
VP: Willie Voss
VP: Frank Warren
Rgnl Mgr: Michael Fleming
IT Man: Chris Milner
VP Opers: Kurt Nelson
Board of Directors: Robert Aiken, David B Eberhardt

D-U-N-S 80-390-0237 IMP
▲ US FOODS HOLDING CORP
9399 W Higgins Rd Ste 500, Rosemont, IL 60018-4992
Tel (847) 720-8000 *Founded/Ownrshp* 2007
Sales 23.1MMM *EMP* 25,000
Tkr Sym USFD *Exch* NYS
SIC 5149 5147 5142 5144 5146 5143 Dried or canned foods; Canned goods: fruit, vegetables, seafood, meats, etc.; Coffee & tea; Seasonings, sauces & extracts; Meats & meat products; Packaged frozen goods; Frozen fish, meat & poultry; Frozen vegetables & fruit products; Poultry & poultry products; Fish & seafoods; Seafoods; Dairy products, except dried or canned
Pr: Pietro Satriano
**Ch Bd:* John C Compton
CFO: Fareed A Khan
Chf Cred: Juliette W Pryor
Chf Mktg O: Steven Guberman
Ofcr: Tiffany Monroe
Ofcr: Mark W Scharbo
Ex VP: Jay Kvasnicka
Ex VP: David Rickard
Ex VP: Gregory Schaffner
Ex VP: Owen Schiano

D-U-N-S 79-514-0433 IMP/EXP
■ US FOODS INC
(*Suby of* US FOODS HOLDING CORP) ★
9399 W Higgins Rd Ste 500, Rosemont, IL 60018-4992
Tel (847) 720-8000 *Founded/Ownrshp* 2007
Sales 23.1MMM *EMP* 25,000
Accts Deloitte & Touche Llp Chicago

SIC 5149 5147 5142 5144 5146 5143 Dried or canned foods; Canned goods: fruit, vegetables, seafood, meats, etc.; Coffee & tea; Seasonings, sauces & extracts; Meats & meat products; Meats, fresh; Packaged frozen goods; Frozen fish, meat & poultry; Frozen vegetables & fruit products; Poultry & poultry products; Fish & seafoods; Seafoods; Dairy products, except dried or canned
Pr: Pietro Satriano
Ch Bd: John C Compton
Pr: Stacie Sopinka
**CFO:* Fareed Khan
**Chf Cred:* Juliette W Pryor
Ofcr: Steven Guberman
**Ofcr:* Tiffany Monroe
Ofcr: Mark Scharbo
Ex VP: Jay Kvasnicka
Ex VP: David Rickard
Ex VP: Gregory Schaffner
Ex VP: Owen Schiano
VP: Dolores Frey
VP: Richard Querci
Dir Bus: Sandra Divito
Dir Bus: Barron Jacobson

US FOODS OF ILLINOIS
See TRANS-PORTE INC

U.S. FOODSERVICE
See E & H DISTRIBUTING LLC

US FOREST SERVICE
See USDA FOREST SERVICE

US FOUNDRY
See UNITED STATES FOUNDRY & MANUFACTURING CORP

D-U-N-S 12-101-9033
■ **US GAS & ELECTRIC INC**
USG&E
(*Suby of* MVC CAPITAL, INC.)
3700 Lakeside Dr Fl 6, Miramar, FL 33027-3264
Tel (305) 947-7880 *Founded/Ownrshp* 2007
Sales 108.3MME *EMP* 128E
SIC 4931 Electric & other services combined
Chf Mktg O: Greg Taffet
COO: Kevin McMinn
**CFO:* David Weinberg
VP: Michelle Mann
QA Dir: Steven Garcia
QA Dir: Michelle Mercier
QA Dir: Dayana Ramos
QA Dir: Sasha Wong
IT Man: Kenneth Hargis
Netwrk Eng: Josh Hollman
Sls Mgr: Brooke Bonelli

D-U-N-S 08-033-3270
US GOLD INC
PREMERIAN
299 S Main St Ste 1800, Salt Lake City, UT 84111-2219
Tel (800) 607-4600 *Founded/Ownrshp* 2016
Sales 1.3MMM *EMP* 35
SIC 6799 Investors
Bd of Dir: Mark Bensen
**Bd of Dir:* K Bensen
Bd of Dir: Jared Gallardo

US GOV GA AERONAUTICAL UAV
See GENERAL ATOMICS AERONAUTICAL SYSTEMS INC

D-U-N-S 07-480-0160 IMP
■ **US GOVERNMENT PUBLISHING OFFICE**
SUPERINTENDENT OF DOCUMENTS
(*Suby of* CONGRESS UNITED STATES) ★
732 N Capitol St Nw, Washington, DC 20401-0002
Tel (202) 512-0000 *Founded/Ownrshp* 1813
Sales NA *EMP* 1,880
Accts Kpmg Llp Washington Dc
SIC 9199 General government administration;
Prin: Davita Vance-Cooks
**CFO:* Steven T Shedd
Dir Teleco: William H Turri
Mng Dir: Lyle Green
Brnch Mgr: Willette Sessomes
Dir IT: Manisha Bhattacharyya
Genl Couns: Roy Potter
**Genl Couns:* Drew Spalding
Counsel: Tom Kelly
Snr Mgr: Charles Kennedy
Snr Mgr: Kevin O'Toole

U.S. GREENFIBER
See GF INVESTORS LLC

D-U-N-S 80-215-8365 IMP/EXP
US GREENFIBER LLC
(*Suby of* US GREENFIBER) ★
5500 77 Center Dr Ste 100, Charlotte, NC 28217-0160
Tel (704) 379-0640 *Founded/Ownrshp* 2013
Sales 145.3MME *EMP* 535
SIC 2679 Building, insulating & packaging paperboard
VP Sls: Steve Gerber

D-U-N-S 10-241-0818
US HEALTH GROUP INC
300 Burnett St Ste 200, Fort Worth, TX 76102-2734
Tel (817) 878-3300 *Founded/Ownrshp* 1982
Sales NA *EMP* 213
SIC 6411 Insurance agents, brokers & service
Ch Bd: Benjamin M Cutler
Pr: Jan Fogg
CFO: Cynthia B Koenig
Ex VP: Patrick H O'Neill
Sr VP: Konrad H Kober
VP: Konnie Davis
VP: Ranita Grauwiler
VP: Jessica Jackson
VP: Bill Shelton
VP: James White Jr
MIS Dir: Rick Watson
Board of Directors: Alan H Freudenstein, Gregory M Grimaldi, George R Hornig, David G Kaytes, Michael A Kramer, Patrick H O'neill, Paul E Suckow, J Grover Thomas Jr

D-U-N-S 96-787-2458
US HEALTH HOLDINGS LTD
U S HEALTH AND LIFE
8220 Irving Rd, Sterling Heights, MI 48312-4621
Tel (586) 693-4400 *Founded/Ownrshp* 1996
Sales NA *EMP* 130E
SIC 6411 Medical insurance claim processing, contract or fee basis
Pr: Anthony Lapiana
Genl Couns: Jim Ford

D-U-N-S 80-559-8211
US HEALTH INC
(*Suby of* BALLY TOTAL FITNESS HOLDING CORP) ★
8700 W Bryn Mawr Ave # 2, Chicago, IL 60631-3512
Tel (773) 399-7626 *Founded/Ownrshp* 2008
Sales 3.9MME *EMP* 1,662E
SIC 7991 Health club
Sr VP: Marc D Bassewitz

D-U-N-S 92-995-6035
US HEALTHWORKS INC
U.S. HEALTHWORKS MEDICAL GROUP
(*Suby of* DIGNITY HEALTH) ★
25124 Springfield Ct, Valencia, CA 91355-1085
Tel (800) 720-2432 *Founded/Ownrshp* 1995
Sales 359.8MME *EMP* 2,355
SIC 8011 Offices & clinics of medical doctors
Pr: Joseph T Mallas
**CFO:* Robert Hutchison
Sr VP: Sherif Hanna
Sr VP: Gregory C Marotta
VP: Michele Alvarez
VP: Angela Donovan
VP: John C Duncan
VP: Angela Fort
VP: Rich Goodin
VP: Therese Hernandez
VP: Kyle Kircher
VP: Deb Kuehn
VP: Scott Lance
VP: Brooks F Marshall
VP: David Oberg
VP: Edward Pucek
VP: Scott Strickland

U.S. HEALTHWORKS MEDICAL GROUP
See US HEALTHWORKS INC

D-U-N-S 07-844-4647
US HISPANIC MEDIA INC
(*Suby of* SOCIEDAD ANONIMA LA NACION)
1 Metrotech Ctr Fl 18, Brooklyn, NY 11201-3949
Tel (212) 885-8000 *Founded/Ownrshp* 2012
Sales 103.5MME *EMP* 566E
SIC 2711 Newspapers: publishing only, not printed on site
Pr: Eduardo Lomanto

US HOME
See US HOME CORP

D-U-N-S 05-157-1438 IMP
■ **US HOME CORP**
US HOME
(*Suby of* LENNAR CORP) ★
10707 Clay Rd, Houston, TX 77041-5630
Tel (305) 559-4000 *Founded/Ownrshp* 2000
Sales 627.9MME *EMP* 2,026
Accts Deloitte & Touche Llp Miami
SIC 1531 6162 6552 Speculative builder, single-family houses; Mortgage brokers, using own money; Land subdividers & developers, residential
Pr: Richard Beckwitt
**Pr:* Craig M Johnson
**Pr:* Stuart A Miller
**COO:* Robert J Strudler
**CFO:* Bruce Gross
Treas: Chester Sadowski
**Treas:* Malcolm Waynewright
VP: Marshall Ames
**VP:* James S Bavouset
**VP:* David B McCain
**VP:* Allan J Pekor
**VP:* Richard G Slaughter

D-U-N-S 09-928-0398
■ **US HOME SYSTEMS INC**
(*Suby of* HOME DEPOT THE) ★
2951 Kinwest Pkwy, Irving, TX 75063-3134
Tel (214) 488-6300 *Founded/Ownrshp* 2012
Sales 106.9MME *EMP* 863E
SIC 3429 5031 1751 Manufactured hardware (general); Kitchen cabinets; Cabinet & finish carpentry
Pr: Murray H Gross
Mng Pt: Brett Maas
CFO: Robert A Defronzo
Chf Mktg O: Steven L Gross
VP: Richard B Goodner
VP: Richard Goodner

D-U-N-S 03-958-1363
US INSTALLATION GROUP INC
951 Brkn Snd Pkwy Nw # 100, Boca Raton, FL 33487-3531
Tel (561) 962-0452 *Founded/Ownrshp* 1999
Sales 86.0MME *EMP* 233
SIC 1752 Floor laying & floor work
Pr: Bruce Deluca
**Pr:* John W Quaintance
**CFO:* Heather Gorrell

D-U-N-S 62-660-5773
US INVESTIGATIONS SERVICES LLC
USIS
(*Suby of* CORPORATE RISK HOLDINGS LLC) ★
125 Lincoln Ave, Grove City, PA 16127-1835
Tel (724) 458-1750 *Founded/Ownrshp* 2002
Sales 476.7MME *EMP* 7,900
SIC 7381 Detective & armored car services
VP: Donald I Buzinkai
Pr: William Mixon
Pr: Jeremy Wensinger
CEO: Sterling Phillips
Sr VP: Francis Meyer
VP: Laura Jones
VP: Mitch Lawrence
VP: Keith R Simmons
Prgrm Mgr: Christy McCampbell

Dist Mgr: Jason Pierret
Opers Mgr: Lee R Montague

D-U-N-S 83-797-7560
US LABORATORIES INC
(*Suby of* BUREAU VERITAS HOLDINGS INC) ★
13773 Icot Blvd Ste 502, Clearwater, FL 33760-3711
Tel (954) 236-8100 *Founded/Ownrshp* 2002
Sales 425.9MME *EMP* 1,660
Accts Pricewaterhousecoopers Llp
SIC 8071 Medical laboratories
Pr: Pedro Guimaraes
**CFO:* Luis Damasceno
**VP:* Heather Bush
VP: Janice Mondello
VP: Roy Moore
Sls&Mrk Ex: Martin B Lowenthal

D-U-N-S 83-267-7525
US LBM HOLDINGS LLC
(*Suby of* LBM BORROWER LLC) ★
1000 Corporate Grove Dr, Buffalo Grove, IL 60089-4550
Tel (877) 787-5267 *Founded/Ownrshp* 2015
Sales 1.9MMME *EMP* 1,207
SIC 5072 5031 5198 Hardware; Kitchen cabinets; Paints, varnishes & supplies
Pr: L T Gibson
COO: Jeff Umosella
CFO: Richard J Kolaczewski
Ex VP: Randy Aardema
VP: Greg Bossert

D-U-N-S 01-694-5920
■ **US LEC COMMUNICATIONS LLC**
PAETEC BUSINESS SERVICES
(*Suby of* PAETEC HOLDING CORP) ★
6801 Morrison Blvd, Charlotte, NC 28211-3599
Tel (704) 319-1000 *Founded/Ownrshp* 2007
Sales 118.5MME *EMP* 1,128
Accts Deloitte & Touche Llp Charlot
SIC 4813 Data telephone communications; Local telephone communications; Long distance telephone communications; Voice telephone communications
CEO: Arunas A Chesonis
Ex VP: Sharon Lamantia
Ex VP: Charlie Sieving
VP: Karl Bergstrom
VP: John Leach
VP: Sean Pflaging
VP: Reginald Scales
Exec: Richard Hyde
Genl Mgr: Tom Coffey
IT Man: Daidre Schweitzer
Mktg Mgr: Jeremiah Needham

D-U-N-S 00-268-8059
US LEGAL SUPPORT INC (TX)
363 N Sam Houston Pkwy E # 1200, Houston, TX 77060-2404
Tel (713) 653-7100 *Founded/Ownrshp* 1996
Sales 150.0MME *EMP* 634E
SIC 8111 Legal services
Pr: Charles F Schugart
**CFO:* Beth Bruce
**CFO:* Vince Ekleberry
Div Pres: Jonathan C Hefler
Div Pres: Daniel K Rothfeld
**Sr VP:* Lee Ann Watson
**VP:* Gayle Hardison
Off Admin: Jennifer Gaul

US LEISURE
See SUNTERRACE CASUAL FURNITURE INC

D-U-N-S 03-629-0125 IMP
US LUMBER GROUP LLC
BOSTON CEDAR
2160 Satellite Blvd # 450, Duluth, GA 30097-4360
Tel (678) 474-4577 *Founded/Ownrshp* 2011
Sales 410.0MM *EMP* 365
SIC 5031 Lumber, plywood & millwork
CEO: Lawerence Newton
Pr: Jeff McLendon
CFO: Ronnie Stroud
CIO: Graham Bishop
Sls Mgr: Dan Wagoner
Sales Asso: Keith Clark
Sales Asso: Brad Daugherty
Sales Asso: Nick Glaser
Sales Asso: Zack Walden

D-U-N-S 11-393-8661 IMP
US MAGNESIUM LLC
USMAG
(*Suby of* RENCO GROUP INC) ★
238 N 2200 W, Salt Lake City, UT 84116-2921
Tel (801) 532-2043 *Founded/Ownrshp* 2002
Sales 122.1MME *EMP* 450
SIC 3356 2819 Magnesium; Magnesium compounds or salts, inorganic
CEO: Mike Legge
VP: Todd Ogaard
Sfty Mgr: Leanard Eayon
VP Mktg: Howard Kaplan

US MARINE
See BRUNSWICK FAMILY BOAT CO INC

US MERCHANT
See MERCHANT OF TENNIS INC

US MERCHANTS
See US MERCHANTS FINANCIAL GROUP INC

D-U-N-S 04-814-2108 IMP
US MERCHANTS FINANCIAL GROUP INC
US MERCHANTS
1118 S La Cienega Blvd, Los Angeles, CA 90035-2519
Tel (310) 855-1946 *Founded/Ownrshp* 1994
Sales 188.0MME *EMP* 1,500
SIC 6719 Investment holding companies, except banks
Pr: Jeff Green
Treas: Marie Green

D-U-N-S 03-722-8939 IMP/EXP
US METALS INC
19102 Gundle Rd, Houston, TX 77073-3514
Tel (281) 443-7473 *Founded/Ownrshp* 1980

Sales 115.0MME *EMP* 76
SIC 5085 Bottler supplies
CEO: Steve Scott

D-U-N-S 88-479-2540
US MOTIVATION INC
U S M
(*Suby of* MARQUETTE GROUP) ★
7840 Roswe Rd Usm Bldg 10, Atlanta, GA 30350
Tel (770) 290-4700 *Founded/Ownrshp* 1994
Sales 96.0MM *EMP* 135E
SIC 8742 Incentive or award program consultant
Pr: Tina Weede
**CEO:* Eric Webb
**CFO:* Theresa Lafontaine
VP: Caren Bigelow
VP: Arthur Bottinick
**VP:* Michael Campbell
VP: Bill Karwoski
**CTO:* Duane Anderson
**VP Sls:* Scott Siewert

D-U-N-S 00-324-1478 IMP
US NEWS & WORLD REPORT INC
4 New York Plz Fl 6, New York, NY 10004-2473
Tel (212) 716-6800 *Founded/Ownrshp* 1933
Sales 109.7MME *EMP* 500
SIC 2721 Magazines: publishing & printing
CEO: Mortimer B Zuckerman
**Co-Ch Bd:* Fred Drasner
**VP:* Bill Frischling
VP: Niel Maheshwari
VP: Donaldson Ross
Sls Mgr: Tina Lopez
Board of Directors: Edward Linde

D-U-N-S 84-706-1520 IMP/EXP
US NONWOVENS CORP
100 Emjay Blvd, Brentwood, NY 11717-3322
Tel (631) 952-0100 *Founded/Ownrshp* 1998
Sales 197.5MME *EMP* 600
SIC 2842 Specialty cleaning, polishes & sanitation goods
Ch Bd: Samuel Mehdizadeh
**CEO:* Shervin Mehdizadeh
**COO:* Rody Mehdizadeh
CFO: Michael Pischel

D-U-N-S 96-976-9020
US NUCLEAR REGULATORY COMMISSION
21 Church St, Rockville, MD 20850-4207
Tel (301) 415-7000 *Founded/Ownrshp* 1975
Sales NA *EMP* 4,000E
SIC 9631 Nuclear energy inspection & regulation office, government
Ch: Gregory Jaczko
Ofcr: Romena Moy
IT Man: Vanessa Cox

D-U-N-S 78-418-7226 IMP/EXP
US OIL TRADING LLC
3001 Marshall Ave, Tacoma, WA 98421-3116
Tel (253) 383-1651 *Founded/Ownrshp* 2006
Sales 179.7MME *EMP* 191
Accts Sweeney Conrad Ps Bellevue
SIC 5172
Pr: Robert B Redd
**CFO:* Thor Nielsen
Treas: Benjamin Kamithi
Treas: Carmen Montero
Sr VP: Pat Hietpas
VP: William Kitto
VP: Bob Redd
VP: Thomas Treichel
Dir Bus: Richard Sawall
Ex Dir: Tommy Smith

D-U-N-S 16-689-1767
■ **US ONCOLOGY HOLDINGS INC**
(*Suby of* MCKESSON CORP) ★
10101 Woodloch Forest Dr, The Woodlands, TX 77380-1975
Tel (281) 863-1000 *Founded/Ownrshp* 2010
Sales 339.5MME *EMP* 4,800E
SIC 8093 8099 8011 Specialty outpatient clinics; Medical services organization; Oncologist
Sr VP: David Young
Ex VP: Asif Ahmad
Ex VP: Grant Bogle
Sr VP: Willie C Bogan
VP: Chuck Dowling
Assoc Dir: Chad Adams
Assoc Dir: Beth Alvarez
Dir Rx: Eric Clarke
Dir Rx: Eileen B Herbeck
Dir Bus: Tommy Pourmahram
Prac Mgr: Amy Velasquez

D-U-N-S 80-164-6514
■ **US ONCOLOGY INC**
(*Suby of* US ONCOLOGY HOLDINGS INC) ★
10101 Woodloch Forest Dr, The Woodlands, TX 77380-1975
Tel (800) 381-2637 *Founded/Ownrshp* 2004
Sales 271.1MME *EMP* 4,800
SIC 8093 8099 8011 Specialty outpatient clinics; Medical services organization; Oncologist; Clinic, operated by physicians; Radiologist
Ch Bd: Bruce Broussard
Pr: Marc Owen
COO: Glen C Laschober
COO: George D Morgan
CFO: Michael A Sicuro
CFO: Jennifer Webster
**V Ch Bd:* Lloyd K Everson MD
Sr VP: Asif Ahmad
Sr VP: Grant Bogle
Sr VP: Donna Bowers
Sr VP: David Bronsweig
Sr VP: Greg Deatkine
Sr VP: Karen Gibson
Sr VP: Willie C Bogan
VP: Matt Brow
VP: Gerardo Castaneda
VP: David Kay
VP: Marc Kerlin
VP: Terry Murdock
Exec: Stephani Meineke
Dir Lab: Susan Barone

Board of Directors: Boone Powell Jr, Russell L Carson, Todd Vannucci, James E Dalton Jr, Francis A Dramis Jr, Yon Y Jorden, Daniel S Lynch, D Scott Mackesy, Mark C Myron MD, Robert A Ortenzio, R Steven Paulson MD

D-U-N-S 62-568-9880
▲ US PHYSICAL THERAPY INC
1300 W Sam Houston Pkwy S # 300, Houston, TX 77042-2454
Tel (713) 297-7000 *Founded/Ownrshp* 1990
Sales 331.3MM *EMP* 3,400ᴱ
Tkr Sym USPH *Exch* NYS
SIC 8049 Physical therapist; Occupational therapist
Pr: Christopher J Reading
**Ch Bd:* Jerald L Pullins
COO: Glenn D McDowell
**CFO:* Lawrence W McAfee
VP: Jeff Todes
Counsel: Leon Pegg
Board of Directors: Mark J Brookner, Harry S Chapman, Bernard A Harris Jr, Marlin W Johnston, Edward L Kuntz, Reginald E Swanson, Clayton K Trier

D-U-N-S 82-617-7024 IMP
US PIPELINE INC
USPL
(*Suby of* DEARBORN RESOURCES INC) ★
950 Echo Ln Ste 100, Houston, TX 77024-2768
Tel (281) 531-6100 *Founded/Ownrshp* 1996
Sales 367.1MM *EMP* 1,500
Accts Laporte Apac Houston Texas
SIC 1623 Oil & gas pipeline construction
Prin: Kelly Osborn
**Ch Bd:* Greg Curran
**CFO:* Bret Roper
**Treas:* Imran Dossani
Board of Directors: F D McCarthy, Alexander Taylor

D-U-N-S 11-880-4319 IMP/EXP
US POLE CO INC
U S ARCHITECTURAL LIGHTING
660 W Avenue O, Palmdale, CA 93551-3610
Tel (800) 877-6537 *Founded/Ownrshp* 1984
Sales 92.7MMᴱ *EMP* 411
SIC 3648 Outdoor lighting equipment
Pr: Joseph Straus

US POST OFFICE
See UNITED STATES POSTAL SERVICE

D-U-N-S 10-198-5930
US POWER GENERATING CO
USPOWERGEN
(*Suby of* TENASKA CAPITAL MANAGEMENT LLC) ★
300 Atlantic St Ste 500, Stamford, CT 06901-3524
Tel (212) 792-0800 *Founded/Ownrshp* 2008
Sales 270.6MMᴱ *EMP* 352ᴱ
SIC 4911 Electric services
Ch Bd: Mark R Sudbey
**CFO:* Theodore A Babcock
**CFO:* Jeff D Hunter
Bd of Dir: Michael Kramer
**Sr VP:* John P Reese
**VP:* Glenn E Camus
**VP:* Katherine C Mason

D-U-N-S 78-476-8009
US RENAL CARE INC
USRC
5851 Legacy Cir Ste 900, Plano, TX 75024-5966
Tel (214) 736-2700 *Founded/Ownrshp* 2012
Sales 452.5MMᴱ *EMP* 2,403ᴱ
SIC 8092 Kidney dialysis centers
CEO: J Christopher Brengard
**Pr:* Stephen Pirri
**Sr VP:* Thomas Weinberg
VP: Tommy Allocco
VP: John Dickenson
VP: Cindy Leyes
VP: Lynelle McLain
VP: Josef Rodriguez
VP: Karen Walton
VP Bus Dev: Richard P Maniscalco
VP Bus Dev: Richard Maniscalco

D-U-N-S 14-994-5573
US SECURITY ASSOCIATES HOLDINGS INC
200 Mansell Ct E Fl 5, Roswell, GA 30076-4856
Tel (770) 625-1500 *Founded/Ownrshp* 1999
Sales 232.6MMᴱ *EMP* 14,514
SIC 7381 7349 Security guard service; Janitorial service, contract basis
Pr: Charles R Schneider
**CFO:* Kenneth W Oringer
**CFO:* Paul M Parrish

D-U-N-S 82-561-6097
US SECURITY ASSOCIATES INC
ADVANCE SECURITY
200 Mansell Ct E Ste 500, Roswell, GA 30076-4852
Tel (770) 625-1500 *Founded/Ownrshp* 2011
Sales 1.7MMMᴱ *EMP* 46,750
SIC 7381 Security guard service
Ch Bd: Charles R Schneider
Pr: Eddie Leitgeb
**CEO:* Richard Wycoff
**CFO:* Karl J Scott
Ofcr: Tramaine Caldwell
Ofcr: Allan Jordan
Ofcr: Bill Quinn
**Ex VP:* Kenneth W Oringer
Sr VP: Alton Harvey
Sr VP: Shirley Schumacher
VP: Michael Baer
VP: Doug Blake
VP: Jaclyn Brecht
VP: John Harrison
VP: Lance Loewenstein
**VP:* L J Paul Lutz
VP: Gregg Wilson

D-U-N-S 02-743-6471
US SECURITY HOLDINGS INC
(*Suby of* US SECURITY ASSOCIATES HOLDINGS INC) ★
200 Mansell Ct E Ste 500, Roswell, GA 30076-4852
Tel (770) 625-1400 *Founded/Ownrshp* 1999
Sales 148.0MMᴱ *EMP* 14,514
SIC 7381 7349 Security guard service; Janitorial service, contract basis
CEO: Charles Schneider
**CFO:* Kenneth Oringer
**Sr VP:* Alton Harvey
**VP:* John O Lear

D-U-N-S 14-778-3765
US SECURITY INSURANCE CO
(*Suby of* HAMILTON RISK MANAGEMENT CO) ★
3155 Nw 77th Ave, Miami, FL 33122-1205
Tel (305) 716-6100 *Founded/Ownrshp* 1985
Sales NA *EMP* 99
SIC 6331 Fire, marine & casualty insurance
Ch Bd: Roberto Espin Jr
Sec: Rachael Aldulaimi
VP: Douglas Campbell
VP: Marco Depompa
VP: Edward Grant
VP: Timothy Lane
VP: Alberto Naon
VP: Kevin Walton
Brnch Mgr: Mike Hunter

D-U-N-S 07-951-2801
US SHALE SOLUTIONS INC
7670 Woodway Dr Ste 250, Houston, TX 77063-1519
Tel (832) 742-7492 *Founded/Ownrshp* 2013
Sales 222.5MMᴱ *EMP* 731ᴱ
SIC 1382 Oil & gas exploration services
Pr: Jarrit M Coward
Ex VP: Mike Stophlet

D-U-N-S 07-838-2104
▲ US SILICA HOLDINGS INC
8490 Progress Dr Ste 300, Frederick, MD 21701-4996
Tel (301) 682-0600 *Founded/Ownrshp* 2008
Sales 642.9MM *EMP* 996ᴱ
Tkr Sym SLCA *Exch* NYS
SIC 1446 Silica mining; Silica sand mining
Pr: Bryan A Shinn
Ch Bd: Charles Shaver
COO: Michael L Winkler
CFO: Donald A Merril
Chf Cred: Bradford Casper
Ofcr: Adam S Yoxtheimer
VP: John P Blanchard
VP: Don D Weinheimer

D-U-N-S 15-103-3180
US SKILLSERVE INC
4115 E Broadway Ste A, Long Beach, CA 90803-1532
Tel (562) 930-0777 *Founded/Ownrshp* 2008
Sales 44.6MMᴱ *EMP* 1,000
SIC 8741 Hospital management; Nursing & personal care facility management
CEO: Simcha Mandeldaum

U.S. SMOKELESS TOBACCO COMPANY
See US SMOKELESS TOBACCO MANUFACTURING CO LLC

D-U-N-S 07-842-6226 EXP
■ US SMOKELESS TOBACCO CO
(*Suby of* ALTRIA GROUP INC) ★
6603 W Broad St, Richmond, VA 23230-1711
Tel (804) 274-2000 *Founded/Ownrshp* 2009
Sales 94.0MMᴱ *EMP* 286ᴱ
SIC 2131 Chewing & smoking tobacco

D-U-N-S 96-245-9173 IMP
■ US SMOKELESS TOBACCO MANUFACTURING CO LLC
U.S. SMOKELESS TOBACCO COMPANY
(*Suby of* US SMOKELESS TOBACCO CO) ★
800 Harrison St, Nashville, TN 37203-3336
Tel (615) 880-4400 *Founded/Ownrshp* 2009
Sales 85.2MMᴱ *EMP* 262ᴱ
SIC 2131 Chewing & smoking tobacco
CEO: Brian W Quigley
**VP:* Jody L Begley
**VP:* Anthony S Helm
**VP:* Greg Ray

US SOCCER
See UNITED STATES SOCCER FEDERATION INC

D-U-N-S 01-423-5760
US STEEL TUBULAR PRODUCTS INC
15660 Dallas Pkwy Ste 500, Dallas, TX 75248-3354
Tel (972) 386-3981 *Founded/Ownrshp* 2008
Sales 464.4MMᴱ *EMP* 10ᴱ
SIC 5051 Iron & steel (ferrous) products
Pr: Douglas R Matthews

U.S SURGICAL
See UNITED STATES SURGICAL CORP

D-U-N-S 08-933-1011 IMP
■ US SYNTHETIC CORP
(*Suby of* DOVER CORP) ★
1260 S 1600 W, Orem, UT 84058-4931
Tel (801) 235-9001 *Founded/Ownrshp* 2004
Sales 301.2MMᴱ *EMP* 1,159
SIC 3915 Lapidary work & diamond cutting & polishing
Ch Bd: Bill J Pope
Pr: Rob Galloway
CFO: John Hardy
VP: Scott Schmidt
VP: Curtis Stucki
Genl Mgr: Robert Farr
Dir IT: Brian Shuey
Sys Mgr: Todd Graham
Prd Mgr: Brett Jensen
Prd Mgr: Jeremy McClellan
Prd Mgr: Steven Pease

D-U-N-S 80-987-5987
US TACTICAL RESPONSE AND INFORMATION SERVICE LLC
2 N Jackson St Ste 605, Montgomery, AL 36104-3821
Tel (888) 315-1113 *Founded/Ownrshp* 2008
Sales 950.0M *EMP* 2,500
SIC 7382 Security systems services
Pr: John Kearney
Pt: Michael Dozier

D-U-N-S 02-472-8946 IMP/EXP
US TELEPACIFIC CORP
TELEPACIFIC COMMUNICATIONS
(*Suby of* US TELEPACIFIC HOLDINGS CORP) ★
515 S Flower St Fl 47, Los Angeles, CA 90071-2208
Tel (213) 213-3000 *Founded/Ownrshp* 1999
Sales 356.6MMᴱ *EMP* 1,100
SIC 4813 Local & long distance telephone communications
Pr: Richard A Jalkut
**Ch Bd:* David Glickman
**CFO:* Timothy Medina
**Sr VP:* Ken Bisnoff
**Sr VP:* Erich Everbach
**Sr VP:* Michael James
**Sr VP:* Rob Madore
**Sr VP:* Russ Shipley
**Sr VP:* David Zahn
**VP:* Michael Cowan
VP: Nancy Lubamersky
VP: Sean McDermott
VP: Andrew Paretti
Exec: Coleridge Stroud

D-U-N-S 78-425-0628
US TELEPACIFIC HOLDINGS CORP
515 S Flower St Fl 47, Los Angeles, CA 90071-2208
Tel (213) 213-3000 *Founded/Ownrshp* 1999
Sales 520.8MMᴱ *EMP* 1,100ᴱ
SIC 4813 Telephone communication, except radio
CEO: Richard A Jalkut
**COO:* Alan Morse
**CFO:* Timothy J Medina
**Sr VP:* Ken Bisnoff
**Sr VP:* Michael James
VP: Bill Blanning

U.S. TOOL GROUP
See U S TOOL GRINDING INC

D-U-N-S 07-914-7726
US TRINITY ENERGY SERVICES LLC (TX)
200 Highland Cir, Argyle, TX 76226-3959
Tel (940) 240-5800 *Founded/Ownrshp* 2013
Sales 144.5MMᴱ *EMP* 500
SIC 1623 Oil & gas line & compressor station construction; Oil & gas pipeline construction

U.S. TRUST, BANK OF AMERICA
See BANK OF AMERICA PVT WEALTH MANAGEMENT

D-U-N-S 05-662-7011 IMP/EXP
US TSUBAKI HOLDINGS INC
U.S.T.H.
(*Suby of* TSUBAKIMOTO CHAIN CO.)
301 E Marquardt Dr, Wheeling, IL 60090-6497
Tel (847) 459-9500 *Founded/Ownrshp* 1971
Sales 354.6MMᴱ *EMP* 900
SIC 5085 3568 Power transmission equipment & apparatus; Drives, chains & sprockets; Sprockets (power transmission equipment)
Pr: Tetsuya Yamamoto
**Pr:* Dan Butterfield
**Sr VP:* Thomas Barton
**VP:* Robert Engelmann
**VP:* Richard Renk

D-U-N-S 07-853-7233
US TSUBAKI POWER TRANSMISSION LLC (FL)
(*Suby of* USTH) ★
301 E Marquardt Dr, Wheeling, IL 60090-6497
Tel (847) 459-9500 *Founded/Ownrshp* 2010
Sales 111.0MMᴱ *EMP* 762ᴱ
SIC 3568 5085 5063 3714 3462 3325 Drives, chains & sprockets; Chain, power transmission; Power transmission equipment & apparatus; Chains, power transmission; Power transmission equipment, electric; Motor vehicle parts & accessories; Iron & steel forgings; Rolling mill rolls, cast steel

D-U-N-S 02-921-8955 IMP
US UNION TOOL INC
(*Suby of* UNION TOOL CO.)
1260 N Fee Ana St, Anaheim, CA 92807-1817
Tel (714) 521-6242 *Founded/Ownrshp* 1995
Sales 150.0MMᴱ *EMP* 60
SIC 3541 Machine tools, metal cutting type
Pr: Hideo Hirano
**Pr:* Robert Smallwood
VP Sls: Jonathan Hay

U.S. UNITED OCEAN SERVICES
See UNITED MARITIME GROUP LLC

D-U-N-S 02-329-1586 IMP
US VENTURE INC
U.S.OIL
425 Better Way, Appleton, WI 54915-6192
Tel (920) 739-6101 *Founded/Ownrshp* 1950
Sales 8.0MMM *EMP* 1,182
Accts Deloitte & Touche Llp Milwau
SIC 5171 5014 5013 Petroleum bulk stations; Automobile tires & tubes; Automotive batteries
Pr: John A Schmidt
CFO: Paul M Bachan
**CFO:* Jay Walters
**Ch:* Thomas A Schmidt
**Treas:* Martin Tomczyk
VP: Mike Koel
Genl Mgr: Bill Renz
Genl Mgr: Albert Selker
Off Admin: Anne Warzyn
Dir IT: Mark Duening
Dir IT: Tom Kriplean

US VISION
See REFAC OPTICAL GROUP

D-U-N-S 07-510-0933 IMP
US VISION INC
J C PENNEY OPTICAL
(*Suby of* US VISION) ★
1 Harmon Dr, Glendora, NJ 08029
Tel (856) 227-8339 *Founded/Ownrshp* 2006
Sales 324.5MMᴱ *EMP* 1,966
SIC 5995 3827 Optical goods stores; Eyeglasses, prescription; Contact lenses, prescription; Optical instruments & lenses
Ex VP: Lynn Romano
VP: Kathy Cullen
VP: Chuck Hahn
VP: Paul Ramsey
Dist Mgr: Jerry Bingham
Dist Mgr: Melissa Byrd
Dist Mgr: Kim Demers
Dist Mgr: Tamara Santangelo
Dist Mgr: Laura Shoup
Dist Mgr: Thomas Spaulding
Store Mgr: Leslie McDevitt

D-U-N-S 17-679-4162
US WASTE INDUSTRIES INC
PUEBLO DISPOSAL
7770 Palmer Park Blvd, Colorado Springs, CO 80951-4605
Tel (719) 535-9041 *Founded/Ownrshp* 1990
Sales 105.2MMᴱ *EMP* 300
SIC 4953 Rubbish collection & disposal
Pr: Victor Divello
**VP:* Dominick Divello

D-U-N-S 13-637-8846
US WATER SERVICES CORP
4939 Cross Bayou Blvd, New Port Richey, FL 34652-3434
Tel (727) 848-8292 *Founded/Ownrshp* 2003
Sales 94.9MMᴱ *EMP* 190ᴱ
SIC 4941 Water supply
Pr: Gary Deremer
**COO:* David B Schultz Sr
**Sec:* Victoria Penick
**VP:* Ralph Amiott
**VP:* Cecil Delcher
**VP:* Jeffrey Dupont
**VP:* Mohammed Kader
VP: Brad Labella
**VP:* Edward Mitchell
IT Man: Melisa R Rotteveel

D-U-N-S 07-844-6215
US WELL SERVICES LLC
770 S Post Oak Ln Ste 405, Houston, TX 77056-6661
Tel (832) 562-3731 *Founded/Ownrshp* 2012
Sales 174.3MM *EMP* 6ᴱ
Accts Kpmg Llp Houston Texas
SIC 1389 Oil field services
CFO: Leonard Travis
**Pr:* Brian Stewart
**CFO:* Kenneth I Sill
Bd of Dir: Matthew Bernard
Bd of Dir: Joel Broussard
**VP:* Jeffrey McPherson
**VP:* Edward S Self III
Snr Mgr: Mark Gainer

D-U-N-S 19-064-6992 IMP
US WIRE & CABLE CORP
FLEXON INDS DIV US WIRE CABLE
1 Flexon Plz, Newark, NJ 07114-1421
Tel (973) 824-5530 *Founded/Ownrshp* 1986
Sales 131.0MMᴱ *EMP* 482
SIC 3052 3315 Garden hose, plastic; Cable, steel: insulated or armored
Pr: David Rauch
**VP:* Joseph Folkman

D-U-N-S 78-562-7555 IMP/EXP
US XPRESS ENTERPRISES INC
(*Suby of* NEW MOUNTAIN LAKE HOLDINGS LLC) ★
4080 Jenkins Rd, Chattanooga, TN 37421-1174
Tel (423) 510-3000 *Founded/Ownrshp* 1989
Sales 1.2MMMᴱ *EMP* 10,885
SIC 4213 4731

D-U-N-S 09-784-1535 IMP
US YACHIYO INC
(*Suby of* YACHIYO OF AMERICA INC) ★
1177 Kellogg Pkwy, Marion, OH 43302-1779
Tel (740) 223-3134 *Founded/Ownrshp* 2007
Sales 159.3MMᴱ *EMP* 232
SIC 3795 Tanks & tank components
Pr: Hiroshi Sasamoto
**VP:* Kazuyoshi Itai
Opers Mgr: Ray Sanders

D-U-N-S 60-274-2850 IMP/EXP
US ZINC CORP
(*Suby of* U S Z) ★
2727 Allen Pkwy Ste 800, Houston, TX 77019-2152
Tel (713) 514-0037 *Founded/Ownrshp* 2008
Sales 105.1MMᴱ *EMP* 282
SIC 3356 Zinc & zinc alloy bars, plates, sheets, etc.
Pr: Rodrigo Daud
VP: Jose Lage Filho

D-U-N-S 80-483-4265
US-LAS COLINAS LIMITED PARTNERSHIP
FOUR SEASONS RESORT & CLUB
9830 Colonnade Blvd # 600, San Antonio, TX 78230-2202
Tel (210) 498-0626 *Founded/Ownrshp* 1991
Sales 17.4MMᴱ *EMP* 1,040
SIC 7011 7997 Hotels; Membership sports & recreation clubs
Prin: Louise Argote
Ex Dir: Hailey Ghalib
Ex Dir: Jason Hans

D-U-N-S 82-762-9978
USA (UNITED SPACE ALLIANCE PENSION)
600 Gemini St, Houston, TX 77058-2754
Tel (281) 212-6200 *Founded/Ownrshp* 2008
Sales 144.8MMᴱ *EMP* 5,000
SIC 3812 Aircraft/aerospace flight instruments & guidance systems
Pr: Ginger Barnes

D-U-N-S 02-062-8132 IMP
USA BOUQUET LLC
CONSOLIDATED FLORAL SOLUTIONS
(*Suby of* FDG ASSOCIATES LLC) ★
1500 Nw 95th Ave, Doral, FL 33172-2800
Tel (786) 437-6500 *Founded/Ownrshp* 2001, 2007

Sales 254.3MM^E *EMP* 400
SIC 5193 Flowers, fresh
Pr: Edgar Lozano
**Pr:* David Gellman
**Pr:* Raj Mangalick
**Pr:* William Trimarco
**VP:* George Barquin
VP: Elida Gutierrez
VP Sls: Scott Hill

D-U-N-S 03-824-6922
USA CABLE INC
SCI-FI
30 Rockefeller Plz Conc28, New York, NY 10112-0009
Tel (212) 413-5000 *Founded/Ownrshp* 1998
Sales 84.6MM^E *EMP* 530
SIC 4841

D-U-N-S 01-989-8997
USA CHILDRENS AND WOMENS HOSPITAL
1700 Center St, Mobile, AL 36604-3301
Tel (251) 415-1000 *Founded/Ownrshp* 1991
Sales 124.6MM *EMP* 85^E
SIC 8069 Children's hospital; Maternity hospital
Pr: Gordon Moulton
VP: Joseph F Busta Jr
VP: Keith Harrison
Dir Rad: Eduardo Rel
CIO: David Blough
Pharmcst: Roy Haywood
Pharmcst: Lisa Young

D-U-N-S 08-045-6776
USA CINEMA INVESTMENT HOLDINGS INC
CINEPOLIS USA
14951 Dallas Pkwy, Dallas, TX 75254-7892
Tel (972) 993-1553 *Founded/Ownrshp* 2010
Sales 78.8MM *EMP* 1,200
SIC 7832 Motion picture theaters, except drive-in
CFO: Luis Orozco
**CEO:* Adrian Mijares Elizondo

D-U-N-S 04-581-5078
USA COMPRESSION PARTNERS LLC
100 Congress Ave Ste 450, Austin, TX 78701-2747
Tel (512) 369-1380 *Founded/Ownrshp* 2008
Sales 342.3MM^E *EMP* 200
SIC 1389 Gas compressing (natural gas) at the fields
Pr: Eric D Long
Pr: Tom Hinsdale
Pr: Brian Nettles
**COO:* Kevin M Bourbonnais
CFO: Hayden Marshall
CFO: Jody Tusa
**CFO:* Joseph C Tusa Jr
Sr VP: Matthew Liuzzi
**VP:* J Gregory Holloway
VP: Eric Scheller
**VP:* David Smith
VP: Mark Story
Dir Bus: William Lehner

D-U-N-S 06-882-7653
▲ USA COMPRESSION PARTNERS LP
100 Congress Ave Ste 450, Austin, TX 78701-2747
Tel (512) 473-2662 *Founded/Ownrshp* 1998
Sales 270.5MM *EMP* 478
Tkr Sym USAC *Exch* NYS
SIC 1389 Gas compressing (natural gas) at the fields; Gas field services
Pr: Eric D Long
Genl Pt: USA Compression GP
COO: William G Manias
CFO: Matthew C Liuzzi
VP: J Gregory Holloway

USA DRUG
See STEPHEN L LAFRANCE PHARMACY INC

USA DRUG
See SUPER D DRUGS ACQUISITION CO

D-U-N-S 80-441-0731
USA ENVIRONMENT LP
316 Georgia Ave, Deer Park, TX 77536-2506
Tel (713) 425-6900 *Founded/Ownrshp* 2001
Sales 95.8MM^E *EMP* 220^E
Accts Ham Langston & Brezina Llp
SIC 8748 Environmental consultant
Mng Pt: Bret Pardue
**Mng Pt:* Russell Herscher
**Mng Pt:* Mike Nalepa
**Mng Pt:* David Whitaker
Ofcr: Lisa Garrett
Ofcr: Steve Prewett
Exec: Linda Dull
Off Mgr: Sondra Parsons
Sfty Dirs: Linda Arreguy
Snr Mgr: Russell Herrscher

USA FOR UNHCR
See UNITED STATES ASSOCIATION FOR UNHCR

D-U-N-S 17-935-5482
USA HEALTHCARE INC
401 Arnold St Ne, Cullman, AL 35055-1967
Tel (256) 739-1239 *Founded/Ownrshp* 1994
Sales 57.3MM^E *EMP* 2,000
SIC 8051 Skilled nursing care facilities
Pr: Frank Brown
CFO: Jeff Hutton
Nrsg Dir: Amanda Jones

USA HQ MICHIGAN
See VARROC LIGHTING SYSTEMS INC

USA JET AIRLINES
See ACTIVE AERO GROUP INC

D-U-N-S 62-113-9484
USA MANAGED HEALTH & WELLNESS RESOURCES GROUP INC
7301 N 16th St Ste 201, Phoenix, AZ 85020-5267
Tel (602) 371-3860 *Founded/Ownrshp* 1987
Sales NA *EMP* 255^E
SIC 6324 6411 Hospital & medical service plans; Insurance agents, brokers & service
Ch Bd: George E Bogle

D-U-N-S 04-452-5921
USA PROPERTIES FUND INC
3200 Douglas Blvd Ste 200, Roseville, CA 95661-4238
Tel (916) 773-6060 *Founded/Ownrshp* 1981
Sales 83.0MM^E *EMP* 200^E
Accts Crowe Horwath Llp Sacramento
SIC 6552 6531 Subdividers & developers; Real estate agents & managers
Pr: Geoffrey C Brown
**Treas:* Kristen Hawkins
**Ex VP:* Edward R Herzog
**Sr VP:* Michael McCleery
**Sr VP:* Karen McCurdy
Dir IT: Michael Stanford

D-U-N-S 07-848-3753 IMP
USA SELLER CO LLC
PET SUPPLIES PLUS
(*Suby of* IRVING PLACE CAPITAL LLC) ★
17197 N Laurel Park Dr # 402, Livonia, MI 48152-2680
Tel (734) 793-6600 *Founded/Ownrshp* 2010
Sales 770.1MM^E *EMP* 4,262^E
SIC 5999 Pets & pet supplies
CFO: Dominic Buccellato
Sr VP: Donna Capichano
Sr VP: Christopher Rowland

USA SHADE & FABRIC STRUCTURES
See SHADE STRUCTURES INC

USA TODAY
See GANNETT SATELLITE INFORMATION NETWORK LLC

D-U-N-S 10-365-8381
▲ USA TRUCK INC
3200 Industrial Park Rd, Van Buren, AR 72956-6110
Tel (479) 471-2500 *Founded/Ownrshp* 1983
Sales 507.9MM *EMP* 2,300^E
Tkr Sym USAK *Exch* NGS
SIC 4213 Trucking, except local
Pr: John R Rogers
**Ch Bd:* Robert A Peiser
V Ch: Thomas M Glaser
Pr: James A Craig
Pr: N Martin Tewari
CFO: Michael Borrows
CFO: James D Reed
VP: Joseph M Kaiser
Brnch Mgr: Patrick Derby
Brnch Mgr: David Joiner
CIO: Christian C Rhodes
Board of Directors: M Susan Chambers, Robert E Creager, Gary R Enzor, Barbara J Faulkenberry, Thomas M Glaser, Alexander D Greene, William H Hanna

D-U-N-S 78-856-3351 EXP
USA UNION INTERNATIONAL INC
26650 The Old Rd Ste 210, Valencia, CA 91381-0751
Tel (661) 286-8801 *Founded/Ownrshp* 1997
Sales NA *EMP* 6^E
SIC 6061 Federal credit unions
Pr: Mark Shiroishi

USAA
See UNITED SERVICES AUTOMOBILE ASSOCIATION

D-U-N-S 60-339-5310
USAA CAPITAL CORP
USAA INVESTMENT MANAGEMENT CO
(*Suby of* USAA) ★
9800 Fredericksburg Rd, San Antonio, TX 78288-0002
Tel (210) 498-2211 *Founded/Ownrshp* 1989
Sales NA *EMP* 2,974^E
SIC 6035 6798 6722 7299 4813 4724 Federal savings banks; Realty investment trusts; Mutual fund sales, on own account; Buyers' club; Local telephone communications; Tourist agency arranging transport, lodging & car rental
Ch Bd: Robert G Davis
Pr: Carl C Liebert III
Pr: Josue Robles Jr
CFO: Kristi A Matus
Treas: Edwin T McQuiston
Ex VP: Steven Alan Bennett
Ex VP: Stuart B Parker
Sr VP: David K Kimball
Sr VP: Bradford W Rich
Sr VP: Kenneth W Smith
Sr VP: Michael D Wagner
VP: Robert L Hoagand
Board of Directors: Clyde D Dean, William J Hybl, Richard D Milligan

D-U-N-S 60-641-0736
USAA FEDERAL SAVINGS BANK
(*Suby of* USAA INVESTMENT MANAGEMENT CO) ★
10750 Mcdermott Fwy, San Antonio, TX 78288-1600
Tel (210) 498-2211 *Founded/Ownrshp* 1983
Sales NA *EMP* 2,718
Accts Ernst & Young Llp San Antonio
SIC 6035 Federal savings banks
Pr: Fritz D Bohne
Ofcr: Thomas Cianelli
Board of Directors: Frederick M Hamilton, John P Abizaid, William J Hybl, Patricia C Barron, Lester L Lyles, John D Buckelew, John H Moellering, Thomas P Carney, Michael E Ryan, Daniel W Christman, Joseph C Strasser Sr, Eileen M Collins, Stephen B Croker, Leslie G Denend, Thomas B Fargo

D-U-N-S 79-299-7231
USAA GENERAL AGENCY INC
(*Suby of* USAA) ★
9800 Fredericksburg Rd, San Antonio, TX 78288-0002
Tel (210) 456-1800 *Founded/Ownrshp* 1983
Sales NA *EMP* 292
SIC 6331 6321 Property damage insurance; Accident & health insurance
Pr: Joseph S Calvelli
**Sec:* Ronald W Holtkamp
Sr VP: David G Peebles
**VP:* John E Ryan Jr

D-U-N-S 79-286-0116
USAA INSURANCE AGENCY INC
(*Suby of* USAA GENERAL AGENCY INC) ★
9800 Fredericksburg Rd B-2e, San Antonio, TX 78288-0002
Tel (210) 498-2211 *Founded/Ownrshp* 1986
Sales NA *EMP* 200^E
SIC 6331 6321 8742 Property damage insurance; Accident & health insurance; Banking & finance consultant
Prin: Barb Davis
CFO: Craig Zenner
**Sr VP:* Ron Holtcamp
Sr VP: R A Rankin
VP: John Brady
**VP:* Cyndi Taylor Krier

USAA INVESTMENT MANAGEMENT CO
See USAA CAPITAL CORP

D-U-N-S 05-511-4169
USAA LIFE INSURANCE CO
(*Suby of* USAA) ★
9800 Fredericksburg Rd, San Antonio, TX 78288-0002
Tel (210) 498-2211 *Founded/Ownrshp* 1963
Sales NA *EMP* 1,050
SIC 6331 6311 Property damage insurance; Life reinsurance
CEO: Robert G Davis
**Pr:* Kristi A Matus
COO: Jason Kaiser
**Treas:* David Holmes
**Sr VP:* John W Douglas
**Sr VP:* Jeff Nordstrom
IT Man: Edward Evans

D-U-N-S 15-470-7020
USAA REAL ESTATE CO
(*Suby of* USAA INVESTMENT MANAGEMENT CO) ★
9830 Colonnade Blvd # 600, San Antonio, TX 78230-2239
Tel (210) 641-8400 *Founded/Ownrshp* 1983
Sales 127.3MM^E *EMP* 134
SIC 6552 Subdividers & developers; Land subdividers & developers, commercial; Land subdividers & developers, residential
CEO: Leonard J Odonnell
CFO: Jim Hime
Assoc VP: Len Magsamen
Assoc VP: Emily Simmons
Sr VP: Michael Merwarth
**Prin:* Pat Duncan
Ex Dir: Ivy Lin
Ex Dir: David Reahl
Ex Dir: Lex Rickenbaker
Ex Dir: Wilson Tyler
Mng Dir: Steve Ames

D-U-N-S 06-249-7453
USAA SAVINGS BANK
(*Suby of* USAA FEDERAL SAVINGS BANK) ★
3773 Howard Hughes Pkwy, Las Vegas, NV 89169-0949
Tel (702) 862-8891 *Founded/Ownrshp* 1996
Sales NA *EMP* 39
SIC 6036 State savings banks, not federally chartered
Pr: Larry R Seedig
**Treas:* Sandra S Weaver

D-U-N-S 10-204-6752
USABLE LIFE
(*Suby of* LSV) ★
17500 Chenal Pkwy, Little Rock, AR 72223-5197
Tel (800) 648-0271 *Founded/Ownrshp* 1987
Sales NA *EMP* 145
SIC 6311 6321 Life insurance carriers; Health insurance carriers
CEO: Jason D Mann
Pt: Julie F Marshall
**COO:* Jim Casey
**CFO:* Mark Langston
**Ex VP:* Kent Boyer
Ex VP: Glenn R Gross
**Ex VP:* Chad Richard
**VP:* Glenn Gross
**VP:* Julie Marshall
Opers Mgr: Christina Glesige

D-U-N-S 06-532-0038
USABLE MUTUAL INSURANCE CO
ARKANSAS BLUE CROSS & BLUE
601 S Gaines St, Little Rock, AR 72201-4007
Tel (501) 378-2000 *Founded/Ownrshp* 1948
Sales NA *EMP* 2,139
SIC 6324 6411 Group hospitalization plans; Medical insurance claim processing, contract or fee basis
CEO: P Mark White
**COO:* Mike Brown
**CFO:* Gray Dillard
Ofcr: Ladonna Lewis
**Ex VP:* David Bridges
**Sr VP:* Jim Bailey
**Sr VP:* Lee Douglas
VP: Ron Deberry
VP: Steve Short
VP: Joseph Smith
Web Dev: Joe Thrasher
Board of Directors: James Thomas May, Robert Lee Shoptaw, Carolyn Blakely, Hayes Candour McClerkin, Patty Fulbright Smith, Susan Brittain, Connie Meeks, Sherman Tate, Sybil Jordan Hampton Ed D, George Key Mitchell M D, Leslie Wyatt, Bradley D Jesson, Robert Donlad Malcom Munro, Leslie Wyatt Phd, Bradley Dean Jesson, Dan Nabholz, Robert Vincent Brothers, James V Kelley, Maria J Norris, Robert V Brothers, James Virgil Kelly, Ben Owens, Mahlon Ogden Maris M D, Ben Edwin Owens, Mahlon O Maris, Carolyn Frazier Blakely Ph

D-U-N-S 93-107-6959
USABLENET INC
142 W 57th St Fl 7, New York, NY 10019-3300
Tel (212) 965-5388 *Founded/Ownrshp* 2000
Sales 84.0MM^E *EMP* 150^E
SIC 4813
CEO: Nick Taylor
**Ch:* Paolo Brajnik

Chf Mktg O: Carin Vuuren
Dir Bus: Patrick Ammann
**Off Mgr:* Kenya Dyer
Mktg Mgr: Karen Yuen
Snr PM: Jugal Daterao

USABLUEBOOK
See HD SUPPLY FACILITIES MAINTENANCE LTD

USAID
See INTERNATIONAL DEVELOPMENT UNITED STATES AGENCY FOR

D-U-N-S 11-394-7233
■ USAID/ASIA & NEAR EAST BUREAU
(*Suby of* USAID) ★
1300 Pa Ave Rnld Raegn, Washington, DC 20523-0001
Tel (202) 712-0200 *Founded/Ownrshp* 2003
Sales NA *EMP* 8,190^E
SIC 9611 Economic development agency, government;
Pr: Gordon West
Snr Ntwrk: David A Boeddeker

D-U-N-S 80-096-5779
USAMERIBANK
(*Suby of* USAMERIBANCORP, INC.)
4770 140th Ave N Ste 401, Clearwater, FL 33762-3897
Tel (727) 475-8780 *Founded/Ownrshp* 2006
Sales NA *EMP* 550
SIC 6029 Commercial banks
Prin: Harrison Steans
Sr VP: Scott McClelland
Sr VP: Linda Orvis
Sr VP: Jeanette Renfrow
VP: Robin Greenlee
VP: Kara Lecomte
VP: John Noellert
VP: Nick Patel
Brnch Mgr: Maria Roman
Dir IT: David Rhodes

D-U-N-S 80-441-3250
▲ USANA HEALTH SCIENCES INC
3838 W Parkway Blvd, Salt Lake City, UT 84120-6336
Tel (801) 954-7100 *Founded/Ownrshp* 1992
Sales 918.5MM *EMP* 1,664
Tkr Sym USNA *Exch* NYS
SIC 2833 Vitamins, natural or synthetic: bulk, uncompounded
CEO: Kevin Guest
**Ch Bd:* Myron W Wentz
Pr: Jim Brown
Pr: Deborah Woo
CEO: Kevin G Guest
CFO: Paul A Jones
Chf Mktg O: Doug Braun
Ofcr: Daniel A Macuga
Ofcr: Rob Sinnott
Creative D: Brian Paul
Ex Dir: Mark Olson
Board of Directors: Robert Anciaux, Gilbert A Fuller, D Richard Williams, Frederic J Winssinger

D-U-N-S 62-315-3249
■ USANI SUB LLC
(*Suby of* HSN LLC) ★
1 Hsn Dr, Saint Petersburg, FL 33729-0001
Tel (727) 872-1000 *Founded/Ownrshp* 2000
Sales 67.1MM^E *EMP* 2,100
SIC 4833 5961 Television broadcasting stations; Catalog & mail-order houses

USARC
See ARMY RESERVE COMMAND UNITED STATES

USCG
See UNITED STATES COAST GUARD

USCIS
See CITIZENSHIP & IMMIGRATION SERVICES US

USD
See UNIVERSITY OF SOUTH DAKOTA

USDA
See AGRICULTURAL MARKETING SERVICE

D-U-N-S 92-933-2450
■ USDA APHIS VETERINARY
ANIMAL PLANT HLTH INSPTN SERVI
(*Suby of* U S D A) ★
4700 River Rd Unit 54, Riverdale, MD 20737-1232
Tel (301) 851-2873 *Founded/Ownrshp* 1976
Sales NA *EMP* 7,299
SIC 9641 Regulation of agricultural marketing;
Pr: Eileen Sullivan
**CIO:* Marylin Holland
Snr Mgr: Nathaniel Pippen

USDA FOOD & NUTRITION SERVICE
See FOOD & NUTRITION SERVICE

D-U-N-S 92-933-2484
■ USDA FOREST SERVICE
US FOREST SERVICE
(*Suby of* U S D A) ★
201 14th St Sw, Washington, DC 20024
Tel (202) 205-1680 *Founded/Ownrshp* 1905
Sales NA *EMP* 33,000
SIC 9512 Land conservation agencies;
Exec: Kartha Ray
Off Mgr: Juanita Tyler
CTO: Grant Dekker
IT Man: Kathy Anderson
IT Man: Corey Betz

USDA NRCS
See NATURAL RESOURCES CONSERVATION SERVICE

D-U-N-S 92-933-0900
■ USDA RURAL DEVELOPMENT
USDA/FAS/OCBD/TSED/CFP
(*Suby of* U S D A) ★
1400 Independence Ave Sw, Washington, DC 20250-0002
Tel (202) 720-9540 *Founded/Ownrshp* 1921
Sales NA *EMP* 6,000
SIC 9641 Regulation of agricultural marketing;
Ex Dir: Norman Brown

Treas: Brad Petersburg
VP: Steve Baker

USDA/FAS/OCBD/TSED/CFP
See USDA RURAL DEVELOPMENT

USEC
See UNITED STATES ENRICHMENT CORP

D-U-N-S 10-587-8610
USER FRIENDLY PHONE BOOK LLC
10200 Grogans Mill Rd # 440, The Woodlands, TX 77380-1134
Tel (281) 465-5400 *Founded/Ownrshp* 2003
Sales 85.6MM^E *EMP* 300
SIC 2741 Telephone & other directory publishing
Area Mgr: Joe Oneal
Sales Exec: Cindy Thomason

USF
See UNIVERSITY OF SAN FRANCISCO INC

USF HOLLAND INC.
See USF HOLLAND LLC

D-U-N-S 00-777-3724
■ **USF HOLLAND LLC**
USF HOLLAND INC.
(*Suby of* YRC REGIONAL TRANSPORTATION INC) ★
700 S Waverly Rd, Holland, MI 49423-9121
Tel (616) 395-5000 *Founded/Ownrshp* 1929, 2005
Sales 690.6MM^E *EMP* 6,600
SIC 4213 Less-than-truckload (LTL) transport
Pr: Scott D Ware
VP: John A Weber
CTO: Roxann Merrill
Dir IT: Joe Carbonaro

D-U-N-S 05-426-0856 IMP
■ **USF REDDAWAY INC**
(*Suby of* YRC REGIONAL TRANSPORTATION INC) ★
7720 Sw Mohawk St Bldg H, Tualatin, OR 97062-8120
Tel (503) 650-1286 *Founded/Ownrshp* 2005
Sales 204.4MM^E *EMP* 2,700
SIC 4213 Less-than-truckload (LTL) transport
Pr: Thomas J O Connor
VP: Terry Gerrond
Genl Mgr: Debbie Fortin
Dir IT: Mike Montgomery
IT Man: Chris Kotchik
S&M/VP: Steve Selvig

USFHP AT MARTIN'S POINT
See MARTINS POINT HEALTH CARE INC

D-U-N-S 12-128-6777
▲ **USG CORP**
550 W Adams St, Chicago, IL 60661-3665
Tel (312) 436-4000 *Founded/Ownrshp* 1901
Sales 3.7MMM *EMP* 8,900^E
Tkr Sym USG *Exch* NYS
SIC 3275 3296 Gypsum products; Gypsum board; Gypsum plaster; Insulating plaster, gypsum; Mineral wool insulation products; Acoustical board & tile, mineral wool
Ch Bd: James S Metcalf
CFO: Matthew F Hilzinger
Ofcr: Brian J Cook
Ex VP: Dominic A Dannessa
Sr VP: Edward M Bosowski
Sr VP: Michelle M Warner
VP: Wayne H Jenkins
VP: Ray Johnson
VP: Chris Lawson
VP: Mary Menina
VP: Jeanette A Press
VP: John Reale
Comm Dir: Robert Williams
Board of Directors: Jose Armario, Thomas A Burke, Matthew Carter Jr, Gretchen R Haggerty, William H Hernandez, Brian A Kenney, Richard P Lavin, Steven F Leer

D-U-N-S 14-831-0014 IMP
■ **USG INTERIORS LLC**
(*Suby of* UNITED STATES GYPSUM CO INC) ★
125 S Franklin St, Chicago, IL 60606-4647
Tel (800) 874-4968 *Founded/Ownrshp* 1986
Sales 869.3MM^E *EMP* 2,300
SIC 5031 Building materials, interior
Pr: James S Metcalf
**COO:* Christopher Griffin
**CFO:* Matthew Hilzinger
**Treas:* Kenneth Banas
Ex VP: Chris Brosz
Sr VP: William H Hernandez
VP: Julian Francis
VP: Chris Rosenthal
Dir Soc: Paulette Clark
Off Mgr: Toni Coates
CTO: Bernard Cale

D-U-N-S 36-163-2342 IMP/EXP
USG INTERNATIONAL LTD
(*Suby of* GYPSUM TRANSPORTATION LIMITED)
125 S Franklin St Ste 4, Chicago, IL 60606-4605
Tel (312) 606-4000 *Founded/Ownrshp* 2014
Sales 121.8MM^E *EMP* 100
SIC 5033 Roofing, siding & insulation
Pr: John H Meister
**VP:* Richard Fleming

USG&E
See US GAS & ELECTRIC INC

USGA
See UNITED STATES GOLF ASSOCIATION

D-U-N-S 80-855-1217
USHEALTH ADMINISTRATORS LLC
300 Burnett St Ste 200, Fort Worth, TX 76102-2734
Tel (817) 878-3307 *Founded/Ownrshp* 1999
Sales NA *EMP* 250
SIC 6321 Accident & health insurance
Treas: Cynthia B Koenig
Sr VP: Konrad H Kober
Sr VP: Travis Yoder

D-U-N-S 07-530-1341 IMP/EXP
USHIO AMERICA INC
(*Suby of* USHIO INC.)
5440 Cerritos Ave, Cypress, CA 90630-4567
Tel (714) 236-8600 *Founded/Ownrshp* 1967
Sales 86.6MM^E *EMP* 200
SIC 5063 Lighting fixtures, commercial & industrial
Pr: Shinji Kameda
**CFO:* Yuichi Asaka
Genl Mgr: Keith Sangiacomo
IT Man: Rez Motamed
Opers Mgr: Rachael Gutierrez
Ql Cn Mgr: Vinay Prakash

D-U-N-S 07-644-0221
USI COLORADO LLC
(*Suby of* USI NORTHEAST) ★
6501 S Fiddlers Ste 100, Greenwood Village, CO 80111
Tel (800) 873-8500 *Founded/Ownrshp* 2013
Sales NA *EMP* 150
SIC 6411 Insurance agents; Insurance brokers
Ch: Michael J Sicard
Treas: Ed Harrington
Treas: Lisa Kammerer
VP: Anita Boissoneau
VP: Dennis Miceli
VP: Michael Van Gilder
Exec: Steve Doss
Exec: John Wells

D-U-N-S 94-426-8259
USI INC
USI INSURANCE SERVICES
200 Summit Lake Dr # 350, Valhalla, NY 10595-1355
Tel (914) 747-6300 *Founded/Ownrshp* 2012
Sales NA *EMP* 4,000
SIC 6411 Insurance information & consulting services; Insurance agents & brokers
Ch Bd: Michael J Sicard
Pr: Robb Pridemore
CFO: Robert Schneider
Ofcr: Joseph Gritzer
Ex VP: Doug Dinjian
Ex VP: Jeff Morgan
Ex VP: Michael Turpin
Ex VP: Ralph M Wilson
Sr VP: Edward J Bowler
Sr VP: Mark Cantin
Sr VP: Stewart H Gibson
Sr VP: Arthur Hall
Sr VP: James P Kane
Sr VP: Robert Meyers
Sr VP: Ernest J Newborn II
Sr VP: Sandra Usleman
Sr VP: Kim Van Orman
Sr VP: Eileen M Webb
VP: Bob Anderson
VP: Tod Anderson
VP: Brian Ball

USI INSURANCE SERVICES
See HENDERSON & PHILLIPS INC

USI INSURANCE SERVICES
See USI INC

D-U-N-S 82-843-1580
USI INSURANCE SERVICES LLC
USI NORTHEAST
(*Suby of* USI INSURANCE SERVICES) ★
200 Summit Lake Dr, Valhalla, NY 10595-1355
Tel (914) 749-8500 *Founded/Ownrshp* 2011
Sales NA *EMP* 732
SIC 6411 Insurance agents, brokers & service
Ex VP: Michael Turnpin
Sr VP: Michael Gilligan
Sr VP: Kevin Racine
VP: Tracy Boss
VP: Scott Gardner
VP: Jessica Hill
VP: Colleen Howland
VP: Erik Liguori
VP: Jennifer Monkiewicz
VP: Ginger Padgett
VP: Jennifer Petterson
VP: Jim Purchase
VP: Louis Ricci
VP: Shari Segall
VP: Jeff Wilson
Dir Bus: James Peveraro

USI NORTHEAST
See USI INSURANCE SERVICES LLC

D-U-N-S 17-135-9917
USI SENIOR HOLDINGS INC
895 W 2600 S, South Salt Lake, UT 84119-2429
Tel (801) 983-0390 *Founded/Ownrshp* 2004
Sales 513.2MM^E *EMP* 1,900
SIC 1742 Insulation, buildings
Pr: Kevin Gilligan
CFO: Brad Fairbanks

D-U-N-S 80-831-8745
USI SERVICE CORP
(*Suby of* USI INSURANCE SERVICES) ★
555 Plsntvlle Rd Ste 160s, Briarcliff Manor, NY 10510
Tel (914) 747-6300 *Founded/Ownrshp* 1993
Sales NA *EMP* 540
SIC 6411 Insurance agents, brokers & service; Insurance brokers
Ch Bd: David L Eslick
**CFO:* Robert Schneider
**Sr VP:* Ed Bowler
Sr VP: H D Wood
VP: Tom Moletto Sr

D-U-N-S 82-504-9364
USI SERVICES GROUP INC
U S I
51 Progress St, Union, NJ 07083-8114
Tel (973) 376-6000 *Founded/Ownrshp* 1993
Sales 182.4MM^E *EMP* 5,000
SIC 7349 Janitorial service, contract basis
Pr: Frederick Goldring
CFO: Barry Golub
Off Admin: Tabitha Iannuzzelli
Dir IT: Paul Murphy
VP Opers: Shaheen Mojibian

D-U-N-S 00-284-8745 EXP
USIBELLI COAL MINE INC
U C M
100 River Rd, Healy, AK 99743
Tel (907) 683-2226 *Founded/Ownrshp* 1943
Sales 84.2MM^E *EMP* 100
SIC 1221 Strip mining, bituminous
Ch Bd: Joe Usibelli
Pr: Joseph Usibelli
Treas: Lanterman Kirk
Sec: A Kirk Lanterman
VP: Rosalie Whyel
Mktg Mgr: John Sims
Board of Directors: Earl Biestline, Marc Langland, Richard Wien

D-U-N-S 82-693-0104
USIC LLC
9045 River Rd Ste 300, Indianapolis, IN 46240-6400
Tel (317) 575-7800 *Founded/Ownrshp* 2008
Sales 1.9MMM^E *EMP* 4,600
SIC 1623 8713 Water, sewer & utility lines; Surveying services
CEO: Rob Tullman
**CFO:* Jim O'Malley
**Sr VP:* Timothy M Seelig
**VP:* Christa Harrell
CIO: Amit Shankar

D-U-N-S 15-060-5418
USIC LOCATING SERVICES LLC
S M & P UTILITY RESOURCES
(*Suby of* USIC LLC) ★
9045 River Rd Ste 300, Indianapolis, IN 46240-6400
Tel (317) 816-2207 *Founded/Ownrshp* 2009
Sales 957.9MM^E *EMP* 3,750
SIC 1623 Water, sewer & utility lines
Pr: Rob Tullman
**CFO:* Jim O'Malley
Sr VP: Timothy M Seelig
**CIO:* Amit Shankar

USIS
See UNITED STATES INFORMATION SYSTEMS INC

USIS
See US INVESTIGATIONS SERVICES LLC

D-U-N-S 00-699-1731
■ **USL SEPARATE ACCOUNT USL VL-R** (NY)
(*Suby of* AGC LIFE INSURANCE CO) ★
1 World Fin Ctr, New York, NY 10281
Tel (800) 874-8743 *Founded/Ownrshp* 1850, 1997
Sales NA *EMP* 906
SIC 6311 6321 Life insurance carriers; Accident insurance carriers; Health insurance carriers
Pr: David J Dietz
Pr: Thomas L Booker
Pr: William M Keeler
Sr VP: Michael Lefante
VP: Ronald Rovner
Corp Couns: William Woods

D-U-N-S 00-479-7507
USLC LLC (SC)
100 Dunbar St Ste 100, Spartanburg, SC 29306-5186
Tel (864) 577-0100 *Founded/Ownrshp* 1997
Sales 83.1MM^E *EMP* 1,200
SIC 7389 Cloth cutting, bolting or winding
Pt: Thomas Hannah

USMAG
See US MAGNESIUM LLC

D-U-N-S 96-892-6746
USMD HOLDINGS INC
(*Suby of* UANT VENTURES LLP) ★
6333 N State Highway 161 # 200, Irving, TX 75038-2229
Tel (214) 493-4000 *Founded/Ownrshp* 2010
Sales 325.1MM *EMP* 1,551
Accts Rsm Us Llp Houston Texas
SIC 8062 General medical & surgical hospitals
Ch Bd: John House
Pr: Gary Rudin
COO: Michael W Bukosky
CFO: Jim Berend
CFO: Carolyn Jones
Ex VP: Greg Cardenas
Ex VP: Richard Johnston
Sr VP: Michelle Speck
VP: Bonnie Lankford
VP: Bren Ori
VP: Michael Wester
Dir Rad: Holly Ragan
Dir Rx: Terry Purcell
Comm Man: Megan Reisig
Board of Directors: John L Larsen, John F Rex

D-U-N-S 13-913-9260
USMD HOSPITAL AT ARLINGTON LP
801 W Interstate 20, Arlington, TX 76017-5851
Tel (817) 472-3400 *Founded/Ownrshp* 2003
Sales 101.0MM *EMP* 500^E
SIC 8062 General medical & surgical hospitals
Pr: Carlos Acosta
Dir Recs: Roni Gonzalez
CFO: Nick Braecino
VP: Bren Ori
VP: John Ortiz
Exec: Anita Lehman
Dir OR: Kathy Mavrakes
Dir Inf Cn: Amelia Macalua
Dir Lab: Charlie White
Dir Rx: Terry Purcell
Dir Rx: Dana Wilkirson

D-U-N-S 08-746-5449 IMP/EXP
USNR LLC
KOCKUMS CANCAR CHIP-N-SAW
1981 Schurman Way, Woodland, WA 98674-9599
Tel (360) 225-8267 *Founded/Ownrshp* 1980
Sales 310.0MM^E *EMP* 1,043
SIC 3585 3553 3625 1221 5084 Air conditioning units, complete: domestic or industrial; Sawmill machines; Control equipment, electric; Strip mining, bituminous; Sawmill machinery & equipment

**Pr:* George Van Hoomissen
**VP:* Donald Bechen

U.S.NRC
See NUCLEAR REGULATORY COMMISSION UNITED STATES

USOC
See UNITED STATES OLYMPIC COMMITTEE INC

U.S.OIL
See US VENTURE INC

D-U-N-S 07-847-6771
USP HOLDINGS INC
6250 N Rver Rd Ste 10100, Des Plaines, IL 60018
Tel (847) 604-6100 *Founded/Ownrshp* 2012
Sales 75.1MM^E *EMP* 1,101
SIC 3321 3491 Cast iron pipe & fittings; Industrial valves
Mng Pt: John A Hatherly
**Pt:* Frank G Hayes
**Pt:* Terry M Theodore

D-U-N-S 96-791-9908
USP INTERNATIONAL HOLDINGS INC
(*Suby of* UNITED SURGICAL PARTNERS INTERNATIONAL INC) ★
15305 Dallas Pkwy, Addison, TX 75001-4637
Tel (972) 713-3500 *Founded/Ownrshp* 2011
Sales 36.8MM^E *EMP* 1,365
SIC 8062 General medical & surgical hospitals
Pr: William H Wilcox
CFO: Mark Kopser

D-U-N-S 09-528-0744
USPHS AK NATIVE MEDICAL CENTER
4315 Diplomacy Dr, Anchorage, AK 99508-5926
Tel (907) 729-2544 *Founded/Ownrshp* 1954
Sales 9.1MM^E *EMP* 1,200
SIC 8062 General medical & surgical hospitals

D-U-N-S 96-363-8213
USPI GROUP HOLDINGS INC
15305 Dallas Pkwy # 1600, Addison, TX 75001-4637
Tel (972) 713-3500 *Founded/Ownrshp* 2007
Sales 645.4MM^E *EMP* 11,000^E
SIC 8011 Offices & clinics of medical doctors
CEO: William H Wilcox

D-U-N-S 07-846-5104
USPI HOLDINGS INC
(*Suby of* USPI GROUP HOLDINGS INC) ★
15305 Dallas Pkwy # 1600, Addison, TX 75001-6491
Tel (972) 713-3500 *Founded/Ownrshp* 2006
Sales 645.4MM^E *EMP* 11,000^E
SIC 8011 Offices & clinics of medical doctors
CEO: William H Wilcox

USPL
See US PIPELINE INC

USPOWERGEN
See US POWER GENERATING CO

USPTO
See UNITED STATES PATENT AND TRADEMARK OFFICE

USRC
See US RENAL CARE INC

D-U-N-S 87-841-6858
USS CAL BUILDERS INC
8051 Main St, Stanton, CA 90680-2452
Tel (714) 828-4882 *Founded/Ownrshp* 1992
Sales 89.5MM^E *EMP* 135
Accts Frazer Frost Llp Brea Ca
SIC 1542 Specialized public building contractors
CEO: Allen Othman
**Pr:* Jennifer Hotrum
Off Mgr: Arlene Bautista
VP Opers: Rabih Elzein
Snr PM: Imad Othman
Board of Directors: Arlene Bautista, Rani Eldjoundi, Jennifer Hotrum

D-U-N-S 15-082-4647 IMP
USS-POSCO INDUSTRIES A CALIFORNIA JOINT VENTURE
900 Loveridge Rd, Pittsburg, CA 94565-2808
Tel (800) 877-7672 *Founded/Ownrshp* 1986
Sales 648.9MM *EMP* 759
Accts Kpmg Llp Sacramento Califor
SIC 3312 Sheet or strip, steel, cold-rolled: own hot-rolled; Tinplate; Iron & steel: galvanized, pipes, plates, sheets, etc.
Pt: United States Steel Corporatio
Ofcr: John Passur
Ex VP: Kevin K SOO
VP: Sungwon Shin
Assoc Dir: Tim Lear
VP Admn: John Berzanski
Dept Mgr: Dean Broglie
Dept Mgr: Will Jones
Genl Mgr: George Kuntz
DP Exec: Jerry Wilson
IT Man: Chris Park

D-U-N-S 05-519-4919
UST GLOBAL INC
5 Polaris Way, Aliso Viejo, CA 92656-5356
Tel (949) 716-8757 *Founded/Ownrshp* 2007
Sales 1.3MMM^E *EMP* 8,700
SIC 7371 Computer software development
Ch: Dan Gupta
**Pr:* Joe Nalkara
**CEO:* Sajan Pillai
**COO:* Arun Narayanan
**COO:* Saurabh Ranjan
VP: Kishor Pillai
VP: Budi Utama
Exec: Jayadivya Vijayan
Genl Mgr: Catharine Gardener
Genl Mgr: Manoj Nair
Genl Mgr: Rich Namerow

D-U-N-S 16-199-6681 IMP/EXP
UST LLC
6 High Ridge Park Bldg A, Stamford, CT 06905-1327
Tel (203) 817-3000 *Founded/Ownrshp* 1986
Sales 108.2MM[E] *EMP* 4,610[E]
SIC 2131 2084 2621 3999

USTA
See UNITED STATES TENNIS ASSOCIATION INC

U.S.T.H.
See USTSUBAKI HOLDINGS INC

USU
See UTAH STATE UNIVERSITY

D-U-N-S 93-251-6966
USV OPTICAL INC
J C PENNEY OPTICAL
(*Suby of* J C PENNEY OPTICAL) ★
1 Harmon Dr Glen Oaks, Glendora, NJ 08029
Tel (856) 228-1000 *Founded/Ownrshp* 1990
Sales 249.7MM[E] *EMP* 1,900
SIC 5995 3851 Optical goods stores; Ophthalmic goods
CEO: William A Schwartz Jr
**Ex VP:* Carmen J Nepa III

USWA
See UNITED STEELWORKERS

UT ELECTRONIC CONTROLS
See UNITED TECHNOLOGIES ELECTRONIC CONTROLS INC

D-U-N-S 82-717-9693
UT FOUNDATION INC
600 Henley St Ste 100, Knoxville, TN 37996-4502
Tel (865) 974-1558 *Founded/Ownrshp* 2010
Sales 121.4MM *EMP* 2
Accts Brown Jake & Mcdaniel Pc Knox
SIC 8699 Charitable organization
Pr: Rickey McCurry

UT HEALTH
See UNIVERSITY OF TEXAS HEALTH SCIENCE CENTER AT HOUSTON

UT HEALTH SAN ANTONIO
See UNIVERSITY OF TEXAS HEALTH SCIENCE CENTER AT SAN ANTONIO

D-U-N-S 11-527-8368
UT MEDICAL GROUP INC
INTERVENTIONAL ASSOCIATES OF M
1407 Union Ave Ste 700, Memphis, TN 38104-3641
Tel (901) 866-8864 *Founded/Ownrshp* 1983
Sales 73.6MM *EMP* 1,207
Accts Cbiz Mhm Llc Memphis Tn
SIC 8011 Offices & clinics of medical doctors
CEO: Juloy Raymer
**CEO:* Charles E Woeppel
**CFO:* Brenda H Jeter
**Chf Mktg O:* J L Smith MD
**VP:* Cassandra Taylor-Wilson
Surgeon: Benjamin S Powell

D-U-N-S 88-423-9380
UT MEDICINE SAN ANTONIO
6126 Wurzbach Rd, San Antonio, TX 78238-1743
Tel (210) 450-9000 *Founded/Ownrshp* 2006
Sales 158.1MM *EMP* 82[E]
Accts Padgett Stratemann & Co Llp S
SIC 8099 Health & allied services

UT MEMORIAL HOSPITAL
See UNIVERSITY HEALTH SYSTEM INC

D-U-N-S 83-899-7971
UT PHYSICIANS
UNIVERSITY CARE PLUS
6410 Fannin St Ste 1500, Houston, TX 77030-5306
Tel (713) 500-5086 *Founded/Ownrshp* 1994
Sales 114.4MM *EMP* 300
Accts Blazek & Vetterlmg Houston T
SIC 8011 General & family practice, physician/surgeon
Ch Bd: Carlos R Hamilton Jr
**V Ch Bd:* Jeffrey Katz
**VP:* Diana Browning
**VP:* Andrew Casas
Exec: Jeannie Molan
**CTO:* James G D

D-U-N-S 79-792-6032
UT SOUTHWESTERN MEDICAL CENTER
5323 Harry Hines Blvd # 7200, Dallas, TX 75390-7200
Tel (214) 648-2508 *Founded/Ownrshp* 2007
Sales 795.6MM *EMP* 14,400
SIC 8059 Personal care home, with health care
Pr: Daniel K Podolsky
**Pr:* J Gregory Fitz
VP: Ruben Esquivel
Dir Lab: Jinchun Zhou
Dir Rx: Brian Cohen
Mng Dir: Vern Cotman
IT Man: Anil John
Netwrk Eng: Lee Brasher
Orthpdst: Jin Jiang
Ansthlgy: Carl Adkins
Ansthlgy: Michael Babiak

UT TYLER
See UNIVERSITY OF TEXAS AT TYLER

D-U-N-S 09-911-4287
UT-BATTELLE LLC
OAK RIDGE NATIONAL LABORATORY
1 Bethel Valley Rd, Oak Ridge, TN 37830-8050
Tel (865) 574-2227 *Founded/Ownrshp* 1999
Sales 98.4MM[E] *EMP* 4,500
SIC 8731 Energy research
**CFO:* Scott Branham
Dir Soc: Budhendra Bhaduri
Prgrm Mgr: Barbara Beckerman
Prgrm Mgr: Jan Berry
Prgrm Mgr: Linda Smith
CIO: Scott Studham
IT Man: John Wagner
Sfty Mgr: John Czachowski
Pgrm Dir: Jenny Keller
Pgrm Dir: Dave Mandl
Pgrm Dir: Michelle Mazerolle

UTAC
See UNITED TACONITE LLC

D-U-N-S 14-844-8954
UTAH ASSOCIATED MUNICIPAL POWER SYSTEMS
UAMPS
155 N 400 W, Salt Lake City, UT 84103-1111
Tel (801) 566-3938 *Founded/Ownrshp* 1980
Sales 187.8MM *EMP* 27
Accts Ernst & Young Llp
SIC 4911 Electric services; Transmission, electric power
Genl Mgr: Doug Hunter
**CFO:* Scott Fox
Bd of Dir: Travis Ball
Bd of Dir: Chris Michaelis
Bd of Dir: Bruce Rigby
Bd of Dir: Jack Taylor
Ex Dir: John Harbert
Ex Dir: Mark Lehnhof
**Plng Mgr:* Marshall Empey
Dir IT: Rusty Schramm
IT Man: Ryan Huntington

D-U-N-S 87-859-3383
UTAH DEPARTMENT OF HUMAN SERVICES
(*Suby of* EXECUTIVE OFFICE OF STATE OF UTAH) ★
195 N 1950 W, Salt Lake City, UT 84116-3100
Tel (801) 538-4001 *Founded/Ownrshp* 1851
Sales 91.3MM[E] *EMP* 4,100
SIC 8322 9441 Individual & family services;
Ex Dir: Ann Williamson
Ofcr: Elizabeth Sollis
Genl Mgr: Kim Turner

D-U-N-S 87-994-1854
UTAH DEPARTMENT OF NATURAL RESOURCES
DNR
(*Suby of* EXECUTIVE OFFICE OF STATE OF UTAH) ★
1594 W North Temple, Salt Lake City, UT 84116-3154
Tel (801) 538-7200 *Founded/Ownrshp* 1967
Sales NA *EMP* 1,308
SIC 9512 Land, mineral & wildlife conservation;
Ex Dir: Mike Styler

D-U-N-S 83-605-4528
UTAH DEPARTMENT OF PUBLIC SAFETY
(*Suby of* EXECUTIVE OFFICE OF STATE OF UTAH) ★
4501 S Constitution Blvd, Taylorsville, UT 84129-5928
Tel (801) 965-4461 *Founded/Ownrshp* 1993
Sales NA *EMP* 2,391
SIC 9229 Public safety bureau, government;
Genl Mgr: Sherry McCusker

D-U-N-S 87-869-0338
UTAH DEPARTMENT OF TRANSPORTATION
(*Suby of* EXECUTIVE OFFICE OF STATE OF UTAH) ★
4501 S Constitution Blvd, Taylorsville, UT 84129-5928
Tel (801) 965-4000 *Founded/Ownrshp* 1911
Sales NA *EMP* 1,800
SIC 9621 Regulation, administration of transportation;
Ex Dir: Carlos Braceras
Mng Dir: Vicki Varela
Prgrm Mgr: Amy Graham
Off Mgr: Laurie Bishop

D-U-N-S 15-595-4126
UTAH DEPT OF WORKFORCE SERVICES
(*Suby of* EXECUTIVE OFFICE OF STATE OF UTAH) ★
140 E Broadway, Salt Lake City, UT 84111-2333
Tel (801) 526-9432 *Founded/Ownrshp* 1933
Sales NA *EMP* 2,000
SIC 9441 Administration of social & manpower programs; ; Public welfare administration: non-operating, government
Ex Dir: Jon Pierpont
**CEO:* William Greer

D-U-N-S 18-669-7579
UTAH HOUSING CORP
UTAH HOUSING FINANCE AGENCY
2479 S Lake Park Blvd, West Valley City, UT 84120-8217
Tel (801) 902-8200 *Founded/Ownrshp* 1975
Sales 96.6MM *EMP* 90
Accts Deloitte & Touche Llp Salt L
SIC 6211 6162 Bond dealers & brokers; Bond & mortgage companies
CEO: Grant Whitaker
**CFO:* Cleon Butterfield
**Sr VP:* Jonathan Hanks
Sls Mgr: Adam Heap

UTAH HOUSING FINANCE AGENCY
See UTAH HOUSING CORP

D-U-N-S 60-357-3580
UTAH NATIONAL SECURITY INC
REAMS 8
2600 W 4700 S, Taylorsville, UT 84129-1806
Tel (801) 963-0397 *Founded/Ownrshp* 1963
Sales 105.0MM *EMP* 700
SIC 5651 Jeans stores
Pr: Paul Ream
**Sec:* Ruby Ream
Genl Mgr: Barry Bessey
Genl Mgr: Carl Willoughby

D-U-N-S 05-421-4689
UTAH RETIREMENT SYSTEMS
UTAH STATE RETIREMENT OFFICE
(*Suby of* EXECUTIVE OFFICE OF STATE OF UTAH) ★
540 E 200 S, Salt Lake City, UT 84102-2044
Tel (801) 366-7700 *Founded/Ownrshp* 1963
Sales NA *EMP* 152
SIC 6371 Pension funds
Ex Dir: Robert V Newman
Ofcr: Ed Archer
Ofcr: Guy Foutz
Dir Sec: John Brinkerhoff
Brnch Mgr: Lynn Baker
CTO: Jeff Bennett
CTO: Bob Newman
Dir IT: Donald Bradshaw
Dir IT: Rick Hanks
Dir IT: Kevin Howard
IT Man: Larry Powell

UTAH STATE RETIREMENT OFFICE
See UTAH RETIREMENT SYSTEMS

D-U-N-S 07-298-3455
UTAH STATE UNIVERSITY
USU
1000 Old Main Hl, Logan, UT 84322-1000
Tel (435) 797-1057 *Founded/Ownrshp* 1888
Sales 382.7MM *EMP* 6,000
SIC 8221 University
Pr: Stan L Albrecht
Trst: David Johnson
VP: Jeff Broadbent
VP: David Cowley
**VP:* Ronald S Godfrey
VP: Fross Peterson
Exec: Peggy Buttars
Exec: Megan Maples
Ex Dir: John Devilbiss
Ex Dir: Aaron Finley
Ex Dir: Katie Nielsen

D-U-N-S 09-776-0433
UTAH STATE UNIVERSITY RESEARCH FOUNDATION
SPACE DYNAMICS LABORATORY
(*Suby of* USU) ★
1695 N Research Pkwy, North Logan, UT 84341
Tel (435) 713-3400 *Founded/Ownrshp* 1967
Sales 128.2MM[E] *EMP* 500
SIC 8711 8734 8733 7371 Engineering services; Testing laboratories; Research institute; Custom computer programming services
Pr: H Scott Hinton
**Treas:* Lyndon B Loosle
Netwrk Eng: Brent Parker
Pgrm Dir: Jennifer Bettencourt
Board of Directors: Niel Holt

D-U-N-S 06-981-6163 IMP
UTAH TRANSIT AUTHORITY (UTA)
U T A
669 W 200 S Bldg 1, Salt Lake City, UT 84101-1015
Tel (801) 262-5626 *Founded/Ownrshp* 1970
Sales 41.5MM *EMP* 2,300
Accts Deloitte & Touche Llp Salt L
SIC 4111 Bus line operations
Pr: Orrin T Colby
COO: Jerry Benson
CFO: Ken Montague
**Treas:* Kenneth D Montague Jr
Trst: Justin Allen
Trst: Necia Christensen
Trst: Larry Ellertson
**VP:* Robert W Davis
VP: Robert A Hunter
VP: Debbie Smart
**Genl Mgr:* John M Inglish

UTAH VALLEY HOSPITAL
See UTAH VALLEY REGIONAL MEDICAL CENTER

D-U-N-S 07-299-9360
UTAH VALLEY REGIONAL MEDICAL CENTER
UTAH VALLEY HOSPITAL
1034 N 500 W, Provo, UT 84604-3380
Tel (801) 357-7850 *Founded/Ownrshp* 1954
Sales 492.9MM *EMP* 3[E]
SIC 8062 General medical & surgical hospitals
Dir Vol: Cheryl Call
Chf Rad: Carl Black
COO: David D Clark
Treas: Wendell Gibby
VP: Clark Bishop
Prgrm Mgr: J Zeeman
Off Mgr: Jackie Durfey
Off Mgr: Kelley Gilson
IT Man: Liz Daniels
Sls&Mrk Ex: Katie Walther
Pathlgst: Paul Urie

D-U-N-S 07-307-6952
UTAH VALLEY UNIVERSITY (UT)
U V U
800 W University Pkwy, Orem, UT 84058-6703
Tel (801) 863-8000 *Founded/Ownrshp* 1941
Sales 184.4MM[E] *EMP* 2,200
SIC 8221 College, except junior
Pr: Matthew S Holland
**VP:* Marc Archambault
**VP:* Cory Duckworth
**VP:* Val Hale
VP: Vanessa Perkins
**VP:* Val Peterson
VP: Douglas E Warner
Dir Lab: Emily Bartlett
Prgrm Mgr: Christian Lindquist
DP Dir: Alan Castle
IT Man: David Andrus

D-U-N-S 07-961-9785
UTAIR - HELICOPTER SERVICES LTD
420 Lexington Ave Rm 300, New York, NY 10170-0399
Tel (212) 297-6207 *Founded/Ownrshp* 2014
Sales 1.0MM *EMP* 1,800[E]
SIC 4513 Air courier services
Pr: Mamed Kasumod

UTC AEROSPACE SYSTEMS
See GOODRICH CORP

D-U-N-S 80-867-7843 IMP/EXP
■ **UTC FIRE & SECURITY AMERICAS CORP INC**
(*Suby of* UNITED TECHNOLOGIES CORP) ★
8985 Town Center Pkwy, Lakewood Ranch, FL 34202-5129
Tel (941) 739-4200 *Founded/Ownrshp* 2001
Sales 1.2MMM[E] *EMP* 3,167
SIC 3669 5065 Burglar alarm apparatus, electric; Fire alarm apparatus, electric; Fire detection systems, electric; Electronic parts & equipment
Pr: Jurgen Timperman
**Treas:* Mark Leite
VP: Barbara Cameron
VP: Rick Falconer
VP: Ray McDermott
CIO: Nick Tullio
Sls Mgr: Gregory Lau

D-U-N-S 79-611-9345
UTC OVERSEAS INC
2 Northpoint Dr Ste 213, Houston, TX 77060-3235
Tel (713) 422-2850 *Founded/Ownrshp* 1989
Sales 99.5MM[E] *EMP* 176
Accts Rsmi Us Llp
SIC 4412 4581 Deep sea foreign transportation of freight; Air freight handling at airports
Pr: Brian Posthumus
**CFO:* Edward Vaz
**VP:* Jim Belby

D-U-N-S 16-145-6363
UTECH INC
(*Suby of* BMS ENTERPRISES INC) ★
303 Arthur St, Fort Worth, TX 76107-2352
Tel (817) 332-2770 *Founded/Ownrshp* 1981
Sales 101.6MM[E] *EMP* 589
SIC 1542 Commercial & office buildings, renovation & repair
Pr: Lloyd E Swiggum
**Treas:* Robert B Smith
**Sr VP:* Bill Boss
Sr VP: Phil Duncan
**Sr VP:* Don Mansir
VP: Tim Draney
Mng Dir: Bernard Connolly

D-U-N-S 00-806-9437 IMP
UTEX INDUSTRIES INC (TX)
10810 Katy Fwy Ste 100, Houston, TX 77043-5013
Tel (713) 559-0203 *Founded/Ownrshp* 1940, 2010
Sales 130.6MM[E] *EMP* 425
SIC 3053 3061 Packing, rubber; Gaskets, all materials; Oil seals, rubber; Oil & gas field machinery rubber goods (mechanical)
CEO: Michael P Balas
**CFO:* Pete Sanchez
**VP:* Mike Blake
**VP:* Chuck Rankin
Plnt Mgr: Dave Lindinger
Prd Mgr: Bill Boenker
Sales Exec: Cindi Hoover

D-U-N-S 16-029-2095
UTF TRUCKING INC
(*Suby of* FRESH DIRECT HOLDINGS INC) ★
2330 Borden Ave, Long Island City, NY 11101-4515
Tel (718) 928-1000 *Founded/Ownrshp* 2006
Sales 58.8MM[E] *EMP* 1,247[E]
SIC 4212 Local trucking, without storage
CEO: Steven Furbush

D-U-N-S 61-408-8453
UTGR INC
TWIN RIVER CASINO
100 Twin River Rd, Lincoln, RI 02865-4635
Tel (401) 723-3200 *Founded/Ownrshp* 2004
Sales 53.5MM[E] *EMP* 1,900
SIC 7011 Casino hotel
Pr: Craig Sculos
**Pr:* Madison Grose
**Pr:* George Papanier
**CFO:* Jay Minas
Exec: Danielle Simone
Snr Ntwrk: James Hunt
IT Man: Tom Willard

D-U-N-S 84-208-1689
UTI (US) HOLDINGS INC
(*Suby of* UTI WORLDWIDE INC.)
400 Sw 6th Ave Ste 906, Portland, OR 97204-1634
Tel (503) 953-1300 *Founded/Ownrshp* 2000
Sales 2.9MMM[E] *EMP* 5,981
Accts Deloitte & Touche Llp Los An
SIC 4731 Freight forwarding; Customhouse brokers
Pr: Christopher Dale
**Treas:* Clinton Smith
**VP:* Mary Anne Henry
VP: Tom Riester
Dir IT: Craig Jarrett
Board of Directors: Robert D Hartman

D-U-N-S 00-337-3719
UTI INTEGRATED LOGISTICS LLC (SC)
(*Suby of* UTI WORLDWIDE INC.)
700 Gervais St Ste 100, Columbia, SC 29201-3061
Tel (803) 771-6785 *Founded/Ownrshp* 1894
Sales 804.8MM[E] *EMP* 4,800
SIC 4226 4213 Textile warehousing; Petroleum & chemical bulk stations & terminals for hire; Trucking, except local
Pr: Doug Walker
Treas: Steven McClure
Treas: James H Walker
Off Mgr: Karen Boyce
Opers Mgr: Herbert Hall

UTI TRANSPORT SOLUTIONS
See INTRANSIT INC

D-U-N-S 08-607-2055 IMP/EXP
UTI UNITED STATES INC
(*Suby of* DSV AIR & SEA HOLDING INC) ★
100 Walnut Ave Ste 405, Clark, NJ 07066-1247
Tel (732) 850-8000 *Founded/Ownrshp* 1976, 2016
Sales 658.1MM[E] *EMP* 1,183[E]
SIC 4731 Freight forwarding; Customhouse brokers
CEO: Edward Feitzinger
CFO: Denise Cotter
Ex VP: Gene T Ochi
Ex VP: Richard Rodick
Sr VP: Lance E D Amico
**VP:* J Thurso Barendse
Brnch Mgr: Neil Howarth
Genl Mgr: Doug Werner
Snr Mgr: Laurie Zech

UTICA BOILERS
See ECR INTERNATIONAL INC

D-U-N-S 05-461-1264
UTICA CITY SCHOOL DISTRICT
UTICA PUBLIC SCHOOLS
106 Memorial Pkwy, Utica, NY 13501-4818
Tel (315) 792-2222 Founded/Ownrshp 1840
Sales 63.4MME EMP 1,500
SIC 8211 Public combined elementary & secondary school
Treas: Nicholas Laino
IT Man: Carla Percia
Pr Dir: Angela Elefante
Teacher Pr: Richard Ambruso

D-U-N-S 07-425-8047
UTICA COMMUNITY SCHOOLS
11303 Greendale Dr, Sterling Heights, MI 48312-2925
Tel (586) 797-1000 Founded/Ownrshp 1948
Sales 154.2MME EMP 2,985
Accts Plante & Moran Pllc Auburn Hi
SIC 8211 Public elementary & secondary schools
Pr: Carol Klenow
*Treas: Robert A Ross
Bd of Dir: Ken Krolczyk
*Trst: Jennifer L Prybys
*VP: Gene L Klida
IT Man: Bill Kirkaldy
IT Man: Paul Rand

D-U-N-S 19-978-5874 IMP
UTICA ENTERPRISES INC
UTICA LAESER SYSTEMS
5750 New King Dr Ste 200, Troy, MI 48098-2611
Tel (586) 726-4300 Founded/Ownrshp 1977
Sales 619.1MME EMP 2,718
SIC 3548 3549 3545 8711 3541 3544 Welding apparatus; Assembly machines, including robotic; Broaches (machine tool accessories); Designing: ship, boat, machine & product; Machine tools, metal cutting type; Broaching machines; Special dies & tools
Ch Bd: Thomas J Carter
*Pr: Stefan Wanczyk
*VP: Dennis Lucas
Prgrm Mgr: Tim Mansfield
Off Mgr: Debbie Connell
Dir IT: Brian Hughes

UTICA LAESER SYSTEMS
See UTICA ENTERPRISES INC

D-U-N-S 15-731-7272
UTICA MUTUAL INSURANCE CO
UTICA NATIONAL INSURANCE GROUP
180 Genesee St, New Hartford, NY 13413-2299
Tel (315) 734-2000 Founded/Ownrshp 1914
Sales NA EMP 1,350
SIC 6331 6311 Fire, marine & casualty insurance: mutual; Life insurance carriers
Ch Bd: J Douglas Robinson
*Ch Bd: William Craig Heston
*Pr: Richard P Creedon
*CFO: Anthony C Paolozzi
VP: Thomas Bonaros
CTO: James P Cahart

UTICA NATIONAL INSURANCE GROUP
See UTICA MUTUAL INSURANCE CO

D-U-N-S 00-697-8407
UTICA NATIONAL INSURANCE GROUP
(Suby of UTICA NATIONAL INSURANCE GROUP) ★
180 Genesee St, New Hartford, NY 13413-2200
Tel (315) 734-2000 Founded/Ownrshp 1914
Sales NA EMP 1,109
SIC 6331 6411 Fire, marine & casualty insurance & carriers; Insurance agents, brokers & service
Ch Bd: J Douglas Robinson
Pr: Michael Austin
*Pr: Richard P Creedon
CFO: Anthony C Paolozzi
Ex VP: Daniel Daly
Sr VP: Raymond E Cox
Sr VP: Kenneth Dedrick
Sr VP: Steven Guski
Sr VP: Brian McCulloch
Sr VP: Andrew E Meehan
Sr VP: Jeffrey C Paige
Sr VP: Clarke Peterson
Sr VP: Albert Ritchie
Sr VP: Robert Slovin
Sr VP: Anthony L Sychtysz
Sr VP: Michael Wolfe
*Sr VP: John R Zapisek
VP: Dane R Austin
VP: William C Bachman
VP: Paul L Cohen
VP: David Cunningham

UTICA PUBLIC SCHOOLS
See UTICA CITY SCHOOL DISTRICT

UTICOR TECHNOLOGY
See AVG ADVANCED TECHNOLOGIES LP

UTILCO DIV
See ILSCO CORP

D-U-N-S 96-173-8163
UTILICON SOLUTIONS LTD
(Suby of ASPLUNDH TREE EXPERT CO) ★
708 Blair Mill Rd, Willow Grove, PA 19090-1701
Tel (215) 784-4200 Founded/Ownrshp 2004
Sales 165.3MME EMP 473
SIC 4939 4923 Combination utilities; Gas transmission & distribution
CEO: Christopher B Asplundh

D-U-N-S 14-278-8806
■ UTILIMAP CORP
(Suby of QUANTA SERVICES INC) ★
10025 Office Center Ave, Saint Louis, MO 63128-1393
Tel (636) 533-0472 Founded/Ownrshp 2011
Sales 92.7MME EMP 300
SIC 7389 Mapmaking services
Pr: Ron Bond
*VP: John Czaicki

D-U-N-S 96-682-2033 IMP/EXP
■ UTILIMASTER SERVICES LLC
(Suby of SPARTAN MOTORS INC) ★
603 Earthway Blvd, Bristol, IN 46507-9182
Tel (574) 848-2000 Founded/Ownrshp 2005
Sales 8.0MMM EMP 3
SIC 7532 Van conversion
Pr: John Forbes
*Treas: Lori Wade
VP: Michael Erickson
VP: Frank Majszak
VP: Stevan Plote
Sfty Mgr: Tony Cuskaden
Sfty Mgr: Jen Molbash
Snr Mgr: Dan Crafts

D-U-N-S 16-722-0081
■ UTILIQUEST LLC
(Suby of DYCOM INDUSTRIES INC) ★
2575 Westside Pkwy # 100, Alpharetta, GA 30004-6410
Tel (678) 461-3900 Founded/Ownrshp 2004
Sales 282.0MME EMP 1,105E
SIC 1623 3812 Communication line & transmission tower construction; Search & navigation equipment
Pr: Dennis Tarosky
CFO: Robert D Amico
CFO: Robert D'Amico
Ex VP: Terry L Fordham
VP: Richard Krauss
VP: Mark Redfern
VP: Thurman Smith
VP: William Stewart
IT Man: Steven Hull
Opers Mgr: Michael Rukavina
Board of Directors: Steven Nielsen

D-U-N-S 03-826-1780
UTILITIES BOARD OF CITY OF FOLEY
RIVIERA UTILITIES
413 E Laurel Ave, Foley, AL 36535-2619
Tel (251) 943-5001 Founded/Ownrshp 1952
Sales 139.1MME EMP 235
Accts Hartmann Blackmon & Kilgore
SIC 4911 1623 4841 Distribution, electric power; Water, sewer & utility lines; Cable & other pay television services
Pr: Michael M Dugger
*CEO: Thomas Dabell
*VP: Robert Schrieber

D-U-N-S 04-390-8193
UTILITIES INC
2335 Sanders Rd, Northbrook, IL 60062-6196
Tel (847) 498-6440 Founded/Ownrshp 1965
Sales 586.6MME EMP 530
SIC 4941 4952 Water supply; Sewerage systems
Pr: Lisa Sparrow
*COO: Lisa Crossett
*COO: John Hoy
*CFO: Jim Japczyk
*VP: John Stover
VP: Carl J Wenz
*Exec: Steve Lubertozzi
Rgnl Mgr: Bob Gilroy
Dir IT: Tom Ostler

D-U-N-S 03-184-5386
UTILITY BOARD OF CITY OF KEY WEST
KEYS ENERGY SERVICE
1001 James St, Key West, FL 33040-6935
Tel (305) 295-1000 Founded/Ownrshp 1980
Sales 91.3MM EMP 164
Accts Oropeza & Parks Key West Flo
SIC 1623 Electric power line construction
CEO: Lynne E Tejeda
Ofcr: Bobby Ruble
Exec: Gricel Owen
*Genl Mgr: Lynne Tejeda
IT Man: Terry Beeman
Plnt Mgr: James Barry

D-U-N-S 80-779-2457
■ UTILITY HOLDING LLC
(Suby of CENTERPOINT ENERGY INC) ★
1111 Louisiana St, Houston, TX 77002-5230
Tel (713) 207-1111 Founded/Ownrshp 2001
Sales 7.4MMME EMP 7,426
SIC 4924 4922 Natural gas distribution; Pipelines, natural gas

D-U-N-S 94-884-4717
UTILITY LINE SERVICES INC
1302 Conshohocken Rd # 100, Conshohocken, PA 19428-1035
Tel (484) 685-3489 Founded/Ownrshp 1996
Sales 114.2MME EMP 225
SIC 1623 Water, sewer & utility lines
Pr: Austin A Meehan
Sfty Dirs: Gary Folk

UTILITY MANAGEMENT AND SUPPLY
See SUNRISE ELECTRIC SUPPLY INC

D-U-N-S 08-000-7296
UTILITY ONE SOURCE LP
7701 Independence Ave, Kansas City, MO 64125-1300
Tel (312) 316-9520 Founded/Ownrshp 2015
Sales 171.8MME EMP 748E
SIC 3713 Utility truck bodies
CEO: Chris Ragot

D-U-N-S 80-999-3202
UTILITY SUPPLY AND CONSTRUCTION CO
420 S Roth St Ste A, Reed City, MI 49677-9115
Tel (231) 832-2297 Founded/Ownrshp 2007
Sales 181.8MME EMP 353
SIC 2411 2491 2631 5063 Logging; Wood preserving; Coated & treated board; Electrical supplies
Pr: Michael Bigford
*CFO: Charles Holmquist
*Prin: Franklin C Wheatlake

D-U-N-S 00-828-6908 IMP/EXP
UTILITY TRAILER MANUFACTURING CO
17295 Railroad St Ste A, City of Industry, CA 91748-1043
Tel (626) 964-7319 Founded/Ownrshp 1914
Sales 1.0MMME EMP 3,000
SIC 3715 Semitrailers for truck tractors
Ch Bd: Paul F Bennett
*Pr: Harold C Bennett
*Sr VP: Craig M Bennett
*VP: Jeffrey J Bennett
VP: Steven Bennett
Sales Exec: David Wallace
Natl Sales: Sal Molina
Mktg Mgr: Des Dugquem
Manager: Shawn McManaway
Manager: Robert Ojeda
Board of Directors: Janet Adler, Melissa Bernal

D-U-N-S 80-947-2053
UTILITY TRAILER OF DALLAS INC
34241 Lyndon B Jhnson Fwy, Dallas, TX 75241-7216
Tel (972) 225-8845 Founded/Ownrshp 1991
Sales 84.0MM EMP 30
Accts Fred J Bastie & Associates P
SIC 5012 5015 5511 Trailers for trucks, new & used; Trailer parts & accessories, used; Trucks, tractors & trailers: new & used
Pr: Patrick W Watson
*VP: Susan D Watson
Sales Asso: Jeff Taylor
Sales Asso: Glen Williams

D-U-N-S 82-468-1584
UTILITY TRAILER SALES OF SOUTHERN CALIFORNIA LLC
15567 Valley Blvd, Fontana, CA 92335-6351
Tel (877) 275-4887 Founded/Ownrshp 1914
Sales 88.1MM EMP 110
SIC 5012 5013 5531 5561 Trailers for passenger vehicles; Automotive supplies & parts; Automobile & truck equipment & parts; Travel trailers: automobile, new & used
Mng Dir: Raymond Gonzalez

D-U-N-S 00-908-9871
UTILITY TRAILER SALES OF UTAH INC
SITE STORAGE
4970 W 2100 S, Salt Lake City, UT 84120-1226
Tel (801) 973-4040 Founded/Ownrshp 1982
Sales 146.8MM EMP 60
Accts Eide Bailly Llp Ogden Utah
SIC 5511 5531 7539 Trucks, tractors & trailers: new & used; Truck equipment & parts; Trailer repair
Pr: Michael E Deputy
*Sec: Clair Heslop
Sls Mgr: Bob Mueller
Sales Asso: Shane Fjeldsted
Sales Asso: Dan Hyde
Sales Asso: Marcus Klug
Sales Asso: Dave McClellan
Sales Asso: Bob Merrill
Sales Asso: Bruce Nielsen
Sales Asso: Jordan Poulsen

UTILITY TRUCK SERVICES
See CONNEXUS ENERGY

D-U-N-S 96-173-8122
UTILITY VEGETATION SERVICES INC
(Suby of ASPLUNDH TREE EXPERT CO) ★
708 Blair Mill Rd, Willow Grove, PA 19090-1701
Tel (215) 784-4200 Founded/Ownrshp 2010
Sales 127.9MME EMP 1,000
SIC 0783 Spraying services, ornamental tree
Prin: Christopher B Asplundh

D-U-N-S 13-147-2680 IMP
UTILX CORP
(Suby of NOVINIUM INC) ★
22820 Russell Rd, Kent, WA 98032-4892
Tel (253) 395-4535 Founded/Ownrshp 2015
Sales 84.6MME EMP 210
SIC 1623 Underground utilities contractor
Pr: Jack Stel
Sr VP: Glenn Bertini
VP: James Adkinson Jr
*VP: Gus Derezes
*VP: Jason French
*VP: Kris Rubino
*VP: Rick Stagi
*CTO: Connie Wheeler
IT Man: Samantha Martin
Opers Mgr: Mike Berry

D-U-N-S 00-957-8693
■ UTLX MANUFACTURING LLC
(Suby of UNION TANK CAR CO) ★
16923 Old Beaumont 90, Houston, TX 77049
Tel (281) 847-8200 Founded/Ownrshp 2010
Sales 122.8MME EMP 550
SIC 3795 Tank recovery vehicles
Pr: Jeremy De La Cerda

D-U-N-S 17-723-9977
UTOPIA HOME CARE INC
60 E Main St, Kings Park, NY 11754-2730
Tel (631) 544-6005 Founded/Ownrshp 1983
Sales 60.1MME EMP 2,000
SIC 8082 8093 Home health care services; Rehabilitation center, outpatient treatment
Ch Bd: Manuel F Martinez
CFO: Thomas Catalanotto
CFO: Andree Grasso
*Sec: Angelena Martinez
*VP: David Martinez
*VP: Diane Martinez
*VP: Manuel G Martinez
Dir Bus: Brent Piepenbring
Genl Mgr: Matthew Hetterich
Off Mgr: Mildred Ortiz
Off Admin: Lisa Hathaway

D-U-N-S 82-568-0598
UTRECHT - AMERICA HOLDINGS INC
RABOBANK NEDERLAND
(Suby of RABOBANK INTERNATIONAL HOLDING B.V.)
245 Park Ave Fl 36, New York, NY 10167-0002
Tel (212) 916-7800 Founded/Ownrshp 1993
Sales NA EMP 2,058
SIC 6022 State commercial banks
Ch Bd: Cor Broekhuyse
VP: Robert Yamasaki
Exec: Brett Delfino
Netwrk Mgr: Tammy Valvo

UTSA
See UNIVERSITY OF TEXAS AT SAN ANTONIO

D-U-N-S 07-943-5062
UTTAM GALVA NORTH AMERICA INC
UGMA
(Suby of UTTAM GALVA STEELS LIMITED)
1500 Broadway Fl 16, New York, NY 10036-4015
Tel (917) 722-8177 Founded/Ownrshp 2014
Sales 100.0MM EMP 5
SIC 5051 Ferroalloys
CEO: Stephan Schoop
*CFO: Daniel Bain

D-U-N-S 01-003-4775 IMP/EXP
UTTERMOST CO
3325 Grassy Hill Rd, Rocky Mount, VA 24151-3911
Tel (540) 483-5103 Founded/Ownrshp 1975
Sales 128.7MM EMP 200
Accts Spencer Hager & Mosdell Pc
SIC 2392 5023 Household furnishings; Home furnishings
Ch: Robert M Cooper Sr
*Pr: Robert M Cooper Jr
*CFO: Tony Doss
Off Admin: Jennifer Preston
VP Opers: Ken Delp
Sfty Mgr: Stephanie Morgan
Opers Mgr: Susan Bowling
Ql Cn Mgr: Larry Forbes
Trfc Mgr: Gary Bowling
Sls Mgr: Scott Doyle
Sls Mgr: Mark Foster

D-U-N-S 00-302-2795 EXP
UTZ QUALITY FOODS LLC
900 High St, Hanover, PA 17331-1639
Tel (800) 367-7629 Founded/Ownrshp 1947
Sales 671.9MME EMP 1,800
SIC 2096 2052 2099 Potato chips & other potato-based snacks; Corn chips & other corn-based snacks; Cheese curls & puffs; Popcorn, already popped (except candy covered); Pretzels; Cookies; Food preparations
Pr: Michael W Rice
Ex VP: Todd Staub
VP: Ed Burda
VP: Brian Greth
VP: Thomas Lawrence
VP: Dylan Lissette
VP: George Neiterer
VP: Larry Racey
VP: Jane Rice
VP: John Warehime
Dist Mgr: Richard Kelly

D-U-N-S 12-972-5797
■ UUNET TECHNOLOGIES INC
VERIZON BUSINESS
(Suby of VERIZON BUSINESS GLOBAL LLC) ★
22001 Loudoun County Pkwy, Ashburn, VA 20147-6105
Tel (703) 726-9240 Founded/Ownrshp 2006
Sales 386.0MME EMP 2,001
SIC 4813
CEO: Michael Capellas

D-U-N-S 82-789-4549
UV LOGISTICS ACQUISITION HOLDING CORP
UNITED VISION LOGISTICS
4021 Abr Csy Py S 200 B A, Lafayette, LA 70503
Tel (337) 291-6700 Founded/Ownrshp 2007
Sales 615.1MME EMP 1,584E
SIC 4213 Trucking, except local
CEO: John Patterson
*Pr: Bentley Burgess
*CEO: Howard Hoffmann
*COO: Rusty Guilbeau
*CFO: Tim Alguire
Ofcr: Mark Southerst
Sr VP: Kurt Antkiewicz
*VP: Tim Daly
VP: Brian Hogan
*VP: Stan Stricklen Sr
Dir IT: Alex Mottram

D-U-N-S 17-488-1524
UV LOGISTICS LLC
UNITED VISION LOGISTICS
(Suby of UNITED VISION LOGISTICS) ★
4021 Ambssdor Cffery Pkwy, Lafayette, LA 70503-5281
Tel (337) 837-4757 Founded/Ownrshp 1987
Sales 112.5MME EMP 210
SIC 4213 1389 Contract haulers; Haulage, oil field
CEO: Rusty Guilbeau
CFO: Tim Alguire
Genl Mgr: Dana Ortego
IT Man: Brent Marceaux
Board of Directors: Steven Guilbeau

UVA CHILDREN'S HOSPITAL SPECIA
See UNIVERSITY OF VIRGINIA PHYSICIANS GROUP

UVAIR
See UNIVERSAL WEATHER AND AVIATION INC

UVE
See UNIVERSAL INSURANCE HOLDINGS INC

UW HEALTH
See UNIVERSITY OF WISCONSIN HOSPITALS AND CLINICS

D-U-N-S 01-709-9416
UW HEALTH
7974 Uw Health Ct, Middleton, WI 53562-5531
Tel (608) 829-5217 Founded/Ownrshp 2008
Sales 680.3MM EMP 5
SIC 8099 Health & allied services
Pr: Donna Katen-Bahensky
VP: Michael Rosencrance

UW HOSPITAL
See REGIONAL DIVISION INC

UW MEDICAL FOUNDATION
See UNIVERSITY OF WISCONSIN MEDICAL FOUNDATION INC

D-U-N-S 07-821-6165
UW MEDICINE/NORTHWEST
(*Suby of* NORTHWEST HOSPITAL & MEDICAL CENTER) ★
1550 N 115th St, Seattle, WA 98133-8401
Tel (206) 364-0500 *Founded/Ownrshp* 1949
Sales 279.3MM^E *EMP* 1,380
SIC 8062

D-U-N-S 96-257-8709
UW MEDICINE/NORTHWEST
NORTHWEST HOSPITAL & MEDICAL C
(*Suby of* NORTHWEST HOSPITAL & MEDICAL CENTER) ★
1550 N 115th St, Seattle, WA 98133-8401
Tel (206) 364-0500 *Founded/Ownrshp* 1949
Sales 293.1MM *EMP* 23^E
SIC 8062

D-U-N-S 02-748-0847 IMP
UWAJIMAYA INC
KUSTOM FOOD
4601 6th Ave S, Seattle, WA 98108-1716
Tel (206) 624-6248 *Founded/Ownrshp* 1965
Sales 153.6MM^E *EMP* 425
SIC 5141 5411 Groceries, general line; Grocery stores, independent
Pr: Tomoko Matsuno
**Treas:* Andy Ike
Genl Mgr: Tommie Oiye
IT Man: Manny Matias
IT Man: David Onishi
Sls Mgr: Alan Kurimura

UWW
See GRAPHIC COMMUNICATIONS HOLDINGS INC

V

D-U-N-S 02-334-2298 IMP
V & H INC
1505 S Central Ave, Marshfield, WI 54449-4904
Tel (715) 387-2545 *Founded/Ownrshp* 1966
Sales 135.0MM^E *EMP* 260
SIC 5511 7513 Automobiles, new & used; Trucks, tractors & trailers: new & used; Truck leasing, without drivers
Pr: Terry Frankland
Pr: Steve Dieringer
**VP:* Robert Wiskerchen
Exec: Mary Ule
Exec: Mary Yule
**Prin:* Jeff Hamus
Brnch Mgr: Brent Janak
**Genl Mgr:* Bill Arndt
CTO: Cindy Gudgeon
Sfty Dirs: Justin Lakies
Prd Mgr: Russ Hagen

D-U-N-S 02-813-7698
V & J EMPLOYMENT SERVICES INC
(*Suby of* V & J HOLDING COMPANIES INC) ★
53223 W Brown Deer Rd, Milwaukee, WI 53223
Tel (414) 365-9003 *Founded/Ownrshp* 1996
Sales 90.0MM *EMP* 25
SIC 5812 Restaurant, family: chain
Pr: Valerie Carter

D-U-N-S 07-160-9155
V & J HOLDING COMPANIES INC (WI)
6933 W Brown Deer Rd Fl 2, Milwaukee, WI 53223-2103
Tel (414) 365-9003 *Founded/Ownrshp* 1984, 1997
Sales 43.4M *EMP* 3,500
SIC 5812 Pizzeria, chain
Ch: John Daniels
**Pr:* Valerie Carter
Rgnl Mgr: Bobbie Santos
IT Man: Tony Weiss

D-U-N-S 36-421-3090
V & J NATIONAL AND UNITED ENTERPRISES LLC
PIZZA HUT
1425 Mount Read Blvd # 1, Rochester, NY 14606-2845
Tel (585) 458-8140 *Founded/Ownrshp* 1997
Sales 11.9MM^E *EMP* 1,300
SIC 5812 Pizzeria, chain
VP: John C Draper

D-U-N-S 04-312-5884
V & J NATIONAL ENTERPRISES LLC (WI)
PIZZA HUT
(*Suby of* V & J HOLDING COMPANIES INC) ★
1425 Mount Read Blvd # 1, Rochester, NY 14606-2844
Tel (585) 458-8140 *Founded/Ownrshp* 1997
Sales 40.1MM^E *EMP* 1,600
SIC 5812 Pizzeria, chain
Pr: Valerie Carter
**VP:* John Daniels
Snr Mgr: Betsy Thomas

D-U-N-S 01-848-0533
V AND V APPLIANCE PARTS INC
27 W Myrtle Ave, Youngstown, OH 44507-1193
Tel (330) 743-5144 *Founded/Ownrshp* 1959
Sales 210.0MM *EMP* 100
SIC 5064 Appliance parts, household
Pr: Bruce Lazar
**Ch Bd:* Victor Lazar
**Treas:* Judy Lazar
**Prin:* Albert E Brennan
**Prin:* Vincent Rypien
Manager: Michael Deonofrio

V B D
See VERA BRADLEY DESIGNS INC

V C E
See VOLVO CONSTRUCTION EQUIPMENT NORTH AMERICA LLC

V C S
See VITALIZE CONSULTING SOLUTIONS INC

V C U
See VIRGINIA COMMONWEALTH UNIVERSITY

V F
See VF SERVICES LLC

V G S
See VEGETABLE GROWERS SUPPLY CO

V GT
See VIDEO GAMING TECHNOLOGIES INC

V H A
See VETERANS HEALTH ADMINISTRATION

V H B
See VANASSE HANGEN BRUSTLIN INC

D-U-N-S 83-642-0000
V H COOPER & CO INC
COOPER FOODS
(*Suby of* COOPER FARMS) ★
2321 State Route 49, Fort Recovery, OH 45846-9501
Tel (419) 375-4116 *Founded/Ownrshp* 1975
Sales 128.2MM^E *EMP* 1,400
SIC 0253 2015 2011 Turkeys & turkey eggs; Chicken slaughtering & processing; Pork products from pork slaughtered on site; Hams & picnics from meat slaughtered on site
Pr: James R Cooper
**COO:* Gary A Cooper
**CFO:* Neil Diller
**Treas:* Anada E Cooper

V I A
See VIA METROPOLITAN TRANSIT

V I P
See VIP HEALTH CARE SERVICES INC

D-U-N-S 04-145-9447
V I P INC
VIP PARTS, TIRES & SERVICE
12 Lexington St, Lewiston, ME 04240-3509
Tel (207) 784-5423 *Founded/Ownrshp* 2001
Sales 348.3MM^E *EMP* 1,000
SIC 5531

D-U-N-S 03-007-6988 IMP
V L H INC
H V L
(*Suby of* ATRIUM INNOVATIONS INC)
600 Boyce Rd, Pittsburgh, PA 15205-9742
Tel (800) 245-4440 *Founded/Ownrshp* 2005
Sales 117.7MM^E *EMP* 400
SIC 2833 5122 2834 Vitamins, natural or synthetic: bulk, uncompounded; Drugs, proprietaries & sundries; Pharmaceutical preparations
Pr: L Douglas Lioon
**Pr:* Harry E Vernacchio
MIS Mgr: Ron Golias
Prd Mgr: Philip White
Natl Sales: Deborah Tew

V M I
See VANTAGE MOBILITY INTERNATIONAL LLC

V N A OF THE BERKSHIRES
See BERKSHIRE MEDICAL CENTER INC

V P H
See VALLEY PRESBYTERIAN HOSPITAL

D-U-N-S 62-305-8161
V P HOLDINGS INC
(*Suby of* COX ENTERPRISES INC) ★
8605 Largo Lakes Dr, Largo, FL 33773-4912
Tel (727) 393-1270 *Founded/Ownrshp* 1991
Sales 105.1MM^E *EMP* 1,660
SIC 7331 Direct mail advertising services
Pr: J R Smith
**Pr:* William Bisbow
**Treas:* William Disbrow
**VP:* P Bradley Barnett
**VP:* Brian G Cooper

D-U-N-S 00-222-3055
V P SUPPLY CORP (NY)
INNOVATIONS BY VP SUPPLY
3445 Winton Pl Ste 101, Rochester, NY 14623-2950
Tel (585) 272-0110 *Founded/Ownrshp* 1960, 1963
Sales 291.2MM^E *EMP* 315
SIC 5074 Plumbing & hydronic heating supplies
Pr: Gary Curwin
**Sec:* Louis Curwin
**VP:* Gary Perkins

V S L
See STRUCTURAL TECHNOLOGIES LLC

D-U-N-S 03-249-7884
V SUAREZ & CO INC
Industrial Luchetti 300 C, Bayamon, PR 00961
Tel (787) 792-1212 *Founded/Ownrshp* 1950
Sales 500.0MM *EMP* 550
SIC 5182 5149 Wine & distilled beverages; Beverages, except coffee & tea
CEO: Diego Surez Jr
**Pr:* Joaqun Dvila
**Ch:* Diego Surez Snchez

D-U-N-S 09-001-0893 IMP
V SUAREZ & CO INC
LIQUORS DIVISION
Industrial Luchetti # 300, Bayamon, PR 00961
Tel (787) 792-1212 *Founded/Ownrshp* 1943
Sales 478.0MM *EMP* 496
SIC 5181 5141 5182 Beer & other fermented malt liquors; Groceries, general line; Bottling wines & liquors
Ch Bd: Diego Suarez Sanchez
Pr: ISA Maire Rivera
**Pr:* Diego Suarez Jr
**Treas:* Vicente Suarez Jr
**VP:* Joaquin Davila
**VP:* Clotilde Perez
**VP:* Jorge Rivera
**VP:* Tomas Rosario
VP Mktg: Raul Armstrong

D-U-N-S 09-967-5253 IMP
V&M STAR A PARTNERSHIP WITH GENERAL AND LIMITED PARTNERS LP
(*Suby of* VALLOUREC TUBES)
8603 Sheldon Rd, Houston, TX 77049-1812
Tel (281) 456-6000 *Founded/Ownrshp* 2002
Sales 141.4MM^E *EMP* 561
SIC 3317 Steel pipe & tubes
Pr: Joel Mastervich

D-U-N-S 15-749-4246
V-B/WILLIAMS FURNITURE CO INC
300 E Grayson St, Galax, VA 24333-2964
Tel (276) 236-6161 *Founded/Ownrshp* 1900
Sales 125.0MM *EMP* 450
SIC 2511 Wood bedroom furniture; Bedside stands: wood
Pr: John D Bassett III
**Pr:* Wayard Bassett

D-U-N-S 02-566-3881 IMP
V-G SUPPLY CO
1400 Renaissance Dr # 309, Park Ridge, IL 60068-1336
Tel (708) 891-1500 *Founded/Ownrshp* 1917
Sales 164.2MM^E *EMP* 80
SIC 5191 5193 Garden supplies; Soil, potting & planting; Flowers & florists' supplies; Flowers & nursery stock; Nursery stock; Florists' supplies
Pr: Kenneth Kotas
Off Mgr: Maria Marketti
VP Opers: Tom Doll

D-U-N-S 00-727-5399 IMP
V-T INDUSTRIES INC
VT INDUSTRIES
1000 Industrial Park, Holstein, IA 51025-7730
Tel (712) 368-4381 *Founded/Ownrshp* 1956
Sales 192.6MM^E *EMP* 534
SIC 3089 3083 4213 2435 2434 2431 Plastic hardware & building products; Doors, folding: plastic or plastic coated fabric; Plastic finished products, laminated; Trucking, except local; Hardwood veneer & plywood; Wood kitchen cabinets; Millwork
Pr: Douglas E Clausen
**Treas:* Randall S Gerritsen
Treas: Randy Gerritsen
Sr VP: Craig Francisco
VP: John Bowling
VP: Jason Farver
VP: Elizabeth A Hansch
VP: Rick Liddell
VP: Ryan Miller
Dir IT: Teri Luebeck
Netwrk Mgr: Terry Christensen

D-U-N-S 14-508-1738
V2SOFT INC
300 Enterprise Ct Ste 100, Bloomfield Hills, MI 48302-0377
Tel (248) 904-1705 *Founded/Ownrshp* 1998
Sales 30.0MM *EMP* 1,000
SIC 7371 Computer software development
CEO: Varchasvi Shankar
**VP:* Nandini S Varchasvi
Snr Mgr: V Kumar

D-U-N-S 02-727-5181 IMP/EXP
VA CELL INC
8400 Nw 33rd St Ste 103, Doral, FL 33122-1937
Tel (305) 592-1367 *Founded/Ownrshp* 2009
Sales 356.1MM *EMP* 11
Accts Glsc & Company Pllc Miami F
SIC 5065 5043 Mobile telephone equipment; Photographic equipment & supplies
CEO: Sunil Agrawal
Pr: Deepak Agrawal

D-U-N-S 11-279-3513
VA HOSPITAL
OVERTON BROOKS VA MEDICAL CTR
510 E Stoner Ave, Shreveport, LA 71101-4243
Tel (318) 221-8411 *Founded/Ownrshp* 2003
Sales 172.0MM *EMP* 99
SIC 8011 Medical centers
Prin: Billy Valentine
Dir Lab: Michael Salinas
CIO: Chris Ponder

D-U-N-S 10-687-9617
VA PORTLAND HEALTH CARE SYSTEM
3710 Sw Us Vtrans Hosp Rd, Portland, OR 97239-2964
Tel (503) 273-5048 *Founded/Ownrshp* 2015
Sales 131.4M^E *EMP* 6,000
SIC 8062 8742 General medical & surgical hospitals; Hospital & health services consultant
COO: Michael E Bays
CFO: Steve Zimmerman
Ofcr: Kathleen M Chapman
Ofcr: Joseph Murley
QA Dir: Beth Keeth
Pathlgst: Marie Rau
Surgeon: H S Floten
Surgeon: William Guyer
Nutrtnst: Marlin Schue
Pharmcst: Donald Love
Resp Thrpy: Helmet Haas

D-U-N-S 05-654-1812
■ **VA SOUTHERN NEVADA HEALTHCARE SYSTEM**
(*Suby of* V H A) ★
6900 Pecos Rd, North Las Vegas, NV 89086-4400
Tel (702) 791-9000 *Founded/Ownrshp* 2010
Sales 83.2MM^E *EMP* 1^E
SIC 8051 9451 Skilled nursing care facilities;
Prin: Teresa Hayden

D-U-N-S 03-884-5673
VACAVILLE UNIFIED SCHOOL DISTRICT
401 Nut Tree Rd Ste 100, Vacaville, CA 95687-3508
Tel (707) 453-6121 *Founded/Ownrshp* 1990
Sales 101.6MM^E *EMP* 2,327
SIC 8211 Public elementary & secondary schools
COO: R Marcia
Ofcr: Walt Simon
VP: Jerry Eaton
Sys Mgr: Phil Jenschke
Teacher Pr: Janet Dieprich

VACO
See VETERANS BENEFITS ADMINISTRATION

D-U-N-S 09-579-3170 IMP/EXP
■ **VACTOR MANUFACTURING INC** (IL)
(*Suby of* FEDERAL SIGNAL CORP) ★
1621 S Illinois St, Streator, IL 61364-3945
Tel (815) 672-3171 *Founded/Ownrshp* 1911, 1994
Sales 228.8MM^E *EMP* 1,500
SIC 3537 Industrial trucks & tractors
Pr: Samuel Miceli
**Pr:* Dan Schueller
VP: Phil Rankin
Genl Mgr: Tammy Luckey
Ql Cn Mgr: Doug Johnson
Sls&Mrk Ex: Brian Halstead

D-U-N-S 08-003-2086
■ **VADNAIS TRENCHLESS SERVICES INC** (CA)
(*Suby of* PRIMORIS SERVICES CORP) ★
26000 Commercentre Dr, Lake Forest, CA 92630-8816
Tel (858) 550-1460 *Founded/Ownrshp* 2014
Sales 118.0MM^E *EMP* 429^E
SIC 1623 1622 Water, sewer & utility lines; Tunnel construction
CEO: Paul Vadnais

VAGABOND INNS
See RPD HOTELS 18 LLC

VAI
See VAN ANDEL RESEARCH INSTITUTE

D-U-N-S 08-039-2483
VAIL CLINIC INC
VAIL VALLEY MEDICAL CENTER
181 W Meadow Dr Ste 100, Vail, CO 81657-5058
Tel (970) 476-2451 *Founded/Ownrshp* 1966
Sales 153.7MM *EMP* 550
SIC 8062 General medical & surgical hospitals
CEO: Doris Kirchner
COO: Stan Anderson
**CFO:* Elizabeth Propp
VP: Diane Botkin
VP: Nicholas Brown
VP: Susan Brozovich
VP: Brian Foster
VP: Sarah Moody
**Prin:* Tom Zellers
CTO: Stuart Read
Dir IT: Mark Lacross

D-U-N-S 80-999-8102
VAIL CORP
390 Interlocken Cres # 1000, Broomfield, CO 80021-8038
Tel (303) 404-1800 *Founded/Ownrshp* 1967
Sales 635.8MM^E *EMP* 19,000^E
SIC 7011 Resort hotel
CEO: Rob A Katz
**Pr:* Richard D Kincaid

D-U-N-S 79-619-2243
▲ **VAIL RESORTS INC**
390 Interlocken Cres, Broomfield, CO 80021-8038
Tel (303) 404-1800 *Founded/Ownrshp* 1997
Sales 1.6MMM *EMP* 5,200
Tkr Sym MTN *Exch* NYS
SIC 7011 6552 Hotels & motels; Ski lodge; Land subdividers & developers, commercial
Ch Bd: Robert A Katz
COO: Patricia Campbell
COO: Christopher E Jarnot
COO: James C O'Donnell
COO: William Rock
COO: Paul G Toner
CFO: Michael Z Barkin
CFO: Michael Barkin
Bd of Dir: Nancy McCoy
Ofcr: Mark R Gasta
Ex VP: Kirsten A Lynch
Ex VP: Randall E Mehrberg
Ex VP: David T Shapiro
Ex VP: Robert N Urwiler
VP: Jeremy Coleman
VP: Gerald Flynn
VP: Angela Korch
VP: Ryan Siurek
VP: Shawn Tebben
VP: Monique Tuttle
Exec: Paul Wade

D-U-N-S 00-290-2815
VAIL SCHOOL DISTRICT
13801 E Benson Hwy Unit B, Vail, AZ 85641-9064
Tel (520) 879-2000 *Founded/Ownrshp* 1903
Sales 102.6MM *EMP* 1,800
Accts Heinfeld Meech & Co PcT
SIC 8211 Public elementary & secondary schools; Public junior high school; School board
Genl Mgr: Stuart Duncan
Off Mgr: Sandra Mooney
Store Mgr: Kathleen Good
MIS Dir: Mark Breen
MIS Dir: Matt Federoff
Psych: Dainah Graham

VAIL VALLEY MEDICAL CENTER
See VAIL CLINIC INC

D-U-N-S 11-415-5141
VAIL VALLEY SURGERY CENTER LLC
181 W Meadow Dr Ste 100, Vail, CO 81657-5058
Tel (970) 476-8872 *Founded/Ownrshp* 2002
Sales 156.2MM *EMP* 25
SIC 8062 General medical & surgical hospitals

VAL D'OR
See CANNON COUNTY KNITTING MILLS INC

D-U-N-S 78-885-4789 IMP/EXP
VAL DOR APPAREL LLC
VALDOR APPAREL
6820 Lyons Technology Pkw, Coconut Creek, FL 33073-4323
Tel (954) 363-7340 *Founded/Ownrshp* 2006
Sales 35.0MM *EMP* 1,800

SIC 2322 2329 2331 2339 2341 Men's & boys' underwear & nightwear; Men's & boys' sportswear & athletic clothing; T-shirts & tops, women's: made from purchased materials; Women's & misses' outerwear; Women's & children's undergarments
CEO: Robert Rothbaum
CFO: Marc Odrobina
Sls Dir: Darlene Arman

D-U-N-S 12-085-6257
VAL VERDE UNIFIED SCH DIS
975 Morgan St, Perris, CA 92571-3103
Tel (951) 940-6100 Founded/Ownrshp 1917
Sales 84.7MM[E] EMP 1,500
SIC 8211 Public elementary & secondary schools
Pr: Shelly Yarbrough
*VP: Wraymond Sawyerr
*Prin: Fredy De Leon
*Prin: Michael M Vargas
Dir Sec: Mark Clark
Dir IT: Robert Delcampo
Pr Dir: Daniel Whitfield

D-U-N-S 02-861-8585 IMP/EXP
VAL-PRO INC
VALLEY FRUIT & PRODUCE CO
1601 E Olympic Blvd # 300, Los Angeles, CA 90021-1942
Tel (213) 627-8736 Founded/Ownrshp 1950
Sales 139.2MM[E] EMP 220
SIC 5148

D-U-N-S 60-281-3768
VALASSIS COMMUNICATIONS INC
(Suby of HARLAND CLARKE HOLDINGS CORP) ★
19975 Victor Pkwy, Livonia, MI 48152-7001
Tel (734) 591-3000 Founded/Ownrshp 2014
Sales 904.4MM[E] EMP 6,400[E]
SIC 7319 7331 7372 Distribution of advertising material or sample services; Direct mail advertising services; Business oriented computer software
Pr: Robert A Mason
*COO: Ronald L Goolsby
*CFO: Grant Fitz
*CFO: Robert L Recchia
*Ch: Alan F Schultz
*Ex VP: James D Parkinson
*Ex VP: Todd L Wiseley
Snr Sftwr: Kevin Swanson
Dir IT: Deb Monahan
IT Man: Ed Anklam
IT Man: David Stewart

D-U-N-S 06-220-0878
VALASSIS DIRECT MAIL INC
(Suby of VALASSIS COMMUNICATIONS INC) ★
1 Targeting Ctr, Windsor, CT 06095-2639
Tel (800) 437-0479 Founded/Ownrshp 2007
Sales 178.9MM[E] EMP 3,800
SIC 7331 Mailing service
Pr: Rob Mason
*COO: Ron Goolsby
*CFO: Steve Mitzel
*CFO: Robert L Recchia
Ofcr: Daniel J Sheehan
*Ex VP: Suzie Brown
*Ex VP: Todd Wiseley
VP: David Hennessey
Genl Mgr: Joel Salomons

D-U-N-S 87-287-4599
VALASSIS INTERNATIONAL INC
(Suby of VALASSIS COMMUNICATIONS INC) ★
19975 Victor Pkwy, Livonia, MI 48152-7001
Tel (734) 591-3000 Founded/Ownrshp 1994
Sales 344.1MM[E] EMP 6,000
SIC 8743 3993 2759 2752 Promotion service; Sales promotion; Signs & advertising specialties; Commercial printing; Commercial printing, lithographic
Pr: Rob Mason
*CEO: Ron Goolsby
Ex VP: Richard Herpich
*Ex VP: Jim Parkinson
*Ex VP: Robert L Recchia
*Ex VP: Todd Wiseley
Sr VP: Eva Kohn
Sftwr Eng: Joel Nelson

D-U-N-S 03-216-0695
VALCO COMPANIES INC
2710 Division Hwy, New Holland, PA 17557-9650
Tel (717) 354-4586 Founded/Ownrshp 2006
Sales 121.4MM[E] EMP 353[E]
SIC 5083 Poultry & livestock equipment
Pr: Joseph A Wetzel
*Treas: Rebecca J Leroy
VP: Fernando Grilo
*VP: Frederick W Steudler
*VP: Richard S Steudler
Dir IT: Mark Robinson
Site Mgr: Kenneth Rinier
Ql Cn Mgr: Fred Hammond
Sales Asso: Thomas Rizzardi

D-U-N-S 00-314-7873 IMP
VALDESE WEAVERS LLC (NC)
(Suby of CENTURY FURNITURE INDUSTRIES) ★
1000 Perkins Rd Se, Valdese, NC 28690-9749
Tel (828) 874-2181 Founded/Ownrshp 1924
Sales 136.2MM[E] EMP 800
SIC 2211 2221 Upholstery fabrics, cotton; Upholstery fabrics, manmade fiber & silk
CEO: Michael Shelton
*Treas: Richard Reese
Sr VP: Bob Walters
VP: Joel Crisp
*VP: Snyder Garrison
VP: Janet Kuck
VP: Blake Millinor
QA Dir: Kathy Duncan
Sys Mgr: Tammy Adams
Web Dev: Chalmer Dill
Software D: Maria Tiso
Board of Directors: Nancy Dowdy, A Alex Shuford II, Charles H Shuford

VALDOR APPAREL
See VAL DOR APPAREL LLC

D-U-N-S 07-081-8642
VALDOSTA CITY SCHOOL DISTRICT
1204 Williams St, Valdosta, GA 31601-4043
Tel (229) 333-8500 Founded/Ownrshp 2011
Sales 33.2MM[E] EMP 1,000[E]
SIC 8211 Public elementary & secondary schools
Netwrk Mgr: Ralph Ward
Pr Dir: Jennifer Steedley
Schl Brd P: Dean Rexroth
Teacher Pr: Owen Clemons

D-U-N-S 87-993-2077
VALDOSTA STATE UNIVERSITY
(Suby of GEORGIA BOARD OF REGENTS) ★
1500 N Patterson St, Valdosta, GA 31698-0001
Tel (229) 333-5800 Founded/Ownrshp 1906
Sales 194.7M[E] EMP 1,956
SIC 8221 College, except junior
Pr: James McKinney
Pr: Traycee F Martin
Assoc Dir: Marsha Walden
*Prin: Patrick Schloss
Brnch Mgr: Steve Blair
Brnch Mgr: Corine Myers
Brnch Mgr: Julie Reffel
CIO: Brian Haugabrook
Sls Dir: Ric Sisler

D-U-N-S 04-223-0623 IMP
VALEANT PHARMACEUTICALS INTERNATIONAL CORP
(Suby of VALEANT PHARMACEUTICALS INTERNATIONAL, INC)
400 Somerset Corp Blvd, Bridgewater, NJ 08807-2867
Tel (908) 927-1400 Founded/Ownrshp 1960
Sales 3.4MMM[E] EMP 4,044
SIC 2834 Pharmaceutical preparations
CEO: J Michael Pearson
Pr: Charles J Bramlage
Pr: Alissa H Lynch
*Pr: G Mason Morfit
COO: Rajiv De Silva
*CFO: Margaret Mulligan
*Ex VP: Robert Chai Onn
*Ex VP: Robert Rosiello
Sr VP: Robert Gelbard
Sr VP: John Julian
Sr VP: Johnson Yiu Nam Lau
Sr VP: John Phillips
VP: Doaa Fathallah
VP: Thomas Hadley
VP: Andrew Saik
VP: Bill Sumner
VP: Sharon Tonetta
VP: Ling Zeng
Dir Risk M: Saberi R Ali
Dir Bus: Rosanna Coveyou
Dir Bus: Warren Lei

D-U-N-S 12-289-3998
VALENCIA COLLEGE
1800 S Kirkman Rd, Orlando, FL 32811-2302
Tel (407) 299-5000 Founded/Ownrshp 1971
Sales 68.3MM EMP 2,839
Accts David W Martin Cpa Tallahas
SIC 8222 Community college
Pr: Sanford C Shugart
COO: Michelle Matis
Ex Dir: Patti Smith
CIO: Daniel Charriez
Opers Mgr: Frank Goodman
Pgrm Dir: John Centko
Pgrm Dir: Ralph Clemente
Pgrm Dir: Terry Miller

D-U-N-S 04-147-8055
■ **VALENT AEROSTRUCTURES LLC**
(Suby of LMI AEROSPACE INC) ★
11064 Strang Line Rd, Lenexa, KS 66215-2113
Tel (816) 423-5600 Founded/Ownrshp 2010, 2012
Sales 123.0MM EMP 700
SIC 3724 Aircraft engines & engine parts
CEO: Ed Dickinson
*Pr: Lawrence E Dickinson
*CEO: Henry Newell
CFO: Mark Deuel

D-U-N-S 18-628-8510 IMP/EXP
VALENT USA CORP
(Suby of SUMITOMO CHEMICAL COMPANY, LIMITED)
1600 Riviera Ave Ste 200, Walnut Creek, CA 94596-3568
Tel (925) 256-2700 Founded/Ownrshp 1988
Sales 750.0MM[E] EMP 289
SIC 2879

D-U-N-S 60-346-1559
VALENTI FLORIDA MANAGEMENT INC
WENDY'S
3930 Premier North Dr, Tampa, FL 33618-8795
Tel (813) 935-8777 Founded/Ownrshp 1979
Sales 57.6MM[E] EMP 1,000
SIC 8741 Restaurant management
*Sr VP: Peter J Grant
*VP: Troy G Valenti

D-U-N-S 01-582-6290
VALENTI MID-ATLANTIC MANAGEMENT LLC (PA)
WENDY'S
1 Rutherford Rd Ste 100, Harrisburg, PA 17109-4540
Tel (717) 652-7822 Founded/Ownrshp 1979
Sales 302.5MM[E] EMP 4,500
SIC 8741 Restaurant management
Pr: Darrell Valenti
*Ex VP: Steven M Nesbitt
*Sr VP: Peter J Grant
*VP: Troy G Valenti

D-U-N-S 07-542-3491 IMP/EXP
VALENTINE ENTERPRISES INC
V.E.I.
1291 Progress Center Ave, Lawrenceville, GA 30043-4801
Tel (770) 995-0661 Founded/Ownrshp 1972
Sales 144.0MM[E] EMP 400
SIC 2023 2099 Dietary supplements, dairy & non-dairy based; Food preparations
Pr: Donald McDaniel
CFO: Stanley Waldheim
Treas: Dwight Adams
Natl Sales: Eric Barber

D-U-N-S 07-828-7758 IMP
VALEO ENGINE COOLING INC
(Suby of VALEO)
1100 Barachel Ln, Greensburg, IN 47240-1200
Tel (812) 663-8541 Founded/Ownrshp 2011
Sales 129.5MM[E] EMP 600
SIC 3714 Motor vehicle parts & accessories
Pr: James Sliker
*Treas: Stephane Barre

D-U-N-S 00-192-9611 IMP
VALEO INC
VALEO INTERIOR CONTROLS
150 Stephenson Hwy, Troy, MI 48083-1116
Tel (248) 619-8300 Founded/Ownrshp 1989
Sales NA EMP 5,000
SIC 3714

VALEO INTERIOR CONTROLS
See VALEO INC

D-U-N-S 00-959-8397 IMP
VALEO LIGHTING SYSTEMS NORTH AMERICA LLC
PLANT 1
1231 A Ave N, Seymour, IN 47274-3364
Tel (812) 524-5021 Founded/Ownrshp 2014
Sales NA EMP 1,000[E]
SIC 3641 3714

D-U-N-S 80-993-1363 IMP/EXP
VALEO NORTH AMERICA INC
VALEO WIPER SYSTEMS
(Suby of VALEO)
150 Stephenson Hwy, Troy, MI 48083-1116
Tel (248) 619-8300 Founded/Ownrshp 1993
Sales 1.1MMM[E] EMP 2,133
SIC 3714 Motor vehicle electrical equipment; Heaters, motor vehicle; Windshield wiper systems, motor vehicle; Air conditioner parts, motor vehicle
Pr: Francoise Colpron
Ex Dir: Jerry Dittrich
Ql Cn Mgr: Dennis Phillips
Snr Mgr: Fernando Dinis
Snr Mgr: Les Ticknor

D-U-N-S 12-432-5429
VALEO RADAR SYSTEMS INC
(Suby of VALEO)
150 Stephenson Hwy, Troy, MI 48083-1116
Tel (248) 619-8300 Founded/Ownrshp 2002
Sales 121.5MM[E] EMP 235
SIC 5731 3714 Radio, television & electronic stores; Motor vehicle electrical equipment
Pr: James Schwyn
*CFO: Nicolas Retailleau
*Prin: Charles Eimers

D-U-N-S 09-786-4917 IMP
VALEO SWITCHES & DETECTION SYSTEMS INC
(Suby of VALEO WIPER SYSTEMS) ★
150 Stephenson Hwy, Troy, MI 48083-1116
Tel (248) 619-8300 Founded/Ownrshp 2001
Sales 161.2MM[E] EMP 1,000
SIC 3714 Motor vehicle parts & accessories
Pr: James Schwyn
VP: Edouard De Pirey
VP: Hyunjoo Kim
Prgrm Mgr: Brad Ryntz
Snr Sftwr: Petr Klapka
CIO: Doris Beckmann
Ql Cn Mgr: David Fipp
Mktg Dir: Jack Corey

VALEO WIPER SYSTEMS
See VALEO NORTH AMERICA INC

D-U-N-S 08-268-6916
▲ **VALERO ENERGY CORP**
1 Valero Way, San Antonio, TX 78249-1616
Tel (210) 345-2000 Founded/Ownrshp 1955
Sales 87.8MMM EMP 10,103
Accts Kpmg Llp San Antonio Texas
Tkr Sym VLO Exch NYS
SIC 2911 2869 Petroleum refining; Gasoline; Ethyl alcohol, ethanol
Ch Bd: Joseph W Gorder
CFO: Michael S Ciskowski
Bd of Dir: Pearl Adams
Bd of Dir: Tira Anderson
Bd of Dir: Grace Batres
Bd of Dir: Lucy Hernandez
Bd of Dir: Chuck Lawton
Bd of Dir: Phoebe McCallum
Bd of Dir: Benny Perriraz
Bd of Dir: Cody Quinn
Bd of Dir: Ramon Riojas
Bd of Dir: Alex Schelanko
Bd of Dir: Jimmy Villarreal
Ex VP: Jay D Browning
Ex VP: R Lane Riggs
Ex VP: Dyfan Williams
VP: Ken Applegate
VP: Gary Arthur
VP: Daniel Collier
VP: Stephanie Davis
VP: Eric Fisher
Board of Directors: Rayford Wilkins Jr, H Paulett Eberhart, Kimberly S Greene, Deborah P Majoras, Donald L Nickles, Philip J Pfeiffer, Robert A Profusek, Susan Kaufman Purcell, Stephen M Waters, Randall J Weisenburger

D-U-N-S 07-922-7072
VALERO ENERGY PARTNERS LP
1 Valero Way, San Antonio, TX 78249-1616
Tel (210) 345-2000 Founded/Ownrshp 2013
Sales 243.6MM EMP 2
Tkr Sym VLP Exch NYS
SIC 4612 4613 4789 Crude petroleum pipelines; Refined petroleum pipelines; Pipeline terminal facilities, independently operated
CEO: Joseph W Gorder
Genl Pt: Valero E LLC
CFO: Donna M Titzman

D-U-N-S 96-355-5222 IMP/EXP
■ **VALERO MARKETING AND SUPPLY CO**
(Suby of VALERO REFINING-NEW ORLEANS LLC) ★
1 Valero Way, San Antonio, TX 78249-1616
Tel (210) 345-2000 Founded/Ownrshp 1995
Sales 1.4MMM[E] EMP 243
SIC 5171 Petroleum bulk stations & terminals
Pr: Joe Gorder
*Ex VP: Jay Browning
*Ex VP: Mike Ciskowski
*Ex VP: Mike Crownover
*Sr VP: Gary Arthur Jr
*Sr VP: Gene Edwards
*Sr VP: George E Kain
*Sr VP: Donna Titzman
*Prin: William R Klesse

D-U-N-S 08-358-0522
■ **VALERO REFINING CO (INC)**
(Suby of VALERO ENERGY CORP) ★
1 Valero Way, San Antonio, TX 78249-1616
Tel (210) 345-2000 Founded/Ownrshp 1997
Sales 651.6MM[E] EMP 1,833[E]
SIC 2911 Petroleum refining; Gasoline
Ch Bd: William E Greehey
*Pr: Joe Gorder
*Ch: Bill Klesse
*Treas: John D Gibbons
*Sr VP: George E Kain
*Sr VP: Kirk Saffell

D-U-N-S 04-365-2424 IMP
■ **VALERO REFINING CO-CALIFORNIA**
(Suby of VALERO REFINING-NEW ORLEANS LLC) ★
1 Valero Way, San Antonio, TX 78249-1616
Tel (210) 345-2000 Founded/Ownrshp 1992
Sales 599.1MM[E] EMP 3,000[E]
SIC 2911 Petroleum refining
CEO: Bill Klesse
*Ch Bd: William E Greehey
*Pr: Joe Gorder
*Ex VP: Gregory C King
*Sr VP: Michael S Ciskowski
*Sr VP: S Eugene Edwards
*VP: Gary L Arthur Jr
*VP: Richard J Marcogliese

D-U-N-S 03-081-4466 EXP
■ **VALERO REFINING CO-NEW JERSEY**
(Suby of VALERO REFINING-NEW ORLEANS LLC) ★
1 Valero Way, San Antonio, TX 78249-1616
Tel (210) 345-2000 Founded/Ownrshp 1981
Sales 119.7MM[E] EMP 992
SIC 2911 6163 Petroleum refining; Loan brokers
Pr: Bill Klesse
*Pr: Joe Gorder
*Treas: Donna Titzman
*Ex VP: Mike Ciskowski
*Ex VP: Gene Edwards
*VP: Gary Arthur Jr

D-U-N-S 17-931-3457 IMP/EXP
■ **VALERO REFINING-NEW ORLEANS LLC**
(Suby of VALERO ENERGY CORP) ★
1 Valero Way, San Antonio, TX 78249-1616
Tel (210) 345-2000 Founded/Ownrshp 1997
Sales 2.7MMM[E] EMP 3,020
SIC 2911 Petroleum refining
*Mng Pt: Jay D Browning
*Mng Pt: S Eugene Edwards
*Mng Pt: John D Gibbons
*Mng Pt: John F Hohnholt
*Mng Pt: Gregory C King
*Mng Pt: William N Latham
*Treas: Donna Tizman
VP: Craig M Schnupp
Sfty Mgr: Drew Owen

D-U-N-S 07-939-1280 IMP/EXP
■ **VALERO REFINING-TEXAS LP**
(Suby of VALERO REFINING-NEW ORLEANS LLC) ★
1 Valero Way, San Antonio, TX 78249-1616
Tel (210) 345-2000 Founded/Ownrshp 1997
Sales 381.5MM[E] EMP 1,572
SIC 2911 Petroleum refining; Gasoline blending plants
Ch Bd: Bill Klesse
*CEO: Joe Gorder
*CFO: Mike Ciskowski
*Sr VP: Wayne Smithers
*VP: Mike Milam
*VP: Mary Morgan
*VP: Dave Parker
*VP: Thomas Shoaf
*VP: Michael Stone
*VP: Wade Upton
Genl Mgr: Jay Browning

D-U-N-S 82-999-0824
■ **VALERO RENEWABLE FUELS CO LLC**
(Suby of VALERO ENERGY CORP) ★
1 Valero Way, San Antonio, TX 78249-1616
Tel (210) 345-2000 Founded/Ownrshp 2009
Sales 90.7MM[E] EMP 235
SIC 2911 Petroleum refining
Ch: William R Klesse
*Ex VP: Kimberly S Bowers
*Ex VP: Michael S Ciskowski
*Ex VP: S Eugene Edwards

D-U-N-S 80-856-3907
VALERO SERVICES INC
1 Valero Way, San Antonio, TX 78249-1616
Tel (210) 345-2000 Founded/Ownrshp 2001
Sales NA EMP 2,400
SIC 2911 5172 5411 Petroleum refining; Petroleum products; Convenience stores
Pr: Joe Gorder
*CEO: Bill Klesse
*Sr VP: Kirk Saffell
*VP: Ellen Williams
*VP: Guy Young

D-U-N-S 00-253-3378 EXP
VALERUS FIELD SOLUTIONS HOLDINGS LLC
(*Suby of* KENTZ CORPORATION LIMITED)
919 Milam St Ste 1000, Houston, TX 77002-5386
Tel (713) 744-6100 *Founded/Ownrshp* 2014
Sales 407.5MM^E *EMP* 60^E
SIC 1382 6719 Oil & gas exploration services; Investment holding companies, except banks
Pr: Christian I Brown
VP: Tush Doshi
VP: Ricardo Moreno
VP: Loren Pieper
VP: Mina Wheless
Dir Bus: Darwin Shaw
Prd Mgr: Lance Behan
Genl Couns: Mark Carlton
Genl Couns: Beto Kuhn

D-U-N-S 08-378-1278
VALET PARKING SERVICE A CALIFORNIA LTD PARTNERSHIP
6933 Hollywood Blvd, Los Angeles, CA 90028-6146
Tel (323) 465-5873 *Founded/Ownrshp* 1946
Sales 22.2MM^E *EMP* 1,400
SIC 7521 7299 Parking lots; Valet parking
CEO: Anthony Policella

D-U-N-S 82-971-8506
■ **VALHI HOLDING CO**
(*Suby of* CONTRAN CORP) ★
5430 Lyndon B Johnson Fwy # 1700, Dallas, TX 75240-2327
Tel (972) 233-1700 *Founded/Ownrshp* 1987
Sales 1.5MMM^E *EMP* 7,175^E
SIC 2816 Inorganic pigments
Pr: Steven L Watson
**CFO:* Bobby D O Brien

D-U-N-S 00-696-7822 IMP/EXP
■ **VALHI INC**
(*Suby of* VALHI HOLDING CO) ★
5430 Lbj Fwy Ste 1700, Dallas, TX 75240-2327
Tel (972) 233-1700 *Founded/Ownrshp* 1932
Sales 1.5MMM *EMP* 2,280^E
Accts Pricewaterhousecoopers Llp Da
Tkr Sym VHI *Exch* NYS
SIC 2816 2899 3429 4953 Titanium dioxide, anatase or rutile (pigments); Chemical preparations; Keys, locks & related hardware; Furniture hardware; Hazardous waste collection & disposal
Ch Bd: Steven L Watson
**Pr:* Bobby D O'Brien
Treas: John A St Wrba
Bd of Dir: Paul Bass
Ex VP: Robert Graham
Ex VP: Kelly D Luttmer
Ex VP: Gregory M Swalwell
Sr VP: Andrew B Nace
VP: Burns Dan
VP: William Lindquist
VP: A Andrew R Louis
VP: Bobby Obrien
Board of Directors: Thomas E Barry, Loretta J Feehan, Elisabeth C Fisher, W Hayden McIlroy, Mary A Tidlund

VALIANT CHAIR MANUFACTURING
See VALIANT PRODUCTS CORP

D-U-N-S 83-125-5430
VALIANT CONSTRUCTION LLC
4229 Bardstown Rd Ste 206, Louisville, KY 40218-4200
Tel (502) 562-0037 *Founded/Ownrshp* 2009
Sales 7.7MMM *EMP* 48
Accts Jones Nale & Mattingly Plc L
SIC 8741 Construction management

VALIANT ENERGY
See ARENA ENERGY LP

D-U-N-S 04-216-9961 IMP
VALIANT PRODUCTS CORP
VALIANT CHAIR MANUFACTURING
2727 W 5th Ave, Denver, CO 80204-4886
Tel (303) 892-1234 *Founded/Ownrshp* 1961
Sales 106.1MM^E *EMP* 150
SIC 5131 5023 7389 2511 2599 1752

D-U-N-S 07-869-1559
VALID USA INC
(*Suby of* VALID SOLUCOES E SERVICOS DE SEGURANCA EM MEIOS DE PAGAMENTO E IDENTIFICACAO S/A)
1011 Warrenville Rd # 450, Lisle, IL 60532-0903
Tel (630) 852-8200 *Founded/Ownrshp* 2012
Sales 175.4MM^E *EMP* 950
SIC 2752 Commercial printing, lithographic
CEO: Carlos Alfonso Seigneur
CEO: Carlos Alfonso Seigneur D'Albu
VP: Gary Hofeldt
VP: Joseph J Taylor
Snr Ntwrk: Dean Sarles
IT Man: Ruben Mendez
Sls Dir: Karen Brooker
Mktg Mgr: Paul Hedlund

VALIDANT
See KINSALE HOLDINGS INC

VALIDEX
See DE FOXX & ASSOCIATES INC

D-U-N-S 79-044-1146
VALIDUS DC SYSTEMS LLC
50 Pocono Rd, Brookfield, CT 06804-3303
Tel (203) 448-3600 *Founded/Ownrshp* 2011
Sales 124.1MM^E *EMP* 15^E
SIC 3679 Static power supply converters for electronic applications
CEO: Rudy Kraus
COO: Ronald Croce
VP: Frank Catapano
VP: Frank J Catapano
VP: Al Dei Maggi

D-U-N-S 02-321-1518
VALIDUS SPECIALTY INC
(*Suby of* VALIDUS HOLDINGS, LTD.)
400 Parsons Pond Dr, Franklin Lakes, NJ 07417-2601
Tel (201) 847-8600 *Founded/Ownrshp* 2006
Sales NA *EMP* 207^E
SIC 6331 Fire, marine & casualty insurance & carriers
CEO: Edward J Noonan
COO: Jonathan P Ritz
CFO: Patrick Boisvert
CFO: Jeffrey D Sangster
Ex VP: Mary Kotch
Ex VP: Andrew E Kudera
Ex VP: Robert F Kuzloski
Ex VP: Kudret Oztap
Ex VP: Romel Salam
Sr VP: Angeline Ang
Sr VP: Florian Lutz
Sr VP: Gary Meserole

D-U-N-S 06-606-0448
VALLARTA FOOD ENTERPRISES INC
VALLARTA SUPERMARKETS
12881 Bradley Ave, Sylmar, CA 91342-3828
Tel (818) 898-0088 *Founded/Ownrshp* 1999
Sales 875.6MM^E *EMP* 5,000
SIC 5411 Grocery stores; Supermarkets
CEO: Enrique Gonzalez Jr
**CFO:* Ray Jones
VP: Rodrigo Gonzalez
Genl Mgr: Alfredo Gonzalez
Genl Mgr: Michael Walker
Dir IT: Alvaro Espinoza
Dir IT: Russ Jones
Mktg Dir: Tony Hernandez

VALLARTA SUPERMARKETS
See VALLARTA FOOD ENTERPRISES INC

D-U-N-S 12-547-3202
VALLARTA SUPERMARKETS INC
10147 San Fernando Rd, Pacoima, CA 91331-2617
Tel (818) 485-0596 *Founded/Ownrshp* 1999
Sales 350.0MM *EMP* 2,500
SIC 5411 Supermarkets
CEO: Miguel Gonzalez
**Pr:* Luis Gonzalez
**VP:* Rodrigo Gonzalez
**VP:* Adolfo Molina

VALLEJO BUILDING MATERIALS
See SYAR INDUSTRIES INC

D-U-N-S 01-463-5429
VALLEJO CITY UNIFIED SCHOOL DISTRICT
665 Walnut Ave, Vallejo, CA 94592-1177
Tel (707) 556-8921 *Founded/Ownrshp* 1921
Sales 133.5MM^E *EMP* 2,000
SIC 8211 Public elementary & secondary schools; Public elementary school
Pr: Steve Samon
Ex Dir: Manuela Miller
Genl Mgr: James Arcala
Pr Dir: Alana Shackelford
Schl Brd P: Tony Ubalde
Teacher Pr: Reynaldo Santacruz
HC Dir: Rayito Farris
HC Dir: Kathy Hahn
Pgrm Dir: Joseph Jones

D-U-N-S 78-280-7804 IMP/EXP
VALLEN DISTRIBUTION INC
HAGEMEYER NORTH AMERICA, INC.
(*Suby of* HAGEMEYER NORTH AMERICA) ★
1460 Tobias Gadson Blvd, Charleston, SC 29407-4793
Tel (843) 745-2400 *Founded/Ownrshp* 2014
Sales 3.7MMM^E *EMP* 1,200
SIC 5085 Electric tools
Pr: Lisa Mitchell
Bd of Dir: Gary McKinsey
Sr VP: Will Lutz
Sr VP: Pat McClure
Sr VP: Per Ohstrom
VP: David Blackwood
VP: David Bolt
VP: Robert Martin
VP: Brian Thompson
VP: David Underkofler
VP Bus Dev: Scott Bierwiler
Exec: Bob Belfiglio
Exec: Bob Gray
Exec: Frank Handwerk
Exec: Matt Kiefer
Exec: Alan Lucas

D-U-N-S 11-175-1954
VALLEN SAFETY SUPPLY CO
521 N Sam Houston Pkwy E # 300, Houston, TX 77060-4035
Tel (281) 500-5000 *Founded/Ownrshp* 2000
Sales 129.4MM^E *EMP* 2,000
SIC 5099 5084 5047 5063 Safety equipment & supplies; Lifesaving & survival equipment (non-medical); Fire extinguishers; Safety equipment; Instruments & control equipment; Measuring & testing equipment, electrical; Noise control equipment; Industrial safety devices: first aid kits & masks; Lighting fixtures; Electric alarms & signaling equipment
CEO: David Gabriel

D-U-N-S 00-427-1177
VALLEY ASPHALT CORP
11641 Mosteller Rd, Cincinnati, OH 45241-1520
Tel (513) 771-0820 *Founded/Ownrshp* 1947
Sales 109.5MM^E *EMP* 150
SIC 1611 2951

D-U-N-S 06-351-3410
VALLEY BAKERS COOPERATIVE ASSOCIATION
VBCA
W6470 Quality Dr, Greenville, WI 54942-8115
Tel (920) 560-3200 *Founded/Ownrshp* 1949
Sales 120.8MM^E *EMP* 71
SIC 5149 5046 Flour; Bakery equipment & supplies
**VP:* Randy Flesch
Exec: Teresa McMahon

D-U-N-S 78-583-3711
VALLEY BAPTIST HEALTH SYSTEM
2101 Pease St, Harlingen, TX 78550-8307
Tel (956) 389-1100 *Founded/Ownrshp* 2000
Sales 1.3MM *EMP* 3,000^E
Accts Bkd Llp Houston Tx
SIC 6719 Personal holding companies, except banks
Pr: James G Springfield
**CFO:* James Eastham
Sr VP: Randy Baker
Dir Rx: Analiza Amaya
Ex Dir: Garner Klein
Pathlgst: Lawrence Dahm

D-U-N-S 07-850-4446 IMP
VALLEY BAPTIST MEDICAL CENTER - BROWNSVILLE (TX)
1040 W Jefferson St, Brownsville, TX 78520-6338
Tel (956) 389-1100 *Founded/Ownrshp* 1925
Sales 235.3MM^E *EMP* 2,500
SIC 8062 General medical & surgical hospitals
CEO: James Eastham
Pr: Teri Retana
**CFO:* Randy McLelland
Ofcr: Manny Vela
VP: Scott Lieberenz

D-U-N-S 82-889-9919
VALLEY BAPTIST MEDICAL CENTER HARLINGEN AUXILIARY INC
2101 Pease St, Harlingen, TX 78550-8307
Tel (956) 389-1100 *Founded/Ownrshp* 2008
Sales 119.7M *EMP* 4,000
Accts Bkd Llp Houston Tx
SIC 8742 Hospital & health services consultant
CEO: Dan McLean
**CEO:* Bill Adams
COO: James Eastham
COO: Scott Manis
VP: Ward Cook
Dir Rad: Kevin P Banks
Dir Rad: Bruce M Berberian
Dir Rad: Harry E Butters
Doctor: Jose Cohen
Doctor: Gerard Desouza
Doctor: Julie Holcher

VALLEY BEHAVIORAL HEALTH
See VALLEY MENTAL HEALTH INC

VALLEY CARE HEALTH SYSTEM, THE
See HOSPITAL COMMITTEE FOR LIVERMORE-PLEASANTON AREAS

VALLEY CARE OLIVE VIEW MEDICAL
See OLIVE VIEW-UCLA MEDICAL CENTER

D-U-N-S 08-011-8328
VALLEY CHILDRENS HEALTHCARE
9300 Valley Childrens Pl, Madera, CA 93636-8761
Tel (559) 353-3000 *Founded/Ownrshp* 2013
Sales 54.0M^E *EMP* 2,800
SIC 8011 8069 Physical medicine, physician/surgeon; Physicians' office, including specialists; Children's hospital
CEO: Todd Suntrapak
**VP:* William Chaltraw

D-U-N-S 07-188-2450
VALLEY CHILDRENS HOSPITAL
9300 Valley Childrens Pl, Madera, CA 93636-8762
Tel (559) 353-3000 *Founded/Ownrshp* 1949
Sales 575.6MM *EMP* 1,800
Accts Moss Adams Llp Stockton Ca
SIC 8069 Children's hospital
Pr: Todd Sunterapak
**Pr:* Gordon Alexander
**COO:* Jessie Hudgins
**CFO:* Michele Waldrin
Bd of Dir: David Krause
Bd of Dir: Jeff Mayer
VP: Carlos Flores
VP: Beverly Hayden-Pugh
VP: David Singh
Ex Dir: Stephanie Vance
QA Dir: Arwa Muraisi

D-U-N-S 05-380-6527
VALLEY CO-OPS INC
VALLEY COUNTRY STORES
1833 S Lincoln Ave, Jerome, ID 83338-6138
Tel (208) 324-8000 *Founded/Ownrshp* 1991
Sales 104.4MM^E *EMP* 160
Accts Moss Adams Llp Yakima Washi
SIC 5171 5191 5251 Petroleum bulk stations; Feed; Fertilizer & fertilizer materials; Hardware
Pr: Carl Pendleton
Genl Mgr: Donn Bordewyk

VALLEY COUNTRY STORES
See VALLEY CO-OPS INC

D-U-N-S 04-167-9515
VALLEY ELECTRIC ASSOCIATION INC
800 E Highway 372, Pahrump, NV 89048-4624
Tel (775) 727-5312 *Founded/Ownrshp* 1965
Sales 91.2MM^E *EMP* 80
SIC 4911 Distribution, electric power
CEO: Thomas Husted
**COO:* Rick Eckert

D-U-N-S 00-398-0638 IMP/EXP
VALLEY FORD TRUCK INC
VALLEY STERLING OF CLEVELAND
5715 Canal Rd, Cleveland, OH 44125-3494
Tel (216) 524-2400 *Founded/Ownrshp* 1964, 2006
Sales 125.0MM *EMP* 80^E
SIC 5013 5511 5521 5531 5012 Truck parts & accessories; Automobiles, new & used; Trucks, tractors & trailers: used; Truck equipment & parts; Automobiles & other motor vehicles
Pr: Brian O'Donnell
**Sec:* Michelle Steibner

VALLEY FORGE INSURANCE BRKG
See MAGUIRE INSURANCE AGENCY INC

D-U-N-S 04-390-9241
■ **VALLEY FORGE LIFE INSURANCE CO INC**
(*Suby of* CNA INSURANCE) ★
333 S Wabash Ave, Chicago, IL 60604-4107
Tel (312) 822-5000 *Founded/Ownrshp* 2008
Sales NA *EMP* 1,141
SIC 6321 6311 Accident insurance carriers; Health insurance carriers; Life insurance carriers
Ch Bd: Dennis Chookaszian
Pr: Philip L Engel
COO: Bernard L Hengesbaugh
CFO: W James Macginnitie
**Chf Mktg O:* William H Sharkey Jr
Sr VP: William J Adamson
Sr VP: Peter P Conway Jr
Sr VP: James P Flood
Sr VP: Micheal C Garner
Sr VP: Peter E Jokiel
Sr VP: Jonathan Kantor
Sr VP: Micheal Mc Gavick
Sr VP: Thomas Taylor
Sr VP: Robert T Van Gieson
Sr VP: Jae L Wittlich
Sr VP: David W Wroe

D-U-N-S 05-324-1204 IMP
VALLEY FRESH FOODS INC
SKYLANE FARMS
3600 E Linwood Ave, Turlock, CA 95380-9109
Tel (209) 669-5600 *Founded/Ownrshp* 1969
Sales 1.4MMM^E *EMP* 287
SIC 0252 2015

VALLEY FRUIT & PRODUCE CO
See VAL-PRO INC

D-U-N-S 11-737-2797
VALLEY HEALTH SYSTEM
1840 Amherst St, Winchester, VA 22601-2808
Tel (540) 536-8000 *Founded/Ownrshp* 1984
Sales 640.5MM^E *EMP* 4,300
SIC 8062 8051 5047 8699 General medical & surgical hospitals; Skilled nursing care facilities; Medical & hospital equipment; Charitable organization
CEO: Mark H Merrill
Chf Rad: Joseph Poe
Chf Rad: Ronald Repasky
Chf Rad: David Snow
**CFO:* Pete Gallagher
CFO: Christine Lowman
Bd of Dir: Byron Brill
Ofcr: Jim Daniel
**Sr VP:* Christopher B Rumpf
VP: Bob Amos
VP: James Dumont
**VP:* Jeffrey Feit
VP: Roy E Fredricksen
VP: Thomas Gibson
VP: Rudy Herndon
VP: Charles Hyre
VP: Ejaz Khan
VP: John Pulizzi
**VP:* Joan Roscoe
VP: Tonya Smith
VP: Paul Ulich
Board of Directors: William F Brandt Jr, Harry F Byrd III, James T Holland, Douglas B Keim MD, Jim Long, William B Major MD, Katherine P Napier, John S Scully IV, Joseph F Silek Jr

D-U-N-S 96-767-6664
VALLEY HEALTH SYSTEM GROUP RETURN
220 Campus Blvd Ste 310, Winchester, VA 22601-2889
Tel (540) 536-4302 *Founded/Ownrshp* 2011
Sales 625.6MM *EMP* 6^E
Accts Valley Health System Winchest
SIC 8062 General medical & surgical hospitals
Ex Dir: Kevin Callanan

D-U-N-S 62-365-3631
VALLEY HEALTH SYSTEM INC
223 N Van Dien Ave, Ridgewood, NJ 07450-2726
Tel (201) 447-8000 *Founded/Ownrshp* 1988
Sales 2.1MM *EMP* 4,000^E
Accts O Connor Davies Llp Paramus
SIC 8062 8099 General medical & surgical hospitals; Childbirth preparation clinic
Pr: Audrey Meyers
Pr: Julia Karcher
**CFO:* Richard D Keenan
VP: Claire Grande
VP: Richard Keenan
VP: Maria Mediago
VP: Mitchell Rubinstein
Ex Dir: Phyllis Marino
CTO: Donna Lagasi
Doctor: Rakesh Patel
Pharmcst: Chris Saco

D-U-N-S 07-415-0830
■ **VALLEY HEALTH SYSTEM LLC**
VALLEY HOSPITAL MEDICAL CENTER
(*Suby of* UNIVERSAL HEALTH SERVICES INC) ★
620 Shadow Ln, Las Vegas, NV 89106-4119
Tel (702) 388-4000 *Founded/Ownrshp* 1971
Sales 269.7MM *EMP* 1,350
SIC 8062 8011 General medical & surgical hospitals; Offices & clinics of medical doctors
CEO: Sam Kaufman
Mng Dir: Cynthia Masalunga
Off Mgr: Sheryl Stevens
IT Man: Steve Shaw
Pathlgst: Jean McKusker
Doctor: Elain Claypool
Doctor: Tina Sprague
Pharmcst: Dan Delnero

D-U-N-S 19-380-4747
VALLEY HEALTH SYSTEMS INC
575 Beech St, Holyoke, MA 01040-2223
Tel (413) 534-2500 *Founded/Ownrshp* 1891
Sales 1.1MM *EMP* 1,550
Accts Pricewaterhouse Coopers Llp H
SIC 8082 8093 8399 8741 8721 Home health care services; Mental health clinic, outpatient; Fund raising organization, non-fee basis; Financial management for business; Accounting, auditing & bookkeeping
Pr: Spiridon Hatiras

Treas: Paul Silva
VP: Jim Keefe
Doctor: Robert Cooper

D-U-N-S 07-999-0850
■ VALLEY HEALTHCARE CENTER LLC
(*Suby of* GENESIS HEALTHCARE LLC) ★
4840 E Tulare Ave, Fresno, CA 93727-3062
Tel (559) 251-7161 *Founded/Ownrshp* 2003
Sales 392.3ME *EMP* 3,238E
SIC 8051 Skilled nursing care facilities
CEO: George V Hagaer Jr

VALLEY HOSPITAL AND MEDICAL CENTER
See SPOKANE VALLEY WASHINGTON HOSPITAL CO LLC

D-U-N-S 07-271-6376
VALLEY HOSPITAL INC (NJ)
(*Suby of* VALLEY HEALTH SYSTEM INC) ★
223 N Van Dien Ave, Ridgewood, NJ 07450-2736
Tel (201) 447-8000 *Founded/Ownrshp* 1925
Sales 621.9MM *EMP* 2,900
SIC 8062 General medical & surgical hospitals
Pr: Audrey Meyers
COO: Peter W Diestel
**VP:* Richard D Keenan
VP: Ann M Leichman
VP: Maria Mediago
VP: Ann Swenson
Nurse Mgr: Cathy Ilardi

VALLEY HOSPITAL MEDICAL CENTER
See VALLEY HEALTH SYSTEM LLC

D-U-N-S 07-191-0038
VALLEY HOSPITAL MEDICAL CENTER
CALEX
(*Suby of* DIGNITY HEALTH) ★
18300 Roscoe Blvd, Northridge, CA 91325-4105
Tel (818) 885-8500 *Founded/Ownrshp* 1978
Sales 403.2MM *EMP* 1,000
SIC 8062 General medical & surgical hospitals
Pr: Patrick Hawthorne
Chf Path: John E Glassco
Exec: Peggy Diller
Prgrm Mgr: Eric Chang
CIO: Psalms McWhorter
HC Dir: Londy Bojorquez
HC Dir: Cheryl Lovett

D-U-N-S 03-872-3581
VALLEY INTERIOR SYSTEMS INC
2203 Fowler St, Cincinnati, OH 45206-2307
Tel (513) 961-0400 *Founded/Ownrshp* 1981
Sales 85.3MME *EMP* 550
SIC 1742 Drywall; Acoustical & ceiling work; Plastering, plain or ornamental
CEO: Mike Strawser
**Pr:* Jeff Hudepohl
**COO:* John Strawser Jr
**CFO:* Steve Dehne
**Ch:* John W Strawser Sr
**Treas:* Anthony Young
**VP:* Jim Melaragno
**VP:* Marcus Taulbee
Brnch Mgr: Troy Vance
Sfty Dirs: John Rudd

VALLEY MEDICAL CENTER
See PUBLIC HOSPITAL DISTRICT 1 OF KING COUNTY

D-U-N-S 80-656-0343
VALLEY MEDICAL FACILITIES INC
HERITAGE VALLEY HEALTH SYSTEM
720 Blackburn Rd, Sewickley, PA 15143-1459
Tel (724) 728-7000 *Founded/Ownrshp* 1990
Sales 369.6MM *EMP* 4,300E
Accts Arnett Carbis Toothman Llp Pi
SIC 8011 Medical centers
CEO: Donald W Spalding
**Pr:* Norman F Mitry
**CFO:* Bryan Randall
CTO: Mindy Hufnagle
Doctor: Susan Guido

D-U-N-S 17-730-4805
VALLEY MENTAL HEALTH INC
VALLEY BEHAVIORAL HEALTH
5965 S 900 E, Salt Lake City, UT 84121-1720
Tel (801) 263-7100 *Founded/Ownrshp* 1981
Sales 50.1MM *EMP* 1,100
Accts Tanner Llc Salt Lake City Ut
SIC 8093 Mental health clinic, outpatient
CEO: Debra Falvo
COO: Christy Calderon
**CFO:* Dale Newton
CFO: Spencer Seaquist
Ex Dir: Bob Gorelik
Prgrm Mgr: Frederick Van Der Veur

D-U-N-S 02-833-7413
VALLEY MILK PRODUCTS LLC
(*Suby of* MARVA MAID DAIRY DIVISION) ★
412 E King St, Strasburg, VA 22657-2433
Tel (540) 465-5113 *Founded/Ownrshp* 1999
Sales 86.0MM *EMP* 32
SIC 2023 2021

D-U-N-S 07-463-8560
VALLEY MOUNTAIN REGIONAL CENTER INC
702 N Aurora St, Stockton, CA 95202-2200
Tel (209) 473-0951 *Founded/Ownrshp* 1974
Sales 150.0MM *EMP* 250
Accts Windes & Mcclaughry Ac Long B
SIC 8322 Multi-service center
CEO: Paul Billodeau
COO: Evonne Lucero
**CFO:* Debra Roth
Bd of Dir: Robert Bianco
VP: Maren Paris
Exec: Cindy Jimenez
Prgrm Mgr: Julie Dediego
Prgrm Mgr: Robin Dickinson
Prgrm Mgr: Wanda Farinelli
Prgrm Mgr: Nikki Gillespie
Prgrm Mgr: Karen Jensen

D-U-N-S 15-428-2792 IMP
▲ VALLEY NATIONAL BANCORP
1455 Valley Rd Ste 3, Wayne, NJ 07470-2089
Tel (973) 305-8800 *Founded/Ownrshp* 1982
Sales NA *EMP* 2,929E
Tkr Sym VLY *Exch* NYS
SIC 6021 National commercial banks
Ch Bd: Gerald H Lipkin
**COO:* Peter Crocitto
**CFO:* Alan D Eskow
Treas: Ira Robbins
Ofcr: Lina Duque
Ofcr: Melissa Scofield
Ex VP: Sherry Ambrosini
Ex VP: Robert J Bardusch
Ex VP: Mitchell L Crandell
Ex VP: Albert L Engel
Ex VP: Dianne M Grenz
Ex VP: Thomas A Iadanza
Ex VP: James G Lawrence
Ex VP: Bernadette M Mueller
Ex VP: Andrea T Onorato
Ex VP: Andrea Onorato
Ex VP: Melissa F Scofield
Sr VP: Carol Diesner
Sr VP: Richard Seguine
VP: Gordon Casanova
VP: Rich Demartino
Board of Directors: Barnett Rukin, Andrew B Abramson, Suresh L Sani, Peter J Baum, Jeffrey S Wilks, Pamela R Bronander, Eric P Edelstein, Mary J Steele Guilfoile, Graham O Jones, Gerald Korde, Michael L Larusso, Marc J Lenner

D-U-N-S 07-516-1448 IMP
■ VALLEY NATIONAL BANK
(*Suby of* VALLEY NATIONAL BANCORP) ★
1455 Valley Rd Ste 3, Wayne, NJ 07470-8448
Tel (973) 696-4020 *Founded/Ownrshp* 1926
Sales NA *EMP* 1,573
SIC 6021 6162

D-U-N-S 07-244-1215 IMP
VALLEY OF SUN UNITED WAY (AZ)
3200 E Camelback Rd # 375, Phoenix, AZ 85018-2328
Tel (602) 631-4800 *Founded/Ownrshp* 1925
Sales 126.4MM *EMP* 81
Accts Lb Ernst & Young Us Llp Phoen
SIC 8699 Charitable organization
Pr: Merl E Waschler
**Ch Bd:* Ken Burbick
Ofcr: Jhenifer Krutz
Sr VP: Brian Spicker
VP: Jeff Kunkel
VP: Warren Whitney
Exec: Tanya Muniz
Comm Dir: Crystal Houston
Ex Dir: Margie Emmermann
Prgrm Mgr: Julie Sater
CIO: Ken Brooks

VALLEY OF THE SUN YMCA
See VALLEY OF SUN YOUNG MENS CHRISTIAN ASSOCIATION

D-U-N-S 02-013-4524
VALLEY OF SUN YOUNG MENS CHRISTIAN ASSOCIATION (AZ)
VALLEY OF THE SUN YMCA
350 N 1st Ave, Phoenix, AZ 85003-1513
Tel (602) 257-5120 *Founded/Ownrshp* 1892
Sales 37.4MM *EMP* 1,500
Accts Cbiz Mhm Llc Phoenix Az
SIC 8641 8322 Youth organizations; Individual & family services
CEO: Gregory W O'Brien
**COO:* George Scobas
**CFO:* George Diflavis
**VP:* Chastity Fermoile
**VP:* Sally Lauro
**VP:* Kerri O'Brien
Ex Dir: Michael Cassidy
Ex Dir: Douglas Grim
Ex Dir: Robin Jordan
Genl Mgr: Sue Suman
CIO: Israel Class

D-U-N-S 07-466-8468
VALLEY PACIFIC PETROLEUM SERVICES INC
152 Frank West Cir # 100, Stockton, CA 95206-4005
Tel (209) 948-9412 *Founded/Ownrshp* 1954
Sales 155.9MME *EMP* 180
SIC 5172 5541 Gasoline; Diesel fuel; Lubricating oils & greases; Gasoline service stations
CEO: Norman Eugene Crum
**Pr:* Dan Elmer
**Pr:* Dale Heinze
**VP:* Nathan Crum
Dir IT: Grant Crum

D-U-N-S 07-478-3515
VALLEY PACKAGING INDUSTRIES INC
110 N Kensington Dr, Appleton, WI 54915-3303
Tel (920) 749-5840 *Founded/Ownrshp* 1955
Sales 6.1MM *EMP* 1,000
SIC 7389 8331 Packaging & labeling services; Vocational rehabilitation agency
Pr: Robert H Russo
CFO: John Hall
Treas: David Gitter
CTO: John Brice
IT Man: Joshua Raymaker
Sls Mgr: Jeffrey Kulibert
Sls Mgr: Ed Schroeder

D-U-N-S 00-966-1638 IMP/EXP
VALLEY POWER SYSTEMS INC
JOHN DEERE AUTHORIZED DEALER
425 S Hacienda Blvd, City of Industry, CA 91745-1123
Tel (626) 333-1243 *Founded/Ownrshp* 1963
Sales 181.1MME *EMP* 700
SIC 3519 5082 Marine engines; Construction & mining machinery
Ch Bd: Hampton Clark Lee
**Pr:* Michael Barnett
**CFO:* Robert K Humphryes
Sr Cor Off: Barbara Webb
**VP:* Richard Kickliter
**VP:* Bruce Noble
CTO: Bob Maconber
Sls Dir: William Wantz

D-U-N-S 07-294-0307
VALLEY PRESBYTERIAN HOSPITAL
V P H
15107 Vanowen St, Van Nuys, CA 91405-4597
Tel (818) 782-6600 *Founded/Ownrshp* 1948
Sales 389.4MM *EMP* 1,600
Accts Moss Adams Llp Los Angeles
SIC 8062 General medical & surgical hospitals
CEO: Gustavo Valdespino
Sr Cor Off: Virginia Napoles
Bd of Dir: Robert C Bills
Ofcr: Jose Claudio
Sr VP: Lori Burnell
Sr VP: Gayathri S Jith
Sr VP: Pegi Matsuda
Sr VP: Norma Resneder
Sr VP: Jean Rico
VP: Jeffrey Allport
VP: Michelle Quigley
Exec: Ganesh Pandian
Exec: Wesley Schmidt
Dir Inf Cn: Jerry Pennington
Comm Man: Lisa Knapp
Board of Directors: Gregory L Kay, Kevin Rice

D-U-N-S 00-321-3311 IMP/EXP
VALLEY PROTEINS (DE) INC
151 Valpro Dr, Winchester, VA 22603-3607
Tel (540) 877-2533 *Founded/Ownrshp* 1956
Sales 430.9MME *EMP* 1,400
SIC 2048 Prepared feeds
Pr: Gerald Smith Jr
**Treas:* William Stuart Hylton
**VP:* Michael A Smith
Genl Mgr: Michael Scheib
Dir IT: Katsias James
Dir IT: Ben Nicholas

D-U-N-S 00-306-3401 EXP
VALLEY PROTEINS INC
151 Valpro Dr, Winchester, VA 22603-3607
Tel (540) 877-2590 *Founded/Ownrshp* 1956
Sales 600.0MM *EMP* 1,450
SIC 2077 Animal & marine fats & oils
Pr: Gerald Smith Jr
VP: Michael Smith
Genl Mgr: Charles H Atkinson
MIS Dir: James Katsias

D-U-N-S 00-616-9791 IMP
VALLEY QUEEN CHEESE FACTORY INC (SD)
200 E Railway Ave, Milbank, SD 57252-1813
Tel (605) 432-4563 *Founded/Ownrshp* 1929
Sales 425.0MM *EMP* 225
SIC 2022

VALLEY RETREADING
See VALLEY TIRE CO INC

D-U-N-S 04-748-6865
VALLEY ROZ ORCHARDS INC
10 E Mead Ave, Yakima, WA 98903-3712
Tel (509) 457-4153 *Founded/Ownrshp* 1967
Sales 28.0MM *EMP* 2,500
SIC 0175 5431 Apple orchard; Cherry orchard; Pear orchard; Prune orchard; Fruit & vegetable markets
Owner: Harley Hansen
**Sec:* Gary Hansen
**VP:* Don Johnson

VALLEY STERLING OF CLEVELAND
See VALLEY FORD TRUCK INC

D-U-N-S 09-952-3995 IMP
VALLEY TIRE CO INC
VALLEY RETREADING
15 Mckean Ave, Charleroi, PA 15022-1436
Tel (724) 489-4483 *Founded/Ownrshp* 1980
Sales 104.1MME *EMP* 252
SIC 5531 7539 5014 7534 Automotive tires; Automotive repair shops; Automobile tires & tubes; Truck tires & tubes; Rebuilding & retreading tires
Pr: James F Stankiewicz
Sls Mgr: David Hollifield

D-U-N-S 00-447-8418
VALLEY VIEW BANCSHARES INC
7500 W 95th St, Shawnee Mission, KS 66212-2202
Tel (913) 381-3311 *Founded/Ownrshp* 1966
Sales NA *EMP* 794
SIC 6712 Bank holding companies
Pr: James Lewis
Ofcr: Lisa Weber
Sr VP: Leo Harris
**VP:* Clay Cloburn
VP: Cherry Cummins
VP: Pat D'Amico
VP: Pat Damico
VP: Tammy Gardner
VP: Edie Hepner
VP: Cathy Keeling
VP: Jeff Teefey

D-U-N-S 13-628-6465
VALLEY VIEW COMMUNITY UNIT SCHOOL DISTRICT 365U
755 Dalhart Ave, Romeoville, IL 60446-1157
Tel (815) 886-2700 *Founded/Ownrshp* 1952
Sales 295.0MM *EMP* 3,000
Accts Wermer Rogers Doran & Ruzon
SIC 8211 Public elementary school; Public junior high school; Public senior high school
**Pr:* Steven Quigly
**Treas:* Joanne R Bourg
Bd of Dir: Elizabeth Campbell
Bd of Dir: Dan Falese
Bd of Dir: Diane Parro
Ofcr: Harris Franklin
**VP:* Richard Gougis
VP: Crystal Hansen
Ex Dir: Erica Ekstrom
Dir Sec: Leroy Brown
Dir IT: Astrid Welch

D-U-N-S 05-656-0493
VALLEY VIEW HOSPITAL ASSOCIATION
1906 Blake Ave, Glenwood Springs, CO 81601-4259
Tel (970) 945-6535 *Founded/Ownrshp* 1955
Sales 192.0MM *EMP* 1,000
SIC 8062

D-U-N-S 00-389-8624
VALLEY WHOLESALE DRUG CO LLC
(*Suby of* SMITH MEDICAL PARTNERS DIV) ★
1401 W Fremont St, Stockton, CA 95203-2627
Tel (209) 466-0131 *Founded/Ownrshp* 1948, 2012
Sales 110.0MME *EMP* 75
SIC 5122 Drugs & drug proprietaries; Cosmetics; Druggists' sundries
CEO: Dale Smith
VP: Angelo Grande
VP: Dan Matteoli
Sls Mgr: Bobby Jones

VALLEY WIDE BEVERAGE COMPANY
See FRESNO BEVERAGE CO INC

D-U-N-S 03-399-9301
VALLEY WIDE COOPERATIVE INC
2114 N 20th St, Nampa, ID 83687-6850
Tel (208) 436-0141 *Founded/Ownrshp* 1947
Sales 721.1MME *EMP* 350
SIC 5191 5251 5541 5171 Fertilizer & fertilizer materials; Hardware; Filling stations, gasoline; Petroleum bulk stations
Pr: Byron Jensen
**CEO:* David Holtom
**Prin:* Jerry Hall
Mktg Mgr: Jason Pollard

VALLEY YELLOW PAGES
See AGI PUBLISHING INC

VALLEYCARE HEALTH
See VALLEYCARE HOSPITAL CORP

VALLEYCARE HEALTH SYSTEM
See HOSPITAL COMMITTEE FOR LIVERMORE-PLEASANTON AREAS

D-U-N-S 84-897-4093
VALLEYCARE HOSPITAL CORP
VALLEYCARE HEALTH
(*Suby of* VALLEY CARE HEALTH SYSTEM) ★
1111 E Stanley Blvd, Livermore, CA 94550-4115
Tel (925) 447-7000 *Founded/Ownrshp* 1988
Sales 85.3MME *EMP* 1,100E
SIC 8011 Primary care medical clinic
Pr: Marcelina L Feit

VALLEYCREST GOLF CRSE MINT INC
See BRIGHTVIEW GOLF MAINTENANCE INC

D-U-N-S 11-809-8235 IMP/EXP
VALLOUREC & MANNESMANN HOLDINGS INC
(*Suby of* VALLOUREC TUBES)
4424 W Sam Houston Pkwy N # 150, Houston, TX 77041-8243
Tel (713) 479-3200 *Founded/Ownrshp* 1984
Sales 649.9MME *EMP* 251
SIC 5082 Oil field equipment
Pr: Olivier Mallet
**VP:* James Herald

D-U-N-S 11-849-5811 IMP
VALLOUREC INDUSTRIES INC
(*Suby of* VALLOUREC & MANNESMANN HOLDINGS INC) ★
19210 E Hardy Rd, Houston, TX 77073-3310
Tel (281) 821-5510 *Founded/Ownrshp* 1984
Sales 120.0MME *EMP* 158
SIC 3498 Tube fabricating (contract bending & shaping)
Pr: Grady Harrison

D-U-N-S 11-570-5589 IMP
VALLOUREC STAR LP
(*Suby of* VALLOUREC)
2669 M L K J Blvd, Youngstown, OH 44510
Tel (330) 742-6300 *Founded/Ownrshp* 2002
Sales 168.8MME *EMP* 570E
SIC 3317 Pipes, seamless steel
Pr: Judson Wallace
CFO: Philippe Lesage

D-U-N-S 10-264-1503 IMP/EXP
VALLOUREC USA CORP
(*Suby of* VALLOUREC & MANNESMANN HOLDINGS INC) ★
4424 W Sm Hstn Pkwy N 1, Houston, TX 77041
Tel (713) 479-3277 *Founded/Ownrshp* 1983
Sales 450.2MME *EMP* 33
SIC 5082 Oil field equipment
Pr: David R Hamrick
CFO: Todd Booth

D-U-N-S 07-062-5116 IMP
VALMET INC
(*Suby of* VALMET OYJ)
2425 Commerce Ave Ste 100, Duluth, GA 30096-8913
Tel (770) 263-7863 *Founded/Ownrshp* 2013
Sales 472.4MME *EMP* 1,418
SIC 3554 5084 Pulp mill machinery; Paper mill machinery: plating, slitting, waxing, etc.; Pulp (wood) manufacturing machinery; Paper manufacturing machinery
Ch Bd: Pasi Laine
**Pr:* William Bohn
**Treas:* Kristen Wald
VP: Mike Gray
VP: Dave King
IT Man: Edythe Griffith
Manager: Mike Gerardi
Sls Mgr: Mark Reynolds
Sls Mgr: Phil Warren

D-U-N-S 00-726-7214
▲ VALMONT INDUSTRIES INC
1 Valmont Plz Ste 500, Omaha, NE 68154-5215
Tel (402) 963-1000 *Founded/Ownrshp* 1946
Sales 2.6MMM *EMP* 10,947
Tkr Sym VMI *Exch* NYS

SIC 3441 3399 3317 3523 3612 Fabricated structural metal; Tower sections, radio & television transmission; Metal powders, pastes & flakes; Steel pipe & tubes; Fertilizing, spraying, dusting & irrigation machinery; Irrigation equipment, self-propelled; Lamp ballasts; Ballasts for lighting fixtures; Fluorescent ballasts
Ch Bd: Mogens C Bay
Pr: Leonard Adams
CFO: Mark C Jaksich
Ex VP: Todd G Atkinson
Ex VP: Barry A Ruffalo
VP: Lee Addams
VP: Michael Banat
VP: Doug Bryson
VP: Jerry Dorman
VP: Timothy Francis
VP: John A Kehoe
VP: Anil Kumar
VP: Wally Pasco
VP: Walter Pasko
VP: Porfirio Sandoval
VP: Aaron M Schapper
VP: Pete Smith
VP: Piet Stevens
VP: Don Vitito
Board of Directors: Theo W Freye, James B Milliken, Daniel P Neary, Catherine James Paglia, Clark T Randt Jr, Walter Scott Jr, Kenneth E Stinson

D-U-N-S 05-105-6984 IMP/EXP
VALMONT INDUSTRIES INC
VALMONT INTERNATIONAL
7002 N 288th St, Valley, NE 68064-8016
Tel (402) 359-2201 *Founded/Ownrshp* 1975
Sales NA *EMP* 6,029
SIC 3523

VALMONT INTERNATIONAL
See VALMONT INDUSTRIES INC

D-U-N-S 10-798-1037 IMP
■ **VALMONT NEWMARK INC**
(*Suby of* VALMONT INDUSTRIES INC) ★
2 Perimeter Park S 475w, Birmingham, AL 35243-3393
Tel (205) 968-7200 *Founded/Ownrshp* 2004
Sales 240.9MM^E *EMP* 1,300
SIC 3272 1731 3317 Poles & posts, concrete; Lighting contractor; Steel pipe & tubes
Pr: Earl R Foust
**CFO:* Larry Price
VP: Doug Sherman
Dir IT: Ron Cochran

D-U-N-S 13-272-8382
VALOR GROUP LLC
F & E TRADING
245 Belmont Dr, Somerset, NJ 08873-1217
Tel (732) 357-2426 *Founded/Ownrshp* 2010
Sales 300.0MM *EMP* 90
SIC 5043 Cameras & photographic equipment
CFO: Gedalia Waxler

D-U-N-S 05-500-8924 IMP/EXP
VALOR LLC
1200 Alsop Ln, Owensboro, KY 42303-0922
Tel (270) 683-2461 *Founded/Ownrshp* 2000
Sales 177.3MM^E *EMP* 152
SIC 5171 5172 Petroleum bulk stations; Lubricating oils & greases
VP: Toby Baptiste
Sales Exec: Beth Bevil

D-U-N-S 01-005-4794
■ **VALOR TELECOMMUNICATIONS ENTERPRISES LLC**
WINDSTREAM STHWEST LONG DSTNCE
(*Suby of* WINDSTREAM SOUTHWEST LONG DISTANCE LP) ★
4001 N Rodney Parham Rd, Little Rock, AR 72212-2459
Tel (501) 748-7000 *Founded/Ownrshp* 2000
Sales 261.7MM *EMP* 1,200
SIC 4813 Voice telephone communications
CFO: Brent K Whittington

D-U-N-S 03-907-4658
■ **VALOR TELECOMMUNICATIONS LLC**
(*Suby of* WINDSTREAM SERVICES LLC) ★
4001 N Rodney Parham Rd, Little Rock, AR 72212-2459
Tel (501) 748-7000 *Founded/Ownrshp* 2006
Sales 3.0MMM *EMP* 1,300
SIC 4813 Voice telephone communications
CFO: Brant Whittington

D-U-N-S 05-939-3926
VALPAK DIRECT MARKETING SYSTEMS INC
COX TARGET MEDIA
(*Suby of* V P HOLDINGS INC) ★
805 Exe Ctr Dr W, Saint Petersburg, FL 33702
Tel (727) 399-3175 *Founded/Ownrshp* 1986
Sales 105.1MM^E *EMP* 1,200
SIC 7331 6794 Direct mail advertising services; Franchises, selling or licensing
Pr: Terry Loebel
Pr: Marylou Armendinger
Pr: Amy King
**CFO:* Jeff Heinicka
**VP:* Nora A Dickinson
VP: David Fox
VP Admn: Todd Leiser
Genl Mgr: Julie Recupero
Software D: Greg Hoch
VP Mktg: Sharon Reeder
S&M/VP: David Szen

VALPAK DIRECT MKTG SYSTEMS
See COX TARGET MEDIA INC

VALPARAISO UNIVERSITY
See LUTHERAN UNIVERSITY ASSOCIATION INC

D-U-N-S 05-073-6453 IMP/EXP
▲ **VALSPAR CORP**
1101 S 3rd St, Minneapolis, MN 55415-1211
Tel (612) 851-7000 *Founded/Ownrshp* 1806
Sales 4.3MMM *EMP* 11,100
Tkr Sym VAL *Exch* NYS
SIC 2851 Paints & allied products; Lacquers, varnishes, enamels & other coatings; Stains: varnish, oil or wax; Putty, wood fillers & sealers
Ch Bd: Gary E Hendrickson
Pr: Michael Brandt
Pr: Les H Ireland
Treas: Deborah Weiss
Treas: Timothy M Wesolowski
Ofcr: James L Muehlbauer
Ex VP: Rolf Engh
Ex VP: Steven Erdahl
Sr VP: Cynthia A Arnold
Sr VP: Anthony L Blaine
Sr VP: Howard C Heckes
Sr VP: John R Wardzel
VP: John Anton
VP: Tony Blaine
VP: Florian Girthofer
VP: Joel C Hart
VP: Andrew Hecker
VP: Alejandro Montoya
VP: Donald A Nolan
VP: Jeff Panchak
VP: Thomas A White
Board of Directors: Ian R Friendly, Jack J Allen, John M Ballbach, John S Bode, William M Cook, Jeffrey H Curler, Shane D Fleming, Janel S Haugarth, Mae C Jemison, David R Lumley

VALTRIS SPECIALTY CHEMICALS
See POLYMER ADDITIVES INC

D-U-N-S 10-681-2951
VALU HOME CENTERS INC
DO IT BEST
45 S Rossler Ave, Buffalo, NY 14206-3417
Tel (716) 824-4150 *Founded/Ownrshp* 1968
Sales 97.8MM^E *EMP* 650
SIC 5211 Home centers
**Ex VP:* Richard C Arena
**VP:* Michael A Amico
**VP:* Grayce Arena
**Prin:* Glenn Izard
Dir IT: Michael Ervolina

D-U-N-S 86-870-3513 IMP
VALU MERCHANDISERS CO
ALWAYS FRESH
(*Suby of* ASSOCIATED GROCERS) ★
5000 Kansas Ave, Kansas City, KS 66106-1135
Tel (913) 319-8500 *Founded/Ownrshp* 1993
Sales 363.4MM^E *EMP* 210^E
SIC 5199 General merchandise, non-durable
Treas: Joe Bush
**Pr:* Dan Funk
**VP:* John Lane

VALUE CITY
See CREST FURNITURE INC

VALUE CITY
See SCHOTTENSTEIN STORES CORP

VALUE CITY
See AMERICAN SIGNATURE INC

D-U-N-S 85-972-3509 IMP
VALUE CITY FURNITURE INC
(*Suby of* VALUE CITY) ★
4300 E 5th Ave, Columbus, OH 43219-1816
Tel (888) 751-8552 *Founded/Ownrshp* 2000
Sales 343.6MM^E *EMP* 4,000
SIC 5712 Furniture stores
Pr: Jay Schottenstein
VP: Joe Bowles
VP: Michael Broidy
VP: Mark Ungar
**Prin:* Pamula A Lillie
Genl Mgr: Joshua Thiele
Genl Mgr: Jessica Twomey
IT Man: Victoria Meyer
Opers Mgr: Damon Rockensuess
Opers Mgr: Jennifer Stemmle
Corp Couns: Melita Garrett

D-U-N-S 01-381-9339 IMP
VALUE DRUG CO
195 Theater Dr, Duncansville, PA 16635-7144
Tel (814) 944-9316 *Founded/Ownrshp* 1936
Sales 779.8MM *EMP* 200
Accts Hill Barth & King Llc Wexfor
SIC 5122 Drugs & drug proprietaries; Druggists' sundries; Patent medicines
Pr: Greg Drew
**Ch Bd:* Rowland Tibbott
**Pr:* John L Letizia
**CFO:* Robert E Tyler
**Treas:* William D Thompson Jr
VP: David Zang
IT Man: Bill Sutton
Mktg Dir: Kathy Kilgore
Advt Mgr: Kelsey Troxell

VALUE FRESH
See RIESBECK FOOD MARKETS INC

VALUE VILLAGE
See TVI INC

VALUE VILLAGE STORES
See SAVERS INC

D-U-N-S 07-911-5785
VALUEACT CAPITAL MANAGEMENT LP
1 Letterman Dr Bldg D, San Francisco, CA 94129-1494
Tel (415) 249-1232 *Founded/Ownrshp* 2005
Sales 160.0MM *EMP* 38
SIC 6722 Money market mutual funds
CEO: Jeffrey Williams Ubben

D-U-N-S 14-955-0993
■ **VALUED SERVICES ACQUISITIONS CO LLC**
(*Suby of* ATLANTICUS HOLDINGS CORPORATION)
5 Concrs Pkwy Ne Ste 1000, Atlanta, GA 30328-6132
Tel (678) 593-1300 *Founded/Ownrshp* 2004
Sales NA *EMP* 750
SIC 6099 Check cashing agencies

VALUEPOINT MATERIAL SOLUTIONS
See HSS LLC

VALUES BY DESIGN
See MARDEL INC

D-U-N-S 60-502-0486 IMP/EXP
■ **VALVOLINE INC**
(*Suby of* ASHLAND LLC) ★
3499 Blazer Pkwy, Lexington, KY 40509-1850
Tel (859) 357-7777 *Founded/Ownrshp* 1918
Sales 1.9MMM *EMP* 5,600
Accts Pricewaterhousecoopers Llp
Tkr Sym VVV *Exch* NYS
SIC 2992 Oils & greases, blending & compounding
Pr: Samuel J Mitchell Jr
Pr: Charles A Quinn
Sr VP: John C Biehl
VP: Peter Freeman
VP: Martin A Kish
VP: John Noal
VP: James V Rocco
Genl Mgr: Gideon Agbeyegbe
Genl Mgr: Dainius Maciuikab
Genl Mgr: Wong Ming
Board of Directors: Richard J Freeland, Stephen F Kirk, Stephen E Macadam, Charles M Sonsteby, Mary J Twinem, Vada O Manager

VALVOLINE INSTANT OIL CHANGE
See VALVOLINE INTERNATIONAL INC

D-U-N-S 86-125-1684 IMP/EXP
■ **VALVOLINE INTERNATIONAL INC**
VALVOLINE INSTANT OIL CHANGE
(*Suby of* VALVOLINE INC) ★
3499 Blazer Pkwy, Lexington, KY 40509-1850
Tel (800) 832-6825 *Founded/Ownrshp* 1992
Sales 406.9MM^E *EMP* 5,000
SIC 7549 5172 Automotive maintenance services; Engine fuels & oils
Pr: S J Mitchell
**CEO:* William A Wulfsohn
CFO: Marvin Quinn

D-U-N-S 08-029-8733
■ **VALVOLINE LLC**
(*Suby of* VALVOLINE US LLC) ★
3499 Blazer Pkwy, Lexington, KY 40509-1850
Tel (859) 357-7777 *Founded/Ownrshp* 2016
Sales 187.9MM^E *EMP* 1,000^E
SIC 2992 Oils & greases, blending & compounding
Pr: Samuel J Mitchell Jr

D-U-N-S 08-029-8718
■ **VALVOLINE US LLC**
(*Suby of* VALVOLINE INC) ★
3499 Blazer Pkwy, Lexington, KY 40509-1850
Tel (859) 357-7777 *Founded/Ownrshp* 2016
Sales 194.7MM^E *EMP* 5,000^E
SIC 2992 Oils & greases, blending & compounding
Pr: Samuel J Mitchell Jr

D-U-N-S 84-014-1621 IMP/EXP
VAM USA LLC
PTS VAM CO
(*Suby of* VALLOUREC INDUSTRIES INC) ★
4424 W S Houston N 150, Houston, TX 77041
Tel (281) 821-5510 *Founded/Ownrshp* 2007
Sales 120.0MM *EMP* 158
SIC 3498 Tube fabricating (contract bending & shaping)
Pr: Eric Shuster
**CFO:* Eric Balgairies
CFO: Adam Shapianski
**Ch:* Didier Hornet
MIS Dir: John Luthern
Dir IT: John Luther
Sls Mgr: Dave Herrmann
Snr Mgr: Claudia Priego

D-U-N-S 94-298-8700
VAN ANDEL INSTITUTE
333 Bostwick Ave Ne, Grand Rapids, MI 49503-2518
Tel (616) 234-5000 *Founded/Ownrshp* 1996
Sales 188.0MM *EMP* 170
Accts Deloitte & Touche Llp Grand R
SIC 8733 Physical research, noncommercial
Ch: David V Andel
**CFO:* Timothy Myers
Bd of Dir: Afton Devos
Bd of Dir: Kaitlyn Disselkoen
VP: Susan Raymond
VP: David Whitescarver
Exec: Ann Schoen
Dir Lab: Glen Alberts
Dir Lab: Anderson Peck
Dir Lab: Megan Senchuk
Assoc Dir: Jim Nicolette
Comm Dir: Nancy Kooienga

D-U-N-S 12-927-3160
VAN ANDEL RESEARCH INSTITUTE
VAI
333 Bostwick Ave Ne, Grand Rapids, MI 49503-2518
Tel (616) 234-5000 *Founded/Ownrshp* 1996
Sales 162.3MM *EMP* 384
Accts Deloitte & Touche Llp Grand R
SIC 8733 Noncommercial research organizations
CEO: David Van Andel
**Pr:* Dr Steven Triezenberg
**CFO:* Timothy J Myers
Assoc Dir: David Ross
CTO: Kuntal Pal
QA Dir: Dana Filkins
IT Man: Dave Drolett

D-U-N-S 00-700-1761 IMP/EXP
VAN ATLAS LINES INC
(*Suby of* ATLAS WORLD GROUP INC) ★
1212 Saint George Rd, Evansville, IN 47711-2364
Tel (812) 424-4326 *Founded/Ownrshp* 1948, 1988
Sales 103.9MM^E *EMP* 606
SIC 4213 4731 Household goods transport; Freight forwarding
Pr: Glen Dunkerson
CFO: Lisa Koch
**CFO:* Richard J Olson
**VP:* David W Coulter
VP: Steve Hermann
**VP:* Dennie Lynn
**VP:* Marian W Sauvey
VP: Mark Spiehler
Plng Mgr: Sherry Bland
Software D: Doreatha Lintzenich
Sls Mgr: Laurie Fellwock

D-U-N-S 10-420-1004
VAN BORTEL FORD INC
71 Marsh Rd, East Rochester, NY 14445-1915
Tel (585) 586-4415 *Founded/Ownrshp* 2001
Sales 109.8MM *EMP* 120
SIC 5531 7539 Automotive parts; Automotive repair shops
Pr: Mary Catherine Van Bortel
Pr: Ruth Perrin
**VP:* Howard Vanbortel

VAN CHEVROLET
See VT MOTORS INC

D-U-N-S 04-502-7083
VAN DE POL ENTERPRISES INC
4895 S Airport Way, Stockton, CA 95206-3915
Tel (209) 465-3421 *Founded/Ownrshp* 1959
Sales 185.1MM^E *EMP* 150
Accts Gallina Llp Rancho Cordova C
SIC 5172 Petroleum products
Ch Bd: Lee Atwater
**Owner:* Paul Gosal
**Owner:* Ted Wysoki
**CEO:* Ronald M Vandepol
**CFO:* Scott Macewan
**VP:* Jon Rosman
**VP:* Curtis Thornhill
**VP:* Mark Volpe
**Prin:* Mike Popari
Genl Mgr: David Atwater

VAN DEVERE BUICK
See VAN DEVERE INC

D-U-N-S 01-749-4733
VAN DEVERE INC
VAN DEVERE BUICK
300 W Market St, Akron, OH 44303-2185
Tel (330) 253-6137 *Founded/Ownrshp* 1970
Sales 103.0MM^E *EMP* 305^E
SIC 5511 7515 Automobiles, new & used; Passenger car leasing
Pr: Michael Van Devere
**Sec:* Shirley A Van Devere
Genl Mgr: Chris Bender
Off Mgr: Kelly McVey

D-U-N-S 00-531-4117 IMP
VAN DIEST SUPPLY CO
1434 220th St, Webster City, IA 50595-7628
Tel (515) 832-2366 *Founded/Ownrshp* 1956
Sales 696.1MM^E *EMP* 500
SIC 5191 2875 2879 Chemicals, agricultural; Fertilizer & fertilizer materials; Fertilizers, mixing only; Agricultural chemicals
Pr: Robert Van Diest
**Pr:* Vandiest Robert
**Treas:* Gregg Olson
**Treas:* Dalene Schlitter
**Sr VP:* Walt Sayer
**VP:* John Van Diest
Area Mgr: Stormy Barricklow
Area Mgr: Gene Triplett
Area Mgr: Brad Weaver
Off Mgr: Brandy Henson
Mfg Dir: Lee Trask

VAN DRUNEN FARMS
See R J VAN DRUNEN & SONS INC

D-U-N-S 18-685-2240
VAN DYK MORTGAGE CORP
PARAMOUNT FUNDING COMPANY
2449 Camelot Ct Se, Grand Rapids, MI 49546-6001
Tel (616) 940-3000 *Founded/Ownrshp* 1987
Sales NA *EMP* 550
SIC 6162 6163 Mortgage bankers & correspondents; Loan brokers
CEO: Tom Van Dyk
**COO:* Jenie Nivison
**CFO:* Justin McDowell
**Sr VP:* Charlie Sundstrom

VAN GUARD TRUCK CENTER ATLANTA
See TOM GRADDY ENTERPRISES INC

D-U-N-S 14-773-3455 IMP
VAN HOOF CORP
1160 N Mayflower Dr, Appleton, WI 54913-9656
Tel (920) 830-5000 *Founded/Ownrshp* 1966
Sales 100.0MM *EMP* 1,200
SIC 4225 General warehousing & storage
Pr: Robert Schroeder
**CFO:* Dan Vandenheuvel
**VP:* Kevin Nixon
**VP:* Dan Sellers
**VP Opers:* Bill Lindeke
Counsel: Ben Haupt

VAN HYGAN & SMYTHE
See BRADFORD EXCHANGE LTD

VAN KEPPEL LIFTRUCK
See G W VAN KEPPEL CO

D-U-N-S 06-018-9172
VAN MANEN PETROLEUM INC
O-305 Lake Michigan Dr Nw, Grand Rapids, MI 49534-3355
Tel (616) 453-6344 *Founded/Ownrshp* 1952

Sales 84.6MM^E EMP 42
SIC 5172 Diesel fuel; Gasoline; Lubricating oils & greases
Ch Bd: Randy Van Manen
*CFO: Doug Van Hattum
Treas: David Beute
Dir IT: Steve Boer

D-U-N-S 94-886-8435
VAN METER INC
850 32nd Ave Sw, Cedar Rapids, IA 52404-3913
Tel (319) 366-5301 Founded/Ownrshp 1995
Sales 181.9MM^E EMP 325
SIC 5063

VAN ROB TECUMSEH
See LENAWEE STAMPING CORP

VAN TUYL GROUP, LLC
See BERKSHIRE HATHAWAY AUTOMOTIVE INC

D-U-N-S 06-232-8844 IMP
VAN WINGERDEN INTERNATIONAL INC
4112 Haywood Rd, Mills River, NC 28759-9740
Tel (828) 696-4500 Founded/Ownrshp 1996
Sales 85.1MM^E EMP 398
SIC 5193 Flowers & florists' supplies
Pr: Kelly Cantrell
IT Man: Kathaleen Lemkes
Mktg Dir: Bert Lemkes

D-U-N-S 09-587-4384
VANASSE HANGEN BRUSTLIN INC (MA)
V H B
101 Walnut St, Watertown, MA 02472-4026
Tel (617) 924-1770 Founded/Ownrshp 1979
Sales 184.7MM EMP 1,085
SIC 8711 Engineering services
Ch Bd: Robert S Brustlin
*Treas: John B Jackson
*Sr VP: Ruth Bonsignore
*Sr VP: Michael Carragher
*Sr VP: Jonathan L Feinstein
*Sr VP: David J Manning
*Sr VP: Francis S O'Callaghan
*Sr VP: Steve Thomas
VP: Jonathan Feinstein
*VP: William Roache
Dir: Victoria Dorokhin
Comm Man: Alexander Shelley

D-U-N-S 04-004-2046
VANCE COUNTY BOARD OF EDUCATION
1724 Graham Ave, Henderson, NC 27536-2904
Tel (252) 492-2127 Founded/Ownrshp 1910
Sales 61.4MM EMP 1,125^E
SIC 8211 School board
Ch Bd: Gloria White

D-U-N-S 96-334-3376
VANCE STREET CAPITAL LLC
11150 Santa Monica Blvd # 750, Los Angeles, CA 90025-0528
Tel (310) 231-7100 Founded/Ownrshp 2007
Sales 86.1MM^E EMP 501
SIC 6799 Investors
VP: John Lerosen

VANCOUVER CLINIC, THE
See VANCOUVER CLINICAL SERVICES PC

D-U-N-S 05-360-3049 IMP
VANCOUVER CLINICAL SERVICES PC
VANCOUVER CLINIC, THE
700 Ne 87th Ave, Vancouver, WA 98664-1913
Tel (360) 397-1500 Founded/Ownrshp 1956
Sales 111.8MM^E EMP 800
SIC 8011 Clinic, operated by physicians; Internal medicine practitioners; Pediatrician; Gynecologist
Ch: Dr Sharon Crowell
*Ch Bd: John Rastall
*CEO: Duane Lucas-Roberts
*CFO: Philip Baker
CFO: June Francisco
Bd of Dir: Yvonne Frei
Bd of Dir: Kevin Meitz
Bd of Dir: Steven Slovic
*Ex Dir: Tom Vansweringen
Dir IT: Thomas O'Neal
Netwrk Mgr: Donavon Nigg
Board of Directors: Michaelann Dir

D-U-N-S 06-060-3941 IMP
VANCOUVER PUBLIC SCHOOLS (WA)
2901 Falk Rd, Vancouver, WA 98661-6392
Tel (360) 313-1000 Founded/Ownrshp 1852
Sales 269.1MM EMP 2,700
SIC 8211 Public elementary & secondary schools
*CFO: Steve Olsen
Dir Sec: Albert Alcanter
Pr Dir: Patricia Nuzzo
Teacher Pr: Kathy Everidge
Psych: Geranios George
Snr Mgr: Greg Ross
Board of Directors: Barb Laurenzo

D-U-N-S 13-350-1556
▲ VANDA PHARMACEUTICALS INC
2200 Penn Ave Nw Ste 300e, Washington, DC 20037-1754
Tel (202) 734-3400 Founded/Ownrshp 2003
Sales 109.9MM EMP 118^E
Tkr Sym VNDA Exch NGM
SIC 2834 8731 Pharmaceutical preparations; Drugs acting on the central nervous system & sense organs; Medical research, commercial
Pr: Mihael H Polymeropoulos
*Ch Bd: H Thomas Watkins
CFO: James P Kelly
Chf Cred: Gian Piero Reverberi
Chf Mktg O: Paolo Baroldi
Sr VP: Richard L Gulino
Board of Directors: Kenneth M Bate, Michael F Cola, Richard W Dugan, Vincent J Milano

D-U-N-S 01-739-5971 IMP
VANDER-BEND MANUFACTURING LLC
2701 Orchard Pkwy, San Jose, CA 95134-2008
Tel (408) 245-5150 Founded/Ownrshp 1999
Sales 184.1MM^E EMP 510
SIC 3679 3444 3549 Harness assemblies for electronic use: wire or cable; Sheet metalwork; Metalworking machinery
Exec: Holly Bugaj
Genl Mgr: John Beebe
Genl Mgr: Steve Wolf
Dir IT: Dennis Wong
Plnt Mgr: Leila Freeman

D-U-N-S 07-871-2110 IMP/EXP
VANDERBILT CHEMICALS LLC
(Suby of RT VANDERBILT HOLDING CO INC) ★
30 Winfield St, Norwalk, CT 06855-1329
Tel (203) 853-1400 Founded/Ownrshp 2012
Sales 103.6MM^E EMP 180
SIC 2819 2869 5169 Industrial inorganic chemicals; Industrial organic chemicals; Chemicals & allied products
Pr: John Benton
*Sec: Stephen Turbak
VP: Richard Davis
Tech Mgr: Marty Sheridan

D-U-N-S 01-684-8504
VANDERBILT CHILDRENS HOSPITAL
MONROE CAROL JR CHILDREN HOSPT
2200 Chld Way Ste 2410, Nashville, TN 37232-0001
Tel (615) 322-7601 Founded/Ownrshp 1998
Sales 159.7MM^E EMP 2,000
SIC 8062 General medical & surgical hospitals
Treas: Beth Moore
Bd of Dir: Monroe Carell
Ofcr: Beth Glascock
Assoc Dir: Patricia Givens
Dir Rad: Rochelle F Andreotti
Off Mgr: Julia Summerlin
Surgeon: Karla G Christian
Pharmcst: Carly Feldott
Pharmcst: Cindy Herzog
Pharmcst: Lori Wright

D-U-N-S 08-120-5155
■ VANDERBILT MORTGAGE AND FINANCE INC
(Suby of CMH SERVICES INC) ★
500 Alcoa Trl, Maryville, TN 37804-5516
Tel (865) 380-3000 Founded/Ownrshp 2012
Sales NA EMP 1,200^E
SIC 6141 Installment sales finance, other than banks
Pr: Eric Hamilton
Treas: Steve Cook
Bd of Dir: George Gunnell
Ex VP: John Kalec
VP: David Barton
VP: Mark Ezzo
Exec: Robert Fox
Genl Mgr: Kim Burnett
Genl Mgr: Jaime Varner
IT Man: John Knight
Plnt Mgr: Steve Sutton

D-U-N-S 00-441-3456
VANDERBILT UNIVERSITY
211 Kirkland Hall, Nashville, TN 37240-0001
Tel (615) 322-5000 Founded/Ownrshp 1873
Sales 1.2MMM EMP 21,000
Accts Pricewaterhousecoopers Llp M
SIC 8221 8062 University; Hospital, medical school affiliation
Ch Bd: Mark Daltrn
Treas: Brett Sweets
Trst: Lee M Bass
Trst: Elizabeth S Bennett
Trst: Camilla D Bergeron
Trst: Cecil D Conlee
Trst: Clairborne P Deming
Trst: Bruce R Evans
Trst: Karen T Fesmire
Trst: Joanne F Hayes
Trst: John R Ingram
Trst: Alice Ji
Trst: Jackson W Moore
Trst: Ayo O Ositelu
Trst: Frederick B Rentschler
Trst: Joe L Roby
Trst: Eugene B Shanks Jr
Trst: Cal Turner Jr
Trst: Levi Watkins Jr
Trst: Andrew M Wilson
Ofcr: Traci K Nordberg

D-U-N-S 02-419-9668
VANDERBILT UNIVERSITY MEDICAL CENTER
1211 Medical Center Dr, Nashville, TN 37232-0004
Tel (615) 875-9396 Founded/Ownrshp 1999
Sales 16.2MM^E EMP 19,000
SIC 8062 Hospital, medical school affiliation
CEO: Jeff Balser
COO: Mitch Edgeworth
CFO: Ray Dziesinski
Treas: Alaine Zachary
Sr VP: Nancy Lane
Dir Rx: Jatika Jordan
Adm Dir: Carol Eck
Ex Dir: Titus Daniels
Pathlgst: Peter Wright
Doctor: Tina Hartert
Doctor: Madan Jagasia

D-U-N-S 03-921-1003
VANDERLANDE INDUSTRIES INC
(Suby of VANDERLANDE INDUSTRIES HOLDING B.V.)
1975 W Oak Cir, Marietta, GA 30062-2249
Tel (770) 250-2800 Founded/Ownrshp 1998
Sales 159.1MM^E EMP 220
SIC 8711 3535 Engineering services; Unit handling conveying systems
Pr: Ewout Cassee
V Ch: Sarah Sucharski
*CFO: Herman Molenaar
*CFO: Herbert Root
*CFO: Bart Wittedeen
Sr VP: Colin Thompson
Mng Dir: Peter Stuer
Genl Mgr: Nick Porter
Sys Mgr: Antonie Vos
Opers Mgr: Chuck Vanzant
Sls Dir: Simon Andary

D-U-N-S 79-560-9382
VANDERRA RESOURCES LLC
1801 Century Park E # 2400, Los Angeles, CA 90067-2326
Tel (817) 439-2220 Founded/Ownrshp 2011
Sales 182.9MM^E EMP 500^E
SIC 1389 Oil field services; Gas field services
COO: Joe Lassister
CFO: Brandon Polk

VANDEVANTER ENGINEERNG
See COGENT INC

D-U-N-S 18-914-8174
■ VANGENT INC
GENERAL-DYNAMICS-IT
(Suby of GENERAL DYNAMICS CORP) ★
3211 Jermantown Rd, Fairfax, VA 22030-2844
Tel (703) 995-2666 Founded/Ownrshp 2007
Sales 522.0M^E EMP 8,728
SIC 8748 7371 7372 7373 7374 7376 Systems analysis & engineering consulting services; Custom computer programming services; Prepackaged software; Computer integrated systems design; Data processing & preparation; Computer facilities management
Pr: S Daniel Johnson
*CFO: James C Reagan
*Sr VP: Kevin T Boyle
*Sr VP: David J Fabianski
Sr VP: John George
Sr VP: Thomas Kirchmaier
*Sr VP: Giovanna Patterson
*VP: Vincent Antonacci
*VP: David Breen
VP: Jerry Calhoun
*VP: Jim Knapp
VP: Tim Turner
Board of Directors: Michael J Bayer, Paul V Lombardi, Robert B McKeon, Ramzi M Musallama, Charles S Ream

D-U-N-S 79-100-5775
VANGUARD CAR RENTAL USA INC
(Suby of ENTERPRISE RENT-A-CAR) ★
6929 N Lakewood Ave # 100, Tulsa, OK 74117-1810
Tel (918) 401-6000 Founded/Ownrshp 2007
Sales 472.2MM^E EMP 14,000
SIC 7514 Rent-a-car service
Pr: Greg Stubblefield
Pr: Robert Connors
COO: Jeffry J Parell
CFO: Thomas C Kennedy
Sr VP: Wesley C Fredenburg
Sr VP: Edward Jones
Sr VP: Paula A Kuykendall
VP: Craig Bonza
VP: David Grace
VP: Mary Morse
VP: Jerry Mosiello
VP: Eugene Pizinger

D-U-N-S 08-204-1562
VANGUARD CHARITABLE ENDOWMENT PROGRAM
100 Vanguard Blvd G19, Malvern, PA 19355-2331
Tel (888) 383-4483 Founded/Ownrshp 1997
Sales 1.0MMM EMP 22
Accts Pricewaterhousecoopers Llp Ph
SIC 7389 Fund raising organizations
Pr: Benjamin R Pierce
COO: John Caswell
*CFO: Kevin Cavanaugh
*Ofcr: David S Ryder
Mktg Mgr: James R Barnes

D-U-N-S 18-591-3258 IMP
VANGUARD EMS INC
3725 Sw Hocken Ave, Beaverton, OR 97005-2413
Tel (503) 644-4808 Founded/Ownrshp 2003
Sales 87.2MM^E EMP 180
SIC 3672 3679

D-U-N-S 16-915-2555
VANGUARD ENERGY SERVICES LLC
(Suby of CONTINUUM ENERGY LLC) ★
850 E Diehl Rd Ste 142, Naperville, IL 60563-8236
Tel (630) 955-1500 Founded/Ownrshp 2003
Sales 129.3MM EMP 28
Accts Grant Thornton Llp Tulsa Ok
SIC 3822 Energy cutoff controls, residential or commercial types
*Genl Mgr: Paul Bougadis

D-U-N-S 94-272-2091
VANGUARD FIDUCIARY TRUST CO INC
VANGUARD PERSONAL TRUST SVCS
(Suby of VANGUARD GROUP INC) ★
100 Vanguard Blvd, Malvern, PA 19355-2331
Tel (610) 669-6000 Founded/Ownrshp 1981
Sales 399.2MM^E EMP 9,000
SIC 6722 Mutual fund sales, on own account
Ch Bd: John J Brennan
*Ch: F William McNabb III
IT Man: Joseph Ford
IT Man: Mia Harkins
Mktg Mgr: Laura Eufrasio
Mktg Mgr: Traci Patel
Mktg Mgr: Theresa Westwood

D-U-N-S 06-007-4812
VANGUARD GROUP INC
100 Vanguard Blvd, Malvern, PA 19355-2331
Tel (610) 669-1000 Founded/Ownrshp 1974
Sales 6.0MMM^E EMP 12,000
Accts Pricewaterhouse Coopers Phila
SIC 6722 Mutual fund sales, on own account
Ch Bd: F William McNabb III
CFO: James Barry
CFO: Thomas Higgins
CFO: Jake Odden
Chf Inves: George U Sater
Ex VP: Annemarie Haddad
Ex Dir: Benjamin Pierce
Mng Dir: James H Gately
Mng Dir: Kathleen C Gubanich
Mng Dir: Martha King
Mng Dir: Michael S Miller

D-U-N-S 17-677-9056
■ VANGUARD HEALTH SYSTEMS INC
(Suby of TENET HEALTHCARE CORP) ★
20 Burton Hills Blvd # 100, Nashville, TN 37215-6409
Tel (615) 665-6000 Founded/Ownrshp 2013
Sales 3.8MMM^E EMP 40,900
SIC 8062 6324 General medical & surgical hospitals; Hospital & medical service plans
CEO: Charles N Martin Jr
Chf Path: Robert Reisman
*Pr: Kent H Wallace
COO: Elaine Mecier
*CFO: Phillip W Roe
Bd of Dir: Dal Bello
*Ofcr: Mark R Montoney MD
Sr VP: Reginald M Ballantyne
Sr VP: Harold H Pilgrim
VP: Harold K Bandy
VP: Richard W Brasher
VP: Robert J Rowntree
VP: Alan J Smith
VP: Peter Tolfa
Dir Rx: Susan Matteson

D-U-N-S 62-161-2167 EXP
VANGUARD INTERNATIONAL INC
22605 Se 56th St Ste 200, Issaquah, WA 98029-5289
Tel (425) 557-8250 Founded/Ownrshp 1990
Sales 135.0MM^E EMP 50
SIC 5148 Fruits; Vegetables
Pr: Craig Stauffer
*CFO: Guy Kisling

D-U-N-S 09-945-2062
VANGUARD LOGISTICS SERVICES (USA) INC
(Suby of DIRECT CONTAINER LINE) ★
5000 Airport Plaza Dr, Long Beach, CA 90815-1271
Tel (310) 847-3000 Founded/Ownrshp 1978
Sales 201.6MM^E EMP 681
SIC 4731 Freight consolidation
Ch: Charles Brennan
Pr: Bruce Ericson
CFO: J Thurso Barendse
Treas: Jeff Alinsangan
Treas: Scott Shellow
VP: Therese Groff
VP: Derek Moore
Exec: Debbie Carr
Off Mgr: Pamela Shaw
IT Man: Calvin Thomas
Software D: Al Hamlin

VANGUARD MARKETING
See THRESHOLD ENTERPRISES LTD

D-U-N-S 13-574-9831 IMP/EXP
VANGUARD NATIONAL TRAILER CORP
(Suby of CHINA INTERNATIONAL MARINE CONTAINERS (GROUP) CO., LTD.)
289 Water Tower Dr, Monon, IN 47959-8160
Tel (219) 253-2000 Founded/Ownrshp 2003
Sales 346.2MM EMP 500
Accts Rsm Us Llp Elkhart Indiana
SIC 3715 3713 Truck trailers; Truck bodies & parts
CEO: Charles Mudd
Rgnl Mgr: Mary Blanchette
Rgnl Mgr: Trent Metzger
Sls Mgr: Bill Fisher

D-U-N-S 79-043-8027
▲ VANGUARD NATURAL RESOURCES LLC
5847 San Felipe St # 1910, Houston, TX 77057-3011
Tel (832) 327-2255 Founded/Ownrshp 2006
Sales 566.6MM EMP 381^E
Tkr Sym VNR Exch NGS
SIC 1311 1382 Crude petroleum & natural gas; Crude petroleum production; Natural gas production; Oil & gas exploration services
Pr: Scott W Smith
*Ch Bd: W Richard Anderson
*CFO: Richard A Robert
Ex VP: Britt Pence
Board of Directors: Bruce W McCullough, Loren Singletary

VANGUARD PERSONAL TRUST SVCS
See VANGUARD FIDUCIARY TRUST CO INC

VANITY FAIR
See VF OUTLET INC

D-U-N-S 04-156-4394 IMP/EXP
■ VANITY FAIR BRANDS LP
(Suby of UNION UNDERWEARR) ★
1 Fruit Of The Loom Dr, Bowling Green, KY 42103-7932
Tel (270) 781-6400 Founded/Ownrshp 2007
Sales 1.2MMM^E EMP 10,303
SIC 2341 2384 2342 Nightgowns & negligees: women's & children's; Robes & dressing gowns; Foundation garments, women's
Pt: Curtis Holtz
Board of Directors: Lawrence R Pugh

D-U-N-S 05-073-6263 IMP
VANITY SHOP OF GRAND FORKS INC (ND)
(Suby of SHAZZAM INC) ★
1001 25th St N, Fargo, ND 58102-3116
Tel (701) 282-0486 Founded/Ownrshp 1966, 1996
Sales 90.0MM EMP 1,200
SIC 5621 Women's clothing stores; Ready-to-wear apparel, women's
Pr: Margaret Quinn
CFO: Jill Motschenbacher
Treas: Jill Shea
Netwrk Eng: Blair Miller
Site Mgr: Lisa Batten
Site Mgr: Tammy Binder
Site Mgr: Jamie Cheney
Site Mgr: Brandi Churchwell
Site Mgr: Anthony Cimolo
Site Mgr: Laura Dougherty
Site Mgr: Laura Gamble

D-U-N-S 78-108-4280
■ VANLINER GROUP INC
(*Suby of* NATIONAL INTERSTATE INSURANCE CO) ★
1 Premier Dr, Fenton, MO 63026-2989
Tel (636) 343-9889 *Founded/Ownrshp* 2010
Sales NA *EMP* 309^E
SIC 6411 8742 Property & casualty insurance agent; General management consultant
Pr: Jonathan Temporiti

VANNOY CONSTRUCTION
See JAMES R VANNOY & SONS CONSTRUCTION CO INC

VANPORT BUILDERS
See VANPORT MANUFACTURING INC

D-U-N-S 04-248-6027 EXP
VANPORT MANUFACTURING INC
VANPORT BUILDERS
28590 Se Wally Rd, Boring, OR 97009-9451
Tel (503) 663-4447 *Founded/Ownrshp* 1967
Sales 100.0MM *EMP* 5
Accts Fellner & Kuhn Portland Or
SIC 2421 5099 Lumber: rough, sawed or planed; Logs, hewn ties, posts & poles
Ch Bd: Adolf Hertrich
**Pr:* Martin Hertrich
**Pr:* Paul Owen
Treas: Jim Everett
**VP:* Edward Harris
Genl Mgr: Chris Ketcham
Sales Asso: Eric Chen

D-U-N-S 02-533-7775 IMP
VANS INC
3730 W 131st St, Alsip, IL 60803-1519
Tel (708) 371-8000 *Founded/Ownrshp* 1961
Sales 86.8MM^E *EMP* 300
SIC 5193 Flowers & florists' supplies; Flowers, fresh; Plants, potted
V Ch Bd: Jack Van Namen
**Pr:* Gary H Schoenfeld
**Pr:* Jacob Van Namen
**COO:* Georgean Summers
**Sr VP:* Curt Van Lonkhuyzen

D-U-N-S 19-713-1865 IMP
■ VANS INC
VANS SHOES
(*Suby of* VF GLOBAL INNOVATION CENTER) ★
6550 Katella Ave, Cypress, CA 90630-5102
Tel (714) 889-6100 *Founded/Ownrshp* 2004
Sales 438.0MM^E *EMP* 2,145^E
SIC 3021 2321 2329 2325 2353 2393 Canvas shoes, rubber soled; Protective footwear, rubber or plastic; Boots, rubber or rubber soled fabric; Men's & boys' sports & polo shirts; Polo shirts, men's & boys': made from purchased materials; Men's & boys' sportswear & athletic clothing; Jackets (suede, leatherette, etc.), sport: men's & boys'; Slacks, dress: men's, youths' & boys'; Shorts (outerwear): men's, youths' & boys'; Hats, caps & millinery; Canvas bags
Sr VP: Arthur I Carver
**CFO:* Scott J Blechman
**Sr VP:* Robert L Nagel
VP: Sarah Crockett
VP: Joseph D Giles
**VP:* Craig E Gosselin
VP: Mark Haskins
VP: Vicki Redding
VP: Chris D Strain
Creative D: Julie Warford
Dist Mgr: Nick Costino

VANS SHOES
See VANS INC

D-U-N-S 82-771-9167 IMP/EXP
VANTAGE DRILLING CO
777 Post Oak Blvd Ste 800, Houston, TX 77056-3215
Tel (281) 404-4700 *Founded/Ownrshp* 2007
Sales 875.5MM *EMP* 1,295^E
SIC 1381

D-U-N-S 15-612-7362
VANTAGE HEALTHCARE CORP
(*Suby of* GOLDEN LIVING CTRS COMMUNITIES) ★
1000 Fianna Way, Fort Smith, AR 72919-9008
Tel (479) 201-2000 *Founded/Ownrshp* 1983
Sales 23.9MM^E *EMP* 1,250
SIC 8741 Nursing & personal care facility management
CEO: William R Floyd

D-U-N-S 04-842-1239 EXP
VANTAGE MOBILITY INTERNATIONAL LLC
V M I
(*Suby of* VMI HOLDINGS LLC)
5202 S 28th Pl, Phoenix, AZ 85040-3799
Tel (602) 243-2700 *Founded/Ownrshp* 2014
Sales 181.3MM^E *EMP* 243
SIC 5012 3559 Automobiles & other motor vehicles; Automotive related machinery
CEO: Doug Eaton
**CFO:* Tim Barone
IT Man: Michael Kell

D-U-N-S 17-591-3656 IMP
VANTAGE OLEOCHEMICALS INC
(*Suby of* HIG CAPITAL LLC) ★
4650 S Racine Ave, Chicago, IL 60609-3321
Tel (773) 376-9000 *Founded/Ownrshp* 1985
Sales 202.5MM^E *EMP* 150^E
SIC 2869 2841 5169 Fatty acid esters, aminos, etc.; Glycerin, crude or refined: from fats; Industrial chemicals
CEO: Julian Steinberg
**Ch Bd:* Robert Drennan
**Pr:* Anthony Tamer
**COO:* Noel Beavis
**CFO:* Helen Scott
**Ex VP:* Don Ciancio
**Ex VP:* Conrad Kempinska
Dir IT: Ian Duncan
Sls Mgr: Ben Baker
Sls Mgr: Joseph Drew

D-U-N-S 82-803-4699
■ VANTAGE ONCOLOGY LLC
(*Suby of* MCKESSON CORP) ★
1500 Rosecrans Ave # 400, Manhattan Beach, CA 90266-3754
Tel (310) 335-4000 *Founded/Ownrshp* 2016
Sales 84.7MM^E *EMP* 515
SIC 8011 Oncologist
CEO: Michael Fiore
Pr: Dee Delapp
**COO:* Marshal Salomon
**CFO:* Brian Rizkallah
**Chf Mktg O:* Leslie E Botnick
**CTO:* Christopher M Rose
VP Opers: Veeral Desai
Genl Couns: Steve Udicious

D-U-N-S 19-134-9898 IMP
VANTAGE SPECIALTIES INC
3938 Porett Dr, Gurnee, IL 60031-1244
Tel (847) 244-3410 *Founded/Ownrshp* 2012
Sales 312.3MM^E *EMP* 338^E
SIC 4925 2869 Mixed natural & manufactured gas, distribution; Fatty acid esters, aminos, etc.
CEO: Julien Steinberg
**COO:* Noel Beavis
**CFO:* Helen Scott
**Ex VP:* Don Ciancio
**Ex VP:* Chris Humberstone
Sr VP: Tiffany Kyllmann
IT Man: Gwen Jones

D-U-N-S 03-154-1878
VANTAGESOUTH BANCSHARES INC
3600 Glenwood Ave Ste 300, Raleigh, NC 27612-4955
Tel (919) 659-9000 *Founded/Ownrshp* 2011
Sales NA *EMP* 467^E
SIC 6022

D-U-N-S 07-741-6480
VANTAGESOUTH BANK
1005 High House Rd, Cary, NC 27513-3586
Tel (919) 460-7770 *Founded/Ownrshp* 1998
Sales NA *EMP* 200
SIC 6022

D-U-N-S 11-281-5790 IMP/EXP
VANTEC HITACHI TRANSPORT SYSTEM (USA) INC
(*Suby of* VANTEC CORPORATION)
991 Francisco St, Torrance, CA 90502-1217
Tel (310) 525-2900 *Founded/Ownrshp* 1983
Sales 138.3MM^E *EMP* 329
SIC 4731 Freight forwarding
CEO: Christopher Haley
**Ch Bd:* Geri Kim
**Treas:* Junko Komiyama
**Prin:* Shinya Hannnya
**Prin:* Toyohiko Sakurai
**Genl Mgr:* Tomoyuki Miyazaki
Opers Mgr: Steven Middleton

D-U-N-S 04-740-7669
■ VANTIV HOLDING LLC
(*Suby of* VANTIV INC) ★
8500 Governors Hill Dr, Symmes Twp, OH 45249-1384
Tel (513) 358-6192 *Founded/Ownrshp* 2008
Sales 1.2MMM^E *EMP* 550^E
SIC 7374 Data processing service
Pr: Charles Drucker
**COO:* Carlos Lima
**CFO:* Mark Heimbouch
VP: Kathy Fitzgerald
**CIO:* Bob Bartlett

D-U-N-S 07-843-3177
▲ VANTIV INC
8500 Governors Hill Dr, Symmes Twp, OH 45249-1384
Tel (513) 900-5250 *Founded/Ownrshp* 1970
Sales 3.1MMM *EMP* 3,313^E
Accts Deloitte & Touche Llp Cincinn
Tkr Sym VNTV *Exch* NYS
SIC 7389 Financial services
Pr: Charles D Drucker
**Ch Bd:* Jeffrey Stiefler
Pr: Kevin Brown
Pr: Sarah Curtsinger
Pr: Robert Demeuse
Pr: Matt Fluegge
Pr: Tracy Hadden
Pr: Raymond Lapid
Pr: Tom Ninos
**COO:* Mark L Heimbouch
CFO: Stephanie Ferris
Treas: Tim Cooper
Ofcr: Ned Greene
Ofcr: Kimberly Martin
Ex VP: John Yarmy
Sr VP: Lynn Rhoads
Sr VP: Nathan Rozof
Sr VP: Paulette Sasso
Sr VP: Christopher Thompson
VP: Kimberly Adams
VP: Bill Andrews
Board of Directors: Lee Adrean, Lars C Anderson, Kevin S Costello, Lisa Hook, David Karnstedt, Gary K Lauer

D-U-N-S 17-469-1527
■ VANTIV LLC
(*Suby of* VANTIV HOLDING LLC) ★
8500 Governors Hill Dr, Symmes Twp, OH 45249-1384
Tel (877) 713-5964 *Founded/Ownrshp* 2009
Sales 1.3MMM^E *EMP* 550
SIC 7374 Data processing service
Pr: Charles Drucker
**Pr:* George A Schafer Jr
Sr VP: Michelle Lund
Sr VP: Jay McCracken
Sr VP: Kevin McKeon
VP: Samuel Adams
VP: Bev Smith
VP: Matthew Theiss
Exec: Diane Howard
Exec: Kim Martin
Mktg Dir: Christina Lohrer

D-U-N-S 02-865-5610 IMP
VAOPTO LLC (NV)
5178 W Patrick Ln, Las Vegas, NV 89118-2829
Tel (702) 979-3582 *Founded/Ownrshp* 2010
Sales 191.0MM^E *EMP* 3,000
SIC 3674 Light emitting diodes

D-U-N-S 83-246-0484
VAPOR ACQUISITION CORP
STANT
1620 Columbia Ave, Connersville, IN 47331-1672
Tel (765) 825-3121 *Founded/Ownrshp* 2009
Sales 123.3MM^E *EMP* 485
SIC 3714 Motor vehicle parts & accessories
CEO: Lou Braga
**CFO:* Michael Saccucci
**Treas:* Tony Showman

D-U-N-S 61-944-1777
VAR RESOURCES LLC
VAR TECHNOLOGY FINANCE
(*Suby of* SUTTON HOLDING CORP) ★
2330 Interstate 30, Mesquite, TX 75150-2720
Tel (972) 755-8200 *Founded/Ownrshp* 1990
Sales 105.0MM *EMP* 61
SIC 7377 Computer rental & leasing; Computer hardware rental or leasing, except finance leasing; Computer peripheral equipment rental & leasing
Pr: Gary Sutton
CFO: David Rieck
VP: Don Archibald
**VP:* Sheree Sutton
Mktg Dir: Robien Christie
Mktg Dir: Aairon Huntley

VAR TECHNOLOGY FINANCE
See VAR RESOURCES LLC

D-U-N-S 00-842-4285 IMP
■ VARCO LP
TUBOSCOPE
(*Suby of* NOV) ★
2835 Holmes Rd, Houston, TX 77051-1023
Tel (713) 799-5272 *Founded/Ownrshp* 2005
Sales 521.2MM^E *EMP* 1,000
SIC 1389 3479 Testing, measuring, surveying & analysis services; Pipe testing, oil field service; Coating or wrapping steel pipe
Pt: John F Lauletta
Pt: J F Maroney
Pt: Joseph C Winkler
Off Mgr: Amanda Keedy
Opers Mgr: Mike Gist
Sls Mgr: Anna Yarbrough

D-U-N-S 78-394-3736 EXP
VARCO PRUDEN HOLDING INC
(*Suby of* BLUESCOPE STEEL LIMITED)
3200 Players Club Cir, Memphis, TN 38125-8843
Tel (901) 748-8000 *Founded/Ownrshp* 2001
Sales 170.2MM^E *EMP* 1,658
SIC 3448 Prefabricated metal buildings
VP: Clifton Hyder
CFO: Terry Finn
Ex VP: Chad Beery
**VP:* Joseph Berryhill
VP: Jeff Jefferies
**VP:* Geoff Miller
CTO: Michael Stanley
IT Man: Jefferys Steve
Netwrk Mgr: Lee Moseley
Mktg Dir: Jim Peckham

D-U-N-S 82-826-9501 IMP
VAREL INTERNATIONAL ENERGY SERVICES INC
(*Suby of* SANDVIK AB)
1625 W Crosby Rd Ste 124, Carrollton, TX 75006-6694
Tel (800) 827-3526 *Founded/Ownrshp* 2014
Sales 338.3MM^E *EMP* 1,300
SIC 1381 3545 Drilling oil & gas wells; Drill bits, metalworking
Pr: Jim Nixon
**CFO:* John Capasso
VP: Chris Byrd
VP: Rod Mackenzie
VP: Bernard Pontneau

D-U-N-S 00-731-9437 IMP
VAREL INTERNATIONAL IND LP
(*Suby of* VAREL INTERNATIONAL ENERGY SERVICES INC) ★
1625 W Crosby Rd Ste 124, Carrollton, TX 75006-6694
Tel (972) 242-1160 *Founded/Ownrshp* 2014
Sales 338.3MM^E *EMP* 984
SIC 3545 3532 1381 Drill bits, metalworking; Bits, except oil & gas field tools, rock; Drilling water intake wells
CEO: Jim Nixon
CFO: Bill Bishkin
CFO: John Capasso
CFO: Linda Earl
CFO: Mike Pisch
**VP:* Guillermo Aponte
**VP:* Speed Collingsworth
**VP:* David Harrington
VP: Colin Hunter
VP: Pat A Neal
Dir IT: Sharon Medor

D-U-N-S 00-692-0565
■ VARIABLE ANNUITY LIFE INSURANCE CO (INC)
AIG VALIC
(*Suby of* AMERICAN GENERAL LIFE INSURANCE CO) ★
2929 Allen Pkwy, Houston, TX 77019-7100
Tel (713) 522-1111 *Founded/Ownrshp* 1979
Sales NA *EMP* 999
SIC 6311 Life insurance
Pr: Bruce R Abrams
Treas: Terry Festervand
Ex VP: Jennifer Cobb
Ex VP: Shawn Duffy
Ex VP: John Lagrasse
Sr VP: Craig Cheyne
VP: Michael Akers
VP: Gregory Broer
VP: Todd Buchanan
VP: Steve Dmytrack
VP: Mark Foster
VP: Don Harris
VP: Tracey Harris
VP: Candy Roach
VP: Bob Taylor
VP: Kevin Toledano
Board of Directors:

D-U-N-S 06-250-5461 IMP/EXP
■ VARIAN INC
(*Suby of* AGILENT TECHNOLOGIES INC) ★
3100 Hansen Way, Palo Alto, CA 94304-1030
Tel (650) 213-8000 *Founded/Ownrshp* 1999
Sales 569.8MM^E *EMP* 3,500
SIC 3826 3845 3829 3827 Analytical instruments; Electromedical equipment; Measuring & controlling devices; Optical instruments & lenses
CEO: Garry W Rogerson
Pr: Dow Wilson
COO: Phillip Criminale
CFO: G Edward McClammy
CFO: Don Woerkom
Treas: Keith Laton
Treas: Sean M Wirtjes
Sr VP: Arthur W Homan
Mktg Dir: Keith La Plain
Mktg Mgr: Laima Baltusis
Sls Mgr: Jamie Bellush

D-U-N-S 00-912-0817
▲ VARIAN MEDICAL SYSTEMS INC
3100 Hansen Way, Palo Alto, CA 94304-1030
Tel (650) 493-4000 *Founded/Ownrshp* 1948
Sales 3.2MMM *EMP* 7,300
Tkr Sym VAR *Exch* NYS
SIC 3845 3844 7372 Electromedical equipment; Electromedical apparatus; Therapeutic X-ray apparatus & tubes; Radiographic X-ray apparatus & tubes; Irradiation equipment; Prepackaged software
Pr: Dow R Wilson
**Ch Bd:* R Andrew Eckert
CFO: Elisha W Finney
**V Ch Bd:* Timothy E Guertin
Sr VP: Jessica L Denecour
Sr VP: John W Kuo
Sr VP: Rafael Torres
Sr VP: Clarence R Verhoef
VP: Steve Hiller
VP: Moataz Karmalawy
VP: Patrick Kupelian
VP: Merna Richardson
VP: Chris Toth
Board of Directors: Susan L Bostrom, Judy Bruner, Regina E Dugan, David J Illingworth, Mark R Laret, Erich R Reinhardt

D-U-N-S 06-240-1570 IMP
■ VARIAN SEMICONDUCTOR EQUIPMENT ASSOCIATES INC (DE)
APPLIED MATERIALS VARIAN
(*Suby of* APPLIED MATERIALS INC) ★
35 Dory Rd, Gloucester, MA 01930-2236
Tel (978) 282-2000 *Founded/Ownrshp* 1999, 2011
Sales 399.4MM^E *EMP* 1,462^E
SIC 5065 3674 Semiconductor devices; Semiconductors & related devices
CEO: Gary E Dickerson
Pr: Thomas Faulkner
**CFO:* Robert J Halliday
Chf Mktg O: Gary Loser
**Ex VP:* Yong-Kil Kim PHD
**Ex VP:* Robert J Perlmutter PHD
Ex VP: Stan Yarbro
VP: Amy Kostka
**VP:* Gary J Rosen PHD
Exec: Brian Gori
Genl Mgr: Craig Chaney

D-U-N-S 96-500-0123
VARIETAL DISTRIBUTION HOLDINGS LLC
(*Suby of* M D P) ★
100 Matsonford Rd, Radnor, PA 19087-4558
Tel (610) 386-1700 *Founded/Ownrshp* 2007
Sales 429.4MM^E *EMP* 8,800^E
SIC 5047 Medical & hospital equipment

D-U-N-S 04-746-9051
VARIETY CHILDRENS HOSPITAL
NICKLAUS CHILDREN'S HOSPITAL
3100 Sw 62nd Ave, Miami, FL 33155-3009
Tel (305) 666-6511 *Founded/Ownrshp* 1963
Sales 618.0MM *EMP* 3,700
SIC 8069 Children's hospital
CEO: Narendra M Kini
Treas: Tim M Birkenstock
Ofcr: April Andrews-Singh
Sr VP: Timothy Birkenstock
Sr VP: Jacqueline L Gonzalez
Sr VP: Edward Martinez
VP: Meschelle Huether
VP: Mario Murgado
VP: Jose Perdomo
VP: Nikole Sanchez-Rubiera
Assoc Dir: Mark Young

D-U-N-S 00-728-7758 IMP/EXP
VARIETY DISTRIBUTORS INC
609 7th St, Harlan, IA 51537-1064
Tel (712) 755-2184 *Founded/Ownrshp* 1946
Sales 162.3MM^E *EMP* 230
SIC 5131 5092 5122 5112 5145 5199 Piece goods & notions; Hobby supplies; Arts & crafts equipment & supplies; Toys & games; Druggists' sundries; Social stationery & greeting cards; Candy; Novelties, paper
Pr: Jerry Koegnis
**Treas:* Dave Minen
**VP:* Merle Honerman
**VP:* Gary Nicola
Genl Mgr: Don Lantz
Mktg Dir: Marlene Brensel

D-U-N-S 00-699-6854 IMP
VARIETY STORES INC
ROSES STORES
(*Suby of* SUPER SAVER) ★
218 S Garnett St, Henderson, NC 27536-4644
Tel (252) 430-2600 *Founded/Ownrshp* 2007

Sales 597.6MM^E *EMP* 6,700
SIC 5331 Variety stores
CEO: James A Pope
**Pr:* Wilson Sawyer
**VP:* Brent Sprunger
Dir IT: Gary Boxler
Trfc Mgr: Jim Wyatt

D-U-N-S 02-456-4577 IMP/EXP
VARIETY WHOLESALERS INC (NC)
SUPER SAVER
218 S Garnett St, Henderson, NC 27536-4644
Tel (252) 430-2800 *Founded/Ownrshp* 1957
Sales 1.4MMM^E *EMP* 6,800
Accts Grant Thornton Co
SIC 5331 Variety stores
CEO: James A Pope
Pr: George A Bellino
**Pr:* Wilson Sawyer
Pr: Barbara Stell
**CFO:* Keith Favreau
Ex VP: Chris Zender
VP: Mark Christenbury
VP: Gerald Frucht
VP: Tim Hedgepeth
VP: David Miles
VP: Mark Zimmerman

D-U-N-S 00-716-5194 IMP
■ **VARIFORM INC**
(*Suby of* PLY GEM HOLDINGS INC) ★
303 W Major St, Kearney, MO 64060-8551
Tel (919) 677-3900 *Founded/Ownrshp* 2004
Sales 134.8MM^E *EMP* 700
SIC 3089 1521 3444 Siding, plastic; Single-family housing construction; Sheet metalwork
Pr: John Wayne
Pr Mgr: Glenda Caldwell

D-U-N-S 60-765-4134
■ **VARISTAR CORP**
(*Suby of* OTTER TAIL CORP) ★
4334 18th Ave S Ste 200, Fargo, ND 58103-7414
Tel (701) 232-6414 *Founded/Ownrshp* 1989
Sales 13.4M *EMP* 2,760
SIC 6719 4899 1623 5047 1731 4213 Personal holding companies, except banks; Data communication services; Telephone & communication line construction; Transmitting tower (telecommunication) construction; Cable laying construction; Medical equipment & supplies; General electrical contractor; Trailer or container on flat car (TOFC/COFC)
CFO: Kevin G Moug
Ch: John Erickson
Sr VP: Michelle Kommer
VP: Charles R Hoge

VARITEC SOLUTIONS
See JAVINE VENTURES INC

D-U-N-S 06-556-3822
VARNER FAMILY LIMITED PARTNERSHIP
5900 E Lerdo Hwy, Shafter, CA 93263-4023
Tel (661) 399-1163 *Founded/Ownrshp* 2000
Sales 111.0MM^E *EMP* 150
SIC 6733 Private estate, personal investment & vacation fund trusts
Genl Pt: James Varner

D-U-N-S 80-120-4012
▲ **VARONIS SYSTEMS INC**
1250 Broadway Fl 29, New York, NY 10001-3720
Tel (877) 292-8767 *Founded/Ownrshp* 2005
Sales 127.2MM *EMP* 947^E
Tkr Sym VRNS *Exch* NGS
SIC 7372 Prepackaged software
Ch Bd: Yakov Faitelson
COO: Eric Mann
CFO: Gili Iohan
Sr VP: James O'Boyle
**CTO:* Ohad Korkus
Mktg Mgr: Maya Ben-Bassat
Mktg Mgr: Inessa Rozenberg
Mktg Mgr: Samantha Telegadis
Sls Mgr: Zachery Botsford
Sales Asso: Justin Lubman
Board of Directors: Fred Van Den Bosch, Kevin Comolli, Rona Segev-Gal, John J Gavin Jr, Thomas F Mendoza, Ofer Segev

D-U-N-S 07-851-6918 IMP
VARROC LIGHTING SYSTEMS INC
USA HQ MICHIGAN
(*Suby of* VARROC ENGINEERING PRIVATE LIMITED)
47828 Halyard Dr, Plymouth, MI 48170-2454
Tel (734) 446-4400 *Founded/Ownrshp* 2010
Sales 847.6MM^E *EMP* 4,200
SIC 3751 Motorcycles, bicycles & parts
Pr: Jeff Stevenson
**VP:* Scott Borovich
Snr Mgr: Dylan Schickel

D-U-N-S 14-783-8689
VARSATEL CORP
2813 Executive Park Dr # 112, Weston, FL 33331-3603
Tel (954) 667-6550 *Founded/Ownrshp* 2002
Sales 221.8MM^E *EMP* 1,429
SIC 5065 Telephone equipment
CEO: Harrison Vargas
**Pr:* Gerardo Riveillas
**CFO:* Gerardo Rivillas
**VP:* Blanca J Hitchcock

D-U-N-S 07-978-7930
VARSITY BRANDS HOLDING CO INC
1901 Diplomat Dr, Farmers Branch, TX 75234-8914
Tel (972) 406-7162 *Founded/Ownrshp* 2014
Sales 1.1MMM *EMP* 3,090
SIC 5091 7299 6719 Watersports equipment & supplies; Party planning service; Investment holding companies, except banks
CFO: John E Pitts
**Ofcr:* Burton Brillhart
**Ex VP:* Terrence Babilla
**Ex VP:* John Nichols
**VP:* Adam Blumenfeld

D-U-N-S 19-634-8577 IMP
VARSITY BRANDS LLC
VARSITY SPIRIT FASHIONS
(*Suby of* VARSITY BRANDS HOLDING CO INC) ★
6745 Lenox Center Ct # 300, Memphis, TN 38115-4300
Tel (901) 387-4306 *Founded/Ownrshp* 2014
Sales 823.5MM^E *EMP* 3,700
SIC 5091 Sporting & recreation goods
CEO: Matthew E Rubel
**Pr:* Jeffrey G Webb
**CFO:* John Nichols
**CFO:* Jhon Nickels
Assoc VP: Braxton Kinser
Ex VP: Denese Pearson
**Sr VP:* J Kristyn Shepherd
VP: Melanie Berry
VP: Jennifer Bond
VP: Kim Carroll
**VP:* Lisa Carter
VP: Craig Davis
VP: Tricia Ferree
**VP:* Karen Halterman
VP: Tracy Hill
VP: Sheila Noone
VP: Bill Patterson
**VP:* Cenie Royal
**VP:* Mary Sparacino
VP: Gary Spencer
VP: Leslie Standlee
Board of Directors: Don R Kornstein, John McConnaughy Jr, Glenn E Schembechler, Arthur N Seessel III

D-U-N-S 05-719-4896
VARSITY CONTRACTORS INC
VARSITY FACILITY SERVICES
315 S 5th Ave, Pocatello, ID 83201-5857
Tel (208) 232-8598 *Founded/Ownrshp* 1957
Sales 97.5MM *EMP* 3,500
SIC 7349

VARSITY FACILITY SERVICES
See VARSITY CONTRACTORS INC

VARSITY SPIRIT FASHIONS
See VARSITY BRANDS LLC

D-U-N-S 07-858-8017
VASARI LLC
550 Bailey Ave Ste 650, Fort Worth, TX 76107-2162
Tel (888) 685-1847 *Founded/Ownrshp* 2012, 2013
Sales 84.2MM^E *EMP* 970
SIC 2024 Dairy based frozen desserts
CEO: Bill Spae
**Pr:* Michael Poates
**CFO:* Jim Berry

D-U-N-S 12-126-7561
▲ **VASCO DATA SECURITY INTERNATIONAL INC**
1901 S Meyers Rd Ste 210, Oakbrook Terrace, IL 60181-5206
Tel (630) 932-8844 *Founded/Ownrshp* 1991
Sales 241.4MM *EMP* 545^E
Tkr Sym VDSI *Exch* NAS
SIC 7373 7371 Computer integrated systems design; Computer software development
Ch Bd: T Kendall Hunt
Pr: Jan Valcke
CFO: Mark S Hoyt
Board of Directors: Michael P Cullinane, John N Fox Jr, Jean K Holley, Matthew Moog

D-U-N-S 60-803-2397
VASCOR LTD
(*Suby of* APL LOGISTICS LTD) ★
100 Farmers Bank Sq # 310, Georgetown, KY 40324-8712
Tel (502) 868-0277 *Founded/Ownrshp* 1987
Sales 117.3MM^E *EMP* 560
SIC 8742 Transportation consultant
CEO: Bill Garrett
Pr: Lee Jones
**CEO:* William Garrett
**Ex VP:* Tomonori Kono
**VP:* Rick Blank
**VP:* Daniel Greenberg
Exec: James Fitzgerald
Genl Mgr: Dan Burbulla
IT Man: David Butts
Snr Mgr: David Goyman
Snr Mgr: Erinn Thompson
Board of Directors: William Villaton

D-U-N-S 00-899-9906
▲ **VASCULAR SOLUTIONS INC** (MN)
6464 Sycamore Ct N, Maple Grove, MN 55369-6032
Tel (763) 656-4300 *Founded/Ownrshp* 1997
Sales 147.2MM *EMP* 568^E
Tkr Sym VASC *Exch* NGS
SIC 3841 Surgical & medical instruments
CEO: Howard Root
CFO: James Hennen
Sr VP: Brent Binkowski
Sr VP: Chad Kugler
Sr VP: Carrie Powers
Sr VP: William Rutstein
Sr VP: Charmaine Sutton
VP: Jonathan Hammond
VP: Gordon Weber
Genl Mgr: Rob Rademacher
IT Man: Mark Plusa
Board of Directors: Martin Emerson, John Erb, Richard Kramp, Richard Nigon, Paul O'connell, Jorge Saucedo

D-U-N-S 01-707-0210 IMP/EXP
VASS PIPE & STEEL CO INC
158 3rd St Ste 2, Mineola, NY 11501-4317
Tel (516) 741-8398 *Founded/Ownrshp* 1982
Sales 180.9MM *EMP* 26
SIC 5051 3317

D-U-N-S 08-046-7954
VASSAR BROTHERS HOSPITAL (NY)
VB MEDICAL CENTER
(*Suby of* HEALTH QUEST SYSTEMS INC) ★
45 Reade Pl, Poughkeepsie, NY 12601-3990
Tel (845) 454-8500 *Founded/Ownrshp* 1888, 1985
Sales 515.2MM *EMP* 1,500
Accts Pricewaterhousecoopers Llp N
SIC 8062 General medical & surgical hospitals
Pr: Daniel Aronzon MD
**Chf Cred:* Janeth Ready
Dir Rx: Bill Silta
Doctor: Manuel M Liu MD

D-U-N-S 08-046-4001
VASSAR COLLEGE
VASSAR COLLEGE STORE
124 Raymond Ave Box 12, Poughkeepsie, NY 12604-0001
Tel (845) 437-7000 *Founded/Ownrshp* 1861
Sales 160.5MM *EMP* 974
Accts Kpmg Llp Albany Ny
SIC 8221 College, except junior
Pr: Catharine Hill
COO: Natalie Friedman
Ofcr: Brian D Springstead
**VP:* Elizabeth Eismeier
Assoc Dir: Catherine Conover
Assoc Dir: Judith Dollenmayer
Assoc Dir: Angela Dysard
Assoc Dir: Seungsook Moon
Assoc Dir: Susan Quade
**Prin:* Donald Barton
Dir Sec: Susan Sheehan

VASSAR COLLEGE STORE
See VASSAR COLLEGE

D-U-N-S 08-561-6964
VASSER BROTHERS MEDICAL CENTER
45 Reade Pl, Poughkeepsie, NY 12601-3947
Tel (845) 454-8500 *Founded/Ownrshp* 2005
Sales 417.3MM^E *EMP* 22^E
SIC 8062 General medical & surgical hospitals
Pr: Daneil Aronzon
Sr VP: Janet L Ready
Pharmcst: Mike Zeolla

D-U-N-S 87-816-2742
VATAMERICA LP
CB VATAMERICA
344 Nassau St, Princeton, NJ 08540-4622
Tel (609) 430-4960 *Founded/Ownrshp* 1993
Sales 100.0MM *EMP* 10
SIC 8741 Financial management for business
Pt: James D Walker

VATTEROTT COLLEGE
See VATTEROTT EDUCATIONAL CENTERS INC

D-U-N-S 07-590-5042
VATTEROTT EDUCATIONAL CENTERS INC
VATTEROTT COLLEGE
7730 Carondelet Ave # 400, Saint Louis, MO 63105-3329
Tel (314) 264-1500 *Founded/Ownrshp* 2002
Sales 49.2MM^E *EMP* 1,001
SIC 8249 Trade school
CEO: Pamela Bell
**CFO:* Dennis Beavers
Bd of Dir: Mary Stewart
Dir IT: Scott Obermeyer
VP Mktg: Scott Schaffer
HC Dir: Deborah Lenihan
Genl Couns: Scott Casanover

D-U-N-S 00-312-4112 IMP/EXP
VAUGHAN-BASSETT FURNITURE CO INC (VA)
300 E Grayson St, Galax, VA 24333-2964
Tel (276) 236-6161 *Founded/Ownrshp* 1919
Sales 298.7MM^E *EMP* 1,564
Accts Smith Leonard Pllc High Point
SIC 2511 Bed frames, except water bed frames: wood; Bedside stands: wood; Dressers, household: wood; Dining room furniture: wood
CEO: John D Bassett III
V Ch: Carlisle W Higgins
**Pr:* Wyatt P E Bassett
**CFO:* Andrew Williamson
Treas: Kenneth H Sharp
**VP:* J Douglas Bassett IV
VP: Alexander G Biggs
VP: C C Carrico
VP: W Doyle Edwards
**VP:* Earl L Morgan
Sfty Mgr: Brian Reavis

VAUGHN CONSTRUCTION
See J T VAUGHN ENTERPRISES INC

D-U-N-S 15-134-3423
VAUGHN INDUSTRIES LLC
1201 E Findlay St, Carey, OH 43316-9686
Tel (419) 396-3900 *Founded/Ownrshp* 1985
Sales 118.2MM^E *EMP* 500
SIC 1731 1711 Electrical work; Mechanical contractor
Ex VP: Gregg Vaughn
Store Mgr: Ryan Fleece
Mtls Mgr: Steve Wilson
Opers Mgr: Peter Barnes

D-U-N-S 14-821-9467 IMP
VAUPELL INDUSTRIAL PLASTICS INC
(*Suby of* HIG CAPITAL MANAGEMENT INC) ★
1144 Nw 53rd St, Seattle, WA 98107-3735
Tel (206) 784-9050 *Founded/Ownrshp* 1957
Sales 195.5MM^E *EMP* 1,200
SIC 3089 Injection molding of plastics
Pr: Joe Jahn
**CFO:* Kelly Schroeder

VB MEDICAL CENTER
See VASSAR BROTHERS HOSPITAL

VBCA
See VALLEY BAKERS COOPERATIVE ASSOCIATION

D-U-N-S 18-297-4881 IMP
VC999 PACKAGING SYSTEMS INC
(*Suby of* VC 999 VERPACKUNGSSYSTEME AG)
419 E 11th Ave, Kansas City, MO 64116-4162
Tel (816) 472-8999 *Founded/Ownrshp* 1985
Sales 96.9MM^E *EMP* 200
SIC 5084 3565 Packaging machinery & equipment; Packaging machinery
Pr: Silvio Weder
VP: Remi Boudot
VP: Thomas Kafski
IT Man: John Lucero
VP Sls: Jim Wright
Mktg Mgr: Josh Wallingford
Manager: Rudy Hueni

D-U-N-S 18-171-1672
▲ **VCA INC**
12401 W Olympic Blvd, Los Angeles, CA 90064-1022
Tel (310) 571-6500 *Founded/Ownrshp* 1986
Sales 2.1MMM *EMP* 12,700
Tkr Sym WOOF *Exch* NGS
SIC 0742 5999 5047 Veterinary services, specialties; Animal hospital services, pets & other animal specialties; Pets & pet supplies; Pet food; Pet supplies; Veterinarians' equipment & supplies
Ch Bd: Robert L Antin
Pr: Josh Drake
COO: Arthur J Antin
CFO: Tomas W Fuller
Sr VP: Neil Tauber
VP: Todd Tams
Dir IT: Bailey Kelly

D-U-N-S 83-322-0945
VCC LLC
600 Las Colinas Blvd E # 1525, Irving, TX 75039-5618
Tel (214) 574-4500 *Founded/Ownrshp* 2008
Sales 597.1MM *EMP* 350
Accts Jpms Cox Pllc Little Rock A
SIC 1542 8711 8742 Commercial & office building, new construction; Construction & civil engineering; Construction project management consultant

D-U-N-S 84-397-9233
VCE CO LLC
1500 N Greenville Ave, Richardson, TX 75081-2265
Tel (972) 656-5300 *Founded/Ownrshp* 2009
Sales 588.8MM^E *EMP* 1,200^E
SIC 3572 Computer storage devices
CEO: Praveen Akkiraju
Sr Pt: Kevin Kennedy
Pr: Frank Hauck
CFO: Robert J Taccini
Chf Mktg O: Nina Hargus
Ex VP: Brian J Miller
Ex VP: Todd Pavone
VP: Tami Booth
VP: Ben Crook
VP: Jamie Erbes
VP: Jeffery Hayward
VP: Michael O'Keefe
VP: Mike O'Malley
VP: Craig P Zajac

D-U-N-S 82-513-9574
VCNA PRAIRIE INC
7601 W 79th St Ste 1, Bridgeview, IL 60455-1409
Tel (708) 458-0400 *Founded/Ownrshp* 1948
Sales NA *EMP* 2,000
SIC 3273 Ready-mixed concrete
Pr: Richard Olsen
**Pr:* David Plummer
Off Mgr: Jonna Kolton

VCNY
See VILLAGE CARE OF NEW YORK INC

VCNY
See VILLAGE CENTER FOR CARE

VCOM-VIRGINIA CAMPUS
See EDWARD VIA VIRGINIA COLLEGE OF OSTEOPATHIC MEDICINE

D-U-N-S 10-388-6180 IMP
VCP MOBILITY INC
SUNRISE MEDICAL NORTH AMERICAN
(*Suby of* SUNRISE MEDICAL HOLDINGS INC) ★
6899 Winchester Cir # 200, Boulder, CO 80301-3507
Tel (303) 218-4500 *Founded/Ownrshp* 2000
Sales 299.9MM^E *EMP* 1,850
SIC 3842 2599 2515 5047 3841 Wheelchairs; Respirators; Hospital furniture, except beds; Mattresses & foundations; Medical & hospital equipment; Surgical & medical instruments; Medical instruments & equipment, blood & bone work
CEO: Thomas Julius Rossnagel
**Pr:* Michael N Cannizzaro
CFO: James L Fetter
Ex VP: Jose Ceto
Ex VP: Christie Guttridge
Ex VP: Thomas H O'Donnell
Sr VP: Bob Hoover
VP: Roberta C Baade
VP: Geoff Cooper
VP: Geoffrey Cooper
VP: Mark Greig
VP: Rita Hostak
VP: Rod Mann
VP: Sam Sinasohn

D-U-N-S 11-805-8424 IMP/EXP
VCS GROUP LLC
CAMUTO GROUP
411 W Putnam Ave Ste 210, Greenwich, CT 06830-6263
Tel (203) 413-6500 *Founded/Ownrshp* 2002
Sales 250.2MM^E *EMP* 726
SIC 5139 Footwear
CEO: Alex Delcielo
**CFO:* Jeff Howald

D-U-N-S 12-497-6937
VCST INC
(*Suby of* VCST INDUSTRIAL PRODUCTS BVBA)
13854 Lakeside Cir 201, Sterling Heights, MI 48313-1316
Tel (586) 685-1747 *Founded/Ownrshp* 2008
Sales 23.3MM^E *EMP* 1,000
SIC 8742 Sales (including sales management) consultant
Sls Mgr: John Podlaski
VP: Ed Goethals
VP Opers: Bill Parry
Plnt Mgr: Greg Boullard

D-U-N-S 01-604-8030
VCU HEALTH SYSTEM AUTHORITY
MEDICAL COLLEGE OF VIRGINIA
1250 E Marshall St, Richmond, VA 23298-5051
Tel (804) 828-9000 *Founded/Ownrshp* 1998
Sales 969.9MM[E] *EMP* 7,399
SIC 8062 Hospital, medical school affiliated with residency
CEO: John Duval
**Pr:* Michael RAO
**COO:* Deborah Davis
**CFO:* Dominic J Puleo
VP: Shirley Gibson
Assoc Dir: Christopher Doern
Nurse Mgr: Mary Coffey
Nurse Mgr: Kym Gee
Opers Mgr: Brooke Krajcir
Sls&Mrk Ex: Carol Morgan
Doctor: William Moskowitz

VDH
See VIRGINIA DEPARTMENT OF HEALTH

D-U-N-S 04-748-6113 IMP
VDM METALS USA LLC
(*Suby of* VDM METALS GMBH)
306 Columbia Tpke, Florham Park, NJ 07932-1217
Tel (973) 437-1664 *Founded/Ownrshp* 1978
Sales 185.2MM *EMP* 230
SIC 3313 Alloys, additive, except copper: not made in blast furnaces
**Pr:* Joseph Fuhrman
Pr: Uwe Schneider
**CFO:* Mark Risse
**Treas:* Michael Dardezed
**Treas:* Michael Zardezed
Sr VP: Rainer Kochanski
Sr VP: Stefan Winkens
VP: Helena Alves
**VP:* Will Harbison
VP: Thomas Josefiak
**VP:* George Kramer
VP: Winfried Sterzl

VDOT
See VIRGINIA DEPARTMENT OF TRANSPORTATION

D-U-N-S 96-480-5662
VEBA TRUST FOR PUBLIC EMPLOYEES IN NORTHWEST
906 W 2nd Ave, Spokane, WA 99201-4538
Tel (509) 838-5571 *Founded/Ownrshp* 2010
Sales 89.2MM *EMP* 2[E]
Accts Schoedel & Schoedel Cpas Pllc
SIC 6733 Trusts
Prin: Mark Wilkerson

VEBATRUST
See STEEL AND PIPE SUPPLY CO INC

D-U-N-S 00-794-4184
VECELLIO & GROGAN INC (WV)
(*Suby of* VECELLIO GROUP INC) ★
2251 Robert C Byrd Dr, Beckley, WV 25801-8790
Tel (304) 252-6575 *Founded/Ownrshp* 1938
Sales 308.2MM[E] *EMP* 1,200
SIC 1611 1622 1629 General contractor, highway & street construction; Highway & street paving contractor; Bridge construction; Golf course construction; Land preparation construction
CEO: Leo A Vecellio Jr
**Sec:* L L Gwinn
**VP:* Dante Castrodale
VP: Paula Puckett
**VP:* Michael A Vecellio
Dir IT: Paula Davis
Board of Directors: Patricia Vecellio Rogers

D-U-N-S 16-233-3079
VECELLIO GROUP INC
101 Sansburys Way, West Palm Beach, FL 33411-3670
Tel (561) 793-2102 *Founded/Ownrshp* 2002
Sales 572.7MM[E] *EMP* 1,200
SIC 1611 Highway & street paving contractor; Grading; General contractor, highway & street construction
CEO: Leo A Vecellio Jr
VP: Paula Burgess
VP: Robert Colozzo
**VP:* Kathryn C Vecellio
**VP:* Michael A Vecellio
**Prin:* Christopher S Vecellio

D-U-N-S 04-156-7595 IMP
VECO CORP
(*Suby of* CH2M HILL COMPANIES LTD) ★
949 E 36th Ave Ste 500, Anchorage, AK 99508-4370
Tel (907) 762-1500 *Founded/Ownrshp* 1946
Sales 384.5MM[E] *EMP* 4,000
SIC 1711 1389 1731 1381 4959 Mechanical contractor; Construction, repair & dismantling services; Electrical work; Drilling oil & gas wells; Toxic or hazardous waste cleanup
Ch Bd: Tammy Kerrigan
**Pr:* Pete Leathard
**CFO:* Roger Chan
VP: Vic Thomas
IT Man: Hammut Ted

D-U-N-S 61-506-0886 EXP
▲ VECTOR GROUP LTD
4400 Biscayne Blvd Fl 10, Miami, FL 33137-3212
Tel (305) 579-8000 *Founded/Ownrshp* 1911
Sales 1.6MMM *EMP* 1,367[E]
Tkr Sym VGR *Exch* NYS
SIC 2111 6552 Cigarettes; Subdividers & developers
Pr: Howard M Lorber
**Ch Bd:* Bennett S Lebow
CFO: J Bryant Kirkland III
Ex VP: Richard J Lampen
VP: Marc N Bell
Board of Directors: Stanley S Arkin, Henry C Beinstein, Ronald J Bernstein, Jeffrey S Podell, Jean E Sharpe

D-U-N-S 19-536-8774
VECTOR RESOURCES INC
VECTORUSA
3530 Voyager St, Torrance, CA 90503-1666
Tel (310) 436-1000 *Founded/Ownrshp* 1988
Sales 83.0MM[E] *EMP* 300[E]
SIC 1731 3651 7373 Communications specialization; Computer installation; Clock radio & telephone combinations; Video camera-audio recorders, household use; Systems engineering, computer related; Turnkey vendors, computer systems; Value-added resellers, computer systems
Pr: David Zukerman
COO: D Zuckerman
Ofcr: Matt Recknagel
**Ex VP:* Robert Messinger
**VP:* John Schuman
**VP:* Jeffrey Zukerman
Genl Mgr: Debi Preece
Off Mgr: Debbie Neil
IT Man: Barb Albanesi
IT Man: Chris Ljungquist
IT Man: Will Smith

D-U-N-S 07-547-5533
VECTOR SECURITY INC
(*Suby of* CONTRIBUTIONSHIP COMPANIES) ★
2000 Ericsson Dr Ste 250, Warrendale, PA 15086-6511
Tel (724) 741-2200 *Founded/Ownrshp* 1988
Sales 233.8MM *EMP* 1,450
Accts Kpmg Llp Pittsburgh Pennsyl
SIC 7382 1731 Burglar alarm maintenance & monitoring; Fire detection & burglar alarm systems specialization
Pr: Pamela J Petrow
**COO:* Jeffrey M Bates
**CFO:* Jeffrey W Hoffman
**Ex VP:* Michael T Grady
Ex VP: Pam Petrow
**VP:* Leslie D Baker
**VP:* Vince Divalerio
**VP:* Thomas P Helisek
VP: Jeff Longmore
**VP:* John Madden
**VP:* Art Miller
**VP:* Anita C Ostrowski
VP: Heidi Varner

D-U-N-S 79-673-1441
VECTOR STEALTH HOLDINGS II LLC
456 Montgomery St Fl 19, San Francisco, CA 94104-1252
Tel (415) 293-5000 *Founded/Ownrshp* 2007
Sales 64.5MM[E] *EMP* 1,030
SIC 7379 Computer related maintenance services
COO: David Baylor

D-U-N-S 07-979-2965
VECTOR TALENT II LLC
1 Market St Ste 2300, San Francisco, CA 94105-1414
Tel (415) 293-5000 *Founded/Ownrshp* 2015
Sales 276.2MM[E] *EMP* 736[E]
SIC 6726 Investment offices
Pr: Alex Slusky

VECTORUSA
See VECTOR RESOURCES INC

D-U-N-S 02-391-6232
VECTRA BANK COLORADO NA
2000 S Colorado Blvd Towe Tower, Denver, CO 80222
Tel (720) 947-7700 *Founded/Ownrshp* 2006
Sales NA *EMP* 538
SIC 6022

D-U-N-S 55-686-9238 IMP/EXP
VECTRA CO
120 S Central Ave Ste 200, Saint Louis, MO 63105-1737
Tel (314) 797-8600 *Founded/Ownrshp* 1991
Sales 1.0MMM[E] *EMP* 6,200
SIC 2819 Metal salts & compounds, except sodium, potassium, aluminum; Cobalt compounds & salts, inorganic; Nickel compounds or salts, inorganic
Ch Bd: Joseph Scaminace
Pr: David B Knowles
CFO: Christopher M Hix
CFO: Manavendra Sial
Treas: Kevin A Durst
Ex VP: Edward Yocum
Sr VP: Gary Westbrook
VP: Gregory J Griffith
VP: Valerie Gentile Sachs
VP: Michael J Scott
VP: Joseph Simeone
Board of Directors: Carl R Christenson, Joseph M Gingo, John A McFarland, Patrick S Mullin, Katherine L Plourde, Allen A Spizzo

VECTREN
See INDIANA GAS CO INC

D-U-N-S 13-550-4913
▲ VECTREN CORP
1 Vectren Sq, Evansville, IN 47708-1209
Tel (812) 491-4000 *Founded/Ownrshp* 1999
Sales 2.4MMM *EMP* 5,600
Tkr Sym VVC *Exch* NYS
SIC 4924 4911 1241 1623 6531 Natural gas distribution; Electric services; Distribution, electric power; Generation, electric power; Transmission, electric power; Coal mining services; Water, sewer & utility lines; Underground utilities contractor; Real estate agents & managers
Ch Bd: Carl L Chapman
Pr: John M Bohls
COO: Eric J Schach
COO: Rick J Schach
CFO: M Susan Hardwick
Ex VP: Ronald E Christian
Sr VP: Dick Lynch
VP: Jon Luttrell
VP: Ellis Redd
Exec: Jerri A Maier
Prd Mgr: Bill Phipps
Board of Directors: Jean L Wojtowicz, James H Degraffenreidt Jr, John D Engelbrecht, Anton H George, Martin C Jischke, Robert G Jones, Patrick K Mullen, R Daniel Sadlier, Michael L Smith, Teresa J Tanner

D-U-N-S 96-379-9981
■ VECTREN ENERGY MARKETING AND SERVICES INC
(*Suby of* VECTREN ENERGY SERVICES INC) ★
1 Vectren Sq, Evansville, IN 47708-1209
Tel (812) 491-4000 *Founded/Ownrshp* 2000
Sales 91.3MM[E] *EMP* 238[E]
SIC 8748 8711 8742 Environmental consultant; Energy conservation engineering; Construction project management consultant
Pr: John Bohls
**Treas:* Robert L Goocher

D-U-N-S 86-946-4123
■ VECTREN ENERGY SERVICES CORP
(*Suby of* VECTREN ENERGY MARKETING AND SERVICES INC) ★
4655 Rosebud Ln, Newburgh, IN 47630-9366
Tel (812) 492-3723 *Founded/Ownrshp* 2000
Sales 91.3MM *EMP* 238
Accts Harding Shymanski & Companyp
SIC 8711 8742 8748 6719 Energy conservation engineering; Construction project management consultant; Energy conservation consultant; Public utility holding companies
Pr: Gregory F Collins
**Treas:* Robert L Goocher
**VP:* Ronald E Christian
VP: Dennis Perrey

D-U-N-S 96-375-1859
■ VECTREN ENERGY SERVICES INC
(*Suby of* VECTREN ENTERPRISES, INC.)
1 Vectren Sq, Evansville, IN 47708-1209
Tel (812) 491-4000 *Founded/Ownrshp* 2000
Sales 109.3MM[E] *EMP* 238[E]
SIC 4924 Natural gas distribution
Pr: John M Bohls
**Treas:* Robert L Goocher

D-U-N-S 14-460-8457
■ VECTREN UTILITY HOLDINGS INC
(*Suby of* VECTREN CORP) ★
1 Vectren Sq, Evansville, IN 47708-1209
Tel (812) 491-4000 *Founded/Ownrshp* 2000
Sales 1.3MMM *EMP* 1,500[E]
Accts Deloitte & Touche Llp Indiana
SIC 4932 4911 4924 Gas & other services combined; Generation, electric power; Transmission, electric power; Distribution, electric power; Natural gas distribution
Ch Bd: Carl L Chapman
**Pr:* Eric J Schach
**CFO:* M Susan Hardwick
**Ex VP:* Ronald E Christian

D-U-N-S 00-259-2467
■ VECTRON INTERNATIONAL INC
SENGENUITY
(*Suby of* KNOWLES CORP) ★
267 Lowell Rd Ste B, Hudson, NH 03051-4937
Tel (603) 598-0070 *Founded/Ownrshp* 1992
Sales 115.8MM[E] *EMP* 622
SIC 3671 Electron tubes
Pr: David W Wightman
**Treas:* Aline A Tomaszewski
**VP:* Edward Grant
VP: Peter Matthews
VP: Scott Murphy
Dir Lab: Dean Kantmann
Dir Lab: Ron L Smith
Opers Mgr: Larry Schiavone
Manager: Jim Elsener

D-U-N-S 07-938-7563
▲ VECTRUS INC
655 Space Center Dr, Colorado Springs, CO 80915-3604
Tel (719) 591-3600 *Founded/Ownrshp* 2014
Sales 1.1MMM *EMP* 6,000[E]
Tkr Sym VEC *Exch* NYS
SIC 8744 Facilities support services
Pr: Kenneth W Hunzeker
**Ch Bd:* Louis J Giuliano
CFO: Matthew M Klein
Ofcr: Francis A Peloso
Sr VP: Charles A Anderson
Sr VP: Kelvin R Coppock
VP: Rene Moline
VP: Janet Oliver
Genl Mgr: Karla Vaudrin
IT Man: Keith Welsh
Board of Directors: Bradford J Boston, Mary L Howell, William F Murdy, Melvin F Parker, Eric M Pillmore, Stephen L Waechter, Phillip C Widman

D-U-N-S 03-046-8243 EXP
■ VECTRUS SYSTEMS CORP
(*Suby of* VECTRUS INC) ★
655 Space Center Dr, Colorado Springs, CO 80915-3604
Tel (719) 591-3600 *Founded/Ownrshp* 1945
Sales 874.8MM[E] *EMP* 5,000
SIC 8744 7376 Facilities support services; Computer facilities management
CEO: Charles Prow
**CFO:* Matthew M Klein
**Treas:* Keith Welsh

D-U-N-S 02-163-4266 IMP
VEDCO INC
5503 Corporate Dr, Saint Joseph, MO 64507-7752
Tel (816) 238-8840 *Founded/Ownrshp* 1979
Sales 263.0MM *EMP* 48
SIC 5047 Veterinarians' equipment & supplies
Pr: Robert Mins
VP: John Graham
Sales Exec: Jeff Hefner
Manager: Tom Campbell
Manager: Jon Claborn

D-U-N-S 60-751-8297 IMP
▲ VEECO INSTRUMENTS INC
1 Terminal Dr, Plainview, NY 11803-2313
Tel (516) 677-0200 *Founded/Ownrshp* 1945
Sales 477.0MM *EMP* 783[E]
Tkr Sym VECO *Exch* NGS
SIC 3559 Semiconductor manufacturing machinery
Ch Bd: John R Peeler
Pr: William J Miller
CFO: Shubham Maheshwari
Sr VP: John P Kiernan
Sr VP: John Kiernan
VP: Ajit Paranjpe
VP: Gregory Robbins
Prgrm Mgr: Jeremy Boyer
Web Dev: John Balat
Sftwr Eng: William Theroux
Mktg Dir: Fran Brennen
Board of Directors: Kathleen Bayless, Edward H Braun, Richard A D'amore, Gordon Hunter, Keith D Jackson, Roger D McDaniel, Peter J Simone, Thomas St Dennis

D-U-N-S 83-062-2713
■ VEECO PROCESS EQUIPMENT INC
(*Suby of* VEECO INSTRUMENTS INC) ★
1 Terminal Dr, Plainview, NY 11803-2313
Tel (516) 677-0200 *Founded/Ownrshp* 2004
Sales 176.9MM[E] *EMP* 800[E]
SIC 3569 Assembly machines, non-metalworking
CEO: John R Peeler
Pr: Russell Low
**CFO:* Shubham Maheshwari
Treas: Cathy Cantasano
**Ex VP:* David Glass
**Ex VP:* Bill Miller
Sr VP: John Kiernan
**Sr VP:* Ken Macwilliams
**Sr VP:* Greg Robbins
VP: Gary Reifert
Rgnl Mgr: Derek Derosia

D-U-N-S 80-879-8417 IMP/EXP
■ VEEDER-ROOT CO
(*Suby of* FORTIVE CORP) ★
125 Powder Forest Dr, Weatogue, CT 06089-9658
Tel (860) 651-2700 *Founded/Ownrshp* 2016
Sales 132.8MM[E] *EMP* 420
SIC 3823 3824 Industrial instrmnts msrmnt display/control process variable; Mechanical measuring meters; Gas meters, domestic & large capacity: industrial
Pr: Brian Burnett
Pr: Dick Lucas
VP: Patrick W Allender
VP: Peter Kolakoski
VP: Darren Mathis
Dir IT: Andrea Mulhall
IT Man: John Flemming
VP Mktg: Kevin Hughes
Sls Dir: Alan Betts

D-U-N-S 79-933-2221
▲ VEEVA SYSTEMS INC
4280 Hacienda Dr, Pleasanton, CA 94588-2719
Tel (925) 452-6500 *Founded/Ownrshp* 2007
Sales 409.2MM *EMP* 1,474[E]
Tkr Sym VEEV *Exch* NYS
SIC 7372 7371 7379 Prepackaged software; Software programming applications; Computer related consulting services
CEO: Peter P Gassner
Ch Bd: Gordon Ritter
Pr: Matthew J Wallach
CFO: Tim Cabral
CFO: Timothy S Cabral
Chf Mktg O: E Nitsa Zuppas
Sr VP: Jonathan W Faddis
Assoc Dir: Melissa Jones
Assoc Dir: Melissa Murphy
Prgrm Mgr: Aaron Neal
Genl Mgr: Avril England
Board of Directors: Timothy C Barabe, Paul E Chamberlain, Ronald E F Codd, Paul Sekhri

D-U-N-S 00-634-0707 IMP/EXP
VEG LIQUIDATION INC
305 E Main St, Siloam Springs, AR 72761-3231
Tel (479) 524-6431 *Founded/Ownrshp* 1926
Sales NA *EMP* 1,500
SIC 2033 5142

D-U-N-S 96-995-0864
VEG-FRESH FARMS LLC
1400 W Rincon St, Corona, CA 92880-9205
Tel (800) 422-5535 *Founded/Ownrshp* 1989
Sales 180.1MM[E] *EMP* 220
SIC 5148 Vegetables; Fruits

D-U-N-S 00-425-3944 IMP/EXP
VEGA AMERICAS INC
OHMART VEGA
(*Suby of* VEGA GRIESHABER KG)
4170 Rosslyn Dr Ste A, Cincinnati, OH 45209-1193
Tel (513) 272-0131 *Founded/Ownrshp* 2008
Sales 145.3MM[E] *EMP* 1,200
SIC 3823 Industrial instrmnts msrmnt display/control process variable
Ofcr: Maruits Hartog
**VP:* Shawn Little
**VP:* Brian Oeder
VP Admn: Carol Ritter
Rgnl Mgr: Dan Stigler
Admn Mgr: Sharlene Burton
IT Man: Neil Wilkie
VP Opers: Ron Hegyesi
Mfg Mgr: Ron Foltz
Opers Mgr: Jim Harness
Ql Cn Mgr: Ken Geiger

D-U-N-S 00-946-4942 IMP
VEGETABLE GROWERS SUPPLY CO
V G S
1360 Merrill St, Salinas, CA 93901-4432
Tel (831) 759-4600 *Founded/Ownrshp* 1948
Sales 102.6MM[E] *EMP* 99
SIC 5199 2449 Packaging materials; Rectangular boxes & crates, wood
CEO: Ron Huff
**Pr:* William J Locke III
CFO: Lisa Erling
Opers Mgr: Bill Locke

D-U-N-S 00-534-8849
VEHICLE PRODUCTION GROUP LLC
VPG
101 Ne 3rd Ave Ste 1500, Fort Lauderdale, FL 33301-1181
Tel (877) 681-3678 *Founded/Ownrshp* 2010
Sales 100.0MM *EMP* 50
SIC 3711

D-U-N-S 83-153-6169 IMP/EXP
■ **VEHICLE SERVICE GROUP LLC**
CHIEF AUTOMOTIVE TECHNOLOGIES
(*Suby of* DOVER CORP) ★
2700 Lanier Dr, Madison, IN 47250-1753
Tel (800) 640-5438 *Founded/Ownrshp* 2007
Sales 113.7MM[E] *EMP* 500[E]
SIC 3711 Chassis, motor vehicle
Pr: Niclas Ytterdahl
CFO: John Podczerwinski
VP: Trinady Abbott
VP: Jim Dirksen
**VP:* James Wysinski
Mktg Dir: Donnie Bruther
Snr Mgr: Chris Bilz

V.E.I.
See VALENTINE ENTERPRISES INC

D-U-N-S 00-885-8185 IMP
VEIT & CO INC
14000 Veit Pl, Rogers, MN 55374-9306
Tel (763) 428-2242 *Founded/Ownrshp* 1966
Sales 165.3MM[E] *EMP* 260
SIC 1611 1795 4953 Grading; Demolition, buildings & other structures; Sanitary landfill operation
CEO: Vaughn A Veit
**Pr:* Greg Boelke
**CFO:* Kevin Brenny
CFO: Mark Nicolay
VP: Russ Reger
Snr PM: Jason Mueller

D-U-N-S 80-413-6646
VEKA HOLDINGS INC
VEKA INNOVATIONS
(*Suby of* VEKA AG)
100 Veka Dr, Fombell, PA 16123-1424
Tel (724) 452-1000 *Founded/Ownrshp* 1998
Sales 216.1MM[E] *EMP* 540[E]
SIC 3089 Extruded finished plastic products
Pr: Joe Peilert
**Treas:* Glenn H Taborski
**Sec:* James H Druschel
Plnt Mgr: Chuck Spaulding
Art Dir: Bob Borkoski

D-U-N-S 10-889-6069 IMP/EXP
VEKA INC
(*Suby of* VEKA INNOVATIONS) ★
100 Veka Dr, Fombell, PA 16123-1424
Tel (800) 654-5589 *Founded/Ownrshp* 1990
Sales 197.2MM[E] *EMP* 500
SIC 3089 Extruded finished plastic products
Pr: Joe Peilert
**CFO:* James H Druschel
**Treas:* Glenn H Taborski
Exec: Carrie Chapman
Genl Mgr: Kevin Seiling
Plnt Mgr: Chuck Spaulding
Sls Mgr: Ian Shearer
Art Dir: Bob Borkoski

VEKA INNOVATIONS
See VEKA HOLDINGS INC

D-U-N-S 00-206-8856 IMP/EXP
VELAN VALVE CORP
(*Suby of* VELAN INC)
94 Avenue C, Williston, VT 05495-9732
Tel (802) 863-2561 *Founded/Ownrshp* 1956
Sales 160.1MM *EMP* 214
SIC 3491 Pressure valves & regulators, industrial
Pr: T Velan
**Pr:* A K Velan
**COO:* S Cherlet
**CFO:* J Ball
**Treas:* G Sabourin
**VP:* V Apostolescu
**VP:* S Bruckert
**VP:* J Del Buey
**VP:* P Dion
**VP:* P Lee
**VP:* G Perez
**VP:* C Pogue
**VP:* A Smith
**VP:* R Sossoyan
**VP:* N Tarfa
**VP:* R Velan
**VP:* G Zarifah
**Exec:* W Maar
**Exec:* I Velan

VELCO
See VERMONT ELECTRIC POWER CO INC

D-U-N-S 60-123-7712 IMP/EXP
VELCRO INC
(*Suby of* VELCRO INDUSTRIES N.V.)
95 Sundial Ave, Manchester, NH 03103-7230
Tel (603) 669-4880 *Founded/Ownrshp* 1985
Sales 316.2MM[E] *EMP* 1,430
SIC 2241 Fabric tapes
Pr: Alain Zijlstra
**Pr:* A John Holton
**Treas:* Fraser Cameron
Sls&Mrk Ex: Kristin Higgins
Sls&Mrk Ex: Judi Mafera
Board of Directors: Roland U Lozeau Jr

D-U-N-S 06-444-1207 IMP/EXP
VELCRO USA INC
(*Suby of* VELCRO INC) ★
95 Sundial Ave, Manchester, NH 03103-7230
Tel (603) 669-4880 *Founded/Ownrshp* 1967
Sales 316.2MM[E] *EMP* 1,000
SIC 2241 3965 Fabric tapes; Fasteners, buttons, needles & pins
Pr: Scott M Filion
**Treas:* Fraser Cameron
**VP:* Boris P Hadshi
VP: Jurjen Jacobs
**VP:* Samantha O'Neil
**Prin:* Thomas Potterfield
Tech Mgr: Pete Leach
Ql Cn Mgr: Donna Leunze

VELDA FARMS DAIRIES
See BORDEN DAIRY CO OF FLORIDA LLC

D-U-N-S 07-923-5397
VELDOS LLC
435 Devon Park Dr Ste 500, Wayne, PA 19087-1939
Tel (610) 254-4121 *Founded/Ownrshp* 2011
Sales 55.2MM[E] *EMP* 1,000
SIC 7389 Telemarketing services

D-U-N-S 80-637-0305
VELO HOLDINGS INC
320 Park Ave Fl 18, New York, NY 10022-6815
Tel (212) 277-1500 *Founded/Ownrshp* 2007
Sales 48.5MM[E] *EMP* 2,371[E]
SIC 7389 Telemarketing services
Ch Bd: Dick Cashin

D-U-N-S 61-030-0766
VELOCITA WIRELESS LLC
SKYTEL
70 Wood Ave S Ste 202, Iselin, NJ 08830-2714
Tel (848) 248-4722 *Founded/Ownrshp* 2007
Sales 86.7MM[E] *EMP* 725
SIC 4899 4812 Data communication services; Radio telephone communication
COO: Eric Eifey
VP: Eric Eife
VP: Sam Reimer
Netwrk Mgr: Michele Girard

D-U-N-S 13-448-7094
VELOCITEL INC
FDH VELOCITEL
1033 Skokie Blvd Ste 320, Northbrook, IL 60062-4199
Tel (224) 757-0001 *Founded/Ownrshp* 2005
Sales 800.0MM[E] *EMP* 600
SIC 7373 8712 Computer-aided design (CAD) systems service; Architectural engineering
CEO: Kevin G Hostetler
Ch Bd: James Estes
Pr: Christopher Murphy
CFO: Joseph M Busky
CFO: Todd A Coke
Ofcr: Terrance Collins
Sr VP: Ken Czosnowski
Sr VP: Robert F Lindyberg
VP: John Meyer
Sfty Mgr: John Kunz
Board of Directors: Jake Macleod, Richard Ruben

D-U-N-S 06-805-6394 IMP
VELOCITY ELECTRONICS LP
2208 Energy Dr, Austin, TX 78758-4970
Tel (512) 973-9500 *Founded/Ownrshp* 1999
Sales 110.4MM[E] *EMP* 60
SIC 5065 Electronic parts & equipment
CEO: Jesper Romell
**Pt:* Frank Bruno
**Pt:* Robert Turner
Sls Mgr: Liz Moody

D-U-N-S 62-107-8711
VELOCITY TECHNOLOGY SOLUTIONS INC
1901 Roxborough Rd 4, Charlotte, NC 28211-3492
Tel (646) 884-6600 *Founded/Ownrshp* 2006
Sales 167.5MM[E] *EMP* 750[E]
SIC 7373 Systems software development services
Pr: Keith Angell
COO: Robert Orshaw
CFO: Steve Shippee
CFO: Marc Vassanelli
Ex VP: Chris Gartner
Sr VP: Paul Cioni
Sr VP: Bryant Gregory
VP: Darian Anderson
VP: Paul Bennett
VP: Peter Nosek
Snr PM: Jody Morrissey

D-U-N-S 12-805-3084
VELTEX CORP
123 W Madison St Ste 1500, Chicago, IL 60602-4612
Tel (312) 235-4014 *Founded/Ownrshp* 1997
Sales 70.0MM *EMP* 1,200
SIC 2211 5199 Broadwoven fabric mills, cotton; Advertising specialties
Pr: Wayne Hanson
**Ch Bd:* R Preston Roberts
COO: Michael Pearl
COO: Robert St-Amant
**Sec:* Stephen Macklem
Board of Directors: Robert Fletcher, James Jacob

D-U-N-S 07-952-0953 IMP/EXP
VELUX AMERICA LLC
(*Suby of* VELUX A/S)
450 Old Brickyard Rd, Greenwood, SC 29649-8681
Tel (864) 941-4700 *Founded/Ownrshp* 2000
Sales 130.8MM[E] *EMP* 400
SIC 5039 Prefabricated structures
Pr: Tim Miller
**CFO:* William D Huber
Mktg Mgr: Stuart Driver
Sls Mgr: Derek Cutler

D-U-N-S 09-764-1997 IMP
VELUX GREENWOOD INC
(*Suby of* VELUX AMERICA LLC) ★
450 Old Brickyard Rd, Greenwood, SC 29649-8681
Tel (864) 941-4700 *Founded/Ownrshp* 2011
Sales 92.2MM[E] *EMP* 380
SIC 3442 Sash, door or window: metal
Pr: John W Pillman
**CFO:* William F Huber

VELVETFLOW
See ORMET PRIMARY ALUMINUM CORP

D-U-N-S 83-611-5808 EXP
VEMMA NUTRITION CO
1621 W Rio Salado Pkwy # 101, Tempe, AZ 85281-2608
Tel (480) 927-8999 *Founded/Ownrshp* 2004
Sales 95.9MM[E] *EMP* 130[E]
SIC 5122 5149 Vitamins & minerals; Groceries & related products; Natural & organic foods; Specialty food items
CEO: Bk Boreyko
COO: Brad Wayment
**COO:* Brad Waynent
CFO: Kevin Heatbrink
Ofcr: Erin Winland
**Ex VP:* Mark Patterson
Ex VP: Peter Reilly
**VP:* Jeff Brademeyer
VP: Connie Ledoux
VP: Court Schilt
VP: Allison Tengan
Exec: Tammy Easton
Exec: Mike Jarrell
Dir Soc: Farah W Abdullah
Dir Soc: Genny Schendl
Creative D: Scott Flatt

D-U-N-S 03-917-9156
VENABLE LLP
575 7th St Nw Ste 1, Washington, DC 20004-1640
Tel (202) 344-4000 *Founded/Ownrshp* 2010
Sales 96.2MM[E] *EMP* 667[E]
SIC 8111 General practice attorney, lawyer
Prin: Philip Horowitz
**Pt:* Alex Weingarten
COO: Bruce Sidell
Telecom Ex: Anna Mattingly
CIO: Cary Arnold
Dir IT: Malke Krammer
Dir IT: Joel Malinowski
IT Man: Diane Traube
Netwrk Mgr: Todd Horn
Counsel: William Agee
Counsel: James Archibald

D-U-N-S 06-938-3529
VENABLE LLP (MD)
750 E Pratt St Ste 900, Baltimore, MD 21202-3157
Tel (410) 244-7400 *Founded/Ownrshp* 1900
Sales 153.2MM[E] *EMP* 784
SIC 8111 General practice law office
**Pt:* Alisa Bergman
Pt: William D Coston
**Pt:* Stuart Ingis
Pt: William R Nordwind
**Pt:* Karl A Racine
Pt: Joseph Ryan
Pt: Judson W Starr
Mng Pt: Lindsay B Meyer
Mng Pt: Robert L Waldman
COO: Charles Morton
CFO: Brian Fyock
Ch: Asa Hutchinson
**Chf Mktg O:* Douglas G Kremer
Board of Directors: Benjamin R Civiletti

D-U-N-S 13-016-2480
VENABLES CONSTRUCTION INC
VENABLE'S WELDING & ROUSTABOUT
7410 Continental Pkwy, Amarillo, TX 79119-6740
Tel (806) 381-2121 *Founded/Ownrshp* 1990
Sales 83.5MM[E] *EMP* 235[E]
Accts Lam & Company Pc Lubbock Tex
SIC 1623 1794 1389 4922 4612 1799 Oil & gas pipeline construction; Excavation work; Roustabout service; Natural gas transmission; Crude petroleum pipelines; Welding on site
Pr: Scott Venable
**CFO:* Kevin Carrier
Off Mgr: Doug Ellis

VENABLE'S WELDING & ROUSTABOUT
See VENABLES CONSTRUCTION INC

D-U-N-S 07-540-7668
■ **VENCARE REHAB SERVICES INC**
(*Suby of* KINDRED HEALTHCARE INC) ★
600 S 4th St, Louisville, KY 40202-2560
Tel (502) 596-7300 *Founded/Ownrshp* 1997
Sales 16.4MM[E] *EMP* 2,000
SIC 8051 Extended care facility
Pr: Edward Kuntz
IT Man: Marty Smith
IT Man: Jared Stivers

D-U-N-S 07-956-3436
VENCORE HOLDING CORP
15052 Conference Ctr Dr, Chantilly, VA 20151-3858
Tel (571) 313-6000 *Founded/Ownrshp* 2010
Sales 306.3MM[E] *EMP* 1,187[E]
SIC 6719 8711 8733 3812 7372 Investment holding companies, except banks; Engineering services; Professional engineer; Consulting engineer; Economic research, noncommercial; Defense systems & equipment; Application computer software; Operating systems computer software
Pr: Steven Omick

D-U-N-S 07-827-9641
VENCORE INC
(*Suby of* VENCORE HOLDING CORP) ★
15052 Conference Ctr Dr, Chantilly, VA 20151-3858
Tel (571) 313-6000 *Founded/Ownrshp* 2010
Sales 1.1MMM *EMP* 3,817
SIC 8711 8733 3812 7372 Engineering services; Professional engineer; Consulting engineer; Economic research, noncommercial; Defense systems & equipment; Application computer software; Operating systems computer software
CEO: Mac Curtis
**CFO:* Jennifer Felix
Sr VP: C Steven Griffin
VP: Rob Carey
Prgrm Mgr: Jeff Gambino
Prgrm Mgr: Bryan McKinney
Genl Mgr: Joe Broadwater
Genl Mgr: John Sutton
IT Man: Jennifer Groves

D-U-N-S 61-319-4799
VENCORE SERVICES AND SOLUTIONS INC
(*Suby of* VENCORE INC) ★
1835 Alexander Bell Dr, Reston, VA 20191-5466
Tel (703) 391-7017 *Founded/Ownrshp* 2005
Sales 521.9MM[E] *EMP* 2,630[E]
SIC 7379 7373 3812 Computer related consulting services; Computer integrated systems design; Defense systems & equipment
Pr: John M Curtis
Pr: Jerry Calhoun
Pr: Stephen Cambone
Treas: Beth Lutz
Sr VP: Stephen C Costalas
Sr VP: Doug Ounanian
VP: Catherine Clark
VP: Robert Polutchko
VP: John Sutton
Prgrm Mgr: Vonnie Craig-Parker
Prgrm Mgr: Todd Odegaard
Board of Directors: Ramzi M Musallam

VENDING SERVICES
See AUXILIARY SERVICES STATE UNIVERSITY COLLEGE AT OSWEGO INC

VENDOR FRIENDS
See LIBERTY USA INC

D-U-N-S 05-135-2961
VENDORS SUPPLY INC
201 Saluda River Rd, Columbia, SC 29210-7835
Tel (803) 772-6390 *Founded/Ownrshp* 1966
Sales 159.4MM[E] *EMP* 175
Accts Knight Gregory & Company Pc
SIC 5141 Food brokers
Pr: Randy Sikes
Area Mgr: Susan Terebo

VENETIAN, THE
See LAS VEGAS SANDS LLC

D-U-N-S 01-114-4412
■ **VENETIAN CASINO RESORT LLC**
VENETIAN RESORT HOTEL CASINO
(*Suby of* VENETIAN) ★
3355 Las Vegas Blvd S, Las Vegas, NV 89109-8941
Tel (702) 414-1000 *Founded/Ownrshp* 1997
Sales 206.1MM[E] *EMP* 8,500
SIC 7011 5812 5813 7299 Casino hotel; Resort hotel; Eating places; Drinking places; Banquet hall facilities
CFO: Robert Rozek
VP: Brad Stone
Ex Dir: Sandra Wild
Dir Sec: Tony Whieddon
CTO: Manjit Singh
DP Exec: Jack Braman
IT Man: Peggy Lundgren
IT Man: Michael Thomas
IT Man: Deborah Wayne
IT Man: Frank Weyer
Sls Dir: Jonathan Young

VENETIAN RESORT HOTEL CASINO
See VENETIAN CASINO RESORT LLC

D-U-N-S 07-999-4273
VENICE REGIONAL HOSPITAL
BON SECOURS VENICE HOSPITAL
540 The Rialto, Venice, FL 34285-2900
Tel (941) 485-7711 *Founded/Ownrshp* 1951
Sales 154.2MM *EMP* 1,305
SIC 8062 Hospital, AMA approved residency
CEO: Pete Wozniak
**Pr:* Michael G Guley
COO: Michael Curran
**COO:* Kristen Gentry
CFO: Osmon Gruhonjk
**CFO:* Brian Hess
Dir Rx: Alok Gupta
MIS Dir: Carroll Wilt
Mtls Mgr: Robert Wildermuth
Pathlgst: Tamara Densmore
Pathlgst: Roy Phillips

D-U-N-S 18-404-2521 IMP
■ **VENTANA MEDICAL SYSTEMS INC**
ROCHE TISSUE DIAGNOSTICS
(*Suby of* ROCHE HOLDING AG)
1910 E Innovation Park Dr, Oro Valley, AZ 85755-1962
Tel (520) 887-2155 *Founded/Ownrshp* 2008
Sales 303.8MM[E] *EMP* 1,200
SIC 3841 2819 3826 Diagnostic apparatus, medical; Chemicals, reagent grade: refined from technical grade; Analytical instruments
Ch Bd: Jack W Schuler
**Ch Bd:* Thomas Grogan
**Pr:* Mara Aspinall
**Pr:* Christopher M Gleeson
**CFO:* Lawrence Mehren
**Treas:* Ann Fonfara
**V Ch Bd:* John Patience
VP: Steve Burnell
VP: Bernard Colombo
**VP:* Jennifer Prescott
Dir Lab: Ethel Macrea
Dir Bus: Philippe Feasson

D-U-N-S 01-742-0550
▲ **VENTAS INC**
353 N Clark St Ste 3300, Chicago, IL 60654-4708
Tel (877) 483-6827 *Founded/Ownrshp* 1998
Sales 3.2MMM *EMP* 1,802[E]
Tkr Sym VTR *Exch* NYS
SIC 6798 Real estate investment trusts
Ch Bd: Debra A Cafaro
Pr: Raymond J Lewis
CFO: Robert F Probst
Ofcr: T Richard Riney
Sr Inv Off: Wilkingson Germain
Sr Inv Off: Carrie Hiebeler
Sr Inv Off: Phil Kayden
Ex VP: John D Cobb
Ex VP: James E Mendelson
Sr VP: John K Hart
Sr VP: Gregory R Liebbe
Sr VP: Brian Wood
VP: James L Andrews
VP: Doug Johnson
VP: Joseph D Lambert
VP: Cindy Liston
Exec: Robin Cherry

D-U-N-S 09-887-6188
VENTECH ENGINEERS INTERNATIONAL CORP
(*Suby of* VENTECH INC) ★
1149 Ellsworth Dr Ofc, Pasadena, TX 77506-4847
Tel (713) 477-0201 *Founded/Ownrshp* 1976
Sales 121.7MM^E *EMP* 300
Accts Tr Moore & Co
SIC 1629 8711 3559 5084 Chemical plant & refinery construction; Construction & civil engineering; Refinery, chemical processing & similar machinery; Petroleum industry machinery
CEO: Bill Stanley
**CFO:* Jerry Stanley
**VP:* Kreg Stanley

D-U-N-S 09-248-0243
VENTECH INC
1149 Ellsworth Dr Ofc, Pasadena, TX 77506-4847
Tel (713) 477-0201 *Founded/Ownrshp* 1977
Sales 122.7MM^E *EMP* 450
SIC 8711 3491 5084 6512 Petroleum engineering; Industrial valves; Industrial machinery & equipment; Commercial & industrial building operation
Pr: Bill Stanley
**CEO:* Kevin Stanley
**VP:* Kreg Stanley

D-U-N-S 55-548-7214
VENTION MEDICAL ADVANCED COMPONENTS INC
29 Northwestern Dr, Salem, NH 03079-4809
Tel (603) 327-0600 *Founded/Ownrshp* 2013
Sales 641.5MM^E *EMP* 300
SIC 3082 3069 3083 Tubes, unsupported plastic; Balloons, advertising & toy: rubber; Laminated plastics plate & sheet
Pr: Dan Croteau
**VP:* Stewart A Fisher
VP: Michael Kilday
Exec: Filomena Meneses
CTO: Nisia Rodrigues
Dir IT: Bob Macmillan

D-U-N-S 09-929-5446 IMP
VENTION MEDICAL INC
(*Suby of* VENTION MEDICAL ADVANCED COMPONENTS INC) ★
6 Century Ln, South Plainfield, NJ 07080-1323
Tel (908) 561-0717 *Founded/Ownrshp* 1979
Sales 630.2MM^E *EMP* 300
Accts Grant Thornton Llp
SIC 3841 Surgical & medical instruments
CEO: Dan Croteau
Pr: Gregory Olson
**CFO:* Thomas Testa
Sr VP: Steven Robertson
VP: David Gorky
VP: Bob Maston
Dir Bus: Paul Trama
MIS Dir: Harriet Blank
Plnt Mgr: Brian Kimble
Plnt Mgr: Robert Meyer
Ql Cn Mgr: Jennifer Weller

D-U-N-S 11-445-3454
VENTIV HEALTH INC
INVENTIVE COMMERCIAL SERVICES
(*Suby of* ADVANCE INSIGHTS) ★
200 Cottontail Ln Ste J, Somerset, NJ 08873-5800
Tel (732) 537-4800 *Founded/Ownrshp* 1998
Sales 98.4MM^E *EMP* 2,800
SIC 8742 Marketing consulting services
CEO: Eran Broshy
**Pr:* Terry Herring
Pr: Susan G Schneider
**CFO:* David Bassin
CFO: John Emery
Ex VP: Grace Duffy
Ex VP: Sam Malik
Ex VP: Chuck Shea
Sr VP: Christopher Crucitti
Sr VP: Eugenia Henry
Sr VP: Ashish Kumar
VP: Sean Burke
VP: Deborah Harder
VP: Bob Melillo
VP: Jeffrey Thomas
Exec: Tim Divane
Exec: Patrice Mason
Exec: Ryan Pirnat
Exec: Jeremy Rochford
Exec: Michelle Warner
Assoc Dir: Glenroy Case

D-U-N-S 83-114-3966 IMP
VENTRA FOWLERVILLE LLC
(*Suby of* FLEX-N-GATE CORP) ★
8887 W Grand River Rd, Fowlerville, MI 48836-9208
Tel (517) 223-5900 *Founded/Ownrshp* 2009
Sales 110.0MM *EMP* 270
SIC 5013 Automotive supplies & parts
Sec: Jim Zsebok

D-U-N-S 83-114-4105
VENTRA GRAND RAPIDS 5 LLC
(*Suby of* FLEX-N-GATE CORP) ★
3075 Breton Rd Se, Grand Rapids, MI 49512-1747
Tel (616) 949-6303 *Founded/Ownrshp* 2009
Sales 117.6MM^E *EMP* 300
SIC 3465 Body parts, automobile: stamped metal
**Treas:* Jim Zsebok

VENTRA GROUP CO
See VENTRA PLASTICS (RUSSELLVILLE) INC

D-U-N-S 83-114-4196 IMP
VENTRA IONIA MAIN LLC
(*Suby of* FLEX-N-GATE CORP) ★
14 Beardsley St, Ionia, MI 48846-9789
Tel (616) 597-3220 *Founded/Ownrshp* 2009
Sales 154.7MM^E *EMP* 585
SIC 3469 3089 5198 Metal stampings; Molding primary plastic; Paints
Sec: Jim Zsebok
VP: Bill Slater
**Genl Mgr:* John Atkinson

VENTRA PLASTICS
See FLEX-N-GATE LLC

D-U-N-S 79-692-6988
VENTRA PLASTICS (RUSSELLVILLE) INC
VENTRA GROUP CO
(*Suby of* VENTRA GROUP CO)
140 Progress Dr, Russellville, KY 42276-9299
Tel (270) 726-4767 *Founded/Ownrshp* 1994
Sales 99.9MM^E *EMP* 250
SIC 3089 Jars, plastic
Pr: Shahid Rafiq Khan
**Ch Bd:* Kenneth Nichols
**Sec:* Dwight Rollins
**Sec:* James David Zsebok
**Plnt Mgr:* Ron Barbe
**Plnt Mgr:* Tim Kelley

D-U-N-S 80-977-3364 IMP
VENTRA SALEM LLC
(*Suby of* FLEX-N-GATE CORP) ★
800 Pennsylvania Ave, Salem, OH 44460-2783
Tel (330) 337-8002 *Founded/Ownrshp* 2008
Sales 179.6MM^E *EMP* 750
SIC 5013 Automotive supplies & parts
Genl Mgr: Scott Tuel

VENTRITEX
See PACESETTER INC

D-U-N-S 07-900-1806
VENTURA COUNTY COMMUNITY COLLEGE DISTRICT
255 W Stanley Ave Ste 150, Ventura, CA 93001-1322
Tel (805) 652-5500 *Founded/Ownrshp* 1962
Sales 64.1MM^E *EMP* 2,000
SIC 8222 8221 Community college; Colleges universities & professional schools
Ofcr: Ryan Hepburn
Ofcr: Vahid Jafroodi
Ofcr: Michael Pallotto
Assoc VP: Patricia Parham
Ex VP: Ed Knudson
Ex VP: Christine Richards
Ex VP: Ramiro Sanchez
Ex Dir: Norbert Tan
Admn Mgr: Catherine Sanchez
Dir IT: Andrew Cawelti
Dir IT: Mark Smith

D-U-N-S 10-178-8599
VENTURA COUNTY MEDICAL CENTER
3291 Loma Vista Rd, Ventura, CA 93003-3099
Tel (805) 652-6000 *Founded/Ownrshp* 2000
Sales 371.8MM *EMP* 413^E
SIC 8011 Medical centers
Prin: Ronald O'Halloran
Prgrm Mgr: Kate Mills
Psych: John Schipper
Nrsg Dir: Meloney R Lcsw

D-U-N-S 95-604-4879 IMP/EXP
VENTURA FOODS LLC
LOU ANA FOODS
40 Pointe Dr, Brea, CA 92821-3652
Tel (714) 257-3700 *Founded/Ownrshp* 1996
Sales 211.0MM^E *EMP* 2,099
SIC 2079 2035 Vegetable shortenings (except corn oil); Cooking oils, except corn: vegetable refined; Pickles, sauces & salad dressings
Pr: Christopher Furman
CFO: Scott Anthony
Ex VP: John Buckles
Ex VP: Andrew Euser
VP: William Bremer
VP: Danielle Conner
VP: David Hochman
VP: Virginia Soderman
VP: Ed Wellmeyer
VP: Fred Zimmermann
VP Bus Dev: Karen Rosenberry

D-U-N-S 14-188-3541
■ VENTURA SYSCO INC
(*Suby of* SYSCO CORP) ★
3100 Sturgis Rd, Oxnard, CA 93030-7276
Tel (805) 205-7000 *Founded/Ownrshp* 2003
Sales 191.1MM^E *EMP* 300
SIC 5141 Food brokers
Pr: Jerry L Barash
**Ch Bd:* Manny Fernandez
**Pr:* Bill Delaney
**CFO:* William Mastrosimone
**VP:* Brian Beach
VP: Alise Churchill
**VP:* Twila Day
**VP:* Kirk Drummond

D-U-N-S 07-798-0621
VENTURA UNIFIED SCHOOL DISTRICT
255 W Stanley Ave Ste 100, Ventura, CA 93001-1331
Tel (805) 641-5000 *Founded/Ownrshp* 1966
Sales 98.2MM^E *EMP* 2,000
SIC 8211 Public elementary school; Public junior high school; Public senior high school; Public special education school
Bd of Dir: Janis Schmutte
Ex VP: Debbie Golden
Exec: Doris Ryder
Dir Sec: Eric Reynolds
Off Mgr: Rosa Salcido
Off Admin: Janice Blackwell
CTO: Claudia Young
Dir IT: Julie Gulick
Dir IT: Rene Rickard
Trfc Dir: Mike McBride
Schl Brd P: Mary Haffner

D-U-N-S 04-758-6581
VENTURE CONSTRUCTION CO INC
5660 Peachtree Indus Blvd, Norcross, GA 30071-1496
Tel (770) 441-2404 *Founded/Ownrshp* 1969
Sales 159.0MM^E *EMP* 177
Accts Braver Schimler Pierce Jenkins
SIC 1542 Commercial & office building, new construction
Pr: E Ray Morris
COO: David Zukerman
Ex VP: L F Holliingsworth
**Ex VP:* L F Hollingsworth
VP: L F Hollinsworth
VP: Christina Kleiner
**VP:* Denise Smith
Snr PM: Will Brickey

D-U-N-S 18-357-9697
VENTURE ELECTRICAL CONTRACTORS
2110 Pewaukee Rd Ste 110, Waukesha, WI 53188-2482
Tel (262) 542-2727 *Founded/Ownrshp* 1988
Sales 16.8MMM *EMP* 100
SIC 1731 General electrical contractor
Pr: Jeff Robertson
Snr PM: Robert Mueller

D-U-N-S 05-109-0801
VENTURE EXPRESS INC (TN)
131 Industrial Blvd, La Vergne, TN 37086-4108
Tel (615) 793-9500 *Founded/Ownrshp* 1980
Sales 121.4MM *EMP* 475
SIC 4213 Trucking, except local
CEO: Brad Allen
**COO:* Shawn Hicklen
**CFO:* Terry Croslow
**CFO:* Frank McMillan
CTO: Bryan Prince
Sfty Dirs: Jason Fucci
Opers Mgr: Todd Burks
Sls Dir: Bobby Lamb

D-U-N-S 02-804-4514
VENTURE LOGISTICS LLC
1101 Harding Ct, Indianapolis, IN 46217-9531
Tel (888) 561-4449 *Founded/Ownrshp* 2000
Sales 131.3MM^E *EMP* 400
SIC 4231 Trucking terminal facilities
Pr: M Douglas Williams
**CFO:* Ernie Krebs
Dir IT: Ken Dwigans
Opers Supe: Daniel Baker
Opers Mgr: Matt Nyman

D-U-N-S 02-062-6738
VENTURE SOLUTIONS INC
(*Suby of* TAYLOR CORP) ★
1170 Grey Fox Rd, Arden Hills, MN 55112-6908
Tel (651) 494-1740 *Founded/Ownrshp* 2011
Sales 88.8MM^E *EMP* 400^E
SIC 2759 Business forms: printing
Pr: Tommie S Braddock
VP: Craig Burma
VP: Wendy Jenkins
Mktg Mgr: Brian Shepley

VENTURE TECHNOLOGIES
See GKR SYSTEMS INC

D-U-N-S 12-159-7538
VENTUREDYNE LTD
THERMOTRON INDUSTRIES
600 College Ave, Pewaukee, WI 53072-3572
Tel (262) 691-9900 *Founded/Ownrshp* 1986
Sales 121.0MM^E *EMP* 800
SIC 3568 3829 3826 3823 3625

D-U-N-S 00-299-2220 IMP/EXP
VENUS LABORATORIES INC
EARTH FRIENDLY PRODUCTS
111 S Rohlwing Rd, Addison, IL 60101-3027
Tel (630) 595-1900 *Founded/Ownrshp* 1962
Sales 91.0MM^E *EMP* 313
SIC 2842 2841 Specialty cleaning preparations; Sanitation preparations; Soap & other detergents
CEO: Kelly Vlahakis-Hanks
**Ch Bd:* Elli Manolas
**Pr:* Van Vlahakis
VP: Nadereh Afsharmanesh
VP: Ruediger Schroeder
**Prin:* John Vlahakis
Genl Mgr: Mike Marrese
Genl Mgr: Zuliana Navarro
Genl Couns: Amber Enriquez
Art Dir: Dennis Murray

D-U-N-S 00-888-2067
VEOLIA ENERGY NORTH AMERICA HOLDINGS INC
53 State St Ste 14, Boston, MA 02109-3205
Tel (617) 849-6612 *Founded/Ownrshp* 2007
Sales 585.1MM^E *EMP* 637
SIC 4939 4961 Combination utilities; Steam & air-conditioning supply
Pr: William Dicroce
Pr: Michael J Marr
CFO: Miller Barry
**CFO:* Jason Salgo
Treas: Stephen Ward
Sr VP: Bill Fahey
Sr VP: Lanita McCauley-Bates
Sr VP: Keavin Nelson
Sr VP: Mark Wagner
Sr VP: John Wood
**VP:* Robert Arendell
VP: Vincent Martin
VP: Michael Smedley
VP: Alexandre Visciglio
VP: Thomas A Witt
Exec: Rene Brangiforte
Dir Risk M: Stephanie Hyde
Dir: Scott Murphy

D-U-N-S 04-007-2261 IMP/EXP
VEOLIA ENVIRONMENTAL SERVICES NORTH AMERICA CORP
200 E Randolph St # 7900, Chicago, IL 60601-6436
Tel (312) 552-2800 *Founded/Ownrshp* 2000
Sales 13.4MMM^E *EMP* 32,950
SIC 4953 Refuse systems; Hazardous waste collection & disposal
Pr: Jeff Adix
Ex VP: Steven Hopper
Ex VP: Augie Schulke
Sr VP: Michael K Slattery
VP: Jean-Marc Bourdin
VP: Martin Demeter
VP: Jim Good
VP: Ferid Grutzner
VP: Gerald Hoffman
VP: George Martin
VP: Greig Seidor
VP: Michael Slattery

D-U-N-S 01-940-5355
■ VEOLIA ENVIRONMENTAL SERVICES NORTH AMERICA LLC
(*Suby of* ADVANCED DISPOSAL SERVICES SOLID WASTE MIDWEST LLC) ★
125 S 84th St Ste 200, Milwaukee, WI 53214-1499
Tel (414) 479-7800 *Founded/Ownrshp* 2007
Sales 4.9MM^E *EMP* 2,925^E
SIC 4953 4212 Refuse systems; Local trucking, without storage
Pr: Jim Long
Pr: Richard Burke
CFO: George K Farr
VP: Ray Bruckert
Plnt Mgr: John H King

D-U-N-S 16-140-9818
VEOLIA ES INDUSTRIAL SERVICES INC
(*Suby of* VEOLIA ENVIRONMENTAL SERVICES NORTH AMERICA CORP) ★
4760 World Houston Pkwy # 100, Houston, TX 77032-2591
Tel (713) 672-8004 *Founded/Ownrshp* 1999
Sales 812.0MM^E *EMP* 3,249
SIC 1799 Steam cleaning of building exteriors
Pr: Darryl Schimeck
**COO:* Gary Noto
**CFO:* Jean-Marc Bourdin
Treas: George K Farr III
**Treas:* Randall Lawson
**Treas:* Brian Sullivan
Ex VP: Dan Ryan
**VP:* Mike Tepatti
VP: Tim Wood
Dir Lab: Raymond Ruth
Area Mgr: Jimmy Starr

D-U-N-S 95-846-6146 IMP/EXP
VEOLIA ES SPECIAL SERVICES INC
W6490b Specialty Dr, Greenville, WI 54942
Tel (800) 932-6216 *Founded/Ownrshp* 1992
Sales 243.6MM^E *EMP* 500
SIC 4953

D-U-N-S 17-511-4255
VEOLIA ES WASTE-TO-ENERGY INC
MONTENAY POWER
1 Penn Plz Ste 4401, New York, NY 10119-4490
Tel (212) 947-5824 *Founded/Ownrshp* 1986
Sales 143.1MM^E *EMP* 600
SIC 4953 Recycling, waste materials
Pr: Stephen Passage
CFO: Thomas Murphy

VEOLIA NORTH AMERICA
See VEOLIA WATER NORTH AMERICA OPERATING SERVICES LLC

D-U-N-S 79-047-3792
VEOLIA NORTH AMERICA LLC
(*Suby of* VEOLIA ENVIRONMENTAL SERVICES NORTH AMERICA CORP) ★
53 State St Ste 14, Boston, MA 02109-3205
Tel (312) 552-2800 *Founded/Ownrshp* 1998
Sales 1.4MMM^E *EMP* 24,950
SIC 8711 Sanitary engineers
Pr: Gregg Macqueen
Ofcr: Mia Javier
Sr VP: Keavin Nelson
Sr VP: Keith Oldewurtel
VP: Karole Colangelo
**VP:* Rob Nicholas
VP: Edwin Piero
Comm Dir: Kirstin Hinchcliff
**Prin:* Sean Hixenbaugh
Rgnl Mgr: Graham Wathen
Div Mgr: Dan Boehm

D-U-N-S 60-835-1466
VEOLIA TRANSPORTATION SERVICES INC
(*Suby of* TRANSDEV SERVICES INC) ★
2015 Spring Rd Ste 750, Oak Brook, IL 60523-3914
Tel (630) 571-7070 *Founded/Ownrshp* 2005
Sales 360.4MM^E *EMP* 6,000
SIC 4111 4141 Local & suburban transit; Local bus charter service
Ch: Ken Westbrook
Pr: Neal Bhimavarapu
**Pr:* Rick Kreiter
**CEO:* Terry Van Der AA
**CFO:* Emmanuel Lenoble
Sr VP: Dick Alexander
**Prin:* Mark T Joseph
Genl Mgr: Ibrahima Toure
Snr Mgr: Yann Leriche

D-U-N-S 16-495-4039
VEOLIA WATER AMERICAS LLC
101 W Washington St # 1400, Indianapolis, IN 46204-3419
Tel (317) 917-3700 *Founded/Ownrshp* 2012
Sales 2.2MMM^E *EMP* 3,200
SIC 4941 4952 Water supply; Sewerage systems
CEO: Terry Mah
**Ex VP:* Frank Benichou
**Ex VP:* Steven L Hopper
Genl Mgr: Frank Crehan

D-U-N-S 17-241-3759
VEOLIA WATER NORTH AMERICA OPERATING SERVICES LLC
VEOLIA NORTH AMERICA
(*Suby of* VEOLIA WATER AMERICAS LLC) ★
101 W Washington St, Indianapolis, IN 46204-3407
Tel (317) 917-3700 *Founded/Ownrshp* 1986
Sales 1.6MMM^E *EMP* 2,425
SIC 4941 Water supply
**CFO:* Jean-Paul Bonnec
**Ex VP:* Frank Benichou
Ex VP: Edwin Pl Ero
**Ex VP:* David L Gadis
VP: Edward Collins

D-U-N-S 55-565-5203
VEOLIA WATER NORTH AMERICA-CENTRAL LLC
53 State St Ste 14, Boston, MA 02109-3205
Tel (617) 849-6600 Founded/Ownrshp 2004
Sales 92.7MM EMP 535
SIC 4952 4941 Sewerage systems; Water supply
IT Man: Marcia Warren

D-U-N-S 19-947-9515
VEOLIA WATER NORTH AMERICA-NORTHEAST LLC
(Suby of VEOLIA NORTH AMERICA) ★
14950 Hathrow Forest Pkwy, Houston, TX 77032-3847
Tel (281) 449-1500 Founded/Ownrshp 2006
Sales 1.6MMM^E EMP 2,000
SIC 4952 4941 Sewerage systems; Water supply
*Pr: Keavin Nelson
Ex VP: Claude Laruelle
Sr VP: Brian Clarke
*VP: Francis X Ferrara
VP: Joyce Harms
*VP: Jeff L Levy
VP: Kevin L McDaniel
VP: William Roach
*VP: Eric Robben
Dir Lab: Pamela London-Exner
Area Mgr: Troy Gratz

D-U-N-S 79-047-3800
VEOLIA WATER TECHNOLOGIES
(Suby of VEOLIA NORTH AMERICA LLC) ★
250 Airside Dr, Moon Township, PA 15108-2793
Tel (412) 809-6000 Founded/Ownrshp 2004
Sales 140.2MM^E EMP 321
SIC 8711 Sanitary engineers
Pr: Finn Nielsen
VP: Lori Meredith
*VP: Remy Philipon
*VP: Frederic Thery
Genl Mgr: Shelly Graham
Genl Mgr: Kirk Schwab
VP Opers: Scott Connor
S&M/VP: James Hall
Mktg Mgr: Carla Robinson
Board of Directors: Jerome Coutant, Jean Michel Herrewyn

D-U-N-S 05-196-8899 IMP
■ VERA BRADLEY DESIGNS INC
V B D
(Suby of VERA BRADLEY INC) ★
12420 Stonebridge Rd, Roanoke, IN 46783-9300
Tel (260) 482-4673 Founded/Ownrshp 2010
Sales 190.5MM^E EMP 450
SIC 5099 Luggage
CEO: Michael C Ray
*Pr: Barbara B Baekgaard
*COO: Jill Nichols
*CFO: Jeffrey A Blade
Bd of Dir: Patricia Miller
Ex VP: Jeffrey Blade
Ex VP: Kim Colby
VP: Steve Bohman
VP: Rosemary Ricketts
VP: Kevin Sierks
Ex Dir: Catherine Hill

D-U-N-S 03-538-7293
VERA BRADLEY INC
3715 Courtwood Dr, Fort Wayne, IN 46815-5907
Tel (260) 482-3250 Founded/Ownrshp 2011
Sales 61.2MM^E EMP 1,427
SIC 3171 Women's handbags & purses
CFO: Jeff Blade

D-U-N-S 19-451-7889
▲ VERA BRADLEY INC
12420 Stonebridge Rd, Roanoke, IN 46783-9300
Tel (877) 708-8372 Founded/Ownrshp 1982
Sales 502.6MM EMP 2,950
Tkr Sym VRA Exch NGS
SIC 3171 3111 2392 2844 Women's handbags & purses; Accessory products, leather; Household furnishings; Blankets, comforters & beddings; Towels, dishcloths & dust cloths; Toilet preparations
Pr: Robert Wallstrom
*Ch Bd: Robert J Hall
CFO: Kevin J Sierks
*Chf Cred: Barbara Bradley Baekgaard
Chf Mktg O: Theresa Palermo
Ex VP: Kimberly F Colby
Ex VP: Sue Fuller
Sr VP: Anastacia S Knapper
Software D: Katherine Kovac
Mktg Mgr: Kris Reese
Board of Directors: Richard Baum, Mary Lou Kelley, John E Kyees, Matthew McEvoy, P Michael Miller, Patricia R Miller, Frances P Philip, Edward M Schmults

VERALLIA NORTH AMERICA
See ARDAGH GLASS INC

D-U-N-S 13-059-8584 IMP/EXP
■ VERATHON INC
(Suby of ROPER TECHNOLOGIES INC) ★
20001 North Creek Pkwy, Bothell, WA 98011-8218
Tel (425) 867-1348 Founded/Ownrshp 2009
Sales 104.3MM^E EMP 400
SIC 3845 Electromedical apparatus; Ultrasonic scanning devices, medical
Pr: Neil Hunn
*Treas: Susan Grieco
*VP: Jack Buhsmer
VP: Mark Cranney
*VP: John R Humphrey
VP: Walt Laboda
Creative D: Michael Miller
*Prin: Daniel Estay
*Prin: Russ Garrison
*Prin: Gerald McMorrow
*Prin: Kendall Stever

D-U-N-S 03-446-6755
VERC ENTERPRISES INC
5 Chestnut St, Duxbury, MA 02332-4419
Tel (781) 934-7300 Founded/Ownrshp 1977
Sales 130.0MM EMP 170
SIC 5541 7542 Filling stations, gasoline; Carwashes
Pr: Leo M Vercollone
*VP: Paul Vercollone

D-U-N-S 96-814-6576
VERDE ENERGY USA HOLDINGS LLC
101 Merritt 7 Ste 2, Norwalk, CT 06851-1060
Tel (203) 663-5700 Founded/Ownrshp 2011
Sales 105.9MM^E EMP 25
SIC 4931 Electric & other services combined
Pr: Thomas Fitzgerald
Ex VP: Richard Riley

D-U-N-S 83-080-7892
VERDE ENERGY USA INC
LOW COST POWER
(Suby of VERDE ENERGY USA HOLDINGS LLC) ★
101 Merritt 7 Ste 2, Norwalk, CT 06851-1060
Tel (203) 663-5700 Founded/Ownrshp 2009
Sales 100.0MM EMP 22
SIC 4931 Electric & other services combined
Pr: Thomas Fitzgerald
*Ch: Lance Lundberg
*Chf Mktg O: Tony Menchaca
Sales Asso: David Motta

D-U-N-S 07-448-3173
VERDE VALLEY MEDICAL CENTER (AZ)
269 S Candy Ln, Cottonwood, AZ 86326-4170
Tel (928) 634-2251 Founded/Ownrshp 1939
Sales 139.8MM EMP 500
SIC 8062 General medical & surgical hospitals
CEO: James J Bleicher
Treas: James E Ledbetter
*Ex VP: Rainy Atkins
*VP: Harry Alberti
Genl Mgr: Bob Yazzie
Cmptr Lab: Dorothy Danielson
Mktg Dir: Margaret Lauri
Pharmcst: John James
Board of Directors: James Bleicher

D-U-N-S 19-527-3636 IMP/EXP
■ VERDUN LLC
(Suby of ILLINOIS TOOL WORKS INC) ★
8860 207th St W, Lakeville, MN 55044-9542
Tel (952) 469-5424 Founded/Ownrshp 2007
Sales 135.4MM^E EMP 350
SIC 3567 Industrial furnaces & ovens; Induction & dielectric heating equipment; Vacuum furnaces & ovens;
Mktg Mgr: Michael Aistrup

D-U-N-S 96-831-5478
▲ VEREIT INC
2325 E Camelback Rd, Phoenix, AZ 85016-3422
Tel (800) 606-3610 Founded/Ownrshp 2010
Sales 1.5MMM EMP 350^E
Tkr Sym VER Exch NYS
SIC 6798 Real estate investment trusts
CEO: Glenn J Rufrano
Mng Pt: Kevin Mansour
*Ch Bd: Hugh R Frater
COO: Paul H McDowell
CFO: Michael J Bartolotta
Ex VP: Lauren Goldberg
Ex VP: Glenn Kindred
Ex VP: William C Miller
Ex VP: Thomas W Roberts
Sr VP: Mike Fitzgerald
Sr VP: Karen Halpert
VP: Alysia Cherry
VP: Sara Grisham
VP: Debbie Hester
VP: Christina Mayo
VP: Tim Schenk
VP: Ninad Tambe
VP: Jim Vlahos
Board of Directors: Bruce D Frank, David B Henry, Mark S Ordan, Eugene A Pinover, Julie G Richardson

D-U-N-S 00-553-6016 IMP
VERICLAIM INC
VRS VERICLAIM
(Suby of T&H GLOBAL HOLDINGS, LLC)
1833 Cntre Pt Cir Ste 139, Naperville, IL 60563
Tel (630) 245-7000 Founded/Ownrshp 2009
Sales NA EMP 320
SIC 6411 Insurance adjusters
Pr: Michael Arbour
Pr: William Breslin
Pr: Clay Humphries
Sr VP: Randy Neal
Sr VP: Scott Richardson
VP: Katherine Gish
VP: Keith Meerholz
VP: C R Neal III
Exec: Steve Astrov
Exec: John Chianese
Exec: Jeff Higgins
Exec: Tom Legrand
Exec: David Lunt
Exec: Richard Martin
Exec: Ron McCartney
Exec: Van W Meredith
Exec: Joseph Patterson
Exec: Gary Slowik

D-U-N-S 13-978-8285
VERIDIAN CREDIT UNION
1827 Ansborough Ave, Waterloo, IA 50701-3629
Tel (319) 236-5600 Founded/Ownrshp 1934
Sales NA EMP 175
SIC 6062 6163 State credit unions, not federally chartered; Loan brokers
CEO: Jean M Trainor
Ofcr: Marcia Correll
Ofcr: Michael Farrell
*Ex VP: Michael Harvey
*VP: Monty Berg
*VP: Becky Hiatt
*VP: Dyann Longseth
VP: Missy Neebel
*VP: Mary Shollenbarger
Ex Dir: Tim Lord
IT Man: Eric Pruess

D-U-N-S 07-886-2194
VERIFINC CORP
12000 Westheimer Rd # 380, Houston, TX 77077-6681
Tel (832) 858-5548 Founded/Ownrshp 2008
Sales 98.4MM^E EMP 5,000
SIC 7371 5734 5122 Computer software development & applications; Computer peripheral equipment; Pharmaceuticals
Pr: Dr Steve AMS

D-U-N-S 01-446-6825 IMP/EXP
■ VERIFONE INC
(Suby of VERIFONE SYSTEMS INC) ★
88 W Plumeria Dr, San Jose, CA 95134-2134
Tel (408) 232-7800 Founded/Ownrshp 1981, 2002
Sales 442.7MM^E EMP 872
SIC 3578 7373 3577 3575 8711 3643 Point-of-sale devices; Operating systems computer software; Application computer software; Computer peripheral equipment; Printers, computer; Computer terminals; Engineering services; Current-carrying wiring devices
CEO: Paul Galant
Pr: Kyle Halkola
Pr: Jim Mauritz
*CFO: Barry Zwarenstein
Ex VP: Isaac Angel
*Ex VP: Alok Bhanot
*Ex VP: Albert Liu
VP: Robert Gonzalez
VP: Clint Jones
VP: Timothy Robinson
*VP: Marc E Rothman

D-U-N-S 17-999-7114
▲ VERIFONE SYSTEMS INC
88 W Plumeria Dr, San Jose, CA 95134-2134
Tel (408) 232-7800 Founded/Ownrshp 1981
Sales 2.0MMM EMP 5,400^E
Accts Ernst & Young Llp San Jose C
Tkr Sym PAY Exch NYS
SIC 3578 7372 Point-of-sale devices; Operating systems computer software; Application computer software
CEO: Paul Galant
CFO: Marc E Rothman
Ex VP: Alok Bhanot
Ex VP: Albert Liu
Ex VP: Albert Y Liu
Ex VP: Patrick McGivern
Ex VP: Glen Robson
VP: Lisa Fernandez
VP: Jay D Parsons
VP: Vik Varma
Dir IT: Patrick Amon
Board of Directors: Robert W Alspaugh, Karen Austin, Alex W Hart, Robert B Henske, Wenda Harris Millard, Eitan Raff, Jonathan I Schwartz, Jane J Thompson

VERIGOLD JEWELRY
See RENAISSANCE JEWELRY NEW YORK INC

VERINT
See KANA SOFTWARE INC

D-U-N-S 01-072-5103
■ VERINT ACQUISITION LLC
(Suby of VERINT SYSTEMS INC) ★
330 S Service Rd Ste 108, Melville, NY 11747-3257
Tel (631) 962-9600 Founded/Ownrshp 2013
Sales 138.6MM^E EMP 25^E
SIC 7371 Computer software development & applications
Pr: Dan Bodner
CFO: Douglas Robinson
Ofcr: Peter Fante

D-U-N-S 78-356-1855
■ VERINT AMERICAS INC
(Suby of VERINT SYSTEMS INC) ★
800 North Point Pkwy, Alpharetta, GA 30005-4124
Tel (770) 754-1900 Founded/Ownrshp 2007
Sales 103.4MM^E EMP 685
SIC 7372 Business oriented computer software
CEO: Dan Bodner
*Ch Bd: David B Gould
*Pr: Nicholas Discombe
Pr: Jeff Iannone
*CFO: William F Evans
Ofcr: Simon Angove
Ofcr: Bill Byron Concevitch
Sr VP: Steve Allen
*Sr VP: John Bourne
Sr VP: Bill Robinson
Sr VP: Nancy Treaster
*Sr VP: Loren Wimpfheimer
VP: Russell E Brown
VP: Hector Brush
VP: Jason Fama
VP: Colin Gallick
VP: Robert Granat
VP: Howard Greenfield
VP: Teresa Haberman
VP: Nigel Hewett
VP: Heather Hogrefe

D-U-N-S 87-827-5817
▲ VERINT SYSTEMS INC
175 Broadhollow Rd # 100, Melville, NY 11747-4910
Tel (631) 962-9600 Founded/Ownrshp 1994
Sales 1.1MMM EMP 5,000
Tkr Sym VRNT Exch NGS
SIC 7382 7372 Security systems services; Prepackaged software
Pr: Dan Bodner
Ch Bd: Victor A Demarines
CFO: Douglas E Robinson
Treas: Glenn Levine
Bd of Dir: Anne Arcand
Ex VP: Julie Beauregard
VP: Garrett Braithwaite
VP: Gabriela Cohen
VP: Yaniv Cohen
VP: Clare Dorrian
VP: Mike Graci
VP: Galit Greenbaum
VP: Paul Harvey
VP: Ryan Hollenbeck
VP: Gabriel Horowitz
VP: Trent Isaacs
VP: Huw Jones
VP: Amit Kerrigan
VP: David Marcus
VP: Michelle Meurer
VP: Masahiro Moriyasu
Board of Directors: John R Egan, Larry Myers, Richard Nottenburg, Howard Safir, Earl Shanks

D-U-N-S 94-379-4214
VERIO INC
(Suby of NTT AMERICA INC) ★
1203 Research Way, Orem, UT 84097-6207
Tel (303) 645-1900 Founded/Ownrshp 1996
Sales 186.6MM^E EMP 412
SIC 4813
CEO: Hideyuki Yamasawa
Pt: Rick Decraene
*Pr: Kiyoshi Madea
CFO: David Stenman
Chf Mktg O: Barb Goworowski
Ex VP: Peter Moss
*Sr VP: Fred Martin
Sr VP: Gus Salamoun
VP: Gwenael Hagan
*VP: Rob Howard
VP: Maria Kernen
VP: Vilia Valentine
Exec: Jason Cavalli
Exec: Victor Logan
Dir Surg: Matt Williams

D-U-N-S 88-389-4040
▲ VERISIGN INC
12061 Bluemont Way, Reston, VA 20190-5684
Tel (703) 948-3200 Founded/Ownrshp 1995
Sales 1.0MMM EMP 1,019
Tkr Sym VRSN Exch NGS
SIC 7375 7372 Information retrieval services; Prepackaged software
Ch Bd: D James Bidzos
COO: Todd B Strubbe
CFO: George E Kilguss III
Ofcr: Barbara Steele
Sr VP: Thomas C Indelicarto
VP: Romain Cholat
VP: Ivor Sequeira
QA Dir: Craig Davies
QA Dir: Rick Vankeuren
Software D: Robin Maxwell
Sales Asso: Samuels James
Board of Directors: Kathleen A Cote, Thomas F Frist III, Jamie S Gorelick, Roger H Moore, Louis A Simpson, Timothy Tomlinson

VERISK ANALYTICS
See INSURANCE SERVICES OFFICE INC

D-U-N-S 82-658-9330
▲ VERISK ANALYTICS INC
545 Washington Blvd, Jersey City, NJ 07310-1607
Tel (201) 469-2000 Founded/Ownrshp 1971
Sales 2.0MMM EMP 7,918
Tkr Sym VRSK Exch NGS
SIC 7375 Information retrieval services
Ch Bd: Scott G Stephenson
Pr: Bill Churney
Pr: Jared Wolovnick
COO: Mark V Anquillare
CFO: Eva F Huston
Ofcr: Jennifer Derfuss
Ex VP: Kenneth E Thompson
Sr VP: Nicholas Daffan
Sr VP: Vincent De P McCarthy
VP: Anthony Canale
VP: Kyle Caswell
VP: Yang Chen
VP: Michael Goodside
VP: Joseph M Izzo
VP: Tayden Judge
VP: Anu Karna
VP: Saurabh Khemka
VP: Chuck Moon
VP: Christopher H Perini
VP: Deborah Purcell
VP: Richard Pursley
Board of Directors: Therese M Vaughan, J Hyatt Brown, David B Wright, Frank J Coyne, Christopher M Foskett, Bruce Hansen, Constantine P Iordanou, John F Lehman Jr, Samuel G Liss, Andrew G Mills, Thomas F Motamed

VERITAS
See SCHNELLER LLC

D-U-N-S 16-061-0809
VERITAS CAPITAL FUND II L P
590 Madison Ave Ste 3501, New York, NY 10022-8527
Tel (212) 415-6700 Founded/Ownrshp 2001
Sales 232.1MM^E EMP 31,029^E
SIC 8742 7374 Management consulting services; Data processing & preparation
Pt: Robert McKeon
Pt: Joe L Benavides
Pt: Hugh D Evans
Pt: Ramzi Musallam
Pt: Jeffrey C Weber

D-U-N-S 79-171-6954
VERITAS CAPITAL MANAGEMENT LLC
9 W 57th St Fl 29, New York, NY 10019-0065
Tel (212) 415-6700 Founded/Ownrshp 1992
Sales 405.7MM^E EMP 1,600
SIC 6799 Venture capital companies
Mng Pt: Ramzi Musallam
Pt: Joe Benavides
Pt: Brian Gorczynski
Pt: Robert B McKeon
Pt: Benjamin Polk
Mng Pt: Hugh Evans
CFO: Jason M Donner
VP: Aneal Krishnan
VP: Daniel H Sugar

D-U-N-S 06-773-8943
VERITAS HEALTH SERVICES INC (CA)
CHINO VALLEY MEDICAL CENTER
(Suby of PRIME HEALTHCARE SERVICES INC) ★
5451 Walnut Ave, Chino, CA 91710-2609
Tel (909) 464-8600 Founded/Ownrshp 2000, 2006
Sales 100.4MM EMP 600

SIC 8062 General medical & surgical hospitals
CEO: Prem Reddy
**Pr:* Irv E Edwards
Dir Lab: Romy Torres
CTO: Allan Tucker

D-U-N-S 07-919-5479
VERITAS STEEL LLC
2300 Cabot Dr Ste 148, Lisle, IL 60532-4615
Tel (630) 423-8708 *Founded/Ownrshp* 2013
Sales 86.4MM *EMP* 718
SIC 3441 Fabricated structural metal for bridges
Pr: Tracy Glende
**Ch Bd:* Henrik Jensen
Pr: Rick Daniels
COO: Mike Sobieski
CFO: Alan Sobel
**Prin:* Richard Phillips
Dir IT: Ronald Soderlund
QI Cn Mgr: Rick Sherman

D-U-N-S 07-976-3288
VERITAS TECHNOLOGIES LLC
(*Suby of* VERITAS US INC) ★
500 E Middlefield Rd, Mountain View, CA 94043-4000
Tel (650) 933-1000 *Founded/Ownrshp* 2014
Sales 130.1MM[E] *EMP* 200[E]
SIC 7371 7375 Computer software development & applications; Information retrieval services; Data base information retrieval
CEO: Bill Coleman
**CFO:* Mick Lopez
**Chf Mktg O:* Ben Gibson
**Ex VP:* John Gannon
Ex VP: Ana Pinczuk
**Ex VP:* Brett Shirk
Sr VP: Gregory King
Sr VP: John Oosterhouse
VP: Janet Coatney
**VP:* Todd Hauschildt
VP: Jeffrey Hofstrand
VP: Yew Ng
VP: Kimberly Stramler

D-U-N-S 08-026-8385
VERITAS US INC
500 E Middlefield Rd, Mountain View, CA 94043-4000
Tel (650) 933-1000 *Founded/Ownrshp* 2014
Sales 1.2MMM *EMP* 200[E]
SIC 7371 Computer software development & applications
CEO: William T Coleman

D-U-N-S 96-358-0944
VERITEXT LEGAL SOLUTIONS
290 W Mount Pleasant Ave, Livingston, NJ 07039-2761
Tel (973) 410-4040 *Founded/Ownrshp* 2016
Sales 88.7MM[E] *EMP* 382[E]
SIC 6719 7338 Investment holding companies, except banks; Court reporting service
CEO: Nancy Josephs
Pr: Jeff Harper
**CFO:* Rich Antoneck
Sr VP: Valerie Berger
Sr VP: Adam Friend
Sr VP: Janet Pawlak
VP: Rita Morriale
Dir Bus: Steve Reymer
Dir Bus: Elyse Smith
Dir Bus: Marj Walker
**CTO:* Tony Donofrio

D-U-N-S 07-929-4494
▲ VERITIV CORP
1000 Abernathy Rd # 1700, Atlanta, GA 30328-5658
Tel (770) 391-8200 *Founded/Ownrshp* 2014
Sales 8.7MMM *EMP* 8,800[E]
Tkr Sym VRTV *Exch* NYS
SIC 5111 5112 5087 Printing & writing paper; Stationery & office supplies; Cleaning & maintenance equipment & supplies
Ch Bd: Mary A Laschinger
CFO: Stephen J Smith
Ofcr: Elizabeth Patrick
Sr VP: Charles B Henry
Sr VP: Mark W Hianik
Sr VP: Timothy D Kutz
Sr VP: Thomas S Lazzaro
Sr VP: Barry R Nelson
Sr VP: Darin W Tang
Sr VP: Adam W Taylor
Sr VP: Daniel J Watkoske
VP: Andrew Magley
Exec: Tim Page
Board of Directors: Allan R Dragone Jr, Matthew J Espe, Daniel T Henry, Tracy A Leinbach, Seth A Meisel, William E Mitchell, Michael P Muldowney, Charles G Ward III, John J Zillmer

D-U-N-S 00-698-9982 IMP/EXP
■ VERITIV OPERATING CO (GA)
(*Suby of* VERITIV CORP) ★
1000 Abernathy Rd, Atlanta, GA 30328-5606
Tel (770) 391-8200 *Founded/Ownrshp* 1975, 2014
Sales 7.3MMM[E] *EMP* 6,400
SIC 5113 5112 5111 Industrial & personal service paper; Shipping supplies; Disposable plates, cups, napkins & eating utensils; Boxes & containers; Computer & photocopying supplies; Computer paper; Photocopying supplies; Laserjet supplies; Printing paper; Writing paper
CEO: Mary A Laschinger
Pr: Tom Shortt
**CFO:* Stephen J Smith
Sr Cor Off: John Carey
VP: Nancy C Geisler
VP: Frank Petsock
Dir Bus: Brent McRae
Div Mgr: Ken Flajs
IT Man: Murali Hegde
Natl Sales: Dave Wright
VP Sls: Jeff Solomon

D-U-N-S 15-161-7446
VERITY HEALTH SYSTEM OF CALIFORNIA INC
203 Redwood Shores Pkwy, Redwood City, CA 94065-1198
Tel (650) 551-6650 *Founded/Ownrshp* 2002
Sales 225.4MM *EMP* 6,000
Accts Grant Thornton Llp San Franci
SIC 8062 General medical & surgical hospitals
CEO: Mitchell Creem
Pr: Robert Walter
**CFO:* Stephen Forney
CFO: Mike Stuart
Ofcr: Gayathri Sellakumar
VP: Candace Caballero
VP: John Omel
VP: Angie Pronio
VP: Analisa Vargas
Assoc Dir: Catalina Salazar
Dir Rx: Norm Fox

VERIZEN
See RICO PUERTO TELEPHONE CO INC

VERIZON
See SUPERMEDIA LLC

VERIZON
See FRONTIER CALIFORNIA INC

VERIZON
See FRONTIER FLORIDA LLC

VERIZON
See TELESECTOR RESOURCES GROUP INC

VERIZON
See NYNEX INFORMATION SOLUTIONS GROUP INC

VERIZON
See BELL ATLANTIC INVESTMENT DEVELOPMENT CORP

VERIZON BUSINESS
See MOTOR COACH INDUSTRIES INC

VERIZON BUSINESS
See MCI INTERNATIONAL SERVICES INC

VERIZON BUSINESS
See MCI COMMUNICATIONS CORP

VERIZON BUSINESS
See MCI COMMUNICATIONS SERVICES INC

VERIZON BUSINESS
See UUNET TECHNOLOGIES INC

VERIZON BUSINESS
See MCI INTERNATIONAL INC

D-U-N-S 60-115-2007 IMP/EXP
■ VERIZON BUSINESS GLOBAL LLC
(*Suby of* VERIZON COMMUNICATIONS INC) ★
22001 Loudoun County Pkwy, Ashburn, VA 20147-6105
Tel (703) 886-5600 *Founded/Ownrshp* 2005
Sales 11.6MMM[E] *EMP* 40,000
SIC 4813 8721 4822 Local & long distance telephone communications; Voice telephone communications; Data telephone communications; Billing & bookkeeping service; Electronic mail
Pr: D Blair Crump
Ex VP: Anastasia Kelly
Sr VP: Martin Burvill
VP: Bill Lumpkin
IT Man: Kelly Bates
IT Man: Annie Coffman
IT Man: Edgar Coss
IT Man: Cowan Dan
IT Man: Mary Dellorto
IT Man: Bryan Humphreys
IT Man: Marshal Jenkins

D-U-N-S 02-028-9070 IMP
■ VERIZON BUSINESS NETWORK SERVICES INC (DE)
(*Suby of* VERIZON BUSINESS) ★
22001 Loudoun County Pkwy, Ashburn, VA 20147-6105
Tel (703) 729-5615 *Founded/Ownrshp* 1973, 1998
Sales 3.8MMM[E] *EMP* 22,930[E]
SIC 4813 Long distance telephone communications; Voice telephone communications; Data telephone communications;
Ch Bd: Nicholas Debelleville
Pr: John Gstratton
CEO: Michael Capellas
Treas: Thomas Quinn
VP: Paul Lmattiola

D-U-N-S 10-721-2169 IMP/EXP
▲ VERIZON COMMUNICATIONS INC
1095 Ave Of The Americas, New York, NY 10036-6704
Tel (212) 395-1000 *Founded/Ownrshp* 1983
Sales 131.6MMM *EMP* 177,700
Tkr Sym VZ *Exch* NYS
SIC 4813 4812 4841 Local & long distance telephone communications; Local telephone communications; Voice telephone communications; ; Cellular telephone services; Cable & other pay television services
Ch Bd: Lowell C McAdam
Pr: Jonathan Lecompte
Pr: John G Stratton
Pr: Marni M Walden
Pr: Kevin Zavaglia
CFO: Matthew D Ellis
CFO: Francis J Shammo
Chf Mktg O: Diego Scotti
Ofcr: Marc C Reed
Ex VP: Roger Gurnani
Ex VP: Robert Mudge
Ex VP: Craig L Silliman
Sr VP: Anthony T Skiadas
Sr VP: Bob Toohey
VP: Shelly Ashwill
VP: Anne Bishop
VP: Richard Black
VP: Philip Burroughs
VP: Maureen Davis
VP: Ian Dillner
VP: John Doherty

D-U-N-S 82-971-3168
■ VERIZON CORPORATE SERVICES GROUP INC
(*Suby of* GTE CORP) ★
295 N Maple Ave, Basking Ridge, NJ 07920-1002
Tel (908) 559-7000 *Founded/Ownrshp* 2005
Sales 179.5MM[E] *EMP* 500[E]
SIC 4813 Telephone communication, except radio
CEO: Virginia Rusterholtz
Chf Cred: Thonis Pe

D-U-N-S 05-350-3983
■ VERIZON DATA SERVICES INC
(*Suby of* GTE WIRELESS INC) ★
1 E Telecom Pkwy, Tampa, FL 33637-0902
Tel (212) 395-1000 *Founded/Ownrshp* 1967
Sales 263.9MM[E] *EMP* 3,800
SIC 7374 7371 Data processing service; Computer software development
Pr: Joseph Castellano
**Treas:* Clifford W Wolf Jr
Sr VP: Gerry Higgins
VP: Michael J Luebke
VP: Richard Ray
**VP:* Kathy A Thompson
IT Man: Brian McGowan

D-U-N-S 00-691-8908
■ VERIZON DELAWARE LLC (DE)
(*Suby of* VERIZON COMMUNICATIONS INC) ★
901 N Tatnall St Fl 2, Wilmington, DE 19801-1644
Tel (302) 571-1571 *Founded/Ownrshp* 1897
Sales 167.7MM[E] *EMP* 930
SIC 4813 4812 7373 2741 Telephone communication, except radio; Local telephone communications; Voice telephone communications; Data telephone communications; Cellular telephone services; Computer integrated systems design; Directories, telephone: publishing only, not printed on site

VERIZON DRECTORIES DISPOSITION
See SUPERMEDIA INC

D-U-N-S 00-694-9895
■ VERIZON MARYLAND LLC (MD)
(*Suby of* VERIZON COMMUNICATIONS INC) ★
1710 Undrpamd Way Ste 401, Hagerstown, MD 21740
Tel (301) 790-7135 *Founded/Ownrshp* 1884, 1984
Sales 1.5MMM[E] *EMP* 5,600
Accts Ernst & Young Llp New York N
SIC 4813 8721 Telephone communication, except radio; Local telephone communications; Voice telephone communications; Data telephone communications; Billing & bookkeeping service
Board of Directors: William R Roberts Christop, David A Hill

VERIZON MIDWEST
See GTE MIDWEST INC

D-U-N-S 00-695-2899
■ VERIZON NEW ENGLAND INC
(*Suby of* VERIZON COMMUNICATIONS INC) ★
185 Franklin St 4th, Boston, MA 02110-1532
Tel (617) 743-9800 *Founded/Ownrshp* 1883, 2001
Sales 2.0MMM[E] *EMP* 18,500
SIC 4813 8721 Telephone communication, except radio; Local telephone communications; Voice telephone communications; Data telephone communications; Billing & bookkeeping service
Ch Bd: Ivan G Seidenberg
**Ch Bd:* Lawrence T Babbio
Pr: Polly Brown
**Sr VP:* Catherine Webster
**VP:* Bruce Beausejour
VP: James McLaughlin
VP: Douglas Schoenberger
Prgrm Mgr: Mark Crichton
Rgnl Mgr: Corey Tarrance
Netwrk Eng: Dino G Imbergamo
Opers Mgr: Ron Reilly
Board of Directors: Gerald Berian

D-U-N-S 00-697-3762
■ VERIZON NEW JERSEY INC (NJ)
(*Suby of* VERIZON COMMUNICATIONS INC) ★
540 Broad St, Newark, NJ 07102-3178
Tel (973) 649-9900 *Founded/Ownrshp* 1904, 1984
Sales 2.2MMM[E] *EMP* 8,300
SIC 4813 8721 Telephone communication, except radio; Local telephone communications; Billing & bookkeeping service
Ch: Lowell C McAdam
CFO: John F Killian
Ex VP: Roy H Chestnutt
Ex VP: Roger Gurnani
Ex VP: Daniel S Mead
Ex VP: Anthony J Melone
Ex VP: Morrison Des Webb
Netwrk Eng: Doug Webb
Board of Directors: Bruce D Cohen, Douglas R Smith

D-U-N-S 00-698-8349 EXP
■ VERIZON NEW YORK INC (NY)
(*Suby of* VERIZON COMMUNICATIONS INC) ★
140 West St, New York, NY 10007-2141
Tel (212) 395-1000 *Founded/Ownrshp* 1896, 2001
Sales 6.9MMM[E] *EMP* 26,800
SIC 4813 7359 Telephone communication, except radio; Local telephone communications; Data telephone communications; Voice telephone communications; Equipment rental & leasing
Ch: W Robert Mudge
**Pr:* Ivan G Seidenberg
Sr VP: Andr S F Irlando
Exec: Raquel Banys
Assoc Dir: Ann Berkowitz
Assoc Dir: Karen Holmes
Ex Dir: Mara S White
Area Mgr: Robert Gross
Snr Ntwrk: Frank Pannacciulli
IT Man: Daryl Allen
Netwrk Eng: Steven Duarte

D-U-N-S 00-794-2287
■ VERIZON NORTHWEST INC
(*Suby of* GTE CORP) ★
600 Hidden Rdg, Irving, TX 75038-3897
Tel (972) 718-5600 *Founded/Ownrshp* 1928, 1964
Sales 746.5MM[E] *EMP* 3,603
SIC 4813 6519 8721 5065 7629 Local & long distance telephone communications; Local telephone communications; Real property lessors; Billing & bookkeeping service; Telephone & telegraphic equipment; Telephone equipment; Telephone set repair; Telecommunication equipment repair (except telephones)
Pr: Eileen O'Neill Odum
Sr VP: Gerald K Dinsmore
VP: Shawne Angelle

D-U-N-S 00-791-3171
■ VERIZON PENNSYLVANIA INC
(*Suby of* VERIZON COMMUNICATIONS INC) ★
1717 Arch St Fl 15, Philadelphia, PA 19103-2787
Tel (215) 466-9900 *Founded/Ownrshp* 1879, 1984
Sales 1.7MMM[E] *EMP* 12,500
SIC 4813 8721 1731 7629 Telephone communication, except radio; Local telephone communications; Voice telephone communications; Data telephone communications; Billing & bookkeeping service; Voice, data & video wiring contractor; Telecommunication equipment repair (except telephones)
Pr: Daniel J Whelan
**Pr:* William B Petersen
**CFO:* Edwin F Hall
IT Man: Vincent Squillacioti
Pgrm Dir: Earl Cohen
Board of Directors: Julia A Conover, William J Mitchell

D-U-N-S 07-934-1476
VERIZON SELECT SERVICES INC
22001 Loudoun County Pkwy, Ashburn, VA 20147-6105
Tel (703) 886-7446 *Founded/Ownrshp* 2000
Sales 264.0MM[E] *EMP* 3,000
SIC 4813 Telephone cable service, land or submarine
**COO:* Barbara Gaskins

D-U-N-S 87-824-5505 IMP
■ VERIZON SELECT SERVICES INC
(*Suby of* GTE CORP) ★
4255 Patriot Dr Ste 400, Grapevine, TX 76051-2304
Tel (972) 724-6000 *Founded/Ownrshp* 1989
Sales 150.5MM[E] *EMP* 305
SIC 4813 Telephone communication, except radio
CEO: Lawrence T Babbio Jr

D-U-N-S 10-673-4213 IMP
■ VERIZON SERVICES CORP
(*Suby of* VERIZON COMMUNICATIONS INC) ★
22001 Loudoun County Pkwy, Ashburn, VA 20147-6105
Tel (703) 729-5931 *Founded/Ownrshp* 1983
Sales 2.3MMM[E] *EMP* 8,539
SIC 4813 Telephone communication, except radio
Pr: W Robert Mudge
**Pr:* Mudge W Robert
**Pr:* John Stratton
CEO: John F Gamba
**CFO:* Steve Smith
**Treas:* Sin Kee Chan
**Ex VP:* Bill Barr
**Ex VP:* Samuel C Ford
**Sr VP:* Martin Burvill
**Sr VP:* A Gray Collins Jr
**Sr VP:* Martha Delehanty
**Sr VP:* Michelle C Ifill
**Sr VP:* Mike Millegan
**VP:* Lawrence T Babbio Jr
**VP:* Robert A Graham
VP: Patrick A Lee
**VP:* Mark J Mathis
**VP:* Mattiola Paul
**VP:* John W Seazholtz
Board of Directors: David Kauffman, Chuck Somes

D-U-N-S 00-699-6433
■ VERIZON SOUTH INC (VA)
(*Suby of* VERIZON COMMUNICATIONS INC) ★
600 Hidden Rdg, Irving, TX 75038-3897
Tel (972) 718-5600 *Founded/Ownrshp* 1947
Sales 987.2MM[E] *EMP* 4,906
SIC 4813 5065 8721 Local & long distance telephone communications; Local telephone communications; Telephone & telegraphic equipment; Telephone equipment; Intercommunication equipment, electronic; Billing & bookkeeping service
Pr: Mudge W Robert
Ch Bd: Lawrence T Babbio Jr
CFO: John F Killian
Treas: Sin Kee Chan
VP: Paul L Mattiola
Ex Dir: Kumar Rajan

D-U-N-S 07-922-9828
■ VERIZON TELEMATICS INC
(*Suby of* VERIZON COMMUNICATIONS INC) ★
2002 Summit Blvd Ste 1800, Brookhaven, GA 30319-1497
Tel (404) 573-5800 *Founded/Ownrshp* 2012
Sales 117.9MM[E] *EMP* 1,024[E]
SIC 7379 4813 Computer related maintenance services; Data telephone communications
CEO: Jeff Leddy
Pr: Erik Goldman
Pr: Keith Schneider
Sr VP: Kevin Link
Sr VP: Mike Vadney
VP: George Ayres
VP: Eric Berkobin
VP: Mike Peterson
VP: Rocco Tricarico
QA Dir: Denise Mericle
Sls Mgr: Jason Billman

D-U-N-S 00-794-1081
■ VERIZON VIRGINIA LLC
(*Suby of* VERIZON COMMUNICATIONS INC) ★
22001 Loudoun County Pkwy, Ashburn, VA 20147-6105
Tel (800) 837-4966 *Founded/Ownrshp* 1905, 1984
Sales 694.2MM^E *EMP* 5,300
Accts Ernst & Young Llp New York N
SIC 4813 Telephone communication, except radio; Local telephone communications; Voice telephone communications; Data telephone communications
Ch Bd: Lawrence T Babbio Jr
* *Pr:* Robert W Woltz Jr
* *Treas:* Neil D Olson
Board of Directors: David R Magnant, Lydia R Pulley, Robert W Woltz Jr

D-U-N-S 00-691-9484
■ VERIZON WASHINGTON DC INC (NY)
(*Suby of* VERIZON COMMUNICATIONS INC) ★
1300 I St Nw, Washington, DC 20005-3314
Tel (202) 392-9900 *Founded/Ownrshp* 1883, 1984
Sales 284.7MM^E *EMP* 1,500
SIC 4813 8721 Local & long distance telephone communications; Billing & bookkeeping service
Pr: William R Roberts
* *CFO:* Lawrence R Whitman
Ex VP: Roy Chestnutt
VP: Joseph L Askew
* *VP:* Mary L Coyne
VP: Andrew Mekelburg
Board of Directors: Glen V Evans, Diana B Gongaware, Marie C Johns, Glen N Jones, Aubrey L Sarvis

VERIZON WIRELESS
See CELLULAR SALES OF KNOXVILLE INC

VERIZON WIRELESS
See 4G WIRELESS INC

VERIZON WIRELESS
See CELLCO PARTNERSHIP

D-U-N-S 88-463-8305 IMP
■ VERIZON WIRELESS INC
(*Suby of* VERIZON COMMUNICATIONS INC) ★
1 Verizon Way, Basking Ridge, NJ 07920-1097
Tel (908) 559-2000 *Founded/Ownrshp* 1997
Sales 387.1MM^E *EMP* 397
SIC 4812 Cellular telephone services
Pr: Russ Preite
Pr: Jonathan Lecompte
Pr: Michelle Miller
Pr: Kevin Zavaglia
Chf Mktg O: Mike Lanman
Div VP: Jerry Smith
Ex VP: David J Small
VP: Joan T Bowyer
VP: Michelle Dutton
VP: Larry Marcus
* *VP:* Philip R Marx
* *VP:* Steven Zipperstein
Assoc Dir: Kathy McDonald
Assoc Dir: Tracy Milo
Assoc Dir: David Neal
Assoc Dir: Zimmerman Tom

D-U-N-S 11-850-9103
■ VERIZON WIRELESS OF EAST LP
(*Suby of* VERIZON WIRELESS) ★
1 Verizon Pl, Alpharetta, GA 30004-8510
Tel (678) 339-4000 *Founded/Ownrshp* 2001
Sales 439.0MM^E *EMP* 600
SIC 4812 Radio telephone communication
CEO: Daniel S Mead
VP: Anthony Bowman
VP: James W Tiller
VP: Steve Zipperstein
Assoc Dir: Jacqueline Blake-Broughton
Assoc Dir: Steven Lyons
Ex Dir: Laura Caragol
IT Man: Praveen Buddiga
Mktg Mgr: Mark Finkelstein

VERIZON WRELESS AUTHORIZED RET
See DIAMOND WIRELESS LLC

VERIZON WIRELESS AUTHORIZED RET
See CAR TOYS INC

D-U-N-S 09-697-8531 IMP
VERLA INTERNATIONAL LTD
463 Temple Hill Rd, New Windsor, NY 12553-5527
Tel (845) 561-2440 *Founded/Ownrshp* 1979
Sales 93.8MM^E *EMP* 400
SIC 2844 Toilet preparations
Pr: Mario F Maffei
* *VP:* Robert R Roth

D-U-N-S 09-241-2188 IMP/EXP
VERMEER EQUIPMENT OF TEXAS INC
VERMEER TEXAS-LOUISIANA
3025 State Highway 161, Irving, TX 75062-2137
Tel (972) 255-3500 *Founded/Ownrshp* 1978
Sales 118.5MM^E *EMP* 140
SIC 5082 7699 7353 General construction machinery & equipment; Construction equipment repair; Heavy construction equipment rental
Pr: Whit Perryman
* *COO:* Mark Krueger
* *CFO:* Darren Tallman
IT Man: Mark Sirois

D-U-N-S 00-527-4071 IMP/EXP
VERMEER MANUFACTURING CO (IA)
1210 E Vermeer Rd, Pella, IA 50219-7660
Tel (641) 628-3141 *Founded/Ownrshp* 1948, 1949
Sales 1.0MMM^E *EMP* 3,292
SIC 3531 3523 Construction machinery; Backhoes, tractors, cranes, plows & similar equipment; Chippers: brush, limb & log; Balers, farm: hay, straw, cotton, etc.
Pr: Andringa Mary
* *CFO:* Steve Van Dusseldorp
VP: Lin Chape
VP: Dell Collins
VP: Dan Langstraat
VP: Steven Willinger
Exec: Dave Elsloo
Exec: Jonathan Hallberg
VP Admn: Vince Newendorp
Ex Dir: Julie Tabatabai
Mng Dir: Nathan Guess

D-U-N-S 03-262-6848 IMP/EXP
VERMEER SOUTHEAST SALES & SERVICE INC
(*Suby of* VERMEER MANUFACTURING CO) ★
4559 Old Winter Garden Rd, Orlando, FL 32811-1735
Tel (407) 295-2020 *Founded/Ownrshp* 1967
Sales 94.2MM^E *EMP* 116
SIC 5082 General construction machinery & equipment; Power shovels
Pr: Merle Den Besten
CFO: Jon Jeffcoat
* *Treas:* Mel R Bokhoven
* *VP:* Todd Bersteer
* *VP:* Kris Den Besten
VP: Kris Besten
VP: Todd V Steeg
Brnch Mgr: Ken Cooper
Brnch Mgr: Cindi Whiteside
Genl Mgr: Craig Sunberg

VERMEER TEXAS-LOUISIANA
See VERMEER EQUIPMENT OF TEXAS INC

D-U-N-S 00-382-1816
VERMILION PARISH SCHOOL BOARD
220 S Jefferson St, Abbeville, LA 70510-5906
Tel (337) 893-3973 *Founded/Ownrshp* 1876
Sales 95.7MM *EMP* 1,250^E
Accts Kolder Champagne Slaven & Co
SIC 8211 School board
Pr: Anthony Fontana
* *CFO:* Phillip J Sellers
VP: Lenita Turner
VP: Maci Viator
Pr Dir: Madeline Dehart
Psych: Ann Abshire
Psych: Angela Lange
Psych: Crystal Wisser
HC Dir: Kelli Romero
Snr Mgr: Christine Hebert

D-U-N-S 80-937-6155
VERMONT AGENCY OF HUMAN SERVICES
(*Suby of* GOVERNORS OFFICE) ★
280 State Dr, Waterbury, VT 05671-9501
Tel (802) 871-3007 *Founded/Ownrshp* 1972
Sales NA *EMP* 2,500^E
SIC 9441 Administration of social & manpower programs;
* *Prin:* Jill Gould
CIO: Margaret Ciechanowicz

D-U-N-S 80-937-6296
VERMONT AGENCY OF TRANSPORTATION
(*Suby of* GOVERNORS OFFICE) ★
1 National Life Dr # 20, Montpelier, VT 05602-3377
Tel (802) 828-2657 *Founded/Ownrshp* 1975
Sales NA *EMP* 1,255
SIC 9621 Regulation, administration of transportation;
Genl Mgr: Carma Flowers
Genl Mgr: Leonard Leblanc

VERMONT CASTINGS GROUP
See MONESSEN HEARTH SYSTEMS CO

VERMONT COLLEGE
See NORWICH UNIVERSITY

D-U-N-S 01-913-8163 IMP
VERMONT COUNTRY STORE INC
BANDSTAND BOOKS & ART
5650 Main St, Manchester Center, VT 05255-9711
Tel (802) 362-4667 *Founded/Ownrshp* 1971
Sales 88.4MM^E *EMP* 405
SIC 5961 5399 5812 General merchandise, mail order; Country general stores; Eating places
VP: Chris Vickers
* *Pr:* William C Shouldice IV
CEO: Lynda Cordett
* *Treas:* Gardner Orton
VP: Laurence A Shaw
Mktg Dir: Jane Brisby
Mktg Mgr: Larry Mishkin
Board of Directors: Coy Clement, Robert Cranshaw, William Cranshaw, Fred Lager

D-U-N-S 00-579-1934 IMP
VERMONT ELECTRIC POWER CO INC (VT)
VELCO
(*Suby of* CENTRAL VERMONT PUBLIC SERVICE CORPORATION)
366 Pinnacle Ridge Rd, Rutland, VT 05701-9386
Tel (802) 773-9161 *Founded/Ownrshp* 1956
Sales 172.9MM *EMP* 150
Accts Kpmg Llp Colchester Vt
SIC 4911 Transmission, electric power
CEO: Thomas Dunn
Pr: John J Donleavy
Pr: Christopher Ldutton
COO: Christopher Root
CFO: Neal Robinson
Treas: Michele Nelson
Bd of Dir: John Cronin
Ofcr: David Haas
VP: Kerrick Johnson
Info Man: Frank Ettori
Genl Couns: Karen O'Neill

D-U-N-S 60-601-1088
VERMONT ENERGY INVESTMENT CORP
EFFICIENCY VERMONT
128 Lakeside Ave Ste 401, Burlington, VT 05401-4894
Tel (802) 860-4095 *Founded/Ownrshp* 1986
Sales 86.8MM *EMP* 275
Accts Johnson Lambert Llp Burlingto
SIC 8748 Energy conservation consultant
Pr: Gus Seelig
* *Treas:* Chip Stone
* *Bd of Dir:* Susan Coakley
Bd of Dir: Jim Merriam
Dir Bus: David Barash
* *Ex Dir:* Scott Johnstone
Genl Mgr: David Bardaglio
Genl Mgr: Fred Holland
Genl Mgr: Katherine Meyers
CTO: Kate Hunter
IT Man: Jules Fishelman

VERMONT FAMILY FARMS
See ST ALBANS COOPERATIVE CREAMERY INC

D-U-N-S 00-793-9598
VERMONT MUTUAL INSURANCE CO
NORTHERN SECURITY INSURANCE CO
89 State St, Montpelier, VT 05602-2954
Tel (802) 223-2341 *Founded/Ownrshp* 1828
Sales NA *EMP* 200
SIC 6331 Property damage insurance; Fire, marine & casualty insurance & carriers
Pr: Thomas J Tierney
* *Pr:* William A Catto
* *CFO:* Brian Eagan
* *VP:* Richard Bland
VP: Joanne Currier
VP: Julia Morgan
VP Mktg: Peter P Fresco
Board of Directors: Richard Belisle, Richard Bland, William Brooks, William Catto, William Gilbert, J Timothy Ide, George Milne, John Hashagen Jr Tom Tier

VERMONT NATIONAL GUARD
See DEPARTMENT OF MILITARY VERMONT

D-U-N-S 07-108-8637
VERMONT STATE COLLEGES
JOHNSON STATE COLLEGE
660 Elm St, Montpelier, VT 05602-4001
Tel (802) 828-2800 *Founded/Ownrshp* 1961
Sales 113.6MM^E *EMP* 2,100
SIC 8221 Colleges universities & professional schools
Ch Bd: Gary W Moore
* *Treas:* Heidi Pelletier
* *VP:* Gordon Winters

D-U-N-S 78-039-9163 IMP
VERMONT TRANSCO LLC
VTTRANSCO
366 Pinnacle Ridge Rd, Rutland, VT 05701-9475
Tel (802) 773-9161 *Founded/Ownrshp* 2006
Sales 172.2MM *EMP* 3
Accts Kpmg Llp Colchester Vt
SIC 1731 Electrical work
Prin: Christopher L Dutton
CFO: Neal Robinson
VP: Kerrick Johnson

D-U-N-S 04-687-7031
VERMONT YANKEE NUCLEAR POWER CORP
(*Suby of* CENTRAL VERMONT PUBLIC SERVICE CORPORATION)
45 Union St, Rutland, VT 05701-3956
Tel (802) 258-4120 *Founded/Ownrshp* 1966
Sales 168.5MM *EMP* 1^E
Accts Kpmg Llp Burlington Vermont
SIC 1731 Electric power systems contractors
Pr: John Boguslawski
* *Ch Bd:* Robert H Young
* *VP:* Bobbi Kilburn

D-U-N-S 00-427-7117 IMP
VERNAY LABORATORIES INC (GA)
VERNAY MANUFACTURING
2077 Cnvntion Ctr Cncurse, Atlanta, GA 30337
Tel (404) 994-2000 *Founded/Ownrshp* 1935
Sales 200.1MM^E *EMP* 500
SIC 3492 Fluid power valves & hose fittings; Electrohydraulic servo valves, metal; Control valves, fluid power: hydraulic & pneumatic; Hose & tube fittings & assemblies, hydraulic/pneumatic
CEO: Ed Urquhart
CFO: Rob Hoglund
* *Ex VP:* Carl Diem
* *Ex VP:* John Madewell
VP Mfg: Greg Gearhart
Sfty Mgr: Ken Carr
Natl Sales: Dale Piper
Mktg Mgr: Joy Brim
Snr Mgr: Paul Grund
Snr Mgr: Jeffer Wright

VERNAY MANUFACTURING
See VERNAY LABORATORIES INC

D-U-N-S 61-065-4477
VERNON HOME HEALTH CARE AGENCY INC
OUTREACH HEALTH SERVICES
(*Suby of* OUTREACH HEALTH SERVICES) ★
2733 Midwestern Pkwy # 120, Wichita Falls, TX 76308-2903
Tel (972) 840-3401 *Founded/Ownrshp* 1990
Sales 29.5MM^E *EMP* 3,000
SIC 8093 8049 8082 Specialty outpatient clinics; Physical therapist; Home health care services
Pr: William Ball
* *VP:* Mary Lou Ball

D-U-N-S 00-632-7266
VERNON L GOEDECKE CO INC
812 E Taylor Ave, Saint Louis, MO 63147-2819
Tel (314) 652-1810 *Founded/Ownrshp* 1947
Sales 97.4MM^E *EMP* 145
SIC 5082 5085 Construction & mining machinery; Industrial supplies
CEO: Ron Peterson
* *Pr:* Mike Rafferty
* *Pr:* Ralph H Wagner
* *VP:* Mike Braun
* *VP:* Eric Peterson
IT Man: Jackie Marler
Sales Asso: Amy Benedick
Sales Asso: Doug Shaiper
Sales Asso: Ed Thomure

D-U-N-S 06-973-6254
VERNON PARISH SCHOOL BOARD
201 Belview Rd, Leesville, LA 71446-2904
Tel (337) 239-3401 *Founded/Ownrshp* 1888
Sales 105.3MM *EMP* 1,333
Accts Allen Green & Williamson Llp
SIC 8211 School board
Pr: Doug Brandon
Genl Mgr: Tim Ward

D-U-N-S 96-403-1236
VERNON PARISH SCHOOL DISTRICT
201 Belview Rd, Leesville, LA 71446-2904
Tel (337) 239-3401 *Founded/Ownrshp* 2010
Sales 3.0MM^E *EMP* 1,323^E
SIC 8211 Public elementary & secondary schools

D-U-N-S 79-998-0912
■ VERNON TELEPHONE CO INC
TDS
(*Suby of* TDS TELECOMMUNICATIONS CORP) ★
1 Curtis Rd, Vernon, NY 13476-3607
Tel (608) 831-1000 *Founded/Ownrshp* 1995
Sales 853.0MM *EMP* 2,700
SIC 4813 Telephone communication, except radio
Pr: David Wittwer

D-U-N-S 08-943-0282
VERONI USA INC
1110 Commerce Blvd # 200, Logan Township, NJ 08085-1765
Tel (609) 970-0320 *Founded/Ownrshp* 2014
Sales 130.7MM *EMP* 28
SIC 2011 Cured meats from meat slaughtered on site
CEO: Antonio Corsano
Pr: Marco Veroni

D-U-N-S 05-209-8332
VERONIS SUHLER & ASSOCIATES INC
VERONIS, SUHLER, STEVENSON
55 E 52nd St Fl 33, New York, NY 10055-0007
Tel (212) 935-4990 *Founded/Ownrshp* 1981
Sales 264.5MM^E *EMP* 2,070
SIC 6211 Investment bankers
Co-CEO: John Veronis
CFO: John R Sinatra
* *Co-CEO:* Jeffrey T Stevenson
* *Co-CEO:* John Suhler
VP: Jack Hartfelder
Mng Dir: David Bainbridge
Mng Dir: Lawrence Crutcher
Mng Dir: Jonathan Drucker
Mng Dir: Hal Greenberg
Mng Dir: David Holland
Mng Dir: Brian Meyer

VERONIS, SUHLER, STEVENSON
See VERONIS SUHLER & ASSOCIATES INC

D-U-N-S 61-163-7047
VERSA CAPITAL MANAGEMENT LLC
2929 Arch St Ste 1650, Philadelphia, PA 19104-2864
Tel (215) 609-3400 *Founded/Ownrshp* 2004
Sales 1.9MMM^E *EMP* 4,032
SIC 6799 Investors
CEO: Gregory Segall
* *COO:* Raymond French
* *COO:* Randall Schultz
Chf Inves: Paul Halpern
Exec: Aaron Headley
Mng Dir: Joel Biran
Mng Dir: Bill Quinn
Off Admin: Gina Cordon

D-U-N-S 61-621-4065
VERSACOLD US INC
(*Suby of* AMERICOLD REALTY TRUST) ★
19840 S Rancho Way, Compton, CA 90220-6320
Tel (310) 632-6265 *Founded/Ownrshp* 2010
Sales 49.4MM^E *EMP* 1,237
SIC 4222 Warehousing, cold storage or refrigerated
CEO: Brent Sugden
* *CFO:* Joel Smith
Rgnl VP: Randy Benish
Rgnl VP: Hal Leddy
VP: Rich Kappmeier

D-U-N-S 06-676-4747
▲ VERSAR INC
6850 Versar Ctr Ste 201, Springfield, VA 22151-4196
Tel (703) 750-3000 *Founded/Ownrshp* 1969
Sales 159.8MM *EMP* 556^E
Tkr Sym VSR *Exch* ASE
SIC 8711 8748 8712 8731 Engineering services; Consulting engineer; Pollution control engineering; Construction & civil engineering; Environmental consultant; Architectural engineering; Natural resource research; Environmental research
CEO: Anthony L Otten
* *Pr:* Jeffrey A Wagonhurst
CFO: Cynthia A Downes
Sr VP: Paul W Kendall
Sr VP: Linda McKnight
Sr VP: Jeff Moran
Sr VP: J Joseph Tyler
Sr VP: James D Villa
VP: Eric Arentsen
VP: Duane Peter
Prgrm Mgr: William Burton
Board of Directors: Robert L Durfee, James L Gallagher, Paul J Hoeper, Frederick M Strader

D-U-N-S 02-272-6965 EXP
VERSATECH AUTOMATION SERVICES LLC
11349 Fm 529 Rd, Houston, TX 77041-3207
Tel (713) 937-3100 *Founded/Ownrshp* 2008
Sales 229.5MM^E *EMP* 600
SIC 5531 5013 Automotive & home supply stores; Automotive supplies & parts; Automotive supplies
Pr: David R Volz Jr
VP: Martin Dworak

D-U-N-S 15-795-0408
VERSATILE PROCESSING GROUP INC
9820 Westpoint Dr Ste 300, Indianapolis, IN 46256-3363
Tel (317) 577-8930 *Founded/Ownrshp* 1999
Sales 92.3MM^E *EMP* 200
SIC 3341 Secondary nonferrous metals
CEO: Rob Van Vliet
* *CFO:* Scott Severson
* *VP:* Ron Rickter

VERSITECH MOLD DIV
See QUALITY MOLD INC

D-U-N-S 82-648-0902
▲ VERSO CORP
6775 Lenox Center Ct # 400, Memphis, TN 38115-4436
Tel (901) 369-4100 *Founded/Ownrshp* 2006
Sales 3.1MMM *EMP* 5,200[E]
Accts Deloitte & Touche Llp Memphis
Tkr Sym VRS *Exch* NYS
SIC 2621 Paper mills; Specialty papers
Pr: David J Paterson
**Ch Bd:* Scott M Kleinman
CFO: Allen J Campbell
Treas: Michael Naumann
Sr VP: Peter H Kesser
Sr VP: Michael Weinhold
VP: Mark Daniel
VP: Patrick Gibney
VP: Benjamin Hinchman IV
VP: Peter Kesser
VP: Craig Liska
VP: Palmi Moller
VP: Dave Schilling
Exec: Sharad Agarwal
Exec: Clarissa Murriel
Exec: Julie Thimmes
Exec: Bob Wilhelm
Board of Directors: Robert M Amen, Richard M Cieri, Michael E Ducey, Thomas Gutierrez, David W Oskin, L H Puckett Jr, Reed B Rayman, David B Sambur, Eric L Press

D-U-N-S 78-398-2866 IMP
■ VERSO PAPER HOLDINGS LLC
(*Suby of* VERSO CORP) ★
6775 Lenox Center Ct # 400, Memphis, TN 38115-4436
Tel (901) 369-4100 *Founded/Ownrshp* 2006
Sales 1.0MMM[E] *EMP* 1,630
Accts Deloitte & Touche Llp Memphis
SIC 2621 Paper mills; Specialty papers; Catalog, magazine & newsprint papers; Catalog paper
VP: Mike Weinhold
VP: Robert M Wilhelm

D-U-N-S 78-421-9383 IMP
■ VERSO PAPER LLC
(*Suby of* VERSO PAPER HOLDINGS LLC) ★
6775 Lenox Center Ct # 400, Memphis, TN 38115-4436
Tel (901) 369-4100 *Founded/Ownrshp* 2006
Sales 327.1MM[E] *EMP* 840
SIC 2621 Paper mills
**CFO:* Robert P Mundy

D-U-N-S 82-926-7777
VERSO PAPER MANAGEMENT LP
60 W 42nd Ste 1942, New York, NY 10165
Tel (212) 599-2700 *Founded/Ownrshp* 2006
Sales 1.0MMM[E] *EMP* 2,901
SIC 2621 Paper mills
Pr: Michael A Jackson
Netwrk Mgr: Jesse Rothfork

D-U-N-S 36-381-8253 IMP
VERST GROUP LOGISTICS INC
300 Shorland Dr, Walton, KY 41094-9328
Tel (859) 485-1212 *Founded/Ownrshp* 2004
Sales 170.7MM *EMP* 1,300
SIC 4225 7389 General warehousing & storage; Labeling bottles, cans, cartons, etc.
CEO: Paul T Verst
**CFO:* James Stadtmiller
**Ch:* William G Verst
VP: Brian Bockman
VP: Dennis Roell
Exec: Tom Morris
Dir Bus: Peter Parker
CTO: Tara Rohan
IT Man: Jason Gindele
Opers Mgr: Mark Clinkenbeard
Opers Mgr: Dale Landrum

D-U-N-S 08-007-4232
▲ VERSUM MATERIALS INC
8555 S River Pkwy, Tempe, AZ 85284-2601
Tel (610) 481-6697 *Founded/Ownrshp* 2016
Sales 624.7MM[E] *EMP* 3,300[E]
Tkr Sym VSM *Exch* NYS
SIC 2842 2891 3569 Ammonia, household; Adhesives; Gas producers, generators & other gas related equipment; Gas separators (machinery); Separators for steam, gas, vapor or air (machinery)
Pr: Guillermo Novo
**CFO:* George Bitto
**Ofcr:* Jessica Feather-Bowman

D-U-N-S 08-007-4257
■ VERSUM MATERIALS US LLC
DELIVERY SYSTEMS AND SERVICES
(*Suby of* VERSUM MATERIALS INC) ★
1919 Vultee St, Allentown, PA 18103-4744
Tel (610) 481-3706 *Founded/Ownrshp* 2015
Sales 621.3MM[E] *EMP* 1,490[E]
SIC 2842 2891 3569 Ammonia, household; Adhesives; Gas producers, generators & other gas related equipment; Gas separators (machinery); Separators for steam, gas, vapor or air (machinery)
Pr: Guillermo Novo

D-U-N-S 14-703-6602
VERTAFORE INC
AMS SERVICES
11724 Ne 195th St, Bothell, WA 98011-3145
Tel (425) 402-1000 *Founded/Ownrshp* 2016
Sales 538.5MM[E] *EMP* 1,200
SIC 7374 Data processing service
CEO: Jeff Hawn
**CFO:* Dave Arkley
**Chf Cred:* Snehal Desai
**Sr VP:* Theo Beack
**Sr VP:* Jenny Guild
Sr VP: Larry Hagerty
**Sr VP:* Joe Magrady
Sr VP: Julia Nenke
Sr VP: Michele Shepard
VP: Mark Craig
Snr Sftwr: Tony Almazan

D-U-N-S 80-815-3634 IMP/EXP
VERTELLUS HEALTH & SPECIALTY PRODUCTS LLC
201 N Illinois St # 1800, Indianapolis, IN 46204-1904
Tel (317) 247-8141 *Founded/Ownrshp* 2006
Sales 201.3MM[E] *EMP* 1,000
SIC 2865

D-U-N-S 08-027-4123
VERTELLUS SPECIALTIES HOLDINGS CORP
(*Suby of* WIND POINT PARTNERS LP) ★
201 N Illinois St # 1800, Indianapolis, IN 46204-1904
Tel (317) 247-8141 *Founded/Ownrshp* 2005
Sales 482.7MM[E] *EMP* 1,000[E]
SIC 2865 6719 Cyclic crudes, coal tar; Tar; Investment holding companies, except banks
Pr: Richard V Preziotti

VERTELLUS SPECIALTIES INC.
See VSI LIQUIDATING INC

D-U-N-S 92-796-9373
VERTEX BUSINESS SERVICES LLC
501 W Pres G Bush Hwy 3, Richardson, TX 75080
Tel (214) 576-1000 *Founded/Ownrshp* 2006
Sales 56.1MM[E] *EMP* 1,000
SIC 7379 Computer related consulting services
Pr: Jason Donahue
**Ch Bd:* David Bieber
Pr: Lance Charlish
CFO: Brad Almond
**Treas:* Charles Michel
Top Exec: Robert Dority
**VP:* Susie Buffam
VP: Sunitha Chamarti
IT Man: Ruth Burns
IT Man: David Paul
IT Man: Atchu Thiru

D-U-N-S 11-744-5338 EXP
VERTEX COMMUNICATIONS CORP
2600 N Longview St, Kilgore, TX 75662-6842
Tel (903) 984-0555 *Founded/Ownrshp* 1984
Sales 226.0MM[E] *EMP* 1,500
SIC 3663

D-U-N-S 79-619-9300
▲ VERTEX ENERGY INC
1331 Gemini St Ste 250, Houston, TX 77058-2764
Tel (866) 660-8156 *Founded/Ownrshp* 2007
Sales 146.9MM *EMP* 205
Tkr Sym VTNR *Exch* NAS
SIC 2911 Petroleum refining
Ch Bd: Benjamin P Cowart
COO: John Strickland
CFO: Chris Carlson
Dir IT: Colin Colvin
Board of Directors: Dan Borgen, James P Gregory, Timothy C Harvey, David L Phillips, Christopher Stratton

D-U-N-S 09-685-3189
VERTEX INC
1041 Old Cassatt Rd, Berwyn, PA 19312-1192
Tel (610) 640-4200 *Founded/Ownrshp* 1978
Sales 207.0MM *EMP* 863
Accts Baker Tilly Virchow Krause Ll
SIC 7372 Business oriented computer software
Pr: David Destefano
Ch Bd: Jeffrey R Westphal
CFO: Lisa Butler
Treas: Stefanie Lucas
VP: Chris Carlson
VP: David Henkin
VP: Chris Kohl
VP: Joanne Leonard
VP: Rajesh Nikam
VP: Steve Richard
VP: Jason Sklar
VP: John Viglione

D-U-N-S 60-247-8257 IMP/EXP
▲ VERTEX PHARMACEUTICALS INC
50 Northern Ave, Boston, MA 02210-1862
Tel (617) 341-6100 *Founded/Ownrshp* 1989
Sales 1.0MMM *EMP* 1,950
Accts Ernst & Young Llp Boston Mas
Tkr Sym VRTX *Exch* NGS
SIC 2834 8731 Pharmaceutical preparations; Biotechnical research, commercial
Ch Bd: Jeffrey M Leiden
CFO: Ian F Smith
Ofcr: Kenneth L Horton
Ex VP: David Altshuler
Ex VP: Stuart A Arbuckle
Ex VP: Peter Mueller
Ex VP: Amit K Sachdev
Sr VP: John J Alam
Sr VP: Paul M Silva
VP: Youssef Bennani
VP: Susan Cameron-Laxton
VP: Robert Castellucci
VP: Sheila Clark
VP: John Condon
VP: Scott Fields
VP: Shelley George
VP: Federico Goodsaid
VP: Jeff Henderson
VP: Lynette Hopkinson
VP: Robert Kauffman
VP: Sylvie Ouellet
Board of Directors: Joshua S Boger, Terrence C Kearney, Margaret G McGlynn, Bruce I Sachs, Elaine S Ullian, William Young

D-U-N-S 80-548-7303
VERTICAL SCREEN INC
251 Veterans Way, Warminster, PA 18974-3534
Tel (215) 396-9870 *Founded/Ownrshp* 1989
Sales 106.7MM[E] *EMP* 400[E]
SIC 7375

VERTICAL V, INC.
See NV5 INC

VERTIV
See LIEBERT CORP

D-U-N-S 60-341-6314
VERTRUE LLC
MEMBER WORKS
20 Glover Ave, Norfolk, CT 06058
Tel (203) 324-7635 *Founded/Ownrshp* 2007
Sales 94.8MM[E] *EMP* 2,371
SIC 7389

D-U-N-S 01-698-7752
VESCO OIL CORP
DIAMOND OIL DISTRIBUTORS
16055 W 12 Mile Rd, Southfield, MI 48076-2979
Tel (800) 527-5358 *Founded/Ownrshp* 1947
Sales 279.1MM[E] *EMP* 210
Accts Rehmann Robson Troy Mi
SIC 5172 Lubricating oils & greases
Pr: Donald R Epstein
CFO: Cheryl R Reitzloff
Mktg Mgr: Mark Halverson

D-U-N-S 88-353-4968
VESTA CORP
11950 Sw Garden Pl, Portland, OR 97223-8248
Tel (503) 639-0235 *Founded/Ownrshp* 1995
Sales 205.1MM[E] *EMP* 600
SIC 3559 3578 Electronic component making machinery; Billing machines
Pr: Douglas Fieldhouse
**CFO:* Sanjay Khare
Bd of Dir: Patrick S Jones
**Sr VP:* Rocky Scales
**VP:* Marshall Behling
VP: Charlton Hamer
VP: Al Markham
VP: James Volpe
**VP:* Xj Wang
VP: Chunrog Zhu
Prgrm Mgr: Sam Canfield

D-U-N-S 09-459-1398
VESTA PROPERTY SERVICES INC (FL)
1021 Oak St, Jacksonville, FL 32204-3905
Tel (904) 355-1831 *Founded/Ownrshp* 1996
Sales 195.5MM[E] *EMP* 650
SIC 6722 6531 Management investment, open-end; Condominium manager
Ch Bd: Frank Surfase
**Pr:* Michael D Hyman
**VP:* Daniel P Armstrong
**VP:* Roy Deary
VP: David Surface

D-U-N-S 19-340-0736
VESTAR CAPITAL PARTNERS INC
245 Park Ave Rm 4100, New York, NY 10167-4196
Tel (212) 351-1600 *Founded/Ownrshp* 1988
Sales 425.4MM[E] *EMP* 50
SIC 6799 Investors
Ch Bd: Daniel S O'Connell
CFO: Brendan Spillan
CFO: Brendon Spillane
VP: Fabrizio Gualdi
VP: Evan Marks
VP: John B Stephens
VP: Takuro Ueji
Prin: Garrick D Bernstein
Mng Dir: James L Elrod
Mng Dir: Jean-Fran Ois Felix
Mng Dir: Giorgio Gandini

D-U-N-S 00-490-1651 IMP/EXP
VESTAS BLADES AMERICA INC
(*Suby of* VESTAS AMERICAS A/S)
1500 E Crown Prince Blvd, Brighton, CO 80603-5885
Tel (303) 655-5800 *Founded/Ownrshp* 2007
Sales 214.8MM[E] *EMP* 650[E]
SIC 3621 Windmills, electric generating
Pr: Jesterser Hans
**Pr:* Jason Barber

VESTAS TECHNOLOGY R D AMERICAS
See VESTAS-AMERICAN WIND TECHNOLOGY INC

D-U-N-S 00-389-8206 IMP
VESTAS TOWERS AMERICA INC
(*Suby of* VESTAS WIND SYSTEMS A/S)
100 Tower Rd, Pueblo, CO 81004-7700
Tel (719) 288-2200 *Founded/Ownrshp* 2008
Sales 202.8MM[E] *EMP* 450
SIC 3443 Wind tunnels; Buoys, metal; Wind & vacuum tunnels
Pr: Ditlev Engel
Pr: Bjarne Hansen
CFO: Dag Andresen
Ex VP: Juan Araluce
Ex VP: Anders Vedel
IT Man: Karen Mealy

D-U-N-S 79-070-2807 IMP/EXP
VESTAS-AMERICAN WIND TECHNOLOGY INC
VESTAS TECHNOLOGY R D AMERICAS
(*Suby of* VESTAS AMERICAS A/S)
1417 Sw Naito Pkwy # 100, Portland, OR 97201-5141
Tel (503) 327-2000 *Founded/Ownrshp* 1992
Sales 404.4MM[E] *EMP* 600[E]
SIC 3523 3511 5084 Farm machinery & equipment; Turbines & turbine generator sets; Industrial machinery & equipment
CEO: Chris Brown
CFO: Christian Venderby
VP: Torben Andersen
VP: Mark Colwell
Off Admin: Angie Lovre
Software D: Zachary Kuzda
Snr Mgr: Jay Judd

D-U-N-S 12-391-3480
VESTCOM INTERNATIONAL INC
2800 Cantrell Rd Ste 400, Little Rock, AR 72202-2049
Tel (501) 663-0100 *Founded/Ownrshp* 2007
Sales 156.1MM[E] *EMP* 700
SIC 8742 7389 Marketing consulting services; Document storage service
Ch Bd: John Lawlor
**Pr:* Tim McKenzie
**CFO:* Bob Bloom
**CFO:* Shannon Palmer
**V Ch Bd:* Joel Cartun
**Sr VP:* Clifton Cook
**Sr VP:* Darrel Risberg
Board of Directors: Steve Bardwell, Stephen Bova, Leonard Fassler, Fred Lafer, Richard White

D-U-N-S 01-178-7347 IMP
VESTIL MANUFACTURING CO
201 Growth Pkwy, Angola, IN 46703-9321
Tel (260) 665-2867 *Founded/Ownrshp* 2007
Sales 95.0MM *EMP* 400
SIC 3537 Aircraft engine cradles
Pr: Ralph Donald Trine

D-U-N-S 04-588-9136 IMP/EXP
VESTIL MANUFACTURING CORP
2999 N Wayne St, Angola, IN 46703-9122
Tel (260) 665-7586 *Founded/Ownrshp* 1967
Sales 87.9MM[E] *EMP* 350[E]
SIC 3999 3535 3069 Dock equipment & supplies, industrial; Conveyors & conveying equipment; Molded rubber products
CEO: Sheri A Trine
**Pr:* Ralph Trine
VP: Barry Trine
VP: Carri Trine
Opers Mgr: Amie Wicker
Plnt Mgr: Roy Edgar
Sales Exec: Serena Van
Mktg Dir: Joshua Sheets
Sales Asso: Renault McHenry

D-U-N-S 07-945-5660
VESTIS RETAIL GROUP LLC
(*Suby of* VERSA CAPITAL MANAGEMENT LLC) ★
160 Corporate Ct, Meriden, CT 06450-7177
Tel (203) 235-5775 *Founded/Ownrshp* 2013
Sales 783.0MM[E] *EMP* 4,032[E]
SIC 7311 Advertising agencies
CEO: Mark Walsh
CFO: Susan J Riley

D-U-N-S 00-432-7847 IMP
VESUVIUS CRUCIBLE CO
(*Suby of* VESUVIUS AMERICA, INC.)
1404 Newton Dr, Champaign, IL 61822-1069
Tel (217) 351-5000 *Founded/Ownrshp* 1916, 1986
Sales 489.9MM[E] *EMP* 2,500
SIC 3297 5051 Nonclay refractories; Foundry products
CFO: Jean P Malherbe
COO: Michael Cunningham
VP: Patrick Bikard
VP: Charles L Turner
Exec: John Cox
Ex Dir: Geoffroy Godin
Genl Mgr: Jerry Taylor
Dir IT: Harold Turpen
Prd Dir: Ken Coulter
Prd Mgr: Tim Faciana
Mktg Mgr: Bruce Winter

D-U-N-S 00-298-2155 IMP/EXP
VESUVIUS U S A CORP
(*Suby of* VESUVIUS CRUCIBLE CO) ★
1404 Newton Dr, Champaign, IL 61822-1069
Tel (217) 402-9204 *Founded/Ownrshp* 1966, 1987
Sales 441.5MM[E] *EMP* 1,500
SIC 3297 5085 Nonclay refractories; Graphite refractories: carbon bond or ceramic bond; Refractory material
Pr: Glenn Cowie
Plnt Mgr: Mike Cunningham
Sls Mgr: Ann Smith

D-U-N-S 15-049-0043 IMP
■ VETCO GRAY INC
GE OIL & GAS
(*Suby of* NUOVO PIGNONE SPA)
4424 W Sam Houston Pkwy N, Houston, TX 77041-8243
Tel (713) 683-2400 *Founded/Ownrshp* 2007
Sales 1.3MMM[E] *EMP* 4,800
SIC 3533 Oil field machinery & equipment
Pr: Claudi Santiago
CFO: Kirk Vincent
Treas: Joan Fontenot
**VP:* Sam Aquillano
Genl Mgr: Peter Condon
Genl Mgr: Bobby Roy
Sales Exec: Matt Castaneda
Sales Exec: Gary Willard
Board of Directors: Kjell Almskog, Bengt Sohlen

D-U-N-S 09-023-6451
VETERANS AFFAIRS PENNSYLVANIA BUREAU FOR
(*Suby of* PA DEPARTMENT OF MILITARY AND VETERANS AFFAIRS) ★
0 47 Ftig Bldg S, Annville, PA 17003
Tel (717) 861-8901 *Founded/Ownrshp* 1998
Sales NA *EMP* 1,800
SIC 9451 Administration of veterans' affairs;
Pr: Cecil Hengeveld

D-U-N-S 92-725-8046
■ VETERANS BENEFITS ADMINISTRATION
VACO
(*Suby of* UNITED STATES DEPT OF VETERANS AFFAIRS) ★
810 Vermont Ave Nw, Washington, DC 20420-0001
Tel (202) 273-5674 *Founded/Ownrshp* 1930
Sales NA *EMP* 1,348
SIC 9451 Administration of veterans' affairs;
Prin: Daniel L Cooper
CFO: James M Bohbach
VP: Carolyn Gray
VP: Dexter Robinson
Assoc Dir: Gracie Specks
**Prin:* Sloan D Gibson
**Prin:* Jose D Riojas
Ex Dir: Lisa J Freeman
Prgrm Mgr: Jacqueline Dennis
Telecom Ex: Richard Culp
CTO: Richard R Wise

D-U-N-S 87-886-5039
VETERANS COMMISSION MISSOURI
(*Suby of* MISSOURI DEPARTMENT OF PUBLIC SAFETY) ★
205 Jefferson St Fl 12, Jefferson City, MO 65101-2901
Tel (573) 751-3779 *Founded/Ownrshp* 1989
Sales NA *EMP* 1,500
SIC 9451 Administration of veterans' affairs;
Ex Dir: Larry D Kay
Ex Dir: Don Taylor

D-U-N-S 92-689-1516
■ **VETERANS HEALTH ADMINISTRATION**
V H A
(*Suby of* UNITED STATES DEPT OF VETERANS AFFAIRS) ★
810 Vermont Ave Nw, Washington, DC 20420-0001
Tel (202) 461-4800 *Founded/Ownrshp* 1930
Sales NA *EMP* 201,000
SIC 9451 Administration of veterans' affairs;
Treas: Jonathan B Perlin
Dir Vol: Stephanie W Burns
CFO: Rick Deckard
CFO: Michael Wolfgang
Ofcr: James P Bagian
Ofcr: Therese Blocher
Ofcr: Margaret Campbell
Ofcr: Everett A Chasen
Ofcr: Joy Hunter
Ofcr: Richard Mirabelli
Ofcr: Alice Powell
VP: Peter Flynn
Exec: Angela Boese
Exec: Vincent Crawford
Exec: Robert Kolodner
Exec: Annamaria Lefchick
Dir Lab: Nolan Clark
Dir Lab: Michael Ittman
Comm Man: Susan Brouchart

D-U-N-S 13-445-3075
VETERANS LIFE INSURANCE CO INC
(*Suby of* PEOPLES BENEFIT LIFE INSURANCE CO) ★
20 Moores Rd, Malvern, PA 19355-1114
Tel (610) 648-5000 *Founded/Ownrshp* 1977
Sales NA *EMP* 500
SIC 6311 6321 Life insurance; Accident & health insurance
Pr: Brian Smith
* *Treas:* Martha Ann McConnell
VP: Sheri Fanaroff
Dir IT: Rich Babyak
Mktg Dir: Doug Sarcia
Cust Svc D: Nancy Crockett

D-U-N-S 01-065-1727 IMP
VETERANS OF FOREIGN WARS OF UNITED STATES (NE)
406 W 34th St Fl 11, Kansas City, MO 64111-2736
Tel (816) 756-3390 *Founded/Ownrshp* 1899
Sales 105.2MM *EMP* 185
Accts Grantthornton Llp Kansas Cit
SIC 8641 Veterans' organization
CFO: Jr H Vander Clute
CFO: Jim Mueller
Treas: John Furgess
Treas: Doug Markley
Sr Cor Off: Suzanne Dicks
Exec: Jack Pope
Ex Dir: Ramon Saiz
Genl Mgr: John Barnes
Genl Mgr: Judy McNeel
Genl Mgr: Ryan Strathman
CIO: Bob Greene

D-U-N-S 04-597-4474
VETERINARY PET INSURANCE SERVICES INC
DVM INSURANCE AGENCY
(*Suby of* SCOTTSDALE INDEMNITY CO) ★
1800 E Emperi Hwy Ste 145, Brea, CA 92821
Tel (714) 989-0555 *Founded/Ownrshp* 2003
Sales NA *EMP* 420[E]
SIC 6411 Insurance agents, brokers & service; Insurance agents & brokers
* *CFO:* Michael Funk
* *Ch:* Mike Miller
* *VP:* Phil Grevin
Dir Bus: Eric Raidmae
* *Prin:* Dennis Drent
Prgrm Mgr: Charysse Sweet
Dir IT: Jeff Sullivan
IT Man: Paresh Valand
Software D: Sunith Pathath
S&M/VP: Rebecca Lewis
Mktg Dir: Brian Iannessa

D-U-N-S 02-869-1988 IMP/EXP
VETERINARY SERVICE INC
4100 Bangs Ave, Modesto, CA 95356-8710
Tel (209) 545-5100 *Founded/Ownrshp* 1960
Sales 180.1MM *EMP* 255
SIC 5047 5199 5083

VETERINARY SPECIALTY
See BLUEPEARL FLORIDA LLC

D-U-N-S 02-210-5530
VETTER EQUIPMENT CO
610 14th Ave S, Denison, IA 51442-2586
Tel (712) 263-6440 *Founded/Ownrshp* 1975
Sales 121.0MM[E] *EMP* 150
SIC 5083 Agricultural machinery & equipment; Farm equipment parts & supplies
Pr: Glen Vetter
Off Mgr: Dick Elliott

D-U-N-S 09-467-9404
VETTER HEALTH SERVICES INC
HERITAGE OF GERING
20220 Harney St, Elkhorn, NE 68022-2063
Tel (402) 895-3932 *Founded/Ownrshp* 1977
Sales 1.1MMM[E] *EMP* 1,150
SIC 8052 Intermediate care facilities
Pr: Glenn Van Ekeren
* *Ex VP:* Bernard A Dana
* *VP:* Eldora Vetter
Ex Dir: Mikeal Loneman
Sfty Dirs: Ed Remm
Nrsg Dir: Maureen Blaylock
Nrsg Dir: Janelle Krzycki
Nrsg Dir: Dan Smith
Nrsg Dir: Diane Villwok
Nrsg Dir: Kevin Vogt

VEXOS
See STACI CORP

D-U-N-S 03-014-6778
VEXOS INC
CLP ST INC.
(*Suby of* CENTRE LANE PARTNERS LLC) ★
60 E 42nd St Ste 1400, New York, NY 10165-1499
Tel (646) 843-0710 *Founded/Ownrshp* 2014
Sales 169.9MM[E] *EMP* 156[E]
SIC 7371 Computer software systems analysis & design, custom
* *Pr:* David Buckley
* *Treas:* Ken Lau
* *Mng Dir:* David Kreilein

D-U-N-S 00-234-4208
▲ **VF CORP** (PA)
105 Corp Ctr Blvd, Greensboro, NC 27408-3194
Tel (336) 424-6000 *Founded/Ownrshp* 1899
Sales 12.3MMM *EMP* 64,000
Accts Pricewaterhousecoopers Llp Gr
Tkr Sym VFC *Exch* NYS
SIC 2325 2321 2329 2339 2331 2369 Jeans: men's, youths' & boys'; Slacks, dress: men's, youths' & boys'; Trousers, dress (separate): men's, youths' & boys'; Men's & boys' dress shirts; Jackets (suede, leatherette, etc.), sport: men's & boys'; Sweaters & sweater jackets: men's & boys'; Jeans: women's, misses' & juniors'; Slacks: women's, misses' & juniors'; Women's & misses' blouses & shirts; Jeans: girls', children's & infants'; Slacks: girls' & children's; Warm-up, jogging & sweat suits: girls' & children's; Bathing suits & swimwear: girls', children's & infants'
Ch Bd: Eric C Wiseman
Pr: Scott H Baxter
Pr: Jim Pisani
Pr: Steven E Rendle
Pr: Karl Heinz Salzburger
CFO: Scott A Roe
Treas: Patrick Guido
Bd of Dir: Garrett Chapman
Bd of Dir: Brandi Cosper
Bd of Dir: Juan De Bedout
Sr VP: Steve E Rendle
VP: Amanda Ballard
VP: Sean Cady
VP: Bill Clodfelter
VP: Linda P Cullum
VP: Stephen F Dull
VP: Nina Floodcampo
VP: Randy Fortenberry
VP: Michael Gannaway
VP: Andy Griffiths
VP: Paul Herron
Board of Directors: Matthew J Shattock, Richard T Carucci, Juliana L Chugg, Juan Ernesto De Bedout, Mark S Hoplamazian, Robert J Hurst, Laura W Lang, W Alan McCollough, W Rodney McMullen, Clarence Otis Jr

VF GLOBAL INNOVATION CENTER
See VF OUTDOOR LLC

D-U-N-S 00-404-8013 IMP/EXP
■ **VF IMAGEWEAR INC**
(*Suby of* VF CORP) ★
545 Marriott Dr Ste 200, Nashville, TN 37214-5077
Tel (615) 565-5000 *Founded/Ownrshp* 1923
Sales 1.0MMM *EMP* 5,650
SIC 2326 5099 2339 2311 Work apparel, except uniforms; Safety equipment & supplies; Women's & misses' outerwear; Men's & boys' suits & coats
CEO: Eric C Wiseman
* *Pr:* Scott Baxter
Pr: Steve Cochran
* *Pr:* Steven E Cochran
* *Pr:* Ed Doran
* *Pr:* Curtis Holtz
* *Pr:* James Pisani
CFO: Marilyn Davidson
* *VP:* George N Derhofer
* *VP:* Patrick Kopf
VP: Frank Pickard
VP: Neal Waters
VP Bus Dev: Brett Barthel

D-U-N-S 04-731-5015 IMP
■ **VF INDUSTRIAL PARK INC**
(*Suby of* VF CORP) ★
801 Hill Ave Ofc, Reading, PA 19610-3028
Tel (610) 378-0408 *Founded/Ownrshp* 1969
Sales 76.7MM[E] *EMP* 1,500
SIC 5611 Clothing, sportswear, men's & boys'
CEO: J Titsworth
* *Pr:* Steve Fritz
* *Treas:* J R Patterson
* *Treas:* Frank C Pickard III
* *VP:* H D McKemy

D-U-N-S 87-271-8192 IMP/EXP
■ **VF JEANSWEAR LIMITED PARTNERSHIP**
(*Suby of* VF CORP) ★
400 N Elm St, Greensboro, NC 27401-2143
Tel (336) 332-3400 *Founded/Ownrshp* 1916
Sales 3.4MMM[E] *EMP* 15,000
SIC 2325 2339 2331 2329 Men's & boys' jeans & dungarees; Men's & boys' dress slacks & shorts; Aprons, except rubber or plastic: women's, misses', juniors'; Hoovers (apron): women's & misses'; Jeans: women's, misses' & juniors'; Blouses, women's & juniors': made from purchased material; Shirts, women's & juniors': made from purchased materials; T-shirts & tops, women's: made from purchased materials; Shirt & slack suits: men's, youths' & boys'
CEO: Eric Weisman
Pr: Steven Birkhold
Pr: Joseph Dzialo
Pr: Angelo Lagrega
CEO: Mackey J McDonald
CFO: Dominic Paul Dascoli
Chf Mktg O: Craig Errington
VP: Tom Glaser
VP: Alan Montgomery
VP: Sam Tucker
Opers Mgr: Anna Chan

D-U-N-S 05-067-4548 IMP
■ **VF OUTDOOR LLC**
VF GLOBAL INNOVATION CENTER
(*Suby of* VF CORP) ★
2701 Harbor Bay Pkwy, Alameda, CA 94502-3041
Tel (510) 618-3500 *Founded/Ownrshp* 1964, 2000
Sales 540.1MM[E] *EMP* 749
SIC 2329 2339 3949 2394 2399 5941 Men's & boys' leather, wool & down-filled outerwear; Ski & snow clothing: men's & boys'; Women's & misses' outerwear; Camping equipment & supplies; Tents: made from purchased materials; Sleeping bags; Camping & backpacking equipment; Skiing equipment
Pr: Scott Baxter
CFO: C Crawford
CFO: Michael Leinwand
Top Exec: Cortney C McDermott
Sr VP: Eric Wiseman
VP: Aaron Carpenter
VP: Jim Gerson
VP: Tucker Hacking
VP: Vicki Redding
VP: Lindsay Rice
VP: Paul Sline
VP: Todd Spaletto
VP: Paul Tabet
Exec: Ruder Finn
Dir Lab: Dilip Lokre

D-U-N-S 80-998-8988
■ **VF OUTLET INC**
VANITY FAIR
(*Suby of* VF CORP) ★
801 Hill Ave Ste 1, Reading, PA 19610-3028
Tel (610) 378-0408 *Founded/Ownrshp* 1991
Sales 216.6MM[E] *EMP* 2,500[E]
SIC 5651 Family clothing stores
Pr: Steve Fritz
* *Treas:* Ryan K Smith
* *VP:* Bradley W Batten
IT Man: Mark Olson
VP Opers: Rick Ott
Sales Exec: Timothy Kenna
VP Merchng: Deborah M Rivera

D-U-N-S 61-843-7859 IMP
■ **VF SERVICES LLC**
V F
(*Suby of* VF CORP) ★
105 Corporate Center Blvd, Greensboro, NC 27408-3194
Tel (336) 424-6000 *Founded/Ownrshp* 1990
Sales 190.8MM[E] *EMP* 484
SIC 2211 Apparel & outerwear fabrics, cotton
CEO: Eric C Wiseman
Pr: David Conn
CFO: B J Bean
* *CFO:* William C Hardy
* *CFO:* Robert K Shearer
CFO: D E Templin
* *Treas:* Frank C Pickard III
* *Sr VP:* Steve Rendle
* *VP:* Jon Eric Anthony
* *VP:* Bradley Batten
* *VP:* Scott Baxter
* *VP:* Candace S Cummings
* *VP:* Cindy F Knoebel
* *VP:* Joseph W Plaster
* *VP:* Boyd Rogers
* *VP:* Karl Heinz Salzburger
VP: Carlos G Tejada

D-U-N-S 00-969-4399 IMP
■ **VF SPORTSWEAR INC**
NAUTICA VF
(*Suby of* VF CORP) ★
545 Wshngton Blvd Fl 8, Jersey City, NJ 07310
Tel (212) 541-5757 *Founded/Ownrshp* 1971
Sales 895.7MM[E] *EMP* 3,300
SIC 2329 2384 5136 5137 5611 6794 Men's & boys' sportswear & athletic clothing; Robes & dressing gowns; Bathrobes, men's & women's: made from purchased materials; Men's & boys' sportswear & work clothing; Men's & boys' robes, nightwear & undergarments; Women's & children's lingerie & undergarments; Clothing, sportswear, men's & boys'; Franchises, selling or licensing
Ch Bd: Karen Murray
* *Pr:* Christopher H Heyn
* *Pr:* Paulette McCready
CFO: Robert A Cordro
* *CFO:* Dave Hall
* *Sr VP:* John Varvatos
VP: Mark Dimuro
VP: Larry Ingram
VP: Larry Warehime
Mng Dir: Tord H Von Dy
Mng Dir: Tord Hellbing Von Dyrssen

VFORCE STAFFING SOLUTIONS
See ACCUIRE LLC

D-U-N-S 07-840-8271
VG HOLDINGS LLC
200 Crescent Ct Ste 1600, Dallas, TX 75201-1829
Tel (314) 727-2087 *Founded/Ownrshp* 2010
Sales NA *EMP* 15,726[E]
SIC 3672

D-U-N-S 16-193-0193
VGM GROUP INC
VGM HOMELINK
1111 W San Marnan Dr, Waterloo, IA 50701-8927
Tel (319) 235-7100 *Founded/Ownrshp* 1986
Sales 144.5MM[E] *EMP* 699[E]
SIC 8748 5047 Business consulting; Medical & hospital equipment
Pr: Matt Waller
* *CEO:* Michael Mallaro
* *COO:* Jim Phillips
Bd of Dir: Brad Werkmeister
VP: Tom Barber
VP: Schultz CAM
VP: Clint Geffert
VP: Mike Hess
VP: Roxann Kouns
VP: Merideth McDonald
VP: Cameron Schultz
Board of Directors: John Adams, Larry Anfinson, John Deery Jr, D Jay Ellis, Van Miller, Jim Phillips, James Walsh

VGM HOMELINK
See VGM GROUP INC

D-U-N-S 80-116-4984
■ **VGR HOLDING LLC**
(*Suby of* VECTOR GROUP LTD) ★
4400 S Biscayne Blvd # 10, Miami, FL 33131-2303
Tel (305) 579-8000 *Founded/Ownrshp* 1999
Sales 114.3MM[E] *EMP* 539[E]
SIC 2111 6552 Cigarettes; Subdividers & developers

D-U-N-S 14-773-4172
VHC INC
3090 Holmgren Way, Green Bay, WI 54304-5736
Tel (920) 336-7278 *Founded/Ownrshp* 1985
Sales 241.5MM[E] *EMP* 1,100
SIC 1731 1542 1541 1521 1711 6512 General electrical contractor; Commercial & office building, new construction; Industrial buildings, new construction; New construction, single-family houses; Process piping contractor; Commercial & industrial building operation
Pr: Dave Van Den Heuvel
* *VP:* Jane Piontek

VHDA
See VIRGINIA HOUSING DEVELOPMENT AUTHORITY

D-U-N-S 06-949-0662
■ **VHS ACQUISITION SUBSIDIARY NUMBER 3 INC**
LOUIS A WEISS MEMORIAL HOSPITAL
(*Suby of* VANGUARD HEALTH SYSTEMS INC) ★
4646 N Marine Dr, Chicago, IL 60640-5759
Tel (773) 878-8700 *Founded/Ownrshp* 2001
Sales 112.1MM *EMP* 1,100
SIC 8062 General medical & surgical hospitals
CEO: Jeffrey Steinberg
Ch Bd: Michael Rosenberg
COO: Frank Molinero
Chf Mktg O: Paula Lane
Dir Lab: Ila Desai
Dir Rad: Bill Quinn
Prac Mgr: Kimberly Field
Netwrk Mgr: William V Pelt
Sfty Mgr: John Lenihan
Opers Mgr: Maggie Sidea
Doctor: Danielle Bass

D-U-N-S 07-172-3969
■ **VHS ACQUISITION SUBSIDIARY NUMBER 9 INC**
METROWEST MEDICAL CENTRE
(*Suby of* VANGUARD HEALTH SYSTEMS INC) ★
115 Lincoln St, Framingham, MA 01702-6358
Tel (508) 383-1000 *Founded/Ownrshp* 1893
Sales 199.1MM[E] *EMP* 1,558
SIC 8062 Hospital, professional nursing school with AMA residency
Pr: Barbara Doyle
* *CEO:* Charles N Martin Jr
* *CFO:* Phillip W Roe
* *CFO:* Roger Wiseman
* *Treas:* Tyler Murphy
* *VP:* Kelvin M Ault
* *VP:* Doug Rabe
Dir Risk M: Judith Barrett
Dir Rad: Thomas Cummings
Dir Rad: Mary L Morris
Prgrm Mgr: Dianne Baskind

D-U-N-S 07-637-7316
■ **VHS CHILDRENS HOSPITAL OF MICHIGAN INC**
(*Suby of* DETROIT MEDICAL CENTER) ★
3901 Beaubien St, Detroit, MI 48201-2119
Tel (313) 745-5437 *Founded/Ownrshp* 1985
Sales 127.6MM[E] *EMP* 2,282
SIC 8069 Children's hospital
CEO: Herman B Gray
Chf Path: Wael Sakr
* *COO:* Lynne Thomas Gordon
CFO: Guy Laprad
CFO: Jay B Rising
Ofcr: Dave Coulter
Ofcr: Stephanie Gregory
Ofcr: Matthew Holland
Ofcr: Lynn Kaiafas
Ofcr: Rosanne Poasky
* *VP:* Luanne Thomas Ewald
VP: Rhonda Foster
* *VP:* Chad Grant
* *VP:* Patrick Kelly
Exec: Theresa Brooks
Assoc Dir: George Westerman
Dir Rad: Lisa Landry
Dir Rx: Dennis Gates

D-U-N-S 03-774-8076
■ **VHS DETROIT RECEIVING HOSPITAL INC**
(*Suby of* DETROIT MEDICAL CENTER) ★
4201 Saint Antoine St, Detroit, MI 48201-2153
Tel (313) 745-3000 *Founded/Ownrshp* 1980
Sales 272.1MM *EMP* 1,741
SIC 8093 8069 8062 Specialty outpatient clinics; Specialty hospitals, except psychiatric; General medical & surgical hospitals
Pr: Iris Taylor PHD
* *Sr VP:* Paul Broughton
VP: Ghulam Saydain
VP: Joe Scallan
IT Man: Lee Martin
VP Mktg: Cheryl Bradley
Snr Mgr: Taylor Thurston

D-U-N-S 62-527-6605 EXP
■ VHS HARPER-HUTZEL HOSPITAL INC
HARPER UNIVERSITY HOSPITAL
(*Suby of* DETROIT MEDICAL CENTER) ★
3980 John R St, Detroit, MI 48201-2018
Tel (313) 745-8040 *Founded/Ownrshp* 1863
Sales 249.1MM[E] *EMP* 2,538
SIC 8062 Hospital, medical school affiliated with nursing & residency
Pr: Thomas A Malone
VP: Janet Houghan
Dir Rx: Marianne Lulic
Dir Rx: Angela Milad
Dir Rx: Carrie Molesa
Dir Rx: Sheila Wihelm
Off Mgr: Monique Walker
Sls Mgr: Linda Hightower
Pathlgst: Fulvio Lonardo
Ansthlgy: Kris Ferguson
Ansthlgy: Wisum George

D-U-N-S 17-011-7530
■ VHS HOLDINGS LLC
(*Suby of* VANGUARD HEALTH SYSTEMS INC) ★
20 Burton Hills Blvd, Nashville, TN 37215-6197
Tel (615) 665-6000 *Founded/Ownrshp* 2004
Sales 141.0MM[E] *EMP* 23,000[E]
SIC 8741 Hospital management
CEO: Charles N Martin Jr
CFO: Phil Roe
CFO: Gary Willis
**Ch:* Keith B Pitts

D-U-N-S 12-199-4842
■ VHS HURON VALLEY-SINAI HOSPITAL INC
(*Suby of* DETROIT MEDICAL CENTER) ★
1 William Carls Dr, Commerce Township, MI 48382-2201
Tel (248) 937-3300 *Founded/Ownrshp* 2011
Sales 163.8MM[E] *EMP* 1,000
SIC 8062 General medical & surgical hospitals
Pr: Lynn Torossian
COO: Lynn Terossian
CFO: Mark Rossman
Dir Risk M: Barb Tofil
Dir Rx: Sabrina Pier
Dir Env Sv: Markia Taylor
Chf Nrs Of: Bette Fitz
Dir Sec: Ken Bale
Off Mgr: Denise Hack

D-U-N-S 17-787-0649
■ VHS OF ILLINOIS INC
MACNEAL HOSPITAL
(*Suby of* VANGUARD HEALTH SYSTEMS INC) ★
3249 Oak Park Ave, Berwyn, IL 60402-3429
Tel (708) 783-9100 *Founded/Ownrshp* 1999
Sales 265.5MM[E] *EMP* 2,500
SIC 8062 General medical & surgical hospitals
CEO: Charles Martin Jr
Chf Rad: Mark Arnett
V Ch: John Jordan
CFO: Emmy Cleary
VP: Esther Delvalle
Dir Rx: Mia Kim
Prgrm Mgr: Deborah Palomino
Off Mgr: Donna Bowles
Snr Ntwrk: Mario Opalka
Doctor: Madalina Ionescu
Doctor: Richard Petrak

D-U-N-S 13-125-8691
■ VHS OF MICHIGAN INC
DETROIT MEDICAL CENTER
(*Suby of* VANGUARD HEALTH SYSTEMS INC) ★
3990 John R St, Detroit, MI 48201-2018
Tel (313) 745-1250 *Founded/Ownrshp* 2010
Sales 1.3MMM[E] *EMP* 13,000
SIC 8062 General medical & surgical hospitals
CEO: Joseph Mullany
Chf Rad: Tom Slovis
Pt: Steven D Grant
Pr: Shawn Levitt
**CEO:* Michael Duggan
**COO:* Andrei Soran
**COO:* Mary L Zuckerman
CFO: Nicholas Fitale
**CFO:* Victor Jordan
CFO: Christopher J Palazzoo
**CFO:* Jay B Rising
**Chf Mktg O:* Suzanne R White
Ofcr: Renee Klien
Ofcr: Conrad L Mallett Jr
**Ex VP:* Conrad Mallet
Ex VP: Suzanne White
Comm Dir: Lisa Strange
Dir Rad: Judy Schaefer
Dir Rx: Dennis Gates

D-U-N-S 12-856-2225
■ VHS SAN ANTONIO PARTNERS LLC
(*Suby of* VANGUARD HEALTH SYSTEMS INC) ★
20 Burton Hills Blvd # 1, Nashville, TN 37215-6197
Tel (615) 665-6036 *Founded/Ownrshp* 2003
Sales 996.5MM[E] *EMP* 14,000
SIC 8741 Hospital management
CEO: Charles Martin
VP: John Geer

D-U-N-S 06-984-0288
■ VHS SINAI-GRACE HOSPITAL INC
(*Suby of* DETROIT MEDICAL CENTER) ★
6071 W Outer Dr, Detroit, MI 48235-2624
Tel (313) 966-3300 *Founded/Ownrshp* 1999
Sales 177.3MM[E] *EMP* 2,300[E]
SIC 8062 Hospital, medical school affiliated with nursing & residency
CEO: Paula R Autry
Pr: Reginald J Eadie MD
CFO: Ken Lipan
Treas: Melissa Dunham-Cragg
VP: Esther Bostick
Dir Rx: Nitin Bhatia
Dir Rx: James Miller
Genl Mgr: Danielle Porter
Off Mgr: Ronald Stavale
QA Dir: Allison Martin
VP Opers: Diane Pressley-Capers

D-U-N-S 13-209-6871
VI LLC INTEGRAL PARTNERS
3 San Joaquin Plz Ste 100, Newport Beach, CA 92660-5944
Tel (949) 720-3612 *Founded/Ownrshp* 2003
Sales 100.0MM *EMP* 2
SIC 6552 Subdividers & developers

D-U-N-S 08-728-6402
VI(Z)RT INC
(*Suby of* VIZRT NORWAY HOLDING AS)
352 7th Ave Fl 14, New York, NY 10001-5012
Tel (212) 560-0708 *Founded/Ownrshp* 1995
Sales 135.0MM[E] *EMP* 45
SIC 7819 Video tape or disk reproduction
Pr: Isaac Hersly
**VP:* Ofra Brown
Genl Mgr: Tom Shelburne
Snr Sftwr: Rachel Hecht
IT Man: Sven Jakobsen
IT Man: Gerry Perral
Manager: David Delaplain

D-U-N-S 08-852-0668 IMP/EXP
VI-JON INC
(*Suby of* VJCS HOLDINGS INC) ★
8515 Page Ave, Saint Louis, MO 63114-6014
Tel (314) 427-1000 *Founded/Ownrshp* 2006
Sales 479.3MM[E] *EMP* 1,350[E]
SIC 2869 2844 Alcohols, non-beverage; Toilet preparations
CEO: Jerry Bowe
**Pr:* Kirk Sanders
MIS Mgr: Tim Schrappen

D-U-N-S 07-330-7498
VIA CHRISTI CLINIC PA
WICHITA CLINIC PHARMACY
(*Suby of* VIA CHRISTI HEALTH INC) ★
3311 E Murdock St, Wichita, KS 67208-3054
Tel (316) 689-9111 *Founded/Ownrshp* 2010
Sales 68.0MM[E] *EMP* 1,200
SIC 8011 Clinic, operated by physicians
Pr: Noel Sanchez MD
Bd of Dir: Steven Taylor
**VP:* Mark L Wencel MD
Dir Lab: Linda Burnside
**Prin:* John Shellipio
Ex Dir: Elaine Simon
Surgeon: Jeremy J Stallbaumer
Ansthlgy: Patricia W Powell
Ansthlgy: Beena M Reddy
Doctor: Frank Cordon
Doctor: Richard Desplinter

D-U-N-S 95-999-3650
VIA CHRISTI HEALTH INC
(*Suby of* ASCENSION HEALTH ALLIANCE) ★
2622 W Central Ave # 102, Wichita, KS 67203-4970
Tel (316) 858-4900 *Founded/Ownrshp* 2013
Sales 131.5MM *EMP* 11,970
Accts Deloitte Tax Llp Cincinnati
SIC 8011 8741 Medical centers; Hospital management
CFO: David Hadley
CFO: Maralee Travis
VP: David Gambino
VP: Robert Harvey
CIO: Diana Hilburn
Mtls Mgr: Mary Lewis

D-U-N-S 01-064-7840
VIA CHRISTI HOSPITAL PITTSBURG INC
1 Mt Carmel Way, Pittsburg, KS 66762-7587
Tel (620) 231-6100 *Founded/Ownrshp* 1979
Sales 85.8MM *EMP* 750
Accts Deloitte Tax Llp Cincinnati
SIC 8062 General medical & surgical hospitals
Pr: Jonathan Davis
Pr: Bill Aquino
Ofcr: Randy Cason
Dir Rad: Debra Regehr
Dir Sec: Gary Falcetto
Dir QC: Carrie Amershek
Dir IT: Chad Pease
Ansthlgy: Jesse Niederklein
Nrsg Dir: Julianna Reischick

D-U-N-S 05-801-3617
VIA CHRISTI HOSPITAL PITTSBURG INC
1 Mt Carmel Way, Pittsburg, KS 66762-7587
Tel (620) 232-9926 *Founded/Ownrshp* 2010
Sales 87.0MM *EMP* 99
SIC 8062 General medical & surgical hospitals
Pr: Randall C Fache
CFO: Ann Buess
Sls Mgr: Mistie Short

D-U-N-S 05-657-7646
VIA CHRISTI HOSPITALS WICHITA INC
(*Suby of* VIA CHRISTI HEALTH INC) ★
929 N Saint Francis St, Wichita, KS 67214-3882
Tel (316) 268-5000 *Founded/Ownrshp* 1995
Sales 538.8MM *EMP* 4,100
SIC 8062 General medical & surgical hospitals
CEO: Jeff Korsmo
VP: Ed Hett
**VP:* Mike Wegner

D-U-N-S 04-975-3494
VIA METROPOLITAN TRANSIT
VIA
800 W Myrtle St, San Antonio, TX 78212-4295
Tel (210) 362-2000 *Founded/Ownrshp* 1978
Sales 26.3MM *EMP* 1,685[E]
Accts Padgett Stratemann & Co Llp
SIC 4111 Bus line operations
Pr: Keith Parker
Exec: Joanne Walsh
Dir IT: Travis E Fagg

D-U-N-S 02-113-8679
VIA MOTORS INC
165 Mountain Way Dr, Orem, UT 84058-5119
Tel (801) 764-9111 *Founded/Ownrshp* 2010
Sales 98.3MM[E] *EMP* 110[E]
SIC 5012 Automobiles
CEO: John Weber

Ch Bd: Bob Lutz
Pr: Alan Perriton
CEO: Peter R Guile
COO: David Muir
CFO: Richard Clayton
CFO: Joseph H Damour
CFO: Brent D Jensen
CFO: Wayne Oliver Jr
VP: Thierry Caussat
VP Sls: Mark Burdge
Board of Directors: Michael Allman, Suzanne H Gilbert, Donald L Runkle

D-U-N-S 61-533-5358
▲ VIACOM INC
1515 Broadway, New York, NY 10036-8901
Tel (212) 258-6000 *Founded/Ownrshp* 2005
Sales 13.2MMM *EMP* 9,200[E]
Tkr Sym VIA *Exch* NGS
SIC 4841 7812 Cable & other pay television services; Motion picture & video production
Pr: Bob Bakish
COO: Alex Ferrari
CFO: Wade Davis
Ofcr: Scott Mills
Ex VP: Tina Exarhos
Ex VP: Carl D Folta
Ex VP: Michael D Fricklas
Ex VP: Tom Gorke
Ex VP: Catherine Houser
Ex VP: David Kline
Ex VP: Dede Lea
Ex VP: Richard Lobel
Ex VP: Jeff Lucas
Ex VP: Scott M Mills
Ex VP: Nancy Newman
Ex VP: Casey Patterson
Ex VP: Chris Pergola
Ex VP: Jim Perry
Sr VP: Katherine Gill-Charest
Sr VP: Julia Phelps
Sr VP: Carole Robinson
Board of Directors: Sumner M Redstone, George S Abrams, Frederic V Salerno, Kenneth Lerer, William Schwartz, Thomas May, Nicole Seligman, Blythe J McGarvie, Judith McHale, Ronald Nelson, Deborah Norville, Charles E Phillips Jr, Shari Redstone

VIACOM INTERNATIONAL
See VIACOM SONGS INC

D-U-N-S 94-996-7603
VIACOM NETWORKS
MTV NETWORKS
2600 Colorado Ave, Santa Monica, CA 90404-3519
Tel (310) 453-4826 *Founded/Ownrshp* 2010
Sales 151.8MM[E] *EMP* 5,000
SIC 7822 Motion picture & tape distribution
Pr: Anthony Disanto
Pr: Jeremy Gonzalez
Sr VP: Duncan Macdonald
VP: Alex Angeledes
VP: Stewart Frey
VP: Bill Hutten
VP: Lisa Tyler
Comm Dir: Allison Olins
Dir IT: Elaine Nefsky
Netwrk Eng: Paul Pink
Mktg Mgr: Candace Bell

D-U-N-S 09-296-1317
■ VIACOM SONGS INC
VIACOM INTERNATIONAL
(*Suby of* VIACOM INC) ★
1515 Broadway Lbby, New York, NY 10036-8901
Tel (212) 258-6000 *Founded/Ownrshp* 1995
Sales 20.6MM[E] *EMP* 1,200
SIC 6531 6519 7359 7941 7812 2731 Real estate agents & managers; Real property lessors; Equipment rental & leasing; Sports field or stadium operator, promoting sports events; Television film production; Book publishing
Pr: Timothy Stevenson

D-U-N-S 94-422-5895
▲ VIAD CORP
1850 N Central Ave # 1900, Phoenix, AZ 85004-4527
Tel (602) 207-1000 *Founded/Ownrshp* 1996
Sales 1.0MMM *EMP* 4,285
Tkr Sym VVI *Exch* NYS
SIC 7389 Convention & show services
Pr: Steven W Moster
Ch Bd: Richard H Dozer
CFO: Ellen M Ingersoll
VP: Gerald L Berner
Ex Dir: Terry Curtis
IT Man: Rajasekhar Velpuru
Corp Couns: Robert Peak

D-U-N-S 83-175-7955
■ VIADS MARKETING & EVENTS GROUP
(*Suby of* VIAD CORP) ★
1850 N Central Ave # 101, Phoenix, AZ 85004-4527
Tel (602) 207-4000 *Founded/Ownrshp* 2009
Sales 42.9MM[E] *EMP* 3,054
SIC 8742 7941 Marketing consulting services; Stadium event operator services

VIAERO WIRELESS
See NE COLORADO CELLULAR INC

D-U-N-S 96-461-6473
VIAFIELD
533 Bradford St, Marble Rock, IA 50653-7727
Tel (641) 315-2515 *Founded/Ownrshp* 2010
Sales 109.2MM[E] *EMP* 184[E]
SIC 5153 Grains
Prin: David Quisley
Snr Mgr: Troy Cummins

D-U-N-S 80-566-3932
VIANT HOLDINGS INC
(*Suby of* MULTIPLAN INC) ★
535 E Diehl Rd Ste 100, Naperville, IL 60563-7723
Tel (630) 649-5000 *Founded/Ownrshp* 2010
Sales 61.4MM[E] *EMP* 1,200
SIC 6719 Investment holding companies, except banks
CEO: Daniel J Thomas

**Pr:* Thomas J Bartlett
**CFO:* Steven A Flack

D-U-N-S 07-810-0380 IMP
■ VIASAT COMMUNICATIONS INC
(*Suby of* VIASAT INC) ★
349 Inverness Dr S, Englewood, CO 80112-5882
Tel (720) 493-6000 *Founded/Ownrshp* 1998, 2009
Sales 103.3MM[E] *EMP* 250[E]
SIC 4899 Data communication services
CEO: David J Leonard
**Pr:* Tom Moore
**COO:* Ken Carroll
**CFO:* Mark D Adolph
**Ex VP:* Erwin Hudson
VP: Jim Elliot
Prgrm Mgr: Kim Greenfield
Prgrm Mgr: Steve Lusk
Snr Sftwr: Julie Williams
Snr Ntwrk: James Colton
QA Dir: Rhonda Daugherty

D-U-N-S 17-509-6619 IMP
▲ VIASAT INC
6155 El Camino Real, Carlsbad, CA 92009-1602
Tel (760) 476-2200 *Founded/Ownrshp* 1986
Sales 1.4MMM *EMP* 3,800[E]
Accts Pricewaterhousecoopers Llp S
Tkr Sym VSAT *Exch* NGS
SIC 3663 Space satellite communications equipment; Receiver-transmitter units (transceiver); Mobile communication equipment; Antennas, transmitting & communications
Ch Bd: Mark Dankberg
Pr: Richard Baldridge
CFO: Shawn Duffy
Treas: Larry Bice
Ex VP: Steven Hart
Ex VP: Steven R Hart
Ex VP: Keven Lippert
Ex VP: Mark Miller
Ex VP: Mark J Miller
Sr VP: Melinda Del Toro
Sr VP: Kevin Harkenrider
Sr VP: Kevin J Harkenrider
Sr VP: Ken Peterman
VP: Kristi Jaska
VP: Mike Kulinski
VP: Thad Mazurczyk
VP: Michael Peterson
VP: Bob Rota
VP: Ric Vandermeulen
VP: John Zlogar
Board of Directors: Frank J Biondi Jr, Robert Bowman, Robert Johnson, B Allen Lay, Jeffrey Nash, John Stenbit, Harvey White

D-U-N-S 00-664-4199 IMP
■ VIASYSTEMS GROUP INC
(*Suby of* TTM TECHNOLOGIES INC) ★
101 S Hanley Rd Ste 400, Saint Louis, MO 63105-3406
Tel (314) 727-2087 *Founded/Ownrshp* 1996
Sales 1.0MMM[E] *EMP* 14,854[E]
SIC 3672 3694 Circuit boards, television & radio printed; Engine electrical equipment
Pr: Thomas Edman
**Treas:* Todd Schull
VP: Christopher Isaak
VP: Antonio Sanchez
**VP:* Daniel Weber

D-U-N-S 12-977-4279 IMP
■ VIASYSTEMS INC
(*Suby of* VIASYSTEMS GROUP INC) ★
520 Maryville Centre Dr # 400, Saint Louis, MO 63141-5820
Tel (314) 727-2087 *Founded/Ownrshp* 1998
Sales 945.6MM[E] *EMP* 11,608[E]
SIC 3672 Printed circuit boards
Pr: Thomas T Edman
**Pr:* Timothy L Conlon
Pr: Steven S L Tang
Pr: Dan Weber
**CEO:* David M Sindelar
**CFO:* Gerald G Sax
**Ex VP:* Canice T K Chung
**Sr VP:* Brian W Barber
**Sr VP:* Richard B Kampf
Sr VP: Rhonda Taylor
VP: Kent Balius
VP: Gary Gagstetter
VP: Cris Isaak
VP: Kelly Jordan
VP: Kelly Wetzler
Exec: Mary Latal
Board of Directors: Robert F Cummings Jr, Jack D Furst, Diane H Gulyas, Edward Herring, Richard A McGinn, Philip Raygorodetsky, Christopher J Steffen, Richard W Vieser

D-U-N-S 07-873-0791
■ VIASYSTEMS NORTH AMERICA INC
(*Suby of* VIASYSTEMS INC) ★
1200 Severn Way, Sterling, VA 20166-8904
Tel (703) 450-2600 *Founded/Ownrshp* 2000
Sales 18.6M[E] *EMP* 1,626
SIC 3672 Printed circuit boards
CEO: David M Sindelar

D-U-N-S 02-281-0311 IMP/EXP
▲ VIAVI SOLUTIONS INC
430 N Mccarthy Blvd, Milpitas, CA 95035-5112
Tel (408) 404-3600 *Founded/Ownrshp* 1979
Sales 906.3MM *EMP* 4,900
Tkr Sym VIAV *Exch* NGS
SIC 3674 3826 Semiconductors & related devices; Optical isolators; Analytical instruments; Laser scientific & engineering instruments
Pr: Oleg Khaykin
**Ch Bd:* Richard E Belluzzo
CFO: Amar Maletira
Ex VP: Paul McNab
Sr VP: Dion Joannou
Sr VP: Ralph Rondinone
Sr VP: Luke Scrivanich
VP: Kevin Siebert
Prgrm Mgr: Satya Ravada
Sftwr Eng: Kwang Chong
Snr Mgr: Ramesh Patil

Board of Directors: Keith Barnes, Tor Braham, Timothy Campos, Donald Colvin, Pamela Strayer

D-U-N-S 07-164-4319
VIB CORP
(*Suby of* RABOBANK NEDERLAND) ★
1498 W Main St, El Centro, CA 92243-2819
Tel (760) 352-5000 *Founded/Ownrshp* 2002
Sales NA *EMP* 1,705
SIC 6022 State commercial banks
Pr: Dennis L Kern
**Ex VP:* Bruce Baccus
**Ex VP:* William Henle
**Ex VP:* Martin E Plourd
**Sr VP:* Jack Stewart Grady
VP: Larry Velasquez
Brnch Mgr: Pamela Fletcher
Dir IT: Mike Lindhorst

D-U-N-S 18-724-4558
VIBRA HEALTHCARE LLC
4550 Lena Dr, Mechanicsburg, PA 17055-4922
Tel (717) 591-5700 *Founded/Ownrshp* 2004
Sales 340.9MM^E *EMP* 4,000
SIC 8051 Skilled nursing care facilities
CEO: Brad Hollinger
Pr: Roger Breed
**COO:* Stephen Marcus
**CFO:* Clint Fegan
Ofcr: Jackie Enck
**Sr VP:* Kraig Couture
Sr VP: Lisa Maclean
Sr VP: Diane Pierce
Sr VP: Douglas Yohe
VP: David Barber
VP: Angelique Culver
VP: Ray Lanas
VP: Wayne Mackey
VP: Paul Mattingly
Exec: Mike Soisson

D-U-N-S 96-188-8638 IMP
VIBRACOUSTIC NORTH AMERICA L P
(*Suby of* VIBRACOUSTIC GMBH)
400 Aylworth Ave, South Haven, MI 49090-1707
Tel (269) 637-2116 *Founded/Ownrshp* 2005
Sales 125.3MM^E *EMP* 340
SIC 2821 3714 3053 3061 Plastics materials & resins; Motor vehicle parts & accessories; Gaskets, packing & sealing devices; Mechanical rubber goods
Pr: Mehdi Ilkhani
**Genl Pt:* Robert G Evans
**Genl Pt:* Ronald S Guest
**Genl Pt:* Leesa Smith
**Genl Pt:* Sergus R Thomas

D-U-N-S 08-043-8780
VICE GROUP HOLDING INC
49 S 2nd St, Brooklyn, NY 11249-5119
Tel (718) 599-3101 *Founded/Ownrshp* 2015
Sales 14.1MM^E *EMP* 2,370
SIC 8748 7812 Business consulting; Motion picture & video production
CEO: Shane Smith
Pr: Andrew Creighton
CFO: Sarah Broderick
Co-Pr: James Schwab
Chf Cred: Eddy Moretti

D-U-N-S 14-195-1322 IMP
VICE MEDIA LLC
49 S 2nd St, Brooklyn, NY 11249-5119
Tel (718) 732-8142 *Founded/Ownrshp* 1999
Sales 109.4MM^E *EMP* 753
SIC 7922 Theatrical producers & services
CEO: Shane Smith
Genl Mgr: Robert Stuart
Mktg Mgr: Shawn Phelan

D-U-N-S 62-690-0898
■ VICEROY INC
(*Suby of* GENERAL ELECTRIC CO) ★
3225 Pasadena Blvd, Pasadena, TX 77503-3101
Tel (713) 475-4518 *Founded/Ownrshp* 1990
Sales 228.5MM *EMP* 523
SIC 1629 3443 1796 8742 8748 7363 Power plant construction; Pipe, standpipe & culverts; Power generating equipment installation; Management consulting services; Business consulting; Engineering help service
Pr: Rl Rives
**Treas:* Bruce Bever
**VP:* Mark Buchanan

VICKERS PETROLEUM DIVISION
See TPI PETROLEUM INC

D-U-N-S 96-495-6098
VICKSBURG HEALTHCARE LLC
MERIT HEALTH RIVER REGION
2100 Highway 61 N, Vicksburg, MS 39183-8211
Tel (601) 883-4287 *Founded/Ownrshp* 1998
Sales 143.1MM^E *EMP* 1,515
SIC 8062 General medical & surgical hospitals
CEO: Greg Pearson
COO: Lorie Ramsey
CFO: John Milazzo
Ofcr: Chuck Hobby
Off Mgr: Michelle Lynn
Dir QC: Mary J Karnes
IT Man: Barbara McKay
HC Dir: Sharon Riddle
Board of Directors: Greg Danielson

D-U-N-S 02-165-5182
VICNRG LLC (TX)
930 S Kimball Ave Ste 100, Southlake, TX 76092-9027
Tel (817) 562-4888 *Founded/Ownrshp* 2009
Sales 88.2MM^E *EMP* 35^E
SIC 5172 Diesel fuel
Snr Mgr: Steve Olive

VICOM
See VIRGINIA INTEGRATED COMMUNICATION INC

D-U-N-S 05-063-5986
▲ VICOR CORP
25 Frontage Rd, Andover, MA 01810-5499
Tel (978) 470-2900 *Founded/Ownrshp* 1981
Sales 220.1MM *EMP* 985^E
Accts Kpmg Llp Boston Massachusett
Tkr Sym VICR *Exch* NGS
SIC 3679 3613 Electronic loads & power supplies; Switches, electric power except snap, push button, etc.
Ch Bd: Patrizio Vinciarelli
**CFO:* James A Simms
VP: Richard Begen
VP: Philip Davies
VP: Lynn Gagnon
VP: Robert Gendron
**VP:* H Allen Henderson
VP: David Hertzberg
**VP:* Barry Kelleher
VP: Michael McNamara
VP: Richard J Nagel Jr
VP: Richard Nagel
VP: Stephen Oliver
VP: Douglas W Richardson
VP: Eddie Rubin
Dir Bus: Keith Nardone
Board of Directors: Samuel J Anderson, Jason L Carlson, Liam K Griffin, David T Riddiford, Claudio Tuozzolo

D-U-N-S 00-213-6117 IMP/EXP
VICTAULIC CO (NJ)
VICTAULIC COMPANY OF AMERICA
4901 Kesslersville Rd, Easton, PA 18040-6714
Tel (610) 559-3300 *Founded/Ownrshp* 1925, 1946
Sales 862.4MM^E *EMP* 3,000
SIC 3321 3491 3494 5085 Ductile iron castings; Industrial valves; Couplings, except pressure & soil pipe; Tools
Pr: John Malloy
Bd of Dir: John Grout
**Ex VP:* Clark R Hale
**Ex VP:* Gary M Moore
**VP:* Brian P Bissey
**VP:* Dennis Brown
VP: Richard Bucher
**VP:* Robert Collevechio
**VP:* John R Diamant
**VP:* Robert Freidl
VP: Maria Happel
VP: Tom Neuhaus
**VP:* John E Perry
**VP:* Lawrence W Thau
VP: Grady Wilkerson
Exec: Scott Walp

VICTAULIC COMPANY OF AMERICA
See VICTAULIC CO

D-U-N-S 01-380-6534
VICTOR ELEMENTARY SCHOOL DISTRICT
12219 Second Ave, Victorville, CA 92395-5770
Tel (760) 245-1691 *Founded/Ownrshp* 1896
Sales 140.9MM *EMP* 575
SIC 8211 Public elementary & secondary schools
MIS Dir: Bill Klopping

D-U-N-S 83-123-7545
VICTOR ELEMENTARY SCHOOL DISTRICT FINANCING CORP
15579 Eighth St, Victorville, CA 92395-3360
Tel (760) 245-1691 *Founded/Ownrshp* 2009
Sales 116.1MM *EMP* 5
Accts Nigro & Nigro Pc Murrieta C
SIC 8699 7389 Charitable organization; Financial services
Prin: Jan Gonzalez
Treas: David North
Bd of Dir: Willie Pringle
Admn Mgr: Steve Benedict

D-U-N-S 82-875-3280
VICTOR ENVELOPE CO
301 Arthur Ct, Bensenville, IL 60106-3381
Tel (630) 616-2750 *Founded/Ownrshp* 1972
Sales 192.1MM^E *EMP* 200
SIC 5111 5112 Printing & writing paper; Envelopes
CEO: Ken Seroka
**Pr:* Kent Dahlgren
Pr: Jeff Thies
**VP:* Kent Gundlach
**VP:* David Nickell
IT Man: Derek Barton
Mktg Dir: Arthur Weingartner

D-U-N-S 01-341-2911 IMP/EXP
■ VICTOR EQUIPMENT CO
VICTOR TECHNOLOGIES
(*Suby of* TWECO-ARCAIR) ★
2800 Airport Rd, Denton, TX 76207-2100
Tel (940) 566-2000 *Founded/Ownrshp* 1913, 1969
Sales 318.5MM^E *EMP* 724
SIC 5088 3541 3548 Transportation equipment & supplies; Plasma process metal cutting machines; Welding & cutting apparatus & accessories
Ch Bd: Paul D Melnuck
**Ch Bd:* Paul D Melnuk
**Pr:* Martin Quinn
COO: Matthew Blake
**CFO:* David L Dyckman
**CFO:* Steve Schumm
Treas: Gus Gast
**VP:* Nick Varsam
**VP:* Patricia Williams
Genl Mgr: Sergio Bustos

D-U-N-S 02-874-3375
VICTOR INSTRUMENTS INC
VICTOR MEDICAL CO
50 Bunsen, Irvine, CA 92618-4210
Tel (949) 855-0337 *Founded/Ownrshp* 1966
Sales 107.3MM^E *EMP* 66
SIC 5122 5047 Pharmaceuticals; Instruments, surgical & medical
Pr: Donald V Louchios
**Ch Bd:* Victor Louchios
**Sec:* Frances Louchios

VICTOR J ANDREW HIGH SCHOOL
See CONSOLIDATED HIGH SCHOOL DISTRICT NO 230 NOT FOR PRO

VICTOR MEDICAL CO
See VICTOR INSTRUMENTS INC

VICTOR TECHNOLOGIES
See VICTOR EQUIPMENT CO

D-U-N-S 18-359-0025 IMP
■ VICTOR TECHNOLOGIES GROUP INC
(*Suby of* COLFAX CORP) ★
16253 Swingley Ridge Rd # 200, Chesterfield, MO 63017-1799
Tel (636) 728-3000 *Founded/Ownrshp* 1987
Sales 583.1MM^E *EMP* 1,941
Accts Kpmg Llp St Louis Missouri
SIC 3541 3423 3613 3443 3621 3548 Machine tools, metal cutting type; Machine tool replacement & repair parts, metal cutting types; Plasma process metal cutting machines; Blow torches; Regulators, power; Cylinders, pressure: metal plate; Inverters, rotating: electrical; Welding apparatus
CEO: Martin Quinn
Ch Bd: Michael A McLain
CFO: Jeffrey S Kulka
Chf Mktg O: E Lee Qualls
Ex VP: David L Dyckman
Ex VP: Jeff Ertel
Ex VP: Terry A Moody
Ex VP: Lee Qualls
Sr VP: David Lindstaedt
VP: Ronald Grim
VP: Mark Jolly
VP: Nick H Varsam

D-U-N-S 07-841-3603
■ VICTOR TECHNOLOGIES HOLDINGS INC
(*Suby of* COLFAX CORP) ★
16052 Swingley Ridge Rd # 300, Chesterfield, MO 63017-2079
Tel (636) 728-3000 *Founded/Ownrshp* 2010, 2014
Sales 120.2MM^E *EMP* 2,000
SIC 3541 Machine tools, metal cutting type
CEO: Martin Quinn

D-U-N-S 00-723-2671
■ VICTOR TECHNOLOGIES INTERNATIONAL INC
TWECO-ARCAIR
(*Suby of* VICTOR TECHNOLOGIES GROUP INC) ★
2800 Airport Rd, Denton, TX 76207-2100
Tel (940) 381-1353 *Founded/Ownrshp* 1987
Sales 318.5MM^E *EMP* 724
SIC 3541 3548 Plasma process metal cutting machines; Welding & cutting apparatus & accessories
Ch Bd: Paul D Melnuk
**COO:* Terry Downes
**Ofcr:* Martin Quinn
**Ofcr:* Steven A Schumm
VP: Steven Fray
**VP:* Nick H Varsam
Dist Mgr: Steve Weaver
CIO: Hank Krey

VICTOR VALLEY COLLEGE
See VICTOR VALLEY COMITY COLGE DIST

D-U-N-S 07-358-3577
VICTOR VALLEY COMITY COLGE DIST
VICTOR VALLEY COLLEGE
(*Suby of* CALIFORNIA COMMUNITY COLLEGES SYSTEM) ★
18422 Bear Valley Rd, Victorville, CA 92395-5850
Tel (760) 245-4271 *Founded/Ownrshp* 1961
Sales 121.9MM^E *EMP* 850
SIC 8222 Community college
Pr: Nicholas L Halisky
Mng Pt: Marie Bloomer
**CFO:* Jim Williams PHD
**VP:* Ron Krimper
**VP:* Willard Lewallen
VP: David Zook
Exec: Marena Campos
Exec: Julie Christiansen
Exec: Virginia Moran
IT Man: Cathleen Rude
IT Man: Dave Steinback

VICTORIA CLASSICS
See TEXTILES FROM EUROPE INC

D-U-N-S 06-946-8114
VICTORIA INDEPENDENT SCHOOL DISTRICT
102 Profit Dr, Victoria, TX 77901-7346
Tel (361) 576-3131 *Founded/Ownrshp* 1898
Sales 142.9MM *EMP* 3,200
Accts Bumgardner Morrison & Company
SIC 8211 Public elementary & secondary schools; High school, junior or senior
Prin: Selina Reyna
Pr Dir: Shawna Currie
Schl Brd P: Tami Keeling
Teacher Pr: Greg Bonewald
HC Dir: Murphey Stuart

D-U-N-S 92-748-6373
■ VICTORIA PARTNERS
MONTE CARLO HOTEL AND CASINO
(*Suby of* MGM RESORTS INTERNATIONAL) ★
3770 Las Vegas Blvd S, Las Vegas, NV 89109-4337
Tel (888) 529-4828 *Founded/Ownrshp* 2005
Sales 90.8MM^E *EMP* 3,000
SIC 7011 5812 7299 5813 Casino hotel; Eating places; Wedding chapel, privately operated; Night clubs
Prin: Jim Thomason
Pr: Raimondo Ascer
CFO: Steve Pierce
Exec: Kathryn Cox
Exec: Alexis Juarez
Exec: Elena Levine
Exec: Pegge Stutzman
Sfty Dirs: David Heath
Sfty Mgr: Anthony Maglicco
Natl Sales: Tara Robinson

D-U-N-S 00-938-6025
■ VICTORIAS SECRET DIRECT HOLDING LLC
(*Suby of* LBRANDS) ★
5 Limited Pkwy E, Reynoldsburg, OH 43068-5300
Tel (614) 577-7111 *Founded/Ownrshp* 1995, 2002
Sales 330.9MM^E *EMP* 1,969^E
SIC 5961 Women's apparel, mail order

D-U-N-S 60-236-3707 IMP
■ VICTORIAS SECRET DIRECT LLC
(*Suby of* VICTORIAS SECRET DIRECT HOLDING LLC) ★
5 Limited Pkwy E, Reynoldsburg, OH 43068-5300
Tel (614) 577-7111 *Founded/Ownrshp* 1995
Sales 330.9MM^E *EMP* 3,700
SIC 5961 5632 5621 Women's apparel, mail order; Lingerie & corsets (underwear); Ready-to-wear apparel, women's
Pr: Steve Conkel
Pr: Vimal Kohli
Assoc VP: Andrea Bozeman
Ex VP: Larry Fultz
VP: Dana Beaumont
VP: Patty Beigel
VP: Eryn Grady
VP: Katie Herzog
VP: Mark Koenig
VP: Brad Kramer
VP: Jackie Sheets
VP: Amy Young
VP: Rachel Ziegler

D-U-N-S 08-722-8177 IMP/EXP
■ VICTORIAS SECRET STORES LLC
(*Suby of* LBRANDS) ★
4 Limited Pkwy E, Reynoldsburg, OH 43068-5300
Tel (614) 577-7111 *Founded/Ownrshp* 2002
Sales 1.6MMM^E *EMP* 18,000
SIC 5632 5621 Lingerie (outerwear); Lingerie & corsets (underwear); Women's clothing stores
CEO: Lori Greeley
Pr: Vimal Kohli
Pr: Jim Pozy
**Pr:* Mark Weikel
Chf Mktg O: Ed Razek
Ex VP: Tracy Brand-Liffey
Ex VP: Wright Margaret
Ex VP: Monica Mitro
Ex VP: Ishan Patel
Ex VP: Randy Whitaker
Ex VP: Margaret Wright
VP: Anne Helm
VP: Brad Hollo
VP: Terri Jameson
VP: Hernandez Jerry
VP: Mark Kirchner
VP: Michele Miller
VP: Daniel Sierzputowski
VP: Cindy Slavik
VP: Amy Stevenson
VP: Brian Van Ooyen

D-U-N-S 07-887-5507 IMP/EXP
VICTORINOX SWISS ARMY INC
(*Suby of* VICTORINOX AG)
7 Victoria Dr, Monroe, CT 06468-1664
Tel (203) 929-6391 *Founded/Ownrshp* 2002
Sales 115.0MM^E *EMP* 250
SIC 5023 5099 5094 5072 Kitchen tools & utensils; Sunglasses; Watches & parts; Cutlery
CEO: Carl Elsener
Treas: Marc A Gold
Sr VP: Jim Anderson
Sr VP: Jim Cary
Sr VP: Dennis Piretra
VP: Herbert M Friedman
Genl Mgr: Geri Arison
CTO: Steve Lynch
VP Sls: Patrick Ehren
VP Sls: Rich Rosenfeld
Mktg Mgr: Kellie Guyeski

VICTORVILLE INDUSTRIAL MNRL
See JAMES HARDIE TRANSITION CO INC

D-U-N-S 07-795-9455
VICTORY CAPITAL HOLDINGS INC
667 Madison Ave Fl 10, New York, NY 10065-8029
Tel (212) 906-0746 *Founded/Ownrshp* 2013
Sales 393.5MM^E *EMP* 1,001^E
SIC 6282 6722 Investment advisory service; Management investment, open-end
Ex Dir: Richard Demartini

D-U-N-S 88-468-4721
VICTORY CAPITAL MANAGEMENT INC
(*Suby of* VICTORY CAPITAL HOLDINGS INC) ★
4900 Tiedeman Rd Fl 4, Brooklyn, OH 44144-2338
Tel (216) 898-2400 *Founded/Ownrshp* 2013
Sales 319.5MM^E *EMP* 1,000
SIC 6282 Investment advice
CEO: David Brown
Pr: Kelly Cliff
**Pr:* Christopher Ohmacht
Pr: Neil Pederson
**CFO:* Michael Policarpo
Chf Mktg O: Caroline Churchill
Chf Inves: Arvid Sachdeva
Ofcr: Linda Meints
VP: Roy W Begley
VP: Robert Cramer
Mng Dir: Jason Dahl

D-U-N-S 18-056-9399
VICTORY FOODS LLC
1100 Airport Pkwy, Gainesville, GA 30501-6816
Tel (678) 343-2070 *Founded/Ownrshp* 2004
Sales 130.7MM^E *EMP* 300
SIC 5144 Poultry & poultry products
Sls Mgr: Scott Sprayberry

D-U-N-S 16-140-2482
VICTORY HEALTH SERVICES
1324 N Sheridan Rd, Waukegan, IL 60085-2161
Tel (847) 360-3000 *Founded/Ownrshp* 1882
Sales 27.9MM^E *EMP* 1,088
SIC 8062 General medical & surgical hospitals
Pr: Timothy J Harrington
**VP:* Jim McNichols

VICTORY HEALTHCARE
See VICTORY PARENT CO LLC

D-U-N-S 05-552-7057
VICTORY HOSPITAL PROPERTIES LLC
2201 Timberloch Pl # 200, The Woodlands, TX 77380-1140
Tel (281) 863-2100 Founded/Ownrshp 2011
Sales 122.4MM^E EMP 1,838^E
SIC 8062 General medical & surgical hospitals

D-U-N-S 82-854-9969
VICTORY INTERNATIONAL GROUP LLC
9800 Irvine Center Dr, Irvine, CA 92618-4353
Tel (949) 407-5888 Founded/Ownrshp 2001
Sales 873.5MM EMP 25
SIC 5092 Toys & hobby goods & supplies
Pr: Jiansheng Fan
*VP: Amanda Meng

D-U-N-S 07-433-2800
VICTORY MEMORIAL HOSPITAL
699 92nd St, Brooklyn, NY 11228-3619
Tel (718) 567-1234 Founded/Ownrshp 1904
Sales 87.5M EMP 1,085
Accts Bederson Llp West Orange Nj
SIC 8062 8051 General medical & surgical hospitals; Skilled nursing care facilities
Pr: J Donald Dicunto
Chf Path: Carmacina Yudis
Chf Rad: John Yakoobhain
*CFO: Oliver Steed
Dir IT: Diane Nardi
Doctor: Mark Beskenstein
Doctor: Peggy Nugent
Doctor: Santosh Sureka
Pharmcst: Emilia Terekhina

D-U-N-S 07-064-0032 IMP/EXP
■ **VICTORY PACKAGING LP**
GOLDEN STATE CONTAINER
(Suby of KAPSTONE PAPER AND PACKAGING CORP) ★
3555 Timmons Ln Ste 1440, Houston, TX 77027-6435
Tel (888) 261-1268 Founded/Ownrshp 2015
Sales 808.3MM^E EMP 900
SIC 5113 5199 Containers, paper & disposable plastic; Corrugated & solid fiber boxes; Packaging materials
CEO: Benjamin H Samuels
Pr: Robert Egan
CFO: Leah Borrello
VP: Rick Bruns
VP: Bryan Burnett
VP: Pat Higgins
VP: John Kaiser
VP: Georgina Lavan
VP: Eric Scorzelli
Exec: Holly Flaniken
Dir Risk M: David San Miguel

D-U-N-S 04-223-1421
VICTORY PARENT CO LLC (TX)
VICTORY HEALTHCARE
2201 Timberloch Pl # 200, The Woodlands, TX 77380-1141
Tel (281) 863-2100 Founded/Ownrshp 2011
Sales 156.3MM^E EMP 710^E
SIC 8062 General medical & surgical hospitals
CIO: Yobi Kasper
QC Dir: Loring Branch

VICTORY STUDIO
See WARNER BROS ENTERTAINMENT INC

VICTORY WHOLESALE GROCERS
See BROTHERS TRADING CO INC

D-U-N-S 80-964-8249
VICTREX USA INC
(Suby of VICTREX PLC)
300 Conshohocken State Rd # 120, Conshohocken, PA 19428-3801
Tel (484) 342-6001 Founded/Ownrshp 1993
Sales 203.4MM^E EMP 550
SIC 5084 Plastic products machinery
Ch: Larry Pentz
*Ch: Anita Frew
IT Man: John Blakely
Mfg Mgr: Dave Buck

VICWEST STEEL
See JENISYS ENGINEERED PRODUCTS INC

D-U-N-S 09-031-7561
■ **VIDA TRIPLE-S INC**
GREAT AMERICAN
(Suby of TRIPLE-S MANAGEMENT CORP) ★
1052 Ave Munoz Rivera, San Juan, PR 00927-5014
Tel (800) 980-7651 Founded/Ownrshp 1969
Sales NA EMP 800
Accts Ernst & Young Llp Hato Rey P
SIC 6311 Life insurance carriers
Pr: Arturo Carrion
*Pr: Arturo Carrin Crespo
Ofcr: Dania Ruiz
*VP: Edgardo Diaz
VP: Luis Gomez

D-U-N-S 16-452-9526
VIDACARE INC
248 W 35th St Fl 7, New York, NY 10001-2505
Tel (917) 637-3780 Founded/Ownrshp 2000
Sales NA EMP 25
Accts Rsm Mcgladrey Inc New York
SIC 6321 Accident & health insurance
Ch Bd: Patrick McGovern
*CEO: Doug Wirth
Med Dir: Jerry Ernst

VIDANT HEALTH
See UNIVERSITY HEALTH SYSTEMS OF EASTERN CAROLINA INC

VIDANT MEDICAL CENTER
See PITT COUNTY MEMORIAL HOSPITAL INC

D-U-N-S 06-685-7486
VIDANT MEDICAL GROUP LLC
104 Mark Dr, Edenton, NC 27932-1756
Tel (252) 482-5171 Founded/Ownrshp 2013
Sales 143.0MM EMP 2

Accts Mcgladrey Llp Chicago Il
SIC 8099 Health & allied services

D-U-N-S 83-699-1950
VIDEO GAMING TECHNOLOGIES INC
VGT
(Suby of ARISTOCRAT LEISURE LIMITED)
308 Mallory Station Rd, Franklin, TN 37067-8210
Tel (615) 372-1000 Founded/Ownrshp 2014
Sales 168.2MM^E EMP 650
SIC 3999 7993 Slot machines; Game machines; Gambling machines
CEO: Jayme Sevigny
Mng Dir: Anne Hey
Prgrm Mgr: Jena Lushbough
Prgrm Mgr: Kristy McCaslin
Prgrm Mgr: Greg Schwartz
Snr Sftwr: Joshua Davis
Software D: David Escue
Sftwr Eng: Chris Bluethman
Sftwr Eng: Brad Bolfing
Sftwr Eng: Alan Condevillamar
Sftwr Eng: Jim Corddry

VIDEOJET SYSTEMS
See VIDEOJET TECHNOLOGIES INC

D-U-N-S 14-753-2147 IMP/EXP
■ **VIDEOJET TECHNOLOGIES INC**
VIDEOJET SYSTEMS
(Suby of DANAHER CORP) ★
1500 N Mittel Blvd, Wood Dale, IL 60191-1072
Tel (630) 860-7300 Founded/Ownrshp 2002
Sales 380.0MM EMP 2,600
SIC 3579 Addressing machines, plates & plate embossers
Pr: Christopher Riley
VP: Fred H Hagedorn
VP: Rip Hoffmann
VP: Scott Mastricola
VP: Christopher Neubauer
VP: Craig B Purse
VP: Jerry Robertson
Exec: Ondrej Kruk
Snr Sftwr: John Buras
Dir IT: Craig Purse
Sfty Mgr: Tim Zernzach

VIE DE FRANCE BAKERY-CAFES
See VIE DE FRANCE YAMAZAKI INC

D-U-N-S 62-624-8173 EXP
VIE DE FRANCE YAMAZAKI INC
VIE DE FRANCE BAKERY-CAFES
(Suby of YAMAZAKI BAKING CO., LTD.)
2070 Chain Bridge Rd # 500, Vienna, VA 22182-2588
Tel (703) 442-9205 Founded/Ownrshp 1991
Sales 2.3MMM^E EMP 12,000
SIC 5142 5461 Bakery products, frozen; Bakeries
Ch Bd: Nobuhiro Iijima
*Pr: Sadao Yasumura
*CFO: Thomas J Rowe
Sr VP: Masaki Saito
VP: Sherry Meyers
VP: Anita Robinson
*VP: Frank Schneider
*VP: Yoshinari Uno
Genl Mgr: Jim Lemieux
QA Dir: Elysee Saint-Elie
IT Man: Greg Rodriquez

D-U-N-S 61-723-3333
■ **VIECORE FEDERAL SYSTEMS DIVISION INC**
(Suby of NUANCE COMMUNICATIONS INC) ★
1 Wayside Rd, Burlington, MA 01803-4609
Tel (781) 565-5000 Founded/Ownrshp 2002
Sales 16.0MM EMP 1,100
SIC 7371 Custom computer programming services; Computer software development
CEO: Paul A Ricci
*COO: Jack L Gumbert II
Dir Bus: Paul Manley
Genl Mgr: Steve Vounessea
Board of Directors: Tanya Rubio, Tanya Amador, Rick Souler, Rich Bormann, Tim Chase, Brett Chisholm, Max Cottrell, Max Cottrell, Pat Hodgson, Ellen Lee, Anthony Lorentzen

D-U-N-S 78-439-2578 IMP
VIEGA LLC
100 N Broadway Ave # 600, Wichita, KS 67202-2206
Tel (316) 425-7400 Founded/Ownrshp 1899
Sales 239.8MM^E EMP 450^E
SIC 5074 Plumbing & hydronic heating supplies
CEO: Dan Schmierer
Pr: Robert Gottermeier
CFO: Nathan Spearman
VP: Robert Boots
VP: Christian Geisthoff
VP: Bob Gottermeier
Dir Bus: Joe Pikus
Dist Mgr: Ted Atkinson
Dist Mgr: Dave Cropper
Dist Mgr: Mike Deminck
Dist Mgr: Dale Heath

D-U-N-S 02-862-0193
VIELE & SONS INC
VIELE & SONS INSTNL GROC
1820 E Valencia Dr, Fullerton, CA 92831-4847
Tel (714) 446-1686 Founded/Ownrshp 1975
Sales 123.4MM^E EMP 90
SIC 5141 Groceries, general line
Pr: Anthony J Viele
*Treas: Joseph Viele
*VP: Anthony Viele Jr
*VP: Mike Viele
Mktg Mgr: Deanna Viele
Sales Asso: Jennifer Klemm

VIELE & SONS INSTNL GROC
See VIELE & SONS INC

D-U-N-S 02-551-8887
VIENNA BEEF LTD (IL)
2501 N Damen Ave, Chicago, IL 60647-2101
Tel (773) 278-7800 Founded/Ownrshp 1893
Sales 90.8MM^E EMP 400

SIC 2013 2035 2053 5411 5149 5147 Prepared beef products from purchased beef; Prepared pork products from purchased pork; Sausages & related products, from purchased meat; Cucumbers, pickles & pickle salting; Relishes, fruit & vegetable; Cakes, bakery: frozen; Delicatessens; Groceries & related products; Meats & meat products
Pr: John P Bodman
*Pr: Howard Eirinberg
*CFO: Richard Steele
*Ch: James Bodman
*Sr VP: Jack P Bodman
*Sr VP: Rick Ewert
*Sr VP: Tom McGlade
*Sr VP: Tim Obrien
*Sr VP: Jeff Walser
VP: Jim Dencek
Exec: Eliot Kaufman

D-U-N-S 03-096-7970
VIENNA CONVALESCENT HOSPITAL INC
800 S Ham Ln, Lodi, CA 95242-3543
Tel (209) 368-7141 Founded/Ownrshp 1971
Sales 827.0MM EMP 131
SIC 8059 Convalescent home
Pr: Kenneth Heffel
CFO: Teresa Stocker
Off Mgr: Sharon Linn
Mktg Dir: Jamie Henderson

D-U-N-S 04-039-0700
VIEWPOINT BANK NA
1309 W 15th St Ste 210, Plano, TX 75075-7244
Tel (972) 578-5000 Founded/Ownrshp 2012
Sales NA EMP 427
SIC 6062

D-U-N-S 79-299-9195 IMP/EXP
■ **VIEWPOINT INTERNATIONAL INC**
ORIGINAL ISLAND SPORT
(Suby of OXFORD INDUSTRIES INC) ★
428 Westlake Ave N # 388, Seattle, WA 98109-5237
Tel (206) 622-8688 Founded/Ownrshp 2003
Sales 269.2MM^E EMP 1,400
SIC 5136 5137 Sportswear, men's & boys'; Women's & children's clothing
Pr: S Anthony Margolis
*Ch Bd: Tony C T Yeung
*CFO: Brian Sherman
*Ex VP: Lucio Dalla Gasperina
*VP: Robert Emmfield

D-U-N-S 17-770-7973 IMP
VIEWSONIC CORP
10 Pointe Dr Ste 200, Brea, CA 92821-7620
Tel (909) 444-8888 Founded/Ownrshp 1987
Sales 172.2MM^E EMP 786^E
SIC 3577 Computer peripheral equipment
Ch Bd: James Chu
*Pr: Jeff Volpe
*CFO: Sung Yi
VP: Mike Holstein
*VP: Brian Igoe
VP: Caroline Lin
Mng Dir: Rebecca Tsen
Genl Mgr: Colleen Browne
Genl Mgr: Bonny Cheng
QA Dir: Peter Yang
Dir IT: Antonio Ramos
Board of Directors: Matthew E Massengill, William J Miller, Bruce L Stein, Luc H Vanhal

D-U-N-S 02-277-6496
VIGEN CONSTRUCTION INC
42247 180th St Sw, East Grand Forks, MN 56721-9267
Tel (218) 773-1159 Founded/Ownrshp 1968
Sales 92.6MM EMP 200
Accts Brady Martz & Associates Pc
SIC 1541 Grain elevator construction
Pr: Jeffrey T Vigen
*Sec: Kimberly D Vigen

VIGO COAL COMPANY
See VIGO COAL OPERATING CO INC

D-U-N-S 09-895-8598
VIGO COAL OPERATING CO INC
VIGO COAL COMPANY
250 N Cross Pointe Blvd, Evansville, IN 47715-4073
Tel (812) 759-8446 Founded/Ownrshp 2005
Sales 95.9MM^E EMP 266
SIC 1221 8748 Surface mining, bituminous; Business consulting
Pr: John C Harman
*Sec: Raymond T Purk

D-U-N-S 07-958-0692
VIGO COUNTY SCHOOL CORP
686 Wabash Ave, Terre Haute, IN 47807-3202
Tel (812) 462-4011 Founded/Ownrshp 1961
Sales 82.5MM^E EMP 1,800
SIC 8211 Public elementary & secondary schools
CFO: Donna Wilson
Prin: Jeffrey Blake
Prin: Karen Bundy
Prin: David A Chapman
Prin: James L Freese
Prin: Alice Fuller
Prin: Mary B Harris
Prin: Mark Miller
Prin: Peggy Pfrank
Prin: Patrick Sheehan
Ex Dir: Stacy Mason

D-U-N-S 00-804-6815 IMP
VIGOBYTE TAPE CORP
2498 Roll Dr Ste 916, San Diego, CA 92154-7213
Tel (866) 803-8446 Founded/Ownrshp 1992
Sales 103.2MM^E EMP 700
SIC 3572

D-U-N-S 10-125-1585 IMP
VIGON INTERNATIONAL INC
127 Airport Rd, East Stroudsburg, PA 18301-7702
Tel (570) 476-4172 Founded/Ownrshp 1998
Sales 93.0MM EMP 75

SIC 2869 5149 2077 Flavors or flavoring materials, synthetic; Perfumes, flavorings & food additives; Flavourings & fragrances; Animal & marine fats & oils
Pr: Stephen Somers
*VP: Steve Somers Jr
QA Dir: Felicia Perryman
IT Man: Peter Crimi
Opers Mgr: Jim Ward
Sls&Mrk Ex: Jeff Milton
Sales Asso: Melanie Vegas
Sales Asso: Marietta Zino

D-U-N-S 07-952-2896
■ **VIGOR ACQUISITION CORP**
(Suby of KROGER CO) ★
1014 Vine St, Cincinnati, OH 45202-1141
Tel (513) 762-4000 Founded/Ownrshp 2011
Sales 206.4MM^E EMP 375,000^E
SIC 5411 Supermarkets, chain
CEO: W Rodney McMullen

D-U-N-S 02-316-8856
VIGOR FAB LLC
(Suby of VIGOR INDUSTRIAL LLC) ★
5555 N Channel Ave, Portland, OR 97217-7655
Tel (503) 247-1777 Founded/Ownrshp 2011
Sales 1.2MM^E EMP 1,000
SIC 3731 Barges, building & repairing
Pr: Frank J Foti
*COO: David R Whitcomb
*CFO: Lon V Leneve
VP: Rene Doiron
Snr PM: Shelton Smith

D-U-N-S 15-372-7818 IMP
VIGOR INDUSTRIAL LLC
5555 N Channel Ave # 71, Portland, OR 97217-7672
Tel (503) 247-1777 Founded/Ownrshp 2000
Sales 462.3MM^E EMP 1,450
SIC 3731 3599 6531 Shipbuilding & repairing; Barges, building & repairing; Machine shop, jobbing & repair; Real estate managers
CEO: Frank J Foti
*COO: David Whitcomb
*CFO: Lon V Levene
Ex Dir: Chad Niemeyer
Rgnl Mgr: Adam Beck
Genl Mgr: Bob Kennedy
Snr Ntwrk: Anthony Wilson

D-U-N-S 62-706-5423 IMP
VIGOR MARINE LLC
(Suby of VIGOR INDUSTRIAL LLC) ★
5555 N Channel Ave # 71, Portland, OR 97217-7672
Tel (503) 247-1804 Founded/Ownrshp 2005
Sales 93.1MM^E EMP 300
SIC 3731 Shipbuilding & repairing
Pr: Frank J Foti
*COO: David R Whitcomb
*CFO: Lon V Leneve
CTO: David Deleon

D-U-N-S 08-641-7136 IMP
VIGOR SHIPYARDS INC
(Suby of PUGET SOUND COMMERCE CENTER INC) ★
1801 16th Ave Sw, Seattle, WA 98134-1017
Tel (206) 623-1635 Founded/Ownrshp 1977
Sales 86.8MM^E EMP 553^E
SIC 3731 Shipbuilding & repairing
Pr: Frank J Foti
*COO: David R Whitcomb
*CFO: Lon V Leneve
*Treas: Berger A Dodge

D-U-N-S 00-902-5891 IMP/EXP
VIGOR WORKS LLC
(Suby of VIGOR INDUSTRIAL LLC) ★
9700 Se Lawnfield Rd, Clackamas, OR 97015-7636
Tel (503) 653-6300 Founded/Ownrshp 2014
Sales 163.3MM^E EMP 350
Accts Van Beek & Co Llc Tigard O
SIC 3441 Boat & barge sections, prefabricated metal; Bridge sections, prefabricated highway; Bridge sections, prefabricated railway; Dam gates, metal plate
CEO: Frank J Foti
*COO: Corey Yraguen
*CFO: Lon V Levene
Treas: Paula Paradis
Genl Mgr: Pat Leaard
QA Dir: Mark Feyder
QA Dir: Jason Wimmer
VP Mfg: Scott Heckman
Mfg Mgr: Dan Miller

D-U-N-S 16-706-4810
VIKING ASSET MANAGEMENT LLC
505 Sansome St Ste 1275, San Francisco, CA 94111-3177
Tel (415) 981-5300 Founded/Ownrshp 2007
Sales 55.6MM^E EMP 1,501
SIC 6282 Investment advice
Pt: Peter Bence

D-U-N-S 00-640-7142 IMP/EXP
VIKING CORP (MI)
(Suby of VIKING GROUP, INC.)
210 Industrial Park Dr, Hastings, MI 49058-9631
Tel (269) 945-9501 Founded/Ownrshp 1897, 1898
Sales 158.7MM^E EMP 471^E
SIC 3499 Fire- or burglary-resistive products
Pr: Thomas G Deegan
CFO: Janice Oshinski
VP: Doug Bensinger
*VP: Gary W Buckley
*VP: Delwin G Dornbos
VP: Scott Martorano
Brnch Mgr: Michael Stewart
Genl Mgr: Harvey Hughey
Opers Mgr: Chris Flandermeyer
Plnt Mgr: Les Raymond
Mktg Mgr: Duane Gilbert

VIKING DISTRIBUTING EAST
See VIKING RANGE LLC

D-U-N-S 02-306-1922
VIKING ELECTRIC SUPPLY INC
(*Suby of* SONEPAR USA) ★
451 Industrial Blvd Ne # 2, Minneapolis, MN 55413-8717
Tel (612) 627-1234 *Founded/Ownrshp* 2000
Sales 300.0MM *EMP* 550
SIC 5063 Electrical apparatus & equipment; Wire & cable
Pr: Greg Hames
Recvr: Blayne Ellson
**CFO:* John Leppa
VP: Rich Passmore
Exec: Stacy Stanslaski
Brnch Mgr: Larry Copeland
Brnch Mgr: Mike Stringer
Genl Mgr: Jay Otterson
Telecom Mg: Susette Smith
IT Man: James Hensley
MIS Mgr: Charkie Peterson

D-U-N-S 03-617-7285
VIKING FOREST PRODUCTS LLC
(*Suby of* FOREST CITY TRADING GROUP LLC) ★
7615 Smetana Ln Ste 140, Eden Prairie, MN 55344-4703
Tel (952) 941-6512 *Founded/Ownrshp* 1982
Sales 350.0MM *EMP* 46
SIC 5031 5051 Lumber: rough, dressed & finished; Plywood; Iron & steel (ferrous) products
Pr: Bruce Johnson
Bd of Dir: Jeff Bump
Bd of Dir: Darren Pursley
Chf Mktg O: Jane Cavanaugh
**VP:* Craig Johnston

VIKING FORMED PRODUCTS
See ALL AMERICAN GROUP INC

D-U-N-S 07-615-0929
VIKING INSURANCE CO OF WISCONSIN
(*Suby of* SENTRY INSURANCE A MUTUAL CO) ★
1800 Northpoint Dr, Stevens Point, WI 54481-1253
Tel (715) 346-6000 *Founded/Ownrshp* 1971
Sales NA *EMP* 404
SIC 6331 Automobile insurance
Pr: Peter G Anhalt
CFO: Mark Hammond

D-U-N-S 00-959-5752 IMP
■ **VIKING OFFICE PRODUCTS INC**
(*Suby of* OFFICE DEPOT INC) ★
3366 E Willow St, Signal Hill, CA 90755-2311
Tel (562) 490-1000 *Founded/Ownrshp* 1998
Sales 1.3MMM^E^ *EMP* 3,226
SIC 5112 5021 5045 5087 5043 5961 Stationery & office supplies; Business forms; Stationery; Office furniture; Computers, peripherals & software; Janitors' supplies; Photographic equipment & supplies; Catalog & mail-order houses
Pr: M Bruce Nelson
**Sr VP:* Ronald W Weissman
**VP:* Mark R Brown
IT Man: James Mandelbaum

D-U-N-S 13-061-5453 IMP/EXP
■ **VIKING PUMP INC**
(*Suby of* IDEX CORP) ★
406 State St, Cedar Falls, IA 50613-3343
Tel (319) 266-1741 *Founded/Ownrshp* 1988
Sales 124.7MM^E^ *EMP* 525
SIC 3561 Industrial pumps & parts
Genl Mgr: Fenton Challgren
CFO: Jeff Ernhardt
Genl Mgr: Bill Canady
Trfc Mgr: Dave Hunt
VP Sls: Kerry Baskins
Sls Dir: India Nair
Board of Directors: John McMurray

D-U-N-S 12-160-9036 IMP/EXP
■ **VIKING RANGE LLC**
VIKING DISTRIBUTING EAST
(*Suby of* MIDDLEBY CORP) ★
111 W Front St, Greenwood, MS 38930-4442
Tel (662) 455-1200 *Founded/Ownrshp* 2012
Sales 259.5MM^E^ *EMP* 575
SIC 3631 5064 Household cooking equipment; Dishwashers; Garbage disposals; Microwave ovens, non-commercial; Refrigerators & freezers
Pr: Selim A Bassoul
Pr: Art Valentine
COO: Steve Ingham
COO: Clint Taylor
**Treas:* Jane Moss
Sr VP: Ron Ussery

VIKING SUPPLY NET
See SUPPLY NETWORK INC

D-U-N-S 00-248-2545 IMP
VIKING YACHT CO
On The Bass Riv Rr 9, New Gretna, NJ 08224
Tel (609) 296-6000 *Founded/Ownrshp* 1986
Sales 245.0MM *EMP* 775^E^
Accts Ernst & Young Llp Philadelphi
SIC 3732 Yachts, building & repairing
CEO: Robert T Healey
Pr: William J Healey
CFO: Gerard D Straub Sr
Ex VP: Patrick Healey
VP: John Kasinski
Exec: Bill Healey
MIS Dir: James Labor
Prd Mgr: Ray Glebock
VP Sls: Joseph Schwab
Sls Mgr: Steve Boerema

D-U-N-S 07-972-2541
VILLA FINANCIAL SERVICES LLC
3755 Chase Ave, Skokie, IL 60076-4008
Tel (847) 440-2660 *Founded/Ownrshp* 2013
Sales 250.0MM *EMP* 100
SIC 8721 Payroll accounting service
CFO: Steve Nagel

D-U-N-S 05-774-7206 EXP
VILLA LIGHTING SUPPLY INC
2929 Chouteau Ave, Saint Louis, MO 63103-2903
Tel (314) 531-2600 *Founded/Ownrshp* 1972
Sales 110.0MM *EMP* 82
SIC 5063 Light bulbs & related supplies; Lighting fixtures
Pr: John Villa
**CFO:* Rick Moore
**Sr VP:* John M Villa
**VP:* Steve Barker
VP: David Foss
**Exec:* Matt Villa
Dir IT: Charles Freukes
Natl Sales: Melissa Cantin
Natl Sales: Dave Christanell
Natl Sales: Kevin Dossett
Natl Sales: Dan Zipf

D-U-N-S 10-133-1676
VILLA PIZZA INC
3 South St, Morristown, NJ 07960-4135
Tel (973) 285-4800 *Founded/Ownrshp* 1982
Sales 49.5MM^E^ *EMP* 1,405
SIC 5812 Pizzeria, chain
CEO: Anthony Scotto
**Pr:* Biagio Scotto
**CFO:* William Niegsch
**Sr VP:* Andrew Steinberg
**Sr VP:* Adam Torine
**VP:* Peter Jurta

D-U-N-S 01-102-0992
VILLAGE CARE OF NEW YORK INC
VCNY
120 Broadway Ste 2840, New York, NY 10271-0009
Tel (212) 337-5816 *Founded/Ownrshp* 1995
Sales 64.9MM^E^ *EMP* 1,193
Accts Loeb & Troper Llp New York N
SIC 8741 8322 Management services; Senior citizens' center or association
Pr: Emma Devito
Pr: Louis Ganim
**COO:* Antoinette Cassetta
**COO:* Lisa Garay
**CFO:* Rachel Amalfitano
**CFO:* Sanjay Dutt
Ofcr: Suzanne Haber
VP: Karl Dehm
VP: Ingrid Jimenez
Dir Bus: Shaun Ruskin
Nurse Mgr: Beverly Greene

D-U-N-S 07-888-5886
VILLAGE CENTER FOR CARE
VCNY
(*Suby of* VCNY) ★
120 Broadway Ste 2840, New York, NY 10271-0009
Tel (212) 367-3748 *Founded/Ownrshp* 1977
Sales 51.6MM *EMP* 1,050
SIC 8051 8082 8322 Skilled nursing care facilities; Home health care services; Adult day care center
Pr: Emma Devito
**CEO:* Arthur A Webb
**CFO:* Rachel Amalfitano
CFO: Sanjay Dutt
**VP:* Lucia Cameron
Dir Sec: Derick Dugan
CIO: David Finkelstein
Dir IT: Michael Gravatt
Netwrk Mgr: Steve Kadish
**Pgrm Dir:* Jessamine Buck

D-U-N-S 93-069-1592 IMP
VILLAGE FARMS LP
195 International Pkwy # 100, Heathrow, FL 32746-5074
Tel (407) 936-1190 *Founded/Ownrshp* 1999
Sales 205.9MM^E^ *EMP* 800
SIC 0161 Cucumber farm; Tomato farm; Pepper farm, sweet & hot (vegetables)
CEO: Michael A Degiglio
**CFO:* Stephen C Ruffini
**Ch:* John R McLernon
**Sr VP:* Douglas Kling
**Sr VP:* Michael Minerva
IT Man: Bill Love

D-U-N-S 07-884-9436
VILLAGE GREEN HOLDING LLC
30833 Northwestern Hwy # 300, Farmington Hills, MI 48334-2583
Tel (248) 851-9600 *Founded/Ownrshp* 2011
Sales 52.0MM *EMP* 1,200
SIC 6719 Investment holding companies, except banks
CEO: Jonathan Holtzman
**COO:* Diane Batayeh
**CFO:* John Woods

D-U-N-S 05-467-2589
VILLAGE GREEN MANAGEMENT CLEARING CO
30833 Northwestern Hwy, Farmington Hills, MI 48334-2551
Tel (248) 851-9600 *Founded/Ownrshp* 1968
Sales 36.1MM^E^ *EMP* 1,100
SIC 6531 Real estate managers
Ch Bd: Jonathan Holtzman
**Pr:* George Quay
**Ex VP:* Steve Bixler

D-U-N-S 00-463-7893 IMP
VILLAGE HOMES OF COLORADO INC (CO)
8480 E Orchard Rd # 1000, Greenwood Village, CO 80111-5015
Tel (303) 795-1976 *Founded/Ownrshp* 1990
Sales 185.0MM *EMP* 230
SIC 1521 New construction, single-family houses
Pr: Cheryl Schuette
**CEO:* John Osborn
**CFO:* Terry Kyger
CFO: Michael Rabon
Sr VP: Matt Osborn
VP: Peter Berson
VP: Ron Hettinger
VP Sls: Rudy Hansch
Mktg Dir: Janet Mitchell

VILLAGE INN RESTAURANT
See CONCORD HOSPITALITY INC

VILLAGE INN RESTAURANT
See AMERICAN BLUE RIBBON HOLDINGS LLC

D-U-N-S 03-899-2637
VILLAGE NURSERIES WHOLESALE LLC
1589 N Main St, Orange, CA 92867-3439
Tel (714) 279-3100 *Founded/Ownrshp* 2001
Sales 171.1MM^E^ *EMP* 600
SIC 5193 Nursery stock
Exec: Terri Cooke
Brnch Mgr: Joseph Jensen
Opers Mgr: Mark Marriott

D-U-N-S 84-761-8410
VILLAGE OF KAUFMAN
421 E 7th St, Kaufman, TX 75142-2938
Tel (972) 962-7328 *Founded/Ownrshp* 1982
Sales 950.0M *EMP* 3,900
SIC 6513 Apartment building operators
Sr VP: Leeann Morein
**Pt:* Matt Caly

D-U-N-S 60-675-9561
VILLAGE OFFICE SUPPLY INC
600 Apgar Dr, Somerset, NJ 08873-1180
Tel (908) 526-0600 *Founded/Ownrshp* 1989
Sales 85.8MM^E^ *EMP* 300
SIC 5112 Computer paper; Data processing supplies
Pr: Rob Mallin

VILLAGE SQUARE
See OAK CREST VILLAGE INC

D-U-N-S 05-351-9450
▲ **VILLAGE SUPER MARKET INC**
733 Mountain Ave, Springfield, NJ 07081-3223
Tel (973) 467-2200 *Founded/Ownrshp* 1937
Sales 1.6MMM *EMP* 6,750^E^
Tkr Sym VLGEA *Exch* NGS
SIC 5411 Supermarkets, chain
Ch Bd: James Sumas
**Pr:* Robert Sumas
**COO:* John J Sumas
CFO: John L Van Orden
**V Ch Bd:* William Sumas
**Chf Mktg O:* Nicholas Sumas
**Ex VP:* John P Sumas
Mktg Mgr: Caitlin Broscius
Board of Directors: Kevin Begley, Steven Crystal, David C Judge, Peter R Lavoy, Stephen F Rooney

D-U-N-S 02-011-9004
VILLAGE VOICE MEDIA HOLDINGS LLC
NEW TIMES WEEKLY
1201 E Jefferson St, Phoenix, AZ 85034-2300
Tel (602) 271-0040 *Founded/Ownrshp* 1991
Sales NA *EMP* 1,400
SIC 2711

VILLAGES, THE
See HOLDING CO OF VILLAGES INC

D-U-N-S 07-726-6245 IMP/EXP
VILLAGES OF LAKE-SUMTER INC
ORANGE BLOSSOM HILLS G&C CLUB
1000 Lake Sumter Lndg, Lady Lake, FL 32162-1695
Tel (352) 753-2270 *Founded/Ownrshp* 1994
Sales 365.8MM^E^ *EMP* 2,500
SIC 6552 1521 7997 5812 7389 Subdividers & developers; New construction, single-family houses; Country club, membership; Eating places; Interior decorating
Pr: H Gary Morse
**Pr:* Martin L Dzuro
**Treas:* W Thomas Brooks
**VP:* Gary L Moyer
**VP:* Jennifer L Parr
IT Man: Dale Borrowman

D-U-N-S 07-925-0665
VILLAGES OPERATING CO (FL)
(*Suby of* VILLAGES) ★
1020 Lake Sumter Lndg, Lady Lake, FL 32162-2699
Tel (352) 753-2270 *Founded/Ownrshp* 2006
Sales 143.3MM *EMP* 100
SIC 6531 Real estate agent, commercial

VILLAGES REGIONAL HOSPITAL
See VILLAGES TRI-COUNTY MEDICAL CENTER INC

D-U-N-S 10-339-4024
VILLAGES TRI-COUNTY MEDICAL CENTER INC
VILLAGES REGIONAL HOSPITAL
1451 El Camino Real, The Villages, FL 32159-0041
Tel (352) 751-8000 *Founded/Ownrshp* 1998
Sales 156.1MM *EMP* 200
SIC 8062 General medical & surgical hospitals
CEO: Donald G Henderson
**Pr:* Terry Upton
**CEO:* Lee Huntley
COO: Saad Ehtisham
**Treas:* Gregory R Lewis
Dir Lab: Diane Treadway
CIO: Dave Steele
Doctor: David Lew

D-U-N-S 07-161-8789
VILLANOVA UNIVERSITY IN STATE OF PENNSYLVANIA
800 E Lancaster Ave, Villanova, PA 19085-1603
Tel (610) 519-4500 *Founded/Ownrshp* 1842
Sales 424.6MM *EMP* 2,022
Accts Pricewaterhousecoopers Llp Ph
SIC 8221 University
Pr: Rev Peter M Donohue
Pr: Heather P Brown
Pr: George Kolb
Ex VP: Daniel McGee
VP: Alexandra Bigelow
VP: Elizabeth Blunt
VP: Kathleen Byrnes
VP: Michael Carlone
VP: Pavankumarrao Cheeti
VP: Robert Devos
VP: Ann E Diebold
VP: Phaneendra Divakaruni
VP: Emily Empel
VP: Steven Fugale
VP: Michael Greco
**VP:* Dorothy Malloy
VP: Bob Morro
VP: Michael J O'Neill
VP: Seri Park
VP: Cathleen Parsons-Nikolic
VP: Jennifer Pohlhaus

D-U-N-S 02-799-0423 IMP
VILLARA CORP
WALK THROUGH VIDEO
4700 Lang Ave, McClellan, CA 95652-2023
Tel (916) 646-2700 *Founded/Ownrshp* 1947
Sales 183.8MM^E^ *EMP* 700
SIC 1711 Heating & air conditioning contractors
**CEO:* Gary Beutler
**VP:* Tom Beutler
VP: John Chanda
VP: Rob Penrod
VP: Scott Sahota
Div Mgr: Ron Lewis
Dir IT: Alex Long
IT Man: Andre Coetser
Sls Mgr: David Ostrander
Sls Mgr: John Petty

D-U-N-S 01-406-0013 IMP
VILLITA AVOCADOS INC
9800 Keystone, Pharr, TX 78577-2722
Tel (956) 843-1118 *Founded/Ownrshp* 2005
Sales 139.0MM *EMP* 14
SIC 5148 Fruits, fresh
Pr: Jose Alfredo Rodriguez
VP: Laura Lemus Murillo

D-U-N-S 10-708-0780 IMP
VILORE FOODS CO INC
3838 Medical Dr Ste 207, San Antonio, TX 78229-2146
Tel (210) 509-9496 *Founded/Ownrshp* 1982
Sales 101.1MM^E^ *EMP* 103
SIC 5149 5169 Groceries & related products; Milk, canned or dried; Juices; Baking supplies; Chemicals & allied products
Pr: Marco A Mena
Div Mgr: William Sneen
IT Man: Matthew Willis
Sls Dir: Andrew Boyer
Sls Dir: Glen Leonard

D-U-N-S 00-609-7430 IMP/EXP
■ **VILTER MANUFACTURING LLC** (WI)
(*Suby of* EMERSUB 14 LLC) ★
5555 S Packard Ave, Cudahy, WI 53110-2623
Tel (414) 744-0111 *Founded/Ownrshp* 2004, 2009
Sales 164.2MM^E^ *EMP* 240
SIC 5078 Refrigeration equipment & supplies
CEO: David N Farr
**CFO:* Richard Cundy
**VP:* Mark Stencel
VP Bus Dev: Wayne Wehber
VP Opers: John Barry

D-U-N-S 07-922-0089 IMP
▲ **VINCE HOLDING CORP**
500 5th Ave Ste 20, New York, NY 10110-2099
Tel (212) 515-2600 *Founded/Ownrshp* 2008
Sales 302.4MM *EMP* 565^E^
Tkr Sym VNCE *Exch* NYS
SIC 5632 5611 5621 Women's accessory & specialty stores; Apparel accessories; Men's & boys' clothing stores; Clothing accessories: men's & boys'; Clothing, sportswear, men's & boys'; Women's clothing stores; Women's sportswear
CEO: Brendan Hoffman
**Ch Bd:* Marc J Leder
CFO: David Stefko
Sr VP: Melissa Wallace
VP: Jill Norton

D-U-N-S 96-890-0485
■ **VINCE LLC**
(*Suby of* VINCE HOLDING CORP) ★
500 5th Ave Ste 20, New York, NY 10110-2099
Tel (212) 515-2600 *Founded/Ownrshp* 2012
Sales 103.8MM^E^ *EMP* 54^E^
SIC 5137 5136 Women's & children's clothing; Men's & boys' clothing
Pr: Karin Gregersen
CFO: Lisa Klinger
CFO: David Stefko
Sr VP: Beth Cohn
Sr VP: Jay Dubiner

VINCENNES DIVISION
See SCHOTT GEMTRON CORP

D-U-N-S 05-759-1448
VINCENNES UNIVERSITY
1002 N 1st St, Vincennes, IN 47591-1500
Tel (812) 888-8888 *Founded/Ownrshp* 1801
Sales 65.0MM *EMP* 1,000
Accts Paul D Joyce Cpa Indianapol
SIC 8221 5942 University; Book stores
Pr: Dick Helton
**Ch:* John R Gaylor
Assoc Dir: Roy Inglis
Genl Mgr: Phil Smith
CIO: Carmen Schnarr
Web Dev: Justin Stanczak
Mktg Dir: Krystal Spencer
HC Dir: Christian Blome

D-U-N-S 04-181-7248
VINELAND BOARD OF EDUCATION
625 E Plum St, Vineland, NJ 08360-3796
Tel (856) 207-6229 *Founded/Ownrshp* 1865
Sales 188.7MM^E^ *EMP* 3,212
SIC 8211 School board
Pr: Scott English
Bd of Dir: Christine Scull
Prin: Joseph Camardo
Prin: Donna Meyers

D-U-N-S 07-989-3859
VINELAND PUBLIC SCHOOLS
625 E Plum St, Vineland, NJ 08360-3708
Tel (856) 794-6700 *Founded/Ownrshp* 2015
Sales 32.4MM^E *EMP* 4,866^E
SIC 8211 Elementary & secondary schools
Bd of Dir: Scott English
Exec: Sylvia Morano
Ex Dir: Kim Friddell
Teacher Pr: Joseph Rossi

D-U-N-S 02-057-1712 IMP
VINEYARD VINES LLC (CT)
181 Harbor Dr Fl 1, Stamford, CT 06902-7498
Tel (203) 661-1803 *Founded/Ownrshp* 1998
Sales 999.7MM^E *EMP* 2,000^E
SIC 5136 5137 5699 5611 5621 Men's & boys' clothing; Women's & children's clothing; Designers, apparel; Men's & boys' clothing stores; Women's clothing stores
VP: Bob Dirr
VP: Renee Heim
VP: Joanne Marciano
VP: Kirsten Oswald
VP: Joann Slattery
Exec: Jeremy Buccolo
Creative D: Brian Devito
Store Mgr: Maribel Keller
CIO: Sunil Verma
CTO: Stephanie Lynn
IT Man: Brian Fogarty

VINEYARDS OF MONTEREY
See JACKSON FAMILY WINES INC

D-U-N-S 00-617-5723
VINFEN CORP
950 Cambridge St, Cambridge, MA 02141-1001
Tel (617) 441-1800 *Founded/Ownrshp* 1977
Sales 125.0MM *EMP* 2,000
Accts Mcgladrey Llp Charlestown Ma
SIC 8361 8331 Self-help group home; Halfway home for delinquents & offenders; Home for the mentally handicapped; Job training services; Vocational training agency
Pr: Bruce L Bird
**Ch Bd:* Philip A Mason
**COO:* Elizabeth K Glaser
**CFO:* Glen A Macitera
**Sr VP:* Susan C Abbott
Sr VP: Joseph Gomes
VP: Liz Cargill
VP: Elizabeth Gluck
VP: John Lind
Comm Dir: Erin Tighe
Dir Bus: Sophie Jones

VINING SPARKS
See VINING-SPARKS IBG LIMITED PARTNERSHIP

D-U-N-S 62-696-6857
VINING-SPARKS IBG LIMITED PARTNERSHIP
VINING SPARKS
775 Ridge Lake Blvd # 200, Memphis, TN 38120-9459
Tel (901) 766-3000 *Founded/Ownrshp* 2009
Sales 133.2MM^E *EMP* 302
SIC 6211 Brokers, security; Dealers, security
Pt: Mark A Medford
Pt: Mark Atwill
Pt: Pete Colin
Pt: John Crawford
Pt: Sherrie Hewlett
Pt: Robert Hiett
Pt: Tim May
Pt: Francis Scott
Pt: Martin Shea Jr
Pt: Randall E Wade
CFO: Allen Riggs
Ofcr: Donna Lillard
Ofcr: Larry May
Ex VP: Kyle Broussard
Ex VP: Craig Dismuke
Ex VP: Randy May
Sr VP: Bill Daniels
Sr VP: Doug McKnight
Sr VP: Brandon Wann
VP: Oscar Adams
VP: Daniel Adler

D-U-N-S 87-907-1058 EXP
VINMAR INTERNATIONAL HOLDINGS LTD
KUVERA INTERNATIONAL
16800 Imperial Valley Dr, Houston, TX 77060-3159
Tel (281) 618-1300 *Founded/Ownrshp* 1994
Sales 407.9MM^E *EMP* 92^E
SIC 5169 Chemicals & allied products
Pr: Hemant Goradia
**CFO:* Anthony Askalany
CFO: Anil Goel
VP: Jim Loughead
VP: Bhuwan Sinha
**Exec:* Resesh Dalal
**Prin:* Vijay Goradia
Genl Mgr: Raul Diaz
CIO: Terry Fields
Manager: Akshat Mehta
Snr Mgr: Kashmira Sutaria

D-U-N-S 82-965-2853 EXP
VINMAR INTERNATIONAL LTD
(*Suby of* KUVERA INTERNATIONAL) ★
16800 Imperial Valley Dr, Houston, TX 77060-3159
Tel (281) 618-1300 *Founded/Ownrshp* 1978
Sales 407.7MM^E *EMP* 92^E
SIC 5169 Chemicals & allied products
CEO: Hemant P Goradia
Pr: Vijay P Goradia
CFO: Anthony Ascalany
Sec: Swatantra V Jain
Exec: Rasesh Dalal
Exec: Jaisimha Sadhanala
Admn Mgr: Kavita Duvvuru
Genl Mgr: Serge Verma
Dir IT: Rakesh Parikh
Sls&Mrk Ex: Everardo Garcia
Sls Dir: Noushin Zarkesh

D-U-N-S 83-255-8519
VINO FARMS LLC
1377 E Lodi Ave, Lodi, CA 95240-0840
Tel (209) 334-6975 *Founded/Ownrshp* 2008
Sales 123.0MM^E *EMP* 700
SIC 5182 Wine

D-U-N-S 07-418-1975
VINSON & ELKINS LLP
1001 Fannin St Ste 2500, Houston, TX 77002-6760
Tel (713) 758-2222 *Founded/Ownrshp* 1917
Sales 347.7MM^E *EMP* 3,200
SIC 8111

D-U-N-S 05-378-0268
VINSON GUARD SERVICE INC
955 Howard Ave, New Orleans, LA 70113-1179
Tel (504) 525-0591 *Founded/Ownrshp* 1963
Sales 52.6MM^E *EMP* 1,400
SIC 7381 Protective services, guard; Security guard service
Pr: Joseph D Vinson Jr
**Treas:* Gail Probst
**VP:* Greg Carter
**VP:* Paul S Wright
IT Man: Todd Tranchina
Opers Mgr: George Jackson

D-U-N-S 01-817-3414 IMP
VINSON PROCESS CONTROLS CO LP
2747 Highpoint Oaks Dr, Lewisville, TX 75067-8190
Tel (972) 459-8200 *Founded/Ownrshp* 1968
Sales 178.5MM^E *EMP* 115
SIC 5084 3533 3498 Instruments & control equipment; Oil well machinery, equipment & supplies; Oil & gas field machinery; Fabricated pipe & fittings; Tube fabricating (contract bending & shaping)
Pr: John C Huskinson
CTO: George Block
MIS Dir: Bob Stevens
IT Man: Stan Parnell
Sls Mgr: Robert Lange
Sales Asso: John Bright
Sales Asso: Reggie Greene

VINTAGE PRODUCTION CALIFORNIA
See CALIFORNIA RESOURCES PRODUCTION CORP

VINTAGE RESERVE METRO DST
See COUNTY OF JEFFERSON

VINTAGE SENIOR LIVING
See SENIOR VINTAGE MANAGEMENT INC

D-U-N-S 16-147-3392
VINTNERS DISTRIBUTORS INC
A R C O
41805 Albrae St, Fremont, CA 94538-3144
Tel (510) 657-9150 *Founded/Ownrshp* 1978
Sales 114.5MM^E *EMP* 280
SIC 5541 Filling stations, gasoline
CEO: Naresh K Goyal
**Pr:* Rajinder K Goyal

VIOGNIER
See DRAEGERS SUPER MARKETS

D-U-N-S 09-869-5323
VION CORP
196 Van Buren St Ste 300, Herndon, VA 20170-5337
Tel (571) 353-6000 *Founded/Ownrshp* 1980
Sales 221.0MM^E *EMP* 220
SIC 5045 Computers, peripherals & software
CEO: Tom Frana
**CFO:* John Lubratich
CFO: Philip J Rouse II
**Ex VP:* Jim Davidson
**Ex VP:* Rob Davies
Sr VP: Jeff Henry
VP: Dan Diltz
VP: Tony Encinias
VP: Carl Fulp
VP: Mike Heath
**VP:* Michael R Jones
**VP:* Michael Jones
VP: Lee Shabe
Dir Bus: Scott Briggs

VIOX SERVICES
See EMCOR FACILITIES SERVICES INC

D-U-N-S 03-865-1832
VIP HEALTH CARE SERVICES INC
V I P
11612 Myrtle Ave, Richmond Hill, NY 11418-1748
Tel (718) 849-2300 *Founded/Ownrshp* 1977
Sales 48.8MM^E *EMP* 2,000
SIC 8082 Home health care services
Pr: Shlomo Appel

VIP PARTS, TIRES & SERVICE
See V I P INC

D-U-N-S 96-872-4117
VIPER HOLDINGS CORP
200 Clarendon St Fl 54, Boston, MA 02116-5021
Tel (617) 619-5400 *Founded/Ownrshp* 1998
Sales 172.4MM^E *EMP* 581^E
SIC 3669 3651 Burglar alarm apparatus, electric; Amplifiers: radio, public address or musical instrument
CEO: Michael Eisenson

D-U-N-S 94-680-6684 IMP/EXP
■ **VIRACON INC**
(*Suby of* APOGEE ENTERPRISES INC) ★
800 Park Dr, Owatonna, MN 55060-4935
Tel (507) 451-9555 *Founded/Ownrshp* 1970
Sales 408.7MM^E *EMP* 1,922
SIC 3211 Laminated glass; Tempered glass; Insulating glass, sealed units
Pr: Kelly Schuller
**Sr VP:* Monte Mitchell
**VP:* Bill Wright
Exec: Jeff Sweet
QA Dir: Brenda Amundsen
IT Man: Al Kolander
IT Man: Terry Larson
Sfty Mgr: Jason Kleeberger
Sfty Mgr: Tom Staska
Opers Mgr: Doug Hunt
Plnt Mgr: Brian Zak

VIRBAC ANIMAL HEALTH
See VIRBAC CORP

D-U-N-S 13-156-8396 IMP/EXP
VIRBAC CORP
VIRBAC ANIMAL HEALTH
(*Suby of* VIRBAC)
3200 Meacham Blvd, Fort Worth, TX 76137-4611
Tel (800) 338-3659 *Founded/Ownrshp* 1984
Sales 95.2MM^E *EMP* 269
SIC 2834 5122 Veterinary pharmaceutical preparations; Animal medicines
Ex VP: Mike O'Bryan
CFO: Jean Nelson
CFO: Joe Rougraff
**Ex VP:* Laurent Cesar
Ex VP: Michael O'Bryan
Ex VP: Mike Obryan
VP: Michael S Bryan
VP: Carole Buys
VP: Henry Haley
VP: Brian Haven
VP: W M Jones
Comm Dir: Michael Albo

D-U-N-S 11-802-6819 EXP
■ **VIRCO INC**
(*Suby of* VIRCO MFG CORP) ★
2027 Harpers Way, Torrance, CA 90501-1524
Tel (310) 533-0474 *Founded/Ownrshp* 1998
Sales 102.5MM^E *EMP* 250^E
SIC 5021 Furniture
CEO: Robert Virtue
VP: Scotty Bell
**VP:* Robert Dose
VP Sls: John Leear

D-U-N-S 00-828-9530 IMP/EXP
▲ **VIRCO MFG CORP**
2027 Harpers Way, Torrance, CA 90501-1524
Tel (310) 533-0474 *Founded/Ownrshp* 1950
Sales 168.6MM *EMP* 695^E
Tkr Sym VIRC *Exch* NGM
SIC 2531 2522 2511 School furniture; Chairs, portable folding; Chairs, table & arm; Office furniture, except wood; Chairs, office: padded or plain, except wood; Tables, office: except wood; Wood household furniture
Ch Bd: Robert A Virtue
**Pr:* Douglas A Virtue
CFO: Robert E Dose
Chf Mktg O: James D Johnson
Sr VP: J Scott Bell
Sr VP: Rob Devers
VP: Bassey Yau
Art Dir: Stan Foster
Board of Directors: Alexander L Cappello, Robert Lind, Donald R Rudkin

D-U-N-S 18-476-1489
▲ **VIRGIN AMERICA INC**
555 Airport Blvd Ste 400, Burlingame, CA 94010-2036
Tel (877) 359-8474 *Founded/Ownrshp* 2004
Sales 1.5MMM *EMP* 2,965^E
Tkr Sym VA *Exch* NGS
SIC 4512 Air passenger carrier, scheduled
Pr: C David Cush
**Ch Bd:* Donald J Carty
**V Ch:* Samuel K Skinner
COO: Stephen A Forte
CFO: Peter D Hunt
Ofcr: David Kelley
Sr VP: Mark Bianchi
Sr VP: John A Macleod
Sr VP: John Macleod
Sr VP: John J Varley
VP: Ross J Bonanno
VP: Luanne Calvert
VP: Dean Cookson
VP: Joe Hill
VP: Jason Lazich
VP: Brad Thomann
VP: Alan Tubbs

D-U-N-S 82-860-1125
VIRGIN GALACTIC LLC
(*Suby of* VIRGIN MANAGEMENT LIMITED)
4022 E Conant St, Long Beach, CA 90808-1777
Tel (562) 384-4400 *Founded/Ownrshp* 2007
Sales 120.4MM^E *EMP* 200^E
SIC 4789 Space flight operations, except government
CEO: George Whitesides
Pr: Steve Isakowitz
Ex VP: Jonathan Firth
Sr VP: Michael P Moses
VP: Tim Buzza
VP: Michael Moses
Dir IT: Mike Cosenza

D-U-N-S 09-010-1080 IMP/EXP
VIRGIN ISLANDS WATER & POWER AUTHORITY
VIWAPA
9702 Estate Thomas, St Thomas, VI 00802-2623
Tel (340) 774-3552 *Founded/Ownrshp* 2016
Sales 412.2MM^E *EMP* 600
SIC 4911 Electric services
CEO: Hugo Hodge Jr
**COO:* Gregory Rhymer
**CFO:* Nellon Bowry
**CFO:* Julio Rhymer
Ex Dir: Alberto Bruno-Vega
Ex Dir: Joseph Thomas

D-U-N-S 11-055-9650
VIRGIN MEDIA HOLDINGS INC
65 Bleecker St Fl 6, New York, NY 10012-2420
Tel (212) 966-2310 *Founded/Ownrshp* 2013
Sales 1.6MMM^E *EMP* 9,820
SIC 4812 4813 4841 Cellular telephone services; Local & long distance telephone communications; ; Cable television services
Pr: Stephen A Burch
**Ch Bd:* James F Mooney
**Ch Bd:* Anthony Stenham
COO: Andrew Barron
**COO:* Neil Berkett

D-U-N-S 80-814-8048
■ **VIRGIN MOBILE USA INC**
(*Suby of* SPRINT COMMUNICATIONS INC) ★
10 Independence Blvd # 200, Warren, NJ 07059-2730
Tel (908) 607-4000 *Founded/Ownrshp* 2000
Sales 104.5MM^E *EMP* 420^E
SIC 4812 Radio telephone communication
Pr: Dow Draper
**COO:* Jonathan H Marchbank
**Ofcr:* David Rj Messenger
**VP:* Jeff Auman
Advt Mgr: Jeremy Agers
Mktg Mgr: Dawn Steingall

D-U-N-S 14-979-8449
■ **VIRGINIA & SOUTHWESTERN RAILWAY CO**
VIRGINIA & SOUTHWESTERN RLWY
(*Suby of* NORFOLK SOUTHERN RAILWAY CO) ★
3 Commercial Pl, Norfolk, VA 23510-2108
Tel (757) 629-2645 *Founded/Ownrshp* 1899
Sales 14.4MM^E *EMP* 1,067^E
SIC 4011 Railroads, line-haul operating
Pr: Stephen C Tobias

VIRGINIA & SOUTHWESTERN RLWY
See VIRGINIA & SOUTHWESTERN RAILWAY CO

VIRGINIA BAPTIST HOSPITAL
See CENTRA HEALTH INC

VIRGINIA BEACH HEATHCARE & REH
See MEDICAL FACILITIES OF AMERICA VI AND XIII (LIMITED PARTNERSHIP)

VIRGINIA BUSINESS MAGAZINE
See MEDIA GENERAL OPERATIONS INC

D-U-N-S 61-081-9026 IMP
VIRGINIA CHAPARRAL INC
GERDAU AMERISTEEL DINWIDDIE CO
25801 Hofheimer Way, North Dinwiddie, VA 23803-8905
Tel (804) 520-0286 *Founded/Ownrshp* 1997
Sales 89.8MM^E *EMP* 410
SIC 3312 Blast furnaces & steel mills
**VP:* Andre Pires
Opers Mgr: Chris Voiles

VIRGINIA COLLEGE AT BIRMINGHAM
See VIRGINIA COLLEGE LLC

D-U-N-S 84-775-4827
VIRGINIA COLLEGE LLC
VIRGINIA COLLEGE AT BIRMINGHAM
3660 Grandview Pkwy # 300, Birmingham, AL 35243-3340
Tel (205) 329-7900 *Founded/Ownrshp* 1999
Sales 134.1MM^E *EMP* 1,200
SIC 8221 Colleges & universities
Pr: Tom Moore
CFO: Steve Miller
VP: Jason Biddy
VP: Pat Foster
Exec: Christine Hurd
Exec: Crystal Jalil
Exec: Bryson W Jones
Pgrm Dir: Jimmy Gonzales
Pgrm Dir: Shauna Mitchell
Pgrm Dir: Charlene Russell
Pgrm Dir: Wayne Sullivan
Board of Directors: Louis Kenter, Rick Tuttle

D-U-N-S 03-255-3682
VIRGINIA COMMERCE BANCORP INC
5350 Lee Hwy, Arlington, VA 22207-1608
Tel (703) 534-0700 *Founded/Ownrshp* 1999
Sales NA *EMP* 330^E
SIC 6022

D-U-N-S 10-530-0446
VIRGINIA COMMONWEALTH UNIVERSITY
V C U
912 W Franklin St, Richmond, VA 23284-9040
Tel (804) 828-0100 *Founded/Ownrshp* 1968
Sales 983.8MM^E *EMP* 11,000
SIC 8221 University
Pr: Eugene P Trani
Ofcr: Amy Chuang
Ofcr: Conan P Phelan
VP: John Bennett
VP: Margaret Gibson
VP: David Hanson
VP: Joe McDonell
Exec: Samantha Marrs
Prin: Vanessa Y Byrd
Ex Dir: Daphne Bryan
Ex Dir: Richard O Bunce

D-U-N-S 12-073-8307
VIRGINIA COMMUNITY COLLEGE SYSTEM OFFICE
(*Suby of* VIRGINIA SECRETARY OF EDUCATION) ★
300 Arboretum Pl Ste 200, North Chesterfield, VA 23236-3473
Tel (804) 819-4901 *Founded/Ownrshp* 2015
Sales 544.3MM *EMP* 4,854
SIC 8222 Community college
CFO: Jaime Tadlock
Ofcr: Vickey Carwile
Ex VP: Karen Petersen
VP: Patsy Joyner
Snr Mgr: James Davis

D-U-N-S 03-742-8166
VIRGINIA CREDIT UNION INC
7500 Boulder View Dr, North Chesterfield, VA 23225-4066
Tel (804) 323-6800 *Founded/Ownrshp* 1928
Sales NA *EMP* 508
SIC 6062 6163 State credit unions, not federally chartered; Loan brokers
Pr: Jane G Watkins
**CFO:* Robert F Warren
**Treas:* Herbert A Parr
Sr VP: Jean Holman

VP: Bill Dodl
VP: Lee Dranoff
VP: Todd Feldman
VP: Paul Hendricks
VP: Stephanie Vick
Brnch Mgr: Brandon Brod
Brnch Mgr: Donald Conner

D-U-N-S 80-939-2053
VIRGINIA DEPARTMENT OF ALCOHOLIC BEVERAGE CONTROL
ABC
(*Suby of* VIRGINIA SECRETARY OF PUBLIC SAFETY AND HOMELAND SECURITY) ★
2901 Hermitage Rd, Richmond, VA 23220-1010
Tel (804) 213-4400 *Founded/Ownrshp* 1934
Sales NA *EMP* 1,500
Accts Commonwealth Of Virginia Rich
SIC 9651 Alcoholic beverage control board, government;
Ch Bd: Susan Swecker
**Ch Bd:* Jeffrey L Painter
**Ch Bd:* Esther H Vassar
**COO:* W Curtis Coleburn
**CFO:* Craig Vanderoand

D-U-N-S 80-974-4444
VIRGINIA DEPARTMENT OF CONSERVATION AND RECREATION
(*Suby of* NATURAL RESOURCES VIRGINIA) ★
600 E Main St Fl 24, Richmond, VA 23219-2440
Tel (804) 371-0099 *Founded/Ownrshp* 1936
Sales NA *EMP* 1,375
SIC 9512 Land, mineral & wildlife conservation;
Dir Vol: Gaston Rouse

D-U-N-S 80-939-2343
VIRGINIA DEPARTMENT OF CORRECTIONS
PUBLIC SAFETY & HOMELND SECRTY
(*Suby of* VIRGINIA SECRETARY OF PUBLIC SAFETY AND HOMELAND SECURITY) ★
6900 Atmore Dr, Richmond, VA 23225-5644
Tel (804) 674-3000 *Founded/Ownrshp* 1908
Sales NA *EMP* 11,840
SIC 9223 Prison, government;

D-U-N-S 80-974-0459
VIRGINIA DEPARTMENT OF HEALTH
VDH
(*Suby of* VIRGINIA SECRETARY OF HEALTH AND HUMAN RESOURCES) ★
109 Governor St Ste 1221, Richmond, VA 23219-3623
Tel (804) 864-7045 *Founded/Ownrshp* 1908
Sales NA *EMP* 3,671
SIC 9431 Administration of public health programs;
**Prin:* Bob McDonnell
Genl Mgr: William Heisey
Genl Mgr: Londilia McCoy-Scott
Pgrm Dir: Nancy Voorhis

D-U-N-S 80-973-9964
VIRGINIA DEPARTMENT OF JUVENILE JUSTICE
(*Suby of* VIRGINIA SECRETARY OF PUBLIC SAFETY AND HOMELAND SECURITY) ★
7th & Franklin Sts, Richmond, VA 23219
Tel (804) 371-0700 *Founded/Ownrshp* 1990
Sales NA *EMP* 2,400
SIC 9223 Prison, government;
Prin: S Pullen Dpty Dir Fin

D-U-N-S 80-987-5321
VIRGINIA DEPARTMENT OF MOTOR VEHICLES
(*Suby of* VIRGINIA SECRETARY OF TRANSPORTATION) ★
2300 W Broad St, Richmond, VA 23220-2051
Tel (804) 367-0538 *Founded/Ownrshp* 1927
Sales NA *EMP* 1,939
SIC 9621 Regulation, administration of transportation;
Prgrm Mgr: Kathy Six
MIS Dir: Cheryl Clark
IT Man: Deborah Dodson

D-U-N-S 80-974-0566
VIRGINIA DEPARTMENT OF SOCIAL SERVICES
DEPUTY COMMISSIONER
(*Suby of* VIRGINIA SECRETARY OF HEALTH AND HUMAN RESOURCES) ★
801 E Main St Fl 3, Richmond, VA 23219-2907
Tel (804) 726-7000 *Founded/Ownrshp* 1974
Sales NA *EMP* 1,850
SIC 9441 Administration of social & human resources;
Ex Dir: Daniela Lewy

D-U-N-S 80-973-9998
VIRGINIA DEPARTMENT OF STATE POLICE
VIRGINIA DEPT STATE POLICE
(*Suby of* VIRGINIA SECRETARY OF PUBLIC SAFETY AND HOMELAND SECURITY) ★
7700 Midlothian Tpke, North Chesterfield, VA 23235-5226
Tel (804) 674-2000 *Founded/Ownrshp* 1942
Sales NA *EMP* 2,600
SIC 9221 State police;
Genl Mgr: James D'Amato
IT Man: Mitzi Hesser
Info Man: Chris Schuessler
Netwrk Eng: Howard Schroeder

D-U-N-S 10-270-8422
VIRGINIA DEPARTMENT OF TRANSPORTATION
VDOT
(*Suby of* OFFICE OF GOVERNOR) ★
1401 E Broad St, Richmond, VA 23219-2052
Tel (804) 786-2836 *Founded/Ownrshp* 2011
Sales 98.4MM[E] *EMP* 9,000
SIC 8711

D-U-N-S 80-987-5263
VIRGINIA DEPARTMENT OF TRANSPORTATION
(*Suby of* VIRGINIA SECRETARY OF TRANSPORTATION) ★
1401 E Broad St, Richmond, VA 23219-2052
Tel (804) 786-2701 *Founded/Ownrshp* 1927
Sales NA *EMP* 10,737
SIC 9621 Regulation, administration of transportation;
CFO: Reta Busher
Genl Mgr: Lisa Pride

VIRGINIA DEPT STATE POLICE
See VIRGINIA DEPARTMENT OF STATE POLICE

D-U-N-S 00-794-1446
■ **VIRGINIA ELECTRIC AND POWER CO**
DOMINION
(*Suby of* DOMINION RESOURCES INC) ★
120 Tredegar St, Richmond, VA 23219-4306
Tel (804) 819-2000 *Founded/Ownrshp* 1909
Sales 7.6MMM *EMP* 6,800
SIC 4911 Electric services; Distribution, electric power; Generation, electric power; Transmission, electric power
Ch Bd: Thomas F Farrell II
Pr: David A Christian
CFO: Mark F McGettrick
Sr VP: Thomas A Hyman
Sr VP: Thomas A Hymn
VP: Michele L Cardiff
Board of Directors: Mark O Webb

D-U-N-S 02-794-4631 IMP
■ **VIRGINIA FOODSERVICE GROUP LLC**
PFG VIRGINIA FOODSERVICE
(*Suby of* P F G) ★
7420 Ranco Rd, Henrico, VA 23228-3702
Tel (804) 237-1001 *Founded/Ownrshp* 1885
Sales 129.0MM[E] *EMP* 200
SIC 5141 5046 Groceries, general line; Commercial cooking & food service equipment
Prin: Mike Morrell

D-U-N-S 01-992-6658
VIRGINIA HOSPITAL CENTER ARLINGTON AUXILIARY INC
1701 N George Mason Dr, Arlington, VA 22205-3610
Tel (703) 558-5668 *Founded/Ownrshp* 1934
Sales 460.3MM *EMP* 2,000
Accts Dixon Hughes Goodman Rockvill
SIC 8062 General medical & surgical hospitals
CEO: James Cole
**Ch Bd:* John R Garrett
**COO:* Carl B Bahnlein
CFO: Robin Norman
**Chf Mktg O:* Jeffrey Dilisi
Assoc VP: Sherri Simons
VP: David Crutchfield
VP: Jeanne Maguire
**VP:* Michael Malone
VP: Steven A Rubloff
IT Man: Mark Rein

D-U-N-S 96-178-8218
VIRGINIA HOSPITAL CENTER ARLINGTON HEALTH SYSTEM
1701 N George Mason Dr, Arlington, VA 22205-3610
Tel (703) 558-5000 *Founded/Ownrshp* 2010
Sales 477.4MM *EMP* 12[E]
Accts Cohen Rutherford Knight Pc Be
SIC 8093 Specialty outpatient clinics
Prin: John R Garrett MD

D-U-N-S 09-960-2369
VIRGINIA HOUSING DEVELOPMENT AUTHORITY
VHDA
601 S Belvidere St, Richmond, VA 23220-6504
Tel (804) 780-0789 *Founded/Ownrshp* 1972
Sales NA *EMP* 300
Accts Kpmg Llp Richmond Va
SIC 6162 Mortgage bankers & correspondents
Ex Dir: Susan F Dewey
Ofcr: Cindy Barrett
Ofcr: Joy Bolling
Ofcr: Jackie Bowen
Ofcr: Maryanne Butler
Ofcr: Bruce Desimone
Ofcr: Amy Dugger
Ofcr: Chris Hilbert
Ofcr: Cindy Holsapple
Ofcr: Danielle Owen
Ofcr: Jackie Patton
Ofcr: Wally Robinson
Ofcr: Cara Wallo
VP: Robert Jackson
VP: Erica Singleton
VP: Shawn Washington

D-U-N-S 04-803-5872
VIRGINIA INTEGRATED COMMUNICATION INC (VA)
VICOM
5361 Cleveland St, Virginia Beach, VA 23462-6524
Tel (757) 490-7777 *Founded/Ownrshp* 2001
Sales 99.8MM[E] *EMP* 89
Accts Mulkey & Company Pc Virgini
SIC 5065 Communication equipment
Pr: Dennis L Schliske
**VP:* Ronald C Hughes III

D-U-N-S 07-474-6793 IMP/EXP
VIRGINIA INTERNATIONAL TERMINALS LLC
(*Suby of* VIRGINIA PORT AUTHORITY) ★
601 World Trade Ctr, Norfolk, VA 23510
Tel (757) 440-7120 *Founded/Ownrshp* 1981
Sales 135.4MM[E] *EMP* 400
Accts Witt Mares Plc New Port Vir
SIC 4491 4213 Marine terminals; Trucking, except local
CEO: Joseph P Ruddy
Pr: Joseph Dorto
COO: Shawn Tiddettes
**Sec:* William M Grace

VP: Wilson S Goode
Counsel: John M Ryan

D-U-N-S 79-040-8504 IMP
VIRGINIA MARUCHAN INC
(*Suby of* MARUCHAN INC) ★
8101 Whitepine Rd, North Chesterfield, VA 23237-2288
Tel (804) 275-0800 *Founded/Ownrshp* 1989
Sales 91.6MM[E] *EMP* 185
SIC 2098 2099 Noodles (e.g. egg, plain & water), dry; Food preparations
Pr: Oda Mutsumiko
Plnt Mgr: Hiro Matsushita

D-U-N-S 07-977-0143
VIRGINIA MASON HEALTH SYSTEM
1100 9th Ave, Seattle, WA 98101-2756
Tel (206) 233-6600 *Founded/Ownrshp* 1985
Sales 16.0MM *EMP* 5,000[E]
Accts Kpmg Llp Seattle Wa
SIC 8741 Hospital management
CEO: Gary Kaplan
Sr VP: Suzanne Anderson

D-U-N-S 19-488-3393
VIRGINIA MASON MEDICAL CENTER
(*Suby of* VIRGINIA MASON HEALTH SYSTEM) ★
1100 9th Ave, Seattle, WA 98101-2756
Tel (206) 223-6600 *Founded/Ownrshp* 1934
Sales 967.2MM *EMP* 5,000
Accts Kpmg Llp Seattle Wa
SIC 8011 8051 6513 8062 Clinic, operated by physicians; Skilled nursing care facilities; Apartment hotel operation; General medical & surgical hospitals
Pr: James Young
Genl Pt: Ryan Drant
**Ch Bd:* Gary S Kaplan
**Pr:* Carolyn Corvi
Pr: Kathleen Paul
**CFO:* Suzanne Anderson
**Treas:* Robert Lemon
Chf Mktg O: Michael Glenn
VP: Katerie Chapman
**VP:* James Orlikoff
**VP:* Evelyn Cruz Sroufe
Dir Risk M: Trian Hutchins

D-U-N-S 07-664-7957
VIRGINIA MASON SEATTLE MAIN CLINIC
(*Suby of* VIRGINIA MASON MEDICAL CENTER) ★
1100 9th Ave, Seattle, WA 98101-2756
Tel (206) 223-6600 *Founded/Ownrshp* 1920
Sales 28.2MM[E] *EMP* 2,200
SIC 8011 Clinic, operated by physicians
Ch Bd: Dr Roger C Lindeman
**V Ch Bd:* Donald Bauermeister

D-U-N-S 15-049-1314
■ **VIRGINIA NATURAL GAS INC**
(*Suby of* SOUTHERN CO GAS) ★
544 S Independence Blvd, Virginia Beach, VA 23452-1104
Tel (757) 466-5400 *Founded/Ownrshp* 2000
Sales 378.7MM[E] *EMP* 500
Accts Pricewaterhousecoopers Llp
SIC 4924 Natural gas distribution
Pr: Robert Duvall
**CFO:* Walter R Hunter
**Treas:* Charles Moore
Genl Mgr: George Faatz

D-U-N-S 07-897-7621
VIRGINIA PALACE NEWSPAPERS INC
150 W Brambleton Ave, Norfolk, VA 23510-2018
Tel (757) 446-2000 *Founded/Ownrshp* 1999
Sales 5.1MM[E] *EMP* 1,100
SIC 8222 Technical institute
Pr: Delmar Carpenter

D-U-N-S 00-313-7015
VIRGINIA POLYTECHNIC INSTITUTE & STATE UNIVERSITY
VIRGINIA TECH
(*Suby of* STATE COUNCIL OF HIGHER EDUCATION FOR VIRGINIA) ★
300 Turner St Nw Ste 4200, Blacksburg, VA 24061-6100
Tel (540) 231-6000 *Founded/Ownrshp* 1872
Sales 1.1MMM *EMP* 6,866
Accts Commonwealth Of Virginia Audit
SIC 8221 University
CEO: John E Dooley
**COO:* Raymond D Smoot Jr
**CFO:* M Dwight Shelton Jr
Assoc VP: Debbie Day
Assoc VP: Karen Sanders
VP: Sherry Albert
VP: Earving L Blythe
**VP:* Elizabeth Flanagin
VP: Terry Herdman
VP: Hal Irvin
VP: Ken C Lssbb
**VP:* Mark McNamee
VP: Scott Midkiff
VP: Patricia A Perillo
VP: Edward F D Spence
VP: Thomas C Tillar
VP: Matthew Winston Jr
Assoc Dir: Katie Reades

D-U-N-S 01-003-9857 IMP
VIRGINIA PORT AUTHORITY
(*Suby of* VIRGINIA SECRETARY OF TRANSPORTATION) ★
600 World Trade Ctr, Norfolk, VA 23510-1781
Tel (757) 683-8000 *Founded/Ownrshp* 1952
Sales NA *EMP* 1,600
Accts Pbmares Llp Harrisonburg Vi
SIC 9621 9111 Port authority or district: government, non-operating; Executive offices
Ex Dir: Jerry Bridges
Opers Mgr: Tyler Supplee
Mktg Mgr: Thomas D Capozzi

D-U-N-S 14-807-0654
VIRGINIA POULTRY GROWERS COOPERATIVE INC
VPGC
6349 Rawley Pike, Hinton, VA 22831-2001
Tel (540) 867-4000 *Founded/Ownrshp* 2004
Sales 104.0MM[E] *EMP* 550
SIC 2015 Chicken slaughtering & processing
Ch Bd: Steve Bazzle
**Pr:* James Mason
**VP:* John King
IT Man: Denise Custer

D-U-N-S 18-695-1443
■ **VIRGINIA POWER SERVICES ENERGY CORP INC**
(*Suby of* DOMINION) ★
120 Tredegar St, Richmond, VA 23219-4306
Tel (804) 819-2000 *Founded/Ownrshp* 1998
Sales 361.1MM[E] *EMP* 100[E]
SIC 4911 Electric services
Pr: David A Christian
**Treas:* G Scott Hetzer
**Sr VP:* J David Rives
**Sr VP:* Paul E Ruppert
**Sr VP:* Fred G Wood III
**VP:* James P Carney
**VP:* C Douglas Holley
**VP:* Carter M Reid

D-U-N-S 92-696-7183
VIRGINIA PREMIER HEALTH PLAN INC
COMMONWEALTH HEALTH PLAN
(*Suby of* MEDICAL COLLEGE OF VIRGINIA) ★
600 E Broad St Ste 400, Richmond, VA 23219-1800
Tel (804) 819-5164 *Founded/Ownrshp* 1994
Sales 969.9MM *EMP* 165
Accts Kpmg Llp Mc Lean Va
SIC 8011 Health maintenance organization
CEO: Linda Hines

D-U-N-S 80-938-7541
VIRGINIA SECRETARY OF COMMERCE AND TRADE
(*Suby of* OFFICE OF GOVERNOR) ★
Ninth St Off Bldg Ste 723, Richmond, VA 23219
Tel (804) 786-7831 *Founded/Ownrshp* 1998
Sales NA *EMP* 1,834
SIC 9611 Administration of general economic programs;

D-U-N-S 80-938-7608
VIRGINIA SECRETARY OF EDUCATION
(*Suby of* OFFICE OF GOVERNOR) ★
1111 E Broad St Fl 5, Richmond, VA 23219-1934
Tel (804) 786-1151 *Founded/Ownrshp* 1870
Sales NA *EMP* 42,400
SIC 9411 Administration of educational programs;

D-U-N-S 80-938-8788
VIRGINIA SECRETARY OF FINANCE
(*Suby of* OFFICE OF GOVERNOR) ★
1111 E Broad St Ste 5035, Richmond, VA 23219-1936
Tel (804) 786-1148 *Founded/Ownrshp* 1971
Sales NA *EMP* 1,031
SIC 9311 Finance, taxation & monetary policy;

D-U-N-S 80-938-7624 IMP
VIRGINIA SECRETARY OF HEALTH AND HUMAN RESOURCES
(*Suby of* OFFICE OF GOVERNOR) ★
202 E 9th St, Richmond, VA 23224-4006
Tel (804) 786-7765 *Founded/Ownrshp* 1908
Sales NA *EMP* 16,235
SIC 9431 9441 Administration of public health programs; ; Administration of social & manpower programs;
VP: Heather Sweitzer

D-U-N-S 80-938-7699
VIRGINIA SECRETARY OF PUBLIC SAFETY AND HOMELAND SECURITY
(*Suby of* OFFICE OF GOVERNOR) ★
1111 E Broad St, Richmond, VA 23219-1934
Tel (804) 786-5351 *Founded/Ownrshp* 1990
Sales NA *EMP* 15,000
SIC 9111 Governors' offices;

D-U-N-S 80-974-0103
VIRGINIA SECRETARY OF TRANSPORTATION
(*Suby of* OFFICE OF GOVERNOR) ★
1111 E Broad St Fl 3, Richmond, VA 23219-1934
Tel (804) 786-8032 *Founded/Ownrshp* 1990
Sales NA *EMP* 13,069
SIC 9621 Regulation, administration of transportation;

D-U-N-S 36-353-5857
VIRGINIA SOUTHSIDE TRAINING CENTER INC
W Washington St, Petersburg, VA 23803
Tel (804) 524-7333 *Founded/Ownrshp* 1939
Sales 29.4MM[E] *EMP* 1,300
SIC 8361 8052 Residential care; Intermediate care facilities
Adm Dir: Bill Hawkins
Off Mgr: Linda Cake

D-U-N-S 07-474-4624 IMP
VIRGINIA STATE UNIVERSITY
1 Hayden Dr, Petersburg, VA 23803-2520
Tel (804) 524-5000 *Founded/Ownrshp* 1882
Sales 90.2MM[E] *EMP* 1,150
SIC 8221 9411 University; Administration of educational programs;
Pr: Dr Keith T Miller
Ofcr: Mike Foster
Ex Dir: Sonya Tann
Prgrm Mgr: Angela James
Off Mgr: Eunice Newton
Dir IT: Robert Calleson
Dir IT: Steven J Ulrich
IT Man: Emmanuel Omojokun
Prd Mgr: Gene Hollingsworth

Prd Mgr: Leslie Moyers
Doctor: Deanne Williams

D-U-N-S 06-997-4772
VIRGINIA SURETY CO INC
(*Suby of* TWG WARRANTY GROUP INC) ★
175 W Jackson Blvd Fl 11, Chicago, IL 60604-2709
Tel (312) 356-3000 *Founded/Ownrshp* 2006
Sales NA *EMP* 1,800
SIC 6351 6399 Liability insurance; Warranty insurance, automobile
Pr: David Lee Cole

VIRGINIA TECH
See VIRGINIA POLYTECHNIC INSTITUTE & STATE UNIVERSITY

D-U-N-S 87-271-9000
VIRGINIA TECH CORPORATE RESEARCH CENTER INC
(*Suby of* VIRGINIA TECH INNOVATIONS CORPORATION)
1715 Pratt Dr Ste 1000, Blacksburg, VA 24060-6386
Tel (540) 961-3600 *Founded/Ownrshp* 1985
Sales 146.0MM *EMP* 75
SIC 8733 Noncommercial research organizations
Pr: Joseph W Meredith
**Ch:* Raymond D Smoot Jr
**Sec:* Kay Hunnings
Genl Mgr: Terri Harris

D-U-N-S 07-937-0736
VIRGINIA TECH FOUNDATION INC (VA)
902 Prices Fork Rd, Blacksburg, VA 24060-3260
Tel (540) 231-2861 *Founded/Ownrshp* 1948
Sales 137.8MME *EMP* 40
Accts Kpmg Llp Mc Lean Va
SIC 7299 Personal financial services
CEO: Dr John E Dooley
**VP:* Dr Elizabeth A Flanagan
**VP:* M Dwight Shelton Jr

D-U-N-S 12-251-5526
VIRGINIA TENASKA PARTNERS L P
(*Suby of* TENASKA INC) ★
14302 Fnb Pkwy, Omaha, NE 68154-4446
Tel (402) 691-9500 *Founded/Ownrshp* 2002
Sales 91.1MM *EMP* 15E
Accts Kpmg Llp Lincoln Ne
SIC 4911 Electric services
Prin: Dave Neubauer
Genl Pt: Herbert Tvp General

D-U-N-S 01-702-9612 IMP
VIRGINIA TILE CO
28320 Plymouth Rd, Livonia, MI 48150-2790
Tel (248) 476-7850 *Founded/Ownrshp* 1929
Sales 117.4MME *EMP* 182
SIC 5032 5023 Brick, stone & related material; Floor coverings
Pr: William H Stephenson
**Cfo:* Mark A Ott
Brnch Mgr: Greg Sott
IT Man: Brian Smith
Manager: James Dean
Sls Mgr: Jack Moulder

VIRGINIA T'S
See HERITAGE SPORTSWEAR INC

D-U-N-S 01-302-0847 EXP
VIRGINIA TS INC
2001 Anchor Ave, Petersburg, VA 23803-2876
Tel (804) 862-2600 *Founded/Ownrshp* 1981
Sales 204.1MME *EMP* 275
SIC 5136 5137 Men's & boys' clothing; Women's & children's clothing
CEO: Dale Call
**Pr:* Jerry Frink Jr
Mktg Dir: Karen Clifton
Sales Asso: Nancy Brandt

D-U-N-S 04-625-3258
VIRGINIA UNITED METHODIST HOMES INC
HERMITAGE AT CEDAR FIELD
5101 Cox Rd Ste 225, Glen Allen, VA 23060-9302
Tel (804) 474-8700 *Founded/Ownrshp* 1945
Sales 60.4MM *EMP* 1,000
Accts Lb Mitchell Wiggins & Company
SIC 8361 Rest home, with health care incidental
Pr: Christopther Henderson
COO: Daniel Oetzel
**Ch:* Stephen Mapp
**Treas:* John B Scott
VP: Richard Bottone
**VP:* Kelli Mansel-Arbuckle
Off Mgr: Angela Petty
Nutrtnst: Christine Lacy

D-U-N-S 06-342-2042
VIRGINIA WESLEYAN COLLEGE
1584 Wesleyan Dr, Norfolk, VA 23502-5599
Tel (757) 455-3200 *Founded/Ownrshp* 1961
Sales 83.0MM *EMP* 585
Accts Cherry Bekaert Llp Charlotte
SIC 8221 College, except junior
Pr: Scott Miller
Pr: Bryan Price
Bd of Dir: Kirsty Green
Ex VP: Joyce B Howell
VP: James Bergdoll
VP: David Buckingham
VP: Tim O'Rourke
VP: Marguerite Vail
Comm Dir: Leona Baker
Genl Mgr: Tim Lockett
Dir IT: Don Stauffer

D-U-N-S 00-794-4622
■ **VIRGINIA WEST AMERICAN WATER CO** (WV)
(*Suby of* AMERICAN WATER WORKS CO INC) ★
1600 Pennsylvania Ave, Charleston, WV 25302-3932
Tel (304) 353-6300 *Founded/Ownrshp* 1926, 1965
Sales 158.8MME *EMP* 450
SIC 4941 Water supply
Pr: Jeffrey McIntyre
**VP:* Mike Miller
IT Man: Carl Sullivan

D-U-N-S 06-876-0156
VIRGINIA WEST UNIVERSITY FOUNDATION INC
1 Waterfront Pl Fl 7, Morgantown, WV 26501-5978
Tel (304) 293-3708 *Founded/Ownrshp* 1954
Sales 174.1MM *EMP* 70
Accts Dixon Hughes Goodman Llp Morg
SIC 6732 Trusts: educational, religious, etc.
Pr: R Wayne King
**Ch Bd:* Marshall Miller
**Pr:* Cynthia L Roth
**COO:* Michael Augustine
**VP:* Dorothy J Dotson
**VP:* Lynn Dotson
**VP:* Jeffrey K Dunn
VP: Rick Kraich
**VP:* Julia Phalunas
**VP:* Craig Walker

D-U-N-S 11-343-3734
VIRGINIA WEST UNIVERSITY HOSPITALS INC
JOHN MICHAEL MOORETRAUMA CTR
1 Medical Center Dr, Morgantown, WV 26506-1200
Tel (304) 598-4000 *Founded/Ownrshp* 1984
Sales 774.0MME *EMP* 6,267E
SIC 8062 General medical & surgical hospitals
Pr: Bruce McClymonds
Dir Recs: Melissa Martin
Dir Vol: Nancy Beckner
Pr: Peggy Cianfrocca
CFO: David Salisberry
VP: Clare Flanagan
Dir Rx: Frank Briggs
Prgrm Mgr: Cindy Jamison
Off Mgr: Linda Mitter
Nurse Mgr: Dan Bazzoli
Nurse Mgr: Ben Campbell

D-U-N-S 10-890-0671
VIRGINIA WEST UNIVERSITY MEDICAL CORP
UNIVERSITY HEALTH ASSOCIATES
1 Stadium Dr, Morgantown, WV 26506-7900
Tel (304) 598-4200 *Founded/Ownrshp* 1971
Sales 272.2MM *EMP* 1,185
SIC 8011 Clinic, operated by physicians
CFO: Robert Milvet
Bd of Dir: Elaine P Bowen
Bd of Dir: Susan Chapman
Bd of Dir: Patricia Crawford
Bd of Dir: Sara J Gainor
Bd of Dir: Jeff Graham
Bd of Dir: Lew Holloway
Bd of Dir: Lynn McCormick
Bd of Dir: Sally Richardson
Bd of Dir: Mazharullah Shaik
Bd of Dir: Michael Thompson
Bd of Dir: Alicia Tyler
**Ofcr:* Melanie Davis
VP: Allen Buthcher

VIRGINIAN PILOT, THE
See VIRGINIAN-PILOT MEDIA COMPANIES LLC

D-U-N-S 00-317-4026 IMP
VIRGINIAN-PILOT MEDIA COMPANIES LLC (VA)
VIRGINIAN PILOT, THE
(*Suby of* LANDMARK MEDIA ENTERPRISES LLC) ★
150 W Brambleton Ave, Norfolk, VA 23510-2018
Tel (757) 446-2056 *Founded/Ownrshp* 1865, 2008
Sales 138.5MME *EMP* 800
SIC 2711 Newspapers, publishing & printing
Pr: Patricia Richardson
**Pr:* David Mele
CFO: Terry Blevins
Ex VP: R Bruce Bradley
Ex VP: Charlie W Hill
Ex VP: Alfred Ritter
VP: L King
Creative D: Julie Richardson
Genl Mgr: Kelly Till
Dir IT: Steve Dandy
Info Man: Roger Berry

D-U-N-S 94-367-7328
VIRONEX INC
4350 W Ohio St, Chicago, IL 60624-1051
Tel (773) 265-0403 *Founded/Ownrshp* 1994
Sales 69.4MME *EMP* 1,000
SIC 4225 General warehousing & storage
Pr: David Schulman
**COO:* Rick Ehrensast

D-U-N-S 60-424-7408
VIRTELA TECHNOLOGY SERVICES INC
(*Suby of* NTT COMMUNICATIONS CORPORATION)
5680 Greenwood Plaza Blvd, Greenwood Village, CO 80111-2414
Tel (720) 475-4000 *Founded/Ownrshp* 2014
Sales 121.8MME *EMP* 220
SIC 4813
Pr: Ron Haigh
CFO: Rui Hou
Sr VP: Ian Dix
**Sr VP:* Ted Studwell
VP: Valko Bryan
VP: Anu Chandra
VP: John Fischer
VP: Paul Hooper
VP: Jane Morrissey
VP: Sudhir Seth
VP: Bryan Valko
Exec: Teggie Bellamy
Exec: Renee Brady
Board of Directors: Rick Smith

D-U-N-S 07-939-2710
▲ **VIRTU FINANCIAL INC**
900 3rd Ave Fl 29, New York, NY 10022-4777
Tel (212) 418-0100 *Founded/Ownrshp* 2013
Sales 796.2MM *EMP* 148E
Tkr Sym VIRT *Exch* NGS
SIC 6211 Brokers, security
CEO: Douglas A Cifu
**Ch Bd:* Vincent Viola
CFO: Joseph Molluso
Sr VP: Venu Palaparthi

D-U-N-S 82-834-0658
VIRTU FINANCIAL LLC
645 Madison Ave Fl 16, New York, NY 10022-1010
Tel (212) 418-0100 *Founded/Ownrshp* 2008
Sales 723.0MM *EMP* 158
Accts Deloitte & Touche Llp New Yor
SIC 6799 Commodity contract trading companies
Ch: Vincent Viola
Mng Pt: Jason Vopni
**Pr:* Chris Concannon
**CEO:* Douglas Cifu
**CFO:* Joseph Molluso
VP: Rex Lewis
Sftwr Eng: Feng Cao

D-U-N-S 06-969-1967
VIRTUA HEALTH INC
NEW BEGINNINGS WEIGHT LOSS PRO
303 Lippincott Dr, Marlton, NJ 08053-4160
Tel (888) 847-8823 *Founded/Ownrshp* 1997
Sales 679.1MME *EMP* 4,116
SIC 8062 8399 General medical & surgical hospitals; Health systems agency
CEO: Richard P Miller
Pr: Stephen Boyle
Pr: Lillian Carson
Pr: Lisa Iacovelli
**COO:* Ninfa Saunders
**CFO:* Robert Segin
**Ch:* Anthony Chigounis
**Ch:* Dennis Flanagan
**Treas:* David Kindlick
Treas: Christopher Warren
Ofcr: Michael E Pepe
**Ex VP:* Alfred Campanella
Ex VP: James Dwyer
**Ex VP:* Michael S Kotzen
**Ex VP:* John M Matsinger
VP: Jane Yepez

D-U-N-S 96-791-3406
VIRTUA MEDICAL GROUP PA
(*Suby of* NEW BEGINNINGS WEIGHT LOSS PRO) ★
301 Lippincott Dr, Marlton, NJ 08053-4197
Tel (856) 355-0340 *Founded/Ownrshp* 2009
Sales 97.4MM *EMP* 1E
SIC 8099 8082 Medical services organization; Home health care services
Ch Bd: Anthony Chigounis
**CEO:* Richard Miller

D-U-N-S 07-550-9794
VIRTUA MEMORIAL HOSPITAL BURLINGTON COUNTY INC (NJ)
(*Suby of* NEW BEGINNINGS WEIGHT LOSS PRO) ★
175 Madison Ave, Mount Holly, NJ 08060-2099
Tel (609) 267-0700 *Founded/Ownrshp* 1880, 1984
Sales 128.8MME *EMP* 1,450
SIC 8062 General medical & surgical hospitals
Pr: Richard P Miller
**Pr:* Richard Miller
**COO:* Tim Selz
**Ex VP:* Alfred Campanella
**Ex VP:* Michael S Kotzen
**Ex VP:* John M Matsinger Do
**Ex VP:* Robert Segin
Dir Rad: John Curtis
VP Opers: Robert Hockel
Doctor: Jagjit Chawla
Doctor: Robert Cowan

D-U-N-S 06-905-7115
VIRTUA-WEST JERSEY HEALTH SYSTEM INC (NJ)
(*Suby of* NEW BEGINNINGS WEIGHT LOSS PRO) ★
1000 Atlantic Ave, Camden, NJ 08104-1132
Tel (856) 246-3000 *Founded/Ownrshp* 1884, 1904
Sales 243.6MME *EMP* 4,100
SIC 8062 General medical & surgical hospitals
Pr: Richard Miller
**CFO:* Robert Segin
**Ch:* Dennis Flanagan
**Treas:* David Kindlick
VP: James Rivard
Ex Dir: Donald Jones

D-U-N-S 83-103-9560
VIRTUAL TECHNOLOGIES GROUP
3820 S Dixie Hwy, Lima, OH 45806-1848
Tel (419) 991-4694 *Founded/Ownrshp* 2008
Sales 87.3MME *EMP* 47E
SIC 5045 Computers
VP: Mike Curtis
CFO: Mike Vansky
Sales Exec: Kelly Davis

VIRTUALCOLOR
See FORT DEARBORN CO

D-U-N-S 02-725-4683
VIRTUS HOLDINGS LLC
540 Prospect St, Combined Locks, WI 54113-1120
Tel (920) 788-3550 *Founded/Ownrshp* 2010
Sales 325.0MME *EMP* 590
SIC 2672 2621 Coated paper, except photographic, carbon or abrasive; Uncoated paper
CEO: Sandra Van Ert

D-U-N-S 78-769-0122 IMP
VIRTUS PARTNERS INC
P X P
100 Pearl St Fl 9, Hartford, CT 06103-4500
Tel (860) 403-5000 *Founded/Ownrshp* 1988
Sales 214.6MME *EMP* 1,079
Accts Pricewaterhousecoopers Llp Ha
SIC 6282 Manager of mutual funds, contract or fee basis
Pr: George R Aylward Jr
COO: Jeannine Vanian
VP: John Beary
VP: Dave Martin
VP: Francis Waltmon
Board of Directors: John T Anderson, Glen D Churchill, Robert W Fiondella, Marilyn E Lamarche, James M Oates, Donna F Tuttle, Ferdinand Lj Verdonck, David A Williams

D-U-N-S 04-827-0180
▲ **VIRTUSA CORP** (MA)
2000 W Park Dr Ste 300, Westborough, MA 01581-3957
Tel (508) 389-7300 *Founded/Ownrshp* 1996
Sales 600.3MM *EMP* 18,226E
Tkr Sym VRTU *Exch* NGS
SIC 7371 7379 Custom computer programming services; Computer related consulting services
Ch Bd: Kris Canekeratne
Pr: Jitin Goyal
COO: Roger Keith Modder
CFO: Ranjan Kalia
Bd of Dir: Al-Noor Ramji
Ofcr: Sundararajan Narayanan
Ex VP: Samir Dhir
Ex VP: Thomas R Holler
VP: Gary Gibbs
VP: Harsha Kumar
VP: Sumita Ohri
VP: Michael Picard
Exec: Devakumar Selvarajan
Board of Directors: Robert E Davoli, Ronald T Maheu, Rowland T Moriarty, Barry R Nearhos, William K O'brien, Martin Trust

D-U-N-S 80-804-0260
▲ **VISA INC**
900 Metro Center Blvd, Foster City, CA 94404-2775
Tel (650) 432-3200 *Founded/Ownrshp* 1958
Sales 13.8MMM *EMP* 11,300
Tkr Sym V *Exch* NYS
SIC 7389 Credit card service
CEO: Charles W Scharf
Ch Bd: Robert W Matschullat
Pr: Ryan McInerney
CFO: Vasant M Prabhu
Ex VP: Robert Alandt
Ex VP: William Sheedy
Ex VP: Rajat Taneja
Ex VP: Kelly Mahon Tullier
Sr VP: James H Hoffmeister
VP: Patrick Collins
VP: Stephen Kehoe
VP: Julie Miller
VP: Abdallah Saoud
VP: M Tilahun
VP: Brian Wood

D-U-N-S 08-385-1147
■ **VISA INTERNATIONAL SERVICE ASSOCIATION**
(*Suby of* VISA INC) ★
900 Metro Center Blvd, Foster City, CA 94404-2172
Tel (650) 432-3200 *Founded/Ownrshp* 1974
Sales 315.0MME *EMP* 1,800
SIC 7389 Financial services
CEO: Charles W Scharf
Ch Bd: William I Campbell
CFO: Byron H Pollitt
Ofcr: Terence Milholland
Ex VP: John Elkins
Ex VP: Thomas M'Guinness
Ex VP: Carol Walsh
VP: Elizabeth Hurvitz
VP: Giovanni Leoni
VP: Eddy Woiski
Prin: Dolores A Ligibel
Board of Directors: Michael Fairey, Yang Bin Ahmad, Peter Hawkins, Peter Ayliffe, Gary Hoffman, Vivian Bartlett, Benjamin P Jenkins III, Alberta G Cefis, Jan Liden, David H Chafey, David Mowat, John Philip Coghlan, Gerard Nebouy, Richard K Davis, Peter Raskind, Charles T Doyle, John G Stumpf, Dr Johannes Evers, Hans Van Der Velde

VISA LIGHTING
See OLDENBURG GROUP INC

D-U-N-S 05-840-7206
■ **VISA USA INC**
(*Suby of* VISA INC) ★
900 Metro Center Blvd, Foster City, CA 94404-2172
Tel (650) 432-3200 *Founded/Ownrshp* 2007
Sales 431.6MME *EMP* 3,800
SIC 7389 Financial services
CEO: Charles W Scharf
**CFO:* Victor W Dahir
CFO: Byron H Pollitt
**Chf Mktg O:* Kevin Burke
Ex VP: Fred Bauer
**Ex VP:* Joshua R Floum
**Ex VP:* Douglas Michelman
**Ex VP:* Kevin J Schultz
Ex VP: Rajat Taneja
Ex VP: Kelly Tullier
VP: Sue Jacobs
VP: Scott Thompson

D-U-N-S 02-002-7447
VISALIA UNIFIED SCHOOL DISTRICT
VISALIA USD
5000 W Cypress Ave, Visalia, CA 93277-8300
Tel (559) 730-7529 *Founded/Ownrshp* 1965
Sales 275.0MM *EMP* 4,000
Accts Crowe Horwath Llp Sacramento
SIC 8211 8299 Public combined elementary & secondary school; Educational services
Ex Dir: Nathan Hernandez
Dir Sec: Mimi Bonds
Dir Sec: Rebecca Peterson
MIS Dir: Al Foytek
Dir IT: Chuck Boone
Schl Brd P: Juan Guerro

VISALIA USD
See VISALIA UNIFIED SCHOOL DISTRICT

D-U-N-S 14-126-0757
■ **VISANT CORP**
(*Suby of* VISANT SECONDARY HOLDINGS CORP) ★
3601 Minnesota Dr Ste 400, Minneapolis, MN 55435-6008
Tel (914) 595-8200 *Founded/Ownrshp* 2003
Sales 831.7MM *EMP* 3,404E

SIC 3911 2741 2389 7221 Rings, finger: precious metal; Yearbooks: publishing & printing; Academic vestments (caps & gowns); School photographer
Ch Bd: Marc L Reisch
CFO: Paul B Carousso
Board of Directors: David F Burgstahler, Webster Chua, Charles W Mooty, Susan C Schnabel

D-U-N-S 17-189-7346 IMP/EXP
■ VISANT HOLDING CORP
(*Suby of* NEWELL BRANDS) ★
3601 Minnesota Dr Ste 400, Minneapolis, MN 55435-6008
Tel (914) 595-8200 *Founded/Ownrshp* 2015
Sales 2.6MMM^E *EMP* 5,250^E
SIC 2741 2759 3911 6719 Yearbooks: publishing & printing; Commercial printing; Invitation & stationery printing & engraving; Announcements: engraved; Stationery: printing; Jewelry, precious metal; Investment holding companies, except banks
Pr: Marc L Reisch
**CFO:* James S Simpson

D-U-N-S 96-979-2139
■ VISANT SECONDARY HOLDINGS CORP
(*Suby of* VISANT HOLDING CORP) ★
357 Main St, Armonk, NY 10504-1808
Tel (914) 595-8200 *Founded/Ownrshp* 2004
Sales 831.7MM^E *EMP* 3,404^E
SIC 2741 Yearbooks: publishing & printing
VP: Paul B Carousso
Sr VP: Marie Hlavaty
Snr Mgr: Marc L Reisch

D-U-N-S 03-411-7908 IMP
VISCARDI INDUSTRIAL SERVICES LLC
815 Lucerne Dr, New Iberia, LA 70563-8980
Tel (337) 367-0824 *Founded/Ownrshp* 2000
Sales 150.3MM *EMP* 440
SIC 1541 Industrial buildings, new construction

VISHAY INTERTECHNOLOGY
See DALE VISHAY ELECTRONICS LLC

D-U-N-S 00-232-7484
▲ VISHAY INTERTECHNOLOGY INC
63 Lancaster Ave, Malvern, PA 19355-2120
Tel (610) 644-1300 *Founded/Ownrshp* 1962
Sales 2.3MMM *EMP* 22,400^E
Accts Ernst & Young Llp Philadelphi
Tkr Sym VSH *Exch* NYS
SIC 3676 3677 3675 3674 3613 3612 Electronic resistors; Resistor networks; Thermistors, except temperature sensors; Electronic coils, transformers & other inductors; Electronic capacitors; Semiconductors & related devices; Switchgear & switchboard apparatus; Transformers, except electric
Pr: Gerald Paul
**Ch Bd:* Marc Zandman
COO: Dieter Wunderlich
CFO: Lori Lipcaman
Ex VP: David Valletta
Ex VP: Johan Vandoom
Sr VP: Peter G Henrici
Sr VP: David L Tomlinson
Sr VP: Clarence TSE
VP: Tony Nguyen
VP: Kyle Terrill
Board of Directors: Abraham Ludomirski, Frank D Maier, Ronald M Ruzic, Ziv Shoshani, Timothy V Talbert, Thomas C Wertheimer

D-U-N-S 96-274-1570
■ VISHAY PRECISION FOIL INC
(*Suby of* VISHAY PRECISION GROUP INC) ★
3 Great Valley Pkwy # 150, Malvern, PA 19355-1478
Tel (484) 321-5300 *Founded/Ownrshp* 2009
Sales 97.5MM^E *EMP* 1,900^E
SIC 3676 Electronic resistors
CEO: Ziv Shoshani
**CFO:* Willian Clancy
**Treas:* Steven Klausner

D-U-N-S 03-117-8695
▲ VISHAY PRECISION GROUP INC
3 Great Valley Pkwy # 150, Malvern, PA 19355-1478
Tel (484) 321-5300 *Founded/Ownrshp* 2009
Sales 232.1MM *EMP* 2,352^E
Tkr Sym VPG *Exch* NYS
SIC 3676 3823 Electronic resistors; Pressure measurement instruments, industrial
Pr: Ziv Shoshani
**Ch Bd:* Marc Zandman
**CFO:* William M Clancy
**VP:* Roland B Desilets
Sls Mgr: Gary Miller
Board of Directors: Janet Clarke, Saul Reibstein, Timothy Talbert, Cary Wood

D-U-N-S 07-813-3902 IMP
■ VISHAY SILICONIX LLC
(*Suby of* SILICONIX INC) ★
2201 Laurelwood Rd, Santa Clara, CA 95054-1516
Tel (408) 988-8000 *Founded/Ownrshp* 1999
Sales 134.6MM^E *EMP* 700
SIC 2869 Silicones
Ch Bd: Felix Zandman
Ex VP: David Valletta
Sr VP: Peter G Henrici
Ql Cn Mgr: Ankur Tyagi
Mktg Mgr: Phil Cohen

VISION 4 LESS
See EYE-MART EXPRESS INC

D-U-N-S 05-596-1338
VISION BUICK GMC LLC
PIEHLER-VISION BUICK GMC
800 Panorama Trl S, Rochester, NY 14625-2310
Tel (585) 586-6940 *Founded/Ownrshp* 2013
Sales 96.0MM *EMP* 53
SIC 5511

D-U-N-S 07-846-1772
■ VISION CARE INSTITUTE LLC
(*Suby of* VISTAKON) ★
7500 Centurion Pkwy, Jacksonville, FL 32256-0517
Tel (904) 443-1086 *Founded/Ownrshp* 2006
Sales 11.0MM^E *EMP* 1,374^E
SIC 8042 Visual training specialist optometrist
Ex Dir: Colleen Jones

D-U-N-S 00-705-7933
VISION INFORMATION TECHNOLOGIES INC (MI)
VISIONIT
3031 W Grand Blvd Ste 600, Detroit, MI 48202-3014
Tel (313) 664-5650 *Founded/Ownrshp* 1997
Sales 189.3MM *EMP* 880^E
Accts Clayton & Mckervey Pc South
SIC 7363 7379 Temporary help service; Computer related maintenance services
CEO: David H Segura
**Pr:* Christine Rice
**CFO:* Larry Kaylor
Dir IT: Gaurang Joshi

D-U-N-S 07-480-2579
VISION PROMOTIONS INC
81 Hobart St, Hackensack, NJ 07601-3912
Tel (908) 333-4213 *Founded/Ownrshp* 2014
Sales 130.0MM *EMP* 43
SIC 7311 Advertising agencies
Pr: David Fisher

D-U-N-S 07-155-4026 IMP
VISION SERVICE PLAN
C V S OPTICAL LAB DIV
3333 Quality Dr, Rancho Cordova, CA 95670-9757
Tel (916) 851-5000 *Founded/Ownrshp* 1955
Sales NA *EMP* 3,055
SIC 6324 5048 Hospital & medical service plans; Ophthalmic goods
CEO: James Robinson Lynch
**COO:* Laura Costa
CFO: Donald J Ball Jr
**Sr VP:* Gary Brooks
VP: Gary Norman Brooks
VP: Maryann Cavanaugh
**VP:* Thomas Fessler
VP: Janet Findlay
VP: Walter E Grubbs
VP: Kate Lawrence
VP: Patrick McClelland
VP: Dan Morgan
VP: Dave Plevyak
VP: Lawrence Donald Price
VP: Kathy Rodine
VP: Frank Romeo
VP: Richard W Steere
VP: Pam Tomlin
Exec: Robin Eisenbeisz
Exec: Devin Farrell
Exec: Cynthia Vonessacos

D-U-N-S 78-653-1624
VISION SOLUTIONS INC
(*Suby of* CLEARLAKE CAPITAL GROUP LP) ★
15300 Barranca Pkwy # 100, Irvine, CA 92618-2256
Tel (949) 253-6500 *Founded/Ownrshp* 2016
Sales 145.0MM *EMP* 650
SIC 7371 7373 Computer software development; Systems integration services
Pr: Nicolaas Vlok
**CFO:* Don Scott
**Chf Mktg O:* Wm Edward Vesely
**Ex VP:* Alan Arnold
**Ex VP:* Robert Johnson
Ex VP: Murray White
VP: Allan Campbell
VP: Marty Gilbert
VP: Craig Johnson
VP: Cathleen Keene
VP: Mike Khattab
VP: Henry Martinez
VP: Pete Robie
VP: Jude Sullivan
VP: Peter SA
Exec: Richard Tee

D-U-N-S 61-779-3364
VISION TECHNOLOGIES ELECTRONICS INC
(*Suby of* VISION TECHNOLOGIES SYSTEMS INC) ★
99 Canal Center Plz # 210, Alexandria, VA 22314-1559
Tel (703) 739-2610 *Founded/Ownrshp* 2000
Sales 243.6MM^E *EMP* 600
SIC 8711 Engineering services
Pr: Edward Szeto
**CEO:* John G Coburn
**CFO:* Suzanne Soh

D-U-N-S 01-763-1941
■ VISION TECHNOLOGIES INC
(*Suby of* BG STAFFING LLC) ★
530 Mccormick Dr Ste G, Glen Burnie, MD 21061-8200
Tel (410) 424-2183 *Founded/Ownrshp* 2015
Sales 108.8MM^E *EMP* 440
SIC 7373 Computer integrated systems design
Pr: John L Shetrone Jr
COO: Bill Tolbert
CFO: S Michael Quade
Sr VP: Kevin Nolan
Sr VP: Albert Saxon
QA Dir: Carolyn Elster
Software D: Tracy Simmons
Netwrk Eng: Weston Brown

D-U-N-S 10-870-2163 IMP
VISION TECHNOLOGIES KINETICS INC
(*Suby of* VISION TECHNOLOGIES SYSTEMS INC) ★
3800 Richardson Rd, Hope Hull, AL 36043-4017
Tel (334) 284-8665 *Founded/Ownrshp* 2002
Sales 168.6MM^E *EMP* 2,000^E
SIC 3714 3795 Motor vehicle parts & accessories; Tanks & tank components
Pr: Julie Briggs
**CFO:* Tom B Dake
VP Admn: Edward Crowell

D-U-N-S 10-347-7845 IMP/EXP
VISION TECHNOLOGIES SYSTEMS INC
(*Suby of* SINGAPORE TECHNOLOGIES ENGINEERING LTD)
99 Canal Center Plz # 220, Alexandria, VA 22314-1559
Tel (703) 739-2610 *Founded/Ownrshp* 2001
Sales 1.2MMM^E *EMP* 2,000^E
SIC 3731 3531 Shipbuilding & repairing; Drags, road (construction & road maintenance equipment)
CEO: John G Coburn
COO: Raymond Mason
CFO: Shaydra Tisdale
**Treas:* Patrick Lee
Sr VP: Pat Macarevey
VP: Richard Fruzzetti
VP: Chin Peh
Genl Mgr: Julian Mallett
MIS Dir: Robin Keyack

VISION-EASE LENS
See INSIGHT EQUITY A P X L P

VISION-EASE LENS
See LENS VISION-EASE CORP

VISION4LESS
See EYEMART EXPRESS LLC

D-U-N-S 11-265-9438
VISIONARY ENTERPRISES INC
6626 E 75th St Ste 100, Indianapolis, IN 46250-2854
Tel (317) 621-4000 *Founded/Ownrshp* 1982
Sales 169.1MM *EMP* 1,645
SIC 6531 8742 8093 Real estate managers; Management consulting services; Specialty outpatient clinics
CEO: Bryan Mills
**Pr:* William Corley
Exec: Linda Hijduke
Exec: Lesia Hills
Ex Dir: Angie Jaynes
Ex Dir: Arnie Starkey

D-U-N-S 03-694-3280
VISIONARY INTEGRATION PROFESSIONALS LLC
VISIONARY INTGRTION PRFSSONALS
(*Suby of* VISIONARY INTEGRATION PROFESSIONALS, INC.)
80 Iron Point Cir Ste 100, Folsom, CA 95630-8592
Tel (916) 608-8320 *Founded/Ownrshp* 2005
Sales 100.0MM *EMP* 625
SIC 8742 7379 Management consulting services; Computer related maintenance services
COO: Jason Marceau
COO: Terry Miller
CFO: Karen Davis
Ex VP: David Perroni
Ex VP: David J Rowe
Sr VP: Vicent Juaristi
VP: Michelle Marshall
VP: Kelli Schnieder
VP: Nell Tomasso
VP: Roger Ward
Exec: Joseph Zippi

VISIONARY INTGRTION PRFSSONALS
See VISIONARY INTEGRATION PROFESSIONALS LLC

VISIONIT
See VISION INFORMATION TECHNOLOGIES INC

D-U-N-S 18-630-0773
VISIONIT SUPPLIES AND SERVICES INC
3031 W Grand Blvd Ste 600, Detroit, MI 48202-3014
Tel (313) 664-5650 *Founded/Ownrshp* 1997
Sales 86.2MM^E *EMP* 1,000
SIC 3577 3955 5734 Printers, computer; Print cartridges for laser & other computer printers; Printers & plotters: computers
CEO: David H Segura
Ex Dir: Stiefel Laboratories

VISIONQUEST LODGEMAKER
See VISIONQUEST NONPROFIT CORP

D-U-N-S 92-987-7314
VISIONQUEST NONPROFIT CORP
VISIONQUEST LODGEMAKER
600 N Swan Rd, Tucson, AZ 85711-2102
Tel (520) 881-3950 *Founded/Ownrshp* 1993
Sales 19.3MM^E *EMP* 1,100
SIC 8361 8211 8322 Residential care; Private senior high school; Youth center
Pr: Peter Ranalli

D-U-N-S 07-729-3348
VISIONS FEDERAL CREDIT UNION
24 Mckinley Ave, Endicott, NY 13760-5415
Tel (607) 754-7900 *Founded/Ownrshp* 1966
Sales NA *EMP* 223
SIC 6061 Federal credit unions
CEO: Frank E Berrish
**CFO:* James Femlet
CFO: Harry Jacobson
Ex VP: Mark R Patterson
**Sr VP:* Charles J Bender
Board of Directors: Frank E Berrish

D-U-N-S 86-690-1721
VISIONWARE INC
(*Suby of* VISIONWORKS OF AMERICA INC) ★
11103 West Ave, San Antonio, TX 78213-1338
Tel (210) 340-3531 *Founded/Ownrshp* 1996
Sales 103.2MM^E *EMP* 800
SIC 5995 Optical goods stores
Pr: Bernard Andrews
Ex VP: George Gebhardt

D-U-N-S 11-890-9647 IMP
VISIONWORKS OF AMERICA INC
(*Suby of* EYE CARE CENTERS OF AMERICA) ★
175 E Houston St, San Antonio, TX 78205-2255
Tel (210) 340-3531 *Founded/Ownrshp* 2005
Sales 1.0MMM^E *EMP* 5,600
SIC 5995 Optical goods stores; Eyeglasses, prescription
Ch Bd: David L Holmberg
Pr: Jim N Eisen
COO: James N Eise
CFO: Jennifer L Taylor
CFO: Alan E Wiley
Ofcr: George E Gebhardt
Ex VP: Jennifer Taylor
Sr VP: Raymond D Carrig Jr
Sr VP: James J Denny
Sr VP: Robert A Niemiec
VP: Jody Anderson
VP: Stuart Bolerjack
VP: Vincent Iavarone
Board of Directors: David A Blandino, Nanette P Deturk, Brett C Moraski, William C Springer

VISIT FLORIDA
See FLORIDA TOURISM INDUSTRY MARKETING CORP

D-U-N-S 07-380-6945 IMP
VISITING NURSE ASSOCIATION OF BOSTON
VNAB
500 Rutherford Ave # 200, Charlestown, MA 02129-1647
Tel (617) 886-6463 *Founded/Ownrshp* 1886
Sales 4.4MM *EMP* 1,670
Accts Rsm Mcgladrey Inc Boston Ma
SIC 8082 Home health care services; Visiting nurse service
Ch Bd: Shephard Remis
**Pr:* Joanne Handy
**Pr:* Raynold Spaboni
CFO: Kim McCalti
**Treas:* John Mc Duffy
VP: Francis Lorion
VP: Kathleen O'Neil
VP: Kathleen Oneil
CIO: Bryan Kaplan

D-U-N-S 07-826-8828
VISITING NURSE ASSOCIATION OF CENTRAL JERSEY INC
VNA OF CENTRAL JERSEY
176 Riverside Ave, Red Bank, NJ 07701-1063
Tel (732) 747-1204 *Founded/Ownrshp* 1912
Sales 71.0MM *EMP* 1,000
Accts Withumsmithbrownpc Red Bank
SIC 8082 Visiting nurse service
CEO: Mary Ann Christopher
**CFO:* Kevin G Rogers
VP: Kathleen McConnell
VP: Loretta Spoltore
Dir Soc: Cammy Tedesco
Dir IT: John Albright

D-U-N-S 07-888-1778 IMP
VISITING NURSE SERVICE OF NEW YORK
5 Penn Plz Ste 1201, New York, NY 10001-1824
Tel (212) 609-6100 *Founded/Ownrshp* 1893
Sales 541.9MM^E *EMP* 11,780
SIC 8082 Visiting nurse service
CEO: Mary Ann Christopher
**CFO:* Sameul Heller
**Ch:* Douglas Broadwater
Sr VP: Michael Bernstein
Sr VP: Kerry Parker
VP: Charles Blum
VP: Thomas Check
VP: Ilaina Edison
VP: Lynda Montella
VP: Neil Pessin
VP: May Schee
VP Bus Dev: Elaine Keane

D-U-N-S 15-770-9452
VISITING NURSE SERVICE OF NEW YORK HOME CARE
(*Suby of* VISITING NURSE SERVICE OF NEW YORK) ★
107 E 70th St, New York, NY 10021-4990
Tel (212) 484-3950 *Founded/Ownrshp* 1984
Sales 32.8MM^E *EMP* 2,000
SIC 8082 Home health care services
Pr: Carol Raphael
COO: Joan Marren
CFO: Samuel Hellar
Bd of Dir: William F Baker

D-U-N-S 96-776-9113
VISITING NURSE SERVICE OF NEW YORK HOME CARE II
5 Penn Plz Fl 12, New York, NY 10001-1810
Tel (212) 609-5716 *Founded/Ownrshp* 2011
Sales 617.1MM *EMP* 8^E
Accts Kpmg Llp Albany Ny
SIC 8082 Visiting nurse service
Pr: Mariane Christopher

D-U-N-S 96-766-5873
VISITING NURSE SERVICE OF NEW YORK HOSPICE CARE
5 Penn Plz Ste 1201, New York, NY 10001-1824
Tel (212) 609-5716 *Founded/Ownrshp* 2011
Sales 83.8MM *EMP* 6^E
Accts Kpmg Llp Albany Ny
SIC 8082 Visiting nurse service
Prin: Jeanne Dennis

D-U-N-S 05-385-5177 IMP/EXP
■ VISKASE COMPANIES INC
(*Suby of* ICAHN ENTERPRISES LP) ★
333 E Butterfield Rd # 400, Lombard, IL 60148-5679
Tel (630) 874-0700 *Founded/Ownrshp* 2010
Sales 343.5MM *EMP* 1,582
Accts Grant Thornton Llp Chicago I
SIC 3089 Celluloid products; Cases, plastic; Battery cases, plastic or plastic combination
Ch Bd: Thomas D Davis
Pr: Jean-Luc Tillon
CFO: John Plescia
Bd of Dir: Chris Williams
Sr VP: Maurice J Ryan
VP: Michael M Blecic
VP: Newton Martins
VP: Myron D Nicholson PHD
Exec: Michael D Schenker
Genl Mgr: Gonzalo Valdez
Snr Ntwrk: James Strait
Board of Directors: Thomas D Davis, Hunter C Gary, Peter Reck, Auguste E Rimpel Jr, Peter K Shea

D-U-N-S 14-830-2698 IMP/EXP
■ VISKASE CORP
(*Suby of* VISKASE COMPANIES INC) ★
333 E Bttrfeld Rd Ste 400, Lombard, IL 60148
Tel (630) 874-0700 *Founded/Ownrshp* 1989
Sales 223.3MM[E] *EMP* 1,350
SIC 3089 Celluloid products
Ch Bd: F Edward Gustafson
**Pr:* John F Weber
Bd of Dir: Robert Dangremond
**VP:* Gordon S Donovan
Off Mgr: Kimberly Diddia
Plnt Mgr: Pat Glarrow

VISTA ALTERNATIVE CAMPUS
See GRAPEVINE - COLLYVILLE INDEPENDENT SCHOOL DIST

D-U-N-S 79-178-6486 EXP
■ VISTA BAKERY INC
LANCE PRIVATE BRANDS
(*Suby of* SNYDERS-LANCE INC) ★
3000 Mount Pleasant St, Burlington, IA 52601-2064
Tel (704) 554-1421 *Founded/Ownrshp* 1934
Sales 190.1MM[E] *EMP* 1,200
SIC 5149 Bakery products
Pr: H D Fields
**Pr:* Dean Fields
Exec: Ron Craft
Exec: Karen S Taylor
Sls Mgr: Tyler Cook

D-U-N-S 83-139-5582
VISTA EQUITY PARTNERS FUND III LP
(*Suby of* VISTA EQUITY PARTNERS LLC) ★
4 Embarcadero Ctr # 2000, San Francisco, CA 94111-5982
Tel (415) 765-6500 *Founded/Ownrshp* 2007
Sales 87.8MM[E] *EMP* 1,030[E]
SIC 6799 Venture capital companies
CFO: John Warnken-Brill
VP: Betty Hung
Prin: Robert F Smith

D-U-N-S 08-024-3845
VISTA EQUITY PARTNERS FUND VI-A LP
(*Suby of* VISTA EQUITY PARTNERS MANAGEMENT, LLC)
4 Embarcadero Ctr Fl 20, San Francisco, CA 94111-5982
Tel (415) 765-6500 *Founded/Ownrshp* 2016
Sales 128.8M[E] *EMP* 5,003[E]
SIC 6722 Money market mutual funds

D-U-N-S 84-833-2354
VISTA EQUITY PARTNERS LLC
(*Suby of* VISTA EQUITY PARTNERS MANAGEMENT, LLC)
4 Embarcadero Ctr # 2000, San Francisco, CA 94111-5982
Tel (415) 765-6500 *Founded/Ownrshp* 2000
Sales 1.0MMM[E] *EMP* 1,609
SIC 6726

D-U-N-S 02-128-5101 IMP
VISTA FOOD EXCHANGE INC
355 Food Center Dr B101, Bronx, NY 10474-7000
Tel (718) 542-4401 *Founded/Ownrshp* 1979
Sales 90.4MM[E] *EMP* 78
SIC 5144 5147 5146 5148 5143 Poultry & poultry products; Meats, fresh; Fish & seafoods; Vegetables, fresh; Dairy products, except dried or canned
Pr: Vincent Pacifico
**CFO:* Allen Butterfast
Off Mgr: Tracy Debus
Dir IT: Michelle Whaley
Sls Mgr: Matthew Gibson

D-U-N-S 07-294-0372
VISTA FORD INC
VISTA LINCOLN
21501 Ventura Blvd, Woodland Hills, CA 91364-1998
Tel (818) 884-7600 *Founded/Ownrshp* 1995
Sales 134.8MM[E] *EMP* 400
SIC 5511 Automobiles, new & used
Pr: Jonathan W Shuken
**Pr:* Victoria A Shuken
**Sec:* Carl Tsai
Ofcr: Tony Fiori
Exec: Chris Sweeney
Genl Mgr: John Schuker
Genl Mgr: Tori Shuken

VISTA GERDE MEDICAL PLAZA
See SHANNON CLINIC

D-U-N-S 92-639-9155
VISTA HEALTH SYSTEM
1324 N Sheridan Rd, Waukegan, IL 60085-2161
Tel (847) 249-3505 *Founded/Ownrshp* 1982
Sales 102.9MM[E] *EMP* 950
SIC 8062 General medical & surgical hospitals
Pr: Timothy J Harrington
**CFO:* David Rothenberger
CIO: Janna Peters
Dir IT: Catherine Marks
VP Mktg: Larry Stanley

VISTA HOST HOTEL MANAGEMENT
See VISTA HOST INC

D-U-N-S 09-194-6968
VISTA HOST INC
VISTA HOST HOTEL MANAGEMENT
10370 Richmond Ave # 150, Houston, TX 77042-4123
Tel (713) 267-5800 *Founded/Ownrshp* 1985
Sales 19.7MM[E] *EMP* 1,000
SIC 7011 Hotels & motels
Ch Bd: Michael V Harrell
**CFO:* Kathie Long
**VP:* Paul Horn
**VP:* Joseph Viglietta
Genl Mgr: Bridgett Stoddard

VISTA LINCOLN
See VISTA FORD INC

VISTA MEDICAL CENTER EAST
See WAUKEGAN ILLINOIS HOSPITAL CO LLC

D-U-N-S 04-310-5071
VISTA NORTH HOSPITAL INC
(*Suby of* PRIME HEALTHCARE SERVICES INC) ★
1409 E Lake Mead Blvd, North Las Vegas, NV 89030-7120
Tel (702) 649-7711 *Founded/Ownrshp* 2015
Sales 89.4MM[E] *EMP* 650
SIC 8062 General medical & surgical hospitals
CEO: Vince Variale
**Chf Rad:* Jeannie Murphy
**CFO:* George Wiley
Dir Sec: Damian Goodrich

D-U-N-S 07-972-8394
▲ VISTA OUTDOOR INC
262 N University Ave, Farmington, UT 84025-2975
Tel (801) 447-3000 *Founded/Ownrshp* 2014
Sales 2.2MMM *EMP* 5,800[E]
Tkr Sym VSTO *Exch* NYS
SIC 3482 3483 3827 3949 3484 3812 Small arms ammunition; Cartridge cases for ammunition, 30 mm. & below; Cartridges, 30 mm. & below; Pellets & BB's, pistol & air rifle ammunition; Ammunition, except for small arms; Ammunition components; Ammunition loading & assembling plant; Binoculars; Archery equipment, general; Decoys, duck & other game birds; Small arms; Search & navigation equipment
Ch Bd: Mark W Deyoung
Pr: Kelly T Grindle
Pr: Robert J Keller
**CFO:* Stephen M Nolan
**Sr VP:* Scott D Chaplin
**Sr VP:* Stephen S Clark
VP: Brett L Merrell
VP: Matthew J Reintjes
VP: David White
Board of Directors: Michael Callahan, April H Foley, Mark A Gottfredson, Gary L McArthur, Robert M Tarola

D-U-N-S 07-933-1239
■ VISTA OUTDOOR SALES LLC
(*Suby of* VISTA OUTDOOR INC) ★
1 Vista Way, Anoka, MN 55303-6794
Tel (763) 323-2414 *Founded/Ownrshp* 2014
Sales 142.2MM[E] *EMP* 320
SIC 3482 3069 Small arms ammunition; Cartridge cases for ammunition, 30 mm. & below; Cartridges, 30 mm. & below; Paper shells: empty, blank or loaded: 30 mm. & below; Rubber hardware
CEO: Mark Deyoung
**CFO:* Stephen Nolan
Opers Mgr: Daniel Aiken

D-U-N-S 00-838-7474 IMP
VISTA PAINT CORP
2020 E Orangethorpe Ave, Fullerton, CA 92831-5327
Tel (714) 680-3800 *Founded/Ownrshp* 1956
Sales 105.3MM[E] *EMP* 475
SIC 5231 2851 Paint; Paints & paint additives
Pr: Eddie R Fischer
CFO: Roger Douglass
CFO: John Jacob
CFO: Dave Reves
**VP:* Jerome Fischer
VP: Joe Windberg
QC Dir: Graham Llera
QC Dir: Graham Swann
Site Mgr: Sandy Strendberg
**VP Sls:* Joe Wittenberg
Sls Mgr: Greg Simpson

D-U-N-S 03-061-0105
VISTA RCHP-SIERRA INC
CANYON VISTA MEDICAL CENTER
(*Suby of* VISTA RCHP-SIERRA HOLDING INC)
5700 E Highway 90, Sierra Vista, AZ 85635-9110
Tel (520) 458-4641 *Founded/Ownrshp* 2013
Sales 97.2MM *EMP* 650
SIC 8062 General medical & surgical hospitals
CEO: Martin S Rash
CFO: Steve Calabrese

D-U-N-S 07-335-5505
VISTA UNIFIED SCHOOL DISTRICT INC
1234 Arcadia Ave, Vista, CA 92084-3404
Tel (760) 726-2170 *Founded/Ownrshp* 1936
Sales 100.3MM[E] *EMP* 1,600
Accts Wilkinson Hadley King & Co L
SIC 8211 Public elementary & secondary schools
VP: Carol W Herrera
VP: Carol Hunley
VP: Akiko Morimoto
Prin: Mike Barnes
Prin: Rodney Goldenberg
Prin: David Lacey
Prin: Hector Menchaca
Ex Dir: Matt Doyle
Ex Dir: Dawn Dully
Dir IT: Dewayne Cossey
Schl Brd P: Elizabeth Jaka

D-U-N-S 83-167-8649 IMP
VISTA-PRO AUTOMOTIVE LLC
22 Century Blvd Ste 410, Nashville, TN 37214-3763
Tel (615) 622-2200 *Founded/Ownrshp* 2009
Sales 386.8MM[E] *EMP* 1,782
SIC 3714

D-U-N-S 11-807-3712
■ VISTACARE INC
(*Suby of* ODYSSEY HEALTHCARE INC) ★
717 N Harwood St Ste 1500, Dallas, TX 75201-6519
Tel (480) 648-4545 *Founded/Ownrshp* 2008
Sales 22.3MM[E] *EMP* 2,555
SIC 8082 Home health care services
Pr: Robert A Lefton
COO: Craig P Goguen
CFO: R Dirk Allison
Ofcr: Todd Cote MD
Sr VP: Brenda A Belger
Sr VP: W Bradley Bickham
Prin: Carla Demichiel
Ex Dir: Joi Bodine
Ex Dir: Rob Zachrich
Sls&Mrk Ex: Elaine Badnais
Sls&Mrk Ex: Molly Meador-Hall

VISTAKON
See JOHNSON & JOHNSON VISION CARE INC

D-U-N-S 00-684-3336
■ VISTAR MIDATLANTIC
(*Suby of* P F G) ★
1109 Commerce Blvd 100, Swedesboro, NJ 08085-1763
Tel (856) 294-0500 *Founded/Ownrshp* 2012
Sales 99.2MM[E] *EMP* 196[E]
SIC 5145 Snack foods
Pr: George Holm

D-U-N-S 01-867-8391 IMP
VISTAR/VSA OF HARTFORD INC
VSA OF NEW ENGLAND
175 Sullivan Ave, South Windsor, CT 06074-1934
Tel (860) 688-7702 *Founded/Ownrshp* 1999
Sales 84.0MM[E] *EMP* 175
SIC 5141 5812 8322

D-U-N-S 16-372-7804
▲ VISTEON CORP
1 Village Center Dr, Van Buren Twp, MI 48111-5711
Tel (800) 847-8366 *Founded/Ownrshp* 2000
Sales 3.2MMM *EMP* 11,000[E]
Tkr Sym VC *Exch* NYS
SIC 3714 Motor vehicle parts & accessories; Motor vehicle engines & parts; Motor vehicle body components & frame; Motor vehicle electrical equipment
CEO: Sachin S Lawande
**Ch Bd:* Francis M Scricco
CFO: Christian Garcia
CFO: Christian A Garcia
Top Exec: Matthew Cole
Top Exec: Robert Vallance
VP: William M Robertson
Assoc Dir: Jim Westropp
CTO: Markus Schupfner
Tech Mgr: Ingo Schneider
Opers Mgr: Laxman Bargav
Board of Directors: Naomi M Bergman, Jeffrey D Jones, Joanne M Maguire, Robert Manzo, David L Treadwell, Harry J Wilson

D-U-N-S 08-045-7910
VISTRA ENERGY CORP
1601 Bryan St, Dallas, TX 75201-3401
Tel (214) 812-4600 *Founded/Ownrshp* 2016
Sales 839.6M[E] *EMP* 8,860
SIC 5722 Electric household appliances, major
Pr: Curtis A Morgan
**COO:* Jim Burke
VP: Molly Sorg

D-U-N-S 14-478-2380
VISUAL PAK CO
1909 S Waukegan Rd, Waukegan, IL 60085-6709
Tel (847) 689-1000 *Founded/Ownrshp* 1983
Sales 220.5MM[E] *EMP* 500
SIC 7389 Packaging & labeling services
CEO: Clayton Bolke
**Pr:* David L Waldron
CFO: John Rubin
**VP:* Dan Brosseau
Dir: Mike Sawant
Genl Mgr: Martin Calvo
CIO: Tim Koers
IT Man: Bob Berg
Plnt Mgr: Dan Clark
Prd Mgr: Martha Avila
Natl Sales: Timothy Goll

VITA COCO
See ALL MARKET INC

D-U-N-S 00-415-3987 IMP/EXP
VITA-MIX CORP
VITAMIX
8615 Usher Rd, Olmsted Twp, OH 44138-2199
Tel (440) 235-4840 *Founded/Ownrshp* 1921
Sales 135.6MM[E] *EMP* 388[E]
SIC 5961 3556

D-U-N-S 79-790-8332
VITAC CORP
101 Hillpointe Dr Ste 200, Canonsburg, PA 15317-9503
Tel (724) 514-4000 *Founded/Ownrshp* 2016
Sales 106.1MM[E] *EMP* 320
SIC 4899 7819 Data communication services; Video tape or disk reproduction
Pr: Pat Prozzi
V Ch: Patricia Hastings
Pr: Timothy Lam
Pr: Timothy Taylor
**COO:* Chuck Karlovits
CFO: Robert Nazarian
**Sr VP:* Darryn Cleary
Sr VP: Richard Leet
**Sr VP:* Deborah Schuste
VP: Yelena Makarczyk
VP: Maggie McDermo
VP: Deborah Schuster

D-U-N-S 94-969-7700 EXP
■ VITACOST.COM INC
(*Suby of* VIGOR ACQUISITION CORP) ★
5400 Broken Sound Blvd # 500, Boca Raton, FL 33487-3521
Tel (561) 982-4180 *Founded/Ownrshp* 2014
Sales 206.4MM[E] *EMP* 790
SIC 5961 Catalog & mail-order houses; Mail order house
CEO: Jeffrey J Horowitz
**CFO:* Brian D Helman
**Chf Mktg O:* Christopher Cavalline
VP: Ellen Finnerty
**CIO:* Joseph R Topper Jr
Opers Mgr: Sharlene Payne
Pr Mgr: Soniya Lambert
Snr PM: Howard Samson

D-U-N-S 10-228-1201
■ VITAL SIGNS MN INC
(*Suby of* VITAL SIGNS, INC.)
5859 Farinon Dr Ste 200, San Antonio, TX 78249-3461
Tel (952) 894-7523 *Founded/Ownrshp* 1992
Sales 57.8MM[E] *EMP* 1,204
SIC 3841 Diagnostic apparatus, medical; Blood pressure apparatus
Genl Mgr: Deb Robertson
MIS Dir: Al Pfeiffer
Board of Directors: Anthony J Dimun, Terry D Wall

D-U-N-S 12-572-4112 IMP/EXP
VITALITY FOODSERVICE INC
NESTLE PROFESSIONAL VITALITY
(*Suby of* WONKA BAMBOOZLE) ★
400 N Tampa St Ste 1700, Tampa, FL 33602-4716
Tel (813) 301-4600 *Founded/Ownrshp* 2009
Sales 325.7MM[E] *EMP* 691
SIC 5149 3586 Juices; Coffee, green or roasted; Measuring & dispensing pumps
CEO: Gary Viljoen
COO: John Minton
CFO: Kim Johnson
VP: Luis Buisson
Rgnl Mgr: Tom Myers
Site Mgr: Bill Anthony

VITALITY GROUP, THE
See DESTINY HEALTH INC

D-U-N-S 12-414-1818
VITALIZE CONSULTING SOLUTIONS INC
V C S
248 Main St Ste 101, Reading, MA 01867-3643
Tel (781) 670-1000 *Founded/Ownrshp* 2011
Sales 196.2MM[E] *EMP* 40,000
SIC 8082 7379

D-U-N-S 04-919-3886 IMP
■ VITALIZE LLC
(*Suby of* LIBERTY INTERACTIVE CORP) ★
5777 N Meeker Ave Ste 500, Boise, ID 83713-1727
Tel (208) 377-3326 *Founded/Ownrshp* 2008
Sales 198.9MM[E] *EMP* 500
SIC 5499 Health & dietetic food stores
CEO: Richard Jalichandra
COO: Kelly Householder
VP: Kandace Hudspeth
VP: Caroline Underwood
Exec: Blossom Barylski
Off Mgr: Nina Dillard
QA Dir: Derlin Staker
Software D: Andrew Lasley
Software D: John Spradlin
Sftwr Eng: Eden Berhe
Sftwr Eng: Bryan Bolles

D-U-N-S 03-195-8655
■ VITAMIN COTTAGE NATURAL FOOD MARKETS INC (CO)
VITAMIN COTTAGE NATURAL GR
(*Suby of* NATURAL GROCERS BY VITAMIN COTTAGE INC) ★
12612 W Alameda Pkwy, Lakewood, CO 80228-2824
Tel (303) 986-4600 *Founded/Ownrshp* 1955
Sales 95.9MM[E] *EMP* 385
SIC 5499 Health foods; Vitamin food stores
Pr: Zephyr Isley
**CFO:* Sandra Buffa
**VP:* Elizabeth Isley
**VP:* Kemper Isley

VITAMIN COTTAGE NATURAL GR
See VITAMIN COTTAGE NATURAL FOOD MARKETS INC

VITAMIN SHOPPE, THE
See VITAMIN SHOPPE INDUSTRIES INC

D-U-N-S 78-824-0153 EXP
▲ VITAMIN SHOPPE INC
300 Harmon Meadow Blvd # 2, Secaucus, NJ 07094-3643
Tel (201) 868-5959 *Founded/Ownrshp* 1977
Sales 1.2MMM *EMP* 5,686
Tkr Sym VSI *Exch* NYS
SIC 5961 5499 Catalog & mail-order houses; Pharmaceuticals, mail order; Vitamin food stores; Spices & herbs
CEO: Anthony N Truesdale
Pr: Michael Beardall
**CEO:* Colin Watts
COO: Jason S Reiser
CFO: Brenda Galgano
CFO: Brenda M Galgano
Sr VP: David M Kastin
Sr VP: Daniel Lamadrid
Sr VP: Richard Tannenbaum
VP: Joseph Weiss
Admn Mgr: Daniel Patasnik

D-U-N-S 00-354-6983
■ VITAMIN SHOPPE INDUSTRIES INC (NY)
VITAMIN SHOPPE, THE
(*Suby of* VITAMIN SHOPPE INC) ★
2101 91st St, North Bergen, NJ 07047-4731
Tel (201) 868-5959 *Founded/Ownrshp* 1977, 2002
Sales 889.8MM[E] *EMP* 4,022
SIC 5961 Pharmaceuticals, mail order
CEO: Anthony Truesdale
V Ch: Rick Markee
**CFO:* Brenda Galgano
Sr VP: Doug Henson
Sr VP: David Kastin
Sr VP: Teresa Orth
VP: Stephen Bontempo
VP: Brian Bootay
VP: James Chavarria
VP: Marsha Furst
**VP:* Dan Lamadrid
**VP:* James Sander
VP: Sherwin Socaransky
VP: Joe Weiss
VP: Suzan Zeitz
Dir Soc: Claudia Cribeiro
Board of Directors: Douglas Korn, Richard L Markee, Richard Perkal

D-U-N-S 10-899-9913 EXP
VITAMIN WORLD INC
(*Suby of* VWRE HOLDINGS INC) ★
4320 Veterans Mem Hwy, Holbrook, NY 11741-4504
Tel (631) 567-9500 *Founded/Ownrshp* 2016
Sales 358.8MM[E] *EMP* 3,000

SIC 5499 Vitamin food stores
Pr: Jack Krause
Sr VP: Nancy Shores

VITAMINSBABY
See CELEBRITY INTERNATIONAL INC

VITAMIX
See VITA-MIX CORP

D-U-N-S 96-055-8609 IMP
VITAQUEST INTERNATIONAL LLC
8 Henderson Dr, West Caldwell, NJ 07006-6608
Tel (973) 575-9200 *Founded/Ownrshp* 1977
Sales 187.7MM^E *EMP* 630
Accts Deloitte & Touche Llp
SIC 2834 5149 5122 8742 Vitamin preparations; Health foods; Vitamins & minerals; Marketing consulting services
Ch Bd: Keith Frankel
* *COO:* David P Illingworth
CFO: John Florian
Sr VP: Gale Morris
VP: Madeline Weisgal
Ex Dir: Diane Raver

VITAS HEALTH CARE
See VITAS HEALTHCARE CORP

D-U-N-S 11-413-6195 IMP
■ **VITAS HEALTHCARE CORP**
VITAS HEALTH CARE
(*Suby of* CHEMED CORP) ★
100 S Biscayne Blvd # 1600, Miami, FL 33131-2021
Tel (305) 374-4143 *Founded/Ownrshp* 2004
Sales 1.1MM *EMP* 9,000
Accts Ernst And Young Llp
SIC 8082 8051 Home health care services; Skilled nursing care facilities
CEO: Nick Westfall
* *Pr:* David A Wester
Ofcr: Karen Peterson
* *Ex VP:* Barry M Kinzbrunner
Ex VP: Timothy S O'Toole
* *Ex VP:* Peggy Pettit
Sr VP: Robert Miller
* *Sr VP:* Christopher Rieder
Sr VP: Mary Zalaznik
VP: Judi Ashline
* *VP:* Tracey Bert
* *VP:* Joe Mack
* *VP:* Peter Ranger
VP: Steven Smith
Assoc Dir: Elizabeth Schultz
Creative D: Beatrice McClelland

D-U-N-S 05-470-1917 IMP/EXP
VITASOY USA INC
(*Suby of* VITASOY INTERNATIONAL HOLDINGS LIMITED)
57 Russell St, Woburn, MA 01801-4707
Tel (781) 430-8988 *Founded/Ownrshp* 1979
Sales 97.4MM^E *EMP* 150^E
SIC 5149 2099 Beverages, except coffee & tea; Tofu, except frozen desserts
CEO: Eugene Lye
Manager: Mark Kim
Manager: Michael Panella

D-U-N-S 00-835-9994 IMP
VITATECH NUTRITIONAL SCIENCES INC
2802 Dow Ave, Tustin, CA 92780-7212
Tel (714) 832-9700 *Founded/Ownrshp* 1980
Sales 111.0MM^E *EMP* 285
SIC 2834

D-U-N-S 88-355-3190
VITECH SYSTEMS GROUP INC
401 Park Ave S Fl 12, New York, NY 10016-8808
Tel (212) 868-0900 *Founded/Ownrshp* 1994
Sales 85.1MM *EMP* 796
Accts Seligson & Giannattasio Llp
SIC 7371 Custom computer programming services
Pr: Frank Vitiello
Sr VP: Stephen Brandt
VP: Chris Lodge
VP: James Vitiello
Assoc Dir: Arvind Gupta
Tech Mgr: Mark Chang
Tech Mgr: Ramandeep Kaur
Tech Mgr: Nikhil Khedlekar
Tech Mgr: Someshwar Veeramaneni
Software D: Marlon Corrales
Software D: Manoj Kumar

D-U-N-S 01-062-7577
VITEL MOBILE INC (FL)
(*Suby of* BROTEX IMPORT & EXPORT S.A.)
8925 Nw 26th St, Doral, FL 33172-1613
Tel (305) 418-9790 *Founded/Ownrshp* 2009
Sales 250.0MM^E *EMP* 20^E
SIC 4812 Cellular telephone services
Pr: Chong Ho Hyo
* *CFO:* Bibi Mrabet
Opers Mgr: Dibi Mardet

D-U-N-S 06-818-3789
VITERBO UNIVERSITY INC (WI)
900 Viterbo Dr, La Crosse, WI 54601-8804
Tel (608) 796-3000 *Founded/Ownrshp* 1890
Sales 45.3MM *EMP* 1,500^E
Accts Wipfli Llp Eau Claire Wiscon
SIC 8221 College, except junior
Pr: Richard B Artman
VP: Diane Brimmer
Comm Dir: Cody Bohl
IT Man: Chad Gilbeck
Info Man: Janice Glass
Mktg Dir: Paul Wilhelmson

D-U-N-S 02-961-5339
■ **VITESSE LLC**
(*Suby of* FACEBOOK INC) ★
1601 Willow Rd, Menlo Park, CA 94025-1452
Tel (650) 543-4800 *Founded/Ownrshp* 2010
Sales 49.9MM^E *EMP* 3,000
SIC 7374 Data processing service
CEO: Christopher R Gardner

D-U-N-S 79-062-0046
VITOL INC
(*Suby of* VITOL SA)
2925 Richmond Ave Ste 11, Houston, TX 77098-3138
Tel (713) 230-1000 *Founded/Ownrshp* 2006
Sales 311.7MM^E *EMP* 185^E
SIC 6211 Oil & gas lease brokers
Pr: Miguel A Loya
VP: Brian Jones
VP: John Zimmerman
Genl Mgr: Marcio Dutra
Corp Couns: Adam Capetillo

D-U-N-S 09-201-0545
VITRAN EXPRESS INC
6500 E 30th St, Indianapolis, IN 46219-1102
Tel (317) 803-6400 *Founded/Ownrshp* 1999
Sales NA *EMP* 2,000
SIC 4213

D-U-N-S 62-422-3020
VITRAN EXPRESS INC
PJAX TRANSPORT
(*Suby of* TRANSFORCE INC)
12225 Stephens Rd, Warren, MI 48089-2010
Tel (317) 803-4000 *Founded/Ownrshp* 2006
Sales 116.1MM^E *EMP* 1,300
SIC 4213 Trucking, except local
Pr: Donald C Hammel
* *Treas:* Mark L Kosovec
* *Sec:* Robert J Tucker
* *VP:* Dave Kimack
Sls&Mrk Ex: Daniel Wolovich

VITRO PACKAGING DE MEXICO
See VITRO PACKAGING LLC

D-U-N-S 61-901-1869 IMP
VITRO PACKAGING LLC
VITRO PACKAGING DE MEXICO
13481 Resource, Laredo, TX 78045-9498
Tel (956) 717-4232 *Founded/Ownrshp* 1979
Sales 257.0MM^E *EMP* 10^E
SIC 3221

D-U-N-S 10-889-2142
VIUS SERVICES CORP
VOITH INDUSTRIAL SERVICES
9395 Kenwood Rd Ste 200, Blue Ash, OH 45242-6819
Tel (513) 731-3590 *Founded/Ownrshp* 2016
Sales 150.0MM *EMP* 3,000
SIC 7349 8741 3714 Building cleaning service; Management services; Motor vehicle parts & accessories
CEO: William Bell
* *CFO:* Donald G Morsch

VIVA INTERNATIONAL GROUP
See MARCOLIN USA EYEWEAR CORP

D-U-N-S 10-330-4358 IMP
VIVENDI HOLDING I LLC
(*Suby of* VIVENDI)
1755 Broadway Fl 2, New York, NY 10019-3743
Tel (212) 572-7000 *Founded/Ownrshp* 2000
Sales 170.1MM^E *EMP* 8,818^E
SIC 7812 7389 Motion picture production; Motion picture production & distribution, television; Television film production; Video production; Music recording producer
CEO: Jean-Ren Fourtou
* *Ch Bd:* Jean Rene Fourtou
CFO: Guillame Hannezo
CFO: Levy John
CFO: Daniel Scolan
Top Exec: Giovanni Tosonotti
Ex VP: Bruno Curis
Ex VP: Eric Looss
Ex VP: Mathieu Peycere
Sr VP: George Bushnell
Sr VP: Robert Greenberg
VP: Rosanna Durruthy
VP: Richard Galvin
VP: Richard P Shaw

D-U-N-S 07-902-0637 IMP
■ **VIVENDI UNIVERSAL ENTERTAINMENT LLLP**
(*Suby of* NECN) ★
30 Rockefeller Plz, New York, NY 10112-0015
Tel (212) 664-4444 *Founded/Ownrshp* 2004
Sales 77.3MM^E *EMP* 15,532^E
SIC 7812 3652 2741 5947 5944 5961 Motion picture production & distribution; Phonograph records, prerecorded; Music, sheet: publishing & printing; Gift shop; Jewelry stores; Gift items, mail order
Ch Bd: Jean-Rene Fourtou
Pr: Ron Meyer

VIVINT
See APX GROUP HOLDINGS INC

D-U-N-S 17-248-6644 IMP
VIVINT INC
APX ALARM SECURITY SOLUTIONS
(*Suby of* VIVINT) ★
4931 N 300 W, Provo, UT 84604-5816
Tel (801) 705-6253 *Founded/Ownrshp* 2005
Sales 1.9MM *EMP* 3,200
SIC 3822 Building services monitoring controls, automatic; Energy cutoff controls, residential or commercial types; Electric heat controls; Air flow controllers, air conditioning & refrigeration
CEO: Todd Pedersen
* *Pr:* Alex Dunn
* *COO:* David Bywater
* *CFO:* Mark Davies
* *Chf Mktg O:* Jeff Lyman
Sr VP: Shawn Brenchley
VP: Paul Dickson
VP: Chris Gera
VP: Richard Guerra
VP: Kristi Knight
VP: Jim Nye
VP: Jeff Thomas
Exec: Keith Nellesen

D-U-N-S 07-859-6904
■ **VIVINT SOLAR DEVELOPER LLC**
(*Suby of* VIVINT SOLAR INC) ★
1800 W Ashton Blvd, Lehi, UT 84043-5490
Tel (801) 377-9111 *Founded/Ownrshp* 2011
Sales 50.2MM^E *EMP* 3,057^E
SIC 1711 Solar energy contractor
CEO: David Bywater
* *Pr:* Greg Butterfield
* *CFO:* Dana Russell
* *Ex VP:* Thomas Plagemann
* *Sr VP:* Chance Allred
* *Sr VP:* Tessa White
* *VP:* Cody Ellis Oram
* *VP:* Dan Rock

D-U-N-S 07-827-0488
▲ **VIVINT SOLAR INC**
1850 W Ashton Blvd, Lehi, UT 84043-5490
Tel (877) 404-4129 *Founded/Ownrshp* 2011
Sales 64.1MM *EMP* 3,685^E
Tkr Sym VSLR *Exch* NYS
SIC 5074 Heating equipment & panels, solar
CEO: David Bywater
* *Ch Bd:* Peter F Wallace
COO: Bryan Christiansen
CFO: Dana C Russell
Chf Mktg O: Chris Lundell
Ex VP: Thomas G Plagemann
Sr VP: L Chance Allred
Sr VP: Paul S Dickson
VP: Chance Allred
Dir Risk M: Paul Dickson
Dist Mgr: Dave Yates
Board of Directors: David F D'alessandro, Alex J Dunn, Bruce McEvoy, Jay D Pauley, Todd R Pederson, Joseph S Tibbetts Jr

D-U-N-S 78-277-2263 IMP
▲ **VIVUS INC**
351 E Evelyn Ave, Mountain View, CA 94041-1530
Tel (650) 934-5200 *Founded/Ownrshp* 1991
Sales 95.4MM *EMP* 94
Tkr Sym VVUS *Exch* NGS
SIC 2834 Pharmaceutical preparations; Proprietary drug products
CEO: Seth H Z Fischer
* *Ch Bd:* David Y Norton
CFO: Mark K Oki
Chf Mktg O: Santosh T Varghese
Sr VP: John L Slebir
Board of Directors: Jorge Plutzky, Eric W Roberts, Herman Rosenman, Allan L Shaw

VIWAPA
See VIRGIN ISLANDS WATER & POWER AUTHORITY

D-U-N-S 08-833-9767
VIZIENT INC
290 E John Carpenter Fwy # 1500, Irving, TX 75062-2752
Tel (972) 830-0000 *Founded/Ownrshp* 1977
Sales 737.8MM^E *EMP* 5,157
SIC 8742

D-U-N-S 12-721-3028 IMP/EXP
VIZIO INC
39 Tesla, Irvine, CA 92618-4603
Tel (949) 428-2525 *Founded/Ownrshp* 2016
Sales 126.1MM^E *EMP* 225
SIC 3651 Television receiving sets; Compact disk players
CEO: William Wang
Pr: Ken Lowe
CFO: Kurt Binder
VP: Francis Ahn
VP: Bartholomew R Brown
VP: Michelle Nguyen
Dir IT: Anthony Chang
IT Man: Nancy Chow
VP Opers: Rob L Brinkman
Opers Mgr: Michael Leshnak
Ql Cn Mgr: Ryan Su

D-U-N-S 79-321-6768
VJCS HOLDINGS INC
8515 Page Ave, Saint Louis, MO 63114-6014
Tel (314) 427-1000 *Founded/Ownrshp* 2006
Sales 171.6MM^E *EMP* 1,350^E
SIC 6719 2844 Investment holding companies, except banks; Toilet preparations
Ch Bd: John G Brunner
* *Pr:* Kirk Sanders

D-U-N-S 02-257-7790 IMP
VM SERVICES INC
(*Suby of* CEBELIAN HOLDINGS PTE LTD)
6701 Mowry Ave, Newark, CA 94560-4927
Tel (510) 744-3720 *Founded/Ownrshp* 1996
Sales 88.1MM^E *EMP* 300
SIC 7371 Computer software development
CEO: Chin Tong Wong
CFO: Wiwit Handayani
CFO: Jennifer Thomas
Exec: Robert Rios
Ql Cn Mgr: Jeffrey Lim

D-U-N-S 14-168-8619 IMP
VMI NUTRITION INC
GENYSIS BRAND SOLUTIONS
391 S Orange St Ste C, Salt Lake City, UT 84104-3525
Tel (801) 954-0471 *Founded/Ownrshp* 2003
Sales 129.0MM *EMP* 250^E
SIC 2087 Powders, drink
CEO: Jeffrey Reynolds
VP: Edgar Grigorian
QC Dir: Daisy Herpin
Ql Cn Mgr: Justine Jennings

D-U-N-S 80-348-0946
VML INC
(*Suby of* W P P) ★
250 Nw Richards Rd # 255, Kansas City, MO 64116-4279
Tel (816) 283-0700 *Founded/Ownrshp* 1992
Sales 120.6MM^E *EMP* 370
SIC 7311 7373 8742 Advertising agencies; Computer integrated systems design; Marketing consulting services
Pt: Jon Cook
* *COO:* Craig Braasch
CFO: Jim Bellinghausen
* *Ch:* Matt Anthony
Ofcr: Eric Baumgartner
* *Ofcr:* Eric Campbell
* *Ofcr:* Scott McCormick
Ofcr: Chuck Searle
Ofcr: Debbi Vandeven
Ofcr: Amy Winger
Ofcr: Brian Yamada
Ofcr: Mike Yardley
Assoc Dir: Tyler Hilker
Creative D: Dave Altis
Creative D: Becky Ervin
Creative D: Andrew McLeod
Creative D: Ryan Simonet
Creative D: Robb Smigielski
Creative D: Mike Wente

D-U-N-S 04-887-0740
■ **VMWARE INC**
(*Suby of* DELL EMC) ★
3401 Hillview Ave, Palo Alto, CA 94304-1383
Tel (650) 427-1000 *Founded/Ownrshp* 2004
Sales 6.5MMM *EMP* 19,000^E
Tkr Sym VMW *Exch* NYS
SIC 7371 7375 Computer software development & applications; Information retrieval services
CEO: Patrick P Gelsinger
* *Ch Bd:* Michael S Dell
* *CFO:* Zane Rowe
* *Ofcr:* Dirk Hohndel
Ex VP: Ray O'Farrell
* *Ex VP:* Sanjay Poonen
Ex VP: Rangarajan Raghuram
Sr VP: Jean-Pierre Brulard
Sr VP: Brett Shirk
VP: Jeff Casale
VP: Bret Connor
VP: Dominick Delfino
VP: John Dolan
VP: Paul Fazzone
VP: Avon Puri
VP: Velchamy Sankarlingam
VP: John Sellers
VP: Pradeep Vancheeswaran
VP: Noah Wasmer
Board of Directors: Anthony J Bates, Michael W Brown, Donald J Carty, Karen Dykstra, Paul Sagan, John R Paul A Maritz

D-U-N-S 13-755-6478
VNA AND HOSPICE OF SOUTH TEXAS
4241 Woodcock Dr Ste A100, San Antonio, TX 78228-1337
Tel (210) 785-5800 *Founded/Ownrshp* 1952
Sales 15.4MM^E *EMP* 1,600
SIC 8082 Home health care services
Ex Dir: Ronnie Harper

D-U-N-S 12-036-3697
VNA CARE NETWORK FOUNDATION INC
120 Thomas St, Worcester, MA 01608-1223
Tel (508) 786-0693 *Founded/Ownrshp* 1983
Sales 8.3MM *EMP* 1,300
SIC 8082 Visiting nurse service
CEO: Karen Green
* *Treas:* Robert Wilson
VP: Diane Bergeron

D-U-N-S 02-785-8716 IMP/EXP
VNA HOLDING INC
(*Suby of* AB VOLVO)
7825 National Service Rd, Greensboro, NC 27409-9667
Tel (336) 393-4890 *Founded/Ownrshp* 1996
Sales NA *EMP* 3,700^E
SIC 6159 3713 5012 5013 Equipment & vehicle finance leasing companies; Truck finance leasing; Machinery & equipment finance leasing; Specialty motor vehicle bodies; Automobile wrecker truck bodies; Commercial vehicles; Truck bodies; Truck tractors; Motor vehicle supplies & new parts; Truck parts & accessories
CEO: Ava Persson
* *Pr:* Eva Pesson
Treas: Don Schumaker
* *VP:* Donald W Shumaker

VNA OF CENTRAL JERSEY
See VISITING NURSE ASSOCIATION OF CENTRAL JERSEY INC

VNAB
See VISITING NURSE ASSOCIATION OF BOSTON

VNAHNC
See SUTTER VISITING NURSE ASSOCIATION & HOSPICE

D-U-N-S 08-034-7384
VNB MORTGAGE SERVICES INC
1720 Rte 23, Wayne, NJ 07470-7524
Tel (973) 696-2813 *Founded/Ownrshp* 1989
Sales NA *EMP* 1,000
SIC 6021 National commercial banks
Pr: Gerald H Lipkin

D-U-N-S 01-796-5523
VNS CHOICE
5 Penn Plz Ste 1201, New York, NY 10001-1824
Tel (212) 609-5600 *Founded/Ownrshp* 2010
Sales 1.3MMM *EMP* 26^E
Accts Kpmg Llp Albany Ny
SIC 8082 Home health care services
Assoc Dir: Deepak N Mathur

D-U-N-S 96-723-6311
VNS CHOICE COMMUNITY CARE
5 Penn Plz Fl 12, New York, NY 10001-1810
Tel (212) 609-5716 *Founded/Ownrshp* 2011
Sales 413.9MM *EMP* 2^E
Accts Kpmg Llp Albany Ny
SIC 8699 Charitable organization
Prin: Holly M Fisher

D-U-N-S 05-311-9889
VNU MARKETING INFORMATION INC
(*Suby of* TNC (US) HOLDINGS INC) ★
770 Broadway Fl 15, New York, NY 10003-9595
Tel (646) 654-5011 *Founded/Ownrshp* 2007
Sales 83.5MM^E *EMP* 1,500
SIC 8732 6282 7374 5045 Market analysis or research; Investment advisory service; Computer time-sharing; Computers; Computer software
CEO: Steven M Schmidt
**Sr VP:* R Ford Dallmeyer
**Sr VP:* Frank D Martell

D-U-N-S 07-689-9475
VOCATIONAL GUIDANCE SERVICES INC
2239 E 55th St, Cleveland, OH 44103-4451
Tel (216) 431-7800 *Founded/Ownrshp* 1890
Sales 12.3MM *EMP* 1,100
Accts Samuel Kellogg & Co Inc Cleve
SIC 8331 Community service employment training program
Pr: Robert E Comben Jr
**CFO:* Donald E Carlson
**VP:* James Hudak
**VP:* Michael Latkovich
Exec: Bill Munshower
**Prin:* Et Al
**Prin:* Nadine Coffinberry
**Prin:* Cornelia Ginn
**Prin:* Miriam Norton
Ex Dir: Shirley Terrell
IT Man: Deric Williams

D-U-N-S 01-750-7091 IMP
▲ VOCERA COMMUNICATIONS INC
525 Race St Ste 150, San Jose, CA 95126-3497
Tel (408) 882-5100 *Founded/Ownrshp* 2000
Sales 104.0MM *EMP* 387^E
Tkr Sym VCRA *Exch* NYS
SIC 3669 Intercommunication systems, electric
Pr: Brent D Lang
**Ch Bd:* Robert J Zollars
CFO: Justin R Spencer
Ofcr: M Bridget Duffy
Ex VP: Jay M Spitzen
Board of Directors: Michael Burkland, John B Grotting, Jeffrey H Hillebrand, Howard E Janzen, Alexa King, John N McMullen, Sharon L O'keefe

D-U-N-S 18-305-6647
■ VOCOLLECT INC
(*Suby of* INTERMEC INC) ★
703 Rodi Rd, Pittsburgh, PA 15235-4558
Tel (412) 829-8145 *Founded/Ownrshp* 2011
Sales 91.9MM^E *EMP* 450
SIC 3577 3571 7372 Encoders, computer peripheral equipment; Electronic computers; Application computer software
Pr: Joe Pajer
Pr: James Dilella
**CFO:* Steven M Barto
**Treas:* Frank S McCallick
**Sr VP:* Laurence R Sweeney
VP: Thomas H Murray
**VP:* Robert I Driessnack
VP: Mike Wills
Genl Mgr: Bruce Arnold
Snr Sftwr: Vanessa Sanchez
CTO: Roger Byford

D-U-N-S 55-689-0622
VOCUS INC
12051 Indian Creek Ct, Beltsville, MD 20705-1246
Tel (301) 459-2590 *Founded/Ownrshp* 2014
Sales 317.2MM^E *EMP* 1,273^E
SIC 7371 7372

D-U-N-S 93-158-8987 IMP
VOESTALPINE ROTEC INC
(*Suby of* VOESTALPINE ELMSTEEL GROUP LIMITED)
3709 Us Highway 52 S, Lafayette, IN 47905-9399
Tel (765) 471-2808 *Founded/Ownrshp* 2000
Sales 103.1MM^E *EMP* 90
SIC 5051 Tubing, metal
Pr: Andrew Ball
Prd Mgr: Simon Ball

D-U-N-S 00-483-7233
VOGEL BROS BUILDING CO (WI)
2701 Packers Ave, Madison, WI 53704-7541
Tel (608) 241-5454 *Founded/Ownrshp* 1875, 1928
Sales 89.7MM^E *EMP* 150
SIC 1542 1541 4941 Commercial & office building, new construction; Commercial & office buildings, renovation & repair; Institutional building construction; Industrial buildings, new construction; Renovation, remodeling & repairs: industrial buildings; Water supply
Ch Bd: David L Vogel
Pr: Peter Vogel
Treas: Ron Ballweg
VP: Ross A Rehfeldt

D-U-N-S 02-627-6263
VOGEL FOREST PRODUCTS LTD
VOGEL LUMBER
138 Canal St Ste 408, Pooler, GA 31322-4049
Tel (912) 348-2233 *Founded/Ownrshp* 2013
Sales 100.2MM *EMP* 2
SIC 5031 Lumber: rough, dressed & finished
Pr: Geraldo Ferreira Da Silva

VOGEL LUMBER
See VOGEL FOREST PRODUCTS LTD

D-U-N-S 00-727-6728 IMP
VOGEL PAINT & WAX CO INC
DIAMOND VOGEL PAINT
1110 Albany Pl Se, Orange City, IA 51041-1982
Tel (712) 737-4993 *Founded/Ownrshp* 1926
Sales 137.4MM^E *EMP* 839
SIC 2851 5198 Paints & paint additives; Lacquers, varnishes, enamels & other coatings; Removers & cleaners; Paints; Varnishes; Paint brushes, rollers, sprayers; Wallcoverings
Pr: Drew Vogel
**Ch:* Franklin Vogel
**Treas:* Bert Aarsen

D-U-N-S 87-822-8352
VOGEL PAINT INC
1110 Albany Pl Se, Orange City, IA 51041-1982
Tel (712) 737-8880 *Founded/Ownrshp* 1971
Sales 177.9MM^E *EMP* 850
SIC 2851 8741 Paints & allied products; Management services
Pr: Drew Vogel
**Sec:* Bert Aarsen
**VP:* Doug Vogel

D-U-N-S 12-642-7785 IMP/EXP
VOGT POWER INTERNATIONAL INC
(*Suby of* BABCOCK POWER INC) ★
13551 Triton Ste 2000, Louisville, KY 40223
Tel (502) 899-4500 *Founded/Ownrshp* 2002
Sales 219.4MM *EMP* 247
Accts Deloitte & Touche Llp Hartfor
SIC 3592 Valves
Pr: Andrew Macgregor
**COO:* Jorge Camacho
COO: Ronald Pancari
Sr VP: Anthony A Thompson
VP: Anthony A Brandano
**VP:* William J Ferguson Jr
VP: David G Hazlett
VP: Nils A Holmblad
VP: Dennie S Hunt
VP: Scott H Leeman
VP: Manfred Pouzar
VP: Dudley Spencer
VP: Christpher Turner
VP: James B Walder

D-U-N-S 07-865-6203
VOICE MEDIA GROUP INC
969 N Broadway, Denver, CO 80203-2705
Tel (303) 296-7744 *Founded/Ownrshp* 2012
Sales 299.1MM^E *EMP* 1,590^E
SIC 6719 Investment holding companies, except banks
CEO: Scott Tobias
Exec: Andy Van De Voorde

VOICE OF AMERICA
See BROADCASTING BOARD OF GOVERNORS

D-U-N-S 07-993-7035
VOICELOTS INC
350 Budd Ave Apt J5, Campbell, CA 95008-4016
Tel (408) 802-4047 *Founded/Ownrshp* 2015
Sales 100.0MM *EMP* 13
SIC 7371 7389 Computer software development & applications;
CEO: Chloe Sledd

D-U-N-S 11-736-5510 IMP
VOIGT & SCHWEITZER LLC
(*Suby of* HILL & SMITH HOLDINGS PLC)
987 Buckeye Park Rd, Columbus, OH 43207-2596
Tel (614) 449-8281 *Founded/Ownrshp* 1984
Sales 85.8MM^E *EMP* 280
SIC 3479 Galvanizing of iron, steel or end-formed products; Hot dip coating of metals or formed products
Pr: Werner Niehaus
Sr VP: Brian Miller
Opers Mgr: James Arahill

D-U-N-S 08-004-7417
VOIP GUARDIAN LLC
405 E 56th St Apt 3g, New York, NY 10022-2469
Tel (212) 421-0888 *Founded/Ownrshp* 2015
Sales NA *EMP* 21
SIC 6153 Working capital financing

D-U-N-S 08-028-9384
VOIP GUARDIAN PARTNERS I LLC
405 E 56th St Apt 3g, New York, NY 10022-2469
Tel (212) 421-0888 *Founded/Ownrshp* 2015
Sales NA *EMP* 5
SIC 6411 Insurance agents, brokers & service

D-U-N-S 12-863-1301 IMP/EXP
VOITH HOLDING INC
(*Suby of* VOITH GMBH)
2200 N Roemer Rd, Appleton, WI 54911-8616
Tel (920) 731-7724 *Founded/Ownrshp* 1867
Sales 879.9MM^E *EMP* 3,000
SIC 5131 3554 2221 6719 Piece goods & other fabrics; Paper industries machinery; Manmade & synthetic broadwoven fabrics; Investment holding companies, except banks
Ch: Bertram Staudenmaier
**Pr:* Otto L Heissenberger
Pr: Thomas Leitner
**CFO:* Jim Heiting
CFO: Alexander Kienle
**CFO:* Egon Kraetschmer
**Treas:* Scott Engmann
Ex VP: Christian Nykiel
Sr VP: Kietaibl Robert
VP: Harald Blank
VP: Alexandre Delrey
**VP:* Robert Matz
**VP:* Laura Wilson

D-U-N-S 78-681-2842 IMP/EXP
VOITH HYDRO INC
(*Suby of* VOITH GMBH)
760 E Berlin Rd, York, PA 17408-8701
Tel (717) 792-7000 *Founded/Ownrshp* 1991
Sales 122.5MM^E *EMP* 580
SIC 3511 7699 Hydraulic turbines; Hydraulic equipment repair
Pr: Robert J Gallo
**COO:* Stanley J Kocon
CFO: Martin Ultsch
VP: Stuart Coulson
IT Man: Christopher Hageman
IT Man: Jeffrey Tome
Opers Mgr: Carl Brewster

VOITH INDUSTRIAL SERVICES
See VIUS SERVICES CORP

D-U-N-S 07-478-7490 IMP
VOITH PAPER INC
(*Suby of* VOITH HOLDING INC) ★
2200 N Roemer Rd, Appleton, WI 54911-8616
Tel (920) 731-0769 *Founded/Ownrshp* 2001
Sales 248.0MM^E *EMP* 975
SIC 3554 Paper industries machinery
CEO: Hubert Lienhard
**Pr:* Robert Gallo
**CFO:* Martin Kaufmann
**Treas:* Scott Engmann
**VP:* Helmut Tausel
QA Dir: Dale Gillespie
IT Man: Ed Delain
Tech Mgr: Jeff Berg
Opers Mgr: James Henry
Manager: Frank Ferlet
Manager: Roberto Zane

D-U-N-S 08-049-3638 IMP
VOITH TURBO INC
(*Suby of* VOITH HOLDING INC) ★
25 Winship Rd, York, PA 17406-8419
Tel (717) 767-3200 *Founded/Ownrshp* 2010
Sales 85.5MM^E *EMP* 125
SIC 5084 5013 Industrial machinery & equipment; Motor vehicle supplies & new parts
CEO: Dr Hubert Lienhard
**Pr:* David M Calveley
Pr: Mark Greening
COO: Soeren Schulze
CFO: Donald Morsch
Ex VP: Antti Kaunonen
Ex VP: Alexander Wassermann
Sr VP: Andreas Brandt
VP: Mark Moline
VP: Kevin Simms
**VP:* Ronald Wilson

D-U-N-S 01-886-0556
VOLCANO CORP
(*Suby of* PHILIPS CONSUMER LIFESTYLE) ★
3721 Vly Cntre Dr Ste 500, San Diego, CA 92130
Tel (800) 228-4728 *Founded/Ownrshp* 2015
Sales 393.6MM^E *EMP* 1,800
SIC 3845 Electromedical equipment; Ultrasonic medical equipment, except cleaning
Pr: R Scott Huennekens
**Ch Bd:* Ronald A Matricaria
**CFO:* John T Dahldorf
Treas: Barbara Taylor
Ex VP: Heather Ace
Ex VP: Joseph M Burnett
**Ex VP:* Darin M Lippoldt
**Ex VP:* John Onopchenko
**Ex VP:* David M Sheehan
VP: Terry Beausir
VP: Terri Dooley
VP: Connie Garrett
VP: Jonathan T Hartmann
VP: Neil Hattangadi
VP: Al Kau
VP: Denise Stearns
VP: Duane Wilder
Board of Directors: Kieran T Gallahue, Lesley H Howe, Alexis V Lukianov, Leslie V Norwalk, Roy T Tanaka, Eric J Topol, Daniel J Wolterman

D-U-N-S 79-662-1191
VOLCOM LLC
STONE ENTERTAINMENT
(*Suby of* KERING)
1740 Monrovia Ave, Costa Mesa, CA 92627-4407
Tel (949) 646-2175 *Founded/Ownrshp* 2011
Sales 120.7MM^E *EMP* 543
SIC 7389 2253 7822 5136 5137 Design services; Music & broadcasting services; Bathing suits & swimwear, knit; Motion picture & tape distribution; Men's & boys' clothing; Women's & children's clothing
CEO: Jason Steris
**Pr:* Richard R Woolcott
CFO: Doug Collier
**CFO:* Douglas P Collier
**CFO:* David Unter
**Ex VP:* Ryan Immegart
**Ex VP:* Tom D Ruiz
**Sr VP:* John W Fearnley
VP: Ryan N Immeg
VP: Ed Shaver
VP: Desiree Swanson

D-U-N-S 09-744-6884 IMP
VOLEX INC
POWERCORDS
(*Suby of* VOLEX PLC)
3110 Coronado Dr, Santa Clara, CA 95054-3205
Tel (669) 444-1740 *Founded/Ownrshp* 1979
Sales 304.2MM^E *EMP* 1,850
SIC 3089 Injection molded finished plastic products
CEO: Christoph Eisenhardt
**Pr:* James Stuart
**CFO:* Nick Parker
Sr VP: Linda Starr
VP: Juan Aguilar

D-U-N-S 19-840-8499
VOLGA DNEPR - UNIQUE AIR CARGO INC
VOLGA DNEPR UNIQUE AIR CARGO
(*Suby of* VOLGA-DNEPR-MOSKVA, OOO)
9400 Grogans Mill Rd, The Woodlands, TX 77380-3642
Tel (832) 585-8611 *Founded/Ownrshp* 2000
Sales 118.0MM *EMP* 23
SIC 4522 Air cargo carriers, nonscheduled
Pr: Alexey Isaikin
**VP:* Konstantin Vekchine

VOLGA DNEPR UNIQUE AIR CARGO
See VOLGA DNEPR - UNIQUE AIR CARGO INC

D-U-N-S 07-260-1123
VOLKERT INC
(*Suby of* DAVID VOLKERT & ASSOCIATES INC) ★
3809 Moffett Rd, Mobile, AL 36618-1299
Tel (251) 342-1070 *Founded/Ownrshp* 1975
Sales 99.8MM *EMP* 800
Accts Wilkins Miller Llc Mobile A
SIC 8711 Consulting engineer
Ch Bd: Perry Hand
**Pr:* Jerry Stump
**CFO:* Thomas Zoghby
Sr VP: Dennis C Morrison
Netwrk Mgr: Tom Gassett
Mktg Dir: Joe Thrasher

D-U-N-S 83-316-1198
VOLKSWAGEN GROUP OF AMERICA CHATTANOOGA OPERATIONS LLC
(*Suby of* AUDI OF AMERICA) ★
2200 Ferdinand Porsche Dr, Herndon, VA 20171-5884
Tel (703) 364-7000 *Founded/Ownrshp* 2008
Sales 266.4MM^E *EMP* 3,200
SIC 5012 5013 Automobiles & other motor vehicles; Automotive supplies & parts
Pr: Michael Horn

D-U-N-S 00-697-2475 IMP/EXP
VOLKSWAGEN GROUP OF AMERICA INC
AUDI OF AMERICA
(*Suby of* VOLKSWAGEN AG)
2200 Ferdinand Porsche Dr, Herndon, VA 20171-5884
Tel (703) 364-7000 *Founded/Ownrshp* 1955
Sales 3.3MMM^E *EMP* 6,000
SIC 5511 5012 5013 6153 6141 4899 New & used car dealers; Automobiles & other motor vehicles; Automotive supplies & parts; Financing of dealers by motor vehicle manufacturers organ.; Installment sales finance, other than banks; Data communication services
CEO: Michael Horn
Pr: Scott Keogh
CFO: Hardy Brennecke
CFO: Christophe Georges
CFO: Frank Witter
Treas: Bjoern Baetge
Treas: Larry Tolep
Ofcr: Nicki Finlayson
Ofcr: Joseph Jacuzzi
Top Exec: Lothar Korn
Ex VP: Mike Beamish
Ex VP: Tony Cervone
Ex VP: David Geanacopoulos
Ex VP: Mario Guerreiro
Ex VP: Stefan Schuller
Ex VP: Scott C Vazin
VP: Kevin Mayer
VP: Vinay R Shahani

D-U-N-S 06-623-7082
VOLKSWAGEN SANTA MONICA INC
LEXUS SANTA MONICA
2440 Santa Monica Blvd, Santa Monica, CA 90404-2039
Tel (310) 829-1888 *Founded/Ownrshp* 1984
Sales 102.0MM^E *EMP* 290
SIC 5511 7532 7538 Automobiles, new & used; Body shop, automotive; General automotive repair shops
Pr: Michael Sullivan
**CEO:* Hazel R Sullivan
**Treas:* Kerry Sullivan
Sls Mgr: Paul Pourhashem
Sls Mgr: Melvante Williams

VOLLRATH
See TVCI HOLDING INC

D-U-N-S 95-806-3489 IMP/EXP
VOLLRATH CO LLC
(*Suby of* VOLLRATH) ★
1236 N 18th St, Sheboygan, WI 53081-3280
Tel (920) 459-6568 *Founded/Ownrshp* 1874
Sales 161.7MM^E *EMP* 800
SIC 3089 3365 3421 3556 3914

D-U-N-S 02-317-1044 IMP
VOLM COMPANIES INC
ULTRATECH
1804 Edison St, Antigo, WI 54409-2438
Tel (715) 627-4826 *Founded/Ownrshp* 1954
Sales 289.5MM^E *EMP* 290
SIC 5113 5199 3565 Bags, paper & disposable plastic; Bags, textile; Packing & wrapping machinery
Pr: Alan Mueller
**CFO:* John Bandsma
**Sec:* William P Volm
IT Man: Mary Thao
Sls Mgr: Mike Vierzba

D-U-N-S 12-361-5630 EXP
VOLOGY INC
4027 Tampa Rd Ste 3900, Oldsmar, FL 34677-3219
Tel (813) 852-6400 *Founded/Ownrshp* 2001
Sales 349.1MM^E *EMP* 391^E
SIC 5065 Electronic parts & equipment
CEO: Barry L Shevlin
**CFO:* Steve Torres
**Sr VP:* John O'Shea
**VP:* Andy Malivuk
**VP:* John Medaska
IT Man: Ryan Codere
Mktg Dir: Jon Godwin

D-U-N-S 00-132-6479
▲ VOLT INFORMATION SCIENCES INC
1133 Avenue Of The Americ, New York, NY 10036-6710
Tel (212) 704-2400 *Founded/Ownrshp* 1950
Sales 1.5MMM *EMP* 27,400
Tkr Sym VISI *Exch* ASE
SIC 7363 4813 4899 Help supply services; Temporary help service; Engineering help service; Telephone communication, except radio; Telephone/video communications; Data communication services
Prin: Dana Messina
**Pr:* Michael D Dean
CFO: Paul Tomkins
Treas: Kevin Hannon
Ex VP: Jerome Shaw
Sr VP: Rhona Driggs
Sr VP: Richard Herring
Sr VP: Sharon H Stern
Board of Directors: James E Boone, Nick S Cyprus, Bruce G Goodman, Theresa A Havell, John C Rudolf, Laurie Siegel

D-U-N-S 80-279-4552
VOLT MANAGEMENT CORP
VOLT WORKFORCE SOLUTIONS
1133 Ave Of The Americas, New York, NY 10036-6710
Tel (212) 704-2400 *Founded/Ownrshp* 1990
Sales 1.1MMM^E *EMP* 32,785
SIC 7363 Help supply services; Domestic help service
Ch Bd: Michael Dean
Sr VP: Ludwig Guarino
VP: Tony Trombetta
Area Mgr: Mike Faulkner
Genl Mgr: Howard B Weinreich
Dir IT: Maryann Hall
Dir IT: Brian Lowes
Sls Mgr: Robert Wolfenden

D-U-N-S 07-843-4121
VOLT SYSTEMS LLC (MO)
618 Spirit Dr, Chesterfield, MO 63005-1258
Tel (636) 393-8658 *Founded/Ownrshp* 2010
Sales 41.2MM^E *EMP* 2,150
SIC 7379 Computer related consulting services
Board of Directors: Jonathan Regalo

VOLT WORKFORCE SOLUTIONS
See VOLT MANAGEMENT CORP

D-U-N-S 01-957-3807
VOLTA OIL CO INC (MA)
1 Roberts Rd Ste 2, Plymouth, MA 02360-5087
Tel (508) 747-3778 *Founded/Ownrshp* 1934, 1976
Sales 220.6MM *EMP* 107
Accts Gray Gray & Gray Llp Westwood
SIC 5172 1799 Diesel fuel; Gasoline; Service station equipment installation, maintenance & repair
Ch: James S Garrett
* *Pr:* Peter Garrett
Off Mgr: Patty Macdonald

VOLTEK DIVISION
See SEKISUI AMERICA CORP

D-U-N-S 79-339-7118 IMP/EXP
VOLUME SERVICES INC
CENTERPLATE
(*Suby of* CENTERPLATE INC) ★
2187 Atlantic St Ste 6, Stamford, CT 06902-6890
Tel (203) 975-5900 *Founded/Ownrshp* 1995
Sales 741.5MM^E *EMP* 28,500
SIC 5812 7999 5947 7993 Concessionaire; Concession operator; Souvenirs; Gambling establishments operating coin-operated machines
CEO: Steve Hammond
* *Pr:* Janet Steinmayer
* *CFO:* Kevin McNamara

D-U-N-S 00-792-1042
VOLUNTEER ENERGY COOPERATIVE (TN)
18359 State Highway 58 N, Decatur, TN 37322-7825
Tel (423) 334-1020 *Founded/Ownrshp* 1935
Sales 243.6MM *EMP* 175
Accts Henderson Hutcherson & Mccullo
SIC 4911 Distribution, electric power
Ch Bd: Gene Carmichael
* *Pr:* Roderick Blevins
* *Pr:* Rody Blevins
* *Sec:* Sammy Norton
VP: Karen Davis
VP: Karen Zitek
Board of Directors: Landon Colvard, V Chm

VOLUNTEER SERVICES OF GOOD SAM
See GOOD SAMARITAN HOSPITAL KEARNEY NEBRASKA

VOLUNTEERTV.COM
See WVLT-TV INC

D-U-N-S 07-984-3985
VOLUNTEERS OF AMERICA
(*Suby of* VOLUNTEERS OF AMERICA OF LOS ANGELES) ★
2100 N Broadway Ste 300, Santa Ana, CA 92706-2624
Tel (714) 426-9834 *Founded/Ownrshp* 2014
Sales 2.5MM^E *EMP* 1,500
SIC 8322 7361 9531 Individual & family services; Employment agencies; Housing programs
Ex Dir: Bob Pratt

D-U-N-S 36-115-7287
VOLUNTEERS OF AMERICA - GREATER NEW YORK INC
340 W 85th St, New York, NY 10024-6265
Tel (212) 873-2600 *Founded/Ownrshp* 1991
Sales 100.8MM *EMP* 1,300^E
SIC 8399 Social service information exchange
Pr: Terry Pettit
CFO: David Fazio
Treas: Herbert L Camp
Assoc Dir: Matthew Richardson
Comm Dir: Rachel Weinstein
* *Prin:* Claire Haaga Altman
Sales Exec: June Murphy
Pgrm Dir: Susan Jackson
Pgrm Dir: Jenny Polanco
Pgrm Dir: Anna Rodriguez
Pgrm Dir: Nadia Wright

D-U-N-S 08-657-5255
VOLUNTEERS OF AMERICA CARE FACILITIES
(*Suby of* VOLUNTEERS OF AMERICA NATIONAL SERVICES) ★
7530 Market Place Dr, Eden Prairie, MN 55344-3636
Tel (952) 941-0305 *Founded/Ownrshp* 1970
Sales 49.2MM *EMP* 1,300
Accts Schechter Dokken Kanter Cpa S
SIC 8322 Individual & family services
Pr: Paula Hart
* *CFO:* Robert Lovegrove

D-U-N-S 07-103-4615
VOLUNTEERS OF AMERICA INC
1660 Duke St Ste 100, Alexandria, VA 22314-3427
Tel (703) 341-5000 *Founded/Ownrshp* 1896
Sales 41.6M *EMP* 3,000^E
Accts Maddox & Associates Apc Baton
SIC 8322 6531 Individual & family services; Social service center; Real estate managers
Pr: Michael King
Dir Vol: Tricia Truwe
V Ch: Don Conley
COO: Bill Jones
COO: Thomas Turnbull
* *Ch:* Dawn Batts
Treas: Robert E Ransom
* *Treas:* Curt Zaske
Ex VP: Jonathan E Baum
Ex VP: David T Bowman
Ex VP: Joseph A Budzynski
Ex VP: Jatrice Martel Gaiter
Ex VP: Margaret Ratcliff
Ex VP: Patrick Sheridan
Ex VP: Jonathan Sherin
VP: Susan Dale
VP: Douglas McAllister
VP: Evelyn Miyasato
VP: Wanda Ozier
Exec: Kimberly Jackson
Board of Directors: Mark T Flaten, Michael Martin, Robert E Wilder Sr, Brian Allen, Jean Galloway, Gerald Mc Fadden, Charlotte Lunsford Berry, D Tyler Gourley, Rubye E Noble, James S Brown, Sandra Trice Gray, Jimmie Paschall, Harlan Cleveland, Lee Grutchfield, Walter C Patterson, Michael Clinton, Frances Hesselbein, Thomas P Perkins, Wallace T Davis, Geneva Johnson, Deborah Ann Perry, Patsy Dow, George Knight, Robert E Ransom, Terrence R Duvernay, Kate Kolbrener

D-U-N-S 12-117-8552
VOLUNTEERS OF AMERICA NATIONAL SERVICES
7530 Market Place Dr, Eden Prairie, MN 55344-3692
Tel (952) 941-0305 *Founded/Ownrshp* 1982
Sales 20.7MM *EMP* 3,000
Accts Schechter Dokken Kanter Cpas
SIC 8051 8052 Extended care facility; Intermediate care facilities
Pr: Charles Gould
* *Ch:* Nancy Feldman
* *Treas:* Ron Patterson

D-U-N-S 07-292-6041 IMP
VOLUNTEERS OF AMERICA OF LOS ANGELES
(*Suby of* VOLUNTEERS OF AMERICA INC) ★
3600 Wilshire Blvd # 1500, Los Angeles, CA 90010-2603
Tel (213) 389-1500 *Founded/Ownrshp* 1896
Sales 87.5MM *EMP* 1,500
Accts Simpson & Simpson Los Angeles
SIC 8322 6531 Social service center; Real estate managers
CEO: Bob Pratt
Ex Dir: Kathryn Ward-Presson

D-U-N-S 13-373-8757
VOLUSIA COUNTY SCHOOL DISTRICT
200 N Clara Ave, Deland, FL 32720-4207
Tel (386) 734-7190 *Founded/Ownrshp* 1854
Sales 343.0MM^E *EMP* 9,021
SIC 8211 School board; Public elementary & secondary schools; Academy
V Ch: Melody Johnson
Bd of Dir: Linda Costello
Bd of Dir: John Hill
Dir Sec: Larry Beals
Netwrk Eng: Tom Finnegan
Trfc Dir: Cindy Humphries
HC Dir: Debbi Fisher

D-U-N-S 02-552-5742 IMP/EXP
VOLVO CARS OF NORTH AMERICA LLC
(*Suby of* VOLVO PERSONVAGNAR AB)
1 Volvo Dr, Rockleigh, NJ 07647-2507
Tel (201) 768-7300 *Founded/Ownrshp* 1957, 1992
Sales 239.8MM^E *EMP* 625
SIC 5511 5013 6159 7515 3714 Automobiles, new & used; Automotive supplies & parts; Automobile finance leasing; Passenger car leasing; Motor vehicle parts & accessories
Pr: Victor H Doolan
CFO: Renzo Landi
CFO: Mats Svensson
Ex VP: Bob Coon
VP: Timothy Fissinger
VP: John Maloney
* *VP:* Robert B Mercer
VP: Stuart Rowley
VP: Michael Thomas
Exec: Kevin Liberman
Creative D: Sarah Atkins

D-U-N-S 10-901-6329 IMP
VOLVO CONSTRUCTION EQUIPMENT NORTH AMERICA LLC
V C E
(*Suby of* VNA HOLDING INC) ★
312 Volvo Way, Shippensburg, PA 17257-9209
Tel (717) 532-9181 *Founded/Ownrshp* 1983
Sales 102.9MM^E *EMP* 220^E
SIC 5082 Bailey bridges
Pr: Goran Lindgren
* *CFO:* Patrick Shannon
VP: Tim Frank
VP: Andrew Knight
VP: Bruce Narveson
VP: Allison Taylor
VP Mktg: Dave Foster
Sls Mgr: Ernesto Gonzalez
Snr Mgr: Sid Chiang

D-U-N-S 93-357-0764 IMP/EXP
VOLVO GROUP NORTH AMERICA LLC
VOLVO TRUCKS NORTH AMERICA
(*Suby of* VNA HOLDING INC) ★
7900 National Service Rd, Greensboro, NC 27409-9416
Tel (336) 393-2000 *Founded/Ownrshp* 2010
Sales 1.7MMM^E *EMP* 3,700
SIC 3713 5012 5013 Specialty motor vehicle bodies; Automobile wrecker truck bodies; Commercial vehicles; Truck bodies; Truck tractors; Motor vehicle supplies & new parts; Truck parts & accessories
Pr: Per Carlsson
CFO: Eddie Brailsford
CFO: Rune Carlsson
CFO: Lars Thor N
* *CFO:* Lars Thoren
CFO: Lars Thortn
CFO: Richard L Wells
Treas: Randy Massey
Sr Cor Off: Patrick Olney
Ofcr: Kathy Hudak
Ex VP: Christopher Patterson
Sr VP: Bill Dawson
VP: Rene Alsterholm
VP: Terry Billings
VP: Grant Derderian
VP: Richard Ferguson
VP: Klass Frisk
VP: Mikael Gisslen
VP: Stan Janis
VP: Dennis Langervik
* *VP:* Therence Pickett

D-U-N-S 80-958-2729 IMP/EXP
VOLVO PENTA OF AMERICAS LLC
(*Suby of* AB VOLVO)
1300 Volvo Penta Dr, Chesapeake, VA 23320-4691
Tel (757) 436-2800 *Founded/Ownrshp* 2004
Sales 83.5MM^E *EMP* 241
SIC 5088 3519 5091 5063 Transportation equipment & supplies; Internal combustion engines; Sporting & recreation goods; Electrical apparatus & equipment
Pr: Ron Huibers
VP: Rustey Farrell
VP: Paul Joergens
Netwrk Mgr: Daphnee Bisschop
Opers Mgr: Rick Moodie
Opers Mgr: Hugh Munro
Opers Mgr: Paul Omahoney

VOLVO TRUCKS NORTH AMERICA
See VOLVO GROUP NORTH AMERICA LLC

D-U-N-S 17-795-6802 IMP/EXP
VOLVO TRUCKS NORTH AMERICA INC
(*Suby of* VNA HOLDING INC) ★
7900 National Service Rd, Greensboro, NC 27409-9416
Tel (336) 393-2000 *Founded/Ownrshp* 1987
Sales 871.4MM^E *EMP* 3,700
SIC 3713 5012 5013 Specialty motor vehicle bodies; Automobile wrecker truck bodies; Commercial vehicles; Truck bodies; Truck tractors; Motor vehicle supplies & new parts; Truck parts & accessories
Pr: Christopher Arnold
Treas: Randy Massey
Bd of Dir: John Muldoon
Sr VP: Philippe Henriette
Sr VP: Karin Hogberg
Sr VP: Scott Kress
VP: Ake B AF Gennas
VP: Jan Hogblom
VP: Magnus Koeck
VP: Dennis Langervik
Exec: Loretta Watson

D-U-N-S 00-616-1459
VOMELA SPECIALTY CO
MASTER PRINT
274 Fillmore Ave E, Saint Paul, MN 55107-1417
Tel (651) 228-2200 *Founded/Ownrshp* 1946
Sales 173.8MM^E *EMP* 1,115
SIC 7336 2396 2752 Graphic arts & related design; Automotive & apparel trimmings; Commercial printing, lithographic
CEO: Mark Auth
* *Ex VP:* Timothy Wieland
Prin: Brian Roux

D-U-N-S 07-105-4415 IMP/EXP
VON DREHLE CORP (NC)
612 3rd Ave Ne Ste 200, Hickory, NC 28601-5100
Tel (828) 322-1805 *Founded/Ownrshp* 1974
Sales 156.7MM^E *EMP* 500
SIC 2621 2676 Paper mills; Towels, napkins & tissue paper products
Ch: Steve Von Drehle
* *Pr:* Randy Bergman
* *CFO:* Craig Keenan
CFO: Carey Latimer
Off Mgr: Tammy Lampley
Dir IT: Phyllis Durmire
Plnt Mgr: Mark Guenin
Natl Sales: Jim Searcy
S&M/VP: Jason Gscheidmeier
Board of Directors: John Davidson, Jeff Pierce, David Underdown, Raymond Von Drehle, Steve Von Drehle

D-U-N-S 00-606-6112 IMP
VON DUPRIN LLC (IN)
GLYNN JOHNSON
(*Suby of* SCHLAGE LOCK CO LLC) ★
2720 Tobey Dr, Indianapolis, IN 46219-1428
Tel (317) 429-2866 *Founded/Ownrshp* 1908, 1980
Sales 90.0MM^E *EMP* 522
SIC 3429 Builders' hardware
Pr: Randy Smith
Pr: Tim Eckersley
VP: Mike Cain

D-U-N-S 00-694-0860 IMP
VON MAUR INC (OK)
6565 N Brady St, Davenport, IA 52806-2054
Tel (563) 388-2200 *Founded/Ownrshp* 1872
Sales 801.6MM^E *EMP* 4,500
Accts Mcgladrey Llp Davenport Ia
SIC 5311 Department stores, non-discount
Ch: Charles R Von Maur
Mng Pt: Sarah Hanks
* *Pr:* James Von Maur
* *CFO:* Robert L Larsen CPA
* *Ch:* Richard B Von Maur Jr
* *Sec:* Terrence Kilburg
VP: Melody Westendorf
Store Dir: Amy Rotert
Dept Mgr: Brett Jones
Store Mgr: Elizabeth Kuebler
Store Mgr: Lisa Magliocco

D-U-N-S 07-144-0218
VONACHEN SERVICES INC
8900 N Pioneer Rd, Peoria, IL 61615-1522
Tel (309) 691-6202 *Founded/Ownrshp* 1968
Sales 27.9MM^E *EMP* 1,200
SIC 7349 4731 8741 7361

D-U-N-S 01-001-9433
▲ **VONAGE HOLDINGS CORP**
23 Main St, Holmdel, NJ 07733-2136
Tel (732) 528-2600 *Founded/Ownrshp* 2000
Sales 895.0MM *EMP* 1,752
Tkr Sym VG *Exch* NYS
SIC 4813 Local & long distance telephone communications
CEO: Alan Masarek
Ch Bd: Jeffrey A Citron
Pr: Clark Peterson
COO: Joseph M Redling
CFO: David T Pearson
Ofcr: Omar Javaid
Ofcr: Susan Quackenbush
Sr VP: Kyle Johnson
VP: Angelique Electra
VP: Craig Wert
CTO: Pablo Calamera
Board of Directors: Stephen Fisher, Carolyn Katz, John J Roberts, Carl Sparks, Gary Steele

D-U-N-S 00-132-5034
VONS COMPANIES INC (MI)
PAVILIONS
(*Suby of* SAFEWAY INC) ★
5918 Stoneridge Mall Rd, Pleasanton, CA 94588-3229
Tel (626) 821-7000 *Founded/Ownrshp* 1906, 2001
Sales 2.3MMM^E *EMP* 29,700
SIC 5411 2026 2024 Grocery stores; Supermarkets; Fluid milk; Ice cream, packaged: molded, on sticks, etc.
Pr: Tom Keller
* *Ex VP:* Bruce Everette
* *Ex VP:* Larree Renda
* *VP:* David Bond
VP: Dandra Calderon
VP: Larry Davis
VP: Dick Gonzales
* *VP:* Richard Gonzales
* *VP:* Richard Goodspeed
* *VP:* Melissa Plaisance
VP: Laree Renda
* *VP:* Harold Rudnick
* *VP:* Peter Scheidt
* *VP:* Rom Schwilke
* *VP:* Jerry Tidwell
* *VP:* David Zylstra

D-U-N-S 12-156-9693
VONTOBEL ASSET MANAGEMENT INC
(*Suby of* VONTOBEL HOLDING AG)
1540 Broadway Fl 38, New York, NY 10036-4039
Tel (212) 415-7000 *Founded/Ownrshp* 1984
Sales 149.6MM *EMP* 55^E
Accts Ernst & Young Llp New York N
SIC 6282 Investment advice
Pr: Heinrich Schlegel
* *COO:* Charles Falck
* *CFO:* Carrie Youngberg
* *Chf Cred:* Joseph Mastoloni
* *Mng Dir:* Rajiv Jain
* *Mng Dir:* Peter H Newell
* *Mng Dir:* Thomas P Wittwer

VOPAK AMERICAS
See VOPAK NORTH AMERICA INC

D-U-N-S 04-810-1364 IMP/EXP
VOPAK NORTH AMERICA INC (DE)
VOPAK AMERICAS
(*Suby of* KONINKLIJKE VOPAK N.V.)
2000 West Loop S Ste 1550, Houston, TX 77027-3527
Tel (713) 561-7200 *Founded/Ownrshp* 1977, 2002
Sales 124.0MM^E *EMP* 454
SIC 4491 4226 4953 4789 Marine terminals; Special warehousing & storage; Chemical detoxification; Hazardous waste collection & disposal; Cleaning railroad ballast
Pr: Dick Richelle
* *VP:* Clinton Roeder
Manager: Michael Patton
Snr Mgr: Rene Stomph

D-U-N-S 00-697-2574 IMP/EXP
VORNADO REALTY TRUST (MD)
888 7th Ave Fl 44, New York, NY 10106-4498
Tel (212) 894-7000 *Founded/Ownrshp* 1986
Sales 2.5MMM *EMP* 4,503
Accts Deloitte & Touche Llp Parsipp
SIC 6798 Real estate investment trusts
Ch Bd: Steven Roth
Pr: Christopher Kennedy
Pr: Mitchell N Schear
COO: Gaston Silva
CFO: Stephen W Theriot
Ex VP: Robert Entin
Ex VP: Michael J Franco
Ex VP: Joseph Macnow
Ex VP: Wendy Silverstein
Sr VP: Paul Sowter
VP: Mark Ambrosone
VP: Shannon Bauer
VP: Robert Byrne
VP: Bridget Cunningham
VP: Amy Farber
VP: Nikhil Gera
VP: Fred Grapstein
VP: Dan E Guglielmone
VP: Paul Heinen
VP: Matt Iocco
VP: Gaurav Khanna
Board of Directors: Candace K Beinecke, Michael D Fascitelli, Robert P Kogod, Michael Lynne, David Mandelbaum, Daniel R Tisch, Richard R West, Russell B Wight Jr

VORTEX OPTICS
See SHELTERED WINGS INC

D-U-N-S 06-359-4360
VORYS SATER SEYMOUR AND PEASE LLP
52 E Gay St, Columbus, OH 43215-3161
Tel (614) 464-6400 *Founded/Ownrshp* 1909
Sales 133.4MM *EMP* 750
SIC 8111

D-U-N-S 15-084-0940
VOS ELECTRIC INC
(*Suby of* VHC INC) ★
3131 Market St, Green Bay, WI 54304-5611
Tel (920) 336-0781 *Founded/Ownrshp* 1985
Sales 90.2MM^E *EMP* 400
SIC 1731 General electrical contractor
Pr: Timothy Van Den Heuvel
**Treas:* Ray Van Den Heuvel II
Treas: Raymond T Van Den II
VP: Bill Bain
**VP:* William C Bain
**VP:* Dean Krueger
**VP:* James Rottier
**Prin:* Ronald Van Den Heuvel

D-U-N-S 03-130-1364
VOSS AUTO NETWORK INC
HOSS
766 Mmsburg Cnterville Rd, Dayton, OH 45459
Tel (937) 428-2400 *Founded/Ownrshp* 1972
Sales 159.3MM^E *EMP* 500
SIC 5511 7538 7515 7513 5521 5012 Automobiles, new & used; General automotive repair shops; Truck rental & leasing, no drivers; Used car dealers; Automobiles & other motor vehicles
Prin: Teresa Haynes
Pr: Chuck Belk
**Pr:* John Voss
Exec: Teresa Haines
Genl Mgr: Dick Lange
Dir IT: Dan Eckert
Mktg Mgr: Stephanie Griffin
Sales Asso: Bob Brown
Sales Asso: John Simpson

D-U-N-S 00-830-7738
VOTAW PRECISION TECHNOLOGIES INC
(*Suby of* BURTEK HOLDINGS INC) ★
13153 Lakeland Rd, Santa Fe Springs, CA 90670-4520
Tel (562) 666-2138 *Founded/Ownrshp* 2014
Sales 110.3MM^E *EMP* 315
SIC 3544 3812 Special dies & tools; Jigs & fixtures; Acceleration indicators & systems components, aerospace
CEO: Jeff Daniel
**Pr:* Scott Wallace
Ex VP: Steve Crisanti
**VP:* Tyler Andersson
VP: Patrick Powers
QA Dir: Nickolas Hirata
VP Mfg: Art Talavera
Ql Cn Mgr: Mark Mancuso
Sls Dir: Mike Petriccione

D-U-N-S 96-798-2641 IMP/EXP
VOTORANTIM METAIS NORTH AMERICA INC
U S Z
(*Suby of* VOTORANTIM EUROPE KORLATOLT FELELOSSEGU TARSASAG)
6020 Navigation Blvd, Houston, TX 77011-1132
Tel (713) 926-1705 *Founded/Ownrshp* 2007
Sales 99.8MM^E *EMP* 282^E
SIC 3356 Zinc & zinc alloy bars, plates, sheets, etc.
Pr: Rodrigo Daud

D-U-N-S 07-865-0240 IMP
VOTORANTIM US INC
(*Suby of* VOTORANTIM GMBH)
3200 Southwest Fwy # 3030, Houston, TX 77027-7539
Tel (832) 726-0160 *Founded/Ownrshp* 2012
Sales 200.0MM *EMP* 14
SIC 1031 1061 Lead & zinc ores; Nickel ore mining
Pr: Christian Hunnicutt

VOUGE
See UNITED FASHIONS OF TEXAS LLC

D-U-N-S 80-046-6695 IMP
■ **VOXX ACCESSORIES CORP**
(*Suby of* VOXX INTERNATIONAL CORP) ★
3502 Wodview Trce Ste 220, Hauppauge, NY 11788
Tel (631) 231-7750 *Founded/Ownrshp* 2007
Sales 153.0MM^E *EMP* 60^E
SIC 5099 Firearms & ammunition, except sporting
Pr: David Geise
**Treas:* Loriann Shelton
VP: Paul Tinaphong
Off Mgr: Claudia Deffenbaugh
Opers Mgr: Rob Standish

D-U-N-S 00-447-1509 IMP
■ **VOXX ELECTRONICS CORP**
(*Suby of* VOXX INTERNATIONAL CORP) ★
150 Marcus Blvd, Hauppauge, NY 11788-3723
Tel (631) 231-7750 *Founded/Ownrshp* 2000
Sales 149.3MM^E *EMP* 400
SIC 5065 5731 Electronic parts & equipment; Sound equipment, automotive
CEO: Patrick M Lavelle
Ch Bd: Patrick Lavelle
**Pr:* Thomas C Malone
Pr: James Tranchina
**CFO:* Charles M Stoehr
**Ch:* John J Salam
VP: Louis Antoniou
VP: James Dario
VP: Patrick Moffett
VP: Dan Murphy
VP: Carl Peters
VP: James Shutowich

D-U-N-S 04-469-4040 IMP/EXP
▲ **VOXX INTERNATIONAL CORP**
2351 J Lawson Blvd, Orlando, FL 32824-4386
Tel (800) 645-7750 *Founded/Ownrshp* 1960
Sales 680.7MM *EMP* 2,100
Accts Grant Thornton Llp Melville
Tkr Sym VOXX *Exch* NGS
SIC 3711 3651 3663 Motor vehicles & car bodies; Household audio & video equipment; Audio electronic systems; Video camera-audio recorders, household use; Radio & TV communications equipment
Pr: Patrick M Lavelle
COO: Loriann Shelton
CFO: Charles M Stoehr
Board of Directors: John Adamovich Jr, Denise Waund Gibson, Paul C Kreuch Jr, Peter A Lesser, Ari M Shalam, John J Shalam

D-U-N-S 12-904-6871
■ **VOYA AMERICA EQUITIES INC**
(*Suby of* SECURITY LIFE OF DENVER INSURANCE COMPANY)
5780 Powers Ferry Rd, Atlanta, GA 30327-4347
Tel (612) 372-5432 *Founded/Ownrshp* 2010
Sales NA *EMP* 700
SIC 6311 6411 Life insurance; Insurance agents, brokers & service
CEO: Margaret B Wall
Pr: Jim Thompson
CFO: Cynthia Grimm

D-U-N-S 09-985-5579
▲ **VOYA FINANCIAL INC**
230 Park Ave Fl 14, New York, NY 10169-1502
Tel (212) 309-8200 *Founded/Ownrshp* 1999
Sales NA *EMP* 7,000
Tkr Sym VOYA *Exch* NYS
SIC 6311 6411 6282 6211 7389 Life insurance; Insurance agents, brokers & service; Investment advice; Security brokers & dealers; Financial services
Ch Bd: Rodney O Martin Jr
Pr: Rob Grubka
Pr: Heather Lavallee
Pr: David Wilken
CEO: Carolyn Johnson
COO: Alain M Karaoglan
CFO: Ewout L Steenbergen
Chf Mktg O: Ann Glover
Ofcr: Chetlur S Ragavan
Ofcr: Kevin D Silva
Ex VP: Nan Ferrara
Sr VP: Miles Edwards
VP: Elizabeth Derby
Board of Directors: Lynne Biggar, Jane P Chwick, Ruth Ann M Gillis, J Barry Griswell, Frederick S Hubbell, Byron H Pollitt Jr, Joseph V Tripodi, Deborah C Wright, David Zwiener

D-U-N-S 14-659-4515
■ **VOYA HOLDINGS INC**
(*Suby of* VOYA FINANCIAL INC) ★
1 Orange Way, Windsor, CT 06095-4773
Tel (860) 580-4646 *Founded/Ownrshp* 1996
Sales 309.0MM^E *EMP* 1,800
SIC 6719 Investment holding companies, except banks
CEO: Robert Leary
**CFO:* Ewout Steenbergen
**Treas:* David Pendergrass
Ofcr: Gary Divan
Sr VP: Chris Eberly
**Sr VP:* Megan Huddleston
VP: James Bogoian
VP: Donald Pegg
VP: Bob Richard
VP: Debra Salvas
VP: Brent Weber

D-U-N-S 60-919-5037
■ **VOYA INSURANCE AND ANNUITY CO**
(*Suby of* VOYA HOLDINGS INC) ★
1475 Dunwoody Dr, West Chester, PA 19380-1478
Tel (610) 425-3400 *Founded/Ownrshp* 2001
Sales NA *EMP* 451
Accts Ernst & Young Llp Boston Mas
SIC 6311 Life insurance; Life insurance carriers
Sr VP: Megan Huddleston
**Ch Bd:* Rodney O Martin Jr
**Pr:* Michael S Smith
CFO: David P Wiland
Sr VP: Tim Billow
Sr VP: Steven T Pierson
Board of Directors: Alain M Karaoglan

D-U-N-S 07-955-5514
■ **VOYA INVESTMENT MANAGEMENT CO LLC**
(*Suby of* VOYA INVESTMENT MANAGEMENT LLC) ★
5780 Powers Ferry Rd, Atlanta, GA 30327-4347
Tel (770) 980-5100 *Founded/Ownrshp* 2012
Sales 112.7MM^E *EMP* 500^E
SIC 6211 Security brokers & dealers
CEO: Jeffrey Becker

D-U-N-S 11-532-0806
■ **VOYA INVESTMENT MANAGEMENT LLC**
(*Suby of* VOYA HOLDINGS INC) ★
5780 Powers Ferry Rd, Atlanta, GA 30327-4347
Tel (770) 980-5100 *Founded/Ownrshp* 2010
Sales 294.0MM^E *EMP* 800
SIC 6211 Security brokers & dealers
CEO: Jeffrey Becker
Pr: Kevin Hill
Ofcr: Stephen Hinck
VP: Glenn Elsey
VP: Scott Frost
VP: Annemarie Hawes
VP: Kathy Martens
VP: Darren Massey

D-U-N-S 96-815-1667
■ **VOYA INVESTMENT TRUST CO**
(*Suby of* VOYA INVESTMENT MANAGEMENT CO LLC) ★
1 Orange Way, Windsor, CT 06095-4773
Tel (860) 580-4646 *Founded/Ownrshp* 1995
Sales 111.3MM^E *EMP* 495^E
SIC 6211 6282 Security brokers & dealers; Investment advisory service
CEO: Jeffrey Becker
Pr: Richard Langevin
VP: Mike Crean
VP: Pat Macken

D-U-N-S 05-518-1770
■ **VOYA RETIREMENT INSURANCE AND ANNUITY CO**
(*Suby of* VOYA HOLDINGS INC) ★
1 Orange Way, Windsor, CT 06095-4773
Tel (860) 580-4646 *Founded/Ownrshp* 2003
Sales NA *EMP* 1,516
Accts Ernst & Young Llp Boston Ma
SIC 6311 Life insurance
Pr: Alain M Karaoglan
**Ch Bd:* Rodney O Martin Jr
Pr: Allison Bryant
Pr: Mark Casper
CFO: Mark B Kaye
Chf Inves: Hans Stoter
Ofcr: Tony Angelico
Sr VP: Steven T Pierson
VP: Marc Altschull
VP: Hans Beekmans
VP: Jodi Beller
VP: Ray Dame
VP: B Ferguson
VP: James Gilbarty
VP: Jason Givens
VP: Bob Guilmette
VP: Scott Hankard
VP: Rory Hart
VP: Scott Hofstedt
VP: Robert Kaplan
VP: Rich Maynes
Board of Directors: Michael S Smith

VOYAGER
See CAMBIUM LEARNING INC

D-U-N-S 00-506-9141
■ **VOYAGER LEARNING CO**
(*Suby of* CAMBIUM LEARNING GROUP INC) ★
17855 Dallas Pkwy Ste 400, Dallas, TX 75287-6857
Tel (214) 932-9500 *Founded/Ownrshp* 1907, 2009
Sales 98.8MM^E *EMP* 399
SIC 2741 2759 Miscellaneous publishing; Commercial printing
Pr: David Cappellucci
COO: John Campbell
**CFO:* Bradley C Almond
**Sr VP:* Todd W Buchardt
VP: Lou Massicci
VP: Mark Trinske
Ex Dir: Mike Isler
Sftwr Eng: Naveen Chinthoju
VP Opers: Debbie Lashbrook
Sales Exec: Lanita Perkins
Sls Mgr: Shelli Rogers

D-U-N-S 01-414-9376
VP HOLDINGS CORP
2514 Fish Hatchery Rd, Madison, WI 53713-2424
Tel (608) 256-1988 *Founded/Ownrshp* 1999
Sales 115.8MM^E *EMP* 269
Accts Mcgladrey & Pullen Llp Madiso
SIC 2048 5191 5153 Feed premixes; Fertilizer & fertilizer materials; Chemicals, agricultural; Grains
Pr: Robert S Tramburg
**CFO:* Mark Miley
**VP:* Alan B Gunderson
**VP:* Allan A Schultz
CTO: Will Klinge
MIS Dir: Dave Simmermon

D-U-N-S 07-864-0973
VPC PIZZA HOLDINGS LLC
227 W Monroe St, Chicago, IL 60606-5055
Tel (312) 701-1777 *Founded/Ownrshp* 2011
Sales 145.5MM^E *EMP* 800^E
SIC 6719 Investment holding companies, except banks
Ch: Richard Levy

VPG
See VEHICLE PRODUCTION GROUP LLC

VPGC
See VIRGINIA POULTRY GROWERS COOPERATIVE INC

D-U-N-S 01-064-7705
VPNE PARKING SOLUTIONS LLC
343 Congress St Ste 3300, Boston, MA 02210-1220
Tel (617) 451-1393 *Founded/Ownrshp* 1990
Sales 81.8MM^E *EMP* 1,250^E
SIC 7521 Parking garage
Ch: Kevin W Leary
Pr: Kevin J Leary
COO: Nick Litton
Sr VP: Thomas Mackinnon
Genl Mgr: Daniel Hession

D-U-N-S 62-280-8657 IMP
VPS COMPANIES INC
310 Walker St, Watsonville, CA 95076-4525
Tel (831) 724-7551 *Founded/Ownrshp* 1966
Sales 299.6MM^E *EMP* 400
SIC 5142 0723 4731 Fruits, frozen; Vegetables, frozen; Crop preparation services for market; Freight transportation arrangement
Ch Bd: Jack Randle
Pr: Ed Fong
**Pr:* Byron Johnson
**CFO:* Ronald Marker
**Sec:* Fred J Haas

VPS CONVENIENCE STORE GROUP
See CENAMA INC

VRS VERICLAIM
See VERICLAIM INC

D-U-N-S 83-275-1932 IMP/EXP
VRUSH INDUSTRIES INC
RUSHFURNITIURE.COM
118 N Wrenn St, High Point, NC 27260-5020
Tel (336) 886-7700 *Founded/Ownrshp* 2009
Sales 300.0MM *EMP* 6,500
SIC 5045 5021 7379 3469 5712 7375 Computer peripheral equipment; Computer software; Furniture; Office & public building furniture; Household furniture; Computer related consulting services; Computer related maintenance services; Furniture components, porcelain enameled; Office furniture; Outdoor & garden furniture; Information retrieval services
Pr: Vicky L Rush
**Ex VP:* Mike Rush

D-U-N-S 15-027-4665
■ **VS HERCULES LLC**
NUTRI-FORCE NUTRITION
(*Suby of* VITAMIN SHOPPE INC) ★
2101 91st St, North Bergen, NJ 07047-4731
Tel (201) 868-5959 *Founded/Ownrshp* 2014
Sales 90.3MM^E *EMP* 124^E
SIC 2834 Vitamin, nutrient & hematinic preparations for human use
CEO: Anthony Truesdale
CFO: Brenda Galgano

D-U-N-S 78-820-6857
VS PARENT INC
(*Suby of* IRVING PLACE CAPITAL LLC) ★
2101 91st St, North Bergen, NJ 07047-4731
Tel (201) 868-5959 *Founded/Ownrshp* 2006
Sales 64.8MM^E *EMP* 3,200
SIC 5961 5499 Catalog & mail-order houses; Vitamin food stores
CEO: Richard Markee
VP: Thomas A Tolworthy
Board of Directors: John H Edmondson, David Edwab, Douglas B Fox, David L Fuente, John D Howard, Douglas Korn, Richard L Perkal

VSA OF NEW ENGLAND
See VISTAR/VSA OF HARTFORD INC

D-U-N-S 60-967-3215
VSC FIRE & SECURITY INC
10343b Kings Acres Rd, Ashland, VA 23005-8059
Tel (804) 459-2200 *Founded/Ownrshp* 1990
Sales 262.7MM^E *EMP* 800
Accts Keiter Glen Allen Virginia
SIC 1711 3494 Fire sprinkler system installation; Sprinkler systems, field
Ch: Martin L Giles
**Pr:* John McDonald
**COO:* Michael Martin
**CFO:* Fritz Mehler
**VP:* Michael Meehan
Genl Mgr: Susan Meador
Sales Exec: Susie Ludwig
Sales Exec: Ron Tidd

D-U-N-S 04-999-7380
▲ **VSE CORP**
6348 Walker Ln, Alexandria, VA 22310-3226
Tel (703) 960-4600 *Founded/Ownrshp* 1959
Sales 533.9MM *EMP* 2,057^E
Tkr Sym VSEC *Exch* NGS
SIC 8711 8742 8741 Engineering services; Mechanical engineering; Maintenance management consultant; Construction management
Pr: Maurice A Gauthier
**Ch Bd:* Clifford M Kendall
Pr: Nancy Margolis
Pr: James E Reed
CFO: Thomas R Loftus
Treas: Richard Hannah
Ex VP: James W Lexo
VP: Bryan Adams
VP: Crystal Douglas
VP: Thomas M Kiernan
VP: Richard Lippert
VP: Crystal R Williams
VP: Crystal Williams
Board of Directors: Ralph E Eberhart, John C Harvey Jr, Calvin S Koonce, James F Lafond, John E Potter, Jack Stultz, Bonnie K Wachtel

D-U-N-S 00-641-8685 IMP/EXP
VSI LIQUIDATING INC
VERTELLUS SPECIALTIES INC.
(*Suby of* VERTELLUS SPECIALTIES HOLDINGS CORP) ★
201 N Illinois St # 1800, Indianapolis, IN 46204-4235
Tel (317) 247-8141 *Founded/Ownrshp* 2007
Sales 482.7MM^E *EMP* 1,000
SIC 2865 Cyclic crudes, coal tar; Tar
Pr: Richard Preziotti
CFO: Stephan A Beitte
**CFO:* Philip Gillespie
Treas: David Schwind
VP: Charles Digioanna
Opers Mgr: Daryl Quinn
Plnt Mgr: Bernard Szalkowski
Board of Directors: Thomas Reilly Jr

D-U-N-S 09-805-5101 IMP
VSM INVESTORS LLC
245 Park Ave Fl 41, New York, NY 10167-0002
Tel (212) 351-1600 *Founded/Ownrshp* 2000
Sales 489.8MM^E *EMP* 4,500
SIC 3842 2599 2515 Wheelchairs; Personal safety equipment; Respirators; Hospital beds; Hospital furniture, except beds; Mattresses & foundations
Mng Dir: John Magliana

D-U-N-S 00-987-8695 IMP
VSM SEWING INC
(*Suby of* VSM GROUP AB)
31000 Viking Pkwy, Westlake, OH 44145-1019
Tel (440) 808-6550 *Founded/Ownrshp* 1997
Sales 129.3MM^E *EMP* 800
SIC 5064 Sewing machines, household: electric
CEO: Charlie Bayer
**Sr VP:* Stan Ingraham
VP: Rick Drainville

D-U-N-S 83-075-7196
VSMA INC
1540 Genessee St, Kansas City, MO 64102-1069
Tel (816) 968-3000 *Founded/Ownrshp* 2009
Sales 415.1MM^E *EMP* 3,813^E

SIC 1542 Commercial & office building, new construction

D-U-N-S 61-643-9170
VSS LLC
382 Galleria Pkwy Ste 400, Madison, MS 39110-6869
Tel (601) 853-8550 Founded/Ownrshp 2006
Sales 138.2MM^E EMP 100
Accts Tann Brown & Russ Co Ltd
SIC 5045 7373 Computers, peripherals & software; Computer integrated systems design
CFO: Bill Grothe
Bd of Dir: Jim Sellinger
Off Mgr: Lucy Sligh

D-U-N-S 80-848-1555
VSS-AHC CONSOLIDATED HOLDINGS CORP
350 Park Ave Fl 7, New York, NY 10022-6080
Tel (212) 935-4990 Founded/Ownrshp 2007
Sales 119.2MM^E EMP 1,050^E
SIC 7389 2721 7331 Trade show arrangement; Magazines: publishing only, not printed on site; Direct mail advertising services

D-U-N-S 96-821-8128
▲ VSS-CAMBIUM HOLDINGS III LLC
55 E 52nd St Fl 33, New York, NY 10055-0007
Tel (212) 308-2281 Founded/Ownrshp 2009
Sales 232.8MM^E EMP 1,193^E
SIC 6726 Investment offices
Mng Pt: Jeffrey T Stevenson

VT GRIFFIN
See CUBE CORP

D-U-N-S 10-425-9234 IMP
VT HACKNEY INC
(Suby of VISION TECHNOLOGIES SYSTEMS INC) ★
911 W 5th St, Washington, NC 27889-4205
Tel (252) 946-6521 Founded/Ownrshp 2005
Sales 146.8MM^E EMP 632
SIC 3713 Beverage truck bodies; Ambulance bodies
Pr: Michael A Tucker
Pr: Curtis Brookshire
*VP: Jeffery T Joyner
Telecom Ex: Jeff Burtner
Info Man: Don Feaster
Plnt Mgr: Sammy Deans

D-U-N-S 11-835-9939 IMP/EXP
VT HALTER MARINE INC
(Suby of VISION TECHNOLOGIES SYSTEMS INC) ★
900 Bayou Casotte Pkwy, Pascagoula, MS 39581-9602
Tel (228) 696-6888 Founded/Ownrshp 2016
Sales 442.2MM^E EMP 2,000
SIC 3731 Shipbuilding & repairing
CEO: William E Skinner
*COO: Paul J Albert
*CFO: Norman D Ballinger
*Ex VP: Rear Admiral John
VP: Robert Mullins
*Prin: D Margaret Gambrell
Prd Mgr: Richard Crimm

D-U-N-S 94-224-3981 IMP/EXP
VT IDIRECT INC
IDIRECT TECHNOLOGIES
(Suby of VISION TECHNOLOGIES ELECTRONICS INC) ★
13861 Sunrise Valley Dr, Herndon, VA 20171-6124
Tel (703) 648-8002 Founded/Ownrshp 2005
Sales 243.6MM^E EMP 600
SIC 3663 Radio & TV communications equipment
CEO: Mary Cotton
Pr: Rick Mantz
*CFO: Chris Norem
*Chf Mktg O: Toni Lee Rudnicki
VP: Kw Chan
VP: Itai Galmor
VP: Jon Gilbert
VP: Wayne Haubner
VP: Andy Hissrich
VP: Karen Reser
VP Bus Dev: Kevin Steen
Exec: Tom Plummer
Dir Bus: Tony Naaman
Dir Bus: Joseph Senhaji
Board of Directors: John G Grimes

VT INDUSTRIES
See V-T INDUSTRIES INC

D-U-N-S 79-937-1166
VT MOTORS INC
VAN CHEVROLET
(Suby of ABC NISSAN) ★
8585 E Frank Lloyd Wright, Scottsdale, AZ 85260-1901
Tel (480) 991-8300 Founded/Ownrshp 2000
Sales 92.3MM^E EMP 260
SIC 5511 Automobiles, new & used
Pr: Larry V Tuyl
*Sec: Alan Cady

D-U-N-S 12-158-8458 IMP/EXP
VT SAN ANTONIO AEROSPACE INC
(Suby of VISION TECHNOLOGIES SYSTEMS INC) ★
9800 John Saunders Rd, San Antonio, TX 78216-4202
Tel (210) 293-3200 Founded/Ownrshp 2002
Sales 107.8MM^E EMP 543^E
SIC 7699 Aircraft & heavy equipment repair services
Pr: Stephen Lim
*Pt: Moh Loong Loh
VP: Tan Shiuan
VP: Pat Stewart
Genl Mgr: Ku K Choon
Genl Mgr: Hwang Ho
Genl Mgr: Kham Joon
Genl Mgr: Cher Keong
Genl Mgr: Brendon McWilliam
Dir IT: Russ Gregory
IT Man: Michael Daly

D-U-N-S 61-195-2255
VT SERVICES INC
(Suby of JORDAN CO L P) ★
529 Viking Dr, Virginia Beach, VA 23452-7306
Tel (912) 573-3671 Founded/Ownrshp 2012
Sales 225.4MM EMP 100
Accts Pricewaterhousecoopers Llp At
SIC 8744 8711 Facilities support services; Aviation &/or aeronautical engineering; Marine engineering
CEO: Terry M Ryan
*Pr: Jonathan F Boucher
*Pr: Walt Yourstone
*CFO: Kent Bridges
*Sec: Allen Garner

VT TRANSCO
See VERMONT TRANSCO LLC

D-U-N-S 05-424-3439
■ VTB HOLDINGS INC
(Suby of TURTLE BEACH CORP) ★
100 Summit Lake Dr, Valhalla, NY 10595-1339
Tel (914) 345-2255 Founded/Ownrshp 2014
Sales 207.1MM EMP 46^E
Accts Freed Maxick Cpas Pc Buffalo
SIC 3651 Sound reproducing equipment
CEO: Juergen Stark
*CFO: John Hanson

D-U-N-S 08-859-6879 IMP
VTECH COMMUNICATIONS INC
(Suby of VTECH HOLDINGS LIMITED)
9590 Sw Gemini Dr Ste 120, Beaverton, OR 97008-7166
Tel (503) 596-1200 Founded/Ownrshp 1989
Sales 97.5MM^E EMP 95
SIC 5065 5064 Communication equipment; Electrical entertainment equipment
Pr: Nicholas P Delany
VP: Graham Williams
VP Opers: Nick Wilson
Natl Sales: Jim Cassidy
Sls Dir: Charles Williams

D-U-N-S 83-135-6055
VUBIQUITY HOLDINGS INC
15301 Ventura Blvd # 3000, Sherman Oaks, CA 91403-5837
Tel (818) 526-5000 Founded/Ownrshp 2006
Sales 300.0MM^E EMP 500
SIC 4841 Cable & other pay television services
CEO: Darcy Antonellis
*Pr: Doug Sylvester
*CFO: William G Arendt
Sr Cor Off: Diane Smith
Chf Mktg O: Brian Matthews
Chf Mktg O: Maria Mendoza
*Ofcr: James P Riley
Ex VP: Pete Bryant
*Ex VP: Anupam Gupta
Ex VP: Adam Poulter
*Ex VP: Brendan Sullivan
Sr VP: Mike Gavigan
VP: Timothy Ainge
VP: Dave Bartolone
VP: Fred Handsman
VP: Robert Poletiek
Board of Directors: Darcy Antonellis, William Darman, Phil Herget Chb, Gary S Howard, Kirby McDonald

D-U-N-S 04-667-6941 IMP
■ VULCAN CONSTRUCTION MATERIALS LLC
VULCAN MATERIALS
(Suby of LEGACY VULCAN LLC) ★
1200 Urban Center Dr, Vestavia, AL 35242-2545
Tel (205) 298-3000 Founded/Ownrshp 1998
Sales 1.0MMM^E EMP 950
SIC 1422 Crushed & broken limestone
Pr: J Thomas Hill
*Ltd Pt: Vulcan A LLC
*Pr: William F Denson III
*Pr: T W Reese
CFO: John Milton
*Ex VP: John R McPherson
*Ex VP: Daniel F Sansone
*Sr VP: Michael R Mills
IT Man: Dan Smart
Tech Mgr: Don Brown
Board of Directors: Melody Synder

D-U-N-S 04-449-6966
VULCAN INC
VULCAN SIGNS
410 E Berry Ave, Foley, AL 36535-2833
Tel (251) 943-7000 Founded/Ownrshp 1966
Sales 110.7MM^E EMP 281
SIC 3469 3993 Metal stampings; Signs, not made in custom sign painting shops
Ch Bd: Robert W Lee
*Pr: Thomas Lee
*Sec: David Mullins
VP: Bob Hamlin
*VP: Robert Hamlin
*VP: James Stewart
Genl Mgr: David Beviacqua
Plnt Mgr: Rocky Stewart
Sls Mgr: Matt Maurin

D-U-N-S 55-691-4729 IMP/EXP
VULCAN INC
505 5th Ave S Ste 900, Seattle, WA 98104-3821
Tel (206) 342-2000 Founded/Ownrshp 1991
Sales 87.8MM^E EMP 200^E
SIC 6531 6722 7941 Real estate managers; Management investment, open-end; Sports clubs, managers & promoters
Pr: Barbara Bennett
COO: Elaine Jones
*Treas: Michael Connor
Bd of Dir: Paul G Allen
Ofcr: Courtney Blodgett
Ofcr: Raechel Waters
Ofcr: Nicki Weston
Ex VP: Gregory P Landis
*Ex VP: Dave Stewart
*VP: Bill Benack
*VP: Susan M Coliton
*VP: Raymond L Colliver
*VP: Steve Crosby
*VP: Susan Drake
*VP: Ada M Healey
*VP: Richard Hutton
*VP: Laura Macdonald
VP: Nathan Troutman
Dir Lab: Michael Lesaius
Assoc Dir: Stuart Nagae

D-U-N-S 00-607-8737
VULCAN INDUSTRIES CORP (WI)
N113w18830 Carnegie Dr, Germantown, WI 53022-3096
Tel (262) 255-1090 Founded/Ownrshp 1945, 1981
Sales 1.2MMM EMP 32
SIC 3469 3498 Metal stampings; Tube fabricating (contract bending & shaping)
Pr: Kurt E Widmann
Site Mgr: Kenneth Burg
Opers Mgr: Gary Koch
Ql Cn Mgr: Michael Burrows
Ql Cn Mgr: John Dohman

VULCAN INFORMATION PACKAGING
See EBSCO INDUSTRIES INC

VULCAN MATERIALS
See CALMAT CO

VULCAN MATERIALS
See VULCAN CONSTRUCTION MATERIALS LLC

D-U-N-S 80-534-4798 IMP/EXP
▲ VULCAN MATERIALS CO
1200 Urban Center Dr, Vestavia, AL 35242-2545
Tel (205) 298-3000 Founded/Ownrshp 1909
Sales 3.4MMM EMP 6,799
Tkr Sym VMC Exch NYS
SIC 1422 1423 2951 1442 3273 3272 Crushed & broken limestone; Limestones, ground; Crushed & broken granite; Asphalt paving mixtures & blocks; Construction sand & gravel; Sand mining; Gravel & pebble mining; Ready-mixed concrete; Concrete products
Ch Bd: J Thomas Hill
CFO: John R McPherson
Ofcr: Michael R Mills
VP: William K Duke
VP: Ejaz A Khan
VP: Jeffery G Lott
VP: Donald McCunniff
VP: David B Pasley
VP: Mark Smith
VP: Rick Vickery
VP: Whittington Worthington
Board of Directors: Vincent J Trosino, Elaine L Chao, Thomas A Fanning, O B Grayson Hall Jr, Cynthia L Hostetler, Douglas J McGregor, Richard T O'brien, James T Prokopanko, Lee J Styslinger, Kathleen Wilson-Thompson

VULCAN MTLS CO VESTAVIA AL
See FLORIDA ROCK INDUSTRIES

D-U-N-S 94-554-7388
■ VULCAN PERFORMANCE CHEMICALS
(Suby of VULCAN MATERIALS CO) ★
1200 Urban Center Dr, Vestavia, AL 35242-2545
Tel (205) 298-3000 Founded/Ownrshp 1972
Sales 226.5MM^E EMP 450
SIC 2819 Industrial inorganic chemicals
Pr: John L Holland
*Ex VP: Daniel Mc Caul
QC Dir: Marty Taylor

VULCAN PLASTICS
See CONSOLIDATED PIPE & SUPPLY CO INC

VULCAN SIGNS
See VULCAN INC

D-U-N-S 02-417-7178 IMP
VVF ILLINOIS SERVICES LLC
(Suby of V V F LIMITED)
2000 Aucutt Rd, Montgomery, IL 60538-1133
Tel (630) 892-4381 Founded/Ownrshp 2008
Sales 209.0MM^E EMP 450
SIC 2841 Soap & other detergents
Exec: Jeanne Keach

D-U-N-S 79-649-0019
VVP HOLDINGS LLC
GLASS CLASS
965 Ridge Lake Blvd # 300, Memphis, TN 38120-9401
Tel (901) 767-7111 Founded/Ownrshp 1992
Sales NA EMP 3,043
SIC 5039 5013 1793 3231 3444 5719

D-U-N-S 05-323-8929
VW CREDIT INC
(Suby of AUDI OF AMERICA) ★
2200 Ferdinand Porsche Dr, Herndon, VA 20171-6243
Tel (248) 340-5000 Founded/Ownrshp 1986
Sales NA EMP 1,200
SIC 6141 Automobile loans, including insurance
Pr: Christian Dahlheim
*Treas: Martin Luedtke
Genl Mgr: Matthew D Darnell
Board of Directors: Kevin Reilly

D-U-N-S 07-957-4445
▲ VWR CORP
100 Matsonford Rd 1-200, Radnor, PA 19087-4569
Tel (610) 386-1700 Founded/Ownrshp 1852
Sales 4.3MMM EMP 9,426^E
Tkr Sym VWR Exch NGS
SIC 2869 2819 3821 5047 Industrial organic chemicals; Chemicals, reagent grade: refined from technical grade; Laboratory apparatus & furniture; Medical laboratory equipment
Ch Bd: Harry Kraemer Jr
Pr: Manuel Brocke-Benz
CFO: Gregory L Cowan
Sr VP: Gerard J Christian
Sr VP: Nils Clausnitzer
Sr VP: Ulf Kepper
Sr VP: Stephan W Labonte
Sr VP: Mark T McLoughlin
Sr VP: George Van Kula
VP: Douglas J Pitts
CTO: Amy Semerad

D-U-N-S 61-538-3739
■ VWR FUNDING INC
(Suby of VWR CORP) ★
100 Matsonford Rd, Radnor, PA 19087-4558
Tel (610) 386-1700 Founded/Ownrshp 2015
Sales 4.3MMM EMP 8,400
Accts Kpmg Llp Philadelphia Penns
SIC 5049 5169 Scientific & engineering equipment & supplies; Laboratory equipment, except medical or dental; Scientific instruments; Chemicals & allied products
Pr: Manuel Brocke-Benz
*Ch Bd: Harry M Jansen Kraemer Jr
CFO: Gregory L Cowan
Sr VP: Gerard J Christian
Sr VP: Stephan W Labont
Sr VP: Theodore C Pulkownik
Sr VP: George Van Kula
VP: John Bloszinsky
VP: Jim Bramwell
VP: Kareem Dossa
VP: Alan Honeycutt
VP: James Kalinovich
VP: Randy Kinkade
VP: Michael Kinzler
VP: David Lechner
VP: Mark McLaughlin
VP: Douglas J Pitts
VP: Peter Vanwalleghem
VP: Rob Welsh
Comm Dir: Valerie C Collado
Board of Directors: Nicholas W Alexos, Robert L Barchi, Edward A Blechschmidt, Thompson Dean, Robert P Decresce, Carlos Del Salto, Pamela Forbes Lieberman, Timothy P Sullivan, Robert J Zollars

D-U-N-S 15-098-2189 IMP/EXP
■ VWR INTERNATIONAL LLC
(Suby of VWR FUNDING INC) ★
100 Matsonford Rd Bldg 1, Radnor, PA 19087-4569
Tel (610) 386-1700 Founded/Ownrshp 2007
Sales 3.4MMM^E EMP 6,535
SIC 5169 5049 Chemicals & allied products; Laboratory equipment, except medical or dental
Pr: Manuel A H Brocke-Benz
Pr: Matt Malenfant
Pr: Peter Schuele
Pr: Eddy Wu
COO: Niels Schwaner
CFO: Walter S Sobon
Treas: Deborah Corr
*Sr VP: Gregory L Cowan
*Sr VP: Mark McLoughlin
*Sr VP: Theodore C Pulkownik
*Sr VP: Peter Schle
VP: Arne Brandon
VP: Manuel Brocke
VP: Bob Dearth
VP: George Gunther
VP: Gretchen Haage
VP: Steve Harsh
VP: Mark Lundahl
VP: Amy McDonald
VP: Adrianne Miller
VP: Hal G Nichter
Board of Directors: Nicholas W Alexos, Harry M Jansen Kraemer Jr, Pamela Forbes Lieberman, Timothy D Sheehan, Timothy P Sullivan

D-U-N-S 96-533-4373
VWR INVESTORS INC
(Suby of VARIETAL DISTRIBUTION HOLDINGS LLC) ★
3 First National Plz, Chicago, IL 60602-5008
Tel (610) 386-1700 Founded/Ownrshp 2007
Sales 429.4MM^E EMP 8,600^E
SIC 6799 Investors

D-U-N-S 08-021-1999
VWRE HOLDINGS INC
105 Orville Dr, Bohemia, NY 11716-2520
Tel (631) 567-9500 Founded/Ownrshp 2016
Sales 76.2MM^E EMP 3,000^E
SIC 6719 5499 Investment holding companies, except banks; Vitamin food stores
Pr: Jack Krause

D-U-N-S 04-138-6504
VXI GLOBAL SOLUTIONS LLC
220 W 1st St Fl 3, Los Angeles, CA 90012-4105
Tel (213) 739-4720 Founded/Ownrshp 1998
Sales 284.7MM^E EMP 2,300
SIC 7389 Telemarketing services
Pr: Eva Yi Hui Wang
Pr: Mark Hauge
*COO: David Zhou
CFO: Stephen Choi
*CFO: Steven Wang
CFO: Roger Wood
Sr VP: Carey Box
Sr VP: Nick Covelli
VP: Armando Castro
VP: Thomas Daviau
VP: Toby Parrish
VP: Carolyn Rivera
VP: Jon Simon
VP: Jayme Steege
*VP: Kit Wan
VP: Gary Witt
VP: Michael Xu
Exec: Eva Wong
Assoc Dir: Julian Pacificador
Dir Bus: Roland Perez

D-U-N-S 12-081-8216 IMP
VYGON CORP
(Suby of VYGON (U.K.) LIMITED)
2750 Morris Rd Ste 200, Lansdale, PA 19446-6012
Tel (215) 390-2002 Founded/Ownrshp 1962
Sales 86.4MM^E EMP 290
SIC 5047 Medical equipment & supplies
Pr: Robert Combs
*CFO: Kenneth Rafferty
Genl Mgr: Sharyn Flores
Mktg Mgr: Micheal Chow
Board of Directors: Philippe Manteau

D-U-N-S 07-086-5134
VYSTAR CREDIT UNION
4949 Blanding Blvd, Jacksonville, FL 32210-7330
Tel (904) 777-6000 *Founded/Ownrshp* 1952
Sales NA *EMP* 1,050
SIC 6061 Federal credit unions
CEO: Terry R West
COO: Richard G Alfirevic
CFO: Lynie Spencer
CFO: John H Turpish
VP: Lori Allen
VP: William Barefield
VP: Bernadette Brown
VP: Judy Campbell
VP: Phil Carter
VP: Tina Davis
VP: Robert Harrington
VP: Kim Hicks
VP: Joan Hill
VP: Ashley Johnson
VP: Laura Lancaster
VP: Benita Lookadoo
VP: Lisa Miller
VP: Gene Moore
VP: Cort Raithel
VP: Bradley Smith
VP: Melissa Thomas

D-U-N-S 15-399-0346
VYTRA HEALTH PLANS LONG ISLAND INC
(*Suby of* EMBLEMHEALTH INC) ★
395 N Service Rd Ste 110, Melville, NY 11747-3140
Tel (631) 694-4000 *Founded/Ownrshp* 2001
Sales NA *EMP* 400
SIC 6324 Health maintenance organization (HMO), insurance only
Pr: Daniel McGowan
**Ch Bd:* Anthony Watson
**Exec:* Philip Gandolfo

W

D-U-N-S 08-571-5977 IMP
W & O SUPPLY INC
(*Suby of* PVI HOLDINGS INC) ★
2677 Port Industrial Dr, Jacksonville, FL 32226-2398
Tel (904) 354-3800 *Founded/Ownrshp* 1975
Sales 160.0MM^E *EMP* 235
SIC 5085 5051 Valves & fittings; Copper sheets, plates, bars, rods, pipes, etc.
Pr: Michael Hume
**Pr:* Jack Guidry
**CFO:* Greg Lechware
**CFO:* Michael Page
VP: Jack B Guidry
**VP:* Michael Mickle
Rgnl Mgr: Carl Herman
Brnch Mgr: Kyle Posey
Brnch Mgr: Dan Sawler
Genl Mgr: Kimberly Hegg
IT Man: Whitney Croxton

D-U-N-S 07-421-3646
W A FOOTE MEMORIAL HOSPITAL
HENRY FORD ALLEGIANCE HEALTH
205 N East Ave, Jackson, MI 49201-1753
Tel (517) 788-4800 *Founded/Ownrshp* 1916
Sales 462.5MM *EMP* 3,500
SIC 8062 General medical & surgical hospitals
Pr: Georgia Fojtasek
COO: Erica Bills
CFO: Hendrik Schuur
Exec: Ginette Busschots
Ex Dir: Tom Lopez
Off Mgr: Ann Brown
Dir IT: Mark Lauteren
Dir IT: Sean RE
Dir IT: Jerry Stassines
IT Man: Jim Hong
Doctor: Naseer Humayun MD

W A I
See WETHERILL ASSOCIATES INC

D-U-N-S 05-622-2037
W A KENDALL AND CO INC
400 Farmer Ct, Lawrenceville, GA 30046-6100
Tel (770) 963-6017 *Founded/Ownrshp* 1970
Sales 159.1MM^E *EMP* 800
SIC 1629

D-U-N-S 08-219-6858
W A RASIC CONSTRUCTION CO INC
4150 Long Beach Blvd, Long Beach, CA 90807-2650
Tel (562) 928-6111 *Founded/Ownrshp* 1978
Sales 168.2MM^E *EMP* 400^E
SIC 1623 Sewer line construction; Water main construction
CEO: Peter L Rasic
VP: Walter Rasic
Div Mgr: Shane Sato
Off Mgr: Zorkita Paschall
CTO: Randall Kulkarni
IT Man: Randall Beck
Snr PM: Jeremy Juarez

D-U-N-S 05-326-7225 IMP
W ATLEE BURPEE CO
BURPEE SEEDS
(*Suby of* BURPEE HOLDING CO INC) ★
300 Park Ave, Warminster, PA 18974-4818
Tel (215) 674-4900 *Founded/Ownrshp* 1876
Sales 117.2MM^E *EMP* 350
SIC 0181 5961 Seeds, vegetable: growing of; Seeds, flower: growing of; Catalog & mail-order houses
Ch Bd: George C Ball Jr
**Pr:* Benjamin Lacson
**Pr:* Christos G Romas
**CFO:* Hans Miller
CIO: Joseph Maloney
IT Man: Ethan Holland
IT Man: Gerald Purcell
Netwrk Mgr: Dick Yowell
Opers Mgr: Steve Wright
Mktg Mgr: Michelle Doyka

D-U-N-S 00-896-7366
W B JOHNSTON GRAIN CO
(*Suby of* WB JOHNSTON GRAIN CO) ★
411 W Chestnut Ave, Enid, OK 73701-2057
Tel (580) 233-5800 *Founded/Ownrshp* 1976
Sales 177.1MM^E *EMP* 275
SIC 5153 5191 4491 4213 0111 0211 Wheat; Fertilizer & fertilizer materials; Feed; Seeds & bulbs; Marine loading & unloading services; Trucking, except local; Wheat; Beef cattle feedlots
CEO: Butch Meibergen
**Pr:* Lew Meibergen
**COO:* Dennis Craig
VP: Roger Henneke
**VP:* Joey Meibergen
Dir IT: Abrahim Guerrero
Snr Mgr: Ed Polk

D-U-N-S 05-180-7493 IMP/EXP
W B MASON CO INC
NEW ENGLAND OFFICE SUPPLY
59 Center St, Brockton, MA 02301-4075
Tel (781) 794-8800 *Founded/Ownrshp* 1975
Sales 580.6MM^E *EMP* 1,200
SIC 5712 5943 Office furniture; Office forms & supplies
Pr: Leo Meehan
**Pr:* Thomas Golden
**CFO:* Tony Dipippa
**Sec:* Steven Greene
**Ex VP:* John Greene
**Sr VP:* Chris Meehan
Prd Mgr: Daniel Hooley
Sls Mgr: Boke Bryant

W C A HOSPITAL
See WOMANS CHRISTIAN ASSOCIATION OF JAMESTOWN NY

W C A HOSPITAL
See WCA GROUP INC

D-U-N-S 09-407-4523 EXP
W C BRADLEY CO
ZEBCO
1017 Front Ave, Columbus, GA 31901-5260
Tel (706) 571-7000 *Founded/Ownrshp* 1989
Sales 236.1MM^E *EMP* 625
SIC 3631 3949 3999 Barbecues, grills & braziers (outdoor cooking); Fishing equipment; Camping equipment & supplies; Candles
CEO: Marc R Olivie
Pr: Connie Warner
**CFO:* James G Hillenbrand
CFO: W B Turner
**CFO:* William Yates
**Ch:* Stephen T Butler
**Treas:* Robert H Wright Jr
VP: Brett Peters
VP: JD Shelton
**VP:* Mathew D Swift
**VP:* J Richard Woodham III
Dir Bus: Gary Butler

W C F
See WORKERS COMPENSATION FUND

W C S
See WASTE CONTROL SPECIALISTS LLC

D-U-N-S 96-488-8424
W C S INC
WENDY'S
1515 N Academy Blvd Ste 4, Colorado Springs, CO 80909-2749
Tel (719) 573-8557 *Founded/Ownrshp* 1985
Sales 68.0MM^E *EMP* 2,800^E
SIC 5812 Fast-food restaurant, chain
CEO: Richard Holland
**Pr:* James Williams
**VP:* Kenneth Lustig

D-U-N-S 10-267-2169 EXP
W CSE INDUSTRIES INC
INC CSE W-INDUSTRIES
(*Suby of* CSE GLOBAL LIMITED)
11500 Charles Rd, Jersey Village, TX 77041-2406
Tel (713) 466-9463 *Founded/Ownrshp* 2000
Sales 147.0MM^E *EMP* 500
SIC 3625 3613 3594 3494 Relays & industrial controls; Control panels, electric; Fluid power pumps & motors; Valves & pipe fittings
CEO: Greg Hanson
**COO:* Salil Gopinath
**VP:* Ken Castlebury

D-U-N-S 08-024-9253
W D LARSON COMPANIES LTD INC
ALLSTATE PETERBILT GROUP
10700 Lyndale Ave S Ste A, Minneapolis, MN 55420-5642
Tel (952) 888-4934 *Founded/Ownrshp* 1974
Sales 119.2MM^E *EMP* 422
SIC 5012 5013 7538 6159 Trucks, commercial; Trailers for trucks, new & used; Motor vehicle supplies & new parts; Truck engine repair, except industrial; Truck finance leasing; Machinery & equipment finance leasing
CEO: Jeff Vanthournout
**Ch Bd:* William D Larson
**Pr:* Glenn D Evans
**CFO:* Kenneth Soltesz
**Sr VP:* Allen T Ofstehage

W D T
See WESTERN DAIRY TRANSPORT LLC

D-U-N-S 07-870-3288 IMP
W DIAMOND GROUP CORP
1680 E Touhy Ave, Des Plaines, IL 60018-3607
Tel (646) 647-2791 *Founded/Ownrshp* 2012
Sales 199.2MM^E *EMP* 600
SIC 2326 5611 Men's & boys' work clothing; Men's & boys' clothing stores
CEO: Doug Williams
**COO:* Kenneth Ragland

D-U-N-S 02-361-8127
W DOUGLASS DISTRIBUTING LTD (TX)
DOUGLAS DISTRIBUTING
325 E Forest Ave, Sherman, TX 75090-8832
Tel (903) 893-1181 *Founded/Ownrshp* 1981
Sales 259.3MM *EMP* 130
SIC 5812 Fast-food restaurant, chain
Genl Pt: William P Douglass
**Pt:* Brad Douglass
**Pt:* Joan Douglass
**Pt:* Diane McCarty
**CFO:* Kim McKinney

D-U-N-S 00-695-4291 IMP
W E AUBUCHON CO INC (MA)
95 Aubuchon Dr, Westminster, MA 01473-1470
Tel (978) 874-0521 *Founded/Ownrshp* 1908
Sales 159.2MM *EMP* 1,252
Accts Rsm Us Llp Boston Massachuse
SIC 5251 5211 5231 5719 Hardware; Lumber & other building materials; Paint; Wallpaper; Housewares
CEO: William E Aubuchon IV
**CFO:* Jeffrey M Aubuchon
**Ex VP:* Bernard W Aubuchon Jr
**VP:* Charles Aubuchon
**VP:* Daniel P Aubuchon
**VP:* Scott D Aubuchon
**VP:* Josiah Gates
**VP:* Joseph Houssan
**VP:* Kenneth S Moore
VP: Greg Moran
IT Man: Lindsay Aubuchon

D-U-N-S 13-024-1144
W E BOWERS & ASSOCIATES INC
W. EBOWERS ASSOCIATES
12401a Kiln Ct Ste A, Beltsville, MD 20705-1315
Tel (800) 989-0011 *Founded/Ownrshp* 1984
Sales 98.8MM^E *EMP* 500
Accts Watkins Meegan Drury & Co L
SIC 1711 Mechanical contractor
Pr: Wayne E Bowers
**CFO:* Rich Harrington
**Sec:* Jim Chilson
**VP:* David J O'Donnell

D-U-N-S 00-693-2032
W E ONEIL CONSTRUCTION CO
(*Suby of* ONEIL INDUSTRIES INC) ★
1245 W Washington Blvd, Chicago, IL 60607-1929
Tel (773) 244-6003 *Founded/Ownrshp* 1981
Sales 189.4MM^E *EMP* 300
Accts Crowe Horwath Llp Oak Brook
SIC 1541 Industrial buildings, new construction
Ch: Mike Faron
Pr: John Finn
Pr: Bruce Hawkins
**Pr:* John A Russell
Pr: Jeff Strom
**Treas:* Conrad L Ott Jr
**VP:* Dennis J Garlick
VP: Wanita Letendre
**VP:* Patrick J McGowan
**VP:* Louis J Reiner
**VP:* James A Sikich
Exec: Jim Sullivan

W. EBOWERS ASSOCIATES
See W E BOWERS & ASSOCIATES INC

W F S CO
See WATONWAN FARM SERVICE INC

W F S I
See WHEATON FRANCISCAN SERVICES INC

D-U-N-S 00-481-5007
W G TOMKO INC (PA)
2559 State Route 88, Finleyville, PA 15332-3504
Tel (724) 348-2000 *Founded/Ownrshp* 1954, 1970
Sales 89.7MM *EMP* 398
SIC 1711 Mechanical contractor
Pr: William G Tomko III
CFO: Scott Tom
**Treas:* Sharee A Waskowiak
Comm Dir: Dean Kollet
Sys Mgr: Ron Miller
VP Opers: Dan White
Sfty Dirs: Cary Ernest
Opers Mgr: Brian McLaughlin
Mktg Mgr: Severino Depasquale
Snr PM: Scott Chorey
Snr PM: George Openko

D-U-N-S 00-403-2132
W G YATES & SONS CONSTRUCTION CO (MS)
(*Suby of* YATES COMPANIES INC) ★
1 Gully Ave, Philadelphia, MS 39350
Tel (904) 714-1376 *Founded/Ownrshp* 1964
Sales 818.4MM *EMP* 2,588
Accts Rea Shaw Giffin & Stuart Ll
SIC 1542 1541 2339 1611 5211 1731 Commercial & office building, new construction; Industrial buildings, new construction; Jeans: women's, misses' & juniors'; Resurfacing contractor; Home centers; General electrical contractor
Pr: William G Yates III
CFO: Brandon Dunn
**Treas:* Marvin Blanks
**Sec:* Alinda Goss
**VP:* E M Johnson III
VP: Mack Johnson
**VP:* Chester Nadolski
VP: Chester J Nadolski
IT Man: Randy Swift
Mktg Mgr: Jodi Tidwell
Counsel: Kenny Bush
Board of Directors: Opal Yates, R Andrew Yates

D-U-N-S 05-371-9126 IMP
W H BRAUM INC
BRAUM'S BAKERY
3000 Ne 63rd St, Oklahoma City, OK 73121-1202
Tel (405) 478-1656 *Founded/Ownrshp* 1940
Sales 129.2MM^E *EMP* 600
SIC 5451 5812 Dairy products stores; Fast-food restaurant, chain
Ch Bd: William H Braum
**Pr:* Drew Braum
**CEO:* W Anthony Bostwick
**CFO:* Anthony Bostwick
**CFO:* Mark A Godwin
**Sec:* Mary Braum
**VP:* Elaine Braum
**VP:* Paul Clark
**VP:* William Ricks
IT Man: Doug Payne
Site Mgr: Mary Black

D-U-N-S 00-819-3013
W H C INC (LA)
300 Industrial Trce, Broussard, LA 70518-3623
Tel (337) 837-4500 *Founded/Ownrshp* 1957
Sales 90.0MM *EMP* 100
SIC 1623 1541 Oil & gas pipeline construction; Industrial buildings, new construction
Pr: Randolph W Warner
**Ch Bd:* George L Crain Jr
**Sr VP:* Rayburn Judice
Sr VP: Kevin Labauve
**Sr VP:* Kevin Lebauve
**Sr VP:* Jerry Martin
VP: Ryan Hebert
Dir Bus: Jack Rizzo

D-U-N-S 02-088-3880
W K KELLOGG FOUNDATION
1 Michigan Ave E, Battle Creek, MI 49017-4012
Tel (269) 968-1611 *Founded/Ownrshp* 1930
Sales 350.9MM *EMP* 200^E
Accts Mitchell & Titus Llp Chicago
SIC 8399 Fund raising organization, non-fee basis
CEO: Sterling K Speirn
**COO:* Linh Nguyen
Trst: Ram N Murgu A
**Ex VP:* Gregory A Lyman
**Sr VP:* James E McHale
**Sr VP:* La June Montgomery-Talley
**VP:* Gail C Christopher
**VP:* Richard M Foster
VP: Dianna Langenburg
**VP:* Paul J Lawler
**VP:* Gail D Mc Clure
VP: Joseph Scantlebury
VP: Cindy Smith
**VP:* Gregory B Taylor
Comm Man: Halcyon C Liew

W K U
See WESTERN KENTUCKY UNIVERSITY

D-U-N-S 87-983-8423
W L BUTLER CONSTRUCTION INC
204 Franklin St, Redwood City, CA 94063-1929
Tel (650) 361-1270 *Founded/Ownrshp* 1994
Sales 106.4MM^E *EMP* 150
SIC 1542 Commercial & office building, new construction; Commercial & office buildings, renovation & repair
CEO: William L Butler
**Pr:* Frank York
VP: Dave Fister
VP: David Fister
VP: Dan Warren
Exec: Joseph Pompili
Dir IT: Gary Sooto
Sfty Mgr: John Kiely
Genl Couns: Trent Morrow
Snr PM: Rick Dion
Snr PM: Andrew Estrin

D-U-N-S 00-233-1536 IMP
W L GORE & ASSOCIATES INC
555 Paper Mill Rd, Newark, DE 19711-7513
Tel (302) 738-4880 *Founded/Ownrshp* 1958
Sales 2.9MMM *EMP* 9,500
SIC 3357 2821 5131 3841 2819 3069

D-U-N-S 03-163-4348
W L HALSEY GROCERY CO INC
HALSEY FOODSERVICE
401 Lanier Rd, Madison, AL 35758-1865
Tel (256) 772-9691 *Founded/Ownrshp* 1879
Sales 85.6MM *EMP* 140
SIC 5141

D-U-N-S 03-407-8139
W L PETREY WHOLESALE CO INC (AL)
PETREY W L WHOLESALE CO
10345 Petrey Hwy, Luverne, AL 36049-4406
Tel (334) 230-5674 *Founded/Ownrshp* 1911
Sales 496.4MM^E *EMP* 650
SIC 5141 5194 Groceries, general line; Tobacco & tobacco products
Ch Bd: James W Jackson Sr
**Pr:* Robert W Jackson
**Sec:* Norman Parks
**VP:* James W Jackson Jr
Off Mgr: Frances Wyrosdick

D-U-N-S 60-382-7908
W LEASE LEWIS CO
2200 Western Ave, Seattle, WA 98121-1921
Tel (206) 622-0500 *Founded/Ownrshp* 1978
Sales 199.1MM^E *EMP* 400^E
SIC 1542 Nonresidential construction; Commercial & office building contractors
Pr: Jeff Cleator
**CFO:* Philo Hall
**Ex VP:* Gary Smith
**VP:* Jay Sorensen

W LEE FLOWERS & CO WHOLESALE
See W LEE FLOWERS AND CO INC

D-U-N-S 00-894-1346 IMP/EXP
W LEE FLOWERS AND CO INC
W LEE FLOWERS & CO WHOLESALE
127 E W Lee Flowers Rd, Scranton, SC 29591-6100
Tel (843) 389-2731 *Founded/Ownrshp* 1977
Sales 181.3MM^E *EMP* 350
SIC 5141 5147 5194

D-U-N-S 04-693-6621
W M AUTOMOTIVE WAREHOUSE INC
208 Penland St, Fort Worth, TX 76111-4697
Tel (817) 834-5559 *Founded/Ownrshp* 1976

Sales 183.5MM[E] EMP 275[E]
SIC 5013 Automotive supplies & parts
Ch Bd: Wilson McMillion
VP: Garry Castle
*VP: Garry Castles
Sales Exec: Jerry Petty

D-U-N-S 14-750-5523
W M GRACE COS INC
7575 N 16th St Ste 1, Phoenix, AZ 85020-4625
Tel (602) 956-8254 Founded/Ownrshp 1978
Sales 75.1MM[E] EMP 1,200[E]
SIC 1542 6512 7011 Nonresidential construction; Auditorium & hall operation; Hotels
Pr: Howard T Grace
CFO: Christine Zeihan
*VP: Ann K Grace
*VP: Matt Grace

D-U-N-S 10-340-2012
W M LYLES CO
(Suby of LYLES DIVERSIFIED, INC.)
1210 W Olive Ave, Fresno, CA 93728-2816
Tel (951) 973-7393 Founded/Ownrshp 1945
Sales 241.8MM EMP 200
Accts Cuttone And Mastro Cpas Fresn
SIC 1623 Pipeline construction; Underground utilities contractor
Pr: Richard E Amigh
VP: Ken Strosnider
Genl Mgr: Rich Nemmer

W N A
See WADDINGTON NORTH AMERICA INC

W O W
See WOW LOGISTICS CO

D-U-N-S 09-716-8277
W P C S FM
PENSACOLA CHRISTIAN COLLEGE
250 Brent Ln, Pensacola, FL 32503-2267
Tel (850) 478-8496 Founded/Ownrshp 1999
Sales 84.4MM EMP 5
Accts Habif Arogeti & Wynne Llp
SIC 4832 Radio broadcasting stations
Pr: AR Horton
VP: Barbi Baer
VP: Paul Ohman
Exec: Donald Brewster

W. P. CAREY FOUNDATION
See CPA 17 LIMITED PARTNERSHIP

D-U-N-S 02-951-3202
▲W P CAREY INC
50 Rockefeller Plz Fl 2, New York, NY 10020-1607
Tel (212) 492-1100 Founded/Ownrshp 1973
Sales 938.3MM EMP 314[E]
Tkr Sym WPC Exch NYS
SIC 6531 6282 Real estate agents & managers; Real estate managers; Real estate leasing & rentals; Investment advice
CEO: Mark J Decesaris
*Ch Bd: Benjamin H Griswold IV
Pr: Jason E Fox
Pr: Mark M Goldberg
COO: Thomas E Zacharias
CFO: Hisham A Kader
Sr VP: Luis Fernandes
VP: Peter Bates
VP: Pam Gonzalez
Board of Directors: Nick J M Van Ommen, Mark Alexander, Karsten Von Koller, Nathaniel S Coolidge, Reginald Winssinger, Peter J Farrell, Axel K A Hansing, Jean Hoysradt, Richard C Marston, Robert E Mittelstaedt Jr, Chris Niehaus, Charles E Parente

W P I
See WORCESTER POLYTECHNIC INSTITUTE

W P I
See WESTERN PARTITIONS INC

W P P
See WPP CLAPTON SQUARE LLC

W P P I
See WPPI ENERGY

W R
See CFI RESORTS MANAGEMENT INC

D-U-N-S 05-608-5533
▲W R BERKLEY CORP
475 Steamboat Rd Fl 1, Greenwich, CT 06830-7144
Tel (203) 629-3000 Founded/Ownrshp 1967
Sales NA EMP 7,621
Tkr Sym WRB Exch NYS
SIC 6331 6321 6351 6311 Fire, marine & casualty insurance: stock; Property damage insurance; Reinsurance carriers, accident & health; Liability insurance; Surety insurance bonding; Life insurance carriers; Life reinsurance
Pr: W Robert Berkley Jr
*Ch Bd: William R Berkley
Pr: Gregory A Douglas
Pr: Naomi Kinderman
Pr: Robert Sabio
CFO: Richard M Baio
Ex VP: Eugene G Ballard
Ex VP: Ira S Lederman
Ex VP: James G Shiel
Sr VP: James Gilbert
Sr VP: Richard M Lowery
Sr VP: Matthew M Ricciardi
Sr VP: Kathleen M Tierney
VP: Steven Cade
VP: Joyce Krech
VP: Carol La Punzina
VP: Jonathan Levine
VP: Gordon J Olver
VP: Stephen Samoskevich
VP: Richard Starkie
Board of Directors: Christopher L Augostini, Ronald E Blaylock, Mark E Brockbank, George G Daly, Mary C Farrell, Jack H Nusbaum, Mark L Shapiro

D-U-N-S 61-060-2245 IMP
W R CASE & SONS CUTLERY CO
(Suby of ZIPPO MANUFACTURING CO INC) ★
50 Owens Way, Bradford, PA 16701-3749
Tel (800) 523-6350 Founded/Ownrshp 1993
Sales 89.4MM[E] EMP 365
SIC 3421 Knives: butchers', hunting, pocket, etc.
CEO: Michael A Schuler
*Pr: Thomas E Arrowsmith
*Pr: George B Duke
Exec: Amy Smith
Mtls Mgr: Linda Butler
Mktg Dir: John Sullivan

D-U-N-S 00-136-7846
▲W R GRACE & CO
7500 Grace Dr, Columbia, MD 21044-4029
Tel (410) 531-4000 Founded/Ownrshp 1854
Sales 3.0MMM EMP 4,900
Accts Pricewaterhousecoopers Llp Ba
Tkr Sym GRA Exch NYS
SIC 2819 3531 2899 2891 3479 Catalysts, chemical; Silica gel; Bituminous, cement & concrete related products & equipment; Waterproofing compounds; Sealants; Coating of metals & formed products
Ch Bd: Alfred E Festa
*Pr: Hudson La Force III
Treas: Donald Spencer
Bd of Dir: Jim Minor
*Ofcr: Elizabeth C Brown
*VP: Keith N Cole
VP: Tony Dondero
VP: Rahul Goturi
VP: Matthew Hellstern
*VP: Mark A Shelnitz
Mktg Dir: Heide Knab
Board of Directors: H Furlong Baldwin, Robert F Cummings Jr, Diane H Gulyas, Julie Fasone Holder, Jeffry N Quinn, Christopher J Steffen, Mark E Tomkins

W. R. GRACE & CO.- CONN.
See W R GRACE & CO-CONN

D-U-N-S 61-296-7141 IMP/EXP
■W R GRACE & CO-CONN
W. R. GRACE & CO.- CONN.
(Suby of W R GRACE & CO) ★
7500 Grace Dr, Columbia, MD 21044-4029
Tel (410) 531-4000 Founded/Ownrshp 1899
Sales 414.1MM[E] EMP 1,050[E]
SIC 2819 3531 2899 2891 3479 Catalysts, chemical; Silica gel; Bituminous, cement & concrete related products & equipment; Waterproofing compounds; Sealants; Coating of metals & formed products
CEO: Fred E Festa
*VP: Mark A Shelnitz
VP: Naren Srinivasan
Site Mgr: Steven Boss
VP Mktg: Joanne Deady
Sls Mgr: Bob Shu
Sls Mgr: Mike Vjestica

D-U-N-S 00-521-2782 IMP/EXP
W R MEADOWS INC
300 Industrial Dr, Hampshire, IL 60140-7722
Tel (847) 214-2100 Founded/Ownrshp 1926
Sales 90.5MM[E] EMP 225
SIC 5031

D-U-N-S 12-645-1736
W R STARKEY MORTGAGE LLP
6101 W Plano Pkwy, Plano, TX 75093-8201
Tel (972) 599-5510 Founded/Ownrshp 2000
Sales NA EMP 275
SIC 6162 Mortgage bankers
Ch: William Starkey Jr
Treas: Linda Preece
Ofcr: Maryann Howard
Ofcr: Mardi White
Ex VP: Todd Bergwall
Ex VP: Sherry Colley
Ex VP: Julie M Gross
Ex VP: Adam Pongrass
Ex VP: David R Williams
Sr VP: Paige Guest
Sr VP: Bill McCracken
Sr VP: Jim Nunn
VP: Christopher Brooks
VP: Michael J Dugan
VP: Scott Dye
VP: Lindsay Ensom
VP: Kevin Johnston
VP: Kelley Shea

D-U-N-S 02-489-7530
W R VERNON PRODUCE CO
1035 N Cherry St, Winston Salem, NC 27101-1422
Tel (336) 725-9741 Founded/Ownrshp 1932
Sales 100.1MM[E] EMP 115
Accts James R Malton Winston-Salem
SIC 5148 Fresh fruits & vegetables
Pr: A E Vernon Sr
*VP: Bill Doss
*VP: A E Vernon Jr
*VP: Pete Vernon
IT Man: Eric Orgain

D-U-N-S 00-793-0936
W S BELLOWS CONSTRUCTION CORP (TX)
1906 Afton St, Houston, TX 77055-2209
Tel (713) 680-2132 Founded/Ownrshp 1914, 1994
Sales 101.1MM[E] EMP 200
SIC 1542 Commercial & office building contractors
Ch Bd: Laura Bellows
*Treas: Thomas Kubin
VP: W S Bellows III
*VP: Steven Imburgia
*VP: Charles Kubin
*VP: David Morris
*VP: Paul Oliver
*VP: John Roberts

D-U-N-S 00-509-4842 IMP/EXP
W S DARLEY & CO
325 Spring Lake Dr, Itasca, IL 60143-2072
Tel (630) 735-3500 Founded/Ownrshp 1908
Sales 169.1MM EMP 245
SIC 3561 5087 5099 3569 3812

W S I
See W SILVER INC

W S I
See WAREHOUSE SERVICES INC

W S S C
See WASHINGTON SUBURBAN SANITARY COMMISSION (INC)

D-U-N-S 00-792-9151 IMP
W SILVER INC (TX)
W S I
9059 Doniphan Dr, Vinton, TX 79821-9372
Tel (915) 886-3553 Founded/Ownrshp 1969
Sales 83.3MM[E] EMP 135
SIC 3312 3462 Bar, rod & wire products; Iron & steel forgings
Prin: Mark Fenenbock
COO: Alfredo Cardona
CFO: Gabriel Santana
Mng Dir: Chris Smith
Mill Mgr: Mike Myers
Plnt Mgr: Luis Garcia
Sales Exec: Martha Montano
Natl Sales: Pete Seaman
Mktg Mgr: Ruben Brito

D-U-N-S 00-297-1703
W SOULE & CO (MI)
W SOULE & CO SERVICE GROUP
7125 S Sprinkle Rd, Portage, MI 49002-9437
Tel (269) 324-7001 Founded/Ownrshp 1920, 1966
Sales 85.8MM[E] EMP 250
SIC 1711 3444 Process piping contractor; Sheet metal specialties, not stamped
Pr: John Soule
*Treas: Howard Dembs

W SOULE & CO SERVICE GROUP
See W SOULE & CO

D-U-N-S 60-087-2191
W T BYLER CO INC
15203 Lillja Rd, Houston, TX 77060-5299
Tel (281) 445-2070 Founded/Ownrshp 2008
Sales 190.0MM EMP 600
SIC 1794 1629 Excavation work; Railroad & railway roadbed construction
CFO: Cliff Atterberry
*VP: Cliff Atteberry
VP: Steve Smith
Off Mgr: Gail Franklin

D-U-N-S 04-341-0158
W T RICH CO INC
29 Crafts St Ste 300, Newton, MA 02458-1392
Tel (617) 467-6010 Founded/Ownrshp 1968
Sales 133.6MM EMP 30
Accts O Brien Fitzgerald Taylor &
SIC 1541 1542 Industrial buildings, new construction; Renovation, remodeling & repairs: industrial buildings; Commercial & office building contractors
CEO: Walter T Rich
*Pr: Ralph W Rich
*CEO: Jonathan Rich
VP: Jonathan W Rich

W V A
See WISCONSIN VISION ASSOCIATES INC

D-U-N-S 00-793-9424
W W CLYDE & CO (UT)
1375 N Main St, Springville, UT 84663-5878
Tel (801) 802-6800 Founded/Ownrshp 1926
Sales 114.3MM[E] EMP 400
SIC 1611 1794 1629 General contractor, highway & street construction; Excavation work; Dam construction
Pr: Jeffrey R Clyde
*VP: A Ray Gammell
IT Man: Jeffrey White
Sfty Mgr: Berke Cheesman

W W F
See WORLD WILDLIFE FUND INC

D-U-N-S 96-449-8401
W W GRAINGER INC GROUP BENEFIT TRUST I
HEALTH AND DENTAL PLAN
100 Grainger Pkwy, Lake Forest, IL 60045-5202
Tel (847) 535-1096 Founded/Ownrshp 2010
Sales 148.3MM EMP 2
SIC 6733 Trusts
Trst Ofcr: Lu Licudine

D-U-N-S 00-128-2565 IMP
W W NORTON & CO INC (NY)
500 5th Ave Fl 6, New York, NY 10110-0054
Tel (212) 354-5500 Founded/Ownrshp 1923
Sales 228.5MM[E] EMP 500
SIC 2731 5192 Textbooks: publishing only, not printed on site; Books: publishing only; Books
Pr: W Drake McFeely
VP: Allen Clawson
VP: Julia Druskin
VP: John Glusman
VP: Michael Levatino
*VP: James L Mairs
VP: Jane Searle
VP: Warren Tiley
Rgnl Mgr: Dennis Fernandes
Rgnl Mgr: Annette Stewart
Web Dev: Patrick Cartelli

W W S
See WENDY WEIHE STORLIE INC

D-U-N-S 11-428-4037
▲W&T OFFSHORE INC
9 Greenway Plz Ste 300, Houston, TX 77046-0908
Tel (713) 626-8525 Founded/Ownrshp 1983
Sales 507.2MM EMP 297[E]
Tkr Sym WTI Exch NYS
SIC 1311 Crude petroleum & natural gas
Ch Bd: Tracy W Krohn
Pr: Jamie L Vazquez
COO: Thomas P Murphy
CFO: John D Gibbons
Sr VP: Stephen L Schroeder
VP: Karen Acree
VP: Paul Baker
VP: Amy Brumfield
VP: David Bump
VP: William S Flores
VP: Steven M Freeman
VP: Thomas F Getten
VP: Todd Grabois
VP: Gregory E Percival
VP: Joe Slattery
VP: Clifford J Williams
Board of Directors: Virginia Boulet, Stuart B Katz, S James Nelson Jr, B Frank Stanley

D-U-N-S 62-276-7911 IMP/EXP
W-H ENERGY SERVICES LLC
(Suby of SCHLUMBERGER) ★
2000 W Sam Houston Pkwy S # 500, Houston, TX 77042-3624
Tel (713) 969-1000 Founded/Ownrshp 2008
Sales 205.5MM[E] EMP 2,959[E]
SIC 1389 7353 Oil field services; Oil field equipment, rental or leasing
COO: Jeffrey L Tepera
CFO: Ernesto Bautista III
CFO: Jeff Tepara
CTO: Sergey Fradkov
Sales Exec: Curtis Bucher

W-H SECURITY
See WRIGHT-HENNEPIN SECURITY CORP

D-U-N-S 96-388-2944
W-INDUSTRIES OF TEXAS LLC
11500 Charles Rd, Jersey Village, TX 77041-2406
Tel (713) 466-9463 Founded/Ownrshp 2001
Sales 112.0MM EMP 408
SIC 6719 Investment holding companies, except banks
*Prin: Greg Hanson

D-U-N-S 14-384-3980 IMP
W/K HOLDING CO INC
2401 Cooper St, Fort Scott, KS 66701-3033
Tel (620) 223-5500 Founded/Ownrshp 2002
Sales 88.9MM[E] EMP 350[E]
SIC 2754 Commercial printing, gravure
Prin: Roger Kraft
Pr: Mark Tucker
Treas: Joe Baker

D-U-N-S 01-066-8361 IMP
W/S PACKAGING GROUP INC
2571 S Hemlock Rd, Green Bay, WI 54229-9508
Tel (920) 866-6300 Founded/Ownrshp 2002
Sales 752.0MM[E] EMP 2,089
SIC 2679 2752 Labels, paper: made from purchased material; Commercial printing, lithographic
CEO: Terrence R Fulwiler
*CEO: Fred C Tinsey
*CFO: Jay K Tomcheck
*Ofcr: William J Smith
Ex VP: Leeann B Foster
*VP: Diane J Biersteker
VP: Bill Cashin
VP: Jerry Denoma
*VP: Scott Fisher
*VP: David A Ghiloni
*VP: David A Groessi
VP: Arshen John
VP: Brenda Jones
VP: Missy Lemmens
*VP: Mark Lutz
VP: Paula Lynch
*VP: Jeff Nyam
*VP: Fred E Polizzi
VP: Louann Sjogren
Exec: Andy Barnes
Exec: Barbara Colotta

D-U-N-S 78-261-0153
W2005 WYN HOTELS LP
545 E J Carpntr Fwy 140, Irving, TX 75062
Tel (972) 444-9700 Founded/Ownrshp 2007
Sales 11.7MM[E] EMP 1,535
SIC 7011 Hotels & motels
Pt: Nina Perry

D-U-N-S 84-793-5194
W2007 GRACE ACQUISITION I INC
(Suby of GRACE I W2007 LLC) ★
7700 Wolf River Blvd, Germantown, TN 38138-1752
Tel (901) 759-6000 Founded/Ownrshp 2007
Sales 179.6MM EMP 146
SIC 6798 Real estate investment trusts
Pr: Howard A Silver
Ch Bd: Phillip H McNeill Sr
VP: Michael K Goforth

D-U-N-S 82-504-8577
W2007/ACEP MANAGERS VOTECO LLC
85 Broad St, New York, NY 10004-2434
Tel (212) 902-1000 Founded/Ownrshp 2007
Sales 351.1MM[E] EMP 5,303
SIC 7011 7999 Casino hotel; Tourist attractions, amusement park concessions & rides; Amusement ride
Prin: Stuart Rothenberg
*Pt: Jonathan Langer
*Mng Dir: Brahm Cramer

D-U-N-S 94-783-2325 IMP
■WA CHESTER LLC
(Suby of PEPCO ENERGY SERVICES INC) ★
4390 Parliament Pl Ste Q, Lanham, MD 20706-1834
Tel (202) 466-1940 Founded/Ownrshp 1995
Sales 131.2MM EMP 139
SIC 1731 General electrical contractor
Bd of Dir: John H Wilson
*Ex VP: Frank Musick

D-U-N-S 00-728-2473
WA STATE COMMUNITY COLLEGE DIST 3
OLYMPIC COLLEGE
1600 Chester Ave, Bremerton, WA 98337-1600
Tel (360) 792-6050 Founded/Ownrshp 1946
Sales 73.7MM[E] EMP 1,500
SIC 8221 Colleges & universities

Pr: David Mitchell
Ex Dir: Cary Bozeman
Prgrm Mgr: Lori Anderson
Dir IT: Brian Bria
Dir IT: Evelyn Evely
Dir IT: Jay Haw
Dir IT: Nancy Patersen
Tech Mgr: Kevin Blackwell
Pgrm Dir: Gayle Dilling

D-U-N-S 01-667-1976
WABASH ELECTRIC SUPPLY INC
1400 S Wabash St, Wabash, IN 46992-4198
Tel (260) 563-2240 *Founded/Ownrshp* 1989
Sales 123.0MM^E *EMP* 166
SIC 5063 Electrical apparatus & equipment; Electrical fittings & construction materials; Electrical supplies; Lighting fixtures
Pr: John Forrester
**Sec:* Gayle Forrester
**VP:* Joseph Dyer
**VP:* Richard White
Brnch Mgr: Cindy McGuire
Brnch Mgr: Cathy Minne
Brnch Mgr: Jerry Smith
Off Mgr: Mick Strange
CTO: Shawn Graff
MIS Dir: Billy Hogge
Opers Mgr: Darren Crandell
Board of Directors: Jack Porter

D-U-N-S 01-340-6834
WABASH INTERMEDIATE HOLDING CORP
3155 W Big Beaver Rd # 209, Troy, MI 48084-3002
Tel (248) 220-5400 *Founded/Ownrshp* 2007
Sales 85.0MM *EMP* 1,200^E
SIC 6719 Investment holding companies, except banks
Pr: Stephen Dow
**CFO:* James Butler

D-U-N-S 12-158-1698
▲ WABASH NATIONAL CORP
1000 Sagamore Pkwy S, Lafayette, IN 47905-4727
Tel (765) 771-5310 *Founded/Ownrshp* 1985
Sales 2.0MMM *EMP* 5,300^E
Tkr Sym WNC *Exch* NYS
SIC 3715 3714 5012 Truck trailers; Trailer bodies; Motor vehicle parts & accessories; Automobiles & other motor vehicles; Trailers for trucks, new & used
Pr: Richard J Giromini
**Ch Bd:* Martin C Jischke
CFO: Jeffery L Taylor
Sr VP: William D Pitchford
Sr VP: Erin J Roth
VP: Ron Gregs
VP: Forrest Held
VP: Steve Miller
VP: Timothy Monahan
VP: Bill Pitchford
VP: Erin Roth
VP: Robert Smith
Board of Directors: James D Kelly, John E Kunz, Larry J Magee, Ann D Murtlow, Scott K Sorensen

D-U-N-S 00-767-3791 EXP
■ WABASH NATIONAL TRAILER CENTERS INC
(*Suby of* WABASH NATIONAL CORP) ★
1000 Sagamore Pkwy S, Lafayette, IN 47905-4727
Tel (765) 771-5300 *Founded/Ownrshp* 1997
Sales 269.2MM^E *EMP* 700
SIC 5012 7539 5013 Trailers for trucks, new & used; Trailer repair; Motor vehicle supplies & new parts; Trailer parts & accessories
Pr: Richard J Giromini
**CFO:* Robert J Smith
**CFO:* Jeffery L Taylor
**Sr VP:* Rodney P Ehrlich
**Sr VP:* Bruce N Ewald
**Sr VP:* Bill Pitchford
VP: Bruce Ewald
Exec: Kathryn Gipe
**Prin:* Robert L Nida
Area Mgr: Kevin Riley

D-U-N-S 13-266-9656 IMP
WABASH TECHNOLOGIES INC
(*Suby of* SENSATA TECHNOLOGIES INDIANA INC) ★
529 Pleasant St, Attleboro, MA 02703-2421
Tel (260) 355-4100 *Founded/Ownrshp* 2014
Sales 260.0MM^E *EMP* 615
SIC 3625 3676 Flow actuated electrical switches; Thermistors, except temperature sensors
Pr: Stephen Dow
**CFO:* Lawrence Denbo
**Sr VP:* Casey Kroll
**VP:* Tom Martin
IT Man: Tammy Scott

D-U-N-S 07-071-9596
WABASH VALLEY POWER ASSOCIATION INC
722 N High School Rd, Indianapolis, IN 46214-3756
Tel (317) 481-2800 *Founded/Ownrshp* 1963
Sales 740.6MM *EMP* 65
Accts Deloitte Tax Llp Indianapolis
SIC 4911 Distribution, electric power
CEO: Rick Coons
**CFO:* Jeffrey A Conrad
**VP:* Katherine A Joyce
**VP:* Curtis E Taylor
VP: Keith Thompson
**VP:* M Keith Thompson
Netwrk Mgr: John C Hambers
Opers Supe: Mindy Myers
Counsel: Brenda Hopkins

D-U-N-S 01-625-9947
WABASH VALLEY PRODUCE INC
4886 E 450n, Dubois, IN 47527-9660
Tel (812) 678-3131 *Founded/Ownrshp* 1958
Sales 117.9MM^E *EMP* 300
SIC 5144 5191 Eggs; Feed
Pr: Bradley Seger
**CFO:* Andrew Seger
**VP:* Thomas W Seger

D-U-N-S 80-673-6588
▲ WABCO HOLDINGS INC
2770 Research Dr Fl 1, Rochester Hills, MI 48309-4901
Tel (248) 270-9299 *Founded/Ownrshp* 1869
Sales 2.6MMM *EMP* 12,429^E
Accts Wim Van Gasse Partner Brusse
Tkr Sym WBC *Exch* NYS
SIC 3714 Motor vehicle brake systems & parts; Motor vehicle steering systems & parts; Motor vehicle transmissions, drive assemblies & parts
Ch Bd: Jacques Esculier
Pr: Leon Liu
CFO: Prashanth Mahendra-Rajah
Ofcr: Mazen Mazraani
Ofcr: Daniel Sebillaut
VP: Lisa Brown
VP: Sean Deason

D-U-N-S 00-651-9633 IMP
WABCO PASSENGER TRANSPORTATION DIVISION
WABTEC PASSENGER TRANSIT
130 Ridgeview Center Dr, Duncan, SC 29334-9635
Tel (864) 433-5900 *Founded/Ownrshp* 1986
Sales 99.2MM^E *EMP* 350
SIC 3799 Trailers & trailer equipment
Pr: Robert Debbi
Mktg Mgr: Jim White

WABTEC
See WESTINGHOUSE AIR BRAKE TECHNOLOGIES CORP

D-U-N-S 85-987-5437 IMP/EXP
■ WABTEC CORP
WABTEC GLOBAL SERVICES
(*Suby of* WABTEC) ★
1001 Airbrake Ave, Wilmerding, PA 15148-1036
Tel (412) 825-1543 *Founded/Ownrshp* 1999
Sales 1.0MMM^E *EMP* 3,400
SIC 3743 Railroad equipment
Pr: Raymond T Betler
Ex VP: Robert J Brooks
Ex VP: Mike McBride
Ex VP: John M Meister
Sr VP: R Mark Cox
Sr VP: Patrick D Dugan
Sr VP: Charles F Kovac
VP: Timothy J Logan
VP: George A Socher
VP: Timothy R Wesley
VP: Ron Witt
Board of Directors: Gary C Valade, Robert J Brooks, Emilio A Fernandez V Chm, Lee B Foster II, Lee B Foster II, Brian P Hehir, Brian P Hehir, Michael Howell, James V Napier, James V Napier, Nickolas W Vande Steeg

WABTEC GLOBAL SERVICES
See WABTEC CORP

WABTEC PASSENGER TRANSIT
See WABCO PASSENGER TRANSPORTATION DIVISION

D-U-N-S 04-054-1070 IMP
■ WABTEC RAILWAY ELECTRONICS INC
(*Suby of* WABTEC) ★
21200 Dorsey Mill Rd, Germantown, MD 20876-6963
Tel (301) 515-2000 *Founded/Ownrshp* 1995
Sales 122.3MM^E *EMP* 300
SIC 3825 3679 3743 3672 Instruments to measure electricity; Tube spacers, mica; Railroad equipment; Printed circuit boards
Pr: Raymond T Betler
**Genl Mgr:* Robert Bourg
Sftwr Eng: Andrew Beard

D-U-N-S 14-619-8515
WACCAMAW COMMUNITY HOSPITAL
GEORGETOWN HOSPITAL SYSTEM
4070 Highway 17 Business, Murrells Inlet, SC 29576-6193
Tel (843) 527-7000 *Founded/Ownrshp* 2002
Sales 157.1MM *EMP* 500
SIC 8062 General medical & surgical hospitals
CEO: Bruce P Bailey
**COO:* Gayle L Resetar
**CFO:* Terry Kiser
Chf Mktg O: Gerald Harmon
**VP:* James F Harper
**VP:* Rick Kaylor
**VP:* Terry L Kiser
Dir Case M: Monica Grey
Pharmcst: Darrell Willm

D-U-N-S 06-945-5182
WACHOVIA A DIVISION OF WELLS F
420 Montgomery St, San Francisco, CA 94104-1207
Tel (415) 571-2832 *Founded/Ownrshp* 2011
Sales NA *EMP* 790^E
SIC 6021 National commercial banks
Prin: John G Stumpf
Ofcr: Eric Irwin
Sr VP: Barbara Angel
Sr VP: Bernie Gacona
Sr VP: Sharon Murphy
Sr VP: Karl Pfeil
Sr VP: Peter Stephenson
VP: Arnie Adkins
VP: Brady Hutka
VP: Anand Jobanputra
VP: Hank Patterson
VP: Elizabeth Seymour
VP: Isaac Washington

D-U-N-S 00-699-6094
■ WACHOVIA BANK NATIONAL ASSOCIATION
(*Suby of* WFC HOLDINGS CORP) ★
301 S Tryon St, Charlotte, NC 28282-1915
Tel (704) 335-5878 *Founded/Ownrshp* 1908, 2010
Sales NA *EMP* 19,000^E
SIC 6021 National trust companies with deposits, commercial
Prin: Ron Fisher
CFO: Christopher Collins
Ex VP: Robert Andersen
Sr VP: Tom Barefoot
Sr VP: Nancy S Jones
VP: Susan Bagdasarian
VP: Joan Bradshaw
VP: Rosalie Brandino
VP: Penny Bruckse
VP: Rebecka Campbell
VP: Doug Dayberry
VP: Carey Hedberg
VP: Gerald Hullinger
VP: Gail Lawrence
VP: Satish Masurkar
VP: Ryoko Mochizuki
VP: Jack Phillips
VP: Prabjeet Rai
VP: Demond Richardson
VP: Theresa Satterlee
VP: Rudi Sykes

D-U-N-S 83-162-7414
■ WACHOVIA INVESTMENT HOLDINGS LLC
(*Suby of* EVEREN CAPITAL CORP) ★
201 S College St Ste 500, Charlotte, NC 28244-0014
Tel (704) 374-2584 *Founded/Ownrshp* 2009
Sales 5.4MM^E *EMP* 1,994^E
SIC 6211 Security brokers & dealers
Pr: Debra Warren
Sr VP: Kevin Slane

D-U-N-S 00-320-2835
■ WACHOVIA MORTGAGE CORP (NC)
(*Suby of* WELLS FARGO BANK NATIONAL ASSOCIATION) ★
201 S College St Fl 16, Charlotte, NC 28244-0002
Tel (704) 374-6161 *Founded/Ownrshp* 1964, 2008
Sales NA *EMP* 1,150
Accts Kpmg Llp Charlotte North Car
SIC 6162 6411 Mortgage bankers; Insurance agents
Pr: James E Maynor
**COO:* Alvin M Brown Jr
Ex VP: Joel McPhee
Sr VP: Robert Bertges
Sr VP: Andrea Esterline
Sr VP: Suzy Yoder
VP: Marc Elliott

D-U-N-S 61-287-0311
■ WACHOVIA OPERATIONAL SERVICES LLC (NORTH CAROLINA)
(*Suby of* WELLS FARGO BANK NATIONAL ASSOCIATION) ★
191 Peachtree St Ne Fl 31, Atlanta, GA 30303-1740
Tel (404) 332-5000 *Founded/Ownrshp* 2008
Sales 71.4MM^E *EMP* 4,132
SIC 7389 Financial services
VP: Joseph Patterson

D-U-N-S 80-954-1407
■ WACHOVIA PREFERRED FUNDING CORP
(*Suby of* WACHOVIA PREFERRED FUNDING HOLDING CORP.)
90 S 7th St Fl 13, Minneapolis, MN 55402-3903
Tel (855) 825-1437 *Founded/Ownrshp* 2008
Sales 870.6MM *EMP* 10^E
SIC 6798 Real estate investment trusts; Mortgage investment trusts
Pr: Michael J Loughlin
CFO: Timothy J Sloan
Ex VP: Richard D Levy

D-U-N-S 36-155-2115
■ WACHOVIA SECURITIES FINANCIAL HOLDINGS LLC
(*Suby of* WACHOVIA SECURITIES HOLDINGS, LLC)
901 E Byrd St Ste 500, Richmond, VA 23219-4066
Tel (804) 782-4174 *Founded/Ownrshp* 2003
Sales 372.7MM^E *EMP* 8,000
SIC 6211 Security brokers & dealers
COO: Marjorie Connelly
Treas: Robert B McGuire
VP: Heather Dautel
VP: Ann Pollard
VP: Lynn N Smith
Comm Dir: Anthony Mattera
Comm Man: Rhonda Washington
Mng Dir: Scott Cohen
Mng Dir: Rick Dowd
Mng Dir: Gloria Gibson
Mng Dir: Darren Langis

D-U-N-S 05-166-2349 EXP
WACHS VALVE AND HYDRANT SERVICES LLC (IL)
WACHS WATER SERVICES
(*Suby of* PURE TECHNOLOGIES LTD)
801 Asbury Dr, Buffalo Grove, IL 60089-4509
Tel (224) 357-2600 *Founded/Ownrshp* 2000
Sales 104.7MM^E *EMP* 115
SIC 4971 Water distribution or supply systems for irrigation
Pr: Cliff Wilson
**CEO:* Edward Wachs
**CFO:* Scott Hales
VP: Ryan McKeon
VP: Wayne Pratt

WACHS WATER SERVICES
See WACHS VALVE AND HYDRANT SERVICES LLC

D-U-N-S 06-120-4384
WACHTELL LIPTON ROSEN & KATZ
51 W 52nd St Fl 29, New York, NY 10019-6150
Tel (212) 403-1000 *Founded/Ownrshp* 1965
Sales 98.4MM^E *EMP* 621
SIC 8111 General practice law office
Sr Pt: Herbert Wachtell
**Sr Pt:* Martin Lipton
Pt: David B Anders
Pt: Martin J Arms
Pt: Wayne M Carlin
Pt: Damian G Didden
Pt: Joshua M Holmes
Pt: David E Kahan
Pt: Jeannemarie O'Brien
Pt: David E Shapiro
Pt: Herbert M Wachtell
COO: Edward Diyanmi

CFO: Constance Monte
VP: Jennifer Reid
Board of Directors: Sheila Barrows

D-U-N-S 00-717-8940
WACHTER INC
WACHTER NETWORK SERVICES
16001 W 99th St, Lenexa, KS 66219-1293
Tel (913) 541-2500 *Founded/Ownrshp* 1930
Sales 229.2MM *EMP* 1,210
Accts Mayer Hoffman Mccann Pc Kansa
SIC 1731 General electrical contractor; Voice, data & video wiring contractor
CEO: Brad Botteron
**COO:* Brian Sloan
COO: Greg Sloan
CFO: Jennifer Botteron
**CFO:* Deanna Gillett
**Sr VP:* Greg K Sloan
Exec: Renee Weaver
Prgrm Mgr: Dee Vincent
Rgnl Mgr: Phil Kennedy
Dir IT: Mike Haas
IT Man: Mark Hufford
Board of Directors: Ann Botteron, Brad Botteron

WACHTER NETWORK SERVICES
See WACHTER INC

D-U-N-S 02-936-1271 IMP
WACKER BIOCHEM CORP
(*Suby of* WACKER CHEMICAL CORP) ★
3301 Sutton Rd, Adrian, MI 49221-9335
Tel (517) 264-8500 *Founded/Ownrshp* 1997
Sales 88.8MM^E *EMP* 500
SIC 2899 Chemical preparations
Pr: Ingo Kavor

D-U-N-S 07-540-0671 IMP
WACKER CHEMICAL CORP
(*Suby of* WACKER CHEMICALS FINANCE B.V.)
3301 Sutton Rd, Adrian, MI 49221-9335
Tel (517) 264-8500 *Founded/Ownrshp* 1974, 2005
Sales 5.0MMM *EMP* 1,400
SIC 2869 5169 Silicones; Industrial chemicals
Pr: David Wilhoit
Sr VP: Joerg Hoffmann
VP: Rolf Hirsenkorn
VP: Thomas Koini
VP: Michael O'Dell
VP: Tristan Saint-Georges
VP: John Tacca
Exec: Peter Tkaczuk
Dir Risk M: Torsten Bohn
CTO: Nadine Baumgartl
Dir IT: Calvin Kilbourn

D-U-N-S 00-178-2176 IMP
WACKER NEUSON CORP
(*Suby of* WACKER NEUSON SE)
N92w15000 Anthony Ave, Menomonee Falls, WI 53051-1504
Tel (262) 255-0500 *Founded/Ownrshp* 1957
Sales 252.6MM^E *EMP* 587
SIC 3531 3621 3561 3546 3423 Backfillers, self-propelled; Vibrators for concrete construction; Tampers, powered; Paving breakers; Motors & generators; Pumps & pumping equipment; Power-driven handtools; Hand & edge tools
Ch Bd: Ulrich Wacker
Pr: Christopher Barnard
COO: Michael Marks
CFO: Willkomm Bob
VP: David Christifulli
VP: William Lahner
VP: Larry O'Toole
VP: Robert Phaneuf
VP: Johannes Vohren
Dist Mgr: Brian Cooke
MIS Dir: David Kosinski
Board of Directors: Werner Schwind, Dr Georg Sick, Klaus Steinle

WACO FOOD STORE
See WARE OIL & SUPPLY CO INC

D-U-N-S 00-314-0597
WACO INC (VA)
5450 Lewis Rd, Sandston, VA 23150-1979
Tel (804) 222-8440 *Founded/Ownrshp* 1963
Sales 116.3MM^E *EMP* 450
Accts Mitchell Wiggins & Company L
SIC 1711 1799 3448 5033 Mechanical contractor; Asbestos removal & encapsulation; Insulation of pipes & boilers; Prefabricated metal buildings; Insulation, thermal
Pr: Daniel M Walker
**Sec:* Thomas B Carswell
**VP:* Larry Battaile
**VP:* Harry Judy
**VP:* Rex H Luzar
**VP:* Ronald J Rost
**VP:* Steve Williams
Brnch Mgr: Tim Cundiff
Off Mgr: Teresa Stawson
Board of Directors: Daniel M Walker

D-U-N-S 07-512-3661
WACO INDEPENDENT SCHOOL DISTRICT
501 Franklin Ave Ofc, Waco, TX 76701-2151
Tel (254) 755-9473 *Founded/Ownrshp* 1948
Sales 157.6MM *EMP* 3,000^E
Accts Belt Harris Pechacek Lllp Ho
SIC 8211 Public elementary & secondary schools
Pr: Pat Atkins
**Pr:* Allen Sykes
**VP:* Avid Schleicher
Ex Dir: Elaine Botello
Genl Mgr: Sheryl Davis
HC Dir: Heather Branch

D-U-N-S 00-192-1089 IMP/EXP
WACOAL AMERICA INC
(*Suby of* WACOAL INTERNATIONAL CORP) ★
1 Wacoal Plz, Lyndhurst, NJ 07071-3400
Tel (201) 933-8400 *Founded/Ownrshp* 1952, 1983
Sales 118.4MM^E *EMP* 800

SIC 2342 2341 Brassieres; Panties: women's, misses', children's & infants'; Women's & children's nightwear
Ch Bd: Seiji Sumi
COO: Stephen Ruzow
COO: John Wilson
VP: Victor Vega
Exec: Dan Castaneda
Dir IT: Carlos Rivas
IT Man: Cherlyn Rice
Plnt Mgr: Jan Levine
Prd Mgr: Margarita Yagudayeva
Trfc Mgr: Inez Delgado
Mktg Dir: Mike Greene

D-U-N-S 19-418-1715 IMP/EXP
WACOAL INTERNATIONAL CORP
(Suby of WACOAL CORP.)
1 Wacoal Plz, Lyndhurst, NJ 07071-3400
Tel (201) 933-8400 Founded/Ownrshp 1981
Sales 132.5MM[E] EMP 900
SIC 2341 Women's & children's undergarments
Pr: Ken Yamamoto

D-U-N-S 02-274-3111 EXP
WADA FARMS MARKETING GROUP LLC
2155 Providence Way, Idaho Falls, ID 83404-4951
Tel (208) 542-2898 Founded/Ownrshp 1997
Sales 181.3MM EMP 39
Accts Vanorden Lund & Cannon Pllc
SIC 5148 Fruits; Vegetables
CEO: Bryan Wada
*Ch Bd: Albert Wada
*Pr: Kevin Stanger

D-U-N-S 80-632-0438
▲ WADDELL & REED FINANCIAL INC
6300 Lamar Ave, Overland Park, KS 66202-4200
Tel (913) 236-2000 Founded/Ownrshp 1937
Sales 1.5MMM EMP 1,691[E]
Tkr Sym WDR Exch NYS
SIC 6211 6282 6411 Security brokers & dealers; Investment advice; Insurance agents, brokers & service
CEO: Philip J Sanders
*Ch Bd: Henry J Herrmann
CFO: Brent K Bloss
Chf Mktg O: Thomas W Butch
Ofcr: John E Sundeen Jr
VP: Jon Baker
VP: Amy Rush
Assoc Dir: John Torola
Board of Directors: Thomas C Godlasky, Alan W Kosloff, Dennis E Logue, Michael F Morrissey, James M Raines, Jerry W Walton

D-U-N-S 15-650-6578
■ WADDELL & REED FINANCIAL SERVICES INC
(Suby of WADDELL & REED FINANCIAL INC) ★
6300 Lamar Ave, Overland Park, KS 66202-4200
Tel (913) 236-2000 Founded/Ownrshp 1990
Sales 154.4MM[E] EMP 900
SIC 6722 6311 6211 6531 Money market mutual funds; Life insurance; Security brokers & dealers; Real estate managers
Pr: Henry Herrmann
Pr: Yvonne Devine
Pr: Jim Turner
COO: John Sundeen
CFO: Douglas Oord
Ofcr: Kristen Richards
Assoc VP: Gina Goldstein
Sr VP: Brent Bloss
Sr VP: Lawrence Cipolla
Sr VP: Philip Sanders
VP: David Burford
VP: Lisa Dale
VP: Frank Dearden
VP: Thomas A Mengel
VP: Grant Sarris
VP: Debra Schmidt
VP: Brian Sullivan
VP: D Towery

D-U-N-S 00-696-6477
■ WADDELL & REED INC (MO)
(Suby of WADDELL & REED FINANCIAL INC) ★
6300 Lamar Ave, Shawnee Mission, KS 66202-4200
Tel (913) 236-2000 Founded/Ownrshp 1937, 1981
Sales 436.5MM[E] EMP 642
SIC 6282 6211 6289 6411 Investment counselors; Underwriters, security; Distributors, security; Security transfer agents; Life insurance agents
CEO: Henry J Herrmann
*Ch Bd: Keith A Tucker
*Pr: Michael L Avery
*Pr: Derek D Burke
*Pr: Robert L Hechler
Sr Ex VP: Steven Anderson
*Ex VP: Thomas W Butch
Ex VP: Mark J Schlafly
VP: David Hui
VP: Mark Nohrenberg
VP: Brian Sullivan
*Dir Risk M: Terry L Lister
Dir Soc: Amanda A McLeish

D-U-N-S 80-944-6164
■ WADDELL & REED INVESTMENT MANAGEMENT CO
(Suby of WADDELL & REED INC) ★
6300 Lamar Ave, Shawnee Mission, KS 66202-4200
Tel (913) 236-2000 Founded/Ownrshp 1937
Sales 112.6MM[E] EMP 600
SIC 6211 Security brokers & dealers
Pr: Henry J Herrmann
Pr: David Jackson
CFO: Daniel P Connealy
Chf Inves: Philip J Sanders
Sr Ex VP: Steve Anderson
VP: Lawrence Cipolla
VP: Michael Gerken
VP: William D Howey Jr
Dist Mgr: Brent Dome
Dist Mgr: William Johnson
Dist Mgr: Brian Willet

D-U-N-S 78-232-0030 IMP/EXP
■ WADDINGTON NORTH AMERICA INC
W N A
(Suby of NEWELL BRANDS) ★
50 E Rivercenter Blvd # 650, Covington, KY 41011-1656
Tel (859) 292-8028 Founded/Ownrshp 2000
Sales 461.5MM[E] EMP 912
SIC 3089 Plastic kitchenware, tableware & houseware; Plastic processing
CEO: Michael G Evans
*COO: Dave Gordon
*CFO: Mike Christopher
VP: David Russell
*CIO: Paul Reed
Sls Mgr: Gina Longo

D-U-N-S 78-198-1832
WADHAMS ENTERPRISES INC
369 Bostwick Rd, Phelps, NY 14532-9309
Tel (800) 334-1314 Founded/Ownrshp 1991
Sales 91.4MM EMP 500
Accts Freed Maxick Cpas Pc Buffa
SIC 4212 4213 Local trucking, without storage; Trucking, except local
CEO: Richard Wadhams
*Pr: Stephen Wadhams
Exec: Eric Klein
Sales Exec: Robert Carr

WADLEY HEALTH SYSTEM
See WADLEY REGIONAL MEDICAL CENTER

WADLEY REGIONAL MEDICAL CENTER
See BRIM HEALTHCARE OF TEXAS LLC

D-U-N-S 06-974-7012 IMP
WADLEY REGIONAL MEDICAL CENTER
WADLEY HEALTH SYSTEM
(Suby of BRIM HOLDINGS INC) ★
1000 Pine St, Texarkana, TX 75501-5100
Tel (903) 798-8000 Founded/Ownrshp 2009
Sales 129.0MM EMP 1,285
SIC 8062 General medical & surgical hospitals
CEO: Thomas Gilbert
CFO: Bryan Hargiss
Treas: Ramona Stanley
Ofcr: Jeanette Akin
Dir Inf Cn: Sher Fomby
Dir Lab: Cindy Parsons
Dir Lab: Tim Powers
Dir Rad: Steven W Holman
Dir Rx: Tammi Hayes
*Prin: Michael A Lieb
CIO: Dan Schumann

D-U-N-S 12-124-5963
WADMAN CORP
2920 S 925 W, Ogden, UT 84401-3800
Tel (801) 621-4185 Founded/Ownrshp 1982
Sales 134.9MM EMP 100
Accts Wood Richards & Associates Pc
SIC 1542 1541 Commercial & office building, new construction; Industrial buildings, new construction
CEO: David L Wadman
*Pr: David Hogan
VP: Keith Buswell
*VP: Perry Stone
Sfty Mgr: Brad Willson

D-U-N-S 96-277-1580 IMP
WAFERTECH LLC
(Suby of TAIWAN SEMICDTR MFG CO LTD) ★
5509 Nw Parker St, Camas, WA 98607-9299
Tel (360) 817-3000 Founded/Ownrshp 1996
Sales 92.2MM[E] EMP 925
SIC 3674 7361 Semiconductor circuit networks; Employment agencies
COO: Ken Smith
Prin: Kuo Chin Hsu
Prin: Spencer Lease
IT Man: Larry Mason

D-U-N-S 04-581-1411 IMP
WAFFLE HOUSE INC (GA)
5986 Financial Dr, Norcross, GA 30071-2988
Tel (770) 729-5700 Founded/Ownrshp 1955
Sales 752.9MM[E] EMP 15,000
SIC 5812 6794 Restaurant, family: chain; Franchises, selling or licensing
CEO: Walter G Ehmer
CFO: Walt Ehmer
*CFO: Robert G Moore
VP: Rob Abney
VP: Don Balfour
VP: Tracy Bradshaw
VP: Mary Ellis
VP: Craig Knight
VP: Vecus Miller
VP: Bob Moore
VP: Randy Wilgus
Assoc Dir: Chris Carter

D-U-N-S 94-006-1927
▲ WAGEWORKS INC
1100 Park Pl Fl 4, San Mateo, CA 94403-1599
Tel (650) 577-5200 Founded/Ownrshp 2000
Sales 334.3MM EMP 1,480
Tkr Sym WAGE Exch NYS
SIC 8742 Compensation & benefits planning consultant
CEO: Joseph L Jackson
*Ch Bd: John W Larson
COO: Edgar O Montes
CFO: Colm M Callan
Ofcr: Jim Lynch
Sr VP: Kimberly L Wilford
VP: Barry Beck
VP: Michael Levin
Snr Sftwr: Bhargavi Chandrasekaran
Snr Sftwr: Rajalakshmi Raman
Mktg Mgr: Shari Wallwork
Board of Directors: Thomas A Bevilacqua, Bruce G Bodaken, Mariann Byerwalter, Jerome D Gramaglia, Robert L Metzger, Edward C Nafus

WAGGENER EDSTROM CMMUNICATIONS
See WAGGENER EDSTROM WORLDWIDE INC

D-U-N-S 11-874-8938
WAGGENER EDSTROM WORLDWIDE INC
WAGGENER EDSTROM CMMUNICATIONS
225 108th Ave Ne Ste 700, Bellevue, WA 98004-5775
Tel (425) 638-7000 Founded/Ownrshp 1983
Sales 84.9MM[E] EMP 800
SIC 8743

D-U-N-S 05-025-5108
WAGGONERS TRUCKING
5220 Midland Rd, Billings, MT 59101-9801
Tel (406) 248-1919 Founded/Ownrshp 1951
Sales 242.1MM[E] EMP 1,400
SIC 4213 Trucking, except local; Automobiles, transport & delivery; Heavy hauling
Ch Bd: Wayne Waggoner
*Pr: David D Waggoner
*VP: Mary L Waggoner
Comm Dir: Robert Lane
Off Mgr: Paula Miller

D-U-N-S 07-816-5081
WAGNER COLLEGE
1 Campus Rd, Staten Island, NY 10301-4495
Tel (718) 390-3100 Founded/Ownrshp 1885
Sales 116.6MM EMP 500
Accts Grant Thornton Llp New York
SIC 8221 Colleges universities & professional schools
Pr: Dr Richard Guarasci
Pr: Lee Manchester
*CFO: William Mae
*Treas: Jim Patterson
Ofcr: James Ferry-Vasquez
Ofcr: Annmarie Lambiasi
*VP: Angelo G Araimo
*VP: Thomas Carroll
Assoc Dir: Laura Barlament
Assoc Dir: Matt Hollingshead
CIO: Frank Cafasso

D-U-N-S 04-072-6978 IMP/EXP
WAGNER EQUIPMENT CO
CATERPILLAR
18000 Smith Rd, Aurora, CO 80011-3511
Tel (303) 739-3000 Founded/Ownrshp 1976
Sales 552.1MM[E] EMP 1,500
SIC 5082 7699 7353

D-U-N-S 88-466-6827 IMP/EXP
WAGNER HOLDINGS INC
(Suby of JOSEF WAGNER-STIFTUNG)
1770 Fernbrook Ln N, Minneapolis, MN 55447-4661
Tel (763) 553-7000 Founded/Ownrshp 1993
Sales 96.3MM[E] EMP 615
SIC 3563 3559 Spraying outfits: metals, paints & chemicals (compressor); Paint making machinery
Pr: Thosdan Koch
VP: Thomas Craig

D-U-N-S 00-718-7032
WAGNER INDUSTRIES INC (MO)
WAGNER LOGISTICS
1201 E 12th Ave, North Kansas City, MO 64116-4306
Tel (816) 421-3520 Founded/Ownrshp 1946
Sales 138.2MM[E] EMP 450
SIC 4225 4214 4731 General warehousing & storage; Local trucking with storage; Truck transportation brokers
Pr: Brian Smith
*Ch Bd: John E Wagner Sr
*CFO: Kevin Service
*Chf Cred: John E Wagner Jr
*VP: Shawn Closser
*VP: Justin Eck
*VP: Joe Johnson
*VP: Michael A Moon

WAGNER LOGISTICS
See WAGNER INDUSTRIES INC

D-U-N-S 78-212-4192
WAGNER-MEINERT LLC
7617 Freedom Way, Fort Wayne, IN 46818-2166
Tel (260) 489-7555 Founded/Ownrshp 2011
Sales 89.6MM[E] EMP 130[E]
SIC 5078 1711 1799 Commercial refrigeration equipment; Mechanical contractor; Food service equipment installation
Pr: Timothy J Wagner
*Treas: Joseph K Deeter
*VP: Joseph T Wagner
Sfty Dirs: Eric Anthony
Snr Mgr: Dan Huelsenbeck
Snr Mgr: Ken Rhoades

D-U-N-S 03-783-7390 IMP
WAGO CORP
(Suby of WAGO KONTAKTTECHNIK GMBH (NACH SCHWEIZER RECHT) & CO. KG)
N120 W 19129 Freistadt Rd N 120 W, Germantown, WI 53022
Tel (262) 255-6333 Founded/Ownrshp 1979
Sales 137.4MM[E] EMP 171
SIC 5063 3643 3678 Electrical apparatus & equipment; Current-carrying wiring devices; Electronic connectors
Ch Bd: Wolfgang Hohorst
*Pr: Thomas J Artmann
*Sec: Gregory Rinn
Mng Dir: Ulrich Bohling
Mng Dir: Sven Hohorst
Mng Dir: Faisal Salem
Mng Dir: Gordon Smith
Rgnl Mgr: Kenneth Gagnon
Rgnl Mgr: Bradley Rosenberg
Rgnl Mgr: Keith Vangilder
Area Mgr: Peter Cashell

D-U-N-S 00-906-5145 IMP/EXP
WAGSTAFF INC
3910 N Flora Rd, Spokane Valley, WA 99216-1720
Tel (509) 922-1404 Founded/Ownrshp 2002
Sales 103.5MM EMP 325
SIC 3542 3364 Machine tools, metal forming type; Nonferrous die-castings except aluminum
CEO: Kevin N Person
*Pr: William G Wagstaff
CFO: Kin Park
*CFO: Kendall Parkes
Ex VP: Michael Wagstaff
*VP: Michael K Anderson
*VP: Michael M Megaard
VP: Kevin Person
*VP: Lee Swartling
Area Mgr: Olivier Gabis
Area Mgr: Dan Payne

D-U-N-S 00-526-3199 IMP/EXP
WAHL CLIPPER CORP (IL)
2900 Locust St, Sterling, IL 61081-9500
Tel (815) 625-6525 Founded/Ownrshp 1911, 1924
Sales 424.0MM[E] EMP 2,000
SIC 3999 Hair clippers for human use, hand & electric
CEO: John Wahl
*Pr: Gregory S Wahl
*CFO: Scott Hamilton
*Ex VP: James O Wahl
*VP: Don Ouellette
S&M/VP: Robert Kelly
S&M/VP: Bruce Kramer

D-U-N-S 00-864-0141 IMP/EXP
WAHLCOMETROFLEX INC
SENIOR FLEXONICS PTHWY
(Suby of SENIOR FLEXONICS) ★
29 Lexington St, Lewiston, ME 04240-3533
Tel (207) 784-2338 Founded/Ownrshp 2010
Sales 91.3MM[E] EMP 300
SIC 3441 3822 8711 Expansion joints (structural shapes), iron or steel; Damper operators: pneumatic, thermostatic, electric; Industrial engineers
Pr: John Powell
*COO: John W Bader
*Prin: Roger Poulin
Prd Mgr: Scott F Hall

D-U-N-S 00-626-7942 IMP
WAINWRIGHT INDUSTRIES INC (MO)
114 Piper Hill Dr Ste 201, Saint Peters, MO 63376-1661
Tel (636) 327-8292 Founded/Ownrshp 1947
Sales 91.1MM[E] EMP 700
SIC 3469 3728 3544

D-U-N-S 08-299-1832
WAITT MEDIA INC
GOLD CIRCLE ENTERTAINMENT
1125 S 103rd St Ste 425, Omaha, NE 68124-6025
Tel (402) 697-8000 Founded/Ownrshp 1998
Sales 86.3MM[E] EMP 862
SIC 6726 Investment offices
Ch Bd: Norm Waitt
*Pr: Michael Delich
*Treas: Annette Sneckenberg
*Ex VP: John Schuele

WAKE COUNTY BOARD OF EDUCATION
See WAKE COUNTY PUBLIC SCHOOL SYSTEM

D-U-N-S 07-558-1884 IMP
WAKE COUNTY PUBLIC SCHOOL SYSTEM
WAKE COUNTY BOARD OF EDUCATION
5625 Dillard Dr, Cary, NC 27518-9226
Tel (919) 431-7343 Founded/Ownrshp 1903
Sales 853.9MM[E] EMP 17,000
SIC 8211 Public elementary & secondary schools
COO: Joel Sweatte
*Ch: Thomas Benton
Ex VP: Ann Collins
VP: Paul Visentin
Exec: Cynthia Keech
Exec: Anthony Muttillo
Dir Surg: Robyn Presley
Ex Dir: Eddie Adams
IT Man: Charlotte Davis
IT Man: Angela Hewitt
Info Man: Pat Augustine

WAKE FOREST BAPTIST EMRGNCY RM
See WAKE FOREST BAPTIST MEDICAL CENTER

WAKE FOREST BAPTIST HEALTH
See WAKE FOREST BAPTIST MEDICAL CENTER

D-U-N-S 00-352-3636
WAKE FOREST BAPTIST MEDICAL CENTER
WAKE FOREST BAPTIST HEALTH
Medical Center Blvd, Winston Salem, NC 27157-0001
Tel (336) 716-2011 Founded/Ownrshp 1921
Sales 2.4MMM[E] EMP 12,563
SIC 8062 General medical & surgical hospitals
CEO: John D McConnell
Ofcr: Eric Tomlinson
Ex VP: Terry G Williams
VP: Teri Hales
VP: Karen H Huey
Dir Lab: Lisha Hunter
Chf Nrs Of: Maureen E Sintich
Prin: John D Long
Prin: Raghunatha Yammani
Cmptr Lab: Bethy Jackle
Dir IT: Mike Slusher

D-U-N-S 03-186-7950
WAKE FOREST BAPTIST MEDICAL CENTER
WAKE FOREST BAPTIST EMRGNCY RM
Medical Center Blvd, Winston Salem, NC 27157-0001
Tel (336) 748-8843 Founded/Ownrshp 1975
Sales 84.9MM EMP 11,000
SIC 8062 General medical & surgical hospitals
CEO: John D McConnell
*COO: Thomas E Sibert
VP: Chad Eckes
VP: Joanne Ruhland
Assoc Dir: Keith Weatherman
Prin: John Crouse
Admn Mgr: Suzanne Simpson
Dir IT: Scott Slater
Info Man: Joel Fisher
Pr Mgr: Rae Bush
Plas Surg: James Thompson

D-U-N-S 04-141-8799 IMP
WAKE FOREST UNIVERSITY
BABCOCK SCHOOL OF BUSINESS
1834 Wake Forest Rd, Winston Salem, NC 27109-6000
Tel (336) 758-5000 Founded/Ownrshp 1834

Sales 1.3MMM *EMP* 4,860
Accts Kpmg Llp Greensboro Nc
SIC 8221 University
Pr: Nathan Hatch
Pr: Reid J Morgan
CFO: B Hofler Milan
Assoc VP: James Alty
Assoc VP: Michele Phillips
Sr VP: William B Applegate
Sr VP: Hof Milam
Sr VP: Edwin G Wilson
VP: Mark Petersen
VP: Sheila M Sanders
VP: Kenneth A Zick
Assoc Dir: Donna Agee
Assoc Dir: Mark Anderson
Assoc Dir: Beverly Essick
Assoc Dir: Beth Fay
Comm Dir: Emily Smith
Comm Man: Julie Horton

D-U-N-S 05-255-1405
WAKE STONE CORP
6821 Knightdale Blvd, Knightdale, NC 27545-9651
Tel (919) 266-1100 *Founded/Ownrshp* 1970
Sales 88.3MM[E] *EMP* 145
SIC 1423 Crushed & broken granite
Pr: Samuel T Bratton
**Ch Bd:* John R Bratton
**CFO:* Theodore D Bratton
COO: Bill Crook
VP: Holt Browning
**VP:* M Holt Browning
**VP:* Thomas B Oxholm
VP: Trent Sherrill
Dir IT: Bo Currie
QC Dir: Chris Gastiger
Sls Mgr: Hunter Jenkins

D-U-N-S 07-201-7668
WAKE TECHNICAL COMMUNITY COLLEGE FOUNDATION INC
(*Suby of* NORTH CAROLINA COMMUNITY COLLEGE SYSTEM) ★
9101 Fayetteville Rd, Raleigh, NC 27603-5655
Tel (919) 866-5000 *Founded/Ownrshp* 1963
Sales 2.9MMM *EMP* 1,000
Accts Langdon & Company Llp Garner
SIC 8222 9411 Community college; Administration of educational programs;
Ex Dir: O Morton Congleon
VP: John Boone
VP: Charles Howe
VP: Mitchell Lavalley
VP: Ursula Nzimiro
VP: Kimberly Stokley
Comm Man: Sara Hassell
Snr Mgr: Margaret Griffin

D-U-N-S 00-697-2418 IMP/EXP
WAKEFERN FOOD CORP
WAKEFERN GENERAL MERCHANDISE
5000 Riverside Dr, Keasbey, NJ 08832-1209
Tel (908) 527-3300 *Founded/Ownrshp* 1946
Sales 12.5MMM *EMP* 3,500
Accts Kpmg Llp Short Hills Nj
SIC 5141 5149 5411 4213 2026 Groceries, general line; Groceries & related products; Supermarkets, chain; Contract haulers; Milk processing (pasteurizing, homogenizing, bottling)
CEO: Joseph Colalillo
**Pr:* Joseph Sheridan
**CFO:* Douglas Wille
**Treas:* Lawrence Inserra Jr
Treas: Doug Wille
Ex VP: Jason Ravitz
**Sr VP:* Chris Lane
**Sr VP:* Bill Mayo
**Sr VP:* Frank Rostan
VP: Mike Ambrosio
VP: Alan Aront
VP: Mukesh Dang
VP: Steve Hening
VP: Larry Kurz
VP: Terry Sharkey
**VP:* James J Sumas
**VP:* Natan Tabak
**VP:* Larri Wolfson

WAKEFERN GENERAL MERCHANDISE
See WAKEFERN FOOD CORP

D-U-N-S 00-105-3131 IMP
WAKEFIELD THERMAL SOLUTIONS INC
WAKEFIELD-VETTE
(*Suby of* HEICO COMPANIES L L C) ★
33 Bridge St, Pelham, NH 03076-3475
Tel (603) 635-2800 *Founded/Ownrshp* 1993, 2012
Sales 85.9MM[E] *EMP* 319
SIC 3354 Shapes, extruded aluminum
Pr: Kevin Kreger
**CFO:* James Polakiewicz
**VP:* Dan Bellerose
VP: Fred Duquette
VP: Jonathan Joyner
**VP:* Steve Lawson
Ql Cn Mgr: Greg Mitchell
Mktg Mgr: Diane Daigle
Manager: Linda Ruggiero
Sls Mgr: Dan Bronson
Sls Mgr: Nadine Frechette

WAKEFIELD-VETTE
See WAKEFIELD THERMAL SOLUTIONS INC

D-U-N-S 07-202-1512
WAKEMED
WAKEMED HEALTH AND HOSPITALS
3000 New Bern Ave G100, Raleigh, NC 27610-1231
Tel (919) 350-8000 *Founded/Ownrshp* 1961
Sales 1.0MMM *EMP* 7,933
Accts Ernst & Young Us Llp Washingt
SIC 8062 General medical & surgical hospitals
CEO: Donald R Gintzig
**Ch Bd:* Jack O Clayton
**COO:* Deborah G Friberg
**COO:* Tom Gettinger
**CFO:* Michael DeVaughn
CFO: Michael D Devaughn
Ofcr: H W Lawson MD
**Ex VP:* Kathleen K Gormley
**Sr VP:* Vicki Block
VP: Rebecca Andrews
VP: Jeremy Beal
VP: Kenneth Bryan
VP: Thomas Cavendar
VP: Betty Gaskins-Mcclaine
VP: Dudley Harrington
VP: Meera Kelley MD
VP: Jeanene R Matin
VP: Kevin P McCarthy
VP: W Stan Taylor
Exec: Mary Custer
Exec: Michael Weinstein

WAKEMED HEALTH AND HOSPITALS
See WAKEMED

D-U-N-S 95-816-8668 IMP/EXP
■ **WAL-MART PUERTO RICO INC**
WALMART
(*Suby of* WALMART) ★
Carr 1 Km 28 7 Bo St Ca, Caguas, PR 00725
Tel (787) 653-7777 *Founded/Ownrshp* 2016
Sales 411.3MM[E] *EMP* 4,500
SIC 5331 5411 5399 Variety stores; Grocery stores; Warehouse club stores
CEO: Renzo Casillo

D-U-N-S 05-195-7769 IMP/EXP
▲ **WAL-MART STORES INC**
WALMART
702 Sw 8th St, Bentonville, AR 72716-6299
Tel (479) 273-4000 *Founded/Ownrshp* 1945
Sales 482.1MMM[E] *EMP* 2,300,000
Tkr Sym WMT *Exch* NYS
SIC 5311 5331 5411 5399 Department stores, discount; Variety stores; Grocery stores; Warehouse club stores
Pr: C Douglas McMillon
Ch Bd: Gregory B Penner
V Ch: Michael Duke
Pr: Rosalind G Brewer
Pr: David Cheesewright
Pr: Gregory Foran
COO: Michael J Bender
CFO: M Brett Biggs
CFO: Michael P Dastugue
Ofcr: Rollin L Ford
Ex VP: Daniel J Bartlett
Ex VP: Jacqueline P Canney
Ex VP: Patricia Curran
Ex VP: John Furner
Ex VP: Jeffrey J Gearhart
Ex VP: Mark Ibbotson
Ex VP: Scott Price
Ex VP: Celia Swanson
Sr VP: Jeremy King
Sr VP: Julie Murphy
Sr VP: Tony Rogers
Board of Directors: Kevin Y Systrom, Aida M Alvarez, Jim C Walton, James I Cash Jr, S Robson Walton, Roger C Corbett, Linda S Wolf, Pamela J Craig, Michael T Duke, Timothy P Flynn, Thomas W Horton, Marissa A Mayer, Steven S Reinemund

D-U-N-S 13-817-3773 EXP
■ **WAL-MART.COM USA LLC**
WALMART
(*Suby of* WALMART) ★
850 Cherry Ave, San Bruno, CA 94066-3031
Tel (650) 837-5000 *Founded/Ownrshp* 2000
Sales 94.9MM[E] *EMP* 300
SIC 5961 5199 General merchandise, mail order; General merchandise, non-durable
CEO: Jeanne Jackson
Pr: Gregory Foran
Pr: Judith McKenna
Ex VP: Pamela K Kohn
VP: Ted Edge
VP: Andy Rendich
VP: Manu Thapar
VP: Ted Tomblinson
VP: Mahesh Tyagarajan
VP: Linda Vytlacil
Ex Dir: Karl Hebert

D-U-N-S 00-653-7161 IMP
WALBRIDGE ALDINGER LLC
(*Suby of* WALBRIDGE GROUP INC) ★
777 Woodward Ave Ste 300, Detroit, MI 48226-3582
Tel (313) 963-8000 *Founded/Ownrshp* 1916
Sales 1.0MMM *EMP* 1,000
SIC 1541 1542 8741 Industrial buildings & warehouses; Nonresidential construction; Construction management
Ch Bd: John Rakolta Jr
**Pr:* Richard Haller
Pr: Wade Herzig
Pr: Chris Morgan
CFO: Vincent J Deangelis
**Treas:* Vincent Deangelis
**V Ch Bd:* Ronald Hausmann
Ofcr: Mildred Kellam
Ofcr: Cynthia Weaver
**Ex VP:* Randy Abdallah
**Ex VP:* Michael Haller
**VP:* Peter Darga
VP: David Hanson
VP: Charlie Pfaifer
VP: Sarah Pinten
VP: Eric Twigg
VP: Ron Vernet
Exec: Sherry Hewett
Dir Bus: Joey Smith

D-U-N-S 14-809-0801
WALBRIDGE GROUP INC
777 Woodward Ave Ste 300, Detroit, MI 48226-3582
Tel (313) 963-8000 *Founded/Ownrshp* 2002
Sales 1.5MMM *EMP* 1,000
Accts Doeren Mayhew Troy Michigan
SIC 1542 Nonresidential construction
Ch Bd: John Rakolta Jr
**Pr:* Michael R Haller
**Ex VP:* Richard J Haller
**Ex VP:* Ronald Hausmann
VP: Peter Darga
**VP:* Vincent J Deangelis
VP: Peter Hellekjaer
VP: Scott Kameg
Exec: Ken Beaudoin
Exec: Doug Weaver
Dir Bus: Andrew Wasiniak

D-U-N-S 07-862-3705
WALBRIDGE INDUSTRIAL PROCESS LLC
(*Suby of* WALBRIDGE GROUP INC) ★
777 Woodward Ave Ste 300, Detroit, MI 48226-3582
Tel (313) 963-8000 *Founded/Ownrshp* 2011
Sales 93.8MM *EMP* 65
SIC 1796 Machine moving & rigging
Mng Pt: John Rokolta III
Treas: Peter Darga

D-U-N-S 01-621-6793
WALBRIDGE INTERNATIONAL LLC
(*Suby of* WALBRIDGE GROUP INC) ★
777 Woodward Ave Fl 3, Detroit, MI 48226-3582
Tel (313) 963-8000 *Founded/Ownrshp* 1994
Sales 320.5MM *EMP* 200
SIC 8741 Construction management
Pr: Richard Haller

D-U-N-S 79-170-1402 IMP
WALBRO LLC
(*Suby of* WALBRO CO.,LTD.)
2015 W River Rd 202, Tucson, AZ 85704-1675
Tel (520) 229-5642 *Founded/Ownrshp* 1991
Sales 548.8MM[E] *EMP* 2,300
SIC 3592 3594 3694 3443 Carburetors; Fluid power pumps & motors; Ignition apparatus, internal combustion engines; Fuel tanks (oil, gas, etc.): metal plate
Pr: Matthew Riddle
CFO: Michael A Shope
**CFO:* Steve Thomson
**Treas:* Carrie Pawlik
**VP:* Ann Guernsey
VP: Anand Pinto
Exec: Dinorah Ochoa
Dir Lab: Paul Verhines
Genl Mgr: Aldo Coley
Genl Mgr: Dave McNaughton
IT Man: Anna Benninghoff

D-U-N-S 80-025-3838 IMP
■ **WALCO INTERNATIONAL INC**
(*Suby of* ANIMAL HEALTH HOLDINGS INC.)
9500 Ray White Rd Ste 200, Fort Worth, TX 76244-9105
Tel (817) 859-3000 *Founded/Ownrshp* 1997
Sales 86.1MM[E] *EMP* 939
SIC 5499 Health foods
CEO: John Adent
**Treas:* Jeff Hyde
**Ex VP:* Kathy Hassentslug
VP: Mark Gray
**VP:* Henry Moomaw
VP: Brian D Motechin
Dir IT: Mark Badgett
Sales Exec: Roger Fanjul

D-U-N-S 00-697-9371 IMP
WALDBAUM INC
WALDBAUM SUPER MARKET
(*Suby of* A & P) ★
2 Paragon Dr, Montvale, NJ 07645-1718
Tel (201) 571-4132 *Founded/Ownrshp* 1904
Sales 843.3MM[E] *EMP* 10,000
SIC 5411 Supermarkets, chain
Pr: David Smithies

WALDBAUM SUPER MARKET
See WALDBAUM INC

WALDEN SECURITY
See METROPOLITAN SECURITY SERVICES INC

D-U-N-S 13-746-1604
WALDINGER CORP
2601 Bell Ave, Des Moines, IA 50321-1189
Tel (515) 284-1911 *Founded/Ownrshp* 1986
Sales 207.1MM *EMP* 900
Accts Mcgladrey Llp
SIC 1711 Mechanical contractor; Plumbing contractors; Warm air heating & air conditioning contractor; Ventilation & duct work contractor
CEO: Thomas K Koehn
Ex Dir: Sheila Riggs

D-U-N-S 07-746-1762
WALDO COUNTY GENERAL HOSPITAL
118 Northport Ave, Belfast, ME 04915-6072
Tel (207) 338-2500 *Founded/Ownrshp* 1989
Sales 86.5MM *EMP* 700
SIC 8062 General medical & surgical hospitals
CEO: Mark Biscone
**Pr:* Lee Woodward Jr
CEO: Laurie McKlein
**Treas:* Catherine Reynolds
**VP:* Dale Kuhnert
**Prin:* Janess Robins
Mktg Mgr: Andrea Walker

D-U-N-S 61-310-1393 IMP
WALDOM ELECTRONICS CORP
GC ELECTRONICS
1801 Morgan St, Rockford, IL 61102-2675
Tel (815) 968-9661 *Founded/Ownrshp* 2003
Sales 144.4MM[E] *EMP* 150
SIC 5065 Electronic parts
Pr: Basel Nizam
**Ex VP:* Thomas Seving
**VP:* Terry Bartsch
VP: Scott Campbell
VP: Peter Rovekamp
**Prin:* Ihsan Nizam
Genl Mgr: Bob Derringer

WALDORF ASTORIA NEW YORK
See AB STABLE LLC

D-U-N-S 87-701-1648
WALDOS HOLDINGS LLC
(*Suby of* WALDO'S DOLAR MART DE MEXICO, S. DE R.L. DE C.V.)
831 Pearl St, Boulder, CO 80302-5007
Tel (303) 381-2640 *Founded/Ownrshp* 1998
Sales 265.4MM[E] *EMP* 4,500[E]
SIC 5411 Grocery stores

WALDRON PUBLIC HOUSE
See BARFLY VENTURES LLC

D-U-N-S 06-439-0131 IMP
■ **WALGREEN ARIZONA DRUG CO** (AZ)
WALGREENS
(*Suby of* WALGREENS) ★
200 Wilmot Rd, Deerfield, IL 60015-4620
Tel (847) 940-2500 *Founded/Ownrshp* 1953
Sales 506.7MM[E] *EMP* 3,500
SIC 5912 Drug stores
Pr: Mark A Wagner
**Pr:* Julian A Oettinger
**VP:* A M Resnick

D-U-N-S 00-896-5063 IMP/EXP
■ **WALGREEN CO**
WALGREENS
(*Suby of* WALGREENS BOOTS ALLIANCE INC) ★
200 Wilmot Rd, Deerfield, IL 60015-4681
Tel (847) 315-2500 *Founded/Ownrshp* 2014
Sales 49.6MMM[E] *EMP* 253,400
SIC 5912 Drug stores
Pr: Gregory D Wasson
Pr: Joseph Magnacca
Pr: Robert Tompkins
Pr: Colin F Watts
**CFO:* Timothy McLevish
Chf Mktg O: Alan E London
Ofcr: Jeremy Kunicki
**Ofcr:* Thomas J Sabatino Jr
Div VP: Richard Cassidy
Ex VP: Kermit R Crawford
Sr VP: Reuben Slone
Sr VP: Kenneth R Weigand
VP: Howard Atlas
VP: Charles Bernard
VP: Kathryn Bronstein
VP: Brian C Demay
VP: Christian Doring
VP: George C Eilers
VP: Mike Ellis
VP: Andrea Farris
VP: Roxanne Flanagan

D-U-N-S 06-438-9273
■ **WALGREEN EASTERN CO INC**
WALGREENS
(*Suby of* WALGREENS) ★
200 Wilmot Rd, Deerfield, IL 60015-4620
Tel (847) 940-2500 *Founded/Ownrshp* 2010
Sales 173.4MM[E] *EMP* 1,160
SIC 5912 Drug stores
Ch Bd: Mark A Wagner
**VP:* Margarita E Kellen

D-U-N-S 06-439-5296
■ **WALGREEN LOUISIANA CO INC**
WALGREENS
(*Suby of* WALGREENS) ★
200 Wilmot Rd, Deerfield, IL 60015-4620
Tel (847) 940-2500 *Founded/Ownrshp* 1935
Sales 146.2MM[E] *EMP* 1,000
SIC 5912 Drug stores; Proprietary (non-prescription medicine) stores
CEO: Stefano Pessina
CFO: Ronald Rubin
**Treas:* Alan Nielsen
Genl Mgr: Mark A Wagner
Cert Phar: Andrew McGuire

D-U-N-S 09-008-1456
■ **WALGREEN OF SAN PATRICIO INC**
WALGREENS
(*Suby of* WALGREENS) ★
580 Marginal Buchanan, Guaynabo, PR 00966-1706
Tel (787) 795-4200 *Founded/Ownrshp* 1963
Sales 440.7MM *EMP* 348
SIC 5912 Drug stores
Genl Mgr: Dennis Santiago
**Treas:* James A Davlin
**VP:* John R Brown
**VP:* Vernon A Brunner
**VP:* L Alan Crotty
**VP:* Gleen S Kraiss
**VP:* John B Seastone
**VP:* William O Shank

WALGREENS
See WALGREEN CO

WALGREENS
See WALGREEN EASTERN CO INC

WALGREENS
See WALGREEN ARIZONA DRUG CO

WALGREENS
See WALGREEN LOUISIANA CO INC

WALGREENS
See WALGREEN OF SAN PATRICIO INC

WALGREENS
See BOND DRUG CO OF ILLINOIS LLC

D-U-N-S 07-960-8595
▲ **WALGREENS BOOTS ALLIANCE INC**
108 Wilmot Rd, Deerfield, IL 60015-5145
Tel (847) 315-2500 *Founded/Ownrshp* 1901
Sales 117.3MMM *EMP* 360,000[E]
Tkr Sym WBA *Exch* NGS
SIC 5912 Drug stores & proprietary stores; Drug stores; Proprietary (non-prescription medicine) stores
CEO: Stefano Pessina
**Ch Bd:* James A Skinner
COO: Ornella Barra
COO: Alex Gourlay
CFO: George R Fairweather
Ex VP: Ken Murphy
Ex VP: Marco Pagni
Sr VP: Jan Stern Reed
Sr VP: Kimberly R Scardino

D-U-N-S 10-284-3331
WALGREENS INFUSION SERVICES INC
OPTION CARE
(*Suby of* M D P) ★
3000 Lakeside Dr Ste 300n, Bannockburn, IL 60015-5405
Tel (312) 940-2500 *Founded/Ownrshp* 2015
Sales 209.7MM^E *EMP* 160^E
SIC 8082 8011 8059 5999 5122 Home health care services; Offices & clinics of medical doctors; Personal care home, with health care; Convalescent equipment & supplies; Pharmaceuticals
CEO: Paul F Mastrapa
**CFO:* Michael Shapiro
**Off Mgr:* Michelle Peterson

WALK THROUGH VIDEO
See VILLARA CORP

D-U-N-S 96-350-1510
▲ WALKER & DUNLOP INC
7501 Wisconsin Ave 1200e, Bethesda, MD 20814-6531
Tel (301) 215-5500 *Founded/Ownrshp* 1937
Sales 468.2MM *EMP* 504
Tkr Sym WD *Exch* NYS
SIC 7389 8741 Financial services; Financial management for business
Ch Bd: William M Walker
**Pr:* Howard W Smith III
Pr: Matthew Sutton
CFO: Stephen P Theobald
Chf Cred: Richard C Warner
Ofcr: Mirra Dersookian
Ofcr: Elizabeth Kieffer
Ex VP: Richard M Lucas
Sr VP: Levi Brooker
VP: Matthew Baldwin
VP: Neil Bane
VP: Chris Botsford
VP: Christopher Forte
VP: Steven Heller
VP: Ralph Lowen
VP: Jeremy Pino
VP: Stephen Smith
VP: Paul Wallace

D-U-N-S 06-235-7538
WALKER AND ASSOCIATES INC
(*Suby of* WALKER GROUP INC) ★
7129 Old Hwy 52, Welcome, NC 27374
Tel (336) 731-6391 *Founded/Ownrshp* 1970
Sales 88.4MM^E *EMP* 140
SIC 4813 5065 8731 8711 3572 3571 Telephone communication, except radio; Electronic parts & equipment; Commercial physical research; Engineering services; Computer storage devices; Electronic computers
Ch Bd: Virginia M Walker
**Pr:* Mark Walker
**CEO:* Chrystie Walker Brown
**CFO:* Douglas Leckie
**Treas:* Marshall Rick Walker
IT Man: Michael Euliss
Snr Mgr: Angie Hunt
Board of Directors: Laura Walker-Michaud

WALKER BAPTIST MEDICAL CENTER
See WALKER REGIONAL MEDICAL CENTER INC

WALKER BARRIER SYSTEMS
See WALKER STAINLESS EQUIPMENT CO LLC

D-U-N-S 00-382-7011
WALKER CO OF KENTUCKY INC (KY)
WALKER CONSTRUCTION
105 Apperson Hts, Mount Sterling, KY 40353-1602
Tel (859) 498-0092 *Founded/Ownrshp* 1959
Sales 85.1MM^E *EMP* 270
SIC 1611 2951 1542 3273 1422

WALKER CONSTRUCTION
See WALKER CO OF KENTUCKY INC

D-U-N-S 07-910-8635
WALKER COUNTY BOARD OF EDUCATION
WALKER COUNTY SCHOOL DISTRICT
1710 Alabama Ave Ste 106, Jasper, AL 35501-5400
Tel (205) 387-2156 *Founded/Ownrshp* 1920
Sales 80.0MM *EMP* 1,135
SIC 8211 Elementary & secondary schools
**CFO:* Margaret Scurlock
IT Man: Marie Fields

D-U-N-S 08-542-3200
WALKER COUNTY BOARD OF EDUCATION
201 S Duke St, La Fayette, GA 30728-3518
Tel (706) 638-1240 *Founded/Ownrshp* 1852
Sales 50.9MM^E *EMP* 1,500
Accts Russell W Hinton Cpa Cgfm
SIC 8211 School board
Pr: Mike Carruth

WALKER COUNTY SCHOOL DISTRICT
See WALKER COUNTY BOARD OF EDUCATION

D-U-N-S 07-935-1346
WALKER COUNTY SCHOOL DISTRICT
201 S Duke St, La Fayette, GA 30728-3518
Tel (706) 638-1240 *Founded/Ownrshp* 2014
Sales 36.1MM^E *EMP* 1,907^E
SIC 8211 Public elementary & secondary schools
Bd of Dir: Charles Wilson
Dir Sec: Tommy Ferguson
Teacher Pr: Heather Holloway

D-U-N-S 00-403-7800 IMP
WALKER DIE CASTING INC (TN)
1125 Higgs Rd, Lewisburg, TN 37091-4408
Tel (931) 359-6206 *Founded/Ownrshp* 1958
Sales 140.0MM *EMP* 655
Accts Marmann & Associates Pc Sh
SIC 3363 Aluminum die-castings
Pr: John R Walker
**Ch:* Robert H Walker
**VP:* Tom Harris
Exec: Josh Winn
Prd Mgr: James Calahan
Ql Cn Mgr: David Salyers

D-U-N-S 04-007-8474
WALKER ENGINEERING INC (TX)
M H TECHNOLOGIES
1505 W Walnut Hill Ln, Irving, TX 75038-3702
Tel (817) 540-7777 *Founded/Ownrshp* 1981
Sales 243.8MM^E *EMP* 900
SIC 1731 General electrical contractor
CEO: Charles F Walker
**Pr:* Wayne Vardell
**CFO:* Thomas Blake
VP: Rod Beckmen
VP: Brent Walker
**VP:* Dutch Wickes
Dir IT: Richard Heard
Opers Mgr: John Healy
VP Mktg: Jonathan Blanscet

D-U-N-S 96-155-9445
■ WALKER GROUP HOLDINGS LLC
(*Suby of* WABASH NATIONAL CORP) ★
625 W State St, New Lisbon, WI 53950-1014
Tel (608) 562-7500 *Founded/Ownrshp* 1998
Sales 195.7MM^E *EMP* 1,200^E
SIC 3443 Vessels, process or storage (from boiler shops): metal plate; Metal parts
**Pr:* Mr Michael J Kays
**CFO:* Brad Walker
**VP:* Thomas Ballon
**VP:* Mr Jim Miller
VP Opers: Dave Nick

D-U-N-S 18-796-6866
WALKER GROUP INC
7129 Old Hwy 52, Welcome, NC 27374
Tel (336) 731-6391 *Founded/Ownrshp* 1985
Sales 90.3MM^E *EMP* 214
SIC 4813 8748 5065 8711 Telephone communication, except radio; Business consulting; Electronic parts & equipment; Engineering services
CEO: Virginia Walker
**Pr:* Mark Walker
**CFO:* Doug Leckie
Treas: Chrystie Brown
**VP:* Hal Sveum
Board of Directors: Christie Brown, Laura Walker-Domin, Douglas Leckie, Mark Walker, Virginia Walker

D-U-N-S 07-867-9404
WALKER METHODIST
3737 Bryant Ave S, Minneapolis, MN 55409-1019
Tel (612) 827-5931 *Founded/Ownrshp* 1915
Sales 15.0MM *EMP* 1,398
Accts Cliftonlarsonallen Llp Minnea
SIC 8361 Geriatric residential care
CEO: Lynn M Starkovich
**COO:* John Huhn
**CFO:* David Brenne
CFO: Todd Willett
Ofcr: Michael Stabs
**VP:* Norma Larson
Exec: Denis Durnev
Ex Dir: Ken Lundeen
Mktg Dir: Lauren Bednar
Sls Dir: Chanda Knoof
Sls Dir: Elizabeth Meyer

D-U-N-S 07-895-9939
WALKER REGIONAL MEDICAL CENTER INC
WALKER BAPTIST MEDICAL CENTER
3400 Highway 78 E, Jasper, AL 35501-8956
Tel (205) 387-4000 *Founded/Ownrshp* 1995
Sales 93.5MM *EMP* 650
SIC 8062 General medical & surgical hospitals
Pr: Joel Tate
Ex VP: Francis Kingsbury
VP: Kimberly McNair
CIO: Kenny Horton

D-U-N-S 08-237-5767
WALKER RESOURCES INC
1343 Hallmark Dr, San Antonio, TX 78216-6020
Tel (210) 341-6000 *Founded/Ownrshp* 1963
Sales 17.7MM^E *EMP* 1,300
SIC 7514 Passenger car rental
CEO: James Walker
**Pr:* Robert Walker
**COO:* Mark Walker

D-U-N-S 00-642-5136 IMP
■ WALKER STAINLESS EQUIPMENT CO LLC (DE)
WALKER BARRIER SYSTEMS
(*Suby of* WABASH NATIONAL CORP) ★
625 W State St, New Lisbon, WI 53950-1014
Tel (608) 562-7500 *Founded/Ownrshp* 1995
Sales 106.9MM^E *EMP* 500^E
SIC 3443 3556 3715 Tanks, lined: metal plate; Food products machinery; Truck trailers
Genl Mgr: Terry Bardell
IT Man: Brent Churchill
Ql Cn Mgr: Marshall Keuhl
Sls Mgr: Michelle Berndt
Sales Asso: Jeffrey Schirmer

WALKIN PAPERS
See PAPER MART INC

D-U-N-S 14-601-1122 IMP
■ WALKING CO
(*Suby of* BIG DOG SPORTSWEAR) ★
25 W Anapamu St, Santa Barbara, CA 93101-5148
Tel (805) 963-8727 *Founded/Ownrshp* 2004
Sales 96.5MM^E *EMP* 530
SIC 5661 Shoe stores
Pr: Andrew Feshbach
**CFO:* Roberta Morris
**Ex VP:* Doug Nilsen
**Ex VP:* Anthony Wall
**VP:* Lee Cox
**VP:* Mike Grenley
VP: Ralph Kimbal
VP: John Otchis
Exec: Stacia Bearman
Dist Mgr: Benjamin Chrislu
Dist Mgr: Denise Lukavic

D-U-N-S 79-027-6331 IMP
▲ WALKING CO HOLDINGS INC
BIG DOG SPORTSWEAR
25 W Anapamu St, Santa Barbara, CA 93101-5148
Tel (805) 963-8727 *Founded/Ownrshp* 1996
Sales 203.4MM^E *EMP* 2,300
Accts Singerlewak Llp Los Angeles
Tkr Sym WALK *Exch* OTC
SIC 5651 5961 5136 5137 5699 Family clothing stores; Clothing, mail order (except women's); Sportswear, men's & boys'; Men's & boys' furnishings; Sportswear, women's & children's; Women's & children's accessories; Sports apparel
CEO: Andrew D Feshbach
**Ch Bd:* Fred Kayne
**CFO:* Roberta J Morris
**Ex VP:* Anthony J Wall
**Sr VP:* Lee M Cox
VP: Joe Cattivera
VP: Lee Cox
VP: Naomi Fujioka
VP: Michael Grenley
VP: Michael Walker
VP: Barry Wise
VP: John Wood
Board of Directors: Skip R Coomber III, Steven C Good, David J Walsh

WALL GROW
See TI AUTOMOTIVE INC

D-U-N-S 18-948-6467
WALL STREET SYSTEMS SERVICES CORP
WALLSTREET SYSTEMS
(*Suby of* ION TRADING IRELAND LIMITED)
1345 Ave Of The, New York, NY 10105
Tel (212) 809-7200 *Founded/Ownrshp* 2011
Sales 97.0MM^E *EMP* 535
SIC 7371 Computer software development
Pr: Alex Tripplett
Off Admin: Stephanie Hvala
CTO: Mark Tirschwell
Software D: Michael Huang
Software D: Laura Solow
Sftwr Eng: Peter Callaway
Sftwr Eng: Shashikant More
Sftwr Eng: Richard Payne
Sftwr Eng: Bing Sun
Sftwr Eng: Cecilia To
Sls Dir: William Burton

D-U-N-S 08-409-5314 IMP/EXP
WALL-TIES & FORMS INC
4000 Bonner Industrial Dr, Shawnee, KS 66226-2103
Tel (913) 441-0073 *Founded/Ownrshp* 1976
Sales 109.7MM^E *EMP* 150
SIC 5082 3444 3443 Contractors' materials; Concrete forms, sheet metal; Fabricated plate work (boiler shop)
CEO: Ross W Worley
**Pr:* Charles Engleken
**VP:* Carl Engleken
**VP:* Janice Jolin
**VP:* Richard Orrison
**VP:* Brent Worley

D-U-N-S 05-058-5777
WALLACE EANNACE ASSOCIATES INC (NY)
50 Newtown Rd, Plainview, NY 11803-4315
Tel (516) 454-9300 *Founded/Ownrshp* 1927, 1969
Sales 88.4MM^E *EMP* 65
SIC 5074 Heating equipment (hydronic); Plumbing fittings & supplies
Pr: Henry J Kunkel
**CFO:* Tim Meegan
**VP:* James Collins
Genl Mgr: Robert Digiovanni

D-U-N-S 60-357-2363
WALLACE FOUNDATION
5 Penn Plz Fl 7, New York, NY 10001-1837
Tel (212) 251-9700 *Founded/Ownrshp* 1988
Sales 131.3MM *EMP* 50
SIC 6732 Educational trust management
Ch Bd: Kevin Kennedy
**Pr:* William Miller
**CFO:* Stacy Martin
Ofcr: Rachel Bork
Ofcr: Claudia Demegret
Ofcr: Nicholas Pelzer
Ofcr: Jessica Schwartz
Ofcr: Christine Yoon
Sr Inv Off: Cfa Thai
**CIO:* Rob D Nagel
IT Man: Erik Williams

D-U-N-S 00-894-3631
WALLACE HARDWARE CO INC
5050 S Davy Crockett Pkwy, Morristown, TN 37813-3962
Tel (423) 586-5650 *Founded/Ownrshp* 1921
Sales 267.3MM^E *EMP* 310
SIC 5072 5074 5085 5083 5211 Hardware; Shelf or light hardware; Plumbing & hydronic heating supplies; Industrial supplies; Farm implements; Farm equipment parts & supplies; Lumber products
Pr: Doyle Wallace
COO: Lee Kimbrough
CFO: Bill Trusler
Ex VP: Lynn Dawson
VP: Eddie Flynn
VP: William A Trusler
VP: William Trusler
IT Man: Anthony Jones
VP Mktg: John Snowden
Advt Mgr: Shirley W Graybeal
Sales Asso: Mike Farthing

WALLACE METAL PRODUCTS
See YORK GROUP INC

D-U-N-S 01-912-2824
■ WALLACE THEATER HOLDINGS INC
HOLLYWOOD THEATERS
(*Suby of* REGAL ENTERTAINMENT GROUP) ★
919 Sw Taylor St Ste 800, Portland, OR 97205-2572
Tel (503) 221-7090 *Founded/Ownrshp* 2013
Sales 1.3MM^E *EMP* 1,300
SIC 7832 Motion picture theaters, except drive-in
Pr: Scott Wallace
**COO:* Clyde Cornell
**CFO:* Charles Kirk

D-U-N-S 04-872-5436
WALLBOARD SUPPLY CO - US LBM LLC
(*Suby of* US LBM HOLDINGS LLC) ★
527 Mammoth Rd, Londonderry, NH 03053-2120
Tel (603) 434-4597 *Founded/Ownrshp* 2014
Sales 83.0MM^E *EMP* 60
SIC 5032 Drywall materials
VP Sls: Michael Cavanaugh

D-U-N-S 80-915-9338
WALLBOARD SYSTEMS HAWAII
696 Turtlewood Pl, Henderson, NV 89052-2854
Tel (702) 233-3654 *Founded/Ownrshp* 1990
Sales 800.0M *EMP* 1,015
SIC 1742

D-U-N-S 04-973-2597
WALLE CORP
200 Hembree Park Dr Ste H, Roswell, GA 30076-3889
Tel (800) 942-6761 *Founded/Ownrshp* 1982
Sales 84.1MM^E *EMP* 275
SIC 2759 2752 2671 Labels & seals: printing; Commercial printing, lithographic; Packaging paper & plastics film, coated & laminated
Pr: Sean M Keeney
**CFO:* Robert Pokowitz
Ofcr: Bob Lawson
VP: Amy Grissen
Exec: Carol Mueller
Off Mgr: Deshone Farley
IT Man: Keih Orego
Prd Mgr: Jamal Shakadih
Ql Cn Mgr: Keith Ortega
Ql Cn Mgr: Mike Podgurski
VP Sls: Brian Metzger

D-U-N-S 04-617-1039
WALLENIUS WILHELMSEN LOGISTICS AMERICAS LLC
(*Suby of* WALLENIUS WILHELMSEN LOGISTICS AS)
188 Broadway Ste 1, Woodcliff Lake, NJ 07677-8072
Tel (201) 307-1300 *Founded/Ownrshp* 1999
Sales 195.7MM *EMP* 1,550
SIC 4412 Deep sea foreign transportation of freight
Pr: Christopher Connor
COO: Erik Nyheim
**CFO:* Mike Hynekamp
**Ex VP:* John Felitto
Sr VP: Gary Jones
VP: Joseph Brereton
VP: Gary Davis
VP: Karim Jumma
VP: Dave Minetti
VP: Doug Peterson
Dir Bus: Nathan Ullrich

D-U-N-S 07-848-1524
WALLICO MAINTENANCE GROUP LLC
(*Suby of* A & A MAINTENANCE ENTERPRISE INC) ★
965 Midland Ave, Yonkers, NY 10704-1027
Tel (914) 595-0664 *Founded/Ownrshp* 2012
Sales 20.0MM^E *EMP* 1,329^E
SIC 7349 Building maintenance services

D-U-N-S 04-350-7821
WALLIS OIL CO (MO)
PUMP HANDLE SNACK SHOPS
106 E Washington St, Cuba, MO 65453-1827
Tel (573) 885-2277 *Founded/Ownrshp* 1968
Sales 241.8MM^E *EMP* 700
SIC 5541 5171 Gasoline service stations; Petroleum bulk stations & terminals
Pr: Lynn Wallis
VP: Rita Baker
VP: Sue Oleary

WALLSTREET SYSTEMS
See WALL STREET SYSTEMS SERVICES CORP

D-U-N-S 00-625-8453 IMP
WALMAN OPTICAL CO (MN)
IMAGEWEAR
801 12th Ave N Ste 1, Minneapolis, MN 55411-4420
Tel (612) 520-6000 *Founded/Ownrshp* 1915
Sales 239.6MM^E *EMP* 970
Accts Boulay Pllp
SIC 5048 3851 Optometric equipment & supplies; Eyes, glass & plastic
CEO: Martin Bassett
**CFO:* Dustin J Lavalley
Ex VP: John Hatcher
**VP:* Charles Pillsbury
VP: Bryan Schueler
VP: Daniel Shirk
Dir Lab: Gerry Hall
Dir Soc: Missy McManigle
Mng Dir: Cheryl Boehm
Brnch Mgr: Tim Davidson
Brnch Mgr: Ethan Dolby

WALMART
See WAL-MART STORES INC

WALMART
See WAL-MART.COM USA LLC

WALMART
See WAL-MART PUERTO RICO INC

D-U-N-S 80-784-2971
WALMART FOUNDATION
702 Sw 8th Stre Dept 8687, Bentonville, AR 72716-0001
Tel (479) 204-2044 *Founded/Ownrshp* 2007
Sales 169.0MM *EMP* 3
Accts Hogantaylor Llp Tulsa Ok
SIC 5411 Supermarkets
Pr: Sylvia Mathews Burwell

WALNUT CREEK FOODS
See COBLENTZ DISTRIBUTING INC

D-U-N-S 05-009-4556 IMP
WALNUT INVESTMENT CORP
AMS
(*Suby of* ALLIED BUILDING PRODUCTS CORP) ★
2940 E White Star Ave, Anaheim, CA 92806-2627
Tel (714) 238-9240 *Founded/Ownrshp* 2007
Sales 88.5MM[E] *EMP* 550
SIC 5031 5039 5072 Building materials, exterior; Ceiling systems & products; Hardware
CEO: Ruben Mendoza
**COO:* Tony Reinders
**CFO:* John Gorey
Brnch Mgr: Tony Van De Walle
Brnch Mgr: Marty Krummer
Brnch Mgr: Paul Lind
Brnch Mgr: John Magana
Brnch Mgr: Steve Manrique
Brnch Mgr: Keri Mowrey
Brnch Mgr: Vanessa Perez
Brnch Mgr: Mario Ramirez

D-U-N-S 04-036-2212
WALNUT VALLEY UNIFIED SCHOOL DISTRICT
880 S Lemon Ave, Walnut, CA 91789-2931
Tel (909) 595-1261 *Founded/Ownrshp* 1890
Sales 146.8MM *EMP* 1,680
Accts Vavrinek Trine Day & Co Ll
SIC 8211 Public elementary & secondary schools; Public junior high school; Public senior high school
Pr: Helen M Hall
**VP:* Y Tony Torng
**Prin:* Larry L Redinger
MIS Dir: Kenny Goodson
Pr Dir: Kelli Gile
Teacher Pr: Danny Kim
Board of Directors: Larry Redinger, Cynthia Ruiz, Tony Torng

D-U-N-S 00-100-6337 IMP
WALPOLE WOODWORKERS INC
767 East St, Walpole, MA 02081-3603
Tel (508) 668-2800 *Founded/Ownrshp* 1976
Sales 103.2MM[E] *EMP* 350
Accts Bonanno Savino & Davies Pc
SIC 2499 Fencing, wood
Pr: Louis A Maglio Jr
**VP:* Sidney A Tildsley

D-U-N-S 00-382-2079 IMP
WALSH CONSTRUCTION CO (IL)
(*Suby of* WALSH GROUP CONSTRUCTION) ★
929 W Adams St, Chicago, IL 60607-3021
Tel (312) 563-5400 *Founded/Ownrshp* 1898, 1983
Sales 1.8MMM[E] *EMP* 3,000
Accts Wolf & Company Llp Oakbrook
SIC 1541 1622 1542 1611 Prefabricated building erection, industrial; Bridge, tunnel & elevated highway; Nonresidential construction; Highway & street construction
Ch Bd: Matthew M Walsh
**Pr:* Daniel J Walsh
Treas: Larry J Kibbon
VP: Hilda Rodriguez
Dir IT: Timothy Nottoli

D-U-N-S 05-361-1034
WALSH CONSTRUCTION CO
2905 Sw 1st Ave, Portland, OR 97201-4705
Tel (503) 228-1190 *Founded/Ownrshp* 1961
Sales 143.2MM[E] *EMP* 242
SIC 1522 1542 Multi-family dwellings, new construction; Apartment building construction; Condominium construction; Commercial & office building contractors; Garage construction
Pr: Robert Walsh
**Pr:* Matthew L Leeding
Treas: Larry Kibbon
**Sec:* John M Wied
**VP:* Andrew Buyer
VP: Robert Forester
**VP:* Robert Forster
VP: Bill Reid
CTO: Donovan Williams
IT Man: Andy Breinholt
QI Cn Mgr: Sharon Libby

D-U-N-S 96-384-9828
WALSH CONSTRUCTION CO II LLC
(*Suby of* WALSH CONSTRUCTION GROUP LLC) ★
929 W Adams St, Chicago, IL 60607-3021
Tel (312) 563-5400 *Founded/Ownrshp* 2009
Sales 130.0MM[E] *EMP* 400[E]
Accts Wolf Company Llp Oakbrook Te
SIC 1542 1611 Nonresidential construction; General contractor, highway & street construction
CFO: Larry Kibbon
IT Man: Forrest Gonzales

D-U-N-S 96-384-9760
WALSH CONSTRUCTION GROUP LLC
(*Suby of* WALSH GROUP CONSTRUCTION) ★
929 W Adams St, Chicago, IL 60607-3021
Tel (312) 563-5400 *Founded/Ownrshp* 2009
Sales 223.5MM[E] *EMP* 600
SIC 1542 Commercial & office building, new construction
CEO: Matthew Walsh
Board of Directors: Matthew Walsh

WALSH GROUP CONSTRUCTION
See WALSH GROUP LTD

D-U-N-S 12-147-6675 IMP
WALSH GROUP LTD
WALSH GROUP CONSTRUCTION
929 W Adams St, Chicago, IL 60607-3021
Tel (312) 563-5400 *Founded/Ownrshp* 1983
Sales 3.5MMM[E] *EMP* 5,000
Accts Wolf & Company Llp Oakbrook T
SIC 1542 1522 1622 1629 1541 Commercial & office building, new construction; Multi-family dwellings, new construction; Highway construction, elevated; Industrial plant construction; Factory construction
CEO: Matthew M Walsh
**Pr:* Daniel Walsh
COO: Bob Greendyke
CFO: Tim Gerken
VP: Michael Gibbons
VP: Matthew Walsh IV
VP: Michael Whelan
Mng Dir: Denis Turner
Prgrm Mgr: Kevin Swain
MIS Dir: Tim Nattoli
Dir IT: Tim Nottoli

D-U-N-S 02-990-5429 EXP
WALSWORTH PUBLISHING CO INC
306 N Kansas Ave, Marceline, MO 64658-2105
Tel (660) 376-3543 *Founded/Ownrshp* 1956
Sales 362.0MM[E] *EMP* 1,000
SIC 2741 2752 Miscellaneous publishing; Yearbooks: publishing & printing; Commercial printing, offset
CEO: Don O Walsworth
**Pr:* Don Walsworth Jr
COO: Jim Mead
CFO: Jeff Vogel
Ex VP: Steve Blair
Ex VP: David Brisa
Ex VP: Joe Cupp
Ex VP: David Grisa
Ex VP: Mark Hatfield
**Ex VP:* Ed Kennedy
VP: Alex Blackwell
VP: Pete Blair
VP: Edward Kennedy

D-U-N-S 87-442-6489
WALT DISNEY ATTRACTIONS
WALT DISNEY WORLD SWAN HOTEL
1500 Epcot Resorts Blvd, Lake Buena Vista, FL 32830-8428
Tel (407) 934-4000 *Founded/Ownrshp* 1992
Sales 137.6MM[E] *EMP* 3,680
SIC 7011 7299 Resort hotel; Banquet hall facilities
Sales Exec: Eric Opron

D-U-N-S 93-266-0376 IMP/EXP
▲ WALT DISNEY CO
500 S Buena Vista St, Burbank, CA 91521-0007
Tel (818) 560-1000 *Founded/Ownrshp* 1925
Sales 55.6MMM *EMP* 185,000
Tkr Sym DIS *Exch* NYS
SIC 4833 4841 7011 7996 7812 2731 Television broadcasting stations; Cable television services; Resort hotel; Amusement parks; Motion picture & video production; Books: publishing only
Ch Bd: Robert A Iger
Pr: Paul Candland
Pr: Leslie Ferraro
CFO: Christine M McCarthy
Treas: Barbara Hafer
Treas: Robert Risteen
Treas: Paul N Saleh
Bd of Dir: James M Kearns
Bd of Dir: Karen A Powers
Chf Mktg O: Anna Hill
Ofcr: Mary Jayne Parker
Ex VP: Karey Burke
Ex VP: Kevin Mayer
Ex VP: Zenia Mucha
Ex VP: Laura Nathanson
Ex VP: John Ryan
Ex VP: Josh Silverman
Ex VP: Jason Taback
Ex VP: Kim Theiss
Ex VP: Norby Williamson
Sr VP: Dorothy Attwood
Board of Directors: Orin C Smith, Susan E Arnold, John S Chen, Jack Dorsey, Maria Elena Lagomasino, Fred H Langhammer, Aylwin B Lewis, Robert W Matschullat, Mark G Parker, Sheryl Sandberg

D-U-N-S 19-369-7216 IMP/EXP
■ WALT DISNEY IMAGINEERING RESEARCH & DEVELOPMENT INC
(*Suby of* DISNEY ENTERPRISES INC) ★
1401 Flower St, Glendale, CA 91201-2421
Tel (818) 544-6500 *Founded/Ownrshp* 1986
Sales 81.7MM[E] *EMP* 1,300
SIC 7819 8712 1542 8741 8711 Visual effects production; Architectural services; Custom builders, non-residential; Management services; Engineering services
CEO: Thomas O Staggs
**V Ch Bd:* Martin A Sklar
**Ex VP:* Craig Russell
**VP:* Markus Gross
**VP:* Jessica Hodgins
**Exec:* Bruce Vaughn
MIS Dir: Jan Oliver

D-U-N-S 04-115-6852
■ WALT DISNEY MUSIC CO
(*Suby of* DISNEY ENTERPRISES INC) ★
500 S Buena Vista St, Burbank, CA 91521-0007
Tel (818) 560-1000 *Founded/Ownrshp* 1947
Sales 123.4MM[E] *EMP* 900[E]
SIC 6794 Music royalties, sheet & record
Pr: Chris Montan
**Ch Bd:* Robert Cavallo
**CEO:* Cathleen M Taff
**Treas:* Cathleen Tass
VP: Luigi-Theo Calabrese
VP: Shelley Miles
VP: Kristin Nolt
VP: Thomas Poulsen
VP: Robert Vanderhyde
Rgnl Mgr: Bruce Austin
Dir IT: Todd Beach

D-U-N-S 04-975-9814 IMP
■ WALT DISNEY PARKS AND RESORTS US INC
EPCOT CENTER
(*Suby of* DISNEY ENTERPRISES INC) ★
1375 E Buena Vista Dr, Lake Buena Vista, FL 32830-8402
Tel (407) 824-2222 *Founded/Ownrshp* 1964
Sales 3.5MMM[E] *EMP* 62,000
SIC 7996 7011 5947 Theme park, amusement; Hotels & motels; Gift, novelty & souvenir shop
CFO: James Hunt
**Pr:* George L Kalogridis
Sr VP: Claire Bilby
Sr VP: Julian Fouche
Sr VP: Tilak Mandadi
**Sr VP:* Dianna Morgan
**Sr VP:* Bill O'Toole
Sr VP: Ken Potrock
VP: Sonia Coleman
VP: Cyndi Cruz
**VP:* Margaret C Giacalone
**VP:* Marsha L Reed
**VP:* Lee Schmudde
**VP:* Jeff Smith
VP: Glen Taylor
VP: Judy Taylor

D-U-N-S 19-727-6140 IMP/EXP
■ WALT DISNEY RECORDS DIRECT
(*Suby of* DISNEY ENTERPRISES INC) ★
500 S Buena Vista St, Burbank, CA 91521-0007
Tel (818) 560-1000 *Founded/Ownrshp* 1983
Sales 76.7MM[E] *EMP* 3,000
SIC 7812 Motion picture production & distribution; Motion picture production & distribution, television; Non-theatrical motion picture production; Non-theatrical motion picture production, television
Sr VP: Alan H Bergman
**CFO:* Rob Moore
**Sr VP:* Nick Franklin

D-U-N-S 62-253-0616
WALT DISNEY WORLD SWAN AND DOLPHIN
WDW SWAN AND DOLPHIN
1500 Epcot Resorts Blvd, Lake Buena Vista, FL 32830-8428
Tel (407) 934-4000 *Founded/Ownrshp* 1987
Sales 113.6MM[E] *EMP* 1,000[E]
SIC 7011 Hostels
Genl Mgr: Fred Sawyers
IT Man: Keith Sweeney
Sls Mgr: Paul Coulter

WALT DISNEY WORLD SWAN HOTEL
See WALT DISNEY ATTRACTIONS

WALTER & WOLF
See WALTERS & WOLF GLASS CO

D-U-N-S 18-135-7286 IMP/EXP
WALTER COKE INC
3500 35th Ave N, Birmingham, AL 35207-2918
Tel (205) 808-7803 *Founded/Ownrshp* 1976
Sales 136.1MM[E] *EMP* 347
SIC 2999

D-U-N-S 02-774-2691
WALTER E NELSON CO
5937 N Cutter Cir, Portland, OR 97217-3940
Tel (503) 285-3037 *Founded/Ownrshp* 1954
Sales 142.7MM[E] *EMP* 150
SIC 5169 5087 Chemicals & allied products; Janitors' supplies
Pr: Michael E Nelson
**CFO:* Robert Wakefield
VP: Dave Henzi
Genl Mgr: Tim Walters
Off Mgr: Julia Castro
Mktg Dir: Monica Cranswick
Sls Dir: John Nelson
Sales Asso: Sue Schroder

D-U-N-S 06-460-9241 IMP/EXP
WALTER E SMITHE FURNITURE INC
1251 W Thorndale Ave, Itasca, IL 60143-1149
Tel (800) 948-4263 *Founded/Ownrshp* 1982
Sales 149.0MM[E] *EMP* 525
SIC 5712 Custom made furniture, except cabinets
Pr: Walter E Smithe III
**Treas:* Mark Smithe
**VP:* Timothy Smithe
**VP:* Walter E Smithe Jr
Genl Mgr: Michelle Rodnick
Netwrk Mgr: Eric Malorny
Mktg Dir: Maryann Curran
Mktg Dir: Pam Johnstone
Advt Mgr: Pamela Johnston

D-U-N-S 18-340-2874 IMP/EXP
WALTER ENERGY INC
3000 Riverchase Galleria # 1700, Hoover, AL 35244-2378
Tel (205) 745-2000 *Founded/Ownrshp* 1972
Sales 1.4MMM *EMP* 2,680
SIC 1241 4925

D-U-N-S 05-608-9126
▲ WALTER INVESTMENT MANAGEMENT CORP
3000 Bayport Dr Ste 1100, Tampa, FL 33607-8405
Tel (813) 421-7600 *Founded/Ownrshp* 1958
Sales NA *EMP* 5,900[E]
Tkr Sym WAC *Exch* NYS
SIC 6162 Mortgage bankers & correspondents
Ch Bd: George M Awad
Pr: Christopher Mullins
COO: David C Schneider
CFO: Gary L Tillett
Ofcr: Gregory A Williamson
Sr VP: Sheryl L Newman
VP: Melissa Henry
Board of Directors: Daniel G Beltzman, Steven R Berrard, Ellyn L Brown, Alvaro G De Molina, William J Meurer, Mark J O'brien, James L Pappas, Shannon E Smith, Michael T Tokarz

D-U-N-S 07-912-8245 EXP
WALTER JIM RESOURCES INC
16243 Highway 216, Brookwood, AL 35444-3058
Tel (205) 554-6150 *Founded/Ownrshp* 1991
Sales 708.9MM[E] *EMP* 1,350
SIC 1222

D-U-N-S 18-848-3069 IMP/EXP
■ WALTER KIDDE PORTABLE EQUIPMENT INC
KIDDE SAFETY
(*Suby of* UNITED TECHNOLOGIES CORP) ★
1016 Corporate Park Dr, Mebane, NC 27302-8368
Tel (919) 563-5911 *Founded/Ownrshp* 2005
Sales 141.6MM[E] *EMP* 450
SIC 3999 Fire extinguishers, portable
Pr: Jim Ward
Ch: Jack Parow
VP: Chris Rovenstine
VP Sls: Joe Fahy
Pr Dir: Amy Rupert

D-U-N-S 02-584-2584
WALTER LAGESTEE INC (IL)
WALTS FOOD CENTERS
16145 State St, South Holland, IL 60473-1287
Tel (708) 596-3166 *Founded/Ownrshp* 1937
Sales 113.2MM[E] *EMP* 820
SIC 5411 5141 Grocery stores, independent; Groceries, general line
Pr: John G Lagestee
**CFO:* Robert Lagestee
**VP:* Willis Lagestee
Genl Mgr: Stan Komperda
Off Mgr: Claudia Petkus
IT Man: Steve Jurgensmeyer

WALTER O BOSWELL MEMORIAL HOSP
See SUN HEALTH CORP

D-U-N-S 00-335-8678
WALTER P RAWL & SONS INC (SC)
824 Fairview Rd, Pelion, SC 29123-9433
Tel (803) 894-1900 *Founded/Ownrshp* 1936
Sales 114.5MM *EMP* 275
Accts Derrick Stubbs & Stith Llp C
SIC 0161 0723 5148 Truck farm; Crop preparation services for market; Fresh fruits & vegetables
Pr: Wayne Rawl
**VP:* Howard Rawl

D-U-N-S 00-610-3162 IMP/EXP
WALTER USA LLC
(*Suby of* SANDVIK AB)
N22 W 23855 Rdg St N 22, Waukesha, WI 53188
Tel (800) 945-5554 *Founded/Ownrshp* 2000
Sales 120.0MM[E] *EMP* 263
SIC 3545 Cutting tools for machine tools; Reamers, machine tool; Drills (machine tool accessories); Boring machine attachments (machine tool accessories)
Pr: Muff Tanriverdi
Sec: Gary Mayer
Genl Mgr: Thomas Benjamin
IT Man: Eric Grunewald
Tech Mgr: Bill Radtke
QI Cn Mgr: Ellen Rothman
Board of Directors: G W Adkins, Charles Kay, Roger Peirce, R H Roerts, D Weselin

D-U-N-S 07-046-4581 IMP
WALTERS & WOLF GLASS CO (CA)
WALTER & WOLF
41450 Boscell Rd, Fremont, CA 94538-3103
Tel (510) 490-1115 *Founded/Ownrshp* 1977
Sales 128.5MM[E] *EMP* 350
SIC 1793 Glass & glazing work
Pr: Randall A Wolf
**CFO:* Jeff Belzer
**VP:* Nick Kocelj
CTO: George Pacheco
Sls Dir: Paul Roy

D-U-N-S 07-828-7694
WALTERS BAYER AUTOMOTIVE GROUP LLC
2030 E Flamingo Rd # 290, Las Vegas, NV 89119-0818
Tel (702) 450-8001 *Founded/Ownrshp* 2009
Sales 92.9MM[E] *EMP* 500
SIC 5012 Automobiles

WALTERS GOLF
See WALTERS GROUP

D-U-N-S 80-942-0722
WALTERS GROUP
WALTERS GOLF
2030 E Flamingo Rd # 290, Las Vegas, NV 89119-0818
Tel (702) 450-8001 *Founded/Ownrshp* 1988
Sales 426.3MM[E] *EMP* 20[E]
Accts Bdo Usa Llp Las Vegas Nv
SIC 6798 Real estate investment trusts
Pt: William T Walters
**Pt:* Bill Walters
**Pt:* Susan Walters
VP: Josh Hill
VP: Lucy Mitchell
Ex Dir: Jeffrey Smith
Admn Mgr: Deb Walsh
Admn Mgr: Lois Watts

D-U-N-S 02-803-8610
WALTERS WHOLESALE ELECTRIC CO
(*Suby of* C E D) ★
2825 Temple Ave, Signal Hill, CA 90755-2212
Tel (562) 988-3100 *Founded/Ownrshp* 2012
Sales 530.0MM[E] *EMP* 475
SIC 5063 3699 1731 Wire & cable; Electrical equipment & supplies; Lighting contractor
CEO: John L Walter
**Pr:* Bill Durkee
**CFO:* Roland Wood
**Treas:* Nancy Nielsen
Dir Soc: Jan Padilla
Brnch Mgr: Steve Barnhart
Brnch Mgr: Dan Golly
Mktg Dir: Kim Crooks
Sls Mgr: Gene Grabast
Sales Asso: Roy Bortolazzo
Sales Asso: John Holmes

D-U-N-S 01-741-5266
WALTERS-DIMMICK PETROLEUM INC (MI)
SHELL SPEE-D-MART
1620 S Kalamazoo Ave, Marshall, MI 49068-9576
Tel (269) 781-4654 *Founded/Ownrshp* 1982, 2012
Sales 392.7MM[E] *EMP* 980
SIC 5541 5411 6512 5172 5171 5983 Filling stations, gasoline; Convenience stores, independent; Commercial & industrial building operation; Lubricating oils & greases; Petroleum bulk stations; Fuel oil dealers
Pr: J P Walters II
**CFO:* Jeff Newhouse
**Treas:* John Walters

*VP: John M Dimmick
Exec: Lori Butler
Area Mgr: Ellen Vipond

D-U-N-S 03-378-5734
WALTHALL OIL CO
UPSON PROPANE
2510 Allen Rd, Macon, GA 31216-6397
Tel (478) 781-1234 Founded/Ownrshp 1952
Sales 185.4MM EMP 130
Accts Meadors Wall & Co Pc Macon
SIC 5172 5541 5411 Petroleum products; Filling stations, gasoline; Convenience stores
CEO: Frank Walthall III
*CFO: Rod Coston
*Sr VP: Charlotte Kennington
VP: Shawn Heacox
*VP: Phillip Sullivan
VP Opers: Matt Rhodes
Sfty Dirs: Thomas Graham
Sls Mgr: Wesley Walthall

D-U-N-S 14-799-0758 IMP
WALTON CONSTRUCTION - A CORE CO LLC
2 Commerce Ct, New Orleans, LA 70123-3225
Tel (504) 733-2212 Founded/Ownrshp 2010
Sales 109.0MM[E] EMP 700
SIC 1541 1542 Industrial buildings, new construction; Commercial & office building, new construction
CFO: Greg Phillip
CFO: Jeffry Stafford
Ofcr: Tom Buddy
Ex VP: Dan Moore
Sr VP: Lotus Millin
VP: Lotus Mellon
Snr PM: Ali Karimi
Snr PM: Doak Stitt

WALTON COUNTY PUBLIC SCHOOLS
See WALTON COUNTY SCHOOL DISTRICT

D-U-N-S 03-004-6510
WALTON COUNTY SCHOOL DISTRICT
WALTON COUNTY PUBLIC SCHOOLS
200 Double Sprng Ch Rd Sw, Monroe, GA 30656-4665
Tel (770) 266-4520 Founded/Ownrshp 1906
Sales 85.3MM[E] EMP 1,900
SIC 8211 Public combined elementary & secondary school
Bd of Dir: Terri Michael
Adm Dir: Bruce Clark
Pr Dir: Callen Moore
Teacher Pr: Lance Young
Psych: Susan Perz

D-U-N-S 00-692-6240
WALTON ELECTRIC MEMBERSHIP CORP
E M C
842 Highway 78 Nw, Monroe, GA 30655-4475
Tel (770) 267-2505 Founded/Ownrshp 1936
Sales 243.8MM EMP 273
Accts Mcnair Mclemore Middlebrooks &
SIC 4911 Distribution, electric power
Pr: D Ronnie Lee
*CFO: Marsha L Shumate

D-U-N-S 87-958-3789
WALTON FAMILY FOUNDATION INC
125 W Central Ave Rm 218, Bentonville, AR 72712-5248
Tel (479) 273-5605 Founded/Ownrshp 1997
Sales 421.8MM EMP 7
SIC 8699 Charitable organization
Ex Dir: Buddy Philpot
Ofcr: Ryan Hale
Ofcr: Cathy N Lund
Ofcr: Moira McDonald
Ofcr: Sandy Nickerson
Ofcr: Kathy Smith
Ofcr: Morgan Snyder
Ofcr: Jessica Young
Opers Mgr: Liz Heimbach

WALTS FOOD CENTERS
See WALTER LAGESTEE INC

D-U-N-S 61-217-9858 IMP/EXP
WALVOIL FLUID POWER CORP
(Suby of WALVOIL SPA)
4111 N Garnett Rd, Tulsa, OK 74116-5022
Tel (918) 858-7100 Founded/Ownrshp 2004
Sales 120.9MM[E] EMP 400
SIC 5085 Pistons & valves
Pr: Ivano Corghi
*CEO: Victor Gottardi

WANDERING WIFI
See AIRWATCH LLC

D-U-N-S 02-172-9033
WANG CENTER FOR PERFORMING ARTS INC
270 Tremont St, Boston, MA 02116-5603
Tel (617) 482-9393 Founded/Ownrshp 2014
Sales 11.5MM EMP 1,000
Accts Moody Famiglietti & Andronico
SIC 7922 Performing arts center production
Ch Bd: Bill Poeuska
V Ch: Charles A Polachi Jr
*Pr: Josiah A Spaulding Jr
*CFO: John Perkins
*Treas: James Distasio
VP: Michael Szczepkowski
*Prin: Sue Dahling Sullivan
*Prin: Anne Taylor

D-U-N-S 96-541-1122
WANG JING
1400 Hermann Pressler Dr, Houston, TX 77030
Tel (713) 794-4190 Founded/Ownrshp 2010
Sales 91.9MM[E] EMP 5,000
SIC 8733 Noncommercial research organizations
Owner: John Mendelsohn

D-U-N-S 78-899-7422 IMP
WANHUA CHEMICAL (AMERICA) CO LTD
(Suby of WANHUA CHEMICAL GROUP CO., LTD.)
3803 West Chester Pike, Newtown Square, PA 19073-2333
Tel (613) 796-1606 Founded/Ownrshp 1998
Sales 250.0MM EMP 25
SIC 5169 Chemicals & allied products
Pr: Jacob Sturgeon

D-U-N-S 93-186-6917 IMP
WANXIANG AMERICA CORP
(Suby of WANXIANG GROUP CORPORATION)
88 Airport Rd, Elgin, IL 60123-9324
Tel (847) 622-8838 Founded/Ownrshp 1993
Sales 350.0MM EMP 6,000
SIC 5013 Motor vehicle supplies & new parts
Pr: Pin Ni
*CFO: Gary E Wetzel
*Ch: Guanqui Lu
Genl Mgr: Michael J Schaal

D-U-N-S 10-671-1062
■ WANZEK CONSTRUCTION INC
(Suby of MASTEC NORTH AMERICA INC) ★
2028 2nd Ave Nw, West Fargo, ND 58078-1317
Tel (701) 282-6171 Founded/Ownrshp 2008
Sales 250.9MM[E] EMP 400[E]
SIC 1542 1623 1622 1799 1541 1629 Nonresidential construction; Sewer line construction; Bridge construction; Swimming pool construction; Industrial buildings & warehouses; Dam construction; Waterway construction; Waste water & sewage treatment plant construction
Pr: Jon Wanzek
Pr: Josh Hahn
*CFO: Kevin Gourde
*Ex VP: Rush Waite
*VP: Arnold Jelinek
Genl Mgr: Rob Fischer
Genl Mgr: Sharon Gammill
CTO: Shane Paulson
QA Dir: Don Keller
IT Man: Kevin Lanners
Sfty Dirs: Randall Tharp

D-U-N-S 06-054-6629
WAPPINGERS CENTRAL SCHOOL DISTRICT
25 Corporate Park Rd, Hopewell Junction, NY 12533-6562
Tel (845) 298-5000 Founded/Ownrshp 1940
Sales 47.3MM[E] EMP 2,100
SIC 8211 Public senior high school; Public elementary school; Public junior high school
Pr: Peggy Kelland
Ofcr: Russell Vanpelt
VP: Kelly Betterton
*VP: Colleen Hardiman
Genl Mgr: Kristen Crandall
Psych: Heather Dahl
Psych: Celeste Jones

D-U-N-S 82-874-9734
WAPSIPINICON WIND PROJECT LLC
(Suby of ENXCO) ★
234 Industrial Park Dr, Dexter, MN 55926-7325
Tel (760) 329-1437 Founded/Ownrshp 2008
Sales 85.9MM[E] EMP 350
SIC 4911 Electric services

D-U-N-S 06-823-6108 IMP/EXP
WARBURG PINCUS LLC
450 Lexington Ave, New York, NY 10017-3904
Tel (212) 878-0600 Founded/Ownrshp 1966
Sales 6.4MMM[E] EMP 19,980
SIC 6799 6211

D-U-N-S 36-154-6604
WARBURG PINCUS PRIVATE EQUITY VIII LP
450 Lexington Ave, New York, NY 10017-3904
Tel (212) 878-0600 Founded/Ownrshp 2001
Sales 1.1MMM[E] EMP 18,420[E]
SIC 6799 Investors
Genl Pt: Lionel Pincus
Genl Pt: John Vogelstein

WARCO
See WEST AMERICAN RUBBER CO LLC

D-U-N-S 02-253-6478 IMP
WARD MACHINERY CO
MARQUIP WARD UNITED
(Suby of BARRY-WEHMILLER COMPANIES INC) ★
10615 Beaver Dam Rd, Cockeysville, MD 21030-2204
Tel (410) 584-7700 Founded/Ownrshp 2002
Sales 121.3MM[E] EMP 652[E]
Accts Ernst & Young Llp St Louis
SIC 3554 Paper industries machinery; Corrugating machines, paper
Ch Bd: Robert H Chapman
Pr: Timothy Sullivan
CFO: James W Lawson
VP: Jim Cummings
VP: William Pratt
VP: John Schultz
Plnt Mgr: Steve Siperko
Natl Sales: Pete Bickford
Manager: Max Rawson
Snr Mgr: Eric Wert

D-U-N-S 15-074-5974 IMP
WARD MANUFACTURING LLC
(Suby of HITACHI METALS AMERICA LTD) ★
117 Gulick St, Blossburg, PA 16912-1001
Tel (570) 638-2131 Founded/Ownrshp 2016
Sales 146.8MM[E] EMP 500[E]
SIC 3321 3322 3498 Cast iron pipe & fittings; Ductile iron castings; Malleable iron foundries; Fabricated pipe & fittings
CEO: Eiji Nakano
Brnch Mgr: Bob Harter
Genl Mgr: Joe Marques
Sfty Mgr: Craig Johnson
Ql Cn Mgr: Jim Belawski
Sls&Mrk Ex: Thomas Heil

D-U-N-S 01-918-6402
WARD PETROLEUM CORP
502 S Fillmore St, Enid, OK 73703-5703
Tel (580) 234-3229 Founded/Ownrshp 1970
Sales 129.8MM[E] EMP 112[E]
SIC 4923 Gas transmission & distribution
Ch Bd: Lew O Ward
*Pr: William C Ward
*Treas: Richard R Tozzi

D-U-N-S 82-987-5421
WARD TRANSPORT & LOGISTICS CORP
1436 Ward Trucking Dr, Altoona, PA 16602-7110
Tel (814) 944-0803 Founded/Ownrshp 1931
Sales 159.0MM[E] EMP 2
Accts Grant Thornton Llp Columbia
SIC 4214 Local trucking with storage
Pr: William Ward
Pr: Jeffrey Heiselmeyer
*Treas: J Richard Ward
VP: Steve Blevins
Opers Mgr: Mike Zinz
Manager: Michael Aiello
Manager: Brad Ashline
Manager: Dwight Derolf
Manager: David Kliem
Manager: Richard Penwell
Manager: Angie Rochester

D-U-N-S 00-790-9500
WARD TRUCKING LLC (PA)
1436 Ward Trucking Dr, Altoona, PA 16602-7110
Tel (814) 944-0803 Founded/Ownrshp 1931, 1947
Sales 153.4MM EMP 1,057
Accts Grant Thornton Columbia Sc
SIC 4213 4214 Trucking, except local; Local trucking with storage
Ch: G William Ward
*Pr: David K Ward
COO: Chuck Delutis
*Genl Mgr: Michael E Ward
Opers Supe: Tim Dunn

D-U-N-S 05-892-9092 IMP
WARD-KRAFT INC
(Suby of W/K HOLDING CO INC) ★
2401 Cooper St, Fort Scott, KS 66701-3033
Tel (800) 821-4021 Founded/Ownrshp 1972
Sales 88.9MM[E] EMP 350
SIC 2761 2672 Manifold business forms; Labels (unprinted), gummed: made from purchased materials
CEO: Roger Kraft
Pr: Mark Tucker
Treas: Kevin Mitchelson
VP: Peter Brody
VP: Kevin Marquardt
VP: Randy Sloan
Brnch Mgr: Cary Mooney
Genl Mgr: Roger Davis
CIO: Ru Holt
CTO: Steve Denton
Prd Mgr: Mikhail Gonzales

D-U-N-S 07-687-3397
WARE GROUP INC
JOHNSTONE SUP S JACKSONVILLE
11710 Central Pkwy, Jacksonville, FL 32224-1400
Tel (904) 641-2282 Founded/Ownrshp 1982
Sales 140.7MM[E] EMP 187
SIC 5075

D-U-N-S 82-978-3385
WARE GROUP LLC
JOHNSTONE SUP AUTHORIZED DLR
11710 Central Pkwy, Jacksonville, FL 32224-1400
Tel (904) 641-2282 Founded/Ownrshp 2006
Sales 125.3MM[E] EMP 195[E]
Accts Ennis Pellum & Associates Pa
SIC 5075 Warm air heating & air conditioning

D-U-N-S 07-539-5160 IMP/EXP
WARE INDUSTRIES INC
MARINO WARE DIVISION
400 Metuchen Rd, South Plainfield, NJ 07080-4807
Tel (908) 757-9000 Founded/Ownrshp 1972, 1989
Sales 155.2MM[E] EMP 420
SIC 3444 Sheet metalwork
Ch Bd: Leroy Schecter
*Pr: Chip Gardner
*COO: Richard Dargel
*CFO: Lori Hagedorn
Exec: Craig Eisenberg
VP Opers: Mark Baker
VP Sls: Michael Fenbert
Mktg Dir: Bill Mayne
Sls Mgr: Barbara Delnero
Sales Asso: Jennifer Cajigas
Sales Asso: Michelle Petrillo

D-U-N-S 03-266-5499
WARE OIL & SUPPLY CO INC
WACO FOOD STORE
2715 S Byron Butler Pkwy, Perry, FL 32348-6329
Tel (850) 838-1852 Founded/Ownrshp 1975
Sales 101.8MM[E] EMP 160
SIC 5172 5087 5411 Gasoline; Diesel fuel; Janitors' supplies; Convenience stores, chain
Pr: Donald R Everett Sr
*Sr VP: Don R Everett Jr
*VP: Douglas M Everett

WAREHOUSE
See PAULS TV LLC

D-U-N-S 60-865-5072
WAREHOUSE DEMO SERVICES INC
1301 4th Ave Nw Ste 202, Issaquah, WA 98027-9371
Tel (425) 889-0797 Founded/Ownrshp 1989
Sales 98.4MM[E] EMP 4,000
SIC 7389 Demonstration service
Pr: Rhonda Levene
*Pr: Ted Koehn
*Treas: Deborah Heslenfield
*VP: Brian Ray Benson
VP Sls: Mindy Paris

D-U-N-S 09-678-7700
WAREHOUSE DIRECT INC
WAREHUSE DRECT WRKPLACE SLTONS
2001 S Mount Prospect Rd, Des Plaines, IL 60018-1808
Tel (847) 952-1925 Founded/Ownrshp 1979
Sales 221.8MM[E] EMP 275
SIC 5112 Office supplies
Ch: Ken Johnson
*Pr: John Moyer
*Ex VP: Kevin S Johnson
*Ex VP: Robert D Swanson
Exec: Sue McHugh
Exec: Hank Paul
Brnch Mgr: Craig Marshak
Trfc Dir: John Garcia
Opers Mgr: Curtis Stokes
Sales Asso: Dave Marr

D-U-N-S 05-954-6119 IMP
WAREHOUSE HOME FURNISHINGS DISTRIBUTORS INC
FARMERS HOME FUNRITURE
1851 Telfair St, Dublin, GA 31021-3118
Tel (800) 456-0424 Founded/Ownrshp 1972
Sales 456.6MM[E] EMP 1,700
SIC 5712 Furniture stores
CEO: Phillip D Faircloth
V Ch: Chan Carter
*Treas: Sam Moore
Sr VP: Graig Lasting
Ex Dir: John Johnson

D-U-N-S 03-314-7885
WAREHOUSE MARKET INC
FAMILY MARKET
6207 S Peoria Ave Ste A, Tulsa, OK 74136-0572
Tel (918) 749-4732 Founded/Ownrshp 1938
Sales 140.8MM[E] EMP 960
SIC 5411 Supermarkets, independent
Pr: Don Olansen
CFO: Clint Cox
Dir IT: Jana Mercer

D-U-N-S 18-730-0124 IMP
WAREHOUSE SERVICES INC
W S I
58 S Burty Rd, Piedmont, SC 29673-8775
Tel (812) 831-4053 Founded/Ownrshp 1986
Sales 396.2MM[E] EMP 975[E]
SIC 1541 4225 Warehouse construction; General warehousing
*VP: Roy Arney
*VP: Brian Richardson
VP: Phil Stephenson
VP Admn: Sam Straub
Sfty Mgr: Seth Wade
Opers Mgr: Mike Crump
Sls Dir: Mike Daniel

WAREHOUSE SHOE SALE
See EUROSTAR INC

D-U-N-S 04-901-8252
WAREHOUSE SPECIALISTS LLC
WSI
(Suby of VAN HOOF CORP) ★
1160 N Mayflower Dr, Appleton, WI 54913-9656
Tel (920) 830-5000 Founded/Ownrshp 1966
Sales 100.0MM EMP 1,200
SIC 4225 General warehousing & storage
Pr: Robert Schroeder
*CFO: Dan Vandenheuvel
*VP Inf Sys: Dan Sellers
IT Man: Chuck Lindberg
*VP Opers: Bill Lindeke
Counsel: Ben Haupt

WAREHUSE DRECT WRKPLACE SLTONS
See WAREHOUSE DIRECT INC

D-U-N-S 01-214-8144
■ WAREX TERMINALS CORP (NY)
(Suby of WARREN EQUITIES INC) ★
1 S Water St, Newburgh, NY 12550-4604
Tel (845) 561-4000 Founded/Ownrshp 1963
Sales 733.9MM EMP 40
SIC 5172

WARM SPRINGS COMPOSITE PDTS
See CONFEDERATED TRIBES OF WARM SPRINGS RESERVATION OF OREGON

D-U-N-S 04-132-6406 IMP
WARMINGTON HOMES
3090 Pullman St, Costa Mesa, CA 92626-7936
Tel (714) 434-4435 Founded/Ownrshp 1972
Sales 129.3MM[E] EMP 375
SIC 1531 Speculative builder, single-family houses
Pr: Timothy P Hogan
*Ch Bd: James P Warmington
Pr: Michael McClellan
Pr: Greg Oberling
Pr: Jack Schwellenbach
Pr: Brian Sinderhoff
Pr: Steve Sutter
*CFO: Michael Riddlesperger
Ex VP: Larry Riggs
VP: Doug Glover
VP: Sara Strange

D-U-N-S 04-127-3889 IMP/EXP
■ WARN INDUSTRIES INC
(Suby of DOVER ENGINEERED SYSTEMS INC) ★
12900 Se Capps Rd, Clackamas, OR 97015-8903
Tel (503) 722-1200 Founded/Ownrshp 2003
Sales 101.1MM[E] EMP 530
SIC 3714 3531 Motor vehicle parts & accessories; Winches
Pr: Jon Stransky
*Pr: Jon Kreitz
*CFO: Eric Winston
*VP: Brendan Anderson
*VP: John Ducharme
*VP: Lawrence Rentz
Dir Risk M: Karl Christensen
Dir Bus: Hugo Burgers
Ex Dir: Marci Jackson

Genl Mgr: Rich Jay
IT Man: Jack Hooper

D-U-N-S 12-205-0438 IMP/EXP
■ WARNACO GROUP INC
(*Suby of* PVH CORP) ★
501 Fashion Ave, NewYork, NY 10018-5903
Tel (212) 287-8000 *Founded/Ownrshp* 2013
Sales 825.5MM^E *EMP* 7,136^E
SIC 2322 2329 2339 2369 2342 2341 Underwear, men's & boys': made from purchased materials; Men's & boys' sportswear & athletic clothing; Women's & misses' outerwear; Bathing suits: women's, misses' & juniors'; Beachwear: women's, misses' & juniors'; Children's bathing suits & beachwear; Bras, girdles & allied garments; Brassieres; Girdles & panty girdles; Panties: women's, misses', children's & infants'; Women's & children's nightwear
CEO: Helen McCluskey
Pr: James B Gerson
Pr: Joanne Kaye
Pr: Martha Olson
Pr: Michael Prendergast
Pr: Janice Sullivan
Pr: Frank Tworecke
CFO: Wallis Brooks
**CFO:* Lawrence R Rutkowski
**Ofcr:* Karyn Hillman
**Ex VP:* Elizabeth Wood
Sr VP: Bob Dakin
**Sr VP:* Jay L Dubiner
VP: Brian Reyes

D-U-N-S 00-116-3856 IMP/EXP
■ WARNACO INC
WARNER S
(*Suby of* WARNACO GROUP INC) ★
501 Fashion Ave Fl 14, NewYork, NY 10018-5942
Tel (212) 287-8000 *Founded/Ownrshp* 1874, 1986
Sales 688.6MM^E *EMP* 4,656
SIC 2342 2341 2321 2329 2322 2323 Bras, girdles & allied garments; Brassieres; Girdles & panty girdles; Panties: women's, misses', children's & infants'; Women's & children's nightwear; Men's & boys' dress shirts; Men's & boys' sportswear & athletic clothing; Underwear, men's & boys': made from purchased materials; Men's & boys' neckwear
Pr: Helen McCluskey
**Ch Bd:* Joseph R Gromek
**Ch Bd:* Charles R Perrin
Pr: Les Hall
**Ex VP:* Larry Rutkowski
**Ex VP:* Stanley Silverstein
Sr VP: Joanna Reeves
VP: Brad Gebhard
VP: J McMullan
VP: Rick Vuich
Ex Dir: Cheryl Turpin
Board of Directors: David A Bell, Robert A Bowmen, Richard Karl Goeltz, Sheila A Hopkins, Charles R Perrin, Don Seeley

D-U-N-S 61-273-6108 IMP
■ WARNER BROS (TRANSATLANTIC) INC
(*Suby of* TW VENTURES, INC)
4000 Warner Blvd, Burbank, CA 91522-0002
Tel (818) 977-0018 *Founded/Ownrshp* 2008
Sales 445.6MM^E *EMP* 9,000
SIC 7822 Distribution, exclusive of production: motion picture
CEO: Barry M Meyer
Pr: Jeremy Williams
CFO: Christina Lee
**Treas:* Ralph Peterson
**Ex VP:* Richard Fox
Sr VP: David B Camp
Sr VP: Dan Crane
Sr VP: Joan Dambros
Sr VP: James Halsey
Sr VP: Darren Higman
Sr VP: Lora Kennedy
Sr VP: Gary Meisel
Sr VP: Lewis Ostrover
Sr VP: Andrew Shipps
VP: Steve Chalk
**VP:* Warren Christie
VP: Nancy L Corshen
VP: Greg Gewickey
VP: Lisa Gregorian
VP: Justin Herz
VP: Darby Oneill

D-U-N-S 13-164-3392 IMP/EXP
■ WARNER BROS ENTERTAINMENT INC
VICTORY STUDIO
(*Suby of* TIME WARNER INC) ★
4000 Warner Blvd, Burbank, CA 91522-0002
Tel (818) 954-6000 *Founded/Ownrshp* 2001
Sales 592.2MM^E *EMP* 7,300
SIC 7812 Motion picture & video production; Television film production
CEO: Kevin Tsujihara
Pr: Alan Horn
Ex VP: Dee Dee Myers
VP: Roseann Cacciola
VP: Brinda Kempton
VP: Maury Leitner
Prin: Barry M Meyer
Ex Dir: Christian Kennel
Genl Mgr: Paul Bufton
Dir IT: Wagner Santos
Dir IT: Mandana Soleimani

D-U-N-S 09-833-9633 IMP
■ WARNER BROS HOME ENTERTAINMENT INC
(*Suby of* VICTORY STUDIO) ★
4000 Warner Blvd Bldg 160, Burbank, CA 91522-0002
Tel (818) 954-6000 *Founded/Ownrshp* 2001
Sales 111.3MM^E *EMP* 600
SIC 3651 Video cassette recorders/players & accessories
Pr: James Cardwell
Sr VP: Christian Davin
Sr VP: David Haddad
**VP:* Jeff Baker
VP: Shari Black
**VP:* Edward Byrnes
**VP:* Jeffrey Calman
**VP:* Brian Jamieson
**VP:* Marsha King
VP: Paul McGuire
VP: Lowell Moore
**VP:* Antonio D Rodriguez
**VP:* Ronald J Sanders
**VP:* Timmy Treu
**VP:* Frank Walsh
VP: Fiona Watts

D-U-N-S 00-962-9841
WARNER BROS RECORDS INC
(*Suby of* WARNER MUSIC INC) ★
3300 Warner Blvd, Burbank, CA 91505-4694
Tel (818) 953-3378 *Founded/Ownrshp* 1990
Sales 135.5MM^E *EMP* 1,300
SIC 7389 Music recording producer; Recording studio, noncommercial records
Pr: Todd Moscowitz
Mng Pt: Maria Gonzales
**Ch Bd:* Rob Cavallo
**Pr:* Livia Tortella
**CFO:* Marty Greenfield
CFO: Hildi Snodgrass
Ex VP: Stu Bergen
**Ex VP:* Murray Gitlin
VP: Marc Cimino
VP: Samantha Maloney
VP: Adam Starr

D-U-N-S 95-720-3177 IMP
WARNER CHILCOTT (US) LLC
WARNER CHILCOTT LABORATORIES
(*Suby of* WARNER CHILCOTT CORP) ★
400 Interpace Pkwy, Parsippany, NJ 07054-1120
Tel (862) 261-7000 *Founded/Ownrshp* 1996
Sales 107.8MM^E *EMP* 520^E
SIC 2834 Pharmaceutical preparations
CEO: Roger Boissonneault
**CFO:* John Goll
**CFO:* Paul Herendeen
**Sr VP:* Leland Cross
**Sr VP:* Izumi Hara
VP: Attio D Musacchio
**VP:* William Poll
Snr Mgr: Grexan Wulff

D-U-N-S 07-835-9571
WARNER CHILCOTT CORP
(*Suby of* ALLERGAN PUBLIC LIMITED COMPANY)
100 Enterprise Dr Ste 280, Rockaway, NJ 07866-2198
Tel (862) 261-7000 *Founded/Ownrshp* 2004
Sales 108.4MM^E *EMP* 542
SIC 2834 6719 Pharmaceutical preparations; Personal holding companies, except banks
Pr: Roger M Boissonneault
**CFO:* Paul Herendeen
VP: Claire Gilligan
VP: Matthew Lamb
Prin: Allison Lombardo
Prgrm Mgr: Tanya Muldoon
CIO: Andrew Fenton
VP Opers: Dominick Musacchio

WARNER CHILCOTT LABORATORIES
See WARNER CHILCOTT (US) LLC

D-U-N-S 01-697-2051
WARNER CHILCOTT PHARMACEUTICALS INC
1 Procter And Gamble Plz, Cincinnati, OH 45202-3315
Tel (513) 983-1100 *Founded/Ownrshp* 1987
Sales 259.8MM^E *EMP* 3,300
SIC 2834 Pharmaceutical preparations
Pr: Mark Collar
**CFO:* Clayton C Daley Jr

D-U-N-S 00-698-8042
■ WARNER COMMUNICATIONS INC (DE)
(*Suby of* ADULT SWIM GAMES) ★
1 Time Warner Ctr, New York, NY 10019-6038
Tel (212) 484-8000 *Founded/Ownrshp* 1961, 1989
Sales 612.6MM^E *EMP* 3,000
SIC 7812 4841 7389 Motion picture production & distribution; Television film production; Motion picture production & distribution, television; Video tape production; Cable television services; Subscription television services; Music distribution systems; Music recording producer
CEO: Jeffrey L Bewkes
V Ch Bd: Kenneth J Novack
Ex VP: Paul T Cappuccio
Ex VP: Patricia Fili-Krushel
Ex VP: Robert M Kimmitt
Ex VP: Michael Lynton
Ex VP: Wayne H Pace
VP: Ernie Enriquez

WARNER ELECTRIC INDUS PDTS
See WARNER ELECTRIC LLC

D-U-N-S 17-785-8383 IMP
■ WARNER ELECTRIC LLC
WARNER ELECTRIC INDUS PDTS
(*Suby of* ALTRA INDUSTRIAL MOTION CORP) ★
449 Gardner St, South Beloit, IL 61080-1397
Tel (815) 389-4300 *Founded/Ownrshp* 1927
Sales 121.8MM^E *EMP* 431
SIC 3714 Clutches, motor vehicle
Sr Cor Off: Richard Czeslawski
VP: Kevin Powell
Exec: Crystal Cochard
Exec: Edouard Haffner
MIS Dir: Rick Coiz
Info Man: Scott Meyers
Ql Cn Mgr: Rick Wiley
Sls Mgr: Ed Astacio
Sls Mgr: Ted Banakis
Sls Mgr: David Loane

D-U-N-S 17-589-2269
WARNER MUSIC GROUP CORP
(*Suby of* AI ENTERTAINMENT HOLDINGS LLC) ★
1633 Broadway, New York, NY 10019-6708
Tel (212) 275-2000 *Founded/Ownrshp* 2011
Sales 3.2MMM *EMP* 4,211^E
SIC 3652 6794 Pre-recorded records & tapes; Music licensing & royalties
CEO: Stephen Cooper
CEO: Stu Bergen
CEO: Cameron Strang
CFO: Eric Levin
**V Ch Bd:* Len Blavatnik
Ex VP: Mike Jbara
Ex VP: Maria Osherova
Ex VP: Paul M Robinson
Ex VP: James Steven
Sr VP: Ann Sweeney
VP: Scott Allender
VP: Beth Appleton
VP: Norma Augenblick
VP: Monique Benjamin
VP: Tristan Boutros
VP: Peter Clancy
VP: Sean Condon
VP: Kevin Conway
VP: Cyndi Goretski
VP: Vanessa Jester
VP: Ben Kline
Board of Directors: Lincoln Benet, Alex Blavatnik, Mathias Dopfner, Thomas H Lee, Jorg Mohaupt, Oliver Slipper, Cameron Strang, Donald A Wagner

D-U-N-S 87-906-8666 EXP
WARNER MUSIC INC
(*Suby of* WMG ACQUISITION CORP) ★
75 Rockefeller Plz Bsmt 1, New York, NY 10019-0011
Tel (212) 275-2000 *Founded/Ownrshp* 2004
Sales 769.2MM^E *EMP* 3,400
SIC 3652 2741 Pre-recorded records & tapes; Phonograph records, prerecorded; Magnetic tape (audio): prerecorded; Compact laser discs, prerecorded; Music, sheet: publishing & printing
Pr: Paul Rene' Albertini
**CFO:* Michael Fleisher
**Ex VP:* David H Johnson
Ex VP: Olafur Olafsson
Sr VP: Jim Noonan
VP: Liz Rosenberg
Mktg Dir: Lisa Cotter
Corp Couns: Paul Lee
Corp Couns: Fred Wistow

WARNER NURSING HOME
See COUNTRYSIDE ESTATES INC

D-U-N-S 11-855-3924
WARNER PACIFIC INSURANCE SERVICES INC
32110 Agoura Rd, Westlake Village, CA 91361-4026
Tel (408) 298-4049 *Founded/Ownrshp* 1984
Sales NA *EMP* 150^E
SIC 6411 Insurance brokers
CEO: John H Nelson
CFO: Matthew Conrow
Bd of Dir: Kim Novak
Bd of Dir: Michelle Taschler
Sr VP: Stephanie Brown
Sr VP: Debbie Vaillancourt
**VP:* David Nelson
Exec: Sioux Cook
QA Dir: Shruti Bulusu
IT Man: Michael Blank
Opers Mgr: Sheri Gabor

WARNER S
See WARNACO INC

WARNER TRUCK CENTER
See FREIGHTLINER OF UTAH A LIMITED LIABILITY CO

D-U-N-S 05-483-4114
WARNER-ELEKTRA-ATLANTIC CORP (NY)
(*Suby of* WARNER BROS RECORDS INC) ★
1633 Broadway Lowr 2c01, New York, NY 10019-6708
Tel (212) 275-2000 *Founded/Ownrshp* 1963, 1990
Sales 32.8MM^E *EMP* 1,200
SIC 7389 Music recording producer
Pr: John Esposito
CFO: John T O'Connell
VP: Bert W Wasserman

D-U-N-S 07-411-5528
WARNER/CHAPPELL MUSIC INC
(*Suby of* WARNER MUSIC INC) ★
10585 Santa Monica Blvd # 300, Los Angeles, CA 90025-0349
Tel (310) 441-8600 *Founded/Ownrshp* 1984, 2002
Sales 103.6MM^E *EMP* 542
SIC 2741 Music book & sheet music publishing
CEO: Cameron Strang
**Pr:* Scott Francis
**COO:* Ira Pianko
**CFO:* Brian Roberts
**Ch:* Edgar Miles Bronfman
Sr VP: Dave Pettigrew
VP: Tim Arnold
VP: Jeremy Blietz
VP: Ron Broitman
VP: Steve Butler
VP: Gary Calderone
VP: Tony Deneri
VP: Sean P Flahaven
VP: Deborah Keegan
VP: Pamela Klein
VP: Scott McDowell
**VP:* Jay Morgenstern
VP: Nancy Taylor
VP: Pat Woods
VP: Annette Yocum
Assoc Dir: Chris Head

D-U-N-S 15-428-1869
WARNOCK AUTOMOTIVE GROUP INC
175 State Route 10, East Hanover, NJ 07936-2104
Tel (973) 884-2100 *Founded/Ownrshp* 1976
Sales 91.1MM^E *EMP* 425
SIC 5511 7515 5012 5013 Automobiles, new & used; Pickups, new & used; Passenger car leasing; Automobiles; Motor vehicle supplies & new parts
Pr: Michael Critchley
**VP:* Richard A Merkt
Sales Exec: Bob Cleaveland
Sls Mgr: Marissa Giovenco

WARR ACRES
See HERTZ TECHNOLOGIES INC

D-U-N-S 11-601-3392
■ WARRANTECH CORP
(*Suby of* AMT WARRANTY CORP) ★
2200 Highway 121, Bedford, TX 76021-5982
Tel (817) 785-6601 *Founded/Ownrshp* 2010
Sales NA *EMP* 335
SIC 6399 Warranty insurance, product; except automobile; Warranty insurance, automobile
Pr: Sean Stapleton
Pr: David J Workman
**COO:* Laurence Tutt
CFO: Richard F Gavino
**CFO:* Steve Knapp
**Treas:* Harry Schlachter
**Ex VP:* Guy Koenig
Ex VP: Chris Murphy
**Sr VP:* Jeanine M Folz
**Sr VP:* James F Morganteen
VP: Mary Aldrich
VP: Mike Burgholzer
VP: Bob Cota
VP Bus Dev: Jon Kohler
Dir Teleco: John Dent

D-U-N-S 83-023-2778
WARRANTY GROUP INC
175 W Jackson Blvd Fl 11, Chicago, IL 60604-2709
Tel (312) 356-3000 *Founded/Ownrshp* 2014
Sales NA *EMP* 2,300^E
SIC 6351 6399 Warranty insurance, home; Warranty insurance, automobile
Pr: Thomas W Warsop III
Pr: Scott McWhinnie
**Pr:* Charles A Robinson IV
Pr: Pamela Schneider
CEO: Gary Jennison
**CFO:* David I Vickers
**Ex VP:* Diana M Chafey
Ex VP: Sophocles Karapass
**Ex VP:* Tom Kilian
**Ex VP:* Colon McLean
Ex VP: Colon S McLean
Ex VP: Manfred Schmoelz
Ex VP: John Serafin
**Ex VP:* Ted Wagner
**Sr VP:* Brian K Ollech
**Sr VP:* Teri Cotton Santos
Sr VP: John H Serafin
VP: Laurie Hubbard
VP: Ronald Markovits
VP: Brian Ollech
VP: Bart Potenzoi

D-U-N-S 07-840-5692
WARREN AVERETT COMPANIES LLC
2500 Acton Rd Ste 200, Vestavia, AL 35243-4226
Tel (205) 979-4100 *Founded/Ownrshp* 2011
Sales 117.1MM^E *EMP* 800
SIC 8721 8741 7363 8742 Certified public accountant; Financial management for business; Help supply services; Compensation & benefits planning consultant
CEO: James W Cunningham
COO: Mary Elliott
CFO: April Harry

WARREN CAT
See WARREN POWER & MACHINERY INC

D-U-N-S 08-059-1654
WARREN CLINIC INC
SAINT FRANCIS HEALTH SYSTEM
6161 S Yale Ave, Tulsa, OK 74136-1902
Tel (918) 488-6000 *Founded/Ownrshp* 1960
Sales 146.7MM *EMP* 1,000
Accts Ernst & Young Us Llp Columbus
SIC 8011 Clinic, operated by physicians
CEO: Jake Henry Jr
COO: Brenda Brown
**Ex VP:* Barry Steichen
**Sr VP:* Lance King M D
**Sr VP:* Peter Aran M D
**Sr VP:* Tom Neff
Sr VP: Bill Schloss
Ex Dir: Randy Mills
Genl Mgr: Jane Walls
Off Mgr: Tina Bulce
Off Mgr: Robert Hauger

D-U-N-S 07-423-2836
WARREN CONSOLIDATED SCHOOLS
31300 Anita Dr, Warren, MI 48093-1646
Tel (586) 825-2400 *Founded/Ownrshp* 1941
Sales 184.4MM *EMP* 1,557^E
Accts Plante & Moran Pllc Clinton
SIC 8211 Elementary school; High school, junior or senior; Preparatory school
**Pr:* Brian White
**CFO:* Robert Carlesso
**Treas:* Megan E Papasian-Broadwell
**VP:* Elaine G Martin
Board of Directors: Peter Mott

D-U-N-S 08-619-4370
WARREN COUNTY PUBLIC SCHOOLS
303 Lovers Ln, Bowling Green, KY 42103-7935
Tel (270) 781-2392 *Founded/Ownrshp* 1900
Sales 71.3MM^E *EMP* 1,400
SIC 8211 Public elementary & secondary schools
Pr Dir: Morgan Watson
Teacher Pr: Michelle Tolbert
HC Dir: Pat Stewart

D-U-N-S 08-944-5076 IMP/EXP
WARREN DISTRIBUTING INC
WDI
8737 Dice Rd, Santa Fe Springs, CA 90670-2513
Tel (562) 789-3360 *Founded/Ownrshp* 1963
Sales 92.3MM^E *EMP* 164
SIC 5013 Automotive supplies & parts
Pr: Jason Pugh
CFO: Linnea Herndon
VP: Dave Erlenbach
Brnch Mgr: North Hollywood
Brnch Mgr: Las Vegas
Genl Mgr: Rick Yount
IT Man: April Tapia
VP Sls: Pat Winters
Sls Mgr: Gustavo Gonzalez

D-U-N-S 00-749-9932 IMP/EXP
WARREN DISTRIBUTION INC (NE)
727 S 13th St, Omaha, NE 68102-3204
Tel (402) 341-9397 *Founded/Ownrshp* 1922
Sales 407.4MM *EMP* 600
Accts Bkd Llp Omaha Nebraska
SIC 2992 Lubricating oils & greases
Ch Bd: Robert N Schlott
**Pr:* Charles P Downey
**CFO:* Donald H Nonnenkamp
VP: Rob Focht
Genl Mgr: David Carrington
Opers Mgr: Margaret Moore
Plnt Mgr: Stan Rogers
Sales Exec: Lynn Braningan
Sales Exec: Ralph Castillo

D-U-N-S 03-789-7402 IMP/EXP
WARREN EQUIPMENT CO
10325 Younger Rd, Midland, TX 79706-2622
Tel (432) 571-8462 *Founded/Ownrshp* 1975
Sales 509.1MM^E *EMP* 1,966
SIC 5082 5084 7699 3563 7359

D-U-N-S 06-520-3164
■ **WARREN EQUITIES INC**
(*Suby of* GLOBAL PARTNERS LP) ★
27 Warren Way, Providence, RI 02905-5000
Tel (401) 781-9900 *Founded/Ownrshp* 2015
Sales 1.5MMM^E *EMP* 1,450
SIC 5172 5541 5411 Petroleum products; Filling stations, gasoline; Convenience stores
Pr: August Schiesser
**CFO:* John Dziedzic
**VP:* Jeffery Walker

D-U-N-S 00-398-2188 IMP/EXP
WARREN FABRICATING CORP (OH)
3240 Mahoning Ave Nw, Warren, OH 44483-2054
Tel (330) 847-0596 *Founded/Ownrshp* 1966
Sales 84.7MM *EMP* 225
SIC 3441 3599 3547 3532 3444 3443 Fabricated structural metal; Machine shop, jobbing & repair; Rolling mill machinery; Mining machinery; Sheet metalwork; Fabricated plate work (boiler shop)
Pr: John C Rebhan
**VP:* David Della Donna
VP: David Donna
**VP:* Paul Theisler
**Prin:* William E Marsteller
**Prin:* Robert M Platt Sr
IT Man: Tom Hinrichs

D-U-N-S 01-417-6296
WARREN FUEL CO
3W WARREN FUELS
1405 United Dr, San Marcos, TX 78666-8277
Tel (512) 395-8557 *Founded/Ownrshp* 1996
Sales 93.0MM *EMP* 5
SIC 5541 Gasoline service stations
Pr: Blake Warren
**Genl Mgr:* Kirt Brumley

D-U-N-S 17-312-6384 EXP
WARREN HENRY AUTOMOBILES INC
WARREN HENRY LAND ROVER N DADE
20800 Nw 2nd Ave, Miami, FL 33169-2104
Tel (305) 690-6010 *Founded/Ownrshp* 1985
Sales 109.9MM^E *EMP* 275
SIC 5511 5531 7538 Automobiles, new & used; Automotive parts; General automotive repair shops
Pr: Warren H Zinn
**Sec:* Erik Day
Exec: Valancia Horne
Genl Mgr: Pedro Palenzuela
Genl Mgr: Larry Zinn
IT Man: Yader Campos
Sales Exec: Fernando Lopez
Mktg Mgr: Alex Cardona
Sls Mgr: Andrew Kipnis
Sls Mgr: Eduardo Molko
Sls Mgr: Ismet Yagci

WARREN HENRY LAND ROVER N DADE
See WARREN HENRY AUTOMOBILES INC

WARREN HOSPITAL
See WARREN ST LUKES HOSPITAL INC

D-U-N-S 07-383-2610 IMP
WARREN INDUSTRIES INC
3100 Mount Pleasant St, Racine, WI 53404-1593
Tel (262) 639-7800 *Founded/Ownrshp* 1973
Sales 118.8MM^E *EMP* 1,000
SIC 7389 Packaging & labeling services; Printing broker
Pr: David Namowicz
**Treas:* Carrie Holat
VP: Garrard David
Plnt Mgr: Steven Namowicz

D-U-N-S 07-555-2810 EXP
WARREN OIL CO INC (NC)
2340 Us Highway 301 N, Dunn, NC 28334-8307
Tel (910) 892-6456 *Founded/Ownrshp* 1975
Sales 167.6MM^E *EMP* 116
Accts Giles Strickland And Associat
SIC 5172 5171 3826 2911 Petroleum products; Lubricating oils & greases; Petroleum bulk stations & terminals; Analytical instruments; Petroleum refining
Pr: William Irvin Warren
**CFO:* Larry Sanderson
VP Sls: Hank Bird

D-U-N-S 00-459-6692
WARREN POWER & MACHINERY INC
WARREN CAT
(*Suby of* WARREN EQUIPMENT CO) ★
10325 Younger Rd, Midland, TX 79706-2622
Tel (432) 571-4200 *Founded/Ownrshp* 2002
Sales 222.3MM^E *EMP* 1,158^E
SIC 3531 Construction machinery
Pr: James Nelson
Exec: John Cjf
Genl Mgr: Paul Holzmer
IT Man: Coby Miller
Mtls Mgr: Joey Redmond
Sls Mgr: Lyle Mashburn

D-U-N-S 00-792-3303 IMP/EXP
WARREN POWER & MACHINERY INC
CATERPILLAR AUTHORIZED DEALER
(*Suby of* WARREN EQUIPMENT CO) ★
10325 Younger Rd, Midland, TX 79706-2622
Tel (432) 563-1170 *Founded/Ownrshp* 1996
Sales 272.9MM^E *EMP* 800
SIC 5082 General construction machinery & equipment
**Pr:* Jim Nelson
CFO: Robert Long
VP: Steven Lindgren
VP: Todd Stucke
Sales Asso: Chance Morgan

D-U-N-S 11-103-6112
WARREN POWER & MACHINERY LP
CATERPILLAR AUTHORIZED DEALER
4501 W Reno Ave, Oklahoma City, OK 73127-6412
Tel (405) 947-6771 *Founded/Ownrshp* 2002
Sales 151.6MM^E *EMP* 313
SIC 5082 Construction & mining machinery
Pt: Richard D Folger
**Pr:* Jim Nelson
IT Man: Shanna Stevens
Mtls Mgr: Phil Hawkins

WARREN RECC
See WARREN RURAL ELECTRIC COOPERATIVE CORP

D-U-N-S 78-111-8260
▲ **WARREN RESOURCES INC**
1331 17th St Ste 720, Denver, CO 80202-1557
Tel (720) 403-8125 *Founded/Ownrshp* 1990
Sales 88.3MM *EMP* 75^E
Accts Grant Thornton Llp Oklahoma C
Tkr Sym WRESQ *Exch* OTO
SIC 1311 Crude petroleum & natural gas; Crude petroleum & natural gas production
Pr: James A Watt
**Ch Bd:* Dominick D'Alleva
CFO: Frank T Smith
Sr VP: Gregory J Fox
VP: John R Powers
VP: Zach Waite
Board of Directors: Chet Borgida, Anthony L Coelho, Leonard Dececchis, Lance Peterson

D-U-N-S 00-695-0752 IMP
WARREN RURAL ELECTRIC COOPERATIVE CORP
WARREN RECC
951 Fairview Ave, Bowling Green, KY 42101-4937
Tel (270) 842-6541 *Founded/Ownrshp* 1938
Sales 182.2MM *EMP* 165
Accts Alexander Thompson Arnold Pllc
SIC 4911 Distribution, electric power
CEO: W Scott Ramsey
CEO: David Anderson
CFO: Roxanne Gray
VP: Tom Martin
VP: Dewayne McDonald
VP: Rick Starks
VP: Neva Whitley
Genl Mgr: Gregg Weathers
Dir IT: Susan Quilles
IT Man: Gary Dunagan

D-U-N-S 07-366-4914
WARREN ST LUKES HOSPITAL INC
WARREN HOSPITAL
(*Suby of* ST LUKES HOSP & HLTH NETWRK) ★
185 Roseberry St, Phillipsburg, NJ 08865-1690
Tel (908) 859-6700 *Founded/Ownrshp* 1921
Sales 110.8MM *EMP* 830
SIC 8062 8093 General medical & surgical hospitals; Rehabilitation center, outpatient treatment
CEO: Thomas Lict
**Pr:* Scott R Wolfe
Trst: Carl Alberto
**VP:* Carl M Alberto
**VP:* Edward A Gilkey
**VP:* Gail Newton
**VP:* Mark Sblendorio
Dir Rad: Angela Collins
Dir Sec: William Eppell
Dir QC: Virginia Domzalski
Site Mgr: Acieta Small

D-U-N-S 14-046-3907 IMP/EXP
WARREN STEEL HOLDINGS LLC
4000 Mahoning Ave Nw, Warren, OH 44483-1924
Tel (330) 847-0487 *Founded/Ownrshp* 2006
Sales 221.9MM^E *EMP* 290
SIC 3567

D-U-N-S 07-077-5655 EXP
WARREN UNILUBE INC
915 E Jefferson Ave, West Memphis, AR 72301-5537
Tel (870) 735-1514 *Founded/Ownrshp* 2003
Sales 122.1MM^E *EMP* 240
SIC 2992 Lubricating oils
CEO: William I Warren
**Pr:* Dale Wells
**CFO:* Larry Sanderson
**VP:* John Massel
**VP:* James H Rone
Plnt Mgr: Rusty Brown
VP Mktg: Lynda Davis

D-U-N-S 11-264-8845
■ **WARRIOR ENERGY SERVICES CORP**
SUPERIOR ENERGY SERVICES
(*Suby of* SESI LLC) ★
5801 Highway 90 E, Broussard, LA 70518-5914
Tel (662) 329-1047 *Founded/Ownrshp* 2006
Sales 260.5MM^E *EMP* 480
SIC 1389 Oil & gas wells: building, repairing & dismantling; Well plugging & abandoning, oil & gas; Perforating well casings; Well logging
Ch: Terry Hall
Pr: Bill Jenkins
CEO: David Dunlap
CFO: Ron E Whitter
Ex VP: Robert J McNally
Ex VP: Robert Taylor

D-U-N-S 11-351-6553
WARTBURG COLLEGE
100 Wartburg Blvd, Waverly, IA 50677-2200
Tel (319) 352-8200 *Founded/Ownrshp* 1931
Sales 94.3MM *EMP* 352
Accts Baker Tilly Virchow Krause Llp
SIC 8221 College, except junior
Ch Bd: Michael McCoy
**Pr:* Darrel Coleson
VP: Loers Deborah
**VP:* Gery Grace
VP: Ferol S Menzel
VP: Leisinger Scott
**VP:* Richard Seggerman
VP: Edith Waldstein
Exec: Penni Pier
Off Admin: Patricia Melver
VP Mktg: Graham Garner

WARTSILA G.A.
See WARTSILA NORTH AMERICA INC

D-U-N-S 14-449-0612 IMP
WARTSILA HOLDING INC
(*Suby of* WARTSILA TECHNOLOGY OY AB)
11710 N Gessner Rd Ste A, Houston, TX 77064-1325
Tel (281) 233-6200 *Founded/Ownrshp* 1997
Sales 249.6MM^E *EMP* 700
SIC 5084 1629 Engines & parts, diesel; Power plant construction
Pr: Aaron Bresnahan
**Sec:* Lea Kellogg
VP: Ralph Lindback
Snr Mgr: Maarit Lautemaki
Board of Directors: Marco Wiren

D-U-N-S 02-102-3643 IMP/EXP
WARTSILA NORTH AMERICA INC
WARTSILA G.A.
(*Suby of* WARTSILA HOLDING INC) ★
11710 N Gessner Rd Ste A, Houston, TX 77064-1325
Tel (281) 233-6200 *Founded/Ownrshp* 1990
Sales 235.5MM^E *EMP* 400
SIC 1629 5084 1382 4789 3731 Power plant construction; Engines & parts, diesel; Aerial geophysical exploration oil & gas; Cargo loading & unloading services; Offshore supply boats, building & repairing
Pr: Aaron Bresnahan
**Treas:* Lea Kellogg
**Prin:* Pierpaolo Barbone
**Prin:* Javier Cavada
**Prin:* Stephan Kuhn
**Prin:* Rakesh Sarin
Mng Dir: Joe Thomas

D-U-N-S 19-345-4022
WARWICK PUBLIC SCHOOLS
34 Warwick Lake Ave, Warwick, RI 02889-2224
Tel (401) 734-3000 *Founded/Ownrshp* 1829
Sales 87.3MM^E *EMP* 2,400
SIC 8211 Public elementary & secondary schools; Public elementary school; Public junior high school; Public senior high school
Ex Dir: Claire Flaherty
IT Man: Bob Callahan
Schl Brd P: Jennifer Ahearn
Teacher Pr: Katherine Duncanson
Teacher Pr: Rosemary Healey
Psych: Paula Decollibus

D-U-N-S 04-949-3828
WASCO INC
CUMBERLAND STONE
1122 2nd Ave N B, Nashville, TN 37208-1702
Tel (615) 244-9090 *Founded/Ownrshp* 1966
Sales 91.1MM^E *EMP* 400
Accts Crowe Horwath Llp Brentwood
SIC 1741 Masonry & other stonework
CEO: Andy Sneed
**COO:* W A Sneed Jr
CFO: Ken Moore
**CFO:* William Tune
Treas: William L Tune III
Sr VP: Malcolm Patton
VP: John Golden
VP: Mike Kincaid
VP: Jason Kinnard
**Prin:* Brad S Procter
Snr PM: Harry Smith

D-U-N-S 96-251-3123
WASH DEPOT AUTO CENTERS LP
SPLASH AUTOWASH
(*Suby of* SPARKLING IMAGE) ★
435 Eastern Ave, Malden, MA 02148-5706
Tel (781) 324-2000 *Founded/Ownrshp* 2002
Sales 32.0MM^E *EMP* 1,000
SIC 7542 5541 5947 Carwashes; Filling stations, gasoline; Gifts & novelties
Pr: Gregory S Anderson
Genl Mgr: Lenny Taterio
Mktg Dir: Joseph Solis
Mktg Mgr: William Chiccarelli

D-U-N-S 17-614-7809
WASH DEPOT HOLDINGS INC
SPARKLING IMAGE
14 Summer St Ste 302, Malden, MA 02148-3994
Tel (781) 324-2000 *Founded/Ownrshp* 2000
Sales 98.3MM^E *EMP* 1,400
SIC 7542 5541 Carwashes; Gasoline service stations
Pr: Gregory S Anderson
**CFO:* Harry Andersen
CFO: Harry Andersen
MIS Dir: Bill Chadwick
Dir IT: Charbel Elkhoury
Mktg Dir: Dan Amirault

D-U-N-S 04-114-1433
WASHBURN UNIVERSITY OF TOPEKA
1700 Sw College Ave, Topeka, KS 66621-1101
Tel (785) 670-1010 *Founded/Ownrshp* 1865
Sales 39.1MM *EMP* 1,000
Accts Rubin Brown Llp Overland Park
SIC 8221 University
Pr: Jerry B Farley
**VP:* Rick Anderson

D-U-N-S 36-409-1439 EXP
WASHING SYSTEMS LLC
167 Commerce Dr, Loveland, OH 45140-7727
Tel (800) 272-1974 *Founded/Ownrshp* 1989
Sales 90.0MM *EMP* 110
SIC 5169 2841 Detergents; Industrial chemicals; Soap & other detergents
Div Mgr: Dean Lewis

D-U-N-S 07-496-4016
WASHINGTON & JEFFERSON COLLEGE
60 S Lincoln St, Washington, PA 15301-4812
Tel (724) 222-4400 *Founded/Ownrshp* 1781
Sales 93.7MM *EMP* 300^E
Accts Schneider Downs & Co Inc Pitt
SIC 8221 College, except junior
Pr: Tori H Smith
**CFO:* Dennis McMaster
**VP:* Alton Newell
Assoc Dir: Michael Timko
Comm Man: W Robert
Web Dev: Gigi Wiltanger
Mktg Dir: Robert Reid

D-U-N-S 04-128-3243
WASHINGTON AND LEE UNIVERSITY
204 W Washington St, Lexington, VA 24450-2554
Tel (540) 458-8400 *Founded/Ownrshp* 1749
Sales 193.9MM *EMP* 700
Accts Kpmg Llp Lexington Va
SIC 8221 University
Pr: Kenneth P Ruscio
**Treas:* Steven G McAllister
Trst: Thomas McJunkin
Trst: Michael Monier
Trst: Glenn Thornhill
Ofcr: Waller T Dudley
Comm Dir: Peter Jetton
Ex Dir: Amy D Barnes
Ex Dir: Brian Eckert
Ex Dir: Jeffery G Hanna
CTO: Richard Peterson

D-U-N-S 02-368-4678
WASHINGTON BANKING CO
450 Sw Bayshore Dr, Oak Harbor, WA 98277-3102
Tel (360) 679-3121 *Founded/Ownrshp* 1996
Sales NA *EMP* 464
SIC 6022

D-U-N-S 09-781-7860 EXP
WASHINGTON BEEF LLC
(*Suby of* AB FOODS LLC) ★
201 Elmwood Rd, Toppenish, WA 98948-9779
Tel (509) 865-2121 *Founded/Ownrshp* 2003
Sales 119.9MM^E *EMP* 670
SIC 2011 Beef products from beef slaughtered on site

WASHINGTON CC DISTRICT 6
See SEATTLE COLLEGES

D-U-N-S 07-427-2134
■ **WASHINGTON CLOSURE CO LLC**
(*Suby of* AECOM ENERGY & CONSTRUCTION INC) ★
720 E Park Blvd Bsmt, Boise, ID 83712-7758
Tel (208) 386-5000 *Founded/Ownrshp* 2002
Sales 27.7MM^E *EMP* 1,050
SIC 4959 1799 1795 4226 Environmental cleanup services; Decontamination services; Wrecking & demolition work; Special warehousing & storage
Prin: Linda Guinn

D-U-N-S 02-256-4314
WASHINGTON COLLEGE
300 Washington Ave, Chestertown, MD 21620-1197
Tel (410) 778-2800 *Founded/Ownrshp* 1959
Sales 110.1MM *EMP* 550^E
Accts Grant Thornton Llp Philadelph
SIC 8221 College, except junior
Pr: Jack S Jay Griswold
Bd of Dir: Jason Bryden
Assoc VP: Sarah Feyerherm
Sr VP: Rebekah Hardy
**VP:* James Manaro
Assoc Dir: Vicky Sawyer
**Prin:* Emily Chamlee-Wright
Prgrm Mgr: Michael Buckley
MIS Dir: Adrian Peterson
Mtls Mgr: Gail Schmidt

WASHINGTON COMPANIES, THE
See WASHINGTON CORPS

D-U-N-S 00-647-3953 IMP/EXP
WASHINGTON CORPS (MT)
WASHINGTON COMPANIES, THE
101 International Dr, Missoula, MT 59808-1549
Tel (406) 523-1300 *Founded/Ownrshp* 1964
Sales 291.8MM *EMP* 1,400^E
SIC 5082 7353 4213 8741 Construction & mining machinery; Heavy construction equipment rental; Trucking, except local; Management services
Pr: Larry Simkins
**COO:* Paul Keiper
**Ex VP:* Karl Swanson
Ex VP: Karl M Swanson
**VP:* John Thee
CIO: Chris Warden
CTO: Larry Ashwell
IT Man: Brian Casman
Software D: Terri Cheff
Software D: Tim Wolsky
Board of Directors: Terry Payne

WASHINGTON COUNTY
See COUNTY OF WASHINGTON

D-U-N-S 07-749-3625
WASHINGTON COUNTY
100 W Beau St Ste 403, Washington, PA 15301-4432
Tel (724) 228-6700 *Founded/Ownrshp* 1781
Sales NA *EMP* 1,100
Accts Maher Duessel Pittsburgh Pen
SIC 9111 County supervisors' & executives' offices;
**Prin:* Harlan G Shober Jr
Genl Mgr: Roger Metcalfe
Dir IT: Steve Tkach

D-U-N-S 07-495-0007
WASHINGTON COUNTY BOARD OF EDUCATION
10435 Downsville Pike, Hagerstown, MD 21740-1732
Tel (301) 766-2800 Founded/Ownrshp 1857
Sales 310.1MM EMP 138E
Accts Smith Elliott Kearns & Company
SIC 8211 School board
Pr: Donna Brightman
*VP: Justin Hartings

D-U-N-S 94-453-1714
WASHINGTON COUNTY BOARD OF EDUCATION
405 W College St, Jonesborough, TN 37659-1009
Tel (423) 753-1100 Founded/Ownrshp 1873
Sales 57.6MM EMP 1,200
SIC 8211 School board
Ch Bd: Todd Ganger

D-U-N-S 60-343-0869
WASHINGTON COUNTY ENDOWMENT FUND (INC)
FINANCIAL OFFICE
251 E Antietam St, Hagerstown, MD 21740-5724
Tel (301) 790-8102 Founded/Ownrshp 1991
Sales 323.5MM EMP 4
SIC 8741 Financial management for business
*Ch: Bradford Downey
*Sec: Steven Barnhart
HC Dir: Frank Dirstilhorst

D-U-N-S 07-962-8932
WASHINGTON COUNTY PUBLIC SCHOOLS
WCPS
10435 Downsville Pike, Hagerstown, MD 21740-1732
Tel (301) 766-2800 Founded/Ownrshp 2014
Sales 308.3MM EMP 2,630E
SIC 8211 Public elementary & secondary schools
Ofcr: Heather Aleshire
Dir Sec: Steve Ganley
Dir Sec: Steve Tanley
Pr Dir: Richard Wright
Psych: Jennifer Bassett
HC Dir: Janice Howells

WASHINGTON COUNTY SCHL DST 23J
See TIGARD-TUALATIN SCHOOL DISTRICT

D-U-N-S 79-922-0405
WASHINGTON COUNTY SCHOOL DISTRICT
121 W Tabernacle St, St George, UT 84770-3338
Tel (435) 673-3553 Founded/Ownrshp 1915
Sales 726.5M EMP 2,700
Accts Savage Esplin & Radmall Pc Sa
SIC 8211
Pr: Curtis Jensen
Bd of Dir: Laura Belnap
*VP: Cal Durfey
*VP: Wes Jensen
Dir IT: Scott Nowling
Psych: Marsha Bowler
Psych: Kate Cirillo
Psych: Staci Glazier
Psych: Stephanie Ibarra
Psych: Danielle Johnson
Psych: Anne Lemmon

D-U-N-S 79-065-8269
■ WASHINGTON DMILITARIZATION LLC
(Suby of AECOM ENERGY & CONSTRUCTION INC) ★
720 E Park Blvd, Boise, ID 83712-7758
Tel (208) 386-5000 Founded/Ownrshp 1992
Sales 36.1MME EMP 1,692
SIC 8711 Engineering services

D-U-N-S 00-290-2088
WASHINGTON ELEMENTARY SCHOOL DISTRICT 6
4650 W Sweetwater Ave, Glendale, AZ 85304-1505
Tel (602) 347-2600 Founded/Ownrshp 1891
Sales 206.8MM EMP 3,014
Accts Heinfeld Meech & Co Pc P
SIC 8211 Public elementary & secondary schools
Genl Mgr: Paul Stanton
Ofcr: Chris Wing
Off Mgr: Tina Cabral
Off Mgr: Ima Dolan
Dir IT: Frank Fraetto
IT Man: Rene Rojas
Pr Dir: Jill Hicks
HC Dir: Benita Loy

D-U-N-S 86-106-5985 EXP
WASHINGTON ENERGY SERVICES CO
BOB'S HEATING & AIR
3909 196th St Sw, Lynnwood, WA 98036-5732
Tel (800) 398-4663 Founded/Ownrshp 2001
Sales 94.6MME EMP 300
SIC 5074 1711 8711 Plumbing & hydronic heating supplies; Heating & air conditioning contractors; Heating & ventilation engineering
Prin: Craig E Olson
VP: Jonathan Dwight
Exec: Leslie Engburge
*Prin: Vern A Olson
Genl Mgr: Jeff Holgate
VP Sls: David Harrison

D-U-N-S 88-490-3857
▲ WASHINGTON FEDERAL INC
425 Pike St Ste 100, Seattle, WA 98101-4062
Tel (206) 624-7930 Founded/Ownrshp 1994
Sales NA EMP 1,838E
Accts Deloitte & Touche Llp Seattle
Tkr Sym WAFD Exch NGS
SIC 6021 National commercial banks
Ch Bd: Roy M Whitehead
Pr: Larry Berg
Pr: Michael Brown
CFO: Vincent L Beatty
Chf Cred: Mark A Schoonover
Ofcr: Brent J Beardall
Ofcr: Linda S Brower
Ofcr: Stacy Hart
Ofcr: Shannon Lee
Ex VP: Cathy Cooper
Ex VP: Jack Jacobson
Ex VP: Angela D Veksler
Sr VP: John Pirtle
VP: Jeff Birkelo
VP: James Goldsmith
VP: Ann Hall
VP: Dave Hasslinger
VP: John Iasonides
VP: Chad Leonard
VP: Jon Little
VP: Lorelei Molitor
Board of Directors: David K Grant, Anna C Johnson, Thomas J Kelley, Erin Lantz, Barbara L Smith, Mark N Tabbutt, Randall H Talbot

D-U-N-S 07-663-3460
■ WASHINGTON FEDERAL NATIONAL ASSOCIATION
(Suby of WASHINGTON FEDERAL INC) ★
425 Pike St, Seattle, WA 98101-3902
Tel (206) 624-7930 Founded/Ownrshp 1917
Sales NA EMP 1,215
SIC 6035 Federal savings & loan associations
Pr: Roy M Whitehead
*CFO: Brent J Beardall
*Ex VP: Linda S Brower
*Ex VP: Ed Hedlund
*Ex VP: Jack Jacobson
Sr VP: Lisa King
VP: Gary Haines
VP: Gerri Seaton
IT Man: Jess Skillings
Netwrk Mgr: John Schliep

D-U-N-S 00-684-4781 IMP/EXP
WASHINGTON FRUIT & PRODUCE CO (WA)
1111 River Rd, Yakima, WA 98902-1304
Tel (509) 457-6177 Founded/Ownrshp 1910, 1955
Sales 106.8MME EMP 200E
SIC 5148 0723 Fruits, fresh; Vegetables, fresh; Crop preparation services for market
Pr: Roderick C Plath
*Treas: Thomas Hamse Jr
Treas: Tommy Hansen
*VP: Daniel Plath
Sls Mgr: Chris Falk

D-U-N-S 13-754-0501
WASHINGTON GAMING INC
711 Powell Ave Sw, Renton, WA 98057-2912
Tel (425) 264-1050 Founded/Ownrshp 2001
Sales 13.5MME EMP 1,350
SIC 7999 Gambling establishment
Pr: Cory Coyle

D-U-N-S 96-546-7223
■ WASHINGTON GAS LIGHT CO
(Suby of WGL HOLDINGS INC) ★
101 Constitution Ave Nw 200w, Washington, DC 20001-2158
Tel (703) 288-3614 Founded/Ownrshp 2010
Sales 5.5MME EMP 1,410
SIC 7519 Utility trailer rental
Pr: Arden Phillips
*VP: George Mank

D-U-N-S 00-692-0607
■ WASHINGTON GAS LIGHT CO INC (DC)
(Suby of WGL HOLDINGS INC) ★
101 Constitution Ave Nw 200w, Washington, DC 20001-2158
Tel (703) 750-4440 Founded/Ownrshp 1848
Sales 1.0MMM EMP 1,529E
SIC 4924 Natural gas distribution
Ch Bd: Terry D McCallister
Pr: Adrian P Chapman
CFO: Vincent L Ammann Jr
Treas: Anthony M Nee
Bd of Dir: Janet Mallory
Ofcr: Louis J Hutchinson III
Sr VP: Gautam Chandra
Sr VP: Luanne S Gutermuth
Sr VP: Douglas A Staebler
Sr VP: Leslie T Thornton
VP: William R Ford
VP: Marcellous P Frye Jr
VP: Mark A Lowe
VP: Richard H Moore
VP: Roberta W Sims
VP: Tracy L Townsend
Board of Directors: Michael D Barnes, Stephen C Beasley, George P Clancy Jr, James W Dyke Jr, Nancy C Floyd, Linda R Gooden, James F Lafond, Debra L Lee, Dale S Rosenthal

D-U-N-S 11-248-8106 IMP
■ WASHINGTON GOVERNMENT ENVIRONMENTAL SERVICES CO LLC
URS
(Suby of AECOM ENERGY & CONSTRUCTION INC) ★
106 Newberry St Sw, Aiken, SC 29801-3852
Tel (803) 502-5710 Founded/Ownrshp 1999
Sales 311.6MME EMP 486
SIC 1622 Bridge construction
Pr: David Pethick
Sr VP: John Hayfield

D-U-N-S 04-847-5920
■ WASHINGTON GROUP INTERNATIONAL INC
(Suby of AECOM ENERGY & CONSTRUCTION INC) ★
1 Morrison Knudsen Plz, Boise, ID 83729-0001
Tel (208) 386-5000 Founded/Ownrshp 1996
Sales 26.2MME EMP 1,000E
SIC 7359 Equipment rental & leasing
Pr: Darrol Norman Groven
*Treas: Lisa Ross
*VP: Douglas L Brigham

D-U-N-S 19-332-0751
WASHINGTON GROUP INTERNATIONAL INC
720 E Park Blvd, Boise, ID 83712-7758
Tel (208) 386-5000 Founded/Ownrshp 1993
Sales NA EMP 1,500
SIC 1611 1629 1221 1081 4959 1475

D-U-N-S 60-438-0337
WASHINGTON HEALTH CARE SERVICES INC
WASHINGTON HOSPITAL
155 Wilson Ave, Washington, PA 15301-3336
Tel (724) 225-7000 Founded/Ownrshp 1985
Sales NA EMP 1,900E
Accts Ernst & Young Us Llp Pittsbur
SIC 6324 Hospital & medical service plans
Pr: Gary Weinsten
*Pr: Telford Thomas
Mktg Mgr: Jamie Ivanac
Sls Mgr: Patty Zink

D-U-N-S 11-907-3443
WASHINGTON HEALTHCARE MARY
2300 Fall Hill Ave # 314, Fredericksburg, VA 22401-3343
Tel (540) 741-2507 Founded/Ownrshp 1983
Sales 75.4MM EMP 4,000
SIC 8741 Hospital management
Pr: Michael P McDermott
Mng Pt: Mark A Butterworth
*CFO: Sean T Barden
CFO: Sean Barden
Treas: Donald H Newlin
Ofcr: Barbara A Kane
*Ex VP: Xavier R Richardson
Ex VP: Tom Ryan
*Ex VP: Kathryn Wall
Ex VP: Kathy Wall
Sr VP: Kevin Van Renan
VP: Eileen Dohmann
VP: Ravi Mathur
VP: Kevin Renan

D-U-N-S 96-790-7598
WASHINGTON HEALTHCARE PHYSICIANS MARY
MARY WASHINGTON HEALTHCARE
(Suby of WASHINGTON HEALTHCARE MARY) ★
2300 Fall Hill Ave # 314, Fredericksburg, VA 22401-3343
Tel (540) 741-1100 Founded/Ownrshp 2010
Sales 584.3MM EMP 91E
SIC 8099 Medical services organization
CEO: Fred M Ryan
*COO: Walter J Kiwall
*CFO: Sean T Barden
Sr VP: Marianna Bedway
Software D: Shawn Sillman

WASHINGTON HOLDINGS
See WASHINGTON REAL ESTATE HOLDINGS LLC

WASHINGTON HOMES
See CITADEL LAND INC

WASHINGTON HOSP SCHL NURSING
See WASHINGTON HOSPITAL

WASHINGTON HOSPITAL
See WASHINGTON HEALTH CARE SERVICES INC

D-U-N-S 07-216-6887
WASHINGTON HOSPITAL
WASHINGTON HOSP SCHL NURSING
155 Wilson Ave, Washington, PA 15301-3398
Tel (724) 225-7000 Founded/Ownrshp 1985
Sales 234.5MM EMP 1,900
SIC 8062 Hospital, medical school affiliated with nursing & residency
CEO: Gary Weinstein
Trst: Dennis Brown
Ofcr: Colleen Allison
Ofcr: Catherine Fischer
VP: Rodney D Louk
VP: Rodney Louke
VP: Ralph Tijerina
Exec: Michael Roney
Dir Rad: Richard Frank
Nurse Mgr: Dorothy Zupancic
CIO: Paul Cullen

D-U-N-S 13-229-6039
WASHINGTON HOSPITAL CENTER CORP
MEDSTAR WASHINGTON HOSP CTR
(Suby of MEDSTAR HEALTH VNA) ★
110 Irving St Nw, Washington, DC 20010-3017
Tel (202) 877-7000 Founded/Ownrshp 1981
Sales 1.1MMM EMP 5,637
SIC 8741 8082 8051 8062 Hospital management; Home health care services; Skilled nursing care facilities; General medical & surgical hospitals
CEO: Harrison J Rider III
COO: Dennis Pullin
CFO: Dan A Macksood
Bd of Dir: Barbara B Allbritton
Bd of Dir: Guy Weigold
Bd of Dir: Margot D Wilson
VP: Colleen Allison
VP: Gregory J Argyros
VP: Robert Di Vito
VP: Frederick Finelli
VP: Karen Jerome
VP: Paul Shapin
VP: Anthony Watkins

D-U-N-S 07-395-6054
WASHINGTON HOSPITAL HEALTHCARE SYSTEM
2000 Mowry Ave, Fremont, CA 94538-1716
Tel (510) 797-3342 Founded/Ownrshp 1948
Sales 205.1MME EMP 1,600
Accts Pricewaterhousecoopers Llp Sa
SIC 8062 General medical & surgical hospitals
CEO: Nancy Farber
CFO: Chris Henry
*Treas: Cathy Messman
Bd of Dir: Macaria C Meyer
Dir Risk M: Kristin K Ferguson
Chf Nrs Of: Stephanie Williams
Nurse Mgr: Sam Avila
Snr Ntwrk: Glenn Abuelhaj
CIO: Lee Herrmann
CIO: Robert Thorwald
CTO: Tasso Argyros

D-U-N-S 06-541-2223
WASHINGTON HOSPITAL INC MARY
DIABETES MGT PRGRAM SPTSYLVNIA
(Suby of WASHINGTON HEALTHCARE MARY) ★
1001 Sam Perry Blvd, Fredericksburg, VA 22401-4453
Tel (540) 741-1100 Founded/Ownrshp 1903
Sales 217.5MME EMP 1,500
SIC 8062 8069 General medical & surgical hospitals; Cancer hospital
Pr: Fred Rankin
*Ex VP: Lester W Abernathy
*VP: White Alda
Dir Lab: Cindy Huffman
Ex Dir: John Burrow
Genl Mgr: Chris King
Off Mgr: Kellie Martino
Sfty Mgr: Andy Holden
Pathlgst: Paul F Hine
HC Dir: Evelyn Bickley

WASHINGTON INVENTORY SERVICE
See WIS

D-U-N-S 04-885-5423
WASHINGTON METROPOLITAN AREA TRANSIT AUTHORITY
WMATA
600 5th St Nw, Washington, DC 20001-2610
Tel (202) 962-1000 Founded/Ownrshp 2013
Sales 734.1MME EMP 11,790
Accts Clifton Gunderson Llp Calvert
SIC 4111 Cable cars, except aerial, amusement & scenic
Genl Mgr: Jack Requa
V Ch: Charles Deegan
*CEO: Paul J Wiedefeld
*CFO: Carol Kissal
*Ofcr: Alexa Dupigny-Samuel
*Ofcr: Delecia Sampson
Prgrm Mgr: Toni Byrd
CIO: Angela Lee
*CIO: Suzanne Peck
IT Man: Azhar Ghori
Sftwr Eng: Thomas Hitaffer
Board of Directors: Mortimer L Downey

D-U-N-S 60-331-7322 IMP/EXP
WASHINGTON MILLS GROUP INC
20 N Main St, North Grafton, MA 01536-1522
Tel (508) 839-6511 Founded/Ownrshp 1988
Sales 170.9MME EMP 600
SIC 3291

D-U-N-S 00-693-3931
■ WASHINGTON NATIONAL INSURANCE CO
(Suby of CNO FINANCIAL GROUP INC) ★
11815 N Pennsylvania St, Carmel, IN 46032-4555
Tel (317) 817-4100 Founded/Ownrshp 1923
Sales NA EMP 517
SIC 6311 6321 Life insurance carriers; Health insurance carriers
CEO: Stephen C Hilbert
*Pr: Barbara Stewart
*Treas: James S Adams
Sls Dir: Terry Monroe
Snr PM: Jason Beheler

WASHINGTON OFFICE
See BUREAU OF LAND MANAGEMENT

D-U-N-S 00-431-8374 IMP/EXP
WASHINGTON PENN PLASTIC CO INC (PA)
(Suby of AUDIA INTERNATIONAL INC) ★
450 Racetrack Rd, Washington, PA 15301-8935
Tel (724) 228-1260 Founded/Ownrshp 1965
Sales 212.1MME EMP 385
SIC 3083 3087 Laminated plastics plate & sheet; Custom compound purchased resins
Pr: Paul Cusolito
*Pr: Martin Devine
COO: Steven Taylor
*Treas: Albert Andy
VP: Earl Throckmorton
Exec: Raymond Blasiak
Exec: Kristi Okleson
Software D: Jason Lewis
Sftwr Eng: James Little
Sfty Dirs: Brandon Schaffer
Plnt Mgr: Joe Spolnik

WASHINGTON POST
See WP CO LLC

WASHINGTON POST
See HARMAN MEDIA LLC

WASHINGTON POTATO COMPANY
See OREGON POTATO CO

D-U-N-S 07-941-7534
▲ WASHINGTON PRIME GROUP INC
180 E Broad St, Columbus, OH 43215-3707
Tel (614) 621-9000 Founded/Ownrshp 2013
Sales 921.6MM EMP 580E
Tkr Sym WPG Exch NYS
SIC 6798 Real estate investment trusts; Realty investment trusts
CEO: Louis G Conforti
*Ch Bd: Robert J Laikin
COO: Butch Knerr
CFO: Mark E Yale
Ex VP: Robert P Demchak
Sr VP: Melissa A Indest

D-U-N-S 12-166-7013
WASHINGTON REAL ESTATE HOLDINGS LLC
WASHINGTON HOLDINGS
600 University St # 2820, Seattle, WA 98101-1176
Tel (206) 613-5300 Founded/Ownrshp 2002
Sales 86.5MME EMP 1,145
SIC 6512 Nonresidential building operators
COO: Ric Anderson
*Ex VP: Mark Barbieri
Ex VP: Brent Lower
VP: Jason Hizer
VP: Tim Holt
Genl Mgr: Casey Holt
Off Admin: Maureen Thacher

D-U-N-S 00-325-7748
▲ WASHINGTON REAL ESTATE INVESTMENT TRUST (MD)
1775 Eye St Nw Ste 1000, Washington, DC 20006-2404
Tel (202) 774-3200 *Founded/Ownrshp* 1960
Sales 288.6MM *EMP* 174[E]
Tkr Sym WRE *Exch* NYS
SIC 6798 Real estate investment trusts
Pr: Paul T McDermott
**Ch Bd:* Charles T Nason
COO: Thomas Q Bakke
CFO: Stephen E Riffee
Board of Directors: Benjamin S Butcher, William G Byrnes, Edward S Civera, Thomas H Nolan Jr, Anthony L Winns

WASHINGTON REGIONAL MED SYS
See WASHINGTON REGIONAL MEDICAL SYSTEM

D-U-N-S 14-472-9373
WASHINGTON REGIONAL MEDICAL CENTER
3215 N Northhills Blvd, Fayetteville, AR 72703-4424
Tel (479) 463-6000 *Founded/Ownrshp* 1988
Sales 245.2MM *EMP* 2,000
SIC 8062 General medical & surgical hospitals
Pr: William L Bradley
Chf Path: Anthony Hui
Chf Rad: Eric Sale
Dir Vol: Jimmie Beauchamp
**Pr:* Mark Bever
**CFO:* Dan Eckels
Sr VP: Bill Rogers
**VP:* Thomas J Olmstead
**VP:* Larry Shackelford
Exec: Steven Singleton
Dir OR: Candy Emanuel
Dir Risk M: Donna Bloyed
Dir Lab: Kathy Miller
Dir Rad: Sissy Peterson
Dir Rx: Ramona McLean

D-U-N-S 79-730-3443
WASHINGTON REGIONAL MEDICAL SYSTEM
WASHINGTON REGIONAL MED SYS
3215 N Northhills Blvd, Fayetteville, AR 72703-4424
Tel (479) 463-1000 *Founded/Ownrshp* 1988
Sales 234.7MM *EMP* 2,100
SIC 8062 8069 General medical & surgical hospitals; Geriatric hospital
Pr: William Bradley
**CFO:* Dan Eckels
**Sr VP:* Tom Olmstead
**Sr VP:* James Shackelford
**VP:* Mark Bevers

D-U-N-S 80-650-0521
■ WASHINGTON RIVER PROTECTION SOLUTIONS LLC
URS
(*Suby of* AECOM ENERGY & CONSTRUCTION INC) ★
2425 Stevens Center Pl, Richland, WA 99354-1874
Tel (509) 376-8103 *Founded/Ownrshp* 2007
Sales 891.3M[E] *EMP* 2,200
SIC 8711 Engineering services
**Pr:* David Olsen

D-U-N-S 36-440-1000 IMP
■ WASHINGTON SAVANNAH RIVER CO LLC
(*Suby of* URS) ★
Savannah River Site Rd 1, Aiken, SC 29808-0001
Tel (803) 725-6211 *Founded/Ownrshp* 1999
Sales 223.5MM[E] *EMP* 406[E]
SIC 4959 Toxic or hazardous waste cleanup
Pr: Leo Sain
**Div Mgr:* Ambrose Schwallie
Dir IT: Jeffrey Krohn
Genl Couns: Victor Franklin

D-U-N-S 13-199-3771 IMP
WASHINGTON SPORTS & ENTERTAINMENT LIMITED PARTNERSHIP
MONUMENTAL SPORTS & ENTRMT
(*Suby of* MONUMENTAL SPORTS & ENTRMT) ★
601 F St Nw, Washington, DC 20004-1605
Tel (202) 661-5000 *Founded/Ownrshp* 2010
Sales 56.0MM[E] *EMP* 1,598[E]
SIC 7941 Stadium event operator services; Professional & semi-professional sports clubs
Sr VP: Kurt Kehl
VP: Rick Moreland
Sls Mgr: David Touhey
Snr Mgr: Jaclyn Benjamin

D-U-N-S 80-888-2385
WASHINGTON STATE DEPARTMENT OF ECOLOGY
(*Suby of* STATE OF WASH OFFICE OF GVRNOR) ★
300 Desmond Dr Se, Olympia, WA 98503-1274
Tel (360) 407-6000 *Founded/Ownrshp* 1970
Sales NA *EMP* 1,600
SIC 9511 Air, water & solid waste management;
Prgrm Mgr: Bill Backous
Prgrm Mgr: Dale Jensen
Prgrm Mgr: Jim Pendowski
Prgrm Mgr: Cullen Stephenson
Prgrm Mgr: Joe Stohr
Prgrm Mgr: Gordon White
Prgrm Mgr: Megan White
Prgrm Mgr: Mike Wilson
IT Man: Sylvester Polzin

D-U-N-S 80-888-2914
WASHINGTON STATE DEPARTMENT OF EMPLOYMENT SECURITY
(*Suby of* STATE OF WASH OFFICE OF GVRNOR) ★
212 Maple Park Ave Se, Olympia, WA 98501-2347
Tel (360) 902-9500 *Founded/Ownrshp* 1937
Sales NA *EMP* 2,500
SIC 9441 Administration of social & manpower programs;
VP: Mike Thomas
Genl Mgr: Trent Howard
Genl Mgr: Joyce Miller
Netwrk Mgr: Dick Noahr

D-U-N-S 05-474-0676
WASHINGTON STATE DEPARTMENT OF ENTERPRISE SERVICES
(*Suby of* STATE OF WASH OFFICE OF GVRNOR) ★
1500 Jefferson St Se, Olympia, WA 98501-2355
Tel (360) 407-2200 *Founded/Ownrshp* 2012
Sales NA *EMP* 1,500
SIC 9111
Ex Dir: Chris Liu
IT Man: Jim Morgan

D-U-N-S 80-888-3052
WASHINGTON STATE DEPARTMENT OF FISH & WILDLIFE
(*Suby of* STATE OF WASH OFFICE OF GVRNOR) ★
600 Capitol Way N, Olympia, WA 98501-1076
Tel (360) 902-2200 *Founded/Ownrshp* 1890
Sales NA *EMP* 1,600
SIC 9512 Wildlife conservation agencies;
Sr Cor Off: Susan Yeager
Ofcr: Jeanette Laws
Genl Mgr: Lee Rolle

D-U-N-S 80-888-3128
WASHINGTON STATE DEPARTMENT OF HEALTH
(*Suby of* STATE OF WASH OFFICE OF GVRNOR) ★
101 Israel Rd Se, Tumwater, WA 98501-5570
Tel (360) 236-4300 *Founded/Ownrshp* 1989
Sales NA *EMP* 1,500
SIC 9431 Administration of public health programs;

D-U-N-S 80-888-3235
WASHINGTON STATE DEPARTMENT OF LABOR AND INDUSTRIES
(*Suby of* STATE OF WASH OFFICE OF GVRNOR) ★
7273 Linderson Way Sw, Tumwater, WA 98501-5414
Tel (360) 902-5743 *Founded/Ownrshp* 1911
Sales NA *EMP* 2,600
SIC 9311 Taxation
IT Man: Bill Harris

D-U-N-S 07-949-9754
WASHINGTON STATE DEPARTMENT OF LICENSING
421 Black Lake Blvd Sw, Olympia, WA 98502-5046
Tel (360) 902-3900 *Founded/Ownrshp* 2014
Sales NA *EMP* 1,300
SIC 9631 Licensing & inspection of utilities, government
CIO: Melissa S Rohwedder

D-U-N-S 08-007-1310
WASHINGTON STATE DEPARTMENT OF LICENSING
1125 Washington St Se, Olympia, WA 98501-2283
Tel (360) 920-3600 *Founded/Ownrshp* 2014
Sales NA *EMP* 1,250[E]
SIC 9111

D-U-N-S 80-888-3375
WASHINGTON STATE DEPARTMENT OF LICENSING
(*Suby of* STATE OF WASH OFFICE OF GVRNOR) ★
1125 Washington St Se, Olympia, WA 98501-2283
Tel (360) 902-3600 *Founded/Ownrshp* 1921
Sales NA *EMP* 1,224
SIC 9651 9621 Regulation, miscellaneous commercial sectors; ; Licensing agencies

D-U-N-S 80-888-3474
WASHINGTON STATE DEPARTMENT OF NATURAL RESOURCES
D N R
(*Suby of* STATE OF WASH OFFICE OF GVRNOR) ★
1111 Washington St Se, Olympia, WA 98501-2283
Tel (360) 902-1000 *Founded/Ownrshp* 1967
Sales NA *EMP* 1,300
SIC 9512 Land conservation agencies;
Ofcr: Steve Sinclair
IT Man: Lonnie Paul

D-U-N-S 80-888-3656
WASHINGTON STATE DEPARTMENT OF REVENUE
(*Suby of* STATE OF WASH OFFICE OF GVRNOR) ★
1025 Union Ave Se Ste 500, Olympia, WA 98501-1539
Tel (360) 570-5900 *Founded/Ownrshp* 1967
Sales NA *EMP* 1,100
SIC 9311 Finance, taxation & monetary policy;

D-U-N-S 80-888-3771
WASHINGTON STATE DEPARTMENT OF SOCIAL AND HEALTH SERVICES
DSHS
(*Suby of* STATE OF WASH OFFICE OF GVRNOR) ★
14th And Jefferson, Olympia, WA 98504-0001
Tel (360) 902-8400 *Founded/Ownrshp* 1970
Sales NA *EMP* 30,816
SIC 9441 Administration of social & manpower programs;
Dir Lab: Robert J Novotney
Off Mgr: Brita Skoog

D-U-N-S 80-888-3995
WASHINGTON STATE DEPARTMENT OF TRANSPORTATION
(*Suby of* STATE OF WASH OFFICE OF GVRNOR) ★
310 Maple Park Ave Se, Olympia, WA 98501-2348
Tel (360) 705-7000 *Founded/Ownrshp* 1977
Sales NA *EMP* 7,100
SIC 9621 Regulation, administration of transportation;
**Prin:* Doug Haight
Prgrm Mgr: Stephens Mike
Admn Mgr: Ed McCallister
IT Man: Ron Westman
IT Man: Jim Wimpee

D-U-N-S 09-287-2043
WASHINGTON STATE EMPLOYEES CREDIT UNION
330 Union Ave Se, Olympia, WA 98501-2062
Tel (360) 943-7911 *Founded/Ownrshp* 1957
Sales NA *EMP* 320
SIC 6062 State credit unions, not federally chartered
Pr: Kevin Foster Keddie
Chf Cred: Mark Allen
Ofcr: Shana Konschuh
**Sr VP:* David Johnson
Sr VP: Ben Morales
VP: Jim Averna
VP: Wilkes Hardin
**VP:* Linda Hollen
VP: David Luchtel
**VP:* George Shipman
VP: Todd Shobert
VP: Lou Stewart

D-U-N-S 87-802-5261 IMP
WASHINGTON STATE LIQUOR CONTROL BOARD
(*Suby of* STATE OF WASH OFFICE OF GVRNOR) ★
3000 Pacific Ave Se, Olympia, WA 98501-8809
Tel (360) 664-1600 *Founded/Ownrshp* 1930
Sales NA *EMP* 1,500
SIC 9651

D-U-N-S 80-888-3854
WASHINGTON STATE PATROL
(*Suby of* STATE OF WASH OFFICE OF GVRNOR) ★
210 11th Ave Sw Rm 116, Olympia, WA 98501-2240
Tel (360) 753-6540 *Founded/Ownrshp* 1921
Sales NA *EMP* 2,100
SIC 9221 State highway patrol;

D-U-N-S 04-148-5301
WASHINGTON STATE UNIVERSITY INC
240 French Adm Bldg, Pullman, WA 99164-0001
Tel (509) 335-2022 *Founded/Ownrshp* 1890
Sales 712.5MM *EMP* 8,000
SIC 8221

D-U-N-S 00-325-8654 IMP/EXP
WASHINGTON SUBURBAN SANITARY COMMISSION (INC) (MD)
W S S C
14501 Sweitzer Ln, Laurel, MD 20707-5901
Tel (301) 206-8000 *Founded/Ownrshp* 1918
Sales 645.6MM *EMP* 2,000
Accts Bca Watson Rice Llp Washingto
SIC 4941 4952 Water supply; Sewerage systems
COO: Michael Crean
V Ch: Adrienne Mandel
**Treas:* Mary J Kirby
**Ofcr:* Wayne Fallin
Top Exec: Craig Thomas
VP: Garry Weiss
Prin: Todd M Curry
Ex Dir: Towanda Livingston
Div Mgr: Nick Delgrosso
Genl Mgr: Shawn D Cooper
**Genl Mgr:* Jerry N Johnson

D-U-N-S 96-479-7950
WASHINGTON TEAMSTERS WELFARE TRUST
2323 Eastlake Ave E, Seattle, WA 98102-3305
Tel (206) 329-4900 *Founded/Ownrshp* 2010
Sales 240.6MM *EMP* 3
Accts Miller Kaplan Arase Llp Seatt
SIC 8631 Labor unions & similar labor organizations
Prin: Dean McInnes

WASHINGTON TIMES NEWSPAPER
See NEWS WORLD COMMUNICATIONS INC

D-U-N-S 07-705-9319
WASHINGTON TOWNSHIP BOARD OF EDUCATION
206 E Holly Ave, Sewell, NJ 08080-2641
Tel (856) 589-6644 *Founded/Ownrshp* 1836
Sales 101.2MM[E] *EMP* 1,600
SIC 8211 School board
Pr: Ginny Murphy

D-U-N-S 03-998-1217
WASHINGTON TOWNSHIP PUBLIC SCHOOL DISTRICT
206 E Holly Ave, Sewell, NJ 08080-2641
Tel (856) 589-6644 *Founded/Ownrshp* 1836
Sales 136.8MM *EMP* 480
SIC 8211 Public elementary & secondary schools
MIS Dir: Joseph Konecki
IT Man: Denise Shaw

D-U-N-S 01-109-4535
WASHINGTON TRACTOR INC
JOHN DEERE AUTHORIZED DEALER
2700 136th Avenue Ct E, Sumner, WA 98390-9228
Tel (253) 863-4436 *Founded/Ownrshp* 2010
Sales 134.7MM[E] *EMP* 582[E]
SIC 3523 5083 5261 7699 7353 Farm machinery & equipment; Farm & garden machinery; Lawnmowers & tractors; Farm machinery repair; Heavy construction equipment rental
Pr: James Hale
**CFO:* Brian Tornow

D-U-N-S 01-977-1468
▲ WASHINGTON TRUST BANCORP INC
23 Broad St Fl 1, Westerly, RI 02891-1868
Tel (401) 348-1200 *Founded/Ownrshp* 1984
Sales NA *EMP* 570[E]
Accts Kpmg Llp Providence Rhode Is
Tkr Sym WASH *Exch* NGS
SIC 6022 State commercial banks
CEO: Joseph J Marcaurele
V Ch: David V Devault
Pr: Edward O Handy III
Pr: John Mohan
Treas: Mark K W Gim
Ofcr: James Hagerty
Ex VP: Kristen L Disanto
VP: Sandra Andrews
VP: Laurel L Bowerman
VP: Kelly Cummings
VP: Al Grant
VP: Bethany Lyons
VP: Peter Miniati
VP: Michael Rauh
VP: L P Sheehan
VP: Linda S Smith
Board of Directors: John F Treanor, John J Bowen, Steven J Crandall, Robert A Dimuccio, Barry G Hittner, Katherine W Hoxsie, Kathleen E McKeough, Victor J Orsinger II, H Douglas Randall III, Edwin J Santos

WASHINGTON TRUST BANK
See WTB FINANCIAL CORP

D-U-N-S 00-794-3756
WASHINGTON TRUST BANK (WA)
(*Suby of* WASHINGTON TRUST BANK) ★
717 W Sprague Ave Fl 7, Spokane, WA 99201-3922
Tel (509) 353-4204 *Founded/Ownrshp* 1902, 1986
Sales NA *EMP* 652
SIC 6022 State commercial banks
CEO: Peter F Stanton
**Pr:* John Heath III
**Treas:* Lawrence V Sorensen
Bd of Dir: Kerri Schoolcraft
Ofcr: Dawn Keeney
Trst Ofcr: Tim Donnelly
**Sr VP:* Albert Buss
Sr VP: Jay Lewis
VP: Diane D Albrethsen
VP: Westfall Alex
VP: Wayne Allert
VP: Nancy L Beauvais
VP: Kelly Bennett
VP: Micheal Brown
VP: Keith Erhart
VP: Beverly Gleason
VP: Kenneth Hill
VP: Kimberly Kasey
VP: Chad Legate
VP: Stuart Linscott
VP: Rod Macrae
Board of Directors: Christopher Ackerley, Dennis Murphy, Jeff Wright

WASHINGTON TRUST COMPANY, THE
See WASHINGTON TRUST CO OF WESTERLY

D-U-N-S 15-361-1710
■ WASHINGTON TRUST CO OF WESTERLY
WASHINGTON TRUST COMPANY, THE
(*Suby of* WASHINGTON TRUST BANCORP INC) ★
23 Broad St Fl 1, Westerly, RI 02891-1868
Tel (401) 348-1200 *Founded/Ownrshp* 1984
Sales NA *EMP* 465
SIC 6022 State trust companies accepting deposits, commercial
CEO: Joseph J Marcaurele
**Pr:* Edward O Handy III
**Pr:* John F Treanor
**CFO:* David V Devault
Chf Cred: James M Vesey
Ofcr: Dennis L Algiere
**Ex VP:* Galan G Daukas
**Ex VP:* Kristen L Disanto
**Ex VP:* Mark K W Gim
Ex VP: Barbara J Perino
Ex VP: B Michael Rauh Jr
**Sr VP:* Stephen M Bessette
Sr VP: Vernon F Bliven
Sr VP: Elizabeth B Eckel
Sr VP: William D Gibson
**Sr VP:* Rick Tjader
VP: Paul A Ceresa
Exec: Chris Sheehan
Board of Directors: H Douglas Randall III, Gary P Bennett, Neil H Thorp, Steven J Crandall, John F Treanor, Larry J Hirsch, John C Warren, Barry G Hittner, Katherine W Hoxsie, Mary E Kennard, Edward M Mazze Phd, Kathleen E McKeough, Victor J Orsinger II

D-U-N-S 06-855-2207
WASHINGTON UNIVERSITY
1 Brookings Dr, Saint Louis, MO 63130-4899
Tel (314) 935-8566 *Founded/Ownrshp* 1853
Sales 2.8MMM *EMP* 9,600
Accts Pricewaterhousecoopers Llp L
SIC 8221 University
Treas: Amy Kweskin
Trst: George W Couch
Trst: David V Habif
Trst: James H Hance
Trst: Louis G Hutt
Trst: Walter L Metcalfe
Dir Lab: Marcia Mannen
Assoc Dir: Robert Browning
Assoc Dir: Karen Heise
Assoc Dir: Konnie Henning
Ex Dir: Roger Phillips

D-U-N-S 02-137-5951
WASHINGTON WESTFIELD SCHOOLS
1143 E 181st St, Westfield, IN 46074-8926
Tel (317) 867-8000 *Founded/Ownrshp* 1964
Sales 110.8MM *EMP* 550
SIC 8211 Public elementary school; Public junior high school; Public senior high school
**Treas:* Marsha L Bohannon
Dir Rx: Nick Verhoff
Teacher Pr: Chris Baldwin

D-U-N-S 80-843-3580
■ WASHINGTONFIRST MORTGAGE CORP
(*Suby of* WASHINGTONFIRST BANKSHARES, INC.)
12700 Fair Lakes Cir, Fairfax, VA 22033-4905
Tel (703) 564-9100 *Founded/Ownrshp* 2015
Sales NA *EMP* 8
SIC 6162 Mortgage brokers, using own money
Ch Bd: Jacques Rebibo
**CEO:* Michael Rebibo
**COO:* Banks Gatchel
**Sec:* Jonathan Holtaway
Ex VP: Patrick Gardner
Opers Mgr: Barbara Evans

D-U-N-S 10-004-9469
WASHOE COUNTY SCHOOL DISTRICT
425 E 9th St, Reno, NV 89512-2800
Tel (775) 348-0200 *Founded/Ownrshp* 1950
Sales 402.8MM^E *EMP* 7,000
SIC 8211 Public elementary & secondary schools
Bd of Dir: Nancy Hollinger
Bd of Dir: Anne Loring
Bd of Dir: Barbara Price
Bd of Dir: Jody Ruggiero
Dir Sec: Jason Trevino
CIO: Darren Osgood
Mktg Mgr: Philip Alba
Teacher Pr: Dawn Huckaby
HC Dir: Dana Balchunas
Genl Couns: John Albrecht
Genl Couns: Tiffany Young

D-U-N-S 07-421-3703
WASHTENAW COMMUNITY COLLEGE
4800 E Huron River Dr, Ann Arbor, MI 48105-4800
Tel (734) 973-3300 *Founded/Ownrshp* 1964
Sales 39.3MM *EMP* 1,300
Accts Rehmann Robson Llc Ann Arbor
SIC 8222 8221 Community college; Colleges universities & professional schools
Pr: Larry Whitworth
COO: Rose B Bellanca
Ofcr: Jeffrey Godbey
VP: Linda Blakey
VP: Steven Hardy
VP: Michelle Mueller
**VP:* Roger Palay
Exec: Judy Wojnowski
Ex Dir: Kathleen Stadtfeld
Ex Dir: Brandon R Tucker
Prgrm Mgr: Marjorie Wells

D-U-N-S 08-160-0751
WASHTENAW INTERMEDIATE SCHOOL DISTRICT
HIGH POINT SCHOOL
1819 S Wagner Rd, Ann Arbor, MI 48103-9715
Tel (734) 994-8100 *Founded/Ownrshp* 1850
Sales 102.8MM *EMP* 600
Accts Plante & Moran Pllc Ann Arbo
SIC 8211 Public combined elementary & secondary school
**Prin:* Brian Marcel
**Prin:* Sarena Shivers
Ex Dir: Naomi Norman
Ex Dir: Alan Oman

WASP
See FAST GLOBAL SOLUTIONS INC

D-U-N-S 10-682-3813
WASSERSTEIN & CO LP
U S EQUITY PARTNERS
(*Suby of* WASSERSTEIN HOLDINGS LLC) ★
1185 Avenue Of The Americ, New York, NY 10036-2603
Tel (212) 702-5600 *Founded/Ownrshp* 2001
Sales 356.2MM^E *EMP* 980
SIC 6799 2721 2741 Investors; Periodicals; Miscellaneous publishing
Ch: Ellis B Jones
Pr: George L Majoros Jr
CFO: Robert Mersten
VP: Nitin Singhal
Prin: Anup Bagaria
Mng Dir: Robert A Fogelson

D-U-N-S 07-924-0812
WASSERSTEIN COSMOS CO-INVEST LP
1301 Ave Of The Americas, New York, NY 10019-6022
Tel (212) 702-5600 *Founded/Ownrshp* 2013
Sales 319.6MM^E *EMP* 453^E
SIC 6799 Investors
Pt: Ellis B Jones

D-U-N-S 07-973-0543
WASSERSTEIN HOLDINGS LLC
1301 Avenue Of The Americ, New York, NY 10019-6090
Tel (212) 702-5600 *Founded/Ownrshp* 2000
Sales 356.2MM^E *EMP* 980
SIC 6799 2721 2741 Investors; Periodicals; Miscellaneous publishing
Ch Bd: Ellis B Jones
**Pr:* George L Majoros Jr
**CFO:* Robert Mersten
**Prin:* Anup Bagaria

D-U-N-S 00-428-9872 IMP/EXP
WASSERSTROM CO (OH)
NATIONAL SMALLWARES
477 S Front St, Columbus, OH 43215-5677
Tel (614) 737-8472 *Founded/Ownrshp* 1902
Sales 821.7MM^E *EMP* 1,100
SIC 5087 3566 5021 5046 5112 5719 Restaurant supplies; Speed changers, drives & gears; Office furniture; Commercial cooking & food service equipment; Office supplies; Kitchenware
Pr: Rodney Wasserstrom
**CFO:* Dennis Blank
**Treas:* Alan Wasserstrom
Ex VP: Bob Stone
**Ex VP:* Reid Wasserstrom
VP: Eric Wasserstrom
Exec: Shelly Myers
**Prin:* David A Tumen
Genl Mgr: Dave Lewellen
Genl Mgr: Mark Medonich
VP Opers: Carl Miller

WASSERSTROM MARKETING DIVISION
See N WASSERSTROM & SONS INC

D-U-N-S 07-835-3143
■ **WASTE AWAY GROUP INC**
(*Suby of* WASTE MANAGEMENT HOLDINGS INC) ★
1001 Fannin St Ste 4000, Houston, TX 77002-6711
Tel (713) 512-6200 *Founded/Ownrshp* 2012
Sales 132.1MM^E *EMP* 699^E
SIC 4953 Refuse systems
Pr: Timothy M Wells

D-U-N-S 36-322-5640
WASTE CONNECTIONS OF CALIFORNIA INC
GREENTEAM OF SAN JOSE
1333 Oakland Rd, San Jose, CA 95112-1364
Tel (408) 282-4400 *Founded/Ownrshp* 1976
Sales 106.4MM^E *EMP* 200
SIC 4953 Garbage: collecting, destroying & processing
VP: Paul Nelson
**CEO:* Ron Mittelstaedt
Ex VP: Michael Harlan
**VP:* Pual Nelson
CTO: Beverley Dokken

WASTE CONNECTIONS OF NEBRASKA
See J & J SANITATION INC

D-U-N-S 79-986-9474 IMP
■ **WASTE CONNECTIONS US INC**
(*Suby of* WASTE CONNECTIONS, INC)
1010 Rogers Bridge Rd, Duncan, SC 29334-9749
Tel (832) 801-1436 *Founded/Ownrshp* 2016
Sales 2.1MMM *EMP* 7,227
Tkr Sym WCN *Exch* NYS
SIC 4953 Refuse systems; Non-hazardous waste disposal sites; Recycling, waste materials
Ch Bd: Ronald J Mittelstaedt
Pr: Steven F Bouck
COO: Darrell W Chambliss
CFO: Worthing F Jackman
Sr VP: David G Eddie
Sr VP: David M Hall
Sr VP: James M Little
Sr VP: Patrick J Shea
VP: Eric O Hansen
VP: Scott I Schreiber
Site Mgr: Nancy Mitchell
Board of Directors: Robert H Davis, Edward E Guillet, Michael W Harlan, William J Razzouk

D-U-N-S 92-688-4032
■ **WASTE CONTROL SPECIALISTS LLC**
W C S
(*Suby of* VALHI INC) ★
5430 Lyndon B Johnson Fwy # 1700, Dallas, TX 75240-2601
Tel (888) 789-2783 *Founded/Ownrshp* 1995
Sales 112.9MM^E *EMP* 185
SIC 4953 Hazardous waste collection & disposal
CEO: Bill Lindquist
**Pr:* Rodney A Baltzer
VP Bus Dev: Tim Blythe

D-U-N-S 03-299-9778
WASTE CORP OF AMERICA INC
1330 Post Oak Blvd Fl 30, Houston, TX 77056-3031
Tel (713) 572-3802 *Founded/Ownrshp* 1998
Sales 389.8MM^E *EMP* 510
SIC 4953 Hazardous waste collection & disposal; Refuse collection & disposal services
CEO: William Caesar
**Ch Bd:* Paul Mitchener
**COO:* Christopher Valerian
**Sr VP:* Michael Roy
**VP:* Robert Bartee
**VP:* Nancy Bryant
**VP:* Scott Lukach
**VP:* Antonio Marin
**VP:* Robert Mecchi
**VP:* Joseph Scarano Jr
**VP:* Derrick Standley
Exec: Nancy Ash
Exec: Tina Melton

D-U-N-S 01-641-7185
WASTE INDUSTRIES LLC
(*Suby of* WASTE INDUSTRIES USA INC) ★
3301 Benson Dr Ste 601, Raleigh, NC 27609-7331
Tel (919) 325-3000 *Founded/Ownrshp* 2000
Sales 838.3MM^E *EMP* 1,225
SIC 4953 Refuse collection & disposal services
V Ch: Phil Carter
Dir Bus: Charles Lee Hicks

D-U-N-S 01-635-6896
WASTE INDUSTRIES USA INC
3301 Benson Dr Ste 601, Raleigh, NC 27609-7331
Tel (919) 325-3000 *Founded/Ownrshp* 2008
Sales 1.2MMM^E *EMP* 1,624
SIC 4953 3443 Rubbish collection & disposal; Dumpsters, garbage
Ch Bd: Lonnie C Poole Jr
Pr: Ven Poole
COO: Greg Yorston
CFO: D Stephen Grissom
VP: Jim Auten
VP: Michael Durham
VP: Michael J Durham
VP: Michael Durham
VP: Steve Grissom
VP: Mike Ingle
VP: Lisa D Inman
VP: Lisa Inman

WASTE MANAGEMENT
See MIDJERSEY DISPOSAL INC

WASTE MANAGEMENT
See NORTHEAST RECYCLING CORP

D-U-N-S 04-939-4799
■ **WASTE MANAGEMENT COLLECTION AND RECYCLING INC**
(*Suby of* WM) ★
1800 S Grand Ave, Santa Ana, CA 92705-4800
Tel (714) 637-3010 *Founded/Ownrshp* 1999
Sales 109.4MM^E *EMP* 350
SIC 7353 4953 Heavy construction equipment rental; Refuse collection & disposal services
Prin: Lee Hicks
Dist Mgr: David Ross
Sls Dir: Eric Rasmussen

D-U-N-S 80-987-5925
■ **WASTE MANAGEMENT COLLECTION AND RECYCLING INC**
(*Suby of* WM) ★
2050 N Glassell St, Orange, CA 92865-3306
Tel (714) 282-0200 *Founded/Ownrshp* 1969
Sales 439.2MM^E *EMP* 1,404
SIC 4953 Refuse systems
Pr: James Teter
**VP:* Ray Burke
Dir IT: Bert Young

D-U-N-S 04-757-7416 IMP/EXP
■ **WASTE MANAGEMENT HOLDINGS INC**
(*Suby of* WM) ★
1001 Fannin St Ste 4000, Houston, TX 77002-6711
Tel (713) 512-6200 *Founded/Ownrshp* 1981
Sales 12.9MMM^E *EMP* 41,350
SIC 4953 Dumps, operation of; Garbage: collecting, destroying & processing; Hazardous waste collection & disposal; Liquid waste, collection & disposal
CEO: David P Steiner
Pr: Don Carpenter
**Pr:* Patrick Derueda
**CFO:* Robert G Simpson
CFO: William Trubek
**VP:* Brent Bell
VP: James Connor
**VP:* Matt Coz
**VP:* John Kelly
**VP:* Karl Mockros
Mng Ofcr: William Bill

D-U-N-S 19-467-2085 EXP
▲ **WASTE MANAGEMENT INC**
WM
1001 Fannin St Ste 4000, Houston, TX 77002-6711
Tel (713) 512-6200 *Founded/Ownrshp* 1987
Sales 12.9MMM *EMP* 41,350
Tkr Sym WM *Exch* NYS
SIC 4953 Refuse systems; Garbage: collecting, destroying & processing; Rubbish collection & disposal; Sanitary landfill operation
Pr: James C Fish Jr
**Ch Bd:* W Robert Reum
COO: James E Trevathan Jr
Treas: Josh Allen
Treas: Devina A Rankin
Bd of Dir: Michael Parrent
Sr VP: Jeff M Harris
Sr VP: John J Morris Jr
Sr VP: Mark E Schwartz
VP: Everett A Bass
VP: Calvin Booker
VP: Barry Caldwell
VP: Don P Carpenter
VP: Chris Desantis
VP: Mary Fisher
VP: Robert Kviklys
VP: David Murphy
VP: Larry Patten
VP: Surya Sahoo
VP: Nikolaj H Sjoqvist
VP: Adam Winston
Board of Directors: Frank M Clark Jr, Andres R Gluski, Patrick W Gross, Victoria M Holt, Kathleen M Mazzarella, John C Pope, David P Steiner, Thomas H Weidemeyer

D-U-N-S 06-361-2006 IMP/EXP
■ **WASTE MANAGEMENT INC OF FLORIDA**
(*Suby of* WM) ★
2859 Paces Ferry Rd Se # 1600, Atlanta, GA 30339-6218
Tel (770) 805-4130 *Founded/Ownrshp* 1964
Sales 234.6MM^E *EMP* 750
SIC 4953 Rubbish collection & disposal

D-U-N-S 00-385-7091
■ **WASTE MANAGEMENT INC OF TENNESSEE** (TN)
(*Suby of* WM) ★
1428 Antioch Pike, Antioch, TN 37013-2775
Tel (615) 831-9600 *Founded/Ownrshp* 1977
Sales 156.4MM^E *EMP* 500
SIC 4953 Refuse systems
VP: Tim Wells
Sfty Mgr: David Day
Sfty Mgr: Ray Litwiler
Sls Dir: William Donaldson
Sls Mgr: Clark Schmidt
Snr Mgr: Julie Bullocks

D-U-N-S 00-691-0053
■ **WASTE MANAGEMENT OF ALAMEDA COUNTY INC**
(*Suby of* WM) ★
172 98th Ave, Oakland, CA 94603-1004
Tel (510) 613-8710 *Founded/Ownrshp* 1986
Sales 270.8MM^E *EMP* 850
SIC 4953 Rubbish collection & disposal
CEO: Barry S Skolnick
Treas: Joe Zanardi
**Ex VP:* James C Fish Jr
**Ex VP:* James E Trevathan
VP: Mike Howell
Exec: Greg Sandborn
CIO: Bob Angell
CTO: Angel Salbana
IT Man: Angel Gallardo
Opers Mgr: Andrea Dillard

D-U-N-S 10-392-3504
■ **WASTE MANAGEMENT OF ARIZONA INC**
(*Suby of* WM) ★
1580 E Elwood St, Phoenix, AZ 85040-1331
Tel (480) 457-4700 *Founded/Ownrshp* 1965
Sales 223.0MM^E *EMP* 713
SIC 4212 Garbage collection & transport, no disposal
Ex Dir: Doreen Sekler

WASTE MANAGEMENT OF ATLANTA
See GEORGIA WASTE SYSTEMS INC

D-U-N-S 00-389-8640
■ **WASTE MANAGEMENT OF CALIFORNIA INC**
(*Suby of* WM) ★
9081 Tujunga Ave, Sun Valley, CA 91352-1516
Tel (877) 836-6526 *Founded/Ownrshp* 1953, 2000
Sales 376.3MM^E *EMP* 1,203
SIC 4953 Garbage: collecting, destroying & processing; Recycling, waste materials
Area Mgr: Keith Schrumpf
Dist Mgr: Andy Esser
Dist Mgr: Scott Slighting

D-U-N-S 05-430-8762
■ **WASTE MANAGEMENT OF COLORADO INC**
(*Suby of* WM) ★
5500 S Quebec St Ste 250, Greenwood Village, CO 80111-1925
Tel (303) 797-1600 *Founded/Ownrshp* 1972
Sales 281.5MM^E *EMP* 900
SIC 4953 Refuse collection & disposal services; Recycling, waste materials
Site Mgr: Jerry Velasquez

D-U-N-S 06-247-4598
■ **WASTE MANAGEMENT OF ILLINOIS INC**
(*Suby of* WM) ★
1001 Fannin St Ste 4000, Houston, TX 77002-6711
Tel (713) 512-6200 *Founded/Ownrshp* 1968
Sales 525.2MM^E *EMP* 1,679
SIC 4953 Rubbish collection & disposal; Recycling, waste materials
Pr: Robert Damico

D-U-N-S 07-443-1446 IMP/EXP
■ **WASTE MANAGEMENT OF INDIANA LLC**
(*Suby of* WM) ★
720 E Butterfield Rd Fl 2, Lombard, IL 60148-5689
Tel (630) 572-8800 *Founded/Ownrshp* 1971
Sales 219.9MM^E *EMP* 703
SIC 4953 Liquid waste, collection & disposal
Sr VP: Bob Damico
Pr: Patrick J Derueda
COO: Lawrence O'Donnell
Sr VP: Duane C Woods
VP: Jack Bernardino
VP: Gregg Hassler
VP: Jim Quirk
VP: Larry Rayburn
VP: Dean Vanderbeaan
Dist Mgr: Chris Pulliam
Dir IT: Chris Foss

D-U-N-S 06-834-7632
■ **WASTE MANAGEMENT OF KENTUCKY LLC**
(*Suby of* WM) ★
7501 Grade Ln, Louisville, KY 40219-3407
Tel (502) 969-2355 *Founded/Ownrshp* 1956, 1984
Sales 93.8MM^E *EMP* 300
SIC 4953 Garbage: collecting, destroying & processing
Genl Mgr: Mary Burnett
Sls&Mrk Ex: Ken Brown

D-U-N-S 15-459-4022
■ **WASTE MANAGEMENT OF MARYLAND INC**
(*Suby of* WM) ★
6994 Columbia Gateway Dr # 200, Columbia, MD 21046-2870
Tel (410) 796-7010 *Founded/Ownrshp* 1998
Sales 191.1MM^E *EMP* 600
SIC 4953 4212 Street refuse systems; Local trucking, without storage
Pr: John Drury
**Pr:* Jim Hitt
**Pr:* Charles A Wilcox
**Treas:* Ronald H Jones
**Treas:* Lee A Mc Cormick
**VP:* Bryan J Blankfield
**VP:* Michael J Cordesman
**VP:* Earl E Defrates
**VP:* Jeffrey A Draper
**VP:* Vahe Gabriel
**VP:* Gregory T Sangalis
**VP:* John S Skoutelas
**VP:* Bruce Snyder

D-U-N-S 18-213-8206
■ **WASTE MANAGEMENT OF MASSACHUSETTS INC**
(*Suby of* WM) ★
4 Liberty Ln W, Hampton, NH 03842-1704
Tel (603) 929-3000 *Founded/Ownrshp* 1985
Sales 121.3MM^E *EMP* 388
SIC 4953 8748 Refuse systems; Refuse collection & disposal services; Recycling, waste materials; Environmental consultant
Pr: Dave Lohnes
**Treas:* Cherie C Rice
**VP:* Robert C Biggs
**VP:* Don P Carpenter
**VP:* Greg A Robertson
**VP:* John S Skoutelas
**VP:* Linda J Smith
Snr Mgr: Garrett Trierweiler

D-U-N-S 06-223-5973
■ **WASTE MANAGEMENT OF MICHIGAN INC** (MI)
ACE SANITATION
(*Suby of* WM) ★
48797 Alpha Dr Ste 100, Wixom, MI 48393-3452
Tel (586) 574-2760 *Founded/Ownrshp* 1944
Sales 508.9MM^E *EMP* 1,627
SIC 4953 Rubbish collection & disposal
Pr: Ron Baker
VP Admn: William Carlson
Prgrm Mgr: Sheri Bienduga

D-U-N-S 06-507-3835
■ WASTE MANAGEMENT OF MISSISSIPPI INC
(Suby of WM) ★
1450 Country Club Dr, Jackson, MS 39209-2509
Tel (601) 922-9647 Founded/Ownrshp 1978
Sales 178.4MM[E] EMP 560
SIC 4953 Refuse collection & disposal services
CEO: Maury Myers
VP: David Myhan
Dist Mgr: Jim Funderburg
Snr Mgr: Ginger Kaladas

D-U-N-S 06-438-4522 EXP
■ WASTE MANAGEMENT OF NEW JERSEY INC
(Suby of WM) ★
107 Silvia St, Ewing, NJ 08628-3200
Tel (609) 434-5200 Founded/Ownrshp 1969
Sales 1.2MMM[E] EMP 4,000
SIC 3087 Custom compound purchased resins
Pr: James E Trevathan
*CFO: William Trubeck
*Sr VP: Jim Dancy
Sftwr Eng: Thomas Utermark
Snr Mgr: Ginger Kaladas

D-U-N-S 14-392-0275
■ WASTE MANAGEMENT OF NEW YORK LLC
(Suby of WM) ★
123 Varick Ave, Brooklyn, NY 11237-1216
Tel (718) 533-5100 Founded/Ownrshp 1998
Sales 400.0MM[E] EMP 1,279[E]
SIC 4953 Refuse systems
Exec: Steve Crawford
IT Man: Bob Eliott

D-U-N-S 00-386-8080
■ WASTE MANAGEMENT OF NORTH DAKOTA INC
(Suby of WM) ★
7007 15th St Nw, Bismarck, ND 58503-8344
Tel (701) 223-2295 Founded/Ownrshp 1997
Sales 125.1MM[E] EMP 400
SIC 4953 Refuse collection & disposal services
Sls Mgr: Mary Robinson

D-U-N-S 85-859-2603
■ WASTE MANAGEMENT OF OKLAHOMA INC
(Suby of WASTE MANAGEMENT HOLDINGS INC) ★
1001 Fannin St Ste 3900, Houston, TX 77002-6717
Tel (713) 512-6200 Founded/Ownrshp 1959
Sales 248.1MM[E] EMP 413
SIC 4953 Refuse collection & disposal services
Pr: David R Hopkins
*CFO: Robert Simpson

D-U-N-S 06-343-5598
■ WASTE MANAGEMENT OF OREGON INC
(Suby of WM) ★
5330 Ne Skyport Way, Portland, OR 97218-1244
Tel (503) 249-8078 Founded/Ownrshp 1970, 1984
Sales 156.4MM[E] EMP 500
SIC 4953 Refuse collection & disposal services
COO: James E Trevathan
*CFO: James C Fish Jr
*Sr VP: Barry H Caldwell
*Sr VP: Jeff M Harris
VP: Gregory Sangalis
IT Man: Dorina V Baggen
Sales Exec: David Tonges

D-U-N-S 61-343-2368
■ WASTE MANAGEMENT OF SOUTH CAROLINA INC
(Suby of WM) ★
390 Innovation Way, Wellford, SC 29385-8900
Tel (864) 232-1537 Founded/Ownrshp 1998
Sales 93.8MM[E] EMP 300
SIC 4953 4212 Sanitary landfill operation; Local trucking, without storage
Pr: Ron Peterson
VP: Amy Bohl
Sls Mgr: Norman Chanler

D-U-N-S 85-872-1285 IMP
■ WASTE MANAGEMENT OF TEXAS INC
(Suby of WM) ★
1001 Fannin St Ste 4000, Houston, TX 77002-6711
Tel (713) 512-6200 Founded/Ownrshp 1990
Sales 1.7MMM[E] EMP 5,600
SIC 4953 Refuse systems
CEO: Amury Myers
*CFO: James C Fish Jr
*Sr VP: Barry H Caldwell
Sr VP: Bob Dees
VP: Harry Lamberton
*VP: James E Trevathan
*Prin: Puneet Bhasin
IT Man: Ed Saenz

D-U-N-S 85-871-9883
■ WASTE MANAGEMENT OF WASHINGTON INC
WASTE MGT HEALTHCARE SOLUTIONS
(Suby of WM) ★
720 4th Ave Ste 400, Kirkland, WA 98033-8136
Tel (425) 823-6164 Founded/Ownrshp 1992
Sales 102.9MM[E] EMP 329
SIC 4953 Refuse systems
Dist Mgr: Jeff McMahon
Genl Mgr: Jamey D Soer

D-U-N-S 00-396-7148
■ WASTE MANAGEMENT OF WISCONSIN INC (WI)
(Suby of WM) ★
N96 W 13600 Cnty Line Rd St N 96, Germantown, WI 53022
Tel (262) 251-4000 Founded/Ownrshp 1956, 1974
Sales 446.0MM[E] EMP 1,400
SIC 4953 4212 Garbage: collecting, destroying & processing; Local trucking, without storage
Pr: Richard Ancelet
Treas: Jodie Landgraf
*VP: Phillip Rooney
*VP: Randy Saltzman
Genl Couns: Dennis Wilt

WASTE MGT HEALTHCARE SOLUTIONS
See WASTE MANAGEMENT OF WASHINGTON INC

D-U-N-S 02-676-3628
WASTE PRO OF FLORIDA INC
2101 W State Rd Ste 301, Longwood, FL 32779
Tel (407) 774-0800 Founded/Ownrshp 2001
Sales 413.5MM[E] EMP 900
SIC 4953 Refuse systems
CEO: John J Jennings
*Pr: David L Danford
*CFO: Don Phillips
*VP: Charles Ewing
*VP: Fred Woods

D-U-N-S 19-057-1773
WASTE PRO USA INC
2101 W State Road 434 # 305, Longwood, FL 32779-5053
Tel (407) 869-8800 Founded/Ownrshp 1986
Sales 715.9MM[E] EMP 1,100
SIC 4953 Refuse systems
CEO: John Jennings
Pr: Tim Dolan
*Pr: Charles Ewing
Pr: Ralph Mills
*COO: Chris Ciaccio
*CFO: Cort Sabina
Bd of Dir: Frank Kelly
Sr VP: Ralph Velocci
VP: Scott Corley
*VP: Robert Hyers
VP: Madhu Sehdev

D-U-N-S 00-766-3820
WASTE SERVICES INC
(Suby of PROGRESSIVE WASTE SOLUTIONS LTD) ★
2301 Eagle Pkwy Ste 200, Fort Worth, TX 76177-2326
Tel (817) 632-4000 Founded/Ownrshp 2003
Sales 282.8MM[E] EMP 400[E]
SIC 4953 Refuse systems
Pr: Kevin Walbridge
*CFO: Stephen Moody
*VP: Thomas Fowler
*VP: Thomas Miller

D-U-N-S 60-856-7756 EXP
WASTEQUIP LLC
6525 Morrison Blvd # 300, Charlotte, NC 28211-0500
Tel (704) 366-7140 Founded/Ownrshp 2012
Sales 498.0MM[E] EMP 1,610
SIC 3443 3537 Dumpsters, garbage; Industrial trucks & tractors
CFO: Steven Svetik
VP: Andrew Bardsley
VP: Monte Clindaniel
VP: Henry Retamal
Exec: Nick Wiseman
Plnt Mgr: Eduardo Pagan
Sls&Mrk Ex: Tom Nero
VP Mktg: Susan Violette
Manager: Charlie Clark
Sls Mgr: Stephanie Sizemore
Sales Asso: Jamie Butler

D-U-N-S 84-923-9041 IMP/EXP
WASTEQUIP MANUFACTURING CO LLC
(Suby of WASTEQUIP LLC) ★
1901 Roxborough Rd # 300, Charlotte, NC 28211-3492
Tel (704) 366-7140 Founded/Ownrshp 1992
Sales 310.6MM[E] EMP 1,100
SIC 3443 Dumpsters, garbage
Pr: Robert Rasmussen
CFO: Brian Meyer
CFO: Steve Svetik
Rgnl Mgr: Steve Ellingboe
Genl Mgr: Margaret Spradlin-Allen
Off Admin: Derrell Doraty
CIO: Rusty Andrews
DP Exec: John Beckwith
Mfg Mgr: Kevin Wiech
Opers Mgr: Jimmy Davis
Plnt Mgr: Ed Reid

D-U-N-S 78-646-7159
WASTREN ADVANTAGE INC
1571 Shyville Rd, Piketon, OH 45661-9201
Tel (970) 254-1277 Founded/Ownrshp 2006
Sales 105.0MM EMP 480
Accts Cherry Bekaert & Holland Llp
SIC 4959 8744 8711 Sanitary services; Facilities support services; Engineering services
Pr: Steve Moore
*COO: Glenn Henderson
*CFO: Thomas Kaupas
*Ex VP: Jim Gardner
*VP: Keith Tucker
Genl Mgr: John Essman
CTO: Keisa Davis
QA Dir: Allison Schaeffer
IT Man: Karl Fleeman

D-U-N-S 07-904-4772
WATAUGA MEDICAL CENTER INC
(Suby of APPALACHIAN REGIONAL HEALTHCARE SYSTEM INC) ★
336 Deerfield Rd, Boone, NC 28607-5008
Tel (828) 262-4100 Founded/Ownrshp 1936
Sales 148.2MM EMP 700[E]
SIC 8062 8011 General medical & surgical hospitals; Offices & clinics of medical doctors
Pr: Richard G Sparks
*CFO: Kevin May
Exec: Mary Long
Dir Rad: Brandy Foster
Chf Nrs Of: June Smith
CTO: Robbie Parker
Doctor: John Shoaf
Doctor: Paul Young

D-U-N-S 02-140-6341
WATCHFIRE ENTERPRISES INC
(Suby of WATCHFIRE TECHNOLOGIES HOLDINGS II INC) ★
1015 Maple St, Danville, IL 61832-3200
Tel (217) 442-0611 Founded/Ownrshp 2013
Sales 130.6MM EMP 344[E]
SIC 3993 Electric signs
CEO: Steve Harriott
*CFO: Frank Dwyer
*CFO: Adam Grimes

D-U-N-S 00-508-3340 IMP/EXP
WATCHFIRE SIGNS LLC
(Suby of WATCHFIRE ENTERPRISES INC) ★
1015 Maple St, Danville, IL 61832-3200
Tel (217) 442-0611 Founded/Ownrshp 2008
Sales 94.0MM[E] EMP 300[E]
SIC 3993 Electric signs
Pr: Steve Harriott
*CFO: Frank Dwyer
VP: Dave Warns

D-U-N-S 16-552-1365
WATCHFIRE TECHNOLOGIES HOLDINGS I INC
1015 Maple St, Danville, IL 61832-3200
Tel (217) 442-6971 Founded/Ownrshp 2013
Sales 130.6MM[E] EMP 357[E]
SIC 3993 Electric signs
CEO: Steve Harriott

D-U-N-S 04-650-3576
WATCHFIRE TECHNOLOGIES HOLDINGS II INC
(Suby of WATCHFIRE TECHNOLOGIES HOLDINGS I INC) ★
1015 Maple St, Danville, IL 61832-3200
Tel (217) 442-0611 Founded/Ownrshp 2013
Sales 130.6MM[E] EMP 351[E]
SIC 3993 Electric signs
CEO: Steve Harriott

D-U-N-S 94-306-9856
WATCHGUARD TECHNOLOGIES INC
505 5th Ave S Ste 500, Seattle, WA 98104-3892
Tel (206) 613-6600 Founded/Ownrshp 1996
Sales 98.4MM[E] EMP 338
SIC 7372 Business oriented computer software
CEO: Prakash Panjwani
CFO: Richard Barber
CFO: Steven Moore
Treas: Steven N Moore
VP: Eric Aarrestad
VP: Kathleen Brush
VP: Keith Clements
VP: Pete Knapp
VP: Michael Martucci
VP: Shari McLaren
VP: Philippe Ortodoro
VP: Sean Price
VP: David Ridout
VP: Scott Robertson
VP: Alex Thurber
VP: Wayson Vannatta
VP: Andrew Young
Board of Directors: Mike Kohlsdorf

WATCHMAN MARKETING
See ROYAL SERVICES INC

D-U-N-S 02-164-8121
WATCO COMPANIES LLC
BATON ROUGE SOUTHERN RAILROAD
315 W 3rd St, Pittsburg, KS 66762-4706
Tel (620) 231-2230 Founded/Ownrshp 2011
Sales 2.0MMM[E] EMP 3,000
SIC 4011 7538 Railroads, line-haul operating; General automotive repair shops
Ch: Gary Lundy
*COO: Terry Towner
*CFO: Matthew McKenzie
*Chf Mktg O: Stefan Loeb
*Ex VP: Arthure McKechnie III
*Sr VP: Jared Radke

D-U-N-S 07-390-1571
WATCO INC
(Suby of BATON ROUGE SOUTHERN RAILROAD) ★
315 W 3rd St, Pittsburg, KS 66762-4706
Tel (208) 734-4644 Founded/Ownrshp 1991
Sales 100.8MM[E] EMP 1,051
SIC 4013 4741 4789 Railroad switching; Rental of railroad cars; Railroad car repair
Ch Bd: Charles R Webb
*Pr: Rick Baden
*CEO: Richard Webb
COO: C Sigley
*Treas: Gary Lundy
Ex VP: Randy Bennett
*Ex VP: Ed McKechnie
*Ex VP: Craig Richey
Ex Dir: Gary C Vaughn
Pdt Mgr: Brandon Elliott

D-U-N-S 05-288-3733
WATER DISTRICT NO1 OF JOHNSON COUNTY KANSAS
WATERONE
10747 Renner Blvd, Lenexa, KS 66219-9624
Tel (913) 895-5500 Founded/Ownrshp 1952
Sales 97.8MM EMP 350
Accts Rubin Brown Llp Overland Park
SIC 4941 Water supply
Ch: Brenda Cherpitel
Treas: Ronald E Appletoft
Treas: Ronald E Appltoft
Treas: Larry Rosenow
Ofcr: Brent Fulton
Genl Mgr: Michael Armstrong
IT Man: Tangie McGlothen
IT Man: Steve Voelker
Snr Mgr: Greg Totzke
Snr Mgr: Curt Vogel

D-U-N-S 03-906-4605
WATER GAS & LIGHT COMMISSION
207 Pine Ave, Albany, GA 31701-2530
Tel (229) 883-8330 Founded/Ownrshp 1912
Sales 209.3MM[E] EMP 290
SIC 4939

WATER ONE QUALITY WTR SYSTEMS
See KINETICO INC

D-U-N-S 00-180-4074 IMP
WATER PIK INC
WATERPIK TECHNOLOGIES
1730 E Prospect Rd, Fort Collins, CO 80525-1310
Tel (800) 525-2774 Founded/Ownrshp 1999, 2007
Sales 123.3MM[E] EMP 800
SIC 3432 3843 Plumbing fixture fittings & trim; Dental equipment & supplies
CEO: Richard P Bisson
VP: Ken Hair
VP: Jay McCulloch
VP: Greg Plummer
VP: Michael Wakeman
VP Opers: Anthony Murphy
Mktg Dir: Scott Headley
Sls Dir: John Herndon
Mktg Mgr: Kelly Carmin
Mktg Mgr: Mike C Codd
Sls Mgr: Keith Hendrickson

WATER PLLUTION CTRL FACILITIES
See METROPOLITAN DISTRICT

D-U-N-S 80-832-1913
WATER RESOURCES CONTROL BOARD CALIFORNIA
STATE WATER RESOURCES
(Suby of CAL/EPA) ★
1001 I St, Sacramento, CA 95814-2828
Tel (916) 341-5250 Founded/Ownrshp 1967
Sales NA EMP 1,200
Accts Pricewaterhousecoopers Llp S
SIC 9511 Water control & quality agency, government;
Ch: Felicia Marcus
Bd of Dir: Arthur G Baggett
Bd of Dir: Charles R Hoppin
Ex Dir: Celeste Cant

D-U-N-S 07-987-1217
■ WATER SOLUTIONS HOLDINGS LLC
KEYSTONE CLEARWATER SOLUTIONS
(Suby of AMERICAN INDUSTRIAL WATER LLC) ★
310 Seven Fields Blvd, Seven Fields, PA 16046-4343
Tel (717) 508-0550 Founded/Ownrshp 2015
Sales 93.9MM[E] EMP 350[E]
SIC 4952 Sewerage systems
CEO: Ned Wehler

WATER SOURCE ONE
See ONE WATER SOURCE LLC

D-U-N-S 62-125-6853
WATER STREET HEALTHCARE PARTNERS LLC
333 W Wacker Dr Ste 2800, Chicago, IL 60606-1336
Tel (312) 506-2900 Founded/Ownrshp 2005
Sales 1.5MMM[E] EMP 978
SIC 6211 Security brokers & dealers
CEO: Brian K Hutchison
*VP: Mike Brennan
VP: Nicklaus Daley
VP: Hilary Dexter
*VP: Katie Ossman
VP: Greg Robitaille
*CIO: Paul T Cottey
Opers Mgr: Carrie Raffin

D-U-N-S 07-896-9144
WATER WORKS BOARD OF CITY OF BIRMINGHAM
BIRMINGHAM WATER WORKS BOARD
3600 1st Ave N, Birmingham, AL 35222-1210
Tel (205) 244-4000 Founded/Ownrshp 1950
Sales 367.5MM[E] EMP 460
Accts Warren Averett Kimbrough & M
SIC 4941 Water supply
Genl Mgr: Mac Underwood
Treas: Miles Creel
Exec: Priscilla Lowry
Comm Man: Binnie Myles
IT Man: Tilden Leigh
IT Man: Rhonda Lewis

WATER WORKS PLUMBING HEATING
See IAP WORLDWIDE SERVICES INC

D-U-N-S 03-504-2474
WATERBROOK WINERY INC
(Suby of PRECEPT WINE) ★
10518 W Highway 12, Walla Walla, WA 99362-6279
Tel (509) 522-1262 Founded/Ownrshp 1983
Sales 89.1MM[E] EMP 207[E]
SIC 5182 Wine
Pr: Mike Williamson
CFO: Tom Sawatzki

D-U-N-S 01-014-2065 IMP
WATERBURY HOSPITAL
WATERBURY HOSPITAL HEALTH CTR
64 Robbins St, Waterbury, CT 06708-2600
Tel (203) 573-6000 Founded/Ownrshp 1986
Sales 192.7MM EMP 1,625
SIC 8062 Hospital, medical school affiliation
Pr: Darlene Stromstad
Chf OB: John M Lewis
*COO: John Evans
COO: Mary B Pryylo
Telecom Ex: Pat Robinson
CIO: Mike Cemeno
Dir IT: Bob Rockhill
IT Man: Joe Alfonzo
IT Man: Juana Clarke
IT Man: Doreen Elnitsky
Sfty Dirs: Ryan Lafleur

WATERBURY HOSPITAL HEALTH CTR
See WATERBURY HOSPITAL

D-U-N-S 10-001-2368
WATERBURY PUBLIC SCHOOL DISTRICT
236 Grand St Ste 1, Waterbury, CT 06702-1930
Tel (203) 574-8004 Founded/Ownrshp 2002
Sales 48.4MM[E] EMP 1,500

SIC 8211 Public elementary & secondary schools; School board
Snr Mgr: Gary Miller

WATERBURY PUBLIC SCHOOL DST
See WATERBURY SCHOOL DISTRICT

D-U-N-S 96-779-8059
WATERBURY SCHOOL DISTRICT
WATERBURY PUBLIC SCHOOL DST
236 Grand St Ste 1, Waterbury, CT 06702-1930
Tel (203) 574-8000 *Founded/Ownrshp* 1894
Sales 3.2MM^E *EMP* 1,500
SIC 8211 Public elementary & secondary schools
Dir Sec: John Herman
IT Man: Ken Ludwig
Pr Dir: Nancy Vaughan
Teacher Pr: Shauna Tucker
HC Dir: Joseph Gorman

D-U-N-S 08-393-9306
WATERFORD SCHOOL DISTRICT
ISAAC E CRARY JUNIOR HIGH SCHL
501 N Cass Lake Rd, Waterford, MI 48328-2307
Tel (248) 682-7800 *Founded/Ownrshp* 1891
Sales 129.2MM *EMP* 1,500
Accts Yeo & Yeo Pc Saginaw Mi
SIC 8211 Public elementary & secondary schools; Public senior high school; Public junior high school; Public elementary school
Off Mgr: Susan Body
Off Admin: Paula Bragan
Off Admin: Cheryl Trosen
IT Man: Jeffrey Spencer

D-U-N-S 83-510-3144 IMP
WATERFRONT ENTERPRISES INC
GATEWAY TERMINAL
400 Waterfront St, New Haven, CT 06512-1717
Tel (203) 467-1997 *Founded/Ownrshp* 1986
Sales 201.0MM^E *EMP* 160
SIC 5172 Fuel oil
Pr: Lawrence E Smith
Ex VP: Scott Shirk
**VP:* Coy Angelo

WATERFURNACE INTERNATIONAL
See WATERFURNACE RENEWABLE ENERGY INC

D-U-N-S 78-617-7949 IMP/EXP
WATERFURNACE RENEWABLE ENERGY INC
WATERFURNACE INTERNATIONAL
9000 Conservation Way, Fort Wayne, IN 46809-9794
Tel (260) 478-5667 *Founded/Ownrshp* 1990
Sales 118.7MM *EMP* 270^E
Accts Grant Thornton Llp Toronto
SIC 4961 Steam supply systems, including geothermal
Ch Bd: Timothy Shields
**Pr:* Tom Huntington
**CFO:* Fred Andriano
Bd of Dir: Chuck Diltz
VP: Bill Dean
IT Man: Dave Fitch
IT Man: Bob Peck
IT Man: Lynn Swing
Ql Cn Mgr: Joseph Bond
Sls Mgr: Tom Atkinson
Sls Mgr: Scott Niesen

WATERHOUSE SECURITIES
See TD AMERITRADE INC

D-U-N-S 00-777-7840
WATERLOO COAL CO INC (OH)
MADISON MINE SUPPLY CO
3675 Dixon Run Rd, Jackson, OH 45640-1474
Tel (740) 286-5633 *Founded/Ownrshp* 1934, 1988
Sales 543.9MM^E *EMP* 125
SIC 1221 1411 1459

D-U-N-S 01-024-6890
WATERLOO COMMUNITY SCHOOL DISTRICT INC
EDUCATION SERVICE CENTER
1516 Washington St, Waterloo, IA 50702-1698
Tel (319) 433-1800 *Founded/Ownrshp* 1851
Sales 26.6MM^E *EMP* 1,488
SIC 8299 Educational services
Pr Dir: Tara Thomas

D-U-N-S 04-314-1418
WATERLOO HOLDINGS INC
(*Suby of* WATERLOO HOLDINGS LLC) ★
1500 Waterloo Dr, Sedalia, MO 65301-1670
Tel (660) 826-0960 *Founded/Ownrshp* 2015
Sales 236.1MM^E *EMP* 1,400
SIC 3429 6719 Manufactured hardware (general); Investment holding companies, except banks
Pr: E J Antonio III

D-U-N-S 08-037-5266
WATERLOO HOLDINGS LLC
(*Suby of* AFI PARTNERS LLC) ★
1500 Waterloo Dr, Sedalia, MO 65301-1670
Tel (660) 826-0960 *Founded/Ownrshp* 2015
Sales 31.7MM^E *EMP* 1,400
SIC 6719 Investment holding companies, except banks
Mng Pt: E J Antonio III

D-U-N-S 00-527-7959 IMP
WATERLOO INDUSTRIES INC (DE)
(*Suby of* WATERLOO HOLDINGS INC) ★
1500 Waterloo Dr, Sedalia, MO 65301-1670
Tel (660) 826-0960 *Founded/Ownrshp* 1986, 2015
Sales 236.1MM^E *EMP* 1,100
SIC 3429 Manufactured hardware (general)
Pr: William Nictakis
**CFO:* Pam Davis
Snr Mgr: Susan Frost

D-U-N-S 15-603-7178
WATERMAN BROADCASTING CORP OF FLORIDA
WBBH TV
3719 Central Ave, Fort Myers, FL 33901-8220
Tel (239) 939-2020 *Founded/Ownrshp* 1983
Sales 100.4MM^E *EMP* 240
SIC 4833 Television broadcasting stations
Pr: Bernard E Waterman
**CFO:* Gerald Poppe
**Sec:* Edith B Waterman
**VP:* Steven H Pontius
Creative D: Todd Schulz
Prd Dir: Sarah Apsey-Barres
Prd Dir: Sarah Caspersen
VP Mktg: Deborah Abbott
Sls Dir: Bob Beville
Sls Mgr: Bill Beard
Sls Mgr: Gayla Wright

D-U-N-S 05-166-4841
WATERMARK MEDICAL HOLDINGS INC
1641 Worthington Rd # 320, West Palm Beach, FL 33409-6704
Tel (561) 283-1191 *Founded/Ownrshp* 2013
Sales 128.5MM^E *EMP* 945
SIC 8099 Medical services organization
CEO: Sean Heyniger
**CFO:* John Fiedor
**VP:* Joe Rose
IT Man: Morgan E Dunn

D-U-N-S 60-667-3127
WATERMARK RETIREMENT COMMUNITIES INC
(*Suby of* FOUNTAINS AFFILIATED COMPANIES, INC.)
2020 W Rudasill Rd, Tucson, AZ 85704-7800
Tel (520) 797-4000 *Founded/Ownrshp* 1996
Sales 122.2MM^E *EMP* 1,528
SIC 8059 Nursing home, except skilled & intermediate care facility; Convalescent home; Rest home, with health care
Pr: David Barnes
**COO:* Rick Kamminga
CFO: Fran Donnellan
CFO: Bruce Frandsen
**Ch:* David Freshwater
**Ofcr:* Mary Beth Farrell
Exec: Brendan Carey
Exec: Josh Marlowe
Dir Risk M: Dennis Johnson
Ex Dir: Robert Miller
Ex Dir: Kristi Roberts

WATERMILL GROUP, THE
See WATERMILL VENTURES LTD

D-U-N-S 84-846-4244 IMP/EXP
WATERMILL VENTURES LTD
WATERMILL GROUP, THE
1 Cranberry Hl 750, Lexington, MA 02421-7394
Tel (781) 891-6660 *Founded/Ownrshp* 1993
Sales 113.2MM^E *EMP* 250
SIC 6799 Investors; Investment clubs
**Genl Pt:* Steven E Karol
**Pt:* Dale Okonow
**Pt:* Benjamin Procter
**CFO:* Michael Fuller
Mktg Dir: Sarah Bowen

WATERONE
See WATER DISTRICT NO1 OF JOHNSON COUNTY KANSAS

D-U-N-S 00-616-6557 IMP/EXP
WATEROUS CO (MN)
(*Suby of* ACIPCO) ★
125 Hardman Ave S, South Saint Paul, MN 55075-1191
Tel (651) 450-5000 *Founded/Ownrshp* 1886, 1989
Sales 235.2MM^E *EMP* 2,000^E
SIC 3491 3561 3494 3321 Water works valves; Fire hydrant valves; Pumps & pumping equipment; Valves & pipe fittings; Gray & ductile iron foundries
Pr: William Smith
**Ch:* Van L Richey
Sr VP: Gail Kincade
Genl Mgr: Matthew Wolf
IT Man: Mike Sterbentz
Sfty Dirs: David Floysand
Sls Mgr: Barry Coe
Sls Mgr: Juan Soto

WATERPIK TECHNOLOGIES
See WATER PIK INC

D-U-N-S 86-770-4355
▲ WATERS CORP
34 Maple St, Milford, MA 01757-3696
Tel (508) 478-2000 *Founded/Ownrshp* 1958
Sales 2.0MMM *EMP* 6,200^E
Accts Pricewaterhousecoopers Llp B
Tkr Sym WAT *Exch* NYS
SIC 3826 3829 7371 7372 Chromatographic equipment, laboratory type; Spectrometers, liquid scintillation & nuclear; Computer software systems analysis & design, custom; Computer software development; Prepackaged software
Pr: Christopher O'Connell
CFO: Eugene G Cassis
Ex VP: Arthur G Caputo
Ex VP: Rick Tarantino
VP: Mark Beaudion
VP: Mark T Beaudoin
VP: Mark T Beaudouin
VP: Asish Chakraborty
VP: Ron Creasia
VP: McCormick Daniel
VP: Rohit Khanna
VP: Jeff Lampert
VP: Larry Maley
VP: Daniel McCormick
VP: Paul Newton
VP: Blais Richard
VP: Mazzarese Robert
VP: Tom Saunders
VP: Terry Shortt
VP: Holleran Susan
VP: Tom Wesley
Board of Directors: Joshua Bekenstein, Michael J Berendt, Douglas A Berthiaume, Edward Conard, Laurie H Glimcher, Christopher A Kuebler, William J Miller, Joann A Reed, Thomas P Salice

D-U-N-S 10-718-6004 IMP
■ WATERS TECHNOLOGIES CORP
(*Suby of* WATERS CORP) ★
34 Maple St, Milford, MA 01757-3696
Tel (508) 478-2000 *Founded/Ownrshp* 1994
Sales 892.9MM^E *EMP* 4,000
SIC 3826 3829 Analytical instruments; Chromatographic equipment, laboratory type; Spectrometers, liquid scintillation & nuclear
CEO: Christopher J O'Connell
**Treas:* John Lynch
Genl Mgr: Marjorie Radlo

D-U-N-S 15-899-8919 IMP
WATERSHED FOODS LLC
202 N Ford St, Gridley, IL 61744-3902
Tel (309) 747-3000 *Founded/Ownrshp* 2005
Sales 96.1MM^E *EMP* 100
SIC 5142 Packaged frozen goods
Pr: Jeremy E Zobrist
CFO: Aaron Anlinker
QA Dir: Jonathan Baner

D-U-N-S 02-023-1894
WATERSTONE BANK
11200 W Plank Ct, Wauwatosa, WI 53226-3250
Tel (414) 459-4211 *Founded/Ownrshp* 2009
Sales NA *EMP* 27
SIC 6029

D-U-N-S 18-633-2172
▲ WATERSTONE FINANCIAL INC
11200 W Plank Ct, Wauwatosa, WI 53226-3250
Tel (414) 761-1000 *Founded/Ownrshp* 2005
Sales NA *EMP* 849^E
Tkr Sym WSBF *Exch* NGS
SIC 6035 Savings institutions, federally chartered
Pr: Douglas S Gordon
**Ch Bd:* Patrick S Lawton
COO: William F Bruss
COO: Kevin P Gillespie
CFO: Mark R Gerke
CFO: Mark Gerke
CFO: Allan R Hosack
VP: Rebecca M Arndt
VP: James Crowley

D-U-N-S 08-817-2119
WATERTON ASSOCIATES LLC (IL)
WATERTON RESIDENTIAL
30 S Wacker Dr Ste 3600, Chicago, IL 60606-7462
Tel (312) 948-4500 *Founded/Ownrshp* 1995
Sales 124.6MM^E *EMP* 460
SIC 6513 6798 Apartment building operators; Real estate investment trusts
CEO: David R Schwartz
**Pr:* Marc Swerdlow
**COO:* Greg Lozinak
**CFO:* Doug Denyer
**Sr VP:* Michelle C Wells
Off Mgr: Christina Shawn

WATERTON RESIDENTIAL
See WATERTON ASSOCIATES LLC

WATERTOWN AREA HEALTH SERVICES
See GREATER WATERTOWN COMMUNITY HEALTH FOUNDATION INC

D-U-N-S 02-439-3167
WATERTOWN COOPERATIVE ELEVATOR ASSOCIATION (SD)
WC
811 Burlington Northern D, Watertown, SD 57201-4111
Tel (605) 886-8333 *Founded/Ownrshp* 1940
Sales 107.5MM *EMP* 45
Accts Carlson Highland & Co Llp C
SIC 5153 5191 4221 Grain elevators; Seeds: field, garden & flower; Farm product warehousing & storage
Pr: Phil Ramal
**VP:* Richard Deberg
**Prin:* Travis Christensen
**Prin:* Jon Hegge
**Prin:* Gordon Little
**Prin:* Steve Schull
**Prin:* Trevor Stieg

D-U-N-S 07-173-9130
WATERVILLE OSTEOPATHIC HEALTH CARE (INC)
200 Kennedy Memorial Dr, Waterville, ME 04901-4526
Tel (207) 873-0731 *Founded/Ownrshp* 1983
Sales 120.0MM *EMP* 300
Accts Berry Dunn Mcneil & Parker
SIC 8069 Specialty hospitals, except psychiatric
CEO: Wilfred Addison

D-U-N-S 05-999-2107
WATERWAY GAS & WASH CO
727 Goddard Ave, Chesterfield, MO 63005-1106
Tel (636) 537-1111 *Founded/Ownrshp* 1970
Sales 318.3MM^E *EMP* 1,000
SIC 5541 7542 Filling stations, gasoline; Carwash, automatic
Ch: Henry W Dubinsky
**Pr:* Robert Dubinsky
**Treas:* David Bunte
**Ex VP:* Karen Patton
VP: Curtis Brown
**VP:* Ken Williams
Exec: Jesse Mayo
Genl Mgr: Steven Agrippino
Genl Mgr: Matt Hofmockel
Genl Mgr: Jim Poelker
Genl Mgr: Brian Wiemann

WATERWAY PLASTICS
See B & S PLASTICS INC

WATERWORKS
See WW LIQUIDATION INC

D-U-N-S 14-665-5126
■ WATHENA HEALTHCARE AND REHABILITATION CENTER LLC
WATHENA HLTHCARE RHBLTTION CTR
(*Suby of* GENESIS HEALTHCARE LLC) ★
2112 Highway 36, Wathena, KS 66090-4126
Tel (785) 989-3141 *Founded/Ownrshp* 2004
Sales 1.5MM^E *EMP* 1,889^E
SIC 8051 Skilled nursing care facilities

WATHENA HLTHCARE RHBLTTION CTR
See WATHENA HEALTHCARE AND REHABILITATION CENTER LLC

WATKINS AND SHEPARD LEASING
See WATKINS AND SHEPARD TRUCKING INC

D-U-N-S 18-351-9867
WATKINS AND SHEPARD TRUCKING INC
WATKINS AND SHEPARD LEASING
(*Suby of* SCHNEIDER NATIONAL INC) ★
N6400 Hwy 10 W, Missoula, MT 59801
Tel (406) 532-6121 *Founded/Ownrshp* 2016
Sales 176.6MM^E *EMP* 1,300
SIC 4213 8299 Trucking, except local; Vehicle driving school
CEO: Ray Kuntz
Pr: Walt Ainsworth
Sec: Daniel Brown

D-U-N-S 04-969-0423
WATKINS ASSOCIATED INDUSTRIES INC (FL)
1958 Monroe Dr Ne, Atlanta, GA 30324-4887
Tel (404) 872-3841 *Founded/Ownrshp* 1980
Sales 507.3MM *EMP* 1,827
SIC 4213 6552 Trucking, except local; Subdividers & developers
Ch Bd: John F Watkins
**Pr:* Michael L Watkins
**Sec:* George W Ready Jr
**Sec:* Eric S Wahlen
**VP:* George Watkins
**VP:* Kimberly M Watkins
**VP:* W B Watkins IV

D-U-N-S 04-108-5135
WATKINS CONSTRUCTION CO LLC
3229 S 15th St, Corsicana, TX 75110
Tel (903) 874-6587 *Founded/Ownrshp* 1957
Sales 196.1MM^E *EMP* 505
SIC 1623 Pipeline construction
Pr: Jerry Watkins
VP: Scott Watkins

D-U-N-S 00-615-8703 IMP
WATKINS INC (DE)
WATKINS PDTS FOR HLTHIER LVING
(*Suby of* JACOBS INTERACTIVE) ★
150 Liberty St, Winona, MN 55987-3707
Tel (507) 457-3300 *Founded/Ownrshp* 1868, 1978
Sales 89.9MM^E *EMP* 260
SIC 2087 2841 Extracts, flavoring; Detergents, synthetic organic or inorganic alkaline; Scouring compounds
Ch Bd: Irwin Jacobs
**Pr:* Mark Jacobs
COO: Michelle Fehr
VP: Delores Antunes
**VP:* James Yenish
MIS Dir: Scott Iverson
IT Man: Randy Drier
Plnt Mgr: Jeff Straight
Mktg Dir: Georgette Moe

D-U-N-S 14-854-7243 IMP/EXP
■ WATKINS MANUFACTURING CORP
A&W CONTRACTORS
(*Suby of* MASCO CORP) ★
1280 Park Center Dr, Vista, CA 92081-8398
Tel (760) 598-6464 *Founded/Ownrshp* 1986
Sales 118.2MM^E *EMP* 516^E
SIC 3999 Hot tubs
Pr: Steve Hammock
COO: Jacquie Matzat
CFO: Chris Peavey
VP: Mike Dunn
VP: Robin French
VP: Leo Hamacher
VP: Roger Lamberson
VP: Tad Vaughn
Dir IT: Joseph Guzman
Dir IT: Jason Joswick
IT Man: Jon Klock

WATKINS PDTS FOR HLTHIER LVING
See WATKINS INC

D-U-N-S 00-627-5481 IMP/EXP
WATLOW ELECTRIC MANUFACTURING CO
WATLOW ELECTRIC MFG CO
12001 Lackland Rd, Saint Louis, MO 63146-4039
Tel (314) 878-4600 *Founded/Ownrshp* 1922
Sales 341.4MM^E *EMP* 1,400
SIC 3699 Electrical equipment & supplies
Ch Bd: Peter T Desloge
Pr: Thomas Lamantia
Treas: Stephen F Desloge
Treas: Thomas Ferris
VP: John A Pennings
VP: Tim Scheib
VP Opers: Jim Rowland
VP Sls: Chris Eichmann

D-U-N-S 78-474-4054 IMP/EXP
WATLOW ELECTRIC MANUFACTURING HOLDINGS CO
WATLOW HEATER TECHNOLOGY CTR
12001 Lackland Rd, Saint Louis, MO 63146-4039
Tel (314) 878-4600 *Founded/Ownrshp* 1922
Sales 630.0MM^E *EMP* 1,400
SIC 6719

WATLOW ELECTRIC MFG CO
See WATLOW ELECTRIC MANUFACTURING CO

WATLOW HEATER TECHNOLOGY CTR
See WATLOW ELECTRIC MANUFACTURING HOLDINGS CO

D-U-N-S 02-302-0597
WATONWAN FARM SERVICE INC
W F S CO
233 W Ciro St, Truman, MN 56088-2018
Tel (507) 776-1244 *Founded/Ownrshp* 1937
Sales 358.6MM *EMP* 255
Accts Gardiner Thompsen Des Moines
SIC 5153 5191 5172 Grains; Fertilizer & fertilizer materials; Chemicals, agricultural; Feed; Seeds: field, garden & flower; Petroleum products
CEO: Ed Bosanko
**Pr:* Todd Ludwig
Treas: Dennis Hunwardsen
**VP:* Craig Kilian
**VP:* Mike Minnehan

D-U-N-S 00-412-3576
▲ WATSCO INC (FL)
2665 S Byshr Dr Ste 901, Miami, FL 33133-5436
Tel (305) 714-4100 *Founded/Ownrshp* 1956
Sales 4.1MMM *EMP* 5,000
Accts Kpmg Llp Miami Florida
Tkr Sym WSO *Exch* NYS
SIC 5075 Air conditioning & ventilation equipment & supplies
Ch Bd: Albert H Nahmad
**Pr:* Aaron J Nahmad
CFO: Ana M Menendez
**Sr VP:* Barry S Logan
VP: Nahmad Aaron
VP: Paul Johnston
VP: Aj Nahmad
VP: Steve Rupp
Dir Risk M: Lisa Robinson
VP Mktg: Ken Connell

D-U-N-S 02-589-9394
WATSEKA RURAL KING SUPPLY INC (IL)
BIG R STORES
200 N Ernest Grove Pkwy, Watseka, IL 60970-1847
Tel (815) 432-3440 *Founded/Ownrshp* 1965
Sales 96.1MM[E] *EMP* 4[E]
SIC 5999 5651 5251 5311

D-U-N-S 03-242-4293
WATSON CLINIC FOUNDATION INC
1600 Lakeland Hills Blvd, Lakeland, FL 33805-3065
Tel (863) 680-7000 *Founded/Ownrshp* 1941
Sales 384.7M[E] *EMP* 1,500
Accts Crowe Horwath Llp Fort Laude
SIC 8011 Clinic, operated by physicians
**CEO:* Louis Saco MD
CFO: Michael Callahan
Dir IT: Howard Gorell
Plas Surg: Peter M Bridge
Doctor: Musa Awan
Doctor: Kevin Browne
Doctor: John Canto
Doctor: Neal Kavesh

D-U-N-S 93-981-2301
WATSON CLINIC LLP
1600 Lakeland Hills Blvd, Lakeland, FL 33805-3065
Tel (863) 680-7000 *Founded/Ownrshp* 1941
Sales 143.2MM[E] *EMP* 1,500[E]
SIC 8011 Internal medicine, physician/surgeon
Pt: Dario M Topolcic
**Pt:* Louis Saco
**Pt:* Jeffrey Scott
CFO: Michael Callaham
Ofcr: Robbin Joachim
Dir Lab: Richard Gould
Surgeon: Marc A Volpe
Ansthlgy: Frances M Harris
Plas Surg: Raam Lakhani
Doctor: Chadi Alkhalil
Doctor: John Bazley

D-U-N-S 13-045-5327
WATSON ELECTRICAL CONSTRUCTION CO LLC
(*Suby of* WECC HOLDINGS, INC.)
1500 Charleston St Se, Wilson, NC 27893-9035
Tel (252) 237-7511 *Founded/Ownrshp* 2003
Sales 106.1MM[E] *EMP* 600
Accts Batchelor Tillery & Roberts
SIC 1731 Electrical work
Pr: Craig Myers
**COO:* Tom Headlee
COO: Susan Lucas
CFO: Richard S Ingram
**Ch:* Stuart Frantz
Ofcr: Craig Taylor
**VP:* David Garren
**VP:* Carroll Lipscombe
VP: Billy Price
Dir Bus: William Robinson
Genl Mgr: Scott Bizzell

WATSON FORD
See WATSON QUALITY FORD INC

D-U-N-S 84-005-4118 IMP/EXP
WATSON LABORATORIES INC
ALLERGAN PHARMACY
(*Suby of* ANDRX CORP) ★
311 Bonnie Cir, Corona, CA 92880-2882
Tel (951) 493-5300 *Founded/Ownrshp* 2014
Sales 241.8MM[E] *EMP* 560
SIC 2834 Pharmaceutical preparations
Ch: Paul M Bisaro
**Pr:* Brenton L Saunders
COO: Albert Paonessa III
**COO:* Robert Stewart
**CFO:* R Todd Joyce
Sr VP: Ranjana B Pathak
Sr VP: Anna Power
VP: Michael Bryner
**VP:* David Hsia
**VP:* Bill Meury
Exec: Linda Adamowicz
Assoc Dir: Debbie Huang
Assoc Dir: Mark Pozatek
Assoc Dir: Anthony Valmores

D-U-N-S 18-056-7570
WATSON QUALITY FORD INC
WATSON FORD
6130 I 55 N, Jackson, MS 39211-2642
Tel (601) 956-7000 *Founded/Ownrshp* 1982
Sales 156.0MM *EMP* 150
SIC 5511 Automobiles, new & used
Pr: Robert H Watson
**Sec:* R J Pizzalato
VP: Dale Foster
Sales Asso: Shune Lowe
Sales Asso: Joshua Smith

WATSONVILLE COMMUNITY HOSPITAL
See WATSONVILLE HEALTHCARE MANAGEMENT LLC

D-U-N-S 78-268-1089
■ WATSONVILLE HEALTHCARE MANAGEMENT LLC
WATSONVILLE COMMUNITY HOSPITAL
(*Suby of* QUORUM HEALTH CORP) ★
75 Neilson St, Watsonville, CA 95076-2468
Tel (831) 724-4741 *Founded/Ownrshp* 2016
Sales 156.2MM *EMP* 1[E]
SIC 8062 General medical & surgical hospitals
CEO: Audra Earl
CFO: Rachel Jones
Ch: Mathias Daniels
Doctor: Frank Ravago

D-U-N-S 62-411-3341 IMP/EXP
WATTS CONSTRUCTORS LLC
(*Suby of* WEITZ CO LLC) ★
6862 Elm St Ste 500, Mc Lean, VA 22101-3838
Tel (703) 358-8800 *Founded/Ownrshp* 2006
Sales 166.9MM[E] *EMP* 500[E]
SIC 1542 1623 Nonresidential construction; Underground utilities contractor
**Mng Dir:* Nick Katsiotis

D-U-N-S 00-100-3268 IMP/EXP
■ WATTS REGULATOR CO
(*Suby of* WATTS WATER TECHNOLOGIES INC) ★
815 Chestnut St, North Andover, MA 01845-6098
Tel (978) 689-6000 *Founded/Ownrshp* 1874
Sales 512.0MM[E] *EMP* 2,249
SIC 3491 3494 Pressure valves & regulators, industrial; Water works valves; Plumbing & heating valves
CFO: William C McCartney

D-U-N-S 04-537-6100
WATTS TRUCKING SERVICE INC
525 17th St, Rock Island, IL 61201-8131
Tel (309) 788-7700 *Founded/Ownrshp* 1964
Sales 354.2MM[E] *EMP* 700
SIC 4953

D-U-N-S 15-216-3093 IMP/EXP
▲ WATTS WATER TECHNOLOGIES INC
815 Chestnut St, North Andover, MA 01845-6009
Tel (978) 688-1811 *Founded/Ownrshp* 1874
Sales 1.4MMM *EMP* 5,000
Tkr Sym WTS *Exch* NYS
SIC 3491 3494 Industrial valves; Pressure valves & regulators, industrial; Water works valves; Plumbing & heating valves
Pr: Robert J Pagano Jr
Pr: Elie Melhem
CFO: Todd A Trapp
Bd of Dir: Robert Ayers
Ofcr: Debra J Ogston
Ex VP: Edward Holtgraver
Ex VP: Kenneth R Lepage
Ex VP: Ram Ramakrishnan
VP: Ernie Elliott
VP: Kari Henrikson
VP: Chris Jamieson
VP: Randy Lambert
VP: Ken Nolan
VP: Timothy O'Neil
VP: Pinja Pirseyedi
VP: Amy Provost
VP: Craig Schmitt
VP: Douglas White
VP: Andrew Windsor
Board of Directors: Robert L Ayers, Bernard Baert, Richard J Cathcart, Christopher L Conway, W Craig Kissel, John K McGillicuddy, Joseph T Noonan, Joseph W Reitmeier

D-U-N-S 07-016-2862
WAUBONSEE COMMUNITY COLLEGE FOUNDATION
At Waubonsee Dr Rr 47, Sugar Grove, IL 60554
Tel (630) 466-7900 *Founded/Ownrshp* 1978
Sales 22.8MM *EMP* 1,502
Accts Sikich Llp Naperville Illino
SIC 8222 Community college
Pr: Christine J Sobek
Ch: Richard W Dickson
VP: Teresa Hummell
Exec: Michele Needham
Off Mgr: Mary Borneman
Netwrk Eng: Christopher C Marczewski
Psych: Kristin Santillan

D-U-N-S 07-456-3354
WAUKEGAN COMMUNITY UNIT SCHOOL DISTRICT 60
1201 N Sheridan Rd, Waukegan, IL 60085-2081
Tel (847) 360-7028 *Founded/Ownrshp* 1970
Sales 60.5MM[E] *EMP* 1,300
SIC 8211 Public elementary & secondary schools

D-U-N-S 78-422-2957
■ WAUKEGAN ILLINOIS HOSPITAL CO LLC
VISTA MEDICAL CENTER EAST
(*Suby of* QUORUM HEALTH CORP) ★
1324 N Sheridan Rd, Waukegan, IL 60085-2161
Tel (847) 360-3000 *Founded/Ownrshp* 2016
Sales 200.2MM *EMP* 3[E]
SIC 8062 General medical & surgical hospitals
Pathlgst: Himani Dalia
Pathlgst: Srinidhi Musunuri

D-U-N-S 00-607-8703 IMP
■ WAUKESHA BEARINGS CORP
WAUKESHA MAGNETIC BEARINGS
(*Suby of* DOVER ENGINEERED SYSTEMS INC) ★
W231n2811 Roundy Cir E, Pewaukee, WI 53072-6245
Tel (262) 506-3000 *Founded/Ownrshp* 1950
Sales 105.3MM[E] *EMP* 650
SIC 3568 3566

D-U-N-S 07-383-6033
WAUKESHA COUNTY AREA TECHNICAL COLLEGE DISTRICT
WCTC
800 Main St, Pewaukee, WI 53072-4601
Tel (262) 691-5566 *Founded/Ownrshp* 1950
Sales 30.6MM *EMP* 1,320
Accts Baker Tilly Virchow Krause Ll
SIC 8222 Technical institute
Pr: Kaylen Betzig
**CFO:* Cary Tessmann
Admn Mgr: Mary K Nicola
Web Dev: Jesse Poser
Psych: Colleen Gonzalez

WAUKESHA ELECTRIC
See SPX TRANSFORMER SOLUTIONS INC

WAUKESHA MAGNETIC BEARINGS
See WAUKESHA BEARINGS CORP

D-U-N-S 07-386-1106
WAUKESHA MEMORIAL HOSPITAL INC
725 American Ave, Waukesha, WI 53188-5099
Tel (262) 928-2292 *Founded/Ownrshp* 1956
Sales 460.1MM *EMP* 2,071
Accts Plante & Moran Pllc Grand Ra
SIC 8062 General medical & surgical hospitals
Pr: John Robertstad
Chf Rad: Gary A Beyer
**CFO:* Robert W Mlynarek
VP: Bob Sievert
Pathlgst: Steven Dubner
Ansthlgy: Robert Purtock
Doctor: Mark D Biehl

D-U-N-S 06-045-8049
WAUKESHA SCHOOL DISTRICT
222 Maple Ave, Waukesha, WI 53186-4725
Tel (262) 970-1038 *Founded/Ownrshp* 2004
Sales 117.3MM[E] *EMP* 1,500
Accts Clifton Gunderson Llp Milwauk
SIC 8211 Public elementary school; Public junior high school; Public senior high school
Bd of Dir: William Baumgart
**Prin:* Rick Nettesheim
Ex Dir: James P Haessly
CTO: Faith E Lincicum
Mktg Mgr: Christopher Schulteis

D-U-N-S 02-359-4377
■ WAUKESHA WHOLESALE FOODS INC
DIERKS WAUKESHA
(*Suby of* US FOODS INC) ★
900 Gale St, Waukesha, WI 53186-2515
Tel (262) 542-8841 *Founded/Ownrshp* 2015
Sales 201.9MM[E] *EMP* 220[E]
SIC 5141 Groceries, general line
CEO: Eric Muehl
**Pr:* Thomas Muehl
**CFO:* Kevin Musser
Ex VP: Wes Muehl
IT Man: Dave Pfannerstill

D-U-N-S 00-793-3195 IMP/EXP
WAUKESHA-PEARCE INDUSTRIES INC (TX)
(*Suby of* PEARCE INDUSTRIES INC) ★
12320 Main St, Houston, TX 77035-6206
Tel (713) 723-1050 *Founded/Ownrshp* 1924, 1976
Sales 423.7MM *EMP* 600
SIC 5084 5082 3621 Engines, gasoline; Compressors, except air conditioning; General construction machinery & equipment; Generators & sets, electric
CEO: Al H Bentley
**Pr:* Laurie Leshin
**Pr:* Louis M Pearce III
**Treas:* Gary M Pearce
Ofcr: Darrel Landry
VP: Jim Adian
**VP:* G Mike Green
**VP:* Robert Lyde
**VP:* Bruce Trusdale
Rgnl Mgr: Frankie Baird
Rgnl Mgr: Scott Lukes

D-U-N-S 00-613-3441 IMP/EXP
WAUPACA FOUNDRY INC
(*Suby of* HITACHI METALS AMERICA LTD) ★
1955 Brunner Dr, Waupaca, WI 54981-8866
Tel (715) 258-6611 *Founded/Ownrshp* 2016
Sales 261.7MM[E] *EMP* 4,396
SIC 3321 Gray iron castings; Ductile iron castings
Pr: Michael Nikolai
**CFO:* Rob Johnson
VP: Darrell Oligney
**VP:* John Wiesbrock
Prgrm Mgr: Mary King
Plnt Mgr: Mark Muszynski
Plnt Mgr: Jeff Walters
Prd Mgr: Brian Schultz
Ql Cn Mgr: Steve Ebert
VP Sls: Kris Pfaehler
Mktg Dir: James Newsome

D-U-N-S 01-937-1517 IMP
WAUSAU COATED PRODUCTS INC
7801 Stewart Ave, Wausau, WI 54401-9379
Tel (715) 848-2741 *Founded/Ownrshp* 1981
Sales 90.0MM[E] *EMP* 200
SIC 2672 3554

D-U-N-S 03-017-9667
■ WAUSAU FINANCIAL SYSTEMS INC (WI)
(*Suby of* DELUXE CORP) ★
400 Westwood Dr, Wausau, WI 54401-7801
Tel (715) 359-0427 *Founded/Ownrshp* 1974, 2014
Sales 123.4MM[E] *EMP* 390
Accts Mcgladrey & Pullen Madison W
SIC 7373 Computer integrated systems design
Pr: Gary Cawthorne
**COO:* Tim Patneaude
**CFO:* Kelly Nansey
Ex VP: Stuart Coppens
**Ex VP:* Mark S Melillo
Ex VP: Mark Melillo
**Ex VP:* Kathy Strasser
Sr VP: Steve Buchberger
Sr VP: J Pitman
VP: Lawrence Buettner
VP: Tom Oberholtzer
VP: Darren Snodgrass
VP Bus Dev: Jeff Macdonald

D-U-N-S 00-613-5792 IMP/EXP
WAUSAU PAPER CORP (WI)
(*Suby of* SCA AMERICAS) ★
100 Paper Pl, Kronenwetter, WI 54455-6000
Tel (715) 693-4470 *Founded/Ownrshp* 2015
Sales 352.0MM *EMP* 900
SIC 2621 Paper mills; Towels, tissues & napkins: paper & stock; Specialty or chemically treated papers
Pr: Donald E Lewis
CFO: Sherri L Lemmer
VP: Tom Craven
**VP:* Kevin S Gorman
VP: Curt Schmidt
Dist Mgr: Charles Adams
IT Man: Ken Hallas
Mfg Mgr: Steven Pearson
Opers Mgr: Dave Meyer
Mktg Mgr: Ronald Boucher
Manager: Doug Jordan

D-U-N-S 79-155-2230 IMP/EXP
WAUSAU PAPER MILLS LLC
100 Paper Pl, Kronenwetter, WI 54455-6000
Tel (715) 693-4470 *Founded/Ownrshp* 2006
Sales NA *EMP* 1,233[E]
SIC 2621

D-U-N-S 79-669-1017 IMP/EXP
WAUSAU PAPER TOWEL & TISSUE LLC
BAY WEST PAPER
(*Suby of* WAUSAU PAPER CORP) ★
1150 Industry Rd, Harrodsburg, KY 40330-9100
Tel (859) 734-0538 *Founded/Ownrshp* 2007
Sales 109.2MM[E] *EMP* 656[E]
SIC 2621 Paper mills
Pr: Matthew Urmanski

D-U-N-S 08-618-8760
WAUSAU SERVICE CORP
(*Suby of* LIBERTY MUTUAL INSURANCE CO) ★
2000 Westwood Dr, Wausau, WI 54401-7802
Tel (715) 845-5211 *Founded/Ownrshp* 1999
Sales NA *EMP* 500
SIC 6331 6311 Fire, marine & casualty insurance & carriers; Life insurance carriers
Pr: Dwight E Davis
**Ch Bd:* Dimon Richard McFerson
Treas: Willard C Sanford
VP: Richard J Byron

D-U-N-S 02-360-3202
WAUSAU SUPPLY CO
7102 Commerce Dr, Schofield, WI 54476-4565
Tel (715) 359-2524 *Founded/Ownrshp* 1946
Sales 607.2MM[E] *EMP* 600
SIC 5033 Roofing, asphalt & sheet metal; Siding, except wood; Insulation, thermal
CEO: Jody Maier
**Pr:* Ronald L Klimisch
COO: Tom Woyak
**CFO:* Charley Hoolig
**Treas:* Tom Thornton
VP: Joe Jordan
**VP:* Joseph Jordan
Mfg Dir: Darin Holt
Sls Mgr: Micah Browning
Sales Asso: Ann Lake

D-U-N-S 02-353-2609 IMP
WAUSAU TILE INC
9001 Business Highway 51, Rothschild, WI 54474-1800
Tel (715) 359-3121 *Founded/Ownrshp* 1953
Sales 86.6MM[E] *EMP* 540
SIC 3272 Tile, precast terrazzo or concrete
Ch Bd: William Creske
**Pr:* Brian Burelle
**CEO:* Edward J Creske
Ofcr: Steve Schinker
Exec: Yvonne Smith
Div Mgr: Todd Treu
Opers Mgr: Dave Ott
Genl Couns: Steve Schnicker

WAUSAU WINDOW AND WALL SYSTEM
See APOGEE WAUSAU GROUP INC

D-U-N-S 10-008-4631
WAUWATOSA SCHOOL DISTRICT
12121 W North Ave, Wauwatosa, WI 53226-2096
Tel (414) 773-1000 *Founded/Ownrshp* 1960
Sales 85.6MM *EMP* 830
Accts Feld Schumacher & Company Ll
SIC 8211 Public elementary & secondary schools
Teacher Pr: Craig Hubbell
Instr Medi: Tim Patten

WAVE
See ARMSTRONG WORTHINGTON VENTURE

WAVE BROADBAND
See WAVEDIVISION HOLDINGS LLC

D-U-N-S 10-210-4689
WAVE ELECTRONICS INC
8648 Glenmont Dr Ste 130, Houston, TX 77036-1930
Tel (713) 849-2710 *Founded/Ownrshp* 2001
Sales 96.9MM *EMP* 100
Accts Eepb Pc Houston Texas
SIC 5064 Electrical appliances, television & radio
CEO: Gary Wermuth
**Pr:* Mark Fukuda
**VP:* Ainslie Fukuda
**VP:* Christopher Hill
**VP:* Susan Sabath
**VP:* Bryan Stewart

D-U-N-S 07-520-5310
WAVEDIVISION HOLDINGS LLC
WAVE BROADBAND
401 Kirkland Prk Pl Ste 500, Kirkland, WA 98033
Tel (425) 576-8200 *Founded/Ownrshp* 2003
Sales 284.9MM *EMP* 817
SIC 4841 Cable television services
CEO: Steven Weed
Pr: Doug Woods
Bd of Dir: Jerry Jacobsen
Ex VP: Patrick Knorr
Ex VP: Charlie Watters
VP: Darren Fry
VP: Jesse Gregory
VP: Angela Higham
VP: David Lampkin
VP: Graham Pugh
Dir Surg: Jody Veeder

D-U-N-S 05-096-4600
WAVERLEY GROUP INC
460 Briarwood Dr Ste 410, Jackson, MS 39206-3026
Tel (601) 956-1013 *Founded/Ownrshp* 1982
Sales 45.4MM[E] *EMP* 1,900
SIC 8051 Convalescent home with continuous nursing care
CEO: Kim Cerny
**Pr:* Bobby Arnold
**VP:* Scott Edwards
Off Mgr: Kim Ahart
Off Mgr: Charlcy York

D-U-N-S 08-011-7548
WAVODYNE THERAPEUTICS INC
150 Lucius Gordon Dr, West Henrietta, NY 14586-9687
Tel (954) 632-6630 *Founded/Ownrshp* 2015
Sales 500.0MM *EMP* 2
SIC 2834 Druggists' preparations (pharmaceuticals)
CEO: James New

D-U-N-S 00-228-4958
WAWA INC
260 W Baltimore Pike, Media, PA 19063-5620
Tel (610) 358-8000 *Founded/Ownrshp* 1969
Sales 9.0MMM *EMP* 15,000
SIC 5411 2026

D-U-N-S 07-916-4395
WAWANESA GENERAL INSURANCE CO
WAWANSEA GENERAL INSURANCE
(*Suby of* WAWANESA MUTUAL INSURANCE COMPANY, THE)
9050 Friars Rd Ste 200, San Diego, CA 92108-5800
Tel (619) 285-6020 *Founded/Ownrshp* 1974
Sales NA *EMP* 500
SIC 6331 Automobile insurance; Property damage insurance
CEO: Jeff Goy
**CFO:* Larry Smith
IT Man: David Johnson

WAWANSEA GENERAL INSURANCE
See WAWANESA GENERAL INSURANCE CO

D-U-N-S 00-921-1160 IMP
WAWONA FROZEN FOODS
100 W Alluvial Ave, Clovis, CA 93611-9176
Tel (559) 299-2901 *Founded/Ownrshp* 1953
Sales 394.0MM[E] *EMP* 2,200
SIC 2037 Fruits, quick frozen & cold pack (frozen)
Pr: William Smittcamp
**Ch Bd:* Earl Smittcamp
**Sec:* Muriel Smittcamp
QA Dir: Duncan Donaldbe
Opers Mgr: Brian Losson
VP Mktg: Blake Smittcamp

D-U-N-S 09-831-9168 EXP
WAWONA PACKING CO LLC
12133 Avenue 408, Cutler, CA 93615-2056
Tel (559) 528-4000 *Founded/Ownrshp* 1999
Sales 57.6MM[E] *EMP* 1,400
SIC 0723 Fruit (fresh) packing services
Sales Exec: Mark Berlinger
Sales Asso: Ben Vived

WAXIE SANITARY SUPPLY
See WAXIES ENTERPRISES INC

D-U-N-S 02-914-2577
WAXIES ENTERPRISES INC
WAXIE SANITARY SUPPLY
9353 Waxie Way, San Diego, CA 92123-1350
Tel (858) 292-8111 *Founded/Ownrshp* 1945
Sales 220.1MM[E] *EMP* 815
SIC 5087

D-U-N-S 00-445-0268 IMP
WAXMAN INDUSTRIES INC (DE)
24460 Aurora Rd, Cleveland, OH 44146-1794
Tel (440) 439-1830 *Founded/Ownrshp* 1962
Sales 100.0MM *EMP* 425
SIC 5072 5074 3494 3491 3432 Hardware; Plumbing & hydronic heating supplies; Valves & pipe fittings; Industrial valves; Plumbing fixture fittings & trim
Pr: Larry Waxman
Ch Bd: Armond Waxman
Ch Bd: Melvin Waxman
Pr: Laurence Waxman
CFO: Mark Wester
Sr VP: Robert Feldman
Sr VP: Steve Hanneman
Sr VP: Michael Pendry
VP: Maureen Crawford
VP: Ben Maibach
VP: Michelle Salimbeni
VP: Suzanne Sharkus
Board of Directors: Irving Z Friedman, John Peters, Mark Reichenbaum, Judy Robins, Todd Waxman

D-U-N-S 00-600-6423
WAY BAKERY (IN)
(*Suby of* AUNT MILLIES BAKERIES) ★
2100 Enterprise St, Jackson, MI 49203-6412
Tel (517) 787-6720 *Founded/Ownrshp* 1884
Sales 56.9MM[E] *EMP* 1,600
Accts Coopers & Lybrand
SIC 2051 Bread, cake & related products; Buns, bread type: fresh or frozen; Pastries, e.g. danish: except frozen; Rolls, bread type: fresh or frozen
Pr: John F Popp
VP: Jay E Miller
Sls Mgr: Frank Marriott

D-U-N-S 07-972-3684
▲ WAYFAIR INC
4 Copley Pl Ste 700, Boston, MA 02116-6513
Tel (617) 532-6100 *Founded/Ownrshp* 2002
Sales 1.3MMM *EMP* 3,000
Tkr Sym W *Exch* NYS
SIC 5961 Catalog & mail-order houses
Ch Bd: Niraj Shah
**Ch Bd:* Steven Conine
COO: James Savarese
CFO: Michael Fleisher
Ofcr: Nicholas Malone
Sr VP: Edmond Macri
Sr VP: John Mulliken
Sr VP: Stephen Oblak
VP: Chad Ghosn
VP: Nancy T Go
VP: Al Gonzalez
VP: Liz Graham
VP: Eric Klose
VP: Michael O'Hanlon
VP: Doran Robinson
VP: Sharif Sleiman
VP: Sarah Whitman
Assoc Dir: Zachary Nicholson
Assoc Dir: Taylor Piersiak
Board of Directors: Julie Bradley, Alex Finkelstein, Robert Gamgort, Michael Kumin, Ian Lane, James R Miller

D-U-N-S 11-208-4681 IMP/EXP
■ WAYFAIR LLC
(*Suby of* WAYFAIR INC) ★
4 Copley Pl Ste 700, Boston, MA 02116-6513
Tel (617) 532-6100 *Founded/Ownrshp* 2008
Sales 601.0MM[E] *EMP* 1,500[E]
SIC 5963 5712 5023 Home related products, direct sales; Furniture stores; Kitchenware
CEO: Niraj Shah
**COO:* James Savarese
**CFO:* Michael Fleisher
**CFO:* Nicholas C Malone
VP: Edmond Macri
VP: John Mulliken
VP: Michael O'Hanlon
Assoc Dir: Michael Beaulieu
Assoc Dir: Mitch Williams
Genl Mgr: Drew Loring
Snr Sftwr: Adam Baratz

D-U-N-S 09-130-7819
WAYNE AUTOMATIC FIRE SPRINKLERS INC (FL)
222 Capitol Ct, Ocoee, FL 34761-3019
Tel (407) 656-3030 *Founded/Ownrshp* 1978
Sales 118.5MM[E] *EMP* 500
Accts Vestal & Wiler Cpas
SIC 1711 Fire sprinkler system installation
CEO: Wayne H Gey
**CFO:* Douglas Eric Morris
Exec: Jackie Hart
Sls Mgr: Troy Bohrer

D-U-N-S 02-445-9109
WAYNE BAILEY INC
WAYNE E BAILEY PRODUCE COMPANY
490 Old Hwy 74, Chadbourn, NC 28431
Tel (910) 654-5163 *Founded/Ownrshp* 1936
Sales 132.5MM[E] *EMP* 250
SIC 5148 0139

WAYNE COUNTY
See COUNTY OF WAYNE

D-U-N-S 14-230-3861
WAYNE COUNTY AIRPORT AUTHORITY
DETROIT METROPOLITAN AIRPORT
1 Detroit Metro Airport, Detroit, MI 48242-1004
Tel (734) 247-7364 *Founded/Ownrshp* 2002
Sales 349.7MM *EMP* 675[E]
Accts Plante & Moran Pllc Southfiel
SIC 4581 Airports, flying fields & services
CEO: Thomas Naughton
Ofcr: Alan Berezansky
Ofcr: Matthew Rager
VP: Arun Gulati
Exec: Danna Fenroy
**Prin:* Lester Robinson
Mng Dir: Matthew McGowan
Dept Mgr: Laura Burns
Dept Mgr: Shantryce Craig
Dept Mgr: Jim Doemer
Counsel: Kevin Clark
Board of Directors: Alfred R Glancy III

D-U-N-S 05-219-9015
WAYNE COUNTY PUBLIC SCHOOLS FOUNDATION INC
2001 Royall Ave, Goldsboro, NC 27534-7407
Tel (919) 705-6117 *Founded/Ownrshp* 1985
Sales 126.0MM[E] *EMP* 3,000
Accts Pittard Perry & Crone Inc G
SIC 8211 Public elementary & secondary schools
Dir Sec: Allen Smith
Pr Dir: Ken Derksen

D-U-N-S 07-979-9673
WAYNE COUNTY SCHOOLS
212 N Court St, Wayne, WV 25570-1141
Tel (304) 272-5116 *Founded/Ownrshp* 2015
Sales 9.9MM[E] *EMP* 1,229[E]
SIC 8211 Public elementary & secondary schools
Dir Sec: Mike D Hart

D-U-N-S 00-391-9172
WAYNE D ENTERPRISES INC
WAYNE WORKWEAR
14300 Hollister St, Houston, TX 77066-5704
Tel (713) 856-0300 *Founded/Ownrshp* 1986
Sales 210.4MM[E] *EMP* 200[E]
SIC 5136 5199 Uniforms, men's & boys'; Gifts & novelties
CEO: Denise Howard
**Pr:* Jim Kirkman
**CFO:* Clay Hughes
**Sec:* Dorothy Kirkman
**Ex VP:* Ronnie Howard
Sales Asso: Steve McClellan

WAYNE DALTON
See HRH DOOR CORP

WAYNE E BAILEY PRODUCE COMPANY
See WAYNE BAILEY INC

D-U-N-S 07-976-9086
WAYNE FARMS INC
(*Suby of* CONTINENTAL GRAIN CO) ★
4110 Continental Dr, Oakwood, GA 30566-2800
Tel (678) 450-3111 *Founded/Ownrshp* 2015
Sales 74.6M[E] *EMP* 9,000
SIC 0751 Poultry services
Pr: Elton Maddox
**Ch Bd:* Michael J Zimmerman
**COO:* Clint Rivers
**Ofcr:* David Malfitano
**VP:* Courtney Fazekas
**VP:* John Flood
Board of Directors: Mitch Adamek, Paul Fribourg, Carl Hausmann, Mark Kehaya, Teresa McCaslin

D-U-N-S 79-761-3275 EXP
WAYNE FARMS LLC
(*Suby of* CONTINENTAL GRAIN CO) ★
4110 Continental Dr, Oakwood, GA 30566-2800
Tel (770) 538-2120 *Founded/Ownrshp* 2000
Sales 2.2MMM[E] *EMP* 9,200
SIC 2015 Poultry slaughtering & processing
CEO: Elton H Maddox
**CFO:* Aaron Leach
**VP:* Chris Baldner
**VP:* Steve Clever
**VP:* Courtney Fazekas
**VP:* John Flood
**VP:* David Malfitano
**VP:* Clint Rivers
Area Mgr: Jack Sherwood
Genl Mgr: Billy Erp
QA Dir: Sarah Clark

D-U-N-S 07-946-0335
WAYNE FUELING SYSTEMS LLC (WV)
3814 Jarrett Way, Austin, TX 78728-1212
Tel (512) 388-8311 *Founded/Ownrshp* 2014
Sales 201.9MM[E] *EMP* 254[E]
SIC 1389 Pipe testing, oil field service
CEO: Neil Thomas
CFO: Jeffrey Lass
Treas: John Hall

D-U-N-S 14-436-2803
WAYNE HEALTH CORP
2700 Wayne Memorial Dr, Goldsboro, NC 27534-9494
Tel (919) 736-1110 *Founded/Ownrshp* 1985
Sales 322.0M *EMP* 1,400
Accts Larsonallen Llp Charlotte Nc
SIC 8741 Hospital management
Pr: William Paugh
CFO: Rebecca Craig
Exec: Kim Anderson

D-U-N-S 07-662-1499
WAYNE J GRIFFIN ELECTRIC INC
116 Hopping Brook Rd, Holliston, MA 01746-1455
Tel (508) 429-8830 *Founded/Ownrshp* 1978
Sales 303.7MM *EMP* 1,100
Accts Kirkland Albrecht & Fredericks
SIC 1731 General electrical contractor
Pr: Wayne J Griffin
**VP:* Jacqueline Griffin
Off Mgr: Sheryl Casey

WAYNE MEMORIAL HEALTH SYSTEM
See WAYNE MEMORIAL HOSPITAL

D-U-N-S 06-959-7250
WAYNE MEMORIAL HOSPITAL
WAYNE MEMORIAL HEALTH SYSTEM
601 Park St, Honesdale, PA 18431-1498
Tel (570) 253-8100 *Founded/Ownrshp* 1900
Sales 84.4MM *EMP* 600[E]
Accts Bkd Llp Springfield Mo
SIC 8062 General medical & surgical hospitals
CEO: David Hoff
**Ch Bd:* Helge Mortensen
COO: John Conte
Dir OR: Elizabeth Korb
Dir Inf Cn: Kay Daley

D-U-N-S 07-557-4855
WAYNE MEMORIAL HOSPITAL INC
2700 Wayne Memorial Dr, Goldsboro, NC 27534-9459
Tel (919) 736-1110 *Founded/Ownrshp* 1885
Sales 196.6MM *EMP* 1,700
SIC 8062 General medical & surgical hospitals
Pr: J William Paugh
COO: Thomas Bradshaw
Dir Bus: Angie Smith
Adm Dir: Jonathan McCarthy
CTO: Debbie Wiggs
IT Man: Rhonda Mercer
Software D: Demarcus Council
Software D: Rose Esposito
Ansthlgy: Christian Hodach
Doctor: Ryan Hoover

D-U-N-S 19-962-5992
WAYNE NEWARK COMMUNITY HOSPITAL
1250 Driving Park Ave, Newark, NY 14513-1057
Tel (315) 332-2244 *Founded/Ownrshp* 1957
Sales 85.9MM *EMP* 600
Accts Ernst & Young Us Llp Buffal
SIC 8062 General medical & surgical hospitals
Chf OB: Abraham Lichtmacher
Sr VP: Richard Gangemi
Dir Bus: Douglas Stark
Chf Nrs Of: Cheryl Sheridan
Adm Dir: Vicki Files
Prac Mgr: Gail Bellanca
Prac Mgr: Lisa Ells
Doctor: Enzo Fallone
Doctor: Fadi Hatem
Doctor: Brooke Henninger
Doctor: Robert Mayo

D-U-N-S 06-428-6495
WAYNE PUBLIC LIBRARY INC
461 Valley Rd, Wayne, NJ 07470-3557
Tel (973) 694-4272 *Founded/Ownrshp* 1940
Sales 83.0MM *EMP* 30
SIC 8231 Public library
Ex Dir: Jody Treadway
**Pr:* Franco Mazzei
**VP:* Micahel Kealy

D-U-N-S 00-196-2224 IMP
WAYNE STATE UNIVERSITY (MI)
656 W Kirby 4200 Faculty, Detroit, MI 48202
Tel (313) 577-2230 *Founded/Ownrshp* 1868
Sales 708.7MM[E] *EMP* 8,500
Accts Plante & Moran Pllc Clinton
SIC 8221 University
Pr: Roy Wilson
Pr: Phil Cunningham
Pr: Christine Hansen
Pr: David W Ripple
CFO: Rick Nork
Ofcr: Fawne Allossery
Ofcr: Rasheeda Zafar
Assoc VP: James Barbret
Assoc VP: Joan Dunbar
Assoc VP: Nabelah Ghareeb
VP: Chacona Johnson
VP: Ryan Kelly
VP: Stephen Lanier
VP: Patrick Lindsey
VP: Joseph Rankin
VP: Hilary Ratner
VP: Joseph F Sawasky
VP: Howard Shapiro
VP: Ayanna Smith
VP: Matthew Theut
VP: Margaret Winters

WAYNE STATE UNIVERSITY PHYSICI
See UNIVERSITY PHYSICIAN GROUP

D-U-N-S 09-686-7643
WAYNE TOWNSHIP BOARD OF EDUCATION
50 Nellis Dr, Wayne, NJ 07470-3555
Tel (973) 633-3000 *Founded/Ownrshp* 1894
Sales 127.8MM[E] *EMP* 2,000
SIC 8211 School board
Pr: Eileen Albanese

D-U-N-S 07-979-9203
WAYNE TOWNSHIP PUBLIC SCHOOLS
50 Nellis Dr, Wayne, NJ 07470-3555
Tel (973) 633-3000 *Founded/Ownrshp* 2015
Sales 20.1MM[E] *EMP* 1,257[E]
SIC 8211 Public elementary & secondary schools
MIS Dir: Mary Deininger
Teacher Pr: Claudia Olivo
HC Dir: Suzanne Koransky

WAYNE WORKWEAR
See WAYNE D ENTERPRISES INC

D-U-N-S 07-276-8195
WAYNE-WESTLAND COMMUNITY SCHOOLS
36745 Marquette St, Westland, MI 48185-3289
Tel (734) 419-2000 *Founded/Ownrshp* 1850
Sales 146.3MM *EMP* 2,000[E]
Accts Plante & Moran Pllc
SIC 8211 Public elementary & secondary schools; High school, junior or senior
Treas: Shawna Walker
Trst: Melandie Hines
VP: Tom Buckalew
Genl Mgr: David Kaumeyer
Pr Dir: Jenny Johnson
Psych: Rose Fricke

D-U-N-S 09-265-7548
WAYNES FOOD MARKET INC (NY)
235 E Division St, Watertown, NY 13601-1511
Tel (315) 493-2854 *Founded/Ownrshp* 2000
Sales 2.5MM *EMP* 2,000
SIC 5411 Grocery stores
Pr: Allen W Williams
**VP:* Barbara Williams

D-U-N-S 04-853-0240
▲ WAYSIDE TECHNOLOGY GROUP INC
1157 Shrewsbury Ave, Shrewsbury, NJ 07702-4321
Tel (732) 389-8950 *Founded/Ownrshp* 1982
Sales 382.0MM *EMP* 132[E]
Tkr Sym WSTG *Exch* NGM
SIC 5045 7373 7379 Computers, peripherals & software; Computer software; Computer integrated systems design; Computer related consulting services
Ch Bd: Simon F Nynens
Ex VP: William Botti
VP: Brian Gilbertson
VP: Vito Legrottaglie
VP: Jacqui Nyborg
VP: Kevin Scull
Board of Directors: Mark T Boyer, Steve Dewindt, Mike Faith, Diana Kurty, F Duffield Meyercord, Allan D Weingarten

D-U-N-S 02-616-9326
WAYZATA INDEPENDENT SCHOOL DISTRICT 284
210 County Road 101 N, Wayzata, MN 55391-2847
Tel (763) 745-5000 *Founded/Ownrshp* 1900
Sales 56.0MM[E] *EMP* 1,527
Accts Larson Allen Llp Minneapolis
SIC 8211 Public elementary & secondary schools
**Ex Dir:* Annie Doughty
Ex Dir: Jim Westrum
Dir Sec: Jordan Curzon
MIS Dir: Jill Schwint
Sls&Mrk Ex: Tika Kude

D-U-N-S 14-848-6934
▲ WAYZATA INVESTMENT PARTNERS LLC
701 Lake St E Ste 300, Wayzata, MN 55391-1894
Tel (952) 345-0700 *Founded/Ownrshp* 2004
Sales 600.7MM[E] *EMP* 2,506[E]

SIC 6799 Investors
Mng Pt: Patrick Halloran
Genl Couns: Steven Adams

WAZEE A TIMKEN BRAND
See TIMKEN MOTOR & CRANE SERVICES LLC

WB
See WILLIAMS BROTHERS CONSTRUCTION CO INC

WB
See WOLVERINE BRASS INC

WB JOHNSTON GRAIN COMPANY
See JOHNSTON ENTERPRISES INC

WB&T
See WILSON BANK AND TRUST

WBA CONSTRUCTION
See WESTERN BUILDERS OF AMARILLO INC

WBBHTV
See WATERMAN BROADCASTING CORP OF FLORIDA

D-U-N-S 06-668-9993 IMP/EXP
WBC GROUP LLC
MEYERPT
6333 Hudson Crossing Pkwy, Hudson, OH 44236-4346
Tel (800) 472-4221 *Founded/Ownrshp* 1997
Sales 88.2MM[E] *EMP* 153[E]
SIC 5122 5047 3843 Vitamins & minerals; Pharmaceuticals; Medical & hospital equipment; Dental equipment & supplies
CEO: Ron Harrington
Treas: Elizabeth Cross

WBCI
See WILLIAMS BROTHERS CONSTRUCTION INC

D-U-N-S 07-865-9451
WBG-PSS HOLDINGS LLC
3231 Se 6th Ave, Topeka, KS 66607-2260
Tel (785) 233-5171 *Founded/Ownrshp* 2012
Sales 3.4MMM[E] *EMP* 30,000[E]
SIC 5499 Health & dietetic food stores
CEO: W Paul Jones

D-U-N-S 13-153-7896
■ WBI ENERGY TRANSMISSION INC
(*Suby of* CENTENNIAL ENERGY HOLDINGS INC) ★
1250 W Century Ave, Bismarck, ND 58503-0911
Tel (701) 530-1601 *Founded/Ownrshp* 1982
Sales 192.2MM[E] *EMP* 277
SIC 4922 1311 Natural gas transmission; Natural gas production
Pr: Steven L Bietz
MIS Dir: Nancy Senger
Dir IT: Tim Michelsen

D-U-N-S 11-470-4849
■ WBI HOLDINGS INC
(*Suby of* CENTENNIAL ENERGY HOLDINGS INC) ★
1250 W Century Ave, Bismarck, ND 58503-0911
Tel (701) 530-1600 *Founded/Ownrshp* 1985
Sales 170.5MM[E] *EMP* 450[E]
SIC 4922 1311 Natural gas transmission; Natural gas production
Pr: Steve Bietz
IT Man: Jeremy Zins

D-U-N-S 96-501-7023 IMP/EXP
WBI INC
MICRO SOLUTIONS ENTERPRISES
8201 Woodley Ave, Van Nuys, CA 91406-1231
Tel (800) 673-4968 *Founded/Ownrshp* 1994
Sales 127.0MM[E] *EMP* 600
SIC 3861

WBJB FM
See BROOKDALE COMMUNITY COLLEGE INC

WBS, INC.
See B S W INC

WC
See WATERTOWN COOPERATIVE ELEVATOR ASSOCIATION

WCA
See WHALLEY COMPUTER ASSOCIATES INC

D-U-N-S 19-871-7407
WCA GROUP INC
W C A HOSPITAL
207 Foote Ave, Jamestown, NY 14701-7077
Tel (716) 487-0141 *Founded/Ownrshp* 1982
Sales 111.7MM[E] *EMP* 1,345
SIC 8062 4119 General medical & surgical hospitals; Ambulance service
CEO: Betsy T Wright
Pr: Mary Bosek
**CFO:* Chuck Iverson
Ofcr: Robert Piede
Off Mgr: Tammara Lchodges
IT Man: Brian Wilshire
Ansthlgy: Mabel T Crosby
HC Dir: Dianne French
Pgrm Dir: Michele Harms

WCA HOSPITAL
See OCCUPATIONAL HEALTH SERVICE

D-U-N-S 14-456-8297
WCA WASTE CORP
(*Suby of* COD INTERMEDIATE LLC) ★
1330 Post Oak Blvd # 3000, Houston, TX 77056-3040
Tel (713) 292-2400 *Founded/Ownrshp* 2012
Sales 761.8MM[E] *EMP* 1,058[E]
SIC 4953 Refuse collection & disposal services; Rubbish collection & disposal; Sanitary landfill operation; Recycling, waste materials
CEO: William K Caesar
**Ch Bd:* Paul Mitchener
**CFO:* Dianna Cervantes
Sr VP: Tom J Fatjo III
**VP:* Joseph J Scarano Jr

D-U-N-S 03-208-8089
WCAMPBELL SUPPLY CO LLC
(*Suby of* W CAMPBELL HOLDINGS LLC)
1015 Cranbury S River Rd, Monroe Township, NJ 08831-3408
Tel (732) 287-8884 *Founded/Ownrshp* 2010
Sales 167.0MM *EMP* 140
SIC 5012 Ambulances
Pr: Neal B Campbell
**CFO:* John R Craft
**Prin:* Chuck Yeoman

WCCHD
See WEST CONTRA COSTA HEALTHCARE DISTRICT

D-U-N-S 07-850-1054
WCE OIL FIELD SERVICES LLC
WCE OIL SERVICES
601 Carlson Pkwy Ste 110, Hopkins, MN 55305-5205
Tel (701) 356-7303 *Founded/Ownrshp* 2014
Sales 204.6MM[E] *EMP* 300
SIC 1389 Construction, repair & dismantling services
CEO: Todd Louis
**COO:* Bert Zibrowski
**VP:* Gilbert Garcia
**VP:* Zach Lamppa

WCE OIL SERVICES
See WCE OIL FIELD SERVICES LLC

WCG WORLD
See WEISSCOMM GROUP LTD

WCH
See WOOD COUNTY HOSPITAL ASSOC

D-U-N-S 00-692-0938 IMP
▲ WCI COMMUNITIES INC
24301 Walden Center Dr, Bonita Springs, FL 34134-4965
Tel (239) 947-2600 *Founded/Ownrshp* 2009
Sales 563.6MM *EMP* 689
Tkr Sym WCIC *Exch* NYS
SIC 1531 6531 Operative builders; Real estate brokers & agents
Pr: Keith E Bass
**Ch Bd:* Stephen D Plavin
**CFO:* Russell Devendorf
Treas: Steven C Adelman
**Sr VP:* Paul J Erhardt
**Sr VP:* Vivien N Hastings
Sr VP: Mitchell C Hochberg
**Sr VP:* Reinaldo L Mesa
Sr VP: Albert F Moscato Jr
Sr VP: Douglas L Schwartz
VP: Richard W Barber
VP: Scott Bowles
VP: WCI Communities
VP: Steven T Jolly
VP: Jim Magnusson
VP: Mike Wolf
Board of Directors: Patrick J Bartels Jr, Michelle Mackay, Darius G Nevin, Charles C Reardon, Christopher E Wilson

D-U-N-S 08-050-0429 IMP
WCM HOLDINGS INC
1150 Canal Rd, Cincinnati, OH 45241
Tel (513) 705-2100 *Founded/Ownrshp* 1978
Sales 123.9MM[E] *EMP* 120[E]
SIC 5099 2381 3842 Safety equipment & supplies; Gloves, work: woven or knit, made from purchased materials; Clothing, fire resistant & protective
CEO: David Herche
**Pr:* Tim Fogarty
**Ch:* Melvyn Fisher

WCMU-TV CHANNEL
See CENTRAL MICHIGAN UNIVERSITY

WCNOC
See WOLF CREEK NUCLEAR OPERATING CORP

D-U-N-S 02-793-0460
■ WCO HOTELS INC
DISNEYLAND HOTEL
(*Suby of* WALT DISNEY CO) ★
1150 W Magic Way, Anaheim, CA 92802-2247
Tel (323) 636-3251 *Founded/Ownrshp* 2007
Sales 49.0MM[E] *EMP* 1,700[E]
SIC 7011 5812 Hotels; Eating places
Pr: Tony Bruno
**Prin:* Cynthia Harriss
Genl Mgr: Dan Coleman
**VP Opers:* Hidel Amemiya

WCP SOLUTIONS
See WEST COAST PAPER CO

WCPS
See WASHINGTON COUNTY PUBLIC SCHOOLS

D-U-N-S 13-106-3299
WCR ENTERPRISES INC
ENGLISH VLG MANOR NURSING HM
111 Sequoyah Ln Ste 7, Altus, OK 73521-1756
Tel (580) 482-4203 *Founded/Ownrshp* 1984
Sales 423.0MM *EMP* 248
SIC 8052 8051 Personal care facility; Skilled nursing care facilities
Pr: William C Ray

WCTC
See WAUKESHA COUNTY AREA TECHNICAL COLLEGE DISTRICT

WCTV 6
See GRAY TELEVISION GROUP INC

WD
See WESTERN DIGITAL TECHNOLOGIES

D-U-N-S 10-277-8750 IMP
■ WD MEDIA LLC
(*Suby of* WESTERN DIGITAL CORP) ★
1710 Automation Pkwy, San Jose, CA 95131-1873
Tel (408) 576-2000 *Founded/Ownrshp* 2007
Sales 90.7MM[E] *EMP* 426
SIC 3695 Magnetic & optical recording media
CEO: Timothy D Harris
**CFO:* Kathleen A Bayless
**Treas:* Mr Jan Schwartz
Bd of Dir: Richard A Kashnow
Bd of Dir: Dennis Wolf
**Ex VP:* Peter S Norris
**Ex VP:* Tsutomu T Yamashita
Sr VP: Ray Martin
VP: Gerardo Bertero
**VP:* Edward J Casey
**VP:* Mr Paul G Judy
VP: Tim Starkey
VP: Eric Tu

D-U-N-S 00-823-2449
▲ WD-40 CO
1061 Cudahy Pl, San Diego, CA 92110-3998
Tel (619) 275-1400 *Founded/Ownrshp* 1953
Sales 380.6MM *EMP* 433[E]
Accts Pricewaterhousecoopers Llp Sa
Tkr Sym WDFC *Exch* NGS
SIC 2992 2851 Lubricating oils; Removers & cleaners
Pr: Garry O Ridge
**Ch Bd:* Linda A Lang
CFO: Jay W Rembolt
Div Pres: Michael L Freeman
Ex VP: Michael J Irwin
VP: Ernest Bernarducci PHD
VP: Richard T Clampitt
VP: Stan Sewitch
VP: Stanley A Sewitch
VP: Rick Soares
Mng Dir: Geoffrey J Holdsworth
Board of Directors: Giles H Bateman, Peter D Bewley, Melissa Claassen, Richard A Collato, Mario L Crivello, Linda A Lang, Daniel E Pittard, Gregory A Sandfort

D-U-N-S 03-768-7373
WDC DEVELOPMENT ASSOCIATES LP
WINN DEVELOPMENT COMPANY
6 Faneuil Hall Market Pl, Boston, MA 02109-6115
Tel (617) 742-4500 *Founded/Ownrshp* 1976
Sales 43.5MM[E] *EMP* 1,000
SIC 6552 Subdividers & developers
Pr: Samuel Ross

WDF FEDERATED FIRE PROTECTION
See WDF INC

D-U-N-S 01-242-0824 IMP
WDF INC
WDF FEDERATED FIRE PROTECTION
30 N Macquesten Pkwy, Mount Vernon, NY 10550-1841
Tel (914) 776-8000 *Founded/Ownrshp* 2011
Sales 243.8MM *EMP* 650
Accts Deloitte & Touche Llp Los Ang
SIC 1711 Plumbing contractors
CEO: Lawrence Roman
**CEO:* Neil Walash
COO: Joseph Locurto
**CFO:* Thomas Soucy
CFO: Jim Tully
Ofcr: Diana Dinunzio
Dir IT: Vince Greayson
Dir IT: Neal Locurto

WDI
See WARREN DISTRIBUTING INC

D-U-N-S 14-484-2726
WDPT FILM DISTRIBUTION LLC
500 S Buena Vista St, Burbank, CA 91521-0001
Tel (818) 560-1000 *Founded/Ownrshp* 2004
Sales 94.1MM[E] *EMP* 176[E]
SIC 5065 Video equipment, electronic
Opers Mgr: Dawn Jonasson

D-U-N-S 82-685-7828
WDS INC
WOMEN'S DISTRIBUTION SERVICES
1632 Village Harbor Dr, Clover, SC 29710-9264
Tel (803) 619-0301 *Founded/Ownrshp* 2008
Sales 165.3MM[E] *EMP* 120
SIC 5085 1541 8742 Industrial supplies; Industrial buildings & warehouses; Management consulting services
Pr: Jennifer Maier
**VP:* Brian Ewert
VP: Ward Norris

WDSOURCE.COM
See CWD LLC

WDW SWAN AND DOLPHIN
See WALT DISNEY WORLD SWAN AND DOLPHIN

D-U-N-S 78-759-7996
WE BOWERS INC
12401 Kiln Ct Ste A, Beltsville, MD 20705-1323
Tel (301) 419-2488 *Founded/Ownrshp* 1991
Sales 137.4MM[E] *EMP* 461
SIC 1711

WE ENERGIES
See WISCONSIN GAS LLC

D-U-N-S 00-794-7385 IMP
■ WE ENERGIES (WI)
(*Suby of* WEC ENERGY GROUP INC) ★
231 W Michigan St, Milwaukee, WI 53203-2918
Tel (414) 221-2345 *Founded/Ownrshp* 1896
Sales 3.8MMM *EMP* 3,653[E]
Accts Deloitte & Touche Llp Milwauk
SIC 4911 4924 4961 Electric services; Distribution, electric power; Generation, electric power; Transmission, electric power; Natural gas distribution; Steam heating systems (suppliers of heat); Steam supply systems, including geothermal
Ch Bd: Gale E Klappa
**Pr:* Allen L Leverett
CFO: Scott J Lauber
**Ex VP:* J Kevin Fletcher
Ex VP: Robert M Garvin
**Ex VP:* Susan H Martin
Ex VP: Joan M Shafer
VP: William J Guc
VP: Tom Metcalfe
Counsel: Lynne English
Board of Directors: J Patrick Keyes

D-U-N-S 96-477-0791
WE R WIRELESS INC
520 Fellowship Rd E508, Mount Laurel, NJ 08054-3417
Tel (443) 735-7500 *Founded/Ownrshp* 2012
Sales 127.1MM[E] *EMP* 3[E]
SIC 5999 Mobile telephones & equipment
Ch: Ricky Singh
CEO: Raj Singh

D-U-N-S 00-377-8057
WE TRANSPORT INC (CT)
75 Commercial St, Plainview, NY 11803-2401
Tel (516) 349-8200 *Founded/Ownrshp* 1959, 1963
Sales 111.8MM[E] *EMP* 1,500
SIC 4151 School buses
CEO: Bart Marksohn
**Pr:* Jerome Marksohn
**Sec:* Helena Marksohn
Ofcr: Louis Donaldson
Ofcr: Pamela Strunk
**VP:* Steven Marksohn
**VP:* Cynthia Reed
**VP:* Carmen Tomeo

D-U-N-S 00-990-1943
WEA INSURANCE CORP
45 Nob Hill Rd, Madison, WI 53713-2195
Tel (608) 276-4000 *Founded/Ownrshp* 1970
Sales NA *EMP* 500
SIC 6324 6311 6321 Hospital & medical service plans; Life insurance; Accident & health insurance
CEO: Mark Moody
VP: Vaughn Vance
Exec: Bob Ceder
Admn Mgr: Rhonda Miller
S&M/VP: Jon Klett
Genl Couns: Michael Stoll
Snr PM: Libby Schmidt

D-U-N-S 08-049-0642
WEA INSURANCE CORP
WEA TRUST
(*Suby of* WEA INSURANCE CORP) ★
45 Nob Hill Rd, Madison, WI 53713-2195
Tel (608) 276-4000 *Founded/Ownrshp* 1970
Sales NA *EMP* 40
SIC 6324 Hospital & medical service plans
Pr: Mark Moody
**CFO:* Paul Lefebvre
**Ex VP:* Peg Smeiser
VP: Mark Blumenfeld
**Prin:* Kim Crowell
**Genl Couns:* Michael Stoll

D-U-N-S 09-296-5466
WEA INTERNATIONAL INC
(*Suby of* WARNER MUSIC INC) ★
75 Rockefeller Plz, New York, NY 10019-6908
Tel (212) 275-1300 *Founded/Ownrshp* 1999
Sales 100.1MM[E] *EMP* 3,400
SIC 3652 Master records or tapes, preparation of
Sr VP: Keith Bruce
VP: Ramon Lopez

WEA TRUST
See WEA INSURANCE CORP

WEABER HARDWOODS
See WEABER INC

D-U-N-S 05-165-4663 EXP
WEABER INC
WEABER HARDWOODS
(*Suby of* WEABER LUMBER) ★
1231 Mount Wilson Rd, Lebanon, PA 17042-4785
Tel (717) 867-2212 *Founded/Ownrshp* 2012
Sales 130.1MM[E] *EMP* 496[E]
SIC 2426 Hardwood dimension & flooring mills; Dimension, hardwood; Flooring, hardwood; Lumber, hardwood dimension
Pr: Matthew Weaber
COO: Sandy Schera
CFO: Bill Campoll
**CFO:* H William Campoll
VP: John Georgelis
Rgnl Mgr: Marty Daigle
Sales Asso: Bryan Eichfeld

WEABER LUMBER
See WT HARDWOODS GROUP INC

WEAR TECHNOLOGY
See MILACRON MARKETING CO LLC

WEATHER CHANNEL, THE
See TWCC HOLDING CORP

D-U-N-S 02-463-8835
WEATHER CHANNEL INC (GA)
TWCC
300 Interstate North Pkwy, Atlanta, GA 30339-2424
Tel (770) 226-0000 *Founded/Ownrshp* 2008
Sales 184.5MM[E] *EMP* 408
SIC 4841 4832

D-U-N-S 00-609-3645 IMP
WEATHER SHIELD MFG INC (WI)
WEATHER SHIELD WINDOWS & DOORS
1 Weathershield Plz, Medford, WI 54451-2206
Tel (715) 748-2100 *Founded/Ownrshp* 1955
Sales 542.9MM[E] *EMP* 2,000
SIC 2431 3089 3442 Window frames, wood; Doors, wood; Windows, plastic; Metal doors, sash & trim
Pr: Edward L Schield
**Sec:* Pamela Schield
**VP:* Kevin L Schield
Sfty Mgr: Craig Schemenauer
Sls Mgr: Deb Berry

WEATHER SHIELD WINDOWS & DOORS
See WEATHER SHIELD MFG INC

WEATHERFORD ARTIFICIAL LIFT
See EPRODUCTION SOLUTIONS LLC

D-U-N-S 02-193-7974 IMP/EXP
WEATHERFORD ARTIFICIAL LIFT SYSTEMS LLC
(*Suby of* WEATHERFORD INTERNATIONAL LLC) ★
2000 Saint James Pl, Houston, TX 77056-4123
Tel (713) 836-4000 *Founded/Ownrshp* 1987
Sales 311.3MM^E *EMP* 570
SIC 3561 5084 Pumps, oil well & field; Pumps & pumping equipment
Pr: Rex Wilson
**Pr:* Keith R Morley
**VP:* Joseph C Henry

WEATHERFORD ARTIFICIAL LIFTS
See U S WEATHERFORD L P

D-U-N-S 06-215-7284 IMP/EXP
WEATHERFORD INTERNATIONAL LLC
(*Suby of* WEATHERFORD INTERNATIONAL PUBLIC LIMITED COMPANY)
2000 Saint James Pl, Houston, TX 77056-4123
Tel (713) 693-4000 *Founded/Ownrshp* 1980
Sales 9.3MMM^E *EMP* 13,980
SIC 1389 Cementing oil & gas well casings
CEO: Bernard J Duroc-Danner
Pr: Dharmesh Bhupatral Mehta
COO: Lee Colley
CFO: John H Briscoe
CFO: Krishna Shivram
Ex VP: Dianne B Ralston
Sr VP: Andrew P Becnel
VP: Chris A Bechtel
VP: A Brent Emerson
VP: Carel Hoyer
VP: Keith Moorley

D-U-N-S 10-682-3131 IMP/EXP
WEATHERFORD LABORATORIES INC
(*Suby of* WEATHERFORD INTERNATIONAL LLC) ★
2000 Saint James Pl, Houston, TX 77056-4123
Tel (832) 237-4000 *Founded/Ownrshp* 2006
Sales 189.9MM^E *EMP* 172
SIC 1389 Oil field services
Pr: Chris A Bechtel
**CFO:* John H Briscoe
**Treas:* Mark M Rothleitner
**Sr VP:* Andrew P Becnel
**Sr VP:* Stuart E Ferguson
**Sr VP:* John M Jameson
**Sr VP:* Dharmesh Bhupatrai Mehta
**Sr VP:* Keith R Morley
Dir Lab: Priyesh Patel
Genl Mgr: Camille Lupton
Genl Mgr: Kimberly Shook

D-U-N-S 11-809-0013
■ **WEATHERFORD REGIONAL MEDICAL CENTER**
(*Suby of* COMMUNITY HEALTH SYSTEMS INC) ★
713 E Anderson St, Weatherford, TX 76086-5705
Tel (682) 582-1000 *Founded/Ownrshp* 2006
Sales 99.1MM^E *EMP* 450
SIC 8062 General medical & surgical hospitals
CEO: David Orcutt
**CFO:* Nancy Cooke
Mktg Dir: Natalie Parish

WEATHERPROOF
See DAVID PEYSER SPORTSWEAR INC

WEATHERTECH
See MAC NEIL AUTOMOTIVE PRODUCTS LIMITED

D-U-N-S 00-604-0604 IMP/EXP
WEAVER POPCORN CO INC
TRAIL'S END POPCORN COMPANY
4485 S Perry Worth Rd, Whitestown, IN 46075-8804
Tel (765) 934-2101 *Founded/Ownrshp* 1936, 1955
Sales 302.3MM^E *EMP* 200
SIC 5145 4213 Popcorn & supplies; Trucking, except local
Ch Bd: Michael E Weaver
CFO: Joe Schneider
CTO: Brady Johns
Board of Directors: Thomas Shoaff

D-U-N-S 78-768-8241 IMP
■ **WEAVEXX LLC**
(*Suby of* XERIUM TECHNOLOGIES INC) ★
14101 Capital Blvd, Youngsville, NC 27596-0166
Tel (919) 556-7235 *Founded/Ownrshp* 1999
Sales 118.7MM^E *EMP* 900
SIC 2221 Specialty broadwoven fabrics, including twisted weaves
CEO: Stephen R Light
Pr: Miguel Quionez
CFO: Jack Frankenfield
CTO: Joan B Ardevol
Plnt Mgr: Mark Parmentier
Secur Mgr: Jerry Smith

D-U-N-S 15-068-5808 IMP
WEB INDUSTRIES INC
377 Simarano Dr Ste 220, Marlborough, MA 01752-3096
Tel (508) 898-2988 *Founded/Ownrshp* 2002
Sales 99.6MM^E *EMP* 250
SIC 2671 5162 3089 2269 3441 Paper coated or laminated for packaging; Plastics film; Injection molded finished plastic products; Finishing plants; Fabricated structural metal
Ch Bd: Robert A Fulton
**Pr:* Mark Pihl
**CEO:* Don Romine
Treas: Jason Anderson
**Ex VP:* Dennis Latimer
**VP:* Carl Rubin
VP: Kevin Young
Admn Mgr: Sharon Morin
Genl Mgr: Josh Chernin
Genl Mgr: John Jaskot
MIS Dir: Kevin Sandberg

D-U-N-S 79-989-1536 IMP
▲ **WEB.COM GROUP INC**
12808 Gran Bay Pkwy W, Jacksonville, FL 32258-4468
Tel (904) 680-6600 *Founded/Ownrshp* 1999
Sales 543.4MM *EMP* 2,200^E
Tkr Sym WEB *Exch* NGS
SIC 7372 7374 Prepackaged software; Computer graphics service
Ch Bd: David L Brown
CFO: Kevin M Carney
Ex VP: Faisal Chughtai
Sr VP: Angela Dunham
Sr VP: Alexander Ross
Sr VP: Helen Rowan
Sr VP: Dafna Sarnoff
Board of Directors: Timothy P Cost, Hugh M Durden, Philip J Facchina, John Giuliani, Timothy I Maudlin, Robert S McCoy Jr, Deborah H Quazzo, Richard Rudman

WEB:WWW.ALTOONAHOSPITAL.ORG
See LEXINGTON HOLDINGS INC

D-U-N-S 06-879-5871 IMP
WEBASTO ROOF SYSTEMS INC
WEBASTO ROOFING
(*Suby of* WEBASTO SE)
1757 Northfield Dr, Rochester Hills, MI 48309-3819
Tel (800) 860-7866 *Founded/Ownrshp* 1974
Sales 500.0MM *EMP* 1,500
SIC 3714 3441 3469 Sun roofs, motor vehicle; Fabricated structural metal; Metal stampings
CEO: Andre Schoenekaes
**CFO:* Philipp Schramm
VP: Andre Bogacz
Ex Dir: Carol Baetz
Ql Cn Mgr: Deborah Adams
Ql Cn Mgr: Jason Naffziger
Sls&Mrk Ex: John Thomas

WEBASTO ROOFING
See WEBASTO ROOF SYSTEMS INC

D-U-N-S 01-646-3642
■ **WEBB AUTOMOTIVE GROUP INC**
(*Suby of* AUTONATION ENTERPRISES INC) ★
200 Sw 1st Ave, Fort Lauderdale, FL 33301-1875
Tel (954) 769-7000 *Founded/Ownrshp* 2008
Sales 127.4MM^E *EMP* 182^E
SIC 7538 General automotive repair shops
Prin: Daniel G Agnew

D-U-N-S 00-641-0740 IMP
WEBB CHEMICAL SERVICE CORP (MI)
2708 Jarman St, Muskegon, MI 49444-2225
Tel (231) 733-2181 *Founded/Ownrshp* 1963, 1964
Sales 99.9MM^E *EMP* 55
SIC 5169 Chemicals & allied products; Chemicals, industrial & heavy
CEO: Brad Hilleary
**Pr:* Charles Stevens
Sls Mgr: Sue Lockhart
Sls Mgr: Mike Siroky

D-U-N-S 36-450-3391 IMP
■ **WEBB WHEEL PRODUCTS INC**
(*Suby of* MARMON GROUP LLC) ★
2310 Industrial Dr Sw, Cullman, AL 35055-6332
Tel (256) 739-6660 *Founded/Ownrshp* 1990
Sales 100.6MM^E *EMP* 500
SIC 3714 Motor vehicle parts & accessories; Brake drums, motor vehicle; Wheels, motor vehicle
Pr: Duane Ricketts
IT Man: Jim Sutherlin
Sfty Mgr: Tom Quick
Manager: Alan Matsumoto

D-U-N-S 60-663-1760 IMP
WEBB-MASON INC
WEBBMASON MARKETING
10830 Gilroy Rd, Hunt Valley, MD 21031-4312
Tel (410) 785-1111 *Founded/Ownrshp* 1989
Sales 117.0MM^E *EMP* 250
SIC 2752 Commercial printing, lithographic; Business form & card printing, lithographic
Pr: Warner Mason
**COO:* Jennifer Moag Black
CFO: Mike Perrera
**CFO:* Ernie Vaile
Bd of Dir: Jim Cullan
**Ex VP:* Bryan Webb
VP: Michelle Bengermino
**VP:* Dan Cahill
VP: Kevin Perzan
VP: Frank Poeschel
**VP:* Doug Traxley

D-U-N-S 18-053-9660
WEBBER LLC
(*Suby of* FERROVIAL SA)
9303 New Trils Dr Ste 200, The Woodlands, TX 77381
Tel (281) 372-0274 *Founded/Ownrshp* 2005
Sales 957.4MM^E *EMP* 1,700
SIC 1611 General contractor, highway & street construction
CEO: Tim Creson
Ex VP: Manuel Costa
Ex VP: Jose Esteban
Sr VP: Tim Muller
VP: Jeff Cormican
VP: Mario Menendez
VP: Ivan Svec
Genl Mgr: Richard Henderson
IT Man: Francisco Hernandez
Sfty Dirs: Sean W Seelbach
Sfty Mgr: Jon Thomas

WEBBMASON MARKETING
See WEBB-MASON INC

D-U-N-S 04-866-2076 IMP
WEBCO HAWAII INC (HI)
ADVANTAGE WEBCO HAWAII
2840 Mokumoa St, Honolulu, HI 96819-4499
Tel (808) 839-4551 *Founded/Ownrshp* 1966
Sales 113.7MM *EMP* 260
Accts Choo Osada & Lee Cpas Inc H
SIC 5122 5199 5141 5064 Cosmetics; Druggists' sundries; General merchandise, non-durable; Groceries, general line; Electric household appliances
Pr: Gregory R Gomes
**Sr VP:* Noel Chang
**Sr VP:* Timothy Doyle
Board of Directors: John Jubinsky

D-U-N-S 03-832-6740 IMP
▲ **WEBCO INDUSTRIES INC**
SOUTHWEST TUBE MFG DIV
9101 W 21st St, Sand Springs, OK 74063-8539
Tel (918) 245-2211 *Founded/Ownrshp* 1969
Sales 480.1MM^E *EMP* 950
Tkr Sym WEBC *Exch* OTO
SIC 3312 5051 Tubes, steel & iron; Tubing, metal
Ch Bd: F William Weber
V Ch: Jerry Honeycutt
Pr: Dana S Weber
CFO: Michael P Howard
Ofcr: Zaldy Prieto
Sr VP: David E Boyer
VP: Lee Beard
VP: Cliburn Orbe
VP: Randy Watson
Exec: Susan Meaux
Genl Mgr: Bobby Floyd
Board of Directors: Dr Kenneth E Case, Christopher Kowalski, Jack D McCarthy, Bradley S Vetal

D-U-N-S 00-477-0392
WEBER DISTRIBUTION WAREHOUSES
13530 Rosecrans Ave, Santa Fe Springs, CA 90670-5087
Tel (562) 356-6300 *Founded/Ownrshp* 1924
Sales 112.0MM^E *EMP* 400
SIC 4214 4225 Local trucking with storage; General warehousing
CEO: Nicholas N Weber
COO: Bob Rubel
CFO: V Osier
CFO: Craig L Smith
Sr VP: Connie Anderson
VP: Sheila Jordan
VP: Robert E Lilja
Prin: Jim Emmerling
VP Opers: Steve Buckman
VP Opers: Tim Regan
Plnt Mgr: Violet Crow

WEBER GRILLS
See WEBER-STEPHEN PRODUCTS LLC

D-U-N-S 00-546-7725 IMP/EXP
WEBER MARKING SYSTEMS INC
WEBER PACKAGING SOLUTIONS
711 W Algonquin Rd, Arlington Heights, IL 60005-4455
Tel (847) 364-8500 *Founded/Ownrshp* 1932
Sales 215.7MM^E *EMP* 700
SIC 3555 2672 2675 Printing trades machinery; Labels (unprinted), gummed: made from purchased materials; Die-cut paper & board
Ch Bd: Joseph A Weber Jr
**Pr:* Glenn C Gilly
VP: Laura McGrath
**VP:* Douglas A Weber
IT Man: Louis Lohman
**VP Mfg:* George Stieber
Mfg Dir: John Oleary

D-U-N-S 00-850-0589 IMP/EXP
WEBER METALS INC
(*Suby of* OTTO FUCHS - KG -)
16706 Garfield Ave, Paramount, CA 90723-5315
Tel (562) 602-0260 *Founded/Ownrshp* 1979
Sales 200.0MM *EMP* 500
SIC 3463 Aluminum forgings
Pr: John R Creed
COO: Pat Moulton
**CFO:* Paul Dennis
VP: Robert Nauman
VP: Bob Naumann
Dir IT: Carren Mann
Manager: Randy Ward

WEBER PACKAGING SOLUTIONS
See WEBER MARKING SYSTEMS INC

D-U-N-S 01-871-7470
WEBER SCHOOL DISTRICT
5320 Adams Ave Pkwy, Ogden, UT 84405-6913
Tel (801) 476-7800 *Founded/Ownrshp* 1915
Sales 230.9MM *EMP* 3,000
Accts Squire & Company Pc Orem Ut
SIC 8211 Public elementary & secondary schools; Secondary school
Bd of Dir: Dean Oborn
VP: Richard Favero
Ex Dir: Cami Alexander
Off Admin: Nancy Spencer
Dir IT: David Brooks
Web Dev: Justin Reeve
Netwrk Eng: John Binder
Netwrk Eng: Jared Ganske
Netwrk Eng: Wayne Hadfield
Netwrk Eng: Brent Pingree

WEBER SHANDWICK WORLDWIDE
See CMGRP INC

D-U-N-S 07-300-0895
WEBER STATE UNIVERSITY
WSU
3848 Harrison Blvd, Ogden, UT 84408-0001
Tel (801) 626-6606 *Founded/Ownrshp* 1933
Sales 102.3MM *EMP* 3,500^E
Accts Office Of The Utah State Audit
SIC 8221 University
Pr: Charles A Wight
**CFO:* Steven E Nabor
**VP:* Bret R Ellis
**VP:* Brad Mortensen
**VP:* Norman Tarbox
**VP:* Janet C Winniford
Prgrm Mgr: Luis Lopez
Admn Mgr: Christina Stice
Genl Mgr: Desiree Larsen
CIO: Don Gardner
Netwrk Mgr: Brooke Chase

D-U-N-S 00-513-5983 IMP/EXP
WEBER-STEPHEN PRODUCTS LLC (DE)
WEBER GRILLS
1415 S Roselle Rd, Palatine, IL 60067-7337
Tel (847) 934-5700 *Founded/Ownrshp* 2010
Sales 1.2MMM^E *EMP* 2,870^E
SIC 3631 Barbecues, grills & braziers (outdoor cooking)
CEO: Thomas D Koos
**Pr:* James C Stephen Sr
**CEO:* Tom Koos
**CFO:* Leonard S Gryn
Ofcr: Alex Hatton
Ex VP: Tom Grana
**Ex VP:* Len Gryn
**Ex VP:* Michael J Kempster
**Ex VP:* Dale Wytiaz
Sr VP: Jim Forbes
VP: William G Krieger

D-U-N-S 05-998-0532 IMP
WEBEX INC
(*Suby of* WH ACQUISITIONS INC) ★
1035 Breezewood Ln, Neenah, WI 54956-4562
Tel (920) 729-6666 *Founded/Ownrshp* 2007
Sales 161.0MM^E *EMP* 300^E
SIC 5084 Industrial machinery & equipment
CEO: Gary Edwards
**Pr:* Paul Schulz
**CFO:* Joey Varkoley
Ofcr: Joseph Varkoly
IT Man: John Zimmer
Info Man: Sue Jodoin
Netwrk Eng: Timo Horn
Mktg Dir: Jeff Keller

WEBEX.COM
See CISCO WEBEX LLC

D-U-N-S 60-267-0742
▲ **WEBMD HEALTH CORP**
395 Hudson St, New York, NY 10014-3669
Tel (212) 624-3700 *Founded/Ownrshp* 2005
Sales 636.4MM *EMP* 1,740^E
Tkr Sym WBMD *Exch* NGS
SIC 7375 4813 Information retrieval services; Online data base information retrieval; ;
CEO: Steven L Zatz
**Ch Bd:* Martin J Wygod
CFO: Blake Desimone
CFO: Anthony Vuolo
Ex VP: Michael B Glick
Ex VP: Gregory Mason
Ex VP: Douglas W Wamsley
Board of Directors: Mark J Adler, Kevin M Cameron, Neil F Dimick, Jerome C Keller, James V Manning, William J Marino, Joseph E Smith, Stanley S Trotman Jr

D-U-N-S 82-871-3821
■ **WEBMD LLC**
(*Suby of* WEBMD HEALTH CORP) ★
395 Hudson St Lbby 3, New York, NY 10014-7450
Tel (212) 624-3700 *Founded/Ownrshp* 2007
Sales 86.6MM^E *EMP* 272^E
SIC 7375 Data base information retrieval
Ex VP: David C Marek
Treas: Anthony Vuolo
Ex VP: Bill Pence
Sr VP: Adam Dublin
Sr VP: John Kritzmacher
VP: Roseann Stampe
QA Dir: Sarath Meepagala
Dir IT: Krishna Bhagavathula
Software D: Dee Madden
VP Opers: Tom Keir
Sls Mgr: Robert Stafford

D-U-N-S 07-991-6743
WEBROOT INC
385 Interlocken Cres # 800, Broomfield, CO 80021-3559
Tel (303) 442-3813 *Founded/Ownrshp* 1998
Sales 121.0MM^E *EMP* 350
SIC 7371 Computer software development
Pr: Dick Williams
COO: Steve Smerey
CFO: John Post
CFO: Cathy Wolff
Bd of Dir: Jake Reynolds
Chf Mktg O: David Duncan
Ex VP: Michael Malloy
Sr VP: Neil Stratz
VP: Chris Benham
VP: Scott Merkle
VP: Kenton Sieckman
VP: Charles Tomeo
VP: Russ Trainor
VP: Steve Tucker
VP: Melanie Williams
Exec: Jay Kirksey
Dir Soc: Cindy McElhiney
Board of Directors: Steve Cakebread, Quentin Gallivan, Greg Myers, Peter Pace, Theresia Gouw Ranzetta, Robin Vasan

D-U-N-S 87-855-3643
■ **WEBSENSE LLC**
(*Suby of* FORCEPOINT LLC) ★
10900 Stonelake Blvd, Austin, TX 78759-5795
Tel (858) 320-8000 *Founded/Ownrshp* 1998
Sales 420.0MM^E *EMP* 2,000
SIC 7372 Prepackaged software
CEO: John McCormack
COO: Robin Bolton
**CFO:* Jim Hagan
CFO: Matthew T Santangelo
Chf Mktg O: John Dillon
**Chf Mktg O:* Neville Letzerich
**Ofcr:* Ed Hammersla
Ex VP: John Giacomini
Ex VP: Heath Thompson
VP: Russell Chadwick
VP: Arturo Gallegos
VP: Don Oldenburg
VP: Shawn Pearson
VP: Devin Redmond
VP: John Starr
Exec: Kimberly Lee
Exec: Douglas Wride

D-U-N-S 00-691-8486 IMP
■ WEBSTER BANK NATIONAL ASSOCIATION
(*Suby of* WEBSTER FINANCIAL CORP) ★
145 Bank St, Waterbury, CT 06702-2211
Tel (203) 578-2230 *Founded/Ownrshp* 1935
Sales NA *EMP* 2,655
SIC 6035 Federal savings & loan associations
Ch Bd: James C Smith
* *Pr:* John R Ciulla
Pr: Sam Hanna
Pr: Jeffrey A Klaus
* *COO:* Gerald P Plush
COO: Teresa Spring
* *CFO:* Glenn Macinnes
* *Treas:* Bruce Wandelmaier
* *Chf Mktg O:* Dawn C Morris
* *Ofcr:* Bernard Garrigues
Ofcr: Peter Pauley
Ofcr: Lizzy Thresher
* *Trst Ofcr:* Thomas N Howe
Assoc VP: Cynthia Saccoman
Ex VP: John Brennan
* *Ex VP:* Nathaniel C Brinn
* *Ex VP:* Jeffrey N Brown
* *Ex VP:* Donald A Cyr
Ex VP: Stephanie Flaherty
* *Ex VP:* Zeynep Fredrick
Ex VP: Scott McBrair
Board of Directors: Sister Marguerite Waite, Achille A Apicella, Joseph A Welna, Joel S Becker, Lauren C States, John J Crawford, Harry Diadamo, Robert A Finkenzeller, Walter R Griffin, J Gregory Hickey, C Michael Jacobi, Allan Kosowsky

D-U-N-S 07-969-4303
WEBSTER CENTRAL SCHOOL DISTRICT (NY)
119 South Ave, Webster, NY 14580-3559
Tel (585) 265-6500 *Founded/Ownrshp* 1949
Sales 64.8MM[E] *EMP* 1,266
SIC 8211 Public elementary & secondary schools
Prin: Glenn Widor
Treas: Jill Sansouci
Dir Sec: Neil Flood
CTO: Bill Ottman
Dir IT: Susan Aeloisio
IT Man: Glenn Drinkwater

D-U-N-S 05-298-9456
■ WEBSTER COUNTY COAL LLC
(*Suby of* ALLIANCE COAL LLC) ★
1758 State Route 874, Clay, KY 42404-9373
Tel (270) 249-2205 *Founded/Ownrshp* 1966, 1974
Sales 57.6MM[E] *EMP* 1,400
SIC 1221 Bituminous coal surface mining
CEO: Joseph W Craft III

D-U-N-S 11-837-3620
▲ WEBSTER FINANCIAL CORP
145 Bank St, Waterbury, CT 06702-2211
Tel (203) 578-2202 *Founded/Ownrshp* 1986
Sales NA *EMP* 2,946[E]
Tkr Sym WBS *Exch* NYS
SIC 6021 National commercial banks
Ch Bd: James C Smith
Pr: John R Ciulla
Pr: Colleen Quinlan
CFO: Glenn I Macinnes
Ex VP: Rosemary Gaidos
Ex VP: Jeff Hubbard
Ex VP: Charles L Wilkins
Sr VP: Chris Rowe
VP: Thomas Woodbury
Board of Directors: Lauren C States, William L Atwell, Joel S Becker, John J Crawford, Elizabeth E Flynn, C Michael Jacobi, Laurence C Morse, Karen R Osar, Mark Pettie, Charles W Shivery

WEBSTER MANAGEMENT
See PATTERSON VETERINARY SUPPLY INC

D-U-N-S 07-198-9727
WEBSTER UNIVERSITY
470 E Lockwood Ave, Saint Louis, MO 63119-3194
Tel (314) 968-6900 *Founded/Ownrshp* 1915
Sales 202.7MM *EMP* 4,500
Accts Bkd Llp Saint Louis Mo
SIC 8221 College, except junior
Pr: Dr Elizabeth Stroble
Pr: Vickie Fredrick
Ofcr: Barbara Carrow
Ofcr: Susan Kerth
Assoc VP: James Myers
VP: Matt Adrignola
VP: Robert Cox
VP: Greg Gunderson
VP: Ted Hoef
VP: John Kennedy
Exec: Russell Viehmann
Dir Soc: Nancy Higgins
Creative D: John Costello

D-U-N-S 87-803-6433
WEBTRENDS INC
(*Suby of* FRANCISCO PARTNERS MANAGEMENT LP) ★
555 Sw Oak St Ste 300, Portland, OR 97204-1775
Tel (503) 294-7025 *Founded/Ownrshp* 2005
Sales 128.5MM[E] *EMP* 325
SIC 7372 Application computer software
CEO: Joe Davis
* *Pr:* Alex Yoder
* *CFO:* Kristen Magnuson
CFO: Valerie McKinney
CFO: Mary Moore
* *Ofcr:* Xavier Le Hericy
VP: John Harrison
VP Bus Dev: Abed Farhan
* *CTO:* Peter Crossley
CTO: Dean Kimball
IT Man: Brian Vanderzanden
Board of Directors: Andre Boisvert

D-U-N-S 82-767-4834
■ WEC BUSINESS SERVICES LLC
(*Suby of* WEC ENERGY GROUP INC) ★
200 E Randolph St # 2200, Chicago, IL 60601-6436
Tel (312) 240-3877 *Founded/Ownrshp* 2007
Sales 239.9MM[E] *EMP* 1,000
SIC 8742 8721 General management consultant; Accounting, auditing & bookkeeping
Ch: Mark Radtke
* *VP:* Linda Kallas
* *VP:* William D Laakso
* *VP:* Phillip M Mikulsky
* *VP:* James F Schott

D-U-N-S 15-730-5780
▲ WEC ENERGY GROUP INC
231 W Michigan St, Milwaukee, WI 53203-2918
Tel (414) 221-2345 *Founded/Ownrshp* 1981
Sales 5.9MMM *EMP* 8,443[E]
Tkr Sym WEC *Exch* NYS
SIC 4911 4924 Electric services; Natural gas distribution
Pr: Allen L Leverett
* *Ch Bd:* Gale E Klappa
Pr: J Kevin Fletcher
CFO: Scott J Lauber
Bd of Dir: Frederick Stratton
Ex VP: Robert M Garvin
Ex VP: Susan H Martin
Ex VP: Tom Metcalfe
Ex VP: Bruce Ramme
VP: William J Guc
Opers Mgr: Bill Mastoris
Board of Directors: Mary Ellen Stanek, John F Bergstrom, Barbara L Bowles, William J Brodsky, Albert J Budney Jr, Patricia W Chadwick, Curt S Culver, Thomas J Fischer, Paul W Jones, Henry W Knueppel

D-U-N-S 17-697-9131
WECTEC GLOBAL PROJECT SERVICES INC
(*Suby of* WESTINGHOUSE ELECTRIC CO LLC) ★
128 S Tryon St Ste 1000, Charlotte, NC 28202-0004
Tel (980) 859-6837 *Founded/Ownrshp* 2015
Sales 2.5MMM *EMP* 1,500
SIC 1731 8712 Electric power systems contractors; Architectural engineering
Pr: David Durham

D-U-N-S 09-944-7427
WEDBUSH INC
1000 Wilshire Blvd # 900, Los Angeles, CA 90017-2457
Tel (213) 688-8080 *Founded/Ownrshp* 1957
Sales 348.9MM[E] *EMP* 641
SIC 7389 Financial services
Pr: Eric D Wedbush
Ofcr: Ryan Sakamoto
VP: Jeff Bell

D-U-N-S 05-010-6749
WEDBUSH SECURITIES INC (CA)
(*Suby of* WEDBUSH INC) ★
1000 Wilshire Blvd # 900, Los Angeles, CA 90017-2457
Tel (213) 688-8000 *Founded/Ownrshp* 1955, 1966
Sales 338.5MM[E] *EMP* 600
Accts Kpmg Llp
SIC 6211 Brokers, security; Stock brokers & dealers; Bond dealers & brokers
Pr: Edward W Wedbush
Pr: Alex Brackman
Pr: Ron Yeager
* *CFO:* Peter Allman-Ward
* *Ch:* Thomas Ringer
Ofcr: Harry Kartolo
* *Ex VP:* Donald W Hultgren
Ex VP: Wesley Long
Ex VP: James Richards
* *Ex VP:* R James Richards
Sr VP: Mark Aquilino
Sr VP: Heather Behanna
Sr VP: Dan Billings
Sr VP: Richard Buckton
Sr VP: Thomas Durkin
* *Sr VP:* Earl I Feldhorn
* *Sr VP:* V Thomas Hale
* *Sr VP:* Steve Kelleher
* *Sr VP:* Richard A Lanni
Sr VP: Ronald D Lehr
Sr VP: Douglas Pryor

D-U-N-S 00-382-3440
WEDDLE BROS CONSTRUCTION CO INC
1201 W 3rd St, Bloomington, IN 47404-5018
Tel (812) 339-9500 *Founded/Ownrshp* 1952
Sales 107.8MM[E] *EMP* 200
SIC 1542 1622 1541 Commercial & office building contractors; Hospital construction; Bridge construction; Industrial buildings, new construction
Pr: Lee E Carmichael
* *CFO:* Steven T Hunt
* *VP:* Robert Carter
* *VP:* Scott Sieboldt
* *VP:* Donald L Turner

D-U-N-S 00-327-5369
WEDGE GROUP INC
1415 La St Ste 3000, Houston, TX 77002
Tel (713) 739-6500 *Founded/Ownrshp* 1979
Sales 1.4MMM[E] *EMP* 900
SIC 1389 1629 1311

WEDGE M & C SERVICES
See WEDGE MEASUREMENT SYSTEMS LLC

D-U-N-S 36-173-7336
WEDGE MEASUREMENT SYSTEMS LLC
WEDGE M & C SERVICES
(*Suby of* WEDGE GROUP INC) ★
1415 La St Ste 1500, Houston, TX 77002
Tel (713) 490-9444 *Founded/Ownrshp* 2004
Sales 165.5MM[E] *EMP* 170
SIC 1389 Measurement of well flow rates, oil & gas
Pr: Thomas D Cathey
CFO: Wilfred Krenek
* *VP:* Gregory J Armstrong
VP: Joe Freeman
* *VP:* Nishith H Patel
Dir IT: Michael Worley

WEDNESDAY AUTO AUCTION
See COLUMBUS FAIR AUTO AUCTION INC

D-U-N-S 05-845-9520
WEEBS INC
APTOS SHOES AND APPAREL
20 Rancho Del Mar, Aptos, CA 95003-3902
Tel (831) 688-8007 *Founded/Ownrshp* 1980
Sales 186.3MM[E] *EMP* 20
SIC 5651 5661 Family clothing stores; Shoe stores
Pr: Ruth Weber
* *VP:* Greg Weber

D-U-N-S 12-583-3798
WEEDEN & CO LP
WEEDEN & CO LTD PARTNERSHIP
(*Suby of* WEEDEN INVESTORS LIMITED PARTNERSHIP) ★
145 Mason St, Greenwich, CT 06830-6605
Tel (203) 861-7670 *Founded/Ownrshp* 1986
Sales 143.1MM *EMP* 135
SIC 6211 Security brokers & dealers
Pr: Robert Demichele
Genl Pt: Camille Barbella
Co-CEO: Lance F Lonergan
VP: Lee Grichuhin
Mng Dir: Mark Howard-Johnson
CTO: Sanjay Kumar

WEEDEN & CO LTD PARTNERSHIP
See WEEDEN & CO LP

D-U-N-S 62-282-7103
WEEDEN INVESTORS LIMITED PARTNERSHIP
145 Mason St, Greenwich, CT 06830-6605
Tel (203) 861-7600 *Founded/Ownrshp* 1986
Sales 144.8MM[E] *EMP* 285
SIC 6799 Investors
Mng Dir: Barry Small
Genl Pt: Weeden Securities Corp
Pt: Michael Mook

WEEKES FOREST PRODUCTS
See MAC ARTHUR CO

D-U-N-S 08-356-2694
WEEKLEY HOMES LLC (IN)
DAVID WEEKLEY HOMES
1111 N Post Oak Rd, Houston, TX 77055-7310
Tel (713) 963-0500 *Founded/Ownrshp* 1976
Sales 837.2MM[E] *EMP* 1,000
SIC 1531 1521 Speculative builder, single-family houses; Single-family housing construction
CEO: David M Weekley
Pr: John Johnson
Chf Mktg O: Natalie Harris
VP: Bill Justus
VP: Bubba Reynolds
Div/Sub He: Jim Feldman
Dir IT: Braden Randy
Sfty Dirs: Ivette Wiswell
VP Mktg: Lyda Akin
Sls Dir: Meghan Bailey
Sls Mgr: Courtney York

D-U-N-S 04-466-5230 IMP/EXP
WEEKS MARINE INC
4 Commerce Dr Fl 2, Cranford, NJ 07016-3520
Tel (908) 272-4010 *Founded/Ownrshp* 1919
Sales 1.1MMM[E] *EMP* 1,500
SIC 1629 Dredging contractor
CEO: Richard S Weeks
* *CFO:* Matthew Reece
* *Ex VP:* Eric Ellefsen
* *Sr VP:* Richard Macdonald
* *Sr VP:* Patrick Whelan
VP: Susan Leech
MIS Mgr: Leon S Trela
Sfty Mgr: Page Ward

D-U-N-S 94-949-8968
WEEKS-LERMAN GROUP LLC
5838 Page Pl, Maspeth, NY 11378-2235
Tel (718) 803-4700 *Founded/Ownrshp* 1995
Sales 205.3MM[E] *EMP* 175
SIC 5112 5021 2752 5044 Stationers, commercial; Office supplies; Office furniture; Commercial printing, offset; Office equipment
VP: Edwin Santana
MIS Dir: Louis Lopez
Dir IT: Eran Bagim
IT Man: Rani Choura
Prd Mgr: Ira Silverstein
Sales Exec: Jeff Siskin
VP Sls: Carol Bleiweiss
VP Sls: Bob Caracci
Sls Dir: Marc Siegel
Manager: Mark Gaeta

D-U-N-S 10-116-0026 IMP
■ WEETABIX CO INC
WEETABIX FOOD COMPANY, THE
(*Suby of* WEETABIX LIMITED)
500 Nickerson Rd Ste 150, Marlborough, MA 01752-4696
Tel (978) 365-1000 *Founded/Ownrshp* 1986
Sales 83.7MM[E] *EMP* 280
SIC 2043 Cereal breakfast foods
CEO: Steve Van Tassel
* *Pr:* Richard George
* *CEO:* Ken Wood
* *Treas:* Joseph Ellis
* *Treas:* Richard Martin
* *VP:* Daniel Dinardo
* *VP:* Edward J Langley
* *VP:* Gary Less
* *VP:* Federico Meade
Plnt Mgr: Jeff Spooner
Sales Exec: Jack Lane

WEETABIX FOOD COMPANY, THE
See WEETABIX CO INC

D-U-N-S 78-270-5669 IMP
WEG ELECTRIC CORP
(*Suby of* WEG S/A.)
6655 Sugarloaf Pkwy, Duluth, GA 30097-4907
Tel (678) 249-2000 *Founded/Ownrshp* 1991
Sales 99.6MM[E] *EMP* 325[E]
SIC 3612 3621 3613 3625 Power & distribution transformers; Electric motor & generator parts; Switchgear & switchboard apparatus; Relays & industrial controls
Pr: Peter Berry
* *VP:* Graham Allen
* *VP:* Ribeiro Luis Fernando
* *VP:* Bayardo Luis
* *VP:* Connolly Randall
VP: Douglas C Stange
Telecom Mg: Michael Serafin
Sls Dir: Antonio Cesar
Sls Dir: Fernando Garcia

D-U-N-S 62-361-4633
WEGE FOUNDATION
99 Monroe Ave Nw Ste 902, Grand Rapids, MI 49503-6210
Tel (616) 957-0480 *Founded/Ownrshp* 1967
Sales 168.9MM *EMP* 3
SIC 8699 Charitable organization
Pr: Peter Wege

D-U-N-S 05-965-0069 IMP
WEGMANS FOOD MARKETS INC
1500 Brooks Ave, Rochester, NY 14624-3589
Tel (585) 328-2550 *Founded/Ownrshp* 1987
Sales 8.0MMM *EMP* 45,000
SIC 5411 Supermarkets, chain
CEO: Danny Wegman
* *Pr:* Colleen Wegman
* *CFO:* James J Leo
CFO: James Leo
Ofcr: Dave D Laus
Ofcr: Angelica Resto
Sr VP: Shari Constantine
* *Sr VP:* John A Depeters II
VP: Ken Cassara
VP: Bill Congdon
VP: Mike Cullen
VP: Larry Damore
VP: Sherwood Deutsch
VP: Joe Divincenzo
VP: Bill Gilley
VP: Mike Hamelink
VP: Mike Keating
VP: Tom Nardo
VP: Kevin Stickles
VP: Nicole Wegman
Exec: Paul Koch

D-U-N-S 00-634-0855
WEHCO MEDIA INC (AR)
115 E Capitol Ave, Little Rock, AR 72201-3819
Tel (501) 378-3529 *Founded/Ownrshp* 1929
Sales 379.9MM[E] *EMP* 2,400
SIC 2711 4841

D-U-N-S 07-125-3983
WEHCO NEWSPAPERS INC (AR)
(*Suby of* WEHCO MEDIA INC) ★
115 E Capital & Scott Sts, Little Rock, AR 72201
Tel (501) 378-3400 *Founded/Ownrshp* 1973, 1974
Sales 126.6MM[E] *EMP* 218[E]
SIC 2711 Newspapers, publishing & printing
Ch Bd: Walter E Hussman Jr
Treas: Allen Berry
Ex Dir: Brenda Hampton
Advt Dir: John Mobbs

WEI
See WORLDCOM EXCHANGE INC

D-U-N-S 06-459-6620 IMP/EXP
WEI-CHUAN USA INC
6655 Garfield Ave, Bell Gardens, CA 90201-1807
Tel (323) 587-2101 *Founded/Ownrshp* 1972
Sales 133.5MM[E] *EMP* 190
SIC 5142 2038 Packaged frozen goods; Dinners, frozen & packaged; Ethnic foods, frozen
Pr: Steve Lin
* *Treas:* William Huang
* *Prin:* Robert Huang
CTO: Jih Chung
IT Man: Huang Christina
Opers Mgr: Wynn Chen
Sls Dir: Jesse Valdez

D-U-N-S 06-497-9016
WEICHERT CO
WEICHERT REALTORS
1625 State Route 10, Morris Plains, NJ 07950-2905
Tel (973) 984-1400 *Founded/Ownrshp* 1969
Sales 90.6MM[E] *EMP* 2,550
SIC 6531 Real estate brokers & agents
Pr: James Weichert
V Ch: Elaine Mosera
Pr: Larry Mueller
VP: Nick Russo
VP: Denise Smith
* *Prin:* Jim Weichert
Brnch Mgr: Karen Contreras
IT Man: John Artigliere
Sls&Mrk Ex: John Way
Mktg Dir: Lawrence Wong
Sls Mgr: Joseph Cubias

WEICHERT REALTORS
See WEICHERT CO

D-U-N-S 80-740-4371
WEIDER PUBLICATIONS LLC
MUSCLE & FITNESS FLEX M&F HERS
(*Suby of* AMERICAN MEDIA INC) ★
6420 Wilshire Blvd # 720, Los Angeles, CA 90048-5502
Tel (818) 884-6800 *Founded/Ownrshp* 2002
Sales 33.9MM[E] *EMP* 1,000
SIC 2721 Magazines: publishing only, not printed on site
VP: John Hartung
CTO: Brenna Pavey
Dir IT: Rebecca Schramm
VP Prd: Daniel Rotstein
Mktg Mgr: Paco Acosta

D-U-N-S 00-554-8029
WEIGAND CONSTRUCTION CO INC
7808 Honeywell Dr, Fort Wayne, IN 46825-6272
Tel (260) 413-6349 *Founded/Ownrshp* 1993

Sales 140.4MM^E *EMP* 300
SIC 1542 Commercial & office building, new construction; Religious building construction; School building construction
Pr: Larry Weigand
**Pr:* Jeremy Ringger
**CFO:* Andrew Binkley
**VP:* David Jankowski
**VP:* Aaron Lybarger
Sfty Mgr: Ryan Hasser

WEIGHT WATCHERS
See WW GROUP INC

D-U-N-S 04-765-7473

▲ WEIGHT WATCHERS INTERNATIONAL INC
675 Ave Americas Fl 6, New York, NY 10010-5117
Tel (212) 589-2700 *Founded/Ownrshp* 1961
Sales 1.1MMM *EMP* 19,000^E
Tkr Sym WTW *Exch* NYS
SIC 7299 7991 Diet center, without medical staff; Weight reducing clubs
Pr: James R Chambers
**Ch Bd:* Raymond Debbane
Pr: Stacey Mowbray
Pr: Corinne Pollier
CFO: Nicholas P Hotchkin
Sr VP: Michael Lysaght
VP: Heidi Bowman
VP: Seth Kaplan
CTO: Dan Crowe
Tech Mgr: Terrence Johnson
Sftwr Eng: Pinal Bhatt
Board of Directors: Steven M Altschuler, Philippe J Amouyal, Cynthia Elkins, Jonas M Fajgenbaum, Denis F Kelly, Sacha Lainovic, Christopher J Sobecki

D-U-N-S 02-050-2530 IMP

■ WEIGHT WATCHERS NORTH AMERICA INC
(*Suby of* WEIGHT WATCHERS INTERNATIONAL INC) ★
300 Jericho Quadrangle # 350, Jericho, NY 11753-2723
Tel (516) 390-1400 *Founded/Ownrshp* 1992
Sales 264.5MM^E *EMP* 6,550
SIC 8093 Weight loss clinic, with medical staff
Pr: James Chambers
**Pr:* Diane Owen
**Pr:* Len Tacconi

D-U-N-S 06-120-4046

WEIL GOTSHAL & MANGES LLP
767 5th Ave Fl Conc1, New York, NY 10153-0119
Tel (212) 310-8000 *Founded/Ownrshp* 1931
Sales 358.3MM^E *EMP* 1,700
SIC 8111 General practice attorney, lawyer
CEO: Barry M Wolf
Sr Pt: Bruce R Rich
Pt: Guillermo Aguilar-Alvarez
Pt: Michael J Aiello
Pt: Stephen J Dannhauser
Pt: Gary D Friedman
Pt: Allan Huss
Pt: Titus Leung
Pt: Stephen Shahida
Pt: David E Wohl
CFO: Norman W Lacroix
CFO: Derek Smyth
Assoc Dir: Simon Okunev
Comm Dir: Elizabeth Ventura

WEIMAN COMPANY DIVISION
See BASSETT FURNITURE INDUSTRIES OF NORTH CAROLINA LLC

D-U-N-S 07-976-9190

WEINBERG CAPITAL GROUP INC
5005 Rockside Rd Ste 1140, Cleveland, OH 44131-6815
Tel (216) 503-8307 *Founded/Ownrshp* 2012
Sales 91.0MM^E *EMP* 96^E
SIC 6799 Investors
CEO: Ronald E Weinberg Jr
Exec: Joyce Schindler

D-U-N-S 78-603-6343

WEINBERG HARRY & JEANETTE FOUNDATION INC
7 Park Center Ct, Owings Mills, MD 21117-4200
Tel (410) 654-8500 *Founded/Ownrshp* 1959
Sales 293.4MM *EMP* 20^E
SIC 8699 Charitable organization
Pr: Shale Stiller
**Ch Bd:* Ellen M Heller
COO: Rachel Monroe
Treas: Robert Kelly
**Treas:* Barry Schloss
Chf Inves: Jonathan Hook
Ofcr: Aaron Merki
Ofcr: Kate Sorestad
Ofcr: Donn Weinberg
Mng Dir: David Gilmore
Pgrm Dir: Zack Dixon

D-U-N-S 00-793-3211

▲ WEINGARTEN REALTY INVESTORS
2600 Citadel Plaza Dr # 125, Houston, TX 77008-1362
Tel (713) 866-6000 *Founded/Ownrshp* 1948
Sales 512.8MM *EMP* 312^E
Tkr Sym WRI *Exch* NYS
SIC 6798 Real estate investment trusts
Pr: Andrew M Alexander
**Ch Bd:* Stanford Alexander
COO: Johnny L Hendrix
CFO: Stephen C Richter
Sr VP: Lee Brody
Sr VP: Gerald Crump
Sr VP: Alan R Kofoed
Sr VP: Miles R Sanchez
Sr VP: Mark D Stout
Sr VP: Steven R Weingarten
VP: Timothy Frakes
VP: Terri Klages
VP: Lee Pearson
Board of Directors: James W Crownover, Stephen A Lasher, Thomas L Ryan, Douglas W Schnitzer, C Park Shaper, Marc J Shapiro

WEINSTEIN SUPPLY
See HAJOCA CORP

D-U-N-S 92-924-0786 IMP/EXP

WEIR GROUP INC
WEIR SPM
(*Suby of* WEIR GROUP (OVERSEAS HOLDINGS) LIMITED)
7601 Wyatt Dr, Fort Worth, TX 76108-2530
Tel (817) 246-2461 *Founded/Ownrshp* 2014
Sales 443.4MM^E *EMP* 1,220
SIC 3561 8711 Pumps & pumping equipment; Engineering services
Pr: Chris Rickard
**Sec:* Dennis Carder
**VP:* R Lynn Marlor
VP: Ronnie Phelps
**VP:* Joseph Roark
MIS Dir: Jeff Russell
IT Man: Jak Deschner
Opers Supe: Chris Aitken
Opers Supe: Phil Portelli
Sfty Mgr: Andy Stephan
Opers Mgr: Rod Bowers

D-U-N-S 09-711-5716 IMP/EXP

WEIR GROUP LP
WEIR SPECIALITY PUMP
(*Suby of* WEIR GROUP PLC(THE))
440 W 800 S, Salt Lake City, UT 84101-2229
Tel (801) 530-7937 *Founded/Ownrshp* 1990
Sales 196.2MM^E *EMP* 1,414
SIC 3561 Pumps & pumping equipment
Pt: Dennis Carder
COO: Gary Pearson
CFO: Linda Beal
VP: Stephen Gee
VP: John Kavalam
VP: Jason Van Orden
Sys Mgr: Linden Mecham
Prd Mgr: Russell Jensen
VP Sls: Don Bowers
Mktg Mgr: Joshua Jensen
Manager: Thomas Horak

WEIR SPECIALITY PUMP
See WEIR GROUP LP

WEIR SPM
See SPM FLOW CONTROL INC

WEIR SPM
See WEIR GROUP INC

D-U-N-S 07-216-6051

WEIRTON MEDICAL CENTER INC
601 Colliers Way, Weirton, WV 26062-5014
Tel (304) 797-6000 *Founded/Ownrshp* 1956
Sales 122.9MM *EMP* 1,100
SIC 8062 8051 General medical & surgical hospitals; Skilled nursing care facilities
CEO: Charles M O'Brien Jr
Chf Path: Lisa Brancazio
Chf Rad: Eric Balzano
**CFO:* Robert Frank
Dir Rad: Janice Bable
Dir Rad: Janice Disario-Bable
Mng Dir: Roger Isla
CIO: Dave Angalich
Surgeon: Carol Slomski
Ansthlgy: Paul M Kempen
Doctor: Virginia Dintini

D-U-N-S 60-504-3066

WEIRTON MEDICAL CORP
601 Colliers Way, Weirton, WV 26062-5014
Tel (304) 797-6000 *Founded/Ownrshp* 1989
Sales 0.0 *EMP* 1,000
Accts Arnett Foster Toothman Pllc Ch
SIC 8062 General medical & surgical hospitals
Pr: Joseph Endrich
Treas: James Thompson
Prin: Marvin Levendorf

D-U-N-S 10-890-8435

WEIRTON STEEL CORP
(*Suby of* ARCELORMITTAL SA)
400 Three Springs Dr, Weirton, WV 26062-4950
Tel (304) 797-2000 *Founded/Ownrshp* 1909
Sales 228.8MM^E *EMP* 2,832
SIC 3312 3316 Sheet or strip, steel, hot-rolled; Sheet or strip, steel, cold-rolled: own hot-rolled; Iron & steel: galvanized, pipes, plates, sheets, etc.; Tinplate; Cold finishing of steel shapes
CEO: D Leonard Wise
**Pr:* Mark E Kaplan
Pr: Richard Reiderer
Pr: John Walker
Treas: David Bordo
Ex VP: James B Bruhn
VP: Thomas W Evans
VP: William R Kiefer
VP: Edward L Scram
VP: Frank G Tluchowski
VP: Mac S White Jr
Board of Directors: Richard R Burt Chairman, Robert J D'anniballe Jr, Mark G Glyptis, Ronald C Whitaker

D-U-N-S 02-300-8949

WEIS BUILDERS INC
7645 Lyndale Ave S # 300, Minneapolis, MN 55423-6009
Tel (612) 243-5000 *Founded/Ownrshp* 1960
Sales 197.1MM^E *EMP* 300
SIC 1522 1541 1542 Apartment building construction; Industrial buildings, new construction; Commercial & office building, new construction
Ch Bd: Jay Weis
Pr: Rick Fenske
**Pr:* Erik Weis
**CFO:* Cassandra Warner
Exec: Dan Rubel
Off Mgr: Gina Curran
QA Dir: Ben Thiel
Sfty Dirs: Doug Happel
Opers Mgr: Dale Worm
Sales Exec: Jeff Reich

D-U-N-S 00-791-7420 IMP

▲ WEIS MARKETS INC (PA)
1000 S 2nd St, Sunbury, PA 17801-3399
Tel (570) 286-4571 *Founded/Ownrshp* 1912
Sales 2.8MMM *EMP* 19,000^E
Accts Ernst & Young Llp Philadelph
Tkr Sym WMK *Exch* NYS
SIC 5411 Supermarkets, chain
Ch Bd: Jonathan H Weis
COO: Kurt A Schertle
CFO: Scott F Frost
Sr VP: David W Gose II
Sr VP: Harold G Graber
Sr VP: Richard A Gunn
Sr VP: Shirl Stroeing
VP: Bob Cline
VP: John Grimes
VP: Jerry Hatch
VP: Dan Kessler
VP: Brad Kochenour
VP: Kevin Small
VP: R Gregory Zeh Jr
Board of Directors: Dennis G Hatchell, Edward J Lauth III, Gerrald B Silverman

D-U-N-S 08-141-8352

WEISER SECURITY SERVICES INC
3939 Tulane Ave 300, New Orleans, LA 70119-6938
Tel (504) 586-4712 *Founded/Ownrshp* 1970
Sales 160.3MM^E *EMP* 3,500
SIC 7381 Security guard service
Pr: Michael L Weiser
**Treas:* Pamela L Weiser
**VP:* Earl L Weiser
Brnch Mgr: Tim Schultz
Brnch Mgr: Mike Tenore

D-U-N-S 07-328-1776

WEISERMAZARS LLP
(*Suby of* MAZARS)
135 W 50th St, New York, NY 10020-1201
Tel (212) 812-7000 *Founded/Ownrshp* 2010
Sales 126.9MM^E *EMP* 731
SIC 8721 Certified public accountant
CEO: Victor Wahba
Pt: Arthur Adams
Pt: Ralph Anderson
Pt: James Blake
Pt: Kathryn Byrne
Pt: Lawrence P Cafasso
Pt: Andrew Cohen
Pt: Anees Din
Pt: Richard S Faltin
Pt: Russell Foster
Pt: Stuart A Gollin
Pt: Barbara S Israel
Pt: Ron Katz
Pt: Arthur R Klampert
Pt: Howard Landsberg
Pt: Bruce A Lev
Pt: Stuart A Nussbaum
Pt: Bernard Patrusky
Pt: Kevin Pianko
Pt: Monica Ranniger
Pt: Stephen J Schwartz

D-U-N-S 13-595-3326 IMP/EXP

WEISS-ROHLIG USA LLC
1601 Estes Ave, Elk Grove Village, IL 60007-5409
Tel (224) 563-3200 *Founded/Ownrshp* 2003
Sales 28.1MM *EMP* 2,018
SIC 4731 Transportation agents & brokers
CEO: Mark McCullough
COO: Preben Pedersen
**CFO:* Richard Labib
CFO: James A McGregor
Ex VP: Andreas Bauermeister
Rgnl Mgr: Russell Kennicott
Brnch Mgr: Brooke Arroyo
Brnch Mgr: Michael Crandall
Brnch Mgr: Yan Jin
Brnch Mgr: Helen Lee
Brnch Mgr: Christian Schubert

D-U-N-S 03-406-9026

WEISSCOMM GROUP LTD
WCG WORLD
50 Francisco St Ste 400, San Francisco, CA 94133-2114
Tel (415) 362-5018 *Founded/Ownrshp* 2001
Sales 125.7MM^E *EMP* 419
SIC 8748 Communications consulting
CEO: James Weiss
**Pr:* Chris Deri
**Pr:* Diane Weiser
**CFO:* Richard Neave
Top Exec: David Fossas
VP: Tim Malone
Dir Sec: Angea Gillespie
IT Man: William Lin
Snr Mgr: Ashley Chatman
Snr Mgr: Alan Garcia
Snr Mgr: Beth Weiss

D-U-N-S 07-838-8264

WEITSMAN SHREDDING
(*Suby of* BEN WEITSMAN AND SON INC) ★
15 W Main St, Owego, NY 13827-1569
Tel (607) 687-2780 *Founded/Ownrshp* 2011
Sales 139.0MM *EMP* 200^E
Accts Chiampou Travis Besaw & Kershn
SIC 5051 5093 5099 Ferrous metals; Nonferrous metals scrap; Containers: glass, metal or plastic

D-U-N-S 00-694-1454

WEITZ CO LLC (IA)
5901 Thornton Ave, Des Moines, IA 50321-2403
Tel (515) 698-4260 *Founded/Ownrshp* 1855
Sales 1.5MMM^E *EMP* 2,000
Accts Kpmg Llp Des Moines Ia
SIC 1542 1541 1629 Commercial & office building, new construction; Commercial & office buildings, renovation & repair; Industrial buildings, new construction; Golf course construction
CEO: Len Martling
**Ch Bd:* Glenn H De Stigter
Pr: Jack Brooks
**Pr:* Craig Damos
**COO:* Leonard W Martling
**CFO:* Donald Blum
**CFO:* Kevin Prust
Ofcr: Amanda Deppe
Ex VP: Bill Hornaday
Sr VP: James McCulloh
**Sr VP:* David Strutt
VP: John E Crain III
VP: Jason Robertson
VP: Jim Wells
VP: James Wenzel
Exec: Jim Gajoch

D-U-N-S 09-682-2291

WEL COMPANIES INC
1625 S Broadway, De Pere, WI 54115-9264
Tel (800) 333-4415 *Founded/Ownrshp* 1975
Sales 108.4MM *EMP* 600
Accts Schenck
SIC 4213 Refrigerated products transport
CEO: Bruce W Tielens
Pr: Rick Schlapman
**CFO:* Greg Bredael
**VP:* Randall M Tielens
MIS Dir: Mike Zeigenbein
IT Man: Chad Schnider
VP Opers: Michael Grover
Trfc Dir: James Gehrke
Sls Dir: Jason Johnson

D-U-N-S 00-801-2957 IMP/EXP

WELBILT WALK-INS LP
KYSOR PANEL SYSTEMS
(*Suby of* KPS GLOBAL LLC) ★
4201 N Beach St, Fort Worth, TX 76137-3212
Tel (817) 281-5121 *Founded/Ownrshp* 1996
Sales 104.1MM^E *EMP* 594
SIC 3089 3585 Panels, building: plastic; Refrigeration & heating equipment
Prin: Jack Bowling

D-U-N-S 19-822-7881 IMP/EXP

■ WELCH ALLYN INC
(*Suby of* HILL-ROM HOLDINGS INC) ★
4341 State Street Rd, Skaneateles Falls, NY 13153-5301
Tel (315) 685-4100 *Founded/Ownrshp* 2015
Sales 723.8MM^E *EMP* 2,602
SIC 3841 2835 3827 Diagnostic apparatus, medical; Otoscopes, except electromedical; Ophthalmic instruments & apparatus; Blood pressure apparatus; In vitro & in vivo diagnostic substances; Optical instruments & lenses
Pr: Stephen Meyer
Pr: Louann Morin
**CFO:* Karen Roscher
**Chf Mktg O:* Scott Gucciardi
Ofcr: Jerri Sawyerfield
**Ex VP:* Mike Ehrhart
**Ex VP:* Dan Fisher
**Ex VP:* Janie Goddard
**Ex VP:* Joseph Hennigan
**Ex VP:* Doug Linquest
**Ex VP:* Louise McDonald
Sr VP: Andy Clapper
VP: Eric Hunt
VP: John Melquist
VP: Brent Murphy
VP: John Tierney
Board of Directors: Vincent C Caponi

D-U-N-S 00-212-6365 IMP/EXP

WELCH FOODS INC A COOPERATIVE (MI)
WELCH'S
(*Suby of* NATIONAL GRAPE CO-OPERATIVE ASSOCIATION INC) ★
300 Baker Ave Ste 101, Concord, MA 01742-2131
Tel (978) 371-1000 *Founded/Ownrshp* 1972
Sales 609.0MM *EMP* 1,000
Accts Kpmg Llp Boston Ma
SIC 2033 2037 Fruit juices: packaged in cans, jars, etc.; Fruit juices: concentrated, hot pack; Tomato juice: packaged in cans, jars, etc.; Jams, jellies & preserves: packaged in cans, jars, etc.; Frozen fruits & vegetables; Fruit juices, frozen; Fruit juice concentrates, frozen
Pr: Bradley Irwin
COO: Carla Loffredo
CFO: Michael Perda
Treas: Rich Brouillette
Chf Mktg O: Tom Dixon
Sr VP: Peter Martin
VP: Delisle Flynn
VP: Ray Gosselin
VP: Wayne D Lutomski
VP: Randy C Papdellis
VP: Vivian Tseng
Board of Directors: Stephen B Morris, William G Barker III, Chris Neugent, Geralyn R Breig, Thomas G Wilkinson, Jerry A Czebotar, Robert T Demartini, Joseph C Falcone, Timothy E Grow, Jon Hinkelman, Bradley C Irwin, Carl E Lee Jr

D-U-N-S 03-185-4032 IMP

WELCH PACKAGING GROUP INC
1020 Herman St, Elkhart, IN 46516-9028
Tel (574) 295-2460 *Founded/Ownrshp* 1997
Sales 146.2MM^E *EMP* 463
SIC 2657 Folding paperboard boxes
Pr: M Scott Welch
**CFO:* Patrick J Baert
Ofcr: Carl Long
Ex VP: Jim Fenner
Genl Mgr: Pete Giczewski

WELCH'S
See WELCH FOODS INC A COOPERATIVE

D-U-N-S 02-888-3788

■ WELCO-CGI GAS TECHNOLOGIES LLC
(*Suby of* PRAXAIR INC) ★
425 Avenue P, Newark, NJ 07105-4800
Tel (973) 589-8795 *Founded/Ownrshp* 2014
Sales 113.1MM^E *EMP* 770
SIC 5085 5169 5999 5084 Welding supplies; Compressed gas; Welding supplies; Propane gas, bottled

D-U-N-S 00-580-2178
WELD COUNTY SCHOOL DISTRICT 6
1025 9th Ave Ste Main, Greeley, CO 80631-4042
Tel (970) 348-6000 *Founded/Ownrshp* 1871
Sales 114.5MM^E *EMP* 2,400
Accts Sample & Bailey Pc Fort Co
SIC 8211 Public elementary & secondary schools; Public elementary school; Public junior high school; Public senior high school
Creative D: Mason Mocabee
**Prin:* Nancy Devine
**Prin:* Wayne Eads

WELD-ON ADHESIVES
See IPS CORP

WELD-TECH ENGINEERING
See RTI ENERGY SYSTEMS INC

D-U-N-S 00-544-3239 IMP
WELDBEND CORP
6600 S Harlem Ave, Argo, IL 60501-1930
Tel (708) 594-1700 *Founded/Ownrshp* 1968
Sales 86.8MM^E *EMP* 200
SIC 3462 Flange, valve & pipe fitting forgings, ferrous
Pr: James J Coulas Jr
Genl Mgr: David Shulman
CIO: James Coulas

D-U-N-S 04-522-3369
WELK GROUP INC
WELK MUSIC GROUP
8860 Lawrence Welk Dr, Escondido, CA 92026-6403
Tel (760) 749-3000 *Founded/Ownrshp* 1955
Sales 119.4MM^E *EMP* 1,350
SIC 7011 5099 Resort hotel; Compact discs; Tapes & cassettes, prerecorded
Pr: Jon Fredricks
**COO:* Marc L Luzzatto
Plnt Mgr: Mario Trejo

WELK MUSIC GROUP
See WELK GROUP INC

D-U-N-S 10-123-0361 IMP/EXP
WELL LUCK CO INC
104 Harbor Dr Ste 1, Jersey City, NJ 07305-4500
Tel (201) 434-1177 *Founded/Ownrshp* 1983
Sales 146.4MM^E *EMP* 150
SIC 5149 Groceries & related products
Pr: Ting Hwa LI
CFO: Ming Blinn

WELL STAR
See KENNESTONE HOSPITAL AT WINDY HILL INC

D-U-N-S 00-139-9815 IMP/EXP
■ **WELLA CORP** (DE)
(*Suby of* PROCTER & GAMBLE DEUTSCHLAND GMBH)
6109 De Soto Ave, Woodland Hills, CA 91367-3709
Tel (818) 999-5112 *Founded/Ownrshp* 1935
Sales 117.0MM^E *EMP* 1,048
SIC 2844

D-U-N-S 03-148-2037 EXP
WELLBORN CABINET INC
38669 Highway 77, Ashland, AL 36251-7366
Tel (256) 354-7151 *Founded/Ownrshp* 1961
Sales 285.2MM^E *EMP* 1,207
SIC 2434 2511 5032 Wood kitchen cabinets; Wood household furniture; Building stone; Granite building stone; Marble building stone
CEO: Paul D Wellborn
COO: Thomas E Halford
CFO: Jeff Uhirn
**CFO:* Jeffrey Uhrin
CTO: Melissa Johnson
Web Dev: Shannon Sewell
Sfty Dirs: Jim Floyd
Sfty Mgr: Wayne Gentry
Sfty Mgr: Sandy Johns
Plnt Mgr: Randy Hurst
Mktg Dir: Angela Oneill

D-U-N-S 19-247-7297
WELLBRIDGE CLUB MANAGEMENT LLC
WELLBRIDGE COMPANY
(*Suby of* WELLBRIDGE CO) ★
6140 Greenwood Plaza Blvd, Greenwood Village, CO 80111-4803
Tel (303) 866-0800 *Founded/Ownrshp* 1982
Sales 100.8MM^E *EMP* 3,000
SIC 7991 Health club
Pr: Ed Williams
Mng Dir: Thad Ross
Rgnl Mgr: Dennis Curtain
Rgnl Mgr: Terri Hebdon
Rgnl Mgr: Ivan Pejic
Rgnl Mgr: Ann Witulski
Genl Mgr: Mark Burke
Genl Mgr: Matthew Gress
Genl Mgr: Jay Nelson
Genl Mgr: Greg Patti
Mktg Dir: Joanna Masloski

WELLBRIDGE COMPANY
See STARMARK MANAGEMENT HOLDINGS LLC

WELLBRIDGE COMPANY
See WELLBRIDGE CLUB MANAGEMENT LLC

D-U-N-S 14-340-0799
▲ **WELLCARE HEALTH PLANS INC**
8735 Henderson Rd, Tampa, FL 33634-1143
Tel (813) 290-6200 *Founded/Ownrshp* 2002
Sales NA *EMP* 6,900^E
Tkr Sym WCG *Exch* NYS
SIC 6324 Hospital & medical service plans; Health maintenance organization (HMO), insurance only
Pr: Kenneth A Burdick
Ch Bd: David J Gallitano
Pr: Cesar D Martinez
Pr: Elizabeth Miller
Pr: Kelly Munson
Pr: Jesse Thomas
COO: Karen M Johnson
CFO: Andrew Asher
CFO: Andrew L Asher
Div Pres: David Reynolds
Bd of Dir: Robert D Graham
Ofcr: Lawrence D Anderson
Sr VP: Darren Ghanayem
Sr VP: Anat Hakim
Sr VP: Rhonda Mims
Sr VP: Michael R Polen
Sr VP: Michael Radu
Sr VP: Blair W Todt
Sr VP: Michael Yount
VP: Larry Anderson
VP: Kathleen Bennett
Board of Directors: Richard C Breon, Carol J Burt, H James Dallas, D Robert Graham, Kevin F Hickey, Christian P Michalik, Glenn D Steele Jr, William L Trubeck, Paul E Weaver

D-U-N-S 11-882-2563
■ **WELLCHOICE INC**
EMPIRE
(*Suby of* ANTHEM INC) ★
1 Liberty Pl, New York, NY 10038-4030
Tel (212) 476-1000 *Founded/Ownrshp* 2005
Sales NA *EMP* 5,500
Accts Ernst & Young Llp New York N
SIC 6321 Health insurance carriers
Pr: Michael Stocker
Ch Bd: Philip Briggs
COO: Gloria McCarthy
CFO: John Remshard
Bd of Dir: Hermes L Ames
Sr VP: Robert W Lawrence
VP: Michael Galvin
VP: Daniel McCarthy
Counsel: Linda V Tiano
Board of Directors: Louis R Tomson, Hermes L Ames III, Faye Wattleton, John R Gunn, John E Zuccotti, Peter Hutchings, Susan L Malley, Edward J Malloy, John F McGillicuddy, Robert F McMillan, Stephen S Scheidt MD, Frederick O Terrell

D-U-N-S 60-837-2541
WELLDYNE INC
7472 S Tucson Way Ste 100, Englewood, CO 80112-3964
Tel (888) 479-2000 *Founded/Ownrshp* 1990
Sales 104.9MM^E *EMP* 386
SIC 8099 Blood related health services
Pr: Damien Lamendola
**COO:* Susan Cain
**Sr VP:* Doug Taylor
**VP:* Jack Feingold
VP: David King
**VP:* Karen Rooks Nauer
**VP:* Sharon Tarnosky
VP: Mike Woodley

D-U-N-S 95-796-0529
WELLDYNERX INC
(*Suby of* WELLDYNE INC) ★
7472 S Tucson Way Ste 100, Centennial, CO 80112-3964
Tel (888) 479-2000 *Founded/Ownrshp* 1999
Sales 104.9MM^E *EMP* 130
SIC 5122 5912 Pharmaceuticals; Drug stores
Pr: Damien Lamendola
**COO:* Susan Cain
Ex VP: Ellen Santilli
Sr VP: Jan Rutherford
VP: Jack Feingold
VP: Cynthia Matthews
VP: Sharon Tarnosky
**VP:* Doug Taylor Sr
VP: Michael Woodley
Assoc Dir: Erik Watts
Dir Rx: Gregg Kello

D-U-N-S 01-710-7061 IMP
WELLER AUTO PARTS INC
FRONTIER RADIATOR
2525 Chicago Dr Sw, Wyoming, MI 49519-1602
Tel (616) 538-5000 *Founded/Ownrshp* 1968
Sales 86.1MM^E *EMP* 150
SIC 5013 5015 5531 Automotive supplies & parts; Automotive supplies, used; Automotive parts
Pr: Harry M Weller
**Treas:* Paul A Weller
**VP:* John Weller

WELLER TRUCK PARTS
See JASPER WELLER LLC

D-U-N-S 07-657-2965
WELLESLEY COLLEGE
106 Central St, Wellesley, MA 02481-8203
Tel (781) 283-1000 *Founded/Ownrshp* 1870
Sales 520.8MM^E *EMP* 2,000^E
Accts Maloney Novotny Llc Cleveland
SIC 8221 College, except junior
Pr: Kimberly Bottomly
Pr: Jane Bachman
**Pr:* H Kim Bottomly
Pr: Deborah Kallman
**Treas:* Ellen Genat Hoffman
VP: Cameran Mason
Assoc Dir: Sumru Erkut
Assoc Dir: Melinda Mangels
Assoc Dir: Peggy McIntosh
Assoc Dir: Lisa Sankowski
Assoc Dir: Laura Till
Assoc Dir: Anna Young
Dir Soc: Elizabeth Tiro
Dir Soc: Sarah Willis

D-U-N-S 07-979-9464
WELLESLEY PUBLIC SCHOOLS
40 Kingsbury St, Wellesley, MA 02481-4831
Tel (781) 446-6200 *Founded/Ownrshp* 2015
Sales 11.6MM^E *EMP* 1,283^E
SIC 8211 Public elementary & secondary schools
Top Exec: Steve Favulli
Off Admin: Cheryl Moy
Dir IT: Sara Groden
Dir IT: Daryl Hedlund
Dir IT: Karen Toomey
Psych: Rebecca Patton
Art Dir: Thom Carter

D-U-N-S 05-700-9821 IMP
WELLINGTON INDUSTRIES INC
39555 S I 94 Servce Dr, Belleville, MI 48111-2877
Tel (734) 942-1060 *Founded/Ownrshp* 2005
Sales 84.1MM^E *EMP* 300
SIC 3465 Automotive stampings
Ch Bd: Marvin Tyghem
CFO: Blaise Flack

D-U-N-S 07-171-9793
WELLINGTON MANAGEMENT GROUP LLP
280 Congress St, Boston, MA 02210-1023
Tel (617) 951-5000 *Founded/Ownrshp* 1996
Sales 886.8MM^E *EMP* 741
SIC 6282 Investment advisory service
Pr: Brendan Joseph Swords
Pt: Nancy T Lukitsh
Pt: Edward Joseph Steinborn
Mng Pt: Kenneth L Abrams
Pr: Matt Alexander
Pr: Ryan Brennan
Pr: Marie Cristoforo
Pr: David Debreceni
Pr: Amit Fernandes
Pr: Kerry Hamson
Pr: Egor Kharakozov
Pr: Adam Saidla
Pr: Matt Ullman
Ofcr: Sandra Eknaian
Sr VP: Cynthia Mary Clarke
Sr VP: Jean Hynes
Sr VP: Phillip H Perelmuter
VP: Nicholas Adams
VP: Joe Agostino
VP: Abigail Babson
VP: Michael Bacevich

WELLINGTON PLACE AT
See UNITED DOMINION REALTY TRUST INC

D-U-N-S 15-130-3468
■ **WELLINGTON REGIONAL MEDICAL CENTER INC**
(*Suby of* UNIVERSAL HEALTH SERVICES INC) ★
10101 Forest Hill Blvd, West Palm Beach, FL 33414-6103
Tel (561) 798-8500 *Founded/Ownrshp* 1986
Sales 174.6MM *EMP* 764
SIC 8062 General medical & surgical hospitals
Pr: Pember Marvin
**CEO:* Jerel Humphrey
COO: Chris Locke
Dir Rad: Bill Dalton
Dir Rx: Jane Massaro
**Prin:* Filton Steve
Ansthlgy: Cary Colter
Ansthlgy: Daylie D Lopez
Doctor: William Dalon
Nrsg Dir: Michelle Epps

D-U-N-S 17-502-2896
WELLIVER MCGUIRE INC
250 N Genesee St, Montour Falls, NY 14865-9647
Tel (704) 454-5500 *Founded/Ownrshp* 1987
Sales 159.2MM^E *EMP* 400
SIC 1542 1541 Commercial & office building, new construction; Commercial & office buildings, renovation & repair; Industrial buildings, new construction; Renovation, remodeling & repairs: industrial buildings
VP: Bob Petrillose
VP: Stephen Welliver

D-U-N-S 82-869-5572 IMP
WELLMAN ADVANCED MATERIALS LLC
(*Suby of* SHANGHAI PRET COMPOSITES CO., LTD.)
520 Kingsburg Hwy, Johnsonville, SC 29555-8011
Tel (843) 386-8152 *Founded/Ownrshp* 2016
Sales 233.5MM^E *EMP* 740^E
SIC 2824 2821 Polyester fibers; Plastics materials & resins
CEO: Robert Fotsch
CFO: Robert K Taylor
VP: Pal Abant
VP: Joe Smith
VP: Robert D Taylor
VP: Scott Taylor
VP: Darrell Turbedille
Dir IT: Tim Carter
VP Mfg: Carroll Burrows
Plnt Mgr: Dal Avant

D-U-N-S 06-521-8737 IMP
WELLMAN DYNAMICS CORP
(*Suby of* FANSTEEL INTERCAST) ★
1746 Commerce Rd, Creston, IA 50801-8191
Tel (641) 782-8521 *Founded/Ownrshp* 1985
Sales 128.8MM^E *EMP* 435
SIC 3369 3365 Magnesium & magnes.-base alloy castings, exc. die-casting; Aluminum & aluminum-based alloy castings
Pr: Brian Cassady
**Sec:* S Downing
**VP:* Mike McCullough

WELLMARK BLUE CROSS
See WELLMARK INC

D-U-N-S 07-584-5545
WELLMARK INC
WELLMARK BLUE CROSS
1331 Grand Ave, Des Moines, IA 50309-2901
Tel (515) 376-4500 *Founded/Ownrshp* 1939
Sales NA *EMP* 1,800
SIC 6324 6411 6321 Hospital & medical service plans; Group hospitalization plans; Insurance agents, brokers & service; Health insurance carriers; Reinsurance carriers, accident & health
CEO: John D Forsyth
CFO: David Brown
Ex VP: Paul Eddy
Ex VP: George B Hanna
Ex VP: Cory R Harris
Ex VP: Ellen Msn
Ex VP: Timothy M Peterson
Ex VP: Vicki Signor
Ex VP: Sameer Sonalkar
Sr VP: Laura Jackson
VP: Michele Druker
VP: Lisa Heffelfinger
VP: McNerney Heintz
VP: Mathew Hosford
VP: Heidi Hoyt
VP: Patricia L Huffman
VP: Stacy Marcusson
VP: Cheryl L McCullough
VP: Dana W McNeill
VP: Sean McTaggart
VP: Lisa Mehle

WELLMED MEDICAL GROUP
See WELLMED MEDICAL MANAGEMENT INC

D-U-N-S 83-987-0966
■ **WELLMED MEDICAL MANAGEMENT INC**
WELLMED MEDICAL GROUP
(*Suby of* UNITEDHEALTH GROUP INC) ★
8637 Fredericksburg Rd # 360, San Antonio, TX 78240-1285
Tel (210) 615-9355 *Founded/Ownrshp* 1996
Sales 83.3MM^E *EMP* 850^E
SIC 8082 Home health care services
Pr: Bryan David Grundhoefer
**Pr:* Carlos Hernandez
**CFO:* Bryan Grundhoefer
**Treas:* Robert Oberrender
VP: Jeff White
**VP:* Joe Zimmerman
IT Man: Kevin Rankin
Pr Dir: Mike Ryan
Pr Mgr: Laura Cisneros
Snr Mgr: Russell Murie

WELLMONT FOUNDATION
See WELLMONT HEALTH SYSTEM

D-U-N-S 95-934-5448
WELLMONT HEALTH SYSTEM
WELLMONT FOUNDATION
1905 American Way, Kingsport, TN 37660-5882
Tel (423) 230-8200 *Founded/Ownrshp* 1996
Sales 675.4MM *EMP* 6,114^E
SIC 8062 8051 8063 General medical & surgical hospitals; Skilled nursing care facilities; Psychiatric hospitals
Prin: Denny Denarvaez
**Ch Bd:* Roger K Mowen Jr
V Ch: R D Crockett Sr
V Ch: T A Scott Jr
Pr: David Brash
Pr: Blaine Douglas
Pr: Bart Hove
Pr: Fred Pelle
Pr: Daniel Wolcott
COO: Eric Deaton
**COO:* Tracey Moffatt
**CFO:* Alice Pope
**CFO:* Beth Ward
Treas: Lee Shillito
**Chf Mktg O:* Dale Sargent
Sr VP: David L Brash
Sr VP: Gary Miller
Sr VP: Will Showalter
VP: Donna Jennings
VP: Kim Whiteaker
Dir OR: Kaye Smith

D-U-N-S 96-803-1174
WELLNEXT LLC
1301 Sawgrs Corp Pkwy, Sunrise, FL 33323-2813
Tel (954) 233-3301 *Founded/Ownrshp* 2014
Sales 192.2MM^E *EMP* 244^E
SIC 8071 Medical laboratories
CEO: Jose Minski
COO: Joel Minski
CFO: George Daulerio
Chf Cred: Ojesh Bhalla
Ex VP: Jim Ford
VP: Sharon Minski
Genl Mgr: Jack Minski

D-U-N-S 00-904-3936 IMP
WELLONS INC
2525 W Firestone Ln, Vancouver, WA 98660-1182
Tel (360) 750-3500 *Founded/Ownrshp* 1972
Sales 83.9MM^E *EMP* 350
Accts Moss-Adams Llp Portland Ore
SIC 3559 3443 Kilns, lumber; Boilers: industrial, power, or marine; Bins, prefabricated metal plate
CEO: Martin Nye
**CFO:* Robert Moore
**VP:* Kenneth Kinsley
Creative D: John Campbell
Netwrk Mgr: Brian Faiman
Sfty Mgr: Scott Carlson
Sales Exec: Andrew Israelson
Board of Directors: Martin Nye

D-U-N-S 00-141-4960
WELLPET LLC
200 Ames Pond Dr Ste 200, Tewksbury, MA 01876-1291
Tel (877) 869-2971 *Founded/Ownrshp* 1961
Sales 98.0MM^E *EMP* 217
SIC 2047 Dog & cat food
CEO: Timothy Callahan
VP: Steve Harris
VP Sls: Roger Parsons

D-U-N-S 79-951-3168
■ **WELLPOINT CALIFORNIA SERVICES INC**
(*Suby of* ANTHEM HOLDING CORP) ★
4553 La Tienda Rd, Westlake Village, CA 91362-3800
Tel (805) 557-6655 *Founded/Ownrshp* 2008
Sales NA *EMP* 80
SIC 6324 Health maintenance organization (HMO), insurance only
Ch Bd: Leonard Schaeffer
**CEO:* Pamela Dianne Kehaly
VP: Robert Glaser
VP: John Siemon
VP: Joan R Sofen

D-U-N-S 00-617-6937
WELLS CONCRETE PRODUCTS CO
210 Inspiration Ln, Albany, MN 56307-4535
Tel (800) 658-7049 *Founded/Ownrshp* 1951

Sales 120.4MM[E] *EMP* 800
SIC 3272 3273

WELLS DAIRY
See WELLS ENTERPRISES INC

D-U-N-S 04-410-3372 IMP/EXP
WELLS ENTERPRISES INC (IA)
WELLS DAIRY
1 Blue Bunny Dr Sw, Le Mars, IA 51031-2207
Tel (712) 546-4000 *Founded/Ownrshp* 1913
Sales 819.8MM[E] *EMP* 2,800
SIC 2024 Ice cream, packaged: molded, on sticks, etc.; Ice milk, packaged: molded, on sticks, etc.; Sherbets, dairy based; Yogurt desserts, frozen
Pr: Michael C Wells
Ch: David Lyons
Sr VP: Bill Baumbach
Sr VP: Thomas D Posey
VP: Mike Crone
Exec: Carol Fischer
Genl Mgr: Dennis Hughes
MIS Dir: Mike Kooistra
QA Dir: Sonya Stroman
IT Man: Scott Grosneheider
IT Man: Dave Sherrill

WELLS FARGO
See NORWEST BANK SOUTH DAKOTA NATIONAL ASSOCIATION

D-U-N-S 00-696-2435 IMP
▲ WELLS FARGO & CO
420 Montgomery St Frnt, San Francisco, CA 94104-1205
Tel (866) 249-3302 *Founded/Ownrshp* 1929
Sales NA *EMP* 264,700[E]
Tkr Sym WFC *Exch* NYS
SIC 6021 6022 6162 6141 7374 National commercial banks; State commercial banks; Mortgage bankers; Consumer finance companies; Data processing service
Pr: Tim Sloan
Pr: Eric Albrecht
Pr: Tony Allred
Pr: Mercedes Armendariz
Pr: Amy Birnbaum
Pr: Frances Brady
Pr: Rory Champagnie
Pr: Valerie Coffin-Mitchell
Pr: Debra Cross
Pr: Elizabeth David
Pr: Tim Dixson
Pr: Daniel Donnelly
Pr: Dolores Erazo
Pr: Vincent Fernandes
Pr: David Flora
Pr: David Geppert
Pr: Samara Gomez
Pr: John Gooch
Pr: Amily H Hanson
Pr: Cindy Harrington
Pr: Marie Henning
Board of Directors: James H Quigley, John Baker II, Susan G Swenson, Elaine L Chao, Suzanne M Vautrinot, John S Chen, Lloyd H Dean, Susan E Engel, Enrique Hernandez Jr, Donald M James, Cynthia M Milligan, Federico F Pena

D-U-N-S 61-035-0290
■ WELLS FARGO ADVISORS LLC
(*Suby of* WELLS FARGO & CO) ★
1 N Jefferson Ave, Saint Louis, MO 63103-2205
Tel (314) 955-3000 *Founded/Ownrshp* 2008
Sales 9.4MMM[E] *EMP* 38,527
SIC 6211 Security brokers & dealers
**Pr:* David Kowach
CEO: Marshall B Wichnack
Ofcr: Jimmie Lenz
Ofcr: Bob Mooney
Assoc VP: Joshua Aylesworth
Assoc VP: Barrett Benton
Assoc VP: Mark Burton
Assoc VP: Bruce R Callender
Assoc VP: Chris Hanaway
Assoc VP: Beth King
Assoc VP: David Materne
Assoc VP: Michele McMahon
Assoc VP: Michael Thomas
Sr VP: Richard M Bagley
Sr VP: Beth Hummels
Sr VP: Chris Moloney

D-U-N-S 96-797-7682
■ WELLS FARGO BANK LTD
(*Suby of* WFC HOLDINGS CORP) ★
333 S Grand Ave Ste 500, Los Angeles, CA 90071-1569
Tel (213) 253-6227 *Founded/Ownrshp* 2013
Sales NA *EMP* 83[E]
SIC 6022 State commercial banks
Brnch Mgr: Randy Reyes
VP: Courtney Cassidy
IT Man: John Brownlee

D-U-N-S 00-691-3404 IMP
■ WELLS FARGO BANK NATIONAL ASSOCIATION
(*Suby of* WELLS FARGO & CO) ★
420 Montgomery St, San Francisco, CA 94104-1298
Tel (415) 396-7392 *Founded/Ownrshp* 1999, 2004
Sales NA *EMP* 19,234
SIC 6021 National trust companies with deposits, commercial
CEO: Timothy J Sloan
Pr: Chris McDaid
Pr: Donna Patterson
COO: Les Biller
CFO: Howard Atkins
V Ch Bd: Terri Dial
V Ch Bd: Michael Gillfillan
V Ch Bd: Charles Johnson
V Ch Bd: Clyde Ostler
V Ch Bd: Paul Watson
Ofcr: Peggy Reingold
Ex VP: John A Berg
Ex VP: Patricia R Callahan
Ex VP: Michael J Heid
Ex VP: Michael James
Ex VP: Richard D Levy
Ex VP: David J Munio
Sr VP: Terri Bethel
Sr VP: Tom Bush
Sr VP: David M Carroll
Sr VP: Ed Gregorio

D-U-N-S 00-697-0636
■ WELLS FARGO BANK NEBRASKA NA (NE)
(*Suby of* WELLS FARGO & CO) ★
1919 Douglas St, Omaha, NE 68102-1316
Tel (402) 536-2022 *Founded/Ownrshp* 1988
Sales NA *EMP* 908
SIC 6021 National commercial banks
Pr: Judy Owen
VP: Sue Moreland

D-U-N-S 07-609-8326
■ WELLS FARGO BANK NEVADA NA
(*Suby of* WELLS FARGO & CO) ★
3300 W Sahara Ave Frnt, Las Vegas, NV 89102-3224
Tel (702) 765-3593 *Founded/Ownrshp* 2001
Sales NA *EMP* 694
Accts Federal Deposit Insurance Corp
SIC 6021 National commercial banks
Pr: Laura Schulte
CFO: Gregory Wilson
VP: Stanley S Stroup
Dir IT: Val Clark
Web Prj Mg: Kole Dunn

D-U-N-S 08-794-1746
■ WELLS FARGO BANK NEW MEXICO NA
(*Suby of* WELLS FARGO & CO) ★
200 Lomas Blvd Nw Ste 100, Albuquerque, NM 87102-9301
Tel (505) 765-5000 *Founded/Ownrshp* 1997
Sales NA *EMP* 270
SIC 6021 National commercial banks
Pr: Larry Willard
**Pr:* John De Graauw
**Pr:* Robert A Jung II
**Pr:* Linda Vega
**Ex VP:* Victor Valdez
**VP:* Pamela Chavec
VP: Pat Sanchez
**VP:* Holly Traver

D-U-N-S 82-648-2262
■ WELLS FARGO BANK SOUTH CENTRAL NATIONAL ASSOCIATION
(*Suby of* WELLS FARGO & CO) ★
2005 Taylor St, Houston, TX 77007-2820
Tel (713) 802-2717 *Founded/Ownrshp* 2008
Sales NA *EMP* 1
SIC 6035 Savings institutions, federally chartered
Prin: Marion Sandler

D-U-N-S 06-819-1956
■ WELLS FARGO BUSINESS CREDIT INC
(*Suby of* WELLS FARGO BANK NATIONAL ASSOCIATION) ★
730 2nd Ave S Fl 8, Minneapolis, MN 55402-3400
Tel (612) 673-8500 *Founded/Ownrshp* 1974
Sales NA *EMP* 500
SIC 6021 6141 National commercial banks; Personal credit institutions
Pr: Martin J Mc Kinley
Ex VP: Kris Klos
Ex VP: Kristine Netjes
Sr VP: Bruce Mc Grath
VP: Terrence Mitchell

D-U-N-S 04-452-5848
■ WELLS FARGO CAPITAL FINANCE LLC
(*Suby of* WELLS FARGO & CO) ★
100 Park Ave Fl 3, New York, NY 10017-5562
Tel (212) 840-2000 *Founded/Ownrshp* 2008
Sales NA *EMP* 400
SIC 6162 7389 Bond & mortgage companies; Financial services
Pr: Guy Fuchs
Pr: Loren Finkelstein
**CEO:* Henry K Jordan
**Ex VP:* Kevin Coyle
Sr VP: Ruben Avilez
Sr VP: Patti Weinberg
VP: Veronica Ferreira
VP: Jennifer Rabinowitz
**Mng Dir:* Barry A Kastner
**Mng Dir:* Michael Lucarelli
Opers Mgr: Irina Mazur

D-U-N-S 02-036-1697
■ WELLS FARGO COMMERCIAL DISTRIBUTION FINANCE LLC
(*Suby of* WELLS FARGO & CO) ★
5595 Trillium Blvd, Hoffman Estates, IL 60192-3405
Tel (847) 747-6800 *Founded/Ownrshp* 2016
Sales NA *EMP* 1,475
SIC 6153 6159 6141 Mercantile financing; Automobile finance leasing; Finance leasing, vehicles: except automobiles & trucks; Machinery & equipment finance leasing; Personal credit institutions
Pr: Robert M Martin
Sr VP: P Frank Limbaugh
Sr VP: Richard L Shirley
VP: James Berry
VP: Timothy Bowen
VP: Leonard F Buchan
VP: Thomas J Grathwohl
VP: Richard M Hinton
VP: James J Keinze
VP: John F Kelly
VP: Ronald L Kozminske
VP: Dennis L V An Leeuwen
VP: Stephen R Leskovsky
VP: Stephen C Monahan
VP: Pat Natale
VP: James M Nolan
VP: Paul R Puma
VP: James D Russell
VP: Emery F Saladin
VP: Lawrence G Schraut
VP: Thomas P Stiffler

D-U-N-S 18-836-9912
■ WELLS FARGO DEALER SERVICES INC
(*Suby of* WELLS FARGO BANK NATIONAL ASSOCIATION) ★
23 Pasteur, Irvine, CA 92618-3816
Tel (949) 727-1002 *Founded/Ownrshp* 2006
Sales NA *EMP* 1,080
SIC 6141 Consumer finance companies
Pr: Thomas A Wolfe
Treas: J Keith Palmer
Chf Cred: Ronald Terry
Chf Mktg O: Robert Galea
**Ex VP:* Dawn M Martin
Ex VP: Cathy J Mungon
Ex VP: David W Prescher
**Sr VP:* Guy Du Bose
Sr VP: Gary Hanson
Sr VP: Mark Marty
Sr VP: Robert E Moore

D-U-N-S 05-274-1907
■ WELLS FARGO EQUIPMENT FINANCE INC (GA)
(*Suby of* WELLS FARGO BANK NATIONAL ASSOCIATION) ★
2345 Rice St Ste 230, Saint Paul, MN 55113-3741
Tel (612) 667-9876 *Founded/Ownrshp* 1968
Sales NA *EMP* 330
SIC 6159 Machinery & equipment finance leasing; Finance leasing, vehicles: except automobiles & trucks; Truck finance leasing
CEO: John M McQueen
Pr: Christopher J Canney
**Pr:* James R Renner
**CFO:* Dan Pocrnich
VP: Jon Eide
VP: Thomas Hooley
**VP:* Mark La Count
VP: John Lande
VP: Randy Lee
VP: Darrel Muzzy
VP: Peter Myhre
VP: Todd Parent
VP: Susan Willmert

D-U-N-S 00-694-1041 IMP
WELLS FARGO FINANCIAL CA INC (NE)
800 Walnut St, Des Moines, IA 50309-3891
Tel (515) 557-7401 *Founded/Ownrshp* 1897
Sales NA *EMP* 9,300
SIC 6141 6153 6351 6159 6531 6021

D-U-N-S 92-892-2343
■ WELLS FARGO FINANCIAL CARDS
(*Suby of* WELLS FARGO BANK NATIONAL ASSOCIATION) ★
3201 N 4th Ave, Sioux Falls, SD 57104-0700
Tel (605) 336-3933 *Founded/Ownrshp* 2014
Sales NA *EMP* 300
SIC 6022 State commercial banks
Pr: John Keilholv
Dir IT: Dawn Saathoff

D-U-N-S 09-478-3677
■ WELLS FARGO FINANCIAL LEASING INC
(*Suby of* WELLS FARGO BANK NATIONAL ASSOCIATION) ★
800 Walnut St, Des Moines, IA 50309-3891
Tel (515) 557-4000 *Founded/Ownrshp* 1977
Sales NA *EMP* 400
SIC 6159 Machinery & equipment finance leasing
Pr: Timothy Reese

D-U-N-S 09-872-6888
■ WELLS FARGO FINANCIAL SECURITY SERVICES INC
(*Suby of* WELLS FARGO & CO) ★
800 Walnut St, Des Moines, IA 50309-3605
Tel (515) 243-2131 *Founded/Ownrshp* 1998
Sales NA *EMP* 11,582
SIC 6141 6153 6351 6159 7374 6021 Consumer finance companies; Installment sales finance, other than banks; Mercantile financing; Purchasers of accounts receivable & commercial paper; Credit & other financial responsibility insurance; Machinery & equipment finance leasing; Data processing service; National commercial banks
Pr: Thomas P Shippee
Pr: Rodney Miller
**CFO:* Dennis E Young
**Ex VP:* Anthony M Padinha
Sr VP: Michael D Dobson
Sr VP: Keith Karpinske
**Sr VP:* Patricia J McFarland
Sr VP: Joseph Willey
VP: Derek Braden
VP: Heidi Goettsch
VP: Ryan Hannam
VP: Jim Kunath
VP: Tracy Lewis
**VP:* William F Mack
VP: Richard Snyder
Exec: Jacki Fultz

D-U-N-S 80-443-4371
WELLS FARGO FINANCING CORP
420 Montgomery St Frnt, San Francisco, CA 94104-1205
Tel (415) 222-4292 *Founded/Ownrshp* 1980
Sales NA *EMP* 158,880[E]
SIC 6022 6021

D-U-N-S 79-932-5410
■ WELLS FARGO FOUNDATION MINNESOTA
N9305-192
(*Suby of* WELLS FARGO & CO) ★
N 9305-192, Minneapolis, MN 55479-0001
Tel (612) 667-1234 *Founded/Ownrshp* 1979
Sales NA *EMP* 4
SIC 6021 National commercial banks
VP: Carolyn Roby

D-U-N-S 78-781-5737
■ WELLS FARGO FUNDING INC
(*Suby of* WELLS FARGO BANK NATIONAL ASSOCIATION) ★
2701 Wells Fargo Way Fl 5, Minneapolis, MN 55467-8000
Tel (800) 328-5074 *Founded/Ownrshp* 1991
Sales NA *EMP* 1,500
SIC 6162 Mortgage bankers
Pr: Eric P Stoddard
**Ex VP:* Daniel T Segersin
Sr VP: Steve Brown
**Sr VP:* Michael S Harter
**Sr VP:* Thomas Navara
**Sr VP:* Susan A Wallace
VP: Terry Bouthilet
VP: Jeanette M Francis
VP: Sharon Johnson
VP: Troy Johnson
VP: Brad Solfest
VP: Julie Williams
Exec: Angelique Anthony

D-U-N-S 00-195-6366 IMP
■ WELLS FARGO HOME MORTGAGE INC
(*Suby of* WELLS FARGO BANK NATIONAL ASSOCIATION) ★
1 Home Campus, Des Moines, IA 50328-0001
Tel (515) 324-3707 *Founded/Ownrshp* 2011
Sales NA *EMP* 4,000
SIC 6162 Mortgage bankers
CEO: Peter J Wissinger
Pr: Colleen Cody
Pr: Lisa Luellen
Pr: Brenda J Wiarda
Treas: John Powers
**Div Pres:* Mike Heid
**Div Pres:* Cara Heiden
Ex VP: Peter Diliberti
Ex VP: John P Gibbons
Ex VP: Jim McCabe
**Ex VP:* Mark Oman
Ex VP: James Richards
Ex VP: William Wood
Sr VP: Nader Nasseh
Sr VP: James F Taylor
VP: Ruben O Avilez
VP: Ted Baxter
VP: Stephanie Binney
VP: Karen C Bolognone
VP: Vince Che
VP: Lori Dahl

D-U-N-S 87-620-0635
■ WELLS FARGO INC
(*Suby of* WELLS FARGO & CO) ★
200 Lomas Blvd Nw Ste 100, Albuquerque, NM 87102-9301
Tel (505) 353-5000 *Founded/Ownrshp* 1993
Sales NA *EMP* 465
SIC 6021 National commercial banks
Pr: Edward T O'Leary
**Ch Bd:* L Scott Nelson
Bd of Dir: Peggy Shifano
Ofcr: Nick Bires
Trst Ofcr: Brent Jordahl
**Trst Ofcr:* Kathy Sporing
**Ex VP:* J Paul Boushelle
**Ex VP:* Scott C Ulbrich
Sr VP: Jeannine Deloche
Sr VP: Joe Lefto
VP: Catharine Carrales
VP: Arthur Cordwell
VP: Mark Demascole
VP: Monique Etheridge
VP: Dolores Kenst
VP: Eleanor Raispis
VP: Prashant Ravani
**VP:* Ross Stenhouse
VP: Carl Tomaselli

D-U-N-S 62-079-2085
■ WELLS FARGO INSURANCE SERVICES INC
(*Suby of* WELLS FARGO & CO) ★
230 W Monroe St Ste 1950, Chicago, IL 60606-4717
Tel (312) 685-4122 *Founded/Ownrshp* 2001
Sales NA *EMP* 8,192
SIC 6411 Insurance agents, brokers & service; Advisory services, insurance
Pr: Kevin T Kenney
Pr: David Zuercher
Treas: Christine M Ostermeier
Ex VP: William Klepp
Ex VP: David Wood
Sr VP: Patrick J Brazill
Sr VP: Vaughn Harris
Sr VP: Roy Musgrove
Sr VP: Mike Taylor
VP: Rick Cassell
VP: Antion Garcia
VP: Christopher Hart
VP: John Moore

D-U-N-S 00-645-3682
■ WELLS FARGO INSURANCE SERVICES OF MINNESOTA INC
(*Suby of* WELLS FARGO INSURANCE SERVICES INC) ★
400 Highway 169 S Ste 800, Minneapolis, MN 55426-1140
Tel (952) 563-0600 *Founded/Ownrshp* 2006
Sales NA *EMP* 5,000
SIC 6411 Insurance agents, brokers & service; Property & casualty insurance agent; Life insurance agents
Pr: Keith Burkhardt
**Ex VP:* Jim Rechtiene
**Sr VP:* Ken Amerman
**Sr VP:* Gary Dennison
**Sr VP:* Tim Dunleavy
**Sr VP:* Jon Ecker
**VP:* John Moore

D-U-N-S 04-557-6485
■ WELLS FARGO INSURANCE SERVICES OF WEST VIRGINIA INC
(*Suby of* WELLS FARGO INSURANCE SERVICES INC) ★
1 Hillcrest Dr E, Charleston, WV 25311-1622
Tel (304) 346-0611 *Founded/Ownrshp* 1993
Sales NA *EMP* 1,500
SIC 6411 Insurance agents, brokers & service
Exec: Kevin Conboy

D-U-N-S 36-421-6726
■ WELLS FARGO INSURANCE SERVICES USA INC
(*Suby of* WELLS FARGO & CO) ★
150 N Michigan Ave # 3900, Chicago, IL 60601-7553
Tel (866) 294-2571 *Founded/Ownrshp* 2008
Sales NA *EMP* 2,037^E^
SIC 6411 Insurance agents, brokers & service
Ch Bd: John E Cay III
**Pr:* Stewart McDowell
**Pr:* Robert N Vlachos Jr
COO: Robert C Kent
CFO: Robert P Cuthbert
**CFO:* Karen J Lehman
CFO: Phil Lombardo
Ex VP: Anne Doss
Ex VP: Laura Schupbach
Sr VP: Nick Blaine
Sr VP: William M Choate
Sr VP: Ray Dorsey
Sr VP: Thomas Hayden
Sr VP: Hale Holden
Sr VP: Jack Matthews
Sr VP: Damian McFadden
Sr VP: Stan Ogden
Sr VP: Julian Smiley
Sr VP: Bill Velin
Sr VP: James S Wylie
VP: Tom Kornelis

D-U-N-S 00-694-1223
■ WELLS FARGO IOWA NA (IA)
(*Suby of* WELLS FARGO & CO) ★
666 Walnut St Ste 1400, Des Moines, IA 50309-3915
Tel (515) 245-3000 *Founded/Ownrshp* 1929
Sales NA *EMP* 2,275^E^
SIC 6021 7389 National commercial banks; Credit card service
Ch Bd: H Lynn Horak
Ofcr: Mary Pudenz
VP: Kristi Boyce
VP: Mark Conway
VP: Judy Corcoran
VP: Becky Gibson
VP: Matt McVey
VP: Deanna Robinson
VP: Scott Snyder
VP: Barb Squire
IT Man: Steve Rahn

D-U-N-S 61-704-9023
■ WELLS FARGO SECURITIES LLC
(*Suby of* WELLS FARGO & CO) ★
301 S Tryon St, Charlotte, NC 28282-1915
Tel (312) 920-9177 *Founded/Ownrshp* 2009
Sales 864.3MM^E^ *EMP* 2,500
SIC 6211 Investment bankers
Pr: Mike Heid
V Ch Bd: Brian Maier
VP: Gloria Sellars

D-U-N-S 07-177-7841
■ WELLS FARGO SERVICES INC
(*Suby of* WELLS FARGO & CO) ★
255 2nd Ave S, Minneapolis, MN 55401-2120
Tel (612) 667-1234 *Founded/Ownrshp* 1968, 1999
Sales 109.2MM^E^ *EMP* 1,161
SIC 7374 Data processing service
Pr: C Webb Edwards
Sr VP: Deborah James
VP: Kevin Beattie
VP: Patricia Herm
VP: Kenneth Hernandez
VP: Mel Reis
Brnch Mgr: Gary Backstrom
Store Mgr: Kevin Krigbaum
CIO: Scott Dillon
IT Man: Paul Rondorf
Sftwr Eng: Glenn Johnson

D-U-N-S 16-198-0222
■ WELLS LAMONT INDUSTRY GROUP LLC
(*Suby of* MARMON INDUSTRIAL LLC) ★
6640 W Touhy Ave, Niles, IL 60714-4587
Tel (800) 247-3295 *Founded/Ownrshp* 1907
Sales 63.8MM^E^ *EMP* 1,400
SIC 2381 Gloves, work: woven or knit, made from purchased materials
VP: Thomas J Palzer
VP: David F Rehm
VP: Jace Suttner
Genl Mgr: Jean Crespin

D-U-N-S 00-607-0320 IMP/EXP
WELLS VEHICLE ELECTRONICS LP
(*Suby of* NGK SPARK PLUG CO., LTD.)
385 W Rolling Meadows Dr, Fond Du Lac, WI 54937-8608
Tel (920) 922-5900 *Founded/Ownrshp* 2005, 2015
Sales 116.2MM^E^ *EMP* 408
SIC 3714 3694 3644 3357

WELLS/BLOOMFIELD INDUSTRIES
See CARRIER COMMERCIAL REFRIGERATION INC

D-U-N-S 78-034-8582
WELLSHIRE FARMS INC
509 Woodstown Rd, Swedesboro, NJ 08085-3156
Tel (877) 467-2331 *Founded/Ownrshp* 2002
Sales 107.4MM *EMP* 2
Accts The Weiss Group Chadds Ford
SIC 5149 Organic & diet foods
Pr: Louis Colameco
COO: Jasmel Sidhu
Sls Dir: Tom Colameco
Sls Mgr: Jim Thomas

WELLSPAN GOOD SAMARITAN HOSP
See GOOD SAMARITAN HOSPITAL OF LEBANON PENNSYLVANIA

WELLSPAN HEALTH
See YORK HOSPITAL

D-U-N-S 14-740-7423
WELLSPAN HEALTH
YORK HOSPITAL
45 Monument Rd, York, PA 17403-5070
Tel (717) 851-2269 *Founded/Ownrshp* 1983
Sales 1.6MMM *EMP* 8,000
Accts Ernst & Young Llp
SIC 5912 Drug stores
Pr: Kevin H Mosser
V Ch: Jeffrey D Lobach
Pr: Bruce Bartels
COO: John M Porter Jr
COO: Bruce A Solomon
CFO: Michael F O'Connor
Ch: William H Kerlin Jr
Treas: D Reed Anderson
Treas: Richard H Brown
Sr VP: Charles H Chodroff
Sr VP: Keith L Gee
Sr VP: Maria Royce
VP: Richard L Ayers
VP: Robert J Batory
VP: Joseph H Edgar
VP: William J Gillespie
VP: Jane Hyde
VP: Glen D Moffett
VP: Michael R Murphy
Exec: Thomas R McGann

D-U-N-S 88-461-2326
WELLSPAN MEDICAL GROUP (INC)
YORK HOSPITAL
(*Suby of* YORK HOSPITAL) ★
140 N Duke St, York, PA 17401-1170
Tel (717) 851-6515 *Founded/Ownrshp* 1993
Sales 336.1MM *EMP* 709
SIC 8011 Primary care medical clinic
CEO: Tom McGann

D-U-N-S 83-675-8573 IMP/EXP
WELLSPRING CAPITAL MANAGEMENT LLC
390 Park Ave Fl 5, New York, NY 10022-4608
Tel (212) 318-9800 *Founded/Ownrshp* 1995
Sales 714.3MM^E^ *EMP* 2,218
SIC 5812 Drive-in restaurant
CEO: William F Dawson Jr
Mng Pt: Carl Stanton
**COO:* William L Ramsey
**Ch:* Greg Feldman
Ofcr: Marlene Reihard
VP: Millet Bartoul
VP: Diane Priola
**Prin:* Alexander E Carles
**Prin:* Joshua C Cascade
**Prin:* John E Morningstar
**Prin:* Carl M Stanton

D-U-N-S 62-404-8745
WELLSPRING CAPITAL PARTNERS III LP
390 Park Ave Fl 5, New York, NY 10022-4608
Tel (212) 318-9800 *Founded/Ownrshp* 2002
Sales 110.5MM^E^ *EMP* 8,285^E^
SIC 5812 5813 7999 7993 Sandwiches & submarines shop; Bar (drinking places); Billiard parlor; Coin-operated amusement devices
Pt: Greg S Feldman
Ex Dir: William Ramsey

D-U-N-S 11-989-0940
WELLSPRING DISTRIBUTION INC
(*Suby of* WELLSPRING CAPITAL MANAGEMENT LLC) ★
390 Park Ave Fl 5, New York, NY 10022-4608
Tel (212) 318-9800 *Founded/Ownrshp* 2002
Sales 160.9MM^E^ *EMP* 2^E^
SIC 6794 5812 Franchises, selling or licensing; Drive-in restaurant
Pr: Greg Feldman
Ofcr: Marleen Richard

D-U-N-S 11-099-9054
WELLSPRING PHARMACEUTICAL CORP
(*Suby of* ANCOR CAPITAL PARTNERS) ★
5911 N Honore Ave Ste 211, Sarasota, FL 34243-2612
Tel (941) 312-4727 *Founded/Ownrshp* 2011
Sales 124.3MM^E^ *EMP* 125^E^
SIC 5122 2834 Pharmaceuticals; Pharmaceutical preparations
Pr: Robert Vukovich PHD
**CEO:* Randall Keene
**COO:* Wendy Shusko
**Ex VP:* Laura Dimichele
**VP:* Bonnie Feeney
IT Man: Peter Lunde

WELLSTAR DOUGLAS HOSPITAL
See DOUGLAS HOSPITAL INC

D-U-N-S 78-741-2154
WELLSTAR HEALTH SYSTEM INC
805 Sandy Plains Rd, Marietta, GA 30066-6340
Tel (770) 956-7827 *Founded/Ownrshp* 1984
Sales 745.9MM *EMP* 11,985
Accts Pricewaterhousecoopers Llp Ph
SIC 8062 General medical & surgical hospitals
CEO: Reynold J Jennings
V Ch: Janie Maddox
Pr: Bradford Newton
CEO: Jim Budzinski
COO: Michael Graue
COO: Monte Wilson
**CFO:* A James Budzinski
CFO: Jim Budzinski
**CFO:* Marsha Burke
CFO: Patty Pate
Trst: Otis Brumby III
Trst: Robert N Cross
Trst: Thomas E Gearhard
Trst: Charles J Jones
Trst: Gary A Miller
Trst: Steven W Oweida
Trst: Walter G Robinson
Trst: Charles Wood
Ofcr: Michael Andrews
Ofcr: Barry Mangel
Ofcr: Bill Mayfield

WELLSTAR PAULDING HOSPITAL
See PAULDING MEDICAL CENTER INC

WELLSTAR WEST GEORGIA MED CTR
See WEST GEORGIA HEALTH SYSTEM INC

D-U-N-S 07-756-4482 IMP
▲ WELLTOWER INC
4500 Dorr St, Toledo, OH 43615-4040
Tel (419) 247-2800 *Founded/Ownrshp* 1970
Sales 3.8MMM *EMP* 476^E^
Tkr Sym HCN *Exch* NYS
SIC 6798 Real estate investment trusts
Pr: Thomas J Derosa
Pr: Charles J Herman Jr
**COO:* Jeffrey H Miller
**CFO:* Scott A Estes
**Treas:* Michael A Crabtree
Chf Inves: Scott M Brinker
**Ex VP:* Erin C Ibele
Ex VP: Mercedes Kerr
**Sr VP:* Matthew McQueen
Sr VP: Paul Nungester
VP: Chris Disalle
VP: Michael Garst
VP: Richard Hansen
VP: Daniel Loftus
VP: Jay Morgan
VP: Greg Schonert
VP: Justin Skiver
VP: Christy C Stone
VP: Kevin Tyler
Board of Directors: Kenneth J Bacon, Jeffrey H Donahue, Fred S Klipsch, Geoffrey G Meyers, Timothy J Naughton, Sharon M Oster, Judith C Pelham, Sergio D Rivera, R Scott Trumbull

D-U-N-S 92-918-9470
WELOCALIZE INC
241 E 4th St Ste 207, Frederick, MD 21701-3612
Tel (301) 668-0330 *Founded/Ownrshp* 1995
Sales 170.0MM *EMP* 1,100
SIC 7389 Translation services
Pr: E Smith Yewell
COO: Gavin Grimes
**COO:* Eugene McGinty
**CFO:* Jeffrey Ash
VP: Olga Beregovaya
VP: Olga Blasco
VP: Jamie Glass
VP: Aaron Heber
VP: Rick Myers
VP: Robert Pfremmer
**VP:* Julia Yewell
Exec: Caroline Gouin
Exec: Mike Ni
Dir Bus: Chris Grebisz

WELSH CARSON ANDERSON & STOWE
See WELSH CARSON ANDERSON & STOWE VI LP

D-U-N-S 80-964-2069
WELSH CARSON ANDERSON & STOWE VI LP
WELSH CARSON ANDERSON & STOWE
320 Park Ave Fl 25, New York, NY 10022-6833
Tel (212) 893-9500 *Founded/Ownrshp* 1993
Sales 1.4MMM^E^ *EMP* 11,416
SIC 6799 Investors
Pt: David Mintz
Genl Pt: John Clark
Genl Pt: Anthony Nicola
Genl Pt: Thomas Scully
Pt: Richard E Aiello
Pt: Jonathan Rather
Pr: Ryan Harper
VP: Darren Battistoni
VP: James Dimitri
VP: Brian Regan
Mktg Mgr: Kate Seward

D-U-N-S 80-881-3252 IMP
WELSPUN PIPES INC
(*Suby of* WELSPUN CORP LIMITED)
9301 Frazier Pike, Little Rock, AR 72206-9280
Tel (501) 301-8800 *Founded/Ownrshp* 2006
Sales 244.8MM^E^ *EMP* 507
Accts Hudson Cisne & Co Llp Littl
SIC 1799 3494 Ornamental metal work; Pipe fittings
Pr: J Barry Leonard
Ofcr: Ashish Bhardwaj
**VP:* Rajesh Chokhani
Cmptr Lab: Vishwanath Gandikota
QA Dir: Ragesh Sheth
Opers Mgr: Manishankar Kumar
Mktg Mgr: Parul Sharma

D-U-N-S 00-408-7386 IMP
WELSPUN TUBULAR LLC
(*Suby of* WELSPUN PIPES INC) ★
9301 Frazier Pike, Little Rock, AR 72206-9280
Tel (501) 301-8800 *Founded/Ownrshp* 2007
Sales 228.8MM^E^ *EMP* 500
Accts Hudson Cisne & Co Llp Little
SIC 3317 Steel pipe & tubes
Pr: David Delie
**VP:* Rajesh Chokhani

D-U-N-S 06-604-7742 IMP
WELSPUN USA INC
(*Suby of* WELSPUN INDIA LIMITED)
295 Textile Bldg 5th Ave, New York, NY 10016
Tel (212) 620-2000 *Founded/Ownrshp* 2000
Sales 193.3MM *EMP* 80
Accts Plante & Moran Pllc Columbus
SIC 5131 Textiles, woven
Ch Bd: Barry Leonard
VP: Pradeep Gandhi
Genl Mgr: Ashish Shukla

D-U-N-S 06-041-4141
WELTMAN WEINBERG & REIS CO LPA (OH)
WW&R
323 W Lkeside Ave Ste 200, Cleveland, OH 44113
Tel (216) 685-1000 *Founded/Ownrshp* 1972, 1951
Sales 155.5MM^E^ *EMP* 1,250
SIC 8111 General practice law office
Pr: Robert B Weltman
Pt: Theresa Fortunato
Pt: Terrence Heffernan
Pt: Alan Hochheiser
Pt: Scott Weltman
Mng Pt: Alan Weinberg
Pr: Holly Anderson
Pr: Therese May
Pr: Leslie Schwarz
COO: Tim Corman
COO: Mark Slavik
CFO: Lloyd Wareham
VP: Allen J Reis
Exec: Tanya Glotz
Assoc Dir: Shawna Bledsoe
Assoc Dir: Keith Fisher
Dir Bus: Robert Hanna

D-U-N-S 78-478-5255
WEMBLEY USA INC
ROCKY MOUNTAIN POSTTIME
10750 E Iliff Ave, Aurora, CO 80014-4707
Tel (303) 751-5918 *Founded/Ownrshp* 2012
Sales 10.5MM^E^ *EMP* 1,006
SIC 7948 Dog race track operation; Horses, racing
CEO: Ty Howard

D-U-N-S 07-991-4485
■ WEN OHIO LLC
WENDY'S
(*Suby of* MERITAGE HOSPITALITY GROUP INC) ★
3310 Eagle Park Dr Ne, Grand Rapids, MI 49525-4574
Tel (616) 988-8751 *Founded/Ownrshp* 2015
Sales 15.4MM^E^ *EMP* 1,700
SIC 5812 Fast-food restaurant, chain
Pr: Robert Schermer Jr
**VP:* Gary A Rose

WENA HOLDING
See WKW ERBSLOEH NORTH AMERICA HOLDING INC

D-U-N-S 07-096-5702
WENATCHEE PUBLIC SCHOOLS
235 Sunset Ave, Wenatchee, WA 98801-1961
Tel (509) 663-8161 *Founded/Ownrshp* 1883
Sales 99.5MM *EMP* 1,100
SIC 8211 Public elementary & secondary schools
Bd of Dir: Jesus Hernandez
Dir Sec: Adam Bergstrom
Schl Brd P: Laura Jaecks

WENATCHEE VALLEY CLINIC
See WENATCHEE VALLEY MEDICAL GROUP PS

D-U-N-S 07-910-2483
WENATCHEE VALLEY HOSPITAL (WA)
820 N Chelan Ave, Wenatchee, WA 98801-2028
Tel (509) 663-8711 *Founded/Ownrshp* 2012
Sales 295.8MM *EMP* 800
SIC 8062 General medical & surgical hospitals
Ch Bd: Thomas Carlson MD
Sec: Edwin Carmack MD
**V Ch Bd:* Mitchell Garrison MD
Med Dir: Stuart Freed MD

D-U-N-S 07-573-0648
WENATCHEE VALLEY MEDICAL GROUP PS
WENATCHEE VALLEY CLINIC
820 N Chelan Ave, Wenatchee, WA 98801-2028
Tel (509) 663-8711 *Founded/Ownrshp* 1990
Sales 96.3MM^E^ *EMP* 240^E^
SIC 8011 Clinic, operated by physicians
Ch Bd: Thomas Carlson MD
Dir Recs: Kristin Walton
CFO: Stephanie Schreiner
**Sec:* Edwin Carmack
**V Ch Bd:* Mitchell Garrison MD
Bd of Dir: Michael Daines
Bd of Dir: Marcus Kubosumi
Ofcr: William Gotthold
IT Man: Bill Dean
IT Man: Matt Warham
Web Dev: Jennifer Blanchard

D-U-N-S 04-471-9144
WENCOR GROUP LLC
416 Dividend Dr, Peachtree City, GA 30269-1906
Tel (678) 490-0140 *Founded/Ownrshp* 2014
Sales 490.2MM^E^ *EMP* 900
SIC 3728 4581 Aircraft parts & equipment; Aircraft maintenance & repair services
CEO: Chris Curtis
**CFO:* Shawn Trogdon
**Treas:* Charles Elder
VP: Andy Shields
Telecom Mg: Mont Erickson
QC Dir: Justin Nelson
Opers Mgr: Chris Wood
Ql Cn Mgr: Andrew Rosenvall
Sales Asso: Michael Cook
Sales Asso: Linda Vargas

D-U-N-S 02-626-1966
WENDCO CORP
WENDY'S
220 W Garden St Ste 500, Pensacola, FL 32502-5745
Tel (850) 433-5425 *Founded/Ownrshp* 1984
Sales 45.4MM^E^ *EMP* 1,200
SIC 5812 Fast-food restaurant, chain
Pr: Roger W Webb

D-U-N-S 09-106-4113 IMP/EXP
WENDCO OF PUERTO RICO INC
WENDY'S
1155 Ave Ponce De Leon, San Juan, PR 00907-3803
Tel (787) 792-2001 *Founded/Ownrshp* 1978
Sales 47.1MM^E^ *EMP* 2,000
Accts Kevane Grant Thornton Llp San
SIC 5812 Fast-food restaurant, chain
Ch Bd: Jorge Colon Nevarez
**Pr:* Jorge Colon
**VP:* Antonia Colon

D-U-N-S 06-342-3648
WENDEL NORTH AMERICA LLC
(*Suby of* WENDEL)
152 W 57th St Fl 55, New York, NY 10019-3310
Tel (212) 557-5100 *Founded/Ownrshp* 2013

Sales 2.1MMM^E *EMP* 7,011^E
SIC 6211 Investment firm, general brokerage
CEO: David Darmon
Off Mgr: Lisa Bruh

D-U-N-S 07-857-8010
WENDELTA INC (TN)
WENDY'S
(*Suby of* CARLISLE LLC) ★
263 Wagner Pl, Memphis, TN 38103-3808
Tel (901) 526-5000 *Founded/Ownrshp* 1975, 1982
Sales 115.4MM^E *EMP* 3,500
SIC 5812 Fast-food restaurant, chain
CEO: Gene D Carlisle
**Pr:* John Hughes
**CFO:* Lewis Geho
VP: Karen Carlisle
VP: G C Chancellor

D-U-N-S 00-877-7476
WENDLING QUARRIES INC (IA)
(*Suby of* MANATTS INC) ★
2647 225th St, De Witt, IA 52742-9123
Tel (563) 659-9181 *Founded/Ownrshp* 1940, 1987
Sales 89.1MM^E *EMP* 200
SIC 1422 1611 1442 Limestones, ground; Agricultural limestone, ground; Highway & street maintenance; Construction sand & gravel
Pr: Anthony J Manatt
Treas: J Miller
**Treas:* Wendell Wuestenberg

D-U-N-S 08-951-5162
WENDORFF BROS CO INC
105 Steelcraft Dr, Hartford, WI 53027-1631
Tel (262) 673-6770 *Founded/Ownrshp* 1998
Sales 87.9MM^E *EMP* 410
SIC 3469 3089 5013 3479 Metal stampings; Injection molding of plastics; Automotive supplies & parts; Painting of metal products
Pr: Gary Wendorff
VP: Gene Wendorff

D-U-N-S 78-678-1021
WENDY WEIHE STORLIE INC
W W S
4032 Shoreline Dr Ste 2, Spring Park, MN 55384-4502
Tel (952) 548-9306 *Founded/Ownrshp* 1992
Sales 95.6MM^E *EMP* 8
Accts Paul Haglund & Co Llc Lakivil
SIC 2079 2077 Margarine & margarine oils; Animal fats, oils & meals; Cargo loading & unloading services; Commercial nonphysical research
Pr: Wendy W Storlie
**COO:* Ted Storlie

WENDY'S
See FFC LIMITED PARTNERSHIP

WENDY'S
See J STANTON DAVID & ASSOCIATES INC

WENDY'S
See VALENTI MID-ATLANTIC MANAGEMENT LLC

WENDY'S
See CALHOUN MANAGEMENT CORP

WENDY'S
See WENDCO CORP

WENDY'S
See B F NASHVILLE INC

WENDY'S
See B F FT MYERS INC

WENDY'S
See DAVCO ACQUISITION HOLDING INC

WENDY'S
See WEN OHIO LLC

WENDY'S
See WENDELTA INC

WENDY'S
See MUY HAMBURGER PARTNERS LLC

WENDY'S
See WENDCO OF PUERTO RICO INC

WENDY'S
See LDF FOOD GROUP INC

WENDY'S
See TAR HEEL CAPITAL CORP NO 2

WENDY'S
See THOMAS FIVE LTD

WENDY'S
See FOURCROWN INC

WENDY'S
See PMD RESTAURANTS LLC

WENDY'S
See DAVCO RESTAURANTS INC

WENDY'S
See FIRST SUN MANAGEMENT CORP

WENDY'S
See VALENTI FLORIDA MANAGEMENT INC

WENDY'S
See PENNANT FOODS LLC

WENDY'S
See CAROLINA RESTAURANT GROUP INC

WENDY'S
See B F SOUTH INC

WENDY'S
See WM LIMITED PARTNERSHIP - 1998

WENDY'S
See EMERALD FOODS INC

WENDY'S
See PISCES FOODS LP

WENDY'S
See W C S INC

D-U-N-S 00-503-8773 IMP/EXP
▲ WENDYS CO
1 Dave Thomas Blvd, Dublin, OH 43017-5452
Tel (614) 764-3100 *Founded/Ownrshp* 1929
Sales 1.8MMM *EMP* 21,200
Tkr Sym WEN *Exch* NGS
SIC 5812 6794 Fast-food restaurant, chain; Franchises, selling or licensing
Pr: Todd A Penegor
**Ch Bd:* Nelson Peltz
**V Ch:* Peter W May
COO: Robert D Wright
CFO: Gunther Plosch
Ofcr: Liliana M Esposito
Ofcr: Kurt A Kane
Ofcr: Scott A Weisberg
Sr VP: Scott A Kriss
VP: Joe Schechinger
CIO: David Trimm
Board of Directors: Emil J Brolick, Janet Hill, Dennis M Kass, Joseph A Levato, Matthew H Peltz, Peter H Rothschild, Michelle J Mathews-Spradli, Arthur B Winkleblack

WENDY'S FOURJAY
See FOURJAY LLC

D-U-N-S 83-044-3573
■ WENDYS INTERNATIONAL LLC
(*Suby of* WENDYS RESTAURANTS LLC) ★
1 Dave Thomas Blvd, Dublin, OH 43017-5452
Tel (614) 764-3100 *Founded/Ownrshp* 1969
Sales 1.3MMM^E *EMP* 37,000^E
Accts Deloitte & Touche Llp Atlanta
SIC 5812 Fast-food restaurant, chain
VP: Denny Lynch
**COO:* Robert D Wright
**Chf Mktg O:* Kenneth Calwell
**Sr VP:* John D Barker
**Sr VP:* Steven B Graham
**Sr VP:* Gerard C Lewis
**Sr VP:* Margaret R Nollen
Sr VP: Raquell Repka
Genl Mgr: Matt Tattrson
Mktg Dir: Bob Stowe
Genl Couns: Mark Inzetta

D-U-N-S 07-022-5669
WENDYS OF BOWLING GREEN INC (KY)
Store 3489 Store3489 St Sto, Bowling Green, KY 42104
Tel (270) 782-6124 *Founded/Ownrshp* 1975
Sales 42.3MM^E *EMP* 1,000
SIC 5812 Fast-food restaurant, chain
Pr: James Smith
**Pr:* Michael O'Malley

D-U-N-S 04-072-5905
WENDYS OF COLORADO SPRINGS INC
(*Suby of* WENDYS) ★
1515 N Academy Blvd # 400, Colorado Springs, CO 80909-2749
Tel (719) 573-8557 *Founded/Ownrshp* 1976
Sales 67.6MM^E *EMP* 1,500
SIC 5812

D-U-N-S 62-380-8321
■ WENDYS OF DENVER INC
(*Suby of* WENDYS INTERNATIONAL LLC) ★
4288 W Dblin Granville Rd, Dublin, OH 43017-1442
Tel (614) 764-3100 *Founded/Ownrshp* 1969
Sales 31.8MM^E *EMP* 1,123^E
SIC 5812 Fast-food restaurant, chain
Prin: John Schuessler
VP: Paul Shreve
VP: Tim Sullivan
Netwrk Eng: Matt Lorenz

D-U-N-S 62-380-9667
■ WENDYS OF NE FLORIDA INC
(*Suby of* WENDYS INTERNATIONAL LLC) ★
4288 W Dblin Granville Rd, Dublin, OH 43017-1442
Tel (614) 764-3100 *Founded/Ownrshp* 1996
Sales 45.4MM^E *EMP* 2,621^E
SIC 5812 Fast-food restaurant, chain
Prin: John Brownley

D-U-N-S 62-381-1671 IMP
■ WENDYS OLD FASHIONED HAMBURGERS OF NEW YORK LLC
(*Suby of* WENDYS INTERNATIONAL LLC) ★
4288 W Dblin Granville Rd, Dublin, OH 43017-1442
Tel (614) 764-3100 *Founded/Ownrshp* 1974
Sales 205.7MM^E *EMP* 13,057^E
SIC 5812 Fast-food restaurant, chain
Prin: Jennifer Smith

WENDYS OLD FASHIONED REST
See BRIDGEMAN FOODS II INC

D-U-N-S 05-285-6671
■ WENDYS RESTAURANTS LLC
(*Suby of* WENDYS CO) ★
1 Dave Thomas Blvd, Dublin, OH 43017-5452
Tel (614) 764-3100 *Founded/Ownrshp* 2008
Sales 1.3MMM^E *EMP* 37,000^E
SIC 5812 6794 Fast-food restaurant, chain; Franchises, selling or licensing
Pr: Emil J Brolick
**CFO:* Todd Pengor
Treas: John F Brownley
Ex VP: Donald F Calhoun
Ex VP: Ed Choe
Ex VP: Kathleen A McGinnis
Sr VP: Ed Austin
Sr VP: John M Deane
Sr VP: Lori Estrada
**Sr VP:* Steven B Graham
Sr VP: Brion G Grube
Sr VP: Jim Hartenstein
Sr VP: Lawrence A Laudick
Sr VP: Neil Lester
Sr VP: Tad Wampfler
Sr VP: Mike Watson
VP: Hanif Adatia
VP: Peter Moses
VP: Gavin Waugh
Board of Directors: Dana Klein, Joseph A Levato, Peter H Rothschild, David E Schwab II, Raymond S Troubh, Jack G Wasserman

D-U-N-S 00-616-7647 IMP/EXP
WENGER CORP (MN)
555 Park Dr, Owatonna, MN 55060-4940
Tel (507) 455-4100 *Founded/Ownrshp* 1946
Sales 113.2MM^E *EMP* 441
SIC 2541 3446 Partitions for floor attachment, prefabricated: wood; Acoustical suspension systems, metal
Pr: Christopher S Simpson
CFO: Joe McCusker
Ofcr: Dixon Gimpel
**VP:* Tom Carmen
**VP:* Jeff Jollay
VP: Jeffrey L Jollay
Dir IT: Scott Blahosky
IT Man: Iris Prissel
**VP Opers:* Jim Kingsley
Mfg Mgr: Rick Bothun
VP Mktg: Dave Bullard

D-U-N-S 01-451-3287 IMP
WENGER FEEDS LLC (PA)
101 W Harrisburg Ave, Rheems, PA 17570
Tel (717) 367-1195 *Founded/Ownrshp* 1948
Sales 99.6MM^E *EMP* 300
SIC 2048 5144 0252

D-U-N-S 01-002-4735 IMP
WENNER BREAD PRODUCTS INC (NY)
33 Rajon Rd, Bayport, NY 11705-1101
Tel (800) 869-6262 *Founded/Ownrshp* 1975
Sales 126.7MM^E *EMP* 425^E
SIC 2051 2053 5461 Bread, all types (white, wheat, rye, etc): fresh or frozen; Frozen bakery products, except bread; Bakeries
CEO: Richard R Wenner
**Sr VP:* Lawrence L Wenner
**VP:* Daniel Wenner
**VP:* William W Wenner Jr
Mktg Mgr: Karen Sarraga
Manager: Michael Costa

D-U-N-S 04-399-3468 IMP
WENNER MEDIA LLC
ROLLING STONE
1290 Ave Of The Amer Fl 2, New York, NY 10104-0295
Tel (212) 484-1616 *Founded/Ownrshp* 1967
Sales 118.1MM^E *EMP* 300
SIC 2721 Magazines: publishing & printing
CEO: Hugh Scogin
**COO:* Katey Distefano
**Ch:* Steven Schwartz
IT Man: Brian McFarland
Ql Cn Mgr: Adam Mardula
Mktg Dir: Mark Neschis
Mktg Dir: John Reese
Sls Dir: Dave Woody

D-U-N-S 00-919-2881 IMP/EXP
WENTE BROS (CA)
WENTE VINEYARDS
5565 Tesla Rd, Livermore, CA 94550-9149
Tel (925) 456-2300 *Founded/Ownrshp* 1883, 1977
Sales 145.1MM^E *EMP* 800
SIC 2084 8742 Wines; Restaurant & food services consultants
CEO: Eric P Wente
**Pr:* Carolyn Wente
CFO: Rich Archer
CFO: Richard Arter
**Ch:* Jean Wente
Treas: Arthur Jeannet
Sr VP: Larry Dipietro
Sr VP: Brendan Finley
Sr VP: Kevin Zollinger
VP: Robert Gundrey
VP: Doug Johnson
**VP:* William Joslin
VP: Shokie Lopez
**VP:* Ralph Riva
VP: Karl Wente
**VP:* Philip Wente

WENTE VINEYARDS
See WENTE BROS

D-U-N-S 04-481-4606
WENTWORTH INSTITUTE OF TECHNOLOGY INC
550 Huntington Ave, Boston, MA 02115-5998
Tel (617) 989-4590 *Founded/Ownrshp* 1904
Sales 172.7MM *EMP* 450
Accts Cbiz Tofias Boston Ma
SIC 8221 Colleges universities & professional schools
Pr: Zorica Pantic
COO: Freedman Jeffrey
Treas: Jerome Cafey
Trst: George C Chryssis
Assoc VP: Peter Maddox
VP: Brenda C Sanchez
Assoc Dir: Greg Abazorius
Assoc Dir: Gregory Jackson
Ex Dir: Maureen Dischino
CIO: Danny Davis
MIS Dir: Patrick Thomas

D-U-N-S 06-990-9281
WENTWORTH-DOUGLASS HOSPITAL
789 Central Ave, Dover, NH 03820-2526
Tel (603) 742-5252 *Founded/Ownrshp* 1906
Sales 322.7MM *EMP* 1,700
Accts Baker Newman & Noyes Llc Man
SIC 8062 General medical & surgical hospitals
Pr: Gregory Walker
**CFO:* Peter Walcek
Treas: Rick Card
Trst: Michael Steinberg
Ofcr: Emily Moore
Exec: Joanie Blinn
VP Admn: Craig Whitney
Adm Dir: Gintautas A Tors
Prac Mgr: Stacey Salinas
Genl Mgr: Scott Monson
Nurse Mgr: Becky Sherburne

D-U-N-S 02-037-1266
WENTZVILLE R-IV SCHOOL DISTRICT
1 Campus Dr, Wentzville, MO 63385-3415
Tel (636) 327-3800 *Founded/Ownrshp* 1860
Sales 162.2MM *EMP* 1,800
Accts Mueller Walla & Albertson P
SIC 8211 Public elementary & secondary schools; Public elementary school; Public junior high school; Public senior high school
CFO: Kari Monsees
Dir IT: Richard Wilson
Pr Dir: Mary Lapak

D-U-N-S 84-920-6628
WERCS
400 E 1st St Ste 100, Casper, WY 82601-2559
Tel (307) 235-6200 *Founded/Ownrshp* 1990
Sales 90.8MM^E *EMP* 600
SIC 6211 6163 6411 6321 6531 6099 Security brokers & dealers; Mortgage brokers arranging for loans, using money of others; Insurance agents & brokers; Life insurance agents; Accident & health insurance; Real estate agent, commercial; Real estate leasing & rentals; Check cashing agencies
Pr: Gail Zimmerman
**Treas:* Bob Moberly
**VP:* Robert K Mc Bride
**VP:* Travis Olsen

D-U-N-S 06-715-4000
WERE READY TO ASSEMBLE INC
IMPACT RESOURCE GROUP
2201 W Royal Ln Ste 230, Irving, TX 75063-3206
Tel (972) 373-9484 *Founded/Ownrshp* 1999
Sales 35.0MM^E *EMP* 1,350^E
SIC 7389 5399 Bicycle assembly service; Army-Navy goods
Pr: Richard J D'Maico
**Treas:* Chris Olson
**VP:* Scott Murphy
Dir Bus: Michael McDonald
Snr Sftwr: Tobe Thompson

D-U-N-S 80-558-3080 IMP/EXP
WERNER CO
(*Suby of* NEW WERNER HOLDING CO INC) ★
93 Werner Rd, Greenville, PA 16125-9434
Tel (724) 588-2000 *Founded/Ownrshp* 2007
Sales 535.1MM^E *EMP* 1,800
SIC 3499 3355 3089 3446 2499 Ladders, portable: metal; Extrusion ingot, aluminum: made in rolling mills; Synthetic resin finished products; Scaffolds, mobile or stationary: metal; Stepladders, wood
CEO: William T Allen
**CFO:* Larry V Friend
CFO: Donald W Resnick
Sr Cor Off: Peter Ocoin
Ex VP: Ignacio Eddie
VP: Jeff Campbell
VP: Rick Meyers
VP: Carlos Perea
VP: Johnathan Remmers
VP: Mark Schell
VP: Tim Slater

WERNER ELECTRIC SUPPLY
See WERNER ELECTRIC VENTURES LLC

D-U-N-S 02-346-5008 IMP
WERNER ELECTRIC SUPPLY CO
4800 W Prospect Ave, Appleton, WI 54914-8900
Tel (920) 337-6700 *Founded/Ownrshp* 1986
Sales 403.0MM^E *EMP* 434
SIC 5063 Electrical apparatus & equipment
CEO: Lynn T Mac Donald
**CFO:* Bradley Klitzke
**VP:* Micahel Ales
**VP:* Robert Stern
**VP:* Ken Stoltzmann

D-U-N-S 08-822-4600
WERNER ELECTRIC VENTURES LLC (WI)
WERNER ELECTRIC SUPPLY
7450 95th St S, Cottage Grove, MN 55016-3949
Tel (651) 458-3701 *Founded/Ownrshp* 2001
Sales 186.5MM^E *EMP* 165
SIC 5063 5084 5085 Electrical apparatus & equipment; Industrial machinery & equipment; Electric tools
Snr Mgr: Ben Granley
Opers Mgr: Steve Hesser
Opers Mgr: Bob Matthew
Sls Mgr: Mike Diepholz
Sales Asso: Chad Dailey
Sales Asso: Jeffrey Larsen
Sales Asso: Gregg Quam

D-U-N-S 02-208-6565
▲ WERNER ENTERPRISES INC
14507 Frontier Rd, Omaha, NE 68138-3875
Tel (402) 895-6640 *Founded/Ownrshp* 1956
Sales 2.0MMM *EMP* 9,192
Tkr Sym WERN *Exch* NGS
SIC 4213 Trucking, except local; Building materials transport; Refrigerated products transport
Pr: Derek J Leathers
COO: H Marty Nordlund
CFO: John J Steele
Ch: Clarence L Werner
Chf Mktg O: Daniel H Cushman
Ofcr: James L Johnson
Assoc VP: Jim Belter
Ex VP: James A Mullen
Ex VP: Jim S Schelble
Ex VP: Robert E Synowicki
VP: Eric Downing
VP: Larry Friend
VP: Dwayne Haug
VP: Randy Kraft
VP: Chris Polenx
Exec: Donna Kalvelage
Assoc Dir: Michele Monaghan
Board of Directors: Kenneth M Bird, Patrick J Jung, Dwaine J Peetz Jr, Duane K Sather, Michael L Steinbach, Gerald H Timmerman

WERNER EXTRUDED PRODUCTS
See OLD LADDER CO

D-U-N-S 00-432-9520
WERNER HOLDING CO (PA) INC (PA)
93 Werner Rd, Greenville, PA 16125-9434
Tel (888) 523-3371 *Founded/Ownrshp* 1922, 1997
Sales 104.3MM^E *EMP* 1,250
SIC 3499 3355 3089 3446 2499 Ladders, portable: metal; Extrusion ingot, aluminum: made in rolling mills; Synthetic resin finished products; Scaffolds, mobile or stationary: metal; Stepladders, wood
CEO: Dennis G Heiner
**Pr:* Steve Richman
**CFO:* Larry V Friend
Sr VP: John J Fiumefreddo
**VP:* Edward W Gericke
**VP:* Robert P Tamburrino
**VP:* Eric J Werner
VP Mfg: Steven R Bentson

D-U-N-S 00-794-5512
■ WESBANCO BANK INC (WV)
(*Suby of* WESBANCO INC) ★
1 Bank Plz, Wheeling, WV 26003-3565
Tel (304) 234-9000 *Founded/Ownrshp* 1870
Sales NA *EMP* 999
SIC 6022 State commercial banks
CEO: Todd Clossin
**Ex VP:* Tom McGaughy
**Ex VP:* John W Moore Jr
**Ex VP:* J B Schmitt
**Sr VP:* David L Pell
VP: Wyatt Hoffman

D-U-N-S 02-215-5626
▲ WESBANCO INC
2100 National Rd, Wheeling, WV 26003-5248
Tel (304) 234-9000 *Founded/Ownrshp* 1968
Sales NA *EMP* 1,682^E
Tkr Sym WSBC *Exch* NGS
SIC 6021 National commercial banks
Pr: Todd F Clossin
**Ch Bd:* James C Gardill
CFO: Robert H Young
Ofcr: Gregory A Dugan
Ofcr: Peter W Jaworski
Ofcr: Michael L Perkins
Sr Tst Off: Kim W Seabright
Ex VP: Lynn D Asensio
Ex VP: Ivan L Burdine
Ex VP: Jonathan D Dargusch
Ex VP: Anthony F Pietranton
Ex VP: Brent E Richmond
VP: Eric Babbert
VP: Traci Boeing
VP: Roanne Burech
VP: Brian Dean
VP: Ryan Digiandomenico
VP: Bob Friend
VP: Rick Givens
VP: Agresta Greg
VP: Wyatt Hoffman
Board of Directors: F Eric Nelson Jr, Stephen J Callen, Ronald W Owen, Christopher V Criss, Richard G Spencer, Abigail M Feinknopf, Kerry M Stemler, Ernest S Fragale, Reed J Tanner, D Bruce Knox, Charlotte A Zuschlag, Lisa A Knutson, Gary L Libs, Paul M Limbert, Jay T McCamic

WESCO
See WESTERN EXPLOSIVES SYSTEMS CO

WESCO AIRCRAFT
See FALCON AEROSPACE HOLDINGS LLC

D-U-N-S 04-848-5478 IMP
■ WESCO AIRCRAFT HARDWARE CORP (CA)
(*Suby of* WESCO AIRCRAFT HOLDINGS INC) ★
24911 Avenue Stanford, Valencia, CA 91355-1281
Tel (661) 775-7200 *Founded/Ownrshp* 1953, 2006
Sales 1.5MMM *EMP* 780
SIC 5088 Aircraft & parts
CEO: Dave Castagnola
**COO:* Alex Murray
CFO: Gregory A Hann
CFO: George Heff
**CFO:* Richard Weller
**Chf Cred:* Todd Renehan
Dept Mgr: Morris Denoun
**CIO:* Dave Currence
QI Cn Mgr: Ben Huhn
QI Cn Mgr: Celina Ramos
S&M/VP: Hal Weinstein

D-U-N-S 80-907-3245
▲ WESCO AIRCRAFT HOLDINGS INC
24911 Avenue Stanford, Valencia, CA 91355-1281
Tel (661) 775-7200 *Founded/Ownrshp* 1953
Sales 1.5MMM *EMP* 2,670^E
Accts Pricewaterhousecoopers Llp Lo
Tkr Sym WAIR *Exch* NYS
SIC 8741 5072 Management services; Hardware
Pr: David J Castagnola
**Ch Bd:* Randy J Snyder
COO: Alex Murray
CFO: Richard J Weller
Chf Cred: Todd Renehan
Act CFO: Lynn Mackison
Ex VP: Dave Currence
Ex VP: Daniel C Snow
VP: Chris King
VP: K Lynn Mackison
VP: Todd Renehart
Board of Directors: Thomas M Bancroft, Paul E Fulchino, Jay L Haberland, Scott E Kuechle, Adam J Palmer, Robert D Paulson, Jennifer M Pollino, Norton A Schwartz

D-U-N-S 82-694-9224 IMP
■ WESCO DISTRIBUTION INC
(*Suby of* WESCO INTERNATIONAL INC) ★
225 W Station Square Dr # 700, Pittsburgh, PA 15219-1151
Tel (412) 454-2200 *Founded/Ownrshp* 1993
Sales 4.9MMM^E *EMP* 5,699
SIC 5063 5085 5065 7389 Electrical apparatus & equipment; Fuses & accessories; Lighting fittings & accessories; Circuit breakers; Industrial supplies; Connectors, electronic; Purchasing service
Pr: John Engel
Treas: Daniel A Brailer
VP: John Hawfield
VP: Mike Ludwig
Exec: Courtney Cabaniss
Rgnl Mgr: Lee Osterman
Brnch Mgr: Dave Boes
Brnch Mgr: Bill Gephart
Brnch Mgr: David Nicholson
Brnch Mgr: Amy Roach
Brnch Mgr: Brent Schultz

D-U-N-S 00-691-0616
■ WESCO FINANCIAL CORP (DE)
(*Suby of* BLUE CHIP STAMPS) ★
301 E Colo Blvd Ste 300, Pasadena, CA 91101
Tel (626) 585-6700 *Founded/Ownrshp* 1959, 2011
Sales 620.4MM^E *EMP* 2,100^E
SIC 7359 6411 7389 Equipment rental & leasing; Property & casualty insurance agent; Scrap steel cutting
Pr: Charles T Munger
Bd of Dir: Robert Flaherty
VP: Robert Sahm

D-U-N-S 08-886-9532
WESCO INC
ON YOUR WAY
1460 Whitehall Rd, Muskegon, MI 49445-1347
Tel (231) 719-4300 *Founded/Ownrshp* 1952
Sales 177.4MM^E *EMP* 1,050
SIC 5411 5541 5145 5149 Convenience stores, independent; Gasoline service stations; Candy; Bakery products; Sandwiches
Co-Pr: James B Westgate
Dir IT: Rachelle Osborn
Pgrm Dir: Kimberley Loniecki

D-U-N-S 10-285-2576 IMP
■ WESCO INTEGRATED SUPPLY INC
(*Suby of* WESCO DISTRIBUTION INC) ★
36 Harbor Park Dr, Port Washington, NY 11050-4651
Tel (516) 484-6070 *Founded/Ownrshp* 1989
Sales 408.4MM^E *EMP* 400^E
SIC 5085 Industrial supplies
CEO: Eli Rosenbaum
Prgrm Mgr: Anessa Chilton
Prgrm Mgr: Miguel Espinosa
Prgrm Mgr: Raul Flores
Prgrm Mgr: Doug Sengillo
Prgrm Mgr: Brandon Updegraff
Prgrm Mgr: Steve Wanke
Area Mgr: Lukasz Szwarc
Genl Mgr: Ashley Kirkbride
IT Man: Luke Jeffrey
Web Dev: Andy Yeh

D-U-N-S 88-405-1616 IMP/EXP
▲ WESCO INTERNATIONAL INC
225 W Station Square Dr # 700, Pittsburgh, PA 15219-1151
Tel (412) 454-2200 *Founded/Ownrshp* 1994
Sales 7.5MMM *EMP* 9,300^E
Tkr Sym WCC *Exch* NYS
SIC 5063 5084 5065 7389 Electrical apparatus & equipment; Fuses & accessories; Lighting fittings & accessories; Circuit breakers; Industrial machinery & equipment; Connectors, electronic; Purchasing service
Ch Bd: John J Engel
CFO: Kenneth S Parks
CFO: David S Schulz
Treas: Brian Begg
Ofcr: Kimberly G Windrow
Sr VP: Diane E Lazzaris
VP: Joseph Astroth
VP: Jim Blais
VP: James Blumhardt
VP: Clarence Dodge
VP: Timothy A Hibbard
VP: Dale Kendall
VP: Mike Ludwig
VP: Kenneth Parks
VP: Scott Render
VP: Jim Westgate
Board of Directors: Bobby J Griffin, Sandra Beach Lin, John K Morgan, James J Obrien, Steven A Raymund, James L Singleton, Robert J Tarr Jr

D-U-N-S 06-038-6059
WESCOM CENTRAL CREDIT UNION
123 S Marengo Ave, Pasadena, CA 91101-2428
Tel (888) 493-7266 *Founded/Ownrshp* 1934
Sales NA *EMP* 604
SIC 6062 State credit unions, not federally chartered
Pr: John Adams
COO: Jane Wood
CFO: Mark Thorpe
Ofcr: Kevin Vogt
Ex VP: Rob Guilford
Sr VP: Susan McCready
Sr VP: Anthony Nowak
Sr VP: Kevin Sarber
VP: Jonathon Bauman
VP: Joel Chavarin
VP: Michelle Esser
VP: Connie Knox
VP: Ron Lenart
VP: Lisa Paul-Hill
VP: Joseph Pazienza
VP: Yesceni Ramirez
VP: Pamela Sullivan
VP: Ron Wilsie
VP: Irving Yu
Exec: Kathie Chism
Board of Directors: Will Brown, Addison D Carter, Gina A Friedrich, Robert Graham, Daniel Kraus, Javier Morales, Norberta N Noguera, Liz Wood

D-U-N-S 03-164-0626
WESFAM RESTAURANTS INC
BURGER KING
206 Gates Ave Se, Huntsville, AL 35801-4213
Tel (256) 533-0211 *Founded/Ownrshp* 1966
Sales 44.7MM *EMP* 1,300
Accts Mda & Associates Huntsville
SIC 5812 Fast-food restaurant, chain
Ch Bd: Jean W Templeton
**Pr:* Rich Wyckoff
**VP:* Tristenne W Robin
**VP:* James Wessel

D-U-N-S 07-692-3143
WESLACO INDEPENDENT SCHOOL DISTRICT
319 W 4th St, Weslaco, TX 78596-6047
Tel (956) 969-6500 *Founded/Ownrshp* 1921
Sales 182.0MM *EMP* 2,500
Accts Noel Garza Cpa Pc Edinburg
SIC 8211 Public elementary school; Public junior high school; Public senior high school
**CFO:* Andres Sanchez
Dir Sec: Melissa Escalon

D-U-N-S 07-194-2197
WESLEY HEALTH SYSTEM LLC
WESLEY MEDICAL CENTER
5001 Hardy St, Hattiesburg, MS 39402-1308
Tel (601) 268-8000 *Founded/Ownrshp* 1997
Sales 88.1MM^E *EMP* 1,590
SIC 8051 8062 8082 8011 Skilled nursing care facilities; General medical & surgical hospitals; Home health care services; General & family practice, physician/surgeon
CEO: Jeff Meigs
**Ch Bd:* Michael May
Pr: James Rosendale
COO: Bill Voloch
CFO: Jim Young
VP: Richard Shaw
Dir Risk M: Debbie Johnson
Dir Lab: Ricky Winstead
Dir Rx: Pam Graham
Chf Nrs Of: Phebe McKay
CTO: Nadine Archuleta

D-U-N-S 88-401-4788
WESLEY LONG COMMUNITY HEALTH SERVICES INC
WESLEY LONG COMMUNITY HOSPITAL
(*Suby of* ANNIE PENN HOSPITAL) ★
501 N Elam Ave, Greensboro, NC 27403-1199
Tel (336) 832-1000 *Founded/Ownrshp* 1984
Sales 1.2MM^E *EMP* 1,000
SIC 8062 General medical & surgical hospitals
Pr: R Timothy Rice
**Pr:* Terrence Akin
**Ex VP:* Theresa Brodrick
**Ex VP:* Mary Jo Cagle
**Ex VP:* Jeffrey Jones
Dir Lab: Esther Ingle

WESLEY LONG COMMUNITY HOSPITAL
See WESLEY LONG COMMUNITY HEALTH SERVICES INC

WESLEY MEDICAL CENTER
See WESLEY HEALTH SYSTEM LLC

D-U-N-S 03-782-4559
■ WESLEY MEDICAL CENTER LLC
(*Suby of* HCA HOLDINGS INC) ★
550 N Hillside St, Wichita, KS 67214-4976
Tel (316) 962-2000 *Founded/Ownrshp* 1998
Sales 545.8MM *EMP* 40^E
SIC 8011 Medical centers
CEO: Hugh Tappan
**COO:* Bill Voloch
**CFO:* Matt Leary
Co-COO: Steve Edgar
Ofcr: Debra McArthur
Exec: Steven Howell
Dir Risk M: Joey Dean
Dir Lab: Bob Hetherington
Dir Rad: Daniel Grantham
Dir Rx: Jack Bond
Dir Rx: Leslie Eidem

D-U-N-S 09-096-1962
WESLEY-JESSEN CORP (DEL) (DE)
(*Suby of* ALCON LABORATORIES INC) ★
333 Howard Ave, Des Plaines, IL 60018-1907
Tel (847) 294-3000 *Founded/Ownrshp* 1995
Sales 90.1MM^E *EMP* 1,000
SIC 3851 Contact lenses
Pr: Glen Bradley
CFO: Edward Kelly
VP: Lawrence L Chapoy
Netwrk Mgr: Martin Fabris
Tech Mgr: Jim McAloon
Board of Directors: Roman Bheinski

D-U-N-S 96-338-7704
WESLEYAN HOMES OF INDIANA INC
34 S Main St, Cloverdale, IN 46120-8531
Tel (765) 795-4260 *Founded/Ownrshp* 2010
Sales 161.4MM *EMP* 8^E
SIC 8051 Skilled nursing care facilities
Prin: David Lawlor

D-U-N-S 06-925-2492
WESLEYAN UNIVERSITY
45 Wyllys Ave, Middletown, CT 06459-3211
Tel (860) 685-2000 *Founded/Ownrshp* 1831
Sales 84.4MM^E *EMP* 900
Accts Kpmg Llp Hartford Ct
SIC 8221 6552 University; Subdividers & developers
Pr: Michael S Roth
V Ch: Irma Gonzalez
**Pr:* Douglas J Bennett Jr
**VP:* Judith Brown
VP: Robert King
**VP:* John C Meerts
VP: Nathan Peters
VP: Barbara-Jan Wilson
Exec: Tessa Bellone
Assoc Dir: Emily Gorlewski
Assoc Dir: Roseann Sillasen
Dir Soc: Laurie Zolty

D-U-N-S 06-131-9026
WESLEYLIFE
HERITAGE HOUSE
5508 Nw 88th St, Johnston, IA 50131-3005
Tel (515) 271-6789 *Founded/Ownrshp* 1947
Sales 6.2MM *EMP* 1,200
Accts Cliftonlarsonallen Llp Minnea
SIC 8059 Rest home, with health care
Ch Bd: Bob Ruch
Pt: Sarah Frost
**Pr:* Rob Kretzinger
VP: Bryan Sanders
Dir Soc: Amber King
Ex Dir: Chris Butters
Off Mgr: Deb Butler
Off Mgr: Rita Nims
CIO: Kevin Wilson
Mktg Dir: Julia Fitzhugh
Pr Dir: Kathy Otterberg

D-U-N-S 07-685-6574
WESPATH BENEFITS AND INVESTMENTS
CENTER FOR HEALTH
1901 Chestnut Ave, Glenview, IL 60025-1604
Tel (847) 869-4550 *Founded/Ownrshp* 1908
Sales NA *EMP* 250
SIC 6371 Pension, health & welfare funds
CEO: Barbara A Boigegrain
**CFO:* Tim Koch
**Ch:* Jeri Sutton

WEST, A THOMSON REUTERS BUS
See WEST PUBLISHING CORP

WEST ADA SCHOOL DISTRICT
See JOINT SCHOOL DISTRICT 2

D-U-N-S 08-984-7107
WEST ALLIS-WEST MILWAUKEE (OR)
WEST ALLS-WEST MLWKEE LRNG CTR
1205 S 70th St, Milwaukee, WI 53214-3167
Tel (414) 604-3033 *Founded/Ownrshp* 1957
Sales 72.4M *EMP* 1,400
Accts Reilly Penner & Benton Llp Mi
SIC 8211 Public senior high school
MIS Dir: Steve Blum
Schl Brd P: Jeff Sikich
HC Dir: Marla Blom

WEST ALLS-WEST MLWKEE LRNG CTR
See WEST ALLIS-WEST MILWAUKEE

D-U-N-S 10-346-2263
■ WEST AMERICA BANK
(*Suby of* WESTAMERICA BANCORPORATION) ★
1108 5th Ave, San Rafael, CA 94901-2916
Tel (707) 863-6113 *Founded/Ownrshp* 1972
Sales NA *EMP* 645
SIC 6022 State commercial banks
Ch Bd: David L Payne
**CFO:* Jennifer Finger
**Treas:* E Joseph Bowler
**Ex VP:* Charles Fritz
**Sr VP:* Robert Entwisle
**Sr VP:* Dennis R Hansen
Sr VP: Bob Silver
**Sr VP:* Hans Tjian
VP: Kris Irvine
VP: Gary Lepiane
VP: Ralph Metzger
VP: Louba Nazaroff

D-U-N-S 00-956-9930 IMP
WEST AMERICAN RUBBER CO LLC
WARCO
1337 W Braden Ct, Orange, CA 92868-1123
Tel (714) 532-3355 *Founded/Ownrshp* 2001
Sales 101.9MM^E *EMP* 400
SIC 3069 3061 3053 Sheets, hard rubber; Mechanical rubber goods; Gaskets, all materials
VP: Timothy Hemstreet
VP: Mark Johnson
Exec: Jim Deleo
IT Man: Michael Escobedo
Sfty Mgr: Shae Howell

WEST ANAHEIM MEDICAL CENTER
See PRIME HEALTHCARE ANAHEIM LLC

WEST AURORA SCHOOL DISTRICT 12
See AURORA WEST SCHOOL DISTRICT 129

D-U-N-S 01-000-6211
WEST BABYLON UNION FREE SCHOOL DISTRICT
10 Farmingdale Rd, West Babylon, NY 11704
Tel (631) 321-3143 *Founded/Ownrshp* 1919
Sales 99.4MM *EMP* 760
Accts Cullen & Danowski Llp Port Je
SIC 8211 Public elementary & secondary schools
**Pr:* Lucy Campasano
**Treas:* Loretta Titolo
**Trst:* James Bocca
**Trst:* Kathleen Jennings
**Trst:* Barbara Kenney
**Trst:* Jerry Nocera

D-U-N-S 07-115-6046
WEST BEND JOINT SCHOOL DISTRICT NO 1
WEST BEND PUBLIC SCHOOLS
735 S Main St Stop 2, West Bend, WI 53095-3962
Tel (262) 335-5435 *Founded/Ownrshp* 1905
Sales 90.0MM *EMP* 1,000
SIC 8211 Public combined elementary & secondary school
MIS Dir: Tim Harder
Teacher Pr: Valley Elliehausen

D-U-N-S 00-643-4245
WEST BEND MUTUAL INSURANCE CO
1900 S 18th Ave, West Bend, WI 53095-9791
Tel (262) 334-5571 *Founded/Ownrshp* 1894
Sales NA *EMP* 1,150
SIC 6331 Fire, marine & casualty insurance: mutual; Property damage insurance
CEO: Kevin Steiner
Pr: Mike Delaney
Pr: Jim Keal
**CFO:* Dale Kent
Treas: Jon Holfeltz
Ofcr: Thomas Reed
**VP:* Jon Duwell
**VP:* Richard L Fox
VP: Paul Hingtgen
**VP:* Robert J Jacques
VP: Rob Jacquesjakes
VP: Gary Klein

VP: Dave Nettum
**VP:* Daniel Roskopf
**VP:* Kelly D Tighe
**VP:* Timothy R Wiedmeyer
**VP:* Christopher Zwygart

WEST BEND PUBLIC SCHOOLS
See WEST BEND JOINT SCHOOL DISTRICT NO 1

D-U-N-S 01-087-8908
WEST BLOOMFIELD SCHOOL DISTRICT
5810 Commerce Rd, West Bloomfield, MI 48324-3200
Tel (248) 865-6420 *Founded/Ownrshp* 1950
Sales 58.5MM^E *EMP* 1,000
Accts Plante & Moran Pplc Clinton T
SIC 8211 Public combined elementary & secondary school; Public elementary & secondary schools; Public senior high school
Dir IT: Jeff Sharp

D-U-N-S 82-919-9699
WEST BOCA MEDICAL CENTER INC
THC
21644 State Road 7, Boca Raton, FL 33428-1899
Tel (561) 488-8000 *Founded/Ownrshp* 1986
Sales 143.0MM *EMP* 835
SIC 8062 General medical & surgical hospitals
CEO: Mitch Feldman
**COO:* Ryan Lee
CFO: Brook Thomas
**Treas:* Tyler Murphy
Dir Risk M: Andrea Nunes
Dir Rad: Richard Pilla
Pgrm Dir: Raymond Mata

D-U-N-S 00-527-7892 IMP
WEST CENTRAL COOPERATIVE (IA)
406 1st St, Ralston, IA 51459-7714
Tel (712) 667-3200 *Founded/Ownrshp* 1933
Sales 455.0MM^E *EMP* 245
SIC 5153 2075 2048 5191

D-U-N-S 07-177-3337 IMP
WEST CENTRAL DISTRIBUTION LLC
2700 Trott Ave Sw, Willmar, MN 56201-2777
Tel (320) 235-8518 *Founded/Ownrshp* 2014
Sales 104.3MM^E *EMP* 39
SIC 5191 Chemicals, agricultural; Fertilizer & fertilizer materials
CEO: Dale J Engan
**Pr:* Dale Engan
**Pr:* Bruce Moen
**CFO:* Craig Trettin
**VP:* Michael Fiebelkorn
**VP:* Pat Maiers
Exec: Nathan Metcalf
Exec: Joy Stengehell
Sls Mgr: Mike Wichmann
Snr Mgr: Steven Roehl

D-U-N-S 02-560-6971
WEST CENTRAL FS INC (DE)
1202 W Piper St, Macomb, IL 61455-2700
Tel (309) 833-2168 *Founded/Ownrshp* 1964
Sales 145.7MM *EMP* 62
Accts Cliftonlarsonallen Llp Normal
SIC 5153 Grains
Genl Mgr: Barry Schmidt
Treas: Kendell Litchfield
Board of Directors: Randy Parks, Darrel Reed, Ron Thompson, John Zimmerman

D-U-N-S 05-803-1980 IMP
WEST CENTRAL PRODUCE INC
12840 Leyva St, Norwalk, CA 90650-6852
Tel (213) 629-3600 *Founded/Ownrshp* 1970
Sales 123.0MM *EMP* 300
SIC 5148 Fresh fruits & vegetables
CEO: Michael Dodo
**CFO:* Jamie Purcell
Manager: Alex Perez

WEST CENTRAL PROVINCE OF THE
See DAUGHTERS OF CHARITY PROVINCE OF ST LOUISE

D-U-N-S 05-967-6171
WEST CENTRAL STEEL INC
110 19th St Nw, Willmar, MN 56201-2427
Tel (320) 235-4070 *Founded/Ownrshp* 1972
Sales 148.3MM^E *EMP* 125
SIC 5051 Metals service centers & offices; Steel; Structural shapes, iron or steel; Concrete reinforcing bars
CEO: Jeffrey Pattison
**CEO:* Delbert A Allinder
Sfty Mgr: Kevin Snyder
Ql Cn Mgr: Brain Lowther
Sales Asso: Marianne Allinder

D-U-N-S 07-161-1693
WEST CHESTER AREA SCHOOL DISTRICT
829 Paoli Pike, West Chester, PA 19380-4551
Tel (484) 266-1000 *Founded/Ownrshp* 1989
Sales 214.0MM *EMP* 1,500
Accts Barbacane Thornton & Company
SIC 8211 Public combined elementary & secondary school
**Pr:* Vince Murphy
Bd of Dir: Pauline Bachtle
Bd of Dir: Mary Howse
Dir IT: June Garwin
Tech Mgr: Martin Friedman
Sfty Dirs: David Flamer
Pr Dir: Tracey Dukert
Schl Brd P: Jeffrey Seagraves
HC Dir: Marilee Giardinieri

WEST CHESTER HOSPITAL
See CHESTER WEST MEDICAL CENTER

WEST CHESTER PROTECTIVE GEAR
See CHESTER WEST HOLDINGS INC

D-U-N-S 62-734-1274
WEST CHESTER UNIVERSITY OF PENNSYLVANIA
STATE SYSTM OF HGHR EDUC OF TH
(*Suby of* STATE SYSTEM HIGHER EDUCATN PA) ★
700 S High St, West Chester, PA 19383-0003
Tel (610) 436-1000 *Founded/Ownrshp* 1871
Sales 204.7MM *EMP* 1,460
Accts Cliftonlarsonallen Llp Plymou
SIC 8221 9411 University; Administration of educational programs;
Pr: Greg Weisenstein
**VP:* Joseph Hammel
VP: Mark Pavlovich
Dir Lab: Brent Thompson
DP Exec: Krupinski Barbara
DP Exec: Pamela Barrows
DP Exec: Sharitz Stephanie

D-U-N-S 07-288-7896
WEST CLERMONT LOCAL SCHOOL DISTRICT
4350 Aicholtz Rd Ste 220, Cincinnati, OH 45245-3501
Tel (513) 943-5000 *Founded/Ownrshp* 1946
Sales 86.2MM *EMP* 1,128
Accts Balestra Harr & Scherer Cpas
SIC 8211 Public elementary school; Public junior high school; Public senior high school; Public vocational/technical school
CFO: Pam Moore
Schl Brd P: John Bantges
Teacher Pr: Bob Walker
HC Dir: Ellie Preston

D-U-N-S 08-658-8050
WEST COAST ARBORISTS INC
2200 E Via Burton, Anaheim, CA 92806-1221
Tel (714) 991-1900 *Founded/Ownrshp* 1972
Sales 263.9MM^E *EMP* 800
SIC 0782

D-U-N-S 02-926-1781 IMP
WEST COAST BEAUTY SUPPLY CO
5001 Industrial Way, Benicia, CA 94510-1033
Tel (707) 748-4800 *Founded/Ownrshp* 2004
Sales 135.3MM^E *EMP* 1,000
SIC 5087 3069

D-U-N-S 61-356-4079
WEST COAST DISTRIBUTING INC
WEST COAST FRESH
350 Main St Fl 1, Malden, MA 02148-5089
Tel (781) 665-0300 *Founded/Ownrshp* 1990
Sales 135.0MM^E *EMP* 75
SIC 4731 5148 Freight transportation arrangement; Fresh fruits & vegetables
Pr: Brian V Bell
Brnch Mgr: Elaine Swaim
CTO: Cynthia Elms
CTO: Thong Phandui
CTO: Jessica Rossello
Dir IT: Jennifer Goree
Dir IT: Anthony Rodriques

WEST COAST FRESH
See WEST COAST DISTRIBUTING INC

D-U-N-S 18-386-1558
WEST COAST GRAPE FARMING INC
800 E Keyes Rd, Ceres, CA 95307-7539
Tel (209) 538-3131 *Founded/Ownrshp* 1987
Sales 53.1MM^E *EMP* 2,500
SIC 0762 Farm management services
Pr: Fred Franzia
**VP:* John Franzia

D-U-N-S 00-895-8118 IMP
WEST COAST PAPER CO
WCP SOLUTIONS
6703 S 234th St Ste 120, Kent, WA 98032-2903
Tel (253) 850-1900 *Founded/Ownrshp* 1930
Sales 258.4MM^E *EMP* 425
SIC 5085 5169 5084 2677 Industrial supplies; Chemicals & allied products; Packaging machinery & equipment; Envelopes
Pr: Teresa Russell
**Pr:* Tom Groves
VP: Stephanie Quinn
VP: Amy Swanson
Genl Mgr: Keith Spurdon
Genl Mgr: Dan Steinke
IT Man: Scott McIver

D-U-N-S 00-367-7012
WEST COAST PRIME MEATS LLC
344 Cliffwood Park St, Brea, CA 92821-4103
Tel (714) 255-8560 *Founded/Ownrshp* 2010
Sales 88.7MM^E *EMP* 120
SIC 5147 Meats & meat products
VP: Nathan Bennett
QA Dir: Samuel Rachal
IT Man: Jamie Carrol

D-U-N-S 96-722-1628
WEST CONSULTANTS-GANNETT FLEMING JOINT VENTURE
11440 W Bernardo Ct # 360, San Diego, CA 92127-1641
Tel (858) 487-9378 *Founded/Ownrshp* 2011
Sales 262.6MM^E *EMP* 39
SIC 8711 Engineering services

D-U-N-S 16-666-2929
WEST CONTRA COSTA HEALTHCARE DISTRICT
WCCHD
2000 Vale Rd, San Pablo, CA 94806-3808
Tel (510) 970-5102 *Founded/Ownrshp* 1948
Sales 100.8MM^E *EMP* 1,202^E
SIC 8082

D-U-N-S 07-169-7015
WEST CONTRA COSTA UNIFIED SCHOOL DISTRICT
1108 Bissell Ave, Richmond, CA 94801-3135
Tel (510) 231-1100 *Founded/Ownrshp* 2004
Sales 251.8MM^E *EMP* 3,800
Accts Crowe Horwath Llp Sacramento
SIC 8211 Elementary & secondary schools
Pr: Charles T Ramsey
**CEO:* Raul Ramirez
IT Man: Chris Hanna
IT Man: David McDonald
IT Man: Mark Terrill
Teacher Pr: Mike Wasilchin
Psych: Karen Aiken
Psych: Emily Santiago
Psych: Rachel Smith
Psych: Kristina Sterling
Snr Mgr: Andrea Melano

D-U-N-S 96-412-6445
▲ WEST CORP
11808 Miracle Hills Dr, Omaha, NE 68154-4403
Tel (402) 963-1200 *Founded/Ownrshp* 1986
Sales 2.2MMM *EMP* 10,630^E
Tkr Sym WSTC *Exch* NGS
SIC 7389 7372 4813 7374 Telephone services; Telephone answering service; Prepackaged software; ; Data processing & preparation; Computer graphics service
Ch Bd: Thomas B Barker
Pr: Ronald Beaumont
Pr: Nancee R Berger
Pr: J Scott Etzler
Pr: Jon R Hanson
Pr: Julie Rutherford
CFO: Jan D Madsen
Bd of Dir: Gregory Alonso
Ofcr: Rod J Kempkes
Ex VP: James Frazer
Ex VP: David C Mussman
Ex VP: Nicole B Theophilus
Ex VP: David J Treinen
VP: David Cottingham
VP: Alyssa R Lotzer
VP: Eric A Robeson
Comm Man: Windell Austin
Board of Directors: Lee Adrean, Donald M Casey Jr, Anthony J Dinovi, Paul R Garcia, Laura A Grattan, Jeanette Horan, Michael A Huber, Diane E Offereins, Gregory T Sloma

WEST COST TOMATO
See MCCLURE PROPERTIES LTD

D-U-N-S 15-064-6073
WEST CUSTOMER MANAGEMENT GROUP LLC
11808 Miracle Hills Dr, Omaha, NE 68154-4403
Tel (402) 571-7700 *Founded/Ownrshp* 2007
Sales NA *EMP* 1,200
SIC 7389

D-U-N-S 06-961-8874
WEST DES MOINES COMMUNITY SCHOOL DISTRICT
3550 Mills Civic Pkwy, West Des Moines, IA 50265-5556
Tel (515) 633-5078 *Founded/Ownrshp* 1898
Sales 117.6MM *EMP* 1,475
Accts Bohnsack & Frommelt Llp Overl
SIC 8211 Public elementary & secondary schools

WEST ENGINEERING SERVICES
See WEST HOU INC

D-U-N-S 10-006-0631
WEST FARGO SCHOOL DISTRICT 6
WEST FRGO SPECIAL EDUCATN UNIT
207 Main Ave W, West Fargo, ND 58078-1725
Tel (701) 356-2000 *Founded/Ownrshp* 1876
Sales 111.0MM *EMP* 700
Accts Robert R Peterson Fargo Nor
SIC 8211 Public special education school
Prin: Dr David Flowers
**Prin:* Mark Lemer

WEST FIELD GROUP
See OHIO FARMERS INSURANCE CO

WEST FLORIDA CANCER INSTITUTE
See WEST FLORIDA HOSPITAL

D-U-N-S 15-822-9653
WEST FLORIDA HOSPITAL
WEST FLORIDA CANCER INSTITUTE
8383 N Davis Hwy, Pensacola, FL 32514-6088
Tel (850) 494-4000 *Founded/Ownrshp* 2001
Sales 233.5MM *EMP* 8^E
SIC 8062 General medical & surgical hospitals
Dir IT: Jeffrey Amerson
Opers Mgr: Scott Weichbrodt

D-U-N-S 13-966-6986
■ WEST FLORIDA REGIONAL MEDICAL CENTER INC
REHABILITATION INSTITUTE W FLA
(*Suby of* HOSPITAL CORPORATION OF AMERICA) ★
8383 N Davis Hwy, Pensacola, FL 32514-6039
Tel (850) 494-4000 *Founded/Ownrshp* 1994
Sales 118.8MM^E *EMP* 1,600
SIC 8062 8093 8063 8051 Hospital, AMA approved residency; Rehabilitation center, outpatient treatment; Psychiatric hospitals; Skilled nursing care facilities
Pr: Samuel N Hazen
**CEO:* Dennis Taylor
**CFO:* Randy Butler
**VP:* David G Anderson
**VP:* Natalie H Cline
**VP:* John M Franck II
**VP:* Donald W Stinnett
Dir Risk M: Sharon Smith
Doctor: Jason Marshall

D-U-N-S 01-834-2555 EXP
WEST FRASER INC
(*Suby of* WEST FRASER TIMBER CO. LTD)
1900 Exeter Rd Ste 105, Germantown, TN 38138-2954
Tel (901) 620-4200 *Founded/Ownrshp* 2000
Sales 620.7MM^E *EMP* 3,400
SIC 2431 0831 Millwork; Forest products
Pr: Edward Seraphim
Exec: Sarah Coker
**Prin:* Henry H Ketchum III
**Ex Dir:* Henry Ketcham
Genl Mgr: Adrian Blocker
Snr Ntwrk: Robert Craig

D-U-N-S 08-483-2094
WEST FRASER WOOD PRODUCTS INC
(*Suby of* WEST FRASER TIMBER CO. LTD)
1900 Exeter Rd Ste 105, Germantown, TN 38138-2954
Tel (901) 620-4200 *Founded/Ownrshp* 2014
Sales 640.0MM *EMP* 320
SIC 2431 Millwork
CEO: Edward Seraphim

WEST FRGO SPECIAL EDUCATN UNIT
See WEST FARGO SCHOOL DISTRICT 6

D-U-N-S 83-317-4571
WEST GEORGIA HEALTH SYSTEM INC
WELLSTAR WEST GEORGIA MED CTR
1514 Vernon Rd, Lagrange, GA 30240-4131
Tel (706) 882-1411 *Founded/Ownrshp* 2006
Sales 175.1MM *EMP* 1,500^E
Accts Dixon Hughes Goodman Llp Atla
SIC 8062 General medical & surgical hospitals
CEO: Gerald N Fulks
Chf Rad: Aparna Velnat
**Sr VP:* Charis Acree
VP Admn: John Flock
Ex Dir: Susan Burdick
Dir Sec: John Whitney
CIO: Sonya Christian
IT Man: Sherry Holliday
Doctor: Clarence Alford
Doctor: William Ayers
Doctor: Robert Copeland MD

WEST HILLS CMNTY COLLEGE DST
See WEST HILLS COMMUNITY COLLEGE DISTRICT FINANCING CORP

D-U-N-S 08-012-1718
WEST HILLS COMMUNITY COLLEGE DISTRICT FINANCING CORP (CA)
WEST HILLS CMNTY COLLEGE DST
9900 Cody Ave, Coalinga, CA 93210-9247
Tel (559) 934-2000 *Founded/Ownrshp* 2002
Sales 28.3MM^E *EMP* 1,004
Accts Vavrinek Trine Day & Co Ll
SIC 8222 Community college
**Pr:* Mark McKean
**VP:* Bill Henry
Off Admin: Graciela Aguerralde
DP Exec: Lori Flory
Psych: Kathleen Trezza

D-U-N-S 87-436-3013
WEST HOU INC
WEST ENGINEERING SERVICES
907 Bains St, Brookshire, TX 77423-4347
Tel (281) 934-1500 *Founded/Ownrshp* 1984
Sales 106.4MM^E *EMP* 150^E
SIC 1389

D-U-N-S 60-701-9338
■ WEST INTERACTIVE CORP
(*Suby of* WEST CORP) ★
11650 Miracle Hills Dr, Omaha, NE 68154-4448
Tel (402) 963-1200 *Founded/Ownrshp* 1996
Sales 76.5MM^E *EMP* 1,015
SIC 7389 Telephone answering service
CEO: Tom Barker
V Ch: Mary West
Pr: Kathy Ritonya
**Pr:* Steven M Stanel
**CFO:* Paul M Mendlik
CFO: Deneen Shadewald
Ex VP: Skip Hanson
Ex VP: David Mussman
Ex VP: David D Treinen
Sr VP: Mark Frei
VP: Gregory G Ablett
VP: Matthew Gargo
VP: Scott Krueger
VP: Jenny Slater

D-U-N-S 11-165-3759
■ WEST IP COMMUNICATIONS INC
(*Suby of* WEST CORP) ★
11808 Miracle Hills Dr, Omaha, NE 68154-4403
Tel (402) 963-1200 *Founded/Ownrshp* 2011
Sales 94.3MM^E *EMP* 170
SIC 4813 Local & long distance telephone communications
**Pr:* Jeff Wellemeyer
**COO:* Shelly Godfrey
**CFO:* Missy Deark
**Treas:* Paul M Mendlik
**Sec:* Susan Diamond
**Sr VP:* Chuck Piazza
VP: Brad Estes
CTO: Jeff Welleymer
Manager: Michael Spartz

WEST JEFFERSON MEDICAL CENTER
See HOSPITAL SERVICE DISTRICT 1 INC

D-U-N-S 00-694-5919
WEST KENTUCKY RURAL ELECTRIC COOP CORP
1218 W Broadway, Mayfield, KY 42066-1944
Tel (270) 247-1321 *Founded/Ownrshp* 1938
Sales 84.2MM *EMP* 86
SIC 4911 Distribution, electric power
Pr: David E Smart
**Ch:* Jamie Potts
Bd of Dir: Benny Adair
Bd of Dir: Troy English
Bd of Dir: Bob Hargrove
Bd of Dir: Eddy Wright
**VP:* Kevin Crider
VP: Ralph Edrington
Sfty Dirs: Kim Grogan

D-U-N-S 96-509-9559 IMP
WEST LIBERTY FOODS LLC
IOWA TURKEY GROWERS COOP
228 W 2nd St, West Liberty, IA 52776-1559
Tel (319) 627-6000 *Founded/Ownrshp* 1996
Sales 616.5MM^E *EMP* 1,650

SIC 2015 Turkey processing & slaughtering
**CFO:* Glenn Elzey
Ofcr: Michele Boney
VP: Michael Quint
VP: Dan Waters
Exec: Brenden Dailey
Dir Bus: Mark Russell
QA Dir: Jessica Bohnenkamp
Dir IT: Diane Beaver
Dir IT: David McDowell
IT Man: Bill Barthel
IT Man: Don Epjgrave

D-U-N-S 02-141-2077
WEST LINN-WILSONVILLE SCHOOL DISTRICT 3JT
WEST LNN-WLSNVILLE SCHL DST 3J
22210 Sw Stafford Rd, Tualatin, OR 97062-7738
Tel (503) 673-7000 *Founded/Ownrshp* 1922
Sales 94.7MM *EMP* 820
SIC 8211 Public elementary & secondary schools
Schl Brd P: Keith Steele
Teacher Pr: Kathy Monroe
Psych: Mike Miller
HC Dir: Jennifer S IAMS

WEST LNN-WLSNVILLE SCHL DST 3J
See WEST LINN-WILSONVILLE SCHOOL DISTRICT 3JT

D-U-N-S 06-913-4179 IMP/EXP
▲ WEST MARINE INC
500 Westridge Dr, Watsonville, CA 95076-4171
Tel (831) 728-2700 *Founded/Ownrshp* 1968
Sales 704.8MM *EMP* 3,796E
Tkr Sym WMAR *Exch* NGS
SIC 5551 5961 5088 5611 5661 5621 Marine supplies; Mail order house; Marine supplies; Clothing, sportswear, men's & boys'; Clothing accessories: men's & boys'; Hats, men's & boys'; Children's shoes; Women's shoes; Men's boots; Ready-to-wear apparel, women's
Pr: Matthew L Hyde
**Ch Bd:* Barbara L Rambo
CFO: Jeffrey L Lasher
Treas: John Zott
Ex VP: Barry Kelley
Ex VP: Paul Rutenis
Sr VP: Debra Radcliff
VP: Andrew Benz
Rgnl Mgr: Dan Matarazzo
Dist Mgr: Brent Lossett
Store Mgr: Eric Sorrell
Board of Directors: Dennis F Madsen, James F Nordstrom Jr, Robert D Olsen, Randolph K Repass, Alice M Richter, Christiana Shi

D-U-N-S 88-387-4000 IMP/EXP
■ WEST MARINE PRODUCTS INC
BOAT US MARINE CENTER
(*Suby of* WEST MARINE INC) ★
500 Westridge Dr, Watsonville, CA 95076-4100
Tel (831) 728-2700 *Founded/Ownrshp* 1968
Sales 557.0MME *EMP* 3,000
SIC 5551 5561 Marine supplies & equipment; Recreational vehicle parts & accessories
CEO: Matt Hyde
Pr: Richard E Everett
CFO: Tom Moran
Sr VP: Eric S Nelson
VP: Joseph Pulford
Prin: Geoff Eisenberg
Genl Mgr: Susan Lynch
Sls Mgr: Pam Wall

D-U-N-S 09-379-4238 IMP
WEST MEMPHIS STEEL & PIPE INC (AR)
1101 Thompson Ave, West Memphis, AR 72301-4066
Tel (870) 735-8244 *Founded/Ownrshp* 1978
Sales 115.3MME *EMP* 65
SIC 5051 Steel; Pipe & tubing, steel; Structural shapes, iron or steel
Pr: Byron P Besser
**COO:* Joe Brackin
**Sec:* Julie Besser
Genl Mgr: Scott Morgan
Sls Dir: Morgan Toline
Sales Asso: Doug Davis
Sales Asso: Andrew Sillyman
Sales Asso: Blake Walpole

D-U-N-S 80-053-4286
WEST NEW YORK SCHOOL DISTRICT
6028 Broadway, West New York, NJ 07093-2808
Tel (201) 553-4000 *Founded/Ownrshp* 2007
Sales 36.3MME *EMP* 1,000E
SIC 8211 Public elementary & secondary schools

D-U-N-S 03-618-6153
WEST OIL INC
MARKETTE STORES, THE
312 Lakeview Blvd, Hartsville, SC 29550-8534
Tel (843) 332-2201 *Founded/Ownrshp* 1991
Sales 183.3MME *EMP* 300E
SIC 5172 5541 5411 Petroleum products; Filling stations, gasoline; Convenience stores, chain
Pr: Alexander C West Jr
**Treas:* Derek Jenner
VP: Bunky Joyce

WEST ONE AUTO CENTER
See WEST ONE AUTOMOTIVE GROUP INC

D-U-N-S 62-568-3487
WEST ONE AUTOMOTIVE GROUP INC
WEST ONE AUTO CENTER
2046 Nw Irving St, Portland, OR 97209-1216
Tel (503) 222-1335 *Founded/Ownrshp* 1991
Sales 182.0MM *EMP* 470
SIC 7514 Rent-a-car service
Pr: Ted L Anderson
**CFO:* Kathy Wigmofta
**Sec:* Doug Kingzeinger

D-U-N-S 93-888-3865
WEST ORANGE HEALTHCARE DISTRICT INC
HEALTH CENRAL
10000 W Colonial Dr Ofc, Ocoee, FL 34761-3493
Tel (407) 296-1000 *Founded/Ownrshp* 1994
Sales 6.5MM *EMP* 1,278
Accts Grant Thornton Llp Orlando F
SIC 8062 General medical & surgical hospitals
CEO: Richard Irwin
**CFO:* Michael Mueller
Trst: Norma Sutton
Trst: Charlie True

D-U-N-S 07-255-9628
WEST ORANGE MEMORIAL HOSPITAL TAX DISTRICT
HEALTH CENTRAL
10000 W Colonial Dr Ofc, Ocoee, FL 34761-3493
Tel (407) 656-3555 *Founded/Ownrshp* 2015
Sales 157.8MME *EMP* 1,600
SIC 8062 General medical & surgical hospitals
Pr: Greg Ohe

D-U-N-S 80-950-7804
WEST OTTAWA PUBLIC SCHOOLS
1138 136th Ave, Holland, MI 49424-7483
Tel (616) 738-5700 *Founded/Ownrshp* 2008
Sales 86.2MM *EMP* 954E
Accts Maner Costerisan Pc Lansing
SIC 8211 Public elementary & secondary schools

D-U-N-S 08-034-9806
WEST OTTAWA SCHOOLS
1138 136th Ave, Holland, MI 49424-7483
Tel (616) 738-5710 *Founded/Ownrshp* 1957
Sales 86.0MM *EMP* 900
SIC 8211 School board

D-U-N-S 06-910-8439 IMP
WEST PAK AVOCADO INC (CA)
AVOCADO PACKER & SHIPPER
38655 Sky Canyon Dr, Murrieta, CA 92563-2536
Tel (951) 296-5757 *Founded/Ownrshp* 1982
Sales 193.9MME *EMP* 120
SIC 0723

D-U-N-S 07-140-6888
WEST PARK HOSPITAL DISTRICT
707 Sheridan Ave, Cody, WY 82414-3409
Tel (307) 527-7501 *Founded/Ownrshp* 1964
Sales 91.3MM *EMP* 450
SIC 8062 General medical & surgical hospitals
CEO: Doug McMillan
**CFO:* Patrick McConnell
IT Man: Wendy Morris
Sls&Mrk Ex: Anne Johnson
Mktg Mgr: Ashly Trudo

D-U-N-S 13-576-2297 IMP
WEST PENN ALLEGHENY HEALTH SYSTEM INC
(*Suby of* HIGHMARK BLUE CRSS-BLUE SHIELD) ★
4800 Friendship Ave, Pittsburgh, PA 15224-1722
Tel (412) 578-5000 *Founded/Ownrshp* 2012
Sales 1.3MMME *EMP* 13,000
SIC 8062 Hospital, affiliated with AMA residency
CEO: John Paul
Pr: Christopher T Olivia
CEO: Connie Cibrone
CFO: Elizabeth Allen
CFO: David Samuel
Ofcr: Jacqueline Bauer
Ofcr: Shariff Zyhier
Ex VP: Robert Brandfass
Ex VP: Michael Devita
Ex VP: Dianne Dismukes
VP: Stephen Brown
VP: Diane Frndak
VP: Paul Jorgensen
VP: Kandy McCloud
VP: Nicholas Valadja
VP: Paul Wheeler
VP: Roger Yost

D-U-N-S 00-791-1050
■ WEST PENN POWER CO (PA)
FIRSTENERGY
(*Suby of* ALLEGHENY ENERGY INC) ★
800 Cabin Hill Dr, Greensburg, PA 15601-1650
Tel (724) 837-3000 *Founded/Ownrshp* 1916, 2006
Sales 491.3MME *EMP* 699
SIC 4911 Distribution, electric power
CEO: Paul J Evanson
Pr: Joseph H Richardson
CEO: Anthony J Alexander
Ex VP: Paul M Barbas
VP: Thomas K Henderson
VP: Ronald A Magnuson
VP: Karl V Pfirrmann

D-U-N-S 00-233-0983 IMP/EXP
▲ WEST PHARMACEUTICAL SERVICES INC (PA)
530 Herman O West Dr, Exton, PA 19341-1147
Tel (610) 594-2900 *Founded/Ownrshp* 1923
Sales 1.4MMM *EMP* 7,100
Accts Pricewaterhousecoopers Llp Ph
Tkr Sym WST *Exch* NYS
SIC 3069 3466 2673 3085 3089 Medical & laboratory rubber sundries & related products; Stoppers, rubber; Atomizer bulbs, rubber; Medical sundries, rubber; Closures, stamped metal; Plastic bags: made from purchased materials; Plastics bottles; Plastic containers, except foam; Closures, plastic
Pr: Eric M Green
**Ch Bd:* Patrick J Zenner
Pr: Warwick Bedwell
Pr: Karen A Flynn
Pr: Heino Lennartz
Pr: John E Paproski
Pr: Christopher G Ryan
CFO: William J Federici
Treas: Michael A Anderson
Ofcr: Annette F Favorite
Sr VP: George L Miller
Sr VP: David A Montecalvo
VP: Joseph Fratinardo
VP: Robert S Hargesheimer
VP: Ken Hornbaker
VP: Daniel Malone
VP: Don O'Callaghan
VP: Eric Resnick
VP: Mike Treadaway
VP Bus Dev: Kenneth Forssell
Assoc Dir: Timothy Meyer
Board of Directors: Mark A Buthman, William F Feehery, Thomas W Hofmann, Paula A Johnson, Douglas A Michels, John H Weiland

D-U-N-S 04-744-8444 IMP
WEST PICO FOODS INC
5201 S Downey Rd, Vernon, CA 90058-3703
Tel (323) 586-9050 *Founded/Ownrshp* 1989
Sales 101.9MME *EMP* 125
Accts Ells Cpa & Business Advisors
SIC 5142 5144 Packaged frozen goods; Poultry: live, dressed or frozen (unpackaged)
Pr: Elias Naghi
CFO: James Ong
**Treas:* Don Lubitz
Exec: Evelyn Cruz

D-U-N-S 07-847-1080 EXP
WEST PLAINS LLC
CT FREIGHT
11500 N Ambassador Dr # 250, Kansas City, MO 64153-1212
Tel (816) 270-4000 *Founded/Ownrshp* 2012
Sales 656.3MM *EMP* 65
Accts Crowe Horwath Llp Elkhart In
SIC 5153 4221 Grain & field beans; Grain elevator, storage only
Pr: John Skelley

WEST POINT
See UNITED STATES MILITARY ACADEMY

WEST POINT CONVALSCENT
See PATRICK HENRY HOSPITAL INC

D-U-N-S 14-850-8286
■ WEST PUBLISHING CORP
WEST, A THOMSON REUTERS BUS
(*Suby of* THOMSON REUTERS CORP) ★
610 620 Opperman Dr, Eagan, MN 55123
Tel (651) 687-7000 *Founded/Ownrshp* 1996
Sales 1.1MMME *EMP* 16,000
SIC 7375 Data base information retrieval
CEO: Peter Warwick
**Pr:* Michael Suchsland
CFO: Melinda Kenealy
**Sr VP:* Ken Ross

D-U-N-S 05-822-6556
WEST QUALITY FOOD SERVICE INC
KFC
220 N 16th Ave, Laurel, MS 39440-4134
Tel (601) 428-4791 *Founded/Ownrshp* 1967
Sales 69.4MME *EMP* 1,889
SIC 5812 Fast-food restaurant, chain
Ch: Victor C West
**Pr:* Richard M West
**CFO:* David T Childress
**Sec:* Louise West
**VP:* Gary West
VP: William West
Genl Mgr: Deryal Crawford
Mktg Mgr: Darlean Willis

D-U-N-S 07-988-1600
■ WEST REVENUE GENERATION SERVICES LLC
(*Suby of* WEST CORP) ★
11808 Miracle Hills Dr, Omaha, NE 68154-4403
Tel (800) 232-0900 *Founded/Ownrshp* 2014
Sales 35.7MME *EMP* 2,000
SIC 7389 Business services
Pr: Michael E Mazour
**CEO:* Thomas B Barker
**COO:* Nancee R Berger
**CFO:* Jan D Madsen
**Sr VP:* Shawn Fliehman

D-U-N-S 13-086-6551
■ WEST SAFETY SERVICES
(*Suby of* WEST CORP) ★
1601 Dry Creek Dr, Longmont, CO 80503-6493
Tel (402) 963-1200 *Founded/Ownrshp* 1993
Sales 237.7MME *EMP* 776
SIC 7373 Computer-aided system services
Pr: Ronald Beaumont
**Pr:* Mary Hester
**CEO:* Stephen M Meer
**Sr VP:* Craig W Donaldson
**Sr VP:* Dami Hummel
**Sr VP:* Steve Lowe
VP: Chandy Ghosh
VP: Marc Offutt
Exec: Joyce Cote
Exec: Deb Mlinar
**Prin:* George K Heinrichs

D-U-N-S 07-929-6557
WEST SAN CARLOS HOTEL PARTNERS LLC
HYATT PLACE SAN JOSE HOTEL
282 Almaden Blvd, San Jose, CA 95113-2003
Tel (408) 998-0400 *Founded/Ownrshp* 2010
Sales 1.0MMM *EMP* 65
SIC 7011 Hotels & motels
Genl Mgr: Michael Lerman

D-U-N-S 04-516-7459
WEST SENECA CENTRAL SCHOOL DISTRICT
1397 Orchard Park Rd # 1, West Seneca, NY 14224-4098
Tel (716) 677-3100 *Founded/Ownrshp* 1948
Sales 61.2MME *EMP* 1,150
SIC 8211 Public elementary & secondary schools; Public elementary school
Genl Mgr: Janice Lewandowski
Pr Dir: Jonathon Dalbo

D-U-N-S 13-350-5094
■ WEST SERVICES INC
(*Suby of* THOMSON REUTERS (LEGAL) INC) ★
610 Opperman Dr, Saint Paul, MN 55123-1340
Tel (651) 687-5882 *Founded/Ownrshp* 2002
Sales 218.0MME *EMP* 2,000E
SIC 2721 Statistical reports (periodicals): publishing only
Pr: Michael Wilens

D-U-N-S 08-486-9825
WEST SHORE SCHOOL BOARD
507 Fishing Creek Rd, New Cumberland, PA 17070-3099
Tel (717) 938-9577 *Founded/Ownrshp* 1966
Sales 96.5MM *EMP* 1,164
SIC 8211 School board
Pr: Ronald Candioto

D-U-N-S 82-920-7278
WEST SHORE SCHOOL DISTRICT
507 Fishing Creek Rd, New Cumberland, PA 17070-3000
Tel (717) 938-9577 *Founded/Ownrshp* 1900
Sales 99.5MM *EMP* 800
Accts Greenawalt & Company Pc Mech
SIC 8211 Public elementary & secondary schools
Adm Dir: Tony McNaughton
Dir Sec: Thomas Ryan
Pr Dir: Ryan Argott
Teacher Pr: Suzanne Tabachini
HC Dir: Thomas Burnheimer

D-U-N-S 01-230-2733 IMP
WEST SIDE FOODS INC (NY)
WESTSIDE POULTRY
355 Food Center Dr A23, Bronx, NY 10474-7580
Tel (718) 842-8500 *Founded/Ownrshp* 1959, 1947
Sales 228.5MME *EMP* 270
SIC 5141 Food brokers
**Sec:* Vincent Pacifico
VP: Jerry Abramson
VP: David Adelson
IT Man: Linda Gonzalez
Sales Asso: David Aronin

WEST SIDE MASONRY
See STEWART RICHEY CONSTRUCTION INC

D-U-N-S 02-568-1164
WEST SIDETRACTOR SALES CO
JOHN DEERE
1400 W Ogden Ave, Naperville, IL 60563-3909
Tel (630) 355-7150 *Founded/Ownrshp* 1962
Sales 186.1MM *EMP* 190
Accts Hansen Plahm & Company Darien
SIC 5082 General construction machinery & equipment; Road construction equipment
Pr: Steven L Benck
**Ch Bd:* Richard W Benck
Mtls Mgr: Bob Bazzetta
Sls Mgr: Kip Bancroft
Sls Mgr: Patricia Fauth
Sls Mgr: Bill Price
Sales Asso: Bill Ettinger
Sales Asso: Brian Levenhagen

D-U-N-S 94-915-6236
WEST SIDETRANSPORT INC
(*Suby of* WESTTRANSPORT) ★
4201 16th Ave Sw, Cedar Rapids, IA 52404-1207
Tel (319) 390-4466 *Founded/Ownrshp* 1978
Sales 120.7MM *EMP* 550E
SIC 4213 Trucking, except local
Pr: Donald A Vogt
Sr Cor Off: Jeanne Vogt
Sfty Dirs: Dave Figler
Manager: Cory Richmond

D-U-N-S 04-219-2765
WEST SIDE UNLIMITED CORP (IA)
WESTTRANSPORT
4201 16th Ave Sw, Cedar Rapids, IA 52404-1207
Tel (319) 390-4466 *Founded/Ownrshp* 1968, 1978
Sales 128.3MM *EMP* 550
Accts Bergan Paulsen & Company Pc
SIC 4213 7389 Trucking, except local; Salvaging of damaged merchandise, service only
Pr: Donald Vogt

D-U-N-S 36-155-6046
WEST SUBURBAN BANCORP INC
711 Westmore Meyers Rd, Lombard, IL 60148-3712
Tel (630) 629-4200 *Founded/Ownrshp* 1986
Sales NA *EMP* 534
SIC 6022 State commercial banks
Ch Bd: Kevin J Acker
**Pr:* Duane G Debs
COO: Keith W Acker
VP: Michael P Brosnahan
Dir IT: William J Jennrich

D-U-N-S 11-820-4908
WEST SUBURBAN MEDICAL CENTER
3 Erie Ct, Oak Park, IL 60302-2519
Tel (708) 383-6200 *Founded/Ownrshp* 1984
Sales 143.0MM *EMP* 2,351
SIC 8011 Medical centers
CEO: Jay E Kreuzer
**Prin:* Douglas F Dean Jr
**Prin:* James Sykes
Prgrm Mgr: Mackenzie Stern

WEST TENNESSEE HEALTH CARE
See JACKSON-MADISON COUNTY GENERAL HOSPITAL DISTRICT

D-U-N-S 06-015-0745
WEST TEXAS GAS INC
GASCARD
211 N Colorado St, Midland, TX 79701-4607
Tel (432) 682-4349 *Founded/Ownrshp* 1976
Sales 178.5MME *EMP* 600
SIC 5411 Convenience stores
Pr: J L Davis
**Sec:* Nancy Chandler
**VP:* David Davis
**VP:* Richard D Hatchett

Exec: Ralph Arrell
Sfty Mgr: Bobby Roach
Opers Mgr: Bart Bean
Opers Mgr: Cindy Lane
Plnt Mgr: Chris Mulkey
Mktg Mgr: Hershel Sorrells

WEST TEXAS PLASTICS
See BRAWLER INDUSTRIES LLC

WEST TRAIL NURSING HOME
See MEBILODDE OF PLYMOUTH

WEST TRANSPORT
See WEST SIDE UNLIMITED CORP

D-U-N-S 79-347-4800
■ **WEST UNIFIED COMMUNICATIONS SERVICES INC**
(*Suby of* WEST CORP) ★
8420 W Bryn Mawr Ave # 1100, Chicago, IL 60631-3479
Tel (773) 399-1600 *Founded/Ownrshp* 2003
Sales 173.3MM^E^ *EMP* 903
SIC 7389 Teleconferencing services
Pr: Paul Nichols
**Pr:* J Scott Etzler
Pr: Kevin Neville
**CFO:* Jan Madsen
**Ex VP:* Marty Dunne
**Ex VP:* Michael Nessler
**Ex VP:* Heather Welborn
VP: David Cottingham
VP: Susan Ferguson
VP: Barbara Gonzalez
VP: Phillip Wilson
Exec: Denise Blanks
Dir Soc: Beth Newlon

WEST VALLEY COLLEGE
See WEST VALLEY-MISSION COMMUNITY COLLEGE DISTRICT

D-U-N-S 00-284-7853
WEST VALLEY CONSTRUCTION CO INC (CA)
580 E Mcglincy Ln, Campbell, CA 95008-4999
Tel (408) 371-5510 *Founded/Ownrshp* 1958
Sales 149.8MM^E^ *EMP* 350
Accts Hood & Strong Llp San Jose C
SIC 1623 Water main construction; Telephone & communication line construction
CEO: Kevin Kelly
**CFO:* David Barnes
**VP:* Jeff Azevedo
**VP:* Jeff Boss
VP: Mike Cadei
**VP:* Jimm Vosburgh
Dist Mgr: Joe Corona
Dist Mgr: John Healey
Dist Mgr: Julie Weinhardt
Dist Mgr: Shawn White
Div Mgr: Mike Renn

D-U-N-S 05-846-6442
WEST VALLEY ENGINEERING INC
WEST VALLEY STAFFING GROUP
390 Potrero Ave, Sunnyvale, CA 94085-4116
Tel (408) 735-1420 *Founded/Ownrshp* 1980
Sales 48.8MM^E^ *EMP* 1,300^E^
SIC 7363 Temporary help service
Pr: Michael F Williams
**CFO:* Teresa Kossayian
CFO: Janet Macaulay
Sr Ex VP: Rovilla Wetle
Sls Dir: Charlie Reynolds
Sls Mgr: Christopher Jensen

D-U-N-S 18-799-6400 IMP
■ **WEST VALLEY MEDICAL CENTER INC**
(*Suby of* HOSPITAL COPORATION OF AMERICA) ★
1717 Arlington Ave, Caldwell, ID 83605-4802
Tel (208) 459-4641 *Founded/Ownrshp* 1995
Sales 103.7MM *EMP* 800
SIC 8062 General medical & surgical hospitals
CEO: Betsy Hunsicker
Pr: Samuel N Hazen
Treas: David G Anderson
VP: Dora A Blackwood
Dir Lab: Mike Lenington
Dir Rx: Taylor Nielson
CIO: Bruk Kammerman
IT Man: John Stone
Software D: Gina Magard
Software D: Julie Taylor
QC Dir: Cheri Samuels

WEST VALLEY STAFFING GROUP
See WEST VALLEY ENGINEERING INC

D-U-N-S 07-630-1530
WEST VALLEY-MISSION COMMUNITY COLLEGE DISTRICT
WEST VALLEY COLLEGE
14000 Fruitvale Ave, Saratoga, CA 95070-5640
Tel (408) 867-2200 *Founded/Ownrshp* 1963
Sales 16.5MM *EMP* 1,184
Accts Vavrinek Trine Day & Co Ll
SIC 8222 8221 Community college; Colleges universities & professional schools
Ofcr: Kuni Hay
Ex VP: Dave Fishbaugh
VP: Ernest Smith
VP: Ernie Smith
Exec: Blaine Harrison
**Prin:* Stan R Arterberry
**Prin:* J Hendrcksn Chancellor
**Prin:* Frank Chong
Prgrm Mgr: Mae Conroy
Prgrm Mgr: Jennifer N Oliver
Off Admin: Kimberley Sharp

D-U-N-S 82-470-0603
WEST VIRGINIA DEPARTMENT OF EDUCATION AND ARTS
(*Suby of* EXECUTIVE OFFICE STATE OF WEST VIRGINIA) ★
1900 Kanawha Blvd E # 358, Charleston, WV 25305-0009
Tel (304) 558-2440 *Founded/Ownrshp* 1989
Sales NA *EMP* 10,489
SIC 9411 Administration of educational programs;
CEO: Kay Goodwin

D-U-N-S 82-470-0611
WEST VIRGINIA DEPARTMENT OF HEALTH AND HUMAN RESOURCES
(*Suby of* EXECUTIVE OFFICE STATE OF WEST VIRGINIA) ★
1 Davis Sq Ste 100e, Charleston, WV 25301-1729
Tel (304) 558-0684 *Founded/Ownrshp* 1989
Sales NA *EMP* 6,000
SIC 9431 9441 Administration of public health programs; ; Administration of social & manpower programs;
CEO: Karen Bowling
Ofcr: Bryan Rosen
**Prin:* Jennifer Taylor
Off Admin: Stephanie Mink
**Doctor:* Micheal Jay Lewis

D-U-N-S 82-470-0645
WEST VIRGINIA DEPARTMENT OF MILITARY AFFAIRS AND PUBLIC SAFETY
NATIONAL GUARD
(*Suby of* EXECUTIVE OFFICE STATE OF WEST VIRGINIA) ★
1900 Kanawha Blvd E Rm 1, Charleston, WV 25305-0001
Tel (304) 558-8045 *Founded/Ownrshp* 1989
Sales NA *EMP* 6,000^E^
SIC 9711 9221 9229 National security; ; Police protection; ; Public order & safety statistics centers;
Board of Directors: Barbara Fish

D-U-N-S 82-470-1155
WEST VIRGINIA DEPARTMENT OF TRANSPORTATION
(*Suby of* EXECUTIVE OFFICE STATE OF WEST VIRGINIA) ★
1900 Kanawha Blvd E # 109, Charleston, WV 25305-0009
Tel (304) 558-0330 *Founded/Ownrshp* 1977
Sales NA *EMP* 5,500
Accts Gibson & Kawash Charleston W
SIC 9621 Regulation, administration of transportation;

D-U-N-S 05-883-7118
WEST VIRGINIA UNITED HEALTH SYSTEM INC
WVUHS
1 Medical Center Dr, Morgantown, WV 26506-1200
Tel (304) 598-4000 *Founded/Ownrshp* 1996
Sales 9.6MM *EMP* 1,613
SIC 8741 Hospital management
CEO: Christophe Colenda MD
**Pr:* J Thomas Jones
**Treas:* Robert D'Alessandri
**VP:* Jeff Gibson
CIO: Richard King

D-U-N-S 92-933-2658
WEST VIRGINIA UNIVERSITY
103 Stewart Hl, Morgantown, WV 26506
Tel (304) 293-2545 *Founded/Ownrshp* 1867
Sales 783.3MM^E^ *EMP* 6,245
Accts Deloitte & Touche Llp Pittsbu
SIC 8221 University
Pr: E Gordon Gee
V Ch: Boyd Edwards
Pr: Anjali Halabe
Bd of Dir: James W Dailey II
Ex VP: John Angotti
Ex VP: Dottie Oakes
VP: Rob Alsop
VP: Margaret Phillips
Exec: Debbie Roman
Assoc Dir: Donna Hylton
Assoc Dir: Elizabeth Vitullo
Comm Dir: Lynn Reinke

D-U-N-S 19-151-0239
WEST VIRGINIA UNIVERSITY RESEARCH CORP
886 Chestnut Ridge Rd, Morgantown, WV 26505-2742
Tel (304) 293-7398 *Founded/Ownrshp* 1985
Sales 131.9MM *EMP* 112
SIC 8733 Educational research agency
Ex Dir: E Gordon Gee
**Pr:* Narvel Weese
**Treas:* Daniel Durbin

WEST WINDSOR CAMPUS
See MERCER COUNTY COMMUNITY COLLEGE

D-U-N-S 04-219-9307 IMP
WEST WINDSOR-PLAINSBORO REGIONAL BOARD OF EDUCATION
321 Village Rd E, Princeton Junction, NJ 08550-2001
Tel (609) 716-5000 *Founded/Ownrshp* 1969
Sales 171.5MM *EMP* 49^E^
Accts Wiss & Company Llp Iselin N
SIC 8211 School board
Pr: Anthony Fleres
Exec: Linda Wiley
Pr Dir: Gerri Hutner

D-U-N-S 08-025-0938
WEST WINDSOR-PLAINSBORO REGIONAL SCHOOL DISTRICT
321 Village Rd E, West Windsor, NJ 08550-2001
Tel (609) 716-5000 *Founded/Ownrshp* 2016
Sales 6.6MM^E^ *EMP* 1,100^E^
SIC 8211 Public elementary & secondary schools
Genl Mgr: Katlyn Schroeck
Schl Brd P: Anthony Fleres

D-U-N-S 00-123-0762 IMP/EXP
WEST-WARD PHARMACEUTICALS CORP
(*Suby of* EUROHEALTH (USA) INC) ★
401 Industrial Way W, Eatontown, NJ 07724-2209
Tel (732) 542-1191 *Founded/Ownrshp* 1946, 1991
Sales 197.6MM^E^ *EMP* 478^E^
SIC 2834 Pharmaceutical preparations
CEO: Michael Raya
**Pr:* Brian Hoffmann
CFO: Fares Awwad
**CFO:* Mohammed Obeidat
**Treas:* George J Muench III
VP: Hal Zenenberg
Dir Risk M: Mauricio Cruz
CTO: Zakaria Barjous
QA Dir: Mary Graham
Opers Mgr: John Dicesare
Opers Mgr: Michael Wherrity
Board of Directors: Hussein Arkhagha, Ali Al Husry, Michael Raya

D-U-N-S 05-283-4694
WESTAIR GASES & EQUIPMENT INC
SAN DIEGO WELDERS SUPPLY
2506 Market St, San Diego, CA 92102-3010
Tel (866) 937-8247 *Founded/Ownrshp* 1970
Sales 101.7MM^E^ *EMP* 160
SIC 5084 Industrial machinery & equipment; Welding machinery & equipment
CEO: Andrew J Castiglione
**Pr:* Steve Castiglione
**CFO:* Tim Van Linge
**Sec:* Sue Castiglione
VP: Mike Fuette
Area Mgr: Victor Flores
Area Mgr: Kody Kearns
Brnch Mgr: Michael Nordquist
Genl Mgr: Michael Crambes
IT Man: Fernando Escamilla
Opers Mgr: Trever Rodgers

D-U-N-S 07-736-6755
▲ **WESTAMERICA BANCORPORATION**
1108 5th Ave, San Rafael, CA 94901-2916
Tel (707) 863-6000 *Founded/Ownrshp* 1972
Sales NA *EMP* 813^E^
Tkr Sym WABC *Exch* NGS
SIC 6021 National commercial banks
Ch Bd: David L Payne
CFO: John Thorson
VP: Gary Lepiane
VP: Tim Shaw
Board of Directors: Etta Allen, Louis E Bartolini, E Joseph Bowler, Arthur C Latno Jr, Patrick D Lynch, Catherine Cope Macmillan, Ronald A Nelson, Edward B Sylvester

D-U-N-S 14-726-8023
WESTAR AEROSPACE & DEFENSE GROUP INC
(*Suby of* VENCORE SERVICES AND SOLUTIONS INC) ★
890 Explorer Blvd Nw, Huntsville, AL 35806-2832
Tel (256) 922-6800 *Founded/Ownrshp* 2004
Sales 41.7MM^E^ *EMP* 1,400
SIC 8733 Noncommercial research organizations; Scientific research agency
Pr: J Garrett Martz
Pr: Charlie Douglas
**CFO:* Bill Goss
**Ex VP:* Randall Tieszen
**Ex VP:* Jim Williford
**VP:* Vanessa Y Chandler
VP: Jim Marsh
IT Man: Stephen Pratt
Secur Mgr: Timothy Hynes

D-U-N-S 60-836-9930
WESTAR CAPITAL ASSOCIATES II LLC
949 S Coast Dr Ste 170, Costa Mesa, CA 92626-7830
Tel (714) 481-5160 *Founded/Ownrshp* 1987
Sales 110.4MM^E^ *EMP* 1,200^E^
SIC 6799 3089 Investors; Injection molded finished plastic products

D-U-N-S 00-694-3781 IMP
▲ **WESTAR ENERGY INC**
818 S Kansas Ave, Topeka, KS 66612-1203
Tel (785) 575-6300 *Founded/Ownrshp* 1924
Sales 2.4MMM *EMP* 2,330
Tkr Sym WR *Exch* NYS
SIC 4911 Electric services; Generation, electric power; Transmission, electric power; Distribution, electric power
Pr: Mark A Ruelle
**Ch Bd:* Charles Q Chandler IV
**CFO:* Anthony D Somma
Sr VP: Bruce A Akin
Sr VP: Jerl L Banning
Sr VP: John T Bridson
Sr VP: Gregory A Greenwood
VP: Jeff Beasley
**VP:* Larry D Irick
**VP:* Kevin L Kongs
QA Dir: Ching Her
Board of Directors: Mollie H Carter, R A Edwards III, Jerry B Farley, Richard L Hawley, B Anthony Isaac, Sandra A J Lawrence, S Carl Soderstrom Jr

D-U-N-S 04-950-8120 IMP
WESTAT INC
1600 Research Blvd, Rockville, MD 20850-3129
Tel (301) 251-1500 *Founded/Ownrshp* 1979
Sales 509.8MM *EMP* 2,000
Accts Rubino & Company Bethesda Md
SIC 8732 7371 7373 8741 8742 8999 Market analysis, business & economic research; Commercial sociological & educational research; Custom computer programming services; Computer integrated systems design; Administrative management; General management consultant; Weather related services; Geological consultant; Lecturing services
Pr: James E Smith
**Ch Bd:* Graham Kalton
Ofcr: Alan Cutler
Ex VP: Tamara Daley
Ex VP: Vasudha Narayanan
Sr VP: Stephen K Dietz
VP: Greg Binzer
VP: Michael Brick
VP: Sue Connor
VP: Doreen Deleonardis
VP: Nancy Dianis
VP: Stephen Durako
VP: Steve Durako
VP: W S Edward
VP: Brad Edwards
VP: Patricia Espey-English
**VP:* Peter Gill
VP: Jim Greenlees
VP: Ron Hirschhorn
VP: Liz Jansky
VP: Kerry Levin

D-U-N-S 06-801-1881
WESTBURY UNION FREE SCHOOL DISTRICT (NY)
2 Hitchcock Ln, Westbury, NY 11568-1615
Tel (516) 876-5000 *Founded/Ownrshp* 1865
Sales 132.2MM *EMP* 299
Accts Coughlin Foundotos Cullen & Da
SIC 8211 Public elementary school; Public senior high school
MIS Dir: Jay Marcucci

D-U-N-S 03-739-6079
WESTCARE FOUNDATION INC
1711 Whitney Mesa Dr # 100, Henderson, NV 89014-2080
Tel (702) 385-3330 *Founded/Ownrshp* 1973
Sales 10.2MM *EMP* 1,400^E^
Accts Roland Roos And Company Fresn
SIC 8322 8611 Substance abuse counseling; Community affairs & services
Pr: Richard E Steinberg
**COO:* Maurice Lee
IT Man: Matt Sunnenberger

D-U-N-S 11-041-8340
WESTCARE HEALTH CORP
68 Hospital Rd, Sylva, NC 28779-2722
Tel (828) 586-7100 *Founded/Ownrshp* 1980
Sales 196.5MM *EMP* 1,200
SIC 8011 General & family practice, physician/surgeon
Pr: Mark Leonard

D-U-N-S 07-316-4357
WESTCARE HEALTH SYSTEM
68 Hospital Rd, Sylva, NC 28779-2722
Tel (828) 586-7000 *Founded/Ownrshp* 1947
Sales 109.7MM^E^ *EMP* 1,200
SIC 8069 Chronic disease hospital
CEO: Steve Heatherly
V Ch: Mark Clasby
**Pr:* Mark Leonard
CFO: Mike McKnight
VP: Deb Bennett
Dir Lab: Kim Saunook
Dir Lab: Kim Saunooke
Dept Mgr: Christie Festa
Opers Mgr: Nora Myers

D-U-N-S 07-871-5430
WESTCHESTER BOCES SCHOOL DISTRICT
WESTCHSTER BD COOP EDUCTL SVCS
17 Berkley Dr, Rye Brook, NY 10573-1422
Tel (914) 937-6107 *Founded/Ownrshp* 1948
Sales 126.9MM^E^ *EMP* 1,296
SIC 8211 Public elementary & secondary schools
Pr: Joseph E Wooley
**VP:* James E Miller
Comm Dir: Brian Howard
Comm Dir: Evelyn McCormack
**Prin:* Cahill Maureen
Off Admin: Chelsea Karp
CTO: Margaret Pesick
Dir IT: Victor Pineiro
Teacher Pr: John Knight

D-U-N-S 07-095-7881 IMP
WESTCHESTER COMMUNITY COLLEGE (NY)
(*Suby of* SUNY ADMINISTRATION) ★
75 Grasslands Rd, Valhalla, NY 10595-1550
Tel (914) 606-6600 *Founded/Ownrshp* 1946
Sales 10.0MM^E^ *EMP* 1,000
Accts D Arcangelo & Co Llp Port Che
SIC 8222 9411 Community college;
Pr: John F M Flynn
**Pr:* Joseph Hankin PHD
CFO: Lisa Mitzner
Bd of Dir: Nickay Piper
VP: Marge Glusker
VP: Robert Schlesinger
Ex Dir: Mitchell Queler
Prgrm Mgr: Stephen Leone
Dept Mgr: Janet Ranucci
Genl Mgr: Laurie M McNeill
Off Mgr: Suzanne Paribello

D-U-N-S 16-006-9399
WESTCHESTER COUNTY HEALTH CARE CORP
WESTCHESTER MEDICAL CENTER
100 Woods Rd, Valhalla, NY 10595-1530
Tel (914) 493-7000 *Founded/Ownrshp* 1998
Sales 1.0MMM *EMP* 3,000^E^
SIC 8062 General medical & surgical hospitals
Pr: Michael D Israel
**CFO:* Gary Brudnicki
**Sr VP:* Anthony Mahler
**Sr VP:* John Morgan
Sr VP: Patricia A Wrobbel
VP: Alan Bey
Exec: Dipak Chandy
Dir Teleco: Carl Pugni
Off Mgr: Gritley Henry
Off Admin: Francine Fizzinoglia
Netwrk Eng: Ron Loscri
Board of Directors: Claudia Edwards, Renee Garrick, Susan Gevertz, John Heimerdinger, Mitchell Hochberg, Patrick McCoy, Steven Rogowsky, Emmeline Rocha-Sinha, Mark Tullis

D-U-N-S 00-699-2226
WESTCHESTER FIRE INSURANCE CO INC
CHUBB
436 Walnut St, Philadelphia, PA 19106-3703
Tel (215) 640-1000 *Founded/Ownrshp* 2015
Sales NA *EMP* 370
SIC 6411 Insurance agents; Real estate insurance agents
VP: Dean M Andrighetto
**CFO:* Robert J Gaffney
**Sr VP:* Eric Thomson Drummond-Hay
**Sr VP:* John Stephen Edack
**Sr VP:* John Michael Intondi
**VP:* Randolph Dale Carey

*VP: Robert Clyde Carscaddon
*VP: William Paul Garrigan
*VP: Edward Keith Hitchcock
*VP: Bruce Arnold Johnston
*VP: John Dennis Madea
*VP: Nancy Annette McCollum
*VP: William Vernon Schmaltz
VP: Linda Williams

WESTCHESTER MEDICAL CENTER
See WESTCHESTER COUNTY HEALTH CARE CORP

D-U-N-S 08-177-2068
WESTCHESTER MEDICAL GROUP PC
WESTMED MEDICAL GROUP
2700 Wstchstr Ave Ste 200, Purchase, NY 10577-2570
Tel (914) 682-0700 Founded/Ownrshp 1996
Sales 111.7MM^E EMP 850
SIC 8011 Physicians' office, including specialists
Pr: Simeon Schwartz MD
COO: Nancy Levesque
*CFO: Clark Yoder
Exec: Christina Blanco
Assoc Dir: Will Saint-Louis
Off Mgr: Lynne Bernstein
Off Mgr: Sha Blakeney
Off Mgr: Yvette Ramirez
Off Mgr: Diane Walsh
CIO: Merin Joseph
Dir IT: Cristiano Dias

WESTCHSTER BD COOP EDUCTL SVCS
See WESTCHESTER BOCES SCHOOL DISTRICT

WESTCO
See WESTERN COOPERATIVE CO INC

WESTCOAST HOSPITALITY
See RED LION HOTELS HOLDINGS INC

D-U-N-S 04-891-2542
WESTCON GROUP INC
COMSTOR
(Suby of DATATEC LTD)
520 White Plains Rd # 200, Tarrytown, NY 10591-5120
Tel (914) 829-7000 Founded/Ownrshp 2001
Sales 3.3MMM^E EMP 3,000
SIC 5045 Mainframe computers
Ch Bd: Dean Douglas
*Ch Bd: Jens Montanana
*CEO: Dolph Westerbos
*COO: Alan Smith
*CFO: Cathy Jessup
*CFO: Chris Leeming
CFO: Charles Thropp
Sr Cor Off: Howie Sun
*Chf Mktg O: Bob Clinton
Ex VP: Andreas Dohmen
Ex VP: Steve Garrou
*Ex VP: William Hurley
Ex VP: John P Malley III
Ex VP: Simon Minett
Ex VP: Lynn S Murphy
*Sr VP: Nancy Saltzman
*Sr VP: Brian Weisfeld
VP: Patty Gray
Dir Bus: Jamie Weiss
Board of Directors: John McCartney, Christopher Seabrooke

D-U-N-S 13-892-2542
WESTCON GROUP NORTH AMERICA INC
(Suby of COMSTOR) ★
520 White Plains Rd # 200, Tarrytown, NY 10591-5102
Tel (914) 829-7000 Founded/Ownrshp 2003
Sales 499.8MM^E EMP 325
SIC 5045 Computers, peripherals & software
CEO: Tom Dolan
*Pr: Dean Douglas
*VP: Charles Thropt
VP: Ayers Tom
VP Admn: Kurt Ruesch

D-U-N-S 04-739-6700
WESTCON INC
BLUE SPRUCE CONSTRUCTION
(Suby of BILFINGER SE)
7401 Yukon Dr, Bismarck, ND 58503-9755
Tel (701) 222-0076 Founded/Ownrshp 2012
Sales 349.3MM^E EMP 800
SIC 1541 3498 8741 Industrial buildings & warehouses; Fabricated pipe & fittings; Construction management
Pr: Mark Peterson
*CFO: Darius Chagnon
*VP: John Benfield
*VP: Dave Hoff
*VP: Steve Sangalis
VP Opers: Kevin Brzezinski
Genl Couns: Melissa Davis
Board of Directors: Harry Lynch, Paul Yeoham

WESTCON INDUSTRIES
See BILFINGER WESTCON INC

D-U-N-S 10-883-4479
WESTCOR LAND TITLE INSURANCE CO
875 Cncrse Pkwy S Ste 200, Maitland, FL 32751
Tel (407) 629-5842 Founded/Ownrshp 1993
Sales NA EMP 180^E
SIC 6311 Life insurance
Pr: Mary O'Donnell
*COO: Scott Chandler
*CFO: Michael Schefstad
VP: Robert T Edwards
*CIO: Mellissa Mesina-Rowe
*Genl Couns: Patricia Bower
Board of Directors: Robbie Graham, Roy Lassiter, Mary O'donnell, David Philipp, Terrence Wright

D-U-N-S 87-798-6208
WESTDALE ASSET MANAGEMENT LTD
3100 Monticello Ave # 600, Dallas, TX 75205-3439
Tel (214) 515-7000 Founded/Ownrshp 1995
Sales 108.0MM^E EMP 1,100
SIC 6531 Real estate agents & managers
Pt: Joseph G Beard
CFO: Cheryl Myrick

D-U-N-S 06-612-1815 IMP/EXP
WESTECH ENGINEERING INC
3665 S West Temple, Salt Lake City, UT 84115-4409
Tel (801) 265-1000 Founded/Ownrshp 1983
Sales 150.0MM^E EMP 529
SIC 3589 Water treatment equipment, industrial
CEO: Rex R Plazier
CFO: Scott Allen
CFO: Greg Howell
Ex VP: Ralph A Cutler
VP: Vincent Hamilton
VP: James R Hanson
VP: Craig Martin
VP: Dwight Mazzone
VP: Guy Roundy
VP Mktg: Rex Plaizier

D-U-N-S 07-465-3882
WESTED
730 Harrison St Ste 500, San Francisco, CA 94107-1242
Tel (415) 565-3000 Founded/Ownrshp 1995
Sales 141.1MM^E EMP 645
SIC 8733 Educational research agency
CEO: Glen H Harvey
Treas: Jeff Kuwabara
Bd of Dir: Tacy C Ashby
Bd of Dir: Jorge O Ayala
Bd of Dir: John M Baracy
Bd of Dir: W B Bowles
Bd of Dir: Christopher Brown
Bd of Dir: Elizabeth J Case
Bd of Dir: Rena Dorph
Bd of Dir: Rex Fortune
Bd of Dir: Carlos A Garcia
Bd of Dir: David Gordon
Bd of Dir: James L Hager
Bd of Dir: Edmond Heatley
Bd of Dir: Tom Horne
Bd of Dir: Beverly Hurley
Bd of Dir: Juan F Lara
Bd of Dir: Myong Leigh
Bd of Dir: Lawrence Lucero
Bd of Dir: Francine Mayfield
Bd of Dir: Jane McCarthy

D-U-N-S 85-917-1134
▲ WESTELL TECHNOLOGIES INC
750 N Commons Dr, Aurora, IL 60504-7940
Tel (630) 898-2500 Founded/Ownrshp 1980
Sales 88.2MM EMP 228
Tkr Sym WSTL Exch NGS
SIC 3661 4813 7389 Telephones & telephone apparatus; Telephone communication, except radio; ; ; Telephone/video communications; Teleconferencing services
CEO: Kirk R Brannock
Ch Bd: Dennis O Harris
CFO: Thomas P Minichiello
Sr VP: Richard E Good
VP: Mark Huntzinger
VP: Mark Tinker
Pgrm Dir: Michelle Cataletto

D-U-N-S 12-615-0502
WESTERN & SOUTHERN FINANCIAL GROUP INC
(Suby of WESTERN & SOUTHERN MUTUAL HOLDING CO) ★
400 Broadway St, Cincinnati, OH 45202-3312
Tel (866) 832-7719 Founded/Ownrshp 2000
Sales 346.1MM EMP 4,000
SIC 6211 Investment firm, general brokerage
Pr: John F Barrett
Pr: Gary Enzweiler
Pr: Lisa Fangman
Pr: Catherine A Huggins
Pr: FSA Hussey
Pr: Patrick Walsh
Pr: Eric Walzer
*CFO: James N Clark
CFO: Bradley J Hunkler
*CFO: Robert L Walker
Chf Mktg O: Jill T McGruder
Ofcr: Joe Davis
Ofcr: David T Henderson
Ofcr: Annette Wallace
Ofcr: Patty Wilson
Ex VP: James Clark
*Sr VP: Troy D Brodie
Sr VP: Troy Brodie
*Sr VP: Herbert R Brown
Sr VP: Karen A Chamberlain
Sr VP: Daniel W Harris

D-U-N-S 00-699-9940
WESTERN & SOUTHERN LIFE INSURANCE CO (OH)
WESTERN-SOUTHERN LIFE
(Suby of WESTERN & SOUTHERN FINANCIAL GROUP INC) ★
400 Broadway St, Cincinnati, OH 45202-3341
Tel (513) 629-1800 Founded/Ownrshp 1888
Sales 359.9MM^E EMP 4,000
SIC 6211 Investment firm, general brokerage
Pr: John F Barrett
Pr: David Dimartino
Pr: Mark Pfefferman
Pr: Elaine Reuss
Pr: Cheryl Stotts
*Treas: James Vance
Chf Cred: Edward Babbitt
Ofcr: Jim Essex
Sr VP: Noreen Hayes
VP: Herb Brown
VP: Jason Bruewer
VP: Keith T Clark
VP: Michael Collier
VP: James Deluca
VP: Jim Deluca
VP: Linda Fieger
VP: Wade Fugate
VP: Stephen Hamilton
VP: Todd Henderson
VP: Benjamin Holman
VP: Carroll Hutchinson

D-U-N-S 96-209-5332
WESTERN & SOUTHERN MUTUAL HOLDING CO
400 Broadway St, Cincinnati, OH 45202-3341
Tel (866) 832-7719 Founded/Ownrshp 2000
Sales 713.1MM^E EMP 4,000
SIC 6211 Investment firm, general brokerage
Pr: John F Barrett
*Sr VP: Jonathan Niemeyer

D-U-N-S 03-986-0929
WESTERN AIRCRAFT INC
(Suby of GREENWICH AEROGROUP INC) ★
4300 S Kennedy St, Boise, ID 83705-8132
Tel (208) 338-1800 Founded/Ownrshp 2007
Sales 136.9MM^E EMP 160
SIC 5088 4581 7359 5172 Aircraft & parts; Aircraft servicing & repairing; Mobile communication equipment rental; Aircraft fueling services
Pr: James Ziegler
*CFO: Michael Maynard
Ch: Allen J Hilde Jr
VP: Colleen Back
*VP: Philip Winters
*Prin: Jeff Mihalic
Genl Mgr: Shontz Austin
IT Man: Peter Woodke
Tech Mgr: Louie Gravel
S&M/VP: Doug Alwine
Manager: Lee Miles

D-U-N-S 01-644-1284
▲ WESTERN ALLIANCE BANCORPORATION
1 E Wshington St Ste 1400, Phoenix, AZ 85004
Tel (602) 389-3500 Founded/Ownrshp 1995
Sales NA EMP 1,446^E
Tkr Sym WAL Exch NYS
SIC 6022 State commercial banks
Ch Bd: Robert Sarver
CFO: Dale Gibbons
Ofcr: Merrill S Wall
Ex VP: Patricia A Taylor
Ex VP: Randall S Theisen
Board of Directors: James E Nave, Bruce D Beach, John P Sande, William S Boyd, Donald D Snyder, Howard N Gould, Sung Won Sohn, Steven J Hilton, Kenneth A Vecchione, Marianne Boyd Johnson, Robert P Latta, Cary Mack, Todd Marshall, M Nafees Nagy

D-U-N-S 03-095-7005
■ WESTERN AREA POWER ADMINISTRATION
(Suby of UNITED STATES DEPT OF ENERGY) ★
12155 W Alameda Pkwy, Lakewood, CO 80228-2802
Tel (720) 962-7000 Founded/Ownrshp 1978
Sales NA EMP 1,314
Accts Kpmg Llp
SIC 9611 Energy development & conservation agency, government;
CFO: Harrison Pease
Sr VP: Ron Moulton
Rgnl Mgr: Brad Warren
Dir IT: Kenny Chu
IT Man: Christina Hayden
Genl Couns: Liova Ju Rez

D-U-N-S 07-411-4638 IMP
■ WESTERN ASSET MANAGEMENT CO
(Suby of LEGG MASON INC) ★
385 E Colorado Blvd # 250, Pasadena, CA 91101-1929
Tel (626) 844-9265 Founded/Ownrshp 1986
Sales 177.2MM^E EMP 238
SIC 6282 Investment advisory service
CEO: James W Hirschmann III
COO: Travis M Carr
Chf Inves: Andrea Mack
Ofcr: Andrew Kang
Ofcr: Vivian Lin
Ofcr: Colette Pontecorvo
Top Exec: Powell Thurston
VP: Alan Nadel
VP: Steve Sibley
*Mng Dir: Stephen Kenneth Leech
*Mng Dir: Stephen A Walsh
Board of Directors: Peter Bain

WESTERN BEEF
See CACTUS HOLDINGS INC

D-U-N-S 06-194-3585
WESTERN BEEF RETAIL INC
(Suby of WESTERN BEEF) ★
4705 Metropolitan Ave, Ridgewood, NY 11385-1046
Tel (718) 417-3770 Founded/Ownrshp 1985
Sales 307.2MM^E EMP 2,000
SIC 5411 Supermarkets
Ch Bd: Richard Fraschilla
COO: James Astuto
CFO: Chris Darrow
*CFO: Tom Moranzoni
Ex VP: Frank Castellana
*VP: Joseph Castellana
Genl Mgr: Donald Bolanco
Genl Mgr: Recio Wagner
IT Man: James Abbene
Plnt Mgr: Santino Montalibano

D-U-N-S 05-779-8936 EXP
WESTERN BOXED MEATS DISTRIBUTORS
WESTERN PRIDE CARRIERS
(Suby of SAND DOLLAR HOLDINGS INC) ★
2401 Ne Argyle St, Portland, OR 97211-1938
Tel (503) 284-3314 Founded/Ownrshp 1998
Sales 97.4MM^E EMP 100
SIC 5147 5142 Meats, fresh; Meat, frozen: packaged
Pr: John Leavy
COO: Tolefson Jeff
*Sec: Eric Doan

D-U-N-S 00-317-7086 IMP/EXP
WESTERN BRANCH DIESEL INC (VA)
JOHN DEERE AUTHORIZED DEALER
3504 Shipwright St, Portsmouth, VA 23703-2428
Tel (757) 673-7000 Founded/Ownrshp 1946, 1987
Sales 84.0MM EMP 303
Accts Dixon Hughes Goodman Llp Norf
SIC 5084 7699 Engines & parts, diesel; Engine repair & replacement, non-automotive
CEO: Herb Haneman
*COO: Rob Miltz
*CFO: Keith Butler
*CFO: Butler R Keith
*VP: Miltz Robert C
*VP: Dan Dixon
*VP: Charles T Gould
Genl Mgr: Jerry Lassiter

D-U-N-S 06-502-9639
WESTERN BUILDERS OF AMARILLO INC (TX)
WBA CONSTRUCTION
700 S Grant St, Amarillo, TX 79101-2528
Tel (806) 376-4321 Founded/Ownrshp 1955, 1991
Sales 121.0MM EMP 150
Accts Stewart Martin Dudley Webb Pc
SIC 1542 Commercial & office building, new construction; Commercial & office buildings, renovation & repair
Pr: Jeremy D Rohane
CFO: Clayton Knapp

D-U-N-S 06-630-0039
WESTERN CAROLINA UNIVERSITY
(Suby of OFFICE OF PRESIDENT) ★
565 H F Robinson, Cullowhee, NC 28723
Tel (828) 227-7211 Founded/Ownrshp 1967
Sales 86.9MM EMP 2,479
Accts Beth A Wood Cpa Raleigh No
SIC 8221 Colleges universities & professional schools
Ofcr: Donna Jones
Ofcr: Holli Thompson
Assoc Dir: Mistie Bibbee
Assoc Dir: Andrew Coburn

D-U-N-S 08-759-5096
WESTERN CONFERENCE OF TEAMSTERS PENSION TRUST FUND
2323 Eastlake Ave E, Seattle, WA 98102-3305
Tel (206) 329-4900 Founded/Ownrshp 1955
Sales 148.8MM EMP 2^E
SIC 6733 Trusts, except educational, religious, charity: management
Owner: Chris Hughes

D-U-N-S 18-749-7649
WESTERN CONNECTICUT HEALTH NETWORK INC
24 Hospital Ave, Danbury, CT 06810-6099
Tel (203) 739-7000 Founded/Ownrshp 1985
Sales 23.4MM EMP 3,000
SIC 8062 General medical & surgical hospitals
Pr: John M Murphy MD
*Pr: Frank J Kelly
*Sec: Arthur N Tedesco
*Sr VP: Steven H Rosenberg
Sr VP: Steven Rosenberg
Dir IT: Mike Hendrick
Anesthlgy: Ronan Romero

D-U-N-S 07-859-5846
WESTERN CONNECTICUT MEDICAL GROUP
14 Research Dr, Bethel, CT 06801-1040
Tel (203) 794-5331 Founded/Ownrshp 1985
Sales 166.9MM EMP 838
SIC 8011 Primary care medical clinic
CFO: Colleen Scott

D-U-N-S 10-225-6856
WESTERN CONSOLIDATED COOPERATIVE
520 County Road 9, Holloway, MN 56249-4000
Tel (320) 394-2171 Founded/Ownrshp 1983
Sales 323.1MM EMP 130
Accts Carlson Highland & Co Llp N
SIC 5153 4221 2875 Grain elevators; Farm product warehousing & storage; Fertilizers, mixing only
Pr: Dean Isaacson
Mktg Dir: Paul Mattson

D-U-N-S 16-109-1111
WESTERN CONSTRUCTION GROUP INC
1637 N Warson Rd, Saint Louis, MO 63132-1027
Tel (314) 427-1637 Founded/Ownrshp 1986
Sales 228.4MM^E EMP 1,043
Accts Rubinbrown Llp Saint Louis M
SIC 1799 1761 1741 1771 Waterproofing; Roofing contractor; Masonry & other stonework; Concrete work
Ch Bd: Benjamin M Bishop Sr
*Pr: Jeffrey Kelley
*CEO: Benjamin Bishop Jr
COO: Eric Olson
*CFO: Paul Gillstrom
*CFO: Michael E Harmon
Treas: William McDonald
*VP: Dennis Ahrenhoersterbaeumer
*VP: Michael R Bishop
VP: Michael Bishop
*VP: Tom Brooks

D-U-N-S 02-193-0011 IMP
■ WESTERN CONTAINER CORP
(Suby of COCA-COLA REFRESHMENTS USA INC) ★
2150 Town Square Pl # 400, Sugar Land, TX 77479-1465
Tel (281) 302-4314 Founded/Ownrshp 1998
Sales 130.3MM^E EMP 610
SIC 3085 Plastics bottles
*Pr: Mike Andrysiak
*CFO: Dale Hosack
*VP: Gregg Johnson
*VP: Roger Kerr

D-U-N-S 19-862-3563
WESTERN CONVENIENCE STORES INC
WESTERN GAS AND CONVENIENCE
9849 E Easter Ave, Centennial, CO 80112-3723
Tel (303) 706-0340 Founded/Ownrshp 1989
Sales 153.8MM^E EMP 400
SIC 5541 Filling stations, gasoline
Pr: Hossein Taraghi
*VP: Debra Taraghi

VP: Chris Wehrle
Dist Mgr: Rhonda Hodson

D-U-N-S 03-497-2976
WESTERN COOPERATIVE CO INC
WESTCO
724 W 3rd St, Alliance, NE 69301-3208
Tel (308) 762-3291 *Founded/Ownrshp* 1942
Sales 152.6MM *EMP* 220
SIC 5172 5541 5191 Petroleum products; Filling stations, gasoline; Fertilizers & agricultural chemicals
Pr: David Briggs
Sales Exec: Chic Keeley
Board of Directors: Mark Buskirk, Tom Jensen, Mark Kimmel, Dan Oligmueller, Scott Schoeneman, Allan Thorson, Joe Van Newkirk

D-U-N-S 80-199-0552
WESTERN DAIRY TRANSPORT LLC
W D T
(*Suby of* B&C HOLDING CO LLC) ★
910 Shelton Dr, Cabool, MO 65689-6310
Tel (417) 962-2300 *Founded/Ownrshp* 2006
Sales 124.7MM[E] *EMP* 800
SIC 4212 4213 Liquid haulage, local; Trucking, except local
Ch: J W Bill Honeycutt Jr
**CEO:* David S Shelton
CFO: Regina Garrabrant
Dir IT: Shawn Watson

D-U-N-S 15-733-1786
WESTERN DENTAL SERVICES INC
530 S Main St Ste 600, Orange, CA 92868-4544
Tel (714) 480-3000 *Founded/Ownrshp* 1986
Sales 342.3MM[E] *EMP* 3,900
SIC 8021 Dentists' office
CEO: Thomas W Erickson
**Pr:* Samuel H Gruenbaum
COO: Stu Gray
**COO:* Stuart Gray
**CFO:* David Joe
Chf Mktg O: Joshua Marder
Ofcr: Theresa Carrara
Ofcr: Bradley Rogers
Sr VP: Louis J Amendola
Sr VP: Bradley Fleiss
VP: Louis Amendola
VP: Kittrick Ireland
VP: Richard Montgomery
VP: Eric Pellkofer
**VP:* Roderick Place
**VP:* Shirley Ritchie
Exec: Kenneth Kirsch

D-U-N-S 00-632-6078 EXP
WESTERN DIESEL SERVICES INC
CK POWER
1100 Research Blvd, Saint Louis, MO 63132-1712
Tel (314) 868-8620 *Founded/Ownrshp* 1960
Sales 118.2MM[E] *EMP* 100
Accts Anders Minkler & Diehl Llp St
SIC 5084 7538 Engines & parts, diesel; Diesel engine repair: automotive
CEO: John R Costello
V Ch: Jim Sida
**Pr:* Paul F Oftby
**CFO:* James P Flynn
Sales Exec: Scott Joachimstaler

WESTERN DIGITAL
See SANDISK CORP

D-U-N-S 05-198-3567 IMP
▲ WESTERN DIGITAL CORP
3355 Michelson Dr Ste 100, Irvine, CA 92612-5694
Tel (949) 672-7000 *Founded/Ownrshp* 1970
Sales 12.9MMM *EMP* 72,878
Accts Kpmg Llp Irvine California
Tkr Sym WDC *Exch* NGS
SIC 3572 Computer storage devices; Disk drives, computer; Magnetic storage devices, computer
CEO: Stephen D Milligan
**Ch Bd:* Matthew E Massengill
Pr: Michael D Cordano
CFO: Mark P Long
Ofcr: Jacqueline M Demaria
Ex VP: Steven G Campbell
Ex VP: Jacqueline Demaria
VP: Robert Blair
VP: Michael Meston
VP: Jim Murphy
Board of Directors: Martin I Cole, Kathleen A Cote, Henry T Denero, Michael D Lambert, Len J Lauer, Sanjay Mehrotra, Paula A Price

D-U-N-S 83-106-9245 IMP
■ WESTERN DIGITAL TECHNOLOGIES
WD
(*Suby of* WESTERN DIGITAL CORP) ★
3355 Michelson Dr Ste 100, Irvine, CA 92612-5694
Tel (949) 672-7000 *Founded/Ownrshp* 1986
Sales 6.5MMM[E] *EMP* 15,050
SIC 3572 Disk drives, computer
**Pr:* John F Coyne
**COO:* Michael D Cordano
**CFO:* Olivier C Leonetti
**VP:* Steven Campbell
**VP:* Jacqueline Demaria

D-U-N-S 03-203-6741 IMP
WESTERN DISTRIBUTING CO
4955 Bannock St, Denver, CO 80216-1815
Tel (303) 388-5755 *Founded/Ownrshp* 1976
Sales 132.9MM[E] *EMP* 340[E]
SIC 5181 5182 Beer & other fermented malt liquors; Liquor
CEO: Vieri Gaines
COO: Grant Bauer
**Treas:* Todd Smith
**VP:* Carlo Gaines

WESTERN DIVISION SCG
See SECURITY CONSULTANTS GROUP INC

D-U-N-S 05-756-2100
■ WESTERN ENERGY CO
(*Suby of* WESTMORELAND MINING LLC) ★
148 Rosebud Ln, Colstrip, MT 59323-9537
Tel (406) 748-5100 *Founded/Ownrshp* 1968
Sales 142.8MM[E] *EMP* 369[E]
SIC 1221 Surface mining, bituminous
CEO: Keith E Alessi
**Pr:* Kent Saltiros
**CFO:* Kevin A Paprzycki
**Ex VP:* Joseph E Micheletti
**Sr VP:* Jennifer S Grafton
**VP:* Morris W Kegley
Prd Mgr: Glenn Logan

D-U-N-S 78-042-3513
WESTERN EXPLOSIVES SYSTEMS CO
WESCO
3135 S Richmond St, Salt Lake City, UT 84106-3053
Tel (801) 484-6557 *Founded/Ownrshp* 2000
Sales 90.0MM *EMP* 190
SIC 5169 1629 1241 1081 1481 2892 Explosives; Blasting contractor, except building demolition; Coal mining services; Metal mining services; Nonmetallic mineral services; Explosives
Pr: Thomas C Fredrick Jr
**COO:* Jared L Fredrick
**CFO:* Paul Fredrick

D-U-N-S 62-122-8019
WESTERN EXPRESS HOLDINGS INC
7135 Centennial Pl, Nashville, TN 37209-1033
Tel (615) 259-9920 *Founded/Ownrshp* 2005
Sales 341.9MM[E] *EMP* 1,660
SIC 4213 Trucking, except local
CEO: Paul L Weick
**COO:* Robert Stachura
**CFO:* Richard L Prickett
**Sr VP:* Geoff Grenier
**VP:* Clarence Easterday
Sfty Dirs: Jim Jackson

D-U-N-S 92-813-8064
WESTERN EXPRESS INC
WESTERN LOGISTICS
(*Suby of* WESTERN EXPRESS HOLDINGS INC) ★
7135 Centennial Pl, Nashville, TN 37209-1033
Tel (615) 259-9920 *Founded/Ownrshp* 1990
Sales 341.9MM[E] *EMP* 1,500
Accts Wayne Wise President By Fax O
SIC 4213 Trucking, except local
Ch: Donna Wise
**Pr:* Paul Wieck
**COO:* Robert Stachura
**CFO:* Rick Preckett
**Treas:* Richard L Prickett Jr
**Ex VP:* Clarence Easterday
**Ex VP:* Richard Prickett
**Sr VP:* Geoff Grenier
**VP:* Steve Binkley
**VP:* John Martin
**Prin:* Andy Brown

D-U-N-S 00-385-4528
WESTERN EXTRALITE CO (MO)
(*Suby of* BORDER STATES ELECTRIC SUPPLY) ★
1470 Liberty St, Kansas City, MO 64102-1018
Tel (816) 421-8404 *Founded/Ownrshp* 1938, 2014
Sales 123.7MM[E] *EMP* 260
SIC 5063

D-U-N-S 02-926-2276 IMP
WESTERN FAMILY FOODS INC
TRUE PALS
(*Suby of* WESTERN FAMILY HOLDING CO) ★
6700 Sw Sandburg St, Portland, OR 97223-8099
Tel (503) 639-6300 *Founded/Ownrshp* 1985
Sales 114.2MM[E] *EMP* 65
SIC 5141 5142

D-U-N-S 19-216-6072
WESTERN FAMILY HOLDING CO
6700 Sw Sandburg St, Tigard, OR 97223-8008
Tel (503) 639-6300 *Founded/Ownrshp* 1983
Sales 182.9MM[E] *EMP* 65[E]
SIC 5141 5142 5199 5122 5149 Groceries, general line; Meat, frozen: packaged; Vegetables, frozen; Dinners, frozen; Fish, frozen: packaged; General merchandise, non-durable; Drugs, proprietaries & sundries; Canned goods: fruit, vegetables, seafood, meats, etc.
Pr: Ronald S King
VP: Gregg Floren
Dept Mgr: Randy Taylor
CTO: Bryan Phillips

D-U-N-S 00-790-5375 IMP
WESTERN FARMERS ELECTRIC COOPERATIVE
WFEC
701 Ne 7th St, Anadarko, OK 73005-2297
Tel (405) 247-3351 *Founded/Ownrshp* 1941
Sales 671.4MM *EMP* 378
Accts Kpmg Llp Oklahoma City Oklah
SIC 4911 ; Generation, electric power; Transmission, electric power
CEO: Gary Roulet
**Pr:* Max Ott
**CEO:* Gary R Roulet
COO: John Parker
**CFO:* Jane Lafferty
**Treas:* Ron Cunningham
**Treas:* Russell Pollard
**VP:* Gary Gilleland
**VP:* Leslie Hinds
**VP:* Brian Hobbs
VP: Ronnie Morgan

WESTERN FINANCE TCA
See WESTERN-SHAMROCK CORP

D-U-N-S 96-852-2771
WESTERN FLYER EXPRESS LLC
5204 W I 40 Service Rd, Oklahoma City, OK 73128-1200
Tel (405) 946-7289 *Founded/Ownrshp* 2013
Sales 91.1MM[E] *EMP* 400
SIC 4231 Trucking terminal facilities

Pr: Rodney Timms
**CFO:* Michael Mattox
VP: Harry L Kimball
VP: April Spurgeon
**VP:* Randy Timms

D-U-N-S 00-709-2513 IMP
WESTERN FORGE INC
(*Suby of* IDEAL INDUSTRIES INC) ★
4607 Forge Rd, Colorado Springs, CO 80907-3577
Tel (719) 598-5070 *Founded/Ownrshp* 1964, 2010
Sales 112.3MM[E] *EMP* 350
SIC 3423 3545 Hand & edge tools; Wrenches, hand tools; Screw drivers, pliers, chisels, etc. (hand tools); Machine tool accessories
CEO: Michael Landreth
**Pr:* Barry Baum
CFO: Scott Wehring
**VP:* Curtis Brown
**VP:* Susan Koenigsknecht
QC Dir: Linda Vigil

WESTERN GAS AND CONVENIENCE
See WESTERN CONVENIENCE STORES INC

D-U-N-S 07-861-9740
■ WESTERN GAS EQUITY PARTNERS LP
(*Suby of* WESTERN GAS RESOURCES INC) ★
1201 Lake Robbins Dr, The Woodlands, TX 77380-1181
Tel (832) 636-6000 *Founded/Ownrshp* 2007
Sales 1.5MMM *EMP* 382[E]
Tkr Sym WGP *Exch* NYS
SIC 1311 Crude petroleum & natural gas
Pr: Donald R Sinclair
Genl Pt: Western Gas Equity Holdings LL
CFO: Benjamin M Fink

D-U-N-S 80-910-7803
■ WESTERN GAS PARTNERS LP
(*Suby of* ANADARKO PETROLEUM CORP) ★
1201 Lake Robbins Dr, The Woodlands, TX 77380-1181
Tel (832) 636-6000 *Founded/Ownrshp* 2007
Sales 1.5MMM *EMP* 364[E]
Tkr Sym WES *Exch* NYS
SIC 4923 4924 4922 Gas transmission & distribution; Natural gas distribution; Natural gas transmission
Pr: Donald R Sinclair
Genl Pt: Western Gas Holdings
CFO: Benjamin M Fink

D-U-N-S 60-641-3052
■ WESTERN GAS RESOURCES INC
(*Suby of* ANADARKO PETROLEUM CORP) ★
1099 18th St, Denver, CO 80202-1908
Tel (303) 452-5603 *Founded/Ownrshp* 2006
Sales 1.6MMM[E] *EMP* 804
SIC 4923 4925 1311 5172 Gas transmission & distribution; Gas production and/or distribution; Crude petroleum & natural gas; Petroleum products
CEO: James T Hackett
CFO: William Krysiak
**CFO:* R A Walker
Treas: Vance Blalock
VP: Paul G Gagnon
VP: Brian E Jeffries
VP: Burton Jones
VP: J Burton Jones
VP: Jeffrey E Jones
VP: David D Keanini
VP: Mark R Petry

D-U-N-S 02-172-8121
WESTERN GENERAL HOLDING CO (CA)
5230 Las Virgenes Rd # 100, Calabasas, CA 91302-3448
Tel (818) 880-9070 *Founded/Ownrshp* 1999
Sales NA *EMP* 250
SIC 6331 Fire, marine & casualty insurance
Ch Bd: Robert M Ehrlich
**Pr:* Daniel Mallut
VP Opers: Mark Goldsmith

D-U-N-S 07-293-0845
WESTERN GENERAL INSURANCE CO INC
(*Suby of* WESTERN GENERAL HOLDING CO) ★
5230 Las Virgenes Rd, Calabasas, CA 91302-3448
Tel (818) 880-9070 *Founded/Ownrshp* 1971
Sales NA *EMP* 165
SIC 6331 Automobile insurance
Ch Bd: Robert M Ehrlich
**CFO:* John Albanese
**Ex VP:* Daniel Mallut

D-U-N-S 12-993-6902
WESTERN GOVERNORS UNIVERSITY
4001 S 700 E Ste 700, Salt Lake City, UT 84107-2533
Tel (801) 274-3280 *Founded/Ownrshp* 1997
Sales 381.0MM *EMP* 208[E]
Accts Mayer Hoffman Mccann Pc Sal
SIC 8299 8221 Educational services; Colleges universities & professional schools
CEO: Robert W Mendenhall
Pr: Sally Johnstone
Bd of Dir: Jim Geringer
Trst: Emily Derocco
VP: Nanette Black
VP: Fred Hurst
VP: Jennifer Smolka
Prgrm Mgr: Laura Creamer
Prgrm Mgr: Margaret Simonis
Prgrm Mgr: Theresa Spicer
Prgrm Mgr: Ryan Wall

D-U-N-S 96-932-4297
WESTERN GROWERS ASSURANCE TRUST
17620 Fitch, Irvine, CA 92614-6022
Tel (800) 777-7898 *Founded/Ownrshp* 2014
Sales NA *EMP* 6[E]
Accts Kpmg Llp Los Angeles Ca
SIC 6331 Agricultural insurance
Ex VP: David Zanze
Sr VP: Jeff Gullickson
VP: Greg Nelson

D-U-N-S 01-687-3205
WESTERN HEALTH ADVANTAGE
2349 Gateway Oaks Dr # 100, Sacramento, CA 95833-4244
Tel (916) 567-1950 *Founded/Ownrshp* 1995
Sales NA *EMP* 100
SIC 6321 Health insurance carriers
Pr: Garry Maisel
CFO: Andrea Richardson
**Treas:* Rita Ruecker
Exec: Heidi Zibull
Web Dev: Fidel Habtezion
Software D: Ali Mashal
Secur Mgr: Ankush Goel
Sales Exec: Bill Figenshu

D-U-N-S 08-379-4917 IMP
WESTERN HYDRO CORP
3449 Enterprise Ave, Hayward, CA 94545-3220
Tel (559) 275-3305 *Founded/Ownrshp* 1977
Sales 262.1MM[E] *EMP* 103
SIC 5084 Pumps & pumping equipment
CEO: Paul R Haderer
**Pr:* Richard A Haderer
Brnch Mgr: Mike Duncan
Sales Asso: Wally Haderer
Sales Asso: Jilverto Lopez
Sales Asso: Jesse Luera

D-U-N-S 00-632-8769
WESTERN ILLINOIS UNIVERSITY INC
1 University Cir, Macomb, IL 61455-1390
Tel (309) 298-1800 *Founded/Ownrshp* 1897
Sales 142.1MM *EMP* 2,048
Accts Ec Ortiz & Collp Chicago
SIC 8221 University
Pr: Dr Jack Thomas
Pr: Ronald Williams
Ofcr: Jerel Jones
VP: Bradley Bainter
VP: Dana Biernbaum
VP: John Biernbaum
VP: Gary Biller
VP: Pamela Bowman
VP: Earl Bracey
VP: John Elfrink
VP: Mary Harris
VP: Garry Johnson
VP: William Oster
VP: Benton Winscott
VP: Alex Zimmermann
Exec: Angela Hyde
Assoc Dir: Mary Lawson

D-U-N-S 00-609-5277 IMP
WESTERN INDUSTRIES INC (WI)
(*Suby of* B-G WESTERN INC) ★
1141 S 10th St, Watertown, WI 53094-6740
Tel (920) 261-0660 *Founded/Ownrshp* 1944
Sales 270.7MM[E] *EMP* 1,100
SIC 3443 3469 3089 3444 1761 3491 Fuel tanks (oil, gas, etc.): metal plate; Stamping metal for the trade; Injection molded finished plastic products; Injection molding of plastics; Sheet metalwork; Sheet metalwork; Automatic regulating & control valves
Pr: Tom Hall
CFO: Michael Saccucci
Sr VP: Rick Hochschild
**VP:* Robert A Schneider
IT Man: Greg Rogge

D-U-N-S 04-867-1416
WESTERN INTEGRATED TECHNOLOGIES INC
13406 Se 32nd St, Kent, WA 98032
Tel (800) 456-6248 *Founded/Ownrshp* 1986
Sales 103.9MM[E] *EMP* 138
SIC 5084 Hydraulic systems equipment & supplies; Pumps & pumping equipment; Controlling instruments & accessories
CEO: William Hill
**VP:* Steve Schwasnick
Brnch Mgr: Garrison Sinclair
Genl Mgr: Rick Robertson
IT Man: Jim Clark
IT Man: Greg Kull
Sls Mgr: Adolf Eppich
Sls Mgr: Eric Lipson
Sales Asso: Jeff Friedman

D-U-N-S 13-763-2030 IMP
WESTERN INTERNATIONAL GAS & CYLINDERS INC
(*Suby of* MATHESON TRI-GAS INC) ★
7173 Highway 159 E, Bellville, TX 77418-5309
Tel (979) 865-5991 *Founded/Ownrshp* 2010
Sales 128.9MM[E] *EMP* 109[E]
SIC 5169 2813 Industrial gases; Acetylene
Ch Bd: Thomas S Kallman
CFO: Michael McWilliams
**Treas:* Dustin Yantis
**Exec:* Denise Haugen
IT Man: Mark Dundore
IT Man: Craig Robertson
Sfty Mgr: Kathy McKenzie
VP Mktg: Wesley Frank

D-U-N-S 03-107-2619 IMP
■ WESTERN KENTUCKY ENERGY CORP
(*Suby of* LG&E AND KU ENERGY LLC) ★
145 N Main St, Henderson, KY 42420-3101
Tel (270) 844-6000 *Founded/Ownrshp* 1998
Sales 170.9MM[E] *EMP* 450
SIC 4911

D-U-N-S 07-787-6258
WESTERN KENTUCKY UNIVERSITY
W K U
1906 College Heights Blvd # 11026, Bowling Green, KY 42101-1001
Tel (270) 745-0111 *Founded/Ownrshp* 1906
Sales 187.1MM *EMP* 2,000
Accts Crowe Horwath Llp Louisville
SIC 8221 University
Pr: Gary A Ransdell
Ofcr: Brian Kitchens
**VP:* Howard Bailey
**VP:* Gordon C Baylis

VP: Kirk Heriot
VP: Richard Kirchmeyer
Exec: Richard Gelderman
Dir Teleco: Edwin Craft
Dir Lab: Cassandra Cantrell
Assoc Dir: Carol White
Dir: Leslie Watkins

WESTERN LOGISTICS
See WESTERN EXPRESS INC

D-U-N-S 18-797-2088
WESTERN MARKETING INC
20 Exit 278, Abilene, TX 79601
Tel (800) 588-4662 *Founded/Ownrshp* 1990
Sales 161.9MM[E] *EMP* 125
SIC 5172 Lubricating oils & greases; Diesel fuel
Ch: Robert Sullivan
**Pr:* Michael Miller
**CFO:* Edward Moulin
**VP:* Vickie Briggs
**VP:* Richard Hasten
**VP:* Jason Reed
IT Man: Nicole McAnelly
Sls Mgr: Payton Ray

D-U-N-S 96-032-4697
WESTERN MARYLAND HEALTH SYSTEM
12500 Willowbrook Rd, Cumberland, MD 21502-6393
Tel (240) 964-7000 *Founded/Ownrshp* 1994
Sales 305.2MM *EMP* 1,879
SIC 8062 General medical & surgical hospitals
CFO: Kimberly S Repac
COO: Nancy D Adams
COO: Beth Evans
Chf Mktg O: Gerald Goldstien
Chf Mktg O: Quamar Zaman
VP: William Bradel
VP Mktg: Chuck Knight
Doctor: Wirasat Hasnain
Doctor: Judy A Stone
Nrsg Dir: Karen Howsare

D-U-N-S 17-937-1448
WESTERN MARYLAND HEALTH SYSTEM REHAB
SACRED HEART HOSPITAL
600 Memorial Ave, Cumberland, MD 21502-3765
Tel (301) 723-4200 *Founded/Ownrshp* 1999
Sales 301.0MM *EMP* 2,200
Accts Kpmg Llp Baltimore Md
SIC 8049 8093 Physical therapist; Rehabilitation center, outpatient treatment
Pr: Barry Ronan MD
Sr VP: Nancy Adams
Sr VP: James Raver
Doctor: Joyce Emerick

D-U-N-S 00-695-6551
■ WESTERN MASSACHUSETTS ELECTRIC CO
EVERSOURCE ENERGY
(*Suby of* EVERSOURCE ENERGY) ★
300 Cadwell Dr, Springfield, MA 01104-1742
Tel (413) 785-5871 *Founded/Ownrshp* 1886
Sales 518.1MM *EMP* 308[E]
SIC 4911 Distribution, electric power; Generation, electric power; Transmission, electric power
CEO: Werner J Schweiger
**Ch Bd:* Thomas J May
**CFO:* James J Judge
**Sr VP:* Gregory B Butler
VP: Jay S Buth
VP: Joseph R Nolan
Exec: Peter Clarke

WESTERN MED CENTER-SANTA ANA
See WESTERN MEDICAL CENTER AUXILIARY

D-U-N-S 07-606-1464
WESTERN MEDICAL CENTER AUXILIARY
WESTERN MED CENTER-SANTA ANA
(*Suby of* KPC HEALTHCARE INC) ★
1301 N Tustin Ave, Santa Ana, CA 92705-8619
Tel (714) 835-3555 *Founded/Ownrshp* 1998
Sales 137.9MM[E] *EMP* 1,300
SIC 8062 General medical & surgical hospitals
CEO: Dan Brothman
**CEO:* Patricia Stites

D-U-N-S 02-414-7087
WESTERN MEDICAL CENTER SANTA ANA
1001 N Tustin Ave, Santa Ana, CA 92705-3502
Tel (714) 953-3664 *Founded/Ownrshp* 2009
Sales 173.1MM[E] *EMP* 4[E]
SIC 8011 Medical centers

WESTERN MICHIGAN UNIV BK STR
See WESTERN MICHIGAN UNIVERSITY

D-U-N-S 06-223-0560 IMP/EXP
WESTERN MICHIGAN UNIVERSITY
WESTERN MICHIGAN UNIV BK STR
1903 W Michigan Ave, Kalamazoo, MI 49008-5200
Tel (269) 387-1000 *Founded/Ownrshp* 1903
Sales 381.9MM *EMP* 861[E]
Accts Plante & Moran Pllc
SIC 8221 Colleges universities & professional schools
CEO: John M Dunn
CFO: Glyn D Lake
Dir Risk M: Cody Ringle
Assoc Dir: Carol Carpenter
Brnch Mgr: Krystin Nichols
DP Exec: Yirong MO
DP Exec: Kimberly Tembreull
Dir IT: George Kohrman
Sls Mgr: Patrick Foley
Sales Asso: Marcus Webb

D-U-N-S 02-432-2062 IMP/EXP
WESTERN MILLING LLC
O.H. KRUSE GRAIN AND MILLING
(*Suby of* KRUSE INVESTMENT CO INC) ★
31120 West St, Goshen, CA 93227
Tel (559) 302-1000 *Founded/Ownrshp* 2000
Sales 571.8MM[E] *EMP* 309
SIC 5191 Animal feeds
Pr: Jeremy Wilhelm

COO: Bob Berczynski
COO: Mark Labounty
CFO: Phil Shanon
Treas: Mark Krebsbach
Opers Supe: Mike Jones
Sales Asso: Cory Anderson
Nutrtnst: Brad Bogdanich

WESTERN NATIONAL INSUR GROUP
See WESTERN NATIONAL MUTUAL INSURANCE CO INC

D-U-N-S 00-792-3808
■ WESTERN NATIONAL LIFE INSURANCE CO
AIG
(*Suby of* AGC LIFE INSURANCE CO) ★
2929 Allen Pkwy Ste 3800, Houston, TX 77019-7104
Tel (713) 522-1111 *Founded/Ownrshp* 1999
Sales NA *EMP* 1,304
SIC 6411 Insurance agents, brokers & service
Ch Bd: Bruce R Abrams
COO: Steve S Poston
CFO: Mary J Fortin
CFO: Scott Gillis
CFO: John Oehmke
CFO: John Poelker
Ofcr: David Marx
Ex VP: Michael Atnip
Ex VP: William Dooley
Ex VP: Marc Gamsin
Ex VP: Bennie Hendrix
Sr VP: Mark Andelin
Sr VP: Rebecca Campbell
Sr VP: Jill Etta
Sr VP: Sharla L Jackson
Sr VP: Monika Machon
Sr VP: Rod Rishel
**VP:* Michael Akers
VP: Stuart Bergoine
VP: Jeffrey Gorton
VP: John Hellyer

D-U-N-S 07-648-1928
WESTERN NATIONAL MUTUAL INSURANCE CO INC
WESTERN NATIONAL INSUR GROUP
5350 W 78th St, Minneapolis, MN 55439-3100
Tel (952) 835-5350 *Founded/Ownrshp* 1900
Sales NA *EMP* 300
SIC 6331 Property damage insurance; Fire, marine & casualty insurance: mutual
Pr: Stuart C Henderson
Pr: Eve Schmidt
Pr: Steven Schmidt
**CFO:* Leon P Smith
**Ex VP:* David L Eide
Sr VP: Brian A Jermeland
VP: Dawn Appollo
VP: Mike Braun
VP: Kevin Christy
VP: Jeff Couchman
VP: Rich Kalina
VP: James Melchior
VP: Steve Richards
VP: John Tollefsrud
Dir Teleco: Dick Connoy
Dir Bus: Stacy Olson

D-U-N-S 03-496-6879 IMP
WESTERN NEVADA SUPPLY CO
BLUE TEAM
950 S Rock Blvd, Sparks, NV 89431-5922
Tel (775) 359-5800 *Founded/Ownrshp* 1964
Sales 328.3MM[E] *EMP* 600
SIC 5074 5083 Plumbing fittings & supplies; Heating equipment (hydronic); Irrigation equipment
Pr: Richard J Reviglio
**Pr:* Jack Reviglio
CFO: Dan Driscoll
**Sec:* Rosalie J Reviglio
Ofcr: Jeffrey Cooper
Ofcr: Jody Hedgcorth
**VP:* Theodore R Reviglio
VP: Tom Reviglio
Ex Dir: Greg Higgins
Brnch Mgr: Lisa Baker
Brnch Mgr: Bill Cassinelli

WESTERN NEW ENGLAND COLLEGE
See WESTERN NEW ENGLAND UNIVERSITY

D-U-N-S 06-698-1333
WESTERN NEW ENGLAND UNIVERSITY
WESTERN NEW ENGLAND COLLEGE
1215 Wilbraham Rd, Springfield, MA 01119-2612
Tel (413) 782-1243 *Founded/Ownrshp* 1919
Sales 108.2MM *EMP* 800[E]
Accts Kpmg Llp Hartford Ct
SIC 8221 College, except junior
Pr: Anthony S Caprio
Bd of Dir: Bret Stothart
VP: Bryan J Gross
VP: Jerry Hirsch
**VP:* William Kelleher
VP: Charles Pollock
Assoc Dir: Joe Sassi
Creative D: Deb Chappell
Off Mgr: Faith Leahy
Dir IT: Kevin Gorman
Dir IT: Christiane Torchia

D-U-N-S 08-842-0054
WESTERN NEW YORK DEVELOPMENTAL DISABILITIES SERVICES OFFICE
(*Suby of* OPWDD) ★
1200 East And West Rd, West Seneca, NY 14224-3604
Tel (716) 517-2000 *Founded/Ownrshp* 1962
Sales NA *EMP* 1,945
SIC 9431
Dir Recs: Betsy Zazycki
Dir Vol: Eileen Grew
Dir Risk M: Ellen Hardy
Dir Soc: Susan Styborski
**Ex Dir:* John Messenger
Nrsg Dir: Linda Guy

D-U-N-S 11-903-7703
WESTERN OIL INC
PETROL-MART
3553 Rider Trl S, Earth City, MO 63045-1127
Tel (314) 738-9900 *Founded/Ownrshp* 1962
Sales 108.8MM[E] *EMP* 200
SIC 5541 5411 7542 4225 Gasoline service stations; Convenience stores; Carwash, self-service; Miniwarehouse, warehousing
Pr: George Eble Jr
**Sec:* Vicki Eble
**VP:* Grant Eble

D-U-N-S 92-996-2413
■ WESTERN PACIFIC REGIONAL FISHERY MANAGEMENT COUNCIL
(*Suby of* NATIONAL OCEANIC AND ATMOSPHERIC ADMINISTRATION) ★
1315 E West Hwy, Silver Spring, MD 20910-6233
Tel (301) 713-2239 *Founded/Ownrshp* 1871
Sales NA *EMP* 1,223
SIC 9611 Administration of general economic programs;
Pr: Eric Schwaab
CFO: Maureen Wylie
CIO: Larry Tymenski
Sftwr Eng: Tom Henderson
Sftwr Eng: Jacques Middlecoff

D-U-N-S 88-376-7972 IMP
WESTERN PAPER DISTRIBUTORS INC
NET WEST
11551 E 45th Ave Unit A, Denver, CO 80239-3160
Tel (303) 371-8710 *Founded/Ownrshp* 1997
Sales 144.8MM[E] *EMP* 115
SIC 5113 5111 5169 Industrial & personal service paper; Printing paper; Chemicals & allied products
CEO: Jim Alexy
**Pr:* Nick Morris
**CFO:* Jeff Farmer
**Sr VP:* Walt Dethlefsen
**VP:* Martin Morris
Telecom Ex: Darin Sorenson
VP Sls: Dirk Goltl
Sls Mgr: Terry Nunn
Sales Asso: Kristopher Gibson
Sales Asso: Lisa Malm
Sales Asso: Gary Sterger

D-U-N-S 07-180-9081 EXP
WESTERN PARTITIONS INC
W P I
8300 Sw Hunziker St, Tigard, OR 97223-8261
Tel (503) 620-1600 *Founded/Ownrshp* 1975
Sales 99.5MM[E] *EMP* 450
SIC 1742 Drywall
Pr: Michael A Roach
**VP:* Angela S Roach
**VP:* Victor A Roach
Board of Directors: Michael Martini

WESTERN PAVING CONSTRUCTION
See LAFARGE WEST INC

D-U-N-S 06-873-5141
WESTERN PENNSYLVANIA HOSPITAL
(*Suby of* ALLEGHENY HEALTH NETWORK) ★
4800 Friendship Ave, Pittsburgh, PA 15224-1722
Tel (412) 578-5000 *Founded/Ownrshp* 1848, 2014
Sales 335.9MM *EMP* 35[E]
SIC 8062 General medical & surgical hospitals
CEO: Dtephen M Patz
Dir Recs: Gerald Sandide
Treas: Laarry Fitzgerald
VP: Barry Deems
VP: Paula Lacher
VP: Robin Zernich
Obsttrcn: Erica B Smith
Ansthlgy: Ashley M Storey

WESTERN PETERBILT
See GWP HOLDINGS LLC

D-U-N-S 12-072-3718
WESTERN PLAINS ENERGY LLC
3022 County Road 18, Oakley, KS 67748-6064
Tel (785) 672-8810 *Founded/Ownrshp* 2001
Sales 120.0MM *EMP* 55[E]
SIC 2869 Ethyl alcohol, ethanol
CEO: Derek Peine
**Pr:* Jeff Torluemke
**CFO:* Curt V Sheldon
**CFO:* Curt Sheldon
Bd of Dir: Dick Sterrett
Genl Mgr: Derek Teine

D-U-N-S 05-025-0620 IMP
WESTERN PNEUMATICS INC (NC)
110 N Seneca Rd, Eugene, OR 97402-6524
Tel (541) 461-2600 *Founded/Ownrshp* 1982
Sales 111.7MM[E] *EMP* 200
SIC 3535 3553 5099 Conveyors & conveying equipment; Sawmill machines; Safety equipment & supplies
Pr: Gary R Warren
**VP:* Bruce H Livesay
**VP:* Robert Marshall
**VP:* Richard F Sanders
VP Sls: Kevin Coffman

D-U-N-S 00-962-3729
WESTERN POWER PRODUCTS INC
(*Suby of* COOPER POWER SYSTEMS LLC) ★
2300 Badger Dr, Waukesha, WI 53188-5931
Tel (262) 896-2400 *Founded/Ownrshp* 1997
Sales 129.4MM[E] *EMP* 4,300
SIC 3644 Insulators & insulation materials, electrical
Pr: William Martino
**Treas:* Alan J Hill
**VP:* Diane K Schumacher
IT Man: Roger Jassart
Plnt Mgr: Ronald Kassing

D-U-N-S 03-394-4612 IMP
WESTERN POWER SPORTS INC
FLY RACING
601 E Gowen Rd, Boise, ID 83716-6607
Tel (208) 376-8400 *Founded/Ownrshp* 1967
Sales 172.9MM[E] *EMP* 185[E]

SIC 5013 Motor vehicle supplies & new parts
Pr: Craig Shoemaker
**CFO:* Randy Lawrence
Web Dev: Austin Maddox
Prd Mgr: Daryn Wessela
Natl Sales: Joe Parr
Natl Sales: Doug Riipinen
Sls Dir: Peter Treadwell
Manager: Joe Galvin
Sls Mgr: Bruce Parry
Sales Asso: Mark Lundgreen
Sales Asso: Mike Picard

WESTERN PRIDE CARRIERS
See WESTERN BOXED MEATS DISTRIBUTORS

WESTERN PRODUCTS
See DOUGLAS DYNAMICS LLC

WESTERN PROTECTORS INSURANCE
See OREGON MUTUAL INSURANCE CO INC

D-U-N-S 84-923-7532
■ WESTERN REFINING CO LP
(*Suby of* WESTERN REFINING INC) ★
123 W Mills Ave Ste 200, El Paso, TX 79901-1575
Tel (915) 534-1400 *Founded/Ownrshp* 2006
Sales 159.0MM[E] *EMP* 350
SIC 2911 Petroleum refining
Pt: Gary Dalke
Pt: Jeff A Stevens
CFO: Gary R Dalke

D-U-N-S 61-506-4776
▲ WESTERN REFINING INC
123 W Mills Ave Ste 200, El Paso, TX 79901-1575
Tel (915) 534-1400 *Founded/Ownrshp* 2005
Sales 15.1MMM *EMP* 5,700[E]
Tkr Sym WNR *Exch* NYS
SIC 2911 5983 Petroleum refining; Fuel oil dealers
Pr: Jeff A Stevens
Ch Bd: Paul L Foster
Pr: Mark Smith
CFO: Gary R Dalke
CFO: Karen B Davis
Treas: Jeffrey S Beyersdorfer
Sr VP: Lowry Barfield
Sr VP: Scott Stevens
VP: Dan Statile
VP: Scott D Weaver
VP: Mike Wheatley
Dir Lab: Monica Mora
Board of Directors: Carin M Barth, Sigmund L Cornelius, L Frederick Francis, Robert J Hassler, Brian J Hogan, William D Sanders

D-U-N-S 07-913-2869
■ WESTERN REFINING LOGISTICS LP
(*Suby of* WESTERN REFINING INC) ★
123 W Mills Ave Ste 200, El Paso, TX 79901-1575
Tel (915) 534-1400 *Founded/Ownrshp* 2013
Sales 2.6MMM *EMP* 870
Tkr Sym WNRL *Exch* NYS
SIC 4613 4612 Refined petroleum pipelines; Crude petroleum pipelines
Pr: Jeff A Stevens
Genl Pt: Western Refining Logistics GP
CFO: Karen B Davis

D-U-N-S 03-590-3194 IMP
■ WESTERN REFINING SOUTHWEST INC
GIANT TRANSPORTATION DIV
(*Suby of* GIANT INDUSTRIES INC) ★
1250 W Washington St # 101, Tempe, AZ 85281-1794
Tel (602) 286-1400 *Founded/Ownrshp* 1968
Sales 137.5MM[E] *EMP* 400
SIC 2911 5171 5411 5541 Petroleum refining; Petroleum bulk stations; Convenience stores, independent; Filling stations, gasoline
Pr: Mark J Smith
Ch Bd: Fredric L Holliger
Pr: Morgan M Gust
Treas: Jeffrey S Beyersdorfer
Sls Mgr: Greg Vasquez

D-U-N-S 07-920-5342
■ WESTERN REFINING TERMINALS LLC
(*Suby of* WESTERN REFINING INC) ★
1250 W Washington St # 101, Tempe, AZ 85281-1794
Tel (602) 286-1401 *Founded/Ownrshp* 2013
Sales 199.7MM[E] *EMP* 1[E]
SIC 5171 Petroleum bulk stations
Prin: Western Refining Trs I

D-U-N-S 00-901-1545
■ WESTERN REFINING WHOLESALE INC
PHOENIX FUEL
(*Suby of* WESTERN REFINING INC) ★
1250 W Washington St # 101, Tempe, AZ 85281-1794
Tel (602) 286-1401 *Founded/Ownrshp* 1953
Sales 460.7MM[E] *EMP* 600
SIC 5171 2911 2992 Petroleum bulk stations; Petroleum refining; Re-refining lubricating oils & greases
Pr: Mark J Smith
**CFO:* Gary R Dalke
**Treas:* Jeffrey S Beyersdorfer
**VP:* Lowry Barfield
**VP:* Andrew Pollak
**VP:* Scott D Weaver
**Prin:* Paul L Foster
**Prin:* Jeff Stevens
Sls Mgr: Greg Vasquez

D-U-N-S 12-619-2447 IMP
WESTERN REFLECTIONS LLC
(*Suby of* O D L) ★
261 Commerce Way, Gallatin, TN 37066-4636
Tel (615) 451-9700 *Founded/Ownrshp* 1999
Sales 124.7MM[E] *EMP* 425
SIC 5031 Doors & windows
CEO: Jess Mulder
**Ch Bd:* David Killoran
**CFO:* Michael Burke
VP: Jeff Balsley
VP: Mark Russell

D-U-N-S 01-759-7006
WESTERN RESERVE FARM COOPERATIVE INC (OH)
DO IT BEST
16003 E High St, Middlefield, OH 44062-7234
Tel (440) 632-0271 *Founded/Ownrshp* 1986
Sales 130.5MM^E *EMP* 95
Accts Balestra Harr & Scherer Cpas
SIC 5191 5983 5211 Farm supplies; Fuel oil dealers; Lumber & other building materials
Pr: Michael L Eastlake
Brnch Mgr: Chris Simyak
IT Man: Curtis Lequyea

D-U-N-S 08-988-8028
WESTERN RESERVE GROUP
1685 Cleveland Rd, Wooster, OH 44691-2335
Tel (330) 262-9060 *Founded/Ownrshp* 1937
Sales NA *EMP* 267
SIC 6331 Fire, marine & casualty insurance: mutual
Ch Bd: Michael Reardon
Pr: David Chandler
Pr: Kevin W Day
Pr: Dennis Manzella
Pr: John P Murphy
CFO: Michael Shutt
V Ch Bd: F Emerson Logee
VP: Diane Agnew
VP: Timothy A Paddock
Genl Mgr: David Jarrett
QA Dir: Joe Hayford

D-U-N-S 00-790-1457
WESTERN RESERVE LIFE ASSURANCE CO (OH)
(*Suby of* FIRST AUSA LIFE INSURANCE CO) ★
570 Carillon Pkwy, Saint Petersburg, FL 33716-1294
Tel (727) 299-1800 *Founded/Ownrshp* 1956, 1991
Sales NA *EMP* 1,150^E
SIC 6311 Life insurance
Ch Bd: John R Kenney
**Pr:* Jerome C Vahl
**COO:* Caroline M Johnson
**CFO:* Alan M Yaeger
**Treas:* Al Hamilton
**Ofcr:* Herb C Collins
**Sr VP:* Terry L Garvin
**Sr VP:* William H Geiger
**Sr VP:* Douglas C Kolsrud
**Sr VP:* Thomas E Pierpan
**Sr VP:* Tim Stonehocker
VP: Alan Yaeger

WESTERN ROCK PRODUCTS
See HANSON AGGREGATES WRP INC

D-U-N-S 00-609-5020 IMP/EXP
WESTERN STATES ENVELOPE CO
WESTERN STATES ENVELOPE LABEL
4480 N 132nd St, Butler, WI 53007-2099
Tel (262) 781-5540 *Founded/Ownrshp* 1908
Sales 209.5MM^E *EMP* 750
SIC 2677 Envelopes
Ch Bd: George F Moss
**Pr:* Mark S Lemberger
**Sr VP:* Thomas J Rewolinski
Genl Mgr: Greg Retzer
Off Mgr: Christina Phillips
CIO: Vineet Shastri
MIS Mgr: Jeanne Schaeffer
Plnt Mgr: Tom Bezoenik
Plnt Mgr: Michael Eddy
Mktg Mgr: Renee Berger
Manager: Chris Neumann

WESTERN STATES ENVELOPE LABEL
See WESTERN STATES ENVELOPE CO

D-U-N-S 16-181-9339 IMP/EXP
WESTERN STATES EQUIPMENT CO
CATERPILLAR AUTHORIZED DEALER
(*Suby of* SLORA CO) ★
500 E Overland Rd, Meridian, ID 83642-6606
Tel (208) 888-2287 *Founded/Ownrshp* 1956
Sales 247.3MM^E *EMP* 534
SIC 5082 7699 5084 General construction machinery & equipment; Industrial machinery & equipment repair; Industrial machinery & equipment
CEO: J L Terteling
**Pr:* Tom Harris
**VP:* Jim D King

D-U-N-S 13-085-8319
WESTERN STATES FIRE PROTECTION CO INC
NATIONAL FIRE SUPPRESSION
(*Suby of* API GROUP INC) ★
7026 S Tucson Way, Centennial, CO 80112-3921
Tel (303) 792-0022 *Founded/Ownrshp* 1989
Sales 274.1MM *EMP* 1,429
Accts Kpmg Llp Minneapolis Mn
SIC 1711 Fire sprinkler system installation
Pr: Gene Postma
**Ch Bd:* Lee R Anderson Sr
Ofcr: Jeremiah Kanizay
VP: June Charles
Opers Mgr: Marinus Both

WESTERN STEER
See CLAREMONT RESTAURANT GROUP LLC

D-U-N-S 05-561-1024 IMP
WESTERN STONE & METAL CORP
8085 S Chester St Ste 300, Centennial, CO 80112-3530
Tel (303) 792-3500 *Founded/Ownrshp* 1971
Sales 114.6MM^E *EMP* 820
SIC 5944 5094

WESTERN STRATEGIC MATERIALS
See STRATEGIC MATERIALS INC

D-U-N-S 06-801-4703
WESTERN SUFFOLK BOCES SECOND SUPERVISORY DISTRICT SUFFOLK COUNTY
507 Deer Park Rd, Dix Hills, NY 11746-5207
Tel (631) 549-4900 *Founded/Ownrshp* 1948
Sales 73.4MM^E *EMP* 1,317
Accts Rs Abrams & Co Llp Island
SIC 8211 Private vocational/technical school; School for physically handicapped; School for the retarded
Pr: Peter Wunsch
CFO: Warren Taylor
**VP:* Mildred Browne
IT Man: Viet Nguyen
Netwrk Mgr: Edward Hengeveld

D-U-N-S 13-972-8406 IMP
WESTERN SUGAR COOPERATIVE
7555 E Hampden Ave # 600, Denver, CO 80231-4837
Tel (303) 830-3939 *Founded/Ownrshp* 2000
Sales 270.8MM^E *EMP* 650
SIC 2063 Beet sugar from beet sugar refinery; Beet pulp, dried: from beet sugar refinery; Molasses from sugar beets
Pr: Rodney Perry
**Ch Bd:* Nicholas Lapaseotes
**CFO:* Jason Bridges
VP: Richard Caluori

D-U-N-S 06-866-5611
■ **WESTERN SURETY CO**
(*Suby of* CNA SURETY CORP) ★
101 S Reid St Ste 300, Sioux Falls, SD 57103-7046
Tel (605) 336-0850 *Founded/Ownrshp* 1986
Sales NA *EMP* 700
SIC 6351 Fidelity or surety bonding
CEO: Mark C Vonnahme
Sr VP: Paul Bruflat
**VP:* John Corcoran
**VP:* Phil Lundy
Opers Mgr: Greg Vinzant
Sls Dir: Kim Gross

D-U-N-S 96-488-7223
WESTERN TEAMSTERS WELFARE TRUST
2323 Eastlake Ave E, Seattle, WA 98102-3305
Tel (206) 329-4900 *Founded/Ownrshp* 2010
Sales 127.3MM *EMP* 3
Accts Miller Kaplan Arase Llp Seatt
SIC 8631 Labor unions & similar labor organizations
Prin: Bob Kromm

D-U-N-S 07-762-4062
WESTERN TECHNICAL COLLEGE
(*Suby of* WISCONSIN TECHNICAL COLLEGE SYSTEM BOARD) ★
400 7th St N, La Crosse, WI 54601-3368
Tel (608) 785-9200 *Founded/Ownrshp* 1912
Sales 28.2MM *EMP* 1,089
Accts Wipfli Llp Eau Claire Wiscon
SIC 8222 8221 Technical institute; Colleges universities & professional schools
Pr: James Lee Rasch
**CFO:* Michael Pieper
Ofcr: Jacquelyn Schreiner
VP: Denise Vujnovich
Dir IT: Bruce Mathew
Psych: Amy L Delagrave
Snr Mgr: Diane Anderson

WESTERN UNION BUS SOLUTIONS
See WESTERN UNION BUSINESS SOLUTIONS (USA) LLC

D-U-N-S 03-879-2016
■ **WESTERN UNION BUSINESS SOLUTIONS (USA) LLC**
WESTERN UNION BUS SOLUTIONS
(*Suby of* WESTERN UNION CO) ★
1152 15th St Nw Ste 700, Washington, DC 20005-1766
Tel (202) 408-1200 *Founded/Ownrshp* 2011
Sales NA *EMP* 380
SIC 6099 Electronic funds transfer network, including switching; Foreign currency exchange
Pr: Kerry Agiasotis
VP: Ben Kavalec
VP: Adam Tiberi
IT Man: Vanessa Pacheco
Ql Cn Mgr: Vrunda Mathur
Manager: Victor Greco
Genl Couns: Cynthia Cross

D-U-N-S 78-780-8950
▲ **WESTERN UNION CO**
12500 Belford Ave, Englewood, CO 80112-5939
Tel (866) 405-5012 *Founded/Ownrshp* 1851
Sales NA *EMP* 10,000
Accts Ernst & Young Llp Denver Col
Tkr Sym WU *Exch* NYS
SIC 6099 Electronic funds transfer network, including switching
Pr: Hikmet Ersek
Pr: Odilon Almeida
CFO: Rajesh K Agrawal
Ch: Ignacio Ramirez
Chf Cred: Bill Chandler
Ofcr: Richard L Williams
Ex VP: Elizabeth G Chambers
Ex VP: Royal Cole
Ex VP: John R Dye
Ex VP: Jean Claude Farah
Ex VP: Ken Liu
Ex VP: Diane Scott
Ex VP: J David Thompson
Sr VP: Molly Shea
VP: Greg Bishop
VP: Fabrice Borsello
VP: Daniel Canning
VP: Scott Coad
VP: Tim Daly
VP: Carol Darland
VP: Kristine Diehl
Board of Directors: Frances Fragos Townsend, Martin I Cole, Solomon D Trujillo, Richard A Goodman, Jack M Greenberg, Betsy D Holden, Jeffrey A Joerres, Linda Fayne Levinson, Roberto G Mendoza, Michael A Miles Jr, Robert W Selander

D-U-N-S 61-270-3322
■ **WESTERN UNION FINANCIAL SERVICES INC**
(*Suby of* WESTERN UNION CO) ★
12510 Belford Ave M22b3, Englewood, CO 80112-5939
Tel (720) 332-1000 *Founded/Ownrshp* 1999
Sales NA *EMP* 5,000
SIC 6099 Electronic funds transfer network, including switching
Pr: Hikmet Ersek
CFO: Brian Pramov
**CFO:* Scott Scheirman
Ofcr: James Keese
Sr VP: Sanjay Gupta
VP: Greg Bishop
VP: Ron Darnall
VP: Robert Deschino
VP: Michael Fell
VP: Bruce Ficke
VP: Darius Jack
VP: Karen Littau
VP: Thomas Moore
VP: Kevin Morrissey
VP: Don Neal
VP: Tom Siekman
VP: Julie Sullivan

D-U-N-S 07-038-1900
WESTERN UNITED ELECTRIC SUPPLY CORP
100 Bromley Business Pkwy, Brighton, CO 80603-8701
Tel (303) 659-2356 *Founded/Ownrshp* 1976
Sales 101.1MM *EMP* 32^E
SIC 5063 Electrical apparatus & equipment
CEO: Michael Prom
**CFO:* Greg Mordini
Sales Asso: Dave Cummins
Sales Asso: Adam Tomczak

D-U-N-S 09-337-3694
WESTERN UNIVERSITY OF HEALTH SCIENCES
309 E 2nd St, Pomona, CA 91766-1854
Tel (909) 623-6116 *Founded/Ownrshp* 1975
Sales 191.6MM *EMP* 1,000
Accts Grant Thornton Llp Los Angele
SIC 8221 College, except junior
Pr: Philip Pumerantz
CFO: Kevin D Shaw
Sr VP: Thomas G Fox
Sr VP: Gary Gugelchuk
VP: Clinton Adams
VP: Dr Tom Fox
VP: Beverly Guidry
VP: Clifford E Holland
Opers Mgr: Earlene Carter
Doctor: Alan Cundari
Doctor: Sebastien L Fuchs

D-U-N-S 15-899-0411
WESTERN VIRGINIA WATER AUTHORITY
601 S Jefferson St # 100, Roanoke, VA 24011-2414
Tel (540) 853-5700 *Founded/Ownrshp* 2004
Sales 117.7MM^E *EMP* 260^E
SIC 4941 Water supply
Ch Bd: Shirley Holland
CFO: Bruce Grant
Bd of Dir: Dareine L Burcham
**Prin:* Gary Robertson
**Ex Dir:* Michael McEvoy
IT Man: Sandra Roberts
Sfty Mgr: Neil Norris

D-U-N-S 07-925-3134
WESTERN WASHINGTON UNIVERSITY
516 High St, Bellingham, WA 98225-5996
Tel (360) 650-3720 *Founded/Ownrshp* 1893
Sales 211.3MM *EMP* 466
Accts Jan M Jutte Cpa Cgfm Olymp
SIC 8221 University
Pr: Sabah Randhawa
Pr: Chyerl Wolfe-Lee
COO: Mark Brovak
COO: Shonda Shipman
Treas: Rebecca Kellow
Ofcr: Stacy Jenkins
VP: Eileen Coughlin
VP: Noemi Ortega
VP: Catherine Riordan
VP: Steve Swan
Assoc Dir: Kurt Willis

D-U-N-S 04-167-8137
■ **WESTERN WASTE OF TEXAS LLC**
(*Suby of* WASTE MANAGEMENT HOLDINGS INC) ★
1001 Fannin St Ste 4000, Houston, TX 77002-6711
Tel (713) 512-6200 *Founded/Ownrshp* 1996
Sales 208.5MM^E *EMP* 1,500
SIC 4953 Refuse systems; Rubbish collection & disposal; Sanitary landfill operation; Recycling, waste materials
Pr: Lawrence O'Donnell III
**CFO:* Earl E De Frates
**Treas:* Ronald H Jones
**Sr VP:* Gregory T Sangalis
VP: Bruce E Snyder

D-U-N-S 02-812-9856
WESTERN WATER WORKS SUPPLY CO
5831 Pine Ave, Chino Hills, CA 91709-6531
Tel (909) 597-7000 *Founded/Ownrshp* 1945
Sales 100.0MM *EMP* 81
SIC 5074

D-U-N-S 00-890-9129 IMP
WESTERN WATERPROOFING CO INC (MO)
BRISK WATERPROOFING COMPANY
(*Suby of* WESTERN CONSTRUCTION GROUP INC) ★
1637 N Warson Rd, Saint Louis, MO 63132-1093
Tel (314) 427-5461 *Founded/Ownrshp* 1915, 1986
Sales 137.9MM^E *EMP* 726
Accts Rubin Brown Llp Saint Louis
SIC 1799 1761 1741 1771 Waterproofing; Roofing contractor; Masonry & other stonework; Concrete work
Prin: Benjamin M Bishop Jr
COO: Jeffery J Kelley
**Ch:* Benjamin M Bishop Sr
Treas: Tim Diehl
Treas: Timothy Dielh
VP: Dennis Ahrenhoersterbaeumer
**VP:* Michael R Bishop
VP: Paul Gillstrom
VP: Michael E Harmon
Brnch Mgr: Taeko Lemke
IT Man: Richard Fitzgerald

D-U-N-S 86-101-5782
■ **WESTERN WIRELESS LLC**
(*Suby of* ALLTEL COMMUNICATIONS LLC) ★
1 Allied Dr, Little Rock, AR 72202-2065
Tel (501) 905-8000 *Founded/Ownrshp* 2005
Sales 213.6MM^E *EMP* 1,500
SIC 4812

D-U-N-S 01-094-6200
WESTERN WORLD INSURANCE CO
(*Suby of* WESTERN WORLD INSURANCE GROUP INC) ★
300 Kimball Dr Ste 500, Parsippany, NJ 07054-2187
Tel (201) 847-8600 *Founded/Ownrshp* 1964
Sales NA *EMP* 204
SIC 6351 Liability insurance
CEO: Thomas F Mulligan
**Pr:* Andrew S Frazier
**CEO:* Thomas Mulligan
Assoc VP: Les Armstrong
Assoc VP: Jason Brooks
Assoc VP: Dean Huntzinger
**Ex VP:* Robert J Livingston
VP: Rosemary D'Aco
VP: Robert Montone
VP: Gregg C Rentko
VP: Bill Rinaldi

D-U-N-S 10-139-9632
WESTERN WORLD INSURANCE GROUP INC
(*Suby of* VALIDUS SPECIALTY INC) ★
300 Kimball Dr Ste 500, Parsippany, NJ 07054-2187
Tel (201) 847-8600 *Founded/Ownrshp* 2014
Sales NA *EMP* 207^E
SIC 6331 Fire, marine & casualty insurance & carriers
Pr: Thomas Mulligan
Assoc VP: Jason Brooks
**Ex VP:* Robert Livingston
Sr VP: Arya Yarpezeshkan
VP: Jim Kelly
VP: Gregg Rentko
VP: Bill Rinaldi
Mng Dir: John Zorn

D-U-N-S 02-679-6987
WESTERN-SHAMROCK CORP
WESTERN FINANCE TCA
801 S Abe St Ste 2a, San Angelo, TX 76903-6735
Tel (325) 653-6814 *Founded/Ownrshp* 1965
Sales NA *EMP* 600
SIC 6141 6159 6153 Personal finance licensed loan companies, small; Agricultural credit institutions; Short-term business credit
Pr: Scott Wisniewski
**VP:* Matthew Conrad
**VP:* Tom Hudgins
VP: Leroy Lamm

WESTERN-SOUTHERN LIFE
See WESTERN & SOUTHERN LIFE INSURANCE CO

D-U-N-S 79-959-1933 IMP/EXP
WESTERNGECO LLC
(*Suby of* SCHLUMBERGER OILFIELD SERVICES) ★
10001 Richmond Ave, Houston, TX 77042-4205
Tel (713) 789-9600 *Founded/Ownrshp* 2001
Sales 5.2MMM^E *EMP* 5,000
SIC 1382 Seismograph surveys
Pr: Thomas Scoulios
**Treas:* David McGarthland
**Ex VP:* Simon Ayat
**VP:* Kevin Deal

D-U-N-S 00-400-0907 IMP
WESTERVELT CO
1400 Jack Warner Pkwy Ne, Tuscaloosa, AL 35404-1002
Tel (205) 562-5295 *Founded/Ownrshp* 1884
Sales 193.7MM^E *EMP* 650
SIC 3553 2421 Sawmill machines; Lumber: rough, sawed or planed
Pr: Michael Case
Ch Bd: Jon Warner
CFO: Gary Bailey
Treas: Mark Hamilton
Treas: Paul Hamilton
VP: Tom Chambers
VP: Alicia Cramer
VP: Gary Dailey
VP: Jim King
VP: Joe Patton
VP: Ray Robbins
Dir Lab: Eddie Bell

D-U-N-S 06-478-9722
WESTERVILLE CITY SCHOOL DISTRICT
936 Eastwind Dr Ste 200, Westerville, OH 43081-3329
Tel (614) 797-5700 *Founded/Ownrshp* 2011
Sales 25.0MM^E *EMP* 1,700^E
SIC 8211 Public elementary & secondary schools
Bd of Dir: Richard Bird
Bd of Dir: Gerrie Cotter
Bd of Dir: Nancy Nestor
MIS Dir: Greg Lewis
Trfc Dir: Jan Horn
Pr Dir: Greg Viebranz
HC Dir: Deborah Meissner

D-U-N-S 07-992-8776
WESTFIELD AMERICA INC
(*Suby of* SCENTRE GROUP LIMITED)
2049 Century Park E Fl 41, Los Angeles, CA 90067-3101
Tel (310) 478-4456 *Founded/Ownrshp* 1924, 1997
Sales 233.2MM^E *EMP* 1,800
SIC 6512 Nonresidential building operators
CEO: Peter S Lowy
COO: Kenneth Wong
**CFO:* Mark A Stefanek
Ofcr: Dimitri Vazelakis
Sr Ex VP: Richard Steets
Ex VP: Bil Giouroukos
Ex VP: Roger Porter
**Sr VP:* Elizabeth Westman

Genl Mgr: Tina Jackson
Genl Mgr: Joanne King

D-U-N-S 96-250-4564
WESTFIELD BANCORP INC
2 Park Cir, Westfield Center, OH 44251-9744
Tel (330) 887-8112 *Founded/Ownrshp* 2004
Sales NA *EMP* 170ᴱ
SIC 6163 Loan brokers
Ch: Jon Park

WESTFIELD GROUP
See WESTFIELD INSURANCE CO

D-U-N-S 00-790-3271
WESTFIELD INSURANCE CO
WESTFIELD GROUP
(*Suby of* WEST FIELD GROUP) ★
1 Park Cir, Westfield Center, OH 44251-9700
Tel (800) 243-0210 *Founded/Ownrshp* 1929
Sales NA *EMP* 50
SIC 6411 6331 Property & casualty insurance agent; Fire, marine & casualty insurance
CEO: James R Clay
* *Pr:* Roger Mc Manus
COO: John Widdup
* *CFO:* Robert Krisowaty
CFO: Mike Skovran
* *Treas:* Joe Kohmann
Ex VP: William Nelson
Ex VP: Michael Prandi
Sr VP: Robert Joyce
VP: Eric Beasley
VP: Matthew Becker
VP: Roger McManus
VP: Kevin P Vonderau
VP: Mary C Weakland
Exec: Brian G Corbett
Exec: Richard Gajda
Exec: Thomas Kranstuber
Exec: Keith Pickering
Exec: Edward Schaefer
Dir Risk M: Eamonn Cunningham

D-U-N-S 93-269-5778
WESTFIELD LLC
(*Suby of* WESTFIELD AMERICA INC) ★
2049 Century Park E # 4100, Los Angeles, CA 90067-3101
Tel (813) 926-4600 *Founded/Ownrshp* 1993
Sales 224.6MMᴱ *EMP* 1,000
SIC 6512 Shopping center, property operation only
CEO: Peter Lowy
* *COO:* Gregory Miles
* *CFO:* Mark Stefanel
Sr Cor Off: Mike Skovran
Ex VP: Katy Dickey
Ex VP: Scott Grossman
Ex VP: Todd Star
Sr VP: Steve Dumas
Sr VP: Larry Green
Sr VP: Ted Kaminski
Sr VP: Hunter Lawrence
Sr VP: Walt Lichtenberg
Sr VP: Craig Tanouye
VP: George Brenner
VP: Kim Brewer
VP: Kendice Briggs
VP: Eric Carlson
VP: Juan Guerro
VP: Stephen Hamilton
VP: John Healy
VP: Jonathan Krausche

D-U-N-S 07-224-1271
WESTFIELD PUBLIC SCHOOLS
94 N Elm St Ste 101, Westfield, MA 01085-1641
Tel (413) 572-6403 *Founded/Ownrshp* 2002
Sales 35.2MMᴱ *EMP* 1,200ᴱ
SIC 8211 Public elementary & secondary schools
Dir Sec: Chris Rogers
Genl Mgr: Shannon Barry
Instr Medi: Rich Starkey

WESTGATE LAKES
See CENTRAL FLORIDA INVESTMENTS INC

D-U-N-S 07-950-7552
WESTGATE LAS VEGAS RESORT LLC
WESTGATE LAS VGAS RSORT CASINO
(*Suby of* WESTGATE LVH LLC) ★
3000 Paradise Rd, Las Vegas, NV 89109-1287
Tel (702) 732-5111 *Founded/Ownrshp* 2014
Sales 697.0Mᴱ *EMP* 1,786ᴱ
SIC 7011 Casino hotel
Sr VP: Don Hinkle

WESTGATE LAS VGAS RSORT CASINO
See WESTGATE LAS VEGAS RESORT LLC

D-U-N-S 07-950-4631
WESTGATE LVH LLC
(*Suby of* WESTGATE RESORTS LTD) ★
3000 Paradise Rd, Las Vegas, NV 89109-1287
Tel (702) 732-5111 *Founded/Ownrshp* 2014
Sales 20.3MMᴱ *EMP* 1,800ᴱ
SIC 7011 Casino hotel

D-U-N-S 12-066-6578
WESTGATE RESORTS LTD
(*Suby of* WESTGATE LAKES) ★
5601 Windhover Dr, Orlando, FL 32819-7914
Tel (407) 351-3350 *Founded/Ownrshp* 1995
Sales 287.1MMᴱ *EMP* 2,603
SIC 7389 Time-share condominium exchange
Mng Pt: David Siegel
CFO: Tom Duggan
VP: Phillip Froehlich
VP: Bobby Fusik
VP: Tim Gissy
VP: Alex Montanarella
VP: Mark Mrozinski
Genl Mgr: Carlos Navarrete
Genl Mgr: Brian Waltrip
IT Man: Yvette Agudelo
IT Man: Kevin Nicholson

WESTGUARD INSURANCE COMPANY
See GUARD INSURANCE GROUP INC

D-U-N-S 08-699-2070
WESTHAVEN NURSING HOME INC
1215 S Western Rd, Stillwater, OK 74074-5151
Tel (405) 743-1140 *Founded/Ownrshp* 1973
Sales 342.0MMᴱ *EMP* 50
SIC 8051 Skilled nursing care facilities

WESTHAVEN REALTY
See LAND SOUTHERN CO LLC

D-U-N-S 15-650-6644
WESTIN HOTELS LIMITED PARTNERSHIP
1111 Westchester Ave, White Plains, NY 10604-3525
Tel (617) 532-4600 *Founded/Ownrshp* 1997
Sales 47.5MMᴱ *EMP* 1,000
SIC 7011 Hotels
Pt: Alan Schnaid
Ex VP: David Norton
Dir Soc: Stephanie Smarsh
CTO: Robert Demaria
Sls Mgr: Jay Pujol
Sls Mgr: Cherie Swanson

WESTIN MAUI RESORT & SPA, THE
See MAUI OPERATING LLC

WESTIN SFO
See MILLBRAE WCP HOTEL I LLC

WESTINGHOUSE
See CBS BROADCASTING INC

D-U-N-S 61-292-6675 IMP
▲ WESTINGHOUSE AIR BRAKE TECHNOLOGIES CORP
WABTEC
1001 Airbrake Ave, Wilmerding, PA 15148-1036
Tel (412) 825-1000 *Founded/Ownrshp* 1869
Sales 3.3MMM *EMP* 13,000
Tkr Sym WAB *Exch* NYS
SIC 3743 Brakes, air & vacuum: railway; Locomotives & parts; Freight cars & equipment; Rapid transit cars & equipment
Pr: Raymond T Betler
* *Ch Bd:* Albert J Neupaver
* *CFO:* Patrick D Dugan
* *V Ch Bd:* Emilio A Fernandez
Sr VP: R Mark Cox
* *Sr VP:* David L Deninno
Sr VP: Scott E Wahlstrom
VP: Jason D Moore
VP: Timothy R Wesley
Exec: Robert Bourg
Exec: Karl-Heinz Colmer
Exec: Michael E Fetsko
Exec: David Meyer
Exec: David J Meyer
Board of Directors: Robert J Brooks, Michael W D Howell, Lee B Foster II, Linda Harty, Brian F Hehir, William E Kassling, Nickolas W Vande Steeg, Gary C Valade

D-U-N-S 14-150-0988
■ WESTINGHOUSE CBS HOLDING CO INC
(*Suby of* CBS CORP) ★
51 W 52nd St Bsmt 1, New York, NY 10019-6100
Tel (212) 975-4321 *Founded/Ownrshp* 1995
Sales 2.2MMMᴱ *EMP* 20,000
SIC 4833 Television broadcasting stations
Pr: Leslie Moonves
* *Sr VP:* Richard M Jones
Sr VP: Chris Simko
Sr VP: Mark Zulli
* *VP:* Anthony G Ambrosio
* *VP:* Louis J Briskman
* *VP:* Martin D Franks
VP: Bill Grubbs
VP: Michael Koczko
Ex Dir: Robin Brendle
Sls Mgr: Jeff Miller

D-U-N-S 06-266-1272 IMP/EXP
WESTINGHOUSE ELECTRIC CO LLC
(*Suby of* TSB NUCLEAR ENERGY USA GROUP INC) ★
1000 Westinghouse Dr, Cranberry Township, PA 16066-5228
Tel (412) 374-2020 *Founded/Ownrshp* 2006
Sales 3.9MMMᴱ *EMP* 12,800
SIC 3829 8711 3823 2819 Measuring & controlling devices; Electrical or electronic engineering; Industrial instrmnts msrmnt display/control process variable; Industrial inorganic chemicals
Pr: Jose E Gutierrez
* *Ch Bd:* Shigenori Shiga
* *Pr:* Jack Allen
* *Pr:* Mark Marano
* *CFO:* Kenichi Ikeda
* *CFO:* Ichiro Sakamoto
CFO: Tsutomu Takahashi
* *Ch:* Danny Roderick
Treas: Michael F Wilson
Ex VP: Tom Nguyen
* *Sr VP:* Jeff Benjamin
* *Sr VP:* Yves Brachet
* *Sr VP:* Jim Brennan
Sr VP: Michele Dewitt
* *Sr VP:* David Durham
* *Sr VP:* Jos Emeterio Gutirrez
* *Sr VP:* David A Howell
* *Sr VP:* Nick Liparulo
VP: Mike Annacone
VP: Aris Candris
VP: Cassie Hagan

D-U-N-S 00-231-9457 IMP/EXP
WESTINGHOUSE LIGHTING CORP
ANGELO BROTHERS CO
12401 Mcnulty Rd Ofc, Philadelphia, PA 19154-1033
Tel (215) 671-2000 *Founded/Ownrshp* 1956
Sales 149.6MMᴱ *EMP* 450
SIC 5063 3641 3645 Electrical apparatus & equipment; Lighting fittings & accessories; Electric lamps; Residential lighting fixtures
Pr: Raymond Angelo
* *Ch Bd:* Stanley Angelo Jr
* *Treas:* Steven Isaacman
* *Ex VP:* John Angelo
* *VP:* Leonard Dubas
VP: Carl Faub

Dir IT: Michael Stevenson
Ql Cn Mgr: Demetrios Karambales
Sls Mgr: Bruce Bell

WESTKUSTE GERMAN SHEPHERDS
See WESTKUSTE INC

D-U-N-S 07-999-0554
WESTKUSTE INC (CA)
WESTKUSTE GERMAN SHEPHERDS
29330 Calle De Caballos, Sun City, CA 92585-9523
Tel (951) 775-2534 *Founded/Ownrshp* 2014
Sales 120.0MM *EMP* 1
SIC 0752 Animal breeding services
CEO: Barbara J Dibernardo

D-U-N-S 78-391-8485
■ WESTLAKE CHEMICAL CORP
(*Suby of* TTWF LP) ★
2801 Post Oak Blvd # 600, Houston, TX 77056-6110
Tel (713) 960-9111 *Founded/Ownrshp* 2016
Sales 4.4MMM *EMP* 10,225
Tkr Sym WLK *Exch* NYS
SIC 2821 Polyethylene resins
Pr: Albert Chao
Ch Bd: James Chao
CFO: M Steven Bender
Ofcr: L Benjamin Ederington
Sr VP: Robert F Buesinger
Sr VP: Michael J Mattina
Sr VP: Lawrence E Teel
VP: Benjamin Ederington
VP: W L Lu
VP: George J Mangieri
VP: Bruce Robertson

D-U-N-S 07-940-7601
■ WESTLAKE CHEMICAL PARTNERS LP
(*Suby of* WESTLAKE CHEMICAL CORP) ★
2801 Post Oak Blvd # 600, Houston, TX 77056-6136
Tel (713) 585-2900 *Founded/Ownrshp* 2014
Sales 1.0MMM *EMP* 142ᴱ
Tkr Sym WLKP *Exch* NYS
SIC 2869 Ethylene; Propylene, butylene; Carbon disulfide
Pr: Albert Chao
Genl Pt: Westlake C LLC
CFO: M Steven Bender

D-U-N-S 09-337-4486 IMP
WESTLAKE DISTRIBUTORS INC
WESTLAKE PRODUCE CO
5301 Rivergrade Rd # 200, Irwindale, CA 91706-1347
Tel (213) 624-8676 *Founded/Ownrshp* 2005
Sales 121.2MMᴱ *EMP* 42
SIC 5148 Fruits, fresh
CEO: William C Brooks
* *COO:* Kent S Pomeroy
* *Ex VP:* Wayne D Giddings
* *Ex VP:* Jeffrey A Miller
Sales Exec: Andrew Bivens

D-U-N-S 15-422-3366 IMP
WESTLAKE HARDWARE INC
ACE HARDWARE
(*Suby of* ACE HARDWARE CORP) ★
14000 Marshall Dr, Lenexa, KS 66215-1221
Tel (913) 888-8438 *Founded/Ownrshp* 2012
Sales 421.1MMᴱ *EMP* 1,700
SIC 5251 Hardware
Pr: George Smith
Pr: Brian Huesers
* *CFO:* Leo Carney
* *Sr VP:* Tom Terrell
Brnch Mgr: Drew Gordon
Genl Mgr: Steve Hall
Dir IT: Tom Lear
Netwrk Mgr: Christy Ruffcorn
Mktg Mgr: Matt McNitt

D-U-N-S 09-192-8924
WESTLAKE HOSPITAL
1225 W Lake St, Melrose Park, IL 60160-4039
Tel (708) 681-3000 *Founded/Ownrshp* 1901
Sales 213.7MM *EMP* 1,000
SIC 8062 General medical & surgical hospitals
Pr: Joan Ormsby
VP: Patrick Durkin
Pr Dir: Marta E Alvarado
Snr Mgr: Mary Harrison

D-U-N-S 61-119-2121 IMP/EXP
■ WESTLAKE OLEFINS CORP
(*Suby of* WESTLAKE CHEMICAL CORP) ★
2801 Post Oak Blvd Fl 6, Houston, TX 77056-6136
Tel (713) 960-9111 *Founded/Ownrshp* 1994
Sales 4.0MMMᴱ *EMP* 480
SIC 2869 2822 Ethylene; Polyethylene, chlorosulfonated (hypalon)
Pr: Albert Chao
VP: David Lu
Tech Mgr: David Hansen

D-U-N-S 15-040-3764 IMP/EXP
■ WESTLAKE POLYMERS LLC
(*Suby of* WESTLAKE OLEFINS CORP) ★
2801 Post Oak Blvd # 650, Houston, TX 77056-6140
Tel (713) 960-9111 *Founded/Ownrshp* 2000
Sales 4.0MMMᴱ *EMP* 430
SIC 2673 2869 Bags: plastic, laminated & coated; Ethylene
Ch Bd: James Chao
CEO: Albert Chao
CFO: M Steven Bender

WESTLAKE PRODUCE CO
See WESTLAKE DISTRIBUTORS INC

D-U-N-S 13-832-9086 IMP/EXP
■ WESTLAKE VINYLS CO LP
(*Suby of* WESTLAKE CHEMICAL CORP) ★
2801 Post Oak Blvd # 600, Houston, TX 77056-6136
Tel (713) 960-9111 *Founded/Ownrshp* 1990
Sales 15.0MMᴱ *EMP* 1,623
SIC 2812 2869 2821 Alkalies & chlorine; Olefins; Plastics materials & resins
Ch: James Chao
CEO: Albert Chao
Sr VP: M Steven Bender

Sr VP: Robert F Buesinger
Sr VP: Wayne Morse

D-U-N-S 17-589-5585
WESTLAND CONSTRUCTION INC
1411 W 1250 S Ste 200, Orem, UT 84058-2224
Tel (801) 374-6085 *Founded/Ownrshp* 2005
Sales 148.9MM *EMP* 63
Accts Wsrp Llc Salt Lake City Uta
SIC 1542 1541 Commercial & office building, new construction; Industrial buildings & warehouses
Pr: Stanley A Houghton
* *CFO:* Lynn J Hawkins
* *VP:* Dale A Houghton
Board of Directors: Lynn Hawkins, Dale Houghton, Stanley Houghton

D-U-N-S 15-220-4756
WESTLEND FINANCING INC
AMERICAN CAPITAL FUNDING
15260 Ventura Blvd # 710, Sherman Oaks, CA 91403-5307
Tel (818) 385-7500 *Founded/Ownrshp* 1996
Sales NA *EMP* 42
SIC 6162 6141 Mortgage bankers; Financing: automobiles, furniture, etc., not a deposit bank
Pr: Danny Ahn
Counsel: Matthew W Goldsby

D-U-N-S 00-487-2578
WESTLIE MOTOR CO
WESTLIE MOTOR LEASING
500 S Broadway, Minot, ND 58701-4451
Tel (701) 852-1354 *Founded/Ownrshp* 1921
Sales 128.5MM *EMP* 190
Accts Brady Martz & Associates Pc
SIC 7513 5511 Truck leasing, without drivers; New & used car dealers
Pr: Steve Blasing
* *CFO:* Darek Zaun
* *Treas:* James H Westlie
Off Mgr: Melanie Backes

WESTLIE MOTOR LEASING
See WESTLIE MOTOR CO

WESTLINK
See STANISLAUS FARM SUPPLY CO

D-U-N-S 14-131-5056 EXP
WESTLINK TRADING LLC
17926 Highway 3, Webster, TX 77598-5351
Tel (832) 295-9778 *Founded/Ownrshp* 2003
Sales 93.0MM *EMP* 4
SIC 5032 5099 5074 5051 5031 Ceramic wall & floor tile; Timber products, rough; Sanitary ware, metal; Steel; Plywood
CFO: Kalpesh Shah

WESTMED MEDICAL GROUP
See WESTCHESTER MEDICAL GROUP PC

D-U-N-S 07-310-6866
WESTMINSTER COLLEGE (UT)
1840 S 1300 E, Salt Lake City, UT 84105-3697
Tel (801) 484-7651 *Founded/Ownrshp* 1896
Sales 96.6MM *EMP* 500ᴱ
SIC 8221 College, except junior
Pr: Steve Morgan
* *Pr:* Brian Levin-Stankevich
* *Treas:* Curtis Ryan
VP: Staci Carson
Ex Dir: Nancy Brown
Off Mgr: Christy Whitman

WESTMINSTER MANAGEMENT
See KUSHNER COMPANIES INC

WESTMINSTER PLACE
See PRESBYTERIAN HOMES

D-U-N-S 96-684-8298
WESTMINSTER PRESERVATION LP
WESTMINSTER VILLAGE
1307 Pawtucket Blvd, Lowell, MA 01854-1801
Tel (212) 506-5885 *Founded/Ownrshp* 2010
Sales 37.3MMᴱ *EMP* 1,828
SIC 6531 Real estate agents & managers
Genl Pt: Jim Brooks

D-U-N-S 01-379-0258
WESTMINSTER PUBLIC SCHOOLS
7002 Raleigh St, Westminster, CO 80030-5914
Tel (303) 428-3511 *Founded/Ownrshp* 1946
Sales 99.4MM *EMP* 1,175
SIC 8211 Public elementary & secondary schools; Public junior high school; Public senior high school
CFO: Sandra Rotellia
Treas: Kevin Massey
Off Admin: Rhonda Saavedra
Psych: Naomi Mathis

D-U-N-S 07-608-2114
WESTMINSTER SCHOOL DISTRICT
14121 Cedarwood St, Westminster, CA 92683-4499
Tel (714) 892-8946 *Founded/Ownrshp* 1872
Sales 75.6MMᴱ *EMP* 1,100
SIC 8211 Public elementary school; Public junior high school
Genl Mgr: Sandra Poteet
Genl Mgr: Tony Wold
IT Man: Christine Fullerton
Pr Dir: Trish Montgomery
Teacher Pr: Louis Fermella

WESTMINSTER VILLAGE
See WESTMINSTER PRESERVATION LP

D-U-N-S 00-791-4930
▲ WESTMORELAND COAL CO
9540 Maroon Cir Unit 200, Englewood, CO 80112-5735
Tel (855) 922-6463 *Founded/Ownrshp* 1854
Sales 1.4MMM *EMP* 3,248
Accts Ernst & Young Llp Denver Co
Tkr Sym WLB *Exch* NGM
SIC 1221 4911 Bituminous coal & lignite-surface mining; Generation, electric power
CEO: Kevin A Paprzycki
* *Ch Bd:* Richard M Klingaman

Pr: John A Schadan
CFO: Gary Kohn
CFO: Jason W Veenstra
**V Ch Bd:* Jan B Packwood
Ofcr: Jennifer S Grafton
Ex VP: Joseph E Micheletti
VP: John Olaughlin
VP: Mark Seglem
Sfty Mgr: Robin Irwin
Board of Directors: Terry J Bachynski, Robert C Flexon, Gail E Hamilton, Michael G Hutchinson, Craig R Mackus, Robert C Scharp, Jeffrey S Stein, Robert A Tinstman

D-U-N-S 07-495-2094
WESTMORELAND COUNTY COMMUNITY COLLEGE EDUCATIONAL FOUNDATION INC
145 Pavilion Ln, Youngwood, PA 15697-1814
Tel (724) 925-4000 *Founded/Ownrshp* 1970
Sales 26.8MM *EMP* 1,600
Accts Schneider Downs & Co Inc P
SIC 8222 Community college
Pr: Daniel Obara
**CFO:* Ron Eberhardt
Ex VP: Alan Tolz
**VP:* Patric Garity
Store Mgr: Chad Seibel
IT Man: John McDonough
Netwrk Mgr: Dennis Pearson
Sls&Mrk Ex: Anna Palatella

D-U-N-S 06-873-7030
WESTMORELAND COUNTY COURTHOUSE
2 N Main St Ste 101, Greensburg, PA 15601-2405
Tel (724) 830-3752 *Founded/Ownrshp* 1773
Sales NA *EMP* 1,925
Accts Zelenkofske Axelrod Llc Pitts
SIC 9121 County commissioner;
Treas: Kathalyn Obrien
Genl Mgr: Meghan McCandless

D-U-N-S 02-033-5894
■ **WESTMORELAND MINING LLC**
(*Suby of* WESTMORELAND COAL CO) ★
490 N 31st St Ste 308, Billings, MT 59101-1256
Tel (719) 442-2600 *Founded/Ownrshp* 2001
Sales 152.9MM^E *EMP* 851
SIC 1241 Coal mining services

WESTMORELAND PLACE
See CHILLICOTHE LONG TERM CARE INC

D-U-N-S 02-236-8968
WESTMORELAND REALTY CORP
1428 Delberts Dr, Monongahela, PA 15063-9752
Tel (724) 258-9009 *Founded/Ownrshp* 1995
Sales 200.0MM^E *EMP* 4^E
SIC 6531 Real estate agents & managers
Pr: Clement Gigliotti

D-U-N-S 00-191-9604
WESTMORELAND REGIONAL HOSPITAL (PA)
EXCELA HEALTH
(*Suby of* EXCELA HEALTH HOLDING CO INC) ★
532 W Pittsburgh St, Greensburg, PA 15601-2282
Tel (724) 832-4000 *Founded/Ownrshp* 1895
Sales 245.3MM *EMP* 2,000^E
Accts Arnett Carbis Toothman Llp Pi
SIC 8062 General medical & surgical hospitals
CEO: David Gallatin
**CEO:* Robert J Rogalski
**CFO:* Jeffrey T Curry
**Treas:* Thomas L Sochacki
Trst: John Robertshaw
Trst: Robert Whipkey
Sr VP: Helen K Burns
Sr VP: John Caverno
VP: Carol Fox
**VP:* Sharon P Smith
Dir Lab: Barbara Day
Dir Lab: Sandra McCoy

D-U-N-S 80-859-0017
■ **WESTMORELAND RESOURCE PARTNERS LP**
(*Suby of* WESTMORELAND COAL CO) ★
9540 Maroon Cir Unit 200, Englewood, CO 80112-5735
Tel (614) 643-0337 *Founded/Ownrshp* 2014
Sales 384.7MM *EMP* 658
Accts Ernst & Young Llp Columbus
Tkr Sym WMLP *Exch* NYS
SIC 1221 Bituminous coal & lignite-surface mining; Bituminous coal surface mining
Pr: Keith E Alessi
Genl Pt: Westmoreland Resources GP
Ch Bd: Kevin A Paprzycki
CFO: Jason W Veenstra

WESTMORELAND SANITARY LANDFILL
See WESTMORELAND WASTE LLC

D-U-N-S 01-752-9665
WESTMORELAND WASTE LLC
WESTMORELAND SANITARY LANDFILL
111 Conner Ln, Belle Vernon, PA 15012-4569
Tel (724) 929-7694 *Founded/Ownrshp* 1997
Sales 200.0MM *EMP* 20
SIC 4953 Refuse systems
Pr: Richard Walton
CFO: Terrance Cunningham

D-U-N-S 80-677-3946
WESTON & SAMPSON INC
5 Centennial Dr Ste 1, Peabody, MA 01960-7985
Tel (978) 532-1900 *Founded/Ownrshp* 2005
Sales 91.3MM^E *EMP* 280
SIC 8711 8748 4953 Engineering services; Business consulting; Liquid waste, collection & disposal
Ch Bd: Michael J Hanlon
**Pr:* Michael J Scipione P
Sr VP: Francis Yanuskiewicz
VP: Patrick J Connelly
VP: Don Gallucci
VP: Bob Horner
VP: Peter M Smith
**VP:* Deirdra Taylor
VP: Francis W Yanuskieicz
Genl Mgr: Bruce Adams
Off Mgr: Angela Gately

D-U-N-S 79-805-9853
WESTON FOODS US INC
MAPLEHURST BAKERIES
(*Suby of* GEORGE WESTON LIMITED)
50 Maplehurst Dr, Brownsburg, IN 46112-9085
Tel (317) 858-9000 *Founded/Ownrshp* 2010
Sales 312.6MM^E *EMP* 1,033
SIC 2051 2052 Bread, all types (white, wheat, rye, etc): fresh or frozen; Rolls, bread type: fresh or frozen; Cakes, bakery: except frozen; Cookies & crackers
Pr: Raymond Baxter
Treas: Edgar Woodle
VP: Donald Niemeyer

D-U-N-S 08-041-2517
▲ **WESTON LAMB HOLDINGS INC**
LAMB WESTON
599 S Rivershore Ln, Eagle, ID 83616-4979
Tel (208) 938-1047 *Founded/Ownrshp* 2016
Sales 1.1MMM^E *EMP* 6,400^E
Tkr Sym LW *Exch* NYS
SIC 2038 Frozen specialties
Pr: Thomas P Werner
**Ch Bd:* Timothy R McLevish
CFO: John F Gehring
Ofcr: Micheline C Carter

D-U-N-S 80-124-2202 IMP/EXP
■ **WESTON LAMB INC**
CONAGRA FOODS LAMB WESTON INC
(*Suby of* LAMB WESTON) ★
8701 W Gage Blvd, Kennewick, WA 99336-1034
Tel (509) 735-4651 *Founded/Ownrshp* 2016
Sales 1.0MMM^E *EMP* 4,500
SIC 2037 Potato products, quick frozen & cold pack
CEO: Thomas P Werner

D-U-N-S 02-140-4884 IMP/EXP
■ **WESTON LAMB SALES INC**
COLUMBIA BASIN BLENDS
(*Suby of* LAMB WESTON) ★
8701 W Gage Blvd, Kennewick, WA 99336-1034
Tel (509) 735-4651 *Founded/Ownrshp* 2016
Sales 108.9MM^E *EMP* 310
SIC 2037 Potato products, quick frozen & cold pack; Fruits, quick frozen & cold pack (frozen)
CEO: Gary Rodkin
Ex VP: Colleen Batcheler
Sr VP: Steve Rummel
CTO: Cliff Stevens

WESTON PRESIDIO CAPITAL
See WESTON PRESIDIO INC

D-U-N-S 82-828-9715
WESTON PRESIDIO CAPITAL MANAGEMENT II LP
200 Clarendon St Fl 50, Boston, MA 02116-5021
Tel (617) 988-2500 *Founded/Ownrshp* 2008
Sales 248.9MM^E *EMP* 3,500^E
SIC 6726 Investment offices
Pt: Mark W Oppegard

D-U-N-S 62-787-6964
WESTON PRESIDIO INC
WESTON PRESIDIO CAPITAL
200 Clarendon St Ste 5000, Boston, MA 02116-5050
Tel (617) 988-2500 *Founded/Ownrshp* 1991
Sales 278.9MM^E *EMP* 1,170
SIC 6799 3944 2519 3085 Venture capital companies; Games, toys & children's vehicles; Fiberglass & plastic furniture; Plastics bottles
Pr: Michael F Cronin
**COO:* Therese Mrozek
CFO: Katherine Lilly
Prin: Julian Alexander
**Prin:* Kevin M Hayes
Prin: Mathew Janopaul

D-U-N-S 11-834-1234
WESTON SOLUTIONS HOLDINGS INC
1400 Weston Way, West Chester, PA 19380-1492
Tel (610) 692-7533 *Founded/Ownrshp* 2003
Sales 627.0MM^E *EMP* 1,800^E
Accts Pricewaterhousecoopers Llp
SIC 8748 Business consulting
Pr: Patrick G McCann
Chf Cred: Peter A Ceribelli
Sr VP: Andrew R Gaddes
Sr VP: Vincent A Laino Jr
Sr VP: Lawrence J Bove Pe

D-U-N-S 04-451-9429
WESTON SOLUTIONS INC
(*Suby of* WESTON SOLUTIONS HOLDINGS INC) ★
1400 Weston Way, West Chester, PA 19380-1492
Tel (610) 701-3000 *Founded/Ownrshp* 2003
Sales 627.0MM^E *EMP* 1,800^E
SIC 8742 8748

D-U-N-S 14-838-6878
WESTON SOLUTIONS OF MICHIGAN INC
(*Suby of* WESTON SOLUTIONS INC) ★
2501 Jolly Rd Ste 100, Okemos, MI 48864-3677
Tel (517) 381-5920 *Founded/Ownrshp* 2004
Sales 35.8MM^E *EMP* 1,897
SIC 8748 Business consulting
Prin: Sally Bartz
**Pr:* Randy Elder
VP Sls: Terri Phiel

D-U-N-S 14-574-0622
■ **WESTOVER DAIRY**
(*Suby of* KROGER CO) ★
2801 Fort Ave, Lynchburg, VA 24501-3309
Tel (434) 528-2560 *Founded/Ownrshp* 2004
Sales 157.9MM^E *EMP* 1^E
SIC 2099 Food preparations
Prin: Roger Miller

D-U-N-S 15-425-8425
■ **WESTOWER COMMUNICATIONS INC**
(*Suby of* MASTEC NETWORK SOLUTIONS LLC) ★
4401 Northside Pkwy Nw # 600, Atlanta, GA 30327-5217
Tel (360) 306-3300 *Founded/Ownrshp* 2014
Sales 191.9MM^E *EMP* 500
SIC 4899 Communication signal enhancement network system
CEO: Steven Pickett
**COO:* Todd Papes
CFO: Michael Carr
**CFO:* Glen Hartwig
**Ex VP:* Bruce Morrison
**Sr VP:* Len Hayes
**Sr VP:* Stephen McKenna
VP: Richard Kirby
VP: Scot Lloyd
VP: Kevin Quick
VP: Richard Seiff
VP: Gary Tavel
VP: Pascal Texier
VP: Robert Whitehorne
**Exec:* Marcel Olson

D-U-N-S 12-826-8641 IMP/EXP
■ **WESTPOINT HOME LLC**
(*Suby of* WESTPOINT INTERNATIONAL INC) ★
28 E 28th St Rm 8, New York, NY 10016-7962
Tel (212) 930-2074 *Founded/Ownrshp* 2012
Sales 629.5MM^E *EMP* 6,000
SIC 2211 2221 Broadwoven fabric mills, cotton; Sheets, bedding & table cloths: cotton; Towels, dishcloths & washcloths: cotton; Bedding, manmade or silk fabric
Sr VP: Christopher N Baker
VP: Billy Harris
VP: Meredith Mele
VP: Stephen Peters
Area Mgr: Jason Mann
Netwrk Mgr: Cullen Edwards
Opers Mgr: Justin Coffey
Snr Mgr: Mike Vinson

D-U-N-S 60-318-7217
■ **WESTPOINT INTERNATIONAL INC**
(*Suby of* ICAHN ENTERPRISES LP) ★
28 E 28th St Bsmt 2, New York, NY 10016-7914
Tel (212) 930-2044 *Founded/Ownrshp* 2005
Sales 629.5MM^E *EMP* 6,000^E
SIC 2211 Broadwoven fabric mills, cotton
CEO: Joseph Pennacchio

WESTPORT ALLENTOWN
See WESTPORT AXLE

D-U-N-S 02-087-9984 IMP
WESTPORT AXLE
WESTPORT ALLENTOWN
650 Boulder Dr Ste 100a, Breinigsville, PA 18031-1536
Tel (610) 366-2900 *Founded/Ownrshp* 2012
Sales 112.3MM^E *EMP* 500
SIC 5015 Automotive supplies, used
Pr: Alex Vanleyen
**VP:* Rena Sharpe

D-U-N-S 15-404-0232 IMP
■ **WESTPORT AXLE CORP**
(*Suby of* UNIVERSAL LOGISTICS HOLDINGS INC) ★
12740 Westport Rd Ste H, Louisville, KY 40245-2121
Tel (502) 425-2103 *Founded/Ownrshp* 2013
Sales 159.6MM^E *EMP* 602
SIC 5051 3463 3714 Forgings, ferrous; Automotive forgings, nonferrous; Machinery forgings, nonferrous; Axles, motor vehicle
Pr: Alexander Leyen
**Treas:* Reinaldo Ferraz De C Moreira
VP: Luciano Bastos
**VP:* Allen Fink
**VP:* Rubens Ribeiro
IT Man: Rich Drake
Ql Cn Mgr: Saloni Pires

D-U-N-S 05-154-8840 IMP/EXP
WESTPORT CORP
MUNDI WESTPORT GROUP
331 Changebridge Rd Ste 3, Pine Brook, NJ 07058-9182
Tel (973) 575-0110 *Founded/Ownrshp* 1968
Sales 126.6MM *EMP* 140
Accts Saxbst Llp Clifton Nj
SIC 5948 5199 Luggage & leather goods stores; Leather goods, except footwear, gloves, luggage, belting
CEO: Richard Florin
**Pr:* Jay Kevin Ross
Pr: Eric Sporn
CFO: Kiomberly Bougas
**CFO:* Anthony J Brain
VP: Paul Berchman
**VP:* Jane Florin
**VP:* John Florin
VP: Paul Kleinheider
**VP:* Robert Lombardi
VP: Matt Morris

D-U-N-S 00-144-6392
WESTPORT INSURANCE CORP
HSB INDUSTRIAL RISK INSURERS
(*Suby of* SWISS RE SOLUTIONS HOLDING CORP) ★
2 Waterside Xing Ste 200, Windsor, CT 06095-1588
Tel (860) 902-7201 *Founded/Ownrshp* 1890
Sales NA *EMP* 920
SIC 6331 6411 Property damage insurance; Loss prevention services, insurance
CEO: Robert Petrilli
**CFO:* James Casey
**Ex VP:* Kerras Campbell
**Ex VP:* Dan Eudy
VP: Edward Kane
**VP:* Seale Tuttle
Corp Couns: Joseph Dombrosky

D-U-N-S 08-084-3246
WESTPORT INSURANCE CORP
(*Suby of* SWISS RE SOLUTIONS HOLDING CORP) ★
5200 Metcalf Ave, Overland Park, KS 66202-1265
Tel (913) 676-5270 *Founded/Ownrshp* 1992
Sales NA *EMP* 600
SIC 6331 Property damage insurance
Sr VP: Steven O'Hern

D-U-N-S 14-766-9667 IMP
WESTPORT PETROLEUM INC
(*Suby of* MITSUI & CO (USA) INC) ★
810 Crescent Centre Dr # 530, Franklin, TN 37067-6298
Tel (615) 771-6800 *Founded/Ownrshp* 1985
Sales 1.0MMM^E *EMP* 14
SIC 5172 Petroleum products; Petroleum brokers
CEO: Keisuke Harigai
CFO: Hiromichi Yoshinaga

D-U-N-S 08-339-8961
WESTPORT SENIOR LIVING INVESTMENT FUND LP
11360 N Jog Rd Ste 102, Palm Beach Gardens, FL 33418-1750
Tel (561) 624-1225 *Founded/Ownrshp* 1998
Sales NA *EMP* 1,250
SIC 9532 Community & rural development
Pt: Susan Rosser

D-U-N-S 07-987-8374
▲ **WESTROCK CO**
504 Thrasher St, Norcross, GA 30071-1967
Tel (678) 291-7456 *Founded/Ownrshp* 1985
Sales 14.1MMM *EMP* 42,000^E
Accts Ernst & Young Llp Atlanta Ge
Tkr Sym WRK *Exch* NYS
SIC 2631 2899 3699 6531 Paperboard mills; Chemical preparations; Electrical equipment & supplies; Real estate agents & managers
Pr: Steven C Voorhees
Pr: Robert K Beckler
Pr: Jeff Chalovich
Pr: Bob Feeser
Pr: James B Porter III
CFO: Ward H Dickson
Ofcr: Jennifer Graham-Johnson
Ex VP: Craig A Gunckel
Ex VP: Robert B McIntosh
Plnt Mgr: Chris Neilson

D-U-N-S 04-758-0006 EXP
WESTROCK CONSUMER PACKAGING GROUP LLC
1950 N Ruby St, Melrose Park, IL 60160-1110
Tel (708) 344-9100 *Founded/Ownrshp* 2010
Sales 141.6MM^E *EMP* 799
SIC 2671

D-U-N-S 00-498-7897 IMP/EXP
■ **WESTROCK CONVERTING CO** (GA)
(*Suby of* WESTROCK RKT CO) ★
504 Thrasher St, Norcross, GA 30071-1967
Tel (770) 246-9982 *Founded/Ownrshp* 1976
Sales 337.9MM^E *EMP* 1,000
SIC 2631 2653 3081 Folding boxboard; Boxes, corrugated: made from purchased materials; Partitions, solid fiber: made from purchased materials; Packing materials, plastic sheet
CEO: Steve Voorhees
**Ex VP:* David Dreibelbis
**Ex VP:* Paul J England
**Ex VP:* Nicholas G George
**Ex VP:* James Hansen
**Ex VP:* Richard Steed
Mktg Dir: John Hughes

D-U-N-S 09-504-7528
WESTROCK CONVERTING CO
ROCKTENN RETAIL SOLUTIONS CO
2464 Amnicola Hwy, Chattanooga, TN 37406-2311
Tel (423) 622-2254 *Founded/Ownrshp* 1958
Sales 104.7MM^E *EMP* 350
SIC 2752 2759 Posters, lithographed; Screen printing; Posters, including billboards: printing
Pr: Phil Harris
CFO: Shawn McDole
Exec: Glenn Amann

D-U-N-S 96-850-5995 EXP
■ **WESTROCK CP LLC**
(*Suby of* WESTROCK MWV LLC) ★
504 Thrasher St, Norcross, GA 30071-1967
Tel (770) 448-2193 *Founded/Ownrshp* 2015
Sales 2.1MMM^E *EMP* 1,600
SIC 5113 Corrugated & solid fiber boxes
CEO: Steve Voorhees
**Pr:* Bob Beckler
**Chf Cred:* Donna Owens Cox
**Ex VP:* Ward Dickson
Ex VP: Owen Glock
Dir Risk M: Douglas Bachman
**Dir Sec:* Nina Butler
Genl Mgr: Jeff Connlain
Genl Mgr: Chuck Johnston
Opers Mgr: Rod Read
Plnt Mgr: Gregg Whitlow

D-U-N-S 60-224-7751 IMP/EXP
■ **WESTROCK DISPENSING SYSTEMS INC**
(*Suby of* WESTROCK MWV LLC) ★
11901 Grandview Rd, Grandview, MO 64030-1109
Tel (816) 986-6000 *Founded/Ownrshp* 1983
Sales 533.0MM^E *EMP* 2,300
SIC 3089 Plastic containers, except foam; Bottle caps, molded plastic; Injection molding of plastics
CEO: John Taylor

D-U-N-S 06-377-7775 IMP
■ **WESTROCK MILL CO LLC**
ROCKTENN
(*Suby of* WESTROCK RKT CO) ★
504 Thrasher St, Norcross, GA 30071-1967
Tel (770) 448-2193 *Founded/Ownrshp* 1973
Sales 181.6MM^E *EMP* 818
SIC 2631 Boxboard
CEO: Steve Vorheese
Pr: Dwight Morris
Pr: Steve York
Ch: James A Rubright
Ex VP: David Dreibelbis
Genl Mgr: Jeff Connlain
IT Man: Robert Slater
Sfty Dirs: Charlie Willie

Sfty Mgr: Ed Hinkel
Sfty Mgr: G Jenkins
Sfty Mgr: Chip Lester

D-U-N-S 13-924-3588 EXP
■ WESTROCK MINNESOTA CORP
(*Suby of* WESTROCK RKT CO) ★
2250 Wabash Ave, Saint Paul, MN 55114-1828
Tel (612) 641-4938 *Founded/Ownrshp* 1997
Sales 23.9M[E] *EMP* 2,200
SIC 2631 Paperboard mills; Folding boxboard; Corrugating medium
Pr: Jay Shuster
Genl Mgr: Jack Greenshields
VP Sls: Gary Vacek
Board of Directors: F Caleb Blodgett, Pierson Grieve, Joseph B Mc Arthur, Morris Sherman, F B Williams

D-U-N-S 10-223-5004 IMP/EXP
■ WESTROCK MWV LLC
(*Suby of* WESTROCK CO) ★
501 S 5th St, Richmond, VA 23219-0501
Tel (804) 444-1000 *Founded/Ownrshp* 2015
Sales 5.0MMM[E] *EMP* 15,000
SIC 2631 2671 2678 2677 2861 2611 Paperboard mills; Linerboard; Container, packaging & boxboard; Coated & treated board; Packaging paper & plastics film, coated & laminated; Plastic film, coated or laminated for packaging; Stationery products; Envelopes; Gum & wood chemicals; Pulp mills
Pr: John A Luke Jr
Pr: Robert Beckler
Pr: Ted Lithgow
CFO: Mark Rajkowski
Ex VP: Robert A Feeser
Ex VP: Raymond W Lane
Sr VP: Richard H Block
Sr VP: Kenneth T Seeger

D-U-N-S 00-328-9725 IMP/EXP
■ WESTROCK RKT CO (GA)
(*Suby of* WESTROCK CO) ★
504 Thrasher St, Norcross, GA 30071-1967
Tel (770) 448-2193 *Founded/Ownrshp* 1936, 2015
Sales 8.9MMM[E] *EMP* 26,600
SIC 2653 2652 2631 Partitions, solid fiber: made from purchased materials; Boxes, corrugated: made from purchased materials; Filing boxes, paperboard: made from purchased materials; Container board; Container, packaging & boxboard
CEO: Steven C Voorhees
Pr: Mike Kiepura
Pr: Jim Porter
CFO: Ward H Dickson
Treas: R E Hardin
Ex VP: Jennifer Graham-Johnson
Ex VP: Robert B McIntosh
VP: Jacqueline M Welch

D-U-N-S 80-837-8546
■ WESTROCK SHARED SERVICES LLC
(*Suby of* WESTROCK RKT CO) ★
504 Thrasher St, Norcross, GA 30071-1967
Tel (770) 448-2193 *Founded/Ownrshp* 2004
Sales NA *EMP* 2,600
SIC 8741 Administrative management
CEO: Steven Voorhees

D-U-N-S 07-943-7580
■ WESTROCK SP CO
(*Suby of* WESTROCK CO) ★
709 Papermill Rd, Dublin, GA 31027-2494
Tel (504) 733-1954 *Founded/Ownrshp* 2015
Sales 201.3MM[E] *EMP* 498[E]
SIC 2621 Kraft paper
CEO: Steeve Voorhees
**Pr:* Bob Beckler
**Pr:* Jim Porter
**Pr:* Ken Seeger
**CEO:* Michael Wilson
**CFO:* Warxd Dickson
**Treas:* Bob McIntosh
**Chf Cred:* Donna Owens Cox
**Ex VP:* Jeff Chalovich
**Ex VP:* Kevin Clark
**Ex VP:* Bob Feeser
**Ex VP:* Craig Gunckel
**Ex VP:* R Zack Smith
**Ex VP:* Tom Stigers

D-U-N-S 06-426-9954 IMP
WESTRUX INTERNATIONAL INC
15555 Valley View Ave, Santa Fe Springs, CA 90670-5718
Tel (562) 404-1020 *Founded/Ownrshp* 1988
Sales 122.9MM[E] *EMP* 205
SIC 5511 5531 7513 7538 Trucks, tractors & trailers: new & used; Truck equipment & parts; Truck rental, without drivers; Truck leasing, without drivers; Truck engine repair, except industrial
Pr: David M Kenney
**CFO:* John M Reynolds
Mktg Dir: Xavier Campos
Mktg Dir: Mike Dendrinos
Sales Asso: Todd Farrell

D-U-N-S 02-783-7889 IMP
WESTSIDE BUILDING MATERIAL CORP
1111 E Howell Ave, Anaheim, CA 92805-6453
Tel (714) 385-1644 *Founded/Ownrshp* 1948
Sales 118.2MM[E] *EMP* 95[E]
SIC 5032 Plastering materials
CEO: Bill Peckham
**Pr:* Geraldine G Peckham
VP: Tony Lee
**VP:* Richard Peckham
Exec: Mona Temple
Dir IT: Joe Zaccari

D-U-N-S 19-345-7686
WESTSIDE COMMUNITY SCHOOL DISTRICT 66
909 S 76th St, Omaha, NE 68114-4519
Tel (402) 390-2100 *Founded/Ownrshp* 1947
Sales 51.8MM[E] *EMP* 1,050[E]
SIC 8211 Public elementary & secondary schools
Exec: Arturo Valenzuela
Off Admin: Betty Karolski
Dir IT: Paul Lindgren
Pr Dir: Brandi Petersen
Schl Brd P: Scott Hazelrigg

WESTSIDE POULTRY
See WEST SIDE FOODS INC

WESTSIDE REGIONAL CENTER
See COASTAL DEVELOPMENTAL SERVICES FOUNDATION

D-U-N-S 36-312-8042
WESTSTAR CINEMAS INC
16530 Ventura Blvd # 500, Encino, CA 91436-4554
Tel (818) 784-6266 *Founded/Ownrshp* 2001
Sales 32.7MM[E] *EMP* 2,000
SIC 7832 Motion picture theaters, except drive-in
Pt: John Watterman

D-U-N-S 07-972-0813
WESTWAY CONSTRUCTION SERVICES LLC
(*Suby of* SATTERFIELD AND PONTIKES CONSTRUCTION INC) ★
8611 Derrington Rd, Houston, TX 77064-6003
Tel (713) 375-2330 *Founded/Ownrshp* 2014
Sales 373.5MM *EMP* 35
SIC 1522 Residential construction
VP: Lorenzo Martinez

WESTWAY GROUP, LLC
See CONTANDA LLC

WESTWIND EQUITY INVESTORS
See WINDJAMMER CAPITAL INVESTORS III LLC

WESTWOOD COLLEGE OF TECHNOLOGY
See TRAV CORP

D-U-N-S 10-663-6652
▲ WESTWOOD HOLDINGS GROUP INC
200 Crescent Ct Ste 1200, Dallas, TX 75201-1855
Tel (214) 756-6900 *Founded/Ownrshp* 1983
Sales 130.9MM *EMP* 168[E]
Tkr Sym WHG *Exch* NYS
SIC 6282 Investment advice; Investment advisory service
Pr: Brian O Casey
**Ch Bd:* Richard M Frank
Pr: Randall L Root
CFO: Bill Hardcastle
CFO: Tiffany B Kice
**V Ch Bd:* Susan M Byrne
Assoc VP: Brian Tully
Ex VP: Mark R Freeman
Sr VP: Julie K Gerron
VP: Gregg Ballew
VP: Marty Brainerd
VP: Jonathan Dale
VP: Hollis Ghobrial
VP: Jeffrey Gubala
VP: Kristie Leatherberry
VP: Crystal Leiva
VP: Thomas Lieu
VP: Matthew Lockridge
VP: Christa Maxwell
VP: Kellie Stark

WESTWOOD MANOR NURSING AND REHABILITATION CENTER
See COMMUNITY CARE CENTER OF WESTWOOD LLC

D-U-N-S 11-311-4219
■ WESTWOOD ONE INC
(*Suby of* CUMULUS MEDIA INC) ★
220 W 42nd St Fl 4, New York, NY 10036-7200
Tel (212) 967-2888 *Founded/Ownrshp* 2013
Sales 203.7MM[E] *EMP* 515[E]
SIC 4832 7922 Radio broadcasting stations; Radio producers; Television program, including commercial producers
CEO: Paul Caine
Pr: Steven Kalin
Pr: Gary Schonfeld
**Pr:* Steve Shaw
**CFO:* Jean B Clifton
Ex VP: Jonathan S Marshall
**VP:* Jack Foley
VP: Chad Seng
VP: Susan Stephens
VP: Ron Werth

WESTWOOD TERRACE
See STANDARD WESTWOOD VENTURE LP

WET SEAL
See SEAL123 INC

D-U-N-S 07-981-3794
WET SEAL LLC
7555 Irvine Center Dr, Irvine, CA 92618-2930
Tel (949) 699-3900 *Founded/Ownrshp* 2015
Sales 251.6MM[E] *EMP* 2,200
SIC 5621 5632 5961 Women's clothing stores; Women's accessory & specialty stores; Women's apparel, mail order
Ch: Gregory Segall
**CEO:* Edmond Thomas
**CFO:* Tom Hillebrandt
**Ex VP:* Christine Lee
**Sr VP:* Kim Bajrech
VP: Nick Dialynas
VP: Alan Flaesgarten
VP: Jon Kubo
Dir Risk M: Jessica Dunn
Info Man: Andy Yu
Site Mgr: Natalie Medrano

WETA TV 26
See GREATER WASHINGTON EDUCATIONAL TELECOMMUNICATIONS ASSOCIATION INC

D-U-N-S 09-287-1110 IMP/EXP
WETHERILL ASSOCIATES INC
W A I
411 Eagleview Blvd # 100, Exton, PA 19341-1167
Tel (484) 875-6600 *Founded/Ownrshp* 1978
Sales 200.0MM *EMP* 420
SIC 5013 Automotive supplies & parts
Pr: Jeffery W Sween
**Pr:* Douglas Moul
Pr: Earl Proud
**Treas:* Deena K Lee
QC Dir: Mathew Badner
Manager: Bryan Haring
Board of Directors: E Gripton

D-U-N-S 01-893-0649
■ WEX INC
WRIGHT EXPRESS FINANCIAL SVCS
(*Suby of* WEX INC) ★
7090 S Union Park Ave # 350, Midvale, UT 84047-4156
Tel (801) 270-8166 *Founded/Ownrshp* 1997
Sales NA *EMP* 35
SIC 6021 National commercial banks
Pr: Kirk Weiler
**CEO:* Melissa D Smith
**CFO:* Darren Haas
**Treas:* Robert L Bendig
Ofcr: Deven Bhatt
Ofcr: Angie Williams
**Sr VP:* Stephen Crowley
**Sr VP:* Steve Elder
**Sr VP:* George Hogan
**Sr VP:* Ken Janosick
VP: Nicole Lengel

D-U-N-S 10-818-5406
▲ WEX INC
97 Darling Ave, South Portland, ME 04106-2301
Tel (207) 773-8171 *Founded/Ownrshp* 1983
Sales 817.6MM *EMP* 2,004[E]
Tkr Sym WEX *Exch* NYS
SIC 7389 7375 Financial services; Credit card service; Information retrieval services
Pr: Melissa D Smith
Sr Pt: Kimberly Bois
Ch Bd: Michael E Dubyak
CFO: Roberto Simon
V Ch Bd: Rowland T Moriarty
Sr VP: Stephen R Crowley
Sr VP: Stephen Crowley
Sr VP: Steven A Elder
Sr VP: George W Hogan
Sr VP: Kenneth Janosick
Sr VP: Kenneth W Janosick
Sr VP: Nicola Morris
Sr VP: Jim Pratt
Sr VP: Hilary A Rapkin
Sr VP: Alison Vanderhoof
Sr VP: Jeff Young
VP: David Maxsiimc
VP: Jill Northrop
Board of Directors: John E Bachman, Eric Duprat, Ronald T Maheu, George L McTavish, Kirk P Pond, Regina O Sommer, Jack Vanwoerkom

D-U-N-S 16-099-6971
WEXCO INC
3490 Board Rd, York, PA 17406-8478
Tel (717) 764-8585 *Founded/Ownrshp* 1986
Sales 106.9MM[E] *EMP* 660
SIC 3089 3149 3999 5091 3081 Extruded finished plastic products; Swimming pools, plastic; Hot tubs; Watersports equipment & supplies; Vinyl film & sheet
Pr: Jeffrey Kurth
**Treas:* Robert E Seitz
**VP:* Linda Luckenbaugh
**VP:* John Schrenk

D-U-N-S 95-912-0544
WEXFORD CAPITAL LP
411 W Putnam Ave Ste 125, Greenwich, CT 06830-6294
Tel (203) 862-7000 *Founded/Ownrshp* 1994
Sales 106.0MM[E] *EMP* 860[E]
SIC 8741 6282 1221 1222 Management services; Investment advice; Bituminous coal surface mining; Bituminous coal-underground mining
Ch: Charles Davidson
Pt: Robert Holtz
Pr: Joseph Jacobs
Treas: John Doyle
VP: Philip Braunstein
VP: Marc Leferman
VP: Lindsay Luger
VP: Paul A Mieyal

D-U-N-S 79-131-0451
WEXFORD HEALTH SOURCES INC
501 Hlday Dr Foster Plz 4, Pittsburgh, PA 15220
Tel (888) 633-6468 *Founded/Ownrshp* 1983
Sales 125.7MM[E] *EMP* 1,525
SIC 8741 Hospital management; Nursing & personal care facility management
Ch Bd: Kevin C Halloran
CFO: Dan Conn
**Sec:* G Norman McCann
VP: John Froehlich
VP: Elaine Gedman
VP: Darius Holmes
VP: Nicholas Little
VP: Diana Malloy
Assoc Dir: Theresa Dronet
CTO: Matthew Jackanic
IT Man: Carlos Correa

WEYANT GREEN
See RELATED COMPANIES L P

D-U-N-S 00-607-7069 IMP/EXP
▲ WEYCO GROUP INC (WI)
333 W Estabrook Blvd # 1, Glendale, WI 53212-1067
Tel (414) 908-1600 *Founded/Ownrshp* 1906
Sales 320.6MM *EMP* 662[E]
Accts Baker Tilly Virchow Krause Ll
Tkr Sym WEYS *Exch* NGS
SIC 5139 5661 Footwear; Shoes; Men's shoes; Women's shoes; Children's shoes
Ch Bd: Thomas W Florsheim Jr
**Pr:* John W Florsheim
CFO: John F Wittkowske
VP: Judy Anderson
VP: Steele Davidoff
VP: Brian Flannery
VP: Beverly Goldberg
Software D: Jeff Schumacher
Sftwr Eng: Peter Grossman
VP Sls: David Polansky
Board of Directors: Tina Chang, Robert Feitler, Thomas W Florsheim, Cory L Nettles, Frederick P Stratton Jr

D-U-N-S 00-130-6992
▲ WEYERHAEUSER CO (WA)
220 Occidental Ave S, Seattle, WA 98104-3120
Tel (253) 924-2345 *Founded/Ownrshp* 1900
Sales 7.0MMM *EMP* 12,600
Tkr Sym WY *Exch* NYS
SIC 6798 0811 2411 2435 2611 2621 Real estate investment trusts; Timber tracts; Logging; Timber, cut at logging camp; Wooden logs; Wood chips, produced in the field; Hardwood veneer & plywood; Pulp mills; Pulp produced from wood base; Paper mills; Newsprint paper
Pr: Doyle R Simons
CFO: Russell S Hagen
Ex VP: Patricia M Bedient
Ex VP: Richard Gozon
Ex VP: Thomas M Lindquist
Sr VP: Adrian Blocker
Sr VP: Adrian M Blocker
Sr VP: James M Branson
Sr VP: Larry Burrows
Sr VP: William C Gaynor
Sr VP: Thomas F Gideon
Sr VP: Marc Grignon
Sr VP: Rhonda C Hunter
Sr VP: Michael A Jackson
Sr VP: James R Kelle
Sr VP: Jim Kilberg
Sr VP: Denise M Merle
Sr VP: Michael R Onustock
Sr VP: Cathy Slater
Sr VP: Devin W Stockfish
VP: Jeanne M Hillman
Board of Directors: D Michael Steuert, David P Bozeman, Kim Williams, Mark A Emmert, Charles Williamson, Rick R Holley, John I Kieckhefer, Sara Grootwassink Lewis, John F Morgan Sr, Nicole W Piasecki, Marc R Racicot, Lawrence A Selzer

D-U-N-S 07-039-7864 EXP
■ WEYERHAEUSER INTERNATIONAL INC
(*Suby of* WEYERHAEUSER CO) ★
33663 Weyerhaeuser Way S, Federal Way, WA 98001-9620
Tel (253) 924-2345 *Founded/Ownrshp* 1965
Sales 244.9MM[E] *EMP* 6,000
SIC 5031 Lumber: rough, dressed & finished
Prin: William C Stivers
CFO: Dick Taggert

D-U-N-S 82-878-9524 IMP/EXP
■ WEYERHAEUSER NR CO
(*Suby of* WEYERHAEUSER CO) ★
220 Occidental Ave S, Seattle, WA 98104-3120
Tel (253) 924-2345 *Founded/Ownrshp* 2008
Sales 84.2MM[E] *EMP* 233[E]
SIC 0811 Timber tracts
CEO: Doyle R Simons
**Pr:* Dan Fulton
**VP:* Patricia M Bedient
Dir IT: J Q Wang

D-U-N-S 87-652-1436
WEYMOUTH PUBLIC SCHOOLS
111 Middle St, East Weymouth, MA 02189-1332
Tel (781) 337-7500 *Founded/Ownrshp* 1862
Sales 42.7MM[E] *EMP* 1,200
SIC 8211 Public elementary & secondary schools
Teacher Pr: Janet Dolan
HC Dir: Jean Afzali

D-U-N-S 05-432-7353
■ WFC HOLDINGS CORP
(*Suby of* WELLS FARGO & CO) ★
420 Montgomery St, San Francisco, CA 94104-1207
Tel (415) 396-7392 *Founded/Ownrshp* 1998
Sales NA *EMP* 19,300
SIC 6021 National commercial banks
Ch Bd: Richard M Kovacevich
VP: Erich Sontag
IT Man: Sandra Duszak
IT Man: Jonathan Morrow

WFEC
See WESTERN FARMERS ELECTRIC COOPERATIVE

D-U-N-S 04-196-6706
WFG NATIONAL TITLE INSURANCE CO
ALLIANCE TITLE
700 N Brand Blvd Ste 1100, Glendale, CA 91203-1208
Tel (818) 476-4000 *Founded/Ownrshp* 1980
Sales NA *EMP* 300
SIC 6361 Title insurance
CEO: Jeffrey Fox
**Pr:* Roberto Olivera
**Pr:* Chris White
**CFO:* James Lokay
**Ex VP:* Art Cheyne
**Ex VP:* Rhio H Weir
VP: Ronald Bearskin
VP: Steve Eagleton
VP: Raymond Gioiosa
Sls Mgr: Phil McCrea

D-U-N-S 96-234-3674
WFG NATIONAL TITLE INSURANCE CO INC
(*Suby of* WILLISTON FINANCIAL GROUP LLC) ★
12909 Sw 68th Pkwy # 350, Portland, OR 97223-8384
Tel (503) 387-3636 *Founded/Ownrshp* 1974
Sales NA *EMP* 550[E]
SIC 6361 Title insurance
CEO: Patrick F Stone
Ofcr: Norma Barker
Ofcr: Taryn Blanton
Ofcr: Nikki Brooke
Ofcr: Leah Burton
Ofcr: Sylvia Diaz
Ofcr: Cherie Gorsuch
Ofcr: Mary Hughes
Ofcr: Dan Kepper
Ofcr: Amanda Rockey
Ofcr: Linda Swayzee
Ex VP: Don O'Neill
Sr VP: Bob Horvat
VP: Geoffrey Blum
VP: Susan McKnight
VP: Todd Wheelen

D-U-N-S 96-809-0295 IMP
WFSR HOLDINGS LLC
(*Suby of* SRC LIQUIDATION LLC) ★
220 E Monument Ave, Dayton, OH 45402-1287
Tel (877) 735-4966 *Founded/Ownrshp* 2013
Sales 156.1MM^{E} *EMP* 2,000
SIC 2752 2754 2759 2761 2789 2791 Commercial printing, lithographic; Commercial printing, gravure; Commercial printing; Manifold business forms; Bookbinding & related work; Typesetting
Pr: Tim Tatman
CFO: Tom Koenig

D-U-N-S 00-699-9817
■ **WFTS**
ABC ACTION NEWS
(*Suby of* JOURNAL MEDIA GROUP INC) ★
4045 N Himes Ave, Tampa, FL 33607-6651
Tel (813) 354-2800 *Founded/Ownrshp* 2015
Sales 147.0MM^{E} *EMP* 1,000^{E}
SIC 4833 Television broadcasting stations
Pr: Richard Boehne
**Pr:* Brian Lawlor

WG
See JOHN WOOD GROUP US HOLDINGS INC

WG GLOBAL, INC.
See WG GLOBAL LLC

D-U-N-S 13-666-1829 IMP/EXP
WG GLOBAL LLC
WG GLOBAL, INC.
(*Suby of* NORICAN HOLDINGS APS)
603 Park Point Dr Ste 200, Golden, CO 80401-5787
Tel (303) 395-2100 *Founded/Ownrshp* 2006
Sales 136.5MM^{E} *EMP* 2,000^{E}
SIC 3569 3559 3629 3625 3443 3412 Blast cleaning equipment, dustless; Metal finishing equipment for plating, etc.; Blasting machines, electrical; Relays & industrial controls; Fabricated plate work (boiler shop); Metal barrels, drums & pails
Pr: Robert Joyce
CFO: Mark Iwan

D-U-N-S 04-341-2295 IMP
WGBH EDUCATIONAL FOUNDATION
CHANNEL 2
1 Guest St, Boston, MA 02135-2104
Tel (617) 300-2000 *Founded/Ownrshp* 1951
Sales 195.4MM *EMP* 1,100
Accts Grant Thornton Llp Boston Ma
SIC 7812 4833 4832 Television film production; Television broadcasting stations; Radio broadcasting stations
Pr: Jonathan C Abbott
V Ch: Ren E M Landers
**Pr:* Henry P Becton Jr
**COO:* Benjamin Godley
**Treas:* Andrew S Griffiths
**VP:* David Bernstein
VP: Bob Kempf
Dir Bus: Marty Blank
Dir IT: Brad Botkin
Pr Mgr: Ellen London
Genl Couns: Jay Fialkov

WGCUTV
See FLORIDA GULF COAST UNIVERSITY

WGES
See WGL ENERGY SERVICES INC

D-U-N-S 80-640-2322
WGH HOLDING CORP
(*Suby of* NORICAN GROUP APS)
350 Indiana St Ste 610, Golden, CO 80401-5098
Tel (706) 884-6884 *Founded/Ownrshp* 2006
Sales 99.6MM^{E} *EMP* 2,000
SIC 3533 Oil field machinery & equipment
CEO: Robert Joyce

D-U-N-S 96-203-4856
■ **WGL ENERGY SERVICES INC**
WGES
(*Suby of* WASHINGTON GAS RESOURCES CORP.)
8614 Westwood Center Dr # 1200, Vienna, VA 22182-2260
Tel (703) 333-3900 *Founded/Ownrshp* 1996
Sales 1.1MMM^{E} *EMP* 100
Accts Deloitte & Touche Llp Mclean
SIC 4931 1711 Electric & other services combined; Solar energy contractor
Pr: Harry A Warren Jr
VP: Phillip Woodyard
Genl Mgr: Jonathan Colpitts
Genl Mgr: Dima Yassin
Off Admin: Markeyta Dwyer
IT Man: Thomas Loy
IT Man: Michael Manos
Sales Exec: Steven Clausman
Sls Dir: Jake S Lee
Mktg Mgr: Peter Dill

D-U-N-S 15-377-6278
▲ **WGL HOLDINGS INC**
101 Constitution Ave Nw 200w, Washington, DC 20001-2158
Tel (703) 750-2000 *Founded/Ownrshp* 1848
Sales 2.3MMM *EMP* 1,529^{E}
Tkr Sym WGL *Exch* NYS
SIC 4924 4923 4922 Natural gas distribution; Gas transmission & distribution; Storage, natural gas
Ch Bd: Terry D McCallister
Pr: Adrian P Chapman
CFO: Vincent L Ammann Jr
Treas: Anthony M Nee
Ofcr: Luanne S Gutermuth
Ofcr: Louis J Hutchinson III
Sr VP: Roberta W Sims
Sr VP: Leslie T Thornton
VP: Gautam Chandra
VP: William R Ford
VP: Marcellous P Frye Jr
VP: Mark A Lowe
VP: Richard H Moore
VP: Tracy L Townsend
Board of Directors: Michael D Barnes, Stephen C Beasley, George P Clancy Jr, James W Dyke Jr, Nancy C Floyd, Linda R Gooden, James F Lafond, Debra L Lee, Dale S Rosenthal

D-U-N-S 00-693-3121
■ **WGN CONTINENTAL BROADCASTING CO**
WGN-CHANNEL 9
(*Suby of* TRIBUNE CABLE) ★
2501 W Bradley Pl, Chicago, IL 60618-4701
Tel (773) 528-2311 *Founded/Ownrshp* 1932
Sales 124.4MM^{E} *EMP* 350
SIC 4832 4833 Radio broadcasting stations; Television broadcasting stations
CEO: Peter Liguori
**Pr:* Dennis J Fitzsimons
**Pr:* Paul Rennie
**Ex VP:* Julio Marenghi
Exec: Rich King
CIO: Marty Wilke
MIS Dir: Bill Henry
Sls Mgr: Jeff Shaw

WGN-CHANNEL 9
See WGN CONTINENTAL BROADCASTING CO

D-U-N-S 82-701-8214
WGS GLOBAL SERVICES LC
6350 Taylor Dr, Flint, MI 48507-4680
Tel (810) 239-4947 *Founded/Ownrshp* 2008
Sales 125.7MM^{E} *EMP* 700^{E}
SIC 3711 Automobile assembly, including specialty automobiles

D-U-N-S 07-939-8534
WH ACQUISITIONS INC
800 Concar Dr Ste 100, San Mateo, CA 94402-7045
Tel (650) 358-5000 *Founded/Ownrshp* 2012
Sales 312.0MM^{E} *EMP* 1,000^{E}
SIC 5084 6719 Industrial machinery & equipment; Investment holding companies, except banks
CEO: Jeff Drazan
**Prin:* Ingrid Swanson
**Prin:* Kevin Yamashita
IT Man: Sanjeev Subbarao

D-U-N-S 08-015-8993
WH FERER CO LLC
2910 N 9th St, Carter Lake, IA 51510-1502
Tel (712) 847-0800 *Founded/Ownrshp* 2016
Sales 95.0MM *EMP* 4
SIC 2816 Metallic & mineral pigments

D-U-N-S 00-537-1257 IMP
WHALLEY COMPUTER ASSOCIATES INC (MA)
WCA
1 Whalley Way, Southwick, MA 01077-9222
Tel (413) 569-4200 *Founded/Ownrshp* 1981, 1986
Sales 99.9MM^{E} *EMP* 104
Accts Aaron Smith Pc East Longme
SIC 5045 7378 Computers, peripherals & software; Computer maintenance & repair
Pr: John Whalley
**VP:* Tom Hanson
**VP:* Paul Whalley
Snr Ntwrk: Richard Gaudreau
Board of Directors: Doug Moglin

D-U-N-S 07-885-4235
WHARTON COUNTY FOODS LLC
4429 Fm 442 Rd, Boling, TX 77420-4061
Tel (979) 657-2891 *Founded/Ownrshp* 2012
Sales 100.0MM *EMP* 300
SIC 5411 Grocery stores; Supermarkets
Genl Mgr: Bruce Montgomery

D-U-N-S 11-515-2639 IMP/EXP
WHARTON-SMITH INC
750 Monroe Rd, Sanford, FL 32771-8877
Tel (407) 321-8410 *Founded/Ownrshp* 1984
Sales 331.6MM^{E} *EMP* 450^{E}
SIC 1542 Nonresidential construction
Ch Bd: George E Smith
**Pr:* Ronald F Davoli
COO: Elyzabeth Morgan
Chf Mktg O: Layla S Krenz
**VP:* Clyde Burgess
VP: Nate Cecil
**VP:* Darin Crafton
**VP:* David Hayes
**VP:* Pat Hewitt
**VP:* John Lyons
VP: Eric Palmer
**VP:* Timothy S Smith
Exec: Gilbert Orcasitas
Exec: Sean White
Dir Bus: Bob McClelland
Dir Bus: David Winters

D-U-N-S 02-618-2394
WHATABURGER RESTAURANTS LLC
300 Concord Plaza Dr, San Antonio, TX 78216-6903
Tel (210) 476-6000 *Founded/Ownrshp* 1950
Sales 713.8MM^{E} *EMP* 20,000
SIC 5812 6794 Fast-food restaurant, chain; Ethnic food restaurants; Franchises, selling or licensing
CEO: Thomas E Dobson
**Pr:* Preston Atkinson
CFO: Julie Gray
Ex VP: Mike McLellan
VP: Peter Opel
Exec: Peggy McCraw
Exec: Angel Merry
Exec: Jessica Zepeda
Prgrm Mgr: Keith McCulloch
Area Mgr: Michael Devito
Genl Mgr: Jeffery Jenings

D-U-N-S 04-296-3223
WHATLEY OIL AND AUTO PARTS CO (GA)
WHATLEY OIL COMPANY
598 Blakely St, Cuthbert, GA 39840-5323
Tel (229) 732-2611 *Founded/Ownrshp* 1955
Sales 163.2MM *EMP* 31
Accts Fountain Arrington Bass Mer
SIC 5171 5013 7389 Petroleum bulk stations; Automotive supplies & parts;
Pr: Steven S Whatley
**Sec:* Sara S Whatley
**VP:* Gregory Whatley

WHATLEY OIL COMPANY
See WHATLEY OIL AND AUTO PARTS CO

WHATSUP GOLD
See IPSWITCH INC

D-U-N-S 00-694-5802 EXP
WHAYNE SUPPLY CO (KY)
(*Suby of* BOYD CO LLC) ★
10001 Linn Station Rd # 112, Louisville, KY 40223-3828
Tel (502) 774-4441 *Founded/Ownrshp* 1913, 2008
Sales 525.0MM^{E} *EMP* 1,300
SIC 5082 4911 General construction machinery & equipment; Excavating machinery & equipment; Generation, electric power
Pr: Monty L Boyd
**Ex VP:* Terry McCarary
**VP:* Joseph Yoerg
Opers Mgr: Tim Embry

D-U-N-S 05-069-6871
WHDH-TV INC
CHANNEL 7
(*Suby of* WSVN MIAMI) ★
7 Bulfinch Pl, Boston, MA 02114-2913
Tel (617) 725-0777 *Founded/Ownrshp* 1995
Sales 117.0MM^{E} *EMP* 448
SIC 4833 Television broadcasting stations
Pr: Edmund N Ansin
**Treas:* Roger Metcalf
**Ex VP:* Robert Leider
Assoc Dir: Alicia Carlson
Ex Dir: John Zannis
MIS Mgr: Edwin Wilk
Trfc Mgr: Patricia Markham

WHEAT MONTANA BAKERY
See WHEAT MONTANA FARMS INC

D-U-N-S 03-280-0484 IMP
WHEAT MONTANA FARMS INC
WHEAT MONTANA BAKERY
10778 Us Highway 287, Three Forks, MT 59752-9518
Tel (406) 285-3614 *Founded/Ownrshp* 1977
Sales 96.8MM^{E} *EMP* 175
SIC 5149 0111 Bakery products; Wheat
Pr: Dean Folkvord
**VP:* Jim Slidmore
Genl Mgr: Hope Folkvord
IT Man: Sandra Seefried
Prd Mgr: Jason Kovnesky
Natl Sales: Dan Scott
Sls&Mrk Ex: Rita Kockl

D-U-N-S 00-478-5663
WHEATLAND ELECTRIC COOPERATIVE INC (KS)
101 N Main St, Scott City, KS 67871-1029
Tel (620) 872-5885 *Founded/Ownrshp* 1948
Sales 124.9MM *EMP* 130
SIC 4911 4812

D-U-N-S 10-539-1130
WHEATLAND ENTERPRISES INC
OVERLAND LIMOUSINE SERVICE
2017 W 104th St, Leawood, KS 66206-2646
Tel (913) 381-3504 *Founded/Ownrshp* 1979
Sales 444.0MM *EMP* 55^{E}
SIC 4119 Limousine rental, with driver
Pr: Diane Forgy

D-U-N-S 87-743-8205 IMP/EXP
WHEATLAND TUBE CO
700 S Dock St, Sharon, PA 16146-1836
Tel (724) 342-6851 *Founded/Ownrshp* 1877
Sales NA *EMP* 1,125
SIC 5051

D-U-N-S 00-791-3981 IMP/EXP
WHEATLAND TUBE LLC (PA)
JMC STEEL GROUP
(*Suby of* ENERGEX TUBE) ★
227 W Monroe St Ste 2600, Chicago, IL 60606-5082
Tel (312) 275-1600 *Founded/Ownrshp* 1877, 2006
Sales 172.8MM^{E} *EMP* 1,300
SIC 3317 3644

D-U-N-S 07-928-7154
WHEATLAND WIND PROJECT LLC
15445 Innovation Dr, San Diego, CA 92128-3432
Tel (888) 903-6926 *Founded/Ownrshp* 2013
Sales 229.6MM^{E} *EMP* 826
SIC 4911 Electric services
Pr: Tristan Grimbert
Sec: Robert Miller
VP: Ryan Pfaff

WHEATON FRANCISCAN
See FRIENDS OF ELMBROOK MEMORIAL HOSPITAL INC

D-U-N-S 96-935-7859
WHEATON FRANCISCAN
3070 N 51st St Ste 601, Milwaukee, WI 53210-1663
Tel (414) 447-2000 *Founded/Ownrshp* 2011
Sales 428.7MM *EMP* 6
SIC 8062 General medical & surgical hospitals
Prin: James Gresham
Snr Mgr: Susan Rusch

WHEATON FRANCISCAN HEALTHCARE
See COVENANT MEDICAL CENTER INC

WHEATON FRANCISCAN HEALTHCARE
See COVENANT HEALTH CARE SYSTEM INC

D-U-N-S 07-383-1075
WHEATON FRANCISCAN HEALTHCARE - ALL SAINTS FOUNDATION INC
(*Suby of* W F S I) ★
400 W River Woods Pkwy, Glendale, WI 53212-1060
Tel (414) 465-3000 *Founded/Ownrshp* 1986
Sales 112.6MM^{E} *EMP* 1,120
SIC 8062 Hospital, AMA approved residency
Pr: Kenneth Buser
Pr: Terri Rocole
VP: Ron Boecker
VP: Rita Hanson
Chf Nrs Of: Mary Ouimet
Off Mgr: Terry Maynard
Doctor: Betsy Berning
HC Dir: Karen Zeka

D-U-N-S 96-621-7585
WHEATON FRANCISCAN HEALTHCARE- ST FRANCIS INC
3237 S 16th St Ste 1005, Milwaukee, WI 53215-4526
Tel (414) 647-5000 *Founded/Ownrshp* 2005
Sales 197.3MM *EMP* 4,000
SIC 8399 Community development groups; Health systems agency
Pr: Dan Mattes
Dir Rx: Eunice B Walker
**Prin:* Vintee Sawhney
Adm Dir: Marc Trznadel
**Ex Dir:* Marc Cohen
Plnt Mgr: Randy Siehr

D-U-N-S 05-606-4314
WHEATON FRANCISCAN HEALTHCARE-FRANKLIN
(*Suby of* WHEATON FRANCISCAN HEALTHCARE) ★
3070 N 51st St Ste 210, Milwaukee, WI 53210-1661
Tel (414) 874-1171 *Founded/Ownrshp* 1883
Sales 468.4MM *EMP* 154^{E}
SIC 8062 General medical & surgical hospitals
Pr: Ron Groepper
Chf Rad: Paul Grebe
Doctor: Steven M Gryniewicz
Doctor: Kari Kluessendorf

D-U-N-S 17-569-9503
WHEATON FRANCISCAN SERVICES INC
W F S I
26w 171 Roosevelt Rd, Wheaton, IL 60189
Tel (414) 465-3000 *Founded/Ownrshp* 1983
Sales 1.8MMM *EMP* 18,000
Accts Kpmg Llp Chicago Il
SIC 8741 5999 Management services; Alarm signal systems
Ch: Joseph Lewis
**Pr:* John D Oliverio
**Treas:* Robert Walker
Sr VP: Robert Strickland
Sr VP: Jon Wachs
VP: Joanne Biesterfeld
VP: Jeffrey Halverson
VP: Michael Lepore
VP: Jim Simaris
Dir IT: Andrew Hillig
IT Man: Matthew Welter

D-U-N-S 00-578-5845 IMP
WHEATON VAN LINES INC
WHEATON WORLD WIDE MOVING
8010 Castleton Rd, Indianapolis, IN 46250-2005
Tel (317) 849-7900 *Founded/Ownrshp* 1945
Sales 90.5MM *EMP* 725
SIC 4213 4731 4214 Household goods transport; Freight forwarding; Local trucking with storage
CEO: Mark Kirschner
**Ch Bd:* Stephen F Burns
**Pr:* Dave Witzerman
VP: Fred McBroom
VP: Jim Reichert
VP: Gary Reynolds
VP: A J Schneider
VP: Rex Swing
VP: John Weissert
Exec: Gerald Holmes
CIO: Jerrod Carter
Board of Directors: Phillip Terry

WHEATON WORLD WIDE MOVING
See WHEATON VAN LINES INC

WHEELABRATOR BRIDGEPORT
See WHEELABRATOR CONNECTICUT INC

D-U-N-S 80-821-7454
WHEELABRATOR CONNECTICUT INC
WHEELABRATOR BRIDGEPORT
(*Suby of* WHEELABRATOR TECHNOLOGIES INC) ★
6 Howard Ave, Bridgeport, CT 06605-1822
Tel (203) 579-2607 *Founded/Ownrshp* 1985
Sales 141.6MM^{E} *EMP* 250
SIC 4953 Refuse systems
**Treas:* Devina A Rankin
**VP:* Mark A Lockett
VP: Cherie Rice

D-U-N-S 62-334-3019 IMP
■ **WHEELABRATOR ENVIRONMENTAL SYSTEMS INC**
(*Suby of* WASTE MANAGEMENT OF TEXAS INC) ★
4 Liberty Ln W, Hampton, NH 03842-1704
Tel (603) 929-3000 *Founded/Ownrshp* 1998
Sales 302.5MM^{E} *EMP* 1,000
SIC 4953 4911 Refuse systems; Generation, electric power
Pr: Mark A Weidman
**VP:* Arthur W Cole
**VP:* Michael F O'Friel
**VP:* Linda J Smith
Snr Mgr: Maureen Harrington

D-U-N-S 96-166-8774 IMP
WHEELABRATOR PORTSMOUTH INC
REFUSE DERIVED FUEL PLANT
(*Suby of* WHEELABRATOR TECHNOLOGIES INC) ★
3809 Elm Ave, Portsmouth, VA 23704-7101
Tel (757) 393-3100 *Founded/Ownrshp* 2010
Sales 113.3MM^{E} *EMP* 200
SIC 4953 4911 Refuse systems; Generation, electric power
VP: Linda J Smith
**Treas:* Cherie C Rice
**VP:* Michael F O'Friel

D-U-N-S 15-086-4767 IMP
WHEELABRATOR TECHNOLOGIES INC
(*Suby of* ENERGY CAPITAL PARTNERS III LLC) ★
100 Arboretum Dr Ste 310, Portsmouth, NH 03801
Tel (603) 929-3156 *Founded/Ownrshp* 2014
Sales 141.6MM *EMP* 250
SIC 4953 Refuse systems
Pr: Robert C Boucher Jr

CFO: Alan Dunlea
VP: Gary Aguinaga
VP: Arthur Cole
VP Opers: William Roberts
S&M/VP: Chris Carey
Sls Mgr: Ken Verhelle
Genl Couns: Michael O'Friel

D-U-N-S 01-004-3957
WHEELCHAIR FOUNDATION
3820 Blackhawk Rd, Danville, CA 94506-4617
Tel (925) 736-8234 *Founded/Ownrshp* 2008
Sales 88.4MM *EMP* 12
SIC 8733 Noncommercial research organizations
Ch: Kenneth Behring
Ex Dir: Steve Largent
Mktg Mgr: Tiffany Camacho

WHEELCHAIR GETAWAYS
See HARRISON WORLDWIDE ENTERPRISES INC

WHEELED COACH INDUSTRIES
See REV AMBULANCE GROUP ORLANDO INC

D-U-N-S 01-458-6911 IMP
■ WHEELER BROS INC
(*Suby of* VSE CORP) ★
384 Drum Ave, Somerset, PA 15501-3400
Tel (814) 443-2444 *Founded/Ownrshp* 2011
Sales 121.5MM^E *EMP* 185
SIC 5013 Motor vehicle supplies & new parts; Automotive supplies & parts; Automotive supplies; Automotive brakes
CEO: David L Wheeler
**Pr:* Randy Davies
**Treas:* Barbara Wheeler Davies
Ex VP: Tina Devers
Ex VP: Charles Thompson
**Ex VP:* Pete Wheeler
Sr VP: Bryan Adams
VP: George Brynd
VP: Christopher Heiple
VP: Christopher N Mowry
Prgrm Mgr: Barry Bruening

D-U-N-S 00-286-9261
WHEELER BROTHERS GRAIN CO LLC
501 Russworm Dr, Watonga, OK 73772
Tel (580) 623-7223 *Founded/Ownrshp* 1948
Sales 136.9MM *EMP* 135
SIC 5153 Grain elevators
Ch: Cinda Wheeler Lafferty
**Pr:* Mike Mahoney
**Ex VP:* Richard Cowan
**VP:* Austin Lafferty
IT Man: Chuck Marquis
Board of Directors: Owen Lafferty

D-U-N-S 00-793-9358 IMP/EXP
WHEELER MACHINERY CO
CATERPILLAR
4901 W 2100 S, Salt Lake City, UT 84120-1200
Tel (801) 974-0511 *Founded/Ownrshp* 1950
Sales 212.7MM^E *EMP* 600
SIC 5082 5084 7359 7353

WHEELER'S
See MANIS LUMBER CO

WHEELING & LAKE ERIE RAILWAY
See WHEELING CORP

D-U-N-S 61-166-7171
WHEELING & LAKE ERIE RAILWAY CO
(*Suby of* WHEELING & LAKE ERIE RAILWAY) ★
100 1st St Se, Brewster, OH 44613-1202
Tel (330) 767-3401 *Founded/Ownrshp* 1990
Sales 100.6MM *EMP* 332
SIC 4011 Railroads, line-haul operating
CEO: Larry R Parsons
**Pr:* William Callison
CFO: Michael D Mokodean
**CFO:* Donna L Phillips
**Ex VP:* Jonathan Chastek
**VP:* James I Northcraft
**VP:* Mike Mokodean
**VP:* Drew A Nelson
VP Mktg: Gregory J Levy

D-U-N-S 62-758-0749
WHEELING CORP
WHEELING & LAKE ERIE RAILWAY
100 1st St Se, Brewster, OH 44613-1202
Tel (330) 767-3401 *Founded/Ownrshp* 1994
Sales 103.5MM^E *EMP* 332
Accts Mayor Hoffman Mccann Pc Akr
SIC 1629 4011 Railroad & railway roadbed construction; Railroads, line-haul operating
Ch Bd: Larry R Parsons
**Pr:* William Callison III
**CFO:* Michael Mokodean

D-U-N-S 06-874-2725
WHEELING HOSPITAL INC (WV)
1 Medical Park, Wheeling, WV 26003-6300
Tel (304) 243-3000 *Founded/Ownrshp* 1850
Sales 339.5MM *EMP* 1,228^E
Accts Deloitte & Touche Llp Pittsbu
SIC 8062 8011 General medical & surgical hospitals; Offices & clinics of medical doctors
CEO: Ronald Viola
Pr: John Pasporius
**Pr:* Kevin M Quirk
**CFO:* James Murdy
CFO: Jim Murdy
Ofcr: Theresa Reese
**VP:* John Pastorius
Chf Nrs Of: Patricia Torbett
Dir Pat Ac: Maryann Kozusnik
Nurse Mgr: Vickie Litman
CIO: Carlene Davies

D-U-N-S 13-019-9172
WHEELING ISLAND GAMING INC
WHEELING ISLAND RACETRACK
(*Suby of* DELAWARE NORTH COMPANIES GAMING & ENTERTAINMENT INC) ★
1 S Stone St, Wheeling, WV 26003-2062
Tel (304) 232-5050 *Founded/Ownrshp* 1900
Sales 31.7MM^E *EMP* 1,000
SIC 7948 7011 5813 Dog race track operation; Horse race track operation; Hotels & motels; Drinking places
Pr: OSI Imomoh
**Pr:* Robert D Marshall Jr
VP: Michael Corbin
**VP:* Mike Maestle
**VP:* Deborah Murray
VP: Ronald Sultemeier
Exec: Jeff Pleta
VP Mktg: Clyde Callicott

WHEELING ISLAND RACETRACK
See WHEELING ISLAND GAMING INC

WHEELING SCHOOL DISTRICT 21
See COMMUNITY CONSOLIDATED SCHOOL DISTRICT 21

D-U-N-S 15-375-6234 IMP
WHEELING-NISSHIN INC
(*Suby of* NISSHIN HOLDING INC) ★
400 Penn St, Follansbee, WV 26037-1412
Tel (304) 527-2800 *Founded/Ownrshp* 1984
Sales 384.3MM *EMP* 175
Accts Ernst & Young Llp
SIC 3312 Coated or plated products
Pr: Noboru Onishi
CFO: Harry Nunokawa
**CFO:* Patstuzo Shiotsuka
**Sec:* Tatsuzo Shiotsuka
**Ex VP:* Pakuya Sashida
Exec: Brian Petrella
Genl Mgr: Walter Kaneko
Genl Mgr: Jeffrey Mc Laughlin
Genl Mgr: Richard Nester
Genl Mgr: Pat J Pendleton
VP Opers: Yogi Hayashi
Board of Directors: Craig Bouchard, James P Bouchard, Fumio Oda

WHEELING-PITTSBURGH
See RG STEEL WHEELING STEEL GROUP LLC

D-U-N-S 00-693-3402 EXP
WHEELS INC (IL)
(*Suby of* FRANK CONSOLIDATED ENTERPRISES INC) ★
666 Garland Pl, Des Plaines, IL 60016-4788
Tel (847) 699-7000 *Founded/Ownrshp* 1939, 1979
Sales 121.5MM^E *EMP* 600
SIC 7515 7513 Passenger car leasing; Truck leasing, without drivers
Pr: James S Frank
COO: Sandra Wilson
**CFO:* Mary Ann O'Dwyer
Top Exec: Heidi Ford
Sr VP: Salvatore Peri
Mng Dir: Clifford Hurd
QA Dir: Poorni Krishnamurthy
QA Dir: Madhuri Yeluri
IT Man: Tim Toporovski
Web Dev: Scott Fogel
Web Dev: Matthew McKinney
Board of Directors: Greg Besio, Scott Pattullo

D-U-N-S 07-696-6191
WHELAN SECURITY CO
1699 S Hanley Rd Ste 350, Saint Louis, MO 63144-2900
Tel (314) 644-3227 *Founded/Ownrshp* 1959
Sales 186.2MM^E *EMP* 5,000
SIC 7382 Security systems services
Ch: Patrick A Twardowski
**Pr:* Greg Twardowski
Div VP: James Schwartz
**Ex VP:* Prentice Robertson
VP: Dan Parisi
VP: Stephen Somers
**VP:* Dan Twardowski
Genl Mgr: Austin Bharadwaja
Board of Directors: Jane F Twardowski

D-U-N-S 02-813-3655
WHELANS INTERNATIONAL CO INC
WHELENS CONTRACT CLEANING
163 Keyland Ct, Bohemia, NY 11716-2621
Tel (631) 244-6962 *Founded/Ownrshp* 1972
Sales 27.5MM^E *EMP* 2,120
SIC 7349 Floor waxing
CEO: Larry Whelan
**Pr:* Mary Whelan Levine

D-U-N-S 00-116-3906 IMP
WHELEN ENGINEERING CO INC (CT)
51 Winthrop Rd, Chester, CT 06412-1036
Tel (860) 526-9504 *Founded/Ownrshp* 1952, 1959
Sales 202.7MM^E *EMP* 666
SIC 3647 3646 3671 3651 3648 3641 Automotive lighting fixtures; Aircraft lighting fixtures; Commercial indusl & institutional electric lighting fixtures; Electron tubes; Household audio & video equipment; Lighting equipment; Electric lamps
Pr: John Olson
CFO: Bob Mitchel
**Treas:* Robert M Mitchell
**Ex VP:* George Whelen IV
VP: Rich Forristall
VP: Mary R Guerrera
VP: Richard Morrow
Software D: Luther Records
Sfty Mgr: Carolyn Greenwood
Sfty Mgr: Steven Kabatznick
Prd Mgr: Ned Scholfield

WHELENS CONTRACT CLEANING
See WHELANS INTERNATIONAL CO INC

D-U-N-S 14-236-6165 EXP
WHEMCO INC
(*Suby of* PARK CORP) ★
5 Hot Metal St Ste 300, Pittsburgh, PA 15203-2351
Tel (412) 390-2700 *Founded/Ownrshp* 2003
Sales 211.4MM^E *EMP* 362
SIC 3312 3462 3731 3325 3441 3369 Blast furnaces & steel mills; Iron & steel forgings; Shipbuilding & repairing; Alloy steel castings, except investment; Fabricated structural metal; Nonferrous foundries
Pr: Charles Novelli
COO: Kevin Marsden
**VP:* Carl Maskiewicz
**VP:* Robert J Peterson
VP: Mark Wolford
DP Dir: Chirs Silinglof
IT Man: Dan Flaherty
Sfty Mgr: Chris Coholick
Opers Mgr: Jennifer Baughman
Plnt Mgr: Ken Hall
Plnt Mgr: Howard Zeigler

D-U-N-S 61-485-8434
WHI CAPITAL PARTNERS
(*Suby of* WILLIAM HARRIS INVESTORS) ★
191 N Wacker Dr Ste 1500, Chicago, IL 60606-1899
Tel (312) 621-0590 *Founded/Ownrshp* 2005
Sales 126.8MM^E *EMP* 275
SIC 6799 3317 Investment clubs; Steel pipe & tubes
Pt: Adam Schecter
Pt: Eric Cohen
Ex VP: Michael Resnick
VP: Michael Schopin

WHIDBEY GENERAL HOSPITAL
See WHIDBEY ISLAND PUBLIC HOSPITAL DISTRICT

D-U-N-S 07-185-2503 IMP
WHIDBEY ISLAND PUBLIC HOSPITAL DISTRICT
WHIDBEY GENERAL HOSPITAL
101 N Main St, Coupeville, WA 98239-3413
Tel (360) 678-5151 *Founded/Ownrshp* 1970
Sales 93.7MM *EMP* 700
SIC 8062 General medical & surgical hospitals
Pr: Anne Tarrant
**CEO:* Tom Tomascino
**COO:* Hank Hanigan
COO: Tom Tomasino
**CFO:* Terry Litke
**CFO:* Joe Vessey
Exec: John Sherman
Dir Rx: Terry Clark
**Prin:* Doug Bishop
Sls&Mrk Ex: Trish Rose
Surgeon: Mario Porras

D-U-N-S 96-961-2162
WHIDDEN MEMORIAL HOSPITAL INC
350 Main St Ste 16, Malden, MA 02148-5023
Tel (781) 306-8872 *Founded/Ownrshp* 2001
Sales 86.6MM *EMP* 800
Accts Pricewaterhousecoopers Llp Bo
SIC 8062 General medical & surgical hospitals
CEO: Patrick Wardell
**CFO:* Gordon Boeudrow Jr
**Dir Surg:* Avril Kane

D-U-N-S 07-888-0610
■ WHIPPANY ACTUATION SYSTEMS LLC
(*Suby of* TRANSDIGM GROUP INC) ★
110 Algonquin Pkwy, Whippany, NJ 07981-1602
Tel (973) 428-9898 *Founded/Ownrshp* 2013
Sales 91.0MM^E *EMP* 236
SIC 3625 3728 Actuators, industrial; Aircraft parts & equipment
Genl Mgr: William Flatley
Genl Mgr: Thomas Pijaca
Opers Mgr: Marc Mastrangelo
Opers Mgr: Fred Stokes

D-U-N-S 01-507-3802 IMP/EXP
WHIRLEY INDUSTRIES INC (PA)
WHIRLEY-DRINKWORKS
618 4th Ave, Warren, PA 16365-4923
Tel (814) 723-7600 *Founded/Ownrshp* 1966
Sales 93.3MM^E *EMP* 280
SIC 3089 Plastic containers, except foam; Cups, plastic, except foam
Pr: Lincoln Sokolski
**VP:* Gregory M Gross
VP: Robert Sokolski
VP: Jennifer Williams
Exec: Sue Borland
Dir IT: Dan Klenck
IT Man: Lana Creal
Sfty Mgr: John Geiger
Opers Mgr: Sherry Sampson
Plnt Mgr: Bruce Shreve
Sales Exec: Alec Conarro

WHIRLEY-DRINKWORKS
See WHIRLEY INDUSTRIES INC

D-U-N-S 00-128-8075
▲ WHIRLPOOL CORP
2000 N M 63, Benton Harbor, MI 49022-2692
Tel (269) 923-5000 *Founded/Ownrshp* 1898
Sales 20.8MMM *EMP* 97,000
Accts Ernst & Young Llp Chicago Il
Tkr Sym WHR *Exch* NYS
SIC 3633 3585 3632 3635 Household laundry equipment; Air conditioning units, complete: domestic or industrial; Refrigerators, mechanical & absorption: household; Freezers, home & farm; Household vacuum cleaners
Ch Bd: Jeff M Fettig
**Pr:* Marc R Bitzer
Pr: Carrick Jay
CFO: Larry M Venturelli
Treas: Blair Clark
Ex VP: Tim Swartz
Ex VP: Dave Szczupak
Ex VP: David T Szczupak
VP: Roy Armes
VP: Andrew Batson
VP: Nancy Berendsen
VP: Anil Berera
VP: David A Binkley
VP: David Binkleysenior
VP: Jean Blanc
VP: David Briskman
VP: Davide Castiglioni
VP: Ann Fandozzi
VP: Brian Hancock
VP: Robert Hardin
VP: Katrina Helmkamp
Board of Directors: Samuel R Allen, Gary T Dicamillo, Diane M Dietz, Geraldine T Elliott, Michael F Johnston, John D Liu, William D Perez, Larry Spencer, Michael D White

WHIRLWIND BUILDING COMPONENTS
See WHIRLWIND HOLDING CO INC

WHIRLWIND BUILDING SYSTEMS
See WHIRLWIND STEEL BUILDINGS INC

D-U-N-S 87-425-2240
WHIRLWIND HOLDING CO INC
WHIRLWIND BUILDING COMPONENTS
8234 Hansen Rd, Houston, TX 77075-1002
Tel (713) 946-7140 *Founded/Ownrshp* 1992
Sales 142.4MM^E *EMP* 417
Accts Gainer Donnelly & Desroches
SIC 3448 Buildings, portable: prefabricated metal; Prefabricated metal components
CEO: Jack Sturdivant
**Pr:* Ty Sturdivant
CFO: Joe Thompson
**Sec:* Julie Friedrich

D-U-N-S 00-807-2258 EXP
WHIRLWIND STEEL BUILDINGS INC
WHIRLWIND BUILDING SYSTEMS
(*Suby of* WHIRLWIND BUILDING COMPONENTS) ★
8234 Hansen Rd, Houston, TX 77075-1002
Tel (713) 946-7140 *Founded/Ownrshp* 1991
Sales 142.4MM^E *EMP* 417
SIC 3448 Buildings, portable: prefabricated metal; Prefabricated metal components
Pr: Jack Sturdivant
**CFO:* Glenn Matthys
CFO: Joe Thompson
**Treas:* Julie Friedrich
**VP:* Dave Fulton
**Prin:* Tyson Sturdivant
Genl Mgr: Scott Ramsey
Plnt Mgr: Mariano Castellano
Plnt Mgr: Shawn Hurst
Ql Cn Mgr: Jose Ortega
VP Sls: Randy Lutz

WHISKEYMILITIA.COM
See BACKCOUNTRY.COM LLC

D-U-N-S 14-436-6366
WHIT-MART INC
APPLEBEE'S
56 Wentworth St, Charleston, SC 29401-6447
Tel (843) 720-5010 *Founded/Ownrshp* 1985
Sales 40.1MM^E *EMP* 1,500
SIC 5812 Restaurant, family: chain
Pr: Gary P Whitman
**CFO:* Michael Wiser

D-U-N-S 00-349-0422 IMP/EXP
WHITAKER OIL CO (GA)
WHITAKER SOLVENTS & CHEMICALS
1557 Marietta Rd Nw, Atlanta, GA 30318-3652
Tel (404) 355-8220 *Founded/Ownrshp* 1958, 1971
Sales 103.6MM^E *EMP* 75
SIC 5169 Industrial chemicals
Pr: C Bart Whitaker III
**Ch Bd:* Colie B Whitaker Jr
**CEO:* Colie B Whitaker III
**CFO:* Victoria R Arce
**CFO:* Victoria Whitaker
**Ex VP:* Ed Steinman
**VP:* Tony Cantrell
Off Mgr: Doug Swift
Plnt Mgr: Camon Worsham
Snr Mgr: Christen Rene

WHITAKER SOLVENTS & CHEMICALS
See WHITAKER OIL CO

D-U-N-S 13-647-9917 IMP
WHITCO SUPPLY LLC
200 N Morgan Ave, Broussard, LA 70518-3904
Tel (337) 837-2440 *Founded/Ownrshp* 2003
Sales 107.1MM^E *EMP* 75
SIC 5084 Oil refining machinery, equipment & supplies
Brnch Mgr: Timmy Boudreaux
Brnch Mgr: Jeff White
Genl Mgr: Brooks Barras
Genl Mgr: Kyle Boudreaux
Store Mgr: John Kulbeth
Trfc Dir: James Bullara
Sales Exec: Jerry Broussard
Sls Mgr: Dustin Dawes
Sls Mgr: Beau Guillory
Sales Asso: Conrad Read
Snr PM: Charles Alexander

D-U-N-S 00-144-3399 IMP
WHITCRAFT LLC
76 County Rd, Eastford, CT 06242
Tel (860) 974-0786 *Founded/Ownrshp* 1960
Sales 85.2MM^E *EMP* 330^E
SIC 3443 3444 3728 Weldments; Sheet metalwork; Aircraft parts & equipment
CEO: Colin Cooper
**Pr:* Jeff Paul
Dir Bus: Leonard Jay
Genl Mgr: Steve Lindsey
CIO: Mike Albert
Dir IT: Allen Roy
IT Man: Deb Gould
Info Man: Don Chrzan
VP Opers: Steve Ruggiero
Ql Cn Mgr: Rick Manwaring
Sls Dir: Richard Martyniak

D-U-N-S 07-771-5209
WHITE & CASE LLP
1155 Avenue Of The Americ, New York, NY 10036-2787
Tel (212) 819-8200 *Founded/Ownrshp* 1997
Sales 689.8MM^E *EMP* 3,662
SIC 8111 General practice law office
Pt: Hugh Verrier
Pt: Emilio Alvarez-Farr
Pt: Emilio J Alvarez-Farre
Pt: Biner Bahr
Pt: Franck De Vita
Pt: Frank Evers
Pt: Christian W Hansen
Pt: Frank-Karl Heuchemer
Pt: Dennis Heuer
Pt: Biner B Hr

Pt: Christopher Kandel
Pt: Eric Laplante
Pt: Andrew Macklin
Pt: Charles R Nairac
Pt: Alexander Reuter
Pt: Carmen Reynolds
Pt: Ivo B Rta
Pt: Arthur Seavone
Pt: G Ran Seborn
Pt: Michael Smith
Pt: Brian G Strawn

D-U-N-S 80-143-3470
■ WHITE BARN CANDLE CO
(*Suby of* LBRANDS) ★
7 Limited Pkwy E, Reynoldsburg, OH 43068-5300
Tel (614) 856-6000 *Founded/Ownrshp* 2002
Sales 214.1MM^E *EMP* 5,000
SIC 5199 Candles
CEO: Diane Neal

WHITE BEAR LAKE AREA SCHOOLS
See INDEPENDENT SCHOOL DISTRICT 624 (INC)

WHITE BIRCH PAPER COMPANY
See BRANT INDUSTRIES INC

D-U-N-S 07-917-3577
■ WHITE CAP CONSTRUCTION SUPPLY
(*Suby of* WHITE CAP CONSTRUCTION SUPPLY INC) ★
1815 Ritchey St, Santa Ana, CA 92705-5127
Tel (949) 794-5300 *Founded/Ownrshp* 2013
Sales 17.0MM^E *EMP* 1,326^E
SIC 5082 Construction & mining machinery
Prin: Jack Karg
VP: Ian Heller
Brnch Mgr: Kevin Burns
Brnch Mgr: Brandon Cook
Dist Mgr: Michael Grecz
Dist Mgr: Shane Louthan
Natl Sales: Richard Nuttall
Sls Mgr: Terry Brown
Sales Asso: Dave Mogstad

D-U-N-S 05-927-1684 IMP
■ WHITE CAP CONSTRUCTION SUPPLY INC
(*Suby of* HD SUPPLY CONSTRUCTION SUPPLY GROUP INC) ★
3100 Cumberland Blvd Se # 1700, Atlanta, GA 30339-5940
Tel (404) 879-7740 *Founded/Ownrshp* 2007
Sales 412.2MM^E *EMP* 2,200^E
SIC 5072 5039 5031 Hardware; Bolts, nuts & screws; Hand tools; Power tools & accessories; Air ducts, sheet metal; Joists; Soil erosion control fabrics; Lumber, plywood & millwork
CEO: John Stegeman
**CFO:* Evan Levitt
Trfc Dir: Anthony West
Sales Asso: Terry Sherrill

D-U-N-S 00-790-2323 IMP
WHITE CASTLE SYSTEM INC
555 W Goodale St, Columbus, OH 43215-1104
Tel (614) 228-5781 *Founded/Ownrshp* 1921
Sales 472.4MM^E *EMP* 10,000
Accts Gbq Partners Llc Columbus Oh
SIC 5812 5142 2051 2013 Fast-food restaurant, chain; Meat, frozen: packaged; Bread, cake & related products; Sausages & other prepared meats
Ch Bd: Edgar W Ingram III
Pr: Bette Everson
**Pr:* Elizabeth Ingram
CFO: Bill Blake
**CFO:* Russell J Meyer
**Treas:* Andrew Prakel
**Ofcr:* John Kelley
VP: Michael S Amburn
**VP:* Kim Bartley
**VP:* Robert Camp
VP: Jeff Carper
VP: Sherrie Foreman
VP: Lisa Ingram
VP: Roger G Post
**VP:* Jamie Richardson
**VP:* Michael Smith
VP: Sean Turner
**VP:* Nicholas Zuk
Dir Teleco: Brian Ingram

D-U-N-S 00-692-0755
WHITE CONSTRUCTION CO INC
WHITE FARMS
2811 N Young Blvd, Chiefland, FL 32626-9189
Tel (352) 493-1444 *Founded/Ownrshp* 1945
Sales 87.9MM^E *EMP* 660
SIC 1611 0241 3531 Highway & street construction; Dairy farms; Asphalt plant, including gravel-mix type
Pr: Luther M White Sr
**Sec:* Juanita M White
**VP:* Nancy W Bennett
**VP:* Luther M White Jr
VP: Nancy White

D-U-N-S 11-888-9237
WHITE COUNTY MEDICAL CENTER
3214 E Race Ave, Searcy, AR 72143-4810
Tel (501) 268-6121 *Founded/Ownrshp* 1967
Sales 198.1MM *EMP* 1,010^E
SIC 8082 8062 Home health care services; General medical & surgical hospitals
CEO: Ray Montgomery
Pr: Scotty Parker
COO: Kevin Burton
**CFO:* Stuart Hill
VP: Ramona Staton
Exec: James H Golleher
IT Man: Jim Poor
Sfty Dirs: Frankie Feltrop
Plnt Mgr: Rick Hare
Nutrtnst: Angela Bradshaw
Nrsg Dir: Peggy Turner

D-U-N-S 07-942-0435
WHITE DEER ENERGY LP II
700 Louisiana St Ste 4770, Houston, TX 77002-2722
Tel (713) 581-6900 *Founded/Ownrshp* 2013
Sales 238.9MM^E *EMP* 280^E
SIC 6726 Investment offices

D-U-N-S 07-074-6896
WHITE EARTH BAND OF CHIPPEWA INDIANS
WHITE EARTH RESERVATION
35500 Eagleview Rd, Ogema, MN 56569-9658
Tel (800) 950-3248 *Founded/Ownrshp* 1934
Sales NA *EMP* 1,500
Accts Frank Johnsoncfo By Fax On Se
SIC 9131 Indian reservation;
Ex Dir: Ron Valiant
**CFO:* Frank Johnson
CFO: Scott Omlid
**Sec:* Franklin Heisler
Genl Mgr: Ken Fox
MIS Dir: Jerry McDonald

WHITE EARTH RESERVATION
See WHITE EARTH BAND OF CHIPPEWA INDIANS

D-U-N-S 80-359-1408
WHITE ENERGY INC
2745 Dallas Pkwy Ste 670, Plano, TX 75093-8710
Tel (972) 715-6490 *Founded/Ownrshp* 2006
Sales 105.0MM^E *EMP* 170
Accts Deloitte & Touche Llp Dallas
SIC 2869 Fuels
CEO: Kevin D Kuykendall
**Pr:* John Neufeld
**Pr:* Omer Sagheer
**CFO:* John Castle
CFO: Dean Reder
Exec: Paula Haley
Genl Mgr: Jon Septerdahl
IT Man: Jason Dimaio
Genl Couns: Geoff Amend

WHITE FARMS
See WHITE CONSTRUCTION CO INC

WHITE GLOVE AGENCY
See WHITE GLOVE PLACEMENT INC

D-U-N-S 95-924-2678
WHITE GLOVE PLACEMENT INC
WHITE GLOVE AGENCY
630 Flushing Ave Fl 2, Brooklyn, NY 11206-5026
Tel (718) 387-8181 *Founded/Ownrshp* 1995
Sales 50.7MM *EMP* 3,100
Accts Bernath & Rosenberg Pc New
SIC 7349 Building maintenance services
Pr: Meir Lefkowitz
VP: Patricia O'Malley
Genl Mgr: Rachel Silberstein

D-U-N-S 17-740-0819
WHITE LODGING SERVICES CORP
701 E 83rd Ave Ste 17, Merrillville, IN 46410-2200
Tel (219) 472-2900 *Founded/Ownrshp* 1986
Sales 710.3MM^E *EMP* 3,510
SIC 8741 6552 Hotel or motel management; Land subdividers & developers, commercial
CEO: Ken Barrett
Pr: Pete Reardon
**Pr:* Bruce W White
COO: Bryan Hayes
**CFO:* Bruce Hoffmann
Sr VP: Chris Anderson
Sr VP: Laura Brouk
Sr VP: Jason Kreul
Sr VP: Dave Montrose
VP: Mark Aftanski
VP: Scott Blalock
VP: Brian Burton
VP: Ron Caldwell
VP: Jason Druso
VP: Cody Feaster
VP: Brandon Frederick
VP: Sherif Guirguis
VP: Bob Jensch
VP: Chris O'Donnell
VP: Thomas Riegelman
VP: Carrie Rosencrans

D-U-N-S 05-386-6851
WHITE MEMORIAL MEDICAL CENTER INC
ADVENTIST HEALTH SYSTEM
(*Suby of* ADVENTIST HEALTH SYSTEM/WEST) ★
1720 E Cesar E Chavez Ave, Los Angeles, CA 90033-2414
Tel (323) 268-5000 *Founded/Ownrshp* 1913
Sales 417.6MM *EMP* 2,000
Accts Ernst & Young Llp Roseville
SIC 8062 General medical & surgical hospitals
CEO: Beth D Zachary
Pr: Mark J Newmyer
**CEO:* John G Raffoul
**CFO:* Terri Day
Treas: Rodney Wehtje
**VP:* Mara C Bryant
**VP:* Mary Anne Chern
VP: Albert Deininger
**VP:* Roland Fargo
Dir Rx: Martin J Torres
Snr Ntwrk: Frank Stevens

D-U-N-S 06-329-3153
WHITE MOUNTAIN APACHE TRIBE
201 E Walnut St, Whiteriver, AZ 85941
Tel (928) 338-4346 *Founded/Ownrshp* 1926
Sales NA *EMP* 1,100
SIC 9131 Indian reservation
Ch Bd: Ronnie Lupe
CTO: Ramon Riley
IT Man: Carleen Johnson
Pgrm Dir: Brenda Begay

D-U-N-S 13-434-6258
WHITE MOUNTAINS CAPITAL INC
(*Suby of* WHITE MOUNTAINS INSURANCE GROUP, LTD.)
265 Franklin St Ste 500, Boston, MA 02110-3170
Tel (617) 330-5310 *Founded/Ownrshp* 2000
Sales NA *EMP* 5,058
SIC 6331 Fire, marine & casualty insurance
Pr: Reid Campbell

WHITE OAK MANAGEMENT
See OAK WHITE MANOR INC

D-U-N-S 01-991-9811
■ WHITE OAK RESOURCES LLC
(*Suby of* ALLIANCE RESOURCE PARTNERS LP) ★
18033 County Road 500 E, Dahlgren, IL 62828-4294
Tel (618) 643-5500 *Founded/Ownrshp* 2015
Sales 57.6MM^E *EMP* 2,574^E
SIC 1241 Coal mining services

WHITE OAK STATION
See PETROMARK INC

D-U-N-S 80-320-1441
■ WHITE PASS & YOKON MOTOR COACHES INC
(*Suby of* HOLLAND AMERCN LINES-WESTOURS) ★
300 Elliott Ave W, Seattle, WA 98119-4198
Tel (206) 281-3535 *Founded/Ownrshp* 2008
Sales 13.4MM^E *EMP* 1,200
SIC 4141 Local bus charter service
Pr: Stein Kruse

D-U-N-S 04-566-3903 IMP
WHITE PLAINS HOSPITAL MEDICAL CENTER
41 E Post Rd, White Plains, NY 10601-4607
Tel (914) 681-0600 *Founded/Ownrshp* 1893
Sales 389.8MM *EMP* 2,000
SIC 8062 General medical & surgical hospitals
Pr: Jon B Schandler
**Ch Bd:* Paul Weissman
**Pr:* Susan Fox
**COO:* Edward F Leonard
COO: Jeffrey Tiesi
**CFO:* John Schiurba
Bd of Dir: Gabriela Guizzo
Bd of Dir: Jill Haskel
Bd of Dir: Barbara Lapp
Bd of Dir: Natalie Webb
VP: Daniel Blum
VP: Susan Krajewski
Dir Rad: Alan L Bernstein

D-U-N-S 08-189-1053
WHITE PLAINS PUBLIC SCHOOLS
5 Homeside Ln, White Plains, NY 10605-4201
Tel (914) 422-2000 *Founded/Ownrshp* 1884
Sales 65.1MM^E *EMP* 1,300
Accts The Government Services Divisi
SIC 8211 Public elementary & secondary schools; School board
**VP:* Charlie Norris
Instr Medi: John Shepeherd

WHITE RIVER COOP
See WHITE RIVER LLC

D-U-N-S 01-650-1041
WHITE RIVER COOPERATIVE INC
416 Church St, Loogootee, IN 47553-1714
Tel (812) 295-4835 *Founded/Ownrshp* 1928
Sales 161.0MM *EMP* 135
Accts C David Harpe Indianapolis
SIC 5191 5171 Feed; Seeds: field, garden & flower; Fertilizer & fertilizer materials; Petroleum bulk stations
Pr: Tom Nugent
Genl Mgr: Mike Riggins
Genl Mgr: Cindy Smith
Off Mgr: Janie Millspaugh

D-U-N-S 07-738-8999
WHITE RIVER HEALTH SYSTEM INC
WHITE RIVER MEDICAL CENTER
1710 Harrison St, Batesville, AR 72501-7303
Tel (870) 262-1200 *Founded/Ownrshp* 1967
Sales 170.0MM *EMP* 1,500
Accts Welch Couch & Company Pa Bate
SIC 8062 General medical & surgical hospitals
Pr: Charles Schaaf
Chf Rad: Charles M Clan
**Pr:* Dick Bernard
**Treas:* James Mack Street
**Treas:* Jim Wann
**VP:* Boris Dover
**VP:* Jay F Shell
Doctor: Steve Alexander
Nrsg Dir: De De Strecker

D-U-N-S 06-702-9889
WHITE RIVER LLC
WHITE RIVER COOP
610 Church St, Loogootee, IN 47553-1311
Tel (812) 295-4835 *Founded/Ownrshp* 2001
Sales 87.8MM *EMP* 87
Accts C David Harpe Cpa Indianapo
SIC 5261 5984 Nurseries & garden centers; Liquefied petroleum gas dealers

WHITE RIVER MEDICAL CENTER
See WHITE RIVER HEALTH SYSTEM INC

D-U-N-S 80-962-2983
WHITE RIVER MEDICAL CENTER
1710 Harrison St, Batesville, AR 72501-7303
Tel (870) 262-1200 *Founded/Ownrshp* 2008
Sales 165.3MM *EMP* 3^E
SIC 8011 General medical & surgical hospitals; Blood related health services
Prin: Michelle Lee Lasiter

WHITE ROSE FOOD DIVISION
See WHITE ROSE INC

WHITE ROSE FOODS
See DI GIORGIO CORP

D-U-N-S 00-914-8248 IMP/EXP
WHITE ROSE INC
WHITE ROSE FOOD DIVISION
380 Middlesex Ave, Carteret, NJ 07008-3445
Tel (732) 541-5555 *Founded/Ownrshp* 2014
Sales NA *EMP* 1,201
SIC 5141 5143 5142 5122 7311 8721

WHITE SATIN SUGAR
See AMALGAMATED SUGAR CO LLC

D-U-N-S 00-693-9706
WHITECO INDUSTRIES INC (NE)
CELEBRATION STATION
1000 E 80th Pl Ste 700n, Merrillville, IN 46410-5676
Tel (219) 769-6601 *Founded/Ownrshp* 1935
Sales 157.0MM^E *EMP* 3,500
SIC 7312 7011 7922 6552 7374 3993 Billboard advertising; Motel, franchised; Inns; Theatrical production services; Land subdividers & developers, commercial; Data processing service; Signs & advertising specialties
Pr: Dean White
Treas: John Peterman
VP: Bill Wellman
Dir IT: Doug Horton

WHITEHALL INDUSTRIES
See SRS INDUSTRIES LLC

D-U-N-S 60-163-3865
■ WHITEHALL STREET INTERNATIONAL REAL ESTATE LIMITED PARTNERSHIP 2001
(*Suby of* GOLDMAN SACHS GROUP INC) ★
85 Broad St, New York, NY 10004-2434
Tel (212) 902-1000 *Founded/Ownrshp* 2001
Sales 602.3MM^E *EMP* 8,100^E
SIC 6719 Investment holding companies, except banks
Pt: Elizabeth Burban

WHITEHOUSE ACQUISITION CO
See ELECTRICAL COMPONENTS INTERNATIONAL INC

D-U-N-S 00-901-0901 IMP
WHITEMAN FAMILY CORP
1725 S Country Club Dr, Mesa, AZ 85210-6003
Tel (480) 633-4413 *Founded/Ownrshp* 1959
Sales 44.5MM^E *EMP* 1,077
SIC 5082 5083 7353 7699 7359 5012 Construction & mining machinery; Agricultural machinery; Heavy construction equipment rental; Aircraft & heavy equipment repair services; Agricultural equipment repair services; Equipment rental & leasing; Automobiles & other motor vehicles
Ch Bd: John O Whiteman
**Pr:* Jeffrey S Whiteman
Board of Directors: Bernard Francois, Anne Christine Standifird, Elden R Strahm, Jack W Whiteman

D-U-N-S 05-590-8586 IMP/EXP
WHITESELL CORP
2703 Avalon Ave, Muscle Shoals, AL 35661-2705
Tel (256) 248-8500 *Founded/Ownrshp* 1985
Sales 158.0MM^E *EMP* 600
SIC 3965 5085 3444 3452 3451 Fasteners; Fasteners & fastening equipment; Forming machine work, sheet metal; Bolts, nuts, rivets & washers; Screw machine products
CEO: Neil Whitesell
**COO:* Robert R Wiese
Plnt Mgr: Ralhp Holt
Prd Mgr: Chris Jones

D-U-N-S 09-415-6429 EXP
▲ WHITEWAVE FOODS CO
1225 17th St Ste 1000, Denver, CO 80202-5599
Tel (303) 635-4500 *Founded/Ownrshp* 2012
Sales 3.8MMM *EMP* 5,300
Tkr Sym WWAV *Exch* NYS
SIC 2026 2023 2021 Fluid milk; Buttermilk, cultured; Cream substitutes; Creamery butter; Milkfat, anhydrous
Ch Bd: Gregg L Engles
Pr: Bernard P J Deryckere
Pr: Kevin C Yost
COO: Blaine E McPeak
CFO: Kelly J Haecker
Ex VP: Edward F Fugger
Ex VP: Roger E Theodoredis
Ex VP: Thomas N Zanetich
Mktg Mgr: Margaret Winter
Board of Directors: Michelle P Goolsby, Stephen L Green, Joseph S Hardin Jr, Anthony J Magro, W Anthony Vernon, Doreen A Wright

D-U-N-S 78-136-3457
WHITFIELD COUNTY SCHOOLS
1306 S Thornton Ave, Dalton, GA 30720-7922
Tel (706) 217-6780 *Founded/Ownrshp* 2006
Sales 25.3MM^E *EMP* 1,608^E
SIC 8211 Public elementary & secondary schools

D-U-N-S 09-930-3083
WHITFIELD EDUCATION FOUNDATION INC
1306 S Thornton Ave, Dalton, GA 30720-7922
Tel (706) 226-3710 *Founded/Ownrshp* 1990
Sales 70.5M *EMP* 1,700
Accts Acree Jinright Leonard & Co
SIC 8211 Public elementary & secondary schools
V Ch: Bill Worley
**CEO:* Tyson Griffin
**CFO:* Carol Knight
CFO: Robert K Sheppard
Bd of Dir: Gary Brock

D-U-N-S 61-971-2227 IMP/EXP
WHITFORD WORLDWIDE CO
47 Park Ave, Elverson, PA 19520-9645
Tel (610) 286-3500 *Founded/Ownrshp* 1969
Sales 113.5MM^E *EMP* 350
SIC 2891 Adhesives & sealants
Pr: David P Willis Jr
**COO:* Michael Miller
**CFO:* Brian E Kilty
Tech Mgr: Kurt Mecray
Opers Mgr: Jimmy Coe
Mktg Dir: Michael Coates
Sls Mgr: Jessica Mannino

D-U-N-S 18-478-8948
■ WHITING CANADIAN HOLDING CO ULC
KODIAK OIL & GAS CORP.
(*Suby of* WHITING PETROLEUM CORP) ★
1700 Broadway Ste 2300, Denver, CO 80290-1703
Tel (303) 837-1661 *Founded/Ownrshp* 2003
Sales 904.6MM^E *EMP* 202
SIC 1381 Drilling oil & gas wells

Ch Bd: James J Volker
COO: Mary Timmins
**CFO:* Michael J Stevens
Treas: Brent P Jensen
Ex VP: Russell Branting

D-U-N-S 00-211-4726 IMP/EXP
WHITING DOOR MFG CORP (NY)
113 Cedar St, Akron, NY 14001-1038
Tel (716) 542-5427 *Founded/Ownrshp* 1953
Sales 124.6MM^E *EMP* 515
SIC 3714 Motor vehicle parts & accessories
Ch Bd: Donald J Whiting
**Ch Bd:* Donald J Whiting
VP: Steve Shelby
VP: Bob Stoll
**VP:* Lauren Whiting
**VP:* Michael T Whiting
Area Mgr: Anthony Goral
Plnt Mgr: Art Gonzales
Board of Directors: Donald J Whiting

WHITING OIL & GAS
See WHITING OIL AND GAS CORP

D-U-N-S 05-238-3064
■ **WHITING OIL AND GAS CORP**
WHITING OIL & GAS
(*Suby of* WHITING PETROLEUM CORP) ★
1700 Broadway Ste 2300, Denver, CO 80290-1703
Tel (303) 837-1661 *Founded/Ownrshp* 2003
Sales 336.0MM^E *EMP* 300
SIC 1311 Crude petroleum production; Natural gas production
CEO: James J Volker
**Pr:* James T Brown
**CFO:* Michael J Stevens
**VP:* D Sherwin Artus
VP: Heather Duncan
VP: Peter W Hagist
VP: Gale N Keithline
VP: James Larson
VP: John E Lodge
VP: Patricia J Miller
VP: Michael A Oestmann
VP: Douglas L Walton
VP: Mark R Williams
Exec: John Keller

D-U-N-S 13-517-5680
▲ **WHITING PETROLEUM CORP**
1700 Broadway Ste 2300, Denver, CO 80290-2300
Tel (303) 837-1661 *Founded/Ownrshp* 1980
Sales 2.0MMM *EMP* 1,200^E
Tkr Sym WLL *Exch* NYS
SIC 1311 1382 Natural gas production; Oil & gas exploration services
Ch Bd: James J Volker
CFO: Michael J Stevens
Treas: Brent P Jensen
Bd of Dir: Philip E Doty
Sr VP: Rick A Ross
Sr VP: Mark R Williams
VP: Bruce R Deboer
VP: Peter W Hagist
VP: Steven A Kranker
VP: David M Seery
Opers Mgr: Jagadeesan Sethuraman
Board of Directors: Thomas L Aller, D Sherwin Artus, James E Catlin, Philip E Doty, William N Hahne, Carin S Knickel, Michael B Walen

D-U-N-S 00-695-0604 IMP
WHITING-TURNER CONTRACTING CO
300 E Joppa Rd Ste 800, Baltimore, MD 21286-3047
Tel (410) 821-1100 *Founded/Ownrshp* 1909, 1955
Sales 5.7MMM *EMP* 2,523
Accts Clifonlarsonallen Timonium M
SIC 1542 1541 1629 8741 Nonresidential construction; Industrial buildings & warehouses; Dams, waterways, docks & other marine construction; Construction management
Pr: Timothy J Regan
Div VP: Espen S Brooks
Div VP: Troy Caldwell
Div VP: Chris Carlson
Div VP: James Martini
Div VP: Robert Mitchell
Div VP: Paul Schmitt
**Ex VP:* Stephen P Duffy
**Ex VP:* Charles Irish Sr
**Ex VP:* Anthony G Moag
**Ex VP:* W Daniel White
**Sr VP:* Daniel M Bauer
Sr VP: Daniel Bauer
Sr VP: Len Cannatelli Jr
**Sr VP:* Leonard A Cannatelli Jr
Sr VP: Jack Dasilva
**Sr VP:* Joaquim Jack Dasilva
**Sr VP:* Keith A Douglas
Sr VP: Keith Douglas
**Sr VP:* Ronald M Eisenberg
**Sr VP:* Michael Ernst

D-U-N-S 80-755-3995
WHITLEY EVERGREEN INC
(*Suby of* WILLIAMS MOBILE OFFICES) ★
201 W 1st St, South Whitley, IN 46787-1256
Tel (260) 723-5131 *Founded/Ownrshp* 1993
Sales 94.7MM^E *EMP* 130
SIC 1542 Commercial & office building, new construction
Pr: Simon Dragan
**CFO:* Robert Jones
**VP:* Mike Ransbottom
**VP:* Andrew Welborn
Genl Mgr: David Black
Sls Mgr: Larry J High

D-U-N-S 05-739-4017
WHITLEY MANUFACTURING CO INC
WILLIAMS MOBILE OFFICES
201 W 1st St, South Whitley, IN 46787-1256
Tel (260) 723-5131 *Founded/Ownrshp* 1993
Sales 105.5MM^E *EMP* 130^E
Accts Dulin Ward & Dewald Inc
SIC 2451 Mobile buildings: for commercial use
Pr: Simon Dragan
Ch Bd: Barry Gossett
CFO: Robert Jones

VP: Randall Holler
VP: Bob Jones
VP: Dan Lipinski
VP: Mike Ransbottom
VP: Andrew Welborn
Genl Mgr: Alan Duer
Genl Mgr: Larry Hammer
Prd Mgr: Bill Gibbs

WHITLOCK GROUP, THE
See AUDIO FIDELITY COMMUNICATIONS CORP

D-U-N-S 02-166-0865 EXP
WHITLOCK PACKAGING CORP
(*Suby of* REFRESCO US HOLDING INC.)
6655 S Lewis Ave Ste 105, Tulsa, OK 74136-1000
Tel (918) 524-4029 *Founded/Ownrshp* 2016
Sales 100.0MM *EMP* 500
SIC 2033

D-U-N-S 01-019-7887
WHITMAN COLLEGE
345 Boyer Ave, Walla Walla, WA 99362-2083
Tel (509) 527-5111 *Founded/Ownrshp* 1859
Sales 87.7MM *EMP* 1,095
SIC 8221 College, except junior
Pr: George Bridges

D-U-N-S 00-179-4163
WHITNEY & CO LLC
J H WHITNEY & CO
130 Main St, New Canaan, CT 06840-5509
Tel (203) 716-6100 *Founded/Ownrshp* 1946
Sales 238.8MM^E *EMP* 1,290
SIC 6211 Investment bankers
Genl Pt: Daniel J O'Brien
CFO: Michael Salvator
**Treas:* David Zatlukal
VP: Micah Meisel
VP: Dima Tkachev
CTO: Dan Anderson
Genl Couns: Kevin Curley

D-U-N-S 00-694-8103 IMP
WHITNEY BANK
WHITNEY COMM. DEVELOPMENT
228 Saint Charles Ave # 228, New Orleans, LA 70130-2628
Tel (504) 586-7272 *Founded/Ownrshp* 2012
Sales NA *EMP* 2,500^E
SIC 6021

D-U-N-S 00-696-4100
■ **WHITNEY BANK** (MS)
(*Suby of* HANCOCK HOLDING CO) ★
1 Hancock Plz Fl 7, Gulfport, MS 39501-1947
Tel (228) 868-4000 *Founded/Ownrshp* 1899
Sales NA *EMP* 750
SIC 6022 State commercial banks
Ch: George Schloegel
Ex VP: Rudi Thompson
**Ex VP:* Charles A Webb
Sr VP: Michael Achary
Sr VP: Trisha Carlson
Sr VP: Geri Kail
Sr VP: Robert Seals
Sr VP: Kelli Stein
VP: Amanda Breland
VP: Marilyn Brown
VP: Corrine Lunsford Buchholz
VP: Debbie Carr
VP: Michele Chaffin
VP: Rick Chatagnier
VP: Amy Corr
VP: Timothy Davis
VP: Beth Elrod
VP: Ford Favre
VP: Resa Frey
VP: Sherrell L Johnson
VP: Toni Miceli

WHITNEY COMM. DEVELOPMENT
See WHITNEY BANK

D-U-N-S 07-327-2122 IMP
WHITNEY MUSEUM OF AMERICAN ART
99 Gansevoort St, New York, NY 10014-1404
Tel (212) 570-3600 *Founded/Ownrshp* 1931
Sales 100.8MM *EMP* 167
Accts Lutz And Carr Cpas Llp New Yo
SIC 8412 Museum
Ch: Leonard A Lauder
**Pr:* Neil G Bluhm
CFO: Idehen Aruede
CFO: Alice Pratt Burns
**Ch:* Robert J Hurst
Treas: Henry Cornell
**Treas:* Richard M Demartini
Ofcr: Courtney Bassett
**VP:* Pamela G Devos
VP: Susan Hess
Assoc Dir: Christy Putnam
Comm Man: Brian Mann Jr

WHITNEY REHAB APARTMENTS
See BUFFALO VILLAGE ASSOC 190 CAROLINA BUF

D-U-N-S 62-153-9790 IMP
WHITSONS FOOD SERVICE CORP
ANDREWS FABULOUS FOODS
1800 Motor Pkwy, Islandia, NY 11749-5216
Tel (631) 424-2700 *Founded/Ownrshp* 1981
Sales 140.4MM^E *EMP* 2,900
SIC 5812 Contract food services
CEO: Robert E Whitcomb
**Pr:* Douglas Whitcomb
**CFO:* Beth Bunster
**VP:* John Whitcomb
VP: William Whitcomb
Comm Dir: Holly Von Seggern
Genl Mgr: Chris Fautas
QA Dir: Bob Whitcomb
Dir IT: Gustavo Monne

D-U-N-S 77-993-6587
WHITTEN GROUP INTERNATIONAL CORP
2622 Lilac St, Longview, WA 98632-3525
Tel (360) 560-3319 *Founded/Ownrshp* 1984
Sales 100.2MM *EMP* 12
SIC 5172 3559 Service station supplies, petroleum; Petroleum refinery equipment
Pr: Ronald W Whitten

D-U-N-S 08-220-5576
WHITTIER UNION HIGH SCHOOL DIST
9401 Painter Ave, Whittier, CA 90605-2729
Tel (562) 698-8121 *Founded/Ownrshp* 1986
Sales 69.7MM^E *EMP* 1,100
SIC 8211 Public elementary & secondary schools
**Pr:* Tim Schneider
**VP:* Dr Ralph Pacheco
Genl Mgr: Julie Johnson
IT Man: Richard Rosenberg
Teacher Pr: Kevin Jamero
Psych: Rosanne Atilano
Psych: Kristin Borzi
Psych: Barney Hein
Psych: Nancy Kahn
Psych: Yolanda Lord
Psych: Lou Munoz

D-U-N-S 96-503-1490
WHITTLESEA BLUE CAB CO
BELL TRANSPORTATION
(*Suby of* WHITTLESEA-BELL) ★
2000 Industrial Rd, Las Vegas, NV 89102
Tel (702) 384-6111 *Founded/Ownrshp* 1970
Sales 39.7MM^E *EMP* 1,000
SIC 4121 Taxicabs
Pr: Brent Bell
**Treas:* Jeanne W O'Doan

D-U-N-S 05-146-2729
WHITTLESEA-BELL
100 Sunshine Ln, Reno, NV 89502-1212
Tel (775) 785-3533 *Founded/Ownrshp* 1972
Sales 39.7MM^E *EMP* 1,065
SIC 8721 Accounting, auditing & bookkeeping
Pr: Brent Bell
**Treas:* Jeanne W O'Doan

D-U-N-S 82-797-9001
■ **WHMC INC**
(*Suby of* HOSPITAL COPORATION OF AMERICA) ★
12141 Richmond Ave, Houston, TX 77082-2408
Tel (281) 558-3444 *Founded/Ownrshp* 1994
Sales 11.0M *EMP* 1,200
Accts Al Zientek Cpa Cfp Pc Houston
SIC 8069 Specialty hospitals, except psychiatric
CEO: Todd Caliva
**Pr:* Samuel N Hazen
COO: Brenda Bowman
CFO: Greg Garrison
**Treas:* David G Anderson
**VP:* Robert A Waterman
Genl Mgr: Douglas Stanley
IT Man: Terry Janis
Psych: Marvin Chang
Psych: Nasrullah Manji
Psych: Nelson Uzquiano

WHME TV 46
See LESEA BROADCASTING CORP

D-U-N-S 80-232-9979 IMP
■ **WHOLE FOODS MARKET CALIFORNIA INC**
(*Suby of* WHOLE FOODS MARKET INC) ★
5980 Horton St Ste 200, Emeryville, CA 94608-2057
Tel (510) 428-7400 *Founded/Ownrshp* 1988
Sales 472.8MM^E *EMP* 3,380
SIC 5411 5149 Supermarkets, chain; Groceries & related products
CEO: David Lannon
**CEO:* Walter E Robb IV
**CFO:* Glenda Flannigan
**VP:* Will Paradise

D-U-N-S 12-288-4583 IMP/EXP
■ **WHOLE FOODS MARKET GROUP INC**
(*Suby of* WHOLE FOODS MARKET INC) ★
7720 Peters Rd, Plantation, FL 33324-4024
Tel (954) 236-0600 *Founded/Ownrshp* 1990
Sales 1.2MMM^E *EMP* 9,800
SIC 5411 Supermarkets, chain
CEO: John Mackey
**Pr:* Roberta Lang
**COO:* A C Gallo
**CFO:* Glenda Flanagan

D-U-N-S 09-373-5686
▲ **WHOLE FOODS MARKET INC**
550 Bowie St, Austin, TX 78703-4644
Tel (512) 477-4455 *Founded/Ownrshp* 1980
Sales 15.7MMM *EMP* 90,900
Tkr Sym WFM *Exch* NGS
SIC 5411 Grocery stores; Supermarkets, chain
Co-CEO: John Mackey
Ch Bd: John B Elstrott
Pr: Anthony C Gallo
CFO: Glenda Flanagan
CFO: Glenda J Flanagan
Co-CEO: Walter Robb
Ex VP: Jason Buechel
Ex VP: David Lannon
Ex VP: Kenneth Meyer
Ex VP: James Sud
VP: Brooke Buchanan
VP: Sonya Gafsi Oblisk
VP: Martin Tracey
Board of Directors: Mary Ellen Coe, Stephanie Kugelman, Jonathan A Seiffer, Morris J Siegel, Jonathan D Sokoloff, Ralph Z Sorenson, Gabrielle Sulzberger, William A Tindell III

D-U-N-S 12-289-3840 IMP
■ **WHOLE FOODS MARKET ROCKY MOUNTAIN/SOUTHWEST LP**
(*Suby of* WHOLE FOODS MARKET INC) ★
11770 Preston Rd Ste 119, Dallas, TX 75230
Tel (214) 361-8887 *Founded/Ownrshp* 2001
Sales 138.2MM^E *EMP* 3,581^E
SIC 5411 Supermarkets, chain
Pt: John Mackey

D-U-N-S 07-920-3701
WHOLE FOODS MARKET SOPAC
MRS GOOCHES
207 N Goode Ave, Glendale, CA 91203-1301
Tel (818) 501-8484 *Founded/Ownrshp* 2013
Sales 244.8MM^E *EMP* 6,000
SIC 5411 Grocery stores
Pr: Patrick Bradley

WHOLESALE
See REGAL DISTRIBUTING CO

WHOLESALE BUILDING MTLS CO
See NC INC

D-U-N-S 02-714-5465
WHOLESALE ELECTRIC SUPPLY CO INC
1400 Waterall St, Texarkana, TX 75501-4964
Tel (903) 794-3404 *Founded/Ownrshp* 1947
Sales 178.7MM^E *EMP* 157
SIC 5063 Electrical apparatus & equipment
Pr: Amos McCulloch Jr
**VP:* Kurt Blumfelder
Sls Mgr: Robert Bright
Sls Mgr: Josh Wolverton
Board of Directors: Robert Bright

D-U-N-S 00-190-4531 IMP/EXP
WHOLESALE ELECTRIC SUPPLY CO OF HOUSTON INC (TX)
4040 Gulf Fwy, Houston, TX 77004-2599
Tel (713) 748-6100 *Founded/Ownrshp* 1949
Sales 248.5MM^E *EMP* 589^E
SIC 5065

WHOLESALE FABRICS
See PINDLER & PINDLER INC

D-U-N-S 00-879-8720
WHOLESALE FUELS INC
2200 E Brundage Ln, Bakersfield, CA 93307-3066
Tel (661) 327-4900 *Founded/Ownrshp* 1982
Sales 111.3MM *EMP* 63
Accts Moss Adams Llp Los Angeles C
SIC 5172 Petroleum products
Pr: Charles McCan
**CFO:* Brian Bucassa
**Sec:* Tom Jamieson
Genl Mgr: Jeff Shultz

D-U-N-S 02-295-2956 IMP
WHOLESALE PRODUCE SUPPLY LLC
752 Kasota Cir Se, Minneapolis, MN 55414-2884
Tel (612) 378-2025 *Founded/Ownrshp* 2007
Sales 150.0MM *EMP* 190
SIC 5148 Fruits; Vegetables
**VP:* Arthur Quiggle

WHOLESALE TIRE DIVISION
See CAPITAL TIRE INC

D-U-N-S 08-982-8644 EXP
WHOLESOME HARVEST BAKING LLC
(*Suby of* CANADA BREAD COMPANY, LIMITED)
1011 E Touhy Ave Ste 500, Des Plaines, IL 60018-5829
Tel (800) 550-6810 *Founded/Ownrshp* 1961
Sales 1.7MMM^E *EMP* 1,200
SIC 2051 Bagels, fresh or frozen
Pr: Dan Curtin
VP Mktg: Orzse Hodi
Mktg Dir: Emily Liang

D-U-N-S 00-562-8136 IMP/EXP
WHOLESOME SWEETENERS INC
(*Suby of* ARLON FOOD AND AGRICULTURE PARTNERS LP) ★
14141 Southwest Fwy # 160, Sugar Land, TX 77478-4630
Tel (281) 275-3199 *Founded/Ownrshp* 1996, 2012
Sales 83.5MM^E *EMP* 56^E
SIC 5141 Food brokers
CEO: Nigel Willerton
**CFO:* Jeff Seidel
VP: Walter Nimocks
Mktg Mgr: Allison Rogers

WHUD
See PAMAL BROADCASTING LTD

D-U-N-S 04-306-3460
WICHITA CITY OF (INC) (KS)
455 N Main St Fl 5, Wichita, KS 67202-1601
Tel (316) 268-4351 *Founded/Ownrshp* 1868
Sales NA *EMP* 2,200^E
Accts Allen Gibbs & Houlik Lc Cpa
SIC 9111 Mayors' offices
Bd of Dir: Michelle Enke
Bd of Dir: Bryan Frye
Ofcr: George Birdwell
Ofcr: Mark Hall
Ofcr: Paul Herman
Ofcr: Mark Manning
Exec: Jane Dean
Ex Dir: Gary Rebenstorf
CTO: Monica Nienstedt

WICHITA CLINIC PHARMACY
See VIA CHRISTI CLINIC PA

D-U-N-S 00-723-2721
■ **WICHITA COCA-COLA BOTTLING CO**
(*Suby of* COCA-COLA REFRESHMENTS USA INC) ★
10001 Industrial Blvd, Lenexa, KS 66215-1209
Tel (316) 612-6400 *Founded/Ownrshp* 1930
Sales 100.3MM^E *EMP* 650
SIC 2086 Bottled & canned soft drinks
CEO: Lowry Kline
Opers Mgr: Cindy Pores

WICHITA FALLS FREIGHTLINER
See LONESTAR FREIGHTLINER GROUP LLC

D-U-N-S 09-426-3704
WICHITA FALLS INDEPENDENT SCHOOL DISTRICT
WICHITA FALLS ISD
1104 Broad St, Wichita Falls, TX 76301-4412
Tel (940) 235-1000 *Founded/Ownrshp* 1890
Sales 72.2MM^E *EMP* 1,500

SIC 8211 Public elementary school; Public junior high school; Public senior high school; Public special education school
Trst: Allyson Flack
Exec: Sandy Camp
Exec: Kathy Dickerson
Ex Dir: Jan Arrington
Ex Dir: Cheryl Pappan
MIS Dir: Leah Horton
Pr Dir: Ashley Thomas
Teacher Pr: January Jones
Teacher Pr: Ciny Kohl

WICHITA FALLS ISD
See WICHITA FALLS INDEPENDENT SCHOOL DISTRICT

WICHITA PUBLIC SCHOOLS
See UNIFIED SCHOOL DISTRICT 259

D-U-N-S 95-958-8633
WICHITA PUBLIC SCHOOLS
201 N Water St, Wichita, KS 67202-1292
Tel (316) 973-4000 *Founded/Ownrshp* 1996
Sales 3.7MM^E *EMP* 5,000
SIC 8211 Catholic elementary & secondary schools
Prin: John Allison
*Prin: Vicki Foss

D-U-N-S 05-307-8127
WICHITA STATE UNIVERSITY
GRADUATE SCHOOL WICHITA STATE
1845 Fairmount St, Wichita, KS 67260-0001
Tel (316) 978-3040 *Founded/Ownrshp* 1895, 1964
Sales 197.4MM *EMP* 3,395
SIC 5999 Hearing aids
Pr: John Bardo
CFO: Kevin Crabtree
Assoc VP: David Wright
VP: Gary Brichacek
VP: Sudeep Ghimire
VP: Joseph Hunter
VP: Terre Johnson
**VP:* Roger D Lowe
VP: Courtney Price
Assoc Dir: Donna Carter
Assoc Dir: Beth Clarkson
Assoc Dir: Pat McLeod

D-U-N-S 78-577-3813 IMP/EXP
WICKED FASHIONS INC
SOUTHPOLE
222 Bridge Plz S, Fort Lee, NJ 07024-5729
Tel (201) 242-5909 *Founded/Ownrshp* 1991
Sales 121.8MM^E *EMP* 400
SIC 5137 5136 Women's & children's clothing; Men's & boys' clothing
CEO: David Khym
**COO:* Keyhyung Lee
**CFO:* Danny Khym
**CFO:* Rudi Lenz
CFO: John Um
CFO: Euikyu Yun
**Treas:* Gary Lim
Genl Mgr: CHI Dam
CIO: Favian Alvarez
Genl Couns: Lisa J Marroni

WICKES LUMBER DIVISION
See BRADCO SUPPLY CORP

D-U-N-S 17-101-9602
WICKS COMMUNICATIONS & MEDIA PARTNERS III LP
WICKS GROUP OF COMPANIES
405 Park Ave Ste 702, New York, NY 10022-9420
Tel (212) 838-2100 *Founded/Ownrshp* 1999
Sales 105.0MM^E *EMP* 900
SIC 6799 Venture capital companies
CEO: Craig Clausk
Mng Pt: Mathew E Gormny III
VP: Thomas Kearney III
Mng Dir: Carter F Bales
Mng Dir: Matthew Gormaly
Mng Dir: Craig Klosk
Mng Dir: Peter Smith

WICKS GROUP OF COMPANIES
See WICKS COMMUNICATIONS & MEDIA PARTNERS III LP

D-U-N-S 78-734-2872
WICKS GROUP OF COMPANIES LLC (DE CORP)
400 Park Ave Fl 12a, New York, NY 10022-9477
Tel (212) 838-2100 *Founded/Ownrshp* 1989
Sales 138.0MM^E *EMP* 234^E
SIC 6211 6282 Investment bankers; Investment advisory service
**Pt:* Daniel L Black
**Pt:* Jamie M Weston
**VP:* Irina I Krasik
Mng Dir: Matthew Gormly

D-U-N-S 07-962-8957
WICOMICO COUNTY PUBLIC SCHOOLS
2424 Northgate Dr Ste 100, Salisbury, MD 21801-7888
Tel (410) 677-4400 *Founded/Ownrshp* 2014
Sales 67.2MM^E *EMP* 3,000^E
SIC 8211 Public elementary & secondary schools
Prin: Donna C Hanlin
Dir Sec: Brian Foret
MIS Dir: Robert Langdon
Pr Dir: Tracy Sahler
Teacher Pr: Vince Pavic

D-U-N-S 02-220-0158
WIDEFIELD SCHOOL DISTRICT 3
1820 Main St, Colorado Springs, CO 80911-1199
Tel (719) 391-3000 *Founded/Ownrshp* 1865
Sales 50.6MM^E *EMP* 1,542
SIC 8211 Public elementary school; Public junior high school; Public senior high school
**Pr:* Chris Velasquez
**Treas:* Theresa Watson
**VP:* Andr Gutierrez
Genl Mgr: Rachel Morse
MIS Dir: Kirsten Toy
IT Man: Landon Finch

Opers Mgr: Dave Allgood
Psych: Eric Thiele

D-U-N-S 04-656-6303
WIDENER UNIVERSITY
1 University Pl, Chester, PA 19013-5792
Tel (610) 499-4000 *Founded/Ownrshp* 1821
Sales 156.5MM *EMP* 1,021
Accts Cliftonlarsonallen Llp Plymou
SIC 8221 College, except junior
Pr: James Thomas Harris III
Pr: Lou Bulik
**CFO:* Joseph J Baker
Treas: James W Hirschmann
Bd of Dir: Diana Vecchio
Ofcr: Rachel Cimino
Assoc VP: Lawrence Lesick
VP: Amy Wilson
Exec: Clayton Sheldon
Ex Dir: John Poulin
Pgrm Dir: Stuart Eimer

D-U-N-S 02-329-3333
WIDEOPENWEST FINANCE LLC
WOW
7887 E Belleview Ave, Englewood, CO 80111-6015
Tel (303) 663-0771 *Founded/Ownrshp* 2001
Sales 1.2MMM *EMP* 1,861
Accts Bdo Usa Llp Atlanta Georgia
SIC 4841 Cable & other pay television services
Prin: Vic Ahmed

D-U-N-S 12-422-9522
WIDEOPENWEST NETWORKS LLC
WOW INTERNET - CABLE - PHONE
(*Suby of* AVISTA CAPITAL HOLDINGS LP) ★
7887 E Belleview Ave, Englewood, CO 80111-6015
Tel (720) 479-3558 *Founded/Ownrshp* 1999
Sales 311.3MM^E *EMP* 1,200
SIC 4813
Pr: Steven Cochran
**COO:* Cathy Kuo
**CFO:* Rich Fish
Ofcr: Cash Hagen
**Sr VP:* Mike Harry
**VP:* Rex Kennedy

WIDOWS, ORPHANS AND DISABLED F
See LOS ANGELES FIREMAN RELIEF ASSOCIATION INC

WIELAND
See SAUDER MANUFACTURING CO

D-U-N-S 19-143-7821 IMP
WIELAND COPPER PRODUCTS LLC
(*Suby of* WIELAND-WERKE AG)
3990 Us 311 Hwy N, Pine Hall, NC 27042-8166
Tel (336) 445-4500 *Founded/Ownrshp* 2010
Sales 150.3MM^E *EMP* 540
SIC 3351 Tubing, copper & copper alloy
VP: Mike Burke
IT Man: Ackim Becker

D-U-N-S 00-648-6468
WIESE HOLDING CO (MO)
1445 Woodson Rd, Saint Louis, MO 63132-2506
Tel (314) 997-4444 *Founded/Ownrshp* 1944
Sales 251.6MM^E *EMP* 950
SIC 5084 7359 Materials handling machinery; Equipment rental & leasing
CEO: Harold E Wiese
**Pr:* Chip Wiese
**COO:* John Baker
Tech Mgr: Joe Anderson
Sls Mgr: Jeff Cramer

D-U-N-S 04-681-7818 IMP
WIESE MATERIAL HANDLING INC
1435 Woodson Rd, Saint Louis, MO 63132-2506
Tel (314) 997-4210 *Founded/Ownrshp* 2000
Sales 246.4MM^E *EMP* 900
SIC 5084 Materials handling machinery
Pr: Harold Wiese
COO: Theron Dodson
**COO:* Pahreon Dudson
**CFO:* Gary Sahrmann
Comm Man: Bob Wright
Brnch Mgr: Lou Espey
Genl Mgr: Kevin Moran
Opers Mgr: Greg Stephenson
Manager: Jay Boston
Sls Mgr: Chuck Griesbeck
Sales Asso: Craig McCallister

D-U-N-S 06-804-6093 IMP
WIESNER PRODUCTS INC
WPI
1333 Brdwy Fl 6, New York, NY 10018
Tel (212) 279-2466 *Founded/Ownrshp* 1974
Sales 100.0MM *EMP* 80
SIC 5139 2252 Footwear; Socks
Pr: Charles Mizrahi
Opers Mgr: David Choi

D-U-N-S 03-262-7622 EXP
WIGINTON CORP
QUALITY FABRICATION & SUPPLY
699 Aero Ln, Sanford, FL 32771-6699
Tel (407) 585-3200 *Founded/Ownrshp* 1967
Sales 107.8MM^E *EMP* 350
SIC 1711 7699 7389 Fire sprinkler system installation; Industrial equipment services; Fire extinguisher servicing
CEO: Donald G Wiginton
**Ch Bd:* Joe E Wiginton
**Pr:* Alan D Wiginton
**COO:* Mark Erickson
**CFO:* Robert Jolly
**Treas:* David M Menzel
Sr VP: Chuck Lake
**Sr VP:* George W Stanley
VP: Steve Browne
VP: Gary Inglis
Area Mgr: Bill Behringer

D-U-N-S 04-446-4584 IMP
WIKA HOLDING L P
(*Suby of* WIKA ALEXANDER WIEGAND SE & CO. KG)
1000 Wiegand Blvd, Lawrenceville, GA 30043-5868
Tel (770) 513-8200 *Founded/Ownrshp* 1967
Sales 176.3MM^E *EMP* 620
SIC 3823 Temperature instruments: industrial process type; Thermometers, filled system: industrial process type
CEO: Alexander Wiegand
**Pr:* Michael Gerster
**Pr:* Dave Wannamaker
**COO:* Klaus Gross
CFO: Steve McCullough
**Ex VP:* Brent Shadix
**VP:* Erich Berninger
Dir IT: Rick Keith
Natl Sales: Tom Piacentini

D-U-N-S 96-311-7416 IMP
WIKA INSTRUMENT LP
(*Suby of* WIKA HOLDING L P) ★
1000 Wiegand Blvd, Lawrenceville, GA 30043-5868
Tel (770) 513-8200 *Founded/Ownrshp* 2008
Sales 126.4MM^E *EMP* 593
SIC 3053 3823 Gaskets, packing & sealing devices; Temperature instruments: industrial process type
Pr: Dave Wannamaker
Pr: Arek Dyrdol
Ex VP: Drew Firestone
VP: Steve McCullough
Ex Dir: Lennie Tuck
IT Man: Rick Keith
IT Man: Oke Sabeni
Sfty Mgr: Cathy Bochenek
Sfty Mgr: Rhonda Williams
Opers Mgr: Scott Horne
Opers Mgr: Andrea Markovic

D-U-N-S 00-315-8938 IMP/EXP
WIKOFF COLOR CORP
1886 Merritt Rd, Fort Mill, SC 29715-7707
Tel (803) 548-2210 *Founded/Ownrshp* 1956
Sales 152.7MM^E *EMP* 450
Accts Dixon Hughes Pllc Charlotte
SIC 2893 2851 Printing ink; Varnishes; Coating, air curing
Ch Bd: Philip L Lambert
**Pr:* Geoffrey A Peters
**CFO:* Frieda Liles
Ofcr: Ron Morin
**VP:* Daryl Collins
VP: Martin Hambrock
Exec: Rodney Landress
Dir Lab: Derek Hines
Off Admin: Lisa Edkins
Off Admin: Beth Mohler
Off Admin: Karen Reposa
Board of Directors: J Patrick Burns, Veda F Clark, Philip L Lambert, Harvey L Lowd, Karl Warnke

D-U-N-S 17-936-4203 IMP
WILBERT FUNERAL SERVICES INC
WILBERT MANUFACTURERS ASSN
10965 Granada Ln Ste 300, Overland Park, KS 66211-1412
Tel (913) 345-2120 *Founded/Ownrshp* 2011
Sales 247.8MM^E *EMP* 720^E
SIC 3272 Burial vaults, concrete or precast terrazzo
Pr: Dennis Welzenbach
CEO: Joseph Suhor
Plnt Mgr: Greg Sisco
S&M/VP: Mike Dvorak

D-U-N-S 04-232-4475 IMP
WILBERT INC
WILBERT PLASTIC SERVICES
2001 Oaks Pkwy, Belmont, NC 28012-5134
Tel (704) 247-3850 *Founded/Ownrshp* 1933
Sales 1.0MMM^E *EMP* 1,500
SIC 5162 3272 Plastics materials; Burial vaults, concrete or precast terrazzo
Pr: Greg Botner
**Ch Bd:* C James Mans
Pr: Denny Knigga
CFO: Bill Cave
VP: Joe Joyner
VP: Allen Whitmer
CIO: Lawrence Demello
Plnt Mgr: Rodney Fye
Plnt Mgr: Andrew Hall
Sales Exec: Bob Gray
Snr Mgr: Larry Moser

WILBERT MANUFACTURERS ASSN
See WILBERT FUNERAL SERVICES INC

WILBERT PLASTIC SERVICES
See WILBERT INC

D-U-N-S 00-824-7397 IMP/EXP
WILBUR CURTIS CO INC
6913 W Acco St, Montebello, CA 90640-5403
Tel (323) 837-2300 *Founded/Ownrshp* 1963
Sales 115.3MM^E *EMP* 275
SIC 3589 Coffee brewing equipment
Pr: Kevin Curtis
**Pr:* Robert A Curtis
**COO:* Joe Laws
**CFO:* Norman Fujitaki
**Ex VP:* Michael A Curtis
VP: Steve Bradley
VP: Scott Grimes
Dir Bus: Thomas Keegan
Genl Mgr: Frederick Reisenduer
CTO: Dan Schneider
VP Mfg: Rick Alumn

D-U-N-S 15-420-9217
WILBUR SMITH ASSOCIATES GROUP INC
(*Suby of* CDM SMITH INC) ★
1301 Gervais St Ste 1600, Columbia, SC 29201-3361
Tel (803) 758-4500 *Founded/Ownrshp* 2011
Sales 52.3MM^E *EMP* 1,319^E
Accts Davis & Company Cpas Columbia
SIC 8711 Engineering services
CEO: M Stevenson Smith
**Pr:* Hollis A Walker
**CFO:* Daniel F Leahy
**VP:* Suzanne Murphy

D-U-N-S 06-505-1922
WILBUR SMITH ASSOCIATES INC
(*Suby of* WILBUR SMITH ASSOCIATES GROUP INC) ★
1301 Gervais St Ste 1600, Columbia, SC 29201-3361
Tel (803) 758-4500 *Founded/Ownrshp* 1986
Sales 52.3MM^E *EMP* 1,217
Accts Pricewaterhousecoopers Llp Sp
SIC 8711 Consulting engineer
Ch: D Ick Fox
**Pr:* Timothy B Wall
**CEO:* M Stevenson Smith
**CFO:* David S Johnson
**Ch:* Dick Fox
**Ex VP:* Thierry Desmaris
**Ex VP:* Edward J Regan III
**Ex VP:* Peter W Tunnicliffe
**Sr VP:* James W Hamann
**Sr VP:* Gerald Stump
VP: Bob Ferrell
VP: Eugene Ryan

D-U-N-S 08-012-4478
WILBUR-ELLIS CO LLC
(*Suby of* WILBUR-ELLIS HOLDINGS II INC) ★
345 California St Fl 27, San Francisco, CA 94104-2644
Tel (415) 772-4000 *Founded/Ownrshp* 2015
Sales 117.3MM^E *EMP* 2,812^E
SIC 5191 0711 Farm supplies; Fertilizer & fertilizer materials; Insecticides; Fertilizer application services
Ch Bd: John P Thacher
Pr: Daniel R Vradenburg
CFO: Michael J Hunter
Treas: Alison J Amonette
VP: Steven J Dietze
VP: David P Granoff
VP: Scott M Hushbeck
VP: Troy W Johnson
VP: Mike P Karasiewicz
VP: Kenneth J Manning
VP: Brent A McGowan
VP: Ron L Pilkinton
VP: Mike D Wilbur
Board of Directors: David P Thacher

D-U-N-S 00-691-3479 IMP/EXP
WILBUR-ELLIS HOLDINGS II INC
345 California St Fl 27, San Francisco, CA 94104-2644
Tel (415) 772-4000 *Founded/Ownrshp* 1921
Sales 1.5MMM^E *EMP* 4,200
Accts Pricewaterhousecoopers
SIC 5999 5191 5169 Feed & farm supply; Chemicals, agricultural; Fertilizer & fertilizer materials; Animal feeds; Industrial chemicals
Pr: John P Thacher
**Ch Bd:* Bruce L Beretta
CFO: James D Crawford
CFO: Michael J Hunter
Treas: Alison J Amonette
VP: Anne Cleary
VP: Steven J Dietze
VP: David P Granoff
VP: Troy Hackett
VP: Scott Hushbeck
Brnch Mgr: Justin Allen
Board of Directors: Alan E Barton, William B Buckner, Richard S Grey, Matthew H Rowland, David J Thacher, Judith F Wilbur

D-U-N-S 02-768-9751 IMP
WILCO FARMERS
200 Industrial Way Ne, Mount Angel, OR 97362-9576
Tel (503) 845-6122 *Founded/Ownrshp* 1967
Sales 267.4MM^E *EMP* 530
SIC 5541 Filling stations, gasoline
Pr: Douglas Hoffman
**COO:* Sam Bugarsky
**CFO:* Randy Moore
Genl Mgr: Bill Hubbell

WILCO HESS
See A T WILLIAMS OIL CO

D-U-N-S 02-017-0577
WILCO LIFE INSURANCE CO
CONSECO
(*Suby of* WILTON REASSURANCE CO) ★
11825 N Pennsylvania St, Carmel, IN 46032-4555
Tel (317) 817-6100 *Founded/Ownrshp* 2014
Sales NA *EMP* 190^E
SIC 6311 Life insurance carriers
Pr: Elizabeth Georgakopoulos
Web Dev: William Thomas
Manager: Michelle Kellogg

D-U-N-S 60-780-6379
WILCO MACHINE & FAB INC
1326 S Broadway St, Marlow, OK 73055-3864
Tel (580) 658-6993 *Founded/Ownrshp* 1973
Sales 112.8MM^E *EMP* 275
SIC 3533 Oil & gas field machinery
CEO: Kris Boles
**Pr:* Brad Boles
**Sec:* Sue Boles
**VP:* Anthony Chandler
**VP:* David McCauley
Admn Mgr: Lucy Parker
IT Man: Roger Calger
IT Man: Roger Neal
IT Man: Gary Reddin
Plnt Mgr: Larry Wortham

D-U-N-S 01-528-1822
WILCOHESS LLC
5446 University Pkwy, Winston Salem, NC 27105-1366
Tel (336) 767-6280 *Founded/Ownrshp* 2001
Sales 754.1MM^E *EMP* 6,000
SIC 5461 5812 5541 Doughnuts; Eating places; Truck stops; Filling stations, gasoline
CFO: Sherry Polowsky

WILCOX & FLEGEL OIL CO
See WILSON OIL INC

D-U-N-S 05-018-3755 IMP
WILCOX FARMS INC
40400 Harts Lake Vly Rd, Roy, WA 98580-9182
Tel (360) 458-7774 *Founded/Ownrshp* 1962

Sales 158.0MM^E *EMP* 600
SIC 0252 2015 2875

D-U-N-S 15-777-6378
WILCOX HEALTH SYSTEM
WILCOX MEMORIAL HOSPITAL
3-3420 Kuhio Hwy, Lihue, HI 96766-1042
Tel (808) 245-1100 *Founded/Ownrshp* 1984
Sales 70.8MM^E *EMP* 1,245
SIC 8741 8011 Hospital management; Clinic, operated by physicians
CEO: Cathy Clark
Ansthlgy: Michael Johnston
Ansthlgy: Robert Oelke

WILCOX MEMORIAL HOSPITAL
See WILCOX HEALTH SYSTEM

D-U-N-S 06-627-8706
WILCOX MEMORIAL HOSPITAL
(*Suby of* HAWAII PACIFIC HEALTH) ★
3-3420 Kuhio Hwy, Lihue, HI 96766-1099
Tel (808) 245-1100 *Founded/Ownrshp* 1936
Sales 105.4MM *EMP* 653
SIC 8062 General medical & surgical hospitals
Pr: Kathy Clark
Exec: Sarah Dillon
Exec: Surendra RAO
Dir OR: Bonnie Clark
Dir Rad: John Culliney
Dir Rad: Allen Johnson
Ansthlgy: Matthew Ruel

D-U-N-S 82-751-7384 IMP/EXP
■ **WILD FLAVORS INC**
A.M. TODD
(*Suby of* ARCHER-DANIELS-MIDLAND CO) ★
1261 Pacific Ave, Erlanger, KY 41018-1260
Tel (859) 342-3600 *Founded/Ownrshp* 2014
Sales 229.5MM^E *EMP* 450
SIC 2869 2819 Flavors or flavoring materials, synthetic; Perfume materials, synthetic; Industrial inorganic chemicals
CEO: Michael H Ponder
**Ch Bd:* Hans-Peter Wild
Pr: Roger Hammond
**COO:* Vince Macciocchi
**CFO:* Gary Massie
Sr VP: Victoria De La Huerga
VP: David Davis
VP: Erik Donhowe
Exec: Peter Kindzierski
Assoc Dir: Marlene Smothers
Dir Bus: Richard Dukes

D-U-N-S 06-071-4755 IMP
■ **WILD WELL CONTROL INC** (TX)
WWCI
(*Suby of* SESI LLC) ★
2202 Oil Center Ct, Houston, TX 77073-3333
Tel (281) 784-4700 *Founded/Ownrshp* 1975, 2001
Sales 1.3MMM^E *EMP* 250
SIC 1389

D-U-N-S 10-407-5916
WILDCAT CONSTRUCTION CO INC
3219 W May St, Wichita, KS 67213-1540
Tel (316) 945-9408 *Founded/Ownrshp* 1983
Sales 85.8MM^E *EMP* 165
SIC 1623 1622 1771 1611 1629 Water, sewer & utility lines; Bridge construction; Concrete work; Grading; Golf course construction
VP: John Curtis
**Pr:* Roger McClellan
COO: Jim Tadtman
**CFO:* Lanny Gridley
**Sec:* Stephen Llamas
**VP:* Alan Farrington
**VP:* Stuart Johnson
**VP:* Paul Sook
Genl Mgr: Joan Haaga

D-U-N-S 08-001-2260
WILDCAT POINT GENERATION FACILITY
(*Suby of* OLD DOMINION ELECTRIC CO-OPERATIVE) ★
179 Old Mill Rd, Conowingo, MD 21918-1146
Tel (724) 422-2169 *Founded/Ownrshp* 2015
Sales 1.2MMM *EMP* 32
SIC 4911 Distribution, electric power
Pr: Jackson E Reasor

WILDE AUTO HONDA
See WILDE AUTOS INC

D-U-N-S 00-788-2074
WILDE AUTOS INC (WI)
WILDE AUTO HONDA
1710a State Road 164 S, Waukesha, WI 53186-3937
Tel (262) 970-5900 *Founded/Ownrshp* 1966, 2001
Sales 140.1MM *EMP* 145
SIC 5511 Automobiles, new & used
Pr: Mark Wilde
**VP:* Pat Donahue
Sales Exec: Joe Perkins

D-U-N-S 08-422-5531
WILDE OF WEST ALLIS INC
TOYOTA-WILDE AUTOMOTIVE GROUP
3225 S 108th St, Milwaukee, WI 53227-4021
Tel (414) 329-6043 *Founded/Ownrshp* 1977
Sales 154.6MM *EMP* 210
SIC 5511 5521 7538 7515 7513 5012 Automobiles, new & used; Used car dealers; General automotive repair shops; Passenger car leasing; Truck rental & leasing, no drivers; Automobiles & other motor vehicles
VP: Patrick Donahue
IT Man: Bill Grunert

D-U-N-S 94-957-7233
WILDFLOWER BREAD CO
7755 E Gray Rd, Scottsdale, AZ 85260-3459
Tel (480) 951-9453 *Founded/Ownrshp* 2012
Sales 166.7MM^E *EMP* 500
SIC 5149 Bakery products
Pr: Louis Basile
**Treas:* Tracy Basile

D-U-N-S 06-149-4969
WILDISH LAND CO
3600 Wildish Ln, Eugene, OR 97408-5003
Tel (541) 485-1700 *Founded/Ownrshp* 1935
Sales 118.8MM^E *EMP* 450
SIC 1611 1542 General contractor, highway & street construction; Nonresidential construction
Pr: James A Wildish
**VP:* Michael C Wildish
**VP:* William R Wildish
Dir IT: Dawn Drury-Odom
Sfty Dirs: Jim Gibson

D-U-N-S 07-520-9650 IMP
WILDLIFE CONSERVATION SOCIETY
NEW YORK ZOOLOGICAL SOCIETY
2300 Southern Blvd, Bronx, NY 10460-1090
Tel (718) 220-5144 *Founded/Ownrshp* 1895
Sales 327.8MM *EMP* 4,000
SIC 8422 8641 Zoological garden, noncommercial; Aquarium; Environmental protection organization
Pr: Christian Samper
**Treas:* John N Irwin III
Trst: Ralph Da Costa Nu EZ
Ofcr: Darren Long
**Ex VP:* James J Breheny
Ex VP: Patricia Calabrese
**Ex VP:* John F Calvelli JD
**Ex VP:* John G Robinson PHD
Sr VP: Christopher J McKenzie
**VP:* Susan A Chin AIA
**VP:* Elizabeth L Bennett PHD
VP: Elizabeth Bennett
**VP:* Robert Calamo
VP: Susan Chin
**VP:* Mary A Dixon
**VP:* Jon Forrest Dohlin
VP: Sergio Furman
**VP:* Linda I Krueger
**VP:* Herman D Smith
**VP:* Laura Stolzenthaler
**VP:* Susan Tressler
Board of Directors: John N Irwin III, Hamilton E James, richard, Anita L Keefe, edith McBea

D-U-N-S 02-808-0125 EXP
WILEMAN BROS & ELLIOTT INC
40232 Road 128, Cutler, CA 93615-2104
Tel (559) 651-8378 *Founded/Ownrshp* 1948
Sales 111.6MM^E *EMP* 75
SIC 0723 2653 0174 0175

D-U-N-S 61-119-3699 IMP
■ **WILEY PUBLISHING INC**
JOHN WILEY AND SONS
(*Suby of* JOHN WILEY & SONS INC) ★
111 River St, Hoboken, NJ 07030-5773
Tel (201) 748-6000 *Founded/Ownrshp* 2001
Sales 268.7MM^E *EMP* 3,200
SIC 2731 Books: publishing & printing
CEO: Stephen M Smith
COO: William Barry
**Sr VP:* William J Arlington
**VP:* Ellis E Cousens
**VP:* Edward J Melando
VP: Natu Patel

D-U-N-S 10-192-3977
WILEY REIN LLP
1776 K St Nw, Washington, DC 20006-2304
Tel (202) 719-7000 *Founded/Ownrshp* 1983
Sales 102.2MM^E *EMP* 575
SIC 8111 General practice law office
Ch: Richard E Wiley
**Pt:* Richard J Bodorff
Pt: Thomas W Brunner
**Pt:* Bert W Rein
**Pt:* Steven Richardson
**Pt:* Richard A Simpson
Pt: Daniel Standish
**Mng Pt:* Peter D Shields
CFO: Ann Hilpert
VP: Kay Nash
Exec: Donna Corini
Exec: James Joehrig
Exec: Nicole Owren
Comm Man: Patricia O'Connell

D-U-N-S 06-712-0196
WILEY SANDERS TRUCK LINES INC
100 Sanders Rd, Troy, AL 36079-2501
Tel (334) 566-5184 *Founded/Ownrshp* 1972
Sales 135.7MM^E *EMP* 1,200
SIC 4213 Trucking, except local
Ch Bd: Wiley C Sanders Jr
**Pr:* Bobby Brown
**CEO:* Driscoll Colquitt
**CFO:* William Colquett
**VP:* Frankie Farris
VP: Jane Hasson
VP: Frankie Sarris
VP: John Smothers
**VP:* Steve Stephens
CIO: Kevin Baker
VP Sls: Frank Esaris

D-U-N-S 00-693-8807
WILHELM CONSTRUCTION INC
F.A. WILHELM CONSTRUCTION
3914 Prospect St, Indianapolis, IN 46203-2344
Tel (317) 359-5411 *Founded/Ownrshp* 1923
Sales 424.0MM *EMP* 1,200
Accts Katz Sapper & Miller Llp Ind
SIC 1542 1541 1761 Commercial & office building, new construction; Industrial buildings, new construction; Roofing, siding & sheet metal work
Pr: Philip Kenney
Pr: Larry Roan
**CFO:* Joseph D Cathcart
**Ex VP:* Jay R Watson
**VP:* Andrew S Lock
**VP:* Larry A Roan
IT Man: James Abner
Opers Mgr: Michael Kerr
Opers Mgr: Andrew Litke
Snr PM: Jason King

D-U-N-S 17-759-0858
▲ **WILHELMINA INTERNATIONAL INC**
200 Crescent Ct Ste 1400, Dallas, TX 75201-7826
Tel (214) 661-7488 *Founded/Ownrshp* 1967
Sales 83.8MM *EMP* 118^E
Tkr Sym WHLM *Exch* NAS
SIC 7363 Modeling service
CEO: William J Wackermann
**Ch Bd:* Mark E Schwarz
CFO: James A McCarthy

D-U-N-S 07-694-7696 IMP/EXP
WILHELMSEN SHIPS SERVICE INC
(*Suby of* WILHELMSEN SHIPS SERVICE AS)
9400 New Century Dr, Pasadena, TX 77507-1832
Tel (281) 867-2000 *Founded/Ownrshp* 1984
Sales 122.9MM^E *EMP* 250
SIC 5551 5088 7699 Marine supplies & equipment; Marine supplies; Nautical repair services
Pr: Colin Hatton
**Sec:* Thomas Flo
Ofcr: Valentina Godinho
VP: Terje Borkenhagen
Exec: Mahesh Chauhan
Exec: Vinayak Korgaonkar
Genl Mgr: Jason Chew
Genl Mgr: Adrian Peterson
Opers Supe: Leslie Caballero
Opers Mgr: Andrey Kolyushko
Ql Cn Mgr: Jane Subramaniam

D-U-N-S 17-439-7968 IMP/EXP
WILIAN HOLDING CO
EFCO
1800 Ne Broadway Ave, Des Moines, IA 50313-2644
Tel (515) 313-4350 *Founded/Ownrshp* 1985
Sales 218.2MM^E *EMP* 1,100
SIC 3444 Concrete forms, sheet metal
Pr: Albert L Jennings
**Treas:* Ryan Loecher
**VP:* Brian West

D-U-N-S 17-665-6742
WILKES COUNTY BOARD OF EDUCATION
613 Cherry St, North Wilkesboro, NC 28659-4229
Tel (336) 667-1121 *Founded/Ownrshp* 1900
Sales 34.6MM^E *EMP* 1,265
SIC 8211 Public elementary & secondary schools
Pr: Barbara England
Pr: Aaron L Fleming
Pr: Geraldine Foy
**Ch:* Coleen T Bush
Bd of Dir: Judith Walsh
**Prin:* Sharron N Huffman
**Prin:* Rick Lankford
Off Admin: Jasson Adkins
Dir IT: Trent Poplin
IT Man: Seth Prevette
Netwrk Eng: Annie Frazier

D-U-N-S 07-979-9738
WILKES COUNTY SCHOOLS
613 Cherry St, North Wilkesboro, NC 28659-4229
Tel (336) 667-1121 *Founded/Ownrshp* 2015
Sales 31.8MM^E *EMP* 10,000^E
SIC 8211 Public elementary & secondary schools
Bd of Dir: Mark Burcham
Ex Dir: Anna Lankford
HC Dir: Wesley Wood

WILKES UNIVERSITY
See COMMUNITY SERVICE OFFICE

D-U-N-S 07-915-8531
WILKES UNIVERSITY
84 W South St, Wilkes Barre, PA 18766-0003
Tel (570) 408-4200 *Founded/Ownrshp* 1947
Sales 116.6MM *EMP* 370
Accts Baker Tilly Virchow Krause Llp
SIC 8221 University
Pr: Patrick F Leahy
**Pr:* Timothy Gilmour
**VP:* Scott Byers
Exec: Jack Chielli
Assoc Dir: Erica Acosta
Assoc Dir: Bridget Giunta
Assoc Dir: Vicki Mayk
Mng Dir: Georgia Costalas
Off Admin: Ann M Feldmeth

D-U-N-S 10-558-6775
WILKES UNIVERSITY SECURITY DEPARTMENT
84 W South St, Wilkes Barre, PA 18766-0003
Tel (570) 408-4999 *Founded/Ownrshp* 2002
Sales 101.7MM *EMP* 25
Accts Kpmg Llp Mclean Va
SIC 7382 Security systems services
MIS Dir: Joseph Bellucci

D-U-N-S 07-599-9623
WILKES-BARRE AREA SCHOOL DISTRICT
730 S Main St, Wilkes Barre, PA 18702-3623
Tel (570) 826-7127 *Founded/Ownrshp* 1971
Sales 54.9MM^E *EMP* 1,200
SIC 8211 Public senior high school; Public junior high school; Public elementary school
Off Mgr: Teresa Popielarski
Teacher Pr: Rochelle Koury
Psych: Beth Owens

WILKES-BARRE GENERAL HOSPITAL
See WYOMING VALLEY HEALTH & EDUCATION FOUNDATION

D-U-N-S 80-443-5063
■ **WILKES-BARRE HOSPITAL CO LLC**
WYOMING VALLEY HEALTH CARE SYS
(*Suby of* COMMUNITY HEALTH SYSTEMS INC) ★
575 N River St, Wilkes Barre, PA 18764-0999
Tel (570) 829-8111 *Founded/Ownrshp* 2009
Sales 252.1MM^E *EMP* 3,500
SIC 8062 8069 General medical & surgical hospitals; Cancer hospital
Ch: David Hochhauser MD
**Pr:* William Moore
**CEO:* Cor Catena
**CEO:* Diane Ljungquist
**COO:* Pam Tahan

**CFO:* Maggie Koehler
**Ch:* Charles D Flack
Ofcr: Cherry Clavette
Ex VP: Mirian Graddick-Weir
VP: Cheryl Kellar
Exec: Tom Moore
Dir Teleco: Justine Tomko
Board of Directors: Mindy Belleman, Gretta Gross, Raymond Kabata, Cindy Turchin

D-U-N-S 82-787-8059
WILKINSON CORP
212 N Naches Ave, Yakima, WA 98901-2438
Tel (866) 914-2403 *Founded/Ownrshp* 1991
Sales 252.6MM^E *EMP* 600
SIC 6552 Subdividers & developers
Ch Bd: Russ Wilkinson
**Pr:* Lonnie Gienger
VP: Doug Ellison
VP: Robert Hall
MIS Dir: Kelli Mattingly

D-U-N-S 02-003-5838
WILL COUNTY
302 N Chicago St, Joliet, IL 60432-4078
Tel (815) 740-4602 *Founded/Ownrshp* 1836
Sales NA *EMP* 2,000
Accts Baket Tilly Virchow Krause Ll
SIC 9111 County supervisors' & executives' offices
Bd of Dir: Mark Ferry
Ofcr: Tara Doggett
Comm Dir: Anastasia Tuskey

D-U-N-S 79-180-7977
WILL PERKINS INC
(*Suby of* PERKINS & WILL GROUP LTD) ★
1250 24th St Nw Ste 800, Washington, DC 20037-1223
Tel (312) 755-0770 *Founded/Ownrshp* 1970
Sales 232.7MM^E *EMP* 1,500
SIC 8712 7389 Architectural services; Interior designer
Pr: Phil Harrison
**CFO:* Dana Waymire
Mktg Mgr: Amie Oberstar

D-U-N-S 03-735-7238
WILLAMETT FALLS HOSPITAL
WILLAMETT FLS HLTH EDUCATN CTR
1500 Division St, Oregon City, OR 97045-1597
Tel (503) 650-6765 *Founded/Ownrshp* 1988
Sales 85.0MM *EMP* 760
Accts Delap Llp Lake Oswego Or
SIC 8062 General medical & surgical hospitals
Pr: Russ Reinhard
**CFO:* Tim Blanchard
**VP:* John Flanders

WILLAMETT FLS HLTH EDUCATN CTR
See WILLAMETT FALLS HOSPITAL

D-U-N-S 04-083-8406
WILLAMETTE DENTAL MANAGEMENT CORP
6950 Ne Campus Way, Hillsboro, OR 97124-5611
Tel (503) 952-2000 *Founded/Ownrshp* 1996
Sales 51.4MM^E *EMP* 1,000
SIC 8021 Dental insurance plan
Pr: Eugene C Skourtes
**Pr:* Stephen Petruzelli
**Treas:* Yuen Chin
VP: Kristen Simmons

D-U-N-S 02-761-2282 IMP
WILLAMETTE EGG FARMS LLC
MOSES LAKES FARMS
31348 S Highway 170, Canby, OR 97013-9596
Tel (503) 651-0000 *Founded/Ownrshp* 1995
Sales 85.4MM *EMP* 200
SIC 5144

D-U-N-S 05-596-8481
WILLAMETTE UNIVERSITY
900 State St, Salem, OR 97301-3930
Tel (503) 370-6728 *Founded/Ownrshp* 1842
Sales 101.5MM *EMP* 700
Accts Kpmg Llp Portland Or
SIC 8221 University
Pr: Stephen E Thorsett
Pt: Ed Warnock
Treas: W Yasinski
**Sr VP:* Monica Rimai
VP: Michael Beseda
VP: Cynthia Chand
VP: Jordan Fickas
VP: Jessica Outhet
VP: Shelby Radcliffe
VP: Debra Ringold
VP: Shana Sechrist
VP: James Sumner
VP: Dan Valles
VP: Edward Whipple
**VP:* W Arnold Yasinski
Exec: Kristen Grainger
Assoc Dir: Rich Dennis

D-U-N-S 00-941-9151 IMP/EXP
WILLAMETTE VALLEY CO
WILVACO
1075 Arrowsmith St, Eugene, OR 97402-9121
Tel (541) 484-9621 *Founded/Ownrshp* 1952
Sales 142.0MM^E *EMP* 265
SIC 5085 2851 2891 5169 Industrial supplies; Wood fillers or sealers; Paints & paint additives; Glue; Chemicals, industrial & heavy
Pr: John R Harrison
CFO: Larry Deck
**CFO:* R Larry Deck
**VP:* Bill Harrison
**VP:* John Murray
VP: Lee Nall
**VP:* Tony Vuksich
Netwrk Eng: Mark Codington
Sfty Mgr: Robin Adair
Ql Cn Mgr: Brian Kuroda
Mktg Mgr: Wally Rowland

D-U-N-S 05-096-2653
WILLAMETTE VALLEY MEDICAL CENTER
(*Suby of* RRCH HEALTHCARE PARTNERS) ★
2700 Se Stratus Ave, McMinnville, OR 97128-6239
Tel (503) 472-6131 *Founded/Ownrshp* 2008
Sales 104.8MM *EMP* 600
SIC 8062 General medical & surgical hospitals
CFO: Cory Rhodes
Dir Lab: Shanna Middaugh
Dept Mgr: Chris Brooker
Software D: Jim Bratcher
Software D: Jerry Thalhamer
Mktg Dir: Julie Geisert
Pathlgst: Pam Smith
HC Dir: Amanda Gilmore
HC Dir: Karl Kamper

WILLAMETTE VALLEY TRTMNT CTR
See CRC HEALTH CORPORATE

WILLAMINA LUMBER COMPANY
See HAMPTON LUMBER MILLS INC

D-U-N-S 82-831-4703
WILLAN INC
(*Suby of* SYNCREON HOLDINGS INC) ★
2851 High Meadow Cir # 250, Auburn Hills, MI 48326-2792
Tel (248) 377-4700 *Founded/Ownrshp* 2000
Sales 12.1MM[E] *EMP* 4,472[E]
SIC 3559 Automotive related machinery
CEO: Willie Lanier

D-U-N-S 13-194-1684
WILLARD HOTEL
WILLARD INTRCNTINENTAL WASH HT
1401 Pennsylvania Ave Nw, Washington, DC 20004-1047
Tel (202) 628-9100 *Founded/Ownrshp* 1980
Sales 48.6MM[E] *EMP* 1,022
SIC 7011 Hotels
CEO: Richard Solomons
**Pt:* Oliver T Carr
Assoc Dir: Daniel Shaffer

WILLARD INTRCNTINENTAL WASH HT
See WILLARD HOTEL

D-U-N-S 79-404-3448 IMP/EXP
WILLBANKS METALS INC
1155 Ne 28th St, Fort Worth, TX 76106-7241
Tel (817) 625-6161 *Founded/Ownrshp* 1974
Sales 100.0MM *EMP* 110[E]
SIC 5051 3449 Steel; Miscellaneous metalwork
CEO: Ryan Letz
**Ch Bd:* Eric Letz
**Pr:* Scott Begin
CFO: Jonathan Putman
**VP:* Joe Culpepper
**VP:* Jim Ely
**VP:* David Freisen
CTO: Kyle McKillip
VP Opers: Clee Jackson
Sales Asso: Todd Weber

D-U-N-S 79-008-5476
■ **WILLBROS CONSTRUCTION (US) LLC**
(*Suby of* WILLBROS UNITED STATES HOLDINGS INC) ★
4400 Post Oak Pkwy # 1000, Houston, TX 77027-3439
Tel (713) 403-8000 *Founded/Ownrshp* 2000
Sales 100.9MM[E] *EMP* 120
SIC 1623 Oil & gas pipeline construction
Pr: Gerrit Coward
**Pr:* Scott Timpone
Sr VP: Mike Futch
VP: Mark Campbell
**VP:* Harry New

D-U-N-S 12-897-0873 IMP/EXP
WILLBROS DOWNSTREAM LLC
INSERV
4300 E 36th St N, Tulsa, OK 74115-1715
Tel (918) 556-3600 *Founded/Ownrshp* 1908
Sales 193.3MM[E] *EMP* 650
SIC 8711 Heating & ventilation engineering
CEO: Andy Farris
VP: Mark Brown
Genl Mgr: Steve Churchill
Genl Mgr: Jeff Stoddard
Sls Mgr: Gene Ward
Snr PM: Rodney Scott
Snr Mgr: James C Lefler Jr

D-U-N-S 83-006-9303
▲ **WILLBROS GROUP INC**
4400 Post Oak Pkwy, Houston, TX 77027-3421
Tel (713) 403-8000 *Founded/Ownrshp* 1908
Sales 908.9MM *EMP* 3,579[E]
Tkr Sym WG *Exch* NYS
SIC 8711 1542 Engineering services; Service station construction
Pr: Michael J Fournier
Pr: Linnie Freeman
COO: Michael Taylor
CFO: Van A Welch
Ex VP: J Robert Berra
Ex VP: Tom Vanhorn
Sr VP: Peter W Arbour
Sr VP: Harry W New
VP: John Allcorn
VP: Peter Arbour
VP: Denny Campos
VP: Stephen Douglas
VP: John Higgins
VP: Chuck Konechne
VP: Rick Reed
VP: Jeff Thetge
VP: Orval Williams
Exec: Johnny M Priest
Board of Directors: Edward J Dipaolo, Michael C Lebens, Daniel E Lonergan, Robert L Sluder, Phil D Wedemeyer, S Miller Williams

D-U-N-S 87-792-4464
WILLBROS INTERNATIONAL INC
WILLBROS MIDDLE EAST
(*Suby of* WILLBROS GLOBAL HOLDING INC)
4400 Post Oak Pkwy # 1000, Houston, TX 77027-3421
Tel (713) 403-8000 *Founded/Ownrshp* 2000
Sales 40.6MM[E] *EMP* 1,200
SIC 8711 Construction & civil engineering
Pr: R Clay Etheridge
Pr: Ronald Coleman

WILLBROS MIDDLE EAST
See WILLBROS INTERNATIONAL INC

D-U-N-S 18-668-6002
■ **WILLBROS UNITED STATES HOLDINGS INC**
(*Suby of* WILLBROS GROUP INC) ★
4400 Post Oak Pkwy # 1000, Houston, TX 77027-3439
Tel (713) 403-8000 *Founded/Ownrshp* 1908
Sales 1.0MMM[E] *EMP* 4,150
SIC 8711 1623 Consulting engineer; Oil & gas pipeline construction
CEO: Michael F Curran
**Pr:* Robert R Harl
**COO:* James L Gibson
**CFO:* Van Welch
**Ex VP:* Jerrit M Coward
**Sr VP:* Peter W Arbour
**Sr VP:* Earl R Collins
Sr VP: R Clay Etheridge
Sr VP: John Higgins
Sr VP: Patrick Schneider
VP: John Allcorn
VP: Matt R Rosser
VP: Jeffery D Thetge

D-U-N-S 07-887-1267
■ **WILLBROS UTILITY T&D HOLDINGS LLC**
(*Suby of* WILLBROS GROUP INC) ★
115 W 7th St Ste 1420, Fort Worth, TX 76102-7015
Tel (682) 233-9010 *Founded/Ownrshp* 2010
Sales 380.9MM[E] *EMP* 1,500[E]
SIC 8711 Engineering services

WILLCARE
See BRACOR INC

D-U-N-S 11-344-0619
▲ **WILLDAN GROUP INC**
2401 E Katella Ave # 300, Anaheim, CA 92806-5909
Tel (800) 424-9144 *Founded/Ownrshp* 1964
Sales 135.1MM *EMP* 688[E]
Tkr Sym WLDN *Exch* NGM
SIC 8711 8748 Civil engineering; Consulting engineer; Urban planning & consulting services
Ch Bd: Thomas D Brisbin
Pr: Michael A Bieber
Pr: Marc Tipermas
CEO: John Rinard
COO: Daniel Chow
COO: Rebekah Smith
CFO: Bill Ellis
CFO: Stacy B McLaughlin
Bd of Dir: Tom D Brisbin
Sr VP: Mike A Bieber
Sr VP: Edward Saltzberg
Sr VP: Frank G Tripepi
VP: Grant Anderson
VP: Jim Bailey
VP: Michael Bieber
VP: Mike Deblieux
VP: Afsaneh House
VP: Elroy Kiepke
VP: Kris Murray
Board of Directors: Steven A Cohen, Raymond W Holdsworth, Douglas J McEachern, Keith W Renken, Mohammed Shahidehpour, John M Toups, Win Westfall

D-U-N-S 00-628-9680 IMP/EXP
WILLERT HOME PRODUCTS INC (MO)
4044 Park Ave, Saint Louis, MO 63110-2320
Tel (314) 772-2822 *Founded/Ownrshp* 1946
Sales 140.3MM[E] *EMP* 350
SIC 3089 2869 2879 2842 Plastic kitchenware, tableware & houseware; Industrial organic chemicals; Insecticides, agricultural or household; Specialty cleaning, polishes & sanitation goods
Pr: Bill Willert
CFO: Brian Warner
Ex VP: Susan Hantak
Ex VP: Brian Willert
VP: Bill Bond
Plnt Mgr: Joe Adamo
Plnt Mgr: Aaron Harris
Mktg Dir: Shelley Cade
Sls Dir: Garnell Lewis
Sls Dir: Sean Tillmon
Sales Asso: Jennifer Thorne

D-U-N-S 02-566-3527 IMP
WILLIAM A RANDOLPH INC (IL)
WM. A. RANDOLPH
820 Lakeside Dr Ste 3, Gurnee, IL 60031-9165
Tel (847) 856-0123 *Founded/Ownrshp* 1958
Sales 110.0MM *EMP* 100
SIC 1542 Commercial & office building, new construction
Pr: Anthony Riccardi
CFO: Jim Gurgone
Treas: Judy Bernstein
**VP:* Eric P Handley
VP: William Hansen
VP: Nobel Heller
VP: Eric Heneley
VP: Kevin Kruckeverg
**VP:* Peter Luedeking
**VP:* Anthony J Riccardi
Genl Mgr: Sharon Bobendrier

D-U-N-S 00-207-0498 IMP/EXP
WILLIAM BARNET & SON LLC (SC)
1300 Hayne St, Spartanburg, SC 29301-5802
Tel (864) 327-4620 *Founded/Ownrshp* 1898
Sales 213.3MM[E] *EMP* 575
SIC 5199 2823 2221 2824 Fabrics, yarns & knit goods; Cellulosic manmade fibers; Broadwoven fabric mills, manmade; Polyester fibers
Pr: Bill McCrary

D-U-N-S 07-636-2110
WILLIAM BEAUMONT HOSPITAL
BEAUMONT HEALTH SYSTEM
(*Suby of* BEAUMONT BOTSFORD OAKWOOD HLTH) ★
3601 W 13 Mile Rd, Royal Oak, MI 48073-6712
Tel (248) 898-5000 *Founded/Ownrshp* 1949
Sales 1.3MMM *EMP* 18,050[E]
SIC 8062 Hospital, affiliated with AMA residency
Pr: Gene Michalski
**Ch Bd:* Stephen R Howard
**V Ch:* Mark Shaevsky
**Pr:* Brian Connolly
**Pr:* Paul Lacasse
**CFO:* John Keuten
**Treas:* Barbara Mahone
Ofcr: Doug Clarkston
Ofcr: Rick Swaine
**Sr VP:* Margaret Casey
VP: David Felten
VP: Steven Richardson
VP: Colette Stimmell
Exec: Edward Gillis

D-U-N-S 00-543-8403 IMP
WILLIAM BLAIR & CO LLC
(*Suby of* WBC HOLDINGS, L.P.)
222 W Adams St Ste 2900, Chicago, IL 60606-5216
Tel (312) 236-1600 *Founded/Ownrshp* 1935
Sales 700.2MM[E] *EMP* 1,100
Accts Ernst & Young Llp Chicago I
SIC 6211 Stock brokers & dealers
CEO: John Ettelson
**CFO:* Jon W Zindel
Bd of Dir: Michael Iancosek
Top Exec: John L Brennan Jr
VP: Mark Birkett
VP: Todd R Cassidy
VP: Brian Doyle
VP: Christopher O Glass
VP: Andrew Hendrie
VP: Stewart Licudi
VP: Walter Prest
VP: Walter Randall
VP: Vice Rollings
VP: Corey P Ryan
VP: Anurag Sharma
VP: Brent Smith
VP: Buck Stebbins
VP: Richard Thivierge
VP: Michael W Trimberger
VP: James Wildman
Exec: John Smith

D-U-N-S 00-102-0684 IMP/EXP
■ **WILLIAM CARTER CO** (GA)
CARTER'S FACTORY OUTLET
(*Suby of* CARTERS INC) ★
3438 Peachtree Rd Ne, Atlanta, GA 30326-1554
Tel (678) 791-1000 *Founded/Ownrshp* 1865
Sales 3.1MMM *EMP* 16,800
SIC 5641 5137 Children's & infants' wear stores; Infants' wear
CEO: Michael Casey
Pr: Brian J Lynch
Treas: Sean McHugh
Ex VP: Kevin D Corning
Ex VP: Peter Smith
Sr VP: Julie A Demilio
Sr VP: William Foglesong
Sr VP: Gill Wilson
Sr VP: Michael C Wu

D-U-N-S 10-237-0830 IMP
WILLIAM CHARLES LTD
1401 N 2nd St, Rockford, IL 61107-3044
Tel (815) 963-7400 *Founded/Ownrshp* 1982
Sales 179.5MM[E] *EMP* 400
SIC 1611 5211 1731 4953 Highway & street paving contractor; Highway & street maintenance; Sand & gravel; General electrical contractor; Sludge disposal sites; Sanitary landfill operation
Pr: Nathan Howard
**Sec:* Wayne Schwalen
**VP:* John Holmstrong

D-U-N-S 84-039-2810
WILLIAM DAVIS REALTY WOODLANDS LLC
17732 Creston Rd, Dallas, TX 75252
Tel (214) 621-9689 *Founded/Ownrshp* 2010
Sales 440.0MM *EMP* 400
SIC 6531 Real estate brokers & agents

D-U-N-S 96-241-4913
■ **WILLIAM GALLAGHER ASSOCIATES INSURANCE BROKERS INC**
(*Suby of* ARTHUR J GALLAGHER & CO) ★
470 Atlantic Ave Fl 13, Boston, MA 02210-2205
Tel (617) 261-6700 *Founded/Ownrshp* 2015
Sales NA *EMP* 250
SIC 6411 8742 Insurance agents, brokers & service; Compensation & benefits planning consultant
CEO: Philip Edmundson
Pr: Laura Handal
Pr: Patrick Veale
Sr VP: Kenneth Ambos
Sr VP: Louisa Bolick
Sr VP: Jeffrey Ursprung
VP: Sara Lavallee
VP: Mike Long
VP: Michael Talmanson

D-U-N-S 01-209-8745 IMP
WILLIAM H KOPKE JR INC
1000 Nthrn Blvd Ste 200, Great Neck, NY 11021
Tel (516) 328-6800 *Founded/Ownrshp* 1937
Sales 230.0MM *EMP* 60
SIC 5148 Fruits
Pr: Peter Kopke Sr
**VP:* Peter Kopke Jr
**VP:* William Kopke
**VP:* Michael Meyers

D-U-N-S 01-101-8611
WILLIAM H PORTER INC
PORTER CHEVROLET/HYUNDAI
414 E Cleveland Ave, Newark, DE 19711-3715
Tel (302) 453-6800 *Founded/Ownrshp* 1952
Sales 83.5MM[E] *EMP* 140
SIC 5511 Automobiles, new & used
Pr: Richard C Porter II
**VP:* Richard C Porter III

WILLIAM HARRIS INVESTORS
See HARRIS WILLIAM & CO INC

D-U-N-S 00-677-1307
WILLIAM HERBERT HUNT TRUST ESTATE
1601 Elm St Ste 3900, Dallas, TX 75201-4708
Tel (214) 880-8400 *Founded/Ownrshp* 1954
Sales 5.0MMM[E] *EMP* 251[E]
SIC 8742 6799 Management consulting services; Investors
Owner: William Herbert Hunt
CFO: Tom Nelson
Dir IT: Dan Robinson

D-U-N-S 00-327-3224 EXP
■ **WILLIAM L BONNELL CO INC**
BONNELL ALUMINUM
(*Suby of* TREDEGAR CORP) ★
25 Bonnell St, Newnan, GA 30263-1603
Tel (770) 253-2020 *Founded/Ownrshp* 1989
Sales 400.0MM *EMP* 1,500
SIC 3354 Shapes, extruded aluminum
CEO: W Brook Hamilton
Telecom Mg: James H Williams
Opers Mgr: Houston Donnie
Opers Mgr: Prather Layman
Sls Dir: Walt Hoban
Mktg Mgr: Guy Charpentier
Manager: Michael Delaney
Manager: Mike Krause
Snr Mgr: Bruce Plumlee
Snr Mgr: Beaman Richard
Snr Mgr: Hemphill Todd
Board of Directors: Norman A Scher

D-U-N-S 79-018-7673
WILLIAM L BONNELL CO INC
1100 Boulders Pkwy, North Chesterfield, VA 23225-4036
Tel (804) 330-1147 *Founded/Ownrshp* 1955
Sales 123.8MM[E] *EMP* 220[E]
SIC 3354 Aluminum extruded products
VP: McAlister C Marshall II

D-U-N-S 78-296-9992
▲ **WILLIAM LYON HOMES**
4695 Macarthur Ct Ste 800, Newport Beach, CA 92660-1863
Tel (949) 833-3600 *Founded/Ownrshp* 1956
Sales 1.1MMM *EMP* 586[E]
Tkr Sym WLH *Exch* NYS
SIC 1531 Operative builders; Speculative builder, single-family houses
Pr: Matthew R Zaist
**Ch Bd:* William H Lyon
CFO: Colin T Severn
Sr VP: Richard S Robinson
VP: Tom Bui
VP: Bryan Cazier
VP: Gary Haddy
VP: Jason R Liljestrom
VP: Rick Puffer
VP: Joe Whittemore
Sales Asso: Julia Giordani
Board of Directors: Douglas K Ammerman, Michael Barr, Thomas F Harrison, Gary H Hunt, William Lyon, Matthew R Niemann, Lynn Carlson Schell

D-U-N-S 80-587-1944
■ **WILLIAM LYON HOMES INC**
(*Suby of* WILLIAM LYON HOMES) ★
4695 Macarthur Ct Ste 800, Newport Beach, CA 92660-1863
Tel (949) 833-3600 *Founded/Ownrshp* 1992
Sales 193.3MM[E] *EMP* 350[E]
SIC 6552 Subdividers & developers
Ch Bd: William H Lyon
**CFO:* Colin Severn
**Sr VP:* Doug Harris
VP: Larry Smith
VP: Alan Uman

D-U-N-S 05-029-9031
WILLIAM MARSH RICE UNIVERSITY INC
6100 Main St, Houston, TX 77005-1827
Tel (713) 348-4055 *Founded/Ownrshp* 1891
Sales 653.3MM *EMP* 2,600
SIC 8221

WILLIAM MORROW PUBLISHING
See HARPERCOLLINS PUBLISHERS LLC

D-U-N-S 79-002-4330
WILLIAM P HEARNE PRODUCE LLC
707 W Lake Dr, Wimauma, FL 33598-3507
Tel (813) 633-8910 *Founded/Ownrshp* 2006
Sales 83.6MM[E] *EMP* 150
SIC 5141 Food brokers
**VP:* Tony Piedimonte

D-U-N-S 17-316-9160
WILLIAM PATERSON UNIVERSITY
300 Pompton Rd, Wayne, NJ 07470-2103
Tel (973) 720-2000 *Founded/Ownrshp* 1992
Sales 151.7MM *EMP* 1,300
Accts Baker Tilly Virchow Krause Ll
SIC 8221 College, except junior
Pr: Kathleen Waldron
**VP:* Stephen Bolyai
**VP:* Miki Cammarata
**VP:* Kristin E Cohen
**VP:* Pamela L Ferguson
VP: Diana Gilmartin
**VP:* 1988-Present Active Here
VP: Casey Lum
VP: Helen Pan
**VP:* Warren Sandmann
Assoc Dir: Karen Hilberg
Assoc Dir: Jane Hutchison
Assoc Dir: Victoria Nauta
Assoc Dir: Patricia Whiteman

D-U-N-S 07-552-0676
WILLIAM PENN FOUNDATION
2 Logan Sq Fl 11, Philadelphia, PA 19103-2763
Tel (215) 988-1830 *Founded/Ownrshp* 1945
Sales 152.3MM *EMP* 27
Accts Kpmg Llp
SIC 6732 Charitable trust management
Pr: Helen Davis Picher
CIO: Madoe Htun
IT Man: Edward Wagner

D-U-N-S 14-420-9269
WILLIAM PRINCE HEALTH SYSTEM
(*Suby of* LAKESIDE FAMILY PHYSICIANS) ★
8650 Sudley Rd Ste 411, Manassas, VA 20110-4416
Tel (703) 369-8270 *Founded/Ownrshp* 1984
Sales 2.6MM *EMP* 1,700
SIC 8741 Hospital management; Nursing & personal care facility management
Pr: Michael Schwartz
Chf Path: Jeffrey Skovronsky
**Ch Bd:* Michael Dailey
**CFO:* Robert W Reily
Off Mgr: Jane Coppage

D-U-N-S 07-827-8702
WILLIAM PRINCE HOSPITAL
(*Suby of* LAKESIDE FAMILY PHYSICIANS) ★
8700 Sudley Rd, Manassas, VA 20110-4418
Tel (703) 369-8484 *Founded/Ownrshp* 2009
Sales 239.0MM *EMP* 1,300
SIC 8062 General medical & surgical hospitals
CEO: Carl Armato
COO: Cynda Tipple
**Prin:* Richard A Belden
CIO: Dolly Ellis

D-U-N-S 96-752-1316
WILLIAM PRINCE HOSPITAL
2085 Frontis Plaza Blvd, Winston Salem, NC 27103-5614
Tel (336) 718-2803 *Founded/Ownrshp* 2011
Sales 235.2MM *EMP* 2
SIC 8699 Charitable organization

D-U-N-S 06-618-9770
WILLIAM RAINEY HARPER COLLEGE EDUCATIONAL FOUNDATION
1200 W Algonquin Rd, Palatine, IL 60067-7373
Tel (847) 925-6490 *Founded/Ownrshp* 1965
Sales 45.9MM *EMP* 1,307
Accts Crowe Horwath Llp Oak Brook
SIC 8399 Fund raising organization, non-fee basis
Pr: Kenneth L Ender
Genl Mgr: Allison Grippe
Netwrk Mgr: Sue Nowakowski

D-U-N-S 08-266-2743
WILLIAM RAVEIS REAL ESTATE INC
KEMPER INSURANCE
7 Trap Falls Rd, Shelton, CT 06484-4601
Tel (203) 926-1090 *Founded/Ownrshp* 1974
Sales NA *EMP* 125
SIC 6411 Insurance agents, brokers & service; Policyholders' consulting service
Ch Bd: William Raveis
**Pr:* Carolyn Deal
Sr VP: Glenn Felson
**Sr VP:* William R Gamelli Jr
Sr VP: John Tarducci
VP: Wayne Edmonds
VP: Lorraine Megenis
Exec: Susan Kelly
Exec: Clifford Slater
Exec: Jeff Whitlock
Ex Dir: Jamie Zdru

D-U-N-S 80-016-3482
WILLIAM S HART UNION HIGH SCHOOL DISTRICT
21380 Centre Pointe Pkwy, Santa Clarita, CA 91350-3050
Tel (661) 259-0033 *Founded/Ownrshp* 2007
Sales 65.5MM^E *EMP* 1,300^E
Accts Christy White Accountancy Corp
SIC 8211 Public elementary & secondary schools
Prgrm Mgr: Nicholas Betty
DP Dir: Ken Harvey
Dir IT: Scott Schultz
Pr Dir: Dave Caldwell
Psych: Laura Ramirez
Psych: Victor Solis
HC Dir: Marty Lieberman

D-U-N-S 00-812-9756
WILLIAM STAMPS FARISH FUND
1100 La St Ste 1200, Houston, TX 77002
Tel (713) 757-7313 *Founded/Ownrshp* 1951
Sales 119.1MM *EMP* 4
SIC 7389 Fund raising organizations
Pr: W S Farish

D-U-N-S 06-925-9398
WILLIAM W BACKUS HOSPITAL
(*Suby of* BACKUS CORP) ★
326 Washington St, Norwich, CT 06360-2740
Tel (860) 889-8331 *Founded/Ownrshp* 1892, 1983
Sales 285.5MM *EMP* 1,300
SIC 8062 General medical & surgical hospitals
Pr: David Whitehead
Pr: Dave Whitehead
Ofcr: Lauren Reil
Sr VP: Dan Lohr
VP: James Healy
VP: Mary Kohanski
Comm Dir: Robert Fraleigh
Dir Bus: Janette Edwards
Adm Dir: James O'Dea
Snr Ntwrk: Bill Jorsz
Site Mgr: Todd Osowski

D-U-N-S 08-433-7229
WILLIAMS & CONNOLLY LLP (DC)
725 12th St Nw, Washington, DC 20005-5901
Tel (202) 434-5800 *Founded/Ownrshp* 1967
Sales 98.4MM^E *EMP* 650
SIC 8111 General practice law office
Mng Pt: Robert Barnett
Pt: Eva Petko Esber
Pt: Bruce R Genderson
Pt: Brendan V Sullivan Jr
Pt: John K Villa
Ofcr: Paul Hourihan
Ex Dir: Lynda Schuler
CIO: Nicole G Minnick
Counsel: Jeremiah Collins
Counsel: Helen I Dooley
Counsel: Mara W Murphy

D-U-N-S 15-101-0675
WILLIAMS BROS HEALTH CARE PHARMACY INC
10 Williams Brothers Dr, Washington, IN 47501-4535
Tel (812) 254-2497 *Founded/Ownrshp* 1990
Sales 91.3MM^E *EMP* 315
SIC 5047 7352 5999 5169 3999 Medical equipment & supplies; Hospital equipment & furniture; Medical equipment rental; Telephone & communication equipment; Oxygen; Wheelchair lifts
Ex VP: Charles C Williams
**VP:* Jeffrey W Williams

D-U-N-S 00-486-2264
WILLIAMS BROTHERS CONSTRUCTION CO INC (TX)
WB
3800 Milam St, Houston, TX 77006-5158
Tel (713) 522-9821 *Founded/Ownrshp* 1955
Sales 505.7MM^E *EMP* 2,331
SIC 1622

D-U-N-S 06-740-8575
WILLIAMS BROTHERS CONSTRUCTION INC
WBCI
1200 E Kelly Ave, Peoria, IL 61616-6579
Tel (309) 688-0416 *Founded/Ownrshp* 1973
Sales 140.0MM *EMP* 75
SIC 1542 Commercial & office building, new construction; Institutional building construction
Pr: David Williams
**Treas:* Jackie Smith
**VP:* Joseph Heck
**VP:* Joseph T Williams
Board of Directors: David Williams

D-U-N-S 00-790-8163 IMP
▲ WILLIAMS COMPANIES INC
1 Williams Ctr, Tulsa, OK 74172-0140
Tel (918) 573-2000 *Founded/Ownrshp* 1908
Sales 7.3MMM *EMP* 6,578
Tkr Sym WMB *Exch* NYS
SIC 4922 4924 1311 1321 Natural gas transmission; Pipelines, natural gas; Natural gas distribution; Natural gas production; Natural gas liquids
Pr: Alan S Armstrong
**Ch Bd:* Kathleen Cooper
CFO: Donald R Chappel
Ofcr: Robyn L Ewing
Sr VP: Walter J Bennett
Sr VP: John R Dearborn
Sr VP: Rory L Miller
Sr VP: Sarah C Miller
Sr VP: Fred E Pace
Sr VP: Brian L Perilloux
Sr VP: Robert S Purgason
Sr VP: James E Scheel
Sr VP: John D Seldenrust
VP: Robert Hatley
VP: Ted T Timmermans
VP: Donald Wicburg
Board of Directors: Murray D Smith, Stephen W Bergstrom, William H Spence, Stephen Chazen, Janice D Stoney, Joseph R Cleveland, Charles Cogut, Michael A Creel, John A Hagg, Juanita H Hinshaw, Peter Ragauss, Scott D Sheffield

D-U-N-S 00-988-1687
■ WILLIAMS CONSOLIDATED I LTD
WILLIAMS INSULATION
(*Suby of* CENTRAL VALLEY INSULATION) ★
1524 N Port Ave, Corpus Christi, TX 78401-1616
Tel (386) 304-2200 *Founded/Ownrshp* 2008
Sales 55.5MM^E *EMP* 4,711^E
SIC 1742

D-U-N-S 04-368-0982 IMP
WILLIAMS DISTRIBUTING CO
WILLLIAMS KITCHEN & BATH
658 Richmond St Nw, Grand Rapids, MI 49504-2036
Tel (616) 771-0505 *Founded/Ownrshp* 1957
Sales 338.9MM^E *EMP* 260
SIC 5075 Warm air heating equipment & supplies; Air conditioning & ventilation equipment & supplies
Ch Bd: James C Williams
**Pr:* Michael J Koster
VP: Marty Fitch

WILLIAMS E & P
See WILLIAMS OLEFINS LLC

D-U-N-S 60-890-6020
■ WILLIAMS ENERGY SERVICES LLC
(*Suby of* WILLIAMS COMPANIES INC) ★
1 One Williams Ctr Bsmt 2, Tulsa, OK 74172-0172
Tel (918) 573-2000 *Founded/Ownrshp* 1999
Sales 638.9MM^E *EMP* 660
SIC 4923 5172 Gas transmission & distribution; Petroleum products; Gases
Pr: Alan S Armstrong
**Sr VP:* Frank E Billings
**Sr VP:* Allison G Bridges
**Sr VP:* Don R Chappel
**Sr VP:* John R Dearborn
Off Admin: Ralph Hill
Opers Supe: Clete Long

D-U-N-S 87-984-7010
■ WILLIAMS FIELD SERVICES CO LLC
(*Suby of* WILLIAMS COMPANIES INC) ★
1 Williams Ctr, Tulsa, OK 74172-0140
Tel (918) 573-2000 *Founded/Ownrshp* 2010
Sales 578.5MM^E *EMP* 450
SIC 1311 Crude petroleum & natural gas
Pr: Steve Malcolm
**Treas:* Travis Campbell
**Sr VP:* Alan S Armstrong

D-U-N-S 80-900-5374
■ WILLIAMS FIELD SERVICES GROUP LLC
(*Suby of* WILLIAMS ENERGY SERVICES LLC) ★
1 One Williams Ctr, Tulsa, OK 74172-0140
Tel (918) 573-2000 *Founded/Ownrshp* 1993
Sales 305.7MM^E *EMP* 500
SIC 4925 Manufactured gas, production & distribution
Pr: Lloyd A Hightower
**Treas:* Travis Campbell
**Sr VP:* Jerry F Gollnick

WILLIAMS FIELD SERVICES-GULF C
See WILLIAMS GAS PIPELINE-TRANSCO

D-U-N-S 06-725-5901 IMP
■ WILLIAMS GAS PIPELINE-TRANSCO
WILLIAMS FIELD SERVICES-GULF C
(*Suby of* WILLIAMS COMPANIES INC) ★
2800 Post Oak Blvd # 300, Houston, TX 77056-6147
Tel (713) 215-2000 *Founded/Ownrshp* 2000
Sales 801.2MM^E *EMP* 1,596
SIC 1321 1221 1222 Natural gas liquids; Surface mining, bituminous; Bituminous coal-underground mining
Pr: Alan S Armstrong
Ch Bd: Keith Bailey
CFO: Rick Rodekohr
Sr VP: Randall Lee Barnard
Sr VP: Frank E Billings
Sr VP: Allison G Bridges
Sr VP: Donald R Chappel
Sr VP: John R Dearborn
VP: Nick Bacile
VP: Edward R Brewer
VP: John Bumgarner
VP: Randall R Conklin
VP: Frank J Ferazzi

D-U-N-S 78-562-8947
■ WILLIAMS INDUSTRIAL SERVICES GROUP LLC
(*Suby of* GLOBAL POWER EQUIPMENT GROUP INC) ★
100 Crescent Center Pkwy # 1240, Tucker, GA 30084-7060
Tel (866) 851-4077 *Founded/Ownrshp* 2005
Sales 160.2MM^E *EMP* 1,304^E
SIC 1799 Asbestos removal & encapsulation
Pr: Ken Robuck

D-U-N-S 00-325-8183 IMP
▲ WILLIAMS INDUSTRIES INC (VA)
1128 Tyler Farms Dr, Raleigh, NC 27603-7949
Tel (919) 604-1746 *Founded/Ownrshp* 1970
Sales 88.9MM^E *EMP* 500
Tkr Sym WMSI *Exch* OTO
SIC 3441 1531 1541 3315 1791 Fabricated structural metal for bridges; Operative builders; Steel building construction; Steel wire & related products; Structural steel erection
Ch Bd: Frank E Williams III
**VP:* Marianne Pastor
VP: Clinton E Williams
**VP Mfg:* Danny C Dunlap
Corp Couns: Daniel Maller
Board of Directors: Stephen N Ashman, William J Sim, Frank E Williams Jr, John A Yerrick

D-U-N-S 00-326-4215
WILLIAMS INSTITUTIONAL FOODS INC (GA)
1325 Bowens Mill Rd Sw, Douglas, GA 31533-3933
Tel (912) 384-5270 *Founded/Ownrshp* 1951, 1972
Sales 92.2MM^E *EMP* 90
SIC 5141 Groceries, general line
Pr: John McCrary
**Ch Bd:* Robert W Williams
**CFO:* Joy W Paulk
Opers Mgr: Steve Crosby

WILLIAMS INSULATION
See WILLIAMS CONSOLIDATED I LTD

D-U-N-S 09-748-8894
■ WILLIAMS INSULATION CO OF AUSTIN INC
AUSTIN CONTRACTOR SERVICES
(*Suby of* B S I HOLDINGS INC) ★
4300 Nixon Ln, Austin, TX 78725-1106
Tel (512) 928-4002 *Founded/Ownrshp* 1980
Sales 72.2MM^E *EMP* 1,400
SIC 1742

D-U-N-S 00-640-1970 IMP
WILLIAMS INTERNATIONAL CO LLC
2280 E West Maple Rd, Commerce Township, MI 48390-3828
Tel (248) 624-5200 *Founded/Ownrshp* 1955, 1995
Sales 208.4MM^E *EMP* 800^E
SIC 3724 3764 Turbines, aircraft type; Engines & engine parts, guided missile
VP: John Becker
VP: Scott Cruzen
VP: Cal Schalk
VP: Frank Smith
QA Dir: John Lentz
IT Man: Mark Csizmadia
IT Man: Lee Kappler
Sftwr Eng: Joe Morris

D-U-N-S 96-160-1473
WILLIAMS LEA INC
(*Suby of* DEUTSCHE POST AG)
381 Park Ave S Fl 5, New York, NY 10016-8806
Tel (212) 351-9000 *Founded/Ownrshp* 1989
Sales 421.6MM^E *EMP* 3,000
SIC 8741 Management services
CEO: Patrick Kelleher
Pr: John Snowdon
CEO: Deb Dulsky
CEO: Todd Handcock
CEO: Tim Rodber
CFO: Liz Catchpole
CFO: Chelsea Gibson
Ofcr: Conor Davey
VP: Edwin Kiernan
VP: Ray Krienke
VP: Christopher Lamb
VP: Adam Lindstrom
VP: Darren O'Meara
VP: David Pennino
VP: Joanne Prifti
VP: Marc Quinlivan
VP: Edward Stone
VP Bus Dev: Andrew Parrish
Exec: Minnie Calo
Exec: Renard Phillips
Dir Bus: Cicely Brown
Board of Directors: Chelsea Gibson, Patrick Kelleher

WILLIAMS MOBILE OFFICES
See WHITLEY MANUFACTURING CO INC

WILLIAMS OIL & PROPANE
See WILLIAMS OIL CO INC

D-U-N-S 01-503-7518
WILLIAMS OIL CO INC
WILLIAMS OIL & PROPANE
44 Reuter Blvd, Towanda, PA 18848-2153
Tel (570) 265-6673 *Founded/Ownrshp* 1983
Sales 184.5MM^E *EMP* 400
SIC 5172 5983 Gasoline; Fuel oil dealers
Pr: Randy B Williams
IT Man: Bill Carmalt

D-U-N-S 78-530-4549
■ WILLIAMS OLEFINS LLC
WILLIAMS E & P
(*Suby of* WILLIAMS COMPANIES INC) ★
1 One Williams Ctr Bsmt 2, Tulsa, OK 74172-0172
Tel (918) 573-2000 *Founded/Ownrshp* 1999
Sales 104.3MM^E *EMP* 147^E
SIC 4922 Natural gas transmission
CEO: Alan S Armstrong
**Sr VP:* Frank E Billings
**Sr VP:* Allison G Bridges
**Sr VP:* John R Dearborn Jr
**Sr VP:* Rory L Miller

D-U-N-S 55-755-6532
WILLIAMS PARTNERS LP
1 Williams Ctr Bsmt 2, Tulsa, OK 74172-0172
Tel (918) 573-2000 *Founded/Ownrshp* 2005
Sales 6.6MMM *EMP* 4,909^E
SIC 4922 1321 4925

D-U-N-S 83-269-5790
▲ WILLIAMS PARTNERS LP
1 Williams Ctr, Tulsa, OK 74172-0140
Tel (918) 573-2000 *Founded/Ownrshp* 2010
Sales 7.3MMM *EMP* 6,578^E
Tkr Sym WPZ *Exch* NYS
SIC 1311 4922 Natural gas production; Natural gas transmission
Ch Bd: Alan S Armstrong
Genl Pt: Wpz GP LLC
Dir Risk M: Jake Murray
Genl Mgr: Ken Access
Snr Ntwrk: Elizabeth Condon
Software D: Chris Victor

D-U-N-S 07-881-5343
WILLIAMS PARTNERS OPERATING LLC
1 Williams Ctr, Tulsa, OK 74172-0140
Tel (918) 573-2000 *Founded/Ownrshp* 2005
Sales 2.0MMM^E *EMP* 1,411
SIC 4923 Gas transmission & distribution
Ch Bd: Alan S Armstrong
CFO: Donald R Chappel

D-U-N-S 78-496-6314
■ WILLIAMS PLANT SERVICES LLC
(*Suby of* WILLIAMS INDUSTRIAL SERVICES GROUP LLC) ★
100 Crescent Center Pkwy # 1240, Tucker, GA 30084-7063
Tel (770) 879-4500 *Founded/Ownrshp* 2003
Sales 100.0MM^E *EMP* 700^E
SIC 1629 8744 Industrial plant construction; Base maintenance (providing personnel on continuing basis)
Pr: Kenneth W Robuck
VP: Jeff Gibbons
Genl Couns: W Herb Johnson

D-U-N-S 00-310-0542 IMP/EXP
WILLIAMS SCOTSMAN INC (MD)
(*Suby of* ALGECO SCOTSMAN) ★
901 S Bond St Ste 600, Baltimore, MD 21231-3348
Tel (410) 931-6000 *Founded/Ownrshp* 1955
Sales 1.4MMM^E *EMP* 1,661
SIC 1531 1541 5039 7359 Operative builders; Industrial buildings & warehouses; Prefabricated structures; Metal buildings; ; Equipment rental & leasing
Pr: Bradley L Soultz
**Treas:* Timothy D Boswell
VP: Andrew Auns
VP: Marty Blanar
VP: Michele Cunningham
VP: Darren C Gould
VP: Jeff Jones
VP: Azuwuike H Ndukwu
VP: Raymond Onofrio
VP: Renee Pisani
VP: Angus Rayner
VP: Terry Richardson
**VP:* Warren Smith

D-U-N-S 79-998-4869
WILLIAMS SCOTSMAN INTERNATIONAL INC
ALGECO SCOTSMAN
(*Suby of* TDR CAPITAL LLP)
901 S Bond St Ste 600, Baltimore, MD 21231-3348
Tel (800) 782-1500 *Founded/Ownrshp* 2008
Sales 1.5MMM^E *EMP* 2,377
SIC 4225 General warehousing & storage
CEO: Jean-Marc Germain
**Pr:* Bradley L Soultz
COO: Seth Schorr
CFO: Michael Richard
Treas: Timothy D Boswell

Top Exec: David Vickers
Ex VP: Jon Veldman
Sr VP: Olga Damiron
Sr VP: Ryan Jurkovic
VP: Rick Bennett
VP: Mark G Delaney
VP: Rick Delvin
VP: Barry Dotson
VP: Philippe Dulou
VP: Dean T Fisher
VP: Andrew Flynn
VP: Brett Kerekffy
VP: Joseph Lopardo
**VP:* Azuwuike H Ndukwu
VP: Ross Perkinson
VP: Patrick Potter
Board of Directors: Victoria Morris

D-U-N-S 02-926-3563
▲ WILLIAMS-SONOMA INC
3250 Van Ness Ave, San Francisco, CA 94109-1012
Tel (415) 421-7900 *Founded/Ownrshp* 1956
Sales 4.9MMM *EMP* 28,100
Accts Deloitte & Touche Llp San Fr
Tkr Sym WSM *Exch* NYS
SIC 5719 5722 5261 5961 Kitchenware; Lighting, lamps & accessories; Beddings & linens; Pictures & mirrors; Household appliance stores; Electric household appliances; Garden supplies & tools; Catalog & mail-order houses; Furniture & furnishings, mail order; General merchandise, mail order
Pr: Laura J Alber
Ch Bd: Adrian D P Bellamy
CFO: Julie P Whalen
Ofcr: Linda Lewis
Ex VP: Marta H Benson
Ex VP: Patrick J Connolly
Ex VP: Bud Cope
Ex VP: Vicki D McWilliams
Ex VP: John F Strain
Sr VP: David R King
Sr VP: Dean A Miller
Board of Directors: Rose Marie Bravo, Adrian T Dillon, Anthony A Greener, Ted W Hall, Sabrina Simmons, Jerry Strizke, Lorraine Twohill

D-U-N-S 17-823-3540 IMP/EXP
■ WILLIAMS-SONOMA STORES INC
POTTERY BARN
(*Suby of* WILLIAMS-SONOMA INC) ★
3250 Van Ness Ave, San Francisco, CA 94109-1012
Tel (415) 421-7900 *Founded/Ownrshp* 1984
Sales 1.8MMM^E *EMP* 5,300
SIC 5023 Fireplace equipment & accessories
CEO: Patrick J Connolly
**Ch Bd:* W Howard Lester
**Pr:* Laura J Alber
**Pr:* Sandra Stangl
**Ex VP:* Julie P Whalen

WILLIAMSBURG COMMUNITY HOSP
See SENTARA WILLIAMSBURG REGIONAL MEDICAL CENTER

D-U-N-S 82-940-8181
WILLIAMSBURG JAMES CITY COUNTY PUBLIC SCHOOLS
WJCC PUBLIC SCHOOLS
117 Ironbound Rd, Williamsburg, VA 23185-2616
Tel (757) 603-6400 *Founded/Ownrshp* 2009
Sales 950.0M *EMP* 2,000
SIC 8299 Schools & educational service
**CFO:* Rene Ewing
Snr Ntwrk: Kevin Blue

D-U-N-S 01-705-5278
WILLIAMSBURG-JAMES CITY COUNTY PUBLIC SCHOOLS
WJCC PUBLIC SCHOOLS
117 Ironbound Rd, Williamsburg, VA 23185-2616
Tel (757) 603-6400 *Founded/Ownrshp* 1870
Sales 57.5MM^E *EMP* 1,800
Accts Goodman & Company Newport New
SIC 8211 Public combined elementary & secondary school
MIS Dir: Brian Landers
Dir IT: Ernie Nucup
Pr Dir: Betsy Overcamp-Smith
Teacher Pr: Tim Baker
HC Dir: Janice Fowler

WILLIAMSON COUNTY BD EDUCATN
See WILLIAMSON COUNTY SCHOOL DISTRICT

D-U-N-S 07-822-5182 IMP
WILLIAMSON COUNTY HOSPITAL INC
WILLIAMSON MEDICAL CENTER
4321 Carothers Pkwy, Franklin, TN 37067-5909
Tel (615) 791-0500 *Founded/Ownrshp* 1957
Sales 168.9MM *EMP* 1,100^E
Accts Lattimore Black Morgan & Cain
SIC 8062 Hospital, affiliated with AMA residency
CEO: Don Webb
**COO:* Julie Miller
**CFO:* Paul Bolin
CFO: Gail Hazelwood
CFO: Donald Webb
VP: Christine Hartman
Dir Inf Cn: Vicki Sweeney
Dir Rx: Angela Dyer
Ex Dir: Steve Smith
CIO: Michael Spivey
Netwrk Mgr: Frederick Eure
Board of Directors: Greg Cook, Steve Smith

D-U-N-S 10-007-3535
WILLIAMSON COUNTY SCHOOL DISTRICT
WILLIAMSON COUNTY BD EDUCATN
1320 W Main St Ste 202, Franklin, TN 37064-3736
Tel (615) 472-4000 *Founded/Ownrshp* 2001
Sales 143.6MM^E *EMP* 2,300
Accts Osborne & Co Pc Brentwood Tn
SIC 8211 Public elementary school; Public junior high school; Public senior high school
Ch: Pj Mezera
**CFO:* Leslie Holman
**Ch:* Pat Anderson
Dir Sec: Michael Fletcher
Admn Mgr: Robin Dickerson
Admn Mgr: Melonye Lowe
Admn Mgr: Reggie Mason
Netwrk Eng: Steve Bethea

WILLIAMSON MEDICAL CENTER
See WILLIAMSON COUNTY HOSPITAL INC

D-U-N-S 03-160-2378
WILLIAMSON OIL CO INC
DISCOUNT FOOD MART
(*Suby of* MAPCO EXPRESS INC) ★
1603 Godfrey Ave Se, Fort Payne, AL 35967-4774
Tel (256) 845-9466 *Founded/Ownrshp* 2004
Sales 121.4MM^E *EMP* 640
Accts Mda Professional Group Pc
SIC 5541 5411 5172 Filling stations, gasoline; Convenience stores; Petroleum products
Pr: Ezra Uzi Yemin
COO: Lynwood Gregory
Treas: John Colling Jr

D-U-N-S 00-802-9498 IMP/EXP
WILLIAMSON-DICKIE MANUFACTURING CO
DICKIES
509 W Vickery Blvd, Fort Worth, TX 76104-1195
Tel (817) 336-7201 *Founded/Ownrshp* 1918, 1998
Sales 2.3MMM^E *EMP* 5,300
SIC 2326 2339 Men's & boys' work clothing; Industrial garments, men's & boys'; Women's & misses' outerwear
CEO: Beverly Allen
**Ch Bd:* Philip Williamson
**Pr:* Cathy Casstevens
**Ex VP:* Marett Cobb
Ex VP: Phil Laster
**Ex VP:* Randy Teuber
VP: Tony Haynie
VP: Marsha Parr
Mfg Dir: Oscar Chavarria
Natl Sales: Ron Kerr
VP Mktg: Matthew McCartin
Board of Directors: Philip Williamson, Daniel Feehan, George Gaines, Geoff Grover, Britt Ingebritson, Jim Kindly, Timothy McKibben, Gail Williamson Raul, Alice Reese, C Donovan Williamson

D-U-N-S 07-917-7739
WILLIAMSPORT HOSPITAL
WILLIAMSPORT REGIONAL MEDICAL CENTER
(*Suby of* SUSQUEHANNA HEALTH SYSTEM) ★
700 High St, Williamsport, PA 17701-3198
Tel (570) 321-1000 *Founded/Ownrshp* 1873
Sales 322.3MM *EMP* 1,300^E
Accts Lb Bkd Llp Springfield Mo
SIC 8062 7389 General medical & surgical hospitals; Financial services
CEO: Steven Johnson
**Pr:* Mary Chaya
**CFO:* Charles Santangelo
**VP:* George Manchester
Dir Teleco: Bill Holmes
Cmptr Lab: Loretta Moffatt
Mktg Dir: Elizabeth Brubaker
Mktg Dir: Greg Harrison
Pathlgst: Jennifer Pryor
Doctor: James Redka

D-U-N-S 03-069-8167
WILLIAMSPORT PATHOLOGY ASSOCS
700 High St, Williamsport, PA 17701-3100
Tel (570) 321-2321 *Founded/Ownrshp* 2012
Sales 285.9MM *EMP* 3
SIC 8011 Pathologist
Prin: Nicholas J Dillman
Off Mgr: Ellen Cero
CTO: Karen Armstrong
Netwrk Mgr: Alan Bird

WILLIAMSPORT REGIONAL MEDICAL CENTER
See WILLIAMSPORT HOSPITAL

D-U-N-S 79-632-4064 IMP
WILLIAMSTON PRODUCTS INC
WPI
845 Progress Ct, Williamston, MI 48895-1658
Tel (517) 655-2131 *Founded/Ownrshp* 2007
Sales 137.8MM^E *EMP* 450
SIC 3089 Automotive parts, plastic
Pr: Frank Remesch
**CFO:* Ed Carpenter
CFO: Mike Isaacs
**VP:* Aashir Patel
**VP:* Ron Phillips
**Prin:* Nigam Tripathi

D-U-N-S 07-400-0969
WILLIAMSVILLE CENTRAL SCHOOL DISTRICT (NY)
Administratiion Center 10 Er Stratiion Cent, East Amherst, NY 14051
Tel (716) 626-8050 *Founded/Ownrshp* 1924
Sales 69.1MM^E *EMP* 1,788
SIC 8211 Public elementary & secondary schools; Public elementary school; Public junior high school; Public senior high school
Prin: William Krone
IT Man: Debbie Radice
Psych: Scott Piotrowski

D-U-N-S 05-525-1821
WILLIS ADMINISTRATIVE SERVICES CORP
WILLIS POOLING
(*Suby of* WILLIS TOWERS WATSON) ★
26 Century Blvd Ste 101, Nashville, TN 37214-4614
Tel (615) 872-3000 *Founded/Ownrshp* 1959
Sales NA *EMP* 468
SIC 6411 Insurance agents, brokers & service
CEO: Dominic Casserley
**Pr:* Nicolas Aubert
**CFO:* John Greene
**Ex VP:* Celia Brown
VP: Karla Hyatt
VP: Shapiro Laurance
IT Man: Rob Wimsatt
Counsel: Kelly Smits
Board of Directors: John R Lamberson, Richard M Miller

WILLIS GUEITS ADAMS
See WILLIS OF NEW YORK INC

D-U-N-S 08-335-3037
▲ WILLIS LEASE FINANCE CORP
773 San Marin Dr Ste 2215, Novato, CA 94945-1366
Tel (415) 408-4700 *Founded/Ownrshp* 1985
Sales NA *EMP* 104^E
Tkr Sym WLFC *Exch* NGM
SIC 6159 5084 Machinery & equipment finance leasing; Industrial machinery & equipment
Ch Bd: Charles F Willis IV
Pr: Brian R Hole
CFO: Scott B Flaherty
Sr VP: Brian Hole
Sr VP: Dean M Poulakidas
Sr VP: Anthony R Spaulding
VP: Marc Pierpoint
Board of Directors: Hans Joerg Hunziker, Robert J Keady, Robert T Morris, Austin C Willis

D-U-N-S 00-698-2466 IMP
WILLIS NORTH AMERICA INC
WILLIS TOWERS WATSON
(*Suby of* WILLIS TOWERS WATSON PUBLIC LIMITED COMPANY)
200 Liberty St Fl 7, New York, NY 10281-0001
Tel (212) 915-8888 *Founded/Ownrshp* 1905, 1990
Sales NA *EMP* 12,574
SIC 6411 8742 8999 8748 Insurance information & consulting services; Insurance agents & brokers; Compensation & benefits planning consultant; Actuarial consultant; Employee programs administration
CEO: Don Bailey
Mng Pt: Charles Steers
CEO: Jim Blaney
**CEO:* Todd Jones
CEO: Brian Parsons
**COO:* Eric Joost
CFO: Sharon Edwards
Treas: Ian Warner
**Ofcr:* Matt Keeping
Ex VP: Matthew Baum
Ex VP: Sara Benolken
Ex VP: Pete Jacqmin
Ex VP: Greg Peterson
Ex VP: Steve Pincus
Ex VP: Ken Sweeney
Ex VP: Jobeth Wells
Sr VP: Adam Cantor
Sr VP: Dana Chapman
Sr VP: Patrick Conroy
Sr VP: Holly Davis
Sr VP: Dee Dickson

D-U-N-S 07-834-6295
WILLIS OF FLORIDA INC
(*Suby of* WILLIS TOWERS WATSON) ★
4211 W Boy Scout Blvd # 4, Tampa, FL 33607-5725
Tel (813) 281-2095 *Founded/Ownrshp* 1994
Sales NA *EMP* 303^E
SIC 6411 Insurance agents, brokers & service
CEO: Joe Plumeri
**Treas:* C W Mooney
VP: Paula Delage
VP: Scott Devine

D-U-N-S 02-037-8188
WILLIS OF NEW YORK INC
WILLIS GUEITS ADAMS
(*Suby of* WILLIS GROUP LIMITED)
335 Madison Ave Fl 20, New York, NY 10017-4633
Tel (212) 938-2439 *Founded/Ownrshp* 2006
Sales NA *EMP* 789
SIC 6411 Insurance brokers
Pr: Gerard Adams
**Treas:* Edward Gueits
**VP:* Regina Addeo
**VP:* Marisa L Green
**VP:* Mary Beth Kelly
**VP:* Barry H Raucher
Off Mgr: Jeanette Victor

D-U-N-S 07-521-5574
WILLIS OF NEW YORK INC
(*Suby of* WILLIS TOWERS WATSON) ★
200 Liberty St, New York, NY 10281-1003
Tel (212) 915-8888 *Founded/Ownrshp* 1971
Sales NA *EMP* 300
SIC 6411 Insurance agents, brokers & service
Pr: Mario Vitale
Mng Pt: Carl Timpanaro
Pr: Jack Geiger
**CEO:* Joseph Blue-Mary
COO: Debra Stanley
Ex VP: Ralph Blust
Ex VP: Celia Brown
Ex VP: John Jacobs
Ex VP: Steven Lewis
Ex VP: Brian Ruane
Ex VP: Mark Rusas
Sr VP: Joe Downey
Sr VP: Frank Freeman
Sr VP: David Gluckman
Sr VP: Rick Hawkinberry
Sr VP: Jim Iacino
Sr VP: Andrew Krasner
Sr VP: Paul Leblanc
Sr VP: Robert Lustberg
Sr VP: David G Oliver
Sr VP: Linda Parker

D-U-N-S 06-909-6022
WILLIS OF TENNESSEE INC
(*Suby of* WILLIS GROUP LIMITED)
26 Century Blvd Ste 101, Nashville, TN 37214-4614
Tel (615) 872-3000 *Founded/Ownrshp* 1973, 1975
Sales NA *EMP* 150^E
SIC 6411 Insurance agents, brokers & service
Pr: J Ronald Ellis
Mng Pt: Linde Hotchkiss
Ex VP: Duncan Ashurst
Ex VP: Howard Bruch
Ex VP: Michael Dellova
Ex VP: Chet Mitrani
Ex VP: Bobby Otte
Ex VP: Bradley Wright
Sr VP: Ron Bussey
Sr VP: Rosemarie Fernicola
Sr VP: Lindsey Frase
Sr VP: Kevin Habash
Sr VP: Bert McKeand
Sr VP: Eileen Reingold
Sr VP: Tosh Siao
VP: Chuck Cernera
VP: Clint Escoe
VP: Vernon Ewing
VP: Marjorie Feit
VP: Jane Haakenstad
VP: Robert Lapinsky

WILLIS POOLING
See WILLIS ADMINISTRATIVE SERVICES CORP

D-U-N-S 00-887-2053
WILLIS SHAW EXPRESS INC (NC)
(*Suby of* COMCAR INDUSTRIES INC) ★
201 N Elm St, Elm Springs, AR 72728
Tel (479) 248-7261 *Founded/Ownrshp* 1914, 1964
Sales 61.0MM^E *EMP* 1,099
SIC 4213

D-U-N-S 92-762-0914
WILLIS STEIN & PARTNERS MANAGEMENT III LLC
1033 Skokie Blvd Ste 360, Northbrook, IL 60062-4137
Tel (312) 422-2400 *Founded/Ownrshp* 1995
Sales 150.9MM^E *EMP* 610^E
SIC 6799 3479 2721 8721 Investors; Painting of metal products; Painting, coating & hot dipping; Magazines: publishing & printing; Payroll accounting service
Mng Pt: Avy Stein
CFO: Todd Smith
Mng Dir: Philip B Pool
Mktg Mgr: Pankaj Jain

WILLIS TOWERS WATSON
See WILLIS NORTH AMERICA INC

D-U-N-S 06-703-8877 IMP
WILLIS-KNIGHTON MEDICAL CENTER
WILLIS-KNIGHTON SOUTH HOSPITAL
2600 Greenwood Rd, Shreveport, LA 71103-3908
Tel (318) 212-4000 *Founded/Ownrshp* 1900
Sales 1.0MMM *EMP* 3,089
Accts Cole Evans & Peterson Shrevep
SIC 8062 General medical & surgical hospitals
Pr: James K Elrod
Chf OB: Kristy M Waltman
**CFO:* Robert Huie
Ofcr: Linda Smith
Sr VP: Charles Daigle
Sr VP: Steve Randall
VP: Rick Cheshier
VP: Margaret Elrod
VP: Ramona Fryer
VP: Peggy Gavin
**VP:* Nila Willhoite
Dir Rx: Tessa Albritton

WILLIS-KNIGHTON SOUTH HOSPITAL
See WILLIS-KNIGHTON MEDICAL CENTER

D-U-N-S 96-580-7634
WILLISTON FINANCIAL GROUP LLC
12909 Sw 68th Pkwy # 350, Portland, OR 97223-8384
Tel (503) 387-3636 *Founded/Ownrshp* 2009
Sales NA *EMP* 551
SIC 6361 Title insurance
CEO: Patrick F Stone
Pr: Tina Arcarese
**COO:* Marshall Haines
**CFO:* Michael T Gallaher
**Ex VP:* Joseph V McCabe Jr
Sr VP: Russell Sugg
VP: Randall D'Arche
**VP:* Susan McKnight
VP: Paulette O'Donnell
VP: Amanda Pursell-Genck
VP: Kevin Rosenberg

D-U-N-S 03-070-1372
WILLISTON HOLDINGS INC
12000 Aerospace Ave # 400, Houston, TX 77034-5576
Tel (832) 300-5858 *Founded/Ownrshp* 1996
Sales 89.5MM^E *EMP* 2,894^E
SIC 5812 6794 5046 Mexican restaurant; Franchises, selling or licensing; Restaurant equipment & supplies
CEO: Marcus Jundt

D-U-N-S 00-682-8099
■ WILLISTON TELEPHONE CO
TDS
(*Suby of* TDS TELECOMMUNICATIONS CORP) ★
4670 West St, Williston, SC 29853-5934
Tel (803) 266-7411 *Founded/Ownrshp* 1991
Sales 867.0MM *EMP* 2,700
SIC 4813 Local telephone communications
VP: Gene S Owens
**Pr:* G Ronnie Barnes
Board of Directors: Dr William B Clark, William O'neal Livingston, Russell W Nix, Betty J Williamson, Lee B Wilson

D-U-N-S 06-494-3814
WILLKIE FARR & GALLAGHER LLP
787 7th Ave Fl 2, New York, NY 10019-6099
Tel (212) 728-8000 *Founded/Ownrshp* 1929
Sales 164.7MM^E *EMP* 1,150
SIC 8111

WILLIAMS KITCHEN & BATH
See WILLIAMS DISTRIBUTING CO

D-U-N-S 00-904-8278
WILLMAR POULTRY CO INC
AG FORTE
1800 Technology Dr Ne, Willmar, MN 56201-2280
Tel (320) 235-8850 *Founded/Ownrshp* 2004
Sales 132.7MM *EMP* 772^E
SIC 0254 0253 Poultry hatcheries; Turkey farm
Ch Bd: Theodore Huisinga
**Pr:* Richard Vanderspek
**CEO:* Richard Huisinga
**CFO:* Beth Wosmek
**VP:* Kevin Lynch

*VP: Scott Norling
Genl Mgr: Ziggy Kotze
Board of Directors: Richard Huisinga, Thomas Huisinga, Kevin Lynch, Rayburn Norling, Scott Norling, Richard Vanderspek

D-U-N-S 08-611-6282 IMP
WILLMAR POULTRY FARMS INC
FARM SERVICE ELEVATOR CO.
3939 1st Ave W, Willmar, MN 56201-4375
Tel (320) 235-8870 Founded/Ownrshp 1963
Sales 120.9MM EMP 64
SIC 0253 2048 Turkey farm; Prepared feeds
CEO: Richard Huisinga
*Pr: Richard Vanderspek
*CFO: Beth Wosmek
*Ch: Theodore Huisinga
*VP: Scott Norling
Board of Directors: Richard Huisinga, Theodore Huisinga, Thomas Huisinga, Timothy Johnson, Rayburn Norling, Scott Norling, Richard Vanderspek

D-U-N-S 01-844-4406
WILLOUGHBY SUPPLY CO (OH)
7433 Clover Ave, Mentor, OH 44060-5211
Tel (440) 942-7939 Founded/Ownrshp 1983
Sales 145.1MM^E EMP 80
SIC 5033 Roofing & siding materials
Pr: Albert Romanini
Brnch Mgr: Dan Colarik
Brnch Mgr: Matthew Digruttolo
Brnch Mgr: Mike Jackson
QA Dir: Terry White
VP Sls: Brad Stalder
Manager: Jeff Aloisi
Manager: Randy Bowlin
Manager: Napolean Givens
Sls Mgr: Chris Meister
Sls Mgr: Mike Stoll

D-U-N-S 07-776-8398
WILLOUGHBY-EASTLAKE CITY SCHOOLS
37047 Ridge Rd, Willoughby, OH 44094-4130
Tel (440) 946-5000 Founded/Ownrshp 1850
Sales 79.5MM^E EMP 1,100
Accts Rea & Associates
SIC 8211 Public elementary & secondary schools; Public elementary school; Public junior high school; Public senior high school
*Treas: Cliff Reinhardt
VP: George J Petric Jr
Off Admin: Frances Maglosky
Off Admin: Debby Patrick

D-U-N-S 07-995-4543
■ **WILLOW CREEK HEALTHCARE CENTER LLC**
(Suby of GENESIS HEALTHCARE LLC) ★
650 W Alluvial Ave, Clovis, CA 93611-6716
Tel (559) 323-6200
Sales 7.3MM^E EMP 2,473^E
SIC 8051 Skilled nursing care facilities
CEO: George V Hager Jr

D-U-N-S 17-520-7687
WILLOW ENTERPRISES INC
PORT HURON HOSPITAL MEDICAL EQ
1221 Pine Grove Ave, Port Huron, MI 48060-3511
Tel (810) 987-2064 Founded/Ownrshp 2010
Sales 178.9MM EMP 25
SIC 8082 5999 Home health care services; Hospital equipment & supplies
Ex Dir: Dan Angeli
*Ch: George Stommel

WILLOW POINT GOLF & COUNTRY CL
See RUSSELL LANDS INC

D-U-N-S 01-333-9684 EXP
WILLOW RUN FOODS INC
1006 Us Route 11, Kirkwood, NY 13795-9600
Tel (607) 338-5221 Founded/Ownrshp 1949
Sales 171.6MM^E EMP 400
SIC 5142 5149 5147 5113 5148 5087

D-U-N-S 11-257-6319
WILLOW VALLEY COMMUNITIES
WILLOW VALLEY LAKES MANOR
100 Willow Vly Lakes Dr, Willow Street, PA 17584-9450
Tel (717) 464-2741 Founded/Ownrshp 1982
Sales 92.9MM EMP 13,000
SIC 8361 8059 8082 Residential care; Convalescent home; Personal care home, with health care; Home health care services
Pr: James Hostetter
CFO: Dennis Griest
Treas: Jill Gilbert
Ex VP: Blaise Holzbauer
VP: Leslie Brant

WILLOW VALLEY LAKES MANOR
See WILLOW VALLEY COMMUNITIES

D-U-N-S 07-382-9699
WILLOWGLEN ACADEMY-WISCONSIN INC
PHOENIX CARE SYSTEMS
(Suby of PHOENIX CARE SYSTEMS INC) ★
1744 N Farwell Ave, Milwaukee, WI 53202-1806
Tel (414) 225-4460 Founded/Ownrshp 1972
Sales 24.7MM^E EMP 1,200
SIC 8361 Residential care for the handicapped
Prin: Donald R Fritz
*Pr: Leonard F Dziubla
*CFO: Richard J Kunath
*Prin: John Yopps

D-U-N-S 15-698-2860
WILLS GROUP INC
6355 Crain Hwy, La Plata, MD 20646-4267
Tel (301) 932-3600 Founded/Ownrshp 1986
Sales 933.3MM EMP 280
Accts Mcgladrey Llp Baltimore Mary
SIC 5541 5983 5172 5411 Filling stations, gasoline; Fuel oil dealers; Fuel oil; Convenience stores, independent
Pr: Lock Wills
*Ch Bd: J Blacklock Wills Jr
*CFO: Jennifer Popescu
Ex VP: Kenneth Halperin
*Ex VP: Mel Strine
*VP: John Cumbs
VP: Kris Demarr
*VP: Stephen J Niven
Opers Mgr: Larry Derrow

WILLY'S FUELS
See APACHE OIL CO INC

WILMAC
See MC WIL GROUP LTD

D-U-N-S 07-120-6015
WILMAC CORP
(Suby of WILMAC) ★
209 N Beaver St, York, PA 17401-5394
Tel (717) 854-7857 Founded/Ownrshp 1957
Sales 74.9MM^E EMP 1,490
SIC 8059 8051 8069 6513 8742 6552 Convalescent home; Skilled nursing care facilities; Substance abuse hospitals; Apartment building operators; Hospital & health services consultant; Land subdividers & developers, commercial
Ch Bd: Webster J Mc Cormack
*Pr: Karen E McCormack
CFO: Dave Friedhofer
*Treas: Vincent T Reigle
*VP: Stephen D Wilson
*VP Admn: Richard W Bricker
Plnt Mgr: Bill Anderson
Board of Directors: Karen E McCormack

D-U-N-S 07-171-5981
WILMER CUTLER PICKERING HALE AND DORR LLP
WILMERHALE
1875 Pennsylvania Ave Nw, Washington, DC 20006-3642
Tel (202) 663-6000 Founded/Ownrshp 1852
Sales 334.3MM^E EMP 1,650
SIC 8111 Specialized law offices, attorneys
Pt: James E Anderson
Sr Pt: Michael Bain
Sr Pt: Michael Bevilacqua
Sr Pt: Jay Bothwick
Sr Pt: John Burgess
Sr Pt: James Burke
Sr Pt: Henry Clinton-Davis
Sr Pt: Michael Fay
Sr Pt: Jeffrey Hermanson
Sr Pt: Neil Jacobs
Sr Pt: Stuart Nayman
Sr Pt: Christopher Prout
Sr Pt: Patrick Rondeau
Sr Pt: Philip Rossetti
Sr Pt: Brent Siler
Sr Pt: Jeff Stein
*Pt: Thomas E Anderson
*Pt: Paul M Architzel
*Pt: Christopher E Babbitt
*Pt: Ambassador Charlene Barshefsky
*Pt: Natalie L Bben

WILMERHALE
See WILMER CUTLER PICKERING HALE AND DORR LLP

D-U-N-S 07-909-6315
WILMINGTON HEALTH PLLC
1202 Medical Center Dr, Wilmington, NC 28401-7307
Tel (910) 341-3300 Founded/Ownrshp 1996
Sales 90.7MM^E EMP 691^E
SIC 8011 Clinic, operated by physicians
CEO: Jeff James
COO: Chris Bunch
CFO: Chasity Chace

WILMINGTON PRODUCTS USA
See NORTHWEST CO LLC

WILMINGTON SAVINGS FUND BANK
See WILMINGTON SAVINGS FUND SOCIETY

D-U-N-S 00-248-4103
■ **WILMINGTON SAVINGS FUND SOCIETY**
WILMINGTON SAVINGS FUND BANK
(Suby of WSFS FINANCIAL CORP) ★
500 Delaware Ave Ste 500, Wilmington, DE 19801-7405
Tel (302) 792-6000 Founded/Ownrshp 1832
Sales NA EMP 375
SIC 6035 Federal savings & loan associations
Ch Bd: Marvin N Schoenhals
CEO: Mark A Turner
COO: Ken Monroe
CFO: Stephen A Fowle
V Ch Bd: Calvert Morgan Jr
Chf Inves: Alice Fredericks
Ofcr: R Abbott
Ofcr: Michael McLaughlin
Assoc VP: Al Cox
Ex VP: Peggy Eddens
Ex VP: Carl Johnston
Ex VP: Rodger Levenson
Ex VP: S James Mazarakis
Ex VP: Patricia A Muldoon
Ex VP: Joseph Murphy
Ex VP: Thomas Stevenson
Ex VP: Richard Wright
Sr VP: Syed Ahmed
Sr VP: Paul Greenplate
Sr VP: David Hargarten
Sr VP: Thomas W Kearney

D-U-N-S 79-433-8087
■ **WILMINGTON TRUST CORP**
(Suby of M&T BANK CORP) ★
1 M And T Plz Ste 1, Buffalo, NY 14203-2301
Tel (302) 651-1000 Founded/Ownrshp 2011
Sales NA EMP 14,243^E
SIC 6712 Bank holding companies
Pr: Mark J Czarnecki
Pr: Philip P Cave
Pr: Larry Gore
Pr: Sharon L Klein
Pr: Peter E Simmons
COO: Jeffrey Culp
COO: Roger Wagner
Treas: Rene F Jones
Trst Ofcr: Robert M Balentine
Ex VP: William Farrell II
VP: John Allenson
VP: Robert Matarese
VP: Ashley Melton
VP: Kirk D Mooneyham

D-U-N-S 62-609-0013
WILMINGTON TRUST SP SERVICES
(Suby of ABARTA INC) ★
1105 N Market St Ste 1300, Wilmington, DE 19801-1241
Tel (302) 427-7650 Founded/Ownrshp 1982
Sales 136.1MM^E EMP 1,300
SIC 2711 Newspapers
VP: Charles Hanlon
Pr: Sania Beven

D-U-N-S 04-654-9150
WILMINGTON UNIVERSITY INC
320 N Dupont Hwy, New Castle, DE 19720-6491
Tel (302) 356-6824 Founded/Ownrshp 1968
Sales 116.4MM EMP 1,200
Accts Gunnip&Company Llp
SIC 8221 College, except junior
Pr: Jack P Varsalona
*CFO: Heather O'Connell
Ofcr: Stephen Duncan
VP: Christine Motta
VP: Carloe Pitcher
Exec: Donald Hagermann
Exec: Misty Williams
Genl Mgr: Gina Garner
Dir IT: Brian Beard
IT Man: Michael S Adams
Web Dev: Ryan J Higgins
Board of Directors: an Eighteen Member Board O

D-U-N-S 00-828-8169 IMP/EXP
WILSEY FOODS INC
(Suby of MITSUI & CO., LTD.)
40 Pointe Dr, Brea, CA 92821-3652
Tel (714) 257-3700 Founded/Ownrshp 1989
Sales 228.8MM^E EMP 2,100
SIC 2079 5149 Cooking oils, except corn: vegetable refined; Vegetable shortenings (except corn oil); Shortening, vegetable
CEO: Takashi Fukunaga
Pr: Steve Takagi
Sec: Yasunari Yamamoto
VP: Hiro Matsumura

D-U-N-S 16-723-3183
WILSHIRE BANCORP INC
3200 Wilshire Blvd, Los Angeles, CA 90010-1333
Tel (213) 387-3200 Founded/Ownrshp 2004
Sales NA EMP 547^E
SIC 6022

D-U-N-S 03-947-0968 IMP
WILSHIRE BANK
WILSHIRE STATE BANK
3200 Wilshire Blvd Fl 10, Los Angeles, CA 90010-1311
Tel (213) 427-1000 Founded/Ownrshp 1980
Sales NA EMP 349
SIC 6022

D-U-N-S 80-041-4455
WILSHIRE HOMES LP
8200 N Mopac Expy Ste 350, Austin, TX 78759-8975
Tel (512) 502-2050 Founded/Ownrshp 2005
Sales 120.0MM EMP 180
SIC 1521 Single-family housing construction
Pt: Edward Horne
Pt: Marvin Galloway
Pt: Win Hansen
Pt: Shelley Ledyard
Opers Mgr: J B Neale

D-U-N-S 94-964-7077 IMP
WILSHIRE PARTNERS
620 Newport Center Dr # 1100, Newport Beach, CA 92660-6420
Tel (800) 285-6038 Founded/Ownrshp 1995
Sales 20.8MM^E EMP 1,604
SIC 5632 5961 Women's accessory & specialty stores; Women's apparel, mail order
Genl Pt: Yan B Haghor

WILSHIRE PHARMACEUTICALS
See ARBOR PHARMACEUTICALS LLC

WILSHIRE STATE BANK
See WILSHIRE BANK

D-U-N-S 16-093-5029
■ **WILSON BANK AND TRUST**
WB&T
(Suby of WILSON BANK HOLDING CO) ★
623 W Main St, Lebanon, TN 37087-3400
Tel (615) 444-2265 Founded/Ownrshp 1987
Sales NA EMP 353
SIC 6022 State trust companies accepting deposits, commercial
CEO: Randall Clemons
*Pr: Elmer Richerson
COO: John Gregory
Bd of Dir: Harold R Patton
Ofcr: Glen Cross
Sr VP: Michael Flanagan
Sr VP: Ralph Mallicoat
Sr VP: Bruce Plummer
*Sr VP: Larry Squires
VP: Sue Bragg
VP: Chad Colwell
VP: Mark Dubarry
VP: Doug Gold
VP: Lisa Gregory
VP: Scott Jasper
VP: Taylor Walker
Exec: Jason Hall

D-U-N-S 87-432-7364
▲ **WILSON BANK HOLDING CO**
623 W Main St, Lebanon, TN 37087-3404
Tel (615) 444-2265 Founded/Ownrshp 1992
Sales NA EMP 406
Accts Maggart & Associates Pc Na
Tkr Sym WBHC Exch OTO
SIC 6021 National commercial banks
Pr: James Randall Clemons
*Ch Bd: James Anthony Patton
CFO: Lisa Pominski
Ofcr: Lois Duke
Ofcr: Janie Kirby
Ofcr: Karen Osment
Ofcr: Amanda Watkins
Assoc VP: Glenda McAdams
*Ex VP: H Elmer Richerson
VP: Cynthia Agee
VP: Lisa Gregory
VP: Jason Hall
VP: Ralph Mallicoat
VP: Bruce Plummer
VP: Sue Shepard
VP: Sue Teat
VP: Jerry Tramel
Board of Directors: Charles Bell, Jack W Bell, James F Comer, Jerry L Franklin, John B Freeman, William P Jordan, Harold R Patton

D-U-N-S 00-399-3482 IMP
WILSON CONSTRUCTION CO (OR)
WILSON UTILITY CONSTRUCTION CO
1190 Nw 3rd Ave, Canby, OR 97013-3441
Tel (503) 263-6882 Founded/Ownrshp 1952
Sales 263.4MM^E EMP 550
Accts Hoffman Stewart & Schmidt Pc
SIC 1623 Electric power line construction
Pr: Donald M Wilson
VP: Jon Oistad
*VP: Stacy Wilson
CTO: Debbie Greene
Dir IT: Scott Carr
Snr PM: Jim Keegan

D-U-N-S 36-108-9238
WILSON COUNTY BOARD OF EDUCATION
WILSON COUNTY SCHOOL DISTRICT
351 Stumpy Ln, Lebanon, TN 37090-5339
Tel (615) 444-3282 Founded/Ownrshp 1934
Sales 139.1MM^E EMP 2,500
SIC 8211 Public elementary & secondary schools
Dir Sec: Steve Spencer
Cmptr Lab: Kristie Davis

WILSON COUNTY SCHOOL DISTRICT
See WILSON COUNTY BOARD OF EDUCATION

D-U-N-S 07-979-8825
WILSON COUNTY SCHOOLS
351 Stumpy Ln, Lebanon, TN 37090-5339
Tel (615) 444-3282 Founded/Ownrshp 2015
Sales 39.5MM^E EMP 1,083^E
SIC 8211 Public elementary & secondary schools
MIS Dir: Mickey Hall
Netwrk Eng: Justin Koehn
Pr Dir: Amber Whitley
Psych: Kristin Sabata
HC Dir: Donna Lawson

D-U-N-S 92-821-5326
WILSON COUNTY SCHOOLS
117 Tarboro St Ne, Wilson, NC 27893-4016
Tel (252) 399-7700 Founded/Ownrshp 1976
Sales 97.0MM EMP 1,600
SIC 8211 Public elementary school; Public junior high school; Public senior high school
*Prin: Larry Price
Opers Mgr: Martha Cayton
Pr Dir: Amber Lynch
Psych: Michelle Dillon

D-U-N-S 07-770-5770
WILSON ELSER MOSKOWITZ EDELMAN & DICKER LLP
150 E 42nd St Fl 23, New York, NY 10017-5636
Tel (212) 490-3000 Founded/Ownrshp 1962
Sales 351.4MM^E EMP 1,500
SIC 8111 General practice law office
COO: Hal Stewart
Pt: Julie R Evans
Pt: Thomas W Hyland
Pt: Gregory S Katz
Pt: Patrick M Kelly
Pt: Harold J Moskowitz
Pt: James C Orr
Mng Pt: Joseph F Bermudez
Mng Pt: William Bogaert
Mng Pt: John W Bussey
Mng Pt: Ricardo J Cata
Mng Pt: Brian Del Gatto
Mng Pt: Michael M Edwards
Mng Pt: David S Eisen
Mng Pt: Sharla J Frost
Mng Pt: William G Gandy
Mng Pt: Robert W Goodson
Mng Pt: Robert W Harrison
Mng Pt: David M Holmes
Mng Pt: Thomas Hyland
Mng Pt: Rodney Janis

WILSON EXPORTS
See DNOW LP

D-U-N-S 60-095-2035
WILSON FARMS INC
1780 Wehrle Dr Ste 110, Williamsville, NY 14221-7000
Tel (716) 204-4300 Founded/Ownrshp 2005
Sales NA EMP 2,200^E
SIC 5199

WILSON HEALTH
See SHELBY COUNTY MEMORIAL HOSPITAL ASSOCIATION

WILSON HEALTH CARE CENTER
See ASBURY ATLANTIC INC

WILSON MEDICAL CENTER
See HEALTH CARE FOUNDATION OF WILSON

D-U-N-S 00-814-8411
WILSON MEMORIAL HOSPITAL
915 Michigan St, Sidney, OH 45365-2491
Tel (937) 498-2311 Founded/Ownrshp 2000
Sales 83.3MM EMP 200
SIC 8062 General medical & surgical hospitals
Dir Recs: Carol Lomason
*Treas: Dave Monnier

VP: Jamie Westfall
**Prin:* Melody Eppley
CIO: Larry J Meyers
Surgeon: Philip A Edwards
Ansthlgy: Roberto Kong
Doctor: Chandulal Ghodasara
Pharmcst: Vera Heitkamp
Pharmcst: Garrett Serr
Cert Phar: Christy Wagner

WILSON N JONES REGIONAL MEDICAL CENTER
See SHERMAN/GRAYSON HOSPITAL LLC

D-U-N-S 05-707-4692
WILSON OIL INC
WILCOX & FLEGEL OIL CO
95 Panel Way, Longview, WA 98632-1023
Tel (360) 575-9222 *Founded/Ownrshp* 1977
Sales 150.6MM^E *EMP* 360^E
SIC 5541 5983 5172 Filling stations, gasoline; Fuel oil dealers; Petroleum products
Pr: Stephen C Wilcox
**VP:* Gary Mellema
Genl Mgr: Bill Hall
DP Exec: Scott Davis
IT Man: Melissa Quick
Plnt Mgr: Lori Barber
Plnt Mgr: Matt Chauncey
Plnt Mgr: Eric Clardy
Plnt Mgr: David Garwood
Plnt Mgr: Tony Guler

D-U-N-S 08-995-9233
WILSON SONSINI GOODRICH & ROSATI PROFESSIONAL CORP (CA)
650 Page Mill Rd, Palo Alto, CA 94304-1001
Tel (650) 493-9300 *Founded/Ownrshp* 1961
Sales 184.4MM^E *EMP* 1,300
SIC 8111 Corporate, partnership & business law
CEO: Steven E Bochner
Pt: James A Diboise
Pt: Jack Sheridan
Pt: Effie Toshav
Mng Pt: Douglas Clark
Mng Pt: John T Sheridan
Ch Bd: Larry W Sonsini
V Ch Bd: Jeff Saper
Bd of Dir: Steve Bochner
Bd of Dir: Katharine A Martin
Bd of Dir: Patrick Schultheis
Sr VP: Sunil Bhardwaj
Sr VP: Courtney Chiang Dorman
VP: Chris Groobey
VP: Phillip Hoare
VP: Christopher W Kirkham

D-U-N-S 02-924-7673 EXP
WILSON SPORTING GOODS CO
(*Suby of* AMER SPORTS CO) ★
8750 W Bryn Mawr Ave Fl 2, Chicago, IL 60631-3721
Tel (773) 714-6400 *Founded/Ownrshp* 2005
Sales 710.5MM^E *EMP* 2,440
SIC 5091 3949 Sporting & recreation goods; Sporting & athletic goods; Golf equipment; Baseball equipment & supplies, general; Tennis equipment & supplies
Pr: Mike Dowse
VP: Armin Boehm
VP: Dan Cougill
VP: John Embree
VP: Tom Gruger
VP: Mary Lally
VP: Kevin McTernan
VP: Jan Thompson
VP: Bob Thurman
Dir Bus: Jeff Christensen
**Prin:* Chris Considine

D-U-N-S 00-645-1165
WILSON TOOL INTERNATIONAL INC (MN)
IMPAX
12912 Farnham Ave N, White Bear Lake, MN 55110-5997
Tel (651) 286-6000 *Founded/Ownrshp* 1966
Sales 149.9MM^E *EMP* 800^E
SIC 3542 3544

D-U-N-S 00-725-7322 EXP
WILSON TRAILER CO
4400 S Lewis Blvd, Sioux City, IA 51106-9518
Tel (712) 252-6500 *Founded/Ownrshp* 1890
Sales 351.8MM^E *EMP* 1,100
SIC 3715 Truck trailers; Semitrailers for truck tractors
Pr: Wilson G Persinger
**Ch Bd:* C Wilson Persinger
COO: Bill Persinger
VP: Dan Howard
VP: Tim Oconnor
Comm Man: Daryl Sheffer
Genl Mgr: West Keller
IT Man: Kevin Christensen
Netwrk Mgr: Chris Church
Opers Mgr: William Pelchat
Plnt Mgr: David Gross

D-U-N-S 00-982-0077
WILSON TRUCKING CORP
137 Wilson Blvd, Fishersville, VA 22939-2227
Tel (540) 949-3200 *Founded/Ownrshp* 1936
Sales 147.5MM *EMP* 1,400
Accts Pbmares Llp Harrisonburg Vi
SIC 4213 Trucking, except local
CEO: C L Wilson
**Pr:* T G Wilson
**CFO:* Michael Herndon
**Sec:* Chris Baldwin
Ex VP: Guy Wilson
VP: John A Kidd
IT Man: Jeffrey A Smith
Sfty Dirs: Fred Lackey

WILSON UTILITY CONSTRUCTION CO
See WILSON CONSTRUCTION CO

D-U-N-S 07-873-0378
WILSONART INTERNATIONAL HOLDINGS LLC
(*Suby of* CLAYTON DUBILIER & RICE LLC) ★
2400 Wilson Pl, Temple, TX 76504-5131
Tel (254) 207-7000 *Founded/Ownrshp* 2012
Sales 200.0MM^E *EMP* 2,036^E
SIC 2541 Counters or counter display cases, wood; Display fixtures, wood; Office fixtures, wood
CEO: Timothy J Obrien
**Ch:* John Krenicki Jr

D-U-N-S 19-816-5458 IMP/EXP
■ **WILSONART INTERNATIONAL INC**
(*Suby of* ILLINOIS TOOL WORKS INC) ★
2501 Wilsonart Dr, Temple, TX 76503
Tel (254) 207-7000 *Founded/Ownrshp* 1994
Sales 470.8MM^E *EMP* 3,402
SIC 2821 2541 Plastics materials & resins; Table or counter tops, plastic laminated
Pr: Kristen Manos
**CFO:* Jeffrey S Lee
Sr VP: Rusty Booth
Assoc Dir: Susanna Kise
IT Man: Terri Arthur
VP Mfg: Sue Rothberg
Opers Mgr: Mike Locke
Ql Cn Mgr: Joey Osborne

D-U-N-S 07-870-4992
WILSONART LLC
(*Suby of* WILSONART INTERNATIONAL HOLDINGS LLC) ★
2501 Wilsonart Dr, Temple, TX 76504
Tel (254) 207-7000 *Founded/Ownrshp* 2012
Sales 188.5MM^E *EMP* 1,794^E
SIC 2541 Counters or counter display cases, wood; Display fixtures, wood; Office fixtures, wood
Pr: Kristen Manos
Exec: Elaine Fisher

D-U-N-S 02-793-0395
■ **WILSONS HOUSE OF SUEDE INC**
WILSONS LEATHER
(*Suby of* G-III APPAREL GROUP LTD) ★
7401 Boone Ave N, Brooklyn Park, MN 55428-1080
Tel (763) 391-4000 *Founded/Ownrshp* 1996
Sales 208.8MM^E *EMP* 4,000
SIC 5699 5948 Leather garments; Leather goods, except luggage & shoes
Pr: David L Rogers
CEO: Joel N Waller
Treas: Daniel Thorson
Ex VP: Carol S Lund
Ex VP: Randy Roland
VP: W Michael Bode
VP: John Fowler
VP: Betty Goff
VP: Jed Jaffe
VP: D Sharp
VP: David B Sharp
VP: D Tidmarsh
VP: David J Tidmarsh
VP: Joel Waller
VP: Steven Waller

WILSONS LEATHER
See WILSONS HOUSE OF SUEDE INC

D-U-N-S 07-997-9650
WILSONS LEATHER EXPERTS INC
7401 Boone Ave N, Brooklyn Park, MN 55428-1080
Tel (763) 391-4000 *Founded/Ownrshp* 2015
Sales 36.9MM^E *EMP* 2,998
SIC 5699 5948 Caps & gowns (academic vestments); Leather goods, except luggage & shoes
CEO: Timothy Becker

WILSONS LEATHER OUTLET
See AM RETAIL GROUP INC

D-U-N-S 82-474-1537 IMP/EXP
WILTON BRANDS LLC
EK SUCCESS BRANDS
(*Suby of* WILTON INDUSTRIES) ★
2240 75th St, Woodridge, IL 60517-2333
Tel (630) 963-7100 *Founded/Ownrshp* 2009
Sales 703.2MM^E *EMP* 1,500
Accts Pricewaterhousecoopers Llp Fl
SIC 5023 2731 2721 7812 5199 Kitchenware; Books: publishing only; Periodicals: publishing only; Video tape production; Candy making goods & supplies
CEO: Sue Buchta
**Ch Bd:* Jerry W Levin
**Pr:* Kevin Fick
**CEO:* Christopher Skinner
**COO:* Mary Cushing Merfeld
**CFO:* Michael Fishoff
Sr VP: Marvin Oakes
Genl Mgr: Dave Ferreira
MIS Dir: Terry Kerestes
Prd Mgr: Challis Yeager
Natl Sales: Michael Sinishta
Board of Directors: John Rice, Gina Bosswell, Christopher Skinner, Aaron D Cohen, Richard Conti, David A Donnini, Kevin Fick, Vincent J Hemmer, Thomas Kasvin, Charls Koppelman, Mary Merfeld

WILTON ENTERPRISES
See WILTON INDUSTRIES INC

D-U-N-S 83-134-0471 EXP
WILTON HOLDINGS INC
WILTON INDUSTRIES
2240 75th St, Woodridge, IL 60517-2333
Tel (630) 963-7100 *Founded/Ownrshp* 1929
Sales 703.2MM^E *EMP* 2,400^E
SIC 5023 2731 2721 7812 5199 Kitchenware; Books: publishing only; Periodicals: publishing only; Video tape production; Candy making goods & supplies
CEO: Steven Fraser
**Pr:* Deborah Bennett
**COO:* Dan Kochenash
**Sr VP:* Rodney Poole

WILTON INDUSTRIES
See WILTON HOLDINGS INC

D-U-N-S 05-253-4799 IMP/EXP
WILTON INDUSTRIES INC
WILTON ENTERPRISES
(*Suby of* EK SUCCESS BRANDS) ★
2240 75th St, Woodridge, IL 60517-2333
Tel (630) 963-7100 *Founded/Ownrshp* 2007
Sales 463.9MM^E *EMP* 755
SIC 5023 2731 2721 7812 5199 Kitchenware; Kitchen tools & utensils; Frames & framing, picture & mirror; Books: publishing only; Periodicals: publishing only; Video tape production; Candy making goods & supplies
Pr: Jeff McLaughlin
COO: Steve Frazer
CFO: Mary Merfield
Ex VP: Eric Tsai
Sales Exec: Marvin G Oakes
Board of Directors: David A Donnini

D-U-N-S 80-862-1655
WILTON RE US HOLDINGS INC
(*Suby of* WILTON RE HOLDINGS LIMITED)
20 Glover Ave Ste 4, Norwalk, CT 06850-1234
Tel (203) 762-4400 *Founded/Ownrshp* 2005
Sales NA *EMP* 200^E
SIC 6311 Life reinsurance
CEO: Chris C Stroup
**COO:* Enrico J Treglia
**CFO:* Michael E Fleitz
**Chf Mktg O:* Donald Araldi
**Ofcr:* David A Van Der Beek
**Sr VP:* Perry H Braun
**Sr VP:* Michael L Greer
**Sr VP:* Mark R Sarlitto
**Sr VP:* Andrew J Wood

D-U-N-S 82-713-3898
WILTON REASSURANCE CO
(*Suby of* WILTON RE US HOLDINGS INC) ★
20 Glover Ave Ste 4, Norwalk, CT 06850-1234
Tel (203) 762-4400 *Founded/Ownrshp* 2004
Sales NA *EMP* 200^E
SIC 6311 Life insurance
CEO: Chris C Stroup
**COO:* Enrico J Treglia
**CFO:* Michael E Fleitz
Treas: Timothy D Rogers
**Chf Mktg O:* Donald Araldi
**Ofcr:* David A Van Der Beek
**Sr VP:* Perry H Braun
**Sr VP:* Michael L Greer
**Sr VP:* Mark R Sarlitto
**Sr VP:* Andrew J Wood

D-U-N-S 60-372-1999
WILTON SURGERY CENTER LLC
AMSURG
(*Suby of* AMSURG CORP) ★
195 Danbury Rd Ste B100, Wilton, CT 06897-6012
Tel (203) 563-9470 *Founded/Ownrshp* 2008
Sales 17.5MM^E *EMP* 1,362^E
SIC 8062 General medical & surgical hospitals

WILVACO
See WILLAMETTE VALLEY CO

WIMCO METALS
See LENMORE INC

D-U-N-S 00-652-7840 IMP
WIMSATT BUILDING MATERIALS CORP
36340 Van Born Rd, Wayne, MI 48184-2071
Tel (734) 722-3460 *Founded/Ownrshp* 1983
Sales 277.0MM^E *EMP* 200
SIC 5033 8742 Roofing & siding materials; Management consulting services
Pr: Robert L Hoffman
**VP:* Alfred P Dechene
**VP:* Charles D Hoffman
**VP:* Gerald Swiney
VP: Jerry Swiney
IT Man: Jon Siedlik
Trfc Dir: Chris Atkinson
Opers Mgr: John Dunckel
Opers Mgr: Michael Erickson
Opers Mgr: Greg Hoffman
Opers Mgr: Bob Martin

D-U-N-S 00-192-6955 IMP
WIN-HOLT EQUIPMENT CORP
WIN-HOLT EQUIPMENT GROUP
20 Crossways Park Dr N # 205, Woodbury, NY 11797-2007
Tel (516) 222-0335 *Founded/Ownrshp* 1946
Sales 90.2MM^E *EMP* 225
SIC 2099 Food preparations
CEO: Jonathan J Holtz
**Pr:* Dominick Scarfogliero
COO: Jose Ponce
Exec: John Cunneen
Genl Mgr: Courtney Guerrero
IT Man: Dina Glover
Opers Mgr: Jane Dunstatter
VP Sls: Jeff Herbert
Mktg Dir: Annette Marsh
Mktg Mgr: Rose Frierson

WIN-HOLT EQUIPMENT GROUP
See WIN-HOLT EQUIPMENT CORP

D-U-N-S 01-353-6164
WIN-SUM SKI CORP
HOLIDAY VALLEY RESORT
6557 Holiday Valley Rd, Ellicottville, NY 14731-9779
Tel (716) 699-2345 *Founded/Ownrshp* 1957
Sales 25.3MM *EMP* 1,350
Accts Buffamante Whipple Buttafaro P
SIC 7011 7997 6531 Hotels & motels; Golf club, membership; Real estate managers
Ch Bd: Dennis Eshbaugh
**CFO:* David Trathen
**VP:* John Northrup
Dir Risk M: Michael Brown
CTO: Christopher Reiley
IT Man: Myers Joseph
IT Man: Joseph Myers
Secur Mgr: Larry Graham
Sales Exec: Heather Adams

D-U-N-S 08-036-0157
WINCHESTER ACQUISITION HOLDINGS CORP
1111 19th St Nw, Washington, DC 20036-3603
Tel (202) 463-4860 *Founded/Ownrshp* 2016
Sales 32.6MM^E *EMP* 1,300^E
SIC 6719 Investment holding companies, except banks
Pr: William Ballhaus

D-U-N-S 16-703-8269 IMP
WINCHESTER ELECTRONICS CORP
KINGS ELECTRONICS
199 Park Road Ext Ste 104, Middlebury, CT 06762
Tel (203) 741-5400 *Founded/Ownrshp* 2004
Sales 337.5MM^E *EMP* 1,350
SIC 3678 Electronic connectors
Pr: Kevin S Perhamus
**CFO:* John Sickler
VP: Dan Hirschnitz
Genl Mgr: Beth Beadle
IT Man: Kevin Bair
Opers Mgr: Jaime Ramirez
Manager: Pat McCauley
Manager: Steve Riddell
Sls Mgr: Torrey Jacobs
Sls Mgr: Et Lee
Sls Mgr: Lauree Letan

D-U-N-S 18-201-1155
WINCHESTER HEALTHCARE MANAGEMENT INC
41 Highland Ave, Winchester, MA 01890-1446
Tel (781) 756-2126 *Founded/Ownrshp* 1987
Sales 25.6M *EMP* 2,113
Accts Deloitte Tax Llp Boston Ma
SIC 8741 Hospital management
Pr: Kevin F Smith
Treas: Kevin Smith
**Treas:* Matthew Woods
VP: Richard J Mazandi Iseke
VP Admn: Philip A Heywood

D-U-N-S 07-213-6468
WINCHESTER HOSPITAL
41 Highland Ave, Winchester, MA 01890-1496
Tel (781) 729-9000 *Founded/Ownrshp* 1906
Sales 262.5MM^E *EMP* 2,500
SIC 8062 General medical & surgical hospitals
Pr: Dale Lodge
Dir Recs: Ellen M Mullin
V Ch: Gerard Polcari
Pr: Robbie Robertson
**Pr:* Kevin F Smith
Treas: Richard J Killigrew
Ex VP: Joseph Taylor
VP: Mary Sweeney
Dir Lab: Lee Coffman
Assoc Dir: Karen Hart
Comm Dir: John Looney

D-U-N-S 79-727-1264
WINCHESTER MEDICAL CENTER
(*Suby of* VALLEY HEALTH SYSTEM) ★
1840 Amherst St, Winchester, VA 22601-2808
Tel (540) 536-8000 *Founded/Ownrshp* 1901
Sales 470.4MM *EMP* 2,500^E
SIC 8059 Nursing home, except skilled & intermediate care facility
Prin: Mark H Merrill
**CEO:* Philips Grady
CFO: Bob Amos
VP: Nicholas Restrepo
**VP:* Nicolas C Restrepo
VP: Terry Sinclair
**VP:* Thurman Suanne
VP: Katherine Tagnesi
Dir OR: Phillip Webb
Dir Risk M: Carla Dallman
Ex Dir: Chuck Coleman

D-U-N-S 07-494-4927
WINCHESTER MEDICAL CENTER AUXILIARY INC
(*Suby of* WINCHESTER MEDICAL CENTER) ★
1840 Amherst St, Winchester, VA 22601-2808
Tel (540) 536-8000 *Founded/Ownrshp* 1984
Sales 124.3MM^E *EMP* 2,046
Accts Arnett & Foster Pllc Cha
SIC 8062 General medical & surgical hospitals
Pr: George B Caley
**CFO:* J Craig Lewis
**Ex VP:* F D Whitworth Jr
**VP:* B J Bartleson
Doctor: Trisha Nashed
Doctor: John Quinn

D-U-N-S 96-353-1723
WINCHESTER PLACE NURSING & REHABILITATION CENTER
(*Suby of* MGM HEALTHCARE) ★
36 Lehman Dr, Winchester, OH 45697
Tel (614) 834-2273 *Founded/Ownrshp* 2010
Sales 1.2MMM *EMP* 1^E
SIC 8051 Skilled nursing care facilities
CEO: Judah Bienstock
Ex Dir: Chris Hudson
Sls&Mrk Ex: Kevin Kilbane

WINCO FOOD STORES
See WINCO FOODS LLC

WINCO FOODS
See WINCO HOLDINGS INC

D-U-N-S 04-051-7028
WINCO FOODS
(*Suby of* WINCO FOOD STORES) ★
80 N Stephanie St, Henderson, NV 89074-8079
Tel (702) 558-5386 *Founded/Ownrshp* 2012
Sales 55.2MM^E *EMP* 1,195^E
SIC 5411 Grocery stores
Pr: Bill Long

D-U-N-S 05-609-8817 IMP
WINCO FOODS LLC
WINCO FOOD STORES
(*Suby of* WINCO FOODS) ★
650 N Armstrong Pl, Boise, ID 83704-0825
Tel (208) 377-0110 *Founded/Ownrshp* 2004
Sales 2.8MMM^E *EMP* 12,000
Accts Kpmg Llp Boise Id
SIC 5411 Supermarkets, chain
Pr: Steven Goddard
**COO:* Rich Charrier
**CFO:* David Butler
VP: Kim Lamborn
VP: Nancy Lebold
**VP:* Gary Piva
VP: Glen Reynolds
VP: Del Ririe
Dir IT: Wendy Bell
Netwrk Eng: Ben Eichelberger

D-U-N-S 60-398-4357
WINCO HOLDINGS INC
WINCO FOODS
650 N Armstrong Pl, Boise, ID 83704-0825
Tel (208) 377-0110 *Founded/Ownrshp* 1968
Sales 2.8MMM^E *EMP* 14,000
Accts Kpmg Llp Boise Id
SIC 5411 Supermarkets; Supermarkets, chain
CEO: Steven Goddard
Recvr: Angie Silva
Pr: David Van Etten
Pr: Dick Vanderlinden
**COO:* Richard Charrier
**CFO:* David Butler
VP: Todd Ashworth
VP: Dave Goodwin
VP: Grant Haag
VP: Jim Parker
VP: Glen Reynolds
VP: Robert Rhodes
VP: Delbert Ririe

D-U-N-S 12-004-6953
■ **WINCOR NIXDORF INC**
(*Suby of* WINCOR NIXDORF INTERNATIONAL GMBH)
12345 N Lamar Blvd # 200, Austin, TX 78753-1306
Tel (512) 676-5000 *Founded/Ownrshp* 2011
Sales 95.7MM^E *EMP* 263^E
SIC 7379 5734 5251 Computer related consulting services; Computer & software stores; Door locks & lock sets
Pr: Stan Holcomb
Pt: Oxana Dovbenko
Pt: Fred Gadalla
Pt: Anja Kegler
Pt: Hilmar Kraft
**CFO:* Gina Miller
Bd of Dir: Khoon H Lim
Ofcr: Jonathan Davison
Ofcr: Werner Kessler
**Sr VP:* Javier Lopez Bartolome
VP: Nyla Braun
VP: Richard Hackle
VP: Lim Khoon Hong
VP: Marco Knuist
**VP:* Patrick Leonard
VP: Javier Pez
VP: Ulrich Seemann
VP: Tad Shepperd
VP: John Tyler
VP: Alan Walsh
VP Bus: Douglas Evans

D-U-N-S 17-436-6823 EXP
WINCORP INTERNATIONAL INC
(*Suby of* JAMAICA BROILERS GROUP LIMITED)
10025 Nw 116th Way Ste 14, Medley, FL 33178-1173
Tel (305) 887-1294 *Founded/Ownrshp* 2006
Sales 92.6MM *EMP* 12
Accts The Sharpton Group Pa Ft La
SIC 5191 5083 5199 7338 5144 Animal feeds; Agricultural machinery & equipment; General merchandise, non-durable; Stenographic services; Eggs
Pr: Stephen Levy
**Ch Bd:* Robert E Levy
**Pr:* Thomas Rahn
VP: Jeff Pierce
VP Mktg: Conley Salmon

D-U-N-S 00-617-7752 IMP/EXP
WINCRAFT INC
LAR LU
960 E Mark St, Winona, MN 55987-4723
Tel (507) 454-5510 *Founded/Ownrshp* 1961
Sales 155.0MM^E *EMP* 600
SIC 3499 2399 3089 3961 3999 3069 Novelties & specialties, metal; Pennants; Novelties, plastic; Costume jewelry, ex. precious metal & semiprecious stones; Badges, metal: policemen, firemen, etc.; Buttons: Red Cross, union, identification; Erasers: rubber or rubber & abrasive combined
Ch Bd: Richard J Pope
**Pr:* John Killen
**Pr:* Philip Welp
Ex VP: Robert Flom
Sr VP: Joe Durand
**VP:* Jack Andresen
VP: Jackie Czatlewski
VP: David Schipper
VP: Kevin Whetstone
Genl Mgr: Kim Pronschinske
Dir IT: Dick Pope
Board of Directors: Richard L Alf

D-U-N-S 15-094-9878
WINCUP INC
4640 Lewis Rd, Stone Mountain, GA 30083-1004
Tel (770) 771-5861 *Founded/Ownrshp* 2006
Sales 353.8MM^E *EMP* 1,100^E
SIC 3086 3089 Cups & plates, foamed plastic; Plastic kitchenware, tableware & houseware
CEO: Jack Brucker
**CFO:* Mark Thomas
**Treas:* Evan Hardin
**Treas:* Douglas Reames
Sr VP: Dan Fischer
**Sr VP:* Mike Revier
VP: Steven McNamee
Genl Mgr: Doug Smith
Prd Mgr: Robert Bobkoskie
Sls Mgr: Henry Bowen
Sls Mgr: Brian Grant

D-U-N-S 60-340-0370
WIND HOTELS HOLDINGS INC
LXR RESORTS
345 Park Ave, New York, NY 10154-0004
Tel (212) 583-5000 *Founded/Ownrshp* 2005
Sales 86.8MM^E *EMP* 500^E
SIC 7011 8741 Hotel, franchised; Resort hotel; Ski lodge; Hotel or motel management
Mng Dir: Kenneth A Caplan
Mng Dir: Peter Koffler
Mng Dir: Vincent Lu

D-U-N-S 15-168-6847 IMP/EXP
WIND POINT PARTNERS LP
676 N Michigan Ave # 3700, Chicago, IL 60611-2838
Tel (312) 255-4800 *Founded/Ownrshp* 1983
Sales 1.7MMM^E *EMP* 5,742
SIC 6799 7363 3089 Venture capital companies; Help supply services; Blister or bubble formed packaging, plastic
Pt: Nathan Brown
Pt: Jim Tenbroek
Pt: Alex Washington
CFO: Cathy Fry
CFO: Leann Kilarski
VP: Rebecca Asfour
VP: Joe Lawler
VP: Matt Moran
VP: Konrad Salaber
Exec: Hannah Yoder
Mng Dir: Bob Cummings

D-U-N-S 78-407-2188
WIND POINT PARTNERS VI LP
(*Suby of* WIND POINT PARTNERS LP) ★
676 N Michigan Ave # 3700, Chicago, IL 60611-2838
Tel (312) 255-4800 *Founded/Ownrshp* 1984
Sales 264.0MM^E *EMP* 1,467^E
SIC 6799 2542 2541 3429 Investors; Partitions & fixtures, except wood; Wood partitions & fixtures; Manufactured hardware (general)
Genl Pt: Jeff Gonyo
Pt: Bob Cummings
Pt: James E Forrest
Pt: Michael Mahoney
Pt: Michael Solot
Pt: James Tenbroek
CFO: Leann Kilarski

D-U-N-S 16-631-5346
WIND RIVER GROUP PT LLC
LEGEND HEALTHCARE
608 Sandau Rd, San Antonio, TX 78216-4131
Tel (210) 564-0100 *Founded/Ownrshp* 2001
Sales 54.6MM^E *EMP* 1,200
SIC 8051 Skilled nursing care facilities
CEO: Doug Preston
**CFO:* Dwight Muse
**Ofcr:* Martin Tomerlin
VP: Kristin Hammon
Exec: Lisa Cavazos
Dir Soc: Sandra Peebles
Dir Bus: Dana Parker
Mktg Dir: Anh Nguyen

D-U-N-S 10-297-5448
■ **WIND RIVER SYSTEMS INC**
(*Suby of* INTEL CORP) ★
500 Wind River Way, Alameda, CA 94501-1162
Tel (510) 748-4100 *Founded/Ownrshp* 1872
Sales 293.9MM^E *EMP* 1,673^E
SIC 7372 7373 Application computer software; Systems software development services
CEO: Elmar Degenhardt
Ch Bd: Kenneth R Klein
Pr: Barry Mainz
Pr: Scot Morrision
COO: Barry R Mainz
CFO: Daniel P Gorey
CFO: Dick Kraber
CFO: Dale Wilde
Chf Mktg O: John J Bruggeman
Sr VP: Christopher Aliberti
Sr VP: Jane E Bone
Sr VP: Jim Douglas
Sr VP: Michael Krutz
Sr VP: Gareth Noyes
VP: Jay Andersen
VP: Damian Artt
VP: Doug Ertz
VP: John C Fogelin
VP: Doreen Lauderback
VP: Duncan Macmurdy
VP: Brad Murdoch

D-U-N-S 11-961-4175 IMP
WIND TURBINE AND ENERGY CABLES CORP
WTEC RNEWABLE ENRGY INNOVATION
1 Bridge Plz N Ste 260, Fort Lee, NJ 07024-7573
Tel (201) 242-9906 *Founded/Ownrshp* 2002
Sales 235.3MM^E *EMP* 100
SIC 5063 Wire & cable
Ch: D Craig Bowman
**Pr:* Robert Singh
**CFO:* Sherie Cho
**CFO:* Bonita Singh
**VP:* Michael Brumbaugh
**VP:* Brian Dick
**VP:* Steve Kim
**VP:* Suren Shah
**VP:* James Wood

WINDANCE COUNTRY CLUB
See GULFSIDE CASINO PARTNERSHIP DBA

D-U-N-S 17-588-3474
WINDGATE FOUNDATION
115 E University St, Siloam Springs, AR 72761-2755
Tel (479) 524-9829 *Founded/Ownrshp* 2005
Sales 108.0MM *EMP* 3
SIC 8733 Noncommercial social research organization
Ex Dir: John Brown

WINDHAM HOUSE OF HATTIESBURG
See LAMAR COMMUNITY CARE CENTER LLC

D-U-N-S 08-831-9892
WINDHAM TOWN OF (INC) (CT)
979 Main St, Willimantic, CT 06226-2200
Tel (860) 465-3000 *Founded/Ownrshp* 1692
Sales NA *EMP* 1,069
Accts Disanto Bertoline & Company P
SIC 9111 City & town managers' offices
Pr: Neal Beets
Genl Mgr: Karen Williams

D-U-N-S 80-906-3519
WINDJAMMER CAPITAL INVESTORS III LLC
WESTWIND EQUITY INVESTORS
610 Newport Center Dr # 1100, Newport Beach, CA 92660-6419
Tel (949) 706-9989 *Founded/Ownrshp* 1990
Sales 114.8MM^E *EMP* 724
SIC 6211 Investment firm, general brokerage
Ch: Robert Bartholomew
**VP:* Matt Anderson
VP: Jeffery J Dunnigan
VP: Andrew Miclot
**Prin:* J Derek Watson
Mng Dir: Derek J Watson

D-U-N-S 07-985-5863
WINDJAMMER CAPITAL INVESTORS IV LP
610 Newport Center Dr, Newport Beach, CA 92660-6419
Tel (919) 706-9989 *Founded/Ownrshp* 2012
Sales 155.9MM^E *EMP* 450^E
SIC 6799 Investors
Pt: Windjammer P LLC

D-U-N-S 07-578-3696
WINDOW PRODUCTS INC
CASCADE WINDOWS
10507 E Montgomery Dr, Spokane Valley, WA 99206-4280
Tel (800) 442-8544 *Founded/Ownrshp* 2016
Sales 84.5MM^E *EMP* 350
SIC 3442 5211

D-U-N-S 02-408-8978
WINDRIVER GRAIN LLC (KS)
2810 E Us Highway 50, Garden City, KS 67846-8528
Tel (620) 275-2101 *Founded/Ownrshp* 1997
Sales 251.7MM *EMP* 24
Accts Lindburg Vogel Pierce Faris C
SIC 5153 Grain & field beans
COO: Robert Tempel

D-U-N-S 78-628-2921 IMP
WINDSOR AJINOMOTO INC
(*Suby of* AJINOMOTO NORTH AMERICA HOLDINGS INC) ★
4200 Concours Ste 100, Ontario, CA 91764-4982
Tel (909) 477-4700 *Founded/Ownrshp* 2013
Sales 87.7MM^E *EMP* 2,500
SIC 2038 2037 Frozen specialties; Frozen fruits & vegetables
Pr: Bernard Kreilmann
**CFO:* Fon Wong
**Ch:* Haruo Kurata
**Treas:* John Gordon
**Ex VP:* George Jurkovich
**Ex VP:* Taro Komura
VP Sls: Neil Ritchey

D-U-N-S 08-172-9188
WINDSOR CAPITAL GROUP INC
WINDSOR MANAGEMENT SERVICES
3250 Ocean Park Blvd # 350, Santa Monica, CA 90405-3257
Tel (310) 566-1100 *Founded/Ownrshp* 1989
Sales 161.5MM^E *EMP* 2,042
SIC 7011 Hotels & motels
CEO: Patrick M Nesbitt
**Pr:* William Upshaw
**COO:* Paul Francisco
**CFO:* Sandy Barnes
**Sr VP:* Craig Stechman
**VP:* Neil Cohen
**VP:* Ken Hassett
Exec: Stacey Wolf
Genl Mgr: Kevin Phipps
Sls Mgr: Brittany Aanestad

WINDSOR COLLECTION
See AMERIMARK DIRECT LLC

WINDSOR CONSTRUCTION
See J & R ASSOCIATES

D-U-N-S 02-786-7498 IMP
WINDSOR FASHIONS INC
9603 John St, Santa Fe Springs, CA 90670-2905
Tel (323) 282-9000 *Founded/Ownrshp* 1959
Sales 118.1MM *EMP* 600
Accts Cohnreznick Llp Los Angeles
SIC 5621 5632 Ready-to-wear apparel, women's; Apparel accessories
Ch Bd: Maurice Zekaria
**Pr:* Leon Zekaria
Ex VP: Robert Sliter
**VP:* Issac Zekaria
Area Mgr: Jovanna Ortega
Dist Mgr: Annalisa Dicesare
Dist Mgr: Molly Meyer
Store Mgr: Joy Cardenas
Dir IT: Curtis Rose
VP Opers: Bob Slatter

WINDSOR FOODS
See WINDSOR QUALITY FOOD CO LTD

D-U-N-S 07-830-6150 IMP/EXP
WINDSOR LOCKS NONWOVENS INC
SUOMINEN NONWOVEN
(*Suby of* SUOMINEN US HOLDING INC) ★
3 Chirnside Rd Bldg D, Windsor Locks, CT 06096-1142
Tel (860) 292-5600 *Founded/Ownrshp* 2011
Sales 115.0MM^E *EMP* 30
SIC 2297 Nonwoven fabrics
CEO: Nina Kopola
**VP:* Petri Rolig

WINDSOR MANAGEMENT SERVICES
See WINDSOR CAPITAL GROUP INC

D-U-N-S 83-701-4919
WINDSOR QUALITY FOOD CO LTD
WINDSOR FOODS
3355 W Alabama St Ste 730, Houston, TX 77098-1866
Tel (713) 843-5200 *Founded/Ownrshp* 1990
Sales 80.3M^E *EMP* 3,300
SIC 2038
Pr: Orry Boscia
VP: Rick Alden
VP: Sarah Chandler
VP: Tom Foegle
Rgnl Mgr: Jim Massaro
Netwrk Mgr: Kirk Mihalkovitz
Sfty Mgr: Ralph Hill
Plnt Mgr: Howard Teufel
Mktg Dir: Anthony Favela
Mktg Mgr: Sarah Salvato
Sls Mgr: Jean Lallana

D-U-N-S 14-482-2124 IMP
WINDSOR WINDOW CO
MONARCH WINDOW
(*Suby of* WOODGRAIN MILLWORK INC) ★
300 Nw 16th St, Fruitland, ID 83619-2218
Tel (800) 452-3801 *Founded/Ownrshp* 2003
Sales 115.0MM *EMP* 666
SIC 2431 Moldings, wood: unfinished & prefinished
Pr: Mark Rieser
**CFO:* Greg Easton
**Treas:* Steve Atkinson
**Prin:* James Burton

WINDSTREAM COMMUNICATION
See XETA TECHNOLOGIES INC

D-U-N-S 78-099-4039
■ **WINDSTREAM COMMUNICATIONS LLC**
(*Suby of* WINDSTREAM SERVICES LLC) ★
4001 N Rodney Parham Rd, Little Rock, AR 72212-2459
Tel (800) 697-8153 *Founded/Ownrshp* 2005
Sales 2.2MMM^E *EMP* 7,400^E
SIC 4813 Telephone communication, except radio
Ex VP: John Fletcher
**COO:* Brent Whittington
**CFO:* Tony Thomas
**Treas:* Robert Clacny
Div VP: John Cheek
Ex VP: Mark Faris
**Sr VP:* Eric Einhorn
**VP:* John Eichler
VP: Stephanie Hinman
Off Admin: Georganne Chevalier
Snr Sftwr: Michael Johnson

D-U-N-S 00-780-9783
■ **WINDSTREAM GEORGIA LLC**
(*Suby of* WINDSTREAM HOLDINGS INC) ★
906 Vista Dr, Dalton, GA 30721-8698
Tel (706) 279-7600 *Founded/Ownrshp* 2006
Sales 210.4MM^E *EMP* 450
SIC 4813 4812 Local & long distance telephone communications; Radio telephone communication
Pr: J Scott Chesbro
Mktg Dir: Terry Moore

D-U-N-S 07-930-5499
▲ **WINDSTREAM HOLDINGS INC**
4001 N Rodney Parham Rd # 101, Little Rock, AR 72212-2490
Tel (501) 748-7000 *Founded/Ownrshp* 2000
Sales 5.7MMM *EMP* 12,326^E
Tkr Sym WIN *Exch* NGS
SIC 4813 5065 Telephone communication, except radio; ; ; Local & long distance telephone communications; Communication equipment
Pr: Anthony W Thomas
Ch Bd: Jeffrey T Hinson
Pr: Jarrod Berkshire
CFO: Robert E Gunderman
Ex VP: John P Fletcher
Sr VP: Beth A Lackey
VP: John C Eichler
CTO: Jeff Small
Board of Directors: Carol B Armitage, Samuel E Beall III, Jeannie H Diefenderfer, William G Laperch, Larry Laque, Michael G Stoltz, Alan L Wells

D-U-N-S 10-918-9071
■ **WINDSTREAM IOWA COMMUNICATIONS LLC**
(*Suby of* WINDSTREAM SERVICES LLC) ★
4001 N Rodney Parham Rd, Little Rock, AR 72212-2459
Tel (501) 748-7000 *Founded/Ownrshp* 2010
Sales 238.9MM^E *EMP* 800
SIC 4813 Telephone communication, except radio; Local telephone communications; Long distance telephone communications;
Pr: Alan L Wells
CFO: Craig A Knock
VP: Donald G Henry
VP Sls: Michael A Struck

D-U-N-S 07-653-4325 IMP
■ **WINDSTREAM NUVOX INC**
(*Suby of* GABRIEL COMMUNICATIONS FINANCE CO) ★
2 N Main St, Greenville, SC 29601-4874
Tel (864) 672-5000 *Founded/Ownrshp* 1998
Sales 350.3MM^E *EMP* 1,800
SIC 4813 Local & long distance telephone communications
Pr: James Akerhielm
Treas: Robert Dilly
VP: Ray Drause
VP: Amy Gardner
VP: Jake Jennings
VP: Anthony Walsh
Exec: Tom Knox
CIO: Victor Gonzalez
CTO: Robert Leithman
Snr Mgr: Derek Davis

D-U-N-S 14-596-6326
■ WINDSTREAM SERVICES LLC
(*Suby of* WINDSTREAM HOLDINGS INC) ★
4001 N Rodney Parham Rd # 101, Little Rock, AR 72212-2490
Tel (501) 748-7000 *Founded/Ownrshp* 2013
Sales 8.0MMM^E^ *EMP* 12,626
SIC 4813 5065 Telephone communication, except radio; ; ; Local & long distance telephone communications; Communication equipment
Pr: Anthony W Thomas
Pr: Tony Thomas
CFO: Robert E Gunderman
Treas: Robert G Clancy
Ex VP: John P Fletcher
Ex VP: Jeffery Howe
Sr VP: Sarah Day
Sr VP: Matt Dement
Sr VP: Kevin Halpin
Sr VP: John Leach
VP: Barry Bishop
VP: Robert Boyd
VP: Cesar Caballero
VP: John C Eichler
VP: Willis Kemp
VP: Ted Thomas
Board of Directors: Carol B Armitage, Samuel E Beall III, Francis X Frantz, Jeffrey T Hinson, Judy K Jones, William A Montgomery, Alan L Wells

D-U-N-S 14-595-7283
■ WINDSTREAM SOUTHWEST LONG DISTANCE LP
(*Suby of* WINDSTREAM SERVICES LLC) ★
201 E John Carpenter Fwy, Irving, TX 75062-2707
Tel (972) 373-1000 *Founded/Ownrshp* 2000
Sales 261.7MM^E^ *EMP* 1,350
SIC 4813 Voice telephone communications
CEO: Kenneth R Cole
**COO:* John J Mueller
**CFO:* John Butler
VP: Keith Terreri
CIO: Cindy Nash

WINDSTREAM STHWEST LONG DSTNCE
See VALOR TELECOMMUNICATIONS ENTERPRISES LLC

D-U-N-S 00-892-8632
■ WINDSTREAM SUPPLY LLC (OH)
(*Suby of* WINDSTREAM SERVICES LLC) ★
13560 Morris Rd Ste 4350, Alpharetta, GA 30004-0002
Tel (678) 381-0984 *Founded/Ownrshp* 1946, 2006
Sales 234.2MM^E^ *EMP* 370
SIC 5065 Telephone equipment
Sr VP: Bob Cori
VP: David L Atwood
VP: Tom C Strangi
VP: Bruce P Thomas

D-U-N-S 04-858-5918
WINDWARD PETROLEUM INC
1064 Goffs Falls Rd, Manchester, NH 03103-6128
Tel (603) 222-2900 *Founded/Ownrshp* 1998
Sales 141.5MM^E^ *EMP* 350
SIC 5531 Automotive parts
Pr: Andy Welcher
**Ch:* Terry Russell
Sr VP: Steve Ruff
**VP:* Mike Spoor

D-U-N-S 13-160-4220 IMP/EXP
WINDWARD PRINT STAR INC
ADPLEX
14950 Hethrw Frst Pkwy # 120, Houston, TX 77032-3847
Tel (281) 821-5522 *Founded/Ownrshp* 2002
Sales 95.0MM^E^ *EMP* 250
SIC 2752 2791 2796 7335 7336 7331 Commercial printing, offset; Typesetting; Color separations for printing; Photographic studio, commercial; Creative services to advertisers, except writers; Mailing service
Ex VP: Edward Raine
**Pr:* Robin Cole
**CEO:* Ed Raine
VP: Bob Newman
VP: Don Smith
**CTO:* John Leonard
IT Man: Devy Chain

D-U-N-S 00-607-6970 IMP/EXP
WINDWAY CAPITAL CORP
630 Riverfront Dr Ste 200, Sheboygan, WI 53081-4629
Tel (920) 457-8600 *Founded/Ownrshp* 1911
Sales 220.8MM^E^ *EMP* 1,080
SIC 3469 2394 3624 3732

WINDY CITY EXPRESS
See EDYS GRAND ICE CREAM

D-U-N-S 06-430-7671 IMP/EXP
WINE GROUP INC
MOGAN DAVID WINE
(*Suby of* WINE GROUP LLC) ★
17000 E State Highway 120, Ripon, CA 95366-9412
Tel (209) 599-4111 *Founded/Ownrshp* 1985
Sales 94.8MM^E^ *EMP* 250
SIC 2084 Wines
CEO: Brian Jay Vos
**Ch Bd:* Arthur Ciocca
CFO: F L Bates
CFO: Richard Mahoney
**VP:* Morris Ball
VP: Armando Bautista
VP: Brad Harrison
**VP:* Stephen Hughes
VP: Sudhir Kumar
VP: Chris Nodland
**VP:* Louis Quaccia
VP: Glenn Spyksma
Exec: Lou Dambrosio

D-U-N-S 19-903-6273 IMP
WINE GROUP INC
4596 Tesla Rd, Livermore, CA 94550-9002
Tel (925) 456-2500 *Founded/Ownrshp* 1981
Sales 25.4MM^E^ *EMP* 1,001
SIC 5921 Wine
CEO: Brian Jay Vos
Pr: David Kent
Ex VP: Matt Henderson
VP: Dave Johnson
VP: Chris Summers
Area Mgr: Cameron Kent
Div Mgr: Brad Anderson
Div Mgr: Matthew Currin

D-U-N-S 55-756-2951 IMP/EXP
WINE GROUP LLC
4596 S Tracy Blvd, Tracy, CA 95377-8106
Tel (415) 986-8700 *Founded/Ownrshp* 1997
Sales 100.5MM^E^ *EMP* 265
SIC 5921 Wine
**Pr:* David Mackesey
CFO: Richard L Mahoney
**CFO:* Jim Page
Chf Mktg O: Laurie Jones
Ex VP: Jeff Dubiel
VP: Dave Johnson
VP: Ken Lizar

D-U-N-S 01-031-6747 IMP
WINE LABELS LLC
STEW LEONARD'S
100 Westport Ave, Norwalk, CT 06851-3915
Tel (203) 847-7213 *Founded/Ownrshp* 2008
Sales 108.5MM^E^ *EMP* 130^E^
SIC 5131 Labels
VP: Bruce Kennedy
VP: Jill Leonard
Exec: Michael Luboff
Exec: Mike Olbrys
Dept Mgr: Robert Luz
Genl Mgr: Marianne Leonard
Store Mgr: Christopher Nemer
Sfty Dirs: Walter Watson
Genl Couns: Drew Kordas
Snr Mgr: Hery Escoto

WINE WAREHOUSE
See BEN MYERSON CANDY CO INC

D-U-N-S 07-955-4546
WINEBOW GROUP LLC
4800 Cox Rd Ste 300, Glen Allen, VA 23060-6524
Tel (804) 752-3670 *Founded/Ownrshp* 2014
Sales 567.5MM^E^ *EMP* 541^E^
SIC 5182 Wine

D-U-N-S 09-848-4975 IMP
WINEBOW INC
LEONARDO LO CASCIO SELECTIONS
(*Suby of* WINEBOW GROUP LLC) ★
75 Chestnut Ridge Rd # 1, Montvale, NJ 07645-1844
Tel (201) 445-0620 *Founded/Ownrshp* 2014
Sales 240.1MM^E^ *EMP* 538
SIC 5182 Wine
CEO: Leonardo Locascio
Pr: Scott Ades
Pr: Frank Shobe
Sr VP: Kristy Heady
VP Admn: Steve Tilstra
Area Mgr: Jamie Beatty
Dist Mgr: Doug D'Auria
VP Mktg: Teresa Low
Pr Mgr: David Greenberg
Mktg Mgr: David Alphonse
Sls Mgr: Bryan Cole

D-U-N-S 80-684-3228 IMP
WINFIELD SOLUTIONS LLC
WINFIELD US
(*Suby of* LAND O'LAKES INC) ★
1080 County Road F W, Saint Paul, MN 55126-2910
Tel (651) 481-2222 *Founded/Ownrshp* 2007
Sales 1.4MMM^E^ *EMP* 800
SIC 5191 Farm supplies
Mktg Mgr: Tyler Grenzow

WINFIELD US
See WINFIELD SOLUTIONS LLC

D-U-N-S 08-308-3720
WINGATE HEALTH CARE HOLDINGS INC
(*Suby of* CONTINENTAL WINGATE CO INC) ★
63 Kendrick St, Needham, MA 02494-2708
Tel (781) 707-9000 *Founded/Ownrshp* 1998
Sales 141.9MM^E^ *EMP* 1,800
SIC 8741 Nursing & personal care facility management
Pr: Scott Schuster
**COO:* Jeff Floyd
**Treas:* Brian Callahan
**Ex VP:* Michael Benjamin
**VP:* Lisa Cappuccilli
**VP:* Tamilyn Levin

D-U-N-S 79-695-3172
WINGATE HEALTH CARE INC
WINGATE HEALTHCARE
(*Suby of* WINGATE HEALTH CARE HOLDINGS INC) ★
589 Highland Ave, Needham, MA 02494-2205
Tel (781) 707-9500 *Founded/Ownrshp* 1998
Sales 129.0MM^E^ *EMP* 1,800^E^
SIC 8741 Nursing & personal care facility management
CEO: Gerald Schuster
**Pr:* Scott Schuster
**Treas:* Tamilyn M Levin
**Ex VP:* Michael Benjamin
**Sr VP:* Jon Gould
**Sr VP:* Tamilyn Levin
VP: Rita Barrett-Cosby
**VP:* Lisa Cappuccilli
Dir IT: John Kokas

WINGATE HEALTHCARE
See WINGATE HEALTH CARE INC

D-U-N-S 18-654-7410 IMP
WINGATE PARTNERS LP
750 N Saint Paul St # 1200, Dallas, TX 75201-3273
Tel (214) 720-1313 *Founded/Ownrshp* 1987
Sales 229.5MM^E^ *EMP* 832
SIC 2621 2672 3645 2519 5021 2521 Paper mills; Coated & laminated paper; Floor lamps; Table lamps; Wall lamps; Wicker furniture: padded or plain; Rattan furniture: padded or plain; Furniture; Wood office furniture
Genl Pt: Frederick B Hegi Jr
**Pt:* Brad Brenneman
**Pt:* Michael B Decker
**Pt:* V Edward Easterling Jr
**Pt:* J I Applebaum
**Pt:* James A Johnson
**Pt:* Jason Reed
VP: Bud Applebaum
VP: Chris Dupr

D-U-N-S 96-040-8727
WINGATE PARTNERS V LP
750 N Saint Paul St # 1200, Dallas, TX 75201-3273
Tel (214) 720-1313 *Founded/Ownrshp* 2013
Sales 146.3MM^E^ *EMP* 600^E^
SIC 6726 3448 Investment offices; Prefabricated metal components

D-U-N-S 07-452-4463
WINGATE UNIVERSITY
220 N Camden Rd, Wingate, NC 28174-9644
Tel (704) 233-8000 *Founded/Ownrshp* 1896
Sales 96.8MM *EMP* 300
Accts Mcgladrey Llp Greensboro Nc
SIC 8221 College, except junior
Pr: Jerry E McGee
CFO: Bill Durham
VP: Steve Poston
**VP:* Charles E Taylor Jr
Exec: Kristen Johnson
Assoc Dir: Nick Delangie
CIO: William Hobbs
Dir IT: Jeanette Bujak
Netwrk Eng: David Thompson
Mtls Mgr: Max Wolfe
HC Dir: Lindsay Kreis

D-U-N-S 00-484-0356 IMP
■ WINGFOOT COMMERCIAL TIRE SYSTEMS LLC (OH)
GOODYEAR COML TIRE & SVC CTRS
(*Suby of* GOODYEAR TIRE & RUBBER CO) ★
1000 S 21st St, Fort Smith, AR 72901-4098
Tel (479) 788-6400 *Founded/Ownrshp* 2000
Sales 354.9MM^E^ *EMP* 2,400
SIC 7534 Tire retreading & repair shops
Pr: Paul Wanstreet
CFO: Ron Carr
**VP:* Todd Tyler

D-U-N-S 07-763-8575
WINGS FINANCIAL CREDIT UNION
14985 Glazier Ave Ste 100, Saint Paul, MN 55124-7490
Tel (952) 997-8000 *Founded/Ownrshp* 1939
Sales NA *EMP* 437
SIC 6061 6282 Federal credit unions; Investment advisory service
CEO: R Frank Weidner
**Ch Bd:* Arlie D Johnson
**COO:* Mark S Everson
**CFO:* Timothy A Keegan
**Sr VP:* Gregory W Higgins
**VP:* Paul L Dinger
**VP:* David E Mason
**VP:* John J Wagner
Brnch Mgr: Ken Olson
Web Dev: Andrew Stoute

D-U-N-S 82-930-3861
WINGSPAN PORTFOLIO HOLDINGS INC
18451 Dallas Pkwy Ste 100, Dallas, TX 75287-5209
Tel (469) 737-2441 *Founded/Ownrshp* 2008
Sales 378.5MM^E^ *EMP* 2,000
SIC 6211 Mortgages, buying & selling
Pr: Steve Horne
**CFO:* Matthew Cassell

D-U-N-S 00-385-3983
WINKLER INC
WINKLER, J & SONS INC DIVISION
535 E Medcalf St, Dale, IN 47523-9384
Tel (812) 937-4421 *Founded/Ownrshp* 1911
Sales 421.4MM^E^ *EMP* 500
SIC 5141 5411 Groceries, general line; Grocery stores, independent
Pr: Lloyd T Winkler
Treas: Lynn Winkler

WINKLER, J & SONS INC DIVISION
See WINKLER INC

WINN DEVELOPMENT COMPANY
See WDC DEVELOPMENT ASSOCIATES LP

D-U-N-S 03-082-2589
WINN MANAGEMENT CO LLC
6 Faneuil Hall Market Pl # 500, Boston, MA 02109-1620
Tel (617) 742-4501 *Founded/Ownrshp* 1972
Sales 27.8MM^E^ *EMP* 1,200
SIC 6531 Real estate managers
CEO: Samual Ross
Pr: Sarah Vinal
COO: Deirdre Kuring
Off Mgr: Deborah Crowley

D-U-N-S 07-849-1430
WINN WB MANAGEMENT CO LLC
6 Faneuil Hall Market Pl # 500, Boston, MA 02109-6108
Tel (617) 742-4500 *Founded/Ownrshp* 2012
Sales 20.0MM^E^ *EMP* 2,620
SIC 6513 Apartment building operators

WINN-DIXIE
See BI-LO HOLDINGS FOUNDATION INC

WINN-DIXIE
See LSF5 BI-LO HOLDINGS LLC

WINN-DIXIE
See BI-LO HOLDING FINANCE LLC

D-U-N-S 00-694-5828
WINN-DIXIE CHARLOTTE INC
(*Suby of* MARKETPLACE) ★
2401 Nevada Blvd, Charlotte, NC 28273-6423
Tel (704) 587-4000 *Founded/Ownrshp* 1945
Sales 457.3MM^E^ *EMP* 7,000
SIC 5411 8741 5141 4226 4222 Supermarkets, chain; Management services; Groceries, general line; Special warehousing & storage; Refrigerated warehousing & storage
Pr: J A Schlosser
**Treas:* David Bragin
**VP:* H E Hess

D-U-N-S 00-692-1902 IMP/EXP
WINN-DIXIE STORES INC
MARKETPLACE
(*Suby of* SOUTHEASTERN GROCERS LLC) ★
8928 Prominence Pkwy # 200, Jacksonville, FL 32256-8264
Tel (904) 783-5000 *Founded/Ownrshp* 2012
Sales 6.8MMM^E^ *EMP* 47,000
SIC 5411 5541 5912 Supermarkets, chain; Gasoline service stations; Drug stores
CEO: R Randall Onstead
CFO: Brian Carney
CFO: Brian P Carney
Treas: Lynn Schweinfurth
Treas: H J Skelton
Ex VP: Lawrence Stablein
Sr VP: Laurence Appel
Sr VP: Bennett L Nussbaum
Sr VP: Christopher L Scott
VP: D Michael Byrum
VP: Mark Cornwell
VP: Dedra Degan
VP: Rich Dubnick
VP: Dan Faketty
VP: John A Fegan
VP: Evelyn V Follit
VP: Eddie Garcia
VP: Sandlin J Grimm
VP: Anita Gutel
VP: Matt Gutermuth
VP: Jim Harper
Board of Directors: Evelyn V Follit, Charles P Garcia, Jeffrey C Girard, Yvonne R Jackson, Gregory P Josefowicz, Ian McLeod, James P Olson, Terry Peets, Richard E Rivera

D-U-N-S 96-998-3568
WINN-DIXIE STORES OF JACKSONVILLE (INC)
(*Suby of* MARKETPLACE) ★
5050 Edgewood Ct, Jacksonville, FL 32254-3601
Tel (904) 783-5000 *Founded/Ownrshp* 1997
Sales 55.1MM^E^ *EMP* 1,000
SIC 5411 Grocery stores
Pr: Wc Calkins

D-U-N-S 80-833-0240
WINNCOMPANIES LLC
6 Faneuil Hall Market Pl, Boston, MA 02109-6115
Tel (617) 742-4500 *Founded/Ownrshp* 2001
Sales 54.5MM^E^ *EMP* 2,600
SIC 6531 Real estate agents & managers
VP: Brett Meringoff
VP: Debra Pratt
VP: Lori J Ricci
Exec: Christopher Fleming

D-U-N-S 00-530-0751 IMP/EXP
▲ WINNEBAGO INDUSTRIES INC (IA)
605 W Crystal Lake Rd, Forest City, IA 50436-2316
Tel (641) 585-3535 *Founded/Ownrshp* 1958
Sales 975.2MM *EMP* 2,900^E^
Tkr Sym WGO *Exch* NYS
SIC 3716 3714 Motor homes; Motor vehicle parts & accessories
Pr: Michael J Happe
Ch Bd: Lawrence A Erickson
Pr: Johnny Hernandez
CFO: Sarah N Nielsen
VP: Scott Degnan
VP: Steven Dummett
VP: Scott C Folkers
VP: Jeff Kubacki
VP Admn: Bret A Woodson
Rgnl Mgr: Dewey Ulbright
Genl Mgr: Jamie Sorenson
Board of Directors: Christopher J Braun, Robert M Chiusano, Robert M Chiusano, Jerry N Currie, William C Fisher, David W Miles, Martha Tomson Rodamaker, Mark T Schroepfer

D-U-N-S 04-164-3834
WINNEBAGO TRIBE OF NEBRASKA
100 Bluff Ave, Winnebago, NE 68071-9787
Tel (402) 878-3100 *Founded/Ownrshp* 1936
Sales 171.5MM^E^ *EMP* 800
SIC 7011 Hotels & motels
Ch: John Blackhawk
**V Ch:* Kennth Mallory
**CFO:* Cheryl Painter
**Treas:* Brian Chamberlain
**Treas:* Thomas Snowball Sr
Ofcr: Joseph Littlegeorge
Doctor: Johnny Jones

D-U-N-S 18-618-1012 IMP
WINNERS ONLY INC
1365 Park Center Dr, Vista, CA 92081-8338
Tel (760) 599-0300 *Founded/Ownrshp* 1988
Sales 90.3MM^E^ *EMP* 200
SIC 5021 Office furniture; Dining room furniture
Ch: Alex Shu
**CEO:* Sheue-Wen Lee
**CFO:* Fred Dizon
CIO: William Lee

D-U-N-S 00-631-4319
WINNRESIDENTIAL LIMITED PARTNERSHIP
6 Faneuil Hall Market Pl, Boston, MA 02109-6115
Tel (617) 742-4500 *Founded/Ownrshp* 2001
Sales 5.3MM^E^ *EMP* 3,000
SIC 6513 Apartment building operators
Pr: Samuel Ross

Pr: William W Wollinger
Sr VP: Lynne Chase

D-U-N-S 07-887-2724
WINNRESIDENTIAL LLC
6 Faneuil Hall Market Pl, Boston, MA 02109-6115
Tel (617) 742-4500 *Founded/Ownrshp* 1971
Sales 135.0MM^E *EMP* 3,000^E
SIC 8741 Management services
Pr: Deirdre A Kuring

D-U-N-S 03-629-5251
WINNSBORO PETROLEUM CO INC
PANTRY EXPRESS
401 S Congress St, Winnsboro, SC 29180-1511
Tel (803) 635-4668 *Founded/Ownrshp* 1946
Sales 83.2MM^E *EMP* 250
SIC 5171 5411 Petroleum bulk stations & terminals; Convenience stores, independent
Pr: F Creighton McMaster
**CFO:* Harper Shull
**Treas:* Quay W McMaster

D-U-N-S 07-652-1533
WINONA HEALTH
855 Mankato Ave, Winona, MN 55987-4868
Tel (507) 454-3650 *Founded/Ownrshp* 1894
Sales 135.8MM^E *EMP* 1,200^E
SIC 8062 8051 Hospital, affiliated with AMA residency; Convalescent home with continuous nursing care
Pr: Rachelle Schultz
Chf Path: Ron England
**CFO:* Jan Brosnahan
Dir IT: Rod Hughbank
Software D: Michal Roskos
Opers Mgr: Kris Cichon
Surgeon: Matthew Broghammer
Doctor: Kari Nelson
Doctor: Kristi Schulte
Doctor: Cullen Schwemer
Doctor: Troy Shelton

D-U-N-S 86-119-3530
WINONA HEALTH SERVICES
859 Mankato Ave, Winona, MN 55987-6435
Tel (507) 454-3650 *Founded/Ownrshp* 1994
Sales 120.9MM *EMP* 850
SIC 8062 8051 General medical & surgical hospitals; Skilled nursing care facilities
CEO: Rachelle Schultz
**CFO:* Mike Allen
CFO: Jan Brosnahan
Sfty Dirs: Kathleen Lanik
Pathlgst: Durga Vege
Obsttrcn: Leann Van Den Bosch
Doctor: Brett Whyte
Diag Rad: Giustino P Albanese

D-U-N-S 80-678-2405
WINONA STATE UNIVERSITY FOUNDATION
(*Suby of* GOVERNORS OFFICE) ★
175 W Mark St, Winona, MN 55987-3384
Tel (507) 457-5000 *Founded/Ownrshp* 2000
Sales 5.6MM *EMP* 1,800
SIC 8221 9199 Colleges universities & professional schools;
Pr: Scott R Olson
**VP:* Kenneth Gorman
VP: Ernie Hughes
VP: Alex Kromminga
Dir Lab: Erika Vail
Assoc Dir: Candice Guenther
Off Mgr: Janet Ruggeberg
Off Mgr: Sandra Stoos
Mktg Dir: Tom Grier
Psych: Lynda Brzezinski

D-U-N-S 05-192-9040 IMP/EXP
WINPAK PORTION PACKAGING INC
(*Suby of* WINPAK LTD)
828a Newtown Yardley Rd # 101, Newtown, PA 18940-4012
Tel (267) 685-8200 *Founded/Ownrshp* 1993
Sales 102.7MM^E *EMP* 227
SIC 3565 2671 Packaging machinery; Plastic film, coated or laminated for packaging
Pr: Tl Johnson
**Pr:* James McMacken
Area Mgr: Kevin McCormick
Prd Mgr: Cliff Bowles
Ql Cn Mgr: Gary Difranco
Sls Dir: Thomas Palilonis
Sls Mgr: Greg Bender
Sls Mgr: Larry Walsh
Snr PM: Dave Kroliczak

D-U-N-S 11-090-7664
WINROC CORP MIDWEST
ALLROC BUILDING PRODUCTS
(*Suby of* SUPERIOR PLUS CORP)
4225 W Glenrosa Ave, Phoenix, AZ 85019-3308
Tel (602) 477-0341 *Founded/Ownrshp* 1997
Sales 111.0MM^E *EMP* 92
SIC 5031 Building materials, interior
Pr: Paul Vandenberg
**Treas:* Jay Bachman
**VP:* Wade Wilson
Brnch Mgr: Josh James
Genl Mgr: Shawn Blacharski
Genl Mgr: Doug Magill
S&M/VP: Scott Cloudy
Sls Dir: Chuck Schattgen
Sales Asso: Estaban Santiago

WINROC-SPI
See SUPERIOR PLUS CONSTRUCTION PRODUCTS CORP

D-U-N-S 12-219-0242
WINROCK INTERNATIONAL INSTITUTE FOR AGRICULTURAL DEVELOPMENT
2101 Riverfront Dr, Little Rock, AR 72202-1748
Tel (501) 280-3000 *Founded/Ownrshp* 1985
Sales 87.3MM *EMP* 187^E
Accts Jpms Cox Pllc Little Rock Ar
SIC 8733 Research institute
CEO: Rodney Ferguson
Bd of Dir: Melissa Dann
Ofcr: Elisabeth Derby
Ofcr: Nona Fisher
Ofcr: Linsley Kinkade
Ofcr: Christopher Kopp
Ofcr: Cindy Martin
Ofcr: Darlene Middleton
Ofcr: Mark Tribble
**VP:* Mary Harris
**VP:* Mike Myers
**VP:* Carol Ann Smith
Comm Dir: Dave Anderson

D-U-N-S 07-231-5799
WINSTON & STRAWN LLP
35 W Wacker Dr Ste 4200, Chicago, IL 60601-1695
Tel (312) 558-5600 *Founded/Ownrshp* 1926
Sales 298.9MM^E *EMP* 1,928
SIC 8111 General practice law office
Mng Pt: Thomas J Fitzgerald
Pt: David L Aronoff
Pt: Thomas P Fitzgerald
Pt: Gayle I Jenkins
Pt: Caryn L Jacobs
Pt: Christopher C Kupec
Pt: C James Levin
Pt: Warren Loui
Pt: Molly McGill
Pt: Patrick M Ryan
Pt: Laura Swihart
Mng Pt: John R Alison
Mng Pt: Gillies Bigot
Mng Pt: Thomas Buchanan
Mng Pt: John H Cobb
Mng Pt: Peter Crowther
Mng Pt: Michael S Elkin
Mng Pt: David P Enzminger
Mng Pt: Joan B Tucker Fife
Mng Pt: Thomas J Frederick
Mng Pt: David G Hall-Jones

D-U-N-S 15-354-9436
WINSTON BRANDS INC
COLLECTIONS ETC
2521 Busse Rd Fl 2, Elk Grove Village, IL 60007-6118
Tel (847) 350-5800 *Founded/Ownrshp* 1997
Sales 200.0MM *EMP* 200^E
SIC 5961 General merchandise, mail order
CEO: Todd Lustbader
COO: Klassman Paul
Sr VP: Kim Hansen
CIO: Erica Greenwood
IT Man: Oakley Masten

WINSTON FURNITURE COMPANY ALA
See BROWN JORDAN INTERNATIONAL INC

D-U-N-S 04-371-4906 IMP/EXP
WINSTON-SALEM INDUSTRIES FOR BLIND INC (NC)
IFB SOLUTIONS
7730 N Point Blvd, Winston Salem, NC 27106-3310
Tel (336) 759-0551 *Founded/Ownrshp* 1936, 1963
Sales 137.0MM *EMP* 600
Accts Dixon Hughes Goodman Llp Wins
SIC 2515 3021 2392 2253 2394 3851 Mattresses, containing felt, foam rubber, urethane, etc.; Protective footwear, rubber or plastic; Bags, laundry: made from purchased materials; Mattress pads; Shower curtains: made from purchased materials; Shirts (outerwear), knit; Liners & covers, fabric: made from purchased materials; Eyeglasses, lenses & frames
Ex Dir: David Horton
**Ch Bd:* Daniel Boucher

D-U-N-S 07-157-9031
WINSTON-SALEM STATE UNIVERSITY FOUNDATION INC
(*Suby of* OFFICE OF PRESIDENT) ★
601 S Martin Lut, Winston Salem, NC 27110-0001
Tel (336) 750-2000 *Founded/Ownrshp* 1970
Sales 6.4MM *EMP* 1,000^E
Accts Beth A Wood Cpa Raleigh Nc
SIC 8221 University
CEO: Elwood Robinson
Ofcr: Norris Gullick
**VP:* Donald J Reaves
Assoc Dir: Margaret Poston
Opers Mgr: Ben Donnelly

D-U-N-S 03-603-1508
WINSTON-SALEM/FORSYTH COUNTY SCHOOLS
4801 Bethania Station Rd, Winston Salem, NC 27105-1202
Tel (336) 727-2635 *Founded/Ownrshp* 1884
Sales 320.2MM^E *EMP* 6,841
SIC 8211 9111 Public elementary & secondary schools; Public elementary school; Public junior high school; Public senior high school; Mayors' offices
Dir IT: Justin Ritchey

D-U-N-S 05-129-9030
WINSUPPLY INC
WSS- DAYTON
3110 Kettering Blvd, Moraine, OH 45439-1924
Tel (937) 294-5331 *Founded/Ownrshp* 2004
Sales 2.7MMM *EMP* 5,200
SIC 1542 5074 5085 Commercial & office building contractors; Plumbing fittings & supplies; Industrial supplies
Ch: Richard W Schwartz
**Pr:* Jack W Johnston
COO: Jim Adcox
**COO:* Jack Osenbaugh
**COO:* Monte Salsman
**CFO:* Grady Collins
CFO: Jeffrey Dice
**CFO:* Roland Gordon
**Treas:* Philip Kremer
Ofcr: Dave Metzger
**VP:* Gary Benaszeski
VP: Steven Coen
VP: Jeff Dice
**VP:* Eddie Gibbs
VP: Roger Gibbs
VP: Bob Guiney

D-U-N-S 18-682-4231 IMP
WINTEC INDUSTRIES INC
8674 Thornton Ave, Newark, CA 94560-3330
Tel (408) 856-0500 *Founded/Ownrshp* 1988
Sales 85.0MM *EMP* 160^E
SIC 3577 3674 3572 Computer peripheral equipment; Semiconductors & related devices; Computer storage devices
CEO: David Jeng
**CFO:* Frank Patchel
**VP:* Kelley Corten
**Dir Surg:* Huey Hall
Prin: Eric Wang
IT Man: Brandon Inabinet
Manager: Gary Fleury
Sales Asso: Vikki Han

D-U-N-S 09-176-3417
WINTER CONSTRUCTION CO
(*Suby of* WINTER GROUP OF COMPANIES INC) ★
191 Peachtree St Ne # 2100, Atlanta, GA 30303-1740
Tel (404) 588-3300 *Founded/Ownrshp* 1997
Sales 130.5MM^E *EMP* 250^E
SIC 1541 Industrial buildings & warehouses; Food products manufacturing or packing plant construction
CEO: S Brent Reid
**CFO:* Ralph Mumme
**CFO:* Brad Reid
**Ex VP:* Gary Ellis
**Ex VP:* Tom Nichols
Exec: Don Bailey
Exec: Ken Smith
Exec: Dale Sparks
CIO: Sean Durkin
Mktg Dir: Amy Moore
Snr PM: Matt Loveless

WINTER GARDEN APARTMENTS
See WINTER GARDEN PRESERVATION LP

D-U-N-S 05-157-8011
WINTER GARDEN PRESERVATION LP
WINTER GARDEN APARTMENTS
5708 Kingsbury Pl, Saint Louis, MO 63112-1641
Tel (314) 361-0251 *Founded/Ownrshp* 2003
Sales 1.3MMM *EMP* 99
SIC 6513 Apartment building operators
Off Mgr: Rebecca Burkerd
Pt: George Buchanan

D-U-N-S 02-408-7749 IMP
WINTER GROUP OF COMPANIES INC
191 Peachtree St Ne, Peachtree Corners, GA 30071
Tel (404) 588-3300 *Founded/Ownrshp* 1997
Sales 130.5MM^E *EMP* 300
SIC 1541 1542 1799 6512 Industrial buildings & warehouses; Commercial & office building contractors; Institutional building construction; Decontamination services; Nonresidential building operators
CEO: S Brent Reid
**CFO:* Ralph Mumme
**Ex VP:* Gary Ellis
**Ex VP:* Tom Nichols
**Ex VP:* Brad Reid

D-U-N-S 07-921-2254 IMP
WINTER HAVEN HOSPITAL INC
BAYCARE EDUCATION SERVICES
(*Suby of* BAYCARE EDUCATION SERVICES) ★
200 Avenue F Ne, Winter Haven, FL 33881-4193
Tel (863) 293-1121 *Founded/Ownrshp* 2013
Sales 257.2MM *EMP* 1,480
SIC 8062 General medical & surgical hospitals
Pr: Steve Nierman
Dir Recs: Carolyn Murphy
**Treas:* William G Burns
Trst: Sharon B Davis
VP: Robert Cassel
VP: Khurram Kamran
VP: Carol Koeppel
Dir Lab: Mark Shumate
Dir Rx: Tiffany M Jones
Nurse Mgr: Debbie Burton
S&M/VP: Jim Seaton

WINTER HEAVEN HOSPITAL
See MID-FLORIDA MEDICAL SERVICES INC

D-U-N-S 07-256-2630
WINTER PARK HEALTHCARE GROUP LTD
200 N Lakemont Ave, Winter Park, FL 32792-3273
Tel (407) 646-7000 *Founded/Ownrshp* 1955
Sales 51.1MM^E *EMP* 1,600
SIC 8062 8011 Hospital, affiliated with AMA residency; Offices & clinics of medical doctors
Pt: J Lindsay Builder
Pt: Peter Lawson

WINTER PARK TOWERS
See PRESBYTERIAN RETIREMENT COMMUNITIES INC

D-U-N-S 17-474-6909
WINTERGREEN RESEARCH INC
6 Raymond St, Lexington, MA 02421-4936
Tel (781) 863-5078 *Founded/Ownrshp* 1986
Sales 350.0M *EMP* 1,099
SIC 8748 8742 Business consulting; Marketing consulting services
Pr: Susan Eustis
COO: Augustus Eustis

D-U-N-S 84-870-6859
WINTERGREEN RESORTS INC
11 Grassy Ridge Dr, Nellysford, VA 22958
Tel (434) 325-8237 *Founded/Ownrshp* 1984
Sales 87.1MM^E *EMP* 1,200
Accts Pkf Witt Mares Plc Fairfax
SIC 8721 7011 5812

D-U-N-S 07-296-4182
WINTERTHUR U S HOLDINGS INC
(*Suby of* QBE HOLDINGS INC) ★
1 General Dr, Sun Prairie, WI 53596-0001
Tel (608) 837-4440 *Founded/Ownrshp* 2007
Sales NA *EMP* 2,200
SIC 6411 6163 Property & casualty insurance agent; Life insurance agents; Loan brokers
Pr: John Pollock
CFO: Laura Hinson
VP: John Schanen
Comm Man: Lee Owen

D-U-N-S 07-105-5214
WINTHROP UNIVERSITY
701 Oakland Ave, Rock Hill, SC 29733-7001
Tel (803) 323-2211 *Founded/Ownrshp* 1886
Sales 90.5MM^E *EMP* 1,100
Accts Cline Brandt Kochenower & Co
SIC 8221 University
Pr: Daniel Mahony
VP: Sherria Johnson
**VP:* J P McKee
Exec: Ann Biggerstaff
Exec: Jamilyn C Larsen
Comm Dir: Monica Bennett
Comm Man: Irish Williams
Adm Dir: Enrico Perez
CIO: James Hammond
Dir IT: Lisa Wilson
Pgrm Dir: Ellin McDonough

D-U-N-S 06-593-7856
WINTHROP-UNIVERSITY HOSPITAL (INC)
259 1st St, Mineola, NY 11501-3987
Tel (516) 663-0333 *Founded/Ownrshp* 1896
Sales 1.2MMM *EMP* 6,000
SIC 8062 Hospital, medical school affiliated with nursing & residency
CEO: John F Collins
**Pr:* Palmira M Cataliotti CPA
Pr: Cathy Ford
**COO:* Garry J Schwall
**Ch:* Charles M Strain
Sr VP: Maureen Gaffney
**Sr VP:* Barbara L Kohart Kleine
**Sr VP:* Maureen Gaffney Rpac Rn
VP: Joe Burke
VP: Barbara Eisenkraft
VP: Barbara L Kohart-Keine
VP: Feliks Koyfman
VP: Stacey Pfeffer
VP: Solomon Torres
Dir Inf Cn: Valsamma Thekkel
Assoc Dir: Faisal Zakaria

D-U-N-S 87-451-0506
■ WINTRUST BANK
NORTH SHORE COMMUNITY BNK & TR
(*Suby of* WINTRUST FINANCIAL CORP) ★
190 S La Salle St # 2200, Chicago, IL 60603-3407
Tel (773) 227-7074 *Founded/Ownrshp* 1997
Sales NA *EMP* 427
SIC 6022 State commercial banks
Pr: William Lynch
Pr: Angela Bentley
Treas: Melissa Omalley
Chf Cred: Dionne Miller
Ofcr: Mark Altstiel
Ofcr: Tracy Anderson
Ofcr: Daniel Ciolino
Ofcr: Brooke Cullen
Ofcr: Timothy Day
Ofcr: Phuong Dinh
Ofcr: Peter Hann
Ofcr: Kam Kniss
Ofcr: Daniel Marino
Ofcr: Luis Medina
Ofcr: Bailey Moore
Ofcr: Judy Rigsby
Ofcr: Anna Rybak
Ofcr: Virginia Sarkis
Ofcr: Shiela Steiner
Ofcr: Heather Vanvleet
Ofcr: Shabnam Warsi

D-U-N-S 96-052-0278
▲ WINTRUST FINANCIAL CORP
9700 W Higgins Rd, Rosemont, IL 60018-4796
Tel (847) 939-9000 *Founded/Ownrshp* 1992
Sales NA *EMP* 3,806^E
Tkr Sym WTFC *Exch* NGS
SIC 6022 6211 6282 State commercial banks; Security brokers & dealers; Investment advisory service
Pr: Edward J Wehmer
Ch Bd: Peter D Crist
Pr: Amy Gulotta
Pr: Joel Macholan
COO: David A Dykstra
CFO: David L Stoehr
Treas: Timothy S Crane
Treas: Karen Moses
Ofcr: Norma Ahlstrand
Ofcr: Melissa Donaldson
Ofcr: John S Fleshood
Ofcr: Leona A Gleason
Ofcr: Pat Gray
Ofcr: Stephen L Madden
Ofcr: Kevin Mitzit
Ofcr: Richard B Murphy
Ofcr: Kay Olenec
Ex VP: Kathleen M Boege
Ex VP: Lloyd M Bowden
Ex VP: Guy W Eisenhuth
Ex VP: Tully F Kari
Board of Directors: Bruce K Crowther, Joseph F Damico, Marla F Glebe, H Patrick Hackett Jr, Scott K Heitmann, Christopher H Perry, Ingrid S Stafford, Gary D Sweeney

D-U-N-S 08-904-0331 IMP
WINZER CORP
4060 E Plano Pkwy, Plano, TX 75074-1800
Tel (800) 527-4126 *Founded/Ownrshp* 1978
Sales 118.8MM^E *EMP* 235
SIC 5072 3452 5251 5169 Bolts, nuts & screws; Bolts, nuts, rivets & washers; Hardware; Industrial chemicals
Ch: Klaus Wuerth
**Pr:* Debbie Bynum
Pr: Rich Unkhouser
Treas: Nola Crane
**VP:* Kipp Bush
**VP:* Richard Funkhouser
**VP:* Rick De La Fuente
**VP:* Jim Leverett
**VP:* Paul Seibert
**VP:* Diane Vanderbilt

*VP: Macy Velasquez
*VP: Kyle Walters
Creative D: Paul Coon

D-U-N-S 07-479-8513
WIPFLI LLP
10000 W Innovation Dr 250-260, Milwaukee, WI 53226-4837
Tel (414) 431-9300 Founded/Ownrshp 1996
Sales 278.8MM[E] EMP 1,135
SIC 8748 8721 Business consulting; Certified public accountant
Mng Pt: Rick Dreher
Pt: Jay Adkisson
Pt: Pamela Branshaw
Pt: Robert Cedergren
Pt: Joann Cotter
Pt: Robert Cottingham
Pt: Claudio J Diaz
Pt: Mark Faanes
Pt: Jeff Greeneway
Pt: Steve Hewitt
Pt: Murali S Iyer
Pt: Ed Koth
Pt: Jeff Kowieski
Pt: Steve Lipton
Pt: Jay Mayer
Pt: Karen Monfre
Pt: Dale Muehl
Pt: Michael Pozielli
Pt: Neal Richardson
Pt: Terry Saber
Pt: John Schwab

D-U-N-S 08-034-1484
WIPRO DATA CENTER AND CLOUD SERVICES INC
(Suby of WIPRO LLC) ★
2 Christie Hts, Leonia, NJ 07605-2233
Tel (201) 840-4772 Founded/Ownrshp 2016
Sales 205.0MM EMP 400
SIC 7379 Computer related consulting services; Data processing consultant
Pr: Raj Bagga
*VP: Sam Matthew

D-U-N-S 11-365-2791
WIPRO LLC
(Suby of WIPRO LIMITED)
2 Tower Center Blvd # 2200, East Brunswick, NJ 08816-1100
Tel (732) 509-1664 Founded/Ownrshp 1998
Sales 220.0MM EMP 490
Accts D Prasanna & Co Basavangudi
SIC 7371 Software programming applications
Pr: Mallathur Balasubramanian
*CFO: Ashish Chawla

D-U-N-S 78-743-6484
WIRE AMERICA INC
1613 E Wallace St, Fort Wayne, IN 46803-2564
Tel (260) 969-1700 Founded/Ownrshp 1988
Sales 91.5MM EMP 43
SIC 4226 3357 Special warehousing & storage; Communication wire
Pr: Lionell Tobin
*Ex VP: Ted Jamison
VP: Richard E Proctor Jr
Opers Mgr: Harold Yon
Ql Cn Mgr: Doug Krall

D-U-N-S 13-549-6839 IMP/EXP
WIRECO WORLDGROUP INC
(Suby of WIRECO WORLDGROUP US HOLDINGS INC) ★
2400 W 75th St, Prairie Village, KS 66208-3509
Tel (816) 270-4700 Founded/Ownrshp 2003
Sales 683.9MM EMP 4,100
SIC 3496 Cable, uninsulated wire: made from purchased wire
Ch Bd: John Anton
*Pr: Christopher L Ayers
*COO: Matthew R Dionne
*CFO: Brian G Block
CFO: Elizabeth Low
*Ofcr: Adrian J Holt
Sr VP: Joaquin Barrios
Sr VP: Miguel Gomez
*Sr VP: Michael J Mastio
Sr VP: Wolfgang Oswald
Sr VP: W Wynne Wister III
VP: Robert Loveall
Board of Directors: Andrew M Freeman, Stephan Kessel, Franklin Myers, W Dexter Paine III, Troy W Thacker

D-U-N-S 82-816-2425 IMP
WIRECO WORLDGROUP US HOLDINGS INC
(Suby of WIRECO WORLDGROUP (CAYMAN) INC.)
2400 W 75th St, Prairie Village, KS 66208-3509
Tel (816) 270-4700 Founded/Ownrshp 2008
Sales 683.9MM[E] EMP 4,561[E]
SIC 3496 Woven wire products
CEO: Christopher L Ayers
*Sr VP: Jos Gramaxo

WIRECUTTER, THE
See NEW YORK TIMES CO

D-U-N-S 00-402-3933
WIREGRASS CONSTRUCTION CO INC (AL)
170 E Main St, Dothan, AL 36301-1722
Tel (334) 699-6800 Founded/Ownrshp 1964
Sales 272.8MM[E] EMP 490
SIC 1611 2951 Highway & street paving contractor; Asphalt & asphaltic paving mixtures (not from refineries)
CEO: Brett Armstrong
*Pr: John L Harper
*CFO: Greg Hoffman
*Ex VP: Randall Epperson
*Sfty Dirs: Tim Beguin
Mtls Mgr: Mike Owen
Plnt Mgr: Jim Seymour

D-U-N-S 17-529-3021
WIRELESS ADVOCATES LLC
(Suby of VERIZON WIRELESS AUTHORIZED RET) ★
400 Fairview Ave N # 900, Seattle, WA 98109-5371
Tel (206) 428-2400 Founded/Ownrshp 2004
Sales 369.1MM[E] EMP 1,500[E]
SIC 5999 Mobile telephones & equipment
VP: Eric Belzer
Dist Mgr: Todd Chinn
Store Mgr: Julia Boyles

D-U-N-S 01-074-2920
WIRELESS CENTER INC
1925 Saint Clair Ave Ne, Cleveland, OH 44114-2028
Tel (216) 503-3777 Founded/Ownrshp 2002
Sales 111.9MM[E] EMP 300[E]
SIC 4812 Cellular telephone services
Prin: Azam Kazmi
VP: Tariq Khan
Prgrm Mgr: Mir Ali
Dist Mgr: Dave Phillips
Dist Mgr: Ali Zaidi
Store Mgr: Amanda Jones

WIRELESS GENERATION
See AMPLIFY EDUCATION INC

D-U-N-S 80-655-4338
WIRELESS NETWORK GROUP INC
WNG
220 W Parkway Ste 10a, Pompton Plains, NJ 07444-1049
Tel (973) 831-4015 Founded/Ownrshp 2000
Sales 24.6MM[E] EMP 1,200[E]
SIC 1623 Communication line & transmission tower construction
Pr: Mike Fox
*CFO: Richard Bosi
*VP: Harry Greisser

D-U-N-S 18-978-3038
WIREMASTERS INC
1788 N Pointe Rd, Columbia, TN 38401-0213
Tel (615) 791-0281 Founded/Ownrshp 2001
Sales 92.9MM EMP 135[E]
SIC 5063 Wire & cable
Pr: David Hill
Trfc Mgr: Terrence Doyle
Sales Exec: Kim Bryant
Sales Exec: Dustin Hargrove
Sales Exec: Chase Thomason
Sales Exec: John Thomason

D-U-N-S 00-114-5143 IMP/EXP
WIREMOLD CO (CT)
(Suby of LEGRAND HOLDING INC) ★
60 Woodlawn St, West Hartford, CT 06110-2383
Tel (860) 233-6251 Founded/Ownrshp 1900, 2005
Sales 329.6MM[E] EMP 1,300
SIC 3644 3643 3496 3315 Noncurrent-carrying wiring services; Raceways; Outlet boxes (electric wiring devices); Current-carrying wiring devices; Miscellaneous fabricated wire products; Steel wire & related products
CEO: John P Selldorff
*Pr: Brian Dibella
*Treas: Steve Schneider
Plnt Mgr: Mike Kijak
Ql Cn Mgr: Robert Britton
VP Mktg: Mario Gonzalez

D-U-N-S 60-172-1566 IMP/EXP
WIREROPE WORKS INC
100 Maynard St, Williamsport, PA 17701-5809
Tel (570) 327-4229 Founded/Ownrshp 2004
Sales 150.1MM[E] EMP 412
SIC 3496 2298 3315 Miscellaneous fabricated wire products; Wire rope centers; Wire, steel: insulated or armored
Pr: Thomas M Saltsgiver
*Treas: William F Huber
Ex VP: Virgil Probasco
*VP: Virgil R Probasco
*VP: Lamar M Richards
VP: Lamar J Richards
Manager: Richard Barnhart
Manager: Jim Klepfer
Board of Directors: Lawrence E Caprous, J Cleveland Sr, William D Davis, William Ughetta

WIRSBO COMPANY
See UPONOR INC

D-U-N-S 14-763-7466 IMP/EXP
WIRTGEN AMERICA INC
(Suby of WIRTGEN GROUP HOLDING GMBH)
6030 Dana Way, Antioch, TN 37013-3116
Tel (615) 501-0600 Founded/Ownrshp 1985
Sales 500.0MM EMP 230
SIC 5082 Road construction & maintenance machinery
Pr: James P McEvoy
CFO: Bob Collins
*Sec: Robert J Collins
Dist Mgr: Jim Holland
Dir IT: James America
IT Man: Edward Asbury
IT Man: Kevin Watts
VP Sls: Mark Stang
Mktg Dir: Ken Snover
Sls Dir: Kelly Graves
Sls Mgr: Rick Brown

WIRTZ BEVERAGE
See BREAKTHRU BEVERAGE ILLINOIS LLC

D-U-N-S 83-624-6103
WIRTZ BEVERAGE GROUP LLC
(Suby of WIRTZ CORP) ★
680 N Lake Shore Dr # 1900, Chicago, IL 60611-4547
Tel (312) 943-7000 Founded/Ownrshp 2010
Sales 181.4MM[E] EMP 783[E]
SIC 5181 5182 Beer & ale; Wine & distilled beverages
Ex VP: Julian Burzynski
Ex VP: Harold Rutstein
Exec: Jessica Quezada
Div Mgr: Susie Andrus
Manager: Tim Clarey
VP Mktg: Danny Wirtz
VP Sls: Brad Redenius
Sls Dir: Kevin Condron
Sls Dir: Adam A Karr
Sls Dir: Tracy Sturm
Mktg Mgr: Michael Roper

D-U-N-S 00-553-1892 IMP
WIRTZ CORP
680 N Lake Shore Dr # 1900, Chicago, IL 60611-4547
Tel (312) 943-7000 Founded/Ownrshp 1922
Sales 766.2MM[E] EMP 2,000
SIC 5181 5182 6513 6512 7011 6411 Beer & ale; Wine & distilled beverages; Apartment building operators; Nonresidential building operators; Hotels & motels; Insurance agents
Pr: W Rockwell Wirtz
Sr VP: Donald Vitek

D-U-N-S 06-616-6018
■ WIS
WASHINGTON INVENTORY SERVICE
(Suby of WESTERN INVENTORY SERVICE LTD)
9265 Sky Park Ct Ste 100, San Diego, CA 92123-4375
Tel (858) 565-8111 Founded/Ownrshp 1963
Sales 82.0MM[E] EMP 1,000
SIC 7389 Inventory computing service
CEO: Jim Rose
*Pr: Howard L Madden
CFO: Trey Graham
*VP: Tom Compogiannis
Rgnl Mgr: Percy Aninakwah
Dist Mgr: Chelsey Boyd
Dist Mgr: Michelle Schneider

D-U-N-S 05-026-5925 IMP
WIS - PAK INC
860 West St, Watertown, WI 53094-3600
Tel (920) 262-6300 Founded/Ownrshp 1969
Sales 277.4MM[E] EMP 600
SIC 2086 Soft drinks: packaged in cans, bottles, etc.
Pr: Barbara Parish
VP: Brenda Koellen
VP: Clayton Kratzer
VP: Julie Kube
VP: Jon Moldenhauer
VP: Stan Staniszewski
Exec: Dave Bradshaw
Off Mgr: Lauren Cutsforth
Dir IT: Kevin Osterhoff
IT Man: Jeff Priegnitz
IT Man: Craig Rainey

D-U-N-S 01-534-0961 IMP
WISCON CORP
WISCONSIN CHEESE
2050 N 15th Ave, Melrose Park, IL 60160-1405
Tel (708) 450-0074 Founded/Ownrshp 1994
Sales 83.1MM[E] EMP 95
SIC 5143 2022 Cheese; Cheese, natural & processed
CEO: Pasquale Caputo
*Pr: Natale Caputo

D-U-N-S 05-290-4810
WISCONSIN ALUMNI RESEARCH FOUNDATION (WI)
614 Walnut St Fl 13, Madison, WI 53726-2336
Tel (608) 263-2500 Founded/Ownrshp 1925
Sales 316.4MM EMP 27[E]
SIC 6799 6794 Investors; Patent buying, licensing, leasing
Comm Dir: Janet Kelly
Pr Mgr: Andrew Cohn

D-U-N-S 00-794-7443
■ WISCONSIN BELL INC
AMERITECH WISCONSIN
(Suby of AT&T INC) ★
722 N Broadway, Milwaukee, WI 53202-4303
Tel (414) 271-9619 Founded/Ownrshp 2009
Sales 955.9MM[E] EMP 4,080
SIC 4813 8721 Local & long distance telephone communications; Local telephone communications; Voice telephone communications; Data telephone communications; Billing & bookkeeping service
Pr: Ellen M Gardner

WISCONSIN BRICK & BLOCK
See COUNTY MATERIALS CORP

D-U-N-S 17-445-1450
WISCONSIN CENTRAL LTD
CANADIAN NATIONAL RAILWAY CO
(Suby of COMPAGNIE DES CHEMINS DE FER NATIONAUX DU CANADA)
17641 Ashland Ave, Homewood, IL 60430-1339
Tel (708) 332-3500 Founded/Ownrshp 2001
Sales 124.7MM[E] EMP 1,900
SIC 4011 Electric railroads
Pr: Jeff Leipelt
*Pr: E Hunter Harrison
*VP: Gordon Traston
*Prin: Nancy Anderson

WISCONSIN CHEESE
See WISCON CORP

D-U-N-S 15-059-6088 IMP
WISCONSIN CHEESE GROUP LLC
CHEESE AMERICA
(Suby of WCG HOLDING CORPORATION)
105 3rd St, Monroe, WI 53566-1028
Tel (608) 325-8342 Founded/Ownrshp 2004
Sales 106.4MM[E] EMP 150
SIC 5143 2022 Cheese; Natural cheese
VP: Dale Losenegger
*CFO: Walter Oldham
*VP: David Petrik

D-U-N-S 80-903-5728
WISCONSIN DEPARTMENT OF ADMINISTRATION
(Suby of GOVERNERS OFFICE) ★
101 E Wilson St Fl 10, Madison, WI 53703-3405
Tel (608) 266-1741 Founded/Ownrshp 1959
Sales NA EMP 1,020
SIC 9611 Administration of general economic programs;
Off Mgr: Sheila Conroy

D-U-N-S 80-903-5975
WISCONSIN DEPARTMENT OF CORRECTIONS
(Suby of GOVERNERS OFFICE) ★
3099 E Washington Ave, Madison, WI 53704-4338
Tel (608) 240-5000 Founded/Ownrshp 1989
Sales NA EMP 10,000
SIC 9223 Prison, government;

D-U-N-S 80-903-6700
WISCONSIN DEPARTMENT OF HEALTH SERVICES
WISCONSIN TITLE XIX
(Suby of GOVERNERS OFFICE) ★
1 W Wilson St Rm 650, Madison, WI 53703-3445
Tel (608) 266-1865 Founded/Ownrshp 1968
Sales NA EMP 6,350
SIC 9431 9441 Administration of public health programs; ; Administration of social & manpower programs;
COO: Joann Oconnor
Ofcr: Henry Anderson III
Ofcr: Kathy A Johnson
Top Exec: Tom Haupt
Nrsg Dir: Lori Monroe

D-U-N-S 80-961-1460
WISCONSIN DEPARTMENT OF TRANSPORTATION
WISDOT
(Suby of GOVERNERS OFFICE) ★
4802 Sheboygan Ave, Madison, WI 53705-2927
Tel (608) 266-2878 Founded/Ownrshp 1967
Sales NA EMP 4,000
SIC 9621 Regulation, administration of transportation;
*Prin: Michael J Berg
*Prin: Steve Krieser
Counsel: Drew Jelinski
Pgrm Dir: Reggie Newson

D-U-N-S 80-944-8012
WISCONSIN DEPARTMENT OF WORKFORCE DEVELOPMENT
(Suby of GOVERNERS OFFICE) ★
201 E Wa Ave Rm 400x, Madison, WI 53703-2866
Tel (608) 266-3131 Founded/Ownrshp 1969
Sales NA EMP 2,800
SIC 9651 Regulation, miscellaneous commercial sectors;
Sec: Reggie Newson
Exec: James Baumann
Exec: James Buell
Exec: Joseph Costa
Exec: Greg Dahl
Exec: Frank Dubois
Comm Dir: John Dipko
Pgrm Dir: Ken Grant

D-U-N-S 80-961-1247
WISCONSIN DEPT OF NATURAL RESOURCES
(Suby of GOVERNERS OFFICE) ★
101 S Webster St, Madison, WI 53703-3474
Tel (608) 266-2621 Founded/Ownrshp 1967
Sales NA EMP 3,340
SIC 9512 Land, mineral & wildlife conservation;

D-U-N-S 96-676-6300
WISCONSIN EDUCATION ASSOCIATION INSURANCE TRUST
(Suby of WEA INSURANCE CORP) ★
45 Nob Hill Rd, Madison, WI 53713-2195
Tel (608) 276-4000 Founded/Ownrshp 2011
Sales NA EMP 2
SIC 6411 Insurance agents, brokers & service

D-U-N-S 87-918-9470
WISCONSIN EDUCATIONAL COMMUNICATIONS BOARD
WISCONSIN PUBLIC TELEVISION
3319 W Beltline Hwy, Madison, WI 53713-4217
Tel (608) 264-9600 Founded/Ownrshp 1954
Sales 103.2MM[E] EMP 342
SIC 4833 4832 Television broadcasting stations; Radio broadcasting stations
Sr Cor Off: Gene Purcell
Sr Cor Off: Rick Krewson
IT Man: James Klas
IT Man: Aimee Wierzba
IT Man: Aimee Wright
Genl Couns: James Pflasterer

D-U-N-S 00-794-7047
■ WISCONSIN GAS LLC (WI)
WE ENERGIES
(Suby of WEC ENERGY GROUP INC) ★
231 W Michigan St, Milwaukee, WI 53203-2918
Tel (414) 221-3236 Founded/Ownrshp 1980
Sales 137.2MM[E] EMP 572[E]
SIC 4924 Natural gas distribution
Web Dev: Connie Helnore

D-U-N-S 07-651-8737
WISCONSIN INDIANHEAD TECHNICAL COLLEGE FOUNDATION INC
WITC
(Suby of WISCONSIN TECHNICAL COLLEGE SYSTEM BOARD) ★
505 Pine Ridge Dr, Shell Lake, WI 54871-8727
Tel (715) 468-2815 Founded/Ownrshp 1972
Sales 630.6M EMP 1,438
Accts Wipfli Llp Eau Claire Wi
SIC 8222 Technical institute
Ch: Morrie Veilleux
*Pr: John Will
*Treas: James Beistle
VP: Mary Carlson
Exec: Diane J Schmitt
Off Mgr: Jane R Minkel
Dir IT: Wayne Erdmond
Psych: Thomas Findlay
Pgrm Dir: Amanda Abrahamson
Pgrm Dir: Kathy Kitter-Carey

D-U-N-S 02-345-0281 IMP
WISCONSIN LIFT TRUCK CORP (WI)
WOLTER GROUP
3125 Intertech Dr, Brookfield, WI 53045-5113
Tel (262) 790-6230 *Founded/Ownrshp* 1962
Sales 136.3MM^E *EMP* 302
SIC 5084 5085 7699 Materials handling machinery; Industrial supplies; Industrial equipment services; Industrial machinery & equipment repair
CEO: Otto J Wolter
**Pr:* Jerry Wiedmann
COO: Jim Dutkiewicz
COO: Jerry Weidmann
**CFO:* Steve Kletzien
VP: Sharon Cerny
VP: Paige Turk
VP: John Wolter
Comm Dir: Julia Williams
Genl Mgr: Christine Emmerich
Genl Mgr: Debbie Schuman

D-U-N-S 07-385-2253
WISCONSIN MILWAUKEE COUNTY
901 N 9th St Ste 306, Milwaukee, WI 53233-1425
Tel (414) 278-4211 *Founded/Ownrshp* 1835
Sales NA *EMP* 4,400
Accts Baker Tilly Virchow Krause
SIC 9111 Executive offices;
CEO: Chris Abele
**Ch Bd:* Marina Dimitrijevic
**Treas:* David Cullen
**Exec:* Scott Walker
**Mng Dir:* Teig Whaley-Smith
Brnch Mgr: Janice Dunn
Brnch Mgr: Chuck McDowell

D-U-N-S 08-668-4339
WISCONSIN PHYSICIANS SERVICE INSURANCE CORP
1717 W Broadway, Monona, WI 53713-1834
Tel (608) 221-4711 *Founded/Ownrshp* 1977
Sales NA *EMP* 2,801
Accts Grant Thornton Llp Madison
SIC 6324 Hospital & medical service plans
Pr: Michael Hamerlik
**CFO:* Thomas Nelson
Ex VP: Jay Martinson
Sr VP: Gartner Stanford
VP: John Driscoll
VP: Dan Edge
VP: Jean Kolowrat
VP: Teri Malsch
VP: Keith Williams
CIO: Kerra Guffey
CIO: Randy Lengyel
Board of Directors: Craig Campbell,chief Admin

D-U-N-S 00-794-6452
■ **WISCONSIN POWER AND LIGHT CO** (WI)
(*Suby of* ALLIANT ENERGY CORP) ★
4902 N Biltmore Ln # 1000, Madison, WI 53718-2148
Tel (608) 458-3311 *Founded/Ownrshp* 1917
Sales 1.4MMM *EMP* 1,277^E
Accts Deloitte & Touche Llp Milwauk
SIC 4931 Electric & other services combined;
Ch Bd: Patricia L Kampling
Pr: John O Larsen
CFO: Thomas L Hanson
Treas: John E Kratchmer
Sr VP: James H Gallegos
Sr VP: Douglas R Kopp
Board of Directors: Patrick E Allen, Michael L Bennett, Darryl B Hazel, Ann K Newhall, Dean C Oestreich, Carol P Sanders, Susan D Whiting

D-U-N-S 00-794-7435
■ **WISCONSIN PUBLIC SERVICE CORP** (WI)
(*Suby of* INTEGRYS HOLDING INC) ★
700 N Adams St, Green Bay, WI 54301-5145
Tel (800) 450-7260 *Founded/Ownrshp* 1883, 2015
Sales 1.4MMM *EMP* 1,333^E
SIC 4931

WISCONSIN PUBLIC TELEVISION
See WISCONSIN EDUCATIONAL COMMUNICATIONS BOARD

D-U-N-S 07-839-6475
WISCONSIN TECHNICAL COLLEGE SYSTEM BOARD
4622 University Ave, Madison, WI 53705-2156
Tel (608) 266-1207 *Founded/Ownrshp* 1911
Sales 424.7MM^E *EMP* 3,500
SIC 8222 Technical institute
Pr: Daniel Clancy
CFO: Greg Wagner
VP: James Zylstra
Genl Mgr: Troy Brown

WISCONSIN TITLE XIX
See WISCONSIN DEPARTMENT OF HEALTH SERVICES

D-U-N-S 10-220-5143
WISCONSIN VISION ASSOCIATES INC
WVA
139 W Chestnut St, Burlington, WI 53105-1255
Tel (262) 763-0100 *Founded/Ownrshp* 1982
Sales 145.6MM^E *EMP* 85
SIC 5048 5122 5047 Ophthalmic goods; Contact lenses; Drugs & drug proprietaries; Surgical equipment & supplies
Pr: Robert Fait
**Sec:* Judy Fait
Top Exec: Dave Snyder
**VP:* Christopher Fait
Web Dev: Matthew Manke
Opers Mgr: Jeffrey Erickson

WISCONSIN-KENWORTH
See CSM COMPANIES INC

D-U-N-S 61-934-4448
▲ **WISDOMTREE INVESTMENTS INC**
245 Park Ave Fl 35, New York, NY 10167-0002
Tel (212) 801-2080 *Founded/Ownrshp* 1985
Sales 298.9MM *EMP* 177^E
Tkr Sym WETF *Exch* NGM
SIC 7389 Financial services
Pr: Jonathan Steinberg
**Ch Bd:* Michael Steinhardt
COO: Gregory Barton
CFO: Amit Muni
Ex VP: Kurt Macalpine
Ex VP: Luciano Siracusano III
Ex VP: Peter M Ziemba
Board of Directors: Steven Begleiter, Anthony Bossone, Bruce Lavine, R Jarrett Lilien, Win Neuger, Frank Salerno

WISDOT
See WISCONSIN DEPARTMENT OF TRANSPORTATION

D-U-N-S 05-475-5504 IMP/EXP
WISE ALLOYS LLC
(*Suby of* WISE METALS GROUP LLC) ★
4805 2nd St, Muscle Shoals, AL 35661-1282
Tel (256) 386-6000 *Founded/Ownrshp* 1999
Sales 338.0MM^E *EMP* 1,007
SIC 3353 Aluminum sheet, plate & foil
CEO: David F D'Addario
V Ch: John J Cameron
**COO:* Wes Oberholzer
CFO: Karen Cassidy
CFO: Kenneth Stastny
Ex VP: Danny Mendelson
**Sr VP:* Joe Pampinto
Sr VP: Phillip Tays
VP: Robert Marion
VP: Thomas Schaefer
VP: Mike Stumpe
VP: Carroll Wills

D-U-N-S 05-113-1779 IMP
WISE BUSINESS FORMS INC
555 Mcfarland 400 Dr, Alpharetta, GA 30004-5691
Tel (770) 442-1060 *Founded/Ownrshp* 1984
Sales 124.4MM^E *EMP* 450
SIC 2761 2752 Manifold business forms; Commercial printing, lithographic
CEO: Bill Prettyman
COO: Charles Teets
**Ex VP:* Jeff Prettyman
Ex VP: Mark A Wells
Genl Mgr: H T Smith
Genl Mgr: Sally Spurr
Plnt Mgr: Jerry Crook

D-U-N-S 10-008-0118
WISE COUNTY PUBLIC SCHOOLS
628 Lake St Ne, Wise, VA 24293-7919
Tel (276) 328-8017 *Founded/Ownrshp* 1999
Sales 55.5MM^E *EMP* 1,100
SIC 8211 Public elementary & secondary schools
**Prin:* Mr B Crutchfield
Adm Dir: Greg Mullens
Plng Mgr: Tony Hill
CTO: Jerrie Adams
MIS Dir: Scott Kiser
MIS Dir: Tonya Porter
Dir IT: Don Mullins
IT Man: Brenda Cuffel
IT Man: Michelle Tiller
IT Man: Joyce Wallace
IT Man: Jason Wamsley

D-U-N-S 94-927-8618 IMP/EXP
WISE FOODS INC
(*Suby of* ARCA CONTINENTAL, S.A.B. DE C.V.)
228 Rasely St, Berwick, PA 18603-4533
Tel (888) 759-4401 *Founded/Ownrshp* 1921
Sales 366.5MM^E *EMP* 876
SIC 2096 Potato chips & similar snacks
CEO: Jolie Weber
VP Mktg: Claire Houang
S&M/VP: Camp Best
Mktg Mgr: Jeff Crowell
Mktg Mgr: Bruce Kadin
Mktg Mgr: Ron Young
Doctor: Rudy Heintzelman

D-U-N-S 06-838-5673
WISE HEALTH FOUNDATION
WISE REGIONAL HEALTH SYSTEM
609 Medical Center Dr, Decatur, TX 76234-3836
Tel (940) 627-5921 *Founded/Ownrshp* 1974
Sales 132.4MM^E *EMP* 850
Accts Bkd Llp Waco Tx
SIC 8062 General medical & surgical hospitals
Pr: Brian Stephens
Dir Recs: Frank Cribbs
**CEO:* Steve Summers
CFO: Leon Fuqua
Bd of Dir: Mickey McMaster
Bd of Dir: Jerhea Nail
Bd of Dir: Judy Wilson
**VP:* Jay Bearden
Dir Inf Cn: Sally Stokes
Adm Dir: Lynn Sherman
Genl Mgr: Travis Fulton

D-U-N-S 02-254-1387 IMP
WISE METALS GROUP LLC
(*Suby of* CONSTELLIUM N.V.)
4805 2nd St, Muscle Shoals, AL 35661-1282
Tel (256) 386-6000 *Founded/Ownrshp* 2014
Sales 651.3MM^E *EMP* 3,196
SIC 3353 3356 Aluminum sheet, plate & foil; Aluminum sheet & strip; Nonferrous rolling & drawing
CEO: David F D'Addario
**COO:* Wes Oberholzer
**CFO:* Monte Schaefer
VP: Freddie Copeland
Exec: Sandra Scarborough
Plnt Mgr: Joe Pampinto

WISE REGIONAL HEALTH SYSTEM
See WISE HEALTH FOUNDATION

D-U-N-S 05-248-2361 IMP
WISENBAKER BUILDER SERVICES INC (TX)
WISENBAKER BUILDERS SERVICES
1703 Westfield Loop Rd, Houston, TX 77073-2705
Tel (281) 233-4000 *Founded/Ownrshp* 1970
Sales 286.8MM^E *EMP* 500
SIC 5023 5084 5031 Floor coverings; Machine tools & metalworking machinery; Lumber, plywood & millwork
VP: Diane Wisenbaker
Ch Bd: John W Wisenbaker Sr
COO: Matt Wisenbaker
CFO: Joseph Chiavone Jr
Sr VP: John Wisenbaker Jr
VP: Russ Bevan
VP: Buddy Billingsley
VP: Lena Gibson
Div Mgr: Aaron Cameron
Div Mgr: Nathan Stroup
MIS Dir: Rick Crouse

WISENBAKER BUILDERS SERVICES
See WISENBAKER BUILDER SERVICES INC

WISH FARMS
See WISHNATZKI INC

D-U-N-S 09-479-6559 IMP
WISHNATZKI INC
WISH FARMS
100 Stearns St, Plant City, FL 33563-5045
Tel (813) 752-5111 *Founded/Ownrshp* 1922
Sales 171.5MM^E *EMP* 250
SIC 5148 Fresh fruits & vegetables
CEO: Gary Wishnatzki
VP: John Brown
VP: Jeremy Burris
Mktg Dir: Amber Kosinsky
Sales Asso: Jason J Deis

D-U-N-S 02-856-6933 IMP/EXP
WISMETTAC ASIAN FOODS INC
WISMETTAC FRESH FISH
(*Suby of* NISHIMOTO COMPANY LIMITED.)
13409 Orden Dr, Santa Fe Springs, CA 90670-6336
Tel (562) 802-1900 *Founded/Ownrshp* 1960
Sales 535.3MM^E *EMP* 1,200
SIC 5149 Groceries & related products
CEO: Takayuki Kanai
**CFO:* Tom Kawaguchi
**VP:* Toshiyoki Nishikawa
Brnch Mgr: Shoichi Kaku
Brnch Mgr: Hiroshi Kikumori
IT Man: Masanori Tabata
Opers Mgr: Jay Yamamoto
Sls Dir: Daryl Asato
Mktg Mgr: Yasuhiko Hamada
Sls Mgr: Clayton Iwaoka
Sales Asso: Masahide Kamimoto

WISMETTAC FRESH FISH
See WISMETTAC ASIAN FOODS INC

D-U-N-S 06-441-1473
WISS JANNEY ELSTNER ASSOCIATES INC
WJE ENGINEERS & ARCHITECTS
330 Pfingsten Rd, Northbrook, IL 60062-2003
Tel (847) 272-2186 *Founded/Ownrshp* 1989
Sales 114.6MM *EMP* 500
Accts Fgmk Llc Bannockburn Illino
SIC 8711 8712 8734 Consulting engineer; Architectural engineering; Testing laboratories
Pr: William J Nugent
**CFO:* Thomas Oczkowski
**Ex VP:* Gary J Klein
**VP:* Ian R Chin
**VP:* Peter Popovic
VP: Predrag L Popovich
VP: R I Chin
VP: Jeffrey N Sutterlin
Genl Mgr: Daniel Eilbeck
Tech Mgr: Matthew Anderson
Sls Mgr: John Lawler

D-U-N-S 03-123-5849
WISSAHICKON SCHOOL DISTRICT
601 Knight Rd, Ambler, PA 19002-3413
Tel (215) 619-8000 *Founded/Ownrshp* 1963
Sales 88.5MM *EMP* 630
SIC 8211 Public elementary & secondary schools; Public junior high school; Public elementary school
**Pr:* Charles McIntyre

WISTRON INFOCOMM
See SMS INFOCOMM CORP

WITC
See WISCONSIN INDIANHEAD TECHNICAL COLLEGE FOUNDATION INC

WITHAM HEALTH SERVICES
See WITHAM MEMORIAL HOSPITAL

D-U-N-S 93-284-5514
WITHAM MEMORIAL HOSPITAL
WITHAM HEALTH SERVICES
2605 N Lebanon St, Lebanon, IN 46052-1476
Tel (765) 485-8000 *Founded/Ownrshp* 1917
Sales 380.3MM *EMP* 725
Accts Blue & Co Llc Indianapolis
SIC 8062 General medical & surgical hospitals
Pr: Raymond Ingham
Chf Rad: Steven Fritsch
Dir Bus: Sharon Keck
Ex Dir: Jane Buroker
Off Mgr: Sandy Anderson
Mktg Dir: Tammy Rabe
Obsttrcn: Ted Winkler
Doctor: Johanna Coughlin
Doctor: Tehniat Haider
Doctor: John Olson
Doctor: Derron Wilson
Board of Directors: Brock Hesler

D-U-N-S 06-000-7432
WITHERS BERGMAN LLP
(*Suby of* WITHERS HK PROFESSIONAL SERVICES LIMITED)
157 Church St Fl 19, New Haven, CT 06510-2100
Tel (203) 789-1320 *Founded/Ownrshp* 1966
Sales 27.6MM^E *EMP* 1,000
SIC 8111 Legal services
Pt: Ivan Sacks
**Pt:* Stanley N Bergman
**Ex VP:* William C Swift Jr
**VP:* David L Reynolds
Off Admin: Susan Ryan
CTO: Marie Zanavich
DP Dir: Barbara Magliola
IT Man: Blaine Cartwright
IT Man: Bob Newton

D-U-N-S 06-467-5648
WITHLACOOCHEE RIVER ELECTRIC COOPERATIVE INC
WREC
14651 21st St, Dade City, FL 33523-2920
Tel (352) 567-5133 *Founded/Ownrshp* 1941
Sales 474.0MM *EMP* 458
Accts Purvis Gray & Company Llp Dad
SIC 4911 Transmission, electric power; Distribution, electric power
Ex VP: Billy E Brown
**Treas:* Charles V Smith
**Sec:* Alan Hingesbach
Genl Mgr: Billy Brown
Dir IT: Larry Darsey

WITHUM SMITH & BROWN CPA
See WITHUMSMITH+BROWN PC

D-U-N-S 09-740-0782 IMP
WITHUMSMITH+BROWN PC
WITHUM SMITH & BROWN CPA
506 Carnegie Ctr Ste 400, Princeton, NJ 08540-6243
Tel (609) 520-1188 *Founded/Ownrshp* 1974
Sales 111.4MM^E *EMP* 490
SIC 8721 Certified public accountant
CEO: William R Hagaman Jr
**Pt:* David A Springsteen
**Pt:* Thomas R Suarez
**Pt:* Daniel J Vitale
**Pr:* Ivan C Brown
CFO: Audra Hamilton
**Treas:* Leonard H Smith
Ex VP: Vankat Krishnaswamy
**VP:* Douglas M Sonier
**VP:* Andrew A Vitale
Exec: Barbara Durning
Dir Bus: Robert Lightman

WITT HEAT TRANSFER PRODUCTS
See HEAT TRANSFER PRODUCTS GROUP LLC

D-U-N-S 96-276-3277
WITT OBRIENS LLC
1201 15th St Nw Ste 600, Washington, DC 20005-2899
Tel (202) 585-0780 *Founded/Ownrshp* 2009
Sales 123.7MM^E *EMP* 230^E
SIC 4959 8748 8322 Environmental cleanup services; Business consulting; Disaster service
CEO: Tim Whipple
**CFO:* Keith Forster
**Treas:* Lisa Manekin
Sr VP: Don Costanzo
VP: Rusty Aaronson
VP: Edward Fry II
VP: Michael Gaines
VP: Mike Gallagher
VP: Anneilia Holton-Williams
VP: Phillip Webber
VP: John Weinfurter
Exec: Bobbi Stewart

WITTENBERG UNIVERSITY
See BOARD OF DIRECTORS OF WITTENBERG COLLEGE

D-U-N-S 04-998-6532
WITTICHEN SUPPLY CO
JOHNSON CONTRLS AUTHORIZED DLR
2912 3rd Ave N, Birmingham, AL 35203-3908
Tel (205) 251-8500 *Founded/Ownrshp* 1986
Sales 163.1MM^E *EMP* 212
SIC 5078 5075 Refrigeration equipment & supplies; Warm air heating equipment & supplies
Pr: David P Henderson
**Treas:* Vicky W Henderson
**VP:* Ivy Wittichen
Brnch Mgr: Marty Waddle
IT Man: Bill Bolin

D-U-N-S 00-609-2498 IMP
WIXON INDUSTRIES INC (WI)
1390 E Bolivar Ave, Milwaukee, WI 53235-4521
Tel (800) 841-5304 *Founded/Ownrshp* 1907
Sales 88.2MM *EMP* 200^E
SIC 2099 2087 2899 Spices, including grinding; Seasonings: dry mixes; Flavoring extracts & syrups; Chemical preparations
Pr: A Peter Gottsacker
**CFO:* Peter Caputa
**Ex VP:* Chuck Ehemann

WIZARDS OF THE COAST, LLC.
See WIZARDS OF COAST LLC

D-U-N-S 78-870-3635 IMP
■ **WIZARDS OF COAST LLC**
WIZARDS OF THE COAST, LLC.
(*Suby of* HASBRO INC) ★
1600 Lind Ave Sw Ste 400, Renton, WA 98057-3374
Tel (425) 226-6500 *Founded/Ownrshp* 1990
Sales 243.8MM^E *EMP* 1,500
SIC 3944 Board games, children's & adults'
CEO: Greg Leeds
VP: Simon Blackwell
Web Dev: Chad Laske
Sftwr Eng: Matt Schroeder

D-U-N-S 93-371-2127
WJ BRADLEY MORTGAGE CAPITAL LLC
MORGAN FINANCIAL
10940 S Parker Rd Ste 506, Parker, CO 80134-7440
Tel (303) 825-5670 *Founded/Ownrshp* 1998
Sales NA *EMP* 705
SIC 6162

D-U-N-S 10-679-8481 IMP
WJ DEUTSCH & SONS LTD
DEUTSCH FAMILY WINE & SPIRITS
201 Tresser Blvd Ste 324, Stamford, CT 06901-3435
Tel (914) 305-5765 *Founded/Ownrshp* 1981
Sales 172.8MM^E *EMP* 220
SIC 5182 Wine
Prin: Peter Deutsch
**Ch Bd:* William J Deutsch
VP: Nick Lavacca
Board of Directors: Kelly Klein

WJCC PUBLIC SCHOOLS
See WILLIAMSBURG-JAMES CITY COUNTY PUBLIC SCHOOLS

WJCC PUBLIC SCHOOLS
See WILLIAMSBURG JAMES CITY COUNTY PUBLIC SCHOOLS

WJE ENGINEERS & ARCHITECTS
See WISS JANNEY ELSTNER ASSOCIATES INC

D-U-N-S 86-010-7270 IMP/EXP
WKI HOLDING CO INC
9525 Bryn Mawr Ave # 300, Rosemont, IL 60018-5252
Tel (847) 233-8600 *Founded/Ownrshp* 1992
Sales 1.4MMM^E *EMP* 2,900
SIC 3229 3469 Pressed & blown glass; Household cooking & kitchen utensils, metal
Pr: Joseph T Mallot
Pr: Ralph Denisco
**Pr:* James A Sharman
**CFO:* Joseph W McGarr
Chf Mktg O: John McLean
**VP:* Raymond J Kulla
**VP:* Jeff MEI
VP: James Wallace

D-U-N-S 80-221-4598
WKW ERBSLOEH NORTH AMERICA HOLDING INC
WENA HOLDING
(*Suby of* ERBSLOH AG)
103 Parkway E, Pell City, AL 35125-2749
Tel (205) 338-4242 *Founded/Ownrshp* 2006
Sales 158.3MM^E *EMP* 530
SIC 6719 Investment holding companies, except banks
Pr: Klaus-Dieter Lengelsen
**Sec:* Ruediger Timm

D-U-N-S 07-936-6095
WKW ERBSLOEH NORTH AMERICA LLC
(*Suby of* WENA HOLDING) ★
103 Parkway E, Pell City, AL 35125-2749
Tel (205) 338-4242 *Founded/Ownrshp* 2006
Sales 90.0MM^E *EMP* 530^E
SIC 3714 Motor vehicle parts & accessories
Pr: Klaus-Dieter Lengelsen
Sec: Ruediger Timm
Prgrm Mgr: Jim Goodson
Prgrm Mgr: David Schultz
Prgrm Mgr: Luis Sommer

D-U-N-S 84-395-7296
WL PLASTICS CORP
575 Lone Star Cir Ste 300, Fort Worth, TX 76177
Tel (682) 831-2701 *Founded/Ownrshp* 2003
Sales 124.0MM^E *EMP* 200
SIC 3084 Plastics pipe
Pr: Mark Wason
**Prin:* Steve Burns

D-U-N-S 60-757-8924
WLG INC
920 E Algonquin Rd # 120, Schaumburg, IL 60173-4184
Tel (773) 416-2803 *Founded/Ownrshp* 2003
Sales 177.9MM *EMP* 353^E
SIC 4731 Freight forwarding
CEO: Andrew Jillings
CEO: Stewart Brown
**CFO:* Edmund Pawelko
VP: Bill Ip
VP: John Ling
VP: Ray Rodriguez
VP: Robert Wong
VP: Tina Zabielski
Genl Mgr: Raymond Chan
Genl Mgr: Alan Kan

D-U-N-S 18-595-5197
WLR RECOVERY ASSOCIATES II LLC
1166 Ave Of The Americas, New York, NY 10036-2708
Tel (212) 826-1100 *Founded/Ownrshp* 2002
Sales 692.4MM^E *EMP* 12,010^E
SIC 6719 Investment holding companies, except banks

D-U-N-S 79-128-0832
WLR RECOVERY FUND II LP
(*Suby of* WLR RECOVERY ASSOCIATES II LLC) ★
1166 6th Ave, New York, NY 10036-2708
Tel (212) 278-9821 *Founded/Ownrshp* 2002
Sales 390.4MM^E *EMP* 12,010^E
SIC 6719 3714 Investment holding companies, except banks; Motor vehicle parts & accessories

WM
See WASTE MANAGEMENT INC

WM. A. RANDOLPH
See WILLIAM A RANDOLPH INC

D-U-N-S 00-819-4664 IMP
WM B REILY & CO INC (LA)
REILY W M B & CO
640 Magazine St, New Orleans, LA 70130-3486
Tel (504) 539-5200 *Founded/Ownrshp* 1903
Sales 386.3MM^E *EMP* 1,454
SIC 2095 2035 2079 5962 5963 2099 Coffee roasting (except by wholesale grocers); Coffee, ground: mixed with grain or chicory; Instant coffee; Mayonnaise; Seasonings, meat sauces (except tomato & dry); Vegetable refined oils (except corn oil); Sandwich & hot food vending machines; Food service, coffee-cart; Tea blending
CEO: W Boatner Reily III
**Pr:* C James McCarthy III
**Sec:* Harold M Herrmann Jr
**VP:* Robert C Maurer
**VP:* Robert D Reily

D-U-N-S 00-701-7288 IMP
WM BARR & CO INC (TN)
KLEAN-STRIP
6750 Lenox Center Ct # 200, Memphis, TN 38115-4281
Tel (901) 775-0100 *Founded/Ownrshp* 1946, 1996
Sales 173.2MM^E *EMP* 350
SIC 2851 Paint removers
Pr: Richard Loomis
**COO:* Esther Geppert
**CFO:* Lawrence Geiger
CFO: Joe Lyons
**VP:* Ann Allard
VP: Leonard Clark
**VP:* Michael Dvorak
**VP:* David Hogber
VP: Loree Horton
VP: Tim Labeau
VP: Stacy Logan
Exec: Ramesh Patel
Exec: Marcia Vargas

D-U-N-S 04-140-8600 IMP
■ WM BOLTHOUSE FARMS INC
(*Suby of* BOLTHOUSE HOLDING CORP) ★
7200 E Brundage Ln, Bakersfield, CA 93307-3016
Tel (661) 366-7205 *Founded/Ownrshp* 2012
Sales 617.1MM^E *EMP* 2,450
SIC 0161 2099 0723 Carrot farm; Onion farm; Ready-to-eat meals, salads & sandwiches; Crop preparation services for market
Pr: Jeff Dunn
CFO: Harleen Singh
**Treas:* Marty Buck
Chf Mktg O: Todd Putnam
Ex VP: Scott Laporta
VP: Rick Hoyt
VP: Anthony Leggio
**VP:* Timothy McCorkle
Creative D: Brenda Spivack
QA Dir: Harjot Gill
Dir IT: Brian Bailey

D-U-N-S 06-745-8562
WM H LEAHY ASSOCIATES INC
CARBOTROL FOODS
2350 Ravine Way Ste 200, Glenview, IL 60025-7621
Tel (847) 904-5250 *Founded/Ownrshp* 1957
Sales 92.3MM^E *EMP* 59
SIC 5141 5142 Groceries, general line; Fruit juices, frozen
Ch Bd: Timothy Leahy
**Pr:* Michael Leahy
**Pr:* Greg Lojkutz
**CFO:* Thomas Banner
**VP:* Marc Justinak
Genl Mgr: Vic Ortega
IT Man: Brenda Delgado
Opers Mgr: Bruce Hesbon
Mktg Mgr: Joe Arends

D-U-N-S 18-721-9212
WM KLORMAN CONSTRUCTION CORP
23047 Ventura Blvd # 200, Woodland Hills, CA 91364-1133
Tel (818) 591-5969 *Founded/Ownrshp* 1985
Sales 100.0MM *EMP* 30
SIC 1521 1542 Single-family housing construction; Commercial & office building, new construction
Pr: William Klorman
VP: Ida Chen
VP: Doug Fowler

D-U-N-S 78-564-8668
■ WM LIMITED PARTNERSHIP - 1998
WENDY'S
(*Suby of* MERITAGE HOSPITALITY GROUP INC) ★
45 Ottawa Ave Sw Ste 600, Grand Rapids, MI 49503-4011
Tel (616) 776-2600 *Founded/Ownrshp* 1998
Sales 60.9MM^E *EMP* 1,500
SIC 5812 Fast-food restaurant, chain
Pt: Robert Schermer Jr
**Pt:* Robert H Potts
**Pt:* James R Saalfeld

D-U-N-S 02-589-7430
WM NOBBE AND CO INC
JOHN DEERE
6469 State Route 3, Waterloo, IL 62298-2825
Tel (618) 939-6717 *Founded/Ownrshp* 1989
Sales 134.8MM *EMP* 102
SIC 5083

D-U-N-S 01-453-8273 EXP
■ WM RECYCLE AMERICA LLC
(*Suby of* WM) ★
1001 Fannin St Ste 4000, Houston, TX 77002-6711
Tel (713) 512-6200 *Founded/Ownrshp* 2002
Sales 450.0MM^E *EMP* 10^E
SIC 5093 Waste paper
Pr: William K Caesar
**COO:* James E Trevathan
**CFO:* James C Fish Jr
**Ex VP:* Puneet Bhasin
**Sr VP:* Barry H Caldwell
**Sr VP:* John J Morris Jr
**Sr VP:* Mark Schwartz
VP: Brian Fielkow
VP: Michael Taylor

D-U-N-S 00-306-1512 IMP/EXP
WMT BURNETT HOLDING LLC (MD)
1500 Bush St, Baltimore, MD 21230-1928
Tel (410) 837-3000 *Founded/Ownrshp* 1937
Sales 168.7MM^E *EMP* 450
SIC 2299 3086 Batting, wadding, padding & fillings; Insulation or cushioning material, foamed plastic
CFO: Jim Rodgers
VP: David Emala
VP: David A Eml
Genl Mgr: Jason Gorger
Opers Mgr: Rodney Manigo
Plnt Mgr: Mike McAllester
Ql Cn Mgr: Matthew Moose

D-U-N-S 00-132-6198 IMP/EXP
WM WRIGLEY JR CO
(*Suby of* MARS INC) ★
930 W Evergreen Ave, Chicago, IL 60642-2437
Tel (312) 280-4710 *Founded/Ownrshp* 1891, 2008
Sales 175.7MM^E *EMP* 16,400
SIC 2067 2064 2087 2899 Chewing gum; Chewing gum base; Candy & other confectionery products; Chewing candy, not chewing gum; Lollipops & other hard candy; Flavoring extracts & syrups; Peppermint oil; Spearmint oil
Pr: Martin Radvan
CFO: Reuben Gamoran
Ofcr: Dushan Petrovich
Sr VP: Peter Hempstead
Sr VP: Howard Malovany
VP: Gary R Bebee
VP: Frank Birkel
VP: Mary Kay Haben
VP: Shaun Kim
VP: Patrick Mitchell
VP: Kathryn Olsen
VP: Kelli Patterson
VP: Rob Peterson
VP: William M Piet
VP: Dennis Schrey
VP: Ralph Scozzafava
VP: Donna L Westerman
Dir Surg: A Rory Finlay

WMATA
See WASHINGTON METROPOLITAN AREA TRANSIT AUTHORITY

D-U-N-S 17-608-6945
WMG ACQUISITION CORP
(*Suby of* WARNER MUSIC GROUP CORP) ★
75 Rockefeller Plz, New York, NY 10019-6908
Tel (212) 275-2000 *Founded/Ownrshp* 2004
Sales 769.2MM^E *EMP* 1,500^E
SIC 2782 2741 7929 Record albums; Music books: publishing & printing; Music, sheet: publishing & printing; Musical entertainers
Pr: Stephen F Cooper
**CFO:* Steven Macri
**Ex VP:* Mark Ansorge
**Ex VP:* Paul M Robinson
**Ex VP:* Will Tanous

D-U-N-S 15-325-3062
WMG HOLDING CO INC
(*Suby of* WARNER MUSIC GROUP CORP) ★
75 Rockefeller Plz, New York, NY 10019-6908
Tel (212) 275-2000 *Founded/Ownrshp* 1977
Sales 134.0MM^E *EMP* 7,810
SIC 3652 2741 Pre-recorded records & tapes; Music books: publishing & printing; Music, sheet: publishing & printing
Ch Bd: Edgar Bronfman Jr
**CFO:* Michael Ward
**VP:* David S Johnson

D-U-N-S 07-861-9985
WMG HOLDINGS CORP
(*Suby of* WARNER MUSIC GROUP CORP) ★
75 Rockefeller Plz Fl 18, New York, NY 10019-6932
Tel (212) 275-2000 *Founded/Ownrshp* 1993
Sales 7.7MM^E *EMP* 3,550
SIC 7929 Musical entertainers
CEO: Steve Cooper

D-U-N-S 87-804-6069
▲ WMI HOLDINGS CORP
800 5th Ave Ste 4100, Seattle, WA 98104-3100
Tel (206) 432-8887 *Founded/Ownrshp* 1889
Sales NA *EMP* 49,403
Accts Burr Pilger Mayer Inc San F
Tkr Sym WMIH *Exch* NAS
SIC 6035 Federal savings banks
Ch: Michael Willingham
Pr: Charles Smith
Pr: Anthony F Vuoto
Pr: Robert J Williams Jr
COO: David Alvarez
CFO: John A Maciel
Treas: Doreen Logan
Ex VP: Daryl David
Ex VP: Bill Ehrlich
Ex VP: Richard Fisher
Ex VP: William Kosturos
Sr VP: Jim Gorzalski
Sr VP: Lewis E Love
Sr VP: Sari L Macrie
VP: Jennifer Etkin
VP: Peter Struck
Board of Directors: William G Reed Jr, Stephen I Chazen, Orin C Smith, Stephen E Frank Chb, James H Stever, Thomas C Leppert, Charles M Lillis, Phillip D Matthews, Margaret Osmer McQuade, Regina T Montoya, Michael K Murphy, Mary E Pugh

D-U-N-S 00-581-0890 IMP
WMJORDAN CO INC
11010 Jefferson Ave, Newport News, VA 23601-2717
Tel (757) 596-6341 *Founded/Ownrshp* 1957
Sales 208.2MM^E *EMP* 340
SIC 1542 1541 School building construction; Hospital construction; Warehouse construction
Pr: John Lawson
**Ch:* Robert T Lawson
**Treas:* Thomas M Shelton
Ex VP: Ken Taylor
**VP:* James M Collins
Exec: Ron Lauster
Div Mgr: Ashley Arrowood
Off Mgr: Paul Galloway
Ql Cn Mgr: Donovan Jacoby

D-U-N-S 14-747-8531 IMP
WMK LLC
MOBILITYWORKS
4199 Kinross Lakes Pkwy # 300, Richfield, OH 44286-9010
Tel (234) 312-2000 *Founded/Ownrshp* 1997
Sales 357.3MM^E *EMP* 727
SIC 5511 7532

D-U-N-S 06-370-7632
WMOG INC
MOSSER GROUP, THE
122 S Wilson Ave, Fremont, OH 43420-2767
Tel (419) 334-3801 *Founded/Ownrshp* 1973
Sales 127.4MM *EMP* 280^E
SIC 1541 7359 1611 Industrial buildings, new construction; Equipment rental & leasing; Highway & street construction
CEO: Robert H Moyer
**Sec:* Al Mehlow
**VP:* J P Boyle
**VP:* Joe Luzar
Sfty Dirs: Mark Prenzlin
Sfty Mgr: George Moore

D-U-N-S 80-003-4183 IMP/EXP
■ WMS GAMING INC
(*Suby of* WMS INDUSTRIES INC) ★
3401 N California Ave, Chicago, IL 60618-5899
Tel (773) 961-1000 *Founded/Ownrshp* 1974
Sales 180.1MM^E *EMP* 630
SIC 3999 Slot machines
CEO: Brian R Gamache
Pr: Sebastian Salat
Pr: Will Smolucha
**CFO:* Scott Schweinfurth
Bd of Dir: Mj Mariani
VP: Rory Block
VP: Lori Miskovic
VP: Norm Wurz
Exec: Kevin Davis
Exec: Michael Sirchio
Dir IT: Brian Yarger

D-U-N-S 01-029-7695
■ WMS INDUSTRIES INC
(*Suby of* SCIENTIFIC GAMES CORP) ★
3401 N California Ave, Chicago, IL 60618-5899
Tel (847) 785-3000 *Founded/Ownrshp* 2013
Sales 697.3MM *EMP* 1,894^E
Accts Ernst & Young Llp Chicago Il
SIC 3999 7999 Coin-operated amusement machines; Lottery operation
Ch Bd: Brian R Gamache
**Pr:* Orrin J Edidin
**COO:* Kenneth Lochiatto
**CFO:* Scott D Schweinfurth
Ex VP: Larry Pacey
VP: Allon Englman
**VP:* Kathleen J McJohn
VP: John P McNicholas
VP: William H Pfund
VP: Paul Quaglia
VP: Rick Riehm
VP: Michael Rutz
Board of Directors: Robert J Bahash, Patricia M Nazemetz, Matthew H Paull, Edward W Rabin Jr, Ira S Sheinfeld, Bobby L Siller, William J Vareschi Jr, Keith R Wyche

D-U-N-S 83-108-8005
WNET
825 8th Ave Fl 14, New York, NY 10019-7435
Tel (212) 560-2000 *Founded/Ownrshp* 2008
Sales 148.0MM *EMP* 350^E
SIC 4833 Television broadcasting stations
CEO: Neal Shapiro
Pr: Lisa Mantone
**CFO:* Caroline Croen
**VP:* Robert A Feinberg
**VP:* Claude Johnson
**VP:* Stephen Segaller
Ex Dir: Hilary Vlachos
Opers Mgr: Erin Roberts

WNG
See WIRELESS NETWORK GROUP INC

D-U-N-S 02-087-1786
WOERNER HOLDINGS LP (FL)
525 Okeechobee Blvd # 720, West Palm Beach, FL 33401-6353
Tel (561) 835-3747 *Founded/Ownrshp* 1948
Sales 94.7MM^E *EMP* 60
Accts Templeton & Company Llp West
SIC 0181 Sod farms
Ch Bd: Lester J Woerner
**COO:* Kathy Miller
**CFO:* Chris Gryskiewicz
**VP:* Brian Choi
VP: Kathy T Miller
**VP:* Trent Woerner

D-U-N-S 00-286-6366
WOHLSEN CONSTRUCTION CO INC
548 Steel Way, Lancaster, PA 17601-3154
Tel (717) 299-2500 *Founded/Ownrshp* 1990
Sales 183.2MM^E *EMP* 275
SIC 1542 1541 8741 School building construction; Commercial & office building, new construction; Hospital construction; Industrial buildings, new construction; Warehouse construction; Construction management
Pr: J Gary Langmuir
**Pr:* John M Thorsen
**Treas:* R Edward Gordon
**Ex VP:* John K Ball
Sr VP: Bernard Grove
**VP:* David B Brodie
VP: Steve Davies
VP: William H Forrey
VP: Ronald Slember

D-U-N-S 07-853-8577
WOK PARENT LLC
7676 E Pinnacle Peak Rd, Scottsdale, AZ 85255-3404
Tel (480) 888-3000 *Founded/Ownrshp* 2012
Sales 1.0MMM^E *EMP* 26,000^E
SIC 5812 Chinese restaurant
Prin: Amar Doshi

D-U-N-S 00-562-4057
WOLF CREEK FEDERAL SERVICES INC
CHUGACH
(*Suby of* CHUGACH GOVERNMENT SOLUTIONS LLC) ★
3800 Cntrpint Dr Ste 1200, Anchorage, AK 99503
Tel (907) 563-8866 *Founded/Ownrshp* 2009
Sales 155.5MM *EMP* 1,600
SIC 3441 Fabricated structural metal
Pr: Kukuk Steven
**CFO:* Angela Astle
**Treas:* McDaniel Matthew
IT Man: Danita Vroman

D-U-N-S 08-029-0725
WOLF CREEK FEDERAL SERVICES INC
(Suby of CHUGACH ALASKA CORP) ★
3800 Cntrpint Dr Ste 1200, Anchorage, AK 99503
Tel (907) 563-8866 Founded/Ownrshp 2009
Sales 155.5MM EMP 1,600
SIC 3441 Fabricated structural metal
Pr: Kukuk Steven
*CFO: Angela Astle
*Treas: McDaniel Matthew

D-U-N-S 17-347-9478 IMP
WOLF CREEK NUCLEAR OPERATING CORP
WCNOC
1550 Oxen Ln, Burlington, KS 66839-9127
Tel (620) 364-4141 Founded/Ownrshp 1986
Sales 4.3MMM^E EMP 1,003
SIC 4911 ; Generation, electric power
Pr: Matt Sunseri
VP: Pat Hawkins
Prin: Bruce Barrett
Dir IT: Rhonda Redding
IT Man: Warren Befort
IT Man: Paul Kesler
Plnt Mgr: Donna Jacobs
Pr Mgr: Cassie Bailey

D-U-N-S 07-749-6917 IMP
WOLF FURNITURE ENTERPRISES INC
1620 N Tuckahoe St, Bellwood, PA 16617-1500
Tel (814) 742-4380 Founded/Ownrshp 1902
Sales 114.9MM^E EMP 430
SIC 5712 5713 5722 5731 5719 Furniture stores; Floor covering stores; Household appliance stores; Radio, television & electronic stores; Lamps & lamp shades
Ch Bd: John J Wolf
*Pr: J Douglas Wolf
*Treas: Charles W McLaughlin
VP: Charles W McLaughin
VP: Doug Shaffer
Genl Mgr: Payman Ahrarian
Genl Mgr: Cindy Cornmesser
Genl Mgr: Randy Lerew
Genl Mgr: Michael Vey
IT Man: Paul Edwards
Mktg Dir: Chris Bertani

D-U-N-S 60-885-5458
WOLF PACKAGING INC
(Suby of BAGCRAFT) ★
2068 303rd Ave, Fort Madison, IA 52627-9751
Tel (319) 372-6643 Founded/Ownrshp 2002
Sales 101.3MM^E EMP 1,128
SIC 2621 2676 2671 Paper mills; Sanitary paper products; Packaging paper & plastics film, coated & laminated
Pr: Tom Wolf
*VP: Mark A Wilcox

D-U-N-S 07-865-8732
WOLF RETAIL SOLUTIONS I INC (FL)
2801 W Busch Blvd Ste 101, Tampa, FL 33618-4500
Tel (813) 280-2946 Founded/Ownrshp 2012
Sales 4.5MM EMP 6,400
SIC 7389 Design services
Pr: Thomas P Robinson III
*Treas: Elizabeth Robinson

D-U-N-S 07-966-7500
WOLF TRANSPORTATION LLC
5204 S Redwood Rd Ste B1, Taylorsville, UT 84123-4273
Tel (801) 759-9465 Founded/Ownrshp 2014
Sales 150.0MM EMP 3
SIC 4212

D-U-N-S 01-817-8301
WOLFF BROS SUPPLY INC
6078 Wolff Rd, Medina, OH 44256-9499
Tel (330) 725-3451 Founded/Ownrshp 1965
Sales 114.4MM EMP 270
SIC 5063 5074 5075

WOLFGANG PUCK CATERING
See H&H CATERING LP

D-U-N-S 00-228-7001 IMP/EXP
WOLFINGTON BODY CO INC
N Off Pa Tpk Exit Rr 100, Exton, PA 19341
Tel (610) 458-8501 Founded/Ownrshp 1990
Sales 134.1MM EMP 109
Accts Narcisi & Company Willow Grov
SIC 3711 3713 5012 Automobile bodies, passenger car, not including engine, etc.; Automobile assembly, including specialty automobiles; Bus bodies (motor vehicles); Hearse bodies; Ambulance bodies; Commercial vehicles
Ex VP: David P Fitzgerald
*Pr: Richard I Wolfington

WOLFSON CHILDREN'S HOSPITAL
See SOUTHERN BAPTIST HOSPITAL OF FLORIDA INC

D-U-N-S 01-712-5980
WOLGAST CORP
4835 Towne Centre Rd # 203, Saginaw, MI 48604-2829
Tel (989) 233-5228 Founded/Ownrshp 1948
Sales 83.7MM^E EMP 135
SIC 1542 1541 Commercial & office building, new construction; Institutional building construction; Industrial buildings, new construction
CEO: Lynn R Wolgast
Pr: Rick Keith
*Pr: Steve Seibert
*Pr: Brian Stadley
*Pr: Jerry Stefano
*COO: Patrick Wolgast
VP: Lloyd Pender
VP: Steve Salyers
VP: Nicholas Seehafer
Dir IT: Tony Wingerter
Opers Mgr: Scott Wilmot

D-U-N-S 01-699-5821 IMP/EXP
WOLPIN CO
GREAT LAKES BEVERAGE
1600 Modern St, Highland Park, MI 48203-2480
Tel (586) 757-4900 Founded/Ownrshp 1958
Sales 90.1MM^E EMP 350
SIC 5181 Beer & other fermented malt liquors
Pr: Walter Wolpin
Off Mgr: Denise Prilo

WOLSELEY FINANCE
See WOLSELEY INVESTMENTS INC

WOLSELEY INDUSTRIAL GROUP
See FRISCHKORN INC

D-U-N-S 14-823-7217 IMP/EXP
WOLSELEY INVESTMENTS INC
WOLSELEY FINANCE
(Suby of WOLSELEY LIMITED)
1904 Ligonier St, Latrobe, PA 15650-3129
Tel (757) 874-7795 Founded/Ownrshp 1982
Sales 3.6MMM^E EMP 32,986
Accts Pricewaterhousecoopers Llp
SIC 5074 5085 5075 5064 5211 5031 Plumbing & hydronic heating supplies; Plumbing & heating valves; Valves & fittings; Industrial tools; Air conditioning & ventilation equipment & supplies; Electrical appliances, major; Lumber & other building materials; Building materials, interior; Building materials, exterior; Lumber: rough, dressed & finished
Pr: Charles A Banks
*VP: Stewart P Mitchell
VP: Steve Petock
Snr Mgr: Kevin Trezise

D-U-N-S 78-738-3819
WOLSELEY REAL ESTATE INC
(Suby of WOLSELEY FINANCE) ★
618 Bland Blvd, Newport News, VA 23602-4310
Tel (757) 874-7795 Founded/Ownrshp 1992
Sales 44.1MM^E EMP 5,014^E
SIC 6531 Real estate leasing & rentals
Pr: David Dibben
DP Exec: Harry Bird
Dir IT: Stephanie Welsh
Natl Sales: John Cassidy
Sales Asso: Robert Mueller

WOLTER GROUP
See WISCONSIN LIFT TRUCK CORP

WOLTERS KLUWER CORP LEGAL SVCS
See CT CORP SYSTEM

D-U-N-S 92-682-8989
WOLTERS KLUWER FINANCIAL SERVICES INC
(Suby of CCH INC) ★
100 S 5th St Ste 700, Minneapolis, MN 55402-1219
Tel (612) 656-7700 Founded/Ownrshp 1999
Sales 304.1MM^E EMP 1,060
SIC 7371 Computer software development
CEO: Richard Flynn
Ch Bd: Patrick Hartford
*CFO: Paul Kuhn
Ex VP: Mark Coronna
*Ex VP: Ken Newton
VP: Greg Alves
VP: George Dessing
VP: Ed Dirocco
VP: Jeff Drais
VP: Dale Dyer
VP: Lisa Fraga
VP: Wayne Miller
VP: Jim Otte
VP: Richard Reeves
VP: Carol Weber
Exec: Timothy R Burniston

D-U-N-S 05-497-0496 IMP
WOLTERS KLUWER HEALTH INC
LIPPINCOTT WILLIAMS & WILKIN
(Suby of WOLTERS KLUWER UNITED STATES INC) ★
2001 Market St Lbby 1, Philadelphia, PA 19103-7048
Tel (215) 521-8300 Founded/Ownrshp 1990
Sales 168.4MM^E EMP 564
SIC 2721 2731 2741 7372 8748 Trade journals: publishing only, not printed on site; Books: publishing only; Miscellaneous publishing; Prepackaged software; Business consulting
CEO: Diana L Nole
*Pr: Robert Becker
CFO: John Pins
Treas: C Lenz
*Sec: Bruce C Lenz
VP: Andra Degutis
VP: Michelle Nedham
*VP: Richard J Parker
VP: Carole Pippin
VP: Julie Stegman
Exec: Karen Lee
Assoc Dir: Julie Oliveras

D-U-N-S 10-113-0540 IMP/EXP
WOLTERS KLUWER UNITED STATES INC
(Suby of WOLTERS KLUWER INTERNATIONAL HOLDING B.V.)
2700 Lake Cook Rd, Riverwoods, IL 60015-3867
Tel (847) 580-5000 Founded/Ownrshp 1990
Sales 3.7MMM^E EMP 7,061
SIC 2731 2721 2741 2759 Books: publishing only; Trade journals: publishing only, not printed on site; Directories: publishing & printing; Commercial printing
Pr: Deidra D Gold
Pr: Steven Hardy
Pr: Brian Kiernan
*Pr: Nancy McKinstry
Pr: Rick Skipton
CEO: Richard Flynn
*CFO: Norm Plaistowe
Bd of Dir: Louise Karam
Bd of Dir: Miriam Youel
Chf Mktg O: Mary A Loustaunau
Ex VP: Scott Gruchot
VP: Dale C Gordon
VP: Michael Radigan
Dir Soc: Tina Frye
Dir Bus: Charles Ross
Comm Man: Albertine Schor

D-U-N-S 78-810-2759 IMP
■ **WOLVERINE ADVANCED MATERIALS LLC**
(Suby of ITT LLC) ★
5850 Mercury Dr Ste 250, Dearborn, MI 48126-2980
Tel (313) 749-6100 Founded/Ownrshp 2015
Sales 189.1MM^E EMP 450
SIC 3559 3694 Automotive related machinery; Automotive electrical equipment
CEO: Grant Beard
*CFO: Michael Beyer
Ex VP: George Caplea
VP: Joseph Conroy
VP: Ronda Coogan
VP: Dana Stonerook
Opers Supe: Christopher Robinson
VP Sls: Eric Denys
Mktg Mgr: Katie Carlson

D-U-N-S 36-151-5679 IMP/EXP
WOLVERINE BRASS INC
WB
(Suby of PROFESSIONAL PLUMBING GROUP INC) ★
2951 E Highway 501, Conway, SC 29526-9515
Tel (843) 347-3121 Founded/Ownrshp 2013
Sales 99.0MM^E EMP 200
SIC 5074 3432 3431 Plumbing fittings & supplies; Plumbing fixture fittings & trim; Metal sanitary ware
CEO: Lloyd W Coppedge
*CFO: Steve David
*VP: Robert J Muser
Rgnl Mgr: Russ Crawford
DP Exec: Bonnie Hardee
*VP Mfg: Philip J Bauer
VP Sls: Russell Dueger
Sls Mgr: Jan Crawford

D-U-N-S 00-289-8088
WOLVERINE BUILDING GROUP INC (MI)
4045 Barden St Se, Grand Rapids, MI 49512-5447
Tel (616) 281-6236 Founded/Ownrshp 1958, 1999
Sales 135.5MM EMP 100
Accts Beene Garter Llp Grand Rapids
SIC 1541 1542 Industrial buildings & warehouses; Commercial & office building, new construction; Institutional building construction
Pr: Michael G Kelly
*Treas: Timothy Gabrielse
Treas: Gerald Houseman
VP: Max Coon
VP: Kurtis Parks
Genl Mgr: Mike Houseman
Sfty Dirs: Theodore Bergin
Sfty Dirs: Pat Livingston
Sls&Mrk Ex: Brandon Hartel
Mktg Mgr: Danielle Millisor
Snr PM: Marc Alexa

WOLVERINE EXECUTION SERVICES
See WOLVERINE TRADING LLC

D-U-N-S 00-536-9343 IMP/EXP
WOLVERINE PACKING CO (MI)
2535 Rivard St, Detroit, MI 48207-2621
Tel (313) 259-7500 Founded/Ownrshp 1934, 1979
Sales 266.8MM^E EMP 275
SIC 5147 2011 5142 Meats, fresh; Veal from meat slaughtered on site; Lamb products from lamb slaughtered on site; Meat, frozen: packaged; Poultry, frozen: packaged
Pr: A James Bonahoom
*VP: Roger P Bonahoom
VP: Roger Bonahoom
Exec: Tom Vogel
Off Mgr: Briyan Bartes
Prd Mgr: Ben Raptoulis
Sls Dir: Rob Thomas
Manager: Pete Curry
Snr Mgr: Aaron Robinson

D-U-N-S 07-670-1465
WOLVERINE PIPE LINE CO
8075 Creekside Dr Ste 210, Portage, MI 49024-6303
Tel (269) 323-2491 Founded/Ownrshp 1952
Sales 95.3MM EMP 75
Accts Bdo Usa Llp Kalamazoo Michig
SIC 4613 Refined petroleum pipelines
Pr: W Allen Sawyer Jr
*VP: John Gurrola

D-U-N-S 00-879-0974
WOLVERINE POWER SUPPLY COOPERATIVE INC (MI)
10125 W Watergate Rd, Cadillac, MI 49601-8458
Tel (231) 775-5700 Founded/Ownrshp 1948, 2006
Sales 376.4MM EMP 110
Accts Plante & Moran Pllc Chicago
SIC 4911 Generation, electric power; Transmission, electric power;
Pr: Eric Baker
*Ch Bd: Dale Farrier
*CFO: Janet Kass
*Treas: Jerry Akers
Ofcr: Michelle Clements
VP: Craig Borr
VP: Dan Dacoeur
Comm Dir: Nancy Tanner
Tech Mgr: Don Heffelfinger
Sfty Dirs: Bruce Welliver
Secur Mgr: Matt Monroe

D-U-N-S 02-518-8132
WOLVERINE TRADING LLC (IL)
WOLVERINE EXECUTION SERVICES
175 W Jackson Blvd # 200, Chicago, IL 60604-3034
Tel (312) 884-4000 Founded/Ownrshp 1994, 2003
Sales 128.0MM^E EMP 300^E
SIC 6211 Security brokers & dealers; Investment firm, general brokerage; Mortgages, buying & selling
Mng Pt: Rob Bellick
Mng Pt: Steven Lund
CFO: Judy Kula
Ofcr: Megan Flaherty
Mng Dir: James Michuda
Mng Dir: Joseph Sacchetti
CIO: Jim Michuda
CTO: Joan Stanek
Dir IT: Steven Finkelshteyn
Dir IT: Rich Holm
Software D: Kasia Dunajewski

D-U-N-S 60-236-2303 EXP
WOLVERINE TUBE INC
2100 Market St Ne, Decatur, AL 35601-2626
Tel (256) 353-1310 Founded/Ownrshp 2013
Sales 298.0MM^E EMP 1,368
SIC 3351 Tubing, copper & copper alloy; Bars & bar shapes, copper & copper alloy
Pr: Harold M Karp
COO: David A Owen
Genl Couns: Jennifer Brinkley

D-U-N-S 00-601-5069 IMP/EXP
▲ **WOLVERINE WORLD WIDE INC**
9341 Courtland Dr Ne, Rockford, MI 49351-0001
Tel (616) 866-5500 Founded/Ownrshp 1883
Sales 2.6MMM EMP 6,550
Tkr Sym WWW Exch NYS
SIC 3143 3149 3144 3111 Men's footwear, except athletic; Athletic shoes, except rubber or plastic; Women's footwear, except athletic; Leather tanning & finishing
Ch Bd: Blake W Krueger
Pr: Ted S Gedra
Pr: Michael Jeppesen
Pr: Mike Jeppesen
Pr: Gillian Meek
Pr: Richard J Woodworth
Pr: James D Zwiers
CFO: Michael D Stornant
Sr VP: Melissa A Howell
VP: Kevin Barker
VP: Brendan M Gibbons
VP: Melissa Howell
VP: Suzanne L Johnson
VP: Deirdre McDonnell
VP: Scott Thomas
VP: Gary Wallen
Exec: Anne Sheffer
Creative D: Marc Loverin
Board of Directors: Michael A Volkema, Jeffrey M Boromisa, Gina R Boswell, Roxane Divol, William K Gerber, Joseph R Gromek, David T Kollat, Brenda J Lauderback, Nicholas T Long, Timothy J O'donovan

D-U-N-S 83-216-2031
WOMACK ELECTRIC & SUPPLY CO INC
GRAVES SUPPLY
518 Newton St, Danville, VA 24541-1428
Tel (434) 793-5134 Founded/Ownrshp 1995
Sales 88.0MM^E EMP 120
SIC 5063 Electrical apparatus & equipment
Pr: Burke Herring
*CFO: Aljon Hancock
*VP: David Womack
*VP: Ray Womack
Genl Mgr: Todd Woodlief
Sales Asso: Eric Payne

D-U-N-S 07-147-4712
WOMANS CHRISTIAN ASSOCIATION OF JAMESTOWN NY
W C A HOSPITAL
(Suby of W C A HOSPITAL) ★
207 Foote Ave, Jamestown, NY 14701-7077
Tel (716) 487-0141 Founded/Ownrshp 1885
Sales 105.5MM EMP 1,345
SIC 8062 8063 8093 8069 General medical & surgical hospitals; Psychiatric hospitals; Specialty outpatient clinics; Specialty hospitals, except psychiatric
Pr: Betsy Wright
CIO: Keith Robison
Sfty Mgr: John Carlson
Doctor: Roberta Gebhard

D-U-N-S 01-040-1966
WOMANS HOSPITAL FOUNDATION INC (LA)
100 Womans Way, Baton Rouge, LA 70817-5100
Tel (225) 927-1300 Founded/Ownrshp 1957
Sales 217.1MM EMP 1,850
SIC 8062 General medical & surgical hospitals
CEO: Teri G Fontenot
V Ch: Dory Binder
V Ch: Laron Nphillips
COO: Marsha Shirey
*CFO: Greg Smith
*Chf Mktg O: Frank Breaux MD
VP: Nancy Crawford
Exec: Robert Earhart
Dir Rx: Peggy Dean
Nurse Mgr: Amye S Reeves
Dir IT: Jason Welch

WOMAN'S HOSPITAL OF TEXAS
See CHCA WOMANS HOSPITAL LP

D-U-N-S 06-030-5166
WOMBLE CARLYLE SANDRIDGE & RICE LLP
1 W 4th St, Winston Salem, NC 27101-3818
Tel (336) 721-3600 Founded/Ownrshp 1876
Sales 197.8MM^E EMP 1,205
SIC 8111

D-U-N-S 05-933-9945
WOMBLE CO INC
12821 Industrial Rd, Houston, TX 77015-6802
Tel (713) 636-8700 Founded/Ownrshp 1977
Sales 197.9MM^E EMP 480
SIC 3479 Painting, coating & hot dipping
Pr: Alice F Womble
Exec: Susan Womble
Genl Mgr: Larry McKinney
Dir IT: Brian Brewer
Dir IT: Chris Heitman
IT Man: Lori Dougan
IT Man: Chris Heitmann
Netwrk Eng: Chris Fontenot
Plnt Mgr: Agustin Ordonez

D-U-N-S 06-985-1913 IMP
WOMEN & INFANTS HOSPITAL OF RHODE ISLAND
101 Dudley St, Providence, RI 02905-2499
Tel (401) 274-1100 Founded/Ownrshp 1987
Sales 428.0MM EMP 2,800

SIC 8062 General medical & surgical hospitals
CEO: Dennis D Keefe
Ex VP: Mark Marcantano
**Ex VP:* Patricia R Recupero
Dir Case M: Rosemary Lasazia
Pathlgst: Rochelle Simon
Surgeon: Michael Weaver
Obsttrcn: Cronin Beth
Obsttrcn: Anne Murray
Obsttrcn: Pablo Rodriguez
Obsttrcn: Reza Shah-Hosseini
Obsttrcn: Vivian Sung

WOMENS AUX OF LK FOREST HOSP
See NORTHWESTERN LAKE FOREST HOSPITAL

WOMENS CENTER
See HUTZEL HOSPITAL

WOMEN'S DISTRIBUTION SERVICES
See WDS INC

WOMEN'S HOSPITAL, THE
See DEACONESS WOMENS HOSPITAL OF SOUTHERN INDIANA LLC

D-U-N-S 79-053-6705
WOMENS HOSPITAL
100 Womans Way, Baton Rouge, LA 70817-5100
Tel (225) 927-1300 *Founded/Ownrshp* 2007
Sales 287.9MM *EMP* 6^E
SIC 8069 Specialty hospitals, except psychiatric
CEO: Teri Fontenot
Dir Rx: Peggy Dean
Sls&Mrk Ex: Kris Muller
Pr Mgr: Jodi Conachen

WOMENS WEAR DAILY
See FAIRCHILD PUBLICATIONS INC

D-U-N-S 60-127-6959 IMP/EXP
WONDERFUL CITRUS PACKING LLC
PARAMOUNT CITRUS PACKING CO
(*Suby of* TELEFLORA) ★
1901 S Lexington St, Delano, CA 93215-9207
Tel (661) 720-2400 *Founded/Ownrshp* 1986
Sales 181.8MM^E *EMP* 600
SIC 0723 0174 2033 Fruit (fresh) packing services; Orange grove; Lemon grove; Fruit juices: fresh

D-U-N-S 05-009-9043 IMP/EXP
WONDERFUL CO LLC
TELEFLORA
11444 W Olympic Blvd # 210, Los Angeles, CA 90064-1559
Tel (310) 966-5700 *Founded/Ownrshp* 2010
Sales 1.7MMM^E *EMP* 1,882
SIC 0723 2084

D-U-N-S 18-177-3268 IMP
WONDERFUL ORCHARDS LLC
PARAMOUNT FARMING
6801 E Lerdo Hwy, Shafter, CA 93263-9610
Tel (661) 399-4456 *Founded/Ownrshp* 1998
Sales 144.6MM^E *EMP* 400
SIC 0173 0179 Almond grove; Olive grove
Ex VP: William D Phillimore
Off Mgr: Elaine Tensley

D-U-N-S 10-696-1345 IMP/EXP
WONDERFUL PISTACHIOS & ALMONDS LLC
PARAMOUNT FARMS
(*Suby of* TELEFLORA) ★
11444 W Olympic Blvd, Los Angeles, CA 90064-1549
Tel (310) 966-4650 *Founded/Ownrshp* 1989
Sales 424.2MM^E *EMP* 1,000
SIC 2068 Salted & roasted nuts & seeds
Pr: Stewart Resnick
Ex VP: Bill Phillimore
Sr VP: Craig B Cooper
VP: Rick Burnes
VP: Curtis Hudson
VP: Mark Masten
Admn Mgr: Sandy Dergazarian
Genl Mgr: Dave Blanchat
QA Dir: Michael Edgeworth
QA Dir: Brenda Leon
Software D: Jason Hester

D-U-N-S 79-452-9651 IMP
WONDERTREATS INC
2200 Lapham Dr, Modesto, CA 95354-3911
Tel (209) 521-8881 *Founded/Ownrshp* 1992
Sales 150.9MM^E *EMP* 315
SIC 5199 5947 Gift baskets; Gift baskets
CEO: Jocelyn Yu Hall
**Pr:* Greg Hall
Sales Exec: Steve Klapak
Sls Mgr: Don Greenland

D-U-N-S 60-303-0958
WONDERWARE CORP
(*Suby of* SCHNEIDER ELECTRIC SOFTWARE LLC) ★
26561 Rancho Pkwy S, Lake Forest, CA 92630-8301
Tel (949) 727-3200 *Founded/Ownrshp* 2014
Sales 132.7MM^E *EMP* 430
SIC 5045 Computer software
VP: Rick Bullotta
COO: Johan Victor
**Sr VP:* Brian Dibenedetto
**Sr VP:* Karen Hamilton
**Sr VP:* Peter Kent
**Sr VP:* Dave Pickett
VP: Silji Abraham
VP: Rick Crider
VP: Alastair Fraser
VP: Stephen Halsey
VP: Norm Thorlakson
Exec: Sue Howard
Exec: Paula Larson
Exec: Ronnie Meredith

WONKA BAMBOOZLE
See NESTLE USA INC

D-U-N-S 08-488-5425 IMP
WOOD CO
WOOD DINING SERVICES
(*Suby of* SODEXO INC) ★
6081 Hamilton Blvd, Allentown, PA 18106-9767
Tel (610) 366-5204 *Founded/Ownrshp* 2006
Sales 249.4MM^E *EMP* 14,000
SIC 5812 Contract food services
Pr: Michel Landel
**Ch Bd:* Robert C Wood
**Treas:* Kevin Nolan
VP: Alison R Lazerwitz

D-U-N-S 07-757-5421
WOOD COUNTY HOSPITAL ASSOC
WCH
960 W Wooster St, Bowling Green, OH 43402-2644
Tel (419) 354-8900 *Founded/Ownrshp* 1951
Sales 109.8MM *EMP* 548
Accts Blue & Co Llc Columbus Oh
SIC 8062 General medical & surgical hospitals
Pr: Stanley Korducki
Chf OB: Gregory Johnson
Chf Rad: Charles Genson
Chf Rad: David Szczesniak
VP: John EBY
Chf Nrs Of: Sandy Beidelschies
Ex Dir: Janette Gee
Off Mgr: Karen Bodeman
Off Mgr: Helen Smarage
Nurse Mgr: David Caprara
CIO: Joanne White

D-U-N-S 02-026-7449
WOOD COUNTY OHIO
1 Court House Sq, Bowling Green, OH 43402-2427
Tel (419) 354-9100 *Founded/Ownrshp* 1820
Sales NA *EMP* 1,250
Accts Dave Yost Columbis Ohio
SIC 9111 County supervisors' & executives' offices
Pr: James F Carter
**Treas:* Jill Engle
**VP:* Doris I Herringshaw

D-U-N-S 07-979-9684
WOOD COUNTY SCHOOLS
1210 13th St, Parkersburg, WV 26101-4144
Tel (304) 420-9663 *Founded/Ownrshp* 1933
Sales 15.0MM^E *EMP* 3,200
SIC 8211 Public elementary & secondary schools
Dir Sec: Donald Brown
Teacher Pr: Sean Francisco
HC Dir: Julie Bertram

WOOD DINING SERVICES
See WOOD CO

D-U-N-S 11-840-2069 IMP/EXP
WOOD GROUP MANAGEMENT SERVICES INC
(*Suby of* JOHN WOOD GROUP P.L.C.)
17325 Park Row, Houston, TX 77084-4932
Tel (281) 828-3500 *Founded/Ownrshp* 1990
Sales 1.9MMM^E *EMP* 6,000
SIC 1389 Oil consultants
Pr: Alan Semple
**CEO:* Allister G Langlands
CFO: Alan G Semple
VP: Bryan Hartman
Genl Mgr: William Stevenson
Info Man: Sheila Crowson
VP Opers: Brandon Stephens
Plnt Mgr: Neil Frey

D-U-N-S 18-273-0937
WOOD GROUP MUSTANG INC
(*Suby of* JOHN WOOD GROUP P.L.C.)
17325 Park Row, Houston, TX 77084-4932
Tel (832) 809-8000 *Founded/Ownrshp* 1987
Sales 1.5MMM^E *EMP* 8,015
SIC 8711 8742 7389 1389 Consulting engineer; Construction project management consultant; Purchasing service; Construction, repair & dismantling services
Prin: Steve R Kowls
COO: Gordon Sterling
CFO: Felix W Covington
CFO: Margaret Laarat
CFO: Meg Lassarat
Ofcr: Yvonne Williams
Ex VP: Gary Baughman
VP: Scott Baker
VP: Terry Boss
VP: John W Dalton
VP: King Fisher
VP: David McMurray

D-U-N-S 07-877-6352
WOOD GROUP PSN INC
PROSAFE
(*Suby of* WOOD GROUP PSN LIMITED)
17325 Park Row, Houston, TX 77084-4932
Tel (281) 647-1041 *Founded/Ownrshp* 2003
Sales 476.7MM^E *EMP* 1,530
SIC 1629 1542 8711 Chemical plant & refinery construction; Institutional building construction; Structural engineering
CEO: Derek S Blackwood
Pr: Mitch Fralick
**Pr:* Graham Levett-Prinsep
**Treas:* Darlene Cameron
**Treas:* Millard D Temple
VP: Ken Anthony
**VP:* John Glithero
Snr PM: Amy Wong

D-U-N-S 09-048-3681
WOOD HOLE OCEANAL GRAPHICS INSTITUTION INC
38 Water St, Woods Hole, MA 02543-1026
Tel (508) 457-2620 *Founded/Ownrshp* 1930
Sales 33.6MM^E *EMP* 1,000
SIC 8731 8733 8221 Environmental research; Noncommercial research organizations; Colleges universities & professional schools

D-U-N-S 85-856-9627
WOOD RANCH BARBECUE AND GRILL INC
WOOD RANCH USA
2835 Townsgate Rd Ste 200, Westlake Village, CA 91361-3079
Tel (805) 719-9000 *Founded/Ownrshp* 1992
Sales 39.0MM^E *EMP* 1,000
SIC 5812 Steak & barbecue restaurants
Owner: Eric Anders
**VP:* Ofer Shemtov
Genl Mgr: Laurel Beattie
Genl Mgr: Elin Fjeldsted
Genl Mgr: Ken Lehman
Genl Mgr: Harry Nguyen
Genl Mgr: Grant Salisbury
Genl Mgr: Brandy Vanderbeck
Genl Mgr: Gary Williams

WOOD RANCH USA
See WOOD RANCH BARBECUE AND GRILL INC

D-U-N-S 00-796-0529 IMP
WOOD-FRUITTICHER GROCERY CO INC (AL)
2900 Alton Rd, Irondale, AL 35210-4393
Tel (205) 836-9663 *Founded/Ownrshp* 1913
Sales 221.8MM^E *EMP* 250
SIC 5142 5141 5147 5087 5046 Packaged frozen goods; Groceries, general line; Meats, fresh; Janitors' supplies; Restaurant equipment & supplies
Ch: David W Wood II
**Pr:* John H Wood
DP Exec: Ronny Huguley
DP Exec: Joe Morris
Sls Mgr: Gregg Champion
Sls Mgr: Tony Cruse
Sls Mgr: Reid Frazier
Sls Mgr: Ronnie Jeffcoat
Sls Mgr: Aimee Price

D-U-N-S 08-703-8451 IMP/EXP
WOOD-MIZER HOLDINGS INC
LASTEC
8180 W 10th St, Indianapolis, IN 46214-2430
Tel (317) 271-1542 *Founded/Ownrshp* 1972
Sales 112.0MM^E *EMP* 370
SIC 3553 3524 3425 2431 Sawmill machines; Lawn & garden mowers & accessories; Saw blades & handsaws; Doors & door parts & trim, wood
COO: Richard Vivers
Ex VP: Scott Laskowski
Dir IT: Stacy Wigginton
QC Dir: Roger Rew
Sls&Mrk Ex: Paul Houghland
Sls Dir: David Mann
Snr Mgr: Lyn Bradbury

D-U-N-S 00-301-9114 IMP
WOOD-MODE INC
1 Second St, Kreamer, PA 17833-5000
Tel (570) 374-2711 *Founded/Ownrshp* 1998
Sales 1.1MMM^E *EMP* 11,000
SIC 2434 Wood kitchen cabinets; Vanities, bathroom: wood
CEO: Robert L Gronlund
**Pr:* R Brooks Gronlund
**Pr:* Fred Richetta
CFO: John K Fairis
CFO: Jeffrey W Jones
VP: Larry Arbogast
**VP:* Theodore B Gronlund
Exec: Brooks Gronlund
Genl Mgr: Robert Gessner
IT Man: Michael Moyer
Sfty Dirs: Butch Hackenberg

D-U-N-S 03-770-8708
WOODARD & CURRAN INC
41 Hutchins Dr, Portland, ME 04102-1973
Tel (800) 426-4262 *Founded/Ownrshp* 1979
Sales 147.0MM *EMP* 821
SIC 8711 8748 Consulting engineer; Business consulting
Ch Bd: Douglas McKeown
**Pr:* Guy Wm Vaillancourt
COO: Mary Michaud
**CFO:* David Remick
Sr VP: Joseph Barbagallo
Sr VP: Michael J Curato
Sr VP: Thomas Francoeur
Sr VP: William Luksha
VP: Dedian David
VP: Seth Garrison
**VP:* James Gorman
VP: Rowina Holden
VP: Tina Hunt
VP: Dan Kelley
VP: Robert Kunze
VP: Kelly Oday
VP: Anne Proctor
VP: Janet Robinson
VP: Michele Shepard
VP: Eric Teittinen
VP: Matt Valentine

D-U-N-S 00-538-7241
WOODARD TECHNOLOGY & INVESTMENTS LLC (OK)
SAGENET
10205 E 61st St Ste D, Tulsa, OK 74133-1513
Tel (918) 270-7000 *Founded/Ownrshp* 1997
Sales 137.9MM *EMP* 263
SIC 5045 Computer peripheral equipment; Computer software
Pr: Daryl Woodard
**CFO:* Rodney Kramer
Chf Mktg O: Rosemary Blum
VP: Donna Helderman
VP: Mark Hogan
Exec: Denyse Pluchel
Genl Mgr: Ronny Hull
**CIO:* Bd Thrower
Sls Dir: Donna Heldermon

D-U-N-S 13-205-2320 IMP/EXP
WOODBOLT DISTRIBUTION LLC
NUTRABOLT
3891 S Traditions Dr, Bryan, TX 77807-7595
Tel (800) 870-2070 *Founded/Ownrshp* 2001
Sales 250.0MM *EMP* 161^E
SIC 5122 Vitamins & minerals
CEO: Doss Cunningham
Dir Bus: Norman Taliaferro
Mktg Dir: Adam Kossoff
Board of Directors: Mike Dimaggio, Andrew Weaver

D-U-N-S 11-411-5942
WOODBRIDGE CORP
LIFETIME COMPOSITES
(*Suby of* WOODBRIDGE HOLDINGS INC) ★
11 Cermak Blvd, Saint Peters, MO 63376-1019
Tel (636) 970-1002 *Founded/Ownrshp* 1984
Sales 303.7MM^E *EMP* 3,000
SIC 2439 Structural wood members
Pr: Robert Magee
**Treas:* Richard Jocsak

D-U-N-S 04-601-4882 IMP
WOODBRIDGE GLASS INC
14321 Myford Rd, Tustin, CA 92780-7022
Tel (714) 838-4444 *Founded/Ownrshp* 1981
Sales 84.6MM^E *EMP* 205
SIC 1793 5231 Glass & glazing work; Glass, leaded or stained
Pr: Virginia Siciliani
**Sec:* Jim Siciliani
**VP:* John Siciliani

D-U-N-S 16-165-9883 IMP
WOODBRIDGE HOLDINGS INC
(*Suby of* WOODBRIDGE FOAM CORPORATION)
1515 Equity Dr, Troy, MI 48084-7129
Tel (248) 288-0100 *Founded/Ownrshp* 1984
Sales 470.4MM^E *EMP* 3,010
SIC 2531 3086 Seats, automobile; Plastics foam products
Pr: Hugh W Sloan Jr
Treas: Richard Jocsak
Ex VP: Robert Magee
VP: Carol Dickson

D-U-N-S 10-796-5134
■ **WOODBRIDGE HOLDINGS LLC**
(*Suby of* HOFFMANS CHOCOLATES) ★
2100 W Cypress Creek Rd, Fort Lauderdale, FL 33309-1823
Tel (954) 950-4950 *Founded/Ownrshp* 2009
Sales 332.9MM^E *EMP* 4,123^E
SIC 1522 Apartment building construction
Pr: Seth M Wise
**V Ch:* John E Abdo
**CFO:* John K Grelle

D-U-N-S 06-786-3548
WOODBRIDGE TOWNSHIP BOARD OF EDUCATION (INC)
WOODBRIDGE TOWNSHIP SCHOOL DIS
428 School St, Woodbridge, NJ 07095-2935
Tel (732) 750-3200 *Founded/Ownrshp* 1876
Sales 233.7MM *EMP* 2,000
Accts Mcenerney Brady & Company Ll
SIC 8211 Public elementary & secondary schools
Pr: Ezio Tamburello
**VP:* Daniel Harris
Cmptr Lab: Delores Guth

WOODBRIDGE TOWNSHIP SCHOOL DIS
See WOODBRIDGE TOWNSHIP BOARD OF EDUCATION (INC)

D-U-N-S 07-979-9796
WOODBRIDGE TOWNSHIP SCHOOL DISTRICT
(*Suby of* WOODBRIDGE TOWNSHIP SCHOOL DIS) ★
428 School St, Woodbridge, NJ 07095-2935
Tel (732) 750-3200 *Founded/Ownrshp* 1875
Sales 57.4MM^E *EMP* 1,684^E
SIC 8211 Public elementary & secondary schools
Dir Sec: Bryan Small
MIS Dir: Robert Ragan
Pr Dir: Joseph Masperi
HC Dir: Kelly Aker

D-U-N-S 00-617-4338 IMP
■ **WOODCRAFT INDUSTRIES INC** (MN)
(*Suby of* WII HOLDING, INC.)
525 Lincoln Ave Se, Saint Cloud, MN 56304-1023
Tel (320) 656-2345 *Founded/Ownrshp* 1953
Sales 263.7MM^E *EMP* 1,500
SIC 2434 2431 2426 Wood kitchen cabinets; Millwork; Dimension, hardwood
Sfty Dirs: Julie Wittrock
Mtls Mgr: Brian Sahlstrom
Opers Mgr: Paul Becker
Plnt Mgr: Steve Lutgen
Art Dir: Teresa Martin

D-U-N-S 01-926-8200 IMP/EXP
WOODCRAFT SUPPLY LLC
1177 Rosemar Rd, Parkersburg, WV 26105-8272
Tel (304) 422-5412 *Founded/Ownrshp* 2006
Sales 228.1MM^E *EMP* 1,000
SIC 5961 5251 Mail order house; Tools, hand
**CFO:* Dawn Knost
VP: Liz Matheny
Store Mgr: Mike Okner
CTO: Jason Guthrie
Advt Mgr: Peter Parker
Sales Asso: Robert Duggins

D-U-N-S 83-171-8056 IMP/EXP
■ **WOODCRAFTERS HOME PRODUCTS HOLDING LLC**
(*Suby of* HOMECREST) ★
3700 Camino De Verdad Rd, Weslaco, TX 78596-7531
Tel (956) 647-8300 *Founded/Ownrshp* 2013
Sales 300.6MM^E *EMP* 1,850
SIC 2434 Vanities, bathroom: wood
CEO: Abraham Tanus
**Pr:* Rick Vazquez
**Ex VP:* Samuel Lugo

D-U-N-S 11-269-8592 IMP/EXP
■ **WOODCRAFTERS HOME PRODUCTS LLC**
(*Suby of* WOODCRAFTERS HOME PRODUCTS HOLDING LLC) ★
3700 Camino De Verdad Rd, Weslaco, TX 78596-7531
Tel (956) 565-6329 *Founded/Ownrshp* 1983

Sales 281.1MM[E] *EMP* 1,800[E]
SIC 2434 Vanities, bathroom: wood
Pr: Rick Vasquez
CFO: Enrique Reynoso
Ex VP: Samuel Lugo
Ex VP: Steve Strasevicz

D-U-N-S 06-323-1255
WOODEN HEART INC
64 Amanda Blvd, New Bloomfield, PA 17068-8026
Tel (717) 834-7144 *Founded/Ownrshp* 2013
Sales 92.0MM *EMP* 52
SIC 5047 Medical equipment & supplies
CEO: Jeffrey Kibe

D-U-N-S 08-629-9435
WOODFIN HEATING INC
WOODFIN OIL CO
1823 N Hamilton St, Richmond, VA 23230-4005
Tel (804) 730-4500 *Founded/Ownrshp* 1977
Sales 373.7MM[E] *EMP* 450
SIC 5172 5983 1711 7382 Fuel oil; Fuel oil dealers; Plumbing, heating, air-conditioning contractors; Security systems services
CEO: Jack Woodfin
**Pr:* Justin R Andress
**Pr:* John H Woodfin Jr
**CFO:* Kevin W Walsh
CFO: Kevin Waltz
**Treas:* David Kibiloski
**VP:* Reaves A Louthan
VP: Andy Sadler
Exec: Davis Farran
Opers Mgr: Steve Walsh
Sls Mgr: Travis Riddle

WOODFIN OIL CO
See WOODFIN HEATING INC

D-U-N-S 87-918-4919
WOODFOREST FINANCIAL GROUP INC
1330 Lake Robbins Dr # 150, The Woodlands, TX 77380-3266
Tel (832) 375-2000 *Founded/Ownrshp* 1985
Sales NA *EMP* 4,500[E]
Accts Grant Thornton Llp Dallas Tx
SIC 6021 National commercial banks
Ch Bd: Robert Marling Jr
**Pr:* Michael Richmond
**COO:* Ann Thomas
Ofcr: Jason Jones
VP: Charlie Adams
VP: Steve Andersen
Ex Dir: Kim Marling
Brnch Mgr: Brandan Baird
Brnch Mgr: Linda O'Dell
Brnch Mgr: Wesley Pack
Brnch Mgr: Vicki Southerland

D-U-N-S 03-883-7266
WOODFOREST NATIONAL BANK
(*Suby of* WOODFOREST FINANCIAL GROUP INC) ★
25231 Grogans Mill Rd # 175, The Woodlands, TX 77380-3103
Tel (713) 455-7000 *Founded/Ownrshp* 1985
Sales NA *EMP* 4,500
SIC 6021 National commercial banks
Pr: Cathleen Nash
**Ch Bd:* Gerald D Cobb
**Pr:* Daniel Hauser
**Pr:* Julie Mayrant
**Pr:* Raymond Sanders
**Pr:* George Sowers
**COO:* James Dreibelbis
**COO:* Andrew Paur
**CFO:* Kelly Holmes
**Ex VP:* Loretta Anderson
**Ex VP:* Lisa Cotton
**Ex VP:* Jim Duke
**Ex VP:* Richard Ferrara
**Ex VP:* Sherra Morris
**Ex VP:* Gayla Puryear
Sr VP: Steve Andersen
Sr VP: Julie Dargani
Sr VP: Lynn McKee
VP: Bruce Bernhoft
VP: Debbie Campbell
VP: Caroline Carithers
Board of Directors: Robert E Marling Jr, Kenneth Babcock, Thomas D McCarley, David L Bratton, James Morrell, E E Chance, Dr Robert H Peterson, Dr Gerald D Cobb, Michael H Richmond, Dr A Dearl Dotson, George V Sowers Jr, James D Dreibelbis, Debra F Sukin, Larry Eichenbaum, Dr B J Westbrook, Joseph V Gillen, Kimberly Marling

D-U-N-S 06-333-4122 IMP/EXP
WOODGRAIN MILLWORK INC (ID)
(*Suby of* PROCESADORA DE MADERAS LOS ANGELES S.A.)
300 Nw 16th St, Fruitland, ID 83619-2218
Tel (208) 452-3801 *Founded/Ownrshp* 1944
Sales 488.0MM *EMP* 2,278
SIC 2431

WOODHARBOR DOORS & CABINETRY
See WOODHARBOR MOLDING & MILLWORKS INC

D-U-N-S 80-812-7419
WOODHARBOR MOLDING & MILLWORKS INC
WOODHARBOR DOORS & CABINETRY
3277 9th St Sw, Mason City, IA 50401-7318
Tel (641) 423-0444 *Founded/Ownrshp* 1993
Sales 97.3MM[E] *EMP* 505
SIC 2431 2521 2517 2434 Doors & door parts & trim, wood; Moldings & baseboards, ornamental & trim; Wood office furniture; Wood television & radio cabinets; Wood kitchen cabinets
Pr: Curtis L Lewerke
**COO:* Jonathan Lewerke
**Treas:* Lisa Koenigs-Heimer
**VP:* Dennis Lewerke
Rgnl Mgr: John Lomacz
IT Man: Christian Schiff
Sftwr Eng: Marjean Gordon
Prd Mgr: Jeff Stokes
Sls Mgr: Rick Tarantowski

WOODHAVEN HEALTH SERVICES
See REMEDI SENIORCARE OF MARYLAND LLC

WOODHEAD INDUSTRIES, INC.
See WOODHEAD INDUSTRIES LLC

D-U-N-S 00-519-5433 IMP
WOODHEAD INDUSTRIES LLC
WOODHEAD INDUSTRIES, INC.
(*Suby of* MOLEX LLC) ★
333 Knightsbridge Pkwy # 200, Lincolnshire, IL 60069-3662
Tel (847) 353-2500 *Founded/Ownrshp* 2006
Sales 103.5MM[E] *EMP* 1,541
SIC 3678 3679 3643 3357 Electronic connectors; Electronic switches; Electronic circuits; Connectors & terminals for electrical devices; Communication wire; Fiber optic cable (insulated)
Ch Bd: Philippe Lemaitre
**CFO:* Robert H Fisher
**Treas:* Joseph P Nogal
VP: Gregory Baker
**VP:* Robert A Moulton
**VP:* Robert J Tortorello
VP: Duane E Wiedor

D-U-N-S 05-396-9361
WOODHULL MEDICAL & MENTAL HEALTH CENTER AUXILIARY INC
NORTH BROOKLYN HEALTH NETWORK
760 Broadway Rm 3cc27, Brooklyn, NY 11206-5317
Tel (718) 963-8467 *Founded/Ownrshp* 1992
Sales 748.7M *EMP* 3,500[E]
SIC 8062 General medical & surgical hospitals
Pr: Ramanathan Raju
**Pr:* Iris Fernandez
**Pr:* Violeta Rivera
COO: Peter Velez
CFO: Michael Anthony
CFO: K C Best
CFO: Milton Nunez
VP: Wesly Mathurin
Dir Lab: Barbara Crooks
Assoc Dir: Yehezkel Lilu
CTO: Jian Liu

WOODLAND CLINIC
See HOLY FAMILY MEMORIAL INC

D-U-N-S 80-354-3313 IMP
WOODLAND FOODS LTD
3751 Sunset Ave, Waukegan, IL 60087-3213
Tel (847) 625-8600 *Founded/Ownrshp* 1992
Sales 124.5MM[E] *EMP* 200[E]
SIC 5149 Groceries & related products; Dried or canned foods; Fruits, dried
Pr: David Moore
QA Dir: Debra Magoon
Ql Cn Mgr: Magdalena Slowinski
Mktg Mgr: Josh Yarnall
Manager: Bob Lapoint

D-U-N-S 01-097-5282
WOODLAND HEALTHCARE
(*Suby of* DIGNITY HEALTH) ★
1325 Cottonwood St, Woodland, CA 95695-5199
Tel (530) 662-3961 *Founded/Ownrshp* 1960
Sales 118.3MM *EMP* 1,000
SIC 8062

WOODLAND HEIGHTS MEDICAL CTR
See PINEY WOODS HEALTHCARE SYSTEM LP

D-U-N-S 04-048-3513
WOODLAND JOINT UNIFIED SCHOOL DISTRICT
435 6th St, Woodland, CA 95695-4109
Tel (530) 662-0201 *Founded/Ownrshp* 1965
Sales 79.7MM[E] *EMP* 1,200
SIC 8211 Public elementary & secondary schools
Pr: Julie Blacklock
**Pr:* Sam Blanco III
**Pr:* Elaine Lytle
Bd of Dir: Babara Mills

D-U-N-S 12-856-1235 IMP/EXP
WOODLAND PULP LLC
144 Main St, Baileyville, ME 04694-3529
Tel (207) 427-3311 *Founded/Ownrshp* 2001
Sales 131.9MM[E] *EMP* 300[E]
SIC 2611 Pulp mills
Sfty Mgr: Collin Beal
Sfty Mgr: Sarah Hood
Opers Mgr: Paul Jack
Opers Mgr: Kevin Merriman

D-U-N-S 96-370-6119
WOODLANDS COMMERCIAL BANK
10350 Park Meadows Dr, Lone Tree, CO 80124-6800
Tel (212) 257-4646 *Founded/Ownrshp* 2010
Sales NA *EMP* 7[E]
SIC 6021 National commercial banks
Prin: Kristen Fletcher

D-U-N-S 10-264-2212
■ WOODLANDS OPERATING CO L P
(*Suby of* HOWARD HUGHES CORP) ★
24 Waterway Ave Ste 1100, The Woodlands, TX 77380-3445
Tel (281) 719-6100 *Founded/Ownrshp* 1997
Sales 132.8MM[E] *EMP* 575[E]
SIC 6552 7997 7389 6513 6512 Subdividers & developers; Membership sports & recreation clubs; Convention & show services; Apartment building operators; Nonresidential building operators
Pr: Alexander Sutton
**Prin:* Timothy J Welbes
Board of Directors: Gary Krow, Allen Model, Steven Shepsman

D-U-N-S 02-327-6231 IMP
WOODMANS FOOD MARKET INC
2631 Liberty Ln, Janesville, WI 53545-0741
Tel (608) 754-8382 *Founded/Ownrshp* 1920
Sales 368.5MM[E] *EMP* 1,950
SIC 5411 Supermarkets, hypermarket; Supermarkets, chain
Pr: Phillip Woodman
Sec: Donna Rusch
VP: Clint Woodman

D-U-N-S 82-767-8710
WOODMEN INSURANCE AGENCY INC
WOODMEN WRLD LIFE INSRNC SOCTY
(*Suby of* WOODMEN OF WORLD LIFE INSURANCE SOCIETY AND/OR OMAHA WOODMEN LIFE INSURANCE SOCIETY) ★
1700 Farnam St Ste 840, Omaha, NE 68102-2025
Tel (402) 342-1890 *Founded/Ownrshp* 2003
Sales NA *EMP* 2,400
SIC 6311 Life insurance
Pr: William J Manifold Jr
Pr: James M Gleason
Sr Cor Off: Russell Lovett
Sr Cor Off: Steve Miller
Sr Cor Off: Cece Walton
Ex VP: James W Bridges
Ex VP: Pat Riedmann
Ex VP: Mark D Theisen
Sr VP: Desi P Doise
VP: James Day
VP: Timothy Fautter
VP: Joseph J Hromadka
VP: Larry Mahagan
VP: Robert T Maher
VP: Jerry Smolinski
Exec: Foust Billie
Exec: William Owen
Comm Man: Christine Hay

D-U-N-S 00-697-0677
WOODMEN OF WORLD LIFE INSURANCE SOCIETY AND/OR OMAHA WOODMEN LIFE INSURANCE SOCIETY
1700 Farnam St Ste 840, Omaha, NE 68102-2025
Tel (402) 342-1890 *Founded/Ownrshp* 1890
Sales NA *EMP* 2,400
SIC 6311 Fraternal life insurance organizations
Ch Bd: James Mounce
CFO: Mark Schreier
Ofcr: Matthew Wells
**Ex VP:* James Bridges
**Ex VP:* Danny E Cummins
Ex VP: Pamela Hernandez
Ex VP: Bridges James
VP: Patrick Dees
VP: Steven Jones
VP: Hromadka Joseph
Exec: Sara Livergood

WOODMEN WRLD LIFE INSRNC SOCTY
See WOODMEN INSURANCE AGENCY INC

WOODRIVER INDUSTRIES
See SEA GULL LIGHTING PRODUCTS LLC

D-U-N-S 08-014-0916
WOODRUFF-SAWYER & CO
50 California St Fl 12, San Francisco, CA 94111-4646
Tel (415) 391-2141 *Founded/Ownrshp* 1966
Sales NA *EMP* 275
SIC 6411 Insurance brokers
CEO: Charles Rosson
COO: Mary Sklarski
Sr VP: Anne Belinn
Sr VP: Megan Colwell
Sr VP: Kristine Furrer
Sr VP: Stephen Gaitley
Sr VP: Stephen Mork
Sr VP: Judy Roberts
Sr VP: Noelle Rodier
Sr VP: Charles Shoemaker
Sr VP: Melody Silberstein
VP: Jacob Decker
VP: Justine Ekstrom
VP: Gene Hacia
VP: Dan Hodges
VP: Linda M Hunter
VP: Candice Jones
VP: Michael Landucci
VP: Harry Rowell
Exec: Matt Gauen
Exec: David Harney
Board of Directors: Christopher Kakel

D-U-N-S 80-179-7374 IMP
WOODS EQUIPMENT CO
(*Suby of* BLOUNT INTERNATIONAL INC) ★
2606 S Il Route 2, Oregon, IL 61061-9685
Tel (815) 732-2141 *Founded/Ownrshp* 2011
Sales 84.4MM[E] *EMP* 540
SIC 3523 3524 3531

D-U-N-S 04-103-0552
WOODS HOLE MARTHAS VINEYARD AND NANTUCKET STEAMSHIP AUTHORITY
STEAMSHIP AUTHORITY, THE
1 Cowdry Rd, Woods Hole, MA 02543-1039
Tel (508) 548-5011 *Founded/Ownrshp* 1961
Sales 100.0MM *EMP* 750
Accts Rsm Us Llp Boston Massachuse
SIC 4482 Intraport transportation
Ch: Robert F Ranney
**Ch Bd:* Marc Hanover
V Ch: Robert Obrien
**Treas:* Robert Davis
Treas: Robert B Davis
**V Ch Bd:* Robert Marshall
**Prin:* Robert L O'Brien
Genl Mgr: Wayne C Lamson
Genl Mgr: Janet Pratt
IT Man: Courtney Oliveira
Genl Couns: Steven Sayers

D-U-N-S 00-176-6682 IMP/EXP
WOODS HOLE OCEANOGRAPHIC INSTITUTION
266 Woods Hole Rd, Woods Hole, MA 02543-1535
Tel (508) 457-2000 *Founded/Ownrshp* 1930
Sales 207.0MM *EMP* 1,000
SIC 8733

D-U-N-S 00-250-3910
WOODS SERVICES INC
40 Martin Gross Dr, Langhorne, PA 19047-1616
Tel (215) 750-4000 *Founded/Ownrshp* 1948
Sales 119.3MM *EMP* 2,300
Accts Grant Thornton Llp Philadelph
SIC 8322 8211 Family location service; Elementary & secondary schools
Pr: Robert G Griffith
**Pr:* Diana L Ramsay
**CFO:* Joseph Zakrzewski
**Ex VP:* Peter M Shubiak

D-U-N-S 02-428-8230
WOODSIDE GROUP INC
IVYWOOD INTERIORS
460 W 50 N Ste 200, Salt Lake City, UT 84101-1023
Tel (801) 299-6700 *Founded/Ownrshp* 2006
Sales 119.1MM[E] *EMP* 400
SIC 1531 Speculative builder, multi-family dwellings
Pr: Scott Nelson
**Treas:* Leonard K Arave
VP: Clay Packer

D-U-N-S 07-456-4295
WOODSTOCK COMMUNITY UNIT SCHOOL DISTRICT 200
227 W Judd St, Woodstock, IL 60098-3126
Tel (815) 338-8200 *Founded/Ownrshp* 1969
Sales 107.5MM *EMP* 900
Accts Evans Marshall & Pease Pc R
SIC 8211 Public elementary & secondary schools; School board
Dir IT: Jerry Swedberg
Pr Dir: Debra Walsdorf
Teacher Pr: Teresa Dailey
HC Dir: Lisa Tate

D-U-N-S 00-301-0006 IMP/EXP
WOODSTREAM CORP (PA)
(*Suby of* VESTAR CAPITAL PARTNERS INC) ★
69 N Locust St, Lititz, PA 17543-1714
Tel (717) 626-2125 *Founded/Ownrshp* 1902
Sales 155.4MM[E] *EMP* 49[E]
SIC 3496 Cages, wire; Traps, animal & fish
Pr: Miguel A Nistal
COO: Steve Lesher
**Treas:* Steven Burk
VP: Steve Polisoto
**VP:* Andrew B Woolworth
Mng Dir: Simon Ragdale
Prgrm Mgr: Tom Daly
Prgrm Mgr: Chad Mateer
Web Prj Mg: Tammy Bernarduci
Natl Sales: Michele White
S&M/VP: William Vaughn

WOODWARD BIZ MEDIA
See WOODWARD COMMUNICATIONS INC

D-U-N-S 00-514-5982 IMP
WOODWARD COMMUNICATIONS INC
WOODWARD BIZ MEDIA
801 Bluff St, Dubuque, IA 52001-4661
Tel (563) 588-5611 *Founded/Ownrshp* 1927
Sales 103.9MM[E] *EMP* 550
SIC 2711 2741 4832 2752 7311 Newspapers: publishing only, not printed on site; Miscellaneous publishing; Radio broadcasting stations; Commercial printing, lithographic; Advertising agencies
Pr: Thomas Woodward
V Ch: Joe Hanson
V Ch: Joe Henry
**CFO:* Steve Larson
CFO: Steven Larson
Dir Soc: Bill Sebastian
Ex Dir: Dan Conness
Genl Mgr: Bob Behrens
Genl Mgr: John Oconnor
Genl Mgr: Jason Sethre
CTO: Tom Marty

D-U-N-S 04-122-2423
WOODWARD DESIGN + BUILD LLC
WOODWARD DESIGN BUILD
1000 S Jffrson Dvis Pkwy, New Orleans, LA 70125-1219
Tel (504) 822-6443 *Founded/Ownrshp* 1949
Sales 137.5MM[E] *EMP* 220[E]
SIC 1541 1542

WOODWARD DESIGN BUILD
See WOODWARD DESIGN + BUILD LLC

D-U-N-S 08-139-8703
■ WOODWARD HEALTH SYSTEMS LLC
WOODWARD REGIONAL HOSPITAL
(*Suby of* COMMUNITY HEALTH SYSTEMS INC) ★
900 17th St, Woodward, OK 73801-2448
Tel (580) 256-2820 *Founded/Ownrshp* 1946, 2012
Sales 551.4MM[E] *EMP* 30,000
SIC 8062 General medical & surgical hospitals
CEO: Dave Wallace
CFO: Tom Earley
Dir OR: Joanna Elliott
QA Dir: Kim Arnold
Surgeon: Jamie Chambers

D-U-N-S 00-851-3152 IMP
■ WOODWARD HRT INC
(*Suby of* WOODWARD INC) ★
25200 Rye Canyon Rd, Santa Clarita, CA 91355-1204
Tel (661) 294-6000 *Founded/Ownrshp* 2009
Sales 203.9MM[E] *EMP* 900
SIC 3625 3492 Actuators, industrial; Electrohydraulic servo valves, metal
CEO: Thomas A Gendron
**Pr:* Martin V Glass
VP: Abdul Bigirumwami
VP: Lisa Tanner
Genl Mgr: Sonia Saldana
IT Man: Michelle Reyles
Sys Mgr: Aaron Quantz
Opers Mgr: Joe Mockenhaupt

D-U-N-S 00-506-9380
▲ WOODWARD INC
1081 Woodward Way, Fort Collins, CO 80524
Tel (970) 482-5811 *Founded/Ownrshp* 1870
Sales 2.0MMM *EMP* 6,900
Tkr Sym WWD *Exch* NGS

SIC 3625 3629 3492 3519 Industrial controls: push button, selector switches, pilot; Electric controls & control accessories, industrial; Industrial electrical relays & switches; Electronic generation equipment; Control valves, aircraft: hydraulic & pneumatic; Parts & accessories, internal combustion engines; Governors, diesel engine
Ch Bd: Thomas A Gendron
Pr: Martin V Glass
Pr: Sagar Patel
Pr: Chad R Preiss
Pr: James D Rudolph
CFO: Robert F Weber Jr
Chf Cred: A Christopher Fawzy
VP: Matt R Cook
VP: Mary F Cox
VP: Steven J Meyer
VP: Dale Sylvan
VP: Matthew F Taylor
VP: John Tysver
Board of Directors: John D Cohn, Paul Donovan, John A Halbrook, Mary L Petrovich, Larry E Rittenberg, James R Rulseh, Ronald M Sega, Gregg C Sengstack, Jonathan W Thayer

WOODWARD MPC, INC.
See MPC PRODUCTS CORP

WOODWARD REGIONAL HOSPITAL
See WOODWARD HEALTH SYSTEMS LLC

D-U-N-S 10-544-7879
WOODWINDS HEALTH CAMPUS
HEALTH EAST WOODWINDS
1925 Woodwinds Dr, Saint Paul, MN 55125-4445
Tel (651) 232-0100 *Founded/Ownrshp* 1998
Sales 150.9MM *EMP* 700
SIC 8069 Specialty hospitals, except psychiatric
Pr: Timothy Hanson
**CEO:* Tom Scmith
VP Opers: Leah Frantzen
Mktg Dir: Dina Fassino

D-U-N-S 00-892-9457
WOOLPERT INC
4454 Idea Center Blvd, Beavercreek, OH 45430-1500
Tel (937) 461-5660 *Founded/Ownrshp* 1935
Sales 99.0MM *EMP* 650
SIC 8711

D-U-N-S 04-389-0276
WOONSOCKET CITY SCHOOL DISTRICT
WOONSOCKET PUBLIC SCHOOLS
108 High St, Woonsocket, RI 02895-4333
Tel (401) 767-4600 *Founded/Ownrshp* 2010
Sales 27.1MM[E] *EMP* 1,056
SIC 8211 Public elementary & secondary schools
Pr: Miriam A Goodman
VP: Roxane Cary
Teacher Pr: James Wolfgang

WOONSOCKET PUBLIC SCHOOLS
See WOONSOCKET CITY SCHOOL DISTRICT

D-U-N-S 82-777-0173
■ WOOT INC
(*Suby of* AMAZON.COM INC) ★
4121 International Pkwy, Carrollton, TX 75007-1907
Tel (972) 417-3959 *Founded/Ownrshp* 2010
Sales 1.6MMM[E] *EMP* 33,720
SIC 7389 Advertising, promotional & trade show services
Pr: Darold Rydl
**CEO:* Matt Rutledge
**CFO:* Derek Chapin
**Treas:* Jim Motley
Sr VP: A Jim Wimpress
**VP:* Amber Beckman
**VP:* Kurt A Lamp
**VP:* Garth Mader
**VP:* Sean Patterson
MIS Dir: Jeff Creasey
Dir IT: Chris Klassen

D-U-N-S 96-736-5649
■ WOOT SERVICES LLC
(*Suby of* WOOT INC) ★
4121 Intl Pkwy Ste 900, Carrollton, TX 75007
Tel (972) 417-3959 *Founded/Ownrshp* 2008
Sales 772.5M[E] *EMP* 33,578[E]
SIC 7389 Advertising, promotional & trade show services
CEO: Matt Rutledge

D-U-N-S 01-553-9902
WORCESTER COUNTY PUBLIC SCHOOLS
6270 Worcester Hwy, Newark, MD 21841-2224
Tel (410) 632-5020 *Founded/Ownrshp* 1999
Sales 43.3M *EMP* 1,071[E]
SIC 8211 Public elementary & secondary schools
IT Man: Sandra Pacella
Pr Dir: Carey Stains
HC Dir: Louis Taylor

D-U-N-S 02-100-9857
WORCESTER EPISCOPAL HOUSING CO LIMITED PARTNERSHIP
CANTERBURY TOWERS
6 Wachusett St, Worcester, MA 01609-2670
Tel (508) 757-1133 *Founded/Ownrshp* 1976
Sales 34.9MM[E] *EMP* 3,900
SIC 6513 Apartment hotel operation
Prin: Maureen McKeown
Sr VP: Leeann Morein

WORCESTER MAGNET SCHOOL
See WORCESTER PUBLIC SCHOOLS

WORCESTER MEDICAL CENTER
See SAINT VINCENT HOSPITAL LLC

D-U-N-S 04-150-8581
WORCESTER POLYTECHNIC INSTITUTE
W P I
100 Institute Rd, Worcester, MA 01609-2280
Tel (508) 831-5000 *Founded/Ownrshp* 1865
Sales 312.0MM *EMP* 873[E]
Accts Pricewaterhousecoopers Llp Ha
SIC 8221 College, except junior
Pr: Dennis D Berkey
**CFO:* Jeffrey Soloman
Chf Mktg O: Amy M Morton
VP: John Miller
Assoc Dir: Connie Aramento
Assoc Dir: Maggie Becker
Assoc Dir: Connie Horwitz
Prgrm Mgr: Monika Maslen
CTO: Benjamin Kurtz
Info Man: Mike Malone
Netwrk Eng: Edward A Clancy

D-U-N-S 10-029-2796
WORCESTER PUBLIC SCHOOLS
WORCESTER MAGNET SCHOOL
20 Irving St, Worcester, MA 01609-2467
Tel (508) 799-3116 *Founded/Ownrshp* 1953
Sales 199.8MM[E] *EMP* 4,391
SIC 8211 Public elementary & secondary schools
Off Mgr: Donna Byrns
Psych: Michelle Cadavid

D-U-N-S 17-508-8657
WORD & BROWN INSURANCE ADMINISTRATORS INC
COBRAPRO
721 S Parker St Ste 300, Orange, CA 92868-4732
Tel (714) 835-5006 *Founded/Ownrshp* 1977
Sales NA *EMP* 800
SIC 6411

D-U-N-S 00-895-1923
WORD CONSTRUCTORS LLC (TX)
1245 River Rd, New Braunfels, TX 78130-4050
Tel (830) 625-2365 *Founded/Ownrshp* 1920
Sales 102.7MM[E] *EMP* 350
SIC 1622 1611 Bridge construction; Highway & street construction
Sr Pt: Timothy D Word

D-U-N-S 13-965-9395 IMP
WORD OF GOD FELLOWSHIP INC
DAYSTAR TELEVISION NETWORK
3901 Highway 121, Bedford, TX 76021-3009
Tel (817) 571-1229 *Founded/Ownrshp* 1995
Sales 125.9MM *EMP* 275[E]
SIC 4833 Television broadcasting stations
Pr: Rev Marcus Lamb
Sr VP: Mark Zinselmeier
**VP:* Joni Lamb
**Prin:* Arnold Torres
Trfc Mgr: Jerry Dorville
Board of Directors: V Pres David Edgar, Arnold Torres

WORK FIT
See HEALTHTRAX INC

D-U-N-S 17-939-8169
WORK RIGHT OCCUPATIONAL HEALTH
330 N Wabash Ave Ste 470, Marion, IN 46952-2685
Tel (765) 662-4198 *Founded/Ownrshp* 1997
Sales 162.5MM *EMP* 10
SIC 8011 Occupational & industrial specialist, physician/surgeon
Doctor: SM Blackmon
Doctor: WD Moore
Doctor: Ae Mueller
Doctor: St Swan

WORK SOURCE
See NEIGHBORHOOD CENTERS INC

D-U-N-S 60-700-9755
▲ WORKDAY INC
6230 Stoneridge Mall Rd, Pleasanton, CA 94588-3260
Tel (925) 951-9000 *Founded/Ownrshp* 2005
Sales 1.1MMM *EMP* 5,200[E]
Accts Ernst & Young Llp San Francis
Tkr Sym WDAY *Exch* NYS
SIC 7371 Custom computer programming services; Computer software development
CEO: Aneel Bhusri
**Ch Bd:* David A Duffield
Pr: Randy Hendricks
Pr: Mark S Peek
Pr: Philip Wilmington
**COO:* Michael A Stankey
CFO: Robynne Sisco
Bd of Dir: Sandra Bazarian
Ex VP: James J Bozzini
Ex VP: Petros Dermetzis
Ex VP: Michael L Frandsen
Sr VP: Jim Bozzini
Sr VP: Christine Cefalo
Sr VP: James P Shaughnessy
VP: Adeyemi Ajao
VP: Craig Butler
VP: Michael Haase
VP: Kendall Tieck
VP: Mike Wendell
Comm Man: Sonia Rose
Board of Directors: A George Battle, Christa Davies, Michael M McNamara, George J Still Jr, Jerry Yang

WORKERS COMPENSATION
See ALABAMA DEPARTMENT OF LABOR

D-U-N-S 62-068-5438
WORKERS COMPENSATION FUND
W C F
100 W Towne Ridge Pkwy, Sandy, UT 84070-5508
Tel (385) 351-8000 *Founded/Ownrshp* 1917
Sales NA *EMP* 320
Accts Ernst & Young Llp Salt Lake C
SIC 6331 Workers' compensation insurance
CEO: Ray D Pickup
Sr VP: Kris McFarland
**Sr VP:* Robert H Short
CIO: Debi Mofford
IT Man: Darren Ashworth
**Genl Couns:* Dennis Lloyd

D-U-N-S 80-274-9457
WORKERS SAFETY INSURANCE
WORKFORCE SAFETY & INSURANCE
(*Suby of* EXECUTIVE OFFICE OF STATE OF NORTH DAKOTA) ★
1600 E Century Ave Ste 1, Bismarck, ND 58503-0649
Tel (701) 328-3800 *Founded/Ownrshp* 1919
Sales NA *EMP* 8,726
SIC 9441 Workmen's compensation office, government;

D-U-N-S 82-808-7932
WORKERS TEMPORARY STAFFING INC
STAFFIRST
(*Suby of* WTS ACQUISITION CORP) ★
5050 W Lemon St Ste 200, Tampa, FL 33609-1104
Tel (813) 637-2220 *Founded/Ownrshp* 2007
Sales 58.2MM[E] *EMP* 15,000
SIC 7363 Temporary help service
Pr: Homas J Bean T
**VP:* Mel Lang

D-U-N-S 96-808-5832 IMP/EXP
WORKFLOWONE LLC
220 E Monument Ave, Dayton, OH 45402-1287
Tel (877) 735-4966 *Founded/Ownrshp* 2013
Sales NA *EMP* 2,000
SIC 2754 2791 4225 4731 2752 2759

D-U-N-S 01-559-4783
WORKFORCE BUSINESS SERVICES INC
1401 Manatee Ave W # 600, Bradenton, FL 34205-6770
Tel (941) 746-6567 *Founded/Ownrshp* 1998
Sales 12.6MM[E] *EMP* 3,047[E]
SIC 7363 Employee leasing service

D-U-N-S 80-992-7098
WORKFORCE COMMISSION LOUISIANA
(*Suby of* EXECUTIVE OFFICE OF STATE OF LOUISIANA) ★
1001 N 23rd St, Baton Rouge, LA 70802-3338
Tel (225) 342-3103 *Founded/Ownrshp* 1950
Sales NA *EMP* 1,200
SIC 9651 Labor regulatory agency;
Ex Dir: Curt Eysink
**CFO:* Renee Ellender Roberie
Ofcr: Christa Davis
Ex Dir: Tim A Barfield Jr
Snr Mgr: Sheral Kellar

D-U-N-S 03-327-8685
WORKFORCE COMMISSION TEXAS
(*Suby of* EXECUTIVE OFFICE OF STATE OF TEXAS) ★
101 E 15th St, Austin, TX 78778-1442
Tel (512) 463-2222 *Founded/Ownrshp* 1845
Sales NA *EMP* 3,600
SIC 9651 Labor regulatory agency
Ex Dir: Larry Temple
**CFO:* Randy Townsend
Comm Dir: Lisa Givens
Ql Cn Mgr: Leangiela Drake

WORKFORCE SAFETY & INSURANCE
See WORKERS SAFETY INSURANCE

D-U-N-S 12-149-8708
WORKFORCE SOFTWARE LLC
38705 7 Mile Rd Ste 300, Livonia, MI 48152-3979
Tel (734) 542-4100 *Founded/Ownrshp* 2011
Sales 92.0MM[E] *EMP* 225
SIC 7372 7371 Prepackaged software; Custom computer programming services
CEO: Mike Morini
COO: David Farquhar
CFO: Bob Feller
Chf Mktg O: Denise Broady
VP: Kathy Cannon
VP: Peter Jackson
VP: Mark Kurowski
VP: Marc Moschetto
Web Dev: Juan Mendes
Software D: Joshua Matz
Sftwr Eng: Spencer Maxfield

D-U-N-S 12-562-7120
WORKFRONT INC
3301 N Thank Way Ste 100, Lehi, UT 84043
Tel (801) 373-3266 *Founded/Ownrshp* 2001
Sales 192.1MM[E] *EMP* 650[E]
SIC 7371 Custom computer programming services
Pr: Alex Shootman
**Ch Bd:* Scott C Johnson
**CEO:* Eric Morgan
**CFO:* Pete Childs
CFO: Michael Olson
**Chf Mktg O:* Bryan Nielson
**Chf Mktg O:* Joe Staples
Ex VP: Sue Fellows
Sr VP: Frank Maylett
VP: Jody Bailey
VP: Karl Clegg
VP: Shane Helget
VP: Bryan D Nielson
Board of Directors: Peter Arrowsmith, Joe Cardenas, Bill Conroy, Steve Erickson, Scott Maxwell

WORKING SOLUTIONS
See WSOL INC

D-U-N-S 02-373-9054
▲ WORKIVA INC
2900 University Blvd, Ames, IA 50010-8665
Tel (888) 275-3125 *Founded/Ownrshp* 2008
Sales 145.2MM *EMP* 1,122
Tkr Sym WK *Exch* NYS
SIC 7372 Prepackaged software
Ch Bd: Matthew M Rizai
**Pr:* Martin J Vanderploeg
CFO: J Stuart Miller
Ex VP: Troy M Calkins
Ex VP: Joseph H Howell
Ex VP: Jeffrey D Trom
Software D: Eric Debusschere
Sftwr Eng: Andrew Perkins
Mktg Dir: Andy Klopstad
Sls Dir: Michelle Amato
Sls Dir: John Beisty
Board of Directors: Michael M Crow, Robert H Herz, Eugene S Katz, David S Mulcahy

D-U-N-S 06-601-3632
WORKMAN OIL CO
MADDOX OIL COMPANY
14670 Forest Rd, Forest, VA 24551-4468
Tel (434) 525-1615 *Founded/Ownrshp* 1974
Sales 212.1MM *EMP* 385
Accts Cherry Bekaert Llp Lynchburg
SIC 5541 Filling stations, gasoline
CEO: Robert M Workman Jr
**Pr:* Warner Hall
VP: Mike Duncan
VP Opers: Larry Bowling
Snr Mgr: Bill Pauley

D-U-N-S 04-417-1403 IMP/EXP
WORKMAN PUBLISHING CO INC
ALGONQUIN BOOKS CHAPEL HL DIV
225 Varick St Fl 9, New York, NY 10014-4381
Tel (212) 254-5900 *Founded/Ownrshp* 1967
Sales 103.2MM[E] *EMP* 225
SIC 2731 Books: publishing only
CEO: Dan Reynolds
Creative D: Vaughna Andrews
Creative D: David Schiller
Ex Dir: Beth Wareham
Mktg Mgr: Molly Frandson
Mktg Mgr: Moira Kerrigan
Sls Mgr: Jenny Lui
Assoc Ed: Samantha O'Brien

D-U-N-S 92-664-3669
WORKPLACE STAFFING SOLUTIONS LLC
13055 Hwy 1, Larose, LA 70373
Tel (985) 798-5111 *Founded/Ownrshp* 1994
Sales 18.0MM *EMP* 3,000
SIC 7363 7361 Temporary help service; Employment agencies
VP: Sam Riley

D-U-N-S 00-463-4585
WORKSPACE DEVELOPMENT LLC (WA)
OPENSQUARE
5601 6th Ave S Ste 470, Seattle, WA 98108-2544
Tel (206) 768-8000 *Founded/Ownrshp* 1934, 2000
Sales 105.3MM[E] *EMP* 200
SIC 5021 Furniture
**Sr VP:* Valarie Schmidt
**Ex Dir:* Scott Harrison

D-U-N-S 60-291-8877
WORKWAY INC
105 Decker Ct Ste 560, Irving, TX 75062-2802
Tel (972) 514-1547 *Founded/Ownrshp* 2011
Sales 20.0MM *EMP* 1,415
SIC 7361 Labor contractors (employment agency)
Ch: John Bowmer
**Pr:* James Bowner
**CFO:* Tom Bowmer
VP: Catherine Anderson
**VP:* Paul Kodros
**VP Opers:* Shanel Avritt
**VP Sls:* Ashley Hoover

D-U-N-S 04-493-9098
▲ WORLD ACCEPTANCE CORP
108 Frederick St, Greenville, SC 29607-2532
Tel (864) 298-9800 *Founded/Ownrshp* 1962
Sales NA *EMP* 4,436[E]
Tkr Sym WRLD *Exch* NGS
SIC 6141 Consumer finance companies; Licensed loan companies, small; Personal finance licensed loan companies, small
CEO: Janet Lewis Matricciani
**Ch Bd:* Ken R Bramlett Jr
CFO: John L Calmes Jr
Ex VP: Daniel Clinton Dyer
Sr VP: Erik T Brown
Sr VP: Tara E Bullock
Sr VP: Francisco Javier Sauza Del Poz
Sr VP: Jeff L Tinney
VP: Brent R Cooler
VP: Marilyn Messer
Board of Directors: James R Gilreath, Scott J Vassalluzzo, Charles D Way, Darrell E Whitaker

D-U-N-S 02-152-4509 IMP/EXP
WORLD AND MAIN (CRANBURY) LLC
(*Suby of* HBC HOLDINGS LLC) ★
324a Half Acre Rd, Cranbury, NJ 08512-3254
Tel (609) 860-9990 *Founded/Ownrshp* 2012
Sales 236.0MM *EMP* 230
Accts Mayer Hoffman Mccann New York
SIC 5072 5087 5074 Hardware; Shelf or light hardware; Security devices, locks; Janitors' supplies; Plumbing & hydronic heating supplies
**CFO:* Benjamin Small
**Treas:* Jack Imszennik

D-U-N-S 08-008-0874
WORLD AND MAIN LLC
324a Half Acre Rd, Cranbury, NJ 08512-3254
Tel (609) 860-9990 *Founded/Ownrshp* 2013
Sales 323.1MM[E] *EMP* 300
SIC 1711 3429 Plumbing contractors; Builders' hardware
Treas: Jack Imszennik

WORLD BANK, THE
See INTERNATIONAL FINANCE CORP

WORLD BANK, THE
See INTERNATIONAL BANK FOR RECONSTRUCTION & DEVELOPMENT (INC)

D-U-N-S 83-214-7487
WORLD BANK GROUP
(*Suby of* WORLD BANK) ★
1818 H St Nw, Washington, DC 20433-0002
Tel (202) 473-1000 *Founded/Ownrshp* 2010
Sales NA *EMP* 13,000[E]
SIC 6082 Foreign trade & international banking institutions
Pr: Jim Yong Kim
CFO: Suprotik Basu
CFO: Vinita Narain
**Treas:* Madelyn Antoncic
Treas: Assaneh M Beschloss
Ofcr: Adel Abouchaev
Ofcr: Santiago Afanador
Ofcr: Behrouz Aghevli
Ofcr: Iskandarsyah Bakri
Ofcr: Yassine Belkhodja
Ofcr: Rodrigo Cabral
Ofcr: Weijen Din
Ofcr: Shelley Fu

Ofcr: Raul Gochez
Ofcr: Nisha Goyal
Ofcr: Heidi Hennrich-Hanson
Ofcr: Rashid Jamal
Ofcr: Andrea James
Ofcr: Miray Kurtay
Ofcr: Robert Lawrence
Ofcr: Graeme Littler

D-U-N-S 10-735-9668
WORLD CLASS AUTOMOTIVE GROUP LP
PLANET FORD
20403 Interstate 45, Spring, TX 77388-5611
Tel (281) 719-3700 *Founded/Ownrshp* 1997
Sales 88.9MM[E] *EMP* 300
SIC 5511 Automobiles, new & used
Pt: Randall L Reed
Pt: Henry M Cimo
Exec: Tony Garrido
Exec: Desmond Stirgis
Genl Mgr: Shawn Burns
Sls Mgr: David Lang
Sls Mgr: Steven Loveless
Sales Asso: Patrick Huygen

WORLD CLASS BEVERAGE DIV
See MONARCH BEVERAGE CO INC

D-U-N-S 96-966-9543
WORLD CLASS DISTRIBUTION INC
TRADER JOE FONTANA WAREHOUSE
10288 Calabash Ave, Fontana, CA 92335-5272
Tel (909) 574-4140 *Founded/Ownrshp* 2009
Sales 106.1MM[E] *EMP* 600[E]
SIC 4225 General warehousing & storage
CEO: Danny Bane
Pr: Robert Camarena
Sec: Sharon A Drabeck
Opers Mgr: Roberto Cortez

D-U-N-S 80-109-2909 IMP
WORLD CLASS INDUSTRIES INC
SUPPLY CHAIN INTEGRATOR
925 N 15th Ave, Hiawatha, IA 52233-2207
Tel (319) 378-1766 *Founded/Ownrshp* 1992
Sales 161.1MM[E] *EMP* 126
SIC 3599 Custom machinery
Pr: Brent Cobb
**Treas:* Sandy Kaloupek
Board of Directors: Patrick Cobb

D-U-N-S 04-803-8181 IMP
■ **WORLD COLOR (USA) HOLDING CO**
(*Suby of* QUAD/GRAPHICS INC) ★
291 State St, North Haven, CT 06473-2131
Tel (203) 288-2468 *Founded/Ownrshp* 2013
Sales 1.0MMM[E] *EMP* 12,893[E]
SIC 2752 2754 Commercial printing, lithographic; Publication printing, gravure
VP: Jon Drews
**V Ch Bd:* Pierre-Karl Peladeau

D-U-N-S 36-413-6390 IMP
WORLD COLOR INC
WORLD COLOR PRINTING DIVISION
10 Sunshine Blvd, Ormond Beach, FL 32174-8754
Tel (386) 672-8388 *Founded/Ownrshp* 1977
Sales 147.5MM[E] *EMP* 2,700
SIC 2759

WORLD COLOR PRINTING DIVISION
See WORLD COLOR INC

D-U-N-S 11-616-3460
■ **WORLD COURIER GROUP INC**
(*Suby of* AMERISOURCEBERGEN CORP) ★
4 High Ridge Park Ste 102, Stamford, CT 06905-1325
Tel (203) 595-0900 *Founded/Ownrshp* 2012
Sales 256.9MM[E] *EMP* 3,000
SIC 4513 Air courier services
CEO: Wayne B Heyland
CFO: Anthony Willsher
Ch: James R Berger
VP: Frances Berger
VP: Carol Lacy
VP: Peter Marcino
Software D: Eduardt Nistor
Manager: Tim Redmond

D-U-N-S 80-762-0372
WORLD CULTURAL ORGANIZATION INC
1330 Avenue Ste 23, New York, NY 10019
Tel (212) 653-0657 *Founded/Ownrshp* 1993
Sales 600.0MM *EMP* 2
SIC 8399 Social change association

D-U-N-S 88-309-7339 IMP
WORLD ELECTRIC SUPPLY INC
(*Suby of* SONEPAR USA) ★
569 Stuart Ln, Jacksonville, FL 32254-3420
Tel (904) 378-4000 *Founded/Ownrshp* 1999
Sales 210.0MM[E] *EMP* 261
SIC 5063 Electrical apparatus & equipment
Pr: Lisa Mitchell
**CFO:* Paul Leveille
**VP:* Dick Caotes
**VP:* Richard Coates
Brnch Mgr: Linda Humphrey
Brnch Mgr: Rusty Spradley
Genl Mgr: Jackie Vasser
Dir IT: Jose Gomez
Opers Mgr: Reggie Osteen
**VP Sls:* William Olson
Sales Asso: Kevin Bennett

WORLD FAMOUS SAN DIEGO ZOO
See ZOOLOGICAL SOCIETY OF SAN DIEGO

D-U-N-S 05-911-5238 IMP
WORLD FINER FOODS LLC
1455 Broad St Ste 4, Bloomfield, NJ 07003-3039
Tel (973) 338-0300 *Founded/Ownrshp* 1988
Sales 210.0MM *EMP* 85
Accts Eisneramper Llp New York Ny
SIC 5149 Specialty food items
Ch Bd: Frank Muchel
Pr: Susan Guerin
VP: Barbara Harloe
VP: Kevin Hubbard
VP: Podd Newstadt
VP: Barry O'Brien
Mng Dir: Dimitrios Stratakis
Rgnl Mgr: Tom Barnes
VP Mktg: Marybeth Depersio
VP Sls: Todd Newstadt
Mktg Dir: Kelly Oshay

D-U-N-S 13-150-4342
▲ **WORLD FUEL SERVICES CORP**
9800 Nw 41st St Ste 400, Doral, FL 33178-2980
Tel (305) 428-8000 *Founded/Ownrshp* 1984
Sales 30.3MMM *EMP* 4,771
Accts Pricewaterhousecoopers Llp Mi
Tkr Sym INT *Exch* NYS
SIC 5172 3519 5541 Petroleum products; Aircraft fueling services; Diesel, semi-diesel or duel-fuel engines, including marine; Gasoline service stations; Filling stations, gasoline; Marine service station; Truck stops
Pr: Michael J Kasbar
Pr: Susan Bolanos
Pr: Joseph Gowen
CFO: Ira M Birns
Treas: Adrienne Urban
Ex VP: Michael J Crosby
Ex VP: Michael Crosby
Ex VP: Francis L Boon Meng
Ex VP: John P Rau
Sr VP: R Alexander Lake
Sr VP: Massoud Sedigh
Sr VP: Mike Stepanovich
Sr VP: Carlos M Velazquez
VP: Amy Abraham
VP: Dorothy Beck
VP: David Black
VP: Tim Bohall
VP: Carlos Cuervo
VP: German Estrada
VP: Ruth Giansante
VP: Piers Gorman
Board of Directors: Ken Bakshi, Jorge L Benitez, Richard A Kassar, Myles Klein, John L Manley, J Thomas Presby, Stephen K Roddenberry, Paul H Stebbins

WORLD FUEL SERVICES FL
See WORLD FUEL SERVICES INC

D-U-N-S 60-603-6481 IMP/EXP
■ **WORLD FUEL SERVICES INC**
WORLD FUEL SERVICES FL
(*Suby of* WORLD FUEL SERVICES CORP) ★
9800 Nw 41st St Ste 400, Doral, FL 33178-2980
Tel (305) 428-8000 *Founded/Ownrshp* 1987
Sales 1.0MMM[E] *EMP* 271
SIC 5172 Aircraft fueling services
Pr: Michael Clementi
**CFO:* Ira Birns
**VP:* Richard Mellone
Sls Mgr: Regina Castro

D-U-N-S 09-366-8226
WORLD INDUSTRIAL RESOURCES CORP
(*Suby of* Q CORP)
13100 56th Ct Ste 710, Clearwater, FL 33760-4021
Tel (727) 572-9991 *Founded/Ownrshp* 1978
Sales 168.5MM[E] *EMP* 3,950
SIC 3999 2542 5113 2671 Music boxes; Fixtures: display, office or store: except wood; Industrial & personal service paper; Waxed paper: made from purchased material
Pr: Leslie Unger
Bd of Dir: Philippe Gastone

D-U-N-S 01-293-5800 IMP
WORLD KITCHEN LLC
(*Suby of* WKI HOLDING CO INC) ★
9525 Bryn Mawr Ave # 300, Rosemont, IL 60018-5252
Tel (847) 233-8600 *Founded/Ownrshp* 2007
Sales 1.4MMM[E] *EMP* 2,900
SIC 3229 3469 3365 3421 5719 Pressed & blown glass; Household cooking & kitchen utensils, metal; Cooking/kitchen utensils, cast aluminum; Cutlery; Kitchenware
CEO: Carl Warschausky
Pr: Kris Malkoski
CFO: Stephen Earhart
Ofcr: Deborah Paskin
Ex VP: Timothy T Johnson
VP: James Aikins
VP: Michelle R Malkin
VP: Marty Straube
VP: James Van Overmeiren
Dir IT: Joe Tokash
IT Man: Chris Brown

D-U-N-S 07-396-1419
WORLD LEARNING INC
SCHOOL FOR INTL TRAINING
(*Suby of* WORLD LEARNING INDIA PRIVATE LIMITED)
1 Kipling Rd, Brattleboro, VT 05301-9079
Tel (802) 257-7751 *Founded/Ownrshp* 1947
Sales 135.9MM *EMP* 450
SIC 8221 8299 College, except junior; Student exchange program
Pr: Sophia Howlett
Ofcr: Amy Fisher
Ofcr: Kevin Giddens
Ofcr: Maka Janikashvili
Ofcr: Holly McCandless
Ofcr: Jessica Mead
Ofcr: Haseena Niazi
Ofcr: Kathryn Schoenberger
**Sr VP:* Nancy Rowden Brock
**Sr VP:* Ross Gibson
VP: Kimberly Abbott
VP: James Bernard
**VP:* Lisa Gurwitch
VP: Reeve Gutsell
**VP:* Scott Lansell
**VP:* John Lucas
**VP:* Lisa Rae
VP: Carlos Sosa
VP: Mark Viso
Assoc Dir: Sean Jones

WORLD MARK
See WYNDHAM RESORT DEVELOPMENT CORP

D-U-N-S 07-873-2728
■ **WORLD MEDIA ENTERPRISES INC**
(*Suby of* BH MEDIA GROUP INC) ★
300 E Franklin St, Richmond, VA 23219-2214
Tel (804) 643-1276 *Founded/Ownrshp* 1986
Sales 81.9MM[E] *EMP* 2,200
SIC 2711 Newspapers, publishing & printing
VP Opers: Sam Hightower

D-U-N-S 07-854-2598
WORLD MEDICAL GOVERNMENT SOLUTIONS LLC
4345 Southpoint Blvd, Jacksonville, FL 32216-6166
Tel (904) 332-3000 *Founded/Ownrshp* 2012
Sales 112.4MM[E] *EMP* 4,133
SIC 5047 Medical & hospital equipment

D-U-N-S 01-649-1573 IMP
■ **WORLD OF JEANS & TOPS** (CA)
TILLY'S
(*Suby of* TILLYS INC) ★
10 Whatney, Irvine, CA 92618-2807
Tel (949) 609-5599 *Founded/Ownrshp* 1984
Sales 516.8MM[E] *EMP* 4,000
Accts Deloitte & Touche Llp Costa M
SIC 5651 Family clothing stores
Ch Bd: Hezy Shaked
Pr: Cheryl Rudich
**CFO:* William Langsdorf

D-U-N-S 07-293-7436
WORLD OIL MARKETING CO
9302 Garfield Ave, South Gate, CA 90280-3805
Tel (562) 928-0100 *Founded/Ownrshp* 1977
Sales 150.5MM[E] *EMP* 475
SIC 2911 4953 2951 5541 4213 4212 Petroleum refining; Asphalt or asphaltic materials, made in refineries; Recycling, waste materials; Paving mixtures; Gasoline service stations; Liquid petroleum transport, non-local; Petroleum haulage, local
Pr: Robert S Roth
**VP:* Florence Roth
**VP:* Richard Roth

D-U-N-S 04-572-0216
WORLD OMNI FINANCIAL CORP
SOUTHEAST TOYOTA FINANCE
(*Suby of* JM & A GROUP) ★
190 Jim Moran Blvd, Deerfield Beach, FL 33442-1702
Tel (954) 429-2200 *Founded/Ownrshp* 1981
Sales NA *EMP* 840
SIC 6141 6159 Automobile loans, including insurance; Automobile finance leasing; Loan institutions, general & industrial
CEO: Colin Brown
**Treas:* Eric M Gebhard
Ofcr: Treyon Bryant
Sr VP: John Sullivan
VP: Rod Arends
VP: Ed Brown
VP: Dan Chait
VP: Brent Sergot
**VP:* Peter J Sheptak
VP: Brick Toifel
Ql Cn Mgr: Angie Lowery

D-U-N-S 96-663-2957
▲ **WORLD POINT TERMINALS LP**
8235 Forsyth Blvd Ste 400, Saint Louis, MO 63105-1621
Tel (314) 889-9660 *Founded/Ownrshp* 2013
Sales 96.1MM *EMP* 145[E]
Tkr Sym WPT *Exch* NYS
SIC 5171 Petroleum bulk stations & terminals
Ch Bd: Paul A Novelly
Genl Pt: Wpt GP LLC
COO: Kenneth E Fenton
COO: Kenneth Fenton
CFO: Steven Twele
Exec: Jonathan Affleck

WORLD SANITARY SUPPLY
See SINGER EQUIPMENT CO INC

D-U-N-S 04-663-0075
WORLD SHIPPING INC
1340 Depot St Ste 200, Cleveland, OH 44116-1741
Tel (440) 356-7676 *Founded/Ownrshp* 1960
Sales 195.8MM[E] *EMP* 450
SIC 4213 4731 Trucking, except local; Agents, shipping
Pr: Frederick M Hunger
**CFO:* John E Hunger
**VP:* Dennis Mahoney

D-U-N-S 07-780-5583
WORLD TECHNOLOGY GROUP INC
8930 Muirfield Ct, Duluth, GA 30097-6618
Tel (404) 697-0985 *Founded/Ownrshp* 1984
Sales 47.5MM[E] *EMP* 1,300
SIC 4813 Voice telephone communications
CFO: Ronald Baptiste

D-U-N-S 80-003-7678 IMP
WORLD TRADING CO INC
6754 Melrose Ln, Oklahoma City, OK 73127-6212
Tel (405) 787-1982 *Founded/Ownrshp* 2003
Sales 13.2MM[E] *EMP* 1,500
SIC 2299 Linen fabrics
Pr: Sohail Ahmed
**Sr VP:* Umair Ahmed
**VP:* Kiran Sohail Ahmed

D-U-N-S 80-764-3036
WORLD TRAVEL PARTNERS GROUP INC
(*Suby of* B C D) ★
6 Concourse Pkwy, Atlanta, GA 30328-6117
Tel (678) 441-5200 *Founded/Ownrshp* 2006
Sales 91.1MM[E] *EMP* 6,000
SIC 4724 Travel agencies
Pr: Jack Alexander
**Pr:* Danny Hood
**CFO:* W Thomas Barham
Snr PM: Maureen Gould

D-U-N-S 07-190-3322 IMP/EXP
WORLD VISION INC
34834 Weyerhaeuser Way S, Federal Way, WA 98001-9523
Tel (253) 815-1000 *Founded/Ownrshp* 1950
Sales 1.0MMM *EMP* 719
SIC 6732

D-U-N-S 61-536-6635
WORLD WIDE TECHNOLOGY
26017 Se 23rd Pl, Sammamish, WA 98075-5947
Tel (425) 269-2678 *Founded/Ownrshp* 1990
Sales 21.0MM *EMP* 1,050
SIC 7371 Custom computer programming services
Pr: David Stuart

D-U-N-S 13-178-4451 IMP
WORLD WIDE TECHNOLOGY HOLDING CO INC
60 Weldon Pkwy, Saint Louis, MO 63101
Tel (314) 919-1400 *Founded/Ownrshp* 1986
Sales 7.4MMM *EMP* 1,052
Accts Ernst & Young Llp St Louis M
SIC 5045 5065 8748 Computers, peripherals & software; Electronic parts & equipment; Business consulting
CEO: James P Kavanaugh
**Ch Bd:* David Steward
**CFO:* Tom Strunk
Rgnl Mgr: Douglas Warner
Netwrk Eng: John Salvatore
Sales Asso: Jamie Stopke

D-U-N-S 61-494-8396 IMP
WORLD WIDE TECHNOLOGY INC
(*Suby of* WORLD WIDE TECHNOLOGY HOLDING CO INC) ★
60 Weldon Pkwy, Maryland Heights, MO 63043-3202
Tel (314) 569-7000 *Founded/Ownrshp* 2002
Sales 5.9MMM *EMP* 1,052
SIC 5045 5065 8741 Computers, peripherals & software; Communication equipment; Management services
CEO: James P Kavanaugh
**Ch Bd:* David L Steward
**Pr:* Joseph G Koenig
**CFO:* Thomas W Strunk
VP: Mark Franke
VP: Matt Horner
VP: Tim Loughman
VP: John Lynch
VP: Leo Makhlin
**VP:* Ann W Marr
**VP:* Robert M Olwig
VP: Dan B Svoboda
VP: Mike P Taylor
VP Bus Dev: Tariq Hafeez
Comm Man: David Rosenblatt

WORLD WIDE TRAVEL SERVICE
See AAA ALLIED GROUP INC

D-U-N-S 07-484-5447
WORLD WILDLIFE FUND INC
W W F
1250 24th St Nw Fl 2, Washington, DC 20037-1193
Tel (202) 293-4800 *Founded/Ownrshp* 1948
Sales 218.0MM *EMP* 2,500[E]
Accts Bdo Usa Llp Mc Lean Va
SIC 8641 Environmental protection organization
CEO: Neville Isdell
**Pr:* Carter Roberts
**COO:* Marcia Marsh
Bd of Dir: Cristi N Samper
Chf Mktg O: Etienne McManus-White
Ofcr: Breen Byrnes
Ofcr: Karen Douthwaite
Ofcr: Wendy Goyert
Ofcr: Rachel Kramer
Ofcr: Ingrid Larson
Ofcr: Mike Osmond
Ofcr: Amy Smith
Ofcr: Martha Stevenson
Ofcr: Annika Terrana
Ofcr: Arianna Vitali
Top Exec: Kah Ng
**Sr VP:* Julie Miller
**VP:* Margaret Ackerley
**VP:* Jason Clay
**VP:* Tom Dillon
**VP:* Ginette Hemley

D-U-N-S 10-116-1263 IMP
▲ **WORLD WRESTLING ENTERTAINMENT INC**
1241 E Main St, Stamford, CT 06902-3520
Tel (203) 352-8600 *Founded/Ownrshp* 1980
Sales 658.7MM *EMP* 840[E]
Tkr Sym WWE *Exch* NYS
SIC 7812 7929 2721 Television film production; Video tape production; Entertainment group; Magazines: publishing only, not printed on site
Ch Bd: Vincent K McMahon
Pr: Michael J Luisi
Pr: Gerrit Meier
CFO: George A Barrios
Ofcr: Michelle D Wilson
Ex VP: Casey Collins
**Ex VP:* Paul Levesque
Sr VP: Blake T Bilstad
VP: Peggy Waldo
Board of Directors: Stuart U Goldfarb, Patricia A Gottesman, Laureen Ong, Joseph H Perkins, Robyn W Peterson, Frank A Riddick III, Jeffrey R Speed

D-U-N-S 60-644-5013
WORLDCOM EXCHANGE INC
WEI
43 Northwestern Dr, Salem, NH 03079-4809
Tel (603) 893-0900 *Founded/Ownrshp* 1993
Sales 178.2MM *EMP* 72
SIC 7373 5045 7379 Computer integrated systems design; Computers; Computer related maintenance services; Computer related consulting services
Pr: Belisario Rosas
**Sec:* Leslie M Rosas
**VP:* Linda L Cronin
Dir IT: Todd Grubbs
VP Mktg: Bill Burke

Mktg Mgr: Kerry Cotter
Sales Asso: Danielle Fredette

D-U-N-S 06-354-8721 IMP
■ WORLDPAC INC
(*Suby of* CARQUEST) ★
37137 Hickory St, Newark, CA 94560-3340
Tel (510) 742-8900 *Founded/Ownrshp* 2004
Sales 819.4MM^E *EMP* 1,175
SIC 5013 5531 Automotive supplies & parts; Automotive parts
CEO: Bob Cushing
Pr: Roy Geddie
Pr: David Heine
Pr: Darius Kondaki
*CFO: John Mosunic
Ex VP: Susan Grass
Ex VP: Mike Hellweg
Ex VP: Steven Sharp
VP: Abbas Banihashemi
VP: Tom Blackney
VP: Chris Frank
VP: Patrick Healy
VP: Peter Klotz
*VP: Steven Murphy
VP: James White
VP: Jason Yurchak
Board of Directors: Patrick Handreke

D-U-N-S 78-027-4155
WORLDPAY US INC
600 Morgan Falls Rd # 260, Atlanta, GA 30350-5813
Tel (770) 396-1616 *Founded/Ownrshp* 2010
Sales 370.4MM^E *EMP* 1,100
SIC 7374

WORLDS BEST CHEESECAKE
See NORTHERN STAR VENTURES LLC

D-U-N-S 00-516-1880 IMP
WORLDS FINEST CHOCOLATE INC
COOK CHOCOLATE COMPANY
(*Suby of* BARRY CALLEBAUT USA LLC) ★
4801 S Lawndale Ave, Chicago, IL 60632-3065
Tel (773) 847-4600 *Founded/Ownrshp* 2015
Sales 230.8MM^E *EMP* 400
SIC 2066 5947 Chocolate & cocoa products; Gift, novelty & souvenir shop
Ch Bd: Edmond F Opler
*Pr: Howard Zodikoff
VP: Rich Mazur
Sls Dir: Larry V Meulen

D-U-N-S 79-094-0451
■ WORLDS FOREMOST BANK
(*Suby of* CABELAS INC) ★
1 Cabelas Dr, Sidney, NE 69162-3028
Tel (402) 323-4300 *Founded/Ownrshp* 2007
Sales NA *EMP* 8^E
SIC 6099 Functions related to deposit banking
Prin: Scott Wanetka
Ofcr: Darcy Wagner

D-U-N-S 79-620-1721 IMP/EXP
▲ WORLDTEX INC
990 3rd Ave Se, Hickory, NC 28602-4009
Tel (828) 322-2242 *Founded/Ownrshp* 1992
Sales 103.8MM^E *EMP* 1,427
Tkr Sym WDTX *Exch* OTO
SIC 2241 Yarns, elastic: fabric covered; Elastic narrow fabrics, woven or braided
Pr: Stewart Little
Treas: Mitchell Setzer
*Sec: Mitchell R Setzer
Genl Mgr: Mac Cheek

D-U-N-S 08-018-2373
■ WORLDWIDE AIR LOGISTICS GROUP INC
(*Suby of* SOUTHERN AIR HOLDINGS INC) ★
7310 Turfway Rd Ste 490, Florence, KY 41042-4871
Tel (859) 568-9300 *Founded/Ownrshp* 2004
Sales 93.7MM^E *EMP* 305^E
SIC 4522 4581 Air cargo carriers, nonscheduled; Airports, flying fields & services
CEO: Daniel McHugh
*Pr: David Soaper
*CFO: Fred Deleeuw
*Chf Cred: Oliver Gritz

D-U-N-S 14-736-7481
WORLDWIDE CORPORATE HOUSING LP
R & B RLTY GRP A CA LTD PRTNRS
(*Suby of* OAKWOOD WORLDWIDE) ★
2222 Corinth Ave, Los Angeles, CA 90064-1602
Tel (877) 902-0832 *Founded/Ownrshp* 2004
Sales 82.7MM^E *EMP* 1,500^E
SIC 7021 Furnished room rental
Prin: Ric Villarreal
VP: Scott McDonald
Opers Mgr: Jay Lavallee
Opers Mgr: Brad Much

D-U-N-S 11-872-2185 IMP
WORLDWIDE DIGITAL CO LLC
(*Suby of* CONTEC LLC) ★
1023 State St, Schenectady, NY 12307-1511
Tel (518) 382-8000 *Founded/Ownrshp* 2004
Sales 221.8MM^E *EMP* 2,200
SIC 5065 Television parts & accessories
CEO: Hari Pillai

D-U-N-S 02-748-6497 IMP
WORLDWIDE DISTRIBUTORS
8211 S 194th St, Kent, WA 98032-1124
Tel (253) 872-8746 *Founded/Ownrshp* 1955
Sales 98.4MM^E *EMP* 53
SIC 5091 5136 5137 5139 5199 5023 Sporting & recreation goods; Men's & boys' clothing; Women's & children's clothing; Shoes; General merchandise, non-durable; Home furnishings
CEO: Mark Williams
*VP: Deb Hammond
Exec: Judy Cyphers

D-U-N-S 14-430-4094 IMP
WORLDWIDE EQUIPMENT ENTERPRISES INC
107 We Dr, Prestonsburg, KY 41653-8809
Tel (606) 874-2772 *Founded/Ownrshp* 1989
Sales 267.9MM^E *EMP* 625
SIC 5511 Automobiles, new & used
Pr: Terry L Dotson
*CFO: J R Polk
*VP: Wendell Wells
Opers Mgr: Bobby Calvert

D-U-N-S 07-680-3360
WORLDWIDE EQUIPMENT INC
(*Suby of* WORLDWIDE EQUIPMENT ENTERPRISES INC) ★
73 We Dr, Prestonsburg, KY 41653-8799
Tel (606) 874-2172 *Founded/Ownrshp* 1985
Sales 197.9MM^E *EMP* 625
SIC 5012 5013 7538 7513 Trucks, commercial; Trailers for trucks, new & used; Truck parts & accessories; Truck engine repair, except industrial; Truck leasing, without drivers
Pr: Terry Dotson
*COO: Scott Blevins
*Sec: Randy Polk
*VP: Robert S Blevins
*VP: Wayne Dyer
*VP: Tom Hjertquist
*VP: Wendell Wells
Off Mgr: Donna Hughes
Opers Mgr: Jim Toussaint
Sls Mgr: Johnny Britton

D-U-N-S 11-744-7417
WORLDWIDE FLIGHT SERVICES INC
AIRLINE SERVICES
1925 W John Carpenter Fwy # 450, Irving, TX 75063-3219
Tel (972) 629-5001 *Founded/Ownrshp* 2015
Sales 2.3MMM^E *EMP* 9,300
SIC 4581 4789 Airports, flying fields & services; Pipeline terminal facilities, independently operated
Pr: Olivier Bijaoui
*COO: Barry D Nassberg
*CFO: Sylvain Rivoire
*Ex VP: John Batten
*Ex VP: Claudine Bonthoux
*Ex VP: Pablo Garcia
*Ex VP: Adolfo Morales
Ex VP: Barry Nassberg
*Ex VP: Jeanette H Quay
*Ex VP: Stewart Sinclair
Info Man: Eddie Wright

D-U-N-S 12-804-0941
WORLDWIDE INFORMATION SYSTEMS LLC
360 Central Ave 2051, Clark, NJ 07066-1108
Tel (908) 272-9430 *Founded/Ownrshp* 1996
Sales 116.0MM *EMP* 1,372
SIC 7371 Computer software development

WORLDWIDE PRODUCE
See GREEN FARMS INC

D-U-N-S 79-609-9778
WORLDWIDE SECURITY ASSOCIATES INC
(*Suby of* WSA GROUP INC) ★
10311 S La Cienega Blvd, Los Angeles, CA 90045-6109
Tel (310) 743-3000 *Founded/Ownrshp* 1991
Sales 23.2MM^E *EMP* 2,000
SIC 7381 Security guard service
Pr: Andres Martinez
VP: Richard Rodriguez
Board of Directors: Kenneth Marker

D-U-N-S 96-633-1451
WORLDWIDE TECHSERVICES LLC
QUALXSERV
(*Suby of* WORLDWIDE TECHSERVICES NETHERLANDS B.V.)
836 North St Unit 5, Tewksbury, MA 01876-1253
Tel (978) 848-9000 *Founded/Ownrshp* 2000
Sales 324.7MM^E *EMP* 3,000^E
SIC 7373 7375 Systems integration services; Information retrieval services
Pr: Dov Horowitz
Pr: Michael J Tracy
*CFO: Nancy Latorre
CFO: Steven M Sieker
VP: Don Crim
Prgrm Mgr: Richard Bowlsby
Prgrm Mgr: Angela Lawson
Prgrm Mgr: Dennis McLaughlin
Prgrm Mgr: Susan Thies
Area Mgr: Shane Carrizosa
CIO: David Hayes

D-U-N-S 78-530-6069 IMP
WORLDWISE INC
(*Suby of* MISTRAL EQUITY PARTNERS LP) ★
6 Hamilton Landing # 150, Novato, CA 94949-8268
Tel (415) 721-7400 *Founded/Ownrshp* 2011
Sales 106.3MM^E *EMP* 100
SIC 5199

WORLEY & OBETZ /FUEL
See WORLEY & OBETZ INC

D-U-N-S 01-435-6463
WORLEY & OBETZ INC
WORLEY & OBETZ /FUEL
85 White Oak Rd, Manheim, PA 17545-8550
Tel (717) 665-6891 *Founded/Ownrshp* 1970
Sales 520.5MM *EMP* 68
Accts Horovitz Rudoy & Roteman Llc
SIC 5983 5541 Fuel oil dealers; Filling stations, gasoline
Pr: Jeffery B Lyons
V Ch: Seth Obetz
COO: Brian Gerhart
CFO: Joel Hagaman
VP: Greg Flory
VP: Michele Kelly
VP: Michele Klusewitz
VP: Jason Mertz
*VP: Robert Seth Obetz
Dir IT: Dena Mitchell
IT Man: Cindi Pratte

D-U-N-S 13-465-6672
WORLEYPARSONS CORP
WORLEYPARSONS LIMITED
(*Suby of* WORLEYPARSONS LIMITED)
575 N Gary Ashford, Houston, TX 77079
Tel (713) 407-5000 *Founded/Ownrshp* 2005
Sales 632.4MM^E *EMP* 4,500
SIC 8711 8742 Engineering services; Management consulting services
CEO: Andrew Wood
*Pr: William E Hall
CFO: Robert Vilce
*Ch: Ron McNeilly
*Treas: Sean Kelleher
*Sr VP: Ashton R Christopher
*Sr VP: Lawrence S Kalban
Sr VP: W J Osborne
VP: Christopher Ashton
VP: Ray Bettis
VP: Thomas Brock
*VP: Robert J Edwards
VP: Robert J Johnson
VP: Daniel L Martin
VP: Francis M McNiff
VP: Richard A Schwanger
VP: Djurica Tankosic

D-U-N-S 03-723-2923
WORLEYPARSONS GROUP INC
(*Suby of* WORLEYPARSONS LIMITED) ★
6330 West Loop S, Bellaire, TX 77401-2928
Tel (713) 407-5000 *Founded/Ownrshp* 1980
Sales 486.8MM^E *EMP* 4,500
SIC 8711 8742

D-U-N-S 00-965-8615
WORLEYPARSONS INTERNATIONAL INC
(*Suby of* WORLEYPARSONS GROUP INC) ★
6330 West Loop S Ste 200, Bellaire, TX 77401-2924
Tel (713) 407-5000 *Founded/Ownrshp* 1980
Sales 140.2MM^E *EMP* 4,500^E
SIC 8742 Management consulting services

WORLEYPARSONS LIMITED
See WORLEYPARSONS CORP

D-U-N-S 61-620-6897
WORLEYPARSONS OF VIRGINIA INC
2675 Morgantown Rd, Reading, PA 19607-9676
Tel (610) 855-2000 *Founded/Ownrshp* 2004
Sales 261.3MM^E *EMP* 6,500
SIC 8712 Architectural engineering
Pr: Christopher L Parker
*CEO: John Grill
*Sr VP: Lawrence S Kalban
*Sr VP: Michael D Robinson
*Sr VP: Harry W Sauer
VP: John Carto
*VP: Sean P Kelleher
Exec: Brad Aanderud
Exec: Charlie Rooth
Mng Dir: Bill Hall
Snr PM: Harvey Goldstein

D-U-N-S 15-085-7043 IMP
WORMSER CORP
TOTAL BEAUTY SOURCE, THE
150 Coolidge Ave, Englewood, NJ 07631-4522
Tel (800) 666-9676 *Founded/Ownrshp* 1985
Sales 97.2MM^E *EMP* 100
SIC 5085 5199 Textile printers' supplies; Packaging materials
Pr: Alan Wormser
Pr: Gary Fagan
*COO: David Wormser
*Sr VP: Diane Hammond
*VP: Robbyn Norman
Exec: Stephen Wormser
Dir IT: Joseph Laboy
Opers Mgr: Allison Lavi

D-U-N-S 14-997-5554
WORNICK CO
WORNICK FOODS
(*Suby of* BAXTERS FOOD GROUP LIMITED)
4700 Creek Rd, Blue Ash, OH 45242-2875
Tel (800) 860-4555 *Founded/Ownrshp* 2003
Sales 248.4MM^E *EMP* 700^E
SIC 2032 Baby foods, including meats: packaged in cans, jars, etc.
Pr: Jon P Geisler
*CFO: Dustin McDulin
Sr Ex VP: Scott Kaylor
*VP: Jack Fields
*VP: Doug Herald
Genl Mgr: Drew Willis
QA Dir: Spencer Chroninger
IT Man: Krista Jung
IT Man: Sandip Singh
Prd Mgr: Earl Herst
Prd Mgr: Randy Powers

WORNICK FOODS
See WORNICK CO

D-U-N-S 83-173-4715
WORNICK HOLDING CO INC
(*Suby of* DDJ TOTAL RETURN FUND) ★
4700 Creek Rd, Blue Ash, OH 45242-2808
Tel (513) 794-9800 *Founded/Ownrshp* 2008
Sales 94.5MM^E *EMP* 1,368
SIC 2032 Canned specialties
Pr: Jon P Geisler
*CFO: Dustin McDulin
*VP: Michael Hyche
*VP: John Kowalchik

D-U-N-S 09-474-3965
WOROCO MANAGEMENT LLC
40 Woodbridge Ave Ste 3, Sewaren, NJ 07077-1335
Tel (732) 855-7720 *Founded/Ownrshp* 1999
Sales 524.1MM *EMP* 14
Accts Aj Santye & Co Somerville N
SIC 5172 Engine fuels & oils

D-U-N-S 01-235-4940
WORTH & CO INC
6263 Kellers Church Rd, Pipersville, PA 18947-1807
Tel (267) 362-1100 *Founded/Ownrshp* 1976
Sales 158.5MM *EMP* 400^E
Accts Kreischer Miller Horsham Pen
SIC 1711 Mechanical contractor
Pr: Stephen Worth
CFO: Jim Denning
*Sec: James A Gillen
*VP: Mark Worth
Opers Mgr: Joe Brown
Snr PM: Joe Stagliano

D-U-N-S 05-647-3564 IMP
WORTH BON INC (NC)
BON WORTH FACTORY OUTLETS
40 Francis Rd, Hendersonville, NC 28792-9314
Tel (828) 697-2216 *Founded/Ownrshp* 1971
Sales 386.9MM^E *EMP* 1,200
SIC 2331 5621 2339 2335 2337 8741 Blouses, women's & juniors': made from purchased material; Ready-to-wear apparel, women's; Slacks: women's, misses' & juniors'; Shorts (outerwear): women's, misses' & juniors'; Dresses, paper: cut & sewn; Skirts, separate: women's, misses' & juniors'; Management services
Pr: Loren W Wells
CFO: Bill M Hale
VP: Bill Hale
Dir IT: Dinah Cannuli

WORTHAM INSURANCE & RISK MGT
See JOHN L WORTHAM & SON LP

D-U-N-S 09-754-5636
WORTHINGTON CITY SCHOOLS
200 E Wilson Bridge Rd # 200, Worthington, OH 43085-2823
Tel (614) 450-6000 *Founded/Ownrshp* 1836
Sales 66.4MM^E *EMP* 1,200
SIC 8211 Elementary & secondary schools
Site Mgr: Janine Caslow
Site Mgr: Nabeth Roehrs

D-U-N-S 19-417-9305 IMP
■ WORTHINGTON CYLINDER CORP
(*Suby of* WORTHINGTON INDUSTRIES INC) ★
200 W Old Wlson Bridge Rd, Worthington, OH 43085-2247
Tel (614) 840-3210 *Founded/Ownrshp* 1982
Sales 483.0MM^E *EMP* 1,336
SIC 3443 Cylinders, pressure: metal plate
Prin: Carol L Barnum
*VP: Jim Knox
Plnt Mgr: Bob Kotarba
Ql Cn Mgr: Sheryl Sorrell
Manager: John Wahl
Sls Mgr: Randi Cox
Sls Mgr: Jim Matteson
Sls Mgr: Mike Norman
Sls Mgr: Brian Ziegler

D-U-N-S 18-813-5008 IMP
■ WORTHINGTON INDUSTRIES ENGINEERED CABS INC
ANGUS-PALM
(*Suby of* WORTHINGTON INDUSTRIES INC) ★
315 Airport Dr, Watertown, SD 57201-5606
Tel (605) 886-5681 *Founded/Ownrshp* 1987
Sales 232.5MM^E *EMP* 1,000
SIC 3537 Cabs, for industrial trucks & tractors
Pr: Robert Kluver
*Pr: John Lamprinakos
*CFO: William Knese
*VP: Knese Bill
*VP: Martin Comes
*VP: Jay Roths
Dir IT: Brian Van Vleet

D-U-N-S 00-431-2401
▲ WORTHINGTON INDUSTRIES INC
200 W Old Wlson Bridge Rd, Worthington, OH 43085-2247
Tel (614) 438-3210 *Founded/Ownrshp* 1955
Sales 2.8MMM *EMP* 10,000
Tkr Sym WOR *Exch* NYS
SIC 3316 3449 3443 3325 Strip steel, cold-rolled: from purchased hot-rolled; Fabricated bar joists & concrete reinforcing bars; Cylinders, pressure: metal plate; Alloy steel castings, except investment
Ch Bd: John P McConnell
Pr: Geoffrey G Gilmore
Pr: John G Lamprinakos
Pr: Mark A Russell
CFO: B Andrew Rose
Sr VP: Virgil L Winland
VP: Dale T Brinkman
VP: Marty Comes
VP: Joseph B Hayek
VP: Catherine M Lyttle
Area Mgr: John Messmer

D-U-N-S 19-387-9988
■ WORTHINGTON INDUSTRIES INC
(*Suby of* WORTHINGTON INDUSTRIES INC) ★
200 W Old Wlson Bridge Rd, Worthington, OH 43085-2247
Tel (614) 438-3077 *Founded/Ownrshp* 1986
Sales 228.8MM^E *EMP* 2,400
SIC 3316 Cold finishing of steel shapes; Cold-rolled strip or wire
CEO: John P McConnell
*Ch Bd: John H McConnell
Sr VP: Virgil Winland
*VP: Edward A Ferkany
VP: Cathy Lyttle
Exec: Jennifer Segrest
Rgnl Mgr: Jeffrey Bell
CTO: Richard Welch
Dir IT: Shawn Johnson
IT Man: Chip Curtis
IT Man: Kathy Lucas

WORTZ BEVERAGE MINNESOTA
See CONSOLIDATED ENTERPRISES INC

D-U-N-S 00-613-8424 IMP
WORZALLA PUBLISHING CO (WI)
3535 Jefferson St, Stevens Point, WI 54481-4379
Tel (715) 344-9600 *Founded/Ownrshp* 1892, 1986
Sales 90.0MM^E *EMP* 570
SIC 2732

D-U-N-S 79-908-6819
WOUNDED WARRIOR PROJECT INC
4899 Belfort Rd Ste 300, Jacksonville, FL 32256-6033
Tel (904) 296-7350 *Founded/Ownrshp* 2007
Sales 342.0MM *EMP* 3[E]
Accts Grant Thornton Llp Jacksonvil
SIC 8641 Veterans' organization
CEO: Steven Nardizzi
**Ch Bd:* Anthony K Odierno
COO: Charlie Fletcher
CFO: Ronald Burgess
**V Ch Bd:* Guy McMichael III
Ex VP: John Hamre
Ex VP: Ayla Hay
Ex VP: John M Molino
Ex VP: Ryan Pavlu
Ex VP: Abby Reiner
Ex VP: Michael Richardson

WOW
See WIDEOPENWEST FINANCE LLC

WOW INTERNET - CABLE - PHONE
See WIDEOPENWEST NETWORKS LLC

D-U-N-S 08-330-2190
WOW LOGISTICS CO
W O W
3040 W Wisconsin Ave, Appleton, WI 54914-1707
Tel (800) 236-3565 *Founded/Ownrshp* 1977
Sales 113.6MM[E] *EMP* 250
SIC 4225 General warehousing
Pr: Howard Kamerer
Pr: Margitta Furnner
Pr: Paul Wow
CFO: Lynda Peters
**Ch:* Donald Utschig
**Treas:* Taul Van Vreede
Bd of Dir: Thomas Pamperin
Ofcr: Dawn Bikin
**VP:* Jen Burkhart
VP: Jamie Hess
VP: Paul Van
Exec: Dan Allen

D-U-N-S 15-065-8565 IMP/EXP
WOZNIAK INDUSTRIES INC
GMP METAL PRODUCTS
2 Mid America Plz Ste 700, Oakbrook Terrace, IL 60181-4796
Tel (630) 954-3400 *Founded/Ownrshp* 1985
Sales 150.0MM[E] *EMP* 300
SIC 3469 3444 3462 Metal stampings; Sheet metal-work; Iron & steel forgings
Pr: Michael Wozniak
**Ch Bd:* Sandra Wozniak
**CFO:* Michael Powers
IT Man: Robert Gamboa

D-U-N-S 78-279-7901
WP CO LLC
WASHINGTON POST
(*Suby of* NASH HOLDINGS LLC) ★
1301 K St Nw, Washington, DC 20071-0004
Tel (202) 334-6242 *Founded/Ownrshp* 2013
Sales 176.9MM[E] *EMP* 795[E]
SIC 2721 2711 Magazines: publishing & printing; Newspapers, publishing & printing
CEO: Katharine Weymouth
VP: Jay Kennedy
VP: Alex Treadway
Exec: Jane L Lockhart
Comm Man: Shani George
Div Mgr: Bryant Despeaux
Netwrk Mgr: Kevin Lockwood
Info Man: Mark Vinyard
Plnt Mgr: Roddy Macpherson
Natl Sales: Sally Ragsdale
Natl Sales: Sheila Wulf

D-U-N-S 07-970-4928
■ **WP GLIMCHER INC**
(*Suby of* WASHINGTON PRIME GROUP INC) ★
180 E Broad St Fl 21, Columbus, OH 43215-3714
Tel (614) 621-9000 *Founded/Ownrshp* 2014
Sales 192.5MM[E] *EMP* 981[E]
SIC 6798 Realty investment trusts
CEO: Michael P Glimcher
**CEO:* Louis G Conforti
**COO:* Butch M Knerr
**CFO:* Mark E Yale
**Ex VP:* Thomas J Drought Jr
Sr VP: Paul Ajdaharian
Sr VP: Lisa Indest
**Sr VP:* Melissa A Indest
Sr VP: Grace Schmitt
Dir Surg: Karen Bailey

D-U-N-S 96-878-1992
■ **WP ROCKET HOLDINGS INC**
(*Suby of* AMR HOLDCO, INC.)
8465 N Pima Rd, Scottsdale, AZ 85258-4489
Tel (800) 352-2309 *Founded/Ownrshp* 2015
Sales 330.2M[E] *EMP* 8,152
SIC 4119 7389 Ambulance service; Fire protection service other than forestry or public
Pr: Sean D Carney

WPI
See WIESNER PRODUCTS INC

WPI
See WILLIAMSTON PRODUCTS INC

D-U-N-S 00-985-3946
■ **WPIX LLC**
WPIX-TV
(*Suby of* TRIBUNE CABLE) ★
80 State St, New York, NY 10017
Tel (212) 949-1100 *Founded/Ownrshp* 1980
Sales 107.8MM[E] *EMP* 301
SIC 4833 Television broadcasting stations
Ch Bd: Ed Willson
**Pr:* John Wielden
VP: Eric Meyrowitz
Adm/Dir: Karen Scott
Genl Mgr: Betty Ellen Berlamino
Art Dir: Louis Schiro

WPIX-TV
See WPIX LLC

D-U-N-S 60-348-8701
WPP CLAPTON SQUARE LLC
W P P
(*Suby of* WPP GROUP USA INC) ★
100 Park Ave Fl 4, New York, NY 10017-5576
Tel (212) 632-2200 *Founded/Ownrshp* 2000
Sales 2.9MMM[E] *EMP* 26,249
SIC 7311 Advertising agencies
Ch: Martin Sorrell
**Pr:* David J Moore
**CFO:* Mary Ellen Howe
CTO: Peter Johnson

D-U-N-S 79-575-2737
WPP GROUP HOLDINGS LLC
(*Suby of* WPP 2012 LIMITED)
100 Park Ave Fl 4, New York, NY 10017-5576
Tel (212) 632-2200 *Founded/Ownrshp* 1987
Sales 6.0MM[E] *EMP* 26,409[E]
SIC 7311 Advertising agencies
CEO: Martin Sorrell
**CFO:* Paul Richardson
Chf Mktg O: Betsy Lazar
Ex VP: Firouzeh Bahrampour
Sr VP: Andrew Garlick
**Sr VP:* Tom Neuman
**VP:* Kevin Farewell
**VP:* Mary Ellen Howe
VP: Graham Russell
CIO: Paul Hughes
Snr Mgr: Carl Hartman

D-U-N-S 11-118-2197
WPP GROUP US INVESTMENTS INC
(*Suby of* WPP 2005 LIMITED)
100 Park Ave, New York, NY 10017-5516
Tel (212) 632-2200 *Founded/Ownrshp* 1985
Sales 336.3MM[E] *EMP* 26,359
SIC 7311 Advertising agencies
CEO: Martin Sorrell
**CFO:* Paul Richardson
**Sr VP:* Tom Neuman
**VP:* Kevin Farewell
**VP:* Mary Ellen Howe

D-U-N-S 08-016-2806
WPP GROUP USA INC
(*Suby of* WPP PLC)
100 Park Ave Fl 4, New York, NY 10017-5576
Tel (212) 632-2200 *Founded/Ownrshp* 2015
Sales 2.9MMM[E] *EMP* 26,250
SIC 7311 Advertising agencies
Pr: Kevin Farewell
VP: Eugene Bauchner
VP: Ronald Pearlroth
VP: Jane Rich
VP: Anthony Sandrik
Exec: Joseph Petyan
Creative D: Aziz Cami
Genl Mgr: Kevin Doherty
Snr Mgr: Robin Dargue

D-U-N-S 96-485-1195
WPP GROUP USA INC
100 Park Ave, New York, NY 10017-5516
Tel (212) 632-2200 *Founded/Ownrshp* 1987
Sales 544.9MM[E] *EMP* 26,409[E]
SIC 7311

D-U-N-S 15-639-8927
WPPI ENERGY
W P P I
1425 Corporate Center Dr, Sun Prairie, WI 53590-9109
Tel (608) 834-4500 *Founded/Ownrshp* 1980
Sales 519.9MM *EMP* 95
SIC 4911

D-U-N-S 00-196-1556 IMP
WPS LEGACY INC (IL)
(*Suby of* ANIMAL SUPPLY CO LLC) ★
6450 Muirfield Dr, Hanover Park, IL 60133-5483
Tel (800) 232-4155 *Founded/Ownrshp* 1955, 2015
Sales 96.7MM[E] *EMP* 110
SIC 5199 Pet supplies
Pr: James D Wilson

D-U-N-S 96-825-7084
▲ **WPX ENERGY INC**
3500 One Williams Ctr, Tulsa, OK 74172-0151
Tel (855) 979-2012 *Founded/Ownrshp* 2011
Sales 1.8MMM *EMP* 1,040[E]
Accts Ernst & Young Llp Tulsa Okla
Tkr Sym WPX *Exch* NYS
SIC 1311 Crude petroleum & natural gas
Pr: Richard E Muncrief
COO: Clay M Gaspar
CFO: J Kevin Vann
Bd of Dir: Ken McQueen
Sr VP: Dennis C Cameron
Sr VP: Michael R Fiser
Sr VP: Bryan K Guderian
VP: Christopher Graves
VP: Chris Griffith
VP: Chad Odegard
VP: Bob Revella
VP: Kelsey Robin
VP: Bob Rock
VP: Sean Terchek
VP: Patsy S Varnell
Board of Directors: John A Carrig, William R Granberry, Robert K Herdman, Karl F Kurz, Henry E Lentz, George A Lorch, William G Lowrie, Kimberly S Lubel, David F Work

WQKT/WKVX
See WWST CORP LLC

D-U-N-S 07-838-4491
WRAPPORTS LLC
350 N Orleans St 10thf, Chicago, IL 60654-1975
Tel (312) 321-3000 *Founded/Ownrshp* 2009
Sales 304.8MM[E] *EMP* 2,330[E]
SIC 7379 2711 ; Newspapers, publishing & printing
Ch: Michael W Ferro Jr
**Pr:* Bradley Phillip Bell
**CEO:* Timothy P Knight
Sls Mgr: Rich Hummel
Counsel: Elaine Taussig

D-U-N-S 00-480-1335
WRD INC (GA)
1641 Sigman Rd Nw, Conyers, GA 30012-3465
Tel (770) 922-8000 *Founded/Ownrshp* 1987
Sales 110.7MM[E] *EMP* 109
SIC 8721 Accounting, auditing & bookkeeping
Pr: James L Respess III
Treas: Theresa Thompson
VP: Todd Greer
**VP:* Jay Moore
**VP:* Ronald L Williams
IT Man: Cindy Murphy

WREC
See WITHLACOOCHEE RIVER ELECTRIC COOPERATIVE INC

D-U-N-S 00-536-8113
WRIGHT & FILIPPIS INC (MI)
NO LIMITS
2845 Crooks Rd, Rochester Hills, MI 48309-3660
Tel (248) 829-8292 *Founded/Ownrshp* 1944
Sales 98.4MM[E] *EMP* 900
SIC 7352 5999 Medical equipment rental; Convalescent equipment & supplies
CEO: Anthony J Filippis
**Pr:* Bob Dewolf
**VP:* Steve Filippis
**VP:* John Wright
Rgnl Mgr: Ron Lupo
Genl Mgr: Kimberly Briesmeister
Off Mgr: Judy Walton
CIO: Michael Homant
CTO: Sharon Myatt
VP Opers: Rob Barrow
Sales Exec: Bill Gumbleton

D-U-N-S 05-361-4426 IMP
WRIGHT BUSINESS FORMS INC
WRIGHT BUSINESS GRAPHICS
18440 Ne San Rafael St, Portland, OR 97230-7009
Tel (503) 661-2525 *Founded/Ownrshp* 1970
Sales 88.7MM[E] *EMP* 296
Accts Ford Black & Co Portland Or
SIC 2761 Manifold business forms
CEO: James T Wright
**Pr:* Daniel C Adkison
**VP:* Brian Cicerchi
**VP:* Gordon Klepec
VP: Jeff Trump
Dir IT: Steve Hart
Dir IT: Stephan Lutter
Netwrk Mgr: Jt Olson
Opers Mgr: Brandon Olson
Prd Mgr: Brad Willard

WRIGHT BUSINESS GRAPHICS
See WRIGHT BUSINESS FORMS INC

WRIGHT EXPRESS FINANCIAL SVCS
See WEX INC

D-U-N-S 02-061-4637
WRIGHT MEDICAL GROUP INC
(*Suby of* WRIGHT MEDICAL GROUP N.V.)
1023 Cherry Rd, Memphis, TN 38117-5423
Tel (800) 238-7117 *Founded/Ownrshp* 2015
Sales 298.0MM *EMP* 898[E]
SIC 3842 Surgical appliances & supplies; Prosthetic appliances; Orthopedic appliances
Pr: Robert J Palmisano
Pr: Kevin D Cordell
Pr: Timothy Davis
**COO:* Pascal Er Girin
**CFO:* Lance A Berry
**Sr VP:* James A Lightman
Sr VP: Edward A Steiger
Sr VP: Jennifer S Walker
**VP:* Julie B Andrews
VP: William Flannery
VP: Karen Harris
VP: Max Mortensen
Exec: Jason Senner
Exec: Julie Tracy

D-U-N-S 80-720-1207 IMP
WRIGHT MEDICAL TECHNOLOGY INC
(*Suby of* WRIGHT MEDICAL GROUP INC) ★
1023 Cherry Rd, Memphis, TN 38117-5423
Tel (901) 867-9971 *Founded/Ownrshp* 1999
Sales 266.5MM[E] *EMP* 898
SIC 3842 3845 Surgical appliances & supplies; Implants, surgical; Electromedical equipment
CEO: Robert Palmisino
Pr: Mike Kaufman
Ex VP: Pascal E Girin
Sr VP: Bill Griffin Jr
Sr VP: Karen Harris
VP: Paul Arrendell
**VP:* Lance Berry
VP: Jean D'Hondt
VP: Timothy E Davis Jr
VP: Angelo De Lollis
**VP:* Daniel J Garen
VP: Essam Helmy
VP: Steven Kahn
VP: Lisa Michels
VP: John Raney
**VP:* Jennifer Walker

D-U-N-S 79-052-3385
WRIGHT SERVICE CORP
5930 Grand Ave Ste 100, West Des Moines, IA 50266-5302
Tel (515) 271-1197 *Founded/Ownrshp* 1985
Sales 443.1MM[E] *EMP* 2,500
SIC 0783 Tree trimming services for public utility lines
CEO: Scott Packard
**Pr:* Will Nutter
**CFO:* Terry McGonegle
**Treas:* McGonegle Terry
**VP:* J Peter Byers
Div Mgr: Mark Harwick

D-U-N-S 04-781-4256
WRIGHT STATE UNIVERSITY
3640 Colonel Glenn Hwy, Dayton, OH 45435-0002
Tel (937) 775-3333 *Founded/Ownrshp* 1961
Sales 233.4MM *EMP* 2,748[E]
Accts Crowe Horwath Llp Columbus O
SIC 8221 University
Pr: David R Hopkins
V Ch: Vishal Soin
Pr: Renee Aitken
Pr: Jeff Ulliman
Trst: Katie L Bullinger
Trst: Don R Graber
Trst: Larry R Klaben
Trst: John C Kunesh
Trst: Timothy R McEwen
Ex VP: Robert J Sweeney
**VP:* Matthew V Filipic
VP: Jacqueline McMillan
VP: Benjamin Salisbury
Exec: Ann Wendt
Dir Lab: Kirby Underwood
Assoc Dir: Terry Anderson
Assoc Dir: Jim Brown
Assoc Dir: Bill Knotts

D-U-N-S 00-785-8129
WRIGHT TREE SERVICE INC (IA)
(*Suby of* WRIGHT SERVICE CORP) ★
5930 Grand Ave Ste 100, West Des Moines, IA 50266-5302
Tel (515) 277-6291 *Founded/Ownrshp* 1933, 1985
Sales 486.4MM[E] *EMP* 2,500
SIC 0783 Tree trimming services for public utility lines
Ch Bd: Scott D Packard
**Pr:* Will Nutter
**CFO:* Terrence J McGongle
Div Mgr: Phil Heinz

D-U-N-S 01-336-8139 IMP
WRIGHT WISNER DISTRIBUTING CORP
3165 Brghtn HnriettaTwn, Rochester, NY 14623-2751
Tel (585) 427-2880 *Founded/Ownrshp* 1953
Sales 145.2MM[E] *EMP* 200
SIC 5181 5149 Beer & other fermented malt liquors; Juices; Soft drinks
CEO: Claude H Wright
VP: Brian Lambert
VP: Larry R Smith

D-U-N-S 00-380-1586
WRIGHT-HENNEPIN COOPERATIVE ELECTRIC ASSOCIATION (MN)
WRIGHT-HENNEPIN ELECTRIC
6800 Electric Dr, Rockford, MN 55373-9386
Tel (763) 477-3000 *Founded/Ownrshp* 1937
Sales 93.4MM *EMP* 145
Accts Brady Martz And Associates Pc
SIC 4911 Distribution, electric power
Pr: Mark Vogt
**Ch:* Chris Lantto
**Sec:* Dale Jans
**VP:* Angela Pirbyl
Sales Asso: Jennifer Virnig

WRIGHT-HENNEPIN ELECTRIC
See WRIGHT-HENNEPIN COOPERATIVE ELECTRIC ASSOCIATION

D-U-N-S 93-290-6084
WRIGHT-HENNEPIN SECURITY CORP
W-H SECURITY
(*Suby of* WRIGHT-HENNEPIN ELECTRIC) ★
6800 Electric Dr, Rockford, MN 55373-9386
Tel (763) 477-3664 *Founded/Ownrshp* 1989
Sales 88.7MM *EMP* 135
SIC 1731 1711 7382 5063 4911 Fire detection & burglar alarm systems specialization; Plumbing, heating, air-conditioning contractors; Security systems services; Burglar alarm systems; Electric services
Pr: Mark Vogt

D-U-N-S 07-127-9939
WRIGHT-PATT CREDIT UNION INC
3560 Pentagon Blvd, Beavercreek, OH 45431-1706
Tel (937) 912-7000 *Founded/Ownrshp* 1932
Sales NA *EMP* 364
SIC 6062 State credit unions, not federally chartered
Pr: Doug Secher
VP: David Bowser
**Prin:* Kim Test
IT Man: Donald Carruth
VP Mktg: Tracy Fors

D-U-N-S 16-061-6525
WRIGHT-PATT FINANCIAL GROUP LTD
2455 Presidential Dr, Beavercreek, OH 45324-6246
Tel (937) 912-7000 *Founded/Ownrshp* 2004
Sales 157.2MM *EMP* 1
SIC 7389 Financial services
Prin: Tim Mislansky

D-U-N-S 04-008-6014 IMP/EXP
WRIGLEY MANUFACTURING CO LLC
WRIGLEY'S
(*Suby of* WM WRIGLEY JR CO) ★
410 N Michigan Ave, Chicago, IL 60611-4213
Tel (312) 644-2121 *Founded/Ownrshp* 1987
Sales 105.6MM[E] *EMP* 2,000
SIC 2067 Chewing gum
Pr: Martin Radvan
**Treas:* Anthony Gedeller
**VP:* Andy Pharoah

WRIGLEY'S
See WRIGLEY MANUFACTURING CO LLC

D-U-N-S 11-424-9923
WRITERS GUILD INDUSTRY HEALTH FUND
1015 N Hollywood Way # 200, Burbank, CA 91505-2541
Tel (818) 846-1015 *Founded/Ownrshp* 1976
Sales 119.3MM *EMP* 21
Accts Ernst & Young Llp Los Angeles
SIC 8742 Compensation & benefits planning consultant
Dir IT: Steve Balman

D-U-N-S 13-211-8964
WRMC HOSPITAL OPERATING CORP
1370 W D St, North Wilkesboro, NC 28659-3506
Tel (336) 651-8100 *Founded/Ownrshp* 2002
Sales 86.1MM *EMP* 35[E]
SIC 8062 General medical & surgical hospitals
Prin: Gaither Kenner
Ex Dir: Ted Chatin
Ex Dir: Gregg Hendren

D-U-N-S 80-701-7228
WRRH INVESTMENTS LP
5747 San Felipe St # 4650, Houston, TX 77057-3101
Tel (713) 782-9100 *Founded/Ownrshp* 2007
Sales 459.2MM[E] *EMP* 5,800
SIC 7011 Hotels & motels
CEO: Joe Wheeling

D-U-N-S 00-692-3031 IMP/EXP
WS BADCOCK CORP (FL)
BADCOCK HOME FURNITURE & MORE
205 Nw 2nd St, Mulberry, FL 33860-2405
Tel (863) 425-4921 *Founded/Ownrshp* 1904
Sales 681.2MM *EMP* 1,000
Accts Kpmg Llp Tampa Fl
SIC 5712 5713 5722 5731 Furniture stores; Floor covering stores; Household appliance stores; Electric household appliances; Electric household appliances, major; Radio, television & electronic stores; Radios, receiver type; Television sets
Pr: Michael J Price
Ch: Wogan S Badcock III
Ex VP: Ben M Badcock
Ex VP: Henry C Badcock
Ex VP: Bill Daughtrey
Ex VP: William Daughtrey
Ex VP: William K Pou Jr
VP: Stephen N Bargamin
VP: Greg A Brinkman
VP: Robert Burnette
VP: Leland Carawan
VP: David Gonyea
VP: Lesley M Hurley
VP: James R Meyer
VP: Mitchell P Stiles
VP: Derrick Taylor
VP: Amy Yeager
VP: Nancy Young

D-U-N-S 61-034-6962
WS MIDWAY HOLDINGS INC
(*Suby of* WELLSPRING CAPITAL PARTNERS III LP) ★
390 Park Ave Fl 6, New York, NY 10022-4623
Tel (212) 318-9800 *Founded/Ownrshp* 2005
Sales 61.4MM[E] *EMP* 8,269[E]
SIC 5812 5813 7999 7993 Eating places; Bar (drinking places); Billiard parlor; Coin-operated amusement devices
Prin: David Mariano

D-U-N-S 55-740-4436
WSA GROUP INC
19208 S Vermont Ave 200, Gardena, CA 90248-4414
Tel (310) 743-3000 *Founded/Ownrshp* 1991
Sales 30.4MM[E] *EMP* 2,000
SIC 7381 7349 Security guard service; Janitorial service, contract basis
Pr: Andres Martinez
Sr VP: William Maggio
**VP:* James E Bush

D-U-N-S 36-445-9602
▲ WSFS FINANCIAL CORP
500 Delaware Ave, Wilmington, DE 19801-1490
Tel (302) 792-6000 *Founded/Ownrshp* 1988
Sales NA *EMP* 762[E]
Tkr Sym WSFS *Exch* NGS
SIC 6021 National commercial banks; National trust companies with deposits, commercial
Pr: Mark A Turner
Ch Bd: Marvin N Schoenhals
CFO: Dominic C Canuso
Ofcr: Thomas W Kearney
Ex VP: Steve Clark
Ex VP: Cynthia Cole
Ex VP: Paul D Geraghty Sr
Ex VP: Rodger Levenson
Sr VP: Vernita L Dorsey
Sr VP: Robert J Hayman
Sr VP: Jason L Spence
VP: Trevor Conlon
VP: Paige Willover
Board of Directors: Anat Bird, Francis B Brake Jr, Jennifer W Davis, Donald W Delson, Calvert A Morgan Jr, David G Turner, Patrick J Ward

WSI
See WAREHOUSE SPECIALISTS LLC

D-U-N-S 88-417-5139
WSNCHS NORTH INC
ST JOSEPH HOSPITAL
(*Suby of* CATHOLIC HLTH SVCS LONG ISLAND) ★
4295 Hempstead Tpke, Bethpage, NY 11714-5713
Tel (516) 579-6000 *Founded/Ownrshp* 2010
Sales 97.2MM *EMP* 756
SIC 8062 General medical & surgical hospitals
Ex VP: Drew Pallas
**Treas:* Joseph Tantillo
Assoc VP: Sandra Clark

D-U-N-S 11-835-0110
WSOL INC
WORKING SOLUTIONS
1820 Preston Park Blvd # 1150, Plano, TX 75093-3669
Tel (972) 964-4800 *Founded/Ownrshp* 2002
Sales 83.3MM[E] *EMP* 800
SIC 7389 Telephone answering service
CEO: Tim Houlne
**Ch Bd:* John Harris
**Pr:* Kim Houlne
**CFO:* Thomas Kim
**Chf Mktg O:* Gail Rigler
Sr VP: Larry Deering
Sr VP: Carlos Zapatero
VP: Joseph Casey
Exec: Kristin Kanger
Prgrm Mgr: Rory Slaughter
Ql Cn Mgr: Tamara Schroer

D-U-N-S 04-483-3333
WSP USA CORP
(*Suby of* WSP USA HOLDINGS INC) ★
1 Penn Plz 250w, New York, NY 10119-0002
Tel (914) 747-1120 *Founded/Ownrshp* 2013
Sales 241.6MM[E] *EMP* 1,056
SIC 8711 8732 Civil engineering; Survey service: marketing, location, etc.
Ch Bd: David Cooper
Treas: Susan Fasnacht
**Sec:* James Nevada
Ex VP: Mose Buonocore
**Ex VP:* Steven Smith
Sr VP: Patrick Chan
Sr VP: Varughese Cherian
Sr VP: Frank Muscarella
VP: Fred Holdorf
VP: Michael Mondshine
Tech Mgr: Pam Groff

D-U-N-S 07-967-0302
WSP USA HOLDINGS INC
(*Suby of* GROUPE WSP GLOBAL INC)
512 7th Ave Fl 13, New York, NY 10018-0807
Tel (212) 532-9600 *Founded/Ownrshp* 2000
Sales 241.6MM[E] *EMP* 1,058
SIC 8711 8732 Civil engineering; Survey service: marketing, location, etc.
Pr: David Cooper

WSS- DAYTON
See WINSUPPLY INC

WSU
See WEBER STATE UNIVERSITY

WSVN MIAMI
See SUNBEAM TELEVISION CORP

WSYM-TV
See JOURNAL BROADCAST GROUP INC

D-U-N-S 07-887-6569
WT HARDWOODS GROUP INC
WEABER LUMBER
(*Suby of* RESILIENCE MANAGEMENT) ★
1231 Mount Wilson Rd, Lebanon, PA 17042-4785
Tel (717) 867-2212 *Founded/Ownrshp* 2010
Sales 130.1MM[E] *EMP* 216[E]
SIC 2426 Hardwood dimension & flooring mills
CEO: Matthew Weaber
**CFO:* H William Campoll

D-U-N-S 96-621-2073
WT WALKER GROUP INC
222 E Erie St Ste 300, Milwaukee, WI 53202-6000
Tel (414) 223-2000 *Founded/Ownrshp* 1950
Sales 105.9MM[E] *EMP* 500
SIC 3462 3398 Iron & steel forgings; Metal heat treating
Prin: Willard T Walker Jr
**CFO:* Robert J Swanson
CFO: Robert Swanson

D-U-N-S 01-203-2678
WTB FINANCIAL CORP
WASHINGTON TRUST BANK
717 W Sprague Ave Fl 7, Spokane, WA 99201-3922
Tel (509) 353-4204 *Founded/Ownrshp* 1902
Sales NA *EMP* 757
SIC 6712 Bank holding companies
CEO: Peter Stanton
**Pr:* Peter F Stanton
**CFO:* Richard W Boutz
Ofcr: Ryne Leonard
**VP:* John Heath

WTEC RNEWABLE ENRGY INNOVATION
See WIND TURBINE AND ENERGY CABLES CORP

D-U-N-S 82-847-3640
WTS ACQUISITION CORP
5050 W Lemon St, Tampa, FL 33609-1104
Tel (813) 637-2220 *Founded/Ownrshp* 2007
Sales 86.2MM[E] *EMP* 15,001
SIC 7363 Temporary help service
Pr: Thomas J Bean

D-U-N-S 06-201-0384
WTS INTERNATIONAL INC
3200 Tower Oaks Blvd # 400, Rockville, MD 20852-4266
Tel (301) 622-7800 *Founded/Ownrshp* 1973
Sales 19.3MM[E] *EMP* 2,000
SIC 7991 7992 Health club; Athletic club & gymnasiums, membership; Public golf courses
Pr: Gary J Henkin
**Treas:* Annette Henkin
Sr VP: Kim Matheson
Exec: Ralph Newman
Netwrk Mgr: Steve Tyng
Mktg Dir: Dwayne Marshall

D-U-N-S 83-315-3732
WTW DELAWARE HOLDINGS LLC
TOWERS WATSON & CO.
(*Suby of* WILLIS TOWERS WATSON PUBLIC LIMITED COMPANY)
901 N Glebe Rd, Arlington, VA 22203-1853
Tel (703) 258-8000 *Founded/Ownrshp* 2016
Sales 2.6MMM[E] *EMP* 16,300[E]
SIC 8742 Management consulting services; Human resource consulting services; Compensation & benefits planning consultant
CEO: John J Haley
Pr: Dominic Casserley
CFO: Roger F Millay
Snr Mgr: Jessica Bassett

WUESTHOFF HOSPITAL
See SCHF NOT-FOR-PROFIT WIND-DOWN INC

D-U-N-S 00-895-3291
WUESTS INC
PIC-N-PAC
9318 Fm 725, Mc Queeney, TX 78123-3504
Tel (830) 379-3442 *Founded/Ownrshp* 1938
Sales 86.7MM[E] *EMP* 150
SIC 5141 5411 0173 Groceries, general line; Grocery stores, independent; Supermarkets; Convenience stores; Pecan grove
Pr: Robert W Wuest
**Sec:* Philip D Wuest
**VP:* Harvey E Wuest Jr

D-U-N-S 01-154-0291 IMP/EXP
WUHL SHAFMAN & LIEBERMAN INC
STATE HOUSE PRODUCE
52 Cornelia St Ste 62, Newark, NJ 07105-4511
Tel (973) 589-3513 *Founded/Ownrshp* 1964, 1979
Sales 136.7MM[E] *EMP* 147[E]
SIC 5148 Fruits
Pr: Aaron Forem

D-U-N-S 02-864-3513
WUNDERLICH SECURITIES INC
6000 Poplar Ave Ste 150, Memphis, TN 38119-3971
Tel (901) 251-1330 *Founded/Ownrshp* 1992
Sales 193.3MM[E] *EMP* 450
SIC 6211 Security brokers & dealers
CEO: Gary Wunderlich
V Ch: Heard Stoddard
Pr: Jim Parrish
COO: Steven Bonnema
CFO: Robert Crone
Ch: Alfred Yolsteb
Chf Cred: James Ritt
Chf Cred: Tracy Wiswell
Ofcr: Jackie McGehee
Ex VP: John Coppeto
Ex VP: Michelle Hoffman
Sr VP: Christopher Freeman
Sr VP: Martin Gaia
Sr VP: Larry Goldsmith
Sr VP: Irene O Haas
Sr VP: Matthew Harrigan
Sr VP: John Hohweiler
Sr VP: Matthew Houston
Sr VP: Michael Kapp
Sr VP: Erik Klefos
Sr VP: Ronald Kramer

D-U-N-S 17-556-2107
WUNDERLICH-MALEC ENGINEERING INC
6101 Blue Circle Dr, Eden Prairie, MN 55343-9108
Tel (952) 933-3222 *Founded/Ownrshp* 1981
Sales 95.5MM[E] *EMP* 163
SIC 8711 Consulting engineer
Pr: Neal Wunderlich
**Treas:* Deborah A Wunderlich
**VP:* Walter Malec
Dir IT: Antony Jones
Sys Mgr: Charles W Waugh
Sftwr Eng: Jerry Dercks
Opers Mgr: Roy Marin
Opers Mgr: Michael Norman
Sls Mgr: Dennis Euers
Snr PM: Benjamin Mark
Snr PM: Jeff Norman

WUNDIES KICKAWAY INNER SECRETS
See DELTA GALIL USA INC

D-U-N-S 09-392-0411 IMP
WURTH ADAMS NUT & BOLT CO
(*Suby of* WURTH GROUP OF NORTH AMERICA INC) ★
9485 Winnetka Ave N, Brooklyn Park, MN 55445-1618
Tel (763) 424-3374 *Founded/Ownrshp* 1978
Sales 85.3MM[E] *EMP* 240
SIC 5072 Miscellaneous fasteners; Nuts (hardware); Bolts; Rivets
Pr: Gary Huck
**CFO:* Jody Fearing Trende
Exec: Alejandra Gutierrez
CTO: Brian Doboszenski
Sls Dir: Michael Mielke

D-U-N-S 00-174-5074 IMP
WURTH BAER SUPPLY CO
(*Suby of* WURTH GROUP OF NORTH AMERICA INC) ★
909 Forest Edge Dr, Vernon Hills, IL 60061-3106
Tel (847) 913-2237 *Founded/Ownrshp* 1957
Sales 177.0MM[E] *EMP* 400
SIC 5072 Builders' hardware; Hand tools
Pr: Thomas O'Neill
**CFO:* Kenneth Cassidy
Treas: Helma Baer
VP: Steve Attman
**VP:* Peter Zinni
IT Man: Frank Cunningham
Mktg Dir: Jim Pacione
Sls Dir: Kevin Blanch
Manager: Tim Morrow

D-U-N-S 62-212-2406 IMP
WURTH GROUP OF NORTH AMERICA INC
(*Suby of* WURTH INTERNATIONAL AG)
93 Grant St, Ramsey, NJ 07446-1105
Tel (201) 818-8877 *Founded/Ownrshp* 1988
Sales 1.3MMM[E] *EMP* 835
SIC 5013 5099 5072 Automotive supplies & parts; Wood & wood by-products; Hardware
CEO: Volker Baer
Sr VP: Satterfield Paul
Rgnl Mgr: David Gibson
Rgnl Mgr: Marco Iven
Dist Mgr: Jason Deangelo
Dist Mgr: Joel Garter
Dist Mgr: Amber Piller
Dist Mgr: Thomas Saak
IT Man: Susie Ebio
Manager: Jenny Castro
Manager: Todd Clabough

D-U-N-S 04-633-8463 IMP
WURTH USA INC
(*Suby of* WURTH GROUP OF NORTH AMERICA INC) ★
93 Grant St, Ramsey, NJ 07446-1179
Tel (201) 825-2710 *Founded/Ownrshp* 1973
Sales 121.4MM[E] *EMP* 503
SIC 5013 Automotive supplies
Pr: Rick Beter
VP: Peter Koukis
**VP:* Volker Paer
VP: Marc Weber
Dist Mgr: Scott Johnson
Dist Mgr: Dominick Lacitignola
Dist Mgr: Greg Mattesen
Dist Mgr: Ryan Snyder
Genl Mgr: Jason Martinelli
Dir IT: Martha Confessore
Opers Mgr: Paul Hughes

D-U-N-S 10-580-4702 IMP
WURTH WOOD GROUP INC
(*Suby of* WURTH GROUP OF NORTH AMERICA INC) ★
4250 Golf Acres Dr, Charlotte, NC 28208-5863
Tel (704) 394-9479 *Founded/Ownrshp* 1999
Sales 90.0MM[E] *EMP* 370
SIC 5211 5031 Lumber products; Lumber: rough, dressed & finished
Pr: Robert H Stolz
**Pr:* Roger Debnam
**VP:* Mike Greenwood
**VP:* Douglas K Lynch
Genl Mgr: Randy Borrego
Genl Mgr: Sarah Cozart
Genl Mgr: Randy Fessler
Genl Mgr: Steve Russell
Genl Mgr: John Venditti
Genl Mgr: Jeff Vincent
Opers Mgr: Steve Bannister

D-U-N-S 00-798-5906 IMP
WURTH/SERVICE SUPPLY INC
(*Suby of* ADOLF WURTH GMBH & CO KG)
4935 W 86th St, Indianapolis, IN 46268-1666
Tel (317) 704-1000 *Founded/Ownrshp* 1948, 1998
Sales 110.0MM[E] *EMP* 240
SIC 5072

WV SUPREME COURT OF APPEALS
See JUDICIARY COURTS OF STATE OF WEST VIRGINIA

D-U-N-S 60-935-9315 IMP
WVA MANUFACTURING LLC
(*Suby of* GLOBE SPECIALTY METALS) ★
Rr 60, Alloy, WV 25002
Tel (304) 779-3200 *Founded/Ownrshp* 2009
Sales 94.6MM[E] *EMP* 200
SIC 3339 2819 Primary nonferrous metals; Industrial inorganic chemicals
CEO: Jeff Bradley
**CEO:* Arden Sims
**VP:* Vickie Hudson

D-U-N-S 19-595-5174
■ WVLT-TV INC
VOLUNTEER TV.COM
(*Suby of* GRAY TELEVISION INC) ★
6450 Papermill Dr, Knoxville, TN 37919-4812
Tel (865) 450-8888 *Founded/Ownrshp* 1996
Sales 468.8MM[E] *EMP* 2,093[E]
SIC 4833 Television broadcasting stations
Pr: Christopher Baker
VP: Tony Bernhardt
Off Mgr: Debbie Helton
Sls Mgr: Valerie Daugherty

WVUHS
See WEST VIRGINIA UNITED HEALTH SYSTEM INC

D-U-N-S 03-237-6709
WW GAY MECHANICAL CONTRACTOR INC
524 Stockton St, Jacksonville, FL 32204-2500
Tel (904) 388-2696 *Founded/Ownrshp* 1962
Sales 190.0MM *EMP* 850
SIC 1711 Mechanical contractor; Fire sprinkler system installation
**Pr:* David D Boree
Treas: James Huntley
VP: Carl Bowles
VP: Mike Bowles
**VP:* Frank C Houser Jr
**VP:* Dean Painter
**VP:* Tom Smith
VP: Michelle Stanley
Genl Mgr: Mike Yuhas
QA Dir: Jamie Webb
Telecom Mg: Mickey Prince

D-U-N-S 00-510-3494
▲ WW GRAINGER INC (IL)
100 Grainger Pkwy, Lake Forest, IL 60045-5202
Tel (847) 535-1000 *Founded/Ownrshp* 1927
Sales 9.9MMM *EMP* 25,800[E]
Accts Ernst & Young Llp Chicago Il
Tkr Sym GWW *Exch* NYS
SIC 5063 5084 5075 5085 5072 Motors, electric; Motor controls, starters & relays: electric; Power transmission equipment, electric; Lighting fixtures; Industrial machinery & equipment; Fans, industrial; Pumps & pumping equipment; Compressors, except air conditioning; Warm air heating equipment & supplies; Air conditioning equipment, except room units; Electric tools; Power tools & accessories; Hand tools
Ch Bd: James T Ryan
COO: Donald G Macpherson
CFO: Ronald L Jadin
Ofcr: Joseph C High
Sr VP: Michael Ali
Sr VP: John L Howard
Sr VP: Dennis Jensen
VP: Chris Chapman
VP: William Chapman
VP: Parris Devine
VP: Michael Dubose
VP: Cindi Evans
VP: William Lomax
VP: Patrick Oneal
VP: Ana Pena
VP: Geoffrey Robertson
VP: Sergio Sanchez
VP: Elizabeth Ubell
Dir Risk M: Ron Cooley
Dir Bus: Kevin Hartler
Board of Directors: James D Slavik, Rodney C Adkins, Brian P Anderson, V Ann Hailey, William K Hall, Stuart L Levenick, Neil S Novich, Michael J Roberts, Gary L Rogers, E Scott Santi

D-U-N-S 06-883-5800
WW GROUP INC
WEIGHT WATCHERS
28555 Orchard Lake Rd # 100, Farmington Hills, MI 48334-2973
Tel (248) 553-8555 *Founded/Ownrshp* 1966, 2000
Sales 24.6MM^E *EMP* 1,000
SIC 7299 Diet center, without medical staff
Pr: Florine Mark
**VP:* Amy Brozgold
**VP:* David M Mark
Mktg Dir: Cheryl Fellows

D-U-N-S 11-822-4575
WW LBV INC
BEST WSTN LK BENA VISTA RESORT
2000 Hotel Plaza Blvd, Lake Buena Vista, FL 32830-8440
Tel (407) 828-2424 *Founded/Ownrshp* 2004
Sales 82.1MM^E *EMP* 1,689
SIC 8741 Hotel or motel management
Pr: Majid Mangalji
Treas: Moez Mangalji
Genl Mgr: Ed Kortum

D-U-N-S 09-722-6047 EXP
WW LIQUIDATION INC
WATERWORKS
60 Backus Ave, Danbury, CT 06810-7329
Tel (203) 546-6000 *Founded/Ownrshp* 2005
Sales 166.3MM^E *EMP* 385
SIC 5074 5999 5211 Plumbing fittings & supplies; Plumbing & heating supplies; Tile, ceramic
CEO: Nancye Gree
**Pr:* Brian Vent
**CFO:* Ralph Bennett
**Ch:* Peter Sallick
VP: Amy Callanan
**VP:* Karen Edwards
**VP:* Lisa Ellis
VP: Barbara Morehouse
**VP:* Daniel Powers
**VP:* Barbara G Sallick
**VP:* Robert J Sallick
**VP:* David Schaefer
**VP:* Michelle Visser

D-U-N-S 00-892-6032
WW WALLWORK INC (ND)
FORD
900 35th St N, Fargo, ND 58102-3089
Tel (701) 282-6700 *Founded/Ownrshp* 1921
Sales 134.7MM^E *EMP* 250
SIC 5511 5012 5013 Trucks, tractors & trailers: new & used; Automobiles; Trucks, commercial; Trailers for trucks, new & used; Automotive supplies & parts
Pr: William W Wallwork III
**Pr:* William Wallwork

WW&R
See WELTMAN WEINBERG & REIS CO LPA

WWCI
See WILD WELL CONTROL INC

D-U-N-S 18-802-1059
■ **WWF OPERATING CO**
(*Suby of* WHITEWAVE FOODS CO) ★
12002 Airport Way, Broomfield, CO 80021-2546
Tel (214) 303-3400 *Founded/Ownrshp* 2012
Sales 789.6MM^E *EMP* 2,500
SIC 2026 2023 Milk & cream, except fermented, cultured & flavored; Cream, whipped; Yogurt; Dry, condensed, evaporated dairy products; Dried nonfat milk
Ch Bd: Gregg L Engles
**CFO:* Kelly J Haecker
**Ex VP:* Edward F Fugger
**Ex VP:* Roger E Theodoredis
**Ex VP:* Thomas N Zanetich

D-U-N-S 05-148-2800
WWL VEHICLE SERVICES AMERICAS INC
(*Suby of* WALLENIUS WILHELMSEN LOGISTICS AMERICAS LLC) ★
188 Broadway Ste 1, Woodcliff Lake, NJ 07677-8072
Tel (201) 505-5100 *Founded/Ownrshp* 1969
Sales 172.9MM^E *EMP* 1,250
SIC 4225 5531 7549 General warehousing & storage; Automotive accessories; Automotive maintenance services
CEO: John Felitto
**CFO:* Mike Hynekamp
Treas: Raimund Brendel
VP: Kevin Killoran

D-U-N-S 83-006-3520 IMP/EXP
WWRD US LLC
(*Suby of* WWRD HOLDINGS LIMITED)
1330 Campus Pkwy, Wall Township, NJ 07753-6811
Tel (732) 938-5800 *Founded/Ownrshp* 2009
Sales 221.8MM^E *EMP* 450
SIC 5023 Home furnishings
CEO: Pierre De Villemejane
COO: Gene Tognela
VP: Robert Shearer
VP: Leigh Taylor
Area Mgr: Nicole Archard
Area Mgr: Donna Bryan
Area Mgr: Rob Essman
Genl Mgr: Kris Bittenbinder
Genl Mgr: Georgina Garrity
Genl Mgr: Gillian Hodgson
CTO: John Perrotto

D-U-N-S 13-209-7051
WWSC HOLDINGS CORP
1730 W Reno Ave, Oklahoma City, OK 73106-3216
Tel (405) 235-3621 *Founded/Ownrshp* 2002
Sales 111.3MM^E *EMP* 1,000
SIC 7389 Personal service agents, brokers & bureaus
Pr: Rick Cooper
**CFO:* J Patrick Hare
**Ch:* Bert Cooper
**VP:* Gary Schnacke
VP Sls: Mike Hankins

D-U-N-S 83-226-3276
WWSC HOLDINGS LLC
(*Suby of* WWSC HOLDINGS CORP) ★
1730 W Reno Ave, Oklahoma City, OK 73106-3216
Tel (405) 235-3621 *Founded/Ownrshp* 2004
Sales 110.5MM^E *EMP* 1,000^E
SIC 3441 Fabricated structural metal
Pr: Rick Cooper
**Ch:* Bert Cooper
**Ex VP:* J Patrick Hare

D-U-N-S 06-717-4313
WWST CORP LLC
WQKT/WKVX
(*Suby of* WOOSTER REPUBLICAN PRINTING CO)
186 S Hillcrest Dr, Wooster, OH 44691-3727
Tel (330) 264-5122 *Founded/Ownrshp* 1996
Sales 50.2MM^E *EMP* 1,605^E
SIC 4833 Television broadcasting stations
Genl Mgr: Craig Walton

WWW.MEDICALALARM.COM
See CONNECT AMERICA.COM LLC

WXIA-TV
See GANNETT BROADCASTING INC

D-U-N-S 00-430-9233 IMP
WYANDOT INC (OH)
135 Wyandot Ave, Marion, OH 43302-1538
Tel (740) 383-4031 *Founded/Ownrshp* 1936
Sales 111.4MM^E *EMP* 350
SIC 2096 Corn chips & other corn-based snacks
CEO: Nick R Chilton
**Pr:* Rex Parrott
**CFO:* Bob Wentz
Ofcr: Dan Mc Grady
VP: Lynn Deeter
VP: Diana Fairclough
**VP:* Bryan Hensel
**VP:* Dan McGrady
VP: Don Mount
Area Mgr: Wayne Cook
Area Mgr: Hank Miller

WYANDOTTE CNTY/KNSAS CTY, UNFD
See UNIFIED GOVERNMENT OF WYANDOTTE COUNTY

D-U-N-S 62-526-0757
■ **WYANDOTTE TELEPHONE CO**
TDS
(*Suby of* TDS TELECOMMUNICATIONS CORP) ★
5 N Main, Wyandotte, OK 74370-4036
Tel (918) 678-8992 *Founded/Ownrshp* 1992
Sales 853.0MM *EMP* 2,700
SIC 4813 Local telephone communications
Pr: David Wittwer

D-U-N-S 10-266-9587 IMP/EXP
WYATT FIELD SERVICE CO
(*Suby of* NOOTER CORP) ★
15415 Katy Fwy Ste 800, Houston, TX 77094-1813
Tel (281) 675-1300 *Founded/Ownrshp* 1985
Sales 165.0MM *EMP* 200
SIC 1791 Structural steel erection
Pr: Roy Cuny
Sec: Derek Falb
Ex VP: David Steinhauser
VP: Morris Dunham
VP: David Heidemeyer
VP: Todd Riedlinger
VP: Jeff Spence
Genl Mgr: James Jordan
Sfty Dirs: Danny L Vara
Sfty Mgr: William Bruce
Sfty Mgr: Frank Herrera

D-U-N-S 08-250-4358 EXP
WYCKOFF FARMS INC (WA)
PEAK SEASON FOODS
160602 Evans Rd, Grandview, WA 98930-9375
Tel (509) 882-3934 *Founded/Ownrshp* 1966
Sales 84.0MM^E *EMP* 550
SIC 0191 General farms, primarily crop
Pr: Clifford D Wyckoff
CFO: Reed McKinlay
**Ofcr:* Reed E McKinley
**Ofcr:* David W Wyckoff
**Ofcr:* Jean T Wyckoff

D-U-N-S 06-608-6307
WYCKOFF HEIGHTS MEDICAL CENTER
374 Stockholm St, Brooklyn, NY 11237-4006
Tel (718) 963-7272 *Founded/Ownrshp* 1889
Sales 229.0MM *EMP* 1,900^E
SIC 8062 General medical & surgical hospitals
Pr: Dominick Gio
**Ch Bd:* Emil Rucigay
**CEO:* Ramon J Rodriguez
CFO: Wahchung Hsu
Sr VP: Nirmal Mattoo
VP: Karen Carey
VP: Cletis Earl
VP: Edward K Freiberg
VP: Kenneth Freiberg
VP: Jose Hernandez
VP: Jebashini Jesursa
VP: Renee Mauriello
**VP:* Harold Mc Donald
VP: Karen Pleines
VP: Teresa Silversmith
**VP:* Kevin Smyley

D-U-N-S 04-990-8759
WYCLIFFE BIBLE TRANSLATORS INC
11221 John Wycliffe Blvd, Orlando, FL 32832-7013
Tel (407) 852-3600 *Founded/Ownrshp* 1942
Sales 186.7MM *EMP* 4,000^E
SIC 8661

D-U-N-S 00-311-0087 IMP
■ **WYETH CONSUMER HEALTHCARE LLC**
(*Suby of* WYETH LLC) ★
1405 Cummings Dr, Richmond, VA 23220-1101
Tel (804) 257-2000 *Founded/Ownrshp* 1866
Sales 187.7MM^E *EMP* 2,735
SIC 2834 Pharmaceutical preparations; Cough medicines; Cold remedies; Lip balms
Pr: John R Stafford
**Treas:* John R Considine
**Sr VP:* H Carlton Townes
**VP:* Stanley F Barshay
**VP:* Robert G Blount
VP: Michael Mead
Ql Cn Mgr: David Anson

WYETH HOLDINGS CORPORATION
See WYETH HOLDINGS LLC

D-U-N-S 82-756-6782 IMP
■ **WYETH HOLDINGS LLC**
WYETH HOLDINGS CORPORATION
(*Suby of* WYETH LLC) ★
5 Giralda Farms, Madison, NJ 07940-1027
Tel (973) 660-5000 *Founded/Ownrshp* 1907
Sales 19.7MM^E *EMP* 1,019^E
SIC 2834 2836 Pharmaceutical preparations; Analgesics; Cough medicines; Veterinary pharmaceutical preparations; Biological products, except diagnostic; Allergens, allergenic extracts; Vaccines; Veterinary biological products
Ch Bd: Greg Norden

D-U-N-S 00-131-7130 IMP/EXP
■ **WYETH LLC**
(*Suby of* PFIZER INC) ★
235 E 42nd St, New York, NY 10017-5703
Tel (973) 660-5000 *Founded/Ownrshp* 1926, 2009
Sales 4.6MMM^E *EMP* 47,426
SIC 2834 2836 Analgesics; Cough medicines; Veterinary pharmaceutical preparations; Biological products, except diagnostic; Allergens, allergenic extracts; Vaccines; Veterinary biological products
CEO: Ian Reid
Pr: Etienne N Attar
Pr: Richard R Deluca
Pr: Michael Kamarck
Pr: Joseph Mahady
Pr: Joseph M Mahady
**Pr:* Bernard Poussot
Pr: Cavan M Redmond
**CFO:* Gregory Norden
CFO: Walid I Mohamed
Treas: Robert E Landry
Bd of Dir: Ulf Wiinberg
**Ex VP:* Charles A Portwood
Ex VP: Robert Power
Sr VP: Timothy P Cost
Sr VP: Kathrin U Jansen
Sr VP: David M Olivier
**Sr VP:* Denise M Peppard
**Sr VP:* Lawrence V Stein
**Sr VP:* Mary Katherine Wold
**VP:* Kevin F Brady

D-U-N-S 07-117-0729 IMP/EXP
■ **WYETH PHARMACEUTICALS CO INC**
(*Suby of* PFIZER INC) ★
1 Carr 3, Guayama, PR 00784-9612
Tel (787) 864-4010 *Founded/Ownrshp* 1998, 2009
Sales 1.1MMM^E *EMP* 2,000^E
SIC 5122 Pharmaceuticals
Pr: Bob Esner
Pr: Geno Germano
**VP:* Jaime Garay

D-U-N-S 11-300-8515 IMP
■ **WYETH PHARMACEUTICALS INC**
PFIZER
(*Suby of* PFIZER INC) ★
500 Arcola Rd, Collegeville, PA 19426-4904
Tel (484) 865-5000 *Founded/Ownrshp* 2002
Sales 1.5MMM^E *EMP* 4,376^E
SIC 5122 8731 Pharmaceuticals; Biological research
Ch Bd: M Anthony Burns
**Pr:* Dennis A Ausiello
**CEO:* W Don Cornwell
**CEO:* Bernard Poussot
**CFO:* Kenneth Martin
VP: Rich Gross
VP: Geoffrey Levitt
VP: Michael Mead
VP: John Quinn
Assoc Dir: Raj Attili
Assoc Dir: Karen Bien
Assoc Dir: William Bohn
Assoc Dir: George Condos
Assoc Dir: James Kelly
Assoc Dir: Karin Sassa
Assoc Dir: Kenneth Scott
Assoc Dir: Brinda Tammara

D-U-N-S 08-007-5822
■ **WYLE INC**
(*Suby of* K B R) ★
1960 E Grand Ave Ste 900, El Segundo, CA 90245-5092
Tel (310) 563-6800 *Founded/Ownrshp* 2016
Sales 737.8MM^E *EMP* 3,400
SIC 8711 7371 8731 Engineering services; Computer software development; Commercial physical research
CEO: Roger Wiederkehr
CFO: Dana Dorsey
VP: Stu Ashton
VP: Andy Zirkelbach
Prgrm Mgr: John Mikelaitis
Prgrm Mgr: Darrell Parker
Prgrm Mgr: Joseph Reiter
Snr Sftwr: Donald Horner
CTO: Jake Jacobs
IT Man: Timothy Tickle

D-U-N-S 87-807-5373 IMP
■ **WYLE LABORATORIES INC**
(*Suby of* WYLE SERVICES CORP) ★
1960 E Grand Ave Ste 900, El Segundo, CA 90245-5092
Tel (310) 563-6800 *Founded/Ownrshp* 2009
Sales 590.5MM^E *EMP* 3,400
SIC 8734 8731 Testing laboratories; Commercial physical research
CEO: George R Melton
**CFO:* Dana Dorsey
CFO: Dana P Dorsey
**Sr VP:* Roger Wiederkehr
VP: Greg Burner
VP: Tom Frey
VP: Harry Hamilton
VP: Doug Kirk
VP: Rich Schwenk
VP: Paul Thomas
**VP:* Doug Van Kirk

D-U-N-S 96-328-1881
■ **WYLE SERVICES CORP**
(*Suby of* WYLE INC) ★
1960 E Grand Ave Ste 900, El Segundo, CA 90245-5092
Tel (310) 563-6800 *Founded/Ownrshp* 2003
Sales 729.9MM^E *EMP* 3,400^E
SIC 8711 7371 Engineering services; Computer software development
Pr: George Melton
Pr: John Jordan
**CFO:* Dana Dorsey
**Sr VP:* Roger Wiederkehr
**VP:* Doug Vankirk
VP: Andy Zirkelbach

D-U-N-S 00-318-5733
WYLIE INDEPENDENT SCHOOL DISTRICT
951 S Ballard Ave, Wylie, TX 75098-4175
Tel (972) 442-5444 *Founded/Ownrshp* 1959
Sales 136.1MM *EMP* 1,000
Accts Edgin Parkman Fleming & Flem
SIC 8211 Public elementary & secondary schools; Public elementary school; Public senior high school
Treas: Pat Bahn
Ofcr: Joe McGriggs
Ofcr: Michael Stewart
Ex Dir: Jordan Adams
Dir IT: Chris Lamb
Schl Brd P: Null S Null Gooch
HC Dir: Amy Hillin

WYMAN PARK MEDICAL CTR
See HOPKINS JOHNS MEDICAL SERVICES CORP

D-U-N-S 00-112-8016 IMP/EXP
■ **WYMAN-GORDON CO** (MA)
(*Suby of* PCC) ★
244 Worcester St, North Grafton, MA 01536-1200
Tel (508) 839-8252 *Founded/Ownrshp* 1883, 1999
Sales 1.3MMM^E *EMP* 3,500
SIC 3463 3462 3324 3728 3317 Nonferrous forgings; Aircraft forgings, nonferrous; Engine or turbine forgings, nonferrous; Iron & steel forgings; Aircraft forgings, ferrous; Machinery forgings, ferrous; Aerospace investment castings, ferrous; Aircraft parts & equipment; Aircraft body & wing assemblies & parts; Pipes, seamless steel
Pr: Kenneth D Buck
Ch: David Guber
**Treas:* Steven C Blackmore
**VP:* Roger P Becker
VP: Jim Houlden
VP: Joe Jenkins
VP: Mark Roskopf
Mng Dir: Kim Glatki
Snr Ntwrk: Bruce McMillian
IT Man: Sebastian Bordron
IT Man: Renelle Chauvin

D-U-N-S 19-585-5556 IMP/EXP
■ **WYMAN-GORDON FORGINGS INC**
WYMAN-GORDON HOUSTON
(*Suby of* PCC) ★
10825 Telge Rd, Houston, TX 77095-5038
Tel (281) 897-2400 *Founded/Ownrshp* 1986
Sales 249.6MM^E *EMP* 850
SIC 3462 Iron & steel forgings; Missile forgings, ferrous; Nuclear power plant forgings, ferrous
CEO: Kenneth D Buck
**VP:* Ruth R Beyer
**VP:* Steven C Blackmore
**VP:* Shawn R Hagel
Genl Mgr: Mike Hall
IT Man: Tammy Aber
IT Man: Narayan Alagappan
IT Man: Sebastian Bordron
Software D: Ronald Wallis
Opers Mgr: Charles Sitterlet
Board of Directors: David Gruber

WYMAN-GORDON HOUSTON
See WYMAN-GORDON FORGINGS INC

WYNDHAM ANATOLE HOTEL
See DALLAS MARKET CENTER DEVELOPMENT CO LTD

WYNDHAM ANATOLE HOTEL
See ANATOLE HOTEL INVESTORS L P

D-U-N-S 80-953-0012
■ **WYNDHAM HOTEL GROUP LLC**
KNIGHTS INN
(*Suby of* WYNDHAM WORLDWIDE CORP) ★
22 Sylvan Way, Parsippany, NJ 07054-3801
Tel (973) 753-6000 *Founded/Ownrshp* 2005
Sales 322.1MM^E *EMP* 5,022^E
SIC 7011 Hotels & motels
Ch Bd: Stephen P Holmes
Pr: Len Carella
Pr: Clyde Guinn
Pr: Daniel Ruff
**Ofcr:* Josh Lesnick
Ex VP: Jim Alderman
**Ex VP:* Thomas G Conforti
Ex VP: Jeff Edwards
Ex VP: Ross Hosking
Ex VP: Flo Lugli
Ex VP: Chip Ohlsson
Ex VP: Keith Pierce
Ex VP: Sean Worker
Sr VP: Margo Happer
VP: Lisa Borromeo Checchio
VP: Don Li
Exec: Eric J Bock Sr
**Dir Risk M:* Duane Elledge

WYNDHAM HOTELS & RESORTS
See WYNDHAM INTERNATIONAL INC

D-U-N-S 05-972-7248 IMP
WYNDHAM INTERNATIONAL INC
WYNDHAM HOTELS & RESORTS
(*Suby of* LXR RESORTS) ★
22 Sylvan Way, Parsippany, NJ 07054-3801
Tel (973) 753-6000 *Founded/Ownrshp* 2005
Sales 86.8MM[E] *EMP* 350[E]
SIC 7011 8741 Hotel, franchised; Resort hotel; Ski lodge; Hotel or motel management
Ch Bd: Fred J Kleisner
CFO: Elizabeth Schroeder
Ex VP: Timothy L Fielding
Ex VP: Michael A Grossman
Ex VP: Mark F Hedley
Ex VP: Judy Hendrick
Ex VP: Andrew Jordan
Ex VP: Mark A Solls
VP: Susy Bell
VP: Marc Damico
VP: William Smith
VP: Mary Watson

D-U-N-S 60-688-5689
■ **WYNDHAM RESORT DEVELOPMENT CORP**
WORLD MARK
(*Suby of* WYNDHAM WORLDWIDE CORP) ★
9805 Willows Rd Ne, Redmond, WA 98052-2540
Tel (425) 498-2500 *Founded/Ownrshp* 2002
Sales 79.9MM[E] *EMP* 2,000
SIC 7389 Time-share condominium exchange
Pr: Franz Hanning
CFO: Michael A Hug
Sr VP: David Herrick
Sr VP: Gary Olmeim
VP: Michael Waring
Board of Directors: Franz Hanning

D-U-N-S 04-965-5624
■ **WYNDHAM VACATION RESORTS INC**
(*Suby of* WYNDHAM WORLDWIDE CORP) ★
6277 Sea Harbor Dr # 400, Orlando, FL 32821-8028
Tel (407) 370-5200 *Founded/Ownrshp* 2001
Sales 169.7MM[E] *EMP* 5,500
SIC 6531 6141 Real estate agents & managers; Time-sharing real estate sales, leasing & rentals; Installment sales finance, other than banks
Pr: Franz S Hanning
Pr: Jeffrey R Cohen
Pr: Emily Ingram
CFO: Michael Hug
Ofcr: Bobby Dedmon
Ex VP: Greg Bendlin
Ex VP: Mary Falvey
Ex VP: Dave Herrick
Ex VP: Bryant Raper
Sr VP: Dianne T Dubois
Sr VP: Jim Hansen
Sr VP: Mark Johnson
VP: Patrick Davis
VP: Peggy Fry
VP: Michael Gussow
VP: Jamie Hildebrand
VP: Lisa Maher
VP: Michael Turolla
Exec: Kim Lowe
Exec: Dianna McCook
Exec: Adina Slyter

D-U-N-S 78-366-1668
▲ **WYNDHAM WORLDWIDE CORP**
22 Sylvan Way, Parsippany, NJ 07054-3801
Tel (973) 753-6000 *Founded/Ownrshp* 1944
Sales 5.5MMM *EMP* 37,700
Accts Deloitte & Touche Llp Parsipp
Tkr Sym WYN *Exch* NYS
SIC 7011 8741 7389 6531 Hotels & motels; Vacation lodges; Hotel, franchised; Hotel or motel management; Time-share condominium exchange; Time-sharing real estate sales, leasing & rentals
Ch Bd: Stephen P Holmes
Pr: Geoffrey A Ballotti
Pr: Franz S Hanning
Pr: Gail Mandel
CFO: Thomas G Conforti
Ofcr: Mary R Falvey
Ex VP: Thomas F Anderson
Ex VP: Scott G McLester
Sr VP: Nicola Rossi
VP: Helen Allison
VP: Clement Bence
VP: Jennifer Braterman
VP: Jodi Campbell
VP: Scott Cavanaugh
VP: Susan Crane
VP: Kirsten Hotchkiss
VP: Jeffrey Leuenberger
VP: Kevin Linder
VP: Ruth Lipshitz
VP: David Mollov
VP: George L Scammell
Board of Directors: Myra J Biblowit, Louise F Brady, James E Buckman, George Herrera, Brian Mulroney, Pauline D E Richards, Michael H Wargotz

WYNIT AND NAVARRE
See WYNIT DISTRIBUTION LLC

D-U-N-S 18-213-5590 IMP/EXP
WYNIT DISTRIBUTION LLC
WYNIT AND NAVARRE
2 W Washington St Ste 500, Greenville, SC 29601-4893
Tel (864) 605-9920 *Founded/Ownrshp* 1987
Sales 307.4MM[E] *EMP* 350
SIC 5045 5043 5046 5199 7372

D-U-N-S 12-517-7373
■ **WYNN LAS VEGAS LLC**
(*Suby of* WYNN RESORTS HOLDINGS LLC) ★
3131 Las Vegas Blvd S, Las Vegas, NV 89109-1967
Tel (702) 770-7555 *Founded/Ownrshp* 2001
Sales 1.6MMM *EMP* 9,600[E]
Accts Ernst & Young Llp Las Vegas
SIC 7011 Hotels & motels; Casino hotel
Pr: Maurice Wooden
**Ch Bd:* Stephen A Wynn
**CFO:* Stephen Cootey
Sr VP: David Carroll
Sr VP: Kim Sinatra
VP: Laura Hemingway
VP: Wilson Ning
VP: Charles Stone
Exec: Brian Kenny
Ex Dir: Todd Moreau
Ex Dir: Roxane Peper
Board of Directors: John Hagenbuch, Ray R Irani, Robert J Miller, Alvin V Shoemaker, J Edward Virtue, D Boone Wayson

D-U-N-S 62-361-0958
■ **WYNN RESORTS HOLDINGS LLC**
(*Suby of* WYNN RESORTS LIMITED) ★
3131 Las Vegas Blvd S, Las Vegas, NV 89109-1967
Tel (702) 770-7555 *Founded/Ownrshp* 2000
Sales 1.6MMM[E] *EMP* 13,000[E]
SIC 7011 Hotels & motels
VP: Pete Lexis
**CFO:* Edward Peterson
VP: Samanta Stewart

D-U-N-S 11-262-0468
▲ **WYNN RESORTS LIMITED**
3131 Las Vegas Blvd S, Las Vegas, NV 89109-1967
Tel (702) 770-7555 *Founded/Ownrshp* 2002
Sales 4.0MMM *EMP* 20,800[E]
Tkr Sym WYNN *Exch* NGS
SIC 7011 Casino hotel; Resort hotel
Ch Bd: Stephen A Wynn
Pr: Matt Maddox
CFO: Stephen Cootey
Treas: Michael Weaver
Bd of Dir: Nicky Chiu
Ofcr: John Strzemp
Ex VP: Chris M Flatt
Ex VP: Debra Nutton
Ex VP: Alex Pariente
Ex VP: Susan Savage
Ex VP: Kim Sinatra
Sr VP: Tom Breitling
Sr VP: Tim Poster
Sr VP: Steve Vollmer
VP: Stephen Battaglini
VP: Cheryl Browning
VP: Teresa Dieguez
VP: Robert Gansmo
VP: Brian Gullbrants
VP: Dean Lawrence
VP: Elaine Lo
Board of Directors: John J Hagenbuch, Ray R Irani, Jay L Johnson, Robert J Miller, Patricia Mulroy, Clark T Randt Jr, Alvin V Shoemaker, J Edward Virtue, D Boone Wayson

D-U-N-S 10-581-2304 IMP
WYNNCHURCH CAPITAL LTD
6250 N Rver Rd Ste 10-100, Rosemont, IL 60018
Tel (847) 604-6100 *Founded/Ownrshp* 1999
Sales 952.6MM[E] *EMP* 2,209
SIC 6733 6799 Private estate, personal investment & vacation fund trusts; Investors
Pr: John Hatherly
**Pt:* Frank G Hayes
**Pt:* Terry M Theodore
**Ch:* Richard J Renaud
Mng Dir: Duncan S Bourne
Mng Dir: Duncan Bourne

D-U-N-S 06-858-7542
WYNRIGHT CORP
(*Suby of* DAIFUKU WEBB HOLDING CO) ★
2500 Elmhurst Rd, Elk Grove Village, IL 60007-6319
Tel (847) 595-9400 *Founded/Ownrshp* 2013
Sales 490.6MM[E] *EMP* 550
SIC 5084 3535 8711 Industrial machinery & equipment; Materials handling machinery; Lift trucks & parts; Conveyors & conveying equipment; Engineering services
CEO: Kevin Ambrose
**COO:* Kenneth Dickerson
COO: Daifuku Webb
**CFO:* Anthony J Caruso
**Div Pres:* Clint Lasher
**Div Pres:* Robert Liebe
Ex VP: Gordon Hellberg
Sr VP: Ron Adams
VP: Dave Beesley
VP: Dane Houston
VP: Randy Marble
VP: Kevin Sosnowski

D-U-N-S 03-733-6757
WYOMING CASING SERVICE INC
198 40th St E, Dickinson, ND 58601-7818
Tel (701) 225-8521 *Founded/Ownrshp* 2004
Sales 249.9MM[E] *EMP* 300
SIC 1389 Oil field services; Gas field services
Pr: Steve Halvorson
**CFO:* Tim Gross
**Sec:* Scott Newson

D-U-N-S 80-991-5796
WYOMING DEPARTMENT OF HEALTH
(*Suby of* EXECUTIVE OFFICE OF STATE OF WYOMING) ★
2300 Capitol Ave Ste 1, Cheyenne, WY 82001-3644
Tel (307) 777-6780 *Founded/Ownrshp* 1990
Sales NA *EMP* 1,520
SIC 9431 Administration of public health programs;
Ex Dir: Brent Sherard
**CFO:* Robert Peck
Ofcr: Jeff Urry
Dir Rx: Jo A Blevens
Dir Sec: Bruce Hayes
IT Man: Eric McVicker

D-U-N-S 80-991-6000
WYOMING DEPARTMENT OF TRANSPORTATION
(*Suby of* EXECUTIVE OFFICE OF STATE OF WYOMING) ★
5300 Bishop Blvd, Cheyenne, WY 82009-3340
Tel (307) 777-4375 *Founded/Ownrshp* 1990
Sales NA *EMP* 2,000
SIC 9621 Regulation, administration of transportation;
Treas: Jerry Rief
Exec: Larry Sheridan
Dist Mgr: Paul Fritzler
Genl Mgr: David Stearns
IT Man: Mike King
IT Man: Bill Oates

WYOMING FOOD BANK OF THE ROCKI
See FOOD BANK OF ROCKIES INC

D-U-N-S 04-812-8227 IMP/EXP
WYOMING MACHINERY CO
5300 W Old Yllowstone Hwy, Casper, WY 82604-1954
Tel (307) 686-1500 *Founded/Ownrshp* 1991
Sales 430.4MM[E] *EMP* 750
SIC 5082 General construction machinery & equipment
CEO: Richard S Wheeler
COO: Keith Cashman
COO: Virginia K Croy
**CFO:* John Kupko
Sr VP: Gail Howard
Admn Mgr: Cindy Tarcha
Sales Exec: Randy Quig
Sales Exec: Larry Sjolin
Sales Exec: John Thompson
Sls Mgr: Clif Bierwagen

D-U-N-S 07-340-0582
WYOMING MEDICAL CENTER
1233 E 2nd St, Casper, WY 82601-2988
Tel (307) 577-7201 *Founded/Ownrshp* 1986
Sales 224.2MM *EMP* 1,033
SIC 8062 Hospital, medical school affiliation
Ch Bd: Chris Muirhead
Dir Vol: Jillian Riddle
V Ch: Mary Macguire
**CEO:* Pam Fulks
COO: Vickie Diamond
**CFO:* Edmond Renenmas
CFO: Werner Studer
Ofcr: Matt Frederiksen
Ofcr: Mary Lynne Shickich
Sr VP: Ed Renemans
VP: Chad Pew
VP: Deb Weaver
Dir Rx: John Arross

D-U-N-S 00-965-8475
WYOMING TRANSACTIONS INC
2373 Cntl Pk Blvd Ste 100, Denver, CO 80238
Tel (303) 803-1397 *Founded/Ownrshp* 2012
Sales 140.4MM[E] *EMP* 300
SIC 8748 7929 Business consulting; Entertainers & entertainment groups
CEO: Issa Ali

D-U-N-S 06-959-4026 IMP
■ **WYOMING VALLEY HEALTH & EDUCATION FOUNDATION**
WILKES-BARRE GENERAL HOSPITAL
(*Suby of* COMMUNITY HEALTH SYSTEMS INC) ★
575 N River St, Wilkes Barre, PA 18702-2634
Tel (570) 829-8111 *Founded/Ownrshp* 1873
Sales 487.2M *EMP* 1,484
SIC 8062 General medical & surgical hospitals
Pr: William Host MD
VP: Joseph McDonald
Doctor: Carol Ragugini
Pharmcst: Molly Bieryla

WYOMING VALLEY HEALTH CARE SYS
See WILKES-BARRE HOSPITAL CO LLC

D-U-N-S 03-595-3827 IMP
■ **WYSE TECHNOLOGY LLC**
DELL WYSE
(*Suby of* DELL COMPUTER) ★
5455 Great America Pkwy, Santa Clara, CA 95054-3645
Tel (800) 438-9973 *Founded/Ownrshp* 2012
Sales 98.8MM[E] *EMP* 530
SIC 5045

D-U-N-S 87-753-2312
WYSS FOUNDATION
1601 Conn Ave Nw Ste 800, Washington, DC 20009-1055
Tel (202) 232-4418 *Founded/Ownrshp* 2007
Sales 1.2MMM *EMP* 3
SIC 8641 Civic social & fraternal associations
Prin: Stephen Vetter
Ofcr: Matt Hollamby

WYTHE WILL TZETZO
See FIRST SOURCE LLC

X O
See XO COMMUNICATIONS SERVICES LLC

D-U-N-S 05-859-6354
X-CHEM INC
(*Suby of* CHEMSEARCH DIVISION) ★
6141 River Rd, Harahan, LA 70123-5129
Tel (504) 733-5806 *Founded/Ownrshp* 1982
Sales 105.0MM[E] *EMP* 120
SIC 5169 Industrial chemicals
Pr: Greg Schwartz
**Treas:* Irena Kildisas
**VP:* Jim Bird
**VP:* Russell L Price
VP: Rich Robinson

X-ES
See EXTREME ENGINEERING SOLUTIONS INC

D-U-N-S 08-011-8850
X.COMMERCE INC
MAGENTO COMMERCE
54 N Central Ave Ste 200, Campbell, CA 95008-2085
Tel (310) 954-8012 *Founded/Ownrshp* 2009
Sales 120.0MM *EMP* 500
SIC 7371 Computer software development & applications
CEO: Mark Lavelle

D-U-N-S 07-976-2718
X5 OPCO LLC
X5 SOLUTIONS NOVATEL
2828 N Harwood St # 1700, Dallas, TX 75201-1518
Tel (214) 932-9293 *Founded/Ownrshp* 2015
Sales 85.0MM *EMP* 130
SIC 4813 Telephone communication, except radio
CEO: Greg Forrest
CFO: John London

X5 SOLUTIONS NOVATEL
See X5 OPCO LLC

XACT
See XCELLENCE INC

D-U-N-S 12-771-8307 IMP/EXP
XANGO LLC
2889 W Ashton Blvd Ste 1, Lehi, UT 84043-4968
Tel (801) 753-3000 *Founded/Ownrshp* 2002
Sales 186.6MM[E] *EMP* 675[E]
SIC 5122 Drugs, proprietaries & sundries
Ch Bd: Aaron Garrity
**Pr:* A Craig Hale
**Pr:* Jason Judge
**Pr:* Kent Wood
CFO: Melissa Bishop
Chf Mktg O: Alma Bustos
**Ex VP:* Gordon Morton
**Ex VP:* Joe Morton
**Sr VP:* Bryan Davis
**Sr VP:* Beverly Hollister
VP: Ryan Anderson
**VP:* Bob Freeze
**VP:* Scott Smith

D-U-N-S 82-714-0950
XANITOS INC
3809 West Chester Pike # 210, Newtown Square, PA 19073-2331
Tel (484) 654-2300 *Founded/Ownrshp* 2008
Sales 58.0MM *EMP* 1,312
SIC 7349 Building cleaning service
CEO: Graeme Crothall
**Pr:* Michael Bailey
**CFO:* Thomas R Morse
**Sr VP:* Dwight Sypolt
VP: Don Schweer

D-U-N-S 12-819-8442
XANTERRA HOLDING CORP
6312 S Fiddlers Green Cir # 600, Greenwood Village, CO 80111-4943
Tel (303) 600-3400 *Founded/Ownrshp* 2001
Sales 385.3MM *EMP* 3,500
SIC 5812 Restaurant, family: chain
Pr: Andrew Todd
**VP:* Michael F Welch

D-U-N-S 02-975-9649
XANTERRA INC
(*Suby of* XANTERRA HOLDING CORP) ★
6312 S Fiddlers Green Cir 600n, Greenwood Village, CO 80111-4920
Tel (303) 600-3400 *Founded/Ownrshp* 2002
Sales 350.7MM *EMP* 3,500
SIC 7011 Hotels & motels
Pr: Andrew N Todd
**VP:* Michael F Welch

D-U-N-S 18-474-8056
XANTERRA SOUTH RIM LLC
1 Main St, Grand Canyon, AZ 86023
Tel (928) 638-2631 *Founded/Ownrshp* 2003
Sales 90.0MM *EMP* 1,500
SIC 7011 5812 Vacation lodges; Eating places

D-U-N-S 18-761-4529
XANTERRA SOUTH RIM LLC
(*Suby of* PARKS XANTERRA & RESORTS INC) ★
6312 S Fiddlers Green Cir, Greenwood Village, CO 80111-4943
Tel (303) 600-3400 *Founded/Ownrshp* 2003
Sales 74.4MM *EMP* 1,000
SIC 7011 5813 7999 Hotels & motels; Tavern (drinking places); Tour & guide services; Tourist attractions, amusement park concessions & rides
Genl Mgr: Gordon Taylor
Ql Cn Mgr: Robert Parmer

D-U-N-S 18-058-1485
XAVIENT INFORMATION SYSTEMS INC
2125 N Madera Rd Ste B, Simi Valley, CA 93065-7710
Tel (805) 955-4111 *Founded/Ownrshp* 2003
Sales NA *EMP* 1,800
SIC 7372 Business oriented computer software
CEO: Rajeev Tandon
Top Exec: Mohd Khan
Sr VP: Kurt Eitz
Sr VP: Alex Salamon
Sr VP: Bob Stankosh
VP: Karen Reser
Exec: Robert Hallahan
Exec: Ankit Rathore
Exec: Sanjay Sharma
Prgrm Mgr: Gaurav Krishna
QA Dir: Ashher Siddiqui

D-U-N-S 07-472-4469
XAVIER UNIVERSITY
3800 Victory Pkwy Unit 1, Cincinnati, OH 45207-1092
Tel (513) 961-0133 *Founded/Ownrshp* 1831
Sales 166.6MM *EMP* 940
Accts Deloitte & Touche Llp Cincin
SIC 8221 University
Pr: Michael J Graham
**CFO:* Maribeth Amyot
Ofcr: Scott Chadwick
Assoc VP: Jeffery Coleman
VP: Eugene Carmichael
VP: Eugene Charmichael
VP: Justin Daffron
VP: David Dodd
VP: Roger A Fortin
VP: John F Kucia
**VP:* Gary Masa
VP: Gary R Massa
VP: Carol Rankin
VP: Terry Richards

VP: Mary Walker
Exec: Jayne McIntosh
Assoc Dir: Lynn Beirl
Assoc Dir: Lauren Cobble

D-U-N-S 02-085-7876
XAVIER UNIVERSITY OF LOUISIANA
XULA
1 Drexel Dr, New Orleans, LA 70125-1098
Tel (504) 520-7411 *Founded/Ownrshp* 1966
Sales 110.4MM *EMP* 600[E]
Accts Bruno & Tervalon Llp Cpas New
SIC 8221 University
Ch: Mr Michael Rue
**Pr:* Dr Norman C Francis
**Sec:* Mr Mark Romig
**VP:* Ed Phillips
**VP:* Sister Patricia Suchalski
Dir Lab: Melyssa Bratton
Dir Rx: Conchetta W Fulton
VP Admn: Ralph Johnson
Adm Dir: Brenda Medley
Doctor: Linda Blakley MD
Doctor: Amne Borghol MD

D-U-N-S 01-745-2397
XAXIS INC
(*Suby of* XAXIS LLC) ★
132 W 31st St Fl 9, New York, NY 10001-3406
Tel (212) 629-7173 *Founded/Ownrshp* 2014
Sales 98.9MM[E] *EMP* 390
SIC 7319 7313 Distribution of advertising material or sample services; Electronic media advertising representatives
Ch: David J Moore
Pr: John Barbera
CEO: Brian Gleason
**CEO:* Brian Lesser
CEO: Matt Sweeney
**COO:* Mark Grether
**CFO:* Christina Van Tassell
**Ofcr:* Anthony Borruso
Ex VP: Irene Bondar
**Ex VP:* Mark E Moran
**Ex VP:* Nicolle Pangis
Ex VP: Akira Yoshikai
Sr VP: James Alla
Sr VP: Stewart Shaw
Sr VP: Jack Smith
Sr VP: Garret Vreeland
VP: Michael Berganovsky
VP: Jerome Fitzgibbons
VP: Max Jaffe
VP: Judy Kendall
VP: John Piccone

D-U-N-S 96-868-3024
XAXIS LLC
(*Suby of* GROUPM) ★
132 W 31st St Fl 9, New York, NY 10001-3406
Tel (646) 259-4200 *Founded/Ownrshp* 2011
Sales 98.9MM[E] *EMP* 600
SIC 7311 Advertising agencies
CEO: Brian Lesser
Pr: Nicolas Bidon
Pr: Paul Dolan
Sr VP: Matthew Haies
Sr VP: Jason Webby
VP: Tim Bagwell
VP: Christina Beaumier
VP: Elizabeth Christensen
VP: Paul Georges-Picot
VP: Sara Hafele
VP: Damien Healy
VP: Max Jaffe
VP: Melissa Kihara
VP: Craig Sofer
VP: Paul Wallace
Assoc Dir: Andrew Arendt

XCEL ENERGY
See PUBLIC SERVICE CO OF COLORADO

XCEL ENERGY
See NORTHERN STATES POWER CO

XCEL ENERGY
See SOUTHWESTERN PUBLIC SERVICE CO

XCEL ENERGY
See NORTHERN STATES POWER CO

D-U-N-S 84-838-1245 IMP
▲ XCEL ENERGY INC
414 Nicollet Mall, Minneapolis, MN 55401-1993
Tel (612) 330-5500 *Founded/Ownrshp* 1909
Sales 11.0MMM *EMP* 11,687
Tkr Sym XEL *Exch* NYS
SIC 4911 4922 Generation, electric power; Transmission, electric power; Distribution, electric power; Natural gas transmission; Pipelines, natural gas
Ch Bd: Ben Fowke
Pr: Christopher B Clark
Pr: David L Eves
Pr: David T Hudson
Pr: Kent T Larson
Pr: Marvin E McDaniel
Pr: Mark E Stoering
CFO: Robert C Frenzel
CFO: Robert Frenzel
Treas: George Tyson
Ofcr: Timothy O'Connor
Ex VP: Scott M Wilensky
Ex VP: Scott M Willensky
Sr VP: David C Harkness
Sr VP: Judy M Poferl
Sr VP: Jeffrey S Savage
VP: Cheryl Campbell
VP: Michael C Connelly
VP: Jim Duevel
VP: Alan Higgins
VP: Aziz Khanifar

D-U-N-S 17-613-9954
■ XCEL ENERGY SERVICES INC
(*Suby of* XCEL ENERGY INC) ★
414 Nicollet Mall Fl 7, Minneapolis, MN 55401-1993
Tel (612) 330-5500 *Founded/Ownrshp* 2000
Sales 4.0MMM[E] *EMP* 10,917[E]
SIC 4931 Electric & other services combined
Pr: Benjamin Gs Fowke III

D-U-N-S 87-742-3277
XCELLENCE INC
XACT
5800 Foxridge Dr Ste 406, Shawnee Mission, KS 66202-2338
Tel (913) 362-8662 *Founded/Ownrshp* 2015
Sales 95.8MM[E] *EMP* 300
SIC 7374 Data processing service
CEO: Robert Polus
Mng Pt: Tim Kilgallen
VP: Carol Purcell
VP: Nick Reizen
**VP:* Tony Scott
Genl Mgr: Bill Anderson
Dir IT: Abby Simon
Software D: Sohel Haider
Prd Mgr: Jose Galvez
Prd Mgr: Sean White
Sls Dir: John Boyer

D-U-N-S 05-077-5804
XCELLERATEHR LLC
702 Civic Center Dr, Oceanside, CA 92054-2504
Tel (602) 571-2187 *Founded/Ownrshp* 2012
Sales 180.0MM *EMP* 24
SIC 7389
CEO: Sheila Guarderas
**COO:* Steve Holmes

D-U-N-S 08-003-1917
▲ XCERRA CORP
825 University Ave, Norwood, MA 02062-2643
Tel (781) 461-1000 *Founded/Ownrshp* 1976
Sales 324.2MM *EMP* 1,722[E]
Tkr Sym XCRA *Exch* NGS
SIC 3825 3429 Semiconductor test equipment; Manufactured hardware (general)
Pr: David G Tacelli
**Ch Bd:* Roger W Blethen
COO: Mark J Gallenberger
Sr VP: Pascal Ronde
VP: Dick McCarthy
Opers Mgr: Mark Distasio
Mktg Mgr: Jin Choi
Board of Directors: Mark S Ain, Roger J Maggs, Jorge L Titinger, Bruce R Wright

D-U-N-S 93-351-8875
▲ XENIA HOTELS & RESORTS INC
200 S Orange Ave Ste 2700, Orlando, FL 32801-6400
Tel (407) 317-6950 *Founded/Ownrshp* 1994
Sales 976.1MM *EMP* 47[E]
Tkr Sym XHR *Exch* NYS
SIC 6798 Real estate investment trusts
Pr: Marcel Verbaas
**Ch Bd:* Jeffrey H Donahue
COO: Barry A N Bloom
CFO: Atish Shah
Sr VP: Joseph S Bello
Sr VP: Joseph T Johnson
Sr VP: Philip A Wade
VP: Taylor Kessel
Board of Directors: John H Alschuler, Keith E Bass, Thomas M Gartland, Beverly K Goulet, Mary E McCormick, Dennis D Oklak

D-U-N-S 05-512-6341
▲ XENITH BANKSHARES INC
901 E Cary St Ste 1700, Richmond, VA 23219-4037
Tel (804) 433-2200 *Founded/Ownrshp* 2001
Sales NA *EMP* 533[E]
Tkr Sym XBKS *Exch* NGS
SIC 6021 National commercial banks
CEO: T Gaylon Layfield III
CFO: Thomas W Osgood
Chf Cred: Wellington W Cottrell III
Ex VP: Ronald E Davis
Sr VP: Judy Gavant
Board of Directors: Scott A Reed, James F Burr, Thomas G Snead, Patrick E Corbin, W Lewis Witt, Henry P Custis Jr, Palmer P Garson, Robert B Goldstein, Edward Grebow, Robert J Merrick, William A Paulette, John S Poelker

D-U-N-S 04-490-8189
XENTEL INC
(*Suby of* IMARKETING SOLUTIONS GROUP INC)
720 W Virginia St, Milwaukee, WI 53204-1539
Tel (954) 522-5200 *Founded/Ownrshp* 1999
Sales 51.6MM[E] *EMP* 1,500
SIC 7389 Fund raising organizations
Ch Bd: Michael Platz
**Pr:* David Winograd
**CFO:* Peter Pielsticker

D-U-N-S 13-982-1222
▲ XERIUM TECHNOLOGIES INC
14101 Capital Blvd, Youngsville, NC 27596-0166
Tel (919) 526-1400 *Founded/Ownrshp* 1999
Sales 477.2MM *EMP* 3,000[E]
Tkr Sym XRM *Exch* NYS
SIC 2221 3069 Broadwoven fabric mills, manmade; Printers' rolls & blankets: rubber or rubberized fabric; Roll coverings, rubber
Pr: Harold C Bevis
**Ch Bd:* James F Wilson
Pr: Eduardo Fracasso
Pr: David Pretty
CFO: Clifford E Pietrafitta
Ex VP: Michael Bly
Ex VP: William Butterfield
CTO: Joan B Ardevol
Board of Directors: Roger A Bailey, April H Foley, Jay J Gurandiano, John F McGovern, Alexander Toeldte

XEROX
See BUCK CONSULTANTS LLC

D-U-N-S 19-419-0609
■ XEROX BUSINESS SERVICES LLC
(*Suby of* XEROX CORP) ★
2828 N Haskell Ave Fl 1, Dallas, TX 75204-2954
Tel (214) 841-6111 *Founded/Ownrshp* 2009
Sales 10.5MMM[E] *EMP* 74,144
SIC 7374 7375 7389 Data processing service; Optical scanning data service; On-line data base information retrieval; Telephone services; Telemarketing services

Pr: Robert Zapfel
Ch Bd: Ursula Burns
CFO: M King
CFO: Brian Walsh
Treas: Doug Henderson
Ofcr: Peter Dowd
Ex VP: Connie Harvey
Ex VP: Bruce Jones
Ex VP: J Michael Peffer
Ex VP: Kevin Warren
Ex VP: Sue Watts
Sr VP: Mark Eugene Brennan
Sr VP: Michael Davis
Sr VP: Doug Mitchell
Sr VP: Ken Philmus
Sr VP: Laura Rossi
Sr VP: Lora Villareal
VP: Raymond Cano
VP: Brian Duffy
VP: Jarrod Johnson
VP: Alison Murray

D-U-N-S 13-211-5846
XEROX CAPITAL SERVICES LLC
100 S Clinton Ave Fl 18, Rochester, NY 14604-1877
Tel (585) 423-3805 *Founded/Ownrshp* 2002
Sales NA *EMP* 1,800[E]
SIC 6211

D-U-N-S 80-634-0100
■ XEROX COMMERCIAL SOLUTIONS LLC
ACS COMMERCIAL SOLUTIONS
(*Suby of* XEROX CORP) ★
2828 N Haskell Ave Fl 9, Dallas, TX 75204-2909
Tel (214) 841-6111 *Founded/Ownrshp* 1990
Sales 208.6MM *EMP* 2,500
SIC 7374 Data processing service; Optical scanning data service

D-U-N-S 04-959-1852
▲ XEROX CORP
45 Glover Ave Ste 700, Norwalk, CT 06850-1238
Tel (203) 968-3000 *Founded/Ownrshp* 1906
Sales 18.0MMM *EMP* 143,600
Tkr Sym XRX *Exch* NYS
SIC 3861 3579 3577 7629 7378 7374 Photocopy machines; Paper handling machines; Computer peripheral equipment; Business machine repair, electric; Computer peripheral equipment repair & maintenance; Data processing & preparation
Ch Bd: Ursula M Burns
Pr: James Burnell
Pr: Manoj Gopi
Pr: Amber Hayes
Pr: Terry Stallcup
CFO: William F Osbourn Jr
Treas: Iskra Gantcheva
Treas: Rohit Philip
Div VP: Bruce Bangert
Div VP: Corey Chapek
Ex VP: Jeffrey Jacobson
Ex VP: Don H Liu
Ex VP: Debbie Redman
Ex VP: Joseph Tumminelli
Ex VP: Chris Weadick
Ex VP: Robert K Zapfel
Sr VP: Lynn Edmonds
Sr VP: George Love
VP: Kristin Baca
VP: Scott Bashrum
VP: William Baxter
Board of Directors: Jonathan Christodoro, Richard J Harrington, William Curt Hunter, Robert J Keegan, Charles Prince, Ann N Reese, Stephen H Rusckowski, Sara Martinez Tucker

D-U-N-S 07-963-1867
■ XEROX EDUCATION SERVICES LLC (DE)
(*Suby of* XEROX BUSINESS SERVICES LLC) ★
2277 E 220th St, Long Beach, CA 90810-1639
Tel (310) 830-9847 *Founded/Ownrshp* 1970, 2002
Sales 123.0MM[E] *EMP* 2,350
SIC 7374 Data processing service
COO: Lynn Blodgett
VP: John Fassbender
VP: Imelda Julian
VP: Bill Krouss
Exec: Gil Guzman
Mng Dir: Richard Schnacker
CTO: Kent Schnacker
Dir IT: Peter Eberling

D-U-N-S 19-601-4372
■ XEROX FEDERAL SOLUTIONS LLC
(*Suby of* XEROX CORP) ★
8260 Willow Oaks Corp Dr, Fairfax, VA 22031-4513
Tel (703) 891-8774 *Founded/Ownrshp* 2010
Sales 85.4MM[E] *EMP* 2,475
SIC 8733 Medical research
Admn Mgr: Chavaughn Stith

D-U-N-S 08-005-7620
■ XEROX HR SOLUTIONS LLC
(*Suby of* A C S HUMAN RESOURCES SOLUTIONS INC) ★
200 Plaza Dr Nj, Secaucus, NJ 07094
Tel (201) 902-2300 *Founded/Ownrshp* 2002
Sales 8.5MM[E] *EMP* 1,075[E]
SIC 8742 Human resource consulting services; Compensation & benefits planning consultant

D-U-N-S 09-366-5359
■ XEROX STATE & LOCAL SOLUTIONS INC
(*Suby of* XEROX BUSINESS SERVICES LLC) ★
8260 Willow Oaks Crprt, Fairfax, VA 22031-4513
Tel (202) 378-2804 *Founded/Ownrshp* 1963
Sales 303.4MM[E] *EMP* 8,000
SIC 7373

D-U-N-S 07-347-1476
■ XEROX STATE HEALTHCARE LLC
(*Suby of* XEROX BUSINESS SERVICES LLC) ★
9040 Roswell Rd Ste 700, Atlanta, GA 30350-7530
Tel (678) 352-7200 *Founded/Ownrshp* 1981
Sales 121.7MM[E] *EMP* 1,200
SIC 7373 Computer integrated systems design
VP: Mary Scanlon

Off Mgr: Marcella Apruitt
MIS Dir: Wendall Turner

D-U-N-S 09-827-8112 IMP/EXP
XERXES CORP
(*Suby of* ZCL COMPOSITES INC)
7901 Xerxes Ave S Ste 201, Minneapolis, MN 55431-1288
Tel (952) 887-1890 *Founded/Ownrshp* 2007
Sales 88.1MM[E] *EMP* 330
SIC 3089 3443 3088 Plastic hardware & building products; Fabricated plate work (boiler shop); Plastics plumbing fixtures
Pr: Roderick W Graham
CEO: Ron Bachmeier
VP: Craig D Peterson
VP: Thomas L Tietjen
Exec: Grace Shaffer
Plnt Mgr: Rudy Tapia
Manager: Ted Cotton
Manager: Dennis Pardy
Board of Directors: Bernie Lafferty

D-U-N-S 06-236-4732
■ XETA TECHNOLOGIES INC
WINDSTREAM COMMUNICATION
(*Suby of* PAETEC HOLDING CORP) ★
4001 N Rodney Parham Rd, Little Rock, AR 72212-2459
Tel (800) 697-8153 *Founded/Ownrshp* 2011
Sales 127.8MM[E] *EMP* 467
SIC 3661 5999 7389 Telephones & telephone apparatus; Telephone equipment & systems; Telephone services
Pr: Greg Forrest
**COO:* Paul Comeau
**CFO:* Robert Wagner
Ofcr: Don Reigel
VP: Mark Scott
VP: Jeanne Shearer
Ex Dir: Scott Davis
Ex Dir: Tom Luce

D-U-N-S 08-010-5953
XFMRS HOLDINGS INC
7570 E Landersdale Rd, Camby, IN 46113-8512
Tel (317) 834-1066 *Founded/Ownrshp* 2004
Sales 67.8M[E] *EMP* 2,000
SIC 3699 Electrical equipment & supplies
Pr: Anthony Imburgia
VP: Joe Huff

D-U-N-S 79-100-9988 IMP
XFMRS INC
7570 E Landersdale Rd, Camby, IN 46113-8512
Tel (317) 834-1066 *Founded/Ownrshp* 1992
Sales 102.5MM[E] *EMP* 1,100
SIC 3677 5065 3612 Electronic transformers; Electronic parts & equipment; Transformers, except electric
Pr: Anthony E Imburia
**Treas:* Randell Barnhorst
**Treas:* Valarie Wareham
**VP:* Tony Imburgia
**Prin:* Cheri Imburgia
Genl Mgr: Buddy Woods
VP Opers: Anthony Imburgia

D-U-N-S 09-701-6364
■ XICOR LLC
(*Suby of* INTERSIL CORP) ★
1001 Murphy Ranch Rd, Milpitas, CA 95035-7912
Tel (408) 432-8888 *Founded/Ownrshp* 2004
Sales 757.0MM *EMP* 1,100[E]
SIC 3674 Microcircuits, integrated (semiconductor)
Ch Bd: Louis Dinardo
**Pr:* David B Bell
**CFO:* David Zinszer
VP: John M Caruso
VP: Michael P Levis
VP: Robert Mahoney
VP: Jim McCreary
VP: Shean O'Malley
**VP:* Sagar Pushpala
Off Mgr: Debbie Reve

D-U-N-S 11-816-8293 IMP
▲ XILINX INC
2100 Logic Dr, San Jose, CA 95124-3400
Tel (408) 559-7778 *Founded/Ownrshp* 1984
Sales 2.2MMM *EMP* 3,458
Accts Ernst & Young Llp San Jose C
Tkr Sym XLNX *Exch* NGS
SIC 3672 3674 7372 Printed circuit boards; Microcircuits, integrated (semiconductor); Application computer software
Pr: Moshe N Gavrielov
**Ch Bd:* Dennis Segers
CFO: Lorenzo A Flores
Ex VP: Victor Peng
Ex VP: Vincent L Tong
Sr VP: Steven L Glaser
Sr VP: Scott R Hover-Smoot
Sr VP: Krishna Rangasayee
VP: Ooi Boon
VP: Lawrence Getman
VP: Liam Madden
Board of Directors: Philip T Gianos, William G Howard Jr, Ronald S Jankov, Thomas H Lee, J Michael Patterson, Albert A Pimentel, Marshall C Turner, Elizabeth W Vanderslice

XIO STORAGE
See XIOTECH CORP

D-U-N-S 83-942-9016
XIOTECH CORP
XIO STORAGE
9950 Federal Dr Unit 100, Colorado Springs, CO 80921-3686
Tel (719) 388-5500 *Founded/Ownrshp* 1995
Sales 88.4MM[E] *EMP* 330
SIC 3572 4226 Computer storage devices; Document & office records storage
CEO: William Miller
**Ch Bd:* Alan Atkinson
**COO:* David Gustavsson
**CFO:* Lawrence D Firestone
**CFO:* Edward Welch

*Ch: Ken Hendrickson
*VP: Gavin McLaughlin
VP: Richard S Nelson
VP: Roger Walton
*Prin: Stephen Sicola
CTO: Stephen J Sicola
Board of Directors: Casey Powell

D-U-N-S 11-431-1074
■ XJT HOLDINGS INC
(Suby of EXPRESSJET HOLDINGS INC) ★
1600 Smith St, Houston, TX 77002-7362
Tel (713) 324-5236 Founded/Ownrshp 2004
Sales 1.6MME EMP 4,540E
SIC 4512 Air transportation, scheduled
Prin: James Beam

D-U-N-S 02-398-7717 IMP
XL AMERICA INC
XL CATLIN
(Suby of XLIT LTD)
70 Seaview Ave Ste 7, Stamford, CT 06902-6040
Tel (203) 964-5200 Founded/Ownrshp 1997
Sales NA EMP 2,775
SIC 6411 6321 6351

XL ASSET FUNDING
See XL SPECIALTY INSURANCE CO

XL CATLIN
See XL GLOBAL SERVICES INC

XL CATLIN
See XL AMERICA INC

D-U-N-S 80-881-6995
XL CONSTRUCTION CORP
851 Buckeye Ct, Milpitas, CA 95035-7408
Tel (408) 240-6000 Founded/Ownrshp 1992
Sales 193.1MME EMP 300E
Accts Ty Llp Danville Ca
SIC 1542 Commercial & office building, new construction; Commercial & office buildings, renovation & repair
Pr: Eric Raff
CFO: Tom Southam
*Ex VP: Dave Beck
*Ex VP: Mario Wijtman
*VP: David Beck
*VP: John Boneso
*VP: Alan Laurlund
*VP: Mario Wijjpman
Exec: Kevin Ng
Exec: Scott Schriefer
Mktg Dir: Patti Larson

D-U-N-S 05-599-4396
XL ENVIRONMENTAL INC
XL GROUP INSURANCE
(Suby of XLIT LTD)
505 Eagleview Blvd # 100, Exton, PA 19341-1199
Tel (800) 327-1414 Founded/Ownrshp 1981, 1982
Sales NA EMP 468
SIC 6411 8748 Insurance agents; Environmental consultant
Prin: Greg Hendrick
*Treas: Oscar Guerrero
Ex VP: Fielding Norton
VP: Michael Archie
VP: Kimberly Macdonald
*VP: J Splain
Exec: Cathy J Jakubowicz
Counsel: Matthew Ford
Counsel: Clifford Keljikian
Counsel: Deidra Moser

D-U-N-S 78-354-4468
XL FOUR STAR BEEF INC
3435 Gomez Ave, Omaha, NE 68107-2561
Tel (402) 731-3370 Founded/Ownrshp 2006
Sales NA EMP 1,000E
SIC 2011

D-U-N-S 00-181-3547
XL GLOBAL SERVICES INC
XL CATLIN
70 Seaview Ave Ste 7, Stamford, CT 06902-6040
Tel (203) 964-5200 Founded/Ownrshp 1998
Sales NA EMP 800
SIC 6331 6282 6351

D-U-N-S 00-699-0238
XL GLOBAL SERVICES INC
XL REINSURANCE AMERICA
(Suby of XL CATLIN) ★
70 Seaview Ave Ste 7, Stamford, CT 06902-6040
Tel (203) 964-5200 Founded/Ownrshp 1929
Sales NA EMP 954
SIC 6411 Insurance agents, brokers & service
Pr: John Welch
Pr: Barbara Luck
*CFO: Peter R Porrino
*Chf Inves: Sarah E Street
Ofcr: Anne Marie Elder
*Ofcr: Myron Hendry
*Ofcr: Eileen Whelley
*Ex VP: Susan L Cross
*Ex VP: Kirtsin Gould
*Ex VP: Gregory S Hendrick
*Ex VP: Jacob D Rosengarten
*Ex VP: Jamie H Veghte

XL GROUP INSURANCE
See XL ENVIRONMENTAL INC

XL MARKETING CORP
See ZETA INTERACTIVE CORP

XL PARTS
See A2 HOLDINGS LTD

XL REINSURANCE AMERICA
See XL GLOBAL SERVICES INC

D-U-N-S 87-907-3161
XL SPECIALIZED TRAILERS INC
(Suby of BULL MOOSE TUBE CO) ★
1086 S 3rd St, Manchester, IA 52057-2004
Tel (563) 927-4900 Founded/Ownrshp 2016
Sales 86.9MME EMP 185
SIC 3715 Semitrailers for truck tractors
Pr: Steve Fairbanks
V Ch: Scott Wall
CFO: Earl White
Genl Mgr: Matt Brunscheon
IT Man: Jeff Ingels
Sls Mgr: Adam Hoefer
Sales Asso: Jesse Wooten

D-U-N-S 18-508-6766
XL SPECIALTY INSURANCE CO
XL ASSET FUNDING
(Suby of XL CATLIN) ★
10 N Martingale Rd # 220, Schaumburg, IL 60173-2289
Tel (847) 517-2990 Founded/Ownrshp 1999
Sales NA EMP 1,600
SIC 6351 6331 Fidelity or surety bonding; Fire, marine & casualty insurance: stock
Pr: Stanley A Galanski
*CFO: David Montgomery
MIS Mgr: Scott Eckman

D-U-N-S 82-683-2011
XL SPECIALTY INSURANCE CO
70 Seaview Ave Ste 5, Stamford, CT 06902-6040
Tel (800) 622-7311 Founded/Ownrshp 2002
Sales NA EMP 1,600
SIC 6321 Accident insurance carriers
CEO: Michael S McGavick
CFO: Peter R Porrino
Chf Inves: Sarah E Street
Ofcr: Myron Hendry
Ofcr: Eileen Whelley
Ex VP: Susan L Cross
Ex VP: Kirtsin Gould
Ex VP: Gregory S Hendrick
Ex VP: Jacob D Rosengarten
Ex VP: Jamie H Veghte

D-U-N-S 07-923-9864
■ XM SATELLITE RADIO HOLDINGS INC
(Suby of SIRIUS XM RADIO INC) ★
1500 Eckington Pl Ne, Washington, DC 20002-2128
Tel (202) 380-4000 Founded/Ownrshp 1997, 2008
Sales 153.4MME EMP 973
Accts Kpmg Llp Mclean Va
SIC 4841 Direct broadcast satellite services (DBS)
Sr VP: Jon Zellner
*CFO: Joseph J Euteneuer
*Treas: David J Frear
*Ex VP: Kelly Baker
*Ex VP: Maritza Disciullo
*Ex VP: Neil Eastman
*Ex VP: Mark Rindsberg
Sr VP: Rebecca Hanson
Sr VP: My-Chau Nguyen
VP: Alex Kondracki
VP: Anh Nguyen
*VP: Chance Patterson
Exec: Mary Malone
Exec: William Olukoya

D-U-N-S 00-220-7843 IMP
XMH-HFI INC
BOBBY JONES SPORTSWEAR
(Suby of HMX OPERATING CO) ★
1155 N Clinton Ave, Rochester, NY 14621-4454
Tel (585) 467-7240 Founded/Ownrshp 2009
Sales 206.8MME EMP 870
SIC 2311 2325 Suits, men's & boys': made from purchased materials; Tailored dress & sport coats: men's & boys'; Slacks, dress: men's, youths' & boys'
Ch Bd: Walter Hickey
*Pr: Mike Cohen
*Pr: Paulette Garafalo
*CFO: Ed Reich
Ex VP: Fruno Castagna
VP: Sean C Fresco
VP: Daniel Marmion
VP: Michael A McGinn
VP: Jon D Morales
VP: Homi B Patel
VP: Brett Schenck
VP: Kenneth M Vojik
VP: Andrew A Zahr

D-U-N-S 04-361-8284
XMULTIPLE TECHNOLOGIES INC (CA)
SLASHPOINT SHARE DRIVE
1060 E Los Angeles Ave, Simi Valley, CA 93065-1827
Tel (805) 579-1100 Founded/Ownrshp 2001
Sales 80.6MME EMP 1,500
SIC 3643 Connectors & terminals for electrical devices
CEO: Alan Pocrass
*Pr: Jeremy Chu
VP Mktg: Rob Rothman
VP Sls: Mr Drew Stoiberg

D-U-N-S 62-360-9935
XO COMMUNICATIONS LLC
(Suby of XO HOLDINGS INC) ★
13865 Sunrise Valley Dr # 400, Herndon, VA 20171-6187
Tel (703) 547-2000 Founded/Ownrshp 2005
Sales 750.0MME EMP 1,500
SIC 4813 Local & long distance telephone communications
CEO: Christopher Ancell
CFO: Phong Le
Ex VP: Robert Geller
Ex VP: Navid Haghighi
Ex VP: Ernest Ortega
Sr VP: Mike Cromwell
Sr VP: Steven Nocella
Sr VP: Debbie Pollock-Berry
Ex Dir: Mark Sweeney
Genl Mgr: David Paul
CTO: Randy Nicklas

D-U-N-S 62-383-3212
XO COMMUNICATIONS SERVICES LLC
X O
(Suby of XO HOLDINGS INC) ★
13865 Sunrise Valley Dr, Herndon, VA 20171-6187
Tel (703) 547-2000 Founded/Ownrshp 2000
Sales 704.8MME EMP 3,670
SIC 4813 Local & long distance telephone communications
Ex VP: Ernie Ortega
*Sr VP: Mike Cromwell
Software D: Gary Chen

D-U-N-S 79-921-8540
▲ XO GROUP INC
195 Broadway Fl 25, New York, NY 10007-3123
Tel (212) 219-8555 Founded/Ownrshp 1996
Sales 141.6MM EMP 641E
Accts Ernst & Young Llp New York N
Tkr Sym XOXO Exch NYS
SIC 7299
Pr: Michael Steib
Ch Bd: David Liu
Pr: Paul Bascobert
Pr: Kristin Savilia
CFO: Gillian Munson
Ofcr: John Reggio
Ex VP: Katherine Brady
Ex VP: Michelle Dvorkin
Ex VP: Jennifer Garrett
Ex VP: Dhanusha Sivajee
Ex VP: Brent Tworetzky
VP: Alison Bernstein
VP: Josh Himwich
VP: Jennifer Perciballi
VP: John Pike
Dir Bus: Sarah Lambert
Board of Directors: Charles Baker, Diane Irvine, Barbara Messing, Peter Sachse, Elizabeth Schimel, Michael Zeisser

D-U-N-S 87-704-3612
XO HOLDINGS INC
(Suby of ACF INDUSTRIES HOLDING CORP) ★
13865 Sunrise Vley Dr 4 Ste 400, Herndon, VA 20171
Tel (703) 547-2000 Founded/Ownrshp 2003
Sales 1.4MMME EMP 3,670
SIC 4813 Local telephone communications; Long distance telephone communications
Pr: Carl C Icahn
Pr: Steven Nocella
CEO: Chris Ancell
CFO: Declaura Thomas
Treas: Kristi Jung
Ex VP: Robert Geller
Ex VP: Navid Haghighi
Ex VP: Ernest Ortega
Sr VP: Mike Cromwell
Sr VP: Debbie Pollock-Berry
VP: Gregory Freiberg

D-U-N-S 00-423-3474 IMP/EXP
■ XOMOX CORP (OH)
TUFLINE
(Suby of CRANE CHEMPHARMA) ★
4526 Res Frest Dr Ste 400, The Woodlands, TX 77381
Tel (936) 271-6500 Founded/Ownrshp 1956, 1972
Sales 187.8MME EMP 963
SIC 3491 3593 3494 Process control regulator valves; Fluid power cylinders & actuators; Valves & pipe fittings
Pr: William C Hayes
Ex VP: Daniel Ritch
VP: Mike McCalmont
VP: William Metz
Genl Mgr: Dale Friemoth

D-U-N-S 09-089-1628
■ XOOM CORP
(Suby of PAYPAL INC) ★
425 Market St Fl 12, San Francisco, CA 94105-5404
Tel (415) 777-4800 Founded/Ownrshp 2015
Sales NA EMP 190E
SIC 6099 Electronic funds transfer network, including switching
Pr: John Kunze
CFO: Ryno Blignaut
Chf Cred: Christopher G Ferro
Sr VP: Julian King
VP: Matt Hibbard
VP: Ramsey Lubbat
VP: Sally Mason
VP: Eugenio Nigro
VP: Joe Raymond
Prgrm Mgr: Tracy Daugherty
Snr Sftwr: Greg Gladman

D-U-N-S 61-064-3843
XORIANT CORP
1248 Reamwood Ave, Sunnyvale, CA 94089-2225
Tel (408) 743-4427 Founded/Ownrshp 1990
Sales 134.6MM EMP 134
Accts Weber And Company Inc San Jo
SIC 7379 7371 Computer related consulting services; Computer software development
CEO: Girish Gaitonde
Pr: Anirban Chakraborty
Pr: Shirish Gosavi
Pr: Raj Nataraj
*CFO: Mahesh Nalavade
VP: Sunil Bidwalkar
VP: Lawrence Brunelle
VP: Max Carnecchia
VP: Peter Elia
VP: Ashwin Honkan
VP: Datta Nadkarni
VP: Achalu Narayanan
VP: Jayaprakashi Ramakrishna
VP: Bhavesh Ved
VP: Ravi Viswanath
Exec: Alan Cade
Exec: Anupam Dash
Exec: Ajay Kumar
Exec: Johnson Mendonsa
Exec: Nripendra Pathak

XPAC
See EXPORT PACKAGING CO INC

XPEDX
See CENTRAL LEWMAR LLC

D-U-N-S 82-968-3171
▲ XPLORE TECHNOLOGIES CORP
8601 Ranch Road 2222 Ii, Austin, TX 78730-2304
Tel (512) 336-7797 Founded/Ownrshp 2007
Sales 100.5MM EMP 114
Tkr Sym XPLR Exch NAS
SIC 3577 Computer peripheral equipment
Ch Bd: Philip S Sassower
Pr: Mark Holleran
CFO: Tom Wilkinson
Chf Mktg O: Peter Poulin

D-U-N-S 00-690-9519 IMP/EXP
■ XPO CNW INC
(Suby of XPO LOGISTICS INC) ★
2211 Old Earhart Rd, Ann Arbor, MI 48105-2963
Tel (253) 926-2251 Founded/Ownrshp 2015
Sales 2.5MMME EMP 30,100
SIC 4213 4731 3715 Trucking, except local; Less-than-truckload (LTL) transport; Trailer or container on flat car (TOFC/COFC); Domestic freight forwarding; Foreign freight forwarding; Customhouse brokers; Truck trailers
Pr: Douglas W Stotlar
*CFO: Stephen L Bruffett
*Ex VP: Stephen K Krull
*Sr VP: Kevin S Coel
*Sr VP: Leslie P Lundberg
Dir IT: Tony Bennett
IT Man: Scott Ruder
IT Man: Elena Smith

D-U-N-S 10-276-6383
■ XPO ENTERPRISE SERVICES INC
(Suby of XPO LOGISTICS INC) ★
2211 Old Earhart Rd # 100, Ann Arbor, MI 48105-2963
Tel (734) 998-4200 Founded/Ownrshp 2015
Sales 1.6MMME EMP 19,000
SIC 4213 Trucking, except local; Heavy hauling; Trailer or container on flat car (TOFC/COFC)
Ch Bd: Douglas W Stotlar
*Pr: Joseph M Dagnese
VP: Jill A Bixby
VP: Lori A Blaney
VP: John P Burton
*VP: Craig Jackson
*VP: Paul Lorensen
VP: Pete Monta O
*VP: Richard Trott
*VP: William R Wynne
*VP Sls: J Edwin Conaway

D-U-N-S 96-550-7882
■ XPO ENTERPRISE SERVICES INC
CON-WAY ENTERPRISE SVCS INC
(Suby of XPO CNW INC) ★
1717 Nw 21st Ave, Portland, OR 97209-1709
Tel (503) 450-2000 Founded/Ownrshp 1996
Sales 98.4MME EMP 1,600
SIC 8721 Accounting, auditing & bookkeeping
VP: Kevin Coel
*Pr: Douglas W Stotlar
*VP: Mitch Plaat
VP: Keith Sawallich
Mng Dir: Margaret Gill

D-U-N-S 07-351-5645 IMP/EXP
■ XPO INTERMODAL INC
(Suby of XPO LOGISTICS INC) ★
5165 Emerald Pkwy 300, Dublin, OH 43017-1063
Tel (614) 923-1400 Founded/Ownrshp 2014
Sales 190.6MME EMP 940
SIC 4731 Freight transportation arrangement
Pr: M Sean Fernandez
Ch Bd: John T Hickerson
Pr: Larry Savage
CEO: Daniel L Gardner
COO: Jeffrey Brashares
CFO: John J Hardig
Ex VP: Peter Baumhefner
Ex VP: Julie A Krehbiel
Ex VP: Doug Matthew
Ex VP: Val Noel
Exec: Peter Ruotsi
Board of Directors: Gordon E Devens, Bradley S Jacobs

D-U-N-S 06-564-7724
■ XPO LAST MILE INC
3PD
(Suby of XPO LOGISTICS INC) ★
1851 W Oak Pkwy Ste 100, Marietta, GA 30062-2285
Tel (866) 373-7874 Founded/Ownrshp 2013
Sales 85.6MME EMP 1,000
SIC 4731 Freight transportation arrangement; Freight rate information service
CEO: Karl F Meyer
*Pr: Bud Workmon
*COO: Charlie Hitt
*CFO: Randy Meyer
*Chf Cred: Russell Marzen
*Sr VP: Mark Elsbey
*CIO: Jonathan Turner

D-U-N-S 60-592-8527
■ XPO LOGISITCS SUPPLY CHAIN HOLDING CO
XPO LOGISTICS - SUPPLY CHAIN
(Suby of XPO LOGISTICS INC) ★
4035 Piedmont Pkwy, High Point, NC 27265-9402
Tel (336) 232-4100 Founded/Ownrshp 2014
Sales 685.2MME EMP 8,000
SIC 4731 Freight transportation arrangement
CEO: Louis Dejoy
VP: Mike Hopkins
VP: Maureen Presner
*VP: Matthew Rogers
*CIO: Ashfaque Chowdhury

XPO LOGISTICS
See JACOBSON WAREHOUSE CO INC

XPO LOGISTICS - SUPPLY CHAIN
See XPO SUPPLY CHAIN INC

XPO LOGISTICS - SUPPLY CHAIN
See XPO LOGISITCS SUPPLY CHAIN HOLDING CO

D-U-N-S 11-131-5813
▲ XPO LOGISTICS INC
5 Greenwich Office Park, Greenwich, CT 06831-5128
Tel (844) 742-5976 Founded/Ownrshp 2001
Sales 7.6MMM EMP 89,000
Tkr Sym XPO Exch NYS

SIC 4731 Freight transportation arrangement; Brokers, shipping; Freight forwarding
Ch Bd: Bradley S Jacobs
COO: Troy A Cooper
CFO: John J Hardig
Ofcr: Gordon E Devens
Ofcr: Scott B Malat
VP: Eric Christian
VP: Thomas Connolly
VP: Lyndon Cron
VP: Paul Gordon
VP: Don Ingersoll
VP: Greg Russo
VP: Brenda Shepherd
VP: Andy Sommers
VP: Brent Stark
VP: Sergio Uribe
VP: Keith Weaver
Exec: Jeffrey Trefil
Board of Directors: Gena L Ashe, Louis Dejoy, Michael G Jesselson, Adrian P Kingshott, Jason D Papastavrou, Oren G Shaffer

D-U-N-S 15-235-6965 IMP/EXP
■ XPO LOGISTICS SUPPLY CHAIN INC
(*Suby of* XPO LOGISTICS - SUPPLY CHAIN) ★
4035 Piedmont Pkwy, High Point, NC 27265-9402
Tel (336) 232-4100 *Founded/Ownrshp* 2001
Sales 441.8MM^E *EMP* 8,000
SIC 4731 Freight transportation arrangement
Pr: Louis Dejoy
Ch Bd: Peter Reyher
Pr: Daniel Bergman
*Treas: John J Hardig
Chf Mktg O: Bryan Smith
Sr VP: Bill Church
Sr VP: John Schneider
VP: Mark Johnson
VP: Maureen Presner
*VP: Matthew Rogers
VP Bus Dev: Jeff Hendricks

D-U-N-S 78-438-0581
■ XPO LOGISTICS WORLDWIDE GOVERNMENT SERVICES LLC
(*Suby of* MENLO WORLDWIDE LOGISTICS) ★
4035 Piedmont Pkwy, High Point, NC 27265-9402
Tel (844) 742-5976 *Founded/Ownrshp* 2003
Sales 52.1MM^E *EMP* 2,200
SIC 4731 4225 4213 8741 Freight transportation arrangement; General warehousing & storage; Less-than-truckload (LTL) transport; Management services
Prin: Ashfaque Chowdhury
*Treas: Stephen K Krull
*VP: K Andrew Dyer

D-U-N-S 78-438-0016 IMP
■ XPO LOGISTICS WORLDWIDE INC
MENLO WORLDWIDE LOGISTICS
(*Suby of* XPO LOGISTICS WORLDWIDE LLC) ★
560 Mission St Ste 2950, San Francisco, CA 94105-3193
Tel (415) 486-2660 *Founded/Ownrshp* 1990
Sales 679.3MM^E *EMP* 2,200
SIC 4731 4225 4213 8741

D-U-N-S 10-719-8108
■ XPO LOGISTICS WORLDWIDE LLC
(*Suby of* XPO CNW INC) ★
4035 Piedmont Pkwy, High Point, NC 27265-9402
Tel (415) 486-2660 *Founded/Ownrshp* 2001
Sales 679.3MM^E *EMP* 2,205
SIC 4731 4512 4213 Domestic freight forwarding; Foreign freight forwarding; Customhouse brokers; Air cargo carrier, scheduled; Trucking, except local; Less-than-truckload (LTL) transport; Trailer or container on flat car (TOFC/COFC)
VP: John C Beckett
VP: Kristi Zaha
Exec: John J Herb
Opers Supe: Tyson Anderson
Opers Mgr: Anthony Marinaro

D-U-N-S 04-401-8518 IMP
■ XPO SUPPLY CHAIN INC
XPO LOGISTICS - SUPPLY CHAIN
(*Suby of* XPO LOGISTICS - SUPPLY CHAIN) ★
4035 Piedmont Pkwy, High Point, NC 27265-9402
Tel (336) 232-4100 *Founded/Ownrshp* 1997
Sales 517.1MM^E *EMP* 8,000
SIC 4731 Freight transportation arrangement
CEO: Louis Dejoy
*Ex VP: Dennis Hunt
*VP: Matthew Rogers
*CIO: Ashfaque Chowdhury

D-U-N-S 15-098-7758 IMP/EXP
XPRESS GLOBAL SYSTEMS LLC
6137 Shallowford Rd # 102, Chattanooga, TN 37421-7801
Tel (706) 673-6551 *Founded/Ownrshp* 2015
Sales 185.7MM^E *EMP* 677
SIC 4213 Trucking, except local
Pr: John Bowes
*CFO: Ray Harlin
*CFO: Jacques Labrie
Brnch Mgr: Mike Hernandez
Genl Mgr: Dean Boyer
Genl Mgr: Wayne Haley
Genl Mgr: John Massetti
VP Opers: Jim Bulman
S&M/VP: Terry Wiseman

D-U-N-S 18-997-0077
XPRESS HOLDINGS INC
(*Suby of* US XPRESS ENTERPRISES INC) ★
3993 Howard Hughes Pkwy # 250, Las Vegas, NV 89169-0961
Tel (702) 866-6001 *Founded/Ownrshp* 2000
Sales 168.6MM^E *EMP* 2,300
SIC 6719 4213 Investment holding companies, except banks; Trucking, except local
Pr: Mindy Riddle
Sec: Jane Greenberg

XPRESS NETWORK SOLUTIONS
See U S XPRESS INC

D-U-N-S 16-185-4054 IMP
XSE GROUP INC
AZTEC
35 Phil Mack Dr, Middletown, CT 06457-1567
Tel (888) 272-8340 *Founded/Ownrshp* 1984
Sales 116.8MM^E *EMP* 70
Accts Tm Byxbee Company Pc Ham
SIC 5112 Office supplies
Pr: Gerald Crean III
*Pr: Aztec Sales
*CFO: Mark Pritchard
*CFO: Jeremy Texeira

D-U-N-S 03-015-1963 IMP
XSTELOS CORP
45 Rockefeller Plz # 2260, New York, NY 10111-2291
Tel (201) 934-2000 *Founded/Ownrshp* 2009
Sales 243.7MM^E *EMP* 3,347
SIC 5661 Footwear, athletic
Pr: Neele E Stearns Jr
Treas: Shaun Murphy

XTANDI
See MEDIVATION INC

D-U-N-S 03-750-0659 IMP/EXP
XTEK INC (OH)
11451 Reading Rd, Cincinnati, OH 45241-2283
Tel (513) 733-7800 *Founded/Ownrshp* 1909
Sales 148.9MM^E *EMP* 469
SIC 3568 3547 3398 3312 Power transmission equipment; Rolling mill machinery; Metal heat treating; Wheels, locomotive & car: iron & steel
*VP: Frank P Petrek
*VP: James J Raible
*VP: Albert Schreiver IV
*Prin: C Jackson Cromer
*Prin: Lewis G Gatch
*Prin: J P Laycock
Genl Mgr: Thomas Ryan
Dir IT: Steve Heart
IT Man: Jamie Judd
Ql Cn Mgr: Dan Engle

D-U-N-S 80-471-2347
■ XTO ENERGY INC
(*Suby of* EXXONMOBIL) ★
810 Houston St Ste 2000, Fort Worth, TX 76102-6298
Tel (817) 870-2800 *Founded/Ownrshp* 2010
Sales 3.6MMM^E *EMP* 3,335
SIC 1311 Crude petroleum production; Natural gas production
CEO: Randy J Cleveland
Pr: Rett Storm
Treas: Brian Givens
*Ex VP: Timothy L Petrus
Ex VP: Dave Scasta
*Sr VP: Bennie G Kniffen
Sr VP: Timothy Petrus
*Sr VP: Gary D Simpson
*Sr VP: Kenneth F Staab
VP: David Burshears
VP: Keith Carwile
VP: Back Delbert Craddock
VP: Robert Gatyhiht
VP: Back Hammond
VP: Jeffrey Heyer
VP: Thomas Johnson
VP: Frank J Marco
VP: Martha Montgomery
VP: F T Perkins
VP: Win Ryan

D-U-N-S 55-543-5663
■ XTRA COMPANIES INC
(*Suby of* XTRA LEASE) ★
7911 Forsyth Blvd Ste 600, Saint Louis, MO 63105-3825
Tel (636) 207-6761 *Founded/Ownrshp* 2004
Sales 119.1MM^E *EMP* 663
SIC 7513 Truck leasing, without drivers
Pr: William H Franz
*CFO: Michael Dreller

D-U-N-S 08-338-0477
■ XTRA CORP
XTRA LEASE
(*Suby of* BERKSHIRE HATHAWAY INC) ★
7911 Forsyth Blvd Ste 600, Saint Louis, MO 63105-3825
Tel (314) 719-0300 *Founded/Ownrshp* 2001
Sales 120.8MM^E *EMP* 663
SIC 7359 Equipment rental & leasing
Pr: William H Franz
CFO: Michael J Dreller
Treas: Stephanie L Johnson
Sr VP: Steve Zaborowski
VP: Bob Keller
VP: John Pomilio
Opers Mgr: Britt Benson
Board of Directors: Leonard Barkan, Robert E Bennett, Marc D Hamburg, Sol Katz, Ruben Lewis, Harry Shapiro

XTRA LEASE
See XTRA CORP

D-U-N-S 87-884-8944
■ XTRA LEASE LLC
(*Suby of* XTRA LLC) ★
7911 Forsyth Blvd Ste 600, Saint Louis, MO 63105-3825
Tel (800) 325-1453 *Founded/Ownrshp* 1969
Sales 119.1MM^E *EMP* 650
SIC 7513 Truck leasing, without drivers
Pr: William H Franz
*CFO: Michael Dreller
*Sr VP: Steve Zaborowski
VP: Mark Backman
VP: Wes Klepper
VP: Andrew Krueger
VP: Georgia Munson
*VP: Kathy O'Leary
*VP: John Pomillio
VP: Stephen Zaborowski
Brnch Mgr: Pete Hoffman

D-U-N-S 09-362-8113
■ XTRA LLC
(*Suby of* XTRA COMPANIES INC) ★
7911 Forsyth Blvd Ste 600, Saint Louis, MO 63105-3825
Tel (314) 719-0400 *Founded/Ownrshp* 2004
Sales 119.1MM^E *EMP* 657
SIC 7513 Truck leasing, without drivers
Pr: William H Franz

XTRA MART
See DRAKE PETROLEUM CO INC

XTREME GRAPHICS
See TRAVEL TAGS INC

XULA
See XAVIER UNIVERSITY OF LOUISIANA

D-U-N-S 79-694-4957
XURA INC
200 Quannapowitt Pkwy, Wakefield, MA 01880-1312
Tel (781) 246-9000 *Founded/Ownrshp* 2016
Sales 270.9MM *EMP* 2,300
SIC 7371 Custom computer programming services; Computer software development
Pr: Philippe Tartavull
CFO: Jacky Wu
Chf Mktg O: James Colby
Ex VP: Nicolas Appert
Ex VP: Kathleen Harris
Ex VP: Roy S Luria
Ex VP: Jim Saunders
Sr VP: Raman Abrol
VP: Alexander Bershadsky
Snr Sftwr: Mahesh Gupta
Snr Sftwr: Anil Soma
Board of Directors: Ronald J De Lange

XYLEM
See FLUID HANDLING LLC

D-U-N-S 08-324-4269 IMP/EXP
■ XYLEM DEWATERING SOLUTIONS INC
JOHN DEERE AUTHORIZED DEALER
(*Suby of* XYLEM INC) ★
84 Floodgate Rd, Bridgeport, NJ 08014-1001
Tel (410) 243-4900 *Founded/Ownrshp* 1976, 2011
Sales 330.0MM *EMP* 790
SIC 7353 3561 5084 Heavy construction equipment rental; Pumps & pumping equipment; Pumps & pumping equipment
Pr: Colin Sobil
*Pr: Grant Salstrom
VP: Nicholas Anthony
VP: Delzingaro Mike
Dir Risk M: Timothy Glazar
Comm Man: Stephanie Morgan
Rgnl Mgr: Reed O Waterbury
Brnch Mgr: Ryan Booth
Brnch Mgr: Nathan Longhurst
Brnch Mgr: Mark O'Sullivan
Dist Mgr: Dean Mills

D-U-N-S 96-884-8734
▲ XYLEM INC
1 International Dr, Rye Brook, NY 10573-1058
Tel (914) 323-5700 *Founded/Ownrshp* 2011
Sales 3.6MMM *EMP* 12,700^E
Tkr Sym XYL *Exch* NYS
SIC 3561 Pumps & pumping equipment
Pr: Patrick K Decker
*Ch Bd: Markos I Tambakeras
Pr: Tomas Brannemo
Pr: David Flinton
Pr: Pak Steven Leung
Pr: Kenneth Napolitano
Pr: Colin R Sabol
CFO: E Mark Rajkowski
CFO: Therese Washburn
Treas: Samir Patel
Ex Ofcr: Shashank Patel
Ofcr: Kairus Tarapore
Sr VP: Jayanthi Iyengar
Sr VP: Claudia S Toussaint
VP: Hyman Buchwald
VP: Mike Delzingaro
VP: Jackie Helfrich
VP: Kelly McAndrew
VP: Christian Wiklund
Board of Directors: Curtis J Crawford, Patrick K Decker, Robert F Friel, Victoria D Harker, Steven R Loranger, Edward J Ludwig, Surya N Mohapatra, Jerome A Peribere

Y

Y, THE
See YMCA OF SAN DIEGO COUNTY

Y A T
See YOROZU AUTOMOTIVE TENNESSEE INC

D-U-N-S 00-797-7770 IMP
Y HATA & CO LIMITED (HI)
CHEFZONE
285 Sand Island Access Rd, Honolulu, HI 96819-2227
Tel (808) 447-4100 *Founded/Ownrshp* 1922
Sales 248.0MM *EMP* 350
SIC 5142 5141 Packaged frozen goods; Groceries, general line
Ch Bd: Russell Hata
*COO: Jim Cremins
*CFO: Brian Marting
Exec: Mona Taga
Dir Soc: Lena Young
IT Man: Glenn Lum

Y M C A
See YOUNG MENS CHRISTIAN ASSOCIATION OF GREATER HOUSTON AREA INC

Y M C A
See YOUNG MENS CHRISTIAN ASSOCIATION OF GREATER NEW YORK

Y M C A OF BROWARD COUNTY, FL
See YOUNG MENS CHRISTIAN ASSOCIATION OF BROWARD COUNTY FLORIDA INC

Y M C A OF GREATER HARTFORD
See YMCA OF METROPOLITAN HARTFORD INC

Y OF CENTRAL MARYLAND
See YMCA OF CENTRAL MARYLAND INC

Y P O
See YOUNG PRESIDENTS ORGANIZATION

Y V Y
See YELED V YALDA EARLY CHILDHOOD CENTER INC

Y-12 NATIONAL SECURITY COMPLEX
See CONSOLIDATED NUCLEAR SECURITY LLC

D-U-N-S 79-203-6449 IMP
YACHIYO OF AMERICA INC
(*Suby of* YACHIYO INDUSTRY CO., LTD.)
2285 Walcutt Rd, Columbus, OH 43228-9575
Tel (614) 876-3220 *Founded/Ownrshp* 1997
Sales 205.2MM^E *EMP* 300^E
SIC 3089 3465 3714 Novelties, plastic; Automotive stampings; Acceleration equipment, motor vehicle
CEO: Poshio Yanada
Admn Mgr: Sherri Spitzer
Ql Cn Mgr: Kirk Bohanan

YACHTS OF SEABOURN, THE
See SEABOURN CRUISE LINE LIMITED

D-U-N-S 07-783-0081
■ YADKIN BANK
(*Suby of* YADKIN FINANCIAL CORP) ★
325 E Front St, Statesville, NC 28677-5906
Tel (704) 924-8815 *Founded/Ownrshp* 1968
Sales NA *EMP* 481^E
SIC 6022 State commercial banks
Pr: Joe H Towell
COO: Mark Demarcus
CFO: Jan H Hollar
CFO: Edwin E Laws
Chf Cred: John R Crysel
Ex VP: John Brubaker
Ex VP: Kristi A Eller
Ex VP: Lestine H Hutchens
Ex VP: Joe K Johnson
Ex VP: Ed Marxen
Ex VP: Ed Shuford
VP: Scott Birkner
VP: Billie Jester
VP: Joanne Jolin
Exec: Joseph M Arundell
Exec: Carol Field

D-U-N-S 80-576-5596
▲ YADKIN FINANCIAL CORP
3600 Glenwood Ave Ste 300, Raleigh, NC 27612-4955
Tel (919) 659-9000 *Founded/Ownrshp* 2006
Sales NA *EMP* 882^E
Tkr Sym YDKN *Exch* NYS
SIC 6022 State commercial banks
Pr: Scott M Custer
*Ch Bd: Joseph H Towell
CFO: Terry S Earley
Chf Cred: Edwin H Shuford III
Ofcr: Robin S Hager
Ex VP: Steven W Jones
Board of Directors: Mary E Rittling, J Adam Abram, Harry C Spell, Michael S Albert, Richard A Urquhart III, David S Brody, Nicolas D Zerbib, Harry M Davis, Barry Z Dodson, Thomas J Hall, Thierry Ho, Steven J Lerner, Michael S Patterson

D-U-N-S 14-419-0089
YADKIN NURSING CARE CENTER INC
(*Suby of* TRIAD MEDICAL SERVICES INC) ★
903 W Main St, Yadkinville, NC 27055-7807
Tel (336) 679-8863 *Founded/Ownrshp* 1977
Sales 632.0MM *EMP* 130
SIC 8082 8051 Home health care services; Skilled nursing care facilities
Pr: Nolan G Brown
*VP: Carson Mooring

D-U-N-S 12-036-0560
YAFFE COMPANIES INC
1200 S G St, Muskogee, OK 74403-6612
Tel (918) 687-7543 *Founded/Ownrshp* 1998
Sales 93.2MM^E *EMP* 450
SIC 5093 5051 Ferrous metal scrap & waste; Steel
Pr: Glenn Yafe
*CFO: Sharla McAfee
*VP: Lyle Bachman
Sfty Dirs: Johnny Johnson

D-U-N-S 00-877-9522
YAGER MATERIALS LLC
OWENSBORO PAVING CO
5001 Highway 2830, Owensboro, KY 42303-9703
Tel (270) 926-0893 *Founded/Ownrshp* 1940
Sales 167.5MM^E *EMP* 225
SIC 1442 1422 1611 3273 4491 3731 Common sand mining; Gravel mining; Limestones, ground; Highway & street paving contractor; Ready-mixed concrete; Loading vessels; Shipbuilding & repairing
Genl Mgr: David Payne
CIO: Pat Yager
IT Man: Jim Yager

D-U-N-S 03-614-7239
YAHNIS CO
CHRIS J. YAHNIS
1440 N Schlitz Dr, Florence, SC 29501-6800
Tel (843) 662-6627 *Founded/Ownrshp* 1999
Sales 104.2MM^E *EMP* 205
SIC 5181 Beer & other fermented malt liquors
Pr: Byron C Yahnis
VP: Ken Emery
*VP: Victoria C Yahnis

D-U-N-S 88-436-4530
▲ YAHOO INC
YAHOOU
701 First Ave, Sunnyvale, CA 94089-1019
Tel (408) 349-3300 *Founded/Ownrshp* 1994

Section I Businesses Alphabetically

Sales 4.9MMM EMP 10,400
Tkr Sym YHOO Exch NGS
SIC 7373 7375 Computer integrated systems design; Systems software development services; Information retrieval services; Data base information retrieval; On-line data base information retrieval
Pr: Marissa A Mayer
Sr Pt: Omar Ansari
*Ch Bd: Maynard G Webb Jr
Pr: Greg Arnold
CFO: Kenneth Goldman
Sr VP: Adam Cahan
Sr VP: Simon Khalaf
VP: Samuel Chou
VP: Angela Gardner
VP: Jeffrey S Hoersch
VP: David Karnstedt
VP: Kenneth Meek
VP: Dan Tepstein
VP: Kirk Williams
Dir Risk M: Lisa Utzschneider
Board of Directors: Jeffrey C Smith, Tor R Braham, Eric K Brandt, Catherine J Friedman, Eddy W Hartenstein, Richard S Hill, Susan M James, Thomas J McInerney, H Lee Scott Jr, Jane E Shaw

YAHOOU
See YAHOO INC

YAK MAT
See DIXIE MAT AND HARDWOOD CO

D-U-N-S 08-020-4206
YAK MAT LLC
2438 Highway 98 E, Columbia, MS 39429-8056
Tel (601) 876-2427 Founded/Ownrshp 2016
Sales 200.0MM EMP 30
SIC 5211 5099 Lumber products; Timber products, rough
CEO: Jonathan Duhon

D-U-N-S 60-590-1219
■YAKIMA HMA LLC
YAKIMA RGIONAL MED CARDIAC CTR
(Suby of CHS PROFESSIONAL SERVICES) ★
110 S 9th Ave, Yakima, WA 98902-3315
Tel (509) 575-5000 Founded/Ownrshp 2014
Sales 91.8MM^E EMP 700^E
SIC 8062 General medical & surgical hospitals
CEO: Veronica Knudson
CFO: Cindy Rios
VP: Beth Gregory
Dir Lab: Caroline Arms
Chf Nrs Of: Ernie Stegall

YAKIMA RGIONAL MED CARDIAC CTR
See YAKIMA HMA LLC

D-U-N-S 05-548-4455
YAKIMA SCHOOL DISTRICT
104 N 4th Ave, Yakima, WA 98902-2636
Tel (509) 573-7000 Founded/Ownrshp 1899
Sales 85.5MM^E EMP 1,500
SIC 8211 Public elementary school; Public junior high school; Public senior high school
Off Mgr: Julee Accardo
Off Mgr: Josie Bryan
Off Mgr: Elsa Perez
Pr Dir: Kristin Fitterer
Teacher Pr: Nick Tobia
Psych: Brice Shipowick
HC Dir: Nancy McHenry
HC Dir: Rebecca Scholl

D-U-N-S 09-461-6935 IMP
YAKIMA VALLEY FARM WORKERS CLINIC INC
YVFWC
518 W 1st Ave, Toppenish, WA 98948-1564
Tel (509) 865-5898 Founded/Ownrshp 1978
Sales 141.4MM EMP 1,568
Accts Cliftonlarsonallen Llp Yakima
SIC 8011 8021 8093 1799 Clinic, operated by physicians; Dental clinic; Mental health clinic, outpatient; Weather stripping
CEO: Carlos Olivares
*Pr: Tom Sak
CFO: Peter Klaus Toop
Treas: Glen Davis
*Treas: Patricia Myers
*VP: Virginia Santillanes
Dir Rx: Thomas Schilling
IT Man: Christy Bracewell
IT Man: James G Ellis II
IT Man: David Perkins

D-U-N-S 02-023-3946 IMP
YAKIMA VALLEY MEMORIAL HOSPITAL ASSOCIATION INC
2811 Tieton Dr, Yakima, WA 98902-3761
Tel (509) 249-5129 Founded/Ownrshp 1950
Sales 361.8MM^E EMP 1,150
Accts Moss-Adams Llp Yakima Washin
SIC 8062 8082 General medical & surgical hospitals; Home health care services
Ch: James Berg
Dir Recs: Jamie Beaman
*CEO: Russ Myers
Bd of Dir: Gail Weaver
VP: Jim Aberle
VP: Randall Cline
VP: Mely Davenport
Dir OR: Tammy Smeback
Dir Risk M: Melanie Gilmore
Comm Dir: Leif Ergeson
Adm Dir: Lynda Boggess

D-U-N-S 00-982-7445 EXP
YALE ELECTRICAL SUPPLY CO
55 Shawmut Rd, Canton, MA 02021-1408
Tel (781) 737-2500 Founded/Ownrshp 1923
Sales 139.4MM^E EMP 50^E
SIC 5063 Electrical supplies; Wiring devices; Lighting fixtures
Pr: Warren Sheinkopf
*VP: Linda Sheinkopf
Brnch Mgr: Todd Sheinkopf

YALE NEW HAVEN HEALTH SYSTEM
See YALE-NEW HAVEN HEALTH SERVICES CORP

D-U-N-S 13-190-8972 IMP/EXP
YALE SECURITY INC
NORTON DOOR CONTROL
(Suby of ASSA ABLOY USA) ★
1902 Airport Rd, Monroe, NC 28110-7396
Tel (704) 283-2101 Founded/Ownrshp 1991
Sales 146.4MM^E EMP 1,100
SIC 3429 3466 Locks or lock sets; Door opening & closing devices, except electrical; Crowns & closures
Pr: Thanasis Molokotos
*Treas: John C Davenport
VP: Jack Adkins
VP: Tom Kaika

D-U-N-S 04-320-7562 IMP
YALE UNIVERSITY
105 Wall St, New Haven, CT 06511-8917
Tel (203) 432-2550 Founded/Ownrshp 1701
Sales 3.1MMM EMP 11,000
Accts Pricewaterhousecoopers Llp Ha
SIC 8221 2731 2721 2741 University; Book publishing; Magazines: publishing & printing; Catalogs: publishing & printing
Pr: Richard C Levin
V Ch: John Geibel
VP: Richard Jacob
*VP: Linda Koch Lorimer
*VP: John E Pepper Jr
VP: John Pepper
*VP: Dorothy Robinson
VP: Charles Turner
Assoc Dir: Heather Allore
Assoc Dir: Elizabeth Bradley
*Prin: Peter Salovey

D-U-N-S 17-483-5397
YALE-NEW HAVEN HEALTH SERVICES CORP
YALE NEW HAVEN HEALTH SYSTEM
789 Howard Ave, New Haven, CT 06519-1300
Tel (888) 461-0106 Founded/Ownrshp 1983
Sales 410.9MM EMP 490
Accts Ernst & Young Us Llp Indianap
SIC 5912 8721 Drug stores; Accounting, auditing & bookkeeping
Pr: Marna P Borgstrom
V Ch: Walter H Monteit
*COO: Richard D'Aquila
COO: Christopher Oconnor
Bd of Dir: Thomas B Ketchum
Ex VP: Gayle L Capozzao
*Ex VP: Frank A Corvino
Ex VP: Richard Daquila
Ex VP: James M Staten
Ex VP: Robert J Trefry
*Sr VP: William S Gedge
Sr VP: Peter N Herbert
VP: Karen Murray
VP: Kevin Myatt

D-U-N-S 07-540-6561
YALE-NEW HAVEN HOSPITAL INC
20 York St, New Haven, CT 06510-3220
Tel (203) 688-4242 Founded/Ownrshp 1985
Sales 2.3MMM EMP 22,000^E
SIC 8351 8062 8741 Child day care services; General medical & surgical hospitals; Hospital management
Pr: Marna P Borgstrom
*Pr: Richard D Aquila
CFO: Vincent Tammaro
Trst: Barrington D Parker Jr
Sr VP: Thomas J Balcezak
Sr VP: Edward Dawling
Sr VP: Patricia Sue Fitzsimons
Sr VP: Abe Lopman
Sr VP: Vin Petrini
Sr VP: Cynthia N Sparer
VP: Kevin A Myatt
Dir Inf Cn: Louise Denbry
Dir Rad: Steve Bencivengo

YALE-NEW HAVEN HOSPITAL SAINT
See HOSPITAL OF ST RAPHAEL PHYSICIANS IPA II INC

D-U-N-S 80-950-7239 IMP
YALE/CHASE EQUIPMENT AND SERVICES INC
2615 Pellissier Pl, City of Industry, CA 90601-1508
Tel (562) 463-8000 Founded/Ownrshp 1993
Sales 94.9MM EMP 200
Accts Windes Inc Irvine California
SIC 5084 7699 7359 Lift trucks & parts; Industrial machinery & equipment repair; Industrial truck rental
Pr: Roger Ketelsleger
*CFO: James Douglas Graven
Ofcr: Teresa Abando
*VP: Michael Ketelsleger
Exec: Teresa Heslip
Admn Mgr: Jana Ketelsleger
MIS Dir: John Rosser
Dir IT: Jana Jamson
Mtls Mgr: Phil Shelton
Mtls Mgr: Greg Wiles
Opers Mgr: Janeen Olsen

D-U-N-S 13-572-8546
YAM SPECIAL HOLDINGS INC
15475 N 84th St, Scottsdale, AZ 85260-1827
Tel (480) 505-8800 Founded/Ownrshp 2001
Sales 503.5MM^E EMP 4,500
SIC 7371 Computer software development
CEO: Blake Irving
*Pr: Robert R Parsons
*CFO: Scott Wagner
CFO: Michael Zimmerman
CFO: Michael J Zimmerman
Ex VP: Christine N Jones
VP: Mike Chadwick
VP: Marianne Curran
VP: Theresa D'Hooge
VP: Lane Jarvis
VP: Miguel Lopez
*VP: Elissa Murphy
VP: Robert Olson

D-U-N-S 18-948-3258 IMP
YAMADA NORTH AMERICA INC
YOTEC
(Suby of YAMADA MANUFACTURING CO., LTD.)
9000 Clmbus Cincinnati Rd, South Charleston, OH 45368-9406
Tel (937) 462-7111 Founded/Ownrshp 1946
Sales 138.9MM^E EMP 350
SIC 3714 Motor vehicle steering systems & parts; Water pump, motor vehicle
Pr: Kiyoshi Osawa
*VP: William Mallory
*Prin: John C Beeler

D-U-N-S 00-959-5463 IMP/EXP
YAMAHA CORP OF AMERICA INC
YAMAHA MUSIC CORPORATION U S A
(Suby of YAMAHA CORPORATION)
6600 Orangethorpe Ave, Buena Park, CA 90620-1396
Tel (714) 522-9011 Founded/Ownrshp 1960
Sales 368.9MM^E EMP 1,000
SIC 5099 5065 5091 3931 Musical instruments; Pianos; Sound equipment, electronic; Sporting & recreation goods; Golf equipment; Musical instruments
CEO: Hitoshi Fukutome
CFO: Karl Bruhn
Treas: R Shimanuki
Treas: Takashi Yabusaki
*Sr VP: Terry Lewis
VP: Philippe Bornstein
VP: Thomas Graham
VP: Dennis McNeal
VP: Mick Umemura
Mng Dir: Mike Matsamoto
Dept Mgr: Kenneth Dill

D-U-N-S 08-558-9307 IMP/EXP
YAMAHA MOTOR CORP USA
(Suby of YAMAHA MOTOR CO., LTD.)
6555 Katella Ave, Cypress, CA 90630-5101
Tel (714) 761-7300 Founded/Ownrshp 1955
Sales 1.1MMM^E EMP 3,700
SIC 5088 5013 5091 5012 Marine crafts & supplies; Golf carts; Motor vehicle supplies & new parts; Boats, canoes, watercrafts & equipment; Motorcycles; Snowmobiles; Motor scooters; Recreation vehicles, all-terrain
CEO: Toshi Kato
Pr: Phil Dyskow
COO: Richard Hinsz
*Sec: Takuwy Watanabe
VP: Dean Burnett
VP: Yoshi Nagami
Exec: Tadakazu Ishibashi
Dept Mgr: Chikage Wong
Dist Mgr: Michael Lamb
Dist Mgr: Jonathan Peirson
Genl Mgr: Kim Ruiz
Board of Directors: Akira Araki, Jun Mori

YAMAHA MUSIC CORPORATION U S A
See YAMAHA CORP OF AMERICA INC

YAMAS IN TURKEY SUBSIDUARY
See ANATOLIA MINERALS DEVELOPMENT LTD

YAMHILL COMMUNITY CARE ORGANIZ
See YAMHILL COUNTY CARE ORGANIZATION INC

D-U-N-S 07-930-7255
YAMHILL COUNTY CARE ORGANIZATION INC
YAMHILL COMMUNITY CARE ORGANIZ
807 Ne 3rd St, McMinnville, OR 97128-4433
Tel (503) 434-7339 Founded/Ownrshp 2012
Sales 96.1MM EMP 4
SIC 8011 Medical insurance plan
CEO: Jim Carlough
Bd of Dir: Jim Rickards

D-U-N-S 01-062-2710
YAMPA VALLEY MEDICAL CENTER
DOAK WALKER CARE CENTER
1024 Central Park Dr, Steamboat Springs, CO 80487-8813
Tel (970) 879-1322 Founded/Ownrshp 1946
Sales 92.2MM EMP 510^E
SIC 8062 8351 General medical & surgical hospitals; Child day care services
CEO: Frank May
CFO: Robert Flake
CFO: Kevin Holman
Dir Lab: Mary Poskus
Dir Rad: Maryjo Wiedel
Chf Nrs Of: Linda Casner
Nurse Mgr: Christy Kopischke
Sls&Mrk Ex: Christine McKelvie
Nutrtnst: Cara Marrs
Nutrtnst: Laura Stout
Nutrtnst: Jennifer Thomsen

D-U-N-S 00-692-5465 IMP/EXP
YANCEY BROS CO
CATERPILLAR AUTHORIZED DEALER
330 Lee Industrial Blvd # 1, Austell, GA 30168-7406
Tel (770) 941-2424 Founded/Ownrshp 1996
Sales 451.2MM^E EMP 750
SIC 5082 5084 7699 7353 Road construction & maintenance machinery; Power plant machinery; Engines & parts, diesel; Construction equipment repair; Heavy construction equipment rental
Pr: James E Stephenson
*Pr: Trey Googe
*CFO: Marshall Ford
Ex VP: Bud Wilfore
VP: Eric Arnold
VP: Chris Burns
VP: Tim McCauley
VP: Sal Minicozzi
VP: Rick Ream
Area Mgr: Scott Angel
Genl Mgr: Chris Hough
Board of Directors: M Bradley Blaylock, Paul W Stephenson

D-U-N-S 17-933-2812 IMP
YANCEYS FANCY INC
(Suby of D & Y CHEESES INC) ★
857 Main Rd, Corfu, NY 14036-9753
Tel (585) 599-4448 Founded/Ownrshp 1996
Sales 106.9MM^E EMP 155
SIC 5143 Dairy products, except dried or canned; Cheese
CEO: Wayne Henry
*VP: Brian Bailey
Sfty Mgr: Ruth Perry
Sfty Mgr: Melifa Phillip
*VP Sls: Michael Wimble
Mktg Mgr: Eric Godlove
Sls Mgr: Mark Saglian

D-U-N-S 07-974-7058
YANFENG US AUTOMOTIVE INTERIOR SYSTEMS I LLC
(Suby of YANFENG HUNGARY AUTOMOTIVE INTERIOR SYSTEMS KORLATOLT FELELOSSEGU TARSASAG)
45000 Helm St, Plymouth, MI 48170-6040
Tel (414) 524-1200 Founded/Ownrshp 2015
Sales 15.1MM^E EMP 4,985^E
SIC 2531 Seats, automobile

D-U-N-S 07-974-7086
YANFENG US AUTOMOTIVE INTERIOR SYSTEMS II LLC
(Suby of YANFENG HUNGARY AUTOMOTIVE INTERIOR SYSTEMS KORLATOLT FELELOSSEGU TARSASAG)
5757 N Green Bay Ave, Milwaukee, WI 53209-4408
Tel (205) 477-4225 Founded/Ownrshp 2015
Sales 140.3MM^E EMP 929^E
SIC 2531 Seats, automobile

D-U-N-S 88-439-5422 IMP
YANFENG USA AUTOMOTIVE TRIM SYSTEMS INC
(Suby of YANFENG AUTOMOTIVE TRIM SYSTEMS CO., LTD.)
42150 Executive Dr, Harrison Township, MI 48045
Tel (586) 354-2101 Founded/Ownrshp 2009
Sales 152.5MM EMP 52
Accts Mellen Smith & Pivoz Plc
SIC 2396 Automotive & apparel trimmings
Pr: David Wang
Opers Mgr: Michael Caringi

D-U-N-S 06-698-3586 IMP
■YANKEE CANDLE CO INC
(Suby of YANKEE HOLDING CORP) ★
16 Yankee Candle Way, South Deerfield, MA 01373-7325
Tel (413) 665-8306 Founded/Ownrshp 2007
Sales 1.4MMM^E EMP 4,100
SIC 3999 2899 5999 Candles; Oils & essential oils; Candle shops
Pr: Hope Margala
*Ch Bd: Craig W Rydin
*CFO: Bruce L Hartman
*CFO: Gregory W Hunt
*Treas: Lisa McCarthy
Bd of Dir: Michael S Ovitz
Bd of Dir: Emily Woods
*Chf Mktg O: Brad Wolansky
*Ex VP: James A Perley
*Sr VP: Paul J Hill
Sr VP: Lori Klimach
Sr VP: Martha S Lacroix
Sr VP: Richard R Ruffolo
VP: Stephen Atwater
VP: Ronald Bohonowicz
*VP: John Capps
VP: Jen Docherty
VP: Gerald Lynch
VP: Dan Purugganan
VP: Thomas Regan
VP: Neal Schuler
Board of Directors: Frank P Bifulco Jr, Terry Burman, Trudy Sullivan

D-U-N-S 96-833-1939
■YANKEE CANDLE INVESTMENTS LLC
(Suby of NEWELL BRANDS) ★
16 Yankee Candle Way, South Deerfield, MA 01373-7325
Tel (413) 665-8306 Founded/Ownrshp 2013
Sales 2.6MMM^E EMP 5,200^E
SIC 3999 5999 Candles; Candle shops
CEO: Harlan M Kent
*CFO: Gregory W Hunt
*Ex VP: Martha S Lacroix
*Ex VP: James A Perley

D-U-N-S 60-366-9193
■YANKEE ENERGY SYSTEM INC
(Suby of EVERSOURCE ENERGY) ★
107 Selden St, Berlin, CT 06037-1616
Tel (860) 665-5000 Founded/Ownrshp 2000
Sales 636.9MM^E EMP 790
SIC 4924 Natural gas distribution
VP: Mary J Healey
Ex VP: Jay S Buth
VP: Thomas J Houde

D-U-N-S 36-166-7371
■YANKEE GAS SERVICES CO
EVERSOURCE ENERGY
(Suby of YANKEE ENERGY SYSTEM INC) ★
107 Selden St, Berlin, CT 06037-1616
Tel (860) 665-5000 Founded/Ownrshp 2000
Sales 700.6MM^E EMP 600
SIC 4924 Natural gas distribution
Pr: Dennis Welch
*Pr: Cheryl W Grise
COO: Murale Gopinathan
*CFO: John H Forsgren
Treas: Randy Shoop
Dir Bus: Christie Bradway
Genl Mgr: Joseph Hobson
Dir IT: Allen Pollock
VP Opers: Marc Andrukiewicz

Opers Supe: Giancarlo Romero
Opers Mgr: John Dugan

D-U-N-S 80-369-0630
■YANKEE HOLDING CORP
(*Suby of* NEWELL BRANDS) ★
16 Yankee Candle Way, South Deerfield, MA 01373-7325
Tel (413) 665-8306 *Founded/Ownrshp* 2013
Sales 2.6MMM^E *EMP* 5,200^E
SIC 3999 2899 Candles; Potpourri; Oils & essential oils
Ch Bd: Craig W Rydin
CFO: Lisa K McCarthy
Ofcr: Martha S Lacroix
Ex VP: James A Perley
VP: Howard Barron
Store Mgr: Lisa McMahen

D-U-N-S 14-752-7717 IMP/EXP
YANMAR AMERICA CORP
(*Suby of* YANMAR CO.,LTD.)
101 International Pkwy, Adairsville, GA 30103-2028
Tel (770) 877-9894 *Founded/Ownrshp* 2010
Sales 236.2MM^E *EMP* 10^E
SIC 5084 7699 5083 3519 Engines & parts, diesel; Construction equipment repair; Agricultural machinery & equipment; Internal combustion engines
Pr: Tim Fernandez
* *CEO:* Theodore Brojar
* *CFO:* Yoshihito Nakamura
* *Ex VP:* Katsumi Deguchi
* *VP:* Jimmy Onishe
* *Genl Mgr:* Seiji Kawahito
CTO: Brian Williams
Snr Mgr: Liston Edge

D-U-N-S 05-069-6327
YANTIS CORP
3611 Paesanos Pkwy # 300, San Antonio, TX 78231-1258
Tel (210) 655-3780 *Founded/Ownrshp* 1975
Sales 190.7MM^E *EMP* 600
SIC 1623 1611 1622 1629 6552 1521 Underground utilities contractor; Highway & street construction; Bridge construction; Land preparation construction; Subdividers & developers; Single-family housing construction
Prin: Blake Yantis
* *Pr:* J Michael Yantis Jr
COO: Justin Allison
VP: Stephen Mark Deering
VP: Scott Finfer
Dir Bus: Todd Compton
IT Man: Jeff Lambert
Sfty Mgr: Sam Delarosa

D-U-N-S 79-516-3518 IMP/EXP
YARA NORTH AMERICA INC
(*Suby of* YARA INTERNATIONAL ASA)
100 N Tampa St Ste 3200, Tampa, FL 33602-5830
Tel (813) 222-5700 *Founded/Ownrshp* 2003
Sales 236.4MM^E *EMP* 218
SIC 5191 5169 Fertilizer & fertilizer materials; Phosphate rock, ground; Ammonia
CEO: Jorgen Ole Haslestad
* *Pr:* Bartolomeo Pescio
* *CFO:* Torgeir Kvidal
* *Treas:* Leesa M Burns
* *Treas:* Rosemary Malarkey
* *VP:* John Ritz
* *VP:* Steve Rodgers

D-U-N-S 02-983-0759
YARCO CO INC
7920 Ward Pkwy, Kansas City, MO 64114-2017
Tel (816) 561-4240 *Founded/Ownrshp* 1923
Sales 102.9MM^E *EMP* 450
SIC 6552 6531 Subdividers & developers; Real estate managers
Pr: Jonathan R Cohn
* *VP:* Clifton R Cohn
Exec: Mickey Carlson
Mktg Mgr: Alison Graff

D-U-N-S 02-232-6057
■YARD HOUSE RESTAURANTS LLC
(*Suby of* DARDEN RESTAURANTS INC) ★
7700 Irvine Center Dr # 300, Irvine, CA 92618-3022
Tel (800) 336-5336 *Founded/Ownrshp* 1995
Sales 16.0MM^E *EMP* 15,000^E
SIC 5812 American restaurant
* *Pr:* Craig Carlyle
Genl Mgr: Ben Benzon
Genl Mgr: Frank Gondermann
Genl Mgr: Courtney Hills
Genl Mgr: David Lory
Genl Mgr: Ed Maclean
Genl Mgr: Raven Maree
Genl Mgr: A J Nemecek

D-U-N-S 06-066-5494 IMP/EXP
■YARDE METALS INC
(*Suby of* RELIANCE STEEL & ALUMINUM CO) ★
45 Newell St, Southington, CT 06489-1424
Tel (860) 406-6061 *Founded/Ownrshp* 2006
Sales 382.0MM^E *EMP* 617
SIC 5051 3499 Metals service centers & offices; Aluminum bars, rods, ingots, sheets, pipes, plates, etc.; Steel; Copper; Safe deposit boxes or chests, metal
CEO: William K Sales Jr
* *Pr:* Matthew L Smith
COO: Smith Matt
COO: Craig Yarde
* *VP:* Carla Lewis
VP: Tom Schittina
Genl Mgr: Jeff Hester
Off Mgr: Rachel Tourville
Dir IT: Marc Rubel
IT Man: Shawn Dell
Opers Mgr: Jerry Hvozdovic

D-U-N-S 12-097-5172
YARDI SYSTEMS INC
430 S Fairview Ave, Santa Barbara, CA 93117-3637
Tel (805) 699-2040 *Founded/Ownrshp* 1982
Sales 665.7MM^E *EMP* 2,831
SIC 7371 Computer software development & applications
Pr: Anant Yardi
Pr: Jonathan Delong
* *COO:* Gordon Morrell
* *Sr VP:* John Pendergast
* *Sr VP:* Fritz Schindelbeck
* *Sr VP:* Robert Teel
Sr VP: Scott Wiener
VP: Arnold Brier
VP: Gennaro Cataldo
VP: Nick Davis
VP: Buck Devashish
VP: Laurie Diaz
VP: Neal Gemassmer
VP: Peter Hill
VP: Michelle Howard
VP: Jones Lang
VP: Alex Stanton
Exec: Julie Lindman
Dir Soc: Erin Harrison
Dir Soc: Jill Jacobs

D-U-N-S 05-162-9558
YARK AUTOMOTIVE GROUP INC
YARK SUBARU
6019 W Central Ave, Toledo, OH 43615-1803
Tel (419) 841-7771 *Founded/Ownrshp* 1971
Sales 144.2MM^E *EMP* 300^E
SIC 5511 7515 Automobiles, new & used; Passenger car leasing
CEO: Douglas Kearns
* *Pr:* John W Yark
* *CFO:* Max Forster
* *Prin:* Jim Yark
Genl Mgr: Dj Yark
Off Mgr: Heather Webster
Sls Mgr: Dave Boehm
Sls Mgr: Travis Dupont
Sls Mgr: Tim Eltschlager
Sls Mgr: Tony Kunisch
Sls Mgr: Ross Lundquist

YARK SUBARU
See YARK AUTOMOTIVE GROUP INC

D-U-N-S 96-925-3319
YASH TECHNOLOGIES INC
605 17th Ave, East Moline, IL 61244-2045
Tel (309) 755-0433 *Founded/Ownrshp* 1996
Sales 200.0MM *EMP* 3,500^E
SIC 7379 Computer related consulting services
Pr: Manoj K Baheti
COO: Venkata Navuluri
COO: Paul Simon
Ex VP: Swaminathan Mani
VP: Kunal Chakravorty
VP: Janaki Cheruvu
VP: Sriram Jayaram
VP: Mukund K Purohit
VP: R Vilayannur
Exec: Darshani Jagirdar
Exec: Sidhartha Kasiraju
Exec: Reena Repe
Exec: Ankur Singhal
Dir Bus: Nimmala Eswar

D-U-N-S 18-722-1515 IMP
■YASHENG GROUP
(*Suby of* GANSU YASHENG SALT INDUSTRIAL (GROUP) CO., LTD.)
805 Veterans Blvd Ste 228, Redwood City, CA 94063-1736
Tel (650) 363-8345 *Founded/Ownrshp* 2004
Sales 938.9MM *EMP* 10,000
Accts Gansu Hongxin Certified Public
Tkr Sym HERB *Exch* OTO
SIC 2879 0111 0115 0116 0112 Agricultural chemicals; Wheat; Corn; Soybeans; Rice
Ch Bd: Weihao Cui
* *CFO:* Zhuang Hai Yun

D-U-N-S 06-448-6434 IMP/EXP
YASKAWA AMERICA INC
DRIVES & MOTION DIVISION
(*Suby of* YASKAWA ELECTRIC CORPORATION)
2121 Norman Dr, Waukegan, IL 60085-6751
Tel (847) 887-7000 *Founded/Ownrshp* 1967
Sales 529.2MM *EMP* 1,000
Accts Ernst & Young Llp Chicago Il
SIC 3621 7694 5063 3566 3823 3625 Motors, electric; Electric motor repair; Motors, electric; Speed changers, drives & gears; Industrial instrmnts msrmnt display/control process variable; Relays & industrial controls
CEO: Gen Kudo
* *Pr:* Steve Barhorst
* *Pr:* Michael Knapek
Pr: Nory Takada
* *CFO:* Tom Schockman
* *Treas:* Akira Hijikuro
VP: Patty Chybowski
Area Mgr: Robert Richard
IT Man: Scott Wohnrade
Software D: Marcin Owczarz
Mfg Mgr: Jason Ormeroid

D-U-N-S 01-704-1232
YATES COMPANIES INC
1 Gully Ave, Philadelphia, MS 39350
Tel (601) 656-5411 *Founded/Ownrshp* 1997
Sales 1.5MMM *EMP* 7,000
Accts Rea Shaw Griffin & Stuart L
SIC 1542 1541 1611 5211 1731 Commercial & office building, new construction; Industrial buildings, new construction; Resurfacing contractor; Home centers; General electrical contractor
Pr: William G Yates Jr
* *CFO:* Brandon Dunn
* *Treas:* Marvin E Blanks III
* *Treas:* Marvin Blanks
* *VP:* William G Yates III
DP Dir: Earnest Harrington
Sfty Dirs: Charles Maness

D-U-N-S 07-921-7074
YATES CONSTRUCTORS LLC
(*Suby of* W G YATES & SONS CONSTRUCTION CO) ★
1855 Data Dr Ste 200, Hoover, AL 35244-1237
Tel (205) 380-8420 *Founded/Ownrshp* 2011
Sales 225.0MM *EMP* 2
SIC 1542 1541 Commercial & office building, new construction; Industrial buildings, new construction
Pr: William G Yates III

D-U-N-S 00-778-5728
YATES PETROLEUM CORP
105 S 4th St, Artesia, NM 88210-2122
Tel (575) 748-1471 *Founded/Ownrshp* 1960
Sales 10.0MMM^E *EMP* 500^E
SIC 1311

D-U-N-S 13-041-0561
YATES SERVICES LLC
(*Suby of* YATES COMPANIES INC) ★
983 Nissan Dr, Smyrna, TN 37167-4405
Tel (615) 459-1701 *Founded/Ownrshp* 2002
Sales 29.8MM^E *EMP* 1,000
SIC 7349 Building maintenance services

D-U-N-S 06-842-2237
YAVAPAI COMMUNITY HOSP ASSN
YAVAPAI REGIONAL MEDICAL CTR
1003 Willow Creek Rd, Prescott, AZ 86301-1641
Tel (928) 445-2700 *Founded/Ownrshp* 1942
Sales 146.9MM *EMP* 1,780
SIC 8062 8011 General medical & surgical hospitals; Offices & clinics of medical doctors
CEO: John Amos
COO: Larry P Burns
Dir Risk M: Lauraine Dupont
Dir Rx: Dave Levos
Chf Nrs Of: Diane Drexler
* *Prin:* Timothy Barnett
Ex Dir: Robbie Nicol
Cmptr Lab: Romeo Canlas
QA Dir: Jimmie Bates
QA Dir: Sandy Tsang
Dir IT: John Rentschler

D-U-N-S 07-244-7105
YAVAPAI COUNTY COMMUNITY COLLEGE DISTRICT
PRESCOTT CAMPUS
1100 E Sheldon St, Prescott, AZ 86301-3220
Tel (928) 445-7300 *Founded/Ownrshp* 1969
Sales 35.7MM^E *EMP* 1,017
SIC 8222 Community college
Pr: Penelope H Wills
Ofcr: Kent Hellman
Exec: Danny Vallo
Genl Mgr: Jody Buckle

D-U-N-S 00-290-0108
YAVAPAI REGIONAL MEDICAL CENTER FOUNDATION (AZ)
1003 Willow Creek Rd, Prescott, AZ 86301-1641
Tel (928) 445-2700 *Founded/Ownrshp* 1942, 1992
Sales 3.2MM *EMP* 1,200
Accts Bkd Llp Colorado Springs Co
SIC 8011 8082 2835 Medical centers; Home health care services; In vitro & in vivo diagnostic substances
CEO: Timothy Barnett
CFO: Kathy Holloway
Treas: Michael T Sharp

YAVAPAI REGIONAL MEDICAL CTR
See YAVAPAI COMMUNITY HOSP ASSN

D-U-N-S 82-488-3912 IMP
YAZAKI INTERNATIONAL CORP
(*Suby of* YAZAKI CORPORATION)
6801 N Haggerty Rd 4707e, Canton, MI 48187-3538
Tel (734) 983-1000 *Founded/Ownrshp* 1992
Sales 2.0MMM^E *EMP* 3,917
SIC 5013 3643 Automotive supplies & parts; Current-carrying wiring devices
* *Treas:* Tatsuo Karasaki
Ex VP: Olga Alavanou
Ex VP: Takashige Miyashita
Ex VP: Jim Romine
Ex VP: Nigel Thompson
* *VP:* Koh Takemoto
VP: Kurt Zielske
Exec: Greg Benjamin
CTO: Ray Ernst
Dir IT: Tom Sutton
IT Man: O'Hara Near

D-U-N-S 00-597-1452 IMP/EXP
YAZAKI NORTH AMERICA INC (IL)
AYC
(*Suby of* YAZAKI INTERNATIONAL CORP) ★
6801 N Haggerty Rd, Canton, MI 48187-3538
Tel (734) 983-1000 *Founded/Ownrshp* 1966, 1992
Sales 1.4MMM^E *EMP* 1,500
SIC 5013 Automotive supplies & parts
CEO: Nigel Thompson
* *Ch Bd:* Max Yamashita
Pr: Nobuhiro Onishi
* *Pr:* George R Perry
Pr: Riku Yazaki
* *Ex VP:* Olga Alavanou
Ex VP: Bob McDonald
Ex VP: Takashige Miyashita
* *Ex VP:* Jim Romine
Ex VP: Ryosuke Yazaki
VP: Lois Bingham
VP: David Conrad
* *VP:* Marcia Goffney
VP: Matt Konyn
VP: Tim Mailley
VP: Mohamad Zahreddine

YBC SUPPLY
See YOUR BUILDING CENTERS INC

D-U-N-S 80-883-7517
■YCC HOLDINGS LLC
(*Suby of* YANKEE CANDLE INVESTMENTS LLC) ★
16 Yankee Candle Way, South Deerfield, MA 01373-7325
Tel (413) 665-8306 *Founded/Ownrshp* 2006
Sales 844.1MM *EMP* 5,200
SIC 3999 2899 5999 Candles; Oils & essential oils; Candle shops
Treas: Lisa K McCarthy

YCSD
See YORK COUNTY SCHOOL DIVISION

YCUSD
See YUBA CITY UNIFIED SCHOOL DISTRICT FINANCING CORP

D-U-N-S 03-570-8973
YEAROUT MECHANICAL INC (NM)
8501 Washington St Ne, Albuquerque, NM 87113-1679
Tel (505) 884-0994 *Founded/Ownrshp* 1964
Sales 96.8MM^E *EMP* 444
SIC 1711 Mechanical contractor
CEO: Kevin Yearout
* *Pr:* Bryan Yearout
* *COO:* Donna Donoghue
VP: Chris Steffen
* *VP:* Lian Yearout
Exec: Marni Goodrich
Rgnl Mgr: Rob Cantey
Genl Mgr: Sal Tortorici
Trfc Dir: Kelly Smith
Sfty Mgr: Dion Jordan
Ql Cn Mgr: James Smouse

D-U-N-S 78-018-9262
YELED VYALDA EARLY CHILDHOOD CENTER INC
YVY
1312 38th St, Brooklyn, NY 11218-3612
Tel (718) 686-3700 *Founded/Ownrshp* 1980
Sales 89.4MM *EMP* 1,500
Accts Loeb & Troper Llp New York
SIC 8351 Head start center, except in conjunction with school
Ch: Jacob Unger
* *CEO:* Solomon Igel
* *CFO:* Rebecca Gutman

YELLOW FINANCIAL CREDIT UNION
See COMMUNITYAMERICA CREDIT UNION

YELLOW JACKET GIFT SHOP
See SOUTH EASTERN REGIONAL MEDICAL INC

D-U-N-S 55-710-0849
YELLOWBOOK CO INC
(*Suby of* HIBU INC) ★
6300 C St Sw, Cedar Rapids, IA 52404-7470
Tel (319) 366-1100 *Founded/Ownrshp* 2002
Sales 67.9MM^E *EMP* 5,000
SIC 7311

D-U-N-S 02-116-5757
YELLOWSTONE LANDSCAPE GROUP INC
(*Suby of* CIVC PARTNERS LP) ★
3235 N State St, Bunnell, FL 32110-4364
Tel (386) 437-6211 *Founded/Ownrshp* 2008, 2015
Sales 169.0MM^E *EMP* 1,100
SIC 0782 0781 Landscape contractors; Landscape counseling & planning
Pr: Tim Portland
Pr: Brian Martin

D-U-N-S 03-411-5860 EXP
YELLOWSTONE LANDSCAPE-SOUTHEAST LLC (FL)
(*Suby of* YELLOWSTONE LANDSCAPE GROUP INC) ★
3235 N State St, Bunnell, FL 32110-4364
Tel (386) 437-6211 *Founded/Ownrshp* 1996, 2009
Sales 137.5MM^E *EMP* 800
SIC 0781 0782 Landscape services; Lawn care services
CFO: Al Lalonde
VP: Travis Walker
Dist Mgr: Paul Lamontaine
Mtls Mgr: Matt Kalasnik

YELLOWSTONE RV
See GULF STREAM COACH INC

D-U-N-S 18-448-8356
▲YELP INC
140 New Montgomery St # 900, San Francisco, CA 94105-3821
Tel (415) 908-3801 *Founded/Ownrshp* 2004
Sales 549.7MM *EMP* 3,826
Tkr Sym YELP *Exch* NYS
SIC 7375 Information retrieval services; On-line data base information retrieval
CEO: Jeremy Stoppelman
* *Ch Bd:* Diane M Irvine
* *COO:* Geoff Donaker
CFO: Charles Baker
Sr VP: Andrea Rubin
Sr VP: Laurence Wilson
VP: Brian Osborn
VP: Eric Singley
Dir Risk M: Joseph R Nachman
Mktg Dir: Kimberly Van
Sls Dir: Spencer Hoekstra
Board of Directors: Fred D Anderson Jr, Peter Fenton, Robert Gibbs, Jeremy Levine, Mariam Naficy

D-U-N-S 80-410-4722
YES MANAGEMENT
1900 16th St Ste 950, Denver, CO 80202-5228
Tel (303) 483-7300 *Founded/Ownrshp* 2007
Sales 343.3MM^E *EMP* 883^E
SIC 6798 Real estate investment trusts
Pr: Charles McDaniel
CFO: Chris Stopps
* *VP:* Chad S McDaniel
Rgnl Mgr: Edward Redmond

YES PREP NORTH FOREST
See YES PREP PUBLIC SCHOOLS INC

D-U-N-S 94-537-9571
YES PREP PUBLIC SCHOOLS INC
YES PREP NORTH FOREST
6201 Bonhomme Rd Ste 168n, Houston, TX 77036-4427
Tel (713) 967-9001 *Founded/Ownrshp* 1998
Sales 90.0MM *EMP* 250E
Accts Gomez & Company Houston Tx
SIC 8211 Public elementary & secondary schools
**Prin:* Christopher L Claflin
**Prin:* Luz E Navarro
**Prin:* Bryan B Reed
**Prin:* Douglas Selman
Dir IT: Richard Charlesworth
Psych: Roberto Trevino

YESCO
See YOUNG ELECTRIC SIGN CO INC

YESHIVA COLLEGE
See YESHIVA UNIVERSITY

D-U-N-S 07-103-6636
YESHIVA UNIVERSITY
YESHIVA COLLEGE
500 W 185th St, New York, NY 10033-3299
Tel (212) 960-5400 *Founded/Ownrshp* 1886
Sales 658.7MM *EMP* 4,500
Accts Pricewaterhousecoopers Llp Ne
SIC 8221 University
Pr: Richard M Joel
V Ch: Ales Cvekl
COO: Norman Adler
CFO: Jacob Harman
CFO: Sheldon Socol
**Treas:* Alan E Goldberg
Ofcr: Jack Zencheck
VP: Mjknoll Finn
VP: Daniel Forman
**VP:* J Michael Gower
VP: Mj Knoll
VP: Marc Milstein
Dir Teleco: Otto Carmelo
Assoc Dir: Marla Keller
Assoc Dir: Helen Panageas

YESMAIL
See INFOGROUP INC

YH AMERICA
See YOKOHAMA INDUSTRIES AMERICAS INC

D-U-N-S 96-372-7982 IMP
YIFANG USA INC
E FUN
136 N Grand Ave Ste 148, West Covina, CA 91791-1728
Tel (909) 593-1562 *Founded/Ownrshp* 2010
Sales 130.0MM *EMP* 8
SIC 5065 Electronic parts
Pr: Bin Wang
Ofcr: Weeliam Yau

D-U-N-S 00-179-2936 IMP
YKK (USA) INC (NY)
(*Suby of* YKK CORP OF AMERICA) ★
1300 Cobb Industrial Dr, Marietta, GA 30066-6607
Tel (770) 427-5521 *Founded/Ownrshp* 1960
Sales 210.5MME *EMP* 1,000
SIC 3452 3965 Bolts, nuts, rivets & washers; Zipper; Fasteners; Buckles & buckle parts
Pr: Kanji Miyatake
**Pr:* Michael Blunt
**Treas:* Ed Renk
Treas: Masahiro Ujihara
VP: Larry Boyd
VP: Satoshi Honda
**VP:* Keith Meyer
Natl Sales: Greg Taylor
Sls Mgr: Scott Jensen

D-U-N-S 78-626-1594 IMP/EXP
YKK AP AMERICA INC
(*Suby of* YKK CORP OF AMERICA) ★
270 Riverside Pkwy Ste A, Austell, GA 30168-7884
Tel (678) 838-6000 *Founded/Ownrshp* 1987
Sales 162.2MME *EMP* 670
SIC 3442 3449 Sash, door or window: metal; Metal doors; Store fronts, prefabricated, metal; Curtain wall, metal
Pr: Mirsuhiro Mizota
**Pr:* Oliver Stepe
Sr VP: Yuichi Toyoshima
VP: Psutum Ito
QA Dir: Greg Brown
Tech Mgr: Bart Harrington
VP Mfg: Greg Holtquist
VP Mfg: Greg Hultquist
Mktg Mgr: Douglas Penn
Sales Asso: Pam Blockmon

D-U-N-S 18-895-5835 IMP
YKK CORP OF AMERICA
(*Suby of* YKK CORPORATION)
1850 Parkway Pl Se # 300, Marietta, GA 30067-8258
Tel (770) 261-6120 *Founded/Ownrshp* 1987
Sales 399.0MME *EMP* 2,500
SIC 3965 3354 Fasteners, buttons, needles & pins; Zipper; Fasteners; Aluminum extruded products
**Treas:* Ed Reck
**Sr VP:* David G Schwartz
VP: Jim Bottomley
VP: Satoshi Honda
Brnch Mgr: Marvin Parker
Corp Couns: Key Wynn

YMCA
See YOUNG MEN S CHRISTIAN ASSOCIATION OF GREATER CHARLOTTE

YMCA
See YOUNG MENS CHRISTIAN ASSOCIATION OF METROPOLITAN MILWAUKEE INC

YMCA
See YOUNG MENS CHRISTIAN ASSOCIATION OF GREATER RICHMOND

YMCA
See YOUNG MENS CHRISTIAN ASSOCIATION OF GREATER CINCINNATI

YMCA
See YOUNG MENS CHRISTIAN ASSOCIATION OF METROPOLITAN LOS ANGELES

YMCA
See GREATER PROVIDENCE YOUNG MENS CHRISTIAN ASSOCIATION

YMCA
See YOUNG MENS CHRISTIAN ASSOCIATION OF CEDAR RAPIDS METROPOLITAN AREA

YMCA
See SARASOTA FAMILY YOUNG MENS CHRISTIAN ASSOCIATION INC

YMCA CENTER
See YOUNG MENS CHRISTIAN ASSOCIATION OF BIRMINGHAM

D-U-N-S 04-878-5208
YMCA GREATER BRANDYWINE
1 E Chestnut St, West Chester, PA 19380-2692
Tel (610) 643-9622 *Founded/Ownrshp* 1901
Sales 32.5MM *EMP* 1,250
Accts Kreischer Miller Horsham Pa
SIC 8641 7991 8351 7032 8322 Youth organizations; Physical fitness facilities; Child day care services; Youth camps; Individual & family services
CEO: Audrey Kain Pedrick
**COO:* Andrea Youndt
**CFO:* Anthony Milano
**CFO:* Tim Walsh
Sr VP: Joe Tankle
**VP:* Donna L Hood
Assoc Dir: Brian Raicich
Ex Dir: Roberto Valera
Pgrm Dir: Kirstan Dolinger

YMCA OF CENTRAL FLORIDA
See CENTRAL FLORIDA YOUNG MENS CHRISTIAN ASSOCIATION INC

D-U-N-S 08-055-3381
YMCA OF CENTRAL MARYLAND INC
Y OF CENTRAL MARYLAND
303 W Chesapeake Ave, Baltimore, MD 21204-4406
Tel (443) 322-9622 *Founded/Ownrshp* 1853
Sales 57.1MM *EMP* 1,751
Accts Rsm Us Llp Baltimore Md
SIC 8641 8351 Youth organizations; Child day care services
Pr: John Hoey
**COO:* Robert J Brosmer
**CFO:* Sherrie Rovnan
Bd of Dir: John Pearson
VP: Suzanne Green
VP: Ruth Heltne
VP: Michelle B Jackson
VP: Bev Landis
VP: Ryan Trexler
Comm Man: Monica Booker
Rgnl Mgr: Charmayne Turner

YMCA OF CENTRAL OHIO
See YOUNG MENS CHRISTIAN ASSOCIATION OF CENTRAL OHIO

YMCA OF DELAWARE
See YOUNG MENS CHRISTIAN ASSOCIATION OF WILMINGTON DELAWARE

D-U-N-S 06-965-3897
YMCA OF FLORIDAS FIRST COAST (FL)
40 E Adams St Ste 210, Jacksonville, FL 32202-3356
Tel (904) 296-3220 *Founded/Ownrshp* 1942
Sales 33.2MM *EMP* 1,500
Accts Lba Certified Public Accountan
SIC 8741 8641 Management services; Civic associations
CEO: Eric K Mann
**CFO:* Tenny Zuber
Dir IT: Shawn Tannen
Site Mgr: Shelia Brown

D-U-N-S 07-658-0216
YMCA OF GREATER BOSTON INC
316 Huntington Ave Ste 1, Boston, MA 02115-5027
Tel (617) 536-6950 *Founded/Ownrshp* 1852
Sales 71.5MM *EMP* 1,500
Accts Kpmg Llp Boston Ma
SIC 8641 7991 8351 7032 8322 Youth organizations; Physical fitness facilities; Child day care services; Youth camps; Individual & family services
Ex Dir: Will Morales
CFO: Ann Tikkanen
**Sr VP:* Leonard Romano
Sr VP: Harold Sparrow
Assoc Dir: Dana Snyder
Prgrm Mgr: Alana Imbaro
Dir IT: Craig Schultze
IT Man: Donna Desmond
Site Mgr: Julian Gomez

YMCA OF GREATER DAYTON
See YOUNG MENS CHRISTIAN ASSOCIATION OF GREATER DAYTON

YMCA OF GREATER LOUISVILLE
See YOUNG MENS CHRISTIAN ASSOCIATION OF GREATER LOUISVILLE

YMCA OF GREATER SAINT LOUIS
See GATEWAY REGION YOUNG MENS CHRISTIAN ASSOCIATION

YMCA OF GREATER SEATTLE
See YOUNG MENS CHRISTIAN ASSOCIATION OF GREATER SEATTLE

YMCA OF GREATER TOLEDO
See YOUNG MENS CHRISTIAN ASSOCIATION OF GREATER TOLEDO

YMCA OF GREATER TWIN CITIES
See YOUNG MENS CHRISTIAN ASSOCIATION OF GREATER TWIN CITIES

YMCA OF METRO WASHINGTON
See YMCA OF METROPOLITAN WASHINGTON

D-U-N-S 02-156-3150
YMCA OF METROPOLITAN CHATTANOOGA
301 W 6th St, Chattanooga, TN 37402-1110
Tel (423) 266-3766 *Founded/Ownrshp* 1991
Sales 14.3MM *EMP* 1,099
Accts Johnson Hickey & Murchison Pc
SIC 8641 7991 8351 7032 8322 Youth organizations; Physical fitness facilities; Child day care services; Youth camps; Individual & family services
CEO: Janet Dunn
**COO:* Rick Madison
**Treas:* Calvin Smith
Pgrm Dir: Rosemary Dworak

YMCA OF METROPOLITAN DETROIT
See YOUNG MENS CHRISTIAN ASSOCIATION OF METROPOLITAN DETROIT

D-U-N-S 01-016-7872
YMCA OF METROPOLITAN HARTFORD INC
Y M C A OF GREATER HARTFORD
50 State House Sq Fl 2, Hartford, CT 06103-3902
Tel (860) 522-9622 *Founded/Ownrshp* 1852
Sales 27.5MM *EMP* 1,182
Accts Blum Shapiro & Company Pc Cpa
SIC 8641 7032 7997 Recreation association; Social club, membership; Youth camps; Membership sports & recreation clubs
Pr: James Morton
**Ch Bd:* Michael Hopkins
**V Ch:* Kathleen Bromage
CFO: Joe Weist
**Treas:* Warren A Hunt
Bd of Dir: Mike Drahota
VP: Barbara Eshoo
Ex Dir: Sharlene Ellovich
Ex Dir: Mitch Mouchabeck
Ex Dir: Becca Polglase
CTO: Krystal Bravo

D-U-N-S 07-263-3621
YMCA OF METROPOLITAN WASHINGTON
YMCA OF METRO WASHINGTON
1112 16th St Nw Ste 720, Washington, DC 20036-4824
Tel (202) 232-6700 *Founded/Ownrshp* 1864
Sales 52.5MME *EMP* 1,400
SIC 8641 Youth organizations
CEO: Angie Reese-Hawkins
**Pr:* Karen Addis
COO: Pam Curran
**COO:* Pamela Curran
**CFO:* Leigh Taylor-Kron
**Sr VP:* Dan Ickes
**Sr VP:* Stacey Leoniak
Sr VP: Ellen Straney
**Sr VP:* Leigh Taylor
**Sr VP:* Janice Williams
Prgrm Mgr: Edward Robinson

YMCA OF MIDDLE TENNESSEE
See YOUNG MENS CHRISTIAN ASSOCIATION OF MIDDLE TENNESSEE

D-U-N-S 09-427-2978
YMCA OF NORTH SHORE INC
245 Cabot St, Beverly, MA 01915-4598
Tel (978) 922-0990 *Founded/Ownrshp* 1984
Sales 46.1MM *EMP* 1,500
Accts Daniel Dennis & Company Llp D
SIC 7021 8322 8351 7999 7032 Dormitory, commercially operated; Individual & family services; Child day care services; Recreation center; Summer camp, except day & sports instructional
CEO: Jack Meany
Dir Vol: Kim Lations
**Pr:* Scott Buyer
**COO:* Chris Lovasco
**CFO:* Diane Linehan
**Treas:* William Leaver
VP: William S Wasserman
Assoc Dir: Paul Busa
Mktg Dir: Alysha Monfette
Pgrm Dir: Christine Sortwell

D-U-N-S 07-783-8373 IMP
YMCA OF NORTHWEST NORTH CAROLINA
METROPOLITAN SERVICES
301 N Main St Ste 1900, Winston Salem, NC 27101-3890
Tel (336) 777-8055 *Founded/Ownrshp* 1888
Sales 31.2MM *EMP* 1,400
Accts Butler & Burke Llp Winston-Sa
SIC 8641 7991 8351 7032 8322 Youth organizations; Physical fitness facilities; Child day care services; Youth camps; Individual & family services
Pr: Curt Hazelbaker
V Ch: Josh Dailey
Ex VP: Rosemary Suess
VP: Karen Bartoletti
VP: Adam McIver
Assoc Dir: Erin Craver
Assoc Dir: Roderick Howard
Comm Dir: Chelsea Cullen
Ex Dir: Jay Sutton
Brnch Mgr: Angela Lanier
Off Mgr: Erin N Johnson

D-U-N-S 07-337-5636
YMCA OF SAN DIEGO COUNTY
Y, THE
3708 Ruffin Rd, San Diego, CA 92123-1812
Tel (858) 292-9622 *Founded/Ownrshp* 1959
Sales 155.5MM *EMP* 5,000E
Accts Cohn Reznick Llp San Diego
SIC 8641 Youth organizations
CEO: Baron Herdelin Doherty
**CFO:* Charmaine Carter
**Sr VP:* John Merritt
VP: Diane Rousseau
IT Man: Joni Terada

YMCA OF SAN FRANCISCO
See YOUNG MENS CHRISTIAN ASSOCIATION OF SAN FRANCISCO

D-U-N-S 07-047-4598
YMCA OF SILICON VALLEY
80 Saratoga Ave, Santa Clara, CA 95051-7303
Tel (408) 351-6400 *Founded/Ownrshp* 1867
Sales 57.6MME *EMP* 1,800
Accts Robert Lee & Associates Llp S
SIC 8641 7991 8351 7032 8322 Youth organizations; Physical fitness facilities; Child day care services; Youth camps; Individual & family services
Pr: Kathy Riggins
**CFO:* Ed Barrantes
Assoc Dir: Anja Oven
Site Mgr: Marisela Herrera

YMCA OF SOUTH HAMPTON ROADS
See YOUNG MENS CHRISTIAN ASSOCIATION OF SOUTH HAMPTON ROADS

YMCA OF THE SUNCOAST
See YOUNG MENS CHRISTIAN ASSOCIATION OF SUNCOAST

YMCA OF THE USA
See NATIONAL COUNCIL OF YOUNG MENS CHRISTIAN ASSOCIATIONS OF UNITED STATES OF AMERICA

YMCA PIERCE AND KITSAP COUNTY
See YOUNG MENS CHRISTIAN ASSOCIATION OF PIERCE AND KITSAP COUNTY

D-U-N-S 14-841-9351
YOCHA DEHE WINTUN NATION
18960 County Rd 75 A, Brooks, CA 95606
Tel (530) 796-2109 *Founded/Ownrshp* 1900
Sales NA *EMP* 2,500E
SIC 9131 Indian reservation
Ch Bd: Marshall McKay
**CFO:* Guy Wolcott
Genl Mgr: Randy Takemoto

YOCRUNCH
See YOFARM CO

YODER TRADING COMPANY
See ARIS HORTICULTURE INC

D-U-N-S 00-200-3484
■**YODLE WEB.COM INC**
(*Suby of* WEB.COM GROUP INC) ★
330 W 34th St Fl 18, New York, NY 10001-2406
Tel (877) 276-5104 *Founded/Ownrshp* 2005, 2016
Sales 214.0MME *EMP* 420E
SIC 4813
CEO: Court Cunningham
Pr: Tim Alvarez
Pr: Tom Calvert
Pr: Steven R Power
CFO: Michael Gordon
VP: John Berkowitz
VP: Kevin Biggs
VP: David McCarthy
VP: Corey O'Donnell
VP: Denise Stott
Area Mgr: Kevin Cogan

D-U-N-S 05-445-6368 IMP
■**YODLEE INC**
(*Suby of* ENVESTNET INC) ★
3600 Bridge Pkwy Ste 200, Redwood City, CA 94065-6139
Tel (650) 980-3600 *Founded/Ownrshp* 2015
Sales 89.0MM *EMP* 451
SIC 8742 Banking & finance consultant
Pr: Anil Arora
CFO: Mike Armsby
Treas: Brad Beals
Chf Cred: Bill Parsons
Bd of Dir: Bruce Felt
Chf Mktg O: David Lee
Sr VP: Marc Blouin
Sr VP: Tim O'Brien
VP: Rosemary Brooks
VP: Jason Eyler
VP: Richard Fitzgerald
VP: Thomas Hempel
VP: Lori Martel
VP: Aditya Palande
VP: Sree Rajan

D-U-N-S 11-279-0126
YOFARM CO
YOCRUNCH
141a Sheridan Dr Ste A, Naugatuck, CT 06770-2038
Tel (203) 720-0000 *Founded/Ownrshp* 1985
Sales 107.9MM *EMP* 100
Accts Mcgladrey & Pullen Llp
SIC 2026 Yogurt
CEO: Todd Siwac
**CFO:* Gary Silver
**VP:* Alfred Lechner

YOGA SAK
See JONAH BROOKLYN INC

D-U-N-S 14-414-7209
YOH SERVICES LLC
(*Suby of* DAY & ZIMMERMANN GROUP INC) ★
1500 Spring Garden St, Philadelphia, PA 19130-4067
Tel (215) 656-2650 *Founded/Ownrshp* 1940
Sales 274.5MME *EMP* 4,000
SIC 7363 Help supply services
Pr: Anthony Bosco
**COO:* Larry Stanczak
**Ch:* William Yoh
VP: Catherine Congleton
**VP:* Jo Johnson
VP: Andy Roane
**VP:* Scott Salantrie
VP: Leslie Tell
VP: Sean Trimble
Brnch Mgr: Michelle Pearce
Brnch Mgr: Stephanie Saxon

YOKE'S FOOD AND DRUG
See YOKES FOODS INC

D-U-N-S 14-425-0164
YOKES FOODS INC
YOKE'S FOOD AND DRUG
3426 S University Rd, Spokane Valley, WA 99206-5855
Tel (509) 921-2292 *Founded/Ownrshp* 1990
Sales 182.7MME *EMP* 950
SIC 5912 Drug stores

Pr: John A Bole
**VP:* Joe A Hanson

D-U-N-S 60-692-5758
YOKOHAMA CORP OF NORTH AMERICA
YOKOHAMA TIRE
(*Suby of* YOKOHAMA RUBBER COMPANY, LIMITED, THE)
1500 Indiana St, Salem, VA 24153-7058
Tel (540) 389-5426 *Founded/Ownrshp* 1917
Sales 833.7MM^E *EMP* 2,100
SIC 3011 5014 Tires & inner tubes; Tires & tubes
CEO: Yasuo Tominaga
**CFO:* Takaharu Fushimi
Treas: Satoshi Miiyata
Ofcr: Shinichi Suzuki
Manager: Brian Aguirre

D-U-N-S 60-313-3463 IMP
YOKOHAMA INDUSTRIES AMERICAS INC
YH AMERICA
(*Suby of* YOKOHAMA TIRE) ★
105 Industry Dr, Versailles, KY 40383-1527
Tel (859) 873-2188 *Founded/Ownrshp* 1989
Sales 123.7MM^E *EMP* 401
SIC 3714 3585 3492 3052 Power steering equipment, motor vehicle; Air conditioner parts, motor vehicle; Refrigeration & heating equipment; Fluid power valves & hose fittings; Rubber & plastics hose & beltings
Pr: Yoku Okamoto
**Pr:* Yasuhiko Tajima
**Treas:* John Devoe
**VP:* Ed Behn
**VP:* Cory Brusman
Genl Mgr: Satoru Fuchise
CTO: Karl Haydon
IT Man: Bill Turner
QC Dir: Caroline Powell
Mtls Mgr: Karen Swigert
Mtls Mgr: Jerry Westrick

YOKOHAMA TIRE
See YOKOHAMA CORP OF NORTH AMERICA

D-U-N-S 05-078-9270 IMP/EXP
YOKOHAMA TIRE CORP
YOKOHAMA TIRE USA
(*Suby of* YOKOHAMA TIRE) ★
1 Macarthur Pl Ste 800, Santa Ana, CA 92707-5948
Tel (714) 870-3800 *Founded/Ownrshp* 1989
Sales 549.0MM^E *EMP* 1,450
SIC 5014 3011

D-U-N-S 07-950-2023
YOKOHAMA TIRE MANUFACTURING VIRGINIA LLC
(*Suby of* YOKOHAMA TIRE USA) ★
1500 Indiana St, Salem, VA 24153-7058
Tel (540) 389-5426 *Founded/Ownrshp* 2013
Sales 210.6MM^E *EMP* 930^E
SIC 3011 Tire & inner tube materials & related products
Pr: Tetsuro Murakami
**CEO:* Yasushi Tanaka

YOKOHAMA TIRE USA
See YOKOHAMA TIRE CORP

YONKERS BOARD OF EDUCATION
See YONKERS CITY SCHOOL DISTRICT

D-U-N-S 13-550-4876
YONKERS CITY SCHOOL DISTRICT
YONKERS BOARD OF EDUCATION
1 Larkin Ctr Fl 3, Yonkers, NY 10701-7044
Tel (914) 376-8000 *Founded/Ownrshp* 1990
Sales 235.6MM^E *EMP* 5,500
SIC 8211 9111 Public elementary school; Public junior high school; Public senior high school; Mayors' offices
Treas: Sophia Wu
**Ofcr:* Joesph J Bracchitta
VP: Teresa Cannady
VP: Karen Doran
VP: Rafael Guerrero
VP: Jose Montas
Dir Sec: Brian Schoulder
Dir IT: Jan Cabbell
Pr Dir: Jerilynne Fierstein
Schl Brd P: Nader Sayegn
Instr Medi: Gina Bell

D-U-N-S 00-699-5682
YONKERS CONTRACTING CO INC
PETMAR BUILDERS DIVISION
969 Midland Ave, Yonkers, NY 10704-1086
Tel (914) 965-1500 *Founded/Ownrshp* 1945
Sales 996.0MM^E *EMP* 2,450
SIC 1611 General contractor, highway & street construction
Ch Bd: Carl E Petrillo
**CFO:* Michael J Keller
**Ex VP:* John Kolaya
VP: Paul Hubert
VP: William Jordan
Dir Bus: Heather Cuffel
Genl Mgr: Greg Petrillo
IT Man: Mike Eannazo
Ql Cn Mgr: Jonathan Pulaski
Board of Directors: Jill Papa

YONKERS RACEWAY
See YONKERS RACING CORP

D-U-N-S 05-630-1138 IMP
YONKERS RACING CORP
YONKERS RACEWAY
810 Yonkers Ave, Yonkers, NY 10704-2030
Tel (914) 968-4200 *Founded/Ownrshp* 1972
Sales 204.1MM *EMP* 1,300
Accts Kpmg Llp New York Ny
SIC 7948 Racing, including track operation; Harness horse racing
CEO: Tim Rooney Jr
**Owner:* Ken Jacobs
**Pr:* Timothy J Rooney Sr
**COO:* Robert Galtiero
**CFO:* Joel Daum
**VP:* Arthur J Rooney Jr
**VP:* Daniel Rooney
Dir Sec: Charlie Cola
Pr Dir: Taryn Duffy
Counsel: Marie Reilly

YORK
See SOUTHERN CALIFORNIA RISK MANAGEMENT ASSOCIATES INC

D-U-N-S 06-867-3102
YORK COLLEGE OF PENNSYLVANIA INC
441 Country Club Rd, York, PA 17403-3651
Tel (717) 815-1780 *Founded/Ownrshp* 1787
Sales 104.4MM *EMP* 660
Accts Grant Thornton Llp Philadelph
SIC 8221 College, except junior
Pr: George W Waldner
Comm Man: Robert Mott
Ex Dir: Jolynn Varano
Dir IT: Gerald Patnode
Dir IT: Bob Robinson
VP Opers: Lindsay Houser

D-U-N-S 12-452-4281
YORK COUNTY SCHOOL DIVISION
YCSD
302 Dare Rd, Yorktown, VA 23692-2716
Tel (757) 898-0300 *Founded/Ownrshp* 1991
Sales 76.0MM^E *EMP* 1,750
SIC 8211 Public elementary & secondary schools
V Ch: Linda Meadows
**COO:* Carl James
**CFO:* Dennis R Jarrett
Bd of Dir: Cindy Kirschke
Bd of Dir: Mark Medford
Prin: Ed Holler
Dir Sec: Russell Payne
Dir IT: Tim Allen
Sfty Dirs: Sandy Hespe
Teacher Pr: James Carroll
Psych: Betty Lasris

D-U-N-S 06-234-3066
■**YORK GROUP INC** (PA)
WALLACE METAL PRODUCTS
(*Suby of* MATTHEWS INTERNATIONAL CORP) ★
2 N Shore Ctr, Pittsburgh, PA 15212-5838
Tel (412) 995-1600 *Founded/Ownrshp* 1996
Sales 71.9MM^E *EMP* 1,667
SIC 7261 Funeral service & crematories
**Pr:* Harry Pontone
**Treas:* David F Beck
**Sr VP:* Sandra A Matson
**Sr VP:* H Joe Trulove
**VP:* Steve Gakenbach
**VP:* Dan E Malone
**VP:* Steven F Nicola
**VP:* Thomas Pontone
Sfty Dirs: Dave Harris
Plnt Mgr: Ray Hughes

YORK HOSPITAL
See WELLSPAN HEALTH

YORK HOSPITAL
See WELLSPAN MEDICAL GROUP (INC)

D-U-N-S 07-121-2153
YORK HOSPITAL
WELLSPAN HEALTH
(*Suby of* YORK HOSPITAL) ★
1001 S George St, York, PA 17403-3645
Tel (717) 851-2345 *Founded/Ownrshp* 1880
Sales 925.9MM *EMP* 6,200
SIC 8062 General medical & surgical hospitals
CEO: Donald B Dellinger
**Pr:* Richard L Seim
**CEO:* Kevin H Mosser
**CFO:* Michael F O'Connor
**Sr VP:* R H Baker MD
**VP:* Richard H Brown
VP: William Gillespie
**VP:* Raymond Rosen
Dir Sec: Kathy Mager
Doctor: Pradeep Alur MD
Doctor: Bruce M Bushwick MD

D-U-N-S 07-746-1549
YORK HOSPITAL
15 Hospital Dr, York, ME 03909-1099
Tel (207) 351-2023 *Founded/Ownrshp* 1905
Sales 159.1MM *EMP* 535
SIC 8062 8051 8069 7361 General medical & surgical hospitals; Skilled nursing care facilities; Drug addiction rehabilitation hospital; Nurses' registry
Ch Bd: Hunt Walton
**Pr:* Jud Knox
**Ch:* Doug Bracy
Chf Mktg O: Jeffrey Lockhart
Dir Risk M: Patricia Novello
CIO: Robin Bonte
CTO: Jennifer Rooney
MIS Dir: John Germero
Dir QC: Erin Graydon Baker
Software D: Lisa Kenney
Software D: Julie Viator

D-U-N-S 19-656-1252 IMP/EXP
YORK INTERNATIONAL CORP
(*Suby of* JOHNSON CONTROLS INC) ★
631 S Richland Ave, York, PA 17403-3445
Tel (717) 771-7890 *Founded/Ownrshp* 2005
Sales 1.9MMM^E *EMP* 8,000
SIC 3585 Refrigeration & heating equipment; Air conditioning units, complete: domestic or industrial; Heat pumps, electric; Compressors for refrigeration & air conditioning equipment
Pr: C David Myers
**Treas:* Stephen Roell
**VP:* Jane B Davis
**VP:* Jerome Okarma
Dir Surg: Cos Caronna
Dir IT: David Mason
Dir IT: Rajiv Vora

D-U-N-S 00-262-6654
YORK NAMI PA COUNTY
140 Roosevelt Ave Ste 200, York, PA 17401-3333
Tel (717) 848-3784 *Founded/Ownrshp* 2007
Sales 96.0MM *EMP* 2
SIC 8299 Educational services
Ex Dir: Kimberly Preske

D-U-N-S 07-121-4472
YORK PENNSYLVANIA HOSPITAL CO LLC
MEMORIAL HOSPITAL
(*Suby of* MEMORIAL HEALTH SYSTEMS CORPORATION)
325 S Belmont St, York, PA 17403-2608
Tel (717) 843-8623 *Founded/Ownrshp* 1995
Sales 97.2MM *EMP* 900
Accts Parentebeard Llc York Pa
SIC 8062 8082 General medical & surgical hospitals; Home health care services
Ch Bd: Chloe Eichelberger
**CEO:* Sally J Dixon
**CFO:* Brent Smith
**VP:* Josette M Myers
Exec: Ann Miller
Dir Sec: Joe Barron
Prac Mgr: Jana Jones
Off Mgr: Carol Raffensberger
Dir IT: Eddie Bender
Dir IT: John Sebastian
Surgeon: Bryan Houseman

D-U-N-S 04-002-7989
YORK PROPERTIES INC OF RALEIGH
1900 Cameron St, Raleigh, NC 27605-1307
Tel (919) 821-1350 *Founded/Ownrshp* 1975
Sales 98.0MM^E *EMP* 125
SIC 6552 6531 Subdividers & developers; Real estate managers; Real estate brokers & agents
Ch Bd: G Smedes York
**Pr:* George S York Jr
**CFO:* Jeff Gregorio
**Sr VP:* Henry Ward
**VP:* John Koonce
**VP:* Hal Worth III
Off Mgr: Elizabeth Boyer

D-U-N-S 08-572-6917
YORK RISK SERVICES GROUP INC
YORK SLA
(*Suby of* FOX HILL HOLDINGS INC) ★
1 Upper Pond Bldg F, Parsippany, NJ 07054
Tel (973) 404-1200 *Founded/Ownrshp* 2008
Sales NA *EMP* 1,832
SIC 6411 Insurance claim adjusters, not employed by insurance company
Pr: Richard H Taketa
Pr: Scott Gaffne
Pr: Randy Thornton
**CFO:* Jeffrey H Marshall
Sr VP: Kerry Anderson
Sr VP: Peter Bellisano
Sr VP: Ritchie Vener
Sr VP: Wm Ritchie Vener
VP: Terry Camp
VP: Raffy Daghlian
VP: Angela Hatley
VP: Leo McCann
VP: Patrick O'Toole
VP: Jim Robert
Exec: Mark Bruaski
Exec: John Couture
Exec: Keith Culley
Exec: Jonathan Drenocky
Exec: David Gabor
Exec: Larry Hutchison
Exec: Cliff Hyde

YORK SCHOOL DISTRICT 4
See FORT MILL SCHOOL DISTRICT 4

YORK SLA
See YORK RISK SERVICES GROUP INC

YORK STREET CAPITAL PARTNERS
See GL CAPITAL PARTNERS LLC

D-U-N-S 13-165-8445 IMP/EXP
YORK TELECOM CORP
YORKTEL
81 Corbett Way, Eatontown, NJ 07724-2264
Tel (732) 413-6000 *Founded/Ownrshp* 1985
Sales 168.5MM^E *EMP* 343
Accts Eisneramper Llp Wall New Jer
SIC 3669 3651 Visual communication systems; Recording machines, except dictation & telephone answering
Ch Bd: York Wang
Pr: Jim Anderson
**CEO:* Ronald Gaboury
CFO: Robert Harris
**CFO:* Judith Pulig
Ex VP: Jim Deblasio
Ex VP: Greg Douglas
Sr VP: Karen Paglia
Sr VP: John Vitale
VP: Joe Arena
VP: Vishal Brown
VP: Victoria Healey
VP: Pete McLain
VP: Dan Missbrenner
VP: Steve Peckman
VP: Aaron Wentzel
VP: Roger Wesenyak

D-U-N-S 13-272-8051
YORKSHIRE GLOBAL RESTAURANTS INC
(*Suby of* A&W RESTAURANT) ★
1648 Mcgrathiana Pkwy, Lexington, KY 40511-1338
Tel (859) 721-1328 *Founded/Ownrshp* 2011
Sales 123.8MM^E *EMP* 1,502
SIC 5812 Drive-in restaurant; Fast-food restaurant, chain
CEO: Kevin Bazner

YORKTEL
See YORK TELECOM CORP

YORKTOWNE CABINETRY
See ELKAY WOOD PRODUCTS CO

D-U-N-S 17-523-7536 IMP
YOROZU AUTOMOTIVE TENNESSEE INC
YAT
(*Suby of* YOROZU NORTH AMERICA INC) ★
395 Mt View Industrial Dr, Morrison, TN 37357-5917
Tel (931) 668-7700 *Founded/Ownrshp* 1986
Sales 121.3MM^E *EMP* 300
SIC 3465 Automotive stampings
Pr: Jack Phillips
**Pr:* Yusuke Kawada
**CFO:* Toshiyuki Yago
**Prin:* Scott Cutrell
**Prin:* Bill Grisard

D-U-N-S 03-665-0752
YOROZU NORTH AMERICA INC (MI)
(*Suby of* YOROZU CORPORATION)
395 Mt View Industrial Dr, Morrison, TN 37357-5917
Tel (931) 668-7700 *Founded/Ownrshp* 1997
Sales 121.3MM^E *EMP* 300
SIC 8711 8742 Engineering services; Merchandising consultant
Pr: Kazumi Sato

D-U-N-S 05-959-1248
YOSEMITE COMMUNITY COLLEGE DISTRICT
COLUMBIA COL/MODESTO JR COLL
2201 Blue Gum Ave, Modesto, CA 95358-1052
Tel (209) 575-7800 *Founded/Ownrshp* 1921
Sales 53.9MM^E *EMP* 1,365
Accts Matson And Isom Chico/Redding
SIC 8222 Community college
Exec: Doug Lau
CIO: Mark Spruiell
CTO: Bob Gauvreau
IT Man: Margo Guzman
Sys Mgr: Larry Weese

YOSEMITE CONCESSION SERVICES
See DNC PARKS & RESORTS AT YOSEMITE INC

D-U-N-S 19-989-2761
YOSEMITE FARM CREDIT ACA
806 W Monte Vista Ave, Turlock, CA 95382-7242
Tel (209) 667-2366 *Founded/Ownrshp* 1920
Sales NA *EMP* 100
SIC 6111 Federal Land Banks
Pr: Leonard Van Eldern
**CFO:* Tracy Sparks
VP: Robert Fuller
VP: Brian Lemons
VP: Galen Miyamoto
Brnch Mgr: Doug Junker
VP Mktg: Melba Miyamoto

YOSHIDA GROUP
See YOSHIDAS INC

D-U-N-S 62-192-7532 IMP
YOSHIDAS INC
YOSHIDA GROUP
8440 Ne Alderwood Rd A, Portland, OR 97220-1471
Tel (503) 731-3702 *Founded/Ownrshp* 1981
Sales 85.7MM^E *EMP* 200
SIC 5149 8741 Groceries & related products; Management services
Pr: Matt Guthrie

D-U-N-S 09-306-9128 IMP
YOSHINOYA AMERICA INC
YOSHINOYA BEEF BOWL
(*Suby of* YOSHINOYA HOLDINGS CO.,LTD.)
991 Knox St, Torrance, CA 90502-1006
Tel (310) 527-6060 *Founded/Ownrshp* 1977, 2003
Sales 52.7MM^E *EMP* 1,300
SIC 5812 Fast-food restaurant, chain
CEO: Hisashi Ikegami
**Pr:* Junichi Umemoto
COO: Atsushi Samura
VP: Andrew Hatzis

YOSHINOYA BEEF BOWL
See YOSHINOYA AMERICA INC

YOTEC
See YAMADA NORTH AMERICA INC

D-U-N-S 55-677-0126
YOUGHIOGHENY COMMUNICATIONS-TEXAS LLC
POCKET COMMUNICATIONS
2118 Fredericksburg Rd, San Antonio, TX 78201-4407
Tel (210) 777-7777 *Founded/Ownrshp* 2005
Sales 113.6MM^E *EMP* 1,000
SIC 4812 Cellular telephone services
CFO: Kelly Simmons
CFO: Burner Snyder

YOUNG & RUBICAM GROUP
See YOUNG & RUBICAM INC

D-U-N-S 00-699-2515
YOUNG & RUBICAM INC
YOUNG & RUBICAM GROUP
(*Suby of* WPP PLC)
3 Columbus Cir Fl 8, New York, NY 10019-8750
Tel (212) 210-3000 *Founded/Ownrshp* 1923, 2000
Sales 1.3MMM^E *EMP* 13,130
SIC 8742 Marketing consulting services
V Ch Bd: June Blocklin
Mng Pt: Katja Skoberne
Pr: Jamie Gallo
**CEO:* Ann Fudge
**CEO:* Lois Jacobs
CEO: Mark Read
CEO: David Sable
COO: Martin Beck
**CFO:* James Bruce
CFO: Peter Law Gisiko
**CFO:* Peter Law-Gisiko
CFO: Marc Sigle
Sr Cor Off: Tim Silvain
Chf Mktg O: Jamie Gutfreund
Ofcr: Yannis Kotziagkiaouridis
Ofcr: Gary S Laben
Ex VP: Bill Manfredi
Ex VP: William J Manfredi
Ex VP: Andrew McLean

Ex VP: Robert Rosiek
Ex VP: Seith Rothstein

D-U-N-S 08-464-1968 IMP/EXP
YOUNG ADULT INSTITUTE INC
460 W 34th St Fl 11, New York, NY 10001-2382
Tel (212) 563-7474 *Founded/Ownrshp* 1964
Sales 225.6MM^E *EMP* 5,000
Accts Grassi & Co Cpas Pc Jericho
SIC 8059 8361 8011 Personal care home, with health care; Home for the mentally retarded; Offices & clinics of medical doctors
CEO: Matthew Sturiale L C S W
**Pr:* Dr Philip H Levy
**CFO:* Karen Wagemann
CFO: Karen Wegmann
Exec: Luz Montalvo
Genl Mgr: Kelly Quinn
Dir IT: Ted Cole
IT Man: Anita Sementilli
Web Dev: George Pappas
Opers Supe: Yolanda Marin
Psych: Richard C Sullivan

D-U-N-S 96-755-5249
YOUNG AUTOMOTIVE GROUP INC
645 N Main St, Layton, UT 84041-2230
Tel (801) 544-1234 *Founded/Ownrshp* 2011
Sales 86.6MM^E *EMP* 283^E
SIC 5511 New & used car dealers

D-U-N-S 18-317-4127
YOUNG BROADCASTING LLC
599 Lexington Ave, New York, NY 10022-6030
Tel (517) 372-8282 *Founded/Ownrshp* 1986
Sales 312.2MM^E *EMP* 1,097^E
Accts Ernst & Young Llp New York N
SIC 4833 Television broadcasting stations
Pr: Deborah A McDermott
**CFO:* James A Morgan
**Ofcr:* Kevin Shea
Board of Directors: Tony Cassara, Tom Sullivan

D-U-N-S 00-908-2918 IMP
YOUNG ELECTRIC SIGN CO INC
YESCO
2401 S Foothill Dr, Salt Lake City, UT 84109-1479
Tel (801) 464-4600 *Founded/Ownrshp* 1920
Sales 363.3MM^E *EMP* 1,501
SIC 3993 7359 1799 6794 Neon signs; Electric signs; Sign rental; Sign installation & maintenance; Franchises, selling or licensing
Ch: Thomas Young Jr
**Pr:* Michael T Young
**Treas:* Clark Smith
**Ex VP:* Paul C Young
**Sr VP:* Lon Searle
**Sr VP:* Neil Smith
VP: Ben Jones
VP: Duane D Wardle
VP: Ken Wilson
VP: Jeffrey Young
Exec: Michelle Zeller
Dir Bus: Jack Larsen

D-U-N-S 07-873-9060
YOUNG INNOVATIONS HOLDINGS LLC
111 S Wacker Dr, Chicago, IL 60606-4302
Tel (312) 506-5600 *Founded/Ownrshp* 2012
Sales 113.3MM^E *EMP* 389^E
SIC 3843 Dental equipment & supplies

D-U-N-S 00-419-3103 IMP
YOUNG INNOVATIONS INC
(*Suby of* YOUNG INNOVATIONS HOLDINGS LLC) ★
2260 Wendt St, Algonquin, IL 60102-1400
Tel (847) 458-5400 *Founded/Ownrshp* 2013
Sales 113.3MM^E *EMP* 389
SIC 3843 Dental equipment & supplies
CEO: Alfred E Brennan
**Pr:* Arthur L Herbst Jr
VP: Julia Carter
VP: Richard G Richmond
Prd Mgr: Tom Richardson

D-U-N-S 05-024-5331
YOUNG LIFE
420 N Cascade Ave, Colorado Springs, CO 80903-3352
Tel (719) 381-1800 *Founded/Ownrshp* 1941
Sales 331.4MM *EMP* 3,100
Accts Capin Crouse Llp Colorado Spr
SIC 8661 7032 Non-church religious organizations; Sporting & recreational camps
Pr: Dennis Rydberg
VP: Reid Estes
VP: John Franklin
VP: Bebe Hobson
VP: Ken Knipp
VP: Lee I Corder
VP: Marty I Caldwell
VP: Angel Ruiz
VP: Ty Saltzgiver
Genl Mgr: Irene Outlar
CTO: Don Stuber

D-U-N-S 02-016-1519
YOUNG MCLARENS INTERNATIONAL INC
(*Suby of* MYI LIMITED)
5555 Triangle Pkwy # 200, Norcross, GA 30092-2597
Tel (770) 448-4680 *Founded/Ownrshp* 2003
Sales NA *EMP* 158
SIC 6411 Insurance adjusters
Pr: Vernon Chalfant
Pr: Gary Brown
CFO: Joseph Faimali
Ex VP: Gary Gabriel
VP: Marco De Leon
VP: Jim Donovan
VP: Paul Dowling
VP: Fred Perez
VP: Christopher Stafford
VP: George Wasielke
Exec: Timothy Bennett
Exec: Jim Carson
Exec: Trent Gillette
Exec: Gerry Griffin
Exec: Matthew Lebrun
Exec: Scott Markey
Exec: David Matias
Exec: Marcus Reath
Exec: Vito Russo
Exec: Robyn Saal
Exec: Russell Umpleby

D-U-N-S 03-051-6694
YOUNG MEN S CHRISTIAN ASSOCIATION OF GREATER CHARLOTTE
YMCA
400 E Morehead St, Charlotte, NC 28202-2610
Tel (704) 716-6200 *Founded/Ownrshp* 1874
Sales 82.7MM *EMP* 3,000
SIC 7032 8641

D-U-N-S 07-546-3208
YOUNG MENS CHRISTIAN ASSOCIATION OF BIRMINGHAM
YMCA CENTER
2101 4th Ave N, Birmingham, AL 35203-3303
Tel (205) 801-9622 *Founded/Ownrshp* 1884
Sales 28.5MM *EMP* 1,100
Accts Carr Riggs & Ingram Llc Birm
SIC 7991 8641 8351 7032 Physical fitness facilities; Youth organizations; Child day care services; Youth camps
CFO: Jon Myer

D-U-N-S 18-316-7600
YOUNG MENS CHRISTIAN ASSOCIATION OF BROWARD COUNTY FLORIDA INC
Y M C A OF BROWARD COUNTY, FL
900 Se 3rd Ave, Fort Lauderdale, FL 33316-1118
Tel (954) 334-9622 *Founded/Ownrshp* 2007
Sales 32.4MM^E *EMP* 1,000
Accts Rsm Mcgladrey Inc Fort Laud
SIC 8641 Youth organizations
Pr: Sheryl A Woods
**Pr:* John M Lass
**COO:* Bruce Griffin
**CFO:* David W Cash
**Treas:* William Penney
**VP:* Andrea Crawford
**VP:* Debbie Metzger
**VP:* Melissa Powers
Off Mgr: Karen Smith

D-U-N-S 09-651-8535
YOUNG MENS CHRISTIAN ASSOCIATION OF CEDAR RAPIDS METROPOLITAN AREA (IA)
YMCA
207 7th Ave Se, Cedar Rapids, IA 52401-2001
Tel (319) 366-6421 *Founded/Ownrshp* 1868
Sales 7.5MM *EMP* 1,608^E
Accts Cliftonlarsonallen Llp Cedar
SIC 8641 8322 Youth organizations; Individual & family services
Ex Dir: Bob Carlson
**VP:* Kathy Lamb
Brnch Mgr: John Buterla
Off Mgr: Kay Schumacher

D-U-N-S 07-503-6962
YOUNG MENS CHRISTIAN ASSOCIATION OF CENTRAL OHIO
YMCA OF CENTRAL OHIO
40 W Long St, Columbus, OH 43215-2817
Tel (614) 224-1142 *Founded/Ownrshp* 1855, 1985
Sales 36.4MM *EMP* 1,800
SIC 8641

D-U-N-S 00-693-3295
YOUNG MENS CHRISTIAN ASSOCIATION OF CHICAGO
1030 W Van Buren St, Chicago, IL 60607-2916
Tel (312) 932-1200 *Founded/Ownrshp* 1861
Sales 113.1MM *EMP* 3,000
Accts Lb Mcgladrey Llp Chicago Il
SIC 8641 7011 8351 8699 8322 7999 Youth organizations; YMCA/YMHA hotel; Child day care services; Charitable organization; Youth center; Squash club, non-membership
Pr: Richard Malone
CFO: Mike Guariao
**Treas:* Noreen St Lawrence
Ofcr: Nicole Camboni
Ex VP: Julie A Burke
Sr VP: Charmaine Williams
VP: Fran J Bell
VP: Kim Kiser
VP: Christina Krasov
Ex Dir: Jeff Tremmel
IT Man: Andrew Adelmann

D-U-N-S 07-289-0486
YOUNG MENS CHRISTIAN ASSOCIATION OF GREATER CINCINNATI
YMCA
1105 Elm St, Cincinnati, OH 45202-7513
Tel (513) 651-2100 *Founded/Ownrshp* 1853
Sales 33.6MM *EMP* 2,821
SIC 8641

D-U-N-S 07-127-8220
YOUNG MENS CHRISTIAN ASSOCIATION OF GREATER DAYTON
YMCA OF GREATER DAYTON
118 W St Ste 300, Dayton, OH 45402
Tel (937) 223-5201 *Founded/Ownrshp* 2014
Sales 26.1MM *EMP* 1,250
Accts Flagel Huber Flagel Certified
SIC 8641 7991 8351 7032 8322 Youth organizations; Physical fitness facilities; Child day care services; Youth camps; Individual & family services
CEO: Dale Brunner
**VP:* Neal Pemberton

D-U-N-S 96-952-7279
YOUNG MENS CHRISTIAN ASSOCIATION OF GREATER HOUSTON AREA
2600 North Loop W Ste 300, Houston, TX 77092-8915
Tel (713) 659-5566 *Founded/Ownrshp* 2011
Sales 109.3MM^E *EMP* 3,500^E
Accts Blazek & Vetterling Houston
SIC 8322

D-U-N-S 05-029-8918
YOUNG MENS CHRISTIAN ASSOCIATION OF GREATER HOUSTON AREA INC
Y M C A
2600 North Loop W Ste 300, Houston, TX 77092-8915
Tel (713) 659-5566 *Founded/Ownrshp* 1886
Sales 95.6MM^E *EMP* 2,500
Accts Blazek & Vetterling Houston
SIC 8641 7991 8351 7032 8322 Youth organizations; Physical fitness facilities; Child day care services; Youth camps; Individual & family services
Pr: Clark D Baker
**COO:* Dale E Walters
**CFO:* Wayne Brewer
Exec: Liz Ramos
Ex Dir: Jeff Watkins

D-U-N-S 03-070-9992
YOUNG MENS CHRISTIAN ASSOCIATION OF GREATER KANSAS CITY (MO)
3100 Broadway Blvd # 1020, Kansas City, MO 64111-2658
Tel (816) 561-9622 *Founded/Ownrshp* 1860
Sales 29.6MM^E *EMP* 1,039
SIC 8641 7993 7991 Civic social & fraternal associations; Coin-operated amusement devices; Physical fitness facilities
CEO: David Byrd
**Pr:* H Eugene Dooley
**COO:* Mark Hulet
COO: John Mikos
**CFO:* Kelli McClure

D-U-N-S 05-956-2710
YOUNG MENS CHRISTIAN ASSOCIATION OF GREATER LOUISVILLE
YMCA OF GREATER LOUISVILLE
545 S 2nd St, Louisville, KY 40202-1801
Tel (502) 587-9622 *Founded/Ownrshp* 1853
Sales 42.8MM *EMP* 1,200
SIC 8641 7991 8351 7032 8322 Youth organizations; Physical fitness facilities; Child day care services; Youth camps; Individual & family services
Pr: Steve Tarber
**Sr VP:* Becky Gamm
**Sr VP:* David Heard
**VP:* Ryan Kingery
**VP:* Kay Manning
**VP:* S Kay Manning
CTO: Sherry Ernst

D-U-N-S 07-280-5419 IMP/EXP
YOUNG MENS CHRISTIAN ASSOCIATION OF GREATER NEW YORK
Y M C A
5 W 63rd St Fl 6, New York, NY 10023-7162
Tel (212) 630-9600 *Founded/Ownrshp* 1852
Sales 196.7MM *EMP* 4,500
Accts Pricewaterhousecoopers Llp Ne
SIC 8641 7991 8351 7032 8322 Youth organizations; Physical fitness facilities; Child day care services; Youth camps; Individual & family services
Pr: Jack Lund
**Ch Bd:* Diana Taylor
**Ch:* Chris Blunt
Ex VP: Sal Maglietta
**Ex VP:* Kenneth Turpin
VP: Lori Rose
VP: Rocksana Subhan
Comm Dir: Sandy Phillips
CTO: Jessica Albizu
VP Opers: Rena McGrevey
Psych: Mark Arena

D-U-N-S 06-602-1361
YOUNG MENS CHRISTIAN ASSOCIATION OF GREATER RICHMOND
YMCA
2 W Franklin St, Richmond, VA 23220-5006
Tel (804) 644-9622 *Founded/Ownrshp* 1854
Sales 41.1MM *EMP* 1,120
Accts Mcgladrey Llp Richmond Virgi
SIC 8641 7991 8351 7032 8322 Youth organizations; Physical fitness facilities; Child day care services; Youth camps; Individual & family services
CEO: Tim Joyce
**Sr VP:* Abby Farris Rogers
VP: Tricia Puryear
Assoc Dir: Andrew Dyson
Assoc Dir: Matthew Roberson
Ex Dir: Justin Guest
Board of Directors: Robert Alexander, Carol Bennett, Carol Bennett, Matthew Clarke, Joseph Dziedzic, Jill Goldfine

D-U-N-S 08-250-6189
YOUNG MENS CHRISTIAN ASSOCIATION OF GREATER SEATTLE
YMCA OF GREATER SEATTLE
909 4th Ave, Seattle, WA 98104-1108
Tel (206) 382-5342 *Founded/Ownrshp* 1876
Sales 74.7MM *EMP* 1,400
Accts Moss Adams Llp Seattle Washi
SIC 8641 8322 Youth organizations; Individual & family services
CEO: Robert B Gilbertson Jr
**Treas:* John F Vynne

D-U-N-S 02-028-5573
YOUNG MENS CHRISTIAN ASSOCIATION OF GREATER TOLEDO
YMCA OF GREATER TOLEDO
1500 N Superior St Fl 2, Toledo, OH 43604-2149
Tel (419) 729-8135 *Founded/Ownrshp* 1865
Sales 29.4MM *EMP* 1,200
Accts Plante & Moran Pllc Southfiel
SIC 8641 7991 8351 7032 8322 Youth organizations; Physical fitness facilities; Child day care services; Youth camps; Individual & family services
Pr: Todd Tibbits
COO: Casey Holck
**CFO:* Brian Keel
**VP:* Stephanie Dames
VP: Wilma Dimanna
VP: Christy Gordon

D-U-N-S 02-049-6519
YOUNG MENS CHRISTIAN ASSOCIATION OF GREATER TWIN CITIES
YMCA OF GREATER TWIN CITIES
2125 E Hennepin Ave, Minneapolis, MN 55413-1766
Tel (612) 465-0450 *Founded/Ownrshp* 1856
Sales 138.0MM *EMP* 7,000
Accts Cliftonlarsonallen Llp Minnea
SIC 8641 Social club, membership; Youth organizations
CEO: Glen Gunderson
**COO:* Todd Tibbits
**CFO:* Greg Waibel
Dir IT: Tim Orpen

D-U-N-S 07-487-5246
YOUNG MENS CHRISTIAN ASSOCIATION OF METROPOLITAN
601 N Akard St, Dallas, TX 75201-3303
Tel (214) 880-9622 *Founded/Ownrshp* 1885
Sales 59.8MM *EMP* 2,000^E
SIC 8641 7991 8351 7032 8322 Youth organizations; Physical fitness facilities; Child day care services; Youth camps; Individual & family services
Pr: Gordon Echtenkamp
**COO:* Phil Dicaslo
**CFO:* Jean A Allen
Sr VP: Carmelita Gallo
Ex Dir: Tony Lokash
Ex Dir: Tricia Meinhold

D-U-N-S 07-587-6375
YOUNG MENS CHRISTIAN ASSOCIATION OF METROPOLITAN ATLANTA INC (GA)
METRO ATLANTA YMCA
100 Edgewood Ave Ne, Atlanta, GA 30303-3026
Tel (404) 588-9622 *Founded/Ownrshp* 1856
Sales 102.7MM *EMP* 5,450
Accts Smith & Howard Atlanta Ga
SIC 8641 7991 8351 7032 8322 Youth organizations; Physical fitness facilities; Child day care services; Youth camps; Individual & family services
CEO: Edward Munster
Pr: Holly Swing
**CFO:* Billy Holley
**CFO:* Kathleen Spencer
Genl Mgr: Nedra Jones
Off Mgr: Regina Colon
Pgrm Dir: Lauren Williams

D-U-N-S 07-632-4029
YOUNG MENS CHRISTIAN ASSOCIATION OF METROPOLITAN DETROIT
YMCA OF METROPOLITAN DETROIT
1401 Broadway St Ste A, Detroit, MI 48226-2112
Tel (313) 267-5300 *Founded/Ownrshp* 1863
Sales 38.1MM *EMP* 1,300
Accts Plante & Moran Pllc Southfie
SIC 7999 8641 Recreation services; Civic associations
Pr: Reid S Thebault
Ex Dir: Lynne Wilcox
CIO: Linda Brooks
Mktg Dir: Anthony Richardson

D-U-N-S 07-412-5949
YOUNG MENS CHRISTIAN ASSOCIATION OF METROPOLITAN LOS ANGELES
YMCA
625 S New Hampshire Ave, Los Angeles, CA 90005-1342
Tel (213) 351-2256 *Founded/Ownrshp* 1889
Sales 103.1MM *EMP* 2,500
Accts Cohnreznick Llp Los Angeles
SIC 8641 Youth organizations
Pr: Alan Hostrup
**Ch Bd:* W J Ellison
**CFO:* Dan Cooper
Exec: Robert Shafer
Assoc Dir: Catherine Knight
Assoc Dir: Melissa Tegeder
Ex Dir: Michael Newton
Ex Dir: Ann Samson
Ex Dir: Donna Termeer

D-U-N-S 06-045-6514
YOUNG MENS CHRISTIAN ASSOCIATION OF METROPOLITAN MILWAUKEE INC
YMCA
161 W Wisconsin Ave, Milwaukee, WI 53203-2602
Tel (414) 291-9622 *Founded/Ownrshp* 1882
Sales 35.1MM *EMP* 3,500
SIC 8641 7991 8351 7032 8322 Youth organizations; Physical fitness facilities; Child day care services; Youth camps; Individual & family services
CEO: Julie A Tolan
**CFO:* James Mellor
**Sr VP:* Jack Takerian
**Sr VP:* Robert Yamacahika
Sr VP: Bob Yamachika
**VP:* Todd Sevenz Coleman
**VP:* Sonja Coster
**VP:* Keelyn Lyon
VP: Boyd Williams
Ex Dir: Jamie Bruning
Dir IT: Mel Johnson

D-U-N-S 07-538-5773
YOUNG MENS CHRISTIAN ASSOCIATION OF MIDDLE TENNESSEE
YMCA OF MIDDLE TENNESSEE
1000 Church St, Nashville, TN 37203-3420
Tel (615) 259-9622 *Founded/Ownrshp* 1875
Sales 90.7MM *EMP* 3,200
Accts Frasier Dean & Howard Pllc Na
SIC 8641 7991 8351 7032 8322 Youth organizations; Physical fitness facilities; Child day care services; Youth camps; Individual & family services
Pr: Dan Dummermuth
CFO: Joey Harwell
**CFO:* Rob Ivy
**Ex VP:* Peter Oldham
Ex Dir: Steve Saxton
Ex Dir: Henry Smith
Board of Directors: Mike Brennan

D-U-N-S 01-944-6822
YOUNG MENS CHRISTIAN ASSOCIATION OF PIERCE AND KITSAP COUNTY
YMCA PIERCE AND KITSAP COUNTY
4717 S 19th St Ste 201, Tacoma, WA 98405-1167
Tel (253) 534-7800 *Founded/Ownrshp* 1883
Sales 49.9MM *EMP* 1,950
Accts Dwyer Pemberton & Coulson Pc
SIC 8699 7991 7032 8322 Charitable organization; Physical fitness facilities; Youth camps; Individual & family services
CEO: Robert Ecklund
**Pr:* Bob Ecklund
**CFO:* Anne Porter
Ex Dir: Andrea Millikan

D-U-N-S 07-877-1466 IMP
YOUNG MENS CHRISTIAN ASSOCIATION OF SAN FRANCISCO
YMCA OF SAN FRANCISCO
50 California St Ste 650, San Francisco, CA 94111-4607
Tel (415) 777-9622 *Founded/Ownrshp* 1998
Sales 74.5MM *EMP* 2,000
SIC 8641 7991 8351 7032 8322 Youth organizations; Physical fitness facilities; Child day care services; Youth camps; Individual & family services
Pr: Charles M Collins
**CFO:* Kathy Cheng
Bd of Dir: Virginia Richardson
**VP:* Linda Griffith
VP: Don Hanna
Assoc Dir: Jane Packer
Ex Dir: Heidi James
Brnch Mgr: Rachel Del Monte
Off Mgr: Jo Himan
Snr Mgr: Matthew Legaspi
Snr Mgr: Angelina Quintana

D-U-N-S 07-792-8653
YOUNG MENS CHRISTIAN ASSOCIATION OF SOUTH HAMPTON ROADS
YMCA OF SOUTH HAMPTON ROADS
920 Corporate Ln, Chesapeake, VA 23320-3406
Tel (757) 624-9622 *Founded/Ownrshp* 1883
Sales 50.8MM *EMP* 2,200
Accts Mcgladrey Llp Richmond Va
SIC 8641 Civic social & fraternal associations
Pr: William H George
**Pr:* Charles Harris
**COO:* Thomas C Flynn
**CFO:* Susan E Ohmsen
**Ch:* James K Diller
VP: Adam Kahrl
VP: Annie Vogt
Ex Dir: Andre Elliott

D-U-N-S 03-750-4714
YOUNG MENS CHRISTIAN ASSOCIATION OF SUNCOAST
YMCA OF THE SUNCOAST
2469 Enterprise Rd, Clearwater, FL 33763-1702
Tel (312) 932-1200 *Founded/Ownrshp* 1956
Sales 27.6MM *EMP* 1,000ᴱ
Accts Cbiz Mhm Llc Clearwater Fl
SIC 8641 7991 8351 7032 8322 Youth organizations; Physical fitness facilities; Child day care services; Youth camps; Individual & family services
Pr: G Scott Goyer
**Ch:* Robinson Charles Jr
**Treas:* Stephen Jefferies
**Ex VP:* Elizabeth Dubuque
VP: Tim Ackerman
VP: Teresa Hibbard
**VP:* Eric Keaton
Ex Dir: Julio Vega
Ex Dir: Stephanie Zagoroza
MIS Dir: Ruby Asquith
Netwrk Eng: Josh Clark

D-U-N-S 07-330-3679
YOUNG MENS CHRISTIAN ASSOCIATION OF WICHITA KANSAS
GREATER WICHITA YMCA
402 N Market St, Wichita, KS 67202-2012
Tel (316) 219-9622 *Founded/Ownrshp* 1885
Sales 46.6MM *EMP* 1,000ᴱ
Accts Bkd Llp Wichita Kansas
SIC 8641 7991 8351 7032 8322 Youth organizations; Physical fitness facilities; Child day care services; Youth camps; Individual & family services
Pr: Ronn McMahon
**CFO:* Bill Schmitz
CFO: William Schmitz
Ex Dir: Casey Garten
Brnch Mgr: John Weber
Genl Mgr: Jennifer Keen
Genl Mgr: Mim McKenzie
Pgrm Dir: Starburst Murphy
Pgrm Dir: Brittani Poland
Pgrm Dir: Kasey Williams

D-U-N-S 07-710-4883
YOUNG MENS CHRISTIAN ASSOCIATION OF WILMINGTON DELAWARE
YMCA OF DELAWARE
100 W 10th St Ste 1100, Wilmington, DE 19801-6607
Tel (302) 221-9622 *Founded/Ownrshp* 1889
Sales 48.4MMᴱ *EMP* 1,055
Accts Gunnip & Company Llp Wilmingt
SIC 7997 7011 Membership sports & recreation clubs; YMCA/YMHA hotel
Pr: Michael P Graves
**Ch:* Lynn Jones
**Treas:* Linda West
**V Ch Bd:* William Farrell II
**V Ch Bd:* Joseph E Johnson

D-U-N-S 00-169-4520
YOUNG PRESIDENTS ORGANIZATION
Y P O
600 Las Colinas Blvd E # 10, Irving, TX 75039-5616
Tel (972) 587-1500 *Founded/Ownrshp* 1951
Sales 96.6MM *EMP* 125ᴱ
Accts Bruce E Bernstien & Assoc Pc
SIC 8621 Professional membership organizations
CEO: George Weathersby
**CEO:* Scott Mordell
**COO:* Mark Foward
**CFO:* Terry Wilson
Comm Man: Brandi Neal
Ex Dir: Karen Craig
Ex Dir: Jeff Klaumann
Ex Dir: Dean Lindal
Rgnl Mgr: Joan Carl
CIO: Dwight Moore
Dir IT: Rick Hornung

D-U-N-S 05-138-6506 IMP/EXP
■YOUNG TOUCHSTONE CO
(*Suby of* WABTEC GLOBAL SERVICES) ★
200 Smith Ln, Jackson, TN 38301-9669
Tel (731) 424-5045 *Founded/Ownrshp* 1999
Sales 403.9MMᴱ *EMP* 600
SIC 4911 3743 Generation, electric power; Locomotives & parts
Pr: James R Jenkins II
VP: Geoff Smith
Prin: Jeff Smith
IT Man: Brian Williams
Sales Exec: Sprenger Michael

D-U-N-S 19-651-2370
YOUNGER BROTHERS GROUP INC
8525 N 75th Ave, Peoria, AZ 85345-7901
Tel (623) 979-1111 *Founded/Ownrshp* 1987
Sales 110.6MMᴱ *EMP* 1,300ᴱ
SIC 1751 Framing contractor
Owner: James A Younger III

D-U-N-S 00-829-1023 IMP/EXP
YOUNGER MFG CO
YOUNGER OPTICS
2925 California St, Torrance, CA 90503-3914
Tel (310) 783-1533 *Founded/Ownrshp* 1955
Sales 171.6MMᴱ *EMP* 850
SIC 3851 Lenses, ophthalmic
CEO: Joseph David Rips
**Pr:* Tom Balch
**CFO:* Roshan Seresinhe
VP: David Ambler
VP: Lingbing Zhao
Area Mgr: Terry Yoneda

YOUNGER OPTICS
See YOUNGER MFG CO

D-U-N-S 07-852-4610
▲YOUNGEVITY INTERNATIONAL INC
2400 Boswell Rd, Chula Vista, CA 91914-3553
Tel (619) 934-3980 *Founded/Ownrshp* 1996
Sales 156.6MM *EMP* 382ᴱ
Tkr Sym YGYI *Exch* OTO
SIC 5499 5999 Health & dietetic food stores; Dietetic foods; Coffee; Vitamin food stores; Cosmetics
Ch Bd: Stephan Wallach
Pr: David Briskie
COO: Michelle Wallach
Bd of Dir: Corey Gold
VP: Cynthia Hernandez
Exec: Tangelia Wiggins
Admn Mgr: Wiley Hurt
Off Mgr: Jonnie Taylor
Board of Directors: Richard Renton, William Thompson

D-U-N-S 02-201-7213
YOUNGS HOLDINGS INC
14402 Franklin Ave, Tustin, CA 92780-7013
Tel (714) 368-4615 *Founded/Ownrshp* 1974
Sales 1.1MMMᴱ *EMP* 1,700
SIC 5182 Wine; Neutral spirits
Pr: Vernon O Underwood Jr
**Pr:* Paul Vert
**Ex VP:* Janet Smith
**VP:* Marry Doidge
VP: Kyle Knower
VP: Damien Pascale
VP: Andrea Pridham

D-U-N-S 61-299-0655 IMP
YOUNGS INTERCO INC
14402 Franklin Ave, Tustin, CA 92780-7013
Tel (714) 368-4615 *Founded/Ownrshp* 1989
Sales 130.2MMᴱ *EMP* 1,606
SIC 5182 Wine & distilled beverages
Ch Bd: Vernon O Underwood
**Pr:* Paul Vert
**CFO:* Dennis Hemann
VP: Mary Goidge
CIO: Karen Eaton

YOUNG'S MARKET COMPANY ARIZONA
See YOUNGS MARKET CO OF ARIZONA LLC

D-U-N-S 00-690-9410 IMP/EXP
YOUNGS MARKET CO LLC
(*Suby of* YOUNGS HOLDINGS INC) ★
14402 Franklin Ave, Tustin, CA 92780-7013
Tel (714) 368-4615 *Founded/Ownrshp* 1989
Sales 972.7MMᴱ *EMP* 1,600
SIC 5182 Wine; Neutral spirits
CEO: Chris Underwood
**CFO:* Dennis Hamann
**CFO:* Kevin Manion
**Ch:* Vern Underwood
Div VP: Darryl Gebo
Ex VP: Philana Bouvier
Ex VP: Donald Robbins
Ex VP: Jason Wooler
Sr VP: Marin Blomquist
Sr VP: Greg Franklin
Sr VP: Jon Scriven
VP: Candida Banti
VP: Jon Barham
VP: Michael Berberian
VP: Michael Berube
VP: Jason Cardoza
VP: Angi Chong
VP: Brian Clelland
VP: Alan Cohen
VP: Roger Cross
VP: Brendon Dahn

D-U-N-S 62-186-8426 IMP
YOUNGS MARKET CO OF ARIZONA LLC
YOUNG'S MARKET COMPANY ARIZONA
(*Suby of* YOUNGS HOLDINGS INC) ★
402 S 54th Pl, Phoenix, AZ 85034-2135
Tel (602) 233-1900 *Founded/Ownrshp* 2011
Sales 152.1MMᴱ *EMP* 300
SIC 5182 Wine & distilled beverages
Brnch Mgr: Stephen Buckmore

D-U-N-S 92-923-4532
YOUNGS TRUCK CENTER INC
ADVANTAGE TRUCK CENTER
3880 Jeff Adams Dr, Charlotte, NC 28206-1259
Tel (704) 597-0551 *Founded/Ownrshp* 1995
Sales 89.1MMᴱ *EMP* 200
SIC 5511 7513 7532

YOUNGSTOWN CITY SCHOOL DST
See YOUNGSTOWN CITY SCHOOLS

D-U-N-S 08-232-9541
YOUNGSTOWN CITY SCHOOLS
YOUNGSTOWN CITY SCHOOL DST
20 W Wood St, Youngstown, OH 44503-1028
Tel (330) 744-6900 *Founded/Ownrshp* 1849
Sales 10.0MM *EMP* 1,500
Accts Dave Yost Columbus Ohio
SIC 8211 Public elementary & secondary schools; Public junior high school; Public senior high school; Vocational high school
**Pr:* Richard Atkinson
**Treas:* William A Johnson
Bd of Dir: Kane Terapia
**VP:* Marcia Haire-Ellis
**Prin:* Lock P Beachum Sr
Dir Sec: William Morvay
Pr Dir: Yvonne Mathis
HC Dir: Bonnie Newton

D-U-N-S 07-313-1237 IMP
YOUNGSTOWN STATE UNIVERSITY INC
1 University Plz, Youngstown, OH 44555-0002
Tel (330) 941-3000 *Founded/Ownrshp* 1908
Sales 207.3MMᴱ *EMP* 2,105ᴱ
Accts Crowe Horwath Llp Columbus O
SIC 8221 University
Pr: Jim Tressel
V Ch: Chander Kohli
Trst: William Bresnahan
Trst: Donald Cagigas
Trst: Millicent S Count
Trst: Charles Cushwa
Trst: Jeffrey Parks
Ofcr: Cheryl Stair
VP: Brittany Bowyer
VP: Jack Fahey
VP: Eugene Grilli
VP: Jim Grilly
VP: Katelyn Kridler
Exec: Craig Bickley
Exec: Edward Krol
Exec: Kevin Reynolds
Assoc Dir: Catherine Cala
Assoc Dir: Gina McHenry
Assoc Dir: James Stanger
Creative D: Ross Morrone

D-U-N-S 60-661-5607
YOUR BUILDING CENTERS INC
YBC SUPPLY
2607 Beale Ave, Altoona, PA 16601-1909
Tel (814) 944-5098 *Founded/Ownrshp* 1989
Sales 100.3MMᴱ *EMP* 340
SIC 5251 Hardware
Pr: Phil Skarada
**Pr:* Dean Conrad
**CFO:* Rich Lender
**Treas:* David E Gardner
Trst: Vincent J Bettwy
**VP:* Tom Miller
Ex Dir: John Bartley
VP Mfg: Tim Leupold
Opers Mgr: Rick Andrews
Sls Mgr: Jeff Tressler

YOUR NAME PROFESSIONAL BRAND
See MANA PRODUCTS INC

D-U-N-S 13-549-9049 IMP/EXP
■YOUR OTHER WAREHOUSE LLC
(*Suby of* HOME DEPOT THE) ★
2455 Paces Ferry Rd Se B8, Atlanta, GA 30339-1834
Tel (770) 433-8211 *Founded/Ownrshp* 2001
Sales 116.2MMᴱ *EMP* 250
SIC 5074 5075 Plumbing fittings & supplies; Warm air heating equipment & supplies
Pr: Francis Blake
Sls Dir: Russ Wheeler
Manager: Charlie Hubert
Sls Mgr: Tippy Thomassie
Snr PM: Chris Thomas

D-U-N-S 07-886-0528
YOURPEOPLE INC
ZENEFITS FTW INSURANCE SVCS
303 2nd St Ste 401, San Francisco, CA 94107-1366
Tel (415) 798-9086 *Founded/Ownrshp* 2010, 2012
Sales NA *EMP* 700
SIC 6411 7372 Insurance brokers; Business oriented computer software
CEO: Parker Conrad
**CEO:* David Sacks
**Ofcr:* Laks Srini
**Prin:* Scott Clark
Sftwr Eng: Keerthi Adusumilli
Sftwr Eng: Scott Balentine
Sftwr Eng: Priyank Bhatnagar
Sftwr Eng: Jin Shieh
VP Sls: Jeff Hazard
Sls Mgr: Jonathan Rothschild
Board of Directors: Antonio Gracias, Bill McGlashan, Peter Theil

D-U-N-S 01-056-8061
YOUTH ADVOCATE PROGRAMS INC
2007 N 3rd St, Harrisburg, PA 17102-1815
Tel (717) 232-7580 *Founded/Ownrshp* 1975
Sales 64.8MM *EMP* 2,250
Accts Baker Tilly Virchow Krause Ll
SIC 8322 Child related social services
CEO: Jeff Fleischer
**CFO:* Richard Stottlemyer
VP: Carla Benway
VP: Lynette Connor
Prgrm Mgr: Kendra White
Admn Mgr: Sheronda Jones
Admn Mgr: Jill Kinser
Admn Mgr: Brenda McCartney
Admn Mgr: Paul McKee
Admn Mgr: Heidi Molina
Admn Mgr: Margaret Nims

D-U-N-S 03-024-0782
YOUTH CONSULTATION SERVICE (INC)
284 Broadway, Newark, NJ 07104-4003
Tel (973) 482-2774 *Founded/Ownrshp* 1919
Sales 75.0MMᴱ *EMP* 1,250
SIC 8093 8361 8211 Mental health clinic, outpatient; Children's home; School for physically handicapped
Pr: Richard Mingoia
**Treas:* Dominic Bratti
Ex VP: Phil Defalco
VP: Hing-Shung Chan
**VP:* Laura Maier
VP: Todd Schaper
Pgrm Dir: Mallory Reichert

D-U-N-S 06-861-3918
YOUTH FOR CHRIST/USA INC
7670 S Vaughn Ct Ste 100, Englewood, CO 80112-4155
Tel (303) 843-9000 *Founded/Ownrshp* 1945
Sales 17.5MM *EMP* 1,400
Accts Capin Crouse Llp Colorado Spr
SIC 8661 Religious organizations
Pr: Daniel Wolgemuth
Assoc VP: Don Talley
Assoc VP: Sean Wallinger
**Sr VP:* John Peterson
VP: Ryan Allen
VP: Royal Benjamin
Exec: Virginia Nurmi

D-U-N-S 17-350-6452
YOUTH VILLAGES INC
3320 Brother Blvd, Memphis, TN 38133-8950
Tel (901) 251-5000 *Founded/Ownrshp* 1979
Sales 12.9MM *EMP* 2,300
Accts Watkins Uiberall Pllc Memphis
SIC 8361 8322 Children's home; Individual & family services
CEO: Patrick Lawler
**CFO:* Greg Gregory
CFO: Keith Mayer
Chf Nrs Of: Gigi Franklin
Ex Dir: Lynne H Saxton
Prgrm Mgr: Heather Savage
Rgnl Mgr: George Edmonds
Rgnl Mgr: Bobbie Hopf
CTO: Shelby Terry
Dir IT: Jill Terry
Opers Supe: Lauren Iapicca

D-U-N-S 10-926-6817
■YP ADVERTISING & PUBLISHING LLC
BELLSOUTH
(*Suby of* YP HOLDINGS LLC) ★
2247 Northlake Pkwy, Tucker, GA 30084-4005
Tel (678) 406-5523 *Founded/Ownrshp* 2012
Sales 2.7MMᴱ *EMP* 3,200
SIC 2741 7313 7311 Directories: publishing only, not printed on site; Radio, television, publisher representatives; Advertising agencies
Ex VP: Michael Wolf
IT Man: Hal Fletcher
Sys Mgr: Ram Durvasula
Mktg Dir: Robert Owens

D-U-N-S 07-849-7225
■YP HOLDINGS LLC
(*Suby of* CERBERUS LP LLC) ★
2247 Northlake Pkwy Fl 10, Tucker, GA 30084-4005
Tel (866) 570-8863 *Founded/Ownrshp* 2012
Sales 607.5M *EMP* 7,200
Accts Deloitte Tax Llp Kansas Ci

SIC 7374 7389 7313 Computer graphics service; Telephone directory distribution, contract or fee basis; Electronic media advertising representatives
CFO: Mark Smith
Ofcr: Allan Richards
Ofcr: Tyrone Tartt
Ex VP: Gale Wickham
CIO: Tyler Best
Sls Dir: Jen Altheide
Sls Mgr: Emily Beck
Sales Asso: Lauren Belling
Board of Directors: Jonathan Miller

D-U-N-S 60-970-2563
■YP.COM LLC
AT&T INTERACTIVE
(*Suby of* CERBERUS CAPITAL MANAGEMENT LP) ★
611 N Brand Blvd Fl 3, Glendale, CA 91203-3286
Tel (818) 937-5500 *Founded/Ownrshp* 2012
Sales 83.8MMᴱ *EMP* 300
SIC 7389 Telephone directory distribution, contract or fee basis; Telephone services
**CFO:* Williams Clenney
Treas: Sandra Barcena
Treas: John Vernagus
Sr VP: Deborah Slavin
VP: Blair Jeffris
Ex Dir: Bill Theisinger
**CTO:* Brad Mohs
Sls Dir: Carey Girvan-Crumpler
Sls Mgr: Paul Wilson
Snr Mgr: Ruben Orr

YRC FREIGHT
See YRC INC

D-U-N-S 00-699-8397 EXP
■YRC INC
YRC FREIGHT
(*Suby of* ROADWAY LLC) ★
10990 Roe Ave, Overland Park, KS 66211-1213
Tel (913) 696-6100 *Founded/Ownrshp* 1954

Sales 4.2MMM[E] *EMP* 20,200
SIC 4213 Trucking, except local; Less-than-truckload (LTL) transport
CEO: James Welch
Pr: Terrence M Gilbert
CFO: Jeff Rogers
Sr VP: Tim Haitz
**Sr VP:* Darren Hawkins
**Sr VP:* Mithcell Lilly
**Sr VP:* Thomas S Palmer
Sr VP: Tom Palmer
VP: Robert Chess
VP: William F Crowe Jr
VP: Charles Delutis
VP: Don Emery
**VP:* Terry Gerrond
VP: Don Hinkle
VP: Christina Lauria
VP: Patrick R Lemons
VP: Paul Lorensen
VP: Paul Marshall
VP: Dan Marsico
VP: Michael W McMillan
VP: William Owen

D-U-N-S 60-871-5673
■YRC REGIONAL TRANSPORTATION INC
(*Suby of* YRC WORLDWIDE INC) ★
10990 Roe Ave, Overland Park, KS 66211-1213
Tel (913) 344-5220 *Founded/Ownrshp* 1991
Sales 813.7MM[E] *EMP* 9,300
SIC 4213 4231 Less-than-truckload (LTL) transport; Trucking terminal facilities
Pr: Jeffrey A Rogers
Ex VP: Greg Reid
**VP:* Terry Gerrond
Sls Mgr: Mark Johnson

D-U-N-S 10-710-1248 IMP/EXP
▲YRC WORLDWIDE INC
10990 Roe Ave, Overland Park, KS 66211-1213
Tel (913) 696-6100 *Founded/Ownrshp* 1924
Sales 4.8MMM *EMP* 32,000
Tkr Sym YRCW *Exch* NGS
SIC 4213 Trucking, except local; Less-than-truckload (LTL) transport
CEO: James L Welch
**Ch Bd:* James E Hoffman
Pr: John Becker
Pr: Donald R Foust
Pr: Darren D Hawkins
Pr: Thomas J O'Connor
Pr: Scott D Ware
CFO: Jamie G Pierson
Treas: Mark D Boehmer
Div VP: Dan Gatta
VP: Chad Clark
VP: Stephanie D Fisher
VP: James A Fry
VP: Bryan McKenzie
VP: Dan Thomas
VP: Tom Ventura
Board of Directors: Raymond J Bromark, Douglas A Carty, William R Davidson, Matthew A Doheny, Robert L Friedman, Michael J Kneeland, Patricia M Nazemetz, James F Winestock

YSD INDUSTRIES
See GUNDERSON RAIL SERVICES LLC

D-U-N-S 08-270-6417
YSLETA INDEPENDENT SCHOOL DISTRICT
YSLETA ISD
9600 Sims Dr, El Paso, TX 79925-7225
Tel (915) 434-0240 *Founded/Ownrshp* 1937
Sales 462.8MM *EMP* 7,155
Accts Whitley Penn Llp Houston Tex
SIC 8211 Public elementary school; Public junior high school; Public senior high school
Board of Directors: Shane Haggerty

YSLETA ISD
See YSLETA INDEPENDENT SCHOOL DISTRICT

D-U-N-S 16-715-5303
YTG LLC
(*Suby of* YATES COMPANIES INC) ★
6222 Saint Louis St, Meridian, MS 39307-7209
Tel (601) 483-2384 *Founded/Ownrshp* 2003
Sales 170.3MM *EMP* 1,228[E]
Accts Rea Shaw Giffin & Stuart Ll
SIC 1731 Electrical work
**CFO:* Brandon Dunn
Opers Mgr: Jimmy Thrash

YU SING
See BELLISIO FOODS INC

D-U-N-S 10-014-4351
YUBA CITY UNIFIED SCHOOL DISTRICT FINANCING CORP
YCUSD
750 N Palora Ave, Yuba City, CA 95991-3627
Tel (530) 822-7601 *Founded/Ownrshp* 1966
Sales NA *EMP* 2,000
SIC 9411 Administration of educational programs;
Pr: Steven Scriven
**VP:* Lonetta Riley
Genl Mgr: Robert Shemwell
Psych: Lisa Marcotte

YUBA COUNTY BOARD SUPERVISORS
See COUNTY OF YUBA

D-U-N-S 19-692-5077
YUCAIPA COMPANIES LLC
9130 W Sunset Blvd, Los Angeles, CA 90069-3110
Tel (310) 789-7200 *Founded/Ownrshp* 1986
Sales 4.3MMM[E] *EMP* 11,000
SIC 8748 6719 6726 Business consulting; Investment holding companies, except banks; Investment offices

D-U-N-S 08-250-8961
YUKON-KUSKOKWIM HEALTH CORP
DELTA HOSPITAL
829 Hospin Hwy Ste 329, Bethel, AK 99559
Tel (907) 543-6300 *Founded/Ownrshp* 1969
Sales 220.5MM *EMP* 3,365
Accts Lb Bdo Usa Llp Bethel Ak
SIC 8062 7363 8069 8093 8042 8021 General medical & surgical hospitals; Medical help service; Alcoholism rehabilitation hospital; Alcohol clinic, outpatient; Offices & clinics of optometrists; Dental clinic
Pr: Gene Peltola
V Ch: James R Charlie Sr
Pr: Christy Christensen
**CFO:* Joseph Demeo
**Treas:* Marvin Deacon
Ofcr: Roger Lowe
**VP:* Daniel J Winkelmanv
Dir Risk M: Jesse Knecht
Dept Mgr: Kerri Drew
Off Mgr: Elaine Simeon
Nurse Mgr: Bernice Cole

D-U-N-S 80-815-6967
YULISTA AVIATION INC
(*Suby of* YULISTA HOLDING LLC) ★
631 Discovery Dr Nw, Huntsville, AL 35806-2801
Tel (256) 319-4621 *Founded/Ownrshp* 2014
Sales 263.0MM[E] *EMP* 938[E]
SIC 3724 Aircraft engines & engine parts
Pr: Darrell Harrison

D-U-N-S 82-956-9156
YULISTA HOLDING LLC
(*Suby of* CALISTA CORP) ★
631 Discovery Dr Nw, Huntsville, AL 35806-2801
Tel (907) 275-2917 *Founded/Ownrshp* 2007
Sales 284.0MM[E] *EMP* 1,300
SIC 8741 Business management
Pr: Joshua Herren
COO: Paul May

D-U-N-S 17-929-4467 IMP/EXP
▲YUM BRANDS INC
1441 Gardiner Ln, Louisville, KY 40213-1914
Tel (502) 874-8300 *Founded/Ownrshp* 1997
Sales 13.1MMM *EMP* 505,000
Tkr Sym YUM *Exch* NYS
SIC 5812 6794 Eating places; Pizzeria, chain; Franchises, selling or licensing
CEO: Greg Creed
**Ch Bd:* David C Novak
Pr: David Gibbs
CEO: Roger Eaton
CEO: Brian Niccol
CEO: Muktesh Pant
COO: Emil Brolick
CFO: Patrick Grismer
CFO: Trip Vornholt
Chf Mktg O: Vipul Chawla
Ofcr: Jonathan D Blum
Sr VP: Peter KAO
VP: Brett Hale
VP: Shaunna Williams
VP: Mary Yamanaka
Board of Directors: Elane Stock, Michael J Cavanagh, Robert D Walter, Brian Cornell, Mirian Graddick-Weir, David W Dorman, Massimo Ferragamo, Jonathan S Linen, Keith Meister, Thomas C Nelson, Thomas M Ryan, Justin Skala

D-U-N-S 60-850-8797
■YUM RESTAURANT SERVICES GROUP INC
(*Suby of* YUM BRANDS INC) ★
1900 Colonel Sanders Ln, Louisville, KY 40213-1970
Tel (502) 874-8300 *Founded/Ownrshp* 1996
Sales 38.4MM[E] *EMP* 1,000[E]
SIC 5812 Fast-food restaurant, chain
CEO: David C Novak
**Pr:* Richard T Carucci
COO: Peter Hearl
**VP:* Sam Su

D-U-N-S 78-610-7990
YUMA CABLEVISION INC
1289 S 2nd Ave, Yuma, AZ 85364-4715
Tel (928) 329-9731 *Founded/Ownrshp* 2006
Sales 200.0MM *EMP* 53
SIC 4841 Cable television services
Pr: Glen Britt

YUMA COUNTY
See COUNTY OF YUMA

D-U-N-S 07-448-5996
YUMA REGIONAL MEDICAL CENTER INC
2400 S Avenue A, Yuma, AZ 85364-7170
Tel (928) 344-2000 *Founded/Ownrshp* 1958
Sales 371.3MM *EMP* 1,600
SIC 8062 General medical & surgical hospitals
CEO: Pat T Walz
Chf Rad: John James
Chf Rad: David Plone
Ch Bd: Victor Smith
CFO: Tony Struck
Sec: Phillip Richemont
Bd of Dir: Wayne Steffey
Ofcr: Divesh Anireddy
Ofcr: Linda Johnson
Ofcr: Margaret Kunes
VP: Jim Hall
VP: Machele Headington
VP: Karen Jensen
VP: Marshall Jones
VP: Carl F Myers
VP: Gene Shaw
Dir Lab: Victor Alvarez
Dir Rx: Tom Vanhassel

D-U-N-S 01-450-0060
YUMA SCHOOL DISTRICT ONE
450 W 6th St, Yuma, AZ 85364-2973
Tel (928) 782-6581 *Founded/Ownrshp* 1900
Sales 69.6MM[E] *EMP* 1,300
Accts Heinfield Meech & Co Pc
SIC 8211 Public elementary school; Public junior high school
IT Man: Ken Lindsey
Tech Mgr: Teresa Middaugh
Teacher Pr: Luciano Munoz
Teacher Pr: Arlene Smith
Psych: Penny Farrar
Psych: Harriet Montaney
HC Dir: Shirley Rodriguez

D-U-N-S 01-991-4952
▲YUME INC
1204 Middlefield Rd, Redwood City, CA 94063-2059
Tel (650) 591-9400 *Founded/Ownrshp* 2004
Sales 173.2MM *EMP* 552[E]
Tkr Sym YUME *Exch* NYS
SIC 7311 Advertising agencies
Pr: Jayant Kadambi
CFO: Anthony Carvalho
Ex VP: Hardeep Bindra
Ex VP: Paul Porrini
**Ex VP:* Ayyappan Sankaran
Ex VP: Jim Soss
VP: Stephanie Gaines
Snr Sftwr: Sivasankar Kandasamy
Board of Directors: Craig Forman, Mitchell Habib, Derek Harrar, Adriel Lares, Christopher Paisley, Daniel Springer

D-U-N-S 18-054-0502 IMP
YUSA CORP
(*Suby of* YAMASHITA RUBBER CO.,LTD.)
151 Jamison Rd Sw, Washington Court Hou, OH 43160
Tel (740) 335-0335 *Founded/Ownrshp* 1987
Sales 228.8MM[E] *EMP* 1,046
SIC 3069 Rubber covered motor mounting rings (rubber bonded); Bushings, rubber; Tubing, rubber
Pr: Takeyoshi Usui
CFO: Greg Niehaus
**Treas:* Yoshiji Iwamoto
Sales Exec: Moe Bagheri
Sls Mgr: Daniel Uttermohlen

YUSEN AIR & SEA SERVICE
See YUSEN LOGISTICS (AMERICAS) INC

D-U-N-S 05-153-2661
YUSEN LOGISTICS (AMERICAS) INC (NY)
YUSEN AIR & SEA SERVICE
(*Suby of* YUSEN LOGISTICS CO., LTD.)
300 Lighting Way Ste 600, Secaucus, NJ 07094-3662
Tel (201) 553-3800 *Founded/Ownrshp* 1968
Sales 1.0MMM[E] *EMP* 2,000
Accts Kpmg Llp New York Ny
SIC 4724 4731 Travel agencies; Freight forwarding
Ch Bd: Kunihiko Miyoshi
**COO:* Michael Noone
**Ch:* Masaki Tanaka
**Ex VP:* Masafumi Soemoto
Sr VP: John Vitolo
VP: Santoso Lessiohadi
VP: Daniel J Reehill
VP: Tom Scorsune
Brnch Mgr: Jesse Garza
Brnch Mgr: Osamu Iwasaki
Brnch Mgr: Mark Nagata

YVFWC
See YAKIMA VALLEY FARM WORKERS CLINIC INC

Z

D-U-N-S 07-999-0519
Z CAPITAL GROUP LLC
1330 Avenue Of The Americ, New York, NY 10019-5483
Tel (212) 595-8400 *Founded/Ownrshp* 2008
Sales 92.2MM[E] *EMP* 70[E]
SIC 6722 Management investment, open-end

Z E E
See ZEE MEDICAL INC

Z G C
See ZEN-NOH GRAIN CORP

D-U-N-S 03-702-5756 IMP/EXP
Z GALLERIE LLC
1855 W 139th St, Gardena, CA 90249-3013
Tel (800) 358-8288 *Founded/Ownrshp* 1979
Sales 214.2MM[E] *EMP* 950
SIC 5719 5999 Housewares; Art dealers
**COO:* Michael Zeiden
VP: Jeffery Bassett
**VP:* Carol Malfatti
Exec: Courtney Fondon
Dist Mgr: Paul Gerrigan
Genl Mgr: Jason Levine

Z HOTEL
See ZIMMER INC

D-U-N-S 05-917-4847 IMP/EXP
■Z MARINE NORTH AMERICA LLC
ZODIAC OF NORTH AMERICA
(*Suby of* MARINE HOLDING US CORP) ★
540 Thompson Creek Rd, Stevensville, MD 21666-2508
Tel (843) 376-3470 *Founded/Ownrshp* 1970
Sales 141.1MM[E] *EMP* 653
SIC 5091 Boats, canoes, watercrafts & equipment; Boat accessories & parts
Pr: Steven Seigel
Pr: Nicole Donaldson
Genl Mgr: Lionel Boudeau
Genl Mgr: James Keller
IT Man: Melanie Hamons
IT Man: Sarah Kidd
IT Man: Bill Priestner
Mktg Mgr: Philip Hughes

Z WIRELESS
See AKA WIRELESS INC

Z- MIKE
See BETA LASERMIKE INC

D-U-N-S 02-155-8440 IMP/EXP
ZACHRY CONSOLIDATED LLC
527 Logwood Ave, San Antonio, TX 78221-1738
Tel (210) 871-2700 *Founded/Ownrshp* 1976
Sales 918.9M[E] *EMP* 15,000
Accts Ernst & Young Llp San Antonio
SIC 1611 1622 1623 1629 3241 1442 General contractor, highway & street construction; Highway & street paving contractor; Bridge construction; Pipeline construction; Dam construction; Portland cement; Construction sand mining; Gravel mining
CEO: John B Zachry
**Pr:* Mark Mills
**Pr:* Henry B Zachry Jr
**Treas:* Charles Ebrom
**Ex VP:* D Kirk McDonald Sr
**VP:* Murray L Johnston Jr
**VP:* Joe J Lozano
**VP:* Tammy Mallaise
**VP:* David S Zachry
Board of Directors: Mollie Steves Zachry

D-U-N-S 80-336-4582
ZACHRY CONSTRUCTION & MATERIALS INC
2330 N Loop 1604 W, San Antonio, TX 78248-4512
Tel (210) 479-1027 *Founded/Ownrshp* 2009
Sales 1.1MMM[E] *EMP* 2,700
SIC 1611 1622 1623 1629 1542 3241 General contractor, highway & street construction; Highway & street paving contractor; Bridge construction; Pipeline construction; Dam construction; Nonresidential construction; Portland cement
CEO: David S Zachry
**Treas:* Warren A Stokes
**Sr VP:* Timothy A Watt
**VP:* Jean J Abiassi
**VP:* Max Frailey
**VP:* Greg W Hale
**VP:* Vivian Garza Steele

D-U-N-S 80-365-8017 IMP
ZACHRY CONSTRUCTION CORP
(*Suby of* ZACHRY CONSTRUCTION & MATERIALS INC) ★
2330 N Loop 1604 W, San Antonio, TX 78248-4512
Tel (210) 871-2700 *Founded/Ownrshp* 2007
Sales 928.9MM[E] *EMP* 2,000[E]
SIC 1623 1611 1622 1629 1542 Pipeline construction; General contractor, highway & street construction; Bridge construction; Dam construction; Nonresidential construction
Ch Bd: David S Zachry
**Pr:* Jean J Abiassi
**Pr:* Vivian Garza-Steele
**Pr:* Leticia Mond
**Pr:* Coyt Webb
**CFO:* Warren A Stokes
**Sr VP:* Kevin McMinniman
**Sr VP:* Timothy A Watt
**Sr VP:* John Young
**VP:* George Laris
**VP:* Paul K Newman
**VP:* Kevin Walker

D-U-N-S 80-340-8843
ZACHRY HOLDINGS INC
527 Logwood Ave, San Antonio, TX 78221-1738
Tel (210) 588-5000 *Founded/Ownrshp* 2007
Sales 6.6MMM[E] *EMP* 15,134
SIC 1541 8711 1629 1623 Investment holding companies, except banks
Ch Bd: John B Zachry
**Pr:* Steven K Brauer
**Pr:* Gerald P Burke
**CFO:* D Kirk McDonald
Sr VP: Kirk D McDonald
VP: Ralph Biediger
VP: Steven Brauer
VP: Cathy O Green
VP: Tom Hannigan
VP: Chris Irwin
**VP:* Glenn D Kloos
VP: Mike Morris
**VP:* David Schwab
Dir Risk M: Susan Gordon
Dir Bus: Terence Hart

D-U-N-S 80-366-7422 IMP
ZACHRY INDUSTRIAL INC
(*Suby of* ZACHRY HOLDINGS INC) ★
527 Logwood Ave, San Antonio, TX 78221-1738
Tel (210) 475-8000 *Founded/Ownrshp* 1998
Sales 5.8MMM[E] *EMP* 13,819
SIC 1541 1629 Industrial buildings & warehouses; Industrial plant construction
Ch Bd: John B Zachry
**CFO:* D Kirk McDonald
**Ex VP:* Keith D Manning
**Sr VP:* Scott Duffy
VP: Arthur Rodriguez
Dir Risk M: Bill Whitaker
Area Mgr: Stanley Tieken
Tech Mgr: Daniel Martinezd
Sfty Dirs: Paul Beck
Sfty Dirs: Don Hurley
Site Mgr: Chad Lacombe

D-U-N-S 02-707-1216 IMP/EXP
ZACHRY INTERNATIONAL INC
(*Suby of* ZACHRY CONSTRUCTION CORP) ★
2330 N Loop 1604 W, San Antonio, TX 78248-4512
Tel (210) 871-2700 *Founded/Ownrshp* 2007
Sales 197.5MM[E] *EMP* 600[E]
SIC 1541 1542 Industrial buildings, new construction; Nonresidential construction
Pr: David S Zachry
Ch: H B Zachry Jr
Treas: Warren A Stokes
Ex VP: Kirk McDonald
Sr VP: Colleen Goff
VP: Norman Thurow
VP: Thomas Coyt Webb
Dir Bus: Bob Atkisson
IT Man: Bryant Revels
Opers Mgr: Larry Johnson
Snr Mgr: Randy Petrosky
Board of Directors: Charles Ebrom, H B Zachry Jr

D-U-N-S 10-332-0552
ZACKS INVESTMENT RESEARCH INC
10 S Riverside Plz # 1600, Chicago, IL 60606-3830
Tel (312) 630-9880 *Founded/Ownrshp* 1981
Sales 116.4MM[E] *EMP* 170
SIC 6282 Investment research

Pr: Leonard Zacks
Pr: Tim Harper
Pr: Charles Ingle
Pr: Alex Insley
Pr: Jon Knotts
Pr: Casper Terpinski
Ofcr: Craig Cook
Ofcr: Thomas Hertog
Ofcr: Frank Lanza
Ex VP: Christine Holman
Ex VP: Daniel Mulcahy
Ex VP: Stephen Reitmeister
Sr VP: Brian Ebling
Sr VP: Tom Schroeder
VP: Mark Deprospero
VP: Seth R Dowling
VP: John Hayes
VP: Kevin Matras
VP: Glenn Meyers
VP: Ed Pawlak
VP: Steve Scala

D-U-N-S 07-975-1214
ZACKY & SONS POULTRY LLC
2020 S East Ave, Fresno, CA 93721-3328
Tel (559) 443-2700 *Founded/Ownrshp* 2013
Sales 115.6MM^E *EMP* 700^E
SIC 2015 Poultry slaughtering & processing
CEO: Lillian Zacky
**CFO:* Kirk Vandergeest

D-U-N-S 79-904-0824 IMP
▲ ZAGG INC
910 W Legacy Center Way, Midvale, UT 84047-5845
Tel (801) 263-0699 *Founded/Ownrshp* 2004
Sales 269.3MM *EMP* 234^E
Tkr Sym ZAGG *Exch* NGS
SIC 5731 6794 Consumer electronic equipment; Franchises, selling or licensing
Pr: Randall L Hales
**Ch Bd:* Cheryl A Larabee
COO: Steve Tarr
CFO: Bradley J Holiday
Web Dev: Jared Ivory
Mktg Dir: Brad Bell
Board of Directors: E Todd Heiner, Daniel R Maurer, P Scott Stubbs

D-U-N-S 07-148-5841
ZAHM & MATSON INC
JOHN DEERE
1756 Lindquist Dr, Falconer, NY 14733-9720
Tel (716) 665-3110 *Founded/Ownrshp* 1994
Sales 88.2MM *EMP* 135
Accts Schaffner Knight Minnaugh Comp
SIC 5261 5999 Lawnmowers & tractors; Lawn & garden equipment; Farm equipment & supplies; Farm machinery
Pr: Tracy Buck
Store Mgr: Andrew Campbell
Store Mgr: James Delizio
Store Mgr: Bill Henry
Store Mgr: Matt Janiga
Pr Dir: Charlie Hirsch
Pr Dir: Mark Holthouse
Sls Mgr: Mike Ames

D-U-N-S 61-288-3483
ZALE CANADA CO
(*Suby of* PIERCING PAGODA) ★
901 W Walnut Hill Ln, Irving, TX 75038-1001
Tel (972) 580-4000 *Founded/Ownrshp* 2000
Sales 223.0MM^E *EMP* 10,000^E
SIC 5944 Jewelry stores
VP: Dominic Guglielmi

D-U-N-S 00-792-8757 IMP
ZALE CORP
PIERCING PAGODA
(*Suby of* SIGNET JEWELERS LIMITED)
901 W Walnut Hill Ln, Irving, TX 75038-1001
Tel (972) 580-4000 *Founded/Ownrshp* 1924, 2014
Sales 1.3MMM^E *EMP* 11,900
SIC 5944 Jewelry stores
CEO: Theo Killion
**CFO:* Thomas A Haubenstricker
Treas: Stephen R Gatne
Sr Cor Off: Ann Carothers
**Chf Mktg O:* Richard A Lennox
**Ofcr:* Matthew W Appel
Ofcr: George Murray
**Ex VP:* Gilbert P Hollander
Ex VP: David L Homberg
Sr VP: Tonya Boyd
Sr VP: T Carroll
Sr VP: Sue Davidson
Sr VP: Philip N Diehl
Sr VP: P Leonard
Sr VP: Michael Lunceford
Sr VP: G W Melton
Sr VP: Stephen C Missanelli
Sr VP: E G Polze
Sr VP: David Rhodes
Sr VP: Nancy O Skinner
VP: Jeff Bourbon

D-U-N-S 06-295-8681 IMP
ZALE DELAWARE INC
PIERCING PAGODA
(*Suby of* PIERCING PAGODA) ★
901 W Walnut Hill Ln, Irving, TX 75038-1001
Tel (972) 580-4000 *Founded/Ownrshp* 1986
Sales 497.5MM^E *EMP* 5,944
SIC 5944 Jewelry stores
Pr: Theo Killion
**CFO:* Rodney Carter
Treas: David Sternblitz
**Ofcr:* William Acevedo
**Ofcr:* Mary Kwan
**Ofcr:* Steven Larkin
**Ex VP:* Gilbert P Hollander
Ex VP: Richard A Lennox
Sr VP: Ken Brumfield
**Sr VP:* Mary Ann Doran
**Sr VP:* Cynthia T Gordon
Sr VP: Paul Leonard
Sr VP: Helen Marsal
**Sr VP:* Stephen C Massanelli
Sr VP: Nancy Skinner
Sr VP: C Stephen

Sr VP: Stephen Strong
Sr VP: John A Zimmermann
VP: Ben Blair
VP: Robert Dinicola
VP: Vincent Price
Board of Directors: Glen Adams, Richard C Breeden, James M Cotter, John B Lowe, Thomas C Shull, Charles M Sonsteby, David M Szymanski

D-U-N-S 07-435-1862
ZANCANELLI MANAGEMENT CORP
BOSTON LE GOURMET PIZZA
11879 W 112th St Ste A, Overland Park, KS 66210-2725
Tel (913) 469-1112 *Founded/Ownrshp* 1999
Sales 21.5MM^E *EMP* 1,000
SIC 5812 Fast-food restaurant, chain
Pr: Gary Zancanelli Jr
CFO: Scott Sullivan

ZANDEX HEALTH CARE
See ZANDEX INC

D-U-N-S 79-180-5385
ZANDEX HEALTH CARE CORP
CEDAR HILL CARE CENTER
(*Suby of* ZANDEX HEALTH CARE) ★
1122 Taylor St, Zanesville, OH 43701-2658
Tel (740) 454-1400 *Founded/Ownrshp* 1984
Sales 37.8MM^E *EMP* 1,200
Accts Plante & Moran Pllc Columbus
SIC 8052 8059 8051 Intermediate care facilities; Rest home, with health care; Skilled nursing care facilities; Extended care facility
Pr: Douglas Ramsey
**CFO:* Lyle Clark
**VP:* Stoey Stout
Off Mgr: Beth Frame

D-U-N-S 07-055-9562
ZANDEX INC
ZANDEX HEALTH CARE
1122 Taylor St, Zanesville, OH 43701-2658
Tel (740) 454-1400 *Founded/Ownrshp* 1968
Sales 38.1MM^E *EMP* 1,200
SIC 8052 8051 Intermediate care facilities; Skilled nursing care facilities
Pr: Douglas L Ramsay
**CFO:* Lyle Clark
**VP:* Stoey Stout
MIS Dir: Donald Williamson

D-U-N-S 07-675-1825
ZANESVILLE COMMUNITY SCHOOL (OH)
401 College Ave, Ashland, OH 44805-3702
Tel (419) 289-5125 *Founded/Ownrshp* 1878
Sales 107.3MM^E *EMP* 620
Accts Gbq Partners Llc Columbus Oh
SIC 8221 College, except junior
Pr: Dr William Crothers
Ex VP: Emmy Hamilton
**VP:* Ron Huiatt
**VP:* James Kirtland
VP: Barb Kiser
VP: Ben Valentine
**VP:* Scott Van Loo
Ex Dir: Rick Ewing II
Ex Dir: Stephen W Krispinsky
Genl Mgr: Frederick Geib
VP Mktg: Colleen Murphy

D-U-N-S 09-871-6132 IMP
■ ZAPPOS.COM INC
(*Suby of* AMAZON.COM INC) ★
400 Stewart Ave Ste A, Las Vegas, NV 89101-2914
Tel (702) 943-7777 *Founded/Ownrshp* 2009
Sales 481.8MM^E *EMP* 3,144
SIC 5661 4813 5632 5611 Shoe stores; ; Apparel accessories; Clothing accessories: men's & boys'
CEO: Anthony Hsieh
**CFO:* Chris Nelson
**Treas:* Sean Patterson
Treas: Daniel Siemens
VP: Rick Byrne
Dir IT: Aki Iida
Software D: Chris Bonafede
Software D: Ed Lim
Opers Mgr: Audrea Hooper
Opers Mgr: Dennis Wegenast
Snr Mgr: Caron Olsen

ZAR APPAREL GROUP
See ZAR GROUP LLC

D-U-N-S 07-925-6601 EXP
ZAR GROUP LLC
ZAR APPAREL GROUP
1375 Broadway Fl 12, New York, NY 10018-7044
Tel (212) 944-2510 *Founded/Ownrshp* 2014
Sales 100.0MM *EMP* 150
SIC 2339 Women's & misses' outerwear
CEO: Bobby Zar
**Pr:* Bruce Bond
**Ch:* Mansour Zar

D-U-N-S 02-575-7337
■ ZARTIC LLC
(*Suby of* ADVANCE PIERRE FOODS) ★
9990 Princeton Glendale Rd, West Chester, OH 45246-1116
Tel (513) 874-8741 *Founded/Ownrshp* 1956, 2006
Sales 58.5MM^E *EMP* 1,000
SIC 2013 2015 Frozen meats from purchased meat; Poultry, processed: frozen

ZATKOFF SEALS & PACKINGS
See ROGER ZATKOFF CO

D-U-N-S 00-153-3637
ZAUSNER FOODS CORP
BC USA
(*Suby of* SAVENCIA SA)
400 S Custer Ave, New Holland, PA 17557-9220
Tel (717) 355-8505 *Founded/Ownrshp* 1946, 1977
Sales 419.2MM^E *EMP* 800
SIC 2022 2032 6794 Cheese, natural & processed; Puddings, except meat: packaged in cans, jars, etc.; Soups & broths: canned, jarred, etc.; Franchises, selling or licensing

Pr: Jessie Hogan
CFO: Oliver Desigalony
**CFO:* Desigalony Olivea
Sr VP: Allen Ezard
Mktg Dir: Rafael Lampon

D-U-N-S 84-913-1545
ZAX INC
ZAXBY'S
1040 Founders Blvd, Athens, GA 30606-6138
Tel (706) 353-8107 *Founded/Ownrshp* 1990
Sales 95.5MM^E *EMP* 2,500
SIC 5812 Eating places
**Sec:* Tony D Townley

ZAXBY'S
See ZAX INC

D-U-N-S 07-831-6565
▲ ZAYO GROUP HOLDINGS INC
1805 29th St Unit 2050, Boulder, CO 80301-1067
Tel (303) 381-4683 *Founded/Ownrshp* 2007
Sales 1.7MMM *EMP* 1,833^E
Tkr Sym ZAYO *Exch* NYS
SIC 4813 3661 Telephone communication, except radio; ; Data telephone communications; Fiber optics communications equipment
Ch Bd: Daniel Caruso
Pr: Jack Waters
COO: Matthew Erickson
COO: Chris Morley
CFO: Ken Desgarennes
Ex VP: Max Clauson
Ex VP: Dan Enright
Ex VP: Greg Friedman
Ex VP: Dave Jones
Ex VP: Glenn Russo
Ex VP: Amanda Tierney
Sr VP: Sandi Mays
Sr VP: Chris Murphy
VP: Emmett Horn
VP: Joe Stockhausen
VP: Jason Tibbs
Exec: Camille Check

D-U-N-S 80-819-3960
■ ZAYO GROUP LLC
(*Suby of* ZAYO GROUP HOLDINGS INC) ★
1805 29th St Unit 2050, Boulder, CO 80301-1067
Tel (303) 381-4683 *Founded/Ownrshp* 2007
Sales 1.7MMM *EMP* 1,513^E
SIC 4813 3661 Telephone communication, except radio; ; Data telephone communications; Fiber optics communications equipment
CEO: Daniel Caruso
CFO: Kenneth Desgarennes
Ex VP: Dave Jones
VP: Greg Friedman
VP: Shawn Graham
VP: Lee Rainey
VP: Michael J Sullivan
Mng Dir: Florian Du Boys
Mng Dir: Alastair Kane
Mng Dir: Michael Strople
Genl Mgr: John Real
Board of Directors: Philip Canfield, Michael Choe, Stephanie Comfort, Rick Connor, Don Gips, Linda Rottenberg

D-U-N-S 00-793-9408
■ ZB NATIONAL ASSOCIATION (UT)
CALIFORNIA BANK & TRUST
(*Suby of* ZIONS BANK) ★
1 S Main St, Salt Lake City, UT 84133-1109
Tel (801) 974-8800 *Founded/Ownrshp* 1873, 1957
Sales NA *EMP* 2,062
SIC 6021 National commercial banks
Pr: A Scott Anderson
**Ch Bd:* Harris H Simmons
COO: Owen Brown
Chf Mktg O: Austin Teri
Ofcr: Christina Clare
Ofcr: Micah Phillips
Ofcr: Eric Saltzman
Ex VP: George Feiger
**Ex VP:* Kay Hall
Ex VP: James Jensen
Ex VP: Peter Morgan
Sr VP: Terry Flynn
Sr VP: Wendy Jones
Sr VP: Greg Nordford
VP: Jerry Barker
VP: Nolan Bellon
VP: Dan Buchannan
VP: Dawn L Craig
VP: David Fuhriman
VP: Brad Herbert
**VP:* James T Jensen
Board of Directors: Susan Johnson, Charley D Jones, Eric O Leavitt, Theresa Martinez, Keith O Rattie, John L Valentine

D-U-N-S 96-463-1030
ZC MANAGEMENT LLC
8600 E Rockcliff Rd, Tucson, AZ 85750-9733
Tel (520) 749-9655 *Founded/Ownrshp* 1996
Sales 41.8MM^E *EMP* 2,000
SIC 7011 Resort hotel

D-U-N-S 11-208-8963 IMP/EXP
ZCO LIQUIDATING CORP
OCZ ENTERPRISE
(*Suby of* TOSHIBA CORPORATION)
6373 San Ignacio Ave, San Jose, CA 95119-1200
Tel (408) 733-8400 *Founded/Ownrshp* 2014
Sales 171.7MM^E *EMP* 597
SIC 3572 Computer storage devices
Pr: Ralph Schmitt
**Ch Bd:* Adam J Epstein
**CFO:* Rafael Torres
**Ex VP:* Alex MEI
Sr VP: Wayne B Eisenberg
Sr VP: Steve Lee
Sr VP: Jason Ruppert
Sr VP: James Tout
Snr Sftwr: Nikhil Dubhashy
Snr Sftwr: Paul Grabinar
Dir IT: Eric Pan
Board of Directors: Richard L Hunter, Russell J Knittel

D-U-N-S 07-877-4410
ZD USA HOLDINGS INC
744 Belleville Ave, New Bedford, MA 02745-6010
Tel (508) 998-4000 *Founded/Ownrshp* 2012
Sales 138.6MM^E *EMP* 400
SIC 3053 Gaskets, packing & sealing devices
CEO: David Slutz

ZEBCO
See W C BRADLEY CO

D-U-N-S 04-901-5696 IMP
▲ ZEBRA TECHNOLOGIES CORP
3 Overlook Pt, Lincolnshire, IL 60069-4302
Tel (847) 634-6700 *Founded/Ownrshp* 1969
Sales 3.6MMM *EMP* 7,000
Tkr Sym ZBRA *Exch* NGS
SIC 3577 2672 2679 5045 Bar code (magnetic ink) printers; Adhesive papers, labels or tapes: from purchased material; Labels (unprinted), gummed: made from purchased materials; Tags, paper (unprinted): made from purchased paper; Computers, peripherals & software
CEO: Anders Gustafsson
**Ch Bd:* Michael A Smith
Pr: Gregory Billings
Pr: Mike Poldino
CFO: Olivier Leonetti
CFO: Michael C Smiley
Chf Mktg O: Jeffrey Schmitz
Ofcr: Gina E Vascsinec
Sr VP: Bill Burns
Sr VP: William J Burns
Sr VP: Hugh K Gagnier
Sr VP: Richard Harrison
Sr VP: Jim Kaput
Sr VP: Jeff Schmitz
VP: Luis Blanco
VP: Bill Cate
VP: Michael Cho
VP: Eileen Eck
VP: Diana Gaddy
VP: Mike Grambo
VP: Joachim Heel
Board of Directors: Richard L Keyser, Andrew K Ludwick, Ross W Manire, Frank B Modruson, Janice M Roberts

ZEDI SOUTHERN FLOW
See ZEDI US INC

D-U-N-S 16-088-2312
ZEDI US INC
ZEDI SOUTHERN FLOW
(*Suby of* ZEDI INC)
208 Roto Park Dr, Broussard, LA 70518-4356
Tel (337) 233-2066 *Founded/Ownrshp* 1992
Sales 190.5MM^E *EMP* 175
SIC 1389 Testing, measuring, surveying & analysis services
VP: Oliver Cummings
VP: Gary Edwards
IT Man: Bill Broussard

D-U-N-S 00-964-5623 IMP
■ ZEE MEDICAL INC
ZEE
(*Suby of* CINTAS CORP) ★
8021 Knue Rd Ste 100, Indianapolis, IN 46250-1972
Tel (949) 252-9500 *Founded/Ownrshp* 1971, 2015
Sales 169.0MM^E *EMP* 830
SIC 8748 8322 Safety training service; First aid service
Pr: Stanton J McComb
**Treas:* Jon W D'Alessio
VP: Lawrence J Burke

D-U-N-S 83-102-5692 EXP
ZEECO USA LLC
22151 E 91st St S, Broken Arrow, OK 74014-3250
Tel (918) 258-8551 *Founded/Ownrshp* 2008
Sales 136.1MM^E *EMP* 700^E
SIC 3433 Gas burners, industrial
Pr: Darton Zink

ZEGNA SPORT
See ERMENEGILDO ZEGNA CORP

D-U-N-S 13-044-0118
ZEIDERS ENTERPRISES INC
2750 Killarney Dr Ste 100, Woodbridge, VA 22192-4124
Tel (703) 496-9000 *Founded/Ownrshp* 1984
Sales 88.2MM *EMP* 635
Accts Bdo Usa Llp Mclean Virginia
SIC 8742 Management consulting services
CEO: Michael D Zeiders
**Pr:* Tamra Avrit
**Treas:* Charlotte A Zeiders
**Sr VP:* Jean Hand
Opers Supe: Jo D Newlon
Psych: Melissa Allen
Psych: Elisabeth Davis

D-U-N-S 82-520-7173
ZEKELMAN INDUSTRIES INC
ENERGEX TUBE
227 W Monroe St Fl 26, Chicago, IL 60606-5055
Tel (312) 275-1600 *Founded/Ownrshp* 2006
Sales 561.5MM^E *EMP* 1,600
SIC 3317 Pipes, seamless steel
CEO: Barry Zekelman
**Pr:* Jim Hays
**CFO:* John Feenan
CFO: Michael J Graham
Ch: Alan Zekelman
Ofcr: Richard Proszowski
**Ex VP:* John C Higgins
**Ex VP:* Michael P McNamara Jr
VP: Helen Davis
**VP:* Andrew Klaus
**VP:* Michael McNamara
**VP:* Michael E Mechley
Board of Directors: Louis Giuliano, Armand Lauzon, Andrew Marino, Alan Zekelman, Barry Zekelman, Clayton Zekelman

D-U-N-S 80-915-2916 IMP
▲ ZELTIQ AESTHETICS INC
4410 Rosewood Dr, Pleasanton, CA 94588-3050
Tel (925) 474-2500 *Founded/Ownrshp* 2005
Sales 255.4MM *EMP* 535E
Tkr Sym ZLTQ *Exch* NGS
SIC 3841 Surgical & medical instruments
Ch Bd: Mark J Foley
CFO: Taylor Harris
CFO: Taylor C Harris
Chf Cred: Keith J Sullivan
Sr VP: Sergio Garcia
VP: Carl H Lamm
Area Mgr: Mario Leone
Area Mgr: Mike Mitchell
Off Admin: Destinee Geasley
Snr Sftwr: Corydon Hinton
CTO: Leonard C Debenedictis
Board of Directors: David J Endicott, Mary M Fisher, D Keith Grossman, Kevin C O'boyle, Andrew N Schiff

D-U-N-S 01-763-9827
ZEN HRO INC
110 Hepler St Ste E, Kernersville, NC 27284-2793
Tel (877) 569-8660 *Founded/Ownrshp* 2009
Sales 71.1MME *EMP* 7,000
SIC 7363 8742 Employee leasing service; Human resource consulting services
CEO: Julius Dizon
**VP:* Marthe Dizon

D-U-N-S 09-858-9419 EXP
ZEN-NOH GRAIN CORP
Z G C
(*Suby of* ZEN-NOH FOODS CO., LTD.)
1127 Hwy 190 E Service Rd, Covington, LA 70433-4929
Tel (985) 867-3500 *Founded/Ownrshp* 1979
Sales 5.7MMM *EMP* 213
Accts Kpmg Llp
SIC 5153 Grain & field beans
CEO: John D Williams
**CFO:* Takuya Yui
**Ex VP:* Osamu Yako
**Sr VP:* Charles E Colbert
Sr VP: Chris Schuster
VP: Robert Cruise
Exec: Karen Hollis
Genl Mgr: Eric Slater
Telecom Ex: Christine Courville
Sls Mgr: Akira Hayashi
Board of Directors: Kevin Adams, Hiroyuki Kawasaki, John D Williams

D-U-N-S 96-191-9805
▲ ZENDESK INC
1019 Market St, San Francisco, CA 94103-1612
Tel (415) 418-7506 *Founded/Ownrshp* 2007
Sales 208.7MM *EMP* 1,268E
Accts Ernst & Young Llp Redwood Cit
Tkr Sym ZEN *Exch* NYS
SIC 7372 Prepackaged software
Ch Bd: Mikkel Svane
CFO: Elena Gomez
CFO: Rick Rigoli
Ofcr: Toke Nygaard
Sr VP: Marcus A Bragg
Sr VP: John Geschke
Sr VP: Amanda Kleha
Sr VP: Matthew Price
Sr VP: Anne Raimondi
VP: Gallant Chen
VP: Ryan Donahue
VP: Aaron Fair
VP: Ryan Gurney
VP: Amir Oren
Dir Risk M: Bryan Cox
Dir Bus: Stewart Townsend
Board of Directors: Carl Bass, Peter Fenton, Caryn Marooney, Elizabeth Nelson, Dana Stalder, Michelle Wilson

ZENEFITS FTW INSURANCE SVCS
See YOURPEOPLE INC

D-U-N-S 08-572-7001
ZENIMAX MEDIA INC
1370 Piccard Dr Ste 120, Rockville, MD 20850-4304
Tel (301) 948-2200 *Founded/Ownrshp* 1999
Sales 89.2MME *EMP* 176
SIC 7371 Computer software development
Ch Bd: Robert A Altman
**Pr:* Ernst Del
**COO:* James L Leder
**CFO:* Cindy L Tallent
**Sr VP:* Denise Kidd
VP: Craig Brown
VP: Pete Hines
**VP:* J Griffin Lesher
QA Dir: Veronika Spiegel
Sls Mgr: Jill Bralove
Counsel: Jeffrey Albertson

ZENITH A FAIRFAX COMPANY, THE
See ZENITH INSURANCE CO

D-U-N-S 19-516-0247
ZENITH AMERICAN SOLUTIONS INC
(*Suby of* HEALTHPLAN HOLDINGS INC) ★
18861 90th Ave Ste A, Mokena, IL 60448-8467
Tel (312) 649-1200 *Founded/Ownrshp* 2011
Sales NA *EMP* 800
SIC 6371 Pension funds; Union welfare, benefit & health funds
CEO: Art Schultz
**Pr:* John Carapi
**CFO:* Joann M Kaminski
**Ex VP:* Jeff Bak
**Ex VP:* Steve Saft
**Sr VP:* Regg Fisher
VP: Keith Saeger
VP: Jay White
CTO: Tai Pham
Mktg Dir: Nate Curry
Board of Directors: Jeff Bak Steve Saft Art Sc

D-U-N-S 00-512-0704
ZENITH ELECTRONICS CORP (DE)
(*Suby of* LG GROUP AIC) ★
2000 Millbrook Dr, Lincolnshire, IL 60069-3630
Tel (847) 941-8000 *Founded/Ownrshp* 1918, 2004
Sales 138.2MME *EMP* 976
SIC 3651 3671 3663 3674 2517 2519 Household audio & video equipment; Television receiving sets; Video cassette recorders/players & accessories; Television tubes; Television broadcasting & communications equipment; Cable television equipment; Microcircuits, integrated (semiconductor); Television cabinets, wood; Television cabinets, plastic
Ch Bd: Tok Joo Lee
CFO: Chun Seok Ho
VP: Ron Snaidauf
VP: Beverley Wyckoff
Natl Sales: Michael Kosla
Board of Directors: Nam Woo

ZENITH INSURANCE COMPANY
See ZENITH NATIONAL INSURANCE CORP

D-U-N-S 06-777-1048
ZENITH INSURANCE CO (CA)
ZENITH A FAIRFAX COMPANY, THE
(*Suby of* ZENITH INSURANCE CO) ★
21255 Califa St, Woodland Hills, CA 91367-5021
Tel (818) 713-1000 *Founded/Ownrshp* 1950, 1977
Sales NA *EMP* 1,600
SIC 6331 Workers' compensation insurance; Automobile insurance; Agricultural insurance; Property damage insurance
Ch Bd: Stanley R Zax
Pr: Todd Cicero
Pr: Jason Clarke
Pr: Tara Flores
Pr: Jack D Miller
CFO: Kari Van Gundy
Ex VP: Wes Heyward
Ex VP: William Owen
Ex VP: Paul Ramont
Ex VP: Craig Thomson
Sr VP: Fred A Hunt
VP: Alan Bub
VP: Duane H Chernow
VP: Jay S Chwanz
VP: Randy Eggers
VP: Pamela Foust
VP: Michael B Gillikin
VP: Michael Gillikin
VP: Sharon Hulbert
VP: Fred Hunt
VP: Charlene Johnson

D-U-N-S 87-943-2557
ZENITH MEDIA SERVICES INC
(*Suby of* PUBLICIS GROUPE S A)
299 W Houston St Fl 11, New York, NY 10014-4876
Tel (212) 989-3034 *Founded/Ownrshp* 2006
Sales 144.6MME *EMP* 800
SIC 7319 Media buying service
CEO: Timothy Jones
**CFO:* Mark Himelfarb
Ex VP: Ava Jordhamo
Sr VP: Joann Accarino
Sr VP: Elizabeth Fox
Sr VP: Allison Shapiro
Sr VP: Brendan Sirhal
Sr VP: Susan Smith
Sr VP: Martha Voyer
VP: Bradley Huff
VP: Larry Hunt
VP: Julie Mark
**VP:* Randy Mayer
**VP:* Thomas McElroy
VP: Vincent Tocci
VP: Neil Vendetti
Exec: Pat Crichlow
Assoc Dir: Marla Katz
Assoc Dir: Rocco Ottomanelli

ZENITH MERCHANDISING
See DIVERSIFIED MOTEL PROPERTIES LIMITED PARTNERSHIP

D-U-N-S 07-190-3314
ZENITH NATIONAL INSURANCE CORP
ZENITH INSURANCE COMPANY
(*Suby of* FAIRFAX FINANCIAL HOLDINGS LIMITED)
21255 Califa St, Woodland Hills, CA 91367-5005
Tel (818) 713-1000 *Founded/Ownrshp* 2010
Sales NA *EMP* 1,600E
SIC 6331 Workers' compensation insurance; Property damage insurance
Pr: Andrew A Barnard
Ch Bd: Stanley R Zax
Pr: Jack D Miller
COO: Davidson M Pattiz
CFO: William J Owen
CFO: Kari L Van Gundy
Ex VP: Michael E Jansen
Ex VP: Paul Ramont
Sr VP: Robert E Meyer
Sr VP: Philip Wein
VP: Diane Heidenreich
VP: Bradley Martin
Exec: Teresa Nielsen
Board of Directors: Robert J Miller, Fabian Nunez, Catherine B Reynolds, Alan I Rothenberg, William S Sessions, Michael Wm Zavis

D-U-N-S 83-315-7451
ZENITH SYSTEMS LLC
5055 Corbin Dr, Cleveland, OH 44128-5462
Tel (216) 587-9510 *Founded/Ownrshp* 2008
Sales 158.5MME *EMP* 500
SIC 1731 Electrical work; Communications specialization
Pr: Paul Francisco
Pr: David Weiland
VP: Bruno Tilenni
**Prin:* Michael Joyce
**Prin:* Aldona Nagy
Genl Mgr: Robert Heiser
CTO: Doug Fortney
IT Man: Ulysses Thomas
Sfty Dirs: Steve Gomez
Snr PM: Jim Koelliker

D-U-N-S 78-587-6962
ZENSAR TECHNOLOGIES INC
(*Suby of* ZENSAR TECHNOLOGIES LIMITED)
1415 W 22nd St Ste 925, Oak Brook, IL 60523-2002
Tel (630) 928-1518 *Founded/Ownrshp* 1991
Sales 86.5MME *EMP* 425
SIC 7371 Computer software development
CEO: Ganesh Natarajan
Assoc VP: Mark Strickland
Assoc VP: Guido Timmerman
**Ex VP:* Vivek Gupta
**Ex VP:* Nitin Parab
Sr VP: Scott Fiore
VP: Prasad Deshpande
VP: Avinash Kale
VP: Ravi Shetty
Exec: Rukmini Augustine
Exec: Geeta Patil
Exec: Yogesh Shah

D-U-N-S 18-622-5319 IMP
ZENSHO AMERICA CORP
ZENSHO USA
(*Suby of* ZENSHO HOLDINGS CO., LTD.)
27261 Las Ramblas Ste 240, Mission Viejo, CA 92691-6468
Tel (760) 585-8455 *Founded/Ownrshp* 2007
Sales NA *EMP* 4,000
SIC 8742 Franchising consultant
CEO: Masaaki Terada
**Pr:* Yasu Nori Hiraguchi

ZENSHO USA
See ZENSHO AMERICA CORP

D-U-N-S 08-036-6943
ZENTRY LLC
200 Crossing Blvd Fl 8, Bridgewater, NJ 08807-2861
Tel (866) 620-3940 *Founded/Ownrshp* 2015
Sales 14.4MM *EMP* 1,200
SIC 7371 Computer software development & applications
CEO: Steve Waldis

D-U-N-S 15-994-7647 IMP
ZEOLYST INTERNATIONAL
300 Lindenwood Dr, Malvern, PA 19355-1740
Tel (610) 651-4200 *Founded/Ownrshp* 1994
Sales 319.6MM *EMP* 115
Accts Pricewaterhousecoopers Llp
SIC 2819 Industrial inorganic chemicals
Mng Pt: Mike Boyce

D-U-N-S 03-047-1374 IMP
ZEP INC
(*Suby of* NM Z PARENT INC) ★
3330 Cumberland Blvd Se # 700, Atlanta, GA 30339-8100
Tel (877) 428-9937 *Founded/Ownrshp* 2015
Sales 920.6MME *EMP* 2,300E
SIC 2841 2879 2842 Soap & other detergents; Detergents, synthetic organic or inorganic alkaline; Scouring compounds; Pesticides, agricultural or household; Degreasing solvent; Sanitation preparations
Pr: William E Redmond Jr
**CFO:* Mark R Bachmann
Ofcr: Jeffrey L Fleck
Ex VP: Carol A Williams
Sr VP: Robert P Collins
VP: Mark Aggerbeck
VP: Mike Clemens
VP: Mari Hayes
VP: William Reitz
VP: Stewart Searle
VP Sls: Tom Moffett

ZEP SALES & SERVICE
See ACUITY SPECIALTY PRODUCTS INC

D-U-N-S 82-876-1325
ZEPHYROS INC
L& L PRODUCTS
160 Mclean, Bruce Twp, MI 48065-4919
Tel (586) 336-1600 *Founded/Ownrshp* 2006
Sales 181.6MME *EMP* 775
SIC 3053 Gaskets & sealing devices; Gaskets, all materials
CEO: John Ligon
**Pr:* Claude Z Demby
**Ch:* Larry R Schmidt
**Treas:* Robert M Ligon

D-U-N-S 82-715-8325 IMP
ZERO MOTORCYCLES INC
380 El Pueblo Rd, Scotts Valley, CA 95066-4212
Tel (831) 438-3500 *Founded/Ownrshp* 2008
Sales 100.1MME *EMP* 95
SIC 5012 Motorcycles
CEO: Richard Michael Walker
**COO:* Karl Wharton
**CFO:* John Boroska
**CFO:* Curt Sacks
VP: Jay Friedland
VP: Scot Harden
VP: Mike Stacy
VP: John Zukoff
CTO: Aaron Cheatham
Prd Mgr: Ronald Brandon
VP Pdt Dev: Dennis Gore

ZEROCHAOS
See APC WORKFORCE SOLUTIONS LLC

D-U-N-S 01-502-8645
ZEROCHAOS LLC (FL)
420 S Orange Ave Ste 600, Orlando, FL 32801-4902
Tel (407) 770-6161 *Founded/Ownrshp* 1999
Sales 214.2MME *EMP* 925
SIC 8721 Payroll accounting service
CEO: Michael Werblun
**COO:* Matthew Levine
**CFO:* Doug Goin
Ofcr: Mark Lowery
**Ex VP:* Anders Gratte
**Ex VP:* Sally Kauffman
VP: John Bennett
VP: Edward Carr
VP: Tavlos Stevenson

Exec: Scott Millson
Ex Dir: Adrian Muhammad

D-U-N-S 00-934-9992
ZETA INTERACTIVE CORP
XL MARKETING CORP
(*Suby of* ZETA INTERACTIVE SYSTEM INDIA PRIVATE LIMITED)
185 Madison Ave, New York, NY 10016-4325
Tel (212) 967-5055 *Founded/Ownrshp* 2009
Sales 3.1MME *EMP* 1,300
SIC 8742 Marketing consulting services
CEO: David A Steinberg
**Pr:* Steve Gerber
Ex VP: Steven Vine
Sr VP: Jeremy Klein
VP: Gillian Ahouanvoheke
Mng Dir: Mike Sheibar
Mktg Mgr: Steven Gerber
Counsel: William Ettenger

D-U-N-S 01-169-0328 IMP/EXP
ZEUS INDUSTRIAL PRODUCTS INC
620 Magnolia St, Orangeburg, SC 29115-6980
Tel (803) 268-9500 *Founded/Ownrshp* 1965
Sales 185.3MME *EMP* 897
SIC 3082 3083

D-U-N-S 95-770-4737 IMP
ZEVACOR PHARMA INC
(*Suby of* DMH CORPORATE HEALTH SERVICES) ★
21000 Atl Blvd Ste 730, Dulles, VA 20166
Tel (703) 547-8161 *Founded/Ownrshp* 2015
Sales 161.0MME *EMP* 400
SIC 5122 5047 Pharmaceuticals; Medical & hospital equipment
Pr: Timothy Stone
**Treas:* Deborah Bragg

D-U-N-S 82-972-9792 IMP
ZF AXLE DRIVES MARYSVILLE LLC
DIVISION P
(*Suby of* DIVISION Z) ★
2900 Busha Hwy, Marysville, MI 48040-2439
Tel (810) 989-8702 *Founded/Ownrshp* 2008
Sales 83.7MME *EMP* 340
SIC 3711 Chassis, motor vehicle
Ql Cn Mgr: Vinicius Cunha

D-U-N-S 03-771-4441 IMP/EXP
ZF CHASSIS COMPONENTS LLC
DIVISION C
(*Suby of* DIVISION Z) ★
3300 John Conley Dr, Lapeer, MI 48446-4301
Tel (810) 245-2000 *Founded/Ownrshp* 2004
Sales 257.5MME *EMP* 800
SIC 3714 Steering mechanisms, motor vehicle; Tie rods, motor vehicle; Ball joints, motor vehicle; Motor vehicle steering systems & parts
VP: Kurt Mueller
COO: James A Stcey
**CFO:* Franz Kleiner
Treas: Gene G Oswalt
**Ofcr:* Allan Currie
**VP:* Bruce Wrenbeck
IT Man: Dave Pittel
Board of Directors: Paul Ballmeier, Bernd Habersac, Dr Peter Holdmann, Carl Petzoldt, Walter Stritzke, E Zeidler

D-U-N-S 09-719-2595 IMP
ZF NORTH AMERICA INC
DIVISION Z
(*Suby of* ZF FRIEDRICHSHAFEN AG)
15811 Centennial Dr, Northville, MI 48168-9629
Tel (734) 416-6200 *Founded/Ownrshp* 1979
Sales 14.5MMME *EMP* 68,037
SIC 3714 5013 Motor vehicle parts & accessories; Automotive supplies & parts
CFO: Hans-Georg Harter
COO: Thomas Dueckers
**Treas:* Kimberly Carnahan
VP: Steven Lash
**Prin:* Michael Hankel
**Prin:* Jrgen Holeksa
**Prin:* Wilhelm Rehm
**Prin:* Konstantin Sauer
Ex Dir: Rod Alberts
Mng Dir: Jennifer Honts
Genl Mgr: Holzner Joachim

D-U-N-S 02-880-2490 IMP/EXP
ZF TRANSMISSIONS GRAY COURT LLC
DIVISION P
(*Suby of* DIVISION Z) ★
2846 N Old Laurens Rd, Gray Court, SC 29645-3157
Tel (864) 601-2500 *Founded/Ownrshp* 2000
Sales 228.8MME *EMP* 800
SIC 3714 Motor vehicle parts & accessories; Power transmission equipment, motor vehicle
Pr: Ludger Reckmann
CFO: Andreas Mailaender
Treas: Bob Capell

D-U-N-S 13-335-7389 IMP/EXP
ZF TRW AUTOMOTIVE HOLDINGS CORP
(*Suby of* ZF FRIEDRICHSHAFEN AG)
12001 Tech Center Dr, Livonia, MI 48150-2122
Tel (734) 855-2600 *Founded/Ownrshp* 2015
Sales 23.8MMME *EMP* 68,037
SIC 3714 3711 Motor vehicle parts & accessories; Motor vehicles & car bodies; Chassis, motor vehicle
CEO: Franz Kleiner
CFO: Joseph S Cantie
CFO: Christophe Marnat
Co-CEO: John Plant
Ex VP: Peter Holdmann
Ex VP: Peter J Lake
Ex VP: Neil E Marchuk
Ex VP: Mark Stewart
VP: Matthew Hett
Snr Mgr: Steve Michaels

D-U-N-S 82-687-4245
ZFUS SERVICES LLC
ZURICH AMERICAN INSURANCE CO
(*Suby of* ZURICH HOLDING CO OF AMERICA INC) ★
1299 Zurich Way, Schaumburg, IL 60196-5870
Tel (847) 605-6000 *Founded/Ownrshp* 2006
Sales NA *EMP* 3
SIC 6351 Credit & other financial responsibility insurance
Ch: Michael Foley
**CEO:* Martin Senn
**CFO:* Dalynn Hoch

D-U-N-S 00-582-0332 IMP/EXP
ZGS INC (NY)
456 W 55th St, New York, NY 10019-4403
Tel (212) 586-1620 *Founded/Ownrshp* 1999
Sales 92.0MM^E *EMP* 200
Accts Rothschild Topal Miller & Kr
SIC 5063 Electrical apparatus & equipment
Pr: Jonathan Resnick
**VP:* Case Lynch
Genl Mgr: Pamela Graber
Genl Mgr: Rick Loudenburg
Genl Mgr: Peter McNamee
Genl Mgr: Fonda Miller
Genl Mgr: Jeff Montgomerie
Off Mgr: Mandy Welch
MIS Dir: Andre Clark
MIS Dir: Dokur Gokcan
MIS Dir: Fernando Gonzalez

D-U-N-S 00-419-3298 IMP
ZHONGDING SEALING PARTS (USA) INC (OH)
ALLIED BALTIC RUBBER
(*Suby of* ANHUI ZHONGDING SEALING PARTS CO., LTD.)
400 Detroit Ave, Monroe, MI 48162-2783
Tel (734) 241-8870 *Founded/Ownrshp* 1946, 2003
Sales 200.0MM *EMP* 500
SIC 3069 Molded rubber products; Rubber automotive products
CEO: Steve Seketa
IT Man: Tom Hamilton

D-U-N-S 08-028-5979
ZHONGLI NEW ENERGY USA CO LLC
25 Metro Dr Ste 228, San Jose, CA 95110-1338
Tel (408) 638-7627 *Founded/Ownrshp* 2015
Sales 100.0MM *EMP* 5
SIC 5074 Heating equipment & panels, solar
Pr: Jianxin Zhou
**CEO:* Hao Sheng
**VP:* Yan Gong

D-U-N-S 07-962-6326 IMP
ZHONGLU AMERICA CORP
6055 E Wash Blvd Ste 412, Commerce, CA 90040-2425
Tel (323) 869-9999 *Founded/Ownrshp* 1997
Sales 100.0MM *EMP* 6
SIC 5142 Fruit juices, frozen
CEO: Hyeon Choi

D-U-N-S 18-549-3079
ZIEGER HEALTH CARE CORP
BEAUMONT BOTSFORD OAKWOOD HEAL
(*Suby of* BEAUMONT BOTSFORD OAKWOOD HLTH) ★
28050 Grand River Ave, Farmington Hills, MI 48336-5919
Tel (248) 471-8000 *Founded/Ownrshp* 2014
Sales 879.8M *EMP* 2,000
SIC 8062 General medical & surgical hospitals
Pr: Paul Lacasse
CFO: Regina Doxtader
Chf Cred: David Walters
VP: Margo Gorchow
VP: Lisa Vandecaveye
Exec: Doug Warren
CIO: Brian McPherson
Pathlgst: Alex Green

D-U-N-S 00-696-2849 EXP
ZIEGLER INC (MN)
CATERPILLAR AUTHORIZED DEALER
901 W 94th St, Minneapolis, MN 55420-4299
Tel (952) 888-4121 *Founded/Ownrshp* 1914, 1970
Sales 566.4MM^E *EMP* 1,045
SIC 5082 5084 Construction & mining machinery; Tractors, construction; Front end loaders; Engines & parts, diesel
CEO: William L Hoeft
**Ch Bd:* Leonard C Hoeft
**CEO:* Stanley Erickson
VP: Dave Clapper
VP: Steve Hron
VP: David M Johnson
**VP:* A E Pearson
VP: Greg Senske
CIO: Christian Anderson
IT Man: Nate Dahl
Opers Mgr: Jim Bjorklund
Board of Directors: Jeffrey Roberts

D-U-N-S 00-847-4579 IMP
■ **ZIEMAN MANUFACTURING CO INC** (CA)
SEATING TECHNOLOGIES
(*Suby of* DREW INDUSTRIES INC) ★
2703 College Ave, Goshen, IN 46528-5040
Tel (574) 535-1125 *Founded/Ownrshp* 1946, 1998
Sales 554.7MM^E *EMP* 2,600
SIC 3715 3441 2451 3799

D-U-N-S 96-548-7353
■ **ZIFF DAVIS LLC**
(*Suby of* J2 CLOUD SERVICES INC) ★
28 E 28th St Fl 11-R, New York, NY 10016-7966
Tel (212) 503-3500 *Founded/Ownrshp* 2010
Sales 95.8MM^E *EMP* 1,760^E
SIC 7319 Media buying service
CEO: Vivek Shah
Pr: Jasmine Alexander
COO: Steven Horowitz
CFO: Brian Stewart
Chf Mktg O: Eric Koepele
Ex VP: Tom McGrade
VP: Kathleen Kincaid
Dir Soc: Joe Maglitta
Dir Soc: Andrea Mahoney
Genl Mgr: Damon Johnson
CTO: Joey Fortuna

ZIFF-DAVIS PUBLISHING
See DAVIS ZIFF PUBLISHING INC

D-U-N-S 17-020-7505 IMP/EXP
ZIJA INTERNATIONAL INC
3300 N Ashton Blvd # 100, Lehi, UT 84043-5339
Tel (801) 494-2300 *Founded/Ownrshp* 2006
Sales 90.7MM^E *EMP* 150^E
SIC 5149 Beverages, except coffee & tea
**Pr:* Bradley Stewart
**CEO:* Rodney Larsen
Sr Ex VP: Kent Fairbanks
**VP:* John Brailsford
VP: Whitney Davis
**VP:* Micheal Hersgberger
**VP:* Cathy Yeates
Exec: Matt Gardner
Mng Dir: Ryan Palmer
Dir IT: Justin Mullen
Genl Couns: Brent Ashworth

D-U-N-S 02-624-3499
ZILLIONAIRE EMPRESS DANIELLE BERHANE MANAGEMENT FIRM
8549 Wilshire Blvd # 817, Beverly Hills, CA 90211-3104
Tel (310) 461-9923 *Founded/Ownrshp* 2012
Sales 44.6MM^E *EMP* 1,000
SIC 6722

D-U-N-S 07-973-1805
▲ **ZILLOW GROUP INC**
1301 2nd Ave Fl 31, Seattle, WA 98101-0003
Tel (206) 470-7000 *Founded/Ownrshp* 2004
Sales 644.6MM *EMP* 2,204^E
Tkr Sym Z *Exch* NGS
SIC 7372 6531 4813 Business oriented computer software; Real estate brokers & agents;
CEO: Spencer M Rascoff
**Ch Bd:* Richard N Barton
**Pr:* Lloyd D Frink
Pr: Paul Levine
COO: Amy C Bohutinsky
Ofcr: Stanley B Humphries
Ofcr: Errol G Samuelson
Ofcr: Greg M Schwartz
CTO: David A Beitel

D-U-N-S 19-387-0669 IMP
■ **ZILLOW INC**
(*Suby of* ZILLOW GROUP INC) ★
1301 2nd Ave Fl 31, Seattle, WA 98101-0003
Tel (206) 470-7000 *Founded/Ownrshp* 2004
Sales 307.4MM^E *EMP* 817^E
SIC 7371 8742 Custom computer programming services; Management consulting services; Real estate consultant
CEO: Spencer M Rascoff
**COO:* Kathleen Philips
**CFO:* Chad M Cohen
**Chf Mktg O:* Amy Bohutinsky
VP: Curt Beardsley
VP: Rob Cross
Prgrm Mgr: Paul Moore
Snr Sftwr: Marius Dumitriu
Snr Sftwr: Joshua Lang
**CTO:* David Beitel
Software D: Justin Baker

D-U-N-S 04-470-8550
ZIM AMERICAN INTEGRATED SHIPPING SERVICES CO INC
ZIM SHIPPING
(*Suby of* ZIM INTEGRATED SHIPPING SERVICES LTD)
5801 Lake Wright Dr, Norfolk, VA 23502-1863
Tel (757) 228-1300 *Founded/Ownrshp* 1948
Sales 96.1MM^E *EMP* 320
SIC 4731 Freight transportation arrangement; Transportation agents & brokers; Agents, shipping
Ch Bd: Nir Gilad
**Pr:* Shaul Cohen Mintz
**CEO:* Rafi Danieli
CFO: Eitan Stern
Sr VP: Gordon Kay
Sr VP: Shaim Shacham
Sr VP: Dan Sutton
Sr VP: Pesach Yoskovitz
**VP:* David Arbel
**VP:* Yakov Baruch
**VP:* Rafael Ben-ARI
VP: Lea Bogatch
VP: Jeff Gill
VP: Thomas Keen
VP: Richard Proumen
VP: Chris Rozon
VP: Joram Shoshan
Exec: Nili Menuhin

ZIM SHIPPING
See ZIM AMERICAN INTEGRATED SHIPPING SERVICES CO INC

D-U-N-S 02-332-9808
ZIMBRICK INC
ISUZU OF MADISON
1601 W Beltline Hwy, Madison, WI 53713-2386
Tel (608) 277-2277 *Founded/Ownrshp* 1965
Sales 228.4MM^E *EMP* 550
SIC 5511 7538 5521 Automobiles, new & used; General automotive repair shops; Used car dealers
CEO: Thomas Zimbrick
**Ch Bd:* John Zimbrick
CFO: Lon Bahr
VP: Kimberly Bauer
VP: Lacey Holland
VP: Jamie Wacek
**VP:* Michael Zimbrick
Exec: Carol Gottinger
Exec: Mary Norgord
Genl Mgr: Brad Barker
Genl Mgr: Jim Campbell

ZIMMER BIOMET
See BIOMET INC

D-U-N-S 02-159-9365
▲ **ZIMMER BIOMET HOLDINGS INC**
345 E Main St, Warsaw, IN 46580-2746
Tel (574) 267-6131 *Founded/Ownrshp* 1927
Sales 6.0MMM *EMP* 17,799^E
Tkr Sym ZBH *Exch* NYS
SIC 3842 Orthopedic appliances; Implants, surgical
Ch Bd: Larry C Glasscock
Pr: David C Dvorak
CFO: Daniel P Florin
Ch: Bruno Melzi
Ex VP: James T Crines
Sr VP: Robin T Barney
Sr VP: Bill Fisher
Sr VP: Chad F Phipps
VP: Michael Barnett
VP: Tony W Collins
VP: Amy Feldman
VP: William Fisher
VP: Joy Goble
VP: Nathan Jones
VP: Roger Klusman
VP: Edwina Payne
VP: Chad Phipps
VP: Randy Sessler
VP: Richard Stair
VP: Randy Verberkmoes
VP: Carol Vierling

D-U-N-S 78-613-3579 IMP
■ **ZIMMER CARIBE INC**
(*Suby of* Z HOTEL) ★
Road 1 Km 123 Hm 4 Bldg 1, Mercedita, PR 00715
Tel (787) 259-5959 *Founded/Ownrshp* 2006
Sales 124.0MM^E *EMP* 681
SIC 3842 Implants, surgical
Pr: Ray Elliot
**CFO:* James T Crines
Genl Mgr: Geraardo Torres

D-U-N-S 05-360-7107
ZIMMER GUNSUL FRASCA ARCHITECTS LLP
1223 Sw Washington St # 200, Portland, OR 97205-2360
Tel (503) 224-3860 *Founded/Ownrshp* 1954
Sales 130.5MM *EMP* 458
SIC 8712 8748 7389 Architectural services; Urban planning & consulting services; Interior designer
Pt: Robert G Packard III
Pt: Brauolio Batista
Pt: Joseph Collins
Pt: Kelly Davis
Pt: Margaret Debolt
Pt: Mark M Foster
Pt: Robert J Frasca
Pt: Ted Hyman
Pt: R Doss Mabe
Pt: Eugene B Sandoval
Pt: Karl Sonnenberg
Pt: Jan C Willemse

D-U-N-S 05-603-8268 IMP/EXP
■ **ZIMMER INC**
Z HOTEL
(*Suby of* ZIMMER BIOMET HOLDINGS INC) ★
1800 W Center St, Warsaw, IN 46580-2304
Tel (330) 343-8801 *Founded/Ownrshp* 2001
Sales 758.4MM^E *EMP* 1,500
SIC 3842 Orthopedic appliances; Implants, surgical; Surgical appliances & supplies
Pr: David C Dvorak
**CFO:* James T Crines
IT Man: Dan Robinson
Sftwr Eng: Eric Nelson
Sfty Mgr: Allen Frutig
VP Mktg: Patric Riewoldt
Mktg Mgr: Leslie Kozar
Mktg Mgr: Judith Rutteman

D-U-N-S 15-465-0261
■ **ZIMMERMAN ADVERTISING LLC**
POWER TRAX
(*Suby of* OMNICOM GROUP INC) ★
6600 N Andrews Ave # 200, Fort Lauderdale, FL 33309-2188
Tel (954) 644-4000 *Founded/Ownrshp* 1985
Sales 105.6MM^E *EMP* 1,100
SIC 7311 Advertising agencies
CEO: Michael Goldberg
**Ch Bd:* Jordan Zimmerman
**Pr:* David Kissell
**Ofcr:* Jim Heidelberg
**Ofcr:* David Nathanson
**Ex VP:* Michael Angelovich
Ex VP: Damon Langdon
Ex VP: Richard Nez
Ex VP: Bryan Sweeney
VP: Gabriela McCoy
VP: Charles Pullen
VP: Lisa Rossi
VP: Joe Shook
VP: Cindy Syracuse

ZINC CORPORATION AMERICA DIV
See HH LIQUIDATING CORP

D-U-N-S 05-336-8937 IMP/EXP
ZINUS INC
(*Suby of* ZINUS INC.)
1951 Fairway Dr Ste A, San Leandro, CA 94577-5643
Tel (925) 417-2100 *Founded/Ownrshp* 1987
Sales 123.8MM *EMP* 70
Accts Jeffrey J Lee Oakland Ca
SIC 2515 Mattresses & bedsprings; Chair & couch springs, assembled; Sofa beds (convertible sofas)
Pr: Youn Jae Lee

D-U-N-S 05-503-8228 IMP/EXP
▲ **ZIONS BANCORPORATION**
ZIONS BANK
1 S Main St Fl 15, Salt Lake City, UT 84133-1109
Tel (801) 844-7637 *Founded/Ownrshp* 1955
Sales NA *EMP* 10,200
Tkr Sym ZION *Exch* NGS
SIC 6022 6021 State commercial banks; National commercial banks
Ch Bd: Harris H Simmons
Pr: A Scott Anderson
Pr: Carson Boss
Pr: Bob Howard
Pr: Leo Howell
Pr: Jeff Newman
Pr: Darrin Zingleman
CFO: Paul E Burdiss
CFO: Ron Lynch
Chf Cred: Michael Morris
Ofcr: Autumn Johnson
Ofcr: Matthew Ketchum
Ofcr: Keith D Maio
Ofcr: Michael J Morris
Ofcr: Kenneth E Peterson
Ofcr: Edward P Schreiber
Ex VP: Lori Chillingworth
Ex VP: Mark Christian
Ex VP: Francis Fisher
Ex VP: W D Hemingway
Ex VP: George B Hofmann III
Board of Directors: Steven C Wheelwright, Jerry C Atkin, Shelley Thomas Williams, Patricia Frobes, Suren K Gupta, J David Heaney, Vivian S Lee, Edward F Murphy, Roger B Porter, Stephen D Quinn, L E Simmons

ZIONS BANK
See ZIONS BANCORPORATION

D-U-N-S 00-909-4400
■ **ZIONS CREDIT CORP** (UT)
(*Suby of* CALIFORNIA BANK & TRUST) ★
310 S Main St Ste 1300, Salt Lake City, UT 84101-2159
Tel (801) 524-2230 *Founded/Ownrshp* 1961, 1997
Sales NA *EMP* 46
SIC 6159 Equipment & vehicle finance leasing companies
Pr: Alan Ralphs
**Treas:* Kay Hall
**VP:* Norman Weldon

D-U-N-S 95-875-9425
ZIONS MOUNTAIN VIEW HOME AND ASSOCIATES LTD
CANYON RIM CARE CENTRE
2730 E 3300 S, Salt Lake City, UT 84109-2819
Tel (801) 487-0896 *Founded/Ownrshp* 1985
Sales 401.9MM *EMP* 80
SIC 8741 Nursing & personal care facility management
Pt: David Dangerfield
Exec: Trista West

D-U-N-S 03-698-2692 IMP
■ **ZIPCAR INC**
(*Suby of* AVIS BUDGET GROUP INC) ★
35 Thomson Pl, Boston, MA 02210-1202
Tel (617) 995-4231 *Founded/Ownrshp* 2013
Sales 85.1MM^E *EMP* 496^E
SIC 7514 Rent-a-car service
Pr: Mark D Norman
Pr: Frerk-Malte Feller
**CFO:* Edward Goldfinger
Chf Mktg O: Sarah Dekin
**Chf Mktg O:* Brian Harrington
**Chf Mktg O:* Robert J Weisberg
**Ex VP:* Lesley Mottla
**Ex VP:* Ciara Smyth
VP: Nichole Mace
VP: David Piperno
VP: Eric Spear
Exec: Kaleb Miller
Exec: Christopher Moulding

D-U-N-S 05-087-9852
ZIPCORP INC (PA)
ZIPPO MANUFACTURING COMPANY
33 Barbour St, Bradford, PA 16701-1973
Tel (814) 368-2700 *Founded/Ownrshp* 1933
Sales 173.1MM^E *EMP* 1,100
SIC 3999 5172 Cigarette lighters, except precious metal; Petroleum products
**VP:* George B Duke

ZIPPO MANUFACTURING COMPANY
See ZIPCORP INC

D-U-N-S 00-210-1301 IMP/EXP
ZIPPO MANUFACTURING CO INC (PA)
(*Suby of* ZIPPO MANUFACTURING CO) ★
33 Barbour St, Bradford, PA 16701-1998
Tel (814) 368-2700 *Founded/Ownrshp* 1932
Sales 173.1MM^E *EMP* 1,020
SIC 3914 3993 5172 3999 3421 3172 Cutlery, stainless steel; Signs & advertising specialties; Petroleum products; Cigarette lighters, except precious metal; Cutlery; Personal leather goods
Prin: George Duke
**Pr:* Gregory W Booth
**CFO:* Don Hall
**CFO:* Richard Roupe
VP: S B Dorn
VP: Bruce Gallagher
VP: Michael Martin
VP: David Mellon
VP: Richard Young
Dir Lab: Scott Bryant
**Prin:* Sarah Dorn
Board of Directors: Richard Dorn, Sarah Dorn, Howard Fesenmyer

ZIPPYS SAIMIN LANAI RESTAURANT
See FCH ENTERPRISES INC

D-U-N-S 02-023-5669
ZIRKLE FRUIT CO
MOXEE RANCH
352 Harrison Rd, Selah, WA 98942-9505
Tel (509) 697-6101 *Founded/Ownrshp* 1976
Sales 805.5MM^E *EMP* 224
SIC 0175 0723 4222

D-U-N-S 80-858-0588
ZOCDOC INC
568 Broadway Fl 9, New York, NY 10012-3217
Tel (866) 962-3621 *Founded/Ownrshp* 2007
Sales 93.5MM^E *EMP* 600^E
SIC 8011 8099 Medical centers; Blood related health services
CEO: Cyrus Massoumi

*COO: Oliver Kharraz
*CFO: Netta Samroengraja
*VP: Joaquin Gamboa
VP: Jade Rothman
*VP: Ori Schnaps
Sftwr Eng: Scott Wilson
Sales Exec: Andrew Bollhoefer
Sales Exec: Sarah Whalley
Sales Exec: Peter Zarrella
Sls Dir: Christine Apold

ZODIAC AEROSYSTEMS
See ZODIAC US CORP

ZODIAC ARLN CABIN & INTR WASH
See HEATHTECNA INC

ZODIAC OF NORTH AMERICA
See Z MARINE NORTH AMERICA LLC

D-U-N-S 01-397-7662
■ ZODIAC POOL SOLUTIONS NORTH AMERICA INC
(Suby of JANDY POOL PRODUCTS) ★
2620 Commerce Way, Vista, CA 92081-8438
Tel (760) 599-9600 Founded/Ownrshp 2007
Sales 141.1MM^E EMP 653
SIC 3589 Swimming pool filter & water conditioning systems
Pr: Francois Mirallie
*CFO: Joel Silva
*VP: Mark Cortell
*VP: Anthony D Prudhomme

D-U-N-S 11-236-2889 IMP/EXP
■ ZODIAC POOL SYSTEMS INC
JANDY POOL PRODUCTS
(Suby of ZODIAC POOL SOLUTIONS)
2620 Commerce Way, Vista, CA 92081-8438
Tel (760) 599-9600 Founded/Ownrshp 2006
Sales 731.6MM^E EMP 1,900
SIC 3589 3999 Swimming pool filter & water conditioning systems; Hot tub & spa covers; Atomizers, toiletry
CEO: Bruce Brooks
Pr: Rick Mills
*COO: Anthony Prudhomme
*CFO: Mike Allanc
Ofcr: Janice Venter
Ex VP: Troy Franzen
VP: Todd Cramer
VP: Scott Frost
VP: Barry Greenwald
VP: Tim Lawrence
Genl Mgr: Brandon Huffman

D-U-N-S 19-740-6374 IMP
ZODIAC SEATS US LLC
(Suby of ZODIAC AEROSYSTEMS) ★
2000 Zodiac Dr, Gainesville, TX 76240
Tel (940) 668-8541 Founded/Ownrshp 2005
Sales 1.4MMM^E EMP 2,300
SIC 5088 3728 Transportation equipment & supplies; Aircraft parts & equipment
Pr: Jeffrey Johnston
COO: Steve Starens
VP: Rakibul Islam
CTO: Karen Summers
Sls Dir: Larry Gaither

D-U-N-S 13-190-8696 IMP
ZODIAC US CORP
ZODIAC AEROSYSTEMS
(Suby of ZODIAC AEROSPACE)
1747 State Route 34, Wall Township, NJ 07727-3935
Tel (732) 681-3527 Founded/Ownrshp 1987
Sales 3.3MMM^E EMP 9,434
SIC 3728 Aircraft landing assemblies & brakes
CEO: Jean-Louis Gerondeau
*COO: Jean-Jacques Jegou
*CFO: John Melone
QA Dir: Michael Mirpour

D-U-N-S 00-638-4978 IMP
ZOELLER CO (KY)
3649 Cane Run Rd, Louisville, KY 40211-1961
Tel (502) 778-2731 Founded/Ownrshp 1939
Sales 164.8MM EMP 300
SIC 3561 5251 3432 3491 Pumps, domestic: water or sump; Pumps & pumping equipment; Plastic plumbing fixture fittings, assembly; Industrial valves
Ch: Robert F Zoeller
*CEO: John Zoeller
*CFO: John Keither
*CFO: John Kuecker
*VP: Gregory Dueffert
VP: Al Smith
Dir Risk M: Bill Zoeller
IT Man: Robert Hentrup
MIS Mgr: Tony Zoeller
VP Mfg: Frank Bailey
Plnt Mgr: Kevin Byrne

D-U-N-S 94-791-7725
▲ ZOES KITCHEN INC
5760 State Highway 121, Plano, TX 75024-6664
Tel (214) 436-8765 Founded/Ownrshp 1995
Sales 171.7MM EMP 3,070^E
Tkr Sym ZOES Exch NYS
SIC 5812 6794 Eating places; Franchises, selling or licensing
Pr: Kevin Miles
*Ch Bd: Greg Dollarhyde
COO: Jeremy Hartley
CFO: Sunil M Doshi
Chf Mktg O: Casey Shilling
Board of Directors: Rahul Aggarwal, Thomas Baldwin, Sue Collyns, Cordia Harrington, Alec Taylor

D-U-N-S 80-044-8800
ZOES KITCHEN USA LLC
5760 State Highway 121 # 250, Plano, TX 75024-6664
Tel (214) 872-4141 Founded/Ownrshp 2004
Sales 20.0MM EMP 1,000^E
SIC 5812 American restaurant
Pr: Kevin Miles
COO: Jeremy Hartley
*CFO: Jason Morgan
*Ch: Greg Dollarhyde
VP: Archie Andrews

D-U-N-S 07-857-9659
▲ ZOETIS INC
10 Sylvan Way Ste 105, Parsippany, NJ 07054-3825
Tel (973) 822-7000 Founded/Ownrshp 2012
Sales 4.7MMM EMP 9,000^E
Accts Kpmg Llp New York New York
Tkr Sym ZTS Exch NYS
SIC 2834 5122 Pharmaceutical preparations; Animal medicines
CEO: Juan Ramon Alaix
*Ch Bd: Michael B McCallister
*CFO: Glenn David
*Ofcr: Roxanne Lagano
Ex VP: Alejandro Bernal
*Ex VP: Heidi C Chen
Ex VP: Catherine A Knupp
Ex VP: Clinton A Lewis Jr
Ex VP: Kristin C Peck
Ex VP: Roman Trawicki
Dir Rx: Russell Dowson
Board of Directors: Paul M Bisaro, Frank A D'amelio, William F Doyle, Sanjay Khosla, Gregory Norden, Louise M Parent, Willie M Reed, Robert W Scully, William C Steere Jr

D-U-N-S 07-881-5825
■ ZOETIS LLC
(Suby of ZOETIS INC) ★
100 Campus Dr, Florham Park, NJ 07932-1020
Tel (800) 601-1357 Founded/Ownrshp 2012
Sales 204.9MM^E EMP 1,194^E
SIC 2834 Pharmaceutical preparations
CEO: Juan Ramon Alaix
Ex VP: Roxanne Lagano
Ex VP: Stefan Weiskopf

D-U-N-S 07-935-5300
■ ZOETIS P&U LLC
(Suby of ZOETIS INC) ★
100 Campus Dr, Florham Park, NJ 07932-1020
Tel (973) 822-7000 Founded/Ownrshp 2012
Sales 92.3MM^E EMP 50^E
SIC 5159 0742 8734 Farm animals; Veterinary services, specialties; Veterinary testing

D-U-N-S 07-095-4094 IMP/EXP
■ ZOETIS PRODUCTS LLC
(Suby of ZOETIS INC) ★
100 Campus Dr Ste 3, Florham Park, NJ 07932-1006
Tel (973) 660-5000 Founded/Ownrshp 2008
Sales 329.7MM^E EMP 2,000
SIC 2833 2834 Medicinals & botanicals; Pharmaceutical preparations
VP: Matthew Farrell
*Pr: Juan Ramon Alaix
*VP: Joseph Del Buono
*VP: David R Jackson
*VP: Clinton Lewis
VP: John S Towler
Assoc Dir: John B Baker
Tech Mgr: Adrian Del Valle
Mktg Dir: Ryan Dunn
Sls Mgr: Karl Wessel

D-U-N-S 94-368-5313
ZOHO CORP
(Suby of ZOHO CORPORATION PRIVATE LIMITED)
4141 Hacienda Dr, Pleasanton, CA 94588-8566
Tel (925) 924-9500 Founded/Ownrshp 1996
Sales 88.2MM^E EMP 1,200
SIC 7372 Application computer software
CEO: Sridhar Vembu
*Ch Bd: Tony Thomas
CFO: Steve Collard
CFO: Maureen Mullarkey
VP: Ken Fenyo
*VP: Sridhar Iyengar
VP: John Joshua
VP: Anthony Sperling
Dir Bus: Kevin Carlsten
Rgnl Mgr: Sumi Jhingon
CIO: Chris Lynch

ZOLL LIFECOR CORPORATION
See ZOLL SERVICES LLC

D-U-N-S 05-536-3428 IMP
ZOLL MEDICAL CORP
(Suby of ASAHI KASEI CORPORATION)
269 Mill Rd, Chelmsford, MA 01824-4105
Tel (978) 421-9100 Founded/Ownrshp 2012
Sales 575.1MM^E EMP 1,908
SIC 3845 7372 Defibrillator; Prepackaged software
CEO: Richard A Packer
*Pr: Marshal W Linder
*Pr: James Palazzolo
*Pr: Jonathan A Rennert
*Treas: John P Bergeron
*Sr VP: Ward M Hamilton
*Sr VP: Ernest Whiton
VP: Don R Bouche
VP: Steven Flora
*VP: Aaron M Grossman
VP: Aaron Grossman
VP: Sharon Kim
VP: Stephen Korn
VP: Scott Martin
VP: Alex N Moghadam
VP: Sean Rollman
VP: Steve Szymkiewicz
VP: Elizabeth Wilson
VP Bus Dev: Hideo Hikami

D-U-N-S 17-420-0907
ZOLL SERVICES LLC
ZOLL LIFECOR CORPORATION
(Suby of ZOLL MEDICAL CORP) ★
121 Gamma Dr, Pittsburgh, PA 15238-2919
Tel (412) 968-3333 Founded/Ownrshp 2006
Sales 228.8MM^E EMP 800
SIC 3845 Electromedical equipment
Pr: Marshal Linder
*VP: Reno Fiolic
*VP: Mike Hardy
*VP: Thomas E Kaib
*VP: Sharon Kim
VP: Jeffrey B Morgan Sr
VP Opers: Jeff Morgan
Ql Cn Mgr: Gene Partin

S&M/VP: Kathleen Higgs
Sls Dir: Stan Belyeu
Sls Mgr: Laura Blair

D-U-N-S 07-989-7393 IMP/EXP
ZOLTEK COMPANIES INC
PANEX
(Suby of TORAY INDUSTRIES,INC.)
3101 Mckelvey Rd, Bridgeton, MO 63044-2552
Tel (314) 291-5110 Founded/Ownrshp 2014
Sales 539.3MM^E EMP 2,123^E
SIC 3624 Fibers, carbon & graphite
Pr: Yoshihiro Takeuchi
COO: Mark Didion
*CFO: Andrew W Whipple
Chf Mktg O: Teri Cook
*Ex VP: Hiroshi Matsuo
VP: Istvan Kinter
VP: Arlene Taich
VP: John White
Genl Mgr: Philip Schell
CIO: Mark Erhardt
CIO: George B Snyder

D-U-N-S 19-559-0237
ZONES INC
1102 15th St Sw Ste 102, Auburn, WA 98001-6524
Tel (253) 205-3000 Founded/Ownrshp 2008
Sales 1.1MMM^E EMP 1,400
SIC 7373 5734 Computer integrated systems design; Computer software & accessories
Ch Bd: Firoz Lalji
*Pt: Derrek Hallock
Pt: Todd Leeson
Pr: Mark Hemenway
*Pr: Murray Wright
CFO: Ronald P McFadden
Sr VP: Dominic Camden
*Sr VP: Anwar Jiwani
Sr VP: Linda Marbena
Sr VP: Robert McGowen
VP: Gary Allen
VP: Jon Allen
VP: Jeremy Clark
VP: Ron Dabrowski
VP: Jim Grass
*VP: Sean Hobday
VP: Asif Hudani
VP: Gregory Malik
*VP: Ronald McFadden
VP: Christopher McNutt
VP: Mark Nehring

D-U-N-S 08-040-2854
ZONES PUBLIC SECTOR LLC (WA)
(Suby of ZONES INC) ★
1102 15th St Sw Ste 102, Auburn, WA 98001-6524
Tel (253) 205-3000 Founded/Ownrshp 2016
Sales 100.0MM EMP 99
SIC 5961 Catalog & mail-order houses
CFO: Ronald McFadden

ZOOK MOLASSES CO
See M SIMON ZOOK CO

D-U-N-S 07-356-0260 IMP/EXP
ZOOLOGICAL SOCIETY OF SAN DIEGO
WORLD FAMOUS SAN DIEGO ZOO
2920 Zoo Dr, San Diego, CA 92101-1646
Tel (619) 231-1515 Founded/Ownrshp 1916
Sales 294.9MM EMP 2,300
Accts Cohnreznick Llp Sacramento C
SIC 8422 5812 5947 Arboreta & botanical or zoological gardens; Eating places; Gift shop
Prin: Berit Durler
*Pr: Richard B Gulley
*CFO: Paula S Brock
*Treas: Frank Alexander
Ofcr: Pam Fein
VP: Paula Beck
VP: Don Leiker
Exec: Frank Lunn
Exec: Chris Mirguet
Assoc Dir: Kelly Craig
Assoc Dir: Susan Farabaugh

D-U-N-S 10-211-0863 IMP
■ ZORAN CORP
(Suby of CSR LIMITED)
1060 Rincon Cir, San Jose, CA 95131-1325
Tel (972) 673-1600 Founded/Ownrshp 2011
Sales 103.3MM^E EMP 1,532^E
SIC 3674 Integrated circuits, semiconductor networks, etc.
CEO: Daniel Willard Gardiner
COO: Lisa Yep
*CFO: Karl Schneider
Sr VP: Gerhard Peinsipp
*Sr VP: Isaac Shenberg PHD
*VP: Robert Kirk
VP: Tom Mager
*VP: David Power
VP: Zoran Suprahd
*VP: Dawn Thompson
Exec: Mati Frenkel
Exec: Desiree Valdez

ZOTEC PARTNERS
See ZOTEC SOLUTIONS INC

D-U-N-S 03-063-4153
ZOTEC SOLUTIONS INC
ZOTEC PARTNERS
11460 N Meridian St Ste X, Carmel, IN 46032-4530
Tel (317) 848-2815 Founded/Ownrshp 1998
Sales 161.2MM^E EMP 553
SIC 7389 Personal service agents, brokers & bureaus
Pr: T Scott Law
Pr: Steve Collins
COO: Taylor Moorehead
Ex VP: Aimee Harvey
Ex VP: Stacy Hiquet
Ex VP: Scott Law Jr
Ex VP: David Stone
Ex VP: Mark Talley
Ex VP: Greg Thomson
VP: Ron Duplessis
VP: Jeff Fowler
*VP: David Law
VP: Jeff McHugh
VP: Victor Sarkissian

Exec: Tracy Reising
Dir Bus: Patrick Holland

D-U-N-S 07-878-7543
ZRAIM INVESTMENTS LLC
400 Sunny Isles Blvd # 190, Sunny Isles Beach, FL 33160-5080
Tel (718) 708-0065 Founded/Ownrshp 2013
Sales 100.0MM EMP 11
SIC 6798 Real estate investment trusts

D-U-N-S 10-400-1367
ZS ASSOCIATES INC
1800 Sherman Ave Ste 37, Evanston, IL 60201-3496
Tel (858) 677-2200 Founded/Ownrshp 1983
Sales 469.9MM^E EMP 3,000
SIC 8742

D-U-N-S 82-802-9566
ZSCALER INC
110 Rose Orchard Way, San Jose, CA 95134-1358
Tel (408) 533-0288 Founded/Ownrshp 2007
Sales 98.4MM^E EMP 600
Accts Pwc Llp
SIC 7371 Computer software development & applications
CEO: Jay Chaudhry
CFO: Greg Pappas
Chf Mktg O: Atri Chatterjee
Ex VP: Dr Amit Sinha
Sr VP: Dr Manoj Apte
VP: Punit Minocha
VP: Rajnish Mishra
VP: Trevis Schuh
Exec: William Welch
Rgnl Mgr: Paula Moeller
CIO: Patrick Foxhoven

D-U-N-S 62-765-5074
ZSL INC
85 State Route 27, Edison, NJ 08820-3561
Tel (877) 800-0975 Founded/Ownrshp 2006
Sales 98.4MM^E EMP 1,500
SIC 7379
CEO: Ram Sesharathnam
Ex VP: Shivakum Kandaswamy
*Ex VP: Shiv Kumar
VP: Shivakumar Kandaswamy
VP: Sirish Rastogi
Exec: Deepika Pandiri
Prgrm Mgr: Praveen Garapati
Rgnl Mgr: Yashwanth Ramesh
Snr Sftwr: Abdul Hameed
Snr Sftwr: Mahesh Mamidala
Software D: Rohit Parulekar

D-U-N-S 07-613-4076 IMP
ZT GROUP INTL INC
ZT SYSTEMS
(Suby of ZT BRAZIL COMERCIO, IMPORTACAO E EXPORTACAO LTDA.)
333 Meadowlands Pkwy Fl 2, Secaucus, NJ 07094-1814
Tel (201) 559-1000 Founded/Ownrshp 1998
Sales 114.9MM^E EMP 250^E
SIC 7379 Computer related consulting services
Ex VP: Bob Anderson
*VP: Rick Garian
VP: Melissa M Massa
*VP: Tom Matson
VP: Matt Partlow
Dir Sec: Tim Jordan
IT Man: James Bateman
Sftwr Eng: Weijie Gong
Sftwr Eng: Feng Liang
Snr PM: Phil Blaustein

ZT SYSTEMS
See ZT GROUP INTL INC

D-U-N-S 12-528-3833 IMP
ZTE (USA) INC
ZTE USA
(Suby of ZTE CORPORATION)
2425 N Central Expy # 600, Richardson, TX 75080-2786
Tel (972) 671-8885 Founded/Ownrshp 1998
Sales 189.5MM^E EMP 294
SIC 5065 5999 Communication equipment; Telephone equipment & systems
Pr: Lixin Cheng
CFO: Ll Zheng
Sr VP: David Britt
VP: Roselyn Blankson
VP: Sean Cai
VP: Dick Chen
*VP: Jie Chen
VP: Wayne Hou
*VP: Daging Liu
VP: Tom Mao
VP: Qin Ni
VP: Sally Song

ZTE USA
See ZTE (USA) INC

D-U-N-S 05-186-8811
ZUAGGUA PARTNERS LLC
4321 Nw 15th Ave, Fort Lauderdale, FL 33309-4507
Tel (772) 501-3594 Founded/Ownrshp 2015
Sales 3.0MMM EMP 5
SIC 6221 Commodity dealers, contracts
Mng Pt: John Howard

D-U-N-S 07-938-0772
ZUEGG USA CORP
(Suby of ZUEGG SPA)
50 Harrison St Ste 214b, Hoboken, NJ 07030-6087
Tel (201) 222-0291 Founded/Ownrshp 2014
Sales 226.7MM EMP 4
SIC 5149 Juices
Pr: Silvano Groppi

D-U-N-S 96-239-9858 EXP
ZULILY INC
2601 Elliott Ave Ste 200, Seattle, WA 98121-1389
Tel (877) 779-5614 Founded/Ownrshp 2009
Sales 1.2MMM EMP 1,110
SIC 5961

D-U-N-S 08-000-8491
■ ZULILY LLC
(*Suby of* LIBERTY INTERACTIVE CORP) ★
2601 Elliott Ave Ste 200, Seattle, WA 98121-1389
Tel (877) 779-5614 *Founded/Ownrshp* 2009
Sales 1.2MMM *EMP* 2,907[E]
SIC 5961 Catalog & mail-order houses; Clothing, mail order (except women's); Women's apparel, mail order
Pr: Darrell Cavens
Pr: Colleen McKeown
COO: Bob Spieth
Sr VP: Dave Atchison
VP: Julie Johnston
VP: Kerry Morris
Snr Sftwr: Kris Craig
Snr Sftwr: Peifeng Ni
Snr Sftwr: Mark Puckett
Snr Sftwr: Matthew Schiros
CIO: Luke Friang

D-U-N-S 09-228-8000 IMP
▲ ZUMIEZ INC
4001 204th St Sw, Lynnwood, WA 98036-6864
Tel (425) 551-1500 *Founded/Ownrshp* 1978
Sales 804.1MM *EMP* 7,000
Tkr Sym ZUMZ *Exch* NGS
SIC 5941 Sporting goods & bicycle shops; Specialty sport supplies; Surfing equipment & supplies; Skateboarding equipment
CEO: Richard M Brooks Jr
**Ch Bd:* Thomas D Campion
CFO: Christopher C Work
Ex VP: Troy R Brown
Ex VP: Chris K Visser
VP: Jim Hume
Dir Soc: Wendy Rork
Rgnl Mgr: Jason Rose
Dist Mgr: Josh Carrico
Dist Mgr: Jon Glover
Dist Mgr: Ryan Runge
Board of Directors: Scott A Bailey, Ernest R Johnson, Sarah G McCoy, Travis D Smith, James M Weber

D-U-N-S 82-464-0424
ZUORA INC
1051 E Hillsdale Blvd # 600, Foster City, CA 94404-1640
Tel (800) 425-1281 *Founded/Ownrshp* 2006
Sales 125.7MM[E] *EMP* 400[E]
SIC 7372 Business oriented computer software
CEO: Tien Tzuo
**Pr:* Marc Diouane
Pr: Zach Keiter
**CFO:* Tyler Sloat
**Chf Mktg O:* David Gee
Sr VP: Marc Aronson
Sr VP: Keith Costello
**Sr VP:* Brent Cromley
**Sr VP:* Tom Krackeler
**Sr VP:* Todd Pearson
**Sr VP:* Jennifer Pileggi
**Sr VP:* Steve Umphreys
Sr VP: Guillaume Vives
VP: Luke Braud
VP: Cheng Che
VP: Rene Cirulli
VP: Mike Donofrio
VP: Dave Frechette
VP: Kevin Kimber
VP: Andrey Kolesnikov
VP: Steven Martello
Board of Directors: Peter Fenton, Tim Haley, Craig Hanson, Jason Pressman, Mike Volpi

D-U-N-S 07-987-9136
ZURICH AGENCY SERVICES INC
ZURICH DIRECT MARKETS
(*Suby of* ZURICH HOLDING CO OF AMERICA INC) ★
7045 College Blvd, Overland Park, KS 66211-1523
Tel (913) 339-1000 *Founded/Ownrshp* 1981
Sales NA *EMP* 885
SIC 6331 6311 Fire, marine & casualty insurance; Property damage insurance; Life insurance
CEO: Michael Foley
**Pr:* Kathleen Savio
**Pr:* Steve R Smith
**Treas:* Robert Burne
VP: Daniel Dorazil
Exec: Gwen Ronen
Prgrm Mgr: Shannon Hindman
Admn Mgr: Lynda Rudesill
Dir IT: Mary McManus
IT Man: Gary Matson
Info Man: Michelle Loya

ZURICH AMERICAN INSURANCE CO
See ZFUS SERVICES LLC

D-U-N-S 06-137-0131
ZURICH AMERICAN INSURANCE CO
(*Suby of* ZURICH HOLDING CO OF AMERICA INC) ★
1299 Zurich Way, Schaumburg, IL 60196-1091
Tel (800) 987-3373 *Founded/Ownrshp* 1872
Sales NA *EMP* 1,500
SIC 6331 Fire, marine & casualty insurance
Pr: Michael Foley
**Treas:* Thomas Buess
Treas: Mary Fran Callahan
Treas: Michael Sullivan
**Ex VP:* Thomas Baumgardner Bosley
**Ex VP:* John Donald Cole
**Ex VP:* Wayne Howard Fisher
**Ex VP:* Robert Morris Fishman
**Ex VP:* Thomas Harry Hite
**Ex VP:* Donald James Hurzeler
**Ex VP:* John Arthur Kelm
**Ex VP:* Frank Anthony Patalano
**Ex VP:* Kenneth Paul Sroka
Ex VP: Diana Joan Whidden
Sr VP: Michael Bond
VP: John Roman
VP: John Shane
VP: Davis Tharayil
Exec: Marcus Cooper
Board of Directors: James William March, Juliet Gloria Nash

ZURICH DIRECT MARKETS
See ZURICH AGENCY SERVICES INC

D-U-N-S 07-847-8780
ZURICH FINANCE (USA) INC
(*Suby of* ZURICH HOLDING CO OF AMERICA INC) ★
1 Liberty Plz Ste 2800, New York, NY 10006-1466
Tel (917) 534-4500 *Founded/Ownrshp* 1998
Sales 34.1MM[E] *EMP* 5,062[E]
SIC 6211 Security brokers & dealers
CEO: Martin Senn
VP: Leslie Weingarten

D-U-N-S 06-454-9959
ZURICH HOLDING CO OF AMERICA INC
(*Suby of* ZURICH INSURANCE GROUP AG)
1299 Zurich Way, Schaumburg, IL 60196-5870
Tel (847) 605-6000 *Founded/Ownrshp* 1980
Sales NA *EMP* 9,500
SIC 6311 6331 6321 6324 6719 Life insurance carriers; Fire, marine & casualty insurance; Health insurance carriers; Hospital & medical service plans; Investment holding companies, except banks
CEO: Martin Senn
**CEO:* Mike Foley
**CEO:* Mike Kerner
Ofcr: Paul McCarthy
VP: John Weber
VP: David Young

D-U-N-S 07-929-8341
ZURICH NORTH AMERICA INC
1299 Zurich Way, Schaumburg, IL 60196-1056
Tel (800) 987-3373 *Founded/Ownrshp* 2014
Sales NA *EMP* 266[E]
SIC 6411 Insurance agents, brokers & service
Ofcr: Jim Black
VP: Cathy Lundgren
Mktg Mgr: Lynne Culberson
Counsel: Douglas Hatlestad

D-U-N-S 92-698-8353
ZURICH SERVICES CORP
(*Suby of* ZURICH HOLDING CO OF AMERICA INC) ★
1299 Zurich Way, Schaumburg, IL 60196-5870
Tel (847) 605-6000 *Founded/Ownrshp* 1992
Sales NA *EMP* 250
SIC 6331 Fire, marine & casualty insurance
CEO: Michael Foley
**Pr:* Dinos Iordanou
COO: Peter Eckert
COO: Bradley S Kass
CFO: Dalynn Hoch
Ofcr: Alfonso Gonzales
Assoc VP: Richard Caby
Sr VP: Denise Deprimo
Sr VP: Lajuanda Johnson
VP: Brandt Karstens
VP: Jean Monestime
VP: Rob Morris
VP: Kathy Olcese
Creative D: John Sauer

D-U-N-S 00-232-5728 IMP/EXP
ZWD PRODUCTS CORP
INDIA INK
(*Suby of* MAYTEX MILLS)
400 Lukens Dr, New Castle, DE 19720-2728
Tel (302) 326-8200 *Founded/Ownrshp* 1939, 2016
Sales 194.4MM[E] *EMP* 510
Accts Ernst & Young Philadelphia
SIC 2434 2514 Vanities, bathroom: wood; Medicine cabinets & vanities: metal
Pr: Richard Benaron
CTO: Jennifer Covin
IT Man: Chuck Honaker

D-U-N-S 00-166-3707 IMP
ZWILLING JA HENCKELS LLC
(*Suby of* ZWILLING J. A. HENCKELS AG)
270 Marble Ave, Pleasantville, NY 10570-3464
Tel (914) 749-3440 *Founded/Ownrshp* 1949
Sales 125.0MM *EMP* 130
SIC 5023 5719 Kitchenware; Kitchen tools & utensils; Kitchenware; Metalware
Pr: Guido Weishaupt
**CFO:* John Henkel
VP Mktg: Howard Ammerman

D-U-N-S 79-146-6878 IMP/EXP
ZXP TECHNOLOGIES LTD
409 Wallisville Rd, Highlands, TX 77562
Tel (281) 426-8800 *Founded/Ownrshp* 2007
Sales 129.4MM[E] *EMP* 250
SIC 2992 2879 7549 Oils & greases, blending & compounding; Agricultural chemicals; Lubrication service, automotive
Pt: Edward C Davis
VP: Rodney Walker

D-U-N-S 15-686-1945 IMP
ZYDUS PHARMACEUTICALS USA INC
(*Suby of* CADILA HEALTHCARE LIMITED)
73 Route 31 N, Pennington, NJ 08534-3601
Tel (609) 730-1900 *Founded/Ownrshp* 2003
Sales 466.3MM *EMP* 31
SIC 2834 Pills, pharmaceutical
CEO: Joseph D Renner
**Pr:* Michael Keenley
**CFO:* Ravi Yadavar
IT Man: Chetan Sakunde
Board of Directors: Dr Mahendra Patel, Dr Sharvil Patel, Joseph D Renner

D-U-N-S 05-253-6570 IMP
■ ZYGO CORP
(*Suby of* AMETEK SENSOR TECHNOLOGY BUS) ★
21 Laurel Brook Rd, Middlefield, CT 06455-1291
Tel (860) 347-8506 *Founded/Ownrshp* 2014
Sales 141.3MM[E] *EMP* 275
SIC 3827 Optical instruments & lenses
Pr: Gary K Willis
Snr Sftwr: David Bolles

D-U-N-S 01-549-5485
▲ ZYNGA INC
699 8th St, San Francisco, CA 94103-4901
Tel (855) 449-9642 *Founded/Ownrshp* 2007
Sales 764.7MM *EMP* 1,669
Tkr Sym ZNGA *Exch* NGS
SIC 7372 7374 Prepackaged software; Application computer software; Data processing & preparation
CEO: Frank Gibeau
**Ch Bd:* Mark Pincus
COO: Matt Bromberg
COO: John Schappert
CFO: Gerard Griffin
CFO: David Lee
CFO: Michelle Quejado
Sr VP: Lincoln Brown
Sr VP: Joe Kaminkow
Sr VP: Tim Letourneau
Sr VP: Devang Shah
VP: Tom Casey
VP: Jamie Davies
VP: Dale Hastings
VP: Pete Hawley
VP: Julie Shumaker
Board of Directors: L John Doerr, Regina E Dugan, William Gordon, Louis J Lavigne Jr, Sunil Paul, Ellen F Siminoff

Section II

Businesses Geographically

ALABAMA

ABBEVILLE, AL

GREAT SOUTHERN WOOD PRESERVING INC p 634
1100 Us Highway 431 S 36310
Tel (334) 585-2291 *SIC* 2491

ADDISON, AL

■ **CAVALIER HOME BUILDERS LLC** p 267
32 Wilson Blvd 100 35540
Tel (256) 747-1575 *SIC* 2451

■ **CAVALIER HOMES INC** p 267
32 Wilson Blvd Ste 100 35540
Tel (256) 747-1575 *SIC* 2451

■ **SOUTHERN ENERGY HOMES INC** p 1348
144 Corporate Way 35540
Tel (256) 747-8589 *SIC* 2451 5271

ALABASTER, AL

BAPTIST HEALTH SYSTEM INC p 153
1000 1st St N 35007
Tel (205) 620-8100 *SIC* 8062

BTC WHOLESALE DISTRIBUTORS INC p 222
100 Airview Ln 35007
Tel (205) 324-2581
SIC 5194 5145 5087 5149 5122

DESHAZO LLC p 432
190 Airpark Industrial Rd 35007
Tel (205) 664-2006 *SIC* 3536

ALBERTVILLE, AL

ALBERTVILLE QUALITY FOODS INC p 47
130 Quality Dr 35950
Tel (256) 840-9923 *SIC* 2015

MITCHELL GROCERY CORP p 977
550 Railroad Ave 35950
Tel (256) 878-4211 *SIC* 5411

■ **PROGRESS RAIL SERVICES CORP** p 1181
1600 Progress Dr 35950
Tel (256) 593-1260 *SIC* 4789 7389

ALEXANDER CITY, AL

RUSSELL LANDS INC p 1259
2544 Willow Point Rd 35010
Tel (256) 329-0835
SIC 5211 6514 4493 7997 7011

SKILSTAF INC p 1330
860 Airport Dr 35010
Tel (256) 234-6208 *SIC* 7363

SL ALABAMA LLC p 1330
2481 Airport Blvd 35010
Tel (256) 397-8140 *SIC* 3714

ANDALUSIA, AL

ANDALUSIA DISTRIBUTING CO INC p 89
117 Allen Ave 36420
Tel (334) 222-3671
SIC 5172 5113 5194 5149

POWERSOUTH ENERGY COOPERATIVE p 1166
2027 E Three Notch St 36421
Tel (334) 427-3000 *SIC* 4911

ANNISTON, AL

B A E SYSTEM p 141
2101 W 10th St 36201
Tel (256) 235-9671 *SIC* 5051

CALHOUN COUNTY SCHOOL DISTRICT p 238
4400 Mcclellan Blvd 36206
Tel (256) 741-7400 *SIC* 8211

NABI BUS LLC p 1006
106 National Dr 36207
Tel (888) 452-7871 *SIC* 3713 5012

REGIONAL MEDICAL CENTER BOARD p 1219
400 E 10th St 36207
Tel (256) 235-5121 *SIC* 8062

ARAB, AL

SYNCRO CORP p 1415
1030 Sundown Dr Nw 35016
Tel (256) 586-6045
SIC 3714 3625 3694 3823 3643

ASHLAND, AL

WELLBORN CABINET INC p 1589
38669 Highway 77 36251
Tel (256) 354-7151 *SIC* 2434 2511 5032

ATHENS, AL

LIMESTONE COUNTY BOARD OF EDUCATION p 866
300 S Jefferson St 35611
Tel (256) 232-5353 *SIC* 8211

LIMESTONE COUNTY SCHOOL DISTRICT p 866
300 S Jefferson St 35611
Tel (256) 232-5353 *SIC* 8211

ATMORE, AL

POARCH BAND OF CREEK INDIANS p 1158
303 Poarch Rd 36502
Tel (251) 368-9136 *SIC* 9131

AUBURN, AL

AUBURN CITY SCHOOL DISTRICT p 130
855 E Samford Ave 36830
Tel (334) 887-2100 *SIC* 8211

AUBURN UNIVERSITY p 130
107 Samford Hall 36849
Tel (334) 844-4539 *SIC* 8221

AUBURN UNIVERSITY FOUNDATION p 130
317 S College St 36849
Tel (334) 844-1124 *SIC* 7389 8641

BORBET ALABAMA INC p 201
979 W Veterans Blvd 36832
Tel (334) 502-9400 *SIC* 3714

DONGHEE ALABAMA LLC p 450
2550 Innovation Dr 36832
Tel (334) 321-2756 *SIC* 3443

SEOHAN-NTN DRIVESHAFT USA CORP p 1305
246 Teague Ct 36832
Tel (334) 707-6863 *SIC* 3559

BAY MINETTE, AL

BALDWIN COUNTY BOARD OF EDUCATION p 147
2600a Hand Ave 36507
Tel (251) 937-0306 *SIC* 8211

BALDWIN COUNTY PUBLIC SCHOOLS p 147
2600a Hand Ave 36507
Tel (251) 937-0306 *SIC* 8211

GULF HEALTH HOSPITALS INC p 646
1815 Hand Ave 36507
Tel (251) 937-5521 *SIC* 8062

QUINCY COMPRESSOR LLC p 1200
701 N Dobson Ave 36507
Tel (251) 937-5900 *SIC* 3519 3563 3561

STANDARD FURNITURE MANUFACTURING CO INC p 1376
801 S Us Highway 31 36507
Tel (251) 937-6741 *SIC* 2511

BESSEMER, AL

SOUTHERN STORE FIXTURES INC p 1350
275 Drexel Rd Se 35022
Tel (205) 428-4800 *SIC* 6719

UAB MEDICAL WEST p 1498
995 9th Ave Sw 35022
Tel (205) 481-7000 *SIC* 8062

BIRMINGHAM, AL

■ **AFFINITY HOSPITAL LLC** p 32
3690 Grandview Pkwy 35243
Tel (205) 592-1000 *SIC* 8062 8011

■ **AGEE STERNE GROUP INC** p 34
800 Shades Creek Pkwy # 700 35209
Tel (205) 949-3500 *SIC* 7389

AGGREGATES USA LLC p 35
3300 Cahaba Rd Ste 302 35223
Tel (205) 777-6340 *SIC* 5032

■ **ALABAMA GAS CORP** p 43
2101 6th Ave N Ste 240 35203
Tel (205) 326-8100 *SIC* 4924

■ **ALABAMA METAL INDUSTRIES CORP** p 43
3245 Fayette Ave 35208
Tel (205) 787-2611
SIC 3446 3449 3089 3441 3316

■ **ALABAMA POWER CO** p 43
600 18th St N 35203
Tel (205) 257-1000 *SIC* 4911

ALABAMA THRIFT STORES INC p 43
1125 Huffman Rd 35215
Tel (205) 856-1234 *SIC* 5331 5932

ALTEC INC p 62
210 Inverness Center Dr 35242
Tel (205) 991-7733 *SIC* 3531 3713 3536

ALTEC INDUSTRIES INC p 62
210 Inverness Center Dr 35242
Tel (205) 991-7733 *SIC* 3531 3536 3713

AMERICAN CANCER SOCIETY MID-SOUTH DIVISION INC p 69
1100 Ireland Way Ste 300 35205
Tel (205) 879-2242 *SIC* 8733

AMERICAN CAST IRON PIPE CO p 70
1501 31st Ave N 35207
Tel (205) 325-7856
SIC 3491 3369 3321 3053 3317

APTALIS HOLDINGS INC p 101
22 Inverness Center Pkwy # 310 35242
Tel (205) 991-8085 *SIC* 2834

APTALIS MIDHOLDINGS LLC p 101
22 Inverness Center Pkwy 35242
Tel (205) 991-8085 *SIC* 2834

APTALIS PHARMA LLC p 101
22 Inverness Center Pkwy # 310 35242
Tel (205) 991-8085 *SIC* 2834

ASSOCIATED GROCERS OF SOUTH INC p 120
3600 Vanderbilt Rd 35217
Tel (205) 841-6781 *SIC* 5141 5411

■ **B E & K ENGINEERING CO (INC)** p 141
2000 International Pk Dr 35243
Tel (205) 972-6000 *SIC* 8711

■ **B E & K INC** p 141
2000 International Pk Dr 35243
Tel (205) 972-6000
SIC 1541 8711 1796 1711

BAPTIST HEALTH SYSTEM INC p 153
1130 22nd St S Ste 1000 35205
Tel (205) 715-5000
SIC 8011 8741 8082 8059

BFW LIQUIDATION LLC p 179
1800 Intl Pk Dr Ste 500 35243
Tel (205) 853-2663 *SIC* 5411 5912 5921

BIG JACK ULTIMATE HOLDINGS LP p 181
124 W Oxmoor Rd 35209
Tel (205) 945-8167 *SIC* 5812

BIRMINGHAM CITY SCHOOLS p 185
2015 Park Pl 35203
Tel (205) 231-4600 *SIC* 8211

BIRMINGHAM FASTENER & SUPPLY INC p 185
931 Avenue W 35214
Tel (205) 595-3511 *SIC* 5085 3452

BL HARBERT HOLDINGS LLC p 186
820 Shades Creek Pkwy # 3000 35209
Tel (205) 802-2800 *SIC* 1542

BL HARBERT INTERNATIONAL LLC p 186
820 Shades Creek Pkwy # 3000 35209
Tel (205) 802-2800 *SIC* 1542

BOOKS-A-MILLION INC p 200
402 Industrial Ln 35211
Tel (205) 942-3737
SIC 5942 5994 5947 5999

BRADLEY ARANT BOULT CUMMINGS LLP p 206
1819 5th Ave N Ste 200 35203
Tel (205) 521-8000 *SIC* 8111

BRASFIELD & GORRIE LLC p 208
3021 7th Ave S 35233
Tel (205) 328-4000 *SIC* 1542

■ **BROOKWOOD BAPTIST MEDICAL CENTER** p 218
2010 Brookwood Med Ctr Dr 35209
Tel (205) 877-1000 *SIC* 8011

BUFFALO ROCK CO p 224
111 Oxmoor Rd 35209
Tel (205) 942-3435 *SIC* 2086 5962 5149

C & C HOLDING INC p 231
2238 Pinson Valley Pkwy 35217
Tel (205) 841-6666 *SIC* 5082 1629 5084

C L P CORP p 232
121 Summit Pkwy 35209
Tel (205) 943-0417 *SIC* 5812

CADENCE BANK NA p 236
2100 3rd Ave N 35203
Tel (205) 326-2265 *SIC* 6021

CAHABA GOVERNMENT BENEFIT ADMINISTRATORS LLC p 237
500 Corporate Pkwy 35242
Tel (205) 220-1900 *SIC* 6324

CARRAWAY METHODIST HEALTH SYSTEMS p 260
1600 Carraway Blvd 35234
Tel (205) 502-4100 *SIC* 8069 8062

CATHOLIC DIOCESE OF BIRMINGHAM IN ALABAMA p 266
2121 3rd Ave N 35203
Tel (205) 838-8307 *SIC* 8661

CHILDRENS HOSPITAL OF ALABAMA p 299
1600 7th Ave S 35233
Tel (205) 939-9100 *SIC* 8069

CITY OF BIRMINGHAM p 313
710 20th St N Ste 600 35203
Tel (205) 254-2000 *SIC* 9111

CITY WHOLESALE GROCERY CO INC p 320
300 Industrial Dr 35211
Tel (205) 795-4533
SIC 5194 5141 5145 5122

COCA-COLA BOTTLING CO UNITED INC p 333
4600 E Lake Blvd 35217
Tel (205) 238-3300 *SIC* 2086 5962

COLONIAL PROPERTIES TRUST p 338
2101 6th Ave N Ste 750 35203
Tel (205) 250-8700
SIC 6798 6552 6531 6513

COMMAND ALKON INC p 344
1800 Intl Pk Dr Ste 400 35243
Tel (205) 879-3282 *SIC* 7371 5045

COMPASS BANK p 350
15 20th St S Ste 100 35233
Tel (205) 297-1986 *SIC* 6021

CONSOLIDATED PIPE & SUPPLY CO INC p 360
1205 Hilltop Pkwy 35204
Tel (205) 323-7261 *SIC* 3494

COWIN EQUIPMENT CO INC p 385
2238 Pinson Valley Pkwy 35217
Tel (205) 841-6666 *SIC* 5082

■ **CRC INSURANCE SERVICES INC** p 390
1 Metroplex Dr Ste 400 35209
Tel (205) 870-7790 *SIC* 6411

DIAGNOSTIC HEALTH CORP p 436
22 Inverness Pkwy Ste 425 35242
Tel (205) 980-2500 *SIC* 8742

DOSTER CONSTRUCTION CO INC p 451
2100 International Pk Dr 35243
Tel (205) 443-3800 *SIC* 1542

■ **DST HEALTH SOLUTIONS INC** p 458
2500 Corporate Dr 35242
Tel (205) 437-6204 *SIC* 8742

DUNN CONSTRUCTION CO INC p 461
3905 Airport Hwy 35222
Tel (205) 592-3866 *SIC* 1611 2951

DUNN INVESTMENT CO p 461
3900 Messer Airport Hwy 35222
Tel (205) 592-3866 *SIC* 1542 1611 3273

EASTERN HEALTH SYSTEM INC p 472
Medical Park E Dr Bldg 1 35235
Tel (205) 838-3996
SIC 8062 8082 8051 8011 8322 8093

EBSCO INDUSTRIES INC p 474
5724 Highway 280 E 35242
Tel (205) 991-6600
SIC 7389 2782 3949 7375 2721 6552

EDUCATION CORP OF AMERICA p 479
3660 Grandview Pkwy # 300 35243
Tel (205) 329-7900 *SIC* 8299

EMARICO INC p 490
146 Resource Center Pkwy 35242
Tel (205) 545-9362 *SIC* 2392

▲ **ENERGEN CORP** p 497
605 Richard Arrington Jr 35203
Tel (205) 326-2700
SIC 1311 4924 4922 1321

■ **ENERGEN RESOURCES CORP** p 497
605 Richard Arrington Jr 35203
Tel (205) 326-2710 *SIC* 1382 1321

GOLDEN ENTERPRISES INC p 620
1 Golden Flake Dr 35205
Tel (205) 458-7316 *SIC* 2096

GOLDEN FLAKE SNACK FOODS INC p 620
1 Golden Flake Dr 35205
Tel (205) 323-6161 *SIC* 2096

HARBERT CORP p 659
2100 3rd Ave N Ste 600 35203
Tel (205) 987-5500 *SIC* 4911 6799

HARBERT MANAGEMENT CORP p 659
2100 3rd Ave N Ste 600 35203
Tel (205) 987-5500 *SIC* 6726 6799

▲ **HEALTHSOUTH CORP** p 677
3660 Grandview Pkwy # 200 35243
Tel (205) 967-7116 *SIC* 8069 8051

■ **HEALTHSOUTH HOME HEALTH CORP** p 677
3660 Grandview Pkwy 35243
Tel (205) 967-7116 *SIC* 8082 8099

■ **HEALTHSOUTH HOME HEALTH HOLDINGS INC** p 677
3660 Grandview Pkwy 35243
Tel (205) 967-7116 *SIC* 8099 8082 6719

■ **HEALTHSOUTH REHABILITATION HOSPITAL OF CYPRESS LLC** p 678
3660 Grandview Pkwy 35243
Tel (205) 967-7116 *SIC* 8093

■ **HIBBETT SPORTING GOODS INC** p 690
2700 Milan Ct 35211
Tel (205) 942-4292 *SIC* 5941 5661 5699

▲ **HIBBETT SPORTS INC** p 690
2700 Milan Ct 35211
Tel (205) 942-4292 *SIC* 5941 5661 5699

■ **HIGHLAND CAPITAL BROKERAGE INC** p 691
3535 Grandview Pkwy Ste 6 35243
Tel (205) 263-4400 *SIC* 6411

HIGHLAND CAPITAL HOLDING CORP p 691
3535 Grandview Pkwy # 600 35243
Tel (205) 263-4400 *SIC* 6411

■ **HILSTAR INSURANCE CO** p 694
2201 4th Ave N 35203
Tel (205) 870-4000 *SIC* 6331

HOAR CONSTRUCTION LLC p 698
2 Metroplex Dr Ste 400 35209
Tel (205) 803-2121 *SIC* 1541

■ **INFINITY CASUALTY INSURANCE CO** p 741
2201 4th Ave N 35203
Tel (205) 870-4000 *SIC* 6331

■ **INFINITY GROUP INC** p 741
2201 4th Ave N 35203
Tel (205) 870-4000 *SIC* 6331

■ **INFINITY INSURANCE AGENCY INC** p 741
2201 4th Ave N 35203
Tel (205) 870-4000 *SIC* 6411

■ **INFINITY INSURANCE CO** p 741
2201 4th Ave N 35203
Tel (205) 870-4000 *SIC* 6331

▲ **INFINITY PROPERTY AND CASUALTY CORP** p 741
3700 Colonnade Pkwy # 600 35243
Tel (205) 870-4000 *SIC* 6331

■ **INFINITY STANDARD INSURANCE CO** p 741
2201 4th Ave N 35203
Tel (205) 870-4000 *SIC* 6331

INTEGRATED MEDICAL SYSTEMS INTERNATIONAL INC p 749
3316 2nd Ave N 35222
Tel (205) 879-3840 *SIC* 3841 7699

JEFFERSON COUNTY ALABAMA p 781
716 Richard Arrington Jr 35203
Tel (205) 731-2880 *SIC* 9111

JEFFERSON COUNTY BOARD OF EDUCATION p 781
2100 Richard Arrington Jr 35209
Tel (205) 379-2000 *SIC* 8211 9111

JEFFERSON COUNTY SCHOOLS p 781
2100 Richard Arrington Jr 35209
Tel (205) 379-2000 SIC 8211

JEFFERSON COUNTY SCHOOLS PUBLIC EDUCATION FOUNDATION p 781
2100 Rich Arrington Jr Bl 35203
Tel (205) 379-2216 SIC 8699

JOE PIPER INC p 787
123 Industrial Dr 35211
Tel (205) 290-2211 SIC 5113

KAMTEK INC p 802
1595 Sterilite Dr 35215
Tel (205) 327-7000 SIC 3714

LIGON INDUSTRIES LLC p 866
1927 1st Ave N Ste 500 35203
Tel (205) 322-3302
SIC 3365 3593 3325 3471 3714 3446

LS1 LLC p 883
331 1st Ave N 35204
Tel (205) 251-9249 SIC 7349

LS1 LLC p 883
331 1st Ave N 35204
Tel (205) 251-9249 SIC 7349

MAYER ELECTRIC SUPPLY CO INC p 923
3405 4th Ave S 35222
Tel (205) 583-3500 SIC 5063 5719

■ **MCGRIFF SEIBELS & WILLIAMS INC** p 929
2211 7th Ave S 35233
Tel (205) 252-9871 SIC 6411

MCWANE INC p 933
2900 Highway 280 S # 300 35223
Tel (205) 414-3100
SIC 3491 1221 3321 3312 3494

■ **MOTION INDUSTRIES INC** p 992
1605 Alton Rd 35210
Tel (205) 956-1122 SIC 5085

MPT OPERATING PARTNERSHIP LP p 996
3500 Colonnade Pkwy # 540 35243
Tel (205) 969-3755 SIC 6798

NCP SOLUTIONS LLC p 1022
5200 E Lake Blvd 35217
Tel (205) 849-5200 SIC 7374

NELSON BROTHERS INC p 1025
820 Shades Creek Pkwy # 2000 35209
Tel (205) 414-2900 SIC 2892 5169

NELSON BROTHERS LLC p 1025
820 Shades Creek Pkwy # 2000 35209
Tel (205) 414-2900 SIC 2892

NOLAND HEALTH SERVICES INC p 1046
600 Corporate Pkwy # 100 35242
Tel (205) 321-5373 SIC 8051

■ **NUCOR STEEL BIRMINGHAM INC** p 1066
2301 Fl Shuttlesworth Dr 35234
Tel (866) 862-4796 SIC 3312

ONEAL INDUSTRIES INC p 1087
2311 Highland Ave S # 200 35205
Tel (205) 721-2880 SIC 5051

ONEAL STEEL INC p 1087
744 41st St N 35222
Tel (205) 599-8000 SIC 5051

ONIN STAFFING LLC p 1088
1 Perimeter Park S 450n 35243
Tel (205) 298-7233 SIC 7361

P J UNITED INC p 1102
2300 Resource Dr 35242
Tel (205) 981-7173 SIC 5812

P&S TRANSPORTATION LLC p 1102
1810 Avenue C 35218
Tel (205) 788-4000 SIC 4213 4789

PLANTATION PATTERNS LLC p 1154
146 Resource Center Pkwy 35242
Tel (205) 545-9229 SIC 2392

POLYMET ALLOYS INC p 1160
1701 Providence Park # 100 35242
Tel (205) 981-2200 SIC 5051

PREFERRED MATERIALS INC p 1169
500 Rvrhills Bus Park 35242
Tel (205) 995-5900
SIC 1611 1771 3531 5032

▲ **PROASSURANCE CORP** p 1178
100 Brookwood Pl Ste 500 35209
Tel (205) 877-4400 SIC 6351 6321

PROTECTIVE LIFE CORP p 1185
2801 Highway 280 S Ofc 35223
Tel (205) 268-1000
SIC 6311 6321 6351 6411

PROTECTIVE LIFE INSURANCE CO p 1185
2801 Highway 280 S 35223
Tel (205) 268-1000 SIC 6311 6411 7389

PS LOGISTICS LLC p 1187
1810 Avenue C 35218
Tel (205) 788-4000 SIC 4214 3537

RAM TOOL & SUPPLY CO INC p 1206
3620 8th Ave S Ste 200 35222
Tel (205) 714-3300 SIC 5085

READY MIX USA LLC p 1213
2657 Ruffner Rd 35210
Tel (205) 967-5211 SIC 5211 3241

■ **REALTYSOUTH ADMIN OFFICE** p 1214
2501 20th Pl S Ste 400 35223
Tel (205) 325-1397 SIC 6531

■ **REGIONS BANK** p 1220
1901 5th Ave N 35203
Tel (205) 326-5300 SIC 6022

▲ **REGIONS FINANCIAL CORP** p 1220
1900 5th Ave N 35203
Tel (205) 581-7890 SIC 6022 6211 6282

ROBINS & MORTON GROUP p 1242
400 Shades Creek Pkwy 35209
Tel (205) 870-1000 SIC 1542

ROYAL CUP INC p 1254
160 Cleage Dr 35217
Tel (205) 849-5836 SIC 2095 5149

SAIIA CONSTRUCTION CO LLC p 1268
4400 Lewisburg Rd 35207
Tel (205) 290-0400 SIC 1794

SAMFORD UNIVERSITY p 1274
800 Lakeshore Dr 35229
Tel (205) 726-2011 SIC 8221

SECURITY ENGINEERS INC p 1299
1617 3rd Ave N 35203
Tel (205) 251-0566 SIC 7381

SHOOK & FLETCHER INSULATION CO INC p 1317
4625 Valleydale Rd 35242
Tel (205) 991-7606 SIC 5033 1799 5085

■ **SMI STEEL LLC** p 1333
101 50th St S 35212
Tel (205) 592-8981 SIC 3312

SOUTHEASTERN CONFERENCE p 1346
2201 Richard Arringtn Jr 35203
Tel (205) 949-8960 SIC 8699

■ **SOUTHERN ELECTRIC GENERATING CO** p 1348
600 18th St N 35203
Tel (205) 257-1000 SIC 4911

■ **SOUTHERN NUCLEAR OPERATING CO INC** p 1350
42 Inverness Center Pkwy 35242
Tel (205) 992-5000 SIC 8741

SOUTHLAND INTERNATIONAL TRUCKS INC p 1351
200 Oxmoor Blvd 35209
Tel (205) 942-6226
SIC 5511 5531 7538 7513

SOUTHLAND TUBE INC p 1351
3525 Richard Arringt 35234
Tel (205) 251-1884 SIC 3317

ST VINCENTS BIRMINGHAM p 1373
810 Saint Vincents Dr 35205
Tel (205) 939-7000 SIC 8062

ST VINCENTS EAST p 1373
50 Medical Park Dr E 35235
Tel (205) 838-3000 SIC 8062 8011

ST VINCENTS HEALTH SYSTEM p 1373
810 Saint Vincents Dr 35205
Tel (205) 939-7000 SIC 8062

STATE FARM INSURANCE p 1381
100 State Farm Pkwy 35209
Tel (205) 916-6000 SIC 6411

■ **STERNE AGEE & LEACH INC** p 1387
800 Shades Creek Pkwy 35209
Tel (205) 226-3397 SIC 6211

SUMMITMEDIA LLC p 1399
2700 Corporate Dr Ste 115 35242
Tel (205) 322-2987 SIC 4832

SUPREME BEVERAGE CO INC p 1408
3217 Messer Airport Hwy 35222
Tel (205) 251-8010 SIC 5181

■ **SURGICAL CARE AFFILIATES LLC** p 1409
569 Brookwood Vlg Ste 901 35209
Tel (205) 545-2572 SIC 8741

TAMERON AUTOMOTIVE GROUP INC p 1423
1675 Montgomery Hwy 35216
Tel (205) 396-3108 SIC 5511 5013

■ **TECHNICAL STAFFING RESOURCES LLC** p 1431
10 Inverness Center Pkwy 35242
Tel (205) 437-7100 SIC 8711 7363

■ **TENNESSEE GAS PIPELINE** p 1438
569 Brookwood Vlg Ste 749 35209
Tel (205) 325-3513 SIC 4922

THEATRES COBB III LLC p 1446
2000b Southbridge Pkwy # 100 35209
Tel (205) 802-7766 SIC 7832

THOMPSON TRACTOR CO INC p 1449
2258 Pinson Valley Pkwy 35217
Tel (334) 215-5000 SIC 5082 5084 5085

TRACTOR & EQUIPMENT CO INC p 1468
5336 Airport Hwy 35212
Tel (205) 591-2131 SIC 5082

TUBULAR PRODUCTS CO p 1490
1400 Red Hollow Rd 35215
Tel (205) 856-1300 SIC 3317

■ **UNITED HEALTHCARE OF ALABAMA INC** p 1509
33 Inverness Center Pkwy # 350 35242
Tel (205) 437-8500 SIC 6324

UNIVERSITY OF ALABAMA AT BIRMINGHAM p 1519
701 20th St S 35233
Tel (205) 934-5493 SIC 8221 8062

UNIVERSITY OF ALABAMA HEALTH SERVICES FOUNDATION PC p 1519
500 22nd St S Ste 100 35233
Tel (205) 731-9600 SIC 8093

■ **VALMONT NEWMARK INC** p 1542
2 Perimeter Park S 475w 35243
Tel (205) 968-7200 SIC 3272 1731 3317

VIRGINIA COLLEGE LLC p 1558
3660 Grandview Pkwy # 300 35243
Tel (205) 329-7900 SIC 8221

WALTER COKE INC p 1574
3500 35th Ave N 35207
Tel (205) 808-7803 SIC 2999

WATER WORKS BOARD OF CITY OF BIRMINGHAM p 1581
3600 1st Ave N 35222
Tel (205) 244-4000 SIC 4941

WITTICHEN SUPPLY CO p 1619
2912 3rd Ave N 35203
Tel (205) 251-8500 SIC 5078 5075

YOUNG MENS CHRISTIAN ASSOCIATION OF BIRMINGHAM p 1638
2101 4th Ave N 35203
Tel (205) 801-9622
SIC 7991 8641 8351 7032

BOAZ, AL

MARSHALL COUNTY HEALTH CARE AUTHORITY p 911
2505 Us Highway 431 35957
Tel (256) 894-6600 SIC 8062

MARSHALL MEDICAL CENTER SOUTH p 911
2505 Us Highway 431 35957
Tel (256) 593-8310 SIC 8011

BRENT, AL

BURKES MECHANICAL INC p 227
2 Industrial Rd 35034
Tel (205) 926-5847 SIC 1711

BREWTON, AL

GEORGIA-PACIFIC BREWTON LLC p 608
32224 Highway 31 36426
Tel (251) 867-3622 SIC 2611 2679

BROOKWOOD, AL

WALTER JIM RESOURCES INC p 1574
16243 Highway 216 35444
Tel (205) 554-6150 SIC 1222

CALERA, AL

■ **SYSCO CENTRAL ALABAMA INC** p 1416
1000 Sysco Dr 35040
Tel (205) 668-0001
SIC 5149 5147 5142 5144 5143

CALVERT, AL

AM/NS CALVERT LLC p 64
1 Am Ns Way 36513
Tel (251) 289-3000 SIC 3312 3449

OUTOKUMPU STAINLESS USA LLC p 1099
1 Steel Dr 36513
Tel (251) 829-3600 SIC 3312 3399

CHUNCHULA, AL

GA WEST & CO INC p 588
12526 Celeste Rd 36521
Tel (251) 679-1965 SIC 1541

LEGACY EQUIPMENT INC p 852
12526 Celeste Rd 36521
Tel (251) 679-1965 SIC 5046

CLANTON, AL

ADIENT CLANTON INC p 22
2541 7th St S 35046
Tel (205) 755-9994 SIC 2531

CLAYTON, AL

BOYD BROS TRANSPORTATION INC p 205
3275 Highway 30 36016
Tel (800) 633-1502 SIC 4213

COLLINSVILLE, AL

JCG FOODS OF ALABAMA LLC p 780
764 George Cagle Dr 35961
Tel (256) 524-2147 SIC 2038

COLUMBIANA, AL

SHELBY CO SCHOOL DISTRICT p 1314
410 E College St 35051
Tel (205) 682-7000 SIC 8211

SHELBY COUNTY BOARD OF EDUCATION p 1314
410 E College St 35051
Tel (205) 682-7000 SIC 8211

COWARTS, AL

HOME OIL CO INC p 703
5744 E Us Highway 84 36321
Tel (334) 793-1544
SIC 5171 5411 5541 5172

CREOLA, AL

DANA TRANSPORT INC p 411
10837 Highway 43 36525
Tel (732) 750-9100 SIC 4213

CULLMAN, AL

ALABAMA CULLMAN YUTAKA TECHNOLOGIES LLC p 43
460 Al Highway 157 35058
Tel (256) 739-3533 SIC 3714

CULLMAN COUNTY BOARD OF EDUCATION p 400
402 Arnold St Ne 35055
Tel (256) 734-2933 SIC 8211

CULLMAN COUNTY SCHOOL DISTRICT p 400
402 Arnold St Ne 35055
Tel (256) 734-2933 SIC 8211

CULLMAN ELECTRIC COOPERATIVE p 400
1749 Eva Rd Ne 35055
Tel (256) 737-3200 SIC 4911

CULLMAN REGIONAL MEDICAL CENTER INC p 400
1912 Al Highway 157 35058
Tel (256) 737-2000 SIC 8062

HEALTH CARE AUTHORITY OF CULLMAN COUNTY p 674
1912 Al Highway 157 35058
Tel (256) 737-2000 SIC 8062

MCGRIFF INDUSTRIES INC p 929
86 Walnut St Ne 35055
Tel (256) 739-0780 SIC 5531 7534

ROD GOLDEN HATCHERY INC p 1246
85 13th St Ne 35055
Tel (256) 734-0941 SIC 0251

RUSKEN PACKAGING INC p 1259
64 Walnut St Nw 35055
Tel (256) 734-0092 SIC 2652

TOPRE AMERICA CORP p 1461
1580 County Rd Ste 222 35057
Tel (256) 735-2600 SIC 2396

USA HEALTHCARE INC p 1534
401 Arnold St Ne 35055
Tel (256) 739-1239 SIC 8051

■ **WEBB WHEEL PRODUCTS INC** p 1586
2310 Industrial Dr Sw 35055
Tel (256) 739-6660 SIC 3714

CUSSETA, AL

CHATTAHOOCHEE OIL CO INC p 292
1405 Lee Road 270 36852
Tel (706) 566-6561 SIC 5172

JOON LLC p 793
1500 County Road 177 36852
Tel (334) 756-8601 SIC 3465 4214

DADEVILLE, AL

PRIME HEALTHCARE LLC p 1175
314 W Columbus St 36853
Tel (256) 825-9273 SIC 8059

SJA INC p 1328
274 Thweatt Indus Blvd 36853
Tel (256) 825-2290 SIC 3089

DAPHNE, AL

BBB INDUSTRIES LLC p 163
29627 Renaissance Blvd 36526
Tel (800) 280-2737 SIC 3694 3714

INTERNATIONAL SHIPHOLDING CORP p 756
29000 Us Highway 98 C201 36526
Tel (251) 243-9100 SIC 4412 4424

DECATUR, AL

AGRI-AFC LLC p 36
121 Somerville Rd Ne 35601
Tel (256) 560-2848
SIC 5159 5153 5083 5191

ALABAMA FARMERS COOPERATIVE INC p 43
121 Somerville Rd Ne 35601
Tel (256) 353-6843 SIC 5191 5153 5159

ALPHAPET INC p 60
1301 Finley Island Rd 35601
Tel (256) 308-1180 SIC 2821

COOKS PEST CONTROL INC p 366
1741 5th Ave Se Ste A 35601
Tel (256) 355-3285 SIC 7342

DECATUR CITY BOARD OF EDUCATION p 420
302 4th Ave Ne 35601
Tel (256) 552-3000 SIC 8211

DECATUR CITY SCHOOLS p 420
302 4th Ave Ne 35601
Tel (256) 552-3000 SIC 8211

DEL MONTE p 423
1200 Market St Ne 35601
Tel (256) 552-7453 SIC 2047

GEMSTONE FOODS p 598
412 8th Ave Ne 35601
Tel (256) 686-3601 SIC 5411 2499

HEALTH CARE AUTHORITY OF MORGAN COUNTY - CITY OF DECATUR p 674
1201 7th St Se 35601
Tel (256) 355-0370 SIC 8062

INDORAMA VENTURES XYLENES & PTA LLC p 739
1401 Finley Island Rd 35601
Tel (256) 340-5200 SIC 2911

MORGAN COUNTY BOARD OF EDUCATION (INC) p 988
302 Fourth Ave 35601
Tel (256) 309-2100 SIC 8211

MORGAN COUNTY SCHOOLS FOUNDATION p 988
235 Highway 67 S 35603
Tel (256) 309-2100 SIC 8211

MUNICIPAL UTILITIES BOARD OF DECATUR MORGAN COUNTY ALABAMA p 1000
1002 Central Pkwy Sw 35601
Tel (256) 552-1440 *SIC* 4911

RENAISSANCE WOODWORKING CO INC p 1223
13 Walnut St Ne 35601
Tel (256) 308-1231 *SIC* 1542 1521

WOLVERINE TUBE INC p 1621
2100 Market St Ne 35601
Tel (256) 353-1310 *SIC* 3351

DOLOMITE, AL

ROBBIE D WOOD INC p 1240
1051 Old Warrior River Rd 35061
Tel (205) 744-8440 *SIC* 4953

DOTHAN, AL

AAA COOPER TRANSPORTATION p 7
1751 Kinsey Rd 36303
Tel (334) 793-2284 *SIC* 4213

ARCHDIOCESE OF MOBILE ED OFF p 105
2700 W Main St 36301
Tel (334) 793-6742 *SIC* 8211

DOTHAN CITY BOARD OF EDUCATION p 452
500 Dusy St 36301
Tel (334) 793-1397 *SIC* 8211

DOTHAN CITY SCHOOLS p 452
500 Dusy St 36301
Tel (334) 793-1397 *SIC* 8211

DOTHAN SECURITY INC p 452
600 W Adams St 36303
Tel (334) 793-5720 *SIC* 7381

G A M INC p 586
900 W Main St 36301
Tel (334) 677-2108 *SIC* 7841 5735

HOUSTON COUNTY HEALTHCARE AUTHORITY p 712
1108 Ross Clark Cir 36301
Tel (334) 793-8111 *SIC* 8062

MARK DUNNING INDUSTRIES p 907
100 Race Track Rd 36303
Tel (334) 983-1506 *SIC* 4953

SUNSOUTH LLC p 1404
4100 Hartford Hwy 36305
Tel (334) 678-7861 *SIC* 5083

■ **TRIAD OF ALABAMA LLC** p 1478
4370 W Main St 36305
Tel (334) 793-5000 *SIC* 8062 8082

WIREGRASS CONSTRUCTION CO INC p 1618
170 E Main St 36301
Tel (334) 699-6800 *SIC* 1611 2951

EASTABOGA, AL

KRONOSPAN INC p 830
1 Kronospan Way 36260
Tel (256) 741-8755 *SIC* 2431 2295

ELBA, AL

▲ **NATIONAL SECURITY GROUP INC** p 1016
661 Davis St E 36323
Tel (334) 897-2273 *SIC* 6311 6331

ENTERPRISE, AL

CARR RIGGS & INGRAM LLC p 260
901 Boll Weevil Cir # 200 36330
Tel (334) 347-0088 *SIC* 8721

HWASEUNG AUTOMOTIVE ALABAMA LLC p 722
100 Sonata Dr 36330
Tel (334) 348-9516 *SIC* 3714 3069

HWASEUNG AUTOMOTIVE AMERICA HOLDINGS INC p 722
100 Sonata Dr 36330
Tel (334) 348-9516 *SIC* 3069 5085

HWASEUNG AUTOMOTIVE USA LLC p 722
101 Development Ln 36330
Tel (334) 348-9516 *SIC* 3714

EUFAULA, AL

■ **AMERICAN BUILDINGS CO** p 69
1150 State Docks Rd 36027
Tel (888) 307-4338 *SIC* 3448

EQUITY GROUP EUFAULA DIVISION LLC p 507
57 Melvin Clark Rd 36027
Tel (334) 687-7790
SIC 2015 2048 2041 2011

FAIRHOPE, AL

COLLEGIATE HOUSING FOUNDA p 337
409 Johnson Ave 36532
Tel (251) 928-9340 *SIC* 7021

COLLEGIATE HOUSING FOUNDATION p 337
409 Johnson Ave 36532
Tel (251) 304-0055 *SIC* 7299

GULF HEALTH HOSPITALS INC p 646
750 Morphy Ave 36532
Tel (251) 928-2375 *SIC* 8062 8011

FLORENCE, AL

AMERICAN PROMOTIONAL EVENTS INC p 78
4511 Helton Dr 35630
Tel (256) 284-1003 *SIC* 5092 5999

ELIZA COFFEE MEMORIAL HOSPITAL p 487
205 Marengo St 35630
Tel (256) 768-9191 *SIC* 8062

HEALTH CARE AUTHORITY OF LAUDERDALE COUNTY AND CITY OF FLORENCE p 674
205 Marengo St 35630
Tel (256) 768-9191 *SIC* 8051 8062

LAUDERDALE COUNTY BOARD OF EDUCATION p 847
355 County Road 61 35634
Tel (256) 760-1300 *SIC* 8211

LAUDERDALE COUNTY SCHOOL SYSTEM p 847
355 County Road 61 35634
Tel (256) 760-1300 *SIC* 8211

MARTIN INC p 912
125 N Court St 35630
Tel (256) 383-3131 *SIC* 5085

FOLEY, AL

BALDWIN JANITORIAL & PAPER LLC p 147
18260 County Road 12 S 36535
Tel (251) 943-7570 *SIC* 7349

■ **FOLEY HOSPITAL CORP** p 563
1613 N Mckenzie St 36535
Tel (251) 949-3400 *SIC* 8062

UTILITIES BOARD OF CITY OF FOLEY p 1537
413 E Laurel Ave 36535
Tel (251) 943-5001 *SIC* 4911 1623 4841

VULCAN INC p 1567
410 E Berry Ave 36535
Tel (251) 943-7000 *SIC* 3469 3993

FORT DEPOSIT, AL

SEJONG ALABAMA LLC p 1301
450 Old Fort Rd E 36032
Tel (334) 227-0821 *SIC* 3714

FORT PAYNE, AL

COOPER HOSIERY MILLS INC p 366
4005 Gault Ave N 35967
Tel (256) 845-1491 *SIC* 2252

■ **CUROTTO-CAN LLC** p 402
4301 Gault Ave N 35967
Tel (256) 845-8359 *SIC* 4953

WILLIAMSON OIL CO INC p 1612
1603 Godfrey Ave Se 35967
Tel (256) 845-9466 *SIC* 5541 5411 5172

FORT RUCKER, AL

■ **ARMY FLEET SUPPORT LLC** p 112
1117 Dilly Branch Rd 36362
Tel (334) 598-0400 *SIC* 7699

GADSDEN, AL

ETOWAH COUNTY BOARD OF EDUCATION p 512
3200 W Meighan Blvd 35904
Tel (256) 549-7560 *SIC* 8211

ETOWAH COUNTY SCHOOLS p 512
3200 W Meighan Blvd 35904
Tel (256) 549-7560 *SIC* 8211

■ **GADSDEN REGIONAL MEDICAL CENTER LLC** p 589
1007 Goodyear Ave 35903
Tel (256) 494-4000
SIC 8062 8082 8011 7352

MID-SOUTH INDUSTRIES INC p 963
2620 E Meighan Blvd 35903
Tel (256) 492-8997
SIC 3672 3089 3824 3714

RIVERVIEW REGIONAL MEDICAL CENTER INC p 1239
600 S 3rd St 35901
Tel (256) 543-5200 *SIC* 8062

GOODWATER, AL

GOODWATER HEALTH CENTER CARE LLC p 624
16 Jones Hill Rd 35072
Tel (256) 839-6711 *SIC* 8059

GORDO, AL

PECO FOODS INC p 1127
145 2nd Ave Nw 35466
Tel (205) 364-7121 *SIC* 0251

GREENVILLE, AL

HWASHIN AMERICA CORP p 722
661 Montgomery Hwy 36037
Tel (334) 382-1100 *SIC* 5531

GULF SHORES, AL

■ **RENAL TREATMENT CENTERS-SOUTHEAST LP** p 1223
3947 Gulf Shores Pkwy 36542
Tel (251) 967-2205 *SIC* 8092

GUNTERSVILLE, AL

ALATRADE FOODS LLC p 45
725 Blount Ave 35976
Tel (256) 571-9696 *SIC* 2015

FACTORY CONNECTION LLC p 523
2300 Highway 79 S 35976
Tel (256) 264-9400 *SIC* 5621

HALEYVILLE, AL

EXXEL OUTDOORS INC p 521
300 American Blvd 35565
Tel (205) 486-5258 *SIC* 2399

HANCEVILLE, AL

ACTION RESOURCES INC p 19
40 County Road 517 35077
Tel (256) 352-2689 *SIC* 4212 4213 1794

HARTSELLE, AL

■ **CERRO WIRE LLC** p 284
1099 Thompson Rd Se 35640
Tel (256) 773-2522 *SIC* 3351

DEVTEK INC p 434
220 Cedar St Nw 35640
Tel (256) 751-9441 *SIC* 5091

HATCHECHUBBEE, AL

CAM BUILDERS LLC p 243
537 Highway 26 36858
Tel (334) 667-6695 *SIC* 1542

HEFLIN, AL

L E BELL CONSTRUCTION CO INC p 834
1226 County Road 11 36264
Tel (256) 253-2434 *SIC* 1623

HOLLY POND, AL

JET PEP INC p 783
9481 Highway 278 W 35083
Tel (256) 796-2237 *SIC* 5541

HOOVER, AL

BLUE CROSS & BLUE SHIELD OF ALABAMA p 191
450 Riverchase Pkwy E 35244
Tel (205) 988-2200 *SIC* 6321 6324

EXPRESS OIL CHANGE LLC p 520
1880 Southpark Dr 35244
Tel (205) 945-1771 *SIC* 7549 7538 6794

HOOVER CITY SCHOOL DISTRICT p 706
2810 Metropolitan Way 35216
Tel (205) 439-1000 *SIC* 8211

■ **KBR CONSTRUCTION CO LLC** p 806
3000 Riverchase Galleria 35244
Tel (205) 972-6538
SIC 1541 1796 1711 1629 1799 1521

■ **LIBERTY NATIONAL LIFE INSURANCE CO** p 862
100 Cncourse Pkwy Ste 350 35244
Tel (205) 325-2722 *SIC* 6321 6311

LONG-LEWIS INC p 877
2551 Highway 150 35244
Tel (205) 989-3673 *SIC* 5511 5072

MJ HARRIS CONSTRUCTION SERVICES LLC p 978
1 Riverchase Rdg Ste 300 35244
Tel (205) 380-6800 *SIC* 1542

UNITED STATES PIPE AND FOUNDRY CO LLC p 1514
2 Chase Corporate Dr # 200 35244
Tel (205) 263-8540 *SIC* 3321

WALTER ENERGY INC p 1574
3000 Riverchase Galleria # 1700 35244
Tel (205) 745-2000 *SIC* 1241 4925

YATES CONSTRUCTORS LLC p 1635
1855 Data Dr Ste 200 35244
Tel (205) 380-8420 *SIC* 1542 1541

HOPE HULL, AL

DAEHAN SOLUTION ALABAMA LLC p 408
9101 County Road 26 36043
Tel (334) 404-5000 *SIC* 3625 2273

VISION TECHNOLOGIES KINETICS INC p 1561
3800 Richardson Rd 36043
Tel (334) 284-8665 *SIC* 3714 3795

HUNTSVILLE, AL

ABACO SYSTEMS INC p 9
12090 S Memorial Pkwy 35803
Tel (256) 382-8200 *SIC* 3571 3672 3577

▲ **ADTRAN INC** p 24
901 Explorer Blvd Nw 35806
Tel (256) 963-8000 *SIC* 3661 3663 4813

ALABAMA A & M UNIVERSITY p 43
4900 Meridian St N 35810
Tel (256) 372-5200 *SIC* 8221

AVIAGEN INC p 137
920 Explorer Blvd Nw 35806
Tel (256) 890-3800 *SIC* 2015

AVIATION & MISSILE SOLUTIONS LLC p 138
1000 Explorer Blvd Nw 35806
Tel (256) 713-5900 *SIC* 7363

AVOCENT CORP p 138
4991 Corporate Dr Nw 35805
Tel (256) 430-4000 *SIC* 3575 3577 7373

AVOCENT HUNTSVILLE CORP p 138
4991 Corporate Dr Nw 35805
Tel (256) 430-4000 *SIC* 3577

■ **BENCHMARK ELECTRONICS HUNTSVILLE INC** p 172
4807 Bradford Dr Nw 35805
Tel (256) 722-6000 *SIC* 3699

BIG SPRINGS INC p 182
2700 Meridian St N 35811
Tel (256) 532-4545 *SIC* 5149

BOCA PHARMACAL LLC p 196
150 Vintage Dr Ne 35811
Tel (800) 444-4011 *SIC* 2834

BRENN DISTRIBUTION INC p 210
130 Vintage Dr Ne 35811
Tel (256) 859-4011 *SIC* 5122

CAMBER CORP p 243
670 Discovery Dr Nw 35806
Tel (256) 922-0200 *SIC* 8731 7371

■ **CAS INC** p 262
100 Quality Cir Nw 35806
Tel (256) 922-4200 *SIC* 8711 7371

CITY OF HUNTSVILLE p 315
308 Fountain Cir Sw Fl 8 35801
Tel (256) 427-5080 *SIC* 9111

CITY OF HUNTSVILLE ELECTRIC SYSTEMS p 315
112 Spragins St Nw 35801
Tel (256) 535-1200 *SIC* 4911

COLSA CORP p 339
6728 Odyssey Dr Nw 35806
Tel (256) 964-5361
SIC 8731 7373 8744 8711

COUNTY OF MADISON p 379
100 Northside Sq 35801
Tel (256) 532-3492 *SIC* 9111

CRESTWOOD HEALTHCARE LP p 392
1 Hospital Dr Sw 35801
Tel (256) 429-4000 *SIC* 8062

■ **DELTACOM LLC** p 427
7037 Old Madison Pike Nw 35806
Tel (256) 382-2100 *SIC* 4813

DYNETICS INC p 465
1002 Explorer Blvd Nw 35806
Tel (256) 964-4000 *SIC* 8731

ENGINEERING RESEARCH AND CONSULTING INC p 499
308 Voyager Way Nw # 200 35806
Tel (256) 430-3080 *SIC* 8731 8711

GENERICS INTERNATIONAL (US) INC p 602
130 Vintage Dr Ne 35811
Tel (256) 859-2575 *SIC* 2834

HEALTH CARE AUTHORITY OF CITY OF HUNTSVILLE p 674
101 Sivley Rd Sw 35801
Tel (256) 265-1000 *SIC* 8011 8062

HUNTSVILLE CITY BOARD OF EDUCATION p 720
200 White St Se 35801
Tel (256) 428-6800 *SIC* 8211

HUNTSVILLE CITY SCHOOLS p 720
200 White St Se 35801
Tel (256) 428-6800 *SIC* 8211

HUNTSVILLE HOSPITAL p 720
101 Sivley Rd Sw 35801
Tel (256) 265-1000 *SIC* 8062

INNOVATIVE XCESSORIES & SERVICES LLC p 745
1862 Sparkman Dr Nw 35816
Tel (877) 330-1331 *SIC* 5012 3711

INTUITIVE RESEARCH AND TECHNOLOGY CORP p 760
5030 Bradford Dr Nw # 205 35805
Tel (256) 922-9300 *SIC* 8711 8748

ITC DELTACOM INC p 767
7037 Old Madison Pike Nw 35806
Tel (256) 382-5900 *SIC* 4813 4899

KWAJALEIN RANGE SERVICES LLC p 832
4975 Bradford Dr Nw # 600 35805
Tel (256) 890-8536 *SIC* 8744

LG ELECTRONICS ALABAMA INC p 860
201 James Record Rd Sw 35824
Tel (256) 772-0623
SIC 3651 3695 5064 5085 5065 4225

MADISON COUNTY BOARD OF EDUCATION p 894
1275 Jordan Rd 35811
Tel (256) 852-2557 *SIC* 8211

MADISON COUNTY SCHOOLS p 894
1275 Jordan Rd 35811
Tel (256) 852-2557 *SIC* 8211

■ **NASA/GEORGE C MARSHALL SPACE FLIGHT CENTER** p 1007
George C Marsha 35812
Tel (256) 544-8620 *SIC* 9661

R M L HUNTSVILLE CHEVROLET LLC p 1202
4930 University Dr Nw 35816
Tel (256) 830-1600 *SIC* 5511

RADIANCE TECHNOLOGIES INC p 1204
350 Wynn Dr Nw 35805
Tel (256) 704-3400
SIC 3721 8711 3429 3812

REED CONTRACTING SERVICES INC p 1217
2512 Triana Blvd Sw 35805
Tel (256) 533-0505
SIC 1771 1794 1623 1629 1611

■ **SANMINA-SCI SYSTEMS (ALABAMA) INC** p 1280
13000 Memorial Pkwy Sw 35803
Tel (256) 882-4800 *SIC* 6719

SCI SYSTEMS INC p 1292
13000 Memorial Pkwy Sw 35803
Tel (256) 882-4800 *SIC* 3571

■ **SCI TECHNOLOGY INC** p 1292
13000 Memorial Pkwy Sw 35803
Tel (256) 882-4800
SIC 3672 3829 8711 3663

SEQUEL TSI HOLDINGS LLC p 1306
1131 Eagletree Ln Sw # 300 35801
Tel (256) 880-3339 *SIC* 8361 8322

SEQUEL YOUTH AND FAMILY SERVICES LLC p 1306
1131 Eagletree Ln Sw 35801
Tel (256) 880-3339 *SIC* 8322 8361

SPENCER COMPANIES INC p 1358
120 Woodson St Nw 35801
Tel (256) 533-1150 *SIC* 5541 5172

SYSTEM STUDIES & SIMULATION INC p 1418
615 Discovery Dr Nw 35806
Tel (256) 539-1700 *SIC* 3761 7379 8711

T - H MARINE SUPPLIES INC p 1419
200 Finney Dr Sw 35824
Tel (256) 772-0164 *SIC* 5551 3999 3429

■ **TELEDYNE BROWN ENGINEERING INC** p 1434
300 Sparkman Dr Nw 35805
Tel (256) 726-1000 *SIC* 8731

■ **TELEDYNE ISOTOPES (INC)** p 1434
300 Sparkman Dr Nw 35805
Tel (256) 726-1000 *SIC* 8734

THREE SPRINGS INC p 1450
1131 Eagletree Ln Sw 35801
Tel (256) 880-3339 *SIC* 8322 8093

TORCH TECHNOLOGIES INC p 1461
4035 Chris Dr Sw Ste C 35802
Tel (256) 319-6000 *SIC* 8711

UNIVERSITY OF ALABAMA IN HUNTSVILLE p 1519
301 Sparkman Dr Nw 35805
Tel (256) 824-6340 *SIC* 8221

WESFAM RESTAURANTS INC p 1593
206 Gates Ave Se 35801
Tel (256) 533-0211 *SIC* 5812

WESTAR AEROSPACE & DEFENSE GROUP INC p 1596
890 Explorer Blvd Nw 35806
Tel (256) 922-6800 *SIC* 8733

YULISTA AVIATION INC p 1640
631 Discovery Dr Nw 35806
Tel (256) 319-4621 *SIC* 3724

YULISTA HOLDING LLC p 1640
631 Discovery Dr Nw 35806
Tel (907) 275-2917 *SIC* 8741

IRONDALE, AL

ATS OPERATING LLC p 129
1900 Crestwood Blvd 35210
Tel (205) 215-9829 *SIC* 5932 5331

G & R MINERAL SERVICES INC p 586
2355 Alton Rd 35210
Tel (205) 956-7300 *SIC* 7349 7699

MARSHALL DURBIN FOOD CORP p 911
2830 Commerce Blvd 35210
Tel (205) 841-7315
SIC 0252 0254 2048 0251 2015 5144

SIMPLY FASHION STORES LTD p 1325
2500 Crestwood Blvd # 100 35210
Tel (205) 951-1700 *SIC* 5621

▲ **TRIAD GUARANTY INC** p 1478
1900 Crestwood Blvd 35210
Tel (205) 951-4012 *SIC* 6351

WOOD-FRUITTICHER GROCERY CO INC p 1622
2900 Alton Rd 35210
Tel (205) 836-9663
SIC 5142 5141 5147 5087 5046

JACKSONVILLE, AL

RMC JACKSONVILLE p 1239
1701 Pelham Rd S 36265
Tel (256) 782-4256 *SIC* 8011

JASPER, AL

WALKER COUNTY BOARD OF EDUCATION p 1573
1710 Alabama Ave Ste 106 35501
Tel (205) 387-2156 *SIC* 8211

WALKER REGIONAL MEDICAL CENTER INC p 1573
3400 Highway 78 E 35501
Tel (205) 387-4000 *SIC* 8062

LEEDS, AL

MARVINS LLC p 914
7480 Parkway Dr Ste 100 35094
Tel (205) 702-7305
SIC 5211 5074 5031 5072

LEESBURG, AL

■ **LEESBURG KNITTING MILLS INC** p 852
400 Industrial Blvd 35983
Tel (256) 526-6522 *SIC* 2281 0724

LINCOLN, AL

HONDA MANUFACTURING OF ALABAMA LLC p 704
1800 Honda Dr 35096
Tel (205) 355-5000 *SIC* 5511

LUVERNE, AL

DONGWON AUTOPART TECHNOLOGY ALABAMA LLC p 450
12970 Montgomery Hwy 36049
Tel (334) 537-5000 *SIC* 3465

DONGWON AUTOPART TECHNOLOGY INC p 450
12970 Montgomery Hwy 36049
Tel (706) 637-9735 *SIC* 3465

SMART ALABAMA LLC p 1332
121 Shin Young Dr 36049
Tel (334) 335-5800 *SIC* 3469 3465

STAMPED METAL AMERICAN RESEARCH TECHNOLOGY INC p 1375
121 Shin Young Dr 36049
Tel (334) 296-5126 *SIC* 3469

W L PETREY WHOLESALE CO INC p 1568
10345 Petrey Hwy 36049
Tel (334) 230-5674 *SIC* 5141 5194

MADISON, AL

ALLIANCE HR INC p 54
9076 Madison Blvd Ste G 35758
Tel (256) 203-6432 *SIC* 8742

CORNERSTONE DETENTION PRODUCTS INC p 371
14000 Al Highway 20 35756
Tel (256) 355-2396 *SIC* 1542

INTERGRAPH CORP p 752
305 Intergraph Way 35758
Tel (256) 730-2000 *SIC* 7372 7373 7379

W L HALSEY GROCERY CO INC p 1568
401 Lanier Rd 35758
Tel (256) 772-9691 *SIC* 5141

MAXWELL AFB, AL

CIVIL AIR PATROL INC p 320
105 S Hansell St Bldg 714 36112
Tel (334) 953-7748 *SIC* 9711

MC CALLA, AL

GESTAMP ALABAMA LLC p 609
7000 Jefferson Metro Pkwy 35111
Tel (205) 477-1412 *SIC* 3465

MIDLAND CITY, AL

COLEMAN WORLD GROUP LLC p 336
1 Eagle Ridge Dr 36350
Tel (334) 803-8888 *SIC* 4214

MILLBROOK, AL

BAJAJ CONEAGLE LLC p 145
1900 Market St 36054
Tel (334) 517-6139 *SIC* 3523

MOBILE, AL

■ **AGENTS ALLIANCE INSURANCE CO** p 34
3800 Sollie Rd 36619
Tel (251) 665-2418 *SIC* 6411

ARCHDIOCESE OF MOBILE p 105
400 Government St 36602
Tel (251) 434-1530 *SIC* 8661

AUSTAL USA LLC p 132
1 Dunlap Dr 36602
Tel (251) 434-8000 *SIC* 3731

BAE SYSTEMS SOUTHEAST SHIPYARDS ALABAMA LLC p 144
Mn Gate Dunlap Dr 36652
Tel (251) 690-7100 *SIC* 3731

BALL HEALTHCARE SERVICES INC p 148
1 Southern Way 36619
Tel (251) 432-5800 *SIC* 8051

BERG SPIRAL PIPE CORP p 174
900 Paper Mill Rd 36610
Tel (251) 330-2900 *SIC* 3317

BOARD OF SCHOOL COMMISSIONERS OF MOBILE COUNTY p 195
1 Magnum Pass 36618
Tel (251) 221-3084 *SIC* 8211

BOARD OF WATER AND SEWER COMMISSIONERS OF CITY OF MOBILE p 196
207 N Catherine St 36604
Tel (251) 694-3100 *SIC* 4952 4941

BORDEN DAIRY CO OF ALABAMA LLC p 201
509 S Craft Hwy 36617
Tel (251) 456-3381 *SIC* 5143

CATHOLIC ARCHDIOCESE OF MOBILE p 265
356 Government St 36602
Tel (251) 434-1585 *SIC* 8661

CITY OF MOBILE p 316
205 Government St 36602
Tel (251) 208-7395 *SIC* 9111

▲ **COMPUTER PROGRAMS AND SYSTEMS INC** p 353
6600 Wall St 36695
Tel (251) 639-8100 *SIC* 7373 7371

CONTINENTAL MOTORS INC p 363
2039 S Broad St 36615
Tel (251) 438-3411 *SIC* 3724

COOPER MARINE & TIMBERLANDS CORP p 367
118 N Royal St 36602
Tel (251) 434-5000 *SIC* 5199 2421

COOPER/T SMITH STEVEDORING CO INC p 367
118 N Royal St Ste 1100 36602
Tel (251) 431-6100 *SIC* 4491

COUNTY OF MOBILE p 380
205 Government St 36644
Tel (251) 574-5077 *SIC* 9111

DAVID VOLKERT & ASSOCIATES INC p 415
3809 Moffett Rd 36618
Tel (251) 342-1070 *SIC* 8711

ENDURACARE THERAPY MANAGEMENT INC p 496
3765a Government Blvd 36693
Tel (251) 666-7867 *SIC* 8049 8741

■ **ENERGYSOUTH INC** p 498
2828 Dauphin St 36606
Tel (251) 450-4774 *SIC* 4924 4922

FLOWERWOOD NURSERY INC p 560
6470 Dauphin Island Pkwy 36605
Tel (251) 443-6540 *SIC* 0181

GAT AIRLINE GROUND SUPPORT INC p 593
8400 Airport Blvd 36608
Tel (251) 633-3888 *SIC* 4581

GLOBAL TEL LINK CORP p 617
2609 Cameron St 36607
Tel (251) 479-4500 *SIC* 4813

GREER AUTRY & SONS INC p 639
2850 W Main St 36612
Tel (251) 342-7964 *SIC* 5411

GTEL HOLDINGS INC p 644
2609 Cameron St 36607
Tel (251) 479-4500 *SIC* 3661 7389

HARGROVE AND ASSOCIATES INC p 661
20 S Royal St 36602
Tel (251) 476-0605 *SIC* 8711

HILLER COMPANIES INC p 693
3751 Joy Springs Dr 36693
Tel (251) 661-1275 *SIC* 1731 5084 5088

HPC LLC p 714
63 S Royal St Ste 800 36602
Tel (251) 441-1990 *SIC* 5122

INFIRMARY HEALTH SYSTEM INC p 741
5 Mobile Infirmary Cir 36607
Tel (251) 435-3030
SIC 8062 6512 1542 7322 5047 7389

■ **METALS USA PLATES AND SHAPES SOUTHEAST INC** p 953
1251 Woodland Ave 36610
Tel (251) 456-4531 *SIC* 5051

MOBILE COUNTY PUBLIC SCHOOLS p 980
1 Magnum Pass 36618
Tel (251) 221-4394 *SIC* 8211

■ **MOBILE GAS SERVICE CORP** p 980
2828 Dauphin St 36606
Tel (251) 476-2720 *SIC* 4924 5722

MOBILE INFIRMARY ASSOCIATION p 980
5 Mobile Infirmary Cir 36607
Tel (251) 435-2400 *SIC* 8062

NORTON LILLY INTERNATIONAL INC p 1061
1 Saint Louis St Ste 5000 36602
Tel (251) 431-6335 *SIC* 4731

OIMO HOLDINGS INC p 1079
2735 Middle Rd 36605
Tel (251) 443-5550 *SIC* 1389

PCH HOTELS AND RESORTS INC p 1124
11 N Water St Ste 8290 36602
Tel (251) 338-5600 *SIC* 7011

PILOT CATASTROPHE SERVICES INC p 1148
1055 Hillcrest Rd 36695
Tel (251) 607-7700 *SIC* 6411

PROVIDENCE HOSPITAL p 1186
6801 Airport Blvd 36608
Tel (251) 633-1000 *SIC* 8062 8011

SAAD ENTERPRISES INC p 1263
1515 S University Blvd 36609
Tel (251) 343-9600
SIC 8082 5047 7352 5912 5621 8741

SMITH COOPER/T CORP p 1333
118 N Royal St Ste 1000 36602
Tel (251) 431-6100
SIC 4499 4492 2421 7692 4491

SOUTHERN MEDICAL HEALTH SYSTEMS INC p 1349
3632 Dauphin St Ste 101b 36608
Tel (251) 460-5280
SIC 8741 8011 7374 7322

SPRINGHILL HOSPITALS INC p 1361
3719 Dauphin St Frnt 36608
Tel (251) 344-9630 *SIC* 8062

SSI GROUP INC p 1363
4721 Morrison Dr 36609
Tel (251) 345-0000 *SIC* 7371 7372

ST AEROSPACE MOBILE INC p 1364
2100 Aerospace Dr Brkley Brookley Complex 36615
Tel (251) 438-8888 *SIC* 4581

TECHNIFY MOTOR (USA) INC p 1431
2039 S Broad St 36615
Tel (251) 438-3411 *SIC* 5088

TURNER SUPPLY CO p 1493
250 N Royal St 36602
Tel (205) 252-6000 *SIC* 5085 5251

UNIVERSITY OF SOUTH ALABAMA p 1525
307 N University Blvd # 380 36608
Tel (251) 460-6101 *SIC* 8221

UNIVERSITY OF SOUTH ALABAMA MEDICAL CENTER p 1525
2451 Fillingim St 36617
Tel (251) 471-7110 *SIC* 8062

USA CHILDRENS AND WOMENS HOSPITAL p 1534
1700 Center St 36604
Tel (251) 415-1000 *SIC* 8069

VOLKERT INC p 1564
3809 Moffett Rd 36618
Tel (251) 342-1070 *SIC* 8711

MONROEVILLE, AL

CROWNE INVESTMENTS INC p 396
501 Whetstone St 36460
Tel (251) 743-3609 *SIC* 8051

ENGLEWOOD HEALTH CARE CENTER LLC p 499
2046 S Alabama Ave 36460
Tel (251) 575-3285 *SIC* 8051

MONTGOMERY, AL

ALABAMA COMMUNITY COLLEGE SYSTEM p 43
135 S Union St 36130
Tel (334) 262-8734 *SIC* 9411

ALABAMA DEPARTMENT OF LABOR p 43
649 Monroe St 36131
Tel (334) 242-8055 *SIC* 9441

ALABAMA DEPARTMENT OF PUBLIC HEALTH p 43
201 Monroe St Ste 1050 36104
Tel (334) 206-5300 *SIC* 9431

ALABAMA DEPT OF CONSERVATION & NATURAL RESOURCES p 43
64 N Union St Rm 458 36130
Tel (334) 242-3468 *SIC* 9512

ALABAMA DEPT OF HUMAN RESOURCES p 43
50 N Ripley St 36130
Tel (334) 242-1310 *SIC* 9441

ALABAMA DEPT OF MENTAL HEALTH p 43
100 N Union St Ste 520 36104
Tel (334) 242-3107 *SIC* 9199

ALABAMA DEPT OF PUBLIC SAFETY p 43
301 S Ripley St 36104
Tel (334) 242-4394 *SIC* 9229

ALABAMA DEPT OF TRANSPORTATION p 43
1409 Coliseum Blvd 36110
Tel (334) 242-6258 *SIC* 9621

ALABAMA JUDICIAL BUILDING AUTHORITY p 43
100 N Union St Rm 224 36104
Tel (334) 353-3328 *SIC* 9111

ALABAMA MUNICIPAL ELECTRIC AUTHORITY p 43
80 Technacenter Dr 36117
Tel (334) 262-1126 *SIC* 4911

ALABAMA STATE UNIVERSITY (INC) p 43
915 S Jackson St 36104
Tel (334) 229-4100 *SIC* 8221

ALABAMA UNIFIED JUDICIAL SYSTEM p 43
300 Dexter Ave 36104
Tel (334) 954-5000 *SIC* 9211

ALFA CORP p 49
2108 E South Blvd 36116
Tel (334) 288-3900 *SIC* 6331 6411 7389

ALFA GENERAL INSURANCE CORP p 49
2108 E South Blvd 36116
Tel (334) 288-0375 *SIC* 6331

ALFA INSURANCE CORP p 49
2108 E South Blvd 36116
Tel (334) 277-6942 *SIC* 6331

ALFA MUTUAL FIRE INSURANCE CO p 49
2108 E South Blvd 36116
Tel (334) 288-3900 *SIC* 6411

ALFA MUTUAL GENERAL INSURANCE CO p 49
2108 E South Blvd 36116
Tel (334) 288-3900 *SIC* 6331

ALFA MUTUAL INSURANCE CO p 49
2108 E South Blvd 36116
Tel (334) 613-4639 *SIC* 6411

ALLSTATE BEVERAGE CO INC p 58
130 6th St 36104
Tel (334) 265-0507 *SIC* 5181

BAPTIST HEALTH p 153
301 Brown Springs Rd 36117
Tel (334) 273-4217 *SIC* 8062

BLOUNT-STRANGE FORD LINCOLN MERCURY INC p 190
4000 Eastern Blvd 36116
Tel (334) 613-5000 *SIC* 5511

CADDELL CONSTRUCTION CO (DE) LLC p 236
2700 Lagoon Park Dr 36109
Tel (334) 272-7723 *SIC* 1542 1541

CADDELL CONSTRUCTION CO INC p 236
2700 Lagoon Park Dr 36109
Tel (334) 272-7723 SIC 1542 1541

CAPITOL BUSINESS EQUIPMENT INC p 251
645 S Mcdonough St 36104
Tel (334) 265-8903
SIC 5045 5044 7699 5065

CCC ASSOCIATES CO p 269
3601 Wetumpka Hwy 36110
Tel (334) 272-2140 SIC 5193 5992

CITY OF MONTGOMERY p 316
103 N Perry St 36104
Tel (334) 625-2025 SIC 9111

COMMUNITY NEWSPAPER HOLDINGS INC p 349
445 Dexter Ave Ste 7000 36104
Tel (334) 293-5800 SIC 2711 4833

CONSTRUCTION MATERIALS INC p 361
4350 Northern Blvd 36110
Tel (334) 272-8200 SIC 5031 5051

DAS NORTH AMERICA INC p 413
840 Industrial Park Blvd 36117
Tel (334) 694-5335 SIC 2211

DEPARTMENT OF CORRECTIONS ALABAMA p 430
301 S Ripley St 36104
Tel (334) 353-3844 SIC 9222

DEPARTMENT OF MILITARY ALABAMA p 430
1720 Congsman Wl Dksn Dr 36109
Tel (334) 271-7435 SIC 9711

DEPT OF REVENUE ALABAMA p 431
50 N Ripley St Fl 4 36130
Tel (334) 242-1170 SIC 9311

EXECUTIVE OFFICE OF STATE OF ALABAMA p 517
600 Dexter Ave Ste S105 36130
Tel (334) 242-7205 SIC 9111

FASTENING SOLUTIONS INC p 531
3075 Selma Hwy 36108
Tel (334) 284-8300 SIC 5085 5072 5051

FOUR STAR FREIGHTLINER INC p 572
3140 Hayneville Rd 36108
Tel (334) 263-1085 SIC 5012 5531

GO GREEN JANITORIAL SERVICES LLC p 619
8448 Crossland Loop 36117
Tel (334) 277-5880 SIC 7699

HEALTHCARE AUTHORITY FOR BAPTIST HEALTH AND AFFILIATE OF UAB HEALTH SYSTEM p 676
2105 E South Blvd 36116
Tel (334) 286-2987 SIC 8062

HYUNDAI MOTOR MANUFACTURING ALABAMA LLC p 724
700 Hyundai Blvd 36105
Tel (334) 387-8000 SIC 5511

JACKSON HOSPITAL & CLINIC INC p 774
1725 Pine St 36106
Tel (334) 293-8000 SIC 8062

KYUNGSHIN-LEAR SALES AND ENGINEERING LLC p 833
100 Smothers Rd 36117
Tel (334) 413-0575 SIC 3714

MOBIS ALABAMA LLC p 980
1395 Mitchell Young Rd 36108
Tel (334) 387-4800 SIC 3714

MOBIS AMERICA INC p 980
1395 Mitchell Young Rd 36108
Tel (334) 387-4840 SIC 3714

MONTGOMERY PUBLIC SCHOOLS p 987
307 S Decatur St 36104
Tel (334) 223-6873 SIC 8211

PUBLIC EMPLOYEES INDIVIDUAL RETIREMENT ACCOUNT FUND/DEFERRED COMPENSATION PLAN p 1189
201 S Union St 36104
Tel (334) 517-7000 SIC 9441

RAYCOM MEDIA INC p 1210
201 Monroe St Fl 20 36104
Tel (334) 206-1400 SIC 4833 4832

REINHARDT MOTORS INC p 1221
720 Eastern Blvd 36117
Tel (334) 272-7147 SIC 5511 7532

SABEL STEEL SERVICE INC p 1263
749 N Court St 36104
Tel (334) 265-6771 SIC 5088 5051

SOUTHEAST WOOD TREATING INC p 1346
3077 Carter Hill Rd 36111
Tel (321) 631-1003 SIC 2421 2491

STATE OF ALABAMA p 1381
300 Dexter Ave 36104
Tel (334) 242-7100 SIC 9111

SYLVEST FARMS INC p 1414
3500 West Blvd 36108
Tel (334) 281-0400 SIC 0251 2015

SYS-CON LLC p 1416
4444 Park Blvd 36116
Tel (334) 281-1520 SIC 1541

THERMASYS GROUP HOLDING CO p 1447
2776 Gunter Park Dr E 36109
Tel (334) 244-9240 SIC 3714 3443

US TACTICAL RESPONSE AND INFORMATION SERVICE LLC p 1533
2 N Jackson St Ste 605 36104
Tel (888) 315-1113 SIC 7382

MOODY, AL

JONES STEPHENS CORP p 792
3249 Moody Pkwy 35004
Tel (205) 640-7200 SIC 5074

RED DIAMOND INC p 1215
400 Park Ave 35004
Tel (205) 577-4000 SIC 5141 2095 2099

MOUNTAIN BRK, AL

JEFFERSON IRON AND METAL BROKERAGE INC p 782
3940 Montclair Rd Ste 300 35213
Tel (205) 803-5200 SIC 5051

▲ SERVISFIRST BANCSHARES INC p 1308
850 Shades Creek Pkwy 35209
Tel (205) 949-0302 SIC 6022

■ SERVISFIRST BANK p 1308
850 Shades Creek Pkwy 35209
Tel (205) 949-0302 SIC 6022

SOUTHERN FOODSERVICE MANAGEMENT INC p 1348
500 Office Park Dr # 210 35223
Tel (205) 871-8000 SIC 5812 5962

MUSCLE SHOALS, AL

CONSTELLIUM METAL PROCUREMENT LLC p 361
2415 Rosedale St Ste H 35661
Tel (256) 443-7435 SIC 7389

DYNAMIC SECURITY INC p 464
1102 Woodward Ave 35661
Tel (256) 383-5798 SIC 7381

SOUTHERN FASTENING SYSTEMS LLC p 1348
635 Fairgrounds Rd 35661
Tel (256) 381-3628
SIC 5084 5085 5251 5072

WHITESELL CORP p 1606
2703 Avalon Ave 35661
Tel (256) 248-8500
SIC 3965 5085 3444 3452 3451

WISE ALLOYS LLC p 1619
4805 2nd St 35661
Tel (256) 386-6000 SIC 3353

WISE METALS GROUP LLC p 1619
4805 2nd St 35661
Tel (256) 386-6000 SIC 3353 3356

NEW HOPE, AL

F & W FARMS INC p 522
177 Woody Cir 35760
Tel (256) 599-6422
SIC 0116 0115 0131 0111

NEW MARKET, AL

MADISON COUNTY COMMISSIONS p 894
783 Coleman Rd 35761
Tel (256) 379-2132 SIC 7999

NORTHPORT, AL

RACON INC p 1203
700 Energy Center Blvd # 404 35473
Tel (205) 333-8500 SIC 1611 1522

ONEONTA, AL

DHS OF BLUNT COUNTY LLC p 435
212 Ellen St 35121
Tel (205) 625-3520 SIC 8051

OPELIKA, AL

DAEWON AMERICA INC p 408
4600 N Park Dr 36801
Tel (334) 364-1600 SIC 3493

EAST ALABAMA HEALTH CARE AUTHORITY p 469
2000 Pepperell Pkwy 36801
Tel (334) 749-3411 SIC 8062

HANWHA ADVANCED MATERIALS AMERICA LLC p 659
4400 N Park Dr 36801
Tel (334) 741-7725 SIC 3714

HANWHA L & C HOLDINGS USA LLC p 659
4400 N Park Dr 36801
Tel (334) 741-7725 SIC 3083 3714

LEE COUNTY SCHOOL DISTRICT p 851
2410 Society Hill Rd 36804
Tel (334) 705-6000 SIC 8211

MANDO AMERICA CORP p 901
4201 N Park Dr 36801
Tel (334) 364-3600 SIC 3714

SCOTT BRIDGE CO INC p 1293
2641 Interstate Dr 36801
Tel (334) 749-5045 SIC 1622

OPP, AL

MFG GALILEO COMPOSITES p 958
18361 Galileo Dr 36467
Tel (334) 493-0014 SIC 5731 3089

ORANGE BEACH, AL

COLUMBIA SOUTHERN EDUCATION GROUP INC p 341
21982 University Ln 36561
Tel (251) 943-2273 SIC 6719

OXFORD, AL

B R WILLIAMS TRUCKING INC p 142
2339 Al Highway 21 S 36203
Tel (256) 831-5580 SIC 4213 4225

FABARC STEEL SUPPLY INC p 523
111 Meadow Ln 36203
Tel (256) 831-8770 SIC 3441

PELHAM, AL

AUTOMATION PERSONNEL SERVICES INC p 134
401 Southgate Dr 35124
Tel (205) 733-3700 SIC 7363

PROCESS EQUIPMENT INC p 1179
2770 Welborn St 35124
Tel (205) 663-5330
SIC 3564 3535 3441 3443

SOUTHEASTERN FOOD MERCHANDISERS INC p 1346
201 Parker Dr 35124
Tel (205) 664-3322 SIC 5141

PELL CITY, AL

WKW ERBSLOEH NORTH AMERICA HOLDING INC p 1620
103 Parkway E 35125
Tel (205) 338-4242 SIC 6719

WKW ERBSLOEH NORTH AMERICA LLC p 1620
103 Parkway E 35125
Tel (205) 338-4242 SIC 3714

PERDUE HILL, AL

ALABAMA RIVER CELLULOSE LLC p 43
2373 Lena Landegger Hwy Cnty 36470
Tel (251) 575-2000 SIC 2611

ALABAMA RIVER WOODLANDS INC p 43
2373 Lena Landegger Hwy 36470
Tel (251) 575-2039 SIC 5099

PHENIX CITY, AL

MEMORY CO LLC p 942
25 Downing Dr 36869
Tel (334) 448-0708 SIC 5199

PIEDMONT, AL

PIEDMONT HEALTH CARE AUTHORITY p 1147
30 Roundtree Dr 36272
Tel (256) 447-8258 SIC 8051

PINE HILL, AL

GD COPPER (USA) INC p 595
405 Gd Copper Dr 36769
Tel (334) 637-0200 SIC 3351 3999

PINSON, AL

D & G ELECTRIC CO LLC p 406
8297 Old Tenn Pike Rd 35126
Tel (205) 365-4074 SIC 1731

PRATTVILLE, AL

AUTAUGA COUNTY SCHOOL BOARD OF EDUCATION p 133
153 W 4th St 36067
Tel (334) 365-5706 SIC 8211

AUTAUGA COUNTY SCHOOL SYSTEM p 133
153 W 4th St 36067
Tel (334) 365-5706 SIC 8211

CENTRAL ALABAMA ELECTRIC COOPERATIVE p 277
1802 Highway 31 N 36067
Tel (334) 365-6762 SIC 4911

RAINSVILLE, AL

DEKALB COUNTY BOARD OF EDUCATION p 423
306 Main St W 35986
Tel (256) 638-7265 SIC 9411

RAINSVILLE TECHNOLOGY INC p 1206
189 Rti Dr 35986
Tel (256) 638-9760 SIC 3089

RED BAY, AL

SUNSHINE MILLS INC p 1404
500 6th St Sw 35582
Tel (256) 356-9541 SIC 2047 2048 5149

TIFFIN MOTOR HOMES INC p 1453
105 2nd St Nw 35582
Tel (256) 356-8661 SIC 3716

RUSSELLVILLE, AL

RUSSELLVILLE HEALTH CARE INC p 1259
705 Gandy St Ne 35653
Tel (256) 332-3773 SIC 8051

SAGINAW, AL

SAGINAW PIPE CO INC p 1268
1980 Hwy 31 S 35137
Tel (205) 664-3670 SIC 5051

SARALAND, AL

SARALAND CITY SCHOOLS p 1282
943 Highway 43 S 36571
Tel (251) 375-5420 SIC 8211

■ TDG OPERATIONS LLC p 1429
716 Bill Myles Dr 36571
Tel (251) 675-9080 SIC 2273

SCOTTSBORO, AL

AMERICAN ASSOCIATED PHARMACIES INC p 68
201 Lnnie E Crawford Blvd 35769
Tel (256) 574-6819 SIC 5122

ASSOCIATED PHARMACIES INC p 121
211 Lonnie Crawford Blvd 35769
Tel (256) 574-6819 SIC 5122

HEAT TRANSFER PRODUCTS GROUP LLC p 679
201 Thomas French Dr 35769
Tel (256) 259-7400 SIC 5084

MAPLES INDUSTRIES INC p 904
2210 Moody Ridge Rd 35768
Tel (256) 259-1327 SIC 2273

SELMA, AL

AMERICAN APPAREL INC p 68
107 Cecil Jackson Byp 36703
Tel (334) 872-6337 SIC 2311 2385

■ BUSH HOG INC p 229
2501 Griffin Ave 36703
Tel (800) 363-6096 SIC 3523

COUGAR OIL INC p 374
1411 Water Ave 36703
Tel (334) 875-2023 SIC 5171 5983 5172

SELMA PUBLIC SCHOOLS p 1302
2194 Broad St 36701
Tel (334) 874-1600 SIC 8211

SEOYON E-HWA INTERIOR SYSTEMS ALABAMA LLC p 1306
200 Craig Industrial Park 36701
Tel (334) 410-7100 SIC 3089

SHEFFIELD, AL

HH HEALTH SYSTEM - SHOALS LLC p 689
1300 S Mongomery Ave 35660
Tel (256) 386-4673 SIC 8062

SHOAL CREEK, AL

■ LEGACY VULCAN LLC p 852
1200 Urban Center Dr 35242
Tel (205) 298-3000
SIC 1422 1423 1442 2951 3273

STEELE, AL

UNIPRES ALABAMA INC p 1505
990 Duncan Farms Rd 35987
Tel (256) 538-1974 SIC 3465

SUMMERDALE, AL

BALDWIN COUNTY ELECTRIC MEMBERSHIP CORP p 147
19600 State Highway 59 36580
Tel (251) 989-6247 SIC 4911

TALLADEGA, AL

ALABAMA INSTITUTE FOR DEAF AND BLIND p 43
205 South St E 35160
Tel (256) 761-3200 SIC 8249 8211

R K ALLEN OIL CO INC p 1202
36002 Al Highway 21 35160
Tel (256) 315-9825 SIC 5172

TALLADEGA COUNTY BOARD OF EDUCATION p 1423
106 South St W Ste A 35160
Tel (256) 362-1401 SIC 8211

TALLASSEE, AL

GKN WESTLAND AEROSPACE INC p 613
3951 Al Highway 229 S 36078
Tel (334) 283-9200 SIC 3728

■ NEPTUNE TECHNOLOGY GROUP INC p 1026
1600 Al Highway 229 S 36078
Tel (334) 283-6555 SIC 3824

THEODORE, AL

BAGBY AND RUSSELL ELECTRIC CO INC p 144
5500 Plantation Rd 36582
Tel (251) 344-5987 SIC 1731

EVONIK CORP p 515
4201 Degussa Rd 36582
Tel (251) 443-4000 SIC 5169

INEOS AMERICAS LLC p 740
7770 Rangeline Rd 36582
Tel (251) 443-3000 SIC 2869 2865

MOBILE PAINT MANUFACTURING CO OF DELAWARE INC p 980
4775 Hamilton Blvd 36582
Tel (251) 443-6110 SIC 2851 5198 5231

TW CRYOGENICS LLC p 1494
4075 Hamilton Blvd 36582
Tel (251) 443-8680 SIC 3443

TRINITY, AL

JOE WHEELER ELECTRIC MEMBERSHIP CORP p 787
25354 Al Highway 24 35673
Tel (256) 552-2300 SIC 4911

JOE WHEELER EMC p 787
25700 Al Highway 24 35673
Tel (256) 552-2300 SIC 6111

■ NUCOR STEEL DECATUR LLC p 1066
4301 Iverson Blvd 35673
Tel (256) 301-3500 SIC 3312

TROY, AL

HB&G BUILDING PRODUCTS INC p 671
1015 S Brundidge Blvd 36081
Tel (334) 566-5000 SIC 2431 2421 2821

PIKE COUNTY BOARD OF EDUCATION p 1148
101 W Love St 36081
Tel (334) 566-1850 SIC 8211

SANDERS LEAD CO INC p 1278
1 Sanders Rd 36079
Tel (334) 566-1563 SIC 3341

TROY UNIVERSITY p 1485
600 University Ave 36082
Tel (334) 670-3179 SIC 8221

WILEY SANDERS TRUCK LINES INC p 1609
100 Sanders Rd 36079
Tel (334) 566-5184 SIC 4213

TRUSSVILLE, AL

MCPHERSON COMPANIES INC p 932
5051 Cardinal St 35173
Tel (205) 661-2799 SIC 5171 5411 5541

TUSCALOOSA, AL

BOONE NEWSPAPERS INC p 200
1060 Fairfax Park Ste B 35406
Tel (205) 330-4100 SIC 2711

CENTURY HEALTH ALLIANCE JOINT VENTURE p 282
809 University Blvd E 35401
Tel (205) 759-7111 SIC 8062 8741

CITY OF TUSCALOOSA p 319
2201 University Blvd 35401
Tel (205) 349-2010 SIC 9111

DCH HEALTH CARE AUTHORITY p 418
809 University Blvd E 35401
Tel (205) 759-7111 SIC 8062 8093

GEOLOGICAL SURVEY OF ALABAMA p 606
420 Hackberry Ln 35487
Tel (205) 247-3592 SIC 9199

HARDIN TAYLOR SECURE MEDICAL FACILITY p 661
1301 Jack Warner Pkwy Ne 35404
Tel (205) 556-7060 SIC 8062 9431

MCABEE CONSTRUCTION INC p 925
5724 21st St 35401
Tel (205) 349-2212
SIC 1629 1791 1796 3443 3498

NHS MANAGEMENT LLC p 1042
931 Fairfax Park 35406
Tel (205) 391-3600 SIC 8082 8059

■ NUCOR STEEL TUSCALOOSA INC p 1067
1700 Holt Rd Ne 35404
Tel (205) 556-1310 SIC 3312

PECO FOODS INC p 1127
1020 Lurleen B Wallace 35401
Tel (205) 345-4711
SIC 0254 0251 2015 2048

PHIFER INC p 1142
4400 Kauloosa Ave 35401
Tel (205) 345-2120
SIC 3496 2221 3357 2295 3442 3354

TUSCALOOSA CITY BOARD OF EDUCATION p 1493
1210 21st Ave 35401
Tel (205) 759-3700 SIC 8211

TUSCALOOSA CITY SCHOOLS p 1493
1210 21st Ave 35401
Tel (205) 759-3560 SIC 8211

TUSCALOOSA COUNTY BOARD OF EDUCATION p 1493
1118 Greensboro Ave 35401
Tel (205) 758-0411 SIC 8211

UNIVERSITY OF ALABAMA p 1519
1202 Coliseum Cir 35487
Tel (205) 348-0628 SIC 8641

UNIVERSITY OF ALABAMA FOUNDATION INC p 1519
301 Rose Adm Bldg 35487
Tel (205) 348-6010 SIC 8221

UNIVERSITY OF ALABAMA SYSTEM p 1519
401 Queen City Ave 35401
Tel (205) 348-5861 SIC 5999

WESTERVELT CO p 1600
1400 Jack Warner Pkwy Ne 35404
Tel (205) 562-5295 SIC 3553 2421

TUSKEGEE INSTITUTE, AL

TUSKEGEE UNIVERSITY p 1493
1200 W Montgomery Rd 36088
Tel (334) 727-8011 SIC 8221

UNION SPRINGS, AL

BONNIE PLANTS INC p 200
1727 Highway 223 36089
Tel (334) 738-3104 SIC 0191

VANCE, AL

MERCEDES-BENZ US INTERNATIONAL INC p 944
1 Mercedes Dr 35490
Tel (205) 507-2252 SIC 3711 3714

VERNON, AL

■ MARATHON EQUIPMENT CO (DELAWARE) p 904
Highway 9 S 35592
Tel (205) 695-9105 SIC 3589

VESTAVIA, AL

CAPELLA HEALTH HOLDINGS LLC p 248
1000 Urban Center Dr # 501 35242
Tel (205) 969-3455 SIC 6798 8062

DRUMMOND CO INC p 457
1000 Urban Center Dr # 300 35242
Tel (205) 945-6500
SIC 1221 1222 3312 5052 5085 5172

INDUSTRIAL CHEMICALS INC p 739
2042 Montreat Dr Ste A 35216
Tel (205) 823-7330 SIC 5169

■ LEGACY VULCAN LLC p 852
1200 Urban Center Dr 35242
Tel (205) 298-3000
SIC 1422 1423 1442 2951 3273

MEDICAL PROPERTIES TRUST INC p 937
1000 Urban Center Dr # 501 35242
Tel (205) 969-3755 SIC 6798

QUALITY RESTAURANT CONCEPTS LLC p 1197
601 Vestavia Pkwy # 1000 35216
Tel (205) 824-5060 SIC 5812

SOUTHERN CARE INC p 1347
1000 Urban Center Dr # 115 35242
Tel (205) 868-4400 SIC 8082

TACALA INC p 1421
4268 Cahaba Heights Ct 35243
Tel (205) 985-9626 SIC 5812

TACALA LLC p 1421
3750 Corporate Woods Dr 35242
Tel (205) 443-9600 SIC 5812

TACALA NORTH INC p 1421
4268 Cahaba Heights Ct 35243
Tel (205) 985-2364 SIC 5812

■ VULCAN CONSTRUCTION MATERIALS LLC p 1567
1200 Urban Center Dr 35242
Tel (205) 298-3000 SIC 1422

▲ VULCAN MATERIALS CO p 1567
1200 Urban Center Dr 35242
Tel (205) 298-3000
SIC 1422 1423 2951 1442 3273 3272

■ VULCAN PERFORMANCE CHEMICALS p 1567
1200 Urban Center Dr 35242
Tel (205) 298-3000 SIC 2819

WARREN AVERETT COMPANIES LLC p 1576
2500 Acton Rd Ste 200 35243
Tel (205) 979-4100
SIC 8721 8741 7363 8742

VINEMONT, AL

RE GARRISON TRUCKING INC p 1212
1103 County Road 1194 35179
Tel (888) 640-8482 SIC 4213

WETUMPKA, AL

ELMORE COUNTY SCHOOL DISTRICT p 489
100 H H Robinson Dr 36092
Tel (334) 567-1200 SIC 8211

WINFIELD, AL

■ CONTINENTAL GLOBAL GROUP INC p 363
438 Industrial Dr 35594
Tel (205) 487-6492 SIC 3535

ALASKA

ANCHORAGE, AK

AFOGNAK NATIVE CORP p 33
3909 Arctic Blvd Ste 500 99503
Tel (907) 222-9500 SIC 0851

AHTNA INC p 37
110 W 38th Ave Ste 100 99503
Tel (907) 868-8250
SIC 1629 7389 1542 1521

■ ALASCOM INC p 44
505 E Bluff Dr 99501
Tel (907) 264-7000 SIC 4813 4833 4832

ALASKA COMMERCIAL CO p 44
550 W 64th Ave Ste 200 99518
Tel (907) 273-4600 SIC 5399

▲ ALASKA COMMUNICATIONS SYSTEMS GROUP INC p 44
600 Telephone Ave 99503
Tel (907) 297-3000 SIC 4813

ALASKA INDUSTRIAL HARDWARE INC p 45
2192 Viking Dr 99501
Tel (907) 279-6691 SIC 5072 5251

ALASKA INTERNATIONAL AIRPORTS SYSTEM p 45
5000 W Intl Airport Rd 99502
Tel (907) 266-2404 SIC 4581

ALASKA NATIONAL CORP p 45
7001 Jewel Lake Rd 99502
Tel (907) 248-2642 SIC 6411

ALASKA NATIONAL INSURANCE CO p 45
7001 Jewel Lake Rd 99502
Tel (907) 248-2642 SIC 6331 6351

ALASKA NATIVE TRIBAL HEALTH CONSORTIUM p 45
4000 Ambassador Dr 99508
Tel (907) 729-1900 SIC 8399 8741

ALASKA RAILROAD CORP p 45
327 W Ship Creek Ave 99501
Tel (907) 265-2494 SIC 4011 6531

ALASKA USA FEDERAL CREDIT UNION p 45
4000 Credit Union Dr 99503
Tel (907) 563-4567 SIC 6061 6163

ALEUT CORP p 48
4000 Old Seward Hwy # 300 99503
Tel (907) 561-4300 SIC 6799 1542 8742

ALUTIIQ LLC p 63
3909 Arctic Blvd Ste 500 99503
Tel (907) 222-9500 SIC 8748

ALUTIIQ PACIFIC LLC p 63
3909 Arctic Blvd Ste 500 99503
Tel (907) 222-9500 SIC 8742 7379

ANCHORAGE MUNICIPALITY OF (INC) p 89
632 W 6th Ave Ste 810 99501
Tel (907) 343-6610 SIC 9111

ANCHORAGE SCHOOL DISTRICT p 89
5530 E Nthrn Lights Blvd 99504
Tel (907) 742-4000 SIC 8211

ARCTIC OFFICE MACHINE INC p 106
100 W Fireweed Ln 99503
Tel (907) 276-2295
SIC 5112 5021 5044 7629

ARCTIC SLOPE REGIONAL CORP p 106
3900 C St Ste 801 99503
Tel (907) 339-6000 SIC 1389 2911 1623

ASRC ENERGY SERVICES LLC p 119
3900 C St Ste 701 99503
Tel (907) 339-6200 SIC 1389

BP TRANSPORTATION (ALASKA) INC p 206
900 E Benson Blvd 99508
Tel (907) 561-5111 SIC 1311

BRISTOL BAY NATIVE CORP p 214
111 W 16th Ave Ste 400 99501
Tel (907) 563-0013 SIC 7011

CALISTA CORP p 242
5015 Bus Pk Blvd Ste 3000 99503
Tel (907) 279-5516 SIC 6512 7363 2711

CARLILE TRANSPORTATION SYSTEMS INC p 257
1800 E 1st Ave 99501
Tel (907) 276-7797 SIC 4212 4213 4731

CH2M HILL ALASKA INC p 286
949 E 36th Ave Ste 500 99508
Tel (907) 762-1500 SIC 1389

CHENEGA CORP p 294
3000 C St Ste 301 99503
Tel (907) 277-5706
SIC 8744 7379 7376 3629 8742

CHUGACH ALASKA CORP p 304
3800 Cntrpint Dr Ste 1200 99503
Tel (907) 563-8866
SIC 8744 4959 7361 0851 7373

CHUGACH ELECTRIC p 304
5601 Electron Dr 99518
Tel (907) 563-7494 SIC 1731

CHUGACH ELECTRIC ASSOCIATION INC p 305
5601 Electron Dr 99518
Tel (907) 563-7494 SIC 4911

CHUGACH FEDERAL SOLUTIONS INC p 305
3800 Cntrpint Dr Ste 1200 99503
Tel (907) 563-8866 SIC 1542

CHUGACH GOVERNMENT SERVICES INC p 305
3800 Cntrpint Dr Ste 1200 99503
Tel (907) 563-8866 SIC 1542

CHUGACH GOVERNMENT SOLUTIONS LLC p 305
3800 Cntrpint Dr Ste 1200 99503
Tel (907) 563-8866 SIC 6719

COOK INLET REGION INC p 366
725 E Fireweed Ln Ste 800 99503
Tel (907) 274-8638
SIC 6552 1382 1389 6519 4832 4833

COPPER RIVER SEAFOODS INC p 368
1118 E 5th Ave 99501
Tel (907) 424-3721 SIC 2091 5146

CPD ALASKA LLC p 387
201 Arctic Slope Ave 99518
Tel (907) 777-5505 SIC 5171

CROWLEY PETROLEUM DIST INC p 395
201 Arctic Slope Ave 99518
Tel (907) 822-3375 SIC 5171

DAVIS CONSTRUCTORS & ENGINEERS INC p 416
6591 A St Ste 300 99518
Tel (907) 562-2336 SIC 1542

DOYON DRILLING INC p 454
11500 C St Ste 200 99515
Tel (907) 563-5530 SIC 1381

FIRST NATIONAL BANK ALASKA p 548
101 W 36th Ave 99503
Tel (907) 777-4362 SIC 6021

■ FRED MEYER OF ALASKA INC p 576
1000 E Nthrn Lights Blvd 99508
Tel (907) 264-9600 SIC 5311

■ G C I HOLDINGS INC p 586
2550 Denali St Ste 1000 99503
Tel (907) 265-5600 SIC 6719

GALEN HOSPITAL ALASKA INC p 589
2801 Debarr Rd 99508
Tel (907) 276-1131 SIC 8062

■ GCI INC p 595
2550 Denali St Ste 1000 99503
Tel (907) 868-5400 SIC 7389

▲ GENERAL COMMUNICATION INC p 599
2550 Denali St Ste 1000 99503
Tel (907) 868-5600 SIC 4813 4841 4812

HARDING HOLDINGS INC p 661
184 E 53rd Ave 99518
Tel (907) 344-1577 SIC 1389 1542

HILCORP ALASKA LLC p 692
3800 Centerpoint Dr 99503
Tel (907) 777-8300 SIC 1382

HOTH INC p 710
4700 Old Intl Airport Rd 99502
Tel (907) 266-8300 SIC 4522 4512

KATMAI GOVERNMENT SERVICES LLC p 804
11001 Omalley Centre Dr # 204 99515
Tel (907) 333-7000 SIC 3812

KONIAG DEVELOPMENT CO LLC p 827
3800 Centerpoint Dr # 502 99503
Tel (907) 561-2668 SIC 8741 6719

NABORS ALASKA DRILLING INC p 1006
2525 C St Ste 200 99503
Tel (907) 263-6000 SIC 1381

NANA DEVELOPMENT CORP p 1007
909 W 9th Ave 99501
Tel (907) 265-4100 SIC 7381 1389

NANA MANAGEMENT SERVICES LLC p 1007
800 E Dimond Blvd 3-450 99515
Tel (907) 273-2400
SIC 5812 7349 7021 7033 7381

NEA - ALASKA HEALTH PLAN TRUST FUND p 1022
4003 Iowa Dr 99517
Tel (907) 274-7526 SIC 8099

NEESER CONSTRUCTION INC p 1024
2501 Blueberry Rd Ste 100 99503
Tel (907) 276-1058 SIC 1542

NORSTAR PIPELINE CO INC p 1049
3000 Spenard Rd 99503
Tel (907) 277-5551 SIC 4922

NORTH STAR UTILITIES GROUP INC p 1054
420 L St Ste 101 99501
Tel (206) 792-0077 SIC 5172

▲ NORTHRIM BANCORP INC p 1058
3111 C St 99503
Tel (907) 562-0062 SIC 6022 6282

OLD HARBOR NATIVE CORP p 1080
2702 Denali St Ste 100 99503
Tel (907) 278-6100 SIC 8748

PEAK OILFIELD SERVICE CO LLC p 1126
5015 Business Park Blvd # 4000 99503
Tel (907) 263-7000 SIC 7699 1389

PENINSULA AIRWAYS INC p 1129
6200 Boeing Ave Ste 300 99502
Tel (907) 771-2500 SIC 4512

RURAL ALASKA COMMUNITY ACTION PROGRAM INC p 1258
731 E 8th Ave 99501
Tel (907) 279-2511 SIC 8399

SAEXPLORATION INC p 1265
8240 Sandlewood Pl # 102 99507
Tel (907) 522-4499 SIC 1389

SAFEWAY SELECT GIFT SOURCE INC p 1267
6401 A St 99518
Tel (907) 561-1944 SIC 5411 5141 5921

■ SCIENCE APPLICATIONS INTERNATIONAL CORP p 1292
1049 W 5th Ave 99501
Tel (907) 792-2700 SIC 7389

SOUTHCENTRAL FOUNDATION p 1345
4501 Diplomacy Dr 99508
Tel (907) 729-4955 SIC 8093 8021 8042

■ SPENARD BUILDERS SUPPLY LLC p 1358
300 E 54th Ave Ste 201 99518
Tel (907) 261-9126 SIC 5211

SWAN EMPLOYER SERVICES p 1411
1306 E 74th Ave Ste 200 99518
Tel (907) 344-7926 SIC 7363 8721

TANADGUSIX CORP p 1424
615 E 82nd Ave Ste 200 99518
Tel (907) 278-2312 SIC 1796 7011 7359

TATITLEK CORP p 1426
561 E 36th Ave 99503
Tel (907) 278-4000 SIC 0811 6552 7361

TYONEK NATIVE CORP p 1496
1689 C St Ste 219 99501
Tel (907) 272-0707 SIC 6552

UDELHOVEN OILFIELD SYSTEMS SERVICES INC p 1499
184 E 53rd Ave 99518
Tel (907) 344-1577 SIC 1541 1542 8711

UNIVERSITY OF ALASKA ANCHORAGE p 1519
3211 Providence Dr 99508
Tel (907) 786-1800 SIC 8221

USPHS AK NATIVE MEDICAL CENTER p 1535
4315 Diplomacy Dr 99508
Tel (907) 729-2544 SIC 8062

VECO CORP p 1546
949 E 36th Ave Ste 500 99508
Tel (907) 762-1500
SIC 1711 1389 1731 1381 4959

WOLF CREEK FEDERAL SERVICES INC p 1620
3800 Cntrpnt Dr Ste 1200 99503
Tel (907) 563-8866 SIC 3441

WOLF CREEK FEDERAL SERVICES INC p 1621
3800 Cntrpnt Dr Ste 1200 99503
Tel (907) 563-8866 SIC 3441

BARROW, AK

NORTH SLOPE BOROUGH p 1054
1274 Agvik St 99723
Tel (907) 852-2611 SIC 9111

UKPEAGVIK INUPIAT CORP p 1500
1250 Agvik St 99723
Tel (907) 852-4460
SIC 1542 6512 6331 1389 4449

BETHEL, AK

YUKON-KUSKOKWIM HEALTH CORP p 1640
829 Hospin Hwy Ste 329 99559
Tel (907) 543-6300
SIC 8062 7363 8069 8093 8042 8021

DELTA JUNCTION, AK

SUMITOMO METAL MINING POGO LLC p 1398
50 Mile Pogo Mile Rd 99737
Tel (907) 895-2740 SIC 1041

DILLINGHAM, AK

BRISTOL BAY AREA HEALTH CORP p 214
6000 Kanakanak Rd 99576
Tel (907) 842-5201 SIC 8062 8011

DOUGLAS, AK

DEPARTMENT OF CORRECTIONS ALASKA p 430
802 3rd St 99824
Tel (907) 465-4652
SIC 9223 8322 9441 8299

FAIRBANKS, AK

BANNER HEALTH SYSTEM p 153
1650 Cowles St 99701
Tel (907) 452-8181 SIC 8082

BRENNTAG PACIFIC INC p 210
4199 Lathrop St 99701
Tel (907) 452-1555 SIC 5169

DENA NENA HENASH p 428
122 1st Ave Ste 600 99701
Tel (907) 452-8251
SIC 8011 8331 8322 8093

DOYON LIMITED p 454
1 Doyon Pl Ste 300 99701
Tel (907) 459-2000 SIC 1381 1382

FAIRBANKS NORTH STAR BOROUGH SCHOOL DISTRICT p 524
520 5th Ave 99701
Tel (907) 452-2000 SIC 8211

FRONTIER ALASKA p 581
5245 Airport Indus Rd 99709
Tel (907) 450-7250 SIC 4512

GOLDEN VALLEY ELECTRIC ASSOCIATION INC p 621
758 Illinois St 99701
Tel (907) 452-1151 SIC 4911

KOYITLOTSINA LIMITED p 828
1603 College Rd Ste 2 99709
Tel (907) 452-8119 SIC 6798 8744 7349

TANANA CHIEFS CONFERENCE p 1424
122 1st Ave Ste 600 99701
Tel (907) 452-8251 SIC 8699

UNIVERSITY OF ALASKA FAIRBANKS p 1520
910 Yukon Dr 202 99775
Tel (907) 474-7211 SIC 8221

UNIVERSITY OF ALASKA SYSTEM p 1520
3295 College Rd 99709
Tel (907) 450-8079 SIC 8221

HEALY, AK

USIBELLI COAL MINE INC p 1535
100 River Rd 99743
Tel (907) 683-2226 SIC 1221

JBER, AK

ALASKA DEPARTMENT OF MILITARY AND VETERANS AFFAIRS p 45
49000 Army Guard Rd Ste 6 99505
Tel (907) 428-6008 SIC 9711 9451

JUNEAU, AK

ALASKA DEPARTMENT OF ADMINISTRATION p 44
333 Willoughby Ave 99801
Tel (907) 465-2200 SIC 9199

ALASKA DEPARTMENT OF FISH AND GAME p 45
1255 W 8th St 99801
Tel (907) 465-4210 SIC 9512

ALASKA DEPARTMENT OF HEALTH AND SOCIAL SERVICES p 45
350 Main St Rm 427 99801
Tel (907) 465-3030 SIC 9431 9441

ALASKA DEPARTMENT OF TRANSPORTATION AND PUBLIC FACILITIES p 45
3132 Channel Dr Ste 300 99801
Tel (907) 465-3900 SIC 9621

ALASKA PERMANENT FUND CORP p 45
801 W 10th St Ste 302 99801
Tel (907) 796-1500 SIC 6733

CITY & BOROUGH OF JUNEAU p 312
155 S Seward St 99801
Tel (907) 789-0819 SIC 9111

EXECUTIVE OFFICE OF STATE OF ALASKA p 517
Capitol Bldg Fl 3 99811
Tel (907) 465-3500 SIC 9111

GOLDBELT INC p 620
3025 Clinton Dr Ste 100 99801
Tel (907) 790-4990 SIC 4489 6512

SEALASKA CORP p 1296
1 Sealaska Plz Ste 400 99801
Tel (907) 586-1512
SIC 5099 8744 7371 8748 1542

SOUTHEAST ALASKA REGIONAL HEALTH CONSORTIUM p 1345
3100 Channel Dr Ste 300 99801
Tel (907) 463-4000 SIC 8011 8062

STATE OF ALASKA p 1381
120 4th St 99801
Tel (907) 465-3500 SIC 9111

KODIAK, AK

KONIAG INC p 827
3800 Cntrpoint Dr Ste 502 99615
Tel (907) 486-2530 SIC 6552 6519 6719

KOTZEBUE, AK

MANIILAQ ASSOCIATION p 901
733 2nd Ave Ferguson Bldg 99752
Tel (907) 442-3311 SIC 8062 8741

NANA REGIONAL CORP INC p 1007
3150 C St Ste 150 99752
Tel (907) 442-3301 SIC 7011

NOME, AK

BERING STRAITS NATIVE CORP p 174
110 Front St Ste 300 99762
Tel (907) 443-5252 SIC 1081

OUZINKIE, AK

OUZINKIE NATIVE CORP p 1099
500 Main St 99644
Tel (907) 680-2208 SIC 6799

PALMER, AK

MATANUSKA ELECTRIC ASSOCIATION INC p 919
163 E Industrial Way 99645
Tel (907) 745-3231 SIC 4911

MATANUSKA SUSITNA BOROUGH SCHOOL DISTRICT p 919
501 N Gulkana St 99645
Tel (907) 746-9255 SIC 8211

SITKA, AK

SHEE ATIKA INC p 1313
315 Lincoln St Ste 300 99835
Tel (907) 747-3534 SIC 6514 6552

SILVER BAY SEAFOODS LLC p 1323
208 Lake St Ste 2e 99835
Tel (907) 966-3110 SIC 5146

SOLDOTNA, AK

CENTRAL PENINSULA GENERAL HOSPITAL INC p 279
250 Hospital Pl 99669
Tel (907) 262-4404 SIC 8062

KENAI PENINSULA BOROUGH SCHOOL DISTRICT p 810
148 N Binkley St 99669
Tel (907) 714-8888 SIC 8211

ARIZONA

AVONDALE, AZ

LIBERTY UTILITIES CO p 863
12725 W Indian School Rd 85392
Tel (905) 465-4500 SIC 4939

BENSON, AZ

ARIZONA ELECTRIC POWER COOPERATIVE INC p 109
1000 S Highway 80 85602
Tel (520) 586-3631 SIC 4911

BISBEE, AZ

COUNTY OF COCHISE p 377
1415 W Melody Ln Bldg G 85603
Tel (520) 432-9200 SIC 9111

BULLHEAD CITY, AZ

MOHAVE ELECTRIC CO-OPERATIVE INC p 982
928 Hancock Rd 86442
Tel (928) 763-4115 SIC 4911 1731

CASA GRANDE, AZ

CASA GRANDE COMMUNITY HOSPITAL p 262
1800 E Florence Blvd 85122
Tel (520) 426-6300 SIC 8062

CHANDLER, AZ

ACHEN-GARDNER INC p 17
550 S 79th St 85226
Tel (480) 940-1300
SIC 1611 1542 1521 1751 6552

ANS HOLDINGS INC p 93
210 S Beck Ave 85226
Tel (480) 966-9630 SIC 2834

ARION CARE SOLUTIONS LLC p 108
1405 N Dobson Rd Ste 3 85224
Tel (480) 323-0468 SIC 8082

ARIZONA NUTRITIONAL SUPPLEMENTS LLC p 109
210 S Beck Ave 85226
Tel (480) 966-9630 SIC 2834

ARMORWORKS INC p 111
7071 W Frye Rd 85226
Tel (480) 517-1150 SIC 3462

ASML US INC p 118
2650 W Geronimo Pl 85224
Tel (480) 696-2888 SIC 5065 7629

BASHAS INC p 158
22402 S Basha Rd 85248
Tel (480) 883-6131
SIC 5411 5149 5148 5147 6512

CHANDLER EARNHARDTS MAZDA p 288
7300 W Orchid Ln 85226
Tel (480) 893-0000 SIC 5511

CHANDLER REGIONAL MEDICAL CENTER p 288
1955 W Frye Rd 85224
Tel (480) 728-3000 SIC 8062

CHANDLER UNIFIED SCHOOL DISTRICT p 288
1525 W Frye Rd 85224
Tel (480) 812-7000 SIC 8211

CHANDLER UNIFIED SCHOOL DISTRICT 80-HHS AFJROTC p 288
3700 S Arizona Ave 85248
Tel (480) 883-5000 SIC 8211

CITY OF CHANDLER p 313
175 S Arizona Ave 85225
Tel (480) 782-2000 SIC 9111

■ COMFORT SYSTEMS USA (SOUTHWEST) INC p 344
6875 W Galveston St 85226
Tel (480) 940-8400 SIC 1711

CRAFCO INC p 388
6165 W Detroit St 85226
Tel (480) 505-8030 SIC 2951 3531

DIGI-KEY CORP p 439
1393 E Powell Way 85249
Tel (480) 294-5709 SIC 7389

■ ERICKSON BUILDING COMPONENTS LLC p 507
250 N Beck Ave 85226
Tel (480) 627-1100 SIC 2439 2452

EXCEPTIONAL EDUCATIONAL SERVICES LLC p 517
5960 S Cooper Rd Ste 1 85249
Tel (480) 398-1994 SIC 8748

EXPRESS MESSENGER SYSTEMS INC p 520
2501 S Price Rd Ste 201 85286
Tel (800) 334-5000 SIC 4215

GILA RIVER GAMING ENTERPRISES p 611
5040 W Wldhorse Pass Blvd 85226
Tel (800) 946-4452 SIC 7993 5812

GLYNLYON INC p 618
300 N Mckemy Ave 85226
Tel (480) 940-0801 SIC 3999

INFUSION SOFTWARE INC p 742
1260 S Spectrum Blvd 85286
Tel (480) 807-0644 SIC 7379 7371

▲ INSYS THERAPEUTICS INC p 748
1333 S Spectrum Blvd 85286
Tel (480) 500-3127 SIC 2836 2834

ISOLA USA CORP p 767
3100 W Ray Rd Ste 301 85226
Tel (480) 893-6527 SIC 3083

KOVACH INC p 828
3195 W Armstrong Pl 85286
Tel (480) 926-9292 SIC 1761

■ MICREL LLC p 961
2355 W Chandler Blvd 85224
Tel (480) 792-7200 SIC 3674

▲ MICROCHIP TECHNOLOGY INC p 962
2355 W Chandler Blvd 85224
Tel (480) 792-7200 SIC 3674

OPTION 1 NUTRITION SOLUTIONS LLC p 1090
2460 E Germann Rd Ste 18 85286
Tel (480) 883-1188 SIC 5047

PACIFIC SCIENTIFIC ENERGETIC MATERIALS CO (CALIFORNIA) LLC p 1105
7073 W Willis Rd Ste 5002 85226
Tel (480) 763-3000
SIC 2892 2899 3483 3489 3699 3728

SOUND PACKAGING LLC p 1342
260 N Roosevelt Ave 85226
Tel (480) 940-2010 SIC 2653

SOUTH BAY CIRCUITS INC p 1342
99 N Mckemy Ave 85226
Tel (480) 940-3125 SIC 3672

COTTONWOOD, AZ

VERDE VALLEY MEDICAL CENTER p 1549
269 S Candy Ln 86326
Tel (928) 634-2251 SIC 8062

DOUGLAS, AZ

TK HOLDINGS INC p 1457
104 E 9th St 85607
Tel (520) 805-4000 SIC 7549

FLAGSTAFF, AZ

COUNTY OF COCONINO p 377
219 E Cherry Ave 86001
Tel (928) 679-7120 SIC 9111

FLAGSTAFF MEDICAL CENTER INC p 554
1200 N Beaver St 86001
Tel (928) 779-3366 SIC 8062

FLAGSTAFF UNIFIED SCHOOL DISTRICT p 554
3285 E Sparrow Ave 86004
Tel (928) 527-6000 SIC 8211

NORTHERN ARIZONA HEALTHCARE CORP p 1055
1200 N Beaver St 86001
Tel (928) 779-3366
SIC 8741 8062 8399 4119

NORTHERN ARIZONA UNIVERSITY p 1055
601 S Knoles Dr Rm 220 86011
Tel (928) 523-9011 SIC 8221

FLORENCE, AZ

COUNTY OF PINAL p 381
31 N Pinal St 85132
Tel (520) 866-6000 SIC 9111

FORT DEFIANCE, AZ

NAVAJO TRIBAL UTILITY AUTHORITY p 1019
Hwy 12 N 86504
Tel (928) 729-5721 SIC 4939 4924 4911

GILBERT, AZ

FISHER FINANCIAL GROUP INC p 552
3303 E Baseline Rd # 113 85234
Tel (480) 461-1111 SIC 6162

GILBERT HOSPITAL LLC p 612
5656 S Power Rd Ste 133 85295
Tel (480) 984-2000 SIC 8062

GILBERT UNIFIED SCHOOL DISTRICT 41 p 612
140 S Gilbert Rd 85296
Tel (480) 497-3452 SIC 8211

HUNTER CONTRACTING CO p 719
701 N Cooper Rd 85233
Tel (480) 892-0521 SIC 1611 1629 1622

ISAGENIX INTERNATIONAL LLC p 766
155 E Rivulon Blvd 85297
Tel (480) 889-5747 SIC 2834

TOWN OF GILBERT p 1465
50 E Civic Center Dr 85296
Tel (480) 503-6000 SIC 9111

TOWN OF GILBERT ARIZONA p 1465
50 E Civic Center Dr 85296
Tel (480) 503-6400 SIC 9111

GLENDALE, AZ

ACHMC INC p 17
18701 N 67th Ave 85308
Tel (623) 561-7170 SIC 8062

ARIZONA DENTAL INSURANCE SERVICE INC p 108
5656 W Talavi Blvd 85306
Tel (602) 588-3617 SIC 6324 6411

CITY OF GLENDALE p 315
5850 W Glendale Ave Fl 4 85301
Tel (623) 930-2000 SIC 9111

CITY OF GLENDALE MUNICIPAL PROPERTY CORP p 315
5850 W Glendale Ave 85301
Tel (623) 930-2820 SIC 7389

DON FORD SANDERSON INC p 450
6400 N 51st Ave 85301
Tel (623) 842-8600 SIC 5511

GLENDALE ELEMENTARY SCHOOL DISTRICT p 615
7301 N 58th Ave 85301
Tel (623) 237-4000 SIC 8211

GLENDALE UNION HIGH SCHOOL DISTRICT p 615
7650 N 43rd Ave 85301
Tel (623) 435-0152 SIC 8211

PEORIA UNIFIED SCHOOL DISTRICT NO11 p 1133
6330 W Thunderbird Rd 85306
Tel (623) 486-6000 SIC 8211

REDFLEX TRAFFIC SYSTEMS INC p 1216
5651 W Talavi Blvd # 200 85306
Tel (623) 207-2000 SIC 8748

SOUTHWEST METAL INDUSTRIES LLC p 1352
4708 W Pasadena Ave 85301
Tel (623) 760-9014 SIC 5051 4953

WASHINGTON ELEMENTARY SCHOOL DISTRICT 6 p 1578
4650 W Sweetwater Ave 85304
Tel (602) 347-2600 SIC 8211

GOODYEAR, AZ

ABRAZO WEST CAMPUS p 12
13677 W Mcdowell Rd 85395
Tel (623) 882-1500 SIC 8062

■ **MCLANE/SUNWEST INC** p 931
14149 W Mcdowell Rd 85395
Tel (623) 935-7500 SIC 5141

GRAND CANYON, AZ

XANTERRA SOUTH RIM LLC p 1630
1 Main St 86023
Tel (928) 638-2631 SIC 7011 5812

GREEN VALLEY, AZ

■ **FREEPORT-MCMORAN SIERRITA INC** p 577
6200 W Duval Mine Rd 85622
Tel (520) 648-8500 SIC 1021

TOHONO OODHAM GAMING ENTERPRISE p 1458
1100 W Pima Mine Rd 85614
Tel (520) 342-3000 SIC 7999 7011

HOLBROOK, AZ

Q K INC p 1194
101 E Hopi Dr 86025
Tel (928) 524-3680 SIC 5812

KINGMAN, AZ

COUNTY OF MOHAVE p 380
700 W Beale St 86401
Tel (928) 753-0729 SIC 9111

KINGMAN HOSPITAL INC p 820
3269 N Stockton Hill Rd 86409
Tel (928) 757-2101 SIC 8062

LAKE HAVASU CITY, AZ

NATIONWIDE HOMES INC p 1018
1100 London Bridge Rd G102 86404
Tel (928) 453-6600 SIC 1521 6531

■ **PHC-LAKE HAVASU INC** p 1141
101 Civic Center Ln 86403
Tel (928) 855-8185 SIC 8062

LEUPP, AZ

TOOH DINEH INDUSTRIES INC p 1460
Leupp School Rd Bldg 4 86035
Tel (928) 686-6477 SIC 3679 3672

LITCHFIELD PARK, AZ

LITCHFIELD ELEMENTARY SCHOOL DISTRICT 79 p 870
272 E Sagebrush St 85340
Tel (623) 535-6000 SIC 8211

MARANA, AZ

MARANA AEROSPACE SOLUTIONS INC p 904
24641 E Pinal Air Park Rd 85653
Tel (520) 682-4181 SIC 4581

MARANA UNIFIED SCHOOL DISTRICT p 904
11279 W Grier Rd 85653
Tel (520) 682-4749 SIC 8211

MARANA UNIFIED SCHOOL DISTRICT PARENT/CITIZEN ORGANIZATION p 904
11279 W Grier Rd 85653
Tel (520) 682-3243 SIC 8211

■ **SILVER BELL MINING LLC** p 1323
25000 W Avra Valley Rd 85653
Tel (520) 682-2420 SIC 1021

TRICO ELECTRIC COOPERATIVE INC p 1479
8600 W Tangerine Rd 85658
Tel (520) 744-2944 SIC 4911

MARICOPA, AZ

AK-CHIN INDIAN COMMUNITY DEVELOPMENT CORP p 41
42507 W Peters & Nall Rd 85138
Tel (520) 568-1000
SIC 0131 0139 5251 7993

MESA, AZ

ACUMEN FISCAL AGENT LLC p 20
4542 E Inverness Ave # 210 85206
Tel (480) 497-1889 SIC 8721

■ **ALPINE VALLEY BREAD CO** p 61
300 W Southern Ave 85210
Tel (480) 483-2774 SIC 2051

■ **AMERICAN TRAFFIC SOLUTIONS INC** p 80
1150 N Alma School Rd 85201
Tel (480) 443-7000 SIC 7374 1731 5084

ANDES INDUSTRIES INC p 90
2260 W Broadway Rd # 101 85202
Tel (480) 813-0925 SIC 5063 3663 3643

BANNER HEALTH SYSTEM p 153
6644 E Baywood Ave 85206
Tel (480) 321-2000 SIC 8062

BERGE FORD INC p 174
460 E Auto Center Dr 85204
Tel (480) 497-7600 SIC 5511

■ **BROWN & BROWN CHEVROLET INC** p 219
145 E Main St 85201
Tel (480) 833-3456 SIC 5511 5521 5012

CITY OF MESA p 316
20 E Main St 85201
Tel (480) 644-2011 SIC 9111

EMPIRE SOUTHWEST LLC p 493
1725 S Country Club Dr 85210
Tel (480) 633-4000 SIC 5082 7353 7699

INTER-TEL TECHNOLOGIES INC p 751
1146 N Alma School Rd 85201
Tel (480) 858-9600
SIC 5999 1731 5065 3661 3577

LONGUST DISTRIBUTING INC p 877
2432 W Birchwood Ave 85202
Tel (480) 820-6244 SIC 5023

LUTHERAN HEART HOSPITAL p 886
6750 E Baywood Ave 85206
Tel (480) 854-5000 SIC 8062

M & O AGENCIES INC p 888
1835 S Extension Rd 85210
Tel (480) 730-4920 SIC 6411

MESA UNIFIED SCHOOL DISTRICT 4 p 951
63 E Main St Ste 101 85201
Tel (480) 472-0000 SIC 8211

MITEL (DELAWARE) INC p 977
1146 N Alma School Rd 85201
Tel (480) 449-8900
SIC 3661 5045 4813 5065 1731 7359

MITEL NETWORKS INC p 977
1146 N Alma School Rd 85201
Tel (480) 961-9000
SIC 3661 7359 1731 7373

MITEL TECHNOLOGIES INC p 977
1146 N Alma School Rd 85201
Tel (480) 449-8900 SIC 5065

MOUNTAIN VISTA MEDICAL CENTER LP p 994
1301 S Crismon Rd 85209
Tel (480) 358-6100 SIC 8062

MOUNTAIN VISTA SURGICAL SPECIALISTS p 994
10238 E Hampton Ave # 402 85209
Tel (480) 354-3200 SIC 8011

NEXTCARE HOLDINGS INC p 1040
1138 N Alma School Rd # 120 85201
Tel (480) 924-8382 SIC 8093 8741 8011

NEXTCARE INC p 1040
2550 N Thunderbird Cir # 303 85215
Tel (480) 924-8382 SIC 8093 8741

PCT INTERNATIONAL INC p 1124
2260 W Broadway Rd # 101 85202
Tel (480) 813-0925 SIC 3663

RISE INC p 1236
4554 E Inverness Ave # 134 85206
Tel (480) 497-1889 SIC 8322

WHITEMAN FAMILY CORP p 1606
1725 S Country Club Dr 85210
Tel (480) 633-4413
SIC 5082 5083 7353 7699 7359 5012

MOHAVE VALLEY, AZ

STEWARTS CONCRETE & BOBCAT p 1389
8771 S Desoto Dr 86440
Tel (928) 788-4453 SIC 1771

NOGALES, AZ

■ **AMPHENOL OPTIMIZE MANUFACTURING CO** p 86
180 N Freeport Dr 10 85621
Tel (520) 397-7015 SIC 3678 3643

DIVINE FLAVOR LLC p 444
766 N Target Range Rd 85621
Tel (520) 281-8328 SIC 5148

EDS MANUFACTURING INC p 479
765 N Target Range Rd 85621
Tel (520) 287-9711 SIC 3679

ORO VALLEY, AZ

ORO VALLEY HOSPITAL LLC p 1095
1551 E Tangerine Rd 85755
Tel (520) 901-3500 SIC 8062

■ **VENTANA MEDICAL SYSTEMS INC** p 1547
1910 E Innovation Park Dr 85755
Tel (520) 887-2155 SIC 3841 2819 3826

PARADISE VALLEY, AZ

STANDARD AERO HOLDINGS INC p 1375
6710 N Scottsdale Rd # 250 85253
Tel (480) 377-3100 SIC 7699

STANDARDAERO AVIATION HOLDINGS INC p 1376
6710 N Scottsdale Rd # 250 85253
Tel (480) 377-3100 SIC 3721

PEORIA, AZ

ANTIGUA ENTERPRISES INC p 94
16651 N 84th Ave 85382
Tel (623) 523-6000 SIC 2329

ANTIGUA GROUP INC p 94
16651 N 84th Ave 85382
Tel (623) 523-6000
SIC 5137 5136 2395 2339 3993

CITY OF PEORIA p 317
8401 W Monroe St 85345
Tel (623) 773-7148 SIC 9111

YOUNGER BROTHERS GROUP INC p 1639
8525 N 75th Ave 85345
Tel (623) 979-1111 SIC 1751

PHOENIX, AZ

11111 NORTH 7TH STREET PROPERTY LLC p 1
11111 N 7th St 85020
Tel (602) 866-7500 SIC 7011

ABEINSA HOLDING INC p 10
2929 N Cent Ave Ste 1100 85012
Tel (602) 265-6870 SIC 1522 1542

ABR PROPERTY LLC p 12
2400 E Missouri Ave 85016
Tel (602) 955-6600 SIC 7011

■ **ABRAZO CENTRAL CAMPUS** p 12
2000 W Bethany Home Rd 85015
Tel (602) 249-0212 SIC 8062

ACE ASPHALT OF ARIZONA INC p 16
3030 S 7th St 85040
Tel (602) 243-4100 SIC 1611

■ **ADVANTAGE LOGISTICS SOUTHWEST INC** p 26
5305 W Buckeye Rd 85043
Tel (602) 477-3100 SIC 5141

AFS TECHNOLOGIES INC p 33
2141 E Highland Ave # 100 85016
Tel (602) 522-8282 SIC 7371

ALHAMBRA SCHOOL DISTRICT 68 p 50
4510 N 37th Ave 85019
Tel (602) 336-2920 SIC 8211

ALLIANCE BEVERAGE DISTRIBUTING CO LLC p 54
1115 N 47th Ave 85043
Tel (602) 760-5500 SIC 5182 5181

ALLIANCE RESIDENTIAL LLC p 55
2415 E Camelback Rd # 600 85016
Tel (602) 778-2800 SIC 6531

■ **ALLIED WASTE INDUSTRIES INC** p 57
18500 N Allied Way # 100 85054
Tel (480) 627-2700 SIC 4953

■ **ALLIED WASTE NORTH AMERICA INC** p 57
18500 N Allied Way # 100 85054
Tel (480) 627-2700 SIC 4953

■ **ALLIED WASTE SYSTEMS INC** p 57
18500 N Allied Way # 100 85054
Tel (480) 627-2700 SIC 4953

■ **AMERICA WEST AIRLINES INC** p 67
4000 E Sky Harbor Blvd 85034
Tel (480) 693-0800 SIC 4512

AMSAFE PARTNERS INC p 87
1043 N 47th Ave 85043
Tel (602) 850-2850 SIC 2399

▲ **APOLLO EDUCATION GROUP INC** p 97
4025 S Riverpoint Pkwy 85040
Tel (480) 966-5394 SIC 8221 8299 8748

ARCH ALUMINUM & GLASS CO OF ARIZONA INC p 104
1825 S 43rd Ave Ste A 85009
Tel (602) 484-9777 SIC 3442 1793

ARIZONA BOARD OF REGENTS p 108
2020 N Central Ave # 230 85004
Tel (602) 229-2500 SIC 8221 9411

ARIZONA COMMUNITY FOUNDATION INC p 108
2201 E Camelback Rd # 405 85016
Tel (928) 348-9649 SIC 6732

ARIZONA DEPARTMENT OF ADMINISTRATION p 108
100 N 15th Ave Ste 401 85007
Tel (602) 542-1500 SIC 9199

ARIZONA DEPARTMENT OF EMERGENCY AND MILITARY AFFAIRS p 109
5636 E Mcdowell Rd 85008
Tel (602) 267-2700 SIC 9711

ARIZONA DEPT OF ECONOMIC SECURITY p 109
1717 W Jefferson St 85007
Tel (602) 542-7166 SIC 9441

ARIZONA DEPT OF TRANSPORTATION p 109
206 S 17th Ave 85007
Tel (602) 712-7227 SIC 9621

ARIZONA PARKING LOT SERVICE p 109
1415 E Bethany Home Rd 85014
Tel (602) 277-8007 SIC 1799 1611

ARIZONA PARTSMASTER INC p 109
7125 W Sherman St 85043
Tel (602) 233-3580 SIC 5087

■ **ARIZONA PUBLIC SERVICE CO** p 109
400 N 5th St Fl 2 85004
Tel (602) 250-1000 SIC 4911

ARIZONA WATER CO p 109
3805 N Black Canyon Hwy 85015
Tel (480) 982-2201 SIC 4941

ASM AMERICA INC p 118
3440 E University Dr 85034
Tel (602) 470-5700 SIC 3559

ASPECT SOFTWARE GROUP HOLDINGS LTD p 118
2325 E Camelback Rd # 700 85016
Tel (602) 282-1500 SIC 7373

ASPECT SOFTWARE INC p 118
2325 E Camelback Rd # 700 85016
Tel (978) 250-7900 SIC 7371

ASTRACO LLC p 122
1411 E Hidalgo Ave 85040
Tel (602) 931-2981 SIC 5136 5699

AUTOMOTIVE INVESTMENT GROUP INC p 134
1300 E Camelback Rd 85014
Tel (602) 264-2332 SIC 5511

■ **AVIATION COMMUNICATION & SURVEILLANCE SYSTEMS LLC** p 138
19810 N 7th Ave 85027
Tel (623) 445-7030 SIC 8711

■ **AVNET ELECTRONICS MARKETING** p 138
2211 S 47th St 85034
Tel (480) 643-2000 SIC 5065

▲ **AVNET INC** p 138
2211 S 47th St 85034
Tel (480) 643-2000 SIC 5065 5045 7379

AXWAY INC p 140
6811 E Mayo Blvd Ste 400 85054
Tel (480) 627-1800 SIC 7372

BAE SYSTEMS p 144
7822 S 46th St 85044
Tel (602) 643-7233 SIC 2531

BAE SYSTEMS PROTECTION SYSTEMS INC p 144
7822 S 46th St 85044
Tel (602) 643-7233
SIC 3721 2353 3795 3842

BANNER HEALTH p 153
2901 N Central Ave # 160 85012
Tel (602) 747-4000
SIC 8062 8051 8082 7361 8011 8093

BANNER-UNIVERSITY MEDICAL GROUP p 153
2901 N Central Ave 85012
Tel (602) 747-4000 SIC 8011

BAR-S FOODS CO p 154
5090 N 40th St Ste 300 85018
Tel (602) 264-7272 SIC 2013

■ **BENCHMARK ELECTRONICS PHOENIX INC** p 172
2222 W Pinnacle Pk Rd # 310 85027
Tel (619) 397-2400 SIC 3577 3672

BEST WESTERN INTERNATIONAL INC p 177
6201 N 24th Pkwy 85016
Tel (602) 957-4200
SIC 7389 7311 5046 8743

■ **BFI WASTE SYSTEMS OF NORTH AMERICA INC** p 179
2394 E Camelback Rd 85016
Tel (480) 627-2700 SIC 4953

BLUE CROSS AND BLUE SHIELD OF ARIZONA INC p 191
2444 W Las Palmaritas Dr 85021
Tel (602) 864-4100 SIC 6324

BLUECROSS AND BLUESHIELD OF AZ p 193
2410 W Royal Palm Rd 85021
Tel (602) 864-4100 SIC 6324

■ **BROWNING-FERRIS INDUSTRIES INC** p 220
18500 N Allied Way # 100 85054
Tel (480) 627-2700 SIC 4953 4959 7359

BURNS CONSULTING INC p 228
15414 N 7th St 8122 85022
Tel (602) 993-3070 SIC 8742 7389

▲ **CABLE ONE INC** p 235
210 E Earll Dr Fl 6 85012
Tel (602) 364-6000 SIC 4813 4841

CAFE VALLEY INC p 237
7000 W Buckeye Rd 85043
Tel (602) 278-2909 SIC 2099

CANYON STATE OIL CO INC p 248
2640 N 31st Ave 85009
Tel (602) 269-7981 SIC 5172 5531

CAPITAL LUMBER CO p 250
5110 N 40th St Ste 242 85018
Tel (602) 381-0709 SIC 5031

CARIOCA CO p 256
2601 W Dunlap Ave Ste 10 85021
Tel (602) 395-2600 SIC 5541 5411

CARTWRIGHT SCHOOL DISTRICT NO83 p 262
5220 W Indian School Rd 85031
Tel (623) 691-4000 SIC 8211

▲ **CAVCO INDUSTRIES INC** p 267
1001 N Central Ave # 800 85004
Tel (602) 256-6263 SIC 2451 5271

CEMEX CORP p 274
4646 E Van Buren St # 250 85008
Tel (602) 416-2600 *SIC* 5032 3273

■ **CENTRAL VALLEY SPECIALTIES INC** p 281
3846 E Winslow Ave 85040
Tel (602) 437-2046 *SIC* 1742 1721

CENTURI CONSTRUCTION GROUP INC p 281
2355 W Utopia Rd 85027
Tel (623) 582-1235 *SIC* 4923

CERTEX USA INC p 284
1721 W Culver St 85007
Tel (602) 271-9048 *SIC* 5084

■ **CIGNA HEALTHCARE OF ARIZONA INC** p 306
25500 N Norterra Dr 85085
Tel (623) 587-4402 *SIC* 6324

CITY OF PHOENIX p 317
200 W Washington St Fl 11 85003
Tel (602) 262-7111 *SIC* 9111

■ **CLEAR CHANNEL OUTDOOR INC** p 324
2325 E Camelback Rd # 400 85016
Tel (602) 381-5700 *SIC* 7312

CLIMATEC LLC p 326
2851 W Kathleen Rd 85053
Tel (602) 944-3330 *SIC* 1731 7373

■ **CLIMAX MOLYBDENUM MARKETING CORP** p 326
333 N Central Ave Ste 100 85004
Tel (602) 366-8100 *SIC* 1061 3313

COPPER STATE BOLT & NUT CO INC p 368
3602 N 35th Ave 85017
Tel (602) 272-2384 *SIC* 5072 3452

COPPERPOINT MUTUAL INSURANCE CO p 368
3030 N 3rd St Ste 110 85012
Tel (602) 631-2300 *SIC* 6331

CORE CONSTRUCTION INC p 369
3036 E Greenway Rd 85032
Tel (602) 494-0800 *SIC* 1542 1541

COUNTY OF MARICOPA p 379
301 W Jefferson St # 960 85003
Tel (602) 506-3011 *SIC* 9111

COURTESY CHEVROLET p 383
1233 E Camelback Rd 85014
Tel (602) 279-3232 *SIC* 5511 5013 7538

COX COMMUNICATIONS INC p 386
1550 W Deer Valley Rd 85027
Tel (404) 269-6736 *SIC* 4841

CREIGHTON SCHOOL DISTRICT p 391
2702 E Flower St 85016
Tel (602) 381-6000 *SIC* 8211

■ **CSK AUTO CORP** p 398
645 E Mazouri Ave Ste 400 85012
Tel (602) 265-9200 *SIC* 5531

CSK AUTO INC p 398
645 E Missouri Ave # 400 85012
Tel (602) 265-9200 *SIC* 5531

CUTTER AVIATION p 403
2802 E Old Tower Rd 85034
Tel (602) 273-1237
SIC 5599 5088 4522 5172 4581

■ **CYPRUS AMAX MINERALS CO** p 405
333 N Central Ave 85004
Tel (602) 366-8100
SIC 1221 1222 1021 1061 1479 1041

■ **CYPRUS CLIMAX METALS CO** p 405
333 N Central Ave 85004
Tel (928) 473-7000 *SIC* 6719

■ **CYPRUS METALS CO** p 406
333 N Central Ave 85004
Tel (928) 473-7000 *SIC* 1021

■ **CYPRUS MINES CORP** p 406
1 N Central Ave 85004
Tel (602) 366-8100
SIC 1221 1021 1031 1061

■ **DBM GLOBAL INC** p 418
3020 E Camelback Rd # 100 85016
Tel (602) 252-7787 *SIC* 3441 1791

DEER VALLEY SCHOOL DISTRICT 97 p 422
20402 N 15th Ave 85027
Tel (623) 445-5000 *SIC* 8211

DEPT OF CORRECTIONS ARIZONA p 431
1601 W Jefferson St 85007
Tel (602) 542-5225 *SIC* 9223

DEPT OF REVENUE ARIZONA p 431
1600 W Monroe St 85007
Tel (602) 542-2054 *SIC* 9311

DESERT SCHOOLS FEDERAL CREDIT UNION p 432
148 N 48th St 85034
Tel (602) 433-7000 *SIC* 6062

DISTRICT MEDICAL GROUP INC p 443
2929 E Thomas Rd 85016
Tel (602) 274-8859 *SIC* 8011

DIVERSIFIED ROOFING CORP p 444
2015 W Mountain View Rd 85021
Tel (602) 850-8218 *SIC* 1761

DREAMERSTRAVELS LLC p 455
830 E Sherman St 85034
Tel (602) 305-6414 *SIC* 7999

ENGHOUSE INTERACTIVE INC p 498
2095 W Pinnacle Peak Rd 85027
Tel (602) 789-2800
SIC 3571 3661 3663 7372 7374

ENTERPRISE CONSULTING SOLUTIONS INC p 502
15458 N 28th Ave 85053
Tel (623) 207-5600 *SIC* 7375

EPCOR WATER (USA) INC p 504
2355 W Pinnacle Peak Rd # 300 85027
Tel (623) 445-2400 *SIC* 4941

ESTRELLA BANNER MEDICAL CENTER p 511
9201 W Thomas Rd 85037
Tel (623) 327-4000 *SIC* 8011

ESTRELLA BANNER SURGERY CENTER p 511
9301 W Thomas Rd 85037
Tel (623) 388-5700 *SIC* 8062

EWING IRRIGATION PRODUCTS INC p 516
3441 E Harbour Dr 85034
Tel (602) 437-9530 *SIC* 5085 5087 5074

EXECUTIVE OFFICE OF STATE OF ARIZONA p 517
1700 W Washington St # 602 85007
Tel (602) 542-4331 *SIC* 9111

EXODYNE INC p 519
8433 N Black Canyon Hwy # 100 85021
Tel (602) 995-3700
SIC 8711 8731 8741 8744 8748

FARMERS INSURANCE CO OF ARIZONA p 529
16001 N 28th Ave 85053
Tel (602) 863-8100 *SIC* 6411 8741

■ **FH GROUP LLC** p 539
1001 N Central Ave # 800 85004
Tel (574) 773-7941 *SIC* 2451

■ **FLEETWOOD HOMES INC** p 555
1001 N Central Ave # 800 85004
Tel (602) 256-6263 *SIC* 2451 5271

FOUNDERS HEALTHCARE LLC p 571
4601 E Hilton Ave Ste 100 85034
Tel (800) 636-2123 *SIC* 7352

■ **FREEPORT MINERALS CORP** p 577
333 N Central Ave 85004
Tel (602) 366-8100
SIC 1061 1021 3312 3351

▲ **FREEPORT-MCMORAN INC** p 577
333 N Central Ave 85004
Tel (602) 366-8100
SIC 1021 1041 1061 1044

■ **FREEPORT-MCMORAN MIAMI INC** p 577
333 N Central Ave 85004
Tel (602) 366-8100 *SIC* 1021

GOODMANS INC p 624
1400 E Indian School Rd 85014
Tel (602) 263-1110 *SIC* 5712 7389

GOODWILL INDUSTRIES OF CENTRAL ARIZONA FOUNDATION INC p 624
2626 W Beryl Ave 85021
Tel (602) 535-4000 *SIC* 8331

▲ **GRAND CANYON EDUCATION INC** p 629
3300 W Camelback Rd 85017
Tel (602) 639-7500 *SIC* 8221

■ **GRAND CANYON UNIVERSITY INC** p 629
3300 W Camelback Rd 85017
Tel (602) 639-7500 *SIC* 8221

GREAT HEARTS ACADEMIES p 633
3102 N 56th St Ste 300 85018
Tel (602) 438-7045 *SIC* 8211

HAYDON BUILDING CORP p 670
4640 E Cotton Gin Loop 85040
Tel (602) 296-1496 *SIC* 1541 1542

HEALTH CHOICE ARIZONA INC p 674
410 N 44th St Ste 900 85008
Tel (480) 968-6866 *SIC* 6321 6411

HEALTH SERVICES DEPARTMENT p 676
150 N 18th Ave Ste 163 85007
Tel (602) 542-1025 *SIC* 9431

HEAVY VEHICLE ELECTRONIC LICENSE PLATE INC p 680
101 N 1st Ave Ste 2275 85003
Tel (602) 412-2240 *SIC* 7538

HIGH-TECH INSTITUTE INC p 691
2250 W Peoria Ave A100 85029
Tel (602) 274-4300 *SIC* 8221

■ **HOLSUM BAKERY INC** p 702
2322 W Lincoln St 85009
Tel (602) 252-2351 *SIC* 2051

■ **HONEYWELL AEROSPACE INC** p 705
1944 E Sky Harbor Cir N 85034
Tel (602) 365-3099 *SIC* 3812 7363 7699

■ **HORIZON DISTRIBUTORS INC** p 707
5214 S 30th St 85040
Tel (480) 337-6700 *SIC* 4971 5083

HOSPICE OF VALLEY p 709
1510 E Flower St 85014
Tel (602) 530-6900 *SIC* 8082

HOTEL CLEANING SERVICES INC p 710
9609 N 22nd Ave 85021
Tel (602) 588-0864 *SIC* 7349

■ **HUNT CONSTRUCTION GROUP INC** p 719
7720 N 16th St Ste 100 85020
Tel (480) 368-4700 *SIC* 8741

■ **INFORMEDRX INC** p 742
4805 E Thistle Landing Dr # 100 85044
Tel (800) 282-3232 *SIC* 8742

■ **INSIGHT DIRECT USA INC** p 746
201 N Central Ave 85004
Tel (480) 333-3000 *SIC* 5045 3571

▲ **INSIGHT ENTERPRISES INC** p 746
201 N Central Ave 85004
Tel (480) 333-3000 *SIC* 5045 7379 5065

INTERSTATE MECHANICAL CORP p 758
1841 E Washington St 85034
Tel (800) 628-0211 *SIC* 1711

▲ **INVENTURE FOODS INC** p 761
5415 E High St Ste 350 85054
Tel (623) 932-6200 *SIC* 2096 2037

IO DATA CENTERS LLC p 762
615 N 48th St 85008
Tel (480) 513-8500 *SIC* 7379

JAVINE VENTURES INC p 779
2851 W Kathleen Rd 85053
Tel (602) 944-3330 *SIC* 5075 1731

JOHN C LINCOLN HEALTH NETWORK p 788
250 E Dunlap Ave 85020
Tel (602) 870-6060 *SIC* 8062 8051

JR MC DADE CO INC p 795
1102 N 21st Ave 85009
Tel (602) 258-7134 *SIC* 5023 1752

JUDICIARY COURTS OF STATE OF ARIZONA p 796
1501 W Washington St 85007
Tel (602) 452-3300 *SIC* 9211

KARSTEN MANUFACTURING CORP p 804
2201 W Desert Cove Ave 85029
Tel (602) 870-5000
SIC 3949 3398 3363 3325 8711 7997

KENYON COMPANIES p 813
2602 N 35th Ave 85009
Tel (602) 233-1191 *SIC* 1742 2819

KENYON CONSTRUCTION INC p 813
4001 W Indian School Rd 85019
Tel (602) 484-0080 *SIC* 1742

KENYON PLASTERING INC p 813
4001 W Indian School Rd 85019
Tel (602) 233-1191 *SIC* 1742

KIEWIT WESTERN CO p 817
3888 E Broadway Rd 85040
Tel (602) 437-7878
SIC 1622 1629 1794 1611 1623

KITCHELL CONTRACTORS INC OF ARIZONA p 822
1707 E Highland Ave # 200 85016
Tel (602) 264-4411 *SIC* 1541 1542 1521

KITCHELL CORP p 822
1707 E Highland Ave # 100 85016
Tel (602) 264-4411
SIC 1542 1541 1521 8711 5078 6552

▲ **KNIGHT TRANSPORTATION INC** p 824
20002 N 19th Ave 85027
Tel (602) 269-2000 *SIC* 4213 4212

KODIAK FRESH PRODUCE LLC p 826
1033 E Maricopa Fwy 85034
Tel (602) 253-2236 *SIC* 5148

KSL ARIZONA HOLDINGS III INC p 831
2400 E Missouri Ave 85016
Tel (602) 955-6600
SIC 7011 5812 7991 5813

LASERMASTERS LLC p 846
4857 W Van Buren St 85043
Tel (602) 278-5234 *SIC* 3861

LEONA GROUP L L C p 856
7878 N 16th St Ste 150 85020
Tel (602) 953-2933 *SIC* 8211

LESLIES HOLDINGS INC p 857
3925 E Broadway Rd # 100 85040
Tel (602) 366-3999 *SIC* 5999

LESLIES POOLMART INC p 857
2005 E Indian School Rd 85016
Tel (602) 366-3999 *SIC* 5091

LINCOLN HERITAGE LIFE INSURANCE CO p 867
4343 E Camelback Rd # 400 85018
Tel (800) 750-6404 *SIC* 6311 6411

LOFTIN EQUIPMENT CO p 874
2111 E Highland Ave # 255 85016
Tel (800) 437-4376 *SIC* 5063 5084 5999

LONDEN INSURANCE GROUP INC p 875
4343 E Camelback Rd # 400 85018
Tel (602) 957-1650 *SIC* 6311 6321 8741

MACAYO RESTAURANTS LLC p 892
1480 E Bethany Home Rd # 130 85014
Tel (602) 264-1831 *SIC* 5813 5812 5149

MAKE-A-WISH FOUNDATION OF AMERICA p 899
4742 N 24th St Ste 400 85016
Tel (602) 279-9474 *SIC* 8322

MARICOPA COUNTY SPECIAL HEALTH CARE DISTRICT p 906
2601 E Roosevelt St 85008
Tel (602) 344-5726 *SIC* 8062

MATRIX ABSENCE MANAGEMENT INC p 920
2421 W Peoria Ave Ste 200 85029
Tel (602) 866-2333 *SIC* 6411

MEADOW VALLEY CORP p 934
3333 E Camelback Rd # 240 85018
Tel (602) 437-5400 *SIC* 1611 5032

MEADOW VALLEY HOLDINGS LLC p 934
4602 E Thomas Rd 85018
Tel (602) 437-5400 *SIC* 1611 5032

MERCY MARICOPA INTEGRATED CARE p 947
4350 E Cotton Center Blvd D 85040
Tel (602) 453-8308 *SIC* 6324

MESA AIR GROUP INC p 951
410 N 44th St Ste 700 85008
Tel (602) 685-4000 *SIC* 4512 4522

MESA AIRLINES INC p 951
410 N 44th St Ste 700 85008
Tel (602) 685-4000 *SIC* 4512 4522 4581

MIDWAY CHEVROLET CO p 966
2323 W Bell Rd 85023
Tel (602) 866-0102 *SIC* 5511

▲ **MOBILE MINI INC** p 980
4646 E Van Buren St # 400 85008
Tel (480) 894-6311
SIC 4225 3448 3441 3412 7359

MODERN INDUSTRIES INC p 981
4747 E Beautiful Ln 85044
Tel (602) 267-7248 *SIC* 3599 3769

MOON VALLEY NURSERY INC p 987
18047 N Tatum Blvd 85032
Tel (602) 493-0403 *SIC* 5193 5261

NAJAFI COMPANIES LLC p 1006
2525 E Camelback Rd 85016
Tel (602) 476-0600 *SIC* 3695

NAUMANN/HOBBS MATERIAL HANDLING CORP II INC p 1019
4335 E Wood St 85040
Tel (602) 437-1331 *SIC* 5084

■ **NPL CONSTRUCTION CO** p 1064
2355 W Utopia Rd 85027
Tel (623) 582-1235 *SIC* 1623

▲ **ON SEMICONDUCTOR CORP** p 1086
5005 E Mcdowell Rd 85008
Tel (602) 244-6600 *SIC* 3674 3825 3651

■ **OXFORD LIFE INSURANCE CO INC** p 1101
2721 N Central Ave Fl 5 85004
Tel (602) 263-6666 *SIC* 6311 6321

■ **PAG WEST LLC** p 1107
7015 E Chauncey Ln 85054
Tel (480) 538-6677 *SIC* 5511

■ **PALM HARBOR HOMES INC** p 1109
1001 N Central Ave # 800 85004
Tel (602) 256-6263 *SIC* 2452 5211 6141

PARADISE VALLEY UNIFIED SCHOOL DISTRICT p 1113
15002 N 32nd St 85032
Tel (602) 867-5100 *SIC* 8211

PARAMOUNT BUILDING SOLUTIONS LLC p 1114
10235 S 51st St Ste 185 85044
Tel (480) 348-1177 *SIC* 7349

■ **PAULEY CONSTRUCTION LLC** p 1121
2021 W Melinda Ln 85027
Tel (623) 581-1200 *SIC* 1623

PENDERGAST ELEMENTARY SCHOOL DISTRICT 92 p 1128
3802 N 91st Ave 85037
Tel (623) 772-2200 *SIC* 8211

PETER PIPER INC p 1138
4745 N 7th St Ste 350 85014
Tel (480) 609-6400 *SIC* 5812 7993 6794

PETSMART INC p 1139
19601 N 27th Ave 85027
Tel (623) 580-6100 *SIC* 5999 0742 0752

■ **PHI AIR MEDICAL LLC** p 1142
2800 N 44th St Ste 800 85008
Tel (602) 224-3500 *SIC* 4522

PHOENIX CHILDRENS HOSPITAL INC p 1144
1919 E Thomas Rd 85016
Tel (602) 546-1000 *SIC* 8069

PHOENIX ELEMENTARY SCHOOL DISTRICT 1 p 1145
1817 N 7th St 85006
Tel (602) 257-3755 *SIC* 8211

■ **PHOENIX NEWSPAPERS INC** p 1145
200 E Van Buren St 85004
Tel (602) 444-8000 *SIC* 2711

PHOENIX RANCH MARKET III p 1145
1602 E Roosevelt St 85006
Tel (602) 254-6676 *SIC* 0291

PHOENIX UNION HIGH SCHOOL DISTRICT NO 210 p 1145
4502 N Central Ave 85012
Tel (602) 271-3302 *SIC* 8211

▲ **PINNACLE WEST CAPITAL CORP** p 1150
400 N 5th St 85004
Tel (602) 250-1000 *SIC* 4911 6552

■ **POINTE HILTON SQUAW PEAK RESORT** p 1159
7677 N 16th St 85020
Tel (602) 997-2626 *SIC* 7011

POWER-ONE INC p 1165
2626 S 7th St 85034
Tel (805) 987-8741 *SIC* 3679

PROGRESSIVE SERVICES INC p 1182
23 N 35th Ave 85009
Tel (602) 278-4900 *SIC* 1761

PUBLIC SAFETY ARIZONA p 1189
2102 W Encanto Blvd 85009
Tel (602) 223-2000 *SIC* 9229

PULICE CONSTRUCTION INC p 1191
2033 W Mountain View Rd 85021
Tel (602) 944-2241 *SIC* 1611 8711

REDBURNTIRE CO p 1216
3801 W Clarendon Ave 85019
Tel (602) 272-7601 *SIC* 5014 7534

▲ **REPUBLIC SERVICES INC** p 1225
18500 N Allied Way # 100 85054
Tel (480) 627-2700 *SIC* 4953

■ **REPUBLIC SERVICES OF FLORIDA LIMITED PARTNERSHIP** p 1225
18500 N Allied Way 85054
Tel (480) 627-2700 SIC 4953

■ **REPWEST INSURANCE CO** p 1226
2721 N Central Ave Fl 8 85004
Tel (602) 263-6755 SIC 6331

RIMROCK PARTNERS LLC p 1235
2415 E Camelback Rd # 700 85016
Tel (602) 954-7085 SIC 6531 6519 6552

ROAD MACHINERY LLC p 1240
4710 E Elwood St Ste 6 85040
Tel (602) 256-5128
SIC 5082 7359 7699 7353 7629

ROGERS BENEFIT GROUP INC p 1246
5110 N 40th St Ste 234 85018
Tel (612) 332-8866 SIC 6411

ROMAN CATHOLIC CHURCH OF DIOCESE OF PHOENIX p 1248
400 E Monroe St 85004
Tel (602) 257-0030 SIC 8661

ROOFING WHOLESALE CO INC p 1249
1918 W Grant St 85009
Tel (602) 258-3794 SIC 5033

ROOMSTORES OF PHOENIX LLC p 1249
3011 E Broadway Rd # 100 85040
Tel (602) 268-1111 SIC 5712

ROOSEVELT SCHOOL DISTRICT NO 66 p 1249
6000 S 7th St 85042
Tel (602) 243-2624 SIC 8211

■ **SAGEPOINT FINANCIAL INC** p 1268
2800 N Central Ave # 2100 85004
Tel (602) 744-3000 SIC 6311 6211

■ **SCHUFF STEEL CO** p 1290
1841 W Buchanan St 85007
Tel (602) 252-7787 SIC 3441

■ **SECURITY TITLE AGENCY INC** p 1299
3636 N Central Ave # 140 85012
Tel (602) 230-6271 SIC 6411 6541

■ **SEMICONDUCTOR COMPONENTS INDUSTRIES LLC** p 1302
5005 E Mcdowell Rd 85008
Tel (602) 244-6600 SIC 3674 3823

SHAMROCK FOODS CO p 1311
3900 E Camelback Rd # 300 85018
Tel (602) 477-2500
SIC 5146 5149 5147 5148 5142 2026

SHASTA INDUSTRIES INC p 1312
6031 N 16th St 85016
Tel (602) 532-3750
SIC 1799 1771 5169 7389 3088 5091

SHELL MEDICAL PLAN p 1314
P.O. Box 53456 85072
Tel (800) 352-3705 SIC 8099

SIMPLIFIED BUSINESS SOLUTIONS INC p 1325
10201 S 51st St Ste 100 85044
Tel (602) 414-0062 SIC 8721

■ **SLC OPERATING LIMITED PARTNERSHIP** p 1331
2231 E Camelback Rd # 400 85016
Tel (602) 852-3900 SIC 6719

SMARTHEALTH INC p 1332
3400 E Mcdowell Rd 85008
Tel (602) 225-9090 SIC 5047

SNELL & WILMER LLP p 1335
400 E Van Buren St Fl 10 85004
Tel (602) 382-6000 SIC 8111

■ **SOUTHERN COPPER CORP** p 1348
1440 E Missouri Ave # 160 85014
Tel (602) 264-1375
SIC 1021 3331 1031 1061 1044

SOUTHERN GLAZERS WINE AND SPIRITS OF ARIZONA LLC p 1348
2375 S 45th Ave 85043
Tel (602) 533-8000 SIC 5181 5182

SOUTHWEST CATHOLIC HEALTH NETWORK CORP p 1351
4350 E Cotton Center Blvd 85040
Tel (602) 263-3000 SIC 8011

SOUTHWEST NETWORK p 1352
2700 N Central Ave # 1050 85004
Tel (602) 266-8402 SIC 8741

SPENCE DRISCOLL & CO LLC p 1358
5050 N 40th St Ste 350 85018
Tel (602) 957-7155 SIC 6411

▲ **SPROUTS FARMERS MARKET INC** p 1361
5455 E High St Ste 111 85054
Tel (480) 814-8016 SIC 5411

ST LUKES MEDICAL CENTER p 1370
1800 E Van Buren St 85006
Tel (602) 251-8100 SIC 8011

ST LUKES MEDICAL CENTER LP p 1370
1800 E Van Buren St 85006
Tel (602) 251-8535 SIC 8062 8063 8051

ST MARYS FOOD BANK ALLIANCE p 1371
2831 N 31st Ave 85009
Tel (602) 242-3663 SIC 8322

STANTEC TECHNOLOGY INTERNATIONAL INC p 1377
8211 S 48th St 85044
Tel (602) 438-2200 SIC 8711

STATE OF ARIZONA p 1381
1700 W Washington St Fl 7 85007
Tel (602) 542-4331 SIC 9111

SUMCO PHOENIX CORP p 1397
19801 N Tatum Blvd 85050
Tel (480) 473-6000 SIC 3674

SUMCO SOUTHWEST CORP p 1397
19801 N Tatum Blvd 85050
Tel (480) 473-6000 SIC 3674

SUNSTATE EQUIPMENT CO LLC p 1404
5552 E Washington St 85034
Tel (602) 275-2398 SIC 7359 7353

SUNTREE LLC p 1405
4502 W Monterosa St 85031
Tel (480) 719-6900 SIC 2068

SUNTREE SNACK FOODS LLC p 1405
4502 W Monterosa St 85031
Tel (480) 719-6900 SIC 2068

SWCA INC p 1411
3033 N Central Ave # 145 85012
Tel (602) 274-3831
SIC 8748 8711 8731 8733

SWIFT LEASING CO INC p 1412
2200 S 75th Ave 85043
Tel (602) 269-9700 SIC 7513

SWIFT LOGISTICS CO INC p 1412
2200 S 75th Ave 85043
Tel (602) 269-9700 SIC 8742

▲ **SWIFT TRANSPORTATION CO** p 1412
2200 S 75th Ave 85043
Tel (602) 269-9700 SIC 4213 4231

SWIFT TRANSPORTATION CO INC p 1412
2200 S 75th Ave 85043
Tel (602) 269-9700 SIC 4213 4225

SYNERGY SOLUTIONS INC p 1415
3141 N 3rd Ave Ste C100 85013
Tel (602) 296-1600 SIC 7389

SYSTEMS SERVICES OF AMERICA INC p 1419
1640 S 39th Ave 85009
Tel (480) 927-4700
SIC 5147 5113 5142 5149 5143

TELGIAN CORP p 1435
10230 S 50th Pl 85044
Tel (480) 753-5444
SIC 1711 8711 1731 8748

TERAMAR STAFFING INC p 1439
1075 N 51st Ave Ste 102 85043
Tel (602) 288-0500 SIC 7363

TEYMA USA & ABENER ENGINEERING AND CONSTRUCTION SERVICES PARTNERSHIP p 1445
57750 S Painted Rock Rd 85012
Tel (303) 928-8500 SIC 3433

TOTAL AIRPORT SERVICES INC p 1462
34406 N 27th Dr Ste 140 85085
Tel (623) 215-9941 SIC 4581

TRANSLATIONAL GENOMICS RESEARCH INSTITUTE p 1472
445 N 5th St 85004
Tel (602) 343-8400 SIC 8731

TRIWEST HEALTHCARE ALLIANCE CORP p 1483
15810 N 28th Ave 85053
Tel (602) 564-2000 SIC 8741 8062

TROXELL COMMUNICATIONS INC p 1485
4675 E Cotton Center Blvd # 155 85040
Tel (602) 437-7240 SIC 5064

TUNGLAND CORP p 1491
4747 N 7th St Ste 300 85014
Tel (602) 224-5052 SIC 6513

■ **TUTOR PERINI BUILDING CORP** p 1493
5055 E Washington St # 210 85034
Tel (602) 256-6777 SIC 1541 1542 8741

TXL HOLDING CORP p 1495
4675 E Cotton Center Blvd 85040
Tel (602) 437-7240 SIC 5064

■ **U-HAUL CO OF DISTRICT OF COLUMBIA INC** p 1497
2727 N Central Ave 85004
Tel (602) 263-6011 SIC 7513

■ **U-HAUL INTERNATIONAL INC** p 1498
2727 N Central Ave 85004
Tel (602) 263-6011
SIC 7513 7519 7359 5531 4226 8741

UFCW AND EMPLOYERS AZ H AND W TRUST p 1499
2400 W Dunlap Ave Ste 250 85021
Tel (602) 249-3582 SIC 8631

UNITED GENERAL BAKERY INC p 1508
3655 W Washington St 85009
Tel (602) 255-0464 SIC 2051

■ **UNIVERSITY OF PHOENIX INC** p 1524
4025 S Riverpoint Pkwy 85040
Tel (480) 966-5394 SIC 8221

USA MANAGED HEALTH & WELLNESS RESOURCES GROUP INC p 1534
7301 N 16th St Ste 201 85020
Tel (602) 371-3860 SIC 6324 6411

VALLEY OF SUN UNITED WAY p 1541
3200 E Camelback Rd # 375 85018
Tel (602) 631-4800 SIC 8699

VALLEY OF SUN YOUNG MENS CHRISTIAN ASSOCIATION p 1541
350 N 1st Ave 85003
Tel (602) 257-5120 SIC 8641 8322

VANTAGE MOBILITY INTERNATIONAL LLC p 1544
5202 S 28th Pl 85040
Tel (602) 243-2700 SIC 5012 3559

▲ **VEREIT INC** p 1549
2325 E Camelback Rd 85016
Tel (800) 606-3610 SIC 6798

▲ **VIAD CORP** p 1554
1850 N Central Ave # 1900 85004
Tel (602) 207-1000 SIC 7389

■ **VIADS MARKETING & EVENTS GROUP** p 1554
1850 N Central Ave # 101 85004
Tel (602) 207-4000 SIC 8742 7941

VILLAGE VOICE MEDIA HOLDINGS LLC p 1557
1201 E Jefferson St 85034
Tel (602) 271-0040 SIC 2711

W M GRACE COS INC p 1569
7575 N 16th St Ste 1 85020
Tel (602) 956-8254 SIC 1542 6512 7011

■ **WASTE MANAGEMENT OF ARIZONA INC** p 1580
1580 E Elwood St 85040
Tel (480) 457-4700 SIC 4212

▲ **WESTERN ALLIANCE BANCORPORATION** p 1597
1 E Wshington St Ste 1400 85004
Tel (602) 389-3500 SIC 6022

WINROC CORP MIDWEST p 1617
4225 W Glenrosa Ave 85019
Tel (602) 477-0341 SIC 5031

YOUNGS MARKET CO OF ARIZONA LLC p 1639
402 S 54th Pl 85034
Tel (602) 233-1900 SIC 5182

PRESCOTT VALLEY, AZ

NCU HOLDINGS LLC p 1022
10000 E University Dr 86314
Tel (928) 541-7777 SIC 6719

PRESCOTT, AZ

CHELTON AVIONICS INC p 293
6400 Wilkinson Dr 86301
Tel (928) 708-1500 SIC 3812

COUNTY OF YAVAPAI p 383
1015 Fair St 86305
Tel (928) 771-3200 SIC 9111

DAVIDSONS INC p 416
6100 Wilkinson Dr 86301
Tel (928) 776-8055 SIC 5091

TIMS BUICK HYUNDAI SUBARU & GMC INC p 1455
1006 Comm Dr 86305
Tel (877) 838-6541 SIC 5511

YAVAPAI COMMUNITY HOSP ASSN p 1635
1003 Willow Creek Rd 86301
Tel (928) 445-2700 SIC 8062 8011

YAVAPAI COUNTY COMMUNITY COLLEGE DISTRICT p 1635
1100 E Sheldon St 86301
Tel (928) 445-7300 SIC 8222

YAVAPAI REGIONAL MEDICAL CENTER FOUNDATION p 1635
1003 Willow Creek Rd 86301
Tel (928) 445-2700 SIC 8011 8082 2835

SAINT DAVID, AZ

APACHE NITROGEN PRODUCTS INC p 96
1436 S Apache Powder Rd 85630
Tel (520) 720-2217
SIC 2873 5169 2875 2819

SAN LUIS, AZ

FACTOR SALES INC p 523
676 N Archibald St 85349
Tel (928) 627-8033 SIC 5411 5651 5141

SCOTTSDALE, AZ

■ **ALLIED WASTE INDUSTRIES (ARIZONA) INC** p 57
15880 N Greenway 85260
Tel (480) 627-2700 SIC 4953

■ **ALLIED WASTE SERVICES OF MASSACHUSETTS LLC** p 57
15880 N Hayden Rd 85260
Tel (480) 627-2700 SIC 4953

AMERICAN PRESIDENT LINES LTD p 77
16220 N Scottsdale Rd 85254
Tel (602) 586-4894 SIC 4412 4424 4491

AMERICAN RELIABLE INSURANCE CO p 78
8655 E Via De Ventura E200 85258
Tel (480) 483-8666 SIC 6331

AMERICAN RESIDENTIAL PROPERTIES LLC p 78
7033 E Greenway Pkwy # 210 85254
Tel (480) 474-4800 SIC 6799

APL LOGISTICS AMERICAS LTD p 97
16220 N Scottsdale Rd 85254
Tel (602) 586-4800 SIC 4731

APL LOGISTICS LTD p 97
16220 N Scottsdale Rd # 300 85254
Tel (602) 586-4800
SIC 4412 4731 4491 4011

APL LOGISTICS WAREHOUSE MANAGEMENT SERVICES INC p 97
16220 N Scottsdale Rd # 300 85254
Tel (480) 483-0886 SIC 4213 4225

▲ **AV HOMES INC** p 135
8601 N Scottsdale Rd # 220 85253
Tel (480) 214-7400 SIC 1531

BLOOD SYSTEMS INC p 189
6210 E Oak St 85257
Tel (480) 946-4201 SIC 8099

BRER SERVICES INC p 210
16260 N 71st St 85254
Tel (949) 794-7900 SIC 6794

■ **CAREFREE COMMUNITIES INC** p 254
6991 E Camelback Rd B310 85251
Tel (480) 423-5700 SIC 6515

▲ **CARLISLE COMPANIES INC** p 257
16430 N Scottsdale Rd 85254
Tel (704) 501-1100
SIC 2952 3714 3312 3357 3263

CHAI BAGEL CORP p 286
14431 N 73rd St 85260
Tel (480) 860-0475
SIC 5149 5461 5812 2052 2051

CITY OF SCOTTSDALE MUNICIPAL PROPERTY CORP p 318
7447 E Indian School Rd R 85251
Tel (480) 312-7859 SIC 9111

COLONY STARWOOD HOMES p 338
8665 E Hartford Dr # 200 85255
Tel (480) 362-9760 SIC 6798

CRA LLC p 388
8901 E Pima Center Pkwy # 230 85258
Tel (480) 889-9900 SIC 8742

■ **DBL DISTRIBUTING LLC** p 418
15880 N Greenwy Hdn Loop # 150 85260
Tel (480) 419-3559 SIC 5065

■ **DEL WEBB COMMUNITIES INC** p 423
15333 N Pima Rd Ste 300 85260
Tel (602) 808-8000 SIC 6552

■ **DEL WEBB CORP** p 423
15111 N Pima Rd 85260
Tel (480) 391-6000 SIC 6552

DEPCOM POWER INC p 430
9200 E Pima Center Pkwy # 180 85258
Tel (480) 270-6910 SIC 1623 5211

DESERT MOUNTAIN PROPERTIES LIMITED PARTNERSHIP p 432
37700 N Desert Mtn Pkwy 85262
Tel (480) 595-4000 SIC 6552 7997

DIAL CORP p 436
7201 E Henkel Way 85255
Tel (480) 754-3425
SIC 2841 2844 2842 2032 2013

DISCOUNT TIRE CO INC p 442
20225 N Scottsdale Rd 85255
Tel (480) 606-6000 SIC 5531

DISCOUNT TIRE CO OF NEW MEXICO INC p 442
20225 N Scottsdale Rd 85255
Tel (480) 606-6000 SIC 5531

DISCOUNT TIRE CO OF TEXAS INC p 442
20225 N Scottsdale Rd 85255
Tel (817) 460-0162 SIC 5531

DMB ASSOCIATES INC p 445
7600 E Doubletree Ste 300 85258
Tel (480) 367-6874
SIC 5999 6512 5961 1542 3446

DOLCE SALON & SPA LLC p 448
7898 E Acoma Dr Ste 108 85260
Tel (602) 515-0420 SIC 5087

DWW AZ INC p 464
7875 E Frank Lloyd Wright 85260
Tel (480) 778-2440 SIC 7389

EAGLE PRODUCE LLC p 468
7332 E Butherus Dr # 200 85260
Tel (480) 998-1444 SIC 0161

■ **EFUNDS CORP** p 481
4900 N Scottsdale Rd # 1000 85251
Tel (602) 431-2700 SIC 7374 7372 7371

FAIRMONT SCOTTSDALE PRINCESS p 525
7575 E Princess Dr 85255
Tel (480) 585-4848 SIC 7011 5812 5813

FENDER MUSICAL INSTRUMENTS CORP p 537
17600 N Perimeter Dr # 100 85255
Tel (480) 596-7195 SIC 3651 3931

FOAM FABRICATORS INC p 562
8722 E San Alberto Dr # 200 85258
Tel (480) 607-7330 SIC 3086

FOOD SERVICES OF AMERICA INC p 564
16100 N 71st St Ste 400 85254
Tel (480) 927-4000
SIC 5148 5142 5146 5141

FOREVER LIVING PRODUCTS US INC p 567
7501 E Mccormick Pkwy # 105 85258
Tel (480) 998-8888 SIC 5122

GENERAL DYNAMICS C4 SYSTEMS INC p 600
8201 E Mcdowell Rd 85257
Tel (480) 441-3033 SIC 8711

GHA TECHNOLOGIES INC p 610
8998 E Raintree Dr 85260
Tel (480) 951-6865 SIC 7373

GLOBAL AGGREGATE LLC p 615
8901 E Mountain View Rd 85258
Tel (480) 414-9400 SIC 6798 7389 5045

GLOBALTRANZ ENTERPRISES INC p 617
7350 N Dobson Rd Ste 135 85256
Tel (480) 339-5600 SIC 4731

■ GO DADDY OPERATING CO LLC p 619
14455 N Hayden Rd Ste 219 85260
Tel (480) 505-8877 SIC 7373 7374

▲ GODADDY INC p 619
14455 N Hayden Rd Ste 100 85260
Tel (480) 505-8800 SIC 7373 4813

GODADDY.COM LLC p 619
14455 N Hayden Rd Ste 219 85260
Tel (480) 505-8800 SIC 7379

HAPPY HOUSE LLC p 659
8116 E Vista Bonita Dr 85255
Tel (480) 854-0788 SIC 1521

HEALTHCARE TRUST OF AMERICA INC p 676
16435 N Scottsdale Rd 85254
Tel (480) 998-3478 SIC 6798

HENKEL CONSUMER GOODS INC p 683
7201 E Henkel Way 85255
Tel (860) 571-5100 SIC 2841

■ HUNT CORP p 719
6720 N Scottsdale Rd # 300 85253
Tel (480) 368-4755 SIC 1541 6531 6552

■ HYPERCOM CORP p 724
8888 E Raintree Dr # 300 85260
Tel (480) 642-5000
SIC 3578 7372 7299 5065

INTERNATIONAL CRUISE & EXCURSION GALLERY INC p 755
15501 N Dial Blvd 85260
Tel (602) 395-1995 SIC 4724

JDA SOFTWARE GROUP INC p 780
15059 N Scottsdale Rd # 400 85254
Tel (480) 308-3000 SIC 7371

JDA SOFTWARE INC p 780
15059 N Scottsdale Rd # 400 85254
Tel (480) 308-3000 SIC 7371 7373

KAHALA BRANDS LTD p 800
9311 E Via De Ventura 85258
Tel (480) 362-4800 SIC 5812 6794

▲ KONA GRILL INC p 827
7150 E Camelback Rd # 220 85251
Tel (480) 922-8100 SIC 5812 6794

L & G MORTGAGEBANC INC p 833
8151 E Evans Rd Ste 10 85260
Tel (408) 905-5140 SIC 6162

▲ MAGELLAN HEALTH INC p 895
4800 N Scottsdale Rd 85251
Tel (602) 572-6050 SIC 8063 8011 5122

MARINE PRESERVATION ASSOCIATION INC p 906
20645 N Pima Rd Ste 100 85255
Tel (480) 991-5500 SIC 8611

MAYO CLINIC ARIZONA p 923
13400 E Shea Blvd 85259
Tel (480) 301-8000 SIC 8011

MCDONOUGH HOLDINGS INC (FN) p 928
21050 N Pima Rd Ste 100 85255
Tel (602) 544-5900
SIC 2431 4449 2426 2421

■ MCKESSON SPECIALTY ARIZONA INC p 930
4343 N Scottsdale Rd # 370 85251
Tel (480) 663-4000 SIC 5122

▲ MERITAGE HOMES CORP p 949
8800 E Raintree Dr # 300 85260
Tel (480) 515-8100 SIC 1521

■ MERITAGE HOMES OF FLORIDA INC p 949
8800 E Raintree Dr # 300 85260
Tel (480) 515-8500 SIC 1521

■ METRO CARE CORP p 954
8465 N Pima Rd 85258
Tel (800) 352-2309 SIC 4119

MNI ENTERPRISES INC p 980
8080 E Gelding Dr Ste 108 85260
Tel (480) 505-4600 SIC 1521

NAI GROUP LLC p 1006
7975 N Hayden Rd Ste D105 85258
Tel (480) 556-6066 SIC 3679

NORTH AMERICAN INTERCONNECT LLC p 1050
7975 N Hayden Rd Ste D105 85258
Tel (480) 556-6066 SIC 2298

▲ NUVERRA ENVIRONMENTAL SOLUTIONS INC p 1068
14624 N Scottsdale Rd 85254
Tel (602) 903-7802 SIC 1389 4953

ON Q FINANCIAL INC p 1086
4800 N Scottsdale Rd 85251
Tel (480) 444-7100 SIC 6282 6162

PEGASUS SOLUTIONS INC p 1127
14000 N Pima Rd Ste 200 85260
Tel (480) 624-6000 SIC 7374

PF CHANGS CHINA BISTRO INC p 1140
7676 E Pinnacle Peak Rd 85255
Tel (480) 888-3000 SIC 5812

PFCCB EDGEWATER LLC p 1140
7676 E Pinnacle Peak Rd 85255
Tel (480) 888-3000 SIC 5812

PHOENICIAN RESORT p 1144
6000 E Camelback Rd 85251
Tel (480) 941-8200 SIC 7011

PLEXUS HOLDINGS INC p 1156
9145 E Pima Center Pkwy 85258
Tel (480) 998-3490 SIC 5149

REDROCK PARTNERS LLC p 1217
8260 E Raintree Dr 85260
Tel (480) 596-5702
SIC 5944 5932 5736 5941 5999

REINALT-THOMAS CORP p 1221
20225 N Scottsdale Rd 85255
Tel (480) 606-6000 SIC 5531

RP CROWN PARENT LLC p 1255
15059 N Scottsdale Rd # 400 85254
Tel (480) 308-3000 SIC 7371

RSC EQUIPMENT RENTAL INC p 1255
6929 E Greenway Pkwy # 200 85254
Tel (480) 905-3300 SIC 7353

■ RURAL/METRO CORP p 1258
8465 N Pima Rd 85258
Tel (480) 606-3886 SIC 4119 7389

■ RURAL/METRO CORP p 1258
8465 N Pima Rd 85258
Tel (480) 606-3345 SIC 4119 7389

■ RURAL/METRO OPERATING CO LLC p 1258
8465 N Pima Rd 85258
Tel (480) 606-3886 SIC 4119

SAGICOR LIFE INSURANCE CO p 1268
4343 N Scottsdale Rd # 300 85251
Tel (480) 425-5100 SIC 6311

SALT RIVER PIMA-MARICOPA INDIAN COMMUNITY EDUCATIONAL SE p 1273
10005 E Osborn Rd 85256
Tel (480) 362-7400 SIC 9131

SALT RIVER SAND & ROCK p 1273
8800 E Chaparral Rd # 155 85250
Tel (480) 850-5757 SIC 5032 1442

SCOTTSDALE HEALTHCARE CORP p 1294
8125 N Hayden Rd 85258
Tel (480) 882-4000 SIC 8062

SCOTTSDALE HEALTHCARE HOSPITALS p 1294
8125 N Hayden Rd 85258
Tel (480) 324-7215 SIC 8062

SCOTTSDALE INSURANCE CO p 1294
8877 N Gainey Center Dr 85258
Tel (480) 365-4000 SIC 6331

SCOTTSDALE UNIFIED SCHOOL DISTRICT p 1294
7575 E Main St 85251
Tel (480) 484-6100 SIC 8211

SERVICES GROUP OF AMERICA INC p 1308
16100 N 71st St Ste 500 85254
Tel (480) 927-4000
SIC 5141 5148 6331 6552

■ SHERATON PHOENICIAN CORP p 1315
6000 E Camelback Rd 85251
Tel (480) 941-8200
SIC 7011 5812 5813 7999 7992

SKBHC HOLDINGS LLC p 1329
8723 E Via De Commercio 85258
Tel (480) 393-0562 SIC 6712

SOUTHERN CALIFORNIA DISCOUNT TIRE CO INC p 1347
5310 E Shea Blvd 85254
Tel (480) 606-6000 SIC 5531

SOUTHWEST FOODSERVICE EXCELLENCE LLC p 1352
9366 E Raintree Dr 101 85260
Tel (480) 551-6550 SIC 5812

SPIRIT REALTY CAPITAL INC p 1359
16767 N Perimeter Dr # 210 85260
Tel (480) 606-0820 SIC 6798

STANDARDAERO BUSINESS AVIATION SERVICES LLC p 1376
6710 N Scottsdale Rd 85253
Tel (480) 377-3100 SIC 7363

STAR BUFFET INC p 1378
2501 N Hayden Rd Ste 103 85257
Tel (480) 425-0397 SIC 5812

STORE CAPITAL CORP p 1391
8501 E Prnceaz Dr Ste 190 85255
Tel (480) 256-1100 SIC 6798

SUNWEST RESTAURANT CONCEPTS INC p 1405
6360 E Thomas Rd Ste 100 85251
Tel (480) 659-1000 SIC 5812

SUPERSHUTTLE INTERNATIONAL INC p 1407
14500 N Northsight Blvd # 329 85260
Tel (480) 609-3000 SIC 4111

▲ TASER INTERNATIONAL INC p 1426
17800 N 85th St 85255
Tel (480) 991-0797 SIC 3489

▲ TAYLOR MORRISON HOME CORP p 1427
4900 N Scottsdale Rd # 2000 85251
Tel (480) 840-8100 SIC 1521

■ TAYLOR MORRISON INC p 1427
4900 N Scottsdale Rd # 2000 85251
Tel (480) 840-8100 SIC 1521

■ TECH GROUP INC p 1430
14677 N 74th St 85260
Tel (480) 281-4500 SIC 3089

■ THERMO FLUIDS INC p 1447
8925 E Pima Center Pkwy # 105 85258
Tel (480) 270-5702 SIC 5093

▲ TPI COMPOSITES INC p 1467
8501 N Scottsdale Rd # 280 85253
Tel (480) 305-8910 SIC 3728

TRANSDEV ON DEMAND INC p 1471
14500 N Northsight Blvd 85260
Tel (480) 609-3000 SIC 4111

TROON GOLF LLC p 1484
15044 N Scottsdale Rd # 300 85254
Tel (480) 606-1000 SIC 8741 6552

▲ UNIVERSAL TECHNICAL INSTITUTE INC p 1517
16220 N Scottsdale Rd # 100 85254
Tel (623) 445-9500 SIC 8249

VT MOTORS INC p 1567
8585 E Frank Lloyd Wright 85260
Tel (480) 991-8300 SIC 5511

WILDFLOWER BREAD CO p 1609
7755 E Gray Rd 85260
Tel (480) 951-9453 SIC 5149

WOK PARENT LLC p 1620
7676 E Pinnacle Peak Rd 85255
Tel (480) 888-3000 SIC 5812

■ WP ROCKET HOLDINGS INC p 1627
8465 N Pima Rd 85258
Tel (800) 352-2309 SIC 4119 7389

YAM SPECIAL HOLDINGS INC p 1634
15475 N 84th St 85260
Tel (480) 505-8800 SIC 7371

SELLS, AZ

TOHONO OODHAM NATION p 1458
Hc 86 85634
Tel (520) 383-6540 SIC 9131

SHOW LOW, AZ

NAVAPACHE REGIONAL MEDICAL CENTER p 1019
2200 E Show Low Lake Rd 85901
Tel (928) 537-4375 SIC 8011

SUMMIT HEALTH CARE REGIONAL MEDICAL CENTER p 1399
2200 E Show Low Lake Rd 85901
Tel (928) 537-6338 SIC 8062

SUMMIT HEALTHCARE ASSOCIATION p 1399
2200 E Show Low Lake Rd 85901
Tel (928) 537-4375 SIC 8621

SUMMIT MEDICAL PLAZA LLC p 1399
2200 E Show Low Lake Rd 85901
Tel (928) 537-4375 SIC 8361

SIERRA VISTA, AZ

PIONEER TITLE AGENCY INC p 1151
580 E Wilcox Dr 85635
Tel (520) 459-4100 SIC 6361 6163

SULPHUR SPRINGS VALLEY ELECTRIC COOPERATIVE INC CHARITABLE p 1397
311 E Wilcox Dr 85635
Tel (520) 384-2221 SIC 4911 1731 1623

VISTA RCHP-SIERRA INC p 1562
5700 E Highway 90 85635
Tel (520) 458-4641 SIC 8062

SUN CITY, AZ

BANNER HEALTH p 153
14502 W Meeker Blvd 85375
Tel (623) 524-4000 SIC 8062

SURPRISE, AZ

DYSART UNIFIED SCHOOL DISTRICT p 465
15802 N Parkview Pl 85374
Tel (623) 876-7000 SIC 8211

SUN HEALTH CORP p 1400
14719 W Grand Ave Ste 113 85374
Tel (623) 876-5350
SIC 8062 8051 8082 7361 8733 6531

TEMPE, AZ

■ AMERICA WEST HOLDINGS CORP p 67
111 W Rio Salado Pkwy 85281
Tel (480) 693-0800 SIC 6719

▲ AMKOR TECHNOLOGY INC p 85
2045 E Innovation Cir 85284
Tel (480) 821-5000 SIC 3674 3825

▲ AMTECH SYSTEMS INC p 87
131 S Clark Dr 85281
Tel (480) 967-5146 SIC 3559

ARIZONA STATE UNIVERSITY p 109
300 E University Dr # 410 85281
Tel (480) 965-2100 SIC 8221

ARIZONA STATE UNIVERSITY FOUNDATION FOR A NEW AMERICAN UNIVE p 109
300 E University Dr 85281
Tel (480) 965-3759 SIC 6732

ARIZONA TILE LLC p 109
8829 S Priest Dr 85284
Tel (480) 991-3066 SIC 5032

ARTESYN EMBEDDED COMPUTING INC p 114
2900 S Diablo Way Ste 190 85282
Tel (602) 438-5720 SIC 3829

ARTESYN EMBEDDED TECHNOLOGIES INC p 114
2900 S Diablo Way Ste 190 85282
Tel (800) 759-1107
SIC 3679 3577 3571 7629 5045

ASTEC AMERICA LLC p 122
2900 S Diablo Way Ste 190 85282
Tel (602) 438-5720 SIC 3679 3629 3621

■ BARD PERIPHERAL VASCULAR INC p 155
1625 W 3rd St 85281
Tel (480) 894-9515 SIC 3842

BRIDGECREST ACCEPTANCE CORP p 211
1720 W Rio Salado Pkwy 85281
Tel (602) 770-1940 SIC 7389

■ CHASE BANKCARD SERVICES INC p 291
100 W University Dr 85281
Tel (480) 902-6000 SIC 6021 6022

CIRCLE K STORES INC p 308
1130 W Warner Rd 85284
Tel (602) 728-8000 SIC 5411 5541

CITY OF TEMPE p 319
31 E 5th St 85281
Tel (480) 350-8355 SIC 9111

CLINICAL RESEARCH ADVANTAGE INC p 326
2141 E Broadway Rd # 120 85282
Tel (480) 820-5656 SIC 8731

■ COMSYS INFORMATION TECHNOLOGY SERVICES LLC p 353
2050 E Asu Cir Ste 120 85284
Tel (877) 626-6797 SIC 7371 7374

CREATIVE TESTING SOLUTIONS p 390
2424 W Erie Dr 85282
Tel (602) 343-7000 SIC 8099

CYTEC ENGINEERED MATERIALS INC p 406
2085 E Tech Cir Ste 300 85284
Tel (480) 730-2000 SIC 3769 5085 2821

DEGENCO MANAGEMENT LLC p 422
825 S 48th St 85281
Tel (480) 829-5090 SIC 5812

DELTA DIVERSIFIED ENTERPRISES INC p 427
425 W Gemini Dr 85283
Tel (480) 831-0532 SIC 1731

DRIVETIME AUTOMOTIVE GROUP INC p 456
1720 W Rio Salado Pkwy 85281
Tel (602) 852-6600 SIC 5521

EARNHARDT FORD SALES CO INC p 469
7300 W Orchid Ln 85284
Tel (480) 893-0000
SIC 5511 5531 7538 5561

■ ELIZABETH ARDEN SALON-HOLDINGS INC p 487
222 S Mill Ave Ste 201 85281
Tel (602) 864-8191 SIC 7231 5999 7299

■ ENSYNCH INC p 501
6820 S Harl Ave 85283
Tel (480) 894-3500 SIC 8748

▲ FIRST SOLAR INC p 549
350 W Washington St # 600 85281
Tel (602) 414-9300 SIC 3674 3433

FNF CONSTRUCTION INC p 562
115 S 48th St 85281
Tel (480) 784-2910 SIC 1611 1794 2951

FRONTIER TECHNOLOGY LLC p 581
8160 S Hardy Dr Ste 101 85284
Tel (480) 366-2000 SIC 7373

■ GIANT INDUSTRIES INC p 611
1250 W Washington St # 101 85281
Tel (915) 534-1400 SIC 2911 5541 5172

■ HEALTH NET OF ARIZONA INC p 675
1230 W Washington St # 401 85281
Tel (602) 286-9242 SIC 6324

HILLMAN GROUP INC p 694
8990 S Kyrene Rd 85284
Tel (800) 800-4900 SIC 3429 5162 3599

INFRASTRUCTURE HOLDINGS CO LLC p 742
115 S 48th St 85281
Tel (480) 784-2910 SIC 1611 1794 2591

IT1 SOURCE LLC p 767
1860 W University Dr # 100 85281
Tel (480) 777-5995 SIC 5734

KYRENE ELEMENTARY DISTRICT p 833
8700 S Kyrene Rd 85284
Tel (480) 541-1000 SIC 8211

KYRENE SCHOOL DISTRICT p 833
8700 S Kyrene Rd 85284
Tel (480) 541-1000 SIC 8211

LABORATORY SCIENCES OF ARIZONA LLC p 836
1255 W Washington St 85281
Tel (602) 685-5000 SIC 8071 8011 8331

▲ LIFELOCK INC p 864
60 E Rio Salado Pkwy # 400 85281
Tel (480) 682-5100 SIC 7382

▲ LIMELIGHT NETWORKS INC p 866
222 S Mill Ave Ste 800 85281
Tel (602) 850-5000 SIC 7372 7375

MACH 1 GLOBAL SERVICES INC p 892
1530 W Broadway Rd 85282
Tel (480) 921-3900 SIC 4731 4212

MARICOPA COUNTY COMMUNITY COLLEGE DISTRICT p 906
2411 W 14th St 85281
Tel (480) 731-8000 SIC 8222

MEDPLAST LLC p 938
405 W Geneva Dr 85282
Tel (480) 553-6400 SIC 6719

MJKL ENTERPRISES LLC p 978
5210 S Priest Dr 85283
Tel (480) 897-7777 SIC 5812

■ MOBILE STORAGE GROUP INC p 980
7420 S Kyrene Rd Ste 101 85283
Tel (480) 894-6311 SIC 5999 7359

MOTOROLA SATELLITE COMMUNICATIONS INC p 993
2900 S Diablo Way 85282
Tel (480) 732-2000 *SIC* 3674

MOUNTAIN RANGE RESTAURANTS LLC p 994
825 S 48th St 85281
Tel (480) 829-5090 *SIC* 5812

MTD SOUTHWEST INC p 997
9235 S Mckemy St 85284
Tel (480) 961-1002 *SIC* 3524 3546 3423

NATIONWIDE CREDIT INC p 1017
1225 W Washington St # 300 85281
Tel (800) 456-4729 *SIC* 7322

■ **NORTHERN TIER ENERGY LP** p 1057
1250 W Washington St # 101 85281
Tel (602) 302-5450 *SIC* 2911

RADIALL USA INC p 1204
8950 S 52nd St Ste 401 85284
Tel (480) 682-9400 *SIC* 3643

■ **RED DOOR SALONS INC** p 1215
222 S Mill Ave Ste 201 85281
Tel (480) 829-8191 *SIC* 7231 5999 7299

ROCKFORD CORP p 1244
600 S Rockford Dr 85281
Tel (480) 967-3565 *SIC* 3651

RUGBY USA INC p 1257
1440 S Priest Dr Ste 103 85281
Tel (480) 968-2208 *SIC* 5031

SALT RIVER PROJECT AGRICULTURAL IMPROVEMENT AND POWER DISTRICT p 1273
1521 N Project Dr 85281
Tel (602) 236-5900 *SIC* 4911

SDB INC p 1295
810 W 1st St 85281
Tel (480) 967-5810 *SIC* 1542

SONORA QUEST LABORATORIES LLC p 1340
1255 W Washington St 85281
Tel (602) 685-5000 *SIC* 8071

SPENCERS AIR CONDITIONING & APPLIANCE INC p 1358
525 W 21st St 85282
Tel (480) 505-2355 *SIC* 5064

■ **STRYKER SUSTAINABILITY SOLUTIONS INC** p 1394
1810 W Drake Dr Ste 101 85283
Tel (888) 888-3433
SIC 5084 5047 7699 3842 3841

SUNDT CONSTRUCTION INC p 1402
2620 S 55th St 85282
Tel (480) 293-3000
SIC 1542 1611 1629 1541 8741

SV PROBE INC p 1410
9185 S Farmer Ave Ste 105 85284
Tel (480) 635-4700 *SIC* 3825

TEMPE ELEMENTARY SCHOOL DISTRICT p 1436
3205 S Rural Rd 85282
Tel (480) 730-7359 *SIC* 8211

TEMPE UNION HIGH SCHOOL DISTRICT 213 (INC) p 1436
500 W Guadalupe Rd 85283
Tel (480) 839-0292 *SIC* 8211

■ **TRIUMPH INSULATION SYSTEMS LLC** p 1483
2925 S Roosevelt St 2 85282
Tel (949) 250-4999 *SIC* 3728

US AIRWAYS INC p 1531
111 W Rio Salado Pkwy # 175 85281
Tel (480) 693-0800 *SIC* 4512

VEMMA NUTRITION CO p 1547
1621 W Rio Salado Pkwy # 101 85281
Tel (480) 927-8999 *SIC* 5122 5149

▲ **VERSUM MATERIALS INC** p 1552
8555 S River Pkwy 85284
Tel (610) 481-6697 *SIC* 2842 2891 3569

■ **WESTERN REFINING SOUTHWEST INC** p 1599
1250 W Washington St # 101 85281
Tel (602) 286-1400
SIC 2911 5171 5411 5541

■ **WESTERN REFINING TERMINALS LLC** p 1599
1250 W Washington St # 101 85281
Tel (602) 286-1401 *SIC* 5171

■ **WESTERN REFINING WHOLESALE INC** p 1599
1250 W Washington St # 101 85281
Tel (602) 286-1401 *SIC* 5171 2911 2992

TOLLESON, AZ

FREIGHTLINER STERLING WESTERN STAR OF ARIZONA LTD p 577
9899 W Roosevelt St 85353
Tel (623) 907-9900 *SIC* 5013 5012 7538

■ **FRYS FOOD STORES OF ARIZONA INC** p 582
500 S 99th Ave 85353
Tel (623) 936-2100 *SIC* 5411

PAPA JOHNS SALADS & PRODUCE INC p 1112
859 S 86th Ave 85353
Tel (480) 894-6885 *SIC* 5148

ROUSSEAU SONS LLC p 1253
102 S 95th Ave 85353
Tel (623) 936-7100 *SIC* 0161 0191

RUSSELL SIGLER INC p 1259
9702 W Tonto St 85353
Tel (623) 388-5100 *SIC* 5064

TUBA CITY, AZ

TUBA CITY REGIONAL HEALTHCARE CORP p 1490
167 N Main St 86045
Tel (928) 283-2501 *SIC* 8062

TUCSON, AZ

▲ **AMERICAS MINING CORP** p 81
1150 N 7th Ave 85705
Tel (520) 798-7500
SIC 1021 1044 1031 1041 3331

■ **AR SILVER BELL INC** p 102
5285 E Williams Cir 85711
Tel (520) 798-7500
SIC 1021 1044 1031 1041 3331 3339

■ **ASARCO LLC** p 115
5285 E Williams Cir # 2000 85711
Tel (520) 798-7500
SIC 1021 1044 1031 1041 3331 3339

BANNER-UNIVERSITY MEDICAL CENTER SOUTH CAMPUS LLC p 153
2800 E Ajo Way 85713
Tel (520) 874-2000 *SIC* 8062

BANNER-UNIVERSITY MEDICAL CENTER TUCSON CAMPUS LLC p 153
1501 N Campbell Ave 85724
Tel (520) 694-0111 *SIC* 8062

BEAUDRY MOTOR CO p 166
4600 E 22nd St 85711
Tel (520) 750-1264 *SIC* 5511 5561

BUFFALO EXCHANGE LTD p 224
203 E Helen St 85705
Tel (520) 622-2711 *SIC* 5621

CARONDELET HEALTH NETWORK p 260
2202 N Forbes Blvd 85745
Tel (520) 872-7542 *SIC* 8062

CITY OF TUCSON p 319
255 W Alameda St 85701
Tel (520) 791-4561 *SIC* 9111

COMMUNITY PROVIDER OF ENRICHMENT SERVICES INC p 350
4825 N Sabino Canyon Rd 85750
Tel (480) 516-0298 *SIC* 8322

CYRACOM INTERNATIONAL INC p 406
5780 N Swan Rd 85718
Tel (520) 745-9447 *SIC* 7389

EL RIO SANTA CRUZ NEIGHBORHOOD HEALTH CENTER INC p 483
839 W Congress St 85745
Tel (520) 792-9890 *SIC* 8093

EVAERO INC p 513
3807 E Kleindale Rd 85716
Tel (520) 327-0053 *SIC* 3599

GOLDEN EAGLE DISTRIBUTORS INC p 620
705 E Ajo Way 85713
Tel (520) 884-5999 *SIC* 5181 5149

■ **HUCK INTERNATIONAL INC** p 716
3724 E Columbia St 85714
Tel (520) 519-7400 *SIC* 3429 3452

JD MELLBERG FINANCIAL p 780
3067 W Ina Rd Ste 105 85741
Tel (520) 731-9000 *SIC* 6311

JIM CLICK INC p 785
780 W Competition Rd 85705
Tel (520) 884-4100 *SIC* 5511

KALIL BOTTLING CO p 801
931 S Highland Ave 85719
Tel (520) 624-1788 *SIC* 2086 7359

LA COSTENA USA INC p 835
8755 S Rita Rd 85747
Tel (520) 663-4720 *SIC* 2032

LEONI WIRING SYSTEMS INC p 856
3100 N Campbell Ave # 101 85719
Tel (520) 741-0895 *SIC* 3643 8741 5063

LEONISCHE HOLDING INC p 856
2861 N Flowing Wells Rd 85705
Tel (520) 741-0895 *SIC* 3679

LOVITT & TOUCHE INC p 881
7202 E Rosewood St # 200 85710
Tel (520) 722-3000 *SIC* 6411

M3 ENGINEERING & TECHNOLOGY CORP p 890
2051 W Sunset Rd Ste 101 85704
Tel (520) 293-1488 *SIC* 8741 8712 8711

■ **MATERION CERAMICS INC** p 919
6100 S Tucson Blvd 85706
Tel (520) 741-3411 *SIC* 3351 3264

NEXTMED HOLDINGS LLC p 1041
6339 E Speedway Blvd 85710
Tel (520) 323-8732 *SIC* 6324

■ **NORTHWEST MEDICAL CENTER** p 1060
6200 N La Cholla Blvd 85741
Tel (520) 742-9000 *SIC* 8062

PIMA COUNTY p 1148
97 E Congress St Fl 3 85701
Tel (520) 243-1800 *SIC* 9111 1623

PIMA COUNTY AMPHITHEATER SCHOOLS p 1148
701 W Wetmore Rd 85705
Tel (520) 696-5000 *SIC* 8211

PIMA COUNTY COMMUNITY COLLEGE DISTRICT INC p 1148
4905 E Broadway Blvd 85709
Tel (520) 206-4500 *SIC* 8222

PIZZA HUT OF ARIZONA INC p 1152
5902 E Pima St 85712
Tel (520) 838-5171 *SIC* 5812

PREMIER BUILDERS LLC p 1170
3191 E 44th St 85713
Tel (520) 293-0300 *SIC* 1521

RAIN BIRD CORP p 1205
6991 E Suthpoint Rd Ste 1 85756
Tel (520) 806-5635 *SIC* 3532

■ **RAYTHEON MISSILE SYSTEMS CO** p 1211
1151 E Hermans Rd 85756
Tel (520) 794-3000 *SIC* 3761

ROMAN CATHOLIC CHURCH OF DIOCESE OF TUCSON p 1248
64 E Broadway Blvd 85701
Tel (520) 792-3410 *SIC* 8661

SAM LEVITZ FURNITURE CO INC p 1274
3430 E 36th St 85713
Tel (520) 624-7443 *SIC* 5712

■ **SARGENT AEROSPACE & DEFENSE LLC** p 1282
5675 W Burlingame Rd 85743
Tel (520) 744-1000
SIC 3728 3724 3568 3492

SOUTHWEST CANNING & PACKAGING INC p 1351
931 S Highland Ave 85719
Tel (520) 622-5811 *SIC* 2086

SUNDT COMPANIES INC p 1402
2015 W River Rd Ste 101 85704
Tel (520) 750-4600 *SIC* 1542 1771 1611

SUNNYSIDE UNIFIED SCHOOL DISTRICT 12 p 1403
2238 E Ginter Rd 85706
Tel (520) 545-2024 *SIC* 8211

■ **SUNQUEST INFORMATION SYSTEMS INC** p 1403
250 S Williams Blvd 85711
Tel (520) 570-2000 *SIC* 7373 7371

TMC HEALTHCARE p 1457
5301 E Grant Rd 85712
Tel (520) 327-5461 *SIC* 8051 8062

TRULY NOLEN OF AMERICA INC p 1486
3636 E Speedway Blvd 85716
Tel (800) 528-3442 *SIC* 7342

TUCSON ELECTRIC POWER CO INC p 1490
88 E Broadway Blvd 85701
Tel (520) 571-4000 *SIC* 4911

TUCSON MEDICAL CENTER p 1490
5301 E Grant Rd 85712
Tel (520) 327-5461
SIC 8062 8051 6513 8741

TUCSON UNIFIED SCHOOL DISTRICT p 1490
1010 E 10th St 85719
Tel (520) 225-6000 *SIC* 8211

UNISOURCE ENERGY SERVICES INC p 1505
88 E Broadway Blvd 85701
Tel (520) 571-4000 *SIC* 4911 4923

UNIVERSAL AVIONICS SYSTEMS CORP p 1516
3260 E Universal Way 85756
Tel (520) 295-2300 *SIC* 3812 3829

UNIVERSITY OF ARIZONA p 1520
888 N Euclid Ave Rm 510 85719
Tel (520) 626-6000 *SIC* 8221

UNIVERSITY OF ARIZONA FOUNDATION p 1520
1111 N Cherry Ave 85721
Tel (520) 621-5494 *SIC* 8699

UNIVERSITY PHYSICIANS HEALTH CARE p 1527
1501 N Campbell Ave 85724
Tel (520) 626-6174 *SIC* 8011

UNS ELECTRIC INC p 1528
88 E Broadway Blvd 901 85701
Tel (928) 681-8966 *SIC* 4911

UNS ENERGY CORP p 1528
88 E Broadway Blvd 85701
Tel (520) 571-4000 *SIC* 4923 4911

VISIONQUEST NONPROFIT CORP p 1561
600 N Swan Rd 85711
Tel (520) 881-3950 *SIC* 8361 8211 8322

WALBRO LLC p 1572
2015 W River Rd 202 85704
Tel (520) 229-5642
SIC 3592 3594 3694 3443

WATERMARK RETIREMENT COMMUNITIES INC p 1582
2020 W Rudasill Rd 85704
Tel (520) 797-4000 *SIC* 8059

ZC MANAGEMENT LLC p 1641
8600 E Rockcliff Rd 85750
Tel (520) 749-9655 *SIC* 7011

VAIL, AZ

VAIL SCHOOL DISTRICT p 1538
13801 E Benson Hwy Unit B 85641
Tel (520) 879-2000 *SIC* 8211

WHITERIVER, AZ

WHITE MOUNTAIN APACHE TRIBE p 1606
201 E Walnut St 85941
Tel (928) 338-4346 *SIC* 9131

WINDOW ROCK, AZ

NAVAJO NATION TRIBAL GOVERNMENT p 1019
2 Miles N Of Hwy 264 86515
Tel (928) 871-6352 *SIC* 9131

YUMA, AZ

AAH MEDICAL LLC p 8
2051 W 25th St 85364
Tel (928) 344-1411 *SIC* 8099

BILL ALEXANDER FORD LINCOLN MERCURY INC p 182
801 E 32nd St 85365
Tel (928) 344-2200 *SIC* 5511

CEMEX CONSTRUCTION MATERIALS SOUTH LLC p 274
2088 E 20th St 85365
Tel (928) 343-4100 *SIC* 3241

CITY OF YUMA p 319
1 City Plz 85364
Tel (928) 373-5187 *SIC* 9111

COUNTY OF YUMA p 383
198 S Main St 85364
Tel (928) 373-1010 *SIC* 9111

SNAKEBITE LEASING INC p 1335
821 S Pacific Ave 85365
Tel (928) 276-3328 *SIC* 5171

YUMA CABLEVISION INC p 1640
1289 S 2nd Ave 85364
Tel (928) 329-9731 *SIC* 4841

YUMA REGIONAL MEDICAL CENTER INC p 1640
2400 S Avenue A 85364
Tel (928) 344-2000 *SIC* 8062

YUMA SCHOOL DISTRICT ONE p 1640
450 W 6th St 85364
Tel (928) 782-6581 *SIC* 8211

ARKANSAS

ALMA, AR

ALMA HEALTHCARE AND REHABILITATION CENTER LLC p 59
401 Heather Ln 72921
Tel (479) 632-4343 *SIC* 8059

ARKADELPHIA, AR

ANTHONY TIMBERLANDS INC p 94
3 Executive Cir 71923
Tel (870) 245-3000 *SIC* 2421

DANFOSS SCROLL TECHNOLOGIES LLC p 411
1 Scroll Dr 71923
Tel (870) 246-0700 *SIC* 3679 3563

ASHDOWN, AR

DOMTAR AW LLC p 449
285 Highway 71 S 71822
Tel (870) 898-2711 *SIC* 2611

BATESVILLE, AR

■ **FUTUREFUEL CHEMICAL CO** p 586
2800 Gap Rd 72501
Tel (870) 698-3000 *SIC* 2819

WHITE RIVER HEALTH SYSTEM INC p 1606
1710 Harrison St 72501
Tel (870) 262-1200 *SIC* 8062

WHITE RIVER MEDICAL CENTER p 1606
1710 Harrison St 72501
Tel (870) 262-1200 *SIC* 8011

BEARDEN, AR

ANTHONY TIMBERLAND INC p 94
111 S Plum St 71720
Tel (870) 687-3611 *SIC* 2421

BEARDEN LEASING CO LTD p 165
111 S Plum St 71720
Tel (870) 687-2246 *SIC* 7359 0811

BENTON, AR

RINECO CHEMICAL INDUSTRIES INC p 1235
819 Vulcan Rd 72015
Tel (501) 778-9089 *SIC* 4953

SALINE COUNTY MEDICAL CENTER p 1272
1 Medical Park Dr 72015
Tel (501) 776-6000 *SIC* 8062

BENTONVILLE, AR

▲ **AMERICAS CAR-MART INC** p 81
802 Se Plaza Ave Ste 200 72712
Tel (479) 464-9944 *SIC* 5521 6141

BENTONVILLE SCHOOL DISTRICT 6 p 173
500 Tiger Blvd 72712
Tel (479) 254-5000 *SIC* 8211

OUTDOOR CAP CO INC p 1098
1200 Melissa Dr 72712
Tel (479) 273-3732 *SIC* 5136

PREMIER CONCEPTS SC p 1170
2701 Se J St 72712
Tel (479) 271-6000 *SIC* 5141

■ **SAMS WEST INC** p 1274
2101 Se Simple Savings Dr 72712
Tel (479) 273-4000 *SIC* 5399

▲ WAL-MART STORES INC p 1572
702 Sw 8th St 72716
Tel (479) 273-4000
SIC 5311 5331 5411 5399

WALMART FOUNDATION p 1573
702 Sw 8th Stre Dept 8687 72716
Tel (479) 204-2044 SIC 5411

WALTON FAMILY FOUNDATION INC p 1575
125 W Central Ave Rm 218 72712
Tel (479) 273-5605 SIC 8699

BERRYVILLE, AR

CARROLL ELECTRIC COOPERATIVE CORP p 261
920 Highway 62 Spur 72616
Tel (870) 423-2161 SIC 4911 5812

BLYTHEVILLE, AR

MISSISSIPPI COUNTY ELECTRIC COOPERATIVE INC p 975
510 N Broadway St 72315
Tel (870) 763-4563 SIC 4911

■ NUCOR-YAMATO STEEL CO (LIMITED PARTNERSHIP) p 1067
5929 E State Highway 18 72315
Tel (870) 762-5500 SIC 3312 3441

BRYANT, AR

BRYANT SCHOOL DISTRICT 25 p 221
200 Nw 4th St 72022
Tel (501) 847-5600 SIC 8211

CABOT, AR

CABOT SCHOOL DISTRICT 4 (INC) p 235
602 N Lincoln St 72023
Tel (501) 843-3363 SIC 8211

CONWAY, AR

■ CENTENNIAL BANK p 275
620 Chestnut St 72032
Tel (501) 328-4663 SIC 6022

CONWAY CORP p 365
1307 Prairie St 72034
Tel (501) 450-6000 SIC 4911 4941 4841

CONWAY REGIONAL MEDICAL CENTER INC p 365
2302 College Ave 72034
Tel (501) 329-3831 SIC 8062

HENDRIX COLLEGE p 683
1600 Washington Ave 72032
Tel (501) 329-6811 SIC 8221

▲ HOME BANCSHARES INC p 703
719 Harkrider St Ste 100 72032
Tel (501) 339-2929 SIC 6022

■ IC BUS LLC p 726
600 Bayford Dr 72034
Tel (501) 327-7761 SIC 3713 3711

NABHOLZ CONSTRUCTION CORP p 1006
612 Garland St 72032
Tel (501) 505-5800 SIC 1541

NABHOLZ INC p 1006
612 Garland St 72032
Tel (501) 505-5800 SIC 5084 7359

RELIANCE HEALTH CARE MANAGEMENT p 1221
824 Salem Rd Ste 210 72034
Tel (501) 932-0050 SIC 8059

UNIVERSITY OF CENTRAL ARKANSAS p 1520
201 Donaghey Ave 72035
Tel (501) 450-5000 SIC 8221

EDGEMONT, AR

DIAMOND HOSPITALITY ENTERPRISES p 436
5 Mystic Isle Rd 72044
Tel (501) 723-5150 SIC 5812 5541 5411

EL DORADO, AR

▲ DELTIC TIMBER CORP p 427
210 E Elm St 71730
Tel (870) 881-9400
SIC 0811 2411 6531 8741

FOREST ANTHONY PRODUCTS CO p 566
309 N Washington Ave 71730
Tel (870) 862-3414 SIC 2421 2452

▲ MURPHY OIL CORP p 1001
300 E Peach St 71730
Tel (870) 862-6411 SIC 1311 1382 2911

■ MURPHY OIL USA INC p 1001
200 E Peach St 71730
Tel (870) 862-6411
SIC 8742 2911 1311 4213

▲ MURPHY USA INC p 1001
200 E Peach St 71730
Tel (870) 875-7600 SIC 5531 5541

SYSTEMS PLANT SERVICES INC p 1419
214 N Wa Ave Ste 700 71730
Tel (870) 862-1315 SIC 1629

ELM SPRINGS, AR

WILLIS SHAW EXPRESS INC p 1612
201 N Elm St 72728
Tel (479) 248-7261 SIC 4213

ENGLAND, AR

BANK OF ENGLAND p 151
123 S Main St 72046
Tel (501) 842-2555 SIC 6022 6021

FAYETTEVILLE, AR

APAC-CENTRAL INC p 95
755 E Millsap Rd 72703
Tel (417) 226-4833 SIC 3272 1611

ARVEST BANK p 114
1 N Mcilroy Ave 72701
Tel (479) 575-1000 SIC 6022

CRAWFORD CR CONSTRUCTION LLC p 389
1102 S Happy Hollow Rd 72701
Tel (479) 251-1161 SIC 1542

FAYETTEVILLE SCHOOL DISTRICT 1 p 532
1000 W Bulldog Blvd 72701
Tel (479) 444-3000 SIC 8211

HANNAS CANDLE CO p 658
2700 S Armstrong Ave 72701
Tel (479) 443-5467 SIC 3999 2844 5999

KPI INTERMEDIATE HOLDINGS INC p 828
481 S Shiloh Dr 72704
Tel (479) 443-1455 SIC 3363 3312

OZARKS ELECTRIC COOPERATIVE CORP p 1101
3641 W Wedington Dr 72704
Tel (479) 521-2900 SIC 4911

PACE INDUSTRIES LLC p 1103
481 S Shiloh Dr 72704
Tel (479) 443-1455 SIC 3363

TWIN RIVERS FOODS INC p 1495
1 E Colt Square Dr 72703
Tel (479) 444-8898 SIC 2015

TWIN RIVERS GROUP INC p 1495
1 E Colt Square Dr 72703
Tel (479) 444-8898 SIC 5142

UNVRSTY OF AR FONDTIN INC p 1528
535 W Research Ctr Blvd 72701
Tel (479) 575-5581 SIC 8399

WASHINGTON REGIONAL MEDICAL CENTER p 1579
3215 N Northhills Blvd 72703
Tel (479) 463-6000 SIC 8062

WASHINGTON REGIONAL MEDICAL SYSTEM p 1579
3215 N Northhills Blvd 72703
Tel (479) 463-1000 SIC 8062 8069

FLIPPIN, AR

ACTRONIX INC p 20
476 W Industrial Prk Rd 72634
Tel (870) 453-8871 SIC 3679

FISHING HOLDINGS LLC p 552
927 Highway 178 N 72634
Tel (870) 453-2222 SIC 3732 5699

MICRO PLASTICS INC p 961
111 Industry Ln 72634
Tel (870) 453-8861 SIC 3965

FORREST CITY, AR

■ FORREST CITY GROCERY CO p 568
3400 Commerce Rd 72335
Tel (870) 633-2044 SIC 5141 5993

FORT SMITH, AR

A O G CORP p 6
115 N 12th St 72901
Tel (479) 783-3181 SIC 4923 4924

■ ABF FREIGHT SYSTEM INC p 11
3801 Old Greenwood Rd 72903
Tel (479) 785-8700 SIC 4213

▲ ARCBEST CORP p 104
3801 Old Greenwood Rd 72903
Tel (479) 785-6000 SIC 4213 4731

ARKANSAS OKLAHOMA GAS CORP p 110
115 N 12th St 72901
Tel (479) 784-2000 SIC 4923

ASERACARE HOSPICE - NEW HORIZONS LLC p 116
1 1000 Beverly Way 72919
Tel (479) 201-2000 SIC 8361

BALDOR ELECTRIC CO p 147
5711 Rs Boreham Jr St 72901
Tel (479) 646-4711
SIC 3621 3566 3463 3366

BEVERLY ENTERPRISES - ALABAMA INC p 179
One Thousand Beverly Way 72919
Tel (479) 201-2000 SIC 8082 8051

BEVERLY ENTERPRISES - ARKANSAS INC p 179
1000 Fianna Way 72919
Tel (479) 636-6285 SIC 8051

BEVERLY ENTERPRISES - INDIANA INC p 179
1000 Fianna Way 72919
Tel (479) 201-2000 SIC 8051

BEVERLY ENTERPRISES - MISSOURI INC p 179
1000 Fianna Way 72919
Tel (479) 201-2000 SIC 8051 8059

BEVERLY ENTERPRISES - VIRGINIA INC p 179
1 1000 Beverly Way 72919
Tel (479) 201-2000 SIC 8082 8051

BEVERLY ENTERPRISES - WISCONSIN INC p 179
1000 Fianna Way 72919
Tel (479) 201-2000 SIC 8051

BEVERLY ENTERPRISES INC p 179
1000 Fianna Way 72919
Tel (479) 201-2000 SIC 8741 8051 8082

BEVERLY ENTERPRISES-OHIO INC p 179
1 Thousand Beverly Way 72919
Tel (479) 201-2000 SIC 8059

BEVERLY ENTERPRISES-PENNSYLVANIA INC p 179
1000 Fianna Way 72919
Tel (479) 201-2000 SIC 8051

BOST INC p 202
7701 S Zero St 72903
Tel (479) 478-5600 SIC 8331 8351

ERC PROPERTIES INC p 507
4107 Massard Rd 72903
Tel (479) 478-5103 SIC 1522 6552 6513

■ FORTH SMITH HMA LLC p 569
1001 Towson Ave 72901
Tel (479) 441-4000 SIC 8062

FURNITURE FACTORY OUTLET LLC p 585
6500 Jenny Lind Rd Spc A 72908
Tel (918) 427-0241 SIC 5712 2515

GGNSC HOLDINGS LLC p 610
1000 Fianna Way 72919
Tel (479) 201-2000
SIC 8059 8051 8082 8322

HOBBS & CURRY FAMILY LIMITED PARTNERSHIP LLLP p 699
4119 Massard Rd 72903
Tel (479) 785-0844 SIC 1542

HOMECARE PREFERRED CHOICE INC p 703
1000 Fianna Way 72919
Tel (479) 201-2000 SIC 8082

K-MAC ENTERPRISES INC p 799
1820 S Zero St 72901
Tel (479) 646-2053 SIC 5812

MERCY HOSPITAL FORT SMITH p 947
7301 Rogers Ave 72903
Tel (479) 314-6000 SIC 8062

MERCY MEDICAL SERVICES INC p 948
5401 Ellsworth Rd 72903
Tel (479) 314-6060 SIC 7363

MPG GEARTECHNOLOGIES p 995
7800 Ball Rd 72908
Tel (479) 646-1662 SIC 3714 3568 3399

O K FOODS INC p 1070
4601 N 6th St 72904
Tel (479) 783-4186 SIC 2015

OK INDUSTRIES INC p 1079
4601 N 6th St 72904
Tel (479) 783-4186 SIC 2048 2015 0251

PROPAK LOGISTICS INC p 1183
1100 Garrison Ave 72901
Tel (479) 478-7800 SIC 7699 4731

RIVERSIDE FURNITURE CORP p 1238
1400 S 6th St 72901
Tel (479) 785-8100 SIC 2511

■ SPARKS REGIONAL MEDICAL CENTER p 1354
1001 Towson Ave 72901
Tel (479) 441-4000 SIC 8062

SPECIAL SCHOOL DISTRICT OF FORT SMITH p 1356
3205 Jenny Lind Rd 72901
Tel (479) 785-2501 SIC 8211

SPECTRA HEALTHCARE ALLIANCE INC p 1357
1000 Fianna Way 72919
Tel (479) 201-2000 SIC 8741

SSW HOLDING CO INC p 1364
3501 Tulsa St 72903
Tel (479) 646-1651 SIC 3496 6719

VANTAGE HEALTHCARE CORP p 1544
1000 Fianna Way 72919
Tel (479) 201-2000 SIC 8741

■ WINGFOOT COMMERCIAL TIRE SYSTEMS LLC p 1616
1000 S 21st St 72901
Tel (479) 788-6400 SIC 7534

GASSVILLE, AR

MAGNESS OIL CO p 896
167 Tucker Cemetery Rd 72635
Tel (870) 425-4353 SIC 5171 5541 5411

HARRISBURG, AR

FARMERS SUPPLY ASSOCIATION p 530
16240 Highway 14 E 72432
Tel (870) 578-2468
SIC 5191 5172 5261 5541 5999

HARRISON, AR

CLARIDGE PRODUCTS AND EQUIPMENT INC p 321
601 Highway 62 65 S 72601
Tel (870) 743-2200
SIC 2531 3354 2541 2542

■ FEDEX FREIGHT INC p 536
2200 Forward Dr 72601
Tel (870) 741-9000 SIC 4213

NORTH ARKANSAS REGIONAL MEDICA p 1050
620 N Main St 72601
Tel (870) 365-2000 SIC 8011

NORTH ARKANSAS REGIONAL MEDICAL CENTER p 1050
620 N Main St 72601
Tel (870) 414-4000 SIC 8062

PETROMARK INC p 1139
308 W Industrial Park Rd 72601
Tel (870) 741-3560 SIC 5541

HEBER SPRINGS, AR

DEFIANCE METAL PRODUCTS OF ARKANSAS INC p 422
944 By Pass Rd 72543
Tel (501) 362-1919
SIC 3465 3443 3544 3469

HOPE, AR

SOUTHERN BAKERIES LLC p 1347
2700 E 3rd St 71801
Tel (870) 777-9031 SIC 5149

HOT SPRINGS VILLAGE, AR

MOUNTAIN VALLEY SPRING CO LLC p 994
283 Mountain Vly Wtr Pl 71909
Tel (501) 623-6671 SIC 5084

HOT SPRINGS, AR

CRACKER BOX LLC p 388
110 Cracker Box Ln 71913
Tel (501) 455-4909 SIC 5411

HOT SPRINGS NATIONAL PARK HOSPITAL HOLDINGS LLC p 710
1910 Malvern Ave 71901
Tel (501) 321-1000 SIC 8062

MOUNTAIN VALLEY SPRING CO LLC p 994
283 Mountain Vly Wtr Pl 71909
Tel (501) 624-7329 SIC 5149 5499

MUNRO & CO INC p 1000
3770 Malvern Rd 71901
Tel (501) 262-6000 SIC 3144 3149

SAINT JOSEPHS HOSPITAL INC p 1269
300 Werner St 71913
Tel (501) 622-1000 SIC 8011

ST JOSEPHS REGIONAL HEALTH CENTER (INC) p 1369
300 Werner St 71913
Tel (501) 622-4500 SIC 8062

JACKSONVILLE, AR

FIRST ELECTRIC CO-OPERATIVE CORP p 546
1000 S Jp Wright Loop Rd 72076
Tel (501) 982-4545 SIC 4911

PATH FINDER SCHOOLS INC p 1120
425 E Trickey Ln 72076
Tel (501) 982-0528 SIC 6513

PATHFINDER INC p 1120
2520 W Main St 72076
Tel (501) 982-0528 SIC 8211

JONESBORO, AR

CITY WATER & LIGHT PLANT OF CITY OF JONESBORO p 320
400 E Monroe Ave 72401
Tel (870) 935-5581 SIC 4931

E C BARTON & CO p 466
2929 Browns Ln 72401
Tel (870) 932-6673 SIC 5031 5211 5713

E RITTER COMMUNICATIONS HOLDINGS INC p 467
2400 Ritter Dr 72401
Tel (870) 336-3434 SIC 4813 4812 5045

FOWLER FOODS INC p 572
139 Southwest Dr 72401
Tel (870) 935-6984 SIC 5812

MID SOUTH SALES INC p 963
243 County Road 414 72404
Tel (870) 933-6457 SIC 5172

NEA BAPTIST CLINIC p 1022
3024 Red Wolf Blvd 72401
Tel (870) 972-7000 SIC 8011

ST BERNARDS HOSPITAL INC p 1365
225 E Jackson Ave 72401
Tel (870) 207-7300 SIC 8062

LITTLE ROCK, AR

▲ ACXIOM CORP p 21
601 E 3rd St 72201
Tel (501) 252-1000 SIC 7374 7375 7371

■ ALLTEL COMMUNICATIONS LLC p 59
1 Allied Dr 72202
Tel (501) 905-8000 SIC 4812

■ ALLTEL COMMUNICATIONS OF VIRGINIA INC p 59
1 Allied Dr 72202
Tel (501) 905-8100 SIC 4812

■ ALLTEL CORP p 59
1001 Technology Dr 72223
Tel (866) 255-8357 SIC 4812 5999

AON CONSULTING INC p 94
315 W 3rd St 72201
Tel (501) 374-9300 SIC 8742

ARKANSAS CHILDRENS HOSPITAL p 109
1 Childrens Way 72202
Tel (501) 364-1100 SIC 8062 8069

ARKANSAS CHILDRENS HOSPITAL FOUNDATION INC p 109
1 Childrens Way 72202
Tel (501) 320-1100 SIC 8699

ARKANSAS DEMOCRAT-GAZETTE INC p 109
121 E Capitol Ave 72201
Tel (501) 378-3400 SIC 2711

ARKANSAS DEPARTMENT OF EDUCATION p 109
4 Capitol Mall 72201
Tel (501) 682-4475 SIC 9411

ARKANSAS DEPARTMENT OF HEALTH p 109
4815 W Markham St 72205
Tel (501) 661-2000 SIC 9431

ARKANSAS DEPARTMENT OF HIGHWAY AND TRANSPORTATION p 109
10324 Interstate 30 72209
Tel (501) 569-2000 SIC 9621

ARKANSAS DEPARTMENT OF HUMAN SERVICES p 109
700 Main St 72201
Tel (501) 682-1001 SIC 9441

ARKANSAS DEPARTMENT OF PARKS AND TOURISM p 109
1 Capitol Mall Ste 900 72201
Tel (501) 682-7777 SIC 9512 9611

ARKANSAS DEPT OF FINANCE AND ADMINISTRATION p 109
1509 W 7th St 72201
Tel (501) 682-2242 SIC 9311

ARKANSAS ELDER OUTREACH OF LITTLE ROCK p 109
12111 Hinson Rd 72212
Tel (225) 906-2274 SIC 8322

ARKANSAS ELECTRIC COOPERATIVE CORP p 109
1 Cooperative Way 72209
Tel (501) 570-2200 SIC 4911

ARKANSAS ELECTRIC COOPERATIVES INC p 109
1 Cooperative Way 72209
Tel (501) 570-2361
SIC 5063 1623 1629 7629

ARKANSAS HEART HOSPITAL LLC p 109
1701 S Shackleford Rd 72211
Tel (501) 219-7000 SIC 8062 8011

ARKANSAS STATE UNIVERSITY p 110
501 Woodlane St Ste 600 72201
Tel (870) 972-2024 SIC 5812

■ ASBURY AUTOMOTIVE ARKANSAS DEALERSHIP HOLDINGS LLC p 115
4400 Landers Rd 72201
Tel (501) 945-1200 SIC 5511

BALDWIN & SHELL CONSTRUCTION CO INC p 147
1000 W Capitol Ave 72201
Tel (501) 374-8677 SIC 1541 1542

▲ BANK OF OZARKS INC p 152
17901 Chenal Pkwy 72223
Tel (501) 978-2265 SIC 6022

BAPTIST HEALTH p 153
11001 Executive Center Dr # 200 72211
Tel (501) 202-2000 SIC 8051

BAPTIST HEALTH MEDICAL CENTER p 153
9601 Baptist Health Dr # 109 72205
Tel (501) 887-3000 SIC 8062

▲ BEAR STATE FINANCIAL HOLDINGS LLC p 165
900 S Shackleford Rd # 200 72211
Tel (501) 320-4862 SIC 6799

BILL HILLARY & CHELSEA CLINTON FOUNDATION p 182
1200 Prsident Clinton Ave 72201
Tel (501) 748-0471 SIC 8399

BLUE ADVANTAGE ADMINISTRATORS OF ARKANSAS p 190
320 W Capitol Ave Ste 500 72201
Tel (501) 378-3600 SIC 6321

■ CARLTON-BATES CO p 258
3600 W 69th St 72209
Tel (501) 562-9100 SIC 5065

■ CDI CONTRACTORS LLC p 271
3000 Cantrell Rd 72202
Tel (501) 666-4300 SIC 1542

CENTRAL ARKANSAS RADIATION THERAPY INSTITUTE INC p 277
8901 Carti Way 72205
Tel (501) 906-3000 SIC 8011 8221

CITY OF LITTLE ROCK p 316
500 W Markham St 72201
Tel (501) 371-4510 SIC 9199

CLARK CONTRACTORS LLC p 322
15825 Cantrell Rd 72223
Tel (501) 868-3133 SIC 1542

CROW-BURLIGAME CO p 394
1901 E Roosevelt Rd 72206
Tel (501) 375-1215 SIC 5013

DAYSPRING SERVICES OF ARKANSAS LLC p 417
1610 W 3rd St 72201
Tel (501) 372-4440 SIC 8093

▲ DILLARDS INC p 439
1600 Cantrell Rd 72201
Tel (501) 376-5200
SIC 5311 5611 5621 5641 5712

DIXIE RESTAURANTS INC p 445
1215 Rebsamen Park Rd 72202
Tel (501) 666-3494 SIC 5812 5813

DYKE INDUSTRIES INC p 464
309 Center St 72201
Tel (501) 376-2921 SIC 5031

■ ENTERGY ARKANSAS INC p 501
425 W Capitol Ave Fl 20 72201
Tel (501) 377-4000 SIC 4911

ESSICK AIR PRODUCTS INC p 510
5800 Murray St 72209
Tel (501) 562-1094 SIC 3534 3585 3634

EXECUTIVE OFFICE OF STATE OF ARKANSAS p 517
State Capitol Ste 250 72201
Tel (501) 682-2345 SIC 9111

HEIFER PROJECT INTERNATIONAL INC p 681
1 World Ave 72202
Tel (501) 907-2600 SIC 8399 6732 9532

HUGG AND HALL EQUIPMENT CO p 717
7201 Scott Hamilton Dr 72209
Tel (501) 562-1262
SIC 5084 5082 7353 7699 5083 3531

JA RIGGS TRACTOR CO p 773
9125 Interstate 30 72209
Tel (501) 570-3100 SIC 5082 5511

JUDICIARY COURTS OF STATE OF ARKANSAS p 796
625 Marshall St Ste 1100 72201
Tel (501) 682-6849 SIC 9211

KINCO CONSTRUCTORS LLC p 819
12600 Lawson Rd 72210
Tel (501) 225-7606 SIC 1542 1541

LEXICON INC p 859
8900 Fourche Dam Pike 72206
Tel (501) 490-4200 SIC 1629 3441

LIFE AND SPECIALTY VENTURES LLC p 863
17500 Chenal Pkwy Ste 500 72223
Tel (501) 378-2910 SIC 6719

LITTLE ROCK SCHOOL DISTRICT p 871
810 W Markham St 72201
Tel (501) 447-1000 SIC 8211

MAIL CONTRACTORS OF AMERICA INC p 897
3800 N Rodney Parham Rd # 301 72212
Tel (501) 280-0500 SIC 4212

MIDCON FUEL SERVICES LLC p 964
8401 Lindsey Rd 72206
Tel (501) 708-2000 SIC 5172

MOUNTAIRE CORP p 994
1901 Napa Valley Dr 72212
Tel (501) 372-6524 SIC 2015

MOUNTAIRE FARMS INC p 994
1901 Napa Valley Dr 72212
Tel (501) 372-6524 SIC 2015

MOUNTAIRE FARMS OF DELAWARE INC p 994
1901 Napa Valley Dr 72212
Tel (501) 372-6524 SIC 0751

PERFECTVISION MANUFACTURING INC p 1135
16101 La Grande Dr 72223
Tel (501) 955-0033 SIC 3679

■ PFG BROADLINE HOLDINGS LLC p 1140
4901 Asher Ave 72204
Tel (501) 568-3141
SIC 5149 5148 5147 5141

PRIORITY WIRE & CABLE INC p 1178
1800 E Roosevelt Rd 72206
Tel (501) 372-5444 SIC 5063

PULASKI COUNTY p 1191
201 Broadway St Ste 440 72201
Tel (501) 340-8381 SIC 9211

PULASKI COUNTY SPECIAL SCHOOL DISTRICT p 1191
925 E Dixon Rd 72206
Tel (501) 490-2000 SIC 8211

■ REGIONS INSURANCE GROUP p 1220
1500 Riverfront Dr # 200 72202
Tel (501) 661-4800 SIC 6411

REPLACEMENT PARTS INC p 1224
1901 E Roosevelt Rd 72206
Tel (501) 375-1215 SIC 5013

ROYSTON HOLDING LLC p 1255
111 Center St Ste 2500 72201
Tel (770) 735-3456 SIC 7389 1751 2542

SI HOLDINGS INC p 1319
111 Center St 72201
Tel (501) 688-8400 SIC 6211

SOUTHWEST POWER POOL INC p 1352
201 Worthen Dr 72223
Tel (501) 614-3200 SIC 4911

ST VINCENT HEALTH SERVICES INC p 1373
2 Saint Vincent Cir 72205
Tel (501) 552-2620 SIC 8062 8099

ST VINCENT INFIRMARY MEDICAL CENTER p 1373
2 Saint Vincent Cir 72205
Tel (501) 552-3000 SIC 8011

STALEY INC p 1375
8101 Fourche Rd 72209
Tel (501) 565-3006 SIC 1731

STATE OF ARKANSAS p 1381
4 Capitol Mall Rm 403a 72201
Tel (501) 682-2345 SIC 9111

STEPHENS CAPITAL PARTNERS LLC p 1386
111 Center St Ste 200 72201
Tel (800) 643-9691 SIC 6211

STEPHENS INC p 1386
111 Center St Ste 200 72201
Tel (501) 377-2000 SIC 6211

STEPHENS LLC p 1386
111 Center St Ste 200 72201
Tel (501) 377-2000 SIC 6719

SUPER D DRUGS ACQUISITION CO p 1405
2100 Brookwood Dr 72202
Tel (501) 296-3300 SIC 5912

UNIVERSITY OF ARKANSAS FOR MEDICAL SCIENCES p 1520
4301 W Markham St 72205
Tel (501) 686-6606 SIC 8221

UNIVERSITY OF ARKANSAS SYSTEM p 1520
2404 N University Ave 72207
Tel (501) 686-2500 SIC 8221

USABLE LIFE p 1534
17500 Chenal Pkwy 72223
Tel (800) 648-0271 SIC 6311 6321

USABLE MUTUAL INSURANCE CO p 1534
601 S Gaines St 72201
Tel (501) 378-2000 SIC 6324 6411

■ VALOR TELECOMMUNICATIONS ENTERPRISES LLC p 1542
4001 N Rodney Parham Rd 72212
Tel (501) 748-7000 SIC 4813

■ VALOR TELECOMMUNICATIONS LLC p 1542
4001 N Rodney Parham Rd 72212
Tel (501) 748-7000 SIC 4813

VESTCOM INTERNATIONAL INC p 1552
2800 Cantrell Rd Ste 400 72202
Tel (501) 663-0100 SIC 8742 7389

WEHCO MEDIA INC p 1587
115 E Capitol Ave 72201
Tel (501) 378-3529 SIC 2711 4841

WEHCO NEWSPAPERS INC p 1587
115 E Capital & Scott Sts 72201
Tel (501) 378-3400 SIC 2711

WELSPUN PIPES INC p 1591
9301 Frazier Pike 72206
Tel (501) 301-8800 SIC 1799 3494

WELSPUN TUBULAR LLC p 1591
9301 Frazier Pike 72206
Tel (501) 301-8800 SIC 3317

■ WESTERN WIRELESS LLC p 1600
1 Allied Dr 72202
Tel (501) 905-8000 SIC 4812

■ WINDSTREAM COMMUNICATIONS LLC p 1615
4001 N Rodney Parham Rd 72212
Tel (800) 697-8153 SIC 4813

▲ WINDSTREAM HOLDINGS INC p 1615
4001 N Rodney Parham Rd # 101 72212
Tel (501) 748-7000 SIC 4813 5065

■ WINDSTREAM IOWA COMMUNICATIONS LLC p 1615
4001 N Rodney Parham Rd 72212
Tel (501) 748-7000 SIC 4813

■ WINDSTREAM SERVICES LLC p 1616
4001 N Rodney Parham Rd # 101 72212
Tel (501) 748-7000 SIC 4813 5065

WINROCK INTERNATIONAL INSTITUTE FOR AGRICULTURAL DEVELOPMENT p 1617
2101 Riverfront Dr 72202
Tel (501) 280-3000 SIC 8733

■ XETA TECHNOLOGIES INC p 1631
4001 N Rodney Parham Rd 72212
Tel (800) 697-8153 SIC 3661 5999 7389

LOWELL, AR

ARVEST BANK GROUP INC p 114
913 W Monroe Ave 72745
Tel (479) 750-1400 SIC 6712

CENTRAL STATES MANUFACTURING INC p 280
302 Jane Pl 72745
Tel (479) 770-0188 SIC 3353 3448 7389

■ J B HUNT TRANSPORT INC p 770
615 J B Hunt Corporate Dr 72745
Tel (479) 820-0000 SIC 4213

▲ JB HUNT TRANSPORT SERVICES INC p 779
615 Jb Hunt Corp Dr 72745
Tel (479) 820-0000 SIC 4213 4731

MAGNOLIA, AR

RELIANCE WELL SERVICE INC p 1222
237 Highway 79 S 71753
Tel (870) 234-2700 SIC 1389

MALVERN, AR

■ KGEN HOT SPRING LLC p 816
696 Black Branch Rd 72104
Tel (501) 609-4600 SIC 4911

MARKED TREE, AR

E RITTER & CO p 466
10 Elm St 72365
Tel (870) 358-7333
SIC 0131 0116 0724 4813 5211 5083

E RITTER AGRIBUSINESS HOLDINGS INC p 466
10 Elm St 72365
Tel (870) 336-7310 SIC 0131 4813

E RITTER SEED CO p 467
300 Adamson St 72365
Tel (870) 358-2130 SIC 5153 5191

RITTER AGRIBUSINESS p 1237
10 Elm St 72365
Tel (870) 336-7310 SIC 6411

MONTICELLO, AR

PRICE COMPANIES INC p 1174
218 Midway Rte 71655
Tel (870) 367-9751 SIC 2421 2426

MOUNTAIN HOME, AR

BAXTER COUNTY REGIONAL HOSPITAL INC p 160
624 Hospital Dr 72653
Tel (870) 508-1000 SIC 8062

NASHVILLE, AR

HUSQVARNA OUTDOOR PRODUCTS INC p 721
1 Poulan Dr 71852
Tel (870) 845-1234 SIC 3524

NEWPORT, AR

ARKANSAS STEEL ASSOCIATES LLC p 110
2803 Van Dyke Rd 72112
Tel (870) 523-3693 SIC 3312 3547

CONMAC INVESTMENTS INC p 356
2301 Mclain St 72112
Tel (870) 523-6576 SIC 5511

NORTH LITTLE ROCK, AR

ARKANSAS DEPARTMENT OF NATIONAL GUARD p 109
Camp Robinson Bldg 6000 72199
Tel (501) 212-5100 SIC 9711

BRUCE OAKLEY INC p 220
3700 Lincoln Ave 72114
Tel (501) 945-0875
SIC 4449 5153 5261 5191 4213

■ COMFORT SYSTEMS USA (ARKANSAS) INC p 344
4806 Rixie Rd 72117
Tel (501) 834-3320 SIC 1711

COULSON OIL CO INC p 374
1434 Pike Ave 38 72114
Tel (501) 376-4222
SIC 5172 5541 5411 6512

FOURJAY LLC p 572
42 Parkstone Cir 72116
Tel (501) 372-2000 SIC 5812

GARVER LLC p 592
4701 Northshore Dr 72118
Tel (501) 376-3633 SIC 8711

HERITAGE CO INC p 686
2402 Wildwood Ave Ste 500 72120
Tel (501) 835-9111 SIC 7389 2721

MAVERICK TRANSPORTATION LLC p 921
13301 Valentine Rd 72117
Tel (501) 955-1222 SIC 4213

MAVERICK USA INC p 921
13301 Valentine Rd 72117
Tel (501) 945-6130 SIC 4213

NORTH LITTLE ROCK SCHOOL DISTRICT p 1053
2700 N Poplar St 72114
Tel (501) 771-8000 SIC 8211

OAKLEY INTERNATIONAL LLC p 1071
3700 Lincoln Ave 72114
Tel (501) 945-0875 SIC 5191

PAT SALMON & SONS INC p 1120
3809 Roundtop Dr 72117
Tel (501) 945-0778 SIC 4213

PINNACLE BUSINESS SOLUTIONS INC p 1149
515 W Pershing Blvd 72114
Tel (501) 210-9000 SIC 6411 7371

RUSSELL CHEVROLET CO p 1259
6100 Landers Rd 72117
Tel (501) 835-8996 SIC 5511

TRAVEL NURSE ACROSS AMERICA LLC p 1473
5020 Northshore Dr Ste 2 72118
Tel (501) 663-5288 SIC 7361

TRL INC p 1483
11700 Valentine Rd 72117
Tel (501) 955-3200 SIC 5012

OSCEOLA, AR

DENSO MANUFACTURING ARKANSAS INC p 428
100 Denso Rd 72370
Tel (870) 622-9500 SIC 3089 7539

OZARK, AR

ARKANSAS VALLEY ELECTRIC COOPERATIVE CORP p 110
1811 W Commercial St 72949
Tel (479) 667-2176 SIC 4911

PARAGOULD, AR

■ **LA DARLING CO LLC** p 835
1401 Highway 49b 72450
Tel (870) 239-9564 *SIC* 2541 2542

THOMAS RONALD HALL OD p 1449
3610 Pruetts Chapel Rd 72450
Tel (870) 236-8500 *SIC* 8011

■ **THORCO INDUSTRIES LLC** p 1450
1401 Highway 49b 72450
Tel (417) 682-3375 *SIC* 5063

PARKDALE, AR

BAYOU GRAIN & CHEMICAL CORP p 162
P.O. Box 67 71661
Tel (870) 473-2281 *SIC* 4221 2873 5153

PINE BLUFF, AR

CENTRAL MOLONEY INC p 279
2400 W 6th Ave 71601
Tel (870) 534-5332 *SIC* 3612

HIXSON LUMBER SALES INC p 697
310 S Tennessee St 71601
Tel (870) 535-1436 *SIC* 2421 5031

JEFFERSON HOSPITAL ASSOCIATION INC p 781
1600 W 40th Ave 71603
Tel (870) 541-7100 *SIC* 8062

KISWIRE PINE BLUFF INC p 822
5100 Industrial Dr S 71602
Tel (870) 247-2444 *SIC* 3312 2296

■ **SIMMONS BANK** p 1324
501 S Main St 71601
Tel (870) 541-1000 *SIC* 6021

▲ **SIMMONS FIRST NATIONAL CORP** p 1324
501 S Main St 71601
Tel (870) 541-1000 *SIC* 6021

STEPHEN L LAFRANCE HOLDINGS INC p 1386
3017 N Midland Dr 71603
Tel (870) 535-5171 *SIC* 5912 6794

■ **STEPHEN L LAFRANCE PHARMACY INC** p 1386
3017 N Midland Dr 71603
Tel (870) 535-5171 *SIC* 5122 5912

UNIVERSITY OF ARKANSAS AT PINE BLUFF p 1520
1200 University Dr 71601
Tel (870) 575-8000 *SIC* 8221

PRAIRIE GROVE, AR

■ **ARKGALV INC** p 110
998 Escue Dr 72753
Tel (479) 846-4500 *SIC* 3312

ROGERS, AR

CCF BRANDS LLC p 270
5211 W Village Pkwy # 101 72758
Tel (479) 464-0544 *SIC* 5144 5142

CHEYENNE INDUSTRIES LLC p 296
5512 W Walsh Ln Ste 201 72758
Tel (501) 812-6590 *SIC* 5063

CHRISTIAN HEALTHCARE OF MISSOURI INC p 302
5305 W Village Pkwy # 12 72758
Tel (479) 464-0200 *SIC* 8059

COOPER COMMUNITIES INC p 366
903 N 47th St 72756
Tel (479) 246-6500 *SIC* 5251

MERCY HEALTH SYSTEM OF NORTHWEST ARKANSAS INC p 946
2710 S Rife Medical Ln 72758
Tel (479) 338-8000 *SIC* 8062

MERCY HOSPITAL ROGERS p 947
2710 S Rife Medical Ln 72758
Tel (479) 338-8000 *SIC* 8062

OZARK MOUNTAIN POULTRY INC p 1101
750 W E St 72756
Tel (479) 633-8700 *SIC* 2015 5144

ROGERS PUBLIC SCHOOLS p 1246
220 S 5th St 72756
Tel (479) 631-3696 *SIC* 8299

ROGERS SCHOOL DISTRICT 30 p 1246
500 W Walnut St 72756
Tel (479) 636-3910 *SIC* 8211

RUSSELLVILLE, AR

ARKANSAS TECH UNIVERSITY p 110
1605 Coliseum Dr 72801
Tel (479) 968-0300 *SIC* 8221

FRIENDSHIP COMMUNITY CARE INC p 580
920 University Dr 72801
Tel (479) 967-2316 *SIC* 8211

■ **HACKNEY LADISH INC** p 652
708 S Elmira Ave 72802
Tel (479) 968-7555 *SIC* 3089 3463

RUSSELLVILLE STEEL CO INC p 1259
280 Steel City Ln 72802
Tel (479) 968-2211 *SIC* 5051

ST MARYS REGIONAL MEDICAL CENTER p 1372
1808 W Main St 72801
Tel (479) 968-2841 *SIC* 8062

■ **TERRA RENEWAL SERVICES INC** p 1439
201 S Denver Ave Ste B 72801
Tel (479) 498-0500 *SIC* 4953 4212

TRANSCO LINES INC p 1471
60 Transco Park Dr 72802
Tel (479) 967-5700 *SIC* 4213

SEARCY, AR

CONVACARE MANAGEMENT INC p 364
2908 Hawkins Dr 72143
Tel (501) 305-3153 *SIC* 8051

FIRST SECURITY BANCORP p 549
314 N Spring St 72143
Tel (501) 279-3400 *SIC* 6022

FIRST SECURITY BANK p 549
314 N Spring St 72143
Tel (501) 279-3400 *SIC* 6022

HARDING UNIVERSITY INC p 661
915 E Market Ave 72149
Tel (501) 279-4000 *SIC* 8221

WHITE COUNTY MEDICAL CENTER p 1606
3214 E Race Ave 72143
Tel (501) 268-6121 *SIC* 8082 8062

SHERWOOD, AR

CRAIN AUTOMOTIVE HOLDINGS LLC p 388
5890 Warden Rd 72120
Tel (501) 542-5000 *SIC* 5511

DELTA DENTAL PLAN OF ARKANSAS INC p 426
1513 Country Club Rd 72120
Tel (501) 992-1666 *SIC* 6324

SILOAM SPRINGS, AR

■ **COBB-VANTRESS INC** p 332
4703 Highway 412 E 72761
Tel (479) 524-3166 *SIC* 0751

LIBERTY BANK p 861
318 E Main St 72761
Tel (479) 524-8101 *SIC* 6022

SAGER CREEK FOODS INC p 1268
305 E Main St 72761
Tel (479) 524-6431 *SIC* 2033

SIMMONS FEED INGREDIENTS INC p 1324
601 N Hico St 72761
Tel (479) 254-8151 *SIC* 2077

SIMMONS FOODS INC p 1324
601 N Hico St 72761
Tel (479) 524-8151 *SIC* 2015

SIMMONS PET FOOD INC p 1324
601 N Hico St 72761
Tel (479) 524-8151 *SIC* 2047

SIMMONS PREPARED FOODS INC p 1324
601 N Hico St 72761
Tel (479) 524-8151 *SIC* 2015

VEG LIQUIDATION INC p 1546
305 E Main St 72761
Tel (479) 524-6431 *SIC* 2033 5142

WINDGATE FOUNDATION p 1615
115 E University St 72761
Tel (479) 524-9829 *SIC* 8733

SPRINGDALE, AR

■ **BNSF LOGISTICS LLC** p 194
2710 S 48th St 72762
Tel (479) 927-5570 *SIC* 4731

GEORGES INC p 606
402 W Robinson Ave 72764
Tel (479) 927-7000 *SIC* 2015 0254 0251

GEORGES PROCESSING INC p 606
402 W Robinson Ave 72764
Tel (479) 927-7000 *SIC* 2015

HARPS FOOD STORES INC p 663
918 S Gutensohn Rd 72762
Tel (479) 751-7601 *SIC* 5411 5122

MULTI-CRAFT CONTRACTORS INC p 999
2300 N Lowell Rd 72764
Tel (479) 751-4330 *SIC* 1711 3441 1731

■ **NORTHWEST HEALTH SYSTEM INC** p 1059
609 W Maple Ave 72764
Tel (479) 751-5711 *SIC* 8062

SPRINGDALE PUBLIC SCHOOL DISTRICT 50 p 1360
804 W Johnson Ave 72764
Tel (479) 750-8800 *SIC* 8211

■ **TYSON BREEDERS INC** p 1496
2200 W Don Tyson Pkwy 72762
Tel (479) 290-4000 *SIC* 0254

■ **TYSON CHICKEN INC** p 1496
2200 W Don Tyson Pkwy 72762
Tel (479) 290-4000
SIC 0252 0253 0254 0251 2015 2013

▲ **TYSON FOODS INC** p 1496
2200 W Don Tyson Pkwy 72762
Tel (479) 290-4000
SIC 2011 2015 2032 2096 2048

STUTTGART, AR

PRODUCERS RICE MILL INC p 1179
518 E Harrison St 72160
Tel (870) 673-4444 *SIC* 2044 5153 2099

RICELAND FOODS INC p 1232
2120 S Park Ave 72160
Tel (870) 673-5500
SIC 2044 2079 5153 2075

TONTITOWN, AR

K & K VETERINARY SUPPLY INC p 798
675 Laura Ln 72770
Tel (479) 361-1516 *SIC* 5199 5047 5072

■ **PAM TRANSPORT INC** p 1110
297 W Henri De Tonti Blvd 72770
Tel (479) 361-9111 *SIC* 4213

▲ **PAM TRANSPORTATION SERVICES INC** p 1110
297 W Henri De Tonti Blvd 72770
Tel (479) 361-9111 *SIC* 4213 4731

TRUMANN, AR

ROACH MANUFACTURING CORP p 1240
808 Highway 463 N 72472
Tel (870) 483-7631 *SIC* 3535

VAN BUREN, AR

FARMERS COOPERATIVE p 529
2105 Industrial Park Rd 72956
Tel (479) 474-8051 *SIC* 5191

TANKERSLEY FOOD SERVICE LLC p 1424
3203 Industrial Park Rd # 303 72956
Tel (479) 471-6800 *SIC* 5142

▲ **USA TRUCK INC** p 1534
3200 Industrial Park Rd 72956
Tel (479) 471-2500 *SIC* 4213

WEINER, AR

GREENWAY EQUIPMENT INC p 638
412 S Van Buren 72479
Tel (870) 684-7740 *SIC* 5999 5082

WEST MEMPHIS, AR

FLASH MARKET INC p 554
105 W Harrison Ave 72301
Tel (870) 732-2242 *SIC* 5541 5411

WARREN UNILUBE INC p 1577
915 E Jefferson Ave 72301
Tel (870) 735-1514 *SIC* 2992

WEST MEMPHIS STEEL & PIPE INC p 1595
1101 Thompson Ave 72301
Tel (870) 735-8244 *SIC* 5051

WHITE HALL, AR

DEPARTMENT OF CORRECTION ARKANSAS p 429
6814 Princeton Pike 71602
Tel (870) 267-6999 *SIC* 9223

MCGEORGE CONTRACTING CO INC p 929
1501 Heartwood St 71602
Tel (870) 534-7120 *SIC* 1611 1423

PINE BLUFF SAND AND GRAVEL CO p 1148
1501 Heartwood St 71602
Tel (870) 534-7120
SIC 2951 3273 1442 5032 1629

CALIFORNIA

ADELANTO, CA

ADELANTO ELEMENTARY SCHOOL DISTRICT p 22
11824 Air Expy 92301
Tel (760) 246-8691 *SIC* 8211

AGOURA HILLS, CA

▲ **AMERICAN HOMES 4 RENT** p 74
30601 Agoura Rd Ste 200 91301
Tel (805) 413-5300 *SIC* 6798

CHATSWORTH PRODUCTS INC p 292
29899 Agoura Rd Ste 120 91301
Tel (818) 735-6100 *SIC* 3499 2542

■ **FIRST AMERICAN MORTGAGE SOLUTIONS LLC** p 544
30005 Ladyface Ct 91301
Tel (800) 333-4510 *SIC* 6163

NATIONAL VETERINARY ASSOCIATES INC p 1016
29229 Canwood St Ste 100 91301
Tel (805) 777-7722 *SIC* 0742

■ **PACIFIC COMPENSATION CORP** p 1104
30301 Agoura Rd Ste 100 91301
Tel (818) 575-8500 *SIC* 6411

PENNYMAC CORP p 1131
27001 Agoura Rd 91301
Tel (818) 878-8416 *SIC* 6163

PRIVATE NATIONAL MORTGAGE ACCEPTANCE CO LLC p 1178
6101 Condor Dr 91301
Tel (818) 224-7401 *SIC* 6162

ALAMEDA, CA

■ **ABBOTT DIABETES CARE INC** p 9
1360 S Loop Rd 94502
Tel (510) 749-5400 *SIC* 2835 3845 3823

ALAMEDA ALLIANCE FOR HEALTH p 44
1240 S Loop Rd 94502
Tel (510) 747-4555 *SIC* 6324

ALAMEDA BUREAU OF ELECTRICITY IMPROVEMENT CORP p 44
2000 Grand St 94501
Tel (510) 748-3901 *SIC* 4911 4899 4841

ALAMEDA UNIFIED SCHOOL DISTRICT p 44
2060 Challenger Dr 94501
Tel (510) 337-7060 *SIC* 8211 8299

CITY OF ALAMEDA p 312
2263 Santa Clara Ave 94501
Tel (510) 747-7400 *SIC* 9111

■ **COST PLUS INC** p 373
1201 Marina Village Pkwy # 100 94501
Tel (510) 893-7300
SIC 5712 5713 5719 5947 5499 5921

PENUMBRA INC p 1132
1351 Harbor Bay Pkwy 94502
Tel (510) 748-3200 *SIC* 3841

STACY AND WITBECK INC p 1374
2800 Harbor Bay Pkwy 94502
Tel (510) 748-1870 *SIC* 1629

TELECARE CORP p 1434
1080 Marina Village Pkwy # 100 94501
Tel (510) 337-7950 *SIC* 8063 8011

■ **VF OUTDOOR LLC** p 1553
2701 Harbor Bay Pkwy 94502
Tel (510) 618-3500
SIC 2329 2339 3949 2394 2399 5941

■ **WIND RIVER SYSTEMS INC** p 1615
500 Wind River Way 94501
Tel (510) 748-4100 *SIC* 7372 7373

ALAMO, CA

RPM MORTGAGE INC p 1255
3240 Stone Valley Rd W 94507
Tel (925) 295-9300 *SIC* 6162

ALHAMBRA, CA

AHMC HEALTHCARE INC p 37
1000 S Fremont Ave Unit 6 91803
Tel (626) 943-7526 *SIC* 8062 8641

ALHAMBRA UNIFIED SCHOOL DISTRICT p 50
1515 W Mission Rd 91803
Tel (626) 943-3000 *SIC* 8211

EASTERN LOS ANGELES REGIONAL CENTER FOR DEVELOPMENTALLY DISABLED INC p 472
1000 S Fremont Ave # 23 91803
Tel (626) 299-4700 *SIC* 8322

▲ **EMCORE CORP** p 491
2015 Chestnut St 91803
Tel (626) 293-3400 *SIC* 3674 3559

ALISO VIEJO, CA

AVANIR PHARMACEUTICALS INC p 136
30 Enterprise Ste 400 92656
Tel (949) 389-6700 *SIC* 2834

CLARIENT DIAGNOSTIC SERVICES INC p 321
31 Columbia 92656
Tel (949) 425-5700 *SIC* 3841 3826 8071

■ **CNT ACQUISITION CORP** p 330
1 Enterprise 92656
Tel (949) 380-6100 *SIC* 3674

COVENANT CARE CALIFORNIA LLC p 384
27071 Aliso Creek Rd # 100 92656
Tel (949) 349-1200 *SIC* 8051

COVENANT CARE LLC p 384
27071 Aliso Creek Rd # 100 92656
Tel (949) 349-1200 *SIC* 8051

■ **FLUOR DANIEL ASIA INC** p 561
3 Polaris Way 92656
Tel (949) 349-2000 *SIC* 6799

■ **FLUOR DANIEL CONSTRUCTION CO** p 561
3 Polaris Way 92656
Tel (949) 349-2000 *SIC* 1622

■ **FLUOR DANIEL VENTURE GROUP INC** p 561
1 Enterprise 92656
Tel (949) 349-2000 *SIC* 6799

■ **FLUOR INDUSTRIAL SERVICES INC** p 561
1 Enterprise 92656
Tel (949) 439-2000 *SIC* 7349

HD SUPPLY DISTRIBUTION SERVICES LLC p 673
26940 Aliso Viejo Pkwy 92656
Tel (949) 643-4700 *SIC* 5072

JMJ FINANCIAL GROUP p 786
26800 Aliso Viejo Pkwy # 200 92656
Tel (949) 340-6336 *SIC* 6162

■ **LENNAR HOMES OF CALIFORNIA INC** p 855
25 Enterprise Ste 400 92656
Tel (949) 349-8000 *SIC* 1521 6552

METAGENICS INC p 952
25 Enterprise Ste 200 92656
Tel (949) 366-0818 *SIC* 5122

▲ **MICROSEMI CORP** p 962
1 Enterprise 92656
Tel (949) 380-6100 *SIC* 3674

▲ **NEW HOME CO INC** p 1031
85 Enterprise Ste 450 92656
Tel (949) 382-7800 *SIC* 1531

ONSITE DENTAL LLC p 1088
85 Argonaut Ste 220 92656
Tel (888) 411-2290 *SIC* 8021

■ **QLOGIC CORP** p 1195
26650 Aliso Viejo Pkwy 92656
Tel (949) 389-6000 *SIC* 3674

QUEST SOFTWARE INC p 1199
4 Polaris Way 92656
Tel (949) 754-8000 *SIC* 7373 7372 7379

■ **SAFEGUARD HEALTH ENTERPRISES INC** p 1266
95 Enterprise Ste 100 92656
Tel (949) 425-4340 SIC 6324

▲ **SUNSTONE HOTEL INVESTORS INC** p 1404
120 Vantis Dr Ste 350 92656
Tel (949) 330-4000 SIC 6798

SUNSTONE HOTEL PROPERTIES INC p 1404
120 Vantis Dr Ste 350 92656
Tel (949) 330-4000 SIC 7011

■ **TELOGIS INC** p 1435
20 Enterprise Ste 100 92656
Tel (949) 389-5500 SIC 7374

UST GLOBAL INC p 1535
5 Polaris Way 92656
Tel (949) 716-8757 SIC 7371

ALVISO, CA

ACME BUILDING MAINTENANCE CO INC p 17
941 Catherine St 95002
Tel (408) 263-5911 SIC 7349

FLEXTRONICS CORP p 556
6201 America Center Dr 95002
Tel (803) 936-5200 SIC 3679 3577 3571

■ **TIVO SOLUTIONS INC** p 1456
2160 Gold St 95002
Tel (408) 519-9100 SIC 7371

ANAHEIM, CA

A AND G INC p 4
1501 E Cerritos Ave 92805
Tel (714) 765-0400 SIC 2329 2253

ADVANTAGE-CROWN SALES & MARKETING LLC p 27
1400 S Douglass Rd # 200 92806
Tel (714) 780-3000 SIC 5141

■ **ALSTYLE APPAREL & ACTIVEWEAR MANAGEMENT CO** p 61
1501 E Cerritos Ave 92805
Tel (714) 765-0400 SIC 2253

■ **ALSTYLE APPAREL LLC** p 61
1501 E Cerritos Ave 92805
Tel (714) 765-0400 SIC 2211

AMPCO CONTRACTING INC p 86
1540 S Lewis St 92805
Tel (949) 955-2255 SIC 4959 1795 1794

ANAHEIM CITY SCHOOL DISTRICT p 88
1001 S East St 92805
Tel (714) 517-7500 SIC 8211

ANAHEIM REGIONAL MEDICAL CENTER p 88
1111 W La Palma Ave 92801
Tel (714) 774-1450 SIC 8069 8062

ANAHEIM UNION HIGH SCHOOL DIST p 88
501 N Crescent Way 92801
Tel (714) 999-3511 SIC 8211

ANGELS BASEBALL LP p 91
2000 E Gene Autry Way 92806
Tel (714) 940-2000 SIC 7941

AQUATIC CO p 101
8101 E Kaiser Blvd # 200 92808
Tel (714) 993-1220 SIC 3088

ARSG INC p 113
3870 E Eagle Dr 92807
Tel (714) 666-6650 SIC 7389

ATLANTA HILL RESTAURANT CORP p 125
4155 E La Palma Ave # 250 92807
Tel (714) 579-3900 SIC 5812

BACE MANUFACTURING INC p 143
3125 E Coronado St 92806
Tel (714) 630-6002 SIC 3089

BENCHMASTER FURNITURE LLC p 172
1481 N Hundley St 92806
Tel (714) 414-0240 SIC 5021

■ **BISCO INDUSTRIES INC** p 185
1500 N Lakeview Ave 92807
Tel (714) 876-2400 SIC 5065

BOMEL CONSTRUCTION CO INC p 199
8195 E Kaiser Blvd 92808
Tel (714) 921-1660 SIC 1541

■ **BRIDGFORD FOODS CORP** p 212
1308 N Patt St 92801
Tel (714) 526-5533
SIC 2045 2099 2015 2013 2022 2038

CARL KARCHER ENTERPRISES INC p 256
1200 N Harbor Blvd 92801
Tel (714) 776-8054 SIC 5812

CIRKS CONSTRUCTION INC p 308
2570 E Cerritos Ave 92806
Tel (714) 632-6717 SIC 1542

CITY OF ANAHEIM p 313
200 S Anaheim Blvd 92805
Tel (714) 765-5162 SIC 9121

CONTROL AIR CONDITIONING CORP p 364
5200 E La Palma Ave 92807
Tel (714) 777-8600 SIC 1711

COUNTRY VILLA SERVICE CORP p 375
2400 E Katella Ave # 800 92806
Tel (310) 574-3733 SIC 8741

▲ **EACO CORP** p 467
1500 N Lakeview Ave 92807
Tel (714) 876-2490 SIC 5065

ECONOLITE CONTROL PRODUCTS INC p 476
3360 E La Palma Ave 92806
Tel (714) 630-3700 SIC 3669

GANAHL LUMBER CO p 590
1220 E Ball Rd 92805
Tel (714) 772-5444 SIC 5211

GEARY PACIFIC CORP p 597
1360 N Hancock St 92807
Tel (714) 279-2950 SIC 5075

GGC ACQUISITION HOLDINGS CORP p 610
3450 E Miraloma Ave 92806
Tel (714) 414-4000 SIC 6719

HARDIN AUTOMOTIVE p 660
1381 S Auto Center Dr 92806
Tel (714) 533-6200 SIC 5511

HARRIS FREEMAN & CO INC p 663
3110 E Miraloma Ave 92806
Tel (714) 765-1190 SIC 5149 2099

ICE BUILDERS INC p 727
421 E Cerritos Ave 92805
Tel (714) 491-1317 SIC 1541

■ **INTERSTATE ELECTRONICS CORP** p 758
602 E Vermont Ave 92805
Tel (714) 758-0500 SIC 3825 3812 3679

ISUZU NORTH AMERICA CORP p 767
1400 S Douglass Rd # 100 92806
Tel (714) 935-9300
SIC 5511 5084 5013 5015

KEENAN HOPKINS SUDER & STOWELL CONTRACTORS INC p 807
5109 E La Palma Ave Ste A 92807
Tel (714) 695-3670
SIC 1742 1751 1743 1741 1721

MAKAR ANAHEIM LLC p 899
777 W Convention Way 92802
Tel (714) 740-4431 SIC 7011

MORPHOTRAK LLC p 990
5515 E La Palma Ave # 100 92807
Tel (714) 238-2000 SIC 7373

NORTH AMERICAN VIDEO CORP p 1050
1041 N Pacificenter Dr 92806
Tel (714) 779-7499 SIC 5065 3812

NORTH ORANGE COUNTY COMMUNITY COLLEGE DISTRICT p 1053
1830 W Romneya Dr 92801
Tel (714) 808-4500 SIC 8222

NORTHGATE GONZALEZ INC p 1057
1201 N Magnolia Ave 92801
Tel (714) 778-3784 SIC 5411

NORTHGATE GONZALEZ LLC p 1057
1201 N Magnolia Ave 92801
Tel (714) 778-3784 SIC 5411

PACIFIC SUNWEAR OF CALIFORNIA LLC p 1106
3450 E Miraloma Ave 92806
Tel (714) 414-4000 SIC 5611 5621 5699

PACIFIC SUNWEAR STORES CORP p 1106
3450 E Miraloma Ave 92806
Tel (714) 414-4000
SIC 5611 5699 5661 5621 5999

PAREX USA INC p 1114
4125 E La Palma Ave 92807
Tel (714) 778-2266 SIC 3299 5031

PENHALL CO p 1128
2121 W Crescent Ave Ste A 92801
Tel (714) 772-6450 SIC 1741 1795

PENHALL INTERNATIONAL CORP p 1129
320 N Crescent Way 92801
Tel (714) 772-6450 SIC 1795 1771

■ **PICK-YOUR-PART AUTO WRECKING** p 1146
1235 S Beach Blvd 92804
Tel (714) 385-1200 SIC 5531 5093

PINNER CONSTRUCTION CO INC p 1150
1255 S Lewis St 92805
Tel (714) 490-4000 SIC 1542

POLLYS INC p 1160
173 E Freedom Ave 92801
Tel (714) 459-0041 SIC 8748

■ **POWER PARAGON INC** p 1165
901 E Ball Rd 92805
Tel (714) 956-9200
SIC 3612 3613 3621 3643

PRIME HEALTHCARE ANAHEIM LLC p 1175
3033 W Orange Ave 92804
Tel (714) 827-3000 SIC 8062

RGB SYSTEMS INC p 1231
1025 E Ball Rd 92805
Tel (714) 491-1500 SIC 3577

RSI HOME PRODUCTS INC p 1256
400 E Orangethorpe Ave 92801
Tel (714) 449-2200
SIC 2514 2541 3281 2434

■ **SMART ELECTRONICS AND ASSEMBLY INC** p 1332
2000 W Corporate Way 92801
Tel (714) 772-2651 SIC 3672

SOURCE REFRIGERATION & HVAC INC p 1342
800 E Orangethorpe Ave 92801
Tel (714) 578-2300 SIC 1711 1731

SPECIALTY RESTAURANTS CORP p 1356
8191 E Kaiser Blvd 92808
Tel (714) 279-6100 SIC 5812 5813

SR BRAY LLC p 1362
1210 N Red Gum St 92806
Tel (714) 765-7551 SIC 1731 7359

STRAUB DISTRIBUTING CO LTD p 1393
4633 E La Palma Ave 92807
Tel (714) 779-4000 SIC 5181

STYLES FOR LESS INC p 1395
1205 N Miller St Ste 120 92806
Tel (714) 400-2525 SIC 5621

■ **SUPERIOR POOL PRODUCTS LLC** p 1407
4900 E Landon Dr 92807
Tel (714) 693-8035 SIC 5091

TARGUS INTERNATIONAL LLC p 1425
1211 N Miller St 92806
Tel (714) 765-5555 SIC 5199

TECHNO COATINGS INC p 1431
1391 S Allec St 92805
Tel (714) 635-1130
SIC 1542 1629 1721 1799

US UNION TOOL INC p 1533
1260 N Fee Ana St 92807
Tel (714) 521-6242 SIC 3541

WALNUT INVESTMENT CORP p 1574
2940 E White Star Ave 92806
Tel (714) 238-9240 SIC 5031 5039 5072

■ **WCO HOTELS INC** p 1585
1150 W Magic Way 92802
Tel (323) 636-3251 SIC 7011 5812

WEST COAST ARBORISTS INC p 1594
2200 E Via Burton 92806
Tel (714) 991-1900 SIC 0782

WESTSIDE BUILDING MATERIAL CORP p 1603
1111 E Howell Ave 92805
Tel (714) 385-1644 SIC 5032

▲ **WILLDAN GROUP INC** p 1610
2401 E Katella Ave # 300 92806
Tel (800) 424-9144 SIC 8711 8748

ANDERSON, CA

LINKUS ENTERPRISES LLC p 869
18631 Lloyd Ln 96007
Tel (530) 229-9197 SIC 1623 5731 4813

SIERRA PACIFIC INDUSTRIES p 1321
19794 Riverside Ave 96007
Tel (530) 378-8000 SIC 2421 2431

ANTIOCH, CA

ANTIOCH UNIFIED SCHOOL DISTRICT p 94
510 G St 94509
Tel (925) 779-7500 SIC 8211

BOND MANUFACTURING CO INC p 200
1700 W 4th St 94509
Tel (925) 252-1135 SIC 5083 3272

APPLE VALLEY, CA

APPLE VALLEY UNIFIED SCHOOL DISTRICT PUBLIC FACILITIES CORP p 99
12555 Navajo Rd 92308
Tel (760) 247-7267 SIC 8211

ST MARY MEDICAL CENTER p 1371
18300 Us Highway 18 92307
Tel (760) 242-2311 SIC 8062

APTOS, CA

BEVERLY FABRICS INC p 179
9019 Soquel Dr Ste 175 95003
Tel (831) 684-4220 SIC 5945 5949

CABRILLO COMMUNITY COLLEGE DISTRICT FINANCING CORP p 235
6500 Soquel Dr 95003
Tel (831) 479-6100 SIC 8222 7922 8221

FIRST ALARM p 544
1111 Estates Dr 95003
Tel (831) 476-1111 SIC 7382

WEEBS INC p 1587
20 Rancho Del Mar 95003
Tel (831) 688-8007 SIC 5651 5661

ARCADIA, CA

METHODIST HOSPITAL OF SOUTHERN CALIFORNIA p 954
300 W Huntington Dr 91007
Tel (626) 898-8000 SIC 8062

PACIFIC CLINICS p 1104
800 S Santa Anita Ave 91006
Tel (626) 254-5000 SIC 8093

ARCATA, CA

SUN VALLEY GROUP INC p 1401
3160 Upper Bay Rd 95521
Tel (707) 822-2885 SIC 0181

ARROYO GRANDE, CA

LUCIA MAR UNIFIED SCHOOL DISTRICT p 884
602 Orchard Ave 93420
Tel (805) 474-3000 SIC 8211

ARVIN, CA

GRIMMWAY ENTERPRISES INC p 640
14141 Di Giorgio Rd 93203
Tel (661) 854-6250 SIC 0723

ATASCADERO, CA

CALIFORNIA DEPARTMENT OF STATE HOSPITALS-ATASCADERO FIRE DEPARTMENT p 240
10333 El Camino Real 93422
Tel (805) 468-2501 SIC 8063

ATWATER, CA

AV THOMAS PRODUCE INC p 135
3900 Sultana Ave 95301
Tel (209) 394-7514 SIC 0161

MERCED UNION HIGH SCHOOL DISTRICT CAPITAL FACILITIES CORP p 944
3430 A St 95301
Tel (209) 385-6400 SIC 8211

TEASDALE FOODS INC p 1430
901 Packers St 95301
Tel (209) 358-5616 SIC 2034 2032

AUBURN, CA

CBM 2012 A CALIFORNIA LIMITED PARTNERSHIP p 268
1010 Racquet Club Dr # 108 95603
Tel (530) 823-2477
SIC 1531 1522 6513 6531 8741

COUNTY OF PLACER p 381
2968 Richardson Dr 95603
Tel (530) 889-4200 SIC 9111

FLYERS ENERGY LLC p 562
2360 Lindbergh St 95602
Tel (530) 885-0401 SIC 5411 5541 5013

MOTHER LODE HOLDING CO p 992
189 Fulweiler Ave 95603
Tel (530) 887-2410 SIC 6361 6531 7389

PLACER TITLE CO p 1153
189 Fulweiler Ave 95603
Tel (530) 887-2410 SIC 6361

UNITED AUBURN INDIAN COMMUNITY p 1506
10720 Indian Hill Rd 95603
Tel (530) 883-2390 SIC 9131

AZUSA, CA

AZUSA PACIFIC UNIVERSITY p 141
901 E Alosta Ave 91702
Tel (626) 969-3434 SIC 8221

AZUSA UNIFIED SCHOOL DISTRICT p 141
546 S Citrus Ave 91702
Tel (626) 967-6211 SIC 8211

AZUSA UNIFIED SCHOOL DISTRICT FACILITIES CORP p 141
546 S Citrus Ave 91702
Tel (626) 858-6159 SIC 8211

MONROVIA NURSERY CO p 985
817 E Monrovia Pl 91702
Tel (626) 334-9321 SIC 0181 5193 5261

MORRIS NATIONAL INC p 990
760 N Mckeever Ave 91702
Tel (626) 385-2000 SIC 5145 5149

RAIN BIRD CORP p 1205
1000 W Sierra Madre Ave 91702
Tel (626) 812-3400 SIC 3494 3432 3523

BAKERSFIELD, CA

AERA ENERGY LLC p 30
10000 Ming Ave 93311
Tel (661) 665-5000 SIC 1381

BAKERSFIELD CITY SCHOOL DISTRICT EDUCATIONAL FOUNDATION p 146
1300 Baker St 93305
Tel (661) 631-4600 SIC 8211

BAKERSFIELD MEMORIAL HOSPITAL p 146
420 34th St 93301
Tel (661) 327-1792 SIC 8062

■ **BOLTHOUSE FARMS** p 199
3200 E Brundage Ln 93304
Tel (661) 366-7205 SIC 0161

■ **BOLTHOUSE HOLDING CORP** p 199
7200 E Brundage Ln 93307
Tel (310) 566-8350 SIC 0161 2099

CALCOT LTD p 238
1900 E Brundage Ln 93307
Tel (661) 327-5961 SIC 5159

■ **CALIFORNIA RESOURCES ELK HILLS LLC** p 241
11109 River Run Blvd 93311
Tel (661) 412-5000 SIC 2911

■ **CALIFORNIA RESOURCES PRODUCTION CORP** p 241
11109 River Run Blvd 93311
Tel (661) 869-8000 SIC 1311 1382

CITY OF BAKERSFIELD p 313
1600 Truxtun Ave Fl 5th 93301
Tel (661) 326-3000 SIC 9111

CLINICA SIERRA VISTA p 326
1430 Truxtun Ave Ste 400 93301
Tel (661) 635-3050 SIC 8011

CONTINENTAL LABOR RESOURCES INC p 363
900 Mohawk St Ste 120 93309
Tel (661) 635-0335 SIC 7363

COUNTY OF KERN p 379
1115 Truxtun Ave Rm 505 93301
Tel (661) 868-3690 SIC 9111

E & B NATURAL RESOURCES MANAGEMENT CORP p 465
1600 Norris Rd 93308
Tel (661) 679-1714 SIC 1311

ESPARZA ENTERPRISES INC p 509
3851 Fruitvale Ave Ste A 93308
Tel (661) 831-0002 SIC 7361 7363

FORD HABERFELDE p 565
2001 Oak St 93301
Tel (661) 328-3600 *SIC* 5511

GREENFIELD UNION SCHOOL DISTRICT p 638
1624 Fairview Rd 93307
Tel (661) 837-6000 *SIC* 8211 9411

JACO OIL CO p 775
3101 State Rd 93308
Tel (661) 393-7000 *SIC* 5541

JAMIESON-HILL A GENERAL PARTNERSHIP p 777
3101 State Rd 93308
Tel (661) 393-7000 *SIC* 5541 6798

JIMS SUPPLY CO INC p 786
3530 Buck Owens Blvd 93308
Tel (661) 324-6514 *SIC* 5051

KEN SMALL CONSTRUCTION INC p 810
6205 District Blvd 93313
Tel (661) 617-1700 *SIC* 1623

KERN COMMUNITY COLLEGE DISTRICT p 813
2100 Chester Ave 93301
Tel (661) 336-5100 *SIC* 8222

KERN COUNTY SUPERINTENDENT OF SCHOOLS EDUCATIONAL SERVICES FOUNDATION p 813
1300 17th St 93301
Tel (661) 636-4000 *SIC* 8211

KERN HIGH SCHOOL DST p 813
5801 Sundale Ave 93309
Tel (661) 827-3100 *SIC* 8211

KERN REGIONAL CENTER p 813
3200 N Sillect Ave 93308
Tel (661) 327-8531 *SIC* 8322

KS INDUSTRIES LP p 831
6205 District Blvd 93313
Tel (661) 617-1700 *SIC* 1623

MP ENVIRONMENTAL SERVICES INC p 995
3400 Manor St 93308
Tel (800) 458-3036
SIC 4953 4213 8748 7699

NESTLE ICE CREAM CO p 1027
7301 District Blvd 93313
Tel (661) 398-3500 *SIC* 5143 5451

NORTH BAKERSFIELD TOYOTA SCION p 1051
19651 Industry Parkway Dr 93308
Tel (661) 615-1100 *SIC* 5511

NTS INC p 1065
8200 Stockdale Hwy Ste M 93311
Tel (661) 588-8514 *SIC* 1623 1541 1771

PACIFIC PROCESS SYSTEMS INC p 1105
7401 Rosedale Hwy 93308
Tel (661) 321-9681 *SIC* 1389 7353 5082

PANAMA-BUENA VISTA UNION SCHOOL DISTRICT p 1111
4200 Ashe Rd 93313
Tel (661) 831-8331 *SIC* 8211

POMWONDERFUL LLC p 1161
4805 Centennial Ste 100 93301
Tel (310) 966-5800 *SIC* 5149 5148 5085

ROBERT HEELY INC p 1241
5401 Woodmere Dr 93313
Tel (661) 617-1400 *SIC* 1623

SAN JOAQUIN COMMUNITY HOSPITAL p 1277
2615 Chester Ave 93301
Tel (661) 395-3000 *SIC* 8062 8011

SELF-INSURED SCHOOLS OF CALIFORNIA p 1302
1300 17th St 5 93301
Tel (661) 636-4000 *SIC* 6371

STURGEON SERVICES INTERNATIONAL INC p 1395
3511 Gilmore Ave 93308
Tel (661) 322-4408 *SIC* 6719

SUN WORLD INTERNATIONAL INC p 1401
16351 Driver Rd 93308
Tel (661) 392-5000
SIC 0723 0172 0174 0175 0179 0161

THREE-WAY CHEVROLET CO p 1450
4501 Wible Rd 93313
Tel (661) 847-6400
SIC 5511 5531 7515 7538 7532

WHOLESALE FUELS INC p 1607
2200 E Brundage Ln 93307
Tel (661) 327-4900 *SIC* 5172

■ **WM BOLTHOUSE FARMS INC** p 1620
7200 E Brundage Ln 93307
Tel (661) 366-7205 *SIC* 0161 2099 0723

BALDWIN PARK, CA

BALDWIN PARK UNIFIED SCHOOL DISTRICT p 147
3699 Holly Ave 91706
Tel (626) 939-4000 *SIC* 8211

CEDARWOOD-YOUNG CO p 272
14620 Joanbridge St 91706
Tel (626) 962-4047 *SIC* 5093

SOURCE ONE STAFFING LLC p 1342
5312 Irwindale Ave Ste 1h 91706
Tel (626) 337-0560 *SIC* 7363

SUPERIOR COMMUNICATIONS INC p 1406
5027 Irwindale Ave # 900 91706
Tel (626) 388-2573 *SIC* 5065

UPM INC p 1528
13245 Los Angeles St 91706
Tel (626) 962-4001 *SIC* 3544 3089

BANNING, CA

GREENTHUMB PRODUCE p 637
2648 W Ramsey St 92220
Tel (951) 849-4711 *SIC* 5148

BEAUMONT, CA

ARROW USA p 113
1105 Highland Ct 92223
Tel (951) 845-6144 *SIC* 5087

BELL GARDENS, CA

BELL GARDENS BICYCLE CLUB INC p 170
888 Bicycle Casino Dr 90201
Tel (562) 806-4646 *SIC* 7999 5812

PARKHOUSE TIRE SERVICE INC p 1116
5960 Shull St 90201
Tel (562) 928-0421 *SIC* 5531

WEI-CHUAN USA INC p 1587
6655 Garfield Ave 90201
Tel (323) 587-2101 *SIC* 5142 2038

BELLFLOWER, CA

BELLFLOWER UNIFIED SCHOOL DISTRICT p 170
16703 Clark Ave 90706
Tel (562) 866-9011 *SIC* 8211

NORMS RESTAURANTS p 1049
17844 Lakewood Blvd 90706
Tel (562) 925-4026 *SIC* 5812

BELL, CA

MARIKA LLC p 906
5553-B Bandini Blvd 90201
Tel (323) 888-7755 *SIC* 2339

PERRIN BERNARD SUPOWITZ INC p 1137
5496 Lindbergh Ln 90201
Tel (323) 981-2800 *SIC* 5141

BELMONT, CA

NIKON PRECISION INC p 1043
1399 Shoreway Rd 94002
Tel (650) 508-4674 *SIC* 5084 5065

▲ **RINGCENTRAL INC** p 1235
20 Davis Dr 94002
Tel (650) 472-4100 *SIC* 7372 4899

■ **SUNEDISON LLC** p 1402
600 Clipper Dr 94002
Tel (650) 453-5600 *SIC* 4911

BELVEDERE TIBURON, CA

NES HOLDINGS INC p 1026
39 Main St 94920
Tel (415) 435-4591 *SIC* 7363

OCADIAN CARE CENTERS LLC p 1072
104 Main St 94920
Tel (415) 789-5427 *SIC* 8051

BENICIA, CA

CYCLE GEAR INC p 405
4705 Industrial Way 94510
Tel (707) 747-5053 *SIC* 5571

WEST COAST BEAUTY SUPPLY CO p 1594
5001 Industrial Way 94510
Tel (707) 748-4800 *SIC* 5087 3069

BERKELEY, CA

BERKELEY UNIFIED SCHOOL DISTRICT p 175
2020 Bonar St Rm 202 94702
Tel (510) 644-4500 *SIC* 8211

CITY OF BERKELEY p 313
2120 Milvia St 94704
Tel (510) 981-7300 *SIC* 9121

GRIFFIN MOTORWERKE INC p 640
1146 6th St 94710
Tel (510) 524-7447 *SIC* 7538 5531

HART CHEMICALS INC p 664
2424 4th St 94710
Tel (510) 549-3535 *SIC* 5191 5169

LAWRENCE BERKELEY NATIONAL LAB p 847
1 Cyclotron Rd 94720
Tel (510) 486-6792 *SIC* 8071

O C JONES & SONS INC p 1070
1520 4th St 94710
Tel (510) 526-3424 *SIC* 1611

SURGERY CENTER OF ALTA BATES SUMMIT MEDICAL CENTER LLC p 1408
2450 Ashby Ave 94705
Tel (510) 204-4444 *SIC* 8062

TOOLOW INC p 1460
4273 Reids Way 94704
Tel (408) 694-2361 *SIC* 7379

UNITED STATES DEPARTMENT OF ENERGY BERKELEY OFFICE p 1512
1 Cyclotron Rd 94720
Tel (510) 486-4000 *SIC* 9611

UNIVERSITY CALIFORNIA BERKELEY p 1518
200 Clfrnia Hall Spc 1500 94720
Tel (510) 642-6000 *SIC* 8221

BEVERLY HILLS, CA

ACADEMY OF MOTION PICTURE ARTS & SCIENCES p 13
8949 Wilshire Blvd 90211
Tel (310) 247-3000 *SIC* 8621 7819 8611

BONERTS INC p 200
273 S Canon Dr 90212
Tel (714) 540-3535 *SIC* 5142

CEDARS-SINAI MEDICAL CARE FOUNDATION p 272
200 N Robertson Blvd # 101 90211
Tel (310) 385-3200 *SIC* 8699

FINN HOLDING CORP p 543
360 N Crescent Dr 90210
Tel (310) 712-1850 *SIC* 4449 3731 4491

G&L REALTY CORP LLC p 587
439 N Bedford Dr 90210
Tel (310) 273-9930 *SIC* 6552

GORES GROUP LLC p 626
9800 Wilshire Blvd 90212
Tel (310) 209-3010 *SIC* 6211

GRAPEMAN FARMS LP p 631
9777 Wilshire Blvd # 918 90212
Tel (310) 273-9540 *SIC* 0172

HILLSTONE RESTAURANT GROUP INC p 694
147 S Beverly Dr 90212
Tel (310) 385-7343 *SIC* 5812 5813

■ **HILTON INNS INC** p 695
9336 Civic Center Dr 90210
Tel (310) 278-4321 *SIC* 7011

JOE TORNANTE-MDP HOLDING LLC p 787
233 S Beverly Dr 90212
Tel (310) 228-6800
SIC 5145 5092 5112 2064

▲ **KENNEDY-WILSON HOLDINGS INC** p 811
151 El Camino Dr 90212
Tel (310) 887-6400 *SIC* 6531 6799

KING HOLDING CORP p 820
360 N Crescent Dr 90210
Tel (586) 254-3900
SIC 3452 3465 3469 3089 5072

LEVINE LEICHTMAN CAPITAL PARTNERS INC p 858
335 N Maple Dr Ste 130 90210
Tel (310) 275-5335 *SIC* 6799

▲ **LIVE NATION ENTERTAINMENT INC** p 871
9348 Civic Center Dr Lbby 90210
Tel (310) 867-7000 *SIC* 7922 7389 7941

MAGIC JOHNSON ENTERPRISES INC p 895
9100 Wilshire Blvd 700e 90212
Tel (310) 247-2033 *SIC* 8743 7389

MAGIC WORKFORCE SOLUTIONS LLC p 895
9100 Wilsh Blvd Ste 700e 90212
Tel (310) 246-6153 *SIC* 8743

MERCHANT OF TENNIS INC p 944
8737 Wilshire Blvd 90211
Tel (310) 228-4000
SIC 5941 5621 5661 5961 5999

METRO-GOLDWYN-MAYER INC p 955
245 N Beverly Dr 90210
Tel (310) 449-3000 *SIC* 7812

MGM HOLDINGS II INC p 958
245 N Beverly Dr 90210
Tel (310) 449-3000 *SIC* 7812

MGM HOLDINGS INC p 958
245 N Beverly Dr 90210
Tel (310) 449-3000 *SIC* 7812

▲ **PACWEST BANCORP** p 1107
9701 Wilshire Blvd # 700 90212
Tel (310) 887-8500 *SIC* 6021

PLATINUM EQUITY LLC p 1155
360 N Crescent Dr Bldg S 90210
Tel (310) 712-1850 *SIC* 6726

PLATINUM EQUITY PARTNERS LLC p 1155
360 N Crescent Dr 90210
Tel (310) 712-1850 *SIC* 6726

PROJECT BOAT HOLDINGS LLC p 1182
360 N Crescent Dr Bldg S 90210
Tel (310) 712-1850 *SIC* 6719

PROJECT SKYLINE INTERMEDIATE HOLDING CORP p 1182
360 N Crescent Dr Bldg S 90210
Tel (310) 712-1850 *SIC* 6719

REALD INC p 1214
100 N Crescent Dr 90210
Tel (424) 702-4327 *SIC* 7812

■ **SHAPELL INDUSTRIES LLC** p 1311
8383 Wilshire Blvd # 700 90211
Tel (323) 655-7330 *SIC* 6552 6514 1522

SPRINKLES CUPCAKES INC p 1361
9635 Santa Monica Blvd 90210
Tel (310) 274-8765 *SIC* 5441

UNICOM SYSTEMS INC p 1502
1143 Summit Dr 90210
Tel (818) 838-0606 *SIC* 7371

ZILLIONAIRE EMPRESS DANIELLE BERHANE MANAGEMENT FIRM p 1643
8549 Wilshire Blvd # 817 90211
Tel (310) 461-9923 *SIC* 6722

BIG BEAR LAKE, CA

SNOW SUMMIT SKI CORP p 1336
880 Summit Blvd 92315
Tel (909) 866-5766 *SIC* 7011 5812

BLOOMINGTON, CA

CHIRO INC p 301
2260 S Vista Ave 92316
Tel (909) 879-1160 *SIC* 5087 7349 5169

BRAWLEY, CA

PIONEERS MEMORIAL HEALTHCARE DISTRICT p 1151
207 W Legion Rd 92227
Tel (760) 351-3333 *SIC* 8062

BREA, CA

AIR TREATMENT CORP p 39
640 N Puente St 92821
Tel (909) 869-7975 *SIC* 5075

AMERICAN FINANCIAL NETWORK INC p 72
10 Pointe Dr Ste 330 92821
Tel (909) 606-3905 *SIC* 6141

AVERY PRODUCTS CORP p 137
50 Pointe Dr 92821
Tel (714) 675-8500
SIC 2678 3951 2672 2891

■ **BECKMAN COULTER INC** p 167
250 S Kraemer Blvd 92821
Tel (714) 993-5321 *SIC* 3826 3841 3821

■ **CALIFORNIA AUTOMOBILE INSURANCE CO** p 239
555 W Imperial Hwy 92821
Tel (714) 232-8669 *SIC* 6331

CAPITALSOURCE BANK p 250
130 S State College Blvd 92821
Tel (714) 989-4600 *SIC* 6022

DIVERSE STAFFING INC p 443
1800 E Lambert Rd Ste 100 92821
Tel (714) 482-0499 *SIC* 7361

FRESH START BAKERIES INC p 579
145 S State Ckkg Blvd 2 Ste 200 92821
Tel (714) 256-8900 *SIC* 2051

GRIFFITH CO p 640
3050 E Birch St 92821
Tel (714) 984-5500 *SIC* 1611

■ **INTERCONTINENTAL EXCHANGE INC** p 752
1415 Moonstone 92821
Tel (770) 857-4700 *SIC* 6231

KIRKHILL AIRCRAFT PARTS CO p 821
3120 Enterprise St 92821
Tel (714) 223-5400 *SIC* 5088 3728

■ **KIRKHILL-TA CO** p 822
300 E Cypress St 92821
Tel (714) 529-4901 *SIC* 3069

LOUIS WURTH AND CO p 880
895 Columbia St 92821
Tel (714) 529-1771 *SIC* 5072 5198

■ **MERCURY CASUALTY CO** p 945
555 W Imperial Hwy 92821
Tel (323) 937-1060 *SIC* 6331 6351

■ **METALS USA BUILDING PRODUCTS LP** p 952
955 Columbia St 92821
Tel (713) 946-9000 *SIC* 3355 5031 1542

NATURES BEST DISTRIBUTION LLC p 1019
6 Pointe Dr Ste 300 92821
Tel (714) 255-4600 *SIC* 5149

NEVELL GROUP INC p 1029
3001 Enterprise St # 200 92821
Tel (714) 579-7501 *SIC* 1542

NORTHSTAR DEMOLITION AND REMEDIATION LP p 1058
404 N Berry St 92821
Tel (714) 672-3500 *SIC* 1795 1799 8744

PENNYSAVER USA PUBLISHING LLC p 1131
2830 Orbiter St 92821
Tel (866) 640-3900 *SIC* 2741

SULLY-MILLER CONTRACTING CO INC p 1397
135 Sstate College Ste 400 92821
Tel (714) 578-9600 *SIC* 1611

SUZUKI MOTOR OF AMERICA INC p 1410
3251 E Imperial Hwy 92821
Tel (714) 996-7040 *SIC* 3751 3519 3799

TP-LINK USA CORP p 1467
145 S State College Blvd # 400 92821
Tel (626) 333-0234 *SIC* 5045

VENTURA FOODS LLC p 1548
40 Pointe Dr 92821
Tel (714) 257-3700 *SIC* 2079 2035

VETERINARY PET INSURANCE SERVICES INC p 1553
1800 E Emperi Hwy Ste 145 92821
Tel (714) 989-0555 *SIC* 6411

VIEWSONIC CORP p 1556
10 Pointe Dr Ste 200 92821
Tel (909) 444-8888 *SIC* 3577

WEST COAST PRIME MEATS LLC p 1594
344 Cliffwood Park St 92821
Tel (714) 255-8560 *SIC* 5147

WILSEY FOODS INC p 1613
40 Pointe Dr 92821
Tel (714) 257-3700 *SIC* 2079 5149

BRENTWOOD, CA

HOT LINE CONSTRUCTION INC p 710
9020 Brentwood Blvd Ste H 94513
Tel (925) 634-9333 *SIC* 1731 1799

BRISBANE, CA

▲ BEBE STORES INC p 167
400 Valley Dr 94005
Tel (415) 715-3900 SIC 2331

BI-RITE RESTAURANT SUPPLY CO INC p 180
123 S Hill Dr 94005
Tel (415) 656-0187
SIC 5141 5147 5148 5023 5046 5963

CRIMSON CAPITAL SILICON VALLEY p 392
1000 Marina Blvd Ste 105 94005
Tel (650) 325-8673 SIC 6799 3429

▲ CUTERA INC p 403
3240 Bayshore Blvd 94005
Tel (415) 657-5500 SIC 3845

LEEMAH CORP p 852
155 S Hill Dr 94005
Tel (415) 394-1288
SIC 3671 3672 3669 3663 3577

MONSTER INC p 985
455 Valley Dr 94005
Tel (415) 840-2000 SIC 5099 4841 3679

NORMAN S WRIGHT MECHANICAL EQUIPMENT CORP p 1049
99 S Hill Dr Ste A 94005
Tel (415) 467-7600 SIC 5075

OAKVILLE PRODUCE PARTNERS LLC p 1071
453 Valley Dr 94005
Tel (415) 647-2991 SIC 5148 5451

BROOKS, CA

CACHE CREEK CASINO RESORT p 235
14455 State Highway 16 95606
Tel (530) 796-3118 SIC 7011

YOCHA DEHE WINTUN NATION p 1636
18960 County Rd 75 A 95606
Tel (530) 796-2109 SIC 9131

BUENA PARK, CA

ACCESS BUSINESS GROUP INTERNATIONAL LLC p 14
5600 Beach Blvd 90621
Tel (714) 521-2853 SIC 2834

AMADA AMERICA INC p 64
7025 Firestone Blvd 90621
Tel (714) 739-2111 SIC 5084 6159

AMCOR PACKAGING (USA) INC p 65
6600 Valley View St 90620
Tel (714) 562-6000 SIC 2653 5113

■ BERRY KNOTTS FARM LLC p 176
8039 Beach Blvd 90620
Tel (714) 827-1776 SIC 2099

■ CONTINENTAL EXCHANGE SOLUTIONS INC p 363
7001 Village Dr Ste 200 90621
Tel (562) 345-2100 SIC 6099

CORDOVA BOLT INC p 369
5601 Dolly Ave 90621
Tel (714) 739-7500 SIC 5072

DR FRESH LLC p 454
6645 Caballero Blvd 90620
Tel (714) 690-1573 SIC 5047 3843

■ LEACH INTERNATIONAL CORP p 850
6900 Orangethorpe Ave 90620
Tel (714) 736-7537 SIC 3679

LEGACY FARMS LLC p 852
6625 Caballero Blvd 90620
Tel (714) 736-1800 SIC 5148

MEDIEVAL TIMES ENTERTAINMENT INC p 938
7662 Beach Blvd 90620
Tel (714) 523-1100 SIC 7041 7996

NORITSU AMERICA CORP p 1048
6900 Noritsu Ave 90620
Tel (714) 521-9040 SIC 5043

OASIS BRANDS INC p 1071
6700 Artesia Blvd 90620
Tel (540) 658-2830 SIC 5113

ORORA PACKAGING SOLUTIONS p 1095
6600 Valley View St 90620
Tel (714) 562-6000 SIC 5113 2653

PHARR-PALOMAR INC p 1141
6781 8th St 90620
Tel (714) 522-4811 SIC 2282 2281

■ RIA ENVIA INC p 1232
6565 Knott Ave 90620
Tel (714) 543-8448 SIC 7389

TAWA SERVICES INC p 1426
6281 Regio Ave Fl 2 90620
Tel (714) 521-8899 SIC 5149 5411

TAWA SUPERMARKET INC p 1426
6281 Regio Ave 90620
Tel (714) 521-8899 SIC 5411

YAMAHA CORP OF AMERICA INC p 1634
6600 Orangethorpe Ave 90620
Tel (714) 522-9011
SIC 5099 5065 5091 3931

BURBANK, CA

■ ABC CABLE NETWORKS GROUP p 10
500 S Buena Vista St 91521
Tel (818) 460-7477 SIC 4832 4833

■ ABC FAMILY WORLDWIDE INC p 10
500 S Buena Vista St 91521
Tel (818) 560-1000 SIC 7812 4841

ALLIANZ GLOBAL RISKS US INSURANCE CO p 55
2350 W Empire Ave 91504
Tel (818) 260-7500 SIC 6331

ANDREWS INTERNATIONAL INC p 90
455 N Moss St 91502
Tel (818) 487-4060 SIC 7381

■ ARAMARK UNIFORM & CAREER APPAREL LLC p 102
115 N First St Ste 203 91502
Tel (818) 973-3700 SIC 7218

BONANZA PRODUCTIONS INC p 199
4000 Warner Blvd 91522
Tel (818) 954-4212 SIC 7929

BURBANK UNIFIED SCHOOL DISTRICT p 226
1900 W Olive Ave 91506
Tel (818) 729-4400 SIC 8211

CITY OF BURBANK p 313
275 E Olive Ave 91502
Tel (818) 238-5800 SIC 9111

CW NETWORK LLC p 404
3300 W Olive Ave Fl 3 91505
Tel (818) 977-2500 SIC 4833

■ DISNEY ENTERPRISES INC p 443
500 S Buena Vista St 91521
Tel (818) 560-1000
SIC 7812 6794 5331 7996 7941

■ DISNEY INTERACTIVE STUDIOS INC p 443
500 S Buena Vista St 91521
Tel (818) 560-1000 SIC 7371

■ DISNEY REGIONAL ENTERTAINMENT INC p 443
500 S Buena Vista St 91521
Tel (818) 560-1000 SIC 7999 5812 5813

■ DISNEY WORLDWIDE SERVICES INC p 443
500 S Buena Vista St 91521
Tel (877) 466-6669 SIC 7812 5736

■ DISNEYLAND INTERNATIONAL INC p 443
500 S Buena Vista St 91521
Tel (818) 560-1000 SIC 7996

FOTO-KEM INDUSTRIES INC p 571
2801 W Alameda Ave 91505
Tel (818) 846-3102 SIC 7819

HASKEL INTERNATIONAL LLC p 667
100 E Graham Pl 91502
Tel (818) 843-4000
SIC 3561 3594 5084 5085 3699

■ HYDRO-AIRE INC p 723
3000 Winona Ave 91504
Tel (818) 526-2600 SIC 3728

KAN-DI-KI LLC p 802
2820 N Ontario St 91504
Tel (818) 549-1880 SIC 8071

■ LAWYERS TITLE CO p 848
7530 N Glenoaks Blvd 91504
Tel (818) 767-0425 SIC 6361 6531

LBI MEDIA HOLDINGS INC p 849
1845 W Empire Ave 91504
Tel (818) 563-5722 SIC 4832 4833

LIBERMAN BROADCASTING INC p 861
1845 W Empire Ave 91504
Tel (818) 729-5300 SIC 4832

LOGIX FEDERAL CREDIT UNION p 875
2340 N Hollywood Way 91505
Tel (888) 718-5328 SIC 6061

PERFORMANCE DESIGNED PRODUCTS LLC p 1135
2300 W Empire Ave # 600 91504
Tel (323) 234-9911 SIC 5092

PROVIDENCE HEALTH & SERVICES FOUNDATION/SAN FERNANDO AND SANTA p 1185
501 S Buena Vista St 91505
Tel (818) 843-5111 SIC 8399

PSI SERVICES LLC p 1188
2950 N Hollywood Way # 200 91505
Tel (818) 847-6180 SIC 8748

RYAN HERCO PRODUCTS CORP p 1260
3010 N San Fernando Blvd 91504
Tel (818) 841-1141 SIC 5074 5162

SCREEN ACTORS GUILD-PRODUCERS ADMINISTRATIVE CORP p 1294
3601 W Olive Ave Ste 200 91505
Tel (818) 954-9400 SIC 6371

SWANER HARDWOOD CO INC p 1411
5 W Magnolia Blvd 91502
Tel (818) 953-5350 SIC 2435 5031

TEAM BENEFITS CORP p 1429
901 W Alameda Ave 100 91506
Tel (818) 558-3261 SIC 8721

TEAM COMPANIES INC p 1429
901 W Alameda Ave Ste 100 91506
Tel (818) 558-3261 SIC 8721

TECHNICOLOR THOMSON GROUP INC p 1431
2233 N Ontario St Ste 300 91504
Tel (818) 260-3600 SIC 7819 7384

▲ WALT DISNEY CO p 1574
500 S Buena Vista St 91521
Tel (818) 560-1000
SIC 4833 4841 7011 7996 7812 2731

■ WALT DISNEY MUSIC CO p 1574
500 S Buena Vista St 91521
Tel (818) 560-1000 SIC 6794

■ WALT DISNEY RECORDS DIRECT p 1574
500 S Buena Vista St 91521
Tel (818) 560-1000 SIC 7812

■ WARNER BROS (TRANSATLANTIC) INC p 1576
4000 Warner Blvd 91522
Tel (818) 977-0018 SIC 7822

■ WARNER BROS ENTERTAINMENT INC p 1576
4000 Warner Blvd 91522
Tel (818) 954-6000 SIC 7812

■ WARNER BROS HOME ENTERTAINMENT INC p 1576
4000 Warner Blvd Bldg 160 91522
Tel (818) 954-6000 SIC 3651

WARNER BROS RECORDS INC p 1576
3300 Warner Blvd 91505
Tel (818) 953-3378 SIC 7389

WDPT FILM DISTRIBUTION LLC p 1585
500 S Buena Vista St 91521
Tel (818) 560-1000 SIC 5065

WRITERS GUILD INDUSTRY HEALTH FUND p 1627
1015 N Hollywood Way # 200 91505
Tel (818) 846-1015 SIC 8742

BURLINGAME, CA

ARES CORP p 107
1440 Chapin Ave Ste 390 94010
Tel (505) 661-6390 SIC 8711

ARES HOLDING CORP p 107
1440 Chapin Ave Ste 390 94010
Tel (650) 401-7100 SIC 8711

CALIFORNIA TEACHERS ASSOCIATION p 241
1705 Murchison Dr 94010
Tel (650) 697-1400 SIC 8621 8631

ENVIRONMENTAL CHEMICAL CORP p 503
1240 Bayshore Hwy 94010
Tel (650) 347-1555 SIC 8711 1542 8744

FCE BENEFIT ADMINISTRATORS INC p 533
887 Mitten Rd Ste 200 94010
Tel (650) 341-0306 SIC 6411

FRANK EDWARDS CO INC p 574
1565 Adrian Rd 94010
Tel (650) 692-2347 SIC 5084 5013

GUITTARD CHOCOLATE CO p 646
10 Guittard Rd 94010
Tel (650) 697-4427 SIC 2066 2064

HANERGY HOLDING AMERICA INC p 657
1350 Bayshore Hwy Ste 825 94010
Tel (650) 288-3722 SIC 4911 6719

JS INTERNATIONAL SHIPPING CORP p 795
1535 Rollins Rd Ste B 94010
Tel (650) 697-3963 SIC 4731

MILLS PENINSULA HOSPITAL INC p 971
1635 Rollins Rd 94010
Tel (650) 652-3807 SIC 8099

MILLS-PENINSULA HEALTH SERVICES p 971
1501 Trousdale Dr 94010
Tel (650) 696-5400 SIC 8062

OBAYASHI USA LLC p 1072
577 Airport Blvd Ste 600 94010
Tel (650) 952-4910 SIC 6531

PRIMROSE ALLOYS INC p 1176
330 Primrose Rd Ste 205 94010
Tel (650) 678-5781 SIC 3317

STANDARD FIBER LLC p 1376
577 Airport Blvd Ste 200 94010
Tel (650) 872-6528 SIC 5021

TREX CORP INC p 1476
851 Burlway Rd Ste 400 94010
Tel (650) 342-7333 SIC 5147

▲ VIRGIN AMERICA INC p 1558
555 Airport Blvd Ste 400 94010
Tel (877) 359-8474 SIC 4512

BUTTONWILLOW, CA

BUTTONWILLOW WAREHOUSE CO INC p 230
125 Front St 93206
Tel (661) 764-5234 SIC 5191

TECH AGRICULTURAL INC p 1430
125 Front St 93206
Tel (661) 323-1001 SIC 5191

CALABASAS HILLS, CA

▲ CHEESECAKE FACTORY INC p 292
26901 Malibu Hills Rd 91301
Tel (818) 871-3000 SIC 5812 2051

CALABASAS, CA

ALE USA INC p 48
26801 Agoura Rd 91301
Tel (818) 878-4816 SIC 3663 3613

BRIGHTVIEW COMPANIES LLC p 213
24151 Ventura Blvd 91302
Tel (818) 223-8500 SIC 1629 0782 0781

BRIGHTVIEW GOLF MAINTENANCE INC p 213
24151 Ventura Blvd 91302
Tel (818) 223-8500 SIC 1629

BRIGHTVIEW LANDSCAPE DEVELOPMENT INC p 213
24151 Ventura Blvd 91302
Tel (818) 223-8500 SIC 0781

BRIGHTVIEW LANDSCAPE SERVICES INC p 213
24151 Ventura Blvd 91302
Tel (818) 223-8500 SIC 0781

■ CHEESECAKE FACTORY RESTAURANTS INC p 292
26901 Malibu Hills Rd 91301
Tel (818) 871-3000 SIC 5812

■ COUNTRYWIDE FINANCIAL CORP p 375
4500 Park Granada 91302
Tel (818) 225-3000
SIC 6162 6211 6361 6411 6163 6799

■ DTS INC p 458
5220 Las Virgenes Rd 91302
Tel (818) 436-1000 SIC 7819 3651

GARCOA INC p 591
26135 Mureau Rd Ste 100 91302
Tel (818) 225-0375 SIC 7389

HARBOR FREIGHT TOOLS USA INC p 659
26541 Agoura Rd 91302
Tel (818) 836-5000 SIC 5251

▲ IXIA p 769
26601 Agoura Rd 91302
Tel (818) 871-1800 SIC 3825 7371

▲ MARCUS & MILLICHAP INC p 905
23975 Park Sorrento # 400 91302
Tel (818) 212-2250 SIC 6531

NATIONAL TECHNICAL SYSTEMS INC p 1016
24007 Ventura Blvd # 200 91302
Tel (818) 591-0776 SIC 8711

▲ NETSOL TECHNOLOGIES INC p 1027
24025 Park Sorrento # 410 91302
Tel (818) 222-9195 SIC 7372 7373 7299

▲ ON ASSIGNMENT INC p 1085
26745 Malibu Hills Rd 91301
Tel (818) 878-7900 SIC 7363 7361

PROLIFICS APPLICATION SERVICES INC p 1182
24025 Park Sorrento # 405 91302
Tel (646) 201-4967 SIC 7379

PROLIFICS INC p 1182
24025 Park Sorrento # 450 91302
Tel (212) 267-7722 SIC 7379 7371

SPIRENT COMMUNICATIONS INC p 1359
27349 Agoura Rd 91301
Tel (818) 676-2300 SIC 3663 3829 3825

WESTERN GENERAL HOLDING CO p 1598
5230 Las Virgenes Rd # 100 91302
Tel (818) 880-9070 SIC 6331

WESTERN GENERAL INSURANCE CO INC p 1598
5230 Las Virgenes Rd 91302
Tel (818) 880-9070 SIC 6331

CALEXICO, CA

COPPEL CORP p 368
503 Scaroni Ave 92231
Tel (760) 357-3707 SIC 5021 5137 5136

LORENZ INC p 878
280 Campillo St Ste G 92231
Tel (760) 356-1019 SIC 3699

CAMARILLO, CA

■ CAMARILLO HEALTHCARE CENTER p 243
205 Granada St 93010
Tel (805) 482-9805 SIC 8741

CENTRAL PURCHASING LLC p 280
3491 Mission Oaks Blvd 93012
Tel (805) 388-1000 SIC 5085 5961 5251

DATA EXCHANGE CORP p 413
3600 Via Pescador 93012
Tel (805) 388-1711 SIC 5045 7378

HOUWELING NURSERIES OXNARD INC p 712
645 Laguna Rd 93012
Tel (805) 488-8832 SIC 5141

■ NEW INSPIRATION BROADCASTING CO INC p 1031
4880 Santa Rosa Rd 93012
Tel (805) 987-0400 SIC 4832 2731

PLEASANT VALLEY SCHOOL DISTRICT p 1156
600 Temple Ave 93010
Tel (805) 445-8637 SIC 8211

PROVIDEA CONFERENCING LLC p 1185
1297 Flynn Rd Ste 100 93012
Tel (805) 384-9995 SIC 4813

RED BLOSSOM SALES INC p 1215
400 W Ventura Blvd # 140 93010
Tel (805) 686-4747 SIC 0171

▲ SALEM MEDIA GROUP INC p 1272
4880 Santa Rosa Rd 93012
Tel (818) 956-0400 SIC 4832 2731 4813

▲ SEMTECH CORP p 1303
200 Flynn Rd 93012
Tel (805) 498-2111 SIC 3674

TECHNICOLOR HOME ENTERTAINMENT SERVICES INC p 1431
3233 Mission Oaks Blvd 93012
Tel (805) 445-1122 SIC 7819

TECHNICOLOR VIDEOCASSETTE OF MICHIGAN INC p 1431
3233 Mission Oaks Blvd 93012
Tel (805) 445-1122 SIC 7819

■ TETRA TECH EMC INC p 1441
100 Camino Ruiz 93012
Tel (805) 484-9082 SIC 8711 7371

■ UNICARE LIFE & HEALTH INSURANCE CO p 1502
5151 Camino Ruiz Ste A 93012
Tel (888) 742-2505 *SIC* 6411 6324

CAMPBELL, CA

24/7 CUSTOMER INC p 2
910 E Hamilton Ave # 240 95008
Tel (650) 385-2247 *SIC* 7379

B C C S INC p 141
1711 Dell Ave 95008
Tel (408) 379-5500 *SIC* 1542

▲ BARRACUDA NETWORKS INC p 156
3175 Winchester Blvd 95008
Tel (408) 342-5400 *SIC* 7372 7373

GROUPWARE TECHNOLOGY INC p 642
541 Division St 95008
Tel (408) 540-0090 *SIC* 7373 5045

PALISADE BUILDERS INC p 1108
1875 S Bascom Ave # 2400 95008
Tel (408) 429-7700 *SIC* 1522

SAN ANDREAS REGIONAL CENTER p 1275
300 Orchard Cy Dr Ste 170 95008
Tel (408) 374-9960 *SIC* 8322

VOICELOTS INC p 1564
350 Budd Ave Apt J5 95008
Tel (408) 802-4047 *SIC* 7371 7389

WEST VALLEY CONSTRUCTION CO INC p 1596
580 E Mcglincy Ln 95008
Tel (408) 371-5510 *SIC* 1623

X.COMMERCE INC p 1630
54 N Central Ave Ste 200 95008
Tel (310) 954-8012 *SIC* 7371

CANOGA PARK, CA

ACCOUNT CONTROL TECHNOLOGY HOLDINGS INC p 15
6918 Owensmouth Ave 91303
Tel (818) 712-4999 *SIC* 7389

■ FIRST AMERICAN HOME BUYERS PROTECTION CORP p 544
8521 Fallbrook Ave # 340 91304
Tel (818) 781-5050 *SIC* 6351

■ INC AEROJET ROCKETDYNE OF DE p 735
8900 De Soto Ave 91304
Tel (818) 586-1000 *SIC* 2869 3724

■ INTERAMERICAN MOTOR CORP p 751
8901 Canoga Ave 91304
Tel (818) 678-6571 *SIC* 5013 5599

CARDIFF BY THE SEA, CA

TRI-ISO TRYLINE LLC p 1477
2187 Newcastle Ave # 101 92007
Tel (909) 626-4855 *SIC* 5169

CARLSBAD, CA

AIH LLC p 38
5810 Van Allen Way 92008
Tel (760) 930-4600 *SIC* 3629 3621 3679

▲ ALPHATEC HOLDINGS INC p 60
5818 El Camino Real 92008
Tel (760) 431-9286 *SIC* 3841

■ ALPHATEC SPINE INC p 60
5818 El Camino Real 92008
Tel (760) 494-6610 *SIC* 3842 8711 5047

■ APPLIED BIOSYSTEMS LLC p 99
5791 Van Allen Way 92008
Tel (650) 638-5000 *SIC* 3826 7372

AVIARA FSRC ASSOCIATES LIMITED p 138
7100 Aviara Resort Dr 92011
Tel (760) 603-6800 *SIC* 7011

AVIARA RESORT ASSOCIATES LIMITED PARTNERSHIP A CALIFORNIA LIMITED PARTNERSHIP p 138
7100 Aviara Resort Dr 92011
Tel (760) 448-1234 *SIC* 7011

BOHICA LIQUIDATION INC p 198
5942 Priestly Dr 92008
Tel (760) 930-0456 *SIC* 5812

■ CALLAWAY GOLF BALL OPERATIONS INC p 242
2180 Rutherford Rd 92008
Tel (760) 931-1771 *SIC* 5091

▲ CALLAWAY GOLF CO p 242
2180 Rutherford Rd 92008
Tel (760) 931-1771
SIC 3949 2329 2339 6794

CAMERON DICKINSON CONSTRUCTION CO INC p 245
6184 Innovation Way 92009
Tel (760) 438-9114 *SIC* 1542 8741

CARECRAFT INC p 254
880 Carlsbad Village Dr # 202 92008
Tel (949) 373-3333 *SIC* 8611

CARLSBAD SD MICHELLE WHS p 257
6225 El Camino Real Ste P 92009
Tel (760) 331-5000 *SIC* 8299

CARLSBAD UNIFIED SCHOOL DISTRICT p 257
6225 El Camino Real 92009
Tel (760) 331-5000 *SIC* 8211

■ ENTROPIC COMMUNICATIONS LLC p 503
5966 La Place Ct Ste 100 92008
Tel (858) 768-3600 *SIC* 3674 7372

GEMOLOGICAL INSTITUTE OF AMERICA INC p 598
5345 Armada Dr 92008
Tel (760) 603-4000 *SIC* 8249 8733

GLANBIA NUTRITIONALS (NA) INC p 614
2840 Loker Ave E Ste 100 92010
Tel (760) 438-0089 *SIC* 5169 2833 8099

GRAND PACIFIC RESORTS INC p 630
5900 Pasteur Ct Ste 200 92008
Tel (760) 431-8500 *SIC* 6531 7011

HISAMITSU PHARMACEUTICAL CO INC p 696
2730 Loker Ave W 92010
Tel (760) 931-1756 *SIC* 8733

HOEHN MOTORS INC p 699
5475 Car Country Dr 92008
Tel (760) 438-4454 *SIC* 5511

INTERIOR SPECIALISTS INC p 753
1630 Faraday Ave 92008
Tel (760) 929-6700 *SIC* 1752 1799

▲ IONIS PHARMACEUTICALS INC p 762
2855 Gazelle Ct 92010
Tel (760) 931-9200 *SIC* 2834 8731 3845

ISLANDS RESTAURANTS LP p 767
5750 Fleet St Ste 120 92008
Tel (760) 268-1800 *SIC* 5812

JENNY CRAIG INC p 782
5770 Fleet St 92008
Tel (760) 696-4000
SIC 7299 6794 5149 5499

JENNY CRAIG WEIGHT LOSS CENTERS INC p 782
5770 Fleet St 92008
Tel (760) 696-4000 *SIC* 7299 7991

■ LIFE TECHNOLOGIES CORP p 864
5781 Van Allen Way 92008
Tel (760) 603-7200 *SIC* 2836 2835

▲ MAXLINEAR INC p 922
5966 La Place Ct Ste 100 92008
Tel (760) 692-0711 *SIC* 3674

▲ NATURAL ALTERNATIVES INTERNATIONAL INC p 1018
1535 Faraday Ave 92008
Tel (760) 744-7340 *SIC* 2833

■ PRANA LIVING LLC p 1167
3209 Lionshead Ave 92010
Tel (866) 915-6457 *SIC* 5136 5137

PRESCRIPTION SOLUTIONS p 1171
2858 Loker Ave E Ste 100 92010
Tel (760) 804-2370 *SIC* 8742

RUBIOS RESTAURANTS INC p 1257
2200 Faraday Ave Ste 250 92008
Tel (760) 929-8226 *SIC* 5812

▲ SEASPINE HOLDINGS CORP p 1297
5770 Armada Dr 92008
Tel (760) 727-8399 *SIC* 3841

SENIOR KISCO LIVING LLC p 1304
5790 Fleet St Ste 300 92008
Tel (760) 804-5900 *SIC* 8322 8741

SYNTERACTHCR CORP p 1416
5759 Fleet St Ste 100 92008
Tel (760) 268-8200 *SIC* 8731

SYNTERACTHCR HOLDINGS CORP p 1416
5759 Fleet St Ste 100 92008
Tel (760) 268-8200 *SIC* 8731

SYNTERACTHCR INC p 1416
5759 Fleet St Ste 100 92008
Tel (760) 268-8200 *SIC* 8731

TAYLORMADE GOLF CO INC p 1427
5545 Fermi Ct 92008
Tel (877) 860-8624 *SIC* 3949

TEG STAFFING INC p 1432
2604 El Camino Real Ste B 92008
Tel (619) 584-3444 *SIC* 7363

UPPER DECK CO LLC p 1529
2251 Rutherford Rd 92008
Tel (800) 873-7332 *SIC* 2752 5947

▲ VIASAT INC p 1554
6155 El Camino Real 92009
Tel (760) 476-2200 *SIC* 3663

CARMEL, CA

■ B S I HOLDINGS INC p 142
100 Clock Tower Pl # 200 93923
Tel (831) 622-1840 *SIC* 1742

CARMICHAEL, CA

ESKATON p 509
5105 Manzanita Ave Ste D 95608
Tel (916) 334-0296 *SIC* 6512 8051

ESKATON PROPERTIES INC p 509
5105 Manzanita Ave Ste A 95608
Tel (916) 334-0810 *SIC* 8361

SAN JUAN UNIFIED SCHOOL DISTRICT p 1277
3738 Walnut Ave 95608
Tel (916) 971-7700 *SIC* 8211

CARPINTERIA, CA

CKE RESTAURANTS HOLDINGS INC p 320
6307 Carpinteria Ave A 93013
Tel (805) 745-7500 *SIC* 5812 6794

DAKO NORTH AMERICA INC p 409
6392 Via Real 93013
Tel (805) 566-6655 *SIC* 5122 3841

FREUDENBERG MEDICAL LLC p 579
1110 Mark Ave 93013
Tel (805) 684-3304 *SIC* 3842

G I A A INC p 587
1155 Eugenia Pl 93013
Tel (805) 566-9191 *SIC* 6411

NUSIL TECHNOLOGY LLC p 1067
1050 Cindy Ln 93013
Tel (805) 684-8780 *SIC* 3069

CARSON, CA

AMPAM PARKS MECHANICAL INC p 86
17036 Avalon Blvd 90746
Tel (310) 835-1532 *SIC* 1711

BAKKAVOR FOODS USA INC p 147
18201 Central Ave 90746
Tel (310) 533-0190 *SIC* 2051 5149

BRENTWOOD ORIGINALS INC p 210
20639 S Fordyce Ave 90810
Tel (310) 637-6804 *SIC* 2392

BRISTOL FARMS p 214
915 E 230th St 90745
Tel (310) 233-4700 *SIC* 5411

CEDARLANE NATURAL FOODS INC p 272
1135 E Artesia Blvd 90746
Tel (310) 886-7720 *SIC* 2038

CWD LLC p 404
21046 Figueroa St Ste B 90745
Tel (310) 218-1082 *SIC* 3714

DERMALOGICA LLC p 431
1535 Beachey Pl 90746
Tel (310) 900-4000 *SIC* 2844

▲ DUCOMMUN INC p 459
23301 Wilmington Ave 90745
Tel (310) 513-7200 *SIC* 3728 3679

KOSHAN INC p 828
23501 Avalon Blvd 90745
Tel (310) 830-8241 *SIC* 5411

KW INTERNATIONAL INC p 832
18655 Bishop Ave 90746
Tel (310) 747-1380 *SIC* 4731 4226 8744

LAKESHORE EQUIPMENT CO INC p 840
2695 E Dominguez St 90895
Tel (310) 537-8600 *SIC* 5999 5961

■ LEINER HEALTH PRODUCTS INC p 854
901 E 233rd St 90745
Tel (631) 200-2000 *SIC* 2834 5122

MAG AEROSPACE INDUSTRIES INC p 895
1500 Glenn Curtiss St 90746
Tel (310) 631-3800 *SIC* 3431 3728

MAINFREIGHT INC p 898
1400 Glenn Curtiss St 90746
Tel (310) 900-1974 *SIC* 4731

MULTIQUIP INC p 1000
18910 Wilmington Ave 90746
Tel (310) 537-3700 *SIC* 5063 5082 3645

SOUTHWIND FOODS LLC p 1353
20644 S Fordyce Ave 90810
Tel (323) 262-8222 *SIC* 5146 5147

▲ US AUTO PARTS NETWORK INC p 1531
16941 Keegan Ave 90746
Tel (310) 735-0085 *SIC* 5961

CASTRO VALLEY, CA

EDEN TOWNSHIP HOSPITAL DISTRICT INC p 477
20400 Lake Chabot Rd # 303 94546
Tel (510) 538-2031 *SIC* 8062 8011

CATHEDRAL CITY, CA

NWT WORLD ARTS INC p 1068
36660 Bankside Dr Ste A 92234
Tel (760) 321-8780 *SIC* 5021

CERES, CA

BRONCO WINE CO p 217
6342 Bystrum Rd 95307
Tel (209) 538-3131 *SIC* 5182 2084

CERES UNIFIED SCHOOL DISTRICT p 283
2503 Lawrence St 95307
Tel (209) 556-1500 *SIC* 8211

WEST COAST GRAPE FARMING INC p 1594
800 E Keyes Rd 95307
Tel (209) 538-3131 *SIC* 0762

CERRITOS, CA

A B C UNIFIED SCHOOL DISTRICT p 5
16700 Norwalk Blvd 90703
Tel (562) 926-5567 *SIC* 8211

■ AIS MANAGEMENT LLC p 41
17785 Center Court Dr N # 250 90703
Tel (562) 345-4247 *SIC* 6411

■ ASPEN EDUCATION GROUP INC p 118
17777 Center Court Dr N # 300 90703
Tel (562) 467-5500 *SIC* 8741 8322

COMMERCIAL CARRIERS INSURANCE AGENCY INC p 345
12641 166th St 90703
Tel (562) 404-4900 *SIC* 6331

ECOLOGY AUTO PARTS INC p 476
14150 Vine Pl 90703
Tel (562) 404-2277 *SIC* 5531

GOLDEN STAR TECHNOLOGY INC p 621
12881 166th St Ste 100 90703
Tel (562) 345-8700 *SIC* 5734 7378 5045

NORM REEVES INC p 1048
18500 Studebaker Rd 90703
Tel (562) 402-3844 *SIC* 5511 5521

CHATSWORTH, CA

1105 MEDIA INC p 1
9201 Oakdale Ave Ste 101 91311
Tel (818) 814-5200
SIC 7313 7389 2721 2741 8748

ALIGN AEROSPACE HOLDING INC p 50
21123 Nordhoff St 91311
Tel (818) 727-7800 *SIC* 3324

ALIGN AEROSPACE LLC p 50
21123 Nordhoff St 91311
Tel (818) 727-7800 *SIC* 5088

▲ CALIFORNIA RESOURCES CORP p 241
9200 Oakdale Ave Fl 9 91311
Tel (888) 848-4754 *SIC* 1311

▲ CAPSTONE TURBINE CORP p 251
21211 Nordhoff St 91311
Tel (818) 734-5300 *SIC* 3511

CBOL CORP p 269
19850 Plummer St 91311
Tel (818) 704-8200
SIC 5065 5072 5013 5088 5084 5162

CHILD CARE RESOURCE CENTER INC p 298
20001 Prairie St 91311
Tel (818) 717-1000 *SIC* 8322

DATADIRECT NETWORKS INC p 414
9351 Deering Ave 91311
Tel (818) 700-7600 *SIC* 3572 7374

EPIC TECHNOLOGIES LLC p 505
9340 Owensmouth Ave 91311
Tel (818) 734-6500 *SIC* 3661 3577 3679

FLAME ENTERPRISES INC p 554
21500 Gledhill St 91311
Tel (301) 668-0636 *SIC* 5065 5063

HYDRAULICS INTERNATIONAL INC p 723
9201 Independence Ave 91311
Tel (818) 998-1231 *SIC* 3728

JOERNS LLC p 787
19748 Dearborn St 91311
Tel (800) 966-6662 *SIC* 5047

JONAH BROOKLYN INC p 792
9673 Topanga Canyon Pl 91311
Tel (877) 964-2725 *SIC* 2673

LAMPS PLUS INC p 841
20250 Plummer St 91311
Tel (818) 886-5267 *SIC* 5719

LUMBER CITY CORP p 885
20525 Nordhoff St Ste 210 91311
Tel (818) 407-3888 *SIC* 5211 5031

M BRADY & ASSOCIATES p 889
9753 Independence Ave 91311
Tel (818) 700-8813 *SIC* 5082

▲ MRV COMMUNICATIONS INC p 996
20520 Nordhoff St 91311
Tel (818) 773-0900 *SIC* 3674

NATEL ENGINEERING CO INC p 1009
9340 Owensmouth Ave 91311
Tel (818) 734-6523 *SIC* 3674 3679

NATROL LLC p 1018
21411 Prairie St 91311
Tel (818) 739-6000 *SIC* 5122 2099

NMB (USA) INC p 1045
9730 Independence Ave 91311
Tel (818) 709-1770
SIC 3562 5063 5084 3728 5065

NNA SERVICES LLC p 1045
9350 De Soto Ave 91311
Tel (818) 739-4071 *SIC* 6411

ONCORE MANUFACTURING LLC p 1086
9340 Owensmouth Ave 91311
Tel (818) 734-6500 *SIC* 3672 8711

ONCORE MANUFACTURING SERVICES INC p 1086
9340 Owensmouth Ave 91311
Tel (510) 360-2222 *SIC* 3672

ONTIC ENGINEERING AND MANUFACTURING INC p 1088
20400 Plummer St 91311
Tel (818) 678-6555 *SIC* 5088 3728 3812

REGENCY ENTERPRISES INC p 1218
9261 Jordan Ave 91311
Tel (818) 901-0255 *SIC* 5063

SEGA HOLDINGS USA INC p 1300
9737 Lurline Ave 91311
Tel (415) 701-6000 *SIC* 3999 5045

STRATEGIC PARTNERS INC p 1392
9800 De Soto Ave 91311
Tel (818) 671-2100
SIC 3143 3144 5139 2339 2389 2329

THIBIANT INTERNATIONAL INC p 1447
20320 Prairie St 91311
Tel (818) 709-1345 *SIC* 2844

CHERRY VALLEY, CA

BEAUMONT UNIFIED SCHOOL DISTRICT p 166
350 W Brookside Ave 92223
Tel (951) 845-1631 *SIC* 8211

CHICO, CA

BUILD.COM INC p 224
402 Otterson Dr Ste 100 95928
Tel (800) 375-3403 *SIC* 5074 5999

CALIFORNIA STATE UNIVERSITY CHICO p 241
400 W 1st St 95929
Tel (530) 898-4636 *SIC* 8221 9411

CHICO CSU RESEARCH FOUNDATION p 298
Csuc Bldg 25 Ste 203 95929
Tel (530) 898-6811 *SIC* 7389

CHICO UNIFIED SCHOOL DISTRICT p 298
1163 E 7th St 95928
Tel (530) 891-3000 *SIC* 8211

ENLOE MEDICAL CENTER p 500
1531 Esplanade 95926
Tel (530) 332-7300 *SIC* 8062

GONZALES ENTERPRISES INC p 623
495 Ryan Ave 95973
Tel (530) 343-8725 *SIC* 5136

SIERRA NEVADA BREWING CO p 1320
1075 E 20th St 95928
Tel (530) 893-3520 *SIC* 2082 5812

■ SMUCKER NATURAL FOODS INC p 1335
37 Speedway Ave 95928
Tel (530) 899-5000 *SIC* 2086 2033 2087

■ TRI COUNTIES BANK p 1476
63 Constitution Dr 95973
Tel (530) 898-0300 *SIC* 6029 6163

▲ TRICO BANCSHARES p 1479
63 Constitution Dr 95973
Tel (530) 898-0300 *SIC* 6022

CHINO HILLS, CA

JACUZZI BRANDS LLC p 775
13925 City Center Dr # 200 91709
Tel (909) 606-1416 *SIC* 3842

PRH PRO INC p 1173
13089 Peyton Dr Ste C362 91709
Tel (714) 510-7226 *SIC* 5085

WESTERN WATER WORKS SUPPLY CO p 1600
5831 Pine Ave 91709
Tel (909) 597-7000 *SIC* 5074

CHINO, CA

AMERICAN BEEF PACKERS INC p 68
13677 Yorba Ave 91710
Tel (909) 628-4888 *SIC* 0751 2011 5147

AMERICAN EAGLE WHEEL CORP p 71
5780 Soestern Ct 91710
Tel (909) 590-8828 *SIC* 5013

AMERICAN FINANCIAL NETWORK INC p 72
3110 Chino Ave Ste 290 91710
Tel (909) 606-3905 *SIC* 6162

CHINO VALLEY UNIFIED SCHOOL DISTRICT p 301
5130 Riverside Dr 91710
Tel (909) 628-1201 *SIC* 8211

CONCEPT GREEN ENERGY SOLUTIONS INC p 354
13824 Yorba Ave 91710
Tel (855) 459-6535 *SIC* 7389 5211

EEP HOLDINGS LLC p 480
4626 Eucalyptus Ave 91710
Tel (909) 597-7861 *SIC* 3089 3544

EL & EL WOOD PRODUCTS CORP p 482
6011 Schaefer Ave 91710
Tel (909) 591-0339 *SIC* 5031

ELITE ONE SOURCE NUTRISCIENCES INC p 487
13840 Magnolia Ave 91710
Tel (909) 902-5005 *SIC* 8049 8099 3999

HARRINGTON INDUSTRIAL PLASTICS LLC p 663
14480 Yorba Ave 91710
Tel (909) 597-8641 *SIC* 5074

INLAND EMPIRE UTILITIES AGENCY A MUNICIPAL WATER DISTRICT (INC) p 743
6075 Kimball Ave 91708
Tel (909) 993-1600 *SIC* 4941

JACUZZI INC p 775
14525 Monte Vista Ave 91710
Tel (909) 606-7733 *SIC* 3088 3589

JACUZZI WHIRLPOOL BATH INC p 775
14525 Monte Vista Ave 91710
Tel (909) 606-1416 *SIC* 3088

QUETICO LLC p 1199
5521 Schaefer Ave 91710
Tel (909) 628-6200 *SIC* 5199 7389

TREND TECHNOLOGIES LLC p 1476
4626 Eucalyptus Ave 91710
Tel (909) 597-7861 *SIC* 3444 3469 3499

TTL HOLDINGS LLC p 1489
4626 Eucalyptus Ave 91710
Tel (909) 597-7861 *SIC* 3089 3544

VERITAS HEALTH SERVICES INC p 1549
5451 Walnut Ave 91710
Tel (909) 464-8600 *SIC* 8062

CHULA VISTA, CA

CHG FOUNDATION p 296
740 Bay Blvd 91910
Tel (619) 422-0422 *SIC* 8699

CHULA VISTA ELEM SCHOOL DISTRICT p 305
84 E J St 91910
Tel (619) 425-9600 *SIC* 8211

CULINARY HISPANIC FOODS INC p 400
805 Bow St 91914
Tel (619) 955-6101 *SIC* 5149

HYSPAN PRECISION PRODUCTS INC p 724
1685 Brandywine Ave 91911
Tel (619) 421-1355 *SIC* 3568 3496 3441

MUTSUTECH LTD p 1003
3130 Bonita Rd Ste 107 91910
Tel (619) 691-7056 *SIC* 5064 5013

■ ROHR INC p 1247
850 Lagoon Dr 91910
Tel (619) 691-4111 *SIC* 3728

SHARP CHULA VISTA AUXILIARY INC p 1312
751 Medical Center Ct 91911
Tel (619) 421-6110 *SIC* 8062

SHARP CHULA VISTA MEDICAL CENTER p 1312
751 Medical Center Ct 91911
Tel (619) 502-5800 *SIC* 8062

SWEETWATER UNION HIGH SCHOOL DISTRICT p 1412
1130 Fifth Ave 91911
Tel (619) 691-5500 *SIC* 8211

TRAFFIC TECH INC p 1469
910 Hale Pl Ste 100 91914
Tel (514) 343-0044 *SIC* 4731

▲ YOUNGEVITY INTERNATIONAL INC p 1639
2400 Boswell Rd 91914
Tel (619) 934-3980 *SIC* 5499 5999

CITRUS HEIGHTS, CA

ROMEO & JULIETTE INC p 1249
7524 Old Auburn Rd 95610
Tel (916) 726-4413 *SIC* 5139

SD DEACON CORP p 1295
7745 Greenback Ln Ste 250 95610
Tel (916) 969-0900 *SIC* 1542

CITY OF INDUSTRY, CA

ACORN ENGINEERING CO p 18
15125 Proctor Ave 91746
Tel (800) 488-8999 *SIC* 3448 3431 3442

■ ALTA-DENA CERTIFIED DAIRY LLC p 61
17637 E Valley Blvd 91744
Tel (626) 964-6401 *SIC* 2026

AMERICA CHUNG NAM (GROUP) HOLDINGS LLC p 67
1163 Fairway Dr 91789
Tel (909) 839-8383 *SIC* 5093

AMERICA CHUNG NAM LLC p 67
1163 Fairway Dr Fl 3 91789
Tel (909) 839-8383 *SIC* 5093

AMERICAN FUTURE TECHNOLOGY CORP p 73
529 Baldwin Park Blvd 91746
Tel (888) 462-3899 *SIC* 5045

AMERICAN PAPER & PLASTICS INC p 77
550 S 7th Ave 91746
Tel (626) 444-0000 *SIC* 5113

ARAKELIAN ENTERPRISES INC p 102
14048 Valley Blvd 91746
Tel (626) 336-3636 *SIC* 4953

BENTLEY MILLS INC p 173
14641 Don Julian Rd 91746
Tel (626) 333-4585 *SIC* 2273 2299

BRIGHTON COLLECTIBLES LLC p 213
14022 Nelson Ave 91746
Tel (626) 961-9381 *SIC* 5632

C&F FOODS INC p 234
15620 E Valley Blvd 91744
Tel (626) 723-1000 *SIC* 5153

CACIQUE INC p 236
14940 Proctor Ave 91746
Tel (626) 961-3399 *SIC* 2022

CLASSIC DISTRIBUTING AND BEVERAGE GROUP INC p 323
120 Puente Ave 91746
Tel (626) 330-8231 *SIC* 5181

CLAYTON MANUFACTURING CO p 323
17477 Hurley St 91744
Tel (626) 443-9381 *SIC* 3569 3829 3511

CLOSET WORLD INC p 327
3860 Capitol Ave 90601
Tel (562) 699-9945 *SIC* 1751 5211

COMMERCIAL LUMBER & PALLET CO INC p 345
135 Long Ln 91746
Tel (626) 968-0631 *SIC* 2448 5031

COMPUCASE CORP p 352
16720 Chestnut St Ste C 91748
Tel (626) 336-6588 *SIC* 3572

CUSTOM ALLOY SALES INC p 403
13191 Crssrds Pkwy N 37 91746
Tel (626) 369-3641 *SIC* 3341 5051

CYBERPOWER INC p 405
730 Baldwin Park Blvd 91746
Tel (626) 813-7730 *SIC* 5045

EMTEK PRODUCTS INC p 495
15250 Stafford St 91744
Tel (626) 961-0413 *SIC* 3429

■ FRESHPOINT OF SOUTHERN CALIFORNIA INC p 579
155 N Orange Ave 91744
Tel (626) 855-1400 *SIC* 5148 5142

GREE USA INC p 636
20035 E Walnut Dr N 91789
Tel (909) 718-0478 *SIC* 5075

HACIENDA-LA PUENTE UNIFIED SCHOOL DISTRICT p 652
15959 Gale Ave 91745
Tel (626) 933-1000 *SIC* 8211

HARALAMBOS BEVERAGE CO p 659
2300 Pellissier Pl 90601
Tel (562) 347-4300 *SIC* 5181 5149

HARMONI INTERNATIONAL SPICE INC CALIFORNIA p 662
881 S Azusa Ave 91748
Tel (626) 330-1550 *SIC* 5148 5149

HOT TOPIC INC p 710
18305 San Jose Ave 91748
Tel (626) 839-4681 *SIC* 2326 5632 5699

JACMAR COMPANIES p 775
300 Baldwin Park Blvd 91746
Tel (800) 834-8806 *SIC* 5141 5812 6552

LANGER JUICE CO INC p 844
16195 Stephens St 91745
Tel (626) 336-3100 *SIC* 2037

LOS ALTOS FOOD PRODUCTS INC p 878
450 Baldwin Park Blvd 91746
Tel (626) 330-6555 *SIC* 5143

MAGNELL ASSOCIATE INC p 896
17560 Rowland St 91748
Tel (562) 695-8823 *SIC* 5045

MARQUEZ BROTHERS ENTERPRISES INC p 910
15480 Valley Blvd 91746
Tel (626) 330-3310 *SIC* 5141

MAX GROUP CORP p 922
17011 Green Dr 91745
Tel (626) 935-0050 *SIC* 5045

MERCADO LATINO INC p 943
245 Baldwin Park Blvd 91746
Tel (626) 333-6862 *SIC* 5141 5148

MERCURY PLASTICS INC p 945
14825 Salt Lake Ave 91746
Tel (626) 369-8457 *SIC* 2673 2759 3089

MIKE CAMPBELL & ASSOCIATES LTD p 968
13031 Temple Ave 91746
Tel (626) 369-3981
SIC 4222 4225 4214 4213

MORROW-MEADOWS CORP p 990
231 Benton Ct 91789
Tel (858) 974-3650 *SIC* 1731

MTC DIRECT INC p 997
17837 Rowland St 91748
Tel (626) 839-6800 *SIC* 5045

NEWEGG INC p 1037
17560 Rowland St 91748
Tel (626) 271-9700 *SIC* 5734

PHFE p 1142
12801 Crossrds Pkwy S 2 200 S 91746
Tel (562) 699-7320 *SIC* 8082

PUBLIC HEALTH FOUNDATION ENTERPRISES INC p 1189
12801 Crossrds Pkwy S 200 91746
Tel (562) 692-4643 *SIC* 8741

QUINN CO p 1200
10006 Rose Hills Rd 90601
Tel (562) 463-4000
SIC 5082 5083 5084 7353

QUINN GROUP INC p 1200
10006 Rose Hills Rd 90601
Tel (562) 463-4000
SIC 5084 5082 7353 7359

QUINN SHEPHERD MACHINERY p 1200
10006 Rose Hills Rd 90601
Tel (562) 463-6000 *SIC* 5082 5084

SAYCO CONTAINER INC p 1285
13400 Nelson Ave 91746
Tel (619) 440-4411 *SIC* 2653 3089 3086

SMURFIT KAPPA NORTH AMERICA LLC p 1335
13400 Nelson Ave 91746
Tel (626) 333-6363 *SIC* 2653 2671 2657

SNAK-KING CORP p 1335
16150 Stephens St 91745
Tel (626) 336-7711 *SIC* 2096

SWEDA CO LLC p 1411
17411 E Valley Blvd 91744
Tel (626) 357-9999 *SIC* 5094 5044

■ TELEDYNE INSTRUMENTS INC p 1434
16830 Chestnut St 91748
Tel (626) 961-9221 *SIC* 3829 3823

TORRID LLC p 1462
18305 San Jose Ave 91748
Tel (626) 839-4681 *SIC* 5621

TRACY INDUSTRIES INC p 1468
3737 Capitol Ave 90601
Tel (562) 692-9034 *SIC* 3519 7538

■ TRIUMPH STRUCTURES-LOS ANGELES INC p 1483
17055 Gale Ave 91745
Tel (626) 965-1642 *SIC* 3599

UNICAL AVIATION INC p 1502
680 S Lemon Ave 91789
Tel (626) 813-1901 *SIC* 5088

US AIRCONDITIONING DISTRIBUTORS INC p 1530
16900 Chestnut St 91748
Tel (626) 854-4500 *SIC* 5075 1711

UTILITY TRAILER MANUFACTURING CO p 1537
17295 Railroad St Ste A 91748
Tel (626) 964-7319 *SIC* 3715

VALLEY POWER SYSTEMS INC p 1541
425 S Hacienda Blvd 91745
Tel (626) 333-1243 *SIC* 3519 5082

YALE/CHASE EQUIPMENT AND SERVICES INC p 1634
2615 Pellissier Pl 90601
Tel (562) 463-8000 *SIC* 5084 7699 7359

CLAREMONT, CA

CLAREMONT GRADUATE UNIVERSITY p 321
150 E 10th St 91711
Tel (909) 607-8632 *SIC* 8221

CLAREMONT MCKENNA COLLEGE FOUNDATION p 321
500 E 9th St 91711
Tel (909) 621-8088 *SIC* 8221

HARVEY MUDD COLLEGE p 667
301 Platt Blvd 91711
Tel (909) 621-8000 *SIC* 8221

PFF BANCORP INC p 1140
2058 N Mills Ave Ste 139 91711
Tel (213) 683-6393 *SIC* 6035

POMONA COLLEGE p 1161
550 N College Ave 91711
Tel (909) 621-8135 *SIC* 8221

■ THERAPAK LLC p 1447
651 Wharton Dr 91711
Tel (909) 267-2000 *SIC* 5047

CLOVIS, CA

CLOVIS UNIFIED SCHOOL DISTRICT p 328
1450 Herndon Ave 93611
Tel (559) 327-9000 *SIC* 8211

PELCO INC p 1128
3500 Pelco Way 93612
Tel (559) 292-1981 *SIC* 3663 7382

WAWONA FROZEN FOODS p 1584
100 W Alluvial Ave 93611
Tel (559) 299-2901 *SIC* 2037

■ WILLOW CREEK HEALTHCARE CENTER LLC p 1613
650 W Alluvial Ave 93611
Tel (559) 323-6200 *SIC* 8051

COACHELLA, CA

COACHELLA VALLEY WATER DISTRICT p 331
85995 Avenue 52 92236
Tel (760) 398-2651
SIC 4941 4971 4952 7389

IMPERIAL WESTERN PRODUCTS INC p 734
86600 Avenue 54 92236
Tel (760) 398-0815 *SIC* 5159 2841 2869

PRIMETIME INTERNATIONAL INC p 1175
86705 Avenue 54 Ste A 92236
Tel (760) 399-4166 *SIC* 5148 4783

SUN AND SANDS ENTERPRISES LLC p 1399
86705 Avenue 54 Ste A 92236
Tel (760) 399-4278 *SIC* 0161

COALINGA, CA

HARRIS FARMS INC p 663
29475 Fresno Coalinga Rd 93210
Tel (559) 884-2435
SIC 0191 0211 2011 7011 5812 5541

WEST HILLS COMMUNITY COLLEGE DISTRICT FINANCING CORP p 1594
9900 Cody Ave 93210
Tel (559) 934-2000 *SIC* 8222

COARSEGOLD, CA

CHUKCHANSI GOLD RESORT & CASINO p 305
711 Lucky Ln 93614
Tel (866) 794-6946 *SIC* 7011

COLTON, CA

ARROWHEAD REGIONAL MEDICAL CENTER p 113
400 N Pepper Ave 92324
Tel (909) 580-1000 *SIC* 8062

C B NICHOLS EGG RANCH p 232
331 W Citrus St 92324
Tel (626) 452-9110 *SIC* 5144 5499

COLTON JOINT UNIFIED SCHOOL DISTRICT p 340
1212 Valencia Dr 92324
Tel (909) 580-5000 *SIC* 8211

COLUSA, CA

COLUSA INDIAN COMMUNITY COUNCIL p 343
3730 State Highway 45 B 95932
Tel (530) 458-8231 *SIC* 9131

COMMERCE, CA

4 EARTH FARMS INC p 3
5555 E Olympic Blvd 90022
Tel (323) 201-5800 *SIC* 5148

99 CENTS ONLY STORES LLC p 4
4000 Union Pacific Ave 90023
Tel (323) 980-8145 *SIC* 5411 5331 5199

ALTAMED HEALTH SERVICES CORP p 62
2040 Camfield Ave 90040
Tel (323) 725-8751 *SIC* 8011 8099

AMERICAN INTERNATIONAL INDUSTRIES p 75
2220 Gaspar Ave 90040
Tel (323) 728-2999 SIC 5122 2844

■ **AMERIFOODS TRADING CO LLC** p 82
600 Citadel Dr 90040
Tel (323) 869-7500 SIC 5141

■ **ATK SPACE SYSTEMS INC** p 125
6033 Bandini Blvd 90040
Tel (323) 722-0222 SIC 3443

BEN MYERSON CANDY CO INC p 172
6550 E Washington Blvd 90040
Tel (800) 331-2829 SIC 5182 5023

CALIFORNIA COMMERCE CLUB INC p 239
6131 Telegraph Rd 90040
Tel (323) 721-2100 SIC 7011 5812

CELLUPHONE INC p 274
6119 E Washington Blvd 90040
Tel (323) 727-9131 SIC 5065 5999

COLOR IMAGE APPAREL INC p 338
6670 Flotilla St 90040
Tel (855) 793-3100 SIC 5137 5136

CORNERSTONE APPAREL INC p 371
5807 Smithway St 90040
Tel (323) 724-3600 SIC 5621

DART TRANSPORTATION SERVICE A CORP p 413
1430 S Eastman Ave Ste 1 90023
Tel (323) 981-8205 SIC 6798 7513

▲ **DIFFERENTIAL BRANDS GROUP INC** p 438
1231 S Gerhart Ave 90022
Tel (323) 890-1800
SIC 2337 2339 2311 2325 3111 2387

ELKAY PLASTICS CO INC p 487
6000 Sheila St 90040
Tel (323) 722-7073 SIC 5113

ERNEST PACKAGING SOLUTIONS INC p 508
5777 Smithway St 90040
Tel (800) 233-7788 SIC 5113 5199 7389

GIBSON OVERSEAS INC p 611
2410 Yates Ave 90040
Tel (323) 832-8900 SIC 5023

GROCERS SPECIALTY CO p 641
5200 Sheila St 90040
Tel (323) 264-5200 SIC 5141

HKF INC p 697
5983 Smithway St 90040
Tel (323) 225-1318
SIC 5075 3873 5064 3567 3643

INTERSTATE MEAT & PROVISION p 758
6114 Scott Way 90040
Tel (323) 838-9400 SIC 5142 5147

JAPAN PULP & PAPER (USA) CORP p 778
5928 S Malt Ave 90040
Tel (323) 889-7750 SIC 5113 5093 5099

JFC INTERNATIONAL INC p 785
7101 E Slauson Ave 90040
Tel (323) 721-6100 SIC 5149

NORSTAR OFFICE PRODUCTS INC p 1049
5353 Jillson St 90040
Tel (323) 262-1919 SIC 2521 2522

▲ **NOVA LIFESTYLE INC** p 1062
6565 E Washington Blvd 90040
Tel (323) 888-9999 SIC 2511 2512

NUMBER HOLDINGS INC p 1067
4000 Union Pacific Ave 90023
Tel (323) 980-8145 SIC 5331 5199

OAKHURST INDUSTRIES INC p 1071
2050 S Tubeway Ave 90040
Tel (323) 724-3000 SIC 2051 5149

PACIFIC VIAL MFG INC p 1106
2738 Supply Ave 90040
Tel (323) 721-7004 SIC 3221

■ **SMART & FINAL INC** p 1332
600 Citadel Dr 90040
Tel (323) 869-7500 SIC 5141 5411

▲ **SMART & FINAL STORES INC** p 1332
600 Citadel Dr 90040
Tel (323) 869-7500 SIC 5411

■ **SMART & FINAL STORES LLC** p 1332
600 Citadel Dr 90040
Tel (323) 869-7500 SIC 5411

SMITH COOPER INTERNATIONAL INC p 1333
2867 Vail Ave 90040
Tel (323) 890-4455 SIC 5085 3494

SUN COAST MERCHANDISE CORP p 1400
6315 Bandini Blvd 90040
Tel (323) 720-9700 SIC 5099

SUPER A FOODS INC p 1405
7200 Dominion Cir 90040
Tel (323) 869-0600 SIC 5411

TIANJIN POOL & SPA CORP p 1452
2701-2711 Garfield Ave 90040
Tel (626) 571-1885 SIC 5169 5091

UNIFIED GROCERS INC p 1503
5200 Sheila St 90040
Tel (323) 264-5200 SIC 5141 6331

UNISERVE FACILITIES SERVICES CORP p 1505
2363 S Atlantic Blvd 90040
Tel (213) 533-1000 SIC 7349

ZHONGLU AMERICA CORP p 1643
6055 E Wash Blvd Ste 412 90040
Tel (323) 869-9999 SIC 5142

COMPTON, CA

AMERICOLD LOGISTICS LLC p 82
19840 S Rancho Way 90220
Tel (310) 635-4993 SIC 4222

AUDIO VIDEO COLOR CORP p 130
17707 S Santa Fe Ave 90221
Tel (424) 213-7500 SIC 2671

COMPTON UNIFIED SCHOOL DISTRICT p 352
501 S Santa Fe Ave 90221
Tel (310) 604-6508 SIC 8211

■ **FOOD 4 LESS HOLDINGS INC** p 563
1100 W Artesia Blvd 90220
Tel (310) 884-9000 SIC 5411

GENERAL PETROLEUM CORP p 601
19501 S Santa Fe Ave 90221
Tel (562) 983-7300 SIC 5172

GOURMET FOODS INC p 627
2910 E Harcourt St 90221
Tel (310) 632-3300 SIC 5141 5812 2099

IPS CORP p 763
455 W Victoria St 90220
Tel (310) 898-3300 SIC 2891

KRACO ENTERPRISES LLC p 829
505 E Euclid Ave 90222
Tel (310) 639-0666 SIC 5531 3069 5013

PECOS INC p 1127
19501 S Santa Fe Ave 90221
Tel (310) 356-2300 SIC 5172

■ **RALPHS GROCERY CO** p 1206
1100 W Artesia Blvd 90220
Tel (310) 884-9000 SIC 5411

TAP OPERATING CO LLC p 1424
400 W Artesia Blvd 90220
Tel (310) 900-5500 SIC 5013

TAP WORLDWIDE LLC p 1424
400 W Artesia Blvd 90220
Tel (310) 900-5500 SIC 5013

TECHMER PM INC p 1431
18420 S Laurel Park Rd 90220
Tel (310) 632-9211 SIC 2821

■ **TRANSAMERICAN DISSOLUTION CO LLC** p 1470
400 W Artesia Blvd 90220
Tel (310) 900-5500 SIC 5531 5013

VERSACOLD US INC p 1551
19840 S Rancho Way 90220
Tel (310) 632-6265 SIC 4222

CONCORD, CA

BEVERAGES & MORE INC p 178
1401 Willow Pass Rd # 900 94520
Tel (925) 609-6000 SIC 5921 5499 5993

BEVMO HOLDINGS LLC p 179
1470 Civic Ct Ste 1600 94520
Tel (925) 609-6000 SIC 5921 5499 5993

CONTRA COSTA WATER DISTRICT INC p 364
1331 Concord Ave 94520
Tel (925) 688-8000 SIC 4941

■ **FIRST AMERICAN TITLE GUARANTY CO** p 544
1355 Willow Way Ste 100 94520
Tel (925) 356-7000 SIC 6361 6531

FRESENIUS USA INC p 578
4040 Nelson Ave 94520
Tel (925) 288-4218
SIC 2834 3841 2835 3842 2836

GILBANE FEDERAL p 611
1655 Grant St Fl 12 94520
Tel (925) 946-3100 SIC 8711 8748

GONSALVES & SANTUCCI INC p 623
5141 Commercial Cir 94520
Tel (925) 685-6799 SIC 1771

LEHIGH SOUTHWEST CEMENT CO p 854
2300 Clayton Rd Ste 300 94520
Tel (972) 653-5500
SIC 3241 2891 5032 5211

MT DIABLO UNIFIED SCHOOL DISTRICT p 997
1936 Carlotta Dr 94519
Tel (925) 682-8000 SIC 8211

■ **NORTH AMERICAN ASSET DEVELOPMENT CORP** p 1049
1855 Gateway Blvd Ste 650 94520
Tel (925) 935-5599 SIC 6361 6531

■ **NORTH AMERICAN TITLE CO INC** p 1050
1855 Gateway Blvd Ste 600 94520
Tel (925) 935-5599 SIC 6361 6531

R & L BROSAMER INC p 1201
1390 Willow Pass Rd # 950 94520
Tel (925) 627-1700 SIC 1611

ROUND TABLE PIZZA INC p 1253
1320 Willow Pass Rd # 600 94520
Tel (925) 969-3900 SIC 5812 6794

SEATEL INC p 1297
4030 Nelson Ave 94520
Tel (925) 798-7979 SIC 3663

CORONA DEL MAR, CA

ROMAN JAMES DESIGN BUILD INC p 1249
3535 E Coast Hwy 145 92625
Tel (949) 375-8618 SIC 7389

CORONA, CA

A & A MANUFACTURING CO INC p 4
1675 Sampson Ave 92879
Tel (951) 371-8090 SIC 3691

AGILE SOURCING PARTNERS INC p 35
2385 Railroad St 92880
Tel (951) 279-4154 SIC 4939

ALL AMERICAN ASPHALT p 51
400 E 6th St 92879
Tel (951) 736-7600 SIC 1611 5032

ALVORD UNIFIED SCHOOL DISTRICT p 63
9 Kpc Pkwy 92879
Tel (951) 509-5000 SIC 8211

AMERICAN ELECTRIC SUPPLY INC p 71
361 S Maple St 92880
Tel (951) 734-7910 SIC 5063

APPA SEAFOOD INC p 97
135 Klug Cir 92880
Tel (951) 278-2772 SIC 5411

COMBUSTION ASSOCIATES INC p 343
555 Monica Cir 92880
Tel (951) 272-6999 SIC 4911 3443

■ **CORE-MARK INTERRELATED COMPANIES INC** p 369
311 Reed Cir 92879
Tel (951) 272-4790 SIC 5199 5122 5087

DART CONTAINER CORP OF CALIFORNIA p 412
150 S Maple St 92880
Tel (951) 739-7791 SIC 3086

CORONADO, CA

L-O CORONADO HOTEL INC p 835
1500 Orange Ave 92118
Tel (619) 435-6611
SIC 7011 5812 5813 5941

■ **SANSPAN CORP** p 1280
1500 Orange Ave 92118
Tel (619) 435-6611 SIC 7011

SHARP CORONADO HOSPITAL & HEALTHCARE CENTER p 1312
250 Prospect Pl 92118
Tel (619) 522-3600 SIC 8062

CORONA, CA

FLEETWOOD ALUMINUM PRODUCTS INC p 555
1 Fleetwood Way 92879
Tel (800) 736-7363 SIC 5031 3442

FLEETWOOD ENTERPRISES INC p 555
1351 Pomona Rd Ste 230 92882
Tel (951) 354-3000 SIC 3799 2451 5561

HP COMMUNICATIONS INC p 714
13341 Temescal Canyon Rd 92883
Tel (951) 572-1200 SIC 1623

HUB DISTRIBUTING INC p 715
1260 Corona Pointe Ct 92879
Tel (951) 340-3149
SIC 5611 5621 5632 5137 5136 5094

IRWIN INTERNATIONAL INC p 765
225 Airport Cir 92880
Tel (951) 372-9555 SIC 5599 5088

KOBELCO COMPRESSORS AMERICA INC p 825
1450 W Rincon St 92880
Tel (951) 739-3030 SIC 1623 3563

LDI MECHANICAL INC p 849
1587 E Bentley Dr 92879
Tel (951) 340-9685 SIC 1711

MCP INDUSTRIES INC p 932
708 S Temescal St Ste 101 92879
Tel (951) 736-1881 SIC 3069 3259 3089

MERRICK ENGINEERING INC p 950
1275 Quarry St 92879
Tel (951) 737-6040 SIC 3089

MINKA LIGHTING INC p 973
1151 Bradford Cir 92882
Tel (951) 735-9220 SIC 5063

■ **MONSTER BEVERAGE 1990 CORP** p 985
1 Monster Way 92879
Tel (951) 739-6200 SIC 2086

▲ **MONSTER BEVERAGE CORP** p 985
1 Monster Way 92879
Tel (951) 739-6200 SIC 2086

■ **MONSTER ENERGY CO** p 985
1 Monster Way 92879
Tel (951) 739-6200 SIC 5149

PET PARTNERS INC p 1137
450 N Sheridan St 92880
Tel (951) 279-9888 SIC 5199

ROBERTSONS READY MIX LTD A CALIFORNIA LIMITED PARTNERSHIP p 1242
200 S Main St Ste 200 92882
Tel (951) 493-6500
SIC 3273 3531 5032 2951 1442

■ **STERNO PRODUCTS LLC** p 1388
1880 Compton Ave Ste 101 92881
Tel (951) 682-9600
SIC 3641 3645 3589 3634 2899

TALCO PLASTICS INC p 1422
1000 W Rincon St 92880
Tel (951) 531-2000 SIC 4953 2821

■ **THERMAL STRUCTURES INC** p 1447
2362 Railroad St 92880
Tel (951) 736-9911 SIC 3724

■ **UHS-CORONA INC** p 1500
800 S Main St 92882
Tel (951) 737-4343 SIC 8062

VEG-FRESH FARMS LLC p 1546
1400 W Rincon St 92880
Tel (800) 422-5535 SIC 5148

WATSON LABORATORIES INC p 1583
311 Bonnie Cir 92880
Tel (951) 493-5300 SIC 2834

CORTE MADERA, CA

IL FORNAIO (AMERICA) CORP p 731
770 Tamalpais Dr Ste 400 94925
Tel (415) 945-0500
SIC 5812 5813 5149 5461 2051

▲ **RESTORATION HARDWARE HOLDINGS INC** p 1228
15 Koch Rd Ste K 94925
Tel (415) 924-1005 SIC 5712

■ **RESTORATION HARDWARE INC** p 1228
15 Koch Rd Ste J 94925
Tel (415) 924-1005 SIC 5712

COSTA MESA, CA

ANNAS LINENS INC p 92
3550 Hyland Ave 92626
Tel (714) 850-0504 SIC 5719 5714 5023

AUTO CLUB ENTERPRISES p 133
3333 Fairview Rd Msa451 92626
Tel (714) 850-5111 SIC 6321

BALBOA CAPITAL CORP p 147
575 Anton Blvd Fl 12 92626
Tel (949) 756-0800 SIC 6141

COAST COMMUNITY COLLEGE DISTRICT ENTERPRISE INC p 331
1370 Adams Ave 92626
Tel (714) 438-4600 SIC 8222 8221

COLLEGE HOSPITAL COSTA MESA MSO INC p 336
301 Victoria St 92627
Tel (949) 642-2734 SIC 8062

DYNAMIC COOKING SYSTEMS INC p 464
695 Town Center Dr # 180 92626
Tel (714) 372-7000 SIC 3589

▲ **EL POLLO LOCO HOLDINGS INC** p 483
3535 Harbor Blvd Ste 100 92626
Tel (714) 599-5000 SIC 5812 6794

■ **EL POLLO LOCO INC** p 483
3535 Harbor Blvd Ste 100 92626
Tel (714) 599-5000 SIC 5812

EMULEX CORP p 495
3333 Susan St 92626
Tel (714) 662-5600 SIC 3577 3661

■ **EPL INTERMEDIATE INC** p 505
3535 Harbor Blvd Ste 100 92626
Tel (714) 599-5000 SIC 5812

EXPERIAN HOLDINGS INC p 520
475 Anton Blvd 92626
Tel (714) 830-7000 SIC 8741

EXPERIAN INFORMATION SOLUTIONS INC p 520
475 Anton Blvd 92626
Tel (714) 830-7000 SIC 7323

FILENET CORP p 542
3565 Harbor Blvd 92626
Tel (800) 345-3638 SIC 7373 7372

FISHER & PAYKEL APPLIANCES USA HOLDINGS INC p 552
695 Town Center Dr # 180 92626
Tel (888) 936-7872 SIC 5064

GRISWOLD INDUSTRIES p 641
1701 Placentia Ave 92627
Tel (949) 722-4800 SIC 3492 3365 3366

■ **HURLEY INTERNATIONAL LLC** p 721
1945 Placentia Ave 92627
Tel (949) 548-9375 SIC 2329 5137

INSIGHT INVESTMENTS CORP p 746
611 Anton Blvd Ste 700 92626
Tel (714) 939-2300 SIC 7377 5045

INSIGHT INVESTMENTS LLC p 746
611 Anton Blvd Ste 700 92626
Tel (714) 939-2300 SIC 7377 5045

JD POWER AND ASSOCIATES p 780
3200 Park Center Dr Fl 13 92626
Tel (714) 621-6200 SIC 8732

KARMA AUTOMOTIVE LLC p 804
3080 Airway Ave 92626
Tel (714) 723-3247 SIC 3711

KINGS SEAFOOD CO LLC p 820
3185 Airway Ave Ste J 92626
Tel (310) 451-4595 SIC 5812

■ **MT SUPPLY INC** p 997
3505 Cadillac Ave Ste K2 92626
Tel (714) 434-4748 SIC 5085 5084

NEWPORT MESA UNIFIED SCHOOL DISTRICT p 1038
2985 Bear St Ste A 92626
Tel (714) 424-5000 SIC 8211

ORANGE COAST COLLEGE p 1091
2701 Fairview Rd 92626
Tel (714) 432-5772 SIC 8221 8299

ORANGE COUNTY SUPERINTENDENT OF SCHOOLS p 1092
200 Kalmus Dr 92626
Tel (714) 966-4000 SIC 8211

QSC LLC p 1195
1675 Macarthur Blvd 92626
Tel (714) 754-6175 *SIC* 3651

SEGERSTROM CENTER FOR ARTS p 1300
600 Town Center Dr 92626
Tel (714) 556-2122 *SIC* 7922

STEARNS LENDING LLC p 1384
555 Anton Blvd Ste 300 92626
Tel (714) 513-7777 *SIC* 6162

SYSPRO IMPACT SOFTWARE INC p 1418
959 S Coast Dr Ste 100 92626
Tel (714) 437-1000 *SIC* 5045 7372 7371

▲ TTM TECHNOLOGIES INC p 1490
1665 Scenic Ave Ste 250 92626
Tel (714) 327-3000 *SIC* 3672

UNIVERSITY RESTAURANT GROUP INC p 1527
3185 Airway Ave Ste J 92626
Tel (714) 432-0400 *SIC* 5812 5813

VOLCOM LLC p 1564
1740 Monrovia Ave 92627
Tel (949) 646-2175
SIC 7389 2253 7822 5136 5137

WARMINGTON HOMES p 1575
3090 Pullman St 92626
Tel (714) 434-4435 *SIC* 1531

WESTAR CAPITAL ASSOCIATES II LLC p 1596
949 S Coast Dr Ste 170 92626
Tel (714) 481-5160 *SIC* 6799 3089

COTATI, CA

PT-1 HOLDINGS LLC p 1189
720 Portal St 94931
Tel (707) 665-4295 *SIC* 6719

COTTONWOOD, CA

NORTH STATE GROCERY INC p 1054
20803 Front St 96022
Tel (530) 347-4621 *SIC* 5411

COVINA, CA

CENTRAL HEALTH PLAN OF CALIFORNIA INC p 278
1055 Park View Dr Ste 355 91724
Tel (626) 938-7120 *SIC* 8082

CHICKS SPORTING GOODS LLC p 298
979 S Village Oaks Dr 91724
Tel (626) 915-1685 *SIC* 5941

CITRUS VALLEY HEALTH PARTNERS INC p 311
210 W San Bernardino Rd 91723
Tel (626) 331-7331 *SIC* 8741

COVINA-VALLEY UNIFIED SCHOOL DISTRICT FACILITIES FINANCE CORP p 385
519 E Badillo St 91723
Tel (626) 974-7000 *SIC* 8211

LERETA LLC p 857
1123 Park View Dr 91724
Tel (626) 543-1765 *SIC* 6211 6541 6361

SOUTHWEST WATER CO p 1353
1325 N Grand Ave Ste 100 91724
Tel (626) 543-2500 *SIC* 4941 4952

CROCKETT, CA

SUGAR C&H CO INC p 1397
830 Loring Ave 94525
Tel (510) 787-2121 *SIC* 2062

CULVER CITY, CA

■ BEATS ELECTRONICS LLC p 166
8600 Hayden Pl 90232
Tel (424) 326-4679 *SIC* 3651 3679

COASTAL DEVELOPMENTAL SERVICES FOUNDATION p 331
5901 Green Valley Cir # 320 90230
Tel (310) 258-4000 *SIC* 8322

COLUMBIA PICTURES INDUSTRIES INC p 341
10202 Washington Blvd 90232
Tel (310) 244-4000 *SIC* 7812

COMPUTER CONSULTING OPERATIONS SPECIALISTS INC p 352
600 Corporate Pointe # 1010 90230
Tel (310) 568-5000
SIC 4813 4899 5045 7378

GLOBECAST AMERICA INC p 618
10525 Washington Blvd 90232
Tel (212) 373-5140 *SIC* 4841

GOLDRICH & KEST INDUSTRIES LLC p 622
5150 Overland Ave 90230
Tel (310) 204-2050 *SIC* 6552

MOLDEX-METRIC INC p 982
10111 Jefferson Blvd 90232
Tel (310) 837-6500 *SIC* 3842

▲ NANTWORKS LLC p 1007
9920 Jefferson Blvd 90232
Tel (310) 405-7539 *SIC* 7373

SERVICON SYSTEMS INC p 1308
3965 Landmark St 90232
Tel (310) 204-5040 *SIC* 8744 7349 1771

SONY PICTURES ENTERTAINMENT INC p 1341
10202 Washington Blvd 90232
Tel (310) 244-4000 *SIC* 7812 7822 7832

SONY PICTURES IMAGEWORKS INC p 1341
9050 Washington Blvd 90232
Tel (310) 840-8000 *SIC* 7374

SOUTHERN CALIFORNIA HOSPITAL AT CULVER CITY p 1347
3828 Delmas Ter 90232
Tel (310) 836-7000 *SIC* 8062

TOPSON DOWNS OF CALIFORNIA INC p 1461
3840 Watseka Ave 90232
Tel (310) 558-0300 *SIC* 5137

UNITED STAFFING SOLUTIONS INC p 1512
12069 Jefferson Blvd 90230
Tel (310) 305-9999 *SIC* 7363

CUPERTINO, CA

▲ AEMETIS INC p 29
20400 Stevens 95014
Tel (408) 213-0940 *SIC* 8731 2911

▲ APPLE INC p 98
1 Infinite Loop 95014
Tel (408) 996-1010
SIC 3663 3571 3575 3577 3651 7372

■ CRC HEALTH CORP p 389
20400 Stevens Creek Blvd 95014
Tel (877) 272-8668
SIC 8069 8099 8322 8093

■ CRC HEALTH CORPORATE p 389
20400 Stevens 95014
Tel (408) 367-0044 *SIC* 8093

■ CRC HEALTH GROUP INC p 389
20400 Stev Creek Blvd 6 95014
Tel (877) 272-8668 *SIC* 8099

CUPERTINO UNION SCHOOL DISTRICT p 401
10301 Vista Dr 95014
Tel (408) 252-3000 *SIC* 8211

MISSION WEST PROPERTIES INC p 975
10050 Bandley Dr 95014
Tel (408) 725-0700 *SIC* 6798

SEAGATE TECHNOLOGY (US) HOLDINGS INC p 1296
10200 S De Anza Blvd 95014
Tel (831) 438-6550 *SIC* 3572

SEAGATE TECHNOLOGY LLC p 1296
10200 S De Anza Blvd 95014
Tel (408) 658-1000 *SIC* 3572

CUTLER, CA

WAWONA PACKING CO LLC p 1584
12133 Avenue 408 93615
Tel (559) 528-4000 *SIC* 0723

WILEMAN BROS & ELLIOTT INC p 1609
40232 Road 128 93615
Tel (559) 651-8378
SIC 0723 2653 0174 0175

CYPRESS, CA

CALIBER CAPITAL GROUP LLC p 239
5900 Katella Ave Ste A101 90630
Tel (714) 507-1998 *SIC* 6282 8111

CHRISTIE DIGITAL SYSTEMS INC p 303
10550 Camden Dr 90630
Tel (714) 236-8610 *SIC* 3861 6719

CHRISTIE DIGITAL SYSTEMS USA INC p 303
10550 Camden Dr 90630
Tel (714) 527-7056 *SIC* 5043

CLARION CORP OF AMERICA p 321
6200 Gateway Dr 90630
Tel (310) 327-9100 *SIC* 5064

DIASORIN MOLECULAR LLC p 437
11331 Valley View St 90630
Tel (562) 240-6500 *SIC* 2835 5047

EXEMPLIS LLC p 519
6415 Katella Ave 90630
Tel (714) 995-4800 *SIC* 2522

FREEWAY INSURANCE p 577
10801 Walker St Ste 250 90630
Tel (714) 252-2500 *SIC* 6411

HYBRID PROMOTIONS LLC p 723
10711 Walker St 90630
Tel (714) 952-3866 *SIC* 5136 5137 5611

MANHATTAN BEACHWEAR INC p 901
10700 Valley View St 90630
Tel (714) 892-7354 *SIC* 2339

MITSUBISHI ELECTRIC US HOLDINGS INC p 977
5900 Katella Ave Ste A 90630
Tel (714) 220-2500
SIC 5065 5045 3651 3663

MITSUBISHI ELECTRIC US INC p 977
5900 Katella Ave Ste A 90630
Tel (714) 220-2500
SIC 5065 5045 1796 3534

MITSUBISHI MOTORS NORTH AMERICA INC p 978
6400 Katella Ave 90630
Tel (714) 799-4730
SIC 5511 5013 6159 6512

■ PACIFICARE HEALTH SYSTEMS LLC p 1106
5995 Plaza Dr 90630
Tel (714) 952-1121 *SIC* 6324

REAL MEX RESTAURANTS INC p 1213
5660 Katella Ave Ste 200 90630
Tel (562) 346-1020 *SIC* 5812

SOUTHERN CAL UNITED FOOD & COMMERCIAL WORKERS UNIONS & FOOD EMPLOYERS PENSION TRUST FUND p 1347
6425 Katella Ave 90630
Tel (714) 220-2297 *SIC* 6371

TOYO TIRE HOLDINGS OF AMERICAS INC p 1466
5900 Katella Ave Ste 200a 90630
Tel (562) 431-6502 *SIC* 3011

■ UHC OF CALIFORNIA p 1500
5995 Plaza Dr 90630
Tel (714) 952-1121 *SIC* 6324 8732

UNITED FOOD AND COMMERCIAL WORKERS UNIONS AND FOOD EMPLOYERS BEN FUND p 1508
6425 Katella Ave 90630
Tel (714) 220-2297 *SIC* 8631

USHIO AMERICA INC p 1535
5440 Cerritos Ave 90630
Tel (714) 236-8600 *SIC* 5063

■ VANS INC p 1544
6550 Katella Ave 90630
Tel (714) 889-6100
SIC 3021 2321 2329 2325 2353 2393

YAMAHA MOTOR CORP USA p 1634
6555 Katella Ave 90630
Tel (714) 761-7300
SIC 5088 5013 5091 5012

DALY CITY, CA

ARMOR DOMAIN INC p 111
235 Westlake Ctr Pmb 518 94015
Tel (415) 637-1817 *SIC* 7381

GENESYS TELECOMMUNICATIONS LABORATORIES INC p 603
2001 Junipero Serra Blvd 94014
Tel (650) 466-1100 *SIC* 7372

SETON MEDICAL CENTER p 1309
1900 Sullivan Ave 94015
Tel (650) 992-4000 *SIC* 8062 8051

DANA POINT, CA

CPH MONARCH HOTEL LLC p 387
1 Monarch Beach Resort 92629
Tel (949) 234-3200 *SIC* 7011

DANVILLE, CA

SAN RAMON VALLEY UNIFIED SCHOOL DISTRICT p 1277
699 Old Orchard Dr 94526
Tel (925) 552-5500 *SIC* 8211

WHEELCHAIR FOUNDATION p 1605
3820 Blackhawk Rd 94506
Tel (925) 736-8234 *SIC* 8733

DAVIS, CA

UNIVERSITY OF CALIFORNIA DAVIS p 1520
1 Shields Ave 95616
Tel (530) 752-1011 *SIC* 8221 9411

DEL MAR, CA

LIQUID INVESTMENTS INC p 870
3840 Via De La Valle # 300 92014
Tel (858) 509-8510 *SIC* 5181 5145 5182

DELANO, CA

WONDERFUL CITRUS PACKING LLC p 1622
1901 S Lexington St 93215
Tel (661) 720-2400 *SIC* 0723 0174 2033

DIAMOND BAR, CA

A P R CONSULTING INC p 6
1370 Valley Vista Dr # 280 91765
Tel (909) 396-5375 *SIC* 7361 7379

■ BIOSENSE WEBSTER INC p 184
3333 S Diamond Canyon Rd 91765
Tel (909) 839-8500 *SIC* 3845 3841

CYCLE LINK (USA) INC p 405
1330 Valley Vista Dr 91765
Tel (909) 861-5888 *SIC* 5093

GARDEN PALS INC p 591
1300 Valley Vista Dr # 209 91765
Tel (909) 605-0200 *SIC* 3423

DINUBA, CA

FRUIT PATCH SALES LLC p 582
38773 Road 48 93618
Tel (559) 591-1170 *SIC* 5148

RUIZ FOOD PRODUCTS INC p 1257
501 S Alta Ave 93618
Tel (559) 591-5510 *SIC* 2038 2099

DIXON, CA

BASALITE CONCRETE PRODUCTS LLC p 158
605 Industrial Way 95620
Tel (707) 678-1901 *SIC* 3272

DOWNEY, CA

DOWNEY REGIONAL MEDICAL CENTER-HOSPITAL INC p 453
11500 Brookshire Ave 90241
Tel (562) 698-0811 *SIC* 8062

DOWNEY UNIFIED SCHOOL DISTRICT p 453
11627 Brookshire Ave 90241
Tel (562) 904-3500 *SIC* 8211

DRMC PROPERTIES INC p 456
11500 Brookshire Ave 90241
Tel (562) 904-5464 *SIC* 5947

JAMES PERSE ENTERPRISES INC p 776
7373 Flores St 90242
Tel (323) 588-2226 *SIC* 5136 5137

LIBERTY UTILITIES (PARK WATER) CORP p 863
9750 Washburn Rd 90241
Tel (562) 923-0711 *SIC* 4941

LOS ANGELES COUNTY OFFICE OF EDUCATION p 878
9300 Imperial Hwy 90242
Tel (562) 922-6111 *SIC* 8211

MERUELO ENTERPRISES INC p 951
9550 Firestone Blvd # 105 90241
Tel (562) 745-2300 *SIC* 1542

PBE WAREHOUSE INC p 1123
12171 Pangborn Ave 90241
Tel (562) 803-4691 *SIC* 5013

RANCHO LOS AMIGOS NATIONAL REHABILIATATION CENTER p 1207
7601 Imperial Hwy 90242
Tel (562) 401-7111 *SIC* 8322

ROCKVIEW DAIRIES INC p 1245
7011 Stewart And Gray Rd 90241
Tel (562) 927-5511 *SIC* 5149 5143 2026

DUARTE, CA

BECKMAN RESEARCH INSTITUTE OF CITY OF HOPE p 167
1500 Duarte Rd 91010
Tel (626) 359-8111 *SIC* 8733

CITY OF HOPE p 315
1500 E Duarte Blvd 91010
Tel (626) 256-4673 *SIC* 8741 8399

CITY OF HOPE p 315
1500 Duarte Rd Fl 4 91010
Tel (626) 256-4673 *SIC* 8069

CITY OF HOPE MEDICAL FOUNDATION p 315
1500 Duarte Rd 91010
Tel (626) 256-4673 *SIC* 8733

CITY OF HOPE NATIONAL MEDICAL CENTER p 315
1500 Duarte Rd 91010
Tel (626) 256-4673 *SIC* 8062

DUBLIN, CA

▲ CALLIDUS SOFTWARE INC p 242
4140 Dublin Blvd Ste 400 94568
Tel (925) 251-2200 *SIC* 7371 7372

CARL ZEISS MEDITEC INC p 256
5160 Hacienda Dr 94568
Tel (925) 557-4100 *SIC* 3827

CHABOT-LAS POSITAS COMMUNITY COLLEGE DISTRICT FINANCING CORP p 286
7600 Dublin Blvd Ste 102 94568
Tel (925) 485-5201 *SIC* 8222

CHALLENGE DAIRY PRODUCTS INC p 286
6701 Donlon Way 94568
Tel (925) 828-6160 *SIC* 5143 5149

DESILVA GATES CONSTRUCTION LP p 432
11555 Dublin Blvd 94568
Tel (925) 361-1380 *SIC* 1611 1794 1542

DUBLIN UNIFIED SCHOOL DISTRICT p 459
7471 Larkdale Ave 94568
Tel (925) 828-2551 *SIC* 8211

HARVEY & MADDING INC p 667
6300 Dublin Blvd 94568
Tel (925) 828-8030
SIC 5511 7538 5015 5013

OLIVER DE SILVA INC p 1082
11555 Dublin Blvd 94568
Tel (925) 829-9220 *SIC* 1429

▲ ROSS STORES INC p 1252
5130 Hacienda Dr 94568
Tel (925) 965-4400
SIC 5651 5661 5944 5632 5611 5999

SYBASE INC p 1413
1 Sybase Dr 94568
Tel (925) 236-5000 *SIC* 7372

■ TALEO CORP p 1422
4140 Dublin Blvd Ste 400 94568
Tel (925) 452-3000 *SIC* 7372

E RNCHO DMNGZ, CA

MURRAY PLUMBING AND HEATING CORP p 1002
18414 S Santa Fe Ave 90221
Tel (310) 637-1500 *SIC* 1711

SONORA MILLS FOODS INC p 1340
3064 E Maria St 90221
Tel (310) 639-5333 *SIC* 2052

EAST PALO ALTO, CA

HGGC LLC p 689
1950 University Ave # 350 94303
Tel (650) 321-4910 *SIC* 6799

EDISON, CA

GIUMARRA VINEYARDS CORP p 613
11220 Edison Hwy 93220
Tel (661) 395-7000 *SIC* 0172 2084 2086

KIRSCHENMAN ENTERPRISES SALES LP p 822
12826 Edison Hwy 93220
Tel (661) 366-5736 *SIC* 7389

EL CAJON, CA

AMS PLASTICS INC p 87
1530 Hilton Head Rd # 205 92019
Tel (619) 713-2000 *SIC* 3089

CAJON VALLEY UNION SCHOOL DISTRICT p 237
750 E Main St 92020
Tel (619) 588-3000 *SIC* 8211

CASS CONSTRUCTION INC p 263
1100 Wagner Dr 92020
Tel (619) 590-0929 *SIC* 1623 1611

GKN AEROSPACE CHEM-TRONICS INC p 613
1150 W Bradley Ave 92020
Tel (619) 448-2320 *SIC* 3724 7699

GROSSMONT UNION HIGH SCHOOL DISTRICT SCHOOL FACILITIES CORP p 641
1100 Murray Dr 92020
Tel (619) 644-8000 *SIC* 8211

GROSSMONT-CUYAMACA COMMUNITY COLLEGE DISTRICT p 641
8800 Grossmont College Dr 92020
Tel (619) 644-7010 *SIC* 8221

K MOTORS INC p 799
965 Arnele Ave 92020
Tel (619) 270-3000 *SIC* 5521 5013 5511

■ PACIFIC GYPSUM SUPPLY INC p 1104
1165 N Johnson Ave 92020
Tel (619) 447-2413 *SIC* 5032 5211

SYCUAN BAND OF KUMEYAAY NATION p 1413
3007 Dehesa Rd 92019
Tel (619) 445-6002 *SIC* 9131

SYCUAN CASINO p 1413
5459 Casino Way 92019
Tel (619) 445-6002 *SIC* 7999 7997

TAYLOR-LISTUG INC p 1427
1980 Gillespie Way 92020
Tel (619) 258-6957 *SIC* 3931

■ UNIVERSITY MECHANICAL & ENGINEERING CONTRACTORS INC p 1519
1168 Fesler St 92020
Tel (619) 956-2500 *SIC* 1711 1623 8741

EL CENTRO, CA

COUNTY OF IMPERIAL p 378
940 W Main St Ste 208 92243
Tel (760) 482-4556 *SIC* 9121

EL CENTRO REGIONAL MEDICAL CENTER INC p 482
1415 Ross Ave 92243
Tel (760) 339-7100 *SIC* 8062

NEW OPTICS USA INC p 1032
510 W Main St 92243
Tel (760) 547-7136 *SIC* 5048

NEW OPTICS USA INC p 1032
653 W Main St Ste 1 92243
Tel (760) 996-9067 *SIC* 5048

NOBLESSE OBLIGE INC p 1046
2015 Silsbee Rd 92243
Tel (760) 353-3336 *SIC* 0722

VIB CORP p 1555
1498 W Main St 92243
Tel (760) 352-5000 *SIC* 6022

EL DORADO HILLS, CA

MCCLONE CONSTRUCTION CO p 926
5170 Hillsdale Cir Ste B 95762
Tel (916) 358-5495 *SIC* 1771 1751

R SYSTEMS INC p 1202
5000 Windplay Dr Ste 5 95762
Tel (916) 939-9696 *SIC* 7379 7373 7374

ROEBBELEN CONTRACTING INC p 1246
1241 Hawks Flight Ct 95762
Tel (916) 939-4000 *SIC* 1542 1541 8741

EL DORADO, CA

CONFORTI PLUMBING INC p 356
6080 Pleasant Valley Rd C 95623
Tel (530) 622-0202 *SIC* 1711

EL MONTE, CA

ACCESS SERVICES p 15
3449 Santa Anita Ave 91731
Tel (213) 270-6000 *SIC* 4111

ATLANTIS SEAFOOD LLC p 127
10501 Valley Blvd # 1820 91731
Tel (626) 626-4900 *SIC* 2092

BROWN JORDAN CO LIMITED PARTNERSHIP p 219
9860 Gidley St 91731
Tel (626) 443-8971 *SIC* 2511 2514

■ CATHAY BANK p 265
9650 Flair Dr 91731
Tel (626) 279-3698 *SIC* 6022

DRIFTWOOD DAIRY INC p 456
10724 Lower Azusa Rd 91731
Tel (626) 444-9591 *SIC* 2026

EL MONTE CITY SCHOOL DISTRICT p 483
3540 Lexington Ave 91731
Tel (626) 453-3700 *SIC* 8211

EL MONTE UNION HIGH SCHOOL DISTRICT p 483
3537 Johnson Ave 91731
Tel (626) 258-4905 *SIC* 8211

GEORGE FISCHER INC p 606
3401 Aero Jet Ave 91731
Tel (626) 571-2770
SIC 3599 5074 3829 3559

GILL CORP p 612
4056 Easy St 91731
Tel (626) 443-6094 *SIC* 3089

LABORERS HEALTH & WELFARE TRUST FUND FOR SOUTHERN p 836
4399 Santa Anita Ave # 200 91731
Tel (626) 279-3000 *SIC* 8631

MOUNTAIN VIEW ELEMENTARY SCHOOL DISTRICT p 994
3320 Gilman Rd 91732
Tel (626) 652-4000 *SIC* 8211

PENSKE MOTOR GROUP LLC p 1131
3534 Peck Rd 91731
Tel (626) 580-6000 *SIC* 5511

SAN GABRIEL VALLEY WATER CO p 1277
11142 Garvey Ave 91733
Tel (626) 448-6183 *SIC* 4941

EL SEGUNDO, CA

ACTIVE INTEREST MEDIA INC p 20
300 Continental Blvd # 650 90245
Tel (310) 356-4100 *SIC* 2721

AERO CALIFORNIA AIRLINES p 30
1960 E Grand Ave Ste 1200 90245
Tel (800) 237-6225 *SIC* 4512

AEROSPACE CORP p 30
2310 E El Segundo Blvd 90245
Tel (310) 336-5000 *SIC* 8733 8731 8711

AVANTI HEALTH SYSTEM LLC p 136
222 N Sepulveda Blvd # 950 90245
Tel (310) 356-0550 *SIC* 8742

AVANTI HOSPITALS LLC p 136
222 N Splvd Blvd Ste 950 90245
Tel (310) 356-0550 *SIC* 7011

BANDAI NAMCO HOLDINGS USA INC p 150
2120 Park Pl Ste 120 90245
Tel (714) 816-9500 *SIC* 3999 7993

■ BIG 5 CORP p 181
2525 E El Segundo Blvd 90245
Tel (310) 536-0611 *SIC* 5941

▲ BIG 5 SPORTING GOODS CORP p 181
2525 E El Segundo Blvd 90245
Tel (310) 536-0611 *SIC* 5941

■ BOEING SATELLITE SYSTEMS INC p 197
900 N Sepulveda Blvd 90245
Tel (310) 791-7450 *SIC* 3663

CETERA FINANCIAL GROUP INC p 284
200 N Sepulveda Blvd # 1200 90245
Tel (800) 879-8100 *SIC* 7389 6282

CHIPTON-ROSS INC (WISCONSIN) p 301
343 Main St 90245
Tel (310) 414-7800 *SIC* 7361

CRUZ BAY PUBLISHING INC p 396
300 Continental Blvd # 650 90245
Tel (310) 356-4100 *SIC* 2721

■ DIRECTV ENTERPRISES LLC p 442
2230 E Imperial Hwy 90245
Tel (310) 535-5000 *SIC* 4841

■ DIRECTV GROUP HOLDINGS LLC p 442
2260 E Imperial Hwy 90245
Tel (310) 964-5000 *SIC* 4841

■ DIRECTV GROUP INC p 442
2260 E Imperial Hwy 90245
Tel (310) 964-5000 *SIC* 4841

■ DIRECTV HOLDINGS LLC p 442
2230 E Imperial Hwy 90245
Tel (310) 964-5000 *SIC* 4841

GUTHY-RENKER LLC p 648
100 N Sepulveda Blvd # 1600 90245
Tel (760) 773-9022
SIC 5099 7812 5999 7389

HCO HOLDING I CORP p 672
999 N Sepulveda Blvd 90245
Tel (323) 583-5000 *SIC* 6719

■ HEALTHCARE PARTNERS LLC p 676
2175 Park Pl 90245
Tel (310) 354-4200 *SIC* 8011

HENRY CO LLC p 684
999 N Sepulveda Blvd 90245
Tel (310) 955-9200 *SIC* 2952 2821 2891

HNC PARENT INC p 698
999 N Sepulveda Blvd 90245
Tel (310) 955-9200 *SIC* 2952 2821 2891

IGNITED LLC p 730
2150 Park Pl Ste 100 90245
Tel (310) 773-3100 *SIC* 7311

INFINEON TECHNOLOGIES AMERICAS CORP p 740
101 N Sepulveda Blvd 90245
Tel (310) 726-8000 *SIC* 3674

INFONET SERVICES CORP p 741
2160 E Grand Ave 90245
Tel (310) 335-2859 *SIC* 4813 7373 7375

INTERNET BRANDS INC p 757
909 N Sepulveda Blvd # 11 90245
Tel (310) 280-4000 *SIC* 7374

KARL STORZ ENDOSCOPY-AMERICA INC p 804
2151 E Grand Ave 90245
Tel (424) 218-8100 *SIC* 3841 5047

KATCH p 804
2381 Rosecrans Ave # 400 90245
Tel (310) 219-6200 *SIC* 7311

■ LIBERTY ENTERTAINMENT INC p 861
2230 E Imperial Hwy 90245
Tel (310) 964-5000 *SIC* 4841

▲ MATTEL INC p 920
333 Continental Blvd 90245
Tel (310) 252-2000 *SIC* 3944 3942

■ MATTEL TOY CO p 920
333 Continental Blvd 90245
Tel (310) 252-2357 *SIC* 5092

■ MULLIN TBG INSURANCE AGENCY SERVICES LLC p 999
100 N Sepulveda Blvd 90245
Tel (310) 203-8770 *SIC* 6411

▲ PCM INC p 1124
1940 E Mariposa Ave 90245
Tel (310) 354-5600
SIC 5734 5961 5731 5045

■ PCM SALES INC p 1124
1940 E Mariposa Ave 90245
Tel (310) 354-5600 *SIC* 5734

PERFORMANCE TEAM FREIGHT SYS INC p 1135
2240 E Maple Ave 90245
Tel (562) 345-2200 *SIC* 4731 4225 4213

PROLOGIC REDEMPTION SOLUTIONS INC p 1182
2121 Rosecrans Ave 90245
Tel (310) 322-7774 *SIC* 7389

■ RENAL TREATMENT CENTERS INC p 1223
601 Hawaii St 90245
Tel (310) 536-2400 *SIC* 8733

RPD HOTELS 18 LLC p 1255
2361 Rosecrans Ave # 150 90245
Tel (213) 746-1531 *SIC* 7011

SOFTSCRIPT INC p 1337
2215 Campus Dr 90245
Tel (310) 451-2110 *SIC* 7338

SPECTRUM CLUBS INC p 1357
840 Apollo St Ste 100 90245
Tel (310) 727-9300 *SIC* 7991

SQUARE ENIX OF AMERICA HOLDINGS INC p 1362
999 N Sepulveda Blvd Fl 3 90245
Tel (310) 846-0400 *SIC* 5045

▲ STAMPS.COM INC p 1375
1990 E Grand Ave 90245
Tel (310) 482-5800 *SIC* 7331 5961 4813

TECHSTYLE INC p 1432
800 Apollo St 90245
Tel (310) 683-0940
SIC 5961 5661 5632 5651

TEN ENTHUSIAST NETWORK LLC p 1436
831 S Douglas St Ste 100 90245
Tel (310) 531-9900 *SIC* 5192

■ TRI-STAR ELECTRONICS INTERNATIONAL INC p 1477
2201 Rosecrans Ave 90245
Tel (310) 536-0444 *SIC* 3643

TRI-UNION FROZEN PRODUCTS INC p 1478
222 N Sepulveda Blvd # 155 90245
Tel (516) 740-4100 *SIC* 5146

■ WYLE INC p 1629
1960 E Grand Ave Ste 900 90245
Tel (310) 563-6800 *SIC* 8711 7371 8731

■ WYLE LABORATORIES INC p 1629
1960 E Grand Ave Ste 900 90245
Tel (310) 563-6800 *SIC* 8734 8731

■ WYLE SERVICES CORP p 1629
1960 E Grand Ave Ste 900 90245
Tel (310) 563-6800 *SIC* 8711 7371

EL TORO, CA

HALLMARK REHABILITATION GP LLC p 655
27442 Portola Pkwy # 200 92610
Tel (949) 282-5900 *SIC* 8322

ELK GROVE, CA

■ CITIZENS TELECOMMUNICATIONS CO OF CALIFORNIA INC p 311
9260 E Stockton Blvd 95624
Tel (916) 686-3000 *SIC* 4813

ELK GROVE AUTO GROUP INC p 487
8575 Laguna Grove Dr 95757
Tel (916) 405-2600 *SIC* 5511

GROVE ELK UNIFIED SCHOOL DISTRICT p 642
9510 Elk Grove Florin Rd 95624
Tel (916) 686-5085 *SIC* 8211

OC COMMUNICATIONS INC p 1072
2204 Kausen Dr Ste 100 95758
Tel (916) 686-3700 *SIC* 4841

SLAKEY BROTHERS INC p 1331
2215 Kausen Dr Ste 1 95758
Tel (916) 478-2000 *SIC* 5075 5074 5078

EMERYVILLE, CA

AAA NORTHERN CALIFORNIA NEVADA AND UTAH p 7
1900 Powell St Ste 1200 94608
Tel (510) 596-3669 *SIC* 6331 8699

AMERICAN AUTOMOBILE ASSOCIATION OF NORTHERN CALIFORNIA NEVADA & UTAH p 68
1900 Powell St Ste 1200 94608
Tel (800) 922-8228 *SIC* 8699

ART SUPPLY ENTERPRISES INC p 113
1375 Ocean Ave 94608
Tel (510) 768-6633 *SIC* 5199

ART.COM INC p 113
2100 Powell St Fl 10th 94608
Tel (510) 879-4700 *SIC* 5999

BERKELEY RESEARCH GROUP LLC p 175
2200 Powell St Ste 1200 94608
Tel (510) 285-3300 *SIC* 8748

CALIFORNIA EMERGENCY PHYSICIANS FOUNDATION p 240
2100 Powell St Ste 900 94608
Tel (510) 350-2700 *SIC* 8621

CHEVYS RESTAURANTS LLC p 296
2000 Powell St Ste 200 94608
Tel (510) 768-1400 *SIC* 5812

CHIRON CORP p 301
4560 Horton St 94608
Tel (510) 655-8730 *SIC* 8099

CLIF BAR & CO p 326
1451 66th St 94608
Tel (510) 596-6300 *SIC* 2052 5149

E-BRANDS RESTAURANTS LLC p 467
6475 Christie Ave Ste 300 94608
Tel (407) 226-1433 *SIC* 5812

■ GRACENOTE INC p 628
2000 Powell St Ste 1500 94608
Tel (510) 428-7200 *SIC* 7371

GROCERY OUTLET INC p 641
5650 Hollis St Ste 100 94608
Tel (510) 845-1999 *SIC* 5411

▲ JAMBA INC p 776
6475 Christie Ave Ste 150 94608
Tel (510) 596-0100 *SIC* 5812 6794

■ JUICE CLUB INC p 797
6475 Christie Ave Ste 150 94608
Tel (510) 596-0100 *SIC* 5812 6794

LEAPFROG ENTERPRISES INC p 850
6401 Hollis St Ste 100 94608
Tel (510) 420-5000 *SIC* 3944

PEETS COFFEE & TEA LLC p 1127
1400 Park Ave 94608
Tel (510) 594-2100 *SIC* 2095 5149

■ PIXAR p 1152
1200 Park Ave 94608
Tel (510) 922-3000 *SIC* 7812 7372 7371

SUTTER VISITING NURSE ASSOCIATION & HOSPICE p 1410
1900 Powell St Ste 300 94608
Tel (866) 652-9178 *SIC* 8082

▲ TUBEMOGUL INC p 1490
1250 53rd St Ste 2 94608
Tel (510) 653-0126 *SIC* 7372

■ WHOLE FOODS MARKET CALIFORNIA INC p 1607
5980 Horton St Ste 200 94608
Tel (510) 428-7400 *SIC* 5411 5149

ENCINITAS, CA

MANA DEVELOPMENT LLC p 900
2339 11th St 92024
Tel (760) 944-1070 *SIC* 5149

ENCINO, CA

COLDWATER CREEK INC p 335
17000 Ventura Blvd # 300 91316
Tel (208) 263-2266 *SIC* 5621 5961

COLDWATER CREEK OUTLET STORES INC p 335
17000 Ventura Blvd # 300 91316
Tel (208) 265-3468 *SIC* 5399

▲ CU BANCORP p 399
15821 Ventura Blvd # 100 91436
Tel (818) 257-7700 *SIC* 6021 6712

FILM MUSICIANS SECONDARY MARKETS FUND p 542
15910 Ventura Blvd # 900 91436
Tel (818) 755-7777 *SIC* 8741 6722

KRAMER-WILSON CO INC p 829
6345 Balboa Blvd Ste 190 91316
Tel (818) 760-0880 *SIC* 6331

KSL MEDIA INC p 831
15910 Ventura Blvd # 900 91436
Tel (212) 468-3395 *SIC* 7319

NATIONAL CEMENT CO INC p 1010
15821 Ventura Blvd # 475 91436
Tel (818) 728-5200 *SIC* 3241 3273

OLS HOTELS & RESORTS LP p 1083
16000 Ventura Blvd # 1010 91436
Tel (818) 905-8280 *SIC* 7011

■ REPUBLIC INDEMNITY CO OF AMERICA p 1225
15821 Ventura Blvd # 370 91436
Tel (818) 990-9860 *SIC* 6331

WESTSTAR CINEMAS INC p 1603
16530 Ventura Blvd # 500 91436
Tel (818) 784-6266 *SIC* 7832

ESCONDIDO, CA

BAKER ELECTRIC INC p 146
1298 Pacific Oaks Pl 92029
Tel (760) 745-2001 *SIC* 1731 8711

ESCONDIDO UNION SCHOOL DISTRICT p 509
2310 Aldergrove Ave 92029
Tel (760) 432-2400 *SIC* 8211

GARRICK MOTORS INC p 592
231 E Lincoln Ave 92026
Tel (760) 746-0601 *SIC* 5511

HENRY AVOCADO CORP p 684
2355 E Lincoln Ave 92027
Tel (760) 745-6632 *SIC* 0179 4213

JR FILANC CONSTRUCTION CO INC p 795
740 N Andreasen Dr 92029
Tel (760) 941-7130 *SIC* 1623 1629

PALOMAR HEALTH p 1110
456 E Grand Ave 92025
Tel (442) 281-5000 *SIC* 8062 8059

RIO VISTA VENTURES LLC p 1236
15651 Old Milky Way 92027
Tel (760) 480-8502 *SIC* 5141

SOLVIS STAFFING SERVICES INC p 1339
500 La Terraza Blvd # 110 92025
Tel (858) 230-8920 *SIC* 7361

SUPERIOR READY MIX CONCRETE LP p 1407
1508 Mission Rd 92029
Tel (760) 745-0556 *SIC* 3273 1611 5032

▲TRUCEPT INC p 1485
500 La Terraza Blvd 92025
Tel (866) 961-5763 *SIC* 8721 8748 8742

WELK GROUP INC p 1589
8860 Lawrence Welk Dr 92026
Tel (760) 749-3000 *SIC* 7011 5099

ETIWANDA, CA

ETIWANDA SCHOOL DISTRICT p 511
6061 East Ave 91739
Tel (909) 899-2451 *SIC* 8211

EUREKA, CA

COUNTY OF HUMBOLDT p 378
825 5th St 95501
Tel (707) 268-2543 *SIC* 9111

ST JOSEPH HOSPITAL p 1368
2700 Dolbeer St 95501
Tel (707) 445-8121 *SIC* 8062

ST JOSEPH HOSPITAL OF EUREKA p 1368
2700 Dolbeer St 95501
Tel (707) 445-8121 *SIC* 8062

EXETER, CA

EXETER PACKERS INC p 519
1250 E Myer Ave 93221
Tel (559) 592-5168 *SIC* 0723

SUN PACIFIC FARMING COOPERATIVE INC p 1400
1250 E Myer Ave 93221
Tel (559) 592-7121 *SIC* 0762

SVENHARDS SWEDISH BAKERY p 1410
701 Industrial Dr 93221
Tel (831) 623-4375 *SIC* 2051

FAIRFIELD, CA

B R FUNSTEN & CO p 142
5200 Watt Ct Ste B 94534
Tel (209) 825-5375 *SIC* 5023

CITY OF FAIRFIELD p 314
1000 Webster St 94533
Tel (707) 428-7569 *SIC* 9111

COUNTY OF SOLANO p 382
675 Texas St Ste 2600 94533
Tel (707) 784-6706 *SIC* 9111

FAIRFIELD-SUISUN UNIFIED SCHOOL DISTRICT p 525
2490 Hilborn Rd 94534
Tel (707) 399-5000 *SIC* 8211

FRANK-LIN DISTILLERS PRODUCTS LTD p 574
2455 Huntington Dr 94533
Tel (408) 259-8900 *SIC* 5182 2085

HALABI INC p 653
2100 Huntington Dr 94533
Tel (707) 402-1600 *SIC* 3281 1799

JELLY BELLY CANDY CO p 782
1 Jelly Belly Ln 94533
Tel (707) 428-2800 *SIC* 2064

LABOR HEALTH & WELTR FNDNE CA p 836
220 Campus Ln 94534
Tel (707) 864-2800 *SIC* 8099

NORTHBAY HEALTHCARE GROUP p 1054
1200 B Gale Wilson Blvd 94533
Tel (707) 646-5000 *SIC* 8062

PARTNERSHIP HEALTH PLAN OF CALIFORNIA p 1118
4665 Business Center Dr 94534
Tel (707) 863-4100 *SIC* 6324

RENO JONES INC p 1224
2373 N Watney Way 94533
Tel (707) 422-4300 *SIC* 5199 5085 3221

S & S TOOL & SUPPLY INC p 1261
2700 Maxwell Way 94534
Tel (925) 335-4000
SIC 5085 7699 5072 7359

SCHURMAN FINE PAPERS p 1291
500 Chadbourne Rd 94534
Tel (707) 425-8006
SIC 5113 2679 2771 5947

FIVE POINTS, CA

HARRIS RANCH BEEF CO p 663
29475 Fresno Coalinga Rd 93624
Tel (559) 884-2435 *SIC* 2011 2013

FOLSOM, CA

CALIFORNIA INDEPENDENT SYSTEM OPERATOR CORP p 240
250 Outcropping Way 95630
Tel (916) 351-4400 *SIC* 4911

CITY OF FOLSOM p 314
50 Natoma St 95630
Tel (916) 355-7200 *SIC* 9111

FPI MANAGEMENT INC p 573
800 Iron Point Rd 95630
Tel (916) 357-5300 *SIC* 6531

SAFE CREDIT UNION p 1265
2295 Iron Point Rd # 100 95630
Tel (916) 979-7233 *SIC* 6062

SIERRA PACIFIC MORTGAGE CO INC p 1321
1180 Iron Point Rd # 200 95630
Tel (916) 932-1700 *SIC* 6162

■ UNITRIN DIRECT INSURANCE CO p 1515
80 Blue Ravine Rd Ste 200 95630
Tel (760) 603-3276 *SIC* 6399

VISIONARY INTEGRATION PROFESSIONALS LLC p 1561
80 Iron Point Cir Ste 100 95630
Tel (916) 608-8320 *SIC* 8742 7379

FONTANA, CA

ADVANCED STEEL RECOVERY LLC p 26
14451 Whittram Ave 92335
Tel (909) 355-2372 *SIC* 5093

BURRTEC WASTE GROUP INC p 229
9890 Cherry Ave 92335
Tel (909) 429-4200 *SIC* 4953

BURRTEC WASTE INDUSTRIES INC p 229
9890 Cherry Ave 92335
Tel (909) 429-4200 *SIC* 4953 4212

CALIFORNIA STEEL INDUSTRIES INC p 241
14000 San Bernardino Ave 92335
Tel (909) 350-6300 *SIC* 3312 3317

CITY OF FONTANA p 314
8353 Sierra Ave 92335
Tel (909) 350-7605 *SIC* 9111

FONTANA UNIFIED SCHOOL DISTRICT p 563
9680 Citrus Ave 92335
Tel (909) 357-7600 *SIC* 8211

■ FORGED METALS INC p 567
10685 Beech Ave 92337
Tel (909) 350-9260 *SIC* 3353

INLAND KENWORTH (US) INC p 743
9730 Cherry Ave 92335
Tel (909) 823-9955
SIC 5012 7538 5013 7513

MATERIAL SUPPLY INC p 919
11700 Industry Ave 92337
Tel (951) 727-2200
SIC 3444 5075 7623 1711

ROTOLO CHEVROLET INC p 1252
16666 S Highland Ave 92336
Tel (866) 756-9776 *SIC* 5511 5521 7538

UTILITY TRAILER SALES OF SOUTHERN CALIFORNIA LLC p 1537
15567 Valley Blvd 92335
Tel (877) 275-4887
SIC 5012 5013 5531 5561

WORLD CLASS DISTRIBUTION INC p 1625
10288 Calabash Ave 92335
Tel (909) 574-4140 *SIC* 4225

FOOTHILL RANCH, CA

BAL SEAL ENGINEERING INC p 147
19650 Pauling 92610
Tel (949) 334-8500 *SIC* 3495

■ BALDWIN HARDWARE CORP p 147
19701 Da Vinci 92610
Tel (949) 672-4000 *SIC* 3429

FUJITSU FRONTECH NORTH AMERICA INC p 584
27121 Towne Centre Dr # 100 92610
Tel (949) 855-5500 *SIC* 7373

HAMPTON PRODUCTS INTERNATIONAL CORP p 656
50 Icon 92610
Tel (949) 472-4256 *SIC* 5072

▲ KAISER ALUMINUM CORP p 800
27422 Portola Pkwy # 200 92610
Tel (949) 614-1740
SIC 3334 3353 3354 3355

■ KAISER ALUMINUM FABRICATED PRODUCTS LLC p 800
27422 Portola Pkwy # 200 92610
Tel (949) 614-1740
SIC 3353 3334 3354 3355

■ KAISER ALUMINUM INVESTMENTS CO p 800
27422 Portola Pkwy # 350 92610
Tel (949) 614-1740
SIC 3353 3334 3354 3355

KAWASAKI MOTORS CORP USA p 805
26972 Burbank 92610
Tel (949) 837-4683
SIC 5012 5013 5084 5091

KWIKSET CORP p 833
19701 Da Vinci 92610
Tel (949) 672-4000 *SIC* 3429

LEOCH BATTERY CORP p 856
19751 Descartes Unit A 92610
Tel (949) 588-5853 *SIC* 3621

LOANDEPOT.COM LLC p 872
26642 Towne Centre Dr 92610
Tel (949) 474-1322 *SIC* 6162

■ NATIONAL MANUFACTURING CO p 1014
19701 Da Vinci 92610
Tel (800) 346-9445 *SIC* 3429

OAKLEY INC p 1071
1 Icon 92610
Tel (949) 951-0991
SIC 3851 2331 2339 3021 3873 3143

OSSUR AMERICAS INC p 1097
27051 Towne Centre Dr 92610
Tel (949) 362-3883 *SIC* 3842

■ PRICE PFISTER INC p 1174
19701 Da Vinci 92610
Tel (949) 672-4000 *SIC* 3432

PROFESSIONAL COMMUNITY MANAGEMENT OF CALIFORNIA p 1180
27051 Towne Centre Dr # 200 92610
Tel (800) 369-7260 *SIC* 6531

SEAL123 INC p 1296
26972 Burbank 92610
Tel (949) 699-3900 *SIC* 5621 5632 5961

■ SKILLED HEALTHCARE LLC p 1330
27442 Portola Pkwy # 200 92610
Tel (949) 282-5800 *SIC* 8051 6513 5122

FOSTER CITY, CA

■ CYBERSOURCE CORP p 405
900 Metro Center Blvd 94404
Tel (650) 432-7350 *SIC* 7374

▲ GILEAD SCIENCES INC p 612
333 Lakeside Dr 94404
Tel (650) 574-3000 *SIC* 2836

▲ GUIDEWIRE SOFTWARE INC p 646
1001 E Hillsdale Blvd # 800 94404
Tel (650) 357-9100 *SIC* 7372

IC COMPLIANCE LLC p 726
1065 E Hillsdale Blvd # 300 94404
Tel (650) 378-4150 *SIC* 7371 8721

LEGACY PARTNERS RESIDENTIAL INC p 852
4000 E 3rd Ave Ste 600 94404
Tel (650) 571-2250 *SIC* 8741

▲ QUINSTREET INC p 1200
950 Tower Ln Ste 600 94404
Tel (650) 578-7700 *SIC* 7389 7372

SAN MATEO-FOSTER CITY SCHOOL DISTRICT p 1277
1170 Chess Dr 94404
Tel (650) 312-7700 *SIC* 8211

▲ SCICLONE PHARMACEUTICALS INC p 1292
950 Tower Ln Ste 900 94404
Tel (650) 358-3456 *SIC* 2834

SONY INTERACTIVE ENTERTAINMENT AMERICA LLC p 1341
2207 Bridgepointe Pkwy 94404
Tel (650) 655-8000 *SIC* 5092

STEELWAVE INC p 1385
4000 E 3rd Ave Ste 600 94404
Tel (650) 571-2200 *SIC* 6552 8741 6531

STEELWAVE LLC p 1385
4000 E 3rd Ave Ste 500 94404
Tel (650) 571-2200 *SIC* 6552 8741 6531

▲ VISA INC p 1560
900 Metro Center Blvd 94404
Tel (650) 432-3200 *SIC* 7389

■ VISA INTERNATIONAL SERVICE ASSOCIATION p 1560
900 Metro Center Blvd 94404
Tel (650) 432-3200 *SIC* 7389

■ VISA USA INC p 1560
900 Metro Center Blvd 94404
Tel (650) 432-3200 *SIC* 7389

ZUORA INC p 1645
1051 E Hillsdale Blvd # 600 94404
Tel (800) 425-1281 *SIC* 7372

FOUNTAIN VALLEY, CA

D-LINK SYSTEMS INC p 407
17595 Mount Herrmann St 92708
Tel (714) 885-6000 *SIC* 5045 3577

■ FOUNTAIN VALLEY REGIONAL HOSPITAL AND MEDICAL CENTER p 571
17100 Euclid St 92708
Tel (714) 966-7200 *SIC* 8062

HYUNDAI MOTOR AMERICA p 724
10550 Talbert Ave 92708
Tel (714) 965-3000 *SIC* 5511 6141 6153

KINGSTON TECHNOLOGY CO INC p 821
17600 Newhope St 92708
Tel (714) 435-2600 *SIC* 3577

KINGSTON TECHNOLOGY CORP p 821
17600 Newhope St 92708
Tel (714) 445-3495 *SIC* 3674

MEMORIAL HEALTH SERVICES p 941
17360 Brookhurst St # 160 92708
Tel (714) 377-6748 *SIC* 8062

MOBIS PARTS AMERICA LLC p 980
10550 Talbert Ave Fl 4 92708
Tel (786) 515-1101 *SIC* 5012

MSEAFOOD CORP p 997
17934 Point Sur St 92708
Tel (714) 842-7900 *SIC* 5146

ORANGE COAST MEMORIAL MEDICAL CENTER p 1091
9920 Talbert Ave 92708
Tel (714) 378-7000 *SIC* 8062

ORANGE COUNTY SANITATION DISTRICT FINANCING CORP p 1092
10844 Ellis Ave 92708
Tel (714) 962-2411 *SIC* 4953

PAN-PACIFIC MECHANICAL LLC p 1111
18250 Euclid St 92708
Tel (949) 474-9170 *SIC* 1711

ROPAK CORP p 1249
10540 Talbert Ave 200w 92708
Tel (714) 845-2845 *SIC* 3089

SUREFIRE LLC p 1408
18300 Mount Baldy Cir 92708
Tel (714) 545-9444 *SIC* 3648 3842 3484

FOWLER, CA

SUNSHINE RAISIN CORP p 1404
626 S 5th St 93625
Tel (559) 834-5981 *SIC* 2064 0723

FREMONT, CA

ACCESS INTERNATIONAL CO p 15
45630 Northport Loop E 94538
Tel (510) 226-1000 *SIC* 5045

ALAMEDA COUNTY WATER DISTRICT INC p 44
43885 S Grimmer Blvd 94538
Tel (510) 668-4200 *SIC* 4941

■ ALZA CORP p 63
6500 Paseo Padre Pkwy 94555
Tel (650) 564-5000 *SIC* 3826

AMAX ENGINEERING CORP p 64
1565 Reliance Way 94539
Tel (510) 651-8886 *SIC* 5045

AMERICAN AIR LIQUIDE INC p 67
46409 Landing Pkwy 94538
Tel (510) 624-4000
SIC 2813 5084 3533 4931

ASI COMPUTER TECHNOLOGIES INC p 117
48289 Fremont Blvd 94538
Tel (510) 226-8000 *SIC* 5045 3577

ASTEELFLASH USA CORP p 122
4211 Starboard Dr 94538
Tel (510) 440-2840 *SIC* 3672 3679

ASUS COMPUTER INTERNATIONAL INC p 123
800 Corp Way 94539
Tel (510) 739-3777 *SIC* 5045 3577

■ ASYST TECHNOLOGIES INC p 123
46897 Bayside Pkwy 94538
Tel (408) 329-6661 *SIC* 3674

▲ AXT INC p 140
4281 Technology Dr 94538
Tel (510) 438-4700 *SIC* 3674

CHRISP CO p 302
43650 Osgood Rd 94539
Tel (510) 656-2840 *SIC* 1611

CITY OF FREMONT p 315
3300 Capitol Ave 94538
Tel (510) 284-4000 *SIC* 9111

CITY OF FREMONT p 315
3300 Capitol Ave 94538
Tel (510) 574-2050 *SIC* 9121

■ CORDIS CORP p 369
6500 Paseo Padre Pkwy 94555
Tel (510) 248-2500 *SIC* 3841 3842

■ CROSSING AUTOMATION INC p 394
46702 Bayside Pkwy 94538
Tel (510) 661-5000 *SIC* 3559

DELTA AMERICA LTD p 426
46101 Fremont Blvd 94538
Tel (510) 668-5100 *SIC* 5065 3679 8731

DELTA PRODUCTS CORP p 427
46101 Fremont Blvd 94538
Tel (510) 668-5100
SIC 5065 5045 8741 5063 3577

DET LOGISTICS USA CORP p 433
46101 Fremont Blvd 94538
Tel (510) 668-5100 *SIC* 5065

DRYCO CONSTRUCTION INC p 457
42745 Boscell Rd 94538
Tel (510) 438-6500 *SIC* 1611 1721 5211

E & E CO LTD p 465
45875 Northport Loop E 94538
Tel (510) 490-9788 *SIC* 5023

▲ ELECTRONICS FOR IMAGING INC p 486
6750 Dumbarton Cir 94555
Tel (650) 357-3500 *SIC* 3577 2899

▲ EXAR CORP p 516
48720 Kato Rd 94538
Tel (510) 668-7000 *SIC* 3674

FREE-FLOW PACKAGING INTERNATIONAL INC p 576
34175 Ardenwood Blvd 94555
Tel (650) 261-5300 *SIC* 3086

FREMONT BANCORPORATION p 577
39150 Fremont Blvd 94538
Tel (510) 792-2300 *SIC* 6712

FREMONT BANK p 577
39150 Fremont Blvd 94538
Tel (510) 505-5226 *SIC* 6022

FREMONT UNIFIED SCHOOL DISTRICT p 578
4210 Technology Dr 94538
Tel (510) 657-2350 *SIC* 8211

GNLD INTERNATIONAL LLC p 619
3500 Gateway Blvd 94538
Tel (510) 651-0405 *SIC* 5122

■ HYVE SOLUTIONS CORP p 724
44201 Nobel Dr 94538
Tel (864) 349-4415 *SIC* 7374

INTELLISWIFT SOFTWARE INC p 750
2201 Walnut Ave Ste 180 94538
Tel (510) 490-9240 *SIC* 7379

KINETIC SYSTEMS INC p 820
48400 Fremont Blvd 94538
Tel (510) 683-6000 *SIC* 1711

▲ LAM RESEARCH CORP p 841
4650 Cushing Pkwy 94538
Tel (510) 572-0200 *SIC* 3674

MAGPIE INTERNET COMMUNICATIONS CORP p 897
2762 Bayview Ct 94538
Tel (510) 344-1200 *SIC* 4813 7379 7374

MATTSON TECHNOLOGY INC p 921
47131 Bayside Pkwy 94538
Tel (510) 657-5900 *SIC* 3559

■ MICROGENICS CORP p 962
46500 Kato Rd 94538
Tel (510) 979-9147 *SIC* 2834

MILESTONE TECHNOLOGIES INC p 969
3101 Skyway Ct 94539
Tel (510) 651-2454 *SIC* 7373 7374

NEW UNITED MOTOR MANUFACTURING INC p 1033
45500 Fremont Blvd 94538
Tel (510) 498-5500 *SIC* 3714 3711

NITINOL DEVICES AND COMPONENTS INC p 1045
47533 Westinghouse Dr 94539
Tel (510) 683-2000 *SIC* 3841 5047

NITTO AMERICAS INC p 1045
48500 Fremont Blvd 94538
Tel (510) 445-5400
SIC 2672 3589 5162 5065

OPLINK COMMUNICATIONS LLC p 1089
46335 Landing Pkwy 94538
Tel (510) 933-7200 *SIC* 3661 4899

PENGUIN COMPUTING INC p 1128
45800 Northport Loop W 94538
Tel (415) 954-2800 *SIC* 5045 7379

PETERSEN-DEAN INC p 1138
39300 Civic Center Dr # 300 94538
Tel (707) 469-7470 *SIC* 1761

PHIHONG USA CORP p 1142
47800 Fremont Blvd 94538
Tel (510) 445-0100 *SIC* 5045 3572

PJS LUMBER INC p 1153
45055 Fremont Blvd 94538
Tel (510) 743-5300 *SIC* 5031 5051

QUANTA COMPUTER USA INC p 1198
45630 Northport Loop E 94538
Tel (510) 226-1371 *SIC* 5045

QUANTA SERVICE INCORPORATION p 1198
45630 Northport Loop E 94538
Tel (510) 226-1000 *SIC* 5045

▲ QUANTENNA COMMUNICATIONS INC p 1198
3450 W Warren Ave 94538
Tel (510) 743-2260 *SIC* 3674

▲ SIGMA DESIGNS INC p 1321
47467 Fremont Blvd 94538
Tel (510) 897-0200 *SIC* 3674

SOLAREDGE TECHNOLOGIES INC p 1338
47505 Seabridge Dr 94538
Tel (877) 360-5292 *SIC* 3629

SONIC MANUFACTURING TECHNOLOGIES INC p 1340
47951 Westinghouse Dr 94539
Tel (510) 580-8500 *SIC* 3672

▲ SYNNEX CORP p 1415
44201 Nobel Dr 94538
Tel (510) 656-3333 *SIC* 5734

■ SYSCO SAN FRANCISCO INC p 1418
5900 Stewart Ave 94538
Tel (510) 226-3000 *SIC* 5141 5147 5142

TEAMSTER BENEFIT TRUST p 1430
39420 Liberty St Ste 260 94538
Tel (510) 796-4676 *SIC* 8631 6411

■ TR MANUFACTURING LLC p 1468
45757 Northport Loop W 94538
Tel (510) 657-3850 *SIC* 3699

■ U-HAUL CO OF CALIFORNIA p 1497
44511 S Grimmer Blvd 94538
Tel (800) 528-0463 *SIC* 7513 7519 4226

UNIGEN CORP p 1503
45388 Warm Springs Blvd 94539
Tel (510) 668-2088 *SIC* 3674 3572

VINTNERS DISTRIBUTORS INC p 1558
41805 Albrae St 94538
Tel (510) 657-9150 *SIC* 5541

WALTERS & WOLF GLASS CO p 1574
41450 Boscell Rd 94538
Tel (510) 490-1115 *SIC* 1793

WASHINGTON HOSPITAL HEALTHCARE SYSTEM p 1578
2000 Mowry Ave 94538
Tel (510) 797-3342 *SIC* 8062

FRENCH CAMP, CA

HEALTH PLAN OF SAN JOAQUIN p 675
7751 S Manthey Rd 95231
Tel (209) 942-6300 *SIC* 6324

SAN JOAQUIN HOSPITAL p 1277
500 W Hospital Rd 95231
Tel (209) 468-6000 *SIC* 8062

FRESNO, CA

AGI PUBLISHING INC p 35
1850 N Gateway Blvd # 152 93727
Tel (559) 251-8888 *SIC* 2741

BRITZ FERTILIZERS INC p 214
3265 W Figarden Dr 93711
Tel (559) 448-8000 *SIC* 5191

BRITZ INC p 214
3265 W Figarden Dr 93711
Tel (559) 448-8000 *SIC* 0723 0724 0191

BRIX GROUP INC p 215
838 N Laverne Ave 93727
Tel (559) 457-4700 *SIC* 5065 5013

CALIFORNIAS VALUED TRUST p 242
520 E Herndon Ave 93720
Tel (559) 437-2960 *SIC* 6733

CALPINE CONTAINERS INC p 242
6425 N Palm Ave Ste 104 93704
Tel (559) 519-7199
SIC 5113 5085 2441 2448

CENTRAL UNIFIED SCHOOL DISTRICT p 280
4605 N Polk Ave 93722
Tel (559) 274-4700 *SIC* 8211

CHARLIES ENTERPRISES p 290
1888 S East Ave 93721
Tel (559) 445-8600 *SIC* 5148

CHUKCHANSI INDIAN HOUSING AUTHORITY p 305
8080 N Palm Ave Ste 207 93711
Tel (559) 370-4141 *SIC* 9531

CITY OF FRESNO p 315
2600 Fresno St 93721
Tel (559) 621-7001 *SIC* 9111

COMMUNITY HOSPITALS OF CENTRAL CALIFORNIA p 349
2823 Fresno St 93721
Tel (559) 459-6000 *SIC* 8069

COMMUNITY MEDICAL CENTER p 349
2823 Fresno St 93721
Tel (559) 459-6000 *SIC* 8062 8011 8051

DAIRYAMERICA INC p 409
7815 N Palm Ave Ste 250 93711
Tel (559) 251-0992 *SIC* 5143

DIBUDUO & DEFENDIS INSURANCE BROKERS LLC p 437
6873 N West Ave 93711
Tel (559) 432-0222 *SIC* 6411

DIOCESE OF FRESNO EDUCATION CORP p 440
1550 N Fresno St 93703
Tel (559) 488-7400 *SIC* 8211 8661

DONAGHY SALES INC p 450
2363 S Cedar Ave 93725
Tel (559) 486-0901 *SIC* 5181

ELECTRIC MOTOR SHOP p 484
253 Fulton St 93721
Tel (559) 233-1153
SIC 5063 1731 7694 7922

ELECTRONIC RECYCLERS INTERNATIONAL INC p 485
7815 N Palm Ave Ste 140 93711
Tel (800) 884-8466 *SIC* 4953

FRESH PACIFIC FRUIT AND VEGETABLE INC p 579
7650 N Palm Ave Ste 103 93711
Tel (559) 432-3500 *SIC* 5148

FRESNO BEVERAGE CO INC p 579
4010 E Hardy Ave 93725
Tel (559) 650-1500 *SIC* 5181

FRESNO COMMUNITY HOSPITAL AND MEDICAL CENTER p 579
2823 Fresno St 93721
Tel (559) 459-6000 *SIC* 8062

FRESNO COUNTY ECONOMIC OPPORTUNITIES COMMISSION p 579
1920 Mariposa Mall # 300 93721
Tel (559) 263-1010 *SIC* 8322 8399

FRESNO COUNTY SUPERINTENDENT OF SCHOOLS p 579
1111 Van Ness Ave 93721
Tel (559) 265-3000 *SIC* 8211

FRESNO TRUCK CENTER p 579
2727 E Central Ave 93725
Tel (559) 486-4310
SIC 5511 5521 5531 5012 5013 6159

FRESNO UNIFIED SCHOOL DISTRICT p 579
2309 Tulare St 93721
Tel (559) 457-3000 *SIC* 8211

INTEGRATED AGRIBUSINESS PROFESSIONALS COOPERATIVE INC p 749
7108 N Fresno St Ste 150 93720
Tel (559) 440-1980 *SIC* 5191

JAMES G PARKER INSURANCE ASSOCIATES p 776
1753 E Fir Ave 93720
Tel (559) 222-7722 *SIC* 6411

JEM RESTAURANT MANAGEMENT CORP p 782
312 W Cromwell Ave 93711
Tel (559) 435-9648 *SIC* 5812

LYONS MAGNUS INC p 888
3158 E Hamilton Ave 93702
Tel (559) 268-5966 *SIC* 2033 2026 2087

MICHAEL CADILLAC INC p 960
50 W Bullard Ave 93704
Tel (559) 431-6000 *SIC* 5511

OLAM AMERICAS INC p 1080
25 Union Pl Ste 3 93720
Tel (559) 447-1390 *SIC* 0723

OLAM WEST COAST INC p 1080
205 E Rver Pk Cir Ste 310 93720
Tel (559) 447-1390 *SIC* 2034

PACIFIC TRELLIS FRUIT LLC p 1106
5108 E Clinton Way # 108 93727
Tel (559) 255-5437 *SIC* 5148

PAPE TRUCKS INC p 1112
2892 E Jensen Ave 93706
Tel (559) 268-4344 *SIC* 5511

PARAGON INDUSTRIES INC p 1113
4285 N Golden State Blvd 93722
Tel (559) 275-5000 *SIC* 5211 5032

PENNY NEWMAN GRAIN CO p 1131
2691 S Cedar Ave 93725
Tel (559) 499-0691 *SIC* 5153

PIONEER FARM EQUIPMENT CO p 1150
2589 N A Fresno Drste 109 93727
Tel (559) 253-0526 *SIC* 5083

PRODUCERS DAIRY FOODS INC p 1179
250 E Belmont Ave 93701
Tel (559) 264-6583 *SIC* 5142 5143

RICHARD HEATH & ASSOCIATES INC p 1232
590 W Locust Ave Ste 103 93650
Tel (559) 447-7000 *SIC* 8748

▲ S&W SEED CO p 1263
7108 N Fresno St Ste 380 93720
Tel (559) 884-2535 *SIC* 0139 0723

SAINT AGNES MEDICAL CENTER p 1268
1303 E Herndon Ave 93720
Tel (559) 450-3000 *SIC* 8062

SALADINOS INC p 1271
3325 W Figarden Dr 93711
Tel (559) 271-3700 *SIC* 5141 2099

SCRIP ADVANTAGE INC p 1294
4273 W Richert Ave # 110 93722
Tel (559) 320-0052 *SIC* 7389

STATE CENTER COMMUNITY COLLEGE DISTRICT p 1380
1525 E Weldon Ave 93704
Tel (559) 226-0720 *SIC* 8222

■ VALLEY HEALTHCARE CENTER LLC p 1541
4840 E Tulare Ave 93727
Tel (559) 251-7161 *SIC* 8051

W M LYLES CO p 1569
1210 W Olive Ave 93728
Tel (951) 973-7393 *SIC* 1623

ZACKY & SONS POULTRY LLC p 1641
2020 S East Ave 93721
Tel (559) 443-2700 *SIC* 2015

FRIANT, CA

TABLE MOUNTAIN CASINO p 1420
8184 Table Mountain Rd 93626
Tel (559) 822-2485 *SIC* 7999

FULLERTON, CA

ALTURA COMMUNICATION SOLUTIONS LLC p 63
1335 S Acacia Ave 92831
Tel (714) 948-8400 *SIC* 5065

ALTURA HOLDINGS LLC p 63
1335 S Acacia Ave 92831
Tel (714) 948-8400 *SIC* 6722

BI TECHNOLOGIES CORP p 180
4200 Bonita Pl 92835
Tel (714) 447-2300 *SIC* 3679 5065 8711

CONSOLIDATED AEROSPACE MANUFACTURING LLC p 359
1425 S Acacia Ave 92831
Tel (714) 521-5060 *SIC* 3812

FULLERTON JOINT UNION HIGH SCHOOL DISTRICT EDUCATIONAL FOUNDATION p 584
1051 W Bastanchury Rd 92833
Tel (714) 870-2800 *SIC* 8211

LUBERSKI INC p 883
310 N Harbor Blvd Ste 205 92832
Tel (714) 680-3447 *SIC* 5144 5143

LUBERSKI INC p 883
310 N Harbor Blvd Ste 205 92832
Tel (714) 680-3447 *SIC* 5144

PROFESSIONAL PLASTICS INC p 1180
1810 E Valencia Dr 92831
Tel (714) 446-6500 *SIC* 5162

PULMUONE FOODS USA INC p 1191
2315 Moore Ave 92833
Tel (714) 578-2800 *SIC* 5149 5141 2075

PULMUONE USA INC p 1191
2315 Moore Ave 92833
Tel (714) 578-2800 *SIC* 5149 5141 2075

SASCO p 1283
2750 Moore Ave 92833
Tel (714) 870-0217 *SIC* 1731

SASCO ELECTRIC INC p 1283
2750 Moore Ave 92833
Tel (714) 870-0217 *SIC* 7373 1731

ST JUDE HOSPITAL p 1369
101 E Valencia Mesa Dr 92835
Tel (714) 871-3280 *SIC* 8062

■ THALES-RAYTHEON SYSTEMS CO LLC p 1446
1801 Hughes Dr 92833
Tel (714) 446-3118 *SIC* 5065

VIELE & SONS INC p 1556
1820 E Valencia Dr 92831
Tel (714) 446-1686 *SIC* 5141

VISTA PAINT CORP p 1562
2020 E Orangethorpe Ave 92831
Tel (714) 680-3800 *SIC* 5231 2851

GALT, CA

BUILDING MATERIAL DISTRIBUTORS INC p 225
225 Elm Ave 95632
Tel (209) 745-3001 *SIC* 5031

GARDEN GROVE, CA

BATTERY SYSTEMS INC p 160
12322 Monarch St 92841
Tel (310) 667-9320 *SIC* 5013

GARDEN GROVE UNIFIED SCHOOL DISTRICT p 591
10331 Stanford Ave 92840
Tel (714) 663-6000 *SIC* 8211

GKN AEROSPACE TRANSPARENCY SYSTEMS INC p 613
12122 Western Ave 92841
Tel (714) 893-7531
SIC 3089 3231 3827 3728 3081 2821

KENNETH CORP p 811
12601 Garden Grove Blvd 92843
Tel (714) 537-5160 *SIC* 8062

■ MICROSEMI CORP - ANALOG MIXED SIGNAL GROUP p 962
11861 Western Ave 92841
Tel (714) 898-8121 *SIC* 3674

■ MODERNHEALTH SPECIALTY (PX) LLC p 981
7373 Lincoln Way 92841
Tel (818) 769-0313 *SIC* 5912

ROMAN CATHOLIC DIOCESE OF ORANGE p 1249
13280 Chapman Ave 92840
Tel (714) 282-3000 *SIC* 8661

SOUTHLAND INDUSTRIES p 1351
7390 Lincoln Way 92841
Tel (800) 613-6240 *SIC* 1711

■ TELETRAC INC p 1435
7391 Lincoln Way 92841
Tel (714) 897-0877 *SIC* 4899

TOMS TRUCK CENTER INC p 1460
12221 Monarch St 92841
Tel (714) 835-5070 *SIC* 5511 5012 7538

GARDENA, CA

ACME METALS & STEEL SUPPLY INC p 18
14930 S San Pedro St 90248
Tel (310) 329-2263 *SIC* 5051

■ AHF-DUCOMMUN INC p 36
268 E Gardena Blvd 90248
Tel (310) 380-5390
SIC 3728 3812 3769 3469

APRO LLC p 100
17311 S Main St 90248
Tel (310) 323-3992 *SIC* 5541

BEST CONTRACTING SERVICES INC p 177
19027 S Hamilton Ave 90248
Tel (310) 328-6969 *SIC* 1761

CAPSTAN CALIFORNIA INC p 251
16100 S Figueroa St 90248
Tel (310) 366-5999 *SIC* 3499

CONSTRUCTION PROTECTIVE SERVICES INC p 361
436 W Walnut St 90248
Tel (800) 257-5512 *SIC* 7381 7382

CPS SECURITY SOLUTIONS INC p 388
436 W Walnut St 90248
Tel (310) 818-1030 *SIC* 7381

■ DESIGNED METAL CONNECTIONS INC p 432
14800 S Figueroa St 90248
Tel (310) 323-6200 *SIC* 3451

■ DUCOMMUN AEROSTRUCTURES INC p 459
268 E Gardena Blvd 90248
Tel (310) 380-5390 *SIC* 3724 3812 3728

GARDENA HOSPITAL LP p 591
1145 W Redondo Beach Blvd 90247
Tel (310) 532-4200 *SIC* 8062 8322 8011

IMPRESA AEROSPACE LLC p 735
344 W 157th St 90248
Tel (310) 354-1200 *SIC* 3728 3444

J & M SALES INC p 770
15001 S Figueroa St 90248
Tel (310) 324-9962
SIC 5651 6531 5311 5611 5621

JK IMAGING LTD p 786
17239 S Main St 90248
Tel (310) 755-6848 *SIC* 5043

JONATHAN LOUIS INTERNATIONAL LTD p 792
544 W 130th St 90248
Tel (323) 770-3330 *SIC* 2512

NATIONAL STORES INC p 1016
15001 S Figueroa St 90248
Tel (310) 324-9962 *SIC* 5651

NISSIN FOODS (USA) CO INC p 1044
2001 W Rosecrans Ave 90249
Tel (310) 327-8478 *SIC* 2098 2038

PAUL R BRILES INC p 1121
1700 W 132nd St 90249
Tel (310) 323-6222 *SIC* 3452

PRIME WHEEL CORP p 1175
17705 S Main St 90248
Tel (310) 516-9126 *SIC* 3714

RAPID GAS INC p 1208
17311 S Main St 90248
Tel (310) 323-3992 *SIC* 5541

■ SOS METALS INC p 1341
201 E Gardena Blvd 90248
Tel (310) 217-8848 *SIC* 5093 5051

SOUTHWEST OFFSET PRINTING CO INC p 1352
13650 Gramercy Pl 90249
Tel (310) 965-9154 *SIC* 2752

TIRECO INC p 1455
500 W 190th St Ste 100 90248
Tel (310) 767-7990 *SIC* 5014 5013 5051

UNITED EL SEGUNDO INC p 1508
17311 S Main St 90248
Tel (310) 323-3992 *SIC* 5172 6531

WSA GROUP INC p 1628
19208 S Vermont Ave 200 90248
Tel (310) 743-3000 *SIC* 7381 7349

Z GALLERIE LLC p 1640
1855 W 139th St 90249
Tel (800) 358-8288 *SIC* 5719 5999

GILROY, CA

CHRISTOPHER RANCH LLC p 303
305 Bloomfield Ave 95020
Tel (408) 847-1100 *SIC* 0139 0175

SAINT LOUISE HOSPITAL p 1270
9400 N Name Uno 95020
Tel (408) 848-2000 *SIC* 8062

GLENDALE, CA

4 OVER LLC p 3
5900 San Fernando Rd D 91202
Tel (818) 246-1170 *SIC* 2759 7336

ACCO ENGINEERED SYSTEMS INC p 15
6265 San Fernando Rd 91201
Tel (818) 244-6571 *SIC* 1711 7623

AMERICAN REALTY ASSOCIATES INC p 78
801 N Brand Blvd Ste 800 91203
Tel (818) 545-1152 *SIC* 6282

▲ AVERY DENNISON CORP p 137
207 N Goode Ave Fl 6 91203
Tel (626) 304-2000
SIC 2672 3081 3497 2678

■ CALMAT CO p 242
500 N Brand Blvd Ste 500 91203
Tel (818) 553-8821
SIC 2951 1442 1429 3273 6512 6552

■ CIGNA HEALTHCARE OF CALIFORNIA INC p 306
400 N Brand Blvd Ste 400 91203
Tel (818) 500-6262 *SIC* 6324

CITY OF GLENDALE p 315
141 N Glendale Ave Fl 2 91206
Tel (818) 548-2085 *SIC* 9111

▲ DINEEQUITY INC p 440
450 N Brand Blvd 91203
Tel (818) 240-6055 *SIC* 5812 6794

DMA CLAIMS INC p 445
330 N Brand Blvd Ste 230 91203
Tel (323) 342-6800 *SIC* 6411

■ DWA HOLDINGS LLC p 463
1000 Flower St 91201
Tel (818) 695-5000 *SIC* 7812

■ EMPLOYERS COMPENSATION INSURANCE CO INC p 494
500 N Brand Blvd Ste 800 91203
Tel (818) 549-4600 *SIC* 6411

FOREST LAWN MEMORIAL-PARK ASSOCIATION p 567
1712 S Glendale Ave 91205
Tel (323) 254-3131 *SIC* 5992 6553 7261

FRONT PORCH COMMUNITIES AND SERVICES - CASA DE MANANA LLC p 580
800 N Brand Blvd Fl 19 91203
Tel (818) 729-8100 *SIC* 8059 8051

GLENAIR INC p 615
1211 Air Way 91201
Tel (818) 247-6000 *SIC* 3643 3825 3357

GLENDALE ADVENTIST MEDICAL CENTER INC p 615
1509 Wilson Ter 91206
Tel (818) 409-8000 *SIC* 8062 8093 8011

GLENDALE COMMUNITY COLLEGE DIST p 615
1500 N Verdugo Rd 91208
Tel (818) 240-1000 *SIC* 8222

GLENDALE MEMORIAL HEALTH CORP p 615
1420 S Central Ave 91204
Tel (818) 502-1900 *SIC* 8062

GLENDALE UNIFIED SCHOOL DISTRICT p 615
223 N Jackson St 91206
Tel (818) 241-3111 *SIC* 8211

GLENOAKS CONVALESCENT HOSPITAL (LP) p 615
409 W Glenoaks Blvd 91202
Tel (818) 240-4300 *SIC* 8062

HOWROYD-WRIGHT EMPLOYMENT AGENCY INC p 714
327 W Broadway 91204
Tel (818) 240-8688 *SIC* 7361

MITSUBISHI KAGAKU IMAGING CORP p 978
655 N Central Ave # 1550 91203
Tel (818) 837-8100 *SIC* 5044 3699

NESTLE HOLDINGS INC p 1026
800 N Brand Blvd 91203
Tel (818) 549-6000
SIC 2023 2032 2038 2033 2064 2026

NESTLE USA INC p 1027
800 N Brand Blvd 91203
Tel (818) 549-6000
SIC 2023 2033 2064 2047 2099 2032

■ OLD REPUBLIC TITLE CO p 1081
101 N Brand Blvd Ste 1400 91203
Tel (818) 240-1936 *SIC* 6361

▲ PS BUSINESS PARKS INC p 1187
701 Western Ave 91201
Tel (818) 244-8080 *SIC* 6798

▲ PUBLIC STORAGE p 1190
701 Western Ave 91201
Tel (818) 244-8080 *SIC* 6798 4225

ROYALTY CAPITAL INC p 1254
1010 N Central Ave 91202
Tel (888) 210-0332 *SIC* 4213

SEGA ENTERTAINMENT USA INC p 1300
600 N Brand Blvd Fl 5 91203
Tel (310) 217-9500 *SIC* 7993

SOUTHERN CALIFORNIA PRESBYTERIAN HOMES p 1347
516 Burchett St 91203
Tel (818) 247-0420 *SIC* 8051

■ STEWART TITLE OF CALIFORNIA INC p 1389
525 N Brand Blvd Ste 100 91203
Tel (818) 291-9145 *SIC* 6361

TSC HOLDINGS INC p 1489
800 N Brand Blvd 91203
Tel (818) 549-6000 *SIC* 2038

■ WALT DISNEY IMAGINEERING RESEARCH & DEVELOPMENT INC p 1574
1401 Flower St 91201
Tel (818) 544-6500
SIC 7819 8712 1542 8741 8711

WFG NATIONAL TITLE INSURANCE CO p 1603
700 N Brand Blvd Ste 1100 91203
Tel (818) 476-4000 *SIC* 6361

WHOLE FOODS MARKET SOPAC p 1607
207 N Goode Ave 91203
Tel (818) 501-8484 *SIC* 5411

■ YP.COM LLC p 1639
611 N Brand Blvd Fl 3 91203
Tel (818) 937-5500 *SIC* 7389

GLENDORA, CA

ANTHONY MANUFACTURING CORP p 94
145 N Grand Ave 91741
Tel (626) 963-9311 *SIC* 3432

ARMSTRONG GARDEN CENTERS INC p 111
2200 E Route 66 Ste 200 91740
Tel (626) 914-1091 *SIC* 5261 0782

CALPORTLAND CO p 243
2025 E Financial Way 91741
Tel (626) 852-6200 *SIC* 3241 3273 5032

CITRUS COMMUNITY COLLEGE DISTRICT p 311
1000 W Foothill Blvd 91741
Tel (626) 963-0323 *SIC* 8222

FOOTHILL HOSPITAL-MORRIS L JOHNSTON MEMORIAL p 564
250 S Grand Ave 91741
Tel (626) 857-3145 *SIC* 8062

NATIONAL HOT ROD ASSOCIATION p 1013
2035 E Financial Way 91741
Tel (626) 914-4761 *SIC* 7948 2711 2741

RIDA INTERNATIONAL INVESTMENTS LLC p 1234
1774 S Barranca Ave 91740
Tel (626) 712-4776 *SIC* 6221

TAIHEIYO CEMENT USA INC p 1421
2025 E Fincl Way Ste 200 91741
Tel (626) 852-6200 *SIC* 3241 3273

UNITED CALIFORNIA DISCOUNT CORP p 1506
2200 E Route 66 Ste 102 91740
Tel (909) 394-5400 *SIC* 6153

GOLETA, CA

CURVATURE LLC p 402
6500 Hollister Ave # 210 93117
Tel (805) 964-9975 *SIC* 4813

▲ DECKERS OUTDOOR CORP p 421
250 Coromar Dr 93117
Tel (805) 967-7611 *SIC* 3021 2389 2339

DIRECT RELIEF p 441
27 S La Patera Ln 93117
Tel (805) 964-4767 *SIC* 8322

■ FLIR COMMERCIAL SYSTEMS INC p 557
6769 Hollister Ave # 100 93117
Tel (805) 690-6685 *SIC* 5065 3699

▲ INOGEN INC p 745
326 Bollay Dr 93117
Tel (805) 562-0500 *SIC* 3841 3842

INTEGRATED PROCUREMENT TECHNOLOGIES INC p 749
7230 Hollister Ave 93117
Tel (805) 682-0842 *SIC* 5088 5065

KARL STORZ IMAGING INC p 804
175 Cremona Dr 93117
Tel (805) 845-3617 *SIC* 3841

SANTA BARBARA TRANSPORTATION CORP p 1280
6414 Hollister Ave 93117
Tel (805) 681-8355 *SIC* 4151 4141

TECOLOTE RESEARCH INC p 1432
420 S Fairview Ave # 201 93117
Tel (805) 571-6366 *SIC* 8742 8731

GOSHEN, CA

KRUSE INVESTMENT CO INC p 830
31120 W St 93227
Tel (559) 302-1000 *SIC* 6799

WESTERN MILLING LLC p 1599
31120 West St 93227
Tel (559) 302-1000 *SIC* 5191

GRANADA HILLS, CA

MAYERLING GROUP INC p 923
12065 Creekview Rd 91344
Tel (323) 707-4748 *SIC* 8742

GRASS VALLEY, CA

GRASS VALLEY INC p 632
125 Crown Point Ct 95945
Tel (530) 478-3000 *SIC* 3663

■ GRASS VALLEY USA LLC p 632
125 Crown Point Ct 95945
Tel (800) 547-8949 *SIC* 3651 3661 3663

SIERRA NEVADA MEMORIAL-MINERS HOSPITAL p 1321
155 Glasson Way 95945
Tel (530) 274-6000 *SIC* 8062

GREENBRAE, CA

MARIN HEALTHCARE DISTRICT p 906
100b Drakes Landing Rd 94904
Tel (415) 464-2090 *SIC* 8062

GROVER BEACH, CA

COMPASS HEALTH INC p 351
200 S 13th St Ste 208 93433
Tel (805) 474-7010 *SIC* 8059

GUADALUPE, CA

■ APIO INC p 97
4575 W Main St 93434
Tel (800) 454-1355 *SIC* 2099 0723

GUERNEVILLE, CA

F KORBEL & BROS p 522
13250 River Rd 95446
Tel (707) 824-7000 *SIC* 2084 0172

HANFORD, CA

ADVENTIST MEDICAL CENTER-HANFORD p 27
115 Mall Dr 93230
Tel (559) 582-9000 *SIC* 8011

BUFORD OIL CO INC p 224
9925 8 3/4 Ave 93230
Tel (559) 582-9028 *SIC* 5172

CENTRAL VALLEY GENERAL HOSPITAL p 280
1025 N Douty St 93230
Tel (559) 583-2100 *SIC* 8062

COUNTY OF KINGS p 379
1400 W Lacey Blvd 93230
Tel (559) 582-0326 *SIC* 9111

HANFORD COMMUNITY HOSPITAL p 657
450 Greenfield Ave 93230
Tel (559) 582-9000 *SIC* 8062

KINGS COUNTY OFFICE OF EDUCATION p 820
1144 W Lacey Blvd 93230
Tel (559) 589-7026 *SIC* 9411

HAWAIIAN GARDENS, CA

HAWAIIAN GARDENS CASINO p 669
21520 Pioneer Blvd # 305 90716
Tel (562) 860-5887 *SIC* 7999

HAWTHORNE, CA

EUREKA RESTAURANT GROUP LLC p 512
12101 Crenshaw Blvd 90250
Tel (310) 331-8233 *SIC* 5812 8741

GOLD STANDARD ASSET MANAGEMENT LLC p 620
5155 W Rosecrans Ave # 238 90250
Tel (310) 644-3600 *SIC* 8741

LITHOGRAPHIX INC p 870
12250 Crenshaw Blvd 90250
Tel (323) 770-1000 *SIC* 2752 2759

■ OSI OPTOELECTRONICS INC p 1096
12525 Chadron Ave 90250
Tel (310) 978-0516
SIC 3674 3827 3812 3672

▲ OSI SYSTEMS INC p 1097
12525 Chadron Ave 90250
Tel (310) 978-0516 *SIC* 3674 3845

SPACE EXPLORATION TECHNOLOGIES CORP p 1354
Rocket Rd 90250
Tel (310) 363-6000 *SIC* 3761

HAYWARD, CA

ALAMEDA ELECTRIC SUPPLY p 44
3875 Bay Center Pl 94545
Tel (510) 786-1400 *SIC* 5063

ALAMEDA NEWSPAPERS INC p 44
22533 Foothill Blvd 94541
Tel (510) 783-6111 *SIC* 2711

■ BERKELEY FARMS LLC p 175
25500 Clawiter Rd 94545
Tel (510) 265-8600 *SIC* 5143 2026 0241

CALIFORNIA STATE UNIVERSITY EAST BAY p 241
25800 Carlos Bee Blvd Sa 94542
Tel (510) 885-3500 *SIC* 8221 9411

COLUMBUS FOODS LLC p 342
30977 San Antonio St 94544
Tel (510) 921-3400 *SIC* 2011 5143 5147

■ DOW CHEMICAL CO p 453
25500 Whitesell St 94545
Tel (510) 786-0100 *SIC* 2819 2821

GCO INC p 595
27750 Industrial Blvd 94545
Tel (510) 786-3333 *SIC* 5074 5087

GILLIG LLC p 612
25800 Clawiter Rd 94545
Tel (510) 785-1500 *SIC* 3713

HAYWARD SISTERS HOSPITAL p 670
27200 Calaroga Ave 94545
Tel (510) 264-4000 *SIC* 8062

HAYWARD UNIFIED SCHOOL DISTRICT p 670
24411 Amador St 94544
Tel (510) 784-2600 *SIC* 8211

HEAT AND CONTROL INC p 679
21121 Cabot Blvd 94545
Tel (510) 259-0500 *SIC* 3556 7699

▲ IMPAX LABORATORIES INC p 734
30831 Huntwood Ave 94544
Tel (510) 240-6000 *SIC* 2834

■ MARCHI THERMAL SYSTEMS INC p 905
3108 Diablo Ave 94545
Tel (510) 300-1500 *SIC* 3826

METRIC EQUIPMENT SALES INC p 954
25841 Industrial Blvd # 200 94545
Tel (510) 264-0887
SIC 5065 5084 7359 3825

MORGAN ADVANCED CERAMICS INC p 988
2425 Whipple Rd 94544
Tel (510) 491-1100 *SIC* 2899 3251 3264

MYGRANT GLASS CO INC p 1004
3271 Arden Rd 94545
Tel (510) 785-4360 *SIC* 5013

PACIFIC CHEESE CO INC p 1104
21090 Cabot Blvd 94545
Tel (510) 784-8800 *SIC* 5143

PLASTIKON INDUSTRIES INC p 1155
688 Sandoval Way 94544
Tel (510) 400-1010 *SIC* 3544 3089

R F MACDONALD CO p 1202
25920 Eden Landing Rd 94545
Tel (510) 784-0110 *SIC* 5084 7699 5074

RJMS CORP p 1239
31010 San Antonio St 94544
Tel (510) 675-0500 *SIC* 5084 5085 7699

SASOL WAX NORTH AMERICA CORP p 1283
3563 Inv Blvd Ste 2 94545
Tel (510) 783-9295 *SIC* 5172 5169

■ SHASTA BEVERAGES INC p 1312
26901 Indl Blvd 94545
Tel (954) 581-0922 *SIC* 2086

■ SKYLAWN p 1330
32992 Mission Blvd 94544
Tel (510) 471-3363 *SIC* 6553 7261

SOLTA MEDICAL INC p 1339
25881 Industrial Blvd 94545
Tel (510) 786-6946 *SIC* 3845

ST ROSE HOSPITAL p 1373
27200 Calaroga Ave 94545
Tel (510) 264-4000 *SIC* 8062

▲ ULTRA CLEAN HOLDINGS INC p 1501
26462 Corporate Ave 94545
Tel (510) 576-4400 *SIC* 3674

■ ULTRA CLEAN TECHNOLOGY SYSTEMS AND SERVICE INC p 1501
26462 Corporate Ave 94545
Tel (510) 576-4400 *SIC* 3823

WESTERN HYDRO CORP p 1598
3449 Enterprise Ave 94545
Tel (559) 275-3305 SIC 5084

HEMET, CA

HEMET UNIFIED SCHOOL DISTRICT p 682
1791 W Acacia Ave 92545
Tel (951) 765-5100 SIC 8211

HEMET VALLEY MEDICAL CENTER-EDUCATION p 682
1117 E Devonshire Ave 92543
Tel (951) 652-2811 SIC 8062

PHYSICIANS FOR HEALTHY HOSPITALS INC p 1145
1117 E Devonshire Ave 92543
Tel (951) 652-2811 SIC 8062

HERCULES, CA

▲ BIO-RAD LABORATORIES INC p 183
1000 Alfred Nobel Dr 94547
Tel (510) 724-7000 SIC 3826 3845 2835

HERMOSA BEACH, CA

MARLIN EQUITY PARTNERS LLC p 909
338 Pier Ave 90254
Tel (310) 364-0100 SIC 6282

HESPERIA, CA

ARIZONA PIPE LINE CO p 109
17372 Lilac St 92345
Tel (760) 244-8212 SIC 1623

HESPERIA UNIFIED SCHOOL DISTRICT p 688
15576 Main St 92345
Tel (760) 244-4411 SIC 8211

R E GOODSPEED AND SONS DISTRIBUTING INC p 1202
11211 G Ave 92345
Tel (760) 949-3356 SIC 5171

HIGHLAND, CA

SAN MANUEL INDIAN BINGO & CASINO p 1277
777 San Manuel Blvd 92346
Tel (909) 864-5050 SIC 7999

HILMAR, CA

HILMAR CHEESE CO INC p 694
8901 Lander Ave 95324
Tel (209) 667-6076 SIC 2022

HOLLISTER, CA

■ PACIFIC SCIENTIFIC ENERGETIC MATERIALS CO (CALIFORNIA) p 1105
3601 Union Rd 95023
Tel (831) 637-3731
SIC 2892 2899 3489 3483 3699 3728

SAN BENITO HEALTH CARE DISTRICT p 1275
911 Sunset Dr Ste A 95023
Tel (831) 637-5711 SIC 8062 8051 8059

HOLTVILLE, CA

KEITHLY-WILLIAMS SEEDS INC p 808
420 Palm Ave 92250
Tel (760) 356-5533 SIC 5191 0721 0181

HUGHSON, CA

DUARTE NURSERY INC p 459
1555 Baldwin Rd 95326
Tel (209) 531-0351 SIC 0181

HUNTINGTON BEACH, CA

▲ BJS RESTAURANTS INC p 186
7755 Center Ave Ste 300 92647
Tel (714) 500-2400 SIC 5812

C&D ZODIAC INC p 234
5701 Bolsa Ave 92647
Tel (714) 934-0000 SIC 3728

CAMBRO MANUFACTURING CO INC p 244
5801 Skylab Rd 92647
Tel (714) 848-1555 SIC 3089

CITY OF HUNTINGTON BEACH p 315
2000 Main St 92648
Tel (714) 536-5202 SIC 9199

CONFIE SEGUROS HOLDING CO p 356
7711 Center Ave Ste 200 92647
Tel (714) 252-2649 SIC 6411

CONFIE SEGUROS INC p 356
7711 Center Ave Ste 200 92647
Tel (714) 252-2500 SIC 6411

CUSTOM BUILDING PRODUCTS INC p 403
7711 Center Ave Fl 5 92647
Tel (800) 272-8786 SIC 2891

DRIESSEN AIRCRAFT INTERIOR SYSTEMS INC p 456
17311 Nichols Ln 92647
Tel (714) 861-7300 SIC 3728

FREEWAY INSURANCE SERVICES INC p 577
7711 Center Ave Ste 200 92647
Tel (714) 252-2500 SIC 6411

G & M OIL CO INC p 586
16868 A Ln 92647
Tel (714) 375-4700 SIC 5541

HARBOR DISTRIBUTING LLC p 659
5901 Bolsa Ave 92647
Tel (714) 933-2400 SIC 5181

HUNTINGTON BEACH UNION HIGH SCHOOL DISTRICT p 720
5832 Bolsa Ave 92649
Tel (714) 903-7000 SIC 8211

OCEAN VIEW SCHOOL DISTRICT (INC) p 1073
17200 Pinehurst Ln 92647
Tel (714) 847-2551 SIC 8211

■ QUIKSILVER INC p 1200
5600 Argosy Ave Ste 100 92649
Tel (714) 889-2200
SIC 2329 2339 3949 5136 5137

■ RAINBOW DISPOSAL CO INC p 1205
17121 Nichols Ln 92647
Tel (714) 847-3581 SIC 4953

RELIABLE WHOLESALE LUMBER INC p 1221
7600 Redondo Cir 92648
Tel (714) 848-8222 SIC 5031 2421

STAFF PRO INC p 1374
15272 Jason Cir 92649
Tel (714) 230-7200 SIC 7382 8741

STATCO ENGINEERING & FABRICATORS INC p 1380
7595 Reynolds Cir 92647
Tel (714) 375-6300 SIC 5084 3556

HUNTINGTON PARK, CA

CITIZENS OF HUMANITY LLC p 311
5715 Bickett St 90255
Tel (323) 923-1240 SIC 2339

CROWN POLY INC p 396
5700 Bickett St 90255
Tel (323) 268-1298 SIC 2673

IMPERIAL BEACH, CA

SOUTH BAY UNION SCHOOL DISTRICT p 1342
601 Elm Ave 91932
Tel (619) 628-1600 SIC 8211

IMPERIAL, CA

IMPERIAL IRRIGATION DISTRICT p 734
333 E Barioni Blvd 92251
Tel (800) 303-7756 SIC 4911 4971 4931

INDIO, CA

CABAZON BAND OF MISSION INDIANS p 234
84245 Indio Springs Dr 92203
Tel (760) 342-2593 SIC 9131

EAST VALLEY TOURIST DEVELOPMENT AUTHORITY p 471
84245 Indio Springs Dr 92203
Tel (760) 342-5000 SIC 7999

INGLEWOOD, CA

AFTER-PARTY6 INC p 33
901 W Hillcrest Blvd 90301
Tel (310) 966-4900 SIC 7359

CITY OF INGLEWOOD p 315
1 W Manchester Blvd 90301
Tel (310) 412-5301 SIC 9111

CLASSIC PARTY RENTALS INC p 323
901 W Hillcrest Blvd 90301
Tel (310) 966-4900 SIC 7359

CP OPCO LLC p 387
901 W Hillcrest Blvd 90301
Tel (310) 966-4900 SIC 7299

GENTLE DENTAL SERVICE CORP p 605
9800 S La Cienega Blvd # 800 90301
Tel (310) 765-2400 SIC 8021

GOODMAN FOOD PRODUCTS INC p 624
200 E Beach Ave Fl 1 90302
Tel (310) 674-3180 SIC 2038

INGLEWOOD UNIFIED SCHOOL DISTRICT p 743
401 S Inglewood Ave 90301
Tel (310) 419-2500 SIC 8211

INTERDENT INC p 752
9800 S La Cienega Blvd # 800 90301
Tel (310) 765-2400 SIC 8021

INTERDENT SERVICE CORP p 752
9800 S La Cienega Blvd # 800 90301
Tel (310) 765-2400 SIC 8021

MARVIN ENGINEERING CO INC p 914
261 W Beach Ave 90302
Tel (310) 674-5030 SIC 3728

PRIME HEALTHCARE CENTINELA LLC p 1175
555 E Hardy St 90301
Tel (310) 673-4660 SIC 8062

IRVINE, CA

3 DAY BLINDS LLC p 2
167 Technology Dr 92618
Tel (855) 569-0087 SIC 5719

4G WIRELESS INC p 3
8871 Research Dr 92618
Tel (949) 748-6100 SIC 4812

511 INC p 3
1360 Reynolds Ave Ste 101 92614
Tel (949) 800-1511
SIC 5699 2231 5139 2393

A CLARK/MCCARTHY JOINT VENTURE p 5
18201 Von Karman Ave # 800 92612
Tel (714) 429-9779 SIC 1521

■ ABM FACILITY SERVICES LLC p 11
152 Technology Dr 92618
Tel (949) 330-1555 SIC 8711

ACCENTCARE HOME HEALTH INC p 14
135 Technology Dr Ste 150 92618
Tel (949) 623-1500 SIC 8082

■ ACCLARENT INC p 15
33 Technology Dr 92618
Tel (650) 687-5888 SIC 3841

ADVANTAGE SALES & MARKETING INC p 26
18100 Von Karman Ave # 900 92612
Tel (949) 797-2900 SIC 5141

ADVANTAGE SALES & MARKETING LLC p 26
18100 Von Karman Ave # 900 92612
Tel (949) 797-2900 SIC 5141 8732

AGILITY HOLDINGS INC p 35
310 Commerce Ste 250 92602
Tel (714) 617-6300 SIC 4731 4213 4214

AGILITY LOGISTICS CORP p 35
240 Commerce 92602
Tel (714) 617-6300
SIC 4731 8742 7372 1381

ALECTO HEALTHCARE SERVICES LLC p 48
16310 Bake Pkwy Ste 200 92618
Tel (323) 938-3161 SIC 8062

ALLERGAN SALES LLC p 53
2525 Dupont Dr 14th 92612
Tel (714) 246-4500 SIC 5122

ALLERGAN SPECIALTY THERAPEUTICS INC p 53
2525 Dupont Dr 92612
Tel (714) 264-4500 SIC 2834

ALLERGAN USA INC p 53
2525 Dupont Dr 92612
Tel (714) 246-4500 SIC 2834

ALLIANCE MEDICAL PRODUCTS INC p 54
9342 Jeronimo Rd 92618
Tel (949) 768-4690 SIC 3841 7819

ALORICA INC p 59
5 Park Plz Ste 1100 92614
Tel (949) 527-4600 SIC 7389

■ ANTECH DIAGNOSTICS INC p 93
17672 Cowan Bldg B 92614
Tel (800) 745-4725 SIC 0742

ARBITECH LLC p 102
15330 Barranca Pkwy 92618
Tel (949) 376-6650 SIC 5045

ASICS AMERICA CORP p 117
80 Technology Dr 92618
Tel (949) 453-8888
SIC 5139 5136 5137 2369 2339 2321

■ ASTRONICS TEST SYSTEMS INC p 122
4 Goodyear 92618
Tel (800) 722-2528 SIC 3825

▲ AUTOBYTEL INC p 133
18872 Macarthur Blvd # 200 92612
Tel (949) 225-4500 SIC 7375

▲ BANC OF CALIFORNIA INC p 149
18500 Von Karman Ave # 1100 92612
Tel (949) 236-5436 SIC 6021

■ BANC OF CALIFORNIA NATIONAL ASSOCIATION p 149
18500 Von Karman Ave 92612
Tel (877) 770-2262 SIC 6035

BDS MARKETING INC p 164
10 Holland 92618
Tel (949) 472-6700 SIC 7311 8743 8732

■ BLIZZARD ENTERTAINMENT INC p 189
16215 Alton Pkwy 92618
Tel (949) 955-1380 SIC 7372 5734 7819

▲ BOOT BARN HOLDINGS INC p 200
15345 Barranca Pkwy 92618
Tel (949) 453-4400 SIC 5661 5641

■ BOOT BARN INC p 200
11251 Beech Ave Ste 200 92618
Tel (714) 288-8181 SIC 5699 5661

BORAL ROOFING LLC p 201
7575 Irvine Center Dr # 100 92618
Tel (949) 756-1605 SIC 1761 3272 3259

BRANDMAN UNIVERSITY p 208
16355 Laguna Canyon Rd 92618
Tel (949) 341-9800 SIC 8221

■ BRER AFFILIATES INC p 210
18500 Von Karman Ave # 400 92612
Tel (949) 794-7900 SIC 6794 6531

■ BRINDERSON LP p 213
19000 Macarthur Blvd # 800 92612
Tel (714) 466-7100 SIC 8711 1629

BROADCOM CORP p 215
5300 California Ave 92617
Tel (949) 926-5000 SIC 3674

BROOKFIELD RELOCATION INC p 217
3333 Michelson Dr # 1000 92612
Tel (949) 794-7900 SIC 6794

BSH HOME APPLIANCES CORP p 222
1901 Main St Ste 600 92614
Tel (949) 440-7100 SIC 3639

BURLEIGH POINT LTD p 227
117 Waterworks Way 92618
Tel (949) 428-3200 SIC 2339 2331 2329

C D LISTENING BAR INC p 232
17822 Gillette Ave Ste A 92614
Tel (949) 225-1170 SIC 5099

▲ CALAMP CORP p 238
15635 Alton Pkwy Ste 250 92618
Tel (949) 600-5600 SIC 3663

▲ CALATLANTIC GROUP INC p 238
15360 Barranca Pkwy 92618
Tel (949) 789-1600
SIC 1531 1521 6162 6541

■ CERADYNE INC p 283
1922 Barranca Pkwy 92606
Tel (714) 549-0421 SIC 3299 3671

■ CERTANCE LLC p 284
141 Innovation Dr 92617
Tel (949) 856-7800 SIC 3572

CITY OF IRVINE p 315
1 Civic Center Plz 92606
Tel (949) 724-6000 SIC 9121 9111

CONCORDIA UNIVERSITY p 355
1530 Concordia 92612
Tel (949) 854-8002 SIC 8221

CONSOLIDATED FIRE PROTECTION LLC p 359
153 Technology Dr Ste 200 92618
Tel (949) 727-3277 SIC 7389

▲ CORELOGIC INC p 369
40 Pacifica Ste 900 92618
Tel (949) 214-1000
SIC 7323 7299 8742 8732

■ CORELOGIC SOLUTIONS LLC p 369
40 Pacifica Ste 900 92618
Tel (949) 214-1000 SIC 7375

CORPORATE RISK HOLDINGS III INC p 372
3349 Michelson Dr Ste 150 92612
Tel (949) 428-5839 SIC 7389

▲ CORVEL CORP p 373
2010 Main St Ste 600 92614
Tel (949) 851-1473 SIC 8741 8011

CREDO 180 CAPITAL PARTNERS p 391
5405 Alton Pkwy 5a 92604
Tel (949) 274-4405 SIC 6282 7373

■ CUMMINS PACIFIC LLC p 401
1939 Deere Ave 92606
Tel (949) 253-6000 SIC 3519 5063 7538

CYBERNET MANUFACTURING INC p 404
5 Holland Ste 201 92618
Tel (949) 600-8000 SIC 3571 3577

CYLANCE INC p 405
18201 Von Karman Ave # 700 92612
Tel (949) 375-3380 SIC 3825 7379

DAHN CORP p 408
18552 Macarthur Blvd # 495 92612
Tel (949) 752-1282 SIC 1531 6531 4225

DELPHI CONNECTION SYSTEMS LLC p 425
30 Corporate Park Ste 303 92606
Tel (949) 458-3100 SIC 3714

DIGIPAS TECHNOLOGIES INC p 439
200 Spectrum Center Dr 92618
Tel (949) 558-0160 SIC 3429 3499 3699

DRAPERS & DAMONS LLC p 455
9 Pasteur Ste 200 92618
Tel (949) 784-3000 SIC 5961 5621 5632

DRYBAR HOLDINGS LLC p 457
125 Technology Dr Ste 150 92618
Tel (310) 776-6330 SIC 6719

EAGLE TOPCO LP p 468
18200 Von Karman Ave 92612
Tel (949) 585-4329 SIC 7372

▲ EDWARDS LIFESCIENCES CORP p 480
1 Edwards Way 92614
Tel (949) 250-2500 SIC 3842

■ EDWARDS LIFESCIENCES LLC p 480
1 Edwards Way 92614
Tel (949) 250-2500 SIC 8011

EGL HOLDCO INC p 481
18200 Von Karman Ave # 1000 92612
Tel (800) 678-7423 SIC 7372

▲ ENDOLOGIX INC p 496
2 Musick 92618
Tel (949) 595-7200 SIC 3841

EXULT INC p 521
121 Innovation Dr Ste 200 92617
Tel (949) 856-8800 SIC 8742

■ FIDELITY NATIONAL TITLE INSURANCE CO p 541
3220 El Camino Real 92602
Tel (949) 622-4600
SIC 6361 8741 6541 6531

FINANCE AMERICA LLC p 542
1901 Main St Ste 150 92614
Tel (949) 440-1000 SIC 6162 6163

FIRST TEAM REAL ESTATE - ORANGE COUNTY p 549
108 Pacifica Ste 300 92618
Tel (888) 236-1943 SIC 6531

FITNESS INTERNATIONAL LLC p 553
3161 Michelson Dr Ste 600 92612
Tel (949) 255-7200 SIC 7991 6794

FOOTHILL / EASTERN TRANSPORTATION CORRIDOR AGENCY p 564
125 Pacifica Ste 100 92618
Tel (949) 754-3400 SIC 1611

FOX HEAD INC p 572
16752 Armstrong Ave 92606
Tel (408) 776-8633 SIC 5136 5137 5961

GATEWAY INC p 594
7565 Irvine Center Dr # 150 92618
Tel (949) 471-7000 SIC 3571 3577

GEM-PACK BERRIES LLC p 598
8 Corporate Park Ste 110 92606
Tel (949) 861-4919 SIC 0171

GENSIA SICOR INC p 604
19 Hughes 92618
Tel (949) 455-4700 SIC 2834 8731

GEORG FISCHER LLC p 606
9271 Jeronimo Rd 92618
Tel (714) 731-8800 SIC 5051 5085

GKK CORP p 613
2355 Main St Ste 220 92614
Tel (949) 250-1500 SIC 8712 8711

GOLDEN STATE FOODS CORP p 621
18301 Von Karman Ave # 1100 92612
Tel (949) 252-2000
SIC 5147 2087 5142 5148 5149

GRAY VESTAR INVESTORS LLC p 632
17622 Armstrong Ave 92614
Tel (949) 863-1171
SIC 2253 2339 2335 2337 3961 2387

▲ HABIT RESTAURANTS INC p 651
17320 Red Hill Ave # 140 92614
Tel (949) 851-8881 SIC 5812

■ HABIT RESTAURANTS LLC p 651
17320 Red Hill Ave # 140 92614
Tel (949) 851-8881 SIC 5812

HAWAII BUSINESS EQUIPMENT INC p 668
2 Musick 92618
Tel (949) 462-6000 SIC 5999 7629 5044

▲ HCP INC p 672
1920 Main St Ste 1200 92614
Tel (949) 407-0700 SIC 6798

HENSEL PHELPS GRANITE HANGAR JOINT VENTURE p 684
18850 Von Kamon 100 92612
Tel (949) 852-0111 SIC 1542 1629

HINES HORTICULTURE INC p 695
12621 Jeffrey Rd 92620
Tel (949) 559-4444 SIC 0181 5261

HIRERIGHT LLC p 695
3349 Michelson Dr Ste 150 92612
Tel (949) 428-5800 SIC 7375 7374

HOAG ORTHOPEDIC INSTITUTE LLC p 698
16250 Sand Canyon Ave 92618
Tel (855) 999-4641 SIC 8011

HORIBA INTERNATIONAL CORP p 706
9755 Research Dr 92618
Tel (949) 250-4811 SIC 3829

HPM CONSTRUCTION LLC p 714
17911 Mitchell S 92614
Tel (949) 474-9170 SIC 1542

HYUNDAI CAPITAL AMERICA p 724
3161 Michelson Dr # 1900 92612
Tel (714) 965-3000 SIC 6141

■ I-FLOW CORP p 725
43 Discovery Ste 100 92618
Tel (800) 448-3569 SIC 3841

▲ IMPAC MORTGAGE HOLDINGS INC p 734
19500 Jamboree Rd 92612
Tel (949) 475-3600 SIC 6798

IN-N-OUT BURGERS p 735
4199 Campus Dr Ste 900 92612
Tel (949) 509-6200 SIC 5812

INFINITE RF HOLDINGS INC p 741
17802 Fitch 92614
Tel (949) 261-1920 SIC 5999 6719

■ INGRAM MICRO INC p 743
3351 Michelson Dr Ste 100 92612
Tel (714) 566-1000 SIC 5045

INTERNATIONAL EDUCATION CORP p 755
16485 Laguna Canyon Rd # 300 92618
Tel (949) 272-7200 SIC 8249

IRVINE APARTMENT COMMUNITIES LP p 765
110 Innovation Dr 92617
Tel (949) 720-5600 SIC 6513 6552 6798

IRVINE RANCH WATER DISTRICT INC p 765
15600 Sand Canyon Ave 92618
Tel (949) 453-5300 SIC 4941 4952

IRVINE UNIFIED SCHOOL DISTICT p 765
5050 Barranca Pkwy 92604
Tel (949) 936-5000 SIC 8211

JAE ELECTRONICS INC p 775
142 Technology Dr Ste 100 92618
Tel (949) 753-2600
SIC 5065 5088 3679 3829 3678

K HOVNANIAN COMPANIES OF CALIFORNIA INC p 798
400 Exchange Ste 200 92602
Tel (949) 222-7700 SIC 1521

KELLEY BLUE BOOK CO INC p 808
195 Technology Dr 92618
Tel (949) 770-7704 SIC 2721

KIA MOTORS AMERICA INC p 816
111 Peters Canyon Rd 92606
Tel (949) 468-4800 SIC 5511 5013 8741

KIMCO STAFFING SERVICES INC p 818
17872 Cowan 92614
Tel (949) 331-1199 SIC 7361

KNOBBE MARTENS OLSON & BEAR LLP p 824
2040 Main St Fl 14 92614
Tel (949) 760-0404 SIC 8111

KOFAX INC p 826
15211 Laguna Canyon Rd 92618
Tel (949) 783-1000 SIC 3577 7371

KOFAX LIMITED p 826
15211 Laguna Canyon Rd 92618
Tel (949) 783-1000 SIC 7372

LIBERTY DENTAL PLAN OF CALIFORNIA INC p 861
340 Commerce Ste 100 92602
Tel (949) 223-0007 SIC 6324

LIFTED RESEARCH GROUP INC p 865
7 Holland 92618
Tel (949) 581-1144 SIC 5136

LINEAGE LOGISTICS HOLDINGS LLC p 868
17911 Von Karman Ave # 400 92614
Tel (800) 678-7271 SIC 4222

LINEAGE LOGISTICS LLC p 868
17911 Von Karman Ave # 400 92614
Tel (800) 678-7271 SIC 4222

LINKSYS LLC p 869
131 Theory 92617
Tel (949) 270-8500 SIC 5065

LOCAL CORP p 872
7555 Irvine Center Dr 92618
Tel (949) 784-0800 SIC 7311

■ LPS REAL ESTATE GROUP INC p 882
2050 Main St Ste 400 92614
Tel (949) 681-4700 SIC 7374

MARUCHAN INC p 913
15800 Laguna Canyon Rd 92618
Tel (949) 789-2300 SIC 2098

▲ MASIMO CORP p 915
52 Discovery 92618
Tel (949) 297-7000 SIC 3845

MAZDA MOTOR OF AMERICA INC p 924
7755 Irvine Center Dr 92618
Tel (949) 727-1990 SIC 5511 5531

■ MEGA BRANDS AMERICA INC p 939
3 Ada Ste 200 92618
Tel (949) 727-9009 SIC 3944

■ MENTOR WORLDWIDE LLC p 943
33 Technology Dr 92618
Tel (800) 636-8678 SIC 3842 3845 3841

MERCHSOURCE LLC p 945
15 Cushing 92618
Tel (949) 900-0900 SIC 5112

■ MESA ENERGY SYSTEMS INC p 951
2 Cromwell 92618
Tel (949) 460-0460 SIC 1711 7623

MIDNITE AIR CORP p 966
2132 Michelson Dr 92612
Tel (310) 330-2300 SIC 4513

■ MISSION ENERGY HOLDING CO p 975
2600 Michelson Dr # 1700 92612
Tel (949) 752-5588 SIC 6719

MOMENTUM TEXTILES LLC p 983
17811 Fitch 92614
Tel (949) 833-8886 SIC 5131 2221

MONTAGE HOTELS & RESORTS LLC p 986
1 Ada Ste 250 92618
Tel (949) 715-5002 SIC 6531

MOTORSPORT AFTERMARKET GROUP INC p 993
17771 Mitchell N Ste A 92614
Tel (949) 440-5500 SIC 3751

MULTI-FINELINE ELECTRONIX INC p 999
8659 Research Dr 92618
Tel (949) 453-6800 SIC 3672

MX HOLDINGS US p 1004
153 Technology Dr Ste 200 92618
Tel (949) 727-3277 SIC 1711 1731 5999

NATIONAL SERVICES GROUP INC p 1016
1682 Langley Ave 92614
Tel (714) 564-7900 SIC 1721

NEUDESIC LLC p 1028
100 Spectrum Center Dr # 1200 92618
Tel (949) 754-4500 SIC 7379

■ NEWPORT CORP p 1038
1791 Deere Ave 92606
Tel (949) 863-3144
SIC 3821 3699 3827 3826

NIKKEN INTERNATIONAL INC p 1043
2 Corporate Park Ste 100 92606
Tel (949) 789-2000 SIC 5199

■ OPTUMRX INC p 1091
2300 Main St 92614
Tel (714) 825-3600 SIC 6324 6321

▲ OPUS BANK p 1091
19900 Macarthur Blvd # 1200 92612
Tel (949) 250-9800 SIC 6029

ORANGE COUNTY FIRE AUTHORITY p 1092
1 Fire Authority Rd 92602
Tel (714) 573-6000 SIC 9224

OWL EDUCATION AND TRAINING INC p 1100
2465 Campus Dr 92612
Tel (949) 797-2000 SIC 8331

PACIFIC DENTAL SERVICES INC p 1104
17000 Red Hill Ave 92614
Tel (714) 845-8500 SIC 8021 6794

PACIFIC PHARMA INC p 1105
18600 Von Karman Ave 92612
Tel (714) 246-4600 SIC 5122

▲ PACIFIC PREMIER BANCORP INC p 1105
17901 Von Karman Ave 92614
Tel (949) 864-8000 SIC 6022

■ PACIFIC PREMIER BANK p 1105
17901 Von Karman Ave 92614
Tel (714) 431-4000 SIC 6531

PACIFIC TRUST BANK p 1106
18500 Von Karman Ave # 1100 92612
Tel (949) 236-5211 SIC 6035

PARKING CONCEPTS INC p 1116
12 Mauchly Ste I 92618
Tel (949) 753-7525 SIC 6531

PETRO-DIAMOND INC p 1139
1100 Main St Fl 2 92614
Tel (949) 553-0112 SIC 5172

POOL WATER PRODUCTS p 1161
17872 Mitchell N Ste 250 92614
Tel (949) 756-1666 SIC 5091 2899 2812

PRINTRONIX LLC p 1177
15345 Barranca Pkwy 92618
Tel (714) 368-2300 SIC 3577

PROOVE MEDICAL LABORATORIES INC p 1183
15326 Elton Pkwy 92618
Tel (949) 427-5303 SIC 8071

PRUDENTIAL OVERALL SUPPLY p 1187
1661 Alton Pkwy 92606
Tel (949) 250-4855 SIC 7218

■ QUADION LLC p 1196
17651 Armstrong Ave 92614
Tel (714) 546-0994 SIC 6282

QUALITY CUSTOM DISTRIBUTION SERVICES INC p 1197
18301 Von Karman Ave 92612
Tel (949) 252-2000 SIC 5087 7319

▲ QUALITY SYSTEMS INC p 1197
18111 Von Karman Ave # 700 92612
Tel (949) 255-2600 SIC 7372 7373

RED.COM INC p 1216
34 Parker 92618
Tel (949) 206-7900 SIC 3861

■ RELS LLC p 1222
40 Pacifica Ste 900 92618
Tel (949) 214-1000 SIC 6531 7323

▲ RESOURCES CONNECTION INC p 1227
17101 Armstrong Ave 92614
Tel (714) 430-6400 SIC 8742 7389 8721

ROLAND DGA CORP p 1247
15363 Barranca Pkwy 92618
Tel (949) 727-2100 SIC 5045 8741

ROYALTY CARPET MILLS INC p 1254
17111 Red Hill Ave 92614
Tel (949) 474-4000 SIC 2273

RYZE SYNTHETICS PORT ARTHUR LLC p 1261
20 Pacifica Ste 1010 92618
Tel (310) 200-2081 SIC 1311

SABRA HEALTH CARE REIT INC p 1264
18500 Von Karman Ave # 550 92612
Tel (949) 255-7100 SIC 6798

SAGE SOFTWARE HOLDINGS INC p 1267
6561 Irvine Center Dr 92618
Tel (866) 530-7243 SIC 7372 7371

SAN JOAQUIN HILLS TRANSPORTATION CORRIDOR AGENCY p 1277
125 Pacifica Ste 100 92618
Tel (949) 754-3400 SIC 1611

■ SAND CANYON CORP p 1278
7595 Irvine Center Dr # 100 92618
Tel (949) 727-9425 SIC 6163 6162

SARES REGIS GROUP p 1282
18802 Bardeen Ave 92612
Tel (949) 756-5959 SIC 6552

SEGA OF AMERICA INC p 1300
6400 Oak Cyn Ste 100 92618
Tel (415) 806-0169 SIC 3999 5092

SENIOR MBK LIVING LLC p 1304
4 Park Plz Ste 400 92614
Tel (949) 242-1400 SIC 8322

SENIOR SILVERADO LIVING INC p 1304
6400 Oak Cyn Ste 200 92618
Tel (949) 240-7200 SIC 8059

■ SHEPLERS INC p 1315
15345 Barranca Pkwy 92618
Tel (316) 946-3835
SIC 5699 5661 5961 5651 5632 5611

SHIMANO AMERICAN CORP p 1316
1 Holland 92618
Tel (949) 951-5003 SIC 5091

SMILE BRANDS GROUP INC p 1333
100 Spectrum Center Dr # 1500 92618
Tel (714) 668-1300 SIC 8741 8021

SOLUTIONS 2 GO LLC p 1339
111 Theory Ste 250 92617
Tel (949) 825-7700 SIC 5092

SOUTH COAST BAKING LLC p 1343
1722 Kettering 92614
Tel (949) 851-9654 SIC 2052 5149

▲ SPECTRUM GROUP INTERNATIONAL INC p 1357
1063 Mcgaw Ave Ste 250 92614
Tel (949) 748-4800 SIC 7389 5094 5944

■ SPECTRUM NUMISMATICS INTERNATIONAL INC p 1357
1063 Mcgaw Ave Ste 250 92614
Tel (949) 955-1250 SIC 5094

ST JOHN KNITS INC p 1367
17522 Armstrong Ave 92614
Tel (949) 863-1171 SIC 2339 2253 2389

ST JOHN KNITS INTERNATIONAL INC p 1367
17622 Armstrong Ave 92614
Tel (949) 863-1171 SIC 2339

ST JOSEPH HEALTH SYSTEM p 1368
3345 Michelson Dr Ste 100 92612
Tel (949) 381-4000 SIC 8082 8741

STEADFAST INCOME REIT INC p 1384
18100 Von Karman Ave # 500 92612
Tel (949) 852-0700 SIC 6798

■ SUN HEALTHCARE GROUP INC p 1400
18831 Von Karman Ave # 400 92612
Tel (949) 255-7100 SIC 8011 8322

SYNERON INC p 1415
3 Goodyear Ste A 92618
Tel (949) 716-6670 SIC 3845

SYNOPTEK INC p 1415
19520 Jamboree Rd Ste 110 92612
Tel (949) 241-8600 SIC 7379

■ SYSCO NEWPORT MEAT CO p 1417
16691 Hale Ave 92606
Tel (949) 399-4200 SIC 5147 5142

■ TACO BELL CORP p 1421
1 Glen Bell Way 92618
Tel (949) 863-4500 SIC 5812 6794

■ TALON THERAPEUTICS INC p 1423
157 Technology Dr 92618
Tel (949) 788-6700 SIC 2834 8731

TCT MOBILE (US) INC p 1428
25 Edelman Ste 200 92618
Tel (949) 892-2990 SIC 5999 5065

TEN-X LLC p 1436
1 Mauchly 92618
Tel (949) 859-2777 SIC 6531

TEVA PARENTERAL MEDICINES INC p 1441
19 Hughes 92618
Tel (949) 455-4700 SIC 2834

THOMAS GALLAWAY CORP p 1448
100 Spectrum Center Dr # 700 92618
Tel (949) 716-9500 SIC 7371 5045

▲ TILLYS INC p 1453
10 Whatney 92618
Tel (949) 609-5599 SIC 5651 5661

TOPAC USA INC p 1460
9740 Irvine Blvd 92618
Tel (949) 462-6000 SIC 5044

TOSHIBA AMERICA BUSINESS SOLUTIONS INC p 1462
9740 Irvine Blvd 92618
Tel (949) 462-6000 SIC 5044

TOSHIBA AMERICA ELECTRONIC COMPONENTS INC p 1462
9740 Irvine Blvd Ste D700 92618
Tel (949) 462-7700
SIC 3651 3631 3674 3679 5065 5064

TOSHIBA BUSINESS SOLUTIONS (USA) INC p 1462
9740 Irvine Blvd 92618
Tel (949) 462-6000 SIC 7629 5044 5999

TRACE3 INC p 1468
7565 Irvine Center Dr # 200 92618
Tel (949) 333-1801 SIC 8742

▲ TRI POINTE GROUP INC p 1476
19540 Jamboree Rd Ste 300 92612
Tel (949) 438-1400 SIC 1531

■ TRI POINTE HOMES INC p 1476
19520 Jamboree Rd Ste 300 92612
Tel (949) 438-1400 SIC 1531

TRIMARAN POLLO PARTNERS LLC p 1480
3333 Michelson Dr 92612
Tel (949) 399-2000 SIC 5812

TROPITONE FURNITURE CO INC p 1484
5 Marconi 92618
Tel (949) 595-2000 SIC 2514 2522

TUTTLE-CLICK INC p 1493
41 Auto Center Dr 92618
Tel (949) 472-7400 SIC 5511

UNITED AGRICULTURAL ASSOCIATION EMP WELFARE BENE PLTR p 1506
54 Corporate Park 92606
Tel (949) 975-1424 SIC 8699

UNITED EDUCATION INSTITUTE p 1508
16485 Laguna Canyon Rd # 300 92618
Tel (949) 272-7200 SIC 8249

UNIVERSITY OF CALIFORNIA IRVINE p 1520
510 Aldrich Hall 92697
Tel (949) 824-8343 SIC 8221 9411

VICTOR INSTRUMENTS INC p 1555
50 Bunsen 92618
Tel (949) 855-0337 SIC 5122 5047

VICTORY INTERNATIONAL GROUP LLC p 1556
9800 Irvine Center Dr 92618
Tel (949) 407-5888 SIC 5092

VISION SOLUTIONS INC p 1561
15300 Barranca Pkwy # 100 92618
Tel (949) 253-6500 SIC 7371 7373

VIZIO INC p 1563
39 Tesla 92618
Tel (949) 428-2525 SIC 3651

■ WELLS FARGO DEALER SERVICES INC p 1590
23 Pasteur 92618
Tel (949) 727-1002 SIC 6141

▲ WESTERN DIGITAL CORP p 1598
3355 Michelson Dr Ste 100 92612
Tel (949) 672-7000 SIC 3572

■ WESTERN DIGITAL TECHNOLOGIES p 1598
3355 Michelson Dr Ste 100 92612
Tel (949) 672-7000 SIC 3572

WESTERN GROWERS ASSURANCE TRUST p 1598
17620 Fitch 92614
Tel (800) 777-7898 SIC 6331

WET SEAL LLC p 1603
7555 Irvine Center Dr 92618
Tel (949) 699-3900 SIC 5621 5632 5961

■ WORLD OF JEANS & TOPS p 1625
10 Whatney 92618
Tel (949) 609-5599 SIC 5651

■ YARD HOUSE RESTAURANTS LLC p 1635
7700 Irvine Center Dr # 300 92618
Tel (800) 336-5336 SIC 5812

IRWINDALE, CA

NELLSON NUTRACEUTICAL INC p 1025
5801 Ayala Ave 91706
Tel (626) 812-6522 SIC 2064

NELLSON NUTRACEUTICAL LLC p 1025
5801 Ayala Ave 91706
Tel (626) 812-6522 SIC 5499

PACIFIC NATIONAL GROUP p 1105
2392 Bateman Ave 91010
Tel (626) 357-4400 SIC 1542

R-RANCH MARKET INC p 1203
13985 Live Oak Ave 91706
Tel (626) 814-2900 SIC 5411

READY PAC FOODS INC p 1213
4401 Foxdale St 91706
Tel (626) 856-8686 SIC 2099 5148

READY PAC PRODUCE INC p 1213
4401 Foxdale St 91706
Tel (800) 800-4088 SIC 2099 5148

WESTLAKE DISTRIBUTORS INC p 1601
5301 Rivergrade Rd # 200 91706
Tel (213) 624-8676 SIC 5148

JACKSON, CA

JACKSON RANCHERIA CASINO & HOTEL p 774
12222 New York Ranch Rd 95642
Tel (209) 223-1677
SIC 7999 5812 7011 5813

JURUPA VALLEY, CA

JURUPA UNIFIED SCHOOL DISTRICT p 797
4850 Pedley Rd 92509
Tel (951) 360-4100 SIC 8211

PAVEMENT RECYCLING SYSTEMS INC p 1122
10240 San Sevaine Way 91752
Tel (951) 682-1091 SIC 5093 1611

KENTFIELD, CA

MARIN COMMUNITY COLLEGE DISTRICT p 906
835 College Ave 94904
Tel (415) 457-8811 SIC 8222 8221

MARIN GENERAL HOSPITAL p 906
250 Bon Air Rd 94904
Tel (415) 925-7000 SIC 8062 8011

KERMAN, CA

HALL MANAGEMENT CORP p 654
759 S Madera Ave 93630
Tel (559) 846-7382 SIC 8741

KING CITY, CA

L A HEARNE CO p 833
512 Metz Rd 93930
Tel (831) 385-5441
SIC 5191 0723 5699 4214 2048 5261

KINGSBURG, CA

KINGSBURG APPLE PACKERS INC p 821
10363 Davis Ave 93631
Tel (559) 897-5132 SIC 5148

SUN-MAID GROWERS OF CALIFORNIA p 1401
13525 S Bethel Ave 93631
Tel (559) 897-6235 SIC 5149

■ SUNBRIDGE CARE ENTERPRISES WEST LLC p 1401
1101 Stroud Ave 93631
Tel (559) 897-5881 SIC 8051

LA CANADA FLINTRIDGE, CA

ALLEN LUND CO INC p 53
4529 Angeles Crest Hwy 91011
Tel (818) 790-8412 SIC 4731

ALLEN LUND CO LLC p 53
4529 Angeles Crest Hwy # 300 91011
Tel (818) 790-1110 SIC 4731

■ NASA/JET PROPULSION LABORATORY INC p 1008
4800 Oak Grove Dr 91011
Tel (818) 354-4321 SIC 9661

LA HABRA, CA

CORPORATE PERSONNEL NETWORK INC p 372
3552 Green Ave Ste 200 90631
Tel (562) 493-1503 SIC 7363

INNOVATIVE STORE SYSTEMS INC p 745
1351 S Beach Blvd Ste L 90631
Tel (562) 947-4101 SIC 2542

LA JOLLA, CA

COPLEY PRESS INC p 368
7776 Ivanhoe Ave 92037
Tel (858) 454-0411 SIC 7383 2711 7011

JC RESORTS LLC p 780
533 Coast Blvd S 92037
Tel (858) 605-2700 SIC 8741 7992 7991

LADEKI RESTAURANT GROUP p 837
7596 Eads Ave Ste 200 92037
Tel (858) 454-2222 SIC 8741

NATIONAL UNIVERSITY p 1016
11355 N Torrey Pines Rd 92037
Tel (858) 642-8000 SIC 8221

▲ PICO HOLDINGS INC p 1146
7979 Ivanhoe Ave Ste 300 92037
Tel (888) 389-3222 SIC 6531

PRICE FAMILY CHARITABLE FUND p 1174
7979 Ivanhoe Ave Ste 520 92037
Tel (858) 551-2327 SIC 8699

SALK INSTITUTE FOR BIOLOGICAL STUDIES SAN DIEGO CALIFORNIA p 1273
10010 N Torrey Pines Rd 92037
Tel (858) 453-4100 SIC 8731

SANFORD BURNHAM PREBYS MEDICAL DISCOVERY INSTITUTE p 1279
10901 N Torrey Pines Rd 92037
Tel (858) 795-5000 SIC 8733

SCHAETZEL CENTER-SCRIPPS MEMORIAL HOSPITAL p 1286
9890 Genesee Ave 92037
Tel (858) 626-7712 SIC 8062

U C SAN DIEGO FOUNDATION p 1497
9500 Gilman Dr 92093
Tel (858) 534-1032 SIC 8699

UNIVERSITY OF CALIFORNIA SAN DIEGO p 1520
9500 Gilman Dr 92093
Tel (858) 534-2230 SIC 8221 9411

LA MESA, CA

GROSSMONT HOSPITAL CORP p 641
5555 Grossmont Center Dr 91942
Tel (619) 740-6000 SIC 8062

GROSSMONT HOSPITAL FOUNDATION p 641
5555 Grossmont Center Dr 91942
Tel (619) 740-4200 SIC 8399

LA MESA-SPRING VALLEY SCHOOL DISTRICT p 835
4750 Date Ave 91942
Tel (619) 668-5700 SIC 8211

RISK MANAGEMENT STRATEGIES INC p 1236
8530 La Mesa Blvd Ste 200 91942
Tel (619) 281-1100 SIC 8748

LA MIRADA, CA

ATV INC p 129
14407 Alondra Blvd 90638
Tel (562) 977-8565 SIC 5531 7538

BIOLA UNIVERSITY INC p 184
13800 Biola Ave 90639
Tel (562) 903-6000 SIC 8221

CALIFORNIA BEES INC p 239
14381 Industry Cir 90638
Tel (714) 228-1999 SIC 5149

ET HORN CO p 467
16050 Canary Ave 90638
Tel (714) 523-8050 SIC 5169

KATANA RACING INC p 804
14407 Alondra Blvd 90638
Tel (562) 977-8565 SIC 5013 5014

LIVING SPACES FURNITURE LLC p 871
14501 Artesia Blvd 90638
Tel (714) 523-2000 SIC 5712 5021

MAKITA USA INC p 899
14930 Northam St 90638
Tel (714) 522-8088 SIC 5072

TOMARCO CONTRACTOR SPECIALTIES INC p 1459
14848 Northam St 90638
Tel (714) 523-1771 SIC 5072

LA PALMA, CA

ATLANTIC RICHFIELD CO INC p 127
4 Centerpointe Dr Ste 200 90623
Tel (800) 333-3991 SIC 5541 1321 2911

INNOVATION INSTITUTE LLC p 744
1 Centerpointe Dr Ste 200 90623
Tel (714) 735-3750 SIC 8099

LA PUENTE, CA

ATHENS DISPOSAL CO INC p 124
14048 Valley Blvd 91746
Tel (626) 336-3636 SIC 4953

CACIQUE DISTRIBUTORS US p 236
14923 Proctor Ave 91746
Tel (626) 961-3399 SIC 5143

LA QUINTA, CA

DESERT SANDS UNIFIED SCHOOL DISTRICT SCHOOL BUILDING CORP p 432
47950 Dune Palms Rd 92253
Tel (760) 771-8567 SIC 8211

KSL RECREATION MANAGEMENT OPERATIONS LLC p 831
50905 Avenida Bermudas 92253
Tel (760) 564-8000 SIC 7992 7011

LA VERNE, CA

UNIVERSITY OF LA VERNE p 1522
1950 3rd St 91750
Tel (909) 593-3511 SIC 8221

LADERA RANCH, CA

STRATEGIC STORAGE TRUST INC p 1392
111 Corporate Dr Ste 120 92694
Tel (949) 429-6600 SIC 6798

LAFAYETTE, CA

BELL-CARTER FOODS INC p 170
3742 Mt Diablo Blvd 94549
Tel (925) 284-5933 SIC 2033

FRANCES MARY ACCESSORIES INC p 573
3732 Mt Diablo Blvd # 260 94549
Tel (925) 962-2111 SIC 3171

FRESH CONNECTION p 578
3722 Mt Diablo Blvd 94549
Tel (925) 299-9939 SIC 5148

SUTTER EAST BAY MEDFNDTN p 1410
3687 Mt Diablo Blvd # 200 94549
Tel (510) 204-6622 SIC 8641

LAGUNA BEACH, CA

LAGUNA WOODS VILLAGE p 838
24351 El Toro Rd 92653
Tel (949) 597-4267 SIC 6531

PAULS TV LLC p 1122
900 Glenneyre St 92651
Tel (949) 596-8800 SIC 5064

LAGUNA HILLS, CA

MANCHA DEVELOPMENT CO LLC p 901
24422 Avenida De La Carlo 92653
Tel (951) 271-4100 SIC 5812

SADDLEBACK MEMORIAL MEDICAL CENTER p 1265
24451 Health Center Dr 92653
Tel (949) 837-4500
SIC 8062 8011 8093 8099 8071 8069

LAKE ELSINORE, CA

LAKE ELSINORE UNIFIED SCHOOL DISTRICT p 839
545 Chaney St 92530
Tel (951) 253-7000 SIC 8211

LAKE FOREST, CA

APRIA HEALTHCARE GROUP INC p 100
26220 Enterprise Ct 92630
Tel (949) 639-2000 SIC 8082

APRIA HEALTHCARE LLC p 100
26220 Enterprise Ct 92630
Tel (949) 616-2606 SIC 5047 7352 5999

■ ARB INC p 102
26000 Commercentre Dr 92630
Tel (949) 598-9242 SIC 1629 1623

■ DEL TACO LLC p 423
25521 Commercentre Dr # 200 92630
Tel (949) 462-9300 SIC 5812

■ DEL TACO HOLDINGS INC p 423
25521 Commercentre Dr # 200 92630
Tel (949) 462-7324 SIC 5812

▲ DEL TACO RESTAURANTS INC p 423
25521 Commercentre Dr # 200 92630
Tel (949) 462-9300 SIC 5812 6794

INSIGHT HEALTH SERVICES HOLDINGS CORP p 746
26250 Entp Ct Ste 100 92630
Tel (949) 282-6000 SIC 8071

INSULECTRO p 747
20362 Windrow Dr Ste 100 92630
Tel (949) 587-3200 SIC 5065

PARSONS GOVERNMENT SERVICES INC p 1118
25531 Commercentre Dr 92630
Tel (949) 768-8161 SIC 8731

REFRIGERATION SUPPLIES DISTRIBUTOR p 1218
26021 Atlantic Ocean Dr 92630
Tel (949) 380-7878 SIC 5078 5075

SCHNEIDER ELECTRIC SOFTWARE LLC p 1288
26561 Rancho Pkwy S 92630
Tel (949) 727-3200 SIC 7373

US CRITICAL LLC p 1531
6 Orchard Ste 150 92630
Tel (800) 884-8945 SIC 3572

■ VADNAIS TRENCHLESS SERVICES INC p 1538
26000 Commercentre Dr 92630
Tel (858) 550-1460 SIC 1623 1622

WONDERWARE CORP p 1622
26561 Rancho Pkwy S 92630
Tel (949) 727-3200 SIC 5045

LAKESIDE, CA

BARONA RESORT & CASINO p 156
1932 Wildcat Canyon Rd 92040
Tel (619) 443-2300 SIC 7011

E M P INTERIORS INC p 466
9902 Channel Rd 92040
Tel (619) 443-7034 SIC 1742

EAGLEBURGMANN KE INC p 468
10038 Marathon Pkwy 92040
Tel (619) 562-6083 SIC 3441

STANDARD DRYWALL INC p 1376
9902 Channel Rd 92040
Tel (619) 443-7034 SIC 1742

LANCASTER, CA

■ AMERICAN MEDICAL RESPONSE OF SOUTHERN CALIFORNIA p 76
1055 W Avenue J 93534
Tel (661) 945-9310 SIC 4119

ANTELOPE VALLEY COMMUNITY COLLEGE DISTRICT p 93
3041 W Avenue K 93536
Tel (661) 722-6300 SIC 8222 8221

ANTELOPE VALLEY HOSPITAL AUXILIARY p 93
1600 W Avenue J 93534
Tel (661) 949-5000 SIC 8062

ANTELOPE VALLEY UNION HIGH SCHOOL DISTRICT p 93
44811 Sierra Hwy 93534
Tel (661) 948-7655 SIC 8211

CARPETERIA FLOORING CENTERS LLC p 260
42212 10th St W Ste 2a 93534
Tel (661) 951-2200 SIC 5713

H W HUNTER INC p 651
1130 Auto Mall Dr 93534
Tel (661) 948-8411 SIC 5511 7538

LANCASTER SCHOOL DISTRICT p 841
44711 Cedar Ave 93534
Tel (661) 948-4661 SIC 8211

Q C S BUILDING SERVICES INC p 1194
41619 Palermo Ct 93536
Tel (661) 267-6211 SIC 7349

LARKSPUR, CA

NORTH COAST MORTGAGE CO p 1052
80 E Sir Francis Drake Bl 94939
Tel (415) 461-2070 SIC 6162

LATHROP, CA

CALIFORNIA NATURAL PRODUCTS p 240
15789 Mckinley Ave 95330
Tel (209) 249-1616 SIC 2099 8731 3612

LEMOORE, CA

SANTA ROSA INDIAN COMMUNITY OF SANTA ROSA RANCHERIA p 1281
16835 Alkali Dr 93245
Tel (559) 924-1278 SIC 9131

TACHI PALACE HOTEL & CASINO p 1421
17225 Jersey Ave 93245
Tel (559) 924-7751 SIC 7011

LINCOLN, CA

JBR INC p 779
1731 Aviation Blvd 95648
Tel (916) 258-8000 SIC 2095 2099

LINDEN, CA

LINDEN UNIFIED SCHOOL DISTRICT p 868
18527 E Highway 26 95236
Tel (209) 887-3894 SIC 8211

MID VALLEY AGRICULTURAL SERVICES INC p 963
16401 E Highway 26 95236
Tel (209) 931-7600 SIC 5191

LIVERMORE, CA

ACCESS INFORMATION MANAGEMENT SHARED SERVICES LLC p 14
6818 Patterson Pass Rd A 94550
Tel (925) 461-5352 SIC 7375

AERO PRECISION INDUSTRIES LLC p 30
201 Lindbergh Ave 94551
Tel (925) 579-5327 SIC 5088

ARCHITECTURAL GLASS & ALUMINUM CO INC p 105
6400 Brisa St 94550
Tel (925) 583-2460
SIC 5051 1793 1791 3442

BUFFINGTON & ASSOCIATES INC p 224
5775 Las Positas Rd 94551
Tel (925) 583-1600 SIC 3423

DAVEY TREE SURGERY CO p 415
2617 S Vasco Rd 94550
Tel (925) 443-1723 SIC 0783

FABCO AUTOMOTIVE CORP p 523
151 Lawrence Dr 94551
Tel (925) 245-4100 SIC 3714

FABCO AUTOMOTIVE CORP p 523
151 Lawrence Dr 94551
Tel (925) 454-9500 SIC 3714

▲ FORMFACTOR INC p 567
7005 Southfront Rd 94551
Tel (925) 290-4000 SIC 3674

H - INVESTMENT CO p 649
6999 Southfront Rd 94551
Tel (925) 245-4300 SIC 5031

HOSKIN & MUIR INC p 708
6611 Preston Ave Ste C 94551
Tel (925) 373-1135 *SIC* 5031

HOSPITAL COMMITTEE FOR LIVERMORE-PLEASANTON AREAS p 709
1111 E Stanley Blvd 94550
Tel (925) 447-7000 *SIC* 8741

JOHN L SULLIVAN INVESTMENTS INC p 789
6200 Northfront Rd 94551
Tel (916) 969-5911 *SIC* 5511 7538

LILJA CORP p 866
229 Rickenbacker Cir 94551
Tel (925) 454-9544 *SIC* 1541

LIVERMORE VALLEY JOINT UNIFIED SCHOOL DISTRICT p 871
685 E Jack London Blvd 94551
Tel (925) 606-3200 *SIC* 8211

▲ MCGRATH RENTCORP p 929
5700 Las Positas Rd 94551
Tel (925) 606-9200 *SIC* 7359 5084

PACKAGING INNOVATORS CORP p 1106
6650 National Dr 94550
Tel (925) 371-2000 *SIC* 5113 2653 3993

▲ PERFORMANT FINANCIAL CORP p 1135
333 N Canyons Pkwy # 100 94551
Tel (925) 960-4800 *SIC* 7375

■ PERFORMANT RECOVERY INC p 1135
333 N Canyons Pkwy # 100 94551
Tel (209) 858-3994 *SIC* 7322 8742 7371

PRODUCE EXCHANGE INC p 1179
7407 Southfront Rd 94551
Tel (925) 454-8700 *SIC* 5148

RETRIEVEX ACQUISITION CORP II p 1229
6818 Patterson Pass Rd 94550
Tel (925) 583-0100 *SIC* 4226 7375

RGW CONSTRUCTION INC p 1231
550 Greenville Rd 94550
Tel (925) 606-2400 *SIC* 1611

SIEGESECURE LLC p 1320
111 Lindbergh Ave Ste E 94551
Tel (925) 963-6548 *SIC* 7389

TOPCON POSITIONING SYSTEMS INC p 1461
7400 National Dr 94550
Tel (925) 245-8300
SIC 3829 3625 3823 3699 8713 1794

TRANS WESTERN POLYMERS INC p 1470
7539 Las Positas Rd 94551
Tel (925) 449-7800 *SIC* 2673 5023 3089

UNITED STATES DEPARTMENT OF ENERGY LIVERMORE OFFICE p 1512
7000 East Ave 94550
Tel (925) 422-1100 *SIC* 9611 8731

VALLEYCARE HOSPITAL CORP p 1541
1111 E Stanley Blvd 94550
Tel (925) 447-7000 *SIC* 8011

WENTE BROS p 1592
5565 Tesla Rd 94550
Tel (925) 456-2300 *SIC* 2084 8742

WINE GROUP INC p 1616
4596 Tesla Rd 94550
Tel (925) 456-2500 *SIC* 5921

LIVINGSTON, CA

FOSTER FARMS LLC p 570
1000 Davis St 95334
Tel (970) 874-7503 *SIC* 0252

FOSTER POULTRY FARMS p 570
1000 Davis St 95334
Tel (209) 394-6914
SIC 0254 2015 5812 0173 5191 4212

LODI, CA

CLARK PEST CONTROL OF STOCKTON INC p 322
555 N Guild Ave 95240
Tel (209) 368-7152 *SIC* 7342

■ COTTAGE BAKERY INC p 374
1831 S Stockton St 95240
Tel (209) 334-3616 *SIC* 5149 2051 2053

▲ FARMERS & MERCHANTS BANCORP p 529
111 W Pine St 95240
Tel (209) 367-2300 *SIC* 6022

■ FARMERS & MERCHANTS BANK OF CENTRAL CALIFORNIA p 529
121 W Pine St 95240
Tel (209) 367-2300 *SIC* 6022 6021

HARO & HARO ENTERPRISES INC p 662
115 W Walnut St Ste 4 95240
Tel (209) 334-2035 *SIC* 0761

KNOX & ASSOCIATES LLC p 825
615 Candlewood Ct 95242
Tel (209) 365-1567 *SIC* 8741 5812

LODI MEMORIAL HOSPITAL ASSOCIATION INC p 874
975 S Fairmont Ave 95240
Tel (209) 334-3411 *SIC* 8062

LODI UNIFIED SCHOOL DISTRICT p 874
1305 E Vine St 95240
Tel (209) 331-7000 *SIC* 8211

PACIFIC COAST PRODUCERS p 1104
631 N Cluff Ave 95240
Tel (209) 367-8800 *SIC* 2033

REYNOLDS PACKING CO p 1231
33 E Tokay St 95240
Tel (209) 369-2725 *SIC* 0723 5148 2449

VIENNA CONVALESCENT HOSPITAL INC p 1556
800 S Ham Ln 95242
Tel (209) 368-7141 *SIC* 8059

VINO FARMS LLC p 1558
1377 E Lodi Ave 95240
Tel (209) 334-6975 *SIC* 5182

LOMA LINDA, CA

LOMA LINDA UNIVERSITY p 875
11060 Anderson St 92350
Tel (909) 558-4540 *SIC* 8221

LOMA LINDA UNIVERSITY HEALTH CARE p 875
11370 Anderson St # 3900 92350
Tel (909) 558-2806
SIC 8062 8011 8051 5999

LOMA LINDA UNIVERSITY HEALTH CARE p 875
11175 Campus St 92350
Tel (909) 558-4729 *SIC* 8011

LOMA LINDA UNIVERSITY MEDICAL CENTER p 875
11234 Anderson St 92354
Tel (909) 558-4000
SIC 8062 8011 8051 5999

LOMPOC, CA

DEN-MAT HOLDINGS LLC p 428
1017 W Central Ave 93436
Tel (805) 346-3700 *SIC* 3843

IMERYS MINERALS CALIFORNIA INC p 733
2500 San Miguelito Rd 93436
Tel (805) 736-1221 *SIC* 1499 3295

LOMPOC UNIFIED SCHOOL DISTRICT p 875
1301 N A St 93436
Tel (805) 742-3300 *SIC* 8211

LONG BEACH, CA

ACAPULCO RESTAURANTS INC p 14
4001 Via Oro Ave Ste 200 90810
Tel (310) 513-7538 *SIC* 5812 5813

■ AES ALAMITOS LLC p 31
690 N Studebaker Rd 90803
Tel (562) 493-7891 *SIC* 3621

ALANT CORP p 44
1850 Outer Traffic Cir 90815
Tel (562) 494-1911 *SIC* 5511

ALLIANCE INSPECTION MANAGEMENT LLC p 54
330 Golden Shore Ste 400 90802
Tel (562) 432-5050 *SIC* 6541

AUDIO VISUAL SERVICES GROUP INC p 131
111 Ocean Beach Blvd Ste 1110 90802
Tel (562) 366-0620 *SIC* 7389 7812 7359

BRAGG INVESTMENT CO INC p 207
6251 N Paramount Blvd 90805
Tel (562) 984-2400 *SIC* 7389 7353 1791

BRIGHTON-BEST INTERNATIONAL INC p 213
5855 Obispo Ave 90805
Tel (562) 808-8000 *SIC* 5072

CALIFORNIA CARTAGE CO LLC p 239
2931 Redondo Ave 90806
Tel (562) 427-1143 *SIC* 4226 8741 8721

CALIFORNIA STATE UNIVERSITY LONG BEACH p 241
1250 N Bellflower Blvd 90840
Tel (562) 985-4111 *SIC* 8221 9411

CALIFORNIA STATE UNIVERSITY SYSTEM p 241
401 Golden Shore 90802
Tel (562) 951-4000 *SIC* 8221 9411

CATHOLIC HEALTHCARE WEST SOUTHERN CALIFORNIA p 267
1050 Linden Ave 90813
Tel (562) 491-9000 *SIC* 8062

CITY OF LONG BEACH p 316
333 W Ocean Blvd Fl 10 90802
Tel (562) 570-6450 *SIC* 9111

■ CONTINENTAL GRAPHICS CORP p 363
4060 N Lakewood Blvd 90808
Tel (714) 503-4200
SIC 3724 7371 7372 7374

DENSO PRODUCTS AND SERVICES AMERICAS INC p 429
3900 Via Oro Ave 90810
Tel (310) 834-6352
SIC 5013 7361 5075 3714

■ EARTHTECH (INFRASTRUCTURE) INC p 469
300 Oceangate Ste 700 90802
Tel (562) 951-2000 *SIC* 8711 8712

■ EDISON MATERIAL SUPPLY LLC p 478
125 Elm Ave 90802
Tel (562) 491-2341 *SIC* 5031

EL TORITO RESTAURANTS INC p 483
4001 Via Oro Ave Ste 200 90810
Tel (562) 346-1200 *SIC* 5812

EPSON AMERICA INC p 506
3840 Kilroy Airport Way 90806
Tel (800) 463-7766 *SIC* 3577

FARMERS & MERCHANTS BANK OF LONG BEACH p 529
302 Pine Ave 90802
Tel (562) 437-0011 *SIC* 6022 6029

FOUNDATION PROPERTY MANAGEMENT INC p 571
911 N Studebaker Rd # 100 90815
Tel (562) 257-5100 *SIC* 8742

HARBOR CHEVROLET CORP p 659
3770 Cherry Ave 90807
Tel (562) 426-3341 *SIC* 5511

INTEX RECREATION CORP p 759
4001 Via Oro Ave Ste 210 90810
Tel (310) 549-5400
SIC 5091 5092 5021 3081

IRWIN INDUSTRIES INC p 765
1580 W Carson St 90810
Tel (310) 233-3000
SIC 1629 1731 1796 7353 1542

JVCKENWOOD USA CORP p 798
2201 E Dominguez St 90810
Tel (310) 639-9000 *SIC* 5064

LD PRODUCTS INC p 849
3700 Cover St 90808
Tel (562) 986-6940 *SIC* 5045 2621

LONG BEACH COMMUNITY COLLEGE DISTRICT p 876
4901 E Carson St 90808
Tel (562) 938-5020 *SIC* 8222

LONG BEACH MEMORIAL MEDICAL CENTER p 876
2801 Atlantic Ave Fl 2 90806
Tel (562) 933-2000 *SIC* 8062

LONG BEACH UNIFIED SCHOOL DISTRICT p 876
1515 Hughes Way 90810
Tel (562) 997-8000 *SIC* 8211

M O DION & SONS INC p 889
1543 W 16th St 90813
Tel (714) 540-5535 *SIC* 5172

MAINTENANCE STAFF INC p 898
122 W 8th St 90813
Tel (562) 493-3982 *SIC* 7349

MEMORIAL HEALTH SERVICES - UNIVERSITY OF CALIFORNIA AT IRVINE CENTER FOR HEALTH EDUCATION p 941
2801 Atlantic Ave 90806
Tel (562) 933-2000 *SIC* 8062 8741

MIECO INC p 968
301 E Ocean Blvd Ste 1100 90802
Tel (562) 435-0085 *SIC* 5172 4925

MOFFATT & NICHOL p 982
3780 Kilroy Arprt Way 90806
Tel (562) 590-6500 *SIC* 8711

▲ MOLINA HEALTHCARE INC p 982
200 Oceangate Ste 100 90802
Tel (562) 435-3666 *SIC* 8011 6324

■ MOLINA HEALTHCARE OF CALIFORNIA PARTNER PLAN INC p 982
200 Oceangate Ste 100 90802
Tel (562) 435-3666 *SIC* 6321 8011

MOLINA INFORMATION SYSTEMS LLC p 982
200 Oceangate Ste 100 90802
Tel (562) 435-3666 *SIC* 8011

■ MOLINA INFORMATION SYSTEMS LLC p 982
200 Oceangate Ste 100 90802
Tel (916) 561-8540 *SIC* 6411

■ MOLINA PATHWAYS LLC p 983
200 Oceangate Ste 100 90802
Tel (562) 491-5773 *SIC* 8011

NACA HOLDINGS INC p 1006
5000 Arprt Plz Dr Ste 200 90815
Tel (650) 872-0800 *SIC* 4731

PIERPASS INC p 1147
444 W Ocean Blvd Ste 700 90802
Tel (562) 437-9112 *SIC* 8399 7322

PIONEER ELECTRONICS (USA) INC p 1150
1925 E Dominguez St 90810
Tel (310) 952-2000 *SIC* 5064

PIONEER NORTH AMERICA INC p 1151
2265 E 220th St 90810
Tel (213) 746-6337 *SIC* 5064 3651

PSAV HOLDINGS LLC p 1188
111 W Ocean Blvd Ste 1110 90802
Tel (562) 366-0138 *SIC* 7359

REDBARN PET PRODUCTS INC p 1216
3229 E Spring St Ste 310 90806
Tel (562) 495-7315 *SIC* 5199 2047

RETIREMENT HOUSING FOUNDATION INC p 1229
911 N Studebaker Rd # 100 90815
Tel (562) 257-5100 *SIC* 6531

SALVATION ARMY p 1273
180 E Ocean Blvd Fl 2 90802
Tel (562) 491-8464 *SIC* 8661

SANDERS INDUSTRIES p 1278
3701 E Conant St 90808
Tel (562) 354-2920 *SIC* 2824

SCAN HEALTH PLAN p 1286
3800 Kilroy Airport Way # 100 90806
Tel (562) 989-5100 *SIC* 6324

SCAN HEALTH PLAN ARIZONA p 1286
3800 Kilroy Airport Way # 100 90806
Tel (602) 778-3300 *SIC* 8099

SCAN LONG TERM CARE p 1286
3800 Kilroy Airport Way 90806
Tel (562) 989-5100 *SIC* 8051

SENIOR CARE ACTION NETWORK FOUNDATION p 1303
3800 Kilroy Airport Way 90806
Tel (562) 989-5100 *SIC* 6324

SHIMADZU PRECISION INSTRUMENTS INC p 1316
3645 N Lakewood Blvd 90808
Tel (562) 420-6226 *SIC* 5088 5047 5084

SHOJI JFE TRADE AMERICA INC p 1317
301 E Ocean Blvd Ste 1750 90802
Tel (562) 637-3500 *SIC* 5051

ST MARY MEDICAL CENTER p 1371
1050 Linden Ave 90813
Tel (562) 491-9000 *SIC* 8062

STEARNS CONRAD AND SCHMIDT CONSULTING ENGINEERS INC p 1384
3900 Kilroy Arprt Way # 100 90806
Tel (562) 426-9544 *SIC* 8711 1541 8748

TA CHEN INTERNATIONAL INC p 1420
5855 Obispo Ave 90805
Tel (562) 808-8000 *SIC* 3452 5051

TABC INC p 1420
6375 N Paramount Blvd 90805
Tel (562) 984-3305 *SIC* 3714 3713 3469

TRISTAR INSURANCE GROUP INC p 1482
100 Oceangate Ste 700 90802
Tel (562) 495-6600 *SIC* 6331 8741

TURELK INC p 1492
3700 Santa Fe Ave Ste 200 90810
Tel (310) 835-3736 *SIC* 1542

US EPSON INC p 1531
3840 Kilroy Airport Way 90806
Tel (562) 290-5678 *SIC* 5045 3577

US SKILLSERVE INC p 1533
4115 E Broadway Ste A 90803
Tel (562) 930-0777 *SIC* 8741

VANGUARD LOGISTICS SERVICES (USA) INC p 1543
5000 Airport Plaza Dr 90815
Tel (310) 847-3000 *SIC* 4731

VIRGIN GALACTIC LLC p 1558
4022 E Conant St 90808
Tel (562) 384-4400 *SIC* 4789

W A RASIC CONSTRUCTION CO INC p 1568
4150 Long Beach Blvd 90807
Tel (562) 928-6111 *SIC* 1623

■ XEROX EDUCATION SERVICES LLC p 1631
2277 E 220th St 90810
Tel (310) 830-9847 *SIC* 7374

LOS ALAMITOS, CA

ARROWHEAD PRODUCTS CORP p 113
4411 Katella Ave 90720
Tel (714) 828-7770 *SIC* 3728

■ BLOOMFIELD BAKERS p 190
10711 Bloomfield St 90720
Tel (626) 610-2253 *SIC* 2052 2064

HANSEN AUTO TRANSPORT INC p 658
3552 Green Ave Ste 201 90720
Tel (562) 430-4100 *SIC* 4213

■ LOS ALAMITOS MEDICAL CENTER INC p 878
3751 Katella Ave 90720
Tel (714) 826-6400 *SIC* 8062

MILLIE AND SEVERSON INC p 971
3601 Serpentine Dr 90720
Tel (562) 493-3611 *SIC* 1541

SEVERSON GROUP INC p 1309
3601 Serpentine Dr 90720
Tel (562) 493-3611 *SIC* 1542 1541

TREND OFFSET PRINTING SERVICES INC p 1476
3701 Catalina St 90720
Tel (562) 598-2446 *SIC* 2752

LOS ALTOS HILLS, CA

FOOTHILL-DE ANZA COMMUNITY COLLEGE DISTRICT FINANCING CORP p 564
12345 S El Monte Rd 94022
Tel (650) 949-6100 *SIC* 8222 8221

IDEA TRAVEL CO p 729
13145 Byrd Ln Ste 101 94022
Tel (650) 948-0207 *SIC* 4724

LOS ALTOS, CA

AMERICAN RESTAURANT GROUP INC p 78
4410 El Camino Real # 201 94022
Tel (650) 949-6400 *SIC* 5812 5813

DAVID AND LUCILE PACKARD FOUNDATION p 415
343 2nd St 94022
Tel (650) 948-7658 *SIC* 2515

DAVID AND LUCILE PACKARD FOUNDATION p 415
300 2nd St 94022
Tel (650) 917-7167 *SIC* 8699

▲ DSP GROUP INC p 458
161 S San Antonio Rd # 10 94022
Tel (408) 986-4300 *SIC* 3674 7371

GUILDERY INC p 646
170 State St Ste A 94022
Tel (650) 257-0157 *SIC* 5231

HARMAN MANAGEMENT CORP p 662
199 1st St Ste 212 94022
Tel (650) 941-5681 *SIC* 8741 5812 5046

LOS ANGELES, CA

■ **ABM JANITORIAL SERVICES - SOUTHWEST INC** p 12
5300 S Eastern Ave 90040
Tel (323) 720-4020 *SIC* 7349

■ **ABM PARKING SERVICES INC** p 12
1150 S Olive St Fl 19 90015
Tel (213) 284-7600 *SIC* 7521 7349

■ **ABRAXIS BIOSCIENCE INC** p 12
11755 Wilshire Blvd Fl 20 90025
Tel (310) 883-1300 *SIC* 2834

■ **ABRAXIS BIOSCIENCE LLC** p 12
11755 Wilshire Blvd Fl 20 90025
Tel (800) 564-0216 *SIC* 2834

ADIR INTERNATIONAL LLC p 22
1605 W Olympic Blvd # 405 90015
Tel (213) 639-2100 *SIC* 5311

ADVANCE PAPER BOX CO p 24
6100 S Gramercy Pl 90047
Tel (323) 750-2550 *SIC* 2653 3082

▲ **AECOM** p 28
1999 Avenue Of The Stars # 2600 90067
Tel (213) 593-8000 *SIC* 8711 8712

■ **AECOM E&C HOLDINGS INC** p 28
1999 Avenue Of Ste 2600 90067
Tel (213) 593-8000
SIC 8711 1611 1629 1623 1541 1622

■ **AECOM GLOBAL II LLC** p 28
1999 Avenue Of The Stars 90067
Tel (213) 593-8100 *SIC* 8711 8712 8741

■ **AECOM SERVICES INC** p 28
555 S Flower St Ste 3700 90071
Tel (213) 593-8000 *SIC* 8712 8741 8711

■ **AECOM TECHNICAL SERVICES INC** p 28
300 S Grand Ave Ste 1100 90071
Tel (213) 593-8000
SIC 4953 8748 8742 8711

AERCAP US GLOBAL AVIATION LLC p 30
10250 Constellation Blvd 90067
Tel (310) 788-1999 *SIC* 3721 4581 6159

AG FACILITIES OPERATIONS LLC p 33
6380 Wilshire Blvd # 800 90048
Tel (323) 651-1808 *SIC* 8059

AIDS HEALTHCARE FOUNDATION p 37
6255 W Sunset Blvd Fl 21 90028
Tel (323) 860-5200 *SIC* 5932 8093 5912

▲ **AIR LEASE CORP** p 38
2000 Avenue Of The Stars 1000n 90067
Tel (310) 553-0555 *SIC* 7359 7389

ALS TESTING SERVICES GROUP INC p 61
818 W 7th St Ste 930 90017
Tel (213) 627-8252 *SIC* 5141 5072 5084

AMERICAN APPAREL LLC p 68
747 Warehouse St 90021
Tel (213) 488-0226 *SIC* 2389 2311 2331

AMERICAN CONTRACTORS INDEMNITY CO p 70
601 S Figueroa St # 1600 90017
Tel (213) 330-1309 *SIC* 6399

AMERICAN GOLF CORP p 73
6080 Center Dr Ste 500 90045
Tel (310) 664-4000
SIC 7997 7999 5812 5941 7992

ANSCHUTZ FILM GROUP p 93
1888 Century Park E # 1400 90067
Tel (310) 887-1000 *SIC* 1742

APP WHOLESALE LLC p 97
3686 E Olympic Blvd 90023
Tel (323) 980-8315 *SIC* 5149

ARES MANAGEMENT HOLDINGS LP p 107
2000 Avenue Of The Stars 90067
Tel (310) 201-4100 *SIC* 6211

■ **ARES MANAGEMENT LLC** p 107
2000 Avenue Of The Stars 90067
Tel (310) 201-4100 *SIC* 6799

▲ **ARES MANAGEMENT LP** p 107
2000 Avenue Of The Stars 90067
Tel (310) 201-4100 *SIC* 6282

ARYZTA HOLDINGS IV LLC p 115
6080 Center Dr Ste 900 90045
Tel (310) 417-4700
SIC 2052 2053 2045 2051

ARYZTA LLC p 115
6080 Center Dr Ste 900 90045
Tel (310) 417-4700 *SIC* 2052 2053 2051

ASSOCIATED STUDENTS UCLA p 121
308 Westwood Plz 90095
Tel (310) 825-4321 *SIC* 8399 5942

ATS NORTHEAST TOW INC p 129
2010 N Figueroa St 90065
Tel (323) 342-0342 *SIC* 7549 5012

AUGE MEDIA CORP p 131
2029 Century Park E Fl 14 90067
Tel (310) 739-8000 *SIC* 2741 7812

AURORA CAPITAL PARTNERS LP p 132
10877 Wilshire Blvd # 2100 90024
Tel (310) 551-0101 *SIC* 6726

AUTOMOBILE CLUB OF SOUTHERN CALIFORNIA p 134
2601 S Figueroa St 90007
Tel (213) 741-3686 *SIC* 6411 8699

AVALON APPAREL LLC p 135
2520 W 6th St Ste 101 90057
Tel (323) 581-3511 *SIC* 2361

BALMORAL FUNDS LLC p 149
11150 Santa Monica Blvd 90025
Tel (310) 473-3065 *SIC* 6282

■ **BANK OF HOPE** p 151
3731 Wilshire Blvd # 400 90010
Tel (213) 639-1700 *SIC* 6021

BBCN BANK p 163
3731 Wilshire Blvd # 1000 90010
Tel (213) 251-2222 *SIC* 6021

■ **BCI COCA-COLA BOTTLING CO OF LOS ANGELES** p 164
1334 S Central Ave 90021
Tel (213) 746-5555 *SIC* 2086

BERBERIAN ENTERPRISES INC p 174
5315 Santa Monica Blvd 90029
Tel (323) 460-4646 *SIC* 5411

BERGELECTRIC CORP p 174
5650 W Centinela Ave 90045
Tel (310) 337-1377 *SIC* 1731

BERRY ECLIPSE FARMS LLC p 176
11812 San Vicente Blvd # 250 90049
Tel (310) 207-7879 *SIC* 0171 5148

BEVERLY HILLS BANCORP INC p 179
333 S Grand Ave Ste 4070 90071
Tel (818) 223-8084 *SIC* 6022

BIOMAT USA INC p 184
2410 Lillyvale Ave 90032
Tel (323) 225-2221 *SIC* 8099

BLACKSTONE CONSULTING INC p 188
11726 San Vicente Blvd # 550 90049
Tel (310) 826-4389 *SIC* 8742

▲ **BOINGO WIRELESS INC** p 198
10960 Wilshire Blvd Fl 23 90024
Tel (310) 586-5180 *SIC* 4813

BREITBURN ENERGY PARTNERS LP p 209
707 Wilshire Blvd # 4600 90017
Tel (213) 225-5900 *SIC* 1311

BROWN AND RIDING INSURANCE SERVICES INC p 219
777 S Figueroa St # 2550 90017
Tel (213) 452-7060 *SIC* 6411

CALIFORNIA COMMUNITY FOUNDATION p 239
221 S Figueroa St Ste 400 90012
Tel (213) 413-4130 *SIC* 6732

CALIFORNIA ENDOWMENT p 240
1000 N Alameda St 90012
Tel (800) 449-4149 *SIC* 8399

CALIFORNIA HOSPITAL MEDICAL CENTER FOUNDATION p 240
1401 S Grand Ave 90015
Tel (213) 748-2411 *SIC* 8062

CALIFORNIA STATE UNIVERSITY LOS ANGELES p 241
5151 State University Dr 90032
Tel (323) 343-3000 *SIC* 8221 9411

■ **CALIFORNIA UNITED BANK** p 241
818 W 7th St Ste 220 90017
Tel (213) 430-7000 *SIC* 6022

CALTIUS PARTNERS IV LP p 243
11766 Wilshire Blvd # 850 90025
Tel (310) 996-9585 *SIC* 6282

CANTON FOOD CO INC p 247
750 S Alameda St 90021
Tel (213) 688-7707
SIC 5141 5146 5411 5421 5149 4222

CAP-MPT p 248
333 S Hope St Fl 8 90071
Tel (213) 473-8600 *SIC* 6351

CAPITAL GROUP COMPANIES INC p 249
333 S Hope St Fl 55 90071
Tel (213) 486-9200
SIC 6282 6091 6722 8741

CAPITAL RESEARCH AND MANAGEMENT CO p 250
333 S Hope St Fl 55 90071
Tel (213) 486-9200 *SIC* 6282

CAPITALSOURCE INC p 250
633 W 5th St Ste 33 90071
Tel (213) 443-7700 *SIC* 6159

CAPITOL RECORDS LLC p 251
1750 Vine St 90028
Tel (213) 462-6252 *SIC* 7389 8999

CAPITOL-EMI MUSIC INC p 251
1750b Vine St 90028
Tel (323) 462-6252 *SIC* 3652

CAREER GROUP INC p 254
10100 Santa Monica Blvd # 900 90067
Tel (310) 277-8188 *SIC* 7361

CARPENTERS HEALTH AND WELFARE TRUST FOR p 260
533 S Fremont Ave Ste 410 90071
Tel (213) 386-8590 *SIC* 1751

CARPENTERS SOUTHWEST ADMINISTRATIVE CORP p 260
533 S Fremont Ave 90071
Tel (213) 386-8590 *SIC* 7011

▲ **CATHAY GENERAL BANCORP** p 265
777 N Broadway 90012
Tel (213) 625-4700 *SIC* 6022

■ **CBRE GLOBAL INVESTORS LLC** p 269
515 S Flower St Ste 3100 90071
Tel (213) 683-4200 *SIC* 8742

▲ **CBRE GROUP INC** p 269
400 S Hope St Ste 25 90071
Tel (213) 613-3333 *SIC* 6531 6162 8742

■ **CBRE INC** p 269
400 S Hope St Ste 25 90071
Tel (310) 477-5876 *SIC* 6726 6531

CHA HEALTH SYSTEMS INC p 286
3731 Wilshire Blvd # 850 90010
Tel (213) 487-3211 *SIC* 8011

CHA HOLLYWOOD MEDICAL CENTER LP p 286
1300 N Vermont Ave 90027
Tel (213) 413-3000 *SIC* 8062 8351

CHARLES DREW UNIVERSITY OF MEDICINE AND SCIENCE p 289
1731 E 120th St 90059
Tel (323) 563-4800 *SIC* 8221

CHILDRENS HOSPITAL LOS ANGELES p 299
4650 W Sunset Blvd 90027
Tel (323) 660-2450 *SIC* 8069 8062

CHILDRENS HOSPITAL LOS ANGELES MEDICAL GROUP INC p 299
6430 W Sunset Blvd # 600 90028
Tel (323) 361-2336 *SIC* 8011

CHURCH OF SCIENTOLOGY INTERNATIONAL p 305
6331 Hollywood Blvd # 801 90028
Tel (323) 960-3500 *SIC* 8661

CIMMS INC p 307
3061 Riverside Dr 90039
Tel (323) 674-0203 *SIC* 5812

CITY NATIONAL BANK p 312
555 S Flower St Ste 2500 90071
Tel (310) 888-6000 *SIC* 6021 6022

CITY OF LOS ANGELES p 316
200 N Spring St Ste 303 90012
Tel (213) 978-0600 *SIC* 9111

CLUB ASSIST US LLC p 328
888 W 6th St Ste 300 90017
Tel (213) 388-4333 *SIC* 5013

▲ **COLONY CAPITAL INC** p 338
515 S Flower St Fl 44 90071
Tel (310) 282-8820 *SIC* 6798

CONNEXITY INC p 358
12200 W Olympic Blvd # 300 90064
Tel (310) 571-1235 *SIC* 4813 7383

COUNTY OF LOS ANGELES p 379
500 W Temple St Ste 375 90012
Tel (213) 974-1101 *SIC* 9111

COX CASTLE & NICHOLSON LLP p 386
2029 Cntury Nicholson Llp 90067
Tel (310) 284-2200 *SIC* 8111

CREATIVE ARTISTS AGENCY LLC p 390
2000 Avenue Of The Stars # 100 90067
Tel (424) 288-2000 *SIC* 7922

CREO CAPITAL PARTNERS LLC p 391
12400 Walsh Ave Ste 1100 90066
Tel (310) 230-8600 *SIC* 6726

CRYSTAL STAIRS INC p 397
5110 W Goldleaf Cir # 150 90056
Tel (323) 299-8998 *SIC* 8322

DATA ANALYSIS INC p 413
12655 Beatrice St 90066
Tel (310) 448-6800 *SIC* 6211 2711 7374

DAVALAN SALES INC p 414
1601 E Olympic Blvd # 325 90021
Tel (213) 623-2500 *SIC* 5148

DCX-CHOL ENTERPRISES INC p 419
12831 S Figueroa St 90061
Tel (310) 516-1692 *SIC* 3671

DEARDENS p 420
700 S Main St 90014
Tel (213) 362-9600
SIC 5712 5722 5731 5944

DECURION CORP p 421
120 N Robertson Blvd Fl 3 90048
Tel (310) 659-9432 *SIC* 7832 7833

DELUXE ENTERTAINMENT SERVICES GROUP INC p 427
2400 W Empire Ave 90027
Tel (323) 462-6171 *SIC* 7819 7313

DEPENDABLE HIGHWAY EXPRESS INC p 430
2555 E Olympic Blvd 90023
Tel (323) 526-2200 *SIC* 4213 4225

■ **DETROIT TELEVISION STATION WKBD INC** p 433
5555 Melrose Ave 90038
Tel (323) 956-5000 *SIC* 4833

DIRECTORS GUILD OF AMERICA - PRODUCER PENSION AND HEALTH PLANS p 442
5055 Wilshire Blvd # 600 90036
Tel (323) 866-2200 *SIC* 6371

E ENTERTAINMENT TELEVISION INC p 466
5750 Wilshire Blvd # 500 90036
Tel (323) 954-2400 *SIC* 4841 4833

■ **EARTH TECHNOLOGY CORP USA** p 469
1999 Avenue Of Ste 2600 90067
Tel (213) 593-8000
SIC 4953 8748 8742 8711

■ **EAST DUBUQUE NITROGEN PARTNERS LP** p 470
10877 Wilshire Blvd Fl 10 90024
Tel (310) 571-9800 *SIC* 2873

ELI AND EDYTHE BROAD FOUNDATION p 486
2121 Avenue Of The Stars 30t 90067
Tel (310) 954-5050 *SIC* 8299

EMSER INTERNATIONAL LLC p 495
8431 Santa Monica Blvd 90069
Tel (323) 650-2000 *SIC* 5032

EMSER TILE LLC p 495
8431 Santa Monica Blvd 90069
Tel (323) 650-2000 *SIC* 5032 5211

EUROSTAR INC p 513
13425 S Figueroa St 90061
Tel (310) 715-9300 *SIC* 5661

FARMERS INSURANCE GROUP p 529
6301 Owensmouth Ave 90010
Tel (888) 327-6335 *SIC* 6411

FARMERS SERVICES LLC p 530
4680 Wilshire Blvd 90010
Tel (323) 932-3200 *SIC* 6411

FIRE INSURANCE EXCHANGE p 543
4680 Wilshire Blvd 90010
Tel (323) 932-3200 *SIC* 6411

FOH GROUP INC p 563
6255 W Sunset Blvd # 2212 90028
Tel (323) 466-5151
SIC 2341 2342 2339 5621 5632

FOREVER 21 INC p 567
3880 N Mission Rd 90031
Tel (213) 741-5100 *SIC* 5632 5661 5621

■ **FOX BROADCASTING CO** p 572
10201 W Pico Blvd 90064
Tel (310) 369-1000 *SIC* 4833

FOX BSB HOLDCO INC p 572
1000 Vin Scully Ave 90090
Tel (323) 224-1500 *SIC* 7941

■ **FOX CABLE NETWORK SERVICES LLC** p 572
10201 W Pico Blvd 90064
Tel (310) 369-2362 *SIC* 4841

FOX HILLS AUTO INC p 572
5880 W Centinela Ave 90045
Tel (310) 649-3673
SIC 5511 7538 5531 5521

■ **FOX INC** p 572
2121 Ave Of The Ste 1100 90067
Tel (310) 369-1000 *SIC* 4833 7812

■ **FOX NETWORKS GROUP INC** p 572
10201 W Pico Blvd 101 90064
Tel (310) 369-9369 *SIC* 4841

FOX RENT A CAR INC p 572
5500 W Century Blvd 90045
Tel (310) 342-5155 *SIC* 7514

■ **FOX TELEVISION STATIONS LLC** p 573
1999 S Bundy Dr 90025
Tel (310) 584-2000 *SIC* 4833 7313

FREEMAN SPOGLI & CO LLC p 577
11100 Santa Monica Blvd # 1900 90025
Tel (310) 444-1822 *SIC* 6211

GARDA CL WEST INC p 591
1612 W Pico Blvd 90015
Tel (213) 383-3611 *SIC* 7381

GENERAL BUSINESS CREDIT p 599
110 E 9th St Ste A1126 90079
Tel (213) 244-9500 *SIC* 6141

GIBSON DUNN & CRUTCHER LLP p 611
333 S Grand Ave Ste 4600 90071
Tel (213) 229-7000 *SIC* 8111

GOLD PARENT LP p 620
11111 Santa Monica Blvd 90025
Tel (310) 954-0444 *SIC* 6211

GOOD SAMARITAN HOSPITAL p 623
1225 Wilshire Blvd 90017
Tel (213) 977-2121 *SIC* 8062

GOOD SAMARITAN HOSPITAL p 623
600 Witmer St 90017
Tel (213) 977-2121 *SIC* 8062

GOOD SAMARITAN HOSPITAL AUXILIARY p 623
1225 Wilshire Blvd 90017
Tel (213) 977-2121 *SIC* 8011

GOODWILL INDUSTRIES OF SOUTHERN CALIFORNIA p 625
342 N San Fernando Rd 90031
Tel (323) 223-1211 *SIC* 5331 8331

GORES RADIO HOLDINGS LLC p 626
10877 Wilshire Blvd # 1805 90024
Tel (310) 209-3010 *SIC* 3699 7382

GRANDPOINT BANK p 630
355 S Grand Ave Ste 2400 90071
Tel (213) 626-0085 *SIC* 6022

GRANDPOINT CAPITAL INC p 630
333 S Grand Ave Ste 4250 90071
Tel (213) 542-4410 *SIC* 6799

GREAT WALL TEXTILE INC p 634
2150 E 10th St 90021
Tel (626) 688-0271 *SIC* 5199

GREEN DOT PUBLIC SCHOOLS CALIFORNIA p 637
1149 S Hill St Ste 600 90015
Tel (323) 565-1600 *SIC* 8211

GREEN DOT PUBLIC SCHOOLS NATIONAL p 637
1149 S Hill St Fl 6 90015
Tel (323) 565-1600 *SIC* 8211

GREEN EQUITY INVESTORS III L P p 637
11111 Santa Monica Blvd # 2000 90025
Tel (310) 954-0444 *SIC* 6211

GREEN EQUITY INVESTORS IV LP p 637
11111 Santa Monica Blvd 90025
Tel (310) 954-0444 *SIC* 5941

GREEN FARMS INC p 637
1661 Mcgarry St 90021
Tel (213) 747-4411 *SIC* 5148

GRIFFIN HOLDINGS LLC p 640
2121 Avenue Of The Stars 90067
Tel (424) 245-4423 SIC 8741

GRIFOLS BIOLOGICALS INC p 640
5555 Valley Blvd 90032
Tel (323) 227-7028 SIC 2836 2834

GRIFOLS SHARED SERVICES NORTH AMERICA INC p 640
2410 Lillyvale Ave 90032
Tel (323) 225-2221 SIC 5122 2834

GRIFOLS USA LLC p 640
2410 Lillyvale Ave 90032
Tel (800) 421-0008 SIC 5047

GRILL CONCEPTS-DC INC p 640
11661 San Vicente Blvd 90049
Tel (310) 820-5559 SIC 5812

GRILL ON ALLEYTHE INC p 640
11661 San Vicente Blvd # 404 90049
Tel (310) 820-5559 SIC 5812

▲ **GUESS INC** p 645
1444 S Alameda St 90021
Tel (213) 765-3100
SIC 2325 2339 5611 5621 5641

H&H CATERING LP p 651
6801 Hollywood Blvd 90028
Tel (323) 491-1250 SIC 5812

HALLMARK AVIATION SERVICES LP p 654
5757 W Century Blvd # 860 90045
Tel (310) 215-0701 SIC 7363

HANCOCK PARK ASSOCIATES II LP p 657
10350 Santa Monica Blvd # 295 90025
Tel (310) 228-6900 SIC 6552

■ **HANMI BANK** p 658
3660 Wilshire Blvd Ph A 90010
Tel (213) 382-2200 SIC 6022

▲ **HANMI FINANCIAL CORP** p 658
3660 Wilshire Blvd Penths Ste A 90010
Tel (213) 382-2200 SIC 6021

HANNAM CHAIN USA INC p 658
2740 W Olympic Blvd 90006
Tel (213) 382-2922 SIC 5046 5411

HARLAND M BRAUN & CO INC p 661
4010 Whiteside St 90063
Tel (323) 263-9275 SIC 5159 5199

HATCHBEAUTY PRODUCTS LLC p 668
10951 W Pico Blvd Ste 300 90064
Tel (310) 396-7070 SIC 5122

HBC SOLUTIONS HOLDINGS LLC p 671
10877 Wilshire Blvd Fl 18 90024
Tel (321) 727-9100 SIC 3663

HEHR INTERNATIONAL INC p 680
3333 Casitas Ave 90039
Tel (323) 663-1261 SIC 3442

HERBALIFE INTERNATIONAL OF AMERICA INC p 685
800 W Olympic Blvd # 406 90015
Tel (310) 410-9600 SIC 5122

HERBALIFE LTD INC p 685
800 W Olympic Blvd # 406 90015
Tel (310) 410-9600 SIC 2833

■ **HOB ENTERTAINMENT LLC** p 698
7060 Hollywood Blvd 90028
Tel (323) 769-4600 SIC 7929

HOLLYWOOD MEDICAL CENTER LP p 701
1300 N Vermont Ave 90027
Tel (213) 413-3000 SIC 8062

▲ **HOPE BANCORP INC** p 706
3731 Wilshire Blvd 90010
Tel (213) 639-1700 SIC 6021

▲ **HOULIHAN LOKEY INC** p 711
10250 Constellation Blvd # 5 90067
Tel (310) 553-8871 SIC 6211 6282

HOUSING AUTHORITY OF CITY OF LOS ANGELES p 711
2600 Wilshire Blvd Fl 2 90057
Tel (213) 252-2500 SIC 9531

HUB INTERNATIONAL OF CALIFORNIA INC p 716
6701 Center Dr W Ste 1500 90045
Tel (310) 568-5900 SIC 6411

▲ **HUDSON PACIFIC PROPERTIES INC** p 717
11601 Wilshire Blvd Fl 6 90025
Tel (310) 445-5700 SIC 6798

IBEW LOCAL 18 p 726
4189 W 2nd St 90004
Tel (213) 387-8274 SIC 8631

ICREST INTERNATIONAL LLC p 728
725 S Figueroa St # 3050 90017
Tel (213) 488-8303 SIC 5148 5147

■ **INSIGNIA/ESG HOTEL PARTNERS INC** p 746
11150 Santa Monica Blvd # 220 90025
Tel (310) 765-2600 SIC 6512

INTERNATIONAL CHURCH OF FOURSQUARE GOSPEL p 754
1910 W Sunset Blvd # 200 90026
Tel (213) 989-4234
SIC 8661 6512 7032 8211 8221

INTERNATIONAL COFFEE & TEA LLC p 754
5700 Wilshire Blvd # 120 90036
Tel (310) 237-2326 SIC 5812 5499 6794

INTERNATIONAL LEASE FINANCE CORP p 755
10250 Constellation Blvd 90067
Tel (310) 788-1999 SIC 7359 8741 5599

INTERNATIONAL MEDICAL CORPS p 756
12400 Wilshire Blvd # 1500 90025
Tel (310) 826-7800 SIC 8322

INTERNET CORP FOR ASSIGNED NAMES AND NUMBERS p 757
12025 Waterfront Dr # 300 90094
Tel (310) 823-9358 SIC 7373

J PAUL GETTYTRUST p 772
1200 Getty Center Dr # 500 90049
Tel (310) 440-7300 SIC 8412

J-M MANUFACTURING CO INC p 772
5200 W Century Blvd 90045
Tel (800) 621-4404 SIC 2821 3491 3084

■ **J2 CLOUD SERVICES INC** p 772
6922 Hollywood Blvd # 500 90028
Tel (323) 860-9200 SIC 4822

▲ **J2 GLOBAL INC** p 772
6922 Hollywood Blvd # 500 90028
Tel (323) 860-9200 SIC 4822

JACK NADEL INC p 773
8701 Bellanca Ave 90045
Tel (310) 815-2600 SIC 8742 5199

JARROW FORMULAS INC p 778
1824 S Robertson Blvd 90035
Tel (310) 204-6936 SIC 5122

JEWISH COMMUNITY FOUNDATION p 784
6505 Wilshire Blvd # 1200 90048
Tel (323) 761-8700 SIC 8699

JOHN HANCOCK LIFE INSURANCE CO (USA) p 788
865 S Figueroa St # 3320 90017
Tel (213) 689-0813
SIC 7389 6351 6371 6321

JOHN S FREY ENTERPRISES p 789
1900 E 64th St 90001
Tel (323) 583-4061 SIC 3441 3444 6719

▲ **KB HOME** p 806
10990 Wilshire Blvd Fl 5 90024
Tel (310) 231-4000 SIC 1531 6351 6162

KECK HOSPITAL OF USC p 807
1500 San Pablo St 90033
Tel (800) 872-2273 SIC 8011

KEOLISTRANSIT AMERICA INC p 813
6053 W Century Blvd # 900 90045
Tel (310) 981-9500 SIC 4119 7699

▲ **KILROY REALTY CORP** p 818
12200 W Olympic Blvd # 200 90064
Tel (310) 481-8400 SIC 6798

KILROY REALTY LP p 818
12200 W Olympic Blvd # 200 90064
Tel (310) 481-8400 SIC 6798

▲ **KORN/FERRY INTERNATIONAL** p 828
1900 Avenue Stars 90067
Tel (310) 552-1834 SIC 8742 7361

LATHAM & WATKINS LLP p 846
355 S Grand Ave Ste 1000 90071
Tel (213) 485-1234 SIC 8111

LEAR CAPITAL INC p 850
1990 S Bundy Dr Ste 600 90025
Tel (310) 571-0190 SIC 6211

LEONARD GREEN & PARTNERS LP p 856
11111 Santa Monica Blvd # 2000 90025
Tel (310) 954-0444 SIC 6211

LEWIS BRISBOIS BISGAARD & SMITH LLP p 858
633 W 5th St Ste 4000 90071
Tel (213) 250-1800 SIC 8111

LINQUEST CORP p 869
5140 W Goldleaf Cir # 400 90056
Tel (323) 924-1600 SIC 8711

LIVHOME INC p 871
5670 Wilshire Blvd # 500 90036
Tel (800) 807-5854 SIC 8322

LOCAL INITIATIVE HEALTH AUTHORITY FOR LOS ANGELES COUNTY p 872
1055 W 7th St Fl 11 90017
Tel (213) 694-1250 SIC 6324

LOCKTON COMPANIES LLC - PACIFIC SERIES p 873
725 S Figueroa St Fl 35 90017
Tel (213) 689-0500 SIC 6411

LONGWOOD MANAGEMENT CORP p 877
4032 Wilshire Blvd Fl 6 90010
Tel (213) 389-6900 SIC 8742 6513

LOS ANGELES CITY COLLEGE p 878
855 N Vermont Ave 90029
Tel (323) 953-4000 SIC 8222

LOS ANGELES COMMUNITY COLLEGE DISTRICT p 878
770 Wilshire Blvd 90017
Tel (213) 891-2000 SIC 8222

LOS ANGELES COUNTY DEVELOPMENTAL SERVICES FOUNDATION p 878
3303 Wilshire Blvd # 700 90010
Tel (213) 383-1300 SIC 8099 8322 8093

LOS ANGELES COUNTY METROPOLITAN TRANSPORTATION AUTHORITY p 878
1 Gateway Plz Fl 25 90012
Tel (323) 466-3876 SIC 4111

LOS ANGELES DEPARTMENT OF WATER AND POWER p 878
111 N Hope St 90012
Tel (213) 367-4211 SIC 4941 4911

LOS ANGELES FIREMAN RELIEF ASSOCIATION INC p 878
2900 W Temple St 90026
Tel (800) 244-3439 SIC 8322

LOS ANGELES PHILHARMONIC ASSOCIATION p 878
151 S Grand Ave 90012
Tel (213) 972-7300 SIC 7929

LOS ANGELES POLICE RELIEF ASSOCIATION INC p 878
600 N Grand Ave 90012
Tel (213) 674-3701 SIC 8641

■ **LOS ANGELESTIMES COMMUNICATIONS LLC** p 879
202 W 1st St Ste 500 90012
Tel (213) 237-3700 SIC 2711

LOS ANGELES UNIFIED SCHOOL DISTRICT p 879
333 S Beaudry Ave Ste 209 90017
Tel (213) 241-1000 SIC 8211

LOTUS COMMUNICATIONS CORP p 879
3301 Barham Blvd Ste 200 90068
Tel (323) 512-2225 SIC 4832

LOVE CULTURE INC p 881
2423 E 23rd St 90058
Tel (614) 625-4781 SIC 5621

LOWE ENTERPRISES INC p 881
11777 San Vicente Blvd # 900 90049
Tel (310) 820-6661 SIC 6531 6552

LOYOLA MARYMOUNT UNIVERSITY INC p 882
1 Lmu Dr Ste 100 90045
Tel (310) 338-2700 SIC 8211

LUCKY BRAND DUNGAREES LLC p 884
540 S Santa Fe Ave 90013
Tel (213) 443-5700 SIC 2325 2339

■ **MADISON/GRAHAM COLOR GRAPHICS INC** p 894
150 N Myers St 90033
Tel (323) 261-7171 SIC 2752 7336 2796

MANATT PHELPS & PHILLIPS LLP p 900
11355 W Olympic Blvd Fl 2 90064
Tel (310) 312-4000 SIC 8111

■ **MARSH RISK & INSURANCE SERVICES INC** p 911
777 S Figueroa St # 2200 90017
Tel (213) 624-5555 SIC 6411

MAURICIO ESPINOSA p 921
3523 Division St 90065
Tel (909) 253-9108 SIC 7389

MEDICAL MANAGEMENT CONSULTANTS INC p 937
8150 Beverly Blvd 90048
Tel (310) 659-3835
SIC 7363 8742 8748 8721

MELLANO & CO p 940
766 Wall St 90014
Tel (213) 622-0796 SIC 5193

MEMORIAL HOSPITAL OF GARDENA p 942
4060 Woody Blvd 90023
Tel (323) 268-5514 SIC 8062

▲ **MERCURY GENERAL CORP** p 945
4484 Wilshire Blvd 90010
Tel (323) 937-1060 SIC 6331 6411

■ **MERCURY INSURANCE CO** p 945
4484 Wilshire Blvd 90010
Tel (323) 937-1060 SIC 6331

■ **MERCURY INSURANCE SERVICES LLC** p 945
4484 Wilshire Blvd 90010
Tel (323) 937-1060 SIC 6331

METRO-GOLDWYN-MAYER STUDIOS INC p 955
10250 Constellation Blvd 90067
Tel (310) 449-3590 SIC 7812

METROPARK USA INC p 955
5750 Grace Pl 90022
Tel (323) 622-3600 SIC 5632 5699

METROPOLITAN WATER DISTRICT OF SOUTHERN CALIFORNIA p 957
700 N Alameda St 90012
Tel (213) 217-6000 SIC 4941

MIDWAY RENT A CAR INC p 967
4751 Wilshire Blvd # 120 90010
Tel (323) 692-4000
SIC 5511 7515 5521 4119 7513

MIKE KELLY FOUNDATION FOR ARTS p 968
7019 N Figueroa St 90042
Tel (323) 257-7853 SIC 8699

MPG OFFICETRUST INC p 995
355 S Grand Ave Ste 3300 90071
Tel (213) 626-3300 SIC 6798

MPOWER COMMUNICATIONS CORP p 995
515 S Flower St 90071
Tel (213) 213-3000 SIC 4813

MUSEUM ASSOCIATES p 1002
5905 Wilshire Blvd 90036
Tel (323) 857-6172 SIC 8412

MUTUALTRADING CO INC p 1003
431 Crocker St 90013
Tel (213) 626-9458 SIC 5149 5141 5023

NATIONWIDETHEATRES CORP p 1018
120 N Robertson Blvd Fl 3 90048
Tel (310) 657-8420 SIC 7833 7832

NEST PARENT INC p 1026
10877 Wilshire Blvd 90024
Tel (310) 551-0101 SIC 6719

OAK PAPER PRODUCTS CO INC p 1070
3686 E Olympic Blvd 90023
Tel (323) 268-0507
SIC 5113 5199 5087 2653

OAKTREE CAPITAL GROUP HOLDINGS LP p 1071
333 S Grand Ave Fl 28 90071
Tel (213) 830-6300 SIC 6282

▲ **OAKTREE CAPITAL GROUP LLC** p 1071
333 S Grand Ave Ste 2800 90071
Tel (213) 830-6300 SIC 6282

■ **OAKTREE CAPITAL MANAGEMENT LP** p 1071
333 S Grand Ave Ste 2800 90071
Tel (213) 830-6300 SIC 6282 6722 6211

OAKTREE HOLDINGS INC p 1071
333 S Grand Ave Ste 2800 90071
Tel (213) 830-6300 SIC 6799

OAKTREE REAL ESTATE OPPORTUNITIES FUND V GP LP p 1071
333 S Grand Ave Fl 28 90071
Tel (213) 830-6300 SIC 6531

OCCIDENTAL COLLEGE p 1072
1600 Campus Rd 90041
Tel (323) 259-2500 SIC 8221

OCCIDENTAL PETROLEUM INVESTMENT CO INC p 1072
10889 Wilshire Blvd Fl 10 90024
Tel (310) 208-8800 SIC 1382 8744

OCM PE HOLDINGS LP p 1074
333 S Grand Ave Fl 28 90071
Tel (213) 830-6213 SIC 3679 3612 3663

OCM REAL ESTATE OPPORTUNITIES FUND II LP p 1074
333 S Grand Ave Fl 28 90071
Tel (213) 830-6300 SIC 6799

OMELVENY & MYERS LLP p 1084
400 S Hope St Fl 19 90071
Tel (213) 430-6000 SIC 8111

OPENGATE CAPITAL LLC p 1089
10250 Constellation Blvd 90067
Tel (310) 432-7000 SIC 2721 6799 8621

P-WAVE HOLDINGS LLC p 1102
10877 Wilshire Blvd 90024
Tel (310) 209-3010 SIC 6799

PABST BREWING CO LLC p 1103
10635 Santa Monica Blvd 90025
Tel (310) 470-0962 SIC 2082

PARACELSUS LOS ANGELES COMMUNITY HOSPITAL INC p 1113
4081 E Olympic Blvd 90023
Tel (323) 267-0477 SIC 8062

■ **PARAMOUNT PICTURES CORP** p 1114
5555 Melrose Ave 90038
Tel (323) 956-5000
SIC 7812 5099 4833 7829

■ **PARAMOUNTTELEVISION SERVICE INC** p 1114
5555 Melrose Ave 90038
Tel (323) 956-5000 SIC 7812

PAUL HASTINGS LLP p 1121
515 S Flower St Fl 25 90071
Tel (213) 683-6000 SIC 8111

POM WONDERFUL HOLDINGS LLC p 1160
11444 W Olympic Blvd # 210 90064
Tel (310) 966-5800 SIC 5149 5148 5085

▲ **PREFERRED BANK** p 1169
601 S Figueroa St # 2900 90017
Tel (213) 891-1188 SIC 6022

PRIME ADMINISTRATION LLC p 1174
357 S Curson Ave 90036
Tel (323) 549-7155 SIC 6798

PROFESSIONAL SECURITY CONSULTANTS p 1180
11454 San Vicente Blvd # 2 90049
Tel (310) 207-7729 SIC 7381 7382

PROPORTION FOODS LLC p 1184
4020 Compton Ave 90011
Tel (323) 231-7777 SIC 2099

PROSPECT ENTERPRISES INC p 1184
625 Kohler St 90021
Tel (213) 599-5700 SIC 5146 2092

PROSPECT MEDICAL HOLDINGS INC p 1184
3415 S Sepulveda Blvd # 9 90034
Tel (310) 943-4500 SIC 8011

PSOMAS p 1188
555 S Flower St Ste 4300 90071
Tel (310) 954-3700 SIC 8713 8711

■ **PVH NECKWEAR INC** p 1193
1735 S Santa Fe Ave 90021
Tel (213) 688-7970 SIC 2323

PW EAGLE INC p 1193
5200 W Century Blvd 90045
Tel (800) 621-4404 SIC 3084

QUEEN OF ANGELS HOLLYWOOD PRESBYTERIAN MEDICAL CENTER p 1198
1300 N Vermont Ave 90027
Tel (213) 413-3000 SIC 8062

QUINN EMANUEL URQUHART & SULLIVAN LLP p 1200
865 S Figueroa St Fl 10 90017
Tel (213) 443-3000 SIC 8111

R & B REALTY GROUP A CALIFORNIA LIMITED PARTNERSHIP p 1201
2222 Corinth Ave 90064
Tel (800) 888-0808 SIC 7021 6531

R & B REALTY GROUP LP p 1201
2222 Corinth Ave 90064
Tel (310) 478-1021 SIC 6531

R W ZANT CO p 1203
1470 E 4th St 90033
Tel (323) 980-5457
SIC 5147 5146 5144 4222

▲ RADNET INC p 1204
1510 Cotner Ave 90025
Tel (310) 445-2800 SIC 8071

■ RADNET MANAGEMENT INC p 1205
1510 Cotner Ave 90025
Tel (310) 445-2800 SIC 8741

▲ READING INTERNATIONAL INC p 1213
6100 Center Dr Ste 900 90045
Tel (213) 235-2240
SIC 7832 7922 6512 6531

▲ RELIANCE STEEL & ALUMINUM CO p 1222
350 S Grand Ave Ste 5100 90071
Tel (213) 687-7700 SIC 5051

RENT A WHEEL p 1224
11726 San Vicente Blvd # 400 90049
Tel (818) 786-7906 SIC 5531

RENT-A-TIRE LP p 1224
11726 San Vicente Blvd # 400 90049
Tel (818) 786-7906 SIC 5531 3312

▲ RENTECH INC p 1224
10880 Wilshire Blvd # 1101 90024
Tel (310) 571-9800 SIC 2999 2873 6794

REXFORD INDUSTRIAL REALTY INC p 1230
11620 Wilshire Blvd # 1000 90025
Tel (310) 966-1680 SIC 6798

RIOT GAMES INC p 1236
12333 W Olympic Blvd 90064
Tel (310) 828-7953 SIC 7371 7993

ROLAND CORP US p 1247
5100 S Eastern Ave 90040
Tel (323) 890-3700 SIC 5099 5045 3931

ROMAN CATHOLIC ARCHBISHOP OF LOS ANGELES p 1248
3424 Wilshire Blvd 90010
Tel (213) 637-7000 SIC 8661

▲ RUBICON PROJECT INC p 1257
12181 Bluff Creek Dr Fl 4 90094
Tel (310) 207-0272 SIC 7311

■ SAFG RETIREMENT SERVICES INC p 1267
1 Sun America Ctr Fl 36 90067
Tel (310) 772-6000 SIC 6411

SAGE HOLDING CO p 1267
3550 Cahuenga Blvd W 90068
Tel (310) 271-3476 SIC 5511

SENTINEL ACQUISITION HOLDINGS INC p 1305
2000 Avenue Of The Stars 90067
Tel (310) 201-4100 SIC 7371 7379

SHEPPARD MULLIN RICHTER & HAMPTON LLP p 1315
333 S Hope St Fl 43 90071
Tel (213) 620-1780 SIC 8111

SIGNAL PRODUCTS INC p 1322
320 W 31st St 90007
Tel (213) 748-0990 SIC 5137

SILVER CINEMAS ACQUISITION CO p 1323
2222 S Barrington Ave 90064
Tel (310) 473-6701 SIC 7832

SKYROCKET TOYS LLC p 1330
12910 Culver Blvd Ste F 90066
Tel (310) 822-6155 SIC 5945

SLAP SHOT HOLDINGS CORP p 1331
11111 Santa Monica Blvd 90025
Tel (310) 954-0444 SIC 5941

SMART & FINAL HOLDINGS LLC p 1332
10205 Constellation Blvd 90067
Tel (310) 843-1900 SIC 5141 5411

SOUTH CENTRAL LOS ANGELES REGIONAL CENTER FOR DEVELOPMENTALLY DISABLED PERSONS INC p 1343
2500 S Western Ave 90018
Tel (213) 744-7000 SIC 8399

■ SOUTHERN CALIFORNIA GAS CO p 1347
555 W 5th St Fl 31 90013
Tel (213) 244-1200 SIC 4924 4922 4932

■ SOUTHERN CALIFORNIA GAS TOWER INC p 1347
555 W 5th St Ste 1700 90013
Tel (213) 244-1200 SIC 4924

SOUTHERN CALIFORNIA HEALTHCARE SYSTEM INC p 1347
3415 S Sepulveda Blvd # 9 90034
Tel (310) 943-4500 SIC 8062

ST VINCENT MEDICAL CENTER p 1373
2131 W 3rd St 90057
Tel (213) 484-7111 SIC 8062

STEINY AND CO INC p 1385
221 N Ardmore Ave 90004
Tel (626) 962-1055 SIC 1731

STOCKBRIDGE/SBE HOLDINGS LLC p 1390
5900 Wilshire Blvd # 3100 90036
Tel (323) 655-8000 SIC 7011

STRAND ENERGY CO p 1392
515 S Flower St Ste 4800 90071
Tel (213) 225-5900 SIC 1311

SULLIVAN GJ & ASSOCIATES INC p 1397
800 W 6th St Ste 1800 90017
Tel (213) 626-1000 SIC 6411

■ SUNAMERICA ANNUITY AND LIFE ASSURANCE CO p 1401
1 Sun America Ctr 90067
Tel (310) 772-6000 SIC 6311

■ SUNAMERICA INC p 1401
1 Sun America Ctr Fl 38 90067
Tel (310) 772-6000
SIC 6091 6311 6211 6282 6411 6371

■ SUNAMERICA INVESTMENTS INC p 1401
1 Sun America Ctr Fl 37 90067
Tel (310) 772-6000
SIC 8741 6211 6282 7311

■ SUNAMERICA LIFE INSURANCE CO p 1401
1 Sun America Ctr Fl 36 90067
Tel (310) 772-6000 SIC 6311

SUNRISE BRANDS LLC p 1403
801 S Figueroa St # 2500 90017
Tel (323) 780-8250
SIC 2339 2331 2335 2337

■ TCW GROUP INC p 1428
865 S Figueroa St # 2100 90017
Tel (213) 244-0000 SIC 6022 6282 6211

TEAM-ONE EMPLOYMENT SPECIALISTS LLC p 1430
2999 Overland Ave Ste 212 90064
Tel (310) 481-4482 SIC 7361

TEAM-ONE STAFFING SERVICES INC p 1430
10801 National Blvd # 104 90064
Tel (310) 481-4480 SIC 7361

TELEPACIFIC COMMUNICATIONS p 1434
515 S Flower St Fl 36 90071
Tel (213) 213-3000 SIC 4813

TENET HEALTH SYSTEMS NORRIS INC p 1437
1441 Eastlake Ave 90089
Tel (323) 865-3000 SIC 8069

THOMAS PROPERTIES GROUP INC p 1449
515 S Flower St Ste 600 90071
Tel (213) 613-1900 SIC 6531

TICKETMASTER CORP p 1452
7060 Hollywood Blvd Ste 2 90028
Tel (323) 769-4600 SIC 7999 7922

TICKETMASTER GROUP INC p 1452
3701 Wilshire Blvd Fl 9 90010
Tel (800) 745-3000 SIC 7999

TICKETMOB LLC p 1452
11833 Mississippi Ave 90025
Tel (800) 927-0939 SIC 8741

TOPA EQUITIES LTD p 1460
1800 Ave Of The Ste 1400 90067
Tel (310) 203-9199 SIC 6163 5181 7538

TORN & GLASSER INC p 1461
1622 E Olympic Blvd 90021
Tel (213) 593-1332
SIC 5149 5153 5145 5191

TRANSAMERICA OCCIDENTAL LIFE INSURANCE CO p 1470
1150 S Olive St Fl 23 90015
Tel (213) 742-2111
SIC 6311 6371 6321 6324 6799

TRANSAMERICA SERVICE CO INC p 1470
1150 S Olive St 90015
Tel (213) 742-2111 SIC 6311

TRANSLATIONAL ONCOLOGY RESEARCH INTERNATIONAL INC p 1472
1033 Gayley Ave Ste 207 90024
Tel (310) 824-1919 SIC 8011 8732 8742

TRANSOM CAPITAL GROUP LLC p 1472
10990 Wilshire Blvd # 440 90024
Tel (424) 293-2818 SIC 6799

TRUCK UNDERWRITERS ASSOCIATION p 1485
4680 Wilshire Blvd 90010
Tel (323) 932-3200 SIC 8621

■ TRUST CO OF WEST p 1487
865 S Figueroa St # 1800 90017
Tel (213) 244-0000 SIC 6211

■ TWENTIETH CENTURY FOX FILM CORP p 1494
10201 W Pico Blvd 90064
Tel (310) 369-1000 SIC 7812

■ TWENTIETH CENTURY FOX HOME ENTERTAINMENT LLC p 1494
10201 W Pico Blvd 90064
Tel (310) 369-1000 SIC 4833

U B O C INSURANCE INC p 1497
445 S Figueroa St 90071
Tel (213) 236-7700 SIC 6411

UCLA FOUNDATION p 1499
10920 Wilshire Blvd # 200 90024
Tel (310) 794-3193 SIC 6732

UCLA HEALTH SYSTEM AUXILIARY p 1499
10920 Wilshire Blvd # 1700 90024
Tel (310) 794-0500 SIC 8082

UNGER FABRIK LLC p 1502
1515 E 15th St 90021
Tel (213) 222-1010 SIC 2339

UNION BANK FOUNDATION p 1504
445 S Figueroa St Ste 710 90071
Tel (213) 236-5000 SIC 6022

UNION BANK OF CALIFORNIA p 1504
445 S Figueroa St Ste 710 90071
Tel (213) 236-6444 SIC 6022

UNIVERSITY OF CALIFORNIA LOS ANGELES p 1520
405 Hilgard Ave 90095
Tel (310) 825-4321 SIC 8221 9411

UNIVERSITY OF SOUTHERN CALIFORNIA p 1525
3720 S Flower St Fl 3 90007
Tel (213) 740-7762 SIC 8221 8071

URS GORES HOLDINGS CORP p 1530
10877 Wilshire Blvd Ste 1 90024
Tel (310) 209-3010 SIC 4213

■ URS GROUP INC p 1530
300 S Grand Ave Ste 1100 90071
Tel (213) 593-8000 SIC 8711 8712 8741

US MERCHANTS FINANCIAL GROUP INC p 1532
1118 S La Cienega Blvd 90035
Tel (310) 855-1946 SIC 6719

US TELEPACIFIC CORP p 1533
515 S Flower St Fl 47 90071
Tel (213) 213-3000 SIC 4813

US TELEPACIFIC HOLDINGS CORP p 1533
515 S Flower St Fl 47 90071
Tel (213) 213-3000 SIC 4813

VAL-PRO INC p 1539
1601 E Olympic Blvd # 300 90021
Tel (213) 627-8736 SIC 5148

VALET PARKING SERVICE A CALIFORNIA LTD PARTNERSHIP p 1540
6933 Hollywood Blvd 90028
Tel (323) 465-5873 SIC 7521 7299

VANCE STREET CAPITAL LLC p 1543
11150 Santa Monica Blvd # 750 90025
Tel (310) 231-7100 SIC 6799

VANDERRA RESOURCES LLC p 1543
1801 Century Park E # 2400 90067
Tel (817) 439-2220 SIC 1389

▲ VCA INC p 1545
12401 W Olympic Blvd 90064
Tel (310) 571-6500 SIC 0742 5999 5047

VOLUNTEERS OF AMERICA OF LOS ANGELES p 1565
3600 Wilshire Blvd # 1500 90010
Tel (213) 389-1500 SIC 8322 6531

VXI GLOBAL SOLUTIONS LLC p 1567
220 W 1st St Fl 3 90012
Tel (213) 739-4720 SIC 7389

WARNER/CHAPPELL MUSIC INC p 1576
10585 Santa Monica Blvd # 300 90025
Tel (310) 441-8600 SIC 2741

WEDBUSH INC p 1587
1000 Wilshire Blvd # 900 90017
Tel (213) 688-8080 SIC 7389

WEDBUSH SECURITIES INC p 1587
1000 Wilshire Blvd # 900 90017
Tel (213) 688-8000 SIC 6211

WEIDER PUBLICATIONS LLC p 1587
6420 Wilshire Blvd # 720 90048
Tel (818) 884-6800 SIC 2721

■ WELLS FARGO BANK LTD p 1590
333 S Grand Ave Ste 500 90071
Tel (213) 253-6227 SIC 6022

WESTFIELD AMERICA INC p 1600
2049 Century Park E Fl 41 90067
Tel (310) 478-4456 SIC 6512

WESTFIELD LLC p 1601
2049 Century Park E # 4100 90067
Tel (813) 926-4600 SIC 6512

WHITE MEMORIAL MEDICAL CENTER INC p 1606
1720 E Cesar E Chavez Ave 90033
Tel (323) 268-5000 SIC 8062

WILSHIRE BANCORP INC p 1613
3200 Wilshire Blvd 90010
Tel (213) 387-3200 SIC 6022

WILSHIRE BANK p 1613
3200 Wilshire Blvd Fl 10 90010
Tel (213) 427-1000 SIC 6022

WONDERFUL CO LLC p 1622
11444 W Olympic Blvd # 210 90064
Tel (310) 966-5700 SIC 0723 2084

WONDERFUL PISTACHIOS & ALMONDS LLC p 1622
11444 W Olympic Blvd 90064
Tel (310) 966-4650 SIC 2068

WORLDWIDE CORPORATE HOUSING LP p 1626
2222 Corinth Ave 90064
Tel (877) 902-0832 SIC 7021

WORLDWIDE SECURITY ASSOCIATES INC p 1626
10311 S La Cienega Blvd 90045
Tel (310) 743-3000 SIC 7381

YOUNG MENS CHRISTIAN ASSOCIATION OF METROPOLITAN LOS ANGELES p 1638
625 S New Hampshire Ave 90005
Tel (213) 351-2256 SIC 8641

YUCAIPA COMPANIES LLC p 1640
9130 W Sunset Blvd 90069
Tel (310) 789-7200 SIC 8748 6719 6726

LOS BANOS, CA

INGOMAR PACKING CO LLC p 743
9950 S Ingomar Grade 93635
Tel (209) 826-9494 SIC 2033

LOS GATOS, CA

AUTO WORLD CAR WASH LLC p 133
15951 Los Gatos Blvd 95032
Tel (408) 345-6532 SIC 7542

BNS HOLDING INC p 194
61 E Main St Ste B 95030
Tel (408) 399-6498 SIC 3711 3713 3531

INFOGAIN CORP p 741
485 Alberto Way Ste 100 95032
Tel (408) 355-6000
SIC 7379 7373 8742 8748 7374 1731

▲ NETFLIX INC p 1027
100 Winchester Cir 95032
Tel (408) 540-3700 SIC 2741 7841

ROKU INC p 1247
150 Winchester Cir 95032
Tel (408) 556-9040 SIC 4841

LYNWOOD, CA

■ EARLE M JORGENSEN CO p 468
10650 Alameda St 90262
Tel (323) 567-1122 SIC 5051

JONES WHOLESALE LUMBER CO INC p 793
10761 Alameda St 90262
Tel (323) 567-1301 SIC 5031

LYNWOOD UNIFIED SCHOOL DISTRICT p 888
11321 Bullis Rd 90262
Tel (310) 639-5627 SIC 8211

ST FRANCIS MEDICAL CENTER p 1366
3630 E Imperial Hwy 90262
Tel (310) 900-8900 SIC 8011

ST FRANCIS MEDICAL CENTER OF LYNWOOD FOUNDATION p 1367
3630 E Imperial Hwy 90262
Tel (310) 900-8900 SIC 8062

MADERA, CA

CHILDRENS HOSPITAL CENTRAL CA p 299
9300 Valley Childrens Pl 93636
Tel (559) 353-6900 SIC 8069

COUNTY OF MADERA p 379
209 W Yosemite Ave 93637
Tel (559) 675-7726 SIC 9111

MADERA COMMUNITY HOSPITAL p 894
1250 E Almond Ave 93637
Tel (559) 675-5555 SIC 8062

MADERA UNIFIED SCHOOL DISTRICT p 894
1902 Howard Rd 93637
Tel (559) 675-4500 SIC 8211

VALLEY CHILDRENS HEALTHCARE p 1540
9300 Valley Childrens Pl 93636
Tel (559) 353-3000 SIC 8011 8069

VALLEY CHILDRENS HOSPITAL p 1540
9300 Valley Childrens Pl 93636
Tel (559) 353-3000 SIC 8069

MALIBU, CA

■ DUN & BRADSTREET EMERGING BUSINESSES CORP p 461
22761 Pacific Coast Hwy # 226 90265
Tel (310) 456-8271 SIC 7389

HUGH DUNCAN & ASSOCIATES INC p 717
26908 Mlibu Cove Colny Dr 90265
Tel (310) 457-7432 SIC 7311

PEPPERDINE UNIVERSITY p 1133
24255 Pacific Coast Hwy # 5000 90263
Tel (310) 506-4000 SIC 8221

MAMMOTH LAKES, CA

MAMMOTH MOUNTAIN SKI AREA LLC p 900
10001 Minaret Rd 93546
Tel (760) 934-2571 SIC 7011 5812

MANHATTAN BEACH, CA

GURU DENIM INC p 648
1888 Rosecrans Ave # 1000 90266
Tel (323) 266-3072 SIC 5137 5611

KINECTA FEDERAL CREDIT UNION p 819
1440 Rosecrans Ave 90266
Tel (310) 643-5400 SIC 6061

KINECTA FINANCIAL & INSURANCE SERVICES LLC p 819
1440 Rosecrans Ave 90266
Tel (310) 643-5400 SIC 6061

▲ SKECHERS USA INC p 1329
228 Manhattan Beach Blvd # 200 90266
Tel (310) 318-3100 SIC 3021 3149

TRUE RELIGION APPAREL INC p 1486
1888 Rosecrans Ave # 1000 90266
Tel (323) 266-3072 SIC 2369 2325 2339

■ VANTAGE ONCOLOGY LLC p 1544
1500 Rosecrans Ave # 400 90266
Tel (310) 335-4000 SIC 8011

MANTECA, CA

■ DOCTORS HOSPITAL OF MANTECA INC p 447
1205 E North St 95336
Tel (209) 823-3111 SIC 8069

KAMPS PROPANE INC p 802
1262 Dupont Ct 95336
Tel (209) 858-6000 SIC 5171

MANTECA UNIFIED SCHOOL DISTRICT p 903
2271 W Louise Ave 95337
Tel (209) 825-3200 SIC 8211

MARINA DEL REY, CA

CFHS HOLDINGS INC p 285
4650 Lincoln Blvd 90292
Tel (310) 823-8911 SIC 8062 8093 8011

▲ **GLOBAL EAGLE ENTERTAINMENT INC** p 616
4553 Glencoe Ave Ste 200 90292
Tel (310) 437-6000 *SIC* 4899 7371 4813

MARTINEZ, CA

CENTRAL CONTRA COSTA SANITARY DISTRICT FACILITIES FINANCING AUTHORITY p 278
5019 Imhoff Pl 94553
Tel (925) 228-9500 *SIC* 4952 4959

CONTRA COSTA COMMUNITY COLLEGE DISTRICT p 364
500 Court St Fl 1 94553
Tel (925) 229-1000 *SIC* 8222

■ **CONTRA COSTA ELECTRIC INC** p 364
825 Howe Rd 94553
Tel (925) 229-4250 *SIC* 1731

COUNTY OF CONTRA COSTA p 377
625 Court St Ste 100 94553
Tel (925) 957-5280 *SIC* 9111

GOLDEN GATE PETROLEUM CO p 621
1340 Arnold Dr Ste 231 94553
Tel (925) 335-3700 *SIC* 5172

SHELL MARTINEZ REFINING CO p 1314
3485 Pacheco Blvd 94553
Tel (925) 313-3000 *SIC* 2911

MARYSVILLE, CA

COUNTY OF YUBA p 383
915 8th St Ste 109 95901
Tel (530) 749-7575 *SIC* 9111

MARYSVILLE JOINT UNIFIED SCHOOL DISTRICT p 915
1919 B St 95901
Tel (530) 741-6000 *SIC* 8211

RIDEOUT MEMORIAL HOSPITAL p 1234
726 4th St 95901
Tel (530) 749-4416 *SIC* 8062 8082

MATHER, CA

BLOODSOURCE INC p 189
10536 Peter A Mccuen Blvd 95655
Tel (916) 456-1500 *SIC* 8099

MAYWOOD, CA

TAPIA ENTERPRISES INC p 1424
6067 District Blvd 90270
Tel (323) 560-7415 *SIC* 5141

MCCLELLAN, CA

SBM MANAGEMENT SERVICES LP p 1285
5241 Arnold Ave 95652
Tel (866) 855-2211 *SIC* 7349

SBM SITE SERVICES LLC p 1285
5241 Arnold Ave 95652
Tel (916) 922-7600 *SIC* 7349

SOMERS BUILDING MAINTENANCE INC p 1339
5241 Arnold Ave 95652
Tel (916) 922-3300 *SIC* 7349

TWIN RIVERS UNIFIED SCHOOL DISTRICT p 1495
5115 Dudley Blvd 95652
Tel (916) 566-1600 *SIC* 8211

VILLARA CORP p 1557
4700 Lang Ave 95652
Tel (916) 646-2700 *SIC* 1711

MENDOTA, CA

S STAMOULES INC p 1262
904 S Lyon Ave 93640
Tel (559) 655-9777 *SIC* 0723

MENLO PARK, CA

ATRIUM CAPITAL CORP p 129
3000 Sand Hill Rd 2-130 94025
Tel (650) 233-7878 *SIC* 6211

BUCK HOLDING LP p 223
2800 Sand Hill Rd Ste 200 94025
Tel (615) 855-5161 *SIC* 5331

CORNERSTONE RESEARCH INC p 371
1000 El Camino Real # 250 94025
Tel (650) 853-1660 *SIC* 8748 7389

▲ **EXPONENT INC** p 520
149 Commonwealth Dr 94025
Tel (650) 326-9400 *SIC* 8711 8742 8999

▲ **FACEBOOK INC** p 523
1 Hacker Way Bldg 10 94025
Tel (650) 543-4800 *SIC* 7375

■ **FACEBOOK PAYMENTS INC** p 523
1601 Willow Rd 94025
Tel (650) 690-3038 *SIC* 7389

GLADIATOR CORP p 614
2882 Sand Hill Rd Ste 280 94025
Tel (650) 233-2900 *SIC* 7372

HEWLETT WILLIAM AND FLORA FOUNDATION (INC) p 688
2121 Sand Hill Rd 94025
Tel (650) 234-4500 *SIC* 8699

■ **KAYTECHNOLOGY HOLDINGS INC** p 805
2500 Sand Hill Rd Ste 300 94025
Tel (650) 289-2481 *SIC* 7372

▲ **LANDEC CORP** p 842
3603 Haven Ave 94025
Tel (650) 306-1650 *SIC* 2033 5148 5999

LELAND STANFORD JUNIOR UNIVERSITY p 854
2575 Sand Hill Rd 94025
Tel (650) 723-2300 *SIC* 8221 8069 8062

MENLO HEALTH ALLIANCE p 943
1300 Crane St 94025
Tel (650) 498-6640 *SIC* 8011

NOVO CONSTRUCTION INC p 1063
1460 Obrien Dr 94025
Tel (650) 701-1500 *SIC* 1542

▲ **PACIFIC BIOSCIENCES OF CALIFORNIA INC** p 1104
1380 Willow Rd 94025
Tel (650) 521-8000 *SIC* 3826

■ **PROTIVITI INC** p 1185
2884 Sand Hill Rd Ste 200 94025
Tel (650) 234-6000 *SIC* 8742 8721

▲ **ROBERT HALF INTERNATIONAL INC** p 1241
2884 Sand Hill Rd Ste 200 94025
Tel (650) 234-6000
SIC 7363 7361 8748 8721

SILVER LAKE PARTNERS II LP p 1323
2775 Sand Hill Rd Ste 100 94025
Tel (650) 233-8120 *SIC* 6726 6211

SRI INTERNATIONAL p 1363
333 Ravenswood Ave 94025
Tel (650) 859-2000 *SIC* 8733 8748

■ **VITESSE LLC** p 1563
1601 Willow Rd 94025
Tel (650) 543-4800 *SIC* 7374

MERCED, CA

CF MERCED LA SIERRA LLC p 285
2424 M St 95340
Tel (209) 723-4224 *SIC* 8051

COUNTY OF MERCED p 379
2222 M St 95340
Tel (209) 385-7511 *SIC* 9111

GOLDEN VALLEY HEALTH CENTERS p 621
737 W Childs Ave 95341
Tel (209) 383-1848 *SIC* 8093

MATER MISERICORDIAE HOSPITAL p 919
333 Mercy Ave 95340
Tel (209) 564-5000 *SIC* 8062

■ **MCLANE/PACIFIC INC** p 931
3876 E Childs Ave 95341
Tel (209) 725-2500 *SIC* 5141

MERCED CITY SCHOOL DISTRICT p 944
444 W 23rd St 95340
Tel (209) 385-6600 *SIC* 8211

MERCED COUNTY OFFICE OF EDUCATION p 944
632 W 13th St 95341
Tel (209) 381-6600 *SIC* 8211

MERCED IRRIGATION DISTRICT p 944
744 W 20th St 95340
Tel (209) 722-5761 *SIC* 4911 4971

MOLDING ACQUISITION CORP p 982
2651 Cooper Ave 95348
Tel (209) 723-5000 *SIC* 2822

MILL VALLEY, CA

ALBECO INC p 46
150 Shoreline Hwy Ste 5 94941
Tel (415) 289-5720 *SIC* 5411

PIATTI RESTAURANT CO LP p 1146
625 Redwood Hwy Frntage Rd 94941
Tel (415) 380-2511 *SIC* 5812

▲ **REDWOODTRUST INC** p 1217
1 Belvedere Pl Ste 300 94941
Tel (415) 389-7373 *SIC* 6798

MILPITAS, CA

ADVANTECH CORP p 27
380 Fairview Way 95035
Tel (408) 519-3800 *SIC* 5045 7379

▲ **AEROHIVE NETWORKS INC** p 30
1011 Mccarthy Blvd 95035
Tel (408) 510-6100 *SIC* 7373

▲ **AVIAT NETWORKS INC** p 138
860 N Mccarthy Blvd 95035
Tel (408) 941-7000 *SIC* 3663

■ **AVIAT US INC** p 138
860 N Mccarthy Blvd 95035
Tel (408) 941-7100 *SIC* 3663 3661

CREATIVE HOLDINGS INC p 390
1901 Mccarthy Blvd 95035
Tel (408) 428-6600
SIC 5045 3577 3931 3674 8711 3651

CREATIVE LABS INC p 390
1901 Mccarthy Blvd 95035
Tel (408) 428-6600 *SIC* 5045 5734 3577

CYBERNET SOFTWARE SYSTEMS INC p 404
1900 Mccarthy Blvd # 210 95035
Tel (408) 615-5700 *SIC* 7371

DEVCON CONSTRUCTION INC p 433
690 Gibraltar Dr 95035
Tel (408) 942-8200 *SIC* 1541

ELOTOUCH SOLUTIONS INC p 489
1033 Mccarthy Blvd 95035
Tel (408) 597-8000 *SIC* 3575

▲ **FIREEYE INC** p 543
1440 Mccarthy Blvd 95035
Tel (408) 321-6300 *SIC* 7372

FLEXTRONICS INTERNATIONAL PA INC p 556
847 Gibraltar Dr 95035
Tel (408) 576-7000 *SIC* 3444

HEADWAY TECHNOLOGIES INC p 673
682 S Hillview Dr 95035
Tel (408) 934-5300 *SIC* 3572

HOYA HOLDINGS INC p 714
680 N Mccarthy Blvd # 120 95035
Tel (408) 654-2300 *SIC* 3861 3825 3827

INFINEON TECHNOLOGIES NORTH AMERICA CORP p 740
640 N Mccarthy Blvd 95035
Tel (866) 951-9519 *SIC* 3674

INFINEON TECHNOLOGIES US HOLDCO INC p 740
640 N Mccarthy Blvd 95035
Tel (408) 956-8960 *SIC* 3674

INTEGRATED SILICON SOLUTION INC p 749
1623 Buckeye Dr 95035
Tel (408) 969-6600 *SIC* 3674

■ **INTERSIL COMMUNICATIONS LLC** p 757
1001 Murphy Ranch Rd 95035
Tel (408) 432-8888 *SIC* 3674

▲ **INTERSIL CORP** p 758
1001 Murphy Ranch Rd 95035
Tel (408) 432-8888 *SIC* 3674 3679

▲ **IXYS CORP** p 769
1590 Buckeye Dr 95035
Tel (408) 457-9000 *SIC* 3674

▲ **KLA-TENCOR CORP** p 822
1 Technology Dr 95035
Tel (408) 875-3000
SIC 3827 3825 7699 7629

▲ **LINEAR TECHNOLOGY CORP** p 869
1630 Mccarthy Blvd 95035
Tel (408) 432-1900 *SIC* 3674

▲ **LUMENTUM HOLDINGS INC** p 885
400 N Mccarthy Blvd 95035
Tel (408) 546-5483 *SIC* 3669 3674 3826

MILPITAS UNIFIED SCHOOL DISTRICT p 972
1331 E Calaveras Blvd 95035
Tel (408) 635-2600 *SIC* 8211

▲ **NANOMETRICS INC** p 1007
1550 Buckeye Dr 95035
Tel (408) 545-6000 *SIC* 3829 3559

PALPILOT INTERNATIONAL CORP p 1110
500 Yosemite Dr 95035
Tel (408) 855-8866 *SIC* 3672 3089

■ **PERICOM SEMICONDUCTOR CORP** p 1136
1545 Barber Ln 95035
Tel (408) 232-9100 *SIC* 3674 3825

PRESTON PIPELINES INC p 1173
133 Bothelo Ave 95035
Tel (408) 262-1418 *SIC* 1623

■ **SANDISK CORP** p 1278
951 Sandisk Dr 95035
Tel (408) 801-1000 *SIC* 3572

■ **SILICON GRAPHICS INTERNATIONAL CORP** p 1323
900 N Mccarthy Blvd 95035
Tel (669) 900-8000 *SIC* 3577 7371

SJ DISTRIBUTORS INC p 1328
625 Vista Way 95035
Tel (888) 988-2328 *SIC* 5142 5148 5149

SPECTRA LABORATORIES INC p 1357
525 Sycamore Dr 95035
Tel (408) 571-1290 *SIC* 8071

▲ **VIAVI SOLUTIONS INC** p 1554
430 N Mccarthy Blvd 95035
Tel (408) 404-3600 *SIC* 3674 3826

■ **XICOR LLC** p 1631
1001 Murphy Ranch Rd 95035
Tel (408) 432-8888 *SIC* 3674

XL CONSTRUCTION CORP p 1632
851 Buckeye Ct 95035
Tel (408) 240-6000 *SIC* 1542

MIRA LOMA, CA

GALASSOS BAKERY p 589
10820 San Sevaine Way 91752
Tel (951) 360-1211 *SIC* 2051

OLIVET INTERNATIONAL INC p 1082
11015 Hopkins St 91752
Tel (951) 681-8888 *SIC* 5099

MISSION HILLS, CA

FACEY MEDICAL FOUNDATION p 523
15451 San Fernando Msn 91345
Tel (818) 365-9531 *SIC* 8099

NATIONAL BUSINESS GROUP INC p 1010
15319 Chatsworth St 91345
Tel (818) 221-6000
SIC 7353 5039 7359 3496 7519

NATIONAL CONSTRUCTION RENTALS INC p 1011
15319 Chatsworth St 91345
Tel (818) 221-6000 *SIC* 7353

PROVIDENCE HOLY CROSS MEDICAL CENTER GUILD p 1186
15031 Rinaldi St 91345
Tel (818) 365-8051 *SIC* 8062

UNICOM GLOBAL INC p 1502
15535 San Fernando Mssion 91345
Tel (818) 838-0606
SIC 8732 6552 7389 7371

MISSION VIEJO, CA

■ **COLDWELL BANKER RESIDENTIAL BROKERAGE CO** p 335
27271 Las Ramblas 92691
Tel (949) 367-1800 *SIC* 6531

■ **COLDWELL BANKER RESIDENTIAL REAL ESTATE** p 335
27271 Las Ramblas 92691
Tel (949) 367-1800 *SIC* 6531

▲ **ENSIGN GROUP INC** p 500
27101 Puerta Real Ste 450 92691
Tel (949) 487-9500 *SIC* 8051

■ **IMMEDIATE CLINIC HEALTHCARE INC** p 734
27101 Puerta Real Ste 450 92691
Tel (949) 487-9500 *SIC* 8082

JAMES HARDIE BUILDING PRODUCTS INC p 776
26300 La Alameda Ste 400 92691
Tel (949) 348-1800 *SIC* 5031

JAMES HARDIE TRANSITION CO INC p 776
26300 La Alameda Ste 400 92691
Tel (949) 348-1800
SIC 3275 3523 3494 5072

JAMES MORIEL p 776
25701 Taladro Cir Ste B 92691
Tel (949) 240-3340 *SIC* 5083

MISSION HOSPITAL REGIONAL MEDICAL CENTER INC p 975
27700 Medical Center Rd 92691
Tel (949) 364-1400 *SIC* 8062

SADDLEBACK VALLEY UNIFIED SCHOOL DISTRICT p 1265
25631 Peter Hartman Way 92691
Tel (949) 586-1234 *SIC* 8211

SIZZLER USA RESTAURANTS INC p 1328
25910 Acero Ste 350 92691
Tel (949) 273-4497 *SIC* 5812

SOUTH ORANGE COUNTY COMMUNITY COLLEGE DISTRICT p 1344
28000 Marguerite Pkwy 92692
Tel (949) 582-4500 *SIC* 8222 8221

ZENSHO AMERICA CORP p 1642
27261 Las Ramblas Ste 240 92691
Tel (760) 585-8455 *SIC* 8742

MODESTO, CA

A B BOYD CO p 4
600 S Mcclure Rd 95357
Tel (800) 554-0200 *SIC* 3069

BASIC RESOURCES INC p 158
928 12th St Ste 700 95354
Tel (209) 521-9771
SIC 1611 3273 2951 3532 3531

BOYD LTI p 205
600 S Mcclure Rd 95357
Tel (800) 554-0200 *SIC* 3549 3053 8711

CENTRAL VALLEY AUTOMOTIVE INC p 280
4460 Mchenry Ave 95356
Tel (209) 526-3300 *SIC* 5511

COUNTY OF STANISLAUS p 382
1010 10th St Ste 5100 95354
Tel (209) 525-6398 *SIC* 9111

■ **DOCTORS MEDICAL CENTER OF MODESTO INC** p 447
1441 Florida Ave 95350
Tel (209) 578-1211 *SIC* 8062

E & J GALLO WINERY p 465
600 Yosemite Blvd 95354
Tel (209) 341-3111 *SIC* 2084 0172

FOSTER DAIRY FARMS p 570
529 Kansas Ave 95351
Tel (209) 576-3400 *SIC* 0241

FOSTER DAIRY PRODUCTS DISTRIBUTING p 570
529 Kansas Ave 95351
Tel (209) 576-3400 *SIC* 5143 2026

FUTTER GOLD MEDICAL FOUNDATION p 585
600 Coffee Rd 95355
Tel (209) 550-4724 *SIC* 8011

G3 ENTERPRISES INC p 588
502 E Whitmore Ave 95358
Tel (209) 341-7515 *SIC* 4731

GALLO GLASS CO p 590
605 S Santa Cruz Ave 95354
Tel (209) 341-3710 *SIC* 3221

HMCLAUSE INC p 697
260 Cousteau Pl Ste 210 95357
Tel (530) 747-3700 *SIC* 0181

JS WEST & COMPANIES p 795
501 9th St 95354
Tel (209) 577-3221
SIC 5172 5211 5251 0723 5499

LTI HOLDINGS INC p 883
600 S Mcclure Rd 95357
Tel (209) 236-1111 *SIC* 3069 2822

MODESTO CITY OF (INC) p 981
1010 10th St Ste 2100 95354
Tel (209) 577-5200 *SIC* 9111

MODESTO CITY SCHOOL DISTRICT p 981
426 Locust St 95351
Tel (209) 576-4011 *SIC* 8211

MODESTO IRRIGATION DISTRICT (INC) p 981
1231 11th St 95354
Tel (209) 526-7337 *SIC* 4911 4971

MSR PUBLIC POWER AGENCY p 997
1231 11th St 95354
Tel (209) 526-7473 SIC 4911

MTC DISTRIBUTING p 997
4900 Stoddard Rd 95356
Tel (209) 523-6449 SIC 5194 5145 5149

OCAT INC p 1072
4306 Sisk Rd 95356
Tel (209) 529-6802 SIC 5812

PACIFIC SOUTHWEST CONTAINER LLC p 1106
4530 Leckron Rd 95357
Tel (209) 526-0444
SIC 2671 2657 3086 2653 2752

RIM CORP p 1235
915 17th St 95354
Tel (209) 523-8331 SIC 8741

SAVE MART SUPERMARKETS p 1284
1800 Standiford Ave 95350
Tel (209) 577-1600
SIC 5411 5141 4213 4212

STAN BOYETT & SON INC p 1375
601 Mchenry Ave 95350
Tel (209) 577-6000 SIC 5172 5541

STANISLAUS FARM SUPPLY CO p 1377
624 E Service Rd 95358
Tel (860) 678-5160 SIC 5191

SUTTER CENTRAL VALLEY HOSPITALS p 1410
1700 Coffee Rd 95355
Tel (209) 526-4500 SIC 8062

SUTTER GOULD MEDICAL FOUNDATION p 1410
1700 Mchenry Ave Ste 60b 95350
Tel (209) 526-4500 SIC 8011

SYLVAN UNION SCHOOL DISTRICT p 1413
605 Sylvan Ave 95350
Tel (209) 574-5000 SIC 8211

VETERINARY SERVICE INC p 1553
4100 Bangs Ave 95356
Tel (209) 545-5100 SIC 5047 5199 5083

WONDERTREATS INC p 1622
2200 Lapham Dr 95354
Tel (209) 521-8881 SIC 5199 5947

YOSEMITE COMMUNITY COLLEGE DISTRICT p 1637
2201 Blue Gum Ave 95358
Tel (209) 575-7800 SIC 8222

MOJAVE, CA

■ SCALED COMPOSITES LLC p 1285
1624 Flight Line 93501
Tel (661) 824-4541 SIC 3721 3999 8711

MONROVIA, CA

■ 3M UNITEK CORP p 3
2724 Peck Rd 91016
Tel (626) 445-7960 SIC 3843

▲ AEROVIRONMENT INC p 31
800 Royal Oaks Dr Ste 210 91016
Tel (626) 357-9983 SIC 3721 8711 3694

CALIFORNIA NEWSPAPERS LIMITED PARTNERSHIP p 241
605 E Huntington Dr # 100 91016
Tel (626) 962-8811 SIC 2711

CHINA MANUFACTURERS ALLIANCE LLC p 301
406 E Huntington Dr # 200 91016
Tel (626) 301-9575 SIC 5014

DECORE-ATIVE SPECIALTIES p 421
2772 Peck Rd 91016
Tel (626) 254-9191 SIC 2431

TRADER JOES CO p 1469
800 S Shamrock Ave 91016
Tel (626) 599-3700 SIC 5411 5921

MONTCLAIR, CA

GIANT INLAND EMPIRE RV CENTER INC p 611
9150 Benson Ave 91763
Tel (909) 981-0444 SIC 5561 7538

NEW AGE INVESTMENTS INC p 1029
9440 Autoplex St 91763
Tel (909) 625-8990 SIC 5511

MONTEBELLO, CA

ALL ACCESS APPAREL INC p 50
1515 Gage Rd 90640
Tel (323) 889-4300 SIC 2331 2361 2335

BEVERLY COMMUNITY HOSPITAL ASSOCIATION p 178
309 W Beverly Blvd 90640
Tel (323) 726-1222 SIC 8062

CFP GROUP INC p 285
1117 W Olympic Blvd 90640
Tel (323) 727-0900 SIC 3556

KATZKIN LEATHER INC p 805
6868 W Acco St 90640
Tel (323) 725-1243 SIC 5199 2531

MONTEBELLO UNIFIED SCHOOL DISTRICT PROTECTIVE LEAGUE p 986
123 S Montebello Blvd 90640
Tel (323) 887-7900 SIC 8211

WILBUR CURTIS CO INC p 1608
6913 W Acco St 90640
Tel (323) 837-2300 SIC 3589

MONTEREY PARK, CA

AHMC GARFIELD MEDICAL CENTER LP p 37
525 N Garfield Ave 91754
Tel (626) 573-2222 SIC 8051 8062

GUARD-SYSTEMS INC p 645
1190 Monterey Pass Rd 91754
Tel (626) 443-0031 SIC 7381

MERCHANTS BUILDING MAINTENANCE CO p 944
1190 Monterey Pass Rd 91754
Tel (323) 881-6701 SIC 7349

MONTEREY, CA

CALIFORNIA CAPITAL INSURANCE CO p 239
2300 Garden Rd 93940
Tel (831) 233-5500 SIC 6331

COMMUNITY HOSPITAL FOUNDATION INC p 349
23625 Holman Hwy 93940
Tel (831) 625-4830 SIC 8741

COMMUNITY HOSPITAL OF MONTEREY PENINSULA p 349
23625 Holman Hwy 93940
Tel (831) 624-5311 SIC 8069 8011

DOLE FRESH VEGETABLES INC p 448
2959 Salinas Hwy 93940
Tel (831) 422-8871 SIC 2099 0723

EXCELLIGENCE LEARNING CORP p 516
2 Lower Ragsda Dr Ste 200 93940
Tel (831) 333-2000 SIC 3944 5999

LANGUAGE LINE HOLDINGS INC p 844
1 Lower Ragsdale Dr # 2 93940
Tel (831) 648-5800 SIC 7389

MONTEREY PENINSULA UNIFIED SCHOOL DISTRICT p 986
700 Pacific St 93940
Tel (831) 392-3915 SIC 8211

■ NAVAL POSTGRADUATE SCHOOL p 1019
1 University Cir Rm M10 93943
Tel (831) 656-7893 SIC 8221 9711

NOVA MANAGEMENT INC p 1062
660 Camino Aguajito # 300 93940
Tel (831) 373-4544 SIC 8711 7361

PRODUCT DEVELOPMENT CORP p 1179
20 Ragsdale Dr Ste 100 93940
Tel (831) 333-1100 SIC 7389

ROMAN CATHOLIC BISHOP MONTEREY p 1248
485 Church St 93940
Tel (831) 373-4666 SIC 8661

MOORPARK, CA

■ BENCHMARK ELECTRONICS MANUFACTURING SOLUTIONS (MOORPARK) INC p 172
200 Science Dr 93021
Tel (805) 532-2800 SIC 3679

CUSTOM SENSORS & TECHNOLOGIES INC p 403
14401 Princeton Ave 93021
Tel (805) 523-2000 SIC 3679

■ MARINE HOLDING US CORP p 906
6000 Condor Dr 93021
Tel (805) 529-2000 SIC 6799

MIKE ROVNER CONSTRUCTION INC p 968
5400 Tech Cir 93021
Tel (805) 584-5961 SIC 1522

MOLLER INVESTMENT GROUP INC p 983
6591 Collins Dr Ste E11 93021
Tel (805) 299-8200 SIC 5541

MURANAKA FARM p 1001
11018 E Los Angeles Ave 93021
Tel (805) 529-6692 SIC 5148

PENNYMAC MORTGAGE INVESTMENT TRUST p 1131
6101 Condor Dr 93021
Tel (818) 224-7442 SIC 6798

PINDLER & PINDLER INC p 1148
11910 Poindexter Ave 93021
Tel (805) 531-9090 SIC 5131

MORAGA, CA

SAINT MARYS COLLEGE OF CALIFORNIA p 1270
1928 Saint Marys Rd 94575
Tel (925) 631-4000 SIC 8221

MORENO VALLEY, CA

MORENO VALLEY UNIFIED SCHOOL DISTRICT p 988
25634 Alessandro Blvd 92553
Tel (951) 571-7500 SIC 8211

MORGAN HILL, CA

ANRITSU CO p 92
490 Jarvis Dr 95037
Tel (408) 201-1551 SIC 5065 3825 3663

ANRITSU US HOLDING INC p 93
490 Jarvis Dr 95037
Tel (408) 778-2000 SIC 3825 3663 5065

■ COAST DISTRIBUTION SYSTEM INC p 331
350 Woodview Ave Ste 100 95037
Tel (408) 782-6686 SIC 5013

LUSAMERICA FOODS INC p 886
16480 Railroad Ave 95037
Tel (408) 294-6622 SIC 5146 5142

PACIFIC STATES INDUSTRIES INC p 1106
10 Madrone Ave 95037
Tel (408) 779-7354 SIC 5031 2421 1751

PARAMIT CORP p 1114
18735 Madrone Pkwy 95037
Tel (408) 782-5600 SIC 3841

SAKATA SEED AMERICA INC p 1271
18095 Serene Dr 95037
Tel (408) 778-7758 SIC 5191 0182

SPECIALIZED BICYCLE COMPONENTS INC p 1356
15130 Concord Cir 95037
Tel (408) 779-6229 SIC 5091

MOUNTAIN VIEW, CA

ACHIEVO CORP p 17
1400 Terra Bella Ave E 94043
Tel (925) 498-8864 SIC 7371

▲ ALPHABET INC p 60
1600 Amphitheatre Pkwy 94043
Tel (650) 253-0000 SIC 7371

■ AUDIENCE INC p 130
331 Fairchild Dr 94043
Tel (650) 254-2800 SIC 3674

BELL INTEGRATOR INC p 170
800 W El Camino Real 94040
Tel (650) 603-0988 SIC 7373 7389

▲ EHEALTH INC p 481
440 E Middlefield Rd 94043
Tel (650) 584-2700 SIC 6411

EL CAMINO HOSPITAL p 482
2500 Grant Rd 94040
Tel (408) 224-6660 SIC 8062

FENWICK & WEST LLP p 537
801 California St 94041
Tel (650) 988-8500 SIC 8111

FIRST TECHNOLOGY FEDERAL CREDIT UNION p 549
1335 Terra Bella Ave 94043
Tel (855) 855-8805 SIC 6061

■ GOOGLE INC p 625
1600 Amphitheatre Pkwy 94043
Tel (650) 253-0000 SIC 4813 7375

■ GOOGLE INTERNATIONAL LLC p 625
1600 Amphitheatre Pkwy 94043
Tel (650) 253-0000 SIC 4813 7375

■ HARMAN CONNECTED SERVICES HOLDING CORP p 662
636 Ellis St 94043
Tel (650) 623-9400 SIC 7373

▲ INTUIT INC p 760
2700 Coast Ave 94043
Tel (650) 944-6000 SIC 7372

▲ LINKEDIN CORP p 869
2029 Stierlin Ct Ste 200 94043
Tel (650) 687-3600 SIC 7375

▲ MOBILEIRON INC p 980
415 E Middlefield Rd 94043
Tel (650) 919-8100 SIC 7372

▲ OMNICELL INC p 1085
590 E Middlefield Rd 94043
Tel (650) 251-6100 SIC 3571

■ PAYPAL GLOBAL HOLDINGS INC p 1122
303 Bryant St 94041
Tel (408) 967-1000 SIC 7374 4813

▲ PURE STORAGE INC p 1192
650 Castro St Ste 400 94041
Tel (800) 379-7873 SIC 3572

▲ QUOTIENT TECHNOLOGY INC p 1201
400 Logue Ave 94043
Tel (650) 605-4600 SIC 7319

▲ SYMANTEC CORP p 1414
350 Ellis St 94043
Tel (650) 527-8000 SIC 7372 7379

▲ SYNOPSYS INC p 1415
690 E Middlefield Rd 94043
Tel (650) 584-5000 SIC 7371

■ TELEDYNE WIRELESS LLC p 1434
1274 Terra Bella Ave 94043
Tel (650) 691-9800 SIC 3679

VERITAS TECHNOLOGIES LLC p 1550
500 E Middlefield Rd 94043
Tel (650) 933-1000 SIC 7371 7375

VERITAS US INC p 1550
500 E Middlefield Rd 94043
Tel (650) 933-1000 SIC 7371

▲ VIVUS INC p 1563
351 E Evelyn Ave 94041
Tel (650) 934-5200 SIC 2834

MURRIETA, CA

MURRIETA VALLEY UNIFIED SCHOOL DISTRICT p 1002
41870 Mcalby Ct 92562
Tel (951) 696-1600 SIC 8211

■ SOUTHWEST HEALTHCARE SYSTEM AUXILIARY p 1352
25500 Medical Center Dr 92562
Tel (951) 696-6000
SIC 8062 8051 8059 4119

WEST PAK AVOCADO INC p 1595
38655 Sky Canyon Dr 92563
Tel (951) 296-5757 SIC 0723

NAPA, CA

BIAGI BROS INC p 181
787 Airpark Rd 94558
Tel (707) 745-8115 SIC 4213 4225

COUNTY OF NAPA p 380
1195 Third St Ste 310 94559
Tel (707) 253-4421 SIC 9111

DOCTORS CO AN INTERINSURANCE EXCHANGE p 447
185 Greenwood Rd 94558
Tel (707) 226-0100 SIC 6321

DOCTORS MANAGEMENT CO p 447
185 Greenwood Rd 94558
Tel (707) 226-0100 SIC 6411

NAPA VALLEY UNIFIED SCHOOL DISTRICT p 1007
2425 Jefferson St 94558
Tel (707) 253-3715 SIC 8211

NORTH BAY DEVELOPMENTAL DISABILITIES SERVICES INC p 1051
10 Executive Ct Ste A 94558
Tel (707) 256-1224 SIC 8331 8322

NOVA GROUP INC p 1062
185 Devlin Rd 94558
Tel (707) 265-1100
SIC 1629 1623 1622 5172

QUEEN OF VALLEY MEDICAL CENTER p 1198
1000 Trancas St 94558
Tel (707) 252-4411 SIC 8062

REGULUS GROUP LLC p 1220
860 Latour Ct 94558
Tel (707) 259-7100 SIC 7374

SYAR INDUSTRIES INC p 1413
2301 Napa Vallejo Hwy 94558
Tel (707) 252-8711
SIC 5032 2951 0762 7992 5932

TREASURY WINE ESTATES AMERICAS CO p 1475
555 Gateway Dr 94558
Tel (707) 259-4500 SIC 2084

NATIONAL CITY, CA

FORNACA INC p 568
2400 National City Blvd 91950
Tel (619) 474-5573 SIC 5511 7532 5531

HARVEST MEAT CO INC p 666
1022 Bay Marina Dr # 106 91950
Tel (619) 477-0185 SIC 5147

NATIONAL SCHOOL DISTRICT p 1016
1500 N Ave 91950
Tel (619) 336-7500 SIC 8211

PARADISE VALLEY HOSPITAL p 1113
2400 E 4th St 91950
Tel (619) 470-4100 SIC 8062

PIONEER SPEAKERS INC p 1151
2427 Transportation Ave 91950
Tel (619) 477-0850 SIC 3679

PLAZA MANOR PRESERVATION LP p 1156
2615 E Plaza Blvd 91950
Tel (619) 475-2125 SIC 6531

SAND DOLLAR HOLDINGS INC p 1278
1022 Bay Marina Dr # 106 91950
Tel (619) 477-0185 SIC 5147

NEEDLES, CA

FORT MOJAVE TRIBAL COUNCIL p 569
500 Merriman St 92363
Tel (760) 629-4591 SIC 9131

NEVADA CITY, CA

COUNTY OF NEVADA p 380
950 Maidu Ave 95959
Tel (530) 265-1480 SIC 9111

NEWARK, CA

▲ DEPOMED INC p 431
7999 Gateway Blvd Ste 300 94560
Tel (510) 744-8000 SIC 2834

FRESH CHOICE LLC p 578
8371 Central Ave Ste A 94560
Tel (510) 857-1241 SIC 5812

HITACHI CONSULTING SOFTWARE SERVICES INC p 696
8000 Jarvis Ave Ste 130 94560
Tel (510) 742-4100 SIC 7299 7371

LOGITECH INC p 875
7700 Gateway Blvd 94560
Tel (510) 795-8500 SIC 3577

MORPHO DETECTION LLC p 989
7151 Gateway Blvd 94560
Tel (510) 739-2400 SIC 3812

RISK MANAGEMENT SOLUTIONS INC p 1236
7575 Gateway Blvd 94560
Tel (510) 505-2500 SIC 6794 6411

SMART MODULAR TECHNOLOGIES (WWH) INC p 1332
39870 Eureka Dr 94560
Tel (510) 623-1231 SIC 3674 3577 3679

UNIVERSITY HEALTHCARE ALLIANCE p 1519
7999 Gateway Blvd Ste 200 94560
Tel (510) 974-8281 SIC 8082

VM SERVICES INC p 1563
6701 Mowry Ave 94560
Tel (510) 744-3720 *SIC* 7371

WINTEC INDUSTRIES INC p 1617
8674 Thornton Ave 94560
Tel (408) 856-0500 *SIC* 3577 3674 3572

■ **WORLDPAC INC** p 1626
37137 Hickory St 94560
Tel (510) 742-8900 *SIC* 5013 5531

NEWBURY PARK, CA

■ **ONYX PHARMACEUTICALS INC** p 1088
1 Amgen Center Dr 91320
Tel (650) 266-0000 *SIC* 2834 8049

NEWCASTLE, CA

A & A STEPPING STONE MFG INC p 4
10291 Ophir Rd 95658
Tel (530) 885-7481 *SIC* 5211 3272

NEWPORT BEACH, CA

ABSOLUTE RETURN PORTFOLIO p 13
700 Newport Center Dr 92660
Tel (800) 800-7646 *SIC* 6722

▲ **ACACIA RESEARCH CORP** p 13
520 Newport Center Dr # 1200 92660
Tel (949) 480-8300 *SIC* 6794

AEROSPACE PARTS HOLDINGS INC p 31
610 Nwport Ctr Dr Ste 950 92660
Tel (949) 877-3630 *SIC* 6719

▲ **ALLIANCE HEALTHCARE SERVICES INC** p 54
100 Bayview Cir Ste 400 92660
Tel (949) 242-5300 *SIC* 8071

ALLIANT INSURANCE SERVICES INC p 55
1301 Dove St Ste 200 92660
Tel (949) 756-0271 *SIC* 6411 8748

ALLIANZ GLOBAL INVESTORS OF AMERICA LP p 55
680 Nwport Ctr Dr Ste 250 92660
Tel (949) 219-2200 *SIC* 6282

▲ **AMERICAN VANGUARD CORP** p 81
4695 Macarthur Ct 92660
Tel (949) 260-1200 *SIC* 2879

CADENCE AEROSPACE LLC p 236
610 Nwport Ctr Dr Ste 950 92660
Tel (949) 877-3630 *SIC* 3728

■ **CLEAN ENERGY** p 323
4675 Macarthur Ct Ste 800 92660
Tel (949) 437-1000 *SIC* 4924

▲ **CLEAN ENERGY FUELS CORP** p 323
4675 Macarthur Ct Ste 800 92660
Tel (949) 437-1000 *SIC* 4924 4922

■ **EDWARDS THEATRES CIRCUIT INC** p 480
300 Newport Center Dr 92660
Tel (949) 640-4600 *SIC* 7832

EUREKA REALTY PARTNERS INC p 512
4100 Macarthur Blvd # 200 92660
Tel (949) 224-4100 *SIC* 6552

■ **EXPERIENCE 1 INC** p 520
5000 Birch St Ste 300 92660
Tel (949) 475-3752 *SIC* 6361 6531

FESTIVAL FUN PARKS LLC p 539
4590 Macarthur Blvd # 400 92660
Tel (949) 261-0404 *SIC* 7999 7993

FLETCHER JONES MOTOR CARS INC p 555
3300 Jamboree Rd 92660
Tel (949) 718-3000 *SIC* 5511

FRANDELI GROUP LLC p 574
20377 Sw Acacia St # 200 92660
Tel (714) 450-7660 *SIC* 6794

H & H AGENCY INC p 649
20351 Sw Acacia St 92660
Tel (949) 260-8840 *SIC* 6331

HEALTHSMART PACIFIC INC p 677
20377 Sw Acacia St # 110 92660
Tel (562) 595-1911 *SIC* 8062

HOAG MEMORIAL HOSPITAL PRESBYTERIAN p 698
1 Hoag Dr 92663
Tel (949) 764-4624 *SIC* 8062

IRVINE CO LLC p 765
550 Newport Center Dr # 160 92660
Tel (949) 720-2000
SIC 6552 6531 0174 0191 4841

IRVINE EASTGATE OFFICE II LLC p 765
550 Newport Center Dr 92660
Tel (949) 720-2000 *SIC* 6798

JAMES R GLIDEWELL DENTAL CERAMICS INC p 777
4141 Macarthur Blvd 92660
Tel (949) 440-2600 *SIC* 8072

JAZZ SEMICONDUCTOR INC p 779
4321 Jamboree Rd 92660
Tel (949) 435-8000 *SIC* 3674

KBS REAL ESTATE INVESTMENT TRUST II INC p 806
800 Nwport Ctr Dr Ste 700 92660
Tel (949) 417-6500 *SIC* 6799

KBS REAL ESTATE INVESTMENT TRUST III INC p 806
620 Newport Center Dr # 1300 92660
Tel (949) 417-6500 *SIC* 6798

KBS STRATEGIC OPPORTUNITY REIT INC p 806
620 Newport Center Dr 92660
Tel (949) 417-6500 *SIC* 6798

KOLL MANAGEMENT SERVICES INC p 826
4343 Von Karman Ave # 150 92660
Tel (949) 833-3030 *SIC* 6531 8741

MAKAR PROPERTIES LLC p 899
4100 Macarthur Blvd # 150 92660
Tel (949) 255-1100 *SIC* 6552 1542

■ **MINDSPEED TECHNOLOGIES INC** p 972
4000 Macarthur Blvd 92660
Tel (949) 579-3000 *SIC* 3674

MSCSOFTWARE CORP p 997
4675 Macarthur Ct Ste 900 92660
Tel (714) 540-8900 *SIC* 7372

NEWTON BIOFUELS LLC p 1039
127 Crystal Ave 92662
Tel (949) 697-3088 *SIC* 2911

ORANGE COUNTY COMMUNITY FOUNDATION p 1092
4041 Macarthur Blvd # 510 92660
Tel (949) 553-4202 *SIC* 6732

OWL COMPANIES p 1100
4695 Macarthur Ct Ste 950 92660
Tel (949) 797-2000 *SIC* 8331 6519 4911

PACIFIC INVESTMENT MANAGEMENT CO LLC p 1105
650 Nwport Ctr Dr Ste 100 92660
Tel (949) 720-6000 *SIC* 6282

PACIFIC LIFE & ANNUITY CO p 1105
700 Newport Center Dr 92660
Tel (949) 219-3011 *SIC* 6311 6411

PACIFIC LIFE FUND ADVISORS LLC p 1105
700 Newport Center Dr 92660
Tel (800) 800-7646 *SIC* 6282

PACIFIC LIFE INSURANCE CO p 1105
700 Newport Center Dr 92660
Tel (949) 219-3011
SIC 6311 6371 6321 7359

PACIFIC LIFECORP p 1105
700 Newport Center Dr 92660
Tel (949) 219-3011
SIC 6371 6311 6321 6035 8111

PACIFIC MUTUAL HOLDING CO p 1105
700 Newport Center Dr 92660
Tel (949) 219-3011 *SIC* 6371 6311 6321

PALACE ENTERTAINMENT INC p 1108
4590 Macarthur Blvd # 400 92660
Tel (949) 261-0404 *SIC* 7999 7993

REALTY FINANCE CORP p 1214
895 Dove St Ste 210 92660
Tel (949) 296-3280 *SIC* 6162

RUBYS DINER INC p 1257
201 Shipyard Way Ste E 92663
Tel (949) 644-7829 *SIC* 5812

SABAL FINANCIAL GROUP LP p 1263
4675 Macarthur Ct Fl 15 92660
Tel (949) 255-2660 *SIC* 6282

SENIOR VINTAGE MANAGEMENT INC p 1304
23 Corporate Plaza Dr # 190 92660
Tel (949) 719-4080 *SIC* 8059

SMART CIRCLE INTERNATIONAL LLC p 1332
4490 Von Karman Ave 92660
Tel (949) 587-9207 *SIC* 5963

SUMMIT REALTY GROUP INC p 1399
177 Riverside Ave Ste F 92663
Tel (619) 987-1630 *SIC* 8742

TARSADIA HOTELS p 1425
620 Newport Center Dr # 1400 92660
Tel (949) 610-8000 *SIC* 7011

■ **TICOR TITLE CO OF CALIFORNIA** p 1452
1500 Quail St Ste 300 92660
Tel (714) 289-7100 *SIC* 6361

■ **TITLE365 CO** p 1456
5000 Birch St Ste 300 92660
Tel (877) 365-9365 *SIC* 6541

TOWER US HOLDINGS INC p 1464
4321 Jamboree Rd 92660
Tel (949) 435-8000 *SIC* 3674

TZ HOLDINGS LP p 1496
567 San Nicolas Dr # 120 92660
Tel (949) 719-2200 *SIC* 7372

VI LLC INTEGRAL PARTNERS p 1554
3 San Joaquin Plz Ste 100 92660
Tel (949) 720-3612 *SIC* 6552

▲ **WILLIAM LYON HOMES** p 1610
4695 Macarthur Ct Ste 800 92660
Tel (949) 833-3600 *SIC* 1531

■ **WILLIAM LYON HOMES INC** p 1610
4695 Macarthur Ct Ste 800 92660
Tel (949) 833-3600 *SIC* 6552

WILSHIRE PARTNERS p 1613
620 Newport Center Dr # 1100 92660
Tel (800) 285-6038 *SIC* 5632 5961

WINDJAMMER CAPITAL INVESTORS III LLC p 1615
610 Newport Center Dr # 1100 92660
Tel (949) 706-9989 *SIC* 6211

WINDJAMMER CAPITAL INVESTORS IV LP p 1615
610 Newport Center Dr 92660
Tel (919) 706-9989 *SIC* 6799

NORCO, CA

HCI INC p 672
3166 Hrseless Carriage Rd 92860
Tel (951) 520-4202 *SIC* 1623

LOMBARDY HOLDINGS INC p 875
3166 Hrseless Carriage Rd 92860
Tel (951) 808-4550 *SIC* 1623 5211

NORTH HIGHLANDS, CA

HERITAGE INTERESTS LLC p 686
4300 Jetway Ct 95660
Tel (916) 481-5030 *SIC* 1751 5031 2431

■ **HOMEQ SERVICING CORP** p 703
4837 Watt Ave 95660
Tel (916) 339-6192
SIC 6162 6163 6111 6159

MCM CONSTRUCTION INC p 932
6413 32nd St 95660
Tel (916) 334-1221 *SIC* 1622

PACIFIC COAST SUPPLY LLC p 1104
4290 Roseville Rd 95660
Tel (916) 971-2301 *SIC* 5031

NORTH HILLS, CA

GALPIN MOTORS INC p 590
15505 Roscoe Blvd 91343
Tel (818) 787-3800
SIC 5511 5521 7538 7515 7514 5531

IMPERIAL TOY LLC p 734
16641 Roscoe Pl 91343
Tel (818) 536-6500 *SIC* 3944

NORTH HOLLYWOOD, CA

■ **AVIBANK MFG INC** p 138
11500 Sherman Way 91605
Tel (818) 392-2100 *SIC* 3452

■ **INTREPID HEALTHCARE SERVICES INC** p 760
4605 Lankershim Blvd 91602
Tel (888) 447-2362 *SIC* 8011

■ **KLUNE HOLDINGS INC** p 823
7323 Coldwater Canyon Ave 91605
Tel (818) 503-8100 *SIC* 3728

■ **KLUNE INDUSTRIES INC** p 823
7323 Coldwater Canyon Ave 91605
Tel (818) 503-8100 *SIC* 3728

■ **O P I PRODUCTS INC** p 1070
13034 Saticoy St 91605
Tel (818) 759-8688 *SIC* 5087 2844

PARK MANAGEMENT GROUP LLC p 1115
1825 Gillespie Way Ste 101 91601
Tel (404) 350-9990 *SIC* 7011

■ **UNIVERSAL STUDIOS INC** p 1517
100 Universal City Plz 91608
Tel (818) 777-1000
SIC 7812 3652 2741 5947 5944 5961

NORTHRIDGE, CA

CONTEMPORARY SERVICES CORP p 362
17101 Superior St 91325
Tel (818) 885-5150 *SIC* 7361

■ **HARMAN PROFESSIONAL INC** p 662
8500 Balboa Blvd 91329
Tel (818) 894-8850 *SIC* 3651

MEDTRONIC MINIMED INC p 939
18000 Devonshire St 91325
Tel (800) 646-4633 *SIC* 3845

MIKUNI AMERICAN CORP p 968
8910 Mikuni Ave 91324
Tel (310) 676-0522 *SIC* 5013 5088

PHARMAVITE LLC p 1141
8510 Balboa Blvd Ste 300 91325
Tel (818) 221-6200 *SIC* 2833 2834

VALLEY HOSPITAL MEDICAL CENTER p 1541
18300 Roscoe Blvd 91325
Tel (818) 885-8500 *SIC* 8062

NORWALK, CA

BALLY TOTAL FITNESS CORP p 149
12440 Imperial Hwy # 300 90650
Tel (562) 484-2000 *SIC* 7991

BALLY TOTAL FITNESS OF CALIFORNIA INC p 149
12440 Imperial Hwy # 300 90650
Tel (562) 484-2000 *SIC* 7991

CERRITOS COMMUNITY COLLEGE DISTRICT p 284
11110 Alondra Blvd 90650
Tel (562) 860-2451 *SIC* 8221 8222

DIANAS MEXICAN FOOD PRODUCTS INC p 437
16330 Pioneer Blvd 90650
Tel (562) 926-5802 *SIC* 2099 5812

DOTY BROS EQUIPMENT CO p 452
11232 Firestone Blvd 90650
Tel (562) 864-6566 *SIC* 1623

NORWALK LA MIRADA UNIFIED SCHOOL DISTRICT p 1061
12820 Pioneer Blvd 90650
Tel (562) 868-0431 *SIC* 8211

WEST CENTRAL PRODUCE INC p 1594
12840 Leyva St 90650
Tel (213) 629-3600 *SIC* 5148

NOVATO, CA

BRADEN PARTNERS LP A CALIFORNIA LIMITED PARTNERSHIP p 206
773 San Marin Dr Ste 2230 94945
Tel (415) 893-1518 *SIC* 8082

CAGWIN & DORWARD p 237
1565 S Novato Blvd 94947
Tel (415) 892-7710 *SIC* 0782

CHARMING TRIM & PACKAGING INC p 290
28 Brookside Ct 94947
Tel (415) 302-7021 *SIC* 5131 3111

FIREMANS FUND INSURANCE CO p 543
777 San Marin Dr Ste 2160 94945
Tel (415) 899-2000 *SIC* 6331 6351 6321

RAPTOR PHARMACEUTICAL CORP p 1209
7 Hamilton Landing # 100 94949
Tel (415) 408-6200 *SIC* 8733 2834

TEIJIN PHARMA USA LLC p 1433
773 San Marin Dr Ste 2230 94945
Tel (415) 893-1518 *SIC* 5131

▲ **WILLIS LEASE FINANCE CORP** p 1612
773 San Marin Dr Ste 2215 94945
Tel (415) 408-4700 *SIC* 6159 5084

WORLDWISE INC p 1626
6 Hamilton Landing # 150 94949
Tel (415) 721-7400 *SIC* 5199

OAKDALE, CA

A L GILBERT CO p 6
304 N Yosemite Ave 95361
Tel (209) 847-1721 *SIC* 5191

OAKHURST, CA

SIERRA TEL COMMUNICATIONS GROUP p 1321
49150 Road 426 93644
Tel (559) 683-4611 *SIC* 4813

OAKLAND, CA

ALAMEDA-CONTRA COSTA TRANSIT DISTRICT p 44
1600 Franklin St 94612
Tel (510) 891-4777 *SIC* 4111

ASPIRE PUBLIC SCHOOLS p 118
1001 22nd Ave Ste 100 94606
Tel (510) 251-1660 *SIC* 8211

BRIGHTSOURCE ENERGY INC p 213
1999 Harrison St Ste 2150 94612
Tel (510) 550-8161 *SIC* 1629

CARPENTER FUNDS ADMINISTRATIVE OFFICE OF NORTHERN CALIFORNIA INC p 260
265 Hegenberger Rd # 100 94621
Tel (510) 639-3996 *SIC* 6733

CHEVRON FEDERAL CREDIT UNION p 296
500 12th St Ste 200 94607
Tel (888) 884-4630 *SIC* 5541

CHILDRENS HOSPITAL & RESEARCH CENTER AT OAKLAND p 299
747 52nd St 94609
Tel (510) 428-3000 *SIC* 8062

CITY OF OAKLAND p 317
150 Frank H Ogawa Plz # 3332 94612
Tel (510) 238-3280 *SIC* 9111

CIVICSOLAR INC p 320
426 17th St Ste 600 94612
Tel (800) 409-2257 *SIC* 5074 5211

▲ **CLOROX CO** p 327
1221 Broadway Ste 1300 94612
Tel (510) 271-7000
SIC 2842 2673 2035 2844 2879

■ **CLOROX INTERNATIONAL CO** p 327
1221 Broadway Ste 13 94612
Tel (510) 271-7000 *SIC* 2842 2879

■ **CLOROX PRODUCTS MANUFACTURING CO** p 327
1221 Broadway Ste 51 94612
Tel (510) 271-7000 *SIC* 2842

■ **CLOROX SALES CO** p 327
1221 Broadway Ste 13 94612
Tel (510) 271-7000 *SIC* 5087

COUNTY OF ALAMEDA p 376
1221 Oak St Ste 555 94612
Tel (510) 272-6691 *SIC* 9111

■ **DASAN ZHONE SOLUTIONS INC** p 413
7195 Oakport St 94621
Tel (510) 777-7000 *SIC* 3661

DREYERS GRAND ICE CREAM HOLDINGS INC p 456
5929 College Ave 94618
Tel (510) 652-8187 *SIC* 5143 5451 2024

EAST BAY MUNICIPAL UTILITY DISTRICT WASTEWATER SYSTEM p 469
375 11th St 94607
Tel (866) 403-2683 *SIC* 4952 4953

EAST BAY MUNICIPAL UTILITY DISTRICT WATER SYSTEM p 469
375 11th St 94607
Tel (866) 403-2683 *SIC* 4941

EAST BAY REGIONAL PARK DISTRICT p 470
2950 Peralta Oaks Ct 94605
Tel (888) 327-2757 *SIC* 7999

EBARA AMERICA CORP p 474
809 Walker Ave Apt 1 94610
Tel (510) 251-0500 *SIC* 3492

EDYS GRAND ICE CREAM p 480
5929 College Ave 94618
Tel (510) 652-8187 *SIC* 2024 5143

ELF BEAUTY INC p 486
570 10th St 94607
Tel (510) 778-7787 *SIC* 5999

FAIRN & SWANSON INC p 525
400 Lancaster St 94601
Tel (510) 533-8260 *SIC* 5122 5182

GIVE SOMETHING BACK INC p 613
7730 Pardee Ln Ste A 94621
Tel (800) 261-2619 *SIC* 5112

■ **GLAD PRODUCTS CO** p 614
1221 Broadway Ste A 94612
Tel (510) 271-7000
SIC 3081 2673 2842 3295

GOLDEN GATE FREIGHTLINER INC p 621
8200 Baldwin St 94621
Tel (559) 486-4310 *SIC* 5511 5531 7538

■ **IAC SEARCH & MEDIA INC** p 725
555 12th St Ste 500 94607
Tel (510) 985-7400 *SIC* 7375

IJOT DEVELOPMENT INC p 731
1300 Clay St Ste 600 94612
Tel (925) 258-9909 *SIC* 2531 2599

JACOBS ENGINEERING GROUP MEDICAL PLAN TRUST p 775
300 Frank H Ogawa Plz # 10 94612
Tel (510) 457-0027 *SIC* 8711

KAISER FDN HEALTH PLAN OF COLORADO p 800
1 Kaiser Plz Ste 15l 94612
Tel (510) 271-6611 *SIC* 8099

KAISER FOUNDATION HEALTH PLAN INC p 800
1 Kaiser Plz 94612
Tel (510) 271-5800 *SIC* 6324

KAISER FOUNDATION HOSPITALS INC p 800
1 Kaiser Plz 94612
Tel (510) 271-6611 *SIC* 8062 8011

KAISER HOSPITAL ASSET MANAGEMENT INC p 800
1 Kaiser Plz 19l 94612
Tel (510) 271-5910 *SIC* 5047

KAISER PERMANENTE INTERNATIONAL p 800
1 Kaiser Plz 94612
Tel (510) 271-5910 *SIC* 8062

KENNETH RAININ FOUNDATION p 811
155 Grand Ave Ste 1000 94612
Tel (510) 625-5200 *SIC* 8999

■ **KINGSFORD PRODUCTS CO LLC** p 821
1221 Broadway Ste 1300 94612
Tel (510) 271-7000
SIC 2861 2099 2035 2033 2879

LA CLINICA DE LA RAZA INC p 835
1450 Fruitvale Ave Fl 3 94601
Tel (510) 535-4000 *SIC* 8099

■ **MATSON NAVIGATION CO INC** p 920
555 12th St 94607
Tel (510) 628-4000 *SIC* 4424 4491 4492

MCGUIRE AND HESTER p 929
9009 Railroad Ave 94603
Tel (510) 632-7676 *SIC* 1623 7353

■ **METTLER-TOLEDO RAININ LLC** p 957
7500 Edgewater Dr 94621
Tel (510) 564-1600 *SIC* 3821 3829

MILLS COLLEGE p 971
5000 Macarthur Blvd 94613
Tel (510) 430-2255 *SIC* 8221

NESTLE DREYERS ICE CREAM CO p 1026
5929 College Ave 94618
Tel (510) 594-9466 *SIC* 5812 2024

OAKLAND UNIFIED SCHOOL DISTRICT p 1071
1000 Broadway Fl 4 94607
Tel (510) 434-7790 *SIC* 8211

OTIS MCALLISTER INC p 1097
300 Frank H Ogawa Plz # 400 94612
Tel (415) 421-6010 *SIC* 5149 5141

▲ **PANDORA MEDIA INC** p 1111
2101 Webster St Ste 1650 94612
Tel (510) 451-4100 *SIC* 4832

PERALTA COMMUNITY COLLEGE DISTRICT p 1134
333 E 8th St 94606
Tel (510) 466-7200 *SIC* 8222

PERMANENTE MEDICAL GROUP INC p 1136
1950 Franklin St Fl 18th 94612
Tel (866) 858-2226 *SIC* 8099

PUBLIC HEALTH INSTITUTE p 1189
555 12th St Ste 1050 94607
Tel (510) 285-5500 *SIC* 8733

REGENTS OF UNIVERSITY OF CALIFORNIA p 1219
1111 Franklin St Fl 12 94607
Tel (510) 987-0700 *SIC* 8221 8733

REGENTS OF UNIVERSITY OF CALIFORNIA p 1219
1111 Franklin St 94607
Tel (619) 543-3713 *SIC* 8062

REGIONAL CENTER OF EAST BAY INC p 1219
7677 Oakport St Ste 300 94621
Tel (510) 383-1200 *SIC* 8322

ROMAN CATHOLIC BISHOP OF OAKLAND p 1248
2121 Harrison St Ste 100 94612
Tel (510) 893-4711 *SIC* 8661

ROMAN CATHOLIC WELFARE CORP OF OAKLAND p 1249
3014 Lakeshore Ave 94610
Tel (510) 893-4711 *SIC* 8211

SALEM CARE CENTER p 1272
2361 E 29th St 94606
Tel (510) 534-3637 *SIC* 8051

SAN FRANCISCO BAY AREA RAPID TRANSIT DISTRICT p 1276
300 Lakeside Dr 94604
Tel (510) 464-6000 *SIC* 4111

SEIU UNITED HEALTHCARE WORKERS-WEST LOCAL 2005 p 1301
560 Thomas L Berkley Way 94612
Tel (510) 251-1250 *SIC* 8631

SHIMMICK CONSTRUCTION CO INC p 1316
8201 Edgewater Dr Ste 202 94621
Tel (510) 777-5000 *SIC* 1629 1623

SIERRA CLUB p 1320
2101 Webster St Ste 1300 94612
Tel (415) 977-5500 *SIC* 8641 8399

SUMMIT MEDICAL CENTER p 1399
350 Hawthorne Ave 94609
Tel (510) 655-4000 *SIC* 8062 8221 5947

SUNGEVITY INC p 1402
66 Franklin St Ste 310 94607
Tel (510) 496-5500 *SIC* 1711 8713

■ **WASTE MANAGEMENT OF ALAMEDA COUNTY INC** p 1580
172 98th Ave 94603
Tel (510) 613-8710 *SIC* 4953

OCEANSIDE, CA

BERGENSONS PROPERTY SERVICES INC p 174
3605 Ocean Ranch Blvd # 200 92056
Tel (760) 631-5111 *SIC* 7349

CITY OF OCEANSIDE p 317
300 N Coast Hwy 92054
Tel (760) 435-3830 *SIC* 9111

FEDERAL HEATH SIGN CO LLC p 534
4602 North Ave 92056
Tel (760) 941-0715 *SIC* 3993

HYDRANAUTICS p 723
401 Jones Rd 92058
Tel (760) 901-2597 *SIC* 2899 3589

OCEANSIDE UNIFIED SCHOOL DISTRICT p 1073
2111 Mission Ave 92058
Tel (760) 966-4000 *SIC* 8211

ONESOURCE DISTRIBUTORS LLC p 1088
3951 Oceanic Dr 92056
Tel (760) 966-4500 *SIC* 5063 3699

TRI-CITY HOSPITAL DISTRICT INC p 1477
4002 Vista Way 92056
Tel (760) 724-8411 *SIC* 8062

XCELLERATEHR LLC p 1631
702 Civic Center Dr 92054
Tel (602) 571-2187 *SIC* 7389

OLANCHA, CA

CG ROXANE LLC p 285
1210 State Hwy 395 93549
Tel (760) 764-2885 *SIC* 2086

OLIVEHURST, CA

SHOEI FOODS USA INC p 1317
1900 Feather River Blvd 95961
Tel (530) 742-7866 *SIC* 5141

ONTARIO, CA

BEAUTY 21 COSMETICS INC p 166
2021 S Archibald Ave 91761
Tel (909) 945-2220 *SIC* 5122 2844

CHAFFEY JOINT UNION HIGH SCHOOL DISTRICT p 286
211 W 5th St 91762
Tel (909) 988-8511 *SIC* 8211

■ **CITIZENS BUSINESS BANK** p 310
701 N Haven Ave Ste 350 91764
Tel (909) 980-4030 *SIC* 6022

CITY OF ONTARIO p 317
303 E B St 91764
Tel (909) 395-2012 *SIC* 9111

CONCORD FOODS INC p 354
4601 E Guasti Rd 91761
Tel (909) 975-2000 *SIC* 5141

▲ **CVB FINANCIAL CORP** p 404
701 N Haven Ave Ste 350 91764
Tel (909) 980-4030 *SIC* 6022

DAMAO LUGGAGE INTERNATIONAL INC p 410
1909 S Vineyard Ave 91761
Tel (909) 923-6531 *SIC* 5099 3161

DPI SPECIALTY FOODS INC p 454
601 S Rockefeller Ave 91761
Tel (909) 390-0892 *SIC* 5149 5143

DPI SPECIALTY FOODS WEST INC p 454
601 S Rockefeller Ave 91761
Tel (909) 975-1019 *SIC* 5141

FIRST MORTGAGE CORP p 548
1131 W 6th St Ste 300 91762
Tel (909) 595-1996 *SIC* 6162

GH DAIRY p 610
14651 Grove Ave 91762
Tel (909) 606-6455 *SIC* 0241

GOLD STAR FOODS INC p 620
3781 E Airport Dr 91761
Tel (909) 843-9600 *SIC* 5142

GROVE LUMBER & BUILDING SUPPLIES INC p 642
1300 S Campus Ave 91761
Tel (909) 947-0277 *SIC* 5031 5211

■ **ICEE CO** p 727
1205 S Dupont Ave 91761
Tel (800) 426-4233
SIC 2038 5145 3559 2087

IDB HOLDINGS INC p 728
601 S Rockefeller Ave 91761
Tel (909) 390-5624 *SIC* 5143 2022

MAG INSTRUMENT INC p 895
2001 S Hellman Ave 91761
Tel (909) 947-1006 *SIC* 3648

■ **MEDEGEN LLC** p 935
4501 E Wall St 91761
Tel (909) 390-9080 *SIC* 3089

MYERS POWER PRODUCTS INC p 1004
2950 E Philadelphia St 91761
Tel (909) 923-1800 *SIC* 3629

NEW-INDY ONTARIO LLC p 1036
5100 Jurupa St 91761
Tel (909) 390-1055 *SIC* 2621

NIAGARA BOTTLING LLC p 1042
2560 E Philadelphia St 91761
Tel (909) 230-5000 *SIC* 2086

ONTARIO-MONTCLAIR SCHOOL DISTRICT p 1088
950 W D St 91762
Tel (909) 459-2500 *SIC* 8211

POOL & ELECTRICAL PRODUCTS INC p 1161
1250 E Francis St 91761
Tel (909) 673-1160 *SIC* 5091

PRIME HEALTHCARE FOUNDATION INC p 1175
3300 E Guasti Rd Fl 3 91761
Tel (909) 235-4400 *SIC* 8011

PRIME HEALTHCARE SERVICES INC p 1175
3300 E Guasti Rd Ste 300 91761
Tel (909) 235-4400 *SIC* 8062

PROS MARKET INC p 1184
1700 S De Soto Pl Ste A 91761
Tel (909) 930-9552 *SIC* 5411

R & B WHOLESALE DISTRIBUTORS INC p 1201
2350 S Milliken Ave 91761
Tel (909) 230-5400 *SIC* 5064

REPLANET LLC p 1224
800 N Haven Ave Ste 120 91764
Tel (951) 520-1700 *SIC* 5084 4953

RIDGESIDE CONSTRUCTION INC p 1234
4345 E Lowell St Ste A 91761
Tel (909) 218-7593 *SIC* 1521

SAVAGE BMW INC p 1283
1301 Auto Center Dr 91761
Tel (909) 390-7888 *SIC* 5511

SIGMANET INC p 1321
4290 E Brickell St 91761
Tel (909) 230-7500 *SIC* 5045 7373

SPECIALTY BRANDS INC p 1356
4200 Concours Ste 100 91764
Tel (909) 477-4851 *SIC* 2038 5142

TEST-RITE PRODUCTS CORP p 1441
1900 Burgundy Pl 91761
Tel (909) 605-9899 *SIC* 5023

TEXAS HOME HEALTH OF AMERICA LP p 1443
1455 Auto Center Dr # 200 91761
Tel (972) 201-3800 *SIC* 8049

TORIN INC p 1461
4355 E Brickell St 91761
Tel (909) 390-8588 *SIC* 5084

WINDSOR AJINOMOTO INC p 1615
4200 Concours Ste 100 91764
Tel (909) 477-4700 *SIC* 2038 2037

ORANGE, CA

ALLIANCE FUNDING GROUP p 54
3745 W Chapman Ave # 200 92868
Tel (714) 940-0653 *SIC* 6159

AMERICAN TECHNOLOGIES INC p 80
210 W Baywood Ave 92865
Tel (714) 283-9990
SIC 1521 1541 1742 1731 1721 1711

AMERIQUEST CAPITAL CORP p 83
1100 W Twn Cntry Rd R 92868
Tel (714) 564-0600 *SIC* 6163

BERGEN BRUNSWIG DRUG CO p 174
4000 W Metropolitan Dr # 200 92868
Tel (714) 385-4000 *SIC* 5122

CASHCALL INC p 263
1 City Blvd W Ste 102 92868
Tel (949) 752-4600 *SIC* 6141

CB TECHNOLOGIES INC p 268
750 The City Dr S Ste 225 92868
Tel (714) 573-7733 *SIC* 7379 7373

CHAPMAN UNIVERSITY p 288
1 University Dr 92866
Tel (714) 997-6815 *SIC* 8221

CHAPMAN UNIVERSITY p 288
283 N Cypress St 92866
Tel (714) 997-6765 *SIC* 8221

CHILDRENS HEALTHCARE OF CALIFORNIA p 299
1201 W La Veta Ave 92868
Tel (714) 997-3000 *SIC* 8069

CHILDRENS HOSPITAL OF ORANGE COUNTY p 300
1201 W La Veta Ave 92868
Tel (714) 997-3000 *SIC* 8069

CHOICE ADMINISTRATORS INSURANCE SERVICES INC p 302
721 S Parker St Ste 200 92868
Tel (714) 542-4200 *SIC* 6411

CONEXIS BENEFIT ADMINISTRATORS LP p 355
721 S Parker St Ste 300 92868
Tel (714) 835-5006 *SIC* 6411

DMG CORP p 446
1110 W Taft Ave Ste A 92865
Tel (562) 692-1277 *SIC* 5075 5078

DON MIGUEL MEXICAN FOODS INC p 450
333 S Anita Dr Ste 1000 92868
Tel (714) 385-4500 *SIC* 2038

ENTERPRISE RENT-A-CAR CO OF LOS ANGELES LLC p 502
333 City Blvd W Ste 1000 92868
Tel (657) 221-4400
SIC 7515 7513 5511 7514

HILL BROTHERS CHEMICAL CO p 693
1675 N Main St 92867
Tel (714) 998-8800 *SIC* 5169 2819

■ **HOLMES & NARVER INC** p 701
999 W Town And Country Rd 92868
Tel (714) 567-2400
SIC 8711 8742 8741 1542

■ **KERR CORP** p 813
1717 W Collins Ave 92867
Tel (714) 516-7400 *SIC* 3843

M S INTERNATIONAL INC p 890
2095 N Batavia St 92865
Tel (714) 685-7500 *SIC* 5032

MEGAMEX FOODS LLC p 940
333 S Anita Dr Ste 1000 92868
Tel (714) 385-4500 *SIC* 5141

NEWPORT CH INTERNATIONAL LLC p 1038
1100 W Town And Country R 92868
Tel (714) 572-8881 *SIC* 5093

ORANGE COUNTY HEALTH AUTHORITY A PUBLIC AGENCY p 1092
505 City Pkwy W 92868
Tel (714) 246-8500 *SIC* 8621 8011

ORANGE COUNTY TRANSPORTATION AUTHORITY p 1092
550 S Main St 92868
Tel (714) 636-7433 *SIC* 4111 8711

ORANGE UNIFIED SCHOOL DISTRICT p 1092
1401 N Handy St 92867
Tel (714) 628-4000 *SIC* 8211

■ **ORMCO CORP** p 1095
1717 W Collins Ave 92867
Tel (714) 516-7400 *SIC* 3843

PLETHORA BUSINESSES p 1156
2117 W Orangewood Ave A 92868
Tel (714) 255-8862 *SIC* 6211

ROTH STAFFING COMPANIES LP p 1252
450 N State College Blvd 92868
Tel (714) 939-8600 *SIC* 7363

SA RECYCLING LLC p 1263
2411 N Glassell St 92865
Tel (714) 632-2000 *SIC* 5093

SISTERS OF ST JOSEPH OF ORANGE p 1327
480 S Batavia St 92868
Tel (714) 633-8121 *SIC* 8661

SKB CORP p 1329
434 W Levers Pl 92867
Tel (714) 637-1252 *SIC* 3089 3161

SOUTHERN COUNTIES OIL CO p 1348
1800 W Katella Ave # 400 92867
Tel (714) 744-7140 *SIC* 5171 5541 5172

ST JOSEPH HOSPITAL OF ORANGE p 1368
1100 W Stewart Dr 92868
Tel (714) 633-9111 *SIC* 8062

STAFFCHEX INC p 1374
790 The City Dr S Ste 180 92868
Tel (714) 912-7500 *SIC* 7361

SWEET CANDY LLC p 1411
929 W Barkley Ave 92868
Tel (877) 817-9338 *SIC* 5441

■ **SYBRON DENTAL SPECIALTIES INC** p 1413
1717 W Collins Ave 92867
Tel (714) 516-7400 *SIC* 3843 2834

ORANGEVALE, CA

■ **SUMMERVILLE AT HAZEL CREEK LLC** p 1398
6125 Hazel Ave 95662
Tel (916) 988-7901 *SIC* 8361

ORANGE, CA

VILLAGE NURSERIES WHOLESALE LLC p 1557
1589 N Main St 92867
Tel (714) 279-3100 *SIC* 5193

■ **WASTE MANAGEMENT COLLECTION AND RECYCLING INC** p 1580
2050 N Glassell St 92865
Tel (714) 282-0200 *SIC* 4953

WEST AMERICAN RUBBER CO LLC p 1593
1337 W Braden Ct 92868
Tel (714) 532-3355 *SIC* 3069 3061 3053

WESTERN DENTAL SERVICES INC p 1598
530 S Main St Ste 600 92868
Tel (714) 480-3000 SIC 8021

WORD & BROWN INSURANCE ADMINISTRATORS INC p 1624
721 S Parker St Ste 300 92868
Tel (714) 835-5006 SIC 6411

ORCUTT, CA

DEN-MAT CORP p 428
236 S Broadway St 93455
Tel (805) 922-8491 SIC 2844 3843

OROSI, CA

MOUNTAIN VIEW AG SERVICES INC p 994
13281 Avenue 416 93647
Tel (559) 528-6004 SIC 0761

OROVILLE, CA

BUTTE COUNTY OFFICE OF EDUCATION p 230
1859 Bird St 95965
Tel (530) 532-5650 SIC 8211

COUNTY OF BUTTE p 376
25 County Center Dr # 110 95965
Tel (530) 538-7701 SIC 9311

OROHEALTH CORP p 1095
2767 Olive Hwy 95966
Tel (530) 533-8500 SIC 8741

OROVILLE HOSPITAL p 1095
2767 Olive Hwy 95966
Tel (530) 533-8500 SIC 8062

OXNARD, CA

AFFINITY GROUP HOLDING LLC p 32
2750 Park View Ct Ste 240 93036
Tel (805) 667-4100 SIC 7997 2721

B & S PLASTICS INC p 141
2200 Sturgis Rd 93030
Tel (805) 981-0262 SIC 3089

BOSKOVICH FARMS INC p 202
711 Diaz Ave 93030
Tel (805) 487-2299 SIC 0723 5812 0161

CITY OF OXNARD p 317
300 W 3rd St Uppr Fl4 93030
Tel (805) 385-7803 SIC 9111

HAAS AUTOMATION INC p 651
2800 Sturgis Rd 93030
Tel (805) 278-1800 SIC 3541

MISSION PRODUCE INC p 975
2500 E Vineyard Ave # 300 93036
Tel (805) 981-3650 SIC 5148

NEW-INDY OXNARD LLC p 1036
5936 Perkins Rd 93033
Tel (805) 986-3881 SIC 2621

OXNARD SCHOOL DISTRICT p 1101
1051 S A St 93030
Tel (805) 487-3918 SIC 8211

OXNARD UNION HIGH SCHOOL DIST p 1101
309 S K St 93030
Tel (805) 385-2500 SIC 8211

RAYPAK INC p 1210
2151 Eastman Ave 93030
Tel (805) 278-5300 SIC 3433

■ **SEMINIS INC** p 1302
2700 Camino Del Sol 93030
Tel (805) 485-7317 SIC 8731 8742 2099

■ **SEMINIS VEGETABLE SEEDS INC** p 1302
2700 Camino Del Sol 93030
Tel (855) 733-3834 SIC 5191 0723

THOMPSON OLDE INC p 1449
3250 Camino Del Sol 93030
Tel (800) 827-1565 SIC 5023 2631 5149

■ **VENTURA SYSCO INC** p 1548
3100 Sturgis Rd 93030
Tel (805) 205-7000 SIC 5141

PACHECO, CA

BAY ALARM CO p 160
60 Berry Dr 94553
Tel (925) 935-1100 SIC 1731 7382 5063

PACOIMA, CA

■ **AMERICAN FRUITS AND FLAVORS LLC** p 73
10725 Sutter Ave 91331
Tel (818) 899-9574 SIC 2087

MOC PRODUCTS CO INC p 980
12306 Montague St 91331
Tel (818) 794-3500 SIC 5169 7549

VALLARTA SUPERMARKETS INC p 1540
10147 San Fernando Rd 91331
Tel (818) 485-0596 SIC 5411

PALA, CA

PALA CASINO SPA & RESORT p 1108
35008 Pala Temecula Rd 92059
Tel (760) 510-5100 SIC 7991

PALM DESERT, CA

QUALITY COLLISION CENTER p 1196
42480 Ritter Cir Ste 5 92211
Tel (760) 779-5054 SIC 7532

PALM SPRINGS, CA

AGUA CALIENTE BAND OF CAHUILLA INDIANS p 36
5401 Dinah Shore Dr 92264
Tel (760) 699-6800 SIC 8699 6552 7999

CFO CONSULTANTS INC p 285
829 E Francis Dr 92262
Tel (760) 899-1919 SIC 8742

■ **DESERT REGIONAL MEDICAL CENTER INC** p 432
1150 N Indian Canyon Dr 92262
Tel (760) 323-6374 SIC 8062

PALM SPRINGS UNIFIED SCHOOL DIST p 1109
980 E Tahquitz Canyon Way 92262
Tel (760) 416-6177 SIC 8211

SPA RESORT CASINO p 1353
401 E Amado Rd 92262
Tel (888) 999-1995 SIC 7011

PALMDALE, CA

■ **PALMDALE REGIONAL MEDICAL CENTER** p 1109
38600 Medical Center Dr 93551
Tel (661) 382-5000 SIC 8011

PALMDALE SCHOOL DISTRICT p 1109
39139 10th St E 93550
Tel (661) 947-7191 SIC 8211

US POLE CO INC p 1533
660 W Avenue O 93551
Tel (800) 877-6537 SIC 3648

PALO ALTO, CA

ACTIAN CORP p 19
2300 Geng Rd Ste 150 94303
Tel (650) 587-5500 SIC 7373 7372

ADAPTIVE INSIGHTS INC p 21
3350 W Bayshore Rd Ste 200 94303
Tel (800) 303-6346 SIC 7372

ALFATECH CAMBRIDGE GROUP GP p 49
345 S California Ave # 3 94306
Tel (650) 543-3030 SIC 8741 8742

ALTAMONT CAPITAL PARTNERS LLC p 62
400 Hamilton Ave Ste 230 94301
Tel (650) 264-7750 SIC 6799

ARIBA INC p 108
3420 Hillview Ave Bldg 3 94304
Tel (650) 849-4000 SIC 7372

BON APPETIT MANAGEMENT CO p 199
100 Hamilton Ave Ste 400 94301
Tel (650) 798-8000 SIC 8741

BROADREACH CAPITAL PARTNERS LLC p 215
248 Homer Ave 94301
Tel (650) 331-2500 SIC 6211

BUSINESS OBJECTS INC p 229
3410 Hillview Ave 94304
Tel (650) 849-4000 SIC 5045

CITY OF PALO ALTO p 317
250 Hamilton Ave 94301
Tel (650) 329-2571 SIC 9111

CLOUDERA INC p 327
1001 Page Mill Rd Bldg 3 94304
Tel (650) 644-3900 SIC 7371 5734 8331

COMMUNICATIONS & POWER INDUSTRIES LLC p 347
607 Hansen Way 94304
Tel (650) 846-2900
SIC 3671 3679 3699 3663

COOLEY LLP p 366
3175 Hanover St 94304
Tel (650) 843-5000 SIC 8111

CPI INTERNATIONAL HOLDING CORP p 387
811 Hansen Way 94304
Tel (650) 846-2900 SIC 3679

CPI INTERNATIONAL INC p 387
811 Hansen Way 94304
Tel (650) 846-2801
SIC 3671 3679 3699 3825

■ **DANISCO US INC** p 412
925 Page Mill Rd 94304
Tel (650) 846-7500
SIC 2835 8731 2899 2869

ELECTRIC POWER RESEARCH INSTITUTE INC p 484
3420 Hillview Ave 94304
Tel (650) 855-2000 SIC 8731

ESSEX PORTFOLIO LP p 510
925 E Meadow Dr 94303
Tel (650) 494-3700 SIC 6798 6513

FOODCOMM INTERNATIONAL p 564
4260 El Camino Real 94306
Tel (650) 813-1300 SIC 5147 5142

GORDON E AND BETTY I MOORE FOUNDATION p 626
1661 Page Mill Rd 94304
Tel (650) 213-3000 SIC 8748

▲ **HERCULES CAPITAL INC** p 685
400 Hamilton Ave Ste 310 94301
Tel (650) 289-3060 SIC 6799

HEWLETT PACKARD p 688
3000 Hanover St 94304
Tel (650) 857-1501 SIC 7371

▲ **HEWLETT PACKARD ENTERPRISE CO** p 688
3000 Hanover St 94304
Tel (650) 857-5817 SIC 7372 7379 3572

■ **HEWLETT-PACKARD ENTERPRISES LLC** p 688
3000 Hanover St 94304
Tel (650) 857-1501 SIC 3571

▲ **HP INC** p 714
1501 Page Mill Rd 94304
Tel (650) 857-1501
SIC 3571 7372 3861 3577 3572 3575

INTEGRATED ARCHIVE SYSTEMS INC p 749
1121 San Antonio Rd D100 94303
Tel (650) 390-9995 SIC 8742 5045

JAZZ PHARMACEUTICALS INC p 779
3180 Porter Dr 94304
Tel (650) 496-3777 SIC 2834

▲ **JIVE SOFTWARE INC** p 786
325 Lytton Ave Ste 200 94301
Tel (650) 319-1920 SIC 7372

JUMIO CORP p 797
268 Lambert Ave 94306
Tel (650) 424-8545 SIC 7371

LUCILE SALTER PACKARD CHILDRENS HOSPITAL AT STANFORD p 884
725 Welch Rd 94304
Tel (650) 497-8000 SIC 8069 8082 5912

MARCUS & MILLICHAP CO p 905
777 S California Ave 94304
Tel (650) 494-1400 SIC 6531

MARCUS & MILLICHAP REAL ESTATE INVESTMENT SERVICES OF INDIANA INC p 905
2626 Hanover St 94304
Tel (650) 494-1400 SIC 6531

MAXIMUS HOLDINGS INC p 922
2475 Hanover St 94304
Tel (650) 935-9500 SIC 7372

MDA COMMUNICATIONS HOLDINGS LLC p 933
3825 Fabian Way 94303
Tel (650) 852-4000 SIC 3663

MEDALLIA INC p 935
395 Page Mill Rd Ste 100 94306
Tel (650) 321-3000 SIC 7372 8732

■ **MERCURY INTERACTIVE LLC** p 945
3000 Hanover St 94304
Tel (650) 857-1501 SIC 7372

METRICSTREAM INC p 954
2600 E Bayshore Rd 94303
Tel (650) 620-2900 SIC 7372

OOMA INC p 1089
1880 Embarcadero Rd 94303
Tel (650) 566-6600 SIC 4813

PALANTIR TECHNOLOGIES INC p 1108
100 Hamilton Ave Ste 300 94301
Tel (650) 815-0200 SIC 7371

PALO ALTO MEDICAL FOUNDATION FOR HEALTH CARE RESEARCH AND EDUCATION (INC) p 1110
795 El Camino Real 94301
Tel (650) 321-4121 SIC 8011

PALO ALTO UNIFIED SCHOOL DISTRICT p 1110
25 Churchill Ave 94306
Tel (650) 329-3804 SIC 8211

SPACE SYSTEMS/LORAL LLC p 1354
3825 Fabian Way 94303
Tel (650) 852-7320 SIC 4899 3663

SYMPHONY TECHNOLOGY GROUP LLC p 1414
2475 Hanover St 94304
Tel (650) 935-9500 SIC 8748 6719

TALL TREE FOODS HOLDINGS INC p 1423
400 Hamilton Ave Ste 230 94301
Tel (650) 264-7750 SIC 2013

▲ **TESLA MOTORS INC** p 1440
3500 Deer Creek Rd 94304
Tel (650) 681-5000 SIC 3711 3714

TIBCO SOFTWARE INC p 1452
3303 Hillview Ave 94304
Tel (650) 846-1000 SIC 7371 7373

■ **VARIAN INC** p 1544
3100 Hansen Way 94304
Tel (650) 213-8000
SIC 3826 3845 3829 3827

▲ **VARIAN MEDICAL SYSTEMS INC** p 1544
3100 Hansen Way 94304
Tel (650) 493-4000 SIC 3845 3844 7372

■ **VMWARE INC** p 1563
3401 Hillview Ave 94304
Tel (650) 427-1000 SIC 7371 7375

WILSON SONSINI GOODRICH & ROSATI PROFESSIONAL CORP p 1614
650 Page Mill Rd 94304
Tel (650) 493-9300 SIC 8111

PALOMAR MOUNTAIN, CA

PALOMAR MOUNTAIN OUTDOOR SCHOOL CAMP p 1110
19452 State Park Rd 92060
Tel (760) 742-2128 SIC 8211

PALOS VERDES ESTATES, CA

DOUGLAS FURNITURE OF CALIFORNIA LLC p 452
809 Tyburn Rd 90274
Tel (310) 749-0003 SIC 2514 2512

PANORAMA CITY, CA

DEANCO HEALTHCARE LLC p 420
14850 Roscoe Blvd 91402
Tel (818) 787-2222 SIC 8063

PARADISE, CA

FEATHER RIVER HOSPITAL p 533
5974 Pentz Rd 95969
Tel (530) 877-9361 SIC 8062 8051

PARAMOUNT, CA

BODEGA LATINA CORP p 197
14601b Lakewood Blvd 90723
Tel (562) 616-8800 SIC 5411

■ **PARAMOUNT PETROLEUM CORP** p 1114
14700 Downey Ave 90723
Tel (562) 531-2060 SIC 2911

PARAMOUNT UNIFIED SCHOOL DISTRICT p 1114
15110 California Ave 90723
Tel (562) 602-6000 SIC 8211

TOTAL-WESTERN INC p 1463
8049 Somerset Blvd 90723
Tel (562) 220-1450 SIC 1389

WEBER METALS INC p 1586
16706 Garfield Ave 90723
Tel (562) 602-0260 SIC 3463

PARLIER, CA

MAXCO SUPPLY INC p 922
605 S Zediker Ave 93648
Tel (559) 646-8449 SIC 5113 2436 3554

PASADENA, CA

■ **AAH HUDSON LP** p 8
1255 N Hudson Ave 91104
Tel (626) 794-9179 SIC 6513

ALEXANDRIA REAL ESTATE EQUITIES INC p 49
385 E Colo Blvd Ste 299 91101
Tel (626) 578-0777 SIC 6798

■ **AMERON INTERNATIONAL CORP** p 84
245 S Los Robles Ave 91101
Tel (626) 683-4000
SIC 3272 3317 3273 1442 3084

ART CENTER COLLEGE OF DESIGN INC p 113
1700 Lida St 91103
Tel (626) 396-2200 SIC 8221

■ **BLUE CHIP STAMPS** p 191
301 E Colo Blvd Ste 300 91101
Tel (626) 585-6700 SIC 5051

BOLTON & CO p 199
3475 E Foothill Blvd # 100 91107
Tel (626) 799-7000 SIC 6411

C W DRIVER INC p 233
468 N Rosemead Blvd 91107
Tel (626) 351-8800 SIC 1542

CALIFORNIA INSTITUTE OF TECHNOLOGY p 240
1200 E California Blvd 91125
Tel (626) 395-6811 SIC 8733

CALIFORNIA IRONWORKERS FIELD WELFARE PLAN p 240
131 N El Molino Ave # 330 91101
Tel (626) 792-7337 SIC 8631

CHARLES PANKOW BUILDERS LTD A CALIFORNIA LIMITED PARTNERSHIP p 289
199 S Los Robles Ave # 300 91101
Tel (626) 304-1190 SIC 1542

■ **CIT BANK NA** p 309
75 N Fair Oaks Ave 91103
Tel (626) 535-4300 SIC 6021

CITY OF PASADENA p 317
100 N Garfield Ave 91101
Tel (626) 744-4386 SIC 9111

COMMUNITY BANK p 347
460 Serra Madre Villa Ave 91107
Tel (626) 577-1700 SIC 6022 6029

■ **CPO COMMERCE LLC** p 387
120 W Bellevue Dr Ste 300 91105
Tel (626) 585-3600 SIC 5072

▲ **EAST WEST BANCORP INC** p 471
135 N Los Robles Ave Fl 7 91101
Tel (626) 768-6000 SIC 6022

■ **EAST WEST BANK** p 471
135 N Ls Rbls Ave 100 91101
Tel (626) 768-6000 SIC 6022

■ **FULL SPECTRUM LENDING INC** p 584
35 N Lake Ave Fl 3 91101
Tel (626) 584-2220 SIC 6162 6163

FULLER THEOLOGICAL SEMINARY p 584
135 N Oakland Ave 91182
Tel (626) 584-5200 SIC 8221

▲ **GENERAL FINANCE CORP** p 600
39 E Union St Ste 206 91103
Tel (626) 584-9722 SIC 7359 5085

▲ **GREEN DOT CORP** p 637
3465 E Foothill Blvd # 100 91107
Tel (626) 765-2000 SIC 6141 7389

▲ **GUIDANCE SOFTWARE INC** p 645
1055 E Colo Blvd Ste 400 91106
Tel (626) 229-9191 SIC 7372 3572

HUNTINGTON HOSPITAL p 720
100 W California Blvd 91105
Tel (626) 397-5000 SIC 8062

IDEALAB p 729
130 W Union St 91103
Tel (626) 356-3654 SIC 5511 6726

IDEALAB HOLDINGS LLC p 729
130 W Union St 91103
Tel (626) 585-6900 SIC 6799 5045 5734

INTER-CON SECURITY SYSTEMS INC p 751
210 S De Lacey Ave # 200 91105
Tel (626) 535-2200 SIC 7381

J G BOSWELL CO p 771
101 W Walnut St 91103
Tel (626) 356-7492 SIC 0131 6552

■ **JACOBS ENGINEERING CO** p 775
1111 S Arroyo Pkwy 91105
Tel (626) 449-2171 SIC 8711 1629

■ **JACOBS ENGINEERING INC** p 775
155 N Lake Ave 91101
Tel (626) 578-3500 SIC 8711

■ **JACOBS INTERNATIONAL LTD INC** p 775
155 N Lake Ave 91101
Tel (626) 578-3500 SIC 8711

LA ASOCIACION NACIONAL PRO PERSONAS MAYORES p 835
234 E Colo Blvd Ste 300 91101
Tel (626) 564-1988 SIC 8322

LOS ANGELES COUNTY EMPLOYEES RETIREMENT ASSOCIATION p 878
300 N Lake Ave Ste 720 91101
Tel (626) 564-6000 SIC 6371

MAX LEON INC p 922
3100 New York Dr 91107
Tel (626) 797-6886 SIC 2339 5632

NAJARIAN FURNITURE CO INC p 1006
265 N Euclid Ave 91101
Tel (626) 839-8700 SIC 5021 5023

ONEWEST BANK GROUP LLC p 1088
888 E Walnut St 91101
Tel (626) 535-4870 SIC 6035

OPENX TECHNOLOGIES INC p 1089
888 E Walnut St Fl 2 91101
Tel (855) 673-6948 SIC 7311

OPERATING ENGINEERS HEALTH & WELFARE FUND p 1089
100 Corson St 91103
Tel (626) 356-1000 SIC 6733

PARSONS CONSTRUCTORS INC p 1118
100 W Walnut St 91124
Tel (626) 440-2000 SIC 8741 8711

PARSONS CORP p 1118
100 W Walnut St 91124
Tel (626) 440-2000
SIC 1629 1611 8711 8741

PARSONS ENGINEERING SCIENCE INC p 1118
100 W Walnut St 91124
Tel (626) 440-2000 SIC 8711

PARSONS GOVERNMENT SERVICES INC p 1118
100 W Walnut St 91124
Tel (626) 440-2000 SIC 8711

PARSONS GOVERNMENT SERVICES INTERNATIONAL INC p 1118
100 W Walnut St 91124
Tel (626) 440-6000 SIC 1542

PARSONS WATER & INFRASTRUCTURE INC p 1118
100 W Walnut St 91124
Tel (626) 440-7000 SIC 8711

PASADENA AREA COMMUNITY COLLEGE DISTRICT p 1119
1570 E Colorado Blvd 91106
Tel (626) 585-7123 SIC 8222

PASADENA HOSPITAL ASSOCIATION LTD p 1119
100 W California Blvd 91105
Tel (626) 397-5000 SIC 8062 8051 8063

PASADENA TOURNAMENT OF ROSES ASSOCIATION p 1119
391 S Orange Grove Blvd 91184
Tel (626) 449-4100 SIC 8641

PASADENA UNIFIED SCHOOL DISTRICT p 1119
351 S Hudson Ave 91101
Tel (626) 396-3600 SIC 8211

SCHAUMBOND GROUP INC p 1286
225 S Lake Ave Ste 300 91101
Tel (626) 215-4998 SIC 6726

SOUTHERN CALIFORNIA PERMANENTE MEDICAL GROUP p 1347
393 Walnut Dr 91107
Tel (626) 405-5704 SIC 6324

SUN PACIFIC MARKETING COOPERATIVE INC p 1400
1095 E Green St 91106
Tel (213) 612-9957 SIC 5148

▲ **TETRA TECH INC** p 1441
3475 E Foothill Blvd 91107
Tel (626) 351-4664 SIC 8711

■ **TICOR TITLE INSURANCE CO INC** p 1452
131 N El Molino Ave 91101
Tel (616) 302-3121 SIC 6361

TPUSA - FHCS INC p 1468
215 N Marengo Ave Ste 160 91101
Tel (213) 873-5100 SIC 7376 7373

UNITED AGENCIES INC p 1506
301 E Colo Blvd Ste 200 91101
Tel (626) 564-2670 SIC 6411

■ **WESCO FINANCIAL CORP** p 1593
301 E Colo Blvd Ste 300 91101
Tel (626) 585-6700 SIC 7359 6411 7389

WESCOM CENTRAL CREDIT UNION p 1593
123 S Marengo Ave 91101
Tel (888) 493-7266 SIC 6062

■ **WESTERN ASSET MANAGEMENT CO** p 1597
385 E Colorado Blvd # 250 91101
Tel (626) 844-9265 SIC 6282

PASO ROBLES, CA

■ **JOSLYN SUNBANK CO LLC** p 794
1740 Commerce Way 93446
Tel (805) 238-2840 SIC 3678 3643 5065

PEBBLE BEACH, CA

I CYPRESS CO p 725
1700 17 Mile Dr 93953
Tel (831) 647-7500 SIC 7011

PEBBLE BEACH RESORT CO DBA LONE CYPRESS SHOP p 1126
2700 17 Mile Dr 93953
Tel (831) 647-7500
SIC 7011 7992 5941 7991

PERRIS, CA

CALIFORNIA TRUSFRAME LLC p 241
23665 Cajalco Rd 92570
Tel (951) 657-7491 SIC 2439

EASTERN MUNICIPAL WATER DISTRICT p 472
2270 Trumble Rd 92572
Tel (951) 928-3777 SIC 4941 4952

SILVER CREEK INDUSTRIES INC p 1323
2830 Barrett Ave 92571
Tel (951) 943-5393 SIC 1542 2452

STARCREST PRODUCTS OF CALIFORNIA INC p 1379
3660 Brennan Ave # 1000 92599
Tel (951) 943-2011 SIC 5961

VAL VERDE UNIFIED SCH DIS p 1539
975 Morgan St 92571
Tel (951) 940-6100 SIC 8211

PETALUMA, CA

AMERICAN INSURANCE CO INC p 75
1465 N Mcdowell Blvd 94954
Tel (415) 899-2000 SIC 6331

ASSOCIATED INDEMNITY CORP p 120
1465 N Mcdowell Blvd # 100 94954
Tel (415) 899-2000
SIC 6311 6321 6331 6351

▲ **CALIX INC** p 242
1035 N Mcdowell Blvd 94954
Tel (707) 766-3000 SIC 3663 4899 4813

COURSECO INC p 383
1670 Corp Cir Ste 201 94954
Tel (707) 763-0335 SIC 7992

CYAN INC p 404
1383 N Mcdowell Blvd # 300 94954
Tel (707) 735-2300 SIC 5065

▲ **ENPHASE ENERGY INC** p 500
1420 N Mcdowell Blvd 94954
Tel (707) 774-7000 SIC 3674

GCX CORP p 595
3875 Cypress Dr 94954
Tel (707) 773-1100 SIC 3429

GOLDEN STATE LUMBER INC p 621
855 Lakeville St Ste 200 94952
Tel (707) 206-4100 SIC 5031 5211

ILLUMINATIONS.COM INC p 733
1736 Corporate Cir 94954
Tel (707) 776-2000 SIC 5961 5947

NATIONAL SURETY CORP p 1016
1465 N Mcdowell Blvd # 100 94954
Tel (415) 899-2000 SIC 6351

SAN FRANCISCO REINSURANCE CO p 1276
1465 N Mcdowell Blvd 94954
Tel (415) 899-2000 SIC 6321

SCANDINAVIAN DESIGNS INC p 1286
2250 S Mcdowell Blvd Ext 94954
Tel (707) 778-1600 SIC 5712

STAR H-R p 1378
3820 Cypress Dr Ste 2 94954
Tel (707) 762-4447 SIC 7363

PICO RIVERA, CA

AMINI INNOVATION CORP p 85
8725 Rex Rd 90660
Tel (562) 222-2500 SIC 5021

BAKEMARK USA LLC p 145
7351 Crider Ave 90660
Tel (562) 949-1054
SIC 2045 5149 3556 2099

PACIFIC LOGISTICS CORP p 1105
7255 Rosemead Blvd 90660
Tel (562) 478-4700 SIC 4731

PITTSBURG, CA

■ **PERFORMANCE MECHANICAL INC** p 1135
701 Willow Pass Rd Ste 2 94565
Tel (925) 432-4080 SIC 1541 1711 8711

PITTSBURG UNIFIED SCHOOL DISTRICT FINANCING CORP p 1152
2000 Railroad Ave 94565
Tel (925) 473-2300 SIC 8211

SSC PITTSBURG OPERATING CO LP p 1363
2351 Loveridge Rd 94565
Tel (925) 427-4444 SIC 8059

USS-POSCO INDUSTRIES A CALIFORNIA JOINT VENTURE p 1535
900 Loveridge Rd 94565
Tel (800) 877-7672 SIC 3312

PLACENTIA, CA

■ **HARTWELL CORP** p 666
900 Richfield Rd 92870
Tel (714) 993-2752 SIC 3429

PLACENTIA-YORBA LINDA UNIFIED SCHOOL DISTRICT p 1153
1301 E Orangethorpe Ave 92870
Tel (714) 986-7000 SIC 8211

SUNRISE GROWERS INC p 1404
701 W Kimberly Ave # 210 92870
Tel (714) 630-2170 SIC 5148 2037

PLACERVILLE, CA

COUNTY OF EL DORADO p 377
330 Fair Ln 95667
Tel (530) 621-5830 SIC 9111

MARSHALL MEDICAL CENTER p 911
1100 Marshall Way 95667
Tel (530) 622-1441 SIC 8062 8071 8082

SHINGLE SPRINGS RANCHERIA p 1317
5168 Honpie Rd 95667
Tel (530) 672-8059 SIC 9131

SHINGLE SPRINGS TRIBAL GAMING AUTHORITY p 1317
1 Red Hawk Pkwy 95667
Tel (530) 677-7000 SIC 7999

PLAYA VISTA, CA

BELKIN INTERNATIONAL INC p 169
12045 Waterfront Dr 90094
Tel (310) 751-5100 SIC 5065 5045

CALIFORNIA PIZZA KITCHEN INC p 241
12181 Bluff Creek Dr Fl 5 90094
Tel (310) 342-5000 SIC 5812

CPL HOLDINGS LLC p 387
12181 Bluff Creek Dr # 250 90094
Tel (310) 348-6800 SIC 5331 6719 5961

HONEST CO INC p 705
12130 Millennium Ste 500 90094
Tel (310) 917-9199 SIC 2341 2833

PLEASANT GROVE, CA

HOC HOLDINGS INC p 699
7310 Pacific Ave 95668
Tel (916) 921-8950
SIC 5082 5084 5083 7359

HOLT OF CALIFORNIA p 702
7310 Pacific Ave 95668
Tel (916) 991-8200
SIC 5082 5084 5083 7359

■ **SYSCO SACRAMENTO INC** p 1418
7062 Pacific Ave 95668
Tel (916) 275-2714 SIC 5141 5142

PLEASANT HILL, CA

DIABLO VALLEY COLLEGE FOUNDATION p 436
321 Golf Club Rd 94523
Tel (925) 685-1230 SIC 7389 8221

NORTHERN CALIFORNIA CONFERENCE OF SEVENTH-DAY ADVENTISTS p 1055
401 Taylor Blvd 94523
Tel (925) 685-4300 SIC 8211 8661

PLEASANTON, CA

AMERICAN BAPTIST HOMES OF WEST p 68
6120 Stoneridge Mall Rd # 300 94588
Tel (925) 924-7100 SIC 8059

AOC TECHNOLOGIES INC p 94
5960 Inglewood Dr 94588
Tel (925) 875-0808 SIC 5051 3357

APEX RESTAURANT MANAGEMENT INC p 96
1024 Serpentine Ln # 101 94566
Tel (925) 233-0006 SIC 5812

ATA RETAIL SERVICES LLC p 123
7133 Koll Center Pkwy # 100 94566
Tel (925) 621-4700 SIC 5199

▲ **BLACKHAWK NETWORK HOLDINGS INC** p 187
6220 Stoneridge Mall Rd 94588
Tel (925) 226-9990 SIC 6099

■ **BLACKHAWK NETWORK INC** p 187
6220 Stoneridge Mall Rd 94588
Tel (925) 226-9990 SIC 6099

CAMEO GLOBAL INC p 245
4695 Chabot Dr Ste 101 94588
Tel (925) 479-7800
SIC 7373 7371 7379 7363 4813 8742

COMMERCE WEST INSURANCE CO p 345
6130 Stoneridge Mall Rd # 400 94588
Tel (925) 730-6400 SIC 6141

▲ **COOPER COMPANIES INC** p 366
6140 Stoneridge Mall Rd # 590 94588
Tel (925) 460-3600 SIC 3851 3842

CORNERSTONE AFFILIATES INC p 370
6120 Stoneridge 94588
Tel (925) 924-7100 SIC 8322

CORNERSTONE STAFFING SOLUTIONS INC p 371
7020 Koll Center Pkwy 94566
Tel (925) 426-6900 SIC 7361

■ **DOCUMENTUM INC** p 447
6801 Koll Center Pkwy 94566
Tel (925) 600-6800 SIC 7372 7371

DOLAN FOSTER ENTERPRISES LLC p 447
5635 W Las Positas Blvd # 406 94588
Tel (925) 621-2600 SIC 5812

■ **E-LOAN INC** p 467
6230 Stoneridge Mall Rd 94588
Tel (925) 847-6200 SIC 6163 6162

▲ **ELLIE MAE INC** p 488
4420 Rosewood Dr Ste 500 94588
Tel (925) 227-7000 SIC 7371

ET SOLAR INC p 511
4900 Hopyard Rd Ste 310 94588
Tel (925) 460-9898 SIC 1711

EXCEL BUILDING SERVICES LLC p 516
1061 Serpentine Ln Ste H 94566
Tel (650) 755-0900 SIC 7349

GOLDEN STATE OVERNIGHT DELIVERY SERVICE INC p 621
7901 Stnridge Dr Ste 400 94588
Tel (800) 322-5555 SIC 4215

■ **GTT COMMUNICATIONS (MP) INC** p 644
6800 Koll Center Pkwy # 200 94566
Tel (925) 201-2500 SIC 4813 7375

HOSPITAL COMMITTEE FOR LIVERMORE-PLEASANTON AREAS p 709
5555 W Las Positas Blvd 94588
Tel (925) 847-3000 SIC 8062 8741

IRONPLANET INC p 765
3825 Hopyard Rd Ste 250 94588
Tel (925) 225-8600 SIC 7389

LEISURE SPORTS INC p 854
4670 Willow Rd Ste 100 94588
Tel (925) 600-1966 SIC 6719

MEGAPATH CLOUD CO LLC p 940
6800 Koll Center Pkwy 94566
Tel (925) 201-2500 SIC 4813

MEGAPATH INC p 940
6800 Koll Center Pkwy # 200 94566
Tel (877) 611-6342 SIC 4813

▲ **NATUS MEDICAL INC** p 1019
6701 Koll Center Pkwy # 150 94566
Tel (925) 223-6700 SIC 3845

NORTHERN CALIFORNIA TPG INC p 1055
6673 Owens Dr 94588
Tel (925) 556-0512 SIC 5141

PACIFIC CONVENIENCE & FUELS LLC p 1104
7180 Koll Center Pkwy 94566
Tel (925) 884-0800 SIC 5411 5541

PATELCO CREDIT UNION p 1120
5050 Hopyard Rd 94588
Tel (800) 358-8228 SIC 6061

PLEASANTON UNIFIED SCHOOL DISTRICT p 1156
4665 Bernal Ave 94566
Tel (925) 462-5500 SIC 8211

QUALITY AUTO CRAFT INC p 1196
3295 Bernal Ave Ste B 94566
Tel (925) 426-0120 SIC 7538 7532

■ **ROCHE MOLECULAR SYSTEMS INC** p 1243
4300 Hacienda Dr 94588
Tel (925) 730-8000 SIC 8731

SAFEWAY CANADA HOLDINGS INC p 1267
5918 Stoneridge Mall Rd 94588
Tel (925) 467-3000 SIC 5411

SAFEWAY DENVER INC p 1267
5918 Stoneridge Mall Rd 94588
Tel (925) 467-3000 SIC 5411

SAFEWAY INC p 1267
5918 Stoneridge Mall Rd 94588
Tel (925) 467-3000 SIC 5411 5912

SAFEWAY STORES 46 INC p 1267
5918 Stoneridge Mall Rd 94588
Tel (925) 467-3000 SIC 5411

SHAKLEE CORP p 1310
4747 Willow Rd 94588
Tel (925) 924-2000 SIC 5499

SHAKLEE US INC p 1311
4747 Willow Rd 94588
Tel (925) 924-2000 SIC 5122

▲ **SIMPSON MANUFACTURING CO INC** p 1325
5956 W Las Positas Blvd 94588
Tel (925) 560-9000 SIC 3441 3399

■ **SIMPSON STRONG-TIE CO INC** p 1325
5956 W Las Positas Blvd 94588
Tel (925) 560-9000 SIC 3449 2891

■ **THORATEC CORP** p 1450
6035 Stoneridge Dr 94588
Tel (925) 847-8600 SIC 3845 3841

▲ **VEEVA SYSTEMS INC** p 1546
4280 Hacienda Dr 94588
Tel (925) 452-6500 SIC 7372 7371 7379

VONS COMPANIES INC p 1565
5918 Stoneridge Mall Rd 94588
Tel (626) 821-7000 SIC 5411 2026 2024

▲ **WORKDAY INC** p 1624
6230 Stoneridge Mall Rd 94588
Tel (925) 951-9000 SIC 7371

▲ ZELTIQ AESTHETICS INC p 1642
4410 Rosewood Dr 94588
Tel (925) 474-2500 *SIC* 3841

ZOHO CORP p 1644
4141 Hacienda Dr 94588
Tel (925) 924-9500 *SIC* 7372

POMONA, CA

CAL POLY POMONA FOUNDATION INC p 237
3801 W Temple Ave Bldg 55 91768
Tel (909) 869-2950 *SIC* 8699

CONTINENTAL AGENCY INC p 362
1768 W 2nd St 91766
Tel (909) 595-8884 *SIC* 4731

FERGUSON FIRE & FABRICATION INC p 538
2750 S Towne Ave 91766
Tel (909) 517-3085 *SIC* 5074 5099

INTER-VALLEY HEALTH PLAN INC p 751
300 S Park Ave Ste 300 91766
Tel (909) 623-6333 *SIC* 6324 8011

KITTRICH CORP p 822
1585 W Mission Blvd 91766
Tel (714) 736-1000 *SIC* 2591 2392 2381

POMONA UNIFIED SCHOOL DISTRICT p 1161
800 S Garey Ave 91766
Tel (909) 397-4700 *SIC* 8211

POMONA VALLEY HOSPITAL MEDICAL CENTER p 1161
1798 N Garey Ave 91767
Tel (909) 865-9500 *SIC* 8062

POWERPLUS GROUP INC USA p 1166
1521 E Grand Ave 91766
Tel (909) 622-5888 *SIC* 3531

ROYAL CABINETS INC p 1254
1299 E Phillips Blvd 91766
Tel (909) 629-8565 *SIC* 2434 2511

SAN GABRIEL/POMONA VALLEYS DEVELOPMENTAL SERVICES INC p 1277
75 Rancho Camino Dr 91766
Tel (909) 620-7722 *SIC* 8322

WESTERN UNIVERSITY OF HEALTH SCIENCES p 1600
309 E 2nd St 91766
Tel (909) 623-6116 *SIC* 8221

PORTERVILLE, CA

CENTRAL VALLEY MORTGAGE SERVICE INC p 280
1987 W Orange Ave 93257
Tel (559) 782-8011 *SIC* 6162

GOOD SHEPHERD LUTHERAN HOME OF WEST p 623
119 N Main St 93257
Tel (559) 791-2000 *SIC* 8361

R M PARKS INC p 1202
1061 N Main St 93257
Tel (559) 784-2384 *SIC* 5171

PORTOLA VALLY, CA

TOSA FOUNDATION p 1462
3130 Alpine Rd 94028
Tel (650) 851-6922 *SIC* 8641

POWAY, CA

ALDILA INC p 48
14145 Danielson St Ste B 92064
Tel (858) 513-1801 *SIC* 3949 3297

BON SUISSE INC p 199
11860 Cmnty Rd Ste 100 92064
Tel (858) 486-0005 *SIC* 5143

▲ COHU INC p 335
12367 Crosthwaite Cir 92064
Tel (858) 848-8100 *SIC* 3825 3663 3699

■ DELTA DESIGN INC p 426
12367 Crosthwaite Cir 92064
Tel (858) 848-8000 *SIC* 3569 3825 3674

GENERAL ATOMICS AERONAUTICAL SYSTEMS INC p 599
14200 Kirkham Way 92064
Tel (858) 312-2810 *SIC* 3721

H M ELECTRONICS INC p 650
14110 Stowe Dr 92064
Tel (858) 535-6000 *SIC* 3669

PALOMAR POMERADO HOSPITAL DISTRICT p 1110
15615 Pomerado Rd 92064
Tel (858) 613-4000 *SIC* 8062

■ SYSCO SAN DIEGO INC p 1418
12180 Kirkham Rd 92064
Tel (858) 513-7300
SIC 5141 5142 5147 5148 5084

QUARTZ HILL, CA

NADONAH MEDICAL SUPPLY p 1006
5021 Columbia Way 93536
Tel (661) 718-3870 *SIC* 5999

RANCHO CORDOVA, CA

▲ AEROJET ROCKETDYNE HOLDINGS INC p 30
2001 Aerojet Rd 95742
Tel (916) 355-4000
SIC 3812 3764 3769 6552 6519

■ AEROJET ROCKETDYNE INC p 30
2001 Aerojet Rd 95742
Tel (916) 355-4000
SIC 3728 3764 3769 3761

AMPAC FINE CHEMICALS LLC p 86
Highway 50 And Hazel Ave Bldg 5019 95741
Tel (916) 357-6880 *SIC* 2834

C C MYERS INC p 232
3286 Fitzgerald Rd 95742
Tel (916) 635-9370 *SIC* 1622

CORDOVA FOLSOM UNIFIED SCHOOL DISTRICT p 369
1965 Birkmont Dr 95742
Tel (916) 294-9000 *SIC* 8211

DIGNITY HEALTH MEDICAL FOUNDATION p 439
3400 Data Dr 95670
Tel (916) 379-2840 *SIC* 8099

FOLSOM-CORDOVA UNIF SCH DIST p 563
1965 Birkmont Dr 95742
Tel (916) 294-9000 *SIC* 8221

■ FRANKLIN TEMPLETON INVESTOR SERVICES LLC p 575
3344 Quality Dr 95670
Tel (916) 463-1500 *SIC* 6211 6282

■ HEALTH NET FEDERAL SERVICES LLC p 675
2025 Aerojet Rd 95742
Tel (916) 935-5000 *SIC* 6324

JUDSON ENTERPRISES INC p 797
2440 Gold River Rd # 100 95670
Tel (916) 631-9300 *SIC* 2431 5031

MERCY HEALTHCARE SACRAMENTO p 947
3400 Data Dr 95670
Tel (916) 379-2871 *SIC* 8062

PABCO BUILDING PRODUCTS LLC p 1103
10600 White Rock Rd # 100 95670
Tel (510) 792-1577 *SIC* 3275 3251 3259

PACIFIC COAST BUILDING PRODUCTS INC p 1104
10600 White Rock Rd # 100 95670
Tel (916) 631-6500
SIC 3275 3271 5031 1761 2952 2426

■ PICK AND PULL AUTO DISMANTLING INC p 1146
10850 Gold Center Dr # 325 95670
Tel (916) 689-2000 *SIC* 5093

■ RENAISSANCE FOOD GROUP LLC p 1223
11020 White Rock Rd # 100 95670
Tel (916) 638-8825 *SIC* 2099

VISION SERVICE PLAN p 1561
3333 Quality Dr 95670
Tel (916) 851-5000 *SIC* 6324 5048

RANCHO CUCAMONGA, CA

▲ AMPHASTAR PHARMACEUTICALS INC p 86
11570 6th St 91730
Tel (909) 980-9484 *SIC* 2834

BRADSHAW INTERNATIONAL INC p 207
9409 Buffalo Ave 91730
Tel (909) 476-3884 *SIC* 5023

CHAFFEY COMMUNITY COLLEGE DISTRICT (INC) p 286
5885 Haven Ave 91737
Tel (909) 652-6560 *SIC* 8222 8221

CU COOPERATIVE SYSTEMS INC p 399
9692 Haven Ave 91730
Tel (909) 948-2500 *SIC* 6099

■ EVOLUTION FRESH INC p 515
11655 Jersey Blvd 91730
Tel (909) 478-0895 *SIC* 5148

INLAND EMPIRE HEALTH PLAN p 743
10801 6th St Ste 120 91730
Tel (909) 890-2000 *SIC* 6321 6324

MILITARY DELI & BAKERY SERVICES INC p 969
10600 N Trademark Pkwy 91730
Tel (909) 373-1344 *SIC* 5812

MONOPRICE INC p 985
11701 6th St 91730
Tel (909) 989-6887 *SIC* 5099

NONGSHIM AMERICA INC p 1047
12155 6th St 91730
Tel (909) 481-3698 *SIC* 5141 2098

NUVI GLOBAL CORP p 1068
8423 Rochester Ave # 101 91730
Tel (844) 740-6938 *SIC* 5122

PAMONA VALLEY MEDICAL GROUP INC p 1110
9302 Pttsbrgh Ave Ste 220 91730
Tel (909) 932-1045 *SIC* 8011 8741

■ RED ROBIN INTERNATIONAL p 1216
12271 Foothill Blvd 91739
Tel (909) 803-2665 *SIC* 5812

SCHLOSSER FORGE CO p 1287
11711 Arrow Rte 91730
Tel (909) 987-4760 *SIC* 3463 3462

STENO EMPLOYMENT SERVICES INC p 1385
8560 Vineyard Ave Ste 208 91730
Tel (909) 476-1404 *SIC* 7363

SUMITOMO RUBBER NORTH AMERICA INC p 1398
8656 Haven Ave 91730
Tel (909) 466-1116 *SIC* 5014

SUPERIOR ELECTRICAL MECHANICAL & PLUMBING INC p 1406
8613 Helms Ave 91730
Tel (909) 357-9400 *SIC* 1731 1711

TAMCO INC p 1423
12459 Arrow Rte 91739
Tel (909) 899-0660 *SIC* 3449

RANCHO DOMINGUEZ, CA

BERRY FRESH LLC p 176
19640 S Rancho Way 90220
Tel (310) 637-2401 *SIC* 5148

CJ KOREA EXPRESS USA CORP p 320
18805 S Laurel Park Rd 90220
Tel (714) 994-1200 *SIC* 4731 4783 4225

DHX-DEPENDABLE HAWAIIAN EXPRESS INC p 435
19201 S Susana Rd 90220
Tel (310) 537-2000 *SIC* 4731

MARIAK INDUSTRIES INC p 906
575 W Manville St 90220
Tel (310) 661-4400 *SIC* 5023 2591

MARS FOOD US LLC p 910
2001 E Cashdan St Ste 201 90220
Tel (310) 933-0670 *SIC* 2044

NEWAY PACKAGING CORP p 1037
1973 E Via Arado 90220
Tel (602) 454-9000 *SIC* 5113 5084

SANTA MONICA SEAFOOD CO p 1281
18531 S Broadwick St 90220
Tel (310) 886-7900 *SIC* 5421 5146 5142

UNION SUPPLY GROUP INC p 1505
2301 E Pacifica Pl 90220
Tel (310) 603-8899 *SIC* 5141 5139 5136

RANCHO MIRAGE, CA

EISENHOWER MEDICAL CENTER p 482
39000 Bob Hope Dr 92270
Tel (760) 340-3911 *SIC* 8062 8082

GOLDEN INTERNATIONAL p 621
36720 Palmdale Rd 92270
Tel (760) 568-1912 *SIC* 6799

RANCHO PALOS VERDES, CA

LONG POINT DEVELOPMENT LLC p 876
100 Terranea Way 90275
Tel (310) 265-2800 *SIC* 7011

RCHO STA MARG, CA

APPLIED MEDICAL CORP p 100
22872 Avenida Empresa 92688
Tel (949) 713-8000 *SIC* 3841

APPLIED MEDICAL RESOURCES CORP p 100
22872 Avenida Empresa 92688
Tel (949) 635-9153 *SIC* 3841

CONTROL COMPONENTS INC p 364
22591 Avenida Empresa 92688
Tel (949) 858-1877 *SIC* 3491

JIPC MANAGEMENT INC p 786
22342 Avenida Empresa # 220 92688
Tel (949) 916-2000 *SIC* 8741

NUCOURSE DISTRIBUTION INC p 1067
22342 Avenida Empresa # 200 92688
Tel (866) 655-4366 *SIC* 5065

OCONNELL LANDSCAPE MAINTENANCE INC p 1074
23091 Arroyo Vis 92688
Tel (949) 589-2007 *SIC* 0782

PARK WEST COMPANIES INC p 1116
22421 Gilberto Ste A 92688
Tel (949) 546-8300 *SIC* 0782 1629 6719

RED BLUFF, CA

ST ELIZABETH COMMUNITY HOSPITAL p 1366
2550 Sster Mary Clumba Dr 96080
Tel (530) 529-7760 *SIC* 8062 6513

REDDING, CA

COUNTY OF SHASTA p 381
1450 Court St Ste 308a 96001
Tel (530) 225-5561 *SIC* 9199

FAR NORTHERN COORDINATING COUNCIL ON DEVELOPMENTAL DISABILITIES p 528
1900 Churn Creek Rd # 31 96002
Tel (530) 222-4791 *SIC* 8322

MERCY HOME SERVICES A CALIFORNIA LIMITED PARTNERSHIP p 947
2175 Rosaline Ave Ste A 96001
Tel (530) 225-6000 *SIC* 8062

PRIME HEALTHCARE SERVICES - SHASTA LLC p 1175
1100 Butte St 96001
Tel (530) 244-5400 *SIC* 8062 8011

REDLANDS, CA

ENVIRONMENTAL SYSTEMS RESEARCH INSTITUTE INC p 503
380 New York St 92373
Tel (909) 793-2853 *SIC* 5045

P & R PAPER SUPPLY CO INC p 1102
1898 E Colton Ave 92374
Tel (909) 389-1811
SIC 5113 5169 5149 5072 5046

PRIME-LINE PRODUCTS CO p 1175
26950 San Bernardino Ave 92374
Tel (909) 887-8118 *SIC* 5072

REDLANDS COMMUNITY HOSPITAL p 1217
350 Terracina Blvd 92373
Tel (909) 335-5500 *SIC* 8069

REDLANDS UNIFIED SCHOOL DISTRICT p 1217
20 W Lugonia Ave 92374
Tel (909) 307-5300 *SIC* 8211

RHS CORP p 1232
350 Terracina Blvd 92373
Tel (909) 335-5500 *SIC* 8741

UNIVERSITY OF REDLANDS p 1524
1200 E Colton Ave 92374
Tel (909) 793-2121 *SIC* 8221

REDONDO BEACH, CA

BICARA LTD p 181
1611 S Catalina Ave 90277
Tel (310) 316-6222 *SIC* 5147 5146 5141

REDWOOD CITY, CA

ABS-CBN INTERNATIONAL p 12
150 Shoreline Dr 94065
Tel (800) 527-2820 *SIC* 4841 7822

■ ARICENT INC p 108
303 Twin Dolphin Dr # 600 94065
Tel (650) 632-4310 *SIC* 7371

▲ BOX INC p 205
900 Jefferson Ave 94063
Tel (877) 729-4269 *SIC* 7372

BRANTNER HOLDING CO p 208
501 Oakside Ave 94063
Tel (650) 361-5292 *SIC* 3678

COUNTY OF SAN MATEO p 381
400 County Ctr 94063
Tel (650) 363-4123 *SIC* 9111

■ DIGITAL INSIGHT CORP p 439
1300 Seaport Blvd Ste 300 94063
Tel (818) 879-1010 *SIC* 7375 7372 7371

DPR CONSTRUCTION A GENERAL PARTNERSHIP p 454
1450 Veterans Blvd 94063
Tel (650) 474-1450 *SIC* 1541

DPR CONSTRUCTION INC p 454
1450 Veterans Blvd Ofc 94063
Tel (650) 474-1450 *SIC* 1541 1542

▲ ELECTRONIC ARTS INC p 485
209 Redwood Shores Pkwy 94065
Tel (650) 628-1500 *SIC* 7372

■ ELECTRONIC ARTS REDWOOD INC p 485
209 Redwood Shores Pkwy 94065
Tel (650) 628-1500 *SIC* 3695

▲ EQUINIX INC p 506
1 Lagoon Dr Ste 400 94065
Tel (650) 598-6000 *SIC* 4813

EVERNOTE CORP p 515
305 Walnut St 94063
Tel (650) 216-7700 *SIC* 4813

▲ GENOMIC HEALTH INC p 604
301 Penobscot Dr 94063
Tel (650) 556-9300 *SIC* 8071 8731

I2C INC p 725
1300 Island Dr Ste 105 94065
Tel (650) 480-5222 *SIC* 5045

▲ IMPERVA INC p 735
3400 Bridge Pkwy Ste 200 94065
Tel (650) 345-9000 *SIC* 7371

INFORMATICA LLC p 741
2100 Seaport Blvd 94063
Tel (650) 385-5000 *SIC* 7372

■ MENLO WORLDWIDE FORWARDING INC p 943
1 Lagoon Dr Ste 400 94065
Tel (650) 596-9600
SIC 4513 4215 4522 4731 6159 6351

▲ N MODEL INC p 1005
1600 Seaport Blvd Ste 400 94063
Tel (650) 610-4600 *SIC* 7371

■ OC ACQUISITION LLC p 1072
500 Oracle Pkwy 94065
Tel (650) 506-7000 *SIC* 7371 7372

OMIDYAR NETWORK SERVICES LLC p 1084
1991 Broadway St Ste 200 94063
Tel (650) 482-2500 *SIC* 8742

■ ORACLE AMERICA INC p 1091
500 Oracle Pkwy 94065
Tel (650) 506-7000
SIC 3571 7379 7373 7372 3674

▲ ORACLE CORP p 1091
500 Oracle Pkwy 94065
Tel (650) 506-7000
SIC 7372 7379 8243 3571 3674

■ ORACLE SYSTEMS CORP p 1091
500 Oracle Pkwy 94065
Tel (650) 506-7000 *SIC* 7372 7379 8243

■ ORACLE USA INC p 1091
500 Oracle Pkwy 94065
Tel (650) 506-7000 *SIC* 7372

PENTAIR THERMAL MANAGEMENT LLC p 1132
899 Broadway St 94063
Tel (650) 474-7414 *SIC* 1711 3822

▲ QUALYS INC p 1198
1600 Bridge Pkwy Ste 201 94065
Tel (650) 801-6100 *SIC* 7371 7372

▲ **ROCKET FUEL INC** p 1244
1900 Seaport Blvd 94063
Tel (650) 595-1300 *SIC* 7379

■ **RUDOLPH AND SLETTEN INC** p 1257
1600 Seaport Blvd Ste 350 94063
Tel (650) 216-3600 *SIC* 1542 1541

S J AMOROSO CONSTRUCTION CO INC p 1262
390 Bridge Pkwy 94065
Tel (650) 654-1900 *SIC* 1542

SABA SOFTWARE INC p 1263
2400 Bridge Pkwy 94065
Tel (650) 581-2500 *SIC* 7372 7371

SEQUOIA HEALTH SERVICES p 1306
170 Alameda De Las Pulgas 94062
Tel (650) 369-5811 *SIC* 8062

SEQUOIA UNION HIGH SCHOOL DISTRICT p 1306
480 James Ave 94062
Tel (650) 369-1411 *SIC* 8211

▲ **SHUTTERFLY INC** p 1319
2800 Bridge Pkwy Ste 100 94065
Tel (650) 610-5200 *SIC* 7384

▲ **SUPPORT.COM INC** p 1408
900 Chesapeake Dr Fl 2 94063
Tel (650) 556-9440 *SIC* 7374 7372

TE CONNECTIVITY MOG INC p 1429
501 Oakside Ave 94063
Tel (650) 361-5292 *SIC* 3229

VERITY HEALTH SYSTEM OF CALIFORNIA INC p 1550
203 Redwood Shores Pkwy 94065
Tel (650) 551-6650 *SIC* 8062

W L BUTLER CONSTRUCTION INC p 1568
204 Franklin St 94063
Tel (650) 361-1270 *SIC* 1542

■ **YASHENG GROUP** p 1635
805 Veterans Blvd Ste 228 94063
Tel (650) 363-8345
SIC 2879 0111 0115 0116 0112

■ **YODLEE INC** p 1636
3600 Bridge Pkwy Ste 200 94065
Tel (650) 980-3600 *SIC* 8742

▲ **YUME INC** p 1640
1204 Middlefield Rd 94063
Tel (650) 591-9400 *SIC* 7311

REEDLEY, CA

MOONLIGHT PACKING CORP p 987
17719 E Huntsman Ave 93654
Tel (559) 638-7799 *SIC* 5148 4783

RIALTO, CA

B & B PLASTICS RECYCLERS INC p 141
3040 N Locust Ave 92377
Tel (909) 829-3606 *SIC* 5093 2673

RIALTO UNIFIED SCHOOL DISTRICT p 1232
182 E Walnut Ave 92376
Tel (909) 820-7700 *SIC* 8211

SRA TRANSPORT INC p 1362
1041 N Willow Ave 92376
Tel (909) 510-2481 *SIC* 4789

RICHMOND, CA

C OVERAA & CO p 233
200 Parr Blvd 94801
Tel (510) 234-0926 *SIC* 1541

CITY OF RICHMOND p 318
450 Civic Center Plaza 94804
Tel (510) 620-6727 *SIC* 9111

JT THORPE & SON INC p 772
1060 Hensley St 94801
Tel (510) 233-2500 *SIC* 1741 8711

■ **MOUNTAIN HARDWEAR INC** p 994
1414 Harbour Way S 94804
Tel (510) 558-3000 *SIC* 2399 2394 5651

OAKLAND PAPER & SUPPLY INC p 1071
3200 Regatta Blvd Ste F 94804
Tel (510) 307-4242 *SIC* 5113 5087

■ **RICHMOND SANITARY SERVICE INC** p 1233
3260 Blume Dr Ste 100 94806
Tel (510) 262-7100 *SIC* 4959

RICHMOND WHOLESALE MEAT CO p 1233
2920 Regatta Blvd 94804
Tel (510) 233-5111 *SIC* 5147

SIMS GROUP USA CORP p 1325
600 S 4th St 94804
Tel (510) 412-5300 *SIC* 5093 4953

T F LOUDERBACK INC p 1419
700 National Ct 94804
Tel (510) 965-6120
SIC 5181 5149 2037 2033

TERRA MILLENNIUM CORP p 1439
1060 Hensley St 94801
Tel (510) 233-2500 *SIC* 1741 8711

WEST CONTRA COSTA UNIFIED SCHOOL DISTRICT p 1594
1108 Bissell Ave 94801
Tel (510) 231-1100 *SIC* 8211

RICHVALE, CA

BUTTE COUNTY RICE GROWERS ASSOCIATION INC p 230
1193 Richvale Hwy 95974
Tel (530) 345-7103 *SIC* 5191 0723 5261

RIDGECREST, CA

RIDGECREST REGIONAL HOSPITAL p 1234
1081 N China Lake Blvd 93555
Tel (760) 446-3551 *SIC* 8062

RIPON, CA

WINE GROUP INC p 1616
17000 E State Highway 120 95366
Tel (209) 599-4111 *SIC* 2084

RIVERSIDE, CA

AMA PLASTICS p 64
1100 Citrus St 92507
Tel (951) 734-5600 *SIC* 3089 3544

■ **AMERICAN MEDICAL RESPONSE** p 76
879 Marlborough Ave 92507
Tel (951) 782-5200 *SIC* 4119

■ **AMERICAN MEDICAL RESPONSE AMBULANCE SERVICE INC** p 76
879 Marlborough Ave 92507
Tel (303) 495-1217 *SIC* 4119

BA HOLDINGS p 143
3016 Kansas Ave Bldg 1 92507
Tel (951) 684-5110 *SIC* 3443 3728

BOURNS INC p 204
1200 Columbia Ave 92507
Tel (951) 781-5500
SIC 3677 3676 3661 3639 3679

CALIFORNIA BAPTIST UNIVERSITY p 239
8432 Magnolia Ave 92504
Tel (951) 689-5771 *SIC* 8221

CITY OF RIVERSIDE p 318
3900 Main St Fl 7 92522
Tel (951) 826-5311 *SIC* 9111

COUNTY OF RIVERSIDE p 381
4080 Lemon St Fl 11 92501
Tel (951) 955-1110 *SIC* 9111

■ **CREST STEEL CORP** p 392
6580 General Rd 92509
Tel (310) 830-2651 *SIC* 5051

DAVID A CAMPBELL CORP p 415
3060 Adams St 92504
Tel (951) 785-4444 *SIC* 5511 7538

DURA COAT PRODUCTS INC p 462
5361 Via Ricardo 92509
Tel (951) 341-6500 *SIC* 3479 2851

ELDORADO NATIONAL (CALIFORNIA) INC p 484
9670 Galena St 92509
Tel (951) 727-9300 *SIC* 3711

FENCEWORKS INC p 537
870 Main St 92501
Tel (951) 788-5620 *SIC* 1799

FLEETWOOD MOTOR HOMES-CALIFINC p 555
3125 Myers St 92503
Tel (951) 354-3000 *SIC* 3716

HERMAN WEISSKER INC p 687
1645 Brown Ave 92509
Tel (951) 826-8800 *SIC* 1623 8711 1731

HUB INTERNATIONAL INSURANCE SERVICES INC p 716
3390 University Ave # 300 92501
Tel (951) 788-8500 *SIC* 6411

■ **INTERNATIONAL LINE BUILDERS INC** p 755
2520 Rubidoux Blvd 92509
Tel (951) 682-2982 *SIC* 1731

JOHNSON MACHINERY CO p 791
800 E La Cadena Dr 92507
Tel (951) 686-4560 *SIC* 5082

K & N ENGINEERING INC p 798
1455 Citrus St 92507
Tel (951) 826-4000 *SIC* 3751 3599 3714

LA CADENA INVESTMENTS INC p 835
3750 University Ave # 610 92501
Tel (909) 733-5000 *SIC* 5411

LA SIERRA UNIVERSITY p 836
4500 Riverwalk Pkwy 92505
Tel (951) 785-2000 *SIC* 8221

LUXFER INC p 887
3016 Kansas Ave Bldg 1 92507
Tel (336) 578-4515 *SIC* 3728 3354

OLDCASTLE PRECAST INC p 1082
2434 Rubidoux Blvd 92509
Tel (951) 788-9720 *SIC* 3089

PARKVIEW COMMUNITY HOSPITAL MEDICAL CENTER p 1117
3865 Jackson St 92503
Tel (951) 354-7404 *SIC* 8062 8011

PRESS-ENTERPRISE CO p 1172
3450 14th St 92501
Tel (951) 684-1200 *SIC* 2711

RIVERSIDE COMMUNITY COLLEGE DISTRICT p 1238
3801 Market St 92501
Tel (951) 328-3663 *SIC* 8222

■ **RIVERSIDE COMMUNITY HEALTH SYSTEMS** p 1238
4445 Magnolia Ave Fl 6 92501
Tel (951) 788-3000 *SIC* 8062 8011

RIVERSIDE COUNTY OFFICE OF EDUCATION p 1238
3939 13th St 92501
Tel (951) 826-6530 *SIC* 8211 8249

RIVERSIDE COUNTY SCHOOLS p 1238
11840 Magnolia Ave Ste G 92503
Tel (951) 788-7274 *SIC* 8211

■ **RIVERSIDE HEALTHCARE SYSTEM LP** p 1238
4445 Magnolia Ave 92501
Tel (951) 788-3000 *SIC* 8062

RIVERSIDE MEDICAL CLINIC INC p 1238
3660 Arlington Ave 92506
Tel (951) 683-6370 *SIC* 8011

RIVERSIDE UNIFIED SCHOOL DISTRICT p 1238
3380 14th St 92501
Tel (951) 788-7135 *SIC* 8211

SKANSKA USA CIVIL WEST CALIFORNIA DISTRICT INC p 1329
1995 Agua Mansa Rd 92509
Tel (951) 684-5360
SIC 1611 1622 1629 8711 2951

SOUTHEASTERN CALIFORNIA CONFERENCE OF SEVENTH-DAY ADVENTISTS p 1346
11330 Pierce St 92505
Tel (951) 509-2200 *SIC* 8211 8661

STRONGHOLD ENGINEERING INC p 1394
2000 Market St 92501
Tel (951) 684-9303 *SIC* 1611

T M COBB CO p 1419
500 Palmyrita Ave 92507
Tel (951) 248-2400 *SIC* 2431 3442

UNIVERSITY OF CALIFORNIA RIVERSIDE ALUMNI ASSOCIATION p 1520
900 University Ave 92521
Tel (951) 827-1012 *SIC* 8221 9411

RLLNG HLS EST, CA

DINCO INC p 440
27520 Hawthorne Blvd # 180 90274
Tel (424) 331-1200 *SIC* 4899

▲ **NATURAL HEALTH TRENDS CORP** p 1018
609 Deep Valley Dr # 390 90274
Tel (310) 541-0888 *SIC* 5122 5961

ROCKLIN, CA

BI WAREHOUSING INC p 180
5404 Pacific St 95677
Tel (916) 624-0654 *SIC* 5531 5013 7539

EDUCATIONAL MEDIA FOUNDATION p 479
5700 West Oaks Blvd 95765
Tel (916) 251-1600 *SIC* 4832

HORIZON WEST HEALTHCARE INC p 707
4020 Sierra College Blvd # 190 95677
Tel (916) 624-6230 *SIC* 8051

HORIZON WEST INC p 708
4020 Sierra College Blvd 95677
Tel (916) 624-6230 *SIC* 8051

PURPLE COMMUNICATIONS INC p 1193
595 Menlo Dr 95765
Tel (888) 600-4780 *SIC* 4812 7389

ROCKLIN UNIFIED SCHOOL DISTRICT p 1245
2615 Sierra Meadows Dr 95677
Tel (916) 624-2428 *SIC* 8211

SIERRA JOINT COMMUNITY COLLEGE DISTRICT p 1320
5000 Rocklin Rd 95677
Tel (916) 624-3333 *SIC* 8222 8221

SLEEP TRAIN INC p 1331
2205 Plaza Dr 95765
Tel (916) 751-4300 *SIC* 5712

SMA SOLAR TECHNOLOGY AMERICA LLC p 1331
6020 West Oaks Blvd 95765
Tel (916) 625-0870 *SIC* 5065

■ **UNITED NATURAL FOODS WEST INC** p 1510
1101 Sunset Blvd 95765
Tel (401) 528-8634 *SIC* 5149 5141

ROHNERT PARK, CA

FEDERATED INDIANS OF GRATON RANCHERIA p 536
6400 Redwood Dr Ste 300 94928
Tel (619) 917-9566 *SIC* 9131

GRATON ECONOMIC DEVELOPMENT AUTHORITY p 632
915 Golf Course Dr 94928
Tel (707) 800-7616 *SIC* 9311

■ **IDEX HEALTH & SCIENCE LLC** p 729
600 Park Ct 94928
Tel (707) 588-2000
SIC 3821 3829 3826 3823 3494

INTERLEMO USA INC p 753
635 Park Ct 94928
Tel (707) 578-8811 *SIC* 5065

LEMO USA INC p 855
635 Park Ct 94928
Tel (707) 206-3700 *SIC* 5065 3678

■ **MARMOT MOUNTAIN LLC** p 909
5789 State Farm Dr # 100 94928
Tel (707) 544-4590 *SIC* 2329

PACE SUPPLY CORP p 1103
6000 State Farm Dr # 200 94928
Tel (707) 303-0320 *SIC* 5074

SOLIGENT DISTRIBUTION LLC p 1338
1500 Valley House Dr # 210 94928
Tel (707) 992-3100 *SIC* 5065

SOLIGENT HOLDINGS INC p 1338
1500 Valley House Dr 94928
Tel (707) 992-3100 *SIC* 5074 7359 1711

ROSAMOND, CA

CATALINA SOLAR LESSEE LLC p 264
11585 Willow Springs Rd 93560
Tel (888) 903-6926 *SIC* 4911

ROSEMEAD, CA

▲ **EDISON INTERNATIONAL** p 478
2244 Walnut Grove Ave 91770
Tel (626) 302-2222 *SIC* 4911

■ **EDISON MISSION GROUP INC** p 478
2244 Walnut Grove Ave 91770
Tel (626) 302-2222
SIC 4931 6799 1629 1531

■ **EDISON MISSION MIDWEST HOLDINGS CO** p 478
2244 Walnut Grove Ave 91770
Tel (626) 302-2222 *SIC* 4911

■ **HCC INDUSTRIES INC** p 672
4232 Temple City Blvd 91770
Tel (626) 443-8933 *SIC* 3679

PANDA EXPRESS INC p 1111
1683 Walnut Grove Ave 91770
Tel (626) 799-9898 *SIC* 5812

PANDA RESTAURANT GROUP INC p 1111
1683 Walnut Grove Ave 91770
Tel (626) 799-9898 *SIC* 5812

■ **SOUTHERN CALIFORNIA EDISON CO** p 1347
2244 Walnut Grove Ave 91770
Tel (626) 302-1212 *SIC* 4911

ROSEVILLE, CA

ADVENTIST HEALTH SYSTEM/WEST p 27
2100 Douglas Blvd 95661
Tel (916) 781-2000 *SIC* 8062

AMERICAN PACIFIC MORTGAGE CORP p 77
3000 Lava Ridge Ct # 200 95661
Tel (916) 960-1325 *SIC* 6162

CITY OF ROSEVILLE p 318
311 Vernon St 95678
Tel (916) 774-5200 *SIC* 9111

ENTERPRISE RENT-A-CAR CO OF SACRAMENTO LLC p 502
150 N Sunrise Ave 95661
Tel (916) 787-4500 *SIC* 7515 7514 5511

FARM CREDIT WEST ACA p 529
1478 Stone Point Dr # 450 95661
Tel (916) 724-4800 *SIC* 6159

FLEXCARE LLC p 556
990 Reserve Dr Ste 200 95678
Tel (866) 564-3589 *SIC* 7363

■ **HD SUPPLY REPAIR & REMODEL LLC** p 673
1695 Eureka Rd 95661
Tel (916) 751-2300 *SIC* 5211

NEW VISION DISPLAY INC p 1033
1430 Blue Oaks Blvd # 100 95747
Tel (916) 786-8111 *SIC* 3679

NORQUIST SALVAGE CORP INC p 1049
2151 Prof Dr Ste 200 95661
Tel (916) 787-1070 *SIC* 5932

NORTHERN CALIFORNIA POWER AGENCY p 1055
651 Commerce Dr 95678
Tel (916) 781-3636 *SIC* 4911

PARAMOUNT EQUITY MORTGAGE LLC p 1114
8781 Sierra College Blvd 95661
Tel (916) 290-9999 *SIC* 6162

PRIDE INDUSTRIES p 1174
10030 Foothills Blvd 95747
Tel (916) 788-2100 *SIC* 4226 7349 3679

PRIDE INDUSTRIES ONE INC p 1174
10030 Foothills Blvd 95747
Tel (916) 788-2100 *SIC* 3999

RABOBANK NATIONAL ASSOCIATION p 1203
915 Highland Pointe Dr 95678
Tel (760) 352-5000 *SIC* 6022

SIERRAPINE A CALIFORNIA LIMITED PARTNERSHIP p 1321
1050 Melody Ln Ste 160 95678
Tel (800) 676-3339 *SIC* 2431

SPI SOLAR INC p 1358
3500 Douglas Blvd Ste 240 95661
Tel (916) 770-8100 *SIC* 3433

SUNRISE OAKS NURSING CENTER p 1404
600 Sunrise Ave 95661
Tel (916) 782-3131 *SIC* 8051

■ **SUREWEST COMMUNICATIONS** p 1408
211 Lincoln St 95678
Tel (916) 786-6141 *SIC* 4813 4812

SUTTER ROSEVILLE MEDICAL CENTER p 1410
1 Medical Plaza Dr 95661
Tel (916) 781-1000 *SIC* 8062

SUTTER ROSEVILLE MEDICAL CENTER FOUNDATION p 1410
1 Medical Plaza Dr 95661
Tel (916) 781-1000 *SIC* 8062

TOMS SIERRA CO INC p 1460
1020 Winding Creek Rd 95678
Tel (916) 218-1600 *SIC* 5541

TRC GROUP INC p 1475
3721 Douglas Blvd Ste 375 95661
Tel (916) 784-7745 *SIC* 5153

USA PROPERTIES FUND INC p 1534
3200 Douglas Blvd Ste 200 95661
Tel (916) 773-6060 *SIC* 6552 6531

ROWLAND HEIGHTS, CA

CELLULAR 123 INC p 274
18414 Colima Rd Ste 0 91748
Tel (626) 913-6788 *SIC* 5999

ROWLAND UNIFIED SCHOOL DISTRICT p 1253
1830 Nogales St 91748
Tel (626) 854-8317 *SIC* 8211

TODAI FRANCHISING LLC p 1458
19481 San Jose Ave 91748
Tel (909) 869-7727 *SIC* 6794

ROYAL OAKS, CA

FALCONTRADING CO p 526
423 Salinas Rd 95076
Tel (831) 786-7000 *SIC* 5149

SACRAMENTO, CA

A TEICHERT & SON INC p 6
3500 American River Dr 95864
Tel (916) 484-3011
SIC 5032 3273 1611 1442 1521

ACCLAMATION INSURANCE MANAGEMENT SERVICES p 15
10445 Old Placerville Rd 95827
Tel (916) 563-1900 *SIC* 6411

AIR RESOURCES BOARD p 39
1001 I St 95814
Tel (916) 322-2990 *SIC* 9511

AIRCO MECHANICAL INC p 40
8210 Demetre Ave 95828
Tel (916) 381-4523 *SIC* 1711 8711

ALSTON CONSTRUCTION CO INC p 61
8775 Folsom Blvd Ste 201 95826
Tel (916) 340-2400 *SIC* 1541 1542

ALTA CALIFORNIA REGIONAL CENTER INC p 61
2241 Harvard St Ste 100 95815
Tel (916) 978-6400 *SIC* 8322

AMERICAN BUILDING SUPPLY INC p 69
8360 Elder Creek Rd 95828
Tel (916) 503-4100 *SIC* 5031 3231

APEXCARE INC p 96
1418 Howe Ave Ste B 95825
Tel (916) 924-9111 *SIC* 8082

APOLLO IDEMITSU CORP p 97
1831 16th St 95811
Tel (916) 443-0890 *SIC* 5172 2911

ARCHITECTURAL BLOMBERG LLC p 105
1453 Blair Ave 95822
Tel (916) 428-8060 *SIC* 3442

ATTORNEY GENERAL CALIFORNIA OFFICE OF p 129
1300 I St Ste 1101 95814
Tel (916) 445-9555 *SIC* 9222

BOB FRINK MANAGEMENT INC p 196
5112 Madison Ave Ste 201 95841
Tel (916) 338-7333 *SIC* 8741 5511

BUSINESS TRANSPORTATION & HOUSING AGENCY STATE OF CALIFORNIA p 230
915 Capitol Mall 95814
Tel (916) 323-5400
SIC 9611 9621 9531 9532

CAHP HEALTH BENEFITS TRUST p 237
2030 V St 95818
Tel (916) 732-2155 *SIC* 6733

CALIFORNIA CASCADE INDUSTRIES p 239
7512 14th Ave 95820
Tel (916) 736-3353 *SIC* 2491 2421

CALIFORNIA COMMUNITY COLLEGES SYSTEM p 239
1102 Q St Fl 4 95811
Tel (916) 445-8752 *SIC* 8221

CALIFORNIA DEPARTMENT OF CONSUMER AFFAIRS p 239
1625 N Market Blvd # 103 95834
Tel (916) 574-7130 *SIC* 9611

CALIFORNIA DEPARTMENT OF CORRECTIONS & REHABILITATION p 239
1515 S St 95811
Tel (916) 341-7066 *SIC* 9223

CALIFORNIA DEPARTMENT OF DEVELOPMENTAL SERVICES p 239
1600 9th St 95814
Tel (916) 654-1690 *SIC* 9431

CALIFORNIA DEPARTMENT OF EDUCATION p 240
1430 N St Ste 5602 95814
Tel (916) 319-0815 *SIC* 9411

CALIFORNIA DEPARTMENT OF EMPLOYMENT DEVELOPMENT p 240
800 Capitol Mall 83 95814
Tel (916) 654-8210 *SIC* 9441

CALIFORNIA DEPARTMENT OF FISH AND WILDLIFE p 240
1416 9th St Fl 12 95814
Tel (916) 445-0411 *SIC* 9512

CALIFORNIA DEPARTMENT OF HOUSING & COMMUNITY DEVELOPMENT p 240
1800 3rd St Fl 1 95811
Tel (916) 445-4782 *SIC* 9531 9532

CALIFORNIA DEPARTMENT OF INSURANCE p 240
300 Capitol Mall Ste 1700 95814
Tel (916) 492-3500 *SIC* 9651

CALIFORNIA DEPARTMENT OF JUSTICE p 240
1300 I St Ste 1142 95814
Tel (916) 324-5437 *SIC* 9222

CALIFORNIA DEPARTMENT OF MOTOR VEHICLES p 240
2415 1st Ave 95818
Tel (916) 657-6847 *SIC* 9621

CALIFORNIA DEPARTMENT OF PARKS AND RECREATION p 240
1416 9th St Ste 1041 95814
Tel (800) 777-0369 *SIC* 9512

CALIFORNIA DEPARTMENT OF PESTICIDE REGULATION p 240
1001 I St 95814
Tel (916) 445-4000 *SIC* 9511

CALIFORNIA DEPARTMENT OF PUBLIC HEALTH p 240
1615 Capitol Ave 95814
Tel (916) 558-1700 *SIC* 9431

CALIFORNIA DEPARTMENT OF REHABILITATION p 240
721 Capitol Mall Fl 6 95814
Tel (916) 558-5683 *SIC* 9431

CALIFORNIA DEPARTMENT OF STATE HOSPITALS p 240
1600 9th St Ste 120 95814
Tel (916) 654-3890 *SIC* 9431

CALIFORNIA DEPARTMENT OF VETERANS AFFAIRS p 240
1227 O St Ste 105 95814
Tel (800) 952-5626 *SIC* 9451

CALIFORNIA DEPARTMENT OF WATER RESOURCES p 240
1416 9th St 95814
Tel (916) 653-9394 *SIC* 9511

CALIFORNIA DEPT OF SOCIAL SERVICES p 240
744 P St 95814
Tel (916) 657-2598 *SIC* 9441

CALIFORNIA DEPT OF TRANSPORTATION p 240
1120 N St 95814
Tel (916) 654-5266 *SIC* 9621

CALIFORNIA ENVIRONMENTAL PROTECTION AGENCY p 240
1001 I St 95814
Tel (916) 323-2514 *SIC* 9511

CALIFORNIA GOVERNMENT OPERATIONS AGENCY p 240
915 Capitol Mall Ste 200 95814
Tel (916) 651-9011 *SIC* 9611

CALIFORNIA HEALTH & HUMAN SERVCS AGENCY p 240
1600 9th St Ste 460 95814
Tel (916) 654-3454 *SIC* 9431 9441

CALIFORNIA NATURAL RESOURCES AGENCY p 240
1416 9th St Ste 1311 95814
Tel (916) 653-5656 *SIC* 9512

CALIFORNIA PUBLIC EMPLOYEES RETIREMENT SYSTEM p 241
400 Q St 95811
Tel (916) 795-3000 *SIC* 6371 9441

CALIFORNIA STATE BOARD OF EQUALIZATION p 241
450 N St 95814
Tel (916) 445-6464 *SIC* 9311

CALVEY INC p 243
7728 Wilbur Way 95828
Tel (916) 681-4800 *SIC* 5113

CITY OF SACRAMENTO p 318
915 I St Fl 5 95814
Tel (916) 808-5300 *SIC* 9111

COMMUNITY COLLEGE FOUNDATION p 348
1901 Royal Oaks Dr # 100 95815
Tel (916) 418-5100 *SIC* 8299 8748

CONTROLLER CALIFORNIA STATE p 364
300 Capitol Mall Ste 1850 95814
Tel (916) 445-2636 *SIC* 9311

COUNTY OF SACRAMENTO p 381
700 H St Ste 7650 95814
Tel (916) 874-5544 *SIC* 9111

CRESTWOOD BEHAVIORAL HEALTH INC p 392
520 Capitol Mall Ste 800 95814
Tel (510) 651-1244 *SIC* 8063

DEPARTMENT OF HEALTH CARE SERVICES p 430
1501 Capitol Ave 95814
Tel (916) 445-4171 *SIC* 9431

DEPARTMENT OF MILITARY CALIFORNIA p 430
9800 Goethe Rd 10 95827
Tel (916) 854-3500 *SIC* 9711

DIAMOND BLUE GROWERS p 436
1802 C St 95811
Tel (916) 442-0771 *SIC* 2099

DONGALEN ENTERPRISES INC p 450
330 Commerce Cir 95815
Tel (916) 422-3110 *SIC* 5162

EXECUTIVE OFFICE OF STATE OF CALIFORNIA p 517
Governors Ofc 95814
Tel (916) 445-2841 *SIC* 9111

FARMERS RICE COOPERATIVE p 530
2566 River Plaza Dr 95833
Tel (916) 923-5100 *SIC* 2044

FOOD & AGRICULTURE CALIFORNIA DEPT p 563
1220 N St Ste 365 95814
Tel (916) 654-0462 *SIC* 9641

FORESTRY AND FIRE PROTECTION CALIFORNIA DEPARTMENT OF p 567
1416 9th St Ste 1535 95814
Tel (916) 653-7772 *SIC* 9512

FRANCHISE TAX BOARD CALIFORNIA p 573
9646 Butterfield Way 95827
Tel (916) 845-3650 *SIC* 9311

GENERAL PRODUCE CO A CALIFORNIA LIMITED PARTNERSHIP p 602
1330 N B St 95811
Tel (916) 441-6431 *SIC* 5148

GO WEST INSURANCE SERVICES INC p 619
2386 Fair Oaks Blvd Ste 2 95825
Tel (916) 487-1102 *SIC* 6411

GOLDEN 1 CREDIT UNION p 620
8945 Cal Center Dr 95826
Tel (916) 732-2900 *SIC* 6062

HIGHWAY PATROL CALIFORNIA p 692
601 N 7th St 95811
Tel (916) 376-3256 *SIC* 9221

INTERNATIONAL UNION OF OPERATING ENGINEERS p 757
1121 L St Ste 401 95814
Tel (916) 444-6880 *SIC* 8631

INTERWEST INSURANCE SERVICES INC p 759
3636 American River Dr # 2 95864
Tel (916) 488-3100 *SIC* 6411

JOHN F OTTO INC p 788
1717 2nd St 95811
Tel (916) 441-6870 *SIC* 1542 1541

JUVENILE JUSTICE DIVISION CALIFORNIA p 798
1515 S St Ste 502s 95811
Tel (916) 323-2848 *SIC* 9223

L LYON WILLIAM & ASSOCIATES INC p 834
3640 American River Dr 95864
Tel (916) 978-4200 *SIC* 8741

LGE ELECTRICAL SALES INC p 860
650 University Ave # 218 95825
Tel (916) 563-2737 *SIC* 5063

LOS RIOS COMMUNITY COLLEGE DISTRICT p 879
1919 Spanos Ct 95825
Tel (916) 568-3041 *SIC* 8222

MARKSTEIN BEVERAGE CO OF SACRAMENTO p 909
60 Main Ave 95838
Tel (916) 920-3911 *SIC* 5181 5149

MATHESON TRUCKING INC p 920
9785 Goethe Rd 95827
Tel (916) 685-2330 *SIC* 4213 4731

▲ MCCLATCHY CO p 926
2100 Q St 95816
Tel (916) 321-1846 *SIC* 2711

MCCLATCHY CO p 926
2100 Q St 95816
Tel (916) 321-1941 *SIC* 8999

■ MCCLATCHY NEWSPAPERS INC p 926
2100 Q St 95816
Tel (916) 321-1000 *SIC* 2711 2759 7375

MERCY METHODIST HOSPITAL p 948
7500 Hospital Dr 95823
Tel (916) 423-6063 *SIC* 8062

MINGS RESOURCE CORP p 973
3316 47th Ave 95824
Tel (916) 421-5054 *SIC* 4953

MYERS & SONS CONSTRUCTION LP p 1004
4600 Northgate Blvd # 100 95834
Tel (916) 283-9950 *SIC* 1611

NATOMAS UNIFIED SCHOOL DISTRICT p 1018
1901 Arena Blvd 95834
Tel (916) 567-5400 *SIC* 8211

OFFICE OF LEGISLATIVE COUNSEL p 1075
State Cpitol Bldg Rm 3021 95814
Tel (916) 341-8000 *SIC* 9121

■ PACIFIC AG PRODUCTS LLC p 1103
400 Capitol Mall Ste 2060 95814
Tel (916) 403-2123 *SIC* 2869

▲ PACIFIC ETHANOL INC p 1104
400 Capitol Mall Ste 2060 95814
Tel (916) 403-2123 *SIC* 2869

QUEST MEDIA & SUPPLIES INC p 1199
5822 Roseville Rd 95842
Tel (916) 338-7070 *SIC* 7373

RADIOLOGICAL ASSOCIATES OF SACRAMENTO MEDICAL GROUP INC p 1204
1500 Expo Pkwy 95815
Tel (916) 646-8300 *SIC* 8071 8011

RAGINGWIRE DATA CENTERS INC p 1205
1200 Striker Ave 95834
Tel (916) 286-3000 *SIC* 7376

REX MOORE ELECTRICAL CONTRACTORS & ENGINEERS INC p 1230
6001 Outfall Cir 95828
Tel (916) 372-1300 *SIC* 1731

REX MOORE GROUP INC p 1230
6001 Outfall Cir 95828
Tel (916) 372-1300 *SIC* 1731 8711

RIVER CITY PETROLEUM INC p 1237
3775 N Freeway Blvd # 101 95834
Tel (916) 371-4960 *SIC* 5172

ROMAN CATHOLIC BISHOP OF SACRAMENTO p 1248
2110 Broadway 95818
Tel (916) 733-0100 *SIC* 8661

RPM LUXURY AUTO SALES INC p 1255
5112 Madison Ave Ste 201 95841
Tel (916) 485-3987 *SIC* 5511

SACRAMENTO AREA SEWER DISTRICT p 1264
10060 Goethe Rd 95827
Tel (916) 876-6000 *SIC* 4953

SACRAMENTO CITY UNIFIED SCHOOL DISTRICT p 1264
5735 47th Ave 95824
Tel (916) 643-7400 *SIC* 8641

SACRAMENTO HOUSING AND REDEVELOPMENT AGENCY p 1265
801 12th St 95814
Tel (916) 440-1390 *SIC* 9532

SACRAMENTO MUNICIPAL UTILITY DISTRICT p 1265
6201 S St 95817
Tel (916) 452-3211 *SIC* 4911

SACRAMENTO REGIONAL COUNTY SANITATION DISTRICT p 1265
10060 Goethe Rd 95827
Tel (916) 876-6000 *SIC* 4959

SACRAMENTO REGIONAL TRANSIT DIST p 1265
1400 29th St 95816
Tel (916) 726-2877 *SIC* 4111

SHAW ENVIRONMENTAL & INFRASTRUCTURE p 1312
1326 N Market Blvd 95834
Tel (916) 928-3300 *SIC* 8711

STATE OF CALIFORNIA p 1381
State Capital 95814
Tel (916) 445-2864 *SIC* 9111

SUTTER CONNECT LLC p 1410
10470 Old Placrvl Rd # 100 95827
Tel (916) 854-6600 *SIC* 8742 8741 8721

SUTTER HEALTH p 1410
2200 River Plaza Dr 95833
Tel (916) 733-8800
SIC 8062 8051 8011 6513

SUTTER HEALTH SACRAMENTO SIERRA REGION p 1410
2200 River Plaza Dr 95833
Tel (916) 733-8800 *SIC* 8062 8063 8052

SUTTER MEDICAL FOUNDATION p 1410
2700 Gateway Oaks Dr 95833
Tel (916) 887-7122 *SIC* 8741

SUTTERCARE CORP p 1410
2200 River Plaza Dr 95833
Tel (916) 733-8800 *SIC* 8051 8062

TEICHERT INC p 1433
3500 American River Dr 95864
Tel (916) 484-3011
SIC 3273 5032 1611 1442 1521 5039

TRANSHUMANCE HOLDING CO INC p 1471
2530 River Plaza Dr # 200 95833
Tel (530) 758-3091 *SIC* 5421 5142

UNGER CONSTRUCTION CO p 1502
910 X St 95818
Tel (916) 325-5500 *SIC* 1542 1541

UNIVERSITY ENTERPRISES INC p 1518
6000 J St 95819
Tel (916) 278-6672 *SIC* 8299 8741

WATER RESOURCES CONTROL BOARD CALIFORNIA p 1581
1001 I St 95814
Tel (916) 341-5250 *SIC* 9511

WESTERN HEALTH ADVANTAGE p 1598
2349 Gateway Oaks Dr # 100 95833
Tel (916) 567-1950 *SIC* 6321

SAINT HELENA, CA

ST HELENA HOSPITAL p 1367
10 Woodland Rd 94574
Tel (707) 963-1882 *SIC* 8062 8063

SUTTER HOME WINERY INC p 1410
100 Saint Helena Hwy S 94574
Tel (707) 963-3104 *SIC* 2084 0172

SALINAS, CA

COUNTY OF MONTEREY p 380
168 W Alisal St Fl 3 93901
Tel (831) 755-5040 *SIC* 9111

DARRIGO BROSCOOF CALIFORNIA p 412
21777 Harris Rd 93908
Tel (831) 455-4500 *SIC* 0161

DON CHAPIN CO INC p 449
560 Crazy Horse Canyon Rd 93907
Tel (831) 449-4273 *SIC* 1623 1611 1771

MANN PACKING CO INC p 902
1333 Schilling Pl 93901
Tel (831) 422-7405 *SIC* 0723 4783 0722

NATIVIDAD HOSPITAL INC p 1018
1441 Constitution Blvd 93906
Tel (831) 755-4111 *SIC* 8062 8011 8093

RAMCO ENTERPRISES LP p 1207
320 Airport Blvd 93905
Tel (831) 758-5272 *SIC* 0171 7361 0723

RIVER RANCH FRESH FOODS LLC p 1237
911 Blanco Cir Ste B 93901
Tel (831) 758-1390 *SIC* 5148

SALINAS UNION HIGH SCHOOL DISTRICT SCHOOL BUILDING CORP p 1272
431 W Alisal St 93901
Tel (831) 796-7000 *SIC* 8211

SALINAS VALLEY MEMORIAL HEALTHCARE SYSTEMS p 1272
450 E Romie Ln 93901
Tel (831) 757-4333 *SIC* 8062

STURDY OIL CO p 1395
1511 Abbott St 93901
Tel (831) 422-8801 *SIC* 5172 5541

TANIMURA & ANTLE FRESH FOODS INC p 1424
1 Harris Rd 93908
Tel (831) 455-2950
SIC 0161 0182 0723 2099

TAYLOR FARMS CALIFORNIA INC p 1427
150 Main St Ste 500 93901
Tel (831) 754-0471 *SIC* 0723

TAYLOR FRESH FOODS INC p 1427
150 Main St Ste 400 93901
Tel (831) 676-9023 *SIC* 0723

VEGETABLE GROWERS SUPPLY CO p 1546
1360 Merrill St 93901
Tel (831) 759-4600 *SIC* 5199 2449

SAN BERNARDINO, CA

CALIFORNIA CITY OF SAN BERNARDINO p 239
300 N D St 92418
Tel (909) 384-5128 *SIC* 9111

CALIFORNIA STATE UNIVERSITY SAN BERNARDINO p 241
5500 University Pkwy 92407
Tel (909) 537-5000 *SIC* 8221 9411

COMMUNITY HOSPITAL OF SAN BERNARDINO p 349
1805 Medical Center Dr 92411
Tel (909) 887-6333 *SIC* 8062

COUNTY OF SAN BERNARDINO p 381
385 N Arrowhead Ave 92415
Tel (909) 387-3841 *SIC* 9111

GOODWILL SOUTHERN CALIFORNIA p 625
8120 Palm Ln 92410
Tel (909) 885-3831 *SIC* 5932 8331

INLAND COUNTIES REGIONAL CENTER INC p 743
1365 S Waterman Ave 92408
Tel (909) 890-3000 *SIC* 8741

L & L NURSERY SUPPLY INC p 833
2552 Shenandoah Way 92407
Tel (909) 591-0461
SIC 5191 2875 2449 5193

LOMA LINDA UNIVERSITY HEALTHCARE p 875
350 Commercial Rd Ste 101 92408
Tel (909) 558-7132 *SIC* 8221

METROPOLITAN AUTOMOTIVE WAREHOUSE p 955
535 Tennis Court Ln 92408
Tel (909) 885-2886 *SIC* 5013

ROMAN CATHOLIC BISHOP OF SAN BERNARDINO p 1248
1201 E Highland Ave 92404
Tel (909) 475-5300 *SIC* 8661

SAN BERNARDINO CITY UNIFIED SCHOOL DISTRICT p 1275
777 N F St 92410
Tel (909) 381-1100 *SIC* 8211

SAN BERNARDINO COMMUNITY COLLEGE DISTRICT p 1275
114 S Del Rosa Dr 92408
Tel (909) 382-4000 *SIC* 8222 4832 4833

SAN BERNARDINO COUNTY SCHOOL DISTRICT p 1275
601 N E St 92415
Tel (909) 386-2417 *SIC* 8211

SAN BERNARDINO HILTON p 1276
285 E Hospitality Ln 92408
Tel (909) 889-0133 *SIC* 7011 6512 5812

STATER BROS HOLDINGS INC p 1383
301 S Tippecanoe Ave 92408
Tel (909) 733-5000 *SIC* 5411

STATER BROS MARKETS INC p 1383
301 S Tippecanoe Ave 92408
Tel (909) 733-5000 *SIC* 5411

SUPERIOR COURT OF CALIFORNIA p 1406
247 W 3rd St 92415
Tel (909) 708-8678 *SIC* 9211

UNIVERSITY ENTERPRISES CORP AT CSUSB p 1518
5500 University Pkwy 92407
Tel (909) 537-5929 *SIC* 5812 5942 8211

SAN BRUNO, CA

HITACHI SOLUTIONS AMERICA LTD p 697
851 Traeger Ave Ste 200 94066
Tel (650) 615-7600 *SIC* 5045 7372 7373

■ RESPONSYS INC p 1228
1100 Grundy Ln Ste 300 94066
Tel (650) 745-1700 *SIC* 7371 7372

T W M INDUSTRIES p 1420
899 Cherry Ave 94066
Tel (650) 583-6491 *SIC* 5812

■ WAL-MART.COM USA LLC p 1572
850 Cherry Ave 94066
Tel (650) 837-5000 *SIC* 5961 5199

SAN CARLOS, CA

CHECK POINT SOFTWARE TECHNOLOGIES INC p 292
959 Skyway Rd Ste 300 94070
Tel (800) 429-4391 *SIC* 7372

INSIDE SOURCE INC p 745
985 Industrial Rd Ste 101 94070
Tel (650) 508-9101 *SIC* 5021

KELLY-MOORE PAINT CO INC p 809
987 Commercial St 94070
Tel (650) 592-8337 *SIC* 2851

MARKLOGIC CORP p 909
999 Skyway Rd Ste 200 94070
Tel (650) 655-2300 *SIC* 7371

▲ NATERA INC p 1009
201 Industrial Rd Ste 410 94070
Tel (650) 249-9090 *SIC* 8071 2835

PENINSULA COMPONENTS INC p 1129
1300 Industrial Rd Ste 21 94070
Tel (650) 593-3288 *SIC* 5085 5065

PENINSULA CORRIDOR JOINT POWERS BOARD p 1129
1250 San Carlos Ave 94070
Tel (650) 508-6200 *SIC* 4111

■ ROVI CORP p 1253
2 Circle Star Way 94070
Tel (408) 562-8400 *SIC* 7372

▲ TIVO CORP p 1456
2 Circle Way 94070
Tel (408) 562-8400 *SIC* 7374 7929

SAN CLEMENTE, CA

ADVANCED MP TECHNOLOGY INC p 26
1010 Calle Sombra 92673
Tel (949) 492-6589 *SIC* 5065

DEALERSOCKET INC p 420
100 Avenida La Pata 92673
Tel (949) 900-0300 *SIC* 7371

EVOLUTION HOSPITALITY LLC p 515
1211 Puerta Del Sol # 170 92673
Tel (949) 325-1350 *SIC* 8741 7011

▲ ICU MEDICAL INC p 728
951 Calle Amanecer 92673
Tel (949) 366-2183 *SIC* 3841 3845

SAN DIEGO, CA

A O REED & CO p 6
4777 Ruffner St 92111
Tel (858) 565-4131 *SIC* 1711

ABF DATA SYSTEMS INC p 11
9020 Kenamar Dr Ste 201 92121
Tel (858) 547-8300 *SIC* 5045 7377

ACCREDITED HOME LENDERS HOLDING CO p 15
15253 Ave Of Science 92128
Tel (858) 676-2100 *SIC* 6798

ACE PARKING MANAGEMENT INC p 16
645 Ash St 92101
Tel (619) 233-6624 *SIC* 7521

AERONAUTICAL SYSTEMS INC p 30
16761 Via Del Campo Ct 92127
Tel (858) 455-2810 *SIC* 3721

■ AGOURON PHARMACEUTICALS INC p 35
10777 Science Center Dr 92121
Tel (858) 622-3000 *SIC* 2834 5122 8731

■ AIG DIRECT INSURANCE SERVICES INC p 37
9640 Gran Rdge Dr Ste 200 92123
Tel (858) 309-3000 *SIC* 6411

AL SHELLCO LLC p 43
9330 Scranton Rd Ste 600 92121
Tel (570) 296-6444 *SIC* 3651 3577

■ ALERE SAN DIEGO INC p 48
9975 Summers Ridge Rd 92121
Tel (858) 455-4808 *SIC* 2835

ALVARADO HOSPITAL LLC p 63
6655 Alvarado Rd 92120
Tel (619) 287-3270 *SIC* 8062

AMERICAN ASSETS TRUST INC p 68
11455 El Camino Real # 200 92130
Tel (858) 350-2600 *SIC* 6798

AMERICAN NEWLAND COMMUNITIES LP p 77
9820 Towne Centre Dr # 100 92121
Tel (858) 455-7503 *SIC* 6552

AMERICAN PROPERTY-MANAGEMENT CORP p 78
8910 University Center Ln # 100 92122
Tel (858) 964-5500 *SIC* 6531

AMERICAN SPECIALTY HEALTH GROUP INC p 79
10221 Wateridge Cir # 201 92121
Tel (858) 754-2000 *SIC* 8082

AMERICAN SPECIALTY HEALTH INC p 79
10221 Wateridge Cir # 201 92121
Tel (858) 754-2000 *SIC* 6411

■ AMETEK PROGRAMMABLE POWER INC p 84
9250 Brown Deer Rd 92121
Tel (858) 450-0085 *SIC* 3679

■ AMN HEALTHCARE INC p 85
12400 High Bluff Dr 92130
Tel (858) 792-0711 *SIC* 8011

▲ AMN HEALTHCARE SERVICES INC p 85
12400 High Bluff Dr 92130
Tel (866) 871-8519 *SIC* 7363

AMYLIN OHIO LLC p 88
9360 Towne Centre Dr 92121
Tel (858) 552-2200 *SIC* 2834

ANA GLOBAL LLC p 88
2360 Marconi Ct 92154
Tel (619) 482-9990 *SIC* 2517 5999

ANDREW LAUREN CO INC p 90
8909 Kenamar Dr Ste 101 92121
Tel (858) 793-5319 *SIC* 5023

ARC OF SAN DIEGO p 103
3030 Market St 92102
Tel (619) 685-1175
SIC 8399 8351 8361 8322

■ ARROWHEAD GENERAL INSURANCE AGENCY INC p 113
701 B St Ste 2100 92101
Tel (619) 881-8600 *SIC* 6331 6411

■ ARROWHEAD MANAGEMENT CO p 113
701 B St Ste 2100 92101
Tel (800) 669-1889 *SIC* 6411 8741

■ ASHFORD UNIVERSITY LLC p 117
8620 Spectrum Center Blvd # 100 92123
Tel (800) 798-0584 *SIC* 8221

ASSOCIATED STUDENTS OF SAN DIEGO STATE UNIVERSITY p 121
5500 Campanile Dr 92182
Tel (619) 594-0234 *SIC* 8699

■ ATK SPACE SYSTEMS INC p 125
7130 Miramar Rd Ste 100b 92121
Tel (937) 490-4145 *SIC* 3769

ATLAS HOTELS INC p 128
500 Hotel Cir N 92108
Tel (619) 291-2232 *SIC* 7011 5812 5813

AUDATEX NORTH AMERICA INC p 130
15030 Ave Of Ste 100 92128
Tel (858) 946-1900 *SIC* 7372

AUTOSPLICE INC p 135
10431 Wtridge Cir Ste 110 92121
Tel (858) 535-0077 *SIC* 3643

■ B OF I FEDERAL BANK p 142
4350 La Jolla Village Dr # 140 92122
Tel (858) 350-6200 *SIC* 6141 6163

BAE SYSTEMS NATIONAL SECURITY SOLUTIONS INC p 144
10920 Technology Pl 92127
Tel (858) 592-5000 *SIC* 3825 7373 3812

BAE SYSTEMS SAN DIEGO SHIP REPAIR INC p 144
2205 E Belt St Foot Of S 92113
Tel (619) 238-1000 *SIC* 3731

■ BARNEY & BARNEY INC p 156
9171 Twne Cntre Dr 500 92122
Tel (800) 321-4696 *SIC* 6411

BARNHART INC p 156
10620 Treena St Ste 300 92131
Tel (858) 635-7400 *SIC* 1542 8741

BEE BUMBLE FOODS LLC p 168
280 10th Ave 92101
Tel (858) 715-4000 *SIC* 2091

BEE BUMBLE HOLDINGS INC p 168
280 10th Ave 92101
Tel (858) 715-4000 *SIC* 2013 2032 2033

BIOMED REALTY LP p 184
17190 Bernardo Center Dr 92128
Tel (858) 485-9840 *SIC* 6798 6531

BIOMED REALTY TRUST INC p 184
17190 Bernardo Center Dr 92128
Tel (858) 485-9840 *SIC* 6798

BIOTIX HOLDINGS INC p 184
9880 Mesa Rim Rd 92121
Tel (858) 875-7681 *SIC* 6719

BLUETECH INC p 192
4025 Hancock St Ste 100 92110
Tel (619) 497-6060 *SIC* 5045

BOB BAKER ENTERPRISES INC p 196
591 Camino De La Reina # 1100 92108
Tel (619) 683-5591 *SIC* 5511

▲ BOFI HOLDING INC p 197
4350 La Jolla Village Dr 92122
Tel (858) 350-6200 *SIC* 6035

BRANDES INVESTMENT PARTNERS INC p 208
11988 El Cmino Real Ste 6 92130
Tel (858) 755-0239 *SIC* 6282

BREHM COMMUNICATIONS INC p 209
16644 W Bernardo Dr # 300 92127
Tel (858) 451-6200 *SIC* 2752 2711

▲ BRIDGEPOINT EDUCATION INC p 211
13500 Evening Creek Dr N 92128
Tel (858) 668-2586 *SIC* 8221

BROADWAY TYPEWRITER CO INC p 216
1055 6th Ave Ste 101 92101
Tel (619) 645-0253 *SIC* 5045 7378

BUMBLE BEE PARENT INC p 225
280 10th Ave 92101
Tel (858) 715-4000 *SIC* 2013 2032 2033

BUMBLE BEE SEAFOODS INC p 225
280 10th Ave 92101
Tel (858) 715-4068 *SIC* 2091 2047

C N L HOTEL DEL PARTNERS LP p 233
1500 Orange Ave 92118
Tel (619) 522-8299 *SIC* 7011

CAL-COMP ELECTRONICS (USA) CO LTD p 237
9877 Waples St 92121
Tel (858) 587-6900 *SIC* 3625

■ CALIFORNIA AMERICAN WATER CO p 239
655 W Broadway Ste 1410 92101
Tel (619) 409-7703 *SIC* 4941

CALIFORNIA BANK & TRUST p 239
11622 El Camino Real # 200 92130
Tel (858) 793-7400 *SIC* 6022

■ CALIFORNIA COMFORT SYSTEMS USA p 239
7740 Kenamar Ct 92121
Tel (858) 564-1100 *SIC* 1711

CALIFORNIA MARINE CLEANING INC p 240
2049 Main St 92113
Tel (619) 231-8788 *SIC* 4953

■ CALPINE ENERGY SOLUTIONS LLC p 242
401 W A St Ste 500 92101
Tel (877) 273-6772 *SIC* 4931 4932

CAMBRIDGE INVESTMENTS LLC p 244
8745 Aero Dr Ste 306 92123
Tel (858) 244-0419 *SIC* 5812

CARE FUSION p 254
10020 Pacific Mesa Blvd 92121
Tel (858) 617-2000 *SIC* 2834

■ CAREFUSION 213 LLC p 255
3750 Torrey View Ct 92130
Tel (800) 523-0502 *SIC* 2834

■ CAREFUSION 303 INC p 255
10020 Pacific Mesa Blvd 92121
Tel (858) 617-2000 *SIC* 3841

■ CAREFUSION CORP p 255
3750 Torrey View Ct 92130
Tel (858) 617-2000 *SIC* 3841 3845 8742

■ CAREFUSION SOLUTIONS LLC p 255
3750 Torrey View Ct 92130
Tel (858) 617-2100 *SIC* 5047

CARL ZEISS VISION INC p 256
12121 Scripps Summit Dr 92131
Tel (858) 790-7700 *SIC* 3827 3851

CATALINA SOLAR 2 LLC p 264
15445 Innovation Dr 92128
Tel (888) 903-6926 *SIC* 4911

CENTER FOR SUSTAINABLE ENERGY p 276
9325 Sky Park Ct Ste 100 92123
Tel (858) 244-1177 *SIC* 8748

CHARLOTTE RUSSE HOLDING INC p 290
5910 Pcf Ctr Blvd Ste 120 92121
Tel (858) 587-1500 *SIC* 5621

CHARLOTTE RUSSE INC p 290
5910 Pcf Ctr Blvd Ste 120 92121
Tel (858) 587-1500 *SIC* 5621

CITY OF SAN DIEGO p 318
202 C St 92101
Tel (619) 236-6330 *SIC* 9111

CLIPPER OIL p 327
2040 Harbor Island Dr # 203 92101
Tel (619) 692-9701 *SIC* 5172 2873 5169

CLUB DEMONSTRATION SERVICES INC p 328
9555 Chesapeake Dr # 100 92123
Tel (858) 581-8700 *SIC* 7389

COAST CITRUS DISTRIBUTORS p 331
7597 Bristow Ct 92154
Tel (619) 661-7950 *SIC* 5148

COMMUNITY FUND OF UNITED JEWISH p 348
4950 Murphy Canyon Rd # 100 92123
Tel (858) 279-2740 *SIC* 8699 8733

COMPETITOR GROUP INC p 351
9477 Waples St Ste 150 92121
Tel (858) 450-6510 *SIC* 2721 7941

CORRUGADOS DE BAJA CALIFORNIA p 373
2475 Paseo De Las A 92154
Tel (619) 662-8672 *SIC* 2653

COUNTY OF SAN DIEGO p 381
1600 Pacific Hwy Ste 209 92101
Tel (619) 531-5880 *SIC* 9111

CPM LTD INC p 387
1855 1st Ave Ste 300 92101
Tel (619) 237-9900 *SIC* 7363

■ CRICKET COMMUNICATIONS LLC p 392
7337 Trade St 92121
Tel (858) 882-6000 *SIC* 4812

CRYDOM INC p 396
2320 Paseo Delas Amer 2 Ste 201 92154
Tel (619) 210-1600
SIC 3625 5065 3674 3643

▲ CUBIC CORP p 399
9333 Balboa Ave 92123
Tel (858) 277-6780 *SIC* 3812 3699 7372

■ CUBIC DEFENSE APPLICATIONS INC p 399
9333 Balboa Ave 92123
Tel (858) 277-6780 *SIC* 3699 3663 3812

■ CUBIC GLOBAL DEFENSE INC p 399
9333 Balboa Ave 92123
Tel (858) 277-6780 *SIC* 7629

■ **CUBIC TRANSPORTATION SYSTEMS INC** p 399
5650 Kearny Mesa Rd 92111
Tel (858) 268-3100 SIC 3829 1731

CYMER INC p 405
17075 Thornmint Ct 92127
Tel (858) 385-7300 SIC 3699 3827

CYMER LLC p 405
17075 Thornmint Ct 92127
Tel (858) 385-7300 SIC 3699 3827

DASSAULT SYSTEMES BIOVIA CORP p 413
5005 Wateridge Vista Dr # 2 92121
Tel (858) 799-5000 SIC 7372

DAYBREAK GAME CO LLC p 417
15051 Avenue Of Science 92128
Tel (858) 577-3100 SIC 7371

▲ **DEXCOM INC** p 434
6340 Sequence Dr 92121
Tel (858) 200-0200 SIC 3841

EDF RENEWABLE ASSET HOLDINGS INC p 477
15445 Innovation Dr 92128
Tel (888) 903-6926 SIC 4911

EDF RENEWABLE ENERGY INC p 477
15445 Innovation Dr 92128
Tel (858) 521-3300 SIC 4911

EDF RENEWABLE SERVICES INC p 477
15445 Innovation Dr 92128
Tel (858) 521-3575 SIC 7539

ELITE SHOW SERVICES INC p 487
2878 Camino Del Rio S # 260 92108
Tel (619) 574-1589 SIC 7381

▲ **ENCORE CAPITAL GROUP INC** p 496
3111 Camino Del Rio N # 103 92108
Tel (877) 445-4581 SIC 6153

ENERGY LABS INC p 497
1695 Cactus Rd 92154
Tel (619) 671-0100 SIC 3585

■ **ENOVA CORP** p 500
101 Ash St 92101
Tel (619) 239-7700 SIC 4911 4924

EPLICA INC p 505
2355 Northside Dr Ste 120 92108
Tel (619) 260-2000 SIC 7363 7361

EPSILON SYSTEMS SOLUTIONS INC p 506
9242 Lightwave Ave # 100 92123
Tel (619) 702-1700 SIC 8711

EVENT NETWORK INC p 513
9606 Aero Dr Ste 1000 92123
Tel (858) 222-6100 SIC 5947

EXCEL TRUST INC p 516
17140 Bernardo Center Dr 92128
Tel (858) 613-1800 SIC 6798

FAIRFIELD DEVELOPMENT INC p 524
5510 Morehouse Dr Ste 200 92121
Tel (858) 457-2123 SIC 1522

FAMILY HEALTH CENTERS OF SAN DIEGO INC p 527
823 Gateway Center Way 92102
Tel (619) 515-2303 SIC 8093

FIRST ALLIED SECURITIES INC p 544
655 W Broadway Fl 11 92101
Tel (619) 702-9600 SIC 6211

FORESTERS EQUITY SERVICES INC p 567
6640 Lusk Blvd Ste A202 92121
Tel (858) 550-4844 SIC 6211

GARDEN FRESH HOLDINGS INC p 591
15822 Bernardo Center Dr A 92127
Tel (858) 675-1600 SIC 5812

GARDEN FRESH RESTAURANT CORP p 591
15822 Bernardo Center Dr A 92127
Tel (858) 675-1600 SIC 5812

GARICH INC p 592
6336 Greenwich Dr Ste A 92122
Tel (858) 453-1331 SIC 7361 8742

■ **GEN-PROBE INC** p 598
10210 Genetic Center Dr 92121
Tel (858) 410-8000 SIC 8731

GENERAL ATOMIC TECHNOLOGIES CORP p 599
3550 General Atomics Ct 92121
Tel (858) 455-3000
SIC 8731 3829 3443 7374 3499 2819

GENERAL ATOMICS p 599
3550 General Atomics Ct 92121
Tel (858) 455-2810 SIC 8731

GENERAL COATINGS CORP p 599
6711 Nancy Ridge Dr 92121
Tel (858) 587-1277 SIC 1721 1799

GERDAU REINFORCING STEEL p 608
3880 Murphy Canyon Rd # 100 92123
Tel (858) 737-7700 SIC 1541

GO-STAFF INC p 619
8798 Complex Dr 92123
Tel (858) 292-8562 SIC 7363 8721

GOFORTH & MARTI p 619
110 W A St Ste 140 92101
Tel (951) 684-0870 SIC 5021

GOLDEN EAGLE INSURANCE CORP p 620
525 B St Ste 1300 92101
Tel (619) 744-6000 SIC 6331

GOODWILL INDUSTRIES OF SAN DIEGO COUNTY p 625
3663 Rosecrans St 92110
Tel (619) 225-2200 SIC 8331

GST AUTOMOTIVE SAFETY COMPONENTS INTERNATIONAL INC p 643
2155 Pseo De Las Americas 92154
Tel (619) 661-9347 SIC 3714

GUILD MORTGAGE CO p 646
5898 Copley Dr Fl 4 92111
Tel (800) 283-8823 SIC 6162 6733

▲ **HALOZYME THERAPEUTICS INC** p 655
11388 Sorrento Valley Rd # 200 92121
Tel (858) 794-8889 SIC 2834 2836

HARPER CONSTRUCTION CO INC p 663
2241 Kettner Blvd Ste 300 92101
Tel (619) 233-7900 SIC 1542 1521

HAWTHORNE MACHINERY CO p 670
16945 Camino San Bernardo 92127
Tel (858) 674-7000
SIC 7353 7699 5082 7359

HELIX ELECTRIC INC p 681
6795 Flanders Dr 92121
Tel (858) 535-0505 SIC 1731

HERITAGE GOLF GROUP LLC p 686
12750 High Bluff Dr # 400 92130
Tel (858) 720-0694 SIC 7992

HIGH RIDGE WIND LLC p 691
15445 Innovation Dr 92128
Tel (888) 903-6926 SIC 4911

HOME BREW MART INC p 703
9045 Carroll Way 92121
Tel (858) 790-6900 SIC 2082 5999

HYUNDAI TRANSLEAD p 724
8880 Rio San Diego Dr # 600 92108
Tel (619) 574-1500 SIC 3443 3715 3412

ICW GROUP HOLDINGS INC p 728
11455 El Camino Real 92130
Tel (858) 350-2400 SIC 6331 6411

▲ **ILLUMINA INC** p 733
5200 Illumina Way 92122
Tel (858) 202-4500 SIC 3826 3821

IMAGE ONE MARKETING GROUP INC p 733
11956 Bernardo Plaza Dr # 525 92128
Tel (858) 673-8299 SIC 7311 5199

INNOVATIVE EMPLOYEE SOLUTIONS INC p 744
9665 Gran Rdge Dr Ste 420 92123
Tel (858) 715-5100 SIC 8721

INOVA DIAGNOSTICS INC p 745
9900 Old Grove Rd 92131
Tel (858) 586-9900 SIC 2835 8731

INSURANCE CO OF WEST p 748
15025 Innovation Dr 92128
Tel (858) 350-2400 SIC 6331

■ **INTEGRAL SYSTEMS INC** p 748
4820 Estgate Mall Ste 200 92121
Tel (443) 539-5330 SIC 7373

INTERNATIONAL TECHNIDYNE CORP p 757
6260 Sequence Dr 92121
Tel (858) 263-2300 SIC 3841 3829

INZI DISPLAY AMERICA INC p 762
7880 Airway Rd Ste B6e 92154
Tel (619) 929-3501 SIC 3651

▲ **JACK IN BOX INC** p 773
9330 Balboa Ave 92123
Tel (858) 571-2121 SIC 5812 6794

JENSEN MEAT CO INC p 782
2550 Britannia Blvd # 101 92154
Tel (619) 754-6450 SIC 5147

JEROMES FURNITURE WAREHOUSE p 783
16960 Mesamint St 92127
Tel (866) 633-4094 SIC 5712

JETMORE WIND LLC p 784
15445 Innovation Dr 92128
Tel (888) 903-6926 SIC 4911

■ **KAPLAN HIGHER EDUCATION LLC** p 803
9055 Balboa Ave 92123
Tel (858) 279-4500 SIC 8249

KELLY CAPITAL GROUP INC p 809
12730 High Bluff Dr # 250 92130
Tel (619) 687-5000 SIC 6733

KLEINFELDER ASSOCIATES p 823
550 W C St Ste 1200 92101
Tel (619) 831-4600 SIC 8748

KLEINFELDER GROUP INC p 823
550 W C St Ste 1200 92101
Tel (619) 831-4600 SIC 8711

KLEINFELDER INC p 823
550 W C St Ste 1200 92101
Tel (619) 831-4600 SIC 8711 8712

■ **KRATOS DEFENSE & ROCKET SUPPORT SERVICES INC** p 829
4820 Estgate Mall Ste 200 92121
Tel (858) 812-7300 SIC 8711

▲ **KRATOS DEFENSE & SECURITY SOLUTIONS INC** p 829
4820 Estgate Mall Ste 200 92121
Tel (858) 812-7300
SIC 3761 8711 8744 7382

KYOCERA AMERICA INC p 833
8611 Balboa Ave 92123
Tel (858) 576-2600 SIC 3674

■ **KYOCERA INTERNATIONAL INC** p 833
8611 Balboa Ave 92123
Tel (858) 576-2600 SIC 5043

LA MESA R V CENTER INC p 835
7430 Copley Park Pl 92111
Tel (858) 874-8001 SIC 5561 7538

LAZ PARKING LTD p 848
9333 Genesee Ave Ste 220 92121
Tel (858) 587-8888 SIC 7521

■ **LEAP WIRELESS INTERNATIONAL INC** p 850
7337 Trade St 92121
Tel (858) 882-6000 SIC 4812

LEDCOR CMI INC p 851
6405 Mira Mesa Blvd # 100 92121
Tel (602) 595-3017
SIC 1541 1611 1629 1623 1522 8999

LEDCOR CONSTRUCTION INC p 851
6405 Mira Mesa Blvd # 100 92121
Tel (858) 527-6400 SIC 1542

LENORE JOHN & CO p 856
1250 Delevan Dr 92102
Tel (619) 232-6136 SIC 5149 5182 5181

LG ELECTRONICS MOBILECOMM USA INC p 860
10225 Willow Creek Rd 92131
Tel (858) 635-5300 SIC 5065 3663

■ **LPL FINANCIAL LLC** p 882
4707 Executive Dr 92121
Tel (800) 877-7210 SIC 6211

■ **LPL HOLDINGS INC** p 882
4707 Executive Dr 92121
Tel (858) 450-9606 SIC 6211

LYTX INC p 888
9785 Towne Centre Dr 92121
Tel (858) 430-4000 SIC 3812

MAD ENGINE INC p 893
6740 Cobra Way Ste 100 92121
Tel (858) 558-5270 SIC 2261

▲ **MAXWELL TECHNOLOGIES INC** p 923
3888 Calle Fortunada 92123
Tel (858) 503-3200 SIC 3629

MCMILLIN COMMUNITIES INC p 932
2750 Womble Rd Ste 200 92106
Tel (619) 561-5275 SIC 6799

MEDIMPACT HEALTHCARE SYSTEMS INC p 938
10181 Scripps Gateway Ct 92131
Tel (858) 566-2727 SIC 8621

MEDIMPACT HOLDINGS INC p 938
10181 Scripps Gateway Ct 92131
Tel (858) 566-2727 SIC 6799

MERCY SCRIPPS HOSPITAL p 948
4077 5th Ave Mer35 92103
Tel (619) 294-8111 SIC 8062

MERIDIAN RACK & PINION INC p 949
6740 Cobra Way Ste 200 92121
Tel (858) 587-8777 SIC 5013 5961

MERRY X-RAY CHEMICAL CORP p 950
4444 Viewridge Ave A 92123
Tel (858) 565-4472 SIC 5047

MERRY X-RAY CORP p 950
4444 Viewridge Ave 92123
Tel (858) 565-4472 SIC 5047

■ **MIDLAND CREDIT MANAGEMENT INC** p 965
3111 Camino Del Rio N 92108
Tel (877) 240-2377 SIC 6153

MILLENNIUM HEALTH LLC p 970
16981 Via Tazon Ste F 92127
Tel (877) 451-3534 SIC 8734

■ **MITCHELL INTERNATIONAL INC** p 977
6220 Greenwich Dr 92122
Tel (858) 368-7000 SIC 7371

■ **MLIM LLC** p 979
350 Camino De La Reina 92108
Tel (619) 299-3131 SIC 2711

■ **MOLECULAR BIOPRODUCTS INC** p 982
9389 Waples St 92121
Tel (858) 453-7551 SIC 4953

MOR FURNITURE FOR LESS INC p 988
8996 Miramar Rd Ste 300 92126
Tel (858) 547-1616 SIC 5712

MPCI HOLDINGS INC p 995
7850 Waterville Rd 92154
Tel (619) 294-2222
SIC 5147 5143 5148 5113

■ **MR COPY INC** p 996
5657 Copley Dr 92111
Tel (858) 573-6300 SIC 5044

■ **NASSCO HOLDINGS INC** p 1009
2798 Harbor Dr 92113
Tel (619) 544-3400 SIC 3731

NATIONAL FUNDING INC p 1012
9820 Towne Centre Dr # 200 92121
Tel (888) 576-4685 SIC 6153 6159 7389

NATIONAL PEN CO LLC p 1015
12121 Scripps Summit Dr # 200 92131
Tel (866) 388-9850 SIC 3951 3993

NATIONAL PEN CORP p 1015
12121 Scripps Summit Dr # 200 92131
Tel (858) 675-3000 SIC 5961

■ **NATIONAL STEEL & SHIPBUILDING CO** p 1016
2798 Harbor Dr 92113
Tel (619) 544-3400 SIC 3731

NEIGHBORHOOD HOUSE ASSOCIATION p 1024
5660 Copley Dr 92111
Tel (858) 715-2642 SIC 8322

NEW ALTERNATIVES INC p 1029
3589 4th Ave 92103
Tel (619) 543-0293 SIC 8322

NEXUS DX INC p 1041
6759 Mesa Ridge Rd 92121
Tel (858) 410-4600 SIC 3841

NISHIBA INDUSTRIES CORP p 1044
2360 Marconi Ct 92154
Tel (619) 661-8866 SIC 3089 3544 5162

NISSAN MOSSY INC p 1044
4625 Brinnell St 92111
Tel (619) 474-7011 SIC 5511

▲ **NOVATEL WIRELESS INC** p 1063
9645 Scranton Rd Ste 205 92121
Tel (858) 812-3400 SIC 3661 7371

NTH GENERATION COMPUTING INC p 1065
17055 Camino San Bernardo 92127
Tel (858) 451-2383 SIC 5045

■ **NURSEFINDERS LLC** p 1067
12400 High Bluff Dr 92130
Tel (858) 314-7427
SIC 7361 8082 7363 8049

▲ **NUVASIVE INC** p 1068
7475 Lusk Blvd 92121
Tel (858) 909-1800 SIC 3841

■ **NYPRO HEALTHCARE BAJA INC** p 1069
2195 Britannia Blvd # 107 92154
Tel (619) 498-9250 SIC 3841 3679

O & S CALIFORNIA INC p 1070
9731 Siempre Viva Rd E 92154
Tel (619) 661-1800 SIC 3699

OASIS REPOWER LLC p 1072
15445 Innovation Dr 92128
Tel (888) 903-6926 SIC 4911

OLIVERMCMILLAN LLC p 1082
733 8th Ave 92101
Tel (619) 321-1111 SIC 6552

OMNITRACS MIDCO LLC p 1085
10182 Telesis Ct Ste 100 92121
Tel (858) 651-5812 SIC 7372

■ **PACIFIC ENTERPRISES** p 1104
101 Ash St 92101
Tel (619) 696-2020 SIC 4924

PACIFIC RIM MECHANICAL CONTRACTORS INC p 1105
7655 Convoy Ct 92111
Tel (858) 974-6500 SIC 1711

PACIFIC SHELLFISH INC p 1106
5040 Cass St 92109
Tel (858) 272-9940 SIC 5146 5421 5812

PACIFICA COMPANIES LLC p 1106
1775 Hancock St Ste 200 92110
Tel (619) 296-9000 SIC 6798 6512

PACIFICA HOSTS INC p 1106
1775 Hancock St Ste 200 92110
Tel (619) 296-9000 SIC 7011

PADRES LP p 1107
100 Pk Blvd Petco Park Petco Pk 92101
Tel (619) 795-5000 SIC 7941

PC SPECIALISTS INC p 1123
10240 Flanders Ct 92121
Tel (858) 566-1900 SIC 5045 5734 7371

PEREGRINE SEMICONDUCTOR CORP p 1134
9380 Carroll Park Dr 92121
Tel (858) 731-9400 SIC 3674

PETCO ANIMAL SUPPLIES INC p 1137
10850 Via Frontera 92127
Tel (858) 453-7845 SIC 0752 5199 5999

PETCO ANIMAL SUPPLIES STORES INC p 1137
9125 Rehco Rd 92121
Tel (858) 453-7845 SIC 5999 0752 5199

PETCO HOLDINGS INC LLC p 1138
10850 Via Frontera 92127
Tel (858) 453-7845 SIC 5999

PGAC CORP p 1140
9630 Ridgehaven Ct Ste B 92123
Tel (858) 560-8213 SIC 2671

PLAZA HOME MORTGAGE INC p 1156
4820 Eastgate Mall # 100 92121
Tel (858) 346-1200 SIC 6162

POINT LOMA NAZARENE UNIVERSITY p 1159
3900 Lomaland Dr 92106
Tel (619) 221-2200 SIC 8221

POWAY UNIFIED SCHOOL DISTRICT p 1164
15250 Ave Of Science 92128
Tel (858) 748-0010 SIC 8211

▲ **PRICESMART INC** p 1174
9740 Scranton Rd Ste 125 92121
Tel (858) 404-8800 SIC 5331

PROMETHEUS LABORATORIES INC p 1183
9410 Carroll Park Dr 92121
Tel (858) 824-0895 SIC 2834 8011

PULSE ELECTRONICS CORP p 1191
12220 World Trade Dr 92128
Tel (858) 674-8100 SIC 3679 3612 3663

PULSE ELECTRONICS INC p 1191
12220 World Trade Dr 92128
Tel (858) 674-8100 SIC 3612 3674 3677

▲ **QUALCOMM INC** p 1196
5775 Morehouse Dr 92121
Tel (858) 587-1121 SIC 3674 7372 6794

■ **QUALCOMM INTERNATIONAL INC** p 1196
5775 Morehouse Dr 92121
Tel (858) 587-1121 SIC 6794

■ **QUALCOMM TECHNOLOGIES INC** p 1196
5775 Morehouse Dr 92121
Tel (858) 587-1121 SIC 3674 7372 6794

▲ **QUIDEL CORP** p 1199
12544 High Bluff Dr # 200 92130
Tel (858) 552-1100 SIC 2835

R W SMITH & CO p 1203
8555 Miralani Dr 92126
Tel (858) 530-1800 *SIC* 5023

RACKS INC p 1203
7565 Siempre Viva Rd 92154
Tel (619) 661-0987 *SIC* 2542 3993 2541

RADY CHILDRENS HOSPITAL AND HEALTH CENTER p 1205
3020 Childrens Way 92123
Tel (858) 576-1700 *SIC* 8069

RADY CHILDRENS HOSPITAL-SAN DIEGO p 1205
3020 Childrens Way 92123
Tel (858) 576-1700 *SIC* 8069

▲ REALTY INCOME CORP p 1214
11995 El Camino Real 92130
Tel (858) 284-5000 *SIC* 6798

REMEC DEFENSE & SPACE INC p 1222
9404 Chesapeake Dr 92123
Tel (858) 560-1301 *SIC* 3812

▲ RESMED INC p 1227
9001 Spectrum Center Blvd 92123
Tel (858) 836-5000 *SIC* 3841

▲ RETAIL OPPORTUNITY INVESTMENTS CORP p 1228
8905 Towne Centre Dr # 108 92122
Tel (858) 677-0900 *SIC* 6798

▲ RETROPHIN INC p 1229
12255 El Camino Real # 250 92130
Tel (760) 260-8600 *SIC* 2834 8731

RIVULIS IRRIGATION INC p 1239
7545 Carroll Rd 92121
Tel (858) 578-1860 *SIC* 3523

ROAD RUNNER SPORTS INC p 1240
5549 Copley Dr 92111
Tel (858) 974-4200 *SIC* 5961 3949 5661

ROEL CONSTRUCTION CO INC p 1246
1615 Murray Canyon Rd # 1000 92108
Tel (619) 297-4156 *SIC* 1541 8741

ROMAN CATHOLIC BISHOP OF SAN DIEGO p 1248
3888 Paducah Dr 92117
Tel (858) 490-8200 *SIC* 8661

ROOSEVELT WIND HOLDINGS LLC p 1249
15445 Innovation Dr 92128
Tel (888) 903-6926 *SIC* 4911

■ RX PRO HEALTH LLC p 1260
12400 High Bluff Dr 92130
Tel (858) 369-4050 *SIC* 7363

SAN DIEGO COMMUNITY COLLEGE DISTRICT p 1276
3375 Camino Del Rio S 92108
Tel (619) 388-6500 *SIC* 8222 8249 8221

SAN DIEGO CONVENTION CENTER CORP INC p 1276
111 W Harbor Dr 92101
Tel (619) 525-5000 *SIC* 6512

SAN DIEGO COUNTY CAPITAL ASSET LEASING C p 1276
1600 Pacific Hwy Ste 163 92101
Tel (336) 733-2728 *SIC* 6799

SAN DIEGO COUNTY CREDIT UNION INC p 1276
6545 Sequence Dr 92121
Tel (877) 732-2848 *SIC* 6062

SAN DIEGO COUNTY OFFICE OF EDUCATION p 1276
6401 Linda Vista Rd 92111
Tel (858) 292-3500 *SIC* 8211

SAN DIEGO COUNTY WATER AUTHORITY p 1276
4677 Overland Ave 92123
Tel (858) 522-6600 *SIC* 4941

SAN DIEGO DATA PROCESSING CORP INC p 1276
202 C St Fl 3 92101
Tel (858) 581-9600 *SIC* 7374

SAN DIEGO FOUNDATION p 1276
2508 Historic Decatur Rd # 200 92106
Tel (619) 235-2300 *SIC* 8322

■ SAN DIEGO GAS & ELECTRIC CO p 1276
8326 Century Park Ct 92123
Tel (619) 696-2000 *SIC* 4931 4911 4924

SAN DIEGO METROPOLITAN TRANSIT SYSTEM p 1276
1255 Imperial Ave # 1000 92101
Tel (619) 231-1466 *SIC* 4111

SAN DIEGO STATE UNIVERSITY p 1276
5500 Campanile Dr 92182
Tel (619) 594-7985 *SIC* 8221 9411

SAN DIEGO STATE UNIVERSITY FOUNDATION p 1276
5250 Campanile Dr Mc1947 92182
Tel (619) 594-1900 *SIC* 8221 9411

SAN DIEGO UNIFIED PORT DISTRICT p 1276
3165 Pacific Hwy 92101
Tel (619) 686-6200 *SIC* 4491

SAN DIEGO UNIFIED SCHOOL DISTRICT p 1276
4100 Normal St 92103
Tel (619) 725-8000 *SIC* 8211

■ SAN DIEGO UNION-TRIBUNE LLC p 1276
600 B St 92101
Tel (619) 299-3131 *SIC* 2711 7313 7383

SAN DIEGO-IMPERIAL COUNTIES DEVELOPMENTAL SERVICES INC p 1276
4355 Ruffin Rd Ste 220 92123
Tel (858) 576-2996 *SIC* 8322

SCRIPPS CLINIC FOUNDATION p 1294
12395 El Camino Real 92130
Tel (858) 554-9000 *SIC* 8741

SCRIPPS HEALTH p 1294
4275 Campus Point Ct 92121
Tel (858) 678-7000
SIC 8051 8082 8062 8049 8042 8043

▲ SEMPRA ENERGY p 1303
488 8th Ave 92101
Tel (619) 696-2000
SIC 4932 4911 5172 4922

■ SEMPRA ENERGY GLOBAL ENTERPRISES p 1303
101 Ash St 92101
Tel (619) 696-2000 *SIC* 4924 4911

■ SEMPRA ENERGY INTERNATIONAL p 1303
101 Ash St 92101
Tel (619) 696-2000 *SIC* 4911

■ SEMPRA GENERATION LLC p 1303
101 Ash St 92101
Tel (619) 696-2000 *SIC* 4931

■ SEQUENOM CENTER FOR MOLECULAR MEDICINE LLC p 1306
3595 John Hopkins Ct 92121
Tel (858) 202-9051 *SIC* 8071

■ SEQUENOM INC p 1306
3595 John Hopkins Ct 92121
Tel (858) 202-9000 *SIC* 8731

SHARP CHULA VISTA MEDICAL CENTER p 1312
8695 Spectrum Center Blvd 92123
Tel (858) 499-5150 *SIC* 8062

SHARP HEALTH PLAN p 1312
8520 Tech Way Ste 200 92123
Tel (858) 499-8300 *SIC* 6324

SHARP HEALTHCARE p 1312
8695 Spectrum Center Blvd 92123
Tel (858) 499-4000 *SIC* 8062 8741 6324

SHARP MEMORIAL HOSPITAL p 1312
7901 Frost St 92123
Tel (858) 939-3636 *SIC* 8062

SHOPCORE PROPERTIES LP p 1318
17140 Bernardo Center Dr 92128
Tel (858) 613-1800 *SIC* 6733

SLATE CREEK WIND PROJECT LLC p 1331
15445 Innovation Dr 92128
Tel (888) 903-6926 *SIC* 4911

■ SMART-TEK AUTOMATED SERVICES INC p 1332
11838 Bernardo Plaza Ct # 250 92128
Tel (858) 798-1644 *SIC* 7372

SMARTDRIVE SYSTEMS INC p 1332
9450 Carroll Park Dr 92121
Tel (866) 933-9930 *SIC* 5099

SMG-PREMIER FOOD SERVICES INC p 1333
8555 Aero Dr Ste 205 92123
Tel (858) 621-5151 *SIC* 5812

■ SOLAR TURBINES INC p 1338
2200 Pacific Hwy 92101
Tel (619) 544-5000 *SIC* 3511

SOLPAC CONSTRUCTION INC p 1338
2424 Congress St 92110
Tel (619) 296-6247 *SIC* 8741 1542 1611

SONY ELECTRONICS INC p 1341
16535 Via Esprillo Bldg 1 92127
Tel (858) 942-2400
SIC 3651 5064 3695 3671 3572 3674

SOUTHERN CAL SCHOOLS VOL EMP BENEFITS ASSOC p 1347
8885 Rio San Diego Dr # 327 92108
Tel (619) 278-0021 *SIC* 8211

STX WIRELESS OPERATIONS LLC p 1395
5887 Copley Dr 92111
Tel (858) 882-6000 *SIC* 4812

SUJA LIFE LLC p 1397
8380 Camino Santa Fe 92121
Tel (855) 879-7852 *SIC* 5149

SULLIVAN INTERNATIONAL GROUP INC p 1397
2750 Womble Rd Ste 100 92106
Tel (619) 260-1432 *SIC* 4959

SUNROAD HOLDING CORP p 1404
4445 Estgate Mall Ste 400 92121
Tel (858) 362-8500 *SIC* 6719

T B PENICK & SONS INC p 1419
15435 Innovation Dr # 100 92128
Tel (858) 558-1800 *SIC* 1541 1542

TCP GLOBAL CORP p 1428
6695 Rasha St 92121
Tel (858) 909-2110 *SIC* 5198 5231

TEGP INC p 1432
2375 Northside Dr Ste 360 92108
Tel (619) 584-3408 *SIC* 7363

THAI UNION INTERNATIONAL INC p 1446
9330 Scranton Rd Ste 500 92121
Tel (858) 558-9662 *SIC* 2091

TOMATOES EXTRAORDINAIRE INC p 1459
1929 Hancock St Ste 150 92110
Tel (619) 295-3172 *SIC* 5149

TRANSWESTERN PUBLISHING CO LLC p 1473
8344 Clairemont Mesa Blvd 92111
Tel (858) 467-2800 *SIC* 2741

TRI-UNION SEAFOODS LLC p 1478
9330 Scranton Rd Ste 500 92121
Tel (858) 558-9662 *SIC* 5146 2091

TRITECH SOFTWARE SYSTEMS p 1483
9477 Waples St Ste 100 92121
Tel (858) 799-7000 *SIC* 7371

▲ TURTLE BEACH CORP p 1493
12220 Scripps Summit Dr # 100 92131
Tel (914) 345-2255 *SIC* 3679

TYLER BLUFF WIND PROJECT LLC p 1496
15445 Innovation Dr 92128
Tel (888) 903-6926 *SIC* 4911

▲ UMAMI SUSTAINABLE SEAFOOD INC p 1501
1230 Columbia St Ste 440 92101
Tel (619) 544-9177 *SIC* 5146 0912

UNIVERSITY OF SAN DIEGO p 1525
5998 Alcala Park Frnt 92110
Tel (619) 260-4600 *SIC* 8221

UNIVESITY OF CALIFORNIA SAN DIEGO HEALTH SYSTEM p 1527
200 W Arbor Dr 8201 92103
Tel (619) 543-3713 *SIC* 8062

■ UPS STORE INC p 1529
6060 Cornerstone Ct W 92121
Tel (858) 455-8800 *SIC* 7389 8742 4783

UPWIND SOLUTIONS INC p 1530
4863 Shawline St Ste A 92111
Tel (866) 927-3142 *SIC* 7374 4931 7373

VIGOBYTE TAPE CORP p 1556
2498 Roll Dr Ste 916 92154
Tel (866) 803-8446 *SIC* 3572

VOLCANO CORP p 1564
3721 Vly Cntre Dr Ste 500 92130
Tel (800) 228-4728 *SIC* 3845

WAWANESA GENERAL INSURANCE CO p 1584
9050 Friars Rd Ste 200 92108
Tel (619) 285-6020 *SIC* 6331

WAXIES ENTERPRISES INC p 1584
9353 Waxie Way 92123
Tel (858) 292-8111 *SIC* 5087

▲ WD-40 CO p 1585
1061 Cudahy Pl 92110
Tel (619) 275-1400 *SIC* 2992 2851

WEST CONSULTANTS-GANNETT FLEMING JOINT VENTURE p 1594
11440 W Bernardo Ct # 360 92127
Tel (858) 487-9378 *SIC* 8711

WESTAIR GASES & EQUIPMENT INC p 1596
2506 Market St 92102
Tel (866) 937-8247 *SIC* 5084

WHEATLAND WIND PROJECT LLC p 1604
15445 Innovation Dr 92128
Tel (888) 903-6926 *SIC* 4911

■ WIS p 1618
9265 Sky Park Ct Ste 100 92123
Tel (858) 565-8111 *SIC* 7389

YMCA OF SAN DIEGO COUNTY p 1636
3708 Ruffin Rd 92123
Tel (858) 292-9622 *SIC* 8641

ZOOLOGICAL SOCIETY OF SAN DIEGO p 1644
2920 Zoo Dr 92101
Tel (619) 231-1515 *SIC* 8422 5812 5947

SAN DIMAS, CA

▲ AMERICAN STATES WATER CO p 80
630 E Foothill Blvd 91773
Tel (909) 394-3600 *SIC* 4941 4911

BONITA UNIFIED SCHOOL DISTRICT p 200
115 W Allen Ave 91773
Tel (909) 971-8200 *SIC* 8211

■ GOLDEN STATE WATER CO p 621
630 E Foothill Blvd 91773
Tel (909) 394-3600 *SIC* 4941 4911

■ SYPRIS DATA SYSTEMS INC p 1416
160 Via Verde 91773
Tel (909) 962-9400 *SIC* 3572 3651

SAN FERNANDO, CA

AHI INVESTMENT INC p 36
675 Glenoaks Blvd 91340
Tel (818) 979-0030 *SIC* 5199 3991

ALL STATE ASSOCIATION INC p 51
11487 San Fernando Rd 91340
Tel (877) 425-2558 *SIC* 8611

BERNARDS BROS INC p 176
555 1st St 91340
Tel (818) 898-1521 *SIC* 1542 1541

TRESIERRAS BROTHERS CORP p 1476
618 San Fernando Rd 91340
Tel (818) 365-8859 *SIC* 5411 5461

SAN FRANCISCO, CA

■ ACHIEVERS LLC p 17
660 3rd St Ste 302 94107
Tel (888) 622-3343 *SIC* 8742

■ ADOBE MACROMEDIA SOFTWARE LLC p 23
601 Townsend St 94103
Tel (415) 832-2000 *SIC* 7372

■ ADVENT SOFTWARE INC p 27
600 Townsend St Fl 5 94103
Tel (415) 543-7696
SIC 7371 7373 7372 6722

AIRBNB INC p 39
888 Brannan St Ste 400 94103
Tel (415) 800-5959 *SIC* 7041

AIRPORT COMMISIONS p 40
San Francisco Intl Arprt 94128
Tel (650) 821-5000 *SIC* 4581

AKQA INC p 42
360 3rd St Ste 500 94107
Tel (415) 645-9400 *SIC* 8742

ALIPHCOM p 50
99 Rhode Island St Fl 3 94103
Tel (415) 230-7600 *SIC* 5065 5999

ALL HALLOWS PRESERVATION LP p 51
54 Navy Rd 94124
Tel (415) 285-3909 *SIC* 6513

AMBER HOLDING INC p 65
150 California St 94111
Tel (415) 765-6500 *SIC* 7371

AMERICAN BECHTEL INC p 68
50 Beale St 94105
Tel (415) 768-1234 *SIC* 8711

■ AMERICAN BUILDING MAINTENANCE CO OF ILLINOIS INC p 69
420 Taylor St 200 94102
Tel (415) 351-4386 *SIC* 7349

■ AMERICAN BUILDING MAINTENANCE CO OF NEW YORK p 69
101 California St 94111
Tel (415) 733-4000 *SIC* 7349

■ AMERICAN BUILDING MAINTENANCE CO-WEST (INC) p 69
75 Broadway Ste 111 94111
Tel (415) 733-4000 *SIC* 7349

■ AMERICAN COMMERCIAL SECURITY SERVICES INC p 70
420 Taylor St Fl 2 94102
Tel (415) 856-1020 *SIC* 7381

AMERICAN INDUSTRIAL PARTNERS LP p 74
1 Maritime Plz Ste 1925 94111
Tel (415) 788-7354 *SIC* 6282

■ AMTECH SERVICES INC p 87
420 Taylor St 200 94102
Tel (415) 733-4000 *SIC* 7349 8742

ANDRE-BOUDIN BAKERIES INC p 90
50 Francisco St Ste 200 94133
Tel (415) 882-1849
SIC 2051 5812 5961 5461

APPDYNAMICS INC p 98
303 2nd St Ste N450 94107
Tel (415) 442-8400 *SIC* 7371

APPIRIO INC p 98
760 Market St Ste 1150 94102
Tel (415) 663-4433 *SIC* 7371 7379

ARLINGTON ENTERPRISES LP p 110
1200 Irving St Ste 2 94122
Tel (415) 753-0403 *SIC* 5411

ARUP NORTH AMERICA LIMITED p 114
560 Mission St Fl 7 94105
Tel (415) 957-9445 *SIC* 8711

ASIA FOUNDATION p 117
465 California St Fl 9 94104
Tel (415) 982-4640 *SIC* 6732

ASSOCIATED MATERIALS GROUP INC p 120
1 Maritime Plz Fl 12 94111
Tel (415) 788-5111
SIC 3089 5033 5031 3442

ASSOCIATED MATERIALS INC p 121
1 Maritime Plz Fl 12 94111
Tel (415) 788-5111
SIC 3089 5033 5031 3442

BABCOCK & BROWN HOLDINGS INC p 143
1 Pier Ste 3 94111
Tel (415) 512-1515 *SIC* 6211

BABCOCK & BROWN RENEWABLE HOLDINGS INC p 143
1 Letterman Dr Ste 216 94129
Tel (415) 512-1515 *SIC* 8711

■ BANANA REPUBLIC LLC p 149
2 Folsom St 94105
Tel (650) 952-4400 *SIC* 5651

■ BANK OF WEST p 152
180 Montgomery St # 1400 94104
Tel (415) 765-4800 *SIC* 6022

■ BANKAMERICA FINANCIAL INC p 152
315 Montgomery St 94104
Tel (415) 622-3521 *SIC* 6153 6141 6282

BARE ESCENTUALS BEAUTY INC p 155
71 Stevenson St Fl 22 94105
Tel (415) 489-5000 *SIC* 5999

BARE ESCENTUALS INC p 155
71 Stevenson St Fl 22 94105
Tel (415) 489-5000 *SIC* 5999

BAYVIEW PRESERVATION LP p 163
5 Commer Ct 94124
Tel (415) 285-7344 *SIC* 6513

BBAM LLC p 163
50 California St Fl 14 94111
Tel (415) 512-1515 *SIC* 6211

BCCI CONSTRUCTION CO p 163
1160 Battery St Ste 250 94111
Tel (415) 817-5100 *SIC* 1542

BECHTEL CAPITAL MANAGEMENT CORP p 167
50 Beale St 94105
Tel (415) 768-1234 *SIC* 8741

BECHTEL CONSTRUCTION OPERATIONS INC p 167
50 Beale St Bsmt 1 94105
Tel (415) 768-1234
SIC 1541 1629 1623 8741 7353

BECHTEL CORP p 167
50 Beale St 94105
Tel (415) 768-1234 *SIC* 8711 1629 8742

BECHTEL ENERGY CORP p 167
50 Beale St Bsmt 1 94105
Tel (415) 768-1234 *SIC* 8711 8741

BECHTEL GROUP INC p 167
50 Beale St Bsmt 1 94105
Tel (415) 768-1234 *SIC* 8711 1629 8742

BECHTEL POWER CORP p 167
50 Beale St Bsmt 2 94105
Tel (415) 768-1234 *SIC* 8711 8742 1629

■ **BIG HEART PET BRANDS** p 181
1 Maritime Plz Fl 2 94111
Tel (415) 247-3000 *SIC* 2047

BIRST INC p 185
45 Fremont St Ste 1800 94105
Tel (415) 766-4800 *SIC* 7371

■ **BLACKROCK GLOBAL INVESTORS** p 188
400 Howard St 94105
Tel (415) 670-2000 *SIC* 6282

■ **BLACKROCK INSTITUTIONAL TRUST CO NATIONAL ASSOCIATION** p 188
400 Howard St 94105
Tel (415) 597-2000 *SIC* 6722

BLUE SHIELD OF CALIFORNIA LIFE & HEALTH INSURANCE CO p 192
50 Beale St Ste 2000 94105
Tel (415) 229-5000 *SIC* 6311 6321

■ **BONDED MAINTENANCE CO** p 200
75 Broadway Ste 111 94111
Tel (415) 733-4000 *SIC* 7349

BOUDIN HOLDINGS INC p 204
221 Main St Ste 1230 94105
Tel (415) 287-1709 *SIC* 5461

BRE PROPERTIES INC p 209
525 Market St Fl 4 94105
Tel (415) 445-6530 *SIC* 6798

BTIG LLC p 222
600 Montgomery St Fl 6 94111
Tel (415) 248-2200 *SIC* 6211

BUILD GROUP INC p 224
457 Minna St Ste 100 94103
Tel (415) 367-9399 *SIC* 1542

BYER CALIFORNIA p 231
66 Potrero Ave 94103
Tel (415) 626-7844 *SIC* 2331

C V STARR & CO p 233
101 2nd St Ste 2500 94105
Tel (415) 216-4000 *SIC* 6411

CAHILL CONTRACTORS INC p 237
425 California St # 2200 94104
Tel (415) 986-0600 *SIC* 1542

▲ **CAI INTERNATIONAL INC** p 237
1 Market Plz Ste 900 94105
Tel (415) 788-0100 *SIC* 7359

CALERA CAPITAL MANAGEMENT INC p 238
580 California St # 2200 94104
Tel (415) 632-5200 *SIC* 6211

CALIFORNIA ACADEMY OF SCIENCES p 239
55 Music Concourse Dr 94118
Tel (415) 379-8000 *SIC* 8422 2721 8412

CALIFORNIA DEPARTMENT OF INDUSTRIAL RELATIONS p 240
455 Golden Gate Ave Fl 8 94102
Tel (415) 557-0100 *SIC* 9651

CALIFORNIA PHYSICIANS SERVICE p 241
50 Beale St Bsmt 2 94105
Tel (415) 229-5000 *SIC* 6324

CALYPSO TECHNOLOGY INC p 243
595 Market St Ste 1800 94105
Tel (415) 817-2400 *SIC* 5734

CANADIAN AMERICAN OIL CO INC p 246
444 Divisadero St 100 94117
Tel (415) 621-8676 *SIC* 5541 6512 6552

CARMEL PARTNERS INC p 258
1000 Sansome St 1 94111
Tel (415) 273-2900 *SIC* 6531 6519

CATHOLIC HEALTHCARE WEST p 266
450 Stanyan St 94117
Tel (415) 668-1000 *SIC* 8062

■ **CBS INTERACTIVE INC** p 269
235 2nd St 94105
Tel (415) 344-2000 *SIC* 7319 7375 4832

■ **CHARLES SCHWAB & CO INC** p 289
211 Main St Fl 17 94105
Tel (415) 636-7000 *SIC* 6211

▲ **CHARLES SCHWAB CORP** p 289
211 Main St Fl 17 94105
Tel (415) 667-7000
SIC 6211 6091 6282 7389

CHECKOUT HOLDING CORP p 292
1 Maritime Plz Ste 1200 94111
Tel (415) 788-5111 *SIC* 7319

CHINESE COMMUNITY HEALTH CARE ASSOCIATION p 301
445 Grant Ave Ste 700 94108
Tel (415) 955-8800 *SIC* 8621

CHINESE COMMUNITY HEALTH PLAN p 301
445 Grant Ave Ste 700 94108
Tel (415) 955-8800 *SIC* 8011

CHINESE HOSPITAL ASSOCIATION p 301
845 Jackson St 94133
Tel (415) 982-2400 *SIC* 8621

CHRISTENSEN FUND p 302
487 Bryant St 94107
Tel (415) 644-0135 *SIC* 8699

CITY & COUNTY OF SAN FRANCISCO p 312
1 Dr Carlton B Goodlett P 94102
Tel (415) 554-7500 *SIC* 9111

CITY COLLEGE OF SAN FRANCISCO p 312
50 Phelan Ave 94112
Tel (415) 239-3000 *SIC* 8221 8222

CLIMATEWORKS FOUNDATION p 326
235 Montgomery St # 1300 94104
Tel (415) 433-0500 *SIC* 8748

CLUB ONE INC p 328
555 Market St Fl 13 94105
Tel (415) 477-3000 *SIC* 7991

CPK HOLDINGS INC p 387
Embarcadero Ctr 94111
Tel (415) 983-2700 *SIC* 5812 6794

CROUSE AND ASSOCIATES INSURANCE BROKERS INC p 394
100 Pine St Ste 2500 94111
Tel (415) 982-3870 *SIC* 6411

CROWN BUILDING MAINTENANCE CO p 395
868 Folsom St 94107
Tel (415) 981-8070 *SIC* 7349 8711

CROWN ENERGY SERVICES INC p 395
868 Folsom St 94107
Tel (415) 546-6534 *SIC* 8711

CUSHMAN & WAKEFIELD OF CALIFORNIA INC p 402
1 Maritime Plz Ste 900 94111
Tel (408) 275-6730 *SIC* 6531

DECKER ELECTRIC CO INC ELECTRICAL CONTRACTORS p 421
1282 Folsom St 94103
Tel (415) 552-1622 *SIC* 1731

DEEM INC p 421
642 Harrison St Fl 2 94107
Tel (415) 590-8300 *SIC* 5961

DELANCEY STREET FOUNDATION p 423
600 The Embarcadero 94107
Tel (415) 957-9800
SIC 8361 5199 8322 4212 5812

DELTA DENTAL INSURANCE CO p 426
100 1st St Fl 4 94105
Tel (415) 972-8400 *SIC* 6411

DELTA DENTAL OF CALIFORNIA p 426
100 1st St Fl 4 94105
Tel (415) 972-8300 *SIC* 6324

DFS GROUP LP p 435
525 Market St Fl 33 94105
Tel (415) 977-2701
SIC 5944 5948 5921 5993 5947 5999

▲ **DIGITAL REALTY TRUST INC** p 439
4 Embarcadero Ctr # 3200 94111
Tel (415) 738-6500 *SIC* 6798

DIGNITY HEALTH p 439
185 Berry St Ste 300 94107
Tel (415) 438-5500 *SIC* 8062

DOCUSIGN INC p 447
221 Main St Ste 1000 94105
Tel (415) 489-4940 *SIC* 7373

DOCUSIGN INC p 447
221 Main St Ste 1000 94105
Tel (415) 489-4940 *SIC* 7373

DODGE & COX p 447
555 California St Fl 40 94104
Tel (415) 981-1710 *SIC* 6722

▲ **DOLBY LABORATORIES INC** p 447
1275 Market St 94103
Tel (415) 558-0200 *SIC* 3663 6794

■ **EDAW INC** p 477
300 California St Fl 5 94104
Tel (415) 955-2800 *SIC* 6552 0781

EDGEWOOD PARTNERS INSURANCE CENTER p 478
135 Main St 21f 94105
Tel (415) 356-3900 *SIC* 6411

EPANTRY LLC p 504
1770 Union St 94123
Tel (657) 444-7837 *SIC* 5961

■ **ESURANCE INSURANCE SERVICES INC** p 511
650 Davis St 94111
Tel (415) 875-4500 *SIC* 6411

EUROMOTORS INC p 512
500 8th St 94103
Tel (415) 673-1700 *SIC* 5511

FAIRMONT HOTEL PARTNERS LLC p 525
950 Mason St 94108
Tel (415) 772-5000 *SIC* 8741

FEDERAL HOME LOAN BANK OF SAN FRANCISCO p 534
600 California St 94108
Tel (415) 616-1000 *SIC* 6111

FEDERAL RESERVE BANK OF SAN FRANCISCO p 535
101 Market St 94105
Tel (415) 974-2000 *SIC* 6011

▲ **FIBROGEN INC** p 540
409 Illinois St 94158
Tel (415) 978-1200 *SIC* 2834

FILLMORE CAPITAL PARTNERS LLC p 542
4 Embarcadero Ctr Ste 710 94111
Tel (415) 834-1477 *SIC* 6799

FINANCIALFORCE.COM INC p 543
595 Market St Ste 2700 94105
Tel (866) 743-2220 *SIC* 7371

▲ **FIRST REPUBLIC BANK** p 549
111 Pine St Ste Bsmt 94111
Tel (415) 392-1400 *SIC* 6022 6282 6162

▲ **FITBIT INC** p 552
405 Howard St Ste 550 94105
Tel (415) 513-1000 *SIC* 3829

FLYNN RESTAURANT GROUP LLC p 562
225 Bush St Ste 1800 94104
Tel (415) 835-9700 *SIC* 5812

FRANCISCO PARTNERS LP p 574
1 Letterman Dr Bldg C 94129
Tel (415) 418-2900 *SIC* 7373 7372

FRANCISCO PARTNERS MANAGEMENT LP p 574
1 Letterman Dr Ste 410 94129
Tel (415) 418-2900 *SIC* 6799 7372

■ **FRITZ COMPANIES INC** p 580
550-1 Eccles Ave 94101
Tel (650) 635-2693 *SIC* 4731

FUSIONSTORM p 585
2 Bryant St Ste 150 94105
Tel (415) 623-2626
SIC 7379 7371 7374 7376

▲ **GAP INC** p 591
2 Folsom St 94105
Tel (415) 427-0100
SIC 5651 5641 5632 5621 5611

GCI INC p 595
875 Battery St Fl 1 94111
Tel (415) 978-2790 *SIC* 1542

GEARY LSF GROUP INC p 597
332 Pine St Fl 6 94104
Tel (877) 616-8226 *SIC* 4813

GENSTAR CAPITAL LLC p 604
4 Embarcadero Ctr # 1900 94111
Tel (415) 834-2350 *SIC* 6799

GERMAN MOTORS CORP p 608
1140 Harrison St 94103
Tel (415) 590-3773 *SIC* 5511 7532

GGC ADMINISTRATION LLC p 610
1 Embarcadero Ctr Fl 39 94111
Tel (415) 983-2700 *SIC* 2591

GIRAFFE HOLDING INC p 613
500 Howard St 94105
Tel (415) 278-7000 *SIC* 5641

GLOBANT LLC p 618
875 Howard St Fl 3 94103
Tel (877) 798-8104 *SIC* 7371

▲ **GLU MOBILE INC** p 618
500 Howard St Ste 300 94105
Tel (415) 800-6100 *SIC* 7371 3944

GOLDEN GATE CAPITAL LP p 620
1 Embarcadero Ctr Fl 39 94111
Tel (415) 983-2700 *SIC* 6211

GOLDEN GATE PRIVATE EQUITY INC p 621
1 Embarcadero Ctr Fl 39 94111
Tel (415) 983-2706 *SIC* 8741 5621

GOLDEN GATE REGIONAL CENTER INC p 621
1355 Market St Ste 220 94103
Tel (415) 546-9222 *SIC* 8322

GRYPHON INVESTORS INC p 643
1 Maritime Plz Ste 2300 94111
Tel (415) 217-7400 *SIC* 6799

■ **GSA PACIFIC RIM REGION OFFICE OF REGIONAL ADMINISTRATOR** p 643
450 Golden Gate Ave Fl 5 94102
Tel (415) 522-3001 *SIC* 9199

GYMBOREE CORP p 649
500 Howard St Fl 2 94105
Tel (415) 278-7000 *SIC* 5641

HAMPTON CREEK INC p 656
2000 Folsom St 94110
Tel (844) 423-6637 *SIC* 2035 2052

HARBOR VIEW HOLDINGS INC p 660
433 California St Fl 7 94104
Tel (415) 982-7777
SIC 1522 1521 6512 8741

HATHAWAY DINWIDDIE CONSTRUCTION CO p 668
275 Battery St Ste 300 94111
Tel (415) 986-2718 *SIC* 1542

HATHAWAY DINWIDDIE CONSTRUCTION GROUP p 668
275 Battery St Ste 300 94111
Tel (415) 986-2718 *SIC* 1542

HEALD CAPITAL LLC p 673
601 Montgomery St Fl 14 94111
Tel (415) 808-1400 *SIC* 6719

HEALTHRIGHT 360 p 677
1735 Mission St Ste 2050 94103
Tel (415) 762-3700 *SIC* 8093 8011

HEARST COMMUNICATIONS INC p 678
901 Mission St 94103
Tel (415) 777-1111 *SIC* 2711

HELLMAN & FRIEDMAN LLC p 681
1 Maritime Plz Fl 12 94111
Tel (415) 788-5111 *SIC* 6726

HELLMUTH OBATA & KASSABAUM INC p 682
1 Bush St Ste 200 94104
Tel (415) 243-0555
SIC 8712 8711 8742 7389 0781

HERRERO BUILDERS INC p 687
2100 Oakdale Ave 94124
Tel (415) 824-7675 *SIC* 1541

HIG MIDDLE MARKET LLC p 690
1 Market Spear Tower 18f 94105
Tel (415) 439-5500 *SIC* 8021

HORIZON HOLDINGS LLC p 707
1 Bush St Ste 650 94104
Tel (415) 788-2000 *SIC* 6799 2053

HORNBLOWER YACHTS LLC p 708
On The Embarcadero Pier 3 St Pier 94111
Tel (415) 788-8866 *SIC* 4489

IGP INDUSTRIES LLC p 730
101 Mission St Ste 1500 94105
Tel (415) 882-4550 *SIC* 7389

ILWU-PMA WELFARE TRUST p 733
1188 Franklin St Ste 101 94109
Tel (415) 673-8500 *SIC* 8699

INSIDEVIEW TECHNOLOGIES INC p 745
444 De Haro St Ste 210 94107
Tel (415) 728-9309 *SIC* 5045

INTERIOR ARCHITECTS INC p 752
500 Sansome St Ste 8th 94111
Tel (415) 434-3305 *SIC* 8712

INTERPACIFIC GROUP INC p 757
576 Beale St 94105
Tel (415) 442-0711 *SIC* 8721

IXONOS USA LIMITED p 769
85 2nd St 94105
Tel (949) 278-1354 *SIC* 7373 8731

J DAVID GLADSTONE INSTITUTES p 771
1650 Owens St 94158
Tel (415) 734-2000 *SIC* 8733

JAMES IRVINE FOUNDATION p 776
1 Bush St Fl 8 94104
Tel (415) 777-2244 *SIC* 6732

JESSICA MCCLINTOCK INC p 783
2307 Broadway St 94115
Tel (415) 553-8200 *SIC* 2361 2335 2844

JEWISH COMMUNITY FEDERATION OF SAN FRANCISCO PENINSULA MARIN & SONOMA COUNTIES p 784
121 Steuart St Fl 7 94105
Tel (415) 777-0411 *SIC* 8399

■ **JMP GROUP INC** p 786
600 Montgomery St # 1100 94111
Tel (415) 835-8900 *SIC* 6211

▲ **JMP GROUP LLC** p 786
600 Montgomery St # 1100 94111
Tel (415) 835-8900 *SIC* 6211

JOHN STEWART CO p 789
1388 Sutter St Ste 1100 94109
Tel (213) 833-1860 *SIC* 6531 6552 6726

JOIE DE VIVRE HOSPITALITY LLC p 792
530 Bush St Ste 501 94108
Tel (415) 835-0300 *SIC* 8741

■ **JP MORGAN H&Q PRINCIPALS LP** p 794
560 Mission St Fl 2 94105
Tel (415) 315-5000
SIC 6211 6799 6282 7389

JUDICIAL COUNCIL OF CALIFORNIA p 796
455 Golden Gate Ave # 1521 94102
Tel (415) 865-4200 *SIC* 9211

KABAM INC p 799
795 Folsom St Fl 6 94107
Tel (415) 391-0817 *SIC* 7371

KENNEDY/JENKS CONSULTANTS INC p 811
303 2nd St Ste 300s 94107
Tel (415) 243-2150 *SIC* 8711

KIKKOMAN SALES USA INC p 817
50 California St Ste 3600 94111
Tel (415) 956-7750 *SIC* 5149 2035

KIMPTON HOTEL & RESTAURANT GROUP LLC p 819
222 Kearny St Ste 200 94108
Tel (415) 397-5572 *SIC* 8741

KINSALE HOLDINGS INC p 821
475 Sansome St Ste 700 94111
Tel (415) 400-2600 *SIC* 5122

■ **KKR FINANCIAL HOLDINGS LLC** p 822
555 California St Fl 50 94104
Tel (415) 315-3620 *SIC* 6798 6282

LEMBI GROUP INC p 855
2101 Market St 94114
Tel (415) 861-1111 *SIC* 6531

▲ **LENDINGCLUB CORP** p 855
71 Stevenson St Ste 300 94105
Tel (415) 632-5600 *SIC* 6153

LEVI STRAUSS & CO p 858
1155 Battery St 94111
Tel (415) 501-6000
SIC 2325 2339 2321 2331 2337 2329

LITTLER MENDELSON PC p 871
333 Bush St Fl 34 94104
Tel (415) 433-1940 *SIC* 8111

M ARTHUR GENSLER JR & ASSOCIATES INC p 889
2 Harrison St Fl 4 94105
Tel (415) 433-3700 *SIC* 8712

MALCOLM DRILLING CO INC p 899
92 Natoma St Ste 400 94105
Tel (415) 901-4400 *SIC* 1799

▲ MARIN SOFTWARE INC *p* 906
123 Mission St Fl 27 94105
Tel (415) 399-2580 *SIC* 7374

MASON STREET OPCO LLC *p* 916
950 Mason St 94108
Tel (415) 772-5000 *SIC* 7011

▲ MCKESSON CORP *p* 930
1 Post St Fl 18 94104
Tel (415) 983-8300
SIC 5122 5047 5199 7372

■ MEDIVATION INC *p* 938
525 Market St Fl 36 94105
Tel (415) 543-3470 *SIC* 2834

MERCHANT SERVICES INC *p* 944
1 S Van Ness Ave Fl 5 94103
Tel (817) 725-0900 *SIC* 7374

MERITAGE GROUP LP *p* 949
The Embarcad Pier 5 St Pier 94111
Tel (415) 399-5330 *SIC* 8741

METROPOLITAN TRANSPORTATION COMMISSION *p* 956
375 Beale St 94105
Tel (510) 817-5700 *SIC* 4111

MICRO HOLDING CORP *p* 961
1 Maritime Plz Fl 12 94111
Tel (415) 788-5111 *SIC* 7374 7389

MILLBRAE WCP HOTEL I LLC *p* 970
335 Powell St 94102
Tel (415) 397-7000 *SIC* 7011

MINTED LLC *p* 974
747 Front St Ste 200 94111
Tel (415) 399-1100 *SIC* 5112

MORGAN LEWIS & BOCKIUS LLP *p* 988
1 Market St Ste 500 94105
Tel (415) 393-2000 *SIC* 8111

MORRISON & FOERSTER LLP *p* 990
425 Market St Fl 30 94105
Tel (415) 268-7000 *SIC* 8111

MUFG UNION BANK NA *p* 999
400 California St 94104
Tel (212) 782-6800 *SIC* 6021

MULESOFT INC *p* 999
77 Geary St Fl 400 94108
Tel (415) 229-2009 *SIC* 7371

▲ NEKTAR THERAPEUTICS *p* 1025
455 Mission Bay Blvd S 94158
Tel (415) 482-5300 *SIC* 2834

NEW FRENCH BAKERY INC *p* 1030
2325 Pine St 94115
Tel (415) 440-0356 *SIC* 5461

▲ NEW RELIC INC *p* 1033
188 Spear St Ste 1200 94105
Tel (650) 777-7600 *SIC* 7372

NEXANT INC *p* 1039
101 2nd St Ste 1000 94105
Tel (415) 369-1000 *SIC* 8748

NORCAL MUTUAL INSURANCE CO INC *p* 1047
560 Davis St Fl 2 94111
Tel (415) 397-9703 *SIC* 6411 6331

NORTH EAST MEDICAL SERVICES *p* 1052
1520 Stockton St 94133
Tel (415) 391-9686 *SIC* 8011

■ OLD NAVY INC *p* 1081
2 Folsom St 94105
Tel (650) 952-4400 *SIC* 5651

■ OLD REPUBLIC TITLE CO *p* 1081
275 Battery St Ste 1500 94111
Tel (415) 421-3500 *SIC* 6361 6531

■ OLD REPUBLIC TITLE HOLDING CO INC *p* 1081
275 Battery St Ste 1500 94111
Tel (415) 421-3500 *SIC* 6361 6531 5045

ON LOK SENIOR HEALTH SERVICES *p* 1086
1333 Bush St 94109
Tel (415) 292-8888 *SIC* 6324 8082

ON24 INC *p* 1086
201 3rd St Fl 3 94103
Tel (877) 202-9599 *SIC* 4813

■ ONE KINGS LANE INC *p* 1086
633 Folsom St Fl 2 94107
Tel (415) 489-9181 *SIC* 5719

■ OPENTABLE INC *p* 1089
1 Montgomery St Ste 700 94104
Tel (415) 344-4200 *SIC* 7389

ORRICK HERRINGTON & SUTCLIFFE LLP *p* 1095
405 Howard St 94105
Tel (415) 773-5700 *SIC* 8111

OTSUKA AMERICA INC *p* 1097
1 Embarcadero Ctr # 2020 94111
Tel (415) 986-5300
SIC 3829 3499 5122 2833 2084 2086

PACIFIC BELL DIRECTORY *p* 1104
101 Spear St Fl 5 94105
Tel (800) 303-3000 *SIC* 2741

■ PACIFIC BELL TELEPHONE CO *p* 1104
430 Bush St Fl 3 94108
Tel (415) 542-9000 *SIC* 4813 2741 4822

■ PACIFIC GAS AND ELECTRIC CO *p* 1104
77 Beale St 94105
Tel (415) 973-7000 *SIC* 4911 4924

PACIFIC MARITIME ASSOCIATION INC *p* 1105
555 Market St Fl 3 94105
Tel (415) 576-3200 *SIC* 8631

PACIFIC STRUCTURES INC *p* 1106
953 Mission St Ste 200 94103
Tel (415) 367-9399 *SIC* 1771

PACIFIC UNION CO *p* 1106
1 Letterman Dr Ste 300 94129
Tel (415) 929-7100 *SIC* 6552 6512 6531

PARKSIDE LENDING LLC *p* 1117
1130 Howard St 94103
Tel (415) 771-3700 *SIC* 6211

PARTHENON DCS HOLDINGS LLC *p* 1118
4 Embarcadero Ctr 94111
Tel (925) 960-4800 *SIC* 8741

PASTA POMODORO INC *p* 1120
1550 Bryant St Ste 100 94103
Tel (415) 431-2681 *SIC* 5812

▲ PATTERN ENERGY GROUP INC *p* 1121
Bay 3 Pier 1 94111
Tel (415) 283-4000 *SIC* 4911

PATTERN ENERGY GROUP LP *p* 1121
Bay 3 Pier 1 94111
Tel (415) 283-4000 *SIC* 4911

PEARL SENIOR CARE LLC *p* 1126
4 Embarcadero Ctr Ste 710 94111
Tel (415) 834-1477 *SIC* 8082

▲ PG&E CORP *p* 1140
77 Beale St 94105
Tel (415) 973-1000 *SIC* 4931 4923

PINTEREST INC *p* 1150
808 Brannan St 94103
Tel (650) 561-5407 *SIC* 7375

PJD CONSTRUCTION INC *p* 1153
447 London St 94112
Tel (415) 218-3031 *SIC* 1542 1522

PLANT CONSTRUCTION CO LP *p* 1154
300 Newhall St 94124
Tel (415) 285-0500 *SIC* 1542

■ POTTERY BARN INC *p* 1164
3250 Van Ness Ave 94109
Tel (415) 421-7900 *SIC* 5719

■ POTTERY BARN KIDS INC *p* 1164
3250 Van Ness Ave 94109
Tel (415) 421-7900 *SIC* 5999

▲ PROLOGIS INC *p* 1183
Bay 1 Pier 1 94111
Tel (415) 394-9000 *SIC* 6798

■ PROLOGIS LP *p* 1183
Bay 1 Pier 1 94111
Tel (415) 394-9000 *SIC* 6798 6799

PROPHET BRAND STRATEGY *p* 1184
1 Bush St Fl 7 94104
Tel (415) 677-0909 *SIC* 8742

PROSPER MARKETPLACE INC *p* 1184
221 Main St Fl 3 94105
Tel (415) 593-5400 *SIC* 6163

RECOLOGY INC *p* 1214
50 California St Fl 24 94111
Tel (415) 875-1000 *SIC* 4953

RED LOBSTER SEAFOOD CO LLC *p* 1215
1 Embarcadero Ctr Fl 39 94111
Tel (415) 983-2706 *SIC* 6726

REES GORDON SCULLY MANSUKHANI LLP *p* 1217
275 Battery St Ste 2000 94111
Tel (415) 986-5900 *SIC* 8111

RETA TRUST *p* 1228
1255 Battery St Ste 450 94111
Tel (415) 546-9300 *SIC* 6733

RIVERBED TECHNOLOGY INC *p* 1237
680 Folsom St Ste 500 94107
Tel (415) 247-8800 *SIC* 3577 5045

ROMAN CATHOLIC ARCHDIOCESE OF SAN FRANCISCO *p* 1248
1 Peter Yorke Way 1 94109
Tel (415) 614-5500 *SIC* 8299

▲ RPX CORP *p* 1255
1 Market Plz Ste 800 94105
Tel (866) 779-7641 *SIC* 6794 8741

S F ADMINISTRATORS INC *p* 1262
642 Harrison St 306 94107
Tel (415) 777-3707 *SIC* 6411

SAINT FRANCIS MEMORIAL HOSPITAL *p* 1269
900 Hyde St 94109
Tel (415) 353-6000 *SIC* 8062

▲ SALESFORCE.COM INC *p* 1272
1 Market Ste 300 94105
Tel (415) 901-7000 *SIC* 7372 7375

SAN FRANCISCO BASEBALL ASSOCIATES LLC *p* 1276
24 Willie Mays Plz 94107
Tel (415) 972-2000 *SIC* 7941 5947

SAN FRANCISCO FOOD BANK *p* 1276
900 Pennsylvania Ave 94107
Tel (415) 282-1900 *SIC* 8322

SAN FRANCISCO FOUNDATION *p* 1276
1 Embarcadero Ctr # 4150 94111
Tel (415) 733-8500 *SIC* 7389

SAN FRANCISCO MUSEUM OF MODERN ART *p* 1276
151 3rd St 94103
Tel (415) 357-4035 *SIC* 8412 5942

SAN FRANCISCO OPERA ASSOCIATION *p* 1276
301 Van Ness Ave 94102
Tel (415) 861-4008 *SIC* 7922

SAN FRANCISCO STATE UNIVERSITY *p* 1276
1600 Holloway Ave 94132
Tel (415) 338-1111 *SIC* 8221 9411

SAN FRANCISCO SYMPHONY INC *p* 1276
201 Van Ness Ave 94102
Tel (415) 552-8000 *SIC* 7929

SAN FRANCISCO UNIFIED SCHOOL DISTRICT *p* 1277
555 Franklin St 94102
Tel (415) 241-6000 *SIC* 8211 8741

SAN FRANCISCO UNIFIED SCHOOL DISTRICT BOARD OF EDUCATION *p* 1277
555 Franklin St 94102
Tel (415) 241-6000 *SIC* 8211

SCHWAB CHARITABLE FUND *p* 1291
211 Main St 94105
Tel (415) 667-9131 *SIC* 8699

■ SCHWAB HOLDINGS INC *p* 1291
211 Main St 94105
Tel (415) 636-7000 *SIC* 6211

SE SCHER CORP *p* 1295
665 3rd St Ste 415 94107
Tel (415) 431-8826 *SIC* 7361

SEDGWICK LLP *p* 1300
333 Bush St Fl 30 94104
Tel (415) 781-7900 *SIC* 8111

SEGA OF AMERICA INC *p* 1300
350 Rhode Island St # 400 94103
Tel (415) 701-6000 *SIC* 5045 5092

SELECTQUOTE INSURANCE SERVICES *p* 1302
595 Market St Fl 10 94105
Tel (415) 543-7338 *SIC* 6411

SEPHORA USA INC *p* 1306
525 Market St Fl 32 94105
Tel (415) 284-3300 *SIC* 5999

▲ SERVICESOURCE INTERNATIONAL INC *p* 1308
760 Market St Fl 4 94102
Tel (415) 901-6030 *SIC* 8742

SHARPER IMAGE CORP *p* 1312
350 The Embarcadero Fl 6 94105
Tel (877) 714-7444
SIC 5731 5941 5999 5719 5945 5961

SKYLINE COMMERCIAL INTERIORS INC *p* 1330
731 Sansome St Fl 4 94111
Tel (415) 908-1020 *SIC* 1542

▲ SPLUNK INC *p* 1359
250 Brannan St 94107
Tel (415) 848-8400 *SIC* 7372

▲ SQUARE INC *p* 1362
1455 Market St Ste 600 94103
Tel (415) 375-3176 *SIC* 7372

SQUARETRADE INC *p* 1362
360 3rd St Fl 6 94107
Tel (415) 541-1000 *SIC* 6411

SR MARY PHILIPPA HEALTH CENTER *p* 1362
2235 Hayes St Fl 5 94117
Tel (415) 750-5500 *SIC* 8099

ST LUKES HOSPITAL *p* 1370
3555 Cesar Chavez 94110
Tel (415) 647-8600 *SIC* 8062

ST MARYS MEDICAL CENTER FOUNDATION *p* 1372
450 Stanyan St 94117
Tel (415) 668-1000 *SIC* 8062

STATE COMPENSATION INSURANCE FUND INC *p* 1380
333 Bush St Fl 8 94104
Tel (888) 782-8338 *SIC* 6331

STEELE INTERNATIONAL INC *p* 1384
1 Sansome St Ste 3500 94104
Tel (415) 781-4300 *SIC* 7381 8742 8748

STEELRIVER INFRASTRUCTURE FUND NORTH AMERICA LP *p* 1384
1 Letterman Dr Ste 500 94129
Tel (415) 848-5448 *SIC* 4924

STEELRIVER INFRASTRUCTURE PARTNERS LP *p* 1384
1 Letterman Dr 94129
Tel (415) 512-1515 *SIC* 6719

STEPHENS INSTITUTE *p* 1386
79 New Montgomery St 94105
Tel (415) 274-2200 *SIC* 8299 8221

■ STUBHUB INC *p* 1394
199 Fremont St Fl 4 94105
Tel (415) 222-8400 *SIC* 7374 7999 7922

SUNBEAM GP LLC *p* 1401
1 Maritime Plz 94111
Tel (615) 665-1283 *SIC* 6719

▲ SUNRUN INC *p* 1404
595 Market St Fl 29 94105
Tel (415) 580-6900 *SIC* 3674

■ SUNRUN SOUTH LLC *p* 1404
595 Market St Fl 29 94105
Tel (415) 580-6900 *SIC* 5074

SUTTER BAY HOSPITALS *p* 1410
633 Folsom St Fl 5 94107
Tel (415) 600-6000 *SIC* 8062 8733

SWINERTON BUILDERS *p* 1412
260 Townsend St 94107
Tel (415) 421-2980 *SIC* 1541 1522 1542

SWINERTON INC *p* 1412
260 Townsend St 94107
Tel (415) 421-2980
SIC 1542 1541 6531 1522

T Y LIN INTERNATIONAL *p* 1420
345 California St Fl 23 94104
Tel (415) 291-3700 *SIC* 8711

TERRENO REALTY CORP *p* 1440
101 Montgomery St Ste 200 94104
Tel (415) 655-4580 *SIC* 6798

TIDES CENTER *p* 1452
The Prsdio 1014 Trney Ave 94129
Tel (415) 561-6400 *SIC* 8399

TIDES FOUNDATION *p* 1452
Presidio Bldg 1014 94129
Tel (415) 561-6400 *SIC* 8399

TOMAHAWK ACQUISITION LLC *p* 1459
150 California St Fl 19 94111
Tel (415) 765-6500 *SIC* 6726 7371

■ TOWNS END STUDIOS LLC *p* 1466
699 8th St 94103
Tel (415) 802-7936 *SIC* 7371

TPG PARTNERS III LP *p* 1467
345 California St # 3300 94104
Tel (415) 743-1500
SIC 1311 1389 4922 5082

TRANSAMERICA FINANCE CORP *p* 1470
600 Montgomery St Fl 16 94111
Tel (415) 983-4000 *SIC* 6153

TRIAGE CONSULTING GROUP *p* 1478
221 Main St Ste 1100 94105
Tel (415) 512-9400 *SIC* 8742 8748

■ TRULIA INC *p* 1486
535 Mission St Fl 7 94105
Tel (415) 648-4358 *SIC* 7374

▲ TWILIO INC *p* 1494
645 Harrison St Fl 3 94107
Tel (415) 390-2337 *SIC* 7372 4812

▲ TWITTER INC *p* 1495
1355 Market St Ste 900 94103
Tel (415) 222-9670 *SIC* 7375

TY LIN INTERNATIONAL GROUP *p* 1496
345 California St Fl 23 94104
Tel (415) 291-3700 *SIC* 8711

UBER TECHNOLOGIES INC *p* 1498
1455 Market St Fl 4 94103
Tel (415) 986-2715 *SIC* 7372

UNIVERSITY OF CALIFORNIA SAN FRANCISCO *p* 1520
505 Parnassus Ave 94143
Tel (415) 476-9000 *SIC* 8221

UNIVERSITY OF CALIFORNIA SAN FRANCISCO FOUNDATION *p* 1520
44 Montgomery St Ste 2200 94104
Tel (415) 476-6922 *SIC* 8699

UNIVERSITY OF SAN FRANCISCO INC *p* 1525
2130 Fulton St 94117
Tel (415) 422-5555 *SIC* 8221

■ URS HOLDINGS INC *p* 1530
600 Montgomery St Fl 25 94111
Tel (415) 774-2700
SIC 8711 7389 6531 8249 4581

VALUEACT CAPITAL MANAGEMENT LP *p* 1542
1 Letterman Dr Bldg D 94129
Tel (415) 249-1232 *SIC* 6722

VECTOR STEALTH HOLDINGS II LLC *p* 1546
456 Montgomery St Fl 19 94104
Tel (415) 293-5000 *SIC* 7379

VECTOR TALENT II LLC *p* 1546
1 Market St Ste 2300 94105
Tel (415) 293-5000 *SIC* 6726

VIKING ASSET MANAGEMENT LLC *p* 1556
505 Sansome St Ste 1275 94111
Tel (415) 981-5300 *SIC* 6282

VISTA EQUITY PARTNERS FUND III LP *p* 1562
4 Embarcadero Ctr # 2000 94111
Tel (415) 765-6500 *SIC* 6799

VISTA EQUITY PARTNERS FUND VI-A LP *p* 1562
4 Embarcadero Ctr Fl 20 94111
Tel (415) 765-6500 *SIC* 6722

VISTA EQUITY PARTNERS LLC *p* 1562
4 Embarcadero Ctr # 2000 94111
Tel (415) 765-6500 *SIC* 6726

WACHOVIA A DIVISION OF WELLS F *p* 1570
420 Montgomery St 94104
Tel (415) 571-2832 *SIC* 6021

WEISSCOMM GROUP LTD *p* 1588
50 Francisco St Ste 400 94133
Tel (415) 362-5018 *SIC* 8748

▲ WELLS FARGO & CO *p* 1590
420 Montgomery St Frnt 94104
Tel (866) 249-3302
SIC 6021 6022 6162 6141 7374

■ WELLS FARGO BANK NATIONAL ASSOCIATION *p* 1590
420 Montgomery St 94104
Tel (415) 396-7392 *SIC* 6021

WELLS FARGO FINANCING CORP *p* 1590
420 Montgomery St Frnt 94104
Tel (415) 222-4292 *SIC* 6022 6021

WESTED *p* 1597
730 Harrison St Ste 500 94107
Tel (415) 565-3000 *SIC* 8733

■ **WFC HOLDINGS CORP** p 1603
420 Montgomery St 94104
Tel (415) 396-7392 *SIC* 6021

WILBUR-ELLIS CO LLC p 1608
345 California St Fl 27 94104
Tel (415) 772-4000 *SIC* 5191 0711

WILBUR-ELLIS HOLDINGS II INC p 1608
345 California St Fl 27 94104
Tel (415) 772-4000 *SIC* 5999 5191 5169

▲ **WILLIAMS-SONOMA INC** p 1612
3250 Van Ness Ave 94109
Tel (415) 421-7900
SIC 5719 5722 5261 5961

■ **WILLIAMS-SONOMA STORES INC** p 1612
3250 Van Ness Ave 94109
Tel (415) 421-7900 *SIC* 5023

WOODRUFF-SAWYER & CO p 1623
50 California St Fl 12 94111
Tel (415) 391-2141 *SIC* 6411

■ **XOOM CORP** p 1632
425 Market St Fl 12 94105
Tel (415) 777-4800 *SIC* 6099

■ **XPO LOGISTICS WORLDWIDE INC** p 1633
560 Mission St Ste 2950 94105
Tel (415) 486-2660
SIC 4731 4225 4213 8741

▲ **YELP INC** p 1635
140 New Montgomery St # 900 94105
Tel (415) 908-3801 *SIC* 7375

YOUNG MENS CHRISTIAN ASSOCIATION OF SAN FRANCISCO p 1639
50 California St Ste 650 94111
Tel (415) 777-9622
SIC 8641 7991 8351 7032 8322

YOURPEOPLE INC p 1639
303 2nd St Ste 401 94107
Tel (415) 798-9086 *SIC* 6411 7372

▲ **ZENDESK INC** p 1642
1019 Market St 94103
Tel (415) 418-7506 *SIC* 7372

▲ **ZYNGA INC** p 1645
699 8th St 94103
Tel (855) 449-9642 *SIC* 7372 7374

SAN GABRIEL, CA

CALIFORNIA SHELLFISH CO INC p 241
818 E Broadway C 91776
Tel (415) 923-7400 *SIC* 2092

NORMANS NURSERY INC p 1049
8665 Duarte Rd 91775
Tel (626) 285-9795 *SIC* 5193 0181

SAN JACINTO, CA

EDELBROCK FOUNDRY CORP p 477
1320 S Buena Vista St 92583
Tel (951) 654-6677 *SIC* 3363 3365 3325

SOBOBA BAND OF LUISENO INDIANS p 1336
23906 Soboba Rd 92583
Tel (951) 654-2765 *SIC* 9131

SAN JOSE, CA

2WIRE INC p 2
1764 Automation Pkwy 95131
Tel (678) 473-2907 *SIC* 4813

40 HRS INC p 3
1669 Flanigan Dr 95121
Tel (408) 414-0158 *SIC* 7361

▲ **8X8 INC** p 4
2125 Onel Dr 95131
Tel (408) 727-1885 *SIC* 4813 7372

▲ **A10 NETWORKS INC** p 7
3 W Plumeria Dr 95134
Tel (408) 325-8668 *SIC* 7373

ACER AMERICA CORP p 17
333 W San Carlos St 95110
Tel (408) 533-7700 *SIC* 7379

ACER AMERICAN HOLDINGS CORP p 17
333 W San Carlos St # 1500 95110
Tel (408) 533-7700 *SIC* 3577 3571

▲ **ADOBE SYSTEMS INC** p 23
345 Park Ave 95110
Tel (408) 536-6000 *SIC* 7372

AIR SYSTEMS INC p 39
940 Remillard Ct Frnt 95122
Tel (408) 280-1666 *SIC* 1711 7623

▲ **ALIGN TECHNOLOGY INC** p 50
2560 Orchard Pkwy 95131
Tel (408) 470-1000 *SIC* 3843

■ **ALTERA CORP** p 62
101 Innovation Dr 95134
Tel (408) 544-7000 *SIC* 3674 7371

ALUM ROCK UNION ELEMENTARY SCHOOL DISTRICT p 63
2930 Gay Ave 95127
Tel (408) 928-6800 *SIC* 8211

■ **APIGEE CORP** p 96
10 Almaden Blvd Ste 1600 95113
Tel (408) 343-7300 *SIC* 7371

ARM INC p 110
150 Rose Orchard Way 95134
Tel (408) 576-1500 *SIC* 3674

■ **ATMEL CORP** p 128
1600 Technology Dr 95110
Tel (408) 441-0311 *SIC* 3674 3714 3545

AURORA NETWORKS INC p 132
1764 Automation Pkwy 95131
Tel (408) 428-9500 *SIC* 3229

AVAGO TECHNOLOGIES US INC p 135
1320 Ridder Park Dr 95131
Tel (800) 433-8778 *SIC* 3674

■ **BEA SYSTEMS INC** p 164
2315 N 1st St 95131
Tel (650) 506-7000 *SIC* 7371 7372

■ **BENCHMARK ELECTRONICS MANUFACTURING SOLUTIONS INC** p 172
5550 Hellyer Ave 95138
Tel (408) 754-9800 *SIC* 3672

BRIDGE BANK NATIONAL ASSOCIATION p 211
55 Almaden Blvd Ste 200 95113
Tel (408) 423-8500 *SIC* 6022 8742

BRISTLECONE INC p 213
10 Almaden Blvd Ste 600 95113
Tel (650) 386-4000 *SIC* 7371 8742

BROADCOM LIMITED p 215
1320 Ridder Park Dr 95131
Tel (408) 433-8000 *SIC* 3674

▲ **BROCADE COMMUNICATIONS SYSTEMS INC** p 216
130 Holger Way 95134
Tel (408) 333-8000 *SIC* 3577 4813

BUCKLES-SMITH ELECTRIC CO p 223
801 Savaker Ave 95126
Tel (408) 280-7777 *SIC* 5084 5063

BURKE INDUSTRIES INC p 227
2250 S 10th St 95112
Tel (408) 297-3500
SIC 3069 2822 2821 3061

▲ **CADENCE DESIGN SYSTEMS INC** p 236
2655 Seely Ave Bldg 5 95134
Tel (408) 943-1234 *SIC* 7372

CALIFORNIA UNITED MECHANICAL INC p 241
2185 Oakland Rd 95131
Tel (408) 232-9000 *SIC* 1711

■ **CALIFORNIA WATER SERVICE CO** p 242
1720 N 1st St 95112
Tel (408) 367-8200 *SIC* 4941

▲ **CALIFORNIA WATER SERVICE GROUP** p 242
1720 N 1st St 95112
Tel (408) 367-8200 *SIC* 4941

CAMPBELL UNION HIGH SCHOOL DIST p 246
3235 Union Ave 95124
Tel (408) 371-0960 *SIC* 8211

▲ **CAVIUM INC** p 267
2315 N 1st St 95131
Tel (408) 943-7100 *SIC* 3674

CHESTER C LEHMANN CO INC p 295
1135 Auzerais Ave 95126
Tel (408) 293-5818 *SIC* 5063

CHILD DEVELOPMENT INC p 298
20 Great Oaks Blvd # 200 95119
Tel (408) 556-7300 *SIC* 8351

▲ **CISCO SYSTEMS INC** p 309
170 W Tasman Dr 95134
Tel (408) 526-4000 *SIC* 3577 7379

■ **CISCO WEBEX LLC** p 309
170 W Tasman Dr 95134
Tel (408) 435-7000 *SIC* 7389 4813

CITY OF SAN JOSE p 318
200 E Santa Clara St 95113
Tel (408) 535-3500 *SIC* 9111

CM MANUFACTURING INC p 328
6321 San Ignacio Ave 95119
Tel (408) 284-7200 *SIC* 3674

CORBRO LLC p 368
4490 Stevens Creek Blvd 95129
Tel (408) 260-9300 *SIC* 5511

COUNTY OF SANTA CLARA p 381
3180 Newberry Dr Ste 150 95118
Tel (408) 299-5105 *SIC* 9199

CRITCHFIELD MECHANICAL INC p 393
1901 Junction Ave 95131
Tel (408) 437-7000 *SIC* 1711

CROWS LLC p 396
1141 S 1st St 95110
Tel (408) 230-4049 *SIC* 5521

■ **CSE HOLDINGS INC** p 397
650 Brennan St 95131
Tel (408) 436-1907
SIC 5087 5084 7699 5113 5199 5112

■ **CSR TECHNOLOGY INC** p 398
1060 Rincon Cir 95131
Tel (408) 523-6500 *SIC* 3679 3812 3674

CUPERTINO ELECTRIC INC p 401
1132 N 7th St 95112
Tel (408) 808-8000 *SIC* 1731

▲ **CYPRESS SEMICONDUCTOR CORP** p 405
5883 Rue Ferrari Ste 100 95138
Tel (408) 943-2600 *SIC* 3674

CYPRESS SEMICONDUCTOR INTERNATIONAL INC p 405
4001 N 1st St 95134
Tel (408) 943-2600 *SIC* 5065

DCHS MEDICAL FOUNDATION p 418
625 Lincoln Ave 95126
Tel (408) 278-3000 *SIC* 8641

DIAMOND MULTIMEDIA SYSTEMS INC p 437
2880 Junction Ave 95134
Tel (408) 868-9613 *SIC* 3672 3577 3661

E-INFOCHIPS INC p 467
2025 Gateway Pl Ste 270 95110
Tel (408) 496-1882 *SIC* 7371 7373

EASTSIDE UNION HIGH SCHOOL DISTRICT p 473
830 N Capitol Ave 95133
Tel (408) 347-5000 *SIC* 8211

▲ **EBAY INC** p 474
2065 Hamilton Ave 95125
Tel (408) 376-7400 *SIC* 5961

EDGES ELECTRICAL GROUP LLC p 477
1135 Auzerais Ave 95126
Tel (408) 293-5818 *SIC* 5063

EVERGREEN SCHOOL DISTRICT p 515
3188 Quimby Rd 95148
Tel (408) 270-6800 *SIC* 8211

▲ **EXTREME NETWORKS INC** p 521
145 Rio Robles 95134
Tel (408) 579-2800 *SIC* 3661 7373 7372

▲ **FAIR ISAAC CORP** p 524
181 Metro Dr Ste 700 95110
Tel (408) 535-1500 *SIC* 7372 8748 7389

FEDEX FREIGHT WEST INC p 536
6411 Guadalupe Mines Rd 95120
Tel (775) 356-7600 *SIC* 4213 4731 4212

FLAGSHIP ENTERPRISES HOLDING INC p 554
1050 N 5th St Ste E 95112
Tel (408) 977-0155 *SIC* 7349

FLAGSHIP FACILITY SERVICES INC p 554
1050 N 5th St Ste E 95112
Tel (408) 977-0155 *SIC* 7349

FLEXTRONICS AMERICA LLC p 556
6201 America Center Dr 95002
Tel (408) 576-7000 *SIC* 3672

FLEXTRONICS HOLDING USA INC p 556
2090 Fortune Dr 95131
Tel (408) 576-7000
SIC 3672 3679 7371 3825

FLEXTRONICS INTERNATIONAL USA INC p 556
6201 America Center Dr 95002
Tel (408) 576-7000 *SIC* 3672

FLEXTRONICS LOGISTICS USA INC p 556
6201 America Center Dr 95002
Tel (408) 576-7000 *SIC* 4783

FORCE10 NETWORKS INC p 565
350 Holger Way 95134
Tel (707) 665-4400 *SIC* 3661

FORESCOUT TECHNOLOGIES INC p 566
190 W Tasman Dr 95134
Tel (408) 213-3191 *SIC* 7371

FRYS ELECTRONICS INC p 582
600 E Brokaw Rd 95112
Tel (408) 350-1484 *SIC* 5999 5734 5731

FUJITSU COMPONENTS AMERICA INC p 584
2290 N 1st St Ste 212 95131
Tel (408) 745-4900 *SIC* 5065

GLOBALLOGIC INC p 617
1741 Tech Dr Ste 400 95110
Tel (408) 273-8900 *SIC* 7371 7379 7373

■ **GOOD SAMARITAN HOSPITAL LP** p 623
2425 Samaritan Dr 95124
Tel (408) 559-2011 *SIC* 8062

GREEN VALLEY CORP p 637
777 N 1st St Fl 5 95112
Tel (408) 287-0246 *SIC* 1542 1522 6512

GREENWASTE RECOVERY INC p 638
625 Charles St 95112
Tel (408) 283-4800 *SIC* 4953

GROVE OAK SCHOOL DISTRICT p 642
6578 Santa Teresa Blvd 95119
Tel (408) 227-8300 *SIC* 8211

▲ **HARMONIC INC** p 662
4300 N 1st St 95134
Tel (408) 542-2500 *SIC* 3663 3823

▲ **HERITAGE COMMERCE CORP** p 686
150 Almaden Blvd Lbby 95113
Tel (408) 947-6900 *SIC* 6022

■ **HGST INC** p 689
3403 Yerba Buena Rd 95135
Tel (800) 801-4618 *SIC* 3572

HITACHI CHEMICAL CO AMERICA LTD p 696
2150 N 1st St Ste 350 95131
Tel (408) 873-2200 *SIC* 5063 5065

HOUSING AUTHORITY OF COUNTY OF SANTA CLARA p 711
505 W Julian St 95110
Tel (408) 275-8770 *SIC* 6531

IMERYS FILTRATION MINERALS INC p 733
1732 N 1st St Ste 450 95112
Tel (805) 562-0200 *SIC* 1499

IMERYS PERLITE USA INC p 733
1732 N 1st St Ste 450 95112
Tel (408) 643-0215 *SIC* 1499

IMERYS TALC AMERICA INC p 733
1732 N 1st St Ste 450 95112
Tel (805) 562-0260 *SIC* 3295 1499

▲ **INTEGRATED DEVICE TECHNOLOGY INC** p 749
6024 Silver Creek Vly Rd 95138
Tel (408) 284-8200 *SIC* 3674

▲ **INVENSENSE INC** p 760
1745 Tech Dr Ste 200 95110
Tel (408) 501-2200 *SIC* 3812

JENSEN CORPORATE HOLDINGS INC p 782
1983 Concourse Dr 95131
Tel (408) 446-1118 *SIC* 0782

KAISER AEROSPACE & ELECTRONICS CORP p 800
2701 Orchard Pkwy Ste 100 95134
Tel (949) 250-1015 *SIC* 3728

KOKUSAI SEMICONDUCTOR EQUIPMENT CORP p 826
2460 N 1st St Ste 290 95131
Tel (408) 456-2750 *SIC* 5065 7629

KSM CORP p 831
1959 Concourse Dr 95131
Tel (408) 514-2400 *SIC* 3674

LEE BROS FOODSERVICES INC p 851
660 E Gish Rd 95112
Tel (408) 275-0700 *SIC* 5141 5142

LSI CORP p 883
1320 Ridder Park Dr 95131
Tel (408) 433-8000 *SIC* 3674

LUMENIS INC p 885
2033 Gateway Pl Ste 200 95110
Tel (408) 764-3000 *SIC* 5047

LUMILEDS LLC p 885
370 W Trimble Rd 95131
Tel (408) 964-2900 *SIC* 3825

MA LABORATORIES INC p 891
2075 N Capitol Ave 95132
Tel (408) 941-0808 *SIC* 5045

MARQUEZ BROTHERS INTERNATIONAL INC p 910
5801 Rue Ferrari 95138
Tel (408) 960-2700 *SIC* 2022

▲ **MAXIM INTEGRATED PRODUCTS INC** p 922
160 Rio Robles 95134
Tel (408) 601-1000 *SIC* 3674

MCLARNEY CONSTRUCTION INC p 931
355 S Daniel Way 95128
Tel (408) 246-8600 *SIC* 1542

MEGAPATH GROUP INC p 940
2510 Zanker Rd 95131
Tel (408) 952-6400 *SIC* 4813

MI PUEBLO LLC p 959
1775 Story Rd Ste 120 95122
Tel (408) 928-1171 *SIC* 5411

MICREL INC p 961
2180 Fortune Dr 95131
Tel (408) 944-0800 *SIC* 3674

■ **MICROSEMI FREQUENCY AND TIME CORP** p 962
3870 N 1st St 95134
Tel (408) 428-6993 *SIC* 3625 7372

■ **MICROSEMI SOC CORP** p 962
3870 N 1st St 95134
Tel (408) 643-6000 *SIC* 3674 7371

▲ **MONOLITHIC POWER SYSTEMS INC** p 984
79 Great Oaks Blvd 95119
Tel (408) 826-0600 *SIC* 3674 8711

■ **MPS INTERNATIONAL LTD** p 996
79 Great Oaks Blvd 95119
Tel (408) 826-0660 *SIC* 3674

NAGARRO INC p 1006
2001 Gateway Pl Ste 100w 95110
Tel (408) 436-6170 *SIC* 7373

■ **NDS SURGICAL IMAGING LLC** p 1022
5750 Hellyer Ave 95138
Tel (408) 776-0085 *SIC* 5047

▲ **NEOPHOTONICS CORP** p 1026
2911 Zanker Rd 95134
Tel (408) 232-9200 *SIC* 3674

▲ **NETGEAR INC** p 1027
350 E Plumeria Dr 95134
Tel (408) 907-8000 *SIC* 3661 3577

▲ **NIMBLE STORAGE INC** p 1043
211 River Oaks Pkwy 95134
Tel (408) 432-9600 *SIC* 3572

■ **NORTHROP GRUMMAN SPACE & MISSION SYSTEMS CORP** p 1058
6377 San Ignacio Ave 95119
Tel (703) 280-2900
SIC 7373 3663 3661 3812 3761

NOVELLUS SYSTEMS INC p 1063
4000 N 1st St 95134
Tel (408) 943-9700 *SIC* 3559

▲ **NUTANIX INC** p 1067
1740 Tech Dr Ste 150 95110
Tel (408) 216-8360 *SIC* 7373

NXP SEMICONDUCTORS USA INC p 1068
411 E Plumeria Dr 95134
Tel (408) 518-5500 *SIC* 3674

▲ **OCLARO INC** p 1074
225 Charcot Ave 95131
Tel (408) 383-1400 *SIC* 3674 3826 3827

OCONNOR HOSPITAL p 1074
2105 Forest Ave 95128
Tel (408) 947-2500 *SIC* 8062

■ **ORCHARD SUPPLY CO LLC** p 1093
6450 Via Del Oro 95119
Tel (408) 281-3500 *SIC* 5251 5261

OSH 1 LIQUIDATING CORP p 1096
6450 Via Del Oro 95119
Tel (408) 281-3500 *SIC* 5251

PACIFIC GROSERVICE INC p 1104
567 Cinnabar St 95110
Tel (408) 727-4826
SIC 5194 5145 5141 5113 5087

▲ PAYPAL HOLDINGS INC p 1123
2211 N 1st St 95131
Tel (408) 967-1000 *SIC* 4813 7374

■ PAYPAL INC p 1123
2211 N 1st St 95131
Tel (877) 981-2163 *SIC* 4813 7374

▲ PDF SOLUTIONS INC p 1124
333 W San Carlos St # 700 95110
Tel (408) 280-7900 *SIC* 7371

PITCO FOODS p 1152
567 Cinnabar St 95110
Tel (916) 372-7772 *SIC* 5141

PLANNED PARENTHOOD MAR MONTE INC p 1154
1691 The Alameda 95126
Tel (408) 287-7532 *SIC* 8093

POLYCOM INC p 1160
6001 America Center Dr 95002
Tel (408) 586-6000 *SIC* 8741

▲ POWER INTEGRATIONS INC p 1165
5245 Hellyer Ave 95138
Tel (408) 414-9200 *SIC* 3674

QCT LLC p 1194
1010 Rincon Cir 95131
Tel (510) 270-6111 *SIC* 7373

■ QUALCOMM ATHEROS INC p 1196
1700 Technology Dr 95110
Tel (408) 773-5200 *SIC* 3674 4899

▲ QUANTUM CORP p 1198
224 Airport Pkwy Ste 300 95110
Tel (408) 944-4000 *SIC* 3572 8731

■ RAE SYSTEMS INC p 1205
3775 N 1st St 95134
Tel (408) 952-8200 *SIC* 3829 3812 3699

REACH AMERICA ESG LTD p 1213
2033 Gateway Pl Ste 500 95110
Tel (408) 573-6170 *SIC* 5169

ROMAN CATHOLIC BISHOP OF SAN JOSE p 1248
1150 N 1st St Ste 100 95112
Tel (408) 983-0100 *SIC* 8661

ROSENDIN ELECTRIC INC p 1251
880 Mabury Rd 95133
Tel (408) 286-2800 *SIC* 1731

SAMSUNG SEMICONDUCTOR INC p 1275
3655 N 1st St 95134
Tel (408) 544-4000 *SIC* 5065 5045

SAN JOSE MEDICAL SYSTEMS LP p 1277
225 N Jackson Ave 95116
Tel (408) 259-5000 *SIC* 8062

SAN JOSE MERCURY-NEWS LLC p 1277
4 N 2nd St Fl 8 95113
Tel (408) 920-5000 *SIC* 2711

SAN JOSE STATE UNIVERSITY p 1277
1 Washington Sq 95192
Tel (408) 924-1000 *SIC* 8221 9411

SAN JOSE UNIFIED SCHOOL DISTRICT p 1277
855 Lenzen Ave 95126
Tel (408) 535-6000 *SIC* 8211

■ SAN JOSE WATER CO p 1277
110 W Taylor St 95110
Tel (408) 288-5314 *SIC* 4941

SAN JOSE/EVERGREEN COMMUNITY COLLEGE DISTRICT FOUNDATION p 1277
40 S Market St 95113
Tel (408) 918-6131 *SIC* 8222

▲ SANMINA CORP p 1280
2700 N 1st St 95134
Tel (408) 964-3500 *SIC* 3672 3674

SANTA CLARA COUNTY OFFICE OF EDUCATION p 1280
1290 Ridder Park Dr 95131
Tel (408) 453-6500 *SIC* 8211

SANTA CLARA VALLEY MEDICAL CENTER p 1280
751 S Bascom Ave 95128
Tel (408) 885-5000 *SIC* 8062 6324

SANTA CLARA VALLEY TRANSPORTATION AUTHORITY p 1280
3331 N 1st St 95134
Tel (408) 321-2300 *SIC* 9621

SANTA CLARA VALLEY WATER DISTRICT PUBLIC FACILITIES FINANCING CORP p 1280
5750 Almaden Expy 95118
Tel (408) 265-2600 *SIC* 4941

SATELLITE HEALTHCARE INC p 1283
300 Santana Row Ste 300 95128
Tel (650) 404-3600 *SIC* 8092

SECOND HARVEST FOOD BANK OF SANTA CLARA & SAN MATEO COUNTIES p 1298
750 Curtner Ave 95125
Tel (408) 266-8866 *SIC* 8322

■ SILICON IMAGE INC p 1323
2115 Onel Dr 95131
Tel (408) 616-4000 *SIC* 3674 7371

SILICON VALLEY EDUCATION FOUNDATION p 1323
1400 Parkmoor Ave Ste 200 95126
Tel (408) 790-9400 *SIC* 8399

▲ SILVER SPRING NETWORKSINC p 1324
230 W Tasman Dr 95134
Tel (669) 770-4000 *SIC* 4899 7372

▲ SJW CORP p 1328
110 W Taylor St 95110
Tel (408) 279-7800 *SIC* 4941 6531

SK HYNIX AMERICA INC p 1328
3101 N 1st St 95134
Tel (408) 232-8000 *SIC* 5065 5045

SMTC MANUFACTURING CORP OF CALIFORNIA p 1335
2302 Trade Zone Blvd 95131
Tel (408) 934-7100 *SIC* 3672

■ SPANSION INC p 1354
198 Champion Ct 95134
Tel (408) 962-2500 *SIC* 3674

STION CORP p 1390
6321 San Ignacio Ave 95119
Tel (408) 284-7200 *SIC* 3674

STRUCTURAL INTEGRITY ASSOCIATES INC p 1394
5215 Hellyer Ave Ste 210 95138
Tel (408) 978-8200 *SIC* 8711

SUMCO USA SALES CORP p 1398
2099 Gateway Pl Ste 400 95110
Tel (408) 352-3880 *SIC* 3674

SUN BASKET INC p 1400
1170 Olinder Ct 95122
Tel (408) 669-4418 *SIC* 2099

■ SUNPOWER CORP p 1403
77 Rio Robles 95134
Tel (408) 240-5500 *SIC* 3674 3679

▲ SUPER MICRO COMPUTER INC p 1405
980 Rock Ave 95131
Tel (408) 503-8000 *SIC* 3571 3572 7372

SUPER TALENT TECHNOLOGY CORP p 1406
2077 N Capitol Ave 95132
Tel (408) 957-8133 *SIC* 5045

▲ SYNAPTICS INC p 1414
1251 Mckay Dr 95131
Tel (408) 904-1100 *SIC* 3577 7372

TAOS MOUNTAIN LLC p 1424
121 Daggett Dr 95134
Tel (408) 324-2800 *SIC* 7379

TCOMT INC p 1428
111 N Market St Ste 670 95113
Tel (408) 351-3340 *SIC* 3663

▲ TESSERA HOLDING CORP p 1441
3025 Orchard Pkwy 95134
Tel (408) 321-6000 *SIC* 3674

■ TESSERA TECHNOLOGIES INC p 1441
3025 Orchard Pkwy 95134
Tel (408) 321-6000 *SIC* 6794 3674

THERMA CORP p 1447
1601 Las Plumas Ave 95133
Tel (408) 347-3400 *SIC* 3444 3448

■ THERMO FINNIGAN LLC p 1447
355 River Oaks Pkwy 95134
Tel (408) 965-6000 *SIC* 3826

■ THERMOQUEST CORP p 1447
355 River Oaks Pkwy 95134
Tel (408) 965-6000 *SIC* 3826 3823

TRANS-PAK INC p 1470
520 Marburg Way 95133
Tel (408) 254-0500 *SIC* 7389

TRIGEM ENTERPRISES INC p 1480
2075 Zanker Rd 95131
Tel (408) 943-9193 *SIC* 5734

▲ UBIQUITI NETWORKS INC p 1498
2580 Orchard Pkwy 95131
Tel (408) 942-3085 *SIC* 7373

■ UCP INC p 1499
99 Almaden Blvd Ste 400 95113
Tel (408) 207-9499 *SIC* 1521 1531 6552

▲ ULTRATECH INC p 1501
3050 Zanker Rd 95134
Tel (408) 321-8835 *SIC* 3559

VANDER-BEND MANUFACTURING LLC p 1543
2701 Orchard Pkwy 95134
Tel (408) 245-5150 *SIC* 3679 3444 3549

■ VERIFONE INC p 1549
88 W Plumeria Dr 95134
Tel (408) 232-7800
SIC 3578 7372 3577 3575 8711 3643

▲ VERIFONE SYSTEMS INC p 1549
88 W Plumeria Dr 95134
Tel (408) 232-7800 *SIC* 3578 7372

▲ VOCERA COMMUNICATIONS INC p 1564
525 Race St Ste 150 95126
Tel (408) 882-5100 *SIC* 3669

WASTE CONNECTIONS OF CALIFORNIA INC p 1580
1333 Oakland Rd 95112
Tel (408) 282-4400 *SIC* 4953

■ WD MEDIA LLC p 1585
1710 Automation Pkwy 95131
Tel (408) 576-2000 *SIC* 3695

WEST SAN CARLOS HOTEL PARTNERS LLC p 1595
282 Almaden Blvd 95113
Tel (408) 998-0400 *SIC* 7011

▲ XILINX INC p 1631
2100 Logic Dr 95124
Tel (408) 559-7778 *SIC* 3672 3674 7372

ZCO LIQUIDATING CORP p 1641
6373 San Ignacio Ave 95119
Tel (408) 733-8400 *SIC* 3572

ZHONGLI NEW ENERGY USA CO LLC p 1643
25 Metro Dr Ste 228 95110
Tel (408) 638-7627 *SIC* 5074

■ ZORAN CORP p 1644
1060 Rincon Cir 95131
Tel (972) 673-1600 *SIC* 3674

ZSCALER INC p 1644
110 Rose Orchard Way 95134
Tel (408) 533-0288 *SIC* 7371

SAN JUAN BAUTISTA, CA

■ EARTHBOUND FARM LLC p 469
1721 San Juan Hwy 95045
Tel (831) 623-7880 *SIC* 0723 2037 2099

■ EARTHBOUND HOLDINGS I LLC p 469
1721 San Juan Hwy 95045
Tel (831) 623-2767 *SIC* 0723 2099

■ EARTHBOUND HOLDINGS II LLC p 469
1721 San Juan Hwy 95045
Tel (831) 623-2767 *SIC* 0723 2099

■ EARTHBOUND HOLDINGS III LLC p 469
1721 San Juan Hwy 95045
Tel (831) 623-7880 *SIC* 0723 2099 6719

■ EB SAV INC p 474
1721 San Juan Hwy 95045
Tel (303) 635-4500 *SIC* 0723 2099

TRUE LEAF FARMS LLC p 1486
1275 San Justo Rd 95045
Tel (831) 623-4667 *SIC* 2034

SAN JUAN CAPISTRANO, CA

CAPISTRANO UNIFIED SCHOOL DISTRICT p 249
33122 Valle Rd 92675
Tel (949) 234-9200 *SIC* 8211

COSCO FIRE PROTECTION INC p 373
29222 Rancho Viejo Rd # 205 92675
Tel (714) 974-8770 *SIC* 1711 1731 5999

EMERALD EXPOSITIONS LLC p 491
31910 Del Obispo St # 200 92675
Tel (949) 226-5700 *SIC* 7389

FLUIDMASTER INC p 561
30800 Rancho Viejo Rd 92675
Tel (949) 728-2000 *SIC* 3432 3089

MERIT INTEGRATED LOGISTICS LLC p 949
29122 Rancho Viejo Rd # 211 92675
Tel (949) 481-0685 *SIC* 4731

■ NICHOLS INSTITUTE REFERENCE LABORATORIES p 1042
33608 Ortega Hwy 92675
Tel (949) 728-4000 *SIC* 8071

■ QUEST DIAGNOSTICS NICHOLS INSTITUTE p 1199
33608 Ortega Hwy 92675
Tel (949) 728-4000 *SIC* 3826 8071

REVENUE PROCESSING SOLUTIONS INC p 1229
28293 Via Del Mar 92675
Tel (949) 481-9080 *SIC* 7371 7389

TECHKO INC p 1431
27301 Calle De La Rosa 92675
Tel (949) 486-0678 *SIC* 3699 3589

SAN LEANDRO, CA

ARYZTA US HOLDINGS I CORP p 115
14490 Catalina St 94577
Tel (800) 938-1900 *SIC* 2052 2053 2051

BIGGE CRANE AND RIGGING CO p 182
10700 Bigge St 94577
Tel (510) 638-8100 *SIC* 1796

GHIRARDELLI CHOCOLATE CO p 610
1111 139th Ave 94578
Tel (510) 483-6970
SIC 5441 2066 5812 5149

INDEPENDENT ELECTRIC SUPPLY INC p 736
2001 Marina Blvd 94577
Tel (520) 908-7900 *SIC* 5063

KENNERLEY-SPRATLING INC p 811
2116 Farallon Dr 94577
Tel (510) 351-8230 *SIC* 3089 3082

KP LLC p 828
13951 Washington Ave 94578
Tel (510) 346-0729
SIC 2752 7334 7331 7374 7389 8742

LA BREA BAKERY CAFE INC p 835
14490 Catalina St 94577
Tel (818) 742-4242 *SIC* 2051 2052 2053

LA BREA BAKERY HOLDINGS INC p 835
14490 Catalina St 94577
Tel (818) 742-4242 *SIC* 2051

OSISOFT LLC p 1097
1600 Alvarado St 94577
Tel (510) 297-5800 *SIC* 7372 7371 7373

PACIFIC COAST CONTAINER INC p 1104
432 Estudillo Ave Ste 1 94577
Tel (510) 346-6100 *SIC* 4789 4225 4222

PETERSON HOLDING CO p 1138
955 Marina Blvd 94577
Tel (510) 357-6200 *SIC* 5082

PETERSON MACHINERY CO p 1138
955 Marina Blvd 94577
Tel (541) 302-9199 *SIC* 7629

PETERSON POWER SYSTEMS INC p 1138
2828 Teagarden St 94577
Tel (510) 618-2921 *SIC* 5084 7353

PETERSON TRACTOR CO p 1138
955 Marina Blvd 94577
Tel (530) 343-1911 *SIC* 5082 5084 5083

RCEB p 1212
500 Davis St Ste 100 94577
Tel (510) 432-7123 *SIC* 8699

SENECA FAMILY OF AGENCIES p 1303
15942 Foothill Blvd 94578
Tel (510) 317-1444 *SIC* 8322 8299 8082

SSMB PACIFIC HOLDING CO INC p 1364
1755 Adams Ave 94577
Tel (510) 836-6100 *SIC* 5012 7699

TEOCAL TRANSPORT INC p 1439
2101 Carden St 94577
Tel (510) 569-3485 *SIC* 4214

▲ TRINET GROUP INC p 1480
1100 San Leandro Blvd # 300 94577
Tel (510) 352-5000 *SIC* 7361 8721

ZINUS INC p 1643
1951 Fairway Dr Ste A 94577
Tel (925) 417-2100 *SIC* 2515

SAN LORENZO, CA

■ AIDELLS SAUSAGE CO INC p 37
2411 Baumann Ave 94580
Tel (510) 614-5450 *SIC* 2013 5147

SAN LORENZO UNIFIED SCHOOL DISTRICT p 1277
15510 Usher St 94580
Tel (510) 317-4600 *SIC* 8211

■ THARCO CONTAINER INC p 1446
2222 Grant Ave 94580
Tel (510) 276-8600 *SIC* 2653

■ THARCO HOLDINGS INC p 1446
2222 Grant Ave 94580
Tel (303) 373-1860 *SIC* 2653 3086 2675

SAN LUIS OBISPO, CA

■ AEE SOLAR INC p 29
775 Fiero Ln Ste 200 93401
Tel (800) 777-6609 *SIC* 5063 3645

CALIFORNIA POLYTECHNIC STATE UNIVERSITY p 241
1 Grand Ave 93407
Tel (805) 756-7414 *SIC* 8221 9411

COUNTY OF SAN LUIS OBISPO p 381
Government Center Rm. 300 93408
Tel (805) 781-5040 *SIC* 9111

FRENCH HOSPITAL MEDICAL CENTER FOUNDATION p 578
1911 Johnson Ave 93401
Tel (805) 543-5353 *SIC* 8062

▲ MINDBODY INC p 972
4051 Broad St Ste 220 93401
Tel (877) 755-4279 *SIC* 7372 8741

■ REC SOLAR COMMERCIAL CORP p 1214
3450 Broad St Ste 105 93401
Tel (844) 732-7652 *SIC* 1623

■ SIERRA VISTA HOSPITAL INC p 1321
1010 Murray Ave 93405
Tel (805) 546-7600 *SIC* 8062

■ SUNRUN INSTALLATION SERVICES INC p 1404
775 Fiero Ln Ste 200 93401
Tel (805) 528-9705 *SIC* 1731

UNIVERSITY OF LAVERNE CENTRAL CAMPUS p 1522
4119 Broad St Ste 200 93401
Tel (805) 788-6200 *SIC* 8221

SAN MARCOS, CA

CALIFORNIA STATE UNIVERSITY SAN MARCOS p 241
333 S Twin Oaks Valley Rd 92096
Tel (760) 750-4000 *SIC* 8221 9411

EDCO WASTE & RECYCLING SERVICES INC p 477
224 S Las Posas Rd 92078
Tel (760) 744-2700 *SIC* 4953 4212

■ ELDORADO STONE LLC p 484
1370 Grand Ave Bldg B 92078
Tel (800) 925-1491 *SIC* 3272

FLATIRON WEST INC p 555
1770 La Costa Meadows Dr 92078
Tel (760) 916-9100 *SIC* 1622 1611

HUNTER INDUSTRIES INC p 719
1940 Diamond St 92078
Tel (800) 383-4747 *SIC* 5087 3084

HUNTER INDUSTRIES L P p 719
1940 Diamond St 92078
Tel (760) 744-5240 *SIC* 1629

LUSARDI CONSTRUCTION CO p 886
1570 Linda Vista Dr 92078
Tel (760) 744-3133 *SIC* 1542 1541

PALOMAR COMMUNITY COLLEGE DISTRICT FINANCING CORP p 1110
1140 W Mission Rd 92069
Tel (760) 744-1150 *SIC* 8222

SAN MARCOS UNIFIED SCHOOL DISTRICT p 1277
255 Pico Ave Ste 250 92069
Tel (760) 744-4776 *SIC* 8211

SAN MARINO, CA

AMERICAN DAIRY INC p 71
2275 Huntington Dr 278 91108
Tel (626) 757-8885 *SIC* 5451

HENRY E HUNTINGTON LIBRARY AND ART GALLERY p 684
1151 Oxford Rd 91108
Tel (626) 405-2100 *SIC* 8231

SAN MATEO, CA

ABD INSURANCE & FINANCIAL SERVICES INC p 10
3 Waters Park Dr Ste 100 94403
Tel (650) 488-8565 *SIC* 6411

ACTUATE CORP p 20
951 Mariners Island Blvd # 600 94404
Tel (650) 645-3000 *SIC* 7372

ANDREINI & CO p 90
220 W 20th Ave 94403
Tel (650) 573-1111 *SIC* 6411

APTTUS CORP p 101
1400 Fashion Island Blvd # 100 94404
Tel (650) 445-7700 *SIC* 7373

ARMCO METALS HOLDINGS INC p 111
1730 S Amphlett Blvd # 230 94402
Tel (650) 212-7630 *SIC* 5051

CALIFORNIA CASUALTY INDEMNITY EXCHANGE p 239
1900 Almeda De Las Pulgas 94403
Tel (650) 574-4000 *SIC* 6331

CALIFORNIA CASUALTY MANAGEMENT CO p 239
1900 Almeda De Las Pulgas 94403
Tel (650) 574-4000 *SIC* 6331 8741

CHILDCARE CAREERS LLC p 298
1700 S El Camino Real # 201 94402
Tel (650) 372-0211 *SIC* 7363 7361

▲ COUPA SOFTWARE INC p 383
1855 S Grant St Fl 4 94402
Tel (650) 931-3200 *SIC* 7372

ESSEX PROPERTY TRUST INC p 510
1100 Park Pl Ste 200 94403
Tel (650) 655-7800 *SIC* 6798

EXTEND HEALTH INC p 521
2929 Campus Dr Ste 400 94403
Tel (650) 288-4800 *SIC* 6411

■ FRANKLIN ADVISERS INC p 574
1 Franklin Pkwy 94403
Tel (650) 312-2000 *SIC* 6282

▲ FRANKLIN RESOURCES INC p 575
1 Franklin Pkwy 94403
Tel (650) 312-2000 *SIC* 6722 6726

■ FRANKLIN TEMPLETON SERVICES LLC p 575
1 Franklin Pkwy 94403
Tel (650) 312-3000 *SIC* 6282

▲ GOPRO INC p 625
3000 Clearview Way 94402
Tel (650) 332-7600 *SIC* 3861 7372

GUCKENHEIMER ENTERPRISES INC p 645
1850 Gateway Dr Ste 500 94404
Tel (650) 592-3800 *SIC* 5812

HATCH REALTY GROUP INC p 667
1611 Lodi Ave 94401
Tel (650) 438-2444 *SIC* 6531

KEYNOTE LLC p 815
777 Mariners Island Blvd 94404
Tel (650) 376-3033 *SIC* 7374 7373

LISI INC p 870
1600 W Hillsdale Blvd # 100 94402
Tel (650) 348-4131 *SIC* 6411

MARKETO INC p 908
901 Mariners Island Blvd 94404
Tel (650) 376-2300 *SIC* 7371 7372

■ NETSUITE INC p 1027
2955 Campus Dr Ste 100 94403
Tel (650) 627-1000 *SIC* 7372

OPEN TEXT INC p 1089
951 Mariners Island Blvd # 7 94404
Tel (650) 645-3000 *SIC* 7379

PENINSULA COMMUNITY FOUNDATION p 1129
1700 S El Camino Real # 300 94402
Tel (650) 358-9369 *SIC* 6732

SAN MATEO COUNTY COMMUNITY COLLEGE DISTRICT p 1277
3401 Csm Dr 94402
Tel (650) 358-6742 *SIC* 8222

■ SOLARCITY CORP p 1338
3055 Clearview Way 94402
Tel (650) 638-1028 *SIC* 1711

SONY MOBILE COMMUNICATIONS (USA) INC p 1341
2207 Bridgepoint Pkwy 94404
Tel (866) 766-9374 *SIC* 3663 5999

SURGICAL STAFF INC p 1409
120 Saint Matthews Ave 94401
Tel (650) 558-3999 *SIC* 7363

▲ WAGEWORKS INC p 1571
1100 Park Pl Fl 4 94403
Tel (650) 577-5200 *SIC* 8742

WH ACQUISITIONS INC p 1604
800 Concar Dr Ste 100 94402
Tel (650) 358-5000 *SIC* 5084 6719

SAN PABLO, CA

DOCTORS MEDICAL CENTER LLC p 447
2000 Vale Rd 94806
Tel (510) 970-5000 *SIC* 8062

WEST CONTRA COSTA HEALTHCARE DISTRICT p 1594
2000 Vale Rd 94806
Tel (510) 970-5102 *SIC* 8082

SAN PEDRO, CA

SEASIDE TRANSPORTATION SERVICES LLC p 1297
389 Terminal Way 90731
Tel (310) 241-1760 *SIC* 4231

SAN RAFAEL, CA

AIRCRAFT FINANCE TRUST p 40
2401 Kerner Blvd 94901
Tel (415) 485-4500 *SIC* 7359

▲ AUTODESK INC p 134
111 Mcinnis Pkwy 94903
Tel (415) 507-5000 *SIC* 7372

▲ BIOMARIN PHARMACEUTICAL INC p 184
770 Lindaro St 94901
Tel (415) 506-6700 *SIC* 2834 2835

CELLMARK INC p 273
22 Pelican Way 94901
Tel (415) 927-1700 *SIC* 5099 5093 5111

CELLMARK PULP & PAPER INC p 273
22 Pelican Way 94901
Tel (415) 927-1700 *SIC* 5099 5111

COUNTY OF MARIN p 379
1600 Los Gamos Dr Ste 200 94903
Tel (415) 473-6358 *SIC* 9111

DOMINICAN UNIVERSITY OF CALIFORNIA p 449
50 Acacia Ave 94901
Tel (415) 457-4440 *SIC* 8221

DUTRA GROUP p 463
2350 Kerner Blvd Ste 200 94901
Tel (415) 258-6876 *SIC* 1629 8711 1429

■ FAIR ISAAC INTERNATIONAL CORP p 524
200 Smith Ranch Rd 94903
Tel (415) 446-6000 *SIC* 7372

GHILOTTI BROS INC p 610
525 Jacoby St 94901
Tel (415) 454-7011 *SIC* 1611 1794 1623

KELLEHER CORP p 808
1543 5th Ave 94901
Tel (415) 454-8861 *SIC* 5031

■ MANAGED HEALTH NETWORK p 900
2370 Kerner Blvd 94901
Tel (415) 460-8168
SIC 6324 8093 8011

MARIN CLEAN ENERGY p 906
1125 Tamalpais Ave 94901
Tel (415) 464-6028 *SIC* 3264

■ MHN SERVICES p 959
2370 Kerner Blvd 94901
Tel (415) 460-8300
SIC 6324 8011 8742 8322

PASHA GROUP p 1119
4040 Civic Center Dr # 350 94903
Tel (415) 927-6400 *SIC* 4731

■ WEST AMERICA BANK p 1593
1108 5th Ave 94901
Tel (707) 863-6113 *SIC* 6022

▲ WESTAMERICA BANCORPORATION p 1596
1108 5th Ave 94901
Tel (707) 863-6000 *SIC* 6021

SAN RAMON, CA

24 HOUR FITNESS USA INC p 2
12647 Alcosta Blvd # 500 94583
Tel (925) 543-3100 *SIC* 7991

24 HOUR FITNESS WORLDWIDE INC p 2
12647 Alcosta Blvd # 500 94583
Tel (925) 543-3100 *SIC* 7991

■ AETNA HEALTH OF CALIFORNIA INC p 31
2409 Camino Ramon 94583
Tel (925) 543-9000 *SIC* 6324

ARMANINO LLP p 111
12657 Alcosta Blvd # 500 94583
Tel (925) 790-2600 *SIC* 8721 8742

BLACKBERRY CORP p 187
3001 Bishop Dr 94583
Tel (972) 650-6126 *SIC* 5999 3661 4812

■ CHEVRON CAPTAIN CO LLC p 295
6001 Bollinger Canyon Rd 94583
Tel (925) 842-1000 *SIC* 2911

▲ CHEVRON CORP p 295
6001 Bollinger Canyon Rd 94583
Tel (925) 842-1000
SIC 2911 1311 1382 1321 5541

■ CHEVRON GLOBAL ENERGY INC p 296
6001 Bollinger Canyon Rd 94583
Tel (925) 842-1000 *SIC* 2911 4731 5172

■ CHEVRON INVESTOR INC p 296
6001 Bollinger Canyon Rd 94583
Tel (925) 842-1000 *SIC* 6799

■ CHEVRON ORONITE CO LLC p 296
6001 Bollinger Canyon Rd 94583
Tel (713) 432-2500
SIC 2821 2899 2869 1311

■ CHEVRON STATIONS INC p 296
6001 Bollinger Canyon Rd 94583
Tel (925) 842-1000 *SIC* 5541 5411

■ CHEVRON USA INC p 296
6001 Bollinger Canyon Rd D1248 94583
Tel (925) 842-1000
SIC 5541 5511 2911 5171

CLAIMS SERVICES GROUP LLC p 321
6111 Bollinger Canyon Rd 94583
Tel (925) 866-1100 *SIC* 6411

EAGLE CANYON CAPITAL LLC p 467
3130 Crow Canyon Pl # 240 94583
Tel (925) 884-0800 *SIC* 5411 5499 2092

ENTERPRISE RENT-A-CAR CO OF SAN FRANCISCO LLC p 502
2633 Camino Ramon Ste 400 94583
Tel (925) 464-5100 *SIC* 7514

▲ FIVE9 INC p 553
4000 Executive Pkwy # 400 94583
Tel (925) 201-2000 *SIC* 7372

MIRION TECHNOLOGIES INC p 974
3000 Executive Pkwy # 518 94583
Tel (925) 543-0800 *SIC* 3829

■ OLD REPUBLIC HOME PROTECTION CO INC p 1081
2 Annabel Ln Ste 112 94583
Tel (925) 866-1500 *SIC* 6411

PACPIZZA LLC p 1107
220 Porter Dr Ste 100 94583
Tel (925) 838-8567 *SIC* 5812

■ SAN RAMON REGIONAL MEDICAL CENTER INC p 1277
6001 Norris Canyon Rd 94583
Tel (925) 275-0634 *SIC* 8062 8093

SHEET METAL WORKERS LOCAL 104 HEALTH CARE PLAN p 1313
2610 Crow Canyon Rd 94583
Tel (925) 208-9999 *SIC* 8631

STRATEGIC RESTAURANTS ACQUISITION CO LLC p 1392
3000 Executive Pkwy 94583
Tel (925) 328-3300 *SIC* 5812

STRAW HAT COOPERATIVE CORP p 1393
18 Crow Canyon Ct Ste 150 94583
Tel (925) 837-3400 *SIC* 5812

■ TEXACO INC p 1441
6001 Bollinger Canyon Rd 94583
Tel (925) 842-1000
SIC 5541 5511 1321 4612 4613 4412

SAN YSIDRO, CA

CENTRO DE SALUD DE LA COMUNIDAD DE SAN YSIDRO INC p 281
4004 Beyer Blvd 92173
Tel (619) 428-4463 *SIC* 8093 8011

SANGER, CA

SANGER UNIFIED SCHOOL DISTRICT p 1279
1905 7th St 93657
Tel (559) 237-3171 *SIC* 8211

SANTA ANA, CA

2100 FREEDOM INC p 1
625 N Grand Ave 92701
Tel (714) 796-7000
SIC 2711 2721 7313 2741 5963 4813

2100 TRUST LLC p 1
625 N Grand Ave 92701
Tel (877) 469-7344 *SIC* 6733

■ ABBOTT MEDICAL OPTICS INC p 9
1700 E Saint Andrew Pl 92705
Tel (714) 247-8200 *SIC* 3841 3845

ACE WIRELESS & TRADING INC p 17
3031 Orange Ave Ste B 92707
Tel (949) 748-5700 *SIC* 5065

ALLIED UNIVERSAL HOLDCO LLC p 57
1551 N Tustin Ave Ste 650 92705
Tel (714) 619-9700 *SIC* 6719 7381

ALLIED UNIVERSAL TOPCO LLC p 57
1551 N Tustin Ave 92705
Tel (714) 619-9700 *SIC* 6719 7381 7349

ALUMINUM PRECISION PRODUCTS INC p 63
3333 W Warner Ave 92704
Tel (714) 546-8125 *SIC* 3463

AMERIQUEST MORTGAGE CO p 83
2677 N Main St Ste 140 92705
Tel (714) 732-9100 *SIC* 6162

■ AMO USA INC p 86
1700 E Saint Andrew Pl 92705
Tel (714) 247-8200 *SIC* 3841 3845

ASCENT AEROSPACE LLC p 116
1395 S Lyon St 92705
Tel (949) 455-0665 *SIC* 3544

ASCENT TOOLING GROUP LLC p 116
1395 S Lyon St 92705
Tel (949) 455-0665 *SIC* 3812

■ BEHR PAINT CORP p 168
3400 W Segerstrom Ave 92704
Tel (714) 545-7101 *SIC* 2851

■ BEHR PROCESS CORP p 168
3400 W Segerstrom Ave 92704
Tel (714) 545-7101 *SIC* 2851

BLOWER-DEMPSAY CORP p 190
4042 W Garry Ave 92704
Tel (714) 481-3800 *SIC* 5111

■ BRASSTECH INC p 208
2001 Carnegie Ave 92705
Tel (949) 417-5207 *SIC* 3432

CITY OF SANTA ANA p 318
20 Civic Center Plz Fl 8 92701
Tel (714) 647-5400 *SIC* 9111

COAST COMPOSITES LLC p 331
1395 S Lyon St 92705
Tel (949) 455-0665 *SIC* 3599

CONTINENTAL CURRENCY SERVICES INC p 363
1108 E 17th St 92701
Tel (714) 569-0300 *SIC* 6099

CONTROLLED MOTION SOLUTIONS INC p 364
911 N Poinsettia St 92701
Tel (661) 324-2260 *SIC* 5085

COUNTY OF ORANGE p 380
333 W Santa Ana Blvd 3f 92701
Tel (714) 834-6200 *SIC* 9431

EASTER SEALS SOUTHERN CALIFORNIA INC p 471
1570 E 17th St 92705
Tel (714) 834-1111 *SIC* 8399

■ EDISON MISSION ENERGY p 478
3 Macarthur Pl Ste 100 92707
Tel (714) 513-8000 *SIC* 4931

ELLIS COMMUNICATIONS KDOC LLC p 488
625 N Grand Ave Fl 1 92701
Tel (949) 442-9800 *SIC* 4833

EXPERIAN CORP p 519
475 Anton Blvd 92704
Tel (714) 830-7000 *SIC* 7323

EXPRESS MANUFACTURING INC p 520
3519 W Warner Ave 92704
Tel (714) 979-2228 *SIC* 3672 3679

F M TARBELL CO p 522
1403 N Tustin Ave Ste 380 92705
Tel (714) 972-0988 *SIC* 6531

▲ FIRST AMERICAN FINANCIAL CORP p 544
1 First American Way 92707
Tel (714) 250-3000 *SIC* 6361 6351

FIRST AMERICAN MORTGAGE SERVICES p 544
3 First American Way 92707
Tel (714) 250-4210 *SIC* 6361

■ FIRST AMERICAN TITLE CO INC p 544
1 First American Way 92707
Tel (505) 881-3300 *SIC* 6361

■ FIRST AMERICAN TITLE INSURANCE CO p 544
1 First American Way 92707
Tel (800) 854-3643 *SIC* 6361

FREEDOM COMMUNICATIONS HOLDINGS INC p 576
625 N Grand Ave 92701
Tel (714) 796-7000
SIC 6719 2711 4813 2721

FREEDOM COMMUNICATIONS INC p 576
625 N Grand Ave 92701
Tel (714) 796-7000
SIC 2711 2721 7313 2741 5963

GENERAL PROCUREMENT INC p 601
800 E Dyer Rd 92705
Tel (949) 679-7960 *SIC* 5045

GOGLANIAN BAKERIES INC p 620
3401 W Segerstrom Ave 92704
Tel (714) 549-1524 *SIC* 5149

GOODWILL INDUSTRIES OF ORANGE COUNTY CALIFORNIA p 625
410 N Fairview St 92703
Tel (714) 547-6308 *SIC* 5932

GRUBB & ELLIS CO p 642
1551 N Tustin Ave Ste 300 92705
Tel (714) 667-8252 *SIC* 6531 8742 6162

GRUBB & ELLIS MANAGEMENT SERVICES INC p 642
1551 N Tustin Ave Ste 300 92705
Tel (412) 201-8200 *SIC* 6531

GUARDSMARK LLC p 645
1551 N Tustin Ave Ste 650 92705
Tel (714) 619-9700 *SIC* 7381 8742 2721

I O INTERCONNECT LTD p 725
1202 E Wakeham Ave 92705
Tel (714) 564-1111 *SIC* 3678 3679

IHP OPERATIONS LLC p 731
2701 S Harbor Blvd 92704
Tel (714) 549-7782 *SIC* 3433

IMPCO TECHNOLOGIES INC p 734
3030 S Susan St 92704
Tel (714) 656-1200 *SIC* 3714 3592 7363

IPC (USA) INC p 763
4 Hutton Cntre Dr Ste 700 92707
Tel (949) 648-5600 *SIC* 5172

KPC HEALTHCARE INC p 828
1301 N Tustin Ave 92705
Tel (714) 953-3652 *SIC* 8062 6719

MAIN ELECTRIC SUPPLY CO p 897
3600 W Segerstrom Ave 92704
Tel (949) 833-3052 *SIC* 5063

MOOREFIELD CONSTRUCTION INC p 987
600 N Tustin Ave Ste 210 92705
Tel (714) 972-0700 *SIC* 1542

ORANGE COAST TITLE CO OF SOUTHERN CALIFORNIA p 1092
640 N Tustin Ave Ste 106 92705
Tel (714) 558-2836 *SIC* 7389 6361 6541

■ **PACIFICARE HEALTH PLAN ADMINISTRATORS INC** p 1106
3120 W Lake Center Dr 92704
Tel (714) 825-5200 SIC 6324

PAVESCAPES p 1122
1340 E Pomona St 92705
Tel (714) 581-5931 SIC 1799

PIONEER PACKING INC p 1151
2430 S Grand Ave 92705
Tel (714) 540-9751 SIC 5113 2653

RANCHO SANTIAGO COMMUNITY COLLEGE DISTRICT INC p 1207
2323 N Broadway Fl 4 92706
Tel (714) 480-7300 SIC 8222 8221

ROBINSON PHARMA INC p 1242
3330 S Harbor Blvd 92704
Tel (714) 241-0235 SIC 2834

SANTA ANA UNIFIED SCHOOL DISTRICT PUBLIC FACILITIES CORP p 1280
1601 E Chestnut Ave 92701
Tel (714) 558-5501 SIC 8211

SCHOOLSFIRST FEDERAL CREDIT UNION p 1290
2115 N Broadway 92706
Tel (714) 258-4000 SIC 6061

SHIELD SECURITY INC p 1316
1551 N Tustin Ave Ste 650 92705
Tel (714) 210-1501 SIC 7381

■ **STEC INC** p 1384
3001 Daimler St 92705
Tel (415) 222-9996 SIC 3572 3674 3577

STREMICKS HERITAGE FOODS LLC p 1393
4002 Westminster Ave 92703
Tel (714) 775-5000 SIC 2026

TARBELL FINANCIAL CORP p 1424
1403 N Tustin Ave Ste 380 92705
Tel (714) 972-0988 SIC 6163 6531 6099

THINK TOGETHER p 1448
2101 E 4th St Ste 200b 92705
Tel (714) 543-3807 SIC 8299

■ **TTM PRINTED CIRCUIT GROUP INC** p 1490
2630 S Harbor Blvd 92704
Tel (714) 327-3000 SIC 3672

UNIVERSAL BUILDING MAINTENANCE LLC p 1516
1551 N Tustin Ave Ste 650 92705
Tel (714) 619-9700 SIC 7349

▲ **UNIVERSAL ELECTRONICS INC** p 1516
201 Sandpointe Ave # 800 92707
Tel (714) 918-9500 SIC 3651 3625 7372

UNIVERSAL PROTECTION GP LLC p 1517
1551 N Tustin Ave Ste 650 92705
Tel (714) 619-9700 SIC 7381

UNIVERSAL PROTECTION SERVICE LP p 1517
1551 N Tustin Ave Ste 650 92705
Tel (714) 619-9700 SIC 7381

UNIVERSAL SERVICES OF AMERICA LP p 1517
1551 N Tustin Ave 92705
Tel (714) 619-9700 SIC 7381 7349

VOLUNTEERS OF AMERICA p 1565
2100 N Broadway Ste 300 92706
Tel (714) 426-9834 SIC 8322 7361 9531

■ **WASTE MANAGEMENT COLLECTION AND RECYCLING INC** p 1580
1800 S Grand Ave 92705
Tel (714) 637-3010 SIC 7353 4953

WESTERN MEDICAL CENTER AUXILIARY p 1599
1301 N Tustin Ave 92705
Tel (714) 835-3555 SIC 8062

WESTERN MEDICAL CENTER SANTA ANA p 1599
1001 N Tustin Ave 92705
Tel (714) 953-3664 SIC 8011

■ **WHITE CAP CONSTRUCTION SUPPLY** p 1606
1815 Ritchey St 92705
Tel (949) 794-5300 SIC 5082

YOKOHAMA TIRE CORP p 1637
1 Macarthur Pl Ste 800 92707
Tel (714) 870-3800 SIC 5014 3011

SANTA BARBARA, CA

ALTA PROPERTIES INC p 61
879 Ward Dr 93111
Tel (805) 967-0171
SIC 3264 3699 3823 3679

BUTLER AMERICA HOLDINGS INC p 230
3820 State St Ste A 93105
Tel (805) 884-9538 SIC 6719

BUTLER AMERICA LLC p 230
3820 State St Ste B 93105
Tel (203) 926-2700 SIC 8711 8748 7361

BUTLER INTERNATIONAL INC p 230
3820 State St Ste A 93105
Tel (805) 882-2200 SIC 7363 8742

BUTLER SERVICE GROUP INC p 230
3820 State St Ste A 93105
Tel (201) 891-5312
SIC 7363 8711 8748 3661 7538

CHANNEL TECHNOLOGIES GROUP LLC p 288
879 Ward Dr 93111
Tel (805) 967-0171 SIC 3812

■ **CHICAGO TITLE INSURANCE CO** p 297
4050 Calle Real 93110
Tel (805) 565-6900 SIC 6361

CITY OF SANTA BARBARA p 318
735 Anacapa St 93101
Tel (805) 564-5334 SIC 9111

COTTAGE HEALTH p 374
400 W Pueblo St 93105
Tel (805) 682-7111 SIC 8399 8062

COUNTY OF SANTA BARBARA p 381
105 E Anapamu St Rm 406 93101
Tel (805) 568-3400 SIC 9111

EMPLOYBRIDGE LLC p 494
3820 State St 93105
Tel (805) 882-2200 SIC 7363

GREEN HILLS SOFTWARE INC p 637
30 W Sola St 93101
Tel (805) 965-6044 SIC 5013

INVEST WEST FINANCIAL CORP p 761
1933 Cliff Dr Ste 1 93109
Tel (805) 957-0095 SIC 6726 6513

JACOB STERN & SONS INC p 775
1464 E Valley Rd 93108
Tel (805) 565-4532 SIC 5169 5191 5199

JORDANOS INC p 793
550 S Patterson Ave 93111
Tel (805) 964-0611
SIC 5181 5182 5149 5141 5142 5148

MARBORG INDUSTRIES p 904
728 E Yanonali St 93103
Tel (805) 963-1852
SIC 4953 7359 7699 4212

MISSION LINEN SUPPLY p 975
717 E Yanonali St 93103
Tel (805) 730-3620 SIC 7218 7213

MOSELEY ASSOCIATES INC p 992
82 Coromar Dr 93117
Tel (805) 968-9621 SIC 3663

NHR NEWCO HOLDINGS LLC p 1042
6500 Hollister Ave # 210 93117
Tel (800) 230-6638 SIC 5045 5065 7379

▲ **QAD INC** p 1194
100 Innovation Pl 93108
Tel (805) 566-6000 SIC 7372 7371

SANSUM CLINIC p 1280
470 S Patterson Ave 93111
Tel (805) 681-7700 SIC 8011

SANTA BARBARA COMMUNITY COLLEGE DISTRICT p 1280
721 Cliff Dr 93109
Tel (805) 965-0581 SIC 8222

SANTA BARBARA COTTAGE HOSPITAL p 1280
400 W Pueblo St 93105
Tel (805) 682-7111 SIC 8062

SANTA BARBARA UNIFIED SCHOOL DISTRICT p 1280
720 Santa Barbara St 93101
Tel (805) 963-4338 SIC 8211

TRI-COUNTIES ASSOCIATION FOR DEVELOPMENTALLY DISABLED INC p 1477
520 E Montecito St 93103
Tel (805) 962-7881 SIC 8322

UNIVERSITY OF CALIFORNIA SANTA BARBARA p 1520
Uc Santa Barbara Mosher A 93106
Tel (805) 893-8000 SIC 8221 9411

■ **WALKING CO** p 1573
25 W Anapamu St 93101
Tel (805) 963-8727 SIC 5661

▲ **WALKING CO HOLDINGS INC** p 1573
25 W Anapamu St 93101
Tel (805) 963-8727
SIC 5651 5961 5136 5137 5699

YARDI SYSTEMS INC p 1635
430 S Fairview Ave 93117
Tel (805) 699-2040 SIC 7371

SANTA CLARA, CA

■ **ABBOTT VASCULAR INC** p 10
3200 Lakeside Dr 95054
Tel (650) 474-3000 SIC 3845

■ **AFFYMETRIX INC** p 33
3420 Central Expy 95051
Tel (408) 731-5000 SIC 3826

▲ **AGILENT TECHNOLOGIES INC** p 35
5301 Stevens Creek Blvd 95051
Tel (408) 345-8886 SIC 3825 3826 7372

■ **AKT AMERICA INC** p 42
3101 Scott Blvd Bldg 91 95054
Tel (408) 563-5455 SIC 3699

ALPS ELECTRIC (NORTH AMERICA) INC p 61
3151 Jay St Ste 101 95054
Tel (408) 361-6400 SIC 5045 5065 5013

AMBARELLA INC p 65
3101 Jay St 95054
Tel (408) 734-8888 SIC 3674

▲ **APPLIED MATERIALS INC** p 99
3050 Bowers Ave 95054
Tel (408) 727-5555 SIC 3559 3674

▲ **APPLIED MICRO CIRCUITS CORP** p 100
4555 Great America Pkwy # 601 95054
Tel (408) 542-8600 SIC 3674

▲ **ARISTA NETWORKS INC** p 108
5453 Great America Pkwy 95054
Tel (408) 547-5500 SIC 3577

ASIAINFO-LINKAGE INC p 117
5201 Great America Pkwy # 356 95054
Tel (408) 970-9788 SIC 4813

AVAYA HOLDINGS CORP p 136
4655 Great America Pkwy 95054
Tel (908) 953-6000 SIC 3661 7372

AVAYA INC p 136
4655 Great America Pkwy 95054
Tel (908) 953-6000 SIC 3661 7372 7371

BANDAI NAMCO ENTERTAINMENT AMERICA INC p 150
2051 Mission College Blvd 95054
Tel (408) 235-2000 SIC 5092

▲ **CHEGG INC** p 292
3990 Freedom Cir 95054
Tel (408) 855-5700 SIC 5942

CITY OF SANTA CLARA p 318
1500 Warburton Ave 95050
Tel (408) 615-2200 SIC 9111

CMT HOLDINGS INC p 329
590 Laurelwood Rd 95054
Tel (408) 734-3339 SIC 5045

COAST PERSONNEL SERVICES INC p 331
2295 De La Cruz Blvd 95050
Tel (408) 653-2100 SIC 7363

▲ **COHERENT INC** p 335
5100 Patrick Henry Dr 95054
Tel (408) 764-4000 SIC 3826 3845 3699

EAG INC p 467
2710 Walsh Ave 95051
Tel (408) 454-4600 SIC 8734

ECS REFINING LLC p 476
705 Reed St 95050
Tel (408) 988-4386 SIC 5093

■ **FILEMAKER INC** p 542
5201 Patrick Henry Dr 95054
Tel (408) 987-7000 SIC 7372

▲ **GIGAMON INC** p 611
3300 Olcott St 95054
Tel (408) 831-4000 SIC 7372 3577

GLOBALFOUNDRIES US INC p 617
2600 Great America Way 95054
Tel (408) 462-3900 SIC 3559 3825 5065

GLODYNE TECHNOSERVE INC p 618
2700 Augustine Dr Ste 190 95054
Tel (408) 340-5017 SIC 7373

■ **HADCO SANTA CLARA INC** p 652
500 El Camino Real 95050
Tel (408) 241-9900 SIC 3672 3679

HITACHI DATA SYSTEMS CORP p 696
2845 Lafayette St 95050
Tel (408) 970-1000
SIC 5045 7378 7379 5734 4225 3571

HITACHI DATA SYSTEMS HOLDING CORP p 696
2845 Lafayette St 95050
Tel (408) 970-1000 SIC 7299

HORTONWORKS INC p 708
5470 Great America Pkwy 95054
Tel (408) 916-4121 SIC 7372

INCEDO INC p 735
2350 Mission College Blvd 95054
Tel (408) 531-6040 SIC 7379

INFOBLOX INC p 741
3111 Coronado Dr 95054
Tel (408) 986-4000 SIC 7374 7371 7379

▲ **INPHI CORP** p 745
2953 Bunker Hill Ln # 300 95054
Tel (408) 217-7300 SIC 3674

▲ **INTEL CORP** p 750
2200 Mission College Blvd 95054
Tel (408) 765-8080 SIC 3674 3577 7372

ITUTOR GROUP INC p 769
3945 Freedom Cir Ste 500 95054
Tel (408) 982-9401 SIC 8299

JOSEPH J ALBANESE INC p 793
851 Martin Ave 95050
Tel (408) 727-5700 SIC 1771

■ **KANA SOFTWARE INC** p 802
2550 Walsh Ave Ste 120 95051
Tel (650) 614-8300 SIC 7372

LUMASENSE TECHNOLOGIES INC p 885
3301 Leonard Ct 95054
Tel (408) 727-1600
SIC 3823 3845 3829 3825

MACAULAY BROWN INC p 891
2933 Bunker Hill Ln # 220 95054
Tel (937) 426-3421 SIC 8711

MARVELL SEMICONDUCTOR INC p 914
5488 Marvell Ln 95054
Tel (408) 222-2500 SIC 3674

MARVELL TECHNOLOGY GROUP LTD p 914
5488 Marvell Ln 95054
Tel (408) 222-2500 SIC 6719

■ **MCAFEE INC** p 925
2821 Mission College Blvd 95054
Tel (408) 346-3832 SIC 7372

■ **MCAFEE SECURITY LLC** p 925
2821 Mission College Blvd 95054
Tel (866) 622-3911 SIC 7372

MERA SOFTWARE SERVICES INC p 943
2350 Mission College Blvd # 340 95054
Tel (650) 703-7226 SIC 7371

MIASOLE p 959
2590 Walsh Ave 95051
Tel (408) 919-5700 SIC 3674

MOBILEUM INC p 980
2880 Lakeside Dr Ste 135 95054
Tel (408) 844-6600 SIC 4899 7373

■ **MOVE INC** p 995
3315 Scott Blvd Ste 250 95054
Tel (408) 558-7100 SIC 6531

NETLOGIC MICROSYSTEMS LLC p 1027
3975 Freedom Cir Ste 900 95054
Tel (408) 454-3000 SIC 3674

▲ **NVIDIA CORP** p 1068
2701 San Tomas Expy 95050
Tel (408) 486-2000 SIC 3674

OMNIVISION TECHNOLOGIES INC p 1085
4275 Burton Dr 95054
Tel (408) 567-3000 SIC 3674

ONE WORKPLACE L FERRARI LLC p 1086
2500 De La Cruz Blvd 95050
Tel (669) 800-2500 SIC 5021 8744

OOYALA HOLDINGS INC p 1089
4750 Patrick Henry Dr 95054
Tel (650) 961-3400 SIC 7812 6719

OOYALA INC p 1089
4750 Patrick Henry Dr 95054
Tel (650) 961-3400 SIC 7371

▲ **PALO ALTO NETWORKS INC** p 1110
4401 Great America Pkwy 95054
Tel (408) 753-4000 SIC 3577 7371

PIVOT INTERIORS INC p 1152
3355 Scott Blvd Ste 110 95054
Tel (408) 432-5600 SIC 5712 7389 7299

PRESIDENT AND BOARD OF TRUSTEES OF SANTA CLARA COLLEGE p 1172
500 El Camino Real 95050
Tel (408) 554-4000 SIC 8221

REDWOOD ELECTRIC GROUP INC p 1217
2775 Northwestern Pkwy 95051
Tel (707) 451-7348 SIC 1731

RENESAS ELECTRONICS AMERICA INC p 1223
2801 Scott Blvd 95050
Tel (408) 588-6000
SIC 5065 8731 5731 5045 8711

ROBINSON OIL CORP p 1242
955 Martin Ave 95050
Tel (408) 327-4300 SIC 5541 5411

ROBINSON OIL SUPPLY & TRANSPORT INC p 1242
955 Martin Ave 95050
Tel (408) 327-4300 SIC 5172

SAN FRANCISCO FORTY NINERS p 1276
4949 Mrie P Debartolo Way 95054
Tel (408) 562-4949 SIC 7941

SANTA CLARA UNIFIED SCHOOL DISTRICT p 1280
1889 Lawrence Rd 95051
Tel (408) 423-2000 SIC 8211

▲ **SERVICENOW INC** p 1308
2225 Lawson Ln 95054
Tel (408) 501-8550 SIC 7379 7372

■ **SILICON VALLEY BANK** p 1323
3003 Tasman Dr 95054
Tel (408) 654-7400 SIC 6029

■ **SILICONIX INC** p 1323
2201 Laurelwood Rd 95054
Tel (408) 988-8000 SIC 3674

■ **SONICWALL LLC** p 1340
5455 Great America Pkwy 95054
Tel (800) 509-1265 SIC 7373

■ **SPECTRA-PHYSICS INC** p 1357
3635 Peterson Way 95054
Tel (650) 961-2550 SIC 3699 8731

▲ **SVB FINANCIAL GROUP** p 1410
3003 Tasman Dr 95054
Tel (408) 654-7400 SIC 6022

TAVANT TECHNOLOGIES INC p 1426
3965 Freedom Cir Ste 750 95054
Tel (408) 519-5400 SIC 7371

▲ **TELENAV INC** p 1434
4655 Great America Pkwy 95054
Tel (408) 245-3800 SIC 3812

TRIANZ p 1478
3979 Freedom Cir Ste 210 95054
Tel (408) 387-5800 SIC 7379

■ **VISHAY SILICONIX LLC** p 1561
2201 Laurelwood Rd 95054
Tel (408) 988-8000 SIC 2869

VOLEX INC p 1564
3110 Coronado Dr 95054
Tel (669) 444-1740 SIC 3089

■ **WYSE TECHNOLOGY LLC** p 1630
5455 Great America Pkwy 95054
Tel (800) 438-9973 SIC 5045

YMCA OF SILICON VALLEY p 1636
80 Saratoga Ave 95051
Tel (408) 351-6400
SIC 8641 7991 8351 7032 8322

SANTA CLARITA, CA

JOHN PAUL MITCHELL SYSTEMS p 789
20705 Centre Pointe Pkwy 91350
Tel (661) 298-0400 SIC 5122

PRINCESS CRUISE LINES LTD p 1176
24305 Town Center Dr 91355
Tel (661) 753-0000 SIC 4481 4725 7011

SANTA CLARITA COMMUNITY COLLEGE DISTRICT p 1280
26455 Rockwell Canyon Rd 91355
Tel (661) 259-7800 SIC 8222 8221

SANTA CLARITA HEALTH CARE ASSOCIATION INC p 1280
23845 Mcbean Pkwy 91355
Tel (661) 253-8000 SIC 8741

SAUGUS UNION SCHOOL DISTRICT p 1283
24930 Avenue Stanford 91355
Tel (661) 294-5300 SIC 8211

SHADOW HOLDINGS LLC p 1310
26455 Ruether Ave 91350
Tel (661) 252-3807 SIC 2844

WILLIAM S HART UNION HIGH SCHOOL DISTRICT p 1611
21380 Centre Pointe Pkwy 91350
Tel (661) 259-0033 SIC 8211

■ WOODWARD HRT INC p 1623
25200 Rye Canyon Rd 91355
Tel (661) 294-6000 SIC 3625 3492

SANTA CRUZ, CA

COUNTY OF SANTA CRUZ p 381
701 Ocean St Rm 520 95060
Tel (831) 454-2100 SIC 9111

DOMINICAN HOSPITAL p 449
1555 Soquel Dr 95065
Tel (831) 462-7700 SIC 8062

HARMONY FOODS CORP p 662
2200 Delaware Ave 95060
Tel (831) 457-3200 SIC 2834 2064

PALO ALTO MEDICAL FOUNDATION STA CRUZ p 1110
2025 Soquel Ave 95062
Tel (831) 458-5670 SIC 8011

▲ PLANTRONICS INC p 1154
345 Encinal St 95060
Tel (831) 426-5858 SIC 3661 3679

SANTA CRUZ SEASIDE CO INC p 1280
400 Beach St 95060
Tel (831) 423-5590
SIC 7996 7011 7933 6531

UNIVERSITY OF CALIFORNIA SANTA CRUZ p 1520
1156 High St 95064
Tel (831) 459-0111 SIC 8221

SANTA FE SPRINGS, CA

ACCURIDE INTERNATIONAL INC p 16
12311 Shoemaker Ave 90670
Tel (562) 903-0200 SIC 3429

ALL-CITY MANAGEMENT SERVICES INC p 51
10440 Pioneer Blvd Ste 5 90670
Tel (310) 202-8284 SIC 8748

ARDEN GROUP INC p 106
13833 Freeway Dr 90670
Tel (310) 638-2842 SIC 5411

ARDEN-MAYFAIR INC p 106
13833 Freeway Dr 90670
Tel (310) 638-2842 SIC 5411

BRENNTAG PACIFIC INC p 210
10747 Patterson Pl 90670
Tel (562) 903-9626 SIC 5169

CHAMPION POWER EQUIPMENT INC p 287
12039 Smith Ave 90670
Tel (877) 338-0999 SIC 5084

COA INC p 330
12928 Sandoval St 90670
Tel (562) 944-7899 SIC 5021

COAST ALUMINUM AND ARCHITECTURAL INC p 331
10628 Fulton Wells Ave 90670
Tel (562) 946-6061 SIC 5051

■ CONSOLIDATED DISPOSAL SERVICE LLC p 359
12949 Telegraph Rd 90670
Tel (562) 347-2100 SIC 4953

CSI ELECTRICAL CONTRACTORS INC p 397
10623 Fulton Wells Ave 90670
Tel (562) 946-0700 SIC 1731

DAY-LEE FOODS INC p 417
10350 Hritg Pk Dr Ste 111 90670
Tel (562) 903-3020 SIC 5147 5144 5146

DIMETRI GARDIKAS PRODUCE CO INC p 440
14811 Marquardt Ave 90670
Tel (562) 404-4779 SIC 5148

E D D INVESTMENT CO p 466
14325 Iseli Rd 90670
Tel (562) 921-5410 SIC 5812

El TAPATIO MARKETS INC p 481
13635 Freeway Dr 90670
Tel (562) 293-4200 SIC 5411

ELLISON MACHINERY CO p 489
9912 Pioneer Blvd 90670
Tel (562) 949-8311 SIC 5084

ELLISON TECHNOLOGIES INC p 489
9912 Pioneer Blvd 90670
Tel (562) 949-8311 SIC 5084

■ EXCEL GARDEN PRODUCTS p 516
10708 Norwalk Blvd 90670
Tel (562) 567-2000 SIC 5191

FUJI FOOD PRODUCTS INC p 583
14420 Bloomfield Ave 90670
Tel (562) 404-2590 SIC 2099

GALLEHER CORP p 590
9303 Greenleaf Ave 90670
Tel (562) 944-8885 SIC 5023

GELSONS MARKETS p 598
13833 Freeway Dr 90670
Tel (310) 638-2842 SIC 5411

HERAEUS PRECIOUS METALS NORTH AMERICA LLC p 685
15524 Carmenita Rd 90670
Tel (562) 921-7464 SIC 3341 2899

KELLY PIPE CO LLC p 809
11680 Bloomfield Ave 90670
Tel (562) 868-0456 SIC 5051

KIK-SOCAL INC p 817
9028 Dice Rd 90670
Tel (562) 946-6427 SIC 2842

LA SPECIALTY PRODUCE CO p 836
13527 Orden Dr 90670
Tel (562) 741-2200 SIC 5148

LAKIN TIRE WEST INC p 840
15305 Spring Ave 90670
Tel (562) 802-2752 SIC 5014 5531

MAXON LIFT CORP p 922
11921 Slauson Ave 90670
Tel (562) 464-0099 SIC 5084 3537 3534

MIAS FASHION MANUFACTURING CO INC p 959
12623 Cisneros Ln 90670
Tel (562) 906-1060 SIC 5137

OIL WELL SERVICE CO p 1079
10840 Norwalk Blvd 90670
Tel (562) 612-0600 SIC 1389

POLLYS INC p 1160
14325 Iseli Rd 90670
Tel (714) 773-9588 SIC 5812

RAYMOND HANDLING SOLUTIONS INC p 1210
9939 Norwalk Blvd 90670
Tel (562) 944-8067 SIC 5084 7699 7359

SOLARIS PAPER INC p 1338
13415 Carmenita Rd 90670
Tel (562) 376-9717 SIC 5093

SPICERS PAPER INC p 1358
12310 Slauson Ave 90670
Tel (562) 698-1199 SIC 5111

SUPER CENTER CONCEPTS INC p 1405
15510 Carmenita Rd 90670
Tel (562) 345-9000 SIC 5411

SWANN COMMUNICATIONS USA INC p 1411
12636 Clark St 90670
Tel (562) 777-2551 SIC 5045 7382

TALLEY INC p 1423
12976 Sandoval St 90670
Tel (562) 906-8000 SIC 5065

THERMAL ENGINEERING INTERNATIONAL (USA) INC p 1447
10375 Slusher Dr 90670
Tel (323) 726-0641 SIC 3443 8711

TORRANCE VAN & STORAGE CO p 1462
12128 Burke St 90670
Tel (562) 567-2100 SIC 4214 4213

TRI-WEST LTD p 1478
12005 Pike St 90670
Tel (562) 692-9166 SIC 5023

TRIANGLE DISTRIBUTING CO p 1478
12065 Pike St 90670
Tel (562) 699-3424 SIC 5181

TROJAN BATTERY CO LLC p 1483
12380 Clark St 90670
Tel (800) 423-6569 SIC 3691 3692

TWIN MED LLC p 1495
11333 Greenstone Ave 90670
Tel (323) 582-9900 SIC 5047

VOTAW PRECISION TECHNOLOGIES INC p 1566
13153 Lakeland Rd 90670
Tel (562) 666-2138 SIC 3544 3812

WARREN DISTRIBUTING INC p 1576
8737 Dice Rd 90670
Tel (562) 789-3360 SIC 5013

WEBER DISTRIBUTION WAREHOUSES p 1586
13530 Rosecrans Ave 90670
Tel (562) 356-6300 SIC 4214 4225

WESTRUX INTERNATIONAL INC p 1603
15555 Valley View Ave 90670
Tel (562) 404-1020
SIC 5511 5531 7513 7538

WINDSOR FASHIONS INC p 1615
9603 John St 90670
Tel (323) 282-9000 SIC 5621 5632

WISMETTAC ASIAN FOODS INC p 1619
13409 Orden Dr 90670
Tel (562) 802-1900 SIC 5149

SANTA MARIA, CA

BETTERAVIA FARMS LLC p 178
1850 W Stowell Rd 93458
Tel (805) 925-2585 SIC 0161

CP DENTAL LLC p 387
2727 Skyway Dr 93455
Tel (800) 433-6628 SIC 3843

GREKA INTEGRATED INC p 639
1700 Sinton Rd 93458
Tel (805) 347-8700 SIC 1382

KENAI DRILLING LIMITED p 810
6430 Cat Canyon Rd 93454
Tel (805) 937-7871 SIC 1381

MARIAN MEDICAL CENTER p 906
1400 E Church St 93454
Tel (805) 739-3000 SIC 8062

SANTA MARIA-BONITA SCHOOL DIST p 1281
708 S Miller St 93454
Tel (805) 928-1783 SIC 8211

SANTA MONICA, CA

▲ ACTIVISION BLIZZARD INC p 20
3100 Ocean Park Blvd 90405
Tel (310) 255-2000 SIC 7372

■ ACTIVISION PUBLISHING INC p 20
3100 Ocean Park Blvd 90405
Tel (310) 255-2000 SIC 7372

ADVANSTAR COMMUNICATIONS INC p 26
2501 Colorado Ave Ste 280 90404
Tel (310) 857-7500 SIC 7389 2721 7331

ANWORTH MORTGAGE ASSET CORP p 94
1299 Ocean Ave Fl 2 90401
Tel (310) 255-4493 SIC 6798

BEACHBODY LLC p 164
3301 Exposition Blvd Fl 3 90404
Tel (310) 883-9000 SIC 7313 7999

CITY OF SANTA MONICA p 318
1685 Main St 90401
Tel (310) 458-8411 SIC 9111

CLEARLAKE CAPITAL GROUP LP p 324
233 Wilshire Blvd Ste 800 90401
Tel (310) 400-8800 SIC 6799

COLONY CAPITAL LLC p 338
2450 Broadway Ste 600 90404
Tel (310) 282-8820
SIC 6799 7999 7011 5813 5812

▲ CORNERSTONE ONDEMAND INC p 371
1601 Cloverfield Blvd 620s 90404
Tel (310) 752-0200 SIC 7372

▲ DEMAND MEDIA INC p 427
1655 26th St 90404
Tel (310) 656-6253 SIC 7313 7336

DOUGLAS EMMETT INC p 452
808 Wilshire Blvd Ste 200 90401
Tel (310) 255-7700 SIC 6798

EDMUNDS HOLDING CO p 478
1620 26th St Ste 400s 90404
Tel (310) 309-6300 SIC 7375

EDMUNDS.COM INC p 478
2401 Colorado Ave 90404
Tel (310) 309-6300 SIC 2731

▲ ENTRAVISION COMMUNICATIONS CORP p 502
2425 Olympic Blvd Ste 600 90404
Tel (310) 447-3870 SIC 4833 4832

FUTURIS GLOBAL HOLDINGS LLC p 586
233 Wilshire Blvd Ste 800 90401
Tel (510) 771-2333 SIC 6719

■ GAME SHOW NETWORK LLC p 590
2150 Colorado Ave Ste 100 90404
Tel (310) 255-6800 SIC 4841

HULU LLC p 718
2500 Broadway Fl 2 90404
Tel (310) 571-4700 SIC 4833 4813

▲ JAKKS PACIFIC INC p 776
2951 28th St Ste 51 90405
Tel (424) 268-9444 SIC 3944

LIONS GATE ENTERTAINMENT INC p 870
2700 Colorado Ave Ste 200 90404
Tel (310) 449-9200 SIC 7812

▲ MACERICH CO p 892
401 Wilshire Blvd Ste 700 90401
Tel (310) 394-6000 SIC 6798

MASTER INTERNATIONAL CORP p 918
1301 Olympic Blvd 90404
Tel (310) 452-1229 SIC 5065

MORLEY BUILDERS INC p 989
3330 Ocean Park Blvd # 101 90405
Tel (310) 399-1600
SIC 1541 1522 1542 1771

NATIONAL GOLF PROPERTIES LLC p 1012
2951 28th St Ste 3000 90405
Tel (310) 664-4000 SIC 6519 8111

■ PACIFIC WESTERN BANK p 1106
456 Santa Monica Blvd 90401
Tel (310) 458-1521 SIC 6021

▲ PRECIOUS A-MARK METALS INC p 1168
429 Santa Monica Blvd # 230 90401
Tel (310) 587-1477 SIC 5094

RAND CORP p 1207
1776 Main St 90401
Tel (310) 393-0411 SIC 8733 8742 8732

RECONSERVE INC p 1214
2811 Wilshire Blvd # 410 90403
Tel (310) 458-1574 SIC 2048

RED BULL DISTRIBUTION CO INC p 1215
1740 Stewart St 90404
Tel (916) 515-3501 SIC 5149

RED BULL NORTH AMERICA INC p 1215
1740 Stewart St 90404
Tel (310) 460-5356 SIC 7929

SAINT JOHNS HEALTH CENTER FOUNDATION p 1269
2121 Santa Monica Blvd 90404
Tel (310) 829-8424 SIC 8062

SANTA MONICA COMMUNITY COLLEGE DISTRICT p 1281
1900 Pico Blvd 90405
Tel (310) 434-4000 SIC 8222

SCOPE INDUSTRIES p 1293
2811 Wilshire Blvd # 410 90403
Tel (310) 458-1574 SIC 4953

SHAPCO INC p 1311
1666 20th St Ste 100 90404
Tel (310) 264-1666 SIC 5051 3317 6799

STONE CANYON INDUSTRIES LLC p 1391
1250 4th St 90401
Tel (310) 570-4869 SIC 6282

TASKUS INC p 1426
3233 Donald 90405
Tel (888) 400-8275 SIC 7374

TCP CAPITAL CORP p 1428
2951 28th St Ste 1000 90405
Tel (310) 566-1000 SIC 6799

TENNENBAUM CAPITAL PARTNERS LLC p 1438
2951 28th St Ste 1000 90405
Tel (310) 396-5451 SIC 6726

▲ TRUECAR INC p 1486
120 Broadway Ste 200 90401
Tel (800) 200-2000 SIC 5012 7299

UNIQUE PREMIUM METALS INC p 1505
3250 Ocean Park Blvd # 350 90405
Tel (213) 622-9995 SIC 5094

UNIVERSAL MUSIC GROUP INC p 1517
2220 Colorado Ave 90404
Tel (310) 865-4000 SIC 7389 2741

VIACOM NETWORKS p 1554
2600 Colorado Ave 90404
Tel (310) 453-4826 SIC 7822

VOLKSWAGEN SANTA MONICA INC p 1564
2440 Santa Monica Blvd 90404
Tel (310) 829-1888 SIC 5511 7532 7538

WINDSOR CAPITAL GROUP INC p 1615
3250 Ocean Park Blvd # 350 90405
Tel (310) 566-1100 SIC 7011

SANTA PAULA, CA

▲ CALAVO GROWERS INC p 238
1141 Cummings Rd Ste A 93060
Tel (805) 525-1245 SIC 5148 5142 5149

▲ LIMONEIRA CO p 866
1141 Cummings Rd Ofc 93060
Tel (805) 525-5541
SIC 0723 0174 0179 6531 6799

SATICOY LEMON ASSOCIATION p 1283
103 N Peck Rd 93060
Tel (805) 654-6500 SIC 0723

SANTA ROSA, CA

AMERICAN AGCREDIT FLCA p 67
400 Aviation Blvd Ste 100 95403
Tel (707) 545-1200 SIC 6159

AMYS KITCHEN INC p 88
2330 Northpoint Pkwy 95407
Tel (707) 578-7188 SIC 2038 2053

B&M RACING & PERFORMANCE PRODUCTS INC p 142
100 Stony Point Rd # 125 95401
Tel (707) 544-4761 SIC 5013

BURBANK LUTHER SAVINGS p 226
500 3rd St 95401
Tel (707) 578-9216 SIC 6036 6035

COUNTY OF SONOMA p 382
585 Fiscal Dr 100 95403
Tel (707) 565-2431 SIC 9111

EXCHANGE BANK p 517
440 Aviation Blvd 95403
Tel (707) 524-3000 SIC 6036 8741 6022

FRIEDMANS HOME IMPROVEMENT p 579
4055 Santa Rosa Ave 95407
Tel (707) 584-7811 SIC 5251 5211 5261

GHILOTTI CONSTRUCTION CO INC p 610
246 Ghilotti Ave 95407
Tel (707) 585-1221 SIC 1629

JACKSON FAMILY WINES INC p 774
421 And 425 Aviation Blvd 95403
Tel (707) 544-4000 SIC 2084 0172 5813

▲ KEYSIGHT TECHNOLOGIES INC p 815
1400 Fountaingrove Pkwy 95403
Tel (707) 577-5030 SIC 3825

LA TORTILLA FACTORY INC p 836
3300 Westwind Blvd 95403
Tel (707) 586-4000 SIC 5149 2051

LUTHER BURBANK CORP p 886
520 3rd St Fl 4 95401
Tel (707) 523-9898 SIC 8211

MEDTRONIC CARDIOVASCULAR p 939
3576 Unocal Pl 95403
Tel (707) 545-1156 SIC 3841

MENDOCINO FOREST PRODUCTS CO LLC p 943
3700 Old Redwood Hwy # 200 95403
Tel (707) 620-2961 SIC 5031 2421

■ OPTICAL COATING LABORATORY LLC p 1090
2789 Northpoint Pkwy 95407
Tel (707) 545-6440 SIC 3479 3577 3827

REDWOOD CREDIT UNION p 1217
3033 Cleveland Ave # 100 95403
Tel (707) 545-4000 SIC 6141

SANTA ROSA CITY OF p 1281
100 Santa Rosa Ave 95404
Tel (707) 543-3010 SIC 9121

SANTA ROSA CITY SCHOOL DIST p 1281
211 Ridgway Ave 95401
Tel (707) 528-5409 *SIC* 8211

SANTA ROSA MEMORIAL HOSPITAL INC p 1281
1165 Montgomery Dr 95405
Tel (707) 546-3210 *SIC* 8062

SONOMA COUNTY JUNIOR COLLEGE DISTRICT p 1340
1501 Mendocino Ave 95401
Tel (707) 527-4011 *SIC* 8222 8221

STEVEN P KIM DPM p 1388
4761 Hoen Ave 95405
Tel (707) 545-0570 *SIC* 8043

SUTTER SANTA ROSA REGIONAL HOSPITAL p 1410
30 Mark West Springs Rd 95403
Tel (707) 576-4000 *SIC* 8062

SANTA YNEZ, CA

CHUMASH CASINO RESORT p 305
3400 E Highway 246 93460
Tel (805) 686-0855 *SIC* 7999 7011

ECHOPOWER CORP p 475
3720 Baseline Ave 93460
Tel (805) 729-4473 *SIC* 4953 5331

SANTEE, CA

SANTEE SCHOOL DISTRICT p 1281
9625 Cuyamaca St 92071
Tel (619) 258-2300 *SIC* 8211

SCANTIBODIES LABORATORY INC p 1286
9336 Abraham Way 92071
Tel (619) 258-9300 *SIC* 2835

SARATOGA, CA

WEST VALLEY-MISSION COMMUNITY COLLEGE DISTRICT p 1596
14000 Fruitvale Ave 95070
Tel (408) 867-2200 *SIC* 8222 8221

SAUSALITO, CA

ACTIVE WELLNESS LLC p 20
4000 Bridgeway Ste 101 94965
Tel (415) 331-1600 *SIC* 8741

C P SHADES INC p 233
403 Coloma St 94965
Tel (415) 331-4581 *SIC* 2339 5621

SCOTTS VALLEY, CA

▲ **FOX FACTORY HOLDING CORP** p 572
915 Disc Dr 95066
Tel (831) 274-6500 *SIC* 3751

MAXTOR CORP p 923
4575 Scotts Valley Dr 95066
Tel (831) 438-6550 *SIC* 3572

THRESHOLD ENTERPRISES LTD p 1451
23 Janis Way 95066
Tel (831) 438-6851 *SIC* 2833

ZERO MOTORCYCLES INC p 1642
380 El Pueblo Rd 95066
Tel (831) 438-3500 *SIC* 5012

SEAL BEACH, CA

BAKERCORP p 146
3020 Old Ranch Pkwy # 220 90740
Tel (562) 430-6262 *SIC* 7359

FTT HOLDINGS INC p 583
3020 Old Ranch Pkwy 90740
Tel (562) 430-6262 *SIC* 3533

SEBASTOPOL, CA

OREILLY MEDIA INC p 1094
1005 Gravenstein Hwy N 95472
Tel (707) 827-7000 *SIC* 2731 2741

TBC SHARED SERVICES INC p 1427
742 S Main St 95472
Tel (707) 829-9864 *SIC* 5531 7534

SHAFTER, CA

BAKERSFIELD PIPE AND SUPPLY INC p 146
3301 Zachary Ave 93263
Tel (661) 589-9141 *SIC* 5051 5085

JDRUSH CO INC p 781
5900 E Lerdo Hwy 93263
Tel (661) 392-1900 *SIC* 5051

VARNER FAMILY LIMITED PARTNERSHIP p 1545
5900 E Lerdo Hwy 93263
Tel (661) 399-1163 *SIC* 6733

WONDERFUL ORCHARDS LLC p 1622
6801 E Lerdo Hwy 93263
Tel (661) 399-4456 *SIC* 0173 0179

SHERMAN OAKS, CA

AVAD LLC p 135
5805 Sepulveda Blvd # 750 91411
Tel (818) 742-4800 *SIC* 5065 7359

LUCKY STRIKE ENTERTAINMENT INC p 884
15260 Ventura Blvd # 1110 91403
Tel (818) 933-3752 *SIC* 3949 5812 5813

LUCKY STRIKE ENTERTAINMENT LLC p 884
15260 Ventura Blvd # 1110 91403
Tel (323) 467-7776 *SIC* 7933

■ **MILLER AUTOMOTIVE GROUP INC** p 970
5425 Van Nuys Blvd 91401
Tel (818) 787-8400 *SIC* 5511 7538 5521

PROSPECT MORTGAGE LLC p 1184
15301 Ventura Blvd D300 91403
Tel (818) 981-0606 *SIC* 6163

▲ **REAL INDUSTRY INC** p 1213
15301 Ventura Blvd # 400 91403
Tel (805) 435-1255 *SIC* 5063 6162

TRITON MEDIA GROUP LLC p 1483
15303 Ventura Blvd # 1500 91403
Tel (323) 290-6900 *SIC* 4832

VUBIQUITY HOLDINGS INC p 1567
15301 Ventura Blvd # 3000 91403
Tel (818) 526-5000 *SIC* 4841

WESTLEND FINANCING INC p 1601
15260 Ventura Blvd # 710 91403
Tel (818) 385-7500 *SIC* 6162 6141

SIGNAL HILL, CA

ALLIED REFRIGERATION INC p 56
2300 E 28th St 90755
Tel (562) 595-5301 *SIC* 5075 5078

EDCO DISPOSAL CORP INC p 477
2755 California Ave 90755
Tel (619) 287-7555 *SIC* 4953

HAR-BRO INC p 659
2750 Signal Pkwy 90755
Tel (562) 528-8000 *SIC* 1542 1521 1522

HOFS HUT RESTAURANT INC p 699
2601 E Willow St 90755
Tel (310) 406-6340 *SIC* 5812

HOFS HUT RESTAURANTS INC p 699
2601 E Willow St 90755
Tel (562) 596-0200 *SIC* 5812

TRAFFIC MANAGEMENT INC p 1469
2435 Lemon Ave 90755
Tel (562) 595-4278 *SIC* 7389 8741

■ **VIKING OFFICE PRODUCTS INC** p 1557
3366 E Willow St 90755
Tel (562) 490-1000
SIC 5112 5021 5045 5087 5043 5961

WALTERS WHOLESALE ELECTRIC CO p 1574
2825 Temple Ave 90755
Tel (562) 988-3100 *SIC* 5063 3699 1731

SIMI VALLEY, CA

■ **ARCONIC GLOBAL FASTENERS & RINGS INC** p 106
3990a Heritage Oak Ct 93063
Tel (310) 530-2220 *SIC* 5085 5072 5065

MEGGITT SAFETY SYSTEMS INC p 940
1785 Voyager Ave Ste 100 93063
Tel (805) 584-4100 *SIC* 3699 3724 3728

MEGGITT-USA INC p 940
1955 Surveyor Ave 93063
Tel (805) 526-5700 *SIC* 3728 3829 3679

PACIFIC SCIENTIFIC CO INC p 1105
1785 Voyager Ave Ste 101 93063
Tel (805) 526-5700
SIC 3812 3669 3621 3694 3823 3625

SIMI VALLEY HOSPITAL AND HEALTH CARE SERVICES p 1324
2975 Sycamore Dr 93065
Tel (805) 955-6000 *SIC* 8049

SIMI VALLEY UNIFIED SCHOOL DISTRICT p 1324
875 Cochran St 93065
Tel (805) 306-4500 *SIC* 8211

SMART LIVING CO p 1332
4100 Guardian St 93063
Tel (805) 578-5500 *SIC* 5199

SPECIAL DEVICES INC p 1356
2655 1st St Ste 300 93065
Tel (805) 387-1000 *SIC* 3714

XAVIENT INFORMATION SYSTEMS INC p 1630
2125 N Madera Rd Ste B 93065
Tel (805) 955-4111 *SIC* 7372

XMULTIPLE TECHNOLOGIES INC p 1632
1060 E Los Angeles Ave 93065
Tel (805) 579-1100 *SIC* 3643

SOLANA BEACH, CA

K2 INSURANCE SERVICES LLC p 799
514 Via De La Valle Ste 3 92075
Tel (858) 866-8966 *SIC* 6411

LAVIDA COMMUNITIES INC p 847
500 Stevens Ave Ste 100 92075
Tel (858) 792-9300
SIC 6513 6512 6531 6553

SENIOR RESOURCE GROUP LLC p 1304
500 Stevens Ave Ste 100 92075
Tel (858) 792-9300
SIC 6513 6512 6531 6553

SONORA, CA

COUNTY OF TUOLUMNE p 382
2 S Green St 95370
Tel (209) 533-5521 *SIC* 9111

SONORA REGIONAL HOSPITAL p 1340
1000 Greenley Rd 95370
Tel (209) 736-0249 *SIC* 8011

SONORA REGIONAL MEDICAL CENTER p 1340
1000 Greenley Rd 95370
Tel (209) 532-5000 *SIC* 8062 8051

SOUTH EL MONTE, CA

■ **INTERNATIONAL MEDICATION SYSTEMS LTD** p 756
1886 Santa Anita Ave 91733
Tel (626) 442-6757 *SIC* 2834 2833 3841

SOUTH GATE, CA

KOOS MANUFACTURING INC p 827
2741 Seminole Ave 90280
Tel (323) 249-1000 *SIC* 7389

■ **SHULTZ STEEL CO** p 1319
5321 Firestone Blvd 90280
Tel (323) 357-3200 *SIC* 3463 3462

WORLD OIL MARKETING CO p 1625
9302 Garfield Ave 90280
Tel (562) 928-0100
SIC 2911 4953 2951 5541 4213 4212

SOUTH LAKE TAHOE, CA

BARTON HEALTHCARE SYSTEM p 158
2170 South Ave 96150
Tel (530) 541-3420 *SIC* 8062

BARTON HOSPITAL p 158
2170 South Ave 96150
Tel (530) 543-5685 *SIC* 8062

BARTON MEMORIAL HOSPITAL p 158
2170 South Ave 96150
Tel (530) 541-3420 *SIC* 8062 8051

SOUTH PASADENA, CA

DMS FACILITY SERVICES INC p 446
1040 Arroyo Dr 91030
Tel (626) 305-8500 *SIC* 7349

DMS FACILITY SERVICES LLC p 446
1040 Arroyo Dr 91030
Tel (626) 305-8500 *SIC* 8711 7349 0781

MERCURY OVERSEAS INC p 945
830 Mission St 91030
Tel (626) 799-9141 *SIC* 5147 5146

SELEY & CO p 1302
1515 Hope St 91030
Tel (626) 799-1196 *SIC* 5191

SOUTH SAN FRANCISCO, CA

AEROGROUND INC p 30
270 Lawrence Ave 94080
Tel (650) 266-6965 *SIC* 4581 4213

▲ **CORE-MARK HOLDING CO INC** p 369
395 Oyster Point Blvd # 415 94080
Tel (650) 589-9445
SIC 5141 5194 5145 5122 5199 5149

■ **CORE-MARK INTERNATIONAL INC** p 369
395 Oyster Point Blvd # 415 94080
Tel (650) 589-9445 *SIC* 5141 5194

■ **CORE-MARK MIDCONTINENT INC** p 369
395 Oyster Point Blvd # 415 94080
Tel (650) 589-9445 *SIC* 5194 5141

DOME CONSTRUCTION CORP p 448
393 E Grand Ave 94080
Tel (650) 416-5600 *SIC* 1542 1541

DRAEGERS SUPER MARKETS p 455
291 Utah Ave 94080
Tel (650) 244-6500 *SIC* 5411

FIVE PRIME THERAPEUTICS INC p 553
2 Corporate Dr 94080
Tel (415) 365-5600 *SIC* 2834 8733

▲ **FLUIDIGM CORP** p 561
7000 Shoreline Ct Ste 100 94080
Tel (650) 266-6000 *SIC* 3826

■ **GENENTECH INC** p 598
1 Dna Way 94080
Tel (650) 225-1000 *SIC* 2834

■ **GENENTECH USA INC** p 599
1 Dna Way 94080
Tel (650) 225-1000 *SIC* 2834

GINO MORENA ENTERPRISES LLC p 612
111 Starlite St 94080
Tel (800) 227-6905 *SIC* 7231

MATAGRANO INC p 919
440 Forbes Blvd 94080
Tel (650) 829-4829 *SIC* 5181 5149

NASSAU-SOSNICK DISTRIBUTION CO LLC p 1009
258 Littlefield Ave 94080
Tel (650) 952-2226 *SIC* 5149 5145 5182

■ **ROCHE HOLDINGS INC** p 1243
1 Dna Way 94080
Tel (625) 225-1000
SIC 2834 2833 2835 2869

■ **SEES CANDIES INC** p 1300
210 El Camino Real 94080
Tel (650) 761-2490 *SIC* 2064 5441

■ **SEES CANDY SHOPS INC** p 1300
210 El Camino Real 94080
Tel (650) 761-2490 *SIC* 2064 5441

SOUTH SAN FRANCISCO UNIFIED SCHOOL DISTRICT p 1345
398 B St 94080
Tel (650) 877-8700 *SIC* 8211

SSF IMPORTED AUTO PARTS LLC p 1363
466 Forbes Blvd 94080
Tel (800) 203-9287 *SIC* 5013

STEVEN ENGINEERING INC p 1388
230 Ryan Way 94080
Tel (650) 588-9200 *SIC* 5085

SUCCESSFACTORS INC p 1396
1 Tower Pl Fl 11 94080
Tel (800) 845-0395 *SIC* 7371

TOSHIBA AMERICA MRI INC p 1462
280 Utah Ave Ste 200 94080
Tel (650) 737-6686 *SIC* 3845 8731

TRICOR AMERICA INC p 1479
717 Airport Blvd 94080
Tel (650) 877-3650 *SIC* 4513

SPRING VALLEY, CA

OTAY WATER DISTRICT (INC) p 1097
2554 Sweetwater Sprng Blvd 91978
Tel (619) 670-2222 *SIC* 4941 1623

STANFORD, CA

STANFORD HEALTH CARE p 1376
300 Pasteur Dr 94305
Tel (650) 723-4000 *SIC* 8062

STANFORD UNIVERSITY p 1376
295 Galvez St 94305
Tel (650) 723-2300 *SIC* 8221

STANTON, CA

CR&R INC p 388
11292 Western Ave 90680
Tel (714) 826-9049 *SIC* 4953 4212 7359

USS CAL BUILDERS INC p 1535
8051 Main St 90680
Tel (714) 828-4882 *SIC* 1542

STEVENSON RANCH, CA

GLOBAL BUILDING SERVICES INC p 616
25129 The Old Rd Ste 102 91381
Tel (661) 288-5733 *SIC* 7349

STOCKTON, CA

■ **AMERICAN MEDICAL RESPONSE WEST** p 76
400 S Fresno St 95203
Tel (209) 948-5136 *SIC* 4119

BANK OF STOCKTON p 152
301 E Miner Ave 95202
Tel (209) 929-1600 *SIC* 6022

CALAMCO p 238
1776 W March Ln Ste 420 95207
Tel (209) 982-1000 *SIC* 5169

CALIFORNIA CEDAR PRODUCTS CO p 239
2385 Arch Airport Rd # 500 95206
Tel (209) 932-5002 *SIC* 2499

CITY OF STOCKTON p 318
425 N El Dorado St 95202
Tel (209) 937-8212 *SIC* 9111

COASTAL PACIFIC FOOD DISTRIBUTORS INC p 332
1015 Performance Dr 95206
Tel (909) 947-2066
SIC 5141 4225 7519 4222

COUNTY OF SAN JOAQUIN p 381
44 N San Joaquin St # 640 95202
Tel (209) 468-3203 *SIC* 9111

DAMERON HOSPITAL ASSOCIATION INC p 410
525 W Acacia St 95203
Tel (209) 944-5550 *SIC* 8621

■ **DIAMOND FOODS LLC** p 436
1050 Diamond St 95205
Tel (415) 445-7444 *SIC* 2068 2096

DIOCESE OF STOCKTON EDUCATIONAL OFFICE p 441
212 N San Joaquin St 95202
Tel (209) 466-0636 *SIC* 8211

DORFMAN-PACIFIC CO p 451
2615 Boeing Way 95206
Tel (209) 982-1400 *SIC* 5136 5137

DURAFLAME INC p 462
2894 Monte Diablo Ave 95203
Tel (209) 461-6600 *SIC* 5099

GRUPE CO p 642
3255 W March Ln Ste 400 95219
Tel (209) 473-6000 *SIC* 6531 1542

HERRICK CORP p 687
3003 E Hammer Ln 95212
Tel (209) 956-4751 *SIC* 3441

MORADA PRODUCE CO LP p 988
500 N Jack Tone Rd 95215
Tel (209) 546-0426 *SIC* 0723

■ **PAQ INC** p 1112
8014 Lower Sacramento Rd I 95210
Tel (209) 957-4917 *SIC* 5411

■ **PDM STEEL SERVICE CENTERS INC** p 1124
3535 E Myrtle St 95205
Tel (209) 943-0555 *SIC* 5051

REDARHCS INC p 1216
4502 Georgetown Pl 95207
Tel (209) 478-0234 *SIC* 5812

SAN JOAQUIN COUNCIL OF GOVERNMENTS p 1277
555 E Weber Ave 95202
Tel (209) 235-0600 *SIC* 8742

ST JOSEPHS MEDICAL CENTER INC p 1369
1800 N California St 95204
Tel (209) 943-2000 *SIC* 8062

ST JOSEPHS MEDICAL CENTER OF STOCKTON p 1369
1800 N California St 95204
Tel (209) 943-2000 *SIC* 8062

STOCKTON UNIFIED SCHOOL DISTRICT p 1390
701 N Madison St 95202
Tel (209) 933-7000 *SIC* 8211

SUPER STORE INDUSTRIES p 1406
2800 W March Ln Ste 210 95219
Tel (209) 473-8100
SIC 2026 2024 5149 5142

UNIVERSITY OF PACIFIC p 1524
3601 Pacific Ave 95211
Tel (209) 946-2401 *SIC* 8221

VALLEY MOUNTAIN REGIONAL CENTER INC p 1541
702 N Aurora St 95202
Tel (209) 473-0951 *SIC* 8322

VALLEY PACIFIC PETROLEUM SERVICES INC p 1541
152 Frank West Cir # 100 95206
Tel (209) 948-9412 *SIC* 5172 5541

VALLEY WHOLESALE DRUG CO LLC p 1541
1401 W Fremont St 95203
Tel (209) 466-0131 *SIC* 5122

VAN DE POL ENTERPRISES INC p 1542
4895 S Airport Way 95206
Tel (209) 465-3421 *SIC* 5172

STUDIO CITY, CA

AMERICAN MERCHANTS INC p 76
3279 Laurel Canyon Blvd 91604
Tel (818) 505-1040 *SIC* 7389

CROWN MEDIA HOLDINGS INC p 395
12700 Ventura Blvd # 100 91604
Tel (888) 390-7474 *SIC* 4841

JERRYS FAMOUS DELI INC p 783
12711 Ventura Blvd # 400 91604
Tel (818) 766-8311 *SIC* 5812

MOTION PICTURE INDUSTRY HEALTH PLAN p 992
11365 Ventura Blvd 91604
Tel (818) 769-0007 *SIC* 6371

MOTION PICTURE INDUSTRY PENSION & HEALTH PLANS p 992
11365 Ventura Blvd # 300 91604
Tel (818) 769-0007 *SIC* 6371

SUN CITY, CA

AEDAN INC p 29
27447 92586
Tel (888) 272-5505
SIC 7371 7381 8733 3812 7382

WESTKUSTE INC p 1601
29330 Calle De Caballos 92585
Tel (951) 775-2534 *SIC* 0752

SUN VALLEY, CA

■ BROWNING-FERRIS INDUSTRIES OF CALIFORNIA INC p 220
9200 Glenoaks Blvd 91352
Tel (818) 790-5410 *SIC* 4953

NORMAN INDUSTRIAL MATERIALS INC p 1049
8300 San Fernando Rd 91352
Tel (818) 729-3333 *SIC* 5051 3441 3449

PLASTIC SERVICES AND PRODUCTS p 1155
12243 Branford St 91352
Tel (818) 896-1101
SIC 3086 3674 2865 2816 3296 2819

PMC GLOBAL INC p 1157
12243 Branford St 91352
Tel (818) 896-1101
SIC 3086 3674 2865 2816 3296 2819

■ WASTE MANAGEMENT OF CALIFORNIA INC p 1580
9081 Tujunga Ave 91352
Tel (877) 836-6526 *SIC* 4953

SUNNYVALE, CA

▲ ACCURAY INC p 16
1310 Chesapeake Ter 94089
Tel (408) 716-4600 *SIC* 3841

▲ ADVANCED MICRO DEVICES INC p 26
1 Amd Pl 94085
Tel (408) 749-4000 *SIC* 3674

ALLIANCE FIBER OPTIC PRODUCTS INC p 54
275 Gibraltar Dr 94089
Tel (408) 736-6900 *SIC* 3229 3661

■ AMAZON LAB126 p 64
1100 Enterprise Way 94089
Tel (650) 426-1100 *SIC* 8731

■ ARUBA NETWORKS INC p 114
1344 Crossman Ave 94089
Tel (408) 227-4500 *SIC* 3577 3663 7371

ATR INTERNATIONAL INC p 129
1230 Oakmead Pkwy Ste 110 94085
Tel (408) 328-8000 *SIC* 7361

BLOOM ENERGY CORP p 189
1299 Orleans Dr 94089
Tel (408) 543-1500 *SIC* 3674

■ BLUE COAT INC p 191
384 Santa Trinita Ave 94085
Tel (408) 220-2200 *SIC* 7372

■ BLUE COAT SYSTEMS LLC p 191
384 Santa Trinita Ave 94085
Tel (408) 220-2200 *SIC* 7372

■ CEPHEID p 283
904 E Caribbean Dr 94089
Tel (408) 541-4191 *SIC* 3826 3841

CHILDRENS CREATIVE LEARNING CENTER INC p 299
794 E Duane Ave 94085
Tel (408) 732-2500 *SIC* 8351

■ DIONEX CORP p 441
1228 Titan Way Ste 1002 94085
Tel (408) 737-0700
SIC 3826 2819 3087 3841

■ FAIRCHILD SEMICONDUCTOR INTERNATIONAL INC p 524
1272 Borregas Ave 94089
Tel (408) 822-2000 *SIC* 3674

▲ FINANCIAL ENGINES INC p 542
1050 Enterprise Way Fl 3 94089
Tel (408) 498-6000 *SIC* 8742 6282 6411

▲ FINISAR CORP p 543
1389 Moffett Park Dr 94089
Tel (408) 548-1000 *SIC* 3661 3663

▲ FORTINET INC p 569
899 Kifer Rd 94086
Tel (408) 235-7700 *SIC* 7372

FUJIKURA AMERICA INC p 583
920 Stewart Dr Ste 150 94085
Tel (408) 748-6991 *SIC* 5063

FUJITSU AMERICA INC p 583
1250 E Arques Ave 94085
Tel (408) 746-6000 *SIC* 7373

FUJITSU COMPUTER PRODUCTS OF AMERICA INC p 584
1250 E Arques Ave 94085
Tel (408) 746-6000 *SIC* 5045

FUJITSU LABORATORIES OF AMERICA INC p 584
1240 E Arques Ave 345 94085
Tel (408) 530-4500 *SIC* 8731

FUJITSU NORTH AMERICA HOLDINGS INC p 584
1250 E Arques Ave 94085
Tel (408) 737-5600 *SIC* 7373

GOOD TECHNOLOGY CORP p 624
430 N Mary Ave Ste 200 94085
Tel (408) 212-7500 *SIC* 7371 7382

HCL AMERICA INC p 672
330 Potrero Ave 94085
Tel (408) 733-0480 *SIC* 7376 7371 8741

▲ INFINERA CORP p 740
140 Caspian Ct 94089
Tel (408) 572-5200 *SIC* 3661 7372

■ INTERWOVEN INC p 759
1140 Enterprise Way 94089
Tel (312) 580-9100 *SIC* 7372

▲ INTUITIVE SURGICAL INC p 760
1020 Kifer Rd 94086
Tel (408) 523-2100 *SIC* 3841

JUNIPER NETWORKS (US) INC p 797
1133 Innovation Way 94089
Tel (408) 745-2000 *SIC* 3577

▲ JUNIPER NETWORKS INC p 797
1133 Innovation Way 94089
Tel (408) 745-2000 *SIC* 3577 7372

LEVEL 10 CONSTRUCTION LP p 858
1050 Entp Way Ste 250 94089
Tel (408) 747-5000 *SIC* 1542

MATERIAL IN MOTION INC p 919
726 Palomar Ave 94085
Tel (650) 967-3300 *SIC* 3571

MEDTRONIC SPINE LLC p 939
1221 Crossman Ave 94089
Tel (408) 548-6500 *SIC* 3841

MELLANOX TECHNOLOGIES INC p 940
350 Oakmead Pkwy 94085
Tel (408) 970-3400 *SIC* 3674

■ MERU NETWORKS INC p 951
894 Ross Dr 94089
Tel (408) 215-5300 *SIC* 3669

■ MICROSEMI STORAGE SOLUTIONS INC p 962
1380 Bordeaux Dr 94089
Tel (408) 239-8000 *SIC* 3674

■ MOLECULAR DEVICES LLC p 982
1311 Orleans Dr 94089
Tel (408) 747-1700 *SIC* 3826 3841

▲ NETAPP INC p 1027
495 E Java Dr 94089
Tel (408) 822-6000 *SIC* 3572 7373 7372

NOKIA INC p 1046
200 S Mathilda Ave 94086
Tel (408) 530-7600
SIC 3663 5065 3661 3577

PALM INC p 1109
950 W Maude Ave 94085
Tel (408) 617-7000 *SIC* 3663

PHARMACYCLICS INC p 1141
995 E Arques Ave 94085
Tel (408) 774-0330 *SIC* 2834

■ PHARMACYCLICS LLC p 1141
999 E Arques Ave 94085
Tel (408) 774-0330 *SIC* 2834

▲ PROOFPOINT INC p 1183
892 Ross Dr 94089
Tel (408) 517-4710 *SIC* 7371

▲ RAMBUS INC p 1207
1050 Entp Way Ste 700 94089
Tel (408) 462-8000 *SIC* 3674 6794

■ RAYTHEON APPLIED SIGNAL TECHNOLOGY INC p 1210
460 W California Ave 94086
Tel (408) 749-1888 *SIC* 3669

RS HUGHES CO INC p 1255
1162 Sonora Ct 94086
Tel (408) 739-3211 *SIC* 5085

■ RUCKUS WIRELESS INC p 1257
350 W Java Dr 94089
Tel (650) 265-4200 *SIC* 4813

▲ SHORETEL INC p 1318
960 Stewart Dr 94085
Tel (408) 331-3300 *SIC* 3661 3663 7372

SILICON VALLEY EXECUTIVE NETWORK p 1323
1336 Nelson Way 94087
Tel (408) 746-5803 *SIC* 8748

STAR ONE CREDIT UNION p 1378
1306 Bordeaux Dr 94089
Tel (408) 543-5202 *SIC* 6061

TRIDENT MICROSYSTEMS INC p 1479
1170 Kifer Rd 94086
Tel (408) 962-5000 *SIC* 3674

▲ TRIMBLE INC p 1480
935 Stewart Dr 94085
Tel (408) 481-8000 *SIC* 3812 3829

WEST VALLEY ENGINEERING INC p 1596
390 Potrero Ave 94085
Tel (408) 735-1420 *SIC* 7363

XORIANT CORP p 1632
1248 Reamwood Ave 94089
Tel (408) 743-4427 *SIC* 7379 7371

▲ YAHOO INC p 1633
701 First Ave 94089
Tel (408) 349-3300 *SIC* 7373 7375

SUSANVILLE, CA

SIERRA-CASCADE NURSERY INC p 1321
472-715 Johnson Rd 96130
Tel (530) 254-6867 *SIC* 0181

SYLMAR, CA

ADVANCED BIONICS LLC p 25
12740 San Fernando Rd 91342
Tel (661) 362-1400 *SIC* 3842

ALLIED BEVERAGES INC p 56
13235 Golden State Rd 91342
Tel (818) 493-6400 *SIC* 5181

■ ANTHONY DOORS INC p 94
12391 Montero Ave 91342
Tel (818) 365-9451 *SIC* 3585

■ DESERT MECHANICAL INC p 432
15870 Olden St 91342
Tel (702) 873-7333 *SIC* 1711

■ FRONTIER-KEMPER CONSTRUCTORS INC p 581
15900 Olden St 91342
Tel (818) 362-2062 *SIC* 1629

MS AEROSPACE INC p 996
13928 Balboa Blvd 91342
Tel (818) 833-9095 *SIC* 3452 3728

OLIVE VIEW-UCLA MEDICAL CENTER p 1082
14445 Olive View Dr 91342
Tel (818) 364-1555 *SIC* 8011

■ PACESETTER INC p 1103
15900 Valley View Ct 91342
Tel (818) 362-6822 *SIC* 3845

■ SIERRACIN CORP p 1321
12780 San Fernando Rd 91342
Tel (818) 741-1656 *SIC* 2851

■ SIERRACIN/SYLMAR CORP p 1321
12780 San Fernando Rd 91342
Tel (818) 362-6711
SIC 3089 3812 3621 3231

SPEARS MANUFACTURING CO p 1355
15853 Olden St 91342
Tel (818) 364-7306 *SIC* 3494 5083

■ SPECTROLAB INC p 1357
12500 Gladstone Ave 91342
Tel (818) 365-4611 *SIC* 3674 3679

▲ TUTOR PERINI CORP p 1493
15901 Olden St 91342
Tel (818) 362-8391
SIC 1542 8741 1611 1791 8711

TUTOR PERINI CORP p 1493
15901 Olden St 91342
Tel (818) 362-8391 *SIC* 1542 1611 1622

■ TUTOR-SALIBA CORP p 1493
15901 Olden St 91342
Tel (818) 362-8391
SIC 1542 1629 7353 1799 6552

VALLARTA FOOD ENTERPRISES INC p 1540
12881 Bradley Ave 91342
Tel (818) 898-0088 *SIC* 5411

TARZANA, CA

AMI-HTI TARZANA ENCINO JOINT VENTURE p 85
18321 Clark St 91356
Tel (818) 881-0800 *SIC* 8062

■ AMISUB OF CALIFORNIA INC p 85
18321 Clark St 91356
Tel (818) 881-0800 *SIC* 8062

PROVIDENCE TARZANA MEDICAL CENTER p 1186
18321 Clark St 91356
Tel (818) 881-0800 *SIC* 8011

TEHACHAPI, CA

■ GE WIND ENERGY LLC p 597
13000 Jameson Rd 93561
Tel (661) 823-6700 *SIC* 3511

TEMECULA, CA

AIRBUS DS COMMUNICATIONS INC p 40
42505 Rio Nedo 92590
Tel (951) 719-2100 *SIC* 3661

COLOR SPOT HOLDINGS INC p 338
27368 Via Industria Ste 2 92590
Tel (760) 695-1430 *SIC* 0181

COLOR SPOT NURSERIES INC p 338
27368 Via Ste 201 92590
Tel (760) 695-1430 *SIC* 0181

FFF ENTERPRISES INC p 539
41093 County Center Dr 92591
Tel (951) 296-2500 *SIC* 5122 5047

PECHANGA DEVELOPMENT CORP p 1126
45000 Pechanga Pkwy 92592
Tel (951) 695-4655 *SIC* 7011 7929 7999

PROFESSIONAL HOSPITAL SUPPLY INC p 1180
42500 Winchester Rd 92590
Tel (951) 699-5000 *SIC* 5047

SOUTHWEST TRADERS INC p 1352
27565 Diaz Rd 92590
Tel (951) 699-7800 *SIC* 5141

■ TEMECULA VALLEY HOSPITAL INC p 1436
31700 Temecula Pkwy 92592
Tel (951) 331-2200 *SIC* 8062

TEMECULA VALLEY UNIFIED SCHOOL DISTRICT p 1436
31350 Rancho Vista Rd 92592
Tel (951) 676-2661 *SIC* 8211

THERMAL, CA

COACHELLA VALLEY UNIFIED SCHDIST p 331
87225 Church St 92274
Tel (760) 399-5137 *SIC* 8211

THOUSAND OAKS, CA

▲ AMGEN INC p 85
1 Amgen Center Dr 91320
Tel (805) 447-1000 *SIC* 2836

■ AMGEN PHARMACEUTICALS INC p 85
1 Amgen Center Dr 91320
Tel (805) 447-1000 *SIC* 8733

BAJA FRESH WESTLAKE VILLAGE INC p 145
100 Moody Ct Ste 200 91360
Tel (805) 495-4704 *SIC* 5812

BEI SENSORS & SYSTEMS CO LLC p 168
1461 Lawrence Dr 91320
Tel (805) 968-0782 *SIC* 3679

CALIFORNIA LUTHERAN UNIVERSITY p 240
60 W Olsen Rd 91360
Tel (805) 493-3135 *SIC* 8221

CONEJO VALLEY UNIFIED SCHOOL DISTRICT p 355
1400 E Janss Rd 91362
Tel (805) 497-9511 *SIC* 8211

■ COUNTRYWIDE HOME LOANS INC p 375
225 W Hillcrest Dr 91360
Tel (818) 225-3000 *SIC* 6162

KAVLICO CORP p 805
1461 Lawrence Dr 91320
Tel (805) 523-2000 *SIC* 3679 3829 3823

■ LOS ROBLES HOSPITAL & MEDICAL CENTER p 879
215 W Janss Rd 91360
Tel (805) 497-2727 *SIC* 8062

PACIFIC UNION ASSOCIATION OF SEVENTH-DAY ADVENTISTS p 1106
2686 Townsgate Rd 91361
Tel (805) 497-9457 *SIC* 8661

SAGE PUBLICATIONS INC p 1267
2455 Teller Rd 91320
Tel (805) 499-0721 *SIC* 2731

■ TELEDYNE SCIENTIFIC & IMAGING LLC p 1434
1049 Camino Dos Rios 91360
Tel (805) 373-4545 *SIC* 8731 8732 8733

▲ TELEDYNE TECHNOLOGIES INC p 1434
1049 Camino Dos Rios 91360
Tel (805) 373-4545
SIC 3679 3761 3519 3724 3812 3674

THOUSAND PALMS, CA

CLK INC p 327
72295 Manufacturing Rd 92276
Tel (760) 341-2992 *SIC* 5812

TORRANCE, CA

ACT 1 GROUP INC p 19
1999 W 190th St 90504
Tel (310) 532-1529 *SIC* 7361 8741

ALPINE ELECTRONICS OF AMERICA INC p 60
19145 Gramercy Pl 90501
Tel (310) 326-8000 *SIC* 5064 3651 3679

AMERICAN HONDA FINANCE CORP p 74
20800 Madrona Ave 90503
Tel (310) 972-2239 *SIC* 6141

AMERICAN HONDA MOTOR CO INC p 74
1919 Torrance Blvd 90501
Tel (310) 783-2000 *SIC* 5012 3732

BINEX LINE CORP p 183
19515 S Vermont Ave 90502
Tel (310) 416-8600 *SIC* 4731 4513

■ **BIOFUSION LLC** p 183
19110 Van Ness Ave 90501
Tel (310) 803-8100 *SIC* 8011

CITIZEN WATCH CO OF AMERICA INC p 310
1000 W 190th St 90502
Tel (310) 532-8463 *SIC* 5094 3829

CITY OF TORRANCE p 319
3031 Torrance Blvd 90503
Tel (310) 328-5310 *SIC* 9111

COMPEX LEGAL SERVICES INC p 351
325 Maple Ave 90503
Tel (310) 782-1801 *SIC* 8111 7338 7334

EDELBROCK HOLDINGS INC p 477
2700 California St 90503
Tel (310) 781-2222 *SIC* 3714 3751

EDELBROCK LLC p 477
2700 California St 90503
Tel (310) 781-2222 *SIC* 3714 3751

EL CAMINO COMMUNITY COLLEGE DISTRICT p 482
16007 Crenshaw Blvd 90506
Tel (310) 532-3670 *SIC* 8222

FARAHMAND ARTA DDS p 528
23326 Hawthorne Blvd # 220 90505
Tel (310) 373-3501 *SIC* 8021

FNS INC p 562
1545 Francisco St 90501
Tel (661) 615-2300 *SIC* 4731

FRESH & EASY NEIGHBORHOOD MARKET INC p 578
20101 Hamilton Ave # 350 90502
Tel (310) 341-1200 *SIC* 5411

HARBOR DEVELOPMENTAL DISABILITIES FOUNDATION INC p 659
21231 Hawthorne Blvd 90503
Tel (310) 540-1711 *SIC* 8399

HARBOR-UCLA MEDICAL CENTER p 660
1000 W Carson St 2 90502
Tel (310) 222-2345 *SIC* 8062

HECNY TRANSPORTATION INC p 680
1416 Francisco St 90501
Tel (310) 347-3400 *SIC* 4731

HERBALIFE INTERNATIONAL INC p 685
990 W 190th St 90502
Tel (310) 410-9600 *SIC* 5499

HI-SHEAR CORP p 689
2600 Skypark Dr 90505
Tel (310) 784-4025 *SIC* 3452 3429

HONDA NORTH AMERICA INC p 704
700 Van Ness Ave 90501
Tel (310) 781-4961 *SIC* 3711 8748

HONDA R&D AMERICAS INC p 705
1900 Harpers Way 90501
Tel (310) 781-5500 *SIC* 5511

HONDA TRADING AMERICA CORP p 705
19210 Van Ness Ave 90501
Tel (310) 787-5000 *SIC* 5013

I C CLASS COMPONENTS CORP p 724
23605 Telo Ave 90505
Tel (310) 539-5500 *SIC* 5065

JTB AMERICAS LTD p 796
19700 Mariner Ave 90503
Tel (310) 303-3750 *SIC* 4724

KEENAN & ASSOCIATES p 807
2355 Crenshaw Blvd # 200 90501
Tel (310) 212-3344 *SIC* 6411

KINGS HAWAIIAN HOLDING CO INC p 820
19161 Harborgate Way 90501
Tel (310) 755-7100 *SIC* 2051 5812

KUBOTA TRACTOR CORP p 831
3401 Del Amo Blvd 90503
Tel (310) 370-3370 *SIC* 5083 3531 3799

KUBOTA USA INC p 831
3401 Del Amo Blvd 90503
Tel (310) 370-3370
SIC 5083 3577 5051 3531 3571

■ **L-3 COMMUNICATIONS ELECTRON TECHNOLOGIES INC** p 834
3100 Lomita Blvd 90505
Tel (310) 517-6000 *SIC* 3671 3764

LITTLE CO OF MARY HOSPITAL p 871
4101 Torrance Blvd 90503
Tel (310) 540-7676 *SIC* 8062 8051

LYNN PRODUCTS INC p 888
2645 W 237th St 90505
Tel (310) 530-5966 *SIC* 3577 3357

MERCURY AIR GROUP INC p 945
2780 Skypark Dr Ste 300 90505
Tel (310) 602-3770 *SIC* 5172 7389 4581

MITSUWA CORP p 978
21515 S Western Ave 90501
Tel (310) 782-6800 *SIC* 5411

▲ **MOTORCAR PARTS OF AMERICA INC** p 993
2929 California St 90503
Tel (310) 212-7910
SIC 3714 3694 3625 5013

NISSIN INTERNATIONAL TRANSPORT USA INC p 1044
1540 W 190th St 90501
Tel (310) 222-8500 *SIC* 4731

PANASONIC PROCUREMENT CORP OF AMERICA p 1111
20000 Mariner Ave Ste 200 90503
Tel (310) 783-4100 *SIC* 6221

PELICAN PRODUCTS INC p 1128
23215 Early Ave 90505
Tel (310) 326-4700 *SIC* 3648 3161 3089

PHENOMENEX INC p 1142
411 Madrid Ave 90501
Tel (310) 212-0555 *SIC* 3826

PROVIDENCE LITTLE CO OF MARY MEDICAL CENTER-TORRANCE p 1186
4101 Torrance Blvd 90503
Tel (310) 540-7676 *SIC* 8741

RESOURCE COLLECTION INC p 1227
3771 W 242nd St Ste 205 90505
Tel (310) 219-3272
SIC 7349 7381 0782 3564

ROBINSON HELICOPTER CO INC p 1242
2901 Airport Dr 90505
Tel (310) 539-0508 *SIC* 3721

SOCIAL VOCATIONAL SERVICES INC p 1336
3555 Torrance Blvd 90503
Tel (310) 944-3303 *SIC* 8361

SURGERY CENTER TORRANCE L P p 1408
23560 Crenshaw Blvd # 104 90505
Tel (310) 784-5880 *SIC* 8011

TORRANCE HEALTH ASSOCIATION INC p 1462
23550 Hawthorne Blvd 90505
Tel (310) 325-9110 *SIC* 8062

TORRANCE MEMORIAL MEDICAL CENTER p 1462
3330 Lomita Blvd 90505
Tel (310) 325-9110 *SIC* 8062

TORRANCE UNIFIED SCHOOL DISTRICT p 1462
2335 Plaza Del Amo 90501
Tel (310) 972-6500 *SIC* 8211

TOWER ENERGY GROUP p 1464
1983 W 190th St Ste 100 90504
Tel (310) 538-8000 *SIC* 5172

TOYOTA FINANCIAL SERVICES INTERNATIONAL CORP p 1466
19001 S Western Ave 90501
Tel (310) 618-4000 *SIC* 5511

TOYOTA MOTOR CREDIT CORP p 1466
19001 S Western Ave 90501
Tel (310) 468-1310 *SIC* 6141

TOYOTA MOTOR SALES USA INC p 1467
19001 S Western Ave 90501
Tel (310) 468-4000 *SIC* 6159 5012 3711

UNIFY FINANCIAL FEDERAL CREDIT UNION p 1503
1899 Western Way Ste 100 90501
Tel (310) 536-5000 *SIC* 6061

VANTEC HITACHI TRANSPORT SYSTEM (USA) INC p 1544
991 Francisco St 90502
Tel (310) 525-2900 *SIC* 4731

VECTOR RESOURCES INC p 1546
3530 Voyager St 90503
Tel (310) 436-1000 *SIC* 1731 3651 7373

■ **VIRCO INC** p 1558
2027 Harpers Way 90501
Tel (310) 533-0474 *SIC* 5021

▲ **VIRCO MFG CORP** p 1558
2027 Harpers Way 90501
Tel (310) 533-0474 *SIC* 2531 2522 2511

YOSHINOYA AMERICA INC p 1637
991 Knox St 90502
Tel (310) 527-6060 *SIC* 5812

YOUNGER MFG CO p 1639
2925 California St 90503
Tel (310) 783-1533 *SIC* 3851

TRACY, CA

CLEARWIRE INC p 324
1490 Holly Dr 95376
Tel (408) 794-8220 *SIC* 8999

TRACY UNIFIED SCHOOL DISTRICT p 1468
1875 W Lowell Ave 95376
Tel (209) 830-3200 *SIC* 8211

WINE GROUP LLC p 1616
4596 S Tracy Blvd 95377
Tel (415) 986-8700 *SIC* 5921

TRUCKEE, CA

TAHOE FOREST HOSPITAL DISTRICT p 1421
10121 Pine Ave 96161
Tel (530) 587-6011 *SIC* 8062

TUJUNGA, CA

DYNASTY FARMS INC p 464
11900 Big Tujunga Cyn Rd 91042
Tel (831) 755-1398 *SIC* 5148

TULARE, CA

J D HEISKELL HOLDINGS LLC p 770
1939 Hillman St 93274
Tel (559) 685-6100 *SIC* 5191 5999

SAPUTO CHEESE USA INC p 1282
800 E Paige Ave 93274
Tel (559) 687-8411 *SIC* 2022

TULARE LOCAL HEALTH CARE DISTRICT p 1491
869 N Cherry St 93274
Tel (559) 685-3462 *SIC* 8062

TURLOCK, CA

ASSOCIATED FEED & SUPPLY CO p 120
5213 W Main St 95380
Tel (209) 667-2708 *SIC* 5191

BONANDER PONTIAC INC p 199
231 S Center St 95380
Tel (209) 632-8871 *SIC* 5511 7539 5012

EMANUEL MEDICAL CENTER AUXILLARY p 490
825 Delbon Ave 95382
Tel (209) 667-4200 *SIC* 5932 5947 8699

■ **EMANUEL MEDICAL CENTER INC** p 490
825 Delbon Ave 95382
Tel (209) 667-4200 *SIC* 8062

FARMLAND MANAGEMENT SERVICES p 530
301 E Main St 95380
Tel (209) 669-0742 *SIC* 0762

GARTON TRACTOR INC p 592
2400 N Golden State Blvd 95382
Tel (209) 632-3931 *SIC* 5999 5083

SELECT HARVEST USA LLC p 1301
14827 W Harding Rd 95380
Tel (209) 668-2471 *SIC* 5159 0173

SENSIENT DEHYDRATED FLAVORS CO p 1304
151 S Walnut Rd 95380
Tel (209) 667-2777 *SIC* 2034

SSI-TURLOCK DAIRY DIVISION p 1364
2600 Spengler Way 95380
Tel (209) 668-2100
SIC 5143 2024 5144 2022

TURLOCK DAIRY & REFRIGERATION INC p 1492
1819 S Walnut Rd 95380
Tel (209) 667-6455 *SIC* 5083 7699 1542

TURLOCK IRRIGATION DISTRICT p 1492
333 E Canal Dr 95380
Tel (209) 883-8222 *SIC* 4911 4971

VALLEY FRESH FOODS INC p 1540
3600 E Linwood Ave 95380
Tel (209) 669-5600 *SIC* 0252 2015

YOSEMITE FARM CREDIT ACA p 1637
806 W Monte Vista Ave 95382
Tel (209) 667-2366 *SIC* 6111

TUSTIN, CA

■ **AB CELLULAR HOLDING LLC** p 9
1452 Edinger Ave 92780
Tel (562) 468-6846 *SIC* 4813

ANSAR GALLERY p 93
2505 El Camino Rd 92782
Tel (949) 220-0000 *SIC* 5141

BROKER SOLUTIONS INC p 217
14511 Myford Rd Ste 100 92780
Tel (800) 450-2010 *SIC* 8742 6162

CARL WARREN & CO p 256
17862 17th St Ste 111 92780
Tel (800) 572-6900 *SIC* 6411

COMPASS WATER SOLUTIONS INC p 351
15542 Mosher Ave 92780
Tel (949) 222-5777 *SIC* 3589

FOUNDATION BUILDING MATERIALS LLC p 571
2552 Walnut Ave Ste 160 92780
Tel (714) 380-3127 *SIC* 1742

HEALTH INVESTMENT CORP p 675
14642 Newport Ave Ste 388 92780
Tel (714) 669-2085 *SIC* 8062

LARGO CONCRETE INC p 845
2741 Walnut Ave Ste 110 92780
Tel (714) 731-3600 *SIC* 1771

LOGOMARK INC p 875
1201 Bell Ave 92780
Tel (714) 675-6100 *SIC* 5199

MANAGEMENT TRUST ASSOCIATION INC p 900
15661 Red Hill Ave # 201 92780
Tel (714) 285-2626 *SIC* 6733

MICROVENTION INC p 962
1311 Valencia Ave 92780
Tel (714) 258-8001 *SIC* 3841

PACIFIC HEALTH CORP p 1104
14642 Newport Ave 92780
Tel (714) 838-9600 *SIC* 8062

RICOH ELECTRONICS INC p 1233
1100 Valencia Ave 92780
Tel (714) 566-2500 *SIC* 3861 3695

TOSHIBA AMERICA MEDICAL SYSTEMS INC p 1462
2441 Michelle Dr 92780
Tel (714) 730-5000 *SIC* 5047

TRINITY CHRISTIAN CENTER OF SANTA ANA INC p 1481
2442 Michelle Dr 92780
Tel (714) 665-3619 *SIC* 4833 7922

TUSTIN UNIFIED SCHOOL DISTRICT p 1493
300 S C St 92780
Tel (714) 730-7515 *SIC* 8211

VITATECH NUTRITIONAL SCIENCES INC p 1563
2802 Dow Ave 92780
Tel (714) 832-9700 *SIC* 2834

WOODBRIDGE GLASS INC p 1622
14321 Myford Rd 92780
Tel (714) 838-4444 *SIC* 1793 5231

YOUNGS HOLDINGS INC p 1639
14402 Franklin Ave 92780
Tel (714) 368-4615 *SIC* 5182

YOUNGS INTERCO INC p 1639
14402 Franklin Ave 92780
Tel (714) 368-4615 *SIC* 5182

YOUNGS MARKET CO LLC p 1639
14402 Franklin Ave 92780
Tel (714) 368-4615 *SIC* 5182

TWENTYNINE PALMS, CA

JACO HILL CO p 775
4960 Adobe Rd 92277
Tel (760) 361-1407 *SIC* 5171

MORONGO UNIFIED SCHOOL DISTRICT p 989
5715 Utah Trl 92277
Tel (760) 367-9191 *SIC* 8211

UKIAH, CA

CALIFORNIA NEWSPAPER LIMITED PARTNERSHIP p 241
194 Ford Rd 95482
Tel (707) 467-9111 *SIC* 2711

COUNTY OF MENDOCINO p 379
501 Low Gap Rd Rm 1010 95482
Tel (707) 463-4441 *SIC* 9111

RINEHART OIL INC p 1235
2401 N State St 95482
Tel (707) 462-8811 *SIC* 5172 5541

UKIAH ADVENTIST HOSPITAL p 1500
275 Hospital Dr 95482
Tel (707) 463-7346 *SIC* 8062

UNION CITY, CA

▲ **ABAXIS INC** p 9
3240 Whipple Rd 94587
Tel (510) 675-6500 *SIC* 3829 2835

ARIAT INTERNATIONAL INC p 108
3242 Whipple Rd 94587
Tel (510) 477-7000
SIC 3199 5139 5137 5136

CHEVYS INC p 296
31100 Courthouse Dr 94587
Tel (510) 675-9620 *SIC* 5812 5813

EMERALD PACKAGING INC p 491
33050 Western Ave 94587
Tel (510) 429-5700 *SIC* 2673

NEW HAVEN UNIFIED SCHOOL DISTRICT p 1030
34200 Alvarado Niles Rd 94587
Tel (510) 471-1100 *SIC* 8211

S C S INC p 1262
2910 Faber St 94587
Tel (510) 477-0008 *SIC* 5146 5147

UNIVERSAL CITY, CA

DW STUDIOS LLC p 463
100 Universal City Plz 91608
Tel (818) 695-5000 *SIC* 7812

NBC STUDIOS INC p 1021
100 Universal City Plz 91608
Tel (818) 777-1000 *SIC* 7922

■ **UNIVERSAL CITY STUDIOS INC** p 1516
100 Universal City Plz 91608
Tel (818) 622-8477 *SIC* 7812 7996

■ **UNIVERSAL CITY STUDIOS PRODUCTIONS LLLP LP** p 1516
100 Universal City Plz 91608
Tel (818) 777-1000
SIC 7812 3652 2741 5947 5944 5961

UPLAND, CA

CAR ENTERPRISES INC p 252
1040 N Benson Ave 91786
Tel (909) 932-9242 *SIC* 5541 5411

SAN ANTONIO COMMUNITY HOSPITAL p 1275
999 San Bernardino Rd 91786
Tel (909) 985-2811 *SIC* 8062 5912

UPLAND UNIFIED SCHOOL DISTRICT p 1528
390 N Euclid Ave Ste 100 91786
Tel (909) 985-1864 *SIC* 8211

VACAVILLE, CA

M&G DURAVENT INC p 890
877 Cotting Ct 95688
Tel (707) 446-1786 *SIC* 3444

MARIANI PACKING CO INC p 906
500 Crocker Dr 95688
Tel (707) 452-2800 *SIC* 0723 2034 5148

TRAVIS CREDIT UNION p 1475
1 Travis Way 95687
Tel (707) 449-4000 *SIC* 6061

VACAVILLE UNIFIED SCHOOL DISTRICT p 1538
401 Nut Tree Rd Ste 100 95687
Tel (707) 453-6121 *SIC* 8211

VALENCIA, CA

ADCO PRODUCTS INC p 21
27615 Avenue Hopkins 91355
Tel (800) 541-2326 *SIC* 2393

ADEPT FASTENERS INC p 22
28709 Industry Dr 91355
Tel (661) 257-6600 *SIC* 5072

ADVANCED BIONICS CORP p 25
28515 Westinghouse Pl 91355
Tel (661) 362-1400 *SIC* 3842

■ **AEROSPACE DYNAMICS INTERNATIONAL INC** p 31
25540 Rye Canyon Rd 91355
Tel (661) 257-3535 *SIC* 3728

ARVATO DIGITAL SERVICES LLC p 114
29011 Commerce Center Dr 91355
Tel (661) 702-2700 *SIC* 5961 7389

C A RASMUSSEN INC p 232
28548 Livingston Ave 91355
Tel (661) 367-9040 *SIC* 1629 1611

CALIFORNIA INSTITUTE OF ARTS p 240
24700 Mcbean Pkwy 91355
Tel (661) 255-1050 *SIC* 8221 8231 8249

DIMENSION DATA p 440
27202 Turnberry Ln # 100 91355
Tel (661) 257-1500 *SIC* 4899

FALCON AEROSPACE HOLDINGS LLC p 526
27727 Avenue Scott 91355
Tel (661) 775-7200 *SIC* 8741

FRUIT GROWERS SUPPLY CO INC p 582
27770 N Entrmt Dr Fl 3 91355
Tel (818) 986-6480
SIC 2653 0811 5191 2448 5113

GOTHIC LANDSCAPING INC p 626
27502 Avenue Scott 91355
Tel (661) 257-1266 *SIC* 0782

HENRY MAYO NEWHALL HOSPITAL p 684
23845 Mcbean Pkwy 91355
Tel (661) 253-8000 *SIC* 8062

HENRY MAYO NEWHALL MEMORIAL HEALTH FOUNDATION INC p 684
23845 Mcbean Pkwy 91355
Tel (661) 253-8000 *SIC* 8062

HENRY MAYO NEWHALL MEMORIAL HOSPITAL p 684
23845 Mcbean Pkwy 91355
Tel (661) 253-8112 *SIC* 8011

LANDSCAPE DEVELOPMENT INC p 843
28447 Witherspoon Pkwy 91355
Tel (661) 295-1970 *SIC* 0782 5039

■ **NOVACAP LLC** p 1062
25111 Anza Dr 91355
Tel (661) 295-5920 *SIC* 3675

■ **PRC - DESOTO INTERNATIONAL INC** p 1168
24811 Ave Rockefeller 91355
Tel (661) 678-4209 *SIC* 2891 3089

■ **PRECISION DYNAMICS CORP** p 1168
27770 N Entrmt Dr Ste 200 91355
Tel (818) 897-1111
SIC 2672 2754 5047 3069

■ **PRINCESS CRUISES AND TOURS INC** p 1177
24305 Town Center Dr # 200 91355
Tel (206) 336-6000 *SIC* 7999

QIAGEN INC p 1195
27220 Turnberry Ln # 200 91355
Tel (661) 702-3598
SIC 3826 5047 8731 2835

QIAGEN NORTH AMERICAN HOLDINGS INC p 1195
27220 Turnberry Ln # 200 91355
Tel (661) 702-3000 *SIC* 5122

■ **SEMCO INSTRUMENTS INC** p 1302
25700 Rye Canyon Rd 91355
Tel (661) 257-2000 *SIC* 3829

STELLAR MICROELECTRONICS INC p 1385
28454 Livingston Ave 91355
Tel (661) 775-3500 *SIC* 5065

STRATASYS DIRECT INC p 1392
28309 Avenue Crocker 91355
Tel (661) 295-4400 *SIC* 3089

SUNKIST GROWERS INC p 1402
27770 N Entertainment Dr # 120 91355
Tel (818) 986-4800
SIC 5148 2033 2037 2899 6794 5046

■ **TRIUMPH ACTUATION SYSTEMS - VALENCIA INC** p 1483
28150 Harrison Pkwy 91355
Tel (661) 295-1015 *SIC* 3823

US HEALTHWORKS INC p 1532
25124 Springfield Ct 91355
Tel (800) 720-2432 *SIC* 8011

USA UNION INTERNATIONAL INC p 1534
26650 The Old Rd Ste 210 91381
Tel (661) 286-8801 *SIC* 6061

■ **WESCO AIRCRAFT HARDWARE CORP** p 1593
24911 Avenue Stanford 91355
Tel (661) 775-7200 *SIC* 5088

▲ **WESCO AIRCRAFT HOLDINGS INC** p 1593
24911 Avenue Stanford 91355
Tel (661) 775-7200 *SIC* 8741 5072

VALLEJO, CA

PETROCHEM INSULATION INC p 1139
110 Corporate Pl 94590
Tel (707) 644-7455 *SIC* 1742 1799

SUTTER SOLANO MEDICAL CENTER INC p 1410
300 Hospital Dr 94589
Tel (707) 554-4444 *SIC* 8062

TIMEC ACQUISITIONS INC p 1454
155 Corporate Pl 94590
Tel (707) 642-2222 *SIC* 1629

TIMEC COMPANIES INC p 1454
155 Corporate Pl 94590
Tel (707) 642-2222 *SIC* 1629 1799

VALLEJO CITY UNIFIED SCHOOL DISTRICT p 1540
665 Walnut Ave 94592
Tel (707) 556-8921 *SIC* 8211

VALLEY CENTER, CA

FENCES4LESS INC p 537
31290 Manzanita Crest Rd 92082
Tel (760) 749-2069 *SIC* 8742

VALLEY VILLAGE, CA

APPAREL CONCEPTS INTERNATIONAL INC p 98
4804 Laurel Canyon Blvd # 59 91607
Tel (626) 233-9198 *SIC* 5136

VAN NUYS, CA

■ **CENTURY-NATIONAL INSURANCE CO** p 282
16650 Sherman Way 91406
Tel (818) 760-0880 *SIC* 6311

CONSOLIDATED FABRICATORS CORP p 359
14620 Arminta St 91402
Tel (818) 901-1005 *SIC* 3443 5051 3444

E & S INTERNATIONAL ENTERPRISES INC p 465
7801 Hayvenhurst Ave 91406
Tel (818) 702-2207 *SIC* 5064

EASTON HOCKEY INC p 473
7855 Haskell Ave Ste 200 91406
Tel (818) 782-6445 *SIC* 5091

ELECTRO RENT CORP p 485
6060 Sepulveda Blvd # 300 91411
Tel (818) 786-2525
SIC 7359 7377 5065 5045

HIRSCH PIPE & SUPPLY CO INC p 696
15025 Oxnard St Ste 100 91411
Tel (818) 756-0900 *SIC* 5074

JERRY LEIGH OF CALIFORNIA INC p 783
7860 Nelson Rd 91402
Tel (818) 909-6200 *SIC* 5137

MGA ENTERTAINMENT INC p 958
16300 Roscoe Blvd Ste 150 91406
Tel (818) 894-2525 *SIC* 5092

NORTH LA COUNTY REGIONAL CENTER INC p 1053
15400 Sherman Way Ste 170 91406
Tel (818) 778-1900 *SIC* 8748

RBG HOLDINGS CORP p 1211
7855 Haskell Ave Ste 350 91406
Tel (818) 782-6445 *SIC* 3949 5091 3751

VALLEY PRESBYTERIAN HOSPITAL p 1541
15107 Vanowen St 91405
Tel (818) 782-6600 *SIC* 8062

WBI INC p 1585
8201 Woodley Ave 91406
Tel (800) 673-4968 *SIC* 3861

VENICE, CA

SNAP INC p 1335
63 Market St 90291
Tel (310) 399-3339 *SIC* 7372

VENTURA, CA

AGI HOLDING CORP p 35
2575 Vista Del Mar Dr 93001
Tel (805) 667-4100 *SIC* 7997 2741

CLINICAS DEL CAMINO REAL INC p 326
200 S Wells Rd Ste 200 93004
Tel (805) 647-6322 *SIC* 8093

COMMUNITY MEMORIAL HEALTH SYSTEM p 349
147 N Brent St 93003
Tel (805) 652-5011 *SIC* 5912

COMMUNITY MEMORIAL HOSPITAL SAN BUENAVENTURA INC p 349
147 N Brent St 93003
Tel (805) 652-5072 *SIC* 8062

COUNTY OF VENTURA p 382
800 S Victoria Ave 93009
Tel (805) 654-2551 *SIC* 9111

DCOR LLC p 418
290 Maple Ct Ste 290 93003
Tel (805) 535-2000 *SIC* 1382

PATAGONIA INC p 1120
259 W Santa Clara St 93001
Tel (805) 643-8616 *SIC* 2329 2339

PATAGONIA WORKS p 1120
259 W Santa Clara St 93001
Tel (805) 643-8616
SIC 5699 2339 2329 5961

■ **SL POWER ELECTRONICS CORP** p 1330
6050 King Dr Ste A 93003
Tel (805) 228-3400 *SIC* 3679

▲ **TRADE DESK INC** p 1468
42 N Chestnut St 93001
Tel (805) 585-3434 *SIC* 7311

VENTURA COUNTY COMMUNITY COLLEGE DISTRICT p 1548
255 W Stanley Ave Ste 150 93001
Tel (805) 652-5500 *SIC* 8222 8221

VENTURA COUNTY MEDICAL CENTER p 1548
3291 Loma Vista Rd 93003
Tel (805) 652-6000 *SIC* 8011

VENTURA UNIFIED SCHOOL DISTRICT p 1548
255 W Stanley Ave Ste 100 93001
Tel (805) 641-5000 *SIC* 8211

VERNON, CA

ARCADIA INC p 103
2301 E Vernon Ave 90058
Tel (323) 269-7300 *SIC* 3355

BAKER COMMODITIES INC p 146
4020 Bandini Blvd 90058
Tel (323) 268-2801 *SIC* 2077 2048

BCBG MAX AZRIA GROUP LLC p 163
2761 Fruitland Ave 90058
Tel (323) 589-2224 *SIC* 5137 5621 2335

CAMINO REAL FOODS INC p 245
2638 E Vernon Ave 90058
Tel (323) 585-6599 *SIC* 2038

■ **CLOUGHERTY PACKING LLC** p 327
3049 E Vernon Ave 90058
Tel (323) 583-4621 *SIC* 2011 2013

CR LAURENCE CO INC p 388
2503 E Vernon Ave 90058
Tel (323) 588-1281 *SIC* 3714 5072 5039

DUNN-EDWARDS CORP p 461
4885 E 52nd Pl 90058
Tel (323) 771-3330 *SIC* 2851 5231

DUTCH LLC p 463
5301 S Santa Fe Ave 90058
Tel (323) 277-3900 *SIC* 5137

E B BRADLEY CO p 466
5602 Bickett St 90058
Tel (323) 585-9917 *SIC* 5072 2452

FISHERMANS PRIDE PROCESSORS INC p 552
4510 S Alameda St 90058
Tel (323) 232-1980 *SIC* 2092

■ **GOLDBERG AND SOLOVY FOODS INC** p 620
5925 Alcoa Ave 90058
Tel (323) 581-6161
SIC 5141 5149 5046 5169

GOLDEN WEST TRADING INC p 622
4401 S Downey Rd 90058
Tel (323) 581-3663 *SIC* 5147 5142

GRAND PACKAGING INC p 630
3840 E 26th St 90058
Tel (323) 980-0918 *SIC* 2673

H & N FOODS INTERNATIONAL INC p 649
5580 S Alameda St 90058
Tel (323) 586-9300 *SIC* 5146

H & N GROUP INC p 649
5580 S Alameda St 90058
Tel (323) 586-9388 *SIC* 5146

■ **J & J SNACK FOODS CORP OF CALIFORNIA** p 770
5353 S Downey Rd 90058
Tel (323) 581-0171 *SIC* 2052 5149

JAYA APPAREL GROUP LLC p 779
5175 S Soto St 90058
Tel (323) 584-3500 *SIC* 2339 2337

KING MEAT SERVICE INC p 820
4215 Exchange Ave 90058
Tel (323) 835-8989 *SIC* 5147

LAWRENCE WHOLESALE LLC p 848
4353 Exchange Ave 90058
Tel (323) 235-7525 *SIC* 5147

MAX RAVE LLC p 922
2761 Fruitland Ave 90058
Tel (201) 861-1416 *SIC* 5621

OVERHILL FARMS INC p 1099
2727 E Vernon Ave 90058
Tel (323) 582-9977 *SIC* 2038

PACIFIC AMERICAN FISH CO INC p 1104
5525 S Santa Fe Ave 90058
Tel (323) 319-1551 *SIC* 5146 2091

RANCHO FOODS INC p 1207
2528 E 37th St 90058
Tel (323) 585-0503 *SIC* 5147 2013

RANDALL FOODS INC p 1207
2905 E 50th St 90058
Tel (323) 261-6565 *SIC* 5147 7299

RCRV INC p 1212
4715 S Alameda St 90058
Tel (323) 235-8070 *SIC* 2673 5137 5136

RED CHAMBER CO p 1215
1912 E Vernon Ave 90058
Tel (323) 234-9000 *SIC* 5146 4222

REHRIG PACIFIC CO p 1220
4010 E 26th St 90058
Tel (800) 421-6244 *SIC* 3089 2821

REHRIG PACIFIC HOLDINGS INC p 1220
4010 E 26th St 90058
Tel (323) 262-5145 *SIC* 3089 2821

SANDBERG FURNITURE MANUFACTURING CO INC p 1278
5685 Alcoa Ave 90058
Tel (323) 582-0711 *SIC* 2511

SEVEN FOR ALL MANKIND LLC p 1309
4440 E 26th St 90058
Tel (323) 406-5300 *SIC* 2325

SHIMS BARGAIN INC p 1316
2600 S Soto St 90058
Tel (323) 881-0099 *SIC* 5199

SOEX WEST USA LLC p 1337
3294 E 26th St 90058
Tel (323) 264-8300 *SIC* 5136

SWEET PEOPLE APPAREL INC p 1411
4715 S Alameda St 90058
Tel (323) 235-7300 *SIC* 5137

UKAS BIG SAVER FOODS INC p 1500
4260 Charter St 90058
Tel (323) 582-7222 *SIC* 5411

WEST PICO FOODS INC p 1595
5201 S Downey Rd 90058
Tel (323) 586-9050 *SIC* 5142 5144

VICTORVILLE, CA

PRIME HEALTHCARE SERVICESFOUNDATION p 1175
16716 Bear Valley Rd 92395
Tel (760) 241-1200 *SIC* 8099

VICTOR ELEMENTARY SCHOOL DISTRICT p 1555
12219 Second Ave 92395
Tel (760) 245-1691 *SIC* 8211

VICTOR ELEMENTARY SCHOOL DISTRICT FINANCING CORP p 1555
15579 Eighth St 92395
Tel (760) 245-1691 *SIC* 8699 7389

VICTOR VALLEY COMITY COLGE DIST p 1555
18422 Bear Valley Rd 92395
Tel (760) 245-4271 *SIC* 8222

VISALIA, CA

CALIFORNIA DAIRIES INC p 239
2000 N Plaza Dr 93291
Tel (559) 625-2200 *SIC* 2026 2021 2023

COUNTY OF TULARE p 382
2800 W Burrel Ave 93291
Tel (559) 636-5005 *SIC* 9111

FAMILY HEALTHCARE NETWORK p 527
305 E Center Ave 93291
Tel (559) 737-4700 *SIC* 8011

KAWEAH DELTA HEALTH CARE DISTRICT GUILD p 805
400 W Mineral King Ave 93291
Tel (559) 624-2000 *SIC* 8062

VISALIA UNIFIED SCHOOL DISTRICT p 1560
5000 W Cypress Ave 93277
Tel (559) 730-7529 *SIC* 8211 8299

VISTA, CA

ALL ONE GOD FAITH INC p 51
1335 Park Center Dr 92081
Tel (844) 937-2551 *SIC* 2841

ALTMAN SPECIALTY PLANTS INC p 62
3742 Blue Bird Canyon Rd 92084
Tel (760) 744-8191 *SIC* 5193 3999

COUNTY FORD NORTH INC p 375
450 W Vista Way 92083
Tel (760) 945-9900
SIC 5511 5521 7538 7515 5531

DEI HOLDINGS INC p 422
1 Viper Way Ste 3 92081
Tel (760) 598-6200 *SIC* 3669 3651

■ **DJO FINANCE LLC** p 445
1430 Decision St 92081
Tel (760) 727-1280 *SIC* 3842

■ **DJO GLOBAL INC** p 445
1430 Decision St 92081
Tel (760) 727-1280 *SIC* 3842

■ **DJO HOLDINGS LLC** p 445
1430 Decision St 92081
Tel (760) 727-1280 *SIC* 3842

■ **DJO LLC** p 445
1430 Decision St 92081
Tel (760) 727-1280 *SIC* 3842

GLACIER WATER SERVICES INC p 614
1385 Park Center Dr 92081
Tel (760) 560-1111 *SIC* 5962

MC TIRES p 925
538 Olive Ave Ste 304 92083
Tel (760) 846-5613 *SIC* 5014 5531

MCCAIN INC p 926
2365 Oak Ridge Way 92081
Tel (760) 727-8100 *SIC* 5084 3444 3669

OFFDUTYOFFICERS.COM p 1075
2365 La Mirada Dr 92081
Tel (888) 408-5900 *SIC* 7381 8742

■ **OUTDOOR SPORTS GEAR INC** p 1098
2320 Cousteau Ct Ste 100 92081
Tel (914) 967-9400
SIC 3949 3069 2339 2329

SANDEL AVIONICS INC p 1278
2401 Dogwood Way 92081
Tel (760) 727-4900 *SIC* 3812

TOTAL SOURCE MANUFACTURING p 1463
1445 Engineer St 92081
Tel (760) 598-2146 SIC 3821

VISTA UNIFIED SCHOOL DISTRICT INC p 1562
1234 Arcadia Ave 92084
Tel (760) 726-2170 SIC 8211

■ **WATKINS MANUFACTURING CORP** p 1582
1280 Park Center Dr 92081
Tel (760) 598-6464 SIC 3999

WINNERS ONLY INC p 1616
1365 Park Center Dr 92081
Tel (760) 599-0300 SIC 5021

■ **ZODIAC POOL SOLUTIONS NORTH AMERICA INC** p 1644
2620 Commerce Way 92081
Tel (760) 599-9600 SIC 3589

■ **ZODIAC POOL SYSTEMS INC** p 1644
2620 Commerce Way 92081
Tel (760) 599-9600 SIC 3589 3999

WALNUT CREEK, CA

ALL ENVIRONMENTAL INC p 51
2500 Camino Diablo 94597
Tel (925) 746-6000 SIC 4959

■ **AMERICAN REPROGRAPHICS CO LLC** p 78
1981 N Broadway Ste 385 94596
Tel (925) 949-5100 SIC 8744 7334

▲ **ARC DOCUMENT SOLUTIONS INC** p 103
1981 N Broadway Ste 385 94596
Tel (925) 949-5100
SIC 7334 7335 7374 7372

ASCENSION INSURANCE INC p 116
1277 Treat Blvd Ste 400 94597
Tel (800) 404-4969 SIC 6411

BASIC AMERICAN INC p 158
2185 N Calif Blvd Ste 215 94596
Tel (925) 472-4000 SIC 2034 2099

BROWN AND CALDWELL p 219
201 N Civic Dr Ste 115 94596
Tel (925) 937-9010 SIC 8711

CALIFORNIA STATE AUTOMOBILE ASSOCIATION INTER-INSURANCE BUREAU p 241
1276 S California Blvd 94596
Tel (925) 287-7600 SIC 6331

CAROLLO ENGINEERS PC p 259
2700 Ygnacio Valley Rd # 300 94598
Tel (925) 932-1710 SIC 8711

▲ **CENTRAL GARDEN & PET CO** p 278
1340 Treat Blvd Ste 600 94597
Tel (925) 948-4000 SIC 5199 5191

CONTRA COSTA NEWSPAPERS INC p 364
175 Lennon Ln Ste 100 94598
Tel (925) 935-2525 SIC 2711

CSAA INSURANCE EXCHANGE p 397
3055 Oak Rd 94597
Tel (800) 922-8228 SIC 6411

■ **CYTOSPORT INC** p 406
1340 Treat Blvd Ste 350 94597
Tel (707) 751-3942 SIC 2023 2086

DEL MONTE FOODS INC p 423
3003 Oak Rd Ste 600 94597
Tel (925) 949-2772 SIC 2033 5149

EPISCOPAL HOMES FOUNDATION p 505
2185 N Calif Blvd Ste 275 94596
Tel (925) 956-7400 SIC 1521

EPISCOPAL SENIOR COMMUNITIES p 505
2185 N Calif Blvd Ste 575 94596
Tel (925) 956-7400 SIC 8361

ERM-WEST INC p 508
1277 Treat Blvd Ste 500 94597
Tel (925) 946-0455 SIC 8711 8742

HEFFERNAN INSURANCE BROKERS p 680
1350 Carlback Ave 94596
Tel (925) 934-8500 SIC 6411

JOHN MUIR HEALTH p 789
1601 Ygnacio Valley Rd 94598
Tel (925) 947-4449 SIC 8062

JOHN MUIR PHYSICIAN NETWORK p 789
1450 Treat Blvd 94597
Tel (925) 296-9700
SIC 8062 8069 8093 7363

KELLEYAMERIT HOLDINGS INC p 808
1331 N Calif Blvd Ste 150 94596
Tel (877) 512-6374 SIC 8741

MECHANICS BANK p 934
1111 Civic Dr Ste 333 94596
Tel (800) 797-6324 SIC 6022

PORTAL INSURANCE AGENCY INC p 1162
1277 Treat Blvd Ste 650 94597
Tel (925) 937-8787 SIC 6411

STEAD MOTORS INC p 1384
1800 N Main St 94596
Tel (925) 937-5060 SIC 5511

VALENT USA CORP p 1539
1600 Riviera Ave Ste 200 94596
Tel (925) 256-2700 SIC 2879

WALNUT, CA

J F SHEA CO INC p 771
655 Brea Canyon Rd 91789
Tel (909) 594-9500 SIC 3273

JF SHEA CONSTRUCTION INC p 785
655 Brea Canyon Rd 91789
Tel (909) 595-4397 SIC 1521 1622 6512

KELLY PAPER CO p 809
288 Brea Canyon Rd 91789
Tel (909) 859-8200 SIC 5111 5943

LIGHTS OF AMERICA INC p 865
611 Reyes Dr 91789
Tel (909) 594-7883
SIC 3645 3646 7629 3641

MARKWINS INTERNATIONAL CORP p 909
22067 Ferrero 91789
Tel (909) 595-8898 SIC 2844

MT SAN ANTONIO COMMUNITY COLLEGE DISTRICT p 997
1100 N Grand Ave 91789
Tel (909) 594-5611 SIC 8222

PORT LOGISTICS GROUP INC p 1162
288 S Mayo Ave 91789
Tel (713) 439-1010 SIC 4214

SHEA HOMES LIMITED PARTNERSHIP A CALIFORNIA LIMITED PARTNERSHIP p 1313
655 Brea Canyon Rd 91789
Tel (909) 594-9500 SIC 1521

■ **SYSCO LOS ANGELES INC** p 1417
20701 Currier Rd 91789
Tel (909) 595-9595 SIC 5141 5084

TREE ISLAND WIRE (USA) INC p 1475
3880 Valley Blvd 91789
Tel (909) 594-7511 SIC 3315

WALNUT VALLEY UNIFIED SCHOOL DISTRICT p 1574
880 S Lemon Ave 91789
Tel (909) 595-1261 SIC 8211

WASCO, CA

PRIMEX FARMS LLC p 1176
16070 Wildwood Rd 93280
Tel (661) 758-7790 SIC 2068

SUNNYGEM LLC p 1403
500 N F St 93280
Tel (661) 758-0491 SIC 2033 3556

WATSONVILLE, CA

AMERI-KLEEN p 67
119 W Beach St 95076
Tel (831) 722-8888 SIC 7349

CB NORTH LLC p 268
480 W Beach St 95076
Tel (831) 786-1642 SIC 0191

DEL MAR FOOD PRODUCTS CORP p 423
1720 Beach Rd 95076
Tel (831) 722-3516 SIC 2033 2099

DRISCOLL STRAWBERRY ASSOCIATES INC p 456
345 Westridge Dr 95076
Tel (831) 424-0506 SIC 5148 5431

■ **GRANITE CONSTRUCTION CO** p 631
585 W Beach St 95076
Tel (831) 724-1011 SIC 1611 1622

▲ **GRANITE CONSTRUCTION INC** p 631
585 W Beach St 95076
Tel (831) 724-1011
SIC 1611 1622 1629 1442

GRANITE ROCK CO p 631
350 Technology Dr 95076
Tel (831) 768-2000
SIC 1442 3273 5032 2951 1611 3271

MONTEREY MUSHROOMS INC p 986
260 Westgate Dr 95076
Tel (831) 763-5300 SIC 0182

PAJARO VALLEY UNIFIED SCHOOL DISTRICT p 1108
294 Green Valley Rd Fl 1 95076
Tel (831) 786-2100 SIC 8211

PLANT SCIENCES INC p 1154
342 Green Valley Rd 95076
Tel (831) 728-3323 SIC 5122 8748 8731

SUPERIOR FOODS INC p 1406
275 Westgate Dr 95076
Tel (831) 728-3691 SIC 5142

VPS COMPANIES INC p 1566
310 Walker St 95076
Tel (831) 724-7551 SIC 5142 0723 4731

■ **WATSONVILLE HEALTHCARE MANAGEMENT LLC** p 1583
75 Neilson St 95076
Tel (831) 724-4741 SIC 8062

▲ **WEST MARINE INC** p 1595
500 Westridge Dr 95076
Tel (831) 728-2700
SIC 5551 5961 5088 5611 5661 5621

■ **WEST MARINE PRODUCTS INC** p 1595
500 Westridge Dr 95076
Tel (831) 728-2700 SIC 5551 5561

WEST COVINA, CA

CITRUS VALLEY MEDICAL CENTER INC p 311
1115 S Sunset Ave 91790
Tel (626) 962-4011 SIC 8062

YIFANG USA INC p 1636
136 N Grand Ave Ste 148 91791
Tel (909) 593-1562 SIC 5065

WEST HILLS, CA

■ **UNILAB CORP** p 1503
8401 Fallbrook Ave 91304
Tel (818) 737-6000 SIC 8071

WEST HOLLYWOOD, CA

CEDARS-SINAI MEDICAL CENTER p 272
8700 Beverly Blvd 90048
Tel (310) 423-3277 SIC 8062

ENDEMOL p 496
9255 W Sunset Blvd # 1100 90069
Tel (310) 860-9914 SIC 7922

■ **TICKETMASTER ENTERTAINMENT LLC** p 1452
8800 W Sunset Blvd 90069
Tel (800) 653-8000 SIC 7922

WEST SACRAMENTO, CA

■ **AMERICAN METALS CORP** p 76
1499 Parkway Blvd 95691
Tel (916) 371-7700 SIC 5051

BROWN CONSTRUCTION INC p 219
1465 Entp Blvd Ste 100 95691
Tel (916) 374-8616 SIC 1522 1542

CALIFORNIA DEPARTMENT OF GENERAL SERVICES p 240
707 3rd St 95605
Tel (916) 376-5000 SIC 9199

CALIFORNIA STATE TEACHERS RETIREMENT SYSTEM p 241
100 Waterfront Pl 95605
Tel (800) 228-5453 SIC 6371 9441

CLARK - PACIFIC CORP p 322
1980 S River Rd 95691
Tel (916) 371-0305 SIC 3272 5032

DBI BEVERAGE SACRAMENTO p 418
3500 Carlin Dr 95691
Tel (916) 373-5700 SIC 5182 5149

NOB HILL GENERAL STORE INC p 1046
500 W Capitol Ave 95605
Tel (916) 373-3333 SIC 5411 5961

NOR-CAL BEVERAGE CO INC p 1047
2150 Stone Blvd 95691
Tel (916) 372-0600 SIC 5181 2086

PHILLIPS PET FOOD AND SUPPLIES p 1144
3885 Seaport Blvd Ste 10 95691
Tel (916) 373-7300 SIC 5149

RALEYS p 1206
500 W Capitol Ave 95605
Tel (916) 373-3333 SIC 5411 5912

RAMOS OIL CO INC p 1207
1515 S River Rd 95691
Tel (916) 371-2570 SIC 5171 5172

■ **TONYS FINE FOODS** p 1460
3575 Reed Ave 95605
Tel (916) 374-4000 SIC 5147 5143 5149

WESTLAKE VILLAGE, CA

APPROVED NETWORKS INC p 100
717 Lakefield Rd Ste A 91361
Tel (800) 590-9535 SIC 3299

■ **BLUE CROSS OF CALIFORNIA** p 192
4553 La Tienda Rd 91362
Tel (805) 557-6050 SIC 6324 6411

■ **CONVERSANT LLC** p 365
30699 Russell Ranch Rd # 250 91362
Tel (818) 575-4500 SIC 7375 4813

DFC HOLDINGS LLC p 435
1 Dole Dr 91362
Tel (818) 879-6600
SIC 0174 0175 0161 5148 2033

DHM HOLDING CO INC p 435
1 Dole Dr 91362
Tel (818) 879-6600
SIC 0179 0174 0175 0161 5148 2033

DOLE FOOD CO INC p 448
1 Dole Dr 91362
Tel (818) 874-4000
SIC 0179 0174 0175 0161 5148 2033

DOLE FRESH FRUIT CO p 448
1 Dole Dr 91362
Tel (818) 874-4000 SIC 5148

DOLE HOLDING CO LLC p 448
1 Dole Dr 91362
Tel (818) 879-6600
SIC 0179 0174 0175 0161 5148 2033

DOLE PACKAGED FOODS LLC p 448
3059 Townsgate Rd 91361
Tel (805) 601-5500 SIC 2037

GUITAR CENTER HOLDINGS INC p 646
5795 Lindero Canyon Rd 91362
Tel (818) 735-8800 SIC 5736

GUITAR CENTER INC p 646
5795 Lindero Canyon Rd 91362
Tel (818) 735-8800 SIC 5736

GUITAR CENTER STORES INC p 646
5795 Lindero Canyon Rd 91362
Tel (818) 735-8800 SIC 5736

IPAYMENT HOLDINGS INC p 763
30721 Russell Ranch Rd # 200 91362
Tel (310) 436-5294 SIC 7389

IPAYMENT INC p 763
30721 Russell Ranch Rd # 200 91362
Tel (212) 802-7200 SIC 7389

K-SWISS INC p 799
31248 Oak Crest Dr 91361
Tel (818) 706-5100 SIC 3021 3911

K-SWISS SALES CORP p 799
31248 Oak Crest Dr # 150 91361
Tel (818) 706-5100 SIC 3021

▲ **LTC PROPERTIES INC** p 883
2829 Townsgate Rd Ste 350 91361
Tel (805) 981-8655 SIC 6798

■ **PACIFIC COMPENSATION INSURANCE CO** p 1104
1 Baxter Way Ste 170 91362
Tel (818) 575-8500 SIC 6331

PENNYMAC FINANCIAL SERVICES INC p 1131
3043 Townsgate Rd 91361
Tel (818) 224-7442 SIC 6162 6282

RYLAND GROUP INC p 1261
3011 Townsgate Rd Ste 200 91361
Tel (805) 367-3800 SIC 1531 1521 6162

WARNER PACIFIC INSURANCE SERVICES INC p 1576
32110 Agoura Rd 91361
Tel (408) 298-4049 SIC 6411

■ **WELLPOINT CALIFORNIA SERVICES INC** p 1589
4553 La Tienda Rd 91362
Tel (805) 557-6655 SIC 6324

WOOD RANCH BARBECUE AND GRILL INC p 1622
2835 Townsgate Rd Ste 200 91361
Tel (805) 719-9000 SIC 5812

WESTMINSTER, CA

WESTMINSTER SCHOOL DISTRICT p 1601
14121 Cedarwood St 92683
Tel (714) 892-8946 SIC 8211

WHITTIER, CA

BRIGHT HEALTH PHYSICIANS p 212
15725 Whittier Blvd # 500 90603
Tel (562) 947-8478 SIC 8011

GEORGIA PACIFIC HOLDINGS INC p 607
13208 Hadley St Apt 1 90601
Tel (626) 926-1474
SIC 2676 2656 2435 2821

INTERHEALTH CORP p 752
12401 Washington Blvd 90602
Tel (562) 698-0811 SIC 8062 8011

OLTMANS CONSTRUCTION CO p 1083
10005 Mission Mill Rd 90601
Tel (562) 948-4242 SIC 1541 1542

■ **ORCHARD - POST ACUTE CARE CENTER** p 1093
12385 Washington Blvd 90606
Tel (562) 693-7701 SIC 8051

PRESBYTERIAN INTERCOMMUNITY HOSPITAL INC p 1171
12401 Washington Blvd 90602
Tel (562) 698-0811 SIC 8062

ROSE HILLS CO p 1250
3888 Workman Mill Rd 90601
Tel (562) 699-0921 SIC 6553

ROSE HILLS HOLDINGS CORP p 1250
3888 Workman Mill Rd 90601
Tel (562) 699-0921 SIC 6553

SANITATION DISTRICT OF LOS ANGELES COUNTY DISTRICT 2 p 1279
1955 Workman Mill Rd 90601
Tel (562) 699-7411 SIC 9511

SANITATION DISTRICTS OF LOS ANGELES COUNTY p 1279
1955 Workman Mill Rd 90601
Tel (562) 908-4288 SIC 4953

WHITTIER UNION HIGH SCHOOL DIST p 1607
9401 Painter Ave 90605
Tel (562) 698-8121 SIC 8211

WILDOMAR, CA

■ **UNIVERSAL HEALTH SERVICES OF RANCHO SPRINGS INC** p 1517
36485 Inland Valley Dr 92595
Tel (951) 677-9712 SIC 8099 8062 8011

WILMINGTON, CA

AL DAHRA ACX GLOBAL INC p 43
920 E Pacific Coast Hwy 90744
Tel (209) 465-3718 SIC 5191

POTENTIAL INDUSTRIES INC p 1164
922 E E St 90744
Tel (310) 807-4466 SIC 4953 5093

WOODLAND HILLS, CA

21ST CENTURY INSURANCE CO p 1
6301 Owensmouth Ave 91367
Tel (877) 310-5687 SIC 6411

21ST CENTURY LIFE AND HEALTH CO INC p 1
21600 Oxnard St Ste 1500 91367
Tel (818) 887-4436 SIC 6321

ANDWIN CORP p 91
6636 Variel Ave 91303
Tel (818) 999-2828
SIC 5113 3842 5199 5087 5047 2835

▲ **B RILEY FINANCIAL INC** p 142
21860 Burbank Blvd 91367
Tel (818) 884-3737 SIC 7389

▲ BLACKLINE INC p 187
21300 Victory Blvd Fl 12 91367
Tel (818) 223-9008 *SIC* 7371

BOETHING TREELAND FARMS INC p 197
23475 Long Valley Rd 91367
Tel (818) 883-1222 *SIC* 0811 5261

CHG-MERIDIAN US HOLDING INC p 296
21800 Oxnard St Ste 400 91367
Tel (818) 702-1800
SIC 7377 6159 5045 7378

CHG-MERIDIAN USA CORP p 296
21800 Oxnard St Ste 400 91367
Tel (818) 702-1800 *SIC* 7373

FARMERS GROUP INC p 529
6301 Owensmouth Ave 91367
Tel (323) 932-3200 *SIC* 6331

FARMERS INSURANCE EXCHANGE p 529
6301 Owensmouth Ave # 300 91367
Tel (323) 932-3200 *SIC* 6311

FIRSTFED FINANCIAL CORP p 550
6320 Canoga Ave 91367
Tel (562) 618-0573 *SIC* 6021

GRILL CONCEPTS INC p 640
6300 Canoga Ave Ste 600 91367
Tel (818) 251-7000 *SIC* 5812

■ HEALTH NET INC p 675
21650 Oxnard St Fl 25 91367
Tel (818) 676-6000 *SIC* 6324 6311

■ HEALTH NET OF CALIFORNIA INC p 675
21281 Burbank Blvd Fl 4 91367
Tel (818) 676-6775
SIC 6324 8062 6311 6321 6331 5912

LIFECARE ASSURANCE CO INC p 864
21600 Oxnard St Fl 16 91367
Tel (818) 887-4436 *SIC* 6321 6411 6311

NATIONAL DIVERSIFIED SALES INC p 1011
21300 Victory Blvd # 215 91367
Tel (559) 562-9888 *SIC* 3089

PANAVISION INC p 1111
6101 Variel Ave 91367
Tel (818) 316-1000
SIC 7359 3861 3648 5063

PANAVISION INTERNATIONAL LP p 1111
6101 Variel Ave 91367
Tel (818) 316-1080 *SIC* 3861

■ REACHLOCAL INC p 1213
21700 Oxnard St Ste 1600 91367
Tel (818) 274-0260 *SIC* 7311 7375

■ SILGAN CONTAINERS CORP p 1323
21800 Oxnard St Ste 600 91367
Tel (818) 348-3700 *SIC* 3411

■ SILGAN CONTAINERS LLC p 1323
21800 Oxnard St Ste 600 91367
Tel (818) 710-3700 *SIC* 3411

■ SILGAN CONTAINERS MANUFACTURING CORP p 1323
21800 Oxnard St Ste 600 91367
Tel (818) 710-3700 *SIC* 3411

THQ INC p 1450
21900 Burbank Blvd # 100 91367
Tel (818) 591-1310 *SIC* 7372

■ UNITED ONLINE INC p 1510
21255 Burbank Blvd # 400 91367
Tel (818) 287-3000 *SIC* 5961 7299

VISTA FORD INC p 1562
21501 Ventura Blvd 91364
Tel (818) 884-7600 *SIC* 5511

■ WELLA CORP p 1589
6109 De Soto Ave 91367
Tel (818) 999-5112 *SIC* 2844

WM KLORMAN CONSTRUCTION CORP p 1620
23047 Ventura Blvd # 200 91364
Tel (818) 591-5969 *SIC* 1521 1542

ZENITH INSURANCE CO p 1642
21255 Califa St 91367
Tel (818) 713-1000 *SIC* 6331

ZENITH NATIONAL INSURANCE CORP p 1642
21255 Califa St 91367
Tel (818) 713-1000 *SIC* 6331

WOODLAND, CA

COUNTY OF YOLO p 383
625 Court St Ste 102 95695
Tel (530) 666-8114 *SIC* 9111

GAYLE MANUFACTURING CO INC p 594
1455 E Kentucky Ave 95776
Tel (707) 226-9136 *SIC* 3441 1541

LIBERTY PACKING CO LLC p 862
724 Main St 95695
Tel (209) 826-7100 *SIC* 5148

LYMAN GROUP INC p 887
201 East St 95776
Tel (530) 662-5442 *SIC* 5191

NATIONAL EWP INC p 1011
500 Main St 95695
Tel (530) 419-2117 *SIC* 1081

NUGGET MARKET INC p 1067
168 Court St 95695
Tel (530) 669-3300 *SIC* 5411

TREMONT GROUP INC p 1476
201 East St 95776
Tel (530) 662-5442 *SIC* 5191

WOODLAND HEALTHCARE p 1623
1325 Cottonwood St 95695
Tel (530) 662-3961 *SIC* 8062

WOODLAND JOINT UNIFIED SCHOOL DISTRICT p 1623
435 6th St 95695
Tel (530) 662-0201 *SIC* 8211

WOODSIDE, CA

FOX PAINE & CO LLC p 572
2105 Woodside Rd Ste D 94062
Tel (650) 235-2075 *SIC* 6211

YORBA LINDA, CA

IMG p 733
4560 Dorinda Rd 92887
Tel (714) 974-1700 *SIC* 7389

NASSER CO INC p 1009
22720 Savi Ranch Pkwy 92887
Tel (714) 279-2100 *SIC* 5141

■ NOBEL BIOCARE USA LLC p 1046
22715 Savi Ranch Pkwy 92887
Tel (714) 282-4800 *SIC* 3843

YOSEMITE NTPK, CA

DNC PARKS & RESORTS AT YOSEMITE INC p 446
9001 Village Dr 95389
Tel (209) 372-1001
SIC 7011 5399 5812 5947 5541 4725

YUBA CITY, CA

FREEMONT RIDEOUT HEALTH GROUP p 577
989 Plumas St 95991
Tel (530) 751-4010 *SIC* 8062

HILBERS INC p 692
1210 Stabler Ln 95993
Tel (530) 673-2947 *SIC* 1542 1541

SUNSWEET GROWERS INC p 1404
901 N Walton Ave 95993
Tel (530) 674-5010 *SIC* 2034 2037 2086

YUBA CITY UNIFIED SCHOOL DISTRICT FINANCING CORP p 1640
750 N Palora Ave 95991
Tel (530) 822-7601 *SIC* 9411

COLORADO

ALAMOSA, CO

SAN LUIS VALLEY HEALTH REGIONAL MEDICAL CENTER p 1277
106 Blanca Ave 81101
Tel (719) 589-2511 *SIC* 8062

ARVADA, CO

ARVADA HOUSE PRESERVATION LIMITED PARTNERSHIP p 114
10175 W 58th Pl Apt 402 80004
Tel (303) 423-8872 *SIC* 6513

COUNTERTRADE PRODUCTS INC p 375
7585 W 66th Ave 80003
Tel (303) 424-7015 *SIC* 5045

MILENDER WHITE CONSTRUCTION CO p 969
12655 W 54th Dr 80002
Tel (303) 216-0420 *SIC* 1542 1522

SORIN GROUP USA INC p 1341
14401 W 65th Way 80004
Tel (303) 425-5508 *SIC* 3845

SUNDYNE LLC p 1402
14845 W 64th Ave 80007
Tel (303) 425-0800 *SIC* 3563 3561

AULT, CO

ALL AROUND ROUSTABOUT LLC p 51
41350 County Road 33 80610
Tel (970) 518-2479 *SIC* 1389

AURORA, CO

ACOSTA SALES & MARKETING CORP p 18
3045 S Parker Rd Ste 255 80014
Tel (303) 752-0030 *SIC* 5141

■ ADVANCED CIRCUITS INC p 25
21101 E 32nd Pkwy 80011
Tel (303) 576-6610 *SIC* 3672

AP MOUNTAIN STATES LLC p 95
797 Ventura St 80011
Tel (303) 363-7101 *SIC* 1542

ASCENDA USA INC p 116
14001 E Iliff Ave Ste 500 80014
Tel (720) 399-2050 *SIC* 7389

AURORA PUBLIC SCHOOLS p 132
15701 E 1st Ave Ste 106 80011
Tel (303) 365-5810 *SIC* 8211

BARTON LEASING INC p 158
14800 E Moncrieff Pl 80011
Tel (303) 576-2200 *SIC* 5032

BEVERAGE DISTRIBUTORS CO LLC p 178
14200 E Moncrieff Pl 80011
Tel (303) 371-3421 *SIC* 5182

BONAKEMI USA INC p 199
2550 S Parker Rd Ste 600 80014
Tel (303) 371-1411
SIC 5198 5169 5023 2851

BROWN STRAUSS INC p 220
2495 Uravan St 80011
Tel (303) 371-2200 *SIC* 5051

BSI HOLDINGS INC p 222
2495 Uravan St 80011
Tel (303) 371-2200
SIC 6719 3589 5093 3715 3823 5051

CHILDRENS HOSPITAL COLORADO p 299
3123 E 16th Ave 80045
Tel (720) 777-1234 *SIC* 8062

CHILDRENS HOSPITAL COLORADO p 299
13123 E 16th Ave 80045
Tel (720) 777-1234 *SIC* 8069

CITY OF AURORA p 313
15151 E Alameda Pkwy 80012
Tel (303) 739-7056 *SIC* 9111 9511

CITYWIDE FINANCIAL INC p 320
13731 E Mississippi Ave 80012
Tel (303) 365-4050 *SIC* 6162

GENERAL ROOFING SERVICES INC p 602
3300 S Parker Rd Ste 500 80014
Tel (303) 923-2200 *SIC* 1761

GRAEBEL COMPANIES INC p 628
16346 Airport Cir 80011
Tel (303) 214-6683 *SIC* 8742

GRAEBEL HOLDINGS INC p 628
16346 Airport Cir 80011
Tel (303) 214-6683 *SIC* 4213 4225 6719

GRAEBEL MOVERS INC p 628
16346 Airport Cir 80011
Tel (303) 214-6683 *SIC* 4213 4214

HEALTHNOTES LLC p 677
1501 S Potomac St 80012
Tel (303) 695-2600 *SIC* 8062

■ MCCANDLESS TRUCK CENTER LLC p 926
16704 E 32nd Ave 80011
Tel (331) 332-5000 *SIC* 5013 7538 5012

SAGE CLIENT 283 LLC p 1267
3155 S Vaughn Way 80014
Tel (303) 595-7200 *SIC* 7011 8741

STEVEN-ROBERT ORIGINALS LLC p 1388
2780 Tower Rd 80011
Tel (303) 375-9925 *SIC* 2053 2024 2099

UNIVERSITY OF COLORADO HEALTH p 1521
12401 E 17th Ave Ste F485 80045
Tel (720) 848-1031 *SIC* 8082

UNIVERSITY OF COLORADO HOSPITALS RETIREMENT PLAN p 1521
2400 S Peoria St Ste 100 80014
Tel (720) 848-4011 *SIC* 6722

WAGNER EQUIPMENT CO p 1571
18000 Smith Rd 80011
Tel (303) 739-3000 *SIC* 5082 7699 7353

WEMBLEY USA INC p 1591
10750 E Iliff Ave 80014
Tel (303) 751-5918 *SIC* 7948

BERTHOUD, CO

DESCO ACQUISITION LLC p 431
230 Commerce Rd 80513
Tel (970) 532-0600 *SIC* 1796 3533 1389

BOULDER, CO

ALFALFAS MARKET INC p 49
1651 Broadway 80302
Tel (303) 449-5343 *SIC* 5499

▲ ARRAY BIOPHARMA INC p 112
3200 Walnut St 80301
Tel (303) 381-6600 *SIC* 2834

AURORA DAIRY CORP p 132
1919 14th St Ste 300 80302
Tel (720) 564-6296 *SIC* 0241

■ BALL AEROSPACE & TECHNOLOGIES CORP p 148
1600 Commerce St 80301
Tel (303) 939-4000 *SIC* 3812

■ BOULDER BRANDS INC p 204
1600 Pearl St Ste 300 80302
Tel (303) 652-0521 *SIC* 2096 6719

■ BOULDER BRANDS USA INC p 204
1600 Pearl St Ste 300 80302
Tel (201) 568-9300 *SIC* 5149

BOULDER CITY OF (INC) p 204
1777 Broadway 80302
Tel (303) 441-3090
SIC 9111 9224 9221 9511

BOULDER COMMUNITY HEALTH p 204
1100 Balsam Ave 80304
Tel (303) 440-2273 *SIC* 8069

BOULDER VALLEY SCHOOL DISTRICT RE-2 p 204
6500 Arapahoe Rd 80303
Tel (303) 447-1010 *SIC* 8211

CORDEN PHARMA COLORADO INC p 369
2075 55th St 80301
Tel (303) 442-1926 *SIC* 2833 8748 2834

COUNTY OF BOULDER p 376
2020 13th St 80302
Tel (303) 441-3500 *SIC* 9111

■ CRISPIN PORTER & BOGUSKY LLC p 392
6450 Gunpark Dr 80301
Tel (303) 628-5100 *SIC* 7311

▲ DMC GLOBAL INC p 446
5405 Spine Rd 80301
Tel (303) 665-5700 *SIC* 3399

GORES ENT HOLDINGS INC p 626
6260 Lookout Rd 80301
Tel (303) 531-3100 *SIC* 3577 7373 3357

GREY MOUNTAIN PARTNERS LLC p 639
1470 Walnut St Ste 400 80302
Tel (303) 449-5692 *SIC* 6726

HEAD USA INC p 673
3125 Sterling Cir Ste 101 80301
Tel (800) 874-3235 *SIC* 5091

HTM USA HOLDINGS INC p 715
3125 Sterling Cir Ste 101 80301
Tel (800) 874-3235 *SIC* 5091 5139 3949

LOGRHYTHM INC p 875
4780 Pearl East Cir 80301
Tel (303) 245-9074 *SIC* 7372

LUND BROWN ENTERPRISES LLC p 885
7490 Clubhouse Rd Ste 200 80301
Tel (303) 530-2900 *SIC* 6794

■ MICRO MOTION INC p 961
7070 Winchester Cir 80301
Tel (303) 530-8400 *SIC* 3824 5084

NATIONAL ECOLOGICAL OBSERVATORY NETWORK INC p 1011
1685 38th St Ste 100 80301
Tel (720) 746-4844 *SIC* 8733

PHARMACA INTEGRATIVE PHARMACY INC p 1141
4940 Pearl East Cir # 301 80301
Tel (303) 442-2304 *SIC* 5912

PIONEER RESTAURANTS LLC p 1151
7490 Clubhouse Rd Fl 2 80301
Tel (720) 485-6841 *SIC* 5812

PRAIRIE MOUNTAIN PUBLISHING CO LLC p 1167
2500 55th St Ste 210 80301
Tel (303) 442-1202 *SIC* 2711

■ RALLY SOFTWARE DEVELOPMENT CORP p 1206
3333 Walnut St 80301
Tel (303) 565-2800 *SIC* 7372

REGENTS OF UNIVERSITY OF COLORADO p 1219
3100 Marine St Ste 48157 80303
Tel (303) 735-6624 *SIC* 8221 8621

RICOH PRODUCTION PRINT SOLUTIONS LLC p 1233
6300 Diagonal Hwy 80301
Tel (303) 924-9348 *SIC* 7389

SAGE V FOODS LLC p 1267
1470 Walnut St Ste 202 80302
Tel (303) 449-5626 *SIC* 2044

SPECTRALINK CORP p 1357
2560 55th St 80301
Tel (303) 441-7500 *SIC* 3663

TUNDRA RESTAURANT SUPPLY INC p 1491
3825 Walnut St Unit E 80301
Tel (303) 440-4142 *SIC* 5046 5074

TUNDRA SPECIALTIES INC p 1491
2845 29th St Unit E 80301
Tel (888) 388-6372 *SIC* 5087

UNIVERSITY CORP FOR ATMOSPHERIC RESEARCH p 1518
3090 Center Green Dr 80301
Tel (303) 497-1000 *SIC* 8733

UNIVERSITY CORP FOR ATMOSPHERIC RESEARCH FOUNDATION p 1518
P.O. Box 3000 80307
Tel (303) 497-8575 *SIC* 8641

VCP MOBILITY INC p 1545
6899 Winchester Cir # 200 80301
Tel (303) 218-4500
SIC 3842 2599 2515 5047 3841

WALDOS HOLDINGS LLC p 1572
831 Pearl St 80302
Tel (303) 381-2640 *SIC* 5411

▲ ZAYO GROUP HOLDINGS INC p 1641
1805 29th St Unit 2050 80301
Tel (303) 381-4683 *SIC* 4813 3661

■ ZAYO GROUP LLC p 1641
1805 29th St Unit 2050 80301
Tel (303) 381-4683 *SIC* 4813 3661

BRECKENRIDGE, CO

PEAK 7 LLC p 1125
100 S Main St 80424
Tel (888) 783-8883 *SIC* 6552

BRIGHTON, CO

BRIGHTON COMMUNITY HOSPITAL ASSOCIATION p 213
1600 Prairie Center Pkwy 80601
Tel (303) 498-1600 *SIC* 8099

COUNTY OF ADAMS p 375
4430 S Adams County Pkwy W5000a 80601
Tel (720) 523-6100 *SIC* 9532

GREENLEAF WHOLESALE FLORIST INC p 638
540 E Bridge St Ste A 80601
Tel (303) 659-8000 *SIC* 5193

ONEAL FLAT ROLLED METALS LLC p 1087
1229 Fulton St 80601
Tel (303) 654-0300 *SIC* 5051

PLATTE VALLEY MEDICAL CENTER FOUNDATION p 1155
1600 Prairie Center Pkwy 80601
Tel (303) 498-1600 *SIC* 8062

SCHOOL DISTRICT 27J CAPITAL FACILITY FEE FOUNDATION p 1289
18551 E 160th Ave 80601
Tel (303) 655-2900 *SIC* 8211

TRANS-WEST INC p 1470
20770 Interstate 76 80603
Tel (303) 289-3161 *SIC* 5511 5012

UNITED POWER INC A COLORADO COOPERATIVE ASSOCIATION p 1511
500 Cooperative Way 80603
Tel (303) 659-0551 *SIC* 4911

VESTAS BLADES AMERICA INC p 1552
1500 E Crown Prince Blvd 80603
Tel (303) 655-5800 *SIC* 3621

WESTERN UNITED ELECTRIC SUPPLY CORP p 1600
100 Bromley Business Pkwy 80603
Tel (303) 659-2356 *SIC* 5063

BROOMFIELD, CO

▲ BALL CORP p 148
10 Longs Peak Dr 80021
Tel (303) 469-3131
SIC 3411 3085 3812 3679

CHECKERS INDUSTRIAL PRODUCTS LLC p 292
620 Compton St 80020
Tel (720) 890-1187 *SIC* 3714 3965

■ CORPORATE EXPRESS US FINANCE INC p 372
1 Environmental Way 80021
Tel (303) 664-2000 *SIC* 5943

■ CORPORATE EXPRESS US INC p 372
1 Environmental Way 80021
Tel (303) 664-2000 *SIC* 5943

CRAFTWORKS RESTAURANTS & BREWERIES GROUP INC p 388
8001 Arista Pl Unit 500 80021
Tel (623) 878-8822 *SIC* 6719

CRAFTWORKS RESTAURANTS & BREWERIES INC p 388
8001 Arista Pl Unit 500 80021
Tel (303) 664-4000 *SIC* 5812

■ CUMMINS ROCKY MOUNTAIN LLC p 401
390 Interlocken Cres # 200 80021
Tel (800) 927-7201 *SIC* 5084 3519

FLATIRON CONSTRUCTION CORP p 554
385 Interlocken Blvd 80021
Tel (303) 485-4050 *SIC* 1622 1629 1611

FLATIRON CONSTRUCTORS INC p 555
385 Interlocken 80021
Tel (303) 485-4050 *SIC* 1611 1622 1629

FLATIRON HOLDING INC p 555
385 Interlocken Cres 80021
Tel (303) 485-4050 *SIC* 1622 1629

HUNTER DOUGLAS WINDOW FASHIONS INC p 719
1 Duette Way 80020
Tel (303) 466-1848 *SIC* 2591

KAISER-HILL CO LLC p 801
11025 Dover St Unit 1000 80021
Tel (303) 966-7000 *SIC* 4953

▲ LEVEL 3 COMMUNICATIONS INC p 858
1025 Eldorado Blvd 80021
Tel (720) 888-1000 *SIC* 4813 7373 7374

■ LEVEL 3 COMMUNICATIONS LLC p 858
1025 Eldorado Blvd 80021
Tel (720) 888-2750 *SIC* 4813 7373

■ LEVEL 3 FINANCING INC p 858
1025 Eldorado Blvd 80021
Tel (720) 888-1000 *SIC* 4813

■ MCDATA CORP p 927
4 Brocade Pkwy 80021
Tel (720) 558-8000
SIC 3679 5045 3825 3577

■ MCDATA SERVICES CORP p 927
4 Brocade Pkwy 80021
Tel (720) 558-8000 *SIC* 7373 3572

MRS FIELDS COMPANIES INC p 996
8001 Arista Pl Unit 600 80021
Tel (720) 599-3374 *SIC* 6794 5461

MRS FIELDS HOLDING CO INC p 996
8001 Arista Pl Unit 600 80021
Tel (720) 599-3350 *SIC* 5461 6794

MWH AMERICAS INC p 1004
370 Interlocken Blvd 80021
Tel (303) 410-4000 *SIC* 8711

MWH CONSTRUCTORS INC p 1004
370 Interlocken Blvd # 300 80021
Tel (303) 439-2800 *SIC* 8711 1629

MWH GLOBAL INC p 1004
370 Interlocken Blvd # 300 80021
Tel (303) 533-1900 *SIC* 8711 8741

NATIONAL ENTERTAINMENT NETWORK LLC p 1011
325 Interlocken Pkwy B 80021
Tel (303) 444-2559 *SIC* 5046 5962

NETWORK GLOBAL LOGISTICS LLC p 1028
320 Interlocken Pkwy # 100 80021
Tel (866) 938-1870 *SIC* 4731

▲ NOODLES & CO p 1047
520 Zang St Ste D 80021
Tel (720) 214-1900 *SIC* 5812

RENEWABLE ENERGY SYSTEMS p 1224
11101 W 120th Ave Ste 400 80021
Tel (303) 439-4200 *SIC* 8731

RES AMERICA CONSTRUCTION INC p 1226
11101 W 120th Ave Ste 400 80021
Tel (512) 617-1960 *SIC* 1629

ROCK BOTTOM RESTAURANTS INC p 1243
8001 Arista Pl Unit 500 80021
Tel (303) 664-4000 *SIC* 5812 5813

SAINT JOHNS HEALTH CTR D6 p 1269
500 Eldorado Blvd # 6300 80021
Tel (913) 895-2800 *SIC* 8099

SISTERS OF CHARITY OF LEAVENWORTH HEALTH SYSTEM INC p 1327
500 Eldorado Blvd # 6300 80021
Tel (303) 813-5000 *SIC* 8062 8011 5912

■ STOLLER NEWPORT NEWS NUCLEAR INC p 1390
105 Technology Dr Ste 190 80021
Tel (303) 546-4300 *SIC* 8744

TRANSFIRST LLC p 1471
12202 Airport Way Ste 100 80021
Tel (800) 654-9256 *SIC* 7374

TRAV CORP p 1473
10249 Church Ranch Way # 200 80021
Tel (303) 426-7000 *SIC* 4724

URBAN SETTLEMENT SERVICES LLC p 1530
11802 Ridge Pkwy Ste 200 80021
Tel (303) 996-8900 *SIC* 6531

VAIL CORP p 1538
390 Interlocken Cres # 1000 80021
Tel (303) 404-1800 *SIC* 7011

▲ VAIL RESORTS INC p 1538
390 Interlocken Cres 80021
Tel (303) 404-1800 *SIC* 7011 6552

WEBROOT INC p 1586
385 Interlocken Cres # 800 80021
Tel (303) 442-3813 *SIC* 7371

■ WWF OPERATING CO p 1629
12002 Airport Way 80021
Tel (214) 303-3400 *SIC* 2026 2023

CANON CITY, CO

SHADOW MOUNTAIN MANAGEMENT CORP p 1310
1401 Phay Ave 81212
Tel (719) 275-8656 *SIC* 8051

CASTLE ROCK, CO

DOUGLAS COUNTY SCHOOL DISTRICT p 452
620 Wilcox St 80104
Tel (303) 387-0100 *SIC* 9411

■ GREAT SOUTHWESTERN CONSTRUCTION INC p 634
1100 Topeka Way 80109
Tel (303) 688-5816 *SIC* 1623

CENTENNIAL, CO

ALLOSOURCE p 58
6278 S Troy Cir 80111
Tel (720) 873-0213 *SIC* 3841

▲ ARROW ELECTRONICS INC p 113
9201 E Dry Creek Rd 80112
Tel (303) 824-4000 *SIC* 5065 5045

COCHLEAR AMERICAS CORP p 333
13059 E Peakview Ave 80111
Tel (303) 790-9010 *SIC* 5047

COLORADO DEPARTMENT OF MILITARY AND VETERANS AFFAIRS p 339
6848 S Revere Pkwy 80112
Tel (720) 250-1530 *SIC* 9711

CORRECTIONAL HEALTHCARE COMPANIES INC p 372
7388 S Revere Pkwy # 707 80112
Tel (615) 312-7286 *SIC* 8011 8744

DIRECT TRAVEL INC p 441
7430 E Caley Ave Ste 220 80111
Tel (952) 746-3575 *SIC* 4724

ENVIRONMENTAL MATERIALS LLC p 503
7306 S Alton Way Ste B 80112
Tel (303) 309-6610 *SIC* 3281

■ FLINT ENERGY SERVICES INC p 557
6901 S Havana St 80112
Tel (918) 294-3030 *SIC* 1389 3594 1623

HASELDEN CONSTRUCTION LLC p 667
6950 S Potomac St Ste 100 80112
Tel (303) 751-1478 *SIC* 1542

IMPACT TELECOM LLC p 734
9000 E Nichols Ave # 230 80112
Tel (866) 557-8919 *SIC* 7389

INTERSTATE HIGHWAY CONSTRUCTION INC p 758
7135 S Tucson Way 80112
Tel (303) 790-7132 *SIC* 1611

JOHNSON STORAGE & MOVING CO HOLDINGS LLC p 791
7009 S Jordan Rd 80112
Tel (303) 785-4300 *SIC* 4213 4214

JOURNEY CHURCH COLORADO p 794
8237 S Holly St Ste C 80122
Tel (303) 921-5595 *SIC* 8661

▲ NATIONAL CINEMEDIA INC p 1010
9110 E Nichols Ave # 200 80112
Tel (303) 792-3600 *SIC* 7311 7389

■ NATIONAL CINEMEDIA LLC p 1010
9110 E Nichols Ave # 200 80112
Tel (303) 792-3600 *SIC* 7311

SAUNDERS CONSTRUCTION INC p 1283
6950 S Jordan Rd 80112
Tel (303) 699-9000 *SIC* 1542

SEAKR ENGINEERING INC p 1296
6221 S Racine Cir 80111
Tel (303) 662-1449 *SIC* 3674 8711

SEMA CONSTRUCTION INC p 1302
7353 S Eagle St 80112
Tel (303) 627-2600 *SIC* 1622 1771

STOLLE MACHINERY CO LLC p 1390
6949 S Potomac St 80112
Tel (303) 708-9044 *SIC* 3542

■ UNITED ARTISTS THEATRE CO p 1506
9110 E Nichols Ave # 200 80112
Tel (303) 792-3600 *SIC* 7832

UNITED LAUNCH ALLIANCE LLC p 1509
9501 E Panorama Cir 80112
Tel (720) 922-7100 *SIC* 3761

WELLDYNERX INC p 1589
7472 S Tucson Way Ste 100 80112
Tel (888) 479-2000 *SIC* 5122 5912

WESTERN CONVENIENCE STORES INC p 1597
9849 E Easter Ave 80112
Tel (303) 706-0340 *SIC* 5541

WESTERN STATES FIRE PROTECTION CO INC p 1600
7026 S Tucson Way 80112
Tel (303) 792-0022 *SIC* 1711

WESTERN STONE & METAL CORP p 1600
8085 S Chester St Ste 300 80112
Tel (303) 792-3500 *SIC* 5944 5094

COLORADO SPRINGS, CO

4 RIVERS EQUIPMENT LLC p 3
1100 E Cheyenne Rd 80905
Tel (800) 364-3029 *SIC* 5084

ACADEMY SCHOOL DISTRICT 20 p 13
1110 Chapel Hills Dr 80920
Tel (719) 234-1200 *SIC* 8211

ACCELLOS INC p 14
90 S Cascade Ave Ste 1200 80903
Tel (719) 433-7000 *SIC* 7373

AEROFLEX COLORADO SPRINGS INC p 30
4350 Centennial Blvd 80907
Tel (719) 594-8000 *SIC* 3674

ALEUT MANAGEMENT SERVICES LLC p 48
5540 Tech Center Dr # 100 80919
Tel (719) 531-9090 *SIC* 8741

BROADMOOR HOTEL INC p 215
1 Lake Ave 80906
Tel (719) 634-7711
SIC 7011 5812 5813 7992 7999 7389

C-USA INC p 234
1005 E Woodmen Rd 80920
Tel (719) 594-4100 *SIC* 5947 5961 2771

CATHOLIC HEALTH INITIATIVES COLORADO p 266
2222 N Nevada Ave 80907
Tel (719) 776-5911 *SIC* 8699

▲ CENTURY CASINOS INC p 282
455 E Pikes Peak Ave # 210 80903
Tel (719) 527-8300 *SIC* 7011 7929 7999

CHERWELL SOFTWARE LLC p 294
10125 Federal Dr Ste 100 80908
Tel (719) 386-7000 *SIC* 7372

CITY OF COLORADO SPRINGS p 314
107 N Nevada Ave Ste 300 80903
Tel (719) 385-2489 *SIC* 5085

COLORADO COLLEGE p 338
14 E Cache La Poudre St 80903
Tel (719) 389-6000 *SIC* 8221

COLORADO DEPARTMENT OF CORRECTIONS p 338
2862 S Circle Dr 80906
Tel (719) 579-9580 *SIC* 9223

COLORADO SPRINGS CITY GOVERNMENT p 339
107 N Nevada Ave 80903
Tel (719) 385-5900 *SIC* 9199

COLORADO SPRINGS SCHOOL DISTRICT 11 p 339
1115 N El Paso St 80903
Tel (719) 520-2000 *SIC* 8211

COLORADO SPRINGS UTILITIES p 339
121 S Tejon St Ste 200 80903
Tel (719) 448-4800 *SIC* 4939

COMPASSION INTERNATIONAL INC p 351
12290 Voyager Pkwy 80921
Tel (719) 487-7000 *SIC* 8399

COUNTY OF EL PASO p 377
200 S Cascade Ave Ste 100 80903
Tel (719) 520-7276 *SIC* 9111

■ DIRECT CHECKS UNLIMITED LLC p 441
8245 N Union Blvd 80920
Tel (719) 531-3900 *SIC* 2782

DISCOVER GOODWILL OF SOUTHERN & WESTERN COLORADO p 442
1460 Grdn Of The Gods Rd 80907
Tel (719) 635-4483 *SIC* 5932 8331

DOSS AVIATION INC p 451
3670 Rebecca Ln Ste 100 80917
Tel (719) 570-9804 *SIC* 5172 4581

ENT FEDERAL CREDIT UNION p 501
7250 Campus Dr Ste 200 80920
Tel (719) 574-1100 *SIC* 6061

FOCUS ON FAMILY p 562
8605 Explorer Dr 80920
Tel (719) 531-3300 *SIC* 8322

G E JOHNSON CONSTRUCTION CO INC p 586
25 N Cascade Ave Ste 400 80903
Tel (719) 473-5321 *SIC* 1542

▲ GOLD RESOURCE CORP p 620
2886 Carriage Manor Pt 80906
Tel (303) 320-7708 *SIC* 1041 1044

HARRISON SCHOOL DISTRICT TWO p 664
1060 Harrison Rd 80905
Tel (719) 579-2000 *SIC* 8211

HEATING AND PLUMBING ENGINEERS INC p 679
407 Fillmore Pl 80907
Tel (719) 633-5571 *SIC* 1711

INDEPENDENT ORDER OF ODD FELLOWS p 736
575 S Union Blvd 80910
Tel (719) 633-2002 *SIC* 8641

■ INTEGRITY URGENT CARE CLINICS INC p 750
4323 Integrity Center Pt 80917
Tel (719) 591-2558 *SIC* 8082 8011 8051

INTELLIGENT SOFTWARE SOLUTIONS USA LLC p 750
5450 Tech Center Dr # 400 80919
Tel (719) 452-7000 *SIC* 7371

MEMORIAL HOSPITAL CORP p 942
1400 E Boulder St 80909
Tel (719) 365-5000 *SIC* 8062

NAVIGATORS p 1020
3820 N 30th St 80904
Tel (719) 598-1212 *SIC* 8661 7032 5942

PENROSE HOSPITAL p 1131
2222 N Nevada Ave Ste 1 80907
Tel (719) 776-5000 *SIC* 8062

PHIL LONG DEALERSHIPS INC p 1142
1114 Motor City Dr 80905
Tel (719) 575-7555 *SIC* 5511 7514 7515

PHIL LONG FORD LLC p 1142
1212 Motor City Dr 80905
Tel (719) 575-7100
SIC 5511 7515 7538 5531

PIONEER SAND CO INC p 1151
5000 Northpark Dr 80918
Tel (719) 599-8100 *SIC* 5211 5031 1794

RAMPART PLUMBING AND HEATING SUPPLY INC p 1207
1801 N Union Blvd 80909
Tel (719) 471-7200 *SIC* 5074

RHODES COLLEGES INC p 1232
1815 Jet Wing Dr 80916
Tel (719) 638-6580 *SIC* 8221 8222

ROCKY MOUNTAIN MATERIALS AND ASPHALT INC p 1245
1910 Rand Ave 80905
Tel (719) 473-3100
SIC 1611 1771 1794 5032

SINTON DAIRY FOODS CO LLC p 1326
3801 Sinton Rd 80907
Tel (719) 633-3821 *SIC* 2026

▲ SPECTRANETICS CORP p 1357
9965 Federal Dr Ste 100 80921
Tel (719) 633-8333 *SIC* 3845

TEPA LLC p 1439
5045 List Dr 80919
Tel (719) 596-8114 *SIC* 5039

UNITED STATES OLYMPIC COMMITTEE INC p 1513
1 Olympic Plz 80903
Tel (719) 632-5551 *SIC* 8699

US WASTE INDUSTRIES INC p 1533
7770 Palmer Park Blvd 80951
Tel (719) 535-9041 *SIC* 4953

▲ VECTRUS INC p 1546
655 Space Center Dr 80915
Tel (719) 591-3600 *SIC* 8744

■ VECTRUS SYSTEMS CORP p 1546
655 Space Center Dr 80915
Tel (719) 591-3600 *SIC* 8744 7376

W C S INC p 1568
1515 N Academy Blvd Ste 4 80909
Tel (719) 573-8557 *SIC* 5812

WENDYS OF COLORADO SPRINGS INC p 1592
1515 N Academy Blvd # 400 80909
Tel (719) 573-8557 *SIC* 5812

WESTERN FORGE INC p 1598
4607 Forge Rd 80907
Tel (719) 598-5070 *SIC* 3423 3545

WIDEFIELD SCHOOL DISTRICT 3 p 1608
1820 Main St 80911
Tel (719) 391-3000 *SIC* 8211

XIOTECH CORP p 1631
9950 Federal Dr Unit 100 80921
Tel (719) 388-5500 *SIC* 3572 4226

YOUNG LIFE p 1638
420 N Cascade Ave 80903
Tel (719) 381-1800 *SIC* 8661 7032

COMMERCE CITY, CO

BAE SYSTEMS POWER INC p 144
5840 Dahlia St 80022
Tel (303) 287-7441
SIC 5084 3531 3999 3569

CENTER FOR TRANSPORTATION SAFETY LLC p 276
5700 E 56th Ave Unit I 80022
Tel (303) 227-0131 *SIC* 7513 7515

DOUGLASS COLONY GROUP INC p 452
5901 E 58th Ave 80022
Tel (303) 288-2635 *SIC* 1761

FLEET-CAR LEASE INC p 555
7563 Dahlia St Unit A 80022
Tel (800) 624-3256 SIC 4213

HONNEN EQUIPMENT CO p 705
5055 E 72nd Ave 80022
Tel (303) 287-7506 SIC 5082 5084

OFFEN PETROLEUM INC p 1075
5100 E 78th Ave 80022
Tel (303) 297-3835 SIC 5172 5541

TIMS AIRBRUSH LLC p 1455
10490 Vaughn Way 80022
Tel (303) 944-9497 SIC 8999 7389

UNITED FOOD SERVICE INC p 1508
5199 Ivy St 80022
Tel (303) 289-3595
SIC 5141 5142 5147 5148 5046

DENVER, CO

A & ETIRE INC p 4
3855 E 52nd Ave 80216
Tel (303) 308-6900 SIC 5014 7534 5531

ACH FOAMTECHNOLOGIES INC p 17
5250 Sherman St 80216
Tel (303) 297-3844 SIC 3086

ACOUSTIC VENTURES LLC p 18
1775 N Sherman St # 2300 80203
Tel (303) 573-7011 SIC 6799

ACT FOR HEALTH INC p 19
500 E 8th Ave 80203
Tel (303) 253-7470 SIC 8011

AD CORP p 21
1551 Wewatta St 80202
Tel (303) 744-1911
SIC 3634 3564 3822 3089 3714 3312

AGRIUM US INC p 36
4582 S Ulster St Ste 1700 80237
Tel (303) 804-4400 SIC 2873

AIMCO PROPERTIES LP p 38
4582 S Ulster St Ste 1100 80237
Tel (303) 757-8101 SIC 6798

■ **AIMCO-GP INC** p 38
4582 S Ulster St Ste 1100 80237
Tel (303) 757-8101 SIC 6798

■ **AIMCO-LP TRUST** p 38
4582 S Ulster St Ste 1100 80237
Tel (303) 757-8101 SIC 6798

ALL COPY PRODUCTS INC p 51
4141 Colorado Blvd 80216
Tel (303) 373-1105 SIC 5044 5112 7371

■ **ALPINE ACCESS INC** p 60
1290 N Broadway Ste 1400 80203
Tel (303) 850-3700 SIC 7361 8742 8748

ALPINE DISPOSAL INC p 60
7373 Washington St 80229
Tel (303) 289-8019 SIC 4953

AMERICAN GUARANTY MORTGAGE LLC p 73
2000 S Colo Blvd Ste 3700 80222
Tel (303) 577-7210 SIC 6282

AMERICAN NATIONAL BANK OF CHEYENNE INC p 76
3033 E 1st Ave Ste 300 80206
Tel (303) 394-5100 SIC 6021

ANSCHUTZ CORP p 93
555 17th St Ste 2400 80202
Tel (303) 298-1000 SIC 2711 1382 7941

ANTERO MIDSTREAM PARTNERS LP p 93
1615 Wynkoop St 80202
Tel (307) 357-7310 SIC 4922

▲ **ANTERO RESOURCES CORP** p 93
1615 Wynkoop St 80202
Tel (303) 357-7310 SIC 1311

ANTERO RESOURCES LLC p 93
1625 17th St Ste 300 80202
Tel (303) 357-7310 SIC 1311

▲ **APARTMENT INVESTMENT & MANAGEMENT CO** p 96
4582 S Ulster St Ste 1100 80237
Tel (303) 757-8101 SIC 6798

ARCHDIOCESE OF DENVER p 105
1300 S Steele St 80210
Tel (303) 722-4687 SIC 8661

ARDENT MILLS LLC p 106
1875 Lawrence St Ste 1400 80202
Tel (800) 851-9618 SIC 2041 4789 8741

ARGUS OF COLORADO INC p 108
720 S Colorado Blvd 600n 80246
Tel (303) 322-4100 SIC 8082 7361

■ **BEAUTYGE BRANDS USA INC** p 166
1515 Wazee St Ste 200 80202
Tel (800) 598-2739 SIC 5122 2844

BIG SUR WATERBEDS INC p 182
5603 Brdwy 80216
Tel (303) 566-8700 SIC 5712 2515 2511

▲ **BILL BARRETT CORP** p 182
1099 18th St Ste 2300 80202
Tel (303) 293-9100 SIC 1311

▲ **BIOSCRIP INC** p 184
1600 Broadway Ste 700 80202
Tel (720) 697-5200 SIC 8059 6411

■ **BLACK HILLS EXPLORATION AND PRODUCTION INC** p 187
1515 Wynkoop St Ste 500 80202
Tel (720) 210-1300 SIC 1382

▲ **BONANZA CREEK ENERGY INC** p 199
410 17th St Ste 1400 80202
Tel (720) 440-6100 SIC 1311

BRANNAN SAND AND GRAVEL CO LLC p 208
2500 Brannan Way 80229
Tel (303) 534-1231 SIC 1611 5032

BRONTAPES INC p 217
875 W Ellsworth Ave 80223
Tel (303) 534-2002 SIC 5085

BROWNSTEIN HYATT FARBER SCHRECK LLP p 220
410 17th St Ste 2200 80202
Tel (303) 223-1100 SIC 8111

BRUNDAGE-BONE CONCRETE PUMPING INC p 221
6461 Downing St 80229
Tel (303) 289-4444 SIC 1771

CALFRAC WELL SERVICES CORP p 238
717 17th St Ste 1445 80202
Tel (303) 293-2931 SIC 1389

CANARY LLC p 246
410 17th St Ste 1320 80202
Tel (303) 309-1185 SIC 1389

CENTURION DISCOVERY INC p 281
518 17th St Ste 925 80202
Tel (303) 645-4555 SIC 8111

▲ **CHIPOTLE MEXICAN GRILL INC** p 301
1401 Wynkoop St Ste 500 80202
Tel (303) 595-4000 SIC 5812 5813

▲ **CIMAREX ENERGY CO** p 307
1700 N Lincoln St # 3700 80203
Tel (303) 295-3995 SIC 1311

CITY & COUNTY OF DENVER p 312
1437 Bannock St Rm 350 80202
Tel (720) 865-9000 SIC 9111

■ **COBIZ BANK** p 332
821 17th St Ste 800 80202
Tel (303) 293-2265 SIC 6021

▲ **COBIZ FINANCIAL INC** p 333
821 17th St 80202
Tel (303) 312-3400 SIC 6021

COLORADO DENTAL SERVICE INC p 338
4582 S Ulster St Ste 800 80237
Tel (303) 741-9300 SIC 6324

COLORADO DEPARTMENT OF HIGHER EDUCATION p 338
1560 Broadway Ste 1600 80202
Tel (303) 866-2723 SIC 9411

COLORADO DEPARTMENT OF HUMAN SERVICE p 338
1575 N Sherman St 80203
Tel (303) 866-5948 SIC 9441

COLORADO DEPARTMENT OF HUMAN SERVICES p 338
1575 N Sherman St Fl 8 80203
Tel (303) 866-5700 SIC 9441

COLORADO DEPARTMENT OF LABOR & EMPLOYMENT p 338
633 17th St Ste 1100 80202
Tel (303) 620-4700 SIC 9651 9441

COLORADO DEPARTMENT OF NATURAL RESOURCES p 339
1313 N Sherman St Ste 718 80203
Tel (303) 866-3311 SIC 9512

COLORADO DEPARTMENT OF PUBLIC HEALTH AND ENVIRONMENT p 339
4300 E Cherry Creek S Dr 80246
Tel (303) 692-2000 SIC 9431 9511

COLORADO DEPARTMENT OF TRANSPORTATION p 339
4201 E Arkansas Ave 80222
Tel (303) 757-9557 SIC 9621

COLORADO FOOD PRODUCTS INC p 339
3600 S Yosemite St # 800 80237
Tel (303) 409-8400 SIC 5147

COLORADO ROCKIES BASEBALL CLUB LTD p 339
2001 Blake St 80205
Tel (303) 292-0200 SIC 7941

COLORADO SEMINARY p 339
2199 S Univ Blvd 80210
Tel (303) 871-2000 SIC 8221

COLORADO STATE UNIVERSITY SYSTEM p 339
475 17th St Ste 1550 80202
Tel (303) 534-6290 SIC 8221

COMMUNITY DEVELOPMENT INSTITUTE HEAD START p 348
10065 E Harvard Ave # 700 80231
Tel (720) 747-5100 SIC 8351

■ **COORS DISTRIBUTING CO** p 368
5400 Pecos St 80221
Tel (303) 433-6541 SIC 5181 4212

■ **CORAM LLC** p 368
555 17th St Ste 1500 80202
Tel (303) 292-4973 SIC 8082

COREPOWERYOGA MANAGEMENT LLC p 369
3001 Brighton Blvd # 269 80216
Tel (303) 813-9020 SIC 8741

■ **CORESITE LLC** p 369
1001 17th St Ste 500 80202
Tel (866) 777-2673 SIC 6798

▲ **CORESITE REALTY CORP** p 369
1001 17th St Ste 500 80202
Tel (866) 777-2673 SIC 6798

CRESTONE PEAK RESOURCES LLC p 392
370 17th St Ste 2170 80202
Tel (720) 410-8500 SIC 1381

CRITIGEN LLC p 393
7604 Tech Way Ste 300 80237
Tel (303) 706-0990 SIC 8748

CROWNE PLAZA DENVER p 396
1450 Glenarm Pl 80202
Tel (303) 573-1450 SIC 7011

▲ **DAVITA INC** p 416
2000 16th St 80202
Tel (303) 405-2100 SIC 8092 8093

DCP MIDSTREAM LLC p 418
370 17th St Ste 2500 80202
Tel (303) 633-2900 SIC 5172

DCP MIDSTREAM LP p 418
370 17th St Ste 2500 80202
Tel (303) 595-3331 SIC 4925

▲ **DCP MIDSTREAM PARTNERS LP** p 418
370 17th St Ste 2500 80202
Tel (303) 595-3331 SIC 4922 4924

DCT INDUSTRIAL TRUST INC p 419
518 17th St Ste 800 80202
Tel (303) 597-2400 SIC 6798

DENCO SALES CO p 428
55 S Yuma St 80223
Tel (303) 733-0607 SIC 5199 5084

DENVER BOARD OF WATER COMMISSIONERS p 429
1600 W 12th Ave 80204
Tel (303) 893-2444 SIC 4941

DENVER FOUNDATION p 429
55 Madison St Ste 800 80206
Tel (303) 300-1790 SIC 6732

DENVER HEALTH AND HOSPITALS AUTHORITY INC p 429
777 Bannock St 80204
Tel (720) 956-2580 SIC 8062

DENVER POST CORP p 429
1560 Broadway Fl 4 80202
Tel (303) 321-7012 SIC 2711

DENVER POST LLC p 429
101 W Colfax Ave 80202
Tel (303) 892-5000 SIC 2711

DENVER PUBLIC SCHOOLS p 429
1860 N Lincoln St 80203
Tel (720) 423-3200 SIC 8211

DENVER WHOLESALE FLORISTS CO p 429
4800 Dahlia St Ste A 80216
Tel (303) 399-0970 SIC 5193

DIVIDEND CAPITAL DIVERSIFIED PROPERTY FUND INC p 444
518 17th St Ste 1200 80202
Tel (303) 228-2200 SIC 6798

DUQUESNE ENERGY SERVCES LLC p 462
4949 S Syracuse St # 550 80237
Tel (832) 278-5980 SIC 2911 5142

■ **DVA HEALTHCARE RENAL CARE INC** p 463
2000 16th St 80202
Tel (253) 280-9501 SIC 8092

EASTERN COLORADO WELL SERVICE LLC p 472
1400 W 122nd Ave Ste 120 80234
Tel (719) 767-5100 SIC 1389

EMERALD OIL INC p 491
200 Columbine St Ste 500 80206
Tel (303) 595-5600 SIC 1311

ENCANA OIL & GAS (USA) INC p 495
370 17th St Ste 1700 80202
Tel (303) 623-2300 SIC 2911 1311

ENERGY CORP OF AMERICA p 497
4643 S Ulster St Ste 1100 80237
Tel (303) 694-2667
SIC 4924 4932 1382 4922 5172

ENSERCO ENERGY LLC p 500
1900 16th St Ste 450 80202
Tel (303) 568-3242 SIC 5172

ENSIGN UNITED STATES DRILLING INC p 500
410 17th St Ste 1200 80202
Tel (303) 292-1206 SIC 1381

■ **EVERGREEN RESOURCES INC** p 515
1401 17th St Ste 1200 80202
Tel (303) 298-8100 SIC 1311 1382 1381

EXECUTIVE OFFICE OF STATE OF COLORADO p 517
136 State Capitol Bldg 80203
Tel (303) 866-2471 SIC 9111 9223

▲ **EXTRACTION OIL & GAS INC** p 521
370 17th St Ste 5300 80202
Tel (720) 557-8300 SIC 1382

FAK INC p 526
10885 E 51st Ave 80239
Tel (303) 289-5433 SIC 4731

■ **FIDELITY EXPLORATION & PRODUCTION CO** p 540
1801 Calif St Ste 2500 80202
Tel (303) 893-3133 SIC 1382

FIDELITY NEWPORT HOLDINGS LLC p 541
400 W 48th Ave 80216
Tel (303) 296-2121 SIC 5812 2051 6719

FILLMORE CCA INVESTMENT LLC p 542
100 Fillmore St Ste 600 80206
Tel (720) 284-6400 SIC 7997

FMH MATERIAL HANDLING SOLUTIONS INC p 562
4105 Globeville Rd 80216
Tel (303) 292-5438 SIC 5084 7353 5013

FOOD BANK OF ROCKIES INC p 564
10700 E 45th Ave 80239
Tel (303) 371-9250 SIC 8322

FOUR WINDS INTERACTIVE LLC p 572
1221 N Broadway 80203
Tel (877) 204-6679 SIC 7372

FREIGHT ALL KINDS INC p 577
10885 E 51st Ave 80239
Tel (800) 321-7182 SIC 4731 4213

FRESHPACK PRODUCE INC p 579
5151 Bannock St Ste 12 80216
Tel (303) 412-6232 SIC 5148

FRONTIER AIRLINES HOLDINGS INC p 580
7001 Tower Rd 80249
Tel (720) 374-4200 SIC 4512

FRONTIER AIRLINES INC p 581
7001 Tower Rd 80249
Tel (720) 374-4200 SIC 4512

■ **FRONTIER REFINING & MARKETING LLC** p 581
8055 E Tufts Ave 80237
Tel (303) 694-0025 SIC 2911

FURNITURE LOW LLC p 585
1333 E 37th Ave 80205
Tel (303) 371-8560 SIC 6512

FURNITURE ROW LLC p 585
5641 Broadway 80216
Tel (303) 576-0787 SIC 5712

GATES CORP p 593
1551 Wewatta St 80202
Tel (303) 744-1911
SIC 3052 3089 3568 5084 4789

GATES GLOBAL LLC p 593
1551 Wewatta St 80202
Tel (303) 744-1911 SIC 1382

GENERAL AIR SERVICE & SUPPLY CO p 599
1105 Zuni St 80204
Tel (303) 892-7003
SIC 5169 5085 5084 5149

GENERAL NOVELTY LTD p 601
420 E 58th Ave Ste 200 80216
Tel (303) 292-5537 SIC 5947

GLOBAL TECHNOLOGY RESOURCES INC p 617
990 S Broadway Ste 300 80209
Tel (303) 455-8800 SIC 7373

GOODWILL INDUSTRIES OF DENVER p 624
6850 Federal Blvd 80221
Tel (303) 650-7700 SIC 8399

▲ **GUARANTY BANCORP** p 644
1331 17th St Ste 200 80202
Tel (303) 296-9600 SIC 6022

■ **GUARANTY BANK AND TRUST CO** p 644
1331 17th St Lbby 80202
Tel (303) 298-6977 SIC 6022

GUIRYS INC p 646
620 Canosa Ct 80204
Tel (720) 360-4840 SIC 5198 5231 5999

▲ **HALLADOR ENERGY CO** p 654
1660 Lincoln St Ste 2700 80264
Tel (303) 839-5504 SIC 1241 1311 1382

HAWKWOOD ENERGY LLC p 670
4582 S Ulster St Ste 500 80237
Tel (303) 823-4175 SIC 1382

■ **HCA-HEALTHONE LLC** p 672
4900 S Monaco St Ste 380 80237
Tel (303) 788-2500 SIC 8062

■ **HIGH SIERRA ENERGY LP** p 691
3773 Cherry Creek N Dr St 80209
Tel (303) 815-1010 SIC 5172

HOLLAND & HART LLP p 700
555 17th St Ste 3200 80202
Tel (303) 295-8000 SIC 8111

HOME BUYERS WARRANTY CORP p 703
10375 E Harvard Ave # 100 80231
Tel (720) 747-6000 SIC 6351 1531

HOSTING.COM INC p 710
900 Suth Broadway Ste 400 80209
Tel (720) 389-3800 SIC 7379

HSS INC p 715
900 S Broadway Ste 100 80209
Tel (303) 603-3000 SIC 8082 7381 7382

HVHTRANSPORTATION INC p 722
181 E 56th Ave Ste 200 80216
Tel (303) 292-3656 SIC 4213

HYLAND HILLS PARK & RECREATION DISTRICT p 724
8801 Pecos St 80260
Tel (303) 427-7873 SIC 7999

INDUSTRIAL INCOMETRUST INC p 740
518 17th St Ste 17 80202
Tel (303) 228-2200 SIC 6091

INTELLISOURCE LLC p 750
1899 Wynkoop St Ste 900 80202
Tel (303) 692-1100 SIC 8742

■ **INTERMOUNTAIN ELECTRIC INC** p 753
5050 Osage St Ste 500 80221
Tel (303) 733-7248 SIC 1542 8742 3671

▲ **INTRAWEST RESORTS HOLDINGS INC** p 760
1621 18th St Ste 300 80202
Tel (303) 749-8200 SIC 7011 7999 6531

▲ **INTREPID POTASH INC** p 760
707 17th St Ste 4200 80202
Tel (303) 296-3006 SIC 1474

JACKSON NATIONAL LIFE DISTRIBUTORS LLC p 774
7601 E Technology Way 80237
Tel (303) 488-3518 *SIC* 6311

■ JACOR BROADCASTING OF COLORADO INC p 775
4695 S Monaco St 80237
Tel (303) 631-2933 *SIC* 7313

■ JANUS CAPITAL CORP p 777
151 Detroit St 80206
Tel (303) 333-3863 *SIC* 6282

▲ JANUS CAPITAL GROUP INC p 778
151 Detroit St 80206
Tel (303) 333-3863 *SIC* 6282 8741

■ JANUS INTERNATIONAL HOLDING LLC p 778
151 Detroit St 80206
Tel (303) 333-3863 *SIC* 6719

■ JOHNS MANVILLE CORP p 790
717 17th St Ste 800 80202
Tel (303) 978-2000 *SIC* 2952 1761 1742

JONAH ENERGY LLC p 792
707 17th St Ste 2700 80202
Tel (720) 577-1000 *SIC* 1382

JUDICIARY COURTS OF STATE OF COLORADO p 796
1300 N Broadway Ste 1200 80203
Tel (303) 837-3741 *SIC* 9211

JUPITER I LLC p 797
9900 E 51st Ave 80238
Tel (303) 574-1115 *SIC* 5021

KAISER FOUNDATION HEALTH PLAN OF COLORADO p 800
10350 E Dakota Ave 80247
Tel (866) 239-1677 *SIC* 6324

KARCHER NORTH AMERICA INC p 804
4555 Airport Way Fl 4 80239
Tel (303) 762-1800 *SIC* 3635 5084

KINROSS GOLD USA INC p 821
5075 S Syracuse St 80237
Tel (775) 829-1666 *SIC* 1041 1044

KRG CAPITAL PARTNERS LLC p 830
1800 Larimer St Ste 2200 80202
Tel (303) 390-5001 *SIC* 6726 8742 6411

KROENKE SPORTS HOLDINGS LLC p 830
1000 Chopper Cir 80204
Tel (303) 405-1100 *SIC* 7941

KSL CAPITAL PARTNERS LLC p 831
100 Saint Paul St Ste 800 80206
Tel (720) 284-6400 *SIC* 6799

LAND TITLE GUARANTEE CO INC p 842
3033 E 1st Ave Ste 600 80206
Tel (303) 321-1880 *SIC* 6411

LENDERLIVE NETWORK INC p 855
710 S Ash St Ste 200 80246
Tel (303) 226-8000 *SIC* 4813 6163

LEPRINO FOODS CO p 857
1830 W 38th Ave 80211
Tel (303) 480-2600 *SIC* 2022

LIBERTY GLOBAL INC p 861
1550 Wewatta St Ste 1000 80202
Tel (303) 220-6600 *SIC* 4841 4813

LIBERTY OILFIELD SERVICES LLC p 862
950 17th St Ste 2000 80202
Tel (303) 515-2800 *SIC* 1382

LOCKHART GEOPHYSICAL CO p 873
1600 Broadway Ste 1660 80202
Tel (303) 592-5220 *SIC* 1382

MANAGEMENT SENIOR LLC MORNINGSTAR p 900
7555 E Hampden Ave # 501 80231
Tel (303) 750-5522 *SIC* 6513

■ MARKWEST ENERGY PARTNERS LP p 909
1515 Arapahoe St 80202
Tel (303) 925-9200 *SIC* 1321 4922 1389

■ MARKWEST HYDROCARBON LLC p 909
1515 Arapahoe St 80202
Tel (303) 290-8700 *SIC* 1321 4924

▲ MDC HOLDINGS INC p 933
4350 S Monaco St Ste 500 80237
Tel (303) 773-1100 *SIC* 1521 6162 7389

MEDIANEWS GROUP INC p 936
101 W Colfax Ave Ste 1100 80202
Tel (303) 954-6360 *SIC* 2711

MENTAL HEALTH CENTER OF DENVER p 943
4141 E Dickenson Pl 80222
Tel (303) 504-6501 *SIC* 8093

MERCY HOUSING INC p 947
1999 Broadway Ste 1000 80202
Tel (303) 830-3300 *SIC* 1522 6531

MERITAGE MIDSTREAM SERVICES II LLC p 949
1331 17th St Ste 1100 80202
Tel (303) 551-8150 *SIC* 1389

METRO WASTEWATER RECLAMATION DISTRICT p 955
6450 York St 80229
Tel (303) 286-3000 *SIC* 4952

METROPOLITAN STATE UNIVERSITY OF DENVER p 956
890 Auraria Pkwy 80204
Tel (303) 556-3030 *SIC* 8221

■ METWEST INC p 957
695 S Broadway 80209
Tel (303) 899-6000 *SIC* 8071

MILE HIGH EQUIPMENT LLC p 969
11100 E 45th Ave 80239
Tel (303) 576-2940 *SIC* 3585

▲ MOLSON COORS BREWING CO p 983
1801 Calif St Ste 4600 80202
Tel (303) 927-2337 *SIC* 2082

MSHC INC p 997
12005 E 45th Ave 80239
Tel (303) 455-2825 *SIC* 8741

▲ MUSCLEPHARM CORP p 1002
4721 Ironton St Unit A 80239
Tel (303) 396-6100 *SIC* 2023

NATIONAL JEWISH HEALTH p 1014
1400 Jackson St 80206
Tel (303) 388-4461 *SIC* 8062

NAVAJO EXPRESS INC p 1019
1400 W 64th Ave 80221
Tel (303) 287-3800 *SIC* 4213

NAVAJO SHIPPERS INC p 1019
1400 W 64th Ave 80221
Tel (303) 287-3800 *SIC* 4213

NEW ERA REALTY INC p 1030
2441 Eliot St 80211
Tel (303) 248-3519 *SIC* 6531

■ NEWFIELD PRODUCTION CO p 1037
1001 17th St Ste 2000 80202
Tel (303) 893-0102 *SIC* 1311

OAKWOOD HOMES LLC p 1071
4908 Tower Rd 80249
Tel (303) 486-8500 *SIC* 1521

OMAHA HOLDINGS LLC p 1083
1551 Wewatta St 80202
Tel (303) 744-1911
SIC 3052 3089 3568 5084 4789

OMAHA INTERMEDIATE HOLDING LLC p 1083
1551 Wewatta St 80202
Tel (303) 744-1911
SIC 3052 3089 3568 5084 4789

OMNITRAX INC p 1085
252 Clayton St Fl 4 80206
Tel (303) 398-4500 *SIC* 4013

OPTIV INC p 1090
1125 17th St Ste 1700 80202
Tel (303) 298-0600
SIC 5045 5065 6719 7381

OPTIV SECURITY INC p 1090
1125 17th St Ste 1700 80202
Tel (888) 732-9406
SIC 5045 7379 7382 5065

OUTDOOR CHANNEL HOLDINGS INC p 1098
1000 Chopper Cir 80204
Tel (951) 699-6991 *SIC* 4841 4833

P2 ACQUISITION LLC p 1103
216 16th St Ste 1700 80202
Tel (303) 390-9400 *SIC* 7389

P2 ENERGY SOLUTIONS INC p 1103
1670 Broadway Ste 2800 80202
Tel (303) 292-0990 *SIC* 1382

P2 NEWCO INC p 1103
216 16th St Ste 1700 80202
Tel (303) 390-9400 *SIC* 7389

PACIFIC ALLIANCE MEDICAL CENTER INC p 1104
2525 S Downing St 80210
Tel (303) 778-1955 *SIC* 8062

PCL CIVIL CONSTRUCTORS INC p 1124
2000 S Colo Blvd Ste 2-50 80222
Tel (303) 365-6500
SIC 1611 1622 1623 1629

PCL CONSTRUCTION ENTERPRISES INC p 1124
2000 S Colorado Blvd 2-500 80222
Tel (303) 365-6500 *SIC* 1542

PCL CONSTRUCTION SERVICES INC p 1124
2000 S Colorado Blvd 2-500 80222
Tel (303) 365-6500 *SIC* 1542 1541

PCL US HOLDINGS INC p 1124
2000 S Colorado Blvd 2-500 80222
Tel (303) 365-6591 *SIC* 1542 1611

▲ PDC ENERGY INC p 1124
1775 N Sherman St # 3000 80203
Tel (303) 860-5800 *SIC* 1311 1381

PEERLESS TYRE CO p 1127
5000 Kingston St 80239
Tel (303) 371-4300 *SIC* 5541 5531

■ PEPSI-COLA METROPOLITAN BOTTLING CO INC p 1134
3801 Brighton Blvd 80216
Tel (303) 292-9220 *SIC* 2086

PETROLEUM PLACE INC p 1139
1670 Broadway Ste 2800 80202
Tel (303) 515-5400 *SIC* 4813 7371

PINNACOL ASSURANCE p 1150
7501 E Lowry Blvd 80230
Tel (303) 361-4000 *SIC* 6331

PLATTE RIVER VENTURES LLC p 1155
200 Fillmore St Ste 200 80206
Tel (303) 292-7300 *SIC* 6799

■ POLICY STUDIES INC p 1159
1515 Wynkoop St Ste 400 80202
Tel (303) 863-0900 *SIC* 8741 8742 7371

PORTERCARE ADVENTIST HEALTH SYSTEM p 1162
2525 S Downing St 80210
Tel (303) 778-5736 *SIC* 8062

■ PROBUILD CO LLC p 1179
7595 E Technology Way # 500 80237
Tel (303) 262-8500 *SIC* 5211 5031

■ PROBUILD HOLDINGS LLC p 1179
7595 Tech Way Ste 500 80237
Tel (303) 262-8500 *SIC* 5031 5211

■ PROLOGIS p 1183
4545 Airport Way 80239
Tel (303) 375-9292 *SIC* 6798 6552

■ PSI SERVICES HOLDING INC p 1188
1515 Wynkoop St Ste 400 80202
Tel (303) 863-0900
SIC 8741 8742 7371 8748

■ PUBLIC SERVICE CO OF COLORADO p 1189
1800 Larimer St Ste 1100 80202
Tel (303) 571-7511 *SIC* 4911 4922 4924

QED INC p 1194
1661 W 3rd Ave 80223
Tel (303) 825-5011 *SIC* 5063

■ QEP ENERGY CO p 1195
1050 17th St Ste 800 80265
Tel (303) 672-6900
SIC 1311 1382 1389 5172

▲ QEP RESOURCES INC p 1195
1050 17th St Ste 800 80265
Tel (303) 672-6900 *SIC* 1311 1321 1382

QUIZNOS CORP p 1200
7595 E Tech Way Ste 200 80237
Tel (720) 359-3300 *SIC* 6794 5812

■ QWEST BUSINESS & GOVERNMENT SERVICES INC p 1201
1801 Calif St Ste 3800 80202
Tel (303) 391-8300
SIC 5999 1731 7629 7373 7371 7622

■ QWEST BUSINESS RESOURCES INC p 1201
1005 17th St 80202
Tel (303) 896-5025 *SIC* 7389 6512

■ QWEST CYBERSOLUTIONS LLC p 1201
1801 California St # 3800 80202
Tel (303) 296-2787 *SIC* 7375

■ QWEST GOVERNMENT SERVICES INC p 1201
931 14th St Ste 1000b 80202
Tel (303) 992-1400 *SIC* 4813 4812

■ QWEST SERVICES CORP p 1201
931 14th St Ste 1000b 80202
Tel (303) 992-1400 *SIC* 4813

▲ RE/MAX HOLDINGS INC p 1212
5075 S Syracuse St 80237
Tel (303) 770-5531 *SIC* 6531 6411

■ RE/MAX LLC p 1212
5075 S Syracuse St 80237
Tel (303) 770-5531 *SIC* 6531

REGIONAL TRANSPORTATION DISTRICT p 1219
1600 Blake St 80202
Tel (303) 628-9000 *SIC* 4111

REGIS 66 INC p 1220
4890 Lowell Blvd 80221
Tel (303) 455-6636 *SIC* 5541

REGIS UNIVERSITY p 1220
3333 Regis Blvd 80221
Tel (303) 458-4100 *SIC* 8221

RENAL CARE GROUP INC p 1223
1 N Broadway Ste 100a 80203
Tel (303) 765-1699 *SIC* 8082

▲ RESOLUTE ENERGY CORP p 1227
1700 N Lincoln St # 2800 80203
Tel (303) 534-4600 *SIC* 1311

■ RESOLUTE NATURAL RESOURCES CO LLC p 1227
1700 N Lincoln St # 2800 80203
Tel (303) 573-4886 *SIC* 1311

■ RICHMOND AMERICAN HOMES OF COLORADO INC p 1233
4350 S Monaco St 80237
Tel (303) 773-1100 *SIC* 1521

RK MECHANICAL INC p 1239
3800 Xanthia St 80238
Tel (303) 576-9696 *SIC* 1711 3498 3441

ROCKPILE ENERGY SERVICES LLC p 1245
1200 17th St Ste 2700 80202
Tel (303) 825-8170 *SIC* 1389

ROCKY QCD MOUNTAIN LLC p 1245
4770 E 51st Ave 80216
Tel (303) 399-6066 *SIC* 5141

ROCKY TEP MOUNTAIN LLC p 1245
1001 17th St Ste 1200 80202
Tel (303) 572-3900 *SIC* 5172

■ ROSE MEDICAL GROUP p 1250
4900 S Monaco St Ste 204 80237
Tel (303) 320-2101 *SIC* 8062 8011 8099

▲ ROYAL GOLD INC p 1254
1660 Wynkoop St Ste 1000 80202
Tel (303) 573-1660 *SIC* 6211

SAGE HOSPITALITY RESOURCES LLC p 1267
1575 Welton St Ste 300 80202
Tel (303) 595-7200 *SIC* 7011

SAINT JOSEPH HOSPITAL INC p 1269
1375 E 19th Ave 80218
Tel (303) 812-2000 *SIC* 8062

SANJEL (USA) INC p 1279
1630 Welton St Ste 400 80202
Tel (303) 893-6866 *SIC* 1389

SCHRYVER MEDICAL SALES AND MARKETING LLC p 1290
12075 E 45th Ave Ste 600 80239
Tel (303) 371-0073 *SIC* 8071 8011

SERVICE SYSTEMS ASSOCIATES INC p 1307
4699 Marion St 80216
Tel (417) 746-0242 *SIC* 5947 5812

SHAW CONSTRUCTION LLC p 1312
300 Kalamath St 80223
Tel (303) 825-4740 *SIC* 1542

SIEGEL OIL CO p 1320
1380 Zuni St 80204
Tel (303) 893-5273 *SIC* 5172 8734

▲ SM ENERGY CO p 1331
1775 N Sherman St # 1200 80203
Tel (303) 861-8140 *SIC* 1311

SMA AMERICA PRODUCTION LLC p 1331
3801 Havana St 80239
Tel (720) 347-6000 *SIC* 3433

SMALLEY & CO p 1332
861 S Jason St 80223
Tel (303) 777-3435 *SIC* 5169

■ SOURCEGAS LLC p 1342
1515 Wynkoop St Ste 500 80202
Tel (303) 243-3400 *SIC* 4924

SQUARETWO FINANCIAL CORP p 1362
4340 S Monaco St Fl 2 80237
Tel (877) 844-5715 *SIC* 7322

ST JOSEPH HOSPITAL INC p 1368
1375 E 19th Ave 80218
Tel (303) 837-7111 *SIC* 8062

■ ST MARY OPERATING CO p 1371
1775 N Sherman St # 1200 80203
Tel (303) 861-8140 *SIC* 1311

STATE BOARD FOR COMMUNITY COLLEGES AND OCCUPATIONAL EDUCATIONAL SYSTEM p 1380
9101 E Lowry Pl 80230
Tel (303) 595-1552 *SIC* 8222

STATE OF COLORADO p 1381
200 E Colfax Ave Ste 91 80203
Tel (303) 866-5000 *SIC* 9111

STURM FINANCIAL GROUP INC p 1395
3033 E 1st Ave Ste 300 80206
Tel (303) 394-5023 *SIC* 6282

SUMMIT MATERIALS CORPS I INC p 1399
1550 Wynkoop St Fl 3 80202
Tel (303) 893-0012 *SIC* 1542 1611

SUMMIT MATERIALS HOLDINGS II LLC p 1399
1550 Wynkoop St Fl 3 80202
Tel (303) 893-0012 *SIC* 1542 1611

SUMMIT MATERIALS HOLDINGS LLC p 1399
1550 Wynkoop St Fl 3 80202
Tel (303) 893-0012 *SIC* 1542 1611

SUMMIT MATERIALS HOLDINGS LP p 1399
1550 Wynkoop St Fl 3 80202
Tel (303) 893-0012 *SIC* 1542 1611

▲ SUMMIT MATERIALS INC p 1399
1550 Wynkoop St Fl 3 80202
Tel (303) 893-0012 *SIC* 1422 1622 1795

SUMMIT MATERIALS INTERMEDIATE HOLDINGS LLC p 1399
1550 Wynkoop St Fl 3 80202
Tel (303) 893-0012 *SIC* 1542 1611

SUMMIT MATERIALS LLC p 1399
1550 Wynkoop St Fl 3 80202
Tel (303) 893-0012 *SIC* 1542 1611

SUNCOR ENERGY (USA) INC p 1402
717 17th St Ste 2900 80202
Tel (303) 793-8000 *SIC* 2911

SYNERGY RESOURCES CORP p 1415
1625 Broadway Ste 300 80202
Tel (720) 616-4300 *SIC* 1381

SYNERGY SERVICES INC p 1415
4601 Dtc Blvd Ste 650 80237
Tel (303) 468-2070 *SIC* 7371

■ T2 MEDICAL INC p 1420
555 17th St Ste 1500 80202
Tel (303) 672-8631 *SIC* 8082

■ TIMKEN MOTOR & CRANE SERVICES LLC p 1455
4850 Moline St 80239
Tel (303) 623-8658
SIC 5063 1731 7694 3613 3536

TOTAL LONGTERM CARE INC p 1463
8950 E Lowry Blvd 80230
Tel (303) 832-1001 *SIC* 8322 8082

■ TOTAL RENAL CARE INC p 1463
2000 16th St 80202
Tel (253) 280-9501 *SIC* 8092

TRANSLOGIC CORP p 1472
10825 E 47th Ave 80239
Tel (303) 371-7770 *SIC* 3535

TRANSMONTAIGNE LLC p 1472
1670 Broadway Ste 3100 80202
Tel (303) 626-8200 *SIC* 5172

▲ TRANSMONTAIGNE PARTNERS LP p 1472
1670 Broadway Ste 3100 80202
Tel (303) 626-8200 *SIC* 4612 5171

TRANSMONTAIGNE PRODUCT SERVICES LLC p 1472
1670 Broadway Ste 3100 80202
Tel (303) 626-8200 *SIC* 4789

▲TRIANGLE PETROLEUM CORP p 1478
1200 17th St Ste 2500 80202
Tel (303) 260-7125 SIC 1311 1382

TRINIDAD/BENHAM CORP p 1481
3650 S Yosemite St # 300 80237
Tel (303) 220-1400
SIC 5149 5153 2034 2099

TRINIDAD/BENHAM HOLDING CO p 1481
3650 S Yosemite St # 300 80237
Tel (303) 220-1400 SIC 5153 5149

TUFF SHED INC p 1491
1777 S Harrison St # 600 80210
Tel (303) 753-8833 SIC 2452

UNITED STATES WELDING INC p 1514
600 S Santa Fe Dr 80223
Tel (303) 777-2475
SIC 5169 5084 5085 5047 7359

UNIVERSITY OF COLORADO FOUNDATION p 1521
1800 N Grant St Ste 725 80203
Tel (303) 813-7935 SIC 8399

UNIVERSITY OF COLORADO HEALTH AND WELFARE TRUST p 1521
1800 N Grant St Ste 800 80203
Tel (303) 860-5600 SIC 6733

UNIVERSITY OF COLORADO HOSPITAL AUTHORITY p 1521
4200 E 9th Ave 80220
Tel (720) 848-0000 SIC 8062

VALIANT PRODUCTS CORP p 1540
2727 W 5th Ave 80204
Tel (303) 892-1234
SIC 5131 5023 7389 2511 2599 1752

VECTRA BANK COLORADO NA p 1546
2000 S Colorado Blvd Towe Tower 80222
Tel (720) 947-7700 SIC 6022

VOICE MEDIA GROUP INC p 1564
969 N Broadway 80203
Tel (303) 296-7744 SIC 6719

▲ WARREN RESOURCES INC p 1577
1331 17th St Ste 720 80202
Tel (720) 403-8125 SIC 1311

WESTERN DISTRIBUTING CO p 1598
4955 Bannock St 80216
Tel (303) 388-5755 SIC 5181 5182

■ WESTERN GAS RESOURCES INC p 1598
1099 18th St 80202
Tel (303) 452-5603
SIC 4923 4925 1311 5172

WESTERN PAPER DISTRIBUTORS INC p 1599
11551 E 45th Ave Unit A 80239
Tel (303) 371-8710 SIC 5113 5111 5169

WESTERN SUGAR COOPERATIVE p 1600
7555 E Hampden Ave # 600 80231
Tel (303) 830-3939 SIC 2063

▲ WHITEWAVE FOODS CO p 1606
1225 17th St Ste 1000 80202
Tel (303) 635-4500 SIC 2026 2023 2021

■ WHITING CANADIAN HOLDING CO ULC p 1606
1700 Broadway Ste 2300 80290
Tel (303) 837-1661 SIC 1381

■ WHITING OIL AND GAS CORP p 1607
1700 Broadway Ste 2300 80290
Tel (303) 837-1661 SIC 1311

▲ WHITING PETROLEUM CORP p 1607
1700 Broadway Ste 2300 80290
Tel (303) 837-1661 SIC 1311 1382

WYOMING TRANSACTIONS INC p 1630
2373 Cntl Pk Blvd Ste 100 80238
Tel (303) 803-1397 SIC 8748 7929

YES MANAGEMENT p 1635
1900 16th St Ste 950 80202
Tel (303) 483-7300 SIC 6798

DURANGO, CO

AKA ENERGY GROUP LLC p 41
65 Mercado St Ste 250 81301
Tel (970) 764-6650 SIC 1389

CATHOLIC HEALTH INITIATIVES COLORADO FOUNDATION p 266
1010 Three Springs Blvd 81301
Tel (970) 247-4311 SIC 8062

CROSSFIRE LLC p 394
820 Airport Rd 81303
Tel (970) 884-4869 SIC 1389

LA PLATA ELECTRIC ASSOCIATION INC p 835
45 Stewart St 81303
Tel (970) 247-5786 SIC 4911

PEAK EXPLORATION & PRODUCTION LLC p 1125
1910 Main Ave 81301
Tel (970) 247-1500 SIC 1382

■ UNITED PIPELINE SYSTEMS USA INC p 1510
135 Turner Dr 81303
Tel (970) 259-0354 SIC 1623

EAGLE, CO

AUSTEN GROUP LLC p 132
679 Founders Ave 81631
Tel (970) 331-2965 SIC 8732

EATON, CO

AGFINITY INC p 34
260 Factory Rd 80615
Tel (970) 454-4000
SIC 5172 2048 7549 5191

ENGLEWOOD, CO

ADVANTEDGE BUSINESS GROUP LLC p 27
9777 Pyramid Ct Ste 220 80112
Tel (303) 734-9424 SIC 8741 7291 7363

▲ AIR METHODS CORP p 39
7301 S Peoria St 80112
Tel (303) 749-1330 SIC 4522

ALACER MANAGEMENT CORP p 43
9635 Maroon Cir Ste 300 80112
Tel (303) 292-1299 SIC 1041

AMERICAN FURNITURE WAREHOUSE CO INC p 73
8820 American Way 80112
Tel (303) 799-9044 SIC 5712

ARCHSTONE COMMUNITIES LLC p 105
9200 E Panorama Cir # 400 80112
Tel (303) 708-5959 SIC 6798 6513

■ ARROW ENTERPRISE COMPUTING SOLUTIONS INC p 113
7459 S Lima St Bldg 2 80112
Tel (303) 824-7650 SIC 5045

BEHAVIORAL HEALTHCARE INC p 168
155 Inverness Dr W 80112
Tel (720) 490-4400 SIC 8099

BEP COLORADO RESTAURANTS LLC p 174
304 Inverness Way S # 305 80112
Tel (303) 671-7333 SIC 5812

■ BLOCKBUSTER LLC p 189
9601 S Meridian Blvd 80112
Tel (702) 262-0703 SIC 7841 5735

CATHOLIC HEALTH INITIATIVES p 266
198 Inverness Dr W 80112
Tel (303) 298-9100 SIC 8062 8051 8741

CATHOLIC HEALTH INITIATIVES COLORADO p 266
198 Inverness Dr W 80112
Tel (303) 290-6500 SIC 8741 8062

CENTURA HEALTH CORP p 281
188 Inverness Dr W # 500 80112
Tel (303) 290-6500 SIC 8069

CH2M HILL COMPANIES LTD p 286
9191 S Jamaica St 80112
Tel (303) 771-0900 SIC 8711

CH2M HILL CONSTRUCTORS INC p 286
9189 S Jamaica St 80112
Tel (720) 286-2000 SIC 8711

CH2M HILL INC p 286
9191 S Jamaica St 80112
Tel (303) 771-0900 SIC 8711

■ CHEVRON MINING INC p 296
116 Invrneco Dr E Ste 207 80112
Tel (303) 930-3600 SIC 1221

CLARK-NEXSEN/CH2M HILL p 322
9191 S Jamaica St 80112
Tel (303) 771-0900 SIC 8711

CRAIG HOSPITAL p 388
3425 S Clarkson St 80113
Tel (303) 789-8000 SIC 8069

▲ CSG SYSTEMS INTERNATIONAL INC p 397
9555 Maroon Cir 80112
Tel (303) 200-2000 SIC 7374

DASCO INC p 413
9785 Maroon Cir Ste 110 80112
Tel (303) 350-5050 SIC 5191

DESTINATION RESIDENCES LLC p 432
10333 E Dry Creek Rd 80112
Tel (303) 799-3830 SIC 7011 8741

■ DISH DBS CORP p 442
9601 S Meridian Blvd 80112
Tel (303) 723-1000 SIC 4841

▲ DISH NETWORK CORP p 442
9601 S Meridian Blvd 80112
Tel (303) 723-1000 SIC 4841

■ DISH NETWORK LLC p 442
9601 S Meridian Blvd 80112
Tel (303) 723-1000 SIC 1799

■ DISH NETWORK SERVICE LLC p 442
9601 S Meridian Blvd 80112
Tel (303) 723-1000 SIC 1799 4841

■ DISH ORBITAL CORP p 442
9601 S Meridian Blvd 80112
Tel (303) 723-1000 SIC 3663 4841

■ ECHOSPHERE LLC p 475
9601 S Meridian Blvd 80112
Tel (303) 723-1000 SIC 5065 4841

▲ ECHOSTAR CORP p 475
100 Inverness Ter E 80112
Tel (303) 706-4000 SIC 3663 4841

■ ECHOSTAR SATELLITE SERVICES LLC p 475
100 Inverness Ter E 80112
Tel (866) 359-8804 SIC 4841

FOODSERVICEWAREHOUSE.COM LLC p 564
84 Inverness Cir E 80112
Tel (303) 801-0629 SIC 5046

■ GAMBRO INC p 590
9540 Maroon Cir Unit 400 80112
Tel (800) 525-2623 SIC 6719

■ GAMBRO RENAL PRODUCTS INC p 590
9540 Maroon Cir Unit 400 80112
Tel (303) 222-6500 SIC 3842

HUGHES SATELLITE SYSTEMS CORP p 717
100 Inverness Ter E 80112
Tel (303) 706-4000 SIC 4813

IHS GLOBAL INC p 731
15 Inverness Way E 80112
Tel (303) 790-0600
SIC 7299 8732 8748 7375 7373

IHS HOLDING INC p 731
15 Inverness Way E 80112
Tel (303) 790-0600
SIC 7299 8732 8748 7375

IHS INC p 731
15 Inverness Way E 80112
Tel (303) 790-0600
SIC 7299 8732 8748 7375

▲ INNOSPEC INC p 744
8310 S Valley Hwy Ste 350 80112
Tel (303) 792-5554 SIC 2911 2869

■ JEPPESEN SANDERSON INC p 783
55 Inverness Dr E 80112
Tel (303) 799-9090 SIC 2741 2731 8748

LGI INTERNATIONAL INC p 860
12300 Liberty Blvd 80112
Tel (720) 875-5800 SIC 4841

LIBERTY BROADBAND CORP p 861
12300 Liberty Blvd 80112
Tel (720) 875-5700 SIC 4841 4899

▲ LIBERTY INTERACTIVE CORP p 862
12300 Liberty Blvd 80112
Tel (720) 875-5300 SIC 4841 5961

■ LIBERTY INTERACTIVE LLC p 862
12300 Liberty Blvd 80112
Tel (720) 875-5400
SIC 5961 4841 7819 4813

▲ LIBERTY MEDIA CORP p 862
12300 Liberty Blvd 80112
Tel (720) 875-5400 SIC 4841

■ LIBERTY QVC HOLDING LLC p 862
12300 Liberty Blvd 80112
Tel (484) 701-3777 SIC 4841 5961

▲ LIBERTY TRIPADVISOR HOLDINGS INC p 862
12300 Liberty Blvd 80112
Tel (720) 875-5200 SIC 7374

■ LIBERTY USA HOLDINGS LLC p 863
12300 Liberty Blvd 80112
Tel (720) 875-5300 SIC 4841

MASTERS INSURANCE AGENCY INC p 918
9785 Maroon Cir Ste 340 80112
Tel (303) 814-1596 SIC 6411 6331 6311

OPERATIONS MANAGEMENT INTERNATIONAL INC p 1089
9193 S Jamaica St Ste 400 80112
Tel (303) 740-0019 SIC 4952 4941

OURAY SPORTSWEAR LLC p 1098
1201 W Mansfield Ave 80110
Tel (303) 798-4035 SIC 5091

■ PENFORD CORP p 1128
345 Inverness Dr S # 200 80112
Tel (303) 649-1900 SIC 2046 2869

PRIMA MARKETING LLC p 1174
21 Inverness Way E 80112
Tel (303) 436-9510 SIC 5411 5541

■ PULTE MORTGAGE LLC p 1192
7390 S Iola St 80112
Tel (303) 740-8800 SIC 6162

SPORTS AUTHORITY INC p 1359
1050 W Hampden Ave 80110
Tel (303) 200-5050 SIC 5941

▲ STARZ p 1379
8900 Liberty Cir 80112
Tel (720) 852-7700 SIC 4841 4813

■ STARZ ENTERTAINMENT LLC p 1380
8900 Liberty Cir 80112
Tel (720) 852-7700 SIC 7812

■ STARZ LLC p 1380
8900 Liberty Cir 80112
Tel (720) 852-7700 SIC 7812

STONEBRIDGE REALTY ADVISORS INC p 1391
9100 E Panorama Dr # 300 80112
Tel (303) 785-3100 SIC 7011

▲ TELETECH HOLDINGS INC p 1435
9197 S Peoria St 80112
Tel (303) 397-8100 SIC 7389

■ TELETECH SERVICES CORP p 1435
9197 S Peoria St 80112
Tel (303) 397-8100 SIC 7389

TIC HOLDINGS INC p 1452
9780 Pyramid Ct Ste 100 80112
Tel (970) 879-2561
SIC 1541 1629 1623 1542

■ TRIZETTO CORP p 1483
9655 Maroon Cir 80112
Tel (303) 495-7000 SIC 7373 8742

TSA STORES INC p 1489
1050 W Hampden Ave 80110
Tel (303) 200-5050 SIC 5941 4832

UNITEDGLOBALCOM INC p 1515
12300 Liberty Blvd 80112
Tel (303) 220-6676 SIC 8999 4813

■ VIASAT COMMUNICATIONS INC p 1554
349 Inverness Dr S 80112
Tel (720) 493-6000 SIC 4899

WELLDYNE INC p 1589
7472 S Tucson Way Ste 100 80112
Tel (888) 479-2000 SIC 8099

▲ WESTERN UNION CO p 1600
12500 Belford Ave 80112
Tel (866) 405-5012 SIC 6099

■ WESTERN UNION FINANCIAL SERVICES INC p 1600
12510 Belford Ave M22b3 80112
Tel (720) 332-1000 SIC 6099

▲ WESTMORELAND COAL CO p 1601
9540 Maroon Cir Unit 200 80112
Tel (855) 922-6463 SIC 1221 4911

■ WESTMORELAND RESOURCE PARTNERS LP p 1602
9540 Maroon Cir Unit 200 80112
Tel (614) 643-0337 SIC 1221

WIDEOPENWEST FINANCE LLC p 1608
7887 E Belleview Ave 80111
Tel (303) 663-0771 SIC 4841

WIDEOPENWEST NETWORKS LLC p 1608
7887 E Belleview Ave 80111
Tel (720) 479-3558 SIC 4813

YOUTH FOR CHRIST/USA INC p 1639
7670 S Vaughn Ct Ste 100 80112
Tel (303) 843-9000 SIC 8661

EVERGREEN, CO

ANATOLIA MINERALS DEVELOPMENT LTD p 88
3721 Hwy 74 Ste 14 80439
Tel (303) 670-9945 SIC 1382 8748

FORT COLLINS, CO

▲ ADVANCED ENERGY INDUSTRIES INC p 25
1625 Sharp Point Dr 80525
Tel (970) 221-4670 SIC 3679 3629 3625

AVAGO TECHNOLOGIES WIRELESS (USA) INC p 135
4380 Ziegler Rd 80525
Tel (970) 288-2575 SIC 3674

BANK OF COLORADO p 151
1609 E Harmony Rd 80525
Tel (970) 206-1159 SIC 6022

CENTER PARTNERS INC p 276
4401 Innovation Dr 80525
Tel (970) 206-9000 SIC 7379 8742 7363

CITY OF FORT COLLINS p 314
215 N Mason St 80524
Tel (970) 221-6770 SIC 9111

COLORADO STATE UNIVERSITY p 339
6003 Campus Delivery 80523
Tel (970) 491-1372 SIC 8221

COUNTY OF LARIMER p 379
200 W Oak St Ste 4000 80521
Tel (970) 498-5930 SIC 9111

FIRST NATIONAL BANK p 548
205 W Oak St 80521
Tel (970) 482-4861 SIC 6021

FORNEY INDUSTRIES INC p 568
2057 Vermont Dr 80525
Tel (800) 521-6038 SIC 5084

LANDMARK EVENT STAFFING SERVICES INC p 842
4131 Harbor Walk Dr 80525
Tel (714) 293-4248 SIC 7381 7389

LIGHTSOURCE CREATIVE SERVICES INC p 865
121 La Porte Ave 80524
Tel (970) 224-2806 SIC 7336

NEENAN CO LLLP p 1024
3325 S Timberline Rd # 100 80525
Tel (970) 493-8747 SIC 1542

NEW BELGIUM BREWING CO INC p 1029
500 Linden St 80524
Tel (970) 221-0524 SIC 2082

OTTER PRODUCTS LLC p 1098
209 S Meldrum St 80521
Tel (970) 493-8446 SIC 3089

PLATTE RIVER POWER AUTHORITY (INC) p 1155
2000 E Horsetooth Rd 80525
Tel (970) 229-5332 SIC 4911

POUDRE SCHOOL DISTRICT p 1164
2407 Laporte Ave 80521
Tel (970) 482-7420 SIC 8211

POUDRE VALLEY HEALTH CARE INC p 1164
2315 E Harmony Rd Ste 200 80528
Tel (970) 495-7000 SIC 8062

TOLMAR HOLDING INC p 1459
701 Centre Ave 80526
Tel (970) 212-4500 SIC 2834

TOLMAR INC p 1459
701 Centre Ave 80526
Tel (970) 212-4500 SIC 2834

WATER PIK INC p 1581
1730 E Prospect Rd 80525
Tel (800) 525-2774 SIC 3432 3843

▲ WOODWARD INC p 1623
1081 Woodward Way 80524
Tel (970) 482-5811
SIC 3625 3629 3492 3519

FORT LUPTON, CO

GOLDEN ALUMINUM INC p 620
1405 14th St 80621
Tel (800) 838-1004 SIC 3353

GRAY OIL CO INC p 632
804 Denver Ave 80621
Tel (303) 857-2288 SIC 5171 5541 5411

LUPTON VENTURES INC p 886
1405 14th St 80621
Tel (303) 659-9767 SIC 3353

FORT MORGAN, CO

NE COLORADO CELLULAR INC p 1022
1224 W Platte Ave 80701
Tel (970) 467-3137 SIC 4812

FOUNTAIN, CO

EL PASO COUNTY SCHOOL DISTRICT 8 p 483
10665 Jimmy Camp Rd 80817
Tel (719) 382-1300 SIC 8211

FREDERICK, CO

■ **PCS FERGUSON INC** p 1124
3771 Eureka Way 80516
Tel (720) 407-3550 SIC 3533 5084

GLENWOOD SPRINGS, CO

ALPINE BANK p 60
2200 Grand Ave 81601
Tel (970) 945-2424 SIC 6022

HOLY CROSS ELECTRIC ASSOCIATION INC p 702
3799 Highway 82 81601
Tel (970) 945-5491 SIC 4911

VALLEY VIEW HOSPITAL ASSOCIATION p 1541
1906 Blake Ave 81601
Tel (970) 945-6535 SIC 8062

GOLDEN, CO

BAILEY CO LLLP p 145
601 Corporate Cir 80401
Tel (303) 384-0200 SIC 5812

■ **BLACK HILLS GAS HOLDINGS LLC** p 187
600 12th St Ste 300 80401
Tel (303) 243-3400 SIC 4924

■ **COLEMAN CO INC** p 336
1767 Denver West Blvd # 200 80401
Tel (316) 832-2653 SIC 3086 5941

COLEMAN NATURAL FOODS LLC p 336
1767 Denver West Blvd # 200 80401
Tel (303) 468-2500 SIC 2011 5147 0251

■ **COORS BREWING CO** p 367
17735 W 32nd Ave 80401
Tel (303) 279-6565 SIC 2082

COORSTEK LLC p 368
16000 Table Mountain Pkwy 80403
Tel (303) 271-7000
SIC 3264 3053 3081 3082 3545

COUNTY OF JEFFERSON p 378
100 Jefferson County Pkwy 80401
Tel (303) 271-8585 SIC 9111

COUNTY OF JEFFERSON p 378
100 Jefferson County Pkwy 80419
Tel (303) 216-2987 SIC 4941

ERIE COUNTY INVESTMENT CO p 508
601 Corporate Cir 80401
Tel (303) 384-0200
SIC 5812 6794 6531 6552 1542 1521

GUY F ATKINSON CONSTRUCTION LLC p 648
350 Indiana St Ste 600 80401
Tel (303) 985-1660 SIC 1611

JACOBS ENTERTAINMENT INC p 775
17301 W Colfax Ave # 250 80401
Tel (303) 215-5196 SIC 7993 7948

JEFFERSON COUNTY SCHOOL DISTRICT NO R-1 p 781
1829 Denver West Dr # 27 80401
Tel (303) 982-6500 SIC 8211

STEVINSON AUTOMOTIVE INC p 1388
1726 Cole Blvd Ste 300 80401
Tel (303) 232-2006 SIC 5511

■ **STRANDED OIL RESOURCES CORP** p 1392
110 N Rubey Dr Unit 120 80403
Tel (512) 279-7870 SIC 8742

TRUSTEES OF COLORADO SCHOOL OF MINES p 1487
1500 Illinois St 80401
Tel (303) 273-3000 SIC 8221

WG GLOBAL LLC p 1604
603 Park Point Dr Ste 200 80401
Tel (303) 395-2100
SIC 3569 3559 3629 3625 3443 3412

WGH HOLDING CORP p 1604
350 Indiana St Ste 610 80401
Tel (706) 884-6884 SIC 3533

GRAND JUNCTION, CO

COLORADO MESA UNIVERSITY p 339
1100 North Ave 81501
Tel (970) 248-1020 SIC 8221

FCI CONSTRUCTORS INC p 533
3070 I 70 Bus Loop Ste A 81504
Tel (970) 434-9093 SIC 1542 1541

MESA COUNTY VALLEY SCHOOL DISTRICT 51 (INC) p 951
2115 Grand Ave 81501
Tel (970) 254-5100 SIC 8211

MONUMENT OIL CO p 987
560 Colorado Ave 81501
Tel (970) 245-3440 SIC 5172

OLDCASTLE SW GROUP INC p 1082
2273 River Rd 81505
Tel (970) 243-4900 SIC 1611 3273 5032

ROCKY MOUNTAIN HEALTH MAINTENANCE ORGANIZATION INC p 1245
2775 Crossroads Blvd 81506
Tel (970) 243-7050 SIC 6321

ST MARYS HOSPITAL & MEDICAL CENTER INC p 1371
2635 N 7th St 81501
Tel (970) 298-2013 SIC 8062

GREELEY, CO

AGU US HOLDINGS INC p 36
7251 W 4th St 80634
Tel (970) 356-4400 SIC 2879 5191

■ **ANIMAL HEALTH INTERNATIONAL INC** p 91
822 7th St Ste 740 80631
Tel (970) 353-2600
SIC 5122 5047 5999 5191 5083 5154

COUNTY OF WELD p 383
1150 O St 80631
Tel (970) 356-4000 SIC 9111

GRANITE HENSEL PHELPS JV p 631
420 6th Ave 80631
Tel (970) 352-6565 SIC 1541 1542

HENSEL PHELPS CONSTRUCTION CO p 684
420 6th Ave 80631
Tel (970) 352-6565
SIC 1542 1521 1771 1522 1541 1622

HENSEL PHELPS SOLTEK JV p 685
420 6th Ave 80631
Tel (970) 352-6565 SIC 1542 1541

HENSEL PHELPS-GRANITE JV p 685
420 6th Ave 80631
Tel (970) 352-6565
SIC 1541 1542 1629 1611

JBS CARRIERS INC p 779
2401 2nd Ave 80631
Tel (866) 298-4573 SIC 4213

JBS FIVE RIVERS CATTLE FEEDING LLC p 779
1770 Promontory Cir 80634
Tel (970) 506-8000 SIC 0211

JBS USA FOOD CO HOLDINGS p 780
1770 Promontory Cir 80634
Tel (970) 506-8000 SIC 2011

JBS USA HOLDINGS LLC p 780
1770 Promontory Cir 80634
Tel (970) 506-8000 SIC 2011 5147

K2D INC p 799
2035 2nd Ave 80631
Tel (970) 313-4400 SIC 5147

NORTH COLORADO MEDICAL CENTER p 1052
1801 16th St 80631
Tel (970) 352-4121 SIC 8011

NORTH COLORADO MEDICAL CENTER FOUNDATION INC p 1052
1801 16th St 80631
Tel (970) 356-9020 SIC 8062

PACKERLAND HOLDINGS INC p 1107
1770 Promontory Cir 80634
Tel (970) 506-8000 SIC 2011 4213

▲ **PILGRIMS PRIDE CORP** p 1148
1770 Promontory Cir 80634
Tel (970) 506-8000
SIC 2015 0254 0252 2048 5999

PROTEIN PROVIDERS INC p 1185
1770 Promontory Cir 80634
Tel (970) 506-7678 SIC 5147 5146

S&C RESALE CO p 1263
1770 Promontory Cir 80634
Tel (970) 506-8000 SIC 5147 5421

SWIFT PORK CO p 1412
1770 Promontory Cir 80634
Tel (970) 506-8000 SIC 5154

UNIVERSITY OF NORTHERN COLORADO p 1524
501 20th St 80639
Tel (970) 351-1890 SIC 8221

WELD COUNTY SCHOOL DISTRICT 6 p 1589
1025 9th Ave Ste Main 80631
Tel (970) 348-6000 SIC 8211

GREENWOOD VILLAGE, CO

ADELPHIA COMMUNICATIONS CORP p 22
5613 Dtc Pkwy Ste 850 80111
Tel (814) 274-6279 SIC 4899

■ **AECOM ENERGY & CONSTRUCTION INC** p 28
6200 S Quebec St 80111
Tel (303) 228-3000
SIC 1622 1629 1081 4953

■ **AMERICAN MEDICAL RESPONSE INC** p 76
6363 S Fiddlers Green Cir # 1400 80111
Tel (303) 495-1200 SIC 4119

▲ **ASCENT CAPITAL GROUP INC** p 116
5251 Dtc Pkwy Ste 1000 80111
Tel (303) 628-5600 SIC 3822 7382

BELLCO CREDIT UNION p 170
7600 E Orchard Rd 400n 80111
Tel (303) 689-7800 SIC 6061

▲ **CENTURY COMMUNITIES INC** p 282
8390 E Crescent Pkwy # 650 80111
Tel (303) 770-8300 SIC 1521

CHERRY CREEK MORTGAGE CO INC p 294
7600 E Orchard Rd 250n 80111
Tel (303) 320-4040 SIC 6162

CHERRY CREEK RADIO LLC p 294
7400 E Orchard Rd # 2800 80111
Tel (303) 468-6500 SIC 4832

CHERRY CREEK SCHOOL DISTRICT 5 p 294
4700 S Yosemite St # 223 80111
Tel (303) 773-1184 SIC 8211

▲ **CIBER INC** p 306
6312 S Fiddlers Green Cir 320n 80111
Tel (303) 220-0100 SIC 7373 7379

■ **CIGNA HEALTHCARE OF COLORADO INC** p 306
8525 E Orchard Rd 80111
Tel (303) 305-1000 SIC 6324

COBANK ACB p 332
6340 S Fiddlers Green Cir 80111
Tel (303) 740-6527 SIC 6111 7359 6159

■ **ENVISION HEALTHCARE CORP** p 504
6363 S Fiddlers Green Cir # 1400 80111
Tel (303) 495-1200 SIC 4119 7363

▲ **ENVISION HEALTHCARE HOLDINGS INC** p 504
6200 S Syracuse Way 80111
Tel (303) 495-1200 SIC 8062 4119

FASCORE LLC p 530
8515 E Orchard Rd 80111
Tel (303) 737-3600 SIC 8741

FIRST DATA HOLDINGS INC p 546
5775 Dtc Blvd Ste 100 80111
Tel (303) 967-8000
SIC 6099 7375 7389 6153

FLAGSHIP FOOD GROUP LLC p 554
6455 S Yosemite St # 140 80111
Tel (303) 954-4979 SIC 2038

GERALD H PHIPPS INC p 608
5995 Greenwood Ste 100 80111
Tel (303) 571-5377 SIC 1542 3399

GIESEN RESTAURANT ENTERPRISES LLC p 611
10 E Belleview Way 80121
Tel (303) 761-7498 SIC 5812

GREAT-WEST LIFE & ANNUITY INSURANCE CO p 635
8515 E Orchard Rd 80111
Tel (303) 737-3000 SIC 6211 6311

GREAT-WEST LIFECO US INC p 635
8515 E Orchard Rd 80111
Tel (303) 737-3000 SIC 6311

GWFS EQUITIES INC p 648
8515 E Orchard Rd 80111
Tel (303) 737-3817 SIC 6211

GWL&A FINANCIAL INC p 648
8515 E Orchard Rd 80111
Tel (303) 737-3000 SIC 6211 6311

■ **INTEGRATED PAYMENT SYSTEMS INC** p 749
6200 S Quebec St Ste 320b 80111
Tel (402) 951-7008 SIC 6099

IQNAVIGATOR INC p 764
6465 Greenwood Plaza Blvd 80111
Tel (303) 563-1500 SIC 7371 7361

ISEC INC p 766
6000 Greenwood Plaza Blvd # 200 80111
Tel (410) 381-6049 SIC 1751

KENTWOOD DTC LLC p 813
5690 Dtc Blvd Ste 600w 80111
Tel (303) 773-3399 SIC 6531 7389

M&C HOTEL INTERESTS INC p 890
6560 Greenwood Plaza Blvd # 300 80111
Tel (303) 779-2000
SIC 8741 8712 6321 6331 7389

M&C HOTEL INTERESTS INC p 890
7600 E Orchard Rd 230s 80111
Tel (303) 779-2000 SIC 7011

▲ **MOLYCORP INC** p 983
5619 Denver Tech Ste 80111
Tel (303) 843-8040 SIC 1099

▲ **NATIONAL BANK HOLDINGS CORP** p 1010
7800 E Orchard Rd Ste 300 80111
Tel (720) 529-3336 SIC 6021

NATIONAL STORAGE AFFILIATES TRUST p 1016
5200 Dtc Pkwy Ste 200 80111
Tel (720) 630-2600 SIC 6798

■ **NEWMONT GOLD CO** p 1038
6363 S Fiddlers Green Cir 80111
Tel (303) 863-7414 SIC 1041

▲ **NEWMONT MINING CORP** p 1038
6363 S Fiddlers Green Cir # 800 80111
Tel (303) 863-7414 SIC 1041 1021

■ **NEWMONT USA LIMITED** p 1038
6363 Sout Fidd Gree Cir 80111
Tel (303) 863-7414 SIC 1041 1021

NEXTMEDIA OPERATING INC p 1041
6312 S Fiddlers Green Cir # 2 80111
Tel (303) 694-9118 SIC 4832

PARKS XANTERRA & RESORTS INC p 1116
6312 S Fiddlers Green Cir 600n 80111
Tel (303) 600-3400 SIC 7011 5947 5812

▲ **RED ROBIN GOURMET BURGERS INC** p 1216
6312 S Fiddlers 80111
Tel (303) 846-6000 SIC 5812 6794

■ **RED ROBIN INTERNATIONAL INC** p 1216
6312 S Fiddlers Green Cir 200n 80111
Tel (303) 846-6000
SIC 5812 6794 5813 5087

REPUBLIC FINANCIAL CORP p 1225
5251 Dtc Pkwy Ste 300 80111
Tel (800) 596-3608 SIC 6726 6159

RICHFIELD HOLDINGS INC p 1233
5775 Dtc Blvd Ste 300 80111
Tel (303) 220-2000
SIC 6321 8712 7389 6331 7011

RICHFIELD HOSPITALITY INC p 1233
7600 E Orchard Rd 230s 80111
Tel (303) 220-2000 SIC 8741

RIO TINTO AMERICA INC p 1236
8051 E Maplewood Ave # 100 80111
Tel (303) 713-5000 SIC 3412 5082 1044

STARMARK MANAGEMENT HOLDINGS LLC p 1379
6140 Greenwood Plaza Blvd 80111
Tel (303) 866-0800 SIC 7997

▲ **STARTEK INC** p 1379
8200 E Maplewood Ave # 100 80111
Tel (303) 262-4500 SIC 7374 7379 8742

■ **STARTEK USA INC** p 1379
8200 E Maplewood Ave # 100 80111
Tel (303) 262-4150 SIC 7372 7379 5045

US BORAX INC p 1531
8051 E Maplewood Ave # 100 80111
Tel (303) 713-5000 SIC 1474 2819

USI COLORADO LLC p 1535
6501 S Fiddlers Ste 100 80111
Tel (800) 873-8500 SIC 6411

VILLAGE HOMES OF COLORADO INC p 1557
8480 E Orchard Rd # 1000 80111
Tel (303) 795-1976 SIC 1521

VIRTELA TECHNOLOGY SERVICES INC p 1560
5680 Greenwood Plaza Blvd 80111
Tel (720) 475-4000 SIC 4813

■ **WASTE MANAGEMENT OF COLORADO INC** p 1580
5500 S Quebec St Ste 250 80111
Tel (303) 797-1600 SIC 4953

WELLBRIDGE CLUB MANAGEMENT LLC p 1589
6140 Greenwood Plaza Blvd 80111
Tel (303) 866-0800 SIC 7991

XANTERRA HOLDING CORP p 1630
6312 S Fiddlers Green Cir # 600 80111
Tel (303) 600-3400 SIC 5812

XANTERRA INC p 1630
6312 S Fiddlers Green Cir 600n 80111
Tel (303) 600-3400 SIC 7011

XANTERRA SOUTH RIM LLC p 1630
6312 S Fiddlers Green Cir 80111
Tel (303) 600-3400 SIC 7011 5813 7999

HAXTUN, CO

GRAINLAND COOPERATIVE p 629
421 S Colorado Ave 80731
Tel (970) 774-6166
SIC 5191 4221 5531 5541

HENDERSON, CO

ASPHALT SPECIALTIES CO INC p 118
10100 Dallas St 80640
Tel (303) 289-8555 SIC 1611

DPI SPECIALTY FOODS ROCKY MOUNTAIN INC p 454
8125 E 88th Ave 80640
Tel (303) 301-1226 SIC 5141

■ **STURGEON ELECTRIC CO INC** p 1395
12150 E 112th Ave 80640
Tel (303) 227-6990 SIC 1731 1623

HIGHLANDS RANCH, CO

■ **ADA-ES INC** p 21
9135 Ridgeline Blvd # 200 80129
Tel (303) 734-1727 SIC 5075

ARCADIS US INC p 103
630 Plaza Dr Ste 200 80129
Tel (720) 344-3500 SIC 8748 8711 8741

CASTLE PARTNERS LLC p 264
6787 Millstone St 80130
Tel (303) 884-1157 SIC 5172 5013

FRANCO-NEVADA US CORP p 574
1745 Shea Center Dr # 310 80129
Tel (303) 317-6335 SIC 6211

SPECIALIZED LOAN SERVICING LLC p 1356
8742 Lucent Blvd Ste 300 80129
Tel (720) 241-7200 SIC 6162

▲ UDR INC p 1499
1745 Shea Center Dr # 200 80129
Tel (720) 283-6120 SIC 6798

■ UNITED DOMINION REALTY LP p 1508
1745 Shea Center Dr # 200 80129
Tel (720) 283-6120 SIC 6531

IGNACIO, CO

SOUTHERN UTE INDIAN TRIBE p 1351
356 Ouray Dr 81137
Tel (970) 563-0100 SIC 9131

LA JARA, CO

CENTURYTEL INC p 282
519 Main St 81140
Tel (719) 274-4437 SIC 4813

LA JUNTA, CO

LEWIS BOLT & NUT CO p 858
30105 6th Ave 81050
Tel (719) 384-5400 SIC 3452

LA SALLE, CO

SUMMIT SLICKLINE INC p 1399
20701 County Road 50 80645
Tel (970) 397-1808 SIC 1389 7389

LAFAYETTE, CO

CTAP LLC p 399
2585 Trailridge Dr E # 200 80026
Tel (303) 661-9475 SIC 5082

GOOD SAMARITAN MEDICAL CENTER FOUNDATION p 623
200 Exempla Cir 80026
Tel (303) 689-4000 SIC 8062

LAKEWOOD, CO

AGGREGATE INDUSTRIES-WCR INC p 35
1687 Cole Blvd Ste 300 80401
Tel (303) 716-5200
SIC 1611 1442 1499 2951

ALLIANCE FOR SUSTAINABLE ENERGY LLC p 54
15013 Denver West Pkwy 80401
Tel (303) 275-3000 SIC 8733

BOSTON MARKET CORP p 203
14103 Denver West Pkwy # 100 80401
Tel (800) 340-2836 SIC 5812

BOSTON MARKET HOLDING CORP p 203
14103 Denver West Pkwy # 100 80401
Tel (303) 278-9500 SIC 5812

CATAMOUNT CONSTRUCTORS INC p 264
1527 Cole Blvd Ste 100 80401
Tel (303) 679-0087 SIC 1542

COLORADO CHRISTIAN UNIVERSITY INC p 338
8787 W Alameda Ave 80226
Tel (303) 963-3000 SIC 8221

COLORADO DEPARTMENT OF PUBLIC SAFETY p 339
700 Kipling St Ste 1000 80215
Tel (303) 239-4400 SIC 9229

▲ COMMAND CENTER INC p 344
3609 S Wadsworth Blvd # 250 80235
Tel (866) 464-5844 SIC 7361

COORSTEK INC p 368
14143 Denver West Pkwy # 400 80401
Tel (303) 271-7000 SIC 3545

EBERL CLAIMS SERVICE LLC p 474
7276 W Mansfield Ave 80235
Tel (303) 988-6286 SIC 6411

EINSTEIN AND NOAH CORP p 482
555 Zang St Ste 300 80228
Tel (303) 568-8000 SIC 5812

EINSTEIN NOAH RESTAURANT GROUP INC p 482
555 Zang St Ste 300 80228
Tel (303) 568-8000 SIC 5812 6794

ENCORE ELECTRIC INC p 496
7125 W Jefferson Ave # 400 80235
Tel (303) 934-1234 SIC 1731

FIRSTBANK p 550
10403 W Colfax Ave # 100 80215
Tel (303) 232-2000 SIC 6021

FIRSTBANK HOLDING CO p 550
12345 W Colfax Ave 80215
Tel (303) 232-3000 SIC 6036

■ INTEGER GROUP L L C p 748
7245 W Alaska Dr 80226
Tel (303) 393-3000 SIC 7311 8742 8743

LINNEA BASEY CANCER RESOURCE CENTER p 869
11600 W 2nd Pl 80228
Tel (773) 484-1000 SIC 8069

▲ MESA LABORATORIES INC p 951
12100 W 6th Ave 80228
Tel (303) 987-8000 SIC 3823 3841

MIDWEST UNITED ENERGY LLC p 968
12687 W Cedar Dr Ste 200 80228
Tel (303) 989-7165 SIC 5172

▲ NATURAL GROCERS BY VITAMIN COTTAGE INC p 1018
12612 W Alameda Pkwy 80228
Tel (303) 986-4600 SIC 5411 5499

■ QDOBA RESTAURANT CORP p 1194
7244 W Bonfils Ln 80226
Tel (720) 898-2300 SIC 5812 6794

■ SERVICEMAGIC INC p 1307
14023 Denver West Pkwy # 2 80401
Tel (303) 963-7200 SIC 4813

TERUMO BCT HOLDING CORP p 1440
10811 W Collins Ave 80215
Tel (303) 232-6800 SIC 3841 6719

TERUMO BCT INC p 1440
10811 W Collins Ave 80215
Tel (303) 232-6800
SIC 8733 3842 3845 5047 7352 7699

TUCANOS DEVELOPMENT LLC p 1490
12345 W Alameda Pkwy 80228
Tel (303) 237-1340 SIC 6799

■ VITAMIN COTTAGE NATURAL FOOD MARKETS INC p 1562
12612 W Alameda Pkwy 80228
Tel (303) 986-4600 SIC 5499

■ WESTERN AREA POWER ADMINISTRATION p 1597
12155 W Alameda Pkwy 80228
Tel (720) 962-7000 SIC 9611

LITTLETON, CO

ALCOHOL MONITORING SYSTEMS INC p 47
1241 W Mineral Ave # 200 80120
Tel (303) 785-7813 SIC 5169 3825

■ ALSTOM RENEWABLE US LLC p 61
7901 Suthpark Plz Ste 110 80120
Tel (303) 730-4000 SIC 3621 3511

AMERICAN CIVIL CONSTRUCTORS HOLDINGS INC p 70
4901 S Windermere St 80120
Tel (303) 795-2582 SIC 1622 0781

AMERICAN CIVIL CONSTRUCTORS LLC p 70
4901 S Windermere St 80120
Tel (303) 795-2582 SIC 1629 0783 0181

ARAPAHOE COMMUNITY COLLEGE FOUNDATION INC p 102
5900 S Santa Fe Dr 80120
Tel (303) 797-4222 SIC 8222

COUNTY OF ARAPAHOE p 376
5334 S Prince St 80120
Tel (303) 795-4620 SIC 9111

CPI CARD GROUP - COLORADO INC p 387
10368 W Centennial Rd A 80127
Tel (303) 973-9311 SIC 3089

CPI CARD GROUP INC p 387
10368 W Centennial Rd A 80127
Tel (303) 973-9311 SIC 6153

CPI HOLDING CO p 387
10368 W Centennial Rd 80127
Tel (303) 973-9311 SIC 2821

GLOBAL EMPLOYMENT HOLDINGS INC p 616
10375 Park Meadows Dr # 475 80124
Tel (303) 216-9500 SIC 7363 6719

GLOBAL EMPLOYMENT SOLUTIONS INC p 616
10375 Park Meadows Dr # 475 80124
Tel (303) 216-9500 SIC 7363

GOLDEN STAR RESOURCES LTD p 621
10901 W Toller Dr Ste 300 80127
Tel (303) 830-9000 SIC 1041

GROUP VOYAGERS INC p 642
5301 S Federal Cir 80123
Tel (303) 703-7000 SIC 4725

IMI AMERICAS INC p 733
5400 S Delaware St 80120
Tel (763) 488-5400 SIC 2542

JONES INTERNATIONAL LTD p 792
300 E Mineral Ave Ste 5 80122
Tel (303) 792-3111
SIC 4832 4841 7371 7372

■ LEVEL 3 TELECOM HOLDINGS LLC p 858
10475 Park Meadows Dr 80124
Tel (303) 566-1000 SIC 4813

■ LEVEL 3 TELECOM LLC p 858
10475 Park Meadows Dr 80124
Tel (303) 566-1000 SIC 4813

LONG BUILDING TECHNOLOGIES INC p 876
5001 S Zuni St 80120
Tel (303) 975-2100 SIC 5075 1711

MAVERICK PUMP SERVICES LLC p 921
9791 Titan Park Cir 80125
Tel (303) 981-8349 SIC 7389

MCDONALD AUTOMOTIVE GROUP LLC p 927
6060 S Broadway 80121
Tel (866) 775-9743 SIC 5511

MOTION & FLOW CONTROL PRODUCTS INC p 992
7941 Shaffer Pkwy 80127
Tel (303) 666-2183 SIC 5085

MOTION AND FLOW CONTROL PRODUCTS INC p 992
7941 Shaffer Pkwy 80127
Tel (303) 762-8012 SIC 5085 5074

NORGREN INC p 1048
5400 S Delaware St 80120
Tel (303) 794-5000 SIC 3492

REPUBLIC NATIONAL DISTRIBUTING CO LLC p 1225
8000 Southpark Ter 80120
Tel (303) 734-2400 SIC 5169

▲ STILLWATER MINING CO p 1390
26 W Dry Creek Cir 80120
Tel (406) 373-8700 SIC 1099

TERRANE METALS CORP p 1439
26 W Dry Creek Cir # 810 80120
Tel (303) 761-8801 SIC 1081

THOMPSON CREEK METALS CO INC p 1449
26 W Dry Creek Cir 80120
Tel (303) 761-8801
SIC 1021 1041 1044 1061

THOMPSON CREEK METALS CO USA p 1449
26 W Dry Creek Cir 80120
Tel (303) 761-8801 SIC 1061

THOMPSON CREEK MINING CO p 1449
26 W Dry Creek Cir # 810 80120
Tel (303) 783-6413 SIC 2899 1061

THOMPSON CREEK MINING LTD p 1449
26 W Dry Creek Cir # 810 80120
Tel (303) 761-8801 SIC 1061 2899 2819

■ TW TELECOM OF COLORADO LLC p 1494
10475 Park Meadows Dr 80124
Tel (636) 625-7000 SIC 4812 4813

LONE TREE, CO

CARDNO INC p 253
10004 Park Meadows Dr # 300 80124
Tel (720) 257-5800
SIC 8711 8748 8742 8741

CARDNO USA INC p 253
10004 Park Meadows Dr # 300 80124
Tel (720) 257-5800 SIC 8711 5045 8748

K & G PETROLEUM LLC p 798
10459 Park Meadows Dr # 101 80124
Tel (303) 792-9467 SIC 5541

WOODLANDS COMMERCIAL BANK p 1623
10350 Park Meadows Dr 80124
Tel (212) 257-4646 SIC 6021

LONGMONT, CO

■ A & W WATER SERVICE INC p 4
1900 S Sunset St Unit 1f 80501
Tel (303) 659-6523 SIC 1389

ABE ORLANDO BUSTAMANTE p 10
7859 Diagonal Hwy 80503
Tel (303) 652-3394 SIC 5099 4789 4212

ALLIANT NATIONAL TITLE INSURANCE CO INC p 55
1831 Lefthand Cir Ste G 80501
Tel (303) 682-9800 SIC 6361

CIRCLE GRAPHICS INC p 308
120 9th Ave Ste B 80501
Tel (303) 532-2370 SIC 2759 7374

DOT HILL SYSTEMS CORP p 452
1351 S Sunset St 80501
Tel (303) 845-3200 SIC 3572 7371

LONGMONT UNITED HOSPITAL p 877
1950 Mountain View Ave 80501
Tel (303) 651-5111 SIC 8062

■ MCLANE/WESTERN INC p 931
2100 E Ken Pratt Blvd 80504
Tel (303) 682-7500 SIC 5141

ST VRAIN VALLEY SCHOOL DISTRICT RE-1J p 1373
395 S Pratt Pkwy 80501
Tel (303) 776-6200 SIC 8211

■ WEST SAFETY SERVICES p 1595
1601 Dry Creek Dr 80503
Tel (402) 963-1200 SIC 7373

LOUISVILLE, CO

BESTOP INC p 177
333 Centennial Pkwy B 80027
Tel (303) 465-1755 SIC 2394 3714

FIT FOR LIFE LLC p 552
833 W S Boulder Rd Bldg G 80027
Tel (303) 222-3600 SIC 5091 5941

▲ GAIA INC p 589
833 W South Boulder Rd 80027
Tel (303) 222-3600 SIC 7299 7812 7999

GLOBAL HEALTHCARE EXCHANGE LLC p 616
1315 W Century Dr Ste 100 80027
Tel (720) 887-7000 SIC 6321

GRAPHIC PACKAGING INTERNATIONAL CORP p 632
1795 Dogwood St Unit 100 80027
Tel (303) 215-4600 SIC 2657 2671 2655

NEN HOLDINGS INC p 1025
397 S Taylor Ave 80027
Tel (303) 444-2559 SIC 5962

ROGUE WAVE SOFTWARE INC p 1246
1315 W Century Dr Ste 150 80027
Tel (303) 473-9118 SIC 7371 7372

LOVELAND, CO

AGRIUM ADVANCED TECHNOLOGIES (US) INC p 36
2915 Rocky Mountain Ave # 400 80538
Tel (970) 292-9000 SIC 2873

CROP PRODUCTION SERVICES INC p 393
3005 Rocky Mountain Ave 80538
Tel (970) 685-3300 SIC 5191

■ HACH CO p 652
5600 Lindbergh Dr 80538
Tel (970) 669-3050
SIC 3826 3823 3231 2819 2869

▲ HESKA CORP p 688
3760 Rocky Mountain Ave 80538
Tel (970) 493-7272 SIC 2834 5122

MEDICAL CENTER OF ROCKIES p 936
2500 Rocky Mountain Ave 80538
Tel (970) 624-2500 SIC 8062

PLATTE CHEMICAL CO p 1155
3005 Rocky Mountain Ave 80538
Tel (970) 685-3300 SIC 2879

THOMPSON SCHOOL DISTRICT R2J p 1449
800 S Taft Ave 80537
Tel (970) 613-5000 SIC 8211

MONTE VISTA, CO

GROWERS SALES AND MARKETING LLC p 642
15 Washington St Ste 207 81144
Tel (719) 852-2600 SIC 5148

MONTROSE, CO

MONTROSE MEMORIAL HOSPITAL INC p 987
800 S 3rd St 81401
Tel (970) 249-2211 SIC 8062 8011

NIWOT, CO

▲ CROCS INC p 393
7477 Dry Creek Pkwy 80503
Tel (303) 848-7000
SIC 3021 5139 3069 5661 2389

SUNRISE MEDICAL HHG INC p 1404
7477 Dry Creek Pkwy 80503
Tel (303) 218-4600 SIC 3842 3844

SUNRISE MEDICAL HOLDINGS INC p 1404
7477 Dry Creek Pkwy 80503
Tel (303) 218-4600 SIC 3842

OAK CREEK, CO

TWENTYMILE COAL LLC p 1494
29515 Routt County Rd 2 # 27 80467
Tel (970) 879-3800 SIC 1222

PARKER, CO

CHUCK LATHAM ASSOCIATES INC p 304
18403 Longs Way Unit 102 80134
Tel (303) 699-2905 SIC 5199

PARKER ADVENTIST HOSPITAL p 1116
9395 Crown Crest Blvd 80138
Tel (303) 269-4000 SIC 8062

WJ BRADLEY MORTGAGE CAPITAL LLC p 1619
10940 S Parker Rd Ste 506 80134
Tel (303) 825-5670 SIC 6162

PEETZ, CO

■ PEETZ TABLE WIND ENERGY LLC p 1127
9500 County Road 78 80747
Tel (970) 334-2230 SIC 4911

PEYTON, CO

FALCON SCHOOL DISTRICT 49 (INC) p 526
10850 E Woodmen Rd 80831
Tel (719) 495-3601 SIC 8211

PUEBLO WEST, CO

ANDREWS PRODUCE INC p 90
717 E Industrial Blvd 81007
Tel (719) 543-3846 SIC 5141 5148

ASI CONSTRUCTORS INC p 117
1850 E Platteville Blvd 81007
Tel (719) 647-2821 SIC 1629

PUEBLO, CO

■ BLACK HILLS/COLORADO ELECTRIC UTILITY CO LP p 187
105 S Victoria Ave 81003
Tel (719) 546-6589 SIC 4911

CF&I STEEL LP p 285
1612 E Abriendo Ave 81004
Tel (719) 561-6000 SIC 3441 3317 3312

COLORADO STATE UNIVERSITY-PUEBLO p 339
2200 Bonforte Blvd 81001
Tel (719) 549-2100 SIC 8221

■ MINI MART INC p 973
442 Keeler Pkwy 81001
Tel (719) 948-3071 SIC 5411

PARK VIEW HOSPITAL p 1116
400 W 16th St 81003
Tel (719) 584-4556 SIC 8741

PARKVIEW HEALTH SYSTEM INC p 1117
400 W 16th St 81003
Tel (719) 584-4000 SIC 8062 7389

PARKVIEW MEDICAL CENTER INC p 1117
400 W 16th St 81003
Tel (719) 584-4000 SIC 8062 8063

PUEBLO COUNTY GOVERNMENT p 1190
215 W 10th St 81003
Tel (719) 583-6000 SIC 9111

PUEBLO SCHOOL DISTRICT 70 p 1191
24951 E Us Highway 50 81006
Tel (719) 542-0220 SIC 8211

PUEBLO SCHOOL DISTRICT NO 60 p 1191
315 W 11th St 81003
Tel (719) 549-7100 SIC 8211

ST MARY-CORWIN HOSPITAL OF PUEBLO CO (INC) p 1371
1008 Minnequa Ave 81004
Tel (719) 557-4000 SIC 8062

T R TOPPERS INC p 1420
320 Fairchild Ave 81001
Tel (719) 948-4902 *SIC* 2066

VESTAS TOWERS AMERICA INC p 1552
100 Tower Rd 81004
Tel (719) 288-2200 *SIC* 3443

RIFLE, CO

STERLING CONSTRUCTION MANAGEMENT LLC p 1387
3158 Baron Ln Unit E 81650
Tel (307) 362-7906 *SIC* 1623

SEDALIA, CO

INTERMOUNTAIN RURAL ELECTRIC ASSOCIATION p 753
5496 N Us Highway 85 80135
Tel (303) 688-3100 *SIC* 4911

STEAMBOAT SPRINGS, CO

ASPEN ELECTRIC AND SUPPLY INC p 118
1890 Loggers Ln Unit C 80487
Tel (970) 879-3905 *SIC* 5719 1731

YAMPA VALLEY MEDICAL CENTER p 1634
1024 Central Park Dr 80487
Tel (970) 879-1322 *SIC* 8062 8351

STRATTON, CO

STRATTON EQUITY COOPERATIVE CO p 1393
98 Colorado Ave 80836
Tel (719) 348-5326
SIC 5153 5191 5171 5541

SUPERIOR, CO

■ KEY EQUIPMENT FINANCE INC p 814
1000 S Mccaslin Blvd 80027
Tel (800) 539-2968 *SIC* 7359

NEXUS BIOENERGY INC p 1041
3026 Castle Peak Ave 80027
Tel (720) 318-2339 *SIC* 4939 7389 8731

TELLURIDE, CO

TSG SKI & GOLF LLC p 1489
565 Mountain Village Blvd 81435
Tel (970) 728-6900 *SIC* 7997

THORNTON, CO

ADAMS 12 FIVE STAR SCHOOLS p 21
1500 E 128th Ave 80241
Tel (720) 972-4000 *SIC* 8211

AMI MECHANICAL INC p 85
12141 Pennsylvania St 80241
Tel (303) 280-1401 *SIC* 1711

HARPEL OIL CO p 662
4204 E 105th Ave 80233
Tel (303) 294-0767 *SIC* 5171 5983 5172

NORTHERN ELECTRIC INC p 1056
12789 Emerson St 80241
Tel (303) 428-6969 *SIC* 1731

VAIL, CO

VAIL CLINIC INC p 1538
181 W Meadow Dr Ste 100 81657
Tel (970) 476-2451 *SIC* 8062

VAIL VALLEY SURGERY CENTER LLC p 1538
181 W Meadow Dr Ste 100 81657
Tel (970) 476-8872 *SIC* 8062

WATKINS, CO

ORICA US SERVICES INC p 1094
33101 E Quincy Ave 80137
Tel (303) 268-5000 *SIC* 2892 5169

ORICA USA INC p 1094
33101 E Quincy Ave 80137
Tel (720) 870-1809 *SIC* 2892 5169

WESTMINSTER, CO

■ ALLOS THERAPEUTICS INC p 58
11000 Westmoor Cir # 150 80021
Tel (303) 426-6262 *SIC* 2834

ALPINE LUMBER CO p 60
10170 Church Ranch Way # 300 80021
Tel (303) 451-8001 *SIC* 5211

ALTA COLLEGES INC p 61
10249 Church Ranch Way # 100 80021
Tel (303) 846-1700 *SIC* 8249

■ BALL METAL BEVERAGE CONTAINER CORP p 148
9300 W 108th Cir 80021
Tel (303) 469-5511 *SIC* 3411

■ BALL METAL FOOD CONTAINER LLC p 148
9300 W 108th Cir 80021
Tel (303) 469-3131 *SIC* 3411

■ BALL PACKAGING LLC p 148
9300 W 108th Cir 80021
Tel (303) 469-5511 *SIC* 3411

CASEY INDUSTRIAL INC p 263
1400 W 122nd Ave Ste 200 80234
Tel (541) 926-8641 *SIC* 1541 8741

▲ DIGITALGLOBE INC p 439
1300 W 120th Ave 80234
Tel (303) 684-4000 *SIC* 4899

EXCLUSIVE STAFFING LTD p 517
8774 Yates Dr Ste 210 80031
Tel (303) 430-1700 *SIC* 7363

LAFARGE WEST INC p 837
10170 Church Ranch Way # 200 80021
Tel (303) 657-4355 *SIC* 5032 1611 3273

TRI-STATE GENERATION AND TRANSMISSION ASSOCIATION INC p 1477
1100 W 116th Ave 80234
Tel (303) 452-6111 *SIC* 4911

WESTMINSTER PUBLIC SCHOOLS p 1601
7002 Raleigh St 80030
Tel (303) 428-3511 *SIC* 8211

WHEAT RIDGE, CO

ELECTRONICS ROW LLC p 486
10601 W I 70 Frntage Rd N 80033
Tel (720) 728-5420 *SIC* 5731

GEORGET SANDERS CO p 606
10201 W 49th Ave 80033
Tel (303) 423-9660 *SIC* 5074

LUTHERAN MEDICAL CENTER p 886
8300 W 38th Ave 80033
Tel (303) 425-4500
SIC 8011 7389 8082 8331

MEDVED CHEVROLET INC p 939
11001 W I 70 Frontage Rd 80033
Tel (303) 421-0100 *SIC* 5511

SCL HEALTH - FRONT RANGE INC p 1292
8300 W 38th Ave 80033
Tel (303) 813-5000 *SIC* 8062 8011 8051

WOODLAND PARK, CO

TRIPLE "R" TRAFFIC CONTROL & BARRICADE RENTAL "LLC p 1482
509 Scott Ave Ste 106 80863
Tel (720) 641-8099 *SIC* 7389

CONNECTICUT

ANSONIA, CT

FARREL CORP p 530
1 Farrell Blvd 06401
Tel (203) 736-5500 *SIC* 3559 1011 3089

AVON, CT

APPLE HEALTH CARE INC p 98
21 Waterville Rd 06001
Tel (860) 678-9755 *SIC* 8093

ITP RAIL ASSOCIATES INC p 768
35 E Main St Ste 415 06001
Tel (860) 693-6120 *SIC* 8742

■ MAGELLAN BEHAVIORAL HEALTH SERVICE LLC p 895
55 Nod Rd 06001
Tel (860) 507-1900 *SIC* 8322

■ MAGELLAN PARTNERS RX INC p 895
55 Nod Rd 06001
Tel (860) 507-1900 *SIC* 8063

ORAFOL AMERICAS INC p 1091
120 Darling Dr 06001
Tel (860) 223-9297 *SIC* 3082

BERLIN, CT

■ CONNECTICUT LIGHT AND POWER CO p 357
107 Selden St 06037
Tel (860) 665-5000 *SIC* 4911

CORBIN RUSSWIN INC p 368
225 Episcopal Rd 06037
Tel (860) 225-7411 *SIC* 3429

■ EVERSOURCE ENERGY SERVICE CO p 515
107 Selden St 06037
Tel (860) 665-5000 *SIC* 1623

■ NORTHEAST NUCLEAR ENERGY CO p 1055
107 Selden St 06037
Tel (860) 665-5000 *SIC* 4911

■ NU ENTERPRISES INC p 1066
107 Selden St 06037
Tel (860) 665-5000 *SIC* 4911

■ YANKEE ENERGY SYSTEM INC p 1634
107 Selden St 06037
Tel (860) 665-5000 *SIC* 4924

■ YANKEE GAS SERVICES CO p 1634
107 Selden St 06037
Tel (860) 665-5000 *SIC* 4924

BETHANY, CT

LATICRETE INTERNATIONAL INC p 846
1 Laticrete Park N 91 06524
Tel (203) 393-0010 *SIC* 2899 2891

BETHEL, CT

ABILITY BEYOND DISABILITY INC p 11
4 Berkshire Blvd 06801
Tel (203) 826-3025 *SIC* 8322 8082

■ DURACELL INC p 462
14 Research Dr 06801
Tel (203) 796-4000 *SIC* 3691

■ DURACELL INTERNATIONAL INC p 462
14 Research Dr 06801
Tel (203) 796-4000 *SIC* 3691

WESTERN CONNECTICUT MEDICAL GROUP p 1597
14 Research Dr 06801
Tel (203) 794-5331 *SIC* 8011

BLOOMFIELD, CT

▲ CIGNA CORP p 306
900 Cottage Grove Rd 06002
Tel (860) 226-6000
SIC 6324 6311 6351 6321

■ CIGNA HEALTH AND LIFE INSURANCE CO p 306
900 Cottage Grove Rd 06002
Tel (860) 226-6000 *SIC* 6311

■ CIGNA HEALTH CORP p 306
900 Cottage Grove Rd 06002
Tel (860) 226-6000 *SIC* 6324

■ CIGNA HEALTH MANAGEMENT INC p 306
900 Cottage Grove Rd 06002
Tel (860) 226-0533 *SIC* 8742

■ CIGNA HEALTHCARE OF CONNECTICUT INC p 306
900 Cottage Grove Rd 06002
Tel (860) 226-2300 *SIC* 6324

■ CONNECTICUT GENERAL CORP p 357
900 Cottage Grove Rd 06002
Tel (860) 226-6000 *SIC* 6311 6321

■ CONNECTICUT GENERAL LIFE INSURANCE CO p 357
900 Cottage Grove Rd 06002
Tel (860) 226-6000 *SIC* 6311 6321

■ JACOBS VEHICLE SYSTEMS INC p 775
22 E Dudley Town Rd 06002
Tel (860) 243-5222 *SIC* 3519

■ KAMAN AEROSPACE CORP p 801
30 Old Windsor Rd 06002
Tel (860) 242-4461 *SIC* 3721 3728

■ KAMAN AEROSPACE GROUP INC p 801
1332 Blue Hills Ave 06002
Tel (860) 243-7100
SIC 3721 3724 3728 3769

▲ KAMAN CORP p 801
1332 Blue Hills Ave 06002
Tel (860) 243-7100 *SIC* 5085 3721 3728

■ KAMAN INDUSTRIAL TECHNOLOGIES CORP p 801
1 Vision Way 06002
Tel (860) 687-5000 *SIC* 3491 5085

■ KAMATICS CORP p 801
1330 Blue Hills Ave 06002
Tel (860) 243-9704
SIC 3451 3562 3724 3728

ROKR DISTRIBUTION US INC p 1247
310 W Newberry Rd 06002
Tel (860) 509-8888 *SIC* 5099 3931

BRANFORD, CT

CANUSA HERSHMAN RECYCLING LLC p 248
45 Ne Industrial Rd # 105 06405
Tel (203) 488-0887 *SIC* 4953

FYC APPAREL GROUP LLC p 586
30 Thompson Rd 06405
Tel (203) 481-2420
SIC 2331 2335 2337 5651

■ TRICOR DIRECT INC p 1479
20 Thompson Rd 06405
Tel (203) 488-8059 *SIC* 3479

BRIDGEPORT, CT

AFFINECO LLC p 32
855 Main St Ste 900 06604
Tel (203) 878-0638 *SIC* 7349 7382

AQUARION WATER CO p 101
835 Main St 06604
Tel (800) 732-9678 *SIC* 4941

BRIDGEPORT CITY SCHOOL DISTRICT p 211
45 Lyon Ter 06604
Tel (203) 576-7291 *SIC* 8211

BRIDGEPORT HOSPITAL p 211
267 Grant St 06610
Tel (203) 384-3000 *SIC* 8062

■ BUSHWICK METALS LLC p 229
560 N Washington Ave # 2 06604
Tel (888) 399-4070 *SIC* 5051

CITY OF BRIDGEPORT p 313
999 Broad St Ste 2 06604
Tel (203) 576-3964 *SIC* 9111

FAIRFIELD COUNTRY RADIOLOGY A p 524
2800 Main St 06606
Tel (203) 576-5033 *SIC* 8011

KOLMAR AMERICAS INC p 827
10 Middle St Ph 06604
Tel (203) 873-2078 *SIC* 5172

LACEY MANUFACTURING CO LLC p 837
1146 Barnum Ave 06610
Tel (203) 336-7427 *SIC* 3841 3089

NORTHEAST MEDICAL GROUP INC p 1055
99 Hawley Ave Fl 3 06606
Tel (203) 339-6499 *SIC* 8011

■ PEOPLES UNITED BANK NATIONAL ASSOCIATION p 1133
850 Main St Fl 6 06604
Tel (203) 338-7171 *SIC* 6022

▲ PEOPLES UNITED FINANCIAL INC p 1133
850 Main St 06604
Tel (203) 338-7171 *SIC* 6411

PRIME RESOURCES CORP p 1175
1100 Boston Ave Bldg 1 06610
Tel (203) 331-9100 *SIC* 3993 2759

■ RBS NATIONAL BANK p 1211
1000 Lafayette Blvd # 600 06604
Tel (203) 551-7270 *SIC* 6021

ST VINCENTS DEVELOPMENT INC p 1373
2800 Main St 06606
Tel (203) 576-6000 *SIC* 8399 6531

ST VINCENTS HEALTH SERVICES CORP p 1373
2800 Main St 06606
Tel (203) 576-6000 *SIC* 8741 8062

ST VINCENTS MEDICAL CENTER FOUNDATION INC p 1373
2800 Main St 06606
Tel (203) 576-6000 *SIC* 8062

TREFZ CORP p 1475
10 Middle St Ste 1701 06604
Tel (203) 367-3621 *SIC* 5812 6531 8721

UNITED SERVICES OF AMERICA INC p 1511
855 Main St Ste 900 06604
Tel (203) 878-0638 *SIC* 7349

UNIVERSITY OF BRIDGEPORT p 1520
126 Park Ave 06604
Tel (203) 576-4000 *SIC* 8221

WHEELABRATOR CONNECTICUT INC p 1604
6 Howard Ave 06605
Tel (203) 579-2607 *SIC* 4953

BRISTOL, CT

AMERICAN CUSTOMER CARE INC p 71
225 N Main St Fl 5 06010
Tel (800) 267-0686 *SIC* 7389

▲ BARNES GROUP INC p 156
123 Main St 06010
Tel (860) 583-7070 *SIC* 3724 3495 3469

BRISTOL HOSPITAL INC p 214
41 Brewster Rd 06010
Tel (860) 585-3000 *SIC* 8062

CITY OF BRISTOL p 313
111 N Main St Ste 17 06010
Tel (860) 584-6100 *SIC* 9111

■ ESPN INC p 509
Espn Plz 06010
Tel (860) 766-2000 *SIC* 4841 4832

■ ESPN PRODUCTIONS INC p 510
545 Middle St 06010
Tel (860) 766-2000 *SIC* 4833

MARK FACEY & CO p 907
225 N Main St Ste 500 06010
Tel (800) 237-0938 *SIC* 7389

BROOKFIELD, CT

▲ PHOTRONICS INC p 1145
15 Secor Rd 06804
Tel (203) 775-9000 *SIC* 3674

VALIDUS DC SYSTEMS LLC p 1540
50 Pocono Rd 06804
Tel (203) 448-3600 *SIC* 3679

CANTON, CT

■ HARKEMA SERVICES INC p 661
305 Albany Tpke 06019
Tel (860) 693-8378 *SIC* 5159

CENTERBROOK, CT

NOBLE ENVIRONMENTAL POWER LLC p 1046
6 Main St Ste 121 06409
Tel (860) 581-5010 *SIC* 4911

CHESHIRE, CT

■ ATLANTIC INERTIAL SYSTEMS INC p 126
250 Knotter Dr 06410
Tel (203) 250-3500 *SIC* 3812

BOZZUTOS INC p 205
275 Schoolhouse Rd 06410
Tel (203) 272-3511 *SIC* 5141 5411

COAST-TO-COAST PRODUCE CO LLC p 331
125 Commerce Ct Ste 2 06410
Tel (203) 271-2006 *SIC* 5148

EDAC TECHNOLOGIES LLC p 477
5 Mckee Pl 06410
Tel (203) 806-2090 *SIC* 3769 3541 3724

LANE CONSTRUCTION CORP p 843
90 Fieldstone Ct 06410
Tel (203) 235-3351
SIC 1622 1611 1629 3272 5032

LANE INDUSTRIES INC p 843
90 Fieldstone Ct 06410
Tel (203) 235-3351
SIC 1629 1611 5032 3272 1622

OSTERMAN & CO INC p 1097
726 S Main St 06410
Tel (203) 272-2233 *SIC* 5162

CHESTER, CT

CHESTERFIELDS LTD p 295
132 Main St 06412
Tel (860) 526-5363 *SIC* 8051

WHELEN ENGINEERING CO INC p 1605
51 Winthrop Rd 06412
Tel (860) 526-9504
SIC 3647 3646 3671 3651 3648 3641

CLINTON, CT

▲ CONNECTICUT WATER SERVICE INC p 357
93 W Main St 06413
Tel (860) 669-8636 *SIC* 4941 6531 1623

COLCHESTER, CT

S & S WORLDWIDE INC p 1261
75 Mill St 06415
Tel (860) 537-3451 *SIC* 5199 5049 3944

DANBURY, CT

ACUREN INSPECTION INC p 20
30 Main St Ste 402 06810
Tel (203) 702-8740 *SIC* 1389 8071

ARMORED AUTOGROUP INC p 111
44 Old Ridgebury Rd # 300 06810
Tel (203) 205-2900 *SIC* 3714

■ ARMORED AUTOGROUP PARENT INC p 111
44 Old Ridgebury Rd # 300 06810
Tel (203) 205-2900 *SIC* 2842 2911 2899

■ ATMI INC p 128
7 Commerce Dr 06810
Tel (952) 942-0855 *SIC* 3674

BARDEN CORP p 155
200 Park Ave 06810
Tel (203) 744-2211
SIC 3562 3469 3842 3089 3399

■ BRANSON ULTRASONICS CORP p 208
41 Eagle Rd Ste 1 06810
Tel (203) 796-0400 *SIC* 3699 3548 3541

■ CARTUS CORP p 262
40 Apple Ridge Rd 06810
Tel (203) 205-3400 *SIC* 7389

DANBURY OFFICE OF PHYSICIAN SERVICES PC p 411
25 Germantown Rd 06810
Tel (203) 794-0090 *SIC* 8011

DANBURY SCHOOL DISTRICT p 411
63 Beaver Brook Rd 06810
Tel (203) 797-4701 *SIC* 8211

DRS CONSOLIDATED CONTROLS INC p 457
21 South St 06810
Tel (203) 798-3000 *SIC* 3823

■ ETHAN ALLEN GLOBAL INC p 511
25 Lake Ave 06810
Tel (203) 743-8000 *SIC* 5712

▲ ETHAN ALLEN INTERIORS INC p 511
Ethan Allen Dr 06811
Tel (203) 743-8000 *SIC* 2511 2512 5712

■ ETHAN ALLEN OPERATIONS INC p 511
Ethan Allen Dr 06813
Tel (203) 743-8496 *SIC* 2511

■ ETHAN ALLEN RETAIL INC p 511
Ethan Allen Dr 06811
Tel (203) 743-8000
SIC 5712 5719 5713 5231 2273

FAG HOLDING CORP p 524
200 Park Ave 06810
Tel (203) 790-5474 *SIC* 3562

▲ FUELCELL ENERGY INC p 583
3 Great Pasture Rd 06810
Tel (203) 825-6000 *SIC* 1629

GENPACT INTERNATIONAL INC p 604
42 Old Ridgebury Rd Ste 1 06810
Tel (203) 730-5100 *SIC* 7371

GENPACT LLC p 604
42 Old Ridgebury Rd Ste 1 06810
Tel (203) 730-5110 *SIC* 8742

■ HEALTHCARE TECHNOLOGY INTERMEDIATE INC p 676
83 Wooster Hts 06810
Tel (203) 448-4600 *SIC* 8742 8732

HOSPITAL DANBURY INC p 709
24 Hospital Ave 06810
Tel (203) 739-7000 *SIC* 8062

ODYSSEY LOGISTICS & TECHNOLOGY CORP p 1075
39 Old Ridgebury Rd Ste 7 06810
Tel (203) 448-3900 *SIC* 4731

■ PRAXAIR DISTRIBUTION INC p 1167
39 Old Ridgebury Rd 06810
Tel (203) 837-2000 *SIC* 2813 5084 5999

▲ PRAXAIR INC p 1168
10 Riverview Dr 06810
Tel (203) 837-2000
SIC 2813 3569 3471 3479

■ PRAXAIR TECHNOLOGY INC p 1168
39 Old Ridgebury Rd 06810
Tel (203) 837-2000
SIC 5172 5084 5169 5085

■ SCHOLASTIC LIBRARY PUBLISHING INC p 1288
90 Sherman Tpke 06816
Tel (203) 797-3500
SIC 2731 5963 5192 2721 5961 7371

■ SHEMIN NURSERIES INC p 1315
42 Old Ridgebury Rd Ste 3 06810
Tel (203) 207-5000 *SIC* 5191 5193

UNION SAVINGS BANK p 1505
226 Main St 06810
Tel (203) 830-4200 *SIC* 6036

WESTERN CONNECTICUT HEALTH NETWORK INC p 1597
24 Hospital Ave 06810
Tel (203) 739-7000 *SIC* 8062

WW LIQUIDATION INC p 1629
60 Backus Ave 06810
Tel (203) 546-6000 *SIC* 5074 5999 5211

DARIEN, CT

▲ GENESEE & WYOMING INC p 602
20 West Ave 06820
Tel (203) 202-8900 *SIC* 4011 4013

HAY ISLAND HOLDING CORP p 670
20 Thorndal Cir 06820
Tel (203) 656-8000 *SIC* 5194 2131

■ RAILAMERICA INC p 1205
20 West Ave 06820
Tel (203) 656-1092 *SIC* 4011

RINGS END INC p 1235
181 West Ave 06820
Tel (203) 655-2525 *SIC* 5031 5211

SWISHER INTERNATIONAL GROUP INC p 1412
20 Thorndal Cir 06820
Tel (203) 656-8000 *SIC* 5194

SWISHER INTERNATIONAL INC p 1412
20 Thorndal Cir 06820
Tel (203) 656-8000 *SIC* 5194

DERBY, CT

GRIFFIN HOSPITAL INC p 640
130 Division St 06418
Tel (203) 735-7421 *SIC* 8062

EAST GRANBY, CT

OPUS INSPECTION INC p 1091
7 Kripes Rd 06026
Tel (860) 392-2100 *SIC* 7371

■ RSCC WIRE & CABLE LLC p 1255
20 Bradley Park Rd 06026
Tel (860) 653-8300 *SIC* 3357 3315

EAST HARTFORD, CT

ALDIN ASSOCIATES LIMITED PARTNERSHIP p 48
77 Sterling Rd 06108
Tel (860) 282-0651 *SIC* 5541 5411

ALLAN S GOODMAN INC p 52
180 Goodwin St 06108
Tel (860) 289-2731 *SIC* 5181 5182

BOOTH WALTZ ENTERPRISES INC p 200
42 Rumsey Rd 06108
Tel (860) 289-7800 *SIC* 5172

■ CELLUTISSUE CORP p 274
2 Forbes St 06108
Tel (860) 289-7496 *SIC* 2621 3842 2676

■ CONNECTICUT NATURAL GAS CORP p 357
77 Hartland St Ste 405 06108
Tel (860) 727-3000 *SIC* 4924

CYIENT INC p 405
330 Roberts St Ste 400 06108
Tel (860) 528-5430 *SIC* 8711

■ DGPM INVESTMENTS INC p 435
300 E River Dr 06108
Tel (860) 528-9981
SIC 5044 5021 5713 1752

■ EM CLARCOR HOLDINGS INC p 490
60 Prestige Park Rd 06108
Tel (860) 920-4200 *SIC* 3714 3492

GOODWIN COLLEGE INC p 625
1 Riverside Dr 06118
Tel (860) 895-8000 *SIC* 8221

JETOBRA INC p 784
700 Connecticut Blvd 06108
Tel (877) 274-8207 *SIC* 5511

KELSER CORP p 809
111 Roberts St Ste D 06108
Tel (860) 610-2200 *SIC* 5045

NEFCO CORP p 1024
411 Burnham St 06108
Tel (860) 290-9044 *SIC* 5085 5072

PRIME MATERIALS RECOVERY INC p 1175
99 E River Dr 06108
Tel (860) 622-7626 *SIC* 5093

■ SOUTHERN CONNECTICUT GAS CO p 1348
77 Hartland St Ste 405 06108
Tel (800) 659-8299 *SIC* 4924

EAST HAVEN, CT

EAST HAVEN BUILDERS SUPPLY - US LBM LLC p 470
193 Silver Sands Rd 06512
Tel (203) 469-2394 *SIC* 5031 5211

TOWN FAIR TIRE CENTERS INC p 1465
460 Coe Ave 06512
Tel (203) 467-8600 *SIC* 5531 5014 5013

EAST WINDSOR, CT

BLAKE GROUP HOLDINGS INC p 188
4 New Park Rd 06088
Tel (860) 243-1491
SIC 5074 5084 7699 8741

SOUTHERN AUTO SALES INC p 1347
161 S Main St 06088
Tel (860) 292-7500 *SIC* 5012

EASTFORD, CT

WHITCRAFT LLC p 1605
76 County Rd 06242
Tel (860) 974-0786 *SIC* 3443 3444 3728

ENFIELD, CT

CONNECTICUT PIE INC p 357
35 Pearl St 06082
Tel (860) 741-3781 *SIC* 5149 5461

EPPENDORF HOLDING INC p 505
175 Freshwater Blvd 06082
Tel (860) 253-3417 *SIC* 3821

LEGO SYSTEMS INC p 853
555 Taylor Rd 06082
Tel (860) 749-2291 *SIC* 3944 5092

FAIRFIELD, CT

▲ ACME UNITED CORP p 18
55 Walls Dr Ste 201 06824
Tel (203) 254-6060
SIC 3421 2499 3842 3579 3069 3999

FAIRFIELD PUBLIC SCHOOLS p 525
501 Kings Hwy E Ste 210 06825
Tel (203) 255-7201 *SIC* 8211

FAIRFIELD UNIVERSITY p 525
1073 N Benson Rd 06824
Tel (203) 254-4000 *SIC* 8221 8211

GE FOUNDATION p 596
3135 Easton Tpke 06828
Tel (203) 373-3216 *SIC* 6722

■ GENERAL ELECTRIC CAPITAL SERVICES INC p 600
3135 Easton Tpke 06828
Tel (203) 373-2211
SIC 6159 6141 7359 6162

RC BIGELOW INC p 1211
201 Black Rock Tpke 06825
Tel (888) 244-3569 *SIC* 2099

SACRED HEART UNIVERSITY INC p 1265
5151 Park Ave 06825
Tel (203) 371-7999 *SIC* 8221

SAVE CHILDREN FEDERATION INC p 1284
501 Kings Hwy E Ste 400 06825
Tel (203) 221-4000 *SIC* 8322 5947

TOWN OF FAIRFIELD p 1465
725 Old Post Rd 06824
Tel (203) 256-3000 *SIC* 9121

FARMINGTON, CT

ALLIED WORLD ASSURANCE INC p 57
1690 New Britain Ave B 06032
Tel (860) 284-1300 *SIC* 6411

BEAZLEY INSURANCE CO INC p 166
30 Batterson Park Rd 06032
Tel (860) 677-3700 *SIC* 6331

■ CARRIER COMMERCIAL REFRIGERATION INC p 260
1 Carrier Pl 06032
Tel (860) 674-3000 *SIC* 3585

■ CARRIER COMMERCIAL REFRIGERATION INC p 260
3 Farm Glen Blvd Ste 301 06032
Tel (336) 245-6400
SIC 3556 3631 3585 3589 3634

CONNECTICARE INC p 356
175 Scott Swamp Rd 06032
Tel (860) 674-5700 *SIC* 6324

CONNECTICUT SPRING AND STAMPING CORP p 357
48 Spring Ln 06032
Tel (860) 677-1341 *SIC* 3469 3495 3493

■ DISCOVER RE MANAGERS INC p 442
5 Batterson Park Rd 06032
Tel (860) 674-2660 *SIC* 6311

DONCASTERS INC p 450
36 Spring Ln 06032
Tel (860) 677-1376
SIC 3511 3356 3728 7699

EBM INDUSTRIES MANAGEMENT GROUP INC p 474
100 Hyde Rd 06032
Tel (860) 674-1515 *SIC* 5084

EBM-PAPST INC p 474
100 Hyde Rd 06032
Tel (860) 674-1515 *SIC* 5084 3564

FAMILYMEDS GROUP INC p 527
312 Farmington Ave Ste B 06032
Tel (888) 787-2800 *SIC* 5912

■ FARMINGTON BANK p 530
1 Farm Glen Blvd 06032
Tel (860) 676-4600 *SIC* 6036 6163

FIP CONSTRUCTION INC p 543
1536 New Britain Ave 06032
Tel (860) 470-1800 *SIC* 1542 1541

▲ FIRST CONNECTICUT BANCORP INC p 546
1 Farm Glen Blvd 06032
Tel (860) 676-4600 *SIC* 6036

KBE BUILDING CORP p 806
76 Batterson Park Rd # 1 06032
Tel (860) 284-7424 *SIC* 1542 1541

MCPHEE ELECTRIC LTD p 932
505 Main St 06032
Tel (860) 677-9797 *SIC* 1731

■ MOORE MEDICAL LLC p 987
1690 New Britain Ave A 06032
Tel (860) 826-3600 *SIC* 5047 5122

■ OTIS ELEVATOR CO p 1097
10 Farm Springs Rd 06032
Tel (860) 676-6000 *SIC* 3534 1796 7699

PHALCON LTD p 1141
505 Main St 06032
Tel (860) 677-9797 *SIC* 1731

PROHEALTH PHYSICIANS INC p 1182
3 Farm Glen Blvd Ste 202 06032
Tel (860) 409-7700 *SIC* 8741

■ STANLEY ACCESS TECHNOLOGIES LLC p 1377
65 Scott Swamp Rd 06032
Tel (860) 409-6502 *SIC* 1751

TRUMPF INC p 1487
111 Hyde Rd 06032
Tel (860) 255-6000 *SIC* 3542 3423 3546

▲ UNITED TECHNOLOGIES CORP p 1514
10 Farm Springs Rd 06032
Tel (860) 728-7000
SIC 3724 3585 3721 3534 3669 3699

GLASTONBURY, CT

AERO-MED LTD p 30
85 Commerce St 06033
Tel (860) 659-0602 *SIC* 5047

FIRSTLIGHT POWER RESOURCES SERVICES LLC p 551
200 Glastonbury Blvd # 303 06033
Tel (860) 430-2110 *SIC* 4911

■ HARPOON ACQUISITION CORP p 663
455 Winding Brook Dr 06033
Tel (860) 815-5736 *SIC* 7372 7373

HEALTHTRAX INC p 678
2345 Main St 06033
Tel (860) 633-5572 *SIC* 7991 7997

HEALTHTRAX INTERNATIONAL INC p 678
2345 Main St 06033
Tel (860) 633-5572 *SIC* 7991

HIGHWAY SAFETY CORP p 692
239 Commerce St Ste C 06033
Tel (860) 659-4330 *SIC* 3444 3479

■ OPEN SOLUTIONS LLC p 1089
455 Winding Brook Dr # 101 06033
Tel (860) 815-5000 *SIC* 7372 7373

▲ UNITED BANK p 1506
45 Glastonbury Blvd # 200 06033
Tel (860) 291-3600 *SIC* 6036

GREENWICH, CT

A&M CAPITAL-GP LP p 7
289 Greenwich Ave Ste 2 06830
Tel (212) 759-4433 *SIC* 8742

AGI NORTH AMERICA LLC p 35
100 Northfield St 06830
Tel (203) 622-9138 *SIC* 2671

AMERICAN INDUSTRIAL ACQUISITION CORP p 74
1465 E Putnam Ave Ste 229 06830
Tel (203) 698-9595 *SIC* 8741

APTUIT (SCIENTIFIC OPERATIONS) LLC p 101
2 Greenwich Office Park 06831
Tel (203) 422-6600 *SIC* 2834

APTUIT LLC p 101
2 Greenwich Office Park 06831
Tel (203) 422-6600 *SIC* 8731

ATLAS AGI HOLDINGS LLC p 127
100 Northfield St 06830
Tel (203) 622-9138 *SIC* 2671

ATLAS HOLDINGS LLC p 128
100 Northfield St 06830
Tel (203) 622-9138
SIC 5031 2491 5039 5153

■ B H SHOE HOLDINGS INC p 142
124 W Putnam Ave Ste 1 06830
Tel (203) 661-2424 *SIC* 3143

■ BERKLEY REGIONAL INSURANCE CO p 175
475 Steamboat Rd Fl 1 06830
Tel (203) 629-3000 *SIC* 6331

BRANT INDUSTRIES INC p 208
80 Field Point Rd 06830
Tel (203) 863-1200 *SIC* 2621

BRIDGEWELL RESOURCES HOLDINGS LLC p 212
1 Sound Shore Dr Ste 302 06830
Tel (203) 622-9138
SIC 5031 2491 5039 5153

BRYNWOOD PARTNERS II LIMITED PARTNERSHIP p 222
8 Sound Shore Dr Ste 265 06830
Tel (203) 622-1790 *SIC* 6282 4731

BRYNWOOD PARTNERS V LIMITED PARTNERSHIP p 222
8 Sound Shore Dr Ste 265 06830
Tel (203) 622-1790
SIC 6282 1751 3442 5031 3354

BRYNWOOD PARTNERS VII LP p 222
8 Sound Shore Dr Ste 265 06830
Tel (203) 622-1790 *SIC* 6211

CAMUTO GROUP LLC p 246
411 W Putnam Ave Ste 210 06830
Tel (203) 413-7100 *SIC* 5139

CAPRICORN INVESTORS II LP p 251
30 E Elm St 06830
Tel (203) 861-6600 *SIC* 2676 5461 6794

CATTERTON PARTNERS CORP p 267
599 W Putnam Ave 06830
Tel (203) 629-4901 *SIC* 6211

DKR CAPITAL INC p 445
10 Glenville St Ste 5 06831
Tel (203) 324-8352 *SIC* 6722

▲ FIFTH STREET ASSET MANAGEMENT INC p 541
777 W Putnam Ave Ste 3 06830
Tel (203) 681-3600 *SIC* 6282

▲ FIFTH STREET FINANCE CORP p 541
777 W Putnam Ave Ste 3 06830
Tel (203) 681-3600 *SIC* 6726

FINCH PAPER HOLDINGS LLC p 543
1 Sound Shore Dr Ste 302 06830
Tel (203) 622-9138 *SIC* 2621

FIRST RESERVE XII ADVISORS LLC p 549
1 Lafayette Pl Ste 3 06830
Tel (203) 661-6601 *SIC* 6799

FRC FOUNDERS CORP p 575
1 Lafayette Pl Ste 3 06830
Tel (203) 661-6601
SIC 8741 1311 1389 8731 5084

GENERAL ATLANTIC CORP p 599
3 Pickwick Plz Ste 200 06830
Tel (203) 629-8600 *SIC* 6211

GENERAL ATLANTIC LLC p 599
600 Steamboat Rd Ste 105 06830
Tel (203) 629-8600 *SIC* 6799

GREENWICH AEROGROUP INC p 638
475 Steamboat Rd Fl 2 06830
Tel (203) 618-4861
SIC 4581 5088 7699 5085

GREENWICH HEALTH CARE SERVICES INC p 639
5 Perryridge Rd 06830
Tel (203) 661-5330 *SIC* 8062

GREENWICH HOSPITAL p 639
5 Perryridge Rd 06830
Tel (203) 863-3000 *SIC* 8062

GREENWICH SCHOOL DISTRICT p 639
290 Greenwich Ave 06830
Tel (203) 625-7400 *SIC* 8211

GRIFFIN MANAGEMENT CO INC p 640
19 Railroad Ave 06830
Tel (203) 869-6700 *SIC* 5511

■ HH BROWN SHOE CO INC p 689
124 W Putnam Ave Ste 1a 06830
Tel (203) 661-2424 *SIC* 3143 3144

■ IBG LLC p 726
1 Pickwick Plz 06830
Tel (203) 618-5800 *SIC* 6211 8732

▲ INTERACTIVE BROKERS GROUP INC p 751
1 Pickwick Plz 06830
Tel (203) 618-5800 *SIC* 6211

■ INTERACTIVE BROKERS LLC p 751
2 Pickwick Plz Ste 210 06830
Tel (203) 618-5700 *SIC* 6211

JACOBS PRIVATE EQUITY LLC p 775
350 Round Hill Rd 06831
Tel (203) 413-4000 *SIC* 4731 6282 6726

JAG FOOTWEAR ACCESSORIES AND RETAIL CORP p 776
411 W Putnam Ave Fl 3 06830
Tel (239) 301-3001 *SIC* 5139

KANDERS & CO INC p 802
2 Sound View Dr Ste 3 06830
Tel (203) 552-9600 *SIC* 6159

LAUREN HOLDING INC p 847
781 North St 06831
Tel (239) 514-7329 *SIC* 6211

LITTLEJOHN & CO LLC p 871
8 Sound Shore Dr Ste 303 06830
Tel (203) 552-3500 *SIC* 6799

LONGVIEW HOLDING CORP p 877
43 Arch St 06830
Tel (203) 869-6734 *SIC* 6719 1389

MRRC HOLD CO p 996
382 Greenwich Ave Apt 1 06830
Tel (203) 987-3500 *SIC* 5812

NORTH CASTLE PARTNERS LLC p 1051
183 E Putnam Ave 06830
Tel (203) 485-0216
SIC 7299 6794 5149 5499

PARTNER REINSURANCE CO OF US p 1118
1 Greenwich Plz Fl 3 06830
Tel (203) 622-1279 *SIC* 6331

PARTNERRE US CORP p 1118
1 Greenwich Plz 06830
Tel (203) 485-4200 *SIC* 6411

ROCKWOOD SERVICE CORP p 1245
43 Arch St 06830
Tel (203) 869-6734 *SIC* 6719

SECURITY CAPITAL CORP p 1299
8 Greenwich Office Park # 2 06831
Tel (203) 625-0770 *SIC* 6411 8211

SHOREWOOD PACKAGING HOLDINGS LLC p 1318
100 Northfield St 06830
Tel (203) 541-8100 *SIC* 2671

SILVER POINT CAPITAL LIMITED PARTNERSHIP p 1324
2 Greenwich Plz 06830
Tel (203) 542-4200 *SIC* 8741 6726

SOUNDVIEW PAPER MILLS LLC p 1342
1 Sound Shore Dr Ste 203 06830
Tel (201) 796-4000 *SIC* 2676

STARWOOD CAPITAL GROUP LLC p 1379
591 W Putnam Ave 06830
Tel (203) 422-7700 *SIC* 6211

STARWOOD PROPERTY TRUST INC p 1379
591 W Putnam Ave 06830
Tel (203) 422-7700 *SIC* 6798

STONE POINT CAPITAL LLC p 1391
20 Horseneck Ln Ste 1 06830
Tel (203) 862-2900 *SIC* 6726

TICC CAPITAL CORP p 1452
8 Sound Shore Dr Ste 255 06830
Tel (203) 983-5275 *SIC* 6726

TONTINE CAPITAL PARTNERS LIMITED PARTNERSHIP p 1460
55 Railroad Ave Ste 103 06830
Tel (203) 769-2000 *SIC* 7389

TOWN OF GREENWICH p 1465
101 Field Point Rd Ste 1 06830
Tel (203) 622-7700 *SIC* 9111

▲ TOWNSQUARE MEDIA INC p 1466
240 Greenwich Ave 06830
Tel (203) 861-0900 *SIC* 4832

TUDOR INVESTMENT CORP p 1490
1275 King St 06831
Tel (203) 863-6700 *SIC* 6282

▲ URSTADT BIDDLE PROPERTIES INC p 1530
321 Railroad Ave Ste 5 06830
Tel (203) 863-8200 *SIC* 6798

VCS GROUP LLC p 1545
411 W Putnam Ave Ste 210 06830
Tel (203) 413-6500 *SIC* 5139

▲ W R BERKLEY CORP p 1569
475 Steamboat Rd Fl 1 06830
Tel (203) 629-3000
SIC 6331 6321 6351 6311

WEEDEN & CO LP p 1587
145 Mason St 06830
Tel (203) 861-7670 *SIC* 6211

WEEDEN INVESTORS LIMITED PARTNERSHIP p 1587
145 Mason St 06830
Tel (203) 861-7600 *SIC* 6799

WEXFORD CAPITAL LP p 1603
411 W Putnam Ave Ste 125 06830
Tel (203) 862-7000
SIC 8741 6282 1221 1222

▲ XPO LOGISTICS INC p 1632
5 Greenwich Office Park 06831
Tel (844) 742-5976 *SIC* 4731

GROTON, CT

■ ELECTRIC BOAT CORP p 484
75 Eastern Point Rd 06340
Tel (860) 433-3000 *SIC* 3731 8711

■ PCC STRUCTURALS GROTON p 1123
839 Poquonnock Rd 06340
Tel (860) 405-3700 *SIC* 3364

HAMDEN, CT

HAMDEN TOWN OF (INC) p 655
2750 Dixwell Ave Fl 2 06518
Tel (203) 287-7100 *SIC* 9111

QUINNIPIAC UNIVERSITY p 1200
275 Mount Carmel Ave 06518
Tel (203) 582-8200 *SIC* 8221

HARTFORD, CT

■ A E PROPERTIES INC p 5
1 Tower Sq 06183
Tel (860) 277-1295 *SIC* 6512

■ ADVEST GROUP INC p 27
90 State House Sq 06103
Tel (860) 509-1000
SIC 6211 6036 6141 6153 6282

■ AETNA FINANCIAL HOLDINGS LLC p 31
151 Farmington Ave 06156
Tel (860) 273-0123 *SIC* 8322

■ AETNA HEALTH HOLDINGS LLC p 31
151 Farmington Ave 06156
Tel (860) 273-0123 *SIC* 6324 6411 6321

■ AETNA HEALTH INC p 31
151 Farmington Ave 06156
Tel (800) 872-3862 *SIC* 6324

■ AETNA HEALTH MANAGEMENT INC p 31
151 Farmington Ave 06156
Tel (860) 273-0123 *SIC* 6324

▲ AETNA INC p 31
151 Farmington Ave 06156
Tel (860) 273-0123
SIC 6324 6321 6371 8011

■ AETNA LIFE INSURANCE CO INC p 31
151 Farmington Ave 06156
Tel (860) 273-0123 *SIC* 6324 6321 8011

■ AHP HOLDINGS INC p 37
151 Farmington Ave 06156
Tel (860) 273-0123 *SIC* 6321 6311 8011

■ AUTOMOBILE INSURANCE CO OF HARTFORD CONNECTICUT p 134
1 Tower Sq 06183
Tel (860) 277-0111 *SIC* 6331

BELL PUMP SERVICE CO p 170
29 Lafayette St 06106
Tel (860) 525-6678 *SIC* 5075 5078 5074

BOARD OF TRUSTEES OF COMMUNITY-TECHNICAL COLLEGE p 196
61 Woodland St Ste 2 06105
Tel (860) 723-0011 *SIC* 8221

CAPITOL LIGHT & SUPPLY CO p 251
270 Locust St 06114
Tel (860) 549-1230 *SIC* 5063

CAPITOL REGION EDUCATION COUNCIL FOUNDATION INC p 251
111 Charter Oak Ave 06106
Tel (860) 524-4068 *SIC* 8299

CCMC CORP p 270
282 Washington St 06106
Tel (860) 545-9490 *SIC* 8069 7389 8299

■ CHARTER OAK FIRE INSURANCE CO p 291
1 Tower Sq 06183
Tel (860) 277-0111 *SIC* 6351 6331

■ CIGNA RE CORP p 306
900 Cottage Grove Rd 06152
Tel (860) 726-6000 *SIC* 6311 6321

CITY OF HARTFORD p 315
550 Main St Ste 1 06103
Tel (860) 757-9311 *SIC* 9111

CM LIFE INSURANCE CO INC p 328
140 Garden St 06105
Tel (860) 987-2676 *SIC* 6311

CONNECTICUT CHILDRENS MEDICAL CENTER p 356
282 Washington St 06106
Tel (860) 545-9000 *SIC* 8069

CONNECTICUT DEPARTMENT OF ADMINISTRATIVE SERVICES p 356
165 Capitol Ave Ste 7 06106
Tel (860) 713-5100 *SIC* 9199

CONNECTICUT DEPARTMENT OF CHILDREN AND FAMILIES p 356
505 Hudson St 06106
Tel (860) 566-2700 *SIC* 9441

CONNECTICUT DEPARTMENT OF DEVELOPMENTAL SERVICES p 356
460 Capitol Ave 06106
Tel (860) 424-3000 *SIC* 9431

CONNECTICUT DEPARTMENT OF ENERGY & ENVIRONMENTAL PROTECTION p 357
79 Elm St Fl 3 06106
Tel (860) 424-4100 *SIC* 9511

CONNECTICUT DEPARTMENT OF MENTAL HEALTH AND ADDICTION SERVICES p 357
410 Capitol Ave Fl 4 06106
Tel (860) 418-7000 *SIC* 9431

CONNECTICUT DEPARTMENT OF PUBLIC WORKS p 357
165 Capitol Ave Ste 6 06106
Tel (860) 713-5790 *SIC* 9511

CONNECTICUT DEPARTMENT OF REVENUE SERVICES p 357
450 Columbus Blvd Ste 1 06103
Tel (860) 297-5962 *SIC* 9311

CONNECTICUT DEPARTMENT OF SOCIAL SERVICES p 357
55 Farmington Ave Fl 1 06105
Tel (860) 424-4908 *SIC* 9441

CONNECTICUT INSTITUTE FOR BLIND INC p 357
120 Holcomb St 06112
Tel (860) 242-2274 *SIC* 8211 8361

CONNECTICUT STATE COLLEGES & UNIVERSITIES BOARD OF REGENTS FOR HIGHER EDUCATION p 357
61 Woodland St 06105
Tel (860) 723-0000 *SIC* 8221

CONNECTICUT STATE UNIVERSITY SYSTEM p 357
61 Woodland St 06105
Tel (860) 493-0000 *SIC* 8221

CONNING & CO p 358
1 Financial Plz Fl 13 06103
Tel (860) 299-2100 *SIC* 6722

DAY PITNEY LLP p 417
242 Trumbull St Fl 5 06103
Tel (617) 345-4600 *SIC* 8111

■ EQUIPOWER RESOURCES CORP p 506
100 Constitution Plz # 10 06103
Tel (203) 676-6700 *SIC* 4911

■ FARMINGTON CASUALTY CO p 530
1 Tower Sq 06183
Tel (860) 277-0111 *SIC* 6411

FIRST TRANSIT INC p 550
249 Wawarme Ave 06114
Tel (860) 247-0050 *SIC* 4111

GOVERNORS OFFICE STATE OF CONNECTICUT p 627
210 Capitol Ave Ste 202 06106
Tel (860) 566-4840 *SIC* 9111

■ HARTFORD ACCIDENT & INDEMNITY CO p 665
1 Hartford Plz 06155
Tel (860) 547-5000 *SIC* 6411

■ HARTFORD CASUALTY INSURANCE CO p 665
690 Asylum Ave 06155
Tel (860) 547-5000 *SIC* 6411 6331

HARTFORD CATHOLIC DEVELOPMENT CORP p 665
134 Farmington Ave 06105
Tel (860) 541-6491 *SIC* 8661

■ HARTFORD COURANT CO LLC p 665
285 Broad St 06115
Tel (860) 241-6200 *SIC* 2711

▲ HARTFORD FINANCIAL SERVICES GROUP INC p 665
1 Hartford Plz 06155
Tel (860) 547-5000
SIC 6331 6311 6351 6321

■ HARTFORD FIRE INSURANCE CO (INC) p 665
1 Hartford Plz 06115
Tel (860) 547-5000
SIC 6411 6311 6351 7373

HARTFORD FOUNDATION FOR PUBLIC GIVING p 665
10 Columbus Blvd Fl 8 06106
Tel (860) 548-1888 *SIC* 6732 8733

HARTFORD HEALTHCARE CORP p 665
1 State St Fl 19 06103
Tel (860) 263-4100 *SIC* 8059

HARTFORD HOSPITAL p 665
80 Seymour St 06102
Tel (860) 545-5000 *SIC* 8062

■ HARTFORD INSURANCE CO OF ILLINOIS p 665
690 Asylum Ave 06105
Tel (860) 547-5000 *SIC* 6411

■ HARTFORD INVESTMENT MANAGEMENT CO p 665
1 Hartford Plz 06155
Tel (860) 297-6700 *SIC* 6282

■ HARTFORD LIFE AND ACCIDENT INSURANCE CO INC p 665
1 Hartford Plz 06115
Tel (860) 547-5000 *SIC* 6311

HARTFORD SCHOOL DISTRICT p 665
960 Main St Fl 9 06103
Tel (860) 695-8400 *SIC* 8211

■ HARTFORD STEAM BOILER INSPECTION AND INSURANCE CO p 665
1 State St Fl 5-12 06103
Tel (860) 722-1866
SIC 6331 8711 7373 8742

■ HSB GROUP INC p 714
1 State St 06102
Tel (860) 722-1866
SIC 6331 6411 6799 8711 8742

INSURITY INC p 748
170 Huyshope Ave 06106
Tel (866) 476-2606 *SIC* 7374

JUDICIAL BRANCH STATE OF CONNECTICUT p 796
231 Capitol Ave 06106
Tel (860) 706-5146 *SIC* 9211

LAZ KARP ASSOCIATES INC p 848
15 Lewis St Fl 5 06103
Tel (860) 522-7641 *SIC* 7521 1799

LAZ KARP ASSOCIATES LLC p 848
15 Lewis St Fl 5 06103
Tel (860) 522-7641 *SIC* 1799

LAZ PARKING LTD LLC p 848
15 Lewis St Fl 5 06103
Tel (860) 713-2030 *SIC* 7521

LEGISLATIVE OFFICE OF STATE OF CONNECTICUT p 853
300 Capitol Ave 06106
Tel (860) 240-0100 *SIC* 9121

METROPOLITAN DISTRICT p 955
555 Main St 06103
Tel (860) 247-6487 *SIC* 4941 4952

MILITARY DEPARTMENT CONNECTICUT p 969
360 Broad St 06105
Tel (860) 524-4953 *SIC* 9711

NEWFIELD CONSTRUCTION INC p 1037
225 Newfield Ave 06106
Tel (860) 953-1477 *SIC* 1541 1542

PHL VARIABLE INSURANCE CO p 1144
1 American Row 06115
Tel (860) 253-1000 *SIC* 6411

PHOENIX COMPANIES INC p 1144
1 American Row 06103
Tel (860) 403-5000 *SIC* 6411

■ PHOENIX INSURANCE CO p 1145
1 Tower Sq 06183
Tel (860) 277-0111 *SIC* 6351 6331

PHOENIX LIFE INSURANCE CO p 1145
1 American Row 06103
Tel (860) 403-5000 *SIC* 6311

PLIMPTON & HILLS CORP p 1156
2 Brainard Rd 06114
Tel (860) 522-4233 *SIC* 5074 5085

PM HOLDINGS INC p 1157
1 American Row 06103
Tel (860) 403-5000
SIC 6411 6162 6722 6282 6211 6552

ROBINSON & COLE LLP p 1242
280 Trumbull St Fl 28 06103
Tel (860) 275-8200 *SIC* 8111

SAINT FRANCIS HOSPITAL AND MEDICAL CENTER FOUNDATION INC p 1269
114 Woodland St 06105
Tel (860) 714-4006 *SIC* 8062 8011 8069

■ **STANDARD FIRE INSURANCE CO** p 1376
1 Tower Ave 06120
Tel (860) 277-0111 *SIC* 6331

STATE OF CONNECTICUT p 1381
210 Capitol Ave Ste 1 06106
Tel (860) 566-4840 *SIC* 9111

■ **TRAVELERS CASUALTY AND SURETY CO** p 1474
1 Tower Sq 8ms 06183
Tel (860) 277-0111 *SIC* 6411 6351

■ **TRAVELERS CASUALTY AND SURETY CO OF AMERICA** p 1474
1 Tower Sq 2ms 06183
Tel (860) 277-0111 *SIC* 6411 6351

■ **TRAVELERS CASUALTY CO OF CONNECTICUT** p 1474
1 Tower Sq 06183
Tel (860) 277-0111 *SIC* 6331 6351 6321

■ **TRAVELERS CASUALTY INSURANCE CO OF AMERICA** p 1474
1 Tower Sq 06183
Tel (860) 277-0111 *SIC* 6411

■ **TRAVELERS COMMERCIAL CASUALTY CO** p 1474
1 Tower Sq 06183
Tel (860) 277-0111 *SIC* 6351 6331

■ **TRAVELERS COMMERCIAL INSURANCE CO** p 1474
1 Tower Sq 06183
Tel (860) 548-9948 *SIC* 6411

TRAVELERS COMPANIES FOUNDATION INC p 1474
1 Tower Sq 06183
Tel (800) 842-5075 *SIC* 6321

■ **TRAVELERS HOME AND MARINE INSURANCE CO** p 1474
1 Tower Sq 2ms 06183
Tel (860) 548-9948 *SIC* 4724

■ **TRAVELERS INDEMNITY CO** p 1474
1 Tower Sq 06183
Tel (860) 277-0111 *SIC* 6411 6331

■ **TRAVELERS INDEMNITY CO OF AMERICA INC** p 1474
1 Tower Sq 06183
Tel (860) 277-0111 *SIC* 6411 6531

■ **TRAVELERS INDEMNITY CO OF CONNECTICUT** p 1474
1 Tower Sq 06183
Tel (860) 548-9948 *SIC* 6411 6331

■ **TRAVELERS PERSONAL SECURITY INSURANCE CO** p 1474
1 Tower Sq 06183
Tel (860) 277-0111 *SIC* 6411

■ **TRAVELERS PROPERTY CASUALTY CORP** p 1474
1 Tower Sq 8ms 06183
Tel (860) 277-0111 *SIC* 6411

■ **TRI STATE BUSINESS SYSTEMS INC** p 1477
1 Tower Sq 06183
Tel (860) 277-0111 *SIC* 6311 6321

TRINITY COLLEGE p 1481
300 Summit St Ste 1 06106
Tel (860) 297-2000 *SIC* 8221

■ **TWIN CITY FIRE INSURANCE CO** p 1495
1 Hartford Plz 06115
Tel (860) 547-5000 *SIC* 6331

UNITED PACIFIC INSURANCE CO p 1510
1 Tower Sq 06183
Tel (860) 277-0995 *SIC* 6411

■ **UNITEDHEALTHCARE INSURANCE CO** p 1515
185 Asylum St 06103
Tel (860) 702-5000 *SIC* 6311 6321

VIRTUS PARTNERS INC p 1560
100 Pearl St Fl 9 06103
Tel (860) 403-5000 *SIC* 6282

YMCA OF METROPOLITAN HARTFORD INC p 1636
50 State House Sq Fl 2 06103
Tel (860) 522-9622 *SIC* 8641 7032 7997

MANCHESTER, CT

ALLIED PRINTING SERVICES INC p 56
1 Allied Way 06042
Tel (860) 643-1101
SIC 2396 2752 2759 2789 2791

BDF HOLDING CORP p 164
428 Tolland Tpke 06042
Tel (860) 474-1200 *SIC* 5712

BOBS DISCOUNT FURNITURE LLC p 196
428 Tolland Tpke 06042
Tel (860) 474-1200 *SIC* 5712

EASTERN CONNECTICUT HEALTH NETWORK INC p 472
71 Haynes St 06040
Tel (860) 533-6565 *SIC* 8062

ECHN ENTERPRISES INC p 475
71 Haynes St 06040
Tel (860) 646-1222 *SIC* 8741

HARTFORD DISTRIBUTORS INC p 665
131 Chapel Rd 06042
Tel (860) 643-2337 *SIC* 5181

▲ **LYDALL INC** p 887
1 Colonial Rd 06042
Tel (860) 646-1233
SIC 2297 3053 2899 2631 3714 3564

MANCHESTER BOARD OF EDUCATION p 901
45 N School St 06042
Tel (860) 647-3442 *SIC* 8211

MANCHESTER MEMORIAL HOSPITAL INC p 901
71 Haynes St 06040
Tel (860) 646-1222 *SIC* 8062

■ **MANCHESTER PARADIGM INC** p 901
967 Parker St 06042
Tel (860) 646-4048 *SIC* 3728

MANCHESTER SCHOOL DISTRICT p 901
45 N School St 06042
Tel (860) 647-3442 *SIC* 8211

MASHANTUCKET, CT

MASHANTUCKET PEQUOT TRIBAL NATION p 915
2 Matts Path 06338
Tel (860) 396-6500 *SIC* 9131

MERIDEN, CT

■ **3M PURIFICATION INC** p 3
400 Research Pkwy 06450
Tel (203) 237-5541 *SIC* 3589 3569

AMHERST NY BOBS INC p 85
160 Corporate Ct 06450
Tel (203) 235-5775
SIC 5651 5611 5699 5621 5641 5661

BI RETAIL INC p 180
160 Corporate Ct 06450
Tel (203) 235-5775
SIC 5651 5611 5699 5621 5641 5661

BS LIQUIDATING LLC p 222
160 Corporate Ct 06450
Tel (203) 235-5775 *SIC* 5651

CANBERRA INDUSTRIES INC p 246
800 Research Pkwy 06450
Tel (203) 238-2351 *SIC* 3829 4813

CARABETTA ENTERPRISES INC p 252
200 Pratt St Ofc 06450
Tel (203) 237-7400
SIC 1522 1542 1521 6512

CITY OF MERIDEN p 316
142 E Main St Rm 218 06450
Tel (203) 630-4124 *SIC* 9111

EASTERN OUTFITTERS LLC p 472
160 Corporate Ct 06450
Tel (203) 235-5775 *SIC* 5611 6719

EVEREST MERGER SUB INC p 514
160 Corporate Ct 06450
Tel (203) 235-5775 *SIC* 5699

H C BOBS INC p 649
160 Corporate Ct 06450
Tel (203) 235-5775
SIC 5651 5611 5699 5621 5641 5661

MERIDEN PUBLIC SCHOOLS p 948
22 Liberty St 06450
Tel (203) 630-4171 *SIC* 8211 9411

MIDSTATE MEDICAL CENTER p 966
435 Lewis Ave 06451
Tel (203) 694-8200 *SIC* 8062

RADIO FREQUENCY SYSTEMS INC p 1204
200 Pond View Dr 06450
Tel (203) 630-3311
SIC 3663 3661 5045 5065

SME HOLDING CO LLC p 1332
160 Corporate Ct 06450
Tel (603) 924-9571 *SIC* 5699 5941

SPORT CHALET LLC p 1359
160 Corporate Ct 06450
Tel (818) 790-2717 *SIC* 5699

TRADEBE TREATMENT AND RECYCLING NORTHEAST LLC p 1468
47 Gracey Ave 06451
Tel (203) 238-8102 *SIC* 4953 1442 4212

VESTIS RETAIL GROUP LLC p 1552
160 Corporate Ct 06450
Tel (203) 235-5775 *SIC* 7311

MIDDLEBURY, CT

■ **CHEMTURA USA CORP** p 294
199 Benson Rd 06762
Tel (203) 573-2000 *SIC* 2879 2869 2822

■ **GREAT LAKES CHEMICAL CORP** p 633
199 Benson Rd 06762
Tel (203) 573-2000 *SIC* 2899 2842

TIMEX GROUP USA INC p 1454
555 Christian Rd 06762
Tel (203) 346-5000 *SIC* 3873

WINCHESTER ELECTRONICS CORP p 1614
199 Park Rad Ext Ste 104 06762
Tel (203) 741-5400 *SIC* 3678

MIDDLEFIELD, CT

■ **ZYGO CORP** p 1645
21 Laurel Brook Rd 06455
Tel (860) 347-8506 *SIC* 3827

MIDDLETOWN, CT

CONNECTICUT DEPARTMENT OF EMERGENCY SERVICES & PUBLIC PROTECTION p 357
1111 Country Club Rd 06457
Tel (860) 685-8000 *SIC* 9221

CONNECTICUT DEPARTMENT OF PUBLIC SAFETY p 357
1111 Country Club Rd 06457
Tel (860) 685-8000 *SIC* 9221 9229

FLO-TECH LLC p 557
699 Middle St 06457
Tel (860) 613-3333 *SIC* 5045 3577

FUTURITY FIRST INSURANCE GROUP INC p 586
101 Centerpoint Dr # 208 06457
Tel (860) 838-4800 *SIC* 6411

LIBERTY BANK p 861
315 Main St 06457
Tel (860) 344-7200 *SIC* 6036 6163 6022

MIDDLESEX HEALTH SYSTEM INC p 965
28 Crescent St 06457
Tel (860) 358-6000 *SIC* 8062

MIDDLESEX HOSPITAL FOUNDATION INC p 965
28 Crescent St 06457
Tel (860) 358-6000 *SIC* 8062

US ELECTRICAL SERVICES INC p 1531
701 Middle St 06457
Tel (860) 522-3232 *SIC* 5063

WESLEYAN UNIVERSITY p 1593
45 Wyllys Ave 06459
Tel (860) 685-2000 *SIC* 8221 6552

XSE GROUP INC p 1633
35 Phil Mack Dr 06457
Tel (888) 272-8340 *SIC* 5112

MILFORD, CT

DONGHIA INC p 450
500 Bic Dr Ste 20 06461
Tel (800) 366-4442
SIC 5198 5131 5021 2342

EASTERN BAG AND PAPER CO INC p 471
200 Research Dr 06460
Tel (203) 878-1814 *SIC* 5113 5087 5046

FRANCHISEE SHIPPING CENTER CO INC p 573
500 Bic Dr Bldg 3 06461
Tel (203) 301-0539 *SIC* 4731 5943

NEOPOST USA INC p 1026
478 Wheelers Farms Rd 06461
Tel (203) 301-3400 *SIC* 3579 7359 7629

■ **SCHICK MANUFACTURING INC** p 1287
10 Leighton Rd 06460
Tel (203) 882-2100 *SIC* 3421

TRI STATE JOINT FUND p 1477
25 Research Dr 06460
Tel (203) 876-3100 *SIC* 6371

MILLDALE, CT

SUPERIOR PRODUCTS DISTRIBUTORS INC p 1407
1403 Meriden Waterbury Rd 06467
Tel (860) 621-3621
SIC 5074 5032 5082 7353

MONROE, CT

AQUARION WATER CO OF CONNECTICUT p 101
200 Monroe Tpke 06468
Tel (203) 445-7310 *SIC* 4941

VICTORINOX SWISS ARMY INC p 1555
7 Victoria Dr 06468
Tel (203) 929-6391
SIC 5023 5099 5094 5072

NAUGATUCK, CT

▲ **EASTERN CO** p 472
112 Bridge St 06770
Tel (203) 729-2255
SIC 3429 3452 3316 2439

YOFARM CO p 1636
141a Sheridan Dr Ste A 06770
Tel (203) 720-0000 *SIC* 2026

NEW BRITAIN, CT

■ **BLACK & DECKER (US) INC** p 186
1000 Stanley Dr 06053
Tel (410) 716-3900 *SIC* 3546 3634

CENTRAL CONNECTICUT HEALTH ALLIANCE INC p 278
100 Grand St 06052
Tel (860) 224-5757 *SIC* 8741

CITY OF NEW BRITAIN p 316
27 W Main St 06051
Tel (860) 826-3415 *SIC* 9111

CONSOLIDATED SCHOOL DISTRICT OF NEW BRITAIN p 360
272 Main St 06051
Tel (860) 827-2200 *SIC* 8211

EMHART TEKNOLOGIES LLC p 492
480 Myrtle St 06053
Tel (800) 783-6427 *SIC* 8711 3541

HOSPITAL FOR SPECIAL CARE p 709
2150 Corbin Ave 06053
Tel (860) 827-4924 *SIC* 8069

HOSPITAL OF CENTRAL CONNECTICUT p 709
100 Grand St 06052
Tel (860) 224-5011 *SIC* 8062

▲ **STANLEY BLACK & DECKER INC** p 1377
1000 Stanley Dr 06053
Tel (860) 225-5111
SIC 3429 3546 3423 3452 3699

TALCOTT GARDENS LIMITED PARTNERSHIP p 1422
135 West St 06051
Tel (860) 229-9554 *SIC* 6513

TILCON CONNECTICUT INC p 1453
642 Black Rock Ave 06052
Tel (860) 224-6010
SIC 5032 1611 3273 2951

NEW CANAAN, CT

GRIDIRON CAPITAL LLC p 640
220 Elm St Fl 2 06840
Tel (203) 972-1100 *SIC* 6726

GRIDIRON TRADING MANAGEMENT CO LLC p 640
81 Hemlock Hill Rd 06840
Tel (704) 872-5231 *SIC* 6221

INVERNESS MANAGEMENT LLC p 761
21 Locust Ave Ste 1d 06840
Tel (203) 966-4177 *SIC* 6799

J H WHITNEY CAPITAL PARTNERS LLC p 771
130 Main St 06840
Tel (203) 716-6100 *SIC* 6799

JH WHITNEY VI LP p 785
130 Main St 06840
Tel (203) 716-6100 *SIC* 6726 5812

SUNLAND TRADING INC p 1403
21 Locust Ave Ste 1a 06840
Tel (203) 966-4166 *SIC* 5149

UNIMIN CORP p 1504
258 Elm St 06840
Tel (203) 966-8880
SIC 1446 1499 1422 1459 4011 1442

WHITNEY & CO LLC p 1607
130 Main St 06840
Tel (203) 716-6100 *SIC* 6211

NEW HAVEN, CT

▲ **ALEXION PHARMACEUTICALS INC** p 49
100 College St 06510
Tel (203) 272-2596 *SIC* 2834 8733

ASSA ABLOY INC p 119
110 Sargent Dr 06511
Tel (203) 624-5225
SIC 5065 5072 3699 3429

■ **AVANGRID INC** p 136
157 Church St 06510
Tel (207) 688-6363 *SIC* 4911 4922 4924

CITY OF NEW HAVEN p 316
165 Church St Fl 2 06510
Tel (203) 946-8200 *SIC* 9111

HIGHER ONE HOLDINGS INC p 691
115 Munson St 06511
Tel (203) 776-7776 *SIC* 7389

HIGHER ONE INC p 691
115 Munson St 06511
Tel (203) 776-7776 *SIC* 7389

HOSPITAL OF ST RAPHAEL PHYSICIANS IPA II INC p 709
1450 Chapel St 06511
Tel (203) 789-3000 *SIC* 8062 8011

KNIGHTS OF COLUMBUS p 824
1 Columbus Plz Ste 1700 06510
Tel (203) 752-4000 *SIC* 6411 8641

NEW HAVEN PUBLIC SCHOOLS p 1030
54 Meadow St Fl 1 06519
Tel (203) 946-8501 *SIC* 8211

PREMIER EDUCATION GROUP LIMITED PARTNERSHIP p 1170
545 Long Wharf Dr Fl 5 06511
Tel (203) 672-2300 *SIC* 8249

PRITCHARD INDUSTRIES (NEW ENGLAND) INC p 1178
111 Court St 06511
Tel (203) 624-3200 *SIC* 7349

SARGENT MANUFACTURING CO p 1282
100 Sargent Dr 06511
Tel (203) 562-2151 *SIC* 3429

SOUTH CENTRAL CONNECTICUT REGIONAL WATER AUTHORITY p 1343
90 Sargent Dr 06511
Tel (203) 562-4020 *SIC* 4941

■ **SOUTHERN NEW ENGLAND TELECOMMUNICATIONS CORP** p 1349
2 Science Park 06511
Tel (203) 771-5200
SIC 4813 4812 5065 6159 2741 4822

■ **SOUTHERN NEW ENGLAND TELEPHONE CO INC** p 1349
310 Orange St 06510
Tel (203) 771-5200 *SIC* 4813 4822

■ **UNITED ILLUMINATING CO** p 1509
157 Church St Fl 16 06510
Tel (203) 499-2000 *SIC* 4911

UNITED STATES SURGICAL CORP p 1514
555 Long Wharf Dr Fl 4 06511
Tel (203) 845-1000 *SIC* 3841 3845 3842

WATERFRONT ENTERPRISES INC p 1582
400 Waterfront St 06512
Tel (203) 467-1997 *SIC* 5172

WITHERS BERGMAN LLP p 1619
157 Church St Fl 19 06510
Tel (203) 789-1320 *SIC* 8111

YALE UNIVERSITY p 1634
105 Wall St 06511
Tel (203) 432-2550
SIC 8221 2731 2721 2741

YALE-NEW HAVEN HEALTH SERVICES CORP p 1634
789 Howard Ave 06519
Tel (888) 461-0106 SIC 5912 8721

YALE-NEW HAVEN HOSPITAL INC p 1634
20 York St 06510
Tel (203) 688-4242 SIC 8351 8062 8741

NEW LONDON, CT

APACHE OIL CO INC p 96
261 Ledyard St 06320
Tel (860) 437-6200 SIC 5172 5541

CONNECTICUT COLLEGE p 356
270 Mohegan Ave 06320
Tel (860) 447-1911 SIC 8221

LAWRENCE & MEMORIAL HOSPITAL INC p 847
365 Montauk Ave 06320
Tel (860) 442-0711 SIC 8011 8062

LAWRENCE + MEMORIAL CORP p 847
365 Montauk Ave 06320
Tel (860) 442-0711 SIC 8741

NEWINGTON, CT

CONNECTICUT DEPARTMENT OF TRANSPORTATION p 357
2800 Berlin Tpke 06111
Tel (860) 594-3000 SIC 9621

DATA-MAIL INC p 414
240 Hartford Ave 06111
Tel (860) 666-0399 SIC 7371

KEENEY MANUFACTURING CO p 807
1170 Main St 06111
Tel (603) 239-6371 SIC 3432 5074

PCX AEROSTRUCTURES LLC p 1124
300 Fenn Rd 06111
Tel (860) 666-2471 SIC 3728

ROWE BROTHERS p 1253
367 Alumni Rd 06111
Tel (203) 265-5533 SIC 5141

TILCON INC p 1453
301 Hartford Ave 06111
Tel (860) 223-3651
SIC 1611 5032 3273 2951

NEWTOWN, CT

TAUNTON INC p 1426
63 S Main St 06470
Tel (203) 426-8171
SIC 2721 2731 7812 5963

NIANTIC, CT

TELAID INDUSTRIES INC p 1433
13 W Main St 06357
Tel (860) 739-4461 SIC 7373

NORFOLK, CT

VERTRUE LLC p 1552
20 Glover Ave 06058
Tel (203) 324-7635 SIC 7389

NORTH FRANKLIN, CT

MOARK LLC p 980
28 Under The Mountain Rd 06254
Tel (951) 332-3300
SIC 5144 2048 0252 2015

NORTH GROSVENORDALE, CT

■ **DRAKE PETROLEUM CO INC** p 455
221 Quinebaug Rd 06255
Tel (860) 935-5200 SIC 5541 5411

NORTH HAVEN, CT

BARTON BRESCOME INC p 158
69 Defco Park Rd 06473
Tel (203) 239-4901 SIC 5182 5181

CONNECTICUT CONTAINER CORP p 356
455 Sackett Point Rd 06473
Tel (203) 248-2161
SIC 2653 3993 3412 2631

HB COMMUNICATIONS INC p 671
60 Dodge Ave 06473
Tel (203) 747-7174 SIC 5064 5065 5731

ULBRICH STAINLESS STEELS & SPECIAL METALS INC p 1500
153 Washington Ave 06473
Tel (203) 239-4481
SIC 3316 3356 5051 3341 3312

UNITED ALUMINUM CORP p 1506
100 United Dr 06473
Tel (203) 575-9771 SIC 3353

■ **WORLD COLOR (USA) HOLDING CO** p 1625
291 State St 06473
Tel (203) 288-2468 SIC 2752 2754

NORTH STONINGTON, CT

A/Z CORP p 7
46 Norwich Westerly Rd 06359
Tel (800) 400-2420 SIC 1541 1542

NORWALK, CT

A GRADE MARKET INC p 5
360 Connecticut Ave 06854
Tel (203) 838-0504 SIC 5411

ADVANCED CENTER FOR REHABILITATION MEDICINE INC p 25
24 Stevens St 06850
Tel (203) 852-2000 SIC 5999

■ **AMG FUNDS LLC** p 85
800 Connecticut Ave Ste 2 06854
Tel (203) 299-3500 SIC 6141

ASEA BROWN BOVERI INC p 116
501 Merritt 7 06851
Tel (203) 750-2200
SIC 3612 3613 5063 3511 3625 8711

CEBAL AMERICAS p 272
101 Merritt 7 Ste 2 06851
Tel (203) 845-6356 SIC 3082

CELLMARK PAPER INC p 273
80 Washington St 06854
Tel (203) 363-7800 SIC 5099 5111

CHARKIT CHEMICAL CORP p 289
32 Haviland St Unit 1 06854
Tel (203) 299-3220 SIC 5169

CITY OF NORWALK p 317
125 East Ave 06851
Tel (203) 854-7900 SIC 9111

CRIUS ENERGY LLC p 393
535 Connecticut Ave # 400 06854
Tel (203) 663-5089 SIC 6719 1731

DATTO INC p 414
101 Merritt 7 Ste 7 06851
Tel (203) 665-6423 SIC 7375

DIAGEO NORTH AMERICA INC p 436
801 Main Ave 06851
Tel (203) 229-2100 SIC 2084 2085

■ **EMCOR CONSTRUCTION SERVICES INC** p 491
301 Merritt 7 Fl 6 06851
Tel (203) 849-7800 SIC 1711 1731

▲ **EMCOR GROUP INC** p 491
301 Merritt 7 Fl 6 06851
Tel (203) 849-7800 SIC 1731 1711 7349

■ **EMCOR MECHANICAL/ELECTRICAL SERVICES (WEST) INC** p 491
301 Merritt 7 06851
Tel (203) 849-7800 SIC 1711 1731

EURPAC SERVICE INC p 513
101 Merritt 7 Corp Park 7 Corporate 06851
Tel (203) 847-0800 SIC 5141 5122

▲ **FACTSET RESEARCH SYSTEMS INC** p 524
601 Merritt 7 06851
Tel (203) 810-1000 SIC 7374

▲ **FRONTIER COMMUNICATIONS CORP** p 581
401 Merritt 7 Ste 1 06851
Tel (203) 614-5600 SIC 4813

■ **FRONTIER FLORIDA LLC** p 581
401 Merritt 7 06851
Tel (813) 483-2011
SIC 4813 6519 8721 5065 7629

■ **GENERAL ELECTRIC CAPITAL CORP** p 600
901 Main Ave 06851
Tel (203) 840-6300 SIC 6159 6141 7359

HEI HOSPITALITY LLC p 680
101 Merritt 7 Corp 06851
Tel (203) 849-8844 SIC 7011

HEIDMAR INC p 680
20 Glover Ave Ste 14 06850
Tel (203) 662-2600 SIC 1389

HOMESERVE USA CORP p 704
601 Merritt 7 Fl 6 06851
Tel (203) 351-4924 SIC 8741 1521

■ **M E S HOLDING CORP** p 889
301 Merritt 7 06851
Tel (203) 849-7800 SIC 1711 1731

MAFCOTE INC p 895
108 Main St Ste 3 06851
Tel (203) 847-8500
SIC 2631 2657 2679 2671

MBI INC p 925
47 Richards Ave 06857
Tel (203) 853-2000 SIC 5961

MERRITT HOSPITALITY LLC p 950
101 Merritt 7 Ste 14 06851
Tel (203) 849-8844 SIC 8741

NORTH AMERICAN POWER AND GAS LLC p 1050
20 Glover Ave Ste 1 06850
Tel (203) 893-4196 SIC 4931

NORWALK HOSPITAL ASSOCIATION p 1061
34 Maple St 06850
Tel (203) 852-2000 SIC 8062

NORWALK PUBLIC SCHOOL DISTRICT p 1061
125 East Ave 06851
Tel (203) 852-9874 SIC 8211 9111

OMEGA ENGINEERING INC p 1084
800 Connecticut Ave 5n01 06854
Tel (203) 359-1660
SIC 3823 3575 3577 3433 3826 2759

■ **PEPPERIDGE FARM INC** p 1134
595 Westport Ave 06851
Tel (203) 846-7000
SIC 5963 2052 2099 2053 5961

▲ **PRICELINE GROUP INC** p 1174
800 Connecticut Ave 3w01 06854
Tel (203) 299-8000 SIC 4724 7375

RT VANDERBILT CO INC p 1203
30 Winfield St 06855
Tel (203) 853-1400
SIC 5169 2869 2819 5052 1499 1459

RT VANDERBILT HOLDING CO INC p 1256
30 Winfield St 06855
Tel (203) 295-2141
SIC 5169 2869 2819 1499 1459

STEW LEONARDS HOLDINGS LLC p 1388
100 Westport Ave 06851
Tel (203) 847-9088 SIC 5411

STOLT-NIELSEN TRANSPORTATION GROUP LTD p 1390
800 Connecticut Ave 4e 06854
Tel (203) 299-3600 SIC 4499 4213

VANDERBILT CHEMICALS LLC p 1543
30 Winfield St 06855
Tel (203) 853-1400 SIC 2819 2869 5169

VERDE ENERGY USA HOLDINGS LLC p 1549
101 Merritt 7 Ste 2 06851
Tel (203) 663-5700 SIC 4931

VERDE ENERGY USA INC p 1549
101 Merritt 7 Ste 2 06851
Tel (203) 663-5700 SIC 4931

WILTON RE US HOLDINGS INC p 1614
20 Glover Ave Ste 4 06850
Tel (203) 762-4400 SIC 6311

WILTON REASSURANCE CO p 1614
20 Glover Ave Ste 4 06850
Tel (203) 762-4400 SIC 6311

WINE LABELS LLC p 1616
100 Westport Ave 06851
Tel (203) 847-7213 SIC 5131

▲ **XEROX CORP** p 1631
45 Glover Ave Ste 700 06850
Tel (203) 968-3000
SIC 3861 3579 3577 7629 7378 7374

NORWICH, CT

BACKUS CORP p 143
326 Washington St 06360
Tel (860) 823-6330 SIC 8741

CONNECTICUT MUNICIPAL ELECTRIC ENERGY COOPERATIVE p 357
30 Stott Ave 06360
Tel (860) 889-4088 SIC 4911

WILLIAM W BACKUS HOSPITAL p 1611
326 Washington St 06360
Tel (860) 889-8331 SIC 8062

OLD GREENWICH, CT

ELLINGTON FINANCIAL LLC p 488
53 Forest Ave 06870
Tel (203) 698-1200 SIC 6162

OLD LYME, CT

LEARN p 850
44 Hatchetts Hill Rd 06371
Tel (860) 434-4800 SIC 8299

OLD SAYBROOK, CT

INFILTRATOR WATER TECHNOLOGIES LLC p 740
4 Business Park Rd 06475
Tel (860) 577-7000 SIC 3089

ORANGE, CT

■ **CONNECTICUT ENERGY CORP** p 357
60 Marsh Hill Rd 06477
Tel (203) 382-8111 SIC 4911 4932

DICHELLO DISTRIBUTORS INC p 437
55 Marsh Hill Rd 06477
Tel (203) 891-2100 SIC 5182 5181

PEZ CANDY INC p 1140
35 Prindle Hill Rd 06477
Tel (203) 795-0531 SIC 5145

▲ **TANGOE INC** p 1424
35 Executive Blvd 06477
Tel (203) 859-9300 SIC 7372

OXFORD, CT

▲ **RBC BEARINGS INC** p 1211
102 Willenbrock Rd Bldg B 06478
Tel (203) 267-7001 SIC 3562

■ **ROLLER BEARING CO OF AMERICA INC** p 1247
102 Willenbrock Rd 06478
Tel (203) 267-7001 SIC 3562

PAWCATUCK, CT

DAVIS-STANDARD HOLDINGS INC p 416
1 Extrusion Dr 06379
Tel (860) 599-1010 SIC 3559

DAVIS-STANDARD LLC p 416
1 Extrusion Dr 06379
Tel (860) 599-1010 SIC 3089

PLAINVILLE, CT

CARLING TECHNOLOGIES INC p 257
60 Johnson Ave 06062
Tel (860) 793-9281 SIC 3643 3613 3612

CWPM LLC p 404
25 Norton Pl 06062
Tel (860) 747-1335 SIC 4953

■ **GEMS SENSORS INC** p 598
1 Cowles Rd 06062
Tel (860) 747-3000
SIC 3824 5084 3812 3625 3613

MANAFORT BROTHERS INC p 900
414 New Britain Ave 06062
Tel (860) 229-4853
SIC 1794 1771 1622 1795 4953

PUTNAM, CT

DAY KIMBALL HEALTHCARE INC p 417
320 Pomfret St 06260
Tel (860) 928-6541 SIC 8062

RIDGEFIELD, CT

BOEHRINGER INGELHEIM CORP p 197
900 Ridgebury Rd 06877
Tel (203) 798-9988 SIC 2834 6221

BOEHRINGER INGELHEIM PHARMACEUTICALS INC p 197
900 Ridgebury Rd 06877
Tel (203) 798-9988 SIC 2834

BOEHRINGER INGELHEIM USA CORP p 197
900 Ridgebury Rd 06877
Tel (203) 798-9988 SIC 2834

▲ **CHEFS WAREHOUSE INC** p 292
100 E Ridge Rd 06877
Tel (203) 894-1345 SIC 5141

■ **NORTHERN TIER ENERGY LLC** p 1057
38c Grove St Ste 5 06877
Tel (203) 244-6550 SIC 1311

SCHIMENTI CONSTRUCTION CO LLC p 1287
650 Danbury Rd Ste 4 06877
Tel (914) 244-9100 SIC 1542

SMARTREVENUE.COM INC p 1332
60 Twin Ridge Rd 06877
Tel (203) 733-9156 SIC 8732

ROCKY HILL, CT

ASSISTIVE TECHNOLOGY GROUP INC p 119
1111 Cromwell Ave Ste 601 06067
Tel (860) 257-3443 SIC 5047

ATG HOLDINGS INC p 124
1111 Cromwell Ave Ste 601 06067
Tel (860) 257-3443 SIC 5047

CONNECTICUT DEPARTMENT OF VETERANS AFFAIRS p 357
287 West St 06067
Tel (860) 721-5891 SIC 9451

HENKEL CORP p 683
1 Henkel Way 06067
Tel (860) 571-5100
SIC 2843 2821 2833 2899 2891

HENKEL OF AMERICA INC p 683
1 Henkel Way 06067
Tel (860) 571-5100
SIC 2869 2843 2821 2833 2899 2891

NORTH AMERICAN MARKETING CORP p 1050
30 Waterchase Dr 06067
Tel (860) 649-3666 SIC 5999

■ **NORTHEAST GENERATION SERVICES CO** p 1054
301 Hammer Mill Rd 06067
Tel (860) 810-1700 SIC 4911

■ **SYSCO CONNECTICUT LLC** p 1417
100 Inwood Rd 06067
Tel (860) 571-5600 SIC 5149 5142

■ **TALEN ENERGY SERVICES NORTHEAST INC** p 1422
50 Inwood Rd Ste 3 06067
Tel (860) 513-1036 SIC 1711 1629

ROGERS, CT

▲ **ROGERS CORP** p 1246
1 Technology Dr 06263
Tel (860) 774-9605 SIC 2891 2821 2824

SANDY HOOK, CT

ULTRA ELECTRONICS AIRPORT SYSTEMS INC p 1501
107 Church Hill Rd Ste G2 06482
Tel (203) 270-3696 SIC 3625

SEYMOUR, CT

THULE HOLDING INC p 1451
42 Silvermine Rd 06483
Tel (203) 881-9600 SIC 3792 3714

THULE INC p 1451
42 Silvermine Rd 06483
Tel (203) 881-9600 SIC 3714 5021

SHELTON, CT

BIC CORP p 181
1 Bic Way Ste 1 06484
Tel (203) 783-2000
SIC 3951 2899 3999 3421 5091 3952

BIC USA INC p 181
1 Bic Way Ste 1 06484
Tel (203) 783-2000
SIC 3951 2899 3999 3421

CAMBRIDGE HOTEL MANAGEMENT LLC p 244
2 Crporate Driveshelton 06484
Tel (203) 925-8370 SIC 7011

CCL INDUSTRIES CORP p 270
15 Controls Dr 06484
Tel (203) 926-1253
SIC 2759 2992 3411 2819 2844

CCL LABEL (DELAWARE) INC p 270
15 Controls Dr 06484
Tel (203) 926-1253 *SIC* 2759

CELLMARK USA LLC p 274
2 Corporate Dr 5 06484
Tel (203) 541-9000 *SIC* 5169 5051 5084

CITY OF SHELTON p 318
54 Hill St 06484
Tel (203) 924-1555 *SIC* 9111

■ CLAYTON HOLDINGS LLC p 323
100 Beard Sawmill Rd # 200 06484
Tel (203) 926-5600 *SIC* 8741 7389 6531

■ DIANON SYSTEMS INC p 437
1 Forest Pkwy 06484
Tel (203) 926-7100 *SIC* 8071

■ EDGEWELL PERSONAL CARE BRANDS LLC p 477
6 Research Dr 06484
Tel (203) 944-5500 *SIC* 3421 2844 2676

GENERAL SUPPLY & SERVICES INC p 602
1000 Bridgeport Ave 5-1 06484
Tel (203) 925-2400 *SIC* 5063 8742

H J BAKER & BRO INC p 650
2 Corporate Dr Ste 545 06484
Tel (203) 682-9200 *SIC* 2048 5191 5052

▲ HUBBELL INC p 716
40 Waterview Dr 06484
Tel (475) 882-4000 *SIC* 3643

IROQUOIS GAS TRANSMISSION SYSTEM LP p 765
1 Corporate Dr Ste 600 06484
Tel (203) 925-7200 *SIC* 4922

■ ITT WATER & WASTEWATER USA INC p 768
1 Greenwich Pl Ste 2 06484
Tel (203) 712-8999 *SIC* 5084

NEVAMAR CO LLC p 1029
20 Progress Dr 06484
Tel (203) 925-1556 *SIC* 3089 5162

NEW CASTLE HOTELS LLC p 1029
2 Corporate Dr Ste 154 06484
Tel (203) 925-8370 *SIC* 7011 8741 8742

PANOLAM INDUSTRIES INC p 1111
20 Progress Dr 06484
Tel (203) 925-1556 *SIC* 3089 3083

PANOLAM INDUSTRIES INTERNATIONAL INC p 1111
20 Progress Dr 06484
Tel (203) 925-1556 *SIC* 2493 3089

PIONEER PLASTICS CORP p 1151
20 Progress Dr 06484
Tel (203) 925-1556 *SIC* 3083 3087

■ PLAYTEX PRODUCTS LLC p 1155
6 Research Dr Ste 400 06484
Tel (203) 944-5500
SIC 2676 3069 2844 3842

PRECISION RESOURCE INC p 1168
25 Forest Pkwy 06484
Tel (203) 925-0012 *SIC* 3469

■ PRUDENTIAL ANNUITIES DISTRIBUTORS INC p 1187
1 Corporate Dr 06484
Tel (203) 926-1888 *SIC* 6411

■ PRUDENTIAL ANNUITIES INC p 1187
1 Corporate Dr Ste 800 06484
Tel (203) 926-1888 *SIC* 6411 8741

■ PRUDENTIAL ANNUITIES LIFE ASSURANCE CORP p 1187
1 Corporate Dr Ste 800 06484
Tel (203) 926-1888 *SIC* 6411

SURESOURCE LLC p 1408
20 Constitution Blvd S 06484
Tel (203) 922-7500 *SIC* 5045

SURVEY SAMPLING INTERNATIONAL LLC p 1409
6 Research Dr Ste 200 06484
Tel (203) 225-6191 *SIC* 8732

TOMRA OF NORTH AMERICA (INC) p 1460
1 Corporate Dr Ste 710 06484
Tel (203) 447-8800 *SIC* 5046

WILLIAM RAVEIS REAL ESTATE INC p 1611
7 Trap Falls Rd 06484
Tel (203) 926-1090 *SIC* 6411

SIMSBURY, CT

CHUBB EXECUTIVE RISK INC p 304
82 Hopmeadow St 06070
Tel (860) 408-2000 *SIC* 6411

EASCO HAND TOOLS INC p 469
125 Powder Forest Dr 06070
Tel (860) 843-7351 *SIC* 3423

ENSIGN-BICKFORD AEROSPACE & DEFENSE CO p 501
640 Hopmeadow St 06070
Tel (860) 843-2289 *SIC* 2892

ENSIGN-BICKFORD INDUSTRIES INC p 501
125 Pwder Frest Dr Fl 3 06070
Tel (860) 843-2000
SIC 3764 2047 2835 3829 2499 6552

■ HARTFORD HOLDINGS INC p 665
200 Hopmeadow St 06070
Tel (860) 547-5000 *SIC* 6311

■ HARTFORD LIFE INC p 665
200 Hopmeadow St 06070
Tel (860) 547-5000 *SIC* 6311

SOUTH WINDSOR, CT

ENGINEERING SERVICES & PRODUCTS CO p 499
1395 John Fitch Blvd 06074
Tel (860) 528-1119 *SIC* 3523 5083 3081

HARTFORD PROVISION CO p 665
625 Nutmeg Rd N 06074
Tel (860) 583-3908 *SIC* 5141

VISTAR/VSA OF HARTFORD INC p 1562
175 Sullivan Ave 06074
Tel (860) 688-7702 *SIC* 5141 5812 8322

SOUTHBURY, CT

GALATA CHEMICALS HOLDING CO LLC p 589
464 Heritage Rd Ste 1 06488
Tel (203) 236-9000 *SIC* 5169 6719

GALATA CHEMICALS LLC p 589
464 Heritage Rd Ste A1 06488
Tel (203) 236-9000 *SIC* 5169 3999

MUNICIPAL EMERGENCY SERVICES INC p 1000
7 Poverty Rd Ste 85h 06488
Tel (203) 364-0620 *SIC* 5087

SOUTHINGTON, CT

CONNECTICUT ON-LINE COMPUTER CENTER INC p 357
100 Executive Blvd Ste 1 06489
Tel (860) 678-0444 *SIC* 7374

■ YARDE METALS INC p 1635
45 Newell St 06489
Tel (860) 406-6061 *SIC* 5051 3499

SOUTHPORT, CT

▲ STURM RUGER & CO INC p 1395
1 Lacey Pl 06890
Tel (203) 259-7843 *SIC* 3484 3324

STAMFORD, CT

AEGEAN BUNKERING (USA) LLC p 29
20 Signal Rd 06902
Tel (212) 430-1100 *SIC* 2911

AFFINION GROUP HOLDINGS INC p 32
6 High Ridge Park Bldg A 06905
Tel (203) 956-1000 *SIC* 8611 6282 8748

AFFINION GROUP INC p 32
6 High Ridge Park Bldg A 06905
Tel (203) 956-1000 *SIC* 7389 5961 6321

AFFINION GROUP LLC p 32
6 High Ridge Park Bldg A 06905
Tel (203) 956-1000
SIC 8699 8748 7319 7331

AGI SHOREWOOD GRAVURE LLC p 35
400 Atlantic St 06901
Tel (203) 541-8100 *SIC* 2671

AGI-SHOREWOOD GROUP US LLC p 35
300 Atlantic St Ste 206 06901
Tel (203) 324-4839 *SIC* 2671 2652 2657

▲ AIRCASTLE LIMITED p 40
300 1st Stamford Pl 9a 06902
Tel (203) 504-1020 *SIC* 7359

ALINDA CAPITAL PARTNERS LLC p 50
1266 E Main St Ste 700r 06902
Tel (203) 930-3800 *SIC* 6726

AMERICARES FOUNDATION INC p 81
88 Hamilton Ave 06902
Tel (203) 658-9500 *SIC* 8322

ASTORIA GENERATING CO LP p 122
300 Atlantic St Ste 500 06901
Tel (212) 792-0800 *SIC* 4911

ATLANTIC STREET CAPITAL MANAGEMENT LLC p 127
281 Tresser Blvd Fl 6 06901
Tel (203) 428-3150 *SIC* 6799

AXEON REFINING LLC p 140
750 Wshngton Blvd Ste 600 06901
Tel (210) 249-9988 *SIC* 2911

AXEON SPECIALTY PRODUCTS LLC p 140
750 Wshngton Blvd Ste 600 06901
Tel (855) 378-4958 *SIC* 2911

AZELIS AMERICAS INC p 140
262 Harbor Dr 06902
Tel (203) 274-8691 *SIC* 5085 5046 5169

CASTLETON COMMODITIES INTERNATIONAL LLC p 264
2200 Atlantic St Ste 800 06902
Tel (203) 564-8100 *SIC* 4923

CASTLETON COMMODITIES TRADING GP LLC p 264
2200 Atlantic St Ste 800 06902
Tel (203) 564-8100 *SIC* 4923

CENTERPLATE INC p 276
2187 Atlantic St 06902
Tel (800) 698-6992
SIC 5812 7999 5947 7993

CENTERPLATE ULTIMATE HOLDINGS CORP p 276
2187 Atlantic St 06902
Tel (800) 698-6992
SIC 5812 7999 5947 7993

■ CENVEO CORP p 283
200 First Stamford Pl # 200 06902
Tel (303) 790-8023 *SIC* 2677 2752 2759

▲ CENVEO INC p 283
200 First Stamford Pl # 200 06902
Tel (203) 595-3000 *SIC* 2677 2679

CHARTER COMMUNICATIONS INC p 290
400 Atlantic St Fl 10 06901
Tel (203) 905-7801 *SIC* 4841 4813

▲ CHARTER COMMUNICATIONS INC p 290
400 Atlantic St 06901
Tel (203) 905-7801 *SIC* 4841 4813

CITY OF STAMFORD p 318
888 Washington Blvd 06901
Tel (203) 977-4150 *SIC* 9111

CLEARVIEW CAPITAL LLC p 324
1010 Washington Blvd # 1 06901
Tel (203) 698-2777 *SIC* 6799

COFCO AMERICAS RESOURCES CORP p 334
4 Stamford Plz 06902
Tel (203) 658-2820
SIC 6221 5153 5149 2099

CONAIR CORP p 354
1 Cummings Point Rd 06902
Tel (203) 351-9000
SIC 3634 3631 3639 3999

■ CRANE AEROSPACE INC p 388
100 Stamford Pl 06902
Tel (203) 363-7300 *SIC* 3492

▲ CRANE CO p 388
100 1st Stamford Pl # 300 06902
Tel (203) 363-7300
SIC 3492 3494 3594 3589 3728 5031

■ CRANE INTERNATIONAL HOLDINGS INC p 389
100 Stamford Pl 06902
Tel (203) 363-7300 *SIC* 3492

CRT CAPITAL GROUP LLC p 396
262 Harbor Dr Fl 2 06902
Tel (203) 569-6400 *SIC* 6211

DANONE HOLDINGS INC p 412
208 Harbor Dr Fl 3 06902
Tel (203) 229-7000 *SIC* 2086

DAYMON WORLDWIDE INC p 417
700 Fairfield Ave Ste 1 06902
Tel (203) 352-7500 *SIC* 8742

■ DESIGN WITHIN REACH INC p 432
711 Canal St Ste 3 06902
Tel (203) 614-0600 *SIC* 5021 5719

DIRECT ENERGY INC p 441
263 Tresser Blvd Fl 8 06901
Tel (800) 260-0300 *SIC* 4911 1311

DKR OASIS MANAGEMENT CO LP p 445
1281 E Main St Ste 3 06902
Tel (203) 324-8400 *SIC* 6722

DMG INFORMATION INC p 446
46 Southfield Ave Ste 400 06902
Tel (203) 973-2940 *SIC* 6719 1731 8748

▲ EAGLE BULK SHIPPING INC p 467
300 Frst Stamford Pl Fl 5 06902
Tel (203) 276-8100 *SIC* 4412

ENCOMPASS DIGITAL MEDIA INC p 495
250 Harbor Dr 06902
Tel (203) 965-6000 *SIC* 4841 8742

F A BARTLETT TREE EXPERT CO p 522
1290 E Main St Ste 2 06902
Tel (203) 323-1131 *SIC* 0783

FINIAL REINSURANCE CO p 543
100 Stamford Pl Ste 201 06902
Tel (203) 564-5273 *SIC* 6411

FREEPOINT COMMODITIES LLC p 577
58 Commerce Rd 06902
Tel (203) 542-6000 *SIC* 6221

FUJIFILM MEDICAL SYSTEMS USA INC p 583
419 West Ave 06902
Tel (203) 324-2000 *SIC* 5047 5043 3861

■ G E COMMERCIAL FINANCE REAL ESTATE p 586
292 Long Ridge Rd 06902
Tel (203) 373-2211 *SIC* 6798

▲ GARTNER INC p 592
56 Top Gallant Rd 06902
Tel (203) 316-1111 *SIC* 8732 8742 8741

GE ASSET MANAGEMENT INC p 595
1600 Summer St Ste 3 06905
Tel (203) 326-2300 *SIC* 6282

■ GE CAPITAL INTERNATIONAL HOLDINGS CORP p 595
260 Long Ridge Rd 06927
Tel (203) 357-4000 *SIC* 6719

■ GE CAPITAL MONTGOMERY WARD p 595
3135 Easton Tpke 06927
Tel (203) 357-4000 *SIC* 6141

■ GE CONSUMER FINANCE INC p 595
777 Long Ridge Rd 06902
Tel (203) 921-1443 *SIC* 8742

GENERAL ELECTRIC INSURANCE PLAN TRUST p 600
1070 High Ridge Rd 06905
Tel (203) 326-2300 *SIC* 6411

■ GENERAL RE CORP p 602
120 Long Ridge Rd 06902
Tel (203) 352-3000 *SIC* 6331

■ GENERAL REINSURANCE CORP p 602
120 Long Ridge Rd 06902
Tel (203) 328-5000
SIC 6331 6351 6411 6321

■ GENERAL STAR INDEMNITY CO p 602
695 Main St Ste 1 06901
Tel (203) 328-5000 *SIC* 6321

GENEVE CORP p 603
96 Cummings Point Rd 06902
Tel (203) 358-8000 *SIC* 5961 3483 6282

GENEVE HOLDINGS INC p 603
96 Cummings Point Rd 06902
Tel (203) 358-8000 *SIC* 3462 6331

GERALD HOLDINGS LLC p 608
680 Washington Blvd Fl 9 06901
Tel (203) 609-8550 *SIC* 6221

GERALD METALS LLC p 608
680 Washington Blvd Fl 9 06901
Tel (203) 609-8300 *SIC* 5051

GLENCORE LTD p 615
301 Tresser Blvd Fl 14 06901
Tel (203) 328-4900 *SIC* 6221

▲ HARMAN INTERNATIONAL INDUSTRIES INC p 662
400 Atlantic St Ste 15 06901
Tel (203) 328-3500 *SIC* 3651

■ HARMAN KG HOLDING LLC p 662
400 Atlantic St Ste 1500 06901
Tel (203) 328-3500 *SIC* 3651

HARVEST HILL BEVERAGE CO p 666
1 High Ridge Park Fl 2 06905
Tel (203) 914-1620 *SIC* 5149

▲ HEXCEL CORP p 688
281 Tresser Blvd Ste 1503 06901
Tel (203) 969-0666
SIC 2821 3728 3089 3624 2891 3469

■ ICON HOLDING CORP p 727
107 Elm St Fl 15 06902
Tel (203) 328-2300 *SIC* 7389 7319

■ ICON INTERNATIONAL INC p 728
4 Stamford Plz 15th 06902
Tel (203) 328-2300 *SIC* 7389 7319

■ INDEPENDENCE HOLDING CO p 736
96 Cummings Point Rd 06902
Tel (203) 358-8000 *SIC* 6311 6321

▲ INFORMATION SERVICES GROUP INC p 742
281 Tresser Blvd Ste 901 06901
Tel (203) 517-3100 *SIC* 8742 7379

INTERLAKE HOLDING CO p 753
1 Landmark Sq Ste 710 06901
Tel (203) 977-8900 *SIC* 4449 4499

LEXA INTERNATIONAL CORP p 859
1 Landmark Sq Ste 407 06901
Tel (203) 326-5200 *SIC* 5171 3822

METRO BUSINESS SYSTEMS INC p 954
11 Largo Dr S 06907
Tel (203) 967-3435 *SIC* 5045

MTM TECHNOLOGIES INC p 998
4 High Ridge Park Ste 102 06905
Tel (203) 588-1981 *SIC* 5045 7379

▲ NAVIGATORS GROUP INC p 1020
400 Atlantic St Fl 8 06901
Tel (203) 905-6090 *SIC* 6331 6351

NESTLE WATERS NORTH AMERICA HOLDINGS INC p 1027
900 Long Ridge Rd Bldg 2 06902
Tel (203) 531-4100 *SIC* 5149

NESTLE WATERS NORTH AMERICA INC p 1027
900 Long Ridge Rd Bldg 2 06902
Tel (203) 531-4100 *SIC* 5149

NOBLE AMERICAS CORP p 1046
107 Elm St Fl 1 06902
Tel (203) 324-8555 *SIC* 5052 1311

NORFALCO LLC p 1048
301 Tresser Blvd 06901
Tel (416) 775-1400 *SIC* 2819

NOVITEX ENTERPRISE SOLUTIONS INC p 1063
300 First Stamford Pl # 2 06902
Tel (844) 668-4839 *SIC* 7334 8741

ODYSSEY RE HOLDINGS CORP p 1075
300 Stamford Pl 06902
Tel (203) 977-8000 *SIC* 6411

ODYSSEY REINSURANCE CO p 1075
300 Stamford Pl Ste 700 06902
Tel (203) 965-0004
SIC 6411 6361 6331 6324 6311

OLYMPUS PARTNERS LP p 1083
1 Station Pl Ste 4 06902
Tel (203) 353-5900 *SIC* 6799

PAVARINI NORTH EAST CONSTRUCTION CO INC p 1122
30 Oak St Fl 3 06905
Tel (203) 327-0100 *SIC* 1542 8741

■ PETRO INC p 1139
9 W Broad St Ste 3 06902
Tel (203) 325-5400 *SIC* 5983 7699

■ PETROLEUM HEAT AND POWER CO INC p 1139
9 W Broad St Ste 3 06902
Tel (800) 645-4328 *SIC* 5983 5172 5722

PHARMACEUTICAL RESEARCH ASSOCIATES INC p 1141
1 Stamford Forum 06901
Tel (203) 588-8000 *SIC* 2834 5122

■ **PHILIP MORRIS CAPITAL CORP** p 1143
225 High Ridge Rd Ste 300 06905
Tel (203) 348-1350 *SIC* 6159

▲ **PITNEY BOWES INC** p 1152
3001 Summer St Ste 3 06905
Tel (203) 356-5000
SIC 3579 7359 3661 8744 7372

PRA HOLDINGS INC p 1167
1 Stamford Forum 06901
Tel (203) 853-0123 *SIC* 2834 5122 8742

▲ **PROVIDENCE SERVICE CORP** p 1186
700 Canal St Ste 3 06902
Tel (203) 307-2800 *SIC* 8322 8742 7389

PURDUE PHARMA LP p 1192
201 Tresser Blvd Fl 1 06901
Tel (203) 588-8000 *SIC* 2834 5122

PURDUE PRODUCTS LP p 1192
1 Stamford Forum 06901
Tel (203) 588-8000 *SIC* 2834

RBS HOLDINGS USA INC p 1211
600 Washington Blvd 06901
Tel (203) 897-2700 *SIC* 6211

RBS SECURITIES INC p 1211
600 Washington Blvd 06901
Tel (203) 897-2700 *SIC* 6282 6211

RESINALL CORP p 1227
3065 High Ridge Rd 06903
Tel (203) 329-7100 *SIC* 2821

▲ **REVOLUTION LIGHTING TECHNOLOGIES INC** p 1229
177 Broad St Fl 12 06901
Tel (203) 504-1111 *SIC* 3674 3641 3993

RON WEBER AND ASSOCIATES INC p 1249
1127 High Ridge Rd 06905
Tel (203) 268-1725 *SIC* 7389

ROYAL BANK OF SCOTLAND PLC p 1254
600 Washington Blvd 06901
Tel (203) 897-2700 *SIC* 6029

SAC CAPITAL ADVISORS LLC p 1264
72 Cummings Point Rd 06902
Tel (203) 890-2000 *SIC* 6799

SAC CAPITAL ADVISORS LP p 1264
72 Cummings Point Rd 06902
Tel (203) 890-2000 *SIC* 6282

■ **SECURITY CAPITAL GROUP INC** p 1299
292 Long Ridge Rd 06902
Tel (203) 373-2211 *SIC* 6799 8742

▲ **SILGAN HOLDINGS INC** p 1323
4 Landmark Sq Ste 400 06901
Tel (203) 975-7110 *SIC* 3411 3085 3089

■ **SILGAN WHITE CAP CORP** p 1323
4 Landmark Sq Ste 400 06901
Tel (630) 515-8383 *SIC* 3411

■ **SPECTRUM MANAGEMENT HOLDING CO LLC** p 1357
400 Atlantic St 06901
Tel (203) 905-7801 *SIC* 4841

STAMFORD CAPITAL GROUP INC p 1375
1266 E Main St Ste 700r 06902
Tel (800) 977-7837 *SIC* 2741 6211

STAMFORD HEALTH SYSTEM INC p 1375
30 Shelburne Rd 06902
Tel (203) 325-7000 *SIC* 8741

STAMFORD HOSPITAL p 1375
1 Hospital Plz 06902
Tel (203) 325-7000 *SIC* 8062

STAR BRANDS NORTH AMERICA INC p 1378
30 Buxton Farm Rd Ste 100 06905
Tel (203) 329-4545 *SIC* 2066

▲ **STAR GAS PARTNERS LP** p 1378
9 W Broad St Ste 3 06902
Tel (203) 328-7310 *SIC* 1711 5172

■ **STARWOOD HOTELS & RESORTS WORLDWIDE LLC** p 1379
1 Star Pt 06902
Tel (203) 964-6000 *SIC* 7011 8741

STATOIL MARKETING & TRADING (US) INC p 1383
120 Long Ridge Rd 3eo1 06902
Tel (203) 978-6900 *SIC* 5172

STATOIL NATURAL GAS LLC p 1383
120 Long Ridge Rd 06902
Tel (203) 978-6900 *SIC* 4924

STATOIL US HOLDINGS INC p 1383
120 Long Ridge Rd 06902
Tel (203) 978-6900 *SIC* 5172 1382

▲ **SYNCHRONY FINANCIAL** p 1414
777 Long Ridge Rd 06902
Tel (203) 585-2400 *SIC* 6021 7389

■ **THOMSON REUTERS US LLC** p 1450
1 Station Pl Ste 6 06902
Tel (203) 539-8000 *SIC* 2711

■ **TIME WARNER CABLE ENTERPRISES LLC** p 1454
400 Atlantic St Ste 6 06901
Tel (877) 495-9201 *SIC* 7812 4841

■ **TIME WARNER ENTERTAINMENT-ADVANCE/NEWHOUSE PARTNERSHIP** p 1454
400 Atlantic St Ste 6 06901
Tel (212) 364-8200 *SIC* 4841

TOWERS WATSON PENNSYLVANIA INC p 1464
263 Tresser Blvd Ste 700 06901
Tel (203) 326-5400 *SIC* 8742 7371

TRONOX INC p 1484
1 Stamford Plz 06901
Tel (203) 705-3800 *SIC* 2819 2421

UBS ENERGY LLC p 1498
677 Washington Blvd 06901
Tel (203) 719-3000 *SIC* 6211 6799

UBS SECURITIES LLC p 1498
677 Washington Blvd 06901
Tel (203) 719-3000
SIC 6211 6221 6289 6311 6091 6282

UBS SECURITIES LLC p 1498
677 Washington Blvd 06901
Tel (203) 719-3000 *SIC* 6211 6282

■ **UNITED RENTALS (NORTH AMERICA) INC** p 1511
100 Frist Stamford 700 06902
Tel (203) 622-3131 *SIC* 7353 7359 5084

▲ **UNITED RENTALS INC** p 1511
100 1st Stamford Pl # 700 06902
Tel (203) 622-3131 *SIC* 7359 7353

US POWER GENERATING CO p 1533
300 Atlantic St Ste 500 06901
Tel (212) 792-0800 *SIC* 4911

UST LLC p 1536
6 High Ridge Park Bldg A 06905
Tel (203) 817-3000
SIC 2131 2084 2621 3999

VINEYARD VINES LLC p 1558
181 Harbor Dr Fl 1 06902
Tel (203) 661-1803
SIC 5136 5137 5699 5611 5621

VOLUME SERVICES INC p 1565
2187 Atlantic St Ste 6 06902
Tel (203) 975-5900
SIC 5812 7999 5947 7993

WJ DEUTSCH & SONS LTD p 1619
201 Tresser Blvd Ste 324 06901
Tel (914) 305-5765 *SIC* 5182

■ **WORLD COURIER GROUP INC** p 1625
4 High Ridge Park Ste 102 06905
Tel (203) 595-0900 *SIC* 4513

▲ **WORLD WRESTLING ENTERTAINMENT INC** p 1625
1241 E Main St 06902
Tel (203) 352-8600 *SIC* 7812 7929 2721

XL AMERICA INC p 1632
70 Seaview Ave Ste 7 06902
Tel (203) 964-5200 *SIC* 6411 6321 6351

XL GLOBAL SERVICES INC p 1632
70 Seaview Ave Ste 7 06902
Tel (203) 964-5200 *SIC* 6331 6282 6351

XL GLOBAL SERVICES INC p 1632
70 Seaview Ave Ste 7 06902
Tel (203) 964-5200 *SIC* 6411

XL SPECIALTY INSURANCE CO p 1632
70 Seaview Ave Ste 5 06902
Tel (800) 622-7311 *SIC* 6321

STORRS, CT

UNIVERSITY OF CONNECTICUT p 1521
343 Mansfield Rd U-1130 06269
Tel (860) 486-2000 *SIC* 8221 9199

STRATFORD, CT

ASHCROFT INC p 117
250 E Main St 06614
Tel (203) 378-8281
SIC 3823 3679 3663 3625

ASHCROFT-NAGANO KEIKI HOLDINGS INC p 117
250 E Main St 06614
Tel (203) 378-8281
SIC 3823 3679 3663 3625

CONNECTICUT DISTRIBUTORS INC p 357
333 Lordship Blvd 06615
Tel (203) 377-1440 *SIC* 5182

■ **DICTAPHONE CORP** p 438
3191 Broadbridge Ave 06614
Tel (203) 381-7000
SIC 3579 3825 3695 3577

HARTLEY & PARKER LIMITED INC p 666
100 Browning St 06615
Tel (203) 375-5671 *SIC* 5182

NATIONS ROOF OF CONNECTICUT LLC p 1017
1400 Honeyspot Road Ext 06615
Tel (203) 335-8109 *SIC* 1761

■ **SIKORSKY AIRCRAFT CORP** p 1322
6900 Main St 06614
Tel (203) 386-4000 *SIC* 3721 4581 5599

■ **SIKORSKY SUPPORT SERVICES INC** p 1322
6900 Main St 06614
Tel (203) 386-4000 *SIC* 5088

STRATFORD SCHOOL DISTRICT p 1392
1000 E Broadway 06615
Tel (203) 381-2012 *SIC* 9411

TOWN OF STRATFORD p 1465
2725 Main St 06615
Tel (203) 385-4001 *SIC* 9111

THOMASTON, CT

ALBEA THOMASTON INC p 46
60 Electric Ave 06787
Tel (860) 283-2000 *SIC* 2844

J R C TRANSPORTATION INC p 772
47 Maple Ave 06787
Tel (860) 283-0207 *SIC* 4213 4212

TOLLAND, CT

GERBER SCIENTIFIC LLC p 608
24 Indl Pk Rd W 06084
Tel (860) 871-8082
SIC 3993 7336 3851 7372 3577

GERBER TECHNOLOGY LLC p 608
24 Industrial Park Rd W 06084
Tel (860) 871-8082 *SIC* 3559 7371

TORRINGTON, CT

CHARLOTTE HUNGERFORD HOSPITAL p 290
540 Litchfield St 06790
Tel (860) 496-6666 *SIC* 8062

O & G INDUSTRIES INC p 1070
112 Wall St 06790
Tel (860) 489-9261
SIC 1542 1541 1611 1623 5032 2951

TECHNICAL INDUSTRIES INC p 1431
336 Pinewoods Rd 06790
Tel (860) 489-2160 *SIC* 3089

TRUMBULL, CT

■ **4 SURE.COM INC** p 3
55 Corporate Dr Ste 5 06611
Tel (203) 615-7000 *SIC* 5045 5734

■ **COOPERSURGICAL INC** p 367
95 Corporate Dr 06611
Tel (203) 601-5200
SIC 5047 3842 3841 3845

GARDNER DENVER NASH LLC p 592
2 Trefoil Dr 06611
Tel (203) 459-3923
SIC 5084 3563 8711 3561

■ **HELICOPTER SUPPORT INC** p 681
124 Quarry Rd 06611
Tel (203) 416-4000 *SIC* 5088 4581 3728

MONROE STAFFING SERVICES LLC p 985
35 Nutmeg Dr Ste 250 06611
Tel (203) 268-8624 *SIC* 7361

OCE-USA HOLDING INC p 1072
100 Oakview Dr 06611
Tel (773) 714-8500 *SIC* 3861 5044

■ **OXFORD HEALTH PLANS (CT) INC** p 1101
48 Monroe Tpke 06611
Tel (203) 459-9100 *SIC* 6324

■ **OXFORD HEALTH PLANS (NY) INC** p 1101
48 Monroe Tpke 06611
Tel (203) 459-9100 *SIC* 6324

■ **OXFORD HEALTH PLANS INC** p 1101
48 Monroe Tpke 06611
Tel (203) 459-9100 *SIC* 6324

THOMAS J LIPTON INC p 1448
75 Merritt Blvd 06611
Tel (206) 381-3500
SIC 2099 2034 2035 2033 2098 2024

TOWN OF TRUMBULL p 1465
5866 Main St 06611
Tel (203) 452-5080 *SIC* 9111

UNCASVILLE, CT

MOHEGAN SUN CASINO p 982
1 Mohegan Sun Blvd 06382
Tel (888) 226-7711 *SIC* 7011

MOHEGAN TRIBAL GAMING AUTHORITY p 982
1 Mohegan Sun Blvd 06382
Tel (860) 862-0777 *SIC* 7011

MTIC LLC p 998
1 Mohegan Sun Blvd 06382
Tel (860) 862-6100 *SIC* 7011

VERNON ROCKVILLE, CT

■ **UNITED BANK FOUNDATION CONNECTICUT INC** p 1506
25 Park St 06066
Tel (860) 291-3705 *SIC* 6036

VERNON, CT

TOWN OF VERNON p 1465
14 Park Pl 06066
Tel (860) 870-3690 *SIC* 9111

WALLINGFORD, CT

▲ **AMPHENOL CORP** p 86
358 Hall Ave 06492
Tel (203) 265-8900 *SIC* 3678 3643 3661

BYK USA INC p 231
524 S Cherry St 06492
Tel (203) 265-2086 *SIC* 2851

CONNECTICUT VNA INC p 357
33 N Plains Industrial Rd 06492
Tel (203) 679-5300 *SIC* 8082 8741

MASONICARE CORP p 916
22 Masonic Ave 06492
Tel (203) 679-5900 *SIC* 8069 8082 8322

THURSTON FOODS INC p 1451
30 Thurston Dr 06492
Tel (203) 265-1525
SIC 5141 5147 5142 5113

■ **TIMES FIBER COMMUNICATIONS INC** p 1454
358 Hall Ave 06492
Tel (203) 265-8500 *SIC* 3357

WATERBURY, CT

CITY OF WATERBURY p 319
236 Grand St 06702
Tel (203) 574-6712 *SIC* 9111

GREATER WATERBURY HEALTH NETWORK INC p 636
64 Robbins St 06708
Tel (203) 573-6000 *SIC* 8741 8093 8011

■ **MACDERMID INC** p 892
245 Freight St 06702
Tel (203) 575-5700
SIC 2899 2842 2874 2992 2752 3577

MERCURY FUEL SERVICE INC p 945
43 Lafayette St 06708
Tel (203) 756-7284
SIC 5172 5541 5411 5983 1711 2911

MICHAELS ENTERPRISES INC p 960
150 Mattatuck Heights Rd # 3 06705
Tel (203) 597-4942 *SIC* 5094

PARADIGM HEALTHCARE DEVELOPMENT LLC p 1113
177 Whitewood Rd 06708
Tel (860) 748-4750 *SIC* 8051

SAINT MARYS HEALTH SYSTEM INC p 1270
56 Franklin St 06706
Tel (203) 709-6000 *SIC* 8062 7011

SAINT MARYS HOSPITAL INC p 1270
56 Franklin St Ste 1 06706
Tel (203) 709-6000 *SIC* 8062

WATERBURY HOSPITAL p 1581
64 Robbins St 06708
Tel (203) 573-6000 *SIC* 8062

WATERBURY PUBLIC SCHOOL DISTRICT p 1581
236 Grand St Ste 1 06702
Tel (203) 574-8004 *SIC* 8211

WATERBURY SCHOOL DISTRICT p 1582
236 Grand St Ste 1 06702
Tel (203) 574-8000 *SIC* 8211

■ **WEBSTER BANK NATIONAL ASSOCIATION** p 1587
145 Bank St 06702
Tel (203) 578-2230 *SIC* 6035

▲ **WEBSTER FINANCIAL CORP** p 1587
145 Bank St 06702
Tel (203) 578-2202 *SIC* 6021

WATERFORD, CT

SONALYSTS INC p 1339
215 Parkway N 06385
Tel (860) 442-4355
SIC 8711 7373 8748 8732 3993

WATERTOWN, CT

■ **BRISTOL INC** p 214
1100 Buckingham St 06795
Tel (860) 945-2200 *SIC* 3823

HOMETOWN AUTO RETAILERS INC p 704
1230 Main St 06795
Tel (203) 756-8908 *SIC* 5511

SIEMON CO p 1320
101 Siemon Company Dr 06795
Tel (860) 945-4200
SIC 3643 3089 3679 3469 3613 3357

WEATOGUE, CT

■ **HARTFORD EQUITY SALES CO INC** p 665
200 Hopmeadow St 06089
Tel (860) 843-8213 *SIC* 6211

■ **HARTFORD LIFE AND ANNUITY INSURANCE CO** p 665
200 Hopmeadow St 06089
Tel (860) 547-5000 *SIC* 6311 6321

■ **HARTFORD LIFE INSURANCE CO** p 665
200 Hopmeadow St 06089
Tel (860) 547-5000 *SIC* 6411

■ **VEEDER-ROOT CO** p 1546
125 Powder Forest Dr 06089
Tel (860) 651-2700 *SIC* 3823 3824

WEST HARTFORD, CT

A H HARRIS & SONS INC p 5
433 S Main St Ste 202 06110
Tel (860) 216-9500 *SIC* 5032

COLT DEFENSE HOLDING LLC p 339
547 New Park Ave 06110
Tel (860) 232-4489 *SIC* 3484

COLT DEFENSE LLC p 339
547 New Park Ave 06110
Tel (860) 232-4489 *SIC* 3484

LEGRAND HOLDING INC p 853
60 Woodlawn St 06110
Tel (860) 233-6251 *SIC* 3643 6719

LEGRAND NORTH AMERICA LLC p 853
60 Woodlawn St 06110
Tel (860) 233-6251 *SIC* 8711

TOWN OF WEST HARTFORD p 1465
50 S Main St Ste 2 06107
Tel (860) 561-7500 *SIC* 9111

■ **TRIUMPH ENGINE CONTROL SYSTEMS LLC** p 1483
1 Charter Oak Blvd 06110
Tel (860) 236-0651 *SIC* 3728 3724 3812

UNIVERSITY OF HARTFORD p 1521
200 Bloomfield Ave 06117
Tel (860) 768-4393 *SIC* 8221

WIREMOLD CO p 1618
60 Woodlawn St 06110
Tel (860) 233-6251
SIC 3644 3643 3496 3315

WEST HAVEN, CT

CITY LINE DISTRIBUTORS INC p 312
20 Industry Dr 06516
Tel (203) 931-3707
SIC 5141 5142 5147 5113

STAR DISTRIBUTORS INC p 1378
460 Frontage Rd 06516
Tel (203) 932-3636 SIC 5181

UNIVERSITY OF NEW HAVEN INC p 1523
300 Boston Post Rd 06516
Tel (203) 932-7000 SIC 8221

WEST SUFFIELD, CT

ROBERT W BAKER NURSERY INC p 1241
1700 Mountain Rd 06093
Tel (860) 668-7371 SIC 5193 5261

WESTBROOK, CT

LEE CO p 851
2 Pettipaug Rd 06498
Tel (860) 399-6281
SIC 3823 3841 3812 3728 3714

WESTPORT, CT

ALLIANZ OF AMERICA INC p 56
55 Greens Farms Rd Ste 1 06880
Tel (203) 221-8500 SIC 6311 6331

BRIDGEWATER ASSOCIATES LP p 212
1 Glendinning Pl 06880
Tel (203) 226-3030 SIC 6282 8742

■ CEHI ACQUISITION CORP p 272
61 Wilton Rd Ste 2 06880
Tel (203) 221-1703 SIC 4959 6719

COMMERCE CONNECT MEDIA INC p 345
830 Post Rd E Fl 2 06880
Tel (800) 547-7377 SIC 2721

▲ COMPASS DIVERSIFIED HOLDINGS p 351
61 Wilton Rd Ste 2 06880
Tel (203) 221-1703 SIC 6211

■ COMPASS GROUP DIVERSIFIED HOLDINGS LLC p 351
60 One Wilton Rd Fl 2 06880
Tel (203) 221-1703 SIC 6726

COMPASS GROUP INTERNATIONAL LLC p 351
61 Wilton Rd Ste 2 06880
Tel (203) 221-1703 SIC 7361 7363

DALIO FOUNDATION INC p 409
1 Glendinning Pl 06880
Tel (203) 291-5130 SIC 8699

■ STERNOCANDLELAMP HOLDINGS INC p 1388
61 Wilton Rd Ste 2 06880
Tel (203) 221-1703 SIC 6211

▲ TEREX CORP p 1439
200 Nyala Farms Rd Ste 2 06880
Tel (203) 222-7170 SIC 3531 3537

■ TEREX USA LLC p 1439
200 Nyala Farms Rd 06880
Tel (203) 222-7170 SIC 3532

TOWN OF WESTPORT p 1465
110 Myrtle Ave 06880
Tel (203) 226-8311 SIC 9111

TRIPLE POINT TECHNOLOGY INC p 1482
57 Greens Farms Rd 06880
Tel (203) 291-7979 SIC 7371

WETHERSFIELD, CT

CONNECTICUT DEPARTMENT OF CORRECTION p 356
24 Wolcott Hill Rd 06109
Tel (860) 692-7481 SIC 9223

WILLIMANTIC, CT

WINDHAM TOWN OF (INC) p 1615
979 Main St 06226
Tel (860) 465-3000 SIC 9111

WILTON, CT

BEIERSDORF INC p 168
45 Danbury Rd 06897
Tel (203) 563-5800 SIC 2844

BEIERSDORF NORTH AMERICA INC p 169
45 Danbury Rd 06897
Tel (203) 563-5800
SIC 2844 5122 3842 2841 2672

■ BLUE BUFFALO CO LTD p 190
11 River Rd Ste 103 06897
Tel (203) 762-9751 SIC 2047 5149

▲ BLUE BUFFALO PET PRODUCTS INC p 191
11 River Rd Ste 103 06897
Tel (203) 762-9751 SIC 2048

CHANNEL 1 CORP p 288
15 River Rd Ste 210 06897
Tel (203) 523-5500 SIC 8742

COMMON FUND FOR NONPROFIT ORGANIZATIONS p 345
15 Old Danbury Rd Ste 200 06897
Tel (203) 563-5000 SIC 6282

COTIVITI CORP p 374
50 Danbury Rd 06897
Tel (203) 642-0727 SIC 8721

COTIVITI LLC p 374
50 Danbury Rd 06897
Tel (203) 529-2000 SIC 8721

COTIVITI USA LLC p 374
50 Danbury Rd 06897
Tel (203) 529-2000 SIC 7389

LD COMMODITIES CITRUS HOLDINGS LLC p 849
40 Danbury Rd 06897
Tel (203) 761-2000 SIC 6221

LOUIS DREYFUS CO HOLDING INC p 879
40 Danbury Rd Ste 3 06897
Tel (203) 761-2000 SIC 6719

LOUIS DREYFUS CO LLC p 879
40 Danbury Rd 06897
Tel (402) 844-2680 SIC 6221

LOUIS DREYFUS CO NA LLC p 879
40 Danbury Rd 06897
Tel (203) 761-2000 SIC 5153

LOUIS DREYFUS HOLDING CO INC p 879
10 Westport Rd Ste 200 06897
Tel (203) 761-2000
SIC 6221 5153 6512 6531 1311

LOUIS DREYFUS US LLC p 879
40 Danbury Rd 06897
Tel (203) 761-2000 SIC 6221

MELISSA & DOUG INC p 940
141 Danbury Rd 06897
Tel (203) 762-4500 SIC 5092

MELISSA & DOUG LLC p 940
141 Danbury Rd 06897
Tel (203) 762-4500 SIC 5092

MUEHLSTEIN INTERNATIONAL LTD p 998
10 Westport Rd Ste 200 06897
Tel (203) 855-6000 SIC 5169 5162

■ NEWS AMERICA MARKETING IN-STORE SERVICES LLC p 1039
20 Westport Rd Ste 320 06897
Tel (203) 563-6600 SIC 7319

NIDERA US LLC p 1043
195 Danbury Rd Ste 240 06897
Tel (203) 834-5700 SIC 5153

■ ONWARD HEALTHCARE INC p 1088
64 Danbury Rd Ste 100 06897
Tel (203) 834-3000 SIC 7361

SIRIUSDECISIONS INC p 1327
187 Danbury Rd 06897
Tel (203) 665-4000 SIC 6282 8742

SUN PRODUCTS CORP p 1400
60 Danbury Rd 06897
Tel (203) 254-6700 SIC 2841

WILTON SURGERY CENTER LLC p 1614
195 Danbury Rd Ste B100 06897
Tel (203) 563-9470 SIC 8062

WINDSOR LOCKS, CT

AHLSTROM NONWOVENS LLC p 37
2 Elm St 06096
Tel (860) 654-8300 SIC 2297

AHLSTROM USA INC p 37
2 Elm St 06096
Tel (860) 654-8300 SIC 2621

ALGONQUIN POWER WINDSOR LOCKS LLC p 50
26 Canal Bank Rd 06096
Tel (860) 627-6616 SIC 4911

■ HAMILTON SUNDSTRAND CORP p 655
1 Hamilton Rd 06096
Tel (860) 654-6000
SIC 3621 3594 3728 3625 3823 3822

HAMILTON SUNDSTRAND SERVICE CORP p 655
1 Hamilton Rd 06096
Tel (860) 654-6000 SIC 3324

HAMILTON SUNDSTRAND SPACE SYSTEMS INTERNATIONAL INC p 655
1 Hamilton Rd 06096
Tel (860) 654-6000 SIC 3841 3826

SUOMINEN US HOLDING INC p 1405
3 Chirnside Rd 06096
Tel (860) 654-8331 SIC 2297

WINDSOR LOCKS NONWOVENS INC p 1615
3 Chirnside Rd Bldg D 06096
Tel (860) 292-5600 SIC 2297

WINDSOR, CT

ALSTOM INC p 61
200 Great Pond Dr 06095
Tel (866) 257-8664 SIC 4911 6719

■ ALSTOM POWER INC p 61
200 Great Pond Dr 06095
Tel (866) 257-8664
SIC 3443 3564 3621 3823 8711

ALSTOM USA INC p 61
2000 Day Hill Rd 06095
Tel (860) 285-3790 SIC 8711

ALVEST (USA) INC p 63
812 Bloomfield Ave 06095
Tel (860) 602-3400 SIC 3585 3535

MORRIS GROUP INC p 990
910 Day Hill Rd 06095
Tel (860) 687-3300 SIC 5084

■ OAKLEAF WASTE MANAGEMENT LLC p 1071
415 Day Hill Rd 06095
Tel (860) 290-1250 SIC 8741 4953

PERMASTEELISA NORTH AMERICA CORP p 1136
123 Day Hill Rd 06095
Tel (860) 298-2000 SIC 1793 1799

SCAPA NORTH AMERICA INC p 1286
111 Great Pond Dr 06095
Tel (860) 688-8000
SIC 2231 3069 2211 2824 2672

SPECIALTY RISK SERVICES INC p 1356
100 Corporate Dr Ste 211 06095
Tel (860) 520-2500 SIC 8741

▲ SS&C TECHNOLOGIES HOLDINGS INC p 1363
80 Lamberton Rd 06095
Tel (860) 298-4500 SIC 7372 7371

■ SS&C TECHNOLOGIES INC p 1363
80 Lamberton Rd 06095
Tel (860) 298-4500 SIC 7372 7371 8741

STANADYNE INTERMEDIATE HOLDINGS LLC p 1375
92 Deerfield Rd 06095
Tel (860) 525-0821 SIC 3714 3492

STANADYNE LLC p 1375
92 Deerfield Rd 06095
Tel (860) 525-0821 SIC 3714

STANADYNE PARENT HOLDINGS INC p 1375
92 Deerfield Rd 06095
Tel (860) 525-0821 SIC 3714

TLD AMERICA CORP p 1457
812 Bloomfield Ave 06095
Tel (860) 602-3400 SIC 5088 3728 7629

■ TRC ENVIRONMENTAL CORP p 1475
21 Griffin Rd N Ste 1 06095
Tel (860) 289-8631 SIC 8748 8711

VALASSIS DIRECT MAIL INC p 1539
1 Targeting Ctr 06095
Tel (800) 437-0479 SIC 7331

■ VOYA HOLDINGS INC p 1566
1 Orange Way 06095
Tel (860) 580-4646 SIC 6719

■ VOYA INVESTMENT TRUST CO p 1566
1 Orange Way 06095
Tel (860) 580-4646 SIC 6211 6282

■ VOYA RETIREMENT INSURANCE AND ANNUITY CO p 1566
1 Orange Way 06095
Tel (860) 580-4646 SIC 6311

WESTPORT INSURANCE CORP p 1602
2 Waterside Xing Ste 200 06095
Tel (860) 902-7201 SIC 6331 6411

WOODSTOCK, CT

CRABTREE & EVELYN LTD p 388
102 Peake Brook Rd 06281
Tel (800) 272-2873 SIC 5122 5149 2844

DELAWARE

BEAR, DE

■ ARLON LLC p 110
1100 Governor Lea Rd 19701
Tel (302) 834-2100 SIC 2822

CLAYMONT, DE

■ CIGNA GLOBAL HOLDINGS INC p 306
590 Naamans Rd 19703
Tel (302) 797-3469 SIC 6311 6512 6411

■ CIGNA HOLDINGS INC p 306
590 Naamans Rd 19703
Tel (215) 761-1000
SIC 6311 6321 6331 6512 6514 6282

CLAYTON, DE

EAGLE GROUP INC p 468
100 Industrial Blvd 19938
Tel (302) 653-3000 SIC 3589 8099

METAL MASTERS FOODSERVICE EQUIPMENT CO INC p 952
100 Industrial Blvd 19938
Tel (302) 653-3000 SIC 3589 3556

DOVER, DE

AUGUST TECHNIC CORP CO p 131
8 The Grn Ste 4934 19901
Tel (302) 223-5215 SIC 5065 5045 7389

BAYHEALTH MEDICAL CENTER INC p 161
640 S State St 19901
Tel (302) 422-3311 SIC 8062

CAPITAL SCHOOL DISTRICT p 250
198 Commerce Way 19904
Tel (302) 672-1500 SIC 8211

▲ CHESAPEAKE UTILITIES CORP p 295
909 Silver Lake Blvd 19904
Tel (302) 734-6799 SIC 4924 4911

DELAWARE DEPARTMENT OF CORRECTION p 424
245 Mckee Rd 19904
Tel (302) 857-5317 SIC 9223

DELAWARE DEPARTMENT OF TRANSPORTATION p 424
800 S Bay Rd Ste 1 19901
Tel (302) 760-2080 SIC 9621

DELAWARE SOLID WASTE AUTHORITY p 424
1128 S Bradford St 19904
Tel (302) 739-5361 SIC 4953

DELAWARE TECHNICAL & COMMUNITY COLLEGE p 424
100 Campus Dr 19904
Tel (302) 857-1000 SIC 8222

DEPARTMENT OF SAFETY AND HOMELAND SECURITY (DSHS) p 430
303 Transportation Cir 19901
Tel (302) 744-2672 SIC 9221 9229

▲ DOVER DOWNS GAMING & ENTERTAINMENT INC p 453
1131 N Dupont Hwy 19901
Tel (302) 674-4600
SIC 7929 7999 7011 7948

EXECUTIVE OFFICE OF GOVERNOR OF DELAWARE p 517
150 Mlk Jr Blvd S Fl 2 19901
Tel (302) 744-4101 SIC 9111

GEORGE & LYNCH INC p 606
150 Lafferty Ln 19901
Tel (302) 736-3031
SIC 1623 1611 1629 1731

KENT GENERAL HOSPITAL p 812
640 S State St 19901
Tel (302) 674-4700 SIC 8062

■ PLAYTEX MANUFACTURING INC p 1155
50 N Dupont Hwy 19901
Tel (302) 678-6000 SIC 2676 2844 2842

STATE OF DELAWARE DNREC p 1381
89 Kings Hwy 19901
Tel (302) 739-9903 SIC 9512

STATE OF DELAWARE DNREC p 1381
89 Kings Hwy 19901
Tel (302) 739-9101 SIC 9511 9512

SUPREME COURT OF STATE OF DELAWARE p 1408
55 The Grn 19901
Tel (302) 739-4155 SIC 9211

FREDERICA, DE

ILC DOVER LP p 731
1 Moonwalker Rd 19946
Tel (302) 335-3911 SIC 3842 3721 7389

NEW ILC DOVER INC p 1031
1 Moonwalker Rd 19946
Tel (302) 335-3911 SIC 3842

GEORGETOWN, DE

OMTRON USA LLC p 1085
22855 Dupont Blvd 19947
Tel (302) 855-7131 SIC 2015

SERVICEXPRESS CORP p 1308
120 N Ray St 19947
Tel (302) 856-3500 SIC 7361

GREENWOOD, DE

DELAWARE ELECTRIC COOPERATIVE INC p 424
14198 Sussex Hwy 19950
Tel (302) 349-9090 SIC 4911

■ DISCOVER BANK p 442
502 E Market St 19950
Tel (302) 349-4512 SIC 6022

HOCKESSIN, DE

PENINSULA UNITED METHODIST HOMES INC p 1129
726 Loveville Rd Ste 3000 19707
Tel (302) 235-6800 SIC 8361

LEWES, DE

BEEBE MEDICAL CENTER INC p 168
424 Savannah Rd 19958
Tel (302) 645-3300 SIC 8062

MIDDLETOWN, DE

■ DELSTAR TECHNOLOGIES INC p 425
601 Industrial Rd 19709
Tel (302) 378-8888 SIC 3081

MILFORD, DE

BURRIS LOGISTICS p 228
501 Se 5th St 19963
Tel (302) 839-4531 SIC 5142 4222 4213

IG BURTON & CO INC p 730
793 Bay Rd 19963
Tel (302) 422-3041 SIC 5511 7538

MILLSBORO, DE

■ INTERVET INC p 759
29160 Intervet Ln 19966
Tel (302) 934-4341 SIC 2836

MOUNTAIRE FARMS OF DELAWARE INC p 994
29005 John J Williams Hwy 19966
Tel (302) 934-1100 SIC 2015

NEW CASTLE, DE

■ **CITICORP BANKING CORP** p 310
1 Penns Way 19721
Tel (302) 323-3140 *SIC* 6162

■ **CITICORP DEL-LEASE INC** p 310
1 Penns Way 19721
Tel (302) 323-3801 *SIC* 6022 6311 6321

COLONIAL SCHOOL DISTRICT p 338
318 E Basin Rd 19720
Tel (302) 323-2700 *SIC* 8211

CORPORATE INTERIORS INC p 372
223 Lisa Dr 19720
Tel (302) 322-1008 *SIC* 5021 2521

COUNTY OF NEW CASTLE p 380
87 Reads Way 19720
Tel (302) 395-5555 *SIC* 9111

DELAWARE DEPT OF HEALTH AND SOCIAL SERVICES p 424
1901 N Dupont Hwy 19720
Tel (302) 255-9040 *SIC* 9431 9441

NATIONAL GUARD DELAWARE p 1013
250 Airport Rd 19720
Tel (302) 326-7160 *SIC* 9711

■ **PRINCETELECOM LLC** p 1176
551 Mews Dr Ste A 19720
Tel (302) 324-1800 *SIC* 1731

PRINTPACK ENTERPRISES INC p 1177
River Rd & Grantham Ln 19720
Tel (302) 323-0900 *SIC* 2673

■ **TA INSTRUMENTS - WATERS LLC** p 1420
159 Lukens Dr 19720
Tel (302) 777-0712 *SIC* 3826

UNITED ELECTRIC SUPPLY CO INC p 1508
10 Bellecor Dr 19720
Tel (800) 322-3374 *SIC* 5063

WILMINGTON UNIVERSITY INC p 1613
320 N Dupont Hwy 19720
Tel (302) 356-6824 *SIC* 8221

ZWD PRODUCTS CORP p 1645
400 Lukens Dr 19720
Tel (302) 326-8200 *SIC* 2434 2514

NEWARK, DE

A JBEK JOINT VENTURE CO p 6
242 Chapman Rd 19702
Tel (302) 452-9000 *SIC* 8711 8741

■ **ATLANTIC CITY ELECTRIC CO** p 126
500 N Wakefield Dr Fl 2 19702
Tel (202) 872-2000 *SIC* 4911

■ **BLACK & DECKER INC** p 186
1423 Kirkwood Hwy 19711
Tel (302) 738-0250
SIC 3429 3452 3579 3423 3949

■ **CHASE BANK USA NATIONAL ASSOCIATION** p 291
200 White Clay Center Dr 19711
Tel (302) 634-1000 *SIC* 6022

CHRISTIANA CARE HEALTH SYSTEM INC p 303
200 Hygeia Dr 19713
Tel (302) 733-1000 *SIC* 8741

■ **DELMARVA POWER & LIGHT CO** p 425
500 N Wakefield Dr Fl 2 19702
Tel (202) 872-2000 *SIC* 4939

■ **EECO INC** p 480
850 Library Ave Ste 204c 19711
Tel (302) 456-1448
SIC 3823 3491 3621 3585 3546 3679

■ **HAPPY HARRYS INC** p 659
326 Ruthar Dr 19711
Tel (302) 366-0335 *SIC* 5912

INTEGRITY STAFFING SOLUTIONS INC p 750
700 Prides Xing 300 19713
Tel (302) 661-8770 *SIC* 7363

■ **J P MORGAN SERVICES INC** p 772
500 Stanton Christiana Rd 19713
Tel (302) 634-1000 *SIC* 7374 8741

■ **MILFORD ANESTHESIA ASSOCIATES LLC** p 969
111 Continental Dr # 412 19713
Tel (302) 783-1831 *SIC* 8011

QPS HOLDINGS LLC p 1195
3 Innovation Way Ste 240 19711
Tel (302) 369-5601 *SIC* 6719

RCP III LLC p 1212
303 E Cleveland Ave 19711
Tel (302) 368-6300 *SIC* 5511

SIGNET US HOLDINGS INC p 1322
850 Library Ave 19711
Tel (302) 738-9652 *SIC* 5944

▲ **SLM CORP** p 1331
300 Continental Dr Ste 1s 19713
Tel (302) 451-0200 *SIC* 6111 6141 7322

TAGHLEEF INDUSTRIES INC p 1421
500 Creek View Rd Ste 301 19711
Tel (302) 326-5500 *SIC* 3081

UNIVERSITY OF DELAWARE p 1521
220 Hullihen Hall 19716
Tel (302) 831-2107 *SIC* 8221

W L GORE & ASSOCIATES INC p 1568
555 Paper Mill Rd 19711
Tel (302) 738-4880
SIC 3357 2821 5131 3841 2819 3069

WILLIAM H PORTER INC p 1610
414 E Cleveland Ave 19711
Tel (302) 453-6800 *SIC* 5511

ODESSA, DE

APPOQUINIMINK SCHOOL DISTRICT INC p 100
118 S 6th St 19730
Tel (302) 376-4128 *SIC* 8211

SEAFORD, DE

ALLEN BIOTECH LLC p 53
126 N Shipley St 19973
Tel (302) 629-9136 *SIC* 2015

ALLEN HARIM FOODS LLC p 53
126 N Shipley St 19973
Tel (302) 629-9136 *SIC* 0251

BIO MEDIC CORP p 183
742 Sussex Ave 19973
Tel (302) 628-4300
SIC 5049 3821 3496 3914 3661

HARIM USA LTD p 661
126 N Shipley St 19973
Tel (302) 629-9136 *SIC* 2015

NANTICOKE HEALTH SERVICES INC p 1007
801 Middleford Rd 19973
Tel (302) 629-6611 *SIC* 8099

NANTICOKE MEMORIAL HOSPITAL INC p 1007
801 Middleford Rd 19973
Tel (302) 629-6611 *SIC* 8062

TRINITY LOGISTICS INC p 1481
50 Fallon Ave 19973
Tel (302) 253-3900 *SIC* 4731

SELBYVILLE, DE

AVALANCHE STRATEGIES LLC p 135
144 Dixon St 19975
Tel (302) 436-7060 *SIC* 5092 5945

INDIAN RIVER SCHOOL DISTRICT p 737
31 Hosier St 19975
Tel (302) 436-1000 *SIC* 8211

■ **MERCANTILE PENINSULA BANK** p 944
1 W Church St 19975
Tel (302) 436-8236 *SIC* 6022

WILMINGTON, DE

21ST CENTURY NORTH AMERICA INSURANCE CO p 2
3 Beaver Valley Rd 19803
Tel (877) 310-5687 *SIC* 6411

■ **A T I FUNDING CORP** p 6
801 N West St Fl 2 19801
Tel (302) 656-8937 *SIC* 3462

AAA CLUB ALLIANCE INC p 7
1 River Pl 19801
Tel (302) 299-4700
SIC 8699 6331 6351 6512 4724

■ **ADP ATLANTIC LLC** p 24
800 Delaware Ave Ste 601 19801
Tel (302) 657-4060 *SIC* 6719

AI DUPONT HOSPITAL FOR CHILDREN p 37
1600 Rockland Rd 19803
Tel (302) 651-4620 *SIC* 8062

ALFRED IDUPONT HOSPITAL FOR CHILDREN p 50
1600 Rockland Rd 19803
Tel (302) 651-4000 *SIC* 8069

■ **AMERICAN LIFE INSURANCE CO** p 75
1 Alico Plz 19801
Tel (302) 594-2000 *SIC* 6411 6321 6324

■ **AMERICAN METER HOLDINGS CORP** p 76
1105 N Market St Ste 1300 19801
Tel (302) 477-0208 *SIC* 3824 3823

AMYLIN PHARMACEUTICALS LLC p 88
1800 Concord Pike 19897
Tel (858) 552-2200 *SIC* 2834 8731

■ **ANDERSON GROUP INC** p 90
3411 Silverside Rd # 103 19810
Tel (302) 478-6160
SIC 5047 5063 5099 7699 3443

ASBURY CARBONS INC p 115
103 Foulk Rd Ste 202 19803
Tel (302) 652-0266
SIC 1499 3295 1241 5051 3952 3069

■ **ASHLAND SPECIALTY INGREDIENTS GP** p 117
8145 Blazer Dr 19808
Tel (302) 594-5000 *SIC* 2869

ASTRAZENECA LP p 122
1800 Concord Pike 19803
Tel (302) 886-3000 *SIC* 2834

ASTRAZENECA PHARMACEUTICALS LP p 122
1800 Concord Pike 19803
Tel (302) 886-3000 *SIC* 2834 5122

ATLAS MANAGEMENT INC p 128
103 Foulk Rd 19803
Tel (302) 576-2749 *SIC* 6726

■ **B WILLIAMS HOLDING CORP** p 142
1403 Foulk Rd Ste 200 19803
Tel (302) 656-8596
SIC 3579 3661 3861 7359 7629 6159

BALFOUR BEATTY LLC p 148
1011 Centre Rd Ste 322 19805
Tel (302) 573-3873 *SIC* 1542 8712 8741

■ **BANCORP BANK** p 150
409 Silverside Rd Ste 105 19809
Tel (302) 385-5000 *SIC* 6022

▲ **BANCORP INC** p 150
409 Silverside Rd Ste 105 19809
Tel (302) 385-5000 *SIC* 6021

BARCLAYS BANK DELAWARE p 154
100 S West St 19801
Tel (302) 255-8000 *SIC* 6035

BARCLAYS FINANCIAL CORP p 155
125 S West St 19801
Tel (302) 622-8990 *SIC* 7389 6282 6211

BARLOWORLD USA INC p 155
1105 N Market St Ste 1300 19801
Tel (302) 427-2765 *SIC* 5084 7699 7359

BMP SUNSTONE CORP p 194
3711 Kennett Pike Ste 200 19807
Tel (610) 940-1675 *SIC* 5122

BRANDYWINE SCHOOL DISTRICT p 208
1311 Brandywine Blvd 19809
Tel (302) 793-5000 *SIC* 8211

BUCCINI/POLLIN GROUP INC p 222
322 A St Ste 300 19801
Tel (302) 691-2100 *SIC* 6552

CAE(US) INC p 236
1011 Ct Rd Ste 322 19805
Tel (813) 885-7481 *SIC* 3559

CATHOLIC DIOCESE OF WILMINGTON INC p 266
1925 Delaware Ave 19806
Tel (302) 573-3100 *SIC* 8661

CAWSL ENTERPRISES INC p 268
3411 Silverside Rd 19810
Tel (302) 478-6160 *SIC* 6211

▲ **CHEMOURS CO** p 293
1007 Market St 19898
Tel (302) 773-1000 *SIC* 2879

■ **CHEMOURS CO FC LLC** p 293
1007 Market St 19898
Tel (302) 774-1000 *SIC* 2879 2816

CHRISTIANA CARE HEALTH SERVICES INC p 303
501 W 14th St 19801
Tel (302) 733-1000 *SIC* 8062

CHRISTINA SCHOOL DISTRICT p 303
600 N Lombard St 19801
Tel (302) 552-2600 *SIC* 8211

CITY OF WILMINGTON p 319
800 N French St Fl 5 19801
Tel (302) 576-2415 *SIC* 9111

■ **CMC STEEL HOLDING CO** p 329
802 N West St Ste 302 19801
Tel (302) 691-6200 *SIC* 3441 3312

■ **CMH CAPITAL INC** p 329
1105 N Market St Ste 1300 19801
Tel (302) 651-7947
SIC 6719 2451 6515 6311

■ **COGENTRIX DELAWARE HOLDINGS INC** p 334
1105 N Market St Ste 1108 19801
Tel (847) 908-2800 *SIC* 4911

■ **COMENITY BANK** p 344
1 Righter Pkwy Ste 100 19803
Tel (614) 729-4000 *SIC* 6022

■ **CONCORD CORPORATE SERVICES INC** p 354
1100 Carr Rd 19809
Tel (302) 791-8200 *SIC* 6099

■ **CONECTIV LLC** p 355
800 N King St Ste 400 19801
Tel (202) 872-2680
SIC 4911 4924 1731 5172

CONNECTIONS COMMUNITY SUPPORT PROGRAMS INC p 357
3821 Lancaster Pike 19805
Tel (302) 984-2302 *SIC* 8322 8361 8049

CONSTRUCTION MANAGEMENT SERVICES INC p 361
3600 Silverside Rd 19810
Tel (302) 478-4200 *SIC* 1731 8741

CORP SERVICE CO INC p 371
2711 Centerville Rd # 400 19808
Tel (302) 636-5400 *SIC* 7389

■ **DELAWARE CAPITAL FORMATION INC** p 423
501 Silverside Rd Ste 5 19809
Tel (302) 793-4921
SIC 5084 3463 3542 3823

■ **DELAWARE CAPITAL HOLDINGS INC** p 423
501 Silverside Rd Ste 5 19809
Tel (302) 793-4921 *SIC* 5084 3533 7699

DELAWARE RACING ASSOCIATION p 424
777 Delaware Park Blvd 19804
Tel (302) 994-2521 *SIC* 7948 7993

DELAWARE SUPERMARKETS INC p 424
501 S Walnut St 19801
Tel (302) 652-3412 *SIC* 5411

DELPHI FINANCIAL GROUP INC p 425
1105 N Market St Ste 1230 19801
Tel (302) 478-5142 *SIC* 6321

DRAGON CLOUD INC p 455
1 Commerce St 19801
Tel (702) 508-2676 *SIC* 2731

■ **DU PONT FOREIGN SALES CORP** p 459
974 Centre Rd 19805
Tel (302) 774-1000 *SIC* 7389

DUPONT PERFORMANCE COATINGS INC p 462
4417 Lncaster Pike Barley 19805
Tel (302) 892-1064 *SIC* 8711

■ **DUPONT PERFORMANCE ELASTOMERS LLC** p 462
4417 Lancaster Pike 19805
Tel (302) 774-1000 *SIC* 2822

▲ **E I DU PONT DE NEMOURS AND CO** p 466
974 Centre Rd 19805
Tel (302) 774-1000
SIC 2879 2824 2865 2821 2834

■ **ERI INVESTMENTS INC** p 507
801 N West St Fl 2 19801
Tel (302) 656-8089 *SIC* 6719

EXCO INC p 517
1007 N Orange St 19801
Tel (905) 477-3065 *SIC* 6719

FEDERAL EXPRESS PACIFIC INC p 534
1209 N Orange St 19801
Tel (901) 369-3600 *SIC* 4513

FEDERAL HOME LOAN ADMINISTRATION INC p 534
1201 N Orange St Ste 600 19801
Tel (855) 345-2669 *SIC* 6162

■ **FIA CARD SERVICES NATIONAL ASSOCIATION** p 539
1100 N King St 19884
Tel (800) 362-6255 *SIC* 7389

FORBO AMERICA INC p 565
103 Foulk Rd Ste 123 19803
Tel (302) 691-6100 *SIC* 5023

FRANKE USA HOLDING INC p 574
1105 N Market St Ste 1300 19801
Tel (615) 462-4000 *SIC* 3589 5023 5084

GB BIOSCIENCES LLC p 594
2200 Concord Pike 19803
Tel (336) 632-6000 *SIC* 2879 2834 2899

GLAXOSMITHKLINE HOLDINGS (AMERICAS) INC p 614
1105 N Market St 19801
Tel (302) 656-5280
SIC 2834 2836 2833 2844 8071

GROUPE SEB HOLDINGS INC p 642
1105 N Market St Ste 1142 19801
Tel (973) 736-0300 *SIC* 5064

H S B C OVERSEAS CORP (DE) p 650
300 Delaware Ave Ste 1400 19801
Tel (302) 657-8400 *SIC* 6722

HATZEL & BUEHLER INC p 668
3600 Silverside Rd Ste A 19810
Tel (302) 478-4200 *SIC* 1731

■ **HERCULES INC** p 685
500 Hercules Rd 19808
Tel (302) 594-5000 *SIC* 2869 2891

HIGHMARKS INC p 692
800 Delaware Ave Ste 900 19801
Tel (302) 421-3000 *SIC* 6321

■ **HONEYWELL SAFETY PRODUCTS USA INC** p 705
2711 Centerville Rd 19808
Tel (302) 636-5401 *SIC* 5099

HORIZON SERVICES INC p 707
320 Century Blvd 19808
Tel (302) 762-1200 *SIC* 1711

HSBC BANK USA p 714
300 Delaware Ave Ste 1400 19801
Tel (302) 778-0169 *SIC* 6022

IKEA HOLDING US INC p 731
1105 N Market St Ste 1044 19801
Tel (302) 655-4126 *SIC* 5021 5712

▲ **INCYTE CORP** p 735
1801 Augustine Cut Off 19803
Tel (302) 498-6700 *SIC* 2834

■ **ING BANK FSB** p 742
802 Delaware Ave 19801
Tel (302) 658-2200 *SIC* 6035 6211

ING USA HOLDING CORP p 742
1 S Orange St 19801
Tel (302) 658-2200 *SIC* 6035

▲ **INTERDIGITAL INC** p 752
200 Bellevue Pkwy Ste 300 19809
Tel (302) 281-3600 *SIC* 3663 5999 6794

INVENSIS INC p 761
1000 N West St Ste 1200 19801
Tel (302) 351-3509 *SIC* 7374

INVISTA CAPITAL MANAGEMENT LLC p 762
2801 Centerville Rd 19808
Tel (302) 683-3000 *SIC* 2869

JUMIO HOLDINGS INC p 797
2711 Centerville Rd # 400 19808
Tel (650) 424-8545 *SIC* 6719 7371

■ **K-TRON INVESTMENT CO** p 799
300 Delaware Ave Ste 900 19801
Tel (856) 589-0500 *SIC* 3823

LABWARE HOLDINGS INC p 836
3 Mill Rd Ste 102 19806
Tel (302) 658-8444 *SIC* 7371 7372 6719

LEXISNEXIS RISK ASSETS INC p 859
1105 N Market St Ste 501 19801
Tel (770) 752-6000
SIC 6411 7375 8721 7323

■ **MBNA MARKETING SYSTEMS INC** p 925
1100 N King St 19884
Tel (302) 456-8588 *SIC* 7389

▲ **NAVIENT CORP** p 1020
123 S Justison St Ste 300 19801
Tel (302) 283-8000 *SIC* 6211 6163

NEW SOURCE ENERGY PARTNERS LP p 1033
300 Delaware Ave Ste 1100 19801
Tel (405) 272-3028 *SIC* 1311 1389

NGK NORTH AMERICA INC p 1041
1105 N Market St Ste 1300 19801
Tel (302) 654-1344
SIC 3714 5013 3264 5063

NGK SPARK PLUGS (USA) HOLDING INC p 1041
1011 Centre Rd 19805
Tel (302) 288-0131 *SIC* 3643 3264

NUCLEAR ELECTRIC INSURANCE LIMITED p 1066
1201 N Market St Ste 1100 19801
Tel (302) 888-3000 *SIC* 6331

■ **PHILLIPS PETROLEUM INTERNATIONAL INVESTMENT CO LLC** p 1144
2711 Centerville Rd # 400 19808
Tel (918) 661-6600 *SIC* 8742

■ **PITNEY BOWES INTERNATIONAL HOLDINGS INC** p 1152
801 N West St Fl 2 19801
Tel (302) 656-8595 *SIC* 6719

■ **PNC BANCORP INC** p 1158
300 Delaware Ave 19801
Tel (302) 427-5896 *SIC* 6021

■ **PNC BANK DELAWARE** p 1158
222 Delaware Ave Lbby 19801
Tel (302) 655-7221 *SIC* 6022

■ **PNC NATIONAL BANK OF DELAWARE** p 1158
300 Bellevue Pkwy Ste 200 19809
Tel (302) 479-4529 *SIC* 6022

RED CLAY CONSOLIDATED SCHOOL DISTRICT p 1215
1502 Spruce Ave 19805
Tel (302) 552-3700 *SIC* 9411

REED ELSEVIER US HOLDINGS INC p 1217
1105 N Market St Ste 501 19801
Tel (302) 427-2672
SIC 2721 7999 8748 6719

RHI REFRACTORIES HOLDING CO p 1231
1105 N Market St Ste 1300 19801
Tel (302) 655-6497
SIC 3297 3255 1459 3546 3272 3589

ROLLINS LEASING LLC p 1247
2200 Concord Pike 19803
Tel (302) 426-2700 *SIC* 7513

■ **SENTINEL TRANSPORTATION LLC** p 1305
3521 Silverside Rd Ste 2a 19810
Tel (302) 477-1640 *SIC* 4212

SEVERN TRENT (DEL) INC p 1309
1011 Centre Rd Ste 320 19805
Tel (302) 427-5990 *SIC* 3589 7371 8741

SEWICKLEY CAPITAL INC p 1309
501 Silverside Rd Ste 67 19809
Tel (302) 793-4964 *SIC* 3559 3822

SHELL ENERGY RESOURCES INC p 1314
1105 N Market St Ste 1300 19801
Tel (302) 658-3676 *SIC* 1311 1382

SIGHTSAVERS INTERNATIONAL INC p 1321
1000 N West St Ste 1200 19801
Tel (800) 707-9746 *SIC* 8069

SMITH & NEPHEW HOLDINGS INC p 1333
1201 N Orange St Ste 788 19801
Tel (302) 884-6720 *SIC* 5047 3841

SOLENIS INTERNATIONAL LP p 1338
500 Hercules Rd 19808
Tel (302) 994-1698 *SIC* 2911 2611 1382

SOLENIS LLC p 1338
3 Beaver Valley Rd # 500 19803
Tel (866) 337-1533 *SIC* 2899

SONEPAR USA HOLDINGS INC p 1339
1011 Centre Rd Ste 327 19805
Tel (302) 573-3807 *SIC* 5063

SPI PHARMA INC p 1358
503 Carr Rd Ste 210 19809
Tel (302) 576-8500 *SIC* 5122

ST FRANCIS HEALTH SERVICES CORP p 1366
7th N Clayton St 19805
Tel (302) 575-8301 *SIC* 8062

ST FRANCIS HOSPITAL INC p 1366
701 N Clayton St 19805
Tel (302) 421-4100 *SIC* 8062

STALEY HOLDINGS INC p 1375
501 Silverside Rd Ste 55 19809
Tel (302) 793-0289 *SIC* 2046

SUEZ NORTH AMERICA INC p 1396
2000 First State Blvd 19804
Tel (302) 633-5670 *SIC* 4941 3569 3589

SYNGENTA CORP p 1415
3411 Silverside Rd # 100 19810
Tel (302) 425-2000 *SIC* 2879 5191 8741

■ **TDY HOLDINGS LLC** p 1429
1403 Foulk Rd Ste 200 19803
Tel (302) 254-4172 *SIC* 3462

▲ **THIRD FEDERAL SAVINGS** p 1448
103 Foulk Rd Ste 101 19803
Tel (302) 661-2009 *SIC* 6035

THOMSON REUTERS (GRC) INC p 1449
2711 Centerville Rd # 400 19808
Tel (212) 227-7357
SIC 7291 8111 8721 8733 8741

THUNDER BASIN CORP p 1451
103 Foulk Rd Ste 151 19803
Tel (610) 962-3770 *SIC* 3566 2298

TUCSON HOTELS LP p 1490
2711 Centerville Rd # 400 19808
Tel (678) 830-2438 *SIC* 7011

UNITED ACQUISITION CORP p 1506
802 N West St 19801
Tel (302) 651-9856 *SIC* 2911 5541 2951

■ **VERIZON DELAWARE LLC** p 1550
901 N Tatnall St Fl 2 19801
Tel (302) 571-1571
SIC 4813 4812 7373 2741

■ **WILMINGTON SAVINGS FUND SOCIETY** p 1613
500 Delaware Ave Ste 500 19801
Tel (302) 792-6000 *SIC* 6035

WILMINGTON TRUST SP SERVICES p 1613
1105 N Market St Ste 1300 19801
Tel (302) 427-7650 *SIC* 2711

▲ **WSFS FINANCIAL CORP** p 1628
500 Delaware Ave 19801
Tel (302) 792-6000 *SIC* 6021

YOUNG MENS CHRISTIAN ASSOCIATION OF WILMINGTON DELAWARE p 1639
100 W 10th St Ste 1100 19801
Tel (302) 221-9622 *SIC* 7997 7011

DISTRICT OF COLUMBIA

WASHINGTON, DC

AARP p 8
601 E St Nw 20049
Tel (202) 434-2277 *SIC* 5192 8399

AARP FOUNDATION p 8
601 E St Nw 20049
Tel (202) 434-2020 *SIC* 8331 8399

ACADEMY FOR EDUCATIONAL DEVELOPMENT INC p 13
1825 Conn Ave Nw Ste 800 20009
Tel (202) 884-8976 *SIC* 8742 8732

ACDI/VOCA p 16
50 F St Nw Ste 1000 20001
Tel (202) 469-6000 *SIC* 8748 8641

ACON INVESTMENTS LLC p 18
1133 Conn Ave Nw Ste 700 20036
Tel (202) 454-1100 *SIC* 6722

ACON SUZO-HAPP LLC p 18
1133 Conn Ave Nw Ste 700 20036
Tel (202) 454-1100 *SIC* 7389

▲ **ADVISORY BOARD CO** p 28
2445 M St Nw Ste 500 20037
Tel (202) 266-5600 *SIC* 8732 8741 7372

AFRICARE p 33
440 R St Nw 20001
Tel (202) 328-5320 *SIC* 8399

■ **AGRICULTURAL MARKETING SERVICE** p 36
1400 Independence Ave Sw 20250
Tel (202) 720-8998 *SIC* 9641

AKIN GUMP STRAUSS HAUER & FELD LLP p 42
1333 New Hampshire Ave Nw # 400 20036
Tel (202) 887-4000 *SIC* 8111

AKIRA TECHNOLOGIES INC p 42
1747 Penn Ave Nw Ste 600 20006
Tel (202) 517-7187 *SIC* 7373 7379

AMERICAN ASSOCIATION FOR ADVANCEMENT OF SCIENCE p 68
1200 New York Ave Nw 20005
Tel (202) 898-0873 *SIC* 8621 2721

AMERICAN BEVERAGE ASSOCIATION p 68
1101 16th St Nw Ste 700 20036
Tel (202) 223-4832 *SIC* 8611

AMERICAN CHEMICAL SOCIETY p 70
1155 16th St Nw 20036
Tel (202) 872-4600 *SIC* 8621 7319

AMERICAN CHEMISTRY COUNCIL INC p 70
700 2nd St Ne Fl 8-10 20002
Tel (202) 249-7000
SIC 8611 8748 8621 8699

AMERICAN COLLEGE OF CARDIOLOGY FOUNDATION p 70
2400 N St Nw 20037
Tel (202) 375-6000 *SIC* 8621

AMERICAN ENTERPRISE INSTITUTE FOR PUBLIC POLICY RESEARCH p 71
1150 17th St Nw Ste 1100 20036
Tel (202) 862-5800 *SIC* 8733 8732

AMERICAN FEDERATION OF LABOR & CONGRESS OF INDUSTRIAL ORGANZATION p 72
815 16th St Nw 20006
Tel (202) 637-5000 *SIC* 8631

AMERICAN FEDERATION OF STATE COUNTY & MUNICIPAL EMPLOYEES p 72
1625 L St Nw 20036
Tel (202) 429-1000 *SIC* 8631

AMERICAN FOREIGN SERVICE PROTECTIVE ASSOCIATION p 72
1620 L St Nw Ste 800 20036
Tel (202) 833-4910 *SIC* 8621

AMERICAN INSTITUTES FOR RESEARCH IN BEHAVIORAL SCIENCES p 75
1000 Thmas Jfferson St Nw 20007
Tel (202) 403-5000 *SIC* 8733

AMERICAN PETROLEUM INSTITUTE INC p 77
1220 L St Nw Ste 900 20005
Tel (202) 682-8000 *SIC* 1389

AMERICAN POSTAL WORKERS UNION p 77
1300 L St Nw Ste 200 20005
Tel (202) 842-4200 *SIC* 8631

AMERICAN PSYCHOLOGICAL ASSOCIATION INC p 78
750 1st St Ne Ste 605 20002
Tel (202) 336-5500 *SIC* 8621

AMERICAN RED CROSS p 78
431 18th St Nw 20006
Tel (202) 737-8300 *SIC* 8322

AMERICAN UNIVERSITY p 81
4400 Massachusetts Ave Nw 20016
Tel (202) 885-1000 *SIC* 8221

AMERICANS FOR PROSPERITY p 81
1728 M St Nw 20036
Tel (866) 730-0150 *SIC* 8299

AMYOTROPHIC LATERAL SCLEROSIS ASSOCIATION p 88
1275 K St Nw Ste 250 20005
Tel (202) 407-8580 *SIC* 8611

APCO WORLDWIDE INC p 96
1299 Penn Ave Nw Ste 300 20004
Tel (202) 638-4082 *SIC* 8748 8742 8732

■ **ARCHITECT OF CAPITOL** p 105
Us Capitol Bldg Rm Sb-16 20515
Tel (202) 228-1793 *SIC* 9121

ARENT FOX LLP p 107
1717 K St Nw Ste B1 20006
Tel (202) 857-6000 *SIC* 8111

ARNOLD & PORTER LLP p 112
601 Massachusetts Ave Nw 20001
Tel (202) 942-5000 *SIC* 8111

ASPEN INSTITUTE p 118
1 Dupont Cir Nw Ste 700 20036
Tel (202) 736-5800 *SIC* 8299

ASSOCIATION OF AMERICAN MEDICAL COLLEGES p 121
655 K St Nw Ste 100 20001
Tel (202) 828-0400 *SIC* 8621

ASSOCIATION OF FLIGHT ATTENDANTS p 121
501 3rd St Nw Fl 10 20001
Tel (202) 387-1968 *SIC* 8631

ASSOCIATION OF UNIVERSITIES FOR RESEARCH IN ASTRONOMY INC p 121
1212 New York Ave Nw # 450 20005
Tel (202) 483-2101 *SIC* 8611

ASTRA CAPITAL MANAGEMENT LLC p 122
1900 K St Nw Ste 1130 20006
Tel (202) 779-9044 *SIC* 6211

BANK FUND STAFF FCU p 150
1725 I St Nw Ste 300 20006
Tel (202) 429-9180 *SIC* 6062

BANK FUND STAFF FEDERAL CREDIT UNION p 150
1725 I St Nw Ste 150 20006
Tel (202) 212-6400 *SIC* 6061

BANK-FUND STAFF FEDERAL CREDIT UNION p 152
1722 I St Nw Ste 200 20006
Tel (202) 458-4350 *SIC* 6062

■ **BLACK ENTERTAINMENT TELEVISION LLC** p 186
1235 W St Ne 20018
Tel (202) 526-4927 *SIC* 4841

BLACKBOARD INC p 187
1111 19th St Nw 20036
Tel (202) 463-4860 *SIC* 7372

BOARD OF GOVERNORS OF FEDERAL RESERVE SYSTEM p 195
20th St Cnsttution Ave Nw 20551
Tel (202) 452-3000 *SIC* 6011

BRIDGEPOINT HEALTHCARE LLC p 211
4601 Martin Luther Jr 20032
Tel (202) 741-4174 *SIC* 8062

■ **BROADCASTING BOARD OF GOVERNORS** p 215
330 Independence Ave Sw # 3360 20237
Tel (202) 203-4000 *SIC* 9721

BROOKINGS INSTITUTION p 218
1775 Massachusetts Ave Nw 20036
Tel (202) 797-6000 *SIC* 8733 2741 8621

■ **BUREAU OF ALCOHOL TOBACCO FIREARMS & EXPLOSIVES** p 226
99 New York Ave Ne # 5514 20002
Tel (202) 648-8500 *SIC* 9651

■ **BUREAU OF CONSULAR AFFAIRS** p 226
2201 C St Nw Ste 6811 20520
Tel (202) 647-9576 *SIC* 9721

■ **BUREAU OF CUSTOMS AND BORDER PROTECTION** p 226
1300 Pennsylvania Ave Nw 20229
Tel (202) 927-0529 *SIC* 9711

■ **BUREAU OF ENGRAVING AND PRINTING** p 226
14th And C St Sw 20228
Tel (202) 874-2361 *SIC* 9311

■ **BUREAU OF IMMIGRATION & CUSTOMS ENFORCEMENT** p 226
500 12th St Sw 20536
Tel (202) 732-2427 *SIC* 9721 9311

■ **BUREAU OF INDIAN AFFAIRS** p 226
1849 C St Nw 20240
Tel (202) 208-6123 *SIC* 9131

■ **BUREAU OF LABOR STATISTICS** p 226
2 Massachusetts Ave Ne 20212
Tel (202) 691-5200 *SIC* 9651

■ **BUREAU OF LAND MANAGEMENT** p 226
1849 C St Nw Rm 5665 20240
Tel (202) 208-3801 *SIC* 9512

■ **BUREAU OF RECLAMATION** p 226
1849 C St Nw 20240
Tel (202) 513-0501 *SIC* 9511

CAPITOL PARTNERS I LP p 251
1808 I St Nw Ste 200 20006
Tel (202) 955-7960 *SIC* 8082 6211

■ **CAPITOL POLICE US** p 251
119 D St Ne 20510
Tel (202) 593-3647 *SIC* 9221

CAREY INTERNATIONAL INC p 255
4530 Wscnsin Ave Nw Ste 5 20016
Tel (202) 895-1200 *SIC* 4119 6794

▲ **CARLYLE GROUP L P** p 258
1001 Pennsylvania Ave Nw 220s 20004
Tel (202) 729-5626 *SIC* 6726 6282

■ **CARLYLE INVESTMENT MANAGEMENT LLC** p 258
1001 Pennsylvania Ave Nw 20004
Tel (202) 729-5385 *SIC* 6282

■ **CARLYLE PARTNERS II LP** p 258
1001 Pennsylvania Ave Nw 20004
Tel (202) 347-2626 *SIC* 3612

■ **CARLYLE PARTNERS III LP** p 258
1001 Penn Ave Nw Ste 220 20004
Tel (202) 347-2626 *SIC* 6719

■ **CARLYLE PARTNERS IV LP** p 258
1001 Pennsylvania Ave Nw 20004
Tel (202) 729-5626 *SIC* 8711 8069 8051

CARNEGIE INSTITUTION OF WASHINGTON p 258
1530 P St Nw 20005
Tel (202) 387-6400 *SIC* 8733

CASSIDYTURLEY INC p 264
2101 L St Nw Ste 700 20037
Tel (202) 463-2100 *SIC* 6531

CATHOLIC UNIVERSITY OF AMERICA p 267
620 Michigan Ave Ne 20064
Tel (202) 319-5000 *SIC* 8221

■ **CFO ACCOUNTING CENTER** p 285
451 7th St Sw 20410
Tel (202) 708-0950 *SIC* 9531

CHEMONICS INTERNATIONAL INC p 293
1717 H St Nw 20006
Tel (202) 955-3300 *SIC* 8742 8748

CHESAPEAKE MANAGEMENT SERVICES INC p 295
1629 K St Nw Ste 300 20006
Tel (202) 600-7678 *SIC* 7373

■ **CHILDREN AND FAMILIES ADMINISTRATION FOR** p 298
330 C St Sw 20201
Tel (202) 401-1822 *SIC* 9441

CHILDRENS HOSPITAL p 299
111 Michigan Ave Nw 20010
Tel (202) 232-0521 *SIC* 8062

CHILDRENS HOSPITAL p 299
1917 C St Ne 20002
Tel (202) 476-5000 *SIC* 8062

CHILDRENS NATIONAL MEDICAL CENTER p 300
111 Michigan Ave Nw 20010
Tel (202) 476-5000 *SIC* 8062

■ **CITIZENSHIP & IMMIGRATION SERVICES US** p 311
20 Ma Ave Nw Rm 3000 20529
Tel (202) 272-1000 *SIC* 9721

CLYDE INC p 328
3236 M St Nw 20007
Tel (202) 333-9180 *SIC* 5812 5813

■ **COGENT COMMUNICATIONS GROUP INC** p 334
2450 N St Nw 20037
Tel (202) 295-4200 *SIC* 8999

▲ **COGENT COMMUNICATIONS HOLDINGS INC** p 334
2450 N St Nw 20037
Tel (202) 295-4200 *SIC* 4813 7372

■ **COGENT COMMUNICATIONS INC** p 334
2450 N St Nw 20037
Tel (202) 295-4200 *SIC* 4813 7375

COLONIAL PARKING INC p 337
1050 Thms Jfrsn St Nw 100 20007
Tel (202) 965-3096 *SIC* 7521

COMMUNICATIONS WORKERS OF AMERICA AFL-CIO CLC p 347
501 3rd St Nw 20001
Tel (202) 434-1100 *SIC* 8631

COMMUNITY FOUNDATION FOR NATIONAL CAPITAL REGION p 348
1201 15th St Nw Ste 420 20005
Tel (202) 263-4799 *SIC* 8699

COMMUNITY PARTNERSHIP FOR PREVENTION OF HOMELESSNESS INC p 349
801 Pennsylvania Ave Se # 31 20003
Tel (202) 543-5298 *SIC* 8322

■ **CONGRESS UNITED STATES** p 356
U S Capitol Senate Office 20510
Tel (202) 225-3121 *SIC* 9121

CONSERVATION INTERNATIONAL FOUNDATION p 358
1003 K St Nw Ste 404 20001
Tel (703) 341-2400 *SIC* 8641

■ CONSOLIDATED EXECUTIVE OFFICE p 359
950 Pennsylvania Ave Nw 20530
Tel (202) 616-6788 *SIC* 9222

CONSORTIUM FOR ELECTIONS & POLITICAL PROCESS STRENGTHENING p 360
1225 I St Nw Ste 700 20005
Tel (202) 408-9450 *SIC* 8651

CORE INC p 369
1201 New York Ave Nw # 420 20005
Tel (202) 332-0063 *SIC* 8733

CORP FOR PUBLIC BROADCASTING p 371
401 9th St Nw Ste 200 20004
Tel (202) 879-9600 *SIC* 7812

CORP FOR TRAVEL PROMOTION p 371
1725 I St Nw Ste 800 20006
Tel (202) 536-2060 *SIC* 7389

▲ COSTAR GROUP INC p 374
1331 L St Nw Ste 2 20005
Tel (202) 346-6500 *SIC* 7375

■ COUNCIL OF INSPECTORS GENERAL ON INTEGRITY AND EFFICIENCY p 374
1717 H St Nw Ste 825 20006
Tel (202) 292-2604 *SIC* 9199

COURT OF APPEALS OF DISTRICT OF COLUMBIA p 383
500 Indiana Ave Nw 20001
Tel (202) 879-2700 *SIC* 9211

■ COURT OF APPEALS UNITED STATES p 383
1 Columbus Cir Ne 20544
Tel (202) 879-1010 *SIC* 9211

COVINGTON & BURLING LLP p 385
1 Citycenter 850 Tenth 20001
Tel (202) 662-6000 *SIC* 8111

CROWELL & MORING LLP p 394
1001 Penn Ave Nw Fl 10 20004
Tel (202) 624-2500 *SIC* 8111

▲ DANAHER CORP p 411
2200 Penn Ave Nw Ste 800w 20037
Tel (202) 828-0850
SIC 3845 3829 3577 3823 3843

DC WATER AND SEWER AUTHORITY p 418
5000 Overlook Ave Sw 20032
Tel (202) 787-2000 *SIC* 4952 4941

■ DEFENSE TECHNOLOGY SECURITY ADMINISTRATION p 422
2000 Defense Pentagon 4b661 20301
Tel (703) 697-3249 *SIC* 9711

■ DH HOLDINGS CORP p 435
1250 24th St Nw 20037
Tel (202) 828-0850 *SIC* 3545

DICKSTEIN SHAPIRO LLP p 438
1825 Eye St Nw Fl 1200 20006
Tel (202) 420-2200 *SIC* 8111

DISTRICT OF COLUMBIA PUBLIC SCHOOLS p 443
1200 1st St Ne Fl 9 20002
Tel (202) 442-5885 *SIC* 8211

DISTRICT OF COLUMBIA WATER & SEWER AUTHORITY p 443
5000 Overlook Ave Sw 20032
Tel (202) 787-2000 *SIC* 9511

DKT INTERNATIONAL INC p 445
1701 K St Nw Ste 900 20006
Tel (202) 223-8780 *SIC* 8322

■ DOD TEST RESOURCE MANGEMENT CENTER p 447
3000 Defense Pentagon 20301
Tel (571) 372-2700 *SIC* 9711

DONOHOE COMPANIES INC p 451
2101 Wisconsin Ave Nw 20007
Tel (202) 333-0880 *SIC* 6552 1542

DOUGLAS DEVELOPMENT CORP p 452
702 H St Nw Ste 400 20001
Tel (202) 638-6300 *SIC* 6552 6531

▲ DUPONT FABROS TECHNOLOGY INC p 462
1212 New York Ave Nw # 900 20005
Tel (202) 728-0044 *SIC* 6798 7374

■ DUPONT FABROS TECHNOLOGY LP p 462
1212 New York Ave Nw # 900 20005
Tel (202) 728-0044 *SIC* 6798

EDISON ELECTRIC INSTITUTE INC p 478
701 Pennsylv Ave Nw Fl 3 20004
Tel (202) 508-5000 *SIC* 8611

ELIZABETH GLASER PEDIATRIC AIDS FOUNDATION p 487
1140 Conn Ave Nw Ste 200 20036
Tel (310) 314-1459 *SIC* 8099 8733

■ EMBASSY OF UNITED STATES OF AMERICA p 490
2201 C St Nw 20520
Tel (202) 895-3500 *SIC* 9721

■ EMPLOYMENT AND TRAINING ADMINISTRATION p 494
200 Constitution Ave Nw S2307 20210
Tel (202) 693-3500 *SIC* 9441

■ EMPLOYMENT STANDARDS ADMINISTRATION p 494
200 Constitution Ave Nw 20210
Tel (202) 541-3610 *SIC* 9651

■ ENVIRONMENTAL PROTECTION AGENCY p 503
1200 Pennsylvania Ave Nw 20460
Tel (202) 272-0167 *SIC* 9511

■ EQUAL EMPLOYMENT OPPORTUNITY COMMISSION p 506
131 M St Ne 20507
Tel (202) 663-4519 *SIC* 9441

■ EXECUTIVE OFFICE OF UNITED STATES GOVERNMENT p 518
1600 Pennsylvania Ave Nw 20006
Tel (202) 456-1414 *SIC* 9111

FACILITY LEADERS IN ARCHITECTURAL/ENGINEERING DESIGN PC p 523
1201 Conn Ave Nw Fl 10 20036
Tel (608) 238-2661 *SIC* 8712 8711

■ FARM SERVICE AGENCY p 529
1400 Independence Ave Sw # 3086 20250
Tel (202) 720-6215 *SIC* 9641

▲ FEDERAL AGRICULTURAL MORTGAGE CORP p 533
1999 K St Nw Fl 4 20006
Tel (202) 872-7700 *SIC* 6111 6159

■ FEDERAL AVIATION ADMINISTRATION p 533
800 Independence Ave Sw 20591
Tel (866) 835-5322 *SIC* 9621

■ FEDERAL BUREAU OF INVESTIGATION p 533
935 Pennsylvania Ave Nw 20535
Tel (202) 324-3000 *SIC* 9221

■ FEDERAL BUREAU OF PRISONS p 533
320 1st St Nw Ste 654 20534
Tel (202) 307-3198 *SIC* 9223

■ FEDERAL COMMUNICATIONS COMMISSION p 533
445 12th St Sw 20554
Tel (202) 418-1925 *SIC* 9631

FEDERAL DEPOSIT INSURANCE CORP p 534
550 17th St Nw 20429
Tel (877) 275-3342 *SIC* 6399 9311

■ FEDERAL EMERGENCY MANAGEMENT AGENCY p 534
500 C St Sw Ocfo 20472
Tel (202) 646-2500 *SIC* 9229

■ FEDERAL ENERGY REGULATORY COMMISSION p 534
888 1st St Ne 20426
Tel (202) 502-6629 *SIC* 9611

■ FEDERAL HIGHWAY ADMINISTRATION p 534
1200 New Jersey Ave Se 20590
Tel (202) 366-0650 *SIC* 9621

▲ FEDERAL NATIONAL MORTGAGE ASSOCIATION p 535
3900 Wisconsin Ave Nw 20016
Tel (202) 752-7000 *SIC* 6111

■ FEDERAL PRISON INDUSTRIES INC p 535
320 1st St Nw 20534
Tel (202) 305-3500 *SIC* 9223

FINANCIAL INDUSTRY REGULATORY AUTHORITY INC p 542
1735 K St Nw 20006
Tel (301) 590-6500 *SIC* 8611

FINNEGAN HENDERSON FARABOW GARRETT & DUNNER LLP p 543
901 New York Ave Nw # 1150 20001
Tel (202) 408-4000 *SIC* 8111

FIRST BOOK p 545
1319 F St Nw Ste 1000 20004
Tel (202) 393-1222 *SIC* 8322

■ FISCAL SERVICE BUREAU OF p 551
401 14th St Sw Rm 548 20227
Tel (202) 622-7000 *SIC* 9311

FORGE CO p 567
1050 Thmas Jfferson St Nw 20007
Tel (202) 295-8100 *SIC* 7521 7011

FRIENDSHIP PUBLIC CHARTER SCHOOL INC p 580
120 Q St Ne Ste 200 20002
Tel (202) 281-1700 *SIC* 8211

▲ FTI CONSULTING INC p 583
1101 K St Nw Ste B100 20005
Tel (202) 312-9100 *SIC* 8742

FUTUREGEN INDUSTRIAL ALLIANCE INC p 586
1101 Penn Ave Nw Fl 6 20004
Tel (202) 756-4520 *SIC* 8711

GALLAUDET UNIVERSITY p 589
800 Florida Ave Ne 20002
Tel (202) 651-5000 *SIC* 8221

GALLUP INC p 590
901 F St Nw Ste 400 20004
Tel (202) 715-3030 *SIC* 8742

■ GEICO CORP p 597
1 Geico Plz 20076
Tel (301) 986-3000 *SIC* 6411

■ GEICO GENERAL INSURANCE CO p 597
1 Geico Plz 20076
Tel (301) 986-3000 *SIC* 6411

■ GEICO INDEMNITY CO p 597
One Geico Plaza 20047
Tel (301) 986-3000 *SIC* 6331 6411

■ GENERAL SERVICES ADMINISTRATION US p 602
1800 F St Nw Rm 6100 20405
Tel (202) 501-8880 *SIC* 9199

GEORGE WASHINGTON UNIVERSITY p 606
2121 I St Nw Ste 601 20052
Tel (202) 242-6600 *SIC* 8221

GEORGE WASHINGTON UNIVERSITY HOSPITAL p 606
900 23rd St Nw 20037
Tel (202) 715-4000 *SIC* 8062

GEORGETOWN UNIVERSITY p 607
37th & O Sts Nw 20057
Tel (202) 687-0100 *SIC* 8221 8062

GOOD BUDDY BUDDY GOOD LLC p 623
300 Anacostia Rd Se # 103 20019
Tel (240) 532-0031 *SIC* 7389

■ GOVERNMENT ACCOUNTABILITY OFFICE p 627
441 G St Nw 20548
Tel (202) 512-3000 *SIC* 9311

GOVERNMENT OF DISTRICT OF COLUMBIA p 627
441 4th St Nw 20001
Tel (202) 727-2277 *SIC* 9111

▲ GOVERNMENT OF UNITED STATES p 627
1600 Pennsylvania Ave Nw 20500
Tel (202) 456-1414 *SIC* 9111

■ GRAIN INSPECTION PACKERS & STOCKYARDS ADMINISTRATION p 629
1400 Independence Ave Sw 20250
Tel (202) 720-0219 *SIC* 9641

GRYPHON TECHNOLOGIES LC p 643
80 M St Se Ste 600 20003
Tel (202) 617-2004
SIC 8741 8711 8731 7371

■ GSA NATIONAL CAPITAL AREA REGION OF REGIONAL ADMINISTRATOR (11A) p 643
7 & D St Sw Ste 7022th 20407
Tel (202) 708-9100 *SIC* 9199

■ GSA NATIONAL CAPITAL REGION p 643
7 & D St Sw Rm 1065th 20407
Tel (202) 708-5891 *SIC* 9199

■ GSA OFFICE OF CHIEF FINANCIAL OFFICER p 643
1800 F St Nw Rm 2140 20405
Tel (202) 501-1721 *SIC* 9199

HARMAN MEDIA LLC p 662
1150 15th St Nw 20071
Tel (202) 334-6000 *SIC* 2721

HEALTH SERVICES FOR CHILDREN WITH SPECIAL NEEDS INC p 676
1101 Vermont Ave Nw # 1002 20005
Tel (202) 467-2737 *SIC* 8322

HERITAGE FOUNDATION p 686
214 Msschstts Ave Ne Bsmt 20002
Tel (202) 546-4400 *SIC* 8733

HOGAN LOVELLS US LLP p 699
555 13th St Nw 20004
Tel (202) 637-5600 *SIC* 8111

HOLLADAY CORP p 700
3400 Idaho Ave Nw Ste 400 20016
Tel (202) 362-2400 *SIC* 1522 6531

■ HOUSE OF REPRESENTATIVES UNITED STATES p 711
The Capitol 20515
Tel (202) 224-3121 *SIC* 9121

HOWARD UNIVERSITY p 713
2400 6th St Nw 20059
Tel (202) 806-6100 *SIC* 8221

HOWARD UNIVERSITY HOSPITAL p 713
2041 Georgia Ave Nw 20060
Tel (202) 865-6100 *SIC* 8062

HOWARD UNIVERSITY HOSPITAL p 713
2041 Georgia Ave Nw 20060
Tel (202) 865-1441 *SIC* 8062

HOWREY LLP p 714
1299 Pennsylvania Ave Nw 20004
Tel (202) 783-0800 *SIC* 8111

HUMANE SOCIETY OF UNITED STATES p 718
1255 23rd St Nw Ste 800 20037
Tel (202) 452-1100 *SIC* 8699

HW HOLDCO LLC p 722
1 Thomas Cir Nw Ste 600 20005
Tel (202) 452-0800 *SIC* 2721 7389

INMARSAT INC p 744
1101 Conn Ave Nw Ste 1200 20036
Tel (202) 248-5150 *SIC* 3663

INTER-AMERICAN DEVELOPMENT BANK p 751
1300 New York Ave Nw 20577
Tel (202) 623-1000 *SIC* 6082

INTERCHURCH MEDICAL ASSISTANCE INC p 752
1730 M St Nw Ste 1100 20036
Tel (202) 888-6200 *SIC* 8661

■ INTERNAL REVENUE SERVICE p 754
1111 Constitution Ave Nw 20224
Tel (202) 803-9000 *SIC* 9311

INTERNATIONAL BANK FOR RECONSTRUCTION & DEVELOPMENT (INC) p 754
1818 H St Nw 20433
Tel (202) 473-1000 *SIC* 6082

INTERNATIONAL BROTHERHOOD OF ELECTRICAL WORKERS p 754
900 7th St Nw Bsmt 1 20001
Tel (202) 833-7000 *SIC* 8631

INTERNATIONAL BROTHERHOOD OF ELECTRICAL WORKERS - PENSION BENEFIT FUND p 754
900 7th St Nw 20001
Tel (202) 728-6200 *SIC* 8631

INTERNATIONAL BROTHERHOOD OF TEAMSTERS p 754
25 Louisiana Ave Nw 20001
Tel (202) 624-6800 *SIC* 8631

INTERNATIONAL CITY MANAGEMENT ASSOCIATION RETIREMENT CORP p 754
777 N Capitol St Ne # 600 20002
Tel (202) 962-4600 *SIC* 7389 6722

■ INTERNATIONAL DEVELOPMENT UNITED STATES AGENCY FOR p 755
1300 Penn Ave Nw 848 20004
Tel (202) 712-0000 *SIC* 9611

INTERNATIONAL FINANCE CORP p 755
1818 H St Nw 20433
Tel (202) 458-2454 *SIC* 6082

INTERNATIONAL FOOD POLICY RESEARCH INSTITUTE p 755
2033 K St Nw Ste 400 20006
Tel (202) 862-5600 *SIC* 8731 8733

INTERNATIONAL MONETARY FUND p 756
700 19th St Nw 20431
Tel (202) 623-7000 *SIC* 6082

■ INTERNATIONAL TRADE ADMINISTRATION p 757
14th /Constitution Ave Nw 20230
Tel (202) 482-2000 *SIC* 9611

JAB BEECH INC p 773
2200 Pennsylvania Ave Nw 20037
Tel (516) 537-1040 *SIC* 6799

JER PARTNERS LLC p 783
1250 Conn Ave Nw Ste 700 20036
Tel (703) 714-8000 *SIC* 6798

JOHN F KENNEDY CENTER FOR PERFORMING ARTS p 788
2700 F St Nw 20566
Tel (202) 416-8000 *SIC* 7922 7929

JOHN I HAAS INC p 789
5185 Mcarthur Blvd Nw # 300 20016
Tel (202) 777-4800 *SIC* 0139 5159

JUST ONE MORE RESTAURANT CORP p 797
1730 Rhode Island Ave Nw # 900 20036
Tel (202) 775-7256 *SIC* 5812 5813

KIPP DC p 821
2600 Virginia Ave Nw # 900 20037
Tel (202) 223-4505 *SIC* 8211

LABORERS INTERNATIONAL UNION OF NORTH AMERICA p 836
905 16th St Nw 20006
Tel (202) 737-8320 *SIC* 8631

LABORERS-EMPLOYERS BENEFIT PLAN COLLECTION TRUST p 836
905 16th St Nw 20006
Tel (202) 393-7344 *SIC* 6411

■ LEGAL SERVICES CORP p 853
3333 K St Nw Ste 1 20007
Tel (202) 295-1500 *SIC* 6732 9199

■ LIBRARY OF CONGRESS p 863
101 Independence Ave Se 20540
Tel (202) 707-5000 *SIC* 8231 9121

▲ LINDBLAD EXPEDITIONS HOLDINGS INC p 868
509 7th St Nw 20004
Tel (202) 654-7060 *SIC* 6799

▲ LIQUIDITY SERVICES INC p 870
1920 L St Nw Fl 6 20036
Tel (202) 467-6868 *SIC* 7389

LIVING SOCIAL INC p 871
1445 New York Ave Nw # 200 20005
Tel (877) 521-4191 *SIC* 5961

LUCY W HAYES TRAINING SCHOOL FOR DECONESSES & MISSIONARIES INC p 884
5255 Loughboro Rd Nw 20016
Tel (202) 537-4257 *SIC* 8062

MCKENNA LONG & ALDRIDGE LLP p 930
1900 K St Nw Ste Ll100 20006
Tel (202) 496-7145 *SIC* 8111

MCN BUILD LLC p 932
1214 28th St Nw 20007
Tel (202) 333-3424 *SIC* 1541 1542

MECCANICA HOLDINGS USA INC p 934
1625 I St Nw Fl 12 20006
Tel (202) 292-2620 *SIC* 6719

MEDICAL FACULTY ASSOCIATES INC p 937
2150 Pennsylvania Ave Nw 20037
Tel (202) 741-3000 *SIC* 8011

MEDSTAR-GEORGETOWN MEDICAL CENTER INC p 939
3800 Reservoir Rd Nw 20007
Tel (202) 444-2000 *SIC* 8062 8221 8069

METROPOLITAN WASHINGTON AIRPORTS AUTHORITY p 957
1 Aviation Cir 20001
Tel (703) 417-8600 *SIC* 4581 4785

NASH HOLDINGS LLC p 1008
1403 Hamlin St Ne 20017
Tel (202) 334-6727 *SIC* 2711 2721

NATIONAL ACADEMY OF SCIENCES OF UNITED STATES OF AMERICA p 1009
2101 Constitution Ave Nw 20418
Tel (202) 334-2000 SIC 8733 8999 8748

■ **NATIONAL AERONAUTICS AND SPACE ADMINISTRATION** p 1009
300 E St Sw Ste 5r30 20546
Tel (202) 358-0000 SIC 9661

■ **NATIONAL AGRICULTURAL STATISTICS SERVICE** p 1009
1400 Independence Ave Sw 20250
Tel (202) 720-2707 SIC 9641

NATIONAL ASSOCIATION OF LETTER CARRIERS p 1010
100 Indana Ave Nw Ste 709 20001
Tel (202) 393-4695 SIC 8631

NATIONAL CAUCUS AND CENTER ON BLACK AGING INC p 1010
1220 L St Nw Ste 800 20005
Tel (202) 637-8400 SIC 8322 8641

■ **NATIONAL CEMETERY ADMINISTRATION** p 1010
810 Vrmont Ave Nw Ste 427 20420
Tel (800) 827-1000 SIC 6553 9451

NATIONAL CONSUMER COOPERATIVE BANK p 1011
2001 Penn Ave Nw Ste 625 20006
Tel (202) 349-7444 SIC 6021

NATIONAL DEMOCRATIC INSTITUTE FOR INTERNATIONAL AFFAIRS p 1011
455 Mdcchstts Ave Nw Fl 8 20001
Tel (202) 728-5500 SIC 8651

NATIONAL EDUCATION ASSOCIATION OF UNITED STATES p 1011
1201 16th St Nw 20036
Tel (202) 833-4000 SIC 8631

NATIONAL ENDOWMENT FOR DEMOCRACY INC p 1011
1025 F St Nw Ste 800 20004
Tel (202) 378-9700 SIC 8399

NATIONAL FISH & WILDLIFE FOUNDATION p 1012
1133 15th St Nw Fl 11 20005
Tel (202) 857-0166 SIC 8641

NATIONAL FOOTBALL LEAGUE PLAYERS ASSOCIATION p 1012
1133 20th St Nw Frnt 1 20036
Tel (202) 756-9100 SIC 7941

■ **NATIONAL GALLERY OF ART** p 1012
6th And Cnsttution Ave Nw 20565
Tel (202) 737-4215 SIC 5942 8412

NATIONAL GEOGRAPHIC SOCIETY p 1012
1145 17th St Nw 20036
Tel (202) 857-7000 SIC 2721

■ **NATIONAL INSTITUTE OF FOOD AND AGRICULTURE** p 1013
1400 Independence Ave Sw 20250
Tel (202) 720-4276 SIC 9641

■ **NATIONAL LABOR RELATIONS BOARD** p 1014
1015 Half St Se 20003
Tel (202) 273-3884 SIC 9651

■ **NATIONAL PARK SERVICE** p 1015
1849 C St Nw 20240
Tel (202) 208-6843 SIC 9512

NATIONAL POSTAL MAIL HANDLERS UNION p 1015
1101 Conn Ave Nw Ste 500 20036
Tel (202) 833-9095 SIC 8631

NATIONAL PUBLIC RADIO INC p 1015
1111 N Capitol St Ne 20002
Tel (202) 513-2000 SIC 8611

■ **NATIONAL RAILROAD PASSENGER CORP** p 1015
60 Massachusetts Ave Ne 20002
Tel (202) 906-3741 SIC 4011 4013

NATIONAL REHABILITATION HOSPITAL INC p 1015
102 Irving St Nw 20010
Tel (202) 877-1000 SIC 8069

■ **NATURAL RESOURCES CONSERVATION SERVICE** p 1018
1400 Independence Ave Sw 20250
Tel (202) 720-7246 SIC 9512

■ **NAVAL RESEARCH LABORATORY** p 1019
4555 Overlook Ave Sw 20375
Tel (202) 767-2370 SIC 9661

NEIGHBORHOOD REINVESTMENT CORP p 1024
999 N Capitol St Ne # 900 20002
Tel (202) 760-4000 SIC 8611

NETWORK FOR GOOD INC p 1028
1140 Conn Ave Nw Ste 700 20036
Tel (202) 627-1600 SIC 4813

NEW VENTURE FUND p 1033
1201 Conn Ave Nw Ste 300 20036
Tel (202) 595-1061 SIC 7389

NEWS WORLD COMMUNICATIONS INC p 1039
3600 New York Ave Ne 20002
Tel (202) 636-3000 SIC 2711

NOT FOR PROFIT HOSPITAL CORP p 1062
1310 Southern Ave Se 20032
Tel (202) 574-6024 SIC 6732

NOT-FOR-PROFIT HOSPITAL CORP p 1062
1310 Southern Ave Se 20032
Tel (202) 574-6000 SIC 8062

NRI INC p 1064
1015 18th St Nw Ste 710 20036
Tel (202) 466-4670 SIC 7363 7361

■ **OCCUPATIONAL SAFETY AND HEALTH ADMINISTRATION** p 1072
200 Constitution Ave Nw N3626 20210
Tel (202) 693-2000 SIC 9651

■ **OFFICE OF ASSISTANT SECRETARY FOR ADMINISTRATION AND MANAGEMENT** p 1075
200 Constitution Ave Nw S-2203 20210
Tel (202) 693-4040 SIC 9651

■ **OFFICE OF THE COMPTROLLER OF THE CURRENCY** p 1076
400 7th St Sw Ste 3e218 20219
Tel (202) 649-6800 SIC 9651

■ **OFFICE OF THE SECRETARY OF DEFENSE** p 1076
1400 Defense Pentagon 20301
Tel (703) 545-6700 SIC 9711

■ **OFFICE OF THRIFT SUPERVISION** p 1076
1700 G St Nw 20552
Tel (202) 906-6900 SIC 9651

PACT INC p 1107
1828 L St Nw Ste 300 20036
Tel (202) 466-5666 SIC 8399 8699

PAGE SOUTHERLAND PAGE INC p 1107
1615 M St Nw Ste 700 20036
Tel (202) 909-4900 SIC 8712 8711

PAN AMERICAN DEVELOPMENT FOUNDATION INC p 1110
1889 F St Nw Fl 2 20006
Tel (202) 458-3969 SIC 8399

PAN AMERICAN HEALTH ORGANIZATION INC p 1110
525 23rd St Nw 20037
Tel (202) 974-3000 SIC 8399

PARALYZED VETERANS OF AMERICA p 1114
801 18th St Nw Frnt 1 20006
Tel (202) 872-1300 SIC 8399 7389 8641

PARSONS BRINCKERHOFF INTERNATIONAL INC p 1118
1401 K St Nw Ste 701 20005
Tel (202) 783-0241 SIC 8711

PARSONS TRANSPORTATION GROUP INC p 1118
100 M St Se Ste 1200 20003
Tel (202) 775-3300 SIC 8711

PARSONS TRANSPORTATION GROUP INC OF VIRGINIA p 1118
1133 15th St Nw Ste 800 20005
Tel (202) 775-3300 SIC 8711

PATIENT-CENTERED OUTCOMES RESEARCH INSTITUTE p 1120
1828 L St Nw Ste 900 20036
Tel (202) 827-7700 SIC 8322

PATTON BOGGS LLP p 1121
2550 M St Nw Ste 200 20037
Tel (202) 457-6000 SIC 8111

■ **PEACE CORPS** p 1125
1111 20th St Nw 20526
Tel (202) 692-2000 SIC 9721

■ **PENTAGON FORCE PROTECTION AGENCY** p 1131
The Pentagon 2e165b 20301
Tel (703) 697-1001 SIC 9711

■ **PEPCO ENERGY SERVICES INC** p 1133
701 9th St Nw Ste 2100 20001
Tel (703) 253-1800
SIC 1711 1731 1623 4961

■ **PEPCO HOLDINGS LLC** p 1133
701 9th St Nw Ste 3 20001
Tel (202) 872-2000 SIC 4931

PHARMACEUTICAL RESEARCH AND MANUFACTURERS OF AMERICA p 1141
950 F St Nw Ste 300 20004
Tel (202) 835-3400 SIC 8611

■ **PHI SERVICE CO** p 1142
701 9th St Nw 20001
Tel (202) 872-2000 SIC 7389

POPULATION SERVICES INTERNATIONAL p 1161
1120 19th St Nw Ste 600 20036
Tel (202) 785-0072 SIC 8733 8732

PORTFOLIO LOGIC LLC p 1163
600 New Hampshire Ave Nw 9f 20037
Tel (202) 266-6519 SIC 6726 8741

POST COMMUNITY MEDIA LLC p 1163
1301 K St Nw 20071
Tel (301) 670-2565 SIC 2711 2732 2721

■ **POTOMAC ELECTRIC POWER CO** p 1164
701 9th St Nw Ste 3 20001
Tel (202) 872-2000 SIC 4911

■ **POTOMAC HOLDING LLC** p 1164
2200 Penn Ave Nw Ste 800w 20037
Tel (202) 828-0850 SIC 3823

■ **PROMONTORY FINANCIAL GROUP LLC** p 1183
801 17th St Nw Ste 1100 20006
Tel (202) 384-1200 SIC 8742

PROVIDENCE HOSPITAL p 1186
1150 Varnum St Ne 20017
Tel (202) 269-7000 SIC 8062

QUADRANGLE DEVELOPMENT CORP p 1196
1001 G St Nw Ste 700w 20001
Tel (202) 667-0014 SIC 6552

QUIVUS SYSTEMS LLC p 1200
3803 T St Nw 20007
Tel (202) 587-5756 SIC 8742

R G A INC p 1202
1001 G St Nw Ste 700w 20001
Tel (202) 393-1999 SIC 6552 7521 6531

REVOLUTION LLC p 1229
1717 Rhode Island Ave Nw # 1000 20036
Tel (202) 776-1400 SIC 6211 7514

RFE/RL INC p 1231
1201 Conn Ave Nw Ste 400 20036
Tel (202) 457-6900 SIC 7922

ROBERT CO INC J E p 1241
1250 Connecticut Ave Nw # 700 20036
Tel (703) 714-8000 SIC 7011

■ **SECURITIES AND EXCHANGE COMMISSION US** p 1299
100 F St Ne 20549
Tel (202) 942-8088 SIC 9651

SECURITIES INVESTOR PROTECTION CORP p 1299
1667 K St Nw Ste 1000 20006
Tel (202) 371-8300 SIC 6289

SECURITY STORAGE CO OF WASHINGTON p 1299
1701 Florida Ave Nw 20009
Tel (202) 797-5659
SIC 4213 4226 4214 4731

■ **SENATE UNITED STATES** p 1303
111 Russell Senate Bldg 20510
Tel (202) 224-3121 SIC 9121

SERVICE EMPLOYEES INTERNATIONAL UNION p 1307
1800 Massachusetts Ave Nw 20036
Tel (202) 730-7000 SIC 8631

SIEMENS CORP p 1320
300 New Jersey Ave Nw # 10 20001
Tel (202) 434-4800
SIC 3661 3641 3844 3612 3357

■ **SMALL BUSINESS ADMINISTRATION US** p 1332
409 3rd St Sw Ste 5000 20416
Tel (202) 205-6770 SIC 9611

SMITHGROUPJJR INC p 1334
1700 New York Ave Nw # 100 20006
Tel (602) 265-2200 SIC 8712

■ **SMITHSONIAN INSTITUTION** p 1334
1000 Jefferson Dr Sw 20560
Tel (202) 633-1000 SIC 8412 8422

SOUTHEASTERN UNIVERSITIES RESEARCH ASSOCIATION INC p 1347
1201 New York Ave Nw # 430 20005
Tel (202) 408-7872 SIC 8741

SPECIAL COUNSEL p 1355
1400 I St Nw Ste 325 20005
Tel (202) 737-3436 SIC 7363 8111 7361

SPECIAL OLYMPICS INC p 1356
1133 19th St Nw Ste 1200 20036
Tel (202) 628-3630 SIC 8322

STEPTOE & JOHNSON LLP p 1386
1330 Connecticut Ave Nw 20036
Tel (202) 429-3000 SIC 8111

■ **SUNRISE CONNECTICUT AVENUE ASSISTED LIVING LLC** p 1403
5111 Connecticut Ave Nw 20008
Tel (202) 966-8020 SIC 6513

■ **SUPREME COURT UNITED STATES** p 1408
1 1st St Ne 20543
Tel (202) 479-3000 SIC 9211

SUTHERLAND ASBILL & BRENNAN LLP p 1409
700 6th St Nw Ste 700 20001
Tel (202) 383-0100 SIC 8111

TE CONNECTIVITY INC p 1429
607 14th St Nw Ste 250 20005
Tel (202) 471-3400 SIC 3678 3643

■ **TEKTRONIX TEXAS LLC** p 1433
2200 Penn Ave Nw Ste 800w 20037
Tel (202) 828-0850 SIC 7372

TEMPUS INC p 1436
1201 New York Ave Nw # 300 20005
Tel (800) 834-2497 SIC 6099

THAYER CAPITAL PARTNERS LP p 1446
1455 Penn Ave Nw Ste 350 20004
Tel (202) 371-0150 SIC 6211

THAYER-BLUM FUNDING III LLC p 1446
1455 Penn Ave Nw Ste 350 20004
Tel (202) 371-0150 SIC 6722 3672 3577

TRANS DIGITAL TECHNOLOGIES LIMITED LIABILITY CO p 1470
1255 23rd St Nw Ste 100 20037
Tel (571) 730-7029 SIC 7373

TRG CUSTOMER SOLUTIONS INC p 1476
1700 Penn Ave Nw Ste 560 20006
Tel (202) 289-9898 SIC 7389

TRG HOLDINGS LLC p 1476
1700 Penn Ave Nw Ste 560 20006
Tel (202) 289-9898 SIC 7323

■ **TRUSTEE PROGRAM UNITED STATES** p 1487
20 Massachusetts 20530
Tel (202) 307-1399 SIC 9222

■ **U S ARMY CORPS OF ENGINEERS** p 1497
441 G Street Nw 20314
Tel (804) 435-9362 SIC 9711

■ **U S OFFICE OF PERSONNEL MANAGEMENT** p 1497
1900 E St Nw Ste 7f14 20415
Tel (202) 606-1800 SIC 9199

ULLICO INC p 1500
1625 I St Nw Fl 5 20006
Tel (202) 682-0900 SIC 6311 6321

UNITED FOOD AND COMMERCIAL WORKERS INTERNATIONAL UNION p 1508
1775 K St Nw 20006
Tel (202) 223-3111 SIC 8631

UNITED NATIONS FOUNDATION INC p 1510
1750 Penn Ave Nw Ste 300 20006
Tel (202) 887-9040 SIC 8621

UNITED NEGRO COLLEGE FUND INC p 1510
1805 7th St Nw Ste 100 20001
Tel (800) 331-2244 SIC 8399

UNITED STATES ASSOCIATION FOR UNHCR p 1512
1775 K St Nw Ste 580 20006
Tel (855) 808-6427 SIC 8322

■ **UNITED STATES COAST GUARD** p 1512
2100 2nd St Sw Stop 7238 20593
Tel (202) 372-4411 SIC 9621

UNITED STATES CONFERENCE OF CATHOLIC BISHOPS p 1512
3211 4th St Ne 20017
Tel (202) 541-3000 SIC 8661 4832 4833

■ **UNITED STATES DEPARTMENT OF AGRICULTURE** p 1512
1400 Independence Ave Sw 20250
Tel (202) 720-3631 SIC 9641

■ **UNITED STATES DEPARTMENT OF COMMERCE** p 1512
1401 Constitution Ave Nw 20230
Tel (202) 482-0267 SIC 9611

■ **UNITED STATES DEPARTMENT OF DEFENSE** p 1512
1000 Defense Pentagon # 3 20301
Tel (703) 692-7100 SIC 9711

■ **UNITED STATES DEPARTMENT OF HEALTH & HUMAN SERVICES** p 1512
200 Independence Ave Sw 20201
Tel (202) 401-2281 SIC 9431

■ **UNITED STATES DEPARTMENT OF HOMELAND SECURITY** p 1512
245 Murray Ln Sw 20528
Tel (202) 282-8000 SIC 9711

■ **UNITED STATES DEPARTMENT OF INTERIOR** p 1512
1849 C St Nw 20240
Tel (202) 208-7351 SIC 9512

■ **UNITED STATES DEPARTMENT OF JUSTICE** p 1512
950 Pennsylvania Ave Nw 20530
Tel (202) 514-2201 SIC 9222 9223

■ **UNITED STATES DEPARTMENT OF LABOR** p 1512
200 Constitution Ave Nw 20210
Tel (202) 693-6002 SIC 9651

■ **UNITED STATES DEPARTMENT OF THE AIR FORCE** p 1512
1000 Air Force Pentagon 20330
Tel (703) 545-6700 SIC 9711

■ **UNITED STATES DEPARTMENT OF THE ARMY** p 1512
1400 Defense Pentagon 20310
Tel (703) 695-1717 SIC 9711

■ **UNITED STATES DEPARTMENT OF THE NAVY** p 1512
1200 Navy Pentagon 20350
Tel (703) 545-6700 SIC 9711

■ **UNITED STATES DEPARTMENT OF TRANSPORTATION** p 1512
1200 New Jersey Ave Se 20590
Tel (202) 366-4000 SIC 9621

■ **UNITED STATES DEPT OF EDUCATION** p 1513
400 Maryland Ave Sw 20202
Tel (202) 245-7468 SIC 9411

■ **UNITED STATES DEPT OF ENERGY** p 1513
1000 Independence Ave Sw 20585
Tel (202) 586-5000 SIC 9611

■ **UNITED STATES DEPT OF HOUSING AND URBAN DEVELOPMENT** p 1513
451 7th St Sw Rm 5256 20410
Tel (202) 708-0417 SIC 9531

■ **UNITED STATES DEPT OF STATE** p 1513
2201 C St Nw 20520
Tel (202) 632-9367 SIC 9721

■ **UNITED STATES DEPT OF TREASURY** p 1513
1500 Pennsylvania Ave Nw 20220
Tel (202) 622-1100 SIC 9311

■ **UNITED STATES DEPT OF VETERANS AFFAIRS** p 1513
810 Vermont Ave Nw 20420
Tel (202) 273-5400 SIC 9451

■ **UNITED STATES HOLOCAUST MEMORIAL MUSEUM** p 1513
100 Raoul Wallenberg Pl Sw 20024
Tel (202) 488-0400 SIC 8412 9411

■ **UNITED STATES MARINE CORPS** p 1513
Pentagon Rm 4b544 20380
Tel (816) 394-7628 SIC 9711

■ **UNITED STATES MINT** p 1513
801 9th St Nw 20220
Tel (202) 756-6468 SIC 9311

UNITED STATES POSTAL SERVICE p 1514
475 Lenfant Plz Sw # 4012 20260
Tel (202) 268-2000 *SIC* 4311

■ **UNITED STATES SECRET SERVICE** p 1514
950 H St Nw 20223
Tel (202) 406-5708 *SIC* 9229

UNITY HEALTH CARE INC p 1515
1220 12th St Se Ste 120 20003
Tel (202) 715-7901 *SIC* 8099

UNIVERSITY OF DISTRICT OF COLUMBIA p 1521
4200 Conn Ave Nw Ste 200 20008
Tel (202) 274-5000 *SIC* 8221

URBAN INSTITUTE p 1530
2100 M St Nw Fl 5 20037
Tel (202) 833-7200 *SIC* 8733

US CHAMBER OF COMMERCE p 1531
1615 H St Nw 20062
Tel (202) 659-6000 *SIC* 8611

■ **US DEPARTMENT OF COMMERCE** p 1531
1401 Constitution Ave Nw 20230
Tel (202) 482-4661 *SIC* 9611

■ **US GOVERNMENT PUBLISHING OFFICE** p 1532
732 N Capitol St Nw 20401
Tel (202) 512-0000 *SIC* 9199

■ **USAID/ASIA & NEAR EAST BUREAU** p 1534
1300 Pa Ave Rnld Raegn 20523
Tel (202) 712-0200 *SIC* 9611

■ **USDA FOREST SERVICE** p 1534
201 14th St Sw 20024
Tel (202) 205-1680 *SIC* 9512

■ **USDA RURAL DEVELOPMENT** p 1534
1400 Independence Ave Sw 20250
Tel (202) 720-9540 *SIC* 9641

▲ **VANDA PHARMACEUTICALS INC** p 1543
2200 Penn Ave Nw Ste 300e 20037
Tel (202) 734-3400 *SIC* 2834 8731

VENABLE LLP p 1547
575 7th St Nw Ste 1 20004
Tel (202) 344-4000 *SIC* 8111

■ **VERIZON WASHINGTON DC INC** p 1551
1300 I St Nw 20005
Tel (202) 392-9900 *SIC* 4813 8721

■ **VETERANS BENEFITS ADMINISTRATION** p 1552
810 Vermont Ave Nw 20420
Tel (202) 273-5674 *SIC* 9451

■ **VETERANS HEALTH ADMINISTRATION** p 1553
810 Vermont Ave Nw 20420
Tel (202) 461-4800 *SIC* 9451

■ **WASHINGTON GAS LIGHT CO** p 1578
101 Constitution Ave Nw 200w 20001
Tel (703) 288-3614 *SIC* 7519

■ **WASHINGTON GAS LIGHT CO INC** p 1578
101 Constitution Ave Nw 200w 20001
Tel (703) 750-4440 *SIC* 4924

WASHINGTON HOSPITAL CENTER CORP p 1578
110 Irving St Nw 20010
Tel (202) 877-7000
SIC 8741 8082 8051 8062

WASHINGTON METROPOLITAN AREA TRANSIT AUTHORITY p 1578
600 5th St Nw 20001
Tel (202) 962-1000 *SIC* 4111

▲ **WASHINGTON REAL ESTATE INVESTMENT TRUST** p 1579
1775 Eye St Nw Ste 1000 20006
Tel (202) 774-3200 *SIC* 6798

WASHINGTON SPORTS & ENTERTAINMENT LIMITED PARTNERSHIP p 1579
601 F St Nw 20004
Tel (202) 661-5000 *SIC* 7941

■ **WESTERN UNION BUSINESS SOLUTIONS (USA) LLC** p 1600
1152 15th St Nw Ste 700 20005
Tel (202) 408-1200 *SIC* 6099

▲ **WGL HOLDINGS INC** p 1604
101 Constitution Ave Nw 200w 20001
Tel (703) 750-2000 *SIC* 4924 4923 4922

WILEY REIN LLP p 1609
1776 K St Nw 20006
Tel (202) 719-7000 *SIC* 8111

WILL PERKINS INC p 1609
1250 24th St Nw Ste 800 20037
Tel (312) 755-0770 *SIC* 8712 7389

WILLARD HOTEL p 1610
1401 Pennsylvania Ave Nw 20004
Tel (202) 628-9100 *SIC* 7011

WILLIAMS & CONNOLLY LLP p 1611
725 12th St Nw 20005
Tel (202) 434-5800 *SIC* 8111

WILMER CUTLER PICKERING HALE AND DORR LLP p 1613
1875 Pennsylvania Ave Nw 20006
Tel (202) 663-6000 *SIC* 8111

WINCHESTER ACQUISITION HOLDINGS CORP p 1614
1111 19th St Nw 20036
Tel (202) 463-4860 *SIC* 6719

WITT OBRIENS LLC p 1619
1201 15th St Nw Ste 600 20005
Tel (202) 585-0780 *SIC* 4959 8748 8322

WORLD BANK GROUP p 1624
1818 H St Nw 20433
Tel (202) 473-1000 *SIC* 6082

WORLD WILDLIFE FUND INC p 1625
1250 24th St Nw Fl 2 20037
Tel (202) 293-4800 *SIC* 8641

WP CO LLC p 1627
1301 K St Nw 20071
Tel (202) 334-6242 *SIC* 2721 2711

WYSS FOUNDATION p 1630
1601 Conn Ave Nw Ste 800 20009
Tel (202) 232-4418 *SIC* 8641

■ **XM SATELLITE RADIO HOLDINGS INC** p 1632
1500 Eckington Pl Ne 20002
Tel (202) 380-4000 *SIC* 4841

YMCA OF METROPOLITAN WASHINGTON p 1636
1112 16th St Nw Ste 720 20036
Tel (202) 232-6700 *SIC* 8641

FLORIDA

ALACHUA, FL

▲ **RTI SURGICAL INC** p 1256
11621 Research Cir 32615
Tel (386) 418-8888 *SIC* 3842

ALTAMONTE SPRINGS, FL

ADVENTIST HEALTH SYSTEM SUNBELT HEALTHCARE CORP p 27
900 Hope Way 32714
Tel (407) 357-1000 *SIC* 5912

ADVENTIST HEALTH SYSTEM/SUNBELT INC p 27
900 Hope Way 32714
Tel (407) 357-1000 *SIC* 8062 8082 8051

AHS/CENTRAL TEXAS INC p 37
900 Hope Way 32714
Tel (407) 357-1000 *SIC* 8062

HAIFA NORTH AMERICA INC p 653
307 Cranes Roost Blvd 32701
Tel (407) 862-6400 *SIC* 5191 5169

JEUNESSE GLOBAL HOLDINGS LLC p 784
650 Douglas Ave Ste 1020 32714
Tel (407) 215-7414 *SIC* 5999

PICERNE DEVELOPMENT CORP OF FLORIDA p 1146
247 N Westmonte Dr 32714
Tel (407) 772-0200 *SIC* 1522

REAL ESTATE IN REAL TIME INC p 1213
100 Lakeshore Dr Ste 96 32714
Tel (321) 312-0748 *SIC* 6531 1542 1522

SUPPORT AVIATION LLC p 1408
208 W Highland St 32714
Tel (407) 731-4118 *SIC* 4581

TOURICO HOLIDAYS INC p 1464
220 E Central Pkwy # 4000 32701
Tel (407) 667-8700 *SIC* 4724

TRAVEL HOLDINGS INC p 1473
220 E Central Pkwy # 4010 32701
Tel (407) 215-7465 *SIC* 4724

TRI-CITY ELECTRICAL CONTRACTORS INC p 1477
430 West Dr 32714
Tel (407) 788-3500 *SIC* 1731

ANNA MARIA, FL

GALATI YACHT SALES LLC p 589
902 Bay Blvd 34216
Tel (941) 778-0755 *SIC* 5551 4493

APOPKA, FL

■ **AQUA UTILITIES FLORIDA INC** p 101
1000 Colour Pl 32703
Tel (386) 740-7174 *SIC* 4941 4952

PENTAIR AQUATIC ECO-SYSTEMS INC p 1131
2395 Apopka Blvd 32703
Tel (407) 886-7575 *SIC* 5074 5999

■ **QORVO FLORIDA INC** p 1195
1818 S Orange Blossom Trl 32703
Tel (407) 886-8860 *SIC* 3674

ATLANTIC BEACH, FL

FLEET LANDING p 555
1 Fleet Landing Blvd 32233
Tel (904) 246-9900 *SIC* 8059

AUBURNDALE, FL

■ **BUCKHEAD BEEF CO** p 223
355 Progress Rd 33823
Tel (863) 508-1050 *SIC* 2011

COLORADO BOXED BEEF CO p 338
302 Progress Rd 33823
Tel (863) 967-0636 *SIC* 5142 5147

COMCAR INDUSTRIES INC p 343
502 E Bridgers Ave 33823
Tel (863) 967-1101
SIC 4213 5521 5013 4212

COMMERCIAL CARRIER CORP p 345
502 E Brdgs Ave 33823
Tel (863) 967-1101 *SIC* 4213

CUTRALE CITRUS JUICES USA INC p 403
602 Mckean St 33823
Tel (863) 528-0396 *SIC* 2037

AVENTURA, FL

CORPAC STEEL PRODUCTS CORP p 372
20803 Biscayne Blvd # 502 33180
Tel (305) 933-8599 *SIC* 5051

GRUPO PHOENIX CORPORATE SERVICES LLC p 643
18851 Ne 29th Ave Ste 601 33180
Tel (954) 241-0023 *SIC* 3089

PROPEMAR INC p 1183
19101 Mystic Pointe Dr # 1709 33180
Tel (954) 775-7002 *SIC* 5146

TFP INTERNATIONAL INC p 1445
20807 Biscayne Blvd # 203 33180
Tel (786) 279-2900 *SIC* 7389

TFS RT INC p 1445
20807 Biscayne Blvd # 203 33180
Tel (416) 240-8404 *SIC* 6082

TRADE FINANCE SOLUTIONS INC p 1468
20807 Biscayne Blvd # 203 33180
Tel (786) 279-2900 *SIC* 7389

ULTRA TRADING INTERNATIONAL LTD p 1501
2875 Ne 191st St Ste 201 33180
Tel (305) 466-4443 *SIC* 5141

BARTOW, FL

PALLETONE INC p 1108
1470 Us Highway 17 S 33830
Tel (863) 533-1147 *SIC* 2448

POLK COUNTY FLORIDA p 1159
330 W Church St 33830
Tel (863) 534-6000 *SIC* 9111

POLK COUNTY SCHOOL DISTRICT p 1159
1915 S Floral Ave 33830
Tel (863) 534-0500 *SIC* 8211

SCHOOL BOARD OF POLK COUNTY p 1289
1915 S Floral Ave 33830
Tel (863) 534-0500 *SIC* 8211

BELLE GLADE, FL

SUGAR CANE GROWERS COOPERATIVE OF FLORIDA p 1397
1500 W Sugar House Rd 33430
Tel (561) 996-5556 *SIC* 2061

BELLEVIEW, FL

SOUTHEAST MILK INC p 1346
1950 Se County Hwy 484 34420
Tel (352) 245-2437 *SIC* 5143 2048

BOCA RATON, FL

ACCOUNTABLE HEALTHCARE HOLDINGS CORP p 15
999 Nw 51st St Ste 210 33431
Tel (561) 235-7813 *SIC* 6719

ACCOUNTABLE HEALTHCARE STAFFING INC p 15
999 Yamato Rd Ste 210 33431
Tel (561) 235-7810 *SIC* 7363

ADT CORP p 24
1501 Yamato Rd 33431
Tel (561) 988-3600 *SIC* 7381 7382 3699

ADT HOLDINGS INC p 24
1501 Nw 51st St 33431
Tel (888) 298-9274 *SIC* 7381 1731

ADT LLC p 24
1501 Yamato Rd 33431
Tel (561) 988-3600 *SIC* 7382

AE INDUSTRIAL PARTNERS LLC p 28
2500 N Military Trl # 470 33431
Tel (561) 372-7820 *SIC* 3369 3324

ALRO METALS SERVICE CENTER CORP p 61
6200 Pk Of Commerce Blvd 33487
Tel (561) 997-6766 *SIC* 5051 5085

■ **AMERICAN HOUSEHOLD INC** p 74
2381 Nw Executive Ctr Dr 33431
Tel (561) 912-4100
SIC 3631 2514 3421 3634 3829 3841

AMERICAN MEDIA INC p 75
301 Yamato Rd Ste 4200 33431
Tel (561) 997-7733 *SIC* 2711 2741

AMERICAN MEDIA OPERATIONS INC p 75
1000 American Media Way 33464
Tel (561) 997-7733 *SIC* 2711 2741

AMERICAN TRAVELER STAFFING PROFESSIONALS LLC p 80
1615 S Federal Hwy # 300 33432
Tel (561) 391-1811 *SIC* 7363 7361

ATI SYSTEMS INTERNATIONAL INC p 124
2000 Nw Corp Blvd Ste 101 33431
Tel (561) 939-7000 *SIC* 7381 4513 4215

BACO RATON COMMUNITY HOSPITAL INC p 143
800 Meadows Rd 33486
Tel (561) 955-5966 *SIC* 8093

BIO-ENGINEERED SUPPLEMENTS & NUTRITION INC p 183
5901 Broken Sound Pkwy Nw 33487
Tel (561) 994-8335 *SIC* 5122 5499

BIOTEST PHARMACEUTICALS CORP p 184
5800 Pk Of Commerce Blvd 33487
Tel (561) 989-5800 *SIC* 8731 2834

■ **BLUEGREEN CORP** p 193
4960 Conference Way N # 100 33431
Tel (561) 912-8000 *SIC* 6531 6552

BOCA RATON REGIONAL HOSPITAL INC p 196
800 Meadows Rd 33486
Tel (561) 395-7100 *SIC* 8062

■ **BOCA RESORTS INC** p 197
501 E Camino Real 33432
Tel (888) 543-1277 *SIC* 7011

BRE SELECT HOTELS OPERATING LLC p 209
501 E Camino Real 33432
Tel (973) 503-9733 *SIC* 7011

BRE/BATON OPERATING LESSEE LLC p 209
501 E Camino Real 33432
Tel (561) 447-3000 *SIC* 7011 7997

BROCKWAY MORAN & PARTNERS INC p 216
225 Ne Mizner Blvd # 700 33432
Tel (561) 750-2000 *SIC* 5812 3599 3728

BRRH CORP p 220
800 Meadows Rd 33486
Tel (561) 395-7100 *SIC* 8062 8082 8099

CAMPUS MANAGEMENT CORP p 246
5201 Congress Ave C220 33487
Tel (561) 923-2500 *SIC* 7373 8741

CANCER TREATMENT CENTERS OF AMERICA INC p 247
5900 Broken Sound Pkwy 33487
Tel (800) 615-3055 *SIC* 8069

CANON FINANCIAL SERVICES INC p 247
5600 Broken Sound Blvd Nw 33487
Tel (561) 997-3100 *SIC* 5045

CAREERS USA INC p 254
6501 Congress Ave Ste 200 33487
Tel (561) 995-7000 *SIC* 7361

CHAMPION SOLUTIONS GROUP INC p 287
791 Park Of Commerce Blvd 33487
Tel (800) 771-7000 *SIC* 5045 5734

CITY OF BOCA RATON p 313
201 W Palmetto Park Rd 33432
Tel (561) 393-7896 *SIC* 9111

CORRECTIONAL SERVICES CORP LLC p 373
621 Nw 53rd St Ste 700 33487
Tel (561) 893-0101 *SIC* 8744

▲ **CROSS COUNTRY HEALTHCARE INC** p 393
6551 Pk Of Cmmrce Blvd Nw 33487
Tel (561) 998-2232 *SIC* 7361 7363

CRT PROPERTIES INC p 396
225 Ne Mizner Blvd # 300 33432
Tel (561) 395-9666 *SIC* 6798

CSL PLASMA INC p 398
900 Broken Sound Pkwy # 4 33487
Tel (561) 981-3700 *SIC* 5122

DCR SYSTEM HOUSE INC p 418
7795 Nw Beacon Sq Blvd 33487
Tel (561) 998-3737 *SIC* 7373

DCR WORKFORCE INC p 418
7795 Nw Beacon Sq 201 33487
Tel (561) 998-3737 *SIC* 7379 7363 8742

DEVCON INTERNATIONAL CORP p 433
595 S Federal Hwy Ste 500 33432
Tel (954) 926-5200
SIC 3699 3273 3281 3271 2951 5032

ECONOMOS PROPERTIES INC p 476
4000 N Federal Hwy # 206 33431
Tel (561) 361-2504 *SIC* 8741

FLORIDA ATLANTIC UNIVERSITY p 557
777 Glades Rd 33431
Tel (561) 297-3000 *SIC* 8221

FLORIDA PENINSULA HOLDINGS LLC p 559
903 Nw 65th St Ste 200 33487
Tel (561) 210-0370 *SIC* 6411

GABLES REALTY LIMITED PARTNERSHIP p 588
225 Ne Mizner Blvd # 400 33432
Tel (561) 997-9700 *SIC* 6798

GARDA CL TECHNICAL SERVICES INC p 591
700 S Federal Hwy Ste 300 33432
Tel (561) 939-7000 *SIC* 6099 7381

GEO CORRECTIONS AND DETENTION LLC p 605
621 Nw 53rd St Ste 700 33487
Tel (561) 999-7490 *SIC* 8744

GEO CORRECTIONS HOLDINGS INC p 605
1 Park Pl 33487
Tel (432) 267-7911 *SIC* 6719

GEO GROUP INC p 605
621 Nw 53rd St Ste 700 33487
Tel (561) 893-0101 *SIC* 6798

GEO REENTRY INC p 605
621 Nw 53rd St Ste 700 33487
Tel (561) 893-0101 *SIC* 8744

GLOBAL FINANCIAL MANAGEMENT SERVICES LLC p 616
925 S Federal Hwy Ste 375 33432
Tel (561) 347-5500 *SIC* 6792

HART JEFFREY GROUP INC p 665
4400 N Federal Hwy 33431
Tel (561) 997-2238 *SIC* 8732 6799

HOLLANDER HOME FASHIONS HOLDINGS LLC p 700
6501 Congress Ave Ste 300 33487
Tel (561) 997-6900 *SIC* 2392

HOLLANDER SLEEP PRODUCTS LLC p 700
6501 Congress Ave Ste 300 33487
Tel (561) 997-6900 *SIC* 2392 2221 5719

ICAN BENEFIT GROUP LLC p 726
5300 Broken Sound Blvd Nw 33487
Tel (800) 530-4226 *SIC* 6411

IHS DIALYSIS INC p 731
6001 Broken Sound Pkwy Nw 33487
Tel (561) 443-0743 *SIC* 8092

JTECH SALES LLC p 772
6531 Park Of Cmrc Blvd Ste 170 33487
Tel (561) 995-0070 *SIC* 5169

■ JARDEN CORP p 778
1800 N Military Trl # 210 33431
Tel (561) 447-2520 *SIC* 3089 3634

LUMBERMENS UNDERWRITING ALLIANCE p 885
1905 Nw Corporate Blvd 33431
Tel (561) 994-1900 *SIC* 6331 6411 6311

LYNN UNIVERSITY INC p 888
3601 N Military Trl 33431
Tel (561) 237-7000 *SIC* 8221

MED-CARE DIABETIC & MEDICAL SUPPLIES INC p 935
901 Yamato Rd Ste 101 33431
Tel (800) 407-0109 *SIC* 5047

■ METROPOLITAN HEALTH NETWORKS INC p 956
2900 N Military Trl 33431
Tel (561) 805-8500 *SIC* 8011

MODERNIZING MEDICINE INC p 981
3600 Fau Blvd Ste 202 33431
Tel (561) 544-0906 *SIC* 7372

■ MOREDIRECT INC p 988
1001 Yamato Rd Ste 200 33431
Tel (561) 237-3300 *SIC* 5045 7373 7376

NATIONAL COUNCIL ON COMPENSATION INSURANCE INC p 1011
901 Peninsula Corp Cir 33487
Tel (561) 893-1000 *SIC* 6331

NCCI HOLDINGS INC p 1021
901 Peninsula Corp Cir 33487
Tel (561) 893-1000 *SIC* 6331

NEWSMAX MEDIA INC p 1039
750 Park Of Commerce Dr # 100 33487
Tel (561) 686-1165 *SIC* 2721 2741

▲ OFFICE DEPOT INC p 1075
6600 N Military Trl 33496
Tel (561) 438-4800
SIC 5943 5044 5734 5045

■ OFFICEMAX INC p 1076
6600 N Military Trl 33496
Tel (630) 438-7800 *SIC* 5943 5021

PACE AMERICAS LLC p 1103
3701 Fau Blvd Ste 200 33431
Tel (561) 995-6000 *SIC* 7371 5065

■ PANTHERS BRHC LLC p 1111
501 E Camino Real 33432
Tel (888) 543-1277 *SIC* 7011 5812 7997

PRO UNLIMITED INC p 1178
7777 Glades Rd Ste 208 33434
Tel (800) 291-1099 *SIC* 8741

PRO UNLIMITED INC p 1178
7777 Glades Rd Ste 208 33434
Tel (561) 994-9500 *SIC* 8741 7372

PROMISE HEALTHCARE INC p 1183
999 Yamato Rd Ste 300 33431
Tel (561) 869-3100 *SIC* 8741

PURITY WHOLESALE GROCERS INC p 1192
5300 Broken Sound Blvd Nw # 110 33487
Tel (561) 997-8302 *SIC* 5141 5122 5199

▲ QEP CO INC p 1194
1001 Brkn Snd Pkwy Nw A 33487
Tel (561) 994-5550 *SIC* 5072 5085 2891

RED HAWK FIRE & SECURITY LLC p 1215
5100 Town Center Cir # 350 33486
Tel (561) 672-3737 *SIC* 3699 7382

SANDOW MEDIA LLC p 1278
3651 Nw 8th Ave Ste 200 33431
Tel (561) 961-7700 *SIC* 2721

▲ SBA COMMUNICATIONS CORP p 1285
8051 Congress Ave Ste 100 33487
Tel (561) 995-7670 *SIC* 4899

■ SBA COMMUNICATIONS INC p 1285
8051 Congress Ave Ste 100 33487
Tel (561) 995-7670 *SIC* 4899

■ SBA SENIOR FINANCE II LLC p 1285
8051 Congress Ave Ste 100 33487
Tel (561) 995-7670 *SIC* 6519

■ SENIOR SBA FINANCE INC p 1304
8051 Congress Ave Ste 100 33487
Tel (561) 995-7670 *SIC* 4899 6519

SENSORMATIC ELECTRONICS LLC p 1305
6600 Congress Ave 33487
Tel (561) 912-6000 *SIC* 7382

SENSORMATIC INTERNATIONAL INC p 1305
6600 Congress Ave 33487
Tel (561) 912-6000 *SIC* 5065

SIMPLEXGRINNELL HOLDINGS LLC p 1325
1501 Nw 51st St 33431
Tel (561) 988-7200
SIC 3579 3669 3699 3822

SIMPLEXGRINNELL LP p 1325
4700 Exchange Ct 33431
Tel (561) 988-7200
SIC 5087 1711 3669 7382

SUN CAPITAL PARTNERS INC p 1400
5200 Town Center Cir # 600 33486
Tel (561) 962-3400
SIC 6799 2672 2671 5812 5411 5311

▲ SUN GORDMANS LP p 1400
5200 Town Center Cir # 600 33486
Tel (561) 394-0550 *SIC* 5651 5963

SUN MACKIE LLC p 1400
5200 Town Center Cir # 470 33486
Tel (561) 394-0550 *SIC* 3651

■ SUNBEAM AMERICAS HOLDINGS LLC p 1401
2381 Nw Executive Ctr Dr 33431
Tel (561) 912-4100
SIC 3631 2514 3421 3634 3829 3841

■ SUNBEAM PRODUCTS INC p 1401
2381 Nw Executive Ctr Dr 33431
Tel (561) 912-4100 *SIC* 3631 3634

SUNTECK HOLDINGS LLC p 1405
6413 Congress Ave Ste 260 33487
Tel (561) 988-9456 *SIC* 4731 6719

SUNTECK INC p 1405
6413 Congress Ave Ste 260 33487
Tel (561) 988-9456 *SIC* 4731

SUNTECK TRANSPORT CO INC p 1405
6413 Congress Ave Ste 260 33487
Tel (561) 988-9456 *SIC* 8741 4731

SUNTECK TRANSPORT GROUP INC p 1405
6413 Congress Ave Ste 260 33487
Tel (561) 988-9456 *SIC* 4731

TAYLOR & FRANCIS GROUP LLC p 1426
6000 Broken Sound Pkwy Nw # 300 33487
Tel (800) 634-7064 *SIC* 2721 2731

TWINLAB CORP p 1495
2255 Glades Rd Ste 342w 33431
Tel (212) 651-8500
SIC 2099 2834 2731 2721 2833

TYCO INTEGRATED SECURITY LLC p 1496
4700 Exchange Ct Ste 300 33431
Tel (561) 226-8201 *SIC* 7382 7381 1731

TYCO SIMPLEXGRINNELL p 1496
1501 Nw 51st St 33431
Tel (561) 988-3658 *SIC* 3569 3491

TYNDALE ENTERPRISES INVESTMENT CORP p 1496
22341 Sw 66th Ave # 1205 33428
Tel (561) 239-5273 *SIC* 5137

UNITED WIRELESS TECHNOLOGIES INC p 1515
300 Se 5th Ave Apt 8180 33432
Tel (561) 302-9350 *SIC* 3571 3663

US INSTALLATION GROUP INC p 1532
951 Brkn Snd Pkwy Nw # 100 33487
Tel (561) 962-0452 *SIC* 1752

■ VITACOST.COM INC p 1562
5400 Broken Sound Blvd # 500 33487
Tel (561) 982-4180 *SIC* 5961

WEST BOCA MEDICAL CENTER INC p 1594
21644 State Road 7 33428
Tel (561) 488-8000 *SIC* 8062

BONITA SPRINGS, FL

▲ HERC HOLDINGS INC p 685
27500 Riverview Ctr Blvd 34134
Tel (239) 301-1000 *SIC* 7359

■ HERC RENTALS INC p 685
27500 Rverview Ctr Bldg 7 34134
Tel (239) 301-1001 *SIC* 7359

SALLYPORT GLOBAL LLC p 1273
27200 Riverview Ste 309 34134
Tel (239) 390-1900 *SIC* 8999

SOLARIS FOUNDATION INC p 1338
9520 Bonita Beach Rd Se 34135
Tel (239) 919-1142 *SIC* 8051 8059

SOURCE INTERLINK COMPANIES INC p 1342
27200 Riverview Center Bl 34134
Tel (866) 276-5584 *SIC* 4731

SOURCE INTERLINK DISTRIBUTION LLC p 1342
27500 Riverview Center Bl 34134
Tel (239) 949-4450 *SIC* 5192

▲ WCI COMMUNITIES INC p 1585
24301 Walden Center Dr 34134
Tel (239) 947-2600 *SIC* 1531 6531

BOYNTON BEACH, FL

APPLE INVESTORS GROUP LLC p 98
303 E Woolbright Rd 33435
Tel (888) 265-7402 *SIC* 5812

BECARRO INTERNATIONAL CORP p 167
1730 Corporate Dr 33426
Tel (561) 737-5585 *SIC* 3171

BETHESDA HOSPITAL INC p 178
2815 S Seacrest Blvd 33435
Tel (561) 737-7733 *SIC* 8062

EARLY LEARNING COALITION OF PALM BEACH COUNTY INC p 469
2300 High Ridge Rd # 115 33426
Tel (561) 214-8000 *SIC* 8351

HEALTHY START COALITION OF PALM BEACH COUNTY IN p 678
2300 High Ridge Rd 33426
Tel (561) 374-7613 *SIC* 8351

BRADENTON, FL

BEALLS DEPARTMENT STORES INC p 165
1806 38th Ave E 34208
Tel (941) 747-2355 *SIC* 5311 5651 5947

BEALLS INC p 165
1806 13th Ave E 34208
Tel (941) 747-2355
SIC 5311 5719 5651 5947

BEALLS OUTLET STORES INC p 165
1806 38th Ave E 34208
Tel (941) 747-2355
SIC 5611 5621 5661 5719

BEALLS WEST GATE CORP p 165
1806 38th Ave E 34208
Tel (941) 744-4330 *SIC* 5651 5661 5719

BURKES OUTLET STORES INC p 227
1806 38th Ave E 34208
Tel (941) 747-2355 *SIC* 5651

CHICAGO 29 INC p 297
7328 Pine Valley St 34202
Tel (419) 621-9002 *SIC* 7231

COUNTY OF MANATEE p 379
1112 Manatee Ave W 34205
Tel (941) 748-4501 *SIC* 9121

EMPLOYEE LEASING SOLUTIONS INC p 494
1401 Manatee Ave W # 600 34205
Tel (941) 746-6567 *SIC* 7363

GOODWILL INDUSTRIES-MANASOTA INC p 625
2705 51st Ave E 34203
Tel (941) 355-2721 *SIC* 8331

■ MANATEE MEMORIAL HOSPITAL p 900
206 2nd St E 34208
Tel (941) 746-5111 *SIC* 8062

■ ROBBYS SPORTING GOODS INC p 1241
311 Manatee Ave W 34205
Tel (941) 748-0577 *SIC* 5941

SCHOOL DISTRICT OF MANATEE COUNTY FLORIDA p 1289
215 Manatee Ave W 34205
Tel (941) 708-8770 *SIC* 8211

TAD PGS INC p 1421
1001 3rd Ave W Ste 460 34205
Tel (941) 746-4434 *SIC* 7363

■ TROPICANA PRODUCTS INC p 1484
1275 26th Ave E 34208
Tel (941) 747-4461
SIC 2033 2037 2086 2048

WORKFORCE BUSINESS SERVICES INC p 1624
1401 Manatee Ave W # 600 34205
Tel (941) 746-6567 *SIC* 7363

BRANDON, FL

AMERICAN SIGNATURE HOME p 79
161 Brandon Town Ctr Dr 33511
Tel (813) 315-1120 *SIC* 5712

■ FLORIDA COCA-COLA BOTTLING CO p 557
521 Lake Kathy Dr 33510
Tel (813) 569-2600 *SIC* 2086

■ GALENCARE INC p 589
119 Oakfield Dr 33511
Tel (813) 681-5551 *SIC* 8062

HOLLAND & KNIGHT LLP p 700
524 Grand Regency Blvd 33510
Tel (813) 901-4200 *SIC* 8111

BROOKSVILLE, FL

COUNTY OF HERNANDO p 378
20 N Main St 34601
Tel (352) 754-4201 *SIC* 9111

HCA HEALTH SERVICES OF FLORIDA INC p 671
11375 Cortez Blvd 34613
Tel (352) 597-3053 *SIC* 8062

■ HERNANDO HEALTHCARE INC p 687
17240 Cortez Blvd 34601
Tel (352) 796-5111 *SIC* 8062

■ HERNANDO HMA INC p 687
17240 Cortez Blvd 34601
Tel (352) 796-5111 *SIC* 8062

■ OAK HILL HOSPITAL MEDICAL STAFF INC p 1070
11375 Cortez Blvd 34613
Tel (352) 596-6632 *SIC* 8062

SCHOOL DISTRICT OF HERNANDO COUNTY FLORIDA p 1289
919 N Broad St 34601
Tel (352) 797-7000 *SIC* 8211

BUNNELL, FL

SCHOOL BOARD OF FLAGLER COUNTY p 1289
1769 E Moody Blvd Bldg 2f 32110
Tel (386) 437-7526 *SIC* 8211 8222

YELLOWSTONE LANDSCAPE GROUP INC p 1635
3235 N State St 32110
Tel (386) 437-6211 *SIC* 0782 0781

YELLOWSTONE LANDSCAPE-SOUTHEAST LLC p 1635
3235 N State St 32110
Tel (386) 437-6211 *SIC* 0781 0782

CAPE CANAVERAL, FL

COMPREHENSIVE HEALTH HOLDINGS INC p 352
8810 Astronaut Blvd 32920
Tel (321) 783-2720 *SIC* 8011

IAP GLOBAL SERVICES LLC p 725
7315 N Atlantic Ave 32920
Tel (321) 784-7100 *SIC* 6726

IAP WORLD SERVICES INC p 725
7315 N Atlantic Ave 32920
Tel (321) 784-7100
SIC 4731 4581 8744 4911 1541 4813

IAP WORLDWIDE SERVICES INC p 725
7315 N Atlantic Ave 32920
Tel (973) 633-5115
SIC 4731 4581 8744 4911

CAPE CORAL, FL

CAPE MEMORIAL HOSPITAL INC p 248
636 Del Prado Blvd S 33990
Tel (239) 424-2000 *SIC* 8062

CITY OF CAPE CORAL p 313
1015 Cultural Park Blvd 33990
Tel (239) 242-3410 *SIC* 9111

CITY OF CAPE CORAL p 313
1015 Cultural Park Blvd 33990
Tel (239) 574-0401 *SIC* 9111

■ LEGACY EDUCATION ALLIANCE INC p 852
1612 Cape Coral Pkwy E 33904
Tel (239) 542-0643 *SIC* 8299

MANAGEMENT CONSULTING INC p 900
2503 Se 17th Ave 33910
Tel (239) 458-3611 *SIC* 5531 5087

■ TIGRENT ENTERPRISES INC p 1453
1612 Cape Coral Pkwy E 33904
Tel (239) 542-0643 *SIC* 8249

▲ TIGRENT INC p 1453
1612 Cape Coral Pkwy E 33904
Tel (239) 542-0643 *SIC* 8249

CASSELBERRY, FL

DYNAFIRE INC p 464
109 Concord Dr Ste B 32707
Tel (407) 740-0232 *SIC* 5063

CHIEFLAND, FL

WHITE CONSTRUCTION CO INC p 1606
2811 N Young Blvd 32626
Tel (352) 493-1444 *SIC* 1611 0241 3531

CLEARWATER BEACH, FL

GOODRICH QUALITY THEATERS INC p 624
31 Island Way Apt 606 33767
Tel (616) 698-7733 *SIC* 7832

CLEARWATER, FL

ABSTRACT ELECTRONICS INC p 13
11526 53rd St N 33760
Tel (727) 540-0236 *SIC* 5065

AMERILIFE GROUP LLC p 82
2650 Mccormick Dr Ste 100 33759
Tel (727) 726-0726 *SIC* 6411

BAYCARE HEALTH SYSTEM INC p 161
2985 Drew St 33759
Tel (727) 519-1200 *SIC* 8741

BOARD OF TRUSTEES ST PETERSBURG COLLEGE p 196
6021 142nd Ave N 33760
Tel (727) 341-3329 *SIC* 8221

BOUCHARD INSURANCE INC p 204
101 Starcrest Dr 33765
Tel (727) 447-6481 *SIC* 6411

CHURCH OF SCIENTOLOGY FLAG SERVICE ORGANIZATION INC p 305
210 S Fort Harrison Ave 33756
Tel (727) 461-1282 *SIC* 8661

CITY OF CLEARWATER p 314
Clearwater Cy Hl Fl 3 33756
Tel (727) 562-4567 *SIC* 9111

COLORGRAPHX INC p 339
4721 110th Ave N 33762
Tel (727) 572-6364 *SIC* 2711

COUNTY OF PINELLAS p 381
315 Court St Rm 300 33756
Tel (727) 464-3485 *SIC* 9121

DEGC ENTERPRISES (US) INC p 422
14255 49th St N Ste 301 33762
Tel (727) 531-9161 *SIC* 5999 5912 5961

ECKERD YOUTH ALTERNATIVES INC p 475
100 Starcrest Dr 33765
Tel (727) 461-2990 *SIC* 8211

▲ HERITAGE INSURANCE HOLDINGS INC p 686
2600 Mccormick Dr Ste 300 33759
Tel (727) 362-7200 *SIC* 6331

HOSPICE OF FLORIDA SUNCOAST p 709
5771 Roosevelt Blvd # 400 33760
Tel (727) 527-4483 *SIC* 8399

■ INSTRUMENT TRANSFORMERS LLC p 747
1907 Calumet St 33765
Tel (727) 461-9413 *SIC* 3612

ION LABS INC p 762
5355 115th Ave N 33760
Tel (727) 527-1072 *SIC* 5122 2834

J T WALKER INDUSTRIES INC p 772
861 N Hercules Ave 33765
Tel (727) 461-0501
SIC 3442 3089 3585 5193

LINCARE HOLDINGS INC p 866
19387 Us Highway 19 N 33764
Tel (727) 530-7700 *SIC* 8082 8093

LINCARE INC p 866
19387 Us Highway 19 N 33764
Tel (727) 530-7700 SIC 8082 5999

LOKEY AUTOMOTIVE GROUP INC p 875
27850 Us Highway 19 N 33761
Tel (888) 275-8388 SIC 5511 7532

LOKEY MOTOR GROUP INC p 875
19820 Us Highway 19 N 33764
Tel (727) 530-1661 SIC 5511

▲ **MARINEMAX INC** p 906
2600 Mccormick Dr Ste 200 33759
Tel (727) 531-1700 SIC 5551

■ **MERCURY INSURANCE CO OF FLORIDA** p 945
1901 Ulmerton Rd Fl 6 33762
Tel (727) 561-4000 SIC 6331

METAL INDUSTRIES INC p 952
1985 Carroll St 33765
Tel (727) 441-2651 SIC 3585

MORGAN TIRE & AUTO LLC p 989
2021 Sunnydale Blvd 33765
Tel (727) 441-3727 SIC 7539 5531 5014

MORTON PLANT HOSPITAL ASSOCIATION INC p 991
300 Pinellas St 33756
Tel (727) 462-7000 SIC 8062 8051

MORTON PLANT MEASE HEALTH CARE INC p 991
300 Pinellas St 33756
Tel (727) 462-7777 SIC 8741 8721

MP DIRECT INC p 995
4800 126th Ave N 33762
Tel (727) 572-8443 SIC 5094 5944 5091

▲ **NICHOLAS FINANCIAL INC** p 1042
2454 N Mcmullen Booth Rd 33759
Tel (727) 726-0763 SIC 6141

PODS ENTERPRISES LLC p 1158
5585 Rio Vista Dr 33760
Tel (727) 538-6300 SIC 4225 6794

PODS HOLDINGS INC p 1159
5585 Rio Vista Dr 33760
Tel (727) 538-6300 SIC 6719

PORPOISE POOL & PATIO INC p 1161
14480 62nd St N 33760
Tel (727) 531-8913
SIC 6794 5999 5712 5091

S2 HR SOLUTIONS 1A LLC p 1263
3001 Executive Dr Ste 340 33762
Tel (727) 565-2950 SIC 8721

SHC HOLDING INC p 1313
311 Park Place Blvd 33759
Tel (727) 533-9700 SIC 6719

SOFT COMPUTER CONSULTANTS INC p 1337
5400 Tech Data Dr 33760
Tel (727) 789-0100 SIC 7373 7371

SUN WHOLESALE SUPPLY INC p 1401
6385 150th Ave N 33760
Tel (727) 524-3299
SIC 5169 5021 5023 5091

SUNCOAST CARING COMMUNITY INC p 1401
5771 Roosevelt Blvd 33760
Tel (727) 586-4432 SIC 6719

TAMPA BAY WATER A REGIONAL WATER SUPPLY AUTHORITY p 1423
2575 Enterprise Rd 33763
Tel (727) 796-2355 SIC 4941

▲ **TECH DATA CORP** p 1430
5350 Tech Data Dr 33760
Tel (727) 539-7429 SIC 5045

■ **TECH DATA PRODUCT MANAGEMENT INC** p 1430
5350 Tech Data Dr 33760
Tel (727) 539-7429 SIC 5045

TECHNOLOGY RESEARCH LLC p 1432
4525 140th Ave N Ste 900 33762
Tel (727) 535-0572 SIC 3613

US LABORATORIES INC p 1532
13773 Icot Blvd Ste 502 33760
Tel (954) 236-8100 SIC 8071

USAMERIBANK p 1534
4770 140th Ave N Ste 401 33762
Tel (727) 475-8780 SIC 6029

WORLD INDUSTRIAL RESOURCES CORP p 1625
13100 56th Ct Ste 710 33760
Tel (727) 572-9991
SIC 3999 2542 5113 2671

YOUNG MENS CHRISTIAN ASSOCIATION OF SUNCOAST p 1639
2469 Enterprise Rd 33763
Tel (312) 932-1200
SIC 8641 7991 8351 7032 8322

CLERMONT, FL

CLERMONT MOTOR SALES LLC p 325
16851 State Road 50 34711
Tel (352) 404-7006 SIC 7549

SOUTH LAKE HOSPITAL INC p 1344
1900 Don Wickham Dr Lbby 34711
Tel (352) 394-4071 SIC 8062

CLEWISTON, FL

UNITED STATES SUGAR CORP p 1514
111 Ponce De Leon Ave 33440
Tel (863) 983-8121
SIC 0133 2061 2062 2033

COCOA BEACH, FL

CAPE CANAVERAL HOSPITAL INC p 248
701 W Cocoa Beach Cswy 32931
Tel (321) 799-7111 SIC 8062

RD AMROSS LLC p 1212
3000 N Atl Ave Ste 207 32931
Tel (321) 613-3902 SIC 3761

COCOA, FL

ALL AMERICAN OIL INC OF BREVARD p 51
402 High Point Dr Ste 102 32926
Tel (321) 690-0807 SIC 5541 5411

EASTERN FLORIDA STATE COLLEGE p 472
1519 Clearlake Rd 32922
Tel (321) 433-7345 SIC 8221

M & R HIGH POINT HOLDINGS INC p 889
402 High Point Dr Ste 101 32926
Tel (321) 631-0245 SIC 6719

M & R UNITED INC p 889
402 High Point Dr Ste 101 32926
Tel (321) 631-0245 SIC 5812 5411

SOUTHEAST PETRO DISTRIBUTORS INC p 1346
402 High Point Dr Ste A 32926
Tel (321) 631-0245 SIC 5172

COCONUT CREEK, FL

FOOD FOR POOR INC p 564
6401 Lyons Rd 33073
Tel (954) 427-2222 SIC 8399

VAL DOR APPAREL LLC p 1538
6820 Lyons Technology Pkw 33073
Tel (954) 363-7340
SIC 2322 2329 2331 2339 2341

CORAL GABLES, FL

3801 FLAGLE SUPERMARKET LLC p 2
3801 W Flagler St 33134
Tel (305) 846-9796 SIC 5411 5912

AERSALE HOLDINGS INC p 31
121 Alhambra Plz Ste 1700 33134
Tel (305) 764-3200 SIC 5088 7359

AERSALE INC p 31
121 Alhambra Plz Ste 1700 33134
Tel (305) 764-3200 SIC 5088

BACARDI USA INC p 143
2701 S Le Jeune Rd 33134
Tel (305) 573-8600 SIC 5182

BAYVIEW FINANCIAL HOLDINGS LP p 162
4425 Ponce De Leon Blvd # 500 33146
Tel (305) 854-8880 SIC 6211

BAYVIEW LENDING GROUP LLC p 163
4425 P De Leon Blvd Fl 3 33146
Tel (305) 854-8880 SIC 6211

BILL USSERY MOTORS BODY SHOP INC p 182
300 Almeria Ave 33134
Tel (305) 445-8593 SIC 5511 7538

BOUNTY FRESH LLC p 204
806 S Douglas Rd Ste 580 33134
Tel (305) 592-6969 SIC 5148

■ **BROTHERS PROPERTY CORP** p 219
2 Alhambra Plz Ste 1280 33134
Tel (305) 285-1035 SIC 6512

■ **CAPITAL BANK NA** p 249
121 Alhambra Plz Ste 1601 33134
Tel (305) 444-1660 SIC 6021

CLUB MED INC (A CAYMAN ISLANDS CORP) p 328
75 Valencia Ave Fl 12 33134
Tel (305) 925-9000 SIC 7011

CODINA PARTNERS LLC p 333
135 San Lorenzo Ave # 750 33146
Tel (305) 529-1300
SIC 6552 6531 1521 8742

COLLECTION INC p 336
200 Bird Rd 33146
Tel (305) 444-5555 SIC 5511

DEL MONTE FRESH PRODUCE CO p 423
241 Sevilla Ave Ste 200 33134
Tel (305) 520-8400 SIC 5148

DEL MONTE FRESH PRODUCE NA INC p 423
241 Sevilla Ave Ste 200 33134
Tel (305) 520-8400 SIC 5148

DOCTORS HOSPITAL INC p 447
5000 University Dr 33146
Tel (305) 666-2111 SIC 8062

EARLY LEARNING COALITION OF MIAMI-DADE MONROE INC p 469
2555 Ponce De Leon Blvd # 5 33134
Tel (305) 646-7220 SIC 8351

EMPIRE INVESTMENT HOLDINGS LLC p 493
1220 Malaga Ave 33134
Tel (305) 403-1111 SIC 6799

FLORIDA EAST COAST INDUSTRIES LLC p 558
2855 S Le Jeune Rd Fl 4 33134
Tel (305) 520-2300 SIC 6552

GABLES ENGINEERING INC p 588
247 Greco Ave 33146
Tel (305) 774-4400 SIC 3679

GRAPHIC CENTER GROUP CORP p 631
2150 Coral Way Fl 1 33145
Tel (305) 961-1649 SIC 7372 7336

▲ **HEMISPHERE MEDIA GROUP INC** p 682
4000 Ponce De Leon Blvd # 650 33146
Tel (305) 421-6364 SIC 4841

▲ **MASTEC INC** p 917
800 S Douglas Rd Ste 1200 33134
Tel (305) 599-1800 SIC 1623 8741

■ **MASTEC NETWORK SOLUTIONS LLC** p 918
806 S Douglas Rd Fl 11 33134
Tel (866) 545-1782 SIC 4812 7373

■ **MASTEC NETWORK SOLUTIONS LLC** p 918
806 S Douglas Rd Fl 11 33134
Tel (866) 545-1782 SIC 4812 7373

■ **MASTEC NORTH AMERICA INC** p 918
800 S Douglas Rd Ste 1200 33134
Tel (305) 599-1800 SIC 1623

MATCON TRADING CORP p 919
2020 Ponce De Leon Blvd # 1204 33134
Tel (305) 442-6333 SIC 6792 2951

MERCANTIL COMMERCEBANK HOLDING CORP p 943
220 Alhambra Cir 33134
Tel (305) 441-5555 SIC 6021 7389 8721

ODEBRECHT CONSTRUCTION INC p 1074
201 Alhambra Cir Ste 1000 33134
Tel (305) 341-8800 SIC 1622 1522

OLE HBO PARTNERS p 1082
396 Alhambra Cir Ste 400 33134
Tel (305) 648-8100 SIC 4841

PESCANOVA INC p 1137
1430 S Dixie Hwy Ste 303 33146
Tel (305) 663-4380 SIC 5142

PREFERRED MEDICAL PLAN INC p 1169
4950 Sw 8th St Fl 4 33134
Tel (305) 324-5585 SIC 6324

QUIRCH FOODS CO p 1200
2701 S Le Jeune Rd 33134
Tel (305) 691-3535
SIC 5147 5142 5144 5146

RENEX CORP p 1224
201 Alhambra Cir Ste 800 33134
Tel (305) 448-2044 SIC 8092

RMET HOLDINGS INC p 1239
133 Sevilla Ave 33134
Tel (305) 567-3582 SIC 5181 5182

SUCRO CAN SOURCING LLC p 1396
2990 Ponce De Leon Blvd # 401 33134
Tel (305) 901-5222 SIC 5159 5149

TRIVEST FUND III LP p 1483
550 S Dixie Hwy Ste 300 33146
Tel (305) 858-2200 SIC 6799 5712

TURBANA CORP p 1492
999 Ponce De Leon Blvd # 900 33134
Tel (305) 445-1542 SIC 5148

UNIVERSITY OF MIAMI p 1523
1320 S Dixie Hwy Ste 150 33146
Tel (305) 284-5155 SIC 8221

CORAL SPRINGS, FL

ABB/CON-CISE OPTICAL GROUP LLC p 9
12301 Nw 39th St 33065
Tel (800) 852-8089 SIC 5048 3851 8741

ALVACO TRADING CO p 63
12301 Nw 39th St 33065
Tel (800) 852-8089 SIC 6719

GLOBAL CONSTRUCTION SERVICES LLC p 616
934 N University Dr 453 33071
Tel (954) 688-6255 SIC 1522

NUBO BOTTLE CO LLC p 1066
3700 Nw 124th Ave Ste 109 33065
Tel (954) 283-9057 SIC 2086

P2P STAFFING CORP p 1103
5810 Coral Ridge Dr # 250 33076
Tel (954) 656-8600 SIC 7361

CRAWFORDVILLE, FL

■ **ST MARKS POWDER INC** p 1370
7121 Coastal Hwy 32327
Tel (850) 577-2824 SIC 2869

CRESTVIEW, FL

■ **CRESTVIEW HOSPITAL CORP** p 392
151 E Redstone Ave 32539
Tel (850) 423-1000 SIC 8062

■ **JUNIOR FOOD STORES OF WEST FLORIDA INC** p 797
619 8th Ave 32536
Tel (850) 587-5023 SIC 5541 5411

CRYSTAL RIVER, FL

■ **CITRUS HMA INC** p 311
6201 N Suncoast Blvd 34428
Tel (352) 563-5488 SIC 8062

MORGAN BROSUPPLY INC p 988
7559 W Gulf To Lake Hwy 34429
Tel (386) 255-2200 SIC 5074

DADE CITY, FL

WITHLACOOCHEE RIVER ELECTRIC COOPERATIVE INC p 1619
14651 21st St 33523
Tel (352) 567-5133 SIC 4911

DANIA BEACH, FL

■ **HULL & CO INC** p 718
1815 Griffin Rd Ste 300 33004
Tel (954) 920-6790 SIC 6411

MAGIC LEAP INC p 895
1855 Griffin Rd Ste B454 33004
Tel (954) 889-7010 SIC 7371

DAVENPORT, FL

▲ **CENTERSTATE BANKS INC** p 276
42745 Highway 27 33837
Tel (863) 419-7750 SIC 6021

■ **HAINES CITY HEALTH MANAGEMENT ASSOCIATION INC** p 653
40100 Highway 27 33837
Tel (863) 422-4971 SIC 8062

DAVIE, FL

ANDRX CORP p 91
4955 Orange Dr 33314
Tel (954) 585-1400 SIC 2834 5122

ANDRX PHARMACEUTICALS INC p 91
4955 Orange Dr 33314
Tel (954) 581-7500 SIC 3826

BANKERS HEALTHCARE GROUP LLC p 152
10234 W State Road 84 33324
Tel (954) 384-9119 SIC 6153

BRISTOL WEST HOLDINGS INC p 214
5701 Stirling Rd 33314
Tel (954) 316-5200 SIC 6331

BRISTOL WEST INSURANCE SERVICE INC p 214
5701 Stirling Rd 33314
Tel (954) 316-5200 SIC 6411

■ **MAKO SURGICAL CORP** p 899
2555 Davie Rd 33317
Tel (866) 647-6256 SIC 3842

NOVA SOUTHEASTERN UNIVERSITY INC p 1062
3301 College Ave 33314
Tel (954) 262-7300 SIC 8221 8211

DAYTONA BEACH, FL

AMERICAN SHRINKWRAP CO p 79
1901 Mason Ave 32117
Tel (800) 229-2904 SIC 5084

■ **ATLANTIC MEDICAL CENTER** p 127
303 N Clyde Morris Blvd 32114
Tel (386) 239-5001 SIC 8062 8011

BETHUNE-COOKMAN UNIVERSITY INC p 178
640 Dr Mary Mcleod Bethun 32114
Tel (386) 481-2000 SIC 8221

▲ **BROWN & BROWN INC** p 219
220 S Ridgewood Ave # 180 32114
Tel (386) 252-9601 SIC 6411

■ **BUILDER SERVICES GROUP INC** p 224
260 Jimmy Ann Dr 32114
Tel (386) 304-2222 SIC 1742

CONRAD YELVINGTON DISTRIBUTORS INC p 358
2328 Bellevue Ave 32114
Tel (386) 257-5504 SIC 5032 5261

COSTA INC p 374
2361 Mason Ave Ste 100 32117
Tel (386) 274-4000 SIC 3851

DEL MAR DESIGNS INC p 423
1821 Holsonback Dr 32117
Tel (386) 767-1997 SIC 5719

EMBRY-RIDDLE AERONAUTICAL UNIVERSITY INC p 490
600 S Clyde Morris Blvd 32114
Tel (386) 226-6000 SIC 8221

FLORIDA HOSPITAL MEMORIAL FOUNDATION p 558
305 Memorial Medical Pkwy # 212 32117
Tel (386) 615-4144 SIC 7389

HALIFAX HEALTH CARE SYSTEMS INC p 654
303 N Clyde Morris Blvd 32114
Tel (386) 254-4000 SIC 8062 8011 8063

■ **HALIFAX MEDIA GROUP LLC** p 654
2339 Beville Rd 32119
Tel (386) 265-6700 SIC 2711

HALIFAX MEDIA HOLDINGS LLC p 654
901 6th St 32117
Tel (386) 681-2404 SIC 2711 2791

HALIFAX STAFFING INC p 654
303 N Clyde Morris Blvd 32114
Tel (386) 226-4560 SIC 7363

▲ **INTERNATIONAL SPEEDWAY CORP** p 757
1 Daytona Blvd 32114
Tel (386) 254-2700 SIC 7948

INTERVEST CONSTRUCTION OF ORLANDO INC p 759
2379 Beville Rd 32119
Tel (386) 788-0820 SIC 1522 1521

LADIES PROFESSIONAL GOLF ASSOCIATION p 837
100 International Golf Dr 32124
Tel (386) 274-6200 SIC 8699

MEMORIAL HEALTH SYSTEMS INC p 941
301 Memorial Medical Pkwy 32117
Tel (386) 231-6000 SIC 8062

■ **NEW YORK TIMES REGIONAL NEWSPAPER GROUP** p 1036
2339 Beville Rd 32119
Tel (212) 556-4673 *SIC* 2711

NEWS-JOURNAL CORP p 1039
901 6th St 32117
Tel (386) 252-1511 *SIC* 2711

PRODUCT QUEST MANUFACTURING LLC p 1179
330 Carswell Ave 32117
Tel (386) 239-8787 *SIC* 2844

■ **TELEDYNE ODI INC** p 1434
1026 N Williamson Blvd 32114
Tel (386) 236-0780 *SIC* 3678

TERRY TAYLOR FORD CO p 1440
1420 N Tomoka Farms Rd 32124
Tel (386) 274-6700 *SIC* 5511 7532

▲ **TOPBUILD CORP** p 1460
260 Jimmy Ann Dr 32114
Tel (386) 304-2200
SIC 1742 1761 1751 5033

■ **TOPBUILD SERVICES GROUP CORP** p 1461
260 Jimmy Ann Dr 32114
Tel (386) 304-2200 *SIC* 1742

■ **TRUTEAM LLC** p 1489
260 Jimmy Ann Dr 32114
Tel (386) 304-2200
SIC 1742 1761 1751 1521

DEERFIELD BEACH, FL

ACQUINITY INTERACTIVE LLC p 18
2200 Sw 10th St 33442
Tel (954) 312-4733 *SIC* 3993

CNA HOLDING CORP p 329
350 Sw 12th Ave 33442
Tel (561) 922-2500 *SIC* 7349 6794

COVERALL NORTH AMERICA INC p 385
350 Sw 12th Ave 33442
Tel (561) 922-2500 *SIC* 6794 7349

■ **GEMAIRE DISTRIBUTORS LLC** p 598
2151 W Hillsboro Blvd # 400 33442
Tel (954) 246-2665 *SIC* 5075

JM FAMILY ENTERPRISES INC p 786
100 Jim Moran Blvd 33442
Tel (954) 429-2000
SIC 5511 5012 5013 5531

LIST INDUSTRIES INC p 870
401 Jim Moran Blvd 33442
Tel (954) 429-9155 *SIC* 2541 5021 2542

MAPEI CORP p 903
1144 E Newport Center Dr 33442
Tel (954) 246-8888 *SIC* 2891

PEOPLES TRUST INSURANCE CO p 1133
18 Peoples Trust Way 33441
Tel (561) 988-9170 *SIC* 6411 6021

REAGAN WIRELESS CORP p 1213
720 S Powerline Rd Ste D 33442
Tel (954) 596-2355 *SIC* 5065 4812

SOUTHEAST TOYOTA DISTRIBUTORS LLC p 1346
100 Jim Moran Blvd 33442
Tel (954) 429-2000 *SIC* 5012

WORLD OMNI FINANCIAL CORP p 1625
190 Jim Moran Blvd 33442
Tel (954) 429-2200 *SIC* 6141 6159

DEFUNIAK SPRINGS, FL

CHOCTAWHATCHEE ELECTRIC COOPERATIVE INC p 302
1350 Baldwin Ave 32435
Tel (850) 892-2111 *SIC* 4911

COUNTY OF WALTON p 382
571 E Nelson Ave Ste 301 32433
Tel (850) 892-8115 *SIC* 9111

DELAND, FL

▲ **ARC GROUP WORLDWIDE INC** p 103
810 Flight Line Blvd 32724
Tel (303) 467-5236 *SIC* 3499 3462 3812

COUNTY OF VOLUSIA p 382
123 W Indiana Ave Ste A 32720
Tel (386) 736-2700 *SIC* 9111

EARL W COLVARD INC p 468
816 S Woodland Blvd 32720
Tel (386) 734-6447 *SIC* 5531 7534

KINGSPAN INSULATED PANELS INC p 821
726 Summerhill Dr 32724
Tel (386) 626-6789 *SIC* 3448

MEMORIAL HOSPITAL - WEST VOLUSIA INC p 942
701 W Plymouth Ave 32720
Tel (386) 943-4522 *SIC* 8062

STETSON UNIVERSITY INC p 1388
421 N Woodland Blvd 32723
Tel (386) 822-7000 *SIC* 8221

VOLUSIA COUNTY SCHOOL DISTRICT p 1565
200 N Clara Ave 32720
Tel (386) 734-7190 *SIC* 8211

DELRAY BEACH, FL

CHILDREN OF AMERICA INC p 298
5300 W Atl Ave Ste 700 33484
Tel (561) 999-0710 *SIC* 8351

■ **DELRAY MEDICAL CENTER INC** p 425
5352 Linton Blvd 33484
Tel (561) 498-4440 *SIC* 8062

FRIENDFINDER NETWORKS INC p 580
1615 S Congress Ave # 103 33445
Tel (561) 912-7000 *SIC* 4813

GREAT AMERICAN BEAUTY INC p 633
124 N Swinton Ave 33444
Tel (561) 496-2730 *SIC* 5122 2844

LIFE CARE HOME HEALTH SERVICES CORP p 863
4723 W Atl Ave Ste 21 33445
Tel (561) 272-5866 *SIC* 8082 7361

MEISNER ELECTRIC INC OF FLORIDA p 940
220 Ne 1st St 33444
Tel (561) 278-8362 *SIC* 1731

MORSE OPERATIONS INC p 991
2850 S Federal Hwy 33483
Tel (561) 276-5000 *SIC* 5511

OCEAN PROPERTIES LTD p 1073
1001 E Atl Ave Ste 202 33483
Tel (603) 559-2100
SIC 7011 6552 1522 5719 5812 5813

■ **OFFICE CLUB INC** p 1075
2200 Germantown Rd 33445
Tel (561) 438-4800 *SIC* 5943 5112

PERO FAMILY FARMS FOOD CO LLC p 1137
14095 Us Highway 441 33446
Tel (561) 498-4533 *SIC* 5148

PERO FAMILY FARMS LLC p 1137
14095 Us Highway 441 33446
Tel (561) 498-4533 *SIC* 5148

TENNIER INDUSTRIES INC p 1438
755 Nw 17th Ave Ste 106 33445
Tel (561) 999-9710 *SIC* 2311

TWIN-STAR INTERNATIONAL INC p 1495
1690 S Congress Ave # 210 33445
Tel (561) 665-8084 *SIC* 5719

DESTIN, FL

■ **RESORTQUEST INTERNATIONAL INC** p 1227
8955 Us Highway 98 W # 203 32550
Tel (850) 837-4774 *SIC* 7011 6519

■ **RESORTQUEST REAL ESTATE OF FLORIDA INC** p 1227
35000 Emerald Coast Pkwy 32541
Tel (850) 837-3700 *SIC* 7011 8741

DORAL, FL

ACCESS TELECOM GROUP INC p 15
1882 Nw 97th Ave 33172
Tel (305) 468-1955 *SIC* 5065 5999

AIR EXPRESS INTERNATIONAL USA INC p 38
1801 Nw 82nd Ave 33126
Tel (786) 264-3500 *SIC* 4731 4513

ALLIED UNIVERSAL CORP p 57
3901 Nw 115th Ave 33178
Tel (305) 888-2623 *SIC* 5169

ALLPLUS COMPUTER SYSTEMS CORP p 58
3075 Nw 107th Ave 33172
Tel (305) 436-3993 *SIC* 5065 5045

AMADEUS AMERICAS INC p 64
3470 Nw 82nd Ave Ste 1000 33122
Tel (305) 499-6000 *SIC* 7371

AMADEUS NORTH AMERICA INC p 64
3470 Nw 82nd Ave Ste 1000 33122
Tel (305) 499-6613 *SIC* 7371 8322

AMERICAN HEALTH CHOICE INC p 73
8350 Nw 52nd Ter Ste 206 33166
Tel (305) 860-2333 *SIC* 8011

ANSA MCAL (US) INC p 93
11403 Nw 39th St 33178
Tel (305) 599-8766 *SIC* 7389 4731

ANSA MCAL TRADING INC p 93
11403 Nw 39th St 33178
Tel (305) 599-8766
SIC 8741 5084 5085 4731

ATKINS NORTH AMERICA INC p 125
2001 Nw 107th Ave 33172
Tel (813) 282-7275 *SIC* 8711

■ **BOSTON SCIENTIFIC MIAMI CORP** p 203
8600 Nw 41st St 33166
Tel (305) 597-4000 *SIC* 3841

■ **CARNIVAL CELEBRATION INC** p 258
3655 Nw 87th Ave 33178
Tel (305) 599-2600 *SIC* 4481

▲ **CARNIVAL CORP** p 259
3655 Nw 87th Ave 33178
Tel (305) 599-2600 *SIC* 4481 4725 7011

EKMAN & CO INC p 482
8750 Nw 36th St Ste 400 33178
Tel (305) 579-1200 *SIC* 5099

EKMAN HOLDING INC p 482
8750 Nw 36th St Ste 400 33178
Tel (305) 579-1200 *SIC* 5099

GOLD COAST BEVERAGE LLC p 620
10055 Nw 12th St 33172
Tel (305) 591-9800 *SIC* 5181

HELLMANN WORLDWIDE LOGISTICS INC p 682
10450 Doral Blvd 33178
Tel (305) 406-4500 *SIC* 4731

IMAGINE SCHOOLS OF DELAWARE INC p 733
8071 Nw 54th St 33166
Tel (305) 648-5962 *SIC* 8211

INNOCO TECHNOLOGY GROUP INC p 744
1608 Nw 84th Ave 33126
Tel (305) 477-8117 *SIC* 5065

■ **INTCOMEX INC** p 748
3505 Nw 107th Ave Ste 1 33178
Tel (305) 477-6230 *SIC* 7371 5045

JG BRANDS INC p 785
10530 Nw 26th St Ste F201 33172
Tel (786) 597-1554 *SIC* 5999

KELLY TRACTOR CO p 809
8255 Nw 58th St 33166
Tel (305) 592-5360
SIC 5082 5083 7359 7353 5084 7699

KW PROPERTY MANAGEMENT LLC p 832
8200 Nw 33rd St Ste 300 33122
Tel (305) 476-9188 *SIC* 6531

■ **M & M AEROSPACE HARDWARE INC** p 888
10000 Nw 15th Ter 33172
Tel (305) 925-2600 *SIC* 5088

MARINE HARVEST USA LLC p 906
8550 Nw 17th St Ste 105 33126
Tel (305) 591-8550 *SIC* 5146

MONTEBIANCO USA LLC p 986
2315 Nw 107th Ave Ste 75 33172
Tel (305) 597-8248 *SIC* 5143

NASA ELECTRONICS CORP p 1007
2330 Nw 102nd Pl 33172
Tel (305) 716-7706 *SIC* 5065

▲ **NEFF CORP** p 1024
3750 Nw 87th Ave Ste 400 33178
Tel (305) 513-3350 *SIC* 7359

NIPRO MEDICAL CORP p 1044
3150 Nw 107th Ave 33172
Tel (305) 599-7174 *SIC* 5047

PANTROPIC POWER INC p 1112
8205 Nw 58th St 33166
Tel (305) 477-3329
SIC 5084 5085 5063 7353

▲ **PERRY ELLIS INTERNATIONAL INC** p 1137
3000 Nw 107th Ave 33172
Tel (305) 592-2830
SIC 2321 2325 2339 2337 5611 5621

■ **PHELPS DODGE INTERNATIONAL CORP** p 1141
9850 Nw 41st St Ste 200 33178
Tel (305) 648-7888 *SIC* 8742 3357 3315

■ **PRESTIGE CRUISES INTERNATIONAL INC** p 1173
8300 Nw 33rd St Ste 100 33122
Tel (305) 514-2300 *SIC* 4449

■ **REGENT SEVEN SEAS CRUISES INC** p 1219
8300 Nw 33rd St Ste 100 33122
Tel (305) 514-4920 *SIC* 4481

■ **SOFTWARE BROKERS OF AMERICA INC** p 1337
3505 Nw 107th Ave Ste 1 33178
Tel (305) 477-5993 *SIC* 5045

STARBOARD CRUISE SERVICES INC p 1378
8400 Nw 36th St Ste 600 33166
Tel (786) 845-7300 *SIC* 5399

■ **SUPREME INTERNATIONAL LLC** p 1408
3000 Nw 107th Ave 33172
Tel (305) 592-2830 *SIC* 2325

TM WIRELESS COMMUNICATION SERVICES INC p 1457
10205 Nw 19th St Ste 101 33172
Tel (305) 421-9938 *SIC* 5065

TWC WISE COMPUTER INC p 1494
3515 Nw 114th Ave 33178
Tel (305) 594-5725 *SIC* 5045

UNIFIED COMMUNICATIONS INTERNATIONAL LLC p 1503
1921 Nw 82nd Ave 33126
Tel (305) 677-7888 *SIC* 5065

UNITED DATA TECHNOLOGIES INC p 1507
8825 Nw 21st Ter 33172
Tel (305) 882-0435 *SIC* 7379

UNIVISION PRODUCTIONS p 1527
9405 Nw 41st St 33178
Tel (305) 597-3097 *SIC* 4833

USA BOUQUET LLC p 1533
1500 Nw 95th Ave 33172
Tel (786) 437-6500 *SIC* 5193

VA CELL INC p 1538
8400 Nw 33rd St Ste 103 33122
Tel (305) 592-1367 *SIC* 5065 5043

VITEL MOBILE INC p 1563
8925 Nw 26th St 33172
Tel (305) 418-9790 *SIC* 4812

▲ **WORLD FUEL SERVICES CORP** p 1625
9800 Nw 41st St Ste 400 33178
Tel (305) 428-8000 *SIC* 5172 3519 5541

■ **WORLD FUEL SERVICES INC** p 1625
9800 Nw 41st St Ste 400 33178
Tel (305) 428-8000 *SIC* 5172

DOVER, FL

TAMPA BAY FISHERIES INC p 1423
3060 Gallagher Rd 33527
Tel (813) 752-8883 *SIC* 2092

DUNEDIN, FL

MEASE HOSPITALS p 934
601 Main St 34698
Tel (727) 734-6354 *SIC* 8071

RAM EXCAVATING INC p 1206
3349 Hannah Way E 34698
Tel (727) 463-6428 *SIC* 1794

TRUSTEES OF MEASE HOSPITAL INC p 1488
601 Main St 34698
Tel (727) 733-1111 *SIC* 8062

EDGEWATER, FL

■ **BOSTON WHALER INC** p 203
100 Whaler Way 32141
Tel (386) 428-0057 *SIC* 3732

ESTERO, FL

■ **HERTZ CORP** p 687
8501 Williams Rd 33928
Tel (239) 301-7000
SIC 7514 7515 7513 7359 5521 6794

HERTZ GLOBAL HOLDINGS INC p 687
8501 Williams Rd Fl 3 33928
Tel (239) 301-7000 *SIC* 7515 7514

HORTIFRUT IMPORTS INC p 708
9450 Corkscrew Palms Cir 33928
Tel (239) 552-4453 *SIC* 5148

FERNANDINA BEACH, FL

A V AMELIA ISLAND PLANTATION p 6
39 Beach Lagoon Rd 32034
Tel (904) 261-6161 *SIC* 7011

AMELIA ISLAND CO p 66
1423 Julia St 32034
Tel (904) 261-6161
SIC 7011 6552 7992 7991 5812

NASSAU COUNTY SCHOOL DISTRICT p 1008
1201 Atlantic Ave 32034
Tel (904) 491-9900 *SIC* 8211

TRI-STARR MANAGEMENT SERVICES INC p 1477
1941 Citrona Dr 32034
Tel (909) 321-0507 *SIC* 8741

FORT LAUDERDALE, FL

ALTADIS HOLDINGS USA INC p 61
5900 N Andrews Ave # 1100 33309
Tel (954) 772-9000 *SIC* 6719

ALTADIS USA INC p 61
5900 N Andrews Ave # 1100 33309
Tel (954) 772-9000 *SIC* 2121

■ **ASE MOTORS HOLDING CORP** p 116
200 Sw 1st Ave 33301
Tel (954) 769-7000 *SIC* 5511

■ **AUTO CO XXVIII INC** p 133
200 Sw 1st Ave 33301
Tel (954) 769-7000 *SIC* 5511

■ **AUTONATION ENTERPRISES INC** p 135
200 Sw 1st Ave Ste 1700 33301
Tel (954) 769-7000 *SIC* 5511

▲ **AUTONATION INC** p 135
200 Sw 1st Ave Ste 1700 33301
Tel (954) 769-6000 *SIC* 5511 5521

■ **AUTONATION MOTORS HOLDING CORP** p 135
200 Sw 1st Ave 33301
Tel (954) 769-7000 *SIC* 5511

BANYAN AIR SERVICES INC p 153
5360 Nw 20th Ter 33309
Tel (954) 491-3170
SIC 5172 4581 5088 4522

■ **BBX CAPITAL CORP** p 163
401 E Las Olas Blvd 33301
Tel (954) 940-4000 *SIC* 6798 6035

▲ **BFC FINANCIAL CORP** p 179
401 E Las Olas Blvd # 800 33301
Tel (954) 940-4900 *SIC* 6035 6531 6552

BODY CENTRAL STORES INC p 197
1883 W State Road 84 # 106 33315
Tel (904) 737-0811 *SIC* 5999

BROWARD COLLEGE p 219
111 E Las Olas Blvd 33301
Tel (954) 201-7400 *SIC* 8222

BROWARD COUNTY PUBLIC SCHOOLS p 219
600 Se 3rd Ave 33301
Tel (754) 321-0000 *SIC* 8211

BROWARD GENERAL MEDICAL CENTER p 219
1600 S Andrews Ave 33316
Tel (954) 355-4400 *SIC* 8011

CHARTER SCHOOLS USA INC p 291
800 Corporate Dr Ste 124 33334
Tel (954) 202-3500 *SIC* 8211

CHILDNET INC p 298
1100 W Mcnab Rd 33309
Tel (954) 414-6000 *SIC* 8322

CHIQUITA BRANDS INTERNATIONAL INC p 301
2051 Se 35th St 33316
Tel (954) 453-1201
SIC 0179 0174 0161 0175 2033

CHIQUITA BRANDS LLC p 301
2051 Se 35th St 33316
Tel (954) 453-1201
SIC 0175 0174 0179 0161 5148 7389

▲ CITRIX SYSTEMS INC p 311
851 W Cypress Creek Rd 33309
Tel (954) 267-3000 SIC 7372

CITY OF FORT LAUDERDALE p 314
100 N Andrews Ave 33301
Tel (954) 828-5013 SIC 9111

CLIFF BERRY INC p 326
851 Eller Dr 33316
Tel (954) 763-3390
SIC 4953 4959 4212 2992 4491

COMMONWEALTH - ALTADIS INC p 345
5900 N Andrews Ave # 1100 33309
Tel (954) 772-9000 SIC 5194

COMMONWEALTH-ALTADIS INC p 346
5900 N Andrews Ave # 1100 33309
Tel (800) 481-5814 SIC 2111 2621 2131

CONSOLIDATED CIGAR HOLDINGS INC p 359
5900 N Andrews Ave # 1100 33309
Tel (954) 772-9000 SIC 2121

CONVEY HEALTH SOLUTIONS INC p 365
1 Financial Plz Fl 14 33394
Tel (954) 903-5000 SIC 5912 5999

COUNTY OF BROWARD p 376
115 S Andrews Ave Ste 409 33301
Tel (954) 357-7050 SIC 9111

CSI INTERNATIONAL INC p 398
6700 N Andrews Ave # 400 33309
Tel (954) 308-4300 SIC 8744 8711

EARLY LEARNING COALITION OF BROWARD COUNTY INC p 469
6301 Nw 5th Way Ste 3400 33309
Tel (954) 377-2188 SIC 8299

EMBRAER AIRCRAFT CUSTOMER SERVICES INC p 490
276 Sw 34th St 33315
Tel (954) 359-3700 SIC 5088

EMBRAER AIRCRAFT HOLDING INC p 490
276 Sw 34th St 33315
Tel (954) 359-3700 SIC 7699

EMBRAER SERVICES INC p 490
276 Sw 34th St 33315
Tel (954) 359-3700 SIC 3721

ENER1 GROUP INC p 497
550 W Cypress Creek Rd 33309
Tel (954) 202-4442 SIC 3577 3069

EVERGLADES COLLEGE INC p 514
1900 W Coml Blvd Ste 180 33309
Tel (954) 776-4476 SIC 8221

FHP MANUFACTURING CO p 539
601 Nw 65th Ct 33309
Tel (954) 776-5471 SIC 3585

■ FIRST INTERNATIONAL EXCHANGE GROUP p 547
2100 W Cypress Creek Rd 33309
Tel (954) 658-3464 SIC 6035 6531

■ FIRSTTEAM AUTOMOTIVE CORP p 549
200 Sw 1st Ave 33301
Tel (954) 769-7000 SIC 5511

■ FLAG INTERMEDIATE HOLDINGS CORP p 554
2400 E Coml Blvd Ste 905 33308
Tel (954) 202-4000 SIC 5051 3354 3315

▲ FLANIGANS ENTERPRISES INC p 554
5059 Ne 18th Ave 33334
Tel (954) 377-1961 SIC 5812 5921

FORT LAUDERDALE TRANSPORTATION INC p 569
1330 Se 4th Ave Ste D 33316
Tel (954) 524-6500 SIC 7299 4789

GA TELESIS LLC p 588
1850 Nw 49th St 33309
Tel (954) 676-3111 SIC 5088 3724

GLOBENET CABOS SUBMARINOS AMERICA INC p 618
200 E Las Olas Blvd 33301
Tel (561) 314-0500 SIC 4813

GREENFIELD WORLD TRADE INC p 638
3355 Entp Ave Ste 160 33331
Tel (954) 202-7419 SIC 5046

GUARANTEE INSURANCE GROUP INC p 644
401 E Las Olas Blvd # 1540 33301
Tel (954) 670-2900 SIC 6411 6331

HBA CORP p 671
5310 Nw 33rd Ave Ste 211 33309
Tel (954) 731-3350 SIC 8051

HOLMAN AUTOMOTIVE INC p 701
12 E Sunrise Blvd 33304
Tel (954) 779-2000 SIC 5511 5531

HOLY CROSS HOSPITAL INC p 702
4725 N Federal Hwy 33308
Tel (954) 771-8000 SIC 8062

HORNERXPRESS INC p 708
5755 Powerline Rd 33309
Tel (954) 772-6966 SIC 5091 3949 3561

HORNERXPRESS-SOUTH FLORIDA INC p 708
5755 Powerline Rd 33309
Tel (800) 432-6966 SIC 5091

HYPOWER INC p 724
5913 Nw 31st Ave 33309
Tel (954) 978-9300 SIC 1623 1731

INTERBOND HOLDING CORP p 751
3200 Sw 42nd St 33312
Tel (954) 797-4000 SIC 7629 3699 5722

INTERMEDIX CORP p 753
6451 N Federal Hwy # 1000 33308
Tel (954) 308-8700 SIC 7372

■ JAMES A CUMMINGS INC p 776
1 E Broward Blvd Ste 1300 33301
Tel (954) 484-1532 SIC 1542 1541

■ KAPLAN INC p 803
6301 Kaplan Univ Ave 33309
Tel (212) 492-5800
SIC 8299 7361 7372 2731

LIFE EXTENSION FOUNDATION INC p 863
3600 W Coml Blvd Ste 100 33309
Tel (954) 766-8433 SIC 8733

■ MAGNIFIQUE PARFUMES AND COSMETICS INC p 896
5900 N Andrews Ave # 500 33309
Tel (954) 335-9100 SIC 5999

MARKSMAN SECURITY CORP p 909
1700 Nw 49th St Ste 110 33309
Tel (954) 771-9755 SIC 7382 7381

■ METALS USA HOLDINGS CORP p 952
2400 E Coml Blvd Ste 905 33308
Tel (954) 202-4000 SIC 5051 3272 3354

■ METALS USA INC p 953
2400 E Coml Blvd Ste 905 33308
Tel (954) 202-4000 SIC 3441

MONTACHEM INTERNATIONAL INC p 986
200 S Andrews Ave Ste 702 33301
Tel (954) 385-9908 SIC 5169

MUVICO THEATERS INC p 1003
2929 E Coml Blvd Ste 408 33308
Tel (954) 564-6550 SIC 7832 8741

NATIONAL MARINE SUPPLIERS INC p 1014
2800 Sw 2nd Ave 33315
Tel (954) 462-3131 SIC 5088

NORTH BROWARD HOSPITAL DISTRICT p 1051
1800 Nw 49th St 33309
Tel (954) 473-7010 SIC 8062

NORTH BROWARD HOSPITAL DISTRICT FEDERAL CREDIT UNION p 1051
303 Se 17th St Ste 106 33316
Tel (954) 355-4400 SIC 6061

▲ PATRIOT NATIONAL INC p 1121
401 E Las Olas Blvd # 1650 33301
Tel (954) 670-2900 SIC 6411

■ PERFUMANIA INC p 1135
5900 N Andrews Ave # 500 33309
Tel (866) 600-3600 SIC 5122 5999

PERNOD RICARD AMERICAS TRAVEL RETAIL INC p 1136
200 E Las Olas Blvd 33301
Tel (954) 940-9000 SIC 5182

PORT CONSOLIDATED INC p 1162
3141 Se 14th Ave 33316
Tel (954) 522-1182 SIC 5172

PROGRESSIVE WASTE SOLUTIONS OF FL INC p 1182
2860 W State Road 84 33312
Tel (954) 888-4300 SIC 4953

PROSPERITY FUNDING INC p 1184
200 S Andrews Ave 201c 33301
Tel (919) 954-0232 SIC 6153

RENAISSANCE CHARTER SCHOOL INC p 1223
6245 N Federal Hwy # 500 33308
Tel (954) 202-3500 SIC 8211

■ REPUBLIC RESOURCES CO p 1225
200 Sw 1st Ave 33301
Tel (954) 769-7000 SIC 5511

RESOLVE MARINE GROUP INC p 1227
1510 Se 17th St Ste 400 33316
Tel (954) 764-8700
SIC 4499 4492 4491 4412 7389

RESORT MARKETING HOLDINGS INC p 1227
2419 E Commercial Blvd 33308
Tel (954) 630-9449 SIC 7011 6719

RESULTS COMPANIES LLC p 1228
100 Ne 3rd Ave Ste 200 33301
Tel (954) 921-2400 SIC 4813

SCHOOL BOARD OF BROWARD COUNTY p 1289
600 Se 3rd Ave 33301
Tel (754) 321-0000 SIC 8211

SCHOOL BOARD OF BROWARD COUNTY (INC) p 1289
600 Se 3rd Ave 33301
Tel (754) 321-0000 SIC 8211 8222

SCRIBEAMERICA LLC p 1294
1200 E Las Olas Blvd # 201 33301
Tel (786) 279-1057 SIC 8099

■ SEABULK INTERNATIONAL INC p 1296
2200 Eller Dr 33316
Tel (954) 828-1701 SIC 4424 4492

▲ SEACOR HOLDINGS INC p 1296
2200 Eller Dr 33316
Tel (954) 523-2200
SIC 4412 4424 4449 4959 8748

SEITLIN & CO p 1301
1000 Corp Dr Ste 400 33334
Tel (305) 591-0090 SIC 6411 8742

SEMINOLE HARD ROCK HOTEL & CASINO p 1302
1 Seminole Way 33314
Tel (954) 327-7625 SIC 7011

SEMINOLE TRIBE OF FLORIDA HARD ROCK p 1302
1 Seminole Way 33314
Tel (954) 327-7625 SIC 7011

SERVICE AMERICA ENTEPRISE INC p 1307
2755 Nw 63rd Ct 33309
Tel (954) 979-1100 SIC 1711 1731

SFN GROUP INC p 1310
2050 Spectrum Blvd 33309
Tel (954) 308-7600 SIC 6794 7363

SFN PROFESSIONAL SERVICES LLC p 1310
2050 Spectrum Blvd 33309
Tel (954) 938-7600 SIC 7363

SIGNATURE CONSULTANTS LLC p 1322
200 W Cypress Creek Rd # 400 33309
Tel (954) 677-1020 SIC 7379 8742

SMF ENERGY CORP p 1332
200 W Cypress Creek Rd # 400 33309
Tel (954) 308-4200 SIC 5172

SOLID RESOURCES INC p 1338
2200 Eller Dr 33316
Tel (941) 928-0958 SIC 8742

STILES CORP p 1389
301 E Las Olas Blvd 33301
Tel (954) 627-9150 SIC 1542 1541

■ SUN-SENTINEL CO INC p 1401
500 E Broward Blvd # 800 33394
Tel (954) 356-4000 SIC 2711

SUZANO PULP AND PAPER AMERICA INC p 1410
800 Corporate Dr Ste 320 33334
Tel (954) 772-7716 SIC 5111

TECHNISOURCE INC p 1431
2050 Spectrum Blvd 33309
Tel (954) 308-7600 SIC 7363 5045 7361

■ TEMPLETON INTERNATIONAL INC p 1436
300 Se 2nd St Ste 600 33301
Tel (954) 527-7500 SIC 6282

■ TEMPLETON WORLDWIDE INC p 1436
500 E Broward Blvd # 900 33394
Tel (954) 527-7500
SIC 6211 6282 8742 8748

TRIVIDIA HEALTH INC p 1483
2400 Nw 55th Ct 33309
Tel (800) 342-7226 SIC 5113

▲ UNIVERSAL INSURANCE HOLDINGS INC p 1517
1110 W Coml Blvd Ste 100 33309
Tel (954) 958-1200 SIC 6411

VEHICLE PRODUCTION GROUP LLC p 1547
101 Ne 3rd Ave Ste 1500 33301
Tel (877) 681-3678 SIC 3711

■ WEBB AUTOMOTIVE GROUP INC p 1586
200 Sw 1st Ave 33301
Tel (954) 769-7000 SIC 7538

■ WOODBRIDGE HOLDINGS LLC p 1622
2100 W Cypress Creek Rd 33309
Tel (954) 950-4950 SIC 1522

YOUNG MENS CHRISTIAN ASSOCIATION OF BROWARD COUNTY FLORIDA INC p 1638
900 Se 3rd Ave 33316
Tel (954) 334-9622 SIC 8641

■ ZIMMERMAN ADVERTISING LLC p 1643
6600 N Andrews Ave # 200 33309
Tel (954) 644-4000 SIC 7311

ZUAGGUA PARTNERS LLC p 1644
4321 Nw 15th Ave 33309
Tel (772) 501-3594 SIC 6221

FORT MYERS, FL

21ST CENTURY ONCOLOGY HOLDINGS INC p 2
2270 Colonial Blvd 33907
Tel (239) 931-7254 SIC 8011

21ST CENTURY ONCOLOGY INC p 2
2270 Colonial Blvd 33907
Tel (239) 931-7333 SIC 8011 7363

▲ ALICO INC p 50
10070 Daniels Interstate 33913
Tel (239) 226-2000
SIC 0174 0212 0133 6519

B & I CONTRACTORS INC p 141
2701 Prince St 33916
Tel (239) 344-3213 SIC 1711 1731

▲ CHICOS FAS INC p 298
11215 Metro Pkwy 33966
Tel (239) 277-6200 SIC 5621

■ CHICOS PRODUCTION SERVICES INC p 298
11215 Metro Pkwy 33966
Tel (239) 277-6200 SIC 5621

CHRISTIAN AND MISSIONARY ALLIANCE FOUNDATION INC p 302
15101 Shell Point Blvd 33908
Tel (239) 466-1111 SIC 6513 8051 8059

COUNTY OF LEE p 379
2115 2nd St 33901
Tel (239) 533-2737 SIC 9111

DOCTORS OSTEOPATHIC MEDICAL CENTER INC p 447
13681 Doctors Way 33912
Tel (239) 768-5000 SIC 8062

FLORIDA GULF COAST UNIVERSITY p 558
10501 Fgcu Blvd S 33965
Tel (239) 590-1000 SIC 8221

GOODWILL INDUSTRIES OF SOUTHWEST FLORIDA INC p 625
5100 Tice St 33905
Tel (239) 995-2106 SIC 5932 5087

GULF COAST MEDICAL CENTRE LTD p 646
13691 Metro Pkwy Ste 110 33912
Tel (239) 343-1000 SIC 8062

HUGHES SUPPLY INC p 717
2920 Ford St 33916
Tel (239) 334-2205
SIC 5063 5074 5075 5085 1711

LEE COUNTY ELECTRIC COOPERATIVE INC p 851
4980 Bayline Dr 33917
Tel (800) 599-2356 SIC 4911

LEE COUNTY PUBLIC SCHOOLS p 851
2855 Colonial Blvd 33966
Tel (239) 337-8523 SIC 8211

LEE COUNTY SHERIFF DEPARTMENT p 851
14750 6 Mile Cypress Pkwy 33912
Tel (239) 477-1000 SIC 9221

LEE MEMORIAL HEALTH SYSTEM p 851
2776 Cleveland Ave 33901
Tel (239) 343-2000 SIC 8011

LEE MEMORIAL HEALTH SYSTEM FOUNDATION INC p 851
2776 Cleveland Ave 33901
Tel (239) 343-2000
SIC 8741 8062 8082 8051

LEE MEMORIAL HOSPITAL INC p 851
2776 Cleveland Ave 33901
Tel (239) 343-2000 SIC 8062

LEE MEMORIAL WOMENS HEALTH PRO p 851
4761 S Cleveland Ave 33907
Tel (239) 343-9734 SIC 8099

LEESAR INC p 852
2727 Winkler Ave 33901
Tel (239) 939-8800 SIC 5047

MASTER PROTECTION HOLDINGS INC p 918
13050 Metro Pkwy Ste 1 33966
Tel (239) 896-1680 SIC 7389 1711 5999

▲ NEOGENOMICS INC p 1026
12701 Commwl Dr Ste 9 33913
Tel (239) 768-0600 SIC 8734 8071

NEOGENOMICS LABORATORIES INC p 1026
12701 Commwl Dr Ste 9 33913
Tel (239) 768-0600 SIC 8071

OBRIEN AUTOMOTIVE OF FLORIDA LLC p 1072
2850 Colonial Blvd 33966
Tel (239) 277-1222 SIC 5511

PAYROLL MADE EASY INC p 1123
11691 Gateway Blvd # 104 33913
Tel (239) 592-9700 SIC 8721

RAYMOND BUILDING SUPPLY p 1210
7751 Bayshore Rd 33917
Tel (941) 429-1212
SIC 5211 2439 2431 3442 2434 3634

■ RJE TELECOM LLC p 1239
4315 Metro Pkwy Ste 300 33916
Tel (239) 454-1944 SIC 4899

ROBB & STUCKY LIMITED LLLP p 1240
14550 Plantation Rd 33912
Tel (239) 437-7997
SIC 5712 5713 5714 5231

SAM GALLOWAY FORD INC p 1274
1800 Boy Scout Dr 33907
Tel (239) 936-3673 SIC 5511

ST ENVIRONMENTAL SERVICES INC (I) p 1366
5726 Corporation Cir 33905
Tel (239) 690-0175 SIC 4959 4941

UNIVERSAL TRAILER CARGO GROUP p 1518
12800 University Dr # 300 33907
Tel (513) 671-3880 SIC 3715

UNIVERSAL TRAILER HOLDINGS CORP p 1518
12800 University Dr # 300 33907
Tel (513) 671-3880 SIC 7513

WATERMAN BROADCASTING CORP OF FLORIDA p 1582
3719 Central Ave 33901
Tel (239) 939-2020 SIC 4833

FORT PIERCE, FL

BERNARD EGAN & CO p 176
1900 N Old Dixie Hwy 34946
Tel (772) 465-7555 SIC 0723 8741 0174

FORT PIERCE UTILITIES AUTHORITY p 569
206 S 6th St 34950
Tel (772) 466-1600
SIC 4931 4941 4924 4813

INDIAN RIVER STATE COLLEGE FOUNDATION INC p 737
3209 Virginia Ave 34981
Tel (772) 462-7340 SIC 8222

■ LAWNWOOD MEDICAL CENTER INC p 847
1700 S 23rd St 34950
Tel (772) 461-4000 SIC 8062 8063 8069

PALMDALE OIL CO INC p 1109
911 N 2nd St 34950
Tel (772) 461-2300 *SIC* 5172

ST LUCIE COUNTY SCHOOL BOARD p 1370
4204 Okeechobee Rd 34947
Tel (772) 429-3600 *SIC* 8211

ST LUCIE PUBLIC SCHOOLS p 1370
4204 Okeechobee Rd 34947
Tel (772) 429-3600 *SIC* 8211

FORT WALTON BEACH, FL

DRS TRAINING & CONTROL SYSTEMS LLC p 457
645 Anchors St Nw 32548
Tel (850) 302-3000 *SIC* 3812 8713

OKALOOSA COUNTY SCHOOL DISTRICT p 1079
120 Lowery Pl Se 32548
Tel (850) 689-7300 *SIC* 8211

PAYROLL MANAGEMENT INC p 1123
348 Miracle Strip Pkwy Sw # 39 32548
Tel (850) 243-5604 *SIC* 7363

■ TYBRIN CORP p 1496
1030 Titan Ct 32547
Tel (850) 337-2500 *SIC* 7371

FROSTPROOF, FL

BEN HILL GRIFFIN INC p 172
700 S Scenic Hwy 33843
Tel (863) 635-2281 *SIC* 2875 0174 2033

GAINESVILLE, FL

ALACHUA COUNTY PUBLIC SCHOOLS p 43
620 E University Ave 32601
Tel (352) 955-7300 *SIC* 8211

ALLCHEM INDUSTRIES HOLDING CORP p 52
6010 Nw 1st Pl 32607
Tel (352) 378-9696 *SIC* 5169

AVMED INC p 138
4300 Nw 89th Blvd Fl 2 32606
Tel (352) 372-8400 *SIC* 6324

CITY OF GAINESVILLE p 315
200 E University Ave 32601
Tel (352) 334-5010 *SIC* 9111

COUNTY OF ALACHUA p 375
12 Se 1st St 2 32601
Tel (352) 374-3605 *SIC* 9111

CROM CORP p 393
250 Sw 36th Ter 32607
Tel (352) 372-3436 *SIC* 1629

▲ EXACTECH INC p 516
2320 Nw 66th Ct 32653
Tel (352) 377-1140 *SIC* 3842

FLORIDA CLINICAL PRACTICE ASSOCIATION INC p 557
1329 Sw 16th St Ste 4250 32608
Tel (352) 265-8017 *SIC* 7322

FLORIDA FARM BUREAU GENERAL INSURANCE CO p 558
5700 Sw 34th St 32608
Tel (352) 378-1321 *SIC* 6411

GAINESVILLE REGIONAL UTILITIES (INC) p 589
301 Se 4th Ave 32601
Tel (352) 334-3400
SIC 4939 4941 4924 4911

GRU p 642
301 Se 4th Ave 32601
Tel (352) 334-3434 *SIC* 4813

GUMBYS PIZZA SYSTEMS INC p 647
3911 W Newberry Rd Ste C 32607
Tel (352) 338-7775 *SIC* 5812

INFINITE ENERGY HOLDINGS INC p 741
7001 Sw 24th Ave 32607
Tel (352) 240-4121 *SIC* 4911 4924

INFINITE ENERGY INC p 741
7001 Sw 24th Ave 32607
Tel (352) 331-1654 *SIC* 4924

LAND OSUN MANAGEMENT CORP p 842
3715 Nw 97th Blvd Ste A 32606
Tel (352) 333-3011 *SIC* 5541 5411

NAYLOR LLC p 1020
5950 Nw 1st Pl 32607
Tel (800) 369-6220 *SIC* 2759 7374

■ NORTH FLORIDA REGIONAL MEDICAL CENTER INC p 1052
6500 W Newberry Rd 32605
Tel (352) 333-4100
SIC 8062 8093 8011 8082 8069

PERRY CHARLES PARTNERS INC p 1137
8200 Nw 15th Pl 32606
Tel (352) 333-9292 *SIC* 1542 1541

SANTA FE COLLEGE p 1280
3000 Nw 83rd St 32606
Tel (352) 395-5000 *SIC* 8222 8221

SANTAFE HEALTHCARE INC p 1281
4300 Nw 89th Blvd 32606
Tel (352) 372-8400 *SIC* 8741

SHANDS TEACHING HOSPITAL AND CLINICS INC p 1311
1600 Sw Archer Rd 32610
Tel (352) 265-0111 *SIC* 8011

SUMTOTAL SYSTEMS LLC p 1399
2850 Nw 43rd St Ste 150 32606
Tel (352) 264-2800 *SIC* 7371

TOWER HILL INSURANCE GROUP INC p 1464
7201 Nw 11th Pl 32605
Tel (352) 332-8800 *SIC* 6331 7371

UNIVERSITY ATHLETIC ASSOCIATION INC p 1518
157 Gale Lemerand Dr 32611
Tel (352) 375-4683 *SIC* 8699

UNIVERSITY OF FLORIDA p 1521
300 Sw 13th St 32611
Tel (352) 392-3261 *SIC* 8221

UNIVERSITY OF FLORIDA FOUNDATION INC p 1521
2012 W University Ave 32603
Tel (352) 392-1691 *SIC* 8399 8641 8221

GREEN COVE SPRINGS, FL

COUNTY OF CLAY p 377
477 Houston St 32043
Tel (904) 269-6376 *SIC* 9111

SCHOOL DISTRICT OF CLAY COUNTY p 1289
900 Walnut St 32043
Tel (904) 284-6500 *SIC* 8211

GROVELAND, FL

CARROLL FULMER HOLDING CORP p 261
8340 American Way 34736
Tel (352) 429-5000 *SIC* 4731

CARROLL FULMER LOGISTICS CORP p 261
8340 American Way 34736
Tel (352) 429-5000 *SIC* 4731

GULF BREEZE, FL

ADAMS HOMES OF NORTHWEST FLORIDA INC p 21
3000 Gulf Breeze Pkwy 32563
Tel (850) 934-0470 *SIC* 1521

INNISFREE HOTELS INC p 744
113 Bay Bridge Dr 32561
Tel (850) 934-3609 *SIC* 7011

HAINES CITY, FL

SOFIDEL AMERICA CORP p 1337
1006 Marley Dr 33844
Tel (863) 547-3920 *SIC* 5113

HALLANDALE BEACH, FL

DIPLOMAT p 441
501 Diplomat Pkwy 33009
Tel (954) 883-4000 *SIC* 7997

LA PLAYA BEACH ASSOCIATES LLC p 835
1000 E Hllandale Bch Blvd 33009
Tel (954) 668-2505 *SIC* 6552

HAVANA, FL

COASTAL FOREST RESOURCES CO p 331
8007 Florida Georgia Hwy 32333
Tel (850) 539-6432
SIC 2436 2491 0811 0851

HEATHROW, FL

AMERICAN AUTOMOBILE ASSOCIATION INC p 68
1000 Aaa Dr Ms28 32746
Tel (407) 444-7000 *SIC* 8699

CENTRAL STATES ENTERPRISES LLC p 280
1275 Lake Heathrow Ln # 101 32746
Tel (407) 333-3503 *SIC* 5153 0213 0723

VILLAGE FARMS LP p 1557
195 International Pkwy # 100 32746
Tel (407) 936-1190 *SIC* 0161

HIALEAH, FL

ARANON CORP p 102
285 W 74th Pl 33014
Tel (305) 557-9004 *SIC* 5048

CITY OF HIALEAH p 315
501 Palm Ave 33010
Tel (305) 883-8075 *SIC* 9111

FOR EYES OPTICAL CO OF COCONUT GROVE INC p 565
285 W 74th Pl 33014
Tel (305) 557-9004 *SIC* 3851 5995

■ LIFEMARK HOSPITALS OF FLORIDA INC p 864
2001 W 68th St 33016
Tel (305) 823-5000 *SIC* 8062

MACMILLAN OIL CO OF FLORIDA INC p 892
2955 E 11th Ave 33013
Tel (305) 691-7814 *SIC* 5172

PALM SPRINGS GENERAL HOSPITAL INC p 1109
1475 W 49th St 33012
Tel (305) 558-2500 *SIC* 8062

SEDANOS MANAGEMENT INC p 1300
3140 W 76th St 33018
Tel (305) 824-1034 *SIC* 5411 5912

■ TELEMUNDO COMMUNICATIONS GROUP INC p 1434
2290 W 8th Ave 33010
Tel (305) 884-8200 *SIC* 4833 7313

■ TENET HIALEAH HEALTHSYSTEM INC p 1437
651 E 25th St 33013
Tel (305) 693-6100 *SIC* 8062

U S HOLDINGS INC p 1497
3200 W 84th St 33018
Tel (305) 885-0301 *SIC* 3321 3543

HOBE SOUND, FL

C & W FISH CO INC p 232
7508 Se Autumn Ln 33455
Tel (772) 283-1184 *SIC* 5199 5146

HOLLY HILL, FL

DAYTONA BEACH AREA ASSOCIATION OF REALTORS FOUNDATION INC p 418
1716 Ridgewood Ave 32117
Tel (386) 677-7131 *SIC* 8611

FLORIDA HEALTH CARE PLAN INC p 558
1340 Ridgewood Ave 32117
Tel (386) 615-4022 *SIC* 6324

METRA ELECTRONICS CORP p 954
460 Walker St 32117
Tel (386) 257-1186 *SIC* 3651

HOLLYWOOD, FL

AG HOLDINGS INC p 33
4601 Sheridan St Ste 500 33021
Tel (954) 987-7180 *SIC* 8051

BARBEQUE INTEGRATED INC p 154
4000 Hollywood Blvd 33021
Tel (407) 355-5800 *SIC* 5812

CAMBRIDGE INTEGRATED SERVICES GROUP INC p 244
7369 Sheridan St Ste 301 33024
Tel (954) 966-4772 *SIC* 8742 7389

CHECKS IN MOTION p 292
11071 Minneapolis Dr 33026
Tel (954) 433-8080 *SIC* 8721

CITY OF HOLLYWOOD p 315
2600 Hollywood Blvd Ste B 33020
Tel (954) 921-3435 *SIC* 9222

DIPLOMAT PROPERTIES LIMITED PARTNERSHIP p 441
3555 S Ocean Dr 33019
Tel (954) 602-6000 *SIC* 7011 7997

FIRST SERVICE RESIDENTIAL FLORIDA INC p 549
2950 N 28th Ter 33020
Tel (954) 925-8200 *SIC* 6531

■ HEICO AEROSPACE CORP p 680
3000 Taft St 33021
Tel (954) 987-6101 *SIC* 3724 3812

■ HEICO AEROSPACE HOLDINGS CORP p 680
3000 Taft St 33021
Tel (954) 987-4000 *SIC* 3724

▲ HEICO CORP p 680
3000 Taft St 33021
Tel (954) 987-4000 *SIC* 3724 3728 7699

■ HEICO ELECTRONIC TECHNOLOGIES CORP p 680
3000 Taft St 33021
Tel (954) 987-6101 *SIC* 3728

HERD ENTERPRISES INC p 685
3500 N 28th Ter 33020
Tel (954) 920-9774 *SIC* 6351

HIP ADMINISTRATORS OF FLORIDA INC p 695
3251 Hollywood Blvd # 401 33021
Tel (954) 893-6400 *SIC* 6324

HOLLYWOOD CITY OF (INC) p 701
2600 Hollywood Blvd Ste B 33020
Tel (954) 921-3231 *SIC* 9111

INTERBOND CORP OF AMERICA p 751
3200 Sw 42nd St 33020
Tel (954) 797-4000 *SIC* 5731 5722

▲ NV5 GLOBAL INC p 1068
200 S Park Rd Ste 350 33021
Tel (954) 495-2112 *SIC* 8711 8748

■ NV5 INC p 1068
200 S Park Rd Ste 350 33021
Tel (954) 495-2112 *SIC* 8711

PHYSICIANS PARTNERS PLUS LLC p 1146
1131 Nw 74th Ter 33024
Tel (352) 622-7000 *SIC* 8748

SEMINOLE TRIBE OF FLORIDA INC p 1302
6300 Stirling Rd 33024
Tel (954) 966-6300
SIC 7999 5194 2011 5182 2911

SEMINOLE TRIBE OF FLORIDA T V INC p 1303
3107 N State Road 7 33021
Tel (954) 966-6300 *SIC* 5812

SOUTH BROWARD HOSPITAL DISTRICT p 1343
3501 Johnson St 33021
Tel (954) 987-2000 *SIC* 8062 8051

TOUSA INC p 1464
4000 Hollywood Blvd # 555 33021
Tel (954) 364-4000
SIC 1521 1522 6162 6541

TRIANGLE AUTO CENTER INC p 1478
1841 N State Road 7 33021
Tel (855) 398-2449 *SIC* 5511 7532

HOMESTEAD, FL

HOMESTEAD HOSPITAL INC p 704
975 Baptist Way 33033
Tel (786) 243-8000 *SIC* 8062

HOMOSASSA, FL

CRYSTAL MOTOR CAR CO INC p 397
1035 S Suncoast Blvd 34448
Tel (352) 795-1515 *SIC* 5511

DSK GROUP INC p 458
6715 W Grver Clvland Blvd 34446
Tel (352) 628-9800 *SIC* 7363

HUDSON, FL

■ HCA HEALTH SERVICES OF FLORIDA INC p 671
14000 Fivay Rd 34667
Tel (727) 819-2929 *SIC* 4789

IMMOKALEE, FL

CUSTOM-PAK INC p 403
315 New Market Rd E 34142
Tel (239) 657-4421 *SIC* 0161

LFC ENTERPRISES INC p 860
315 New Market Rd E 34142
Tel (239) 657-3117 *SIC* 5431

LIPMAN-TEXAS LLC p 870
315 New Market Rd E 34142
Tel (239) 657-4421 *SIC* 5148

SIX LS PACKING CO INC p 1328
315 New Market Rd E 34142
Tel (239) 657-3117 *SIC* 5148

INDIALANTIC, FL

■ RAYTHEON CYBER SOLUTIONS INC p 1211
1220 N Hwy A1a Ste 123 32903
Tel (321) 253-7841 *SIC* 7379

INVERNESS, FL

CITRUS COUNTY SCHOOL BOARD LEASING CORP p 311
1007 W Main St 34450
Tel (352) 726-1931 *SIC* 8211

CITRUS COUNTY SCHOOLS p 311
1007 W Main St 34450
Tel (352) 726-1931 *SIC* 8211

FOUNDATION RESOLUTION CORP p 571
502 W Highland Blvd 34452
Tel (352) 726-1551 *SIC* 8062

JACKSONVILLE, FL

ACOSTA INC p 18
6600 Corporate Ctr Pkwy 32216
Tel (904) 332-7986 *SIC* 5141

ACOSTA SALES CO INC p 18
6600 Corporate Ctr Pkwy 32216
Tel (904) 281-9800 *SIC* 5149 5141

ADECCO USA INC p 22
10151 Deerwood Bldg 200 32256
Tel (904) 359-4710
SIC 7363 7361 8742 6794

ADVANTAGE SALES LLC p 26
7411 Fullerton St Ste 101 32256
Tel (904) 292-9009 *SIC* 5141

ALFA SMARTPARKS INC p 49
1 W Adams St Ste 200 32202
Tel (904) 358-1027 *SIC* 7996

AMERI-FORCE INC p 67
9485 Regency Square Blvd 32225
Tel (904) 633-9918 *SIC* 7363

■ AMERICAN HERITAGE LIFE INSURANCE CO INC p 74
1776 Amercn Heritg Lf Dr 32224
Tel (904) 992-1776 *SIC* 6321 6311 6351

■ AMERICAN HERITAGE LIFE INVESTMENT CORP p 74
1776 Amercn Heritg Lf Dr 32224
Tel (904) 992-1776
SIC 6311 6321 6351 7374

AMERICAN HOSPICE HOLDINGS LLC p 74
50 N Laura St Ste 1800 32202
Tel (904) 493-6745 *SIC* 8059

AMPORTS INC p 86
10201 Centurion Pkwy N # 401 32256
Tel (904) 652-2962 *SIC* 4491

AON RISK SERVICES INC OF FLORIDA p 95
13901 Sutton Park Dr S # 360 32224
Tel (904) 724-2001 *SIC* 6411

APR ENERGY LLC p 100
3600 Prt Jcksnvl Pkwy 32226
Tel (904) 223-2278 *SIC* 4911

ARIZONA CHEMICAL CO LLC p 108
4600 Touchton Rd E # 1500 32246
Tel (904) 928-8700 *SIC* 2861 2911

BAE SYSTEMS AH INC p 144
13386 International Pkwy 32218
Tel (904) 741-5400
SIC 3711 3842 3312 3728

BAE SYSTEMS SOUTHEAST SHIPYARDS AMHC INC p 144
8500 Heckscher Dr 32226
Tel (904) 251-3111 *SIC* 3731

■ BAKER DISTRIBUTING CO LLC p 146
14610 Breakers Dr Ste 100 32258
Tel (904) 407-4500 *SIC* 5075 5078

BAPTIST HEALTH SYSTEM FOUNDATION INC p 153
841 Prudential Dr # 1300 32207
Tel (904) 202-2919 *SIC* 8322

BAPTIST HEALTH SYSTEM INC p 153
800 Prudential Dr 32207
Tel (904) 202-2000 SIC 8741

BAPTIST MEDICAL CENTER OF BEACHES INC p 154
1350 13th Ave S 32250
Tel (904) 247-2900 SIC 8062

BAPTIST MEDICAL CENTER OF BEACHES INC p 154
3563 Phillips Hwy 32207
Tel (704) 202-1797 SIC 8062

BEAVER STREET FISHERIES INC p 166
1741 W St Beaver 32209
Tel (904) 354-5661 SIC 5142 5141

BEELINE.COM INC p 168
12724 Gran Bay Pkwy W # 200 32258
Tel (904) 527-5700 SIC 7371

BI-LO HOLDING FINANCE LLC p 180
5050 Edgewood Ct 32254
Tel (904) 783-5000 SIC 5411

BI-LO HOLDING LLC p 180
5050 Edgewood Ct 32254
Tel (904) 783-5000 SIC 5411

BI-LO HOLDINGS FOUNDATION INC p 180
5050 Edgewood Ct 32254
Tel (904) 783-5000 SIC 5411

BI-LO LLC p 180
8928 Prominence Pkwy # 200 32256
Tel (904) 783-5000 SIC 5411

▲ BLACK KNIGHT FINANCIAL SERVICES INC p 187
601 Riverside Ave 32204
Tel (904) 854-5100 SIC 7372

■ BLACK KNIGHT FINANCIAL SERVICES LLC p 187
601 Riverside Ave 32204
Tel (904) 854-8100
SIC 6361 6331 6531 8741

■ BLACK KNIGHT HOLDINGS INC p 187
601 Riverside Ave 32204
Tel (904) 854-8100
SIC 6361 6331 6531 8741

■ BLACK KNIGHT INFOSERV LLC p 187
601 Riverside Ave 32204
Tel (904) 854-5100 SIC 7389 7374

BLUE CROSS AND BLUE SHIELD OF FLORIDA INC p 191
4800 Deerwood Campus Pkwy 32246
Tel (904) 905-0000 SIC 6324

BODY CENTRAL CORP p 197
6225 Powers Ave 32217
Tel (904) 737-0811 SIC 5621 5961

BRUMOS MOTOR CARS INC p 221
10231 Atlantic Blvd 32225
Tel (904) 724-1080 SIC 5511

■ BUILDERS FIRSTSOURCE - FLORIDA LLC p 225
6550 Roosevelt Blvd 32244
Tel (904) 772-6100 SIC 5031

BUSH INDUSTRIES CORP p 229
9850 Atlantic Blvd 32225
Tel (904) 725-0911 SIC 5511

■ C AND C POWER LINE INC p 232
12035 Palm Lake Dr 32218
Tel (904) 751-6020 SIC 4911 1731

CARIB ENERGY (USA) LLC p 256
9487 Regency Square Blvd 32225
Tel (904) 727-2559 SIC 3533

CCP MANAGEMENT INC p 270
3401 Phillips Hwy 32207
Tel (904) 398-7177 SIC 5032 5169

■ CEVA LOGISTICS US GROUP INC p 285
10751 Deerwood Park Blvd 32256
Tel (904) 928-1400 SIC 4213 4226

■ CEVA LOGISTICS US HOLDINGS INC p 285
10751 Deerwood Park Blvd # 201 32256
Tel (904) 928-1400 SIC 4213 4226

CHAMPION BRANDS INC p 287
5571 Fl Min Blvd S 32257
Tel (660) 885-8151 SIC 5181

■ CHICAGO TITLE INSURANCE CO p 297
601 Riverside Ave 32204
Tel (904) 854-8100 SIC 6361

CITY OF JACKSONVILLE p 315
117 W Duval St Fl Mess 32202
Tel (904) 630-1776 SIC 9111

CITY OF JACKSONVILLE p 315
501 E Bay St 32202
Tel (904) 630-0500 SIC 9221

■ COGGIN AUTOMOTIVE CORP p 334
7245 Blanding Blvd 32244
Tel (904) 779-8030 SIC 5511

■ COMCAST OF FLORIDA/GEORGIA/ILLINOIS/MICHIGAN LLC p 343
4600 Touchton Rd E # 2200 32246
Tel (904) 374-8000 SIC 4813 4841

COMMUNITY HOSPICE OF NORTHEAST FLORIDA INC p 349
4266 Sunbeam Rd Ste 100 32257
Tel (904) 268-5200 SIC 8082 8051

CROWLEY AMERICAN TRANSPORT INC p 394
9487 Regency Square Blvd 32225
Tel (904) 727-2200 SIC 4424

CROWLEY HOLDINGS INC p 394
9487 Regency Square Blvd # 101 32225
Tel (904) 727-2200
SIC 4412 4424 5171 5172 5541 4492

CROWLEY LINER SERVICES INC p 395
9487 Regency Square Blvd # 101 32225
Tel (904) 727-2200 SIC 4424

CROWLEY MARITIME CORP p 395
9487 Regency Square Blvd 32225
Tel (904) 727-2200
SIC 4412 4424 5171 5172 5541 4492

CROWLEY PETROLEUM SERVICES INC p 395
9487 Regency Square Blvd 32225
Tel (904) 727-2200 SIC 4412 4424

CSI COMPANIES INC p 397
9995 Gate Pkwy N Ste 100 32246
Tel (904) 338-9515 SIC 7361

▲ CSX CORP p 398
500 Water St Fl 15 32202
Tel (904) 359-3200 SIC 4011

■ CSX INTERMODAL INC p 398
500 Water St 32202
Tel (904) 633-1000 SIC 4213 4011 4225

■ CSX TECHNOLOGY INC p 398
550 Water St 32202
Tel (904) 633-1000 SIC 7371

■ CSX TRANSPORTATION INC p 398
500 Water St 32202
Tel (904) 359-3100 SIC 4011

CUSTOMIZED DISTRIBUTION LLC p 403
5545 Shawland Rd 32254
Tel (904) 783-0848 SIC 5141 7319

CYPRESS TRUCK LINES INC p 405
1414 Lindrose St 32206
Tel (904) 353-8641 SIC 4213

DIOCESE OF ST AUGUSTINE INC p 440
11625 Old St Augustine Rd 32258
Tel (904) 824-2806 SIC 8661 6531

DIVERSIFIED HEALTH SERVICES INC p 444
4800 Deerwood Campus Pkwy 32246
Tel (904) 791-6111 SIC 6311

DIVERSIFIED SERVICE OPTIONS INC p 444
532 Riverside Ave 32202
Tel (904) 791-6305 SIC 6719

DUVAL COUNTY PUBLIC SCHOOLS p 463
1701 Prudential Dr 32207
Tel (904) 390-2000 SIC 8211

DUVAL MOTOR CO INC p 463
1616 Cassat Ave 32210
Tel (904) 387-6541 SIC 5521 5511

ELKINS CONSTRUCTORS INC p 488
701 W Adams St Ste 1 32204
Tel (904) 353-6500 SIC 1542

ENHANCED RECOVERY CO LLC p 499
8014 Bayberry Rd 32256
Tel (904) 371-1005 SIC 7322

■ EVERBANK p 513
501 Riverside Ave Fl 1 32202
Tel (904) 623-8408 SIC 6035

▲ EVERBANK FINANCIAL CORP p 513
501 Riverside Ave 32202
Tel (904) 281-6000 SIC 6035 7389

■ EVERHOME MORTGAGE CO p 515
301 W Bay St Ste 2600 32202
Tel (904) 281-6000 SIC 6162

EXPERIENCED MAIL TRANSPORT INC p 520
1072 Leeda Dr 32254
Tel (904) 354-4855 SIC 4212

FANATICS INC p 527
8100 Nations Way 32256
Tel (904) 421-8143 SIC 5941 5699

FECR RAIL CORP p 533
7411 Fullerton St Ste 100 32256
Tel (800) 342-1131 SIC 4011

■ FIDELITY INFORMATION SERVICES LLC p 540
601 Riverside Ave 32204
Tel (888) 323-0310 SIC 7374

■ FIDELITY NATIONAL EUROPE LLC p 540
601 Riverside Ave Fl 4 32204
Tel (904) 854-8100 SIC 6361

▲ FIDELITY NATIONAL FINANCIAL INC p 540
601 Riverside Ave Fl 4 32204
Tel (904) 854-8100
SIC 6361 6331 6531 8741 3699

▲ FIDELITY NATIONAL INFORMATION SERVICES INC p 541
601 Riverside Ave 32204
Tel (904) 438-6000 SIC 7389 7374

FIREHOUSE SUBS INC p 543
3400-8 Kori Rd 32257
Tel (904) 886-8300 SIC 5812

FIRST COAST ENERGY LLP p 545
7014 A C Skinner Pkwy # 290 32256
Tel (904) 596-3200 SIC 5541 5411 5172

FIRST COAST SERVICE OPTIONS INC p 545
532 Riverside Ave 32202
Tel (904) 791-8000 SIC 8742

■ FIS FINANCIAL SYSTEMS LLC p 551
601 Riverside Ave 32204
Tel (904) 438-6000 SIC 7374 7372

■ FIS WEALTH MANAGEMENT SERVICES INC p 551
601 Riverside Ave 32204
Tel (904) 854-5000 SIC 7389 7374

FLIGHTSTAR AIRCRAFT SERVICES LLC p 557
6025 Flightline Dr 32221
Tel (904) 741-0300 SIC 4581 3728

FLORIDA EAST COAST HOLDINGS CORP p 558
7411 Fullerton St Ste 300 32256
Tel (800) 342-1131 SIC 6719

FLORIDA EAST COAST RAILWAY LLC p 558
7411 Fullerton St Ste 300 32256
Tel (904) 538-6100 SIC 4011

■ FLORIDA ROCK & TANK LINES INC p 559
200 W Forsyth St 7th 32202
Tel (904) 396-5733 SIC 4213 4212

■ FLORIDA ROCK INDUSTRIES p 559
4707 Gordon St 32216
Tel (904) 355-1781 SIC 1422

FLORIDA SCHOOL CHOICE p 559
4655 Salisbury Rd Ste 400 32256
Tel (800) 447-1636 SIC 8211

FLORIDA STATE COLLEGE AT JACKSONVILLE p 559
501 W State St Ste 307 32202
Tel (904) 632-3251 SIC 8221

FOODONICS INTERNATIONAL INC p 564
5139 Edgewood Ct 32254
Tel (904) 783-0950 SIC 5144

■ FOREST RAYONIER RESOURCES LP p 567
50 N Laura St Ste 1900 32202
Tel (904) 357-9100 SIC 0851

■ FORTEGRA FINANCIAL CORP p 569
10151 Deerwood Park Blvd # 330 32256
Tel (866) 961-9529 SIC 6411

GATE PETROLEUM CO p 593
9540 San Jose Blvd 32257
Tel (904) 730-3470
SIC 5541 3272 5411 7997

GATE PRECAST CO p 593
9540 San Jose Blvd 32257
Tel (904) 732-7668 SIC 3272

GENESIS HEALTH INC p 603
3599 University Blvd S # 1 32216
Tel (904) 858-7600 SIC 8069 8011 8741

GENESIS REHABILITATION HOSPITAL INC p 603
3599 University Blvd S # 1 32216
Tel (904) 858-7600 SIC 8063 8069 8051

■ GULF SOUTH MEDICAL SUPPLY INC p 647
4345 Sthpint Blvd Ste 100 32216
Tel (904) 332-3000 SIC 5047

HARRIS DENISE ANN TRUST p 663
301 W Bay St Ste 14117 32202
Tel (888) 504-0994 SIC 6733

HASKELL CO p 667
111 Riverside Ave 32202
Tel (904) 791-4500
SIC 1541 1542 1522 1623 8712 3272

HASKELL CO INC p 667
111 Riverside Ave 32202
Tel (904) 791-4500
SIC 1541 1542 1522 1623 8712 3272

HEALOGICS INC p 673
5220 Belfort Rd Ste 130 32256
Tel (904) 296-6526 SIC 8093

HEALTH OPTIONS INC p 675
4800 Deerwood Campus Pkwy 32246
Tel (904) 564-5700 SIC 6324

HOSPICE TREASURE CHEST p 709
4266 Sunbeam Rd Ste 100 32257
Tel (904) 596-6278 SIC 5932

IDEA INTEGRATION CORP p 728
12724 Gran Bay Pkwy W 32258
Tel (877) 727-8234 SIC 7373

■ INTERLINE BRANDS INC p 753
801 W Bay St 32204
Tel (904) 421-1400 SIC 5074 5063 5072

■ INTERLINE BRANDS INC p 753
701 San Marco Blvd 32207
Tel (904) 421-1400 SIC 5074 5063 5072

JACKSONVILLE UNIVERSITY p 774
2800 University Blvd N 32211
Tel (904) 256-8000 SIC 8221

JEA p 781
21 W Church St Fl 1 32202
Tel (904) 665-6000 SIC 4911 1623

■ JOHNSON & JOHNSON VISION CARE INC p 790
7500 Centurion Pkwy 32256
Tel (904) 443-1000 SIC 3851

KELLEY-CLARKE LLC p 808
6600 Corporate Ctr Pkwy 32216
Tel (904) 281-9800 SIC 5141

■ KEMPER INDEPENDENCE INSURANCE CO p 810
12926 Gran Bay Pkwy W 32258
Tel (904) 245-5600 SIC 6411

■ LANDSTAR GLOBAL LOGISTICS INC p 843
13410 Sutton Park Dr S 32224
Tel (904) 390-4751 SIC 4731

■ LANDSTAR LIGON INC p 843
13410 Sutton Park Dr S 32224
Tel (904) 398-9400 SIC 4213

■ LANDSTAR SYSTEM HOLDINGS INC p 843
13410 Sutton Park Dr S 32224
Tel (904) 398-9400 SIC 4213

▲ LANDSTAR SYSTEM INC p 843
13410 Sutton Park Dr S 32224
Tel (904) 398-9400 SIC 4789

■ LAWYERS TITLE INSURANCE CORP p 848
601 Riverside Ave 32204
Tel (888) 866-3684 SIC 6361 7372 5734

LSF5 BI-LO HOLDINGS LLC p 883
5050 Edgewood Ct 32254
Tel (904) 783-5000 SIC 5411

MAC PAPERS INC p 891
3300 Phillips Hwy 32207
Tel (904) 396-5312 SIC 5112 5111

MAIN STREET AMERICA GROUP INC p 897
4601 Touchton Rd E # 3300 32246
Tel (904) 642-3000 SIC 6411

MALNOVE INC OF FLORIDA p 900
10500 Canada Dr 32218
Tel (904) 696-1600 SIC 2657

MAUI ACQUISITION CORP p 921
13386 International Pkwy 32218
Tel (904) 741-5400 SIC 3069 2389

MAYO CLINIC JACKSONVILLE (A NONPROFIT CORP) p 924
4500 San Pablo Rd S 32224
Tel (904) 953-2000 SIC 8062

MEDTRONIC XOMED INC p 939
6743 Southpoint Dr N 32216
Tel (904) 296-9600 SIC 3842 3841

■ MEMORIAL HOSPITAL JACKSONVILLE INC p 942
3625 University Blvd S 32216
Tel (904) 399-6111 SIC 8062

■ METAVANTE HOLDINGS LLC p 953
601 Riverside Ave 32204
Tel (904) 438-6000 SIC 3578 5049 7374

MILLER ELECTRIC CO p 970
2251 Rosselle St 32204
Tel (904) 388-8000 SIC 1731

MILTON J WOOD CO p 972
3805 Faye Rd 32226
Tel (904) 353-5527 SIC 1711 1542

MODIS INC p 981
10151 Deerwood Pkwy Bldg 32256
Tel (904) 360-2300 SIC 7371

MORRIS HOLDINGS INC p 990
1650 County Road 210 W 32259
Tel (904) 829-3946 SIC 5541 5812 5411

MPS GROUP INC p 995
10151 Deerwood Park Blvd 200-400 32256
Tel (904) 360-2000 SIC 7363 8742 7361

NEMOURS FOUNDATION p 1025
10140 Centurion Pkwy N 32256
Tel (904) 697-4100 SIC 8069 8093

NEMOURS FOUNDATION PENSION PLAN p 1025
10140 Centurion Pkwy N 32256
Tel (904) 697-4100 SIC 6371

NETWORK FOB INC p 1028
6622 Sthpint Dr S Ste 210 32216
Tel (651) 256-1000 SIC 4731

NEXTRAN CORP p 1041
1986 W Beaver St 32209
Tel (904) 354-3721 SIC 5511 5531 7538

NGM INSURANCE CO p 1041
4601 Touchton Rd E # 3400 32246
Tel (904) 380-7282 SIC 6331

ONE CALL MEDICAL INC p 1086
841 Prudential Dr Ste 900 32207
Tel (904) 646-0199 SIC 8742 7389

PARC MANAGEMENT LLC p 1114
7892 Baymeadows Way 32256
Tel (904) 732-7272 SIC 7996

▲ PATRIOT TRANSPORTATION HOLDING INC p 1121
200 W Forsyth St Fl 7 32202
Tel (904) 858-9100 SIC 4212

■ PATRIOT TRANSPORTATION INC p 1121
200 W Forsyth St Ste 700 32202
Tel (904) 356-6110 SIC 4213 6531 6519

PAVILION HEALTH SERVICES INC p 1122
3563 Phillips Hwy Ste 106 32207
Tel (904) 202-5887 SIC 5912

PILOT CORP OF AMERICA p 1148
3855 Regent Blvd 32224
Tel (904) 645-9999 SIC 5112 3951

■ PSS WORLD MEDICAL INC p 1188
4345 Southpoint Blvd # 110 32216
Tel (904) 332-3000 SIC 5122 5047

■ RAILAMERICA TRANSPORTATION CORP p 1205
7411 Fullerton St Ste 300 32256
Tel (904) 538-6100 SIC 4011

RALEIGH WINN-DIXIE INC p 1206
5050 Edgewood Ct 32254
Tel (904) 783-5000 SIC 5411

■ RANGER LANDSTAR INC p 1208
13410 Sutton Park Dr S 32224
Tel (800) 872-9400 SIC 4213

RAVEN TRANSPORT CO INC p 1209
6800 Broadway Ave 32254
Tel (904) 880-1515 SIC 4213

▲ RAYONIER ADVANCED MATERIALS INC p 1210
1301 Riverplace Blvd # 2300 32207
Tel (904) 357-4600 SIC 2821 2823

▲ RAYONIER INC p 1210
225 Water St Ste 1400 32202
Tel (904) 357-9100
SIC 6798 5099 6552 5031

■ RAYONIER PERFORMANCE FIBERS LLC p 1210
1301 Riverplace Blvd 32207
Tel (912) 427-5000 *SIC* 3081

▲ REGENCY CENTERS CORP p 1218
1 Independent Dr Ste 114 32202
Tel (904) 598-7000 *SIC* 6798

■ REGENCY CENTERS LP p 1218
1 Independent Dr Ste 114 32202
Tel (904) 598-7000 *SIC* 6798

ROUX LABORATORIES INC p 1253
5344 Overmyer Dr 32254
Tel (904) 366-2602 *SIC* 2844

ROYAL SERVICES INC p 1254
4526 Lenox Ave 32205
Tel (904) 386-6436 *SIC* 7349 7371

RS&H INC p 1255
10748 Deerwood Park Blvd 32256
Tel (904) 256-2500 *SIC* 8711 8712

SAFARILAND LLC p 1265
13386 International Pkwy 32218
Tel (904) 741-5400 *SIC* 3842 3199

■ SAFT AMERICA INC p 1267
13575 Waterworks St 32221
Tel (904) 861-1501 *SIC* 3691 5063

SCOTT-MCRAE AUTOMOTIVE GROUP INC p 1294
701 Riverside Park Pl # 120 32204
Tel (904) 354-4000 *SIC* 5511 7515 6159

■ SERVICELINK HOLDINGS LLC p 1307
601 Riverside Ave Bldg 5 32204
Tel (904) 854-8100
SIC 6361 6331 6531 8741 3699

SHANDS JACKSONVILLE HEALTHCARE INC p 1311
655 W 8th St 32209
Tel (904) 244-0411 *SIC* 8062

SHANDS JACKSONVILLE MEDICAL CENTER INC p 1311
655 W 8th St 32209
Tel (904) 244-5576 *SIC* 8062

SOUTHEASTERN GROCERS LLC p 1346
8928 Prominence Pkwy # 200 32256
Tel (904) 783-5000 *SIC* 5411

SOUTHERN BAPTIST HOSPITAL OF FLORIDA INC p 1347
800 Prudential Dr 32207
Tel (904) 202-2000 *SIC* 8062

■ SOUTHLAND ENVIRONMENTAL SERVICES INC p 1351
8619 Western Way 32256
Tel (904) 731-2456 *SIC* 4953

SPECIAL COUNSEL INC p 1355
10201 Centurion Pkwy N 32256
Tel (904) 360-2251 *SIC* 7363

ST JOHNS RIVER POWER PARK p 1368
21 W Church St 32202
Tel (904) 751-7700 *SIC* 4911

ST LUKES HOSPITAL ASSOCIATION p 1370
4201 Belfort Rd 32216
Tel (904) 296-3700 *SIC* 8062

ST VINCENTS HEALTH SYSTEM INC p 1373
4203 Belfort Rd Ste 155 32216
Tel (904) 308-7300 *SIC* 8741

ST VINCENTS MEDICAL CENTER INC p 1373
4205 Belfort Rd Ste 4030 32216
Tel (904) 308-7300 *SIC* 8062

■ STEIN MART BUYING CORP p 1385
1200 Riverplace Blvd # 1000 32207
Tel (904) 346-1500 *SIC* 5199

▲ STEIN MART INC p 1385
1200 Riverplace Blvd # 1000 32207
Tel (904) 346-1500 *SIC* 5311 5651

STELLAR COMPANIES INC p 1385
2900 Hartley Rd 32257
Tel (904) 899-9393 *SIC* 1542 8711 1541

STEP UP FOR STUDENTS INC p 1386
4655 Salisbury Rd Ste 400 32256
Tel (877) 735-7837 *SIC* 8299

STEWART & STEVENSON FDDA LLC p 1389
5040 University Blvd W 32216
Tel (904) 737-7330 *SIC* 5084 7699

STILLWATER INSURANCE SERVICES INC p 1389
4905 Belfort Rd Ste 110 32256
Tel (904) 997-7336 *SIC* 6331

SUDDATH COMPANIES p 1396
815 S Main St Ste 400 32207
Tel (904) 390-7100 *SIC* 4214 4731

SUDDATH VAN LINES INC p 1396
815 S Main St Ste 400 32207
Tel (904) 390-7100 *SIC* 4213 4731 4214

SUMMIT CONTRACTING GROUP INC p 1398
1000 Rverside Ave Ste 800 32204
Tel (904) 268-5515 *SIC* 1522

SUPERIOR CONSTRUCTION CO SOUTHEAST LLC p 1406
7072 Business Park Blvd N 32256
Tel (904) 292-4240 *SIC* 1611

■ SYSCO JACKSONVILLE INC p 1417
1501 Lewis Industrial Dr 32254
Tel (904) 781-5070
SIC 5149 5147 5144 5963

TAX DEFENSE NETWORK LLC p 1426
9000 Southside Blvd # 11000 32256
Tel (904) 421-4410 *SIC* 7299

TOM BUSH VOLKSWAGEN INC p 1459
9850 Atlantic Blvd 32225
Tel (904) 725-0911 *SIC* 5511

TOM NEHL TRUCK CO p 1459
417 Edgewood Ave S 32254
Tel (904) 389-3653 *SIC* 5511 5531 7538

TPH ACQUISITION LLLP p 1467
10321 Fortune Pkwy 32256
Tel (904) 731-3034 *SIC* 5013

TRUENET COMMUNICATIONS CORP p 1486
7666 Blanding Blvd 32244
Tel (904) 777-9052 *SIC* 4899

■ UNISON INDUSTRIES LLC p 1505
7575 Baymeadows Way 32256
Tel (904) 739-4000 *SIC* 3694

UNIVERSITY OF FLORIDA JACKSONVILLE HEALTHCARE INC p 1521
3122 New Berlin Rd 32226
Tel (904) 244-9500 *SIC* 8011

UNIVERSITY OF FLORIDA JACKSONVILLE PHYSICIANS INC p 1521
653 W 8th St 32209
Tel (904) 244-9500 *SIC* 8011

UNIVERSITY OF NORTH FLORIDA p 1524
1 U N F Dr 32224
Tel (904) 620-1000 *SIC* 8221

US ASSURE INC p 1531
8230 Nations Way 32256
Tel (904) 398-3907 *SIC* 6399

VESTA PROPERTY SERVICES INC p 1552
1021 Oak St 32204
Tel (904) 355-1831 *SIC* 6722 6531

■ VISION CARE INSTITUTE LLC p 1561
7500 Centurion Pkwy 32256
Tel (904) 443-1086 *SIC* 8042

VYSTAR CREDIT UNION p 1568
4949 Blanding Blvd 32210
Tel (904) 777-6000 *SIC* 6061

W & O SUPPLY INC p 1568
2677 Port Industrial Dr 32226
Tel (904) 354-3800 *SIC* 5085 5051

WARE GROUP INC p 1575
11710 Central Pkwy 32224
Tel (904) 641-2282 *SIC* 5075

WARE GROUP LLC p 1575
11710 Central Pkwy 32224
Tel (904) 641-2282 *SIC* 5075

▲ WEB.COM GROUP INC p 1586
12808 Gran Bay Pkwy W 32258
Tel (904) 680-6600 *SIC* 7372 7374

WINN-DIXIE STORES INC p 1616
8928 Prominence Pkwy # 200 32256
Tel (904) 783-5000 *SIC* 5411 5541 5912

WINN-DIXIE STORES OF JACKSONVILLE (INC) p 1616
5050 Edgewood Ct 32254
Tel (904) 783-5000 *SIC* 5411

WORLD ELECTRIC SUPPLY INC p 1625
569 Stuart Ln 32254
Tel (904) 378-4000 *SIC* 5063

WORLD MEDICAL GOVERNMENT SOLUTIONS LLC p 1625
4345 Southpoint Blvd 32216
Tel (904) 332-3000 *SIC* 5047

WOUNDED WARRIOR PROJECT INC p 1627
4899 Belfort Rd Ste 300 32256
Tel (904) 296-7350 *SIC* 8641

WW GAY MECHANICAL CONTRACTOR INC p 1628
524 Stockton St 32204
Tel (904) 388-2696 *SIC* 1711

YMCA OF FLORIDAS FIRST COAST p 1636
40 E Adams St Ste 210 32202
Tel (904) 296-3220 *SIC* 8741 8641

JUNO BEACH, FL

■ ENERGY DUANE ARNOLD LLC p 497
700 Universe Blvd 33408
Tel (561) 691-7171 *SIC* 4911

ESI ENERGY LLC p 509
700 Universe Blvd 33408
Tel (561) 691-7171 *SIC* 4911

■ FLORIDA POWER & LIGHT CO INC p 559
700 Universe Blvd 33408
Tel (561) 694-4000 *SIC* 4911

■ GENESIS SOLAR LLC p 603
700 Universe Blvd 33408
Tel (561) 691-3062 *SIC* 4911

■ NEXTERA ENERGY CAPITAL HOLDINGS INC p 1040
700 Universe Blvd 33408
Tel (561) 694-6311 *SIC* 6799

▲ NEXTERA ENERGY INC p 1040
700 Universe Blvd 33408
Tel (561) 694-4000 *SIC* 4911

■ NEXTERA ENERGY OPERATING SERVICES LLC p 1040
700 Universe Blvd 33408
Tel (561) 691-7171 *SIC* 4911

▲ NEXTERA ENERGY PARTNERS LP p 1040
700 Universe Blvd 33408
Tel (561) 694-4000 *SIC* 4911

■ NEXTERA ENERGY POWER MARKETING LLC p 1040
700 Universe Blvd 33408
Tel (561) 691-7171 *SIC* 4911

■ NEXTERA ENERGY RESOURCES LLC p 1040
700 Universe Blvd 33408
Tel (561) 691-7171 *SIC* 4911

NEXTERA ENERGY SERVICES HOLDINGS LLC p 1040
700 Universe Blvd 33408
Tel (561) 691-7171 *SIC* 4911

NEXTERA ENERGY SERVICES LLC p 1040
700 Universe Blvd 33408
Tel (561) 691-7171 *SIC* 4911

JUPITER, FL

AUDIO AMERICA INC p 130
15132 Park Of Commerce Bl 33478
Tel (561) 863-7704 *SIC* 5099

■ CARRIER CORP p 260
17900 Bee Line Hwy 33478
Tel (561) 796-2000 *SIC* 3585

G4S HOLDING ONE INC p 588
1395 University Blvd 33458
Tel (561) 622-5656
SIC 7381 7382 8744 8748 8742

G4S SECURE SOLUTIONS (USA) INC p 588
1395 University Blvd 33458
Tel (561) 622-5656
SIC 7381 8744 8748 8742

G4S SECURE SOLUTIONS INTERNATIONAL INC p 588
1395 University Blvd 33458
Tel (561) 622-5656 *SIC* 7382 7381

G4S TECHNOLOGY HOLDINGS (USA) INC p 588
1395 University Blvd 33458
Tel (561) 622-5656 *SIC* 7381

HOLTEC INTERNATIONAL p 702
1001 N Us Highway 1 33477
Tel (561) 745-7772 *SIC* 2819 8711

JENOPTIK NORTH AMERICA INC p 782
16490 Innovation Dr 33478
Tel (561) 881-7400 *SIC* 3827

JJTAYLOR COMPANIES INC p 786
655 N Highway A1a 33477
Tel (813) 247-4000 *SIC* 5181

JUPITER MEDICAL CENTER INC p 797
1210 S Old Dixie Hwy 33458
Tel (561) 747-2234 *SIC* 8062 8051

POWER SYSTEMS MFG LLC p 1165
1440 W Indiantown Rd # 200 33458
Tel (561) 354-1100 *SIC* 3463

QUICKTEST INC p 1199
1061 E Indiantown Rd # 300 33477
Tel (561) 748-0931 *SIC* 7375

RONCO CONSULTING CORP p 1249
1395 University Blvd 33458
Tel (571) 551-2934 *SIC* 1794 7389 7382

KENNEDY SPACE CENTER, FL

UNITED SPACE ALLIANCE LLC p 1512
Launch Equipment Support 32899
Tel (321) 861-0733 *SIC* 7389

KEY WEST, FL

■ LOWER KEYS MEDICAL CENTER p 881
5900 College Rd 33040
Tel (305) 294-5531 *SIC* 8062

MONROE COUNTY SCHOOL DISTRICT p 985
241 Trumbo Rd 33040
Tel (305) 293-1400 *SIC* 8211

UTILITY BOARD OF CITY OF KEY WEST p 1537
1001 James St 33040
Tel (305) 295-1000 *SIC* 1623

KEYSTONE HEIGHTS, FL

CLAY ELECTRIC COOPERATIVE INC p 323
225 W Walker Dr 32656
Tel (352) 473-8000 *SIC* 4911

KISSIMMEE, FL

AV COOLING SOLUTIONS INC p 135
803 E Donegan Ave 34744
Tel (407) 572-8739 *SIC* 5999

COUNTY OF OSCEOLA p 380
1 Courthouse Sq 34741
Tel (407) 742-2000 *SIC* 9111

DARNGAVIL ENTERPRISES LLC p 412
3103 Riachuelo Ln 34744
Tel (407) 288-2776 *SIC* 4213

FITNESS CENTRE AT CELEBRATION HEALTH p 552
400 Celebration Pl 34747
Tel (407) 303-4400 *SIC* 7991

GOSPEL OF PEACE INC p 626
215 Celebration Pl # 200 34747
Tel (321) 939-4700 *SIC* 6552

INTERNATIONAL CONSORTIUM FOR ADVANCED MANUFACTURING RESEARCH INC p 755
3 Courthouse Sq Fl 2 34741
Tel (407) 742-4252 *SIC* 8731

JR DAVIS CONSTRUCTION CO INC p 795
210 S Hoagland Blvd 34741
Tel (407) 870-0066 *SIC* 1629 1521

KISSIMMEE UTILITY AUTHORITY (INC) p 822
1701 W Carroll St 34741
Tel (407) 933-7777 *SIC* 4911

ORANGE LAKE COUNTRY CLUB INC p 1092
8505 W Irlo Bronson Hwy 34747
Tel (407) 239-0000
SIC 7011 6552 7997 5812 5813

OSCEOLA COUNTY SCHOOL BOARD p 1096
817 Bill Beck Blvd 34744
Tel (407) 870-4600 *SIC* 8211

OSCEOLAK12FL p 1096
817 Bill Beck Blvd 34744
Tel (407) 870-4630 *SIC* 8211

SCHOOL DISTRICT OF OSCEOLA COUNTY FL p 1289
817 Bill Beck Blvd 34744
Tel (407) 870-4600 *SIC* 8211

STERLING HOSPITALITY INC p 1387
2950 Reedy Creek Blvd 34747
Tel (407) 997-3481 *SIC* 8741 8721

LABELLE, FL

HENDRY COUNTY SCHOOL DISTRICT p 683
25 E Hickpochee Ave 33935
Tel (863) 674-4642 *SIC* 8211

LADY LAKE, FL

VILLAGES OF LAKE-SUMTER INC p 1557
1000 Lake Sumter Lndg 32162
Tel (352) 753-2270
SIC 6552 1521 7997 5812 7389

VILLAGES OPERATING CO p 1557
1020 Lake Sumter Lndg 32162
Tel (352) 753-2270 *SIC* 6531

LAKE BUENA VISTA, FL

WALT DISNEY ATTRACTIONS p 1574
1500 Epcot Resorts Blvd 32830
Tel (407) 934-4000 *SIC* 7011 7299

■ WALT DISNEY PARKS AND RESORTS US INC p 1574
1375 E Buena Vista Dr 32830
Tel (407) 824-2222 *SIC* 7996 7011 5947

WALT DISNEY WORLD SWAN AND DOLPHIN p 1574
1500 Epcot Resorts Blvd 32830
Tel (407) 934-4000 *SIC* 7011

WW LBV INC p 1629
2000 Hotel Plaza Blvd 32830
Tel (407) 828-2424 *SIC* 8741

LAKE CITY, FL

ANDERSON COLUMBIA CO INC p 89
871 Nw Guerdon St 32055
Tel (386) 752-7585 *SIC* 1611 2951

COLUMBIA COUNTY SCHOOL BOARD p 340
372 W Duval St 32055
Tel (386) 755-8010 *SIC* 8211

COLUMBIA COUNTY SCHOOL DISTRICT p 340
372 W Duval St 32055
Tel (386) 755-8000 *SIC* 8211 9411

SCAFFS INC p 1285
134 Se Colburn Ave 32025
Tel (386) 752-7344 *SIC* 5411

LAKE MARY, FL

ACCESS MEDIQUIP LLC p 15
255 Primera Blvd Ste 230 32746
Tel (713) 985-4850 *SIC* 5047

ASSUREDPARTNERS GULF COAST INSURANCE AGENCY LLC p 122
200 Colonial Center Pkwy 32746
Tel (407) 804-5222 *SIC* 6321

ASSUREDPARTNERS INC p 122
200 Colonial Center Pkwy 32746
Tel (407) 804-5222 *SIC* 6411

BUNKERS INTERNATIONAL CORP p 226
1071 S Sun Dr Ste 3 32746
Tel (407) 328-7757 *SIC* 7389 5172

D+H USA CORP p 407
605 Crescent Executive Ct # 600 32746
Tel (407) 804-6600 *SIC* 7372

D+H USA HOLDINGS INC p 407
605 Crescent Executive Ct # 600 32746
Tel (407) 804-6600 *SIC* 6719

EDUCATION AMERICA INC p 479
7131 Bus Pk Ln Ste 300 32746
Tel (407) 562-5500 *SIC* 8222

▲ FARO TECHNOLOGIES INC p 530
250 Technology Park 32746
Tel (407) 333-9911 *SIC* 3829

MITSUBISHI HITACHI POWER SYSTEMS AMERICAS INC p 977
400 Colonial Center Pkwy # 400 32746
Tel (407) 688-6100 *SIC* 5084 1796

■ PRIORITY HEALTHCARE DISTRIBUTION INC p 1177
255 Technology Park 32746
Tel (407) 833-7000 *SIC* 5122 5047

REMINGTON COLLEGES INC p 1222
7131 Bus Pk Ln Ste 300 32746
Tel (407) 562-5500 *SIC* 8221 8222

■ SCHOLASTIC BOOK FAIRS INC p 1288
1080 Greenwood Blvd 32746
Tel (407) 829-7300 *SIC* 5192 5199 5942

■ SUNGARD PUBLIC SECTOR INC p 1402
1000 Business Center Dr 32746
Tel (407) 304-3235 *SIC* 5045

LAKE WALES, FL

CITRUS WORLD INC p 311
20205 Hwy 27 33853
Tel (863) 676-1411 *SIC* 2037

LANGFORD SERVICES INC p 844
6480 State Road 60 E 33898
Tel (863) 528-2242 *SIC* 8999

OAKLEY TRANSPORT INC p 1071
101 Abc Rd 33859
Tel (863) 638-1435 *SIC* 4213 6531

LAKE WORTH, FL

MELTON MANAGEMENT INC p 941
6342 Lantana Rd 33463
Tel (561) 641-6717 *SIC* 5812

PALM BEACH STATE COLLEGE p 1109
4200 S Congress Ave 33461
Tel (561) 868-3350 *SIC* 8222 8351 8221

LAKELAND, FL

CITY OF LAKELAND p 316
228 S Massachusetts Ave 33801
Tel (863) 834-6000 *SIC* 9111

■ DISCOUNT AUTO PARTS LLC p 442
4900 Frontage Rd S 33815
Tel (863) 248-2056 *SIC* 5531

FAIRWAYS GOLF CORP p 525
5385 Gateway Blvd Ste 12 33811
Tel (407) 589-7200 *SIC* 7992

FLEETWING CORP p 555
742 S Combee Rd 33801
Tel (863) 665-7557 *SIC* 5172 5411

FLORIDA SOUTHERN COLLEGE p 559
111 Lake Hollingsworth Dr 33801
Tel (863) 680-4111 *SIC* 8221

HARRELLS INC p 663
720 Kraft Rd 33815
Tel (863) 687-2774 *SIC* 2875 5191

HARRELLS LLC p 663
5105 New Tampa Hwy 33815
Tel (863) 687-2774 *SIC* 2875 5191

INTEGRATED SUPPLY NETWORK LLC p 749
2727 Interstate Dr 33805
Tel (863) 603-0777 *SIC* 5013 5072

JBT FOODTECH CITRUS SYSTEMS p 780
400 Fairway Ave 33801
Tel (863) 683-5411 *SIC* 5169

JJJTB INC p 786
3200 Flightline Dr 33811
Tel (863) 607-5600 *SIC* 4731

LAKELAND REGIONAL HEALTH SYSTEMS INC p 840
1324 Lakeland Hills Blvd 33805
Tel (863) 687-1100 *SIC* 8062

LAKELAND REGIONAL MEDICAL CENTER INC p 840
1324 Lakeland Hills Blvd 33805
Tel (863) 687-1100 *SIC* 8062

MCGEE TIRE STORES INC p 929
3939 Us Highway 98 S # 101 33812
Tel (863) 667-3347 *SIC* 5531 7538

MEADOWBROOK GOLF GROUP INC p 934
5385 Gateway Blvd Ste 12 33811
Tel (407) 589-7200
SIC 8742 8741 7992 5941

MUTZ MOTORS LTD PARTNERSHIP p 1003
1430 W Memorial Blvd 33815
Tel (863) 682-1100
SIC 5511 7538 7532 7515 5531 5521

PUBLIX SUPER MARKETS INC p 1190
3300 Publix Corp Pkwy 33811
Tel (863) 688-1188 *SIC* 5411

SADDLE CREEK CORP p 1265
3010 Saddle Creek Rd 33801
Tel (863) 665-0966 *SIC* 4225

SCHWARZ PARTNERS PACKAGING LLC p 1291
2808 New Tampa Hwy 33815
Tel (863) 682-0123 *SIC* 2653

■ SOUTHERN BAKERIES INC p 1347
3355 W Memorial Blvd 33815
Tel (863) 682-1155 *SIC* 2051 5149

■ SUMMIT CONSULTING LLC p 1398
2310 Commerce Point Dr 33801
Tel (863) 665-6060 *SIC* 6331 6411

TAMPA MAID FOODS LLC p 1423
1600 Kathleen Rd 33805
Tel (863) 687-4411 *SIC* 2092

TRADING CORP p 1469
5516 Scott View Ln 33813
Tel (754) 900-7666 *SIC* 5045 5961

WATSON CLINIC FOUNDATION INC p 1583
1600 Lakeland Hills Blvd 33805
Tel (863) 680-7000 *SIC* 8011

WATSON CLINIC LLP p 1583
1600 Lakeland Hills Blvd 33805
Tel (863) 680-7000 *SIC* 8011

LAKEWOOD RANCH, FL

DENTAL CARE ALLIANCE LLC p 429
6240 Lake Osprey Dr 34240
Tel (888) 876-4531 *SIC* 8021

GOLD COAST EAGLE DISTRIBUTING LIMITED LIABILITY LIMITED PARTNERSHIP p 620
7051 Wireless Ct 34240
Tel (941) 355-7685 *SIC* 5181

K NEAL PATRICK & ASSOCIATES INC p 799
8210 Lakewood Ranch Blvd 34202
Tel (941) 328-1111 *SIC* 6531

■ UTC FIRE & SECURITY AMERICAS CORP INC p 1536
8985 Town Center Pkwy 34202
Tel (941) 739-4200 *SIC* 3669 5065

LAND O LAKES, FL

DISTRICT SCHOOL BOARD OF PASCO COUNTY p 443
7227 Land O Lakes Blvd 34638
Tel (813) 794-2000 *SIC* 8211

PASCO COUNTY SCHOOLS p 1119
7227 Land O Lakes Blvd 34638
Tel (813) 794-2651 *SIC* 8211

TRAILER COUNTRY INC p 1469
5326 Land O Lakes Blvd 34639
Tel (813) 929-0700 *SIC* 5599

LANTANA, FL

PARAMOUNT FUNDING GROUP INC p 1114
212 E Ocean Ave 33462
Tel (561) 586-6290 *SIC* 6163

LARGO, FL

AGORA MARKETING SOLUTIONS INC p 35
8285 Bryan Dairy Rd # 150 33777
Tel (727) 369-2700 *SIC* 7331 7389

BAYCARE HOME CARE INC p 161
8452 118th Ave 33773
Tel (727) 394-6461 *SIC* 8082 7352

BCH MECHANICAL INC p 164
6354 118th Ave 33773
Tel (727) 546-3561 *SIC* 1711 3444

CITY OF LARGO p 316
201 Highland Ave N 33770
Tel (727) 587-6700 *SIC* 9111

FLORIDA DEPARTMENT OF VETERANS AFFAIRS p 558
11351 Ulmerton Rd Rm 311k 33778
Tel (727) 319-7427 *SIC* 9451 9111

HIT PROMOTIONAL PRODUCTS INC p 696
7150 Bryan Dairy Rd 33777
Tel (727) 541-5561 *SIC* 2759 3993

■ LARGO MEDICAL CENTER INC p 845
201 14th St Sw 33770
Tel (727) 588-5200 *SIC* 8062

■ LINVATEC CORP p 869
11311 Concept Blvd 33773
Tel (727) 392-6464 *SIC* 3842 3841 2821

■ NESTOR SALES LLC p 1027
7337 Bryan Dairy Rd 33777
Tel (727) 544-6114 *SIC* 5013 5085

PINELLAS COUNTY PUBLIC SCHOOLS p 1149
301 4th St Sw 33770
Tel (727) 588-6000 *SIC* 8211

PINELLAS COUNTY SCHOOL BOARD p 1149
301 4th St Sw 33770
Tel (727) 588-6000 *SIC* 8211 4832

TREMAYNE ANTONIO WILLIAMS GLOBAL ESTATE ENTRUST TRUST p 1476
12955 Walsingham Rd # 197 33774
Tel (727) 218-0199 *SIC* 6733

V P HOLDINGS INC p 1538
8605 Largo Lakes Dr 33773
Tel (727) 393-1270 *SIC* 7331

LAUDERDALE LAKES, FL

EDUCATION TRAINING CORP p 479
3383 N State Road 7 33319
Tel (954) 400-2000 *SIC* 8243

FCC HOLDINGS INC p 533
3383 N State Road 7 33319
Tel (954) 535-8700 *SIC* 8243

HIGH-TECH INSTITUTE HOLDINGS INC p 691
3383 N State Road 7 33319
Tel (602) 328-2800 *SIC* 6719

LEESBURG, FL

CENTRAL FLORIDA HEALTH ALLIANCE INC p 278
600 E Dixie Ave 34748
Tel (352) 323-5000 *SIC* 8741

LEESBURG REGIONAL MEDICAL CENTER INC p 852
600 E Dixie Ave 34748
Tel (352) 323-5762 *SIC* 8062

RO-MAC LUMBER & SUPPLY INC p 1240
700 E Main St 34748
Tel (352) 787-4545 *SIC* 5211 5031

LITHIA, FL

CENTRAL MAINTENANCE AND WELDING INC p 279
2620 E Keysville Rd 33547
Tel (813) 229-0012 *SIC* 3443 1791 7692

■ MOSAIC FERTILIZER LLC p 991
13830 Circa Crossing Dr 33547
Tel (813) 500-6300 *SIC* 2874

QGS DEVELOPMENT INC p 1195
17502 County Road 672 33547
Tel (813) 634-3326 *SIC* 0782 0781 1711

LONGWOOD, FL

INSURANCE OFFICE OF AMERICA INC p 748
1855 W State Road 434 32750
Tel (407) 788-3000 *SIC* 6411

J RAYMOND & ASSOCIATES INC p 772
465 W Warren Ave 32750
Tel (407) 339-2988 *SIC* 1542

LONGWOOD LINCOLN-MERCURY INC p 877
3505 N Us Highway 17 92 32750
Tel (407) 322-4884 *SIC* 5511

NORTH SOUTH FOODS GROUP INC p 1054
3373 Sterling Ridge Ct 32779
Tel (407) 805-9075 *SIC* 5144 5147 5146

■ SEARS HOME IMPROVEMENT PRODUCTS INC p 1297
1024 Florida Central Pkwy 32750
Tel (407) 767-0990 *SIC* 1521

SUNNILAND CORP p 1403
1735 State Road 419 32750
Tel (407) 322-2421 *SIC* 5033 5191

WASTE PRO OF FLORIDA INC p 1581
2101 W State Rd Ste 301 32779
Tel (407) 774-0800 *SIC* 4953

WASTE PRO USA INC p 1581
2101 W State Road 434 # 305 32779
Tel (407) 869-8800 *SIC* 4953

LOXAHATCHEE, FL

J & J PRODUCE INC p 770
4003 Seminole Pratt 33470
Tel (561) 422-9777 *SIC* 5148 0161

■ PALMS WEST HOSPITAL LIMITED PARTNERSHIP p 1109
13001 Southern Blvd 33470
Tel (561) 798-3300 *SIC* 8062

LUTZ, FL

■ OVATIONS FOOD SERVICES LP p 1099
18228 N Us Highway 41 33549
Tel (813) 948-6900 *SIC* 8742 7922

ST JOSEPHS HOSPITAL-NORTH p 1369
4211 Van Dyke Rd 33558
Tel (813) 443-7000 *SIC* 8099

MACCLENNY, FL

LV HIERS INC p 887
253 Florida Ave 32063
Tel (904) 259-2314 *SIC* 5171

MAITLAND, FL

ADCS CLINICS LLC p 21
151 Southhall Ln Ste 300 32751
Tel (407) 875-2080 *SIC* 8011

ADH 702 INC p 22
203 Lookout Pl Ste A 32751
Tel (407) 629-9311 *SIC* 5812

CONCORD MANAGEMENT CO INC p 354
1551 Sandspur Rd 32751
Tel (407) 741-8600 *SIC* 6513

CONCORD MANAGEMENT LTD p 354
1551 Sandspur Rd 32751
Tel (407) 741-8600 *SIC* 6531

CONCURRENT PARTNERS LLLP p 355
800 Cncrse Pkwy S Ste 200 32751
Tel (407) 571-1550 *SIC* 8051

CONSULATE HEALTH CARE LLC p 361
800 Concourse Pkwy S 32751
Tel (407) 571-1550 *SIC* 8051

CONSULATE MANAGEMENT CO LLC p 361
800 Concourse Pkwy S 32751
Tel (407) 571-1550
SIC 8051 8059 8071 8093

DIGITAL RISK LLC p 439
2301 Maitland Center Pkwy # 165 32751
Tel (407) 215-2900 *SIC* 8748

FLORIDA HOSPITAL MEDICAL GROUP INC p 558
2600 Westhall Ln 32751
Tel (407) 200-2700 *SIC* 8011

INDUSTRIAL CONTAINER SERVICES LLC p 739
2400 Maitland Center Pkwy 32751
Tel (800) 273-3786 *SIC* 3443 3411 3412

LSQ FUNDING GROUP LC p 883
2600 Lucien Way Ste 100 32751
Tel (407) 206-0022 *SIC* 6153

LSQ GROUP LLC p 883
2600 Lucien Way Ste 100 32751
Tel (407) 206-0022 *SIC* 6153

SEA CREST HEALTH CARE MANAGEMENT LLC p 1295
800 Concourse Pkwy S 32751
Tel (813) 744-2800 *SIC* 8059

SPECIALTY RESTAURANT DEVELOPMENT LLC p 1356
2600 Westhall Ln Ste 100 32751
Tel (407) 661-3151 *SIC* 8741

■ UNITED HEALTHCARE OF FLORIDA INC p 1509
495 N Keller Rd Ste 200 32751
Tel (407) 659-6900 *SIC* 6321

WESTCOR LAND TITLE INSURANCE CO p 1597
875 Cncrse Pkwy S Ste 200 32751
Tel (407) 629-5842 *SIC* 6311

MARCO ISLAND, FL

HYDRAPOWER INTERNATIONAL INC p 723
950 N Collier Blvd # 202 34145
Tel (239) 642-5379 *SIC* 3542

MARGATE, FL

GL STAFFING SERVICES INC p 613
1709 Banks Rd Bldg A 33063
Tel (954) 973-8350 *SIC* 7361

GLOBAL RESPONSE CORP p 617
777 S State Road 7 33068
Tel (954) 973-7300 *SIC* 7389

MARIANNA, FL

JACKSON COUNTY PUBLIC SCHOOLS p 773
2903 Jefferson St 32446
Tel (850) 482-1200 *SIC* 8211

MEDLEY, FL

ABBOUD TRADING CORP p 10
10910 Nw 92nd Ter 33178
Tel (786) 235-7007 *SIC* 5065

ALL AMERICAN CONTAINERS INC p 51
9330 Nw 110th Ave 33178
Tel (305) 887-0797 *SIC* 5085 5099

■ BRIGHTSTAR CORP p 213
9725 Nw 117th Ave Ste 105 33178
Tel (305) 421-6000 *SIC* 5065

CENTRO INTERNACIONAL DE AGRICULTURA TROPICAL p 281
7343 Nw 79th Ter 33166
Tel (305) 863-9127 *SIC* 8731

CIAT p 305
7343 Nw 79th Ter 33166
Tel (305) 863-9126 *SIC* 5099

COMMUNITY ASPHALT CORP p 347
9675 Nw 117th Ave Ste 108 33178
Tel (305) 884-9444 *SIC* 1611 2951

CONDOTTE AMERICA INC p 355
10790 Nw 127th St 33178
Tel (305) 670-7585 *SIC* 1611 1622 1542

DADE PAPER & BAG CO p 408
9601 Nw 112th Ave 33178
Tel (305) 805-2600 *SIC* 5113

DP DISTRIBUTION LLC p 454
9601 Nw 112th Ave 33178
Tel (305) 777-6108 *SIC* 5149 5963

INTRADECO APPAREL INC p 759
9500 Nw 108th Ave 33178
Tel (305) 264-8888 *SIC* 2389

INTRADECO INC p 759
9500 Nw 108th Ave 33178
Tel (305) 264-6022 *SIC* 5136 5199 5065

■ NAVARRO DISCOUNT PHARMACIES LLC p 1019
9675 Nw 117th Ave 202 33178
Tel (305) 805-1076 *SIC* 5912

REGAL WORLDWIDE TRADING LLC p 1218
9500 Nw 108th Ave 33178
Tel (305) 714-7425 *SIC* 5064

■ RYDER INTEGRATED LOGISTICS INC p 1260
11690 Nw 105th St 33178
Tel (305) 500-3726 *SIC* 7513

▲ RYDER SYSTEM INC p 1260
11690 Nw 105th St 33178
Tel (305) 500-3726 *SIC* 7513 4212

■ RYDER TRUCK RENTAL INC p 1260
11690 Nw 105th St 33178
Tel (305) 500-3726 *SIC* 7513

■ SEABOARD MARINE LTD INC p 1295
8001 Nw 79th Ave 33166
Tel (305) 863-4444 *SIC* 4412

SENATOR INTERNATIONAL FREIGHT FORWARDING LLC p 1303
10201 Nw 112th Ave Ste 10 33178
Tel (305) 593-5520 *SIC* 4731

SENATOR INTERNATIONAL HOLDING LLC p 1303
10201 Nw 112th Ave Ste 10 33178
Tel (305) 593-5520 *SIC* 4731

■ SYSCO SOUTH FLORIDA INC p 1418
12500 Nw 112th Ave 33178
Tel (305) 651-5421
SIC 5149 5147 5142 5113 5143 5144

TRACFONE WIRELESS INC p 1468
9700 Nw 112th Ave 33178
Tel (305) 640-2000 *SIC* 4813 4812

TROPIC OIL CO p 1484
9970 Nw 89th Ct 33178
Tel (305) 888-4611 *SIC* 5172

UNITED STATES FOUNDRY & MANUFACTURING CORP p 1513
8351 Nw 93rd St 33166
Tel (305) 885-0301 SIC 3321 3441 3322

URBIETA OIL INC p 1530
9701 Nw 89th Ave 33178
Tel (305) 884-0008 SIC 5171 5172

WINCORP INTERNATIONAL INC p 1615
10025 Nw 116th Way Ste 14 33178
Tel (305) 887-1294
SIC 5191 5083 5199 7338 5144

MELBOURNE, FL

DRS NETWORK & IMAGING SYSTEMS LLC p 457
100 N Babcock St 32935
Tel (321) 309-1500 SIC 3674

FLORIDA INSTITUTE OFTECHNOLOGY INC p 559
150 W University Blvd Ofc 32901
Tel (321) 674-8000 SIC 8221 4581 8299

▲ GOLDFIELD CORP DEL p 622
1684 W Hibiscus Blvd 32901
Tel (321) 724-1700 SIC 1623 1731

▲ HARRIS CORP p 663
1025 W Nasa Blvd 32919
Tel (321) 727-9100
SIC 3812 3663 3699 3661 3674

HOLIDAY BUILDERS INC p 700
2293 W Eau Gallie Blvd 32935
Tel (321) 610-5156 SIC 1521

HOLMES REGIONAL MEDICAL CENTER INC p 702
1350 Hickory St 32901
Tel (321) 434-7000 SIC 8062

KELLY MANAGEMENT CORP p 809
2415 S Babcock St Ste C 32901
Tel (321) 768-2424 SIC 5511

■ KINDRED DEVELOPMENT 17 LLC p 819
765 W Nasa Blvd 32901
Tel (321) 409-4044 SIC 8062

M CTEST SERVICE INC p 889
425 North Dr 32934
Tel (321) 956-3052 SIC 3672 8734

MC ASSEMBLY HOLDINGS INC p 925
425 North Dr 32934
Tel (321) 253-0541 SIC 8734 3672

MC ASSEMBLY INTERNATIONAL LLC p 925
425 North Dr 32934
Tel (321) 253-0541 SIC 3825 1389

PSA HEALTHCARE p 1188
760 North Dr Ste D 32934
Tel (321) 254-4254 SIC 8099

SATCOM DIRECT INC p 1283
1050 Satcom Ln 32940
Tel (321) 777-3000 SIC 3663

SOUTHEAST AEROSPACE INC p 1345
1399 General Aviation Dr 32935
Tel (321) 255-9877
SIC 5088 3812 3728 3721 4581

SPACE COAST CREDIT UNION p 1354
8045 N Wickham Rd 32940
Tel (321) 259-6219 SIC 6062

■ SPACE COAST HEALTH FOUNDATION INC p 1354
6905 N Wickham Rd Ste 301 32940
Tel (321) 241-6600 SIC 8399

SPACE GATEWAY SUPPORT LLC p 1354
1235 Evans Rd 32904
Tel (321) 853-3393 SIC 1531

MIAMI BEACH, FL

CITY OF MIAMI BEACH p 316
1700 Convention Center Dr # 3 33139
Tel (305) 673-7000 SIC 9111

LNR PROPERTY LLC p 872
1601 Washington Ave # 800 33139
Tel (305) 695-5500 SIC 6513

MOUNT SINAI MEDICAL CENTER OF FLORIDA INC p 994
4300 Alton Rd 33140
Tel (305) 674-2121 SIC 8062 8741

MIAMI GARDENS, FL

EL DORADO FURNITURE CORP p 482
4200 Nw 167th St 33054
Tel (305) 624-9700 SIC 5712

MIAMI LAKES, FL

■ BANCO POPULAR NORTH AMERICA INC p 150
P.O. Box 4906 33014
Tel (847) 994-5400 SIC 6022

▲ BANKUNITED INC p 152
14817 Oak Ln 33016
Tel (305) 569-2000 SIC 6022

BLUMBERG INDUSTRIES INC p 193
5770 Miami Lakes Dr E 33014
Tel (305) 821-3850 SIC 3645 3646

■ CORDIS INTERNATIONAL CORP p 369
14201 Nw 60th Ave 33014
Tel (305) 824-2000 SIC 2834

■ FDC VITAMINS LLC p 533
14620 Nw 60th Ave 33014
Tel (305) 468-1600 SIC 2833

GRAHAM COMPANIES p 628
6843 Main St 33014
Tel (305) 821-1130
SIC 1531 7011 0212 6552 6512 2711

GRAHAM COMPANIES p 628
6843 Main St 33014
Tel (305) 821-1130 SIC 6552

INKTEL HOLDINGS CORP p 743
13975 Nw 58th Ct 33014
Tel (305) 523-1100 SIC 7389

ISACO INTERNATIONAL CORP p 766
5980 Miami Lakes Dr E 33014
Tel (305) 594-4455 SIC 5136

KELLSTROM AEROSPACE LLC p 809
14400 Nw 77th Ct Ste 306 33016
Tel (847) 233-5800 SIC 5088

■ N A BANKUNITED p 1005
14817 Oak Ln 33016
Tel (305) 231-6400 SIC 6035 6163 6111

PLANET AUTOMOTIVE GROUP INC p 1154
6200 Nw 167th St B 33014
Tel (305) 728-5000 SIC 5511

MIAMI SHORES, FL

ARCHDIOCESE OF MIAMI INC p 105
9401 Biscayne Blvd 33138
Tel (305) 757-6241 SIC 8661

BARRY UNIVERSITY INC p 157
11300 Ne 2nd Ave 33161
Tel (305) 899-3050 SIC 8221

MIAMI SPRINGS, FL

CENTURION AIR CARGO INC p 281
4500 Nw 36th St Bldg 916 33166
Tel (305) 871-0130 SIC 4581 4522

MIAMI, FL

4701 NORTH MERIDIAN LLC p 3
4218 Ne 22nd Ave Fl 2 33137
Tel (305) 573-3900 SIC 6531

■ ADP TOTALSOURCE GROUP INC p 24
10200 Sw 72nd St 33173
Tel (305) 630-1000 SIC 8742

AKERMAN LLP p 42
98 Se 7th St Ste 1100 33131
Tel (305) 374-5600 SIC 8111

ALL AMERICAN GROUP HOLDINGS LLC p 51
1450 Brickell Ave # 3100 33131
Tel (305) 379-2322 SIC 6719

ALL AMERICAN SEMICONDUCTOR LLC p 51
3100 Nw 36th St 33142
Tel (305) 626-4183 SIC 5065

■ AMERICAN BANKERS INSURANCE CO OF FLORIDA p 68
11222 Quail Roost Dr 33157
Tel (305) 253-2244 SIC 6411 6331

■ AMERICAN BANKERS INSURANCE GROUP INC p 68
11222 Quail Roost Dr 33157
Tel (305) 253-2244
SIC 6331 6311 6351 6321 6324

■ AMERICAN BANKERS LIFE ASSURANCE CO OF FLORIDA p 68
11222 Quail Roost Dr 33157
Tel (305) 253-2244 SIC 6311

AMERICAN NICARAGUAN FOUNDATION INC p 77
1000 Nw 57th Ct Ste 770 33126
Tel (305) 374-3391 SIC 8399 8641

AMERICAN SALES AND MANAGEMENT ORGANIZATION LLC p 79
7200 Corp Ctr Dr Ste 206 33126
Tel (305) 269-2700 SIC 7382 7349 7363

AMERIJET HOLDINGS INC p 82
3401 Nw 72nd Ave Ste A 33122
Tel (800) 927-6059
SIC 4512 8741 4581 4213

AREAS USA INC p 106
5301 Blue Lagoon Dr # 690 33126
Tel (305) 264-1709 SIC 5399 5812

ARMOR CORRECTIONAL HEALTH SERVICES INC p 111
4960 Sw 72nd Ave Ste 400 33155
Tel (305) 662-8522 SIC 8099

ATLAS PAPER MILLS LLC p 128
3301 Nw 107th St 33167
Tel (800) 562-2860 SIC 2621

BAKER NORTON US INC p 146
74 Nw 176th St 33169
Tel (305) 575-6000 SIC 2834

■ BANCO SANTANDER INTERNATIONAL p 150
1401 Brickell Ave Ste 200 33131
Tel (305) 530-2900 SIC 6029

BAPTIST HOSPITAL OF MIAMI INC p 154
8900 N Kendall Dr 33176
Tel (786) 596-1960 SIC 8062

BAYSIDE CAPITAL INC p 162
1450 Brickell Ave Fl 31 33131
Tel (305) 379-8686 SIC 6799

BENIHANA INC p 173
21500 Biscayne Blvd # 100 33180
Tel (305) 593-0770 SIC 5812 6794

BEST DOCTORS INSURANCE HOLDINGS LLC p 177
5201 Blue Lagoon Dr # 300 33126
Tel (305) 269-2521 SIC 8011 6719

BLUMAR USA LLC p 193
6303 Blue Lagoon Dr 385 33126
Tel (305) 261-2417 SIC 5146 5142

BTS GROUP INC p 222
2620 Sw 27th Ave 33133
Tel (305) 358-5850 SIC 6159

BURGER KING CAPITAL HOLDINGS LLC p 227
5505 Blue Lagoon Dr 33126
Tel (305) 378-3000 SIC 5812

BURGER KING CORP p 227
5505 Blue Lagoon Dr 33126
Tel (305) 378-3000 SIC 5812 6794

BURGER KING HOLDCO LLC p 227
5505 Blue Lagoon Dr 33126
Tel (305) 378-3000 SIC 5812

BURGER KING HOLDINGS INC p 227
5505 Blue Lagoon Dr 33126
Tel (305) 378-3000 SIC 5812 6794

BURGER KING WORLDWIDE INC p 227
5505 Blue Lagoon Dr 33126
Tel (305) 378-3000 SIC 5812

BUSINESS TELECOMMUNICATIONS SERVICES INC p 230
2620 Sw 27th Ave 33133
Tel (305) 358-5850 SIC 4813 5999 8748

C C 1 LIMITED PARTNERSHIP p 232
3201 Nw 72nd Ave 33122
Tel (305) 599-2337 SIC 2086

CAMANCHACA INC p 243
7200 Nw 19th St Ste 410 33126
Tel (305) 406-9560 SIC 5146

CARIBBEAN FINANCIAL GROUP INC p 256
20807 Biscayne Blvd # 200 33180
Tel (305) 933-6601 SIC 6141

■ CELEBRITY CRUISES INC p 273
1050 Caribbean Way 33132
Tel (305) 262-6677 SIC 4729

CHILDRENS TRUST p 300
3150 Sw 3rd Ave Fl 8 33129
Tel (305) 571-5700 SIC 6732

CITY NATIONAL BANK p 312
25 W Flagler St Fl 3 33130
Tel (305) 577-7333 SIC 6021

CITY OF MIAMI p 316
3500 Pan American Dr Fl 2 33133
Tel (305) 250-5300 SIC 9111

CLC ENTERPRISES INC p 323
11231 Nw 20th St Unit 133 33172
Tel (305) 640-1803 SIC 5065

CLUB MED SALES INC p 328
6505 Blue Lagoon Dr # 225 33126
Tel (305) 925-9000
SIC 4724 4725 7011 8741

COSTA FARMS LLC p 374
21800 Sw 162nd Ave 33170
Tel (305) 247-3248 SIC 0181

COUNTY OF MIAMI-DADE p 380
111 Nw 1st St Ste 2550 33128
Tel (305) 375-5147 SIC 9111

DE MOYA GROUP INC p 419
14600 Sw 136th St 33186
Tel (305) 255-5713 SIC 1611 1622

■ DEAN DAIRY HOLDINGS LLC p 420
6851 Ne 2nd Ave 33138
Tel (305) 795-7700 SIC 5143

DESA AGI LLC p 431
1450 Brickell Ave # 2080 33131
Tel (786) 315-4680 SIC 6221

DFA HOLDINGS INC p 435
6100 Hllywood Blvd Fl 7 33180
Tel (954) 986-7700 SIC 5182 5399

DIANA FOODS INC p 437
13300 Nw 25th St 33182
Tel (305) 593-8317 SIC 5141 5149

DOWNRITE HOLDINGS INC p 453
14241 Sw 143rd Ct 33186
Tel (305) 232-2340
SIC 1611 1623 8711 1794

EAGLE BRANDS WEDCO LIMITED PARTNERSHIP p 467
3201 Nw 72nd Ave 33122
Tel (305) 599-2337 SIC 5182

ELANDIA INTERNATIONAL INC p 483
8333 Nw 53rd St Ste 400 33166
Tel (305) 415-8830
SIC 4813 4899 7371 5044

ELITE FLOWER SERVICES INC p 487
3200 Nw 67th Ave Bldg 2s 33122
Tel (305) 436-7400 SIC 5193

ELLER-ITO STEVEDORING CO LLC p 488
1007 N America Way # 501 33132
Tel (305) 379-3700 SIC 7999 4491

EUROTIRE INC p 513
200 S Biscayne Blvd # 5500 33131
Tel (212) 262-2251 SIC 3011

EXPOCREDIT LLC p 520
1450 Brickell Ave # 2660 33131
Tel (305) 347-9222 SIC 6153

FALCON FARMS INC p 526
2330 Nw 82nd Ave 33122
Tel (305) 477-8088 SIC 5992 5193

FARM STORES CORP p 529
2937 Sw 27th Ave Ste 203 33133
Tel (800) 726-3276 SIC 5411

FLORIDA INTERNATIONAL UNIVERSITY p 559
11200 Sw 8th St 33199
Tel (305) 348-2494 SIC 8221

FLORIDA VEG INVESTMENTS LLC p 559
7350 Nw 30th Ave 33147
Tel (305) 836-3152 SIC 5148

■ FLOWERS BAKING CO OF MIAMI LLC p 560
17800 Nw Miami Ct 33169
Tel (305) 652-3416 SIC 2051 5461

FONTAINEBLUEAU FLORIDA HOTEL LLC p 563
4441 Collins Ave 33140
Tel (305) 538-2000
SIC 6519 7011 5812 7991

GENERAL ASPHALT CO INC p 599
4850 Nw 72nd Ave 33166
Tel (305) 592-6005 SIC 3531

GEORGIAN AMERICAN ALLOYS INC p 608
200 S Biscayne Blvd # 5500 33131
Tel (305) 375-7560 SIC 1061

GLF CONSTRUCTION CORP p 615
528 Nw 7th Ave 33136
Tel (305) 371-5228
SIC 1611 1622 1542 1541 1522

GLOBE SPECIALTY METALS INC p 618
600 Brickell Ave Ste 3100 33131
Tel (786) 509-6900 SIC 3339 3313

GOODWILL INDUSTRIES OF SOUTH FLORIDA INC p 625
2121 Nw 21st St 33142
Tel (305) 325-9114 SIC 8331

GREENBERG TRAURIG PA p 637
333 Se 2nd Ave Ste 4100 33131
Tel (305) 579-0500 SIC 8111

▲ HACKETT GROUP INC p 652
1001 Brickell Bay Dr # 3000 33131
Tel (305) 375-8005 SIC 8742

HAMILTON RISK MANAGEMENT CO p 655
3155 Nw 77th Ave 33122
Tel (305) 716-6000
SIC 6331 7323 6141 6541 6411

HARVARD MAINTENANCE INC p 666
2 S Biscayne Blvd # 3650 33131
Tel (305) 351-7300 SIC 7349

HERRERA PETROLEUM CORP p 687
5209 Nw 74th Ave Ste 279 33166
Tel (786) 267-5467 SIC 5983

HIG CAPITAL INC p 690
1450 Brickell Ave # 3100 33131
Tel (305) 379-2322 SIC 8742 6211

HIG CAPITAL LLC p 690
1450 Brickell Ave Fl 31 33131
Tel (305) 379-2322 SIC 6211

HIG CAPITAL MANAGEMENT INC p 690
1450 Brickell Ave Fl 31 33131
Tel (305) 379-2322 SIC 6211

HIG CAPITAL PARTNERS III LP p 690
1450 Brickell Ave # 3100 33131
Tel (305) 379-2322
SIC 6211 5084 7352 7699 8748 3842

▲ HIG SURGERY CENTERS LLC p 690
1450 Brickell Ave Fl 31 33131
Tel (305) 379-2322 SIC 8062 3851

HIG TRANSPORT HOLDINGS INC p 690
1450 Brickell Ave Fl 31 33131
Tel (305) 379-2322 SIC 8742

HILTON INTERNATIONAL CO p 695
5201 Blue Lagoon Dr # 600 33126
Tel (305) 444-3444 SIC 7011 5812

INDEPENDENT PURCHASING COOPERATIVE INC p 737
9200 S Dadeland Blvd # 800 33156
Tel (305) 670-0041 SIC 7389

INTERFOOD INC p 752
777 Brickell Ave Ste 702 33131
Tel (786) 953-8320 SIC 5143

INTERFOODS OF AMERICA INC p 752
9500 S Dadeland Blvd # 800 33156
Tel (305) 670-0746 SIC 5812 6794

INTERNATIONAL RESTAURANT MANAGEMENT GROUP INC p 756
4531 Pnc De Leon Blvd 3 Ste 300 33146
Tel (305) 476-1611 SIC 5812

IVAX CORP p 769
4400 Biscayne Blvd 33137
Tel (305) 329-3795 SIC 2834

IVAX PHARMACEUTICALS LLC p 769
74 Nw 176th St 33169
Tel (305) 575-6000 SIC 2834

J & B IMPORTERS INC p 769
11925 Sw 128th St 33186
Tel (305) 238-1866 SIC 5091

JACKSON MEMORIAL HOSPITAL p 774
1611 Nw 12th Ave 33136
Tel (305) 585-1111 SIC 8062

JOHN S AND JAMES L KNIGHT FOUNDATION INC p 789
200 S Biscayne Blvd # 3300 33131
Tel (305) 358-1061 SIC 8399

JOSE MASSUH REVOCABLE TRUST p 793
825 Brickell Bay Dr 33131
Tel (305) 358-1900 SIC 5162

■ KENDALL HEALTHCARE GROUP LTD p 810
11750 Sw 40th St 33175
Tel (305) 227-5500 SIC 8062

KENDALL IMPORTS LLC p 810
10943 S Dixie Hwy 33156
Tel (305) 666-1784 SIC 5511 5521

KENDALL REGIONAL MEDICAL CENTER INC p 810
11750 Sw 40th St 33175
Tel (305) 223-3000 SIC 8011

KENDALL WEST BAPTIST HOSPITAL INC p 810
9555 Sw 162nd Ave 33196
Tel (786) 467-2000 SIC 8062

KEYSTONE HOLDINGS LLC p 815
10 Nw 42nd Ave Ste 700 33126
Tel (305) 567-1577
SIC 8711 3053 3081 3082 3545

KONING RESTAURANTS INTERNATIONAL LC p 827
15600 Nw 15th Ave 33169
Tel (305) 430-1200 SIC 5812

▲ LADENBURG THALMANN FINANCIAL SERVICES INC p 837
4400 Biscayne Blvd Fl 12 33137
Tel (305) 572-4100 SIC 6211 6282

LAN CARGO SA p 841
6500 Nw 22nd St 33122
Tel (786) 265-6000 SIC 4789

LATAM AIRLINES GROUP SA INC p 846
6500 Nw 22nd St 33122
Tel (786) 265-6050 SIC 4512

LATAMSCIENCE LLC p 846
2151 S Le Jeune Rd # 307 33134
Tel (305) 871-0701 SIC 8731 8999

LEHMAN DEALERSHIP ENTERPRISES INC p 854
21400 Nw 2nd Ave 33169
Tel (305) 653-7111 SIC 5511

▲ LENNAR CORP p 855
700 Nw 107th Ave Ste 400 33172
Tel (305) 559-4000 SIC 1531 6552 6163

■ LENNAR FINANCIAL SERVICES LLC p 855
700 Nw 107th Ave Ste 400 33172
Tel (305) 559-4000
SIC 6162 6153 6361 6411 7382

■ LENNAR HOMES INC p 855
730 Nw 107th Ave Ste 300 33172
Tel (305) 559-4000 SIC 1531

■ LENNAR HOMES LLC p 855
700 Nw 107th Ave Ste 400 33172
Tel (305) 559-4000 SIC 1531

LEON FLAGLER HOLDINGS LLC p 856
7950 Nw 5th Ct 33150
Tel (305) 631-3900 SIC 8011

LEON MANAGEMENT INTERNATIONAL INC p 856
11501 Sw 40th St Fl 2 33165
Tel (305) 642-5366 SIC 8741

LEON MEDICAL CENTERS INC p 856
11501 Sw 40th St 33165
Tel (305) 559-2881 SIC 8011

LIMECOM INC p 866
6303 Blue Lagoon Dr 33126
Tel (786) 408-6743 SIC 4899

M-SKO IAS HOLDINGS INC p 890
1395 Brickell Ave Ste 800 33131
Tel (786) 871-2904 SIC 5084

MAT CONCESSIONAIRE LLC p 918
860 Macarthur Cswy 33132
Tel (305) 929-0560 SIC 5812

■ MERCY HOSPITAL INC p 947
3663 S Miami Ave 33133
Tel (305) 854-4400 SIC 8062

■ MIAMI BEACH HEALTHCARE GROUP LTD p 959
20900 Biscayne Blvd 33180
Tel (305) 682-7000 SIC 8062

MIAMI DADE COLLEGE p 959
300 Ne 2nd Ave Rm 3116 33132
Tel (305) 237-3000 SIC 8222 9411 8221

MIAMI JEWISH HEALTH SYSTEMS INC p 959
5200 Ne 2nd Ave 33137
Tel (305) 751-8626 SIC 8051

MIAMI-DADE COUNTY PUBLIC SCHOOLS-158 p 959
1450 Ne 2nd Ave 33132
Tel (305) 995-1000 SIC 8211

MICCOSUKEE TRIBE OF INDIANS OF FLORIDA p 959
Sw 8th St & Us Hwy 41 33194
Tel (305) 223-8380
SIC 5812 5331 8412 5947 4489

MULTIEXPORT FOODS INC p 999
703 Nw 62nd Ave Ste 510 33126
Tel (305) 364-0009 SIC 5146

NATIONAL DELI LLC p 1011
7250 Nw 35th Ter Tce 33122
Tel (305) 592-0300 SIC 5147

■ NCL (BAHAMAS) LTD A BERMUDA CO p 1022
7665 Corporate Center Dr 33126
Tel (305) 436-4000 SIC 4729

■ NCL CORP LTD p 1022
7665 Corporate Center Dr 33126
Tel (305) 436-4000 SIC 4481

■ NEIGHBORHOOD HEALTH PARTNERSHIP INC p 1024
7600 Nw 19th St Ste 100 33126
Tel (305) 715-2200 SIC 6324 6321

NEORIS USA INC p 1026
703 Waterford Way Ste 700 33126
Tel (305) 728-6000 SIC 4813

■ NORTH AMERICAN TITLE GROUP INC p 1050
700 Nw 107th Ave Ste 300 33172
Tel (305) 552-1102 SIC 6361

■ NORTH SHORE MEDICAL CENTER INC p 1053
1100 Nw 95th St 33150
Tel (305) 835-6000 SIC 8062

▲ NORWEGIAN CRUISE LINE HOLDINGS LTD p 1061
7665 Corp Ctr Dr 33126
Tel (305) 436-4000 SIC 4481

NOVEN PHARMACEUTICALS INC p 1063
11960 Sw 144th St 33186
Tel (305) 964-3393 SIC 2834

OCEAN BANK p 1072
780 Nw 42nd Ave Ste 300 33126
Tel (305) 448-2265 SIC 6022

OCEAN BANKSHARES INC p 1073
780 Nw 42nd Ave Ste 626 33126
Tel (305) 442-2660 SIC 6712

■ OCEANIA CRUISES INC p 1073
7665 Nw 19th St 33126
Tel (305) 514-2300 SIC 4481

▲ OPKO HEALTH INC p 1089
4400 Biscayne Blvd 33137
Tel (305) 575-4100 SIC 2834 2835 8731

OPTIMA SPECIALTY STEEL INC p 1090
200 S Biscayne Blvd # 5500 33131
Tel (877) 289-2277 SIC 3317

OUR KIDS OF MIAMI-DADE/MONROE INC p 1098
401 Nw 2nd Ave Ste S212 33128
Tel (305) 455-6000 SIC 8322

PACIFIC LTD CORP p 1105
825 Brickell Bay Dr 33131
Tel (305) 358-1900 SIC 5162

PAN AMERICAN HOSPITAL CORP p 1110
5959 Nw 7th St 33126
Tel (305) 261-2273 SIC 8062

PARBEL OF FLORIDA INC p 1114
6100 Blue Lagoon Dr # 200 33126
Tel (305) 262-7500 SIC 5122

PASSION GROWERS LLC p 1120
7499 Nw 31st St 33122
Tel (305) 935-6657 SIC 5193

PATAGONIA SEAFARMS INC p 1120
7205 Corp Cntr Dr Ste 402 33126
Tel (786) 693-8711 SIC 5146

PEREZ TRADING CO INC p 1135
3490 Nw 125th St 33167
Tel (305) 769-0761 SIC 5199

PERKO INC p 1136
16490 Nw 13th Ave 33169
Tel (305) 621-7525 SIC 3429

PHINEAS CORP p 1144
9040 Sw 72nd St 33173
Tel (305) 596-9040 SIC 8361 8399 6531

POLLO OPERATIONS INC p 1160
7300 N Kendall Dr Fl 8 33156
Tel (305) 671-1225 SIC 5812

■ POOLE & KENT CO OF FLORIDA p 1161
1781 Nw North River Dr 33125
Tel (305) 325-1930 SIC 1611

■ PRESTIGE CRUISE HOLDINGS INC p 1173
7665 Nw 19th St 33126
Tel (305) 514-2300 SIC 4481

RC ALUMINUM INDUSTRIES INC p 1211
2805 Nw 75th Ave 33122
Tel (305) 592-1515 SIC 3442 1751

REFRICENTER OF MIAMI INC p 1218
7101 Nw 43rd St 33166
Tel (305) 477-8880 SIC 5075 5078

RELIANT INVENTORY GROUP LLC p 1222
2601 S Byshr Dr Ste 725 33133
Tel (786) 268-4520 SIC 7374

RESOLUTE FP FLORIDA INC p 1227
3301 Nw 107th St 33167
Tel (800) 562-2860 SIC 2621

▲ ROYAL CARIBBEAN CRUISES LTD p 1254
1050 Caribbean Way 33132
Tel (305) 539-6000 SIC 4481

SABADELL UNITED BANK NATIONAL ASSOCIATION p 1263
1111 Brickell Ave 33131
Tel (305) 358-4334 SIC 6021

SAILORMEN INC p 1268
9500 S Dadeland Blvd # 800 33156
Tel (305) 670-4112 SIC 5812

SCHENKER AMERICAS INC p 1286
1000 Nw 57th Ct Ste 700 33126
Tel (786) 388-4300 SIC 4731

SCHOOL BOARD OF MIAMI-DADE COUNTY p 1289
1450 Ne 2nd Ave 33132
Tel (305) 995-1000 SIC 8211

SEIDLE ENTERPRISES INC p 1301
2900 Nw 36th St 33142
Tel (305) 635-8000 SIC 5511 7538 7532

SERVISAIR USA & CARRIBEAN p 1308
6065 Nw 18th St Bldg 716d 33126
Tel (305) 262-4059 SIC 4581

SGWSNHC LLC p 1310
1600 Nw 163rd St 33169
Tel (305) 625-4171 SIC 5182

SHAMI MEDIA GROUP INC p 1311
1395 Brickell Ave Ste 800 33131
Tel (347) 549-2710 SIC 7389

■ SIMPLY HEALTHCARE HOLDINGS INC p 1325
9250 W Flagler St Ste 600 33174
Tel (877) 915-0551 SIC 6321 6719

■ SIMPLY HEALTHCARE PLANS INC p 1325
9250 W Flagler St Ste 600 33174
Tel (305) 408-5700 SIC 6321

SOUTH MOTOR CO OF DADE COUNTY p 1344
16165 S Dixie Hwy 33157
Tel (888) 418-3508 SIC 5511 5521

SOUTHERN GLAZERS WINE AND SPIRITS LLC p 1348
1600 Nw 163rd St 33169
Tel (305) 625-4171 SIC 5182 5181

▲ SPANISH BROADCASTING SYSTEM INC p 1354
7007 Nw 77th Ave 33166
Tel (305) 441-6901 SIC 4832 4833

STYLE-VIEW PRODUCTS INC p 1395
1800 N Bayshore Dr # 4001 33132
Tel (305) 634-9688
SIC 3442 3444 3443 3354

SUCDEN AMERICAS CORP p 1396
701 Brickell Ave Ste 1200 33131
Tel (305) 374-4440 SIC 6221

SUNRISE COMMUNITY INC p 1403
9040 Sw 72nd St 33173
Tel (305) 275-3365 SIC 8052 8331 8322

SURGERY CENTER HOLDINGS INC p 1408
1450 Brickell Ave Fl 31 33131
Tel (813) 514-9571 SIC 6799

■ TECH DATA LATIN AMERICA INC p 1430
2200 Nw 112th Ave 33172
Tel (305) 593-5000 SIC 5045

TELEFONICA USA p 1434
1111 Brickell Ave # 1000 33131
Tel (305) 925-5300 SIC 7375 7374 4813

TELEFONICA USA INC p 1434
1111 Brickell Ave # 1000 33131
Tel (305) 925-5298 SIC 5065 4813

■ TERREMARK WORLDWIDE INC p 1440
2 S Biscayne Blvd # 2800 33131
Tel (305) 961-3200 SIC 4813 8742

■ TIGERDIRECT INC p 1453
7795 W Flagler St Ste 35 33144
Tel (305) 415-2200 SIC 5961 5734

TIM HORTONS USA INC p 1453
5505 Blue Lagoon Dr 33126
Tel (888) 376-4835 SIC 6794 5812

TOTALBANK p 1463
100 Se 2nd St 33131
Tel (305) 982-3310 SIC 6022 6163

TRANSPORTATION AMERICA INC p 1472
2766 Nw 62nd St 33147
Tel (305) 308-8110 SIC 4212

TROPIC SUPPLY INC p 1484
151 Ne 179th St 33162
Tel (305) 652-7717 SIC 5078 5075

TRUJILLO & SONS INC p 1486
3325 Nw 62nd St 33147
Tel (305) 633-6482 SIC 5141

TURNBERRY ASSOCIATES p 1492
19501 Biscayne Blvd # 3400 33180
Tel (305) 937-6262 SIC 6512 6552

UNITED AUTOMOBILE INSURANCE GROUP INC p 1506
3909 Ne 163rd St Ste 308 33160
Tel (305) 940-5022 SIC 6411

UNIVERSITY OF MIAMI MILLER SCHOOL OF MEDICINE p 1523
900 Nw 17th St Ste 1 33136
Tel (305) 326-6000 SIC 8069

US SECURITY INSURANCE CO p 1533
3155 Nw 77th Ave 33122
Tel (305) 716-6100 SIC 6331

VARIETY CHILDRENS HOSPITAL p 1544
3100 Sw 62nd Ave 33155
Tel (305) 666-6511 SIC 8069

▲ VECTOR GROUP LTD p 1546
4400 Biscayne Blvd Fl 10 33137
Tel (305) 579-8000 SIC 2111 6552

■ VGR HOLDING LLC p 1553
4400 S Biscayne Blvd # 10 33131
Tel (305) 579-8000 SIC 2111 6552

■ VITAS HEALTHCARE CORP p 1563
100 S Biscayne Blvd # 1600 33131
Tel (305) 374-4143 SIC 8082 8051

WARREN HENRY AUTOMOBILES INC p 1577
20800 Nw 2nd Ave 33169
Tel (305) 690-6010 SIC 5511 5531 7538

▲ WATSCO INC p 1583
2665 S Byshr Dr Ste 901 33133
Tel (305) 714-4100 SIC 5075

MIDWAY, FL

AJAX BUILDING CORP p 41
1080 Commerce Blvd 32343
Tel (850) 224-9571 SIC 1542

MILTON, FL

COUNTY OF SANTA ROSA BOARD OF PUBLIC INSTRUCTION p 381
5086 Canal St 32570
Tel (850) 983-5000 SIC 8211

MIRAMAR, FL

AMERICAN HEALTH ASSOCIATES INC p 73
2831 Corporate Way 33025
Tel (954) 919-5005 SIC 8071

AVEVA DRUG DELIVERY SYSTEMS INC p 137
3250 Commerce Pkwy 33025
Tel (954) 430-3340 SIC 2834

COMPUPAY HOLDINGS CORP p 352
3450 Lakeside Dr Ste 400 33027
Tel (469) 791-3300 SIC 6719

■ EMERGING MARKETS COMMUNICATIONS LLC p 492
3044 N Commerce Pkwy 33025
Tel (954) 538-4000 SIC 4841

■ ENERGY SERVICES PROVIDERS INC p 498
3700 Lakeside Dr 6 33027
Tel (305) 947-7880 SIC 2211

JL AUDIO INC p 786
10369 N Commerce Pkwy 33025
Tel (954) 443-1100 SIC 5065 2519

PREMIER BEVERAGE CO LLC p 1170
9801 Premier Pkwy 33025
Tel (954) 436-9200 SIC 5181 5182

REGAL SPRINGS TRADING CO p 1218
2801 Sw 149th Ave Ste 270 33027
Tel (954) 283-9035 SIC 5146

SANARE LLC p 1277
3620 Enterprise Way 33025
Tel (305) 438-9696 SIC 5047

SHAW-ROSS INTERNATIONAL IMPORTERS INC p 1313
2900 Sw 149th Ave Ste 200 33027
Tel (954) 430-5020 SIC 5182

SHAW-ROSS INTERNATIONAL IMPORTERS LLC p 1313
2900 Sw 149th Ave Ste 200 33027
Tel (954) 430-5020 SIC 5182

SOMERSET NEIGHBORHOOD SCHOOL INC p 1339
12425 Sw 53rd St 33027
Tel (305) 829-2406 SIC 8211

SOUTHEAST FROZEN FOODS CO LP p 1345
3261 Executive Way 33025
Tel (954) 882-1044 SIC 5142 4222 5411

SOUTHEAST FROZEN FOODS INC p 1346
3261 Executive Way 33025
Tel (866) 289-1198 SIC 2038

▲ SPIRIT AIRLINES INC p 1359
2800 Executive Way 33025
Tel (954) 447-7920 SIC 4512

UNIVITA OF FLORIDA INC p 1528
15800 Sw 25th St 33027
Tel (305) 826-0244 SIC 5047 7352

■ US GAS & ELECTRIC INC p 1532
3700 Lakeside Dr Fl 6 33027
Tel (305) 947-7880 SIC 4931

MULBERRY, FL

AMZ HOLDING CORP p 88
4800 State Road 60 E 33860
Tel (863) 578-1206 SIC 5169

ARR-MAZ CUSTOM CHEMICALS INC p 112
4800 State Road 60 E 33860
Tel (863) 578-1206 SIC 2869

ARR-MAZ PRODUCTS LP p 112
4800 State Road 60 E 33860
Tel (863) 578-1206 SIC 2899 2869

WS BADCOCK CORP p 1628
205 Nw 2nd St 33860
Tel (863) 425-4921
SIC 5712 5713 5722 5731

NAPLES, FL

▲ ACI WORLDWIDE INC p 17
3520 Kraft Rd Ste 300 34105
Tel (239) 403-4600 SIC 7372 5045

ARTHREX INC p 114
1370 Creekside Blvd 34108
Tel (239) 643-5553 SIC 3841

ASG TECHNOLOGIES GROUP INC p 116
708 Goodlette Rd N 34102
Tel (239) 435-2200 SIC 7372

▲ BEASLEY BROADCAST GROUP INC p 166
3033 Riviera Dr Ste 200 34103
Tel (239) 263-5000 SIC 4832

CC-NAPLES INC p 269
704 Village Cir 34110
Tel (239) 596-4702 SIC 8741

COLLIER COUNTY PUBLIC SCHOOLS p 337
5775 Osceola Trl 34109
Tel (239) 377-0001 SIC 8211

COUNTY OF COLLIER p 377
3299 Tamiami Trl E # 700 34112
Tel (239) 252-8999 SIC 9111

GARGIULO INC p 592
15000 Old Hwy 41 N 34110
Tel (239) 597-3131 SIC 5148

■ **GREATER MEDIA INC** p 635
3033 Riviera Dr Ste 200 34103
Tel (239) 263-5000 SIC 2711 8999 4832

■ **HEALTH MANAGEMENT ASSOCIATES INC** p 675
5811 Pelican Bay Blvd # 500 34108
Tel (239) 598-3131 SIC 8062

MANHATTAN CONSTRUCTION (FLORIDA) INC p 901
3705 Westview Dr Ste 1 34104
Tel (239) 643-6000
SIC 1542 8712 1531 1521 8741

NAPLES COMMUNITY HOSPITAL INC p 1007
350 7th St N 34102
Tel (239) 436-5000 SIC 8062

NCH HEALTHCARE SYSTEM INC p 1022
350 7th St N 34102
Tel (239) 624-5000 SIC 8062

■ **PHYSICIANS REGIONAL MEDICAL CENTER** p 1146
6101 Pine Ridge Rd 34119
Tel (239) 348-4400 SIC 8011 8062

ROONEY HOLDINGS INC p 1249
3705 Westview Dr Ste 1 34104
Tel (239) 403-0375 SIC 1542

■ **TIB FINANCIAL CORP** p 1452
599 Tamiami Trl N Ste 101 34102
Tel (239) 263-3344 SIC 6022

NEW PORT RICHEY, FL

COMMUNITY HOSPITAL OF NEW PORT RICHEY p 349
5637 Marine Pkwy 34652
Tel (727) 845-9127 SIC 8062

COUNTY OF PASCO p 380
8731 Citizens Dr 34654
Tel (727) 847-2411 SIC 9111

HYUNDAI OF NEW PORT RICHEY LLC p 724
3936 Us Highway 19 34652
Tel (727) 569-0999 SIC 5511 7549

■ **PALL AEROPOWER CORP** p 1108
10540 Ridge Rd Ste 100 34654
Tel (727) 849-9999 SIC 3569

PASCO SHERIFFS OFFICE p 1119
8700 Citizens Dr 34654
Tel (727) 847-5878 SIC 9221

US WATER SERVICES CORP p 1533
4939 Cross Bayou Blvd 34652
Tel (727) 848-8292 SIC 4941

NEW SMYRNA BEACH, FL

SOUTHEAST VOLUSIA HEALTHCARE CORP p 1346
401 Palmetto St 32168
Tel (386) 424-5000 SIC 8062

NORTH BAY VILLAGE, FL

SUNBEAM TELEVISION CORP p 1401
1401 79th Street Cswy 33141
Tel (305) 751-6692 SIC 4833 6512

NORTH LAUDERDALE, FL

ANSWER GROUP INC p 93
7562 Southgate Blvd 33068
Tel (954) 720-4002 SIC 7371 8748

FAMILY CENTRAL INC p 526
840 N Lauderdale Ave 33068
Tel (954) 720-1000 SIC 8322

NORTH MIAMI BEACH, FL

JACKSON NORTH MEDICAL CENTER p 774
160 Nw 170th St 33169
Tel (305) 651-1100 SIC 8011 8062

METRO PARKING CORP p 955
8300 Nw 7th Ave 33160
Tel (305) 579-5300 SIC 7521 4119

NORTH MIAMI, FL

AMERICAN INVESTMENT GROUP p 75
1549 Ne 123rd St 33161
Tel (561) 714-6157 SIC 6799

KENT SECURITY SERVICES INC p 812
14600 Biscayne Blvd 33181
Tel (305) 919-9400 SIC 7381 7299

NORTH PALM BEACH, FL

DRIFTWOOD HOSPITALITY MANAGEMENT LLC p 456
11770 Us Highway 1 # 202 33408
Tel (561) 833-9979 SIC 7011

JACOBS INVESTMENTS INC p 775
11770 Us Highway 1 # 600 33408
Tel (561) 776-6050 SIC 6211 7011

NORTH VENICE, FL

AJAX PAVING INDUSTRIES OF FLORIDA LLC p 41
1 Ajax Dr 34275
Tel (941) 486-3600 SIC 1611 2951

▲ **PGT INC** p 1140
1070 Technology Dr 34275
Tel (941) 480-1600 SIC 3442 2431 3211

■ **PGT INDUSTRIES INC** p 1140
1070 Technology Dr 34275
Tel (352) 335-5556 SIC 3442 2431 3231

TERVIS TUMBLER CO p 1440
201 Triple Diamond Blvd 34275
Tel (941) 966-2114 SIC 3089

OAKLAND PARK, FL

ORIX USA CORP p 1095
676 W Prospect Rd 33309
Tel (214) 237-2000 SIC 8741

PEARL PAINT CO INC p 1126
1033 E Oakland Park Blvd 33334
Tel (954) 564-5700
SIC 5999 5199 7699 5112 5947 7311

STEEL FABRICATORS LLC p 1384
721 Ne 44th St 33334
Tel (954) 772-0440 SIC 5051

SUNSHINE CLEANING SYSTEMS INC p 1404
3445 Ne 12th Ter 33334
Tel (954) 772-0884 SIC 7349

OCALA, FL

CITY OF OCALA p 317
110 Se Watula Ave 34471
Tel (352) 401-3914 SIC 9111

■ **CLOSETMAID CORP** p 327
650 Sw 27th Ave 34471
Tel (352) 401-6000 SIC 2511

CUSTOM WINDOW SYSTEMS INC p 403
1900 Sw 44th Ave 34474
Tel (352) 368-6922 SIC 3442

CWS HOLDING CO LLC p 404
1900 Sw 44th Ave 34474
Tel (352) 368-6922 SIC 2431 3211

DAVE CARTER & ASSOCIATES INC p 415
3530 Sw 7th St 34474
Tel (352) 732-3317 SIC 5063 5039

DELUCA INC p 427
1719 Sw College Rd 34471
Tel (352) 732-0770 SIC 5511

DJ PROPERTY INVESTMENTS INC p 445
1602 Sw College Rd 34471
Tel (352) 620-2264 SIC 5511

E-ONE INC p 467
1601 Sw 37th Ave 34474
Tel (352) 237-1122 SIC 3711

ESD WASTE2WATER INC p 509
495 Oak Rd 34472
Tel (800) 277-3279 SIC 3589

GOODMAN DISTRIBUTION INC p 624
1426 Ne 8th Ave 34470
Tel (352) 620-2727 SIC 5075

■ **MARION COMMUNITY HOSPITAL INC** p 907
1431 Sw 1st Ave 34471
Tel (352) 401-1000 SIC 8062

MARION COUNTY BOARD OF COUNTY COMMISSIONERS p 907
601 Se 25th Ave 34471
Tel (352) 438-2323 SIC 9111

MARION COUNTY PUBLIC SCHOOLS p 907
512 Se 3rd St 34471
Tel (352) 671-7700 SIC 8211

MARION COUNTY SCHOOL BOARD p 907
512 Se 3rd St 34471
Tel (352) 671-7700 SIC 8211

■ **MARION WEST COMMUNITY HOSPITAL** p 907
4600 Sw 46th Ct 34474
Tel (352) 291-3000 SIC 8062

MONROE REGIONAL HEALTH SYSTEM p 985
131 Sw 15th St 34471
Tel (352) 351-7200 SIC 8011

MUNROE REGIONAL MEDICAL CENTER INC p 1000
1500 Sw 1st Ave 34471
Tel (352) 351-7200 SIC 8062

ON TOP OF WORLD COMMUNITIES INC p 1086
8445 Sw 80th St 34481
Tel (352) 854-3600 SIC 6552 1522

SIGNATURE BRANDS LLC p 1322
808 Sw 12th St 34471
Tel (352) 622-3134 SIC 2064

■ **SPX FLOW TECHNOLOGY USA INC** p 1362
4647 Se 40th Ave 34474
Tel (352) 237-1220 SIC 3569

OCOEE, FL

ORLANDO HEALTH CENTRAL INC p 1095
10000 W Colonial Dr 34761
Tel (407) 296-1820 SIC 8062

■ **SYSCO CENTRAL FLORIDA INC** p 1416
200 W Story Rd 34761
Tel (407) 877-8500 SIC 5149

WAYNE AUTOMATIC FIRE SPRINKLERS INC p 1584
222 Capitol Ct 34761
Tel (407) 656-3030 SIC 1711

WEST ORANGE HEALTHCARE DISTRICT INC p 1595
10000 W Colonial Dr Ofc 34761
Tel (407) 296-1000 SIC 8062

WEST ORANGE MEMORIAL HOSPITAL TAX DISTRICT p 1595
10000 W Colonial Dr Ofc 34761
Tel (407) 656-3555 SIC 8062

OLDSMAR, FL

BEAM ASSOCIATES LLC p 165
301 Commerce Blvd Ste 2 34677
Tel (813) 855-5695 SIC 3585

MI METALS INC p 959
301 Commerce Blvd 34677
Tel (813) 855-5695 SIC 3585

TRINITY SERVICES GROUP INC p 1482
477 Commerce Blvd 34677
Tel (813) 854-4264 SIC 8744

VOLOGY INC p 1564
4027 Tampa Rd Ste 3900 34677
Tel (813) 852-6400 SIC 5065

ORANGE CITY, FL

SOUTHWEST VOLUSIA HEALTHCARE CORP p 1352
1055 Saxon Blvd 32763
Tel (386) 917-5000 SIC 8062

ORANGE PARK, FL

BRIDGESTONE HOSEPOWER LLC p 211
50 Industrial Loop N 32073
Tel (904) 264-1267 SIC 5085 3542

ORANGE PARK MEDICAL CENTER p 1092
2001 Kingsley Ave 32073
Tel (904) 276-8500 SIC 8069

ORLANDO, FL

AA METALS INC p 7
11616 Landstar Blvd 32824
Tel (407) 377-0246 SIC 5051

ABC LIQUORS INC p 10
8989 S Orange Ave 32824
Tel (407) 851-0000 SIC 5921

ACOUSTI ENGINEERING CO OF FLORIDA p 18
4656 Sw 34th St 32811
Tel (407) 425-3467 SIC 1742 5713

ACTION NISSAN INC p 19
12785 S Ornge Blossom Trl 32837
Tel (407) 926-7050 SIC 5511

ADVANTA REALTY LLC p 26
3956 Town Ctr Blvd 329 32837
Tel (407) 697-6604 SIC 6531

ADVENTIST UNIVERSITY OF HEALTH SCIENCES INC p 27
671 Winyah Dr 32803
Tel (407) 303-7742 SIC 8249

AIRCRAFT SERVICE INTERNATIONAL INC p 40
201 S Orange Ave Ste 1100 32801
Tel (407) 648-7373 SIC 4581 5172

■ **AIRTRAN HOLDINGS INC** p 41
9955 Airtran Blvd 32827
Tel (407) 318-5600 SIC 4512

ALE HOUSE MANAGEMENT INC p 48
5750 Major Blvd Ste 400 32819
Tel (407) 547-1120 SIC 8741

ALLIED CONVENTION SERVICE INC p 56
2502 Lake Orange Dr 32837
Tel (407) 851-0261 SIC 7389

ANIXTER POWER SOLUTIONS LLC p 92
501 W Church St Ste 100 32805
Tel (407) 841-4755 SIC 5063

APC WORKFORCE SOLUTIONS LLC p 96
420 S Orange Ave Ste 600 32801
Tel (407) 770-6161 SIC 7363

ARR INVESTMENTS INC p 112
2600 E Jackson St 32803
Tel (407) 894-8401 SIC 8351 8211

ATTORNEYS TITLE INSURANCE FUND INC p 129
6545 Corp Center Blvd # 100 32822
Tel (407) 240-3863 SIC 6361

BAGGAGE AIRLINE GUEST SERVICES INC p 145
6751 Forum Dr Ste 200 32821
Tel (407) 447-5547 SIC 4212

BAR HARBOR LOBSTER CO INC p 154
2000 Premier Row 32809
Tel (407) 851-4001 SIC 5146 5812

BARNIES COFFEE & TEA CO INC p 156
29 S Orange Ave 32801
Tel (407) 854-6600 SIC 5499 5812

BBA US HOLDINGS INC p 163
201 S Orange Ave Ste 1425 32801
Tel (407) 648-7230 SIC 3728 2399 3052

BELV PARTNERS LP p 171
9801 International Dr 32819
Tel (407) 352-4000 SIC 7011

BUCA INC p 222
4700 Millenia Blvd # 400 32839
Tel (407) 903-5500 SIC 5812

CAMPUS CRUSADE FOR CHRIST INC p 246
100 Lake Hart Dr 32832
Tel (407) 826-2000 SIC 8661

CENTRAL FLORIDA EXPRESSWAY AUTHORITY p 278
4974 Orl Tower Rd 32807
Tel (407) 690-5000 SIC 4785

CENTRAL FLORIDA INVESTMENTS INC p 278
5601 Windhover Dr Ofc 32819
Tel (407) 354-3040 SIC 6552 7011 6531

CENTRAL FLORIDA REGIONAL TRANSPORTATION AUTHORITY p 278
455 N Garland Ave 32801
Tel (407) 841-2279 SIC 4111

CENTRAL FLORIDA YOUNG MENS CHRISTIAN ASSOCIATION INC p 278
433 N Mills Ave 32803
Tel (407) 896-9220 SIC 8641

CFI RESORTS MANAGEMENT INC p 285
5601 Windhover Dr 32819
Tel (407) 351-3350 SIC 8741

CHEP RECYCLED PALLET SOLUTIONS LLC p 294
8517 Suthpark Cir Ste 140 32819
Tel (713) 332-6145 SIC 2448 0831

CHRISTENSEN ENTERPRISES INC p 302
333 Thorpe Rd 32824
Tel (407) 830-6401 SIC 5531 7538 7532

CITY BEVERAGES LLC p 312
10928 Florida Crown Dr 32824
Tel (407) 851-7100 SIC 5181

CITY OF ORLANDO p 317
1 City Cmmns 400 S Orange 32801
Tel (407) 246-2121 SIC 9111

CNL FINANCIAL GROUP INC p 330
450 S Orange Ave Ste 300 32801
Tel (407) 650-1000 SIC 6141 6719

CNL HEALTHCARE PROPERTIES INC p 330
450 S Orange Ave 32801
Tel (407) 650-1000 SIC 6798

CNL LIFESTYLE PROPERTIES INC p 330
450 S Orange Ave 32801
Tel (407) 650-1000 SIC 6798

COLEMAN TECHNOLOGIES LLC p 336
5337 Millenia Lakes Blvd 32839
Tel (407) 481-8600 SIC 4813

COMMUNITY COORDINATED CARE FOR CHILDREN INC p 348
3500 W Colonial Dr 32808
Tel (407) 522-2252 SIC 8322

■ **CONNEXTIONS INC** p 358
9395 S John Young Pkwy 32819
Tel (407) 926-2411 SIC 7379 7331

CORPORATE CAPITAL TRUST INC p 372
450 S Orange Ave 32801
Tel (866) 933-1960 SIC 6733

COUNTY OF ORANGE p 380
201 S Rosalind Ave Fl 5 32801
Tel (407) 836-7390 SIC 9111

■ **CURASCRIPT INC** p 401
6272 Lee Vista Blvd 32822
Tel (407) 852-4903 SIC 5122

DANIEL J NEWLIN PA p 411
7335 W Sand Lake Rd # 200 32819
Tel (407) 888-8000 SIC 8111

▲ **DARDEN RESTAURANTS INC** p 412
1000 Darden Center Dr 32837
Tel (407) 245-4000 SIC 5812

■ **DART INDUSTRIES INC** p 413
14901 S Orange Blossom Tr 32837
Tel (407) 826-5050 SIC 3089

■ **DATAMAX-ONEIL CORP** p 414
4501 Pkwy Commerce Blvd 32808
Tel (407) 578-8007 SIC 3577 2754

DIOCESE OF ORLANDO HUMAN CONCERNS FOUNDATION INC p 440
50 E Robinson St 32801
Tel (407) 246-4800 SIC 8661

DISCOVERY MARKETING AND DISTRIBUTING INC p 442
6505 Edgewater Dr 32810
Tel (407) 523-0775 SIC 5999 7389

EAST ORLANDO HEALTH & REHAB CENTER INC p 470
250 S Chickasaw Trl 32825
Tel (407) 380-3466 SIC 8051

ENTEC POLYMERS LLC p 501
1900 Summit Tower Blvd # 900 32810
Tel (407) 875-9595 SIC 5162 1459

FAMILY PHYSICIANS OF WINTER PARK PA p 527
6416 Old Winter Garden Rd 32835
Tel (407) 293-2930 SIC 8011

FLORIDA HOSPITAL MEDICAL CENTER INC p 558
601 E Rollins St 32803
Tel (407) 303-5600 SIC 8062

FLORIDA MUNICIPAL POWER AGENCY p 559
8553 Commodity Cir 32819
Tel (407) 355-7767 SIC 4911

FLORIDA VIRTUAL SCHOOL p 559
5401 S Kirkman Rd Ste 550 32819
Tel (407) 857-6588 SIC 8211

FLORIDAS BLOOD CENTERS INC p 560
8669 Commodity Cir Lbby 32819
Tel (407) 226-3800 SIC 8099

FORD GREENWAY INC p 565
9001 E Colonial Dr 32817
Tel (407) 275-3200 SIC 5511 5012

FRENCH FURNITURE ORLANDO LLC p 578
901 Centr Flori Pkwy Unit 32824
Tel (407) 270-1111 SIC 5712

■ **FRESHPOINT CENTRAL FLORIDA INC** p 579
8801 Exchange Dr 32809
Tel (407) 383-8427 SIC 5148 5431

■ **GMRI INC** p 619
1000 Darden Center Dr 32837
Tel (407) 245-4000 SIC 5812

GOODWILL INDUSTRIES OF CENTRAL FLORIDA INC p 624
7531 S Orange Blossom Trl 32809
Tel (407) 857-0659 SIC 8331 8741

GREATER ORLANDO AVIATION AUTHORITY p 635
1 Jeff Fuqua Blvd 32827
Tel (407) 825-2001 SIC 4581

HARD ROCK CAFE FOUNDATION INC p 660
6100 Old Park Ln Ste 100 32835
Tel (407) 445-7625
SIC 5812 5813 7011 6794

HARD ROCK CAFE INTERNATIONAL (USA) INC p 660
6100 Old Park Ln Ste 100 32835
Tel (407) 445-7625 SIC 5812

HD AMERICAN ROAD LLC p 672
3770 37th St 32805
Tel (407) 423-0346 SIC 5571

■ **HD SUPPLY POWER SOLUTIONS GROUP INC** p 673
501 W Church St Ste 100 32805
Tel (407) 841-4755 SIC 5063

■ **HD SUPPLY WATERWORKS GROUP INC** p 673
501 W Church St Ste 100 32805
Tel (407) 841-4755
SIC 5051 5074 5084 5099

■ **HILTON GRAND VACATIONS CO LLC** p 695
5323 Millenia Lakes Blvd # 400 32839
Tel (407) 722-3100 SIC 6552

■ **HYATT HOTELS OF FLORIDA INC** p 723
9801 International Dr 32819
Tel (407) 284-1234 SIC 7011 5812 5813

ISI DESIGN AND INSTALLATION SOLUTIONS INC p 766
6321 Emperor Dr Ste 201 32809
Tel (407) 872-1865
SIC 7389 1752 1799 1751

ISLAND ONE INC p 766
7345 Greenbriar Pkwy 32819
Tel (407) 859-8900 SIC 1522

JACKSON NURSE PROFESSIONALS LLC p 774
3452 Lake Lynda Dr # 200 32817
Tel (205) 968-7500 SIC 7363

KESSLER ENTERPRISE INC p 813
4901 Vineland Rd Ste 650 32811
Tel (407) 996-9999 SIC 8741 7011

KEYSTONE GROUP HOLDINGS INC p 815
4901 Vineland Rd Ste 350 32811
Tel (813) 225-4650 SIC 7389 7261

KONY INC p 827
7380 W Sand Lake Rd # 390 32819
Tel (407) 730-5669 SIC 7372

■ **KROGER SPECIALTY PHARMACY HOLDINGS I INC** p 830
6435 Hazeltine National 32822
Tel (626) 932-1600 SIC 6719

■ **LOCKHEED MARTIN TRAINING SOLUTIONS** p 873
100 Global Innovation Cir 32825
Tel (407) 306-4000 SIC 3728

LOYAL SOURCE GOVERNMENT SERVICES LLC p 882
12612 Challenger Pkwy # 365 32826
Tel (407) 306-8441 SIC 8062

MARGARITAVILLE ENTERPRISES LLC p 906
6900 Turkey Lake Rd # 200 32819
Tel (407) 224-3213 SIC 5087

■ **MARRIOTT CORP** p 910
4040 Central Florida Pkwy 32837
Tel (407) 206-2300 SIC 7011

■ **MARRIOTT OWNERSHIP RESORTS INC** p 910
6649 W Wood Blvd Ste 500 32821
Tel (863) 688-7700 SIC 7011

■ **MARRIOTT RESORTS HOSPITALITY CORP** p 910
6649 W Wood Blvd Ste 500 32821
Tel (407) 206-6000 SIC 7011

▲ **MARRIOTT VACATIONS WORLDWIDE CORP** p 910
6649 Westwood Blvd 32821
Tel (407) 206-6000 SIC 6531 7011

MASSEY SERVICES INC p 917
315 Groveland St 32804
Tel (407) 645-2500 SIC 7342

MILLERS ALE HOUSE INC p 971
5750 Major Blvd Ste 400 32819
Tel (407) 547-1120 SIC 5812

MORGAN & MORGAN PA p 988
20 N Orange Ave Ste 1607 32801
Tel (407) 420-1414 SIC 8111

■ **MSR HOTELS & RESORTS INC** p 997
450 S Orange Ave 32801
Tel (407) 650-1000 SIC 7011

NATIONAL AIR CARGO HOLDINGS INC p 1009
5955 T G Lee Blvd Ste 200 32822
Tel (716) 631-0011 SIC 4731

▲ **NATIONAL RETAIL PROPERTIES INC** p 1015
450 S Orange Ave Ste 900 32801
Tel (407) 265-7348 SIC 6798

NATIONS ROOF OF FLORIDA LLC p 1017
1313 E Landstreet Rd 32824
Tel (407) 649-1333 SIC 1761

NAUTIQUE BOAT CO INC p 1019
14700 Aerospace Pkwy 32832
Tel (407) 855-4141 SIC 3799 3732

NEMOURS CHILDRENS HOSPITAL p 1025
13535 Nemours Pkwy 32827
Tel (407) 567-4000 SIC 8069

NEPHRON PHARMACEUTICALS CORP p 1026
4121 Sw 34th St 32811
Tel (407) 246-1389 SIC 2834

ODC CONSTRUCTION LLC p 1074
5701 Carder Rd 32810
Tel (407) 447-5999 SIC 1521

ONEBLOOD FOUNDATION INC p 1087
8669 Commodity Cir 32819
Tel (407) 248-5480 SIC 8099

ONEBLOOD INC p 1087
8669 Commodity Cir 32819
Tel (407) 455-7551 SIC 8099

ORANGE COUNTY GOVERNMENT p 1092
21 S Roseland Ave 32801
Tel (407) 836-7370 SIC 9199

ORANGE COUNTY PUBLIC SCHOOLS p 1092
445 W Amelia St 32801
Tel (407) 317-3200 SIC 8211

ORLANDO HEALTH INC p 1095
52 W Underwood St 32806
Tel (321) 843-7000 SIC 8062 8741 8069

ORLANDO UTILITIES COMMISSION p 1095
100 W Anderson St 32801
Tel (407) 246-2121
SIC 4941 4931 4939 4911

PARKWAY PROPERTIES INC p 1117
390 N Orange Ave Ste 2400 32801
Tel (407) 650-0593 SIC 6798

PINELOCH FAMILY CARE p 1149
2898 S Osceola Ave 32806
Tel (407) 812-8110 SIC 8011

PLANET HOLLYWOOD INTERNATIONAL INC p 1154
4700 Millenia Blvd # 400 32839
Tel (407) 903-5500 SIC 5812 6794 5699

PRESBYTERIAN RETIREMENT COMMUNITIES INC p 1171
80 W Lucerne Cir 32801
Tel (407) 839-5050 SIC 8361 8052 8051

QUALITY ONE WIRELESS LLC p 1197
1500 Tradeport Dr Ste B 32824
Tel (407) 857-3737 SIC 5065

■ **RARE HOSPITALITY INTERNATIONAL INC** p 1209
7469 Brokerage Dr 32809
Tel (407) 245-5042 SIC 5812

RAVAGO AMERICAS LLC p 1209
1900 Summit Tower Blvd 32810
Tel (407) 875-9595 SIC 5162

RAVAGO HOLDINGS AMERICA INC p 1209
1900 Summit Tower Blvd 32810
Tel (407) 875-9595 SIC 5162

RED LOBSTER HOSPITALITY LLC p 1215
450 S Orange Ave Ste 800 32801
Tel (407) 734-9000 SIC 5812

RED LOBSTER MANAGEMENT LLC p 1215
450 S Orange Ave Ste 800 32801
Tel (407) 734-9000 SIC 5812

REGAL MARINE INDUSTRIES INC p 1218
2300 Jetport Dr 32809
Tel (407) 851-4360 SIC 3732

RESOURCE EMPLOYMENT SOLUTIONS LLC p 1227
5900 Lake Ellenor Dr # 100 32809
Tel (866) 412-6535 SIC 7361 7363

ROMACORP INC p 1248
11315 Corp Blvd Ste 100 32817
Tel (214) 343-7800 SIC 5812

ROSEN 9939 INC p 1251
9840 International Dr 32819
Tel (407) 996-9939
SIC 7011 5812 5813 7992 7389

ROSEN HOTELS AND RESORTS INC p 1251
9840 International Dr 32819
Tel (407) 996-1706
SIC 7011 5812 5813 7389 8011 7992

ROTECH HEALTHCARE INC p 1252
3600 Vineland Rd Ste 114 32811
Tel (407) 822-4600 SIC 7352

SCHOOL BOARD OF ORANGE COUNTY FLORIDA p 1289
445 W Amelia St Lbby 32801
Tel (407) 317-3200 SIC 8211

SCOTT + CORMIA ARCHITECTURE AND INTERIORS LLC p 1293
429 S Keller Rd Ste 200 32810
Tel (407) 660-2766 SIC 8712

■ **SEA WORLD LLC** p 1295
9205 Southpark Ctr Loop 32819
Tel (407) 226-5011 SIC 7996

■ **SEA WORLD OF FLORIDA LLC** p 1295
9205 Southpark Ctr Loop 32819
Tel (407) 226-5011 SIC 7996

▲ **SEAWORLD ENTERTAINMENT INC** p 1298
9205 Southpark Center Loo 32819
Tel (407) 226-5011 SIC 7996

■ **SEAWORLD PARKS & ENTERTAINMENT INC** p 1298
9205 Southpark Center Loo 32819
Tel (407) 226-5011 SIC 7996

SECOND HARVEST FOOD BANK OF CENTRAL FLORIDA INC p 1298
411 Mercy Dr 32805
Tel (407) 295-1066 SIC 8699

■ **SENTINEL COMMUNICATIONS NEWS VENTURES INC** p 1305
633 N Orange Ave 32801
Tel (407) 420-5000 SIC 2711

SENTIO HEALTHCARE PROPERTIES INC p 1305
189 S Orange Ave Ste 1700 32801
Tel (407) 999-7679 SIC 6798

SIEMENS ENERGY INC p 1320
4400 N Alafaya Trl 32826
Tel (407) 736-5183 SIC 3511

SIGNATURE FLIGHT SUPPORT CORP p 1322
201 S Orange Ave Ste 1100 32801
Tel (407) 648-7200 SIC 5541

■ **STARWOOD VACATION SERVICES INC** p 1379
8801 Vistana Centre Dr 32821
Tel (407) 903-4640 SIC 7041

■ **SUNTRUST BANKS OF FLORIDA INC** p 1401
200 S Orange Ave 32801
Tel (407) 237-4141 SIC 6021 6022

■ **SVO MANAGEMENT INC** p 1410
9002 San Marco Ct 32819
Tel (407) 239-3100 SIC 6531

TAYLOR FARMS FLORIDA INC p 1427
7492 Chancellor Dr 32809
Tel (407) 515-8436 SIC 3523

■ **TEKTRONIX SERVICE SOLUTIONS INC** p 1433
6120 Hanging Moss Rd 32807
Tel (407) 678-6900
SIC 3812 3674 8734 7699

TEMPUS RESORTS INTERNATIONAL LTD p 1436
7345 Greenbriar Pkwy 32819
Tel (407) 363-1717 SIC 7011 6531

TRIAD ISOTOPES INC p 1478
4205 Vineland Rd Ste L1 32811
Tel (407) 872-8455 SIC 5912

▲ **TUPPERWARE BRANDS CORP** p 1492
14901 S Orange Blossom Tr 32837
Tel (407) 826-5050 SIC 3089 2844

■ **TUPPERWARE US INC** p 1492
14901 S Ornge Blossom Trl 32837
Tel (407) 826-5050 SIC 3089

■ **UCF HOTEL VENTURE** p 1499
6800 Lakewood Plaza Dr 32819
Tel (407) 503-9000 SIC 7011 5813 5812

■ **UNIVERSAL CITY DEVELOPMENT PARTNERS LTD** p 1516
1000 Unversal Studios Plz 32819
Tel (407) 363-8000 SIC 7996

UNIVERSAL CITY FLORIDA PARTNERS p 1516
1000 Unversal Studios Plz 32819
Tel (407) 363-8000 SIC 7996 7819

■ **UNIVERSAL CITY TRAVEL PARTNERS** p 1516
1000 Unversal Studios Plz 32819
Tel (407) 363-8000 SIC 7996

■ **UNIVERSAL ORLANDO ONLINE MERCHANDISE STORE** p 1517
1000 Unversal Studios Plz 32819
Tel (407) 363-8000 SIC 7996

UNIVERSITY OF CENTRAL FLORIDA BOARD OF TRUSTEES p 1520
4000 Central Florida Blvd 32816
Tel (407) 823-2000 SIC 8221

UNR HOLDINGS INC p 1528
301 E Pine St 32801
Tel (407) 210-6541 SIC 6719

VALENCIA COLLEGE p 1539
1800 S Kirkman Rd 32811
Tel (407) 299-5000 SIC 8222

VERMEER SOUTHEAST SALES & SERVICE INC p 1551
4559 Old Winter Garden Rd 32811
Tel (407) 295-2020 SIC 5082

▲ **VOXX INTERNATIONAL CORP** p 1566
2351 J Lawson Blvd 32824
Tel (800) 645-7750 SIC 3711 3651 3663

WESTGATE RESORTS LTD p 1601
5601 Windhover Dr 32819
Tel (407) 351-3350 SIC 7389

WYCLIFFE BIBLE TRANSLATORS INC p 1629
11221 John Wycliffe Blvd 32832
Tel (407) 852-3600 SIC 8661

■ **WYNDHAM VACATION RESORTS INC** p 1630
6277 Sea Harbor Dr # 400 32821
Tel (407) 370-5200 SIC 6531 6141

▲ **XENIA HOTELS & RESORTS INC** p 1631
200 S Orange Ave Ste 2700 32801
Tel (407) 317-6950 SIC 6798

ZEROCHAOS LLC p 1642
420 S Orange Ave Ste 600 32801
Tel (407) 770-6161 SIC 8721

ORMOND BEACH, FL

FLORIDA PRODUCTION ENGINEERING INC p 559
2 E Tower Cir 32174
Tel (386) 677-2566 SIC 3465 3089

STONEWOOD HOLDINGS LLC p 1391
780 W Granada Blvd # 100 32174
Tel (386) 760-2282 SIC 5812

WORLD COLOR INC p 1625
10 Sunshine Blvd 32174
Tel (386) 672-8388 SIC 2759

OVIEDO, FL

A DUDA & SONS INC p 5
1200 Duda Trl 32765
Tel (407) 365-2111
SIC 0161 5148 2033 0133 6552 0174

DUDA FARM FRESH FOODS INC p 459
1200 Duda Trl 32765
Tel (407) 365-2111 SIC 5148 0161 0174

PALATKA, FL

COUNTY OF PUTNAM p 381
2509 Crill Ave Ste 900 32177
Tel (386) 329-0205 SIC 9111

SCHOOL DISTRICT OF PUTNAM COUNTY FLORIDA p 1290
200 Reid St Ste 1 32177
Tel (386) 329-0653 SIC 8211

PALM BAY, FL

PALM BAY HOSPITAL INC p 1109
1425 Malabar Rd Ne 32907
Tel (321) 434-8000 SIC 8062

PALM BEACH GARDENS, FL

■ **AMERIPATH HOLDINGS INC** p 83
7111 Fairway Dr Ste 101 33418
Tel (561) 845-1850 SIC 8071

■ **AMERIPATH INC** p 83
7111 Fairway Dr Ste 101 33418
Tel (561) 712-6200 SIC 8071

AUDIOLOGY DISTRIBUTION LLC p 131
10455 Riverside Dr 33410
Tel (561) 478-8770 SIC 5999

AURORA DIAGNOSTICS HOLDINGS LLC p 132
11025 Rca Center Dr # 300 33410
Tel (561) 626-5512 SIC 8071

■ **BIOMET 3I LLC** p 184
4555 Riverside Dr 33410
Tel (561) 775-9928 SIC 3843

CENTERRA GROUP LLC p 276
7121 Fairway Dr Ste 301 33418
Tel (561) 472-0600 SIC 7381 8744

■ **CHROMALLOY GAS TURBINE LLC** p 304
3999 Rca Blvd 33410
Tel (561) 935-3571
SIC 3724 7699 4581 3764 3769 3533

CON EL OF DIOCESE OF PALM BEACH INC p 354
9995 N Military Trl 33410
Tel (561) 775-9500 SIC 8661

CROSS MATCH TECHNOLOGIES INC p 393
3950 Rca Blvd Ste 5001 33410
Tel (561) 622-1650 SIC 3999

■ **DIVOSTA HOMES LP** p 444
4500 Pga Blvd Ste 400 33418
Tel (561) 691-9050 SIC 6552

DUFFYS HOLDINGS INC p 459
4440 Pga Blvd Ste 201 33410
Tel (561) 804-7676 SIC 5812

▲ **DYCOM INDUSTRIES INC** p 464
11780 Us Highway 1 # 600 33408
Tel (561) 627-7171 SIC 1623 1731

■ **DYCOM INVESTMENTS INC** p 464
11770 Us Highway 1 # 101 33408
Tel (561) 627-7171 SIC 1623

KSF ACQUISITION CORP p 831
11780 Us Highway 1 400n 33408
Tel (561) 231-6548 SIC 5122

KSF INTERMEDIATE CORP p 831
11780 Us Highway 1 400n 33408
Tel (866) 726-2272 SIC 6733

LGL RECYCLING LLC p 860
2401 Pga Blvd 33410
Tel (561) 582-6688 SIC 4953

MIDAS INC p 964
4300 Tbc Way 33410
Tel (630) 438-3000 SIC 7533 6794

NATIONAL DENTEX CORP p 1011
11601 Kew Gardens Ave 33410
Tel (877) 942-5871 SIC 8072

PROFESSIONAL GOLFERS ASSOCIATION OF AMERICA INC p 1180
100 Avenue Of Champions 33418
Tel (561) 624-8400 SIC 7941 5961

R H G ACQUISITION CORP p 1202
4440 Pga Blvd Ste 201 33410
Tel (561) 804-7676 SIC 5812

■ **SEQUA CORP** p 1306
3999 Rca Blvd 33410
Tel (201) 343-1122
SIC 3724 3764 3812 3699 3845 3542

TBC CORP p 1427
4300 Tbc Way 33410
Tel (561) 227-0955 SIC 5014

TBC RETAIL GROUP INC p 1427
4280 Prof Ctr Dr Ste 400 33410
Tel (561) 383-3000 SIC 7538 5531 7534

WESTPORT SENIOR LIVING INVESTMENT FUND LP p 1602
11360 N Jog Rd Ste 102 33418
Tel (561) 624-1225 SIC 9532

PALM BEACH, FL

FLAGLER SYSTEM INC p 554
1 S County Rd 33480
Tel (561) 655-6611 SIC 7041 7997

ITALIAN RESTAURANT p 767
1 S County Rd 33480
Tel (561) 655-6611 SIC 5812

OSCEOLA FARMS CO p 1096
340 Royal Poinciana Way # 315 33480
Tel (561) 655-6303 SIC 2099

PALM BEACH CAPITAL FUND II LP p 1109
180 Royal Palm Way 33480
Tel (561) 659-9022 SIC 6799 2621

PALM CITY, FL

ARMELLINI INDUSTRIES INC p 111
3446 Sw Armellini Ave 34990
Tel (772) 287-0575 SIC 4213 5193 4731

IVOX SOLUTIONS LLC p 769
4485 Sw Port Way 34990
Tel (772) 286-8183 SIC 5065 4812

PALM COAST, FL

FRIENDS OF LIBRARY FLAGLER COUNTY INC p 580
2500 Palm Coast Pkwy Nw 32137
Tel (386) 445-1389 SIC 8231

MEMORIAL HOSPITAL FLAGLER INC p 942
60 Memorial Medical Pkwy 32164
Tel (386) 586-2000 SIC 8062

PALM HARBOR, FL

IF MUSIC INC p 730
401 Orange St 34683
Tel (727) 515-3004 SIC 2741

NATIONWIDE TITLE CLEARING INC p 1018
2100 Alt 19 34683
Tel (727) 771-4000 SIC 6162 6541

PALM SPRINGS, FL

STANTON OPTICAL FLORIDA LLC p 1377
3801 S Congress Ave 33461
Tel (561) 275-2020 SIC 5995

PALMETTO BAY, FL

BUPA INSURANCE CO p 226
17901 Old Cutler Rd 33157
Tel (305) 275-1400 SIC 6321

PALMETTO, FL

FELD ENTERTAINMENT INC p 537
800 Feld Way 34221
Tel (941) 721-1200 SIC 7999 7929 5945

MCCLURE PROPERTIES LTD p 927
502 6th Ave W 34221
Tel (941) 722-4545 SIC 0161

PACIFIC TOMATO GROWERS LTD p 1106
503 10th St W 34221
Tel (941) 729-8410 SIC 0161 0174 0723

■ **SYSCO WEST COAST FLORIDA INC** p 1418
3000 69th St E 34221
Tel (941) 721-1450 SIC 5149 5141

PANAMA CITY BEACH, FL

EAGLE CONSTRUCTION & ENVIRONMENTAL SERVICES LLC p 468
600 Grand Panama Blvd 32407
Tel (254) 442-1553 SIC 8744

PROGRESSIVE ENVIRONMENTAL SERVICES INC p 1181
1619 Moylan Rd 32407
Tel (850) 234-8428 SIC 4959

SWS ENVIRONMENTAL SERVICES p 1413
1619 Moylan Rd 32407
Tel (850) 234-8428 SIC 1794

PANAMA CITY, FL

BAY COUNTY HEALTH SYSTEM LLC p 160
615 N Bonita Ave 32401
Tel (850) 769-1511 SIC 8011

BAY DISTRICT SCHOOL BOARD p 160
1311 Balboa Ave 32401
Tel (850) 767-4100 SIC 8211

BAY DISTRICT SCHOOLS p 161
1311 Balboa Ave 32401
Tel (850) 767-4101 SIC 8211

BAY MEDICAL CENTER p 161
615 N Bonita Ave 32401
Tel (850) 769-1511 SIC 8062 8011

EASTERN SHIPBUILDING GROUP INC p 472
2200 Nelson Ave 32401
Tel (850) 763-1900 SIC 3731

EDGEWATER BEACH RESORT LLC p 477
11212 Front Beach Rd 32407
Tel (850) 235-4044
SIC 1531 7011 5813 5812

FOLKS RESTAURANTS LTD p 563
508 Harmon Ave 32401
Tel (850) 763-0501 SIC 5812

GAC CONTRACTORS INC p 588
4116 N Highway 231 32404
Tel (850) 785-4675 SIC 1611 1629

JENSEN USA INC p 783
99 Aberdeen Loop 32405
Tel (850) 271-8464 SIC 5087

PEOPLES FIRST PROPERTIES INC p 1132
1002 W 23rd St Ste 400 32405
Tel (850) 769-8981 SIC 1522 6552

RESORT HOSPITALITY ENTERPRISES LTD p 1227
1002 W 23rd St Ste 400 32405
Tel (321) 953-7272 SIC 8741

PEMBROKE PINES, FL

■ **AN MOTORS OF PEMBROKE LLC** p 88
8600 Pines Blvd 33024
Tel (954) 433-3377 SIC 5511

CITY OF PEMBROKE PINES p 317
10100 Pines Blvd Fl 5 33026
Tel (954) 431-4330 SIC 9111

CLAIRES BOUTIQUES INC p 321
11401 Pines Blvd 33026
Tel (954) 438-0433
SIC 5632 5699 5999 5943 5947

CLAIRES STORES INC p 321
3 Sw 129th Ave 33027
Tel (954) 433-3900 SIC 5632

■ **ELIZABETH ARDEN INC** p 487
880 Sw 145th Ave Ste 200 33027
Tel (954) 364-6900 SIC 2844

PENSACOLA, FL

BAPTIST HEALTH CARE CORP p 153
1000 W Moreno St 32501
Tel (850) 434-4080 SIC 8741

BAPTIST HOSPITAL INC p 154
1000 W Moreno St 32501
Tel (850) 434-4011 SIC 8062

BAYBEACH HOTELS LLC p 161
51 Gulf Breeze Pkwy 32507
Tel (850) 932-2214 SIC 7011

COUNTY OF ESCAMBIA p 378
221 Palafox Pl Ste 200 32502
Tel (850) 595-3000 SIC 9111

ELIZABETHTOWN WATER CO INC p 487
7303 Plantation Rd 32504
Tel (251) 656-9857 SIC 4941

EMERALD COAST UTILITIES AUTHORITY p 491
9255 Sturdevant St 32514
Tel (850) 476-5110 SIC 4959 4952 4941

ESCAMBIA COUNTY SCHOOL BOARD p 509
75 N Pace Blvd 32505
Tel (850) 432-6121 SIC 8211

ESCAMBIA COUNTY SCHOOL DISTRICT p 509
75 N Pace Blvd 32505
Tel (850) 432-6121 SIC 8211

GULF COAST HEALTH CARE LLC p 646
40 Palafox Pl Ste 400 32502
Tel (800) 881-9907 SIC 8051

■ **GULF POWER CO** p 646
1 Energy Pl 32520
Tel (850) 444-6111 SIC 4911

LAKEVIEW CENTER INC p 840
1221 W Lakeview Ave 32501
Tel (850) 432-1222
SIC 8069 8093 7389 7371 7373

MASTER-TEC FLOORS INC p 918
3109 N T St 32505
Tel (850) 454-0008 SIC 1752 5713

OFFSHORE INLAND MARINE & OILFIELD SERVICES INC p 1076
700 S Barracks St 32502
Tel (251) 443-5550 SIC 1389

PENSACOLA CHRISTIAN COLLEGE INC p 1131
250 Brent Ln 32503
Tel (850) 478-8496 SIC 8221

SACRED HEART HEALTH SYSTEM INC p 1265
5151 N 9th Ave 32504
Tel (850) 416-1600 SIC 8062 8011

SANDERS BROTHERS ELECTRIC INC p 1278
8195 Kipling St 32514
Tel (850) 857-0701 SIC 1731

SOUTHERN ENVIRONMENTAL INC p 1348
6690 W Nine Mile Rd 32526
Tel (850) 944-4475 SIC 3822

UNIVERSITY OF WEST FLORIDA p 1526
11000 University Pkwy # 10 32514
Tel (850) 474-2000 SIC 8221

W P C S FM p 1569
250 Brent Ln 32503
Tel (850) 478-8496 SIC 4832

WENDCO CORP p 1591
220 W Garden St Ste 500 32502
Tel (850) 433-5425 SIC 5812

WEST FLORIDA HOSPITAL p 1594
8383 N Davis Hwy 32514
Tel (850) 494-4000 SIC 8062

■ **WEST FLORIDA REGIONAL MEDICAL CENTER INC** p 1594
8383 N Davis Hwy 32514
Tel (850) 494-4000
SIC 8062 8093 8063 8051

PERRY, FL

BUCKEYE FLORIDA LIMITED PARTNERSHIP p 223
1 Buckeye Dr 32348
Tel (850) 584-1121 SIC 2611

FOLEY CELLULOSE LLC p 563
3510 Contractors Rd 32348
Tel (850) 584-1121 SIC 2611

WARE OIL & SUPPLY CO INC p 1575
2715 S Byron Butler Pkwy 32348
Tel (850) 838-1852 SIC 5172 5087 5411

PINELLAS PARK, FL

A & M SUPPLY CORP p 4
6701 90th Ave N 33782
Tel (727) 541-6631 SIC 5031

KANE FURNITURE CORP p 802
5700 70th Ave N 33781
Tel (727) 545-9555 SIC 5712

TRANSITIONS OPTICAL INC p 1472
9251 Belcher Rd N 33782
Tel (727) 545-0400 SIC 3229 3851

PLANT CITY, FL

AG-MART PRODUCE INC p 34
4006 Airport Rd 33563
Tel (877) 606-5003 SIC 0171

CAR WASH PARTNERS INC p 252
1503 S Collins St 33563
Tel (813) 754-0777 SIC 7542 7549

LINDER INDUSTRIAL MACHINERY CO p 868
1601 S Frontage Rd # 100 33563
Tel (813) 754-2727 SIC 5082 7353

LINDER INDUSTRIAL MACHINERY CO p 868
1601 S Frontage Rd # 100 33563
Tel (813) 754-2727 SIC 5082

MARIO CAMACHO FOODS LLC p 907
2502 Walden Woods Dr 33566
Tel (813) 305-4534 SIC 5148

SOUTH FLORIDA BAPTIST HOSPITAL INC p 1344
301 N Alexander St 33563
Tel (813) 757-1200 SIC 8062

SUNSHINE STATE DAIRY FARMS LLC p 1404
3304 Sydney Rd 33566
Tel (813) 754-1847 SIC 5143 2048

■ **SYSCO INTERNATIONAL FOOD GROUP INC** p 1417
2401 Police Center Dr 33566
Tel (813) 707-6161 SIC 5144 5149

WISHNATZKI INC p 1619
100 Stearns St 33563
Tel (813) 752-5111 SIC 5148

PLANTATION, FL

C3/CUSTOMERCONTACTCHANNELS INC p 234
1200 S Pine Island Rd # 200 33324
Tel (954) 849-0622 SIC 7389

CASTLE MANAGEMENT INC p 264
12270 Sw 3rd St Ste 200 33325
Tel (800) 337-5850 SIC 6512

CHETU INC p 295
10167 W Sunrise Blvd # 200 33322
Tel (954) 342-5676 SIC 7379

■ **CIGNA DENTAL HEALTH INC** p 306
300 Nw 82nd Ave Ste 700 33324
Tel (954) 514-6600 SIC 6324

■ **COLUMBIA HOSPITAL CORP OF SOUTH BROWARD** p 341
8201 W Broward Blvd 33324
Tel (954) 473-6600 SIC 8062

DHL EXPRESS (USA) INC p 435
1210 S Pine Island Rd 33324
Tel (954) 888-7000 SIC 4513 7389 4731

DPWN HOLDINGS (USA) INC p 454
1210 S Pine Island Rd 33324
Tel (954) 888-7000 SIC 4513 4731

IBS PARTNERS LTD p 726
1 N University Dr Ut400a 33324
Tel (954) 581-0922 SIC 2086

KERZNER INTERNATIONAL NORTH AMERICA INC p 813
1000 S Pine Island Rd 33324
Tel (954) 809-2000 SIC 7011

LS ENERGIA INC p 882
1200 S Pine Island Rd # 420 33324
Tel (954) 628-3059 SIC 1731

▲ **NATIONAL BEVERAGE CORP** p 1010
8100 Sw 10th St Ste 4000 33324
Tel (954) 581-0922 SIC 2086

■ **NEWBEVCO INC** p 1037
1 N University Dr 33324
Tel (954) 581-0922 SIC 2086

■ **PLANTATION GENERAL HOSPITAL LP** p 1154
401 Nw 42nd Ave 33317
Tel (954) 587-5010 SIC 8062

PRC LLC p 1168
8151 Peters Rd Ste 4000 33324
Tel (954) 693-3700 SIC 8741

SOLSTICE BENEFITS INC p 1339
7901 Sw 6th Ct Ste 400 33324
Tel (954) 370-1700 SIC 6324

SOUTH AFRICAN AIRWAYS SOC LIMITED INC p 1342
1200 S Pine Isl Rd 650 33324
Tel (800) 722-9675 SIC 4512

STAR GLOBE NETWORK ENTERPRISES INC p 1378
1331 Nw 80th Ter 33322
Tel (561) 771-2053 SIC 7389

TRADESTATION GROUP INC p 1469
8050 Sw 10th St Ste 4000 33324
Tel (954) 652-7000 SIC 6211

■ **WHOLE FOODS MARKET GROUP INC** p 1607
7720 Peters Rd 33324
Tel (954) 236-0600 SIC 5411

POMPANO BEACH, FL

ASSOCIATED GROCERS OF FLORIDA INC p 120
1141 Sw 12th Ave 33069
Tel (954) 876-3000 SIC 8699

AYCO FARMS INC p 140
1501 Nw 12th Ave 33069
Tel (954) 788-6800 SIC 5148 0161

B C S S LTD p 141
1801 W Atlantic Blvd 33069
Tel (954) 971-3000 SIC 5511

BAERS FURNITURE CO INC p 144
1589 Nw 12th Ave 33069
Tel (954) 946-8001 SIC 5712

BENNETT AUTO SUPPLY INC p 173
3141 Sw 10th St 33069
Tel (954) 335-8700 SIC 5531 5013 3711

CROSS INTERNATIONAL INC p 393
600 Sw 3rd St Ste 2201 33060
Tel (954) 657-9000 SIC 8322

CURRENT BUILDERS CONSTRUCTION SERVICES INC p 402
2251 Blount Rd 33069
Tel (954) 977-4211 SIC 1522 1542

EDWIN B STIMPSON CO INC p 480
1515 Sw 13th Ct 33069
Tel (954) 946-3500 SIC 3452 3469

FLEXSOL HOLDING CORP p 556
1531 Nw 12th Ave 33069
Tel (954) 941-6333 SIC 2673 3082 3081

FLEXSOL PACKAGING CORP OF POMPANO BEACH p 556
1531 Nw 12th Ave 33069
Tel (800) 325-7740 SIC 3089

■ **FRESHPOINT SOUTH FLORIDA INC** p 579
2300 Nw 19th St 33069
Tel (954) 917-7272 SIC 5148 5143

HOERBIGER COMPRESSION TECHNOLOGY AMERICA HOLDING INC p 699
3350 Gateway Dr 33069
Tel (954) 974-5700 SIC 3494 7699

HOERBIGER CORP OF AMERICA INC p 699
3350 Gateway Dr 33069
Tel (954) 974-5700 SIC 3491

HUTCHINGS AUTOMOTIVE PRODUCTS INC p 721
2041 Nw 15th Ave 33069
Tel (954) 958-9866 SIC 3465

INTERACTIVE RESPONSE TECHNOLOGIES INC p 751
895 Sw 30th Ave Ste 201 33069
Tel (954) 484-4973 SIC 7389

IUPAT DISTRICT COUNCIL 78 p 769
1300 Sw 12th Ave 33069
Tel (954) 946-9311 SIC 8631

■ **LAND N SEA DISTRIBUTING INC** p 842
3131 N Andrews Avenue Ext 33064
Tel (954) 792-9971
SIC 5088 5091 5046 5531

▲ **PETMED EXPRESS INC** p 1139
1441 Sw 29th Ave 33069
Tel (954) 979-5995 SIC 5999 5122

POINT BLANK ENTERPRISES INC p 1159
2102 Sw 2nd St 33069
Tel (954) 630-0900
SIC 3842 3462 3728 8711

POINT BLANK SOLUTIONS INC p 1159
2101 Sw 2nd St 33069
Tel (800) 413-5155 SIC 3842

PRIDE AIR CONDITIONING & APPLIANCE INC p 1174
2150 Nw 18th St 33069
Tel (954) 977-7433 SIC 6399 7623

▲ **STONEGATE BANK** p 1391
400 N Federal Hwy 33062
Tel (954) 315-5500 SIC 6022

STUART BUILDING PRODUCTS LLC p 1394
1341 Nw 15th St 33069
Tel (954) 971-7264 SIC 5032

SUN COMMODITIES INC p 1400
2230 Sw 2nd St 33069
Tel (954) 972-8383 *SIC* 5148

PONTE VEDRA BEACH, FL

ATP TOUR INC p 128
201 Atp Tour Blvd 32082
Tel (904) 285-9886 *SIC* 8621

PGA TOUR HOLDINGS INC p 1140
112 Pga Tour Blvd 32082
Tel (904) 285-3700 *SIC* 7992 7997

PGA TOUR INC p 1140
112 Pga Tour Blvd 32082
Tel (904) 285-3700 *SIC* 7997

PONTE VEDRA, FL

■ ADVANCED DISPOSAL SERVICES INC p 25
90 Fort Wade Rd Ste 200 32081
Tel (904) 737-7900 *SIC* 4953

■ ADVANCED DISPOSAL SERVICES MIDWEST LLC p 25
90 Fort Wade Rd Ste 200 32081
Tel (904) 737-7900 *SIC* 4953

■ ADVANCED DISPOSAL SERVICES SOLID WASTE MIDWEST LLC p 25
90 Fort Wade Rd Ste 200 32081
Tel (904) 737-7900 *SIC* 7699 4953 4959

■ ADVANCED DISPOSAL SERVICES SOLID WASTE SOUTHEAST INC p 25
90 Fort Wade Rd Ste 200 32081
Tel (904) 737-7900 *SIC* 4953

■ ADVANCED DISPOSAL SERVICES SOUTH LLC p 25
90 Fort Wade Rd Ste 200 32081
Tel (904) 737-7900 *SIC* 4953 6719

▲ ADVANCED DISPOSAL WASTE HOLDINGS CORP p 25
90 Fort Wade Rd Ste 200 32081
Tel (904) 737-7900 *SIC* 4953

■ MWSTAR WASTE HOLDINGS CORP p 1004
90 Fort Wade Rd Ste 200 32081
Tel (904) 737-7900 *SIC* 1629 4953

PORT CHARLOTTE, FL

CHARLOTTE COUNTY PUBLIC SCHOOLS p 290
1445 Education Way 33948
Tel (941) 255-0808 *SIC* 8211

COUNTY OF CHARLOTTE p 377
18500 Murdock Cir Ste 423 33948
Tel (941) 637-2199 *SIC* 9111

■ FAWCETT MEMORIAL HOSPITAL INC p 532
21298 Olean Blvd 33952
Tel (941) 629-1181 *SIC* 8062

■ PEACE RIVER REGIONAL MEDICAL CENTER p 1125
2500 Harvard Blvd 33952
Tel (941) 766-4122 *SIC* 8062

SCHOOL BOARD OF CHARLOTTE COUNTY FLORIDA p 1289
1445 Education Way 33948
Tel (941) 255-0808 *SIC* 8211

ST JOSEPH PREFERRED HEALTHCARE INC p 1368
2500 Harbor Blvd 33952
Tel (941) 625-4122 *SIC* 8741

PORT ORANGE, FL

HALIFAX HOME HEALTH p 654
3800 Woodbriar Trl 32129
Tel (386) 322-4700 *SIC* 8082 7361

■ POWER CORP OF AMERICA p 1165
4647 Clyde Morris Blvd 32129
Tel (386) 333-6441 *SIC* 1731 1623

PORT SAINT LUCIE, FL

ATLS MEDICAL SUPPLY INC p 128
8881 Liberty Ln 34952
Tel (772) 398-5842 *SIC* 5961

■ LIBERTY HEALTHCARE GROUP INC p 861
8881 Liberty Ln 34952
Tel (772) 398-7257 *SIC* 5961

■ QVC SAINT LUCIE INC p 1201
300 Nw Peacock Blvd 34986
Tel (772) 873-4300 *SIC* 5963

QUINCY, FL

GADSDEN COUNTY SCHOOLS p 588
35 Martin Luther King 32351
Tel (850) 627-9651 *SIC* 8211

TALQUIN ELECTRIC COOPERATIVE INC p 1423
1640 W Jefferson St 32351
Tel (850) 627-7651 *SIC* 4931

RIVERVIEW, FL

■ PROGRESSIVE BAYSIDE INSURANCE CO p 1181
4030 Crescent Park Dr B 33578
Tel (813) 487-1000 *SIC* 6331

■ PROGRESSIVE SOUTHEASTERN INSURANCE CO INC p 1182
4030 Crescent Park Dr B 33578
Tel (813) 487-1000 *SIC* 6331

TAMPA ARMATURE WORKS INC p 1423
6312 S 78th St 33578
Tel (813) 621-5661 *SIC* 5063 3613 3621

RIVIERA BEACH, FL

■ BIRDSALL INC p 185
5 E 11th St 33404
Tel (561) 881-3900 *SIC* 4412

CHENEY BROS INC p 294
1 Cheney Way 33404
Tel (561) 845-4700
SIC 5141 5087 5113 5169 5149

■ PEPSI COLA BOTTLING FORT LAUNDERDALE p 1134
7305 Garden Rd 33404
Tel (561) 848-1000 *SIC* 2086

■ SYSCO SOUTHEAST FLORIDA LLC p 1418
1999 Dr M Lthr Kng Jr Bld Martin 33404
Tel (561) 842-1999 *SIC* 5149

TROPICAL SHIPPING USA LLC p 1484
501 Avenue P 33404
Tel (561) 863-5737 *SIC* 4412 4789

ROCKLEDGE, FL

HEALTH FIRST HEALTH PLANS INC p 674
6450 Us Highway 1 32955
Tel (321) 434-5600 *SIC* 6324

HEALTH FIRST INC p 674
6450 Us Highway 1 32955
Tel (321) 434-4300
SIC 8062 8011 8082 8069 7991 6324

RENCO ELECTRONICS INC p 1223
595 International Pl 32955
Tel (321) 637-1000 *SIC* 5065 3677

■ ROCKLEDGE HMA LLC p 1245
110 Longwood Ave 32955
Tel (321) 636-2211 *SIC* 8062

■ SCHF NOT-FOR-PROFIT WIND-DOWN INC p 1287
110 Longwood Ave 32955
Tel (321) 636-2211 *SIC* 8062

ROCKY POINT, FL

ARMA GLOBAL CORP p 110
2701 N Rocky Point Dr # 1150 33607
Tel (866) 554-9333 *SIC* 5045 8748 8742

■ CIGNA HEALTHCARE OF FLORIDA INC p 306
2701 N Rocky Point Dr # 178 33607
Tel (215) 761-1000 *SIC* 6324

CUNNINGHAM LINDSEY US INC p 401
3030 N Rocky Point Dr W # 530 33607
Tel (813) 830-7100 *SIC* 6719

MCNICHOLS CO p 932
2502 N Rocky Point Dr # 750 33607
Tel (877) 884-4653 *SIC* 5051

SHRINERS INTERNATIONAL HEADQUARTERS INC p 1319
2900 N Rocky Point Dr 33607
Tel (813) 281-0300 *SIC* 8082

ROYAL PALM BEACH, FL

PINNACLE HOTEL MANAGEMENT CO LLC p 1150
1480 Royal Palm Bch Blvd 33411
Tel (561) 242-9066 *SIC* 8741

SAFETY HARBOR, FL

BUFKOR INC p 224
1801 Stonebrook Ln 34695
Tel (727) 572-9991 *SIC* 5199 2084

SAINT AUGUSTINE, FL

BROWN JORDAN INTERNATIONAL INC p 220
475 W Town Pl Ste 200 32092
Tel (336) 622-2201 *SIC* 2512 2514

■ CARLISLE INTERCONNECT TECHNOLOGIES INC p 257
100 Tensolite Dr 32092
Tel (904) 829-5600
SIC 3679 3399 3678 3357 3643 5063

COUNTY OF ST JOHNS p 382
500 San Sebastian Vw 32084
Tel (904) 209-0300 *SIC* 9111

DENT J GREGG & ASSOCICATES PLC p 429
400 Health Park Blvd 32086
Tel (904) 819-4565 *SIC* 8031

FLAGLER HEALTHCARE SYSTEMS INC p 554
400 Health Park Blvd 32086
Tel (904) 819-5155 *SIC* 8062

FLAGLER HOSPITAL INC p 554
400 Health Park Blvd 32086
Tel (904) 819-5155 *SIC* 8062

FLORIDA DEPARTMENT OF MILITARY p 558
190 San Marco Ave 32084
Tel (904) 823-4748 *SIC* 9711

POSTAL FLEET SERVICES INC p 1164
2808 N 5th St Ste 501 32084
Tel (904) 824-2007 *SIC* 4214

RING POWER CORP p 1235
500 World Commerce Pkwy 32092
Tel (904) 201-7400 *SIC* 5082 5084 7353

RPC INC p 1255
500 World Commerce Pkwy 32092
Tel (904) 448-1055 *SIC* 5082

ST JOHNS COUNTY SCHOOL BOARD p 1367
40 Orange St 32084
Tel (904) 547-7500 *SIC* 8211

ST JOHNS COUNTY SCHOOL BOARD OF PUBLIC INSTRUCTION p 1367
2980 Collins Ave 32084
Tel (904) 824-4401 *SIC* 8211

ST JOHNS COUNTY SCHOOL DISTRICT p 1367
40 Orange St 32084
Tel (904) 547-7500 *SIC* 8211

■ TENSOLITE LLC p 1438
100 Tensolite Dr 32092
Tel (904) 829-5600 *SIC* 3357 3643 3679

SAINT JOHNS, FL

JMJ CONSULTING GROUP INC p 786
1197 Perregrine Cir E 32259
Tel (904) 538-0944 *SIC* 5141

SAINT LEO, FL

SAINT LEO UNIVERSITY INC p 1270
33701 State Road 52 33574
Tel (352) 588-8200 *SIC* 8221

SAINT PETERSBURG, FL

AEGON USA SECURITIES INC p 29
570 Carillon Pkwy 33716
Tel (727) 299-1800 *SIC* 6211

AMERICA II ELECTRONICS INC p 67
2600 118th Ave N 33716
Tel (727) 573-0900 *SIC* 5065

AMERICAN MANAGED CARE LLC p 75
100 Central Ave Ste 200 33701
Tel (866) 690-4842 *SIC* 6411

AMERICAN STRATEGIC INSURANCE CORP p 80
1 Asi Way N 33702
Tel (727) 821-8765 *SIC* 6331

ANDERSON GROUP LLC p 90
111 2nd Ave Ne Ste 105 33701
Tel (248) 645-8000 *SIC* 6799 6719

BANKERS FINANCIAL CORP p 152
11101 Roosevelt Blvd N 33716
Tel (727) 823-4000 *SIC* 6411

BANKERS INSURANCE CO p 152
11101 Roosevelt Blvd N 33716
Tel (727) 823-4000 *SIC* 6331

BANKERS INSURANCE GROUP INC p 152
11101 Roosevelt Blvd N 33716
Tel (727) 823-4000 *SIC* 6411

BANKERS INTERNATIONAL FINANCIAL CORP p 152
11101 Roosevelt Blvd N 33716
Tel (727) 823-4000 *SIC* 6411

BAYFRONT HMA MEDICAL CTR LLC p 161
701 6th St S 33701
Tel (727) 823-1234 *SIC* 8011

■ BAYFRONT MEDICAL CENTER INC p 161
701 6th St S 33701
Tel (727) 893-6111 *SIC* 8062

CATALINA MARKETING CORP p 264
200 Carillon Pkwy 33716
Tel (727) 579-5000 *SIC* 7319

CELOTEX CORP p 274
10301 Dr Martn L Kng Jr S 33716
Tel (727) 563-5100
SIC 3086 3275 3296 2493 2952

CERIDIAN BENEFITS SERVICES p 283
3201 34th St S 33711
Tel (800) 689-7893 *SIC* 8742

CITY OF SAINT PETERSBURG p 318
175 5th St N 33701
Tel (727) 893-7111 *SIC* 9111

COMPULINK CORP p 352
1205 Gandy Blvd N 33702
Tel (727) 579-1065 *SIC* 3679

COXTARGET MEDIA INC p 386
1 Valpak Ave N 33716
Tel (727) 399-3000
SIC 7331 8741 8742 2759

CROWN AUTO DEALERSHIPS INC p 395
6001 34th St N 33714
Tel (727) 525-4990 *SIC* 5511

CURANT INC p 401
11001 Roosevelt Blvd N # 1400 33716
Tel (770) 437-8040 *SIC* 5912

DIOCESE OF ST PETERSBURG INC p 441
6363 9th Ave N 33710
Tel (727) 345-3338 *SIC* 8661

■ DUKE ENERGY FLORIDA LLC p 460
299 1st Ave N 33701
Tel (704) 382-3853 *SIC* 4911

■ FIDELITY NATIONAL GLOBAL CARD SERVICES INC p 541
11601 Roosevelt Blvd N 33716
Tel (727) 556-9000 *SIC* 7389

FIRST CONTACT LLC p 546
200 Central Ave Ste 600 33701
Tel (727) 369-0850 *SIC* 7389

GA FOOD SERVICES OF PINELLAS COUNTY INC p 588
12200 32nd Ct N 33716
Tel (727) 573-2211 *SIC* 2038 5812

■ GALEN OF FLORIDA INC p 589
6500 38th Ave N 33710
Tel (727) 341-4055 *SIC* 8062

■ GENERAL DYNAMICS ORDNANCE AND TACTICAL SYSTEMS INC p 600
11399 16th Ct N Ste 200 33716
Tel (727) 578-8100
SIC 3483 3482 2892 3489

■ GENERAL DYNAMICS-OTS INC p 600
11399 16th Ct N Ste 200 33716
Tel (727) 578-8100 *SIC* 3728 3812

GOODWILL INDUSTRIES-SUNCOAST INC p 625
10596 Gandy Blvd N 33702
Tel (727) 523-1512 *SIC* 5932 8093

GOODWILL INDUSTRIES-SUNCOAST INC p 625
10596 Gandy Blvd N 33702
Tel (727) 523-1512 *SIC* 7361 5932

GREAT BAY DISTRIBUTORS INC p 633
2750 Eagle Ave N 33716
Tel (727) 584-8626 *SIC* 5181

■ HALKEY-ROBERTS CORP p 654
2700 Halkey Roberts Pl N 33716
Tel (727) 471-4200 *SIC* 3842

▲ HSN INC p 715
1 Hsn Dr 33729
Tel (727) 872-1000 *SIC* 5961 5331 5712

■ HSN LLC p 715
1 Hsn Dr 33729
Tel (727) 872-1000 *SIC* 5961

■ HSNI LLC p 715
1 Hsn Dr 33729
Tel (727) 872-1000 *SIC* 5961

IQOR GLOBAL SERVICES LLC p 764
1 Progress Plz Ste 7 33701
Tel (727) 369-0878 *SIC* 8748 4731

IQOR US INC p 764
1 Progress Plz Ste 170 33701
Tel (866) 657-2057 *SIC* 7322

▲ JABIL CIRCUIT INC p 773
10560 Dr Martin Luther 33716
Tel (727) 577-9749 *SIC* 3672

■ JABIL CIRCUIT LLC p 773
10560 Dr Martin 33716
Tel (727) 577-9749 *SIC* 3672

JOHNS HOPKINS ALL CHILDRENS HOSPITAL INC p 790
501 6th Ave S 33701
Tel (727) 898-7451 *SIC* 8069 8062

MORTGAGE INVESTORS CORP p 991
6090 Central Ave 33707
Tel (727) 347-1930 *SIC* 6162

■ MTS MEDICATION TECHNOLOGIES INC p 998
2003 Gandy Blvd N Ste 800 33702
Tel (727) 576-6311 *SIC* 3565 3089

■ NORTHSIDE HOSPITAL p 1058
6000 49th St N 33709
Tel (727) 521-4411
SIC 8031 8011 8069 8062

POWER DESIGN INC p 1165
11600 9th St N 33716
Tel (727) 210-0492 *SIC* 1731

PROGRESS ENERGY SERVICE CO LLC p 1181
299 1st Ave N 33701
Tel (727) 820-5151 *SIC* 4911

■ PROGRESS FUELS CORP p 1181
1 Progress Plz Fl 11 33701
Tel (727) 824-6600 *SIC* 1221

PSCU INC p 1188
560 Carillon Pkwy 33716
Tel (727) 572-8822 *SIC* 7389

QUANTUM SPATIAL INC p 1198
10033 Mlk St N Ste 200 33716
Tel (920) 457-3631 *SIC* 2741 8713

■ RAYMOND JAMES & ASSOCIATES INC p 1210
880 Carillon Pkwy 33716
Tel (727) 567-1000 *SIC* 6211 6722 8741

■ RAYMOND JAMES BANK NATIONAL ASSOCIATION p 1210
710 Carillon Pkwy 33716
Tel (727) 567-8000 *SIC* 6035

▲ RAYMOND JAMES FINANCIAL INC p 1210
880 Carillon Pkwy 33716
Tel (727) 567-1000 *SIC* 6211

■ RAYMOND JAMES FINANCIAL SERVICES INC p 1210
880 Carillon Pkwy 33716
Tel (727) 567-1000
SIC 6211 6282 6712 6091 6035

■ RENZ NICHOLS FAMILY LIMITED PARTNERSHIP p 1224
11601 Roosevelt Blvd N 33716
Tel (727) 573-7848 *SIC* 7389

ST ANTHONYS HOSPITAL INC p 1364
1200 7th Ave N 33705
Tel (727) 825-1100 *SIC* 8062

TAMPA BAY SPORTS ENTERTAINMENT LLC p 1423
490 1st Ave S 33701
Tel (727) 893-8111 *SIC* 2711

TIMES PUBLISHING CO p 1454
490 1st Ave S 33701
Tel (727) 893-8111 *SIC* 2711 2721

TRIAD DIGITAL MEDIA LLC p 1478
100 Carillon Pkwy Ste 100 33716
Tel (727) 231-5041 *SIC* 7311

■ **USANI SUB LLC** p 1534
1 Hsn Dr 33729
Tel (727) 872-1000 *SIC* 4833 5961

VALPAK DIRECT MARKETING SYSTEMS INC p 1542
805 Exe Ctr Dr W 33702
Tel (727) 399-3175 *SIC* 7331 6794

WESTERN RESERVE LIFE ASSURANCE CO p 1600
570 Carillon Pkwy 33716
Tel (727) 299-1800 *SIC* 6311

SANFORD, FL

ADAPCO INC p 21
550 Aero Ln 32771
Tel (407) 330-4800 *SIC* 5191

■ **CENTRAL FLORIDA REGIONAL HOSPITAL INC** p 278
1401 W Seminole Blvd 32771
Tel (407) 321-4500 *SIC* 8062

COUNTY OF SEMINOLE p 381
1101 E 1st St 32771
Tel (407) 665-7664 *SIC* 9111

DEL-AIR HEATING AIR CONDITIONING & REFRIGERATION CORP p 423
531 Codisco Way 32771
Tel (866) 796-4874 *SIC* 1711

FATHERSTABLE L L C p 531
2100 Country Club Rd 32771
Tel (407) 324-1200 *SIC* 2099

FLORIDA IRRIGATION SUPPLY INC p 559
300 Central Park Dr 32771
Tel (407) 425-6669 *SIC* 5084

NEWTRIBES MISSION INC p 1033
1000 E 1st St 32771
Tel (407) 323-3430 *SIC* 8661

PARADIES GIFTS INC p 1113
2305 W Airport Blvd 32771
Tel (407) 290-5288 *SIC* 5199

SANFORD AUTO DEALERS EXCHANGE INC p 1279
2851 Saint Johns Pkwy 32771
Tel (407) 328-7300 *SIC* 5012

SEMINOLE COUNTY PUBLIC SCHOOLS p 1302
400 E Lake Mary Blvd 32773
Tel (407) 320-0000 *SIC* 8211

SEMINOLE STATE COLLEGE OF FLORIDA p 1302
100 Weldon Blvd 32773
Tel (407) 708-4722 *SIC* 8221

WHARTON-SMITH INC p 1604
750 Monroe Rd 32771
Tel (407) 321-8410 *SIC* 1542

WIGINTON CORP p 1608
699 Aero Ln 32771
Tel (407) 585-3200 *SIC* 1711 7699 7389

SANTA ROSA BEACH, FL

ANGELINAS PIZZERIA & PASTA INC p 91
4005 E County Highway 30a 32459
Tel (850) 231-2500 *SIC* 5812

SARASOTA, FL

ADVANTAGETRIM & LUMBER CO INC p 26
7524 Commerce Pl 34243
Tel (941) 388-9299 *SIC* 5031 5211

ALLIED AVIATION LLC p 56
4120 Higel Ave 34242
Tel (212) 868-5593 *SIC* 5172

BOARS HEAD PROVISIONS CO INC p 196
1819 Main St Ste 800 34236
Tel (941) 955-0994 *SIC* 5147

COUNTY OF SARASOTA p 381
1660 Ringling Blvd 34236
Tel (941) 861-5165 *SIC* 9111

DAYHAGAN FINANCIAL RJFS p 417
1000 S Tamiami Trl 34236
Tel (941) 330-1702 *SIC* 6282

FCCI GROUP INC p 533
6300 University Pkwy 34240
Tel (941) 907-3224 *SIC* 6331

FCCI INSURANCE CO p 533
6300 University Pkwy 34240
Tel (941) 907-3224 *SIC* 6331

FCCI INSURANCE GROUP INC p 533
6300 University Pkwy 34240
Tel (941) 907-2515 *SIC* 6411

FCCI MUTUAL INSURANCE HOLDING CO p 533
6300 University Pkwy 34240
Tel (941) 907-3224 *SIC* 6331

FCCI SERVICES INC p 533
6300 University Pkwy 34240
Tel (941) 556-3345 *SIC* 6411

FINANCIAL INSURANCE MANAGEMENT CORP p 542
1440 Main St 34236
Tel (941) 952-5522 *SIC* 6411 8742

■ **FLOWERS BAKING CO OF BRADENTON LLC** p 560
6490 Parkland Dr 34243
Tel (941) 758-5656 *SIC* 2051

FRANK BRUNCKHORST CO LLC p 574
1819 Main St Ste 800 34236
Tel (941) 955-0994 *SIC* 5147

HOVEROUND CORP p 713
6010 Cattleridge Dr 34232
Tel (941) 739-6200 *SIC* 3842

INTERTAPE POLYMER CORP p 759
100 Paramount Dr Ste 300 34232
Tel (941) 727-5788 *SIC* 2672

IPG (US) HOLDINGS INC p 763
100 Paramount Dr Ste 300 34232
Tel (941) 727-5788 *SIC* 2672 3953

IPG (US) INC p 763
100 Paramount Dr Ste 300 34232
Tel (941) 727-5788 *SIC* 2672 3953

JCI JONES CHEMICALS INC p 780
1765 Ringling Blvd 34236
Tel (941) 330-1537 *SIC* 5169 2842

LEXJET LLC p 860
1605 Main St Ste 400 34236
Tel (941) 330-1210
SIC 5045 5112 5111 2672 5043

▲ **ROPER TECHNOLOGIES INC** p 1250
6901 Prof Pkwy E Ste 200 34240
Tel (941) 556-2601
SIC 3823 3563 3491 3826 3829

SARASOTA COUNTY PUBLIC HOSPITAL DISTRICT p 1282
1700 S Tamiami Trl 34239
Tel (941) 917-9000 *SIC* 8062 7372

SARASOTA COUNTY SCHOOLS p 1282
1960 Landings Blvd 34231
Tel (941) 927-9000 *SIC* 8211

■ **SARASOTA DOCTORS HOSPITAL INC** p 1282
5731 Bee Ridge Rd 34233
Tel (941) 342-1100 *SIC* 8062

SARASOTA FAMILY YOUNG MENS CHRISTIAN ASSOCIATION INC p 1282
1 S School Ave Ste 301 34237
Tel (941) 951-2916
SIC 8641 8351 8322 7997 7991

SCHOOL BOARD OF SARASOTA COUNTY p 1289
1960 Landings Blvd 34231
Tel (941) 927-9000 *SIC* 8211

▲ **SUN HYDRAULICS CORP** p 1400
1500 W University Pkwy 34243
Tel (941) 362-1200 *SIC* 3492

SUNCOASTTECHNICAL COLLEGE p 1402
4748 Beneva Rd 34233
Tel (941) 361-6590 *SIC* 8249

TIDEWELL HOSPICE INC p 1452
5955 Rand Blvd 34238
Tel (941) 552-7500 *SIC* 8082

▲ **UNIROYAL GLOBAL ENGINEERED PRODUCTS INC** p 1505
1800 2nd St Ste 970 34236
Tel (941) 906-8580 *SIC* 2824 2396

UNIVERSAL INSURANCE MANAGERS INC p 1517
101 Paramount Dr Ste 220 34232
Tel (941) 378-8851 *SIC* 6411

WELLSPRING PHARMACEUTICAL CORP p 1591
5911 N Honore Ave Ste 211 34243
Tel (941) 312-4727 *SIC* 5122 2834

SEBASTIAN, FL

■ **SEBASTIAN RIVER MEDICAL CENTER** p 1298
13695 Us Highway 1 32958
Tel (772) 589-3186 *SIC* 8062

SEBRING, FL

FLORIDA HOSPITAL HEARTLAND MEDICAL CENTER p 558
4200 Sun N Lake Blvd 33872
Tel (863) 314-4466 *SIC* 8062

HIGHLANDS COUNTY SCHOOLS p 691
426 School St 33870
Tel (863) 471-5564 *SIC* 8211

SCHOOL BOARD OF HIGHLANDS COUNTY p 1289
426 School St 33870
Tel (863) 471-5555 *SIC* 8211

SEFFNER, FL

LDRV HOLDINGS CORP p 849
6130 Lazy Days Blvd 33584
Tel (813) 246-4333 *SIC* 5561

RTG FURNITURE CORP p 1256
11540 E Us Highway 92 33584
Tel (813) 623-5400 *SIC* 5712

RTG FURNITURE CORP OF GEORGIA p 1256
11540 E Us Highway 92 33584
Tel (813) 623-5400 *SIC* 5712

RTG FURNITURE OF TEXAS LP p 1256
11540 E Us Highway 92 33584
Tel (813) 628-9724 *SIC* 5712 5021

SEMINOLE, FL

SHAMROCK ACQUISITION CORP p 1311
10540 Belcher Rd S 33777
Tel (727) 209-0553 *SIC* 7349

▲ **SUPERIOR UNIFORM GROUP INC** p 1407
10055 Seminole Blvd 33772
Tel (727) 397-9611 *SIC* 2389 3999 7389

SOUTH MIAMI, FL

BAPTIST HEALTH SOUTH FLORIDA INC p 153
6855 S Red Rd 33143
Tel (305) 596-1960 *SIC* 8062 8011 8082

CARGO FORCE INC p 255
6705 Sw 57th Ave Ste 700 33143
Tel (305) 740-3252 *SIC* 4581

▲ **ILG** p 731
6262 Sunset Dr 33143
Tel (305) 666-1861 *SIC* 8699

■ **INTERVAL ACQUISITION CORP** p 759
6262 Sunset Dr Ste 400 33143
Tel (954) 431-0060 *SIC* 4724

■ **INTERVAL HOLDING CO INC** p 759
6262 Sunset Dr Fl 6 33143
Tel (305) 666-1861 *SIC* 8699 8721 6531

■ **INTERVAL INTERNATIONAL INC** p 759
6262 Sunset Dr Ste 400 33143
Tel (305) 666-1861 *SIC* 8699

LARKIN COMMUNITY HOSPITAL INC p 845
7031 Sw 62nd Ave 33143
Tel (305) 757-5707 *SIC* 8062

MOTCO INC p 992
7900 Sw 57th Ave Ste 10 33143
Tel (305) 662-8814 *SIC* 5182 5122 5199

MUNILLA CONSTRUCTION MANAGEMENT LLC p 1000
6201 Sw 70th St Fl 2 33143
Tel (305) 541-0000 *SIC* 1622 1542

SOUTH MIAMI HOSPITAL INC p 1344
6200 Sw 73rd St 33143
Tel (786) 662-4000 *SIC* 8062

STUART, FL

DYNAMIC PRECISION GROUP INC p 464
3651 Se Commerce Ave 34997
Tel (772) 287-7770 *SIC* 3724 3444

MARTIN COUNTY SCHOOL DISTRICT p 912
500 Se Ocean Blvd 34994
Tel (772) 219-1200 *SIC* 8211

MARTIN MEMORIAL HEALTH SYSTEMS INC p 912
200 Se Hospital Ave 34994
Tel (772) 287-5200 *SIC* 8741 8062

MARTIN MEMORIAL MEDICAL CENTER INC p 912
200 Se Hospital Ave 34994
Tel (772) 287-5200 *SIC* 8062

■ **NUCO2 INC** p 1066
2800 Se Market Pl 34997
Tel (772) 221-1754 *SIC* 5169

■ **SEACOAST BANK OF FLORIDA INC** p 1296
815 Colorado Ave Lbby 34994
Tel (772) 221-2760 *SIC* 6021

▲ **SEACOAST BANKING CORP OF FLORIDA** p 1296
815 Colorado Ave 34994
Tel (772) 287-4000 *SIC* 6022

TURBOCOMBUSTOR TECHNOLOGY INC p 1492
3651 Se Commerce Ave 34997
Tel (772) 287-7770 *SIC* 3724 3728 3444

SUMTERVILLE, FL

SUMTER ELECTRIC COOPERATIVE INC p 1399
330 S Us 301 33585
Tel (352) 237-4107 *SIC* 4911

SUNNY ISLES BEACH, FL

TRANS-RESOURCES INC p 1470
17780 Collins Ave 33160
Tel (305) 933-8301 *SIC* 2873 2819 2879

ZRAIM INVESTMENTS LLC p 1644
400 Sunny Isles Blvd # 190 33160
Tel (718) 708-0065 *SIC* 6798

SUNRISE, FL

AERO HARDWARE & SUPPLY INC p 30
300 International Pkwy 33325
Tel (954) 845-1040 *SIC* 5084 5085

AGROYCE METAL MARKETING LLC p 36
1381 Sawgrs Corp Pkwy 33323
Tel (954) 561-3607 *SIC* 5051

ALLIANCE ENTERTAINMENT HOLDING CORP p 54
1401 Nw 136th Ave Ste 100 33323
Tel (954) 255-4000 *SIC* 5199 6719

ALLIANCE ENTERTAINMENT LLC p 54
1401 Nw 136th Ave Ste 100 33323
Tel (954) 255-4403 *SIC* 5199 3651

BROADSPIRE SERVICES INC p 215
1391 Nw 136th Ave 33323
Tel (954) 452-4000 *SIC* 8099 6331

BUREAU VERITAS HOLDINGS INC p 226
1601 Sawgrafl Corporate S Ste 400 33323
Tel (954) 835-9309
SIC 7389 8748 8711 8742

BUREAU VERITAS NORTH AMERICA INC p 227
1601 Sawgrs Corp Pkwy 33323
Tel (954) 236-8100
SIC 7389 8748 8734 8711 8742

CITY OF SUNRISE p 318
10770 W Oakland Park Blvd 33351
Tel (954) 746-3297 *SIC* 9111

■ **COVENTRY HEALTH PLAN OF FLORIDA INC** p 385
1340 Concord Ter 33323
Tel (954) 858-3000 *SIC* 6324

CROSS COUNTRY HOME HOLDINGS INC p 393
1625 Nw 136th Ave Ste 200 33323
Tel (954) 835-1900 *SIC* 6351

CROSS COUNTRY HOME SERVICES INC p 393
1625 Nw 136th Ave Ste 200 33323
Tel (954) 835-1900 *SIC* 6351

▲ **FEDERATED NATIONAL HOLDING CO** p 536
14050 Nw 14th St Ste 180 33323
Tel (954) 581-9993 *SIC* 6331 6411

G L HOMES OF FLORIDA CORP p 587
1600 Sawgrs Corp Pkwy # 400 33323
Tel (954) 753-1730 *SIC* 1521

INTERIM HEALTHCARE INC p 752
1601 Swgrs Corp Pkwy # 100 33323
Tel (800) 338-7786 *SIC* 6794 7363 8082

INTERNATIONAL BULLION AND METAL BROKERS (USA) INC p 754
14051 Nw 14th St Ste 3 33323
Tel (954) 660-6900 *SIC* 5094

▲ **MEDNAX INC** p 938
1301 Concord Ter 33323
Tel (954) 384-0175 *SIC* 8011

NATURES PRODUCTS INC p 1019
1301 Sawgrs Corp Pkwy 33323
Tel (954) 233-3300 *SIC* 5122 5499

ONECIS INSURANCE CO p 1087
1601 Sawgrs Corp Pkwy 33323
Tel (954) 236-8100 *SIC* 7389 6331

PET SUPERMARKET INC p 1137
1100 International Pkwy # 200 33323
Tel (866) 434-1990 *SIC* 5999 3999 5199

■ **SHERIDAN HEALTHCARE INC** p 1315
1613 Harrison Pkwy # 200 33323
Tel (954) 838-2371 *SIC* 8011

SHERIDAN HEALTHCORP INC p 1316
1613 Nw 136th Ave 33323
Tel (954) 838-2371 *SIC* 8741

SUNSHINE RESTAURANT MERGER SUB LLC p 1404
13650 Nw 8th St Ste 103 33325
Tel (305) 931-5454 *SIC* 5812

TEAM FOCUS INSURANCE GROUP LLC p 1429
1300 Sawgrs Corp Pkwy # 300 33323
Tel (954) 331-4800 *SIC* 6719 6411

UNITED STATES PHARMACEUTICAL GROUP LLC p 1514
13621 Nw 12th St Ste 100 33323
Tel (954) 903-5000 *SIC* 5047

WELLNEXT LLC p 1589
1301 Sawgrs Corp Pkwy 33323
Tel (954) 233-3301 *SIC* 8071

TALLAHASSEE, FL

ACCUIRE LLC p 16
2001 Thomasville Rd 32308
Tel (850) 893-7710 *SIC* 7361

BOARD OF GOVERNORS STATE UNIVERSITY SYSTEM OF FLORIDA p 195
325 W Gaines St Ste 1625 32399
Tel (850) 245-0466 *SIC* 8221

C W ROBERTS CONTRACTING INC p 233
3372 Capital Cir Ne 32308
Tel (850) 385-5060 *SIC* 1611

■ **CAPITAL CITY BANK** p 249
217 N Monroe St 32301
Tel (850) 402-7700 *SIC* 6022

▲ **CAPITAL CITY BANK GROUP INC** p 249
217 N Monroe St 32301
Tel (850) 402-7000 *SIC* 6022

CAPITAL HEALTH PLAN INC p 249
2140 Centerville Rd 32308
Tel (850) 383-3333 *SIC* 8011

CITIZENS PROPERTY INSURANCE CORP p 311
2101 Maryland Cir 32303
Tel (888) 685-1555 *SIC* 6311

EXECUTIVE OFFICE OF GOVERNOR OF FLORIDA p 517
400 S Monroe St 32399
Tel (850) 488-4505 *SIC* 9111

FISH & WILDLIFE CONSERVATION COMMISSION FLORIDA p 551
620 S Meridian St 32399
Tel (850) 487-3796 *SIC* 9512

FLORIDA A & M UNIVERSITY p 557
1601 S M L King Jr Blvd 32307
Tel (850) 599-3000 *SIC* 8221

FLORIDA DEPARTMENT OF AGRICULTURE AND CONSUMER SERVICES p 558
10 The Capitol 32399
Tel (850) 617-7700 *SIC* 9641 9611 9111

FLORIDA DEPARTMENT OF CHILDREN & FAMILIES p 558
1317 Winewood Blvd Rm 306 32399
Tel (850) 488-2840 *SIC* 9441 9411

FLORIDA DEPARTMENT OF CORRECTIONS p 558
501 S Calhoun St 32399
Tel (850) 488-7480 SIC 9223

FLORIDA DEPARTMENT OF ECONOMIC OPPORTUNITY p 558
107 E Madison St St120 32399
Tel (850) 245-7362 SIC 9199

FLORIDA DEPARTMENT OF EDUCATION p 558
325 W Gaines St Ste 101 32399
Tel (850) 245-0505 SIC 9411

FLORIDA DEPARTMENT OF ENVIRONMENTAL PROTECTION p 558
3900 Commwl Blvd 32399
Tel (850) 245-2112 SIC 9512

FLORIDA DEPARTMENT OF FINANCIAL SERVICES p 558
200 E Gaines St 32399
Tel (850) 413-3100 SIC 9651

FLORIDA DEPARTMENT OF HEALTH p 558
4052 Bald Cypress Way 32399
Tel (850) 245-4500 SIC 9431 8399

FLORIDA DEPARTMENT OF HIGHWAY SAFETY AND MOTOR VEHICLES p 558
2900 Apalachee Pkwy 32399
Tel (850) 617-3100 SIC 9621

FLORIDA DEPARTMENT OF JUVENILE JUSTICE p 558
2737 Centerview Dr # 1225 32399
Tel (850) 921-3048 SIC 9223

FLORIDA DEPARTMENT OF LABOR AND EMPLOYMENT SECURITY p 558
2012 Capital Cir Se 32399
Tel (850) 942-8341 SIC 9651 9111

FLORIDA DEPARTMENT OF LAW ENFORCEMENT p 558
2331 Phillips Rd 32308
Tel (850) 410-7000 SIC 9221

FLORIDA DEPARTMENT OF LEGAL AFFAIRS p 558
107 W Gaines St 32399
Tel (850) 414-3300 SIC 8111 9222

FLORIDA DEPARTMENT OF REVENUE p 558
2450 Oak Blvd 32399
Tel (850) 617-8600 SIC 9311 9111

FLORIDA DEPARTMENT OF TRANSPORTATION p 558
605 Suwannee St 32399
Tel (850) 414-4500 SIC 9621

FLORIDA DIVISION OF ADMINISTRATIVE HEARINGS p 558
1230 Apalachee Pkwy 32301
Tel (850) 488-9675 SIC 9211

FLORIDA HEALTHY KIDS CORP p 558
661 E Jefferson St # 200 32301
Tel (850) 701-6160 SIC 6321

FLORIDA HOUSING FINANCE CORP p 559
227 N Bronough St # 5000 32301
Tel (850) 488-4197 SIC 6162

FLORIDA OFFICE OF ATTORNEY GENERAL p 559
Pl-01 The Capitol 32399
Tel (850) 414-3300 SIC 9222

FLORIDA STATE UNIVERSITY p 559
600 W College Ave 32306
Tel (850) 644-5482 SIC 8221

FLORIDA TOURISM INDUSTRY MARKETING CORP p 559
2450 W Exec Ctr Cir 200 32301
Tel (850) 488-5607 SIC 4724 8743 8742

ICONIC GROUP INC p 728
3490 Martin Hurst Rd 32312
Tel (800) 628-4509 SIC 7335

LEGISLATIVE OFFICE OF FLORIDA p 853
400 S Monroe St 32399
Tel (850) 488-4505 SIC 9121

LEON COUNTY SCHOOL BOARD p 856
2757 W Pensacola St 32304
Tel (850) 487-7100 SIC 8211

LEON COUNTY SCHOOL DISTRICT p 856
2757 W Pensacola St 32304
Tel (850) 487-7100 SIC 8211

MAINLINE INFORMATION SYSTEMS INC p 898
1700 Summit Lake Dr 32317
Tel (850) 219-5000 SIC 7373 7379 7371

MCKENZIE TANK LINES INC p 930
1966 Commonwealth Ln 32303
Tel (850) 576-1221 SIC 4213 3715 3443

PHYSICIANS UNITED PLAN INC p 1146
2020 Capital Cir Se 310 32301
Tel (888) 827-5787 SIC 6321

STATE OF FLORIDA p 1381
400 S Monroe St 32399
Tel (850) 488-7146 SIC 9111

STATE OF FLORIDA OF JUDICIARY COURTS p 1381
500 S Duval St 32399
Tel (850) 922-5081 SIC 9211

TALLAHASSEE CITY OF (INC) p 1423
300 S Adams St 32301
Tel (850) 891-8441 SIC 9111

■ **TALLAHASSEE MEDICAL CENTER INC** p 1423
2626 Capital Medical Blvd 32308
Tel (850) 325-5000 SIC 8062

TALLAHASSEE MEMORIAL HEALTHCARE INC p 1423
1300 Miccosukee Rd 32308
Tel (850) 431-1155 SIC 8062

TAMARAC, FL

CITY FURNITURE INC p 312
6701 Hiatus Rd 33321
Tel (954) 597-2200 SIC 5712

FLORIDA A&G CO INC p 557
10200 Nw 67th St 33321
Tel (800) 432-8132 SIC 3442 5039

SONNYS ENTERPRISES INC p 1340
5605 Hiatus Rd 33321
Tel (954) 720-4100 SIC 5087 3589

■ **UNIVERSITY HOSPITAL LTD** p 1519
7201 N University Dr 33321
Tel (954) 721-2200 SIC 8062

TAMPA, FL

AAA AUTO CLUB SOUTH INC p 7
1515 N West Shore Blvd 33607
Tel (813) 289-5000
SIC 4724 6331 8699 6311

ADAMS AIR & HYDRAULICS INC p 21
7209 E Adamo Dr 33619
Tel (813) 626-4128 SIC 5084

ADVANTAGE SALES & MARKETING p 26
3922 Coconut Palm Dr # 300 33619
Tel (813) 281-8080 SIC 5141

ADVANTAGE WAYPOINT LLC p 27
13521 Prestige Pl 33635
Tel (813) 358-5900 SIC 5141

AETNA MAINTENANCE INC p 31
101 E Kennedy Blvd G102 33602
Tel (813) 621-6878 SIC 7349

AMALIE OIL CO p 64
1601 Mcclosky Blvd 33605
Tel (813) 248-1988 SIC 2992 3085

AMERICAN INTEGRITY INSURANCE GROUP LLC p 75
5426 Bay Center Dr # 650 33609
Tel (813) 880-7000 SIC 6331

■ **AMERIGROUP FLORIDA INC** p 82
4200 W Cypress St 900-1000 33607
Tel (813) 830-6900 SIC 6324

ANCHOR GLASS CONTAINER CORP p 89
401 E Jackson St Ste 1100 33602
Tel (813) 884-0000 SIC 3221

AQUA VENTURE HOLDINGS LLC p 101
14400 Carlson Cir 33626
Tel (813) 855-8636 SIC 8741

■ **AT&T GLOBAL NETWORK SERVICES LLC** p 123
3405 W Dr Martin Lthr Kng 33607
Tel (813) 878-3000 SIC 4899

ATKINS NORTH AMERICA HOLDINGS CORP p 125
4030 W Boy Scout Blvd 33607
Tel (813) 282-7275 SIC 8712 6519 8711

AUDIO VISUAL INNOVATIONS INC p 130
6301 Benjamin Rd Ste 101 33634
Tel (813) 884-7168
SIC 3669 5064 3861 3663 3651 5043

AUTO CLUB SOUTH INSURANCE CO p 133
14055 Riveredge Dr # 500 33637
Tel (800) 289-1325 SIC 6411

AVI-SPL EMPLOYEE EMERGENCY RELIEF FUND INC p 137
6301 Benjamin Rd Ste 101 33634
Tel (813) 884-7168
SIC 3669 3861 3663 3651 5043 5064

AVI-SPL HOLDINGS INC p 137
6301 Benjamin Rd Ste 101 33634
Tel (866) 708-5034
SIC 3669 3861 3663 3651 1731 5064

AVI-SPL INC p 137
6301 Benjamin Rd Ste 101 33634
Tel (866) 708-5034 SIC 7359 5999

BILL CURRIE FORD INC p 182
5815 N Dale Mabry Hwy 33614
Tel (813) 872-5555 SIC 5511 7538

▲ **BLOOMIN BRANDS INC** p 190
2202 N West Shore Blvd # 500 33607
Tel (813) 282-1225 SIC 5812

BLUEPEARL FLORIDA LLC p 193
3000 Busch Lake Blvd 33614
Tel (813) 933-8944 SIC 0742

BMP INTERNATIONAL INC p 194
5139 W Idlewild Ave 33634
Tel (727) 458-0544 SIC 1542

■ **BONEFISH GRILL INC** p 200
2202 N West Shore Blvd # 5 33607
Tel (813) 282-1225 SIC 5812

BUCCANEER HOLDINGS LLC p 222
8125 Highwoods Palm Way 33647
Tel (813) 637-5000 SIC 4813 4812

BUDDYS NEWCO LLC p 223
6608 E Adamo Dr 33619
Tel (813) 623-5461 SIC 7359 6794

BUSINESS JOURNAL PUBLICATIONS INC p 229
4350 W Cypress St Ste 800 33607
Tel (813) 342-2472 SIC 2711

CAE USA INC p 236
4908 Tampa West Blvd 33634
Tel (813) 885-7481
SIC 3699 7373 8299 8249 8711

■ **CARRABBAS ITALIAN GRILL INC** p 260
2202 N West Shore Blvd # 5 33607
Tel (813) 288-8286 SIC 5812

CARTER VALIDUS MISSION CRITICAL REIT INC p 262
4890 W Kennedy Blvd # 650 33609
Tel (813) 287-0101 SIC 6798

CASUAL RESTAURANT CONCEPTS INC p 264
205 S Hoover Blvd Ste 402 33609
Tel (813) 286-2006 SIC 5813 5812

CENTRAL FLORIDA BEHAVIORAL HEALTH NETWORK INC p 278
719 S Us Highway 301 33619
Tel (813) 740-4811 SIC 8322

CHADWELL SUPPLY INC p 286
4907 Joanne Kearney Blvd 33619
Tel (888) 341-2423 SIC 5031 1752

CHECKERS DRIVE-IN RESTAURANTS INC p 292
4300 W Cypress St Ste 600 33607
Tel (813) 283-7000 SIC 5812 6794

CITRUS HEALTH CARE INC p 311
101 S Hoover Blvd Ste 100 33609
Tel (813) 490-7931 SIC 6324

CITY OF TAMPA p 319
306 E Jackson St Fl 7 33602
Tel (813) 274-8211 SIC 9111

COAST DENTAL SERVICES INC p 331
4010 W Boy Scout Blvd # 1100 33607
Tel (813) 288-1999 SIC 8021

■ **COCA-COLA BEVERAGES FLORIDA LLC** p 333
10117 Princess Plm Ave # 400 33610
Tel (813) 327-7294 SIC 2086

COLONIAL GROCERS INC p 337
4001 E Lake Ave 33610
Tel (813) 621-8880 SIC 0132 5141

■ **COMPREHENSIVE HEALTH MANAGEMENT INC** p 352
8735 Henderson Rd 33634
Tel (813) 206-1033 SIC 8741

COTT BEVERAGES INC p 374
5519 W Idlewild Ave 33634
Tel (813) 313-1800 SIC 2086

COTT CORP p 374
5519 W Idlewild Ave 33634
Tel (813) 313-1800 SIC 2086

COUNTY OF HILLSBOROUGH p 378
601 E Kennedy Blvd Fl 23 33602
Tel (813) 276-2720 SIC 9111

DEDC INC p 421
8603 E Adamo Dr 33619
Tel (813) 626-5195 SIC 5065

DEX IMAGING INC p 434
5109 W Lemon St 33609
Tel (813) 288-8080 SIC 5044

DIVERSIFIED MAINTENANCE SYSTEMS LLC p 444
5110 Sunforest Dr Ste 250 33634
Tel (800) 351-1557 SIC 7349

DRUG SHOPPE INC p 457
4060 N Armenia Ave 33607
Tel (813) 870-3939 SIC 5912

ELECTRIC SUPPLY OF TAMPA INC p 485
4407 N Manhattan Ave 33614
Tel (813) 872-1894 SIC 5063

ENTERPRISE LEASING CO OF FLORIDA LLC p 502
3505 E Fontage Ste 200 Rd 33607
Tel (813) 887-4299 SIC 7514 7515

FERMAN MOTOR CAR CO INC p 538
1306 W Kennedy Blvd 33606
Tel (813) 251-2765 SIC 5511

FLORIDA HEALTH SCIENCES CENTER INC p 558
1 Tampa General Cir 33606
Tel (813) 844-7000 SIC 8062

FLORIDA LIFT SYSTEMS LLC p 559
115 S 78th St 33619
Tel (904) 764-7662 SIC 5084 7359 7699

G4S YOUTH SERVICES LLC p 588
6302 Benjamin Rd Ste 400 33634
Tel (813) 514-6275 SIC 8322

GARDNER ASPHALT CORP p 592
4161 E 7th Ave 33605
Tel (813) 248-2441 SIC 3531

GARDNER-GIBSON INC p 592
4161 E 7th Ave 33605
Tel (813) 248-2101 SIC 2951 2851 2952

GARDNER-GIBSON MANUFACTURING INC p 592
4161 E 7th Ave 33605
Tel (813) 248-2101 SIC 2951 2891 2952

GERDAU AMERISTEEL CORP p 608
4221 W Boy Scout Blvd # 600 33607
Tel (813) 286-8383 SIC 3312

GERDAU AMERISTEEL US INC p 608
4221 W Boy Scout Blvd # 600 33607
Tel (813) 286-8383 SIC 3312 3449 3315

GERDAU USA INC p 608
4221 W Boy Scout Blvd 33607
Tel (813) 286-8383 SIC 3312 3449 3315

■ **GLOBAL IMAGING SYSTEMS INC** p 616
3903 Northdale Blvd 200w 33624
Tel (813) 960-5508 SIC 5044 5045 7629

GOOD TIMES USA LLC p 624
8408 Temple Terrace Hwy 33637
Tel (813) 621-8702 SIC 5194

■ **GRANITE SERVICES INTERNATIONAL INC** p 631
201 N Franklin St # 1000 33602
Tel (813) 242-7400 SIC 7363

GREYSTONE HEALTHCARE MANAGEMENT CORP p 640
4042 Park Oaks Blvd # 300 33610
Tel (813) 635-9500 SIC 8741

GRUDEN ACQUISITION INC p 642
4041 Park Oaks Blvd # 200 33610
Tel (800) 282-2031 SIC 4213

GULFSIDE SUPPLY INC p 647
2900 E 7th Ave Ste 200 33605
Tel (813) 636-9808 SIC 5033

GUNNALLEN FINANCIAL INC p 648
5002 W Waters Ave 33634
Tel (800) 713-4046 SIC 6211

H LEE MOFFITT CANCER CENTER & RESEARCH INSTITUTE p 650
12902 Usf Magnolia Dr 33612
Tel (813) 745-4673 SIC 8062

H LEE MOFFITT CANCER CENTER & RESEARCH INSTITUTE HOSPITAL INC p 650
12902 Usf Magnolia Dr 33612
Tel (813) 745-4673 SIC 8733

H LEE MOFFITT CANCER CENTER AND RESEARCH INSTITUTE INC p 650
12902 Usf Magnolia Dr 33612
Tel (813) 745-4673 SIC 8011

▲ **HCI GROUP INC** p 672
5300 W Cypress St Ste 100 33607
Tel (813) 849-9500 SIC 6331 6411

HEALTH E SYSTEMS LLC p 674
5100 W Lemon St Ste 311 33609
Tel (813) 463-1235 SIC 6411

▲ **HEALTH INSURANCE INNOVATIONS INC** p 675
15438 N Florida Ave # 201 33613
Tel (877) 376-5831 SIC 6411

HEALTHPLAN HOLDINGS INC p 677
3501 E Frontage Rd 33607
Tel (813) 289-1000 SIC 6399

HEALTHPLAN SERVICES INC p 677
3501 E Frontage Rd # 125 33607
Tel (813) 289-1000 SIC 8741

HELM FERTILIZER CORP (FLORIDA) p 682
401 E Jackson St Ste 1400 33602
Tel (813) 621-8846 SIC 5191 6221

HI DEVELOPMENT CORP p 689
111 W Fortune St 33602
Tel (813) 229-6686 SIC 8741

HILLSBOROUGH COMMUNITY COLLEGE INC p 694
39 Columbia Dr 33606
Tel (813) 253-7000 SIC 8222

HILLSBOROUGH COUNTY PUBLIC SCHOOLS p 694
901 E Kennedy Blvd 33602
Tel (813) 272-4050 SIC 8211

HILLSBOROUGH COUNTY SCHOOL DISTRICT p 694
901 E Kennedy Blvd 33602
Tel (813) 272-4000 SIC 8211

■ **HORIZON BAY MANAGEMENT LLC** p 707
5426 Bay Center Dr # 600 33609
Tel (813) 287-3900 SIC 8611 6531 1522

INTEGRAL HEALTH PLAN INC p 748
4631 Woodland Corp Blvd 33614
Tel (866) 258-4326 SIC 8099

■ **INTERMEDIA COMMUNICATIONS INC** p 753
3608 Queen Palm Dr 33619
Tel (800) 940-0011 SIC 4813

JOHNSON BROTHERS OF FLORIDA INC p 790
4520 S Church Ave 33611
Tel (813) 832-4477 SIC 5182 5149

JTS ENTERPRISES OF TAMPA LIMITED p 796
4908 W Nassau St 33607
Tel (813) 287-2231 SIC 5812

KEENAN HOPKINS SCHMIDT AND STOWELL CONTRACTORS INC p 807
5422 Bay Center Dr # 200 33609
Tel (813) 627-2219 SIC 1542 1742

■ **KFORCE GOVERNMENT HOLDINGS INC** p 816
1001 E Palm Ave 33605
Tel (813) 552-5000 SIC 6719

▲ **KFORCE INC** p 816
1001 E Palm Ave 33605
Tel (813) 552-5000 SIC 7363 7361

KFORCE SERVICES CORP p 816
1001 E Palm Ave 33605
Tel (813) 552-3734 SIC 7361

KIMMINS CONTRACTING CORP p 819
1501 E 2nd Ave 33605
Tel (813) 248-3878 SIC 1623

KIMMINS CORP p 819
1501 E 2nd Ave 33605
Tel (813) 248-3878 SIC 1799 1795 1522

LIFELINK FOUNDATION INC p 864
9661 Delaney Creek Blvd 33619
Tel (813) 253-2640 SIC 8099

LIGHTNING HOCKEY LP p 865
401 Channelside Dr 33602
Tel (813) 301-6500 *SIC* 7941

LUTHERAN SERVICES FLORIDA INC p 886
3627a W Waters Ave 33614
Tel (813) 868-4438 *SIC* 8322

LYKES BROS INC p 887
400 N Tampa St Ste 1900 33602
Tel (813) 223-3911 *SIC* 0174 6331

■ **MASONITE CORP** p 916
1 Tampa City Center 20 33602
Tel (813) 877-2726 *SIC* 2431 3469

MASONITE HOLDINGS INC p 916
201 N Franklin St Ste 300 33602
Tel (813) 877-2726 *SIC* 2431 3442

▲ **MASONITE INTERNATIONAL CORP** p 916
201 N Franklin St 33602
Tel (813) 877-2726 *SIC* 2431 3442

MATRIX HEALTHCARE SERVICES INC p 920
3111 W Dr Martin 33607
Tel (813) 247-2077 *SIC* 6411

MCS OF TAMPA INC p 932
8510 Sunstate St 33634
Tel (813) 872-0217
SIC 1731 7373 4813 7378

N E WHERE TRANSPORT INC p 1005
3808 E Dr M L King Jr Blv Martin Luther 33610
Tel (813) 363-0959 *SIC* 4212

■ **NORTRAX INC** p 1061
4042 Park Oaks Blvd # 200 33610
Tel (813) 635-2300 *SIC* 5082

■ **ORION MARINE CONSTRUCTION INC** p 1095
5440 W Tyson Ave 33611
Tel (813) 839-8441 *SIC* 1629

■ **OS PRIME INC** p 1096
2202 N West Shore Blvd # 50 33607
Tel (813) 282-1225 *SIC* 5812

■ **OSI RESTAURANT PARTNERS LLC** p 1097
2202 N West Shore Blvd # 5 33607
Tel (813) 282-1225 *SIC* 5812 5813

■ **OUTBACK STEAKHOUSE OF FLORIDA LLC** p 1098
2202 N West Shore Blvd # 500 33607
Tel (813) 282-1225 *SIC* 5812

PEMCO WORLD AIR SERVICES INC p 1128
4102 N West Shore Blvd 33614
Tel (813) 322-9600 *SIC* 4581 3728

PEOPLES GAS p 1133
702 N Franklin St Ste 516 33602
Tel (727) 824-0990 *SIC* 4923

PEPIN DISTRIBUTING CO p 1133
4121 N 50th St 33610
Tel (813) 626-6176 *SIC* 5181

■ **PEPSI-COLA BOTTLING CO OF TAMPA** p 1134
11315 N 30th St 33612
Tel (813) 971-2550 *SIC* 2086

■ **PHARMERICA LONG-TERM CARE LLC** p 1141
3625 Queen Palm Dr 33619
Tel (877) 975-2273
SIC 5912 5961 8082 5122

PMSI LLC p 1157
175 Kelsey Ln 33619
Tel (813) 626-7788 *SIC* 6331

■ **PRIMUS TELECOMMUNICATIONS INC** p 1176
3903 Northdale Blvd 220e 33624
Tel (703) 902-2800 *SIC* 4813

PRINCE CONTRACTING LLC p 1176
10210 Highland Manor Dr # 110 33610
Tel (813) 699-5900 *SIC* 1611

PRODUCE EXCHANGE CO INC p 1179
2801 E Hillsborough Ave 33610
Tel (813) 237-3374 *SIC* 5148

QUALAWASH HOLDINGS LLC p 1196
1302 N 19th St Ste 300 33605
Tel (813) 321-6485 *SIC* 7699

QUALITY CARRIERS INC p 1196
4041 Park Oaks Blvd # 200 33610
Tel (800) 282-2031 *SIC* 4213

QUALITY DISTRIBUTION INC p 1197
4041 Park Oaks Blvd # 200 33610
Tel (813) 630-5826 *SIC* 4213

QUALITY DISTRIBUTION LLC p 1197
4041 Park Oaks Blvd # 200 33610
Tel (813) 630-5826 *SIC* 4213 7699 4212

RADIANT GROUP LLC p 1204
1320 E 9th Ave Ste 211 33605
Tel (813) 247-4731 *SIC* 5171 5411

ROBBINS MANUFACTURING CO INC p 1241
13001 N Nebraska Ave 33612
Tel (813) 971-3030 *SIC* 2491

SANWA GROWERS INC p 1281
2801 E Hillsborough Ave 33610
Tel (813) 642-5159 *SIC* 5147 5148

SEMINOLE ELECTRIC COOPERATIVE INC p 1302
16313 N Dale Mabry Hwy 33618
Tel (813) 963-0994 *SIC* 4911

SENIOR CARE GROUP INC p 1304
1240 Marbella Plaza Dr 33619
Tel (813) 341-2700 *SIC* 8051

SEVEN-ONE-SEVEN PARKING SERVICES INC p 1309
1410 N Florida Ave 33602
Tel (813) 228-7722
SIC 7299 6519 7521 4119 8742

SHIP L TAMPA L C p 1317
1130 Mcclosky Blvd 33605
Tel (813) 248-9310 *SIC* 3731

SHRINERS HOSPITALS FOR CHILDREN p 1319
12502 Usf Pine Dr 33612
Tel (813) 972-2250 *SIC* 8069

SMITHS INTERCONNECT INC p 1334
4726 Eisenhower Blvd 33634
Tel (813) 901-7200 *SIC* 3679

ST JOSEPHS HOSPITAL INC p 1369
3001 W Dr Mrtn Lthr Kng B Martin Luther 33607
Tel (813) 554-8500 *SIC* 8062

SUNCOAST CREDIT UNION p 1401
6801 E Hillsborough Ave 33610
Tel (800) 999-5887 *SIC* 6062 6061

SUPERIOR BANK p 1406
4350 W Cypress St Ste 102 33607
Tel (813) 350-6728 *SIC* 6021

■ **SYKES ACQUISITION LLC** p 1413
400 N Ashley Dr 33602
Tel (813) 274-1000 *SIC* 7379

▲ **SYKES ENTERPRISES INC** p 1413
400 N Ashley Dr Ste 2800 33602
Tel (813) 274-1000 *SIC* 7379 7389

SYNERGY HEALTH NORTH AMERICA INC p 1415
401 E Jackson St Ste 3100 33602
Tel (813) 891-9550 *SIC* 5047 7213

SYNIVERSE HOLDINGS INC p 1415
8125 Highwoods Palm Way 33647
Tel (813) 637-5000 *SIC* 4812 3663

SYNIVERSE TECHNOLOGIES LLC p 1415
8125 Highwoods Palm Way 33647
Tel (813) 637-5000 *SIC* 4812 3663

■ **SYPRIS ELECTRONICS LLC** p 1416
10421 Univ Ctr Dr Ste 100 33612
Tel (813) 972-6000 *SIC* 3672 3679

TAMPA ELECTRIC CO p 1423
702 N Franklin St 33602
Tel (813) 228-1111 *SIC* 4911 4924

TAMPA GENERAL HOSPITAL p 1423
1 Tampa General Cir 33606
Tel (813) 844-4527 *SIC* 8062

TAMPA MEDIA GROUP INC p 1423
202 S Parker St 33606
Tel (813) 259-7711 *SIC* 2711

TAMPA METROPOLITAN AREA YOUNG MENS CHRISTIAN ASSOCIATION INC p 1423
110 E Oak Ave 33602
Tel (813) 224-9622 *SIC* 8641

TAMPA PIPELINE CORP p 1423
5802 Hartford St 33619
Tel (813) 623-2431 *SIC* 4613

TECO DIVERSIFIED INC p 1432
702 N Franklin St 33602
Tel (813) 228-4111 *SIC* 1221

TECO ENERGY INC p 1432
702 N Franklin St 33602
Tel (813) 228-1111
SIC 4911 4924 4424 1221 1222

■ **TIME CUSTOMER SERVICE INC** p 1454
1 N Dale Mabry Hwy # 150 33609
Tel (813) 878-6427 *SIC* 7389 7374

■ **TRADEMARK METALS RECYCLING LLC** p 1468
The Lincoln Center 5401 W 33609
Tel (813) 226-0088 *SIC* 5093 1081

TRIBRIDGE HOLDINGS LLC p 1479
4830 W Kennedy Blvd # 890 33609
Tel (813) 287-8887 *SIC* 6719

TRIBUNE CO p 1479
202 S Parker St 33606
Tel (813) 259-7711 *SIC* 2711

TRUCK COMPONENTS INC p 1485
8819 N Brooks St 33604
Tel (813) 933-1166 *SIC* 5013

UNITED MARITIME GROUP LLC p 1510
601 S Harbour Island Blvd 33602
Tel (813) 209-4200 *SIC* 4449 4424

UNIVERSITY COMMUNITY HOSPITAL INC p 1518
3100 E Fletcher Ave 33613
Tel (813) 615-7887 *SIC* 8062

UNIVERSITY MEDICAL SERVICE ASSOCIATION INC p 1519
12901 Brc Dwns Blvd Mdc62 33612
Tel (813) 974-2124 *SIC* 8621

UNIVERSITY OF SOUTH FLORIDA BOARD OF TRUSTESS p 1525
4202 E Fowler Ave 33620
Tel (813) 974-2011 *SIC* 8221

UNIVERSITY OF SOUTH FLORIDA FOUNDATION INC p 1525
3802 Spectrum Blvd # 100 33612
Tel (813) 974-5095 *SIC* 8699

UNIVERSITY OF SOUTH FLORIDA MEDICAL SERVICES SUPPORT CORP p 1525
12901 Brc Dwns Blvd Mdc62 33612
Tel (813) 974-2201 *SIC* 8011 8741

UNIVERSITY OF TAMPA INC p 1525
401 W Kennedy Blvd 33606
Tel (813) 253-3333 *SIC* 8221

VALENTI FLORIDA MANAGEMENT INC p 1539
3930 Premier North Dr 33618
Tel (813) 935-8777 *SIC* 8741

■ **VERIZON DATA SERVICES INC** p 1550
1 E Telecom Pkwy 33637
Tel (212) 395-1000 *SIC* 7374 7371

VITALITY FOODSERVICE INC p 1562
400 N Tampa St Ste 1700 33602
Tel (813) 301-4600 *SIC* 5149 3586

▲ **WALTER INVESTMENT MANAGEMENT CORP** p 1574
3000 Bayport Dr Ste 1100 33607
Tel (813) 421-7600 *SIC* 6162

▲ **WELLCARE HEALTH PLANS INC** p 1589
8735 Henderson Rd 33634
Tel (813) 290-6200 *SIC* 6324

■ **WFTS** p 1604
4045 N Himes Ave 33607
Tel (813) 354-2800 *SIC* 4833

WILLIS OF FLORIDA INC p 1612
4211 W Boy Scout Blvd # 4 33607
Tel (813) 281-2095 *SIC* 6411

WOLF RETAIL SOLUTIONS I INC p 1621
2801 W Busch Blvd Ste 101 33618
Tel (813) 280-2946 *SIC* 7389

WORKERS TEMPORARY STAFFING INC p 1624
5050 W Lemon St Ste 200 33609
Tel (813) 637-2220 *SIC* 7363

WTS ACQUISITION CORP p 1628
5050 W Lemon St 33609
Tel (813) 637-2220 *SIC* 7363

YARA NORTH AMERICA INC p 1635
100 N Tampa St Ste 3200 33602
Tel (813) 222-5700 *SIC* 5191 5169

TARPON SPRINGS, FL

FERMAN CHEVROLET OF TARPON SPRINGS p 538
43520 Us Highway 19 N 34689
Tel (727) 942-4800
SIC 5511 7538 7515 7513 5521

HAWKINS CONSTRUCTION INC p 670
1430 L&R Industrial Blvd 34689
Tel (727) 937-2690 *SIC* 1542

TARPON SPRINGS HOSPITAL FOUNDATION INC p 1425
1395 S Pinellas Ave 34689
Tel (727) 942-5000 *SIC* 8062

TAVARES, FL

COUNTY OF LAKE p 379
315 W Main St 32778
Tel (352) 343-9808 *SIC* 9111

FLORIDA HOSPITAL WATERMAN INC p 559
1000 Waterman Way 32778
Tel (352) 253-3333 *SIC* 8062

LAKE COUNTY SCHOOLS p 838
201 W Burleigh Blvd 32778
Tel (352) 253-6500 *SIC* 8211

SCHOOL BOARD OF LAKE COUNTY (INC) p 1289
201 W Burleigh Blvd 32778
Tel (352) 253-6500 *SIC* 8211

TAVERNIER, FL

FLORIDA KEYS ELECTRIC COOPERATIVE ASSOCIATION INC p 559
91630 Overseas Hwy 33070
Tel (305) 852-2431 *SIC* 4911 1731 1623

TEMPLE TERRACE, FL

SCHOOL DISTRICT OF HILLSBOROUGH COUNTY p 1289
129 Glen Ridge Ave 33617
Tel (813) 817-4507 *SIC* 8211

THE VILLAGES, FL

HOLDING CO OF VILLAGES INC p 700
1000 Lake Sumter Lndg 32162
Tel (352) 753-2270 *SIC* 6531

VILLAGES TRI-COUNTY MEDICAL CENTER INC p 1557
1451 El Camino Real 32159
Tel (352) 751-8000 *SIC* 8062

TITUSVILLE, FL

BREVARD NORTH COUNTY HOSPITAL p 210
951 N Washington Ave 32796
Tel (321) 268-6333 *SIC* 8062

■ **JOHN F KENNEDY SPACE CENTER** p 788
6225 Vectorspace Blvd 32780
Tel (321) 867-5000 *SIC* 9661

■ **SMART CHOICE AUTOMOTIVE GROUP INC** p 1332
5130 S Washington Ave 32780
Tel (321) 269-9680 *SIC* 5521 3714 6141

■ **SOUTHEAST POWER CORP** p 1346
1805 Hammock Rd 32796
Tel (321) 268-0540 *SIC* 1731

TRENTON, FL

■ **TRI-COUNTY BANK** p 1477
350 E Wade St 32693
Tel (352) 463-1547 *SIC* 6022

TRINITY, FL

■ **KYSOR INDUSTRIAL CORP** p 833
2227 Welbilt Blvd 34655
Tel (727) 376-8600 *SIC* 3585 3714

■ **MANITOWOC FOODSERVICE COMPANIES LLC** p 902
2227 Welbilt Blvd 34655
Tel (727) 375-7010 *SIC* 6719

▲ **MANITOWOC FOODSERVICE INC** p 902
2227 Welbilt Blvd 34655
Tel (727) 375-7010 *SIC* 3585 3589

NEWPORT RICHEY HOSPITAL INC p 1038
9330 State Road 54 34655
Tel (727) 834-4000 *SIC* 8011

UNIVERSITY PARK, FL

FIRST WATCH OF OHIO INC p 550
8027 Cooper Creek Blvd # 103 34201
Tel (941) 907-6657 *SIC* 5812

VENICE, FL

COAST PUMP & SUPPLY CO INC p 331
610 Groveland Ave 34285
Tel (352) 258-2291 *SIC* 0721

■ **FIRST GUARD INSURANCE CO** p 547
200 Nokomis Ave S Fl 4 34285
Tel (941) 485-6210 *SIC* 6411

VENICE REGIONAL HOSPITAL p 1547
540 The Rialto 34285
Tel (941) 485-7711 *SIC* 8062

VENUS, FL

DELRAY PLANTS CO p 425
956 Old State Road 8 33960
Tel (800) 854-5393 *SIC* 5193

VERO BEACH, FL

ARMOUR RESIDENTIAL REIT INC p 111
3001 Ocean Dr Ste 201 32963
Tel (772) 617-4340 *SIC* 6798

GEORGE E WARREN CORP p 606
3001 Ocean Dr Ste 203 32963
Tel (772) 778-7100 *SIC* 5171

INDIAN RIVER COUNTY p 737
1800 27th St Bldg B 32960
Tel (772) 567-8000 *SIC* 9111

INDIAN RIVER MEMORIAL HOSPITAL INC p 737
1000 36th St 32960
Tel (772) 567-4311 *SIC* 8062 8011

■ **OPTEUM FINANCIAL SERVICES LLC** p 1090
3305 Flamingo Dr 32963
Tel (772) 231-1245 *SIC* 6162

PIPER AIRCRAFT INC p 1151
2926 Piper Dr 32960
Tel (772) 567-4361 *SIC* 3721 3728

SCHOOL DISTRICT OF INDIAN RIVER COUNTY p 1289
6500 57th St 32967
Tel (772) 564-3000 *SIC* 8211

SHAVER PROPERTIES INC p 1312
6010 Old Dixie Hwy Ste K 32967
Tel (772) 569-3466 *SIC* 2431

SOUTHERN FULFILLMENT SERVICES LLC p 1348
1650 90th Ave 32966
Tel (772) 226-3500 *SIC* 5148 5149

VIERA, FL

ATHLETIC DEALERS LLC p 124
5423 Village Dr 32955
Tel (321) 254-0091 *SIC* 8611

BREVARD COUNTY CO p 210
2725 Jdge Fran Jmeson Way 32940
Tel (321) 633-2046 *SIC* 9111

BREVARD COUNTY SCHOOLS p 210
2700 Jdge Fran Jmeson Way 32940
Tel (321) 633-1000 *SIC* 8211

SCHOOL BOARD OF BREVARD COUNTY p 1289
2700 Jdge Fran Jmeson Way 32940
Tel (321) 633-1000 *SIC* 8211

WATERSOUND, FL

▲ **ST JOE CO** p 1367
133 S Watersound Pkwy A 32461
Tel (850) 231-6400
SIC 6531 6552 6512 0811 0851

WAUCHULA, FL

PEACE RIVER ELECTRIC COOPERATIVE INC p 1125
210 Metheny Rd 33873
Tel (800) 282-3824 *SIC* 4911

WELLINGTON, FL

▲ **B/E AEROSPACE INC** p 142
1400 Corporate Center Way 33414
Tel (561) 791-5000 *SIC* 2531 3728 3647

▲ KLX INC p 823
1300 Corporate Center Way # 200 33414
Tel (561) 383-5100 *SIC* 3728 2911 1381

PEGASUS BUILDERS INC p 1127
3340 Frlane Frms Rd Ste 8 33414
Tel (561) 791-7037 *SIC* 1521 1542

WESLEY CHAPEL, FL

AMERICAN STAFF MANAGEMENT INC p 79
27613 Cashford Cir # 102 33544
Tel (813) 994-1200 *SIC* 7363

FLORIDA HOSPITAL WESLEY CHAPEL INC p 559
2600 Bruce B Downs Blvd 33544
Tel (813) 929-5000 *SIC* 8062

WEST PALM BEACH, FL

ACCOMPLISH THERAPY LLC p 15
1665 Palm Beach Lks 33401
Tel (561) 223-4332 *SIC* 8093

▲ AFFILIATED MANAGERS GROUP INC p 32
777 S Flagler Dr 33401
Tel (800) 345-1100 *SIC* 6722 6282

BAYVIEW CADILLAC NEW CARS & SERVICE LLC p 162
1240 N Federal Hwy 33403
Tel (954) 537-6200 *SIC* 5511

BRAMAN MOTOR CARS p 207
2901 Okeechobee Blvd 33409
Tel (561) 615-4800 *SIC* 5511

BROWN DISTRIBUTING CO INC p 219
1300 Allendale Rd 33405
Tel (561) 655-3791 *SIC* 5181

CEMEX CONSTRUCTION MATERIALS ATLANTIC LLC p 274
1501 Belvedere Rd 33406
Tel (561) 833-5555 *SIC* 3272

CEMEX CONSTRUCTION MATERIALS PACIFIC LLC p 274
1501 Belvedere Rd 33406
Tel (561) 833-5555 *SIC* 3272

CEMEX MATERIALS LLC p 274
1501 Belvedere Rd 33406
Tel (561) 833-5555
SIC 3271 3273 3272 1422

▲ CHATHAM LODGING TRUST p 291
222 Lakeview Ave Ste 200 33401
Tel (561) 802-4477 *SIC* 6798

CITY OF WEST PALM BEACH p 319
401 Clematis St 33401
Tel (561) 822-1200 *SIC* 9111

COMVEST INVESTMENT PARTNERS III LP p 353
525 Okeechobee Blvd # 1050 33401
Tel (561) 727-2000
SIC 4731 5912 5999 3652 8742 1731

COMVEST NATIONSHEALTH HOLDINGS LLC p 353
525 Okeechobee Blvd # 1050 33401
Tel (561) 727-2000 *SIC* 5912 5999

COMVEST PARTNERS p 353
525 Okeechobee Blvd # 1050 33401
Tel (561) 727-2000 *SIC* 6799

COMVEST VELOCITY ACQUISITION I LLC p 354
525 Okeechobee Blvd # 1050 33401
Tel (561) 727-2000 *SIC* 6719

COUNTY OF PALM BEACH p 380
301 N Olive Ave Frnt 33401
Tel (561) 355-2959 *SIC* 9111

CREATIVE CHOICE HOMES INC p 390
8895 N Military Trl 206e 33410
Tel (561) 627-7988 *SIC* 6552 4813

DIGITY COMPANIES LLC p 439
701 Nrthpint Pkwy Ste 500 33407
Tel (561) 616-4600 *SIC* 4832

FANJUL CORP p 527
1 N Clematis St Ste 200 33401
Tel (561) 655-6303
SIC 0133 2061 2099 6552

FEDELITY FEDERAL BANK & TRUST p 533
205 Datura St 33401
Tel (561) 803-9900 *SIC* 6141

FIRST BANK OF PALM BEACHES p 545
415 5th St 33401
Tel (561) 651-7266 *SIC* 6022

FLORIDA CRYSTALS CORP p 557
1 N Clematis St Ste 200 33401
Tel (561) 655-6303
SIC 2061 2062 2044 4911

GULFSTREAM GOODWILL INDUSTRIES INC p 647
1715 E Tiffany Dr 33407
Tel (561) 848-7200 *SIC* 8399

HEDRICK BROTHERS CONSTRUCTION CO INC p 680
2200 Centre Park West Dr # 100 33409
Tel (561) 689-8880 *SIC* 1542

HOSPICE OF PALM BEACH COUNTY INC p 709
5300 East Ave 33407
Tel (561) 848-5200 *SIC* 8059

INTERCOASTAL HEALTH SYSTEMS INC p 752
1309 N Flagler Dr 33401
Tel (561) 650-6272 *SIC* 8741 8069

ION MEDIA NETWORKS INC p 762
601 Clearwater Park Rd 33401
Tel (561) 659-4122 *SIC* 4833

ISLAND HOSPITALITY MANAGEMENT LLC p 766
222 Lakeview Ave Ste 200 33401
Tel (561) 832-6132 *SIC* 8741

KAST CONSTRUCTION CO LLC p 804
701 Nrthpint Pkwy Ste 400 33407
Tel (561) 689-2910 *SIC* 1531

MYERS AUTO GROUP LLC p 1004
915 S Dixie Hwy 33401
Tel (561) 659-6206 *SIC* 5511

NATIONAL OAK DISTRIBUTORS INC p 1014
6529 Southern Blvd Ste 6 33413
Tel (561) 478-2711 *SIC* 5013 5198

OASIS OUTSOURCING INC p 1071
2054 Vista Pkwy Ste 300 33411
Tel (561) 227-6500 *SIC* 8721 8742 7363

▲ OCWEN FINANCIAL CORP p 1074
1661 Worthington Rd # 100 33409
Tel (561) 682-8000 *SIC* 6162

■ OCWEN LOAN SERVICING LLC p 1074
1661 Worthington Rd # 100 33409
Tel (561) 682-8000 *SIC* 6162

OXBOW CARBON & MINERALS HOLDINGS INC p 1100
1601 Forum Pl Ste 1400 33401
Tel (561) 907-5400 *SIC* 5052 1222

OXBOW CARBON LLC p 1100
1601 Forum Pl Ste 1400 33401
Tel (561) 907-5400 *SIC* 1241 2999 5052

OXBOW CORP p 1100
1601 Forum Pl Ste 1400 33401
Tel (561) 907-5422 *SIC* 8731

OXBOW ENERGY SOLUTIONS LLC p 1100
1601 Forum Pl Ste 1400 33401
Tel (561) 907-4300 *SIC* 5052

PALM BEACH ATLANTIC UNIVERSITY ALUMNI ASSOCIATION p 1109
901 S Flagler Dr 33401
Tel (561) 803-2000 *SIC* 8641

PALM BEACH ATLANTIC UNIVERSITY INC p 1109
901 S Flagler Dr 33401
Tel (561) 803-2000 *SIC* 8221

PALM BEACH CAPITAL FUND I LP p 1109
525 S Flagler Dr Ste 208 33401
Tel (561) 659-9022 *SIC* 6211

PALM BEACH NEWSPAPERS INC p 1109
2751 S Dixie Hwy 33405
Tel (561) 820-4100 *SIC* 2711 2721

PENINSULAR ELECTRIC DISTRIBUTORS INC p 1129
1301 Okeechobee Rd 33401
Tel (561) 832-1626 *SIC* 5063

PERSONNEL SERVICES INC p 1137
2260 Palm Bch Lks 210 33409
Tel (561) 965-7070 *SIC* 7363

PGA RESORT & SPA p 1140
1555 Palm Beach Lks 33401
Tel (561) 686-2000
SIC 8741 7377 7513 7515

▲ PLATFORM SPECIALTY PRODUCTS CORP p 1155
1450 Centrepark Blvd 33401
Tel (561) 207-9600 *SIC* 2869 2899

RANGER CONSTRUCTION INDUSTRIES INC p 1208
101 Sansburys Way 33411
Tel (561) 793-9400 *SIC* 1611

ROGER DEAN ENTERPRISES INC p 1246
2235 Okeechobee Blvd 33409
Tel (561) 683-8100
SIC 5511 5521 7538 7532 7515

RREMC LLC p 1255
1800 Okeechobee Rd # 100 33409
Tel (561) 684-2101 *SIC* 5812

SCHOOL BOARD OF PALM BEACH COUNTY p 1289
3300 Forest Hill Blvd C316 33406
Tel (561) 434-8000 *SIC* 8211

SCHOOL DISTRICT OF WEST PALM BEACH COUNTY p 1290
3300 Forest Hill Blvd 33406
Tel (561) 434-8747 *SIC* 8211

SHOES FOR CREWS LLC p 1317
250 S Australian Ave # 1700 33401
Tel (561) 683-5090 *SIC* 5139

SOUTH FLORIDA WATER MANAGEMENT DISTRICT LEASING CORP p 1344
3301 Gun Club Rd 33406
Tel (561) 686-8800 *SIC* 4941

■ ST MARYS MEDICAL CENTER p 1371
901 45th St 33407
Tel (561) 844-6300 *SIC* 8062

TANDEM HEALTHCARE OF WEST PALM BEACH INC p 1424
1626 Davis Rd 33406
Tel (561) 439-8897 *SIC* 8059 8051

■ TENET GOOD SAMARITAN HOSPITAL INC p 1437
1309 N Flagler Dr 33401
Tel (561) 655-5511 *SIC* 8062

■ THERMO ELECTRON NORTH AMERICA LLC p 1447
770 Northpoint Pkwy # 100 33407
Tel (561) 688-8700 *SIC* 3826

TOOJAYS MANAGEMENT LLC p 1460
3654 Georgia Ave 33405
Tel (561) 659-9011 *SIC* 8741

VECELLIO GROUP INC p 1546
101 Sansburys Way 33411
Tel (561) 793-2102 *SIC* 1611

WATERMARK MEDICAL HOLDINGS INC p 1582
1641 Worthington Rd # 320 33409
Tel (561) 283-1191 *SIC* 8099

■ WELLINGTON REGIONAL MEDICAL CENTER INC p 1589
10101 Forest Hill Blvd 33414
Tel (561) 798-8500 *SIC* 8062

WOERNER HOLDINGS LP p 1620
525 Okeechobee Blvd # 720 33401
Tel (561) 835-3747 *SIC* 0181

WESTON, FL

ALTEGRA HEALTH INC p 62
1725 N Commerce Pkwy 33326
Tel (305) 779-6070 *SIC* 7374

ANDA INC p 89
2915 Weston Rd 33331
Tel (954) 217-4500 *SIC* 5122

CLEVELAND CLINIC FLORIDA FOUNDATION p 325
3100 Weston Rd 33331
Tel (954) 689-5000 *SIC* 8062

▲ FCB FINANCIAL HOLDINGS INC p 532
2500 Weston Rd Ste 300 33331
Tel (954) 984-3313 *SIC* 6022

■ FLORIDA COMMUNITY BANK NA p 557
2500 Weston Rd Ste 300 33331
Tel (866) 764-0006 *SIC* 6022

FSA NETWORK INC p 582
1545 N Park Dr Ste 101 33326
Tel (954) 745-2120 *SIC* 4212 7641

GLOBAL MAIL INC p 617
2700 S Comm Pkwy Ste 300 33331
Tel (800) 805-9306 *SIC* 4513

▲ ULTIMATE SOFTWARE GROUP INC p 1501
2000 Ultimate Way 33326
Tel (800) 432-1729 *SIC* 7372

VARSATEL CORP p 1545
2813 Executive Park Dr # 112 33331
Tel (954) 667-6550 *SIC* 5065

WILLISTON, FL

SEABRING MARINE INDUSTRIES INC p 1296
1579 Sw 18th St 32696
Tel (352) 529-9161 *SIC* 5091 3732

WILTON MANORS, FL

■ IMPSAT FIBER NETWORKS INC p 735
2040 N Dixie Hwy 33305
Tel (954) 779-7171 *SIC* 4899

MOSS & ASSOCIATES LLC p 992
2101 N Andrews Ave 33311
Tel (954) 524-5678 *SIC* 1542

WIMAUMA, FL

WILLIAM P HEARNE PRODUCE LLC p 1610
707 W Lake Dr 33598
Tel (813) 633-8910 *SIC* 5141

WINDERMERE, FL

FRESH EXPRESS INC p 578
4757 The Grove Dr Ste 260 34786
Tel (980) 636-5530 *SIC* 0723 2099

WINTER GARDEN, FL

LOUIS DREYFUS CITRUS INC p 879
355 9th St 34787
Tel (407) 656-1000 *SIC* 2037 2033

WINTER HAVEN, FL

BORDEN DAIRY CO OF FLORIDA LLC p 201
308 Avenue G Sw 33880
Tel (863) 297-7300
SIC 5143 2026 2024 2022 2021

CARPENTER CONTRACTORS OF AMERICA INC p 260
3900 Ave D Nw 33880
Tel (863) 294-6449 *SIC* 1751 2439 2431

CENTER FOR PSYCHIATRY AT WINTER HAVEN INC p 276
200 Avenue F Ne 33881
Tel (863) 297-1744 *SIC* 8011

■ CENTERSTATE BANK OF FLORIDA NATIONAL ASSOCIATION p 276
7722 State Road 544 33881
Tel (863) 422-8990 *SIC* 6022

■ FIRST NATIONAL BANK OF POLK COUNTY INC p 548
7722 State Road 544 Fl 1 33881
Tel (863) 422-8990 *SIC* 6022

■ FLORIDA PUBLIC UTILITIES CO p 559
331 W Central Ave Ste 200 33880
Tel (352) 447-2790 *SIC* 4911 4922 5984

G ROE WM & SONS INC p 587
500 Avenue R Sw 33880
Tel (863) 294-3577 *SIC* 2033

INDIAN RIVER TRANSPORT CO p 738
2580 Executive Rd 33884
Tel (863) 324-2430 *SIC* 4213

MID-FLORIDA MEDICAL SERVICES INC p 963
200 Avenue F Ne 33881
Tel (863) 297-1895 *SIC* 8741 8062 8082

WINTER HAVEN HOSPITAL INC p 1617
200 Avenue F Ne 33881
Tel (863) 293-1121 *SIC* 8062

WINTER PARK, FL

BONNIER CORP p 200
460 N Orlando Ave Ste 200 32789
Tel (407) 622-1014 *SIC* 2721

■ CEMETERY MANAGEMENT INC p 274
1201 S Orlando Ave # 365 32789
Tel (407) 740-7000 *SIC* 6553 6531

CHILDRENS HOME SOCIETY OF FLORIDA p 299
1485 S Semoran Blvd 32792
Tel (407) 657-2197 *SIC* 8322 8361

CRDENTIA CORP p 390
1964 Howell Branch Rd # 103 32792
Tel (520) 327-2651 *SIC* 7363

DINGMAN GROUP INC p 440
1051 W Webster Ave 32789
Tel (407) 644-6043 *SIC* 5511 5531 7539

FLORIDA CONFERENCE ASSOCIATION OF SEVENTH-DAY ADVENTISTS p 557
655 N Wymore Rd 32789
Tel (407) 644-5000
SIC 8661 8211 5942 6513

FULL SAIL LLC p 584
3300 University Blvd 32792
Tel (407) 679-0100 *SIC* 8222 7389

GECOS INC p 597
1936 Lee Rd 32789
Tel (407) 645-5500 *SIC* 1611 2951 1623

HANDEX CONSULTING AND REMEDIATION LLC p 657
1350 Orange Ave Ste 101 32789
Tel (352) 735-1800 *SIC* 4959

HUBBARD CONSTRUCTION CO p 716
1936 Lee Rd Ste 101 32789
Tel (407) 645-5500 *SIC* 1611 2951 1623

HUBBARD GROUP INC p 716
1936 Lee Rd Ste 101 32789
Tel (407) 645-5500 *SIC* 1611 2951 1623

MERCANTILE BANK p 943
1560 Orange Ave Ste 300 32789
Tel (407) 622-3528 *SIC* 6022

ORANGE COUNTY FIRE & RESCUE p 1092
6590 Amory Ct 32792
Tel (407) 836-9112 *SIC* 9224

QUINCO ELECTRICAL INC p 1200
4224 Metric Dr 32792
Tel (407) 478-6005 *SIC* 1731

REV AMBULANCE GROUP ORLANDO INC p 1229
2737 Forsyth Rd 32792
Tel (407) 677-7777 *SIC* 3711

ROLLINS COLLEGE p 1247
1000 Holt Ave 2718 32789
Tel (407) 646-2000 *SIC* 8221

RSR GROUP INC p 1256
4405 Metric Dr 32792
Tel (407) 677-6114 *SIC* 5099

▲ RUTHS HOSPITALITY GROUP INC p 1260
1030 W Canton Ave Ste 100 32789
Tel (407) 333-7440 *SIC* 5812 6794

WINTER PARK HEALTHCARE GROUP LTD p 1617
200 N Lakemont Ave 32792
Tel (407) 646-7000 *SIC* 8062 8011

ZELLWOOD, FL

INDUSTRIAL CONTAINER SERVICES - FL LLC p 739
2400 Maitland Ctr 32798
Tel (407) 930-4182 *SIC* 5085

ZEPHYRHILLS, FL

FLORIDA HOSPITAL ZEPHYRHILLS p 559
37924 Medical Arts Ct 33541
Tel (813) 779-1900 *SIC* 8062

FLORIDA HOSPITAL ZEPHYRHILLS INC p 559
7050 Gall Blvd 33541
Tel (813) 788-0411 *SIC* 8062

FLORIDA MEDICAL CLINIC PA p 559
38135 Market Sq 33542
Tel (813) 780-8440 *SIC* 8011

GEORGIA

ACWORTH, GA

DAYS CHEVROLET INC p 417
3693 Cobb Pkwy Nw 30101
Tel (770) 974-4242 *SIC* 5511

ADAIRSVILLE, GA

YANMAR AMERICA CORP p 1635
101 International Pkwy 30103
Tel (770) 877-9894
SIC 5084 7699 5083 3519

ALBANY, GA

BRAD LANIER OIL CO INC p 206
611 W Roosevelt Ave 31701
Tel (229) 436-0131 SIC 5171 5541 5411

CITY OF ALBANY p 312
222 Pine Ave Ste 560 31701
Tel (229) 883-6955 SIC 9121

DOUGHERTY COUNTY SCHOOL SYSTEM p 452
200 Pine Ave 31701
Tel (229) 431-1264 SIC 8211

FLINT EQUIPMENT HOLDINGS INC p 557
1206 Blaylock St 31705
Tel (229) 888-1212 SIC 5084

HERITAGE FINANCIAL GROUP INC p 686
721 N Westover Blvd 31707
Tel (229) 420-0000 SIC 6035

MEDIACOM SOUTHEAST LLC p 936
1104 N Westover Blvd 31707
Tel (229) 888-0242 SIC 4841 4813

METROPOWER INC p 957
798 21st Ave 31701
Tel (229) 432-7345 SIC 1731

OXFORD CONSTRUCTION CO p 1101
3200 Palmyra Rd 31707
Tel (229) 883-3232 SIC 1611 1629

PHOEBE PUTNEY MEMORIAL HOSPITAL INC p 1144
2000 Palmyra Rd 31701
Tel (229) 434-2000 SIC 8062

PHOEBE PUTNEY MEMORIAL HOSPITAL INC p 1144
417 W 3rd Ave 31701
Tel (229) 312-1000 SIC 8062

WATER GAS & LIGHT COMMISSION p 1581
207 Pine Ave 31701
Tel (229) 883-8330 SIC 4939

ALMA, GA

SATILLA RURAL ELECTRIC MEMBERSHIP CORP p 1283
928 Ga Highway 32 E 31510
Tel (912) 632-7222 SIC 4911

ALPHARETTA, GA

■ ACCU-TECH CORP p 16
11350 Old Roswell Rd # 100 30009
Tel (770) 740-2240 SIC 5065 5063

AGC AMERICA INC p 34
11175 Cicero Dr Ste 400 30022
Tel (404) 446-4200
SIC 6719 3211 2869 5169 3229

AGC FLAT GLASS NORTH AMERICA INC p 34
11175 Cicero Dr Ste 400 30022
Tel (404) 446-4200 SIC 3231 3211

AHLSTROM ATLANTA LLC p 36
3820 Mansell Rd Ste 200 30022
Tel (770) 650-2100 SIC 2621

ALLNEX USA INC p 58
9005 Westside Pkwy 30009
Tel (800) 433-2873 SIC 2821

AMEC E&I HOLDINGS INC p 66
1105 Lakewood Pkwy # 300 30009
Tel (770) 360-0600 SIC 8744 8711

AMEC E&I INC p 66
1105 Lakewood Pkwy # 300 30009
Tel (770) 360-0600 SIC 8711

AMEC FOSTER WHEELER ENVIRONMENT & INFRASTRUCTURE INC p 66
1105 Lakewood Pkwy # 300 30009
Tel (770) 360-0600 SIC 8748 8711

AMERIFLEET TRANSPORTATION INC p 82
1111 Alderman Dr 30005
Tel (770) 442-0222 SIC 4789

ANDRITZ (USA) INC p 91
5405 Windward Pkwy 100 30004
Tel (770) 640-2500 SIC 3554 3523

ANGELICA CORP p 91
1105 Lakewood Pkwy # 210 30009
Tel (678) 823-4100 SIC 7213 5699 5661

ANGELICA TEXTILE SERVICES INC p 91
1105 Lakewood Pkwy # 210 30009
Tel (678) 823-4100 SIC 7213 7211

APTEAN INC p 101
4325 Alexander Dr Ste 100 30022
Tel (770) 351-9600 SIC 5045

ARCH CHEMICALS INC p 104
1200 Bluegrass Lakes Pkwy 30004
Tel (678) 624-5800 SIC 2819 2899

ARGOS READY MIX (SOUTH CENTRAL) CORP p 107
3015 Wndward Pl Dr Ste 30 30005
Tel (678) 368-4300 SIC 3273

ARGOS USA LLC p 107
3015 Windward Plz 30005
Tel (678) 368-4300 SIC 3272

ARGOS USA LLC p 107
3015 Windward Plz Ste 300 30005
Tel (678) 368-4300 SIC 3272 5032

ATRIUM HOSPITALITY LP p 129
12735 Morris Road Ext # 400 30004
Tel (678) 762-0005 SIC 7011

■ AUTOTOTE SYSTEMS INC p 135
1500 Bluegrass Lakes Pkwy 30004
Tel (770) 664-3700
SIC 3578 7373 7359 8711

AXIS SPECIALTY US HOLDINGS INC p 140
11680 Great Oaks Way # 500 30022
Tel (678) 746-9000 SIC 6719

AXIS SPECIALTY US SERVICES INC p 140
11680 Great Oaks Way # 500 30022
Tel (678) 746-9000 SIC 6331

■ BANK OF NORTH GEORGIA p 152
8025 Westside Pkwy # 150 30009
Tel (770) 569-9660 SIC 6022

■ BRIGHTSTAR DEVICE PROTECTION LLC p 213
2325 Lkeview Pkwy Ste 700 30009
Tel (843) 548-0120 SIC 6411

CDC SOFTWARE INC p 270
4325 Alexander Dr 30022
Tel (770) 351-9600 SIC 5045

■ CELLU TISSUE HOLDINGS INC p 274
12725 Morris Road Ext # 210 30004
Tel (678) 393-2651 SIC 2621

■ CHECKFREE CORP p 292
2900 Westside Pkwy 30004
Tel (678) 375-3000 SIC 7389

■ CHECKFREE SERVICES CORP p 292
2900 Westside Pkwy 30004
Tel (678) 375-3000 SIC 7374

CHEP (USA) INC p 294
5897 Windward Pkwy 30005
Tel (770) 379-6900 SIC 7359

CIOX HEALTH LLC p 308
925 North Point Pkwy # 350 30005
Tel (800) 367-1500 SIC 7375

CIVES CORP p 320
3700 Mansell Rd Ste 500 30022
Tel (770) 993-4424 SIC 3441 3713 3443

COLONIAL PIPELINE CO p 338
1185 Sanctuary Pkwy # 100 30009
Tel (678) 762-2200
SIC 4613 4612 4226 1389 5171

CONVERGENT RESOURCES HOLDINGS LLC p 365
555 N Point Ctr E Ste 175 30022
Tel (866) 867-0179 SIC 8741

CONVERGENT RESOURCES INC p 365
555 N Point Ctr E Ste 175 30022
Tel (770) 512-3670 SIC 7322

DOLMAR GMBH (INC) p 448
1005 Alderman Dr Ste 106 30005
Tel (770) 569-4945 SIC 5072

EASYLINK SERVICES INTERNATIONAL CORP p 473
11720 Amberpark Dr # 200 30009
Tel (678) 533-8000 SIC 4813

ENDOCHOICE INC p 496
11405 Old Roswell Rd 30009
Tel (888) 682-3636 SIC 5047

EXECUTRAIN CORP p 518
2500 Northwinds Pkwy # 460 30009
Tel (770) 667-7700 SIC 6794 8243

GLOBAL CELLULAR INC p 616
6485 Shiloh Rd Ste B100 30005
Tel (678) 513-4020 SIC 5065

■ GOLDEN PEANUT CO LLC p 621
100 N Point Ctr E Ste 400 30022
Tel (770) 752-8160 SIC 0723

HAGEMEYER NORTH AMERICA HOLDINGS INC p 652
11680 Great Oaks Way 30022
Tel (843) 745-2400 SIC 5085

▲ HALYARD HEALTH INC p 655
5405 Windward Pkwy 30004
Tel (678) 425-9273 SIC 3842 3841 3845

■ HALYARD SALES LLC p 655
5405 Windward Pkwy # 100 30004
Tel (678) 425-9273 SIC 3845 3841

■ HANSGROHE INC p 658
1490 Bluegrass Lakes Pkwy 30004
Tel (770) 360-9880 SIC 3432 5074 3431

HEALTHPORT INC p 677
925 North Point Pkwy # 350 30005
Tel (770) 360-1700 SIC 6324 7373 7374

HONEY BAKED HAM CO LLC p 705
3875 Mansell Rd Ste 100 30022
Tel (678) 966-3100 SIC 5421

INFOR (US) INC p 741
13560 Morris Rd Ste 4100 30004
Tel (678) 319-8000 SIC 7372

INGENICO CORP (DELAWARE) p 742
3025 Windward Plz Ste 600 30005
Tel (678) 456-1200 SIC 3577

INTEGRA LOGISTICS LLC p 748
4400 Alexander Dr 1w 30022
Tel (678) 775-5140 SIC 4731

JACKSON HEALTHCARE LLC p 774
2655 Northwinds Pkwy 30009
Tel (770) 643-5500 SIC 7361

JACKSON HEALTHCARE STAFFING HOLDINGS LLC p 774
2655 Northwinds Pkwy 30009
Tel (770) 643-5500 SIC 8099

■ KAPLAN HIGHER EDUCATION LLC p 803
900 North Point Pkwy # 250 30005
Tel (770) 360-6100 SIC 8221 8244

LANDIS+GYR HOLDCO2 LLC p 842
30000 Mill Creek Ave 30022
Tel (678) 258-1500 SIC 7389

LANDIS+GYR INC p 842
30000 Mill Creek Ave 30022
Tel (678) 258-1500 SIC 3825

LAZER SPOT INC p 849
6525 Shiloh Rd Ste 900 30005
Tel (770) 886-6851 SIC 0762 4212

LEASE PLAN USA INC p 850
1165 Sanctuary Pkwy 30009
Tel (770) 933-9090 SIC 7515 8741

LEXISNEXIS RISK SOLUTIONS INC p 860
1000 Alderman Dr 30005
Tel (678) 694-6000 SIC 8748

LIAISON TECHNOLOGIES INC p 861
3157 Royal Dr Ste 200 30022
Tel (770) 642-5000 SIC 7373

LIN R ROGERS ELECTRICAL CONTRACTORS INC p 866
2050 Marconi Dr Ste 100 30005
Tel (770) 772-3400 SIC 1731

■ MAGNATRAX CORP p 896
1220 Old Alpharetta Rd # 310 30005
Tel (678) 455-3360
SIC 3448 3442 3479 4213 3444

MAGNITUDE PARENT HOLDINGS LLC p 896
200 N Point Ctr E Ste 200 30022
Tel (678) 323-2500 SIC 6719

MARKETSOURCE INC p 908
11700 Great Oaks Way 30022
Tel (770) 674-5000 SIC 8742

■ MCKESSON INFORMATION SOLUTIONS LLC p 930
5995 Windward Pkwy 30005
Tel (404) 338-6000 SIC 7373

■ MCKESSON TECHNOLOGIES INC p 930
11475 Great Oaks Way # 400 30022
Tel (404) 338-6000
SIC 7374 8741 8721 7322 7373

MEDASSETS INC p 935
200 N Point Ctr E Ste 200 30022
Tel (678) 323-2500 SIC 8742

MEDASSETS NET REVENUE SYSTEMS LLC p 935
200 N Point Ctr E Ste 400 30022
Tel (678) 248-8200 SIC 8742 7371

MEDQUEST INC p 938
3480 Preston Ridge Rd # 500 30005
Tel (678) 992-7200 SIC 8071

■ MICROTEK MEDICAL HOLDINGS INC p 962
13000 Drfeld Pkwy Ste 300 30004
Tel (678) 896-4400 SIC 3842

MQ ASSOCIATES INC p 996
3480 Preston Ridge Rd # 600 30005
Tel (770) 300-0101 SIC 8099

NATIONAL CHRISTIAN CHARITABLE p 1010
11625 Rainwater Dr # 500 30009
Tel (404) 252-0100 SIC 8699

▲ NEENAH PAPER INC p 1024
3460 Preston Ridge Rd # 150 30005
Tel (678) 566-6500 SIC 2621 2741

PCL INDUSTRIAL CONSTRUCTION CO p 1124
6445 Shiloh Rd Ste E 30005
Tel (678) 965-3100 SIC 1629 1541

PEXCO LLC p 1140
2500 Northwinds Pkwy # 472 30009
Tel (404) 564-8560 SIC 3089

PRECISION CONCRETE CONSTRUCTION INC p 1168
2075 Brandon Trl 30004
Tel (770) 751-9158 SIC 1771

PRIME RISK PARTNERS INC p 1175
2475 Northwinds Pkwy 30009
Tel (770) 856-9332 SIC 6411

PRIMETALS TECHNOLOGIES USA LLC p 1175
5895 Windward Pkwy Fl 2 30005
Tel (770) 740-3800 SIC 3312

PRO MARKETING INC p 1178
1350 Bluegrass Lakes Pkwy 30004
Tel (770) 521-1421 SIC 5072 5085

PROMETHEAN INC p 1183
1165 Sanctuary Pkwy # 400 30009
Tel (678) 762-1500 SIC 5049 5045

PYRAMID CONSULTING INC p 1193
11100 Atlantis Pl 30022
Tel (678) 514-3500 SIC 7379 7371

■ RADIANT SYSTEMS INC p 1204
3925 Brookside Pkwy 30022
Tel (877) 794-7237 SIC 5734 7373

ROLTA INTERNATIONAL INC p 1248
5865 N Point Pkwy Ste 300 30022
Tel (678) 942-5000 SIC 7389 7371 7372

▲ SCHWEITZER-MAUDUIT INTERNATIONAL INC p 1291
100 N Point Ctr E Ste 600 30022
Tel (800) 514-0186 SIC 2141 2111 2621

SCIENTIFIC GAMES FINANCE CORP p 1292
1500 Bluegrass Lakes Pkwy 30004
Tel (770) 664-3700 SIC 2754

■ SCIENTIFIC GAMES INTERNATIONAL INC p 1292
1500 Bluegrass Lakes Pkwy 30004
Tel (770) 664-3700 SIC 7389 7999

SELECT MANAGEMENT RESOURCES LLC p 1301
3440 Preston Ridge Rd # 500 30005
Tel (678) 823-4700 SIC 8741

SOLVAY SPECIALTY POLYMERS USA LLC p 1339
4500 Mcginnis Ferry Rd 30005
Tel (770) 772-8200 SIC 3089

SOUTHERN INSURANCE UNDERWRITERS INC p 1349
4500 Mansell Rd 30022
Tel (678) 498-4500 SIC 6411

SPORTECH RACING LLC p 1359
1095 Windward Ridge Pkwy 30005
Tel (678) 566-1021 SIC 7373

TENSAR CORP GEORGIA p 1438
2500 Northwinds Pkwy # 50 30009
Tel (770) 344-2090 SIC 3089 8711

TENSAR INTERNATIONAL CORP p 1438
2500 Northwinds Pkwy # 500 30009
Tel (770) 344-2090 SIC 8711 3089

THYSSENKRUPP ELEVATOR AMERICAS CORP p 1451
11605 Haynes Bridge Rd 30009
Tel (678) 319-3240 SIC 7699 3534 1796

THYSSENKRUPP ELEVATOR CORP p 1451
11605 Haynes Bridge Rd # 650 30009
Tel (678) 319-3240 SIC 3534 1796 7699

TM RESTAURANT GROUP LLC p 1457
6220 Shiloh Rd Ste 100 30005
Tel (678) 679-1210 SIC 5812

■ UPS SUPPLY CHAIN SOLUTIONS INC p 1529
12380 Morris Rd 30005
Tel (800) 742-5727 SIC 8742

■ UPS WORLDWIDE LOGISTICS INC p 1529
12380 Morris Rd 30005
Tel (678) 746-4100 SIC 7389

■ UTILIQUEST LLC p 1537
2575 Westside Pkwy # 100 30004
Tel (678) 461-3900 SIC 1623 3812

■ VERINT AMERICAS INC p 1549
800 North Point Pkwy 30005
Tel (770) 754-1900 SIC 7372

■ VERIZON WIRELESS OF EAST LP p 1551
1 Verizon Pl 30004
Tel (678) 339-4000 SIC 4812

■ WINDSTREAM SUPPLY LLC p 1616
13560 Morris Rd Ste 4350 30004
Tel (678) 381-0984 SIC 5065

WISE BUSINESS FORMS INC p 1619
555 Mcfarland 400 Dr 30004
Tel (770) 442-1060 SIC 2761 2752

AMERICUS, GA

HABITAT FOR HUMANITY INTERNATIONAL INC p 651
121 Habitat St 31709
Tel (800) 422-4828
SIC 8399 8661 8322 1521 1531

ATHENS, GA

CLARKE COUNTY SCHOOL DISTRICT p 322
240 Mitchell Bridge Rd 30606
Tel (706) 546-7721 SIC 8211

COMMUNITY NEWSPAPERS INC p 349
2365 Prince Ave A 30606
Tel (706) 548-0010 SIC 2752

ISLAND APPAREL p 766
135 Renfrew Dr 30606
Tel (706) 548-3420 SIC 2325

■ MCLANE/SOUTHEAST p 931
300 Highway 29 N 30601
Tel (706) 549-4520 SIC 5141

PBR INC p 1123
335 Athena Dr 30601
Tel (706) 354-3700 SIC 2297 2221 3089

PIEDMONT ATHENS REGIONAL MEDICAL CENTER INC p 1146
1510 Prince Ave 30606
Tel (706) 475-7000 SIC 8062

POWER PARTNERS INC p 1165
200 Newton Bridge Rd 30607
Tel (706) 548-3121 SIC 3612

ST MARYS HEALTH CARE SYSTEM INC p 1371
1230 Baxter St 30606
Tel (706) 389-3000 SIC 8062 8051

UNIFIED GOVERNMENT OF ATHENS-CLARKE COUNTY p 1503
301 College Ave Ste 300 30601
Tel (706) 613-3010 SIC 9111

UNIVERSITY OF GEORGIA p 1521
424 E Broad St 30602
Tel (706) 542-2786 SIC 8221

UNIVERSITY OF GEORGIA p 1521
415 Boyds Graduate Studie 30602
Tel (706) 542-2911 SIC 5734

UNIVERSITY OF GEORGIA ATHLETIC ASSOCIATION INC p 1521
1 Selig Cir B 30602
Tel (706) 542-1306 SIC 8699

UNIVERSITY OF GEORGIA FOUNDATION p 1521
394 S Milledge Ave # 100 30605
Tel (706) 542-6677 SIC 8699

UNIVERSITY OF GEORGIA RESEARCH FOUNDATION INC p 1521
310 E Campus Rd 409 30602
Tel (706) 542-5939 SIC 6732

ZAX INC p 1641
1040 Founders Blvd 30606
Tel (706) 353-8107 SIC 5812

ATLANTA, GA

A A G STUCCHI NORTH AMERICA INC p 4
3400 Peachtree Rd Ne # 945 30326
Tel (404) 806-5399 SIC 3678

■ A S A HOLDINGS INC p 6
100 Hartsfield Ctr Pkwy 30354
Tel (404) 766-1400 SIC 4512

▲ AARONS INC p 8
400 Galleria Pkwy Se # 300 30339
Tel (404) 231-0011
SIC 7359 5712 5731 5722 5932 6794

ABB ENTERPRISE SOFTWARE INC p 9
400 Perimeter Ctr Ter 5 30346
Tel (678) 830-1000 SIC 7372

ACCESS INSURANCE HOLDINGS INC p 14
3 Ravinia Dr Ste 400 30346
Tel (770) 234-3631 SIC 6411

ACTION CAPITAL CORP p 19
230 Peachtree St Nw # 810 30303
Tel (404) 524-3181 SIC 6153

▲ ACUITY BRANDS INC p 20
1170 Peachtree St Ne 30309
Tel (404) 853-1400 SIC 3648 3646 3645

ACUITY SPECIALTY PRODUCTS INC p 20
1310 Sboard Indus Blvd Nw 30318
Tel (404) 352-1680
SIC 2841 2879 2842 5169

■ AGL RESOURCES SERVICE CO p 35
10 Peachtree Pl Ne # 1000 30309
Tel (404) 584-9470
SIC 8742 8721 8744 4924

■ AIR SERV CORP p 39
3399 Peachtree Rd Ne 30326
Tel (404) 926-4200 SIC 4581 4111

AIR SERV SECURITY INC p 39
3399 Peachtree Rd Ne # 1800 30326
Tel (404) 926-4200 SIC 4581

■ AIRWATCH LLC p 41
1155 Perimeter Ctr # 100 30338
Tel (470) 247-4312 SIC 7371

AJC INTERNATIONAL INC p 41
1000 Abernathy Rd Ste 600 30328
Tel (404) 252-6750
SIC 5144 5147 5148 5146

ALDRIDGE PITE LLP p 48
3575 Piedmont Rd Ne # 500 30305
Tel (404) 994-7400 SIC 8111

■ ALERE HEALTH LLC p 48
3200 Windy Hill Rd Se 100b 30339
Tel (770) 767-4500 SIC 8099

ALEXANDER GALLO HOLDINGS LLC p 49
101 Marietta St Nw # 2700 30303
Tel (404) 495-0777 SIC 7311

ALLCONNECT INC p 52
980 Hammond Dr Ste 1000 30328
Tel (404) 260-2200 SIC 4812

ALLIED AUTOMOTIVE GROUP INC p 56
2302 Parklake Dr Ne # 600 30345
Tel (404) 373-4285 SIC 4213

ALLIED SYSTEMS HOLDINGS INC p 57
2302 Parkl Dr Bldg 15ste 30345
Tel (404) 373-4285 SIC 4213

ALSTON & BIRD LLP p 61
1201 W Peachtree St Ne # 4000 30309
Tel (404) 881-7654 SIC 8111

ALTISOURCE HOLDINGS LLC p 62
1000 Abernathy Rd 30328
Tel (877) 839-7118 SIC 6794 6519

ALTISOURCE SOLUTIONS INC p 62
1000 Abernathy Rd Ste 200 30328
Tel (770) 612-7007 SIC 6162

AMERICAN CANCER SOCIETY INC p 69
250 Williams St Nw # 6000 30303
Tel (404) 320-3333 SIC 8621

■ AMERICAN SECURITY INSURANCE CO p 79
260 Interstate N Cir Se 30339
Tel (770) 763-1000 SIC 6331

▲ AMERICAN SOFTWARE INC p 79
470 E Paces Ferry Rd Ne 30305
Tel (404) 261-4381 SIC 7372

AMERICOLD LOGISTICS LLC p 82
10 Glenlake Pkwy Ste 324 30328
Tel (678) 441-1400
SIC 4222 4899 8742 7389

AMERICOLD REALTY TRUST p 82
10 Glenlk Pkwy Ste 600 30328
Tel (404) 394-1312 SIC 4222

AMERIPARK LLC p 82
3200 Cobb Galleria Pkwy # 299 30339
Tel (404) 364-0342 SIC 7521 7299

AMERISAVE MORTGAGE CORP p 83
3350 Peachtree Rd Ne # 1000 30326
Tel (866) 970-7283 SIC 6163

AOT BEDDING INTERMEDIATE HOLDINGS LLC p 95
1 Concrs Pkwy Ne Ste 800 30328
Tel (770) 512-7700 SIC 2515

APAC HOLDINGS INC p 95
900 Ashwood Pkwy Ste 700 30338
Tel (770) 392-5300 SIC 1611 3531 5032

APAC-SOUTHEAST INC p 95
900 Ashwood Pkwy Ste 700 30338
Tel (770) 392-5300 SIC 1611 1622 2951

APARTMENTIME COM LLC p 96
2025 Peachtree Rd Ne 30309
Tel (404) 961-0603 SIC 7299

APTOS INC p 101
945 E Paces Ferry Rd Ne 30326
Tel (866) 493-7037
SIC 5044 5045 7378 7699

■ AQUILEX SPECIALTY REPAIR AND OVERHAUL LLC p 102
3344 Peachtree Rd Ne 30326
Tel (800) 868-9353 SIC 3699

ARBOR PHARMACEUTICALS LLC p 103
6 Cncurse Pkwy Ste 1800 30328
Tel (678) 334-2420 SIC 5122

ARBYS RESTAURANT GROUP p 103
1155 Perimeter Ctr 30338
Tel (678) 514-4100 SIC 5812

ARBYS RESTAURANT GROUP INC p 103
1155 Perimeter Ctr 30338
Tel (678) 514-4100 SIC 5812

ARCAPITA INC p 103
1180 Peachtree St Ne # 3000 30309
Tel (404) 920-9000 SIC 6798

ARCHER WESTERN CONTRACTORS LLC p 105
2410 Paces Ferry Rd Se # 600 30339
Tel (404) 495-8700
SIC 1542 1622 1611 1629

ARG HOLDING CORP p 107
1180 Peachtree St Ne 30309
Tel (404) 591-5200 SIC 5812

ARG IH LLC p 107
1180 Peachtree St Ne 30309
Tel (404) 591-5200 SIC 5812

ARGONNE CAPITAL GROUP LLC p 107
3060 Peachtree Rd Nw # 400 30305
Tel (404) 364-2984 SIC 6799

ARROW EXTERMINATORS INC p 113
8613 Roswell Rd Bldg 4 30350
Tel (770) 993-8705
SIC 1742 7342 1521 1542

ATLANTA BEVERAGE CO p 125
5000 Fulton Indus Blvd Sw 30336
Tel (404) 699-6700 SIC 5181

ATLANTA BOARD OF EDUCATION p 125
130 Trinity Ave Sw 30303
Tel (404) 802-3500 SIC 8211

ATLANTA CLARK UNIVERSITY INC p 125
223 James P Brawley Dr Sw 30314
Tel (404) 880-8000 SIC 8221

ATLANTA COMMUNITY FOOD BANK INC p 125
732 Jseph E Lwery Blvd Nw 30318
Tel (404) 892-9822 SIC 8322 4783

■ ATLANTA GAS LIGHT CO p 125
10 Peachtree Pl Ne # 1000 30309
Tel (630) 388-2781 SIC 4924

■ ATLANTA MEDICAL CENTER p 125
303 Parkway Dr Ne 30312
Tel (404) 265-4000 SIC 8062

■ ATLANTA NATIONAL LEAGUE BASEBALL CLUB INC p 125
755 Hank Aaron Dr Sw 30315
Tel (404) 522-7630 SIC 7941

ATLANTA NETWORK TECHNOLOGIES INC p 125
710 Morgan Falls Rd 30350
Tel (877) 293-9797 SIC 5045 5065

ATLANTA ORIENTAL FOOD WHOLESALE CO p 125
5600 Buford Hwy Ne 30340
Tel (770) 455-0770
SIC 5146 5421 5046 5719

ATLANTA OUTPATIENT PEACHTREE DUNWOODY CENTER p 125
5730 Glenridge Dr Ste 400 30328
Tel (404) 847-0893 SIC 8093

ATLANTA PUBLIC SCHOOLS p 125
130 Trinity Ave Sw 30303
Tel (404) 802-3500 SIC 8211

ATLANTIC TRUST CO NA p 127
1555 Peachtree St Ne # 1100 30309
Tel (404) 881-3400 SIC 6733

AVANGATE INC p 136
3500 Lenox Rd Ne Ste 710 30326
Tel (650) 249-5280 SIC 7373

■ AWS HOLDINGS LLC p 139
1155 Perimeter Ctr # 100 30338
Tel (404) 478-7500 SIC 7371

■ AXIALL CORP p 140
1000 Abernathy Rd # 1200 30328
Tel (770) 395-4500
SIC 2812 2821 2865 2861 2873

■ AXIALL LLC p 140
1000 Abernathy Rd # 1200 30328
Tel (770) 395-4500 SIC 2821

BALFOUR BEATTY INFRASTRUCTURE INC p 148
999 Peachtree St Ne # 900 30309
Tel (404) 875-0356 SIC 1611

BCD TRAVEL USA LLC p 164
6 Concourse Pkwy Ste 2400 30328
Tel (678) 441-5200 SIC 4724 7372

BEAVEX INC p 166
2120 Powers Ferry Rd Se 30339
Tel (404) 260-0961 SIC 4215 4513

■ BEAZER HOMES CORP p 166
1000 Abernathy Rd 30328
Tel (770) 829-3700 SIC 1531

▲ BEAZER HOMES USA INC p 166
1000 Abernathy Rd Ste 260 30328
Tel (770) 829-3700 SIC 1521 1522

■ BEECHER CARLSON HOLDINGS INC p 168
6 Concourse Pkwy Ste 2300 30328
Tel (404) 460-1400 SIC 6411

■ BELLSOUTH CORP p 171
675 W Peach St Ste 4300 30375
Tel (404) 420-6126
SIC 4813 4812 2741 5065

■ BELLSOUTH TELECOMMUNICATIONS INC p 171
675 W Peach St Ne St Ne 30375
Tel (912) 526-3440
SIC 4813 4812 2741 5065

BENCHMARK BRANDS INC p 172
1375 Peachtree St Ne Fl 6 30309
Tel (770) 242-1254 SIC 5139

BENTON GLOBAL LLC p 173
1045 S Rver Indus Blvd Se 30315
Tel (404) 267-2200 SIC 4213

BIGMOUTHBEN CONVENIENCE STORE LLC p 182
370 Auburn Ave Ne Ste A 30312
Tel (404) 331-3973 SIC 5411 5947

BIRCH COMMUNICATIONS INC p 185
320 Interstate North Pkwy 30339
Tel (866) 424-5100 SIC 4813 5045

■ BLUE CROSS AND BLUE SHIELD OF GEORGIA INC p 191
3350 Peachtree Rd Ne # 300 30326
Tel (404) 842-8000 SIC 6324 6321

■ BLUELINX CORP p 193
4300 Wildwood Pkwy 30339
Tel (770) 953-7000 SIC 5031

■ BLUELINX HOLDINGS INC p 193
4300 Wildwood Pkwy 30339
Tel (770) 953-7000 SIC 5031 5211

▲ BMC STOCK HOLDINGS INC p 193
980 Hammond Dr Ste 500 30328
Tel (678) 222-1219
SIC 5211 2431 5031 5713 5251

BOARD OF REGENTS OF UNIVERSITY SYSTEM OF GEORGIA p 195
270 Washington St Sw Fl 7 30334
Tel (404) 962-3050 SIC 8221

BOYS & GIRLS CLUBS OF AMERICA p 205
1275 Peachtree St Ne # 500 30309
Tel (404) 527-7100 SIC 8322

BRISTOL HOTEL & RESORTS INC p 214
3 Ravinia Dr Ste 100 30346
Tel (770) 604-2000 SIC 8741

BURKS COMPANIES p 227
191 Peachtree St Ne # 800 30303
Tel (404) 589-4600
SIC 1752 5085 7349 4953 8999

BURNS GROUP UNLIMITED LLC p 228
833 Piedmont Ave Ne Ste B 30308
Tel (404) 873-0772 SIC 8743

BWAY CORP p 230
8607 Roberts Dr Ste 250 30350
Tel (770) 645-4800 SIC 3411 3089

BWAY HOLDING CO p 231
8607 Roberts Dr Ste 250 30350
Tel (770) 645-4800 SIC 3411 3089

BWAY INTERMEDIATE CO INC p 231
8607 Roberts Dr Ste 250 30350
Tel (770) 645-4800 SIC 3411 3089

BYERS ENGINEERING CO p 231
6285 Barfield Rd Fl 4 30328
Tel (404) 843-1000 SIC 8711 7371

■ CABLE NEWS NETWORK INC p 235
1 Cnn Ctr Nw 12 30303
Tel (404) 878-2276 SIC 4833

■ CABLE NEWS NETWORK LP LLLP p 235
1 Cnn Ctr Nw 30303
Tel (404) 522-8873 SIC 4833

CAJUN OPERATING CO p 237
980 Hammond Dr Ste 1100 30328
Tel (770) 350-3800 SIC 5812

■ CALPHALON CORP p 242
3 Glenlake Pkwy 30328
Tel (770) 418-7100 SIC 3365 3469

CARROLLS LLC p 261
4281 Old Dixie Hwy 30354
Tel (404) 366-5476 SIC 5014 5013

CARTER CENTER COLABORATIVE INC p 261
453 Freedom Pkwy Ne 30307
Tel (404) 420-5100 SIC 8221

CARTER CENTER INC p 261
453 Freedom Pkwy Ne 30307
Tel (404) 420-5100 SIC 8651 8412

▲ CARTERS INC p 262
3438 Peachtree Rd Ne # 1800 30326
Tel (678) 791-1000 SIC 2361 2369

■ CARTERS RETAIL INC p 262
3438 Peachtree Rd Ne 30326
Tel (203) 926-5000 SIC 5641

CBEYOND INC p 268
320 Interstate N Pkwy 500 30339
Tel (678) 424-2400
SIC 4813 7389 4899 1731

CDC SOFTWARE HOLDINGS INC p 270
Two Cncourse Pkwy Ste 800 39901
Tel (770) 351-9600 SIC 7372 7379 8243

CENTENNIAL HEALTHCARE CORP p 275
400 Perimeter Ctr Ter Ne 30346
Tel (770) 698-9040
SIC 8051 8069 8052 8741

■ CENTERS FOR DISEASE CONTROL AND PREVENTION p 276
1600 Clifton Rd Ne 30329
Tel (404) 639-3311 SIC 9431

CENTRAL VALLEY GAS STORAGE LLC p 280
10 Peachtree Pl Ne 30309
Tel (404) 584-3733 SIC 4924

■ CERTUSHOLDINGS INC p 284
1170 Peachtree St Nw 2400 30309
Tel (704) 973-3917 SIC 6022

CHARTER GLOBAL INC p 291
7000 Central Pkwy # 1100 30328
Tel (888) 326-9933 SIC 7371

CHICK-FIL-A INC p 298
5200 Buffington Rd 30349
Tel (404) 765-8038 SIC 5812 8741

CHILDRENS HEALTHCARE OF ATLANTA FOUNDATION INC p 299
1405 Clifton Rd Ne 30322
Tel (404) 785-7300 SIC 8069

CHILDRENS HEALTHCARE OF ATLANTA INC p 299
1600 Tullie Cir Ne 30329
Tel (404) 785-7000 SIC 8069

CHOATE CONSTRUCTION CO p 301
8200 Roberts Dr Ste 600 30350
Tel (678) 892-1200 SIC 1522 1531 1542

■ CINER ENTERPRISES INC p 308
5 Concourse Pkwy Ste 2500 30328
Tel (770) 375-2300 SIC 1474 2812

■ CINER RESOURCES CORP p 308
5 Concourse Pkwy 30328
Tel (770) 375-2300 SIC 1474 2812

■ CINER RESOURCES LP p 308
5 Concourse Pkwy Ste 2500 30328
Tel (770) 375-2300 SIC 1474

■ CINER WYOMING HOLDING CO p 308
5 Concourse Pkwy 30328
Tel (770) 375-2300 SIC 1474 2812

■ CITADEL BROADCASTING CORP p 309
3280 Peachtree Rd Ne # 2300 30305
Tel (404) 949-0700 SIC 4832

CITY OF ATLANTA p 313
55 Trinity Ave Sw # 3900 30303
Tel (404) 330-6100 SIC 9111

CKS PACKAGING INC p 320
350 Great Sw Pkwy Sw 30336
Tel (404) 691-8900 SIC 3089

CLEVELAND ELECTRIC CO INC p 325
1281 Fulton Indus Blvd Nw 30336
Tel (404) 696-4550 SIC 1731 1711 1796

CLEVELAND GROUP INC p 325
1281 Fulton Indus Blvd Nw 30336
Tel (404) 696-4550 SIC 1731 8741 1711

CLOUD SHERPAS INC p 327
3525 Piedmont Rd Ne 8-710 30305
Tel (404) 665-3556 SIC 7371

CMPC USA INC p 329
1040 Crown Pointe Pkwy # 800 30338
Tel (770) 551-2640 SIC 5099

▲ COCA-COLA CO p 333
1 Coca Cola Plz Nw 30313
Tel (404) 676-2121
SIC 2087 2086 2033 2037

COCA-COLA ENTERPRISES INC p 333
2500 Windy Ridge Pkwy Se # 700 30339
Tel (678) 260-3000 SIC 2086

■ COCA-COLA EXPORT CORP p 333
1 Coca Cola Plz Nw 30313
Tel (404) 676-2121 SIC 5149

■ COCA-COLA INTERAMERICAN CORP p 333
1 Coca Cola Plz Nw 30313
Tel (404) 676-2121 SIC 2086

■ COCA-COLA REFRESHMENTS USA INC p 333
2500 Windy Ridge Pkwy Se 30339
Tel (770) 989-3000 SIC 2086 2087

COLUMBIA PROPERTY TRUST INC p 341
1 Glenlake Pkwy Ste 1200 30328
Tel (404) 465-2200 SIC 6798

COMMERCIAL ROOFING SPECIALTIES INC p 345
2703 Peachtree Sq 30360
Tel (770) 458-0539 SIC 5033

COMMUNITY & SOUTHERN BANK p 347
3333 Rvrwood Pkwy Se # 350 30339
Tel (770) 832-3557 SIC 6022

COMMUNITY FOUNDATION FOR GREATER ATLANTA INC p 348
191 Peachtree St Ne # 1000 30303
Tel (404) 688-5525 SIC 6732

COMMUNITY LOANS OF AMERICA INC p 349
8601 Dunwoody Pl Ste 406 30350
Tel (770) 587-1901 *SIC* 8741

CONCESSIONS INTERNATIONAL LLC p 354
566 Wells St Sw 30312
Tel (404) 681-0300 *SIC* 5812 5963 5947

CONSOLIDATED CONTAINER CO LLC p 359
3101 Towercreek Pkwy Se 30339
Tel (678) 742-4600 *SIC* 3089

CONSOLIDATED CONTAINER CO LP p 359
3101 Towercreek Pkwy Se 30339
Tel (678) 742-4600 *SIC* 3089 3999

CONSOLIDATED CONTAINER HOLDINGS LLC p 359
3101 Towercreek Pkwy Se P 30339
Tel (678) 742-4600 *SIC* 2671 7389 5113

CONSOLIDATED CONTAINER INTERMEDIARY LLC p 359
3101 Towercreek Pkwy Se 30339
Tel (678) 742-4600 *SIC* 5113 2671

COOPERATIVE FOR ASSISTANCE AND RELIEF EVERYWHERE INC p 367
151 Ellis St Ne 30303
Tel (404) 681-2552 *SIC* 8641 8322

CORTLAND IMPROVEMENTS LLC p 373
3424 Peachtree Rd Ne # 300 30326
Tel (404) 965-3988 *SIC* 6531

▲ **COTIVITI HOLDINGS INC** p 374
115 Prmter Ctr Pl Ste 700 30346
Tel (770) 379-2800 *SIC* 8721

COUNTY OF FULTON p 378
141 Pryor St Sw 30303
Tel (404) 612-4000 *SIC* 9111

▲ **COUSINS PROPERTIES INC** p 383
191 Peachtree St Ne # 500 30303
Tel (404) 407-1000 *SIC* 6798

COX COMMUNICATIONS ARIZONA LLC p 386
6305 Pchtree Dunwoody Rd 30328
Tel (404) 843-5000 *SIC* 4841

COX COMMUNICATIONS CALIFORNIA LLC p 386
6205 Pachtree Dunwoody Rd 30328
Tel (404) 843-5000 *SIC* 4841

COX COMMUNICATIONS INC p 386
6205 B Pchtree Dunwody Ne 30328
Tel (404) 843-5000 *SIC* 4841 4813

COX COMMUNICATIONS LAS VEGAS INC p 386
6205 Pachtree Dunwoody Rd 30328
Tel (404) 269-7898 *SIC* 4841

COX ENTERPRISES INC p 386
6205 Pachtree Dunwoody Rd 30328
Tel (678) 645-0000
SIC 4841 4813 2711 4833 7389 4832

COX MEDIA GROUP LLC p 386
6205 Pachtree Dunwoody Rd 30328
Tel (678) 645-0000
SIC 4833 4832 7922 7313

COX NEWSPAPERS INC p 386
6205 Peachtree Dunwoody 30328
Tel (678) 645-0000 *SIC* 2711

COX RADIO INC p 386
6205 Pachtree Dunwoody Rd 30328
Tel (678) 645-0000 *SIC* 4832

COX TEXAS PUBLICATIONS INC p 386
6205 Pachtree Dunwoody Rd 30328
Tel (404) 843-5000 *SIC* 2711

CP KELCO US INC p 387
3100 Cumberland Blvd Se # 600 30339
Tel (678) 247-7300 *SIC* 2899

CREATIVE SURFACES INC p 390
1400 W Marietta St Nw 30318
Tel (205) 988-3246 *SIC* 2541 1799

CRH AMERICA INC p 392
900 Ashwood Pkwy Ste 600 30338
Tel (770) 804-3363 *SIC* 3272

■ **CTC COMMUNICATIONS CORP** p 399
1170 Peachtree St Ne # 900 30309
Tel (404) 815-0770 *SIC* 4813

■ **CUMULUS BROADCASTING LLC** p 401
3280 Peachtree Rd Nw Ste 30305
Tel (404) 949-0700 *SIC* 4832

■ **CUMULUS MEDIA HOLDINGS INC** p 401
3280 Peachtree Rd Ne # 2300 30305
Tel (404) 949-0700 *SIC* 4832

▲ **CUMULUS MEDIA INC** p 401
3280 Peachtree Rd Ne Ne2300 30305
Tel (404) 949-0700 *SIC* 4832

■ **DAL GLOBAL SERVICES LLC** p 409
980 Virginia Ave 4th 30354
Tel (404) 715-4300
SIC 7361 8331 7382 5088

DATA BLUE LLC p 413
1117 Perimeter Ctr 30338
Tel (727) 412-8470 *SIC* 7379

DAVIDSON HOTEL CO p 416
1 Ravinia Dr Ste 1600 30346
Tel (678) 349-0909 *SIC* 8741 7011

DAVIDSON HOTEL CO LLC p 416
1 Ravinia Dr Ste 1600 30346
Tel (901) 821-4117 *SIC* 7011

DAVIDSON HOTEL PARTNERS LP p 416
1 Ravinia Dr Ste 1600 30346
Tel (901) 761-4664 *SIC* 7011

▲ **DELTA AIR LINES INC** p 426
1030 Delta Blvd 30354
Tel (404) 715-2600 *SIC* 4512

DELTA COMMUNITY CREDIT UNION p 426
1025 Virginia Ave 30354
Tel (404) 715-4725 *SIC* 6061 6163

■ **DELTA TECHNOLOGY LLC** p 427
1001 International Blvd 30354
Tel (404) 714-1500 *SIC* 7373

DEPARTMENT OF BEHAVIORAL HEALTH AND DEVELOPMENTAL DISABILITIES p 429
2 Peachtree St Nw 30303
Tel (404) 657-1650 *SIC* 9431

DIAZ WHOLESALE & MFG CO INC p 437
5501 Fulton Indus Blvd Sw 30336
Tel (404) 346-9312 *SIC* 5141

▲ **DLH HOLDINGS CORP** p 445
3565 Piedmont Rd Ne 30305
Tel (770) 554-3545 *SIC* 7363 8742

DOCUMENT TECHNOLOGIES LLC p 447
2 Ravinia Dr Ste 850 30346
Tel (770) 390-2700 *SIC* 7389

DS SERVICES HOLDINGS INC p 457
5660 New Northside Dr # 500 30328
Tel (770) 933-1400 *SIC* 5499 5149

DS SERVICES OF AMERICA INC p 457
2300 Windy Ridge Pkwy Se 500n 30339
Tel (770) 933-1400 *SIC* 5963

DS WATERS HOLDINGS LLC p 457
5660 New Northside Dr # 500 30328
Tel (770) 933-1400 *SIC* 2086

■ **EAGLE SPINCO INC** p 468
115 Perimeter Center Pl 30346
Tel (770) 395-4500 *SIC* 2812 5169

■ **EARTHLINK BUSINESS LLC** p 469
1170 Pchtree S Ne Ste 900 30309
Tel (404) 815-0770 *SIC* 4899

▲ **EARTHLINK HOLDINGS CORP** p 469
1170 Peachtree St Ne # 900 30309
Tel (404) 815-0770 *SIC* 4813

EARTHLINK INC p 469
1375 Peachtree St Ne A9 30309
Tel (404) 815-0770 *SIC* 4813

■ **EARTHLINK LLC** p 469
1170 Peachtree St Ne # 900 30309
Tel (877) 355-1501 *SIC* 4813

EB SUBHOLDINGS I INC p 474
1040 Crown Pointe Pkwy 30338
Tel (770) 671-1900 *SIC* 7363

■ **EIS INC** p 482
2018 Powers Ferry Rd Se # 500 30339
Tel (678) 255-3600 *SIC* 5065

■ **ELAVON INC** p 483
2 Cncourse Pkwy Ste 800 30328
Tel (678) 731-5000 *SIC* 7375 7374

ELEKTA HOLDINGS US INC p 486
400 Perimeter Center Ter 30346
Tel (770) 300-9725 *SIC* 5047 3841

ELLIS ATLANTA JIM INC p 488
5901 Peachtree Indus Blvd 30341
Tel (770) 454-8200 *SIC* 5511 5521

EMORY CLINIC INC p 493
1365 Clifton Rd Ne 30322
Tel (404) 778-5000 *SIC* 8062

EMORY HEALTHCARE INC p 493
1440 Clifton Rd Ne 30322
Tel (404) 778-7777 *SIC* 8062

EMORY UNIVERSITY p 493
201 Dowman Dr Ne 30322
Tel (404) 727-6013 *SIC* 8221 8082

EMORY UNIVERSITY HOSPITAL MIDTOWN p 493
550 Peachtree St Ne 30308
Tel (404) 686-7100 *SIC* 8062

■ **EMPIRE DISTRIBUTORS INC** p 493
3755 Atlanta Indus Pkwy 30331
Tel (404) 572-4100 *SIC* 5182

EMPLOYBRIDGE HOLDING CO p 494
1040 Crown Pointe Pkwy # 1040 30338
Tel (770) 671-1900 *SIC* 7361

EMPLOYBRIDGE SOUTHWEST LLC p 494
3050 Peachtree Rd Nw 30305
Tel (404) 816-3255 *SIC* 7363

EMPLOYMENT SOLUTIONS MANAGEMENT INC p 494
1040 Crown Pointe Pkwy 30338
Tel (770) 671-1900 *SIC* 8741

ENTERPRISE LEASING CO OF GEORGIA LLC p 502
5909 Peachtree Ind 30341
Tel (770) 821-0399 *SIC* 7514 7515 5521

EQUICORP PARTNERS LLC p 506
75 14th St Ne Unit 4610 30309
Tel (404) 442-1530 *SIC* 6282

▲ **EQUIFAX INC** p 506
1550 Peachtree St Nw 30309
Tel (404) 885-8000
SIC 7323 7389 8732 8741

■ **EQUIFAX INFORMATION SERVICES LLC** p 506
1550 Peachtree St Ne 30309
Tel (404) 885-8000 *SIC* 7323

EQUITY MSOUTH PARTNERS L P p 507
3050 Peachtree Rd Nw 30305
Tel (404) 816-3255 *SIC* 6799 7363

ESQUIRE DEPOSITION SERVICES LLC p 510
2700 Centennial Twr 30303
Tel (404) 495-0777 *SIC* 7338

EXAMWORKS GROUP INC p 516
3280 Peachtree Rd Ne # 2625 30305
Tel (404) 952-2400 *SIC* 8099

EXAMWORKS INC p 516
3280 Peachtree Rd Ne # 2625 30305
Tel (404) 952-2400 *SIC* 7389

EXECUTIVE OFFICE OF STATE OF GEORGIA p 517
203 State Capitol Sw 30334
Tel (404) 656-1776 *SIC* 9111

■ **EXPRESSJET AIRLINES INC** p 520
100 Hartsfield Ctr 700 30354
Tel (404) 856-1000 *SIC* 4512

FACILITY HOLDINGS CORP p 523
2700 Cumberland Pkwy Se 30339
Tel (770) 437-2700 *SIC* 1541

FEDERAL HOME LOAN BANK OF ATLANTA p 534
1475 Peachtree St Ne # 400 30309
Tel (404) 888-8000 *SIC* 6111

FEDERAL RESERVE BANK OF ATLANTA p 535
1000 Peachtree St Ne 30309
Tel (404) 498-8500 *SIC* 6011

▲ **FIDELITY SOUTHERN CORP** p 541
3490 Piedmont Rd Ne # 1550 30305
Tel (404) 639-6500 *SIC* 6022

■ **FINANCIAL SERVICE CORP** p 543
2300 Windy Ridge Pkwy Se 1100s 30339
Tel (770) 916-6500
SIC 6722 6411 8742 6211

FIRST ADVANTAGE CORP p 544
1 Concourse Pkwy Ste 200 30328
Tel (800) 888-5773
SIC 7323 8742 7372 7389 7381

■ **FIRST DATA MERCHANT SERVICES CORP** p 546
5565 Glenridge Connector 30342
Tel (404) 890-3000
SIC 7374 7389 7375 6153 6099

FISHER & PHILLIPS LLP p 552
1075 Peachtree St Ne # 3500 30309
Tel (404) 231-1400 *SIC* 8111

FOCUS BRANDS INC p 562
5620 Glenridge Dr 30342
Tel (404) 255-3250 *SIC* 5461 5143 6794

FORMATION CAPITAL LLC p 567
3500 Lenox Rd Ne Ste 510 30326
Tel (770) 754-9660 *SIC* 6211 8742

FORT JAMES CORP p 569
133 Peachtree St Ne 30303
Tel (404) 652-4000 *SIC* 2621

■ **FSC CORP** p 582
2300 Windy Ridge Pkwy Se # 1100 30339
Tel (770) 916-6500
SIC 6722 6411 8742 6211

■ **FSC SECURITIES CORP** p 582
2300 Windy Ridge Pkwy Se # 1100 30339
Tel (770) 916-6500 *SIC* 6411 6211

FULTON COUNTY BOARD OF EDUCATION p 584
6201 Powers Ferry Rd 30339
Tel (404) 768-3600 *SIC* 8211

FULTON COUNTY SCHOOL SYSTEM p 584
6201 Powers Ferry Rd 30339
Tel (470) 254-3600 *SIC* 8211

FULTON DEKALB HOSPITAL AUTHORITY p 584
191 Peachtree St Ne # 820 30303
Tel (404) 600-4097 *SIC* 8062

GABLES RESIDENTIAL SERVICES INC p 588
3399 Peachtree Rd Ne # 600 30326
Tel (404) 923-5500 *SIC* 6531

■ **GE ENERGY MANAGEMENT SERVICES LLC** p 596
4200 Wildwood Pkwy 30339
Tel (678) 844-6000 *SIC* 4911

■ **GE ENERGY PARTS INC** p 596
4200 Wildwood Pkwy 30339
Tel (678) 844-6000 *SIC* 5065 3612

■ **GE GRID SOLUTIONS LLC** p 596
4200 Wildwood Pkwy 30339
Tel (877) 605-6777 *SIC* 3612

■ **GEIGER INTERNATIONAL INC** p 597
6095 Fulton Indus Blvd Sw 30336
Tel (404) 344-1100 *SIC* 2521

GENERAL WHOLESALE CO p 602
1271 Tacoma Dr Nw 30318
Tel (404) 352-1041 *SIC* 5182 5181

■ **GENON AMERICAS INC** p 604
1155 Perimeter Ctr # 100 30338
Tel (678) 579-5000 *SIC* 4924

■ **GENON NORTH AMERICA LLC** p 604
1155 Perimeter Ctr # 100 30338
Tel (678) 579-5000 *SIC* 4924 4911 6221

■ **GENTIVA HEALTH SERVICES INC** p 605
3350 Riverwood Pkwy Se # 1400 30339
Tel (770) 951-6450 *SIC* 8082

▲ **GENUINE PARTS CO** p 605
2999 Wildwood Pkwy 30339
Tel (770) 953-1700
SIC 5013 5531 3714 5084 5085 5021

GEORGIA BANKERS ASSOCIATION INSURANCE TRUST INC p 607
50 Hurt Plz Se Ste 1050 30303
Tel (404) 522-1501 *SIC* 6411

GEORGIA BANKERS ASSOCIATION INSURANCE TRUST INC p 607
50 Hurt Plz Se Ste 1050 30303
Tel (404) 522-1501 *SIC* 6411

GEORGIA BAPTIST HEALTH CARE SYSTEM INC p 607
100 10th St Nw Ste 700 30309
Tel (404) 814-4477 *SIC* 8741

GEORGIA DEPARTMENT OF EDUCATION p 607
205 Jesse Hill Jr Dr Se 30334
Tel (404) 656-2497 *SIC* 8211 9411

GEORGIA DEPARTMENT OF HUMAN SERVICES p 607
2 Peachtree St Nw 30303
Tel (404) 651-9361 *SIC* 9441

GEORGIA DEPARTMENT OF LABOR p 607
148 Andrew Yng Intl Blvd # 100 30303
Tel (404) 232-3540 *SIC* 9651

GEORGIA DEPARTMENT OF NATURAL RESOURCES p 607
2 Martin Luther King Jr 30334
Tel (404) 656-3500 *SIC* 9512

GEORGIA DEPARTMENT OF PUBLIC HEALTH p 607
2 Peachtree St Nw Fl 15 30303
Tel (404) 657-2700 *SIC* 9431

GEORGIA DEPARTMENT OF PUBLIC SAFETY p 607
959 E Confederate Ave Se 30316
Tel (404) 624-7739 *SIC* 9229

GEORGIA DEPARTMENT OF REVENUE p 607
1800 Century Blvd Ne # 1200 30345
Tel (877) 423-6711 *SIC* 9311

GEORGIA DEPARTMENT OF TRANSPORTATION p 607
600 W Peachtree St Nw 30308
Tel (404) 631-1014 *SIC* 9621

GEORGIA INSTITUTE OF TECHNOLOGY p 607
225 North Ave Nw 30332
Tel (404) 894-2000 *SIC* 8221

GEORGIA MUNICIPAL ASSOCIATION INC p 607
201 Pryor St Sw 30303
Tel (404) 688-0472 *SIC* 2711 2741 8611

■ **GEORGIA POWER CO** p 607
241 Ralph Mcgill Blvd Ne 30308
Tel (404) 506-6526 *SIC* 4911

GEORGIA STATE UNIVERSITY p 607
30 Courtland St Se 30303
Tel (404) 413-2000 *SIC* 8221

GEORGIA TECH APPLIED RESEARCH CORP p 607
505 10th St Nw 30318
Tel (404) 894-4819 *SIC* 8731

GEORGIA TECH RESEARCH CORP p 607
505 10th St Nw 30318
Tel (404) 894-4819 *SIC* 8732

GEORGIA TECHNOLOGY AUTHORITY p 607
47 Trinity Ave Sw 30334
Tel (404) 463-2300 *SIC* 4899 9199

GEORGIA-PACIFIC HOLDINGS LLC p 608
133 Peachtree St Ne # 4810 30303
Tel (404) 652-4000 *SIC* 6719

GEORGIA-PACIFIC LLC p 608
133 Peachtree St Ne # 4810 30303
Tel (404) 652-4000
SIC 2676 2656 2653 2435 2821 3275

GEORGIA-PACIFIC PACKAGING LLC p 608
133 Peachtree St Ne # 4810 30303
Tel (404) 652-4000 *SIC* 2656

GEORGIA-PACIFIC WOOD PRODUCTS SOUTH LLC p 608
133 Peachtree St Ne 30303
Tel (404) 652-4000 *SIC* 2656

GEORGIAS OWN CREDIT UNION p 608
1155 Peachtree St Ne # 400 30309
Tel (404) 874-1166 *SIC* 6062

GERBER AGRI INTERNATIONAL LLC p 608
1000 Parkwood Cir Se # 335 30339
Tel (770) 952-4187 *SIC* 5144 5147

GFG MANAGEMENT LLC p 610
5555 Glenridge Connector # 850 30342
Tel (770) 514-4871 *SIC* 5461

GLOBAL FRANCHISE GROUP LLC p 616
5555 Glenridge Connector # 850 30342
Tel (770) 514-4500 *SIC* 5461 6794

▲ **GLOBAL PAYMENTS INC** p 617
10 Glenlake Pkwy N Tower 30328
Tel (770) 829-8000 *SIC* 7389

GNN INVESTOR LLC p 619
133 Peachtree St Ne 30303
Tel (404) 652-4000
SIC 2621 2611 2631 2653 5111 2677

GOLDCO LLC p 620
100 Ashford Ctr N Ste 130 30338
Tel (334) 792-1267 *SIC* 5812

GOLDER ASSOCIATES INC p 622
3730 Chamblee Tucker Rd 30341
Tel (770) 496-1893 *SIC* 8711

■ **GOODY PRODUCTS INC** p 625
3 Glenlake Pkwy 30328
Tel (770) 418-7300 SIC 3999 3089 3069

GP BUILDING PRODUCTS OPERATIONS LLC p 627
133 Peachtree St Ne 30303
Tel (404) 652-4000 SIC 2656

GP CELLULOSE LLC p 627
133 Peachtree St Ne # 1 30303
Tel (404) 652-6630 SIC 2611

GP CHEMICALS EQUITY LLC p 627
55 Park Pl Ne 30303
Tel (404) 652-4000 SIC 5169

■ **GPI HOLDINGS INC** p 627
1500 Riveredge Pkwy # 100 30328
Tel (770) 240-7200
SIC 2631 2653 2449 4922

GPS HOSPITALITY LLC p 628
2100 Riveredge Pkwy # 850 30328
Tel (770) 933-5023 SIC 5812

■ **GRACO CHILDRENS PRODUCTS INC** p 628
3 Glenlake Pkwy 30328
Tel (770) 418-7200 SIC 2514

GRADY HEALTH SYSTEM p 628
80 Jesse Hill Jr Dr Se 30303
Tel (404) 616-4360 SIC 8062

GRANCARE LLC p 629
1 Ravinia Dr Ste 1400 30346
Tel (770) 393-0199
SIC 8051 8052 8093 8071

▲ **GRAPHIC PACKAGING HOLDING CO** p 632
1500 Riveredge Pkwy # 100 30328
Tel (770) 240-7200 SIC 2631 2653 2671

■ **GRAPHIC PACKAGING INTERNATIONAL INC** p 632
1500 Riveredge Pkwy # 100 30328
Tel (770) 240-7200 SIC 2657 2631 7389

■ **GREAT LAKES COCA-COLA DISTRIBUTION LLC** p 633
1 Coca Cola Plz Nw 30313
Tel (404) 374-8969 SIC 2086

GREENSKY LLC p 638
5565 Glenridge Connector 30342
Tel (404) 832-4000 SIC 6141

■ **GRID SOLUTIONS (US) LLC** p 640
4200 Wildwood Pkwy # 2018 30339
Tel (877) 605-6777 SIC 4911

GSMA LTD p 643
1000 Abernathy Rd Ste 450 30328
Tel (678) 281-6600 SIC 7389

H J RUSSELL & CO p 650
171 17th St Nw Ste 1600 30363
Tel (404) 330-1000
SIC 1542 8741 7389 8742

HALPERNS STEAK AND SEAFOOD CO LLC p 655
4685 Welcome All Rd Sw 30349
Tel (404) 767-9229 SIC 5147

HANSON AGGREGATES SOUTHEAST INC p 659
2310 Parklake Dr Ne # 550 30345
Tel (770) 491-2777 SIC 1423 1442

HARDEN HEALTHCARE SERVICES LLC p 660
3350 Riverwood Pkwy Se # 1 30339
Tel (512) 634-4965 SIC 8082

▲ **HAVERTY FURNITURE COMPANIES INC** p 668
780 Johnson Ferry Rd 30342
Tel (404) 443-2900
SIC 5712 5722 5713 5021

HBW INSURANCE SERVICES LLC p 671
4501 Circ 75 Pkwy Sef6200 30339
Tel (678) 742-6300 SIC 6411

■ **HD BUILDER SOLUTIONS GROUP LLC** p 672
2455 Paces Ferry Rd Se C9 30339
Tel (770) 443-8211 SIC 5023 1752 1799

■ **HD SUPPLY CONSTRUCTION SUPPLY GROUP INC** p 673
3100 Cumberland Blvd Se 30339
Tel (770) 852-9000 SIC 5072 5039 5031

■ **HD SUPPLY CONSTRUCTION SUPPLY LTD** p 673
3100 Cumberland Blvd Se # 1700 30339
Tel (770) 852-9000 SIC 5031 5039 5072

HD SUPPLY FACILITIES MAINTENANCE GROUP INC p 673
3100 Cumberland Blvd Se 30339
Tel (770) 852-9000 SIC 5087

■ **HD SUPPLY FACILITIES MAINTENANCE LTD** p 673
3100 Cumberland Blvd Se # 1700 30339
Tel (770) 852-9000 SIC 5087

▲ **HD SUPPLY HOLDINGS INC** p 673
3100 Cumberland Blvd Se # 1480 30339
Tel (770) 852-9000 SIC 5087 5072 5085

■ **HD SUPPLY HOLDINGS LLC** p 673
3100 Cumberland Blvd Se # 1700 30339
Tel (770) 852-9000
SIC 5051 5074 5084 5099

■ **HD SUPPLY INC** p 673
3100 Cumberland Blvd Se # 1700 30339
Tel (770) 852-9000 SIC 5031 5033

■ **HD SUPPLY WATERWORKS LTD** p 673
3100 Cumberland Blvd Se 30339
Tel (770) 852-9000 SIC 5074

■ **HDS HOLDING CORP** p 673
3100 Cumberland Blvd Se 30339
Tel (770) 852-9000 SIC 5087 5072 5085

HEALTH CARE CAPITAL INC p 674
2 Ravinia Dr Ste 1350 30346
Tel (770) 393-3355 SIC 6162 8051 8741

HEELY-BROWN CO p 680
1280 Chattahoochee Ave Nw 30318
Tel (404) 352-0022 SIC 5033

HEERY INTERNATIONAL INC p 680
999 Peachtree St Ne # 300 30309
Tel (404) 881-9880 SIC 8712 8711 8742

HENNESSY CADILLAC INC p 683
3040 Piedmont Rd Ne 30305
Tel (404) 261-5700 SIC 5511

HILLTOPPER HOLDING CORP p 694
303 Perimeter Ctr N # 500 30346
Tel (770) 698-9040 SIC 8051 8741

HOLDER CONSTRUCTION CO p 700
3333 Riverwood Pkwy Se # 400 30339
Tel (770) 988-3000 SIC 1542

HOLDER CONSTRUCTION GROUP LLC p 700
3333 Riverwood Pkwy Se # 400 30339
Tel (770) 988-3000 SIC 1542

HOLDER CORP p 700
3300 Cumberland Blvd Se # 400 30339
Tel (770) 988-3000 SIC 6552 1542

▲ **HOME DEPOT INC** p 703
2455 Paces Ferry Rd Se 30339
Tel (770) 433-8211
SIC 5261 5211 5231 5251 1751 1752

■ **HOME DEPOT INTERNATIONAL INC** p 703
2455 Paces Ferry Rd Se 30339
Tel (770) 384-3889 SIC 5211

■ **HOME DEPOT USA INC** p 703
2455 Paces Ferry Rd Se 30339
Tel (770) 433-8211 SIC 5023 5999

HOOTERS OF AMERICA LLC p 706
1815 The Exchange Se 30339
Tel (770) 951-2040 SIC 5812 6794

HOTEL EQUITIES INC p 710
41 Perimeter Ctr E # 510 30346
Tel (770) 934-2170 SIC 6799 8741

ICS CONTRACT SERVICES LLC p 728
1251 Marietta Blvd Nw 30318
Tel (404) 367-8286 SIC 7349

IDHASOFT INC p 729
6 Concourse Pkwy Ste 500 30328
Tel (770) 248-2999 SIC 7379

IMEDX INC p 733
3560 Lenox Rd Ne Ste 3000 30326
Tel (404) 418-0096 SIC 7338

IN TOUCH MINISTRIES INC p 735
3836 Dekalb Tec Pkwy 30340
Tel (770) 451-1001 SIC 7922

INCOMM HOLDINGS INC p 735
250 Williams St Nw Fl 5 30303
Tel (770) 240-6100 SIC 6099

INDUSTRIAL DEVELOPMENTS INTERNATIONAL LLC p 739
1100 Peachtree S 30309
Tel (404) 479-4000 SIC 6552 6531

INFOSYS MCCAMISH SYSTEMS LLC p 742
6425 Powers Ferry Rd 30339
Tel (770) 690-1500 SIC 6399 7373

INNOVATIVE SERVICE TECHNOLOGY MANAGEMENT SERVICES INC p 745
934 Glenwood Ave Se # 250 30316
Tel (404) 582-8850 SIC 8744

INSTITUTE OF NUCLEAR POWER OPERATIONS p 747
700 Galleria Pkwy Se # 100 30339
Tel (770) 644-8000 SIC 8999

INTEGRAL GROUP LLC p 748
191 Peachtree St Ne # 4100 30303
Tel (404) 224-1860
SIC 6552 8748 6798 6799 6722

INTELLIGENT CONSUMER HOLDINGS LLC p 750
980 Hammond Dr Ste 1000 30328
Tel (404) 260-2200 SIC 7299

INTER-CONTINENTAL HOTELS CORP p 751
3 Ravinia Dr Ste 100 30346
Tel (770) 604-5000 SIC 7011

INTERACTIVE COMMUNICATIONS INTERNATIONAL INC p 751
250 Williams St Nw # 5000 30303
Tel (770) 240-6100 SIC 6099

▲ **INTERCONTINENTAL EXCHANGE INC** p 752
5660 New Northside Dr # 300 30328
Tel (770) 857-4700 SIC 6231

INTERCONTINENTAL HOTELS GROUP RESOURCES INC p 752
3 Ravinia Dr Ste 100 30346
Tel (770) 604-5000 SIC 7011 8741 6794

■ **INTERFACE AMERICAS INC** p 752
2859 Pcs Frry St 2000 30339
Tel (770) 437-6800 SIC 2273

INTERFACE FLOORING SYSTEMS INC p 752
2859 Paces Ferry Rd Se 30339
Tel (800) 336-0225 SIC 3272 1771 3999

▲ **INTERFACE INC** p 752
2859 Paces Ferry Rd Se # 2000 30339
Tel (770) 437-6800 SIC 2273

INTERIOR LOGIC GROUP INC p 753
3050 Peachtree Rd Nw 30305
Tel (770) 560-7186 SIC 7389

▲ **INTERNAP CORP** p 754
1 Ravinia Dr Ste 1300 30346
Tel (404) 302-9700 SIC 7373 7375

INTERRA GROUP INC p 757
400 Interstate N Pkwy Ste 30339
Tel (770) 612-8101 SIC 5141 6719

INTERSTATE NATIONAL DEALER SERVICES INC p 758
6120 Powers Ferry Rd S 30339
Tel (678) 894-3500 SIC 6399 6221

INTOWN HOLDING CO LLC p 759
2727 Paces Fery Rd 2 1200 30339
Tel (770) 799-5000 SIC 6712

INTOWN HOSPITALITY INVESTORS LP p 759
980 Hammond Dr Ste 1400 30328
Tel (770) 799-5000 SIC 7011

INVESCO AGENCY SECURITIES INC p 761
1360 Peachtree St Ne # 600 30309
Tel (404) 892-0896 SIC 6798

▲ **INVESCO LTD** p 761
1555 Peachtree St Ne 18 30309
Tel (404) 892-0896 SIC 6282

INVESCO MORTGAGE CAPITAL INC p 761
1555 Peachtree St Ne 30309
Tel (404) 892-0896 SIC 6798

ISD HOLDINGS INC p 766
4715 Frederick Dr Sw 30336
Tel (404) 691-7400
SIC 7389 2542 2759 2752

JAMESON INNS INC p 777
41 Perimeter Ctr E # 4100 30346
Tel (770) 512-0462 SIC 7011 1522

JAS AMERICA HOLDING INC p 778
5424 Glenridge Dr 30342
Tel (770) 688-1240 SIC 4731

JAS FORWARDING (USA) INC p 778
6165 Barfield Rd 30328
Tel (770) 688-1206 SIC 4731

JINNY BEAUTY SUPPLY CO INC p 786
3587 Oakcliff Rd 30340
Tel (770) 734-9222 SIC 5087

JP TURNER & CO LLC p 795
1 Buckhead Plz 3060 30305
Tel (404) 479-8300 SIC 6211

KABBAGE INC p 799
730 Peachtree St Ne # 350 30308
Tel (855) 278-7084 SIC 6153

KAISER FOUNDATION HEALTH PLAN OF GEORGIA INC p 800
3495 Piedmont Rd Ne # 9 30305
Tel (404) 364-7000 SIC 6324

KAJIMA INTERNATIONAL INC p 801
3475 Piedmont Rd Ne # 1600 30305
Tel (404) 564-3900 SIC 1541 3446 1542

KAJIMA REAL ESTATE DEVELOPMENT INC p 801
3475 Pdmn Rd Ne Ste 1600 30305
Tel (404) 564-3900 SIC 6552

KAJIMA USA INC p 801
3475 Piedmont Rd Ne 30305
Tel (404) 564-3900
SIC 1542 1541 6531 1522 6552 1622

KEMIRA CHEMICALS INC p 809
1000 Parkwood Cir Se # 500 30339
Tel (863) 533-5990 SIC 2869 2819

KEMIRA WATER SOLUTIONS INC p 809
1000 Parkwood Cir Se # 500 30339
Tel (770) 436-1542 SIC 2899

KILPATRICK TOWNSEND & STOCKTON LLP p 818
1100 Peachtree St Ne 30309
Tel (404) 815-6500 SIC 8111

KING & SPALDING LLP p 820
1180 Peachtree St 30309
Tel (404) 572-4600 SIC 8111

KURT SALMON US LLC p 832
1355 Peachtree St Ne # 900 30309
Tel (404) 892-0321 SIC 8742

LANE SERVICES LLC p 843
303 Perimeter Ctr N # 200 30346
Tel (678) 681-7200 SIC 6512

LANIER PARKING HOLDINGS INC p 844
233 Peachtree St Ne # 2600 30303
Tel (404) 881-6076 SIC 7521

LAVOI CORP p 847
1749 Tullie Cir Ne 30329
Tel (404) 325-1016
SIC 2045 2053 2051 5149

LEGAL ACQUISITIONS SUPPORT SERVICES LLC p 853
1170 Peachtree St Ne # 1200 30309
Tel (404) 546-7290 SIC 6531

LG HAUSYS AMERICA INC p 860
900 Circle 75 Pkwy Se # 15 30339
Tel (678) 486-8210 SIC 2541

LION GABLES REALTY LIMITED PARTNERSHIP p 869
3399 Peachtree Rd Ne 30326
Tel (404) 923-5500 SIC 6531

■ **LOGISTICARE SOLUTIONS LLC** p 874
1275 Peachtree St Ne Fl 6 30309
Tel (404) 888-5800 SIC 4731

LOR INC p 878
2170 Piedmont Rd Ne 30324
Tel (404) 486-5600 SIC 6799 5084 3443

■ **MACDERMID PRINTING SOLUTIONS LLC** p 892
5210 Phillip Lee Dr Sw 30336
Tel (404) 472-0072 SIC 3555

MAG MUTUAL INSURANCE AGENCY LLC p 895
3525 Piedmont Rd Ne 8-600 30305
Tel (404) 842-5600 SIC 6351 6411

▲ **MANHATTAN ASSOCIATES INC** p 901
2300 Windy Ridge Pkwy Se 1000n 30339
Tel (770) 955-7070 SIC 7373 7372 5045

MANHEIM INVESTMENTS INC p 901
6205 Pachtree Dunwoody Rd 30328
Tel (866) 626-4346 SIC 5012

MANHEIM REMARKETING INC p 901
6325 Pchtree Dnwody Rd Ne 30328
Tel (678) 645-2067 SIC 5012

MARINER HEALTH CARE INC p 907
1 Ravinia Dr Ste 1500 30346
Tel (678) 443-7000
SIC 5912 8051 8093 8741 8062 3443

MARTIN ENGLE & ASSOCIATES INC p 912
5565 Glenridge Connector # 900 30342
Tel (678) 553-4400 SIC 6411

MATRIX RESOURCES INC p 920
1000 Abernathy Rd Ste 500 30328
Tel (770) 677-2400 SIC 8742

MCKENNEYS INC p 930
1056 Moreland Indus Blvd 30316
Tel (404) 622-5000 SIC 1711 8711

■ **MEAD PACKAGING INTERNATIONAL INC** p 933
3423 Piedmont Rd Ne 30305
Tel (404) 875-2711 SIC 6719

MERCEDES-BENZ USA LLC p 944
303 Perimeter Ctr N 30346
Tel (201) 573-0600
SIC 5012 5013 7538 5511

MERCHANDISING SOLUTIONS GROUP INC p 944
260 Peachtree St Nw 30303
Tel (800) 417-1320 SIC 5199 1542

MERCHANTS METALS LLC p 945
211 Perimeter Center Pkwy 30346
Tel (770) 741-0300 SIC 3496 3446 5031

METROPOLITAN ATLANTA RAPID TRANSIT AUTHORITY p 955
2424 Piedmont Rd Ne 30324
Tel (404) 848-5000 SIC 4111

MILLER ZELL INC p 971
6100 Fulton Indus Blvd Sw 30336
Tel (404) 691-7400
SIC 7389 2542 2759 2752

■ **MLT VACATIONS LLC** p 979
700 S Central Ave 30354
Tel (651) 289-8500 SIC 4725

MONDI BAGS USA LLC p 984
1200 Abernathy Rd Ste 450 30328
Tel (770) 243-5410 SIC 2621

MOREHOUSE COLLEGE (INC) p 988
830 Westview Dr Sw 30314
Tel (404) 681-2800 SIC 8221

MOREHOUSE SCHOOL OF MEDICINE INC p 988
720 Westview Dr Sw 30310
Tel (404) 752-1500 SIC 8322 8221

MORRISON MANAGEMENT SPECIALISTS INC p 990
5801 Pachtree Dunwoody Rd 30342
Tel (404) 845-3330 SIC 8099

MOSCOW CAMDEN AND SAN AUGUSTINE RAILROAD LLC p 992
133 Peachtree St Ne 30303
Tel (404) 652-4000 SIC 2656

■ **MUELLER GROUP LLC** p 998
1200 Abernathy Rd 30328
Tel (770) 206-4200
SIC 3823 3321 3533 7699

▲ **MUELLER WATER PRODUCTS INC** p 998
1200 Abernathy Rd # 1200 30328
Tel (770) 206-4200
SIC 3491 3492 3494 3443 3321 3823

■ **MUNICH AMERICAN REASSURANCE CO PAC INC** p 1000
56 Perimeter Ctr E # 200 30346
Tel (770) 350-3200 SIC 6331

MUNICIPAL ELECTRIC AUTHORITY OF GEORGIA p 1000
1470 Riveredge Pkwy 30328
Tel (770) 563-0300 SIC 1623

NATIONAL DISTRIBUTING CO INC p 1011
1 National Dr Sw 30336
Tel (404) 696-1681 SIC 5182 5181

NATIONAL FURNITURE LIQUIDATORS I LLC p 1012
2865 Log Cabin Dr Se 30339
Tel (404) 872-7280 SIC 5021 5712 5932

■ **NATIONAL GENERAL LENDER SERVICES INC** p 1012
210 Interstate N Pkwy 30339
Tel (770) 690-8400 SIC 6719

NATIONAL SENIOR CARE INC p 1016
1 Ravinia Dr Ste 1500 30346
Tel (678) 443-7000
SIC 5912 8051 8093 8741 8062 3443

■ **NATURALLY FRESH INC** p 1018
1000 Naturally Fresh Blvd 30349
Tel (404) 765-9000 SIC 2035 2099

NAVIGATION CAPITAL PARTNERS INC p 1020
3060 Peachtree Rd Nw 30305
Tel (404) 504-4070 SIC 6726

NCP 2 LP p 1022
3060 Peachtree Rd Nw # 780 30305
Tel (404) 504-4080 SIC 6211

NEW MANHEIM AUTO AUCTIONS LIMITED (INC) p 1032
6205 Pachtree Dunwoody Rd 30328
Tel (678) 645-0000 SIC 5012

NEW SOUTH CONSTRUCTION CO INC p 1033
1180 W Peachtree St Nw # 70 30309
Tel (404) 443-4000 SIC 1541 8741

NEWELL RECYCLING OF ATLANTA LLC p 1037
1359 Central Ave 30344
Tel (404) 766-1621 SIC 4953

NEXXLINX CORP INC p 1041
3565 Piedmont Rd Ne 2-104 30305
Tel (877) 747-0658 SIC 7389 8742

NIIT TECHNOLOGIES INC p 1043
1050 Crown Pinte Pkwy 5th # 5 30338
Tel (770) 551-9494 SIC 7379 7371

NOBLE INVESTMENT GROUP LLC p 1046
3424 Peachtree Rd Ne # 2000 30326
Tel (404) 262-9660 SIC 6726

NOBLE SYSTEMS CORP p 1046
1200 Ashwood Pkwy Ste 300 30338
Tel (404) 851-1331 SIC 3661

NORDIC LOGISTICS AND WAREHOUSING LLC p 1048
4300 Pleasantdale Rd 30340
Tel (770) 448-7400 SIC 4222

NORTH GEORGIA CONFERENCE OF METHODIST CHURCH INC p 1052
159 Ralph Mcgill Blvd Ne 30308
Tel (706) 548-6616 SIC 8661

NORTH HIGHLAND CO LLC p 1052
3333 Piedmont Rd Ne # 1000 30305
Tel (404) 233-1015 SIC 8742 7379

NORTH HIGHLAND HOLDING CO INC p 1052
3333 Piedmont Rd Ne # 1000 30305
Tel (404) 233-1015 SIC 8742

NORTHSIDE HOSPITAL INC p 1058
1000 Johnson Ferry Rd 30342
Tel (404) 851-8000 SIC 8062

NOVELIS CORP p 1063
3560 Lenox Rd Ne Ste 2000 30326
Tel (404) 760-4000 SIC 3353

NOVELIS INC p 1063
3560 Lenox Rd Ne Ste 2000 30326
Tel (404) 760-4000 SIC 3355

■ **NUANCE TRANSCRIPTION SERVICES INC** p 1066
1 Glenlake Pkwy Ste 800 30328
Tel (800) 205-7047 SIC 7338

▲ **NUMEREX CORP** p 1067
400 Interstate North Pkwy 30339
Tel (770) 693-5950 SIC 3669 7371

■ **ODWALLA INC** p 1074
1 Coca Cola Plz Nw 30313
Tel (479) 721-6260 SIC 2033

OLDCASTLE ARCHITECTURAL INC p 1081
900 Ashwood Pkwy Ste 600 30338
Tel (770) 804-3363 SIC 3251

OLDCASTLE BUILDING PRODUCTS INC p 1082
900 Ashwood Pkwy Ste 600 30338
Tel (770) 804-3363 SIC 5031

OLDCASTLE INC p 1082
900 Ashwood Pkwy Ste 600 30338
Tel (770) 804-3363
SIC 3273 3272 3271 3255

OLDCASTLE MATERIALS INC p 1082
900 Ashwood Pkwy Ste 700 30338
Tel (770) 522-5600
SIC 3272 1622 1611 2951 5032

OMNI INSURANCE CO p 1084
2018 Powers Ferry Rd Se # 100 30339
Tel (770) 952-4500 SIC 6331

OMNI INSURANCE GROUP INC p 1085
20018 Powers Ferry Rd 30339
Tel (770) 952-4500 SIC 6331

■ **ORKIN LLC** p 1095
2170 Piedmont Rd Ne 30324
Tel (404) 888-2000 SIC 7342

▲ **OXFORD INDUSTRIES INC** p 1101
999 Peachtree St Ne # 688 30309
Tel (404) 659-2424 SIC 2321 2325 2311

PARADIES SHOPS LLC p 1113
2849 Paces Ferry Rd Se 30339
Tel (404) 344-7905
SIC 5947 5994 5621 5611 5912 5941

PAVESTONE LLC p 1122
3490 Piedmont Rd Ne # 1300 30305
Tel (404) 926-3167
SIC 3251 3241 3255 3272

■ **PEACH STATE HEALTH PLAN INC** p 1125
1100 Circle 75 Pkwy Se # 1100 30339
Tel (678) 556-2300 SIC 6324

PIEDMONT HEALTHCARE INC p 1147
1800 Hwll Mll Rd Nw 850 30318
Tel (770) 801-2550 SIC 8059

PIEDMONT HOSPITAL INC p 1147
1968 Peachtree Rd Nw 30309
Tel (404) 605-5000 SIC 8062

PIEDMONT MEDICAL CENTER INC p 1147
1968 Peachtree Rd Nw 30309
Tel (404) 605-5000 SIC 8011

PIEDMONT NATIONAL CORP p 1147
1561 Southland Cir Nw 30318
Tel (404) 351-6130 SIC 5199 5113

PIKSEL INC p 1148
2100 Powers Ferry Rd Se # 400 30339
Tel (646) 553-4845 SIC 4813

■ **PILGRIMS PRIDE CORP OF GEORGIA INC** p 1148
244 Perimeter Ctr Pkwy Ne 30346
Tel (770) 393-5000 SIC 2015 0254

PLACE PROPERTIES LP p 1153
3445 Peachtree Rd Ne # 1400 30326
Tel (404) 495-7500 SIC 6552

▲ **POPEYES LOUISIANA KITCHEN INC** p 1161
400 Perimeter Ctr Ter 30346
Tel (404) 459-4450 SIC 5812 6794

PORSCHE CARS NORTH AMERICA INC p 1161
1 Porsche Dr 30354
Tel (770) 290-3500 SIC 5511 5013

POST APARTMENT HOMES LP p 1163
4401 Northsde Pkwy 800 30327
Tel (404) 846-5000 SIC 6798 6513

POST PROPERTIES INC p 1164
4401 Northside Pkwy Nw # 800 30327
Tel (404) 846-5000 SIC 6798 6531

■ **POST SERVICES LLC** p 1164
4401 Northside Pkwy Nw # 800 30327
Tel (404) 846-5000 SIC 6531

▲ **PREFERRED APARTMENT COMMUNITIES INC** p 1169
3284 Northside Pkwy Nw # 150 30327
Tel (770) 818-4100 SIC 6798

PREMIERE GLOBAL SERVICES INC p 1171
3280 Peachtree Rd Ne # 1000 30305
Tel (404) 262-8400 SIC 7372 7389

▲ **PRGX GLOBAL INC** p 1173
600 Galleria Pkwy Se # 100 30339
Tel (770) 779-3900 SIC 8721

PRINCIPLE SOLUTIONS GROUP LLC p 1177
5 Concourse Pkwy Ste 2700 30328
Tel (770) 399-4500 SIC 7363

PRINTPACK HOLDINGS INC p 1177
2800 Overlook Pkwy Ne 30339
Tel (404) 460-7000 SIC 2673

PRINTPACK INC p 1177
2800 Overlook Pkwy Ne 30339
Tel (404) 460-7000 SIC 2673 3081

PROGRESSIVE LOGISTICS SERVICES LLC p 1181
6 Piedmont Ctr Ne Ste 606 30305
Tel (404) 495-5300 SIC 4213

PROMINA HEALTH SYSTEM INC p 1183
2727 Paces Ferry Rd Se 30339
Tel (404) 541-1111 SIC 8741 8062

PROMMIS SOLUTIONS LLC p 1183
400 Northridge Rd 30350
Tel (800) 275-7171 SIC 6111

PUBLIC TELECOMMUNICATIONS COMMISSION GEORGIA p 1190
260 14th St Nw 30318
Tel (404) 685-4788 SIC 4833

■ **PULTE DIVERSIFIED COMPANIES INC** p 1192
3350 Peachtree Rd Ne 30326
Tel (248) 647-2750 SIC 1521

■ **PULTE HOME CORP** p 1192
3350 Peachtree Rd Ne # 150 30326
Tel (248) 647-2750 SIC 1531 6552 6162

▲ **PULTEGROUP INC** p 1192
3350 Peachtree Rd Ne # 150 30326
Tel (404) 978-6400 SIC 1531 6552 6162

PURCHASING POWER LLC p 1192
1349 W Peachtree St Nw # 1100 30309
Tel (404) 609-5100 SIC 5961

■ **QBE FIRST INSURANCE AGENCY INC** p 1194
210 Interstate North Pkwy 30339
Tel (770) 690-8400 SIC 6411

QUIKRETE COMPANIES LLC p 1200
3490 Piedmont Rd Ne 30305
Tel (404) 634-9100
SIC 3272 3255 3251 3241

QUIKRETE HOLDINGS INC p 1200
3490 Piedmont Rd Ne # 1300 30305
Tel (404) 926-3167 SIC 3272 3241 3255

RACETRAC PETROLEUM INC p 1203
3225 Cumberland Blvd Se # 100 30339
Tel (770) 850-3491 SIC 5541 5411 5172

■ **RAILSERVE INC** p 1205
1691 Phoenix Blvd Ste 250 30349
Tel (770) 996-6838 SIC 4013

RAM PARTNERS LLC p 1206
3284 Northside Pkwy Nw # 300 30327
Tel (770) 437-5200 SIC 8741 8742

RANDSTAD NORTH AMERICA INC p 1208
3625 Cumberland Blvd Se 30339
Tel (770) 937-7000 SIC 7363 7361

RANDSTAD US LP p 1208
3625 Cumberland Blvd Se 30339
Tel (770) 937-7000 SIC 7361 7363

■ **REFRESHMENT PRODUCT SERVICES INC** p 1217
1 Coca Cola Plz Nw 30313
Tel (404) 676-2121 SIC 2086

REGAN INTERNATIONAL INC p 1218
2141 Whittier Pl Nw 30318
Tel (603) 624-9615 SIC 5153

RENTPATH INC p 1224
950 E Paces Ferry Rd Ne # 2600 30326
Tel (678) 421-3000 SIC 6531

RESOURCE HEALTHCARE OF AMERICA INC p 1227
1819 Peachtree Rd Ne # 520 30309
Tel (404) 364-2900 SIC 6531

RFPS MANAGEMENT CO II LP p 1231
2170 Piedmont Rd Ne 30324
Tel (404) 888-2000 SIC 1389

RHEEM MANUFACTURING CO INC p 1231
1100 Abernathy Rd # 1700 30328
Tel (770) 351-3000 SIC 3585 3433

RHEEM SALES CO INC p 1231
1100 Abernathy Rd # 1400 30328
Tel (770) 351-3016 SIC 3585

ROARK CAPITAL GROUP INC p 1240
1180 Peachtree St Ne # 2500 30309
Tel (404) 591-5200
SIC 6726 3993 7331 6794 5261

ROBERT W WOODRUFF ARTS CENTER INC p 1241
1280 Peachtree St Ne 30309
Tel (404) 733-4200
SIC 7929 8412 6512 8299

ROBERT W WOODRUFF ARTS CENTER INC p 1241
1280 Peachtree St Ne 30309
Tel (404) 733-4200 SIC 8412

ROBERT W WOODRUFF FOUNDATION INC p 1241
191 Peachtree St Ne 30303
Tel (404) 522-6755 SIC 6733

▲ **ROLLINS INC** p 1247
2170 Piedmont Rd Ne 30324
Tel (404) 888-2000 SIC 7342

■ **ROLLINS SUPPLY INC** p 1247
2170 Piedmont Rd Ne 30324
Tel (404) 888-2000 SIC 7389

ROYAL CAPITAL CORP p 1254
255 E Paces Ferry Rd Ne # 300 30305
Tel (404) 239-0808 SIC 6719

ROYAL FOOD SERVICE CO INC p 1254
3720 Zip Indus Blvd Se 30354
Tel (404) 366-4299 SIC 5148 5142

ROYAL HOSPITALITY CORP p 1254
255 E Paces Ferry Rd Ne # 300 30305
Tel (404) 239-0329 SIC 6794 8741 5812

■ **RSUI GROUP INC** p 1256
945 E Paces Ferry Rd Ne # 1800 30326
Tel (404) 231-2366 SIC 6331 6321

■ **RUBBERMAID INC** p 1256
3 Glenlake Pkwy 30328
Tel (770) 418-7000
SIC 3089 2519 3944 2369 2392

RUSSELL MCCALLS INC p 1259
255 Ted Turner Dr Sw 30303
Tel (404) 954-7600 SIC 5149 5143 5147

■ **SAFE-GUARD PRODUCTS INTERNATIONAL LLC** p 1266
2 Concourse Pkwy Ste 500 30328
Tel (404) 816-3221 SIC 6411

SAGE SOFTWARE INC p 1267
271 17th St Nw Ste 1100 30363
Tel (866) 996-7243 SIC 7372

SAINT JOSEPHS HOSPITAL OF ATLANTA INC p 1269
5665 Pchtr Dunwoody Rd Ne 30342
Tel (404) 851-7001 SIC 8062

SAINT JOSEPHS PRIMARY CARE NETWORK INC p 1269
5673 Peachtree Dunwdy 30342
Tel (404) 778-6100 SIC 8741

SAINT JOSEPHS SERVICE CORP p 1270
5665 Pachtree Dunwoody Rd 30342
Tel (404) 851-7001 SIC 8062

SATAIR USA INC p 1283
3993 Tradeport Blvd 30354
Tel (404) 675-6333 SIC 5088

SAVASENIORCARE LLC p 1284
1 Ravinia Dr Ste 1500 30346
Tel (770) 829-5100 SIC 8742

■ **SCHNITZER SOUTHEAST LLC** p 1288
906 Adamson St Sw 30315
Tel (404) 332-1750 SIC 5093

SCIENTIFIC RESEARCH CORP p 1292
2300 Windy Ridge Pkwy Se 400s 30339
Tel (770) 859-9161 SIC 8732 8711

SECURAMERICA LLC p 1298
3399 Peachtree Rd Ne # 1050 30326
Tel (404) 926-4222 SIC 7381

■ **SECUREWORKS CORP** p 1298
1 Concrse Pkwy Ne Ste 500 30328
Tel (404) 327-6339 SIC 7371

■ **SECUREWORKS INC** p 1298
1 Concourse Pkwy Ste 500 30328
Tel (770) 396-5767 SIC 7371

SERTA SIMMONS BEDDING LLC p 1307
1 Concourse Pkwy Ste 800 30328
Tel (770) 512-7700 SIC 2515

SHEPARD EXPOSITION SERVICES INC p 1315
1424 Hills Pl Nw 30318
Tel (404) 720-8600 SIC 7389

SHEPHERD CENTER INC p 1315
2020 Peachtree Rd Nw 30309
Tel (404) 352-2020 SIC 8069

■ **SILVERPOP SYSTEMS INC** p 1324
6303 Barfield Rd 30328
Tel (404) 348-9600 SIC 7374

SIMMONS HOLDINGS LLC p 1324
1 Concrs Pkwy Ne Ste 800 30328
Tel (770) 512-7700 SIC 2515

SIMMONS MANUFACTURING CO LLC p 1324
1 Concrse Pkwy Ne Ste 800 30328
Tel (770) 512-7700 SIC 2515

SITA INFORMATION NETWORKING COMPUTING USA INC p 1327
3100 Cumberland Blvd Se 30339
Tel (770) 850-4500 SIC 4899

SIX CONTINENTS HOTELS INC p 1328
3 Ravinia Dr Ste 100 30346
Tel (770) 604-2000 SIC 7011 6794 8741

SOFTWARE PARADIGMS INTERNATIONAL GROUP LLC p 1337
5 Concourse Pkwy Ste 500 30328
Tel (770) 904-7720 SIC 7379

SOUTHEASTRANS INC p 1347
4751 Best Rd Ste 140 30337
Tel (404) 209-4000 SIC 8742

▲ **SOUTHERN CO** p 1347
30 Ivan Allen Jr Blvd Nw 30308
Tel (404) 506-5000 SIC 4911

■ **SOUTHERN CO GAS** p 1347
10 Peachtree Pl Ne 30309
Tel (404) 584-4000 SIC 4922 4924

■ **SOUTHERN CO SERVICES INC** p 1347
30 Ivan Allen Jr Blvd Nw 30308
Tel (404) 506-5000 SIC 8711

■ **SOUTHERN COMMUNICATIONS SERVICES INC** p 1348
5555 Glenridge Connector 30342
Tel (678) 443-1500 SIC 4813 4812

■ **SOUTHERN POWER CO** p 1350
30 Ivan Allen Jr Blvd Nw 30308
Tel (404) 506-5000 SIC 4911

■ **SOUTHLAND LIFE INSURANCE CO** p 1351
5780 Powers Ferry Rd 30327
Tel (770) 980-5100 SIC 6311

SOUTO FOODS LLC p 1353
3077 Mccall Dr Ste 5 30340
Tel (404) 317-0674 SIC 5141

SOVEREIGN HEALTHCARE LLC p 1353
5887 Glenridge Dr Ste 150 30328
Tel (404) 574-2033 SIC 8051

SPECTRA METAL SALES INC p 1357
6104 Boat Rock Blvd Sw 30336
Tel (404) 344-4305
SIC 5051 3354 3355 3479 3444 2952

SPELMAN COLLEGE p 1358
350 Spelman Ln Sw 589 30314
Tel (404) 681-3643 SIC 8221

SPG HOLDINGS LLC p 1358
133 Peachtree St Se 30303
Tel (404) 652-4000 SIC 2621 5199

SSB MANUFACTURING CO p 1363
1 Concourse Pkwy Ste 800 30328
Tel (770) 512-7700 SIC 2515

STAFFING SOLUTIONS OF CENTRAL TEXAS INC p 1374
1040 Crown Pointe Pkwy 30338
Tel (770) 671-1900 SIC 7363

STAFFING SOLUTIONS SOUTHWEST INC p 1374
1040 Crown Pointe Pkwy 30338
Tel (678) 443-4200 SIC 7361 7363

STAG-PARKWAY INC p 1374
6320 Boat Rock Blvd Sw 30336
Tel (404) 349-7800 SIC 5013

■ **STATE BANK AND TRUST CO** p 1380
3399 Peachtree Rd Ne # 1900 30326
Tel (800) 414-4177 SIC 6022

▲ **STATE BANK FINANCIAL CORP** p 1380
3399 Peachtree Rd Ne 30326
Tel (404) 475-6599
SIC 6022 6712 6311 6141 6331

STATE OF GEORGIA p 1381
206 Washington St Sw # 111 30334
Tel (404) 656-1776 SIC 9111

STRONGHAVEN INC p 1394
2727 Paces Ferry Rd Se 1-1850 30339
Tel (678) 235-2713 SIC 2653

SUN SUITES INTERESTS LLLP p 1400
4770 S Atlanta Rd Se 30339
Tel (404) 350-9990 SIC 6719

▲ **SUNLINK HEALTH SYSTEMS INC** p 1403
900 Cir 75 Pkwy Se # 650 30339
Tel (770) 933-7000 SIC 8062 8051 5912

■ **SUNLINK HEALTHCARE CORP** p 1403
900 Circle 75 Pkwy Se # 13 30339
Tel (770) 850-1109 SIC 8051 8062

■ SUNTRUST BANK p 1405
303 Peachtree St Ne Fl 30 30308
Tel (877) 782-0175 *SIC* 6021

▲ SUNTRUST BANKS INC p 1405
303 Peachtree St Ne 30308
Tel (800) 786-8787
SIC 6021 6022 6211 6091 6282

■ SUNTRUST EQUITY FUNDING LLC p 1405
25 Park Pl Ne Lbby 2 30303
Tel (404) 477-6818 *SIC* 6021

SUPERIOR ESSEX HOLDING CORP p 1406
150 Interstate N Pkwy 30339
Tel (770) 657-6000 *SIC* 3357

SUPERIOR ESSEX INC p 1406
6120 Powers Ferry Rd # 150 30339
Tel (770) 657-6000 *SIC* 3357

SUPERIOR ESSEX INTERNATIONAL LP p 1406
6120 Powers Ferry Rd # 150 30339
Tel (770) 657-6000 *SIC* 3357

SWETT & CRAWFORD OF GEORGIA INC p 1412
3350 Riverwood Pkwy Se # 1100 30339
Tel (404) 240-5200 *SIC* 6411

SWIFT DENIM SERVICES INC p 1412
5 Concourse Pkwy Ste 2 30328
Tel (770) 901-6300 *SIC* 2211

SYBRA LLC p 1413
1155 Perimeter Ctr # 1100 30338
Tel (678) 514-4100 *SIC* 5812

■ SYMCOR INC p 1414
3399 Peachtree Rd Ne # 850 30326
Tel (404) 504-0100 *SIC* 7374

■ TEAVANA CORP p 1430
3630 Peachtree Rd Ne # 1480 30326
Tel (404) 495-0760 *SIC* 5499

■ TEAVANA HOLDINGS INC p 1430
3393 Peachtree Rd Ne # 317 30326
Tel (404) 995-8200 *SIC* 5499

TECHNICAL COLLEGE SYSTEM OF GEORGIA FOUNDATION INC p 1431
1800 Century Pl Ne # 550 30345
Tel (404) 679-1600 *SIC* 8211 9199

TEDS MONTANA GRILL INC p 1432
133 Luckie St Nw Ste 200 30303
Tel (404) 521-9796 *SIC* 5812

■ TEN NETWORK HOLDING INC p 1436
1 Cnn Ctr Nw 30303
Tel (404) 827-1700 *SIC* 4833

TEXAS WINGS INC p 1445
1815 The Exchange Se 30339
Tel (770) 799-2241 *SIC* 5812

■ THD AT-HOME SERVICES INC p 1446
2690 Cumberland Pkwy Se # 300 30339
Tel (770) 779-1423 *SIC* 8741

THOMAS CONCRETE INDUSTRIES INC p 1448
2500 Cumberland Pkwy Se # 200 30339
Tel (770) 431-3300 *SIC* 3273 5032

THOMAS CONCRETE OF GEORGIA INC p 1448
2500 Cumbrld Pkwy Se 20 Ste 200 30339
Tel (770) 969-8545 *SIC* 3273

TIN LIZZYS CONSOLIDATED LLC p 1455
2030 Powers Ferry Rd Se 30339
Tel (678) 681-9503 *SIC* 6719

TOM GRADDY ENTERPRISES INC p 1459
3348 Peachtree Rd Ne 30326
Tel (404) 363-8390
SIC 5531 5511 7538 5012

TOSCA SERVICES LLC p 1462
303 Peachtree Center Ave 30303
Tel (920) 569-5335 *SIC* 7359 5144

TOTAL RESOURCE AUCTIONS INC p 1463
6205 Pachtree Dunwoody Rd 30328
Tel (678) 645-0000 *SIC* 5012

TRANSITIONAL HEALTH PARTNERS p 1472
400 Perimeter Ctr Ter Ne 30346
Tel (770) 698-9040 *SIC* 8051

TRAVELPORT LIMITED p 1474
300 Galleria Pkwy Se 30339
Tel (770) 563-7400 *SIC* 4724

TRAVELPORT LP p 1475
300 Galleria Pkwy Se 30339
Tel (770) 563-7400 *SIC* 7374

■ TRIARC ACQUISITION LLC p 1478
1155 Perimeter Ctr 30338
Tel (678) 514-4101 *SIC* 5812

TRIMONT REAL ESTATE ADVISORS INC p 1480
3424 Peachtree Rd Ne # 2200 30326
Tel (404) 420-5600 *SIC* 6531

TROUTMAN SANDERS LLP p 1484
600 Peachtree St Ne # 5200 30308
Tel (404) 885-3000 *SIC* 8111

TROUTMAN SANDERS LLP POLITICAL ACTION COMMITTEE INC p 1484
600 Peachtree St Ne Ste 5 30308
Tel (404) 885-3000 *SIC* 8651

■ TURNER BROADCASTING SYSTEM INC p 1492
1 Cnn Ctr Nw 14sw 30303
Tel (404) 575-7250
SIC 7822 4833 4841 7812

■ TWCC HOLDING CORP p 1494
300 Interstate N Pkwy Se 30339
Tel (770) 226-0000
SIC 4833 4813 7812 8999

■ UHS OF PEACHFORD LP p 1500
2151 Peachford Rd 30338
Tel (770) 455-3200 *SIC* 8011

UNIPRO FOODSERVICE INC p 1505
2500 Cumbrld Pkwy Se 60 Ste 600 30339
Tel (770) 952-0871
SIC 5147 5141 5146 5142

■ UNITED PARCEL SERVICE CO p 1510
55 Glenlake Pkwy 30328
Tel (404) 828-6000 *SIC* 4512

UNITED PARCEL SERVICE INC p 1510
55 Glenlake Pkwy 30328
Tel (404) 828-6000 *SIC* 4215

▲ UNITED PARCEL SERVICE INC p 1510
55 Glenlake Pkwy 30328
Tel (404) 828-6000 *SIC* 4215 4513 4522

■ UNITED PARCEL SERVICE INC (OH) p 1510
55 Glenlake Pkwy 30328
Tel (404) 828-6000 *SIC* 7389

■ UPS FUEL SERVICES INC p 1529
55 Glenlake Pkwy 30328
Tel (678) 339-3250 *SIC* 5172

■ UPS LOGISTICS GROUP INC p 1529
55 Glenlake Pkwy 30328
Tel (678) 746-4100
SIC 7389 7513 4731 4513

■ UPS SUPPLY CHAIN SOLUTIONS GENERAL SERVICES INC p 1529
55 Glenlake Pkwy 30328
Tel (404) 828-6000 *SIC* 4215

US MOTIVATION INC p 1532
7840 Roswe Rd Usm Bldg 10 30350
Tel (770) 290-4700 *SIC* 8742

■ VALUED SERVICES ACQUISITIONS CO LLC p 1542
5 Concrs Pkwy Ne Ste 1000 30328
Tel (678) 593-1300 *SIC* 6099

▲ VERITIV CORP p 1550
1000 Abernathy Rd # 1700 30328
Tel (770) 391-8200 *SIC* 5111 5112 5087

■ VERITIV OPERATING CO p 1550
1000 Abernathy Rd 30328
Tel (770) 391-8200 *SIC* 5113 5112 5111

VERNAY LABORATORIES INC p 1551
2077 Cnvntion Ctr Cncurse 30337
Tel (404) 994-2000 *SIC* 3492

■ VOYA AMERICA EQUITIES INC p 1566
5780 Powers Ferry Rd 30327
Tel (612) 372-5432 *SIC* 6311 6411

■ VOYA INVESTMENT MANAGEMENT CO LLC p 1566
5780 Powers Ferry Rd 30327
Tel (770) 980-5100 *SIC* 6211

■ VOYA INVESTMENT MANAGEMENT LLC p 1566
5780 Powers Ferry Rd 30327
Tel (770) 980-5100 *SIC* 6211

■ WACHOVIA OPERATIONAL SERVICES LLC (NORTH CAROLINA) p 1570
191 Peachtree St Ne Fl 31 30303
Tel (404) 332-5000 *SIC* 7389

■ WASTE MANAGEMENT INC OF FLORIDA p 1580
2859 Paces Ferry Rd Se # 1600 30339
Tel (770) 805-4130 *SIC* 4953

WATKINS ASSOCIATED INDUSTRIES INC p 1582
1958 Monroe Dr Ne 30324
Tel (404) 872-3841 *SIC* 4213 6552

WEATHER CHANNEL INC p 1585
300 Interstate North Pkwy 30339
Tel (770) 226-0000 *SIC* 4841 4832

■ WESTOWER COMMUNICATIONS INC p 1602
4401 Northside Pkwy Nw # 600 30327
Tel (360) 306-3300 *SIC* 4899

WHITAKER OIL CO p 1605
1557 Marietta Rd Nw 30318
Tel (404) 355-8220 *SIC* 5169

■ WHITE CAP CONSTRUCTION SUPPLY INC p 1606
3100 Cumberland Blvd Se # 1700 30339
Tel (404) 879-7740 *SIC* 5072 5039 5031

■ WILLIAM CARTER CO p 1610
3438 Peachtree Rd Ne 30326
Tel (678) 791-1000 *SIC* 5641 5137

WINTER CONSTRUCTION CO p 1617
191 Peachtree St Ne # 2100 30303
Tel (404) 588-3300 *SIC* 1541

WORLD TRAVEL PARTNERS GROUP INC p 1625
6 Concourse Pkwy 30328
Tel (678) 441-5200 *SIC* 4724

WORLDPAY US INC p 1626
600 Morgan Falls Rd # 260 30350
Tel (770) 396-1616 *SIC* 7374

■ XEROX STATE HEALTHCARE LLC p 1631
9040 Roswell Rd Ste 700 30350
Tel (678) 352-7200 *SIC* 7373

YOUNG MENS CHRISTIAN ASSOCIATION OF METROPOLITAN ATLANTA INC p 1638
100 Edgewood Ave Ne 30303
Tel (404) 588-9622
SIC 8641 7991 8351 7032 8322

■ YOUR OTHER WAREHOUSE LLC p 1639
2455 Paces Ferry Rd Se B8 30339
Tel (770) 433-8211 *SIC* 5074 5075

ZEP INC p 1642
3330 Cumberland Blvd Se # 700 30339
Tel (877) 428-9937 *SIC* 2841 2879 2842

AUGUSTA, GA

ACC CONSTRUCTION CO INC p 14
635 Nw Frontage Rd Ste A 30907
Tel (706) 868-1037 *SIC* 1542 1541

AU MEDICAL CENTER INC p 130
1120 15th St 30912
Tel (706) 721-6569 *SIC* 8062

AUGUSTA NEWSPRINT CO EMPLOYEES RECREATION ASSOCIATION INC p 131
2434 Doug Barnard Pkwy 30906
Tel (706) 798-3440 *SIC* 2621

AUGUSTA UNIVERSITY p 131
1120 15th St 30912
Tel (706) 721-0011 *SIC* 8221

CARESOUTH HEALTH SYSTEM INC p 255
1 10th St Ste 500 30901
Tel (706) 855-5533 *SIC* 8099

CARESOUTH HOME HEALTH SERVICES LLC p 255
1 10th St Ste 500 30901
Tel (706) 855-5533 *SIC* 8082

CAROLE FABRICS CORP p 259
633 Nw Frontage Rd 30907
Tel (706) 863-4742
SIC 2221 2591 5131 5949 2392 2391

COUNTY OF AUGUSTA-RICHMOND p 376
535 Telfair St 30901
Tel (706) 821-2429 *SIC* 9111

CSLCS LLC p 398
1 10th St Ste 100 30901
Tel (855) 458-5500 *SIC* 8082

■ DOCTORS HOSPITAL OF AUGUSTA LLC p 447
3651 Wheeler Rd 30909
Tel (706) 651-3232 *SIC* 8062 8049

DSM FINANCE USA INC p 458
1408 Columbia Nitrogen Dr 30901
Tel (706) 849-6515
SIC 2891 2816 3089 3083 5169

EAST CENTRAL REGIONAL HOSPITAL p 470
3405 Mike Padgett Hwy 30906
Tel (706) 792-7105 *SIC* 8062

FIBRANT LLC p 540
1408 Columbia Nitrogen Dr 30901
Tel (706) 849-6600 *SIC* 2819 2899

FPL FOOD LLC p 573
1301 New Savannah Rd 30901
Tel (706) 722-2694 *SIC* 2011

GEORGIA HEALTH SCIENCES FOUNDATION INC p 607
1120 15th St 30912
Tel (800) 869-1113 *SIC* 8062 8221

INTERNATIONAL MANAGEMENT SERVICES CO INC p 756
3633 Wheeler Rd Ste 350 30909
Tel (706) 855-1014 *SIC* 8742

MANAGEMENT ANALYSIS & UTILIZATION INC p 900
501 Greene St Ste 100 30901
Tel (706) 722-6806 *SIC* 7361

MERRY LAND PROPERTIES LLC p 950
209 7th St Ste 300 30901
Tel (706) 722-6756 *SIC* 6798

MORRIS COMMUNICATIONS CO LLC p 990
725 Broad St 30901
Tel (706) 724-0851
SIC 2711 5199 2721 2731

MORRIS PUBLISHING GROUP LLC p 990
725 Broad St 30901
Tel (706) 724-0851 *SIC* 2711

MPG NEWSPAPER HOLDING LLC p 995
725 Broad St 30901
Tel (706) 724-0851 *SIC* 2711

■ MURRAY BISCUIT CO LLC p 1001
1550 Marvin Griffin Rd 30906
Tel (706) 798-8600 *SIC* 2052 2051

PHYSICIANS PRACTICE GROUP p 1146
1499 Walton Way Ste 1400 30901
Tel (706) 724-6100 *SIC* 8011

QUESTO INC p 1199
725 Broad St 30901
Tel (706) 724-0851 *SIC* 2711

RICHMOND COUNTY BOARD OF EDUCATION p 1233
864 Broad St 30901
Tel (706) 826-1000 *SIC* 8211

RICHMOND COUNTY SCHOOL SYSTEM p 1233
864 Broad St 30901
Tel (706) 826-1000 *SIC* 8211

SHIVERS TRADING & OPERATING CO p 1317
725 Broad St 30901
Tel (706) 724-0851
SIC 2711 2721 2731 4832 7312 6512

SIZEMORE INC p 1328
2116 Walton Way 30904
Tel (706) 736-1456 *SIC* 7381 7363 7349

SOUTHEASTERN NEWSPAPERS CO LLC p 1346
725 Broad St 30901
Tel (706) 722-0011 *SIC* 2711

TFE LOGISTICS GROUP INC p 1445
3633 Wheeler Rd Ste 350 30909
Tel (706) 855-1014 *SIC* 1541

THERMAL CERAMICS INC p 1447
2102 Old Savannah Rd 30906
Tel (706) 796-4200
SIC 3299 3255 5085 3296 3264 3053

UNIVERSITY HEALTH INC p 1518
1350 Walton Way 30901
Tel (706) 722-9011 *SIC* 8062

UNIVERSITY HEALTH RESOURCES INC p 1518
1350 Walton Way 30901
Tel (706) 722-9011 *SIC* 8741

UNIVERSITY HEALTH SERVICES INC p 1518
1350 Walton Way 30901
Tel (706) 722-9011 *SIC* 8062

AUSTELL, GA

CARAUSTAR CUSTOM PACKAGING GROUP INC p 252
5000 Austell Powder Sprin 30106
Tel (770) 948-3101 *SIC* 2657

CARAUSTAR INDUSTRIES INC p 252
5000 Astell Pwdr Sprng Rd 30106
Tel (770) 948-3101
SIC 2655 2631 2679 2656 2652

COBB HOSPITAL INC p 332
3950 Austell Rd 30106
Tel (770) 792-7600 *SIC* 8062

PLATEAU EXCAVATION INC p 1155
375 Lee Industrial Blvd 30168
Tel (770) 944-0205 *SIC* 1794

UNITED FORMING INC p 1508
470 Riverside Pkwy 30168
Tel (678) 945-4224 *SIC* 1771

YANCEY BROS CO p 1634
330 Lee Industrial Blvd # 1 30168
Tel (770) 941-2424
SIC 5082 5084 7699 7353

YKK AP AMERICA INC p 1636
270 Riverside Pkwy Ste A 30168
Tel (678) 838-6000 *SIC* 3442 3449

BAINBRIDGE, GA

DECATUR COUNTY SCHOOL DISTRICT p 420
100 S West St 39817
Tel (229) 248-2200 *SIC* 8211

ELBERTA CRATE & BOX CO p 483
606 Dothan Rd 39817
Tel (229) 243-1268 *SIC* 2449 5023 2448

SOUTHWEST GEORGIA OIL CO INC p 1352
1711 E Shotwell St 39819
Tel (229) 246-1553
SIC 5171 5541 5411 5921

BALDWIN, GA

FIELDALE FARMS CORP p 541
555 Broiler Blvd 30511
Tel (706) 778-5100 *SIC* 2015 2013 0751

BERKELEY LAKE, GA

TRANSCENTRA INC p 1471
4855 Peachtree Industrial 30092
Tel (678) 728-2500 *SIC* 7373

BETHLEHEM, GA

HARRISON POULTRY INC p 664
107 Star St W 30620
Tel (770) 867-9105
SIC 0254 2015 5984 2013 2011

BLACK CREEK, GA

BRYAN COUNTY SCHOOLS p 221
8810 Us Highway 280 E 31308
Tel (912) 851-4000 *SIC* 8211

BLAIRSVILLE, GA

■ UNITED COMMUNITY BANK p 1507
177 Highway 515 E 30512
Tel (706) 745-2151 *SIC* 6022

UNITED COMMUNITY BANKS INC p 1507
125 Highway 515 E 30512
Tel (581) 807-3041 *SIC* 6022

▲ UNITED COMMUNITY BANKS INC p 1507
125 Highway 515 E 30512
Tel (706) 781-2265 *SIC* 6022

BOSTON, GA

AG-PRO LLC p 34
19595 Us Hwy 84 31626
Tel (229) 498-8833 *SIC* 3523 5082

BRASELTON, GA

ELAN CHATEAU RESORTS LLC p 483
100 Rue Charlemagne Dr 30517
Tel (678) 425-0900
SIC 2084 5812 7992 7011

FOUNTAINHEAD DEVELOPMENT LLC p 571
100 Rue Charlemagne Dr 30517
Tel (770) 867-0903
SIC 7992 7991 5921 5812 7011

HITACHI KOKI USA LTD p 696
1111 Broadway Ave 30517
Tel (770) 925-1774 SIC 5084

BREMEN, GA

HL-A CO p 697
101 Thomas B Mur Ind Blvd 30110
Tel (678) 309-2000 SIC 3429 3714

BROOKHAVEN, GA

■ AT&T MOBILITY LLC p 123
1025 Lenox Park Blvd Ne 30319
Tel (425) 580-6014 SIC 4812 4813 5999

▲ ATLANTIC AMERICAN CORP p 125
4370 Peachtree Rd Ne # 200 30319
Tel (404) 266-5500 SIC 6311 6321 6331

AUTOTRADER.COM INC p 135
3003 Summit Blvd Fl 200 30319
Tel (404) 568-8000 SIC 5521

■ BELLSOUTH BUSINESS SYSTEMS INC p 171
2180 Lake Blvd Ne 30319
Tel (404) 829-8000 SIC 4813 4812

COX ARIZONA TELCOM LLC p 386
1400 Lake Hearn Dr Ne 30319
Tel (404) 843-5000 SIC 4841

COX AUTOMOTIVE INC p 386
3003 Summit Blvd Fl 200 30319
Tel (404) 843-5000 SIC 5012

COX BUSINESS SERVICES LLC p 386
1400 Lake Hearn Dr Ne 30319
Tel (404) 843-5000 SIC 4813

COX HOLDINGS INC p 386
1400 Lake Hearn Dr Ne 30319
Tel (404) 843-5000 SIC 4841 4813

COX MEDIA LLC p 386
1400 Lake Hearn Dr Ne 30319
Tel (404) 843-5000 SIC 4841 7313

COX NEVADA TELCOM LLC p 386
1400 Lake Hearn Dr Ne 30319
Tel (404) 269-7898 SIC 4841

COXCOM LLC p 386
1400 Lake Hearn Dr Ne 30319
Tel (404) 843-5000 SIC 4841 4813

CRAWFORD & CO p 389
1001 Summit Blvd Ste 500 30319
Tel (404) 300-1000
SIC 6411 8111 8099 6331

CRAWFORD & CO HEALTHCARE MANAGEMENT INC p 389
1001 Summit Blvd 30319
Tel (404) 256-0830 SIC 6411

■ FIDELITY BANK p 540
3 Corporate Blvd Ne # 110 30329
Tel (404) 325-3935 SIC 6029

FRI HOLDING CO LLC p 579
4170 Ashford Dunwoody Rd 30319
Tel (404) 865-3356 SIC 5812

■ GRAY TELEVISION GROUP INC p 632
4370 Peachtree Rd Ne # 500 30319
Tel (404) 266-8333 SIC 4833

▲ GRAY TELEVISION INC p 632
4370 Peachtree Rd Ne # 500 30319
Tel (404) 504-9828 SIC 4833

HLSS MANAGEMENT LLC p 697
2002 Summit Blvd Fl 6 30319
Tel (561) 682-7561 SIC 6162

IG STAFFING HOLDINGS LLC p 730
4170 Ashford Dnwody Rd Ne 30319
Tel (404) 257-7900 SIC 7361

INSIGHT GLOBAL LLC p 746
4170 Ashford Dunwoody 250 30319
Tel (404) 257-7900 SIC 7361

LODGIAN INC p 873
2002 Summit Blvd Ste 300 30319
Tel (404) 364-9400 SIC 7011 5813

▲ MARINE PRODUCTS CORP p 906
2801 Buford Hwy Ne # 520 30329
Tel (404) 321-7910 SIC 3732

■ NDCHEALTH CORP p 1022
1564 Northeast Expy Ne 30329
Tel (404) 728-2000 SIC 7374 8742

▲ RPC INC p 1255
2801 Buford Hwy Ne # 520 30329
Tel (404) 321-2140 SIC 1389

SALVATION ARMY p 1273
1424 Northeast Expy Ne 30329
Tel (404) 728-1300 SIC 8661 8322

SOFTTEK INTEGRATION SYSTEMS INC p 1337
2002 Summit Blvd Ste 300 30319
Tel (404) 460-5040 SIC 7379 7371 7373

■ VERIZON TELEMATICS INC p 1550
2002 Summit Blvd Ste 1800 30319
Tel (404) 573-5800 SIC 7379 4813

BRUNSWICK, GA

BRUNSWICK CELLULOSE LLC p 221
1400 9th St 31520
Tel (912) 265-5780
SIC 2611 2421 2899 2631

GLYNN COUNTY BOARD OF EDUCATION p 618
1313 Egmont St 31520
Tel (912) 267-4100 SIC 8211

GLYNN COUNTY SCHOOL SYSTEM p 618
1313 Egmont St 31520
Tel (912) 267-4100 SIC 8211

GLYNN-BRUNSWICK MEMORIAL HOSPITAL AUTHORITY p 618
2415 Parkwood Dr 31520
Tel (912) 466-7000 SIC 8062 8011

INTERNATIONAL AUTO PROCESSING INC p 754
1 Joe Frank Harris Blvd 31523
Tel (912) 554-8432
SIC 5012 7542 7538 7532

KING & PRINCE SEAFOOD CORP p 820
1 King And Prince Blvd 31520
Tel (912) 261-7025 SIC 2092

MAP INTERNATIONAL (INC) p 903
4700 Glynco Pkwy 31525
Tel (912) 265-6010 SIC 8399

PINOVA HOLDINGS INC p 1150
2801 Cook St 31520
Tel (888) 807-2958 SIC 2869

PINOVA INC p 1150
2801 Cook St 31520
Tel (888) 807-2958 SIC 2861

BUFORD, GA

LUND INC p 886
4325 Hamilton Mill Rd # 400 30518
Tel (678) 804-3767 SIC 3714

LUND INTERNATIONAL HOLDING CO p 886
4325 Hamilton Mill Rd 30518
Tel (678) 804-3767 SIC 3714 3713

MAKITA CORP OF AMERICA p 899
2650 Buford Hwy 30518
Tel (770) 932-2901 SIC 3546

THERAGENICS CORP p 1447
5203 Bristol Indus Way 30518
Tel (770) 271-0233 SIC 2834 3842

CAIRO, GA

IRA HIGDON GROCERY CO p 764
150 Iga Way 39828
Tel (229) 377-1272
SIC 5141 5147 5142 5143 2111 5194

CALHOUN, GA

ADVENTIST HEALTH SYSTEM GEORGIA INC p 27
1035 Red Bud Rd Ne 30701
Tel (706) 879-4714 SIC 8062

■ ALADDIN MANUFACTURING CORP p 43
160 S Industrial Blvd 30701
Tel (706) 629-7721 SIC 2273

APACHE MILLS INC p 96
197 Royal Dr Se 30701
Tel (706) 629-7791 SIC 2273

■ DAL-TILE SERVICES INC p 409
160 S Industrial Blvd 30701
Tel (706) 629-7721 SIC 3253

FIELDTURF USA INC p 541
175 N Industrial Blvd Ne 30701
Tel (706) 625-6533 SIC 3999

■ MOHAWK CARPET DISTRIBUTION INC p 982
160 S Industrial Blvd 30701
Tel (706) 695-9743 SIC 2273

■ MOHAWK CARPET LLC p 982
160 S Industrial Blvd 30701
Tel (706) 629-7721 SIC 2273

▲ MOHAWK INDUSTRIES INC p 982
160 S Industrial Blvd 30701
Tel (706) 629-7721 SIC 2273 3253

CAMILLA, GA

EQUITY GROUP - GEORGIA DIVISION LLC p 506
7220 Us Highway 19 31730
Tel (229) 336-1001 SIC 2015 0254 2048

GOLDEN PEANUT & TREE NUTS p 621
275 Industrial Blvd 31730
Tel (229) 336-7282 SIC 5159 2068

KEYSTONE FOODS EQUITY GROUP p 815
7220 Us Highway 19 31730
Tel (229) 336-9747 SIC 2099

CANTON, GA

CHEROKEE COUNTY BOARD OF EDUCATION p 294
110 Academy St 30114
Tel (770) 479-1871 SIC 8211

CHEROKEE COUNTY SCHOOL DISTRICT p 294
110 Academy St 30114
Tel (770) 479-1871 SIC 8211

CHEROKEE COUNTY WATER & SEWERAGE AUTHORITY p 294
391 W Main St 30114
Tel (770) 591-7156 SIC 4941 4952

COUNTY OF CHEROKEE p 377
1130 Bluffs Pkwy 30114
Tel (678) 493-6000 SIC 9111

NORTHSIDE HOSPITAL - CHEROKEE INC p 1058
201 Hospital Rd 30114
Tel (770) 720-5100 SIC 8062

CARROLLTON, GA

AUBREY SILVEY ENTERPRISES INC p 130
371 Hamp Jones Rd 30117
Tel (770) 834-0738
SIC 1629 1541 3643 7389 3699 5063

CARROLL COUNTY BOARD OF EDUCATION p 261
164 Independence Dr 30116
Tel (770) 834-3348 SIC 8211

CARROLL COUNTY SCHOOLS p 261
164 Independence Dr 30116
Tel (770) 832-3568 SIC 8211

CARROLL ELECTRIC MEMBERSHIP CORP p 261
155 N Highway 113 30117
Tel (770) 832-3552 SIC 4911

CUBS ACQUISITION CORP p 400
1 Southwire Dr 30119
Tel (770) 832-4242 SIC 3357 3661 3643

DECOSTAR INDUSTRIES INC p 421
1 Decoma Dr 30117
Tel (770) 801-2900 SIC 3714

GREENWAY HEALTH p 638
100 Greenway Blvd 30117
Tel (770) 836-3100 SIC 7373 7371

GREENWAY HEALTH LLC p 638
100 Greenway Blvd 30117
Tel (877) 932-6301 SIC 5734

SOUTHWIRE CO LLC p 1353
1 Southwire Dr 30119
Tel (770) 832-4242
SIC 3351 3355 3357 3599

TANNER MEDICAL CENTER INC p 1424
705 Dixie St 30117
Tel (770) 836-9666 SIC 8062

UNIVERSITY OF WEST GEORGIA p 1526
1601 Maple St 30118
Tel (678) 839-4780 SIC 8221

CARTERSVILLE, GA

AQUAFIL USA INC p 101
1 Aquafil Dr 30120
Tel (678) 605-8100 SIC 5199

BARTOW COUNTY BOARD OF EDUCATION p 158
65 Gilreath Rd Nw 30121
Tel (770) 606-5800 SIC 8211

BARTOW COUNTY SCHOOL SYSTEM p 158
65 Gilreath Rd Nw 30121
Tel (770) 606-5800 SIC 8211

■ CARTERSVILLE MEDICAL CENTER LLC p 262
960 Joe Frank Harris 30120
Tel (770) 382-1530 SIC 8361

CEDARTOWN, GA

POLK SCHOOL DISTRICT p 1159
612 S College St 30125
Tel (770) 748-3821 SIC 8211

CHATSWORTH, GA

MURRAY COUNTY SCHOOLS p 1001
1006 Green Rd 30705
Tel (706) 695-4531 SIC 8211

CLARKESVILLE, GA

HABERSHAM COUNTY BOARD OF EDUCATION p 651
132 Stanford Mill Rd 30523
Tel (706) 754-2110 SIC 8211

CLARKSTON, GA

■ ANSCO & ASSOCIATES LLC p 93
736 Park North Blvd 30021
Tel (404) 508-5700 SIC 1623

CLAXTON, GA

FRIES FARMS LLC p 580
8816 Us Highway 301 30417
Tel (912) 739-3181 SIC 0251 2015

NORMAN W FRIES INC p 1049
8816 Us Highway 301 30417
Tel (912) 739-1158 SIC 2015

COLLEGE PARK, GA

■ BUCKHEAD BEEF CO INC p 223
4500 Wickersham Dr 30337
Tel (404) 355-4400 SIC 5142 5146 5421

OLAM US HOLDINGS INC p 1080
2077 Convention Ctr 150 30337
Tel (404) 209-2676 SIC 0723

■ SYSCO ATLANTA LLC p 1416
2225 Riverdale Rd 30337
Tel (404) 765-9900 SIC 5141

COLUMBUS, GA

▲ AFLAC INC p 33
1932 Wynnton Rd 31999
Tel (706) 323-3431 SIC 6321 6311

■ AMERICAN FAMILY LIFE ASSURANCE CO OF COLUMBUS p 72
1932 Wynnton Rd 31999
Tel (706) 323-3431 SIC 6311

■ BB & T FINANCIAL FSB A FEDERAL SAVINGS BANK p 163
4 Bradley Park Ct Ste 1c 31904
Tel (706) 653-7885 SIC 8742

BLADES TECHNOLOGY INTERNATIONAL INC p 188
8801 Macon Rd 31908
Tel (706) 568-5900 SIC 3728

▲ CARMIKE CINEMAS INC p 258
1301 1st Ave 31901
Tel (706) 576-3400 SIC 7832

CHILD DEVELOPMENT SCHOOLS INC p 298
6053 Veterans Pkwy # 300 31909
Tel (706) 562-8600 SIC 8351

COLUMBUS GEORGIA CONSOLIDATED GOVERNMENT p 342
100 10th St 31901
Tel (706) 653-4000 SIC 9111

COLUMBUS REGIONAL HEALTHCARE SYSTEM INC p 342
707 Center St Ste 300 31901
Tel (706) 571-1495 SIC 8062

CONCRETE CO p 355
1030 1st Ave 31901
Tel (706) 256-5700 SIC 1442 3272

CONSOLIDATED GOVERMENT OF GA INC p 359
814 Linwood Blvd 31901
Tel (706) 653-4410 SIC 4111

DMI COLUMBUS LLC p 446
1600 Northside Indus Blvd 31904
Tel (248) 728-8642 SIC 3465

FLOURNOY DEVELOPMENT CO p 560
900 Brookstone Ctr Pkwy 31904
Tel (706) 324-4000 SIC 6552 1522 8741

FOLEY PRODUCTS CO p 563
1030 1st Ave 31901
Tel (706) 563-7882 SIC 3272

■ GA H IMPORTS LLC p 588
3000 N Lake Pkwy Ste 400 31909
Tel (706) 522-2090 SIC 5511

■ GEORGE G KERASOTES CORP p 606
1301 1st Ave 31901
Tel (706) 576-3400 SIC 7832

MASTERBUILT MANUFACTURING LLC p 918
1 Masterbuilt Ct 31907
Tel (706) 327-5622 SIC 3631 3714

MEDICAL CENTER p 936
710 Center St 31901
Tel (706) 660-6255 SIC 8062

MUSCOGEE COUNTY SCHOOL DISTRICT p 1002
2960 Macon Rd 31906
Tel (706) 748-2000 SIC 8211

PANASONIC ENERGY CORP OF AMERICA p 1111
1 Panasonic Dr 31907
Tel (706) 561-7730 SIC 3691 5531

PEZOLD MANAGEMENT ASSOCIATES INC p 1140
600 Brokstone Centre Pkwy 31904
Tel (706) 576-6400 SIC 5812

SCHUSTER ENTERPRISES INC p 1291
3530 Macon Rd 31907
Tel (706) 568-2657 SIC 5812

■ ST FRANCIS HOSPITAL INC p 1366
2122 Manchester Expy 31904
Tel (706) 596-4000 SIC 8062

STANDARD CONCRETE PRODUCTS INC p 1376
945 Broadway Ste 300 31901
Tel (706) 322-3274 SIC 3272

■ SYNOVUS BANK p 1415
1148 Broadway 31901
Tel (706) 649-4900 SIC 6022

▲ SYNOVUS FINANCIAL CORP p 1415
1111 Bay Ave Ste 500 31901
Tel (706) 649-2311 SIC 6021 6022 7389

■ SYNOVUS TRUST CO NA p 1415
1148 Broadway 31901
Tel (706) 649-2311 SIC 6733 6282

▲ TOTAL SYSTEM SERVICES INC p 1463
1 Tsys Way 31901
Tel (706) 644-6081 SIC 7374

W C BRADLEY CO p 1568
1017 Front Ave 31901
Tel (706) 571-7000 SIC 3631 3949 3999

COMMERCE, GA

■ ROPER PUMP CO p 1250
3475 Old Maysville Rd 30529
Tel (706) 336-3459 SIC 3823 3561

CONYERS, GA

■ ACUITY BRANDS LIGHTING INC p 20
1 Acuity Way 30012
Tel (800) 922-9641 SIC 3646 3645 3641

CELLOFOAM NORTH AMERICA INC p 274
1917 Rockdale Indstrl Blv 30012
Tel (770) 929-3688 SIC 3089 2821

FIREFIGHTERS PENSION FUND GEORGIA p 543
2171 Eastview Pkwy 30013
Tel (770) 388-5757 SIC 8631 9651

■ HILL PHOENIX INC p 693
2016 Gees Mill Rd Ne 30013
Tel (770) 285-3264 SIC 3632

HSBC SECURITIES (USA) INC p 715
107 Iris Glen Dr Se 30013
Tel (212) 525-5000 SIC 6211

HSBC USA INC p 715
107 Iris Glen Dr Se 30013
Tel (212) 525-5000 SIC 6021

JET CORR INC p 783
1800 Sarasot Bus Pkwy Ne B 30013
Tel (770) 929-1300 SIC 2653

LATEX CONSTRUCTION CO INC p 846
1353 Farmer Rd Nw 30012
Tel (770) 760-0820 SIC 1623

MADISON INDUSTRIES INC OF GEORGIA p 894
1035 Iris Dr Sw 30094
Tel (770) 483-4401 SIC 1541 3444

PRATT (JET CORR) INC p 1167
1800 Sarasot Bus Pkwy Ne B 30013
Tel (770) 929-1300 SIC 2653

PRATT INDUSTRIES (USA) INC p 1167
1800-A Sarasota Pkwy 30013
Tel (770) 918-5678 SIC 2621

PRATT PAPER (NY) INC p 1167
1800 Sarasota Business 30013
Tel (770) 918-5678 SIC 2611

ROCKDALE COUNTY BOARD OF EDUCATION p 1243
954 N Main St Nw 30012
Tel (770) 483-4713 SIC 8211

ROCKDALE COUNTY PUBLIC SCHOOLS p 1243
954 N Main St Nw 30012
Tel (770) 483-4713 SIC 8211

■ **ROCKDALE HOSPITAL LLC** p 1244
1412 Milstead Ave Ne 30012
Tel (770) 918-3101 SIC 8062

■ **ROCKDALE MEDICAL CENTER INC** p 1244
1412 Milstead Ave Ne 30012
Tel (770) 918-3000 SIC 8062

SOUTHEAST CONNECTIONS LLC p 1345
2720 Dogwood Dr Se 30013
Tel (678) 509-0165 SIC 1623

TEIJIN ARAMID USA INC p 1433
801 Blacklawn Rd Sw Ste F 30012
Tel (770) 929-0781 SIC 5131

TIMBER PRODUCTS INSPECTION INC p 1454
1641 Sigman Rd Nw 30012
Tel (770) 922-8000 SIC 0851 8734

■ **UNIFIED BRANDS INC** p 1503
2016 Gees Mill Rd Ne 30013
Tel (601) 372-3903 SIC 3469

WRD INC p 1627
1641 Sigman Rd Nw 30012
Tel (770) 922-8000 SIC 8721

CORNELIA, GA

COMMUNITY BANKSHARES INC p 347
400 N Main St 30531
Tel (706) 778-3900 SIC 6712

COVINGTON, GA

BRIDGESTONE GOLF INC p 211
15320 Indsrial Pk Blvd Ne 30014
Tel (770) 787-7400 SIC 5091 3949

CLEAR GROUP LLC p 324
90 Summer Walk Ct 30016
Tel (404) 403-0274 SIC 5812

FIBERVISIONS MANUFACTURING CO p 539
7101 Alcovy Rd Ne 30014
Tel (770) 784-3402 SIC 2821 2823

LENDMARK FINANCIAL SERVICES LLC p 855
2118 Usher St Nw 30014
Tel (678) 625-6500 SIC 6162

NEWTON COUNTY BOARD OF EDUCATION p 1039
2109 Newton Dr Ne 30014
Tel (770) 787-1330 SIC 8211

NEWTON COUNTY SCHOOLS p 1039
2109 Newton Dr Ne 30014
Tel (770) 787-1330 SIC 8211

■ **SGD NORTH AMERICA INC** p 1310
9141 Technology Dr 30014
Tel (770) 385-3800 SIC 3221

SIMS ENTERPRISES OF GEORGIA LLC p 1325
205 Creekview Blvd 30016
Tel (770) 385-3461 SIC 3585

SNAPPING SHOALS ELECTRIC MEMBERSHIP CORP p 1335
14750 Brown Bridge Rd 30016
Tel (770) 786-3484 SIC 1731

SNAPPING SHOALS ELECTRIC TRUST INC p 1335
14750 Brown Bridge Rd 30016
Tel (770) 786-3484 SIC 4911

CUMMING, GA

AMERICAN BOA INC p 69
1420 Redi Rd 30040
Tel (678) 513-3348 SIC 3494

AUTOMATIONDIRECT.COM INC p 134
3505 Hutchinson Rd 30040
Tel (770) 889-2858 SIC 5084

COUNTY OF FORSYTH p 378
110 E Main St Ste 210 30040
Tel (770) 781-2101 SIC 9111

FORSYTH COUNTY BOARD OF EDUCATION p 568
1120 Dahlonega Hwy 30040
Tel (770) 887-2461 SIC 8211

FORSYTH COUNTY SCHOOLS p 568
1120 Dahlonega Hwy 30040
Tel (770) 887-2461 SIC 8211

HOOVER PRECISION PRODUCTS INC p 706
2200 Pendley Rd 30041
Tel (770) 889-9223 SIC 3399

SAWNEE ELECTRIC MEMBERSHIP CORP p 1284
543 Atlanta Rd 30040
Tel (770) 887-2363 SIC 4911

CUTHBERT, GA

WHATLEY OIL AND AUTO PARTS CO p 1604
598 Blakely St 39840
Tel (229) 732-2611 SIC 5171 5013 7389

DAHLONEGA, GA

UNIVERSITY OF NORTH GEORGIA p 1524
82 College Ln 30533
Tel (706) 864-1400 SIC 8221

DALLAS, GA

PAULDING COUNTY BOARD OF EDUCATION p 1121
3236 Atlanta Hwy 30132
Tel (770) 443-8000 SIC 8211

PAULDING COUNTY SCHOOL DISTRICT p 1121
3236 Atlanta Hwy 30132
Tel (770) 443-8000 SIC 8211

PAULDING MEDICAL CENTER INC p 1121
600 W Memorial Dr 30132
Tel (770) 445-4411 SIC 8062 8051

DALTON, GA

BEAULIEU GROUP LLC p 166
1502 Coronet Dr 30720
Tel (706) 259-4511 SIC 2273 2281

BEAULIEU OF AMERICA INC p 166
1502 Coronet Dr 30720
Tel (706) 278-6666 SIC 2273

BROWN INDUSTRIES INC p 219
205 W Industrial Blvd 30720
Tel (706) 277-1977
SIC 2759 5131 2273 3552 3315 2671

COLUMBIA RECYCLING CORP p 341
1001 Chattanooga Ave 30720
Tel (706) 278-4701 SIC 2299

DALTON PUBLIC SCHOOLS p 410
300 W Waugh St 30720
Tel (706) 876-4000 SIC 8211

▲ **DIXIE GROUP INC** p 444
475 Reed Rd 30720
Tel (706) 876-5800 SIC 2273

ENGINEERED FLOORS LLC p 499
3510 Corporate Dr 30721
Tel (706) 625-4334 SIC 2273

HAMILTON HEALTH CARE SYSTEM INC p 655
1200 Memorial Dr 30720
Tel (706) 278-2105 SIC 8322 8062

HAMILTON MEDICAL CENTER INC p 655
1200 Memorial Dr 30720
Tel (706) 272-6000 SIC 8062

J & J INDUSTRIES INC p 770
818 J And J Dr 30721
Tel (706) 529-2100 SIC 2273

LEXMARK CARPET MILLS INC p 860
285 Kraft Dr 30721
Tel (706) 277-3000 SIC 2273

MARKETING ALLIANCE GROUP INC p 908
2830 N Dug Gap Rd Sw 30720
Tel (706) 277-9707 SIC 2752

NORTH GEORGIA ELECTRIC MEMBERSHIP FOUNDATION INC p 1052
1850 Cleveland Hwy 30721
Tel (706) 259-9441 SIC 4911

■ **SHAW CONTRACT FLOORING SERVICES INC** p 1312
616 E Walnut Ave 30721
Tel (706) 278-3812 SIC 1752

■ **SHAW INDUSTRIES GROUP INC** p 1313
616 E Walnut Ave 30721
Tel (800) 441-7429 SIC 5023

■ **SHAW INDUSTRIES INC** p 1313
616 E Walnut Ave 30721
Tel (706) 278-3812 SIC 2273

TANDUS CENTIVA INC p 1424
311 Smith Industrial Blvd 30721
Tel (706) 259-9711 SIC 2273

TANDUS GROUP INC p 1424
311 Smith Industrial Blvd 30721
Tel (706) 259-9711 SIC 2273

TEXTILE RUBBER AND CHEMICAL CO INC p 1445
1300-1350 Tiarco Dr Sw 30721
Tel (706) 277-1300 SIC 5169 2821

US FLOORS INC p 1531
3580 Corporate Dr 30721
Tel (706) 278-9491 SIC 5713

WHITFIELD COUNTY SCHOOLS p 1606
1306 S Thornton Ave 30720
Tel (706) 217-6780 SIC 8211

WHITFIELD EDUCATION FOUNDATION INC p 1606
1306 S Thornton Ave 30720
Tel (706) 226-3710 SIC 8211

■ **WINDSTREAM GEORGIA LLC** p 1615
906 Vista Dr 30721
Tel (706) 279-7600 SIC 4813 4812

DAWSONVILLE, GA

GOLD CREEK FOODS LLC p 620
686 Highway 9 N 30534
Tel (706) 216-8640 SIC 5144

DECATUR, GA

COUNTY OF DEKALB p 377
1300 Commerce Dr 30030
Tel (404) 371-2881 SIC 9532

DEKALB FARMERS MARKET INC p 423
3000 E Ponce De Leon Ave 30030
Tel (404) 377-6400
SIC 5431 5421 5461 5451 5921 5812

DEKALB MEDICAL CENTER INC p 423
2701 N Decatur Rd 30033
Tel (404) 501-1000 SIC 8062

DEKALB REGIONAL HEALTH SYSTEM INC p 423
2701 N Decatur Rd 30033
Tel (404) 501-1000 SIC 8741

GEORGIA DEPARTMENT OF JUVENILE JUSTICE p 607
3408 Covington Hwy 30032
Tel (404) 508-6500 SIC 9222

GEORGIA PERIMETER COLLEGE p 607
3251 Panthersville Rd 30034
Tel (678) 891-2300 SIC 8222

GLOBAL HEALTH SOLUTIONS INC p 616
325 Swanton Way 30030
Tel (404) 592-1430 SIC 8099

GOODWILL INDUSTRIES OF NORTH GEORGIA INC p 624
2201 Lawrenceville Hwy 30033
Tel (404) 420-9914 SIC 8331

GOODWILL OF NORTH GEORGIA INC p 625
2201 Lawrenceville Hwy 30033
Tel (404) 420-9900 SIC 5932 8331

JOHN H HARLAND CO p 788
2939 Miller Rd 30035
Tel (770) 593-5050
SIC 2782 2752 2761 7371 7379

NRD HOLDINGS LLC p 1064
625 Dekalb Ste 100 30033
Tel (404) 499-1960 SIC 6719

DOUGLAS, GA

BROOKS AUTO PARTS INC p 218
402 Peterson Ave S 31533
Tel (912) 384-7818 SIC 5531

COFFEE COUNTY SCHOOL DISTRICT p 334
1311 Peterson Ave S 31533
Tel (912) 384-2086 SIC 8211

COFFEE REGIONAL MEDICAL CENTER INC p 334
1101 Ocilla Rd 31533
Tel (912) 384-1900 SIC 8062

DOUGLASVILLE, GA

DOUGLAS COUNTY BOARD OF EDUCATION p 452
9030 Highway 5 30134
Tel (770) 651-2000 SIC 8211

DOUGLAS COUNTY SCHOOL SYSTEM p 452
9030 Highway 5 30134
Tel (770) 651-2000 SIC 8211

DOUGLAS HOSPITAL INC p 452
8954 Hospital Dr Frnt 30134
Tel (770) 949-1500 SIC 8062

GREYSTONE POWER CORP AN ELECTRIC MEMBERSHIP CORP p 640
4040 Bankhead Hwy 78 30134
Tel (770) 942-6576 SIC 4911

SEASONS-4 INC p 1297
4500 Industrial Access Rd 30134
Tel (770) 489-0716 SIC 3585 3567

DOUGLAS, GA

WILLIAMS INSTITUTIONAL FOODS INC p 1611
1325 Bowens Mill Rd Sw 31533
Tel (912) 384-5270 SIC 5141

DUBLIN, GA

■ **FAIRVIEW PARK LIMITED PARTNERSHIP** p 525
200 Industrial Blvd 31021
Tel (478) 274-3990 SIC 8062

■ **SP FIBER TECHNOLOGIES SOUTHEAST LLC** p 1353
709 Papermill Rd 31027
Tel (478) 272-1600 SIC 2621

WAREHOUSE HOME FURNISHINGS DISTRIBUTORS INC p 1575
1851 Telfair St 31021
Tel (800) 456-0424 SIC 5712

■ **WESTROCK SP CO** p 1603
709 Papermill Rd 31027
Tel (504) 733-1954 SIC 2621

DULUTH, GA

▲ **AGCO CORP** p 34
4205 River Green Pkwy 30096
Tel (770) 813-9200 SIC 3523 6159

ALLSTAFF MANAGEMENT INC p 58
6650 Sugarloaf Pkwy # 300 30097
Tel (770) 339-0000 SIC 7363

AMERICAN CYBERSYSTEMS INC p 71
2400 Meadowbrook Pkwy 30096
Tel (770) 493-5588 SIC 7373 7371 7372

AMERISURE MUTUAL INSURANCE CO p 84
2160 Satellite Blvd # 200 30097
Tel (770) 813-3300 SIC 6411

■ **ASBURY AUTOMOTIVE ATLANTA LLC** p 115
3039 Premiere Pkwy # 900 30097
Tel (404) 622-1921
SIC 5511 7515 5013 6159 5521

▲ **ASBURY AUTOMOTIVE GROUP INC** p 115
2905 Premiere Pkwy 30097
Tel (770) 418-8200 SIC 5511

BAILY INTERNATIONAL OF ATLANTA INC p 145
3312-B N Berkeley Lk Rd 30096
Tel (770) 452-8212 SIC 5087

BARCO INC p 155
3059 Premiere Pkwy # 400 30097
Tel (408) 400-4100 SIC 3575 3669

CURTIS 1000 INC p 402
1725 Breckinridge Park 30096
Tel (770) 925-4500
SIC 2761 2759 2791 2789 2752

DATAPATH INC p 414
2205 Northmont Pkwy 100 30096
Tel (678) 597-0300 SIC 3663

DIVERSITECH CORP p 444
6650 Sugarloaf Pkwy # 100 30097
Tel (678) 542-3600 SIC 3272

DULUTH TRAVEL INC p 461
2860 Peachtree Industrial 30097
Tel (770) 813-9895 SIC 4724

▲ **EBIX INC** p 474
1 Ebix Way Ste 100 30097
Tel (678) 281-2020 SIC 7371 7372

EVERCARE CO p 513
3885 Crestwd Pkwy Nw # 175 30096
Tel (770) 570-5000 SIC 3991

FIBERVISIONS CORP p 539
3700 Crestwood Pkwy Nw 30096
Tel (678) 578-7240 SIC 2899

GROUP RESOURCES INC p 642
3080 Premiere Pkwy # 100 30097
Tel (770) 623-8383 SIC 6411

■ **HEALTHCARE SOLUTIONS INC** p 676
2736 Meadow Church Rd # 300 30097
Tel (866) 810-4332 SIC 8742

ICONEX LLC p 728
3097 Satellite Blvd 30096
Tel (917) 282-0861 SIC 5111 2621

INTRALOT INC p 760
11360 Technology Cir 30097
Tel (678) 473-7200 SIC 7379

KURANI PIZZA INC p 832
2825 Breckinridge Blvd # 150 30096
Tel (770) 923-2313 SIC 5812

■ **MACYS SYSTEMS AND TECHNOLOGY INC** p 893
5985 State Bridge Rd 30097
Tel (678) 474-2000 SIC 7374

MERIAL INC p 948
3239 Satellite Blvd 30096
Tel (678) 638-3000 SIC 5122

MERIAL LIMITED p 948
3239 Satellite Blvd 500 30096
Tel (678) 638-3000 SIC 2836

MERIAL UK LLC p 948
3239 Satellite Blvd 30096
Tel (678) 638-3000 SIC 2836 2834 3841

METSO AUTOMATION p 957
2425 Commerce Ave Ste 100 30096
Tel (770) 476-3641 SIC 5084

MOORIM USA INC p 988
3700 Crestwood Pkwy Nw 30096
Tel (303) 770-8809 SIC 5111

NATIONAL DCP LLC p 1011
3805 Crestwood Pkwy Nw 30096
Tel (770) 369-8600 SIC 5461

NATIONAL VISION INC p 1017
2435 Commerce Ave # 2200 30096
Tel (770) 822-3600 SIC 5995 8042

▲ **NCR CORP** p 1022
3097 Satellite Blvd # 100 30096
Tel (937) 445-5000
SIC 3575 3578 7379 7374 7371

■ **NISCAYAH INC** p 1044
2400 Commerce Ave Ste 500 30096
Tel (678) 474-1720 SIC 5065

ORDNER CONSTRUCTION CO INC p 1093
1600 Executive Dr Ste 100 30096
Tel (678) 380-7400 SIC 1542

PIKE NURSERY HOLDING LLC p 1148
3555 Koger Blvd Ste 360 30096
Tel (770) 921-1022 SIC 5261

PILGRIMS PRIDE CORP p 1148
1965 Evergreen Blvd # 100 30096
Tel (770) 232-4200 SIC 2015 5144 5141

■ PRIMERICA FINANCIAL SERVICES INC p 1175
3120 Breckinridge Blvd 30099
Tel (800) 544-5445 SIC 6411

▲ PRIMERICA INC p 1175
1 Primerica Pkwy 30099
Tel (770) 381-1000 SIC 6411

PRIMERICA LIFE INSURANCE CO p 1175
1 Primerica Pkwy 30099
Tel (770) 381-1000 SIC 6311

■ SAIA MOTOR FREIGHT LINE LLC p 1268
11465 Johns Creek Pkwy # 400 30097
Tel (770) 232-5067 SIC 4213

SOUTHEAST TESTING & ENGINEERING INC p 1346
2870 N Berkeley Lk Rd Nw 30096
Tel (678) 377-1234 SIC 7389

TANDBERG TELEVISION INC p 1424
4500 River Green Pkwy 30096
Tel (678) 812-6300 SIC 4841

TRAVEL INC p 1473
4355 River Green Pkwy 30096
Tel (770) 291-4100 SIC 4724

US LUMBER GROUP LLC p 1532
2160 Satellite Blvd # 450 30097
Tel (678) 474-4577 SIC 5031

VALMET INC p 1541
2425 Commerce Ave Ste 100 30096
Tel (770) 263-7863 SIC 3554 5084

WEG ELECTRIC CORP p 1587
6655 Sugarloaf Pkwy 30097
Tel (678) 249-2000
SIC 3612 3621 3613 3625

WORLD TECHNOLOGY GROUP INC p 1625
8930 Muirfield Ct 30097
Tel (404) 697-0985 SIC 4813

DUNWOODY, GA

KRYSTAL CO p 830
1455 Lincoln Pkwy E # 600 30346
Tel (423) 757-1550 SIC 5812 6794

PS ENERGY GROUP INC p 1187
4480 N Shallowford Rd # 100 30338
Tel (770) 350-3000 SIC 8742 5172 4924

EASTMAN, GA

MONDI BAGS USA LLC p 984
281 Hemphill Blvd 31023
Tel (478) 374-7032 SIC 2393 2621

EATONTON, GA

HORTON INDUSTRIES INC p 708
101 Industrial Blvd 31024
Tel (706) 485-8506 SIC 2451 5271

HORTON VANS INC p 708
130 Coleman Dr 31024
Tel (706) 923-2900 SIC 3713 3792

ELLAVILLE, GA

■ TCI INC p 1428
734 Dixon Dr 31806
Tel (229) 937-5411 SIC 2851

ELLENWOOD, GA

KAUFFMAN TIRE INC p 805
2832 Anvil Block Rd 30294
Tel (404) 762-4944 SIC 5014 5531

EVANS, GA

CLUB CAR LLC p 328
4125 Washington Rd 30809
Tel (706) 863-3000 SIC 3799

COLUMBIA COUNTY SCHOOL DISTRICT p 340
4781 Hereford Farm Rd 30809
Tel (706) 541-0650 SIC 8211

FAIRBURN, GA

POREX CORP p 1161
500 Bohannon Rd 30213
Tel (800) 241-0195 SIC 3082 3842 3841

FAYETTEVILLE, GA

BRENT SCARBROUGH & CO INC p 210
155 Robinson Dr 30214
Tel (770) 461-8603 SIC 1623

FAYETTE COMMUNITY HOSPITAL INC p 532
1255 Highway 54 W 30214
Tel (770) 719-7000 SIC 8062

FAYETTE COUNTY BOARD OF EDUCATION p 532
210 Stonewall Ave W 30214
Tel (770) 460-3520 SIC 8211

FAYETTE COUNTY PUBLIC SCHOOLS p 532
210 Stonewall Ave W 30214
Tel (770) 460-3535 SIC 8211

M B FAYETTE SPECIALISTS INC p 889
1588 Highway 85 N 30214
Tel (770) 461-3784 SIC 7538

FOREST PARK, GA

ATLANTA COMMERCIAL TIRE INC p 125
5067 Old Kennedy Rd 30297
Tel (404) 351-8016 SIC 5014 5531

FOC ACQUISITION LLC p 562
146 Forest Pkwy Ste B 30297
Tel (404) 361-2201
SIC 5142 5421 5144 2092

■ FRESHPOINT INC p 579
16 Forest Pkwy Bldg H 30297
Tel (404) 362-6100 SIC 5148

GPI LIQUIDATION INC p 627
16 Forest Pkwy Bldg M 30297
Tel (404) 361-0215 SIC 5148

SUTHERLANDS FOODSERVICE INC p 1410
16 Forest Pkwy Bldg K 30297
Tel (404) 366-8550
SIC 5144 5148 5147 5143 5141

FORSYTH, GA

GEORGIA DEPARTMENT OF CORRECTIONS p 607
300 Patrol Rd 31029
Tel (404) 656-4593 SIC 9223

GRESCO UTILITY SUPPLY INC p 639
1135 Rumble Rd 31029
Tel (478) 315-0800 SIC 5063

FORT VALLEY, GA

■ BIRD BLUE CORP p 185
402 Bluebird Blvd 31030
Tel (478) 822-2801 SIC 3713

BLUE BIRD BODY CO p 190
402 Bluebird Blvd 31030
Tel (478) 825-2021 SIC 4111

BLUE BIRD GLOBAL CORP p 190
402 Bluebird Blvd 31030
Tel (478) 822-2811 SIC 3713 3711

PEACH COUNTY HOLDINGS INC p 1125
402 Bluebird Blvd 31030
Tel (478) 825-2021 SIC 3713 3711

FRANKLIN, GA

FRANKLIN ALUMINUM CO INC p 574
266 Mary Johnson Dr 30217
Tel (706) 675-3341 SIC 3354

GAINESVILLE, GA

AMERICAS HOME PLACE INC p 81
2144 Hilton Dr 30501
Tel (770) 532-1128 SIC 1521

■ COTTRELL INC p 374
2125 Candler Rd 30507
Tel (770) 532-7251 SIC 3713

HALL COUNTY BOARD OF EDUCATION p 654
711 Green St Nw Ste 100 30501
Tel (770) 534-1080 SIC 8211

HALL COUNTY OF GEORGIA p 654
2875 Browns Bridge Rd 30504
Tel (770) 535-8288 SIC 9111

HALL COUNTY SCHOOL DISTRICT p 654
711 Green St Nw Ste 100 30501
Tel (770) 534-1080 SIC 8211

HEARST BUSINESS MEDIA CORP p 678
2620 Barrett Rd 30507
Tel (770) 532-4111 SIC 2721

JOHN SOULES ACQUISITIONS LLC p 789
311 Green St Nw Ste 500 30501
Tel (770) 532-3058 SIC 2015

KUBOTA MANUFACTURING OF AMERICA CORP p 831
2715 Ramsey Rd 30501
Tel (770) 532-0038 SIC 3524 3537

LONGSTREET CLINIC P C p 877
725 Jesse Jewell Pkwy Se 30501
Tel (770) 718-1122 SIC 8011

MANSFIELD ENERGY CORP p 903
1025 Airport Pkwy 30501
Tel (678) 450-2000 SIC 5172 4212 1796

MANSFIELD OIL CO OF GAINESVILLE INC p 903
1025 Airport Pkwy 30501
Tel (678) 450-2000 SIC 5172

MAR-JAC POULTRY INC p 904
1020 Aviation Blvd 30501
Tel (770) 531-5000 SIC 0254

MAREL STORK POULTRY PROCESSING INC p 905
1024 Airport Pkwy 30501
Tel (770) 532-7041 SIC 3556 3535

MARJAC HOLDINGS LLC p 907
1020 Aviation Blvd 30501
Tel (770) 531-5000 SIC 2015

MARTIN CAR FINANCING INC p 912
3150 Mlton Mrtn Tyota Way 30507
Tel (770) 532-4355 SIC 5511

MERIAL SELECT INC p 948
1168 Airport Pkwy 30501
Tel (770) 536-8787 SIC 5122 2836

NORTHEAST GEORGIA HEALTH SYSTEM INC p 1054
743 Spring St Ne 30501
Tel (770) 219-9000 SIC 8062

NORTHEAST GEORGIA MEDICAL CENTER INC p 1054
743 Spring St Ne 30501
Tel (770) 219-9000 SIC 8062

VICTORY FOODS LLC p 1555
1100 Airport Pkwy 30501
Tel (678) 343-2070 SIC 5144

GLENNVILLE, GA

ROTARY CORP p 1252
801 W Barnard St 30427
Tel (912) 654-3433 SIC 5083 3469 5013

GRAY, GA

ETHICA HEALTH & RETIREMENT COMMUNITIES p 511
1005 Boulder Dr 31032
Tel (478) 621-2100 SIC 8051

HEALTH SCHOLARSHIPS INC p 675
1005 Boulder Dr 31032
Tel (478) 742-6569 SIC 6732

HEALTH SYSTEMS FACILITIES INC p 676
1005 Boulder Dr 31032
Tel (478) 621-2100 SIC 7389

GREENSBORO, GA

■ LINGER LONGER DEVELOPMENT CO p 869
100 Linger Longer Rd 30642
Tel (888) 298-3119 SIC 6552 7997

GRIFFIN, GA

GRIFFIN-SPALDING COUNTY SCHOOLS SYSTEM p 640
216 S 6th St 30224
Tel (770) 229-3700 SIC 8211

INNVISION HOSPITALITY INC p 745
504 Carver Rd 30224
Tel (888) 875-6202 SIC 5131 5021 7389

■ KOPPERS PERFORMANCE CHEMICALS INC p 828
1016 Everee Inn Rd 30224
Tel (770) 228-8434 SIC 2491

PEACE OFFICERS ANNUITY & BENEFITS FUND OF GEORGIA INC p 1125
1208 Greenbelt Dr 30224
Tel (770) 228-8461 SIC 8399

■ TENET HEALTH SYSTEM SPALDING INC p 1437
601 S 8th St 30224
Tel (770) 228-2721 SIC 8062

GROVETOWN, GA

AUGUSTA SPORTSWEAR INC p 131
425 Park 20 W 30813
Tel (706) 860-4633
SIC 2329 2339 2393 2399

GIW INDUSTRIES INC p 613
5000 Wrightsboro Rd 30813
Tel (706) 863-1011 SIC 3561 3559

HAMPTON, GA

SOUTHERN STATES LLC p 1350
30 Georgia Ave 30228
Tel (770) 946-4562 SIC 3613 4013 1731

HAWKINSVILLE, GA

AGE GOLDEN PROPERTIES LTD p 34
19 Merritt St 31036
Tel (478) 783-1438 SIC 8059

HAZLEHURST, GA

FOREST BEASLEY PRODUCTS INC p 566
712 Uvalda Hwy 31539
Tel (912) 375-5174 SIC 5031

HINESVILLE, GA

LIBERTY COUNTY BOARD OF EDUCATION p 861
200 Bradwell St 31313
Tel (912) 876-2162 SIC 8211

LIBERTY COUNTY SCHOOL SYSTEM p 861
200 Bradwell St 31313
Tel (912) 876-2161 SIC 8211

JACKSON, GA

CENTRAL GEORGIA ELECTRIC MEMBERSHIP CORP p 278
923 S Mulberry St 30233
Tel (770) 775-7857 SIC 4911 1711

JASPER, GA

ROYSTON LLC p 1255
1 Pickroy Rd 30143
Tel (770) 735-3456 SIC 7389 2542 1751

JEFFERSON, GA

JACKSON COUNTY SCHOOL DISTRICT p 773
1660 Winder Hwy 30549
Tel (706) 367-5151 SIC 8211

JACKSON ELECTRIC MEMBERSHIP CORP p 773
850 Commerce Rd 30549
Tel (706) 367-5281 SIC 4911

JOHNS CREEK, GA

BLUE EAGLE HOLDINGS LP p 192
6465 E Johns Xing 30097
Tel (678) 584-4000 SIC 7389 7374 8742

EHCA JOHNS CREEK LLC p 481
6325 Hospital Pkwy 30097
Tel (770) 813-0438 SIC 8062

▲ PIEDMONT OFFICE REALTY TRUST INC p 1147
11695 Johns Creek Pkwy 30097
Tel (770) 418-8800 SIC 6798

■ POLYVISION CORP p 1160
10700 Abbotts Bridge Rd # 100 30097
Tel (678) 542-3100 SIC 3281 3993

RADIAL SOUTH LP p 1204
6465 E Johns Xing 30097
Tel (678) 584-4000 SIC 7389 7374 8742

▲ SAIA INC p 1268
11465 Johns Creek Pkwy # 400 30097
Tel (770) 232-5067 SIC 4213

JONESBORO, GA

CLAYTON COUNTY BOARD OF EDUCATION p 323
1058 5th Ave 30236
Tel (770) 473-2700 SIC 8211

CLAYTON COUNTY PUBLIC SCHOOLS p 323
1058 5th Ave 30236
Tel (678) 817-3076 SIC 8211

CLAYTON COUNTY SCHOOL DISTRICT p 323
1058 5th Ave 30236
Tel (770) 473-2700 SIC 8211

CORESLAB STRUCTURES (ATLANTA) INC p 370
1655 Noahs Ark Rd 30236
Tel (770) 471-1150 SIC 3272 1771

COUNTY OF CLAYTON p 377
112 Smith St 30236
Tel (770) 477-3208 SIC 9111

LAY MANAGEMENT CORP OF GEORIGA p 848
790 Dixon Rd Apt J7 30238
Tel (678) 558-5631 SIC 8741

KENNESAW, GA

AMREST LLC p 86
2045 Attic Pkwy Nw 30152
Tel (770) 850-8816 SIC 5812

■ AUTOMATED LOGIC CORP p 134
1150 Roberts Blvd Nw 30144
Tel (770) 429-3000 SIC 3822

BRAND ENERGY & INFRASTRUCTURE HOLDINGS INC p 207
1325 Cobb Intl Dr Nw A1 30152
Tel (678) 285-1400 SIC 1799

BRAND ENERGY & INFRASTRUCTURE SERVICES INC p 207
1325 Cobb Intl Dr Nw A1 30152
Tel (678) 285-1400 SIC 1799

BRAND ENERGY SOLUTIONS LLC p 207
1325 Cobb International D 30152
Tel (678) 285-1400
SIC 1751 1742 1799 1721

BRAND SERVICES LLC p 208
1325 Cobb Intl Dr Nw A1 30152
Tel (678) 285-1400 SIC 1799

BRECKENRIDGE IS INC p 209
245 Townpark Dr Nw # 200 30144
Tel (678) 322-3536 SIC 6411

▲ CRYOLIFE INC p 396
1655 Roberts Blvd Nw 30144
Tel (770) 419-3355 SIC 3841

ENERCON SERVICES INC p 497
500 Townpark Ln Nw # 275 30144
Tel (770) 919-1930 SIC 8711

HCC LIFE INSURANCE CO p 672
225 Townpark Dr Nw # 145 30144
Tel (770) 973-9851 SIC 6411

HEIDELBERG AMERICAS INC p 680
1000 Gutenberg Dr Nw 30144
Tel (770) 419-6500 SIC 5084

HEIDELBERG USA INC p 680
1000 Gutenberg Dr Nw 30144
Tel (770) 419-6500 SIC 5084 3555

INFRATECH CORP p 742
2036 Baker Ct Nw 30144
Tel (770) 792-8700 SIC 1623

KENNESAW STATE UNIVERSITY p 811
1000 Chastain Rd Nw 30144
Tel (770) 423-6000 SIC 8221

KNAPP LOGISTICS AUTOMATION INC p 824
2124 Barrett Park Dr Nw # 100 30144
Tel (678) 388-2880 SIC 3559

MAGIC WORKFORCE SOLUTIONS LLC p 895
840 Ernest W Barrett Pkwy 30144
Tel (770) 420-4759 SIC 7361

MAIN STREET NATURAL GAS INC p 898
104 Townpark Dr Nw 30144
Tel (770) 590-1000 SIC 4922

MUNICIPAL GAS AUTHORITY OF GEORGIA p 1000
104 Townpark Dr Nw 30144
Tel (770) 590-1000 SIC 5172

PACESETTER STEEL SERVICE INC p 1103
1045 Big Shanty Rd Nw 30144
Tel (770) 919-8000 SIC 5051

RYLA INC p 1261
2120 Barrett Park Dr Nw 30144
Tel (678) 322-5000 SIC 7389

SIGNAL POINT SYSTEMS INC p 1322
1270 Shiloh Rd Nw Ste 100 30144
Tel (770) 499-0439 SIC 1623

■TUG MANUFACTURING CORP p 1491
2652 S Main St Nw 30144
Tel (770) 422-7230 SIC 3537

■TUG TECHNOLOGIES CORP p 1491
1995 Duncan Dr Nw 30144
Tel (770) 422-7230 SIC 3537

UNI-SELECT USA INC p 1502
1155 Roberts Blvd Nw # 175 30144
Tel (770) 701-5000 SIC 5013

KINGSLAND, GA

CAMDEN COUNTY BOARD OF EDUCATION p 244
311 S East St 31548
Tel (912) 729-5687 SIC 8211

CAMDEN COUNTY SCHOOL DISTRICT p 244
311 S East St 31548
Tel (912) 729-5687 SIC 8211

LA FAYETTE, GA

■ ROPER CORP p 1250
1507 Broomtown Rd 30728
Tel (706) 638-3559 SIC 3631 3634

WALKER COUNTY BOARD OF EDUCATION p 1573
201 S Duke St 30728
Tel (706) 638-1240 SIC 8211

WALKER COUNTY SCHOOL DISTRICT p 1573
201 S Duke St 30728
Tel (706) 638-1240 SIC 8211

LAGRANGE, GA

DIVERSE POWER INC AN ELECTRIC MEMBERSHIP CORP p 443
1400 S Davis Rd 30241
Tel (706) 845-2000 SIC 4911

GEORGIA L SEJONG L C p 607
1641 Lukken Indl Dr W 30240
Tel (706) 845-7091 SIC 3714

HANIL E HWA INTERIOR SYSTEMS GEORGIA INC p 657
104 Wiley Rd 30240
Tel (706) 298-9701 SIC 3089

■ INTERFACEFLOR LLC p 752
1503 Orchard Hill Rd 30240
Tel (706) 882-1891 SIC 2273

KLEEN-TEX INDUSTRIES INC p 823
101 N Greenwood St Ste C 30240
Tel (706) 882-0111 SIC 3069 2273 2392

LA GRANGE TROUP COUNTY HOSPITAL AUTHORITY p 835
1514 Vernon Rd 30240
Tel (706) 882-1411 SIC 8062 8051

MCDONALD OIL CO INC p 927
1700 Lukken Indus Dr W 30240
Tel (706) 884-6191 SIC 5541 5921 6519

MOUNTVILLE MILLS INC p 995
1729 S Davis Rd 30241
Tel (706) 882-2961 SIC 2273 2211 2221

SEWON AMERICA INC p 1309
1000 Sewon Blvd 30240
Tel (706) 298-5800 SIC 3711

TROUP COUNTY BOARD OF EDUCATION p 1484
100 N Davis Rd Ste C 30241
Tel (706) 812-7900 SIC 8211

TROUP COUNTY SCHOOL SYSTEM p 1484
100 N Davis Rd 30241
Tel (706) 812-7900 SIC 8211

WEST GEORGIA HEALTH SYSTEM INC p 1594
1514 Vernon Rd 30240
Tel (706) 882-1411 SIC 8062

LAKE CITY, GA

DIXIEN LLC p 445
5286 Circle Dr 30260
Tel (478) 929-4121 SIC 3089

LAVONIA, GA

CARRY-ON TRAILER INC p 261
101 Joe Harvey St 30553
Tel (706) 356-5379 SIC 3799

LAWRENCEVILLE, GA

AIRGAS CARBONIC INC p 40
2530 Sever Rd Ste 300 30043
Tel (770) 717-2210 SIC 2813 7359 5088

AMERICAN LUBEFAST LLC p 75
1550 N Brown Rd Ste 140 30043
Tel (770) 995-6312 SIC 6794 7549

AMERICAS BEST CONTACTS & EYEGLASSES INC p 81
296 Grayson Hwy 30046
Tel (770) 822-2036 SIC 5995

BIO-LAB INC p 183
1725 N Brown Rd 30043
Tel (678) 502-4000 SIC 2812 2819 2899

■ BIOLAB WATER ADDITIVES p 184
N Brown Rd 30045
Tel (678) 502-4699 SIC 5169

BRAND BANKING CO p 207
106 Crogan St 30046
Tel (770) 963-9224 SIC 6036

CONSOLIDATED VISION GROUP INC p 360
296 Grayson Hwy 30046
Tel (770) 822-3600 SIC 5995

ENCOMPASS SUPPLY CHAIN SOLUTIONS INC p 496
775 Tipton Industrial Dr 30046
Tel (800) 432-8542 SIC 8741

GWINNETT COUNTY GOVERNMENT p 648
75 Langley Dr 30046
Tel (770) 822-8000 SIC 9111

GWINNETT HEALTH SYSTEM INC p 648
1000 Medical Center Blvd 30046
Tel (678) 312-1000 SIC 8062

GWINNETT HOSPITAL SYSTEM INC p 648
1000 Medical Center Blvd 30046
Tel (678) 343-3428 SIC 8062

HAYES CHRYSLER-DODGE-JEEP INC p 670
719 Duluth Hwy 30046
Tel (770) 963-5251 SIC 5511

PEACH STATE ROOFING INC p 1125
1655 Spectrum Dr Ste A 30043
Tel (770) 962-7885 SIC 1761

PEACHTREE SOFTWARE INC p 1125
1715 N Brown Rd 30043
Tel (770) 682-1542 SIC 7372 7371

PLUMBING DISTRIBUTORS INC p 1156
1025 Old Norcross Rd 30046
Tel (770) 963-9231 SIC 5074

■ SCIENTIFIC-ATLANTA LLC p 1292
5030 Sugarloaf Pkwy 30044
Tel (678) 277-1000
SIC 3663 3661 3577 3825

▲ SED INTERNATIONAL HOLDINGS INC p 1299
2150 Cedars Rd Ste 200 30043
Tel (678) 878-2600 SIC 5045 5065

■ SED INTERNATIONAL INC p 1299
2150 Cedars Rd Ste 200 30043
Tel (844) 501-5858 SIC 5045

STAFFING CONCEPTS INTERNATIONAL OF GEORGIA INC p 1374
2435 Tech Center Pkwy 30043
Tel (770) 623-9143 SIC 7363

VALENTINE ENTERPRISES INC p 1539
1291 Progress Center Ave 30043
Tel (770) 995-0661 SIC 2023 2099

W A KENDALL AND CO INC p 1568
400 Farmer Ct 30046
Tel (770) 963-6017 SIC 1629

WIKA HOLDING L P p 1608
1000 Wiegand Blvd 30043
Tel (770) 513-8200 SIC 3823

WIKA INSTRUMENT LP p 1608
1000 Wiegand Blvd 30043
Tel (770) 513-8200 SIC 3053 3823

LEESBURG, GA

CHEM-NUT INC p 293
800 Business Park Dr 31763
Tel (229) 883-7050 SIC 5191 8611

LITHIA SPRINGS, GA

NATIONS ROOF LLC p 1017
1633 Blairs Bridge Rd 30122
Tel (678) 567-1533 SIC 1761

LITHONIA, GA

BROWN INTEGRATED LOGISTICS INC p 219
6908 Chapman Rd 30058
Tel (770) 482-6521
SIC 4225 4213 4731 7359

JAMES BROWN CO p 776
6908 Chapman Rd 30058
Tel (770) 482-6521 SIC 4213

SOUTHERN PAN SERVICES CO p 1350
2385 Lithonia Indus Blvd 30058
Tel (678) 301-2400 SIC 1542

MABLETON, GA

BROOKS-BERRY-HAYNIE & ASSOCIATES INC p 218
600 Discovery Pl 30126
Tel (770) 874-1162 SIC 1731

FIRST AMERICAN RESOURCES CO LLC p 544
2030 Rverview Indus Dr Se 30126
Tel (404) 505-3499 SIC 5051 3479

I & S ACQUISITION CORP p 724
5200 Riverview Rd Se 30126
Tel (404) 881-1199 SIC 1731

INGLETT & STUBBS LLC p 743
5200 Riverview Rd Se 30126
Tel (404) 881-1199 SIC 1731

MACON, GA

ALLIED BUSINESS SYSTEMS LLC p 56
4848 Mercer University Dr 31210
Tel (800) 727-7534 SIC 7371 5734

BEARINGS & DRIVES INC p 166
607 Lower Poplar St 31201
Tel (478) 746-7623 SIC 5085

BIBB COUNTY BOARD OF EDUCATION p 181
484 Mulberry St Ste 300 31201
Tel (478) 765-8711 SIC 8211

BIBB COUNTY SCHOOL DISTRICT p 181
484 Mulberry St Ste 300 31201
Tel (478) 765-8711 SIC 8211

CITY OF MACON p 316
700 Poplar St 31201
Tel (478) 751-7258 SIC 9111

■ COLISEUM PARK HOSPITAL INC p 336
350 Hospital Dr 31217
Tel (478) 765-7000 SIC 8062

CORP OF MERCER UNIVERSITY p 371
1400 Coleman Ave 31207
Tel (478) 301-2700 SIC 8221

GEORGIA FARM BUREAU FEDERATION INC p 607
1620 Bass Rd 31210
Tel (478) 474-8411
SIC 6111 5154 8699 5191

GEORGIA FARM BUREAU MUTUAL INSURANCE CO p 607
1620 Bass Rd 31210
Tel (478) 474-0679 SIC 6411

KAMIN LLC p 802
822 Huber Rd 31217
Tel (478) 750-5410 SIC 3295

KIMCO FACILITY SERVICES LLC p 818
6055 Lakeside Commons Dr 31210
Tel (478) 752-7000 SIC 7349

LINTECH INTERNATIONAL LLC p 869
7705 Ne Industrial Blvd 31216
Tel (877) 546-8324 SIC 5169

MACON WATER AUTHORITY p 893
790 2nd St 31201
Tel (478) 464-5600 SIC 4941 4952

MEDICAL CEN p 936
691 Cherry St Fl 5 31201
Tel (478) 633-6831 SIC 8099

MEDICAL CENTER OF CENTRAL GEORGIA INC p 936
777 Hemlock St 31201
Tel (478) 633-1000 SIC 8062

MIDCOUNTRY FINANCIAL CORP p 964
201 2nd St Ste 950 31201
Tel (478) 746-8222 SIC 7389

MIDDLE GEORGIA STATE UNIVERSITY p 964
100 University Pkwy 31206
Tel (478) 471-2700 SIC 8221

NAVICENT HEALTH INC p 1020
777 Hemlock St 31201
Tel (478) 633-1000 SIC 8741

PROFESSIONAL SYSTEMS LLC p 1180
6055 Lakeside Ste 440 31210
Tel (478) 752-7000 SIC 7349 7361

REEVES CONSTRUCTION CO p 1217
101 Sheraton Ct 31210
Tel (478) 474-9092 SIC 1611

TRIANGLE CHEMICAL CO p 1478
206 Lower Elm St 31206
Tel (478) 743-1548 SIC 5191

WALTHALL OIL CO p 1575
2510 Allen Rd 31216
Tel (478) 781-1234 SIC 5172 5541 5411

MADISON, GA

HOPS GRILL & BAR INC p 706
Hancock At Washington St 30650
Tel (706) 342-4552 SIC 5813 5812

■ PENNINGTON SEED INC p 1130
1280 Atlanta Hwy 30650
Tel (706) 342-1234
SIC 5261 2873 5191 6799 0723

MARIETTA, GA

AKZO NOBEL PULP AND PERFORMANCE CHEMICALS INC p 43
1850 Parkway Pl Se # 1200 30067
Tel (770) 578-0858 SIC 2899 2819

AMREP INC p 86
425 Franklin Gtwy Se # 530 30067
Tel (770) 590-5960
SIC 2842 2079 2911 2869 2841 2819

APPLIED TECHNICAL SERVICES INC p 100
1049 Triad Ct 30062
Tel (770) 423-1400 SIC 8734 8711 8731

BALDWIN PAVING CO INC p 147
1014 Kenmill Dr Nw 30060
Tel (770) 425-9191 SIC 1611 2951

BENEVIS LLC p 173
1090 Northchase Pkwy Se 30067
Tel (770) 916-9000 SIC 8741 7389

BOARD OF LIGHTS AND WATER p 195
675 N Marietta Pkwy Ne 30060
Tel (770) 794-5150 SIC 4911 4941

CITY OF MARIETTA p 316
205 Lawrence St Ne 30060
Tel (770) 794-5507 SIC 9111

COBB COUNTY BOARD OF EDUCATION p 332
514 Glover St Se 30060
Tel (770) 426-3300 SIC 8211

COBB COUNTY PUBLIC SCHOOLS p 332
514 Glover St Se 30060
Tel (770) 426-3300 SIC 8211

COBB ELECTRIC MEMBERSHIP CORP p 332
1000 Emc Pkwy Ne 30060
Tel (770) 429-2100 SIC 4911

COLUMBIAN CHEMICALS CO p 342
1800 W Oak Commons Ct 30062
Tel (770) 792-9400 SIC 2895

COLUMBIAN INTERNATIONAL CHEMICALS CORP p 342
1800 W Oak Commons Ct 30062
Tel (770) 792-9400 SIC 6719

CONLAN CO p 356
1800 Parkway Pl Se # 1010 30067
Tel (770) 423-8000 SIC 1542 1541

COUNTY OF COBB p 377
100 Cherokee St Ste 400 30090
Tel (770) 528-3300 SIC 9512

CW MATTHEWS CONTRACTING CO INC p 404
1600 Kenview Dr Nw 30060
Tel (770) 422-7520 SIC 2891 2951

DOUGLAS HOSPITAL INC p 452
805 Sandy Plains Rd 30066
Tel (770) 792-5023 SIC 8062

ENERGY CONSULTING GROUP p 497
1000 Emc Pkwy Ne 30060
Tel (678) 355-3190 SIC 8748

INSURANCE HOUSE INC p 748
1904 Leland Dr Se 30067
Tel (770) 952-0080 SIC 6331 6411 6141

KENNESTONE HOSPITAL AT WINDY HILL INC p 811
677 Church St Ne 30060
Tel (770) 793-5000 SIC 8062

KENNESTONE HOSPITAL INC p 811
805 Sandy Plains Rd 30066
Tel (770) 792-5023 SIC 8062

■ LOCKHEED MARTIN AERONAUTICAL CO p 873
86 S Cobb Dr Se 30063
Tel (770) 494-4411
SIC 3721 3812 7699 3769

MARIETTA CITY SCHOOLS (INC) p 906
250 Howard St Ne 30060
Tel (770) 422-3500 SIC 8211

MARIETTA DRAPERY & WINDOW COVERINGS CO INC p 906
22 Trammell St Sw 30064
Tel (770) 428-3335
SIC 5023 2391 2591 2392

▲ MIMEDX GROUP INC p 972
1775 W Oak Commons Ct 30062
Tel (770) 651-9100 SIC 3842 3841

NORTH AMERICAN CONTAINER CORP p 1050
1811 W Oak Pkwy Ste D 30062
Tel (770) 431-4858 SIC 3443

OCAMPOS INC p 1072
480 Tam Oshanter Dr Se 30067
Tel (770) 509-2595 SIC 5084

ONEPATH SYSTEMS LLC p 1088
2053 Franklin Way Se 30067
Tel (678) 695-5500
SIC 7389 8744 7378 7376 7382

REDI-FLOORS INC p 1217
1791 Williams Dr 30066
Tel (770) 590-7334 SIC 5023 5032

SIVICA HOMES INC p 1328
1640 Pwrs Fy Rd Se 18-300 30067
Tel (770) 645-5559 SIC 1521

SOUTHERN POLYTECHNIC STATE UNIVERSITY FOUNDATION INC p 1350
1100 S Marietta Pkwy Se 30060
Tel (678) 915-7778 SIC 8221

TIP TOP POULTRY INC p 1455
327 Wallace Rd 30062
Tel (770) 973-8070 SIC 2015

TRILOK INDUSTRIES INC p 1480
670 Village Trce Ne 30067
Tel (678) 325-2960 SIC 1799 1742

VANDERLANDE INDUSTRIES INC p 1543
1975 W Oak Cir 30062
Tel (770) 250-2800 SIC 8711 3535

WELLSTAR HEALTH SYSTEM INC p 1591
805 Sandy Plains Rd 30066
Tel (770) 956-7827 SIC 8062

■ XPO LAST MILE INC p 1632
1851 W Oak Pkwy Ste 100 30062
Tel (866) 373-7874 SIC 4731

YKK (USA) INC p 1636
1300 Cobb Industrial Dr 30066
Tel (770) 427-5521 SIC 3452 3965

YKK CORP OF AMERICA p 1636
1850 Parkway Pl Se # 300 30067
Tel (770) 261-6120 SIC 3965 3354

MCDONOUGH, GA

BENNETT INTERNATIONAL GROUP LLC p 173
1001 Industrial Pkwy 30253
Tel (770) 957-1866 SIC 4213

BENNETT MOTOR EXPRESS LLC p 173
1001 Industrial Pkwy 30253
Tel (770) 957-1866 SIC 4213 4212 4215

COUNTY OF HENRY p 378
140 Henry Pkwy 30253
Tel (770) 288-6000 SIC 9111

DOWLING TEXTILE CO p 453
615 Macon Rd 30253
Tel (770) 957-3981 SIC 2326 2337 2389

ENCOMPASS GROUP LLC p 495
615 Macon St 30253
Tel (770) 957-3981 *SIC* 2326 2337 2389

GEORGIA CROWN DISTRIBUTING CO p 607
100 Georgia Crown Dr 30253
Tel (770) 302-3000 *SIC* 5182 5181

HENRY COUNTY BOARD OF EDUCATION p 684
33 N Zack Hinton Pkwy 30253
Tel (770) 957-6601 *SIC* 8211

HENRY COUNTY SCHOOLS p 684
33 N Zack Hinton Pkwy 30253
Tel (770) 957-6601 *SIC* 8211

MIDLAND, GA

PRECISION COMPONENTS INTERNATIONAL INC p 1168
8801 Macon Rd 31820
Tel (706) 568-5900 *SIC* 3728 5088 3724

MIDWAY, GA

INTERNATIONAL GREETINGS USA INC p 755
338 Industrial Blvd 31320
Tel (912) 884-9727 *SIC* 2679

MILTON, GA

EXIDETECHNOLOGIES p 519
13000 Deerfield Pkwy # 200 30004
Tel (678) 566-9000 *SIC* 3691

MONROE, GA

WALTON COUNTY SCHOOL DISTRICT p 1575
200 Double Sprng Ch Rd Sw 30656
Tel (770) 266-4520 *SIC* 8211

WALTON ELECTRIC MEMBERSHIP CORP p 1575
842 Highway 78 Nw 30655
Tel (770) 267-2505 *SIC* 4911

MORROW, GA

ALLAN VIGIL FORD LINCOLN INC p 52
6790 Mount Zion Blvd 30260
Tel (678) 364-3675 *SIC* 5511

CLAYTON COUNTY WATER AUTHORITY p 323
1600 Battle Creek Rd 30260
Tel (770) 961-2130 *SIC* 4941 4952

■ **NISSAN CONYERS INC** p 1044
1420 Iris Dr 30260
Tel (770) 922-7600 *SIC* 5511

TOTO USA HOLDINGS INC p 1463
1155 Southern Rd 30260
Tel (770) 960-8531 *SIC* 3088 3431 3261

MOULTRIE, GA

■ **AMERICAN BANKING CO** p 68
225 S Main St 31768
Tel (229) 985-2222 *SIC* 6022 6021

▲ **AMERIS BANCORP** p 83
310 1st St Se 31768
Tel (229) 890-1111 *SIC* 6022

■ **AMERIS BANK** p 83
310 1st St Se 31768
Tel (800) 845-5219 *SIC* 6022

COLQUITT COUNTY BOARD OF EDUCATION p 339
710 28th Ave Se 31768
Tel (229) 985-1550 *SIC* 8211

COLQUITT COUNTY SCHOOLS p 339
710 28th Ave Se 31768
Tel (229) 890-6200 *SIC* 8211

COLQUITT ELECTRIC MEMBERSHIP CORP p 339
15 Rowland Dr 31768
Tel (229) 985-3620 *SIC* 4911

COLQUITT REGIONAL MEDICAL CENTER p 339
3131 S Main St 31768
Tel (229) 985-3420 *SIC* 8011

HOSPITAL AUTHORITY OF COLQUITT COUNTY p 709
3131 S Main St 31768
Tel (229) 985-3420 *SIC* 8062

NASHVILLE, GA

■ **CHAPARRAL BOATS INC** p 288
300 Industrial Park Blvd 31639
Tel (229) 686-7481 *SIC* 3732

JH HARVEY CO LLC p 785
107 S Davis St 31639
Tel (704) 633-8250 *SIC* 5411

NEWNAN, GA

■ **BON L MANUFACTURING CO** p 199
25 Bonnell St 30263
Tel (770) 253-2020 *SIC* 3354

COWETA COUNTY SCHOOL SYSTEM p 385
237 Jackson St 30263
Tel (770) 254-2800 *SIC* 8211

COWETA COUNTY SCHOOL SYSTEM BOARD OF EDUCATION p 385
237 Jackson St 30263
Tel (770) 254-2801 *SIC* 8211

EGO NORTH AMERICA INC p 481
83 Hillwood Cir 30263
Tel (770) 251-3980 *SIC* 3634 5065

KASON INDUSTRIES INC p 804
57 Amlajack Blvd 30265
Tel (770) 251-1422 *SIC* 3589

PIEDMONT NEWNAN HOSPITAL INC p 1147
745 Poplar Rd 30265
Tel (770) 253-2330 *SIC* 8062

■ **WILLIAM L BONNELL CO INC** p 1610
25 Bonnell St 30263
Tel (770) 253-2020 *SIC* 3354

NORCROSS, GA

ACE INDUSTRIES INC p 16
6295 Mcdonough Dr 30093
Tel (770) 441-0898 *SIC* 5084

ACS ACQUISITION CORP p 18
6575 The Corners Pkwy 30092
Tel (678) 268-1300 *SIC* 5045 7374

■ **AFTER HOURS FORMALWEAR INC** p 33
4444 Shackleford Rd # 100 30093
Tel (770) 448-8381 *SIC* 5611

■ **ALBECCA INC** p 46
3900 Steve Reynolds Blvd 30093
Tel (770) 279-5210 *SIC* 2499 3499

AMERICAN MEGATRENDS INC p 76
5555 Okbrook Pkwy Ste 200 30093
Tel (770) 246-8600 *SIC* 3572

AQUILEX HOLDINGS LLC p 101
2225 Skyland Ct 30071
Tel (678) 728-9100 *SIC* 7349

AQUILEX LLC p 101
2225 Skyland Ct 30071
Tel (404) 869-6677 *SIC* 6712

ASAP SOLUTIONS GROUP LLC p 115
3885 Holcomb Bridge Rd 30092
Tel (770) 246-1718 *SIC* 7379 8742

ASSET MANAGEMENT OUTSOURCING RECOVERIES INC p 119
5655 Peachtree Pkwy # 213 30092
Tel (678) 259-9600 *SIC* 8741

ATLANTIX GLOBAL SYSTEMS LLC p 127
1 Sun Ct 30092
Tel (770) 248-7700 *SIC* 8731

AUTOMOBILE PROTECTION CORP-APCO p 134
6010 Atlantic Blvd 30071
Tel (678) 225-1001 *SIC* 6411

■ **AZZ WSI LLC** p 141
2225 Skyland Ct 30071
Tel (678) 728-9200 *SIC* 1799

BRAMBLES USA INC (DEL) p 207
180 Technology Pkwy # 600 30092
Tel (770) 776-1900
SIC 4953 4212 7353 8741 7359

CAPE ENVIRONMENTAL MANAGEMENT INC p 248
500 Pinnacle Ct Ste 100 30071
Tel (770) 908-7200 *SIC* 1542 1541

CAPSTONE LOGISTICS LLC p 251
6525 The Corners Pkwy 30092
Tel (770) 414-1929 *SIC* 4789

■ **CHECKFREE INVESTMENT CORP** p 292
4411 E Jones Bridge Rd 30092
Tel (678) 375-3000 *SIC* 7374

COMVERGE INC p 353
5390 Triangle Pkwy # 300 30092
Tel (678) 802-8011 *SIC* 3822

CONSUMER SOURCE INC p 361
3585 Engrg Dr Ste 100 30092
Tel (678) 421-3000 *SIC* 2741

DEUTZ CORP p 433
3883 Steve Reynolds Blvd 30093
Tel (770) 564-7100 *SIC* 5084

EAGLE ROCK DISTRIBUTING CO LLC p 468
6205 Best Friend Rd 30071
Tel (770) 498-5500 *SIC* 5181 5182

■ **EMS TECHNOLOGIES INC** p 495
660 Engineering Dr 30092
Tel (770) 263-9200 *SIC* 3663 7373

EURAMAX HOLDINGS INC p 512
303 Research Dr Ste 400 30092
Tel (770) 449-7066 *SIC* 3444

EURAMAX INTERNATIONAL INC p 512
303 Research Dr Ste 400 30092
Tel (770) 449-7066 *SIC* 3471

▲ **FLEETCOR TECHNOLOGIES INC** p 555
5445 Triangle Pkwy # 400 30092
Tel (770) 449-0479 *SIC* 7389

■ **FLEETCOR TECHNOLOGIES OPERATING CO LLC** p 555
655 Engineering Dr # 300 30092
Tel (770) 449-0479 *SIC* 7389

FMK HOLDINGS LLC p 562
3081 Holcom Ste H 1 30071
Tel (413) 736-4554 *SIC* 2631 2621 2672

FURUKAWA ELECTRIC TECHNOLOGIES INC p 585
2000 Northeast Expy 30071
Tel (770) 798-2082 *SIC* 5051

■ **GOLDLEAF FINANCIAL SOLUTIONS INC** p 622
350 Technology Pkwy # 200 30092
Tel (678) 966-0844 *SIC* 8721 8741

GREAT AMERICAN COOKIE CO INC p 633
4685 Frederick Dr Sw 30093
Tel (877) 639-2361 *SIC* 5461

HERSCHEND ENTERTAINMENT CO LLC p 687
5445 Triangle Pkwy # 200 30092
Tel (770) 441-1940 *SIC* 7999 5947 5812

INITIAL CONTRACT SERVICES INC p 743
1780 Corporate Dr Ste 440 30093
Tel (678) 812-3079 *SIC* 7349

■ **INTERCEPT INC** p 751
3150 Holcomb Bridge Rd 30071
Tel (770) 248-9600 *SIC* 6099 7374

■ **ISAAC FAIR CORP** p 766
3550 Engrg Dr Ste 200 30092
Tel (770) 810-8000 *SIC* 7371

■ **KAWNEER CO INC** p 805
555 Guthridge Ct Tech 30092
Tel (770) 449-5555 *SIC* 3442 3446

■ **LARSON-JUHL US LLC** p 845
3900 Steve Reynolds Blvd 30093
Tel (770) 279-5200 *SIC* 2499 3499 2431

LMS INTELLIBOUND INC p 872
6525 The Corners Pkwy 30092
Tel (770) 724-0564 *SIC* 4225

MCNAUGHTON-MCKAY SOUTHEAST INC p 932
6685 Best Friend Rd 30071
Tel (770) 825-8600 *SIC* 5063

MDSA LLC p 933
650 Engineering Dr 30092
Tel (770) 448-3900 *SIC* 5013 6794

MILNER INC p 972
5125 Peachtree Indus Blvd 30092
Tel (770) 458-0999
SIC 7372 5999 7389 5065 5049 5044

MINGLEDORFFS INC p 973
6675 Jones Mill Ct 30092
Tel (770) 446-6311 *SIC* 5075

MOLNLYCKE HEALTH CARE US LLC p 983
5550 Peachtree Pkwy # 500 30092
Tel (678) 250-7900 *SIC* 5047

NETWORK COMMUNICATIONS INC p 1028
2 Sun Ct Ste 300 30092
Tel (678) 346-9300 *SIC* 2731 2721

■ **NEXTEL SOUTH CORP** p 1040
6575 The Corners Pkwy 30092
Tel (703) 592-7422 *SIC* 4812

OFS BRIGHTWAVE LLC p 1076
2000 Northeast Expy 30071
Tel (770) 798-3000 *SIC* 3357 3229

OFS FITEL LLC p 1076
2000 Northeast Expy 30071
Tel (770) 798-2000 *SIC* 3229 3357

OLE MEXICAN FOODS INC p 1082
6585 Crescent Dr 30071
Tel (770) 582-9200 *SIC* 2099 2032

PEDIATRIA HEALTHCARE LLC p 1127
5185 Peachtree Pkwy # 350 30092
Tel (770) 840-1966 *SIC* 8082 8741

PEDIATRIC SERVICES HOLDING CORP p 1127
3720 Da Vinci Ct 30092
Tel (770) 441-1580 *SIC* 8082 6719

PEDIATRIC SERVICES OF AMERICA INC p 1127
3720 Davinci Ct Ste 200 30092
Tel (770) 441-1580 *SIC* 8082

PEDIATRIC SERVICES OF AMERICA INC (DE) p 1127
3720 Davinci Ct Ste 200 30092
Tel (770) 441-1580 *SIC* 8082

PP&A-GA CORP p 1166
5425 Peachtree Pkwy 30092
Tel (678) 906-2806 *SIC* 7361

PROGRESSIVE LOGISTICS SERVICES LLC p 1181
6525 The Corners Pkwy # 520 30092
Tel (404) 564-1222 *SIC* 8631

PROSYS INC p 1185
6575 The Corners Pkwy # 300 30092
Tel (678) 268-1300 *SIC* 5045 7374

PROSYS INFORMATION SYSTEMS INC p 1185
6575 The Corners Pkwy # 300 30092
Tel (678) 268-1300 *SIC* 5045 7373

PRUITT CORP p 1187
1626 Jeurgens Ct 30093
Tel (706) 552-1699 *SIC* 8621

RECALL CORP p 1214
180 Technology Pkwy # 100 30092
Tel (770) 776-1000 *SIC* 8741

■ **REVENUEMED INC** p 1229
3740 Davinci Ct Ste 300 30092
Tel (770) 246-9797 *SIC* 8748

■ **RTS PACKAGING LLC** p 1256
504 Thrasher St 30071
Tel (800) 558-6984 *SIC* 2493

■ **S1 CORP** p 1263
705 Westech Dr 30092
Tel (678) 966-9499 *SIC* 7372 7371

SBS SERVICES CORP p 1285
3091 Holcomb Bridge Rd 30071
Tel (678) 534-4861 *SIC* 8741

SIDEL INC p 1319
5600 Sun Ct 30092
Tel (678) 221-3000 *SIC* 5084

SOUTHERN UNION CONFERENCE ASSOCIATION OF SEVENTH-DAY ADVENTISTS p 1350
302 Research Dr 30092
Tel (404) 299-1832 *SIC* 8661

SUNIVA INC p 1402
5765 Peachtree Indus Blvd 30092
Tel (404) 477-2700 *SIC* 3674 3433

VENTURE CONSTRUCTION CO INC p 1548
5660 Peachtree Indus Blvd 30071
Tel (770) 441-2404 *SIC* 1542

WAFFLE HOUSE INC p 1571
5986 Financial Dr 30071
Tel (770) 729-5700 *SIC* 5812 6794

▲ **WESTROCK CO** p 1602
504 Thrasher St 30071
Tel (678) 291-7456
SIC 2631 2899 3699 6531

■ **WESTROCK CONVERTING CO** p 1602
504 Thrasher St 30071
Tel (770) 246-9982 *SIC* 2631 2653 3081

■ **WESTROCK CP LLC** p 1602
504 Thrasher St 30071
Tel (770) 448-2193 *SIC* 5113

■ **WESTROCK MILL CO LLC** p 1602
504 Thrasher St 30071
Tel (770) 448-2193 *SIC* 2631

■ **WESTROCK RKT CO** p 1603
504 Thrasher St 30071
Tel (770) 448-2193 *SIC* 2653 2652 2631

■ **WESTROCK SHARED SERVICES LLC** p 1603
504 Thrasher St 30071
Tel (770) 448-2193 *SIC* 8741

YOUNG MCLARENS INTERNATIONAL INC p 1638
5555 Triangle Pkwy # 200 30092
Tel (770) 448-4680 *SIC* 6411

OAKWOOD, GA

PERFORMANCE FOOD GROUP OF GEORGIA LLC p 1135
3501 Old Oakwood Rd 30566
Tel (770) 532-7779 *SIC* 5141

WAYNE FARMS INC p 1584
4110 Continental Dr 30566
Tel (678) 450-3111 *SIC* 0751

WAYNE FARMS LLC p 1584
4110 Continental Dr 30566
Tel (770) 538-2120 *SIC* 2015

OCHLOCKNEE, GA

■ **OIL-DRI CORP OF GEORGIA** p 1079
28990 Hwy 3 31773
Tel (229) 574-5131 *SIC* 3295 3564 2842

PEACHTREE CITY, GA

AMCOR TOBACCO PACKAGING AMERICAS LLC p 66
445 Dividend Dr 30269
Tel (770) 486-9095 *SIC* 2671

COOPER LIGHTING LLC p 367
1121 Highway 74 S 30269
Tel (770) 486-4800 *SIC* 3648 3646

COOPER WIRING DEVICES INC p 367
203 Cooper Cir 30269
Tel (770) 631-2100 *SIC* 3643 3613

GLOBAL AVIATION HOLDINGS INC p 615
101 World Dr 30269
Tel (770) 632-8000 *SIC* 4522

HOSHIZAKI AMERICA INC p 708
618 Highway 74 S 30269
Tel (770) 487-2331 *SIC* 3585 5078

■ **MORGAN SOUTHERN INC** p 988
700 Westpark Dr Ste 250 30269
Tel (404) 366-1345 *SIC* 4213

OSMOSE UTILITIES SERVICES INC p 1097
635 Highway 74 S 30269
Tel (770) 632-6700 *SIC* 8741 8711 1623

TRULITE GLASS & ALUMINUM SOLUTIONS LLC p 1486
403 Westpark Ct Ste 201 30269
Tel (678) 593-9200 *SIC* 3354 3449

WENCOR GROUP LLC p 1591
416 Dividend Dr 30269
Tel (678) 490-0140 *SIC* 3728 4581

PEACHTREE CORNERS, GA

CENTRICSIT LLC p 281
3140 Northwoods Pkwy 30071
Tel (678) 495-4732 *SIC* 5045

CUSTARD INSURANCE ADJUSTERS INC p 402
4875 Avalon Ridge Pkwy 30071
Tel (770) 263-6800 *SIC* 6411

HARP BUSINESS SERVICES INC p 662
2725 Northwoods Pkwy A2 30071
Tel (678) 482-0675 *SIC* 2759 4225 5699

IMMUCOR INC p 734
3130 Gateway Dr 30071
Tel (770) 441-2051 *SIC* 2835

IVD HOLDINGS INC p 769
3130 Gateway Dr 30071
Tel (770) 441-2051 *SIC* 2835

IVD INTERMEDIATE HOLDINGS B INC p 769
3130 Gateway Dr 30071
Tel (770) 441-2051 *SIC* 2835

MCSI INC p 933
2975 Northwoods Pkwy 30071
Tel (770) 441-5263 *SIC* 1731 5065 7359

■ PHOENIX CORP p 1144
4685 Buford Hwy 30071
Tel (770) 447-4211 *SIC* 5051

STRATIX CORP p 1392
4920 Avalon Ridge Pkwy 30071
Tel (770) 326-7580 *SIC* 4812

WINTER GROUP OF COMPANIES INC p 1617
191 Peachtree St Ne 30071
Tel (404) 588-3300
SIC 1541 1542 1799 6512

PENDERGRASS, GA

NICOLON CORP p 1043
365 S Holland Dr 30567
Tel (706) 693-2226 *SIC* 2221 5949

ROYAL TEN CATE (USA) INC p 1254
365 S Holland Dr 30567
Tel (706) 693-2226 *SIC* 2299

SIGNATURE FOOD MARKETING LLC p 1322
5786 Us Highway 129 N 30567
Tel (706) 693-0095 *SIC* 5141

TAKEUCHI MFG (US) LTD p 1422
519 Bonnie Valentine Way 30567
Tel (706) 693-3600 *SIC* 5082

TOYOTA INDUSTRIES COMPRESSOR PARTS AMERICA CO p 1466
500 Valentine Indus Pkwy 30567
Tel (706) 693-7200 *SIC* 5075

PERRY, GA

HOUSTON COUNTY BOARD OF EDUCATION p 712
1100 Main St 31069
Tel (478) 988-6200 *SIC* 8211

HOUSTON COUNTY SCHOOL SYSTEM p 712
1100 Main St 31069
Tel (478) 988-6200 *SIC* 8211

PARRISH CONSTRUCTION GROUP INC p 1117
221 Industrial Park Dr 31069
Tel (478) 987-5544 *SIC* 1542

POOLER, GA

BEST TRUCKING LOGISTICS INC p 177
126 Pine Meadow Dr 31322
Tel (912) 349-6869 *SIC* 4789

JCB INC p 780
2000 Bamford Blvd 31322
Tel (912) 447-2000
SIC 5082 5084 3531 3537

JCB MANUFACTURING INC p 780
2000 Bamford Blvd 31322
Tel (912) 447-2000 *SIC* 5084

VOGEL FOREST PRODUCTS LTD p 1564
138 Canal St Ste 408 31322
Tel (912) 348-2233 *SIC* 5031

QUITMAN, GA

BROOKS COUNTY HOSPITAL AUTHORITY p 218
903 N Court St 31643
Tel (229) 263-4171 *SIC* 8062

REYNOLDS, GA

FLINT ELECTRIC MEMBERSHIP CORP p 557
3 S Macon St 31076
Tel (478) 847-3415 *SIC* 4911

RICEBORO, GA

CHEMTALL INC p 293
1 Chemical Plant Rd 31323
Tel (912) 884-3366 *SIC* 2869

INTERSTATE PAPER LLC p 758
2366 Interstate Rd Ste 1 31323
Tel (912) 884-3371 *SIC* 2631

SNF HOLDING CO p 1335
1 Chemical Plant Rd 31323
Tel (912) 884-3366 *SIC* 2822 2899

SNF INC p 1335
1 Chemical Plant Rd 31323
Tel (912) 884-3366 *SIC* 2822

RICHMOND HILL, GA

SOMMERS CO p 1339
1000 Sommers Blvd 31324
Tel (800) 654-6466 *SIC* 5172 5541 7033

RINGGOLD, GA

CATOOSA COUNTY PUBLIC SCHOOLS p 267
307 Cleveland St 30736
Tel (706) 965-3977 *SIC* 8211 9411

FIVE STAR HOLDING CO INC p 553
248 Rollins Industrial Ct 30736
Tel (706) 937-5077
SIC 5962 5812 5963 2099

RIVERDALE, GA

PRIME HEALTHCARE FOUNDATION - SOUTHERN REGIONAL LLC p 1175
11 Upper Riverdale Rd Sw 30274
Tel (770) 991-8000 *SIC* 8062

SOUTHERN REGIONAL HEALTH SYSTEM INC p 1350
11 Upper Riverdale Rd Sw 30274
Tel (770) 991-8175 *SIC* 8062

SOUTHERN REGIONAL MEDICAL CENTER p 1350
11 Upper Riverdale Rd Sw 30274
Tel (770) 991-8520 *SIC* 8011

ROCKMART, GA

MEGGITT (ROCKMART) INC p 940
669 Goodyear Ave 30153
Tel (770) 684-7855 *SIC* 3728

ROME, GA

BERRY COLLEGE INC p 176
2277 Martha Berry Hwy Nw 30161
Tel (706) 232-5374 *SIC* 8221

BIG TIME PRODUCTS LLC p 182
2 Wilbanks Rd Se 30161
Tel (706) 295-3770 *SIC* 2259

FLOYD COUNTY BOARD OF EDUCATION p 560
600 Riverside Pkwy Ne 30161
Tel (706) 234-1031 *SIC* 8211

FLOYD COUNTY SCHOOLS p 560
600 Riverside Pkwy Ne 30161
Tel (706) 234-1031 *SIC* 8211

FLOYD HEALTHCARE MANAGEMENT INC p 561
304 Turner Mccall Blvd Sw 30165
Tel (706) 509-5000 *SIC* 8062

HARBIN CLINIC LLC p 659
221 Technology Pkwy Nw 30165
Tel (706) 295-5331 *SIC* 8011

MANIS LUMBER CO p 901
15 Old Airport Rd Nw 30165
Tel (706) 232-2400 *SIC* 5031 5211

PIRELLI TIRE LLC p 1151
100 Pirelli Dr Se 30161
Tel (706) 368-5800 *SIC* 3011

■ REDMOND PARK HOSPITAL LLC p 1217
501 Redmond Rd Nw 30165
Tel (706) 291-0291 *SIC* 8062 8011

SOUTHEASTERN MILLS INC p 1346
333 Old Lindale Rd Se 30161
Tel (706) 291-6528
SIC 2099 2041 5149 2045

SYNTEC INDUSTRIES LLC p 1416
438 Lavender Dr Nw 30165
Tel (706) 235-1158 *SIC* 2273 5023

ROSSVILLE, GA

NECA IBEW FAMILY MEDICAL CARE PLAN p 1023
410 Chickamauga Ave # 301 30741
Tel (877) 937-9602 *SIC* 6371

ROSWELL, GA

ADAMS OUTDOOR ADVERTISING LIMITED PARTNERSHIP p 21
500 Colonial Center Pkwy 30076
Tel (770) 333-0399 *SIC* 7312

ANDREWS INTERNATIONAL p 90
200 Mansell Ct E Ste 500 30076
Tel (661) 775-8400 *SIC* 7381

ARCLIN USA LLC p 105
1000 Holcomb Woods Pkwy 30076
Tel (678) 999-2100 *SIC* 2821 2891

BORAL BRICKS INC p 201
200 Mansell Ct E Ste 310 30076
Tel (770) 645-4500 *SIC* 3251 5211 3271

BORAL INDUSTRIES INC p 201
200 Mansell Ct E Ste 310 30076
Tel (770) 645-4500
SIC 3251 3272 3275 5032 3271 2899

C-E MINERALS INC p 234
100 Mansell Ct E Ste 615 30076
Tel (770) 225-7900
SIC 1099 1446 3295 6512

COMPDENT OF GEORGIA INC p 351
100 Mansell Ct E Ste 400 30076
Tel (770) 998-8936 *SIC* 6324 6311

DYNAMIX GROUP INC p 464
1905 Woodstock Rd # 4150 30075
Tel (770) 643-8877 *SIC* 7373 8731

FELDSPAR CORP p 537
100 Mansell Ct E Ste 300 30076
Tel (770) 594-0660 *SIC* 1459 1442

IMERYS USA INC p 733
100 Mansell Ct E Ste 300 30076
Tel (770) 645-3300
SIC 1455 1459 1429 1422 2819

KEYSTON BROS (INC) p 815
1000 Holcomb Wds Pkwy # 111 30076
Tel (770) 587-2555 *SIC* 5199 5131 5191

KIMBERLY-CLARK PROFESSIONAL p 818
1400 Holcomb Bridge Rd 30076
Tel (800) 241-3146 *SIC* 3589

KLOCKNER NAMASCO HOLDING CORP p 823
500 Colonial Center Pkwy # 500 30076
Tel (678) 259-8800 *SIC* 5051

KLOCKNER USA HOLDING INC p 823
500 Colonial Center Pkwy # 500 30076
Tel (678) 259-8800 *SIC* 6799 5051

KLOECKNER METALS CORP p 823
500 Colonial Center Pkwy # 500 30076
Tel (678) 259-8800 *SIC* 5051

KUDZU FABRICS INC p 831
2154 River Cliff Dr 30076
Tel (770) 641-0379 *SIC* 5199 5131 5191

MYCOM NORTH AMERICA INC p 1004
1080 Holcomb Bridge Rd # 200210 30076
Tel (770) 776-0000 *SIC* 4899

NOLAN TRANSPORTATION GROUP LLC p 1046
85 Mill St Ste 214 30075
Tel (770) 509-9611 *SIC* 4731

NORTH FULTON MEDICAL CENTER VOLUNTEER SERVICES ORGANIZATION INC p 1052
3000 Hospital Blvd 30076
Tel (770) 751-2500 *SIC* 8062

ROYAL OAK ENTERPRISES LLC p 1254
1 Royal Oak Ave 30076
Tel (678) 461-3200 *SIC* 2999 2899

S & A COMPUTER SERVICES INC p 1261
1125 Northmeadow Pkwy # 120 30076
Tel (770) 569-2828 *SIC* 7379

S&B INDUSTRIAL MINERALS NORTH AMERICA INC p 1263
100 Mansell Ct E Ste 200 30076
Tel (610) 647-1123 *SIC* 5052

SINGLE SOURCE INC p 1326
601 W Crssvlle Rd Ste 100 30075
Tel (770) 840-7877 *SIC* 5013 7532

■ SITEONE LANDSCAPE SUPPLY HOLDING LLC p 1328
300 Colonial Center Pkwy 30076
Tel (770) 255-2100
SIC 5083 5191 5193 5032 5063

▲ SITEONE LANDSCAPE SUPPLY INC p 1328
300 Colonial Center Pkwy 30076
Tel (770) 255-2100
SIC 5083 5191 5193 5032 5063

■ SITEONE LANDSCAPE SUPPLY LLC p 1328
300 Colonial Center Pkwy # 600 30076
Tel (770) 255-2100 *SIC* 5063 5193 5083

US SECURITY ASSOCIATES HOLDINGS INC p 1533
200 Mansell Ct E Fl 5 30076
Tel (770) 625-1500 *SIC* 7381 7349

US SECURITY ASSOCIATES INC p 1533
200 Mansell Ct E Ste 500 30076
Tel (770) 625-1500 *SIC* 7381

US SECURITY HOLDINGS INC p 1533
200 Mansell Ct E Ste 500 30076
Tel (770) 625-1400 *SIC* 7381 7349

WALLE CORP p 1573
200 Hembree Park Dr Ste H 30076
Tel (800) 942-6761 *SIC* 2759 2752 2671

SAINT MARYS, GA

GILMAN BUILDING PRODUCTS LLC p 612
2500 Saint Marys Rd 31558
Tel (912) 576-0300 *SIC* 2421

SANDERSVILLE, GA

JET FOOD STORES OF GEORGIA INC p 783
1106 S Harris St 31082
Tel (478) 552-2588 *SIC* 5411

SANDY SPRINGS, GA

CSM BAKERY SOLUTIONS LLC p 398
5775 Glenridge Dr Bldg A 30328
Tel (404) 478-5400 *SIC* 2052

SAVANNAH, GA

ATLANTIC WOOD INDUSTRIES INC p 127
405 E Perry St 31401
Tel (912) 966-7008 *SIC* 2491 3272

BOARD OF EDUCATION FOR CITY OF SAVANNAH AND COUNTY OF CHATHAM (INC) p 195
208 Bull St 31401
Tel (912) 395-1000 *SIC* 8211

BRADLEY PLYWOOD CORP p 206
204 Old West Lathrop Ave 31415
Tel (912) 447-7000 *SIC* 5031

CANDLER HOSPITAL INC p 247
5353 Reynolds St 31405
Tel (912) 819-6000 *SIC* 8062

CAPITOL MATERIALS OF SAVANNAH INC p 251
305 Telfair Rd 31415
Tel (912) 232-0952 *SIC* 5082

CATHOLIC DIOCESE OF SAVANNAH p 266
2170 E Victory Dr 31404
Tel (912) 201-4100 *SIC* 8661 8211

CHATHAM COUNTY BOARD OF EDUCATION p 291
208 Bull St 31401
Tel (912) 395-1000 *SIC* 8211

■ CHATHAM STEEL CORP p 291
501 W Boundary St 31401
Tel (912) 233-4182 *SIC* 5051 3317

CHEMOIL CORP p 293
101 N Lathrop Ave 31415
Tel (912) 236-1331 *SIC* 5172

▲ CITITRENDS INC p 310
104 Coleman Blvd 31408
Tel (912) 236-1561
SIC 5611 5621 5641 5632

CITY OF SAVANNAH p 318
2 E Bay St 31401
Tel (912) 651-6415 *SIC* 9111

COLONIAL GROUP INC p 337
101 N Lathrop Ave 31415
Tel (800) 944-3835
SIC 5171 5169 5172 4924 4492 4226

COLONIAL OIL INDUSTRIES INC p 337
101 N Lathrop Ave 31415
Tel (904) 396-1388 *SIC* 5171 5541

CRYSTAL DIAMOND BRANDS INC p 396
3000 Tremont Rd 31405
Tel (912) 651-5112 *SIC* 7389 2099

■ DERST BAKING CO LLC p 431
1311 W 52nd St 31405
Tel (912) 233-2235 *SIC* 2051 5461

FUJI VEGETABLE OIL INC p 583
120 Brampton Rd 31408
Tel (912) 966-5900 *SIC* 2076

GREAT DANE TRAILERS INC p 633
602 E Lathrop Ave 31415
Tel (912) 644-2100 *SIC* 5013 5012

■ GULFSTREAM AEROSPACE CORP p 647
500 Gulfstream Rd 31408
Tel (912) 965-3000 *SIC* 3721 4581

■ GULFSTREAM AEROSPACE CORP (GEORGIA) p 647
500 Gulfstream Rd 31408
Tel (912) 965-3000 *SIC* 3721

■ GULFSTREAM DELAWARE CORP p 647
500 Gulfstream Rd 31408
Tel (912) 965-3000 *SIC* 3721 5088

MEMORIAL HEALTH INC p 941
4700 Waters Ave 31404
Tel (912) 350-8000 *SIC* 8062

MEMORIAL HEALTH UNIVERSITY MEDICAL CENTER INC p 941
4700 Waters Ave 31404
Tel (912) 350-8000 *SIC* 8062 8011

MORRIS MULTIMEDIA INC p 990
27 Abercorn St 31401
Tel (912) 233-1281 *SIC* 4833 2752

ORTHOPEDIC SURGERY CENTER L P p 1096
210 E Derenne Ave 31405
Tel (912) 644-5300 *SIC* 8011

PETER BRASSELER HOLDINGS LLC p 1138
1 Brasseler Blvd 31419
Tel (912) 925-8525 *SIC* 5047 3841 3843

PROVIDENT HEALTH SERVICES INC p 1186
4700 Waters Ave 31404
Tel (912) 350-8000 *SIC* 8082 4119

ROGER WOOD FOODS INC p 1246
7 Alfred St 31408
Tel (912) 652-9600 *SIC* 2013 5147

SAINT JOSEPHS HOSPITAL INC p 1269
5353 Reynolds St 31405
Tel (912) 355-9967 *SIC* 8062

SAINT JOSEPHS HOSPITAL INC p 1269
11705 Mercy Blvd 31419
Tel (912) 819-4100 *SIC* 8062

SAVANNA-CHATHAM COUNTY PUBLIC SCHOOL SYSTEM p 1284
208 Bull St 31401
Tel (912) 395-5600 *SIC* 8211

SAVANNAH CITY WATER SUPPLY p 1284
6183 Hwy 21 N 31407
Tel (912) 964-4473 *SIC* 4941

SAVANNAH COLLEGE OF ART AND DESIGN INC p 1284
126 E Gaston St 31401
Tel (912) 525-5000 *SIC* 8221

SAVANNAH COLLEGE OF ART AND DESIGN INC p 1284
115 E York St 31401
Tel (912) 525-5800 *SIC* 8748

■ SAVANNAH ELECTRIC AND POWER CO p 1284
600 E Bay St 31401
Tel (912) 644-7171 *SIC* 4911

SAVANNAH WOOD PRESERVING CO INC p 1284
501 Stiles Ave 31415
Tel (912) 236-4875 *SIC* 2491

SPIRIT CONSTRUCTION SERVICES INC p 1359
118 Coleman Blvd 31408
Tel (912) 748-8055 *SIC* 1541 1542

ST JOSEPHS/CANDLER HEALTH SYSTEM INC p 1369
5353 Reynolds St Ste 101 31405
Tel (912) 819-6000 *SIC* 8062

SULLIVAN GROUP p 1397
37 W Fairmont Ave # 100 31406
Tel (912) 352-3800 *SIC* 7361

TITLEMAX OF TEXAS INC p 1456
15 Bull St Ste 200 31401
Tel (912) 525-2675 *SIC* 6141

TMX FINANCE HOLDINGS INC p 1458
15 Bull St Ste 200 31401
Tel (912) 525-2675 *SIC* 6719

TMX FINANCE LLC p 1458
15 Bull St Ste 200 31401
Tel (912) 525-2675 *SIC* 6141

TRONOX LLC p 1484
1 Kerr Mcgee Rd 31404
Tel (912) 652-1000 *SIC* 2816 2819 5198

SEA ISLAND, GA

SEA ISLAND ACQUISITION LP p 1295
100 Cloister Dr 31561
Tel (912) 638-3611 *SIC* 7011 0781 7992

SEA ISLAND ACQUISITIONS LLC p 1295
100 Cloister Dr 31561
Tel (912) 638-3611 *SIC* 7011

SEA ISLAND CO p 1295
100 Cloister Dr 31561
Tel (888) 732-4752 *SIC* 7011 0781 7992

SEA ISLAND SERVICES INC p 1295
100 Hudson Pl 31561
Tel (912) 638-3611 *SIC* 4111 4941

SMYRNA, GA

ALLISON-SMITH CO LLC p 58
1869 S Cobb Indus Blvd Se 30082
Tel (404) 351-6430 *SIC* 1731 7389

BUILDER SUPPORT SERVICES INC p 224
4125 Atlanta Rd Se 30080
Tel (770) 907-3400 *SIC* 1531 6531

CATHOLIC FOUNDATION OF NORTH GEORGIA INC p 266
2401 Lake Park Dr Se # 100 30080
Tel (404) 920-7300 *SIC* 8661

COMPASS CHEMICAL INTERNATIONAL LLC p 351
5544 Oakdale Rd Se 30082
Tel (404) 696-6711 *SIC* 5169 3589

■ CORE-MARK DISTRIBUTORS INC p 369
4820 N Church Ln 30080
Tel (404) 792-2000
SIC 5194 5141 5145 5113

CURANT HEALTH GEORGIA LLC p 401
200 Technology Ct Se B 30082
Tel (770) 437-8040 *SIC* 5122

CYTEC SURFACE SPECIALTIES INC p 406
1950 Lake Park Dr Se 30080
Tel (770) 434-6188
SIC 3086 5169 5191 5162 3081 2823

FACILITY DESIGN/BUILDERS INC p 523
2233 Lake Park Dr Se # 450 30080
Tel (770) 437-2700 *SIC* 1541

FLOOR AND DECOR OUTLETS OF AMERICA INC p 557
2233 Lake Park Dr Se # 400 30080
Tel (404) 471-1634 *SIC* 5713 1771

HUMPHRIES AND CO LLC p 718
4581 S Cobb Dr Se Ste 200 30080
Tel (770) 434-1890 *SIC* 1542

MURATA ELECTRONICS NORTH AMERICA INC p 1001
2200 Lake Park Dr Se 30080
Tel (770) 436-1300 *SIC* 5065 3675 3679

■ PRINTEGRA CORP p 1177
5040 Highlands Pkwy Se 30082
Tel (770) 487-5151
SIC 2761 2782 2677 2678 2679

■ S P RICHARDS CO p 1262
6300 Highlands Pkwy Se 30082
Tel (770) 434-4571 *SIC* 5112 5021

SANDVIK MINING AND CONSTRUCTION USA LLC p 1279
300 Technology Ct Se 30082
Tel (404) 589-3800 *SIC* 5082

TNG GP p 1458
1955 Lake Park Dr Se # 400 30080
Tel (770) 863-9000 *SIC* 5192

UCB CHEMICALS CORP p 1498
2000 Lake Park Dr Se 30080
Tel (770) 434-6188 *SIC* 5169 5191 5162

UCB INC p 1498
1950 Lake Park Dr Se 30080
Tel (770) 970-7500 *SIC* 5122 8731 8732

UNISTAN INC p 1505
5500 United Dr Se 30082
Tel (678) 305-2080 *SIC* 5182 5181

UNITED DISTRIBUTORS INC p 1507
5500 United Dr Se 30082
Tel (678) 305-2000 *SIC* 5182

SNELLVILLE, GA

E R SNELL CONTRACTOR INC p 466
1785 Oak Rd 30078
Tel (770) 985-0600 *SIC* 1611

■ EHCA EASTSIDE OCCUPATIONAL MEDICINE CENTER LLC p 481
1700 Medical Way 30078
Tel (770) 979-0200 *SIC* 8062

SOCIAL CIRCLE, GA

STANDRIDGE COLOR CORP p 1376
1196 E Hightower Trl 30025
Tel (770) 464-3362 *SIC* 2865 2816 3083

SPRINGFIELD, GA

EFFINGHAM COUNTY BOARD OF EDUCATION p 480
405 N Ash St 31329
Tel (912) 754-6491 *SIC* 8211

EFFINGHAM COUNTY SCHOOLS p 480
405 N Ash St 31329
Tel (912) 754-6491 *SIC* 8211

STATESBORO, GA

AGSOUTH FARM CREDIT ACA p 36
26 S Main St 30458
Tel (912) 764-9091 *SIC* 6159

BLAKEWOOD PROPERTIES ASSOCIATES p 188
620 E Olliff St 30458
Tel (912) 764-3330 *SIC* 6531

BULLOCH COUNTY BOARD OF EDUCATION p 225
150 Williams Rd Ste A 30458
Tel (912) 764-6201 *SIC* 8211

BULLOCH COUNTY SCHOOLS p 225
150 Williams Rd Ste A 30458
Tel (912) 212-8500 *SIC* 8211

EAST GEORGIA REGIONAL MEDICAL CENTER p 470
1499 Fair Rd 30458
Tel (912) 486-1000 *SIC* 8748

GEORGIA SOUTHERN UNIVERSITY p 607
1582 Southern Dr 30458
Tel (912) 681-5224 *SIC* 8221

■ STATESBORO HMA INC p 1383
1499 Fair Rd 30458
Tel (912) 486-1000 *SIC* 8062

STILLMORE, GA

CRIDER INC p 392
1 Plant Ave 30464
Tel (912) 562-4435 *SIC* 2099

STOCKBRIDGE, GA

ALL AMERICAN QUALITY FOODS INC p 51
125 Eagles Landing Pkwy 30281
Tel (770) 474-5904 *SIC* 5411

GRESHAM WOFTAM INC p 639
1 Gresham Lndg 30281
Tel (770) 389-1600 *SIC* 6411

PIEDMONT HENRY HOSPITAL INC p 1147
1133 Eagles Landing Pkwy 30281
Tel (678) 604-1001 *SIC* 8062

STONE MOUNTAIN, GA

DEKALB COUNTY BOARD OF EDUCATION p 423
1701 Mountain Indus Blvd 30083
Tel (678) 676-1200 *SIC* 8211

DEKALB COUNTY SCHOOLS p 423
1701 Mountain Indus Blvd 30083
Tel (678) 676-1200 *SIC* 8211

DNK SALES LLC p 446
949 Stephenson Rd Ste B 30087
Tel (678) 704-7300 *SIC* 6311 7291 5699

■ HEATCRAFT REFRIGERATION PRODUCTS LLC p 679
2175 W Park Place Blvd 30087
Tel (770) 465-5600 *SIC* 3585

MED-ACOUSTICS INC p 935
1685 E Park Place Blvd 30087
Tel (770) 498-8075 *SIC* 5047 1742

NEW WINCUP HOLDINGS INC p 1033
4640 Lewis Rd 30083
Tel (770) 938-5281 *SIC* 3086

WINCUP INC p 1615
4640 Lewis Rd 30083
Tel (770) 771-5861 *SIC* 3086 3089

SUWANEE, GA

ARINSO INTERNATIONAL INC p 108
3965 Johns Creek Ct Ste A 30024
Tel (678) 259-0500 *SIC* 7379

ARRIS GROUP INC p 112
3871 Lakefield Dr Ste 300 30024
Tel (678) 473-2907
SIC 7372 3663 3357 7373 3661

ARRIS INTERNATIONAL INC p 112
3871 Lakefield Dr Ste 300 30024
Tel (678) 473-2000 *SIC* 3663

ARRIS SOLUTIONS INC p 112
3871 Lakefield Dr Ste 300 30024
Tel (678) 473-2000 *SIC* 3661 3663 3357

ARRIS TECHNOLOGY INC p 113
3871 Lakefield Dr 30024
Tel (678) 473-2907 *SIC* 7372 3825

CONTROL SOUTHERN INC p 364
3850 Lakefield Dr 30024
Tel (770) 495-3100 *SIC* 5084

DOOSAN INDUSTRIAL VEHICLE AMERICA CORP p 451
2905 Shawnee Indus Way 30024
Tel (770) 831-2200 *SIC* 5084

DOOSAN INFRACORE AMERICA CORP p 451
2905 Shawnee Industrial W 30024
Tel (770) 831-2200 *SIC* 5084 5082

DOOSAN INFRACORE INTERNATIONAL INC p 451
2905 Shawnee Industrial W 30024
Tel (770) 831-2200 *SIC* 3531

GWINNETT COUNTY PUBLIC SCHOOLS p 648
437 Old Peachtree Rd Nw 30024
Tel (678) 301-6000 *SIC* 8211

HABASIT AMERICA INC p 651
805 Satellite Blvd Nw 30024
Tel (678) 288-3600 *SIC* 3566

HISENSE USA CORP p 696
7310 Mcginnis Ferry Rd 30024
Tel (678) 318-9060 *SIC* 7622

MEGGITT TRAINING SYSTEMS INC p 940
296 Brogdon Rd 30024
Tel (678) 288-1090 *SIC* 3699

PAI INDUSTRIES INC p 1107
950 Northbrook Pkwy 30024
Tel (770) 822-1000 *SIC* 3714 5013

PRICE INDUSTRIES INC p 1174
2975 Shawnee Ridge Ct 30024
Tel (770) 623-8050 *SIC* 3444

QUALITY TECHNOLOGY SERVICES LLC p 1197
300 Satellite Blvd Nw 30024
Tel (678) 546-0064
SIC 7373 4813 7378 7374

SWETT & CRAWFORD GROUP INC p 1412
7230 Mcginnis Ferry Rd # 300 30024
Tel (404) 240-5200 *SIC* 6411

SYLVANIA, GA

KING AMERICA FINISHING INC p 820
1351 Scarboro Hwy 30467
Tel (912) 863-4511 *SIC* 2211 2261

TALLAPOOSA, GA

HONDA PRECISION PARTS OF GEORGIA LLC p 705
550 Honda Pkwy 30176
Tel (770) 574-3400 *SIC* 3089

TEMPLE, GA

JANUS INTERNATIONAL GROUP LLC p 778
135 Janus Intl Blvd 30179
Tel (770) 562-2850 *SIC* 3442

THOMASVILLE, GA

ARCHBOLD MEDICAL CENTER INC p 104
Gordon Ave At Mimosa Dr 31792
Tel (229) 228-2739 *SIC* 8741 8062

CLEAVER-BROOKS INC p 325
221 Law St 31792
Tel (229) 226-3024
SIC 3589 3569 3561 3433 3443

■ FLOWERS BAKERIES LLC p 560
1919 Flowers Cir 31757
Tel (229) 226-9110 *SIC* 2051 2053

■ FLOWERS BAKING CO OF THOMASVILLE INC p 560
1919 Flowers Cir 31757
Tel (229) 226-9110 *SIC* 2051

▲ FLOWERS FOODS INC p 560
1919 Flowers Cir 31757
Tel (229) 226-9110 *SIC* 2051 2052

JOHN D ARCHBOLD MEMORIAL HOSPITAL p 788
915 Gordon Ave 31792
Tel (229) 228-2000 *SIC* 8062

TURBINE ENGINE COMPONENTS TECHNOLOGIES CORP p 1492
1211 Old Albany Rd 31792
Tel (229) 228-2600
SIC 3463 3724 3714 3469

THOMSON, GA

THOMSON PLASTICS INC p 1449
130 Quality Dr 30824
Tel (706) 828-7508 *SIC* 3949 3089

TIFTON, GA

TIFT COUNTY BOARD OF EDUCATION p 1453
207 Ridge Ave N 31794
Tel (229) 387-2400 *SIC* 8211

TIFT COUNTY HOSPITAL AUTHORITY p 1453
901 18th St E 31794
Tel (229) 382-7120 *SIC* 8062

TIFT COUNTY SCHOOLS p 1453
207 Ridge Ave N 31794
Tel (229) 387-2400 *SIC* 8211

TIFT REGIONAL MEDICAL CENTER p 1453
901 18th St E 31794
Tel (229) 382-7120 *SIC* 8062

TIFT REGIONAL MEDICAL CENTER p 1453
901 18th St E 31794
Tel (229) 382-7120 *SIC* 8062

TOCCOA, GA

1ST FRANKLIN FINANCIAL CORP p 1
135 E Tugalo St 30577
Tel (706) 886-7571 *SIC* 6141

GEM INDUSTRIES INC p 598
Hwy 123 N 30577
Tel (706) 886-8431
SIC 3429 2531 2511 3446 2821 2515

■ PATTERSON PUMP CO p 1121
2129 Ayersville Rd 30577
Tel (706) 886-2101 *SIC* 3561 3511 3559

PRUITTHEALTH CORP p 1187
209 E Doyle St 30577
Tel (706) 886-8493 *SIC* 8741

TUCKER, GA

AMEC FOSTER WHEELER E&C SERVICES INC p 66
1979 Lkeside Pkwy Ste 400 30084
Tel (770) 688-2500 *SIC* 8711

AMEC FOSTER WHEELER VENTURES INC p 66
1979 Lkeside Pkwy Ste 400 30084
Tel (770) 688-2500 *SIC* 8748 8711

GEORGIA ENERGY COOPERATIVE (AN ELECTRIC MEMBERSHIP CORP) p 607
2100 E Exch Pl Ste 300 30084
Tel (770) 270-7500 *SIC* 4911

GEORGIA TRANSMISSION CORP p 607
2100 E Exchange Pl 30084
Tel (770) 270-7400 *SIC* 4911

▲ GMS INC p 619
100 Crescent Center Pkwy 30084
Tel (800) 392-4619 *SIC* 3275 5031 5039

■ GYPSUM MANAGEMENT AND SUPPLY INC p 649
100 Crescent Center Pkwy # 800 30084
Tel (770) 939-1711 *SIC* 5032 8742

INLAND FRESH SEAFOOD CORP OF AMERICA INC p 743
1651 Montreal Cir 30084
Tel (404) 350-5850 *SIC* 5146 5144 5147

LANIER WORLDWIDE INC p 844
4667 N Royal Atlanta Dr 30084
Tel (770) 493-2100
SIC 5044 5999 7359 7629

OGLETHORPE POWER CORP p 1077
2100 E Exch Pl Ste 203 30084
Tel (770) 270-7600 *SIC* 4911

■ WILLIAMS INDUSTRIAL SERVICES GROUP LLC p 1611
100 Crescent Center Pkwy # 1240 30084
Tel (866) 851-4077 *SIC* 1799

■ WILLIAMS PLANT SERVICES LLC p 1611
100 Crescent Center Pkwy # 1240 30084
Tel (770) 879-4500 *SIC* 1629 8744

■ YP ADVERTISING & PUBLISHING LLC p 1639
2247 Northlake Pkwy 30084
Tel (678) 406-5523 *SIC* 2741 7313 7311

■ YP HOLDINGS LLC p 1639
2247 Northlake Pkwy Fl 10 30084
Tel (866) 570-8863 *SIC* 7374 7389 7313

UNION CITY, GA

SOUTHERN MILLS INC p 1349
6501 Mall Blvd 30291
Tel (770) 969-1000 *SIC* 2221 2297

UNION CITY CITY OF INC p 1504
5047 Union St 30291
Tel (770) 964-2288 *SIC* 9111 9221

VALDOSTA, GA

AMBLING MANAGEMENT CO LLC p 65
348 Enterprise Dr 31601
Tel (866) 777-7228
SIC 1522 6552 6531 6513

C TERRY HUNT INDUSTRIES INC p 233
5420 Perimeter Rd 31601
Tel (229) 244-6707 *SIC* 1629

FRESH BEGINNINGS INC p 578
4001 Coleman Rd N 31602
Tel (229) 242-0237 *SIC* 5199 2052 2064

HOSPITAL AUTHORITY OF VALDOSTA AND LOWNDES COUNTY GEORGIA p 709
2501 N Patterson St 31602
Tel (229) 333-1000 *SIC* 8062

LANGDALE CO p 844
1202 Madison Hwy 31601
Tel (229) 242-7450
SIC 2421 2491 7011 7699 5031 5171

LOWNDES COUNTY BOARD OF EDUCATION INC p 882
1592 Norman Dr 31601
Tel (229) 245-2250 *SIC* 8211

LOWNDES COUNTY SCHOOLS p 882
1592 Norman Dr 31601
Tel (229) 245-2250 *SIC* 8211

SOUTH GEORGIA MEDICAL CENTER p 1344
2501 N Patterson St 31602
Tel (229) 333-1000 *SIC* 8062

VALDOSTA CITY SCHOOL DISTRICT p 1539
1204 Williams St 31601
Tel (229) 333-8500 *SIC* 8211

VALDOSTA STATE UNIVERSITY p 1539
1500 N Patterson St 31698
Tel (229) 333-5800 *SIC* 8221

VIDALIA, GA

MEADOWS HEALTHCARE ALLIANCE INC p 934
1 Meadows Pkwy 30474
Tel (912) 538-5866 *SIC* 8099 8062

MEADOWS REGIONAL MEDICAL CENTER INC p 934
1703 Meadows Ln 30474
Tel (912) 537-8921 *SIC* 8062 8051

VILLA RICA, GA

■ FLOWERS BAKING CO OF VILLA RICA LLC p 560
134 Doyle Mcclain Dr 30180
Tel (770) 459-2883 SIC 2051

WARNER ROBINS, GA

DSL XPRESS LLC p 458
2006 Karl Dr Apt 1602 31088
Tel (706) 945-9542 SIC 4213

HOUSTON HEALTHCARE SYSTEM INC p 712
1601 Watson Blvd 31093
Tel (478) 922-4281 SIC 8062

HOUSTON HOSPITALS INC p 712
1601 Watson Blvd 31093
Tel (478) 929-9544 SIC 8062

WATKINSVILLE, GA

GOLDEN PANTRY FOOD STORES INC p 621
1150 Wall St 30677
Tel (800) 533-3816 SIC 5411 5541

WAYCROSS, GA

CAROLINA SKIFF LLC p 259
3231 Fulford Rd 31503
Tel (912) 287-0547 SIC 5091 3732

■ FLASH FOODS LLC p 554
215 Pendleton St 31501
Tel (912) 285-4011 SIC 5541 5411

GENERAL HOUSING INC p 601
2255 Industrial Blvd 31503
Tel (912) 285-5068 SIC 2451

JONES CO p 792
215 Pendleton St Ste A 31501
Tel (912) 285-4011 SIC 5541 5411 5172

LEWIS AND RAULERSON INC p 858
1759 State St 31501
Tel (912) 283-5951 SIC 5171

MAYO CLINIC HEALTH SYSTEM IN WAYCROSS INC p 923
1900 Tebeau St 31501
Tel (912) 283-3030 SIC 8062 8051

WEST POINT, GA

BATSON-COOK CO p 159
817 4th Ave 31833
Tel (706) 643-2500 SIC 1542 5211 1541

DAEHAN SOLUTION GEORGIA LLC p 408
791 S Progress Pkwy 31833
Tel (706) 902-5200 SIC 5013 8711 3714

J SMITH LANIER & CO p 772
300 W 10th St 31833
Tel (706) 645-2211 SIC 6411

KIA MOTORS MANUFACTURING GEORGIA INC p 816
7777 Kia Pkwy 31833
Tel (706) 902-7777 SIC 5511

KNOLOGY BROADBAND INC p 825
1241 Og Skinner Dr 31833
Tel (706) 645-8553 SIC 4841

KNOLOGY INC p 825
1241 Og Skinner Dr 31833
Tel (334) 644-2611 SIC 4813 4841

KYUNGSHIN AMERICA CORP p 833
1201 Og Skinner Dr 31833
Tel (706) 645-1595 SIC 3714

POWERTECH AMERICA INC p 1166
6801 Kia Pkwy 31833
Tel (706) 902-6800 SIC 5012 3714

POWERTECH AMERICA SALES LLC p 1166
6801 Kia Pkwy 31833
Tel (706) 902-6800 SIC 5013

WHITE, GA

SURYA CARPET INC p 1409
1 Surya Dr 30184
Tel (706) 625-4823 SIC 5023 2273

TOYO TIRE NORTH AMERICA MANUFACTURING INC p 1466
3660 Highway 411 Ne 30184
Tel (678) 721-7200 SIC 3011

WINDER, GA

BARROW COUNTY BOARD OF EDUCATION p 157
179 W Athens St 30680
Tel (770) 867-4527 SIC 8211

BARROW COUNTY SCHOOL SYSTEM p 157
179 W Athens St 30680
Tel (770) 867-4527 SIC 8211

MAGBEE BROS LUMBER AND SUPPLY CO INC p 895
1065 Bankhead Hwy 30680
Tel (678) 425-2600
SIC 2431 5211 3531 2439

WINTERVILLE, GA

NAKANISHI MANUFACTURING CORP p 1006
1225 Voyles Rd 30683
Tel (706) 353-0006 SIC 5085 3562

WOODSTOCK, GA

PRIMUS BUILDERS INC p 1176
8294 Highway 92 Ste 210 30189
Tel (770) 928-7120 SIC 1542

YOUNG HARRIS, GA

BLUE RIDGE MOUNTAIN ELECTRIC MEMBERSHIP CORP p 192
875 Main St 30582
Tel (706) 379-3121 SIC 4911

HAWAII

AIEA, HI

MOMI PALI MEDICAL CENTER p 983
98-1079 Moanalua Rd # 680 96701
Tel (808) 486-6000 SIC 8011

EWA BEACH, HI

HAWAII MEDICAL CENTER WEST LLC p 669
91-2141 Fort Weaver Rd 96706
Tel (808) 678-7000 SIC 8062

HILO, HI

CMU & ASSOCIATES INC p 329
55 Holomua St 96720
Tel (808) 961-0877 SIC 5146 5148 5142

COUNTY OF HAWAII p 378
25 Aupuni St Ste 107 96720
Tel (808) 961-8211 SIC 9111

■ HAWAII ELECTRIC LIGHT CO INC p 669
54 Halekauila St 96720
Tel (808) 935-1171 SIC 4911

HAWAII SCHOOL DISTRICT p 669
75 Aupuni St Rm 203 96720
Tel (808) 974-6600 SIC 8211 9411

HILO MEDICAL CENTER p 694
1190 Waianuenue Ave 96720
Tel (808) 932-3000 SIC 8011

ISEMOTO CONTRACTING CO LTD p 766
648 Piilani St 96720
Tel (808) 935-7194 SIC 1629 1542 1541

PUNA PLANTATION HAWAII LIMITED p 1192
50 E Puainako St 96720
Tel (808) 959-9111 SIC 5411

SUISAN CO p 1397
333 Kilauea Ave Ste 202 96720
Tel (808) 935-8511 SIC 5142 5146

HONOLULU, HI

▲ ALEXANDER & BALDWIN INC p 49
822 Bishop St 96813
Tel (808) 525-6611 SIC 6512 2062

■ ALEXANDER & BALDWIN LLC p 49
822 Bishop St 96813
Tel (808) 525-6611
SIC 6531 0133 0179 6552

■ ALOHA PETROLEUM LTD p 59
1132 Bishop St Ste 1700 96813
Tel (808) 833-3249 SIC 5172 5541 5411

AMBULATORY SERVICES INC p 65
1301 Punchbowl St 96813
Tel (808) 538-9011 SIC 8031

■ AMERICAN SAVINGS BANK FSB p 79
915 Fort Street Mall 96813
Tel (808) 627-6900 SIC 6035

■ AMFAC HAWAII LLC A HAWAII LIMITED LIABILITY CO p 85
700 Bishop St Ste 2002 96813
Tel (808) 543-8900
SIC 6531 6552 0133 0179

■ AQUA HOTELS AND RESORTS INC p 101
1850 Ala Moana Blvd 96815
Tel (808) 943-9291 SIC 7011

■ AQUA-ASTON HOSPITALITY LLC p 101
2155 Kalakaua Ave Fl 5 96815
Tel (808) 931-1400 SIC 7389 7011

■ BANK OF HAWAII p 151
130 Merchant St 96813
Tel (888) 643-3888 SIC 6022 6411 6211

▲ BANK OF HAWAII CORP p 151
130 Merchant St 96813
Tel (888) 643-3888 SIC 6022

BOARD OF WATER SUPPLY p 196
630 S Beretania St 96843
Tel (808) 748-5100 SIC 4941

■ CENTRAL PACIFIC BANK p 279
220 S King St 96813
Tel (808) 544-0500 SIC 6022

▲ CENTRAL PACIFIC FINANCIAL CORP p 279
220 S King St 96813
Tel (808) 544-0500 SIC 6022

CITY & COUNTY OF HONOLULU p 312
530 S King St Rm 208 96813
Tel (808) 523-4141 SIC 9111

CITY MILL CO LIMITED p 312
660 N Nimitz Hwy 96817
Tel (808) 533-3811 SIC 5211

■ COFFEE PARTNERS HAWAII p 334
210 Ward Ave Ste 105 96814
Tel (808) 545-1149 SIC 8742

CUTTER MANAGEMENT CO p 403
1100 Alakea St Steth2 96814
Tel (808) 529-2000 SIC 5511 7515

DAWSON TECHNICAL LLC p 417
900 Fort Street Mall # 1850 96813
Tel (808) 536-5500 SIC 8711 1542

DCK PACIFIC CONSTRUCTION LLC p 418
707 Richards St Ste 410 96813
Tel (808) 533-5000 SIC 1542

DON QUIJOTE (USA) CO LTD p 450
801 Kaheka St 96814
Tel (808) 973-4800
SIC 5411 5331 6512 5912

ELITE PACIFIC PROPERTIES LLC p 487
4211 Waialae Ave Ste 106 96816
Tel (808) 589-2040 SIC 6512 6531

EXECUTIVE OFFICE OF STATE OF HAWAII p 517
415 S Beretania St Fl 5 96813
Tel (808) 586-0034 SIC 9111

FCH ENTERPRISES INC p 533
1765 S King St 96826
Tel (808) 973-0877 SIC 5812

■ FIRST HAWAIIAN BANK p 547
999 Bishop St Ste 3200 96813
Tel (808) 525-6340 SIC 6022

FIRST HAWAIIAN BANK p 547
2339 Kamehameha Hwy # 447 96819
Tel (808) 844-4444 SIC 6029

■ FIRST HAWAIIAN INC p 547
999 Bishop St Fl 29 96813
Tel (808) 525-7000 SIC 6022

FIRST INSURANCE CO OF HAWAII LTD p 547
1100 Ward Ave 96814
Tel (808) 527-7777 SIC 6331 6411

FOOD PANTRY LTD p 564
3536 Harding Ave Ste 500 96816
Tel (808) 732-5515 SIC 5411 5947

FOODLAND SUPER MARKET LIMITED p 564
3536 Harding Ave Fl 1 96816
Tel (808) 732-0791 SIC 5411

■ GAS CO LLC p 593
745 Fort Street Mall # 1800 96813
Tel (808) 594-5530
SIC 4932 4925 5172 5984

■ HA 3049 UALENA STREET LLC p 651
3375 Koapaka St Ste G350 96819
Tel (808) 835-3700 SIC 4111

HAWAI I PACIFIC HEALTH p 668
55 Merchant St Ste 2500 96813
Tel (808) 535-7350 SIC 8062 8011

HAWAII DENTAL SERVICE p 668
700 Bishop St Ste 700 96813
Tel (808) 521-1431 SIC 6324

HAWAII DEPARTMENT OF HUMAN RESOURCES DEVELOPMENT p 668
235 S Beretania St # 1400 96813
Tel (808) 587-1100 SIC 9199

HAWAII DEPARTMENT OF HUMAN SERVICES p 668
1390 Miller St Ste 209 96813
Tel (808) 586-4997 SIC 9441

HAWAII DEPARTMENT OF PUBLIC SAFETY p 668
919 Ala Moana Blvd # 407 96814
Tel (808) 587-1288 SIC 9221 9229

HAWAII DEPARTMENT OF TRANSPORTATION p 668
869 Punchbowl St Rm 509 96813
Tel (808) 587-1830 SIC 9621

HAWAII ENERGY RESOURCES INC p 669
733 Bishop St Fl 28 96813
Tel (808) 547-3111 SIC 5172 2911 5171

HAWAII FOODSERVICE ALLIANCE LLC p 669
2720 Waiwai Loop 96819
Tel (808) 839-2004 SIC 5141 5812

HAWAII HEALTH SYSTEMS CORP p 669
3675 Kilauea Ave 96816
Tel (808) 733-4020 SIC 8082

HAWAII MEDICAL CENTER p 669
2230 Liliha St Ste 227 96817
Tel (808) 547-6881 SIC 8062

HAWAII MEDICAL SERVICE ASSOCIATION p 669
818 Keeaumoku St Ste 200 96814
Tel (808) 948-6111 SIC 6321 6324

HAWAII PACIFIC UNIVERSITY p 669
1164 Bishop St Ste 800 96813
Tel (808) 544-0200 SIC 8221

HAWAII PIZZA HUT INC p 669
828 Fort Street Mall # 130 96813
Tel (808) 566-3200 SIC 5812

HAWAII STATE DEPARTMENT OF EDUCATION p 669
1390 Miller St Rm 305309 96813
Tel (808) 586-3310 SIC 9411

■ HAWAIIAN AIRLINES INC p 669
3375 Koapaka St Ste G350 96819
Tel (808) 835-3700 SIC 4512

HAWAIIAN DREDGING CONSTRUCTION CO INC p 669
201 Merchant St Ste 900 96813
Tel (808) 735-3211
SIC 1542 1611 1522 1521

■ HAWAIIAN ELECTRIC CO INC p 669
900 Richards St 96813
Tel (808) 543-7771 SIC 4911

▲ HAWAIIAN ELECTRIC INDUSTRIES INC p 669
1001 Bishop St Ste 2900 96813
Tel (808) 543-5662 SIC 4911 6035

▲ HAWAIIAN HOLDINGS INC p 669
3375 Koapaka St Ste G350 96819
Tel (808) 835-3700 SIC 4512

HAWAIIAN NATIVE CORP p 669
900 Fort Street Mall # 1850 96813
Tel (808) 536-5500 SIC 8699

■ HAWAIIAN TELCOM COMMUNICATIONS INC p 669
1177 Bishop St 96813
Tel (808) 546-4511 SIC 4813 4812

▲ HAWAIIAN TELCOM HOLDCO INC p 669
1177 Bishop St 96813
Tel (808) 546-4511 SIC 4813

■ HAWAIIAN TELCOM INC p 669
1177 Bishop St 96813
Tel (808) 643-3456 SIC 4813 5065 7629

HIE HOLDINGS INC p 690
2839 Mokumoa St 96819
Tel (808) 833-2244 SIC 2095 7993

■ HILTON HAWAIIAN VILLAGE LLC p 695
2005 Kalia Rd 96815
Tel (808) 949-4321 SIC 7011 5812 5813

HONOLULU SCHOOL DISTRICT p 705
4967 Kilauea Ave 96816
Tel (808) 733-4950 SIC 8211

HONPA HONGWANJI HAWAII BETSUIN p 705
1727 Pali Hwy 96813
Tel (808) 536-7044 SIC 8661

HTH CORP p 715
1668 S King St Fl 2 96826
Tel (808) 469-4111 SIC 7011 5812 6512

ISLAND HOLDINGS INC p 766
1022 Bethel St Fl 4 96813
Tel (808) 531-1311 SIC 6512

ISLAND INSURANCE CO LIMITED p 766
1022 Bethel St 96813
Tel (808) 564-8200 SIC 6331 6411

JARDINE HAWAII MOTOR HOLDINGS LTD p 778
818 Kapiolani Blvd 96813
Tel (808) 592-5600 SIC 5511

JUDICIARY COURTS OF STATE OF HAWAII p 796
417 S King St 96813
Tel (808) 539-4700 SIC 9211

KAPIOLANI MEDICAL CENTER AT PALI MOMI p 803
55 Merchant St 96813
Tel (808) 486-6000 SIC 8322

KAPIOLANI MEDICAL CENTER FOR WOMEN AND CHILDREN p 803
1319 Punahou St 96826
Tel (808) 535-7401 SIC 8069

KAZI FOODS CORP OF HAWAII p 805
560 N Nimitz Hwy Ste 214 96817
Tel (808) 550-4100 SIC 5812

■ KOKO OHA INVESTMENTS INC p 826
1100 Alakea St Fl 8 96813
Tel (808) 535-5999 SIC 5172 6719

KUAKINI HEALTH SYSTEM p 831
347 N Kuakini St 96817
Tel (808) 536-2236 SIC 8062

KUAKINI MEDICAL CENTER p 831
347 N Kuakini St 96817
Tel (808) 547-9231 SIC 8062

KYO-YA HOTELS & RESORTS LP p 833
2255 Kalakaua Ave Fl 2 96815
Tel (808) 931-8600 SIC 7011 5812 5813

MARYL GROUP INC p 914
55 Merchant St Ste 2000 96813
Tel (808) 545-2920 SIC 6552 1542

▲ MATSON INC p 920
1411 Sand Island Pkwy 96819
Tel (808) 848-1211 SIC 4499

MAUI DIVERS OF HAWAII LIMITED p 921
1520 Liona St 96814
Tel (808) 946-7979 SIC 3911 5944 5094

■ MID PAC PETROLEUM LLC p 963
1132 Bishop St Ste 2500 96813
Tel (808) 535-5999 SIC 5984 5172

MNS LTD p 980
766 Pohukaina St 96813
Tel (808) 591-1063 SIC 5099

NAN INC p 1007
636 Laumaka St 96819
Tel (808) 842-4929 SIC 1542

OAHU PUBLICATIONS INC p 1070
500 Ala Moana Blvd 96813
Tel (808) 529-4700 SIC 2711

OAHU TRANSIT SERVICES INC p 1070
811 Middle St Rm 225 96819
Tel (808) 848-4400 SIC 4111

OUTRIGGER HOTELS HAWAII p 1099
2375 Kuhio Ave Fl 4 96815
Tel (808) 921-6510 SIC 7011

PACIFIC GUARDIAN LIFE INSURANCE CO LIMITED p 1104
1440 Kalani St Ste 1700 96817
Tel (808) 942-6541 SIC 6311 6321

PHOENIX V LLC p 1145
311 Pacific St 96817
Tel (808) 532-7400 SIC 5169 8748

POMARE LTD p 1160
670 Auahi St Ste I03 96813
Tel (808) 524-3966 SIC 5651

PUNAHOU SCHOOL p 1192
1601 Punahou St 96822
Tel (808) 944-5711 SIC 8211

QSI INC p 1195
3375 Koapaka St Ste D108 96819
Tel (808) 831-0811 SIC 5411

QUEENS HEALTH SYSTEMS p 1198
1301 Punchbowl St 96813
Tel (808) 691-5900 SIC 8062

QUEENS MEDICAL CENTER p 1198
1301 Punchbowl St 96813
Tel (808) 547-4329 SIC 8062 8621

RESEARCH CORP OF UNIVERSITY OF HAWAII p 1226
2800 Woodlawn Dr Ste 200 96822
Tel (808) 988-8311 SIC 8733

ROBERTS HAWAII INC p 1242
680 Iwilei Rd Ste 700 96817
Tel (808) 523-7750
SIC 4119 4724 7011 4489

ROBERTS TOURS AND TRANSPORTATION INC p 1242
680 Iwilei Rd Ste 700 96817
Tel (808) 523-7750 SIC 4119

ROMAN CATHOLIC CHURCH IN STATE OF HAWAII p 1248
1184 Bishop St 96813
Tel (808) 536-7036 SIC 8661

■ **SCHULER HOMES INC** p 1290
828 Fort Street Mall 4th 96813
Tel (808) 521-5661 SIC 6552

SERVCO PACIFIC INC p 1307
2850 Pukoloa St Ste 300 96819
Tel (808) 564-1300 SIC 5013 5064 5511

SEVEN-ELEVEN HAWAII INC p 1309
1755 Nuuanu Ave Fl 2 96817
Tel (808) 526-1711 SIC 5411

ST FRANCIS HEALTHCARE SYSTEM OF HAWAII p 1366
2226 Liliha St Ste 227 96817
Tel (808) 547-6883 SIC 8051 8082

STATE HAWAII DEPARTMENT OF HEALTH p 1381
1250 Punchbowl St 96813
Tel (808) 586-4400 SIC 9431

STATE OF HAWAII p 1381
201 Merchant St Ste 1805 96813
Tel (808) 586-1735 SIC 9111

STRAUB CLINIC & HOSPITAL p 1393
888 S King St 96813
Tel (808) 522-4000 SIC 8011 8062

SUASIN CANCER CARE INC p 1395
1301 Punchbowl St 96813
Tel (512) 583-0205 SIC 8011

TD FOOD GROUP INC p 1429
828 Fort Street Mall # 130 96813
Tel (808) 566-3200 SIC 5812 6794

TERUYA BROS LIMITED p 1440
1276 Young St Ste B 96814
Tel (808) 591-8946 SIC 5411

TITLE GUARANTY OF HAWAII INC p 1456
235 Queen St Fl 2nd 96813
Tel (808) 533-6261 SIC 6361

TRUSTEES OF ESTATE OF BERNICE PAUAHI BISHOP p 1487
567 S King St Ste 200 96813
Tel (808) 523-6200 SIC 8211

UNIVERSITY OF HAWAII SYSTEMS p 1521
2444 Dole St 96822
Tel (808) 956-8278 SIC 8221 8222

WEBCO HAWAII INC p 1586
2840 Mokumoa St 96819
Tel (808) 839-4551
SIC 5122 5199 5141 5064

Y HATA & CO LIMITED p 1633
285 Sand Island Access Rd 96819
Tel (808) 447-4100 SIC 5142 5141

KAHULUI, HI

EXCEPTIONAL INC p 517
111 Hana Hwy Ste 111 96732
Tel (808) 877-6555 SIC 7363 5941 7361

■ **MAUI ELECTRIC CO LIMITED** p 921
210 W Kamehameha Ave 96732
Tel (808) 871-8461 SIC 4911

KAILUA KONA, HI

HUALALAI INVESTORS LLC p 715
100 Kaupulehu Dr 96740
Tel (808) 325-8400 SIC 6552

KAILUA, HI

CASTLE MEDICAL CENTER p 264
640 Ulukahiki St 96734
Tel (808) 263-5500 SIC 8062

KAPOLEI, HI

■ **COVANTA HONOLULU RESOURCE RECOVERY VENTURE** p 384
91-174 Hanua St 96707
Tel (808) 682-2099 SIC 4911

GRACE PACIFIC LLC p 628
949 Kamokila Blvd Ste 200 96707
Tel (808) 674-8383 SIC 1611 1429 3272

HONSADOR LUMBER LLC p 705
91-151 Malakole St 96707
Tel (808) 479-3071 SIC 5031 5211

LEEWARD OAHU SCHOOL DISTRICT p 852
601 Kamokila Blvd Ste 418 96707
Tel (808) 564-6066 SIC 8211 9411

KIHEI, HI

SANDY PAGES p 1279
1794 S Kihei Rd Ste 4 96753
Tel (808) 205-0321 SIC 5192 5092

KOLOA, HI

KAWAILOA DEVELOPMENT LLP p 805
1571 Poipu Rd Ste 3063 96756
Tel (808) 742-1234 SIC 7011 7992

LAHAINA, HI

■ **KAPALUA LAND CO LTD** p 803
1000 Kapalua Dr 96761
Tel (808) 669-5622 SIC 6552 6512

■ **MAUI OPERATING LLC** p 921
2365 Kaanapali Pkwy 96761
Tel (808) 661-2588 SIC 7011 7389

■ **MAUI PINEAPPLE CO LTD** p 921
200 Village Rd 96761
Tel (808) 877-1624 SIC 2033

LAIE, HI

BRIGHAM YOUNG UNIVERSITY-HAWAII p 212
55-220 Kulanui St 96762
Tel (808) 293-3211 SIC 8221

POLYNESIAN CULTURAL CENTER INC p 1160
55-370 Kamehameha Hwy 96762
Tel (808) 293-3000 SIC 7999 5812 5947

LANAI CITY, HI

LANAI RESORTS LLC p 841
1311 Fraser Ave 96763
Tel (808) 565-3000 SIC 6552 6512

LIHUE, HI

COUNTY OF KAUAI p 379
4444 Rice St Ste 150 96766
Tel (808) 241-4200 SIC 9111

KAUAI ISLAND UTILITY COOPERATIVE p 805
4463 Pahee St Ste 1 96766
Tel (808) 246-4300 SIC 4911

KAUAI SCHOOL DISTRICT p 805
3060 Eiwa St Ste 305 96766
Tel (808) 274-3502 SIC 8211 9411

WILCOX HEALTH SYSTEM p 1609
3-3420 Kuhio Hwy 96766
Tel (808) 245-1100 SIC 8741 8011

WILCOX MEMORIAL HOSPITAL p 1609
3-3420 Kuhio Hwy 96766
Tel (808) 245-1100 SIC 8062

MILILANI, HI

■ **AMERICA SAVING BANK** p 67
200 Kahelu Ave 96789
Tel (808) 627-6900 SIC 6035

PEARL CITY, HI

HAWAIIAN HOUSEWARES LTD p 669
96-1282 Waihona St 96782
Tel (808) 453-8000
SIC 5199 5194 5141 5145

PUUNENE, HI

■ **HAWAIIAN COMMERCIAL & SUGAR CO** p 669
1 Hansen St 96784
Tel (808) 877-0081 SIC 2061

SCHOFIELD BARRACKS, HI

ISLAND PALM COMMUNITIES LLC p 766
215 Duck Rd Bldg 950 96857
Tel (808) 275-3100 SIC 6531

WAILUKU, HI

COUNTY OF MAUI p 379
200 S High St 96793
Tel (808) 270-7855 SIC 9111

MAUI MEMORIAL MEDICAL CENTER p 921
221 Mahalani St 96793
Tel (808) 244-9056 SIC 8062

MAUI SCHOOL DISTRICT p 921
54 S High St Fl 4 96793
Tel (808) 984-8001 SIC 8211 9411

WAIPAHU, HI

ALBERT C KOBAYASHI INC p 46
94-535 Ukee St Ste 101 96797
Tel (808) 671-6460 SIC 1542 1521 1522

HAWTHORNE PACIFIC CORP p 670
94-025 Farrington Hwy 96797
Tel (808) 676-0227 SIC 5084 7353

PARADISE BEVERAGES INC p 1113
94-1450 Moaniani St 96797
Tel (808) 678-4000 SIC 5181 5182 5149

IDAHO

ATHOL, ID

IDAHO FOREST GROUP LLC p 728
4447 E Chilco Rd 83801
Tel (208) 255-3200 SIC 2421

BLACKFOOT, ID

BINGHAM COOPERATIVE INC p 183
477 W Highway 26 83221
Tel (208) 785-3440 SIC 5191 5171 5541

BMH INC p 194
98 Poplar St 83221
Tel (208) 785-4100 SIC 8062 8051

IDAHO POTATO PACKERS CORP p 728
40 N 400 W 83221
Tel (208) 785-3030 SIC 5148

NONPAREIL CORP p 1047
411 W Collins Rd 83221
Tel (208) 785-5880 SIC 2099

BOISE, ID

AB ACQUISITION LLC p 9
250 E Parkcenter Blvd 83706
Tel (208) 395-6200 SIC 5411

ABS FINANCE CO INC p 12
250 E Parkcenter Blvd 83706
Tel (208) 395-6200 SIC 5141

AGRI BEEF CO p 36
1555 W Shoreline Dr # 320 83702
Tel (208) 338-2500 SIC 2011 0212

ALBERTSONS COMPANIES INC p 46
250 E Parkcenter Blvd 83706
Tel (208) 395-6200 SIC 5912 5499

ALBERTSONS COMPANIES LLC p 46
250 E Parkcenter Blvd 83706
Tel (208) 395-6200 SIC 5912 5499

ALBERTSONS HOLDINGS LLC p 46
250 E Parkcenter Blvd 83706
Tel (208) 395-6200 SIC 5411

ALBERTSONS LLC p 46
250 E Parkcenter Blvd 83706
Tel (208) 395-6200 SIC 5499 5912

ALLIANCE TITLE & ESCROW CORP p 55
380 E Parkcenter Blvd # 105 83706
Tel (208) 388-8881 SIC 6411

AMALGAMATED SUGAR CO LLC p 64
1951 S Saturn Way Ste 100 83709
Tel (208) 383-6500 SIC 2063

AMERICAN DRUG STORES LLC p 71
250 E Parkcenter Blvd 83706
Tel (208) 395-6200 SIC 5912

▲ **BOISE CASCADE CO** p 198
1111 W Jefferson St # 300 83702
Tel (208) 384-6161 SIC 2421

BOISE CASCADE HOLDINGS LLC p 198
1111 W Jefferson St # 300 83702
Tel (208) 384-6161 SIC 5031 8744

■ **BOISE CASCADE WOOD PRODUCTS LLC** p 198
1111 W Jefferson St # 300 83728
Tel (208) 384-6161 SIC 5099

■ **BOISE INC** p 198
1111 W Jefferson St # 50 83702
Tel (208) 384-7000 SIC 2671 2621 2631

■ **BOISE PAPER HOLDINGS LLC** p 198
1111 W Jefferson St # 200 83702
Tel (208) 384-7501 SIC 2621

BOISE STATE UNIVERSITY p 198
1910 University Dr 83725
Tel (208) 426-1011 SIC 8221

■ **BOISE WHITE PAPER LLC** p 198
1111 W Jefferson St # 200 83702
Tel (208) 384-7000 SIC 2621

BUILDING MATERIALS HOLDING CORP p 225
720 E Park Blvd Ste 115 83712
Tel (208) 331-4300 SIC 5211 5031

BZ INTERMEDIATE HOLDINGS LLC p 231
1111 W Jefferson St 83702
Tel (208) 384-7000 SIC 8211

C STEIN INC p 233
4719 S Market St 83705
Tel (208) 378-0550
SIC 5181 5182 5149 4941 5921

CITY OF BOISE p 313
150 N Capitol Blvd 83702
Tel (208) 384-4422 SIC 9111

CLICK SALES INC p 326
917 S Lusk St Ste 200 83706
Tel (208) 472-9400 SIC 5734

COUNTY OF ADA p 375
200 W Front St 83702
Tel (208) 287-7080 SIC 9121

DELTA DENTAL PLAN OF IDAHO INC p 426
555 E Parkcenter Blvd 83706
Tel (208) 489-3580 SIC 6324 8021

DEPARTMENT OF CORRECTION IDAHO p 429
1299 N Orchard St Ste 110 83706
Tel (208) 658-2000 SIC 9223

DNIS DLN ATOPRK&TRCK CNTR p 446
2573 S Orchard St 83705
Tel (208) 336-6000 SIC 5511

EMPLOYERS RESOURCE MANAGEMENT CO p 494
1301 S Vista Ave Ste 200 83705
Tel (208) 376-3000 SIC 7363

EUGENIA CHANG MD p 512
100 E Idaho St 83712
Tel (208) 381-2711 SIC 8011

EXECUTIVE OFFICE OF STATE OF IDAHO p 517
700 W Jefferson St 83720
Tel (208) 334-2100 SIC 9111

FOREST PRODUCTS HOLDINGS LLC p 567
1111 W Jefferson St # 300 83702
Tel (208) 384-6161 SIC 5031 8744

FUTURE FOUNDATION INC p 585
380 E Parkcenter Blvd # 230 83706
Tel (208) 336-0150 SIC 3354 5013 6361

▲ **IDACORP INC** p 728
1221 W Idaho St 83702
Tel (208) 388-2200 SIC 4911

IDAHO DEPARTMENT OF HEALTH AND WELFARE p 728
450 W State St Fl 9 83702
Tel (208) 334-5500 SIC 9431

IDAHO DEPARTMENT OF TRANSPORTATION p 728
3311 W State St 83703
Tel (208) 334-8000 SIC 9621

■ **IDAHO POWER CO** p 728
1221 W Idaho St 83702
Tel (208) 388-2200 SIC 4911

INDEPENDENT SCHOOL DISTRICT OF BOISE CITY p 737
8169 W Victory Rd 83709
Tel (208) 854-4000 SIC 8211

■ **INTERMOUNTAIN GAS CO** p 753
555 S Cole Rd 83709
Tel (208) 377-6000 SIC 4924

INTERMOUNTAIN INDUSTRIES INC p 753
555 S Cole Rd 83709
Tel (208) 377-6000 SIC 4924

JOAH INC p 787
250 E Parkcenter Blvd 83706
Tel (208) 395-6200 SIC 5411

JR SIMPLOT CO p 795
999 W Main St Ste 1300 83702
Tel (208) 336-2110
SIC 0211 2879 2037 2874 2873

■ **MICRON SEMICONDUCTOR PRODUCTS INC** p 962
8000 S Federal Way 83716
Tel (208) 368-4000 SIC 5065

▲ **MICRON TECHNOLOGY INC** p 962
8000 S Federal Way 83716
Tel (208) 368-4000 SIC 3674

MILITARY DIVISION OF STATE OF IDAHO p 969
4040 W Guard St Bldg 600 83705
Tel (208) 422-5507 SIC 9711

■ **MOTIVEPOWER INC** p 992
4600 S Apple St 83716
Tel (208) 947-4800 SIC 3743

MOUNTAIN STATES TUMOR INSTITUTE INC p 994
190 E Bannock St 83712
Tel (208) 381-2222 SIC 8093

■ **MWI ANIMAL HEALTH** p 1004
3041 W Pasadena Dr 83705
Tel (208) 955-8930 SIC 5047 5149

■ **MWI VETERINARY SUPPLY CO** p 1004
3041 W Pasadena Dr 83705
Tel (208) 955-8930
SIC 5047 2834 2835 2836

■ **NATIONAL PROJECTS INC** p 1015
720 E Park Blvd 83712
Tel (208) 386-5000 SIC 1629 1542 1541

NEW ALBERTSONS INC p 1029
250 E Parkcenter Blvd 83706
Tel (208) 395-6200 SIC 5411

NORCO INC p 1047
1125 W Amity Rd 83705
Tel (208) 336-1643
SIC 5084 5169 7352 5999 3548 2813

OCHOA AG UNLIMITED FOODS INC p 1073
910 W Main St Ste 248 83702
Tel (208) 343-6882 SIC 5142

RECORD STEEL AND CONSTRUCTION INC p 1214
333 W Rossi St Ste 200 83706
Tel (208) 887-1401 SIC 1542 1791

SAINT ALPHONSUS REGIONAL MEDICAL CENTER INC p 1268
1055 N Curtis Rd 83706
Tel (208) 367-2121 SIC 8062

■ **SELECTBUILD CONSTRUCTION INC** p 1301
720 E Park Blvd Ste 115 83712
Tel (208) 331-4300
SIC 1521 1771 1751 2431 5031 5211

SIMPLOT PHOSPHATES LLC p 1325
999 W Main St Ste 1300 83702
Tel (208) 336-2110 SIC 2874

SMALL MINE DEVELOPMENT LLC p 1332
670 E Riverpark Ln # 100 83706
Tel (208) 338-8880 SIC 1081

SNAKE RIVER SUGAR CO p 1335
1951 S Saturn Way Ste 100 83709
Tel (208) 383-6500 SIC 8611 2063

ST LUKES HEALTH SYSTEM LTD p 1370
190 E Bannock St 83712
Tel (208) 381-2222 *SIC* 8062

ST LUKES REGIONAL MEDICAL CENTER LTD p 1370
190 E Bannock St 83712
Tel (208) 381-5500 *SIC* 8062 8011

STINKER STORES INC p 1390
3184 W Elder St 83705
Tel (208) 375-0942 *SIC* 5541

TERTELING HOLDING CO INC p 1440
3858 N Garden Center Way 83703
Tel (208) 342-0018 *SIC* 5082

TITLEONE EXCHANGE CO p 1456
1101 W River St Ste 201 83702
Tel (208) 424-8511 *SIC* 6541

▲ **US ECOLOGY INC** p 1531
251 E Front St Ste 400 83702
Tel (208) 331-8400 *SIC* 4953

■ **VITALIZE LLC** p 1562
5777 N Meeker Ave Ste 500 83713
Tel (208) 377-3326 *SIC* 5499

■ **WASHINGTON CLOSURE CO LLC** p 1577
720 E Park Blvd Bsmt 83712
Tel (208) 386-5000
SIC 4959 1799 1795 4226

■ **WASHINGTON DMILITARIZATION LLC** p 1578
720 E Park Blvd 83712
Tel (208) 386-5000 *SIC* 8711

■ **WASHINGTON GROUP INTERNATIONAL INC** p 1578
1 Morrison Knudsen Plz 83729
Tel (208) 386-5000 *SIC* 7359

WASHINGTON GROUP INTERNATIONAL INC p 1578
720 E Park Blvd 83712
Tel (208) 386-5000
SIC 1611 1629 1221 1081 4959 1475

WESTERN AIRCRAFT INC p 1597
4300 S Kennedy St 83705
Tel (208) 338-1800
SIC 5088 4581 7359 5172

WESTERN POWER SPORTS INC p 1599
601 E Gowen Rd 83716
Tel (208) 376-8400 *SIC* 5013

WINCO FOODS LLC p 1615
650 N Armstrong Pl 83704
Tel (208) 377-0110 *SIC* 5411

WINCO HOLDINGS INC p 1615
650 N Armstrong Pl 83704
Tel (208) 377-0110 *SIC* 5411

BUHL, ID

CLEAR SPRINGS FOODS INC p 324
4424 N 1500 E 83316
Tel (208) 543-4316 *SIC* 0273 2048

CALDWELL, ID

D&B SUPPLY CO p 407
3303 E Linden St 83605
Tel (208) 459-7446
SIC 5191 5699 5251 5261 5999 5531

■ **WEST VALLEY MEDICAL CENTER INC** p 1596
1717 Arlington Ave 83605
Tel (208) 459-4641 *SIC* 8062

COEUR D ALENE, ID

COEUR D ALENE SCHOOL DISTRICT 271 p 333
1400 N Northwood Ctr Ct 83814
Tel (208) 664-8241 *SIC* 8211

■ **COEUR-ROCHESTER INC** p 334
505 E Front Ave 83814
Tel (312) 489-5800 *SIC* 1044

GREAT FLOORS LLC p 633
524 E Sherman Ave 83814
Tel (208) 664-5405 *SIC* 1752 5713

HAGADONE INVESTMENT CO INC p 652
111 S 1st St 83814
Tel (208) 667-3431 *SIC* 2711 7011

▲ **HECLA MINING CO** p 680
6500 N Mineral Dr Ste 200 83815
Tel (208) 769-4100
SIC 1041 1044 1031 1081

IDAHO FOREST GROUP LLC p 728
687 W Cnfield Ave Ste 100 83815
Tel (208) 255-3200 *SIC* 5211

KOOTENAI HOSPITAL DISTRICT p 827
2003 Kootenai Health Way 83814
Tel (208) 625-4000
SIC 8062 8063 8093 8734

EAGLE, ID

DICKINSON FROZEN FOODS INC p 438
1205 E Iron Eagle Dr B 83616
Tel (208) 938-7540 *SIC* 5142

LANDSCAPE INNOVATIONS LLC p 843
11101 Fairview 189 83616
Tel (208) 841-7666 *SIC* 0781

▲ **WESTON LAMB HOLDINGS INC** p 1602
599 S Rivershore Ln 83616
Tel (208) 938-1047 *SIC* 2038

EDEN, ID

STANDLEE HAY TRUCKING CO INC p 1376
990 S 1690 E 83325
Tel (208) 825-5117 *SIC* 5191

FRUITLAND, ID

ADVANCED HEALTH CARE CORP p 25
215 N Whitley Dr Ste 1 83619
Tel (208) 452-6392 *SIC* 8082

WINDSOR WINDOW CO p 1615
300 Nw 16th St 83619
Tel (800) 452-3801 *SIC* 2431

WOODGRAIN MILLWORK INC p 1623
300 Nw 16th St 83619
Tel (208) 452-3801 *SIC* 2431

GENESEE, ID

PACIFIC NORTHWEST FARMERS COOPERATIVE INC p 1105
117 W Chestnut 83832
Tel (208) 285-1141 *SIC* 5153 2099

GRAND VIEW, ID

SIMPLOT LIVESTOCK CO p 1325
1301 Highway 67 83624
Tel (208) 834-2231 *SIC* 0211

HAILEY, ID

POWER ENGINEERS INC p 1165
3940 Glenbrook Dr 83333
Tel (208) 788-3456 *SIC* 8711

HAMER, ID

BLAINE LARSEN FARMS INC p 188
2650 N 2375 E 83425
Tel (208) 662-5501
SIC 5148 2099 0111 0139

HAYDEN LAKE, ID

MANITO SUPER 1 FOODS INC p 902
240 W Hayden Ave 83835
Tel (208) 772-5722 *SIC* 5411

IDAHO FALLS, ID

BATTELLE ENERGY ALLIANCE LLC p 159
2525 Fremont Ave 83402
Tel (208) 533-7606 *SIC* 8731 7382

BONNEVILLE JOINT SCHOOL DISTRICT NO 93 p 200
3497 N Ammon Rd 83401
Tel (208) 525-4400 *SIC* 8211

C-A-L STORES COMPANIES INC p 234
665 E Anderson St 83401
Tel (208) 523-3359 *SIC* 5191

CIRI DEVELOPMENT CORP p 308
1425 Higham St 83402
Tel (208) 528-8718 *SIC* 6519 6552

CONRAD & BISCHOFF INC p 358
2251 N Holmes Ave 83401
Tel (208) 522-8174 *SIC* 5171 5411 5541

DOUG ANDRUS DISTRIBUTING LLC p 452
6300 S 45th W 83402
Tel (208) 523-1034 *SIC* 4213

EAGLE EYE PRODUCE INC p 468
4050 E Lincoln Rd 83401
Tel (208) 522-2343 *SIC* 5148

EASTERN IDAHO REGIONAL MEDICAL CENTER AUXILIARY INC p 472
3100 Channing Way 83404
Tel (208) 529-6111 *SIC* 8011

FIRST CALL JEWEL INC p 545
1410 Hollipark Dr 83401
Tel (208) 522-7777
SIC 1731 1711 5078 5063

IDAHO FALLS SCHOOL DISTRICT NO 91 EDUCATION FOUNDATION INC p 728
690 John Adams Pkwy 83401
Tel (208) 525-7500 *SIC* 8211

IDAHOAN FOODS LLC p 728
357 Constitution Way 83402
Tel (208) 542-3700 *SIC* 2034

INTERMOUNTAIN NATURAL LLC p 753
1740 S Yellowstone Hwy 83402
Tel (208) 227-9000 *SIC* 5147 2013

MELALEUCA INC p 940
4609 W 65th S 83402
Tel (208) 522-0700
SIC 2833 5122 2844 2841 2834

MOUNTAIN VIEW HOSPITAL LLC p 994
2325 Coronado St 83404
Tel (208) 557-2700 *SIC* 8062

POTANDON PRODUCE LLC p 1164
1210 Pier View Dr 83402
Tel (208) 419-4200 *SIC* 5148 0161 0722

WADA FARMS MARKETING GROUP LLC p 1571
2155 Providence Way 83404
Tel (208) 542-2898 *SIC* 5148

JEROME, ID

RITE STUFF FOODS INC p 1236
2155 S Lincoln Ave 83338
Tel (208) 324-8410 *SIC* 5149

VALLEY CO-OPS INC p 1540
1833 S Lincoln Ave 83338
Tel (208) 324-8000 *SIC* 5171 5191 5251

KENDRICK, ID

■ **POTLATCH TELEPHONE CO** p 1164
702 E Main 83537
Tel (208) 289-5701 *SIC* 4813

KUNA, ID

KUNA GOOD NEIGHBORS INC p 832
12689 S Five Mile Rd 83634
Tel (208) 362-1907 *SIC* 8611

LACLEDE, ID

RILEY CREEK LUMBER CO p 1235
30 Riley Creek Rd 83841
Tel (208) 255-3200 *SIC* 5099

LEWISTON, ID

ATK SPORTING GROUP p 125
2299 Snake River Ave 83501
Tel (208) 746-2351 *SIC* 5099

EUCON CORP p 512
4201 Snake River Ave 83501
Tel (509) 533-1615 *SIC* 1442 1611

REGENCE BLUESHIELD OF IDAHO INC p 1218
1602 21st Ave 83501
Tel (208) 743-0320 *SIC* 6324

ST JOSEPH REGIONAL MEDICAL CENTER INC p 1368
415 6th St 83501
Tel (208) 743-2511 *SIC* 8062

MACKAY, ID

MACKAY JOINT SCHOOL DIST 182 p 892
411 Rose Ave 83251
Tel (208) 588-2896 *SIC* 8211

MERIDIAN, ID

BLUE CROSS OF IDAHO CARE PLUS INC p 192
3000 E Pine Ave 83642
Tel (208) 345-4550 *SIC* 6321

BLUE CROSS OF IDAHO HEALTH SERVICE INC p 192
3000 E Pine Ave 83642
Tel (208) 331-7408 *SIC* 6321

COMMERCIAL TIRE INC p 345
2095 E Commercial St 83642
Tel (208) 888-8800 *SIC* 5531 5014

ENGINEERED STRUCTURES INC p 499
3330 E Louise Dr Ste 300 83642
Tel (208) 362-3040 *SIC* 1542 1531

ES-O-EN CORP p 509
455 W Amity Rd 83642
Tel (208) 888-6428 *SIC* 5812

IDAHO PACIFIC LUMBER CO INC p 728
1770 S Spanish Sun Way 83642
Tel (208) 375-8052 *SIC* 5031

■ **IDAHO TIMBER LLC** p 728
3540 E Longwing Ln # 270 83646
Tel (208) 377-3000 *SIC* 0831

JACKSONS FOOD STORES INC p 774
3450 E Commercial Ct 83642
Tel (208) 888-6061 *SIC* 5541 5411

JOINT SCHOOL DISTRICT p 792
1303 E Central Dr 83642
Tel (208) 350-5093 *SIC* 8211

JOINT SCHOOL DISTRICT 2 p 792
1303 E Central Dr 83642
Tel (208) 855-4500 *SIC* 8211

PERFORMANCE SYSTEMS INC p 1135
2204 E Lanark St 83642
Tel (208) 287-0800 *SIC* 1542

SCENTSY INC p 1286
2701 E Pine Ave 83642
Tel (208) 472-0800 *SIC* 3999

THOMAS MANAGEMENT CORP p 1449
700 E Franklin Rd 83642
Tel (208) 884-5766 *SIC* 5963

UNITED HERITAGE FINANCIAL GROUP INC p 1509
707 E United Heritage Ct 83642
Tel (208) 493-6100 *SIC* 6311

UNITED HERITAGE LIFE INSURANCE CO p 1509
707 E Untd Heritage Ct # 130 83642
Tel (208) 475-0932 *SIC* 6311

WESTERN STATES EQUIPMENT CO p 1600
500 E Overland Rd 83642
Tel (208) 888-2287 *SIC* 5082 7699 5084

MOSCOW, ID

REGENTS OF UNIVERSITY OF IDAHO p 1219
875 Perimeter Dr Ms3020 83844
Tel (208) 885-6174 *SIC* 8221

NAMPA, ID

COLLEGE OF WESTERN IDAHO p 337
6056 Birch Ln 83687
Tel (208) 562-3200 *SIC* 8299

GAA HOLDINGS INC p 588
216 8th St N 83687
Tel (208) 465-5111 *SIC* 2038

GREAT AMERICAN SNACKS INC p 633
216 8th St N 83687
Tel (208) 465-5111 *SIC* 2038

HANSEN-RICE INC p 658
1717 E Chisholm Dr 83687
Tel (208) 465-0200 *SIC* 1541

NAMPA SCHOOL DISTRICT 131 p 1007
619 S Canyon St 83686
Tel (208) 468-4600 *SIC* 8211

SAINT ALPHONSUS MEDICAL CENTER - NAMPA HEALTH FOUNDATION INC p 1268
1512 12th Ave Rd 83686
Tel (208) 467-1171 *SIC* 8062 8011

VALLEY WIDE COOPERATIVE INC p 1541
2114 N 20th St 83687
Tel (208) 436-0141
SIC 5191 5251 5541 5171

PLUMMER, ID

COEUR DALENE TRIBE p 333
850 A St 83851
Tel (208) 686-1800 *SIC* 9131

POCATELLO, ID

AMI SEMICONDUCTOR INC p 85
2300 W Buckskin Rd 83201
Tel (208) 233-4690 *SIC* 3674 8711

FARM BUREAU MUTUAL INSURANCE CO OF IDAHO p 528
275 Tierra Vista Dr 83201
Tel (208) 232-7914 *SIC* 6331

IDAHO STATE UNIVERSITY p 728
921 S 8th Ave 83209
Tel (208) 282-0211 *SIC* 8221

IDAHO STATE UNIVERSITY p 728
1455 Flightline 83204
Tel (208) 232-8485 *SIC* 8249

POCATELLO HEALTH SYSTEM LLC p 1158
777 Hospital Way 83201
Tel (208) 239-1000 *SIC* 8062

POCATELLO/CHUBBUCK SCHOOL DISTRICT 25 p 1158
3115 Pole Line Rd 83201
Tel (208) 235-3295 *SIC* 8211

PORTNEUF MEDICAL CENTER INC p 1163
651 Memorial Dr 83201
Tel (208) 239-1000 *SIC* 8062

VARSITY CONTRACTORS INC p 1545
315 S 5th Ave 83201
Tel (208) 232-8598 *SIC* 7349

POST FALLS, ID

RAYCAP INC p 1210
806 S Clearwater Loop 83854
Tel (208) 457-0895 *SIC* 3643 5063

■ **SYSCO SPOKANE INC** p 1418
300 N Baugh Way 83854
Tel (208) 777-9511 *SIC* 5046 5141

REXBURG, ID

ARTCO (US) INC p 114
1 Stationery Pl 83441
Tel (208) 359-1000 *SIC* 5112 2759

BRIGHAM YOUNG UNIVERSITY-IDAHO p 212
525 S Center St 83460
Tel (208) 496-1901 *SIC* 8221

MOUNTAIN WEST LLC p 994
4212 S Highway 191 83440
Tel (208) 359-5640 *SIC* 1429

PREMIER PERFORMANCE LLC p 1170
278 Dividend Dr 83440
Tel (208) 356-0106 *SIC* 4923

RIGBY, ID

BROULIMS SUPER MARKET INC p 219
182 N State St 83442
Tel (208) 745-9201 *SIC* 5912

■ **IDAHO-PACIFIC CORP** p 728
4723 E 100 N 83442
Tel (208) 538-6971 *SIC* 2034

RUPERT, ID

LAND VIEW INC p 842
20504 4th St 83350
Tel (208) 531-4100
SIC 2879 2873 2874 5999 5261 5169

SANDPOINT, ID

LITEHOUSE INC p 870
100 Litehouse Dr 83864
Tel (208) 920-2000 *SIC* 2035 2033

SODA SPRINGS, ID

NU-WEST INDUSTRIES INC p 1066
3010 Conda Rd 83276
Tel (208) 547-4381 *SIC* 2874

SUN VALLEY, ID

SUN VALLEY CO p 1401
1 Sun Valley Rd 83353
Tel (208) 622-4111 *SIC* 7011 7996

TWIN FALLS, ID

EXTREME STAFFING OF IDAHO LLC p 521
651 Blue Lakes Blvd N 83301
Tel (208) 733-5627 *SIC* 7363

GLANBIA INC p 614
121 4th Ave S 83301
Tel (208) 733-7555 *SIC* 2022

RIDLEYS FOOD CORP p 1234
621 Washington St S 83301
Tel (208) 324-4633 *SIC* 5411 2099

ST LUKES MAGIC VALLEY INC p 1370
801 Pole Line Rd W 83301
Tel (208) 737-2000 *SIC* 8062 8063

TWIN FALLS SCHOOL DISTRICT 411 p 1495
201 Main Ave W 83301
Tel (208) 733-0134 *SIC* 8211

WILDER, ID

CTI FOODS ACQUISITION LLC p 399
22303 Highway 95 83676
Tel (208) 482-7844 *SIC* 2656

CTI FOODS HOLDING CO LLC p 399
22303 Highway 95 83676
Tel (208) 482-7844 *SIC* 2013 2032 2035

CTI-SSI FOOD SERVICES LLC p 399
22303 Highway 95 83676
Tel (208) 602-0937 *SIC* 2013

WORLEY, ID

SCOTT KRAMER p 1293
Hwy 95 83876
Tel (800) 523-2464 *SIC* 7011

ILLINOIS

ABBOTT PARK, IL

▲ ABBOTT LABORATORIES p 9
100 Abbott Park Rd 60064
Tel (224) 667-6100
SIC 2834 2835 3841 3826

■ ABBOTT LABORATORIES INC p 9
200 Abbott Park Rd 60064
Tel (224) 668-2076 *SIC* 2834 3841

ADDISON, IL

ARJOHUNTLEIGH INC p 109
2349 W Lake St Ste 250 60101
Tel (630) 785-4490 *SIC* 5047

ASSOCIATED MATERIAL HANDLING INDUSTRIES INC p 120
133 N Swift Rd 60101
Tel (630) 588-8800 *SIC* 5084 7699 7353

B2B COMPUTER PRODUCTS LLC p 143
313 S Rohlwing Rd 60101
Tel (630) 627-1400 *SIC* 5045

DUPAGE HIGH SCHOOL DISTRICT 88 p 462
2 Friendship Plz 60101
Tel (630) 530-3990 *SIC* 8211

■ INSIGHT PUBLIC SECTOR INC p 746
2250 W Pinehurst Blvd # 200 60101
Tel (630) 924-6801 *SIC* 5045

JD NORMAN INDUSTRIES INC p 780
787 W Belden Ave 60101
Tel (630) 458-3700 *SIC* 3469 3496 3495

■ PAMPERED CHEF LTD p 1110
140 N Swift Rd 60101
Tel (630) 261-8900 *SIC* 5963

PARTS TOWN LLC p 1118
1150 N Swift Rd Ste A 60101
Tel (708) 865-7278 *SIC* 5084

PLZ AEROSCIENCE CORP p 1157
1005 S Westgate St 60101
Tel (636) 334-9100 *SIC* 2813

PT HOLDINGS LLC p 1189
1150 N Swift Rd Ste A 60101
Tel (800) 438-8898
SIC 5084 5046 7699 6719

STAINLESS SALES CORP p 1374
2301 W Windsor Ct Unit B 60101
Tel (773) 247-9060 *SIC* 5051

STS OPERATING INC p 1394
2301 W Windsor Ct 60101
Tel (630) 317-2700 *SIC* 5084

SUNRISE ELECTRIC SUPPLY INC p 1404
130 S Addison Rd 60101
Tel (630) 543-1111 *SIC* 5063 5211

SYNCREON TECHNOLOGY (USA) LLC p 1415
1200 N Greenbriar Dr 60101
Tel (630) 261-3100 *SIC* 7389 4222

TURTLE WAX INC p 1493
2250 W Pinehurst Blvd # 150 60101
Tel (630) 455-3700 *SIC* 2842

VENUS LABORATORIES INC p 1548
111 S Rohlwing Rd 60101
Tel (630) 595-1900 *SIC* 2842 2841

ALBION, IL

CHAMPION LABORATORIES INC p 287
200 S 4th St 62806
Tel (618) 445-6011 *SIC* 3714

MCLEAN IMPLEMENT INC p 931
793 Illinois Route 130 62806
Tel (618) 445-3676 *SIC* 5083

ALGONQUIN, IL

CONSOLIDATED SCHOOL DISTRICT 158 p 360
650 Academic Dr 60102
Tel (847) 659-6158 *SIC* 8211 8741

YOUNG INNOVATIONS INC p 1638
2260 Wendt St 60102
Tel (847) 458-5400 *SIC* 3843

ALSIP, IL

ADVERTISING RESOURCES INC p 27
11601 S Central Ave 60803
Tel (708) 293-1926 *SIC* 7389

GRIFFITH FOODS GROUP INC p 640
1 Griffith Ctr 60803
Tel (708) 371-0900 *SIC* 2099

GRIFFITH FOODS INC p 640
12200 S Central Ave 60803
Tel (708) 371-0900 *SIC* 2099

GRIFFITH FOODS INTERNATIONAL INC p 640
1 Griffith Ctr 60803
Tel (708) 371-0900 *SIC* 2099 7389

GRIFFITH FOODS WORLDWIDE INC p 640
12200 S Central Ave 60803
Tel (708) 371-0900 *SIC* 2099

NUFARM AMERICAS INC p 1067
11901 S Austin Ave Ste A 60803
Tel (708) 377-1330 *SIC* 2869 2879

ULBRICH OF ILLINOIS INC p 1500
12340 S Laramie Ave 60803
Tel (708) 489-9500 *SIC* 5051

VANS INC p 1544
3730 W 131st St 60803
Tel (708) 371-8000 *SIC* 5193

ALTON, IL

ALTON MEMORIAL HOSPITAL FOUNDATION p 62
1 Memorial Dr 62002
Tel (618) 463-7311 *SIC* 8062 8059

ALTON STEEL INC p 62
5 Cut St 62002
Tel (618) 463-4490 *SIC* 3312

COPE PLASTICS INC p 368
4441 Indl Dr 62002
Tel (618) 466-0221 *SIC* 5162 3599

ANTIOCH, IL

ALUMA SYSTEMS p 63
1020 Anita Ave 60002
Tel (847) 838-4366 *SIC* 7359

ARENZVILLE, IL

BEARD IMPLEMENT CO (INC) p 165
216 W Frederick St 62611
Tel (217) 997-5514 *SIC* 5083 7699

ARGO, IL

WELDBEND CORP p 1589
6600 S Harlem Ave 60501
Tel (708) 594-1700 *SIC* 3462

ARLINGTON HEIGHTS, IL

ALEXIAN BROTHERS OF AMERICA INC p 49
3040 W Salt Creek Ln 60005
Tel (847) 640-7550 *SIC* 8742 8062 8361

BENEFICIAL CO LLC p 172
1421 W Shure Dr Ste 100 60004
Tel (708) 453-6502
SIC 6141 6351 6162 6021 6552 6311

COMMUNITY CONSOLIDATED SCHOOL DISTRICT 59 p 348
2123 S Arlington Hts Rd 60005
Tel (847) 593-4300 *SIC* 8211

COMPOSITES ONE LLC p 351
85 W Algonquin Rd Ste 600 60005
Tel (847) 437-0200 *SIC* 5162

■ DAVITA ARLINGTON HEIGHTS RENAL CENTER p 416
17 W Golf Rd 60005
Tel (847) 437-2188 *SIC* 8092

E3 DIAGNOSTICS INC p 467
3333 N Kennicott Ave 60004
Tel (847) 459-1770 *SIC* 5999

■ EUROPEAN IMPORTS INC p 513
600 E Brook Dr 60005
Tel (800) 323-3464 *SIC* 5141 5149 5147

■ GE HEALTHCARE HOLDINGS INC p 596
3350 N Ridge Ave 60004
Tel (847) 398-8400
SIC 2835 2833 5169 5122

GLS COMPOSITES DISTIBUTION CORP p 618
85 W Algonquin Rd Ste 600 60005
Tel (800) 621-8003 *SIC* 5169

GREAT LAKES SYNERGY CORP p 634
85 W Algonquin Rd Ste 600 60005
Tel (847) 437-0200 *SIC* 5084 4226 4213

GURTZ ELECTRIC CO p 648
77 W Seegers Rd 60005
Tel (847) 734-2400 *SIC* 1731

HSBC FINANCE CORP p 714
1421 W Shure Dr Ste 100 60004
Tel (224) 880-7000 *SIC* 6141

INTERTEK p 759
545 E Algonquin Rd Ste F 60005
Tel (847) 871-1020 *SIC* 8748

LUTHERAN LIFE COMMUNITIES p 886
800 W Oakton St 60004
Tel (847) 368-7400 *SIC* 8052

NORTHWEST COMMUNITY HOSPITAL FOUNDATION p 1059
800 W Central Rd 60005
Tel (847) 618-1000 *SIC* 8062

NORTHWEST COMMUNITY HOSPITAL INC p 1059
800 W Central Rd 60005
Tel (847) 618-1000 *SIC* 8062

PACE SUBURBAN BUS DIVISION OF REGIONAL TRANSPORTATION AUTHORITY p 1103
550 W Algonquin Rd 60005
Tel (847) 364-7223 *SIC* 4111

PADDOCK PUBLICATIONS INC p 1107
155 E Algonquin Rd 60005
Tel (847) 427-4300 *SIC* 2711

▲ PAYLOCITY HOLDING CORP p 1122
3850 N Wilke Rd 60004
Tel (847) 463-3200 *SIC* 7372

SYNERGY55 INC p 1415
85 W Algonquin Rd Ste 600 60005
Tel (847) 437-0200 *SIC* 8741

TOWNSHIP HIGH SCHOOL DISTRICT 214 p 1466
2121 S Goebbert Rd 60005
Tel (847) 718-7600 *SIC* 8211

WEBER MARKING SYSTEMS INC p 1586
711 W Algonquin Rd 60005
Tel (847) 364-8500 *SIC* 3555 2672 2675

ARTHUR, IL

■ C H I OVERHEAD DOORS INC p 232
1485 Sunrise Dr 61911
Tel (217) 543-2135 *SIC* 3442

■ CHI DOORS HOLDINGS INC p 296
1485 Sunrise Dr 61911
Tel (217) 543-2135 *SIC* 3442

ASHKUM, IL

MEIER OIL SERVICE INC p 940
405 N Second St 60911
Tel (815) 698-2343 *SIC* 5171 5172

ASHTON, IL

CREST FOODS CO INC p 392
905 Main St 61006
Tel (800) 435-6972 *SIC* 2023 7336

ASSUMPTION, IL

■ GSI GROUP LLC p 643
1004 E Illinois St 62510
Tel (217) 226-4421 *SIC* 5039

■ GSI HOLDINGS CORP p 643
1004 E Illinois St 62510
Tel (217) 226-4421 *SIC* 3523

SLOAN IMPLEMENT CO INC p 1331
120 N Business 51 62510
Tel (217) 226-4411 *SIC* 5083

ATLANTA, IL

CENTRAL ILLINOIS AG INC p 278
200 E Sharon St 61723
Tel (217) 648-2307 *SIC* 5999 7699

AURORA, IL

ANDY FRAIN SERVICES INC p 91
761 Shoreline Dr 60504
Tel (630) 820-3820 *SIC* 7381 7363

AURORA WEST SCHOOL DISTRICT 129 p 132
1877 W Downer Pl Ste 100 60506
Tel (630) 301-5000 *SIC* 8211

■ BRK BRANDS INC p 215
3901 Liberty St 60504
Tel (630) 851-7330 *SIC* 3669

▲ CABOT MICROELECTRONICS CORP p 235
870 N Commons Dr 60504
Tel (630) 375-6631 *SIC* 2842

CITY OF AURORA p 313
44 E Downer Pl 60505
Tel (630) 892-8811 *SIC* 9111

COPLEY MEMORIAL HOSPITAL INC p 368
2000 Ogden Ave 60504
Tel (630) 978-6200 *SIC* 8062

DRYER CANCER CENTER p 457
1221 N Highland Ave 60506
Tel (630) 264-8656 *SIC* 5047 8011

EAST AURORA SCHOOL DISTRICT 131 p 469
417 5th St 60505
Tel (630) 299-8355 *SIC* 8211

■ FIRST ALERT INC p 544
3901 Liberty St 60504
Tel (630) 851-7330
SIC 3669 3999 3446 3499 3829 3648

FOX VALLEY PRESS INC p 573
495 N Commons Dr Ste 200 60504
Tel (815) 439-5300 *SIC* 2759

HANCHETT PAPER CO p 656
4000 Ferry Rd 60502
Tel (630) 978-1000 *SIC* 5084 5199

■ HENRY PRATT CO LLC p 684
401 S Highland Ave 60506
Tel (630) 844-4000 *SIC* 3491

ILLINOIS AUTO ELECTRIC CO p 732
700 Enterprise St 60504
Tel (630) 862-3300
SIC 5084 5013 5083 5078 7699 3519

INDIAN PRAIRIE COMMUNITY UNIT SCHOOL DISTRICT p 737
780 Shoreline Dr 60504
Tel (630) 375-3000 *SIC* 8211

INEOS STYROLUTION AMERICA LLC p 740
4245 Meridian Pkwy # 151 60504
Tel (630) 820-9500 *SIC* 2869

■ LEHIGH CONSUMER PRODUCTS LLC p 853
3901 Liberty St 60504
Tel (630) 851-7330
SIC 3965 2298 3462 3452 8742

MAGNETROL INTERNATIONAL INC p 896
705 Enterprise St 60504
Tel (630) 723-6600
SIC 3823 3699 3643 3625 3541

MITUTOYO AMERICA CORP p 978
965 Corporate Blvd 60502
Tel (630) 820-9666 *SIC* 5084 7373

MIZAR HOLDING CO INC p 978
3702 Prairie Lake Ct 60504
Tel (630) 978-2500 *SIC* 5064

▲ OLD SECOND BANCORP INC p 1081
37 S River St 60506
Tel (630) 892-0202 *SIC* 6022

■ OLD SECOND NATIONAL BANK OF AURORA p 1081
37 S River St 60506
Tel (630) 844-3555 *SIC* 6021

OSI GROUP LLC p 1096
1225 Corp Blvd Ste 300 60505
Tel (630) 851-6600 *SIC* 2099

OSI INDUSTRIES LLC p 1096
1225 Corp Blvd Ste 105 60505
Tel (630) 851-6600 *SIC* 2099

RUSH-COPLEY MEDICAL CENTER INC p 1259
2000 Ogden Ave 60504
Tel (630) 978-6200 *SIC* 8062

UNITE HERE HEALTH p 1506
711 N Commons Dr 60504
Tel (630) 236-5100 *SIC* 6371

▲ WESTELL TECHNOLOGIES INC p 1597
750 N Commons Dr 60504
Tel (630) 898-2500 *SIC* 3661 4813 7389

BALDWIN, IL

■ DYNEGY MIDWEST GENERATION LLC p 465
10901 Baldwin Rd 62217
Tel (618) 785-2294 *SIC* 4911

BANNOCKBURN, IL

BAXALTA INC p 160
1200 Lakeside Dr 60015
Tel (224) 940-2000 *SIC* 2834

LTD COMMODITIES LLC p 883
2800 Lakeside Dr 60015
Tel (847) 295-6058 *SIC* 5961 5947

OPTION CARE ENTERPRISES INC p 1090
3000 Lakeside Dr Ste 300n 60015
Tel (847) 964-4950
SIC 8082 5122 6794 5912 8049

TWINS INTERNATIONAL INC p 1495
2275 Half Day Rd Ste 300 60015
Tel (847) 374-1200 *SIC* 5812

WALGREENS INFUSION SERVICES INC p 1573
3000 Lakeside Dr Ste 300n 60015
Tel (312) 940-2500
SIC 8082 8011 8059 5999 5122

BARRINGTON, IL

ALTERNATIVE RESOURCES CORP p 62
600 Hart Rd Ste 300 60010
Tel (847) 381-6701 *SIC* 7363

BARRINGTON 220 COMMUNITY UNIT SCHOOL DISTRICT p 157
310 James St 60010
Tel (847) 381-6300 *SIC* 8211

■ BARRINGTON BANK & TRUST CO NATIONAL ASSOCIATION p 157
201 S Hough St 60010
Tel (847) 842-4500 *SIC* 6022

BARRINGTON VENTURE HOLDING CO LLC p 157
6000 Garlands Ln Ste 120 60010
Tel (847) 756-3000 *SIC* 6552

MOTOR WERKS PARTNERS LP p 993
1475 S Barrington Rd 60010
Tel (847) 842-1352 *SIC* 5511 7515

ORIUS CORP p 1095
1000 Hart Rd Ste 140 60010
Tel (847) 277-8444 *SIC* 4813

BARTLETT, IL

AUTO TRUCK GROUP LLC p 133
1420 Brewster Creek Blvd 60103
Tel (630) 860-5600 *SIC* 3713 1541

CHEESE MERCHANTS OF AMERICA LLC p 292
1301 Schiferl Rd 60103
Tel (630) 221-0580 *SIC* 5143 2022

GET FRESH PRODUCE INC p 609
1441 Brewster Creek Blvd 60103
Tel (630) 837-9700 *SIC* 5148

GRECO & SONS INC p 636
1550 Hecht Dr 60103
Tel (630) 668-1000 *SIC* 5149

SENIOR HOLDINGS INC p 1304
300 E Devon Ave 60103
Tel (630) 837-1811 *SIC* 3599 2821

SENIOR OPERATIONS LLC p 1304
300 E Devon Ave 60103
Tel (630) 837-1811 *SIC* 3599

BATAVIA, IL

ALDI INC p 47
1200 N Kirk Rd 60510
Tel (630) 879-8100 *SIC* 5411

FERMI RESEARCH ALLIANCE LLC p 538
Ms 105 Wilson & Kirk Rds 60510
Tel (630) 406-7901 *SIC* 8731

FERMILAB p 538
Wilson Str And Kirk Rd 60510
Tel (630) 840-3000 *SIC* 8731

FLINN SCIENTIFIC INC p 557
770 N Raddant Rd 60510
Tel (800) 452-1261 *SIC* 3821 5049

PARKSITE INC p 1117
1563 Hubbard Ave 60510
Tel (630) 761-9490 *SIC* 5031 5162

STCHARLES TRUCKING INC p 1383
650 N Raddant Rd 60510
Tel (630) 584-4285 *SIC* 4214

SUNCAST CORP p 1401
701 N Kirk Rd 60510
Tel (630) 879-2050 *SIC* 2519 3052 3432

BEDFORD PARK, IL

HELIGEAR ACQUISITION CO p 681
6006 W 73rd St 60638
Tel (708) 728-2000 *SIC* 3724 7699

M BLOCK & SONS INC p 889
5020 W 73rd St 60638
Tel (708) 728-8400 *SIC* 5064 5023

POWER STOP LLC p 1165
6112 W 73rd St Unit C 60638
Tel (708) 575-9745 *SIC* 5013

PRAIRIE PACKAGING INC p 1167
7200 S Mason Ave 60638
Tel (708) 496-1172 *SIC* 3089 3421

PREFERRED RISK INSURANCE SERVICES INC p 1169
6640 S Cicero Ave Ste 400 60638
Tel (708) 552-2424 *SIC* 7389

BELLEVILLE, IL

BELLEVILLE BOOT CO p 170
100 Premier Dr 62220
Tel (618) 233-5600 *SIC* 3143

DICKERSON PETROLEUM INC p 438
920 N Illinois St 62220
Tel (618) 233-0786 *SIC* 5172

DICKERSON STATIONS INC p 438
920 N Illinois St 62220
Tel (618) 233-0786 *SIC* 5541 5411

EGYPTIAN AREA SCHOOLS EMPLOYEE BENEFIT TRUST p 481
1109 Hartman Ln 62221
Tel (618) 973-8221 *SIC* 8211

FKG OIL CO p 554
721 W Main St 62220
Tel (618) 233-6754 *SIC* 5541

■ **ILLINOIS-AMERICAN WATER CO** p 733
300 N Water Works Dr 62223
Tel (618) 236-1181 *SIC* 4941

PROTESTANT MEMORIAL MEDICAL CENTER INC p 1185
4500 Memorial Dr 62226
Tel (618) 233-7750 *SIC* 8062 8051

SOUTHWESTERN ILLINOIS COLLEGE COMMUNITY COLLEGE DISTRICT NO 522 p 1353
2500 Carlyle Ave 62221
Tel (618) 235-2700 *SIC* 8222 8221

ST ELIZABETHS HOSPITAL OF BELLEVILLE INC p 1366
211 S 3rd St 62220
Tel (618) 234-2120 *SIC* 8062

ST ELIZABETHS HOSPITAL OFTHIRD ORDER OF ST FRANCIS p 1366
211 S 3rd St 62220
Tel (618) 234-2120 *SIC* 8641

BENSENVILLE, IL

VICTOR ENVELOPE CO p 1555
301 Arthur Ct 60106
Tel (630) 616-2750 *SIC* 5111 5112

BERKELEY, IL

PREFERRED MEAL SYSTEMS INC p 1169
5240 Saint Charles Rd 60163
Tel (309) 697-4550 *SIC* 5963

BERWYN, IL

CHICAGO PASTRY INC p 297
6501 Roosevelt Rd 60402
Tel (708) 788-5320 *SIC* 5149 5461

■ **MAC NEAL MEMORIAL HOSPITAL ASSOCIATION** p 891
3249 Oak Park Ave 60402
Tel (708) 783-9100 *SIC* 8062

■ **VHS OF ILLINOIS INC** p 1554
3249 Oak Park Ave 60402
Tel (708) 783-9100 *SIC* 8062

BLOOMINGDALE, IL

BRIDGESTONE RETAIL OPERATIONS LLC p 211
333 E Lake St Ste 300 60108
Tel (630) 259-9000 *SIC* 5531 7534 5014

■ **INSIGHT NORTH AMERICA INC** p 746
444 Scott Dr 60108
Tel (630) 924-6700 *SIC* 5045

NOW HEALTH GROUP INC p 1064
244 Knollwood Dr Ste 300 60108
Tel (630) 545-9098 *SIC* 2834

▲ **PC-TEL INC** p 1123
471 Brighton Ct 60108
Tel (630) 372-6800 *SIC* 5731 4812 7372

BLOOMINGTON, IL

A MICHAEL OWENS INC p 6
814 W Chestnut St 61701
Tel (309) 828-7750 *SIC* 5541 4213

AFNI INC p 33
404 Brock Dr 61701
Tel (309) 828-5226 *SIC* 8742 7322

AMBERJACK LTD p 65
3 State Farm Plz 61791
Tel (309) 766-6920 *SIC* 6512 6513

BIAGGIS RISTORANTE ITALIANO LLC p 181
1705 Clearwater Ave Ste A 61704
Tel (309) 664-2148 *SIC* 5812

CC SERVICES INC p 269
1701 Towanda Ave 61701
Tel (309) 821-3372 *SIC* 8742 6411

CORN BELT ENERGY CORP p 370
1 Energy Way 61705
Tel (309) 661-1004 *SIC* 4911 4924

COUNTRY LIFE INSURANCE CO p 375
1701 Towanda Ave 61701
Tel (309) 557-3000 *SIC* 6311 6321

COUNTRY MUTUAL INSURANCE CO INC p 375
1701 Towanda Ave 61701
Tel (309) 821-3000 *SIC* 6411

FREEDOM OIL CO p 576
814 W Chestnut St 61701
Tel (309) 828-7750 *SIC* 5541

GROWMARK INC p 642
1701 Towanda Ave 61701
Tel (309) 557-6000 *SIC* 5191

HEARTLAND BANK ANDTRUST p 679
401 N Hershey Rd 61704
Tel (309) 662-4444 *SIC* 6022

HERITAGE ENTERPRISES INC p 686
115 W Jefferson St # 401 61701
Tel (309) 828-4361 *SIC* 8051

ILLINOIS AGRICULTURAL ASSOCIATION p 732
1701 Towanda Ave 61701
Tel (309) 557-2111
SIC 8611 6722 8742 6311 7514

MIDWEST FOOD BANK NFP p 967
1703 S Veterans Pkwy 61701
Tel (309) 663-5350 *SIC* 8322

OSF ST JOSEPH MEDICAL CENTER BLOOMINGTON p 1096
2200 E Washington St 61701
Tel (309) 662-3311 *SIC* 8011

STARK EXCAVATING INC p 1379
1805 W Washington St 61701
Tel (309) 828-5034 *SIC* 1611 1794

STATE FARM BANK FSB p 1380
1 State Farm Plz E 6 61701
Tel (877) 734-2265 *SIC* 6411

STATE FARM FIRE AND CASUALTY CO p 1380
Three State Frm Plz S H-4 61710
Tel (309) 766-2311 *SIC* 6411

STATE FARM FLORIDA INSURANCE CO p 1380
1 State Farm Plaza D 2 61701
Tel (309) 766-2311 *SIC* 6411

STATE FARM GENERAL INSURANCE CO INC p 1380
1 State Farm Plz 61701
Tel (309) 766-2311 *SIC* 6411

STATE FARM LIFE AND ACCIDENT ASSURANCE CO (INC) p 1381
1 State Farm Plz 61701
Tel (309) 766-2311 *SIC* 6411

STATE FARM LIFE INSURANCE CO INC p 1381
1 State Farm Plz 61701
Tel (309) 766-2311 *SIC* 6311

STATE FARM MUTUAL AUTOMOBILE INSURANCE CO p 1381
1 State Farm Plz 61710
Tel (309) 766-2311
SIC 6321 6311 6036 6331

BLUE ISLAND, IL

■ **BLUE ISLAND HOSPITAL CO LLC** p 192
12935 Gregory St 60406
Tel (708) 597-2000 *SIC* 8062

BOLINGBROOK, IL

ADVENTIST BOLINGBROOK HOSPITAL p 27
500 Remington Blvd 60440
Tel (630) 312-5000 *SIC* 8062

ATI HOLDINGS LLC p 124
790 Remington Blvd 60440
Tel (630) 296-2222 *SIC* 8049

■ **CHICAGO OFFICE TECHNOLOGY GROUP INC** p 297
3 Territorial Ct 60440
Tel (630) 378-9339 *SIC* 5044 5112

COVENANT AVIATION SECURITY LLC p 384
400 Quadrangle Dr Ste A 60440
Tel (630) 771-0800 *SIC* 7381

COVENANT SECURITY SERVICES LTD p 384
400 Quadrangle Dr Ste A 60440
Tel (630) 771-0800 *SIC* 7381

COVENANT SERVICES WORLDWIDE LLC p 384
400 Quadrangle Dr Ste A 60440
Tel (630) 771-0800 *SIC* 7381

DYWIDAG SYSTEMS INTERNATIONAL USA INC p 465
320 Marmon Dr 60440
Tel (630) 739-1100 *SIC* 5051

G & W ELECTRIC CO p 586
305 W Crossroads Pkwy 60440
Tel (708) 388-5010 *SIC* 3613 3643

MAC NEIL AUTOMOTIVE PRODUCTS LIMITED p 891
1 Macneil Ct 60440
Tel (630) 769-1500 *SIC* 5531 5013

PRESENCE HOSPITALS PRV p 1172
1000 Remington Blvd # 100 60440
Tel (877) 737-4636 *SIC* 8062

QUANTUM FOODS LLC p 1198
750 S Schmidt Rd 60440
Tel (319) 627-6000 *SIC* 8742

S&S ACTIVEWEAR LLC p 1263
581 Territorial Dr 60440
Tel (630) 679-9940 *SIC* 5136

■ **SALISBURY ELECTRICAL SAFETY LLC** p 1272
101 E Crssrads Pkwy Ste A 60440
Tel (877) 406-4501 *SIC* 3842

SCRIP HOLDING CORP p 1294
360 Veterans Pkwy Ste 115 60440
Tel (630) 771-7400 *SIC* 5047

SOUTHERN GLAZERS WINE AND SPIRITS OF ILLINOIS LLC p 1348
300 E Crossroads Pkwy 60440
Tel (630) 685-3000 *SIC* 5182

▲ **ULTA SALON COSMETICS & FRAGRANCE INC** p 1500
1000 Remington Blvd # 120 60440
Tel (630) 410-4800 *SIC* 5999 5632 5961

BOURBONNAIS, IL

■ **NUCOR STEEL KANKAKEE INC** p 1066
1 Nucor Way 60914
Tel (815) 937-3131 *SIC* 3312 3547 3449

OLIVET NAZARENE UNIVERSITY p 1082
1 University Ave 60914
Tel (815) 939-5247 *SIC* 8221

BRADLEY, IL

MONICAL PIZZA CORP p 984
530 N Kinzie Ave 60915
Tel (815) 937-1890 *SIC* 5812 6794

PEDDINGHAUS CORP p 1127
300 N Washington Ave 60915
Tel (815) 937-3800 *SIC* 3541

BREESE, IL

HAAG FOOD SERVICE INC p 651
300 N Haag St 62230
Tel (618) 526-7120 *SIC* 5142 5144 5141

POETTKER CONSTRUCTION CO p 1159
380 S Germantown Rd 62230
Tel (314) 994-0004 *SIC* 1542

BRIDGEPORT, IL

RUCKERS WHOLESALE & SERVICE CO p 1257
777 E State St 62417
Tel (618) 945-2411 *SIC* 5145

BRIDGEVIEW, IL

BRIDGEVIEW BANK GROUP p 212
7940 S Harlem Ave 60455
Tel (708) 594-7400 *SIC* 6022

▲ **MANITEX INTERNATIONAL INC** p 901
9725 Industrial Dr 60455
Tel (708) 430-7500 *SIC* 3537 3536

STAMPEDE MEAT INC p 1375
7351 S 78th Ave 60455
Tel (773) 376-4300 *SIC* 2013

VCNA PRAIRIE INC p 1545
7601 W 79th St Ste 1 60455
Tel (708) 458-0400 *SIC* 3273

BROADVIEW, IL

HEADCO INDUSTRIES INC p 673
2601 Parkes Dr 60155
Tel (708) 681-4400 *SIC* 5085 3599 5084

HUEN ELECTRIC INC p 717
1801 W 16th St 60155
Tel (708) 343-5511 *SIC* 1731

MULLINS FOOD PRODUCTS INC p 999
2200 S 25th Ave 60155
Tel (708) 344-3224 *SIC* 2033 2035

PRINCIPAL MANUFACTURING CORP p 1177
2800 S 19th Ave 60155
Tel (708) 865-7500 *SIC* 3469

ROBERT BOSCH LLC p 1241
2800 S 25th Ave 60155
Tel (248) 876-1000
SIC 3714 3694 5013 5064 3565 3541

BUFFALO GROVE, IL

ANGUS CHEMICAL CO p 91
1500 E Lake Cook Rd 60089
Tel (847) 215-8600 *SIC* 2869 2899

ARLINGTON COMPUTER PRODUCTS INC p 110
851 Commerce Ct 60089
Tel (847) 541-2475 *SIC* 5045

■ **ASAP SOFTWARE EXPRESS INC** p 115
850 Asbury Dr 60089
Tel (847) 465-3700 *SIC* 5045

■ **BPREX HEALTHCARE PACKAGING INC** p 206
600 Deerfield Pkwy 60089
Tel (800) 537-0178 *SIC* 3565

EDWARD HINES LUMBER CO p 480
1050 Corporate Grove Dr 60089
Tel (847) 353-7700 *SIC* 5031 5211

ESSEX RENTAL CORP p 510
1110 W Lake Cook Rd # 220 60089
Tel (847) 215-6500 *SIC* 7353 5082

FCC ENTERPRISES INC p 533
1641 Barclay Blvd 60089
Tel (847) 279-7360 *SIC* 7349

GLOBAL MATERIAL TECHNOLOGIES INC p 617
750 W Lake Cook Rd # 480 60089
Tel (847) 495-4700 *SIC* 3291

INDECK ENERGY SERVICES INC p 735
600 N Buffalo Grove Rd # 300 60089
Tel (847) 520-3212 *SIC* 4911

INTERNATIONAL SERVICES INC p 756
1250 Barclay Blvd 60089
Tel (847) 808-5590 *SIC* 8742

LBM BORROWER LLC p 849
1000 Corporate Grove Dr 60089
Tel (877) 787-5267 *SIC* 5031

■ **LEICA MICROSYSTEMS INC** p 854
1700 Leider Ln 60089
Tel (847) 405-0123 *SIC* 3827 3841 3821

MID OAKS INVESTMENTS LLC p 963
750 W Lake Cook Rd # 460 60089
Tel (847) 215-3475 *SIC* 6726 3089

MNJ TECHNOLOGIES DIRECT INC p 980
1025 Busch Pkwy 60089
Tel (847) 634-0700 *SIC* 5734 5045 7373

MORSE AUTOMOTIVE CORP p 990
750 W Lake Cook Rd # 480 60089
Tel (773) 843-9000 *SIC* 3714

NEMERA BUFFALO GROVE LLC p 1025
600 Deerfield Pkwy 60089
Tel (847) 541-7900 *SIC* 3841

NEMERA US HOLDING INC p 1025
600 Deerfield Pkwy 60089
Tel (847) 325-3620 *SIC* 3841

PRODUCE ALLIANCE LLC p 1179
100 Lexington Dr Ste 201 60089
Tel (847) 808-3030 *SIC* 5148

RUBY ROBINSON CO INC p 1257
100 Lexington Dr Ste 201 60089
Tel (847) 808-3030 *SIC* 5148

SIEMENS INDUSTRY INC p 1320
1000 Deerfield Pkwy 60089
Tel (847) 215-1000
SIC 3822 5063 3669 1731 7382 3625

US LBM HOLDINGS LLC p 1532
1000 Corporate Grove Dr 60089
Tel (877) 787-5267 *SIC* 5072 5031 5198

WACHS VALVE AND HYDRANT SERVICES LLC p 1570
801 Asbury Dr 60089
Tel (224) 357-2600 *SIC* 4971

BURNHAM, IL

SCRAP METAL SERVICES LLC p 1294
13830 S Brainard Ave 60633
Tel (708) 730-1400 *SIC* 5093

BURR RIDGE, IL

ANTARCTIC MECHANICAL SERVICES INC p 93
140 Tower Dr 60527
Tel (630) 887-7700 *SIC* 1711 1731

BROOKFIELD GLOBAL RELOCATION SERVICES LLC p 217
150 Harvester Dr Ste 201 60527
Tel (630) 972-2250 *SIC* 7389

DILLON TRANSPORT INC p 440
901 Mcclintock Dr Ste 300 60527
Tel (630) 281-7093 *SIC* 4212

HUMAN FACTORS APPLICATIONS INC p 718
1000 Burr Ridge Pkwy 60527
Tel (630) 850-6900 *SIC* 7363 8748

TUTHILL CORP p 1493
8500 S Madison St 60527
Tel (630) 382-4900 *SIC* 3561 3586 3524

CALUMET CITY, IL

PLASTICS COLOR CORP p 1155
14201 Paxton Ave 60409
Tel (708) 868-3800 *SIC* 3559

CAMBRIDGE, IL

GOLD STAR FS INC p 620
101 N East St 61238
Tel (309) 937-3369
SIC 5171 5153 5039 5191

CARBONDALE, IL

SOUTHERN ILLINOIS HEALTHCARE E p 1348
2370 N Mcroy Dr 62901
Tel (618) 457-5200 *SIC* 8099

SOUTHERN ILLINOIS HEALTHCARE ENTERPRISES INC p 1348
1239 E Main St Ste C 62901
Tel (618) 457-5200 *SIC* 8062

SOUTHERN ILLINOIS HOSPITAL SERVICES p 1348
1239 E Main St Ste C 62901
Tel (618) 457-5200 *SIC* 8062

SOUTHERN ILLINOIS UNIVERSITY INC p 1349
1400 Douglas Dr 62901
Tel (618) 536-3475 *SIC* 8221

SOUTHERN ILLINOIS UNIVERSITY SYSTEM p 1349
1400 Douglas Dr 62901
Tel (618) 536-3331 *SIC* 8221

CARLINVILLE, IL

M & M SERVICE CO INC p 888
130 N Chiles St 62626
Tel (217) 854-4516 *SIC* 5153 5191 5171

P F D SUPPLY CORP p 1102
1100 Broadway 62626
Tel (217) 854-2547 *SIC* 5143

PRAIRIE FARMS DAIRY INC p 1167
1100 Broadway 62626
Tel (217) 854-2547 *SIC* 2026

CARLYLE, IL

MASCHHOFFS LLC p 915
7475 State Route 127 62231
Tel (618) 594-2125 *SIC* 0213

CARMI, IL

MARTIN & BAYLEY INC p 912
1311a W Main St 62821
Tel (618) 382-2334 *SIC* 5411

CAROL STREAM, IL

AMERICAN LITHO INC p 75
175 Mercedes Dr 60188
Tel (630) 462-1700 *SIC* 2752

AVG ADVANCED TECHNOLOGIES LP p 137
343 Saint Paul Blvd 60188
Tel (630) 668-3900
SIC 3672 3661 3824 3822 3625

BLACK HORSE CARRIERS INC p 187
150 Village Ct 60188
Tel (630) 690-8900 *SIC* 4212 5159

CAPUTOS NEW FARM PRODUCE INC p 252
520 E North Ave 60188
Tel (630) 620-4444
SIC 5431 5411 5148 5149

■ **COMMUNICATIONS SUPPLY CORP** p 347
200 E Lies Rd 60188
Tel (630) 221-6400 *SIC* 4899

FIC AMERICA CORP p 540
485 E Lies Rd 60188
Tel (630) 871-7609 *SIC* 3469

INTER LOCAL PENSION FUND INC p 751
455 Kehoe Blvd Ste 100 60188
Tel (630) 752-8400 *SIC* 6371

NTA PRECISION AXLE CORP p 1065
795 Kimberly Dr 60188
Tel (630) 690-6300 *SIC* 3714

■ **PRINCE CASTLE LLC** p 1176
355 Kehoe Blvd 60188
Tel (630) 462-8800 *SIC* 3589

PRINOVA HOLDINGS LLC p 1177
285 Fullerton Ave 60188
Tel (630) 868-0300 *SIC* 8049

PRINOVA US LLC p 1177
285 Fullerton Ave 60188
Tel (630) 868-0300 *SIC* 5141

SCHMOLZ + BICKENBACH USA INC p 1287
365 Village Dr 60188
Tel (630) 682-3900 *SIC* 5051

SPECIALTY ROLLED METALS LLC p 1356
423 Saint Paul Blvd 60188
Tel (630) 871-5765 *SIC* 5051

CARPENTERSVILLE, IL

COMMUNITY UNIT SCHOOL DISTRICT 300 p 350
2550 Harnish Dr 60110
Tel (847) 426-1300 *SIC* 8211

OTTO ENGINEERING INC p 1098
2 E Main St 60110
Tel (847) 428-7171 *SIC* 3643

POLYNT COMPOSITES USA INC p 1160
99 E Cottage Ave 60110
Tel (847) 428-2657 *SIC* 2821

REVCOR INC p 1229
251 Edwards Ave 60110
Tel (847) 428-4411 *SIC* 3564 3089

TRIM-RITE FOOD CORP INC p 1480
801 Commerce Pkwy 60110
Tel (847) 649-3400 *SIC* 5147

CARRIER MILLS, IL

SOUTHEASTERN ILLINOIS ELECTRIC COOPERATIVE INC p 1346
100 Cooperative Way 62917
Tel (618) 273-2611 *SIC* 4911

CARY, IL

■ **SAGE PRODUCTS LLC** p 1267
3909 3 Oaks Rd 60013
Tel (815) 455-4700 *SIC* 3842 5047

CENTRALIA, IL

ST MARYS-GOOD SAMARITAN INC p 1372
400 N Pleasant Ave 62801
Tel (618) 436-8000 *SIC* 8062

CHAMPAIGN, IL

BIRKEYS FARM STORE INC p 185
2102 W Park Ct 61821
Tel (217) 693-7200 *SIC* 5083 5082 5511

■ **BUSEY BANK** p 229
100 W University Ave # 100 61820
Tel (217) 365-4500 *SIC* 6022

CHAMPAIGN COMMUNITY UNIT SCHOOL DISTRICT 4 (INC) p 287
703 S New St 61820
Tel (217) 351-3800 *SIC* 8211 8351

CHRISTIE CLINIC LLC p 303
101 W University Ave 61820
Tel (217) 366-1200 *SIC* 8011

▲ **FIRST BUSEY CORP** p 545
100 W University Ave 61820
Tel (217) 365-4544 *SIC* 6022

HOBBICO INC p 698
1608 Interstate Dr 61822
Tel (217) 398-3630 *SIC* 5092 5961

HORIZON HOBBY LLC p 707
4105 Fieldstone Rd 61822
Tel (217) 352-1913 *SIC* 5092

MIDWEST UNDERGROUND TECHNOLOGY INC p 968
2626 Midwest Ct 61822
Tel (217) 819-3040 *SIC* 1731 1623

PREMIER COOPERATIVE INC p 1170
2104 W Park Ct 61821
Tel (217) 355-1983 *SIC* 5153 5191

TRI STAR MARKETING INC p 1477
2211 W Bradley Ave 61821
Tel (217) 367-8386 *SIC* 5541 5411 5172

VESUVIUS CRUCIBLE CO p 1552
1404 Newton Dr 61822
Tel (217) 351-5000 *SIC* 3297 5051

VESUVIUS U S A CORP p 1552
1404 Newton Dr 61822
Tel (217) 402-9204 *SIC* 3297 5085

CHANNAHON, IL

DIVERSIFIED CPC INTERNATIONAL INC p 444
24338 W Durkee Rd 60410
Tel (815) 423-5991 *SIC* 2813 5169

LODERS CROKLAAN USA LLC p 873
24708 W Durkee Rd 60410
Tel (815) 730-5200 *SIC* 2079

CHARLESTON, IL

EASTERN ILLINOIS UNIVERSITY p 472
600 Lincoln Ave 61920
Tel (217) 581-5000 *SIC* 8221 5812

CHATHAM, IL

HENRY TECHNOLOGIES INC p 684
701 S Main St 62629
Tel (217) 483-2406
SIC 3491 3585 3567 3564 3545 3494

CHESTER, IL

GILSTER-MARY LEE CORP p 612
1037 State St 62233
Tel (618) 826-2361
SIC 2043 2098 2099 2045 3089

CHICAGO HEIGHTS, IL

CHS ACQUISITION CORP p 304
211 E Main St 60411
Tel (708) 756-5648 *SIC* 3312

ESMARK STEEL GROUP LLC p 509
2500 Euclid Ave 60411
Tel (708) 756-0400 *SIC* 5051

JDM STEEL SERVICE INC p 781
330 E Joe Orr Rd Unit 3 60411
Tel (708) 757-2092 *SIC* 5051 4225

K R DRENTH TRUCKING INC p 799
20340 Stoney Island Ave 60411
Tel (708) 757-3333 *SIC* 4212

■ **SUGAR STEEL CORP** p 1397
2521 State St Ste 1 60411
Tel (708) 757-9500 *SIC* 5051

CHICAGO RIDGE, IL

RESOURCE MANAGEMENT ENTERPRISES INC p 1227
9999 Anderson Ave 60415
Tel (708) 425-8565 *SIC* 4953

CHICAGO, IL

A B M INC p 5
180 N Lasalle St Ste 1700 60601
Tel (312) 469-1643 *SIC* 7349

A EPSTEIN AND SONS INTERNATIONAL INC p 5
600 W Fulton St Ste 800 60661
Tel (312) 454-9100
SIC 8711 8712 7389 1542 1541 8742

A FINKL & SONS CO p 5
1355 E 93rd St 60619
Tel (773) 975-2510 *SIC* 3312

A T KEARNEY INC p 6
227 W Monroe St 60606
Tel (312) 648-0111 *SIC* 8742

ABN AMRO CLEARING CHICAGO LLC p 12
175 W Jackson Blvd # 400 60604
Tel (312) 604-8000 *SIC* 6289

ACCENTURE INC p 14
161 N Clark St Ste 1100 60601
Tel (312) 737-8842 *SIC* 7379 7389 8742

ACCENTURE LLC p 14
161 N Clark St Ste 1100 60601
Tel (312) 693-0161 *SIC* 7379 7389 8742

ACCENTURE LLP p 14
161 N Clark St Ste 1100 60601
Tel (312) 693-0161 *SIC* 8742

ACCENTURE SUB INC p 14
161 N Clark St Ste 1100 60601
Tel (312) 693-0161 *SIC* 8742

ACCESS COMMUNITY HEALTH NETWORK p 14
600 W Fulton St Ste 200 60661
Tel (312) 526-2200 *SIC* 8011

ACCRETIVE HEALTH INC p 15
401 N Michigan Ave # 2700 60611
Tel (312) 324-7820 *SIC* 8741

ACCRETIVE SOLUTIONS INC p 16
1 S Wacker Dr Ste 950 60606
Tel (312) 994-4600 *SIC* 8721

ACCRETIVE SOLUTIONS OPERATING CORP p 16
1 S Wacker Dr Ste 950 60606
Tel (312) 994-4600 *SIC* 8721 7363 7361

ADDISON PROFESSIONAL FINANCIAL SEARCH LLC p 22
125 S Wacker Dr Fl 27 60606
Tel (312) 424-0300 *SIC* 7363

■ **ADM INVESTOR SERVICES INC** p 23
141 W Jackson Blvd 2100a 60604
Tel (312) 242-7000 *SIC* 6221

ADVANCE ELECTRICAL SUPPLY CO LLC p 24
263 N Oakley Blvd 60612
Tel (312) 421-2300 *SIC* 5063

ADVANCED EQUITIES FINANCIAL CORP p 25
200 S Wacker Dr Ste 3200 60606
Tel (312) 377-5300 *SIC* 6211

ADVOCATE HEALTH CENTERS INC p 28
2545 S Mrtn Lther King Dr 60616
Tel (312) 842-7117 *SIC* 8011

■ **AERIAL COMMUNICATIONS INC** p 30
8410 W Bryn Mawr Ave 60631
Tel (773) 399-4200 *SIC* 4812

■ **AETNA HEALTH OF ILLINOIS INC** p 31
100 N Riverside Plz Fl 20 60606
Tel (312) 928-3000 *SIC* 6324

AJINOMOTO HEARTLAND INC p 41
8430 W Bryn Mawr Ave 60631
Tel (773) 380-7000 *SIC* 5159

AKZO NOBEL CHEMICALS LLC p 42
525 W Van Buren St # 1600 60607
Tel (312) 544-7000 *SIC* 2841

AKZO NOBEL FUNCTIONAL CHEMICAL LLC p 42
525 W Van Buren St # 1600 60607
Tel (312) 544-7000 *SIC* 2869

AKZO NOBEL INC p 42
525 W Van Buren St Fl 16 60607
Tel (312) 544-7000
SIC 2869 2851 2834 3841 3826 2819

AKZO NOBEL POLYMER CHEM LLC p 42
525 W Van Buren St # 1600 60607
Tel (312) 544-7000 *SIC* 2869

ALDEN MANAGEMENT SERVICES INC p 47
4200 W Peterson Ave # 142 60646
Tel (773) 282-8183 *SIC* 8051 8741

ALDEN-WENTWORTH NURSING CENTER INC p 47
201 W 69th St 60621
Tel (773) 487-1200 *SIC* 8051

ALFRED BENESCH & CO p 49
205 N Michigan Ave # 2400 60601
Tel (312) 565-2497 *SIC* 8711

ALLIANT CREDIT UNION FOUNDATION p 55
11545 W Touhy Ave 60666
Tel (800) 328-1935 *SIC* 6062 6061

▲ **ALLSCRIPTS HEALTHCARE SOLUTIONS INC** p 58
222 Merchandise Mart Plz 60654
Tel (312) 506-1200 *SIC* 7372

ALPHA BAKING CO INC p 60
5001 W Polk St 60644
Tel (773) 489-5400 *SIC* 2051

AMER SPORTS CO p 66
8750 W Bryn Mawr Ave 60631
Tel (773) 714-6400 *SIC* 3949

AMERICAN BAR ASSOCIATION p 68
321 N Clark St Ste Ll2 60654
Tel (312) 988-5000 *SIC* 8621 2721 2731

■ **AMERICAN CASUALTY CO OF READING PENNSYLVANIA INC** p 70
333 S Wabash Ave Fl 22 60604
Tel (312) 822-5000 *SIC* 6411

AMERICAN COLLEGE OF SURGEONS INC p 70
633 N Saint Clair St # 2600 60611
Tel (312) 202-5000 *SIC* 8621

AMERICAN DENTAL ASSOCIATION p 71
211 E Chicago Ave 60611
Tel (312) 440-2500 *SIC* 8621

AMERICAN HOSPITAL ASSOCIATION p 74
155 N Wacker Dr Ste 400 60606
Tel (312) 422-3000 *SIC* 2721 2731 8099

■ **AMERICAN IMAGING MANAGEMENT INC** p 74
8600 W Bryn Mawr Ave 800s 60631
Tel (773) 864-4600 *SIC* 6321

AMERICAN MEDICAL ASSOCIATION INC p 76
330 N Wabash Ave # 39300 60611
Tel (312) 464-5000
SIC 8621 2721 6321 6282

AMERICAN TRANSPORT GROUP LLC p 80
1900 W Kinzie St 60622
Tel (773) 235-9600 *SIC* 4731

■ **AMERITECH PAYPHONE SERVICES OF MICHIGAN INC** p 84
225 W Randolph St 60606
Tel (708) 458-8460 *SIC* 4813

■ **AMERITECH SERVICES INC** p 84
208 S Lasalle St Ste 814 60604
Tel (847) 248-2000
SIC 7389 4225 8742 8721

■ **AMLI RESIDENTIAL PROPERTIES LP** p 85
141 W Jackson Blvd # 300 60604
Tel (312) 283-4700 *SIC* 6798

AMOCO OIL HOLDING CO p 86
200 E Randolph St 60601
Tel (312) 856-4650 *SIC* 8699 4953

AMSTED INDUSTRIES INC p 87
180 N Stetson Ave 60601
Tel (312) 645-1700
SIC 3443 3325 3585 3321 3743

AMSTED RAIL CO INC p 87
311 S Wacker Dr Ste 5300 60606
Tel (312) 922-4501 *SIC* 3743

ANN & ROBERT H LURIE CHILDRENS HOSPITAL OF CHICAGO p 92
225 E Chicago Ave 60611
Tel (312) 227-7132 *SIC* 8011 8069

ANTHONY MARANO CO p 94
3000 S Ashland Ave # 100 60608
Tel (773) 321-7500 *SIC* 5148

AON BENFIELD FAC INC p 94
200 E Randolph St Fl 15 60601
Tel (312) 381-5300 *SIC* 6321 6311

AON CORP p 95
200 E Randolph St 60601
Tel (312) 381-1000 *SIC* 6411 8742

AON GROUP INC p 95
200 E Randolph St Fl 5 60601
Tel (312) 381-2738 *SIC* 6311 8742 6411

AON HEWITT LLC p 95
200 E Randolph St Ll3 60601
Tel (312) 381-1000 *SIC* 8742 8999

AON RISK SERVICES COMPANIES INC p 95
200 E Randolph St Fl 14 60601
Tel (312) 381-1000 *SIC* 6411 8111

AON SOLUTIONS INC p 95
200 E Randolph St 60601
Tel (312) 381-1000 *SIC* 6411

AON US HOLDINGS INC p 95
200 E Randolph St 60601
Tel (312) 381-1000 *SIC* 6411 6799 8741

ARBOR PRIVATE INVESTMENT CO LLC p 103
676 N Michigan Ave # 3410 60611
Tel (312) 981-3770 *SIC* 6726

ARCELOR USA HOLDING INC p 104
1 S Dearborn St Ste 1800 60603
Tel (312) 899-3400 *SIC* 5051

ARCELORMITTAL USA LLC p 104
1 S Dearborn St Ste 1800 60603
Tel (312) 346-0300
SIC 3312 3325 3356 3316

ARCHER WESTERN CONSTRUCTION LLC p 105
929 W Adams St 60607
Tel (312) 563-5400
SIC 1521 1622 1629 1542

▲ ARCHER-DANIELS-MIDLAND CO p 105
77 W Wacker Dr Ste 4600 60601
Tel (312) 634-8100
SIC 2046 2041 2075 2074 5153 2083

ARDAGH METAL BEVERAGE USA INC p 106
8770 W Bryn Mawr Ave # 175 60631
Tel (773) 399-3000 *SIC* 3411

ART INSTITUTE OF CHICAGO p 113
111 S Michigan Ave 60603
Tel (312) 443-3600 *SIC* 8412 8299

ASSISTED LIVING CONCEPTS LLC p 119
330 N Wabash Ave Ste 3700 60611
Tel (888) 252-5001
SIC 8052 8051 8059 8082

ASSOCIATED GROUP HOLDINGS LLC p 120
30 S Wacker Dr Ste 1600 60606
Tel (312) 662-5488 *SIC* 3448

■ AT&T TELEHOLDINGS INC p 123
30 S Wacker Dr Fl 34 60606
Tel (800) 257-0902
SIC 4813 4812 2741 5065 6159 7382

ATLAS HOLDING INC p 128
1855 E 122nd St 60633
Tel (773) 646-4500 *SIC* 3317

ATLAS TUBE (CHICAGO) LLC p 128
1855 E 122nd St 60633
Tel (773) 646-4500 *SIC* 3317 3644

AVANT INC p 136
222 N Lsalle St Ste 1700 60601
Tel (312) 448-8685 *SIC* 6141

AVIV HEALTHCARE PROPERTIES LIMITED PARTNERSHIP p 138
303 W Madison St 60606
Tel (312) 855-0930 *SIC* 8099

AVIV REIT INC p 138
303 W Madison St Ste 2400 60606
Tel (312) 855-0930 *SIC* 6798

B C S INSURANCE CO p 141
676 N Saint Clair St # 1500 60611
Tel (312) 371-6006 *SIC* 6321

BADGER FARMS INC p 143
652 N Western Ave 60612
Tel (773) 278-9100
SIC 5143 5149 5147 5144 5142 5087

BAGCRAFTPAPERCON I LLC p 144
3900 W 43rd St 60632
Tel (620) 856-2800
SIC 2671 2674 2673 3497 2759

BAGCRAFTPAPERCON LLC p 144
3900 W 43rd St 60632
Tel (773) 843-8000 *SIC* 8741

BAKER & MCKENZIE LLP p 145
300 E Randolph St # 5000 60601
Tel (312) 861-8000 *SIC* 8111

BAKER TILLY VIRCHOW KRAUSE LLP p 146
205 N Michigan Ave # 2800 60601
Tel (312) 729-8000 *SIC* 8721

BALLY TOTAL FITNESS HOLDING CORP p 149
8700 W Bryn Mawr Ave 620n 60631
Tel (773) 380-3000 *SIC* 7991

■ BANC ONE CAPITAL MARKETS INC p 149
1 Bank One Plz 60670
Tel (800) 992-7169 *SIC* 6211 6282

■ BANC ONE FINANCIAL LLC p 149
1 Chase Tower 60670
Tel (312) 732-5531 *SIC* 6211 6153

■ BANKERS LIFE & CASUALTY CO p 152
111 E Wacker Dr Ste 2100 60601
Tel (312) 396-6000 *SIC* 6321 6311 6324

BARCODES LLC p 155
200 W Monroe St Ste 1050 60606
Tel (312) 588-5960 *SIC* 5065

BARRY CALLEBAUT USA LLC p 157
600 W Chicago Ave Ste 860 60654
Tel (312) 496-7491 *SIC* 2066 8741

BATHXCESSORIES INC p 159
1481 N Larrabee St 60610
Tel (312) 951-2885 *SIC* 5099

BATTAGLIA DISTRIBUTING CORP INC p 159
2500 S Ashland Ave 60608
Tel (312) 738-1111 *SIC* 5141

BDO USA LLP p 164
130 E Randolph St # 2800 60601
Tel (312) 240-1236 *SIC* 8721

BDT CAPITAL PARTNERS LLC p 164
401 N Michigan Ave # 3100 60611
Tel (312) 660-7311 *SIC* 6799

BEECKEN PETTY OKEEFE & CO LLC p 168
131 S Dearborn St Ste 122 60603
Tel (312) 435-0300 *SIC* 6799 3841

BEL BRANDS USA INC p 169
30 S Wacker Dr Ste 3000 60606
Tel (312) 462-1500 *SIC* 2022

BELAIR HD STUDIOS LLC p 169
2233 S Throop St 60608
Tel (312) 254-5188 *SIC* 7335 2711

BERGLUND CONSTRUCTION CO p 174
8410 S South Chicago Ave 60617
Tel (773) 374-1000 *SIC* 1542

BERLIN PACKAGING LLC p 175
525 W Monroe St Ste 1400 60661
Tel (312) 876-9292 *SIC* 5085

BEST FOOD SERVICES INC p 177
7131 W 61st St 60638
Tel (773) 966-1123 *SIC* 5149

BLUE CROSS & BLUE SHIELD ASSOCIATION p 191
225 N Michigan Ave Fl 5 60601
Tel (312) 297-6000 *SIC* 8621 6324

BMM LOGISTICS INC p 194
209 W Jackson Blvd # 903 60606
Tel (312) 730-7495 *SIC* 4731

BMO BANKCORP INC p 194
111 W Monroe St 60603
Tel (312) 461-2121 *SIC* 6021 6211

BMO FINANCIAL CORP p 194
111 W Monroe St Ste 1200 60603
Tel (312) 461-2121 *SIC* 6021 6082 6211

BOARD OF EDUCATION OF CITY OF CHICAGO p 195
125 S Clark St Fl 14 60603
Tel (773) 553-2760 *SIC* 8211

BOARD OF EDUCATION OF CITY OF CHICAGO p 195
42 W Madison St Fl 2 60602
Tel (773) 553-1000 *SIC* 8211

■ BOARD OF TRADE OF CITY OF CHICAGO p 195
141 W Jackson Blvd 756 60604
Tel (312) 435-3500 *SIC* 6231

BOARD OF TRUSTEES OF COMMUNITY COLLEGE DISTRICT 508 (INC) p 196
226 W Jackson Blvd # 103 60606
Tel (312) 553-2752 *SIC* 8221 8222

▲ BOEING CO p 197
100 N Riverside Plz 60606
Tel (312) 544-2000
SIC 3721 3663 3761 3764 3812 3728

■ BOEING IRVING CO p 197
100 N Riverside Plz Fl 35 60606
Tel (312) 544-2000 *SIC* 3663

BRAIN HURRICANE LLC p 207
2510 S Christiana Ave 60623
Tel (312) 577-0066 *SIC* 8299

BRANDENBURG INDUSTRIAL SERVICE CO p 208
2625 S Loomis St 60608
Tel (312) 326-5800 *SIC* 4959 1795 5093

■ BRIDGFORD FOODS CORP p 212
170 N Green St 60607
Tel (312) 733-0300 *SIC* 2013

■ BRUSS CO p 221
3548 N Kostner Ave 60641
Tel (773) 282-2900
SIC 5147 5142 2013 2011

■ BSWIFT LLC p 222
10 S Riverside Plz # 1100 60606
Tel (312) 261-5750 *SIC* 6371 7373

BULLEY & ANDREWS p 225
1755 W Armitage Ave 60622
Tel (773) 235-2433 *SIC* 1542 1541

BULLEY & ANDREWS LLC p 225
1755 W Armitage Ave 60622
Tel (312) 207-2100 *SIC* 1541 1542

■ BUSINESS PROPERTY LENDING INC p 229
500 W Monroe St 60661
Tel (312) 441-7000
SIC 6153 6799 6162 6159

BWAY INTERMEDIATE CO INC p 231
3 First National Plz 60602
Tel (312) 895-1000 *SIC* 6719

BWAY PARENT CO INC p 231
3200 S Kilbourn Ave 60623
Tel (773) 890-3300 *SIC* 3411 3089

BYLINE BANCORP INC p 231
180 N La Salle St Ste 300 60601
Tel (773) 843-7800 *SIC* 6712 6162

BYLINE BANK p 231
3639 N Broadway St 60613
Tel (773) 244-7000 *SIC* 6022 6163 6021

CARE CAPITAL PROPERTIES INC p 254
191 N Wacker Dr Ste 1200 60606
Tel (312) 881-4700 *SIC* 6798

■ CAREERBUILDER LLC p 254
200 N La Salle St # 1100 60601
Tel (773) 527-3600 *SIC* 7361

■ CARS.COM LLC p 261
175 W Jackson Blvd Fl 8 60604
Tel (312) 601-5000 *SIC* 7313

CARYLON CORP p 262
2500 W Arthington St 60612
Tel (312) 666-7700
SIC 7699 1629 7349 8748 4959

CATHOLIC BISHOP OF CHICAGO p 265
835 N Rush St 60611
Tel (312) 534-8200 *SIC* 8661

CATHOLIC CHARITIES OF ARCHDIOCESE OF CHICAGO p 266
721 N La Salle Dr 60654
Tel (312) 655-7000 *SIC* 8399

CATHOLIC CHURCH EXTENSION SOCIETY OF UNITED STATES OF AMERICA p 266
150 S Wacker Dr Ste 2000 60606
Tel (312) 236-7240 *SIC* 8661

▲ CBOE HOLDINGS INC p 269
400 S Lasalle St 60605
Tel (312) 786-5600 *SIC* 6231

■ CBOT HOLDINGS INC p 269
141 W Jackson Blvd 60604
Tel (312) 435-3500 *SIC* 6231

CC INDUSTRIES INC p 269
222 N La Salle St # 1000 60601
Tel (312) 855-4000 *SIC* 6552

CCC INFORMATION SERVICES INC p 269
222 Mchds Mart Plz 900 60654
Tel (312) 222-4636 *SIC* 7371

■ CELTIC GROUP INC p 274
233 S Wacker Dr Ste 700 60606
Tel (312) 332-5401 *SIC* 6321 6311

■ CELTIC INSURANCE CO p 274
233 S Wacker Dr Ste 700 60606
Tel (312) 332-5401 *SIC* 6311

▲ CENTRAL STEEL AND WIRE CO p 280
3000 W 51st St 60632
Tel (773) 471-3800 *SIC* 5051

▲ CENTURY ALUMINUM CO p 281
1 S Wacker Dr Ste 1000 60606
Tel (312) 696-3101 *SIC* 3334

CHAPMAN AND CUTLER LLP p 288
111 W Monroe St Ste 1700 60603
Tel (312) 845-3000 *SIC* 8111

CHICAGO & ILLINOIS RIVER MARKETING LLC p 297
141 W Jackson Blvd Ste 2800 60604
Tel (312) 341-3174 *SIC* 5153

■ CHICAGO BOARD OPTIONS EXCHANGE INC p 297
400 S La Salle St Fl 1 60605
Tel (312) 786-5600 *SIC* 6211 6231

CHICAGO CHARTER SCHOOL FOUNDATION p 297
11 E Adams St Ste 600 60603
Tel (312) 455-7890 *SIC* 7389

CHICAGO COMMUNITY TRUST p 297
225 N Michigan Ave # 2200 60601
Tel (312) 616-8000 *SIC* 8641

CHICAGO GROWTH PARTNERS II LP p 297
222 Merchandise Mart Plz # 1871 60654
Tel (312) 698-6300 *SIC* 6799

CHICAGO HOUSING AUTHORITY p 297
60 E Van Buren St Fl 10 60605
Tel (312) 791-8500 *SIC* 9531

CHICAGO MEAT AUTHORITY INC p 297
1120 W 47th Pl 60609
Tel (773) 254-3811 *SIC* 2011

■ CHICAGO MERCANTILE EXCHANGE INC p 297
20 S Wacker Dr 60606
Tel (312) 930-1000 *SIC* 6231

CHICAGO METALLIC CO LLC p 297
4849 S Austin Ave 60638
Tel (708) 563-4600 *SIC* 3446 5033

CHICAGO METALLIC CORP p 297
4849 S Austin Ave 60638
Tel (708) 563-4600 *SIC* 3446 5033

CHICAGO PARK DISTRICT p 297
541 N Fairbanks Ct # 300 60611
Tel (312) 742-7529 *SIC* 7999

CHICAGO PUBLIC SCHOOLS p 297
42 W Madison St 60602
Tel (773) 553-1000 *SIC* 8211

CHICAGO REVIEW PRESS INC p 297
814 N Franklin St Ste 100 60610
Tel (312) 337-0747 *SIC* 5192 2731

CHICAGO SCHOOL OF PROFESSIONAL PSYCHOLOGY p 297
325 N Wells St Fl 4 60654
Tel (312) 379-1699 *SIC* 8221

CHICAGO STATE UNIVERSITY p 297
9501 S King Dr 60628
Tel (773) 995-2000 *SIC* 8221

CHICAGO SUN-TIMES FEATURES INC p 297
350 N Orleans St Fl 10 60654
Tel (312) 321-3000 *SIC* 2711 2752

■ CHICAGO TITLE AND TRUST CO p 297
10 S La Salle St Ste 3100 60603
Tel (312) 223-2000 *SIC* 6361

■ CHICAGO TITLE INSURANCE CO p 297
10 S Lasalle St Ste 2850 60603
Tel (312) 223-2402 *SIC* 6411 6361

CHICAGO TRANSIT AUTHORITY p 298
567 W Lake St Ste Cta 60661
Tel (312) 664-7200 *SIC* 4111 4789

■ CHICAGO TRIBUNE CO p 298
435 N Michigan Ave # 200 60611
Tel (312) 222-3232
SIC 2711 7383 7389 7331

■ CHICAGO TRIBUNE NEWSPAPERS INC p 298
435 N Michigan Ave # 200 60611
Tel (312) 222-3232 *SIC* 7313

CHILDRENS HOSPITAL OF CHICAGO MEDICAL CENTER p 299
225 E Chicago Ave 60611
Tel (312) 227-4000 *SIC* 8062 8733

CHRISTIAN BROTHERS INVESTMENT SERVICES INC p 302
20 N Wacker Dr Ste 2000 60606
Tel (312) 526-3343 *SIC* 6282

CHS CAPITAL LLC p 304
300 N La Salle Dr # 4925 60654
Tel (312) 876-1840 *SIC* 5084

CHS PRIVATE EQUITY V LP p 304
300 N La Salle Dr # 4925 60654
Tel (312) 876-1840 *SIC* 5085

■ CIGNA HEALTHCARE OF ILLINOIS INC p 306
525 W Monroe St Ste 1800 60661
Tel (312) 496-5340 *SIC* 6324

CIM TRUCKING INC p 307
2232 S Blue Island Ave 60608
Tel (773) 927-6611 *SIC* 4212

CISION US INC p 309
130 E Randolph St Fl 7 60601
Tel (312) 922-2400 *SIC* 7389 2741 7331

CITADEL LLC p 309
131 S Dearborn St Ste 200 60603
Tel (312) 395-2100 *SIC* 6211

CITY OF CHICAGO p 314
121 N La Salle St 60602
Tel (312) 744-5000 *SIC* 9111

CITY POINT REALTY LLC p 319
1275 N Clybourn Ave 60610
Tel (312) 255-1500 *SIC* 6531

CIVC PARTNERS LP p 320
191 N Wacker Dr Ste 1100 60606
Tel (312) 521-2000 *SIC* 8742 6799

CLASSIC RIVERDALE INC p 323
200 W Madison St Ste 3700 60606
Tel (312) 803-8800 *SIC* 7011

CLAYCO INC p 323
35 E Wacker Dr Ste 1300 60601
Tel (312) 658-0747 *SIC* 1541

CLUNE CONSTRUCTION CO LP p 328
10 S Riverside Plz # 2200 60606
Tel (312) 609-3635 *SIC* 1542

▲ CME GROUP INC p 329
20 S Wacker Dr 60606
Tel (312) 930-1000 *SIC* 6231

■ CNA FINANCIAL CORP p 329
333 S Wabash Ave Ste 300 60604
Tel (312) 822-5000 *SIC* 6411 6331 6311

■ CNA FOUNDATION p 329
333 S Wabash Ave Fl 1 60604
Tel (312) 822-5000 *SIC* 6331

■ CNA SURETY CORP p 330
333 S Wabash Ave Ste 41s 60604
Tel (312) 822-5000 *SIC* 6411

CNLC-STC INC p 330
350 N Orleans St 60654
Tel (312) 321-3000 *SIC* 2711

COBRA ELECTRONICS CORP p 333
6500 W Cortland St 60707
Tel (773) 889-8870 *SIC* 5999

▲ COEUR MINING INC p 333
104 S Michigan Ave # 900 60603
Tel (312) 489-5800 *SIC* 1041 1044

COLOR COMMUNICATIONS INC p 338
4000 W Fillmore St 60624
Tel (773) 638-1400 *SIC* 2752 3993

COLSON ASSOCIATES INC p 339
1 N Franklin St Ste 2420 60606
Tel (312) 980-1100 *SIC* 8748

COLSON GROUP INC p 339
1 N Franklin St Ste 2420 60606
Tel (312) 980-1100 *SIC* 3429

COLUMBIA COLLEGE CHICAGO p 340
600 S Michigan Ave Fl 5 60605
Tel (312) 663-1600 *SIC* 8221

COLUMBIA PIPE & SUPPLY CO p 341
1120 W Pershing Rd 60609
Tel (773) 927-6600 *SIC* 5051 5085 5074

COMBINED INSURANCE CO OF AMERICA p 343
200 E Randolph St Lbby 10 60601
Tel (800) 225-4500 *SIC* 6321 6311

■ COMMAND TRANSPORTATION LLC p 344
600 W Chicago Ave Ste 725 60654
Tel (847) 213-2200 *SIC* 4731

■ COMMONWEALTH EDISON CO p 346
440 S La Salle St 60605
Tel (312) 394-4321 *SIC* 4911

COMMUNITY AND ECONOMIC DEVELOPMENT ASSOCIATION OF COOK COUNTY INC p 347
567 W Lake St Ste 1200 60661
Tel (312) 795-8844 *SIC* 8748

COMMUNITY FIRST MEDICAL CENTER p 348
5645 W Addison St 60634
Tel (773) 282-7000 *SIC* 8062

COMPSYCH EMPLOYEE ASSISTANCE PROGRAMS INC p 352
455 N Ctyfrnt Plz Dr # 1300 60611
Tel (312) 595-4000 *SIC* 8742

COMPUTERSHARE LLC p 353
2 N La Salle St Ste 200 60602
Tel (312) 588-4992 *SIC* 6289

▲ CONAGRA BRANDS INC p 354
222 Merchandise Mart Plz 60654
Tel (312) 549-5000 *SIC* 2099 2038 2013

■ CONAGRA DAIRY FOODS CO INC p 354
222 Merchandise Mart Plz 60654
Tel (630) 848-0975 *SIC* 2022

CONSOLIDATED ENTERPRISES INC p 359
680 N Lake Shore Dr Fl 19 60611
Tel (312) 943-7000 *SIC* 5182

CONTINENTAL ASSURANCE CO p 362
333 S Wabash Ave Fl 43 60604
Tel (312) 822-5000 *SIC* 6411 6371 6321

■ CONTINENTAL CASUALTY CO INC p 363
333 S Wabash Ave Ste 300 60604
Tel (312) 822-5000 *SIC* 6331

▲ CONTINENTAL MATERIALS CORP p 363
440 S La Salle St # 3100 60605
Tel (312) 541-7200 *SIC* 3585 3273 5031

CONTINENTAL PAPER GRADING CO p 363
1623 S Lumber St 60616
Tel (312) 226-2010 *SIC* 5093

COOK COUNTY BUREAU OF HEALTH SERVICES p 365
1900 W Polk St Ste 220 60612
Tel (312) 864-7571 *SIC* 9431

COUNTY OF COOK p 377
118 N Clark St 60602
Tel (312) 603-5500 *SIC* 9111

COVERIS HOLDING CORP p 385
8600 W Bryn Mawr Ave 60631
Tel (773) 877-3300 *SIC* 6719 2673 2631

■ COYOTE LOGISTICS LLC p 387
2545 W Diversey Ave Fl 3 60647
Tel (877) 626-9683 *SIC* 4731

CPI BUYER LLC p 387
300 N La Salle Dr # 5600 60654
Tel (312) 382-2200 *SIC* 5049

CROWE HORWATH LLP p 394
225 W Wacker Dr Ste 2600 60606
Tel (312) 899-7000 *SIC* 8721

CROWN GOLF PROPERTIES LP p 395
222 N La Salle St # 2000 60601
Tel (312) 395-7701 *SIC* 8742 1629

■ CROWN IMPORTS LLC p 395
1 S Dearborn St Ste 1700 60603
Tel (312) 873-9600 *SIC* 5181

CT ASSOCIATES OF ILLINOIS LP p 399
2061 N Campbell Ave Ofc 60647
Tel (773) 486-3666 *SIC* 6531 6513

CT TECHNOLOGIES HOLDINGS INC p 399
875 N Michigan Ave 60611
Tel (770) 360-1700 *SIC* 6719

CUSHMAN & WAKEFIELD INC p 402
77 W Wacker Dr Ste 1800 60601
Tel (312) 424-8000 *SIC* 6531 8742 8732

CZARNOWSKI DISPLAY SERVICE INC p 406
2287 S Blue Island Ave 60608
Tel (773) 247-1500 *SIC* 7389

DANIEL J EDELMAN HOLDINGS INC p 411
200 E Randolph St Fl 63 60601
Tel (312) 240-3000 *SIC* 7313 8743

DANIEL J EDELMAN INC p 411
200 E Randolph St Fl 63 60601
Tel (312) 240-3000 *SIC* 7313 8743

DANIELS SHARPSMART INC p 411
111 W Jackson Blvd # 720 60604
Tel (312) 546-8900 *SIC* 4953 2834

DE PAUL UNIVERSITY p 419
1 E Jackson Blvd 60604
Tel (312) 362-6714 *SIC* 8221

DEARBORN WHOLESALE GROCERS LP p 420
2455 S Damen Ave Ste 100 60608
Tel (773) 254-4300 *SIC* 5141

DELOITTE CORPORATE FINANCE LLC p 425
111 S Wacker Dr 60606
Tel (312) 486-1400 *SIC* 7389

DENTONS US LLP p 429
233 S Wacker Dr Ste 5900 60606
Tel (312) 876-8000 *SIC* 8111

DESTINY HEALTH INC p 432
200 W Monroe St Ste 1900 60606
Tel (312) 224-7100 *SIC* 6321 8399

DRW HOLDINGS LLC p 457
540 W Madison St Ste 2500 60661
Tel (312) 542-1000 *SIC* 6719

DUTCH FARMS INC p 463
700 E 107th St 60628
Tel (773) 660-0900 *SIC* 5143

ECHELON CAPITAL LLC p 475
121 W Wacker Dr 60601
Tel (312) 263-0263 *SIC* 6799

▲ ECHO GLOBAL LOGISTICS INC p 475
600 W Chicago Ave Ste 725 60654
Tel (800) 354-7993 *SIC* 4731 4813

EDSAL MANUFACTURING CO INC p 479
4400 S Packers Ave 60609
Tel (773) 475-3020 *SIC* 2599 2542 2522

EL-MILAGRO INC p 483
3050 W 26th St 60623
Tel (773) 579-6120 *SIC* 2099 5812

ELECTRICAL INSURANCE TRUSTEES p 485
221 N La Salle St Ste 200 60601
Tel (312) 782-5442 *SIC* 6371 6282

ELITE LABOR SERVICES LTD p 487
1400 W Hubbard St Ste 2 60642
Tel (773) 235-3000 *SIC* 7363

ENCYCLOPAEDIA BRITANNICA INC p 496
325 N Lasalle St Ste 200 60654
Tel (847) 777-2241 *SIC* 2731

■ ENOVA FINANCIAL HOLDINGS LLC p 500
200 W Jackson Blvd # 2400 60606
Tel (312) 568-4200 *SIC* 6163

▲ ENOVA INTERNATIONAL INC p 500
175 W Jackson Blvd Fl 10 60604
Tel (312) 568-4200 *SIC* 7389

ENTERTAINMENT CRUISES INC p 502
455 N Ctyfrnt Plz Dr # 2600 60611
Tel (312) 321-7600 *SIC* 4489

■ ENVESTNET ASSET MANAGEMENT INC p 503
35 E Wacker Dr Ste 2400 60601
Tel (312) 827-2800 *SIC* 6282

▲ ENVESTNET INC p 503
35 E Wacker Dr Ste 2400 60601
Tel (312) 827-2800 *SIC* 7389 6282 7372

EON CLIMATE & RENEWABLES NORTH AMERICA LLC p 504
353 N Clark St Fl 30 60654
Tel (312) 245-3035 *SIC* 4911

EQUITY COMMONWEALTH p 506
2 N Riverside Plz Ste 600 60606
Tel (312) 646-2800 *SIC* 6798

▲ EQUITY LIFESTYLE PROPERTIES INC p 507
2 N Riverside Plz Ste 800 60606
Tel (312) 279-1400 *SIC* 6798 6531

EQUITY RESIDENTIAL p 507
2 N Rverside Plz Ste 1100 60606
Tel (312) 474-1300 *SIC* 6798

ERP OPERATING LIMITED PARTNERSHIP p 508
2 N Riverside Plz Ste 400 60606
Tel (312) 474-1300 *SIC* 6798

EVANGELICAL COVENANT CHURCH p 513
8303 W Higgins Rd Fl 1 60631
Tel (773) 907-3303 *SIC* 8661

EVRAZ INC NA p 516
200 E Randolph St # 7800 60601
Tel (312) 533-3621 *SIC* 3312 3317 3325

■ EXELON BUSINESS SERVICES CO LLC p 518
10 S Dearborn St 60603
Tel (800) 483-3220 *SIC* 7389

▲ EXELON CORP p 518
10 S Dearborn St Fl 53 60603
Tel (800) 483-3220 *SIC* 4911 4924

■ EXELON ENERGY DELIVERY CO LLC p 519
10 S Dearborn St Fl 53 60603
Tel (312) 394-7399 *SIC* 4931

EXP US SERVICES INC p 519
205 N Mich Aveste 3600 60601
Tel (312) 616-0000 *SIC* 8711 8712

FAIRLIFE LLC p 525
1001 W Adams St 60607
Tel (312) 624-9444 *SIC* 5149

FAIRPLAY INC p 525
4640 S Halsted St 60609
Tel (773) 247-3077 *SIC* 5411

FAMILY HEALTH NETWORK INC p 527
322 S Green St Ste 400 60607
Tel (312) 243-5235 *SIC* 8011

FEDERAL HOME LOAN BANK OF CHICAGO p 534
200 E Randolph St # 1700 60601
Tel (312) 565-5700 *SIC* 6111

FEDERAL RESERVE BANK OF CHICAGO p 535
230 S La Salle St Ste 1 60604
Tel (312) 322-2128 *SIC* 6011

FEEDING AMERICA p 537
35 E Wacker Dr Ste 2000 60601
Tel (312) 263-2303 *SIC* 8322

■ FERALLOY CORP p 537
8755 W Higgins Rd Ste 970 60631
Tel (503) 286-8869
SIC 5051 3471 3444 3312

FH PASCHEN SN NIELSEN INC p 539
5515 N East River Rd 60656
Tel (773) 444-3474
SIC 1611 1622 1522 1542

■ FIDELITY & CASUALTY CO OF NEW YORK p 540
333 S Wabash Ave Fl 1 60604
Tel (312) 822-5000 *SIC* 6411

FIELD MUSEUM OF NATURAL HISTORY p 541
1400 S Lake Shore Dr 60605
Tel (312) 922-9410 *SIC* 8412

FIELDGLASS INC p 541
111 N Canal St Ste 600 60606
Tel (312) 763-4800 *SIC* 7373

FIRST INDUSTRIAL LP p 547
311 S Wacker Dr Ste 3900 60606
Tel (312) 344-4300 *SIC* 6798

FIRST INDUSTRIAL REALTY TRUST INC p 547
311 S Wacker Dr Ste 3900 60606
Tel (312) 344-4300 *SIC* 6798

FLAT OUT CRAZY LLC p 554
303 W Erie St Ste 600 60654
Tel (312) 284-6500 *SIC* 8741 5812

FLEXPOINT PARTNERS LLC p 556
676 N Michigan Ave # 3300 60611
Tel (312) 327-4520 *SIC* 5511

■ FLORIDA RSA 8 INC p 559
8410 W Bryn Mawr Ave # 700 60631
Tel (773) 399-8900 *SIC* 4812

FLS TRANSPORTATION SERVICES INC p 561
180 N La Salle St # 2950 60601
Tel (877) 744-7357 *SIC* 8742 4731

FLYING FOOD FARE INC p 562
212 N Sangamon St Ste 1a 60607
Tel (312) 243-2122 *SIC* 5812 5149 5947

FLYING FOOD GROUP INC p 562
212 N Sangamon St Ste 1a 60607
Tel (312) 243-2122 *SIC* 5812

FORWARD SPACE LLC p 570
1142 N North Branch St 60642
Tel (312) 942-1100 *SIC* 5021 7389

FRED TEITELBAUM CONSTRUCTION CO p 576
5526 N Kedzie Ave 60625
Tel (954) 971-1700 *SIC* 1522

FREEDMAN SEATING CO p 576
4545 W Augusta Blvd 60651
Tel (773) 524-2440 *SIC* 2531

▲ FREIGHTCAR AMERICA INC p 577
2 N Rverside Plz Ste 1300 60606
Tel (800) 458-2235 *SIC* 3743

GATEWAY FOUNDATION INC p 593
55 E Jackson Blvd # 1500 60604
Tel (312) 663-1130 *SIC* 8093

■ GATORADE CO p 594
555 W Monroe St Fl 1 60661
Tel (312) 821-1000 *SIC* 2086 5149

▲ GATX CORP p 594
222 W Adams St 60606
Tel (312) 621-6200 *SIC* 4741 7359 4491

■ GE HEALTHCARE FINANCIAL SERVICES INC p 596
500 W Monroe St Fl 19 60661
Tel (312) 697-3999 *SIC* 6141

GEM REALTY CAPITAL INC p 598
900 N Michigan Ave # 1450 60611
Tel (312) 915-2900 *SIC* 6799

GENERAL ELECTRIC RAILCAR SERVICES CORP p 600
161 N Clark St Fl 7 60601
Tel (312) 853-5000
SIC 7359 3743 4789 3462

▲ GENERAL GROWTH PROPERTIES INC p 601
110 N Wacker Dr 60606
Tel (312) 960-5000 *SIC* 6798

■ GETZ BROS& CO INC p 609
225 W Washington St # 1900 60606
Tel (312) 845-5686
SIC 5047 5031 5141 5065 5082

■ GGP INC p 610
110 N Wacker Dr 60606
Tel (312) 960-5000 *SIC* 6798

GO GROUP LLC p 619
1200 W 35th St 60609
Tel (844) 787-1670 *SIC* 4111

▲ GOGO INC p 620
111 N Canal St Ste 1500 60606
Tel (312) 517-5000 *SIC* 4899

■ GOGO LLC p 620
111 N Canal St Fl 15 60606
Tel (630) 647-1400
SIC 3663 4812 4813 4899

GOLD EAGLE CO p 620
4400 S Kildare Ave Front 60632
Tel (773) 376-4400 *SIC* 5013

■ GOLIN/HARRIS INTERNATIONAL INC p 622
875 N Michigan Ave # 2600 60611
Tel (312) 729-4000 *SIC* 8743

▲ GOLUB CAPITAL BDC INC p 622
150 S Wacker Dr Ste 800 60606
Tel (312) 205-5050 *SIC* 6726

GRANT THORNTON LLP p 631
171 N Clark St Ste 200 60601
Tel (312) 856-0200 *SIC* 8721 8742

GREAT DANE LIMITED PARTNERSHIP p 633
222 N Lasalle St Ste 920 60601
Tel (773) 254-5533 *SIC* 3715

GREATER CHICAGO FOOD DEPOSITORY p 635
4100 W 42nd Pl 60632
Tel (773) 247-3663 *SIC* 8322

GREELEY AND HANSEN LLC p 636
100 S Wacker Dr Ste 1400 60606
Tel (312) 558-9000 *SIC* 8711

GREEN COUCH CORP p 636
231 S La Salle St Fl 8 60604
Tel (312) 263-1177 *SIC* 7379 7371

GREEN COURTE PARTNERS LLC p 637
303 W Madison St Ste 1500 60606
Tel (847) 615-1631 *SIC* 6798

▲ GROUPON INC p 642
600 W Chicago Ave Ste 400 60654
Tel (312) 334-1579 *SIC* 7311 7319

▲ GRUBHUB INC p 642
111 W Washington St # 2100 60602
Tel (877) 585-7878 *SIC* 5961

GTCR GOLDER RAUNER LLC p 644
300 N La Salle Dr # 5600 60654
Tel (312) 329-0225 *SIC* 6726

GTCR LLC p 644
300 N La Salle Dr # 5600 60654
Tel (312) 382-2200 *SIC* 5049

GTCR VALOR COMPANIES INC p 644
300 N La Salle Dr # 5600 60654
Tel (312) 382-2200 *SIC* 7389

GUARANTEED RATE INC p 644
3940 N Ravenswood Ave 60613
Tel (866) 934-7283 *SIC* 6162

GUGGENHEIM CAPITAL LLC p 645
227 W Monroe St Ste 4900 60606
Tel (312) 827-0100 *SIC* 6726

H GROUP HOLDING INC p 650
222 W Adams St Ste 250 60606
Tel (312) 750-1234
SIC 4512 7011 5812 5813

H W LOCHNER INC p 651
225 W Washington St # 1200 60606
Tel (312) 372-7346 *SIC* 8711 8742

HABITAT CO LLC p 651
350 W Hubbard St Ste 500 60654
Tel (312) 955-0413 *SIC* 6531

HARBORQUEST INC p 660
14 E Jackson Blvd # 1210 60604
Tel (312) 612-7600 *SIC* 7363 4119 7361

HARDIN SCHIFF LLP p 660
233 S Wacker Dr Ste 6600 60606
Tel (312) 258-5500 *SIC* 8111

■ HARLEY-DAVIDSON FINANCIAL SERVICES INC p 661
222 W Adams St Ste 2000 60606
Tel (312) 368-9501 *SIC* 6141 6411

■ HARMONY HEALTH SYSTEMS INC p 662
200 W Adams St Ste 800 60606
Tel (312) 372-3471 *SIC* 6324 8011

HARRIS BMO BANK NATIONAL ASSOCIATION p 663
111 W Monroe St Ste 1200 60603
Tel (312) 461-2323 *SIC* 6021

HARRIS WILLIAM & CO INC p 664
191 N Wacker Dr Ste 1500 60606
Tel (312) 621-0590 *SIC* 6799 3317

HAYES MECHANICAL LLC p 670
5959 S Harlem Ave 60638
Tel (773) 784-0000 *SIC* 1711

HCSC INSURANCE SERVICES CO p 672
300 E Randolph St 60601
Tel (312) 653-6000 *SIC* 6311

HEALTH CARE SERVICE CORP A MUTUAL LEGAL RESERVE CO p 674
300 E Randolph St Fl 4 60601
Tel (312) 653-6000 *SIC* 6324 6321 6411

HEALTH CARE SERVICE CORP ILLINOIS STATE PAC NFP p 674
300 E Randolph St Fl 4 60601
Tel (312) 653-6000 *SIC* 6321

HEALTHCARE INFORMATION AND MANAGEMENT SYSTEMS SOCIETY p 676
33 W Monroe St Ste 1700 60603
Tel (312) 664-4467 *SIC* 8099

HEICO COMPANIES L L C p 680
5600 Three First Nat Plz 60602
Tel (312) 419-8220
SIC 3315 3589 3448 3531 1731 3663

▲ HEIDRICK & STRUGGLES INTERNATIONAL INC p 680
233 S Wacker Dr Ste 4900 60606
Tel (312) 496-1200 *SIC* 7361

HELP AT HOME LLC p 682
1 N State St Ste 800 60602
Tel (312) 762-9999 *SIC* 8082

HENRY CROWN AND CO p 684
222 N La Salle St # 2000 60601
Tel (312) 236-6300 *SIC* 2514

HERE HOLDING CORP p 685
425 W Randolph St 60606
Tel (312) 894-7000 *SIC* 7379

HERE NORTH AMERICA LLC p 685
425 W Randolph St 60606
Tel (312) 894-7000 *SIC* 7371

▲ HILL-ROM HOLDINGS INC p 693
2 Prudential Plz Ste 4100 60601
Tel (312) 819-7200 *SIC* 3841 7352

■ HILLSHIRE BRANDS CO p 694
400 S Jefferson St Fl 1 60607
Tel (312) 614-6000 *SIC* 2013 2051 2053

HINCKLEY & SCHMITT INC p 695
6055 S Harlem Ave 60638
Tel (773) 586-8600 *SIC* 2086 5149 7359

HINSHAW & CULBERTSON LLP p 695
222 N La Salle St Ste 300 60601
Tel (312) 704-3000 *SIC* 8111

■ HOLLY HUNT ENTERPRISES INC p 701
801 W Adams St Ste 700 60607
Tel (312) 329-5999 *SIC* 5021

HOME PRODUCTS INTERNATIONAL - NORTH AMERICA INC p 703
4501 W 47th St 60632
Tel (773) 890-1010 *SIC* 3089 3499

HOME PRODUCTS INTERNATIONAL INC p 703
4501 W 47th St 60632
Tel (773) 890-1010 *SIC* 6719

HOMETOWN AMERICA LLC p 704
150 N Wacker Dr Ste 2800 60606
Tel (312) 604-7500 *SIC* 6512

HOMETOWN AMERICA MANAGEMENT CORP p 704
150 N Wacker Dr Ste 2800 60606
Tel (312) 604-7500 *SIC* 6515

HOSTWAY CORP p 710
100 N Riverside Plz # 800 60606
Tel (312) 238-0125 *SIC* 4813

HU-FRIEDY MFG CO LLC p 715
3232 N Rockwell St 60618
Tel (773) 975-3975 *SIC* 3843

HUB INTERNATIONAL LIMITED p 716
300 N La Salle Dr Ste 17 60654
Tel (312) 596-7522 *SIC* 6411

HUB INTERNATIONAL MIDWEST LTD p 716
55 E Jackson Blvd 1400a 60604
Tel (312) 922-5000 *SIC* 6411

HUB INTERNATIONAL OF ILLINOIS LIMITED p 716
300 N Lslle St Fl 17 60654
Tel (312) 922-5000 *SIC* 6411

▲ HURON CONSULTING GROUP INC p 721
550 W Van Buren St # 1600 60607
Tel (312) 583-8700 *SIC* 8742 8748

■ HURON CONSULTING SERVICES LLC p 721
550 W Van Buren St # 1600 60607
Tel (312) 583-8700 *SIC* 8748

■ HYATT CORP p 723
150 N Riverside Plz 60606
Tel (312) 750-1234 *SIC* 7011

■ HYATT EQUITIES LLC p 723
71 S Wacker Dr Fl 14 60606
Tel (312) 750-1234 *SIC* 7011

▲ HYATT HOTELS CORP p 723
71 S Wacker Dr Ste 1000 60606
Tel (312) 750-1234 *SIC* 7011 6794

■ HYATT HOTELS MANAGEMENT CORP p 723
71 S Wacker Dr Ste 1000 60606
Tel (312) 750-1234 *SIC* 7011

■ HYATT INTERNATIONAL CORP p 723
71 S Wacker Dr 12 60606
Tel (312) 750-1234 *SIC* 7011

■ ILLINOIS BELL TELEPHONE CO p 732
225 W Randolph St Fl Ll 60606
Tel (618) 344-9077 *SIC* 4813 8721 6512

ILLINOIS DEPARTMENT OF HUMAN SERVICES p 732
401 S Clinton St 60607
Tel (312) 793-1547 *SIC* 9431

ILLINOIS INSTITUTE OF TECHNOLOGY p 732
10 W 35th St 60616
Tel (312) 567-3000 *SIC* 8221

ILLINOIS MASONIC MEDICAL CENTER p 732
836 W Wellington Ave 60657
Tel (773) 975-1600 *SIC* 8062

ILLINOIS STATE MEDICAL SOCIETY p 732
20 N Michigan Ave Ste 700 60602
Tel (312) 782-2749 *SIC* 8621

IMC-CHICAGO LLC p 733
233 S Wacker Dr Ste 4300 60606
Tel (312) 244-3300 *SIC* 6231

INFORMATION RESOURCES INC p 742
150 N Clinton St 60661
Tel (312) 726-1221 *SIC* 7372

▲ INNERWORKINGS INC p 744
600 W Chicago Ave Ste 850 60654
Tel (312) 642-3700 *SIC* 2752 7374 7372

INSTITUTE FOR INTERNATIONAL EDUCATION OF STUDENTS p 747
33 W Monroe St Ste 2300 60603
Tel (312) 944-1750 *SIC* 8299

INTEGRYS ENERGY GROUP INC p 750
200 E Randolph St # 2200 60601
Tel (312) 228-5400 *SIC* 4931 5172 4911

▲ INTELIQUENT INC p 750
550 W Adams St Fl 9 60661
Tel (312) 384-8000 *SIC* 4813

INTERNATIONAL FELLOWSHIP OF CHRISTIANS & JEWS INC p 755
30 N La Salle St Ste 2600 60602
Tel (312) 641-7200 *SIC* 8661

INVENERGY LLC p 760
1 S Wacker Dr Ste 1800 60606
Tel (312) 224-1400 *SIC* 8711

IOWA PACIFIC HOLDINGS LLC p 763
118 S Clinton St Ste 400 60661
Tel (312) 466-0900 *SIC* 4011

IPSOS PUBLIC AFFAIRS INC p 764
222 S Rverside Plz Fl 4 60606
Tel (312) 526-4000 *SIC* 8732 8731

ISMIE MUTUAL INSURANCE CO p 767
20 N Michigan Ave Ste 700 60602
Tel (312) 782-2749 *SIC* 6351

ITR CONCESSION CO HOLDINGS LLC p 768
8801 S Anthony Ave 60617
Tel (312) 552-7100 *SIC* 4785 6719

JACKSON PARK HOSPITAL FOUNDATION p 774
7531 S Stony Island Ave # 1 60649
Tel (773) 947-7500 *SIC* 8062

JAMES MCHUGH CONSTRUCTION CO p 776
1737 S Michigan Ave 60616
Tel (312) 986-8000 *SIC* 1542 1522 1622

JCG INDUSTRIES INC p 780
4404 W Berteau Ave 60641
Tel (847) 384-5940 *SIC* 5144

JEFFREY L LONDON p 782
70 W Madison St Ste 4200 60602
Tel (312) 583-2339 *SIC* 8111

JENNER & BLOCK LLP p 782
353 N Clark St Ste 3200 60654
Tel (312) 222-9350 *SIC* 8111

■ JERNBERG INDUSTRIES LLC p 783
328 W 40th Pl 60609
Tel (773) 268-3004 *SIC* 3462 3463

JEWISH FEDERATION OF METROPOLITAN CHICAGO p 784
30 S Wells St 60606
Tel (312) 357-4790 *SIC* 8399

JEWISH UNITED FUND OF METROPOLITAN CHICAGO p 785
30 S Wells St 60606
Tel (312) 357-4805 *SIC* 8399

▲ JOHN BEAN TECHNOLOGIES CORP p 787
70 W Madison St Ste 4400 60602
Tel (312) 861-5900 *SIC* 3556 3585 3537

JOHN CRANE INC p 788
227 W Monroe St Ste 1800 60606
Tel (312) 605-7800 *SIC* 3053

JOHN D AND CATHERINE T MACARTHUR FOUNDATION p 788
140 S Dearborn St 60603
Tel (312) 332-0101 *SIC* 7011

■ JONES LANG LASALLE AMERICAS INC p 792
200 E Randolph St # 4300 60601
Tel (312) 782-5800 *SIC* 6282 1542

▲ JONES LANG LASALLE INC p 792
200 E Randolph St # 4300 60601
Tel (312) 782-5800 *SIC* 6512 6531

■ JOSEPH T RYERSON & SON INC p 794
227 W Monroe St Fl 27 60606
Tel (312) 292-5000 *SIC* 5051 5162

■ JPMORGAN CAPITAL CORP p 795
55 W Monroe St 60603
Tel (614) 248-5800 *SIC* 8748 6726

■ JT CO INC p 796
7401 S Cicero Ave 60629
Tel (773) 838-3400 *SIC* 7389

K+S MONTANA HOLDINGS LLC p 799
123 N Wacker Dr 60606
Tel (312) 807-2000 *SIC* 2899

K+S SALT LLC p 799
123 N Wacker Dr Fl 6 60606
Tel (844) 789-3991 *SIC* 2899 5149 5169

KATO KAGAKU CO LTD p 804
151 E Wacker Dr 60601
Tel (312) 565-1234 *SIC* 6512 7011

KATTEN MUCHIN ROSENMAN LLP p 804
525 W Monroe St Ste 1900 60661
Tel (312) 902-5200 *SIC* 8111

▲ KEMPER CORP p 809
1 E Wacker Dr 60601
Tel (312) 661-4600
SIC 6331 6321 6311 6141

KENNICOTT BROS CO p 811
1638 W Hubbard St 60622
Tel (312) 492-8200 *SIC* 5193

■ KERASOTES SHOWPLACE THEATRES LLC p 813
224 N Des Plns Ste 200 60661
Tel (312) 756-3360 *SIC* 7832

KINGPIN HOLDINGS LLC p 820
10 S Wacker Dr Ste 3175 60606
Tel (312) 876-1275 *SIC* 7933

KINGPIN INTERMEDIATE CORP p 820
10 S Wacker Dr 60606
Tel (312) 876-1275 *SIC* 7933

KIRBY FOODS INC p 821
8745 W Higgins Rd 60631
Tel (217) 352-2600 *SIC* 5411

KIRKLAND & ELLIS LLP p 822
300 N La Salle Dr # 2400 60654
Tel (312) 862-2000 *SIC* 8111

L & W SUPPLY CORP p 833
550 W Adams St 60661
Tel (312) 606-4000 *SIC* 5032

LAFARGE BUILDING MATERIALS INC p 837
8700 W Bryn Mawr Ave 300n 60631
Tel (678) 746-2000
SIC 3241 3274 3273 3271

LAFARGE NORTH AMERICA INC p 837
8700 W Bryn Mawr Ave Ll 60631
Tel (703) 480-3600
SIC 3241 3273 3272 3271 1442 2951

LAKE CAPITAL MANAGEMENT LLC p 838
676 N Michigan Ave # 3900 60611
Tel (312) 640-7050 *SIC* 6799

LAKESHORE MANAGEMENT GROUP INC p 840
70 E Lake St Ste 1600 60601
Tel (773) 981-1452 *SIC* 7991

LAPHAM-HICKEY STEEL CORP p 845
5500 W 73rd St 60638
Tel (708) 496-6111
SIC 5051 3398 3355 3317 3316

LASALLE INCOME & GROWTH FUND IV p 846
200 E Randolph St Fl 44 60601
Tel (312) 228-2087 *SIC* 6531

■ LASALLE INVESTMENT MANAGEMENT INC p 846
333 W Wacker Dr Ste 2000 60606
Tel (312) 782-5800 *SIC* 6531

▲ LAWSON PRODUCTS INC p 848
8770 W Bryn Mawr Ave # 639 60631
Tel (773) 304-5050
SIC 5072 5085 5084 5013

LAWTER INC p 848
200 N La Salle St # 2600 60601
Tel (312) 662-5700 *SIC* 2899 2851

LE PETIT PAIN HOLDINGS LLC p 849
676 N Michigan Ave 60611
Tel (312) 981-3770 *SIC* 2051

LEARNING CARE GROUP INC p 850
130 S Jefferson St # 300 60661
Tel (312) 469-5656 *SIC* 8351

LEO BURNETT CO INC p 856
35 W Wacker Dr Fl 21 60601
Tel (312) 220-5959 *SIC* 7311 3993

LEONAS PIZZERIA INC p 856
3931 S Leavitt St 60609
Tel (773) 843-0050 *SIC* 5812 5813

LETTUCE ENTERTAIN YOU ENTERPRISES INC p 857
5419 N Sheridan Rd 60640
Tel (773) 878-7340 *SIC* 5812 8741

LETTUCE ENTERTAIN YOU TOO INC p 858
5419 N Sheridan Rd # 116 60640
Tel (773) 878-7340 *SIC* 5812 5813

LEVY R & H LIMITED PARTNERSHIP p 858
980 N Michigan Ave # 400 60611
Tel (312) 664-8200 *SIC* 5812

LIBERTY HAMPSHIRE CO LLC p 861
227 W Monroe St 60606
Tel (312) 827-0100 *SIC* 6141

LINCOLN INTERNATIONAL LLC p 867
500 W Madison St Ste 3900 60661
Tel (312) 580-8339 *SIC* 6211

LINCOLN PROVISION INC p 868
824 W 38th Pl 60609
Tel (773) 254-2400 *SIC* 5142 5147

LINDEN LLC p 868
111 S Wacker Dr Ste 3350 60606
Tel (312) 506-5657 *SIC* 6726

▲ LITTELFUSE INC p 870
8755 W Higgins Rd Ste 500 60631
Tel (773) 628-1000 *SIC* 3613 3679

LIVINGSTON INTERNATIONAL INC p 871
141 W Jackson Blvd 1510a 60604
Tel (630) 766-0202 *SIC* 7389

▲ LKQ CORP p 872
500 W Madison St Ste 2800 60661
Tel (312) 621-1950 *SIC* 5093 5015

LLOYDS ILLINOIS INC p 872
181 W Madison St Ste 3870 60602
Tel (312) 407-6200 *SIC* 6411

LOCAL 25 SEIU WELFARE FUND p 872
111 E Wacker Dr Ste 1700 60601
Tel (312) 240-1600 *SIC* 6371

LOGAN SQUARE ALUMINUM SUPPLY INC p 874
2500 N Pulaski Rd 60639
Tel (773) 235-2500 *SIC* 5211 3089

LOYOLA UNIVERSITY OF CHICAGO INC p 882
1032 W Sheridan Rd 60660
Tel (773) 274-3000 *SIC* 8221

LSC COMMUNICATIONS US LLC p 883
35 W Wacker Dr 60601
Tel (844) 572-5720 *SIC* 1623

LUNAN CORP p 885
414 N Orleans St Ste 402 60654
Tel (312) 645-9898 *SIC* 5812

LYRIC OPERA OF CHICAGO p 888
20 N Wacker Dr Ste 860 60606
Tel (312) 332-2244 *SIC* 7922

MADISON CAPITAL FUNDING LLC p 894
30 S Wacker Dr Ste 3700 60606
Tel (312) 596-6900 *SIC* 6163

MADISON CAPITAL PARTNERS CORP p 894
500 W Madison St Ste 3890 60661
Tel (312) 277-0323 *SIC* 3542 8741

MADISON DEARBORN PARTNERS IV LP p 894
70 W Madison St Ste 3800 60602
Tel (312) 895-1000 *SIC* 5031 8744

MADISON DEARBORN PARTNERS LLC p 894
70 W Madison St Ste 4600 60602
Tel (312) 895-1000 *SIC* 6726 6722

MADISON INDUSTRIES HOLDINGS LLC p 894
500 W Madison St Ste 3890 60661
Tel (312) 277-0156
SIC 6719 5051 3443 3316

MAGNUM INSURANCE AGENCY CO INC p 896
4259 N Western Ave 60618
Tel (773) 539-2102 *SIC* 6411

MARATHON MEDIA GROUP LLC p 904
737 N Michigan Ave # 2060 60611
Tel (312) 640-9700 *SIC* 4832

■ MARIO TRICOCIS HAIR SALON & DAY SPA p 907
900 N Michigan Ave # 1850 60611
Tel (800) 874-2624 *SIC* 7231

MARKET TRACK LLC p 908
233 S Wacker Dr 60606
Tel (312) 529-5102 *SIC* 8742

MARKETING STORE WORLDWIDE L L C p 908
55 W Monroe St Fl 14 60603
Tel (312) 614-4600 *SIC* 7311 8742

■ MARMON GROUP LLC p 909
181 W Madison St Ste 2600 60602
Tel (312) 372-9500 *SIC* 3452 5072

■ MARMON GROUP LLC p 909
181 W Madison St Ste 2600 60602
Tel (312) 372-9500 *SIC* 8748

■ MARMON HOLDINGS INC p 909
181 W Madison St Ste 2600 60602
Tel (312) 372-9500
SIC 5051 3351 3743 4741 3423 3589

■ MARMON INDUSTRIAL LLC p 909
181 W Madison St Fl 26 60602
Tel (312) 372-9500
SIC 3743 4741 3589 6159 3965 3492

■ MARMON RETAIL & END USER TECHNOLOGIES INC p 909
181 W Madison St Fl 26 60602
Tel (312) 372-9500 *SIC* 2599

■ MARMON RETAIL SERVICES INC p 909
181 W Madison St 60602
Tel (312) 332-0317 *SIC* 2541 2542

MARSH MCLENNAN p 911
540 W Madison St Ste 1200 60661
Tel (312) 627-6000 *SIC* 6411

MARVEL GROUP INC p 913
3843 W 43rd St 60632
Tel (773) 523-4804 *SIC* 2522

■ MATERIAL SERVICE RESOURCES CORP p 919
222 N La Salle St # 1200 60601
Tel (630) 325-7736 *SIC* 1442 1221

MAYER BROWN LLP p 923
71 S Wacker Dr Ste 1000 60606
Tel (312) 782-0600 *SIC* 8111

■ MB FINANCIAL BANK p 924
936 N Western Ave 60622
Tel (773) 772-4500 *SIC* 6035

▲ MB FINANCIAL INC p 924
800 W Madison St 60607
Tel (888) 422-6562 *SIC* 6035

MCDERMOTT WILL & EMERY LLP INC p 927
227 W Monroe St Ste 4400 60606
Tel (312) 372-2000 *SIC* 8111

MCHUGH ENTERPRISES INC p 929
1737 S Michigan Ave 60616
Tel (312) 986-8000
SIC 1542 1522 1622 1771 1742 6552

MERCHANDISE MART PROPERTIES INC p 944
222 Merchandise Mart Plz # 470 60654
Tel (312) 527-4141 *SIC* 6531

MERCY HOSPITAL AND MEDICAL CENTER p 947
2525 S Michigan Ave 60616
Tel (312) 567-2201 *SIC* 8062

■ MERGE HEALTHCARE INC p 948
71 S Wacker Dr Ste 2 60606
Tel (312) 565-6868 *SIC* 7373 3841

MERISANT CO p 949
125 S Wacker Dr Ste 3150 60606
Tel (312) 840-6000 *SIC* 2869

MERISANT US INC p 949
125 S Wacker Dr Ste 3150 60606
Tel (312) 840-6000 *SIC* 2869

MESIROW FINANCIAL HOLDINGS INC p 951
353 N Clark St Lowr Level 60654
Tel (312) 595-6000
SIC 6211 6282 6531 6552 6411

MESIROW FINANCIAL INC p 951
353 N Clark St Lowr Level 60654
Tel (312) 595-6000 *SIC* 6211

METAL MANAGEMENT INC p 952
2500 S Paulina St 60608
Tel (312) 645-0700 *SIC* 5093 1795

METAL MANAGEMENT MIDWEST INC p 952
2500 S Paulina St 60608
Tel (773) 254-1200 *SIC* 5093

▲ METHODE ELECTRONICS INC p 953
7401 W Wilson Ave 60706
Tel (708) 867-6777
SIC 3678 3674 3676 3672 3825 3643

METROPOLITAN PIER AND EXPOSITION AUTHORITY p 956
301 Ecermak Rd Fl 5 60616
Tel (312) 791-7000 *SIC* 7389 7999 7011

METROPOLITAN WATER RECLAIMATION DISTRICT OF GREATER CHICAGO p 957
100 E Erie St 60611
Tel (312) 751-5600 *SIC* 9511

■ MHC OPERATING LIMITED PARTNERSHIP p 959
2 N Riverside Plz Ste 800 60606
Tel (312) 279-1400 *SIC* 6515 6531

MID-CITY TRUCK DRIVING ACADEMY INC p 963
6740 W Belmont Ave 60634
Tel (773) 725-3000 *SIC* 8299 5511

MID-WEST INSTITUTIONAL FOOD DISTRIBUTORS INC p 964
3100 W 36th St 60632
Tel (773) 927-8870
SIC 5142 5143 5144 5147 5148

MIDWEST CANVAS CORP p 967
4635 W Lake St 60644
Tel (773) 287-4400 SIC 3081 3089

■ MIDWEST GENERATION EME LLC p 967
440 Suth La Salle St 3500 60605
Tel (312) 583-6000 SIC 4911

■ MILLERCOORS LLC p 971
250 S Wacker Dr Ste 800 60606
Tel (312) 496-2700 SIC 2082

MISERICORDIA HOME p 975
6300 N Ridge Ave 60660
Tel (773) 973-6300 SIC 8052

MMS USA HOLDINGS INC p 979
35 W Wacker Dr 60601
Tel (800) 933-3622 SIC 8742

MOLD-RITE PLASTICS LLC p 982
30 N La Salle St Ste 2425 60602
Tel (518) 561-1812 SIC 3089

MONTERREY SECURITY CONSULTANTS INC p 986
2232 S Blue Island Ave 60608
Tel (773) 843-0434 SIC 8742

MOODY BIBLE INSTITUTE OF CHICAGO p 987
820 N La Salle Dr 60610
Tel (312) 329-4000
SIC 8661 8299 8221 4832 2731

▲ MORNINGSTAR INC p 989
22 W Washington St # 600 60602
Tel (312) 696-6000 SIC 6282 6722 7375

MORTON INTERNATIONAL LLC p 991
123 N Wacker Dr Ste 2400 60606
Tel (312) 807-2696
SIC 2891 2851 2822 1479 2899

MORTON SALT INC p 991
123 N Wacker Dr Fl 24 60606
Tel (800) 725-8847
SIC 2891 2851 2822 1479 2899

MORTONS OF CHICAGO/BOCA RATON INC p 991
350 W Hubbard St 60654
Tel (713) 850-1010 SIC 5812

MOTOROLA MOBILITY HOLDINGS LLC p 993
222 Merchandise Mart Plz 60654
Tel (800) 668-6765 SIC 3663

MOTOROLA MOBILITY LLC p 993
222 Merchandise Mart Plz 60654
Tel (800) 866-6765 SIC 3663 4812

▲ MOTOROLA SOLUTIONS INC p 993
500 W Monroe St 60661
Tel (847) 576-5000 SIC 3663 3661

MOUNT SINAI HOSPITAL MEDICAL CENTER OF CHICAGO p 994
1501 S California Ave 60608
Tel (773) 542-2000 SIC 8062

MUSCULAR DYSTROPHY ASSOCIATION INC p 1002
222 S Riverside Plz # 1500 60606
Tel (520) 529-2000 SIC 8733

NAMASTE LABORATORIES LLC p 1007
310 S Racine Ave Fl 8 60607
Tel (708) 824-1393 SIC 2844

NATIONAL ASSOCIATION OF REALTORS p 1010
430 N Michigan Ave Lowr 2 60611
Tel (800) 874-6500 SIC 8611 2721 8299

NATIONAL COUNCIL OF YOUNG MENS CHRISTIAN ASSOCIATIONS OF UNITED STATES OF AMERICA p 1011
101 N Wacker Dr Ste 1600 60606
Tel (312) 977-0031 SIC 7997 8399 8322

NATIONAL EQUIPMENT SERVICES INC p 1011
8420 W Bryn Mawr Ave 60631
Tel (773) 695-3999 SIC 7359

NATIONAL EQUITY TITLE AGENCY INC p 1011
415 N La Salle Dr Ste 202 60654
Tel (312) 782-4290 SIC 6361

■ NATIONAL FIRE INSURANCE CO OF HARTFORD p 1012
Cna Plz 60604
Tel (312) 822-5000 SIC 6331

NATIONAL FUTURES ASSOCIATION (INC) p 1012
300 S Riverside Plz # 1800 60606
Tel (312) 781-1300 SIC 8611

NATIONAL LOUIS UNIVERSITY p 1014
122 S Michigan Ave # 600 60603
Tel (312) 261-3599 SIC 8221 8211

NATIONAL OPINION RESEARCH CENTER p 1014
1155 E 60th St 60637
Tel (773) 753-7500 SIC 8732

NATIONAL SURGICAL HOSPITALS INC p 1016
250 S Wacker Dr Ste 500 60606
Tel (312) 627-8400 SIC 8062 8093

■ NATIONAL WASTE SERVICE INC p 1017
2608 S Damen Ave 60608
Tel (773) 579-3600 SIC 4953

NATIONAL YMCA EMPLOYEE BENEFITS TRUST p 1017
101 N Wacker Dr Ste 1500 60606
Tel (312) 977-0031 SIC 8641

NATIONWIDE FOODS INC p 1017
700 E 107th St 60628
Tel (773) 787-4900 SIC 2013 5142 5147

▲ NAVIGANT CONSULTING INC p 1020
30 S Wacker Dr Ste 3550 60606
Tel (312) 573-5600 SIC 8742

NAVY PIER INC p 1020
600 E Grand Ave Ste 134 60611
Tel (312) 595-5333 SIC 6519 7999

NEAR NORTH NATIONAL GROUP INC p 1023
875 N Michigan Ave # 3100 60611
Tel (312) 867-0064 SIC 6411

NES RENTALS HOLDINGS INC p 1026
8420 W Bryn Mawr Ave # 310 60631
Tel (773) 695-3999 SIC 7359 7699 5082

NESBITT BURNS SECURITIES INC p 1026
115 S La Salle St Ste 20w 60603
Tel (312) 461-6220 SIC 6211

NEW WORLD VAN LINES INC p 1033
5875 N Rogers Ave 60646
Tel (773) 685-3399 SIC 4213

■ NEWARK CORP p 1037
300 S Riverside Plz # 2200 60606
Tel (773) 784-5100 SIC 5065

■ NEWARK ELECTRONICS CORP p 1037
300 S Riverside Plz 60606
Tel (773) 784-5100 SIC 5065 5063 5961

NEWLY WEDS FOODS INC p 1038
4140 W Fullerton Ave 60639
Tel (773) 489-7000 SIC 2099

NLFH ACCT PAYABLE BILL CH p 1045
541 N Fairbanks Ct Fl 16 60611
Tel (312) 926-2094 SIC 8721

NOBLE NETWORK OF CHARTER SCHOOLS p 1046
1 N State St Fl 7 60602
Tel (773) 278-6895 SIC 8211

NORTH ADVOCATE SIDE HEALTH NETWORK p 1049
836 W Wellington Ave 60657
Tel (773) 296-5699 SIC 8741 8721

NORTH AMERICAN CO FOR LIFE & HEALTH INSURANCE p 1049
525 W Van Buren St # 1200 60607
Tel (312) 648-7600 SIC 6311 6321

NORTH PARK UNIVERSITY p 1053
2543 W Cullom Ave 60618
Tel (773) 244-6200 SIC 8221

■ NORTH SHORE GAS CO p 1053
200 E Randolph St # 2200 60601
Tel (312) 240-4000 SIC 4924

NORTHEAST ILLINOIS REGIONAL COMMUTER RAILROAD CORP p 1055
547 W Jackson Blvd Ste 1 60661
Tel (312) 322-6900 SIC 4111 4011

NORTHEASTERN ILLINOIS UNIVERSITY p 1055
5500 N Saint Louis Ave 60625
Tel (773) 442-4000 SIC 8221

■ NORTHERN TRUST CO p 1057
50 S La Salle St 60603
Tel (312) 630-6000 SIC 6021

▲ NORTHERN TRUST CORP p 1057
50 S La Salle St 60603
Tel (312) 630-6000 SIC 6022

NORTHWEST INSURANCE NETWORK INC p 1060
515 N State St Ste 2100 60654
Tel (312) 427-1777 SIC 6411

NORTHWESTERN MEDICAL FACULTY FOUNDATION INC p 1060
680 N Lake Shore Dr Ste 1 60611
Tel (312) 926-2630 SIC 8011

NORTHWESTERN MEMORIAL HEALTHCARE p 1060
251 E Huron St Ste 3-710 60611
Tel (312) 926-2000
SIC 8082 6513 7389 8099

NORTHWESTERN MEMORIAL HOSPITAL p 1060
251 E Huron St 60611
Tel (312) 755-0604 SIC 8062

NORWEGIAN AMERICAN HOSPITAL INC p 1061
1044 N Francisco Ave 60622
Tel (773) 278-8800 SIC 8062

NOVA CAPITAL MANAGEMENT USA LLC p 1062
401 N Michigan Ave # 1200 60611
Tel (312) 822-3380 SIC 6799

NUVEEN INVESTMENTS INC p 1068
333 W Wacker Dr 60606
Tel (312) 917-7700 SIC 6282 6211

NUVEEN JOHN & CO INC (DEL) p 1068
333 W Wacker Dr Fl 33 60606
Tel (312) 917-7700 SIC 6211 8742

OFC MANAGEMENT INC p 1075
446 E Ontario St 10-100 60611
Tel (312) 642-0031 SIC 7991

▲ OIL-DRI CORP OF AMERICA p 1079
410 N Michigan Ave # 400 60611
Tel (312) 321-1515 SIC 2842 3295

▲ OLD REPUBLIC INTERNATIONAL CORP p 1081
307 N Michigan Ave 60601
Tel (312) 346-8100 SIC 6351

■ OLD REPUBLIC MORTGAGE GUARANTEE GROUP INC p 1081
307 N Michigan Ave # 1400 60601
Tel (312) 346-8100 SIC 6361

■ OLD REPUBLIC SECURITY HOLDINGS INC p 1081
307 N Michigan Ave # 1400 60601
Tel (312) 346-8100 SIC 6411 6361

■ OLD REPUBLIC SURETY GROUP INC p 1081
307 N Michigan Ave # 1400 60601
Tel (312) 346-8100 SIC 6411 6361

■ OLD REPUBLIC TITLE INSURANCE GROUP INC (DEL) p 1081
307 N Michigan Ave # 1400 60601
Tel (312) 346-8100 SIC 6361 6531

ONEIL INDUSTRIES INC p 1087
1245 W Washington Blvd 60607
Tel (773) 244-6003 SIC 1542 1541

OPPORTUNITY INTERNATIONAL INC p 1090
550 W Van Buren St # 200 60607
Tel (630) 242-4100 SIC 8399

OPTIONS CLEARING CORP p 1090
1 N Wacker Dr Fl 5 60606
Tel (312) 322-6200 SIC 6289

■ ORBITZ INC p 1092
200 S Wacker Dr 60606
Tel (312) 894-5000 SIC 4724

■ ORBITZ LLC p 1092
500 W Madison St Ste 1000 60661
Tel (312) 894-5000 SIC 4724

■ ORBITZ WORLDWIDE INC p 1093
500 W Madison St Ste 1000 60661
Tel (312) 894-5000 SIC 4724

ORGANICLIFE LLC p 1094
445 W Erie St Ste 110 60654
Tel (312) 929-2005 SIC 5812

OXFORD CAPITAL GROUP LLC p 1101
350 W Hubbard St Ste 440 60654
Tel (312) 755-9500 SIC 6719

OXFORD CAPITAL PARTNERS INC p 1101
350 W Hubbard St Ste 440 60654
Tel (312) 755-9500 SIC 6719

PACKAGING DYNAMICS CORP p 1106
3900 W 43rd St 60632
Tel (773) 254-8000 SIC 2671

PARKING SERVICE INC p 1116
180 N La Salle St # 1700 60601
Tel (312) 819-5050 SIC 7521

PEAK6 INVESTMENTS LP p 1126
141 W Jackson Blvd # 500 60604
Tel (312) 362-2401 SIC 6211

■ PEOPLES ENERGY LLC p 1132
200 E Randolph St Fl 22 60601
Tel (312) 240-4000 SIC 4924 4925 4911

■ PEOPLES GAS LIGHT AND COKE CO p 1133
200 E Randolph St # 2200 60601
Tel (312) 744-7000 SIC 4925

■ PEOPLESCOUT INC p 1133
860 W Evergreen Ave 60642
Tel (312) 915-0505 SIC 7361

PEPPER COMPANIES INC p 1133
643 N Orleans St 60654
Tel (312) 266-4703 SIC 1542 1541

PEPPER CONSTRUCTION CO p 1133
643 N Orleans St 60654
Tel (312) 266-4700 SIC 1542 1541

PEPPER CONSTRUCTION GROUP LLC p 1133
643 N Orleans St 60654
Tel (312) 266-4700 SIC 1542

PERKINS & WILL GROUP LTD p 1136
410 N Michigan Ave # 1600 60611
Tel (312) 755-0770 SIC 8712 7389

PETES FRESH MARKET 4700 CORP p 1138
4333 S Pulaski Rd 60632
Tel (773) 927-4300 SIC 5148 5431

PFINGSTEN PARTNERS LLC p 1140
300 N Lasalle St 5400 60654
Tel (312) 222-8707
SIC 5065 6211 3679 3578

PHOENIX INTERNATIONAL PUBLICATIONS INC p 1145
8501 W Higgins Rd Ste 300 60631
Tel (773) 739-4400 SIC 5942 2731

PIPE FITTERS RETIREMENT FUND LOCAL 597 p 1151
45 N Ogden Ave Fl 1 60607
Tel (312) 829-4191 SIC 6371

PLS FINANCIAL SERVICES INC p 1156
1 S Wacker Dr Fl 36 60606
Tel (312) 491-7300 SIC 7389 6798

PLS GROUP INC p 1156
1 S Wacker Dr Fl 36 60606
Tel (312) 491-7300 SIC 6719

▲ POTBELLY CORP p 1164
111 N Canal St Ste 850 60606
Tel (312) 951-0600 SIC 5812

■ POWER CO USA LLC p 1165
1165 N Clark St Ste 400 60610
Tel (312) 496-3729 SIC 8748

POWER CONSTRUCTION CO LLC p 1165
8750 W Bryn Mawr Ave 60631
Tel (312) 596-6960 SIC 1541 1542

PPM AMERICA INC p 1166
225 W Wacker Dr Ste 1200 60606
Tel (312) 634-2500 SIC 6282

PRESENCE CHICAGO HOSPITALS NETWORK p 1172
7435 W Talcott Ave 60631
Tel (773) 737-4636 SIC 8062

PRESENCE CHICAGO HOSPITALS NETWORK p 1172
7435 W Talcott Ave 60631
Tel (773) 774-8000 SIC 8062 8059

PRESENCE HEALTH NETWORK p 1172
200 S Wacker Dr Fl 12 60606
Tel (773) 774-8000
SIC 8082 8062 8011 8051

PRESENCE SAINT JOSEPH HOSPITAL - CHICAGO p 1172
2900 N Lake Shore Dr 60657
Tel (773) 665-3000 SIC 8062

PRESENCE SAINTS MARY AND ELIZABETH MEDICAL CENTER p 1172
2233 W Division St 60622
Tel (312) 770-2000 SIC 8062

PRITZKER GROUP- CHICAGO LLC p 1178
111 S Wacker Dr Ste 4000 60606
Tel (312) 447-6000 SIC 8111

PRITZKER ORGANIZATION LLC p 1178
71 S Wacker Dr Fl 47 60606
Tel (312) 873-4900 SIC 6159

▲ PRIVATEBANCORP INC p 1178
120 S Lasalle St Ste 400 60603
Tel (312) 564-2000 SIC 6022

■ PRIVATEBANK AND TRUST CO p 1178
120 S La Salle St 60603
Tel (312) 564-2000 SIC 6022

PROFESSIONAL CONVENTION MANAGEMENT ASSOCIATION p 1180
35 E Wacker Dr Ste 500 60601
Tel (312) 423-7262 SIC 8611

PROFESSIONAL NATIONAL TITLE NETWORK p 1180
70 W Madison St Ste 1600 60602
Tel (312) 621-1105 SIC 6361

PROFESSIONAL NURSING INC p 1180
325 N Wells St Ste 900 60654
Tel (312) 527-1839 SIC 7361 7363

PROTEIN BAR INC p 1185
200 N Lasalle Ste 1880 60601
Tel (312) 300-2566 SIC 5812

PULLMAN WHEEL WORKS ASSOCIATES p 1191
901 E 104th St Ste 2 60628
Tel (773) 785-1300 SIC 6513

QST INDUSTRIES INC p 1195
550 W Adams St Ste 200 60661
Tel (312) 930-9400 SIC 2396 2392 2752

■ QUAKER OATS CO p 1196
555 W Monroe St Fl 1 60661
Tel (312) 821-1000
SIC 2086 2043 2045 2052 2064 2099

■ QUAKER SALES & DISTRIBUTION INC p 1196
555 W Monroe St 60661
Tel (312) 821-1000 SIC 5963

QUINNOX INC p 1200
400 N Michigan Ave # 1300 60611
Tel (630) 548-4800 SIC 7379 7371

R & R GOLDMAN & ASSOCIATES INC p 1201
4300 N Knox Ave 60641
Tel (773) 777-4494 SIC 5621

■ RAILROAD RETIREMENT BOARD UNITED STATES p 1205
844 N Rush St 60611
Tel (877) 772-5772 SIC 9441

RAPID DISPLAYS INC p 1208
4300 W 47th St 60632
Tel (773) 927-5000 SIC 2675 3944

REGIONAL TRANSPORTATION AUTHORITY p 1219
175 W Jackson Blvd # 1650 60604
Tel (312) 913-3200 SIC 4111

REHABILITATION INSTITUTE OF CHICAGO p 1220
345 E Superior St 60611
Tel (312) 238-1000 SIC 8069

RESEARCH INTERNATIONAL USA p 1226
222 Merchandise Mart Plz # 250 60654
Tel (312) 787-4060 SIC 8732

REWARDS NETWORK INC p 1229
2 N Riverside Plz # 200 60606
Tel (312) 756-0021 SIC 7389

REX ELECTRIC & TECHNOLOGIES LLC p 1230
200 W Monroe St Ste 1700 60606
Tel (312) 251-3620 SIC 1731

REXAM BEVERAGE CAN CO p 1230
8770 W Bryn Mawr Ave Fl 8 60631
Tel (773) 399-3000 SIC 3411

RIVERBED HOLDINGS INC p 1237
300 N La Salle Dr # 4350 60654
Tel (312) 254-3300 SIC 6719

RJ OBRIEN & ASSOCIATES LLC p 1239
222 S Riverside Plz # 1200 60606
Tel (312) 373-5000 SIC 6221 6211

RJ OBRIEN HOLDINGS INC p 1239
222 S Riverside Plz # 900 60606
Tel (312) 373-5000 SIC 6282

ROADSAFE TRAFFIC SYSTEMS INC p 1240
8750 W Bryn Mawr Ave # 400 60631
Tel (773) 724-3300 SIC 1721 1611 7389

ROBERT R MCCORMICK FOUNDATION p 1241
205 N Michigan Ave # 4300 60601
Tel (312) 445-5000 *SIC* 8641 8699

ROOSEVELT UNIVERSITY p 1249
430 S Michigan Ave 60605
Tel (312) 341-3500 *SIC* 8221

ROSENTHAL COLLINS GROUP LLC p 1251
216 W Jackson Blvd # 400 60606
Tel (312) 460-9200
SIC 6221 6289 6231 6211

▲ RR DONNELLEY & SONS CO p 1255
35 W Wacker Dr Ste 3650 60601
Tel (312) 326-8000
SIC 2754 2759 2752 2732 7331 7336

■ RR DONNELLEY PRINTING CO LP p 1255
111 S Wacker Dr Ste 3500 60606
Tel (312) 326-8000 *SIC* 2754 2752 5085

RSM US LLP p 1256
1 S Wacker Dr Ste 800 60606
Tel (312) 634-3400 *SIC* 8721 8742 7291

RUSH SYSTEM FOR HEALTH p 1258
1645 W Jackson Blvd Ste 5 60612
Tel (312) 942-4061 *SIC* 8741 8062

RUSH UNIVERSITY MEDICAL CENTER p 1259
1653 W Congress Pkwy 60612
Tel (312) 942-5000 *SIC* 8062

▲ RYERSON HOLDING CORP p 1260
227 W Monroe St Fl 27 60606
Tel (312) 292-5000 *SIC* 5051

RYERSON INC p 1261
227 W Monroe St Ste 2700 60606
Tel (312) 292-5000 *SIC* 5051

■ RYERSON PROCUREMENT CORP p 1261
227 W Monroe St Fl 27 60606
Tel (312) 292-5000 *SIC* 5051

S & C ELECTRIC CO p 1261
6601 N Ridge Blvd 60626
Tel (773) 338-1000
SIC 3613 3643 3625 8711

SAC WIRELESS LLC p 1264
540 W Madison St Ste 1600 60661
Tel (847) 944-1600 *SIC* 8741 8742

SAINT ANTHONY HOSPITAL p 1268
2875 W 19th St 60623
Tel (773) 484-1000 *SIC* 8062

SAINT XAVIER UNIVERSITY p 1271
3700 W 103rd St 60655
Tel (773) 298-3000 *SIC* 8221

SAMMONS FINANCIAL GROUP INC p 1274
525 W Van Buren St # 1200 60607
Tel (312) 648-7600 *SIC* 6311

SARGENT & LUNDY LLC p 1282
55 E Monroe St Ste 2700 60603
Tel (312) 269-2000 *SIC* 8711

SCHULZE AND BURCH BISCUIT CO p 1291
1133 W 35th St 60609
Tel (773) 927-6622 *SIC* 2051 2052 2099

■ SELECT HOTELS GROUP LLC p 1301
71 S Wacker Dr 60606
Tel (312) 750-1234 *SIC* 7011

SENIOR LIFESTYLE CORP p 1304
303 E Wacker Dr Ste 2400 60601
Tel (312) 673-4333 *SIC* 8052

SENIOR RESURRECTION SERVICES p 1304
7435 W Talcott Ave 60631
Tel (773) 774-8000 *SIC* 8059

SERVICE EMPLOYEES INTERNATIONAL UNION LOCAL 1 p 1307
111 E Wacker Dr Ste 2500 60601
Tel (312) 240-1600 *SIC* 8631

SEYFARTH SHAW LLP p 1309
131 S Dearborn St # 2400 60603
Tel (312) 460-5000 *SIC* 8111

SIDLEY AUSTIN LLP p 1319
1 S Dearborn St Ste 900 60603
Tel (312) 853-7000 *SIC* 8111

SILKROAD TECHNOLOGY INC p 1323
100 S Wacker Dr Ste 425 60606
Tel (866) 329-3363 *SIC* 7371

■ SIMPLER NORTH AMERICA LLC p 1325
1 N Dearborn St Ste 1400 60602
Tel (312) 533-3500 *SIC* 8742 7379

SINAI CHILDRENS HOSPITAL p 1326
1500 S Cal Ave K435 435 K 60608
Tel (773) 542-2000 *SIC* 8011 8062

SINAI HEALTH SYSTEM p 1326
1500 S Fairfield Ave 60608
Tel (773) 542-2000 *SIC* 6512 8741

SKENDER CONSTRUCTION CO p 1329
200 W Madison St Ste 1300 60606
Tel (312) 781-0265 *SIC* 1542

SKIDMORE OWINGS & MERRILL LLP p 1329
224 S Michigan Ave # 1000 60604
Tel (312) 554-9090 *SIC* 8712

SMITHBUCKLIN CORP p 1333
330 N Wabash Ave 60611
Tel (312) 644-6610 *SIC* 8742 8743 4724

SMT TELECOM INC p 1335
5219 N Harlem Ave 60656
Tel (773) 842-4412 *SIC* 8748

SMX LLC p 1335
860 W Evergreen Ave 60642
Tel (312) 915-0900 *SIC* 7361

SOFTCHOICE CORP p 1337
314 W Superior St Ste 400 60654
Tel (416) 588-9002 *SIC* 5045

▲ SP PLUS CORP p 1353
200 E Randolph St # 7700 60601
Tel (312) 274-2000 *SIC* 7521 7514

SPSS INC p 1362
200 W Madison St Ste 2300 60606
Tel (312) 651-3000 *SIC* 7372

SRAM LLC p 1362
1000 W Fulton Market # 400 60607
Tel (312) 664-8800 *SIC* 3751

ST BERNARD HOSPITAL p 1365
326 W 64th St 60621
Tel (773) 962-3900 *SIC* 8062

■ STAFF MANAGEMENT SOLUTIONS LLC p 1374
860 W Evergreen Ave 60642
Tel (312) 915-0900 *SIC* 7363 8741

STARCOM MEDIAVEST GROUP INC p 1379
35 W Wacker Dr Fl 9 60601
Tel (312) 220-3535 *SIC* 7311

■ STONE SOUTHWEST INC p 1391
150 N Michigan Ave 60601
Tel (312) 346-6600
SIC 2631 2611 2621 2435 2436 2421

STRATEGIC HOTELS & RESORTS INC p 1392
200 W Madison St Ste 1700 60606
Tel (312) 658-5000 *SIC* 6798

SUN-TIMES MEDIA GROUP INC p 1401
350 N Orleans St Fl 10 60654
Tel (312) 321-2299 *SIC* 2711

SUN-TIMES MEDIA HOLDINGS LLC p 1401
350 N Orleans St Fl 10 60654
Tel (312) 321-2299 *SIC* 2711

SUPERIOR GRAPHITE CO p 1406
10 S Riverside Plz # 1470 60606
Tel (312) 559-2999 *SIC* 3295

SUZLON WIND ENERGY CORP p 1410
8750 W Bryn Mawr Ave # 900 60631
Tel (773) 328-5073 *SIC* 3511

SWEDISH COVENANT HOSPITAL p 1411
5145 N California Ave 60625
Tel (773) 878-8200 *SIC* 8062 8059

SWISSOTEL MANAGEMENT CORP p 1413
323 E Wacker Dr 60601
Tel (312) 565-0565 *SIC* 7011

SYSTEM PARKING INC p 1418
180 N La Salle St # 1700 60601
Tel (312) 819-5050 *SIC* 7521

SYSTEM SOFTWARE ASSOCIATES INC DEL p 1418
500 W Madison St Ste 1600 60661
Tel (312) 258-6000 *SIC* 7372 7373

T & J FOODS LLC p 1419
233 S Wacker Dr Ste 8325 60606
Tel (312) 357-5137 *SIC* 5147

TCA TOLEDO LLC p 1428
3611 N Kedzie Ave Fl 2 60618
Tel (773) 463-1234 *SIC* 7991

▲ TELEPHONE AND DATA SYSTEMS INC p 1434
30 N La Salle St Ste 4000 60602
Tel (312) 630-1900 *SIC* 4812 4813

TEMPEL STEEL CO p 1436
5500 N Wolcott Ave 60640
Tel (773) 250-8000
SIC 3469 3313 3316 3398 5051

TENNIS CORP OF AMERICA p 1438
3611 N Kedzie Ave Fl 2 60618
Tel (773) 463-1234 *SIC* 7991

TESTA PRODUCE INC p 1441
4555 S Racine Ave 60609
Tel (312) 226-3237 *SIC* 5148 5812

TEYS (USA) INC p 1445
770 N Halsted St Ste 202 60642
Tel (312) 492-7163 *SIC* 2011

THOMA BRAVO LLC p 1448
300 N La Salle Dr # 4350 60654
Tel (312) 254-3300 *SIC* 6799

THOMA CRESSEY BRAVO INC p 1448
300 N La Salle Dr # 4350 60654
Tel (312) 254-3300
SIC 6799 8711 6311 6321 6531 7373

THOR PALMER HOUSE HOTEL LLC p 1450
17 E Monroe St Lbby 10 60603
Tel (312) 726-7500 *SIC* 7011

THOUGHTWORKS INC p 1450
200 E Randolph St # 2500 60601
Tel (312) 373-1000 *SIC* 8741

THRALL ENTERPRISES INC p 1450
180 N Stetson Ave 60601
Tel (312) 621-8200 *SIC* 2893

THYSSENKRUPP NORTH AMERICA INC p 1451
111 W Jackson Blvd # 2400 60604
Tel (312) 525-2800 *SIC* 6719 3714

■ TOOTSIE ROLL CO INC p 1460
7401 S Cicero Ave 60629
Tel (773) 838-3400 *SIC* 2064

▲ TOOTSIE ROLL INDUSTRIES INC p 1460
7401 S Cicero Ave 60629
Tel (773) 838-3400 *SIC* 2064

■ TOOTSIE ROLL INDUSTRIES LLC p 1460
7401 S Cicero Ave 60629
Tel (773) 245-4202 *SIC* 2064

TOYOTA TECHNOLOGICAL INSTITUTE AT CHICAGO p 1467
6045 S Kenwood Ave 60637
Tel (773) 834-2500 *SIC* 8221

TPS PARKING MANAGEMENT LLC p 1467
200 W Monroe St Ste 1500 60606
Tel (312) 781-9396 *SIC* 7521

TRADING TECHNOLOGIES INTERNATIONAL INC p 1469
222 S Riverside Plz # 1000 60606
Tel (312) 476-1000 *SIC* 7371

TRAFFIC TECH HOLDING CORP p 1469
180 N Michigan Ave # 700 60601
Tel (514) 343-0044 *SIC* 4731

TRANSCO INC p 1471
200 N La Salle St # 1550 60601
Tel (312) 896-8527
SIC 4789 3743 3296 1742

TRANSLOGIX LLC p 1472
2001 E 122nd St 60633
Tel (773) 646-8300 *SIC* 4731

■ TRANSPORTATION INSURANCE CO p 1472
333 S Wabash Ave 60604
Tel (312) 822-5000 *SIC* 6411

▲ TRANSUNION p 1473
555 W Adams St Fl 1 60661
Tel (312) 985-2000 *SIC* 7323

■ TRANSUNION INTERACTIVE INC p 1473
555 W Adams St 60661
Tel (805) 782-8282 *SIC* 7323

■ TRANSUNION INTERMEDIATE HOLDINGS INC p 1473
555 W Adams St Fl 2 60661
Tel (312) 258-1717 *SIC* 7323

■ TRANSUNION LLC p 1473
555 W Adams St Fl 1 60661
Tel (312) 985-2000 *SIC* 8741

TREASURE ISLAND FOODS INC p 1475
3460 N Broadway St 60657
Tel (773) 327-3880 *SIC* 5411 5921

■ TRIBUNE BROADCASTING CO LLC p 1479
435 N Michigan Ave Fl 2 60611
Tel (312) 222-3333 *SIC* 4833 4832

■ TRIBUNE INTERACTIVE INC p 1479
435 N Michigan Ave Fl 2 60611
Tel (312) 222-3232 *SIC* 4813

▲ TRIBUNE MEDIA CO p 1479
435 N Michigan Ave Fl 2 60611
Tel (212) 210-2786
SIC 4833 4832 7922 7941

■ TRIBUNE PUBLISHING CO LLC p 1479
435 N Michigan Ave Fl 2 60611
Tel (312) 222-9100 *SIC* 2711

TRIMARK MARLINN INC p 1480
6100 W 73rd St Ste 1 60638
Tel (708) 496-1700 *SIC* 5046

TRIPPE MANUFACTURING CO p 1482
1111 W 35th St Fl 12 60609
Tel (773) 869-1111 *SIC* 3577

▲ TRONC INC p 1484
435 N Michigan Ave 60611
Tel (312) 222-9100 *SIC* 2711

TRUE VALUE CO p 1486
8600 W Bryn Mawr Ave 100s 60631
Tel (773) 695-5000 *SIC* 5072 2851 3991

TRUSTWAVE CORP p 1488
70 W Madison St Ste 1050 60602
Tel (312) 873-7500 *SIC* 7299 7373

TRUSTWAVE HOLDINGS INC p 1488
70 W Madison St Ste 1050 60602
Tel (312) 750-0950 *SIC* 7373 7372

TTX CO p 1490
101 N Wacker Dr 60606
Tel (312) 853-3223 *SIC* 4741

TWG HOLDINGS INC p 1494
175 W Jackson Blvd Fl 11 60604
Tel (312) 356-3000 *SIC* 6399 8721 6411

TWG WARRANTY GROUP INC p 1494
175 W Jackson Blvd Fl 11 60604
Tel (312) 356-3000 *SIC* 6399 8721 6411

UBS ASSET MANAGEMENT (AMERICAS) INC p 1498
1 N Wacker Dr Ste 3700 60606
Tel (312) 525-4111 *SIC* 6211

UCHICAGO ARGONNE LLC p 1499
5801 S Ellis Ave Ste 601 60637
Tel (773) 702-9476 *SIC* 8733

UHY ADVISORS INC p 1500
30 S Wacker Dr Ste 1330 60606
Tel (312) 578-9600 *SIC* 8721

ULTIMA HOSPITALITY LLC p 1500
30 S Wacker Dr Ste 3600 60606
Tel (312) 948-4500 *SIC* 8741

ULTRA STORES INC p 1501
122 S Michigan Ave # 800 60603
Tel (312) 922-3800 *SIC* 5944

UNI CARE p 1502
233 S Wacker Dr 60606
Tel (312) 234-7000 *SIC* 8011

UNIFIED MANAGEMENT CORP p 1503
1 E Wacker Dr Ste 3504 60601
Tel (312) 828-9480 *SIC* 7363

■ UNION TANK CAR CO p 1505
175 W Jackson Blvd # 2100 60604
Tel (312) 431-3111
SIC 3743 4741 4789 5051

■ UNITED AIRLINES INC p 1506
233 S Wacker Dr Ste 430 60606
Tel (872) 825-4000 *SIC* 4512 4513 4729

UNITED CENTER JOINT VENTURE p 1507
1901 W Madison St 60612
Tel (312) 455-4112 *SIC* 7941

▲ UNITED CONTINENTAL HOLDINGS INC p 1507
233 S Wacker Dr 60606
Tel (872) 825-4000 *SIC* 4512

■ UNITED STATES CELLULAR CORP p 1512
8410 W Bryn Mawr Ave # 700 60631
Tel (773) 399-8900 *SIC* 4812 4813

■ UNITED STATES GYPSUM CO INC p 1513
550 W Adams St Ste 1300 60661
Tel (312) 606-4000 *SIC* 3275

UNITED STATES SOCCER FEDERATION INC p 1514
1801 S Prairie Ave 60616
Tel (312) 808-1300 *SIC* 8699

UNITED TEMPS INC p 1514
1550 S Ind Ave Ste 300 60605
Tel (312) 922-8558 *SIC* 7361

UNIVERSITY OF CHICAGO p 1520
5801 S Ellis Ave Ste 1 60637
Tel (773) 702-1234 *SIC* 8221

UNIVERSITY OF CHICAGO p 1520
1414 E 59th St 60637
Tel (773) 753-2270 *SIC* 7021

UNIVERSITY OF CHICAGO MEDICAL CENTER p 1520
5841 S Maryland Ave 60637
Tel (773) 702-1000 *SIC* 8062

UNLIMITED ADVACARE INC p 1528
2939 N Pulaski Rd 60641
Tel (773) 725-8858 *SIC* 5047

UNO CHARTER SCHOOL NETWORK INC p 1528
209 W Jackson Blvd # 500 60606
Tel (312) 637-3900 *SIC* 8211

URBAN PENNSYLVANIA INVESTMENT MEMBER LLC p 1530
445 N Wells St Ste 200 60654
Tel (312) 222-0777 *SIC* 6799

US HEALTH INC p 1532
8700 W Bryn Mawr Ave # 2 60631
Tel (773) 399-7626 *SIC* 7991

▲ USG CORP p 1535
550 W Adams St 60661
Tel (312) 436-4000 *SIC* 3275 3296

■ USG INTERIORS LLC p 1535
125 S Franklin St 60606
Tel (800) 874-4968 *SIC* 5031

USG INTERNATIONAL LTD p 1535
125 S Franklin St Ste 4 60606
Tel (312) 606-4000 *SIC* 5033

■ VALLEY FORGE LIFE INSURANCE CO INC p 1540
333 S Wabash Ave 60604
Tel (312) 822-5000 *SIC* 6321 6311

VANTAGE OLEOCHEMICALS INC p 1544
4650 S Racine Ave 60609
Tel (773) 376-9000 *SIC* 2869 2841 5169

VELTEX CORP p 1547
123 W Madison St Ste 1500 60602
Tel (312) 235-4014 *SIC* 2211 5199

▲ VENTAS INC p 1547
353 N Clark St Ste 3300 60654
Tel (877) 483-6827 *SIC* 6798

VEOLIA ENVIRONMENTAL SERVICES NORTH AMERICA CORP p 1548
200 E Randolph St # 7900 60601
Tel (312) 552-2800 *SIC* 4953

■ VHS ACQUISITION SUBSIDIARY NUMBER 3 INC p 1553
4646 N Marine Dr 60640
Tel (773) 878-8700 *SIC* 8062

VIENNA BEEF LTD p 1556
2501 N Damen Ave 60647
Tel (773) 278-7800
SIC 2013 2035 2053 5411 5149 5147

VIRGINIA SURETY CO INC p 1560
175 W Jackson Blvd Fl 11 60604
Tel (312) 356-3000 *SIC* 6351 6399

VIRONEX INC p 1560
4350 W Ohio St 60624
Tel (773) 265-0403 *SIC* 4225

VPC PIZZA HOLDINGS LLC p 1566
227 W Monroe St 60606
Tel (312) 701-1777 *SIC* 6719

VWR INVESTORS INC p 1567
3 First National Plz 60602
Tel (610) 386-1700 *SIC* 6799

W E ONEIL CONSTRUCTION CO p 1568
1245 W Washington Blvd 60607
Tel (773) 244-6003 *SIC* 1541

WALSH CONSTRUCTION CO p 1574
929 W Adams St 60607
Tel (312) 563-5400
SIC 1541 1622 1542 1611

WALSH CONSTRUCTION CO II LLC p 1574
929 W Adams St 60607
Tel (312) 563-5400 *SIC* 1542 1611

WALSH CONSTRUCTION GROUP LLC p 1574
929 W Adams St 60607
Tel (312) 563-5400 *SIC* 1542

WALSH GROUP LTD p 1574
929 W Adams St 60607
Tel (312) 563-5400
SIC 1542 1522 1622 1629 1541

WARRANTY GROUP INC p 1576
175 W Jackson Blvd Fl 11 60604
Tel (312) 356-3000 *SIC* 6351 6399

WATER STREET HEALTHCARE PARTNERS LLC p 1581
333 W Wacker Dr Ste 2800 60606
Tel (312) 506-2900 *SIC* 6211

WATERTON ASSOCIATES LLC p 1582
30 S Wacker Dr Ste 3600 60606
Tel (312) 948-4500 *SIC* 6513 6798

■ **WEC BUSINESS SERVICES LLC** p 1587
200 E Randolph St # 2200 60601
Tel (312) 240-3877 *SIC* 8742 8721

■ **WELLS FARGO INSURANCE SERVICES INC** p 1590
230 W Monroe St Ste 1950 60606
Tel (312) 685-4122 *SIC* 6411

■ **WELLS FARGO INSURANCE SERVICES USA INC** p 1591
150 N Michigan Ave # 3900 60601
Tel (866) 294-2571 *SIC* 6411

■ **WEST UNIFIED COMMUNICATIONS SERVICES INC** p 1596
8420 W Bryn Mawr Ave # 1100 60631
Tel (773) 399-1600 *SIC* 7389

■ **WGN CONTINENTAL BROADCASTING CO** p 1604
2501 W Bradley Pl 60618
Tel (773) 528-2311 *SIC* 4832 4833

WHEATLAND TUBE LLC p 1604
227 W Monroe St Ste 2600 60606
Tel (312) 275-1600 *SIC* 3317 3644

WHI CAPITAL PARTNERS p 1605
191 N Wacker Dr Ste 1500 60606
Tel (312) 621-0590 *SIC* 6799 3317

WILLIAM BLAIR & CO LLC p 1610
222 W Adams St Ste 2900 60606
Tel (312) 236-1600 *SIC* 6211

WILSON SPORTING GOODS CO p 1614
8750 W Bryn Mawr Ave Fl 2 60631
Tel (773) 714-6400 *SIC* 5091 3949

WIND POINT PARTNERS LP p 1615
676 N Michigan Ave # 3700 60611
Tel (312) 255-4800 *SIC* 6799 7363 3089

WIND POINT PARTNERS VI LP p 1615
676 N Michigan Ave # 3700 60611
Tel (312) 255-4800
SIC 6799 2542 2541 3429

WINSTON & STRAWN LLP p 1617
35 W Wacker Dr Ste 4200 60601
Tel (312) 558-5600 *SIC* 8111

■ **WINTRUST BANK** p 1617
190 S La Salle St # 2200 60603
Tel (773) 227-7074 *SIC* 6022

WIRTZ BEVERAGE GROUP LLC p 1618
680 N Lake Shore Dr # 1900 60611
Tel (312) 943-7000 *SIC* 5181 5182

WIRTZ CORP p 1618
680 N Lake Shore Dr # 1900 60611
Tel (312) 943-7000
SIC 5181 5182 6513 6512 7011 6411

WM WRIGLEY JR CO p 1620
930 W Evergreen Ave 60642
Tel (312) 280-4710
SIC 2067 2064 2087 2899

■ **WMS GAMING INC** p 1620
3401 N California Ave 60618
Tel (773) 961-1000 *SIC* 3999

■ **WMS INDUSTRIES INC** p 1620
3401 N California Ave 60618
Tel (847) 785-3000 *SIC* 3999 7999

WOLVERINE TRADING LLC p 1621
175 W Jackson Blvd # 200 60604
Tel (312) 884-4000 *SIC* 6211

WORLDS FINEST CHOCOLATE INC p 1626
4801 S Lawndale Ave 60632
Tel (773) 847-4600 *SIC* 2066 5947

WRAPPORTS LLC p 1627
350 N Orleans St 10thf 60654
Tel (312) 321-3000 *SIC* 7379 2711

WRIGLEY MANUFACTURING CO LLC p 1627
410 N Michigan Ave 60611
Tel (312) 644-2121 *SIC* 2067

YOUNG INNOVATIONS HOLDINGS LLC p 1638
111 S Wacker Dr 60606
Tel (312) 506-5600 *SIC* 3843

YOUNG MENS CHRISTIAN ASSOCIATION OF CHICAGO p 1638
1030 W Van Buren St 60607
Tel (312) 932-1200
SIC 8641 7011 8351 8699 8322 7999

ZACKS INVESTMENT RESEARCH INC p 1640
10 S Riverside Plz # 1600 60606
Tel (312) 630-9880 *SIC* 6282

ZEKELMAN INDUSTRIES INC p 1641
227 W Monroe St Fl 26 60606
Tel (312) 275-1600 *SIC* 3317

CHILLICOTHE, IL

MH EQUIPMENT CO p 958
2001 Hartman 61523
Tel (309) 579-8020 *SIC* 5084

MH LOGISTICS CORP p 958
2001 Hartman 61523
Tel (309) 579-8030 *SIC* 5084

CICERO, IL

ALTERNATIVE STAFFING INC p 62
5620 W Cermak Rd 60804
Tel (708) 652-3636 *SIC* 7361

BREAKTHRU BEVERAGE ILLINOIS LLC p 209
3333 S Laramie Ave 60804
Tel (708) 298-3333 *SIC* 5182

▲ **BROADWIND ENERGY INC** p 216
3240 S Central Ave 60804
Tel (708) 780-4800 *SIC* 3511

CICERO PUBLIC SCHOOL DISTRICT 99 p 306
5110 W 24th St 60804
Tel (708) 863-4856 *SIC* 8211

COREY STEEL CO p 370
2800 S 61st Ct 60804
Tel (800) 323-2750 *SIC* 3316 5051

ROYAL BOX GROUP LLC p 1254
1301 S 47th Ave 60804
Tel (708) 656-2020 *SIC* 2653

UNITED SCRAP METAL INC p 1511
1545 S Cicero Ave 60804
Tel (708) 780-6800 *SIC* 5093

COAL CITY, IL

D CONSTRUCTION INC p 406
1488 S Broadway St 60416
Tel (815) 634-2555 *SIC* 1611

COLLINSVILLE, IL

■ **AMEREN ILLINOIS CO** p 66
6 Executive Dr 62234
Tel (618) 343-8150 *SIC* 4924 4911

COLUMBIA, IL

LUHR BROS INC p 884
250 W Sand Bank Rd 62236
Tel (618) 281-4106 *SIC* 1629

■ **MAVERICK TECHNOLOGIES HOLDINGS LLC** p 921
265 Admiral Trost Rd 62236
Tel (618) 281-9100 *SIC* 8711 8748 1731

■ **MAVERICK TECHNOLOGIES LLC** p 921
265 Admiral Trost Rd 62236
Tel (618) 281-9100 *SIC* 8711 8748 1731

COUNTRYSIDE, IL

CONTRACTING & MATERIAL CO p 364
9550 W 55th St Ste A 60525
Tel (708) 588-6000
SIC 4922 1623 4612 1731

COOPERS HAWK INTERMEDIATE HOLDING LLC p 367
5325 9th Ave 60525
Tel (708) 839-2920
SIC 8741 2084 5182 5812

MEADE ELECTRIC CO INC p 933
9550 W 55th St Ste A 60525
Tel (708) 588-2500 *SIC* 1731

MIDWEST OPERATING ENGINEERS FRINGE BENEFIT FUND p 967
6150 Joliet Rd 60525
Tel (708) 482-0589 *SIC* 6371

MIDWEST OPERATING ENGINEERS WELFARE FUND p 967
6150 Joliet Rd 60525
Tel (708) 482-7300 *SIC* 6722

CREST HILL, IL

EDWARD MEDICAL GROUP p 480
16151 Weber Rd Ste 201 60403
Tel (815) 773-7827 *SIC* 8099

CRETE, IL

CRETE-MONEE SCHOOL DISTRICT NO 201-U p 392
1500 S Sangamon St 60417
Tel (708) 367-8300 *SIC* 8211

HOLLAND LP p 700
1000 Holland Dr 60417
Tel (708) 672-2300 *SIC* 2899 3743

CRYSTAL LAKE, IL

▲ **APTARGROUP INC** p 101
475 W Terra Cotta Ave E 60014
Tel (815) 477-0424 *SIC* 3089 3499

CENTEGRA HEALTH SYSTEM p 275
385 Millennium Dr Ste A 60012
Tel (815) 788-5800 *SIC* 8062

CRYSTAL LAKE COMMUNITY CONSOLIDATED SCHOOL DISTRICT 47 p 397
300 Commerce Dr 60014
Tel (815) 459-6070 *SIC* 8211 8741

CURRAN GROUP INC p 402
286 Memorial Ct 60014
Tel (815) 455-5100 *SIC* 1799 3253 1611

MCHENRY COUNTY COLLEGE p 929
8900 Us Highway 14 60012
Tel (815) 455-3700 *SIC* 8222 8221 9411

TC INDUSTRIES INC p 1428
3703 S Il Route 31 60012
Tel (815) 459-2401 *SIC* 3499 3398

TERRA COTTA HOLDINGS CO p 1439
3703 S Il Route 31 60012
Tel (815) 459-2400 *SIC* 3499 3398 6531

DAHLGREN, IL

■ **WHITE OAK RESOURCES LLC** p 1606
18033 County Road 500 E 62828
Tel (618) 643-5500 *SIC* 1241

DAKOTA, IL

BERNER FOOD & BEVERAGE LLC p 176
2034 E Factory Rd 61018
Tel (815) 563-4222
SIC 2022 2026 2095 2086 2033

DANVILLE, IL

CANNON COCHRAN MANAGEMENT SERVICES INC p 247
2 E Main St Towne Ctr 61832
Tel (217) 446-1089 *SIC* 6411

CCMSI HOLDINGS INC p 270
2 E Main St Ste 208 61832
Tel (217) 446-1089 *SIC* 8748

KIK CUSTOM PRODUCTS INC p 817
1 W Hegeler Ln 61832
Tel (217) 442-1400
SIC 2841 2842 2843 2844

■ **MCLANE/MIDWEST INC** p 931
3400 E Main St 61834
Tel (217) 477-7500 *SIC* 5141

MERVIS INDUSTRIES INC p 951
3295 E Main St Ste C 61834
Tel (217) 442-5300 *SIC* 5093

THYSSENKRUPP CRANKSHAFT CO LLC p 1451
1000 Lynch Rd 61834
Tel (217) 431-0060 *SIC* 3714 3462

THYSSENKRUPP PRESTA DANVILLE LLC p 1451
75 Walz Crk 61834
Tel (217) 444-5500 *SIC* 3714

WATCHFIRE ENTERPRISES INC p 1581
1015 Maple St 61832
Tel (217) 442-0611 *SIC* 3993

WATCHFIRE SIGNS LLC p 1581
1015 Maple St 61832
Tel (217) 442-0611 *SIC* 3993

WATCHFIRE TECHNOLOGIES HOLDINGS I INC p 1581
1015 Maple St 61832
Tel (217) 442-6971 *SIC* 3993

WATCHFIRE TECHNOLOGIES HOLDINGS II INC p 1581
1015 Maple St 61832
Tel (217) 442-0611 *SIC* 3993

DARIEN, IL

ROTATION DYNAMICS CORP p 1252
8140 Cass Ave 60561
Tel (630) 769-9255 *SIC* 3069

SINGLE SOURCE INC p 1326
8160 Cass Ave 60561
Tel (630) 324-5982 *SIC* 5141

DECATUR, IL

ADM COCOA INC p 23
4666 E Faries Pkwy 62526
Tel (217) 424-5200 *SIC* 5169

ADM EDIBLE BEAN SPECIALTIES INC p 23
4666 E Faries Pkwy 62526
Tel (217) 424-5200 *SIC* 5191

■ **ADM GRAIN RIVER SYSTEM INC** p 23
4666 E Faries Pkwy 62526
Tel (312) 634-8100 *SIC* 5153

■ **ADM TRUCKING INC** p 23
2501 N Brush College Rd 62526
Tel (217) 424-5200 *SIC* 4213

■ **AMERICAN RIVER TRANSPORTATION CO LLC** p 78
4666 E Faries Pkwy 62526
Tel (217) 424-5200 *SIC* 4449

CONTINENTAL CARBONIC PRODUCTS INC p 363
3985 E Harrison Ave 62526
Tel (217) 428-2068 *SIC* 2813

DECATUR MEMORIAL FOUNDATION p 420
2300 N Edward St 62526
Tel (217) 876-8121 *SIC* 6732

DECATUR MEMORIAL HOSPITAL p 421
2300 N Edward St 62526
Tel (217) 877-8121 *SIC* 8062

DECATUR SCHOOL DISTRICT 61 INC p 421
101 W Cerro Gordo St 62523
Tel (217) 362-3000 *SIC* 8211

DMH CORPORATE HEALTH SERVICES p 446
2300 N Edward St 62526
Tel (217) 876-8121 *SIC* 8062

HOWARD G BUFFETT FOUNDATION p 713
145 N Merchant St Apt 1 62523
Tel (217) 429-3988 *SIC* 7389

MCLEOD EXPRESS LLC p 931
5002 Cundiff Ct 62526
Tel (217) 706-5045 *SIC* 4213

MORGAN DISTRIBUTING INC p 988
3425 N 22nd St 62526
Tel (217) 877-3570 *SIC* 5171

NECA IBEW WELFARE TRUST FUND p 1023
2120 Hubbard Ave 62526
Tel (800) 765-4239 *SIC* 8631

RATHJE ENTERPRISES INC p 1209
1845 N 22nd St 62526
Tel (217) 423-2593 *SIC* 1731 7694 5063

ST MARYS HOSPITAL p 1371
1800 E Lake Shore Dr 62521
Tel (217) 464-2984 *SIC* 8062

ST MARYS HOSPITAL DECATUR OF HOSPITAL SISTERS OF THIRD ORDER OF ST FRANCIS p 1371
1800 E Lake Shore Dr 62521
Tel (217) 464-2966 *SIC* 8062

TATE & LYLE INGREDIENTS AMERICAS LLC p 1426
2200 E Eldorado St 62521
Tel (217) 423-4411 *SIC* 2046

DEERFIELD, IL

AMERICAN CHEMET CORP p 70
740 Waukegan Rd Ste 202 60015
Tel (847) 948-0800 *SIC* 2819 2816

BAXALTA US INC p 160
1 Baxter Pkwy 60015
Tel (224) 948-2000 *SIC* 7389

■ **BAXTER HEALTHCARE CORP** p 160
1 Baxter Pkwy 60015
Tel (224) 948-2000
SIC 3841 2835 2389 3842 5047

▲ **BAXTER INTERNATIONAL INC** p 160
1 Baxter Pkwy 60015
Tel (224) 948-2000
SIC 2834 3841 2835 3842

■ **BAXTER WORLD TRADE CORP** p 160
1 Baxter Pkwy 60015
Tel (224) 948-2000 *SIC* 2834 3841

BEAM GLOBAL SPIRITS & WINE LLC p 165
510 Lake Cook Rd 60015
Tel (847) 948-8888 *SIC* 2085

BEAM SUNTORY INC p 165
510 Lake Cook Rd 60015
Tel (847) 948-8888 *SIC* 2085

■ **BOND DRUG CO OF ILLINOIS LLC** p 200
200 Wilmot Rd 60015
Tel (847) 914-2500 *SIC* 5912

■ **CATAMARAN PBM OF ILLINOIS II INC** p 264
1417 Lake Cook Rd Ste 100 60015
Tel (847) 374-2640 *SIC* 5961

▲ **CF INDUSTRIES HOLDINGS INC** p 285
4 Parkway N Ste 400 60015
Tel (847) 405-2400 *SIC* 2873 2874

■ **CF INDUSTRIES INC** p 285
4 Parkway N Ste 400 60015
Tel (847) 405-2400 *SIC* 2873 2874

■ **CF INDUSTRIES NITROGEN LLC** p 285
4 Parkway N Ste 400 60015
Tel (847) 405-2400 *SIC* 2875 2873

■ **CF INDUSTRIES SALES LLC** p 285
4 Parkway N Ste 400 60015
Tel (847) 405-2400 *SIC* 2873

CHARLES AND MARGERY BARANCIK FOUNDATION p 289
520 Lake Cook Rd 60015
Tel (847) 948-9340 *SIC* 8699

CRITICAL CARE SYSTEMS INC p 393
108 Wilmot Rd 60015
Tel (847) 914-2500 *SIC* 8082

■ **ESSENDANT CO** p 510
1 Parkway North Blvd # 100 60015
Tel (847) 627-7000 *SIC* 5112

▲ **ESSENDANT INC** p 510
1 Parkway North Blvd # 100 60015
Tel (847) 627-7000
SIC 5112 5111 5021 5044 5087 5045

■ **ESSENDANT MANAGEMENT SERVICES LLC** p 510
1 Parkway N Ste 100 60015
Tel (847) 627-7000 *SIC* 5943 7373

■ **EVANSTON INSURANCE CO** p 513
10 Parkway N Ste 100 60015
Tel (847) 572-6000 *SIC* 6351 6331

▲ **FORTUNE BRANDS HOME & SECURITY INC** p 570
520 Lake Cook Rd 60015
Tel (847) 484-4400
SIC 2531 2599 3429 3469

GCG FINANCIAL INC p 595
3 Parkway N Ste 500 60015
Tel (847) 457-3000 *SIC* 6411 8742 6211

GLENWOOD TREE EXPERTS p 615
21457 Milwaukee Ave 60015
Tel (847) 459-0200 *SIC* 0783 0782

HOLDEN INDUSTRIES INC p 700
500 Lake Cook Rd Ste 400 60015
Tel (847) 940-1500
SIC 2752 2672 3545 3589 3541 3441

JIM BEAM BRANDS CO p 785
510 Lake Cook Rd Ste 200 60015
Tel (847) 948-8903 *SIC* 2085

JORDAN INDUSTRIES INC p 793
1751 Lake Cook Rd Ste 550 60015
Tel (847) 945-5591
SIC 3621 3625 3714 3089 2759 5999

JORDAN SPECIALTY PLASTICS INC p 793
1751 Lake Cook Rd Ste 550 60015
Tel (847) 945-5591 *SIC* 3089 3081

■ LAGASSE INC p 838
1 Parkway North Blvd # 100 60015
Tel (847) 627-7000 SIC 5087 5141

LUNDBECK LLC p 886
6 Parkway N Ste 400 60015
Tel (847) 282-1000 SIC 2834 5122

■ MARKEL MIDWEST p 908
10 Parkway N Ste 100 60015
Tel (847) 572-6000 SIC 6351

MEREX TECHNOLOGY LEASING CORP p 948
570 Lake Cook Rd Ste 300 60015
Tel (847) 940-1200 SIC 6159 5045

MERIDIAN GROUP INTERNATIONAL INC p 948
9 Parkway N Ste 500 60015
Tel (847) 940-1200 SIC 8742 6159

MERIDIAN IT INC p 949
9 Parkway N Ste 500 60015
Tel (847) 964-2664 SIC 5045

MERIDIAN LEASING CORP p 949
9 Parkway N Ste 500 60015
Tel (847) 964-2700 SIC 6159

■ MONDELEZ GLOBAL LLC p 983
3 Parkway N Ste 300 60015
Tel (847) 943-4000
SIC 2052 2066 3999 2067 2022 2087

▲ MONDELEZ INTERNATIONAL INC p 983
3 Parkway N Ste 300 60015
Tel (847) 943-4000
SIC 2022 2013 2095 2043 2035 2087

NCH MARKETING SERVICES INC p 1022
155 N Pfingsten Rd # 200 60015
Tel (847) 317-9039 SIC 7389

OUTOKUMPU STAINLESS INC p 1099
2275 Half Day Rd Ste 300 60015
Tel (847) 317-1400 SIC 5051

PREGIS HOLDING I CORP p 1170
1650 Lake Cook Rd Ste 400 60015
Tel (847) 597-2200 SIC 2671 5199 7336

PREGIS LLC p 1170
1650 Lake Cook Rd Ste 400 60015
Tel (847) 597-9330 SIC 3086

PREGIS LLC p 1170
1650 Lake Cook Rd Ste 400 60015
Tel (847) 597-2200 SIC 2671 2673 3086

SIMONTON HOLDINGS INC p 1325
520 Lake Cook Rd 60015
Tel (304) 428-8261
SIC 3089 5961 3086 5963

SPIRE HOSPITALITY LLC p 1359
111 S Pfingsten Rd # 425 60015
Tel (847) 498-6650 SIC 8741

STERIGENICS HOLDINGS LLC p 1386
3 Parkway N Ste 100n 60015
Tel (847) 607-6060 SIC 6719

STERIGENICS US LLC p 1386
3 Parkway N Ste 100n 60015
Tel (847) 607-6060 SIC 7389

▲ SURGICAL CARE AFFILIATES INC p 1409
510 Lake Cook Rd Ste 400 60015
Tel (847) 236-0921 SIC 8093

TAKEDA DEVELOPMENT CENTER AMERICAS INC p 1422
1 Takeda Pkwy 60015
Tel (224) 554-6500 SIC 2834

TAKEDA PHARMACEUTICALS AMERICA INC p 1422
1 Takeda Pkwy 60015
Tel (224) 554-6500 SIC 2834

TAKEDA PHARMACEUTICALS USA INC p 1422
1 Takeda Pkwy 60015
Tel (224) 554-6500 SIC 2834

▲ TERRA NITROGEN CO LP p 1439
4 Parkway N Ste 400 60015
Tel (847) 405-2400 SIC 2873

■ TEXTURA CORP p 1445
1405 Lake Cook Rd 60015
Tel (866) 839-8872 SIC 7372

■ WALGREEN ARIZONA DRUG CO p 1572
200 Wilmot Rd 60015
Tel (847) 940-2500 SIC 5912

■ WALGREEN CO p 1572
200 Wilmot Rd 60015
Tel (847) 315-2500 SIC 5912

■ WALGREEN EASTERN CO INC p 1572
200 Wilmot Rd 60015
Tel (847) 940-2500 SIC 5912

■ WALGREEN LOUISIANA CO INC p 1572
200 Wilmot Rd 60015
Tel (847) 940-2500 SIC 5912

▲ WALGREENS BOOTS ALLIANCE INC p 1572
108 Wilmot Rd 60015
Tel (847) 315-2500 SIC 5912

DEKALB, IL

KISHWAUKEE COMMUNITY HOSPITAL p 822
1 Kish Hospital Dr 60115
Tel (815) 756-1521 SIC 8062

NORTHERN ILLINOIS UNIVERSITY ALUMNI ASSOCIATION p 1056
1425 W Lincoln Hwy 60115
Tel (815) 753-9500 SIC 8221

■ TEGRANT ALLOYD BRANDS INC p 1432
1401 Pleasant St 60115
Tel (815) 756-8451 SIC 3089 3565

■ TEGRANT CORP p 1433
1401 Pleasant St 60115
Tel (815) 756-8451 SIC 2671

■ TEGRANT HOLDING CORP p 1433
1401 Pleasant St 60115
Tel (815) 756-8451 SIC 3089 3565

DES PLAINES, IL

BIG TEN CONFERENCE INC p 182
5440 Park Pl 60018
Tel (847) 696-1010 SIC 8699

CAROLINA DESIGNS LTD p 259
999 E Touhy Ave Ste 500 60018
Tel (847) 294-1100 SIC 3999

CHICAGO FAUCET CO p 297
2100 Clearwater Dr 60018
Tel (847) 803-5000 SIC 3432

CIBA VISION INC p 305
333 Howard Ave 60018
Tel (847) 294-3000 SIC 3851

DSC LOGISTICS INC p 457
1750 S Wolf Rd 60018
Tel (847) 390-6800
SIC 4225 4213 4212 4731

FILTRAN HOLDINGS LLC p 542
875 Seegers Rd 60016
Tel (847) 635-6670 SIC 3433

FILTRAN LLC p 542
875 Seegers Rd 60016
Tel (847) 635-6670 SIC 3433

FRANK CONSOLIDATED ENTERPRISES INC p 574
666 Garland Pl 60016
Tel (847) 699-7000 SIC 8742

ILLINOIS BONE AND JOINT INSTITUTE LLC p 732
900 Rand Rd Ste 200 60016
Tel (847) 375-3000 SIC 8011

IMS COMPANIES LLC p 735
1 Innovation Dr 60016
Tel (847) 391-8100
SIC 3469 8711 3679 3714 3444

JUNO LIGHTING LLC p 797
1300 S Wolf Rd 60018
Tel (847) 827-9880 SIC 3646 3645

LORIG CONSTRUCTION CO p 878
250 E Touhy Ave 60018
Tel (847) 298-0360 SIC 1622

LUTHERAN SOCIAL SERVICES OF ILLINOIS p 886
1001 E Touhy Ave Ste 50 60018
Tel (847) 635-4600 SIC 8322 6514 6513

MOTOR COACH INDUSTRIES INTERNATIONAL INC p 993
200 E Oakton St 60018
Tel (847) 285-2000 SIC 3713 3711 3714

OAKTON COMMUNITY COLLEGE p 1071
1600 E Golf Rd Rm 1505 60016
Tel (847) 635-1600 SIC 8221 8222

PRESENCE HOLY FAMILY MEDICAL CENTER p 1172
100 N River Rd 60016
Tel (847) 297-1800 SIC 8062

PROSPECT AIRPORT SERVICES INC p 1184
2130 S Wolf Rd Fl 2 60018
Tel (847) 299-3636 SIC 4581 7349

■ SGK LLC p 1310
1600 Sherwin Ave 60018
Tel (847) 827-9494 SIC 8748

■ SYSCO CHICAGO INC p 1416
250 Wieboldt Dr 60016
Tel (847) 699-5400 SIC 5149 5142

TOTAL SWEETENERS INC p 1463
1700 E Higgins Rd Ste 300 60018
Tel (847) 299-1999 SIC 5149

■ U O P EQUITEC SERVICES INC p 1497
25 E Algonquin Rd 60016
Tel (847) 391-2000 SIC 3533

■ UOP LLC p 1528
25 E Algonquin Rd 60016
Tel (847) 391-2000
SIC 2819 8711 8731 8999 3823 3479

USP HOLDINGS INC p 1535
6250 N Rver Rd Ste 10100 60018
Tel (847) 604-6100 SIC 3321 3491

W DIAMOND GROUP CORP p 1568
1680 E Touhy Ave 60018
Tel (646) 647-2791 SIC 2326 5611

WAREHOUSE DIRECT INC p 1575
2001 S Mount Prospect Rd 60018
Tel (847) 952-1925 SIC 5112

WESLEY-JESSEN CORP (DEL) p 1593
333 Howard Ave 60018
Tel (847) 294-3000 SIC 3851

WHEELS INC p 1605
666 Garland Pl 60016
Tel (847) 699-7000 SIC 7515 7513

WHOLESOME HARVEST BAKING LLC p 1607
1011 E Touhy Ave Ste 500 60018
Tel (800) 550-6810 SIC 2051

DIXON, IL

KATHERINE SHAW BETHEA HOSPITAL p 804
403 E 1st St 61021
Tel (815) 288-5531 SIC 8062

NEISEWANDER ENTERPRISES INC p 1025
1101 E River Rd 61021
Tel (815) 288-1431 SIC 3442 2431 3429

RAYNOR MFG CO p 1210
1101 E River Rd 61021
Tel (815) 288-1431
SIC 3442 7011 3699 2431

DOWNERS GROVE, IL

■ ADDUS HEALTHCARE INC p 22
2300 Warrenville Rd 60515
Tel (630) 296-3400 SIC 8082

▲ ADDUS HOMECARE CORP p 22
2300 Warrenville Rd # 100 60515
Tel (630) 296-3400 SIC 8082 8361

ADVOCATE HEALTH AND HOSPITALS CORP p 28
3975 Highland Ave 60515
Tel (630) 572-9393 SIC 8062

ADVOCATE HEALTH CARE NETWORK p 28
3075 Highland Pkwy Fl 6 60515
Tel (630) 572-9393 SIC 8621

AMBITECH ENGINEERING CORP p 65
1411 Opus Pl Ste 200 60515
Tel (630) 963-5800 SIC 8711

■ ARAMARK MANAGEMENT SERVICES LIMITED PARTNERSHIP p 102
2300 Warrenville Rd 60515
Tel (630) 271-2000 SIC 7349

■ BECKER PROFESSIONAL DEVELOPMENT CORP p 167
3005 Highland Pkwy # 700 60515
Tel (630) 515-7700 SIC 8299

COMMUNITY HIGH SCHOOL DISTRICT 99 p 349
6301 Springside Ave 60516
Tel (630) 795-7100 SIC 8211

■ COVENTRY HEALTH CARE WORKERS COMPENSATION INC p 385
3200 Highland Ave 60515
Tel (630) 737-7900 SIC 5047

▲ DEVRY EDUCATION GROUP INC p 434
3005 Highland Pkwy # 700 60515
Tel (630) 515-7700
SIC 8221 8299 8249 8243

■ DEVRY UNIVERSITY INC p 434
3005 Highland Pkwy # 700 60515
Tel (630) 515-7700 SIC 8221

■ DOVER ARTIFICIAL LIFT INTERNATIONAL LLC p 453
3005 Highland Pkwy 60515
Tel (630) 743-2563
SIC 3559 3535 3533 3561

▲ DOVER CORP p 453
3005 Highland Pkwy # 200 60515
Tel (630) 541-1540
SIC 3632 3586 3533 3577 3674

■ DOVER ENGINEERED SYSTEMS INC p 453
3005 Highland Pkwy # 200 60515
Tel (630) 743-2505
SIC 3568 3443 3441 3561 3491 3492

■ DOVER PRINTING & IDENTIFICATION INC p 453
3005 Highland Pkwy # 200 60515
Tel (630) 541-1540
SIC 3556 3565 3593 7699

DOWNERS GROVE IMPORTS LTD p 453
2020 Ogden Ave 60515
Tel (630) 964-9500 SIC 5511

DU PAGE MEDICAL GROUP LTD p 458
1100 31st St Ste 300 60515
Tel (630) 545-6000 SIC 8011

ELGIN EQUIPMENT GROUP LLC p 486
2001 Bttrfeld Rd Ste 1020 60515
Tel (630) 434-7200 SIC 3532

ELGIN NATIONAL INDUSTRIES INC p 486
2001 Bttrfeld Rd Ste 1020 60515
Tel (630) 434-7200 SIC 3532 8711

■ FIRST HEALTH GROUP CORP p 547
3200 Highland Ave 60515
Tel (630) 737-7900
SIC 8742 6324 6321 6411

■ FIRST HEALTH STRATEGIES INC p 547
3200 Highland Ave 60515
Tel (630) 737-7900 SIC 6411

FLEXIBLE STEEL LACING CO INC p 556
2525 Wisconsin Ave 60515
Tel (630) 971-0150 SIC 3429

■ FLORISTS TRANSWORLD DELIVERY INC p 560
3113 Woodcreek Dr 60515
Tel (630) 719-7800 SIC 5193 7389 2771

▲ FTD COMPANIES INC p 582
3113 Woodcreek Dr 60515
Tel (630) 719-7800 SIC 5992 5947 5961

■ FTD GROUP INC p 582
3113 Woodcreek Dr 60515
Tel (630) 719-7800 SIC 5193 7389

■ FTD INC p 582
3113 Woodcreek Dr 60515
Tel (630) 719-7800 SIC 5193 7389

■ GIBSON ELECTRIC CO INC p 611
3100 Woodcreek Dr 60515
Tel (630) 288-3800 SIC 1731

GLANBIA PERFORMANCE NUTRITION INC p 614
3500 Lacey Rd 60515
Tel (630) 236-0097 SIC 2833 5149 5122

HAVI GLOBAL SOLUTIONS LLC p 668
3500 Lacey Rd Ste 600 60515
Tel (630) 493-7400 SIC 8748

HAVI GROUP LIMITED PARTNERSHIP p 668
3500 Lacey Rd Ste 600 60515
Tel (630) 353-4200 SIC 5113 5142 5199

HEARTHSIDE FOOD SOLUTIONS LLC p 678
3250 Lacey Rd Ste 200 60515
Tel (630) 967-3600 SIC 2043 2038

HEARTLAND HOME FOODS INC p 679
1400 Opus Pl Ste 900 60515
Tel (800) 492-5592 SIC 5812 8741

ILLINOIS STATE OF TOLL HIGHWAY AUTHORITY p 732
2700 Ogden Ave 60515
Tel (630) 241-6800 SIC 9621

MIDWESTERN UNIVERSITY p 968
555 31st St 60515
Tel (630) 515-7300 SIC 8221

NEOVIA LOGISTICS SERVICES LLC p 1026
2001 Bttrfeld Rd Ste 1400 60515
Tel (469) 513-7000 SIC 6719

NEUCO INC p 1028
5101 Thatcher Rd 60515
Tel (630) 960-3800 SIC 5075

PAYONEER INC p 1122
5300 Katrine Ave 60515
Tel (331) 777-2622 SIC 6153

PLUMROSE USA INC p 1157
1901 Butterfield Rd # 305 60515
Tel (732) 257-6600
SIC 2011 5147 2013 5149

■ RALCORP FROZEN BAKERY PRODUCTS INC p 1206
3250 Lacey Rd Ste 600 60515
Tel (630) 455-5200
SIC 2051 2053 2041 2035 2656

RALCORP FROZEN BAKERY PRODUCTS INC p 1206
3250 Lacey Rd Ste 600 60515
Tel (630) 455-5200 SIC 2053 2045

RESCAR INDUSTRIES INC p 1226
1101 31st St Ste 250 60515
Tel (630) 963-1114 SIC 3743

■ SANFORD LP p 1279
3500 Lacey Rd 60515
Tel (770) 418-7000 SIC 2891 3951 3952

SENTINEL TECHNOLOGIES INC p 1305
2550 Warrenville Rd 60515
Tel (630) 769-4300 SIC 7378 1731

■ SILGAN WHITE CAP LLC p 1323
1140 31st St 60515
Tel (630) 515-8383 SIC 5199

■ T-SYSTEMS NORTH AMERICA INC p 1420
1901 Butterfield Rd # 700 60515
Tel (630) 493-6100 SIC 7379 8748

TRI CITY FOODS OF ILLINOIS INC p 1476
1400 Opus Pl Ste 900 60515
Tel (630) 598-3300 SIC 5812

▲ UNIVAR INC p 1516
3075 Highland Pkwy # 200 60515
Tel (331) 777-6000 SIC 5169 5191 8741

DUNLAP, IL

PROCTOR HEALTH CARE INC p 1179
12529 N Fillyside Dr 61525
Tel (309) 691-1000 SIC 8741

DUPO, IL

KUNA MEAT CO INC p 832
704 Kuna Industrial Ct 62239
Tel (618) 286-4000
SIC 5144 5142 5147 5169 5149 5148

DWIGHT, IL

ARENDS HOGAN WALKER LLC p 106
27688 E 3200 North Rd 60420
Tel (217) 388-7717 SIC 5999 5082

EAST ALTON, IL

■ GBC METALS LLC p 594
427 N Shamrock St 62024
Tel (618) 258-2350 SIC 3351 3341 3469

■ GLOBAL BRASS AND COPPER INC p 615
305 Lewis And Clark Blvd 62024
Tel (618) 258-5000
SIC 3351 3341 3469 1542

EAST DUBUQUE, IL

CRESCENT ELECTRIC SUPPLY CO p 391
7750 Timmerman Dr 61025
Tel (815) 747-3145 SIC 5063

EAST MOLINE, IL

YASH TECHNOLOGIES INC p 1635
605 17th Ave 61244
Tel (309) 755-0433 SIC 7379

EAST PEORIA, IL

FEDERAL WAREHOUSE CO p 536
200 National St 61611
Tel (309) 694-4500 SIC 4225 4213 4212

RIVER CITY CONSTRUCTION LLC p 1237
101 Hoffer Ln 61611
Tel (309) 694-3120 SIC 1542 1629

SISTERS OF THIRD ORDER OF ST FRANCIS p 1327
1175 Saint Francis Ln 61611
Tel (309) 699-7215 SIC 8661

EAST SAINT LOUIS, IL

BEELMAN TRUCK CO p 168
1 Racehorse Dr 62205
Tel (618) 646-5300 SIC 4214

CASINO QUEEN INC p 263
200 Front St 62201
Tel (618) 874-5000 SIC 7999 7011

EAST ST LOUIS SCHOOL DISTRICT 189 p 470
1005 State St 62201
Tel (618) 646-3000 SIC 8211

PILOT TRAVEL CENTERS LLC p 1148
1340 Piggott Ave 62201
Tel (618) 875-5800 SIC 5541

EASTON, IL

SUNRISE AG SERVICE CO p 1403
104 S 1st St 62633
Tel (309) 562-7296 SIC 5191 5171 5541

EDELSTEIN, IL

AKRON SERVICES INC p 42
17705 N Elevator Rd 61526
Tel (309) 243-7533 SIC 5153 5191

EDWARDSVILLE, IL

CASSENS TRANSPORT CO p 263
145 N Kansas St 62025
Tel (618) 656-3006 SIC 4213 4231

COUNTY OF MADISON p 379
157 N Main St Rm 382 62025
Tel (618) 692-7040 SIC 9111

EDWARDSVILLE COMMUNITY SCHOOL DISTRICT 7 p 480
708 Saint Louis St 62025
Tel (618) 659-3672 SIC 8211

JF ELECTRIC INC p 785
100 Lake Front Pkwy 62025
Tel (618) 797-5353 SIC 1731

R P LUMBER CO INC p 1202
514 E Vandalia St 62025
Tel (618) 656-1514 SIC 5211 5251

EFFINGHAM, IL

EFFINGHAM EQUITY p 480
201 W Roadway Ave 62401
Tel (217) 342-4101 SIC 5999 5251

▲ MIDLAND STATES BANCORP INC p 966
1201 Network Centre Dr 62401
Tel (217) 342-7321 SIC 6022

■ MIDLAND STATES BANK p 966
1201 Network Centre Dr 62401
Tel (217) 342-2141 SIC 6022

SOUTH CENTRAL FS INC p 1343
405 S Banker St 62401
Tel (217) 342-9231 SIC 5171 5191 2875

ST ANTHONYS MEMORIAL HOSPITAL OF HOSPITAL SISTERS OF THE THIRD ORDER OF ST FRANCIS p 1364
503 N Maple St 62401
Tel (217) 342-2121 SIC 8062

ELBURN, IL

ILLINOIS CONSTRUCTORS CORP p 732
39w866 Fabyan Pkwy 60119
Tel (630) 232-7280 SIC 1611

ELDORADO, IL

SOUTHEASTERN ILLINOIS ELECTRIC COOPERATIVE p 1346
P.O. Box 251 62930
Tel (618) 273-2611 SIC 4911

ELGIN, IL

AMERICAN NTN BEARING MANUFACTURING CORP p 77
1525 Holmes Rd 60123
Tel (847) 741-4545 SIC 3562

BOHLER-UDDEHOLM CORP p 198
2505 Millennium Dr 60124
Tel (877) 992-8764 SIC 5051

CAPSONIC AUTOMOTIVE INC p 251
460 2nd St 60123
Tel (847) 888-7300 SIC 3625 3679 3674

■ COLEMAN FLOOR LLC p 336
1331 Davis Rd 60123
Tel (847) 907-3109 SIC 1752

ELGIN COMMUNITY COLLEGE p 486
1700 Spartan Dr 60123
Tel (847) 697-1000 SIC 8222 8221 9411

■ ELGIN SWEEPER CO p 486
1300 W Bartlett Rd 60120
Tel (847) 741-5370 SIC 3711

ENRIQUE MENDOZA p 500
2350 Nantucket Ln 60123
Tel (630) 364-1808 SIC 7379 5045

■ FCC ENVIRONMENTAL LLC p 533
2175 Point Blvd Ste 375 60123
Tel (281) 668-3300 SIC 4953

▲ HERITAGE-CRYSTAL CLEAN INC p 686
2175 Point Blvd Ste 375 60123
Tel (847) 836-5670 SIC 7699 8734

■ HERITAGE-CRYSTAL CLEAN LLC p 686
2175 Point Blvd Ste 375 60123
Tel (847) 836-5670 SIC 4953

▲ JOHN B SANFILIPPO & SON INC p 787
1703 N Randall Rd 60123
Tel (847) 289-1800
SIC 2068 2064 2099 2096 2066

LENDING SOLUTIONS INC p 855
2200 Point Blvd Ste 110 60123
Tel (847) 844-2200 SIC 6153 7389

■ MARSHALL MIDDLEBY INC p 911
1400 Toastmaster Dr 60120
Tel (847) 289-0204 SIC 3556 3585 3631

MAZAK OPTONICS CORP p 924
2725 Galvin Ct 60124
Tel (847) 252-4500 SIC 5084

▲ MIDDLEBY CORP p 965
1400 Toastmaster Dr 60120
Tel (847) 741-3300 SIC 3556 3589

MR CHIPS INC p 996
1380 Gateway Dr Ste 7 60124
Tel (847) 468-9000 SIC 5092 5047

QUANTUM PLASTICS LLC p 1198
1000 Davis Rd 60123
Tel (847) 695-9700 SIC 7389

SCHOOL DISTRICT U-46 p 1290
355 E Chicago St 60120
Tel (847) 888-5000 SIC 8211

SHERMAN ADVOCATE HOSPITAL p 1316
1425 N Randall Rd 60123
Tel (847) 742-9800 SIC 8062

SUBURBAN PLASTICS CO p 1396
340 Renner Dr 60123
Tel (847) 741-4900 SIC 3089

WANXIANG AMERICA CORP p 1575
88 Airport Rd 60123
Tel (847) 622-8838 SIC 5013

ELK GROVE VILLAGE, IL

ALEXIAN BROTHERS HEALTH SYSTEM INC p 49
3040 Salt Creek Ln 60007
Tel (847) 437-5500 SIC 8062

ALEXIAN BROTHERS MEDICAL CENTER INC p 49
800 Biesterfield Rd Fl 1 60007
Tel (847) 437-5500 SIC 8062

AMERICAN ACADEMY OF PEDIATRICS p 67
141 Northwest Point Blvd 60007
Tel (847) 228-5005 SIC 8621

▲ ATLAS FINANCIAL HOLDINGS INC p 128
150 Northwest Point Blvd # 3 60007
Tel (847) 472-6700 SIC 6331

■ CITICORP CREDIT SERVICES INC p 310
50 Northwest Point Blvd 60007
Tel (847) 597-3000
SIC 7374 7389 7379 6141

■ CITICORP DINERS CLUB INC p 310
50 Northwest Point Blvd 60007
Tel (847) 472-6041 SIC 6021

CLEAR LAM PACKAGING INC p 324
1950 Pratt Blvd 60007
Tel (847) 439-8570 SIC 2671

D&W FINE PACK HOLDINGS LLC p 407
1900 Pratt Blvd 60007
Tel (847) 378-1200 SIC 3089

D&W FINE PACK LLC p 407
1900 Pratt Blvd 60007
Tel (847) 378-1200 SIC 3089

DAYTON SUPERIOR CORP p 418
2400 Arthur Ave 60007
Tel (847) 391-4700 SIC 3444

FIRST AMERICAN BANK p 544
700 Busse Rd 60007
Tel (847) 228-9300 SIC 6022

FIRST AMERICAN BANK CORP (DEL) p 544
1650 Lewis Ave 60007
Tel (847) 228-5505 SIC 6712

FORT DEARBORN CO p 568
1530 Morse Ave 60007
Tel (847) 357-9500 SIC 2752 2759

GROOT INDUSTRIES INC p 641
2500 Landmeier Rd 60007
Tel (847) 734-6400 SIC 4953

ICON IDENTITY SOLUTIONS INC p 727
1418 Elmhurst Rd 60007
Tel (847) 364-2250 SIC 3993

KINETEK INC p 819
25 Northwest Point Blvd # 900 60007
Tel (224) 265-1290 SIC 3621 3566 3613

LADY LITTLE FOODS INC p 837
2323 Pratt Blvd 60007
Tel (847) 806-1440 SIC 2038 2099

LAWRENCE FOODS INC p 847
2200 Lunt Ave 60007
Tel (847) 437-2400 SIC 2033 2099

LIFT SOURCE INC p 865
1815 Landmeier Rd 60007
Tel (847) 678-3450 SIC 5999 5084

MAIN STEEL LLC p 897
2200 Pratt Blvd 60007
Tel (847) 916-1220 SIC 3312

MATERIAL SCIENCES CORP p 919
2250 Pratt Blvd 60007
Tel (888) 603-1553 SIC 3312 5051

■ MEDALIST INDUSTRIES INC p 935
2700 Elmhurst Rd 60007
Tel (847) 766-9000 SIC 3452

NATIONAL MATERIAL LP p 1014
1965 Pratt Blvd 60007
Tel (847) 806-7200
SIC 5051 3469 3354 5093 4911 4924

NATIONAL MATERIAL TRADING LLC p 1014
1965 Pratt Blvd 60007
Tel (847) 806-0990 SIC 5051

ROLLEX CORP p 1247
800 Chase Ave 60007
Tel (847) 437-3000 SIC 3444

▲ SIGMATRON INTERNATIONAL INC p 1321
2201 Landmeier Rd 60007
Tel (847) 956-8000
SIC 3672 3677 3679 3549 3825

STEINER ELECTRIC CO p 1385
1250 Touhy Ave 60007
Tel (847) 228-0400 SIC 5065 5063

TIGERFLEX CORP p 1453
801 Estes Ave 60007
Tel (847) 439-1766 SIC 3052

TIGERS (USA) GLOBAL LOGISTICS INC p 1453
25 Northwest Point Blvd # 1025 60007
Tel (516) 825-4774
SIC 4731 4581 4522 4512

TOPCO ASSOCIATES LLC p 1461
150 Northwest Point Blvd # 6 60007
Tel (847) 676-3030 SIC 5141

TOPCO HOLDINGS INC (COOPERATIVE) p 1461
150 Northwest Point Blvd 60007
Tel (847) 676-3030 SIC 5141 8699

WEISS-ROHLIG USA LLC p 1588
1601 Estes Ave 60007
Tel (224) 563-3200 SIC 4731

WINSTON BRANDS INC p 1617
2521 Busse Rd Fl 2 60007
Tel (847) 350-5800 SIC 5961

WYNRIGHT CORP p 1630
2500 Elmhurst Rd 60007
Tel (847) 595-9400 SIC 5084 3535 8711

ELMHURST, IL

BOYD GROUP U S INC p 205
500 W Lake St Ste 1 60126
Tel (630) 832-0670 SIC 7549 7538

CHAMBERLAIN GROUP INC p 287
845 N Larch Ave 60126
Tel (630) 279-3600 SIC 3699

CHAMBERLAIN MANUFACTURING CORP p 287
845 N Larch Ave 60126
Tel (630) 279-3600 SIC 3651 3625 3699

DISCOUNT MEDIA PRODUCTS LLC p 442
845 N Church Ct 60126
Tel (630) 834-3113 SIC 5065 5999

DUCHOSSOIS GROUP INC p 459
845 N Larch Ave 60126
Tel (630) 279-3600 SIC 3699

ELM HURST AUTO GROUP p 489
466 W Lake St 60126
Tel (630) 833-7945 SIC 5511

ELMHURST COLLEGE p 489
190 S Prospect Ave 60126
Tel (630) 279-4100 SIC 8221

ELMHURST MEMORIAL HEALTHCARE p 489
155 E Brush Hill Rd 60126
Tel (331) 221-1000 SIC 8011

ELMHURST MEMORIAL HOSPITAL INC p 489
133 E Brush Hill Rd 60126
Tel (331) 221-9003 SIC 8062

ELMHURST-CHICAGO STONE CO p 489
400 W 1st St 60126
Tel (630) 832-4000 SIC 1442 3273 3272

GERBER GLASS (DISTRICT 1) LLC p 608
500 W Lake St 60126
Tel (800) 826-8682 SIC 7549

GRAPHIC CONVERTING INC p 631
877 N Larch Ave 60126
Tel (630) 758-4100 SIC 2675

MCMASTER-CARR SUPPLY CO p 932
600 N County Line Rd 60126
Tel (630) 834-9600 SIC 5085 5075

MEDSPEED LLC p 939
655 W Grand Ave Ste 320 60126
Tel (630) 617-5050 SIC 4731

PATTEN INDUSTRIES INC p 1121
635 W Lake St 60126
Tel (630) 279-4400 SIC 5084 5082 7353

PENDUM LLC p 1128
558 W Lamont Rd 60126
Tel (800) 422-6835 SIC 6099 7381

S & S AUTOMOTIVE INC p 1261
740 N Larch Ave 60126
Tel (630) 279-1613
SIC 5013 5999 5065 1731

EVANSTON, IL

EVANSTON CONSOLIDATED COMMUNITY SCHOOL DISTRICT 65 p 513
1500 Mcdaniel Ave 60201
Tel (847) 859-8000 SIC 8211

EVANSTON TOWNSHIP HIGH SCHOOL DISTRICT 202 p 513
1600 Dodge Ave 60201
Tel (847) 424-7000 SIC 8211

NORTH SHORE UNIVERSITY HEALTH SYSTEM p 1053
2650 Ridge Ave 60201
Tel (847) 570-2640 SIC 8011

NORTHSHORE UNIVERSITY HEALTHSYSTEM p 1058
1301 Central St 60201
Tel (847) 570-5295 SIC 5912

NORTHWESTERN UNIVERSITY p 1061
633 Clark St 60208
Tel (847) 491-3741 SIC 8221

NORTHWESTERN UNIVERSITY INFORMATION TECHNOLOGIES p 1061
1800 Sherman Ave Ste 7 60201
Tel (847) 467-1766 SIC 4813 7374 4812

ONE ROTARY CENTER p 1086
1560 Sherman Ave Ste Ll1 60201
Tel (847) 869-5417 SIC 8621

PRESBYTERIAN HOMES p 1171
3200 Grant St 60201
Tel (847) 492-4800 SIC 8361

PRESENCE SAINT FRANCIS HOSPITAL p 1172
355 Ridge Ave 60202
Tel (847) 316-4000 SIC 8062 8059

ROTARY FOUNDATION OF ROTARY INTERNATIONAL p 1252
1560 Sherman Ave Ste 1111 60201
Tel (847) 866-3000 SIC 8699

ROTARY INTERNATIONAL p 1252
1 Rotary Ctr 60201
Tel (847) 866-3000 SIC 8641

SILVER OAK SERVICES PARTNERS LLC p 1324
1560 Sherman Ave Ste 1200 60201
Tel (847) 492-1700 SIC 6722

ZS ASSOCIATES INC p 1644
1800 Sherman Ave Ste 37 60201
Tel (858) 677-2200 SIC 8742

EVERGREEN PARK, IL

LITTLE CO OF MARY HOSPITAL AND HEALTH CARE CENTERS p 871
2800 W 95th St 60805
Tel (708) 422-6200 SIC 8062

LITTLE CO OF MARY HOSPITAL AND HEALTH CARE CENTERS p 871
2800 W 95th St 60805
Tel (708) 422-6200 SIC 8062

PHYSICIAN MATCH p 1145
2800 W 95th St 60805
Tel (708) 423-3070 SIC 8062

FAIRFIELD, IL

AIRTEX PRODUCTS LP p 40
407 W Main St 62837
Tel (618) 842-2111 SIC 5013

FARMER CITY, IL

HOWE-OTTO INC p 713
951 E 3300 North Rd 61842
Tel (309) 928-9730 SIC 0116 0115 7389

FOREST PARK, IL

ESSENTRA COMPONENTS INC p 510
7400 Industrial Dr 60130
Tel (773) 539-4060 SIC 3089

FARMINGTON FOODS INC p 530
7419 Franklin St 60130
Tel (708) 771-3600 SIC 2013

FRANKFORT, IL

PRESENCE CENTRAL AND SUBURBAN HOSPITALS NETWORK p 1172
9223 W Saint Francis Rd 60423
Tel (312) 308-3200 SIC 8062

FRANKLIN PARK, IL

HILL MECHANICAL CORP p 693
11045 Gage Ave 60131
Tel (847) 451-5000 SIC 1711

JJI LIGHTING GROUP INC p 786
11500 Melrose Ave 60131
Tel (847) 451-3258 SIC 3646 3648 3645

MULTI GROUP LOGISTICS INC p 999
10900 Belmont Ave Ste 400 60131
Tel (847) 621-3333 SIC 4213

OLYMPIA FOOD INDUSTRIES INC p 1083
9501 Nevada Ave 60131
Tel (847) 349-9358 SIC 5149

RCM INDUSTRIES INC p 1212
3021 Cullerton St 60131
Tel (847) 455-1950 SIC 3363

SLOAN VALVE CO p 1331
10500 Seymour Ave 60131
Tel (847) 671-4300 SIC 3494 3432

TRANSCENDIA INC p 1471
9201 Belmont Ave 60131
Tel (847) 678-1800 SIC 3081 5162

FREEPORT, IL

FREEPORT MEMORIAL HOSPITAL INC p 577
1045 W Stephenson St 61032
Tel (815) 599-0000 SIC 8062

FREEPORT REGIONAL HEALTH CARE FOUNDATION p 577
1045 W Stephenson St 61032
Tel (815) 599-6000 SIC 8011

FURST-MCNESS CO p 585
120 E Clark St 61032
Tel (800) 435-5100 SIC 2048 5191

HELM GROUP INC p 682
2283 Business Us 20 E 61032
Tel (815) 235-2244 SIC 1611 1622 1629

MORSE ELECTRIC INC p 990
500 W South St 61032
Tel (815) 266-4200 SIC 1731

MORSE GROUP INC p 990
500 W South St 61032
Tel (815) 266-4200 SIC 1731

■ **NEWELL OPERATING CO** p 1037
29 E Stephenson St 61032
Tel (815) 235-4171
SIC 3365 3991 3089 2591 3965 3596

NORTHERN ILLINOIS HEALTH PLAN p 1056
773 W Lincoln St Ste 402 61032
Tel (815) 599-7050 SIC 8741 8721

RUBBERMAID SPECIALTY PRODUCTS INC p 1256
29 E Stephenson St 61032
Tel (815) 235-4171 SIC 3089

GALATIA, IL

AMERICAN COAL CO p 70
9085 Highway 34 N 62935
Tel (618) 268-6311 SIC 1222 5052

GALESBURG, IL

COMMUNITY UNIT SCHOOL DISTRICT 205 p 350
932 Harrison St 61401
Tel (309) 343-3623 SIC 8211 8741

MARTIN SULLIVAN INC p 913
250 E Main St Ste 402 61401
Tel (309) 343-1423 SIC 5083 5261

UNLIMITED DEVELOPMENT INC p 1528
285 S Farnham St 61401
Tel (309) 343-1550 SIC 8741

GALVA, IL

BIG RIVER RESOURCES GALVA LLC p 181
1100 Se 2nd St 61434
Tel (309) 932-2033 SIC 2869

GENEVA, IL

BURGESS-NORTON MFG CO INC p 227
737 Peyton St 60134
Tel (630) 232-4100 SIC 3399 3592 3452

COUNTY OF KANE p 379
719 S Batavia Ave 60134
Tel (630) 232-3400 SIC 9111

DELNOR-COMMUNITY HOSPITAL p 425
300 Randall Rd 60134
Tel (630) 208-3000 SIC 8062

FONA INTERNATIONAL INC p 563
1900 Averill Rd 60134
Tel (630) 578-8600 SIC 2087

GENEVA COMMUNITY UNIT SCHOOL DISTRICT 304 p 603
227 N 4th St 60134
Tel (630) 463-3000 SIC 8211

NORTHERN ILLINOIS FOOD BANK p 1056
273 Dearborn Ct 60134
Tel (630) 443-6910 SIC 8322

PEACOCK FOODS LLC p 1125
1800 Averill Rd 60134
Tel (630) 845-9400 SIC 4783 7389

GLEN ELLYN, IL

BURPEE HOLDING CO INC p 228
800 Roosevelt Rd Ste 216 60137
Tel (215) 674-4900 SIC 0181 5191

COMMUNITY COLLEGE DISTRICT 502 p 348
425 Fawell Blvd 60137
Tel (630) 942-2800 SIC 8222

GLENBARD TOWNSHIP HIGH SCHOOL DISTRICT 87 p 615
596 Crescent Blvd 60137
Tel (630) 469-9100 SIC 8211

GLENCOE, IL

ASC COMMUNICATIONS INC p 115
315 Vernon Ave 60022
Tel (800) 417-2035 SIC 4899

GLENDALE HEIGHTS, IL

ADVENTIST GLENOAKS HOSPITAL p 27
701 Winthrop Ave 60139
Tel (630) 545-8000 SIC 8062

CHICAGO BLOWER CORP p 297
1675 Glen Ellyn Rd 60139
Tel (630) 858-2600 SIC 3564 1711

■ **CORNELIUS INC** p 370
101 Regency Dr 60139
Tel (630) 539-6850 SIC 3585 3556 3586

EPKO INDUSTRIES INC p 505
400 High Grove Blvd 60139
Tel (847) 437-4000 SIC 5198

EXOVA INC p 519
194 Internationale Blvd 60139
Tel (630) 221-0385 SIC 8734

KRONOS FOODS CORP p 830
1 Kronos 60139
Tel (773) 847-2250
SIC 2013 2051 5141 5963

SPRAYING SYSTEMS CO p 1360
200 W North Ave 60139
Tel (630) 665-5000 SIC 3499

SPRENGER ENTERPRISES INC p 1360
2198 Gladstone Ct 60139
Tel (630) 529-0700 SIC 8741

GLENVIEW, IL

ABT ELECTRONICS INC p 13
1200 Milwaukee Ave 60025
Tel (847) 967-8830 SIC 5722 5731

ADELPHI ENTERPRISES LIMITED PARTNERSHIP p 22
2000 Waukegan Rd 60025
Tel (847) 698-3700 SIC 5511

■ **ANIXTER INC** p 92
2301 Patriot Blvd 60026
Tel (224) 521-8000 SIC 5063 4899

ANIXTER INC p 92
2301 Patriot Blvd 60026
Tel (800) 323-8167 SIC 3641

▲ **ANIXTER INTERNATIONAL INC** p 92
2301 Patriot Blvd 60026
Tel (224) 521-8000 SIC 5063 5085

GUARANTEE TRUST LIFE INSURANCE CO p 644
1275 Milwaukee Ave # 100 60025
Tel (847) 699-0600 SIC 6321 6311

▲ **ILLINOIS TOOL WORKS INC** p 732
155 Harlem Ave 60025
Tel (847) 724-7500
SIC 3089 3965 3499 2891 3585

KRAFT PIZZA CO INC p 829
1 Kraft Ct 60025
Tel (847) 646-2000 SIC 2038

LOREN BUICK & PONTIAC INC p 878
1610 Waukegan Rd 60025
Tel (847) 729-8900 SIC 5511 5521

▲ **MEAD JOHNSON NUTRITION CO** p 933
2701 Patriot Blvd 60026
Tel (847) 832-2420 SIC 2023 2834

NORTH AMERICAN CORP OF ILLINOIS p 1050
2101 Claire Ct 60025
Tel (847) 832-4000 SIC 5113 5169

OPTIMAS OE SOLUTIONS HOLDING LLC p 1090
2651 Compass Rd 60026
Tel (224) 521-8000 SIC 5063

OPTIMAS OE SOLUTIONS INTERMED LLC p 1090
2651 Compass Rd 60026
Tel (224) 521-8000 SIC 5063

PARK GLENVIEW DISTRICT p 1115
1930 Prairie St 60025
Tel (847) 657-3215 SIC 7997 7992

R A ZWEIG INC p 1201
2500 Ravine Way 60025
Tel (847) 832-9001 SIC 5013

RDG CHICAGO INC p 1212
1840 Pickwick Ln 60026
Tel (847) 510-2037 SIC 8741

■ **SIGNODE CORP** p 1322
3600 W Lake Ave 60026
Tel (800) 527-1499 SIC 3565 3499

SIGNODE INDUSTRIAL GROUP LLC p 1322
3650 W Lake Ave 60026
Tel (847) 724-7500 SIC 2671

■ **SUREPAYROLL INC** p 1408
2350 Ravine Way Ste 100 60025
Tel (847) 676-8420 SIC 8721

WESPATH BENEFITS AND INVESTMENTS p 1593
1901 Chestnut Ave 60025
Tel (847) 869-4550 SIC 6371

WM H LEAHY ASSOCIATES INC p 1620
2350 Ravine Way Ste 200 60025
Tel (847) 904-5250 SIC 5141 5142

GLENWOOD, IL

▲ **LANDAUER INC** p 842
2 Science Rd 60425
Tel (708) 755-7000 SIC 8734 5047 3829

GRANITE CITY, IL

GATEWAY PACKAGING CO p 594
20 Central Industrial Dr 62040
Tel (618) 451-0010 SIC 2674 2679

■ **GRANITE CITY HOSPITAL CORP** p 631
2100 Madison Ave 62040
Tel (618) 798-3000 SIC 8062

TOTALL METAL RECYCLING INC p 1463
2700 Missouri Ave 62040
Tel (618) 877-0585 SIC 5093

GRAYSLAKE, IL

COLLEGE OF LAKE COUNTY p 337
19351 W Washington St 60030
Tel (847) 543-2000 SIC 8222

GRIDLEY, IL

WATERSHED FOODS LLC p 1582
202 N Ford St 61744
Tel (309) 747-3000 SIC 5142

GURNEE, IL

■ **DYNAPAR CORP** p 464
1675 N Delany Rd 60031
Tel (847) 662-2666 SIC 3824

ILLINOIS BONE & JOINT INSTITUTE p 732
350 S Greenleaf St # 405 60031
Tel (847) 336-2344 SIC 8011

ROSEN MOTOR SALES INC p 1251
7000 Grand Ave 60031
Tel (847) 856-8439 SIC 5511

VANTAGE SPECIALTIES INC p 1544
3938 Porett Dr 60031
Tel (847) 244-3410 SIC 4925 2869

WILLIAM A RANDOLPH INC p 1610
820 Lakeside Dr Ste 3 60031
Tel (847) 856-0123 SIC 1542

HAMPSHIRE, IL

W R MEADOWS INC p 1569
300 Industrial Dr 60140
Tel (847) 214-2100 SIC 5031

HANOVER PARK, IL

ROUND GROUND METALS INC p 1252
4825 Turnberry Dr 60133
Tel (630) 539-5300 SIC 5051 7389

WPS LEGACY INC p 1627
6450 Muirfield Dr 60133
Tel (800) 232-4155 SIC 5199

HARTFORD, IL

HWRT OIL CO LLC p 722
1 Piasa Ln 62048
Tel (618) 254-2855 SIC 5172

HARVEY, IL

■ **AFC CABLE SYSTEMS INC** p 32
16100 Lathrop Ave 60426
Tel (508) 998-1131
SIC 3429 3444 3599 5085

■ **ALLIED TUBE & CONDUIT CORP** p 57
16100 Lathrop Ave 60426
Tel (708) 339-1610 SIC 3317

▲ **ATKORE INTERNATIONAL GROUP INC** p 125
16100 Lathrop Ave 60426
Tel (708) 339-1610
SIC 3441 1791 3446 3448 3496

■ **ATKORE INTERNATIONAL HOLDINGS INC** p 125
16100 Lathrop Ave 60426
Tel (708) 225-2051
SIC 6719 3441 1791 3446 3448 3496

■ **ATKORE INTERNATIONAL INC** p 125
16100 Lathrop Ave 60426
Tel (708) 339-1610 SIC 3317

FUCHS CORP p 583
17050 Lathrop Ave 60426
Tel (800) 323-7755 SIC 2992 5172 2899

INGALLS HEALTH SYSTEM p 742
1 Ingalls Dr 60426
Tel (708) 333-2333 SIC 8062

INGALLS MEMORIAL HOSPITAL p 742
1 Ingalls Dr 60426
Tel (708) 333-2300 SIC 8062

LB STEEL LLC p 849
15700 Lathrop Ave 60426
Tel (708) 331-2600 SIC 3599

THORTON TOWNSHIP HIGH SCHOOL DISTRICT 205 p 1450
15001 Broadway Ave 60426
Tel (708) 225-4036 SIC 8211

■ **UNISTRUT INTERNATIONAL CORP** p 1505
16100 Lathrop Ave 60426
Tel (800) 882-5543
SIC 3441 1791 3446 3448 3496 3429

HAZEL CREST, IL

ADVOCATE SOUTH SUBURBAN HOSPITAL p 28
17800 Kedzie Ave 60429
Tel (708) 799-8000 SIC 8062

LANCO INTERNATIONAL INC p 842
3111 167th St 60429
Tel (708) 596-5200
SIC 3531 8711 5084 3536 7353 3537

MI-JACK PRODUCTS INC p 959
3111 167th St 60429
Tel (708) 596-5200 SIC 3531 8711

HEBRON, IL

■ **FILTERTEK INC** p 542
11411 Price Rd 60034
Tel (815) 648-2410 SIC 3089 3564

HERSCHER, IL

HERSCHER SCHOOL DISTRICT 2 p 687
501 N Main St 60941
Tel (815) 426-2162 SIC 8211

HICKORY HILLS, IL

STANDARD BANK & TRUST CO (INC) p 1375
7800 W 95th St Ste 101 60457
Tel (708) 499-2062 SIC 6022

HIGHLAND PARK, IL

DEERE PARK ASSOCIATES INC p 422
240 N Deere Park Dr W 60035
Tel (847) 509-1000 SIC 8742

DICK BLICK CO p 438
1849 Green Bay Rd Ste 310 60035
Tel (847) 681-6800 SIC 5945

DICK BLICK HOLDINGS INC p 438
1849 Green Bay Rd Ste 310 60035
Tel (847) 681-6800 SIC 5961

GVW GROUP LLC p 648
625 Roger Williams Ave 60035
Tel (847) 681-8417 SIC 3713

NORTHSHORE SCHOOL DST 112 p 1058
1936 Green Bay Rd 60035
Tel (224) 765-3000 SIC 8211

SOLO CUP INVESTMENT CORP p 1338
1700 Old Deerfield Rd 60035
Tel (847) 831-4800 SIC 3089 2656 3421

SUNSET FOOD MART INC p 1404
777 Central Ave Ste 2 60035
Tel (847) 234-8380 SIC 5411 5921

HIGHLAND, IL

BASLER ELECTRIC CO p 159
12570 State Route 143 62249
Tel (618) 654-2341 SIC 3679 3612 3672

COOPER B-LINE INC p 366
509 W Monroe St 62249
Tel (618) 654-2184
SIC 3441 3443 3452 3444 3429 3356

PLOCHER CONSTRUCTION CO INC p 1156
2808 Thole Plocher Rd 62249
Tel (618) 654-9408 SIC 1542

HINSDALE, IL

ADVENTIST MIDWEST HEALTH p 27
120 N Oak St 60521
Tel (630) 856-9000 SIC 8062 5947 8011

■ **MCDONALDS RESTAURANTS OF FLORIDA INC** p 928
1 Mcdonalds Dr 60523
Tel (630) 623-3000 SIC 5812

PETCO PETROLEUM CORP p 1138
108 E Ogden Ave Ste 100 60521
Tel (630) 654-1740 SIC 1389

RML HEALTH PROVIDERS LIMITED PARTNERSHIP p 1239
5601 S County Line Rd 60521
Tel (708) 783-5800 SIC 8062

ROWELL CHEMICAL CORP p 1253
15 Salt Creek Ln Ste 205 60521
Tel (630) 920-8833 SIC 5169

SEVERSTAL US HOLDINGS II INC p 1309
907 N Elm St Ste 100 60521
Tel (708) 756-0400 SIC 3291

SHAMROCK CO p 1311
15 Spinning Wheel Rd # 110 60521
Tel (630) 655-8274 SIC 5812

HODGKINS, IL

ARRO CORP p 113
7440 Santa Fe Dr 60525
Tel (708) 352-8200 SIC 5141

HOFFMAN ESTATES, IL

■ **AMCOL INTERNATIONAL CORP** p 65
2870 Forbs Ave 60192
Tel (847) 851-1500
SIC 1459 5032 4213 4731

■ **AMERICAN COLLOID CO** p 70
2870 Forbs Ave 60192
Tel (847) 851-1700 SIC 1459 2899

BARRINGTON BROADCASTING LLC p 157
500 W Higgins Rd Ste 880 60195
Tel (847) 884-1877 SIC 4833

▲ **CDK GLOBAL INC** p 271
1950 Hassell Rd 60169
Tel (847) 397-1700 SIC 7372

CENTRAL TERRITORIAL OF SALVATION ARMY p 280
5550 Prairie Stone Pkwy # 130 60192
Tel (847) 294-2000 SIC 8661 8322

CLAIRES INC p 321
2400 W Central Rd 60192
Tel (847) 765-1100 SIC 5632 5947

■ **COLLOID ENVIRONMENTAL TECHNOLOGIES CO LLC** p 337
2870 Forbs Ave 60192
Tel (847) 851-1500 SIC 3259 2899

DMG MORI USA INC p 446
2400 Huntington Blvd 60192
Tel (847) 593-5400 *SIC* 3541 3545

■ **INNOVEL SOLUTIONS INC** p 745
3333 Beverly Rd 60179
Tel (847) 286-2500 *SIC* 4731 8741 8742

■ **KMART CORP** p 824
3333 Beverly Rd 60179
Tel (847) 286-2500 *SIC* 5311 5912 5399

■ **KMART HOLDING CORP** p 824
3333 Beverly Rd 60179
Tel (847) 286-2500 *SIC* 5311

LEOPARDO COMPANIES INC p 856
5200 Prairie Stone Pkwy 60192
Tel (847) 783-3000 *SIC* 1542 8741

NATIONAL BEDDING CO LLC p 1010
2600 Forbs Ave 60192
Tel (847) 645-0200 *SIC* 2515

OMRON ELECTRONICS LLC p 1085
2895 Greenspt Pkwy 200 60169
Tel (847) 843-7900 *SIC* 5065 3699

OMRON MANAGEMENT CENTER OF AMERICA INC p 1085
2895 Greenspoint Pkwy # 100 60169
Tel (224) 520-7650
SIC 5044 5046 5065 5047 5045 8732

▲ **SEARS HOLDINGS CORP** p 1297
3333 Beverly Rd 60179
Tel (847) 286-2500
SIC 5311 5411 5531 5961

■ **SEARS HOLDINGS MANAGEMENT CORP** p 1297
3333 Beverly Rd 60179
Tel (847) 286-2500 *SIC* 6531 6719

▲ **SEARS HOMETOWN AND OUTLET STORES INC** p 1297
5500 Trillium Blvd # 501 60192
Tel (847) 286-2500 *SIC* 5251 5261 5722

■ **SEARS ROEBUCK AND CO** p 1297
3333 Beverly Rd 60179
Tel (847) 286-2500 *SIC* 5311

SERTA INC p 1306
2600 Forbs Ave 60192
Tel (847) 645-0200 *SIC* 2515

ST ALEXIUS MEDICAL CENTER p 1364
1555 Barrington Rd Bldg 1 60169
Tel (847) 884-9800 *SIC* 8062

STAR SU CO LLC p 1378
5200 Prairie Stone Pkwy 60192
Tel (847) 649-1450 *SIC* 5084

■ **WELLS FARGO COMMERCIAL DISTRIBUTION FINANCE LLC** p 1590
5595 Trillium Blvd 60192
Tel (847) 747-6800 *SIC* 6153 6159 6141

HOMER GLEN, IL

RICHARDS BUILDING SUPPLY CO p 1232
12070 W 159th St 60491
Tel (773) 586-7777 *SIC* 5033 5211

HOMEWOOD, IL

CARL BUDDIG AND CO p 256
950 175th St 60430
Tel (708) 798-0900 *SIC* 2013 2022

CCBC INC p 269
1 Mi Jack Way 60430
Tel (708) 206-0500 *SIC* 6719

EAGLE EXPRESS LINES INC p 468
925 175th St 60430
Tel (708) 333-8401 *SIC* 4213 4215 4212

GRAND TRUNK CORP p 630
17641 Ashland Ave 60430
Tel (708) 332-3500 *SIC* 4011

GRAND TRUNK WESTERN RAILROAD CO p 630
17641 Ashland Ave 60430
Tel (708) 332-3500 *SIC* 4011

ILLINOIS CENTRAL RAILROAD CO p 732
17641 Ashland Ave 60430
Tel (708) 332-3500 *SIC* 4011

WISCONSIN CENTRAL LTD p 1618
17641 Ashland Ave 60430
Tel (708) 332-3500 *SIC* 4011

ITASCA, IL

AIT WORLDWIDE LOGISTICS INC p 41
701 N Rohlwing Rd 60143
Tel (630) 766-0711 *SIC* 4731

ALLMETAL INC p 58
1 Pierce Pl Ste 900 60143
Tel (630) 250-8090 *SIC* 3699 3089

▲ **ARTHUR J GALLAGHER & CO** p 114
2 Pierce Pl 60143
Tel (630) 773-3800 *SIC* 6411 6282 8741

■ **ARTHUR J GALLAGHER & CO (ILLINOIS)** p 114
2 Pierce Pl Ste 100 60143
Tel (630) 773-3800 *SIC* 6411

BOLER CO p 198
500 Park Blvd Ste 1010 60143
Tel (630) 773-9111 *SIC* 3714 3493

DOMINICKS FINER FOODS LLC p 449
150 E Pierce Rd Ste 400 60143
Tel (630) 990-2880 *SIC* 5411

ENESCO LLC p 498
225 Windsor Dr 60143
Tel (630) 875-5300 *SIC* 5947

EQUIPMENT DEPOT OF ILLINOIS INC p 506
751 Expressway Dr 60143
Tel (847) 836-5005
SIC 5084 5087 5063 7699

FELLOWES INC p 537
1789 Norwood Ave 60143
Tel (630) 893-1600
SIC 2522 3589 2653 3577 3572 3579

▲ **FIRST MIDWEST BANCORP INC** p 548
1 Pierce Pl Ste 1500w 60143
Tel (630) 875-7450 *SIC* 6021

■ **FIRST MIDWEST BANK** p 548
1 Pierce Pl Ste 1500w 60143
Tel (630) 875-7450 *SIC* 6021

FLEXERA HOLDINGS LP p 556
300 Park Blvd Ste 500 60143
Tel (847) 466-4000 *SIC* 7371 7372

FLEXERA SOFTWARE LLC p 556
300 Park Blvd Ste 500 60143
Tel (847) 466-4000 *SIC* 7371 7372

■ **GALLAGHER BASSETT SERVICES INC** p 589
2 Pierce Pl Ste 100 60143
Tel (630) 773-3800 *SIC* 6411 8741

■ **GALLAGHER BENEFIT SERVICES INC** p 589
2 Pierce Pl 60143
Tel (630) 773-3800 *SIC* 6411

■ **GOGO INTERMEDIATE HOLDINGS LLC** p 620
1250 N Arlington Rd 60143
Tel (630) 647-1400 *SIC* 3663

HENDRICKSON USA LLC p 683
500 Park Blvd Ste 450 60143
Tel (630) 874-9700 *SIC* 3537

HENRICKSEN & CO INC p 683
1101 W Thorndale Ave 60143
Tel (630) 250-9090 *SIC* 5021 7389

IFS NORTH AMERICA INC p 730
300 Park Blvd Ste 555 60143
Tel (888) 437-4968 *SIC* 7372 7379 8243

INFINITY RESOURCES INC p 741
900 N Rohlwing Rd 60143
Tel (630) 735-1000 *SIC* 5961

JEWEL OSCO INC p 784
150 E Pierce Rd Ste 200 60143
Tel (630) 551-2672 *SIC* 5411 2834

■ **KESTER INC** p 814
800 W Thorndale Ave 60143
Tel (630) 616-4000 *SIC* 3356

▲ **KNOWLES CORP** p 825
1151 Maplewood Dr 60143
Tel (630) 250-5100 *SIC* 3651 3675

■ **KNOWLES ELECTRONICS HOLDINGS INC** p 825
1151 Maplewood Dr 60143
Tel (630) 250-5100
SIC 3679 3625 3651 8731 6159

■ **KNOWLES ELECTRONICS LLC** p 825
1151 Maplewood Dr 60143
Tel (630) 250-5100 *SIC* 3679 3842

■ **KNOWLES INTERMEDIATE HOLDING INC** p 825
1151 Maplewood Dr 60143
Tel (630) 250-5100 *SIC* 6799

MID-AMERICA OVERSEAS INC p 963
650 E Devon Ave Ste 150 60143
Tel (630) 285-9083 *SIC* 4731

MR DAVIDS FLOORING INTERNATIONAL LLC p 996
865 W Irving Park Rd 60143
Tel (847) 250-4600 *SIC* 1752

NEW ALBERTSONS INC p 1029
150 E Pierce Rd Ste 200 60143
Tel (630) 948-6000 *SIC* 5411 5912 5331

NNR GLOBAL LOGISTICS USA INC p 1045
450 E Devon Ave Ste 260 60143
Tel (630) 773-1490 *SIC* 4731

PRISM COMPANIES INC p 1178
248 Spring Lake Dr 60143
Tel (630) 216-5788 *SIC* 8742

■ **RISK PLACEMENT SERVICES INC** p 1236
2 Pierce Pl Fl 25 60143
Tel (630) 773-3800 *SIC* 6411

ROBERTSHAW CONTROLS CO p 1242
1222 Hamilton Pkwy 60143
Tel (630) 260-3400 *SIC* 3823 3822 3492

SEKO GLOBAL LOGISTICS NETWORK LLC p 1301
1100 Arlington Ste 600 60143
Tel (630) 919-4800 *SIC* 4731

SEKO WORLDWIDE LLC p 1301
1100 N Arlingtn Hts 600 60143
Tel (630) 919-4800 *SIC* 4731

SOURCELINK ACQUISITION LLC p 1342
500 Park Blvd Ste 1425 60143
Tel (866) 947-6872 *SIC* 7374 7331

W S DARLEY & CO p 1569
325 Spring Lake Dr 60143
Tel (630) 735-3500
SIC 3561 5087 5099 3569 3812

WALTER E SMITHE FURNITURE INC p 1574
1251 W Thorndale Ave 60143
Tel (800) 948-4263 *SIC* 5712

JACKSONVILLE, IL

CGB DIVERSIFIED SERVICES INC p 285
1608b W Lafayette Ave 62650
Tel (217) 245-4599 *SIC* 5153

PASSAVANT MEMORIAL AREA HOSPITAL ASSOCIATION p 1120
1600 W Walnut St 62650
Tel (217) 245-4640 *SIC* 8062

JERSEYVILLE, IL

JERSEY COUNTY GRAIN CO p 783
426 E Exchange St 62052
Tel (618) 498-2183 *SIC* 5153 5191

JOLIET, IL

■ **ANDREW INTERNATIONAL SERVICES CORP** p 90
2700 Ellis Rd 60433
Tel (779) 435-6000 *SIC* 3663

BROCK INDUSTRIAL SERVICES LLC p 216
2210 Oak Leaf St 60436
Tel (815) 730-3350 *SIC* 1721 1799

CARLSON BROS INC p 257
17250 New Lenox Rd B 60433
Tel (815) 727-2200 *SIC* 1542

CENTRAL GROCERS INC p 278
2600 Haven Ave 60433
Tel (815) 553-8800
SIC 5141 5147 5142 5148 5143 5122

CIT INC p 309
103 S Larkin Ave 60436
Tel (815) 741-7500 *SIC* 5511

■ **EMPRESS CASINO JOLIET CORP** p 495
777 Hollywood Blvd 60436
Tel (815) 744-9400 *SIC* 7999

FILTRATION GROUP CORP p 542
912 E Washington St Ste 1 60433
Tel (815) 726-4600 *SIC* 3564

FILTRATION GROUP LLC p 542
912 E Washington St Ste 1 60433
Tel (815) 726-4600 *SIC* 3564

ILLINOIS CENTRAL SCHOOL BUS LLC p 732
78 N Chicago St 2 60432
Tel (815) 744-4800 *SIC* 4151

JOLIET JUNIOR COLLEGE DISTRICT 525 p 792
1215 Houbolt Rd 60431
Tel (815) 280-6767 *SIC* 8222

JOLIET PUBLIC SCHOOLS DISTRICT 86 p 792
420 N Raynor Ave 60435
Tel (815) 740-3196 *SIC* 8211

ROMAN CATHOLIC DIOCESE OF JOLIET p 1249
425 Summit St 60435
Tel (815) 722-6606 *SIC* 8661

SUPERMERCADO LA HACIENDA INC p 1407
224 S Larkin Ave 60436
Tel (815) 724-0200 *SIC* 5411

WILL COUNTY p 1609
302 N Chicago St 60432
Tel (815) 740-4602 *SIC* 9111

JOPPA, IL

■ **ELECTRIC ENERGY INC** p 484
2100 Portland Rd 62953
Tel (618) 543-7531 *SIC* 4911

KANKAKEE, IL

MIDWEST TRANSIT EQUIPMENT INC p 968
146 W Issert Dr 60901
Tel (815) 933-2412 *SIC* 5012

RIVERSIDE HEALTH SYSTEM p 1238
350 N Wall St 60901
Tel (815) 933-1671
SIC 8082 8062 5912 5047

RIVERSIDE MEDI-CENTER INC p 1238
350 N Wall St 60901
Tel (815) 933-1671 *SIC* 8082 5912 5999

RIVERSIDE MEDICAL CENTER p 1238
350 N Wall St 60901
Tel (815) 933-1671 *SIC* 8062

SMALL NEWSPAPER GROUP p 1332
8 Dearborn Sq 60901
Tel (815) 937-3300 *SIC* 2711 2791 2752

KINCAID, IL

■ **KINCAID GENERATION LLC** p 819
4 Miles W Of Kincaid 62540
Tel (217) 237-4311 *SIC* 4911

LA GRANGE, IL

GRAYHILL INC p 632
561 W Hillgrove Ave 60525
Tel (708) 354-1040
SIC 3613 3625 3679 3643 3575

LA GRANGE MEMORIAL HOSPITAL INC p 835
5101 Willow Springs Rd 60525
Tel (708) 352-1200 *SIC* 8062

LAFOX, IL

▲ **RICHARDSON ELECTRONICS LTD** p 1232
40w267 Keslinger Rd 60147
Tel (630) 208-2316 *SIC* 5065 7373 3671

LAKE BLUFF, IL

COBALT HOLDINGS INC p 332
101 Waukegan Rd Ste 990 60044
Tel (773) 230-3219 *SIC* 4812 4813

KARL KNAUZ MOTORS INC p 804
775 Rockland Rd 60044
Tel (847) 615-3670 *SIC* 5511

TERLATO WINE GROUP LTD p 1439
900 Armour Dr 60044
Tel (847) 604-8900 *SIC* 5182 2084 8743

LAKE FOREST, IL

▲ **AKORN INC** p 42
1925 W Field Ct Ste 300 60045
Tel (847) 279-6100 *SIC* 2834 5047

AUTOPARTS HOLDINGS LTD p 135
1900 W Field Ct 60045
Tel (203) 830-7800 *SIC* 3714

▲ **BRUNSWICK CORP** p 221
1 N Field Ct 60045
Tel (847) 735-4700
SIC 3519 3732 3949 7933 5091

CHICAGO DAIRY CORP p 297
27820 Irma Lee Cir # 200 60045
Tel (847) 680-0300 *SIC* 5143

CORESOURCE INC p 370
400 N Field Dr 60045
Tel (847) 615-1500 *SIC* 6324 6411

■ **DAYTON ELECTRIC MFG CO** p 417
100 Grainger Pkwy 60045
Tel (847) 535-1000 *SIC* 5063 5084 5072

EBHI HOLDINGS INC p 474
1000 Field Dr Ste 240 60045
Tel (312) 251-3430
SIC 5611 5699 5941 5719 5947 5961

FOREST LAKE HOSPITAL p 567
660 N Westmoreland Rd 60045
Tel (847) 234-5600 *SIC* 8062

FRAM GROUP OPERATIONS LLC p 573
1900 W Field Ct 60045
Tel (800) 890-2075 *SIC* 3694 3714

■ **GRAINGER INTERNATIONAL INC** p 629
100 Grainger Pkwy 60045
Tel (847) 535-1000
SIC 5074 5084 5085 5072

HORIZON PHARMA INC p 707
150 Saunders Rd Ste 130 60045
Tel (224) 383-3000 *SIC* 2834

HORIZON THERAPEUTICS INC p 707
150 Saunders Rd Ste 150 60045
Tel (224) 383-3000 *SIC* 2834

■ **HOSPIRA INC** p 709
275 N Field Dr 60045
Tel (224) 212-2000 *SIC* 2834 3841

HSBC NORTH AMERICA HOLDINGS INC p 715
452 5th Ave 7 60045
Tel (224) 544-4400 *SIC* 6351

▲ **IDEX CORP** p 729
1925 W Field Ct Ste 200 60045
Tel (847) 498-7070 *SIC* 3561 3563 3594

INTERNATIONAL PRECISION COMPONENTS CORP p 756
28468 N Ballard Dr 60045
Tel (847) 247-2050 *SIC* 3089

■ **LAKE FOREST BANK AND TRUST CO** p 839
727 N Bank Ln Fl 1 60045
Tel (847) 234-2882 *SIC* 6022

LAKE FOREST COLLEGE p 839
555 N Sheridan Rd 60045
Tel (847) 234-3100 *SIC* 8221

LAKE FOREST HOSPITAL FOUNDATION p 839
660 N Westmoreland Rd 60045
Tel (847) 234-5600 *SIC* 8062

NORTHWESTERN LAKE FOREST HOSPITAL p 1060
660 N Westmoreland Rd 60045
Tel (847) 234-0945
SIC 8062 5947 5932 5812

▲ **PACKAGING CORP OF AMERICA** p 1106
1955 W Field Ct 60045
Tel (847) 482-3000 *SIC* 2631 2653

PACTIV LLC p 1107
1900 W Field Ct 60045
Tel (847) 482-2000 *SIC* 5113 3089 2673

■ **PHOSPHATE RESOURCE PARTNERS LIMITED PARTNERSHIP** p 1145
100 Saunders Rd Ste 300 60045
Tel (847) 739-1200
SIC 2874 1311 1475 2819 1094

PRESTONE PRODUCTS CORP p 1173
1900 W Field Ct 60045
Tel (847) 482-2045 *SIC* 2899

RENAISSANCE ACQUISITION HOLDINGS LLC p 1223
272 E Deerpath Ste 206 60045
Tel (847) 283-7772 *SIC* 5122

RENAISSANCE SSP HOLDINGS INC p 1223
272 E Deerpath Ste 350 60045
Tel (210) 476-8194 *SIC* 2834

REYNOLDS CONSUMER PRODUCTS HOLDINGS INC p 1230
1900 W Field Ct 60045
Tel (847) 482-3050 *SIC* 7389

REYNOLDS CONSUMER PRODUCTS LLC p 1230
1900 W Field Ct 60045
Tel (847) 482-3500 *SIC* 3353

ROUNDTABLE HEALTHCARE PARTNERS LP p 1253
272 E Deerpath Ste 350 60045
Tel (847) 482-9275 *SIC* 6722 3699 2834

SCC HOLDING CO LLC p 1286
150 Saunders Rd Ste 150 60045
Tel (847) 444-5000 *SIC* 3089 2656 3421

▲ STERICYCLE INC p 1386
28161 N Keith Dr 60045
Tel (847) 367-5910 *SIC* 4953

TAP PHARMACEUTICAL PRODUCTS INC p 1424
675 N Field Dr 60045
Tel (847) 582-2000 *SIC* 5122

■ TENNECO AUTOMOTIVE OPERATING CO INC p 1437
500 N Field Dr 60045
Tel (847) 482-5000 *SIC* 3714 3699

▲ TENNECO INC p 1437
500 N Field Dr 60045
Tel (847) 482-5000 *SIC* 3714

TRICOR PACIFIC CAPITAL PARTNERS (FUND IV) US LP p 1479
1 Westminster Pl Ste 100n 60045
Tel (847) 295-4410 *SIC* 6211

TRUSTMARK INSURANCE CO (MUTUAL) p 1488
400 N Field Dr 60045
Tel (847) 283-4145 *SIC* 6321 6311

TRUSTMARK LIFE INSURANCE CO p 1488
400 N Field Dr 60045
Tel (847) 615-1500 *SIC* 6321

TRUSTMARK MUTUAL HOLDING CO p 1488
400 N Field Dr 60045
Tel (847) 615-1500 *SIC* 7991 8099

UCI INTERNATIONAL INC p 1499
1900 W Field Ct 60045
Tel (812) 867-4156 *SIC* 3714

UNITED COMPONENTS LLC p 1507
1900 W Field Ct 60045
Tel (812) 867-4516 *SIC* 5013 3714

US BUILDER SERVICES LLC p 1531
272 E Deerpath Ste 308 60045
Tel (847) 735-2066 *SIC* 1742 1731 1711

W W GRAINGER INC GROUP BENEFIT TRUST I p 1569
100 Grainger Pkwy 60045
Tel (847) 535-1096 *SIC* 6733

▲ WW GRAINGER INC p 1628
100 Grainger Pkwy 60045
Tel (847) 535-1000
SIC 5063 5084 5075 5085 5072

LAKE ZURICH, IL

▲ ACCO BRANDS CORP p 15
4 Corporate Dr 60047
Tel (847) 541-9500
SIC 2782 3083 2761 2672

■ ACCO BRANDS INC p 15
4 Corporate Dr 60047
Tel (847) 541-9500 *SIC* 2542

■ ACCO BRANDS USA LLC p 15
4 Corporate Dr 60047
Tel (800) 222-6462
SIC 3089 2761 3496 2675

CAPITAL BUILDING SERVICES GROUP INC p 249
540 Capital Dr Ste 100 60047
Tel (847) 847-3800 *SIC* 7349

COMMUNITY UNIT SCHOOL DISTRICT 95 p 350
400 S Old Rand Rd 60047
Tel (847) 438-2831 *SIC* 8211

DOVENMUEHLE MORTGAGE INC p 452
1 Corporate Dr Ste 360 60047
Tel (847) 550-7300 *SIC* 6162 6411

ECHO INC p 475
400 Oakwood Rd 60047
Tel (847) 540-8400 *SIC* 3524

FENWAL HOLDINGS INC p 537
3 Corporate Dr Ste 300 60047
Tel (847) 550-2300 *SIC* 3069 5047

FENWAL INC p 537
3 Corporate Dr Ste 300 60047
Tel (847) 550-2300 *SIC* 5047 3069

FRESENIUS KABI USA INC p 578
3 Corporate Dr Ste 300 60047
Tel (847) 969-2700 *SIC* 2834

FRESENIUS KABI USA LLC p 578
3 Corporate Dr Ste 300 60047
Tel (847) 550-2300 *SIC* 2834

GENERAL BINDING CORP p 599
4 Corporate Dr 60047
Tel (847) 541-9500
SIC 5044 2782 3559 3589 7629 3579

LANSING, IL

LEXINGTON CORPORATE ENTERPRISES INC p 859
17725 Volbrecht Rd 60438
Tel (708) 418-0700 *SIC* 5075 1711

NATIONAL PASTEURIZED EGGS INC p 1015
2963 Bernice Rd Ste 1 60438
Tel (708) 418-8500 *SIC* 5144

NB COATINGS INC p 1021
2701 E 170th St 60438
Tel (800) 323-3224 *SIC* 2851 2865

TEMPERATURE EQUIPMENT CORP p 1436
17725 Volbrecht Rd Ste 1 60438
Tel (708) 418-0900 *SIC* 5075

LAWRENCEVILLE, IL

TOYOTA BOSHOKU ILLINOIS LLC p 1466
100 Trim Masters Dr 62439
Tel (618) 943-5300 *SIC* 3714

LEMONT, IL

FRANCISCAN COMMUNITIES INC p 573
11500 Theresa Dr 60439
Tel (708) 647-6500 *SIC* 8051

FRANCISCAN SISTER OF CHICAGO p 573
11500 Theresa Dr 60439
Tel (708) 647-6500 *SIC* 8661 8011

K-FIVE CONSTRUCTION CORP p 799
13769 Main St 60439
Tel (630) 257-5600 *SIC* 1611

OSCO INC p 1096
13351 Main St 60439
Tel (630) 257-8000 *SIC* 5172

PDV MIDWEST REFINING LLC p 1125
135th St New Ave 60439
Tel (630) 257-7761
SIC 2992 2911 5171 4213

■ US DEPT OF ENERGY CHICAGO OFFICE p 1531
9800 S Cass Ave Ste 1 60439
Tel (630) 252-2442 *SIC* 9611

LIBERTYVILLE, IL

ADVOCATE CONDELL MEDICAL CENTER p 28
801 S Milwaukee Ave 60048
Tel (847) 362-2900 *SIC* 8062

ALDRIDGE ELECTRIC INC p 48
844 E Rockland Rd 60048
Tel (847) 680-5200 *SIC* 2899 4789 3643

■ BRIGHTSTAR US INC p 213
850 Technology Way 60048
Tel (847) 573-2600 *SIC* 5065

HOLLISTER INC p 701
2000 Hollister Dr 60048
Tel (847) 680-1000 *SIC* 3841 3842

SNAP-ON CREDIT LLC p 1335
950 Technology Way # 301 60048
Tel (847) 782-7700 *SIC* 6153

LINCOLN, IL

CHRISTIAN HOMES INC p 302
200 N Postville Dr 62656
Tel (217) 732-9651 *SIC* 8052 8051

LINCOLNSHIRE, IL

ADCO GLOBAL INC p 21
100 Tri State Intl # 135 60069
Tel (847) 282-3485 *SIC* 2891

ADLAI E STEVENSON HIGH SCHOOL DISTRICT 125 p 23
1 Stevenson Dr 60069
Tel (847) 415-4000 *SIC* 8211

AON CONSULTING WORLDWIDE INC p 95
100 Half Day Rd 2 60069
Tel (312) 381-4800
SIC 6311 6321 6331 8742 6411 6351

▲ CAMPING WORLD HOLDINGS INC p 246
250 Parkway Dr Ste 270 60069
Tel (847) 808-3000 *SIC* 7513 6159 7539

▲ CDW CORP p 271
75 Tri State Intl 60069
Tel (847) 465-6000
SIC 5963 5045 5734 5961

■ CDW LLC p 271
75 Tri State Intl 60069
Tel (847) 465-6000 *SIC* 5045

FOCUS PRODUCTS GROUP INTERNATIONAL LLC p 563
300 Knightsbridge Pkwy 60069
Tel (800) 238-2253 *SIC* 5023

FREEDOMROADS HOLDING CO LLC p 576
250 Parkway Dr Ste 270 60069
Tel (847) 808-3000 *SIC* 8743

FREEDOMROADS LLC p 576
250 Parkway Dr Ste 270 60069
Tel (866) 838-5304 *SIC* 5561

GF MACHINING SOLUTIONS LLC p 609
560 Bond St 60069
Tel (847) 913-5300 *SIC* 5084

GOOD SAM ENTERPRISES LLC p 623
250 Parkway Dr Ste 270 60069
Tel (847) 229-6720 *SIC* 5561 7997 2721

■ HONEYWELL ANALYTICS INC p 705
405 Barclay Blvd 60069
Tel (847) 955-8200 *SIC* 3491 3829

HYDRAFORCE INC p 723
500 Barclay Blvd 60069
Tel (847) 793-2300 *SIC* 3492

I3 GROUP INC p 725
550 Bond St 60069
Tel (847) 325-1000 *SIC* 5021 1799

KLEIN TOOLS INC p 823
450 Bond St 60069
Tel (847) 821-5500 *SIC* 3423 3199

LSIS USA INC p 883
2000 Millbrook Dr 60069
Tel (847) 941-8240 *SIC* 5063

PURE METAL RECYCLING LLC p 1192
100 Tri State Intl # 215 60069
Tel (773) 523-4500 *SIC* 5093

■ QUILL CORP p 1200
100 Schelter Rd 60069
Tel (847) 634-6690 *SIC* 5943

SAPUTO CHEESE USA INC p 1282
1 Overlook Pt Ste 300 60069
Tel (847) 267-1100 *SIC* 2022

SF HOLDINGS GROUP INC p 1310
300 Tr State Intl Ste 200 60069
Tel (847) 831-4800 *SIC* 2656

SOLO CUP CO p 1338
300 Tri State Intl # 200 60069
Tel (847) 831-4800 *SIC* 3089 3421 2656

SOLO CUP CO LLC p 1338
300 Tri State Intl # 200 60069
Tel (847) 444-5000 *SIC* 3089 2656 3421

SOLO CUP OPERATING CORP p 1338
300 Tr State Intl Ste 200 60069
Tel (847) 444-5000 *SIC* 3089 2656 3556

SYSMEX AMERICA INC p 1418
577 Aptakisic Rd 60069
Tel (847) 996-4500 *SIC* 5047 3841

WOODHEAD INDUSTRIES LLC p 1623
333 Knightsbridge Pkwy # 200 60069
Tel (847) 353-2500
SIC 3678 3679 3643 3357

▲ ZEBRA TECHNOLOGIES CORP p 1641
3 Overlook Pt 60069
Tel (847) 634-6700
SIC 3577 2672 2679 5045

ZENITH ELECTRONICS CORP p 1642
2000 Millbrook Dr 60069
Tel (847) 941-8000
SIC 3651 3671 3663 3674 2517 2519

LINCOLNWOOD, IL

GROSSINGER AUTOPLEX INC p 641
6900 N Mccormick Blvd # 1 60712
Tel (847) 674-9000 *SIC* 5511

ITEX DEVELOPMENT CORP p 768
6633 N Lincoln Ave 60712
Tel (847) 674-2383 *SIC* 8742

LOEBER MOTORS INC p 874
4255 W Touhy Ave 60712
Tel (847) 675-1000 *SIC* 5511

MILLARD GROUP INC p 969
7301 N Cicero Ave 60712
Tel (847) 674-4100 *SIC* 7349

LISLE, IL

ARMOUR-ECKRICH MEATS LLC p 111
4225 Naperville Rd # 600 60532
Tel (630) 281-5000 *SIC* 3556

BENEDICTINE UNIVERSITY p 172
5700 College Rd 60532
Tel (630) 829-6000 *SIC* 8221

CLARK BRANDS LLC p 322
4200 Commerce Ct Ste 350 60532
Tel (630) 355-8918
SIC 6794 7389 5541 5812

▲ CTS CORP p 399
2375 Cabot Dr 60532
Tel (630) 577-8800
SIC 3678 3829 3676 3679 3674

■ CTS ELECTRONIC COMPONENTS INC p 399
2375 Cabot Dr 60532
Tel (630) 577-8800 *SIC* 3724

FOOTPRINT ACQUISITION LLC p 564
2200 Western Ct Ste 150 60532
Tel (630) 324-3400 *SIC* 7389

GLORY GLOBAL SOLUTIONS INC p 618
3333 Warrenville Rd # 310 60532
Tel (920) 262-3300 *SIC* 5087 5046 5044

HPR PARTNERS LLC p 714
801 Warrenville Rd # 550 60532
Tel (630) 737-0788 *SIC* 5141

KANTAR OPERATIONS p 803
3333 Warrenville Rd # 400 60532
Tel (630) 505-0066 *SIC* 8732

LANTMANNEN UNIBAKE USA INC p 844
5007 Lincoln Ave Ste 300 60532
Tel (630) 963-4781 *SIC* 5142

MCCAIN FOODS USA INC p 926
2275 Cabot Dr 60532
Tel (630) 955-0400 *SIC* 2037

MCCAIN USA INC p 926
2275 Cabot Dr 60532
Tel (800) 938-7799 *SIC* 2037 2038 5411

MOLEX LLC p 982
2222 Wellington Ct 60532
Tel (630) 969-4550 *SIC* 3679 3643 3357

MOLEX PREMISE NETWORKS INC p 982
2222 Wellington Ct 60532
Tel (866) 733-6659 *SIC* 3679 3643 3357

MOLEX U S INC p 982
2222 Wellington Ct 60532
Tel (630) 969-4550
SIC 3678 3679 3643 3357

■ NAVISTAR INC p 1020
2701 Navistar Dr 60532
Tel (331) 332-5000
SIC 3711 3714 3519 6153 6159 6331

▲ NAVISTAR INTERNATIONAL CORP p 1020
2701 Navistar Dr 60532
Tel (331) 332-5000
SIC 3711 3714 3713 3519 6159

SSAB ENTERPRISES LLC p 1363
801 Warrenville Rd # 800 60532
Tel (630) 810-4800 *SIC* 3312

SSAB US HOLDING INC p 1363
801 Warrenville Rd # 800 60532
Tel (630) 810-4800 *SIC* 3312

▲ SUNCOKE ENERGY INC p 1402
1011 Warrenville Rd # 600 60532
Tel (630) 824-1000 *SIC* 3312 1241

■ SUNCOKE ENERGY PARTNERS LP p 1402
1011 Warrenville Rd # 600 60532
Tel (630) 824-1000 *SIC* 3312

TALARIS INC p 1422
3333 Warrenville Rd # 310 60532
Tel (630) 577-1000 *SIC* 3578 3499

TRANSITIONAL CARE MANAGEMENT LLC p 1472
3333 Warrenville Rd # 200 60532
Tel (847) 720-8700 *SIC* 8051

■ UNITED HEALTHCARE OF ILLINOIS INC p 1509
550 Warrenville Rd # 300 60532
Tel (630) 725-7204 *SIC* 6324

VALID USA INC p 1540
1011 Warrenville Rd # 450 60532
Tel (630) 852-8200 *SIC* 2752

VERITAS STEEL LLC p 1550
2300 Cabot Dr Ste 148 60532
Tel (630) 423-8708 *SIC* 3441

LITCHFIELD, IL

■ MARINE ACQUISITION CORP p 906
1 Sierra Pl 62056
Tel (217) 324-9400 *SIC* 5088

SIERRA INTERNATIONAL INC p 1320
1 Sierra Pl 62056
Tel (217) 324-9400 *SIC* 5088 3519

LOMBARD, IL

■ CINCH CONNECTIVITY SOLUTIONS INC p 307
1700 S Finley Rd 60148
Tel (847) 739-0300 *SIC* 3678 3679

■ CINCH CONNECTORS INC p 307
1700 S Finley Rd 60148
Tel (630) 705-6001 *SIC* 3643 3678

CORPORATE TRAVEL CONSULTANTS INC p 372
450 E 22nd St Ste 100 60148
Tel (630) 691-9100 *SIC* 4724

DENTAL NETWORK OF AMERICA LLC p 429
701 E 22nd St Ste 300 60148
Tel (630) 691-0290 *SIC* 6324

ENTERPRISE LEASING CO OF CHICAGO LLC p 502
1050 N Lombard Rd 60148
Tel (630) 693-2916 *SIC* 7515 7514

HARRY J KLOEPPEL & ASSOCIATES INC p 664
246 E Janata Blvd Ste 300 60148
Tel (630) 206-5810 *SIC* 5049

MOL (AMERICA) INC p 982
700 E Bttrfeld Rd Ste 250 60148
Tel (630) 424-3480 *SIC* 4731 7373 4412

OLD HF LLC p 1081
1000 N Rohlwing Rd Ste 46 60148
Tel (630) 261-3900 *SIC* 5712

ONYX ENVIRONMENTAL SERVICES LLC p 1088
700 E Bttrfeld Rd Ste 201 60148
Tel (630) 218-1500
SIC 8711 4953 2869 1799 1629

■ PERNIX BUILDING GROUP LLC p 1136
151 E 22nd St Ste 101e 60148
Tel (630) 620-4787 *SIC* 1521

▲ PERNIX GROUP INC p 1136
151 E 22nd St Ste 101e 60148
Tel (630) 620-4787 *SIC* 1542 4911

RECYCLE AMERICA ALLIANCE LLC p 1215
720 E Butterfield Rd Fl 2 60148
Tel (630) 572-8800 *SIC* 4953

ROYAL MANAGEMENT CORP p 1254
665 W North Ave Ste 500 60148
Tel (630) 495-1700 *SIC* 8059

TRANSDEV NORTH AMERICA INC p 1471
720 E Bttrfeld Rd Ste 300 60148
Tel (630) 571-7070 *SIC* 4111 4131 4173

TRANSDEV SERVICES INC p 1471
720 E Bttrfeld Rd Ste 300 60148
Tel (630) 571-7070 *SIC* 4119 4121

TRP ACQUISITION CORP p 1485
1000 N Rohlwing Rd Ste 46 60148
Tel (630) 261-2380 *SIC* 2512

■ VISKASE COMPANIES INC p 1561
333 E Butterfield Rd # 400 60148
Tel (630) 874-0700 *SIC* 3089

■ VISKASE CORP p 1562
333 E Bttrfeld Rd Ste 400 60148
Tel (630) 874-0700 *SIC* 3089

■ **WASTE MANAGEMENT OF INDIANA LLC** p 1580
720 E Butterfield Rd Fl 2 60148
Tel (630) 572-8800 *SIC* 4953

WEST SUBURBAN BANCORP INC p 1595
711 Westmore Meyers Rd 60148
Tel (630) 629-4200 *SIC* 6022

LONG GROVE, IL

AMERICAN MANUFACTURERS MUTUAL INSURANCE CO p 75
1 Kemper Dr 60047
Tel (847) 320-2000 *SIC* 6331

AMERICAN MOTORISTS INSURANCE CO p 76
1 Kemper Dr 60047
Tel (847) 320-2000 *SIC* 6411

AMERICAN PROTECTION INSURANCE CO INC p 78
1 Kemper Dr 60047
Tel (847) 320-2000 *SIC* 6411

GRI ENGINEERING & DEVELOPMENT LLC p 640
6700 Wildlife Way 60047
Tel (847) 383-8478 *SIC* 5013

MAT HOLDINGS INC p 918
6700 Wildlife Way 60047
Tel (847) 821-9630 *SIC* 2842 3714 3563

MAT INDUSTRIES LLC p 918
6700 Wildlife Way 60047
Tel (847) 821-9630 *SIC* 3563

MIDWEST AIRTECHNOLOGIES INC p 967
6700 Wildlife Way 60047
Tel (847) 821-9630
SIC 5072 5191 5063 5051 5031

LOVES PARK, IL

CIMCO RESOURCES INC p 307
1616 Windsor Rd 61111
Tel (815) 986-7211 *SIC* 5093 7389

TH FOODS INC p 1446
2134 Harlem Rd 61111
Tel (800) 896-2396 *SIC* 2052

MACHESNEY PARK, IL

HARLEM SCHOOL DISTRICT 122 p 661
8605 N 2nd St 61115
Tel (815) 654-4500 *SIC* 8211 8741

MACOMB, IL

NTN-BOWER CORP p 1065
711 Bower Rd 61455
Tel (309) 837-0440 *SIC* 3562

WEST CENTRAL FS INC p 1594
1202 W Piper St 61455
Tel (309) 833-2168 *SIC* 5153

WESTERN ILLINOIS UNIVERSITY INC p 1598
1 University Cir 61455
Tel (309) 298-1800 *SIC* 8221

MADISON, IL

CUSTOM STEEL PROCESSING INC p 403
1001 College St 62060
Tel (618) 876-7276 *SIC* 5051

MAHOMET, IL

FARM CREDIT ILLINOIS ACA p 528
1100 Farm Credit Dr 61853
Tel (217) 590-2222 *SIC* 6159 6153 6111

MAPLE PARK, IL

HFI ENTERPRISES INC p 689
2s181 County Line Rd 60151
Tel (630) 557-2406 *SIC* 5172 5191

MARENGO, IL

UNICARRIERS AMERICAS CORP p 1502
240 N Prospect St 60152
Tel (800) 871-5438 *SIC* 3537 3519 5084

MARION, IL

AISIN MFG ILLINOIS LLC p 41
11000 Redco Dr 62959
Tel (618) 998-8333 *SIC* 3714

■ **MARION HOSPITAL CORP** p 907
3333 W Deyoung St 62959
Tel (618) 998-7800 *SIC* 8062 8011

MARION VA MEDICAL CENTER p 907
2401 W Main St 62959
Tel (618) 993-1122 *SIC* 8062

PEPSI MIDAMERICA CO p 1134
2605 W Main St 62959
Tel (618) 997-1377 *SIC* 2086

SHAWNEE VILLAGE PRESERVATION LP p 1313
1304 W Boulevard St 62959
Tel (618) 997-5365 *SIC* 6531

SOUTHERN ILLINOIS POWER CO-OPERATIVE p 1349
11543 Lake Of Egypt Rd 62959
Tel (618) 964-1448 *SIC* 4911

MARISSA, IL

PRAIRIE STATE GENERATING CO LLC p 1167
3872 County Highway 12 62257
Tel (618) 824-7600 *SIC* 4911

MARK, IL

MENNIES MACHINE CO p 943
Mennie Dr Rr 71 61340
Tel (815) 339-2226 *SIC* 3544 8742

MARYVILLE, IL

SOUTHWESTERN ILLINOIS HEALTH FACILITIES INC p 1353
6800 State Route 162 62062
Tel (618) 288-5711 *SIC* 8062

MASCOUTAH, IL

CABLOFIL INC p 235
8319 State Route 4 62258
Tel (618) 566-3230 *SIC* 3443

MATTESON, IL

A & R SECURITY SERVICES INC p 4
600 Holiday Plaza Dr # 500 60443
Tel (708) 389-3830 *SIC* 7381

ROGERS ENTERPRISES INC p 1246
20821 S Cicero Ave 60443
Tel (708) 679-7588 *SIC* 5944

SUTTON FORD INC p 1410
21315 Central Ave 60443
Tel (708) 720-8000 *SIC* 5511

MATTOON, IL

▲ **CONSOLIDATED COMMUNICATIONS HOLDINGS INC** p 359
121 S 17th St 61938
Tel (217) 235-3311 *SIC* 4813

■ **CONSOLIDATED COMMUNICATIONS INC** p 359
121 S 17th St 61938
Tel (217) 235-3311 *SIC* 4813

■ **CONSOLIDATED COMMUNICATIONS OF ILLINOIS CO** p 359
121 S 17th St 61938
Tel (217) 235-3311 *SIC* 4813

LAKE LAND COLLEGE p 839
5001 Lake Land Blvd 61938
Tel (217) 234-5253 *SIC* 8222 8221

MATTOON RURAL KING SUPPLY INC p 921
4216 Dewitt Ave 61938
Tel (217) 254-6678 *SIC* 5399

SARAH BUSH LINCOLN HEALTH CENTER p 1282
1000 Health Center Dr 61938
Tel (217) 258-2525 *SIC* 8011 8062

MAYWOOD, IL

LOYOLA UNIVERSITY MEDICAL CENTER p 882
2160 S 1st Ave 60153
Tel (708) 216-9000 *SIC* 8011

MC COOK, IL

CAPITOL WHOLESALE MEATS INC p 251
8751 W 50th St 60525
Tel (708) 485-4800 *SIC* 2013

MICHAEL LEWIS CO p 960
8900 W 50th St 60525
Tel (708) 688-2200
SIC 5113 5141 5142 2782 2759 2621

■ **PROGRESS RAIL LOCOMOTIVE INC** p 1181
9301 W 55th St 60525
Tel (800) 255-5355 *SIC* 3621 3519 3647

MCHENRY, IL

BPI HOLDINGS INTERNATIONAL INC p 206
4400 Prime Pkwy 60050
Tel (815) 363-9000 *SIC* 3714

BRAKE PARTS INC LLC p 207
4400 Prime Pkwy 60050
Tel (815) 363-9000 *SIC* 3714

FABRIK INDUSTRIES INC p 523
5213 Prime Pkwy 60050
Tel (815) 385-9480 *SIC* 3089 3544

FOLLETT SCHOOL SOLUTIONS INC p 563
1340 Ridgeview Dr 60050
Tel (815) 759-1700 *SIC* 5192

MEDCOR INC p 935
4805 Prime Pkwy 60050
Tel (815) 363-9500 *SIC* 8099

MEDELA INC p 935
1101 Corporate Dr 60050
Tel (800) 435-8316 *SIC* 5047 3596

NIMED CORP p 1043
4201 W Medical Center Dr 60050
Tel (815) 344-5555 *SIC* 8062

NORTHERN ILLINOIS MEDICAL CENTER p 1056
4201 W Medical Center Dr 60050
Tel (815) 344-5000 *SIC* 8062

MELROSE PARK, IL

ANNING-JOHNSON CO p 92
1959 Anson Dr 60160
Tel (708) 681-1300
SIC 1742 1752 1799 1761

ANSON INDUSTRIES INC p 93
1959 Anson Dr 60160
Tel (708) 681-1300
SIC 1742 1752 1761 1799

CHAS LEVY CIRCULATING CO p 291
1930 George St Ste 4 60160
Tel (708) 356-3600 *SIC* 4213 4214 5192

DYNAMIC MANUFACTURING INC p 464
1930 N Mannheim Rd 60160
Tel (708) 343-8753 *SIC* 3714

■ **FANNIE MAY CONFECTIONS BRANDS INC** p 527
2457 W North Ave 60160
Tel (773) 693-9100 *SIC* 2064 5441

GOTTLIEB HEALTH RESOURCES INC p 626
701 W North Ave 60160
Tel (708) 681-3200 *SIC* 8741

GOTTLIEB MEMORIAL HOSPITAL p 626
701 W North Ave 60160
Tel (708) 681-3200 *SIC* 8062

■ **H J M P CORP** p 650
1930 George St Ste 2 60160
Tel (708) 345-5370
SIC 2033 5149 0174 2037

■ **IMPAC GROUP INC** p 734
1950 N Ruby St 60160
Tel (708) 344-9100 *SIC* 2657

INTERLAKE MECALUX INC p 753
1600 N 25th Ave 60160
Tel (708) 344-9999 *SIC* 5084 2542

KREHER STEEL CO LLC p 829
1550 N 25th Ave 60160
Tel (708) 345-8180 *SIC* 5051

MECHANICAL SERVANTS LLC p 934
2755 Thomas St 60160
Tel (708) 486-1500 *SIC* 5122

WESTLAKE HOSPITAL p 1601
1225 W Lake St 60160
Tel (708) 681-3000 *SIC* 8062

WESTROCK CONSUMER PACKAGING GROUP LLC p 1602
1950 N Ruby St 60160
Tel (708) 344-9100 *SIC* 2671

WISCON CORP p 1618
2050 N 15th Ave 60160
Tel (708) 450-0074 *SIC* 5143 2022

MENDOTA, IL

NORTHERN PARTNERS COOPERATIVE p 1056
1000 6th Ave 61342
Tel (815) 539-6772 *SIC* 5153

MILAN, IL

BI-STATE PACKAGING INC p 181
4905 77th Ave E 61264
Tel (309) 736-8500 *SIC* 5199 5084

COUNTRY STONE INC p 375
6300 75th Ave Ste A 61264
Tel (309) 787-1744
SIC 2499 2875 3273 3281

ELLIOTT AVIATION INC p 488
6601 74th Ave 61264
Tel (309) 799-3183 *SIC* 4581 5599

EXPORT PACKAGING CO INC p 520
525 10th Ave E 61264
Tel (309) 756-4288 *SIC* 4783 2448 2441

GROUP O INC p 642
4905 77th Ave E 61264
Tel (309) 736-8100
SIC 8742 7389 4226 5085

LYNCO DISTRIBUTION INC p 887
1410 11th St W 61264
Tel (309) 787-2300 *SIC* 5199

R & O SPECIALTIES INC p 1201
120 4th Ave E 61264
Tel (309) 736-8660 *SIC* 5085 5013 3479

MOKENA, IL

OZINGA BROS INC p 1102
19001 Old Lagrange Rd # 30 60448
Tel (708) 326-4200 *SIC* 3273 5032

PRESENCE LIFE CONNECTIONS p 1172
18927 Hickory Creek Dr # 300 60448
Tel (708) 478-7900 *SIC* 8052

PRESENCE PRV HEALTH p 1172
19827 Hickory Crk Dr 30 Ste 300 60448
Tel (815) 741-7137 *SIC* 8051 8062

REVERE ELECTRIC SUPPLY CO p 1229
8807 187th St 60448
Tel (312) 738-3636 *SIC* 5063

UNITED ROAD TOWING INC p 1511
9550 Bormet Dr Ste 304 60448
Tel (708) 390-2200 *SIC* 7549

ZENITH AMERICAN SOLUTIONS INC p 1642
18861 90th Ave Ste A 60448
Tel (312) 649-1200 *SIC* 6371

MOLINE, IL

▲ **DEERE & CO** p 422
1 John Deere Pl 61265
Tel (309) 765-8000
SIC 3523 3531 3524 6159

■ **DEERE PAYROLL SERVICES INC** p 422
1 John Deere Pl 61265
Tel (309) 765-8000 *SIC* 8721

FCA INC p 532
7601 John Deere Pkwy 61265
Tel (309) 792-3222 *SIC* 5085 5031

FCA LLC p 532
7601 John Deere Pkwy 61265
Tel (309) 792-3444
SIC 4783 5031 5085 2448

HEART OF AMERICA MANAGEMENT LLC p 678
1501 River Dr 61265
Tel (309) 797-9300 *SIC* 8741 5812 7011

■ **JOHN DEERE CONSTRUCTION & FORESTRY CO** p 788
1 John Deere Pl 61265
Tel (309) 765-8000 *SIC* 5084 5082

JOHN DEERE INSURANCE GROUP INC p 788
3400 80th St 61265
Tel (309) 765-8000 *SIC* 6331 6321 6311

■ **JOHN DEERE SHARED SERVICES INC** p 788
1515 5th Ave Ste 200 61265
Tel (309) 765-0260 *SIC* 5082

KONE ELEVATOR p 827
1 Kone Ct 61265
Tel (309) 764-6771 *SIC* 7699 3534

KONE INC p 827
1 Kone Ct 61265
Tel (309) 764-6771 *SIC* 7699 3534 1796

MOLINE DISPATCH PUBLISHING CO p 983
1720 5th Ave 61265
Tel (309) 764-4344 *SIC* 2711 2752

MOLINE-COAL VALLEY COMMUNITY UNIT SCHOOL DISTRICT 40 p 983
1619 11th Ave 61265
Tel (309) 743-1600 *SIC* 8211

▲ **QCR HOLDINGS INC** p 1194
3551 7th St Ste 204 61265
Tel (309) 736-3584 *SIC* 6022

RIVERSTONE GROUP INC p 1238
1701 5th Ave 61265
Tel (309) 757-8250 *SIC* 1422

STANDARD WESTWOOD VENTURE LP p 1376
2200 1st St Ste A 61265
Tel (309) 797-4327 *SIC* 6513

■ **UNITEDHEALTHCARE SERVICES CO OF RIVER VALLEY INC** p 1515
1300 River Dr Ste 200 61265
Tel (952) 936-1300 *SIC* 6324

MOMENCE, IL

R J VAN DRUNEN & SONS INC p 1202
300 W 6th St 60954
Tel (815) 472-3100
SIC 2034 2037 0161 2099

MONEE, IL

G K ENTERPRISES INC p 587
26000 S Whiting Way Ste 2 60449
Tel (708) 587-2150
SIC 3743 3443 3559 3556 3536

MONTGOMERY, IL

AURORA BEARING CO p 131
901 Aucutt Rd 60538
Tel (630) 897-8941 *SIC* 3568

■ **FOX RIVER FOODS INC** p 572
5030 Baseline Rd 60538
Tel (630) 896-1991
SIC 5142 5149 5148 5147

LYON LLC p 888
420 N Main St 60538
Tel (630) 892-8941 *SIC* 2542

LYON WORKSPACE PRODUCTS LLC p 888
420 N Main St 60538
Tel (630) 892-8941 *SIC* 2542

TOGO PACKING CO INC p 1458
2125 Rochester Rd 60538
Tel (800) 575-3365 *SIC* 2011

VVF ILLINOIS SERVICES LLC p 1567
2000 Aucutt Rd 60538
Tel (630) 892-4381 *SIC* 2841

MONTICELLO, IL

TOP FLIGHT GRAIN MONTICELLO CO p 1460
420 W Marion St 61856
Tel (217) 762-2163 *SIC* 5153 5191 4221

MORRIS, IL

AUX SABLE LIQUID PRODUCTS LP p 135
6155 E Us Route 6 60450
Tel (815) 941-5800 *SIC* 1321

MORRIS HOSPITAL p 990
150 W High St 60450
Tel (815) 942-2932 *SIC* 8011 8062

MORTON GROVE, IL

CRAWFORD SUPPLY GROUP INC p 389
8150 Lehigh Ave Ste A 60053
Tel (847) 967-0550 *SIC* 5074

LAKESHORE RECYCLING SYSTEMS LLC p 840
6132 Oakton St 60053
Tel (773) 685-8811 *SIC* 4953

▲ **LIFEWAY FOODS INC** p 865
6431 Oakton St 60053
Tel (847) 967-1010 *SIC* 2023 2026

MORTON GROVE PHARMACEUTICALS INC p 991
6451 Main St 60053
Tel (847) 967-5600 SIC 2834

PUBLICATIONS INTERNATIONAL LTD p 1190
8140 Lehigh Ave 60053
Tel (847) 676-3470 SIC 2731 2721

SCHWARZ PAPER CO LLC p 1291
8338 Austin Ave 60053
Tel (847) 966-2550 SIC 2621 5199 4225

MORTON, IL

■ **CAT LOGISTICS INC** p 264
500 N Morton Ave 61550
Tel (309) 675-1000 SIC 4225 5045 4213

■ **CATERPILLAR LOGISTICS INC** p 265
500 N Morton Ave 61550
Tel (309) 266-3591 SIC 4225

CORE CONSTRUCTION GROUP LTD p 369
866 N Main St 61550
Tel (309) 263-0808 SIC 8741

G&D INTEGRATED TRANSPORTATION INC p 587
50 Commerce Dr 61550
Tel (309) 284-6700 SIC 4213

MMC PRECISION HOLDINGS CORP p 979
1021 W Birchwood St 61550
Tel (309) 266-7176 SIC 3449

MORTON BUILDINGS INC p 991
252 W Adams St 61550
Tel (309) 263-7474 SIC 2452

MORTON COMMUNITY BANK INC p 991
721 W Jackson St 61550
Tel (309) 263-8126 SIC 6022 6021

MORTON INDUSTRIAL GROUP INC p 991
1021 W Birchwood St 61550
Tel (309) 266-7176 SIC 3449

MORTON INDUSTRIES LLC p 991
70 Commerce Dr 61550
Tel (309) 263-2590 SIC 3498

STAR TRANSPORT INC p 1378
240 W Ashland St 61550
Tel (309) 266-7613 SIC 4213 4731

MOUNT PROSPECT, IL

■ **ATLAS MATERIAL TESTING TECHNOLOGY LLC** p 128
1500 Bishop Ct 60056
Tel (773) 327-4520
SIC 3823 3569 3599 8734 3825 3821

CUMMINS - ALLISON CORP p 401
852 Feehanville Dr 60056
Tel (847) 759-6403 SIC 3578 3519

DIVERSIFIED FOODSERVICE SUPPLY INC p 444
607 Dempster St 60056
Tel (847) 966-9700 SIC 5046 7699

MIZKAN AMERICA HOLDINGS INC p 978
1661 Feehanville Dr # 300 60056
Tel (847) 590-0059 SIC 2099

MIZKAN AMERICA INC p 978
1661 Feehanville Dr # 200 60056
Tel (847) 590-0059 SIC 2099 2035

NTN BEARING CORP OF AMERICA p 1065
1600 Bishop Ct 60056
Tel (847) 298-7500 SIC 5085

NTN USA CORP p 1065
1600 Bishop Ct 60056
Tel (847) 298-4652 SIC 5085 3562 3568

RAULAND-BORG CORP p 1209
1802 W Central Rd 60056
Tel (847) 590-7100 SIC 3661 3663

ROBERT BOSCH TOOL CORP p 1241
1800 W Central Rd 60056
Tel (224) 232-2000 SIC 3546

SCHUMACHER ELECTRIC CORP p 1291
801 E Business Center Dr 60056
Tel (847) 385-1600 SIC 3629 3677

SUMITOMO ELECTRIC CARBIDE INC p 1398
1001 E Business Center Dr 60056
Tel (847) 635-0044 SIC 5084

MOUNT STERLING, IL

DOT FOODS INC p 451
1 Dot Way 62353
Tel (217) 773-4411 SIC 5141 5142

GRABBER HOLDINGS LLC p 628
1 Dot Way 62353
Tel (217) 773-4411 SIC 5072 5211 6719

MOUNT VERNON, IL

GOOD SAMARITAN REGIONAL HEALTH CENTER p 623
1 Good Samaritan Way 62864
Tel (618) 242-4600 SIC 8062

NATIONAL RAILWAY EQUIPMENT CO p 1015
1100 Shawnee St 62864
Tel (618) 242-6590 SIC 5088 3743

MUNDELEIN, IL

AMCOR FLEXIBLES LLC p 65
1919 S Butterfield Rd 60060
Tel (847) 362-9000
SIC 2671 2621 2821 3081 3466

CERTIFIED POWER INC p 284
970 Campus Dr 60060
Tel (847) 573-3800 SIC 3714 7539 5013

MAC LEAN-FOGG CO p 891
1000 Allanson Rd 60060
Tel (847) 566-0010
SIC 3678 3452 3089 3061 3492 3451

RUPRECHT CO p 1258
1301 Allanson Rd 60060
Tel (312) 829-4100 SIC 5147

NAPERVILLE, IL

APPLICATIONS SOFTWARE TECHNOLOGY CORP p 99
1755 Park St Ste 100 60563
Tel (630) 778-0707 SIC 4813

BILL JACOBS MOTORSPORT HOLDINGS INC p 182
1564 W Ogden Ave 60540
Tel (630) 357-1200 SIC 5511 5521

BP AMOCO CHEMICAL CO p 205
150 W Warrenville Rd 60563
Tel (630) 420-5111
SIC 2221 2821 2869 2819 2865

▲ **CALAMOS ASSET MANAGEMENT INC** p 238
2020 Calamos Ct Ofc 60563
Tel (630) 245-7200 SIC 6211 6282

■ **CALAMOS INVESTMENTS LLC** p 238
2020 Calamos Ct Ofc 60563
Tel (630) 245-7200 SIC 6211 6282

CATHOLIC ORDER OF FORESTERS INC p 267
355 Shuman Blvd 60563
Tel (630) 983-4900 SIC 6311

CITY OF NAPERVILLE p 316
400 S Eagle St 60540
Tel (630) 420-6111 SIC 9111

CORIANT INTERNATIONAL INC p 370
1415 W Diehl Rd 60563
Tel (630) 798-8800 SIC 4813

CORIANT NORTH AMERICA LLC p 370
1415 W Diehl Rd 60563
Tel (630) 798-4238 SIC 5065

CORIANT OPERATIONS INC p 370
1415 W Diehl Rd 60563
Tel (847) 382-8817 SIC 3661

DELTA DENTAL OF ILLINOIS p 426
111 Shuman Blvd Ste 100 60563
Tel (630) 718-4700 SIC 6324

EBY-BROWN CO LLC p 474
1415 W Diehl Rd Ste 300 60563
Tel (630) 778-2800
SIC 5194 5145 5141 5122 5149

EDWARD HOSPITAL p 480
801 S Washington St 60540
Tel (630) 355-0450 SIC 8062

EDWARD-ELMHURST HEALTHCARE p 480
801 S Washington St 60540
Tel (630) 355-0450 SIC 8062

■ **FACTORY CARD & PARTY OUTLET CORP** p 523
2727 W Diehl Rd 60563
Tel (630) 579-2000 SIC 5947

GEA FARM TECHNOLOGIES INC p 597
1880 Country Farm Dr 60563
Tel (630) 548-8200
SIC 5083 3523 2841 2842

HALLMARK SERVICES CORP p 655
1000 E Warrenville Rd # 400 60563
Tel (630) 328-4400 SIC 6321

ILONA FINANCIAL GROUP INC p 733
1807 S Washington St 60565
Tel (630) 699-6147 SIC 6311

KEHE DISTRIBUTORS HOLDINGS LLC p 807
1245 E Diehl Rd Ste 200 60563
Tel (630) 343-0000 SIC 5149

KEHE DISTRIBUTORS LLC p 807
1245 E Diehl Rd Ste 200 60563
Tel (630) 343-0000 SIC 5149

LAIDLAW INTERNATIONAL INC p 838
55 Shuman Blvd Ste 400 60563
Tel (214) 849-8100 SIC 4151 4131

■ **MONONA HOLDINGS LLC** p 984
1952 Mc Dowell Rd Ste 207 60563
Tel (630) 946-0630 SIC 3694 5063

■ **NALCO CO LLC** p 1006
1601 W Diehl Rd 60563
Tel (630) 305-1000
SIC 3559 2899 2992 2891

■ **NALCO HOLDING CO** p 1007
1601 W Diehl Rd 60563
Tel (630) 305-1000 SIC 2899 2992

■ **NALCO HOLDINGS LLC** p 1007
1601 W Diehl Rd 60563
Tel (630) 305-1000 SIC 2899 2992 3559

NAPERVILLE COMMUNITY UNIT SCHOOL DISTRICT 203 p 1007
203 W Hillside Rd 60540
Tel (630) 420-6300 SIC 8211

■ **NICOR SERVICES** p 1043
1751 W Diehl Rd Ste 200 60563
Tel (630) 718-2707 SIC 4924

NORTH CENTRAL COLLEGE p 1051
30 N Brainard St 60540
Tel (630) 637-5100 SIC 8221

■ **NORTHERN ILLINOIS GAS CO** p 1056
1844 W Ferry Rd 60563
Tel (630) 983-8676 SIC 4924 4922

■ **OFFICEMAX CONTRACT INC** p 1076
263 Shuman Blvd 60563
Tel (630) 438-7800
SIC 5021 5112 5044 5111 5943 5712

■ **OTTAWA ACQUISITION LLC** p 1098
1844 W Ferry Rd 60563
Tel (888) 642-6748 SIC 4924

PARK NAPERVILLE DISTRICT p 1115
320 Jackson Ave 60540
Tel (630) 848-5000
SIC 7992 7999 8322 8741

■ **RSA MEDICAL LLC** p 1255
2135 City Gate Ln Ste 600 60563
Tel (630) 416-7150 SIC 6321

SIKICH LLP p 1322
1415 W Diehl Rd Ste 400 60563
Tel (630) 566-8400 SIC 8721

■ **STANLEY CONVERGENT SECURITY SOLUTIONS INC** p 1377
55 Shuman Blvd Ste 900 60563
Tel (630) 245-7100 SIC 7382

■ **SYX DISTRIBUTION INC** p 1419
175 Ambassador Dr 60540
Tel (516) 608-7000 SIC 5734

TELLABS INC p 1435
1415 W Diehl Rd 60563
Tel (630) 798-8800 SIC 3661 1731

■ **TRADEWINDS HEATING & AIR CONDITIONING** p 1469
2019 Corporate Ln Ste 159 60563
Tel (630) 718-2700 SIC 1711

VANGUARD ENERGY SERVICES LLC p 1543
850 E Diehl Rd Ste 142 60563
Tel (630) 955-1500 SIC 3822

VERICLAIM INC p 1549
1833 Cntre Pt Cir Ste 139 60563
Tel (630) 245-7000 SIC 6411

VIANT HOLDINGS INC p 1554
535 E Diehl Rd Ste 100 60563
Tel (630) 649-5000 SIC 6719

WEST SIDE TRACTOR SALES CO p 1595
1400 W Ogden Ave 60563
Tel (630) 355-7150 SIC 5082

NASHVILLE, IL

NASCOTE INDUSTRIES INC p 1008
18310 Enterprise Ave 62263
Tel (618) 327-3286 SIC 3714

NAUVOO, IL

COLUSA ELEVATOR CO p 343
13 Broadway 62354
Tel (217) 453-2216 SIC 5153

NEPONSET, IL

MARTIN ENGINEERING CO p 912
1 Martin Pl 61345
Tel (309) 852-2384 SIC 3829 3532

NEW LENOX, IL

SILVER CROSS HEALTH SYSTEM p 1323
1900 Silver Cross Blvd 60451
Tel (815) 300-1100 SIC 8059

SILVER CROSS HOSPITAL AND MEDICAL CENTERS p 1323
1900 Silver Cross Blvd 60451
Tel (815) 300-1100 SIC 8062

TRINITY SERVICES INC p 1482
301 Veterans Pkwy 60451
Tel (815) 485-6197 SIC 8211 8322

NILES, IL

AFN LLC p 33
7230 N Caldwell Ave 60714
Tel (847) 498-8885 SIC 4731

ALP LIGHTING & CEILING PRODUCTS INC p 60
6333 W Gross Point Rd 60714
Tel (773) 774-9550
SIC 3089 3354 5162 3496 3442 3229

BRADFORD EXCHANGE LTD p 206
9333 N Milwaukee Ave 60714
Tel (847) 966-2770 SIC 5961 5199

GARVEY GROUP LLC p 593
7400 N Lehigh Ave 60714
Tel (847) 647-1900 SIC 6719

▲ **MFRI INC** p 958
6410 W Howard St 60714
Tel (847) 966-1000 SIC 3677 3564 3569

■ **MPC PRODUCTS CORP** p 995
6300 W Howard St 60714
Tel (847) 673-8300
SIC 3728 3621 3676 3812 3625

■ **PERMA-PIPE INC** p 1136
7720 N Lehigh Ave 60714
Tel (847) 966-2190 SIC 3498

RICO INDUSTRIES INC p 1233
7000 N Austin Ave 60714
Tel (312) 427-0313
SIC 5199 3172 2396 3993

SHURE INC p 1319
5800 W Touhy Ave 60714
Tel (847) 600-2000 SIC 3651 3679 3661

SPECIALTY PROMOTIONS INC p 1356
6019 W Howard St 60714
Tel (847) 588-2580 SIC 2752

■ **WELLS LAMONT INDUSTRY GROUP LLC** p 1591
6640 W Touhy Ave 60714
Tel (800) 247-3295 SIC 2381

NORMAL, IL

BOARD OF TRUSTEES OF ILLINOIS STATE UNIVERSITY p 196
302 Hovey Hall 61790
Tel (309) 438-2111 SIC 8221

BROMENN REGIONAL MEDICAL CENTER p 217
1304 Franklin Ave 61761
Tel (309) 454-1400 SIC 8093

BROMENN SERVICE AUXILIARY GIFT SHOP p 217
Franklin Ave Virginia St 61761
Tel (309) 454-1400 SIC 5947 5641 5621

CENTRAL ILLINOIS TRUCKS INC p 278
200 W Northtown Rd 61761
Tel (800) 322-5017 SIC 5013 7538 5012

MCLEAN COUNTY UNIT DISTRICT NO 5 p 931
1809 Hovey Ave 61761
Tel (309) 557-4000 SIC 8211

NORTH AURORA, IL

OBERWEIS DAIRY INC p 1072
951 Ice Cream Dr 60542
Tel (630) 801-6100 SIC 5963 5451

NORTH CHICAGO, IL

▲ **ABBVIE INC** p 10
1 N Waukegan Rd 60064
Tel (847) 932-7900 SIC 2834 2836

ROSALIND FRANKLIN UNIVERSITY OF MEDICINE AND SCIENCE p 1250
3333 Green Bay Rd 60064
Tel (847) 578-3000 SIC 8221

NORTHBROOK, IL

▲ **ALLSTATE CORP** p 58
2775 Sanders Rd 60062
Tel (847) 402-5000
SIC 6411 6351 6311 6371

■ **ALLSTATE DISTRIBUTORS LLC** p 58
2775 Sanders Rd 60062
Tel (847) 402-5000 SIC 6411

■ **ALLSTATE INDEMNITY CO** p 58
2775 Sanders Rd F9 60062
Tel (847) 402-5000 SIC 6411

■ **ALLSTATE INSURANCE CO** p 58
2775 Sanders Rd 60062
Tel (847) 402-5000 SIC 6411

■ **ALLSTATE LIFE INSURANCE CO** p 58
3075 Sanders Rd 60062
Tel (847) 402-5000 SIC 6411 6311

■ **ALLSTATE NON INSURANCE HOLDINGS INC** p 58
2775 Sanders Rd Ste D 60062
Tel (847) 402-5000 SIC 6411

AMARI METALS EUROPE LTD p 64
555 Skokie Blvd Ste 555 60062
Tel (847) 480-4690 SIC 6719

ARMON INC p 111
2265 Carlson Dr 60062
Tel (847) 498-4800 SIC 1711 7515 6552

ASTELLAS PHARMA US INC p 122
1 Astellas Way 60062
Tel (800) 888-7704 SIC 5122

ASTELLAS US HOLDING INC p 122
1 Astellas Way 60062
Tel (224) 205-8800 SIC 2834

■ **CAREMARK INTERNATIONAL LLC** p 255
2211 Sanders Rd 60062
Tel (847) 559-4700
SIC 5961 6411 8099 8092 8093

■ **CAREMARK LLC** p 255
2211 Sanders Rd 60062
Tel (847) 559-4700
SIC 5961 6411 8099 8092 8093 8742

CENSEA INC p 275
650 Dundee Rd Ste 180 60062
Tel (224) 723-5800 SIC 5146

CENTRAL SEAWAY CO INC p 280
650 Dundee Rd Ste 180 60062
Tel (224) 723-5800 SIC 5146

D D G INC p 407
1955 Shermer Rd Ste 300 60062
Tel (847) 412-0277 SIC 3317 2511 6512

EUROMARKET DESIGNS INC p 512
1250 Techny Rd 60062
Tel (847) 272-2888
SIC 5719 5947 5712 5961 2599

F E MORAN INC p 522
2265 Carlson Dr 60062
Tel (847) 498-4800 SIC 1711

■ **FIRST INSURANCE FUNDING CORP** p 547
450 Skokie Blvd Ste 1000 60062
Tel (847) 374-3000 SIC 6159

HENLEY MANAGEMENT CO p 683
555 Skokie Blvd Ste 555 60062
Tel (847) 480-4690 SIC 6719

HIGHLAND BAKING CO INC p 691
2301 Shermer Rd 60062
Tel (847) 677-2789 *SIC* 5149 2051

HILCO INC p 692
5 Revere Dr Ste 430 60062
Tel (847) 714-1288 *SIC* 7389 6531

■ **KAPSTONE KRAFT PAPER CORP** p 803
1101 Skokie Blvd Ste 300 60062
Tel (252) 533-6000 *SIC* 2621

▲ **KAPSTONE PAPER AND PACKAGING CORP** p 803
1101 Skokie Blvd Ste 300 60062
Tel (847) 239-8800 *SIC* 2621

■ **KAPSTONE RECEIVABLES LLC** p 804
1101 Skokie Blvd Ste 300 60062
Tel (270) 393-2559 *SIC* 7322

KEMPER SPORTS INC p 810
500 Skokie Blvd Ste 444 60062
Tel (847) 850-1818 *SIC* 8743 7941 7992

KEMPER SPORTS MANAGEMENT INC p 810
500 Skokie Blvd Ste 444 60062
Tel (847) 850-1818 *SIC* 7999

■ **KENNY CONSTRUCTION A GRANITE CO** p 811
2215 Sanders Rd Ste 400 60062
Tel (847) 919-8200
SIC 1622 1611 1629 1623 1541

■ **KENNY INDUSTRIES INC** p 811
2215 Sanders Rd Ste 400 60062
Tel (847) 919-8200
SIC 1611 1622 1629 1623 1541 6552

LANE CLEARWATER LIMITED PARTNERSHIP p 843
1200 Shermer Rd 60062
Tel (847) 498-6650 *SIC* 7011

M HOLLAND CO p 889
400 Skokie Blvd Ste 600 60062
Tel (847) 272-7370 *SIC* 5162

MAURICE SPORTING GOODS INC p 921
1910 Techny Rd 60062
Tel (847) 715-1500 *SIC* 5091

MAYLINE INVESTMENTS INC p 923
555 Skokie Blvd 60062
Tel (847) 948-9340 *SIC* 2522 2521

MERIT HEALTH SYSTEMS LLC p 949
1033 Skokie Blvd Ste 360 60062
Tel (502) 753-0890 *SIC* 8741

■ **METALS USA SPECIALTY METALS NORTHCENTRAL INC** p 953
3000 Shermer Rd 60062
Tel (847) 291-2400 *SIC* 5051

MU SIGMA INC p 998
3400 Dundee Rd Ste 160 60062
Tel (847) 919-0445 *SIC* 7378 7374

OLD WORLD INDUSTRIES LLC p 1081
4065 Commercial Ave 60062
Tel (847) 559-2000 *SIC* 5013 5169

OPTICSPLANET INC p 1090
3150 Commercial Ave 60062
Tel (847) 513-6190 *SIC* 5995 5049

PCS NITROGEN FERTILIZER OPERATIONS INC p 1124
1101 Skokie Blvd Ste 400 60062
Tel (847) 849-4200 *SIC* 2873

PCS NITROGEN INC p 1124
1101 Skokie Blvd Ste 400 60062
Tel (847) 849-4200 *SIC* 2873 2874

PCS PHOSPHATE CO INC p 1124
1101 Skokie Blvd Ste 400 60062
Tel (847) 849-4200
SIC 1475 1474 2874 2819

PCS SALES (USA) INC p 1124
1101 Skokie Blvd Ste 400 60062
Tel (847) 849-4200 *SIC* 5191

R L C ENTERPRISES INC p 1202
155 Revere Dr Ste 5 60062
Tel (847) 498-7888 *SIC* 5812

■ **ST PAUL PROTECTIVE INSURANCE CO** p 1372
Allstate S Barrington Plz 60062
Tel (847) 402-5000 *SIC* 6331

UL LLC p 1500
333 Pfingsten Rd 60062
Tel (847) 272-8800 *SIC* 8734

UNDERWRITERS LABORATORIES INC p 1502
333 Pfingsten Rd 60062
Tel (847) 272-8800 *SIC* 8734

UTILITIES INC p 1537
2335 Sanders Rd 60062
Tel (847) 498-6440 *SIC* 4941 4952

VELOCITEL INC p 1547
1033 Skokie Blvd Ste 320 60062
Tel (224) 757-0001 *SIC* 7373 8712

WILLIS STEIN & PARTNERS MANAGEMENT III LLC p 1612
1033 Skokie Blvd Ste 360 60062
Tel (312) 422-2400
SIC 6799 3479 2721 8721

WISS JANNEY ELSTNER ASSOCIATES INC p 1619
330 Pfingsten Rd 60062
Tel (847) 272-2186 *SIC* 8711 8712 8734

NORTHFIELD, IL

BODINE ELECTRIC CO p 197
201 Northfield Rd 60093
Tel (773) 478-3515 *SIC* 5063 3625 3621

COLLEGE OF AMERICAN PATHOLOGISTS p 336
325 Waukegan Rd 60093
Tel (800) 323-4040 *SIC* 8621

KARLIN FOODS CORP p 804
1845 Oak St Ste 19 60093
Tel (847) 441-8330 *SIC* 2034

KRAFT FOODS GROUP INC p 829
3 Lakes Dr 60093
Tel (847) 646-2000
SIC 2022 3411 2095 2043 2035 2087

MEDLINE INDUSTRIES INC p 938
3 Lakes Dr 60093
Tel (847) 949-5500 *SIC* 3841 5047 5999

SELECT REHABILITATION-MIDWEST LLC p 1301
550 W Frontage Rd # 2415 60093
Tel (847) 441-5593 *SIC* 8093

▲ **STEPAN CO** p 1386
22 W Frontage Rd 60093
Tel (847) 446-7500
SIC 2843 2821 2087 2865

NORTHLAKE, IL

CUSTOM COMPANIES INC p 403
317 W Lake St 60164
Tel (708) 344-5555 *SIC* 4731 4214

EMPIRETODAY LLC p 494
333 Northwest Ave 60164
Tel (847) 583-5238 *SIC* 5713

NORKOL INC p 1048
11650 W Grand Ave 60164
Tel (708) 531-1000 *SIC* 2679

SCHOLLE IPN CORP p 1288
200 W North Ave 60164
Tel (708) 562-7290
SIC 2819 3081 2821 3089

SCHOLLE IPN PACKAGING INC p 1288
200 W North Ave 60164
Tel (708) 562-7290 *SIC* 3089

OAK BROOK, IL

1888 MILLS LLC p 1
1520 Kensington Rd # 115 60523
Tel (630) 620-5222 *SIC* 5023 5131

▲ **A M CASTLE & CO** p 6
1420 Kensington Rd # 220 60523
Tel (847) 455-7111 *SIC* 5051 5162

ACE HARDWARE CORP p 16
2200 Kensington Ct 60523
Tel (630) 990-6600
SIC 5251 5198 5063 5074 5083

ADVOCATE NORTHSIDE HEALTH p 28
2025 Windsor Dr 60523
Tel (630) 572-9393 *SIC* 8062

COOK-ILLINOIS CORP p 366
2100 Clearwater Dr # 250 60523
Tel (708) 560-9840 *SIC* 4151

COSATECH INC p 373
1415 W 22nd St Towe Flr 60523
Tel (630) 684-2331 *SIC* 7373

DOMINICKS FINER FOODS INC p 449
711 Jorie Blvd Ms-4000 60523
Tel (630) 891-5000 *SIC* 5411

ELKAY MANUFACTURING CO INC p 487
2222 Camden Ct 60523
Tel (630) 574-8484
SIC 3431 3585 3432 2434

ELKAY PLUMBING PRODUCTS CO p 487
2222 Camden Ct 60523
Tel (630) 574-8484 *SIC* 3431

EVANGELICAL SERVICES CORP p 513
2025 Windsor Dr 60523
Tel (630) 572-9393 *SIC* 8741

▲ **FEDERAL SIGNAL CORP** p 536
1415 W 22nd St Ste 1100 60523
Tel (630) 954-2000
SIC 3711 3647 3669 3559 3544 3545

■ **GREAT LAKES DREDGE & DOCK CO LLC** p 633
2122 York Rd Ste 200 60523
Tel (630) 574-3000 *SIC* 1629

▲ **GREAT LAKES DREDGE & DOCK CORP** p 633
2122 York Rd Ste 200 60523
Tel (630) 574-3000 *SIC* 1629 1741

GREAT LAKES REIT p 634
823 Commerce Dr Ste 300 60523
Tel (708) 848-5216 *SIC* 6798 6531

HENIFF TRANSPORTATION SYSTEMS LLC p 683
2015 Spring Rd Ste 780 60523
Tel (630) 230-2100 *SIC* 4213

HTS ACQUISITION INC p 715
915 Harger Rd 60523
Tel (630) 368-0920 *SIC* 3646 3229 3645

▲ **HUB GROUP INC** p 715
2000 Clearwater Dr 60523
Tel (630) 271-3600 *SIC* 4731

■ **HUB GROUP TRUCKING INC** p 716
2000 Clearwater Dr 60523
Tel (630) 271-3600 *SIC* 4212

ILLINOIS MUNICIPAL RETIREMENT FUND p 732
2211 York Rd Ste 500 60523
Tel (630) 368-1010 *SIC* 6371

INLAND BANCORP INC p 743
2805 Butterfield Rd # 370 60523
Tel (630) 218-8000 *SIC* 6719

INLAND DIVERSIFIED REAL ESTATE TRUST INC p 743
2901 Butterfield Rd 60523
Tel (630) 218-8000 *SIC* 6798

INLAND REAL ESTATE GROUP OF COMPANIES p 743
2901 Butterfield Rd 60523
Tel (630) 218-8000
SIC 6513 6512 6162 6282 1522 1542

INLAND REAL ESTATE INVESTMENT CORP p 743
2901 Butterfield Rd 60523
Tel (630) 218-8000 *SIC* 6211 6798

INLAND SECURITIES CORP p 744
2901 Butterfield Rd 60523
Tel (630) 218-8000 *SIC* 6211

INTERNATIONAL EQUIPMENT SOLUTIONS LLC p 755
2211 York Rd Ste 320 60523
Tel (630) 570-6880 *SIC* 3531

INVENTRUST PROPERTIES CORP p 761
2809 Butterfield Rd 60523
Tel (855) 377-0510 *SIC* 6798

IRC RETAIL CENTERS LLC p 764
814 Commerce Dr Ste 300 60523
Tel (877) 206-5656 *SIC* 6798

L & H CO INC p 833
2215 York Rd Ste 304 60523
Tel (630) 571-7200
SIC 1731 1611 1623 3621

LIFELINK HOUSING CORP p 864
1900 Spring Rd Ste 300 60523
Tel (630) 368-0817 *SIC* 6513

▲ **MCDONALDS CORP** p 928
1 Mcdonalds Dr 60523
Tel (630) 623-3000 *SIC* 5812 6794

■ **MCDONALDS RESTAURANT OPERATIONS INC** p 928
2111 Mcdonalds Dr 60523
Tel (630) 623-3000 *SIC* 5812 8741

■ **MCDONALDS RESTAURANTS OF ALASKA INC** p 928
2111 Mcdonalds Dr 60523
Tel (630) 623-3000 *SIC* 5812

■ **MCDONALDS RESTAURANTS OF CALIFORNIA INC** p 928
1 Mcdonalds Dr 60523
Tel (630) 623-3000 *SIC* 5812

■ **MCDONALDS RESTAURANTS OF COLORADO INC** p 928
1 Mcdonalds Dr 60523
Tel (630) 623-3000 *SIC* 5812

■ **MCDONALDS RESTAURANTS OF CONNECTICUT INC** p 928
1 Mcdonalds Dr 60523
Tel (630) 623-3000 *SIC* 5812

■ **MCDONALDS RESTAURANTS OF DISTRICT OF COLUMBIA INC** p 928
1 Mcdonalds Dr 60523
Tel (630) 623-3000 *SIC* 5812

■ **MCDONALDS RESTAURANTS OF GEORGIA INC** p 928
1 Mcdonalds Dr 60523
Tel (630) 623-3000 *SIC* 5812

■ **MCDONALDS RESTAURANTS OF ILLINOIS INC** p 928
21 Mcdonalds Dr 60523
Tel (630) 623-3000 *SIC* 5812

■ **MCDONALDS RESTAURANTS OF INDIANA INC** p 928
2111 Mcdonalds Dr 60523
Tel (630) 623-3000 *SIC* 5812

■ **MCDONALDS RESTAURANTS OF MARYLAND INC** p 928
1 Mcdonalds Dr 60523
Tel (630) 623-3000 *SIC* 5812

■ **MCDONALDS RESTAURANTS OF MASSACHUSETTS INC** p 928
1 Mcdonalds Dr 60523
Tel (630) 623-3000 *SIC* 5812

■ **MCDONALDS RESTAURANTS OF MICHIGAN INC** p 928
1 Mcdonalds Dr 60523
Tel (630) 623-3000 *SIC* 5812

■ **MCDONALDS RESTAURANTS OF MINNESOTA INC** p 928
1 Mcdonalds Dr 60523
Tel (630) 623-3000 *SIC* 5812

■ **MCDONALDS RESTAURANTS OF MISSOURI INC** p 928
1 Mcdonalds Dr 60523
Tel (630) 623-3000 *SIC* 5812

■ **MCDONALDS RESTAURANTS OF NEVADA INC** p 928
1 Mcdonalds Dr 60523
Tel (630) 623-3000 *SIC* 5812

■ **MCDONALDS RESTAURANTS OF NEW JERSEY INC** p 928
1 Mcdonalds Dr 60523
Tel (630) 623-3000 *SIC* 5812

■ **MCDONALDS RESTAURANTS OF NEW YORK INC** p 928
1 Mcdonalds Dr 60523
Tel (630) 623-3000 *SIC* 5812

■ **MCDONALDS RESTAURANTS OF NORTH CAROLINA INC** p 928
1 Mcdonalds Dr 60523
Tel (630) 623-3000 *SIC* 5812

■ **MCDONALDS RESTAURANTS OF OHIO INC** p 928
1 Mcdonalds Dr 60523
Tel (630) 623-3000 *SIC* 5812

■ **MCDONALDS RESTAURANTS OF OKLAHOMA INC** p 928
1 Mcdonalds Dr 60523
Tel (630) 623-3000 *SIC* 5812

■ **MCDONALDS RESTAURANTS OF PENNSYLVANIA INC** p 928
1 Mcdonalds Dr 60523
Tel (630) 623-3000 *SIC* 5812

■ **MCDONALDS RESTAURANTS OF SOUTH CAROLINA INC** p 928
1 Mcdonalds Dr 60523
Tel (630) 623-3000 *SIC* 5812

■ **MCDONALDS RESTAURANTS OF TENNESSEE INC** p 928
1 Mcdonalds Dr 60523
Tel (630) 623-3000 *SIC* 5812

■ **MCDONALDS RESTAURANTS OF TEXAS INC** p 928
1 Mcdonalds Dr 60523
Tel (630) 623-3000 *SIC* 5812

■ **MCDONALDS RESTAURANTS OF VIRGINIA INC** p 928
1 Mcdonalds Dr 60523
Tel (630) 623-3000 *SIC* 5812

■ **MCDONALDS RESTAURANTS OF WASHINGTON INC** p 928
1 Mcdonalds Dr 60523
Tel (630) 623-3000 *SIC* 5812 8741

■ **MCDONALDS RESTAURANTS OF WISCONSIN INC** p 928
1 Mcdonalds Dr 60523
Tel (630) 623-3000 *SIC* 5812

■ **MCDONALDS USA LLC** p 928
2111 Mcdonalds Dr 60523
Tel (630) 623-3000 *SIC* 5812

MTL INSURANCE CO p 998
1200 Jorie Blvd Ste 100 60523
Tel (630) 990-1000 *SIC* 6311

NATIONWIDE OF CHICAGO-FOOD BROKERS INC p 1018
915 Harger Rd Ste 110 60523
Tel (630) 286-1500 *SIC* 5142

NORTH AMERICA PACKAGING CORP p 1049
1515 W 22nd St Ste 550 60523
Tel (630) 203-4100 *SIC* 3089

NOVIPAX LLC p 1063
2215 York Rd Ste 504 60523
Tel (630) 686-2735 *SIC* 2821 2299

■ **PLANETECHS LLC** p 1154
1520 Kensington Rd # 311 60523
Tel (630) 468-1766 *SIC* 7363

PORTILLOS HOT DOGS INC p 1163
2001 Spring Rd Ste 400 60523
Tel (630) 954-3773 *SIC* 5812 5813

PURECIRCLE USA INC p 1192
915 Harger Rd Ste 250 60523
Tel (866) 960-8242 *SIC* 2869

RAHAL FOODS INC p 1205
915 Harger Rd Ste 110 60523
Tel (630) 286-1500 *SIC* 5149 5431

RASMUSSEN INC p 1209
1415 W 22nd St Ste 400 60523
Tel (630) 366-2800 *SIC* 8299

READERLINK DISTRIBUTION SERVICES LLC p 1213
1420 Kensington Rd # 300 60523
Tel (708) 356-3717 *SIC* 5192

READERLINK LLC p 1213
1420 Kensington Rd # 300 60523
Tel (708) 356-3600 *SIC* 5192

▲ **RETAIL PROPERTIES OF AMERICA INC** p 1228
2021 Spring Rd Ste 200 60523
Tel (630) 634-4200 *SIC* 6798

STERIGENICS INTERNATIONAL LLC p 1386
2015 Spring Rd Ste 650 60523
Tel (630) 928-1700 *SIC* 7389

SUPERIOR BULK LOGISTICS INC p 1406
711 Jorie Blvd Ste 101n 60523
Tel (630) 573-2555 *SIC* 4213

TOMY HOLDINGS INC p 1460
2015 Spring Rd Ste 400 60523
Tel (630) 573-7200 *SIC* 5092 5945

TRANSPORT SERVICE CO p 1472
2001 Spring Rd Ste 400 60523
Tel (630) 472-5900 *SIC* 4213 4731

▲ **TREEHOUSE FOODS INC** p 1475
2021 Spring Rd Ste 600 60523
Tel (708) 483-1300
SIC 2035 2023 2032 2033 2087

UNION PARTNERS I LLC p 1505
1400 16th St Ste 250 60523
Tel (630) 822-7000 *SIC* 8741 7389

VEOLIA TRANSPORTATION SERVICES INC p 1548
2015 Spring Rd Ste 750 60523
Tel (630) 571-7070 *SIC* 4111 4141

ZENSAR TECHNOLOGIES INC p 1642
1415 W 22nd St Ste 925 60523
Tel (630) 928-1518 *SIC* 7371

OAK PARK, IL

CITIZENS RX LLC p 311
1144 Lake St Ste 401 60301
Tel (888) 545-1120 *SIC* 8742

IYPAD INTERNATIONAL INC NFP p 769
419 S East Ave 60302
Tel (773) 654-7141 *SIC* 9441

OAK PARK & RIVER FOREST HIGH SCHOOL DIST 200 p 1070
201 N Scoville Ave 60302
Tel (708) 383-0700 *SIC* 8211

RUSH OAK PARK HOSPITAL INC p 1258
520 S Maple Ave 60304
Tel (708) 383-9300 *SIC* 8051 8062

SYNERGON HEALTH SYSTEM INC p 1415
520 S Maple Ave 60304
Tel (708) 660-6661 *SIC* 8062 8051 8082

WEST SUBURBAN MEDICAL CENTER p 1595
3 Erie Ct 60302
Tel (708) 383-6200 *SIC* 8011

OAKBROOK TERRACE, IL

B C S LIFE INSURANCE CO (INC) p 141
2 Mid America Plz Ste 200 60181
Tel (630) 472-7700 *SIC* 6321 6311

BALDWIN RICHARDSON FOODS CO p 147
1 Tower Ln 60181
Tel (815) 464-9994 *SIC* 2024

BCS FINANCIAL CORP p 164
2 Mid America Plz 60181
Tel (630) 472-7700 *SIC* 6331 6311 6211

FERRARA CANDY CO p 538
1 Tower Ln Ste 2700 60181
Tel (708) 366-0500 *SIC* 2064

GRAYCOR INC p 632
2 Mid America Plz Ste 400 60181
Tel (630) 684-7110 *SIC* 1541 1542

GRAYCOR INDUSTRIAL CONSTRUCTORS INC p 632
2 Mid America Plz Ste 400 60181
Tel (630) 684-7110 *SIC* 1542 1541

JOINT COMMISSION ON ACCREDITATION OF HEALTHCARE ORGANIZATIONS p 792
1 Renaissance Blvd 60181
Tel (630) 792-5000 *SIC* 8621

MAKE CORP p 899
1 S 450 Smmit Ave Ste 165 60181
Tel (630) 376-0646 *SIC* 7379

■ **MATSON LOGISTICS INC** p 920
1815 S Meyers Rd Ste 700 60181
Tel (630) 203-3500 *SIC* 4731

PROFESSIONAL SERVICE INDUSTRIES HOLDING INC p 1180
1901 S Meyers Rd Ste 400 60181
Tel (630) 691-1490 *SIC* 8711 8734

PROFESSIONAL SERVICE INDUSTRIES INC p 1180
1901 S Meyers Rd Ste 400 60181
Tel (630) 691-1490 *SIC* 8711 8734

PSI ACQUISITION INC p 1188
1901 S Meyers Rd Ste 400 60181
Tel (630) 691-1490 *SIC* 6719

■ **PUMP SOLUTIONS GROUP** p 1192
1815 S Meyers Rd Ste 670 60181
Tel (630) 487-2240 *SIC* 3561

■ **REDBOX AUTOMATED RETAIL LLC** p 1216
1 Tower Ln Ste 1200 60181
Tel (630) 756-8700 *SIC* 7841

SIRVA INC p 1327
1 Parkview Plz 60181
Tel (630) 570-3047
SIC 4213 4214 4731 7513 6331

SIRVA WORLDWIDE INC p 1327
1 Parkview Plz Ste 300 60181
Tel (630) 570-3047
SIC 4213 4214 4731 7513 6331

TRI-MEATS INC p 1477
17 W 662 Butterfi 60181
Tel (630) 705-2800 *SIC* 5147

▲ **VASCO DATA SECURITY INTERNATIONAL INC** p 1545
1901 S Meyers Rd Ste 210 60181
Tel (630) 932-8844 *SIC* 7373 7371

WOZNIAK INDUSTRIES INC p 1627
2 Mid America Plz Ste 700 60181
Tel (630) 954-3400 *SIC* 3469 3444 3462

OKAWVILLE, IL

TOP AG COOPERATIVE INC p 1460
702 S Elevator St 62271
Tel (618) 243-5293 *SIC* 5153 5191

OLYMPIA FIELDS, IL

ST JAMES HOSPITAL & HEALTH CENTERS INC p 1367
20201 Crawford Ave 60461
Tel (708) 747-4000 *SIC* 8062 5912

OREGON, IL

E D ETNYRE & CO p 466
1333 S Daysville Rd 61061
Tel (815) 732-2116 *SIC* 3531

GENWOODS HOLDCO LLC p 605
2606 S Il Route 2 61061
Tel (815) 732-2141 *SIC* 3523

WOODS EQUIPMENT CO p 1623
2606 S Il Route 2 61061
Tel (815) 732-2141 *SIC* 3523 3524 3531

ORLAND PARK, IL

BERKOT LTD p 175
11333 W 159th St 60467
Tel (708) 590-4088 *SIC* 5411

CONSOLIDATED HIGH SCHOOL DISTRICT NO 230 NOT FOR PRO p 360
15100 S 94th Ave Uppr 60462
Tel (708) 349-5759 *SIC* 8211

HORTON GROUP INC p 708
10320 Orland Pkwy 60467
Tel (708) 845-3000
SIC 6411 6331 6321 6311

TOTAL RENAL CARE INC p 1463
13155 S La Grange Rd 60462
Tel (800) 424-6589 *SIC* 8092

OTTAWA, IL

4L TECHNOLOGIES INC p 3
4200 Columbus St 61350
Tel (815) 431-8100 *SIC* 3555

CLOVER TECHNOLOGIES GROUP LLC p 328
4200 Columbus St 61350
Tel (815) 431-8100 *SIC* 5943 3861

PALATINE, IL

ARLINGTON AUTOMOTIVE GROUP INC p 110
2095 N Rand Rd 60074
Tel (847) 394-5100
SIC 7538 5521 5511 5531 7532

COMMUNITY CONSOLIDATED SCHOOL DISTRICT 15 COOK COUNTY p 348
580 N 1st Bank Dr 60067
Tel (847) 963-3000 *SIC* 8211

HARPER COLLEGE p 663
1200 W Algonquin Rd 60067
Tel (847) 925-6707 *SIC* 8221

INTEC GROUP INC p 748
666 S Vermont St 60067
Tel (847) 358-0088 *SIC* 3089

JASONS FOODS p 778
208 E Helen Rd 60067
Tel (847) 358-9901 *SIC* 5144 5147 5142

JEVIC TRANSPORTATION INC p 784
1540 E Dundee Rd Ste 240 60074
Tel (856) 764-1909 *SIC* 4213

PARK PALATINE DISTRICT p 1115
250 E Wood St 60067
Tel (847) 991-0333 *SIC* 7999

PROBIDDER LLC p 1178
945 E Kenilworth Ave 60074
Tel (847) 962-3140 *SIC* 8742 7371

TELVENT USA LLC p 1435
1415 S Roselle Rd 60067
Tel (717) 944-5460 *SIC* 7379 8748

TOWNSHIP HIGH SCHOOL DISTRICT 211 FOUNDATION p 1466
1750 S Roselle Rd Ste 100 60067
Tel (708) 359-3300 *SIC* 8211

WEBER-STEPHEN PRODUCTS LLC p 1586
1415 S Roselle Rd 60067
Tel (847) 934-5700 *SIC* 3631

WILLIAM RAINEY HARPER COLLEGE EDUCATIONAL FOUNDATION p 1611
1200 W Algonquin Rd 60067
Tel (847) 925-6490 *SIC* 8399

PALOS HEIGHTS, IL

PALOS COMMMUNITY HOSPITAL p 1110
12251 S 80th Ave 60463
Tel (708) 923-4000 *SIC* 8062

PALOS HILLS, IL

MORAINE VALLEY COMMUNITY COLLEGE p 988
9000 W College Pkwy 60465
Tel (708) 974-4300 *SIC* 8222

SOUTHFIELD CORP p 1351
8995 W 95th St 60465
Tel (708) 344-1000
SIC 3273 1442 3241 4212 4213 5032

PARIS, IL

NORTH AMERICAN LIGHTING INC p 1050
2275 S Main St 61944
Tel (217) 465-6600 *SIC* 3647

PARK FOREST, IL

CONTINENTAL/MIDLAND LLC p 364
24000 S Western Ave 60466
Tel (708) 747-1200 *SIC* 3452

PARK RIDGE, IL

ADVOCATE HEALTH AND HOSPITALS CORP p 28
1775 Dempster St 60068
Tel (847) 723-6610 *SIC* 8062

KOCH MEAT CO INC p 825
1300 Higgins Rd Ste 100 60068
Tel (847) 384-8018 *SIC* 5142 5144

LUTHERAN GENERAL MEDICAL GROUP S C p 886
1775 Dempster St Ste 10 60068
Tel (847) 795-2800 *SIC* 8093

MAINE TOWNSHIP HIGH SCHOOL DISTRICT 207 p 898
1177 S Dee Rd 60068
Tel (847) 696-3600 *SIC* 8211

MESSINA GROUP INC p 951
200 S Prospect Ave 60068
Tel (847) 825-8000 *SIC* 7361 7379

SIERRA SYSTEMS INC p 1321
200 S Prospect Ave 60068
Tel (847) 384-2000 *SIC* 7363

V-G SUPPLY CO p 1538
1400 Renaissance Dr # 309 60068
Tel (708) 891-1500 *SIC* 5191 5193

PEKIN, IL

■ **AVENTINE RENEWABLE ENERGY HOLDINGS LLC** p 136
1300 S 2nd St 61554
Tel (309) 347-9200 *SIC* 2869

▲ **FARMERS AUTOMOBILE INSURANCE ASSOCIATION (INC)** p 529
2505 Court St 61558
Tel (309) 346-1161 *SIC* 6411 6311

■ **FARMERS AUTOMOBILE MANAGEMENT CORP** p 529
2505 Court St 61554
Tel (309) 346-1161 *SIC* 6311 6321

■ **ILLINOIS CORN PROCESSING LLC** p 732
1301 S Front St 61554
Tel (309) 353-3990 *SIC* 2085

■ **PACIFIC ETHANOL PEKIN INC** p 1104
1300 S 2nd St 61554
Tel (309) 347-9200 *SIC* 2869

■ **PEKIN INSURANCE** p 1128
2505 Court St 61558
Tel (888) 735-4611 *SIC* 6411

■ **PEKIN LIFE INSURANCE CO** p 1128
2505 Court St 61554
Tel (309) 346-1161 *SIC* 6311 6321

PEORIA, IL

ADVANCED TECHNOLOGY SERVICES INC p 26
8201 N University St # 1 61615
Tel (309) 693-4000 *SIC* 7699 7629 7378

AHC p 36
121 Ne Jefferson Ave # 100 61602
Tel (888) 568-3137 *SIC* 7322

BRADLEY UNIVERSITY p 206
1501 W Bradley Ave 61625
Tel (309) 677-3150 *SIC* 8221

■ **CATERPILLAR BRAZIL LLC** p 265
100 Ne Adams St 61629
Tel (309) 675-1000 *SIC* 3523

▲ **CATERPILLAR INC** p 265
100 Ne Adams St 61629
Tel (309) 675-1000
SIC 3531 3519 3511 6531 6321 6331

■ **CATERPILLAR S A R L LLC** p 265
100 Ne Adams St 61629
Tel (309) 675-1000 *SIC* 5082

■ **CILCORP INC** p 307
300 Liberty St 61602
Tel (309) 677-5271 *SIC* 4911 4924

CITIZENS EQUITY FIRST CREDIT UNION p 311
5401 W Everett M Dirksen 61607
Tel (309) 633-3603 *SIC* 6062

CONNOR CO p 358
2800 Ne Adams St 61603
Tel (309) 693-7229 *SIC* 5074 5075

COULTER COMPANIES INC p 374
4700 N Sterling Ave Ste 2 61615
Tel (309) 686-8033 *SIC* 4953 8711

COUNTY OF PEORIA p 381
324 Main St 61602
Tel (309) 672-6056 *SIC* 9111

ELM ENTERPRISES LLC p 489
60 State St Ste 201 61602
Tel (309) 671-4300 *SIC* 8748 8713

GENERAL YELLOW PAGES CONSULTANTS INC p 602
222 Ne Monroe St Ste 800 61602
Tel (309) 677-0400 *SIC* 7311

■ **GREATER PEORIA SPECIALTY HOSPITAL LLC** p 635
500 W Romeo B Garrett Ave 61605
Tel (309) 680-1500 *SIC* 8062 8099

HAGERTY BROTHERS CO p 652
1506 W Detweiller Dr 61615
Tel (309) 589-0200 *SIC* 5072

HGS (USA) LLC p 689
1901 E War Memorial Dr 61614
Tel (309) 679-4261 *SIC* 7389

ILLINOIS CENTRAL COLLEGE p 732
1 College Dr 61635
Tel (309) 694-5011 *SIC* 8222

ILLINOIS MUTUAL LIFE INSURANCE CO p 732
300 Sw Adams St 61634
Tel (309) 674-8255 *SIC* 6321 6311

MAUI JIM USA INC p 921
1 Aloha Ln 61615
Tel (309) 589-6158 *SIC* 5099 3851

METHODIST HEALTH SERVICES CORP p 953
221 Ne Glen Oak Ave 61636
Tel (309) 672-5522 *SIC* 8062

METHODIST MEDICAL CENTER FOUNDATION p 954
221 Ne Glen Oak Ave 61636
Tel (309) 672-4895 *SIC* 8082

METHODIST MEDICAL CENTER OF ILLINOIS p 954
221 Ne Glen Oak Ave 61636
Tel (309) 672-5522 *SIC* 8062

ONE CALL LOCATORS LTD p 1086
60 State St Ste 201 61602
Tel (309) 673-2851 *SIC* 7389

OSF HEALTHCARE SYSTEM p 1096
800 Ne Glen Oak Ave 61603
Tel (309) 655-2850 *SIC* 8062 8051

OSF SAINT FRANCIS MEDICAL CENTER p 1096
530 Ne Glen Oak Ave 61637
Tel (309) 655-2000 *SIC* 8011

P J HOERR INC p 1102
107 N Commerce Pl 61604
Tel (309) 688-9567 *SIC* 1542

PEARL & ASSOCIATES LTD p 1126
1200 E Glen Ave 61616
Tel (309) 688-9000 *SIC* 6411

PEORIA BOARD OF EDUCATION (INC) p 1133
3202 N Wisconsin Ave 61603
Tel (309) 672-6512 *SIC* 8211

PERORIA DISPOSAL CO p 1137
4700 N Sterling Ave Ste 2 61615
Tel (309) 686-8033 *SIC* 4953

PETERSEN HEALTH CARE INC p 1138
830 W Trailcreek Dr 61614
Tel (309) 691-8113 *SIC* 8059

PROCTOR HOSPITAL p 1179
5409 N Knoxville Ave # 1 61614
Tel (309) 691-1000 *SIC* 8062

▲ **RLI CORP** p 1239
9025 N Lindbergh Dr 61615
Tel (309) 692-1000 *SIC* 6411

■ **RLI INSURANCE CO (INC)** p 1239
9025 N Lindbergh Dr 61615
Tel (309) 692-1000 *SIC* 6331

SUPERIOR CONSOLIDATED INDUSTRIES INC p 1406
801 Sw Jefferson Ave 61605
Tel (309) 677-5980 *SIC* 7389 1721

VONACHEN SERVICES INC p 1565
8900 N Pioneer Rd 61615
Tel (309) 691-6202
SIC 7349 4731 8741 7361

WILLIAMS BROTHERS CONSTRUCTION INC p 1611
1200 E Kelly Ave 61616
Tel (309) 688-0416 *SIC* 1542

PERCY, IL

KNIGHT HAWK COAL LLC p 824
500 Cutler Trico Rd 62272
Tel (618) 426-3662 *SIC* 1241 1222

PERU, IL

CARUS GROUP INC p 262
315 5th St 61354
Tel (815) 223-1500 *SIC* 2819

EAKAS CORP p 468
6251 State Route 251 61354
Tel (815) 223-8811 *SIC* 3089

ILLINOIS VALLEY COMMUNITY HOSPITAL INC p 732
925 West St 61354
Tel (815) 223-3300 *SIC* 8062

IV HEALTHCORP INC p 769
925 West St 61354
Tel (815) 223-3300 *SIC* 8062 8741 5912

PHOENIX, IL

STERLING LUMBER CO p 1387
501 E 151st St 60426
Tel (708) 388-2223 *SIC* 5031 7389 2448

PLAINFIELD, IL

CBI SERVICES INC p 268
14107 S Route 59 60544
Tel (815) 439-6668 *SIC* 1629 8741

LOGOPLASTE USA INC p 875
14420 N Van Dyke Rd 60544
Tel (815) 230-6961 *SIC* 3085

PLAINFIELD COMMUNITY CONSOLIDATED SCHOOL DISTRICT 202 p 1153
15732 S Howard St 60544
Tel (815) 439-5482 *SIC* 8211

PRINCETON, IL

BUREAU SERVICE CO p 226
22069 Us Highway 34 61356
Tel (815) 875-2800
SIC 5191 5172 5153 5411 7542

PROSPECT HEIGHTS, IL

HOUSEHOLD FINANCE CORP p 711
2700 Sanders Rd 60070
Tel (847) 790-1590
SIC 6141 6162 6351 6153 6159 6311

HOUSEHOLD REALTY CORP p 711
2700 Sanders Rd Fl 1 60070
Tel (847) 790-1590 SIC 6141

HSBC INVESTMENTS (NORTH AMERICA) INC p 715
2700 Sanders Rd 60070
Tel (847) 564-5000
SIC 6141 7389 6351 6159 6162 6311

QUINCY, IL

ADM ALLIANCE NUTRITION INC p 23
1000 N 30th St 62301
Tel (217) 231-2674 SIC 2048 5154

BLESSING CORPORATE SERVICES INC p 189
Broadway At 11th 62305
Tel (217) 223-1200 SIC 8741

BLESSING HOSPITAL p 189
Broadway At 11th St 62301
Tel (217) 223-1200 SIC 8062

GARDNER DENVER HOLDINGS INC p 592
1800 Gardner Expy 62305
Tel (217) 222-5400 SIC 3564 3563

HOLLISTER-WHITNEY ELEVATOR CORP p 701
2603 N 24th St 62305
Tel (217) 222-0466 SIC 3534

KIRLINS INC p 822
532 Maine St 62301
Tel (217) 222-0813 SIC 5947

N KOHL GROCER CO p 1005
130 Jersey St 62301
Tel (217) 222-5000 SIC 5141 5113 5046

NIEMANN FOODS FOUNDATION p 1043
923 N 12th St 62301
Tel (217) 221-5600 SIC 5411 5541

QUINCY MEDIA INC p 1200
130 S 5th St 62301
Tel (217) 223-5100
SIC 2711 4833 2752 2741

REFRESHMENT SERVICES INC p 1218
1121 Locust St 62301
Tel (217) 223-8600 SIC 2086

SHARKEY TRANSPORT SERVICES INC p 1312
3803 Dye Rd 62305
Tel (217) 228-6555 SIC 4213

▲ TITAN INTERNATIONAL INC p 1456
2701 Spruce St 62301
Tel (217) 228-6011 SIC 3312 3714 3011

■ TITAN WHEEL CORP OF ILLINOIS p 1456
2701 Spruce St 62301
Tel (217) 228-6023 SIC 3499

RICHMOND, IL

LEICA BIOSYSTEMS RICHMOND INC p 854
5205 Rte 12 60071
Tel (815) 678-2000 SIC 3842

RIVER FOREST, IL

DOMINICAN UNIVERSITY p 449
7900 Division St 60305
Tel (708) 366-2490 SIC 8221

RIVERDALE, IL

ARCELORMITTAL RIVERDALE INC p 104
13500 S Perry Ave 60827
Tel (708) 849-8803 SIC 3316

RIVERSIDE, IL

TEXOR PETROLEUM CO INC p 1445
3340 Harlem Ave 60546
Tel (708) 447-1999 SIC 5172 5541

RIVERWOODS, IL

CCH INC p 270
2700 Lake Cook Rd 60015
Tel (847) 267-7000
SIC 2721 2731 7389 7338 8732 7371

■ DFS CORPORATE SERVICES LLC p 435
2500 Lake Cook Rd 2 60015
Tel (224) 405-0900 SIC 6153

▲ DISCOVER FINANCIAL SERVICES p 442
2500 Lake Cook Rd 60015
Tel (224) 405-0900 SIC 6022 6141 7389

WOLTERS KLUWER UNITED STATES INC p 1621
2700 Lake Cook Rd 60015
Tel (847) 580-5000
SIC 2731 2721 2741 2759

ROBINSON, IL

MIDWEST TRANSPORT INC p 968
11385 N Trimble Rd 62454
Tel (618) 544-3399 SIC 4213

ROCHELLE, IL

MAPLEHURST FARMS INC p 904
936 S Moore Rd 61068
Tel (815) 562-8723 SIC 5153 2879 4212

NEWS MEDIA CORP p 1039
211 E Il Route 38 61068
Tel (815) 562-2061 SIC 2711

■ ROCHELLE FOODS LLC p 1243
1001 S Main St 61068
Tel (815) 562-4141 SIC 2013 2011

ROCK ISLAND, IL

■ BITUMINOUS CASUALTY CORP p 185
320 18th St 61201
Tel (309) 786-5401 SIC 6331

MODERN WOODMEN OF AMERICA p 981
1701 1st Ave 61201
Tel (309) 793-5537 SIC 6311

PERFORMANCE FOOD SERVICE TPC p 1135
8001 51st St W 61201
Tel (309) 787-1234 SIC 5149

PLANT EQUIPMENT CO p 1154
2515 5th Ave 61201
Tel (309) 786-3369 SIC 5084

RILCO INC p 1235
1320 1st St 61201
Tel (309) 788-5631 SIC 5172 5169

ROCK ISLAND/MILAN SCHOOL DISTRICT 41 p 1243
2101 6th Ave 61201
Tel (309) 793-5900 SIC 8211

ROYAL NEIGHBORS OF AMERICA p 1254
230 16th St 61201
Tel (309) 788-4561 SIC 6411 6311

TRINITY MEDICAL CENTER p 1481
2701 17th St 61201
Tel (309) 779-5000 SIC 8062

TRINITY REGIONAL HEALTH SYSTEM p 1481
2701 17th St 61201
Tel (309) 779-5000 SIC 8062 8741

WATTS TRUCKING SERVICE INC p 1583
525 17th St 61201
Tel (309) 788-7700 SIC 4953

ROCKFORD, IL

ANDERSONBRECON INC p 90
4545 Assembly Dr 61109
Tel (815) 484-8900 SIC 7389

BERGSTROM CLIMATE SYSTEMS LLC p 174
2390 Blackhawk Rd 61109
Tel (815) 874-7821 SIC 3585

BERGSTROM INC p 174
2390 Blackhawk Rd 61109
Tel (815) 874-7821 SIC 3531

BILL DORAN CO p 182
707 W Jefferson St 61101
Tel (815) 965-8791 SIC 5193

CATHOLIC DIOCESE OF ROCKFORD p 266
555 Colman Center Dr 61108
Tel (815) 399-4300
SIC 8661 8322 8361 8211 6553

CITY OF ROCKFORD p 318
425 E State St 61104
Tel (779) 348-7300 SIC 9111

COUNTY OF WINNEBAGO p 383
404 Elm St Ste 104 61101
Tel (815) 319-4444 SIC 9111

■ ECLIPSE COMBUSTION INC p 475
1665 Elmwood Rd 61103
Tel (815) 877-3031 SIC 3433

■ ECLIPSE INC p 475
1665 Elmwood Rd 61103
Tel (815) 877-3031
SIC 3564 3433 3822 3823 3443 3494

EMERY AIR INC p 492
46 Airport Dr 61109
Tel (815) 987-4100 SIC 4731

ESTWING MANUFACTURING CO INC p 511
2647 8th St 61109
Tel (815) 397-9521
SIC 3423 3546 3545 3429 3421 3425

GOELLNER INC p 619
2500 Latham St 61103
Tel (815) 962-6076 SIC 3599

■ GREENLEE TEXTRON INC p 638
4455 Boeing Dr 61109
Tel (815) 397-7070 SIC 3549 3541 3546

GUNITE CORP p 647
302 Peoples Ave 61104
Tel (815) 964-3301 SIC 3714

GYPSUM SUPPLY CO p 649
1125 Harrison Ave 61104
Tel (815) 397-5718 SIC 5032

JOSEPH BEHR & SONS INC p 793
1100 Seminary St 61104
Tel (815) 987-2755 SIC 5093

KELLEY WILLIAMSON CO p 808
1132 Harrison Ave 61104
Tel (815) 397-9410 SIC 5541 5411 5171

■ LIEBOVICH BROS INC p 863
2116 Preston St 61102
Tel (815) 987-3200 SIC 5051

■ LIEBOVICH STEEL & ALUMINUM CO p 863
2116 Preston St 61102
Tel (815) 987-3200 SIC 5051

MERCY HEALTH CORP p 946
2400 N Rockton Ave 61103
Tel (815) 971-5000 SIC 8062

MID-WEST DAIRYMENS CO p 964
4313 W State St 61102
Tel (815) 968-0504 SIC 5143

REOPCO INC p 1224
4930 E State St Ste 1 61108
Tel (815) 387-1700 SIC 5411 5541

ROCKFORD BOARD OF EDUCATION p 1244
501 7th St 61104
Tel (815) 966-3000 SIC 8211

ROCKFORD CONCENTRIC INC p 1244
2222 15th St 61104
Tel (815) 398-4400 SIC 3594 3629

ROCKFORD HEALTH PHYSICIANS p 1244
2300 N Rockton Ave 61103
Tel (815) 971-2000 SIC 8011

ROCKFORD HEALTH SYSTEM p 1244
2400 N Rockton Ave 61103
Tel (815) 971-5000 SIC 8741

ROCKFORD MEMORIAL HOSPITAL p 1244
2400 N Rockton Ave 61103
Tel (815) 971-5000
SIC 8062 8011 8071 8099

ROCKFORD PARK DISTRICT p 1244
401 S Main St Ste 101 61101
Tel (815) 987-8800 SIC 7999

ROCKFORD PRODUCTS LLC p 1244
707 Harrison Ave 61104
Tel (815) 397-6000 SIC 3462

RUBLOFF CONSTRUCTION INC p 1257
6723 Weaver Rd Ste 108 61114
Tel (815) 316-5410 SIC 1542

SCHNEIDER ELECTRIC BUILDINGS LLC p 1287
839 N Perryville Rd 61107
Tel (815) 381-5000
SIC 3822 1711 3625 3823 3621

SOUTHERN IMPERIAL INC p 1349
1400 Eddy Ave 61103
Tel (815) 877-7041 SIC 5046 2542

SUPPLYCORE INC p 1407
303 N Main St Ste 800 61101
Tel (815) 997-1624 SIC 5072 5085

SWEDISHAMERICAN HEALTH SYSTEM CORP p 1411
1401 E State St 61104
Tel (815) 968-4400
SIC 8743 6512 8742 8099 8082 8062

SWEDISHAMERICAN HOSPITAL p 1411
1401 E State St 61104
Tel (815) 968-4400 SIC 8062

WALDOM ELECTRONICS CORP p 1572
1801 Morgan St 61102
Tel (815) 968-9661 SIC 5065

WILLIAM CHARLES LTD p 1610
1401 N 2nd St 61107
Tel (815) 963-7400
SIC 1611 5211 1731 4953

ROCKTON, IL

■ CHEMTOOL INC p 293
801 W Rockton Rd 61072
Tel (815) 957-4140
SIC 2992 2899 2842 2841

ROLLING MEADOWS, IL

A H MANAGEMENT GROUP INC p 5
1151 Rohlwing Rd 60008
Tel (847) 342-8065
SIC 5962 7993 5963 7389 5046

BEAR CONSTRUCTION CO p 165
1501 Rohlwing Rd 60008
Tel (847) 222-1900 SIC 1542

CHARLES INDUSTRIES LTD p 289
5600 Apollo Dr 60008
Tel (847) 806-6300 SIC 3661 3629 3677

ENVIRONMENTAL RESOURCES MANAGEMENT - NORTH CENTRAL INC p 503
1701 Golf Rd Ste 1-700 60008
Tel (610) 524-3500 SIC 8748

KIMBALL HILL INC p 818
5999 New Wilke Rd Ste 306 60008
Tel (847) 364-7300 SIC 1521 1531

KOMATSU AMERICA CORP p 827
1701 Golf Rd Ste 1-100 60008
Tel (847) 437-5800 SIC 5082 3532 3531

KOMATSU AMERICA INDUSTRIES LLC p 827
1701 Golf Rd Ste 1-100 60008
Tel (847) 437-5800 SIC 5084

■ L E MYERS CO p 834
1701 Golf Rd Ste 3-1012 60008
Tel (847) 290-1891 SIC 1623

▲ MYR GROUP INC p 1004
1701 Golf Rd Ste 3-1012 60008
Tel (847) 290-1891 SIC 1623 1731

NISSHIN HOLDING INC p 1044
1701 Golf Rd 60008
Tel (847) 290-5100 SIC 8742

■ PLIANT LLC p 1156
1701 Golf Rd Ste 2-900 60008
Tel (812) 424-2904 SIC 3081 2673 3089

RTC INDUSTRIES INC p 1256
2800 Golf Rd 60008
Tel (847) 640-2400 SIC 2599 5211

T & T REPROGRAPHICS INC p 1419
5100 Newport Dr Ste 1 60008
Tel (847) 398-5855 SIC 7334

ROMEOVILLE, IL

BARRY-WEHMILLER CONTAINER SYSTEMS INC p 157
1305 Lakeview Dr 60446
Tel (630) 759-6800 SIC 3535

BOSCH AUTOMOTIVE AFTER MARKET SERVICE SOLUTIONS p 202
1385 N Weber Rd 60446
Tel (815) 407-3903 SIC 5013

■ CHICAGO TUBE AND IRON CO p 298
1 Chicago Tube Dr 60446
Tel (815) 834-2500 SIC 5051 3441

CHRISTIAN BROTHERS EMPLOYEE BENEFIT TRUST p 302
1205 Windham Pkwy 60446
Tel (630) 378-2900 SIC 6411

LESAINT LOGISTICS LLC p 857
868 W Crossroads Pkwy 60446
Tel (630) 243-5950 SIC 4731 4225 8742

LEWIS UNIVERSITY p 859
1 University Pkwy 60446
Tel (815) 838-0500 SIC 8221

MAGID GLOVE & SAFETY MANUFACTURING CO LLC p 895
1300 Naperville Dr 60446
Tel (773) 384-2070
SIC 3151 2381 5699 3842 2326

■ MIDWEST GENERATION LLC p 967
529 E Romeo Rd 60446
Tel (609) 524-4526 SIC 4911

PROTECTION ONE INC p 1185
1267 Windham Pkwy 60446
Tel (877) 938-2214 SIC 7382

VALLEY VIEW COMMUNITY UNIT SCHOOL DISTRICT 365U p 1541
755 Dalhart Ave 60446
Tel (815) 886-2700 SIC 8211

ROSELLE, IL

CASE FOUNDATION CO p 263
1325 Lake St 60172
Tel (630) 529-2911 SIC 1629

GROHE AMERICA INC p 641
200 N Gary Ave Ste G 60172
Tel (630) 582-7711 SIC 2499

JON-DON INC p 792
400 Medinah Rd 60172
Tel (630) 872-5401 SIC 5087

KELLSTROM COMMERCIAL AEROSPACE INC p 809
450 Medinah Rd 60172
Tel (630) 351-8813 SIC 5088

M & R PRINTING EQUIPMENT INC p 889
440 Medinah Rd 60172
Tel (800) 736-6431 SIC 3555 3552 5084

M&R HOLDINGS INC p 890
440 Medinah Rd 60172
Tel (630) 858-6101 SIC 3552

RIM LOGISTICS LTD p 1235
200 N Gary Ave Ste B 60172
Tel (630) 595-0610 SIC 4731

TRANSCARGOBG INC p 1471
812 Oregon Trl 60172
Tel (847) 980-3779 SIC 4212

UNISTAFF PRO INC p 1505
344 E Irving Park Rd 60172
Tel (708) 450-1600 SIC 7361

ROSEMONT, IL

■ APPLETON GRP LLC p 99
9377 W Higgins Rd 60018
Tel (847) 268-6000
SIC 3644 3643 3613 3646 3699

BRG SPORTS INC p 211
9801 W Higgins Rd 60018
Tel (831) 461-7500 SIC 3949 3751

CAPGEMINI FINANCIAL SERVICES INTERNATIONAL INC p 248
6400 Shafer Ct Ste 100 60018
Tel (847) 384-6100 SIC 7371

CAPGEMINI FINANCIAL SERVICES USA INC p 249
6400 Shafer Ct Ste 100 60018
Tel (847) 384-6100 SIC 7373

CENTRAL STATES SOUTHEAST & SOUTHWEST AREAS HEALTH & WELFARE FUND p 280
9377 W Higgins Rd 60018
Tel (847) 518-9800 SIC 6371

CENTRAL STATES SOUTHEAST AND SOUTHWEST AREAS PENSION FUND p 280
9377 W Higgins Rd Fl 2 60018
Tel (847) 518-9800 SIC 6371

COILPLUS INC p 335
6250 N River Rd Ste 6050 60018
Tel (847) 384-3000 SIC 5051

COLE TAYLOR BANK p 336
9550 W Higgins Rd Fl 5 60018
Tel (847) 653-7000 SIC 6022

CULLIGAN INTERNATIONAL CO p 400
9399 W Higgins Rd # 1100 60018
Tel (847) 430-2800 SIC 3589

DAIRY MANAGEMENT INC p 409
10255 W Higgins Rd # 900 60018
Tel (847) 803-2000 SIC 8611

FIRST HOSPITALITY GROUP INC p 547
10275 W Higgins Rd # 300 60018
Tel (847) 299-9040 SIC 7011

HELIX ACQUISITION HOLDINGS INC p 681
9501 Tech Blvd Ste 401 60018
Tel (847) 349-5760 SIC 6719

IPC INTERNATIONAL CORP p 763
10255 W Hggi 60018
Tel (847) 444-2000
SIC 7381 8742 2389 3199

■ **LIFE FITNESS INC** p 863
9525 Bryn Mawr Ave Fl 6 60018
Tel (847) 288-3300 SIC 3949

LIFEWATCH CORP p 865
10255 W Higgins Rd # 100 60018
Tel (847) 720-2100 SIC 8099 5047 3845

LIFEWATCH SERVICES INC p 865
10255 W Higgins Rd # 100 60018
Tel (847) 720-2100
SIC 5047 8099 3845 8071

MARTIN-BROWER CO L L C p 913
6250 N River Rd Ste 9000 60018
Tel (847) 227-6500
SIC 5142 5113 5149 5087

MATTHEW WARREN INC p 920
9501 Tech Blvd Ste 401 60018
Tel (847) 349-5760 SIC 3493

■ **MB FINANCIAL BANK NA** p 924
6111 N River Rd Ste 800 60018
Tel (847) 653-4800 SIC 6021

MCSHANE DEVELOPMENT CO LLC p 932
9500 Bryn Mawr Ave 60018
Tel (847) 292-4300 SIC 6552

METAL ONE HOLDINGS AMERICA INC p 952
6250 N River Rd Ste 6055 60018
Tel (847) 318-0019 SIC 5085 5051

MONTCLAIR HOTELS MB LLC p 986
6600 Mannheim Rd 60018
Tel (847) 457-3900 SIC 7011

MW INDUSTRIES INC p 1004
9501 Tech Blvd Ste 401 60018
Tel (847) 349-5760 SIC 6719 5085

MWI HOLDINGS INC p 1004
9501 Tech Blvd Ste 401 60018
Tel (847) 349-5760 SIC 6719

NATIONAL DAIRY PROMOTION AND RESEARCH BOARD p 1011
10255 W Higgins Rd # 900 60018
Tel (847) 803-2000 SIC 8611

RANDA ACCESSORIES LEATHER GOODS LLC p 1207
5600 N River Rd Ste 500 60018
Tel (847) 292-8300 SIC 5136 5948 3172

REINHART FOODSERVICE LOUISIANA LLC p 1221
6250 N River Rd 60018
Tel (847) 227-6500 SIC 5149

REYES HOLDINGS LLC p 1230
6250 N River Rd Ste 9000 60018
Tel (847) 227-6500 SIC 5181 5142

RIDDELL INC p 1234
9801 W Higgins Rd Ste 800 60018
Tel (847) 292-1472 SIC 5091 3949

ROSEMONT EXPOSITION SERVICES INC p 1251
9291w Bryn Mawr Ave 60018
Tel (847) 696-2208 SIC 7389

SAPA EXTRUSIONS INC p 1281
6250 N River Rd Ste 5000 60018
Tel (877) 710-7272 SIC 3354

■ **STANDARD CAR TRUCK CO INC** p 1375
6400 Shafer Ct Ste 450 60018
Tel (847) 692-6050 SIC 3743 3321

TAYLOR CAPITAL GROUP INC p 1427
9550 W Higgins Rd 60018
Tel (847) 653-7978 SIC 6022

TECTA AMERICA CORP p 1432
9450 Bryn Mawr Ave 60018
Tel (847) 581-3888 SIC 1761

TECTA HOLDING INC p 1432
6450 Brayn Mawr Ste 500 60018
Tel (847) 581-3888 SIC 1761

■ **TRANS-PORTE INC** p 1470
9399 W Higgins Rd 60018
Tel (847) 720-8000 SIC 5812

TRIMEGA PURCHASING ASSOCIATION p 1480
5600 N River Rd Ste 700 60018
Tel (847) 699-3330 SIC 7389

▲ **US FOODS HOLDING CORP** p 1531
9399 W Higgins Rd Ste 500 60018
Tel (847) 720-8000
SIC 5149 5147 5142 5144 5146 5143

■ **US FOODS INC** p 1531
9399 W Higgins Rd Ste 500 60018
Tel (847) 720-8000
SIC 5149 5147 5142 5144 5146 5143

▲ **WINTRUST FINANCIAL CORP** p 1617
9700 W Higgins Rd 60018
Tel (847) 939-9000 SIC 6022 6211 6282

WKI HOLDING CO INC p 1620
9525 Bryn Mawr Ave # 300 60018
Tel (847) 233-8600 SIC 3229 3469

WORLD KITCHEN LLC p 1625
9525 Bryn Mawr Ave # 300 60018
Tel (847) 233-8600
SIC 3229 3469 3365 3421 5719

WYNNCHURCH CAPITAL LTD p 1630
6250 N Rver Rd Ste 10-100 60018
Tel (847) 604-6100 SIC 6733 6799

SAINT CHARLES, IL

AMERICAN TRISTAR INC p 80
525 Dunham Rd 60174
Tel (920) 872-2181 SIC 2099

AQUASCAPE DESIGNS INC p 101
901 Aqualand Way 60174
Tel (630) 659-2000
SIC 5191 1629 0782 0781

COMMUNITY UNIT SCHOOL DISTRICT 303 p 350
201 S 7th St 60174
Tel (630) 513-3030 SIC 8211

OMRON AUTOMOTIVE ELECTRONICS INC p 1085
3709 Ohio Ave 60174
Tel (630) 443-6800
SIC 5065 3625 3714 8742

POWER PACKAGING INC p 1165
525 Dunham Rd Ste 3 60174
Tel (630) 377-3838 SIC 7389

QUALITY BAKERIES LLC p 1196
1750 E Main St Ste 260 60174
Tel (630) 553-7377 SIC 2053

ST CHARLES COMMUNITY UNIT SCHOOL DISTRICT 303 p 1365
201 S 7th St 60174
Tel (331) 228-2000 SIC 8211

SYSTEM SENSOR LTD p 1418
3825 Ohio Ave 60174
Tel (630) 377-6674 SIC 3669

SALEM, IL

RADIAC ABRASIVES INC p 1204
1015 S College St 62881
Tel (618) 548-4200 SIC 3291

SAUGET, IL

BRANDING IRON HOLDINGS INC p 208
1682 Sauget Business Blvd 62206
Tel (618) 337-8400 SIC 2013 5147

■ **CERRO FLOW PRODUCTS LLC** p 284
3000 Mississippi Ave 62206
Tel (618) 337-6000
SIC 3351 3331 3498 3585 5051

SAVANNA, IL

J B SULLIVAN INC p 770
425 1st St Ste 1 61074
Tel (815) 273-4511 SIC 5411

SCHAUMBURG, IL

ACS AUXILIARIES GROUP INC p 18
1100 E Woodfield Rd # 550 60173
Tel (847) 273-7700 SIC 8748

AEC INC p 28
1100 E Wdfield Rd Ste 588 60173
Tel (847) 273-7700
SIC 3585 3823 3559 3443 3535

AMERICAN CHARTERED BANK p 70
1199 E Higgins Rd 60173
Tel (847) 517-5400 SIC 6022 6021

AMERICAN FARM BUREAU INSURANCE SERVICES INC p 72
1501 E Wdfeld Rd Ste 300w 60173
Tel (847) 969-2900 SIC 6411

■ **AMERICAN GENERAL ASSURANCE CO** p 73
1000 E Wdfield Rd Ste 300 60173
Tel (847) 517-6000 SIC 6311

ANDREWS STAFFING INC p 90
1834 Walden Office Sq # 150 60173
Tel (847) 995-9300 SIC 7363

ASSURANCE AGENCY LTD p 121
1750 E Golf Rd 60173
Tel (847) 944-9087 SIC 6411

▲ **CAREER EDUCATION CORP** p 254
231 N Martingale Rd # 100 60173
Tel (847) 781-3600 SIC 8221 8244 8299

■ **CATAMARAN CORP** p 264
1600 Mcconnor Pkwy Fl 1 60173
Tel (800) 282-3232 SIC 8742

CHEF SOLUTIONS HOLDINGS LLC p 292
20 N Martingale Rd # 600 60173
Tel (847) 762-8500 SIC 2099

CHICAGO FREIGHT CAR LEASING CO p 297
425 N Martingale Rd Fl 6 60173
Tel (847) 318-8000 SIC 4741 3643

CONVERGINT TECHNOLOGIES LLC p 365
1 Commerce Dr 60173
Tel (847) 620-5000 SIC 7382

■ **FEDERAL KEMPER LIFE ASSURANCE CO** p 535
1600 Mcconnor Pkwy 60173
Tel (847) 874-4000 SIC 6311

▲ **GLOBAL BRASS AND COPPER HOLDINGS INC** p 615
475 N Marti Rd Ste 1050 60173
Tel (847) 240-4700 SIC 3351 3341 3469

GONNELLA BAKING CO p 623
1117 Wiley Rd 60173
Tel (312) 733-2020
SIC 2051 5812 2099 2038

HITACHI HIGH TECHNOLOGIES AMERICA INC p 696
10 N Martingale Rd # 500 60173
Tel (847) 273-4141 SIC 5065

HOSTMARK INVESTORS LIMITED PARTNERSHIP p 710
1300 E Wdfield Rd Ste 400 60173
Tel (847) 517-9100 SIC 8741

INTERACTIVE HEALTH HOLDINGS CORP p 751
1700 E Golf Rd Ste 900 60173
Tel (847) 590-0200 SIC 8099

INTERACTIVE HEALTH SOLUTIONS INC p 751
1700 E Golf Rd Ste 900 60173
Tel (866) 279-1636 SIC 8099

INX GROUP LTD p 762
150 N Martingale Rd # 700 60173
Tel (630) 382-1800 SIC 2893

INX INTERNATIONAL INK CO p 762
150 N Martingale Rd # 700 60173
Tel (630) 382-1800 SIC 2893

J-POWER USA DEVELOPMENT CO LTD p 772
1900 E Golf Rd Ste 1030 60173
Tel (847) 908-2800 SIC 4911

JX NIPPON OIL & ENERGY USA INC p 798
20 N Martingale Rd # 300 60173
Tel (847) 413-2188 SIC 5172

KURIYAMA OF AMERICA INC p 832
360 E State Pkwy 60173
Tel (847) 755-0360 SIC 5085 3052

MCI SERVICE PARTS INC p 930
1700 E Golf Rd Fl 3 60173
Tel (847) 285-2000 SIC 5013

MCII HOLDINGS INC p 930
1700 E Golf Rd 60173
Tel (866) 624-2622 SIC 6512

MERCURY PRODUCTS CORP p 945
1201 Mercury Dr 60193
Tel (847) 524-4400 SIC 3465 3469 3714

MISUMI USA INC p 976
1717 N Penny Ln Ste 200 60173
Tel (800) 681-7475 SIC 5084

■ **MOTOROLA SOLUTIONS SALES AND SERVICES** p 993
1303 E Algonquin Rd 60196
Tel (847) 576-1000 SIC 5065

NATION PIZZA PRODUCTS LP p 1009
601 E Algonquin Rd 60173
Tel (847) 397-3320 SIC 2038 2045 2033

NETWORK ASSOCIATES INC p 1028
1100 E Wdfield Rd Ste 200 60173
Tel (847) 803-4888 SIC 8742 5113

NETWORK SERVICES CO p 1028
1100 E Wdfield Rd Ste 200 60173
Tel (847) 803-4888 SIC 5113

OERLIKON BALZERS COATING USA INC p 1075
1475 E Wdfield Rd Ste 201 60173
Tel (847) 619-5541 SIC 3479 3471

■ **OPTUMRX PBM OF ILLINOIS INC** p 1091
1600 Mcconnor Pkwy 60173
Tel (224) 231-1743 SIC 6371

PATRICK SCHAUMBURG AUTOMOBILES INC p 1120
526 Mall Dr 60173
Tel (847) 605-4000
SIC 5511 7539 7538 7532 5531 5013

■ **PEPSI-COLA GENERAL BOTTLERS INC** p 1134
1475 E Wdfield Rd Ste 1300 60173
Tel (847) 598-3000 SIC 2086 5149

RITTAL CORP p 1237
425 N Martingale Rd # 400 60173
Tel (847) 240-4600 SIC 3469 5065

ROANOKE COMPANIES INC p 1240
1475 E Woodfield Rd 60173
Tel (847) 969-1420 SIC 6411

ROANOKE INSURANCE GROUP INC p 1240
1475 E Wdfield Rd Ste 500 60173
Tel (847) 969-1420 SIC 6411

ROBERT V ROHRMAN INC p 1241
750 E Golf Rd 60173
Tel (847) 884-6632 SIC 5511 6159

SAGENT PHARMACEUTICALS INC p 1268
1901 N Roselle Rd Ste 700 60195
Tel (847) 908-1600 SIC 2834 5122

SCHAUMBURG COMMUNITY CONSOLIDATED SCHOOL DISTRICT 54 p 1286
524 E Schaumburg Rd 60194
Tel (847) 357-5000 SIC 8211

SCHNEIDER ELECTRIC HOLDINGS INC p 1287
200 N Martingale Rd # 100 60173
Tel (717) 944-5460
SIC 3822 1711 3625 3823 3621

▲ **SPARTON CORP** p 1355
425 N Martingale Rd 60173
Tel (847) 762-5800 SIC 3674 3672

■ **SPARTON EMT LLC** p 1355
425 N Martingale Rd Ste 2 60173
Tel (800) 772-7866 SIC 3674

STERLING PRODUCTS INC p 1387
1100 E Woodfield Rd # 550 60173
Tel (847) 273-7700 SIC 3559 3823 3542

SUNSTAR AMERICAS INC p 1404
301 E Central Rd 60195
Tel (773) 777-4000 SIC 3843

WLG INC p 1620
920 E Algonquin Rd # 120 60173
Tel (773) 416-2803 SIC 4731

XL SPECIALTY INSURANCE CO p 1632
10 N Martingale Rd # 220 60173
Tel (847) 517-2990 SIC 6351 6331

ZFUS SERVICES LLC p 1643
1299 Zurich Way 60196
Tel (847) 605-6000 SIC 6351

ZURICH AMERICAN INSURANCE CO p 1645
1299 Zurich Way 60196
Tel (800) 987-3373 SIC 6331

ZURICH HOLDING CO OF AMERICA INC p 1645
1299 Zurich Way 60196
Tel (847) 605-6000
SIC 6311 6331 6321 6324 6719

ZURICH NORTH AMERICA INC p 1645
1299 Zurich Way 60196
Tel (800) 987-3373 SIC 6411

ZURICH SERVICES CORP p 1645
1299 Zurich Way 60196
Tel (847) 605-6000 SIC 6331

SCHILLER PARK, IL

AUDIO VISUAL SERVICES GROUP INC p 131
5100 River Rd Ste 300 60176
Tel (847) 222-9800 SIC 7359

PSAV INC p 1188
5100 River Rd Ste 300 60176
Tel (847) 222-9800 SIC 7371 7359

SUN BELLE INC p 1400
3810 Rose St 60176
Tel (708) 343-4545 SIC 5149

SUN BELLE INC p 1400
3810 Rose St 60176
Tel (708) 343-4545 SIC 5148

SHANNON, IL

EASTLAND FEED AND GRAIN INC p 473
210 N Stanton St 61078
Tel (815) 864-2723 SIC 5191 5153

SILVIS, IL

GENESIS HEALTH SYSTEMS p 603
1455 Hospital Rd 61282
Tel (309) 281-3270 SIC 8051 8059

SKOKIE, IL

COVENANT RETIREMENT COMMUNITIES INC p 384
5700 Old Orchard Rd 60077
Tel (773) 878-2294 SIC 8741

FORSYTHE SOLUTIONS GROUP INC p 568
7770 Frontage Rd 60077
Tel (847) 213-7000 SIC 7379

FORSYTHE TECHNOLOGY INC p 568
7770 Frontage Rd 60077
Tel (847) 213-7000 SIC 7377 5045 7373

FORSYTHE/MCARTHUR ASSOCIATES INC p 568
7770 Frontage Rd 60077
Tel (847) 213-7000 SIC 7377 7373 5045

■ **HOMESERVICES OF ILLINOIS LLC** p 704
1370 Meadow Rd 60076
Tel (847) 853-5000 SIC 6162

PEAPOD LLC p 1126
9933 Woods Dr 60077
Tel (847) 583-9400 SIC 5411

SKOKIE HOSPITAL p 1330
9600 Gross Point Rd 60076
Tel (847) 677-9600 SIC 8062

TECH LIGHTING LLC p 1431
7400 Linder Ave 60077
Tel (847) 410-4400 SIC 5063

VILLA FINANCIAL SERVICES LLC p 1557
3755 Chase Ave 60076
Tel (847) 440-2660 SIC 8721

SOUTH BELOIT, IL

FORTERRA PRESSURE PIPE INC p 569
4416 Prairie Hill Rd 61080
Tel (815) 389-4800 SIC 3272 3317

■ **WARNER ELECTRIC LLC** p 1576
449 Gardner St 61080
Tel (815) 389-4300 SIC 3714

SOUTH ELGIN, IL

HOFFER PLASTICS CORP p 699
500 N Collins St 60177
Tel (847) 741-5740 *SIC* 3089

SOUTH HOLLAND, IL

ED MINIAT LLC p 476
16250 Vincennes Ave 60473
Tel (708) 589-2400 *SIC* 5147 5144

MINIAT COMPANIES INC p 973
16250 Vincennes Ave 60473
Tel (708) 589-2400 *SIC* 5147 5144

MINIAT HOLDINGS LLC p 973
16250 Vincennes Ave 60473
Tel (708) 589-2400 *SIC* 5147 5144

SOUTH CHICAGO PACKING LLC p 1343
16250 Vincennes Ave 60473
Tel (708) 589-2400 *SIC* 2079

UNIVERSAL POOL CO INC p 1517
300 W Armory Dr 60473
Tel (708) 339-6060 *SIC* 5021 5091

WALTER LAGESTEE INC p 1574
16145 State St 60473
Tel (708) 596-3166 *SIC* 5411 5141

SOUTH JACKSONVILLE, IL

HERTZBERG-NEW METHOD INC p 688
617 E Vandalia Rd 62650
Tel (217) 243-5451 *SIC* 5192

SPARTA, IL

SPARTAN LIGHT METAL PRODUCTS INC p 1355
510 E Mcclurken Ave 62286
Tel (618) 443-4346
SIC 3363 3364 3369 3365

SPRING GROVE, IL

INTERMATIC INC p 753
7777 Winn Rd 60081
Tel (815) 675-2321 *SIC* 3612 3645

SCOT FORGE CO p 1293
8001 Winn Rd 60081
Tel (815) 675-1000 *SIC* 3462

SPRINGFIELD, IL

■ **ALLEGIANCE INSURANCE CO** p 53
1 Horace Mann Plz 62715
Tel (217) 789-2500 *SIC* 6331

■ **AMERICAN GENERAL LIFE INSURANCE** p 73
1 Franklin Sq 62703
Tel (217) 528-2011 *SIC* 6411 6321 6211

BRANDT CONSOLIDATED INC p 208
2935 S Koke Mill Rd 62711
Tel (217) 547-5800 *SIC* 2875 5191

BUNN-O-MATIC CORP p 226
5020 Ash Grove Dr 62711
Tel (217) 529-6601 *SIC* 3589

CDS OFFICE SYSTEMS INC p 271
612 S Dirksen Pkwy 62703
Tel (800) 367-1508
SIC 5044 5999 7629 7378 3861 3577

CITY OF SPRINGFIELD p 318
800 E Monroe St Ste 300 62701
Tel (217) 789-2200 *SIC* 9111

COMMUNITY CARE SYSTEMS INC p 347
405 N Macarthur Blvd 62702
Tel (217) 698-0200 *SIC* 8082

DEPARTMENT OF CORRECTIONS ILLINOIS p 430
1301 Concordia Ct 62702
Tel (217) 557-1030 *SIC* 9223 9111

DEPARTMENT OF REVENUE ILLINOIS p 430
101 W Jefferson St 62702
Tel (217) 782-3336 *SIC* 9311

EXECUTIVE OFFICE OF GOVERNOR p 517
207 S State St 62704
Tel (217) 782-6832 *SIC* 9111

■ **FREEMAN ENERGY CORP** p 576
3008 Happy Landing Dr 62711
Tel (217) 698-3949 *SIC* 1241

FREESEN INC p 577
3151 Robbins Rd Ste A 62704
Tel (217) 546-6192 *SIC* 1622 1771 1629

H D SMITH LLC p 650
3063 Fiat Ave 62703
Tel (866) 232-1222 *SIC* 5122 8082

▲ **HORACE MANN EDUCATORS CORP** p 706
1 Horace Mann Plz 62715
Tel (217) 789-2500 *SIC* 6311 6331 6411

■ **HORACE MANN LIFE INSURANCE CO** p 706
1 Horace Mann Plz 62715
Tel (217) 789-2500 *SIC* 6411

■ **HORACE MANN PROPERTY & CASUALTY INSURANCE CO** p 706
1 Horace Mann Plz 62715
Tel (217) 789-2500 *SIC* 6331

■ **HORACE MANN SERVICE CORP** p 706
1 Horace Mann Plz 62715
Tel (217) 789-2500 *SIC* 6411

HOSPITAL SISTERS HEALTH SYSTEM p 710
4936 Laverna Rd 62707
Tel (217) 523-4747 *SIC* 8082

HSHS MEDICAL GROUP INC p 715
3051 Hollis Dr 200 62704
Tel (217) 492-9696 *SIC* 8011

ILLINOIS COMMUNITY COLLEGE SYSTEM p 732
401 E Capitol Ave 62701
Tel (217) 528-2858 *SIC* 8221 9411

ILLINOIS DEPARTMENT OF MILITARY AFFAIRS p 732
1301 N Macarthur Blvd 62702
Tel (217) 761-3910 *SIC* 9711

ILLINOIS DEPARTMENT OF NATURAL RESOURCES p 732
1 Natural Resources Way # 100 62702
Tel (217) 782-6302 *SIC* 9512 9111

ILLINOIS DEPARTMENT OF PUBLIC HEALTH p 732
535 W Jefferson St Lbby 62702
Tel (217) 785-4302 *SIC* 9431

ILLINOIS DEPARTMENT OF TRANSPORTATION p 732
2300 S Dirksen Pkwy 62764
Tel (217) 782-7820 *SIC* 9621

ILLINOIS DEPARTMENT OF VETERANS AFFAIRS p 732
833 S Spring St 62704
Tel (217) 782-6641 *SIC* 9451

ILLINOIS ENVIRONMENTAL PROTECTION AGENCY p 732
1021 North Grand Ave E 62702
Tel (217) 782-3397 *SIC* 9511

ILLINOIS MASONIC CHARITIES FUND p 732
2866 Via Verde St 62703
Tel (217) 529-8900 *SIC* 8322

ILLINOIS MUNICIPAL ELECTRIC AGENCY p 732
3400 Conifer Dr 62711
Tel (217) 789-4632 *SIC* 4911

ILLINOIS STATE BOARD OF EDUCATION p 732
100 N 1st St Ste 1 62702
Tel (217) 782-4321 *SIC* 9411

ILLINOIS STATE OF STATE POLICE p 732
801 S 7th St 62703
Tel (217) 782-7263 *SIC* 9221

JUDICIAL COURTS OF STATE OF ILLINOIS p 796
Clerk Supreme Court Bldg 62704
Tel (217) 782-2035 *SIC* 9111 9211

LEVI RAY & SHOUP INC p 858
2401 W Monroe St 62704
Tel (217) 793-3800 *SIC* 7371 5045 7379

LINCOLN HERITAGE LIFE INSURANCE CO p 867
920 S Spring St 62704
Tel (602) 957-1650 *SIC* 6311

MEMORIAL HEALTH SYSTEM p 941
701 N 1st St 62781
Tel (217) 788-3000 *SIC* 8741 8062

MEMORIAL MEDICAL CENTER p 942
701 N 1st St 62781
Tel (217) 788-3000 *SIC* 8062

MIDSTATES VIDEO CORP p 966
1022 E Adams St 62703
Tel (217) 544-8433 *SIC* 7389 7841

PRAIRIE POWER INC p 1167
3130 Pleasant Run 62711
Tel (217) 245-6161 *SIC* 4911

ROLAND MACHINERY CO p 1247
816 N Dirksen Pkwy 62702
Tel (217) 789-7711 *SIC* 7353 5082

SIU PHYSICIANS & SURGEONS INC p 1328
801 N Rutledge St # 2050 62702
Tel (217) 545-8065 *SIC* 8011

SPRINGFIELD CLINIC LLP p 1360
1025 S 6th St 62703
Tel (217) 528-7541 *SIC* 8011

SPRINGFIELD ELECTRIC SUPPLY CO p 1360
700 N 9th St 62702
Tel (217) 788-2100 *SIC* 5063 5719

SPRINGFIELD SCHOOL DISTRICT 186 p 1361
1900 W Monroe St 62704
Tel (217) 525-3000 *SIC* 8211

ST JOHNS HOSPITAL SISTERS OF THIRD ORDER OF ST FRANCIS p 1367
800 E Carpenter St 62769
Tel (217) 544-6464 *SIC* 8062

STATE OF ILLINOIS p 1381
207 State House 62706
Tel (217) 782-6830 *SIC* 9111

■ **TEACHERS INSURANCE CO INC** p 1429
1 Horace Mann Plz 62715
Tel (217) 789-2500 *SIC* 6311

TEACHERS RETIREMENT SYSTEM OF STATE OF ILLINOIS p 1429
2815 W Washington St # 200 62702
Tel (217) 753-0370 *SIC* 6371 9199

TOM LANGE CO INC p 1459
755 Apple Orchard Rd 62703
Tel (217) 786-3300 *SIC* 5148

UNITED CONTRACTORS MIDWEST INC p 1507
3151 Robbins Rd Ste A 62704
Tel (217) 546-6192 *SIC* 8742 1622 5082

STERLING, IL

CANDLELIGHT INVESTMENT HOLDINGS INC p 247
1980 Industrial Dr 61081
Tel (815) 632-6800 *SIC* 5199

CGH MEDICAL CENTER p 285
100 E Le Fevre Rd 61081
Tel (815) 625-0400 *SIC* 8062

HALO BRANDED SOLUTIONS INC p 655
1980 Industrial Dr 61081
Tel (815) 632-6988 *SIC* 5199

HALO HOLDING CORP p 655
1980 Industrial Dr 61081
Tel (815) 632-6800 *SIC* 5199

■ **STERLING STEEL CO LLC** p 1387
101 Avenue K 61081
Tel (815) 548-7000 *SIC* 3312

WAHL CLIPPER CORP p 1571
2900 Locust St 61081
Tel (815) 625-6525 *SIC* 3999

STREATOR, IL

■ **VACTOR MANUFACTURING INC** p 1538
1621 S Illinois St 61364
Tel (815) 672-3171 *SIC* 3537

SUGAR GROVE, IL

WAUBONSEE COMMUNITY COLLEGE FOUNDATION p 1583
At Waubonsee Dr Rr 47 60554
Tel (630) 466-7900 *SIC* 8222

SULLIVAN, IL

AGRI-FAB INC p 36
809 S Hamilton St 61951
Tel (217) 728-8388 *SIC* 3469 3429 5083

HYDRO-GEAR INC p 723
1411 S Hamilton St 61951
Tel (217) 728-2581 *SIC* 3594

SYCAMORE, IL

IDEAL INDUSTRIES INC p 729
1375 Park Ave 60178
Tel (815) 895-5181 *SIC* 3825 3643

TAYLORVILLE, IL

DRIVELINE RETAIL MERCHANDISING INC p 456
1141 E 1500 North Rd 62568
Tel (704) 663-7741 *SIC* 8742

TEUTOPOLIS, IL

SIEMER MILLING CO p 1320
111 W Main St 62467
Tel (217) 857-3131 *SIC* 2041

STEVENS INDUSTRIES INC p 1388
704 W Main St 62467
Tel (217) 540-3100 *SIC* 2531 2679 2511

THREE-Z PRINTING CO p 1451
902 W Main St 62467
Tel (217) 857-3153 *SIC* 2752

TINLEY PARK, IL

CONGLOBAL INDUSTRIES LLC p 356
8200 185th St Ste A 60487
Tel (925) 543-0977
SIC 3743 4213 4231 1799 7699

ITS TECHNOLOGIES & LOGISTICS LLC p 768
8200 185th St Ste A 60487
Tel (708) 225-2400 *SIC* 4789

ITS TECHNOLOGIES & LOGISTICS LLC p 768
8200 185th St Ste A 60487
Tel (708) 225-2400 *SIC* 4789

PANDUIT CORP p 1111
18900 Panduit Dr 60487
Tel (708) 532-1800 *SIC* 3699 3644 5063

PROVEN BUSINESS SYSTEMS LLC p 1185
18450 Crossing Dr Ste D 60487
Tel (708) 614-1770 *SIC* 5044 5999

REST HAVEN ILLIANA CHRISTIAN CONVALESCENT HOME p 1228
18601 North Creek Dr A 60477
Tel (708) 342-8100 *SIC* 8051 8361

UGN INC p 1499
18410 Crossing Dr Ste C 60487
Tel (773) 437-2400 *SIC* 3714

TOLEDO, IL

BEN TIRE DISTRIBUTORS LTD p 172
203 E Madison St 62468
Tel (800) 252-8961
SIC 5014 5013 5531 7534

TROY, IL

TRUCK CENTERS INC p 1485
2280 Formosa Rd 62294
Tel (618) 667-3454
SIC 5531 5511 7538 5012 4522 7699

UNION, IL

BAGMAKERS INC p 145
6606 S Union Rd 60180
Tel (815) 923-2247 *SIC* 2673 2674

INTREN INC p 760
18202 W Union Rd 60180
Tel (815) 923-2300 *SIC* 1623

UNIVERSITY PARK, IL

APPLIED SYSTEMS INC p 100
200 Applied Pkwy 60484
Tel (708) 534-5575 *SIC* 7371 7372

BARREL ACCESSORIES AND SUPPLY CO INC p 156
2595 Palmer Ave 60484
Tel (708) 534-0900 *SIC* 5085 5084

BIMBA MANUFACTURING CO INC p 183
25150 S Governors Hwy 60484
Tel (708) 534-8544 *SIC* 3593

GOVERNORS STATE UNIVERSITY p 627
1 University Pkwy 60484
Tel (708) 534-5000 *SIC* 8221

NATIONAL TUBE SUPPLY CO p 1016
925 Central Ave 60484
Tel (708) 534-2700 *SIC* 5051

URBANA, IL

CARLE FOUNDATION p 256
611 W Park St 61801
Tel (217) 383-3311 *SIC* 8062

CARLE FOUNDATION HOSPITAL p 256
611 W Park St 61801
Tel (217) 326-2900 *SIC* 8062

CARLE HEALTH CARE INC p 257
611 W Park St 61801
Tel (217) 383-3206 *SIC* 8099

CARLE HOLDING CO INC p 257
602 W University Ave 61801
Tel (217) 383-3311 *SIC* 8011

COUNTY OF CHAMPAIGN p 376
1776 E Washington St Ofc 61802
Tel (217) 384-3772 *SIC* 9199

FLEX-N-GATE CORP p 555
1306 E University Ave 61802
Tel (217) 384-6600 *SIC* 3714

HEALTH ALLIANCE MEDICAL PLANS INC p 674
301 S Vine St 61801
Tel (217) 337-8000 *SIC* 6321 6324

UNIVERSITY OF ILLINOIS p 1521
506 S Wright St Rm 364 61801
Tel (217) 333-1000 *SIC* 8221

UNIVERSITY OF ILLINOIS FOUNDATION p 1521
1305 W Green St 61801
Tel (217) 333-0810 *SIC* 8699

VERNON HILLS, IL

ALI GROUP NORTH AMERICA CORP p 50
101 Corporate Woods Pkwy 60061
Tel (847) 215-6565 *SIC* 3589

AMERICAN HOTEL REGISTER CO p 74
100 S Milwaukee Ave # 100 60061
Tel (847) 743-3000
SIC 5046 5023 5021 5113

BAXTER CREDIT UNION p 160
340 N Milwaukee Ave 60061
Tel (847) 522-8600 *SIC* 6062

■ **CDW GOVERNMENT LLC** p 271
230 N Milwaukee Ave 60061
Tel (847) 465-6000 *SIC* 5961 5065 5734

CDW HOLDINGS LLC p 271
3 First National Pl 60061
Tel (847) 465-6000
SIC 5963 5045 5734 5961

COLE-PARMER INSTRUMENT CO LLC p 336
625 Bunker Ct 60061
Tel (847) 549-7600 *SIC* 5049

DELUXE MEDIA SERVICES INC p 427
568 Atrium Dr 60061
Tel (847) 990-4100 *SIC* 7819 7822

DERINGER-NEY INC p 431
616 Atrium Dr Ste 100 60061
Tel (847) 566-4100
SIC 3643 3542 3469 3452 3316

GRAHAM ENTERPRISE INC p 629
750 Bunker Ct Ste 100 60061
Tel (847) 837-0777 *SIC* 5172 5411

HAND2MIND INC p 657
500 Greenview Ct 60061
Tel (847) 816-5060 *SIC* 5049 5169

HH GLOBAL USA INC p 689
175 E Hawthorn Pkwy # 325 60061
Tel (847) 816-6303 *SIC* 8742

RICHARD WOLF MEDICAL INSTRUMENTS CORP p 1232
353 Corporate Woods Pkwy 60061
Tel (847) 913-1113 *SIC* 5047 3841

■ **RUST-OLEUM CORP** p 1260
11 E Hawthorn Pkwy 60061
Tel (847) 367-7700
SIC 2891 2899 2816 2842 2851

SAYERS TECHNOLOGY LLC p 1285
825 Corporate Woods Pkwy 60061
Tel (847) 391-4802 *SIC* 5734 7378

SCOTSMAN INDUSTRIES INC p 1293
101 Corporate Woods Pkwy 60061
Tel (847) 215-4501 *SIC* 3585 3632

TETRA PAK MATERIALS LP p 1441
101 Corporate Woods Pkwy 60061
Tel (847) 955-6000 *SIC* 2671

TETRA PAK US HOLDINGS INC p 1441
101 Corporate Woods Pkwy 60061
Tel (940) 565-8800 *SIC* 2656

WURTH BAER SUPPLY CO p 1628
909 Forest Edge Dr 60061
Tel (847) 913-2237 *SIC* 5072

VILLA PARK, IL

SUPREME LOBSTER AND SEAFOOD CO p 1408
220 E North Ave 60181
Tel (630) 834-3474 *SIC* 5146

WARRENVILLE, IL

B P OIL PIPELINE CO p 142
28301 Ferry Rd 60555
Tel (630) 420-5111 *SIC* 4612

BP AMERICA INC p 205
4101 Winfield Rd Ste 200 60555
Tel (630) 420-5111
SIC 2911 5171 4612 4613 4424

BP OIL SUPPLY CO p 205
28100 Torch Pkwy 60555
Tel (630) 836-5000 *SIC* 5172

BP PIPELINES (NORTH AMERICA) INC p 206
28100 Torch Pkwy Ste 600 60555
Tel (630) 836-5100 *SIC* 4612 4613

DURHAM SCHOOL SERVICES L P p 463
4300 Weaver Pkwy Ste 100 60555
Tel (630) 836-0292 *SIC* 4151

EN ENGINEERING LLC p 495
28100 Torch Pkwy Ste 400 60555
Tel (630) 353-4000 *SIC* 8711

HEICO HOLDING INC p 680
27501 Bella Vista Pkwy 60555
Tel (630) 353-5000 *SIC* 6719

NATIONAL EXPRESS LLC p 1011
4300 Weaver Pkwy Ste 100 60555
Tel (800) 950-0485 *SIC* 4119

OHMITE HOLDING LLC p 1078
27501 Bella Vista Pkwy 60555
Tel (847) 258-0300 *SIC* 3625 5065

■ **PATTERSON MEDICAL PRODUCTS INC** p 1121
28100 Torch Pkwy 60555
Tel (630) 393-6671 *SIC* 3841

PETTIBONE LLC p 1140
27501 Bella Vista Pkwy 60555
Tel (630) 353-5000 *SIC* 6719

PHONAK LLC p 1145
4520 Weaver Pkwy Ste 1 60555
Tel (630) 821-5000 *SIC* 3842 5999

PLYMOUTH TUBE CO p 1157
29w 150 Warrenville Rd 60555
Tel (630) 393-3550 *SIC* 3317 3354

STANDARD OIL CO p 1376
4101 Winfield Rd Ste 100 60555
Tel (630) 836-5000 *SIC* 2911

WATERLOO, IL

WM NOBBE AND CO INC p 1620
6469 State Route 3 62298
Tel (618) 939-6717 *SIC* 5083

WATSEKA, IL

WATSEKA RURAL KING SUPPLY INC p 1583
200 N Ernest Grove Pkwy 60970
Tel (815) 432-3440
SIC 5999 5651 5251 5311

WAUCONDA, IL

ACRES ENTERPRISES INC p 18
610 W Liberty St 60084
Tel (847) 526-4554 *SIC* 0782 0781 4959

FIDELITONE INC p 540
1260 Karl Ct 60084
Tel (847) 487-3300 *SIC* 4214

LACOSTA INC p 837
440 W Bonner Rd 60084
Tel (847) 526-9556 *SIC* 7349

WAUKEGAN, IL

ARLINGTON INDUSTRIES INC p 110
1616 S Lakeside Dr 60085
Tel (847) 689-2754 *SIC* 5112

■ **CARDINAL HEALTH 200 LLC** p 253
3651 Birchwood Dr 60085
Tel (847) 578-9500 *SIC* 5047

COLEMAN CABLE LLC p 336
1530 S Shields Dr 60085
Tel (847) 672-2300 *SIC* 3661 3357 3643

■ **COMCAST OF ILLINOIS III INC** p 343
1585 S Waukegan Rd 60085
Tel (847) 856-5239 *SIC* 4841

COUNTY OF LAKE p 379
18 N County St Fl 8 60085
Tel (847) 377-2373 *SIC* 9111

DEUBLIN CO p 433
2050 Norman Dr 60085
Tel (847) 689-8600
SIC 3498 3492 3568 3494

HORIZONS HOLDINGS LLC p 708
1705 S Waukegan Rd 60085
Tel (800) 858-2352 *SIC* 5023

JST CORP p 796
1957 S Lakeside Dr 60085
Tel (847) 473-1957 *SIC* 5065

LAKE COUNTY PRESS INC p 838
98 Noll St 60085
Tel (847) 336-4333 *SIC* 2791 7334

NOSCO INC p 1062
651 S Ml King Jr Ave 60085
Tel (847) 336-4200 *SIC* 2752 2657

TRU-SPEC METALS INC p 1485
3075 N Oak Grove Ave 60087
Tel (847) 360-8400 *SIC* 5051

UCC HOLDINGS CORP p 1499
2100 Norman Dr 60085
Tel (847) 473-5900 *SIC* 3443 8711

UNITED CONVEYOR CORP p 1507
2100 Norman Dr 60085
Tel (847) 473-5900 *SIC* 3535

VICTORY HEALTH SERVICES p 1555
1324 N Sheridan Rd 60085
Tel (847) 360-3000 *SIC* 8062

VISTA HEALTH SYSTEM p 1562
1324 N Sheridan Rd 60085
Tel (847) 249-3505 *SIC* 8062

VISUAL PAK CO p 1562
1909 S Waukegan Rd 60085
Tel (847) 689-1000 *SIC* 7389

WAUKEGAN COMMUNITY UNIT SCHOOL DISTRICT 60 p 1583
1201 N Sheridan Rd 60085
Tel (847) 360-7028 *SIC* 8211

■ **WAUKEGAN ILLINOIS HOSPITAL CO LLC** p 1583
1324 N Sheridan Rd 60085
Tel (847) 360-3000 *SIC* 8062

WOODLAND FOODS LTD p 1623
3751 Sunset Ave 60087
Tel (847) 625-8600 *SIC* 5149

YASKAWA AMERICA INC p 1635
2121 Norman Dr 60085
Tel (847) 887-7000
SIC 3621 7694 5063 3566 3823 3625

WAVERLY, IL

FARMERS ELEVATOR CO OF LOWDER p 529
10955 North St 62692
Tel (217) 435-9023 *SIC* 5153

WAYNE CITY, IL

CONSOLIDATED GRAIN & BARGE CO p 359
Washington & Water St 62895
Tel (618) 895-2181
SIC 4221 5153 4449 4491

WENONA, IL

OAK STATE PRODUCTS INC p 1070
775 State Route 251 61377
Tel (815) 853-4348 *SIC* 2051

WEST CHICAGO, IL

■ **ASPEN MARKETING SERVICES LLC** p 118
1240 W North Ave 60185
Tel (630) 293-9600 *SIC* 8743 8748 5199

BALL HORTICULTURAL CO p 148
622 Town Rd 60185
Tel (630) 231-3600 *SIC* 0181

■ **BULK MOLDING COMPOUNDS INC** p 225
1600 Powis Ct 60185
Tel (630) 377-1065 *SIC* 3087

JEL SERT CO p 782
Conde St Rr 59 60185
Tel (630) 231-7590
SIC 2087 2024 2099 5499 5143

WEST FRANKFORT, IL

LEISURE PROPERTIES LLC p 854
11884 Country Club Rd 62896
Tel (618) 937-6426 *SIC* 3732

WESTCHESTER, IL

A & R JANITORIAL SERVICE INC p 4
10127 W Roosevelt Rd 60154
Tel (708) 656-8300 *SIC* 7349

■ **AXLE HOLDINGS INC** p 140
2 Westbrook Corporate Ctr 60154
Tel (708) 492-7000 *SIC* 5012

BRAINLAB INC p 207
5 Westbrook Corp Ctr 60154
Tel (800) 784-7700 *SIC* 5047 3841

■ **COMMSCOPE TECHNOLOGIES LLC** p 346
4 Westbrook Corporate Ctr 60154
Tel (708) 236-6000
SIC 3663 3357 3679 3812 3699

FOLLETT CORP p 563
3 Westbrook Ctr Ste 200 60154
Tel (708) 884-0000 *SIC* 5942 5192

FOLLETT HIGHER EDUCATION GROUP INC p 563
3 Westbrook Corp Ctr # 200 60154
Tel (800) 365-5388 *SIC* 5942 5943 5947

▲ **INGREDION INC** p 743
5 Westbrook Corporate Ctr # 500 60154
Tel (708) 551-2600 *SIC* 2046

■ **INSURANCE AUTO AUCTIONS INC** p 747
2 Westbrook Corporate Ctr # 1000 60154
Tel (708) 492-7000 *SIC* 5012

LABORERS PENSION & WELFARE FUNDS p 836
11465 W Cermak Rd 60154
Tel (708) 562-0200 *SIC* 6371

MATERIAL SERVICE CORP p 919
2235 Entp Dr Ste 3504 60154
Tel (708) 731-2600 *SIC* 1422 1442

WESTMONT, IL

EMPLOYCO USA II INC p 494
350 E Ogden Ave 60559
Tel (630) 920-0000 *SIC* 7361

HA-INTERNATIONAL LLC p 651
630 Oakmont Ln 60559
Tel (630) 575-5700 *SIC* 2869

HA-USA INC p 651
630 Oakmont Ln 60559
Tel (630) 575-5700 *SIC* 2869

JOHNSON SERVICE GROUP INC p 791
1 E Oakhill Dr Ste 200 60559
Tel (630) 655-3500 *SIC* 7363 8711

PORTFOLIO HOTELS & RESORTS LLC p 1162
601 Oakmont Ln Ste 420 60559
Tel (630) 366-2018 *SIC* 7011

TY INC p 1496
280 Chestnut Ave 60559
Tel (630) 920-1515 *SIC* 5092

WHEATON, IL

COMMUNITY UNIT SCHOOL DISTRICT 200 p 350
130 W Park Ave 60189
Tel (630) 682-2000 *SIC* 8211

COUNTY OF DU PAGE p 377
421 N County Farm Rd 60187
Tel (630) 407-6000 *SIC* 9111

FIRST TRUST PORTFOLIOS LP p 550
120 E Liberty Dr Ste 400 60187
Tel (800) 621-1675 *SIC* 6211

■ **TOUCHSENSOR TECHNOLOGIES LLC** p 1463
203 N Gables Blvd 60187
Tel (630) 221-9000 *SIC* 5065 3674

TRUSTEES OF WHEATON COLLEGE p 1488
501 College Ave 60187
Tel (630) 752-5000 *SIC* 8221

WHEATON FRANCISCAN SERVICES INC p 1604
26w 171 Roosevelt Rd 60189
Tel (414) 465-3000 *SIC* 8741 5999

WHEELING, IL

ANGIOTECH PHARMACEUTICALS (US) INC p 91
241 W Palatine Rd 60090
Tel (847) 637-3333
SIC 3841 3541 3842 8731

BOWE BELL + HOWELL HOLDINGS INC p 204
760 S Wolf Rd 60090
Tel (312) 541-9300 *SIC* 3579

COMMUNITY CONSOLIDATED SCHOOL DISTRICT 21 p 348
999 W Dundee Rd 60090
Tel (847) 520-2700 *SIC* 8211

DOALL CO p 446
1480 S Wolf Rd 60090
Tel (847) 495-6800 *SIC* 5085 5084

DOALL INDUSTRIAL SUPPLY CORP p 446
1480 S Wolf Rd 60090
Tel (800) 923-6255 *SIC* 5085

DURABLE INC p 462
750 Northgate Pkwy 60090
Tel (847) 541-4400 *SIC* 3497 3354

■ **FLUID MANAGEMENT INC** p 561
1023 Wheeling Rd 60090
Tel (847) 537-0880 *SIC* 3559

HANDI-FOIL CORP p 657
135 E Hintz Rd 60090
Tel (847) 520-1000 *SIC* 3497

HFA INC p 689
135 E Hintz Rd 60090
Tel (847) 520-1000 *SIC* 3497

INDECK POWER EQUIPMENT CO p 736
1111 Willis Ave 60090
Tel (847) 541-8300 *SIC* 5084 5074 7359

LEWIS PAPER INTERNATIONAL INC p 859
1400 S Wolf Rd Ste 100 60090
Tel (847) 520-3386 *SIC* 5111

MANAN TOOL & MANUFACTURING INC p 900
241 W Palatine Rd 60090
Tel (847) 637-3333 *SIC* 3541 3841

MIDLAND PAPER CO p 966
101 E Palatine Rd 60090
Tel (847) 777-2700 *SIC* 5111

SEGERDAHL CORP p 1300
1351 Wheeling Rd 60090
Tel (847) 541-1080 *SIC* 2752

SEGERDAHL GRAPHICS INC p 1300
1351 Wheeling Rd 60090
Tel (847) 541-1080 *SIC* 2752 8742

US TSUBAKI HOLDINGS INC p 1533
301 E Marquardt Dr 60090
Tel (847) 459-9500 *SIC* 5085 3568

US TSUBAKI POWER TRANSMISSION LLC p 1533
301 E Marquardt Dr 60090
Tel (847) 459-9500
SIC 3568 5085 5063 3714 3462 3325

WILLOWBROOK, IL

FAGOR ARRASATE USA INC p 524
636 Executive Dr 60527
Tel (630) 920-0422 *SIC* 5051 5064

NEW YORK BLOWER CO p 1034
7660 S Quincy St 60527
Tel (630) 794-5700 *SIC* 3564

PLASTICS GROUP INC p 1155
7409 S Quincy St 60527
Tel (630) 325-1210 *SIC* 3089

WINFIELD, IL

CDH-DELNOR HEALTH SYSTEM p 271
25 N Winfield Rd 60190
Tel (630) 933-1600 *SIC* 8071 8741

CENTRAL DUPAGE HOSPITAL ASSOCIATION p 278
25 N Winfield Rd 60190
Tel (630) 933-1600 *SIC* 8062

WOOD DALE, IL

▲ **AAR CORP** p 8
1100 N Wood Dale Rd 60191
Tel (630) 227-2000
SIC 3724 4581 3537 5599 7359

■ **AAR INTERNATIONAL INC** p 8
1100 N Wood Dale Rd 60191
Tel (630) 227-2000 *SIC* 5088

■ **AAR MANUFACTURING INC** p 8
1100 N Wood Dale Rd 60191
Tel (630) 227-2000 *SIC* 7629

■ **AAR SUPPLY CHAIN INC** p 8
1100 N Wood Dale Rd 60191
Tel (630) 227-2000 *SIC* 5088 3728

■ **AWW 10 INC** p 139
1441 N Wood Dale Rd 60191
Tel (630) 595-0000 *SIC* 3452 5072

■ **CH ROBINSON FREIGHT SERVICES LTD** p 286
1501 N Mittel Blvd Ste A 60191
Tel (630) 766-4445 *SIC* 4731 4225

CHAMPION CONTAINER CORP p 287
1455 N Michael Dr 60191
Tel (630) 279-4600 *SIC* 5113

CNA INTERNATIONAL INC p 330
940 N Central Ave 60191
Tel (630) 238-9800 *SIC* 5063 5064

MADDEN COMMUNICATIONS INC p 893
901 Mittel Dr 60191
Tel (630) 787-2200 *SIC* 2752

■ **POWER SOLUTIONS INC** p 1165
201 Mittel Dr 60191
Tel (630) 350-9400 *SIC* 5084

▲ **POWER SOLUTIONS INTERNATIONAL INC** p 1165
201 Mittel Dr 60191
Tel (630) 350-9400 *SIC* 5084

SIMU LTD p 1326
201 Mittel Dr 60191
Tel (630) 350-1060
SIC 5113 5141 5142 2782 2759 2621

TEMPCO ELECTRIC HEATER CORP p 1436
607 N Central Ave 60191
Tel (630) 350-2252 *SIC* 3567 3369 3829

TOYO INK INTERNATIONAL CORP p 1466
1225 N Michael Dr 60191
Tel (866) 969-8696 *SIC* 2893 5112

■ **VIDEOJET TECHNOLOGIES INC** p 1556
1500 N Mittel Blvd 60191
Tel (630) 860-7300 *SIC* 3579

WOOD RIVER, IL

MERS LLC p 951
200 S Amoco Cutoff 62095
Tel (618) 254-4500 *SIC* 5172

WOODRIDGE, IL

APL LOGISTICS AMERICAS LTD p 97
2649 Internationale Pkwy 60517
Tel (630) 783-0200 *SIC* 3531

BEAVERS HOLDINGS LLC p 166
3550 Hobson Rd Fl 3 60517
Tel (630) 963-2736 *SIC* 8741 6531

CHAMPION PACKAGING & DISTRIBUTION INC p 287
1840 Internationale Pkwy 60517
Tel (630) 755-4220 *SIC* 2842 2812

CLEARSTAFF INC p 324
7501 Lemont Rd Ste 220 60517
Tel (630) 985-0100 *SIC* 7363

DON EDWARD & CO p 449
9801 Adam Don Pkwy 60517
Tel (708) 442-9400
SIC 5021 5046 5087 5113 5169

E K SUCCESS LTD p 466
2240 75th St 60517
Tel (630) 963-7100 *SIC* 5199 2679

FOLLETT SCHOOL SOLUTIONS INC p 563
1433 Internationale Pkwy 60517
Tel (630) 972-5600 *SIC* 5192

GERBER PLUMBING FIXTURES LLC p 608
2500 Intrntonale Pkwy 60517
Tel (630) 679-1420 *SIC* 3261

GKN AMERICA CORP p 613
2715 Davey Rd Ste 300 60517
Tel (630) 972-9300 *SIC* 3714

GKN NORTH AMERICA SERVICES INC p 613
2715 Davey Rd Ste 300 60517
Tel (630) 972-9300 SIC 3714 5013 7359

GLOBE UNION GROUP INC p 618
2500 Internationale Pkwy 60517
Tel (630) 679-1420 SIC 3261 3432 7699

GOSS INTERNATIONAL CORP p 626
9018 Heritage Pkwy # 1200 60517
Tel (630) 796-7560 SIC 3555 5084

H C SCHAU & SON INC p 649
10350 Argonne Dr Ste 400 60517
Tel (630) 783-1000 SIC 5147 2099

HENDRICKSON USA LLC p 683
800 S Frontage Rd 60517
Tel (630) 910-2844 SIC 5012

INVENTUS POWER INC p 761
1200 Internationale Pkwy 60517
Tel (630) 410-7900 SIC 3629

NETCO INC (IL) p 1027
7501 Lemont Rd Ste 305 60517
Tel (312) 782-4290 SIC 6361

ORBUS LLC p 1093
9033 Murphy Rd 60517
Tel (630) 226-1155 SIC 3999

PLUS GROUP INC p 1157
7425 Janes Ave Ste 201 60517
Tel (630) 515-0500 SIC 7361 7363

RJW LOGISTICS INC p 1239
11240 Katherines Xing 60517
Tel (630) 424-2400 SIC 4731

SAMUEL STRAPPING SYSTEMS INC p 1275
1401 Davey Rd Ste 300 60517
Tel (630) 783-8900 SIC 3499 5085

TRANSPORT DRIVERS INC p 1472
3540 Seven Bridges Dr # 300 60517
Tel (630) 766-2721 SIC 7363

WILTON BRANDS LLC p 1614
2240 75th St 60517
Tel (630) 963-7100
SIC 5023 2731 2721 7812 5199

WILTON HOLDINGS INC p 1614
2240 75th St 60517
Tel (630) 963-7100
SIC 5023 2731 2721 7812 5199

WILTON INDUSTRIES INC p 1614
2240 75th St 60517
Tel (630) 963-7100
SIC 5023 2731 2721 7812 5199

WOODSTOCK, IL

■ CATALENT PHARMA SOLUTIONS LLC p 264
2210 Lake Shore Dr 60098
Tel (815) 338-9500 SIC 5084

CONSERV FS INC p 358
1110 Mcconnell Rd 60098
Tel (815) 334-5950 SIC 5171 5191

EPS SOLUTIONS INC p 505
1525 W Lake Shore Dr 60098
Tel (815) 206-0868 SIC 2676

KELCO INDUSTRIES INC p 808
1425 Lake Ave 60098
Tel (815) 334-3600
SIC 3599 3069 3494 3585 3544 3625

MEMORIAL MEDICAL CENTER-WOODSTOCK p 942
3701 Doty Rd 60098
Tel (815) 334-3880 SIC 8062 8051

WOODSTOCK COMMUNITY UNIT SCHOOL DISTRICT 200 p 1623
227 W Judd St 60098
Tel (815) 338-8200 SIC 8211

WORTH, IL

FOUNDERS GROUP INC p 571
6825 W 111th St 60482
Tel (708) 448-6500 SIC 6712

ZION, IL

MIDWESTERN REGIONAL MEDICAL CENTER INC p 968
2501 Emmaus Ave 60099
Tel (847) 731-1364 SIC 8069

INDIANA

ALBION, IN

BUSCHE PERFORMANCE GROUP INC p 229
1563 E State Road 8 46701
Tel (260) 636-7030 SIC 3599

ANDERSON, IN

CARTER EXPRESS INC p 262
4020 W 73rd St 46011
Tel (765) 778-6961 SIC 4213 4212

CARTER LOGISTICS LLC p 262
4020 W 73rd St 46011
Tel (765) 778-6960 SIC 4731

COMMUNITY HOSPITAL OF ANDERSON AND MADISON COUNTY INC p 349
1515 N Madison Ave 46011
Tel (765) 298-4242 SIC 8062 8011

E & B PAVING INC p 465
286 W 300 N 46012
Tel (765) 643-5358 SIC 1611 2951 1794

HOOSIER PARK LLC p 706
4500 Dan Patch Cir Xxx 46013
Tel (765) 642-7223 SIC 7948

JP HOLDING CO INC p 794
4020 W 73rd St 46011
Tel (765) 778-6960 SIC 4213

KEIHIN NORTH AMERICA INC p 808
2701 Enterprise Dr # 100 46013
Tel (765) 298-6030 SIC 3714

RICKER OIL CO INC p 1233
30 W 11th St 46016
Tel (765) 643-3016 SIC 5171

S&S STEEL SERVICES INC p 1263
444 E 29th St 46016
Tel (765) 622-4545 SIC 5051 3316

ST VINCENT ANDERSON REGIONAL HOSPITAL INC p 1373
2015 Jackson St 46016
Tel (765) 649-2511 SIC 8062 5047

ANGOLA, IN

EJ BROOKS CO p 482
409 Hoosier Dr 46703
Tel (800) 348-4777 SIC 3679

TYDEN GROUP HOLDINGS CORP p 1496
409 Hoosier Dr 46703
Tel (740) 420-6777 SIC 3953 2891

VESTIL MANUFACTURING CO p 1552
201 Growth Pkwy 46703
Tel (260) 665-2867 SIC 3537

VESTIL MANUFACTURING CORP p 1552
2999 N Wayne St 46703
Tel (260) 665-7586 SIC 3999 3535 3069

ATTICA, IN

HARRISON STEEL CASTINGS CO p 664
900 S Mound St 47918
Tel (765) 762-2481 SIC 3325

AUBURN, IN

METAL TECHNOLOGIES OF INDIANA INC p 952
1401 S Grandstaff Dr 46706
Tel (260) 925-4717 SIC 3321 3443

AUSTIN, IN

MORGAN FOODS INC p 988
90 W Morgan St 47102
Tel (812) 794-1170 SIC 2032

AVON, IN

AVON COMMUNITY SCHOOL CORP p 139
7203 E Us Highway 36 46123
Tel (317) 272-2920 SIC 8211

CO-ALLIANCE LLP p 330
5250 E Us Hwy 3 46123
Tel (317) 745-4491
SIC 5191 5171 5153 2875

HARLAN BAKERIES LLC p 661
7597 E Us Highway 36 46123
Tel (317) 272-3600 SIC 5149 2051 2045

HARLAN BAKERIES-AVON LLC p 661
7597 E Us Highway 36 46123
Tel (317) 272-3600 SIC 5149 2051 2045

HENDRICKS COUNTY RURAL ELECTRIC MEMBERSHIP CORP p 683
86 N County Road 500 E 46123
Tel (317) 745-5473 SIC 4911

IU HEALTH WEST HOSPITAL p 769
1111 Ronald Reagan Pkwy # 223 46123
Tel (317) 217-3000 SIC 8062

BATESVILLE, IN

■ BATESVILLE CASKET CO INC p 159
1 Batesville Blvd 47006
Tel (812) 934-7500 SIC 3995

■ BATESVILLE SERVICES INC p 159
1 Batesville Blvd 47006
Tel (812) 934-7000 SIC 3995

BATESVILLE TOOL & DIE INC p 159
177 Six Pine Ranch Rd 47006
Tel (812) 934-5616 SIC 3469 3544

BTD MANUFACTURING INC p 222
177 Six Pine Ranch Rd 47006
Tel (812) 934-5616 SIC 3469 3544

FORETHOUGHT LIFE INSURANCE CO p 567
1 Forethought Ctr 47006
Tel (812) 934-7139 SIC 6311

■ HILL-ROM CO INC p 693
1069 State Road 46 E 47006
Tel (812) 934-7777 SIC 7352

■ HILL-ROM INC p 693
1069 State Route 46 E 47006
Tel (812) 934-7777 SIC 7352 2599

▲ HILLENBRAND INC p 693
1 Batesville Blvd 47006
Tel (812) 934-7500 SIC 3535 3995

BLOOMINGTON, IN

CARDON & ASSOCIATES INC p 253
2749 E Covenanter Dr 47401
Tel (812) 332-2265 SIC 8741 6513 8742

COOK GROUP INC p 365
750 N Daniels Way 47404
Tel (812) 339-2235
SIC 3841 3821 3845 6411 6512 6211

COOK INC p 366
750 N Daniels Way 47404
Tel (812) 339-2235 SIC 3841

HOOSIER ENERGY RURAL ELECTRIC COOPERATIVE INC p 706
2501 S Cooperative Way 47403
Tel (812) 876-2021 SIC 4911

INDIANA UNIVERSITY FOUNDATION INC p 739
1500 N State Road 46 Byp 47408
Tel (812) 855-8311 SIC 8299

INDIANA UNIVERSITY HEALTH BLOOMINGTON INC p 739
601 W 2nd St 47403
Tel (812) 353-5252 SIC 8062

MONROE COUNTY COMMUNITY SCHOOL CORP p 985
315 E North Dr 47401
Tel (812) 330-7700 SIC 8211

NATIONAL SALVAGE & SERVICE CORP p 1016
6755 S Old State Road 37 47401
Tel (812) 339-8437
SIC 5088 1629 1795 5099 5093

TRUSTEES OF INDIANA UNIVERSITY p 1488
509 E 3rd St 47401
Tel (812) 855-0516 SIC 8221

WEDDLE BROS CONSTRUCTION CO INC p 1587
1201 W 3rd St 47404
Tel (812) 339-9500 SIC 1542 1622 1541

BLUFFTON, IN

PRETZELS INC p 1173
123 W Harvest Rd 46714
Tel (260) 824-4838 SIC 2052 2099

BREMEN, IN

BREMEN CASTINGS INC p 209
500 N Baltimore St 46506
Tel (574) 546-2411 SIC 3321

BRISTOL, IN

■ AMERI KART CORP p 67
17196 State Road 120 46507
Tel (574) 848-7462
SIC 3089 3537 2821 5162

DIVERSIFIED MACHINE BRISTOL LLC p 444
51650 County Road 133 46507
Tel (248) 728-8642 SIC 3465

ROBERT WEED PLYWOOD CORP p 1241
705 Maple St 46507
Tel (574) 848-7631 SIC 5031 2435 2431

UNIVERSAL TRAILER CARGO GROUP INC p 1518
14054 C R 4 46507
Tel (574) 264-9661 SIC 3715

■ UTILIMASTER SERVICES LLC p 1537
603 Earthway Blvd 46507
Tel (574) 848-2000 SIC 7532

BROWNSBURG, IN

BADGER DAYLIGHTING CORP p 143
8930 Motorsports Way 46112
Tel (317) 456-1432 SIC 1389

BADGER DAYLIGHTING USA INC p 143
8930 Motorsports Way 46112
Tel (317) 456-1050 SIC 1389

MAPLEHURST BAKERIES LLC p 904
50 Maplehurst Dr 46112
Tel (317) 858-9000 SIC 2051

WESTON FOODS US INC p 1602
50 Maplehurst Dr 46112
Tel (317) 858-9000 SIC 2051 2052

BURNS HARBOR, IN

ARCELORMITTAL BURNS HARBOR LLC p 104
250 W Us Highway 12 46304
Tel (219) 787-2120 SIC 3312

BUTLER, IN

INDIANA MULTIMATIC MFG INC p 738
201 Re Jones Rd 46721
Tel (260) 868-1000 SIC 3465

CAMBY, IN

XFMRS HOLDINGS INC p 1631
7570 E Landersdale Rd 46113
Tel (317) 834-1066 SIC 3699

XFMRS INC p 1631
7570 E Landersdale Rd 46113
Tel (317) 834-1066 SIC 3677 5065 3612

CAMDEN, IN

■ CAMDEN TELEPHONE CO INC p 245
210 W Main St 46917
Tel (608) 831-1000 SIC 4813

CARMEL, IN

■ ADESA CORP LLC p 22
13085 Hamilton Crossing B 46032
Tel (317) 249-4550 SIC 5012 6153

ALLEGION S&S US HOLDING CO INC p 53
11819 N Pennsylvania St 46032
Tel (317) 810-3700 SIC 3429

ALLIANCE FOR COOPERATIVE ENERGY SERVICES POWER MARKETING LLC p 54
4140 W 99th St 46032
Tel (317) 344-7000 SIC 4911

ALLIED SOLUTIONS LLC p 57
1320 City Center Dr # 300 46032
Tel (317) 706-7600 SIC 6321 6351 6159

■ AUTOMOTIVE FINANCE CORP p 134
13085 H Croining Blvd 3 Ste 300 46032
Tel (317) 815-9645 SIC 6153

▲ BALDWIN & LYONS INC p 147
111 Congressional Blvd # 500 46032
Tel (317) 636-9800 SIC 6331 6411

BYRIDER SALES OF INDIANA S LLC p 231
12802 Hmlton Crssing Blvd 46032
Tel (317) 249-3000 SIC 5521

CARMEL CLAY SCHOOLS p 258
5201 E Main St 46033
Tel (317) 844-9961 SIC 8211

CELLULAR CONNECTION LLC p 274
525 Congressional Blvd 46032
Tel (765) 651-2001
SIC 5065 1731 5999 5731

■ CICH INC p 306
11825 N Pennsylvania St 46032
Tel (317) 817-6100 SIC 6311

▲ CNO FINANCIAL GROUP INC p 330
11825 N Pennsylvania St 46032
Tel (317) 817-6100 SIC 6311 6321 6331

■ CNO SERVICES LLC p 330
11825 N Pennsylvania St 46032
Tel (317) 817-6100 SIC 6411

CONSECO VARIABLE INSURANCE CO p 358
11825 N Pennsylvania St 46032
Tel (317) 817-6100 SIC 6311

ELECTRONIC TECHNOLOGIES CORP USA p 486
11819 N Pennsylvania St 46032
Tel (317) 810-3177 SIC 5065 5063 7382

HERITAGE MANAGEMENT GROUP INC p 686
2384 Glebe St 46032
Tel (317) 569-0877 SIC 7389

INDIANA MUNICIPAL POWER AGENCY p 738
11610 N College Ave 46032
Tel (317) 573-9955 SIC 4911

INDIANA SECONDARY MARKET FOR EDUCATION LOANS INC p 738
11595 N Meridian St # 200 46032
Tel (317) 715-9000 SIC 6111

ITT EDUCATIONAL SERVICES INC p 768
13000 N Meridian St 46032
Tel (317) 706-9200 SIC 8221

JD BYRIDER SYSTEMS LLC p 780
12802 Hmlton Crssing Blvd 46032
Tel (317) 249-3000
SIC 6794 5734 7538 7515 5521

▲ KAR AUCTION SERVICES INC p 804
13085 Hmlton Crssing Blvd 46032
Tel (800) 923-3725 SIC 5012 6153 5521

KAR HOLDINGS II LLC p 804
13085 Hamil Cross Blvd St Ste 500 46032
Tel (317) 815-1100 SIC 5012 6153

MIDCONTINENT INDEPENDENT SYSTEM OPERATOR INC p 964
720 City Center Dr 46032
Tel (317) 249-5400 SIC 4911

NEXTGEAR CAPITAL INC p 1040
11799 N College Ave 46032
Tel (317) 571-3721 SIC 6159

SCHLAGE LOCK CO LLC p 1287
11819 N Pennsylvania St 46032
Tel (317) 810-3700 SIC 3429

SEEMAC INC p 1300
11350 N Meridian St # 450 46032
Tel (317) 844-3995 SIC 5031

■ SENIOR CONSECO HEALTH INSURANCE CO p 1304
11825 N Pennsylvania St 46032
Tel (317) 817-6100 SIC 6321

SHEPHERD INSURANCE LLC p 1315
111 Congressional Blvd # 100 46032
Tel (317) 846-5554 SIC 6411

ST VINCENT CARMEL HOSPITAL p 1373
13500 N Meridian St 46032
Tel (317) 582-7000 SIC 8093

TC HEARTLAND LLC p 1428
14300 Clay Terrace Blvd 46032
Tel (317) 566-9750 SIC 2099

TELAMON CORP p 1433
1000 E 116th St 46032
Tel (317) 818-6888 SIC 4813 8711 3357

TELAMON TECHNOLOGIES CORP p 1433
1000 E 116th St 46032
Tel (317) 818-6888 SIC 3661

■ WASHINGTON NATIONAL INSURANCE CO p 1578
11815 N Pennsylvania St 46032
Tel (317) 817-4100 SIC 6311 6321

WILCO LIFE INSURANCE CO p 1608
11825 N Pennsylvania St 46032
Tel (317) 817-6100 SIC 6311

ZOTEC SOLUTIONS INC p 1644
11460 N Meridian St Ste X 46032
Tel (317) 848-2815 SIC 7389

CHESTERTON, IN

ADS LOGISTICS CO LLC p 24
116 E 1100 N 46304
Tel (219) 836-3900 SIC 4731

URSCHEL LABORATORIES INC p 1530
1200 Cutting Edge Dr 46304
Tel (219) 464-4811 SIC 3556 7374

CHURUBUSCO, IN

C & A TOOL ENGINEERING INC p 231
4100 N Us 33 N 46723
Tel (260) 693-2167 SIC 3544 3545

CLINTON, IN

INFRASTRUCTURE AND ENERGY ALTERNATIVES LLC p 742
3900 White Ave 47842
Tel (708) 397-4200 SIC 8731 1731

CLOVERDALE, IN

WESLEYAN HOMES OF INDIANA INC p 1593
34 S Main St 46120
Tel (765) 795-4260 SIC 8051

COLUMBIA CITY, IN

80/20 INC p 4
1701 S 400 E 46725
Tel (260) 248-8030 SIC 3354

COUPLED PRODUCTS LLC p 383
2651 S 600 E 46725
Tel (260) 248-3200 SIC 3714

NORTHEASTERN REMC p 1055
4901 E Park Dr Fl 30 46725
Tel (260) 625-3700 SIC 4911

NORTHEASTERN RURAL ELECTRIC MEMBERSHIP CORP p 1055
4901 E Park 30 Dr 46725
Tel (260) 625-3700 SIC 4911

UNDERSEA SENSOR SYSTEMS INC p 1502
4868 E Park 30 Dr 46725
Tel (260) 244-3500 SIC 3812

COLUMBUS, IN

BARTHOLOMEW CONSOLIDATED SCHOOL FOUNDATION INC p 157
1200 Central Ave 47201
Tel (812) 376-4234 SIC 8399

COLUMBUS REGIONAL HOSPITAL p 342
2400 17th St 47201
Tel (812) 379-4441 SIC 8062

COLUMBUS REGIONAL HOSPITAL p 342
2400 17th St 47201
Tel (812) 379-4441 SIC 8062

COSCO INC p 373
2525 State St 47201
Tel (812) 372-0141 SIC 3944 2511 2514

COUCHE-TARD US INC p 374
4080 W Jnathan Moore Pike 47201
Tel (812) 379-9227 SIC 5411

▲ CUMMINS INC p 401
500 Jackson St 47201
Tel (812) 377-5000
SIC 3519 3714 3694 3621

DOREL JUVENILE GROUP INC p 451
2525 State St 47201
Tel (800) 457-5276
SIC 3089 3069 3429 3699 3648

DOREL USA INC p 451
2525 State St 47201
Tel (812) 372-0141 SIC 3944 2511 2514

ELWOOD STAFFING SERVICES INC p 490
4111 Central Ave 47203
Tel (812) 372-6200 SIC 7361

ENKEI AMERICA INC p 499
2900 Inwood Dr 47201
Tel (812) 373-7000 SIC 3714 3365

FAURECIA EMISSIONS CONTROL TECHNOLOGIES USA LLC p 531
950 W 450 S 47201
Tel (812) 341-2000 SIC 3714

IMPACT FORGE GROUP LLC p 734
2805 Norcross Dr 47201
Tel (812) 342-4437 SIC 3462 3463

MACS CONVENIENCE STORES LLC p 893
4080 W Jnathan Moore Pike 47201
Tel (812) 379-9227 SIC 5411

NTN DRIVESHAFT INC p 1065
8251 S International Dr 47201
Tel (812) 342-5414 SIC 3568

PREMIER AG CO-OP INC p 1170
785 S Marr Rd 47201
Tel (812) 379-9501
SIC 5153 5191 5172 5411 2429

TOYOTA INDUSTRIAL EQUIPMENT MFG INC p 1466
5555 Inwood Dr 47201
Tel (812) 342-0060 SIC 3537

TOYOTA INDUSTRIES NORTH AMERICA INC p 1466
3030 Barker Dr 47201
Tel (812) 341-3810 SIC 3585 5084

TOYOTA MATERIAL HANDLING USA INC p 1466
5559 Inwood Dr 47201
Tel (800) 381-5879 SIC 5084

CONNERSVILLE, IN

STANT CORP p 1377
1620 Columbia Ave 47331
Tel (765) 825-3121 SIC 3714

STANT MANUFACTURING INC p 1377
1620 Columbia Ave 47331
Tel (870) 247-5480 SIC 3491

STANT USA CORP p 1377
1620 Columbia Ave 47331
Tel (765) 825-3121 SIC 3714

VAPOR ACQUISITION CORP p 1544
1620 Columbia Ave 47331
Tel (765) 825-3121 SIC 3714

CRAWFORDSVILLE, IN

CERES SOLUTIONS LLP p 283
2112 Indianapolis Rd 47933
Tel (765) 362-6108 SIC 5191

HERITAGE PRODUCTS INC p 686
2000 Smith Ave 47933
Tel (765) 364-9002 SIC 3465

RAYTECH COMPOSITES INC p 1210
1204 Darlington Ave 47933
Tel (765) 362-3500 SIC 3714

CROTHERSVILLE, IN

■ MARMON RETAIL PRODUCTS INC p 909
1002 Industrial Way 47229
Tel (812) 793-2929 SIC 3357 3351

CROWN POINT, IN

FRANCISCAN COMMUNITIES INC p 573
203 W Franciscan Dr 46307
Tel (219) 661-5100 SIC 8059

■ ILLIANA DISPOSAL SERVICE INC p 732
865 Wheeler St 46307
Tel (219) 662-8600 SIC 4953

LAKE COUNTY OF INDIANA p 838
2293 N Main St 46307
Tel (219) 755-3465 SIC 9111

SAMC INC p 1274
1201 S Main St 46307
Tel (219) 738-2100 SIC 8062

CULVER, IN

CULVER EDUCATIONAL FOUNDATION p 400
1300 Academy Rd 46511
Tel (574) 842-8222 SIC 8699

DALE, IN

WINKLER INC p 1616
535 E Medcalf St 47523
Tel (812) 937-4421 SIC 5141 5411

DANVILLE, IN

HENDRICKS COUNTY HOSPITAL p 683
1000 E Main St 46122
Tel (317) 745-4451 SIC 8062 8051

HENDRICKS REGIONAL HEALTH GUILD INC p 683
1000 E Mn St 46122
Tel (317) 745-4451 SIC 8062

DECATUR, IN

AIP/FW FUNDING INC p 38
1031 E Us Highway 224 46733
Tel (212) 627-2360 SIC 3716

ALLIED RECREATION GROUP INC p 56
1031 E Us Highway 224 46733
Tel (260) 728-2121 SIC 3716

GOLDSHIELD FIBER GLASS INC p 622
2004 Patterson St 46733
Tel (260) 728-2476 SIC 2221

DELPHI, IN

INDIANA PACKERS CORP p 738
Hwy 421 S & Cr 100 N 46923
Tel (765) 564-3680 SIC 2011 2013

DUBOIS, IN

WABASH VALLEY PRODUCE INC p 1570
4886 E 450n 47527
Tel (812) 678-3131 SIC 5144 5191

DYER, IN

SAINT MARGARET MERCY HEALTHCARE CENTER p 1270
24 Joliet St 46311
Tel (219) 865-2141 SIC 8062 8063

EAST CHICAGO, IN

■ AMERISTAR EAST CHICAGO HOLDINGS LLC p 83
777 Ameristar Blvd 46312
Tel (219) 378-3000 SIC 7999

ARCELORMITTAL HOLDINGS LLC p 104
3210 Watling St 46312
Tel (219) 399-1200 SIC 3312 1011

ARCELORMITTAL MINORCA MINE INC p 104
3210 Watling St 46312
Tel (219) 399-1200 SIC 1011

INDIANA ARCELORMITTAL HARBOR LLC p 738
3210 Watling St 46312
Tel (219) 399-1200 SIC 3312

■ RIH ACQUISITIONS IN LLC p 1235
777 Resorts Blvd 46312
Tel (219) 378-3000 SIC 7999

SCHOOL CITY OF EAST CHICAGO p 1289
1401 E 144th St 46312
Tel (219) 391-4100 SIC 8211

ST CATHERINE HOSPITAL INC p 1365
4321 Fir St 46312
Tel (219) 392-1700 SIC 8062

TRADEBE GP p 1468
4343 Kennedy Ave 46312
Tel (800) 388-7242 SIC 4953 7699 1389

TRADEBE TREATMENT AND RECYCLING LLC p 1468
4343 Kennedy Ave 46312
Tel (219) 397-3951 SIC 4953

ELIZABETH, IN

■ CAESARS RIVERBOAT CASINO LLC p 237
11999 Casino Center Dr Se 47117
Tel (812) 969-6000 SIC 7011

ELKHART, IN

AACOA INC p 8
2551 County Road 10 W 46514
Tel (574) 262-4685 SIC 3471

ALL AMERICAN GROUP INC p 51
2831 Dexter Dr 46514
Tel (574) 262-0123
SIC 3716 3792 2452 3714 1521

AS HOLDINGS INC p 115
5120 Beck Dr 46516
Tel (574) 295-8384
SIC 5033 5169 5031 5162

ASA ELECTRONICS LLC p 115
2602 Marina Dr 46514
Tel (574) 264-3135 SIC 5099

ATWOOD MOBILE PRODUCTS INC p 130
1120 N Main St 46514
Tel (574) 264-2131 SIC 3714

ATWOOD MOBILE PRODUCTS LLC p 130
1120 N Main St 46514
Tel (574) 264-2131 SIC 3714

BRISTOL LASALLE CORP p 214
601 County Road 17 46516
Tel (574) 295-4400
SIC 5023 5021 5051 5033 3645 3089

CONN-SELMER INC p 356
600 Industrial Pkwy 46516
Tel (574) 522-1675 SIC 3931 5736

DEHCO INC p 422
3601 Charlotte Ave 46517
Tel (574) 294-2684
SIC 2891 5031 5074 5014 5084

DEXTER AXLE CO p 434
2900 Industrial Pkwy 46516
Tel (574) 295-7888 SIC 3714

DOMETIC CORP p 449
2320 Industrial Pkwy 46516
Tel (574) 294-2511 SIC 5561

▲ DREW INDUSTRIES INC p 455
3501 County Road 6 E 46514
Tel (574) 535-1125
SIC 3711 3714 3715 3442 3431

ELKHART COMMUNITY SCHOOLS p 488
2720 California Rd 46514
Tel (574) 262-5500 SIC 8211

ELKHART GENERAL HOSPITAL INC p 488
600 East Blvd 46514
Tel (574) 294-2621 SIC 8062

ELKHART PRODUCTS CORP p 488
1255 Oak St 46514
Tel (574) 264-3181 SIC 3498

■ FOREST RIVER INC p 567
900 County Road 1 N 46514
Tel (574) 389-4600 SIC 5561 3715

FURRION LLC p 585
2612 Glenview Dr 46514
Tel (888) 354-5792 SIC 3663

■ HEARTLAND RECREATIONAL VEHICLES LLC p 679
2831 Dexter Dr 46514
Tel (574) 266-8726 SIC 3799

■ HOMETTE CORP p 704
2520 Bypass Rd 46514
Tel (574) 294-6521 SIC 2452 3792

KEM KREST LLC p 809
3221 Magnum Dr 46516
Tel (574) 389-2650
SIC 5169 5013 5085 4783 4225

■ KINRO MANUFACTURING INC p 821
3501 County Road 6 E 46514
Tel (574) 535-1125 SIC 3442

■ LIPPERT COMPONENTS INC p 870
3501 County Road 6 E 46514
Tel (800) 551-9149
SIC 3711 3469 3444 3714

NIBCO INC p 1042
1516 Middlebury St 46516
Tel (574) 295-3000 SIC 3494 3491 3089

▲ PATRICK INDUSTRIES INC p 1120
107 W Franklin St 46516
Tel (574) 294-7511
SIC 3275 2493 2435 5031 5033 2891

PONTOON BOAT LLC p 1161
2805 Decio Dr 46514
Tel (574) 264-6336 SIC 3069

▲ SKYLINE CORP p 1330
2520 Bypass Rd 46514
Tel (574) 294-6521 SIC 2451 2452 3792

■ SKYLINE HOMES INC p 1330
2520 Bypass Rd 46514
Tel (574) 294-6521 SIC 2451 3792

STEINWAY PIANO CO INC p 1385
600 Industrial Pkwy 46516
Tel (574) 522-1675 SIC 3931

▲ THOR INDUSTRIES INC p 1450
601 E Beardsley Ave 46514
Tel (574) 970-7460 SIC 3799 3711

■ THOR MOTOR COACH INC p 1450
520 County Road 15 46516
Tel (574) 266-1111 SIC 3716 3792

TREDIT TIRE & WHEEL CO INC p 1475
3305 Charlotte Ave 46517
Tel (574) 293-0581 SIC 5014 5013

TRUCK ACCESSORIES GROUP LLC p 1485
28858 Ventura Dr 46517
Tel (574) 522-5337 SIC 3713

WELCH PACKAGING GROUP INC p 1588
1020 Herman St 46516
Tel (574) 295-2460 SIC 2657

ELWOOD, IN

ELSA CORP p 489
1240 S State Road 37 46036
Tel (765) 552-5200 SIC 3714

RED GOLD INC p 1215
1500 Tomato Country Way 46036
Tel (765) 557-5500 SIC 2033 2035

TRIPLE S TIRE CO INC p 1482
405 S 9th St 46036
Tel (765) 552-5765 SIC 5014 5531

EVANSVILLE, IN

ACCURIDE CORP p 16
7140 Office Cir 47715
Tel (812) 962-5000 SIC 3714 3713

AMERIQUAL GROUP LLC p 83
18200 Highway 41 N 47725
Tel (812) 867-1300 SIC 2099

ARMOR PARENT CORP p 111
7140 Office Cir 47715
Tel (812) 962-5000 SIC 6719

ATLAS WORLD GROUP INC p 128
1212 Saint George Rd 47711
Tel (812) 424-2222 SIC 4213 4731

■ AZTAR INDIANA GAMING CO LLC p 140
421 Nw Riverside Dr 47708
Tel (812) 433-4000 SIC 7011

■ BERRY PLASTICS CORP p 176
101 Oakley St 47710
Tel (812) 424-2904 SIC 3089 3081

▲ BERRY PLASTICS GROUP INC p 176
101 Oakley St 47710
Tel (812) 424-2904
SIC 3089 3085 2673 3081 3083

■ BPREX CLOSURES LLC p 206
101 Oakley St 47710
Tel (812) 424-2904 SIC 3089

BRAKE SUPPLY CO INC p 207
5501 Foundation Blvd 47725
Tel (812) 467-1000
SIC 5082 5084 5088 5013 3532

■ CAPTIVE PLASTICS INC p 252
101 Oakley St 47710
Tel (812) 424-2904 SIC 3089

CITY OF EVANSVILLE p 314
1 Nw Martin Luther 47708
Tel (812) 436-4994 SIC 9121

■ COVALENCE SPECIALTY ADHESIVES LLC p 383
101 Oakley St 47710
Tel (812) 424-2904 SIC 2891

■ COVALENCE SPECIALTY COATINGS LLC p 383
101 Oakley St 47710
Tel (812) 424-2904 SIC 2672

CRESLINE PLASTIC PIPE CO INC p 391
600 N Cross Pointe Blvd 47715
Tel (812) 428-9300 SIC 3084

D-PATRICK INC p 407
200 N Green River Rd 47715
Tel (812) 473-6500 SIC 5511

DEACONESS HEALTH SYSTEM INC p 419
600 Mary St 47710
Tel (812) 450-5000 SIC 8741

DEACONESS HOSPITAL INC p 419
600 Mary St 47710
Tel (812) 450-5000 SIC 8062

DSM ENGINEERING PLASTICS INC p 458
2267 W Mill Rd 47720
Tel (812) 435-7500 SIC 2821 3087 3083

▲ ESCALADE INC p 509
817 Maxwell Ave 47711
Tel (812) 467-4449 SIC 3949 3579

EVANSVILLE-VANDERBURGH SCHOOL DISTRICT p 513
951 Walnut St 47713
Tel (812) 435-8477 SIC 8211

FLANDERS ELECTRIC MOTOR SERVICE INC p 554
8101 Baumgart Rd 47725
Tel (812) 867-7421 SIC 7694 5063

■ INDIAN INDUSTRIES INC p 737
817 Maxwell Ave 47711
Tel (812) 467-1200 SIC 3949

■ INDIANA GAS CO INC p 738
20 Nw 4th St 47708
Tel (812) 491-4000 SIC 4924

INDUSTRIAL CONTRACTORS SKANSKA INC p 739
401 Nw 1st St 47708
Tel (812) 423-7832 SIC 1541 1542

KOCH AIR LLC p 825
1900 W Lloyd Expy 47712
Tel (812) 962-5200 SIC 5075

KOCH ENTERPRISES INC p 825
14 S 11th Ave 47712
Tel (812) 465-9800
SIC 3363 5075 3559 5084 2891 3069

KOCH HVAC DISTRIBUTION INC p 825
1900 W Lloyd Expy 47712
Tel (812) 962-5200 SIC 5075

LEWIS BROTHERS BAKERIES INC p 858
500 N Fulton Ave 47710
Tel (812) 425-4642 SIC 2051 5149

■ LUCENT POLYMERS INC p 884
1700 Lynch Rd 47711
Tel (812) 421-2216 SIC 5162

■ MATRIXX GROUP INC p 920
15000 Highway 41 N 47725
Tel (812) 421-3600 SIC 5162

■ MEAD JOHNSON & CO LLC p 933
2400 W Lloyd Expy 47712
Tel (812) 429-5000 SIC 2099 2834 2032

■ MERIT LIFE INSURANCE CO p 949
601 Nw 2nd St Unit 1 47708
Tel (812) 424-8031 SIC 6311

■ MOREQUITY INC p 988
7116 Eagle Crest Blvd 47715
Tel (800) 345-0187 SIC 6162

▲ OLD NATIONAL BANCORP p 1081
1 Main St 47708
Tel (812) 464-1294 SIC 6021

■ OLD NATIONAL BANK p 1081
1 Main St 47708
Tel (800) 731-2265 SIC 6021 6022

▲ ONE MAIN FINANCIAL SERVICES p 1086
601 Nw 2nd St 47708
Tel (800) 961-5577 SIC 6141 6351 6331

■ ONEMAIN HOLDINGS INC p 1087
601 Nw 2nd St 47708
Tel (812) 424-8031 SIC 6141

PEABODY BEAR RUN MINING LLC p 1125
7100 Eagle Crest Blvd 47715
Tel (812) 659-7126 SIC 1221

■ POLY-SEAL LLC p 1160
101 Oakley St 47710
Tel (812) 306-2573 SIC 3089

PROFESSIONAL TRANSPORTATION INC p 1180
3700 E Morgan Ave 47715
Tel (812) 471-2440 SIC 4011

■ Q-COMM CORP p 1194
3701 Communications Way 47715
Tel (812) 253-7000 SIC 4813 4812

RABEN TIRE CO LLC p 1203
2100 N New York Ave 47711
Tel (812) 465-5565 SIC 5531 5014

RED SPOT PAINT & VARNISH CO INC p 1216
1107 E Louisiana St 47711
Tel (812) 428-9100 SIC 2851

■ ROYAL CROWN BOTTLING CORP p 1254
1100 Independence Ave 47714
Tel (812) 424-7978 SIC 2086

SAINT MARYS RIVERSIDE p 1270
37 Washington Ave 47713
Tel (812) 485-8000 SIC 8062

▲ SHOE CARNIVAL INC p 1317
7500 E Columbia St 47715
Tel (812) 867-6471 SIC 5661

SKANSKA US CIVIL MIDWEST INC p 1329
401 Nw 1st St 47708
Tel (812) 423-7832 SIC 1611

■ SOUTHERN INDIANA GAS & ELECTRIC CO p 1349
1 Vectren Sq 47708
Tel (812) 424-6411 SIC 4911 4924 4932

■ SPRINGLEAF FINANCE CORP p 1361
601 Nw 2nd St 47708
Tel (812) 424-8031 SIC 6141

■ SPRINGLEAF FINANCE INC p 1361
601 Nw 2nd St 47708
Tel (812) 424-8031
SIC 6153 6351 6331 7389

■ SPRINGLEAF MORTGAGE LOAN TRUST 2012-2 p 1361
601 Nw 2nd St 47708
Tel (812) 424-8031 SIC 6733

SRG GLOBAL TRIM INC p 1363
601 N Congress Ave 47715
Tel (812) 473-6200 SIC 3089

ST MARYS HEALTH INC p 1371
3700 Washington Ave 47714
Tel (812) 485-4000 SIC 8062

ST MARYS HEALTH INC p 1371
3700 Washington Ave 47714
Tel (812) 485-7623 SIC 8062

STERLING BOILER AND MECHANICAL INC p 1387
1420 Kimber Ln 47715
Tel (812) 479-5447 SIC 1711 3443

TRANSPORTATION TECHNOLOGIES INDUSTRIES INC p 1473
7140 Office Cir 47715
Tel (812) 962-5000
SIC 2531 3714 3321 4741 3471

TRAYLOR BROS INC p 1475
835 N Congress Ave 47715
Tel (812) 477-1542 SIC 1622

TRI-STATE REFRACTORIES CORP p 1478
1127 E Virginia St 47711
Tel (812) 425-3466 SIC 1741 5085

UCI ACQUISITION HOLDINGS (NO 1) CORP p 1499
14601 Highway 41 N 47725
Tel (812) 867-4156 SIC 3714

UNIVERSITY OF SOUTHERN INDIANA p 1525
8600 University Blvd 47712
Tel (812) 464-8600 SIC 8221

VAN ATLAS LINES INC p 1542
1212 Saint George Rd 47711
Tel (812) 424-4326 SIC 4213 4731

▲ VECTREN CORP p 1546
1 Vectren Sq 47708
Tel (812) 491-4000
SIC 4924 4911 1241 1623 6531

■ VECTREN ENERGY MARKETING AND SERVICES INC p 1546
1 Vectren Sq 47708
Tel (812) 491-4000 SIC 8748 8711 8742

■ VECTREN ENERGY SERVICES INC p 1546
1 Vectren Sq 47708
Tel (812) 491-4000 SIC 4924

■ VECTREN UTILITY HOLDINGS INC p 1546
1 Vectren Sq 47708
Tel (812) 491-4000 SIC 4932 4911 4924

VIGO COAL OPERATING CO INC p 1556
250 N Cross Pointe Blvd 47715
Tel (812) 759-8446 SIC 1221 8748

FERDINAND, IN

BEST CHAIRS INC p 177
1 Best Dr 47532
Tel (812) 367-1761 SIC 2512

FISHERS, IN

■ HEARTHMARK LLC p 678
9999 E 121st St 46037
Tel (765) 557-3000 SIC 3221

MAINSCAPE INC p 898
13418 Britton Park Rd 46038
Tel (317) 577-3155 SIC 0781

MEYER & NAJEM CONSTRUCTION LLC p 957
11787 Lantern Rd Ste 100 46038
Tel (317) 577-0007 SIC 1542

MEYER & NAJEM INC p 957
11787 Lantern Rd Ste 100 46038
Tel (317) 577-0007 SIC 1542

NATIONAL CATASTROPHE ADJUSTERS INC p 1010
9725 Windermere Blvd 46037
Tel (317) 915-8888 SIC 6411

STRATOSPHERE QUALITY LLC p 1393
12024 Exit 5 Pkwy 46037
Tel (317) 578-1455 SIC 7389

FLOYDS KNOBS, IN

NETSHAPE TECHNOLOGIES INC p 1027
3620 Paoli Pike Ste 8 47119
Tel (812) 248-9273 SIC 3339

NST HOLDINGS GROUP INC p 1065
3620 Paoli Pike Ste 8 47119
Tel (812) 248-9273 SIC 6289

FORT WAYNE, IN

ALLIED DOMESTIC FORWARDING LLC p 56
5001 Us Highway 30 W 46818
Tel (260) 429-2511 SIC 4212

ALPHA RAE PERSONNEL INC p 60
347 W Berry St Ste 700 46802
Tel (260) 426-8227 SIC 8742

ANTHONY WAYNE REHABILITATION CENTER FOR HANDICAPPED AND BLIND INC p 94
8515 Bluffton Rd 46809
Tel (260) 744-6145
SIC 8331 7331 3441 3412 2449 2448

ASH BROKERAGE CORP p 116
888 S Harrison St 46802
Tel (260) 459-0823 SIC 6411

AW HOLDINGS LLC p 139
8515 Bluffton Rd 46809
Tel (260) 744-6145 SIC 8331

BRC RUBBER & PLASTICS INC p 209
1029a W State Blvd 46808
Tel (260) 693-2171 SIC 3061 3714 3053

BROOKS CONSTRUCTION CO INC p 218
6525 Ardmore Ave 46809
Tel (260) 478-1990 SIC 1611

BROTHERHOOD MUTUAL INSURANCE CO p 219
6400 Brotherhood Way 46825
Tel (260) 482-8668 SIC 6331

BUCHANAN HAULING & RIGGING INC p 222
4625 Industrial Rd 46825
Tel (260) 471-1877 SIC 4212

BUCHANAN LOGISTICS INC p 222
4625 Industrial Rd 46825
Tel (260) 471-1877 SIC 4731

CADILLAC COFFEE CO p 236
7221 Innovation Blvd 46818
Tel (248) 545-2266 SIC 5149 7389

■ CHINA FW INC p 301
1300 S Clinton St 46802
Tel (260) 455-2000 SIC 6311

CITY OF FORT WAYNE p 314
200 E Berry St 46802
Tel (260) 427-1111 SIC 9111

COUNTY OF ALLEN p 376
Courthouse Rm 201 46802
Tel (260) 449-7245 SIC 9111

■ DANA LIGHT AXLE PRODUCTS LLC p 410
2100 W State Blvd 46808
Tel (260) 483-7174 SIC 3714

DIOCESE OF FORT WAYNE-SOUTH BEND INVESTMENT TRUST INC p 440
915 S Clinton St 46802
Tel (260) 422-4611 SIC 8661

DO IT BEST CORP p 446
6502 Nelson Rd 46803
Tel (260) 748-5300 SIC 5072 5031 5063

ESSEX GROUP INC p 510
1601 Wall St 46802
Tel (260) 461-4000 SIC 3357

■ FIRST PENN-PACIFIC LIFE INSURANCE CO p 548
1300 S Clinton St 46802
Tel (260) 455-6408 SIC 6411

FORT WAYNE COMMUNITY SCHOOLS p 569
1200 S Clinton St 46802
Tel (260) 467-2160 SIC 8211

FORT WAYNE METALS RESEARCH PRODUCTS CORP p 569
9609 Ardmore Ave 46809
Tel (260) 747-4154 SIC 3315

■ FORT WAYNE POOLS p 569
6930 Gettysburg Pike 46804
Tel (260) 459-4100 SIC 5091 3949

▲ FRANKLIN ELECTRIC CO INC p 575
9255 Coverdale Rd 46809
Tel (260) 824-2900 SIC 3621 3561

GLADIEUX TRADING AND MARKETING CO LP p 614
4133 New Haven Ave 46803
Tel (260) 423-4477 SIC 5171

HERITAGE FOOD SERVICE GROUP INC p 686
5130 Executive Blvd 46808
Tel (260) 482-1444 SIC 5087

HOLSUM OF FORT WAYNE INC p 702
136 Murray St 46803
Tel (260) 456-2130 SIC 2051

INDIANA INSTITUTE OF TECHNOLOGY INC p 738
1600 E Washington Blvd 46803
Tel (260) 422-5561 SIC 8221

INTERSTATE WAREHOUSING OF VIRGINIA LLC p 758
9009 Coldwater Rd Ste 300 46825
Tel (260) 490-3000 SIC 4222

IOM HEALTH SYSTEM LP p 762
7950 W Jefferson Blvd 46804
Tel (260) 435-7001 SIC 8062

LASSUS BROS OIL INC p 846
1800 Magnavox Way 46804
Tel (260) 436-1415 SIC 5541 5411

■ LINCOLN FINANCIAL ADVISORS CORP p 867
1300 S Clinton St 46802
Tel (800) 237-3813
SIC 6311 6282 8748 8742

■ LINCOLN NATIONAL INVESTMENT COMPANIES INC p 867
200 E Berry St 46802
Tel (260) 455-2000 SIC 6282 6722

■ LINCOLN NATIONAL LIFE INSURANCE CO p 867
1300 S Clinton St 46802
Tel (260) 455-2000 SIC 6411

■ LINCOLN NATIONAL RISK MANAGEMENT INC p 867
1670 Magnavox Way 46804
Tel (260) 455-2000 SIC 6411

■ LUTHERAN HEALTH NETWORK OF INDIANA LLC p 886
2123 Lincolnway Ct 46819
Tel (260) 479-3550 SIC 6719

■ LUTHERAN HOSPITAL OF INDIANA LP p 886
7950 W Jefferson Blvd 46804
Tel (260) 479-3434 SIC 8062

■ MEDICAL PROTECTIVE CO p 937
5814 Reed Rd 46835
Tel (260) 485-9622 SIC 6351 6411

■ MEDPRO GROUP INC p 938
5814 Reed Rd 46835
Tel (800) 463-3776 SIC 6351

MULLINIX PACKAGES INC p 999
3511 Engle Rd 46809
Tel (260) 747-3149 SIC 3089

■ NEWS PUBLISHING CO INC p 1039
600 W Main St 46802
Tel (260) 461-8444 SIC 2711

NORTH AMERICAN VAN LINES INC p 1050
5001 Us Highway 30 W 46818
Tel (260) 429-1682
SIC 4213 4731 4214 6331 7389 4212

ODANIEL AUTOMOTIVE INC p 1074
5611 Illinois Rd 46804
Tel (260) 435-5300 SIC 5511

■ OMNISOURCE CORP p 1085
7575 W Jefferson Blvd 46804
Tel (260) 422-5541 SIC 5093 3462 3399

PARKVIEW FOUNDATION INC p 1117
2200 Randallia Dr 46805
Tel (260) 373-4000 SIC 8062

PARKVIEW HEALTH SYSTEM INC p 1117
10501 Corporate Dr 46845
Tel (260) 484-6636 SIC 8741 8062

PARKVIEW HOSPITAL INC p 1117
10501 Corporate Dr 46845
Tel (260) 373-4000 SIC 8062

PERFECTION BAKERIES INC p 1135
350 Pearl St 46802
Tel (260) 424-8245 SIC 2051

PETROLEUM TRADERS CORP p 1139
7120 Pointe Inverness Way 46804
Tel (260) 432-6622 SIC 5172

PHYSICIANS HEALTH PLAN OF NORTHERN INDIANA INC p 1145
8101 W Jefferson Blvd 46804
Tel (260) 432-6690 SIC 6321 8011 6411

PRECISION SOYA LLC p 1169
6501 Constitution Dr 46804
Tel (260) 459-9353 SIC 0723

REA MAGNET WIRE CO INC p 1213
3600 E Pontiac St 46803
Tel (260) 421-7321 SIC 3357

RENAISSANCE HEALTH CARE CORP p 1223
6050 S 800 E-92 46814
Tel (260) 625-3545 SIC 8052 8051

RIVERSIDE MFG LLC p 1238
14510 Lima Rd 46818
Tel (260) 637-4470 SIC 3714

■ SHAMBAUGH & SON LP p 1311
7614 Opportunity Dr 46825
Tel (260) 487-7777
SIC 1711 1799 1731 1796 1629

SHAMBAUGH & SON LP p 1311
7614 Opportunity Dr 46825
Tel (260) 487-7814 SIC 8711 3556 5122

SMITH ACADEMY FOR EXCELLENCE INC p 1333
2625 Belvedere Dr Ste 108 46802
Tel (260) 749-5832 SIC 8211

■ ST JOSEPH HEALTH SYSTEM LLC p 1368
700 Broadway 46802
Tel (260) 425-3000 SIC 8099

STAR FINANCIAL GROUP INC p 1378
127 W Berry St Fl 2 46802
Tel (260) 467-5500 SIC 6712

▲ STEEL DYNAMICS INC p 1384
7575 W Jefferson Blvd 46804
Tel (260) 969-3500 SIC 3312 3316 7389

SWEETWATER SOUND INC p 1412
5501 Us Highway 30 W 46818
Tel (260) 432-8176 SIC 7389 5736 5999

TIPPMANN CONSTRUCTION LLC p 1455
9009 Coldwater Rd Ste 300 46825
Tel (260) 490-3000 SIC 1541 1796

TIPPMANN PROPERTIES INC p 1455
9009 Coldwater Rd Ste 300 46825
Tel (260) 490-3000 SIC 8741

■ TRANSWORKS OF INDIANA INC p 1473
9910 Dupont Circle Dr E 46825
Tel (260) 487-4400 SIC 4011

TRELLEBORG SEALING SOLUTIONS US INC p 1476
2531 Bremer Rd 46803
Tel (260) 749-9631 SIC 3089

VERA BRADLEY INC p 1549
3715 Courtwood Dr 46815
Tel (260) 482-3250 SIC 3171

WAGNER-MEINERT LLC p 1571
7617 Freedom Way 46818
Tel (260) 489-7555 SIC 5078 1711 1799

WATERFURNACE RENEWABLE ENERGY INC p 1582
9000 Conservation Way 46809
Tel (260) 478-5667 SIC 4961

WEIGAND CONSTRUCTION CO INC p 1587
7808 Honeywell Dr 46825
Tel (260) 413-6349 SIC 1542

WIRE AMERICA INC p 1618
1613 E Wallace St 46803
Tel (260) 969-1700 SIC 4226 3357

FRANKLIN, IN

KYB AMERICAS CORP p 833
2625 N Morton St 46131
Tel (317) 736-7774 SIC 3714 8711

SHIPSTON ALUMINUM TECHNOLOGIES INTERNATIONAL LLC p 1317
1450 Commerce Pkwy 46131
Tel (317) 738-0282 *SIC* 3365

FRENCH LICK, IN

FRENCH LICK SPRINGS RESORT INC p 578
8670 W State Road 56 47432
Tel (888) 936-9360 *SIC* 7011

GARRETT, IN

CENTURION INDUSTRIES INC p 281
1107 N Taylor Rd 46738
Tel (260) 357-6665 *SIC* 3444 1796

GROUP DEKKO HOLDINGS INC p 641
2505 Dekko Dr 46738
Tel (260) 347-0700 *SIC* 3496

■ GROUP DEKKO INC p 641
2505 Dekko Dr 46738
Tel (260) 357-3621
SIC 3479 3469 3643 3315 3089

GARY, IN

BUFFINGTON HARBOR RIVERBOAT LLC p 224
21 Buffington Harbor Dr 46406
Tel (219) 977-9999 *SIC* 5812 7993

CITY OF GARY p 315
401 Broadway Ste 100 46402
Tel (219) 881-1301 *SIC* 9121

CONSOLIDATED FABRICATION AND CONSTRUCTORS INC p 359
3851 Ellsworth St 46408
Tel (219) 884-6150 *SIC* 1623

CROWN CORR INC p 395
7100 W 21st Ave 46406
Tel (219) 944-7537 *SIC* 1542 1761

GARY COMMUNITY SCHOOLS CORP p 593
1988 Polk St 46407
Tel (219) 886-6400 *SIC* 8211

INDIANA SUGARS INC p 738
911 Virginia St 46402
Tel (219) 886-9151 *SIC* 5149

MAJESTIC HOLDCO LLC p 898
1 Buffington Harbor Dr 46406
Tel (702) 388-2400 *SIC* 7011

METHODIST HOSPITALS INC p 954
600 Grant St 46402
Tel (219) 886-4000 *SIC* 8062

GOSHEN, IN

COMMODORE CORP p 345
1423 Lincolnway E 46526
Tel (574) 533-7100 *SIC* 2452

DELORO STELLITE HOLDINGS CORP p 425
1201 Eisenhower Dr N 46526
Tel (574) 534-2585 *SIC* 3479

■ DMI HOLDING CORP p 446
2164 Caragana Ct 46526
Tel (574) 534-1224 *SIC* 3792 5012

■ DUTCHMEN MANUFACTURING INC p 463
2164 Caragana Ct 46526
Tel (574) 537-0600 *SIC* 5511

EVERENCE ASSOCIATION INC p 514
1110 N Main St 46528
Tel (574) 533-9511 *SIC* 6321

GOSHEN COMMUNITY SCHOOLS p 626
613 E Purl St 46526
Tel (574) 533-8631 *SIC* 8211

GOSHEN HEALTH SYSTEM INC p 626
200 High Park Ave 46526
Tel (574) 533-2141 *SIC* 5912

GOSHEN HOSPITAL ASSOCIATION INC p 626
200 High Park Ave 46526
Tel (574) 533-2141 *SIC* 8062

■ H-C LIQUIDATING CORP p 651
1002 Eisenhower Dr N 46526
Tel (574) 535-9300 *SIC* 2434

■ KEYSTONE RV CO p 816
2642 Hackberry Dr 46526
Tel (574) 534-9430 *SIC* 3792

MOBILE CLIMATE CONTROL CORP p 980
17103 State Road 4 46528
Tel (574) 534-1516 *SIC* 5075 3714

RIETH-RILEY CONSTRUCTION CO INC p 1234
3626 Elkhart Rd 46526
Tel (574) 875-5183 *SIC* 1611 1771 1622

■ SUPREME CORP p 1408
2581 Kercher Rd 46528
Tel (574) 642-4888 *SIC* 3713 3792 3585

▲ SUPREME INDUSTRIES INC p 1408
2581 Kercher Rd 46528
Tel (574) 642-3070 *SIC* 3537 3713 3799

TF INTER-HOLDINGS INC p 1445
17141 State Road 4 46528
Tel (574) 533-0302 *SIC* 5147 4213 5144

TROYER FOODS INC p 1485
17141 State Road 4 46528
Tel (574) 533-0302
SIC 5147 5144 5141 5146

■ ZIEMAN MANUFACTURING CO INC p 1643
2703 College Ave 46528
Tel (574) 535-1125
SIC 3715 3441 2451 3799

GRANGER, IN

ITR CONCESSION CO LLC p 768
52551 Ash Rd 46530
Tel (574) 674-8836 *SIC* 1611

GREENCASTLE, IN

CHIYODA USA CORP p 301
2200 E State Road 240 46135
Tel (765) 653-2993 *SIC* 5013

DEPAUW UNIVERSITY p 430
313 S Locust St 46135
Tel (765) 658-4800 *SIC* 8221

HEARTLAND AUTOMOTIVE INC p 679
300 S Warren Dr 46135
Tel (765) 653-4263 *SIC* 3714

GREENFIELD, IN

BASTIAN AUTOMATION ENGINEERING LLC p 159
2155 Fields Blvd 46140
Tel (317) 467-2583 *SIC* 3579 7699

FLODRAULIC GROUP INC p 557
3539 N 700 W 46140
Tel (317) 890-3700 *SIC* 5084

GASAMERICA SERVICES INC p 593
2700 W Main St 46140
Tel (317) 468-2515 *SIC* 5541 5171

HANCOCK REGIONAL HOSPITAL p 657
801 N State St 46140
Tel (317) 462-5544 *SIC* 8062

INDIANA AUTOMOTIVE FASTENERS INC p 738
1300 Anderson Blvd 46140
Tel (317) 467-0100 *SIC* 3452 3714

IRVING MATERIALS INC p 765
8032 N State Road 9 46140
Tel (317) 326-3101
SIC 3273 3271 5032 2951

KEIHIN IPT MFG LLC p 808
400 W New Rd 46140
Tel (317) 462-3015 *SIC* 3714

NAHI LLC p 1006
3539 N 700 W 46140
Tel (317) 890-3700 *SIC* 5084

ONLINE TRANSPORT INC p 1088
6311 W Stoner Dr 46140
Tel (317) 894-6860 *SIC* 4213

■ PRECOAT METALS CORP p 1169
1950 E Main St 46140
Tel (317) 462-7761 *SIC* 3479

SPECTRA PREMIUM (USA) CORP p 1357
3052 N Distribution Way 46140
Tel (317) 891-1700 *SIC* 5013

GREENSBURG, IN

G E C O M CORP p 586
1025 Barachel Ln 47240
Tel (812) 663-2270 *SIC* 3714

HONDA MANUFACTURING OF INDIANA LLC p 704
2755 N Michigan Ave 47240
Tel (812) 222-6000 *SIC* 3711

■ MAINSOURCE BANK p 898
201 N Broadway St 47240
Tel (812) 663-4711 *SIC* 6035

▲ MAINSOURCE FINANCIAL GROUP INC p 898
2105 N State Road 3 Byp 47240
Tel (812) 663-0157 *SIC* 6022

VALEO ENGINE COOLING INC p 1539
1100 Barachel Ln 47240
Tel (812) 663-8541 *SIC* 3714

GREENWOOD, IN

ENDRESS + HAUSER FLOWTEC AG INC p 496
2330 Endress Pl 46143
Tel (317) 535-7138 *SIC* 3823

ENDRESS + HAUSER INC p 496
2350 Endress Pl 46143
Tel (317) 535-7138 *SIC* 8711

■ INDIANA-AMERICAN WATER CO INC p 739
555 E County Line Rd # 201 46143
Tel (800) 492-8373 *SIC* 4941

PHOENIX GROUP INC p 1145
164 S Park Blvd 46143
Tel (317) 884-3600 *SIC* 8742 6719

GRIFFITH, IN

BULKMATIC TRANSPORT CO INC p 225
2001 N Cline Ave 46319
Tel (219) 972-7630 *SIC* 4213 4731 4212

HAGERSTOWN, IN

AUTOCAR LLC p 134
551 S Washington St 47346
Tel (765) 489-5499 *SIC* 3713

HAMMOND, IN

AL WARREN OIL CO INC p 43
1646 Summer St 46320
Tel (773) 735-6900 *SIC* 5172 5541

CITY OF HAMMOND p 315
5925 Calumet Ave 46320
Tel (219) 853-6301 *SIC* 9111

HAMMOND PUBLIC SCHOOLS p 656
41 Williams St 46320
Tel (219) 933-2400 *SIC* 8211

■ HORSESHOE HAMMOND LLC p 708
777 Casino Center Dr 46320
Tel (866) 711-7463 *SIC* 7999 5947 5812

INDIANA HARBOR BELT RAILROAD CO p 738
2721 161st St 46323
Tel (219) 989-4703 *SIC* 4013 4011

K2 INDUSTRIAL SERVICES INC p 799
4527 Columbia Ave 2 46327
Tel (708) 928-4765 *SIC* 2842 1799

MORRISON CONSTRUCTION CO INC p 990
1834 Summer St 46320
Tel (219) 932-5036 *SIC* 1541

NIAGARA LASALLE CORP p 1042
1412 150th St 46327
Tel (219) 853-6000 *SIC* 3316

ST MARGARET MERCY HEALTHCARE CENTERS INC p 1370
5454 Hohman Ave 46320
Tel (219) 932-2300 *SIC* 8062 8052 8051

HIGHLAND, IN

FIRST BANCSHARES INC p 545
9701 Indpls Blvd 46322
Tel (219) 659-0043 *SIC* 6022

STRACK AND VAN TIL SUPER MARKET INC p 1392
9632 Cline Ave 46322
Tel (219) 924-6932 *SIC* 5411 8741 4226

HILLSBORO, IN

■ MERCHANTS AND FARMERS TELEPHONE CO p 944
125 W Main St 47949
Tel (765) 798-2145 *SIC* 4813

HOBART, IN

ITR NORTH AMERICA LLC p 768
6301 Northwind Pkwy 46342
Tel (219) 947-8230 *SIC* 5084

ST MARY MEDICAL CENTER INC p 1371
1500 S Lake Park Ave 46342
Tel (219) 942-0551 *SIC* 8062

HOWE, IN

EXO-S US LLC p 519
6505 N State Road 9 46746
Tel (260) 562-4100 *SIC* 3089

HUNTINGBURG, IN

FARBEST FOODS INC p 528
4689 S 400w 47542
Tel (812) 683-4200 *SIC* 2015

OFS BRANDS HOLDINGS INC p 1076
1204 E 6th St 47542
Tel (800) 521-5381
SIC 2521 2522 2511 2599

HUNTINGTON, IN

HUNTINGTON COUNTY COMMUNITY SCHOOL CORP p 720
2485 Waterworks Rd 46750
Tel (260) 356-8312 *SIC* 8211

■ UNITED TECHNOLOGIES ELECTRONIC CONTROLS INC p 1514
3650 W 200 N 46750
Tel (260) 359-3514 *SIC* 3822

INDIANAPOLIS, IN

ABC EMPLOYMENT HOLDINGS LLC p 10
6610 N Shadeland Ave 46220
Tel (866) 674-7678 *SIC* 7361

ACA SPARROW CORP p 13
2937 N Kenwood Ave Apt B 46208
Tel (317) 920-1374 *SIC* 6519

ACORN DISTRIBUTORS INC p 18
5820 Fortune Cir W 46241
Tel (317) 243-9234
SIC 5113 5087 5169 5046 5023

ADVANCED PHYSICAL THERAPY PC p 26
5949 W Raymond St 46241
Tel (317) 486-2186 *SIC* 8093

ADVANTAGE HEALTH SOLUTIONS INC p 26
9045 River Rd Ste 200 46240
Tel (317) 573-2700 *SIC* 6324

■ AEARO TECHNOLOGIES LLC p 28
5457 W 79th St 46268
Tel (317) 692-6666 *SIC* 3842 3851 3643

■ AGRIGENETICS INC p 36
9330 Zionsville Rd 46268
Tel (317) 337-3000 *SIC* 5191

▲ ALLISON TRANSMISSION HOLDINGS INC p 58
1 Allison Way 46222
Tel (317) 242-5000 *SIC* 3714

■ ALLISON TRANSMISSION INC p 58
1 Allison Way 46222
Tel (317) 242-5000 *SIC* 3714

AMERICAN ECONOMY INSURANCE CO INC p 71
500 N Meridian St 46204
Tel (317) 423-9920 *SIC* 6331

AMERICAN HEALTH NETWORK INC p 73
10689 N Pennsylvna St # 200 46280
Tel (317) 580-6309 *SIC* 8011

AMERICAN HEALTH NETWORK OF INDIANA INC p 73
10689 N Pennsylvna St # 200 46280
Tel (317) 580-6314 *SIC* 6324 8011

AMERICAN HEALTH NETWORK OF INDIANA LLC p 73
10689 N Pennsylvna St # 200 46280
Tel (317) 580-6309 *SIC* 8011

AMERICAN UNITED LIFE INSURANCE CO INC p 81
1 American Sq Ste 368 46282
Tel (317) 285-1877 *SIC* 6371 6311 6321

AMERICAN UNITED MUTUAL INSURANCE HOLDING CO p 81
1 American Sq 46282
Tel (317) 285-1877
SIC 6211 6311 6371 6351 6331

■ AMERITECH p 84
240 N Meridian St 46204
Tel (317) 265-2266 *SIC* 4813 8721

▲ ANGIES LIST INC p 91
1030 E Washington St 46202
Tel (888) 888-5478 *SIC* 7311

■ ANTHEM HOLDING CORP p 93
120 Monument Cir Ste 200 46204
Tel (317) 488-6000 *SIC* 6321

▲ ANTHEM INC p 93
120 Monument Cir Ste 200 46204
Tel (317) 488-6000 *SIC* 6324 6321

■ ANTHEM INSURANCE COMPANIES INC p 94
120 Monument Cir Ste 200 46204
Tel (317) 488-6000
SIC 6324 6411 6321 6331 6159 7371

■ ANTHEM SOUTHEAST INC p 94
120 Monument Cir Ste 200 46204
Tel (317) 488-6000 *SIC* 6411 6311 6321

APPLE AMERICAN INDIANA LLC p 98
6515 E 82nd St Ste 109 46250
Tel (317) 577-8334 *SIC* 5812 5813

APTEAN HOLDINGS INC p 101
450 E 96th St Ste 300 46240
Tel (317) 249-1700 *SIC* 7371 5045

ASPHALT MATERIALS INC p 118
5400 W 86th St 46268
Tel (317) 872-6010 *SIC* 2951 1442

■ ASSOCIATED GROUP INC p 120
120 Monument Cir Ste 200 46204
Tel (317) 488-6000 *SIC* 6324

ATA AIRLINES INC p 123
7337 W Washington St 46231
Tel (317) 898-3110 *SIC* 4581

AUCTION BROADCASTING CO LLC p 130
1919 S Post Rd 46239
Tel (317) 862-7325 *SIC* 5012

■ BALKAMP INC p 148
2601 S Holt Rd 46241
Tel (317) 244-7241 *SIC* 5013

BARNES & THORNBURG LLP p 156
11 S Meridian St Ste 1313 46204
Tel (317) 236-1313 *SIC* 8111

BASTIAN SOLUTIONS LLC p 159
10585 N Meridian St Fl 3 46290
Tel (317) 575-9992 *SIC* 8711

BELL AMERICAN GROUP LLC p 169
8930 Bash St Ste L 46256
Tel (317) 788-0374 *SIC* 5812

BELL INDUSTRIES INC p 170
4400 W 96th St 46268
Tel (866) 782-2355 *SIC* 7379 5734

BELL TECHLOGIX INC p 170
4400 W 96th St 46268
Tel (317) 333-7777 *SIC* 7379

BFS DIVERSIFIED PRODUCTS INC p 179
250 W 96th St Ste 150 46260
Tel (317) 575-7000 *SIC* 5031 5013 5169

BMWC GROUP INC p 194
1740 W Michigan St 46222
Tel (317) 267-0400 *SIC* 1629

BOWEN ENGINEERING CORP p 204
8802 N Meridian St Ste X 46260
Tel (219) 661-9770 *SIC* 1629 1623 1541

BUCHER AND CHRISTIAN CONSULTING INC p 222
9777 N College Ave 46280
Tel (317) 493-2000 *SIC* 7379

BUTLER UNIVERSITY p 230
4600 Sunset Ave 46208
Tel (317) 940-8000 *SIC* 8221

CAITO FOODS SERVICE INC p 237
3120 N Post Rd 46226
Tel (800) 652-8165 *SIC* 5148

■ CALUMET LUBRICANTS CO LIMITED PARTNERSHIP p 243
2780 Waterfront Pkwy Ste 200 E 46214
Tel (317) 328-5660 *SIC* 2992

■ CALUMET OPERATING LLC p 243
2780 Waterfront Pkwy 46214
Tel (317) 328-5660 *SIC* 2992

▲ CALUMET SPECIALTY PRODUCTS PARTNERS LP p 243
2780 Waterfront Pkwy Ste 200 E 46214
Tel (317) 328-5660 *SIC* 2911 2992

CARE GROUP LLC p 254
8333 Naab Rd Ste 340 46260
Tel (317) 338-5050 *SIC* 8011 8093

▲ CELADON GROUP INC p 273
9503 E 33rd St 46235
Tel (317) 972-7000 *SIC* 4212 4225

■ CELADON TRUCKING SERVICES INC p 273
9503 E 33rd St 46235
Tel (317) 972-7000 *SIC* 4213 4212

CENTAUR ACQUISITION LLC p 275
111 Monument Cir Ste 777 46204
Tel (317) 656-8787 *SIC* 7011 7948

CENTAUR HOLDINGS LLC p 275
111 Monument Cir 46204
Tel (317) 656-8787 *SIC* 6719

CENTAUR INC p 275
111 Monument Cir 46204
Tel (317) 656-8787 *SIC* 7948

CENTAUR LLC p 275
10 W Market St Ste 200 46204
Tel (317) 656-8787 *SIC* 7948

CENTRAL PRODUCTS LLC p 280
7750 Georgetown Rd 46268
Tel (317) 634-2550 *SIC* 5046 5021

CENTRAL SUPPLY CO INC p 280
8900 E 30th St 46219
Tel (317) 898-2411
SIC 5074 5063 5085 5719

■ CERULEAN COMPANIES INC p 284
120 Monument Cir Ste 200 46204
Tel (317) 488-6000 *SIC* 6321

CHAUTAUQUA AIRLINES INC p 292
8909 Purdue Rd Ste 300 46268
Tel (317) 484-6000 *SIC* 4512 4522

CITIZENS ENERGY GROUP p 311
2020 N Meridian St 46202
Tel (317) 924-3341 *SIC* 4925

CITIZENS ENERGY SERVICES CO LLC p 311
2020 N Meridian St 46202
Tel (317) 927-6110 *SIC* 4924

CITIZENS WATER p 311
2020 N Meridian St 46202
Tel (317) 631-1431 *SIC* 4941

CITY OF INDIANAPOLIS p 315
200 E Washington St # 2501 46204
Tel (317) 327-3601 *SIC* 9111

CLOSURE SYSTEMS INTERNATIONAL HOLDINGS INC p 327
7702 Woodland Dr Ste 200 46278
Tel (317) 876-0173 *SIC* 7389

CLOSURE SYSTEMS INTERNATIONAL INC p 327
7702 Woodland Dr Ste 200 46278
Tel (317) 390-5000 *SIC* 3334 3565

COMLUX AMERICA LLC p 344
2910 S High School Rd 46241
Tel (317) 472-7370 *SIC* 1799

COMMUNITY HEALTH NETWORK FOUNDATION INC p 348
7321 Shadeland Sta # 100 46256
Tel (317) 621-1282 *SIC* 7389

COMMUNITY HEALTH NETWORK INC p 348
1500 N Ritter Ave 46219
Tel (317) 355-1411 *SIC* 8062

COMMUNITY PHYSICIANS OF INDIANA INC p 350
7240 Shadeland Sta # 300 46256
Tel (317) 621-7455 *SIC* 8011

CORE BTS INC p 369
10201 N Illinois St # 240 46290
Tel (317) 566-6200 *SIC* 7373

COUNTRYMARK COOPERATIVE HOLDING CORP p 375
225 S East St Ste 144 46202
Tel (800) 808-3170
SIC 5172 2911 1382 1311 6719

COUNTY OF MARION p 379
200 E Washington St # 801 46204
Tel (317) 327-3001 *SIC* 9111

CRYSTAL FLASH PETROLEUM LLC p 396
5221 Ivy Tech Dr 46268
Tel (317) 879-2849 *SIC* 5541 5411 5171

■ CUMMINS CROSSPOINT LLC p 401
2601 Fortune Cir E 300c 46241
Tel (317) 243-7979
SIC 5084 7538 5063 3519

■ CUMMINS CROSSPOINT LLC p 401
2601 Fortune Cir E Ste 30 46241
Tel (317) 243-7979 *SIC* 5084 7538 3519

DEEM LLC p 421
6831 E 32nd St Ste 200 46226
Tel (317) 860-2990 *SIC* 1731 1711

DEFENDERS INC p 422
3750 Priority Way S Dr 46240
Tel (317) 810-4720 *SIC* 7382

■ DEFENSE FINANCE & ACCOUNTING SERVICE p 422
8899 E 56th St 46249
Tel (317) 212-0585 *SIC* 9311

DEFLECTO LLC p 422
7035 E 86th St 46250
Tel (317) 849-9555 *SIC* 3089

DEPARTMENT OF CHILD SERVICES p 429
302 W Washington St E306 46204
Tel (317) 234-5739 *SIC* 9611

■ DOW AGROSCIENCES LLC p 453
9330 Zionsville Rd 46268
Tel (317) 337-3000
SIC 2879 5191 0721 8731

DUKE REALTY CORP p 460
600 E 96th St Ste 100 46240
Tel (317) 808-6000 *SIC* 6798 1542

DUKE REALTY LIMITED PARTNERSHIP p 460
600 E 96th St Ste 100 46240
Tel (317) 808-6000 *SIC* 6798

EAGLE CARE p 467
6900 Gray Rd 46237
Tel (317) 788-2500 *SIC* 6512

EDUCATIONAL MANAGEMENT CORP p 479
550 E Washington St 46204
Tel (317) 264-5656 *SIC* 8221

▲ ELI LILLY AND CO p 486
Lilly Corporate Center 46285
Tel (317) 276-2000 *SIC* 2834

■ ELI LILLY INTERNATIONAL CORP p 487
893 S Delaware St 46225
Tel (317) 276-2000
SIC 8742 2834 8731 3841 2879

▲ EMMIS COMMUNICATIONS CORP p 493
40 Monument Cir Ste 700 46204
Tel (317) 266-0100 *SIC* 4832 2721

EQUIAN LLC p 506
5975 Castle Crk Pkwy 10 Ste 100 46250
Tel (800) 962-6831 *SIC* 6324

ERMCO INC p 508
1625 W Thompson Rd 46217
Tel (317) 780-2923 *SIC* 1731

ESKENAZI HEALTH CENTER INC p 509
720 Eskenazi Ave Fl 2 46202
Tel (317) 880-0000 *SIC* 8062 8093 8099

■ EXACTTARGET INC p 516
20 N Meridian St Ste 200 46204
Tel (317) 423-3928 *SIC* 7372

EXECUTIVE MANAGEMENT SERVICES OF INDIANA INC p 517
4177 N Ems Blvd 46250
Tel (317) 813-1490 *SIC* 7349

EXECUTIVE OFFICE OF STATE OF INDIANA p 517
200 W Washington St # 206 46204
Tel (317) 232-4567 *SIC* 9111

FAEGRE BAKER DANIELS LLP p 524
300 N Meridian St # 2700 46204
Tel (317) 237-0300 *SIC* 8111

FEDERAL HOME LOAN BANK OF INDIANAPOLIS p 534
8250 Wdfld Xing Blvd 46240
Tel (317) 465-0200 *SIC* 6111

■ FIFTH THIRD BANK INDIANA p 542
251 N Illinois St # 1000 46204
Tel (317) 383-2300 *SIC* 6022

▲ FINISH LINE INC p 543
3308 N Mitthoefer Rd 46235
Tel (317) 899-1022 *SIC* 5661 5699 5941

FINISHMASTER INC p 543
115 W Washington St Fl 7 46204
Tel (317) 237-3678 *SIC* 5013

FIRESTONE BUILDING PRODUCTS CO LLC p 544
250 W 96th St Ste 150 46260
Tel (317) 575-7000 *SIC* 5033

FIRESTONE INDUSTRIAL PRODUCTS CO LLC p 544
250 W 96th St Ste 150 46260
Tel (317) 818-8600
SIC 5531 3469 3714 3495

FLAHERTY & COLLINS CONSTRUCTION INC p 554
8900 Keystone Xing # 1200 46240
Tel (317) 816-9300 *SIC* 1542

GENE B GLICK CO INC p 598
8801 River Crossing Blvd # 200 46240
Tel (317) 469-0400 *SIC* 1522 6531 6513

GLAZERS DISTRIBUTORS OF INDIANA LLC p 614
5337 W 78th St 46268
Tel (317) 876-1188 *SIC* 5182

■ GOLDEN RULE FINANCIAL CORP p 621
7440 Woodland Dr 46278
Tel (317) 297-4123 *SIC* 6321 6311

■ GOLDEN RULE INSURANCE CO p 621
7440 Woodland Dr 46278
Tel (317) 297-4123 *SIC* 6321 6311

GOODWILL INDUSTRIES OF CENTRAL INDIANA INC p 624
1635 W Michigan St 46222
Tel (317) 564-4313
SIC 5932 4783 8331 4953

■ GREGG APPLIANCES INC p 639
4151 E 96th St 46240
Tel (317) 848-8710 *SIC* 5731 5722 5719

GSF USA INC p 643
2701 Fortune Cir E Ste D 46241
Tel (317) 262-4958 *SIC* 7349

GUGGENHEIM LIFE AND ANNUITY CO p 645
401 Penn Pkwy Ste 300 46280
Tel (317) 574-6213 *SIC* 6311

H P PRODUCTS CORP p 650
4220 Saguaro Trl 46268
Tel (317) 298-9957 *SIC* 5087

HALO LLC p 655
10585 N Meridian St Fl 3 46290
Tel (317) 575-9992 *SIC* 8711 3535

HARRIS & FORD LLC p 663
9307 E 56th St 46216
Tel (317) 591-0000 *SIC* 5169 5085

■ HAVERSTICK CONSULTING INC p 668
8770 Guion Rd Ste A 46268
Tel (317) 218-1700 *SIC* 7371 7373

HEALTH & HOSPITAL CORP OF MARION COUNTY p 674
3838 N Rural St Fl 8 46205
Tel (317) 221-2000 *SIC* 8062

HERFF JONES LLC p 685
4501 W 62nd St 46268
Tel (800) 837-4235 *SIC* 3911 2721 2741

HERITAGE ENVIRONMENTAL SERVICES INC p 686
7901 W Morris St 46231
Tel (317) 243-0811
SIC 5093 4213 8731 7389 1799 8711

HERITAGE ENVIRONMENTAL SERVICES LLC p 686
7901 W Morris St 46231
Tel (317) 243-0811
SIC 5093 4213 8731 7389 1799 8711

▲ HHGREGG INC p 689
4151 E 96th St 46240
Tel (317) 848-8710 *SIC* 5731 5722 5712

HIGHPOINT GLOBAL LLC p 692
300 N Meridian St Ste 190 46204
Tel (317) 576-4500 *SIC* 8742

HIRATA CORP OF AMERICA p 695
5625 Decatur Blvd 46241
Tel (317) 856-8600 *SIC* 3535 3537 8711

▲ HURCO COMPANIES INC p 721
1 Technology Way 46268
Tel (317) 293-5309 *SIC* 3823 7372

ICE MILLER LLP p 727
1 American Sq Ste 2900 46282
Tel (317) 236-2100 *SIC* 8111

IEA RENEWABLE ENERGY INC p 729
2647 Wtrfrnt Pw E Dr # 100 46214
Tel (765) 832-8526 *SIC* 8711 8748

IF&P FOODS INC p 730
4501 Massachusetts Ave 46218
Tel (317) 546-2425 *SIC* 5148

INDEPENDENT STATIONERS INC p 737
250 E 96th St Ste 510 46240
Tel (317) 845-9155 *SIC* 5021 5112

INDIANA ANNUAL UNITED METHODIST CHURCH p 738
301 Pennsylvania Pkwy 46280
Tel (317) 924-1321 *SIC* 8661

INDIANA DEPARTMENT OF NATURAL RESOURCES p 738
402 W Washington St W299 46204
Tel (317) 232-4020 *SIC* 9512

INDIANA DEPARTMENT OF TRANSPORTATION p 738
100 N Senate Ave Rm N758 46204
Tel (317) 232-3166 *SIC* 9621

INDIANA DEPT OF CORRECTION p 738
302 W Washington St E334 46204
Tel (317) 232-2430 *SIC* 9223

INDIANA DEPT OF WORKFORCE DEVELOPMENT p 738
10 N Senate Ave 46204
Tel (317) 233-5661 *SIC* 9111

INDIANA FAMILY AND SOCIAL SERVICES ADMINISTRATION p 738
402 W Washington St W461 46204
Tel (317) 233-4454 *SIC* 9441

INDIANA FARM BUREAU INC p 738
225 S East St 46202
Tel (317) 692-7851 *SIC* 6411

■ INDIANA NEWSPAPERS LLC p 738
130 S Meridian St 46225
Tel (317) 444-4000 *SIC* 2711 2752

INDIANA OFFICE OF ADJUTANT GENERAL p 738
2002 S Holt Rd 46241
Tel (317) 247-3559 *SIC* 9711

INDIANA ORTHOPAEDIC HOSPITAL LLC p 738
8450 Northwest Blvd 46278
Tel (317) 956-1000 *SIC* 8069

INDIANA POLICE STATE p 738
100 N Senate Ave Rm N340 46204
Tel (317) 232-8241 *SIC* 9221

INDIANA STATE DEPARTMENT OF HEALTH p 738
2 N Meridian St Ste 1 46204
Tel (317) 233-1325 *SIC* 9431

INDIANA UNIVERSITY HEALTH INC p 739
1701 Senate Blvd 46202
Tel (317) 962-2000 *SIC* 8062 6324

INDIANAPOLIS AIRPORT AUTHORITY p 739
7800 Col Weir Cook Dr # 100 46241
Tel (317) 487-9594 *SIC* 4581

■ INDIANAPOLIS POWER & LIGHT CO p 739
1 Monument Cir 46204
Tel (317) 261-8261 *SIC* 4911

INDIANAPOLIS PUBLIC SCHOOLS p 739
120 E Walnut St 46204
Tel (317) 226-4000 *SIC* 8211

INTERACTIVE INTELLIGENCE GROUP INC p 751
7601 Interactive Way 46278
Tel (317) 872-3000 *SIC* 7372

■ INTERACTIVE INTELLIGENCE INC p 751
7601 Interactive Way 46278
Tel (800) 267-1364 *SIC* 7372 7371

■ IPALCO ENTERPRISES INC p 763
1 Monument Cir 46204
Tel (317) 261-8261 *SIC* 4911

IVY TECH COMMUNITY COLLEGE OF INDIANA p 769
50 W Fall Creek Pkwy N Dr 46208
Tel (317) 921-4882 *SIC* 8221

JACKSON OIL & SOLVENTS INC p 774
1970 Kentucky Ave 46221
Tel (317) 481-2244
SIC 5172 5541 5983 5531

JUBILEE CENTER p 796
10330 N Meridian St 46290
Tel (317) 415-5300 *SIC* 8748

JUDICIARY COURTS OF STATE OF INDIANA p 796
200 W Washington St # 217 46204
Tel (317) 232-1930 *SIC* 9211

KEY BENEFIT ADMINISTRATORS INC p 814
8330 Allison Pointe Trl 46250
Tel (317) 284-7100 *SIC* 6371

KITE REALTY GROUP TRUST p 822
30 S Meridian St Ste 1100 46204
Tel (317) 577-5600 *SIC* 6798

KITTLES HOME FURNISHINGS CENTER INC p 822
8600 Allisonville Rd 46250
Tel (317) 849-5300 *SIC* 5712 5719

KOORSEN FIRE & SECURITY INC p 827
2719 N Arlington Ave 46218
Tel (317) 542-1800
SIC 5099 7389 5199 5063 1731

LACY DISTRIBUTION INC p 837
54 Monument Cir Ste 800 46204
Tel (317) 237-5400 *SIC* 5015

LDI LOGISTICS INC p 849
54 Monument Cir Ste 800 46204
Tel (317) 237-5400 *SIC* 4731

LDI LTD LLC p 849
54 Monument Cir Ste 800 46204
Tel (317) 237-5400 *SIC* 6719

LEE SUPPLY CORP p 852
6610 Guion Rd 46268
Tel (317) 290-2500
SIC 5074 5075 5064 5085 5031

■ LIDS CORP p 863
7555 Woodland Dr 46278
Tel (888) 564-4287 *SIC* 5699

LILY CARES FOUNDATION INC p 866
Lilly Corporate Center 46285
Tel (317) 277-9109 *SIC* 8699

LIQUID TRANSPORT CORP p 870
8470 Allison Pointe Blvd # 400 46250
Tel (317) 841-4200 *SIC* 4213

LONE STAR INDUSTRIES INC p 875
10401 N Meridian St # 400 46290
Tel (317) 706-3314 *SIC* 3241 3273

M D WISE INC p 889
1200 Madison Ave Ste 400 46225
Tel (317) 822-7300 *SIC* 8621

M S D WAYNE TOWNSHIP p 889
1220 S High School Rd 46241
Tel (317) 243-8251 *SIC* 9111

M-PLAN INC p 890
8802 N Meridian St # 100 46260
Tel (317) 963-9700 *SIC* 6324 6411

MACALLISTER MACHINERY CO INC p 891
7515 E 30th St 46219
Tel (317) 545-2151 *SIC* 5082 7699 5013

MAGNOLIA HEALTH SYSTEMS INC p 896
9480 Prority W Dr 46240
Tel (317) 818-1240 *SIC* 8099

MAHOMED SALES & WAREHOUSING LLC p 897
8258 Zionsville Rd 46268
Tel (317) 472-5800 *SIC* 4225 3714

■ MALL AT MONTGOMERYVILLE LP p 899
115 W Washington St 46204
Tel (215) 362-1600 *SIC* 6512

MARSH SUPERMARKETS CO LLC p 911
9800 Crosspoint Blvd 46256
Tel (317) 594-2406 *SIC* 5411

MARSH SUPERMARKETS HOLDING LLC p 911
9800 Crosspoint Blvd 46256
Tel (317) 594-2100 *SIC* 5411

MASCO BATH CORP p 915
8445 Keystone Xing # 100 46240
Tel (317) 254-5959 *SIC* 3088 3842

■ MASCO CORP OF INDIANA p 915
55 E 111th St 46280
Tel (317) 848-1812 *SIC* 3432

MATERIALS PROCESSING INC p 919
3500 Depauw Blvd 46268
Tel (317) 803-3010 *SIC* 6719

MAYS CHEMICAL CO INC p 924
5611 E 71st St 46220
Tel (317) 842-8722 *SIC* 5169 4731

MCFARLING FOODS INC p 928
333 W 14th St 46202
Tel (317) 687-6827
SIC 5147 5149 5144 5146

MCL INC p 930
2730 E 62nd St 46220
Tel (317) 257-5425 SIC 5812

MDWISE INC p 933
1200 Madison Ave Ste 400 46225
Tel (317) 630-2828 SIC 6324

MERIDIAN CITIZENS MUTUAL INSURANCE CO p 948
2955 N Meridian St 46208
Tel (317) 931-7000 SIC 6331

METHODIST HEALTH GROUP INC p 953
1701 Senate Blvd 46202
Tel (317) 962-2000 SIC 8062 6321

METHODIST HOSPITAL p 953
1900 N Capitol Ave Fl 3 46202
Tel (317) 962-2000 SIC 8062

METROPOLITAN SCHOOL DISTRICT OF LAWRENCE TOWNSHIP p 956
6501 Sunnyside Rd 46236
Tel (317) 423-8200 SIC 8211

METROPOLITAN SCHOOL DISTRICT OF WARREN TOWNSHIP p 956
975 N Post Rd 46219
Tel (317) 869-4300 SIC 8211

METROPOLITAN SCHOOL DISTRICT OF WAYNE TOWNSHIP p 956
1220 S High School Rd 46241
Tel (317) 988-8600 SIC 8211

METROPOLITAN SCHOOL DISTRICT WASHINGTON TOWNSHIP p 956
8550 Wdfld Xing Blvd 46240
Tel (317) 845-9400 SIC 8211

MICRO METL CORP p 961
3035 N Shadeland Ave # 300 46226
Tel (800) 662-4822 SIC 3444

MILESTONE CONTRACTORS LP p 969
5950 S Belmont Ave 46217
Tel (317) 788-6885 SIC 1611

■ MILLER PIPELINE LLC p 971
8850 Crawfordsville Rd 46234
Tel (317) 293-0278 SIC 1623

MONARCH BEVERAGE CO INC p 983
9347 Pendleton Pike 46236
Tel (317) 612-1310 SIC 5181 5182

■ MYCOGEN CORP p 1004
9330 Zionsville Rd 46268
Tel (317) 337-3000
SIC 5191 2879 0721 8731

■ MYCOGEN PLANT SCIENCE INC p 1004
9330 Zionsville Rd 46268
Tel (317) 337-3000 SIC 5191

NATIONAL COLLEGIATE ATHLETIC ASSOCIATION p 1011
700 W Washington St 46204
Tel (317) 917-6222 SIC 8699

■ NATIONAL GOVERNMENT SERVICES INC p 1012
8115 Knue Rd 46250
Tel (317) 841-4400 SIC 8099

NATIONAL WINE & SPIRITS INC p 1017
733 S West St 46225
Tel (317) 636-6092 SIC 5182

NEW CENTAUR LLC p 1029
10 W Market St Ste 2700 46204
Tel (317) 656-8787 SIC 8741

ONEAMERICA FINANCIAL PARTNERS INC p 1087
1 American Sq 46282
Tel (317) 285-1877 SIC 6371 6311 6321

ONEAMERICA RETIREMENT SERVICES LLC p 1087
1 American Sq 46282
Tel (317) 285-1877 SIC 6411

ONI RISK PARTNERS INC p 1088
600 E 96th St Ste 400 46240
Tel (317) 706-9500 SIC 6411

PALMER TRUCKS INC p 1109
2929 S Holt Rd 46241
Tel (317) 243-1668
SIC 5511 5531 7538 7513 5012

PEPPER CONSTRUCTION CO OF INDIANA LLC p 1133
1850 W 15th St 46202
Tel (317) 681-1000 SIC 1542 1541

PERRY TOWNSHIP SCHOOLS p 1137
6548 Orinoco Ave 46227
Tel (317) 789-3700 SIC 8211

PIAZZA PRODUCE INC p 1146
5941 W 82nd St 46278
Tel (317) 872-0101 SIC 5148

PIAZZA PRODUCE LLC p 1146
5941 W 82nd St 46278
Tel (317) 872-0101 SIC 5148

PINNACLE OIL HOLDINGS LLC p 1150
5009 W 81st St 46268
Tel (317) 875-9465 SIC 2992 5172 8742

■ PRAXAIR SURFACE TECHNOLOGIES INC p 1168
1500 Polco St 46222
Tel (317) 240-2500 SIC 3479 3548 3563

PROTRANS INTERNATIONAL INC p 1185
8311 N Perimeter Rd 46241
Tel (317) 240-4100 SIC 4731

RELIANT SERVICE LLC p 1222
8850 Crawfordsville Rd 46234
Tel (317) 295-6407 SIC 1623

RENAISSANCE CHARITABLE FOUNDATION INC p 1223
8910 Purdue Rd Ste 550 46268
Tel (317) 843-5400 SIC 8699

■ REPUBLIC AIRLINE INC p 1225
8909 Purdue Rd Ste 300 46268
Tel (317) 484-6000 SIC 4512

▲ REPUBLIC AIRWAYS HOLDINGS INC p 1225
8909 Purdue Rd Ste 300 46268
Tel (317) 484-6000 SIC 4512

■ ROCHE DIAGNOSTICS CORP p 1243
9115 Hague Rd 46256
Tel (800) 428-5076 SIC 2835

ROLLS-ROYCE CORP p 1247
450 S Meridian St 46225
Tel (317) 230-2000
SIC 3724 3443 3462 3731 3743 3732

ROMAN CATHOLIC ARCHDIOCESE OF INDIANAPOLIS INC p 1248
1400 N Meridian St 46202
Tel (317) 236-1400 SIC 8661 8211

SCHWARZ PARTNERS LP p 1291
3600 Woodview Trce # 300 46268
Tel (317) 290-1140 SIC 2679

■ SENSIENT FLAVORS LLC p 1304
5600 W Raymond St 46241
Tel (317) 243-3521 SIC 2087

SHIEL SEXTON CO INC p 1316
902 N Capitol Ave 46204
Tel (317) 423-6000 SIC 1542 1541

▲ SIMON PROPERTY GROUP INC p 1325
225 W Washington St 46204
Tel (317) 636-1600 SIC 6798 6512

■ SIMON PROPERTY GROUP LP p 1325
225 W Washington St 46204
Tel (317) 636-1600 SIC 6798 6512

SOLAR SOURCES INC p 1338
6755 Gray Rd 46237
Tel (317) 788-0084 SIC 1221

SPG-FCM VENTURES LLC p 1358
225 W Washington St 46204
Tel (317) 636-1600 SIC 6798

ST BARNABAS SCHOOL p 1365
8300 Rahke Rd 46217
Tel (317) 881-7422 SIC 8211

ST VINCENT HEALTH INC p 1373
10330 N Meridian St 46290
Tel (317) 338-2345 SIC 8011

ST VINCENT HEART CENTER OF INDIANA LLC p 1373
10580 N Meridian St 46290
Tel (317) 583-5000 SIC 8069

ST VINCENT HOSPITAL AND HEALTH CARE CENTER INC p 1373
2001 W 86th St Ste 200 46260
Tel (317) 338-7000 SIC 8062

STANDARD LIFE INSURANCE CO OF INDIANA p 1376
10689 N Pennsylvna St # 200 46280
Tel (317) 574-6201 SIC 6324

■ STANLEY SECURITY SOLUTIONS INC p 1377
9998 Crosspoint Blvd # 3 46256
Tel (317) 849-2255 SIC 3699

STATE LIFE INSURANCE CO p 1381
1 American Sq 46282
Tel (317) 285-2300 SIC 6311 6321

STATE OF INDIANA p 1381
200 W Washington St # 201 46204
Tel (317) 232-4567 SIC 9111

■ STEAK N SHAKE INC p 1384
36 S Pennsylvania St # 500 46204
Tel (317) 633-4100 SIC 5812 6794

STERLING FLUID SYSTEMS (USA) LLC p 1387
2005 Dr Mrtn Lthr Kng Jr 46202
Tel (317) 925-9661 SIC 3561

▲ STONEGATE MORTGAGE CORP p 1391
9190 Priority Way West Dr 46240
Tel (317) 663-5100 SIC 6162

SUPERIOR OIL CO INC p 1406
1402 N Capitol Ave # 100 46202
Tel (317) 781-4400 SIC 5169 5162

■ SYSCO INDIANAPOLIS LLC p 1417
4000 W 62nd St 46268
Tel (317) 291-2020 SIC 5149 5046 5411

TECHNICAL YOUTH LLC p 1431
8365 Keystone Xing # 104 46240
Tel (317) 475-0079 SIC 7379

TECHNIKS LLC p 1431
9930 E 56th St 46236
Tel (317) 803-8000 SIC 5084 5049

TRIMEDX INDIA LLC p 1480
5451 Lakeview Pkwy S Dr 46268
Tel (877) 874-6339 SIC 7699

TRUCK COUNTRY OF INDIANA INC p 1485
1851 W Thompson Rd 46217
Tel (317) 788-1533
SIC 5511 5531 7538 7539

TUBE PROCESSING CORP p 1490
604 E Legrande Ave 46203
Tel (317) 787-1321
SIC 3498 3356 3469 7692 3444 3728

UNITED FARM FAMILY LIFE INSURANCE CO p 1508
225 S East St Ste 144 46202
Tel (317) 692-7200 SIC 6311 6411

UNITED FARM FAMILY MUTUAL INSURANCE CO p 1508
225 S East St 46202
Tel (317) 692-7200 SIC 6331

UNIVERSITY OF INDIANAPOLIS p 1521
1400 E Hanna Ave 46227
Tel (317) 788-3368 SIC 8221

USIC LLC p 1535
9045 River Rd Ste 300 46240
Tel (317) 575-7800 SIC 1623 8713

USIC LOCATING SERVICES LLC p 1535
9045 River Rd Ste 300 46240
Tel (317) 816-2207 SIC 1623

VENTURE LOGISTICS LLC p 1548
1101 Harding Ct 46217
Tel (888) 561-4449 SIC 4231

VEOLIA WATER AMERICAS LLC p 1548
101 W Washington St # 1400 46204
Tel (317) 917-3700 SIC 4941 4952

VEOLIA WATER NORTH AMERICA OPERATING SERVICES LLC p 1548
101 W Washington St 46204
Tel (317) 917-3700 SIC 4941

VERSATILE PROCESSING GROUP INC p 1551
9820 Westpoint Dr Ste 300 46256
Tel (317) 577-8930 SIC 3341

VERTELLUS HEALTH & SPECIALTY PRODUCTS LLC p 1552
201 N Illinois St # 1800 46204
Tel (317) 247-8141 SIC 2865

VERTELLUS SPECIALTIES HOLDINGS CORP p 1552
201 N Illinois St # 1800 46204
Tel (317) 247-8141 SIC 2865 6719

VISIONARY ENTERPRISES INC p 1561
6626 E 75th St Ste 100 46250
Tel (317) 621-4000 SIC 6531 8742 8093

VITRAN EXPRESS INC p 1563
6500 E 30th St 46219
Tel (317) 803-6400 SIC 4213

VON DUPRIN LLC p 1565
2720 Tobey Dr 46219
Tel (317) 429-2866 SIC 3429

VSI LIQUIDATING INC p 1566
201 N Illinois St # 1800 46204
Tel (317) 247-8141 SIC 2865

WABASH VALLEY POWER ASSOCIATION INC p 1570
722 N High School Rd 46214
Tel (317) 481-2800 SIC 4911

WHEATON VAN LINES INC p 1604
8010 Castleton Rd 46250
Tel (317) 849-7900 SIC 4213 4731 4214

WILHELM CONSTRUCTION INC p 1609
3914 Prospect St 46203
Tel (317) 359-5411 SIC 1542 1541 1761

WOOD-MIZER HOLDINGS INC p 1622
8180 W 10th St 46214
Tel (317) 271-1542
SIC 3553 3524 3425 2431

WURTH/SERVICE SUPPLY INC p 1628
4935 W 86th St 46268
Tel (317) 704-1000 SIC 5072

■ ZEE MEDICAL INC p 1641
8021 Knue Rd Ste 100 46250
Tel (949) 252-9500 SIC 8748 8322

JASPER, IN

ARIENS SPECIALTY BRANDS LLC p 108
1919 Hospitality Dr 47546
Tel (800) 457-7444 SIC 5084

BUEHLER FOODS INC p 224
1100 W 12th Ave 47546
Tel (812) 482-1366 SIC 5411

■ GERMAN AMERICAN BANCORP p 608
711 Main St 47546
Tel (812) 482-1314 SIC 6022

▲ GERMAN AMERICAN BANCORP INC p 608
711 Main St 47546
Tel (812) 482-1314 SIC 6022

JASPER ENGINE & TRANSMISSION EXCHANGE INC p 778
815 Wernsing Rd 47546
Tel (812) 482-1041 SIC 5013

JASPER ENGINE & TRANSMISSION EXCHANGE INC p 778
815 Wernsing Rd 47546
Tel (812) 482-1041 SIC 5013

JASPER ENGINE & TRANSMISSION EXCHANGE INC (KY) p 778
815 Wernsing Rd 47546
Tel (812) 482-1041 SIC 5013 7537

JASPER ENGINE EXCHANGE INC p 778
815 Wernsing Rd 47546
Tel (812) 482-1041 SIC 3714 7538 6512

JASPER RUBBER PRODUCTS INC p 778
1010 1st Ave W 47546
Tel (812) 482-3242 SIC 3061

JASPER SEATING CO INC p 778
225 Clay St 47546
Tel (812) 482-3204 SIC 2521 2531 2522

■ KIMBALL ELECTRONICS GROUP LLC p 818
1205 Kimball Blvd 47546
Tel (812) 634-4000 SIC 3571

▲ KIMBALL ELECTRONICS INC p 818
1205 Kimball Blvd 47546
Tel (812) 634-4000 SIC 3672

■ KIMBALL ELECTRONICS MANUFACTURING INC p 818
1600 Royal St 47549
Tel (812) 482-1600 SIC 3679

■ KIMBALL ELECTRONICS TAMPA INC p 818
1205 Kimball Blvd 47546
Tel (812) 634-4000 SIC 3679 3672

■ KIMBALL FURNITURE GROUP LLC p 818
1600 Royal St 47549
Tel (812) 482-1600 SIC 2521 2522

▲ KIMBALL INTERNATIONAL INC p 818
1600 Royal St 47549
Tel (812) 482-1600
SIC 2511 2512 2521 2522 2517

■ KIMBALL OFFICE INC p 818
1600 Royal St 47549
Tel (812) 482-1600 SIC 2522

■ MASTERBRAND CABINETS INC p 918
1 Masterbrand Cabinets Dr 47546
Tel (812) 482-2527 SIC 2434

MEMORIAL HOSPITAL AND HEALTH CARE CENTER p 942
800 W 9th St 47546
Tel (812) 482-2345 SIC 8062

MEYER DISTRIBUTING INC p 957
560 E 25th St 47546
Tel (812) 482-5102 SIC 5013 5012

■ NATIONAL OFFICE FURNITURE INC p 1014
1610 Royal St 47549
Tel (812) 482-1600 SIC 5712

SERVUS p 1308
4201 Mannheim Rd Ste A 47546
Tel (812) 482-3212 SIC 5812

JEFFERSONVILLE, IN

ACBL RIVER OPERATIONS LLC p 14
1701 E Market St 47130
Tel (636) 530-2100 SIC 4449

■ ACCENT MARKETING SERVICES LLC p 14
4550 Town Center Blvd 47130
Tel (812) 941-1112 SIC 7331 7389 8748

ACL TRANSPORTATION SERVICES LLC p 17
1701 E Market St 47130
Tel (800) 899-7195 SIC 4449

AMERICAN BARGE LINE CO p 68
1701 E Market St 47130
Tel (812) 288-0100 SIC 4449 3731 4491

AMERICAN COMMERCIAL BARGE LINE p 70
1701 E Market St 47130
Tel (812) 288-0100 SIC 4449 3731 4491

AMERICAN COMMERCIAL LINES INC p 70
1701 E Market St 47130
Tel (812) 288-0100 SIC 4449 3731 4491

AMERICAN COMMERCIAL LINES INTERNATIONAL LLC p 70
1701 E Market St 47130
Tel (800) 899-7195 SIC 4449

■ CLARCOR AIR FILTRATION PRODUCTS INC p 321
100 River Ridge Cir 47130
Tel (502) 969-2304 SIC 3564

CLARK MEMORIAL HOSPITAL p 322
1220 Missouri Ave 47130
Tel (812) 282-6631 SIC 8062 8063

COMMERCIAL BARGE LINE CO p 345
1701 E Market St 47130
Tel (812) 288-0100 SIC 3731 4449 4491

GREATER CLARK COUNTY SCHOOLS p 635
2112 Utica Sellersburg Rd 47130
Tel (812) 283-0701 SIC 8211

IDEMITSU LUBRICANTS AMERICA CORP p 729
701 Port Rd 47130
Tel (812) 284-3300 SIC 2992

LOUISIANA DOCK CO LLC p 880
1701 Utica Pike 47130
Tel (812) 288-0100 SIC 7389

■ PUROLATOR PRODUCTS AIR FILTRATION CO p 1192
100 River Ridge Cir 47130
Tel (866) 925-2247 SIC 3564 3433

■ RHN CLARK MEMORIAL HOSPITAL LLC p 1231
1220 Missouri Ave 47130
Tel (812) 282-6631 SIC 8062 8063

SHOE SENSATION INC p 1317
253 America Pl 47130
Tel (812) 288-7659 SIC 5661

SOUTHERN INDIANA WASTE SYSTEMS LLC p 1349
6108 Sable Mill Ct 47130
Tel (502) 935-1130 SIC 5722

KENDALLVILLE, IN

COLWELL INC p 343
2605 Marion Dr 46755
Tel (260) 347-1981 SIC 2752

■ **COURIER KENDALLVILLE INC** p 383
2500 Marion Dr 46755
Tel (260) 347-3044 SIC 2732

DEKKO ACQUISITION PARENT INC p 423
6928 N 400 E 46755
Tel (260) 347-0700 SIC 3496

FLINT & WALLING INC p 557
95 N Oak St 46755
Tel (260) 347-1781 SIC 3561

KENTLAND, IN

CPX INC p 388
410 E Kent St 47951
Tel (219) 474-5280 SIC 3089 3694

KOKOMO, IN

FIRST NATIONAL BANK AND TRUST p 548
2206 W Sycamore St 46901
Tel (765) 868-3551 SIC 6021

▲ **HAYNES INTERNATIONAL INC** p 670
1020 W Park Ave 46901
Tel (765) 456-6000 SIC 3356

HOWARD COMMUNITY HOSPITAL p 713
3500 S Lafountain St 46902
Tel (765) 453-0702 SIC 8062 8063

IMAGING CENTER OF N CENTRAL INDIANA p 733
2201 W Boulevard 46902
Tel (765) 452-0808 SIC 8071

KOKOMO SCHOOL CORP p 826
1500 S Washington St 46902
Tel (765) 455-8000 SIC 8211

ST JOSEPH MEMORIAL HOSPITAL p 1368
1907 W Sycamore St 46901
Tel (765) 456-5433 SIC 8062

SYNDICATE SALES INC p 1415
2025 N Wabash Ave 46901
Tel (765) 457-7277 SIC 3089

LA PORTE, IN

AMERICAN LICORICE CO p 75
1900 Whirlpool Dr S 46350
Tel (510) 487-5500 SIC 2064

IUHLP LIQUIDATION INC p 769
1007 Lincolnway 46350
Tel (219) 326-1234 SIC 8062

■ **LA PORTE HOSPITAL CO LLC** p 835
1007 Lincolnway 46350
Tel (219) 326-1234 SIC 8062

LAPORTE HOSPITAL INC p 845
Tunnel 7 Lincoln Way 46350
Tel (219) 326-2305 SIC 8062

LAFAYETTE, IN

ARNETT PHYSICIAN GROUP PC p 112
2600 Greenbush St 47904
Tel (765) 448-8000 SIC 8011

FAIRFIELD MANUFACTURING CO INC p 525
2400 Sagamore Pkwy S 47905
Tel (765) 772-4000 SIC 3462 3714 5085

GEO SPECIALTY CHEMICALS INC p 605
401 S Earl Ave Ste 3 47904
Tel (765) 448-9412 SIC 2819

GREATER LAFAYETTE HEALTH SERVICES p 635
1501 Hartford St 47904
Tel (765) 423-6011 SIC 8062

GREATER LAFAYETTE HEALTH SERVICES INC p 635
1501 Hartford St 47904
Tel (765) 423-6011 SIC 8062

KIRBY RISK CORP p 821
1815 Sagamore Pkwy N 47904
Tel (765) 448-4567
SIC 5063 7694 3599 3679 3629

LAFAYETTE SCHOOL CORP p 838
2300 Cason St 47904
Tel (765) 771-6000 SIC 8211

OSCAR WINSKI CO INC p 1096
2407 N 9th Street Rd 47904
Tel (765) 742-1102 SIC 5051 5093

SUBARU OF INDIANA AUTOMOTIVE INC p 1395
5500 State Road 38 E 47905
Tel (765) 449-1111 SIC 3711

TIPPECANOE SCHOOL CORP p 1455
21 Elston Rd 47909
Tel (765) 474-2481 SIC 8211

VOESTALPINE ROTEC INC p 1564
3709 Us Highway 52 S 47905
Tel (765) 471-2808 SIC 5051

▲ **WABASH NATIONAL CORP** p 1570
1000 Sagamore Pkwy S 47905
Tel (765) 771-5310 SIC 3715 3714 5012

■ **WABASH NATIONAL TRAILER CENTERS INC** p 1570
1000 Sagamore Pkwy S 47905
Tel (765) 771-5300 SIC 5012 7539 5013

LAWRENCEBURG, IN

■ **INDIANA GAMING CO LP** p 738
777 Hollywood Blvd 47025
Tel (812) 539-8000 SIC 7011

LEBANON, IN

AURORA PARTS & ACCESSORIES LLC p 132
500 S Enterprise Blvd 46052
Tel (765) 483-5622 SIC 5013

SKJODT-BARRETT CONTRACT PACKAGING LLC p 1330
401 S Enterprise Blvd 46052
Tel (765) 482-6856 SIC 2099

WITHAM MEMORIAL HOSPITAL p 1619
2605 N Lebanon St 46052
Tel (765) 485-8000 SIC 8062

LEESBURG, IN

MAPLE LEAF INC p 903
101 E Church St 46538
Tel (574) 453-4455 SIC 0259 2015 5159

LIGONIER, IN

MILLENNIUM INDUSTRIES CORP p 970
925 N Main St 46767
Tel (260) 894-3163 SIC 3469

LOGANSPORT, IN

CAL-COMP USA (INDIANA) INC p 237
1 Technology Way 46947
Tel (574) 739-2929 SIC 3672

CARTER FUEL SYSTEMS LLC p 262
101 E Industrial Blvd 46947
Tel (800) 342-6125 SIC 3714 5989

SMALL PARTS INC p 1332
600 Humphrey St 46947
Tel (574) 753-6323 SIC 3443

LOOGOOTEE, IN

WHITE RIVER COOPERATIVE INC p 1606
416 Church St 47553
Tel (812) 295-4835 SIC 5191 5171

WHITE RIVER LLC p 1606
610 Church St 47553
Tel (812) 295-4835 SIC 5261 5984

LOWELL, IN

SACO INDUSTRIES INC p 1264
17151 Morse St 46356
Tel (219) 690-9900 SIC 2434

LYNNVILLE, IN

PEABODY MIDWEST MINING LLC p 1125
566 Dickeyville Rd 47619
Tel (812) 434-8500 SIC 1221 1222 1241

MADISON, IN

ARVIN SANGO INC p 114
2905 Wilson Ave 47250
Tel (812) 265-2888 SIC 3714

BETHANY CIRCLE OF KINGS DAUGHTERS OF MADISON INDIANA INC p 178
1373 E Sr 62 47250
Tel (812) 801-0800 SIC 8062 8011 8082

GROTE INDUSTRIES INC p 641
2600 Lanier Dr 47250
Tel (812) 273-2121 SIC 3231 3647

GROTE INDUSTRIES LLC p 641
2600 Lanier Dr 47250
Tel (812) 265-8273 SIC 3647 3231

MADISON PRECISION PRODUCTS INC p 894
94 E 400 N 47250
Tel (812) 273-4702 SIC 3363 3365

■ **VEHICLE SERVICE GROUP LLC** p 1547
2700 Lanier Dr 47250
Tel (800) 640-5438 SIC 3711

MARION, IN

HARTSON-KENNEDY CABINET TOP CO INC p 666
522 W 22nd St 46953
Tel (765) 673-0451 SIC 3083

INDIANA WESLEYAN UNIVERSITY p 739
4201 S Washington St 46953
Tel (765) 674-6901 SIC 8221

MARION COMMUNITY SCHOOLS p 907
750 W 26th St 46953
Tel (765) 662-2546 SIC 8211

MARION GENERAL HOSPITAL INC p 907
441 N Wabash Ave 46952
Tel (765) 660-6000 SIC 8062

TLC MANAGEMENT INC p 1457
1800 N Wabash Rd Ste 300 46952
Tel (765) 671-2282 SIC 8741

WORK RIGHT OCCUPATIONAL HEALTH p 1624
330 N Wabash Ave Ste 470 46952
Tel (765) 662-4198 SIC 8011

MARKLE, IN

NOVAE CORP p 1062
1 Novae Pkwy 46770
Tel (260) 758-9800 SIC 5084 3524

MARTINSVILLE, IN

DAN ENNIS FARMS INC p 410
6910 Egbert Rd 46151
Tel (765) 342-2711 SIC 0191

■ **DANIEL INDUSTRIES INC** p 411
8460 Valley View Dr 46151
Tel (317) 442-5294 SIC 1522

MEDORA, IN

MITCHELL & STARK CONSTRUCTION CO INC p 976
170 W 1st St 47260
Tel (812) 966-2151 SIC 1623 1629

MENTONE, IN

MIDWEST POULTRY SERVICES LP p 967
9951 W State Road 25 46539
Tel (574) 353-7232 SIC 0751 2015

MERRILLVILLE, IN

CELEBRATION STATION PROPERTIES INC p 273
1000 E 80th Pl Ste 420n 46410
Tel (219) 757-3500 SIC 7999

DIRECTBUY INC p 441
8450 Broadway 46410
Tel (219) 736-1100
SIC 5021 5064 5023 5961 6794 7299

■ **NISOURCE CORPORATE SERVICES CO** p 1044
801 E 86th Ave 46410
Tel (219) 647-4222 SIC 8741

▲ **NISOURCE INC** p 1044
801 E 86th Ave 46410
Tel (877) 647-5990 SIC 4939 4922

■ **NORTHERN INDIANA PUBLIC SERVICE CO** p 1056
801 E 86th Ave 46410
Tel (877) 647-5990 SIC 4924 4911

TRADEBE ENVIRONMENTAL SERVICES LLC p 1468
1433 E 83rd Ave Ste 200 46410
Tel (800) 388-7242 SIC 4953 7699 1389

WHITE LODGING SERVICES CORP p 1606
701 E 83rd Ave Ste 17 46410
Tel (219) 472-2900 SIC 8741 6552

WHITECO INDUSTRIES INC p 1606
1000 E 80th Pl Ste 700n 46410
Tel (219) 769-6601
SIC 7312 7011 7922 6552 7374 3993

MICHIGAN CITY, IN

DWYER INSTRUMENTS INC p 464
102 Indiana Highway 212 46360
Tel (219) 879-8868
SIC 3823 3824 3822 3829 3491 3625

▲ **HORIZON BANCORP** p 707
515 Franklin St 46360
Tel (219) 879-0211 SIC 6021

■ **HORIZON BANK NATIONAL ASSOCIATION** p 707
515 Franklin St 46360
Tel (219) 873-2640 SIC 6021

MICHIGAN CITY AREA SCHOOLS p 960
408 S Carroll Ave 46360
Tel (219) 873-2000 SIC 8211

■ **PALL FILTER SPECIALISTS INC** p 1108
100 Anchor Rd 46360
Tel (219) 879-3307 SIC 3569

SAINT ANTHONY MEMORIAL HEALTH CENTERS p 1268
301 W Homer St 46360
Tel (219) 877-1710 SIC 8093

SULLAIR LLC p 1397
3700 E Michigan Blvd 46360
Tel (219) 879-5451 SIC 3569 3563

TONN AND BLANK CONSTRUCTION LLC p 1460
1623 Greenwood Ave 46360
Tel (219) 879-7321 SIC 1542

MIDDLEBURY, IN

HALLMARK BUILDERS INC p 654
520 S Main St 46540
Tel (574) 825-9850 SIC 1521

■ **JAYCO INC** p 779
903 S Main St 46540
Tel (574) 825-5861 SIC 5013 3716 3792

MILFORD, IN

■ **CTB INC** p 399
410 N Higbee St 46542
Tel (574) 658-4191 SIC 3443 3523

MAPLE LEAF FARMS INC p 903
9166 N 200 E 46542
Tel (574) 453-4500 SIC 0259 2015

MISHAWAKA, IN

BRAVOGRAND INC p 209
4220 Edison Lakes Pkwy # 300 46545
Tel (574) 271-4600 SIC 5812

FRANCISCAN ALLIANCE INC p 573
1515 W Dragoon Trl 46544
Tel (574) 256-3935 SIC 8062 8051

GRAYLING CORP p 632
4220 Edison Lkes Pkwy 100 46545
Tel (856) 384-1212 SIC 5812 5813 6531

NYLONCRAFT INC p 1069
616 W Mckinley Ave 46545
Tel (574) 256-1521 SIC 3089

QUALITY DINING INC p 1197
4220 Edison Lakes Pkwy # 300 46545
Tel (574) 271-4600 SIC 5812 6794

SAINT JOSEPH MEDICAL CENTER INC p 1269
5215 Holy Cross Pkwy 46545
Tel (574) 335-5000 SIC 8062

SAINT JOSEPH REGIONAL MEDICAL CENTER-SOUTH BEND CAMPUS INC p 1269
5215 Holy Cross Pkwy 46545
Tel (574) 335-5000 SIC 8011

■ **SCHURZ COMMUNICATIONS INC** p 1291
1301 E Douglas Rd 46545
Tel (574) 247-7237 SIC 4833 2711

MONON, IN

CIMC USA INC p 307
289 Water Tower Dr 47959
Tel (219) 253-2054 SIC 1541

VANGUARD NATIONAL TRAILER CORP p 1543
289 Water Tower Dr 47959
Tel (219) 253-2000 SIC 3715 3713

MONTICELLO, IN

JORDAN MANUFACTURING CO INC p 793
1200 S 6th St 47960
Tel (574) 583-6008 SIC 2392 5021

MARIAN INC p 906
2787 S Freeman Rd 47960
Tel (574) 583-3464 SIC 3699

MOORESVILLE, IN

TOA (USA) LLC p 1458
2000 Pleiades Dr 46158
Tel (317) 834-0522 SIC 3714

MOUNT VERNON, IN

POSEY COUNTY FARM BUREAU COOPERATIVE ASSOCIATION INC p 1163
817 W 4th St 47620
Tel (812) 838-4468 SIC 5191 5172 5153

POSEY COUNTY LLC p 1163
817 W 4th St 47620
Tel (812) 838-4468 SIC 5191

SABIC INNOVATIVE PLASTICS MT VERNON LLC p 1264
1 Lexan Ln 47620
Tel (812) 838-4385 SIC 2821 3087 3081

MUNCIE, IN

ARDAGH GLASS INC p 106
1509 S Macedonia Ave 47302
Tel (765) 741-7000 SIC 3221

BALL STATE UNIVERSITY p 148
2000 W University Ave 47306
Tel (765) 289-1241 SIC 8221

DIY/GROUP INC p 445
2401 W 26th St 47302
Tel (765) 284-9000 SIC 1541

■ **FIRST MERCHANTS BANK NATIONAL ASSOCIATION** p 547
200 E Jackson St 47305
Tel (765) 747-1500 SIC 6029

▲ **FIRST MERCHANTS CORP** p 547
200 E Jackson St 47305
Tel (765) 747-1500 SIC 6021 6331

INDIANA UNIVERSITY HEALTH BALL MEMORIAL HOSPITAL INC p 739
2401 W University Ave 47303
Tel (765) 751-1449 SIC 8062

MUNCIE COMMUNITY SCHOOLS p 1000
2501 N Oakwood Ave 47304
Tel (765) 747-5205 SIC 8211

TOWNSEND CORP p 1466
1015 W Jackson St 47305
Tel (765) 468-3007 SIC 0783

MUNSTER, IN

COMMUNITY FOUNDATION OF NORTHWEST INDIANA INC p 348
905 Ridge Rd 46321
Tel (219) 836-0130 SIC 8741 8062

COMMUNITY HOSPITAL p 349
901 Macarthur Blvd 46321
Tel (219) 836-1600 SIC 8062

MUNSTER MEDICAL RESEARCH FOUNDATION INC p 1001
901 Macarthur Blvd 46321
Tel (219) 836-1600 SIC 8062

NAPPANEE, IN

ASCOT ENTERPRISES INC p 116
503 S Main St 46550
Tel (877) 773-7751 SIC 2391 2591 2392

■ **FAIRMONT HOMES LLC** p 525
502 S Oakland Ave 46550
Tel (574) 773-7941 SIC 2451

GULF STREAM COACH INC p 647
503 S Oakland Ave 46550
Tel (574) 773-7761
SIC 3716 3792 3714 2451

KOUNTRY WOOD PRODUCTS LLC p 828
352 Shawnee St 46550
Tel (574) 773-5673 SIC 2434 5211 5031

NEWMAR CORP p 1038
355 Delaware St 46550
Tel (574) 773-7791 *SIC* 3716 3792

NEW ALBANY, IN

ALCHEMY AROMATICS LLC p 47
621 Park East Blvd 47150
Tel (812) 755-6660 *SIC* 5169 5122

BEACH MOLD & TOOL INC p 164
999 Progress Blvd 47150
Tel (812) 945-2688 *SIC* 3089 3544

FKI SECURITY GROUP LLC p 554
101 Security Pkwy 47150
Tel (812) 948-8400
SIC 2522 5044 3499 3429

FLOYD MEMORIAL HOSPITAL AND HEALTH SERVICES p 561
1850 State St 47150
Tel (812) 944-7701 *SIC* 8062

MAC CONSTRUCTION & EXCAVATING INC p 891
1908 Unruh Ct 47150
Tel (812) 284-4250 *SIC* 1623 1622 1794

NEW ALBANY FLOYD COUNTY CONSOLIDATED SCHOOL CORP p 1029
2813 Grant Line Rd 47150
Tel (812) 949-4200 *SIC* 8211

SAMTEC INC p 1275
520 Park East Blvd 47150
Tel (812) 944-6733 *SIC* 3679

NEW CARLISLE, IN

I/N TEK LP p 725
30755 Edison Rd 46552
Tel (574) 654-1000 *SIC* 3316

NEW HAVEN, IN

EAST ALLEN COUNTY SCHOOLS p 469
1240 State Road 930 E 46774
Tel (260) 446-0100 *SIC* 8211

NEW PARIS, IN

■ **BETTER WAY PARTNERS LLC** p 178
70891 County Road 23 46553
Tel (574) 831-3340 *SIC* 3089

SMOKER CRAFT INC p 1334
68143 Clunette St 46553
Tel (574) 831-2103 *SIC* 3732 5551 3731

NEWBURGH, IN

DEACONESS GATEWAY HOSPITAL p 419
4011 Gateway Blvd 47630
Tel (812) 842-2000 *SIC* 8062

DEACONESS WOMENS HOSPITAL OF SOUTHERN INDIANA LLC p 419
4199 Gateway Blvd 47630
Tel (812) 842-4200 *SIC* 8062

■ **ENERGY SYSTEMS GROUP LLC** p 498
4655 Rosebud Ln 47630
Tel (812) 492-3734 *SIC* 8711 1711 1629

■ **VECTREN ENERGY SERVICES CORP** p 1546
4655 Rosebud Ln 47630
Tel (812) 492-3723
SIC 8711 8742 8748 6719

NOBLESVILLE, IN

AMBU INC p 65
15011 Herriman Blvd 46060
Tel (317) 776-6823 *SIC* 3841

INDUSTRIAL DIELECTRICS HOLDINGS INC p 740
407 S 7th St 46060
Tel (317) 773-1766 *SIC* 3644

INTRA AMERICAN METALS INC p 759
14297 Bergen Blvd Ste 200 46060
Tel (317) 219-4444 *SIC* 5093

RIVERVIEW HOSPITAL p 1238
395 Westfield Rd 46060
Tel (317) 773-0760 *SIC* 8062

NOTRE DAME, IN

UNIVERSITY OF NOTRE DAME DU LAC p 1524
805 Grace Hall 46556
Tel (574) 631-6401 *SIC* 8221

ORLAND, IN

CRYSTAL VALLEY FARMS LLC p 397
9622 W 350 N 46776
Tel (260) 829-6550 *SIC* 5144

PINE MANOR INC p 1149
9622 W 350 N 46776
Tel (800) 532-4186 *SIC* 2048 2015 0254

ORLEANS, IN

■ **LAYNE HEAVY CIVIL INC** p 848
4520 N State Road 37 47452
Tel (812) 865-3232 *SIC* 1623 1781 1629

■ **LAYNE INLINER LLC** p 848
4520 N State Rd State 37 47452
Tel (812) 865-3232 *SIC* 1623

■ **PAOLI LLC** p 1112
201 E Martin St 47452
Tel (800) 457-7415 *SIC* 2521

PENDLETON, IN

■ **BALLANTRAE INC** p 148
600 Corporation Dr 46064
Tel (800) 372-3555 *SIC* 3714 3694

■ **BORGWARNER PDS (INDIANA) INC** p 201
600 Corporation Dr 46064
Tel (800) 372-3555 *SIC* 3694 3714

■ **MAGNEQUENCH INC** p 896
237 S Pendleton Ave Ste C 46064
Tel (765) 778-7809 *SIC* 3499

■ **NEW PDS CORP** p 1032
600 Corporation Dr 46064
Tel (800) 372-3555 *SIC* 3694 3714

■ **REMAN HOLDINGS LLC** p 1222
600 Corporation Dr 46064
Tel (800) 372-5131 *SIC* 3714 3694

■ **REMY HOLDINGS INC** p 1223
600 Corporation Dr 46064
Tel (765) 778-6499 *SIC* 3694 3714

■ **REMY INC** p 1223
600 Corporation Dr 46064
Tel (765) 778-6499
SIC 3714 3694 3625 3621 5013

■ **REMY INTERNATIONAL HOLDINGS INC** p 1223
600 Corporation Dr 46064
Tel (765) 778-6499 *SIC* 6712

■ **REMY POWER PRODUCTS LLC** p 1223
600 Corporation Dr 46064
Tel (765) 778-6499 *SIC* 3625 3694 3621

PERU, IN

APERION CARE PERU LLC p 96
1850 W Matador St 46970
Tel (765) 689-5000 *SIC* 8051

PIERCETON, IN

PARAGON MEDICAL INC p 1113
8 Matchett Dr 46562
Tel (574) 594-2140 *SIC* 3089 3841 7371

PLAINFIELD, IN

■ **BRIGHTPOINT INC** p 213
501 Airtech Pkwy 46168
Tel (317) 707-2355 *SIC* 5065

■ **BRIGHTPOINT NORTH AMERICA LLC** p 213
501 Airtech Pkwy 46168
Tel (317) 707-2355 *SIC* 5065

■ **BRIGHTPOINT NORTH AMERICA LP** p 213
501 Airtech Pkwy 46168
Tel (317) 707-2355 *SIC* 5065

■ **CLOUDBLUE TECHNOLOGIES INC** p 327
501 Airtech Pkwy 46168
Tel (866) 437-4258 *SIC* 7379

■ **DUKE ENERGY INDIANA LLC** p 460
1000 E Main St 46168
Tel (704) 382-3853 *SIC* 4911

■ **ISD PLAINFIELD LLC** p 766
8110 Network Dr 46168
Tel (317) 838-8089 *SIC* 8092

■ **TOUCHSTONE WIRELESS REPAIR AND LOGISTICS LP** p 1464
501 Airtech Pkwy 46168
Tel (317) 707-2355 *SIC* 4812 5065

PORTAGE, IN

G W BERKHEIMER CO INC p 587
6000 Southport Rd 46368
Tel (219) 764-5200 *SIC* 5075 5078

NLMK INDIANA LLC p 1045
6500 S Boundary Rd 46368
Tel (219) 787-8200 *SIC* 3312

PORTAGE TOWNSHIP SCHOOLS p 1162
6240 Us Highway 6 46368
Tel (219) 762-6511 *SIC* 8211

RESTAURANT MANAGEMENT CORP p 1228
1575 Adler Cir Ste C 46368
Tel (219) 764-3355 *SIC* 5812

SUPERIOR CONSTRUCTION CO INC p 1406
1455 Louis Sullivan Dr 46368
Tel (219) 886-3728 *SIC* 1541 1629 1622

PORTLAND, IN

INDIANA FCC INC p 738
555 Industrial Dr 47371
Tel (260) 726-8023 *SIC* 3714

JAY PETROLEUM INC p 779
533 S 200 W 47371
Tel (260) 726-9374 *SIC* 5411 5172

PRINCETON, IN

TOYOTA MOTOR MANUFACTURING INDIANA INC p 1466
4000 S Tulip Tree Dr 47670
Tel (812) 387-2000 *SIC* 3711

REMINGTON, IN

FBI BUILDINGS INC p 532
3823 W 1800 S 47977
Tel (219) 261-2157 *SIC* 1542 5031 1541

REMINGTON HYBRID SEED CO INC p 1222
4746 W Us Highway 24 47977
Tel (219) 261-3444 *SIC* 0191

SCHILLI LEASING INC p 1287
6358 W Us Highway 24 47977
Tel (888) 233-1919 *SIC* 7513 7359

RICHMOND, IN

■ **BELDEN WIRE & CABLE CO LLC** p 169
2200 Us Highway 27 S 47374
Tel (765) 983-5200 *SIC* 3357

CINRAM INC p 308
1600 Rich Rd 47374
Tel (416) 298-8190 *SIC* 3652 3695

COLOR-BOX LLC p 338
623 S G St 47374
Tel (765) 966-7588 *SIC* 2653

EARLHAM COLLEGE p 469
801 National Rd W 47374
Tel (765) 983-1200 *SIC* 8221

HARVEST LAND CO-OP INC p 666
1435 Nw 5th St 47374
Tel (765) 962-1527 *SIC* 5191 5153

MOSEY MANUFACTURING CO INC p 992
262 Fort Wayne Ave 47374
Tel (765) 983-8800 *SIC* 3541

PRIMEX PLASTICS CORP p 1176
1235 N F St 47374
Tel (765) 966-7774 *SIC* 3081 2821

REID HOSPITAL & HEALTH CARE SERVICES FOUNDATION INC p 1220
1100 Reid Pkwy 47374
Tel (765) 983-3102 *SIC* 8062

REID HOSPITAL & HEALTH CARE SERVICES INC p 1221
1100 Reid Pkwy 47374
Tel (765) 983-3000 *SIC* 8069

REID HOSPITAL & HEALTH CARE SERVICES INC p 1221
1100 Reid Pkwy 47374
Tel (765) 983-3000 *SIC* 8062

REID PHYSICIAN ASSOCIATES INC p 1221
1100 Reid Pkwy 47374
Tel (765) 983-3000 *SIC* 8011

ROANOKE, IN

■ **VERA BRADLEY DESIGNS INC** p 1549
12420 Stonebridge Rd 46783
Tel (260) 482-4673 *SIC* 5099

▲ **VERA BRADLEY INC** p 1549
12420 Stonebridge Rd 46783
Tel (877) 708-8372
SIC 3171 3111 2392 2844

ROCHESTER, IN

ROCHESTER METAL PRODUCTS CORP p 1243
616 Indiana Ave 46975
Tel (574) 223-3164 *SIC* 3321

RUSHVILLE, IN

INTAT PRECISION INC p 748
2148 N State Road 3 46173
Tel (765) 932-5323 *SIC* 3321

SAINT JOHN, IN

LAKE CENTRAL SCHOOL CORP p 838
8260 Wicker Ave 46373
Tel (219) 365-8507 *SIC* 8211

SCHERERVILLE, IN

MCCOLLY REALTORS INC p 927
850 Deer Creek Dr 46375
Tel (219) 322-5508 *SIC* 6531

SCOTTSBURG, IN

ILPEA INDUSTRIES INC p 733
745 S Gardner St 47170
Tel (812) 837-6616 *SIC* 3053 3089

ILPEA INDUSTRIES INC p 733
745 S Gardner St 47170
Tel (812) 752-2526 *SIC* 5085

NORTH ELECTRIC INC p 1052
2438 W Robin Rd 47170
Tel (812) 752-4804 *SIC* 1731

SELLERSBURG, IN

■ **MANITOWOC BEVERAGE SYSTEMS INC** p 902
2100 Future Dr 47172
Tel (419) 861-0800 *SIC* 3585

SELMA, IN

ECO-PAK p 476
9211 E Jackson St 47383
Tel (765) 287-2093 *SIC* 5999

SEYMOUR, IN

AISIN HOLDINGS OF AMERICA INC p 41
1665 E 4th Street Rd 47274
Tel (812) 524-8144 *SIC* 5013

AISIN USA MFG INC p 41
1700 E 4th Street Rd 47274
Tel (812) 523-1969 *SIC* 3714

JACKSON COUNTY SCHNECK MEMORIAL HOSPITAL p 773
411 W Tipton St 47274
Tel (812) 522-2349 *SIC* 8062

JOHN C GROUB CO INC p 787
900 A Ave E 47274
Tel (812) 522-1998 *SIC* 5411

KOCOLENE MARKETING LLC p 826
2060 1st Ave 47274
Tel (812) 522-2224 *SIC* 5541 5411

■ **KREMERS URBAN PHARMACEUTICALS INC** p 829
1101 C Ave W 47274
Tel (812) 523-5347 *SIC* 2834

ROSE ACRE FARMS INC p 1250
6874 N Base Rd 47274
Tel (812) 497-2557 *SIC* 0252

SEYMOUR TUBING INC p 1309
1515 E 4th Street Rd 47274
Tel (812) 523-0842 *SIC* 3312

SWIFTY OIL LLC p 1412
1515 W Tipton St 47274
Tel (812) 522-1640 *SIC* 5541 5411

VALEO LIGHTING SYSTEMS NORTH AMERICA LLC p 1539
1231 A Ave N 47274
Tel (812) 524-5021 *SIC* 3641 3714

SHELBYVILLE, IN

KNAUF INSULATION INC p 824
1 Knauf Dr 46176
Tel (317) 398-4434 *SIC* 3229

MAJOR HOSPITAL p 899
150 W Washington St 46176
Tel (317) 392-3211 *SIC* 8062 8011

PK USA INC p 1153
600 Northridge Dr 46176
Tel (317) 395-5500
SIC 3465 3089 3714 3429

RYOBI DIE CASTING (USA) INC p 1261
800 W Mausoleum Rd 46176
Tel (317) 398-3398
SIC 3714 3444 3365 3363

SHERIDAN, IN

JBS UNITED INC p 780
4310 W State Road 38 46069
Tel (317) 758-4495 *SIC* 2048 5153 0213

SOUTH BEND, IN

■ **1ST SOURCE BANK** p 1
100 N Michigan St Ste 800 46601
Tel (574) 235-2000 *SIC* 6022

▲ **1ST SOURCE CORP** p 1
100 N Michigan St 46601
Tel (574) 235-2000 *SIC* 6022

3-D CONCRETE CORRECTION INC p 2
20115 Jackson Rd 46614
Tel (574) 291-0771 *SIC* 1771

ADAMS REMCO INC p 21
2612 Foundation Dr 46628
Tel (574) 288-2113 *SIC* 5044 7629 8243

AM GENERAL HOLDINGS LLC p 63
105 N Niles Ave 46617
Tel (574) 237-6222 *SIC* 3714 3711 8711

AM GENERAL LLC p 63
105 N Niles Ave 46617
Tel (574) 237-6222 *SIC* 3711 3714 8711

BEACON HEALTH SYSTEM INC p 164
615 N Michigan St 46601
Tel (574) 647-1000 *SIC* 8741 8399 8082

BEACON MEDICAL GROUP INC p 165
615 N Michigan St 46601
Tel (574) 647-1000 *SIC* 8741 8399 8082

CITY OF SOUTH BEND p 318
227 W Jefferson Blvd 46601
Tel (574) 235-9216 *SIC* 9111

■ **CLP TOWNE INC** p 328
24805 Us Highway 20 46628
Tel (574) 233-3183 *SIC* 4731

ELKHART PLASTICS p 488
3300 N Kenmore St 46628
Tel (574) 232-8066 *SIC* 3089

HMR ACQUISITION CO INC p 698
1501 N Ironwood Dr 46635
Tel (574) 272-5922 *SIC* 5812 5813

■ **HUBBELL INC (DELAWARE)** p 716
3902 W Sample St 46619
Tel (574) 234-7151 *SIC* 3644 3699 3613

INTERNATIONAL BRAKE INDUSTRIES INC p 754
4300 Quality Dr 46628
Tel (419) 905-7468 *SIC* 3713 3714

KW SERVICES LLC p 832
3801 Voorde Dr Ste B 46628
Tel (574) 232-2051 *SIC* 6719 1799 5063

LESEA BROADCASTING CORP p 857
61300 Ironwood Rd 46614
Tel (574) 291-8200 *SIC* 4833 4832

MARTINS SUPER MARKETS INC p 913
760 Cotter St 46613
Tel (574) 234-5848 *SIC* 5411

MEMORIAL HOSPITAL OF SOUTH BEND INC p 942
615 N Michigan St 46601
Tel (574) 647-7751 *SIC* 8062

MERIDIAN TITLE CORP p 949
202 S Michigan St Ste 300 46601
Tel (574) 232-5845 *SIC* 6361

PEOPLELINK LLC p 1132
431 E Colfax Ave Ste 200 46617
Tel (574) 232-5400 *SIC* 7361

PRESS GANEY ASSOCIATES INC p 1172
404 Columbia St 46601
Tel (574) 232-3387 *SIC* 8742

ROYAL ADHESIVES AND SEALANTS LLC p 1254
2001 W Washington St 46628
Tel (574) 246-5000 *SIC* 2891 7389 8711

ROYAL HOLDINGS INC p 1254
2001 W Washington St 46628
Tel (574) 246-5000 *SIC* 2891

SANCTUARY AT HOLY CROSS p 1278
17475 Dugdale Dr 46635
Tel (574) 247-7500 *SIC* 8322 8052

SOUTH BEND CHOCOLATE CO INC p 1343
3300 W Sample St Ste 110 46619
Tel (574) 233-2577
SIC 5149 2066 5441 5812

SOUTH BEND COMMUNITY SCHOOL CORP RILEY SCHOOL BUILDING p 1343
215 S Saint Joseph St 46601
Tel (574) 283-8000 *SIC* 8211

SOUTH BEND MEDICAL FOUNDATION INC p 1343
530 N Lafayette Blvd 46601
Tel (574) 234-4176 *SIC* 8071

STANZ CHEESE CO INC p 1377
1840 Commerce Dr 46628
Tel (574) 232-6666
SIC 5142 5141 5148 5113 5087 5085

STEEL WAREHOUSE CO LLC p 1384
2722 Tucker Dr 46619
Tel (574) 236-5100 *SIC* 5051

TIRE RACK INC p 1455
7101 Vorden Pkwy 46628
Tel (888) 541-1777 *SIC* 5014 3714

TOWNE HOLDINGS INC p 1466
24805 Us Highway 20 46628
Tel (574) 233-3183 *SIC* 4213

SOUTH WHITLEY, IN

AG PLUS INC p 33
401 N Main St 46787
Tel (260) 723-5141 *SIC* 5191 2041 5153

STUMP PRINTING CO INC p 1395
101 Carroll Rd 46787
Tel (260) 723-5171
SIC 5199 2679 5961 2759

WHITLEY EVERGREEN INC p 1607
201 W 1st St 46787
Tel (260) 723-5131 *SIC* 1542

WHITLEY MANUFACTURING CO INC p 1607
201 W 1st St 46787
Tel (260) 723-5131 *SIC* 2451

SPICELAND, IN

DRAPER INC p 455
411 S Pearl St 47385
Tel (765) 987-7999 *SIC* 3861 2591 3651

TELL CITY, IN

MULZER CRUSHED STONE INC p 1000
534 Mozart St 47586
Tel (812) 547-7921
SIC 1422 3273 5191 5085

TERRE HAUTE, IN

CERES SOLUTIONS p 283
2600 S 13th St 47802
Tel (812) 235-8123 *SIC* 5153 5172 5191

COMPANHIA SIDERURGICA NACIONAL LLC p 350
455 W Industrial Dr 47802
Tel (812) 299-4157 *SIC* 3316 3312

■ **FIRST FINANCIAL BANK NA** p 546
1 First Financial Plz 47807
Tel (812) 238-6000 *SIC* 6021

▲ **FIRST FINANCIAL CORP** p 546
1 First Financial Plz 47807
Tel (812) 238-6000 *SIC* 6022

INDIANA LABORERS WELFARE FUND p 738
413 Swan St 47807
Tel (812) 238-2551 *SIC* 6371

INDIANA LLC ADVICS MANUFACTURING p 738
10550 James Adams St 47802
Tel (812) 298-1617 *SIC* 3714

INDIANA STATE UNIVERSITY p 738
200 N 7th St 47809
Tel (800) 468-6478 *SIC* 8221

■ **KINDRED NURSING CENTERS LIMITED PARTNERSHIP** p 819
3500 Maple Ave 47804
Tel (502) 596-7300 *SIC* 8051

ROSE-HULMAN INSTITUTE OF TECHNOLOGY INC p 1250
5500 Wabash Ave 47803
Tel (812) 877-1511 *SIC* 8221

SONY DADC US INC p 1341
1800 N Fruitridge Ave 47804
Tel (812) 462-8100
SIC 3695 3652 3651 3577 3572

SUNRISE COAL LLC p 1403
1183 E Canvasback Dr 47802
Tel (812) 299-2800 *SIC* 1222

TEMPLETON COAL CO INC p 1436
701 Wabash Ave Ste 501 47807
Tel (812) 232-7037
SIC 5074 3567 3961 5049 3089

THOMPSON THRIFT CONSTRUCTION INC p 1449
901 Wabash Ave Ste 300 47807
Tel (812) 235-5959 *SIC* 1542 6531

THYSSENKRUPP PRESTA NORTH AMERICA LLC p 1452
1597 E Industrial Dr 47802
Tel (812) 299-5000 *SIC* 5013

UNION HOSPITAL INC p 1504
1606 N 7th St 47804
Tel (812) 238-7000 *SIC* 8062

VIGO COUNTY SCHOOL CORP p 1556
686 Wabash Ave 47807
Tel (812) 462-4011 *SIC* 8211

TIPTON, IN

PARK 100 FOODS INC p 1115
326 E Adams St 46072
Tel (765) 675-3480 *SIC* 2013 2032 2035

■ **TIPTON TELEPHONE CO INC** p 1455
117 E Washington St 46072
Tel (765) 675-4185 *SIC* 4813

TOPEKA, IN

■ **CROSSROADS RV INC** p 394
305 Hawpatch Dr 46571
Tel (260) 593-3850 *SIC* 3711

NISHIKAWA COOPER LLC p 1044
324 Morrow St 46571
Tel (260) 593-2156 *SIC* 3069

NISHIKAWA OF AMERICA INC p 1044
324 Morrow St 46571
Tel (260) 593-2156 *SIC* 3069

UNION CITY, IN

CARDINAL ETHANOL LLC p 252
1554 N County Rd 600 E 47390
Tel (765) 964-3137 *SIC* 2869 2085

UPLAND, IN

AVIS INDUSTRIAL CORP p 138
1909 S Main St 46989
Tel (765) 998-8100
SIC 3429 3462 3312 3531 3714 3569

PIERCE CO INC p 1147
35 N 8th St 46989
Tel (765) 998-8100 *SIC* 3714

VALPARAISO, IN

FAMILY EXPRESS CORP p 526
213 S State Road 49 46383
Tel (219) 531-6490 *SIC* 5541 5411

LUTHERAN UNIVERSITY ASSOCIATION INC p 886
1700 Chapel Dr 46383
Tel (219) 464-5000 *SIC* 8221

■ **MCGILL MANUFACTURING CO INC** p 929
2300 Evans Ave 46383
Tel (219) 465-2200 *SIC* 3562

■ **PORTER FOUNDATION INC** p 1162
802 Laporte Ave 46383
Tel (219) 465-4600 *SIC* 8062

■ **PORTER HEALTH SERVICES INC** p 1162
814 Laporte Ave 46383
Tel (219) 477-1013 *SIC* 6324

PORTER REGIONAL HOSPITAL p 1162
85 E Us 6 Frontage Rd 46383
Tel (219) 263-4600 *SIC* 8062

QUALITY OIL INC p 1197
55 N 400 E 46383
Tel (219) 462-2951 *SIC* 5171 5172

US 1 INDUSTRIES INC p 1530
336 W Us Highway 30 # 201 46385
Tel (219) 476-1300 *SIC* 4213 4731

VERSAILLES, IN

JOHN E RETZNER OIL CO INC p 788
630 S Adams St 47042
Tel (812) 609-4178 *SIC* 5983

VINCENNES, IN

FUTABA INDIANA OF AMERICA CORP p 585
3320 S Keller Rd 47591
Tel (812) 895-4700 *SIC* 3089 3465 2396

KNOX COUNTY HOSPITAL p 825
305 S 5th St 47591
Tel (812) 882-5220 *SIC* 8062

NC INC p 1021
1023 Main St 47591
Tel (812) 886-4412 *SIC* 5031 5211

VINCENNES UNIVERSITY p 1557
1002 N 1st St 47591
Tel (812) 888-8888 *SIC* 8221 5942

WABASH, IN

■ **FIRST MERCHANTS BANK** p 547
189 W Market St 46992
Tel (260) 563-4116 *SIC* 6022

FORD METER BOX CO INC p 565
775 Manchester Ave 46992
Tel (260) 563-3171 *SIC* 3494

HARVEY INDUSTRIES LLC p 667
3837 Mill St 46992
Tel (260) 563-8371 *SIC* 3463 3365

NORTH CENTRAL COOPERATIVE INC p 1051
2025 S Wabash St 46992
Tel (800) 992-3495 *SIC* 5172 5153 5191

WABASH ELECTRIC SUPPLY INC p 1570
1400 S Wabash St 46992
Tel (260) 563-2240 *SIC* 5063

WARSAW, IN

■ **BIOMET INC** p 184
56 E Bell Dr 46582
Tel (574) 267-6639 *SIC* 3842 3841 3845

■ **BIOMET ORTHOPEDICS LLC** p 184
56 E Bell Dr 46582
Tel (574) 267-6639 *SIC* 3842

DALTON CORP p 410
1900 E Jefferson St 46580
Tel (574) 267-8111 *SIC* 3321

■ **DEPUY ORTHOPAEDICS INC** p 431
700 Orthopaedic Dr 46582
Tel (574) 267-8143 *SIC* 3842

■ **DEPUY PRODUCTS INC** p 431
700 Orthopaedic Dr 46582
Tel (574) 267-8143 *SIC* 3842

■ **LAKE CITY BANK** p 838
202 E Center St 46580
Tel (574) 267-6144 *SIC* 6022 6163

▲ **LAKELAND FINANCIAL CORP** p 840
202 E Center St 46580
Tel (574) 267-6144 *SIC* 6022

LVB ACQUISITION HOLDING LLC p 887
56 E Bell Dr 46582
Tel (574) 267-6639 *SIC* 3842 3841 3845

■ **LVB ACQUISITION INC** p 887
56 E Bell Dr 46582
Tel (574) 267-6639 *SIC* 3842 3841 3845

MILLERS HEALTH SYSTEMS INC p 971
1690 S County Farm Rd 46580
Tel (574) 267-7211 *SIC* 8052 8051 8361

NEW DALTON FOUNDRY LLC p 1029
1900 E Jefferson St 46580
Tel (574) 267-8111 *SIC* 3321

SYMMETRY MEDICAL INC p 1414
3724 N State Road 15 46582
Tel (574) 268-2252 *SIC* 3841 3842

▲ **ZIMMER BIOMET HOLDINGS INC** p 1643
345 E Main St 46580
Tel (574) 267-6131 *SIC* 3842

■ **ZIMMER INC** p 1643
1800 W Center St 46580
Tel (330) 343-8801 *SIC* 3842

WASHINGTON, IN

WILLIAMS BROS HEALTH CARE PHARMACY INC p 1611
10 Williams Brothers Dr 47501
Tel (812) 254-2497
SIC 5047 7352 5999 5169 3999

WATERLOO, IN

METALX LLC p 953
295 S Commerce Dr 46793
Tel (260) 232-3000 *SIC* 5093

WAWAKA, IN

FRICK SERVICES INC p 579
3154 Depot St 46794
Tel (260) 761-3311
SIC 5191 5153 5261 4221 2048 4213

WEST LAFAYETTE, IN

LAFAYETTE VENETIAN BLIND INC p 838
3000 Klondike Rd 47906
Tel (765) 464-2500 *SIC* 2591 2391

PURDUE RESEARCH FOUNDATION p 1192
1281 Win Hentschel Blvd 47906
Tel (765) 588-3470 *SIC* 8733

PURDUE UNIVERSITY p 1192
401 S Grant St 47907
Tel (765) 494-8000 *SIC* 8221

WEST TERRE HAUTE, IN

MICHAELS G L CONSTRUCTION INC p 960
554 W Cedarwood Ave 47885
Tel (812) 478-3154 *SIC* 1542 1541

WESTFIELD, IN

AGRELIANT GENETICS LLC p 35
1122 E 169th St 46074
Tel (317) 896-5552 *SIC* 5191

INDIANA MILLS & MANUFACTURING INC p 738
18881 Immi Way 46074
Tel (317) 896-9531 *SIC* 3714

REVERE INDUSTRIES LLC p 1229
16855 Suthpark Dr Ste 100 46074
Tel (317) 580-2420
SIC 3089 3399 3363 3497

WASHINGTON WESTFIELD SCHOOLS p 1579
1143 E 181st St 46074
Tel (317) 867-8000 *SIC* 8211

WHITESTOWN, IN

WEAVER POPCORN CO INC p 1586
4485 S Perry Worth Rd 46075
Tel (765) 934-2101 *SIC* 5145 4213

WHITING, IN

CENTIER BANK p 277
1500 119th St 46394
Tel (219) 659-0043 *SIC* 6022

WINAMAC, IN

BRAUN CORP p 208
631 W 11th St 46996
Tel (574) 946-6153 *SIC* 3999

WINCHESTER, IN

■ **SILVERTOWNE LP** p 1324
120 E Union City Pike 47394
Tel (765) 584-7481 *SIC* 5999 5094

IOWA

ALBERT CITY, IA

AG PARTNERS LLC p 33
30 Main St 50510
Tel (712) 843-2291 *SIC* 5153 5191 2048

ALGONA, IA

PHARMACISTS MUTUAL INSURANCE CO p 1141
808 Highway 18 W 50511
Tel (515) 295-2461 *SIC* 6331

ALTOONA, IA

HARRISON TRUCK CENTERS INC p 664
3601 Adventureland Dr 50009
Tel (515) 967-3500 *SIC* 5511 7538

PRAIRIE MEADOWS RACETRACK AND CASINO INC p 1167
1 Prairie Meadows Dr 50009
Tel (515) 967-1000
SIC 7948 7993 7999 5947 5812 5813

RACING ASSOCIATION OF CENTRAL p 1203
1 Prairie Meadows Dr 50009
Tel (515) 967-1000 *SIC* 8611

AMES, IA

ALIGNED AG DISTRIBUTORS LLC p 50
224b S Bell Ave 50010
Tel (641) 858-2341 *SIC* 5191

CITY OF AMES p 313
515 Clark Ave 50010
Tel (515) 239-5140 *SIC* 9111

DANFOSS POWER SOLUTIONS (US) CO p 411
2800 E 13th St 50010
Tel (515) 239-6000 *SIC* 3594

DANFOSS POWER SOLUTIONS INC p 411
2800 E 13th St 50010
Tel (515) 239-6000 *SIC* 1731

IOWA DEPARTMENT OF TRANSPORTATION p 762
800 Lincoln Way 50010
Tel (515) 239-1111 *SIC* 9621

IOWA STATE UNIVERSITY FOUNDATION p 763
2505 University Blvd 50010
Tel (515) 294-4607 *SIC* 8399

IOWA STATE UNIVERSITY OF SCIENCE AND TECHNOLOGY p 763
1350 Beardshear Hall 50011
Tel (515) 294-6162 *SIC* 8221

LANDUS COOPERATIVE p 843
2321 N Loop Dr Ste 220 50010
Tel (515) 817-2100 *SIC* 5153

MARY GREELEY MEDICAL CENTER p 914
1111 Duff Ave 50010
Tel (515) 239-6730 *SIC* 8062

MARY GREELEY MEDICAL CENTER FOUNDATION p 914
1111 Duff Ave 50010
Tel (515) 239-2011 *SIC* 8062

MCFARLAND CLINIC PC p 928
1215 Duff Ave 50010
Tel (515) 239-4400 *SIC* 8011

NATIONAL FARMERS ORGANIZATION p 1011
528 Billy Sunday Rd # 100 50010
Tel (515) 292-2000 *SIC* 8631

NFO INC p 1041
528 Billy Sunday Rd # 100 50010
Tel (515) 292-2000 *SIC* 8631

■ **REG BIOFUELS LLC** p 1218
416 S Bell Ave 50010
Tel (515) 239-8000 *SIC* 2911

▲ **RENEWABLE ENERGY GROUP INC** p 1223
416 S Bell Ave 50010
Tel (515) 239-8000 *SIC* 2911 2869

SARGENT GROUP INC p 1282
2905 Se 5th St 50010
Tel (515) 232-0442 *SIC* 1541 1796

STORY CONSTRUCTION CO p 1392
300 S Bell Ave 50010
Tel (515) 232-4358 *SIC* 1542 1629

TODD & SARGENT INC p 1458
2905 Se 5th St 50010
Tel (515) 232-0442 SIC 1541 1542

UNITED STATES DEPARTMENT OF ENERGY AMES OFFICE p 1512
111 Tasf Iowa State Univ 50011
Tel (515) 294-5643 SIC 9611

▲ WORKIVA INC p 1624
2900 University Blvd 50010
Tel (888) 275-3125 SIC 7372

ANAMOSA, IA

J&P CYCLES LLC p 772
13225 Circle Dr 52205
Tel (319) 462-4817 SIC 5571 5013

ANKENY, IA

AGRI INDUSTRIES INC p 36
700 Se Dalbey Dr 50021
Tel (515) 964-2200 SIC 5153 7359

ALBAUGH LLC p 46
1525 Ne 36th St 50021
Tel (515) 964-9444 SIC 2879

ANKENY COMMUNITY SCHOOLS INC p 92
306 Sw School St 50023
Tel (515) 965-9600 SIC 8211

▲ CASEYS GENERAL STORES INC p 263
1 Se Convenience Blvd 50021
Tel (515) 965-6100 SIC 5411 5541

■ CASEYS MARKETING CO p 263
1 Se Convenience Blvd 50021
Tel (515) 965-6100
SIC 5411 5172 5141 5812

■ CASEYS RETAIL CO p 263
1 Se Convenience Blvd 50021
Tel (515) 965-6100 SIC 5411

DES MOINES AREA COMMUNITY COLLEGE p 431
2006 S Ankeny Blvd 50023
Tel (515) 964-6214 SIC 8221

LAURIDSEN GROUP INC p 847
2425 Se Oak Tree Ct 50021
Tel (515) 289-7600 SIC 2099

OMG MID WEST INC p 1084
2401 Se Tones Dr Ste 13 50021
Tel (515) 266-9928 SIC 1442 1422

PERISHABLE DISTRIBUTORS OF IOWA LTD p 1136
2741 Se Pdi Pl 50021
Tel (515) 965-6300 SIC 5146 5144 5147

PURFOODS LLC p 1192
3210 Se Corp Woods Dr 50021
Tel (515) 963-0641 SIC 2099

■ SYSCO IOWA INC p 1417
1 Sysco Dr 50021
Tel (515) 289-5300
SIC 5149 5147 5142 5144 5113 5143

TONE BROTHERS INC p 1460
2301 Se Tones Dr 50021
Tel (515) 965-2711 SIC 2087 2099

ARCADIA, IA

FARMERS COOPERATIVE ELEVATOR CO p 529
12543 190th St 51430
Tel (712) 689-2296 SIC 5191 5153

ATLANTIC, IA

ATLANTIC BOTTLING CO p 126
4 E 2nd St 50022
Tel (515) 987-1931 SIC 2086

BETTENDORF, IA

JMF CO p 786
2735 62nd Street Ct 52722
Tel (563) 332-9200 SIC 5074

■ OLYMPIC STEEL IOWA INC p 1083
6425 State St 52722
Tel (563) 332-7785 SIC 5051 3444

RESTAURANTS RESOURCES INC p 1228
1805 State St Ste 201 52722
Tel (563) 243-7571 SIC 5812

SIVYER STEEL CORP p 1328
225 33rd St 52722
Tel (563) 355-1811 SIC 3325

TRINITY MEDICAL CENTER p 1481
4500 Utica Ridge Rd 52722
Tel (563) 742-2000 SIC 8062

BOONE, IA

FAREWAY STORES INC p 528
715 8th St 50036
Tel (515) 432-2623 SIC 5411

BROOKLYN, IA

MANATTS INC p 900
1775 Old 6 Rd 52211
Tel (641) 522-9206
SIC 1611 1442 2951 3273

BURLINGTON, IA

HOPE HAVEN AREA DEVELOPMENT CENTER CORP p 706
828 N 7th St Ste 1 52601
Tel (319) 752-0110 SIC 8361

REIF OIL CO p 1221
801 N 3rd St 52601
Tel (319) 758-1240 SIC 5172 5411

SHEARERS FOODS BURLINGTON LLC p 1313
3000 Mount Pleasant St 52601
Tel (319) 754-6551 SIC 2052

■ VISTA BAKERY INC p 1562
3000 Mount Pleasant St 52601
Tel (704) 554-1421 SIC 5149

BURT, IA

STATELINE COOPERATIVE p 1383
120 Walnut St 50522
Tel (515) 885-2642 SIC 5191 5172 5031

CALMAR, IA

NORTHEAST IOWA COMMUNITY COLLEGE FOUNDATION p 1055
1625 Highway 150 52132
Tel (563) 562-3263 SIC 8222

CAMBRIDGE, IA

R J PETERSON COMPANIES INC p 1202
32364 585th Ave 50046
Tel (515) 360-3337 SIC 1521

CARROLL, IA

CROSS OVER LLC p 393
621 Alta Vista Dr 51401
Tel (712) 790-4549 SIC 8733 7389

FARNER-BOCKEN CO p 530
1751 E Us Highway 30 51401
Tel (712) 792-7454 SIC 5145 5194

CARTER LAKE, IA

OWEN INDUSTRIES INC p 1099
501 Avenue H 51510
Tel (800) 831-9252 SIC 5051 3441

WH FERER CO LLC p 1604
2910 N 9th St 51510
Tel (712) 847-0800 SIC 2816

CEDAR FALLS, IA

BOSSARD NORTH AMERICA INC p 202
6521 Production Dr 50613
Tel (319) 268-3700 SIC 5085

CBE COMPANIES INC p 268
1309 Technology Pkwy 50613
Tel (319) 226-5161 SIC 8742

CBE GROUP INC p 268
1309 Technology Pkwy 50613
Tel (319) 234-6686 SIC 7322 8742

MARTIN BROTHERS DISTRIBUTING CO INC p 912
6623 Chancellor Dr 50613
Tel (319) 266-1775
SIC 5141 5169 5046 5087

UNIVERSITY OF NORTHERN IOWA p 1524
1227 W 27th St 50614
Tel (319) 242-7325 SIC 8221

■ VIKING PUMP INC p 1557
406 State St 50613
Tel (319) 266-1741 SIC 3561

CEDAR RAPIDS, IA

ACCESS DIRECT TELEMARKETING SERVICES INC p 14
4515 20th Ave Sw Ste B 52404
Tel (319) 390-8900 SIC 7389 7361

■ ADDISON INSURANCE CO p 22
118 2nd Ave Se 52401
Tel (319) 399-5700 SIC 6331

AEGON US HOLDING CORP p 29
4333 Edgewood Rd Ne 52499
Tel (319) 355-8511
SIC 6311 6321 6351 6159

AEGON USA INVESTMENT MANAGEMENT LLC p 29
4333 Edgewood Rd Ne 52499
Tel (319) 398-8511 SIC 6282

AEGON USA LLC p 29
4333 Edgewood Rd Ne 52499
Tel (319) 355-8511 SIC 6311

■ ALLIANT INDUSTRIES INC p 55
200 1st St Se 52401
Tel (398) 786-4268
SIC 4011 4741 4911 4924

APACHE HOSE & BELTING CO INC p 96
4805 Bowling St Sw 52404
Tel (319) 365-0471 SIC 3496 3052 5085

CADET HOLDING CORP p 236
4333 Edgewood Rd Ne 52499
Tel (319) 398-8511 SIC 6311

CEDAR RAPIDS COMMUNITY SCHOOL DISTRICT p 272
2500 Edgewood Rd Nw 52405
Tel (319) 558-2000 SIC 8211

CEDAR RAPIDS COMMUNITY SCHOOL DISTRICT FOUNDATION p 272
2500 Edgewood Rd Nw 52405
Tel (319) 558-2000 SIC 8399

CENTRAL IOWA POWER COOPERATIVE p 278
1400 Highway 13 52403
Tel (319) 366-8011 SIC 4911

CITY OF CEDAR RAPIDS p 313
101 1st St Se 52401
Tel (319) 286-5080 SIC 9111

COMMONWEALTH GENERAL CORP p 346
4333 Edgewood Rd Ne 52499
Tel (502) 560-2000 SIC 6311

CRST EXPEDITED INC p 396
1332 Edgewood Rd Sw 52404
Tel (319) 396-4400 SIC 4213

CRST INTERNATIONAL INC p 396
3930 16th Ave Sw 52404
Tel (319) 396-4400 SIC 4213

D C TAYLOR CO p 406
312 29th St Ne 52402
Tel (319) 363-2073 SIC 1761

DATA LINK SOLUTIONS LLC p 413
350 Collins Rd Ne 52498
Tel (319) 295-8144 SIC 3812

GAZETTE CO p 594
500 3rd Ave Se 52401
Tel (319) 398-8211 SIC 2711 2752 4833

GREATAMERICA FINANCIAL SERVICES CORP p 635
625 1st St Se Ste 800 52401
Tel (319) 365-8000 SIC 6159

GREEN COMPANIES INC p 636
8710 Earhart Ln Sw 52404
Tel (319) 841-4000
SIC 8711 8748 8713 4911 1623

HEDGES ASSOCIATES INC p 680
5408 Blairs Forest Way Ne 52402
Tel (319) 378-8760 SIC 6531

■ INTERSTATE POWER AND LIGHT CO p 758
200 1st St Se 52401
Tel (319) 398-4411 SIC 4911 4924 4961

■ KAPSTONE CONTAINER CORP p 803
1601 Blairs Ferry Rd Ne 52402
Tel (319) 393-3610 SIC 2653

KIRKWOOD COMMUNITY COLLEGE FOUNDATION p 822
6301 Kirkwood Blvd Sw 52404
Tel (319) 398-5411 SIC 8222

MCGRATH AUTOMOTIVE GROUP INC p 929
4610 Center Point Rd Ne 52402
Tel (319) 688-2937 SIC 5511

■ MCLEODUSA INC p 932
6400 C St Sw 52404
Tel (319) 364-0000 SIC 4813 4812

MERCY CARE MANAGEMENT INC p 945
701 10th St Se 52403
Tel (319) 398-6011 SIC 8011 8741 8322

MERCY FLOWERS & GIFTS p 946
701 10th St Se 52403
Tel (319) 398-6124 SIC 5992 5947

MERCY HOSPITAL CEDAR RAPIDS IOWA p 947
701 10th St Se 52403
Tel (319) 398-6011 SIC 8062

MERCYCARE SERVICE CORP p 948
701 10th St Se 52403
Tel (319) 398-6011 SIC 8011

NRG MEDIA LLC p 1064
2875 Mount Vernon Rd Se 52403
Tel (319) 862-0300 SIC 4832

■ PENFORD PRODUCTS CO p 1128
1001 1st St Sw 52404
Tel (319) 398-3700 SIC 2046

PMX INDUSTRIES INC p 1158
5300 Willow Creek Dr Sw 52404
Tel (319) 368-7700
SIC 3366 5051 3444 3364 3351 3331

▲ ROCKWELL COLLINS INC p 1245
400 Collins Rd Ne 52498
Tel (319) 295-1000 SIC 3812 3663

■ ROCKWELL COLLINS SALES & SERVICES INC p 1245
400 Collins Rd Ne 52498
Tel (319) 295-8899 SIC 5065

■ ROCKWELL COLLINS SIMULATION & TRAINING SOLUTIONS LLC p 1245
400 Collins Rd Ne 52498
Tel (319) 295-1000 SIC 3699 8744

RUFFALO NOEL LEVITZ LLC p 1257
1025 Kirkwood Pkwy Sw 52404
Tel (800) 876-1117 SIC 7389

SAINT LUKES METHODIST HOSPITAL INC p 1270
1026 A Ave Ne 52402
Tel (319) 369-7209 SIC 8049

SCHIMBERG CO p 1287
1106 Shaver Rd Ne 52402
Tel (319) 365-9421 SIC 5074 3498

■ SPECIALTY BLENDING CO LLC p 1356
1000 Wenig Rd Ne 52402
Tel (319) 298-3360 SIC 6163

ST LUKES METHODIST HOSPITAL INC p 1370
1026 A Ave Ne 52402
Tel (319) 369-7211 SIC 8062

STONERIVER INC p 1391
222 3rd Ave Se Ste 405 52401
Tel (319) 378-5773 SIC 7371

THOMPSON TRUCK & TRAILER INC p 1449
2740 6th St Sw 52404
Tel (319) 364-2491 SIC 5012

TOP SHOP LLC p 1460
5515 Council St Ne 52402
Tel (319) 393-1041 SIC 2541

TRANSAMERICA ADVISORS LIFE INSURANCE CO p 1470
4333 Edgewood Rd Ne 52499
Tel (800) 346-3677 SIC 6311

TRANSAMERICA CORP p 1470
4333 Edgewood Rd Ne 52499
Tel (319) 398-8511 SIC 6311

TRANSAMERICA INSURANCE CORP p 1470
4333 Edgewood Rd Ne 52499
Tel (319) 355-4883 SIC 6321

TRANSAMERICA LIFE INSURANCE CO p 1470
4333 Edgewood Rd Ne 52499
Tel (319) 398-8511 SIC 6371 6311

TRANSAMERICA PREMIER LIFE INSURANCE CO p 1470
4333 Edgewood Rd Ne 52499
Tel (319) 355-8511 SIC 6311 6321

TRUENORTH COMPANIES LC p 1486
500 1st St Se 52401
Tel (319) 364-5193 SIC 6411

■ UNITED FIRE & CASUALTY CO p 1508
118 2nd Ave Se 52401
Tel (319) 399-5700 SIC 6331 6311 6321

▲ UNITED FIRE GROUP INC p 1508
118 2nd Ave Se 52401
Tel (319) 399-5700 SIC 6411 6311

■ UNITED LIFE INSURANCE CO INC p 1510
118 2nd Ave Se 52401
Tel (319) 399-5700 SIC 6311

VAN METER INC p 1543
850 32nd Ave Sw 52404
Tel (319) 366-5301 SIC 5063

WEST SIDE TRANSPORT INC p 1595
4201 16th Ave Sw 52404
Tel (319) 390-4466 SIC 4213

WEST SIDE UNLIMITED CORP p 1595
4201 16th Ave Sw 52404
Tel (319) 390-4466 SIC 4213 7389

YELLOWBOOK CO INC p 1635
6300 C St Sw 52404
Tel (319) 366-1100 SIC 7311

YOUNG MENS CHRISTIAN ASSOCIATION OF CEDAR RAPIDS METROPOLITAN AREA p 1638
207 7th Ave Se 52401
Tel (319) 366-6421 SIC 8641 8322

CHARLES CITY, IA

■ CAMBREX CHARLES CITY INC p 244
1205 11th St 50616
Tel (641) 257-1000
SIC 2834 2899 2865 2048

CHEROKEE, IA

FIRST COOPERATIVE ASSOCIATION p 546
960 Riverview Dr 51012
Tel (712) 225-5400 SIC 5191 5153

CLARION, IA

HAGIE HOLDING CO p 653
721 Central Ave W 50525
Tel (515) 532-2861 SIC 3523

NORTH CENTRAL COOPERATIVE p 1051
221 4th Ave Nw 50525
Tel (515) 532-2881 SIC 5153 5191 5172

CLEAR LAKE, IA

AREA EDUCATION AGENCY 267 p 106
9184b 265th St Ste B 50428
Tel (641) 357-6125 SIC 8211

DEAN SNYDER CONSTRUCTION CO p 420
913 N 14th St 50428
Tel (641) 357-2283 SIC 1542 1521 1541

CLINTON, IA

CUSTOM-PAK INC p 403
86 16th Ave N 52732
Tel (563) 659-2100 SIC 3089

MERCY MEDICAL CENTER-CLINTON INC p 948
1410 N 4th St 52732
Tel (563) 244-5555 SIC 8062 8051 5122

CLIVE, IA

ARCHITECTURAL WALL SYSTEMS CO p 105
12345 University Ave # 100 50325
Tel (515) 255-1556 SIC 1542

JACOBSON TRANSPORTATION CO INC p 775
1275 Nw 128th St 50325
Tel (515) 262-1236 SIC 4213 4731

JHCI HOLDINGS INC p 785
1275 Nw 128th St 50325
Tel (515) 265-6171 SIC 4226 4221 4225

CONRAD, IA

MID IOWA COOPERATIVE p 963
201 S Main St 50621
Tel (641) 366-2740 SIC 5153 5191 2048

CORALVILLE, IA

INTEGRATED DNA TECHNOLOGIES INC p 749
1710 Commercial Park 52241
Tel (319) 626-8400 *SIC* 8733 5047

COUNCIL BLUFFS, IA

■ **AMERISTAR CASINO COUNCIL BLUFFS LLC** p 83
2200 River Rd 51501
Tel (712) 328-8888
SIC 7011 7991 5813 5812

COUNCIL BLUFFS COMMUNITY SCHOOL DISTRICT p 374
300 W Broadway Ste 1600 51503
Tel (712) 328-6419 *SIC* 8211

ECHO GROUP INC p 475
1851 Madison Ave Ste 710 51503
Tel (712) 322-4120 *SIC* 5063

FUTURE FOAM INC p 585
1610 Avenue N 51501
Tel (712) 323-9122 *SIC* 3086

■ **HARVEYS IOWA MANAGEMENT CO INC** p 667
1 Harrahs Blvd 51501
Tel (712) 329-6000 *SIC* 7011

HAWK JIM GROUP INC p 669
3119 S 9th St 51501
Tel (712) 366-2241 *SIC* 5012 7539

JENNIE EDMUNDSON MEMORIAL HOSPITAL p 782
933 E Pierce St 51503
Tel (712) 396-6000 *SIC* 8062

JIM HAWK TRUCK TRAILER INC p 785
3119 S 9th St 51501
Tel (712) 366-2241 *SIC* 5012

OMAHA STANDARD LLC p 1083
3501 S 11th St Ste 1 51501
Tel (712) 328-7444 *SIC* 3713 3536 3537

SOUTHWEST IOWA RENEWABLE ENERGY LLC p 1352
10868 189th St 51503
Tel (712) 366-0392 *SIC* 2869 2085 2046

CRESCO, IA

FEATHERLITE INC p 533
13380 Highways 63 & 9 52136
Tel (563) 547-6000 *SIC* 3716 3799 3714

CRESTON, IA

FANSTEEL INC p 527
1746 Commerce Rd 50801
Tel (641) 782-8521
SIC 3463 3728 3365 3369 3769 3545

WELLMAN DYNAMICS CORP p 1589
1746 Commerce Rd 50801
Tel (641) 782-8521 *SIC* 3369 3365

DAVENPORT, IA

■ **BITCO CORP** p 185
3700 Market Square Cir 52807
Tel (309) 786-5401 *SIC* 6411 6331

■ **BITCO NATIONAL INSURANCE CO** p 185
3700 Market Square Cir 52807
Tel (309) 786-5401 *SIC* 6331

CARLETON LIFE SUPPORT SYSTEMS INC p 257
2734 Hickory Grove Rd 52804
Tel (563) 383-6000 *SIC* 3679

DAVENPORT COMMUNITY SCHOOL DISTRICT p 415
1606 Brady St Ste 100 52803
Tel (563) 336-5000 *SIC* 8211

GENESIS HEALTH SYSTEM p 603
1227 E Rusholme St 52803
Tel (563) 421-1000 *SIC* 8741 8399 7218

GENESIS MEDICAL CENTER p 603
1227 E Rusholme St 52803
Tel (563) 421-6000 *SIC* 8062

▲ **LEE ENTERPRISES INC** p 851
201 N Harrison St Ste 600 52801
Tel (563) 383-2100 *SIC* 2711

■ **LEE PUBLICATIONS INC** p 851
201 N Harrison St Ste 600 52801
Tel (563) 383-2100 *SIC* 2711

MARCO GROUP INTERNATIONAL INC p 905
3425 E Locust St 52803
Tel (563) 324-2519 *SIC* 5084 5032

NETWORK IMAGING SOLUTIONS INC p 1028
242 E 90th St 52806
Tel (563) 285-6123 *SIC* 4225

PER MAR SECURITY AND RESEARCH CORP p 1134
1910 E Kimberly Rd 52807
Tel (563) 359-3200
SIC 8732 7381 5099 7389 7382

QUAD CITY AUTOMOTIVE GROUP LLC p 1195
3700 N Harrison St 52806
Tel (563) 386-1511 *SIC* 5511 5521

■ **R K DIXON CO** p 1202
5700 Utica Ridge Rd 52807
Tel (563) 344-9100 *SIC* 5044 7629 7359

RUSSELL CONSTRUCTION CO INC p 1259
4600 E 53rd St 52807
Tel (563) 355-1845 *SIC* 1542

S J SMITH CO INC p 1262
3707 W River Dr 52802
Tel (563) 324-5237 *SIC* 5169 5084 5999

SEARS MANUFACTURING CO p 1297
1718 S Concord St 52802
Tel (563) 383-2800 *SIC* 2531

ST AMBROSE UNIVERSITY p 1364
518 W Locust St 52803
Tel (563) 333-6000 *SIC* 8221

SWISS VALLEY FARMS COOPERATIVE p 1413
247 Research Pkwy 52806
Tel (563) 468-6600
SIC 5143 2022 5191 2023

TRI-CITY ELECTRIC CO OF IOWA p 1477
6225 N Brady St 52806
Tel (563) 322-7181 *SIC* 1731

VON MAUR INC p 1565
6565 N Brady St 52806
Tel (563) 388-2200 *SIC* 5311

DE WITT, IA

WENDLING QUARRIES INC p 1592
2647 225th St 52742
Tel (563) 659-9181 *SIC* 1422 1611 1442

DECORAH, IA

■ **INFASTECH DECORAH LLC** p 740
1304 Kerr Dr 52101
Tel (563) 382-4216 *SIC* 3452 3965

DENISON, IA

AMAIZING ENERGY HOLDING CO LLC p 64
2404 Highway 30 51442
Tel (712) 263-2676 *SIC* 2869

VETTER EQUIPMENT CO p 1553
610 14th Ave S 51442
Tel (712) 263-6440 *SIC* 5083

DES MOINES, IA

ALLIED CONSTRUCTION SERVICES INC p 56
2122 Fleur Dr 50321
Tel (515) 288-4855
SIC 1742 1752 1721 1751 1542

ALLIED GROUP INC p 56
1100 Locust St 50391
Tel (515) 280-4211 *SIC* 6331 6211 5112

ALLIED PROPERTY AND CASUALTY INSURANCE CO p 56
1100 Locust St 50391
Tel (515) 280-4211 *SIC* 6331

AMCO INSURANCE CO p 65
1100 Locust St 50391
Tel (515) 280-4211 *SIC* 6411

AMERICAN ENTERPRISE MUTUAL HOLDING CO p 71
601 6th Ave 50309
Tel (515) 245-2000 *SIC* 6321 6411

AMERICAN REPUBLIC INSURANCE CO p 78
601 6th Ave 50309
Tel (515) 245-2000 *SIC* 6324

ANDERSON ERICKSON DAIRY CO p 90
2420 E University Ave 50317
Tel (515) 265-2521 *SIC* 0241

ANNETT HOLDINGS INC p 92
6115 Leland Ave 50321
Tel (515) 287-6380 *SIC* 4213

ARLO TRANSPORTATION INC p 110
3811 Dixon St 50313
Tel (515) 265-6171 *SIC* 4731

ARNOLD LOGISTICS LLC p 112
3811 Dixon St 50313
Tel (515) 265-6171 *SIC* 4789

BAKER ELECTRIC INC p 146
111 Jackson Ave 50315
Tel (515) 288-6774 *SIC* 1731

BAKER MECHANICAL INC p 146
4224 Hubbell Ave 50317
Tel (515) 262-4000 *SIC* 1711 3444

BANKERS TRUST CO p 152
453 7th St 50309
Tel (515) 245-2863 *SIC* 6022

BARTON SOLVENTS INC p 158
1920 Ne 46th Ave 50313
Tel (515) 265-7998 *SIC* 5169

■ **BERKSHIRE HATHAWAY ENERGY CO** p 175
666 Grand Ave Ste 500 50309
Tel (515) 242-4300 *SIC* 4911 4924 6531

BROADLAWNS MEDICAL CENTER GUILD p 215
1801 Hickman Rd 50314
Tel (515) 282-2200 *SIC* 8062

CATHOLIC HEALTH INITIATIVES - IOWA CORP p 266
1111 6th Ave 50314
Tel (515) 247-3121 *SIC* 8062

CDS GLOBAL INC p 271
1901 Bell Ave Ste 19 50315
Tel (866) 897-7987 *SIC* 7389 7375 7374

CENTRAL IOWA HOSPITAL CORP p 278
1200 Pleasant St 50309
Tel (515) 241-6212 *SIC* 8062

CHANNEL PRIME ALLIANCE LLC p 288
1803 Hull Ave 50313
Tel (515) 264-4110 *SIC* 5169

CITY OF DES MOINES p 314
400 Robert D Ray Dr Ste B 50309
Tel (515) 283-4500 *SIC* 9111

CONSTRUCTION PRODUCTS INC p 361
1800 Ne 46th Ave 50313
Tel (515) 313-4253 *SIC* 3536 3544

COUNTY OF POLK p 381
111 Court Ave Ste 390 50309
Tel (515) 286-3200 *SIC* 9111

DEE ZEE INC p 421
1572 Ne 58th Ave 50313
Tel (515) 265-7331 *SIC* 3714

DES MOINES INDEPENDENT COMMUNITY SCHOOL DISTRICT p 431
2323 Grand Ave 50312
Tel (515) 242-7911 *SIC* 8211

DRAKE UNIVERSITY p 455
2507 University Ave 50311
Tel (515) 271-2011 *SIC* 8221

E M C NATIONAL LIFE MUTUAL HOLDING CO p 466
699 Walnut St 50309
Tel (515) 225-8197 *SIC* 6311

EFCO CORP p 480
1800 Ne 46th Ave 50313
Tel (515) 266-1141 *SIC* 3523

ELECTRO MANAGEMENT CORP p 485
111 Jackson Ave 50315
Tel (515) 288-6774 *SIC* 1731

■ **EMC INSURANCE GROUP INC** p 490
717 Mulberry St 50309
Tel (515) 345-2902 *SIC* 6331 6351 6321

EMC NATIONAL LIFE CO p 491
699 Walnut St Ste 1100 50309
Tel (515) 237-2000 *SIC* 6311 6411

■ **EMC REINSURANCE CO** p 491
717 Mulberry St 50309
Tel (515) 345-4541 *SIC* 6411

EMCO ENTERPRISES INC p 491
2121 E Walnut St 50317
Tel (515) 264-4283 *SIC* 5031

▲ **EMPLOYERS MUTUAL CASUALTY CO** p 494
717 Mulberry St 50309
Tel (515) 280-2511
SIC 6411 6321 6311 6519

FARMLAND MUTUAL INSURANCE CO INC p 530
1100 Locust St 50391
Tel (515) 508-3300 *SIC* 6411

FEDERAL HOME LOAN BANK OF DES MOINES p 534
801 Walnut St Ste 200 50309
Tel (515) 281-1000 *SIC* 6019

■ **FIDELITY & GUARANTY LIFE** p 540
601 Locust St Fl 2 50309
Tel (800) 445-6758 *SIC* 6311

■ **FIDELITY ACCEPTANCE CORP** p 540
800 Walnut St 50309
Tel (515) 557-8279 *SIC* 6021

FOODS INC p 564
4343 Merle Hay Rd 50310
Tel (515) 278-1657 *SIC* 5912

GIT-N-GO CONVENIENCE STORES INC p 613
2716 Indianola Ave 50315
Tel (515) 288-8565 *SIC* 5411 5541 6722

HALO GROUP INC p 655
814 33rd St 50312
Tel (515) 974-6908 *SIC* 6163

IOWA DEPARTMENT OF CORRECTIONS p 762
510 E 12th St Rm 4 50319
Tel (515) 725-5701 *SIC* 9223

IOWA DEPARTMENT OF EXECUTIVE OFFICE p 762
State Capital 50319
Tel (515) 281-5211 *SIC* 9111

IOWA DEPARTMENT OF HUMAN SERVICES p 762
1305 E Walnut St Rm 114 50319
Tel (515) 281-5454 *SIC* 9441

IOWA FINANCE AUTHORITY p 762
2015 Grand Ave Ste 200 50312
Tel (515) 725-4900 *SIC* 6163

IOWA PHYSICIANS CLINIC MEDICAL FOUNDATION p 763
1221 Pleasant St Ste 200 50309
Tel (515) 241-6212 *SIC* 8011

JACOBSON WAREHOUSE CO INC p 775
3811 Dixon St 50313
Tel (515) 265-6171
SIC 4226 4221 4225 8741 6552 4783

JENSEN CONSTRUCTION CO p 782
5550 Ne 22nd St 50313
Tel (515) 266-5173 *SIC* 1622 1629

JHCI ACQUISITION INC p 785
3811 Dixon St 50313
Tel (515) 265-6171 *SIC* 4225

JUDICIARY COURTS OF STATE OF IOWA p 796
1111 E Court Ave 50319
Tel (515) 281-5241 *SIC* 9211

KBC GROUP INC p 806
3400 109th St 50322
Tel (515) 270-2417 *SIC* 1542 5083

KEMIN INDUSTRIES INC p 809
2100 Maury St 50317
Tel (515) 559-5100 *SIC* 2834

LIFESPACE COMMUNITIES INC p 864
100 E Grand Ave Ste 200 50309
Tel (515) 288-5805 *SIC* 8059

LOFFREDO GARDENS INC p 874
4001 Sw 63rd St 50321
Tel (816) 421-7480 *SIC* 5148

LOMAR DISTRIBUTING INC p 875
2500 Dixon St 50316
Tel (515) 244-3105 *SIC* 5143 5149

MCANINCH CORP p 926
4001 Delaware Ave 50313
Tel (515) 267-2500 *SIC* 1623 1794

MERCY COLLEGE OF HEALTH SCIENCES p 946
928 6th Ave 50309
Tel (515) 643-3180 *SIC* 8221

▲ **MEREDITH CORP** p 948
1716 Locust St 50309
Tel (515) 284-3000 *SIC* 2721 2731 4833

■ **MHC INC** p 959
666 Grand Ave Ste 500 50309
Tel (515) 242-4300 *SIC* 4924 4911

■ **MIDAMERICAN ENERGY CO** p 964
666 Grand Ave Ste 500 50309
Tel (515) 242-4300 *SIC* 4931

■ **MIDAMERICAN FUNDING LLC** p 964
666 Grand Ave Ste 500 50309
Tel (515) 242-4300 *SIC* 4911 4924

MITTERA GROUP INC p 978
1312 Locust St Ste 202 50309
Tel (515) 343-5353 *SIC* 2752 7319

NATIONAL PORK BOARD p 1015
1776 Nw 114th St 50325
Tel (515) 223-2600 *SIC* 5147

PLUMB SUPPLY CO LLC p 1156
1622 Ne 51st Ave 50313
Tel (515) 262-9511 *SIC* 5074 5075

■ **PPW HOLDINGS LLC** p 1166
666 Grand Ave Ste 500 50309
Tel (515) 242-4300 *SIC* 4911 4924 6531

▲ **PRINCIPAL FINANCIAL GROUP INC** p 1177
711 High St 50392
Tel (515) 247-5111
SIC 6321 6799 6722 6311

■ **PRINCIPAL FINANCIAL SERVICES INC** p 1177
711 High St 50392
Tel (515) 247-5111 *SIC* 6311

■ **PRINCIPAL GLOBAL INVESTORS LLC** p 1177
801 Grand Ave 50309
Tel (515) 247-6582 *SIC* 6311

■ **PRINCIPAL INTERNATIONAL INC** p 1177
711 High St 50392
Tel (515) 247-5013
SIC 6282 6311 6321 6331

■ **PRINCIPAL LIFE INSURANCE CO** p 1177
711 High St 50392
Tel (515) 247-5111
SIC 6311 6211 6162 6321 6411

RASMUSSEN GROUP INC p 1209
5550 Ne 22nd St 50313
Tel (515) 266-5173 *SIC* 1622 1611 3272

RUAN LOGISTICS CORP p 1256
666 Grand Ave Ste 3100 50309
Tel (515) 245-2500 *SIC* 8742

RUAN TRANSPORT CORP p 1256
666 Grand Ave Ste 3100 50309
Tel (515) 245-2500 *SIC* 4213

RUAN TRANSPORTATION MANAGEMENT SYSTEMS INC p 1256
666 Grand Ave Ste 3100 50309
Tel (515) 245-2500 *SIC* 4213 7513

STATE OF IOWA p 1381
1007 E Grand Ave Rm 105 50319
Tel (515) 281-5211 *SIC* 9111

■ **TITAN TIRE CORP** p 1456
2345 E Market St 50317
Tel (515) 265-9200 *SIC* 3011

UNITED SERVICES ASSOCIATION INC p 1511
11280 Aurora Ave 50322
Tel (515) 276-6763 *SIC* 5191

WALDINGER CORP p 1572
2601 Bell Ave 50321
Tel (515) 284-1911 *SIC* 1711

WEITZ CO LLC p 1588
5901 Thornton Ave 50321
Tel (515) 698-4260 *SIC* 1542 1541 1629

WELLMARK INC p 1589
1331 Grand Ave 50309
Tel (515) 376-4500 *SIC* 6324 6411 6321

WELLS FARGO FINANCIAL CA INC p 1590
800 Walnut St 50309
Tel (515) 557-7401
SIC 6141 6153 6351 6159 6531 6021

■ **WELLS FARGO FINANCIAL LEASING INC** p 1590
800 Walnut St 50309
Tel (515) 557-4000 *SIC* 6159

■ **WELLS FARGO FINANCIAL SECURITY SERVICES INC** p 1590
800 Walnut St 50309
Tel (515) 243-2131
SIC 6141 6153 6351 6159 7374 6021

■ WELLS FARGO HOME MORTGAGE INC p 1590
1 Home Campus 50328
Tel (515) 324-3707 *SIC* 6162

■ WELLS FARGO IOWA NA p 1591
666 Walnut St Ste 1400 50309
Tel (515) 245-3000 *SIC* 6021 7389

WILIAN HOLDING CO p 1609
1800 Ne Broadway Ave 50313
Tel (515) 313-4350 *SIC* 3444

DUBUQUE, IA

A Y MCDONALD INDUSTRIES INC p 7
4800 Chavenelle Rd 52002
Tel (800) 292-2737
SIC 3432 3561 3494 5074 5075 5031

CHILDBIRTH EDUCATION p 298
350 N Grandview Ave 52001
Tel (563) 589-2406 *SIC* 8062

CONLON CONSTRUCTION CO OF IOWA p 356
1100 Rockdale Rd 52003
Tel (563) 583-1724 *SIC* 1542 8741 1541

COTTINGHAM & BUTLER INC p 374
800 Main St 52001
Tel (800) 793-5235 *SIC* 6411

■ DUBUQUE BANK AND TRUST CO p 459
1398 Central Ave 52001
Tel (563) 589-2000 *SIC* 6022

DUBUQUE COMMUNITY SCHOOL DISTRICT p 459
2300 Chaney Rd 52001
Tel (563) 552-3000 *SIC* 8211

EAGLE WINDOW & DOOR INC p 468
2045 Kerper Blvd 52001
Tel (563) 556-2270 *SIC* 2431

FINLEY HOSPITAL p 543
350 N Grandview Ave 52001
Tel (563) 582-1881 *SIC* 8011

▲ FLEXSTEEL INDUSTRIES INC p 556
385 Bell St 52001
Tel (563) 556-7730 *SIC* 2512 2515 2511

FOODLINER INC p 564
2099 Southpark Ct Ste 1 52003
Tel (563) 584-2670 *SIC* 4213

▲ HEARTLAND FINANCIAL USA INC p 679
1398 Central Ave 52001
Tel (563) 589-2000 *SIC* 6022

MCCOY GROUP INC p 927
2099 Southpark Ct 52003
Tel (563) 556-3773 *SIC* 5012 7538 4213

MULGREW OIL CO p 999
10314 Silverwood Dr 52003
Tel (563) 583-7386 *SIC* 5171 5172 5541

■ PENINSULA GAMING LLC p 1129
301 Bell St 52001
Tel (563) 690-4975 *SIC* 7999 7011

PENINSULA GAMING PARTNERS LLC p 1129
600 Star Brewery Dr # 110 52001
Tel (563) 690-4975 *SIC* 7999 7011

ROUSSELOT DUBUQUE INC p 1253
2350 Kerper Blvd 52001
Tel (262) 363-6050 *SIC* 2899

THEISENS INC p 1446
6201 Chavenelle Rd 52002
Tel (563) 556-4738
SIC 5531 5999 5699 5261

TRUCK COUNTRY OF IOWA INC p 1485
2099 Southpark Ct Ste 2 52003
Tel (563) 556-3773 *SIC* 5012 5531 7538

WOODWARD COMMUNICATIONS INC p 1623
801 Bluff St 52001
Tel (563) 588-5611
SIC 2711 2741 4832 2752 7311

DYERSVILLE, IA

BIG RIVER UNITED ENERGY LLC p 181
3294 Vine Rd 52040
Tel (563) 875-5500 *SIC* 2869

TOMY CORP p 1460
2021 9th St Se 52040
Tel (563) 875-2000 *SIC* 5092

TOMY INTERNATIONAL INC p 1460
2021 9th St Se 52040
Tel (563) 875-2000 *SIC* 5092

ELDORA, IA

UNITED SUPPLIERS INC p 1514
224 S Bell Ave 50627
Tel (515) 509-2400 *SIC* 5191

FAIRFIELD, IA

CAMBRIDGE INVESTMENT RESEARCH INC p 244
1776 Pleasant Plain Rd 52556
Tel (641) 472-5100 *SIC* 6211

DEXTER APACHE HOLDINGS INC p 434
2211 W Grimes Ave 52556
Tel (641) 472-5131 *SIC* 3321 3582

SOMEBODY CARES INC p 1339
57 N Court St 52556
Tel (641) 472-5352 *SIC* 5947 7699 5999

FLOYD, IA

FARMCHEM CORP p 529
616 Madison 50435
Tel (800) 247-1854 *SIC* 5083

FOREST CITY, IA

▲ WINNEBAGO INDUSTRIES INC p 1616
605 W Crystal Lake Rd 50436
Tel (641) 585-3535 *SIC* 3716 3714

FORT DODGE, IA

DECKER COMPANIES p 421
4000 5th Ave S 50501
Tel (515) 576-4141 *SIC* 4213

NEW CO-OPERATIVE INC p 1029
2626 1st Ave S 50501
Tel (515) 955-2040 *SIC* 5153 5191

NEW CO-OPERATIVE INC p 1029
2626 1st Ave S 50501
Tel (515) 955-2040 *SIC* 5153

TRINITY REGIONAL MEDICAL CENTER p 1481
802 Kenyon Rd Ste 1 50501
Tel (515) 574-6800 *SIC* 8062 8093

FORT MADISON, IA

■ PINNACLE FOODS LLC p 1149
2467 Henry Ladyn Dr 52627
Tel (319) 463-7111 *SIC* 2011

WOLF PACKAGING INC p 1621
2068 303rd Ave 52627
Tel (319) 372-6643 *SIC* 2621 2676 2671

FREDERICKSBURG, IA

FARMERS WIN COOPERATIVE p 530
110 N Jefferson Ave 50630
Tel (563) 237-5324 *SIC* 5191

GARNER, IA

■ IOWA MOLD TOOLING CO INC p 763
500 W Us Highway 18 50438
Tel (641) 923-3711 *SIC* 3531 3713 3563

GOLDFIELD, IA

CENTRAL IOWA RENEWABLE ENERGY LLC p 278
415 Locust St 50542
Tel (515) 825-3161 *SIC* 8731

CORN LP p 370
1303 Highway 3 E 50542
Tel (515) 825-3161 *SIC* 2869

GRIMES, IA

■ BLACK HILLS/IOWA GAS UTILITY CO LLC p 187
1205 Sw 37th St 50111
Tel (515) 224-1404 *SIC* 4924

RYKO SOLUTIONS INC p 1261
1500 Se 37th St 50111
Tel (515) 986-3700 *SIC* 3589 1796 7699

STAR OF DAVID ARMS INDUSTRIES INC p 1378
304 Se 2nd St Apt B 50111
Tel (888) 491-0307 *SIC* 3484 7389

GRINNELL, IA

ENGINEERED PLASTIC COMPONENTS INC p 499
1408 Zimmerman Dr 50112
Tel (641) 236-3100 *SIC* 3089

GRINNELL MUTUAL REINSURANCE CO p 641
4215 Highway 146 50112
Tel (641) 269-8000 *SIC* 6411

TRUSTEES OF GRINNELL COLLEGE p 1488
733 Broad St 50112
Tel (641) 269-3500 *SIC* 8221

HAMPTON, IA

ABCM CORP p 10
1320 4th St Ne 50441
Tel (641) 456-5636 *SIC* 8741 6519 7011

HARLAN, IA

FARM SERVICE COOPERATIVE p 529
2308 Pine St 51537
Tel (712) 755-2207 *SIC* 5153

VARIETY DISTRIBUTORS INC p 1544
609 7th St 51537
Tel (712) 755-2184
SIC 5131 5092 5122 5112 5145 5199

HARRIS, IA

SUNRISE FARMS INC p 1404
2060 White Ave 51345
Tel (712) 735-6010 *SIC* 0252

HIAWATHA, IA

IOWA FIRE PROTECTION INC p 762
735 Robins Rd 52233
Tel (319) 378-0820 *SIC* 1711

■ MCLEODUSA HOLDINGS INC p 932
1770 Boyson Rd 52233
Tel (319) 364-0000 *SIC* 4813 4812

WORLD CLASS INDUSTRIES INC p 1625
925 N 15th Ave 52233
Tel (319) 378-1766 *SIC* 3599

HILLS, IA

ELDON C STUTSMAN INC p 484
121 Lassie 52235
Tel (319) 679-2281 *SIC* 5191 3523

▲ HILLS BANCORPORATION p 694
131 Main St 52235
Tel (319) 679-2291 *SIC* 6022

■ HILLS BANK AND TRUST CO p 694
131 Main St 52235
Tel (319) 679-2291 *SIC* 6022

HOLSTEIN, IA

V-T INDUSTRIES INC p 1538
1000 Industrial Park 51025
Tel (712) 368-4381
SIC 3089 3083 4213 2435 2434 2431

HOUGHTON, IA

CHEM GRO OF HOUGHTON INC p 293
504 Main St 52631
Tel (319) 469-2611 *SIC* 5153 5191

HUDSON, IA

EAST CENTRAL IOWA COOP p 470
602 Washington St 50643
Tel (319) 988-3257 *SIC* 5153 5191

HUMBOLDT, IA

CORN BELT POWER COOPERATIVE p 370
1300 13th St N 50548
Tel (515) 332-7700 *SIC* 4911

IDA GROVE, IA

GODBERSEN-SMITH CONSTRUCTION CO INC p 619
121 E State Highway 175 51445
Tel (712) 364-3388 *SIC* 3531 1622

IOWA CITY, IA

ACT INC p 19
500 Act Dr 52243
Tel (319) 337-1000 *SIC* 8748

IOWA CITY COMMUNITY SCHOOL DISTRICT p 762
1725 N Dodge St 52245
Tel (319) 688-1000 *SIC* 8211

MERCY HOSPITAL IOWA CITY IOWA INC p 947
500 E Market St 52245
Tel (319) 339-0300
SIC 8062 8011 6512 8399

MERCY SERVICES IOWA CITY INC p 948
500 E Market St 52245
Tel (319) 339-3541 *SIC* 8011 8082

▲ MIDWESTONE FINANCIAL GROUP INC p 968
102 S Clinton St 52240
Tel (319) 356-5800 *SIC* 6022 6331

STATE UNIVERSITY OF IOWA FOUNDATION p 1383
1 W Park Rd 52242
Tel (319) 335-3305 *SIC* 8399 7371 7359

UNIVERSITY OF IOWA p 1521
101 Jessup Hall 52242
Tel (319) 335-3500 *SIC* 8221

UNIVERSITY OF IOWA HOSPITALS AND CLINICS p 1522
200 Hawkins Dr 52242
Tel (319) 356-1616 *SIC* 8062

IOWA FALLS, IA

IOWA SELECT FARMS LLP p 763
811 S Oak St 50126
Tel (641) 648-4479 *SIC* 0213

JOHNSTON, IA

■ AGCO FINANCE LLC p 34
8001 Birchwood Ct C 50131
Tel (515) 251-2800 *SIC* 6159

■ DEERE CREDIT INC p 422
6400 Nw 86th St 50131
Tel (515) 224-2800 *SIC* 6153

DELTA DENTAL OF IOWA p 426
9000 Northpark Dr 50131
Tel (515) 331-4594 *SIC* 6321

IOWA BANKERS BENEFIT PLAN p 762
8800 Nw 62nd Ave 50131
Tel (515) 286-4300 *SIC* 6411

IOWA DEPARTMENT OF PUBLIC DEFENSE p 762
7105 Nw 70th Ave 50131
Tel (515) 252-4211 *SIC* 9711

■ JOHN DEERE FINANCIAL SERVICES INC p 788
6400 Nw 86th St 50131
Tel (515) 267-3000 *SIC* 6141

■ OPTIMUM QUALITY GRAINS LLC p 1090
7100 Nw 62nd Ave 50131
Tel (515) 270-3200 *SIC* 5153

■ PIONEER HI-BRED INTERNATIONAL INC p 1150
7100 Nw 62nd Ave 50131
Tel (515) 535-3200 *SIC* 5191

■ PIONEER OVERSEAS CORP p 1151
7100 Nw 62nd Ave 50131
Tel (515) 535-3200 *SIC* 5191

SHAZAM INC p 1313
6700 Pioneer Pkwy 50131
Tel (515) 288-2828 *SIC* 7374

WESLEYLIFE p 1593
5508 Nw 88th St 50131
Tel (515) 271-6789 *SIC* 8059

KEOKUK, IA

HENNIGES AUTOMOTIVE IOWA INC p 683
3200 Main St 52632
Tel (319) 524-4560
SIC 3069 3442 3429 2295

ROQUETTE AMERICA INC p 1250
1003 S 5th St 52632
Tel (319) 524-5757 *SIC* 2046 2869

LAMONI, IA

GRACELAND UNIVERSITY p 628
1 University Pl 50140
Tel (641) 784-5000 *SIC* 8221

LAWLER, IA

HOMELAND ENERGY SOLUTIONS LLC p 703
2779 Highway 24 52154
Tel (563) 238-5555 *SIC* 2869 2085 2046

LE MARS, IA

NORTHWEST IOWA POWER COOPERATIVE p 1060
31002 C38 51031
Tel (712) 546-4141 *SIC* 4911

WELLS ENTERPRISES INC p 1590
1 Blue Bunny Dr Sw 51031
Tel (712) 546-4000 *SIC* 2024

MANCHESTER, IA

■ HENDERSON PRODUCTS INC p 682
1085 S 3rd St 52057
Tel (563) 927-2828 *SIC* 3537

XL SPECIALIZED TRAILERS INC p 1632
1086 S 3rd St 52057
Tel (563) 927-4900 *SIC* 3715

MARBLE ROCK, IA

VIAFIELD p 1554
533 Bradford St 50653
Tel (641) 315-2515 *SIC* 5153

MARCUS, IA

LITTLE SIOUX CORN PROCESSORS LLC p 871
4808 F Ave 51035
Tel (712) 376-2800 *SIC* 2869

LSCP LLLP p 883
4808 F Ave 51035
Tel (712) 376-2800 *SIC* 4925 5191

MARION, IA

LINN CO-OPERATIVE OIL CO p 869
325 35th St 52302
Tel (319) 377-4881 *SIC* 5153 5171 5191

MARSHALLTOWN, IA

■ FISHER CONTROLS INTERNATIONAL LLC p 552
205 S Center St 50158
Tel (641) 754-3011
SIC 3491 3823 3625 3612 3494

■ INSTRUMENT & VALVE SERVICES CO p 747
205 S Center St 50158
Tel (641) 754-3011 *SIC* 3494 3825 7699

MASON CITY, IA

AADG INC p 8
1502 12th St Nw 50401
Tel (641) 423-1334 *SIC* 3442

GOLDEN GRAIN ENERGY LLC p 621
1822 43rd St Sw 50401
Tel (641) 423-8525 *SIC* 2869

MERCY MEDICAL CENTER FOUNDATION - NORTH IOWA p 947
1000 4th St Sw 50401
Tel (641) 428-7000 *SIC* 8062

WOODHARBOR MOLDING & MILLWORKS INC p 1623
3277 9th St Sw 50401
Tel (641) 423-0444
SIC 2431 2521 2517 2434

MIDDLETOWN, IA

AMERICAN ORDNANCE LLC p 77
17575 Hwy 79 52638
Tel (319) 753-7004 *SIC* 3483

MONONA, IA

■ MONONA WIRE CORP p 984
301 W Spruce St 52159
Tel (563) 539-2012 *SIC* 3679 3694

MONTEZUMA, IA

BROWNELLS INC p 220
200 S Front St 50171
Tel (641) 623-5401 SIC 5091 5941

MONTICELLO, IA

INNOVATIVE AG SERVICES CO p 744
2010 S Main St 52310
Tel (319) 465-3501 SIC 5999

MOUNT PLEASANT, IA

METROGROUP CORP p 955
1805 E Washington St 52641
Tel (319) 385-5135 SIC 7331 7389

METROGROUP HOLDING LLC p 955
1805 E Washington St 52641
Tel (319) 385-5135 SIC 6719

PACKERS HOLDINGS LLC p 1107
1010 E Washington St # 202 52641
Tel (800) 881-9558 SIC 7342 7349

MUSCATINE, IA

■ ALLSTEEL INC p 58
2210 2nd Ave 52761
Tel (563) 272-4800 SIC 2522

BRIDGESTONE BANDAG LLC p 211
2000 Bandag Dr 52761
Tel (563) 262-2511
SIC 7534 3559 5014 3011 7549 6794

EASTERN IOWA COMMUNITY COLLEGE DISTRICT p 472
152 Colorado St 52761
Tel (563) 264-2088 SIC 8222 8221

GRAIN PROCESSING CORP p 629
1600 Oregon St 52761
Tel (563) 264-4265 SIC 2869 2085 2082

▲ HNI CORP p 698
408 E 2nd St 52761
Tel (563) 272-7400
SIC 2522 2542 2521 2541 3433 3429

■ HON CO LLC p 704
200 Oak St 52761
Tel (563) 272-7100 SIC 2521

KENT CORP p 812
2905 N Highway 61 52761
Tel (563) 264-4211
SIC 2869 2085 2046 2048

KENT NUTRITION GROUP INC p 812
1600 Oregon St 52761
Tel (866) 647-1212 SIC 2048

■ MAXON FURNITURE INC p 922
2210 2nd Ave 52761
Tel (800) 876-4274 SIC 2522

MUSCATINE COMMUNITY SCHOOL DISTRICT p 1002
2900 Mulberry Ave 52761
Tel (563) 263-7223 SIC 8211

MUSCATINE POWER & WATER (INC) p 1002
3205 Cedar St 52761
Tel (563) 263-2631 SIC 4911 4941

RAYMOND-MUSCATINE INC p 1210
3305 N Highway 38 52761
Tel (563) 262-7700 SIC 3537

SC COMPANIES INC p 1285
225 Iowa Ave 52761
Tel (563) 264-6600 SIC 8711

SSAB IOWA INC p 1363
1770 Bill Sharp Blvd 52761
Tel (563) 381-5300 SIC 3312

STANLEY CONSULTANTS INC p 1377
225 Iowa Ave 52761
Tel (563) 264-6600 SIC 8711

NEVADA, IA

LINCOLNWAY ENERGY LLC p 868
59511 Lincoln Hwy 50201
Tel (515) 232-1010 SIC 2869 2861

PARAGON INTERNATIONAL INC p 1113
731 W 18th St 50201
Tel (515) 382-8000 SIC 3589 3556 3431

NEW HAMPTON, IA

FIVE STAR COOPERATIVE p 553
1949 N Linn Ave 50659
Tel (641) 394-3052 SIC 5153 5191

NEWTON, IA

■ TPI IOWA LLC p 1467
2300 N 33rd E 50208
Tel (641) 791-3500 SIC 3083

NORTH LIBERTY, IA

CENTRO INC p 281
950 N Bend Dr 52317
Tel (319) 626-3200 SIC 3089

▲ HEARTLAND EXPRESS INC p 679
901 N Kansas Ave 52317
Tel (319) 626-3600 SIC 4213

■ HEARTLAND EXPRESS INC OF IOWA p 679
901 N Kansas Ave 52317
Tel (319) 626-3600 SIC 4213

NORWAY, IA

FRONTIER COOPERATIVE p 581
3021 78th St 52318
Tel (319) 227-7996 SIC 5122 2099 5149

OAKLAND, IA

OAKLAND FOODS LLC p 1071
21876 Highway 59 51560
Tel (712) 482-6640 SIC 2013

OAKVILLE, IA

TRIOAK FOODS INC p 1482
103 W Railroad St 52646
Tel (319) 766-2230 SIC 0213 5153

ORANGE CITY, IA

DIAMOND-VOGEL PAINT CO p 437
1110 Albany Pl Se 51041
Tel (712) 737-8880 SIC 2851 5231

PIZZA RANCH INC p 1153
204 19th St Se 51041
Tel (712) 707-8800 SIC 5812 6794

VOGEL PAINT & WAX CO INC p 1564
1110 Albany Pl Se 51041
Tel (712) 737-4993 SIC 2851 5198

VOGEL PAINT INC p 1564
1110 Albany Pl Se 51041
Tel (712) 737-8880 SIC 2851 8741

OSKALOOSA, IA

MUSCO CORP p 1002
100 1st Ave W 52577
Tel (641) 676-1746
SIC 7359 3648 3646 3641 3545 3423

MUSCO SPORTS LIGHTING LLC p 1002
100 1st Ave W 52577
Tel (641) 673-0411 SIC 3648

OSSIAN, IA

FARMERS UNION COOPERATIVE p 530
1913 County Road B32 52161
Tel (563) 532-9381 SIC 5153 5261 5983

REILLY CONSTRUCTION CO INC p 1221
110 E Main St 52161
Tel (563) 532-9211 SIC 1611

PELLA, IA

PELLA CORP p 1128
102 Main St 50219
Tel (641) 621-1000 SIC 2431

PRECISION INC p 1168
300 Se 14th St 50219
Tel (641) 628-3115 SIC 2499 3429

VERMEER MANUFACTURING CO p 1551
1210 E Vermeer Rd 50219
Tel (641) 628-3141 SIC 3531 3523

PEOSTA, IA

MI-T-M CORP p 959
50 Mitm Dr 52068
Tel (563) 556-7484 SIC 3569

POCAHONTAS, IA

PRO COOPERATIVE p 1178
17 3rd Ave Ne 50574
Tel (712) 335-3060 SIC 5153 5191 5172

POSTVILLE, IA

INDUSTRIAL LAMINATES/NORPLEX INC p 740
665 Lybrand St 52162
Tel (563) 864-7321 SIC 3089 3081

RALSTON, IA

WEST CENTRAL COOPERATIVE p 1594
406 1st St 51459
Tel (712) 667-3200
SIC 5153 2075 2048 5191

RED OAK, IA

UNITED FARMERS MERCANTILE COOPERATIVE p 1508
203 W Oak St 51566
Tel (712) 623-5453
SIC 5153 5191 5541 5211 2048

REINBECK, IA

PETERSON CONTRACTORS INC p 1138
104 Blackhawk St 50669
Tel (319) 345-2713 SIC 1611

ROCK VALLEY, IA

COOPERATIVE FARMERS ELEVATOR p 367
1219 Main St 51247
Tel (712) 476-5321 SIC 5153 5191

ROLAND, IA

KEY COOPERATIVE p 814
13585 620th Ave 50236
Tel (515) 388-4341
SIC 5153 5541 2048 5191

SERGEANT BLUFF, IA

GELITA NORTH AMERICA INC p 598
2445 Port Neal Rd 51054
Tel (712) 943-5516 SIC 5169 2099

SHEFFIELD, IA

SUKUP MANUFACTURING CO p 1397
1555 255th St 50475
Tel (641) 892-4222 SIC 3523

SHELDON, IA

ROSENBOOM MACHINE & TOOL INC p 1251
1530 Western Ave 51201
Tel (712) 324-4854 SIC 3593 3492 3594

SIOUX CENTER, IA

FARMERS COOPERATIVE SOCIETY p 529
317 3rd St Nw 51250
Tel (712) 722-2671 SIC 5153 5191 5211

HARBOR GROUP INC p 659
1520 N Main Ave 51250
Tel (712) 722-1661 SIC 1731

INTERSTATES CONSTRUCTION SERVICES INC p 758
1520 N Main Ave 51250
Tel (712) 722-1662 SIC 1731 3629

SIOUXLAND FARMERS COOPERATIVE p 1326
317 3rd St Nw 51250
Tel (712) 722-2671 SIC 5153 5191

SIOUX CITY, IA

BOMGAARS SUPPLY INC p 199
1805 Zenith Dr 51103
Tel (712) 226-5000 SIC 5311 5999 5651

CHESTERMAN CO p 295
4700 S Lewis Blvd 51106
Tel (712) 252-2653 SIC 2086

CSD INC p 397
5101 Harbor Dr 51111
Tel (712) 255-6927 SIC 5191

DIOCESE OF SIOUX CITY p 440
1821 Jackson St 51105
Tel (712) 255-7933 SIC 8661

■ FLO KAY INDUSTRIES INC p 557
1919 Grand Ave 51106
Tel (712) 277-2011 SIC 2873 2048 2816

KLINGER COMPANIES INC p 823
2015 7th St 51101
Tel (712) 277-3900 SIC 1542 1541

NORTHWEST IOWA HOSPITAL CORP p 1060
2800 Pierce St Ste 410 51104
Tel (712) 279-3500 SIC 8062 8051

SABRE COMMUNICATIONS CORP p 1264
7101 Southbridge Dr 51111
Tel (712) 258-6690 SIC 3663 3441 1731

SIOUX CITY COMMUNITY SCHOOL DISTRICT INC p 1326
627 4th St Ofc 51101
Tel (712) 279-6667 SIC 8211

SIOUX CITY FOUNDRY CO p 1326
801 Division St 51105
Tel (712) 252-4181
SIC 5051 3443 3321 3316 3444 3441

SIOUX CITY TRUCK SALES INC p 1326
2601 Voyager Ave 51111
Tel (712) 234-2728 SIC 5511

■ TERRA INDUSTRIES INC p 1439
600 4th St Terra Ctr 51102
Tel (712) 943-5501 SIC 2873

TUR-PAK FOODS INC p 1492
6201 Macarthur St 51111
Tel (712) 258-9354 SIC 5147

UNITY POINT HEALTH ST LUKE p 1515
2720 Stone Park Blvd 51104
Tel (712) 279-3500 SIC 8741

WILSON TRAILER CO p 1614
4400 S Lewis Blvd 51106
Tel (712) 252-6500 SIC 3715

SPENCER, IA

EATON HYDRAULICS INC p 473
803 32nd Ave W 51301
Tel (712) 264-3269 SIC 1799

SHINE BROS CORP p 1317
225 10th Ave Se 51301
Tel (712) 262-5579 SIC 5093 3341

SPENCER MUNICIPAL HOSPITAL p 1358
1200 1st Ave E Ste 1 51301
Tel (712) 264-6198 SIC 8062 8011

SPIRIT LAKE, IA

REMBRANDT ENTERPRISES INC p 1222
1521 18th St 51360
Tel (712) 759-1800 SIC 2015 3556

STORM LAKE, IA

■ METABANK p 952
121 E 5th St 50588
Tel (712) 732-4117 SIC 6035

STRAWBERRY POINT, IA

SEEDORFF MASONRY INC p 1300
408 W Mission St 52076
Tel (563) 933-2296 SIC 1741 2448

TAMA, IA

SAC & FOX TRIBAL OFFICES p 1264
349 Meskwaki Rd 52339
Tel (641) 484-4678 SIC 9532

URBANDALE, IA

■ CONTINENTAL WESTERN INSURANCE CO p 364
11201 Douglas Ave 50322
Tel (515) 473-3000 SIC 6331

DSI DISTRIBUTING INC p 457
3601 109th St 50322
Tel (515) 276-9181 SIC 5063 5731

IOWA LIMESTONE CO p 763
3301 106th Cir 50322
Tel (515) 243-3160 SIC 1422 5191

LOGAN CONTRACTORS SUPPLY INC p 874
4101 106th St 50322
Tel (515) 253-9048 SIC 5082

UNITYPOINT AT HOME p 1515
11333 Aurora Ave 50322
Tel (515) 557-3100 SIC 8082

WALCOTT, IA

IOWA 80 GROUP INC p 762
515 Sterling Dr 52773
Tel (563) 468-5500
SIC 5541 5399 7542 5812

IOWA 80 TRUCKSTOP INC p 762
755 W Iowa 80 Rd I-80 52773
Tel (563) 284-6961
SIC 5541 5399 7542 5812

RIVER VALLEY COOPERATIVE p 1237
102 S Main St 52773
Tel (563) 284-6223 SIC 5153 5191

WATERLOO, IA

ALLEN HEALTH SYSTEMS INC p 53
1825 Logan Ave 50703
Tel (319) 235-3941 SIC 8741

ALLEN MEMORIAL HOSPITAL CORP p 53
1825 Logan Ave 50703
Tel (319) 235-3941 SIC 8062

COVENANT HEALTH SYSTEM INC p 384
3421 W 9th St 50702
Tel (319) 236-4111 SIC 8062

COVENANT MEDICAL CENTER INC p 384
3421 W 9th St 50702
Tel (319) 272-7296 SIC 8062

CPM ACQUISITION CORP p 387
2975 Airline Cir 50703
Tel (319) 232-8444 SIC 3523

CPM HOLDINGS INC p 387
2975 Airline Cir 50703
Tel (336) 248-5181 SIC 5084

HAWKEYE COMMUNITY COLLEGE p 669
1501 E Orange Rd 50701
Tel (319) 296-4201 SIC 8222

■ OMEGA CABINETS LTD p 1084
1205 Peters Dr 50703
Tel (319) 235-5700 SIC 2434 5211

PROFESSIONAL OFFICE SERVICES INC p 1180
2757 Burton Ave 50703
Tel (319) 235-6777 SIC 2761

VERIDIAN CREDIT UNION p 1549
1827 Ansborough Ave 50701
Tel (319) 236-5600 SIC 6062 6163

VGM GROUP INC p 1553
1111 W San Marnan Dr 50701
Tel (319) 235-7100 SIC 8748 5047

WATERLOO COMMUNITY SCHOOL DISTRICT INC p 1582
1516 Washington St 50702
Tel (319) 433-1800 SIC 8299

WAVERLY, IA

CUNA MUTUAL LIFE INSURANCE CO p 401
2000 Heritage Way 50677
Tel (319) 352-4090 SIC 6411 6321 8742

■ TEREX MHPS CORP p 1439
106 12th St Se 50677
Tel (877) 794-5284 SIC 3536

WARTBURG COLLEGE p 1577
100 Wartburg Blvd 50677
Tel (319) 352-8200 SIC 8221

WEBSTER CITY, IA

VAN DIEST SUPPLY CO p 1542
1434 220th St 50595
Tel (515) 832-2366 SIC 5191 2875 2879

WEST BEND, IA

MAXYIELD COOPERATIVE p 923
313 3rd Ave Nw 50597
Tel (515) 887-7211
SIC 5153 5191 2999 0723

WEST BURLINGTON, IA

BIG RIVER RESOURCES LLC p 181
15210 103rd St 52655
Tel (319) 753-1100 SIC 2869

BIG RIVER RESOURCES WEST BURLINGTON LLC p 181
15210 103rd St 52655
Tel (319) 753-1100 SIC 2869

GREAT RIVER HEALTH SYSTEMS INC p 634
1221 S Gear Ave 52655
Tel (319) 768-1000 SIC 8062

GREAT RIVER MEDICAL CENTER p 634
1221 S Gear Ave 52655
Tel (319) 768-1000 SIC 8062

WEST DES MOINES, IA

▲ AMERICAN EQUITY INVESTMENT LIFE HOLDING CO p 71
6000 Westown Pkwy 50266
Tel (515) 221-0002 SIC 6311

■ AMERICAN EQUITY INVESTMENT LIFE INSURANCE CO p 71
5000 Westown Pkwy Ste 440 50266
Tel (515) 221-0002 SIC 6311

ATHENE ANNUITY AND LIFE CO p 124
7700 Mills Civic Pkwy 50266
Tel (888) 266-8489 SIC 6311

ATHENE USA CORP p 124
7700 Mills Civic Pkwy 50266
Tel (515) 342-3413 SIC 6311

BRIGGS MEDICAL SERVICE CO p 212
7300 Westown Pkwy Ste 100 50266
Tel (515) 327-6400 SIC 5047

CARE INITIATIVES p 254
1611 Westlakes Pkwy 50266
Tel (515) 224-4442 SIC 8051 8052

CEDAR CREEK LLC p 272
5034 Grand Ridge Dr 50265
Tel (405) 917-8300 SIC 2431 5031

EQUITRUST LIFE INSURANCE CO INC p 506
7100 Westown Pkwy Ste 200 50266
Tel (888) 400-5759 SIC 6411

FARM BUREAU MULTI-STATE SERVICES INC p 528
5400 University Ave 50266
Tel (515) 225-5400 SIC 6411

FARM BUREAU PROPERTY & CASUALTY INSURANCE CO p 528
5400 University Ave 50266
Tel (515) 225-5400 SIC 6411 2711 6211

FARMERS MUTUAL HAIL INSURANCE CO OF IOWA p 529
6785 Westown Pkwy 50266
Tel (515) 282-9104 SIC 6331

▲ FBL FINANCIAL GROUP INC p 532
5400 University Ave 50266
Tel (515) 225-5400 SIC 6311 6411

GUIDEONE AMERICA INSURANCE CO p 645
1111 Ashworth Rd 50265
Tel (515) 267-5000 SIC 6331

GUIDEONE INC p 645
1111 Ashworth Rd 50265
Tel (515) 267-5000 SIC 6311

GUIDEONE MUTUAL INSURANCE CO p 645
1111 Ashworth Rd 50265
Tel (515) 267-5000 SIC 6331

GUIDEONE MUTUAL INSURANCE CO p 645
1111 Ashworth Rd 50265
Tel (515) 267-5000 SIC 6411

HEARTLAND CO-OP p 679
2829 Westown Pkwy Ste 350 50266
Tel (515) 225-1334 SIC 5153 0762 2048

HIRSH INDUSTRIES INC p 696
3636 Westown Pkwy Ste 100 50266
Tel (515) 299-3200 SIC 2522 2541

HMA INC p 697
3001 Westown Pkwy Stop 1 50266
Tel (515) 223-6800 SIC 6411 6321 8742

HOLMES MURPHY AND ASSOCIATES LLC p 701
3001 Westown Pkwy 50266
Tel (800) 247-7756 SIC 6411

HOMESTEADERS LIFE CO p 704
5700 Westown Pkwy Ofc 50266
Tel (515) 440-7777 SIC 6311

HY-LINE NORTH AMERICA LLC p 722
1755 West Lakes Pkwy A 50266
Tel (515) 225-6030 SIC 0254

HY-VEE AND AFFILIATES BENEFIT PLAN AND TRUST p 723
5820 Westown Pkwy 50266
Tel (515) 267-2800 SIC 6411

HY-VEE INC p 723
5820 Westown Pkwy 50266
Tel (515) 267-2800 SIC 5411 5912 5921

IMT INSURANCE CO p 735
4445 Corporate Dr Ste 100 50266
Tel (515) 327-2777 SIC 6331 7374

IOWA FARM BUREAU FEDERATION p 762
5400 University Ave 50266
Tel (515) 225-5400
SIC 8699 5154 6311 6321 6411

IOWA HEALTH SYSTEM p 762
1776 West Lakes Pkwy # 400 50266
Tel (515) 241-6161 SIC 8062 8721 8741

IOWA NETWORK SERVICES INC p 763
7760 Office Plaza Dr S 50266
Tel (515) 830-0110 SIC 4813

IOWA STUDENT LOAN LIQUIDITY CORP p 763
6775 Vista Dr 50266
Tel (515) 243-5626 SIC 6111 6141

ITA GROUP INC p 767
4600 Westown Pkwy Ste 100 50266
Tel (515) 326-3400 SIC 8742 4724

KRAUSE HOLDINGS INC p 829
6400 Westown Pkwy 50266
Tel (515) 226-0128 SIC 5411

KUM & GO LC p 832
6400 Westown Pkwy 50266
Tel (515) 226-0128 SIC 5411

■ MARSH AFFINITY GROUP SERVICES p 910
12421 Meredith Dr 50398
Tel (515) 243-1900 SIC 6411

MERCHANTS BONDING CO (MUTUAL) p 944
6700 Westown Pkwy 50266
Tel (515) 243-8171 SIC 6351

MERCY HEALTH NETWORK INC p 946
1755 59th Pl 50266
Tel (515) 247-3121 SIC 8741

SNI COMPANIES p 1335
4500 Westown Pkwy Ste 120 50266
Tel (727) 577-4294 SIC 7361

■ UNION SECURITY INSURANCE CO p 1505
6941 Vista Dr 50266
Tel (651) 361-4000 SIC 6321 6324

WEST DES MOINES COMMUNITY SCHOOL DISTRICT p 1594
3550 Mills Civic Pkwy 50265
Tel (515) 633-5078 SIC 8211

WRIGHT SERVICE CORP p 1627
5930 Grand Ave Ste 100 50266
Tel (515) 271-1197 SIC 0783

WRIGHT TREE SERVICE INC p 1627
5930 Grand Ave Ste 100 50266
Tel (515) 277-6291 SIC 0783

WEST LIBERTY, IA

WEST LIBERTY FOODS LLC p 1594
228 W 2nd St 52776
Tel (319) 627-6000 SIC 2015

WILLIAMSBURG, IA

KINZE MANUFACTURING INC p 821
2172 M Ave 52361
Tel (319) 668-1300 SIC 3523

WINDSOR HEIGHTS, IA

ELECTRICAL ENGINEERING AND EQUIPMENT CO p 485
953 73rd St 50324
Tel (515) 273-0100 SIC 5063 8711

KANSAS

ARKANSAS CITY, KS

ARKANSAS CITY PRESBYTERIAN MANOR INC p 109
1711 N 4th St 67005
Tel (620) 442-8700 SIC 8051

CFPB HOLDINGS LLC p 285
604 Goff Industrial Pk Rd 67005
Tel (620) 741-3100 SIC 8731

CREEKSTONE FARMS PREMIUM BEEF LLC p 391
604 Goff Industrial Pk Rd 67005
Tel (620) 741-3100 SIC 2011

ATCHISON, KS

BLISH-MIZE CO p 189
223 S 5th St 66002
Tel (913) 367-1250 SIC 5072

BRADKEN - ATCHISON/ST JOSEPH INC p 206
400 S 4th St 66002
Tel (913) 367-2121 SIC 3325

▲ MGP INGREDIENTS INC p 958
100 Commercial St 66002
Tel (913) 367-1480 SIC 2085 2041

■ MGPI PROCESSING INC p 958
100 Commercial St 66002
Tel (913) 367-1480 SIC 2085 2041

BELOIT, KS

AGMARK LLC p 35
118 W Main St 67420
Tel (785) 738-9641 SIC 4221

CARRICO IMPLEMENT CO INC p 260
3160 Us 24 Hwy 67420
Tel (785) 738-5744 SIC 5083

SUNFLOWER MANUFACTURING CO INC p 1402
3154 Hallie Trl 67420
Tel (785) 738-2261 SIC 3523

BONNER SPRINGS, KS

BERKEL & CO CONTRACTORS INC p 175
2649 S 142nd St 66012
Tel (913) 422-5125 SIC 1771 1741

BURLINGTON, KS

WOLF CREEK NUCLEAR OPERATING CORP p 1621
1550 Oxen Ln 66839
Tel (620) 364-4141 SIC 4911

CHANUTE, KS

CONSOLIDATED OIL WELL SERVICES LLC p 360
1322 S Grant Ave 66720
Tel (620) 431-9210 SIC 1389

Q CONSOLIDATED OIL WELL SERVICES LLC p 1194
1322 S Grant Ave 66720
Tel (620) 431-9210 SIC 1389

COFFEYVILLE, KS

MEDICALODGES INC p 937
201 W 8th St 67337
Tel (620) 251-6700 SIC 8051

COLUMBUS, KS

CROSSLAND CONSTRUCTION CO INC p 394
833 S East Ave 66725
Tel (620) 429-1414 SIC 1542

COLWICH, KS

ICM INC p 727
310 N 1st St 67030
Tel (316) 796-0900 SIC 8748 8711

CONCORDIA, KS

F&A FOOD SALES INC p 522
2221 Lincoln St 66901
Tel (785) 243-2301 SIC 5141

DE SOTO, KS

AIRTEX MANUFACTURING LLLP p 40
32050 W 83rd St 66018
Tel (913) 583-3181
SIC 3585 5075 3564 3433

HUHTAMAKI AMERICAS INC p 718
9201 Packaging Dr 66018
Tel (913) 583-3025 SIC 3089

HUHTAMAKI FILMS INC p 718
9201 Packaging Dr 66018
Tel (913) 583-3025 SIC 3089

HUHTAMAKI INC p 718
9201 Packaging Dr 66018
Tel (913) 583-3025 SIC 2656 3565

DERBY, KS

DERBY PUBLIC SCHOOLS p 431
120 E Washington St 67037
Tel (316) 788-8400 SIC 8211

EDWARDSVILLE, KS

EARP MEAT CO p 469
2730 S 98th St 66111
Tel (913) 287-3311 SIC 5142 5141 5113

EL DORADO, KS

■ HOLLYFRONTIER EL DORADO REFINING LLC p 701
1401 Douglas Rd 67042
Tel (316) 321-2200 SIC 2911

ELWOOD, KS

SNORKEL INTERNATIONAL INC p 1336
2009 Roseport Rd 66024
Tel (785) 989-3000 SIC 3537

EMPORIA, KS

EMPORIA STATE UNIVERSITY p 494
1 Kellogg Cir 66801
Tel (620) 341-1200 SIC 8221

EMPORIA UNIFIED SCHOOL DISTRICT 253 p 494
1700 W 7th Ave 66801
Tel (620) 341-2200 SIC 8211

HOPKINS MANUFACTURING CORP p 706
428 Peyton St 66801
Tel (620) 342-7320 SIC 3714

NEWMAN MEMORIAL HOSPITAL FOUNDATION p 1038
1201 W 12th Ave 66801
Tel (620) 343-6800 SIC 8062 5047 8011

S&S QUALITY MEATS LLC p 1263
1542 S Highway 99 66801
Tel (620) 342-6354 SIC 2011 2013

SIMMONS PET FOOD KS INC p 1324
1400 E Logan Ave 66801
Tel (620) 342-1323 SIC 2047

FORT LEAVENWORTH, KS

ARMED FORCES BANK NATIONAL ASSOCIATION p 111
320 Kansas Ave 66027
Tel (913) 682-9090 SIC 6021

FORT SCOTT, KS

W/K HOLDING CO INC p 1569
2401 Cooper St 66701
Tel (620) 223-5500 SIC 2754

WARD-KRAFT INC p 1575
2401 Cooper St 66701
Tel (800) 821-4021 SIC 2761 2672

FRONTENAC, KS

TRIPLE - T FOODS INC p 1482
1601 W Mckay St 66763
Tel (620) 231-7779 SIC 2047

GALENA, KS

CELLTRON INC p 274
1110 W 7th St 66739
Tel (620) 783-1333 SIC 3679

GARDEN CITY, KS

AMERICAN IMPLEMENT INC p 74
2611 W Jones Ave 67846
Tel (620) 275-4114 SIC 5083

GARDEN CITY CO-OP INC p 591
106 N 6th St 67846
Tel (620) 275-6161 SIC 5153 5191 5172

GARDEN CITY PUBLIC SCHOOLS p 591
1205 Fleming St 67846
Tel (620) 805-7000 SIC 8211

ST CATHERINE HOSPITAL p 1365
401 E Spruce St 67846
Tel (620) 272-2222 SIC 8062

WINDRIVER GRAIN LLC p 1615
2810 E Us Highway 50 67846
Tel (620) 275-2101 SIC 5153

GARDNER, KS

GARDNER EDGERTON UNIFIED SCHOOL DISTRICT 231 p 592
231 E Madison St 66030
Tel (913) 856-7102 SIC 8211

GREAT BEND, KS

BECKER TIRE & TREADING INC p 167
904 Washington St 67530
Tel (620) 793-5414 SIC 5014 5531

FULLER BRUSH CO INC p 584
1 Fuller Way 67530
Tel (620) 792-1711 SIC 2842 2844 3991

GREAT BEND COOPERATIVE ASSOCIATION p 633
606 Main St 67530
Tel (620) 793-3531
SIC 5153 5191 5171 4221

STRAUB INTERNATIONAL INC p 1393
214 Sw 40 Ave 67530
Tel (620) 792-5256 SIC 5083 5531

HAYS, KS

FORT HAYS STATE UNIVERSITY p 568
600 Park St 67601
Tel (785) 628-4000 SIC 8221

HAYS MEDICAL CENTER INC p 670
2220 Canterbury Dr 67601
Tel (785) 623-5000 SIC 8062 8051

MIDLAND MARKETING CO-OP INC p 966
219 E 9th St 67601
Tel (785) 625-5138
SIC 5153 5191 5541 5171 4221

MIDWEST ENERGY INC p 967
1330 Canterbury Dr 67601
Tel (785) 625-3437 SIC 4911 8611

ST JOHNS REST HOME INC p 1368
2225 Canterbury Dr 67601
Tel (785) 735-2208 SIC 8361

SUNFLOWER ELECTRIC HOLDINGS INC p 1402
301 W 13th St 67601
Tel (785) 628-2845 SIC 4911

SUNFLOWER ELECTRIC POWER CORP p 1402
301 W 13th St 67601
Tel (785) 628-2845 SIC 4911

HAYSVILLE, KS

■ AIR PRODUCTS MANUFACTURING CORP p 39
6601 S Ridge Rd 67060
Tel (316) 522-8181 SIC 2813 2819

HOPE, KS

AGRI TRAILS COOP INC p 36
508 N Main St 67451
Tel (785) 366-7213 SIC 5999 5261

HUMBOLDT, KS

▲ MONARCH CEMENT CO p 983
449 1200th St 66748
Tel (620) 473-2222 SIC 3241 3273

HUTCHINSON, KS

COLLINS BUS CORP p 337
415 W 6th Ave 67505
Tel (620) 662-9000 SIC 3711

COLLINS INDUSTRIES INC p 337
15 Compound Dr 67502
Tel (620) 663-5551 SIC 4522

CONKLIN CARS SALINA LLC p 356
1400 E 11th Ave 67501
Tel (785) 825-8271 SIC 5511

CONKLIN FANGMAN INVESTMENT CO INC p 356
1400 E 11th Ave 67501
Tel (620) 662-4467
SIC 7515 5511 7538 5521

■ **DILLON COMPANIES INC** p 439
2700 E 4th Ave 67501
Tel (620) 665-5511 *SIC* 5411

HEALTH CARE INC p 674
1701 E 23rd Ave 67502
Tel (620) 665-2000 *SIC* 8062 7352 6512

HUTCHINSON REGIONAL MEDICAL CENTER INC p 722
1701 E 23rd Ave 67502
Tel (620) 665-2000 *SIC* 8062

■ **KWIK SHOP INC** p 832
734 E 4th Ave 67501
Tel (620) 669-8504 *SIC* 5411

IUKA, KS

KANZA COOPERATIVE ASSOCIATION p 803
102 N Main St 67066
Tel (620) 546-2231
SIC 5153 5191 5541 4221

JAMESTOWN, KS

CHEYENNE LODGE INC p 296
716 Cedar St 66948
Tel (785) 439-6211 *SIC* 8052

JOHNSON, KS

JOHNSON COOPERATIVE GRAIN CO INC p 791
304 E Highland Ave 67855
Tel (620) 492-6210 *SIC* 5153 5191 5172

JUNCTION CITY, KS

GEARY COUNTY UNIFIED SCHOOL DISTRICT 475 p 597
123 N Eisenhower Dr 66441
Tel (785) 717-4000 *SIC* 8211

KANSAS CITY, KS

ARCHDIOCESE OF KANSAS CITY IN KANSAS p 105
12615 Parallel Pkwy 66109
Tel (913) 721-1570
SIC 8661 8211 8222 2711

ASSOCIATED WHOLESALE GROCERS INC p 121
5000 Kansas Ave 66106
Tel (913) 288-1000
SIC 5141 5143 5142 5147 5146 5148

B & J FOOD SERVICE EQUIPMENT INC p 141
236 N 7th St 66101
Tel (913) 621-6165 *SIC* 5046

BOARD OF EDUCATION OF KANSAS CITY KS (INC) p 195
2010 N 59th St 66104
Tel (913) 551-3200 *SIC* 8211

BOILERMAKER BLACKSMITH NATIONAL PENSION TRUST p 198
754 Minnesota Ave Ste 522 66101
Tel (913) 342-6555 *SIC* 6371

BOILERMAKERS NATIONAL HEALTH AND WELFARE FUND p 198
754 Minnesota Ave Ste 424 66101
Tel (866) 342-6555 *SIC* 6722

C&M TIRE INC p 234
401 S 42nd St 66106
Tel (913) 321-3003
SIC 5531 7534 5014 3312

■ **COFFEYVILLE RESOURCES LLC** p 334
10 E Cambridge Circle Dr 66103
Tel (913) 982-0500 *SIC* 1623

CONSPEC MARKETING AND MFG CO p 360
636 S 66th Ter 66111
Tel (913) 287-1700 *SIC* 2819

■ **DEFFENBAUGH INDUSTRIES INC** p 422
2601 Midwest Dr 66111
Tel (913) 631-3300 *SIC* 4212 4953

EPIQ SYSTEMS INC p 505
501 Kansas Ave 66105
Tel (913) 621-9500 *SIC* 7371 8748

G W VAN KEPPEL CO p 587
1801 N 9th St 66101
Tel (913) 281-4800
SIC 5082 7699 5084 7359

HARCROS CHEMICALS INC p 660
5200 Speaker Rd 66106
Tel (913) 321-3131 *SIC* 5169 2869

HEARTLAND IMAGING COMPANIES INC p 679
1211 W Cambridge Cir Dr 66103
Tel (913) 621-1211 *SIC* 5043

KANSAS CITY BOARD OF PUBLIC UTILITIES p 802
540 Minnesota Ave 66101
Tel (913) 573-9000 *SIC* 4931 4941

KANSAS UNIVERSITY PHYSICIANS INC p 803
3901 Rainbow Blvd 66160
Tel (913) 362-2128 *SIC* 8011

L G BARCUS AND SONS INC p 834
1430 State Ave 66102
Tel (913) 621-1100 *SIC* 1629 1622

LIBERTY FRUIT CO INC p 861
1247 Argentine Blvd 66105
Tel (913) 238-4606 *SIC* 5148

MEL STEVENSON & ASSOCIATES INC p 940
2840 Roe Ln 66103
Tel (913) 262-0505 *SIC* 5033 5082 5023

PROVIDENCE MEDICAL CENTER p 1186
8929 Parallel Pkwy 66112
Tel (913) 596-4870 *SIC* 8062

PROVIDENCE/SAINT JOHN FOUNDATION INC p 1186
8929 Parallel Pkwy 66112
Tel (913) 596-4000 *SIC* 8062 8741 8011

RIVERSIDE TRANSPORT INC p 1238
5400 Kansas Ave 66106
Tel (913) 233-5500 *SIC* 4212 4213

ROAD BUILDERS MACHINERY & SUPPLY CO INC p 1240
1001 S 7th St 66105
Tel (913) 371-3822 *SIC* 5082 7353 7699

UNBOUND p 1502
1 Elmwood Ave 66103
Tel (913) 384-6500 *SIC* 8399

UNIFIED GOVERNMENT OF WYANDOTTE COUNTY p 1503
701 N 7th St 66101
Tel (913) 573-5000 *SIC* 9111

UNIVERSITY OF KANSAS HOSPITAL p 1522
3901 Rainbow Blvd 66160
Tel (913) 588-5000 *SIC* 8062

UNIVERSITY OF KANSAS MEDICAL CENTER p 1522
3901 Rainbow Blvd 66160
Tel (913) 588-1443 *SIC* 8733

UNIVERSITY OF KANSAS MEDICAL CENTER RESEARCH INSTITUTE INC p 1522
3901 Rainbow Blvd 66160
Tel (913) 588-5000 *SIC* 8221

VALU MERCHANDISERS CO p 1542
5000 Kansas Ave 66106
Tel (913) 319-8500 *SIC* 5199

LAWRENCE, KS

GARAGE DOOR GROUP INC p 591
3800 Greenway Cir 66046
Tel (800) 503-3667 *SIC* 3442

KANSAS ATHLETICS INC p 802
1651 Naismith Dr 66045
Tel (785) 864-7050 *SIC* 8699

KANSAS UNIVERSITY ENDOWMENT ASSOCIATION p 803
1891 Constant Ave 66047
Tel (785) 832-7400 *SIC* 6732

LAWRENCE MEMORIAL HOSPITAL p 848
325 Maine St 66044
Tel (785) 505-5000 *SIC* 8062

LAWRENCE MEMORIAL HOSPITAL ENDOWMENT ASSOCIATION p 848
330 Arkansas St Ste 201 66044
Tel (785) 505-3318 *SIC* 8051 8062

LAWRENCE PUBLIC SCHOOLS p 848
110 Mcdonald Dr 66044
Tel (785) 832-5000 *SIC* 8211

■ **PACKERWARE LLC** p 1107
2330 Packer Rd 66049
Tel (785) 331-4236 *SIC* 3089

PEOPLES BANK p 1132
4831 W 6th St 66049
Tel (785) 842-4004 *SIC* 6712

PROTECTION ONE ALARM MONITORING INC p 1185
1035 N 3rd St Ste 101 66044
Tel (785) 856-5500 *SIC* 7382

UNIVERSITY OF KANSAS p 1522
1450 Jayhawk Blvd Rm 225 66045
Tel (785) 864-4868 *SIC* 8221

UNIVERSITY OF KANSAS CENTER FOR RESEARCH INC p 1522
2385 Irving Hill Rd 66045
Tel (785) 864-3441
SIC 8733 8732 8741 8731

LEAVENWORTH, KS

HEATRON INC p 679
3000 Wilson Ave 66048
Tel (913) 651-4420 *SIC* 3567 3634

SISTERS OF CHARITY OF LEAVENWORTH p 1327
4200 S 4th St Traffic Way 66048
Tel (913) 682-5151 *SIC* 8661

LEAWOOD, KS

AGSPRING LLC p 36
5250 W 116th Pl Ste 200 66211
Tel (913) 333-3035 *SIC* 0191 8748

■ **AMC ENTERTAINMENT HOLDINGS INC** p 65
1 Amc Way 11500 Ash St 66211
Tel (913) 213-2000 *SIC* 7832

■ **AMC ENTERTAINMENT INC** p 65
11500 Ash St 66211
Tel (913) 213-2000 *SIC* 7832

AMERICAN ACADEMY OF FAMILY PHYSICIANS p 67
11400 Tomahawk Creek Pkwy 66211
Tel (913) 906-6000 *SIC* 8621

■ **AMERICAN MULTI-CINEMA INC** p 76
1 Amc Way 66211
Tel (913) 213-2000 *SIC* 7832 5812 8741

ASCEND LEARNING LLC p 115
11161 Overbrook Rd 66211
Tel (800) 667-7531 *SIC* 8249

COLORADO KENWORTH INC p 339
11120 Tomahawk Creek Pkwy 66211
Tel (720) 941-0833 *SIC* 5511

DD TRADERS INC p 419
5000 W 134th St 66209
Tel (913) 402-6800 *SIC* 5199

▲ **EURONET WORLDWIDE INC** p 512
3500 College Blvd 66211
Tel (913) 327-4200 *SIC* 6099 7372 4813

GRAFTON INC p 628
4501 College Blvd Ste 160 66211
Tel (913) 498-0701 *SIC* 7363 7361

HOULIHANS RESTAURANTS INC p 711
8700 State Line Rd # 100 66206
Tel (913) 901-2500 *SIC* 5812 5813

MASSMAN CONSTRUCTION CO p 917
4400 W 109th St Ste 300 66211
Tel (913) 291-2600 *SIC* 1629 1622

MURPHY-HOFFMAN CO p 1001
11120 Tomahawk Creek Pkwy 66211
Tel (816) 483-6444
SIC 5012 7513 7538 6159 5511

SCOR GLOBAL LIFE USA REINSURANCE CO p 1293
11625 Rosewood St Ste 300 66211
Tel (913) 901-4600 *SIC* 6311 6321

STAR FUEL CENTERS INC p 1378
11161 Overbrook Rd 66211
Tel (913) 652-9400
SIC 5172 7542 5541 5411

TALLGRASS DEVELOPMENT LP p 1423
4200 W 115th St Ste 350 66211
Tel (513) 941-0500 *SIC* 4922

TALLGRASS ENERGY GP LP p 1423
4200 W 115th St Ste 350 66211
Tel (913) 928-6060 *SIC* 4922

▲ **TALLGRASS ENERGY PARTNERS LP** p 1423
4200 W 115th St Ste 350 66211
Tel (913) 928-6060 *SIC* 4922 4923

TALLGRASS OPERATIONS LLC p 1423
4200 W 115th St Ste 350 66211
Tel (913) 928-6060 *SIC* 4922

TEVA NEUROSCIENCE INC p 1441
11100 Nall Ave 66211
Tel (913) 777-3000 *SIC* 2834

WHEATLAND ENTERPRISES INC p 1604
2017 W 104th St 66206
Tel (913) 381-3504 *SIC* 4119

LENEXA, KS

ALENCO INC p 48
16201 W 110th St 66219
Tel (913) 438-1902 *SIC* 1521 1751 1761

AMERICAN DIRECT PROCUREMENT INC p 71
11000 Lakeview Ave 66219
Tel (913) 677-5588 *SIC* 5031

AXELACARE HOLDINGS INC p 140
15529 College Blvd 66219
Tel (877) 342-9352 *SIC* 8082

BATS GLOBAL MARKETS INC p 159
8050 Marshall Dr Ste 120 66214
Tel (913) 815-7000 *SIC* 6231

CARAVAN INGREDIENTS INC p 252
7905 Quivira Rd 66215
Tel (913) 890-5500
SIC 2099 2821 5084 2087

CIMARRON UNDERGROUND INC p 307
8375 Melrose Dr 66214
Tel (913) 438-2981 *SIC* 1623 1731

CITY WIDE HOLDING CO INC p 320
15447 W 100th Ter 66219
Tel (913) 888-5700
SIC 1542 1522 5087 7349

COMMUNITYAMERICA CREDIT UNION p 350
9777 Ridge Dr 66219
Tel (913) 905-7000 *SIC* 6062 6163

CORBION AMERICA HOLDINGS INC p 368
7905 Quivira Rd 66215
Tel (913) 890-5500
SIC 2819 2869 2041 2023

FEDERATED RURAL ELECTRIC INSURANCE EXCHANGE p 536
11875 W 85th St 66214
Tel (913) 541-0150 *SIC* 6331

GENESH INC p 602
8831 Long St 66215
Tel (913) 492-0007 *SIC* 5812

HEART TO HEART INTERNATIONAL INC p 678
13250 W 98th St 66215
Tel (913) 764-5200 *SIC* 8399

INKCYCLE INC p 743
11100 W 82nd St 66214
Tel (913) 894-8387
SIC 3955 7699 7378 5045 8249 5734

KCG INC p 806
15720 W 108th St Ste 100 66219
Tel (913) 438-4142 *SIC* 5032 2992

■ **LABONE INC** p 836
10101 Renner Blvd 66219
Tel (913) 888-1770 *SIC* 8071 6411

LEXMARK ENTERPRISE SOFTWARE LLC p 860
8900 Renner Blvd 66219
Tel (913) 422-7525 *SIC* 7371 7372

MAREL INC p 905
8145 Flint St 66214
Tel (913) 888-9110 *SIC* 5046

MEDIWARE INFORMATION SYSTEMS INC p 938
11711 W 79th St 66214
Tel (913) 307-1000 *SIC* 7372

OCONNOR CO INC p 1074
16910 W 116th St 66219
Tel (913) 894-8788 *SIC* 5075

P1 GROUP INC p 1103
13605 W 96th Ter 66215
Tel (913) 529-5000 *SIC* 1711 1731

PERFORMANCE CONTRACTING GROUP INC p 1135
11145 Thompson Ave 66219
Tel (913) 888-8600 *SIC* 1799 1742

PERFORMANCE CONTRACTING INC p 1135
11145 Thompson Ave 66219
Tel (913) 888-8600 *SIC* 1742 8711

POWER SALES AND ADVERTISING p 1165
9909 Lakeview Ave 66219
Tel (913) 324-4900 *SIC* 5199

PURAC AMERICA INC p 1192
7905 Quivira Rd 66215
Tel (847) 634-6330 *SIC* 2869

RAILCREW XPRESS LLC p 1205
9867 Widmer Rd 66215
Tel (913) 928-5000 *SIC* 4131

REGAL DISTRIBUTING CO p 1218
17201 W 113th St 66219
Tel (913) 894-8787 *SIC* 5112 5113 5046

■ **REMEL INC** p 1222
12076 Santa Fe Trail Dr 66215
Tel (800) 255-6730 *SIC* 2836

RENZENBERGER INC p 1224
14325 W 95th St 66215
Tel (913) 631-0450 *SIC* 4131 4119

SAFC BIOSCIENCES INC p 1265
13804 W 107th St 66215
Tel (913) 469-5580 *SIC* 2836

■ **VALENT AEROSTRUCTURES LLC** p 1539
11064 Strang Line Rd 66215
Tel (816) 423-5600 *SIC* 3724

WACHTER INC p 1570
16001 W 99th St 66219
Tel (913) 541-2500 *SIC* 1731

WATER DISTRICT NO1 OF JOHNSON COUNTY KANSAS p 1581
10747 Renner Blvd 66219
Tel (913) 895-5500 *SIC* 4941

WESTLAKE HARDWARE INC p 1601
14000 Marshall Dr 66215
Tel (913) 888-8438 *SIC* 5251

■ **WICHITA COCA-COLA BOTTLING CO** p 1607
10001 Industrial Blvd 66215
Tel (316) 612-6400 *SIC* 2086

LENORA, KS

RURAL TELEPHONE SERVICE CO INC p 1258
145 N Main St 67645
Tel (785) 567-4281 *SIC* 4813 5734 5045

LIBERAL, KS

HIGH PLAINS PIZZA INC p 690
7 W Parkway Blvd 67901
Tel (620) 624-5638 *SIC* 5812

LIBERAL SCHOOL DISTRICT p 861
401 N Kansas Ave 67901
Tel (620) 604-1010 *SIC* 8211

MANHATTAN, KS

FARM BUREAU MUTUAL INSURANCE CO INC p 528
2627 Kfb Plz 66503
Tel (785) 587-6000 *SIC* 6331

ITS GREEK TO ME INC p 768
520 Mccall Rd Ste A 66502
Tel (785) 537-8822
SIC 5136 5699 5137 5947 2759

KANSAS STATE UNIVERSITY p 803
110 Anderson Hall 66506
Tel (785) 532-6210 *SIC* 8221

KANSAS STATE UNIVERSITY FOUNDATION INC p 803
1800 Kimball Ave Ste 200 66502
Tel (785) 532-6266 *SIC* 7389

LEISZLER OIL CO INC p 854
8228 Southport Dr 66502
Tel (785) 632-5648 *SIC* 5171 5411 5541

MANKO WINDOW SYSTEMS INC p 902
800 Hayes Dr 66502
Tel (785) 776-9643 *SIC* 3442 1799 5039

MERCY REGIONAL HEALTH CENTRE AUXILLIARY p 948
1823 College Ave 66502
Tel (785) 776-2802 *SIC* 5947

STEEL AND PIPE SUPPLY CO INC p 1384
555 Poyntz Ave Ste 122 66502
Tel (800) 521-2345 *SIC* 5051

UNIFIED SCHOOL DISTRICT 383 p 1503
2031 Poyntz Ave 66502
Tel (785) 587-2000 *SIC* 8211 8249

MARYSVILLE, KS

KANEQUIP INC p 802
1152 Pony Express Hwy 66508
Tel (785) 562-2377 *SIC* 5046 5083

LANDOLL CORP p 843
1900 North St 66508
Tel (785) 562-5381
SIC 3728 3715 3523 3537

MAYETTA, KS

PRAIRIE BAND POTAWATOMI NATION p 1167
16281 Q Rd 66509
Tel (785) 966-2255 *SIC* 9131

MCPHERSON, KS

■ CHS MCPHERSON REFINERY INC p 304
2000 S Main St 67460
Tel (620) 241-2340 *SIC* 2911 4612 4213

FARMERS ALLIANCE MUTUAL INSURANCE CO p 529
1122 N Main St 67460
Tel (620) 241-2200 *SIC* 6331

MERRIAM, KS

■ LEE JEANS CO INC p 851
9001 W 67th St 66202
Tel (913) 384-4000 *SIC* 2325 2339 2369

MYRON GREEN CORP p 1005
8500 Shawnee Mission Pkwy 66202
Tel (913) 384-4900 *SIC* 5962

▲ SEABOARD CORP p 1295
9000 W 67th St 66202
Tel (913) 676-8800
SIC 2011 0133 4412 6221 0723 0213

TREAT AMERICA MANAGEMENT CO LLC p 1475
8500 Shawnee Mission Pkwy # 100 66202
Tel (913) 268-5800 *SIC* 5963

MOUNDRIDGE, KS

MID-KANSAS COOPERATIVE ASSOCIATION p 963
307 W Cole St 67107
Tel (620) 345-6328 *SIC* 5153 5191

MORIDGE MANUFACTURING INC p 989
105 Old Us Highway 81 67107
Tel (620) 345-6301 *SIC* 3524 3523

TEAM MARKETING ALLIANCE LLC p 1430
307 W Cole St 67107
Tel (620) 345-3560 *SIC* 5153

NEODESHA, KS

COBALT BOATS LLC p 332
1715 N 8th St 66757
Tel (620) 325-2653 *SIC* 3732

NEW CENTURY, KS

■ DANISCO USA INC p 412
4 New Century Pkwy 66031
Tel (913) 764-8100 *SIC* 2099

KGP PRODUCTS INC p 816
600 New Century Pkwy 66031
Tel (800) 755-1950 *SIC* 3661

NEWTON, KS

■ B N S F INC p 142
616 S Boyd Ave 67114
Tel (316) 284-3260 *SIC* 4011

OAKLEY, KS

FRONTIER AG INC p 580
415 W 2nd St 67748
Tel (785) 462-2063 *SIC* 5153 5191

PIONEER FEEDYARD LLC p 1150
1021 County Road Cc 67748
Tel (785) 672-3257
SIC 0111 0211 0115 0212

WESTERN PLAINS ENERGY LLC p 1599
3022 County Road 18 67748
Tel (785) 672-8810 *SIC* 2869

OLATHE, KS

COUNTY OF JOHNSON p 378
111 S Cherry St Ste 1200 66061
Tel (913) 715-0435 *SIC* 9111

D H PACE CO INC p 407
1901 E 119th St 66061
Tel (816) 221-0543 *SIC* 5211 7699

EBY GROUP INC p 474
13795 S Mur Len Rd # 301 66062
Tel (913) 782-3200 *SIC* 6719

EE NEWCOMER ENTERPRISES INC p 480
1901 E 119th St 66061
Tel (816) 221-0543 *SIC* 5031 5211 7699

■ ENCORE RECEIVABLE MANAGEMENT INC p 496
400 N Rogers Rd 66062
Tel (913) 782-3333 *SIC* 7322

FORD OLATHE SALES INC p 566
1845 E Santa Fe St 66062
Tel (913) 782-0881 *SIC* 5511 5561 5012

GARMIN INTERNATIONAL INC p 592
1200 E 151st St 66062
Tel (913) 397-8200 *SIC* 3812 3669 8713

GERSON CO p 609
1450 S Lone Elm Rd 66061
Tel (913) 262-7400
SIC 5193 5199 5023 5094

GRUNDFOS PUMPS CORP p 642
17100 W 118th Ter 66061
Tel (913) 227-3400 *SIC* 5084

HUSQVARNA CONSTRUCTION PRODUCTS NORTH AMERICA INC p 721
17400 W 119th St 66061
Tel (913) 928-1000
SIC 3541 3291 5085 5082 3425 2951

▲ NIC INC p 1042
25501 W Valley Pkwy # 300 66061
Tel (877) 234-3468 *SIC* 7371

OLATHE HEALTH SYSTEM INC p 1080
20333 W 151st St 66061
Tel (913) 791-4200 *SIC* 5912

OLATHE MEDICAL CENTER INC p 1080
20333 W 151st St 66061
Tel (913) 791-4200 *SIC* 8082 8062

OLATHE UNIFIED SCHOOL DISTRICT 233 p 1080
14160 S Blackbob Rd 66062
Tel (913) 780-7000 *SIC* 8211

■ SYSCO KANSAS CITY INC p 1417
1915 E Kansas City Rd 66061
Tel (913) 829-5555 *SIC* 5149 5141

TERRACON CONSULTANTS INC p 1439
18001 W 106th St Ste 300 66061
Tel (913) 599-6886
SIC 8742 8711 8748 8741

TRANSAM TRUCKING INC p 1470
15910 S Us 169 Hwy 66062
Tel (913) 782-5300 *SIC* 4213

TSVC INC p 1489
18001 W 106th St Ste 300 66061
Tel (913) 599-6886 *SIC* 7389

TVH PARTS CO p 1494
16355 S Lone Elm Rd 66062
Tel (913) 829-1000 *SIC* 5084

OSBORNE, KS

MIDWAY CO-OP ASSOCIATION p 967
210 W Harrison St 67473
Tel (785) 346-5451 *SIC* 5153 5171

OTTAWA, KS

CARGOTEC HOLDING INC p 255
415 E Dundee St 66067
Tel (785) 242-2200 *SIC* 3593 3537

KALMAR SOLUTIONS LLC p 801
415 E Dundee St 66067
Tel (785) 242-2200
SIC 3537 3714 3713 3643

OTTAWA COOPERATIVE ASSOCIATION INC p 1098
302 N Main St 66067
Tel (785) 242-5170 *SIC* 5191 5171 5153

OVERLAND PARK, KS

■ ADM MILLING CO p 23
8000 W 110th St Ste 300 66210
Tel (913) 491-9400 *SIC* 2041

AGREX INC p 36
10975 Grandview Dr # 200 66210
Tel (913) 851-6300 *SIC* 5153

ALEXANDER OPEN SYSTEMS INC p 49
12980 Foster St Ste 300 66213
Tel (913) 307-2300
SIC 5045 7373 8748 7376 3577 1731

APAC-KANSAS INC p 95
7415 W 130th St Ste 300 66213
Tel (913) 371-1003
SIC 1611 1771 2951 7353 1622

ASCENSION INSURANCE INC p 116
9225 Indian Creek Pkwy # 700 66210
Tel (816) 842-1332 *SIC* 6411

ASH GROVE CEMENT CO p 116
11011 Cody St Ste 300 66210
Tel (913) 451-8900
SIC 3241 3273 1422 3271

ASH GROVE MATERIALS CORP p 117
11011 Cody St Ste 300 66210
Tel (913) 345-2030
SIC 3273 3272 1411 7389 4212

B&V - GENSLER JV p 142
6800 W 115th St Ste 2200 66211
Tel (913) 458-6650 *SIC* 8711

B&V-BAKER GUAM JV p 142
6601 College Blvd 66211
Tel (913) 458-4300 *SIC* 8711

■ BHA ALTAIR LLC p 180
11501 Outlook St Ste 100 66211
Tel (816) 356-8400 *SIC* 3564

BLACK & VEATCH CORP p 186
11401 Lamar Ave 66211
Tel (913) 458-2000 *SIC* 8711

BLACK & VEATCH HOLDING CO p 186
11401 Lamar Ave 66211
Tel (913) 458-2000 *SIC* 8711 8741

■ BUSHNELL HOLDINGS INC p 229
9200 Cody St 66214
Tel (913) 752-3400 *SIC* 3851 5049 5091

■ BUSHNELL INC p 229
9200 Cody St 66214
Tel (913) 752-3400 *SIC* 3827

BVH INC p 230
11401 Lamar Ave 66211
Tel (913) 458-2000 *SIC* 8711 8741

CENTRAL STATES THERMO KING INC p 280
7200 W 132nd St Ste 270 66213
Tel (888) 566-5743 *SIC* 5078 7623 5084

■ CLEARWIRE CORP p 324
6200 Sprint Pkwy 66251
Tel (425) 216-7600 *SIC* 4813

■ COMPASS MINERALS AMERICA INC p 351
9900 W 109th St Ste 600 66210
Tel (913) 344-9100 *SIC* 2899 1479

■ COMPASS MINERALS GROUP INC p 351
9900 W 109th St Ste 600 66210
Tel (913) 344-9100 *SIC* 2819 2899

▲ COMPASS MINERALS INTERNATIONAL INC p 351
9900 W 109th St Ste 100 66210
Tel (913) 344-9200 *SIC* 1474 2899 2819

■ COVENTRY HEALTH CARE OF KANSAS INC p 385
9401 Indian Creek Pkwy # 1300 66210
Tel (800) 969-3343 *SIC* 6324 8011

FAVORITE HEALTHCARE STAFFING INC p 531
7255 W 98th Ter Ste 150 66212
Tel (913) 383-9733 *SIC* 7363

FERRELL COMPANIES INC p 538
7500 College Blvd # 1000 66210
Tel (913) 661-1500 *SIC* 1311 5984

FERRELLGAS INC p 538
7500 College Blvd # 1000 66210
Tel (913) 661-1500 *SIC* 5084 5172

■ FERRELLGAS LP p 538
7500 College Blvd # 1000 66210
Tel (913) 661-1500 *SIC* 5984

▲ FERRELLGAS PARTNERS LP p 538
7500 College Blvd # 1000 66210
Tel (913) 661-1500 *SIC* 5084 5172

FQSR LLC p 573
8900 Indian Creek Pkwy # 100 66210
Tel (913) 469-1112 *SIC* 5812

GREAT-WEST FINANCIAL RETIREMENT PLAN SERVICES LLC p 635
11500 Outlook St 66211
Tel (847) 857-3000 *SIC* 6411

HANTOVER INC p 659
5200 W 110th St Ste 200 66211
Tel (913) 214-4800 *SIC* 5099 5084

INLAND TRUCK PARTS CO INC p 744
4400 College Blvd Ste 145 66211
Tel (913) 345-9664 *SIC* 5013 7538

INTOUCH SOLUTIONS INC p 759
7045 College Blvd Ste 300 66211
Tel (913) 317-9700 *SIC* 8742

JOHNSON COUNTY COMMUNITY COLLEGE p 791
12345 College Blvd 66210
Tel (913) 469-8500 *SIC* 8222 8221

KARNAVATI HOLDINGS INC p 804
9401 Indian Creek Pkwy # 1000 66210
Tel (913) 344-9500 *SIC* 1479

KUNI ENTERPRISES LLC p 832
8035 Lenexa Dr 66214
Tel (360) 553-7350 *SIC* 5511

LANSING TRADE GROUP LLC p 844
10975 Benson Dr Ste 400 66210
Tel (913) 748-3000 *SIC* 5153 6221

MENORAH MEDICAL CENTER INC p 943
5721 W 119th St 66209
Tel (913) 498-6000 *SIC* 8011 8062

■ MIDLAND LOAN SERVICES A DIVISION OF PNC BANK NATIONAL ASSOCIATION p 965
10851 Mastin St Ste 700 66210
Tel (913) 253-9000 *SIC* 6162

MIDWEST AIR TRAFFIC CONTROL SERVICE INC p 967
7285 W 132nd St Ste 340 66213
Tel (913) 782-7082 *SIC* 4581

MIQ HOLDINGS INC p 974
11501 Outlook St Ste 500 66211
Tel (913) 696-7363 *SIC* 4225 4731 8741

MIQ LOGISTICS LLC p 974
11501 Outlook St Ste 500 66211
Tel (913) 696-7100 *SIC* 4731 8741

MMC CORP p 979
10955 Lowell Ave Ste 350 66210
Tel (913) 469-0101 *SIC* 1542 1711

NETSMART TECHNOLOGIES INC p 1027
4950 College Blvd 66211
Tel (913) 327-7444 *SIC* 7371 7372

■ NEXTEL OF CALIFORNIA INC p 1040
6200 Sprint Pkwy 66251
Tel (866) 505-2385 *SIC* 4812

■ NEXTEL PARTNERS OPERATING CORP p 1040
6200 Sprint Pkwy 66251
Tel (800) 829-0965 *SIC* 4812

NPC INTERNATIONAL HOLDINGS INC p 1064
7300 W 129th St 66213
Tel (913) 327-3109 *SIC* 5812

NPC INTERNATIONAL INC p 1064
7300 W 129th St 66213
Tel (913) 632-0300 *SIC* 5812

NPC RESTAURANT HOLDINGS LLC p 1064
7300 W 129th St 66213
Tel (913) 327-5555 *SIC* 5812 6794

OVERLAND PARK REGIONAL MEDICAL CENTER INC p 1099
10500 Quivira Rd 66215
Tel (913) 541-0000 *SIC* 8062

■ OVERLAND SOLUTIONS INC p 1099
10975 Grandview Dr # 400 66210
Tel (913) 451-3222 *SIC* 6411

QC HOLDINGS INC p 1194
9401 Indian Creek Pkwy # 1500 66210
Tel (866) 660-2243 *SIC* 6141 7389

QTS REALTY TRUST INC p 1195
12851 Foster St 66213
Tel (913) 814-9988 *SIC* 7375 7374

QUALITY GROUP OF COMPANIES LLC p 1197
12851 Foster St Ste 205 66213
Tel (913) 814-9988 *SIC* 6531

QUALITY TECHNOLOGY SERVICES HOLDING LLC p 1197
12851 Foster St Ste 205 66213
Tel (913) 814-9988 *SIC* 6719

QUALITY TECHNOLOGY SERVICES LLC p 1197
12851 Foster St 66213
Tel (913) 814-9988 *SIC* 7376 8741

QUALITYTECH LP p 1197
12851 Foster St 66213
Tel (877) 787-3282 *SIC* 7374

■ ROADWAY LLC p 1240
10990 Roe Ave 66211
Tel (913) 344-3000 *SIC* 4213

SEARLES VALLEY MINERALS INC p 1297
9401 Indn Crk Pkwy # 1000 66210
Tel (913) 344-9500 *SIC* 1479

SHAMROCK TRADING CORP p 1311
9300 Metcalf Ave 66212
Tel (913) 310-2200
SIC 4731 6153 8742 7323

SHAWNEE MISSION UNIFIED SCHOOL DISTRICT p 1313
7235 Antioch Rd 66204
Tel (913) 993-6200 *SIC* 8211

■ SPRINT COMMUNICATIONS CO LP p 1361
6391 Sprint Pkwy 66251
Tel (800) 829-0965 *SIC* 4813

■ SPRINT COMMUNICATIONS INC p 1361
6200 Sprint Pkwy 66251
Tel (855) 848-3280 *SIC* 4813 4812 5999

■ SPRINT CORP p 1361
6200 Sprint Pkwy 66251
Tel (855) 848-3280 *SIC* 4813 4812

■ SPRINT SPECTRUM LP p 1361
6800 Sprint Pkwy 66251
Tel (703) 433-4000 *SIC* 4813

■ SPRINT/UNITED MANAGEMENT CO p 1361
6200 Sprint Pkwy 66251
Tel (800) 697-6000 *SIC* 8741

■ SPX COOLING TECHNOLOGIES INC p 1362
7401 W 129th St 66213
Tel (913) 664-7400 *SIC* 3443

SVM MINERALS HOLDINGS INC p 1410
9401 Indian Creek Pkwy 66210
Tel (913) 344-9500 *SIC* 1479

SWISS RE AMERICA HOLDING CORP p 1412
5200 Metcalf Ave 66202
Tel (913) 676-5200 *SIC* 6331 6311

SWISS RE SOLUTIONS HOLDING CORP p 1413
5200 Metcalf Ave 66202
Tel (913) 676-5200 *SIC* 6331

SWISS REINSURANCE AMERICA CORP p 1413
5200 Metcalf Ave 66202
Tel (913) 676-5200 *SIC* 6311

▲ WADDELL & REED FINANCIAL INC p 1571
6300 Lamar Ave 66202
Tel (913) 236-2000 *SIC* 6211 6282 6411

■ WADDELL & REED FINANCIAL SERVICES INC p 1571
6300 Lamar Ave 66202
Tel (913) 236-2000
SIC 6722 6311 6211 6531

WESTPORT INSURANCE CORP p 1602
5200 Metcalf Ave 66202
Tel (913) 676-5270 *SIC* 6331

WILBERT FUNERAL SERVICES INC p 1608
10965 Granada Ln Ste 300 66211
Tel (913) 345-2120 *SIC* 3272

■ YRC INC p 1639
10990 Roe Ave 66211
Tel (913) 696-6100 *SIC* 4213

■ YRC REGIONAL TRANSPORTATION INC p 1640
10990 Roe Ave 66211
Tel (913) 344-5220 *SIC* 4213 4231

▲ YRC WORLDWIDE INC p 1640
10990 Roe Ave 66211
Tel (913) 696-6100 *SIC* 4213

ZANCANELLI MANAGEMENT CORP p 1641
11879 W 112th St Ste A 66210
Tel (913) 469-1112 *SIC* 5812

ZURICH AGENCY SERVICES INC p 1645
7045 College Blvd 66211
Tel (913) 339-1000 *SIC* 6331 6311

PAOLA, KS

MID-WEST FERTILIZER INC p 964
1105 Baptiste Dr 66071
Tel (913) 294-5555 *SIC* 5191

PARK CITY, KS

MURPHY TRACTOR & EQUIPMENT CO INC p 1001
5375 N Deere Rd 67219
Tel (855) 246-9124 *SIC* 5082

PARSONS, KS

BEACHNER GRAIN INC p 164
2600 Flynn Dr 67357
Tel (620) 449-8500 *SIC* 5153

TANK CONNECTION LLC p 1424
3609 N 16th St 67357
Tel (620) 423-0251 *SIC* 5084 3443

PERRY, KS

HAMM INC p 656
609 Perry Pl 66073
Tel (785) 597-5111 *SIC* 1411 1771 1611

PHILLIPSBURG, KS

BROOKE HOLDINGS INC p 217
205 F St 67661
Tel (785) 543-3199 *SIC* 6411

GREAT PLAINS HEALTH ALLIANCE INC p 634
625 3rd St 67661
Tel (785) 543-2111 *SIC* 8742

PITTSBURG, KS

LEISURETIME PRODUCTS LLC p 854
3001 N Rouse St 66762
Tel (620) 232-2400 *SIC* 3089 3949 2452

MILLERS INC p 971
610 E Jefferson St 66762
Tel (620) 231-8050 *SIC* 7384

VIA CHRISTI HOSPITAL PITTSBURG INC p 1554
1 Mt Carmel Way 66762
Tel (620) 231-6100 *SIC* 8062

VIA CHRISTI HOSPITAL PITTSBURG INC p 1554
1 Mt Carmel Way 66762
Tel (620) 232-9926 *SIC* 8062

WATCO COMPANIES LLC p 1581
315 W 3rd St 66762
Tel (620) 231-2230 *SIC* 4011 7538

WATCO INC p 1581
315 W 3rd St 66762
Tel (208) 734-4644 *SIC* 4013 4741 4789

PRAIRIE VILLAGE, KS

AMERICRAFT CARTON INC p 82
7400 State Line Rd # 206 66208
Tel (913) 387-3700 *SIC* 2657

WIRECO WORLDGROUP INC p 1618
2400 W 75th St 66208
Tel (816) 270-4700 *SIC* 3496

WIRECO WORLDGROUP US HOLDINGS INC p 1618
2400 W 75th St 66208
Tel (816) 270-4700 *SIC* 3496

PRATT, KS

STANION WHOLESALE ELECTRIC CO INC p 1377
812 S Main St 67124
Tel (620) 672-5678 *SIC* 5063

SALINA, KS

BLUE BEACON USA LP II p 190
500 Graves Blvd 67401
Tel (785) 825-2221 *SIC* 7542

FARMERS RANCHERS LIVSTOCK COMMUNITY INC p 530
1500 W Old Highway 40 67401
Tel (785) 825-0211 *SIC* 5154

GREAT PLAINS MANUFACTURING INC p 634
1525 E North St 67401
Tel (785) 823-3276 *SIC* 3523

SAINT FRANCIS COMMUNITY SERVICES INC p 1269
509 E Elm St 67401
Tel (785) 825-0541 *SIC* 8741 8361

SALINA PUBLIC SCHOOLS p 1272
1511 Gypsum Ave 67401
Tel (785) 309-4700 *SIC* 8211

SALINA REGIONAL HEALTH CENTER INC p 1272
400 S Santa Fe Ave 67401
Tel (785) 452-7000 *SIC* 8062

SCOTT CITY, KS

SCOTT COOPERATIVE ASSOCIATION INC p 1293
410 E 1st St 67871
Tel (620) 872-5823
SIC 5153 5541 5191 4221

WHEATLAND ELECTRIC COOPERATIVE INC p 1604
101 N Main St 67871
Tel (620) 872-5885 *SIC* 4911 4812

SENECA, KS

FAIRVIEW MILLS LLC p 525
604 Nemaha St 66538
Tel (785) 336-2148 *SIC* 3999

NEMAHA COUNTY COOPERATIVE ASSOCIATION p 1025
223 E Main St 66538
Tel (785) 336-6153 *SIC* 5153 5191 5541

SHAWNEE MISSION, KS

CHARLES WALKER NORTH AMERICA p 289
9400 W 55th St 66203
Tel (913) 236-9233 *SIC* 5085

■ **EMBARQ MANAGEMENT CO** p 490
5454 W 110th St 66211
Tel (913) 323-4637 *SIC* 4813 4812

FIRST EXCESS AND REINSURANCE CORP p 546
6329 Glenwood St Ste 300 66202
Tel (913) 676-5524 *SIC* 6331

GOURMET SYSTEMS OF KANSAS INC p 627
4551 W 107th St Ste 100 66207
Tel (913) 967-4000 *SIC* 5812 5813

HILLCREST BANCSHARES INC p 693
11111 W 95th St 66214
Tel (913) 492-7500 *SIC* 6022

HSG RESOURCES INC p 715
9660 Legler Rd 66219
Tel (913) 492-5920 *SIC* 1442

IBT INC p 726
9400 W 55th St 66203
Tel (913) 677-3151 *SIC* 5085 5084

■ **LEE APPAREL CO INC** p 851
1 Lee Dr 66202
Tel (913) 789-0330 *SIC* 2325 2339

MW BUILDERS GROUP INC p 1003
10955 Lowell Ave Ste 350 66210
Tel (913) 345-0007 *SIC* 1542

PENTON BUSINESS MEDIA INC p 1132
9800 Metcalf Ave 66212
Tel (913) 341-1300 *SIC* 2721

QC FINANCIAL SERVICES INC p 1194
9401 Indian Creek Pkwy # 1500 66210
Tel (913) 439-1100 *SIC* 6141 6099

SAINT LUKES SOUTH HOSPITAL INC p 1270
12300 Metcalf Ave 66213
Tel (913) 317-7000 *SIC* 8062

SANDEN NORTH AMERICA INC p 1278
9900 Pflumm Rd Ste 22 66215
Tel (913) 888-6667 *SIC* 7389

SCRIPTPRO LLC p 1295
5828 Reeds Rd 66202
Tel (913) 384-1008 *SIC* 3559 3586

SCRIPTPRO USA INC p 1295
5828 Reeds Rd 66202
Tel (913) 384-1008 *SIC* 5087

■ **SEABOARD FOODS LLC** p 1295
9000 W 67th St Ste 200 66202
Tel (913) 261-2600 *SIC* 0213 5147 2011

SHAWNEE MISSION BOARD OF EDUCATION p 1313
7235 Antioch Rd 66204
Tel (913) 993-6200 *SIC* 8211

SHAWNEE MISSION MEDICAL CENTER INC p 1313
9100 W 74th St 66204
Tel (913) 676-2000 *SIC* 8062

SHAWNEE MISSION SCHOOL DISTRICT p 1313
7235 Antioch Rd 66204
Tel (913) 993-6200 *SIC* 8211

SKC COMMUNICATION PRODUCTS LLC p 1329
8320 Hedge Lane Ter 66227
Tel (913) 422-4222 *SIC* 5065 5999

SMITH AND LOVELESS INC p 1333
14040 Santa Fe Trail Dr 66215
Tel (913) 888-5201 *SIC* 3589 5074

■ **SPRINT SPECTRUM HOLDING CO LP** p 1361
6160 Sprint Pkwy 66251
Tel (800) 829-0965 *SIC* 4813

VALLEY VIEW BANCSHARES INC p 1541
7500 W 95th St 66212
Tel (913) 381-3311 *SIC* 6712

■ **WADDELL & REED INC** p 1571
6300 Lamar Ave 66202
Tel (913) 236-2000
SIC 6282 6211 6289 6411

■ **WADDELL & REED INVESTMENT MANAGEMENT CO** p 1571
6300 Lamar Ave 66202
Tel (913) 236-2000 *SIC* 6211

XCELLENCE INC p 1631
5800 Foxridge Dr Ste 406 66202
Tel (913) 362-8662 *SIC* 7374

SHAWNEE, KS

I2 ASIA LLC p 725
21983 W 83rd St 66227
Tel (913) 422-1600 *SIC* 5084

NAZDAR CO p 1021
8501 Hedge Lane Ter 66227
Tel (913) 422-1888 *SIC* 2893

WALL-TIES & FORMS INC p 1573
4000 Bonner Industrial Dr 66226
Tel (913) 441-0073 *SIC* 5082 3444 3443

SOLOMON, KS

SOLOMON TRANSFORMERS LLC p 1338
103 W Main St 67480
Tel (785) 655-2191 *SIC* 3612 5093

SPEARVILLE, KS

ALLIANCE AG AND GRAIN LLC p 53
313 N Main 67876
Tel (620) 385-2898 *SIC* 0723

TOPEKA, KS

ADJUTANT GENERALS DEPARTMENT KANSAS p 23
2800 Sw Topeka Blvd 66611
Tel (785) 274-1000 *SIC* 9711

BLUE CROSS AND BLUE SHIELD OF KANSAS INC p 191
1133 Sw Topeka Blvd 66629
Tel (785) 291-7000 *SIC* 6321 6324

▲ **CAPITOL FEDERAL FINANCIAL INC** p 251
700 S Kansas Ave Fl 1 66603
Tel (785) 235-1341 *SIC* 6035

■ **CAPITOL FEDERAL SAVINGS BANK** p 251
700 S Kansas Ave Fl 1 66603
Tel (785) 235-1341 *SIC* 6035

CITY OF TOPEKA EMPLOYEES FRIENDSHIP FUND p 319
620 Se Madison St Ste 203 66607
Tel (785) 368-3749 *SIC* 9199

COUNTY OF SHAWNEE p 381
200 Se 7th St 66603
Tel (785) 233-8200 *SIC* 9111

EXECUTIVE OFFICE OF STATE OF KANSAS p 517
300 Sw 10th Ave 66612
Tel (785) 296-6240 *SIC* 9111

FEDERAL HOME LOAN BANK p 534
1 Sw Sec Bnft Pl Ste 100 66606
Tel (785) 233-0507 *SIC* 6019

■ **HILLS PET NUTRITION INC** p 694
400 Sw 8th Ave Ste 101 66603
Tel (785) 354-8523 *SIC* 5149 2048 2047

JUDICIARY COURTS OF STATE OF KANSAS p 796
301 Sw 10th Ave 66612
Tel (785) 296-4873 *SIC* 9211

KANSAS DEPARTMENT FOR CHILDREN AND FAMILIES p 803
915 Sw Harrison St 66612
Tel (785) 368-6358 *SIC* 9441 9431

KANSAS DEPARTMENT OF CORRECTIONS p 803
714 Sw Jackson St Fl 3 66603
Tel (785) 296-3317 *SIC* 9223

KANSAS DEPARTMENT OF TRANSPORTATION p 803
700 Sw Harrison St # 500 66603
Tel (785) 296-3501 *SIC* 9621

KANSAS ELECTRIC POWER COOPERATIVE INC p 803
600 Sw Corporate Vw 66615
Tel (785) 273-7010 *SIC* 4911

KOSS CONSTRUCTION CO p 828
5830 Sw Drury Ln 66604
Tel (785) 228-2928 *SIC* 1611

PAYLESS INC p 1122
3231 Se 6th Ave 66607
Tel (785) 233-5171 *SIC* 5661 5632

PAYLESS SHOESOURCE INC p 1122
3231 Se 6th Ave 66607
Tel (785) 233-5171 *SIC* 5661

PTMW INC p 1189
5040 Nw Us Highway 24 66618
Tel (785) 232-7792 *SIC* 3441

RESTAURANT SERVICES INC p 1228
5877 Sw 29th St 66614
Tel (785) 273-1805 *SIC* 5812

SECURITY BENEFIT CORP p 1299
1 Sw Security Benefit Pl 66636
Tel (785) 438-3000 *SIC* 6211

SECURITY BENEFIT GROUP INC p 1299
1 Sw Security Benefit Pl 66636
Tel (785) 438-3000 *SIC* 6211 7311 6411

SECURITY BENEFIT LIFE INSURANCE CO p 1299
1 Sw Security Benefit Pl 66636
Tel (785) 438-3000
SIC 6311 6722 6091 6211 8748

ST FRANCIS HEALTH CENTER INC p 1366
1700 Sw 7th St 66606
Tel (785) 295-8000 *SIC* 8062 8011

STATE OF KANSAS p 1381
300 Sw 10th Ave Ste 222s 66612
Tel (785) 354-1388 *SIC* 9111

STORMONT-VAIL HEALTHCARE INC p 1392
1500 Sw 10th Ave 66604
Tel (785) 354-6000 *SIC* 8062

TOPEKA UNIFIED SCHOOL DISTRICT 501 p 1461
624 Sw 24th St 66611
Tel (785) 295-3000 *SIC* 8211

WASHBURN UNIVERSITY OF TOPEKA p 1577
1700 Sw College Ave 66621
Tel (785) 670-1010 *SIC* 8221

WBG-PSS HOLDINGS LLC p 1585
3231 Se 6th Ave 66607
Tel (785) 233-5171 *SIC* 5499

▲ **WESTAR ENERGY INC** p 1596
818 S Kansas Ave 66612
Tel (785) 575-6300 *SIC* 4911

WAMEGO, KS

■ **CATERPILLAR WORK TOOLS INC** p 265
400 Work Tool Rd 66547
Tel (904) 786-8700 *SIC* 3531

KANEQUIP INC p 802
18035 E Us Highway 24 66547
Tel (785) 456-2041 *SIC* 5999 5083

TALLGRASS COMMODITIES LLC p 1423
420 Lincoln St 66547
Tel (855) 494-8484 *SIC* 0119

WATHENA, KS

■ **WATHENA HEALTHCARE AND REHABILITATION CENTER LLC** p 1582
2112 Highway 36 66090
Tel (785) 989-3141 *SIC* 8051

WESTWOOD, KS

■ **SPRINT INTERNATIONAL INC** p 1361
2330 Shawnee Mission Pkwy 66205
Tel (913) 624-3000 *SIC* 4813

WICHITA, KS

AEROFLEX WICHITA INC p 30
10200 W York St 67215
Tel (316) 522-4981 *SIC* 4581

AHI HOLDINGS INC p 36
3050 N Saint Francis St 67219
Tel (316) 832-3484 *SIC* 3585 3444

AIRXCEL INC p 41
3050 N Saint Francis St 67219
Tel (316) 832-3400 *SIC* 3585

AMERICAN PIZZA PARTNERS LP p 77
7700 E Polo Dr 67206
Tel (316) 634-1190 *SIC* 5812

▲ **AMERICAN RESTAURANT PARTNERS LP** p 78
3020 N Cypress St Ste 100 67226
Tel (316) 634-1190 *SIC* 5812

APPLE CORPS LP p 98
1877 N Rock Rd 67206
Tel (316) 683-2611 *SIC* 5812

■ **BALCO INC** p 147
2626 S Sheridan Ave 67217
Tel (800) 767-0082
SIC 3441 3089 3496 3446 3443

■ **BEECHCRAFT CORP** p 168
10511 E Central Ave 67206
Tel (316) 676-7111 *SIC* 3728 3721

■ **BEECHCRAFT HOLDINGS LLC** p 168
10511 E Central Ave 67206
Tel (316) 676-7111 *SIC* 3721 3728 6719

BEREXCO LLC p 174
2020 N Bramblewood St 67206
Tel (316) 265-3311 *SIC* 1382 1311

BERRY COMPANIES INC p 176
3223 N Hydraulic St 67219
Tel (316) 838-3321
SIC 5082 7353 7699 5084

BOMBARDIER LEARJET INC p 199
1 Learjet Way 67209
Tel (316) 946-2000 *SIC* 3721

CARGILL MEAT SOLUTIONS CORP p 255
151 N Main St Ste 900 67202
Tel (316) 291-2500 *SIC* 2011 5147 4213

CATHOLIC DIOCESE OF WICHITA INC p 266
424 N Broadway Ave 67202
Tel (316) 269-3900 *SIC* 8661 8051

■ **CESSNA AIRCRAFT CO** p 284
1 Cessna Blvd 67215
Tel (316) 517-6000 *SIC* 3721

CHAMPPS OPERATING CORP p 287
151 S Whittier St Ofc 67207
Tel (800) 229-2118 *SIC* 5812 5813

CLEAN HARBORS WICHITA LLC p 324
2824 N Ohio St 67219
Tel (316) 832-0151 *SIC* 2992 5169 5172

CONTINENTAL AMERICAN CORP p 362
5000 E 29th St N 67220
Tel (316) 685-2266 *SIC* 2759 3069

CORNEJO & SONS LLC p 370
2060 E Tulsa St 67216
Tel (316) 522-5100
SIC 1542 1794 1795 1611

COUNTY OF SEDGWICK p 381
525 N Main St Ste 823 67203
Tel (316) 660-9000 *SIC* 9111

DELTA DENTAL OF KANSAS INC p 426
1619 N Waterfront Pkwy 67206
Tel (316) 264-4511 *SIC* 6324

DONDLINGER & SONS CONSTRUCTION CO INC p 450
2656 S Sheridan Ave 67217
Tel (316) 945-0555 *SIC* 1622 1541 1542

EBY CORP p 474
2525 E 36th Cir N 67219
Tel (316) 268-3500
SIC 1629 1623 1622 1541 1542 7353

ENVISION INC p 504
2301 S Water St 67213
Tel (316) 267-2244 *SIC* 2673 2676

ETHANOL PRODUCTS LLC p 511
3939 N Webb Rd 67226
Tel (316) 303-1380 *SIC* 5172 5169

FIDELITY FINANCIAL CORP p 540
100 E English St 67202
Tel (316) 265-2261 *SIC* 6035

FLINT HILLS RESOURCES LLC p 557
4111 E 37th St N 67220
Tel (316) 828-5500 *SIC* 5169 5084

FLINT HILLS RESOURCES LP p 557
4111 E 37th St N 67220
Tel (800) 292-3133
SIC 5172 4612 1382 2911

FOLEY EQUIPMENT CO p 563
1550 S West St 67213
Tel (316) 943-4211 *SIC* 5084 5082 5083

FOLEY INDUSTRIES INC p 563
1550 S West St 67213
Tel (316) 943-4211
SIC 5082 5084 7353 6512

FOX & HOUND RESTAURANT GROUP p 572
1421 N Waterfront Pkwy 67206
Tel (316) 634-0505 *SIC* 5812

GT SALES & MANUFACTURING INC p 587
2202 S West St 67213
Tel (316) 943-2171 *SIC* 5085 3053 3052

HAMPEL OIL DISTRIBUTORS INC p 656
3727 S West St 67217
Tel (316) 529-1162 *SIC* 5171

■ **HAWKER BEECHCRAFT GLOBAL CUSTOMER SUPPORT LLC** p 669
10511 E Central Ave 67206
Tel (316) 676-7111 *SIC* 7699

■ **HCA HOSPITAL SERVICES OF SAN DIEGO** p 672
550 N Hillside St 67214
Tel (316) 962-2000 *SIC* 8062

HUTTON CONSTRUCTION CORP p 722
2229 S West St 67213
Tel (316) 942-8855 *SIC* 1542

IFR SYSTEMS INC p 730
10200 W York St 67215
Tel (316) 522-4981 *SIC* 4581

INLAND CRUDE PURCHASING LLC p 743
727 N Waco Ave Ste 400 67203
Tel (316) 263-3201 *SIC* 5172

INTEGRATED HEALTHCARE SYSTEMS INC p 749
3311 E Murdock St 67208
Tel (316) 689-9111 *SIC* 7359

INTRUST BANK NA p 760
105 N Main St 67202
Tel (316) 383-1111 *SIC* 6021

INTRUST FINANCIAL CORP p 760
105 N Main St 67202
Tel (316) 383-1111 *SIC* 6712 6022

JS VENTURES INC p 795
2400 N Woodlawn Blvd # 230 67220
Tel (316) 683-7799 *SIC* 5812

■ **KANSAS GAS AND ELECTRIC CO** p 803
120 E 1st St N 67202
Tel (316) 721-1899 *SIC* 4911

KANSAS TURNPIKE AUTHORITY p 803
9401 E Kellogg Dr 67207
Tel (316) 682-4537 *SIC* 4785

KEY CONSTRUCTION INC p 814
741 W 2nd St N 67203
Tel (316) 263-9515 *SIC* 1542 1541

KMS INC p 824
811 E Waterman St Ste 1 67202
Tel (316) 264-8833 *SIC* 5199 5141

KOCH AG & ENERGY SOLUTIONS LLC p 825
4111 E 37th St N 67220
Tel (316) 828-8310 *SIC* 5191

KOCH BUSINESS SOLUTIONS LP p 825
4111 E 37th St N 67220
Tel (316) 828-5500 *SIC* 8748

KOCH CHEMICAL TECHNOLOGY GROUP LLC p 825
4111 E 37th St N 67220
Tel (316) 828-8515 *SIC* 3443

KOCH FERTILIZER LLC p 825
4111 E 37th St N 67220
Tel (316) 828-5010 *SIC* 2873 5169 2813

KOCH INDUSTRIES INC p 825
4111 E 37th St N 67220
Tel (316) 828-5500 *SIC* 5172 2911 5169

KOCH RESOURCES LLC p 826
4111 E 37th St N 67220
Tel (316) 828-5500 *SIC* 6221 2911

KOCH SUPPLY & TRADING LP p 826
4111 E 37th St N 67220
Tel (316) 828-5500 *SIC* 2911

KOCH-GLITSCH LP p 826
4111 E 37th St N 67220
Tel (316) 828-5110 *SIC* 3443

KS&T INTERNATIONAL HOLDINGS LP p 831
4111 E 37th St N 67220
Tel (316) 828-5500 *SIC* 2911

LAW CO INC p 847
345 N Rverview St Ste 300 67203
Tel (316) 268-0200 *SIC* 1542 1522

LDF FOOD GROUP INC p 849
10610 E 26th Cir N 67226
Tel (316) 630-0677 *SIC* 5812

LDF SALES & DISTRIBUTING INC p 849
10610 E 26th Cir N 67226
Tel (316) 636-5575 *SIC* 5181

LEARJET INC p 850
1 Learjet Way 67209
Tel (316) 946-2000 *SIC* 3721 3812

LODGING ENTERPRISES LLC p 874
8080 E Central Ave # 180 67206
Tel (316) 630-6300 *SIC* 7011 8741 6552

LONE STAR STEAKHOUSE & SALOON OF OHIO INC p 876
224 E Douglas Ave Ste 700 67202
Tel (972) 295-8600 *SIC* 5812

MARCUS FOOD CO p 905
240 N Rock Rd Ste 246 67206
Tel (316) 686-7649 *SIC* 5144 5142

MARTIN K EBY CONSTRUCTION CO INC p 912
2525 E 36th Cir N 67219
Tel (316) 268-3500 *SIC* 1542

MELROSE US 3 LLC p 941
2600 S Custer Ave 67217
Tel (859) 887-6390 *SIC* 3089

MERRY TECHNOLOGY INC p 950
315 N Rverview St Apt 615 67203
Tel (316) 371-9533 *SIC* 1521 1542

MIDWEST DRYWALL CO INC p 967
1351 S Reca Ct Ste 101 67209
Tel (316) 722-9559 *SIC* 1742

MINNESOTA PIPE LINE CO LLC p 974
4111 E 37th St N 67220
Tel (316) 828-5500 *SIC* 4612

MURFIN DRILLING CO INC p 1001
250 N Water St Ste 300 67202
Tel (316) 267-3241
SIC 1381 1382 5082 6512 6514

MVP HOLDINGS LLC p 1003
8301 E 21st St N Ste 370 67206
Tel (316) 262-2819 *SIC* 6719

PRATT (LOVE BOX) LLC p 1167
700 E 37th St N 67219
Tel (316) 838-0851 *SIC* 2653 2448 4213

■ **PREFERRED HEALTH SYSTEMS INC** p 1169
8535 E 21st St N 67206
Tel (316) 609-2345 *SIC* 6324

■ **PREFERRED PLUS OF KANSAS INC** p 1169
8535 E 21st St N 67206
Tel (316) 609-2345 *SIC* 8011

PRESBYTERIAN MANORS INC p 1171
2414 N Woodlawn Blvd 67220
Tel (316) 685-1100 *SIC* 8051

RAGE ADMINISTRATIVE AND MARKETING SERVICES INC p 1205
1313 N Webb Rd Ste 200 67206
Tel (316) 634-1888 *SIC* 5812

RESTAURANT MANAGEMENT CO OF WICHITA INC p 1228
7700 E Polo Dr 67206
Tel (316) 634-1190 *SIC* 5812

RUSTY ECK FORD INC p 1260
7310 E Kellogg Dr 67207
Tel (316) 685-9211 *SIC* 5511

SHELL TOPCO LP p 1314
2533 S West St 67217
Tel (316) 942-7266 *SIC* 3625 1711

■ **SHEPLERS HOLDING CORP** p 1315
6501 W Kellogg Dr 67209
Tel (316) 946-3800 *SIC* 5699 5661

SHERWOOD CONSTRUCTION CO INC p 1316
3219 W May St 67213
Tel (316) 943-0211 *SIC* 1794 4522

SPEEDY CASH HOLDINGS CORP p 1358
3527 N Ridge Rd 67205
Tel (316) 722-3801 *SIC* 6162

▲ **SPIRIT AEROSYSTEMS HOLDINGS INC** p 1359
3801 S Oliver St 67210
Tel (316) 526-9000 *SIC* 3728 3724

■ **SPIRIT AEROSYSTEMS INC** p 1359
3801 S Oliver St 67210
Tel (316) 526-9000 *SIC* 3728

STAR LUMBER & SUPPLY CO INC p 1378
325 S West St 67213
Tel (316) 942-2221 *SIC* 5211 5713

TACO TICO INC p 1421
505 S Broadway Ave # 205 67202
Tel (316) 683-6621 *SIC* 6794

TAVISTOCK RESTAURANTS LLC p 1426
2024 N Woodlawn St # 417 67208
Tel (510) 594-4262 *SIC* 5812

■ **TEXTRON AVIATION INC** p 1445
1 Cessna Blvd 67215
Tel (316) 517-6000 *SIC* 4581

UNIFIED SCHOOL DISTRICT 259 p 1503
201 N Water St 67202
Tel (316) 973-4000 *SIC* 8211 8249 8331

UNIVERSAL COMPANIES INC p 1516
2824 N Ohio St 67219
Tel (316) 832-0151
SIC 5171 5541 6512 8741 6099 2992

VIA CHRISTI CLINIC PA p 1554
3311 E Murdock St 67208
Tel (316) 689-9111 *SIC* 8011

VIA CHRISTI HEALTH INC p 1554
2622 W Central Ave # 102 67203
Tel (316) 858-4900 *SIC* 8011 8741

VIA CHRISTI HOSPITALS WICHITA INC p 1554
929 N Saint Francis St 67214
Tel (316) 268-5000 *SIC* 8062

VIEGA LLC p 1556
100 N Broadway Ave # 600 67202
Tel (316) 425-7400 *SIC* 5074

■ **WESLEY MEDICAL CENTER LLC** p 1593
550 N Hillside St 67214
Tel (316) 962-2000 *SIC* 8011

WICHITA CITY OF (INC) p 1607
455 N Main St Fl 5 67202
Tel (316) 268-4351 *SIC* 9111

WICHITA PUBLIC SCHOOLS p 1608
201 N Water St 67202
Tel (316) 973-4000 *SIC* 8211

WICHITA STATE UNIVERSITY p 1608
1845 Fairmount St 67260
Tel (316) 978-3040 *SIC* 5999

WILDCAT CONSTRUCTION CO INC p 1609
3219 W May St 67213
Tel (316) 945-9408
SIC 1623 1622 1771 1611 1629

YOUNG MENS CHRISTIAN ASSOCIATION OF WICHITA KANSAS p 1639
402 N Market St 67202
Tel (316) 219-9622
SIC 8641 7991 8351 7032 8322

KENTUCKY

ALBANY, KY

EQUITY GROUP - KENTUCKY DIVISION LLC p 507
2294 Ky Highway 90 W 42602
Tel (606) 387-2300 *SIC* 2048 5144

ASHLAND, KY

ASHLAND HOSPITAL CORP p 117
2201 Lexington Ave 41101
Tel (606) 408-4000 *SIC* 8062

KINGS DAUGHTERS HEALTH SYSTEM INC p 820
2201 Lexington Ave 41101
Tel (606) 408-4000 *SIC* 8062

KINGS DAUGHTERS MEDICAL CENTER p 820
2201 Lexington Ave 41101
Tel (606) 408-4000 *SIC* 8062

OUR LADY OF BELLEFONTE HOSPITAL INC p 1098
1000 Saint Christopher Dr 41101
Tel (606) 833-3333
SIC 8062 8082 8011 5999

BARDSTOWN, KY

AMERICAN FUJI SEAL INC p 73
1051 Bloomfield Rd 40004
Tel (502) 348-9211 *SIC* 8748 2671

HEAVEN HILL DISTILLERIES INC p 679
1064 Loretto Rd 40004
Tel (502) 348-3921 *SIC* 2085

MITSUBA BARDSTOWN INC p 977
901 Withrow Ct 40004
Tel (502) 348-1409 *SIC* 3714

NEWCOMB OIL CO LLC p 1037
901 Withrow Ct 40004
Tel (502) 348-3961 *SIC* 5411 5171

SALT RIVER ELECTRIC COOPERATIVE CORP p 1273
111 W Brashear Ave 40004
Tel (502) 348-3931 *SIC* 4911

TOYOTA BOSHOKU KENTUCKY LLC p 1466
1051 Withrow Ct 40004
Tel (502) 349-6000 *SIC* 5511

BEAVER DAM, KY

DAICEL SAFETY SYSTEMS AMERICA LLC p 408
720 Old Liberty Church Rd 42320
Tel (270) 274-0062 *SIC* 3069

BELCHER, KY

CAMBRIAN COAL CORP p 244
15888 Ferrells Creek Rd 41513
Tel (606) 754-9898 *SIC* 1081

BEREA, KY

BEREA COLLEGE p 174
101 Chestnut St 40403
Tel (859) 985-3000 *SIC* 8221

BETSY LAYNE, KY

KENTUCKY OIL AND REFINING CO p 812
156 Ky Oil Vlg 41605
Tel (606) 478-2303 *SIC* 5171 5541

BOWLING GREEN, KY

BARREN RIVER DEVELOPMENT COUNCIL INC p 157
177 Graham Ave 42101
Tel (270) 781-2381 *SIC* 8748

BOWLING GREEN METALFORMING LLC p 204
111 Cosma Dr 42101
Tel (270) 901-1555 *SIC* 3499 3715

BOWLING GREEN-WARREN COUNTY COMMUNITY HOSPITAL CORP p 204
250 Park St 42101
Tel (270) 745-1000 *SIC* 8062

CAMPING WORLD INC p 246
650 Three Springs Rd 42104
Tel (270) 781-2718 *SIC* 5561 5961

COMMONWEALTH HEALTH CORP INC p 346
800 Park St 42101
Tel (270) 745-1500 *SIC* 8062 6513

CWI INC p 404
650 Three Springs Rd 42104
Tel (270) 781-2718 *SIC* 5941

■ **FRUIT OF LOOM INC** p 582
1 Fruit Of The Loom Dr 42103
Tel (270) 781-6400 *SIC* 2254 2253

GREENVIEW REGIONAL HOSPITAL p 638
1801 Ashley Cir 42104
Tel (270) 793-1000 *SIC* 8011

HIGH PERFORMANCE INDUSTRIES HOLDINGS INC p 690
1801 Russellville Rd 42101
Tel (270) 782-2900 *SIC* 3592 3714

HOLLEY PERFORMANCE PRODUCTS INC p 700
1801 Russellville Rd 42101
Tel (270) 782-2900 *SIC* 3714 3592

HOUCHENS FOOD GROUP INC p 710
700 Church St 42101
Tel (270) 843-3252 *SIC* 5411 5541 5093

HOUCHENS INDUSTRIES INC p 711
700 Church St 42101
Tel (270) 843-3252 *SIC* 6719

MARTIN MANAGEMENT GROUP INC p 912
1048 Ashley St Ste 401 42103
Tel (270) 783-8080 *SIC* 5511

RAFFERTYS INC p 1205
1750 Scottsville Rd Ste 2 42104
Tel (270) 781-2834 *SIC* 5812 5813

ROSEWOOD HEALTH CARE CENTER p 1251
550 High St 42101
Tel (270) 843-3296 *SIC* 8051 8093

■ **RUSSELL BRANDS LLC** p 1259
1 Fruit Of The Loom Dr 42103
Tel (270) 781-6400
SIC 2253 2211 2329 2339 3949 5091

SCOTTYS CONTRACTING AND STONE LLC p 1294
2300 Barren River Rd 42101
Tel (270) 781-3998 *SIC* 1629 1611 2951

STEWART RICHEY CONSTRUCTION INC p 1389
2137 Glen Lily Rd 42101
Tel (270) 842-5184 *SIC* 1542 1521 1541

SUMITOMO ELECTRIC WIRING SYSTEMS INC p 1398
1018 Ashley St 42103
Tel (270) 782-7397 *SIC* 3714 5063 3694

TRACE DIE CAST INC p 1468
140 Graham Ave 42101
Tel (270) 781-0049 *SIC* 3363

■ **UNION UNDERWEAR CO INC** p 1505
1 Fruit Of The Loom Dr 42103
Tel (270) 781-6400 *SIC* 8661

■ **VANITY FAIR BRANDS LP** p 1543
1 Fruit Of The Loom Dr 42103
Tel (270) 781-6400 *SIC* 2341 2384 2342

WARREN COUNTY PUBLIC SCHOOLS p 1576
303 Lovers Ln 42103
Tel (270) 781-2392 *SIC* 8211

WARREN RURAL ELECTRIC COOPERATIVE CORP p 1577
951 Fairview Ave 42101
Tel (270) 842-6541 *SIC* 4911

WENDYS OF BOWLING GREEN INC p 1592
Store 3489 Store3489 St Sto 42104
Tel (270) 782-6124 *SIC* 5812

WESTERN KENTUCKY UNIVERSITY p 1598
1906 College Heights Blvd # 11026 42101
Tel (270) 745-0111 *SIC* 8221

BRANDENBURG, KY

MONUMENT CHEMICAL KENTUCKY LLC p 987
2450 Olin Rd 40108
Tel (270) 422-2101 *SIC* 2911

CALVERT CITY, KY

CC METALS AND ALLOYS LLC p 269
1542 N Main St 42029
Tel (270) 395-7631 *SIC* 3313 3341 3295

■ **ISP CHEMICALS LLC** p 767
455 N Main St 42029
Tel (270) 395-4165 *SIC* 2869

CAMPBELLSVILLE, KY

COX INTERIOR INC p 386
1751 Old Columbia Rd 42718
Tel (270) 789-3129 *SIC* 2431

MURAKAMI MANUFACTURING USA INC p 1001
575 Watertower Byp 42718
Tel (270) 469-3939 *SIC* 3231

CATLETTSBURG, KY

■ **CATLETTSBURG REFINING LLC** p 267
11631 Us Route 23 41129
Tel (606) 921-3333 *SIC* 2911

CLAY, KY

■ **WEBSTER COUNTY COAL LLC** p 1587
1758 State Route 874 42404
Tel (270) 249-2205 *SIC* 1221

COLD SPRING, KY

DISABLED AMERICAN VETERANS p 442
3725 Alexandria Pike 41076
Tel (859) 441-7300 *SIC* 8641

■ **GRIFFIN INDUSTRIES LLC** p 640
4221 Alexandria Pike 41076
Tel (859) 781-2010 *SIC* 2077

COLUMBIA, KY

■ **FAMILY HOME HEALTH CARE INC** p 527
937 Campbellsville Rd R 42728
Tel (270) 384-6411 *SIC* 8082

CORBIN, KY

FORCHT GROUP OF KENTUCKY LLC p 565
200 S Kentucky Ave 40701
Tel (606) 528-9600 *SIC* 6141

PLM HOLDING CO LLC p 1156
200 Allison Blvd 40701
Tel (606) 523-4444 *SIC* 1222

COVINGTON, KY

▲ **ASHLAND GLOBAL HOLDINGS INC** p 117
50 E Rivercenter Blvd 41011
Tel (859) 815-3333 *SIC* 5169

■ **ASHLAND LLC** p 117
50 E Rivercenter Blvd # 1600 41011
Tel (859) 815-3333
SIC 2899 2851 2821 2911 5169 7549

CLUB CHEF LLC p 328
3776 Lake Park Dr Unit 1 41017
Tel (859) 578-3100 *SIC* 5148

COMMONWEALTH HOTELS LLC p 346
100 E Rivercenter Blvd # 1050 41011
Tel (859) 392-2264 *SIC* 7011 8741

CORPOREX COMPANIES LLC p 372
100 E Rivercntr Blvd 11 Ste 1100 41011
Tel (859) 292-5500 *SIC* 6798

CORPOREX REALTY & INVESTMENT LLC p 372
100 E Riverctr Ste 1100 41011
Tel (859) 292-5500
SIC 1542 6531 6552 8741 6512

COVINGTON BOARD OF EDUCATION p 385
25 E 7th St 41011
Tel (859) 292-5800 *SIC* 8211

DIOCESE OF COVINGTON p 440
1125 Madison Ave 41011
Tel (859) 392-1500 *SIC* 8211 8661

FBM OHIO LLC p 532
2048 Rolling Hills Dr 41017
Tel (859) 431-0626 *SIC* 5031

PRO MACH INC p 1178
50 E Rivercntr Blvd 180 Ste 1800 41011
Tel (513) 831-8778 *SIC* 3565

RA JONES & CO p 1203
2701 Crescent Springs Rd 41017
Tel (859) 341-0400 *SIC* 3565 3823

■ **WADDINGTON NORTH AMERICA INC** p 1571
50 E Rivercenter Blvd # 650 41011
Tel (859) 292-8028 *SIC* 3089

CRESTVIEW HILLS, KY

APPLE SAUCE INC p 99
741 Centre View Blvd # 100 41017
Tel (859) 331-3900 *SIC* 5812

BANK OF KENTUCKY FINANCIAL CORP p 151
111 Lookout Farm Dr 41017
Tel (859) 371-2340 *SIC* 6035

C J APPLE II INC p 232
741 Centre View Blvd # 100 41017
Tel (859) 331-3900 *SIC* 5812

COLUMBIA SUSSEX CORP p 342
740 Centre View Blvd 41017
Tel (859) 331-0091 *SIC* 7011 5812

ST ELIZABETH PHYSICIAN SERVICES LLC p 1366
334 Thomas More Pkwy 41017
Tel (859) 344-3737 *SIC* 8011

SUMMIT MEDICAL GROUP INC p 1399
334 Thomas More Pkwy 41017
Tel (859) 344-3737 *SIC* 8011

TROPICANA ENTERTAINMENT INTERMEDIATE HOLDINGS LLC p 1484
740 Centre View Blvd 41017
Tel (859) 578-1100 *SIC* 7011

TROPICANA ENTERTAINMENT LLC p 1484
740 Centre View Blvd 41017
Tel (859) 669-1500 *SIC* 7929

CRESTWOOD, KY

OLDHAM COUNTY SCHOOL DISTRICT p 1082
6165 W Highway 146 40014
Tel (502) 241-3500 *SIC* 8211

DANVILLE, KY

CENTER COLLEGE p 275
600 W Walnut St 40422
Tel (859) 238-5369 *SIC* 5812

CENTRE COLLEGE OF KENTUCKY p 281
600 W Walnut St 40422
Tel (859) 238-5200 *SIC* 8221

EPHRAIM MCDOWELL REGIONAL MEDICAL CENTER INC p 504
217 S 3rd St 40422
Tel (859) 239-1000 *SIC* 8062

DUNNVILLE, KY

TARTER GATE CO LLC p 1425
10739 S Us 127 42528
Tel (435) 744-0770 *SIC* 3446 0219

TARTER GATE WOOD PRODUCTS INC p 1425
10739 S Us 127 42528
Tel (606) 787-2081
SIC 3446 2448 2499 2426 2421

EAST BERNSTADT, KY

ELMO GREER & SONS LLC p 489
3138 N Us Highway 25 40729
Tel (606) 862-4233 *SIC* 1611 2951

EDGEWOOD, KY

SAINT ELIZABETH MEDICAL CENTER INC p 1269
1 Medical Village Dr 41017
Tel (859) 301-2000 *SIC* 8062 8069 8093

ELIZABETHTOWN, KY

AKEBONO BRAKE ELIZABETHTOWN PLANT p 42
300 Ring Rd 42701
Tel (270) 737-4906 *SIC* 3714

AMBRAKE MANUFACTURING LTD p 65
300 Ring Rd 42701
Tel (270) 737-4906 *SIC* 3714

FLEX AMERICA INC p 555
1221 N Black Branch Rd 42701
Tel (270) 982-3456 *SIC* 5199

HARDIN COUNTY BOARD OF EDUCATION p 660
65 W A Jenkins Rd 42701
Tel (270) 369-7370 *SIC* 8211

HARDIN MEMORIAL HOSPITAL FOUNDATION INC p 660
913 N Dixie Ave 42701
Tel (270) 737-1212 *SIC* 8062

ERLANGER, KY

AQUIONICS INC p 102
1455 Jamike Ave Ste 100 41018
Tel (859) 341-0710 *SIC* 5074

■ **COMAIR HOLDINGS LLC** p 343
82 Comair Blvd 41018
Tel (859) 767-2550 *SIC* 4512

CORPORATE CLEANING SYSTEMS INC p 372
3370 Turfway Rd Ste 190 41018
Tel (859) 371-5252 *SIC* 7349

FISCHER HOMES INC p 551
3940 Olympic Blvd Ste 100 41018
Tel (859) 341-4709 *SIC* 1522

MEGGITT (ERLANGER) LLC p 940
1400 Jamike Ave 41018
Tel (859) 525-8040 *SIC* 3369

PERFETTI VAN MELLE USA INC p 1135
3645 Turfway Rd 41018
Tel (859) 283-1234 *SIC* 5145 2064

REMKE MARKETS INC p 1222
1299 Cox Ave 41018
Tel (859) 594-3400 *SIC* 5912

TOYOTA BOSHOKU AMERICA INC p 1466
1360 Dolwick Rd Ste 125 41018
Tel (859) 817-4000 *SIC* 3711 5013

TOYOTA MOTOR ENGINEERING & MANUFACTURING NORTH AMERICA INC p 1466
25 Atlantic Ave 41018
Tel (469) 292-1074 *SIC* 3711 3713 8741

TRANSFREIGHT LLC p 1471
3940 Olympic Blvd Ste 500 41018
Tel (859) 372-5930 *SIC* 4213 8742

TRIM MASTERS INC p 1480
1360 Dolwick Rd Ste 125 41018
Tel (859) 887-6000 *SIC* 2531

■ **UNITED STATES PLAYING CARD CO** p 1514
300 Gap Way 41018
Tel (859) 815-7300 *SIC* 2752 5092

■ **WILD FLAVORS INC** p 1609
1261 Pacific Ave 41018
Tel (859) 342-3600 *SIC* 2869 2819

FLORENCE, KY

BOONE COUNTY BOARD OF EDUCATION p 200
8330 Us Highway 42 41042
Tel (859) 283-1003 *SIC* 8211

BOONE COUNTY SCHOOLS p 200
8330 Us Highway 42 41042
Tel (859) 283-1003 *SIC* 8211

CORKEN STEEL PRODUCTS CO p 370
7920 Kentucky Dr 41042
Tel (859) 291-4664
SIC 5075 3444 5051 8742 6411

DURO BAG MANUFACTURING CO p 463
7600 Empire Dr 41042
Tel (859) 371-2150 *SIC* 2674

EMERSON POWER TRANSMISSION CORP p 492
7120 New Buffington Rd 41042
Tel (859) 342-7900
SIC 3429 3052 3568 3562 3566 3462

■ **FIFTH THIRD BANK OF NORTHERN KENTUCKY** p 542
8100 Burlington Pike 41042
Tel (859) 283-8500 *SIC* 6022

■ **HENNEGAN CO** p 683
7455 Empire Dr 41042
Tel (859) 282-3600 *SIC* 2752 2789

KRAUSS-MAFFEI CORP p 829
7095 Industrial Rd 41042
Tel (859) 283-0200 *SIC* 5084 3559

MAZAK CORP p 924
8025 Production Dr 41042
Tel (859) 342-1700 *SIC* 3541 5084

MUBEA INC p 998
6800 Industrial Rd 41042
Tel (859) 746-5300
SIC 3493 3312 3495 3429 3714

ROBERT BOSCH AUTOMOTIVE STEERING LLC p 1241
15 Spiral Dr 41042
Tel (859) 568-1143 *SIC* 3714

■ **SOUTHERN AIR HOLDINGS INC** p 1347
7310 Turfway Rd Ste 400 41042
Tel (859) 568-9200 *SIC* 4522 4581

■ **SOUTHERN AIR INC** p 1347
7310 Turfway Rd Ste 400 41042
Tel (859) 568-9200 *SIC* 4522

■ **WORLDWIDE AIR LOGISTICS GROUP INC** p 1626
7310 Turfway Rd Ste 490 41042
Tel (859) 568-9300 *SIC* 4522 4581

FORT MITCHELL, KY

DREES CO p 455
211 Grandview Dr Ste 300 41017
Tel (859) 578-4200 *SIC* 1531 1522 1521

■ **RIVER METALS RECYCLING LLC** p 1237
334 Beechwood Rd Ste 401 41017
Tel (859) 292-8400 *SIC* 5093 3341

FRANKFORT, KY

CITY OF FRANKFORT p 315
1200 Kentucky Ave 40601
Tel (502) 875-8500 *SIC* 7389

COMMONWEALTH OF KENTUCKY p 346
700 Capital Ave Ste 100 40601
Tel (502) 564-2611 *SIC* 9111

DEPARTMENT OF COMMUNITY BASED SERVICES p 429
275 E Main St Ste 3wa 40601
Tel (502) 564-3703 *SIC* 9431 9441

DEPARTMENT OF CORRECTIONS KENTUCKY p 430
275 E Main St Rm 36 40601
Tel (502) 564-4726 *SIC* 9223

DEPARTMENT OF HIGHWAYS KENTUCKY p 430
200 Mero St 40601
Tel (502) 564-4890 *SIC* 9621

ELECTRIC & WATER PLANT BOARD OF CITY OF FRANKFORT KY p 484
317 W 2nd St 40601
Tel (502) 352-4372
SIC 4941 4911 7382 5063 4841 4813

ENERGY AND ENVIRONMENT CABINET p 497
500 Mero St Ste 4 40601
Tel (502) 564-3350 *SIC* 8641 9611

EXECUTIVE OFFICE OF COMMONWEALTH OF KENTUCKY p 517
State Cptl 700 Cpitol Ave State Capitol 40601
Tel (502) 564-2611 *SIC* 9111

▲ **FARMERS CAPITAL BANK CORP** p 529
202 W Main St Ste 100 40601
Tel (502) 227-1668 *SIC* 6021 7374 6411

■ **FRANKFORT REGIONAL MEDICAL CENTER** p 574
299 Kings Daughters Dr 40601
Tel (502) 875-5240 *SIC* 8062 8011

FRANKLIN COUNTY BOARD OF EDUCATION p 575
190 Kings Daughters Dr B-300 40601
Tel (502) 695-6700 *SIC* 8211

HEALTH & FAMILY SERVICES KENTUCKY CABINET FOR p 673
275 E Main St B 40601
Tel (502) 564-5497 *SIC* 9431

JUDICIARY COURTS OF COMMONWEALTH OF KENTUCKY p 796
700 Capital Ave Rm 231 40601
Tel (502) 564-6753 *SIC* 9211

JUSTICE AND PUBLIC SAFETY CABINET OF KENTUCKY p 797
125 Holmes St Fl 2 40601
Tel (502) 564-7554 *SIC* 9229

KENTUCKY DEPARTMENT OF PARKS p 812
Capital Plaza Tower 10th 40601
Tel (502) 564-2172 *SIC* 9512

KENTUCKY DEPT OF TECHNICAL EDUCATION p 812
500 Mero St Ste 2 40601
Tel (502) 564-4286 *SIC* 9411 9441

KENTUCKY EDUCATION AND WORK FORCE DEVELOPMENT CABINET p 812
500 Mero St Ste 3 40601
Tel (502) 564-6606 *SIC* 9441 9111

KENTUCKY EDUCATION AND WORKFORCE DEVELOPMENT CABINET p 812
500 Mero St Ste 3 40601
Tel (502) 564-0372 *SIC* 9411

KENTUCKY OFFICE OF ATTORNEY GENERAL p 812
Capitol Building Rm 100 40601
Tel (502) 696-5615 *SIC* 9199

MONTAPLAST OF NORTH AMERICA INC p 986
2011 Hoover Blvd 40601
Tel (502) 695-7766 *SIC* 3714 3089

TOPY AMERICA INC p 1461
980 Chenault Rd 40601
Tel (502) 783-1250 *SIC* 3714

TOURISM ARTS AND HERITAGE CABINET p 1464
500 Mero St Fl 24 40601
Tel (502) 564-4270 *SIC* 9512

TRANSPORTATION CABINET KENTUCKY p 1472
200 Mero St 40601
Tel (502) 564-3020 *SIC* 9621

FRANKLIN, KY

FRANKLIN PRECISION INDUSTRY INC p 575
3220 Bowling Green Rd 42134
Tel (270) 598-4300 *SIC* 3714

KEYSTOPS LLC p 816
376 Reasonover Ave 42134
Tel (270) 586-8283 *SIC* 5541 5171

FT WRIGHT, KY

KENTON COUNTY SCHOOL DISTRICT p 812
1055 Eaton Dr 41017
Tel (859) 344-8888 *SIC* 8211

KENTON COUNTY SCHOOL DISTRICT EDUCATIONAL FOUNDATION INC p 812
1055 Eaton Dr 41017
Tel (859) 344-8888 *SIC* 8399

GEORGETOWN, KY

GEORGETOWN METAL PROCESSING LLC p 607
650 Triport Rd 40324
Tel (502) 868-3450 *SIC* 3317

INTERNATIONAL CRANKSHAFT INC p 755
101 Carley Ct 40324
Tel (502) 868-0003 *SIC* 3714

MINOVA HOLDING INC p 974
150 Carley Ct 40324
Tel (502) 863-6800 *SIC* 2821 3564 2439

ORICA GROUND SUPPORT INC p 1094
150 Summer Ct 40324
Tel (502) 863-6800
SIC 5082 3564 2439 7699

SCOTT COUNTY BOARD OF EDUCATION p 1293
2168 Frankfort Rd 40324
Tel (502) 863-3663 *SIC* 8211

SCOTT COUNTY SCHOOLS p 1293
2168 Frankfort Rd 40324
Tel (502) 863-3663 *SIC* 8211

TOYOTA MOTOR MANUFACTURING KENTUCKY INC p 1466
1001 Cherry Blossom Way 40324
Tel (502) 868-2000 *SIC* 5511

VASCOR LTD p 1545
100 Farmers Bank Sq # 310 40324
Tel (502) 868-0277 *SIC* 8742

GHENT, KY

NORTH AMERICAN STAINLESS p 1050
6870 Us Highway 42 E 41045
Tel (502) 347-6000 *SIC* 3316 3312

GLASGOW, KY

ACK CONTROLS INC p 17
2600 Happy Valley Rd 42141
Tel (270) 678-6200 SIC 5013 3625 3357

AMAK BRAKE LLC p 64
1765 Cleveland Ave 42141
Tel (270) 678-1765 SIC 3714

T J SAMPSON COMMUNITY HOSPITAL p 1419
1301 N Rise St 42141
Tel (270) 651-1305 SIC 8062

TJ SAMSON COMMUNITY HOSPITAL p 1457
1301 N Race St 42141
Tel (270) 651-4444 SIC 8062

HAGERHILL, KY

CHRISTIAN APPALACHIAN PROJECT INC p 302
6550 S Ky Route 321 41222
Tel (606) 789-9791 SIC 8322

SLEDHEAD TRUCKING LLC p 1331
115 Denver Br 41222
Tel (606) 297-5391 SIC 4212

HALLIE, KY

EASTERN KENTUCKY UNIVERSITY p 472
91 Lilley Cornett Br 41821
Tel (606) 633-5828 SIC 8221

HARRODSBURG, KY

HITACHI AUTOMOTIVE SYSTEMS AMERICAS INC p 696
955 Warwick Rd 40330
Tel (859) 734-9451
SIC 3694 3714 3699 3625

LP HARRODSBURG LLC p 882
853 Lexington Rd 40330
Tel (859) 734-7791 SIC 8051

WAUSAU PAPER TOWEL & TISSUE LLC p 1583
1150 Industry Rd 40330
Tel (859) 734-0538 SIC 2621

HAWESVILLE, KY

■ CENTURY ALUMINUM OF KENTUCKY LLC p 281
1627 State Rte 271 N 42348
Tel (270) 685-2493 SIC 3354

HAZARD, KY

LESLIE RESOURCES INC p 857
1021 Tori Dr 41701
Tel (606) 439-0946 SIC 1221

NEIGHBORHOOD RESTAURANTS INC p 1024
601 Main St Ste 102 41701
Tel (606) 436-0736 SIC 5812

HEBRON, KY

BOGE RUBBER & PLASTICS USA LLC p 197
1102 Aviation Blvd 41048
Tel (859) 689-5900 SIC 5013

FIVES MACHINING SYSTEMS INC p 553
2200 Litton Ln 41048
Tel (859) 534-4600 SIC 3559

POMEROY GROUP HOLDINGS INC p 1160
1020 Petersburg Rd 41048
Tel (859) 586-6000
SIC 7373 7374 7361 6719

POMEROY IT SOLUTIONS INC p 1160
1020 Petersburg Rd 41048
Tel (859) 586-0600 SIC 7373 5045 7378

POMEROY IT SOLUTIONS SALES CO INC p 1160
1020 Petersburg Rd 41048
Tel (859) 586-0600 SIC 7373 7374 7361

ROSS ACQUISITION CO p 1251
3380 Langley Dr 41048
Tel (859) 538-8000 SIC 5145 6211

UNITED RADIO INC p 1511
3345 Point Pleasant Rd 41048
Tel (859) 371-4423 SIC 5046

HENDERSON, KY

AUDUBON METALS LLC p 131
3055 Ohio Dr 42420
Tel (270) 830-6622 SIC 3341

BIG RIVERS ELECTRIC CORP p 182
201 3rd St 42420
Tel (270) 827-2561 SIC 4911

BRENNTAG MID-SOUTH INC p 210
1405 State Route 136 W 42420
Tel (270) 827-3545 SIC 5169

COMMUNITY UNITED METHODIST HOSPITAL INC p 350
1305 N Elm St 42420
Tel (270) 827-7700 SIC 8062

FORTIS PLASTICS LLC p 569
390 Community Dr 42420
Tel (270) 827-9801 SIC 5031

GIBBS DIE CASTING CORP p 611
369 Community Dr 42420
Tel (270) 827-1801 SIC 3364 3363 3542

HENDERSON COUNTY SCHOOL DISTRICT p 682
1805 2nd St 42420
Tel (270) 831-5000 SIC 8211

KENERGY CORP p 810
6402 Old Corydon Rd 42420
Tel (270) 926-4141 SIC 4911

■ WESTERN KENTUCKY ENERGY CORP p 1598
145 N Main St 42420
Tel (270) 844-6000 SIC 4911

HIGHLAND HEIGHTS, KY

CASTELLINI CO LLC p 264
2 Plum St 41076
Tel (800) 233-8560 SIC 5148 4212 4213

CASTELLINI HOLDING CO LLC p 264
2 Plum St 41076
Tel (859) 442-4673 SIC 5148

■ G K TECHNOLOGIES INC p 587
4 Tesseneer Dr 41076
Tel (859) 572-8000 SIC 3357 3315

▲ GENERAL CABLE CORP p 599
4 Tesseneer Dr 41076
Tel (859) 572-8000 SIC 3351 3357

■ GENERAL CABLE INDUSTRIES INC p 599
4 Tesseneer Dr 41076
Tel (859) 572-8000 SIC 3351 3315 3357

■ GENERAL CABLE TECHNOLOGIES CORP p 599
4 Tesseneer Dr 41076
Tel (859) 572-8000 SIC 3357

HOPKINSVILLE, KY

■ ABM GOVERNMENT SERVICES LLC p 12
101 Walton Way 42240
Tel (270) 885-4642 SIC 8748

CHRISTIAN COUNTY SCHOOL DISTRICT FINANCE CORP p 302
200 Glass Ave 42240
Tel (270) 887-7000 SIC 8211

FLYNN ENTERPRISES LLC p 562
2203 S Walnut St 42240
Tel (270) 886-0223 SIC 2325 2339 2337

GRUPO ANTOLIN KENTUCKY INC p 643
208 Commerce Ct 42240
Tel (270) 885-2703 SIC 3559 2399

JENNIE STUART MEDICAL CENTER INC p 782
320 W 18th St 42240
Tel (270) 887-0100 SIC 8062

MARTINREA HOPKINSVILLE LLC p 913
1500 Frank Yost Ln 42240
Tel (270) 475-2000 SIC 5013

MAX ARNOLD & SONS LLC p 922
702 N Main St 42240
Tel (270) 885-8488
SIC 5171 5541 5411 5812

PENNYRILE RURAL ELECTRIC COOPERATIVE CORP p 1131
2000 Harrison St 42240
Tel (270) 886-2555 SIC 4911

TG AUTOMOTIVE SEALING KENTUCKY LLC p 1445
501 Frank Yost Ln 42240
Tel (270) 475-1400 SIC 3465

TRAD NORTH AMERICA INC p 1468
750 Frank Yost Ln 42240
Tel (270) 885-9116 SIC 3433

HYDEN, KY

■ LESLIE COUNTY TELEPHONE CO p 857
22076 Main St 41749
Tel (606) 672-2303 SIC 4813

INDEPENDENCE, KY

CROSSET CO LLC p 394
10295 Toebben Dr 41051
Tel (859) 283-5830 SIC 5148

IVEL, KY

EAST KENTUCKY NETWORK LLC p 470
101 Technology Trl 41642
Tel (606) 477-2355 SIC 4812 1731

LA GRANGE, KY

RAWLINGS CO LLC p 1209
1 Eden Pkwy 40031
Tel (502) 587-1279 SIC 8748 8111

STAINLESS STEEL ACQUISITION CO LLC p 1374
2615 E Highway 146 40031
Tel (502) 805-1120 SIC 4953

STAINLESS STEEL MIDWEST LLC p 1374
2615 E Highway 146 40031
Tel (502) 805-1120 SIC 5093

LEBANON, KY

CURTIS-MARUYASU AMERICA INC p 402
665 Metts Dr 40033
Tel (270) 692-2109 SIC 3714 3498

LEXINGTON, KY

A & W RESTAURANTS INC p 4
1648 Mcgrathiana Pkwy # 380 40511
Tel (859) 219-0019 SIC 5812 6794

A GREAT AMERICAN BRAND LLC p 5
1648 Mcgrathiana Pkwy 40511
Tel (859) 219-0019 SIC 5812 6794

ALL STAR DAIRY ASSOCIATION INC p 51
1050 Monarch St Ste 101 40513
Tel (859) 255-3644
SIC 5149 5169 5113 5199

■ AMAZON.COMKYDC LLC p 65
1850 Mercer Rd 40511
Tel (859) 381-2102 SIC 4226

AMTECK OF KENTUCKY INC p 87
2421 Fortune Dr Ste 150 40509
Tel (859) 255-9546 SIC 1731

APPALACHIAN REGIONAL HEALTHCARE INC p 98
2260 Executive Dr 40505
Tel (859) 226-2440 SIC 8062

BLACKHAWK MINING LLC p 187
3228 Summit Square Pl # 180 40509
Tel (859) 543-0515 SIC 1241

BLUEGRASS FAMILY HEALTH p 193
651 Perimeter Dr Ste 300 40517
Tel (859) 269-4475 SIC 6321 6411

BLUEGRASSORG p 193
1351 Newtown Pike 40511
Tel (859) 253-1686 SIC 8322

BOARD OF EDUCATION FAYETTE COUNTY KY p 195
701 E Main St Ste 107 40502
Tel (859) 381-4141 SIC 8211

BUDSGUNSHOP.COM LLC p 224
1105 Industry Rd 40505
Tel (859) 368-0371 SIC 5941

CENTRAL BANK & TRUST CO p 277
300 W Vine St Ste 3 40507
Tel (859) 253-6222 SIC 6022

CENTRAL BAPTIST HOSPITAL p 277
1740 Nicholasville Rd 40503
Tel (859) 260-6100 SIC 8069

DAVIS H ELLIOT CONSTRUCTION CO INC p 416
673 Blue Sky Pkwy 40509
Tel (859) 263-5148 SIC 1623 1731

DENHAM-BLYTHE CO INC p 428
100 Trade St Ste 250 40511
Tel (859) 255-7405 SIC 1541 1542

FAYETTE COUNTY PUBLIC SCHOOLS p 532
701 E Main St Rm 219 40502
Tel (859) 381-4159 SIC 8211

FAYETTE COUNTY PUBLIC SCHOOLS p 532
1126 Russell Cave Rd 40505
Tel (859) 381-4000 SIC 8211

FAZOLIS RESTAURANTS LLC p 532
2470 Palumbo Dr 40509
Tel (859) 268-1668 SIC 5812

FLORIDA TILE INC p 559
998 Governors Ln Ste 300 40513
Tel (859) 219-5200 SIC 3253

GALLS LLC p 590
1340 Russell Cave Rd 40505
Tel (859) 266-7227 SIC 5961 5399 2395

GLOBAL FITNESS HOLDINGS LLC p 616
1056 Wellington Way # 200 40513
Tel (859) 252-5993 SIC 7991

GRAY CONSTRUCTION INC p 632
10 Quality St 40507
Tel (859) 281-5000 SIC 1541 1542 8712

GRAY INC p 632
10 Quality St 40507
Tel (859) 281-5000 SIC 1541 1542

HNRC DISSOLUTION CO p 698
201 E Main St 100 40507
Tel (606) 327-5450 SIC 1222

KEENELAND ASSOCIATION INC p 807
4201 Versailles Rd 40510
Tel (859) 288-4236 SIC 5154 7948 0751

KENTUCKY EMPLOYERS MUTUAL INSURANCE AUTHORITY p 812
250 W Main St Ste 900 40507
Tel (859) 425-7800 SIC 6331

KENTUCKY MEDICAL SERVICES FOUNDATION INC p 812
2333 Alumni Park Plz # 200 40517
Tel (859) 257-7910 SIC 8721

■ KENTUCKY UTILITIES CO INC p 812
1 Quality St 40507
Tel (502) 627-2000 SIC 4911

LEXINGTON-FAYETTE URBAN COUNTY GOVERNMENT p 859
200 E Main St 40507
Tel (859) 258-3100 SIC 9121 9111

LEXMARK INTERNATIONAL INC p 860
740 W New Circle Rd 40511
Tel (859) 232-2000 SIC 3577

LICKING RIVER RESOURCES INC p 863
6301 Old Richmond Rd 40515
Tel (859) 223-8820 SIC 1241

LINK-BELT CONSTRUCTION EQUIPMENT CO LP LLLP p 869
2651 Palumbo Dr 40509
Tel (859) 263-5200 SIC 3531

■ MARSHALL PHYSICIAN SERVICES LLC p 911
1792 Alysheba Way Ste 150 40509
Tel (877) 601-6372 SIC 8011

MEDICAL REHABILITATION CENTERS LLC p 937
1050 Chinoe Rd Ste 300 40502
Tel (859) 255-0075 SIC 8742

NEW LEXINGTON CLINIC PSC p 1032
1221 S Broadway 40504
Tel (859) 258-4950 SIC 8011

RHINO RESOURCE PARTNERS LP p 1231
424 Lewis Hargett Cir # 250 40503
Tel (859) 389-6500 SIC 1221 1222

S & S FIRESTONE INC p 1261
1475 Jingle Bell Ln 40509
Tel (859) 281-8500 SIC 5531

SAINT JOSEPH HEALTH SYSTEM INC p 1269
1 Saint Joseph Dr 40504
Tel (859) 313-1000 SIC 8062 8099 8011

SEED RESTAURANT GROUP INC p 1300
2470 Palumbo Dr 40509
Tel (859) 268-1668 SIC 6794 5812

SOFTWARE INFORMATION SYSTEMS LLC p 1337
165 Barr St 40507
Tel (859) 977-4747 SIC 5045 7379

▲ TEMPUR SEALY INTERNATIONAL INC p 1436
1000 Tempur Way 40511
Tel (800) 878-8889 SIC 2515 2392

■ TEMPUR WORLD LLC p 1436
1713 Jaggie Fox Way 40511
Tel (859) 259-4838 SIC 2515

■ TEMPUR-PEDIC NORTH AMERICA LLC p 1436
1000 Tempur Way 40511
Tel (888) 811-5053 SIC 5021

THOMAS AND KING INC p 1448
249 E Main St Ste 101 40507
Tel (859) 254-2180 SIC 5812

THOMAS AND KING OF ARIZONA INC p 1448
249 E Main St Ste 101 40507
Tel (859) 254-2180 SIC 5812 5813

UK HEALTHCARE GOODSAMARITAN HOSPITAL p 1500
310 S Limestone 40508
Tel (859) 226-7000 SIC 8062 8011

UNIVERSITY OF KENTUCKY p 1522
411 S Limestone 40508
Tel (859) 257-4759 SIC 8221

UNIVERSITY OF KENTUCKY p 1522
203 Brcknrdg Hl 168 Fnkhs 40506
Tel (859) 257-9185 SIC 5122

UNIVERSITY OF KENTUCKY HOSPITAL AUXILIARY INC p 1522
800 Rose St 40536
Tel (859) 323-5000 SIC 8062

UNIVERSITY OF KENTUCKY RESEARCH FOUNDATION p 1522
102 Kinkead Hall 40506
Tel (859) 257-4758 SIC 8733

US COAL CORP p 1531
6301 Old Richmond Rd 40515
Tel (859) 223-8820 SIC 1241

■ VALVOLINE INC p 1542
3499 Blazer Pkwy 40509
Tel (859) 357-7777 SIC 2992

■ VALVOLINE INTERNATIONAL INC p 1542
3499 Blazer Pkwy 40509
Tel (800) 832-6825 SIC 7549 5172

■ VALVOLINE LLC p 1542
3499 Blazer Pkwy 40509
Tel (859) 357-7777 SIC 2992

■ VALVOLINE US LLC p 1542
3499 Blazer Pkwy 40509
Tel (859) 357-7777 SIC 2992

YORKSHIRE GLOBAL RESTAURANTS INC p 1637
1648 Mcgrathiana Pkwy 40511
Tel (859) 721-1328 SIC 5812

LONDON, KY

AISIN AUTOMOTIVE CASTING LLC p 41
4870 E Highway 552 40744
Tel (606) 878-6523 SIC 3363

BORDEN DAIRY CO OF KENTUCKY LLC p 201
221 W Highway 80 40741
Tel (606) 878-7301 SIC 5143

LAUREL COUNTY BOARD OF EDUCATION p 847
718 N Main St 40741
Tel (606) 862-4608 SIC 8211

LAUREL GROCERY CO LLC p 847
129 Barbourville Rd 40744
Tel (606) 878-6601
SIC 5141 5147 5122 5143

SENTURE LLC p 1305
460 Industrial Blvd 40741
Tel (606) 878-4205
SIC 7379 7389 7374 7373 8742

SHAMROCK COAL CO INC p 1311
1374 Highway 192 E 40741
Tel (606) 878-7411 SIC 1222

LOUISA, KY

BROWN FOODSERVICE INC p 219
500 E Clayton Ln 41230
Tel (606) 638-1139
SIC 5142 5141 5084 5087

LOUISVILLE, KY

A&R LOGISTICS INC p 7
600 N Hurstbourne Pkwy # 110 40222
Tel (815) 941-5200 *SIC* 8742 4731

AAF-MCQUAY GROUP INC p 8
9920 Corporate Campus Dr # 2200 40223
Tel (502) 637-0111
SIC 5075 3585 3564 7623

ABEL CONSTRUCTION CO INC p 11
3401 Bashford Avenue Ct 40218
Tel (502) 451-2235 *SIC* 1541 1542

■ **ADP BENEFIT SERVICES KY INC** p 24
11405 Bluegrass Pkwy 40299
Tel (888) 421-7477 *SIC* 8741

■ **AFAM ACQUISITION LLC** p 32
9510 Ormsby Station Rd 40223
Tel (502) 640-9318 *SIC* 8082

AL J SCHNEIDER CO p 43
325 W Main St Ste 1800 40202
Tel (502) 584-5984 *SIC* 7011 5031

▲ **ALMOST FAMILY INC** p 59
9510 Ormsby Station Rd # 103 40223
Tel (502) 423-4336 *SIC* 8082

AMERICAN AIR FILTER CO INC p 67
9920 Corporate Campus Dr # 2200 40223
Tel (502) 637-0011 *SIC* 3564

AMERICAN INCOME LIFE INSURANCE p 74
10000 Shelbyville Rd # 211 40223
Tel (812) 280-1360 *SIC* 6411

AMERICAN SYNTHETIC RUBBER CO LLC p 80
4500 Camp Ground Rd 40216
Tel (502) 449-8300 *SIC* 2822 2821

ASSURED NL INSURANCE AGENCY INC p 122
2305 River Rd 40206
Tel (502) 894-2100 *SIC* 6411

B F FT MYERS INC p 141
3309 Collins Ln 40245
Tel (502) 254-7130 *SIC* 5812

B F SOUTH INC p 142
3309 Collins Ln 40245
Tel (502) 254-7130 *SIC* 5812

■ **BA MERCHANT SERVICES** p 143
1231 Durrett Ln 40213
Tel (502) 315-2000 *SIC* 7374

■ **BA MERCHANT SERVICES LLC** p 143
1231 Durrett Ln 40213
Tel (502) 315-2000 *SIC* 7374

BAPTIST HEALTHCARE AFFILIATES INC p 154
2701 Eastpoint Pkwy 40223
Tel (502) 896-5008 *SIC* 8062

BAPTIST HEALTHCARE SYSTEM INC p 154
2701 Eastpoint Pkwy 40223
Tel (502) 896-5000 *SIC* 8062 8011 8741

BOWIE RESOURCE PARTNERS LLC p 204
6100 Dutchmans Ln Ste 902 40205
Tel (502) 584-6022 *SIC* 1221

BOWIE RESOURCES LLC p 204
6100 Dutchmans Ln Ste 902 40205
Tel (502) 584-6022 *SIC* 1221

BOYD CO LLC p 205
1400 Cecil Ave 40211
Tel (502) 774-4441 *SIC* 5082

BRAMCO INC p 207
1801 Watterson Trl 40299
Tel (502) 493-4300 *SIC* 5082 7353

▲ **BROWN-FORMAN CORP** p 220
850 Dixie Hwy 40210
Tel (502) 585-1100 *SIC* 2085 2084 2449

BUFFALO CONSTRUCTION INC p 224
2700 Stanley Gault Pkwy # 130 40223
Tel (502) 327-4686 *SIC* 1542

▲ **CAFEPRESS INC** p 237
11909 Shelbyville Rd 40243
Tel (502) 995-2268 *SIC* 4813 5961

CALDWELL GROUP LLC p 238
4000 Tower Rd 40219
Tel (502) 964-3361 *SIC* 3443

CALDWELL TANKS INC p 238
4000 Tower Rd 40219
Tel (502) 964-3361 *SIC* 3443 5084 3441

CALIFORNIA SQUARE LIMITED PARTNERSHIP p 241
1600 Garland Ave 40210
Tel (502) 589-9034 *SIC* 6513

■ **CAMBRIDGE HOME HEALTH CARE INC** p 244
9510 Ormsby Station Rd # 300 40223
Tel (330) 270-8661 *SIC* 8082

CANYON FUEL CO LLC p 248
6100 Dutchmans Ln Fl 9 40205
Tel (502) 584-6022 *SIC* 1241

CARBIDE INDUSTRIES LLC p 252
4400 Bells Ln 40211
Tel (502) 775-4100 *SIC* 2813 2819

CARDINAL CARRYOR INC p 252
1055 Grade Ln 40213
Tel (502) 363-6641
SIC 5084 7699 7359 5085 3535

CAUDILL SEED AND WAREHOUSE CO INC p 267
1402 W Main St 40203
Tel (502) 583-4402 *SIC* 5191 5261

■ **CDR MANUFACTURING INC** p 271
10200 Forest Green Blvd 40223
Tel (502) 625-0760 *SIC* 3679 3672 3699

CENTRAL CARBIDE LLC p 277
4400 Bells Ln 40211
Tel (502) 775-4100 *SIC* 2819

CHARAH INC p 288
12601 Plantside Dr 40299
Tel (502) 245-1353 *SIC* 1081 4953

▲ **CHURCHILL DOWNS INC** p 305
600 N Hurstbourne Pkwy 40222
Tel (502) 636-4400 *SIC* 7948 7993 3578

CHURCHILL INSURANCE ASSOCIATES INC p 305
1700 Eastpoint Pkwy 40223
Tel (502) 244-1343 *SIC* 6411

COMMUNITY MEDICAL ASSOCIATES INC p 349
224 E Broadway Fl 5 40202
Tel (502) 588-9490 *SIC* 8011

■ **CONSTELLATION NEWENERGY - GAS DIVISION LLC** p 361
9960 Corporate Campus Dr 40223
Tel (502) 426-4500 *SIC* 4924

CORHART REFRACTORIES CORP p 370
10300 Ormsby Park Pl # 450 40223
Tel (502) 423-6324 *SIC* 3255 3297

■ **COURIER-JOURNAL INC** p 383
525 W Broadway 40202
Tel (502) 582-4011 *SIC* 2711

DELTA DENTAL OF KENTUCKY INC p 426
10100 Linn Station Rd # 700 40223
Tel (502) 736-5000 *SIC* 6324

DERBY INDUSTRIES LLC p 431
4451 Robards Ln 40218
Tel (502) 451-7373
SIC 4225 7389 4222 4226

DOMETIC CORP p 448
13551 Triton Park Blvd # 1000 40223
Tel (502) 873-3524
SIC 3089 3443 3444 3822 3823 3999

ENOVAPREMIER LLC p 500
1630 Lyndon Farm Ct # 100 40223
Tel (502) 412-4406 *SIC* 3089

EVERGREEN REHABILITATION LLC p 515
136 Saint Matthews Ave # 300 40207
Tel (502) 897-1700 *SIC* 8049

FAMILY ROOTS USA INC p 527
4211 Produce Rd 40218
Tel (502) 964-0063 *SIC* 5999

FARM CREDIT MID-AMERICA p 528
1601 Ups Dr 40223
Tel (502) 420-3700 *SIC* 6159 6141

FIFTEENINONE OPCO GROUP LLC p 541
7400 New La Grange Rd 40222
Tel (502) 429-8062 *SIC* 8051

■ **FIFTH THIRD BANK OF KENTUCKY INC** p 542
401 S 4th St Ste 1000 40202
Tel (502) 562-5215 *SIC* 6021

FOUR COURTS INC p 571
2100 Millvale Rd 40205
Tel (502) 451-0990 *SIC* 8052

HAIER US APPLIANCE SOLUTIONS INC p 653
4000 Buechel Bank Rd 40225
Tel (502) 452-4666 *SIC* 3639

HALL CONTRACTING OF KENTUCKY INC p 654
3800 Crittenden Dr 40209
Tel (502) 367-6151
SIC 1541 1623 1761 1731

HANSON AGGREGATES MIDWEST LLC p 659
207 Old Harrods Creek Rd 40223
Tel (502) 244-7550 *SIC* 1422 1611

HARSHAW SERVICE INC p 664
12700 Plantside Dr 40299
Tel (502) 499-7000 *SIC* 5075 1711 5074

HILLIARD-LYONS INC p 693
500 W Jefferson St # 700 40202
Tel (502) 588-8400 *SIC* 7389

HL FINANCIAL SERVICES LLC p 697
500 W Jefferson St 40202
Tel (502) 588-8400 *SIC* 7389

HOLT EQUIPMENT CO LLC p 702
4508 River Rd 40222
Tel (502) 899-7513 *SIC* 5082

HORTON FRUIT CO INC p 708
4701 Jennings Ln 40218
Tel (502) 969-1371 *SIC* 5148

■ **HUMANA GOVERNMENT BUSINESS INC** p 718
305 N Hurstbourne Pkwy 1b 40222
Tel (502) 318-0935 *SIC* 6321

■ **HUMANA HEALTH PLAN OF KANSAS INC** p 718
500 W Main St Ste 300 40202
Tel (502) 580-1000 *SIC* 6324 6321

▲ **HUMANA INC** p 718
500 W Main St Ste 300 40202
Tel (502) 580-1000 *SIC* 6324 6321 6411

■ **HUMANA INSURANCE CO OF KENTUCKY** p 718
500 W Main St Ste 300 40202
Tel (502) 580-1000 *SIC* 6321 8741

■ **HUMCO INC** p 718
500 W Main St Ste 300 40202
Tel (502) 580-1000 *SIC* 6321

ICAP ENERGY LLC p 726
9931 Corporate Campus Dr 40223
Tel (502) 327-1400 *SIC* 5172

IMI SOUTH LLC p 734
1440 Selinda Ave 40213
Tel (502) 456-6930 *SIC* 3273

INTERLOCK INDUSTRIES INC p 753
545 S 3rd St Ste 310 40202
Tel (502) 569-2007
SIC 3341 4121 3444 3354 2653

ISCO INDUSTRIES INC p 766
100 Witherspoon St 40202
Tel (502) 318-6626 *SIC* 5085 5083

J J B HILLIARD W L LYONS LLC p 771
500 W Jefferson St # 700 40202
Tel (502) 588-8400 *SIC* 6211

JEFFERSON COUNTY BOARD OF EDUCATION p 781
3332 Newburg Rd 40218
Tel (502) 485-3011 *SIC* 8211 8741

JEFFERSON COUNTY PUBLIC SCHOOL DISTRICT p 781
3332 Newburg Rd 40218
Tel (502) 485-3011 *SIC* 8211

JEWISH HOSPITAL & ST MARYS HEALTHCARE INC p 784
200 Abraham Flexner Way # 1 40202
Tel (502) 587-4011 *SIC* 8062 8082

JEWISH HOSPITAL HEALTHCARE SERVICES INC p 784
200 Abraham Flexner Way # 1 40202
Tel (502) 587-4011 *SIC* 8062 8082

JONES PLASTIC AND ENGINEERING CO LLC p 792
2410 Plantside Dr 40299
Tel (502) 491-3785 *SIC* 3089

KELLEY CONSTRUCTION INC p 808
12550 Lake Station Pl 40299
Tel (502) 239-2848 *SIC* 1542

KENTUCKY ASSOCIATION OF ELECTRIC COOPERATIVES INC p 812
4515 Bishop Ln 40218
Tel (502) 451-2430
SIC 3612 2721 7629 5063

KENTUCKY FARM BUREAU INSURANCE AGENCY INC p 812
9201 Bunsen Pkwy 40220
Tel (502) 495-5000 *SIC* 6411

KENTUCKY FARM BUREAU MUTUAL INSURANCE CO p 812
9201 Bunsen Pkwy 40220
Tel (502) 495-5000 *SIC* 6411

■ **KENTUCKY FRIED CHICKEN CORP** p 812
1441 Gardiner Ln 40213
Tel (502) 874-8300 *SIC* 5812 6794

■ **KENTUCKY FRIED CHICKEN OF LOUISVILLE INC** p 812
1441 Gardiner Ln 40213
Tel (502) 874-8300 *SIC* 5812

KENTUCKY-INDIANA LUMBER CO INC p 812
4010 Collins Ln 40245
Tel (502) 637-1401 *SIC* 5031 2439 2431

KENTUCKYONE HEALTH INC p 813
200 Abraham Flexner Way 40202
Tel (502) 587-4011 *SIC* 8099

KENTUCKYONE HEALTH MEDICAL GRO p 813
100 E Liberty St Ste 100 40202
Tel (502) 315-1458 *SIC* 8099

■ **KFC CORP (DE)** p 816
1900 Colonel Sanders Ln 40213
Tel (502) 874-8300 *SIC* 5812 6794

■ **KFC ENTERPRISES INC** p 816
1441 Gardiner Ln 40213
Tel (502) 895-3227 *SIC* 5812

■ **KFC NATIONAL MANAGEMENT CO** p 816
1441 Gardiner Ln 40213
Tel (502) 874-8300 *SIC* 5812

▲ **KINDRED HEALTHCARE INC** p 819
680 S 4th St 40202
Tel (502) 596-7300
SIC 8062 8051 8322 8082

■ **KINDRED HEALTHCARE OPERATING INC** p 819
680 S 4th St 40202
Tel (502) 596-7300 *SIC* 8051

■ **KINDRED HOSPITALS LIMITED PARTNERSHIP** p 819
1313 Saint Anthony Pl 40204
Tel (502) 587-7001 *SIC* 8069

■ **KINDRED NURSING CENTERS EAST LLC** p 819
680 S 4th St 40202
Tel (502) 596-7300 *SIC* 8051

KOSAIR CHILDRENS HOSPITAL p 828
231 E Chestnut St Ste 100 40202
Tel (502) 629-6000 *SIC* 8062

LABORATORY SUPPLY CO p 836
1951 Bishop Ln Ste 300 40218
Tel (800) 888-5227 *SIC* 5047

LANTECH.COM LLC p 844
11000 Bluegrass Pkwy 40299
Tel (502) 267-4200 *SIC* 3565

■ **LG&E AND KU ENERGY LLC** p 860
220 W Main St Ste 1400 40202
Tel (502) 627-2000
SIC 4911 4931 4932 4924

■ **LG&E AND KU SERVICES CO** p 860
220 W Main St Ste 1400 40202
Tel (502) 627-2000 *SIC* 4911

LLFLEX LLC p 872
1225 W Burnett Ave 40210
Tel (502) 635-6331 *SIC* 2672

LOGO HOLDINGS I CORP p 875
626 W Main St 40202
Tel (502) 637-5443 *SIC* 3577

LOGO HOLDINGS II CORP p 875
626 W Main St 40202
Tel (502) 637-5443 *SIC* 6719 7336

LONG JOHN SILVERS RESTAURANT INC p 876
1441 Gardiner Ln 40213
Tel (502) 874-3000 *SIC* 5812 6794

LOUISVILLE & JEFFERSON COUNTY METROPOLITAN SEWER DISTRICT p 880
700 W Liberty St 40203
Tel (502) 540-6000 *SIC* 4952

LOUISVILLE BEDDING CO INC p 880
10400 Bunsen Way 40299
Tel (502) 491-3370 *SIC* 2392 3949

■ **LOUISVILLE GAS AND ELECTRIC CO** p 880
220 W Main St Ste 1400 40202
Tel (502) 627-2000 *SIC* 4931 4911 4924

LOUISVILLE HOSPITAL p 881
217 E Chestnut St 40202
Tel (502) 587-1100 *SIC* 8062

LOUISVILLE LADDER INC p 881
7765 National Tpke # 190 40214
Tel (502) 636-2811 *SIC* 2499

LOUISVILLE TILE DISTRIBUTORS INC p 881
4520 Bishop Ln 40218
Tel (502) 452-2037 *SIC* 5032 5211 1743

LOUISVILLE WATER CO p 881
550 S 3rd St 40202
Tel (502) 569-3600 *SIC* 4941

LOUISVILLE-JEFFERSON COUNTY METRO GOVERNMENT p 881
527 W Jefferson St 40202
Tel (502) 574-2003 *SIC* 9111

MATERIAL HANDLING SYSTEMS INC p 919
3955 E Blue Lick Rd 40229
Tel (502) 636-0690 *SIC* 5084

MERCER TRANSPORTATION CO INC p 944
1128 W Main St 40203
Tel (502) 584-2301 *SIC* 4213

MESA FOODS LLC p 951
3701 W Magnolia Ave 40211
Tel (502) 772-2500 *SIC* 2096 2045 2099

N GLANTZ & SON LLC p 1005
2501 Constant Comment Pl 40299
Tel (502) 426-4473 *SIC* 5046

■ **NATIONAL HEALTH INDUSTRIES INC** p 1013
9510 Ormsby Station Rd # 300 40223
Tel (502) 448-5862 *SIC* 8082

NL OF KY INC p 1045
2305 River Rd 40206
Tel (502) 894-2100 *SIC* 6411

■ **NORTH ATLANTIC TRADING CO INC** p 1051
5201 Interchange Way 40229
Tel (502) 778-4421 *SIC* 2131

NORTON AUDUBON HOSPITAL p 1061
1 Audubon Plaza Dr 40217
Tel (502) 636-7111 *SIC* 8062

NORTON HEALTHCARE FOUNDATION INC p 1061
4967 Us Highway 42 # 100 40222
Tel (502) 629-8000 *SIC* 7389

NORTON HEALTHCARE INC p 1061
200 E Chestnut St 40202
Tel (502) 629-8000 *SIC* 8741 8062

NORTON HOSPITAL p 1061
200 E Chestnut St Frnt 40202
Tel (502) 629-8159 *SIC* 8062

NORTON HOSPITALS INC p 1061
200 E Chestnut St 40202
Tel (502) 629-8000
SIC 8062 8011 8093 8071

■ **NPC GROUP INC** p 1064
5100 Interchange Way 40229
Tel (312) 627-6000 *SIC* 7389

NUMIT LLC p 1067
15415 Shelbyville Rd 40245
Tel (502) 245-2110 *SIC* 3316

■ **OMNI HOME HEALTH SERVICES LLC** p 1084
9510 Ormsby Station Rd # 300 40223
Tel (615) 712-2248 *SIC* 8082

ORR CORP p 1095
11601 Interchange Dr 40229
Tel (502) 774-5791 *SIC* 5084

ORR SAFETY CORP p 1095
11601 Interchange Dr 40229
Tel (502) 774-5791 *SIC* 5099

PACKAGING UNLIMITED LLC p 1107
1729 Mccloskey Ave 40210
Tel (502) 515-3900 SIC 2653

▲ PAPA JOHNS INTERNATIONAL INC p 1112
2002 Papa Johns Blvd # 100 40299
Tel (502) 261-7272 SIC 5812 6794 2099

■ PAPA JOHNS INTERNATIONAL INC p 1112
2002 Papa Johns Blvd # 100 40299
Tel (502) 261-7272 SIC 5812

PAPERCONE CORP p 1112
3200 Fern Valley Rd 40213
Tel (502) 961-9493 SIC 2677

PAYMENT ALLIANCE INTERNATIONAL INC p 1122
1 Paragon Ctr 6060 Dutchm 40205
Tel (502) 212-4000 SIC 6099

PAYMENT ALLIANCE PROCESSING CORP p 1122
6060 Dutchmans Ln Ste 320 40205
Tel (502) 212-4000 SIC 8742

PCA-CORRECTIONS LLC p 1123
2701 Chestnut Station Ct 40299
Tel (502) 526-0375 SIC 5122

▲ PHARMERICA CORP p 1141
1901 Campus Pl 40299
Tel (502) 627-7000 SIC 5912 5122

PHYSICIAN GROUP p 1145
6801 Dixie Hwy Ste 133 40258
Tel (502) 937-3864 SIC 8011

■ PJ FOOD SERVICE INC p 1153
2002 Papa Johns Blvd 40299
Tel (502) 261-7272 SIC 5149 5087 2045

PLUMBERS SUPPLY CO p 1156
1000 E Main St 40206
Tel (502) 582-2261 SIC 5074 5085

PREMIER PACKAGING LLC p 1170
3900 Produce Rd 40218
Tel (502) 935-8786 SIC 5085 5113 3086

PRESBYTERIAN CHURCH (USA) A CORP p 1171
100 Witherspoon St 40202
Tel (800) 728-7228 SIC 8661

PSC INDUSTRIES INC p 1188
1100 W Market St 40203
Tel (502) 625-7700 SIC 3411

RECOVERCARE LLC p 1215
1920 Stanley Gault Pkwy # 100 40223
Tel (502) 489-9449 SIC 5047 8099

■ REHABCARE GROUP INC p 1220
680 S 4th St 40202
Tel (502) 596-7300
SIC 8093 8099 8049 8051

▲ REPUBLIC BANCORP INC p 1225
601 W Market St Ste 100 40202
Tel (502) 584-3600 SIC 6022

■ REPUBLIC BANK & TRUST CO INC p 1225
601 W Market St Ste 100 40202
Tel (502) 584-3600 SIC 6022 6163

RES-CARE INC p 1226
9901 Linn Station Rd 40223
Tel (502) 394-2100 SIC 8052 8331 7363

RESTAURANT SUPPLY CHAIN SOLUTIONS LLC p 1228
950 Breckenridge Ln # 300 40207
Tel (502) 896-5900
SIC 5812 5046 5141 5149

REV-A-SHELF CO LLC p 1229
12400 Earl Jones Way 40299
Tel (502) 499-5835 SIC 3823 5063

RMD CORP p 1239
2509 Plantside Dr 40299
Tel (502) 499-9991 SIC 5812 5813

ROAD & RAIL SERVICES INC p 1240
4233 Bardstown Rd Ste 200 40218
Tel (502) 365-5361 SIC 4789 4013

ROLLER DIE AND FORMING CO INC p 1247
1172 Industrial Blvd 40219
Tel (502) 969-1327 SIC 3355 3544

ROMAN CATHOLIC BISHOP OF LOUISVILLE p 1248
212 E College St 40203
Tel (502) 585-3291 SIC 8661

RUDD EQUIPMENT CO INC p 1257
4344 Poplar Level Rd 40213
Tel (502) 456-4050 SIC 5082 7353

SAM SWOPE AUTO GROUP LLC p 1274
10 Swope Autocenter Dr 40299
Tel (502) 499-5000 SIC 5511 5012 7532

SENIOR CARE INC p 1304
700 N Hurstbourne Pkwy # 200 40222
Tel (502) 753-6000 SIC 8082

■ SENIOR HOME CARE INC p 1304
680 S 4th St 40202
Tel (502) 596-7300 SIC 8082

SEVEN COUNTIES SERVICES INC p 1309
101 W Muhammad Ali Blvd 40202
Tel (502) 589-8600
SIC 8399 8011 8093 8322 8031

SGS INTERNATIONAL LLC p 1310
626 W Main St Ste 500 40202
Tel (502) 637-5443 SIC 6719

SHPS FULFILLMENT SERVICES p 1319
3900 Collins Ln 40245
Tel (502) 267-3423 SIC 3555

SHPS HOLDINGS INC p 1319
9200 Shelbyville Rd # 100 40222
Tel (502) 267-4900 SIC 6411 8742

SIEMENS RAIL AUTOMATION CORP p 1320
2400 Nelson Miller Pkwy 40223
Tel (502) 244-7400 SIC 3743 3669

SIGNATURE HEALTHCARE LLC p 1322
12201 Bluegrass Pkwy 40299
Tel (502) 568-7800 SIC 8051

SOURCECORP HEALTHSERVE RADIOLOGY INC p 1342
602 N English Station Rd 40223
Tel (502) 244-0035 SIC 7334 8748 8721

SOUTHERN GRAPHIC SYSTEMS LLC p 1348
626 W Main St Ste 500 40202
Tel (502) 637-5443 SIC 2796

SOUTHERN GRAPHICS INC p 1348
626 W Main St 40202
Tel (502) 637-5443 SIC 7336 7389

■ SPECIALTY HEALTHCARE SERVICES INC p 1356
680 S 4th St 40202
Tel (502) 596-7300 SIC 8741

SPECTRACARE INC p 1357
9000 Wessex Pl Ste 100 40222
Tel (800) 467-5410 SIC 8082

STEEL TECHNOLOGIES LLC p 1384
700 N Hurstbourne Pkwy 40222
Tel (502) 245-2110 SIC 3312 3316

▲ STOCK YARDS BANCORP INC p 1390
1040 E Main St 40206
Tel (502) 582-2571 SIC 6022

■ STOCK YARDS BANK & TRUST CO INC p 1390
1040 E Main St 40206
Tel (502) 625-1790 SIC 6022

SUD-CHEMIE INC p 1396
1600 W Hill St 40210
Tel (502) 634-7361 SIC 2819

■ SUNCREST HEALTHCARE INC p 1402
9510 Ormsby Station Rd # 300 40223
Tel (615) 627-9267 SIC 8082

▲ SYPRIS SOLUTIONS INC p 1416
101 Bullitt Ln Ste 450 40222
Tel (502) 329-2000
SIC 3672 3679 3812 3674 3462

■ SYPRIS TECHNOLOGIES INC p 1416
2820 W Broadway 40211
Tel (502) 774-6011 SIC 3462

■ SYSCO LOUISVILLE INC p 1417
7705 National Tpke 40214
Tel (502) 367-6131 SIC 5141

TAG HOLDINGS INC p 1421
6901 Riverport Dr Ste B 40258
Tel (214) 469-3300 SIC 2321 2339 2369

TASMAN INDUSTRIES INC p 1426
930 Geiger St 40206
Tel (502) 785-7477 SIC 3111 5159

■ TEXAS ROADHOUSE HOLDINGS LLC p 1444
6040 Dutchmans Ln Ste 400 40205
Tel (502) 426-9984 SIC 5812 6794

▲ TEXAS ROADHOUSE INC p 1444
6040 Dutchmans Ln Ste 200 40205
Tel (502) 426-9984 SIC 5812 6794

THORNTONS INC p 1450
10101 Linn Station Rd # 200 40223
Tel (502) 425-8022 SIC 5461 5411

TRILOGY REHAB SERVICES LLC p 1480
2701 Chestnut Station Ct 40299
Tel (800) 335-1060
SIC 8059 1542 8741 8051

TROVER SOLUTIONS INC p 1485
9390 Bunsen Pkwy 40220
Tel (502) 214-1340 SIC 6411 7322

TUMBLEWEED INC p 1491
2301 River Rd Ste 200 40206
Tel (502) 893-0323 SIC 5812

▲ TURNING POINT BRANDS INC p 1493
5201 Interchange Way 40229
Tel (502) 778-4421 SIC 2131

UNDERWRITERS SAFETY AND CLAIMS INC p 1502
1700 Eastpoint Pkwy 40223
Tel (502) 244-1343 SIC 6411

UNITED REHAB LLC p 1511
9510 Ormsby Station Rd # 101 40223
Tel (502) 426-2242 SIC 8052 8051 8059

UNITED UTILITY SUPPLY COOPERATIVE INC p 1515
4515 Bishop Ln 40218
Tel (502) 459-4011 SIC 5063

UNIVERSITY HEALTH CARE INC p 1518
5100 Cmmerce Crossings Dr 40229
Tel (502) 585-7900 SIC 8011 6411

UNIVERSITY HEALTHCARE INC p 1519
5100 Cmmerce Crossings Dr 40229
Tel (800) 691-5566 SIC 6324

UNIVERSITY MEDICAL CENTER INC p 1519
530 S Jackson St 40202
Tel (502) 562-3000 SIC 8062

UNIVERSITY OF LOUISVILLE p 1522
2301 S 3rd St 40292
Tel (502) 852-5555 SIC 8221

■ UPS CUSTOMHOUSE BROKERAGE INC p 1529
1930 Bishop Ln Ste 200 40218
Tel (502) 485-2600 SIC 4731

VALIANT CONSTRUCTION LLC p 1540
4229 Bardstown Rd Ste 206 40218
Tel (502) 562-0037 SIC 8741

■ VENCARE REHAB SERVICES INC p 1547
600 S 4th St 40202
Tel (502) 596-7300 SIC 8051

VOGT POWER INTERNATIONAL INC p 1564
13551 Triton Ste 2000 40223
Tel (502) 899-4500 SIC 3592

■ WASTE MANAGEMENT OF KENTUCKY LLC p 1580
7501 Grade Ln 40219
Tel (502) 969-2355 SIC 4953

■ WESTPORT AXLE CORP p 1602
12740 Westport Rd Ste H 40245
Tel (502) 425-2103 SIC 5051 3463 3714

WHAYNE SUPPLY CO p 1604
10001 Linn Station Rd # 112 40223
Tel (502) 774-4441 SIC 5082 4911

YOUNG MENS CHRISTIAN ASSOCIATION OF GREATER LOUISVILLE p 1638
545 S 2nd St 40202
Tel (502) 587-9622
SIC 8641 7991 8351 7032 8322

▲ YUM BRANDS INC p 1640
1441 Gardiner Ln 40213
Tel (502) 874-8300 SIC 5812 6794

■ YUM RESTAURANT SERVICES GROUP INC p 1640
1900 Colonel Sanders Ln 40213
Tel (502) 874-8300 SIC 5812

ZOELLER CO p 1644
3649 Cane Run Rd 40211
Tel (502) 778-2731
SIC 3561 5251 3432 3491

LOVELY, KY

BEECH FORK PROCESSING INC p 168
Rr 292 41231
Tel (606) 395-6841 SIC 1222

MADISONVILLE, KY

AHLSTROM FILTRATION LLC p 36
215 Nebo Rd 42431
Tel (270) 821-0140 SIC 2621

BAPTIST HEALTH MADISONVILLE INC p 153
900 Hospital Dr 42431
Tel (270) 825-5100 SIC 8011 8062

HOPKINS COUNTY SCHOOL DISTRICT p 706
320 S Seminary St 42431
Tel (270) 825-6000 SIC 8211

TROVER CLINIC FOUNDATION p 1484
200 Clinic Dr 42431
Tel (270) 825-7200 SIC 8093

MAYFIELD, KY

DAIRYMANS SUPPLY CO INC p 409
3114 State Route 45 S 42066
Tel (270) 247-5641 SIC 5031

WEST KENTUCKY RURAL ELECTRIC COOP CORP p 1594
1218 W Broadway 42066
Tel (270) 247-1321 SIC 4911

MAYSVILLE, KY

DIRECTECH HOLDING CO INC p 441
33 W 2nd St Ste 504 41056
Tel (606) 564-0007 SIC 5731

DIRECTECH OF KENTUCKY INC p 441
33 W 2nd St Ste 504 41056
Tel (606) 564-0007 SIC 7389

MC KEE, KY

JACKSON ENERGY COOPERATIVE CORP p 774
115 Jackson Energy Ln 40447
Tel (606) 364-1000 SIC 4911

MOREHEAD, KY

MOREHEAD STATE UNIVERSITY p 988
207 Hal Mcdowell 40351
Tel (606) 783-2053 SIC 8221

ST CLAIRE MEDICAL CENTER INC p 1365
222 Medical Cir 40351
Tel (606) 783-6500 SIC 8062 8011

MOUNT STERLING, KY

WALKER CO OF KENTUCKY INC p 1573
105 Apperson Hts 40353
Tel (859) 498-0092
SIC 1611 2951 1542 3273 1422

MUNFORDVILLE, KY

HART COUNTY SCHOOLS p 664
25 Quality St 42765
Tel (270) 524-2631 SIC 8211

MURRAY, KY

INTERSTATE PERSONNEL SERVICES INC p 758
3443 Us Highway 641 S 42071
Tel (270) 753-1717 SIC 4213

KENTUCKY LAKE OIL CO INC p 812
620 S 4th St 42071
Tel (270) 753-1323
SIC 5541 5571 5171 5411

MURRAY STATE UNIVERSITY p 1002
102 Curris Ctr 42071
Tel (270) 809-3774 SIC 8221

MURRAY-CALLOWAY COUNTY PUBLIC HOSPITAL CORP p 1002
803 Poplar St 42071
Tel (270) 762-1100 SIC 8062

PASCHALL TRUCK LINES INC p 1119
3443 Us Highway 641 S 42071
Tel (270) 753-1717 SIC 4213

NEWPORT, KY

DIVISIONS INC p 444
1 Riverfront Pl Ste 500 41071
Tel (859) 448-9730 SIC 7349

■ LOCAL TV LLC p 873
300 Dave Cowans Dr 41071
Tel (859) 448-2700 SIC 4833

NORTHERN KENTUCKY UNIVERSITY p 1056
Nunn Dr 41099
Tel (859) 572-5100 SIC 8221

NICHOLASVILLE, KY

ALLTECH INC p 58
3031 Catnip Hill Rd 40356
Tel (859) 885-9613
SIC 2869 2048 3821 2819

BLUE GRASS ENERGY COOPERATIVE CORP p 192
1201 Lexington Rd 40356
Tel (859) 885-4191 SIC 4911

JESSAMINE COUNTY BOARD OF EDUCATION (INC) p 783
871 Wilmore Rd 40356
Tel (859) 885-4179 SIC 8211

R J CORMAN RAILROAD GROUP LLC p 1202
1 Jay Station Rd 40356
Tel (859) 881-7521 SIC 4011

OAKLAND, KY

CLARK DISTRIBUTING CO INC p 322
300 Oakland Flatrock Rd 42159
Tel (270) 563-4735 SIC 5149 5181

OWENSBORO, KY

■ BOARDWALK PIPELINES HOLDING CORP p 196
610 W 2nd St 42301
Tel (270) 926-8686 SIC 4922 4923

COOPERATIVE HEALTH SERVICES INC p 367
811 E Parrish Ave 42303
Tel (270) 688-3075 SIC 8071

DAVIESS COUNTY BOARD OF EDUCATION p 416
1622 Southeastern Pkwy 42303
Tel (270) 852-7000 SIC 8211

FIELD PACKING CO LLC p 541
6 Dublin Ln 42301
Tel (270) 926-2324 SIC 2011

MODERN WELDING CO INC p 981
2880 New Hartford Rd 42303
Tel (270) 685-4400
SIC 3443 5051 3441 5085

MPD INC p 995
316 E 9th St 42303
Tel (270) 685-6200
SIC 3671 3829 3812 3663 3643 3053

OWENSBORO GRAIN EDIBLE OILS LLC p 1100
822 E 2nd St 42303
Tel (270) 926-2032 SIC 2079

OWENSBORO HEALTH INC p 1100
1201 Pleasant Valley Rd 42303
Tel (270) 688-2000 SIC 8062

OWENSBORO MUNICIPAL UTILITIES p 1100
2070 Tamarack Rd 42301
Tel (270) 926-3200 SIC 4911

OWENSBORO MUNICIPAL UTILITIES ELECTRIC LIGHT & POWER SYSTEM p 1100
2070 Tamarack Rd 42301
Tel (270) 926-3200 SIC 4911 4941

■ RENAL TREATMENT CENTERS-ILLINOIS INC p 1223
1930 E Parrish Ave 42303
Tel (270) 926-0120 SIC 8092

SOUTHERN STAR CENTRAL CORP p 1350
4700 Highway 56 42301
Tel (270) 852-5000 SIC 4923

SOUTHERN STAR CENTRAL GAS PIPELINE INC p 1350
4700 Highway 56 42301
Tel (270) 852-5000 SIC 4923

SPECIALTY FOODS HOLDINGS INC p 1356
6 Dublin Ln 42301
Tel (757) 952-1200 SIC 2013

■ TEXAS GAS TRANSMISSION LLC p 1443
610 W 2nd St 42301
Tel (270) 926-8686 SIC 4922

TITAN CONTRACTING & LEASING CO INC p 1456
2205 Ragu Dr 42303
Tel (270) 683-6564 SIC 1711

VALOR LLC p 1542
1200 Alsop Ln 42303
Tel (270) 683-2461 SIC 5171 5172

YAGER MATERIALS LLC p 1633
5001 Highway 2830 42303
Tel (270) 926-0893
SIC 1442 1422 1611 3273 4491 3731

OWENTON, KY

OWEN ELECTRIC COOPERATIVE INC p 1099
8205 Highway 127 S 40359
Tel (502) 484-3471 *SIC* 4911

OWINGSVILLE, KY

CTI FOODS LLC p 399
59 Custom Foods Dr 40360
Tel (310) 637-0900 *SIC* 2013

PADUCAH, KY

A & K CONSTRUCTION INC p 4
100 Calloway Ct 42001
Tel (270) 441-7752 *SIC* 1542 1541

COMPUTER SERVICES INC p 353
3901 Technology Dr 42001
Tel (800) 545-4274 *SIC* 7374

HARPER INDUSTRIES INC p 663
960 N Hc Mathis Dr 42001
Tel (270) 442-2753
SIC 3273 1711 1611 1542

HENRY A PETTER SUPPLY CO LLC p 684
5110 Charter Oak Dr 42001
Tel (270) 575-6922 *SIC* 5085

JAMES MARINE INC p 776
4500 Clarks River Rd 42003
Tel (270) 898-7392
SIC 3731 4492 5541 3732

MCCRACKEN COUNTY PUBLIC SCHOOLS p 927
5347 Benton Rd 42003
Tel (270) 538-4000 *SIC* 8211

MERCY HEALTH PARTNERS - LOURDES INC p 946
1530 Lone Oak Rd Int24 42003
Tel (270) 444-2444 *SIC* 8062

NATIONAL RAILWAY EQUIPMENT CO p 1015
1300 Kentucky Ave 42003
Tel (270) 444-4555 *SIC* 3743

PAXTON MEDIA GROUP LLC p 1122
100 Television Ln 42003
Tel (270) 575-8630 *SIC* 2711 4833

TREES N TRENDS INC p 1475
3229 Benton Rd 42003
Tel (270) 443-5100
SIC 5999 3999 5947 5193

PARIS, KY

CENTRAL MOTOR WHEEL OF AMERICA INC p 279
150 Wheat Dr 40361
Tel (859) 987-0500 *SIC* 3714

HINKLE CONTRACTING CORP p 695
395 N Middletown Rd 40361
Tel (859) 987-3670
SIC 1611 1422 3273 3272 3271 2951

■ **MONESSEN HEARTH SYSTEMS CO** p 984
149 Cleveland Dr 40361
Tel (859) 987-0740 *SIC* 3433

REVSTONE INDUSTRIES LLC p 1229
2008 Cypress St Ste 100 40361
Tel (859) 294-5590 *SIC* 2821 3086 3341

PHILPOT, KY

HINES PRECISION INC p 695
5680 Old Highway 54 42366
Tel (270) 729-4242 *SIC* 3469 3444

PIKEVILLE, KY

▲ **COMMUNITY TRUST BANCORP INC** p 350
346 N Mayo Trl 41501
Tel (606) 432-1414 *SIC* 6022

■ **COMMUNITY TRUST BANK INC** p 350
346 N Mayo Trl 41501
Tel (606) 432-1414 *SIC* 6021

PIKE COUNTY SCHOOLS p 1148
316 S Mayo Trl 41501
Tel (606) 432-7700 *SIC* 8211

PIKEVILLE MEDICAL CENTER INC p 1148
911 Bypass Rd 41501
Tel (606) 218-3500 *SIC* 8062

PRESTONSBURG, KY

FLOYD COUNTY SCHOOLS p 560
106 N Front Ave 41653
Tel (606) 886-2354 *SIC* 8211

■ **KENTUCKY WEST VIRGINIA GAS CO** p 812
748 N Lake Dr 41653
Tel (606) 886-2311 *SIC* 1311 1389 4922

WORLDWIDE EQUIPMENT ENTERPRISES INC p 1626
107 We Dr 41653
Tel (606) 874-2772 *SIC* 5511

WORLDWIDE EQUIPMENT INC p 1626
73 We Dr 41653
Tel (606) 874-2172
SIC 5012 5013 7538 7513

PROSPECT, KY

BRITTHAVEN OF KENTUCKY INC p 214
6301 Bass Rd 40059
Tel (502) 228-9440 *SIC* 8051

RICHMOND, KY

EASTERN KENTUCKY UNIVERSITY p 472
521 Lancaster Ave 40475
Tel (859) 622-1791 *SIC* 8221

MADISON COUNTY SCHOOL DISTRICT p 894
550 S Keeneland Dr 40475
Tel (859) 624-4500 *SIC* 8211

ROBARDS, KY

BIG RIVERS ELECTRIC CORP p 182
9000 Hwy 2096 42452
Tel (270) 827-2561 *SIC* 4911

■ **CENTURY ALUMINUM SEBREE LLC** p 282
9404 State Route 2096 42452
Tel (270) 521-7811 *SIC* 3334

RUSSELL SPRINGS, KY

BRANSCUM CONSTRUCTION CO/ROBINS & MORTON A JOINT VENTURE p 208
90 Key Village Rd 42642
Tel (270) 866-5107 *SIC* 1541 8741 1542

STEPHENS PIPE & STEEL LLC p 1386
2224 E Highway 619 42642
Tel (270) 866-3331 *SIC* 5051 3315

RUSSELLVILLE, KY

LOGAN ALUMINUM INC p 874
200 Gate Two Rd 2rd 42276
Tel (270) 755-6000 *SIC* 3355

VENTRA PLASTICS (RUSSELLVILLE) INC p 1548
140 Progress Dr 42276
Tel (270) 726-4767 *SIC* 3089

SALEM, KY

■ **SALEM TELEPHONE CO** p 1272
221 E Main St 42078
Tel (608) 831-1000 *SIC* 4813

SHELBYVILLE, KY

LANDMARK COMMUNITY NEWSPAPERS LLC p 842
601 Taylorsville Rd 40065
Tel (502) 633-4334 *SIC* 2711 2759

LANDMARK COMMUNITY NEWSPAPERS OF KENTUCKY LLC p 842
601 Taylorsville Rd 40065
Tel (502) 633-4334 *SIC* 2711 2752

OHIO VALLEY ALUMINUM CO II LLC p 1078
1100 Brooks Industrial Rd 40065
Tel (502) 633-2783 *SIC* 3341

OMEGA PLASTIC CORP p 1084
901 Commerce Cir 40065
Tel (502) 633-0168 *SIC* 2673

SHEPHERDSVILLE, KY

BULLITT COUNTY PUBLIC SCHOOLS p 225
1040 Highway 44 E 40165
Tel (502) 869-8000 *SIC* 8211

BULLITT COUNTY PUBLIC SCHOOLS p 225
1040 Highway 44 E 40165
Tel (502) 869-8000 *SIC* 8211

PUBLISHERS PRINTING CO LLC p 1190
100 Frank E Simon Ave 40165
Tel (502) 955-6526 *SIC* 2752 2791 2789

SIMPSONVILLE, KY

BROWN JORDAN CO p 219
20 Kingbrook Pkwy 40067
Tel (323) 686-0951 *SIC* 2514 2511

NEFF PACKAGING SOLUTIONS INC p 1024
10 Kingbrook Pkwy 40067
Tel (502) 722-5020 *SIC* 2657

SOMERSET, KY

■ **LAKE CUMBERLAND REGIONAL HOSPITAL LLC** p 839
305 Langdon St 42503
Tel (606) 679-7441 *SIC* 8031

■ **LIFEPOINT OF LAKE CUMBERLAND LLC** p 864
305 Langdon St 42503
Tel (606) 679-7441 *SIC* 8062 8082

MODERN DISTRIBUTORS INC p 981
817 W Columbia St 42501
Tel (606) 679-1178
SIC 5194 5962 5145 5064

PULASKI COUNTY SCHOOL DISTRICT FINANCE CORP p 1191
501 E University Dr 42503
Tel (606) 679-1123 *SIC* 8211 8741

PULASKI COUNTY SCHOOLS p 1191
501 E University Dr 42503
Tel (606) 679-1123 *SIC* 8211

SOMERSET HARDWOOD FLOORING INC p 1339
70 W Racetrack Rd 42503
Tel (606) 678-2842 *SIC* 2426

SOUTH KENTUCKY RURAL ELECTRIC CO-OPERATIVE CORP p 1344
925-929 N Main St 42503
Tel (606) 678-4121 *SIC* 4911

SOUTHERN PETROLEUM INC p 1350
600 Monticello St 42501
Tel (606) 678-5127 *SIC* 5171

TOYOTETSU AMERICA INC p 1467
100 Pin Oak Dr 42503
Tel (606) 274-9005 *SIC* 3465 3714 3429

STEARNS, KY

OUTDOOR VENTURE CORP p 1099
30 Venture Dr 42647
Tel (606) 376-5021 *SIC* 2394

STURGIS, KY

■ **ERVIN CABLE CONSTRUCTION LLC** p 508
450 Pryor Blvd 42459
Tel (270) 333-3366 *SIC* 1623

TAYLOR MILL, KY

L B INDUSTRIES INC p 833
8770 Railroad Dr 41015
Tel (859) 431-8300 *SIC* 5051

LALLY PIPE & TUBE CO p 841
8770 Railroad Dr 41015
Tel (606) 371-5600 *SIC* 5014

VERSAILLES, KY

KENTUCKY COMMUNITY AND TECHNICAL COLLEGE SYSTEM p 812
300 N Main St 40383
Tel (859) 256-3100 *SIC* 8222

YOKOHAMA INDUSTRIES AMERICAS INC p 1637
105 Industry Dr 40383
Tel (859) 873-2188
SIC 3714 3585 3492 3052

WALTON, KY

VERST GROUP LOGISTICS INC p 1552
300 Shorland Dr 41094
Tel (859) 485-1212 *SIC* 4225 7389

WHITESBURG, KY

CHILDERS OIL CO p 298
51 Highway 2034 41858
Tel (606) 633-2525 *SIC* 5171

■ **COMMUNITY TRUST BANK** p 350
155 Main St 41858
Tel (606) 633-0161 *SIC* 6022 6021

HOMETOWN CONVENIENCE LLC p 704
51 Highway 2034 41858
Tel (606) 633-2525 *SIC* 5172

WILLIAMSBURG, KY

CHARTWELLS CATERING p 291
Cumberland Col Dining 40769
Tel (606) 539-4358 *SIC* 5812

WINCHESTER, KY

APOLLO OIL LLC p 97
1175 Early Dr 40391
Tel (859) 744-5444 *SIC* 5172 5013

EAST KENTUCKY POWER COOPERATIVE p 470
4775 Lexington Rd 40391
Tel (859) 744-4812 *SIC* 4911

EAST KENTUCKY POWER COOPERATIVE INC p 470
4775 Lexington Rd 40391
Tel (859) 744-4812 *SIC* 4911

UNIVANCE INC p 1516
3400 Corporate Dr 40391
Tel (859) 737-2306 *SIC* 3568 3714 5012

LOUISIANA

ABBEVILLE, LA

COASTAL CHEMICAL CO LLC p 331
3520 Veterans Memorial Dr 70510
Tel (337) 898-0001 *SIC* 5172 5169

VERMILION PARISH SCHOOL BOARD p 1551
220 S Jefferson St 70510
Tel (337) 893-3973 *SIC* 8211

ALEXANDRIA, LA

AFCO INDUSTRIES INC p 32
3400 Roy Ave 71302
Tel (318) 448-1651 *SIC* 3354 3083 3442

CHRISTUS HEALTH CENTRAL LOUISIANA p 303
3330 Masonic Dr 71301
Tel (318) 487-1122 *SIC* 8062

DIAMOND B CONSTRUCTION CO INC p 436
2090 Industrial Park Rd 71303
Tel (318) 427-1300 *SIC* 1611

GILCHRIST CONSTRUCTION CO LLC p 612
5709 New York Ave 71302
Tel (318) 448-3565 *SIC* 1771

MARTCO LLC p 911
2189 Memorial Dr 71301
Tel (318) 448-0405 *SIC* 2493 2435

MARTIN COMPANIES LLC ROM p 912
2189 Memorial Dr 71301
Tel (318) 445-1973 *SIC* 0811

MARTIN SUSTAINABLE RESOURCES LLC p 913
2189 Memorial Dr 71301
Tel (318) 448-0405 *SIC* 2493 2435

■ **RAPIDES HEALTHCARE SYSTEM LLC** p 1208
211 4th St 71301
Tel (318) 473-3150 *SIC* 8062 5047

RAPIDES PARISH SCHOOL DISTRICT p 1208
619 6th St 71301
Tel (318) 487-0888 *SIC* 8211

RAPIDES REGIONAL MEDICAL CENTER p 1208
211 4th St 71301
Tel (318) 473-3000 *SIC* 8062

T & D SOLUTIONS LLC p 1419
6411 Masonic Dr 71301
Tel (318) 442-8138 *SIC* 1623

AMELIA, LA

BOLLINGER MARINE FABRICATORS INC p 198
816 Bollinger Ln 70340
Tel (985) 631-5300 *SIC* 3731

AMITE, LA

TANGIPAHOA PARISH SCHOOL BOARD INC p 1424
59656 Puleston Rd 70422
Tel (985) 748-2433 *SIC* 8211

TANGIPAHOA PARISH SCHOOL SYSTEM p 1424
59656 Puleston Rd 70422
Tel (985) 748-2416 *SIC* 8211

ARCADIA, LA

HOUSE OF RAEFORD FARMS OF LOUISIANA LLC p 711
3867 2nd St 71001
Tel (318) 263-9004 *SIC* 0251 2015

ARNAUDVILLE, LA

■ **INTERNATIONAL SNUBBING SERVICES LLC** p 756
190 Industries Ln 70512
Tel (337) 754-7233 *SIC* 1389 7353

AVONDALE, LA

■ **AVONDALE INDUSTRIES OF NEW YORK INC** p 139
5100 River Rd 70094
Tel (504) 654-5254 *SIC* 3731

BAKER, LA

PALISADES HOLDINGS INC p 1108
2266 Groom Rd 70714
Tel (225) 236-1440 *SIC* 5051

BASTROP, LA

MOREHOUSE BIOENERGY LLC p 988
7070 Carl Rd 71220
Tel (770) 743-4300 *SIC* 2493

BATON ROUGE, LA

ABMB-HNTB JOINT VENTURE LLC p 12
500 Main St 70801
Tel (225) 765-7400 *SIC* 8711

ADVANCED HEALTH CONCEPTS p 25
134 Mcgehee Dr 70815
Tel (225) 275-1660 *SIC* 8082

AFFIRMATIVE LLC p 32
2900 Westfork Dr Ste 600 70827
Tel (225) 928-9000 *SIC* 6311 6141

ALL STAR AUTOMOTIVE GROUP p 51
13000 Florida Blvd 70815
Tel (225) 298-3210 *SIC* 5511

■ **AMEDISYS HOME HEALTH INC OF FLORIDA** p 66
5959 S Shrwood Frest Blvd 70816
Tel (225) 292-2031 *SIC* 8082

■ **AMEDISYS HOME HEALTH INC OF VIRGINIA** p 66
5959 S Shrwood Frest Blvd 70816
Tel (225) 292-2031 *SIC* 8082

▲ **AMEDISYS INC** p 66
3854 American Way Ste A 70816
Tel (225) 292-2031
SIC 8082 8051 8049 8361

■ **AMEDISYS HOME HEALTH INC OF SOUTH CAROLINA** p 66
5959 S Shrwood Frest Blvd 70816
Tel (225) 292-2031 *SIC* 8082

ARKEL INTERNATIONAL LLC p 110
1048 Florida Blvd 70802
Tel (225) 343-0500 *SIC* 1542

ASSOCIATED GROCERS INC p 120
8600 Anselmo Ln 70810
Tel (225) 444-1000 *SIC* 5141

■ **AUDUBON INSURANCE CO** p 131
4000 S Shrwd Frst Blvd Ste 401 70816
Tel (225) 293-5900 *SIC* 6331 6411

AWC INC p 139
6655 Exchequer Dr 70809
Tel (225) 752-3939 *SIC* 1731

BATON ROUGE GENERAL MEDICAL CENTER p 159
8490 Picardy Ave Ste 200 70809
Tel (225) 237-1547 SIC 3949

BATON ROUGE GENERAL MEDICAL CENTER p 159
3600 Florida Blvd 70806
Tel (225) 387-7000 SIC 8062

CAJUN CONSTRUCTORS LLC p 237
15635 Airline Hwy 70817
Tel (225) 753-5857
SIC 1623 4952 1541 1542

CAJUN DEEP FOUNDATIONS LLC p 237
15635 Airline Hwy 70817
Tel (225) 753-5857 SIC 1389

CAJUN INDUSTRIES LLC p 237
15635 Airline Hwy 70817
Tel (225) 753-5857 SIC 1389

CAPITAL CITY PRESS LLC p 249
10705 Reiger Rd 70809
Tel (225) 383-1111 SIC 2711 2752

CB&I CONTRACTORS INC p 268
4171 Essen Ln 70809
Tel (225) 932-2500 SIC 1541

CB&I ENVIRONMENTAL & INFRASTRUCTURE INC p 268
3867 Plaza Tower Dr 70816
Tel (225) 932-2500
SIC 8748 1794 1795 8744 8741

CB&I GOVERNMENT SOLUTIONS INC p 268
4171 Essen Ln 70809
Tel (225) 932-2500
SIC 8711 8734 8748 1541 1542 1611

CCC HOLDING LLC p 269
3332 Partridge Ln Bldg A 70809
Tel (225) 368-3900 SIC 2095 5149 5812

CHAMPION INDUSTRIES INC p 287
10848 Airline Hwy 70816
Tel (225) 291-9090
SIC 2542 2759 2791 2789 2752

CITY OF BATON ROUGE p 313
222 Saint Louis St Rm 301 70802
Tel (225) 389-3061 SIC 9111

CMC AMERICAS INC p 328
4354 S Shrwd Forst Bl 175 70816
Tel (225) 296-8440 SIC 7374 7379

COASTAL BRIDGE CO LLC p 331
4825 Jamestown Ave 70808
Tel (225) 766-0244 SIC 1622

COMMUNITY COFFEE CO LLC p 348
3332 Partridge Ln Bldg A 70809
Tel (800) 688-0990 SIC 2095

DEEP SOUTH CRANE AND RIGGING LLC p 421
15324 Airline Hwy 70817
Tel (225) 753-4371 SIC 7353

EAST BATON ROUGE MEDICAL CENTER LLC p 469
17000 Medical Center Dr 70816
Tel (225) 752-2470 SIC 8062

EAST BATON ROUGE PARISH SCHOOL DISTRICT p 469
1050 S Foster Dr 70806
Tel (225) 922-5400 SIC 8211

EAST WEST COPOLYMER LLC p 471
5955 Scenic Hwy 70805
Tel (225) 267-3400 SIC 2822

EDGEN GROUP INC p 477
18444 Highland Rd 70809
Tel (225) 756-9868 SIC 5051

EMPIRE SCAFFOLD LLC p 493
9680 S Choctaw Dr 70815
Tel (225) 924-3170 SIC 1799

ENTERGY TEXAS INC p 502
446 North Blvd 70802
Tel (800) 368-3749 SIC 4911

EXCEL CONTRACTORS INC p 516
8641 United Plaza Blvd 70809
Tel (225) 408-1300 SIC 1731

EXECUTIVE OFFICE OF STATE OF LOUISIANA p 517
900 N 3rd St Fl 4 70802
Tel (225) 342-7015 SIC 9111

FORD BACON & DAVIS LLC p 565
12021 Lakeland Park Blvd # 212 70809
Tel (225) 297-3431 SIC 8711 1541 1623

FRANCISCAN MISSIONARIES OF OUR LADY HEALTH SYSTEM INC p 573
4200 Essen Ln 70809
Tel (225) 526-4500 SIC 8741

GENERAL HEALTH SYSTEM p 601
8585 Picardy Ave 70809
Tel (225) 387-7000 SIC 8741 6324

GENERAL HEALTH SYSTEM p 601
5757 Corp Blvd Ste 200 70808
Tel (225) 237-1500 SIC 8071 7991

GENERAL HEALTH SYSTEM MANAGEMENT INC p 601
8585 Picardy Ave 70809
Tel (225) 237-1700 SIC 6324

■ **GEORGIA L AMEDISYS L C** p 607
5959 S Shrwood Frest Blvd 70816
Tel (225) 292-2031 SIC 8082

GERRY LANE ENTERPRISES INC p 609
6505 Florida Blvd 70806
Tel (225) 926-4600 SIC 5511

▲ **H&E EQUIPMENT SERVICES INC** p 651
7500 Pecue Ln 70809
Tel (225) 298-5200 SIC 7359 5082

■ **H&J CAPITAL LLC** p 651
8485 Goodwood Blvd 70806
Tel (225) 926-2888 SIC 6719

HMO OF LOUISIANA INC p 698
5525 Reitz Ave 70809
Tel (225) 295-3307 SIC 6324

IBERVILLE INSULATIONS LLC p 726
11621 Sun Belt Ct 70809
Tel (225) 752-2194 SIC 1799

ISC CONSTRUCTORS LLC p 766
20480 Highland Rd 70817
Tel (225) 756-8001 SIC 1731

ISC GROUP L L C p 766
20480 Highland Rd 70817
Tel (225) 756-8001 SIC 1731

■ **JACOBS CONSTRUCTORS INC** p 775
4949 Essen Ln 70809
Tel (225) 769-7700 SIC 1629

■ **JAMES CONSTRUCTION GROUP LLC** p 776
18484 E Petroleum Dr 70809
Tel (225) 293-0274 SIC 1611 1622

JB JAMES CONSTRUCTION LLC p 779
1881 Wooddale Blvd 70806
Tel (225) 927-3131 SIC 1611

JOHN H CARTER CO INC p 788
17630 Perkins Rd Ste West 70810
Tel (225) 751-3788 SIC 5084

▲ **LAMAR ADVERTISING CO** p 841
5321 Corporate Blvd 70808
Tel (225) 926-1000 SIC 7312 6798

■ **LAMAR MEDIA CORP** p 841
5321 Corporate Blvd 70808
Tel (225) 926-1000 SIC 7312

LAMAR TEXAS LIMITED PARTNERSHIP p 841
5321 Corporate Blvd 70808
Tel (800) 235-2627 SIC 7312

LCR-M LIMITED PARTNERSHIP p 849
6232 Siegen Ln 70809
Tel (225) 292-9910 SIC 5074

LIPSEYS LLC p 870
7277 Exchequer Dr 70809
Tel (225) 755-1333 SIC 5091

LOFTON CORP p 874
9414 Interline Ave 70809
Tel (225) 924-0200 SIC 7361

LOFTON SECURITY SERVICE INC p 874
9405 Interline Ave 70809
Tel (225) 906-2200 SIC 7381

LOUISIANA BOARD OF REGENTS p 880
1201 N 3rd St Ste 6-200 70802
Tel (225) 342-4253 SIC 9411

LOUISIANA DEPARTMENT OF CHILDREN AND FAMILY SERVICES p 880
627 N 4th St 70802
Tel (225) 342-4220 SIC 9441

LOUISIANA DEPARTMENT OF ENVIRONMENTAL QUALITY p 880
602 N 5th St 70802
Tel (225) 219-3953 SIC 9511

LOUISIANA DEPARTMENT OF HEALTH AND HOSPITALS p 880
628 N 4th St 70802
Tel (225) 342-9500 SIC 9431

LOUISIANA DEPARTMENT OF PUBLIC EDUCATION p 880
1201 N 3rd St 70802
Tel (225) 342-3836 SIC 9411

LOUISIANA DEPARTMENT OF PUBLIC SAFETY & CORRECTIONS p 880
7919 Independence Blvd 70806
Tel (225) 925-6006 SIC 9221

LOUISIANA DEPARTMENT OF PUBLIC SAFETY AND CORRECTIONS p 880
504 Mayflower St 70802
Tel (225) 342-6740 SIC 9229 9223

LOUISIANA DEPARTMENT OF TRANSPORTATION AND DEVELOPMENT p 880
1201 Capitol Access Rd 70802
Tel (225) 379-1232 SIC 9111

LOUISIANA DIVISION OF ADMINISTRATION p 880
1201 N 3rd St Ste 7-20 70802
Tel (225) 342-7000 SIC 9199

LOUISIANA FARM BUREAU CASUALTY INSURANCE CO p 880
9516 Airline Hwy 70815
Tel (225) 922-6200 SIC 6411

LOUISIANA HEALTH SERVICE AND INDEMNITY CO p 880
5525 Reitz Ave 70809
Tel (225) 295-3307 SIC 6321 6324 6411

LOUISIANA STATE UNIVERSITY p 880
202 Himes Hall 70803
Tel (225) 578-2760 SIC 8221

LOUISIANA STATE UNIVERSITY p 880
3810 W Lkshore Dr Ste 111 70808
Tel (225) 578-2760 SIC 8221

LOUISIANA WORKERS COMPENSATION CORP p 880
2237 S Acadian Thruway 70808
Tel (225) 924-7788 SIC 6331

MAPP CONSTRUCTION LLC p 904
344 3rd St 70801
Tel (225) 757-0111 SIC 1542

MID CITY MEDICAL CENTER p 962
3600 Florida Blvd 70806
Tel (225) 387-7000 SIC 8062

MMR CONSTRUCTORS INC p 979
15961 Airline Hwy 70817
Tel (225) 756-5090 SIC 1731

MMR GROUP INC p 979
15961 Airline Hwy 70817
Tel (225) 756-5090 SIC 1731

MOCKLER BEVERAGE CO p 980
11811 Reiger Rd 70809
Tel (225) 408-4283 SIC 5181 5921

MOODY-PRICE LLC p 987
18320 Petroleum Dr 70809
Tel (225) 751-7001 SIC 5084

MURRAY EDGEN CORP p 1001
18444 Highland Rd 70809
Tel (225) 756-9868 SIC 5051

MURRAY EDGEN II L P p 1001
18444 Highland Rd 70809
Tel (225) 756-9868 SIC 5051

NEWTRON GROUP L L C p 1039
8183 W El Cajon Dr 70815
Tel (225) 927-8921 SIC 1731

NEWTRON HOLDINGS LLC p 1039
8183 W El Cajon Dr 70815
Tel (225) 927-8921 SIC 1731

ORION INSTRUMENTS LLC p 1095
2105 Oak Villa Blvd 70815
Tel (225) 906-2343 SIC 3823

OUR LADY OF LAKE HOSPITAL INC p 1098
5000 Hennessy Blvd 70808
Tel (225) 765-7709 SIC 8062

PALA GROUP INC p 1108
16347 Old Hammond Hwy 70816
Tel (225) 272-5194 SIC 1629 1541

PALA INTERSTATE LLC p 1108
16347 Old Hammond Hwy 70816
Tel (225) 272-5194 SIC 1541 8711

PERFORMANCE CONTRACTORS INC p 1135
9901 Pecue Ln 70810
Tel (225) 490-2000 SIC 1541 3498

PICCADILLY RESTAURANTS LLC p 1146
4150 S Shrwood Frest Blvd 70816
Tel (225) 293-9440 SIC 5812

PROVIDENT RESOURCES GROUP INC p 1186
5565 Bankers Ave 70808
Tel (225) 766-3977 SIC 8051

RAISING CANES RESTAURANTS LLC p 1206
400 Convention St Ste 550 70802
Tel (225) 383-7400 SIC 5812

REPUBLIC FINANCE LLC p 1225
7031 Commerce Cir Ste 100 70809
Tel (225) 927-0005 SIC 6141

ROMAN CATHOLIC CHURCH OF DIOCESE OF BATON ROUGE p 1248
1800 S Acadian Thruway 70808
Tel (225) 387-0561 SIC 8661

SETPOINT INTEGRATED SOLUTIONS INC p 1309
19011 Highland Rd 70809
Tel (225) 753-3290 SIC 5085 5084

SHAW GROUP INC p 1312
4171 Essen Ln 70809
Tel (225) 932-2500
SIC 8711 8734 1629 3498

SOUTHERN UNIVERSITY AGRICULTURAL & MECHANICAL COLLEGE p 1350
G Leon Netherville Dr 70813
Tel (225) 771-5021 SIC 8221 9411

SOUTHERN UNIVERSITY AND A&M COLLEGE SYSTEM p 1350
J S Clark Adm Bldg 3rd Fl 70813
Tel (225) 771-4680 SIC 8221

STARMOUNT LIFE INSURANCE CO INC p 1379
8485 Goodwood Blvd 70806
Tel (225) 400-9100 SIC 6311

STATE OF LOUISIANA p 1381
900 N 3rd St Fl 4 70802
Tel (225) 342-0991 SIC 9111

TRIAD E&C HOLDINGS LLC p 1478
8183 W El Cajon Dr 70815
Tel (225) 927-8921 SIC 1731

TRIAD ELECTRIC & CONTROLS INC p 1478
2288 N Airway Dr 70815
Tel (225) 923-0604 SIC 1731

TURNER INDUSTRIAL MAINTENANCE LLC p 1492
8687 United Plaza Blvd 70809
Tel (225) 922-5050 SIC 7349

TURNER INDUSTRIES GROUP LLC p 1493
8687 United Plaza Blvd 70809
Tel (225) 922-5050 SIC 7359 7699

TURNER INDUSTRIES OF CALIFORNIA p 1493
8687 United Plaza Blvd 70809
Tel (225) 922-5050 SIC 1541

TURNER SPECIALTY SERVICES LLC p 1493
8687 United Plaza Blvd 70809
Tel (225) 922-5050 SIC 1541 7699

UNITED SCAFFOLDING INC p 1511
12021 Lakeland Park Blvd # 120 70809
Tel (225) 774-1480 SIC 1799

UNIVERSITIES OF LOUISIANA SYSTEM p 1518
1201 N 3rd St Ste 7300 70802
Tel (225) 342-6950 SIC 9411

WOMANS HOSPITAL FOUNDATION INC p 1621
100 Womans Way 70817
Tel (225) 927-1300 SIC 8062

WOMENS HOSPITAL p 1622
100 Womans Way 70817
Tel (225) 927-1300 SIC 8069

WORKFORCE COMMISSION LOUISIANA p 1624
1001 N 23rd St 70802
Tel (225) 342-3103 SIC 9651

BELLE CHASSE, LA

OIL MOP LLC p 1079
131 Keating Dr 70037
Tel (504) 394-6110 SIC 4959

POWCO OF LOUISIANA LLC p 1164
208 Gunther Ln 70037
Tel (504) 394-6005 SIC 3593

UNITED SITE SERVICES OF MISSISSIPPI LLC p 1511
9486 Highway 23 70037
Tel (866) 356-5615 SIC 7349

BENTON, LA

BOSSIER PARISH SCHOOL BOARD INC p 202
410 N Sibley St 71006
Tel (318) 549-5000 SIC 8211

BOSSIER PARISH SCHOOLS p 202
410 N Sibley St 71006
Tel (318) 549-5000 SIC 8211

BERWICK, LA

BERRY BROS GENERAL CONTRACTORS INC p 176
1414 River Rd 70342
Tel (985) 384-8770 SIC 1629 4959

BOSSIER CITY, LA

CELLXION LLC p 274
5031 Hazel Jones Rd 71111
Tel (318) 213-2900
SIC 4812 1623 3448 3441

HARDWARE RESOURCES INC p 661
4319 Marlena St 71111
Tel (318) 742-0660 SIC 5072 2499

HARRISON CO LLC p 664
4801 Viking Dr 71111
Tel (318) 747-0700 SIC 5194 5145 5141

■ **HORSESHOE ENTERTAINMENT** p 708
711 Horseshoe Blvd 71111
Tel (318) 742-0711 SIC 7011

LOUISIANA RIVERBOAT GAMING PARTNERSHIP p 880
711 Diamondjacks Blvd 71111
Tel (318) 678-7633 SIC 7999

MCELROY METAL MILL INC p 928
1500 Hamilton Rd 71111
Tel (318) 747-8000 SIC 3448

RED RIVER MOTOR FREIGHT LLC p 1216
451050 Marlena St 71111
Tel (318) 884-9994 SIC 4789

TIM ICENHOWER OIL AND GAS INC p 1454
5916 Industrial Drive Ext 71112
Tel (318) 752-2293 SIC 1382

BREAUX BRIDGE, LA

ST MARTIN PARISH SCHOOL BOARD p 1370
625 Corporate Blvd 70517
Tel (337) 394-6261 SIC 8211

ST MARTIN PARISH SCHOOL DISTRICT p 1370
P.O. Box 1000 70517
Tel (337) 394-6261 SIC 8211

BROUSSARD, LA

CHARTER SUPPLY CO p 291
8100 Ambssdor Cffery Pkwy 70518
Tel (337) 837-2724 SIC 5084

DELMAR SYSTEMS INC p 425
8114 Highway 90 E 70518
Tel (337) 365-0180 SIC 1389

DOERLE FOOD SERVICES LLC p 447
113 Kol Dr 70518
Tel (337) 252-8551
SIC 5142 5141 5087 5148

HUTCO INC p 722
114 Park Center Dr 70518
Tel (337) 837-5594 SIC 7363

OFFSHORE ENERGY SERVICES p 1076
5900 Highway 90 E 70518
Tel (337) 837-1024 SIC 1389

■ **SUPERIOR ENERGY SERVICES LLC** p 1406
5801 Highway 90 E 70518
Tel (337) 714-4545 SIC 1389 7353

W H C INC p 1568
300 Industrial Trce 70518
Tel (337) 837-4500 SIC 1623 1541

■ **WARRIOR ENERGY SERVICES CORP** p 1577
5801 Highway 90 E 70518
Tel (662) 329-1047 SIC 1389

WHITCO SUPPLY LLC p 1605
200 N Morgan Ave 70518
Tel (337) 837-2440 SIC 5084

ZEDI US INC p 1641
208 Roto Park Dr 70518
Tel (337) 233-2066 SIC 1389

BURNSIDE, LA

ALMATIS BURNSIDE LLC p 59
41237 Hwy 22 70738
Tel (225) 474-1700 SIC 2819

CARENCRO, LA

OMNI ENERGY SERVICES CORP p 1084
4500 Ne Evangeline Trwy 70520
Tel (337) 896-6664 SIC 1382 1389 7349

CENTERVILLE, LA

ST MARY PARISH SCHOOL BOARD p 1371
474 Hwy 317 70522
Tel (337) 836-9661 SIC 8211

ST MARY PARISH SCHOOLS p 1371
474 Hwy 317 70522
Tel (337) 836-9661 SIC 8211

CHALMETTE, LA

■ **CHALMETTE REFINING LLC** p 287
500 W Saint Bernard Hwy 70043
Tel (504) 281-1212 SIC 2911

CHARENTON, LA

CHITIMACHA TRIBE OF LOUISIANA p 301
155 Chitimacha Loop 70523
Tel (337) 923-4973 SIC 9131

CYPRESS BAYOU CASINO p 405
832 Martin Luther King Rd 70523
Tel (337) 923-7284 SIC 7999

CHOUDRANT, LA

ORIGIN BANK p 1094
3921 Elm St 71227
Tel (318) 255-2222 SIC 6022

COVINGTON, LA

■ **ARDENT SERVICES LLC** p 106
170 New Camellia Blvd 70433
Tel (985) 792-3000 SIC 1731

CARI INVESTMENT CO LLC p 256
222 N Vermont St 70433
Tel (985) 635-6009
SIC 6211 4424 3731 5146

■ **CETCO ENERGY SERVICES CO LLC** p 284
1001 Ochsner Blvd Ste 425 70433
Tel (985) 871-4700 SIC 1389 2869 3533

CGB ENTERPRISES INC p 285
1127 Hwy 190 E Service Rd 70433
Tel (985) 867-3500 SIC 4221 5191 4491

CONSOLIDATED GRAIN & BARGE INC p 360
1001 Highway 190 E Svc Rd 70433
Tel (985) 867-3500 SIC 5153

FOREST MANOR INC p 567
71338 Highway 21 70433
Tel (985) 892-6900 SIC 8051

GILSBAR INC p 612
2100 Covington Centre 70433
Tel (985) 892-3520 SIC 6411

▲ **GLOBALSTAR INC** p 617
300 Holiday Square Blvd # 300 70433
Tel (985) 335-1500 SIC 4813

▲ **HORNBECK OFFSHORE SERVICES INC** p 708
103 Northpark Blvd # 300 70433
Tel (985) 727-2000 SIC 4499

■ **HORNBECK OFFSHORE SERVICES LLC** p 708
103 Northpark Blvd # 300 70433
Tel (985) 727-2000 SIC 1382

LAKEVIEW REGIONAL MEDICAL CENTER p 840
95 Judge Tanner Blvd 70433
Tel (985) 867-3800 SIC 8069

LLOG EXPLORATION CO LLC p 872
1001 Ochsner Blvd Ste 200 70433
Tel (504) 833-7700 SIC 1311 1382

LLOG EXPLORATION OFFSHORE LLC p 872
1001 Ochsner Blvd Ste 200 70433
Tel (985) 801-4300 SIC 1382

LOOP LLC p 877
137 Northpark Blvd 70433
Tel (985) 632-6970 SIC 1389

▲ **POOL CORP** p 1161
109 Northpark Blvd # 400 70433
Tel (985) 892-5521 SIC 5091

SAINT TAMMANY PARISH HOSPITAL SERVICE DISTRICT 1 p 1270
1202 S Tyler St 70433
Tel (985) 898-4000 SIC 8062

SAINT TAMMANY PARISH SCHOOL BOARD p 1270
321 N Theard St 70433
Tel (985) 892-2276 SIC 8211

■ **SCP DISTRIBUTORS LLC** p 1294
109 Northpark Blvd 70433
Tel (985) 892-5521 SIC 5091

ST TAMMANY PARISH PUBLIC SCHOOL SYSTEM p 1373
321 N Theard St 70433
Tel (985) 892-2276 SIC 8211

ZEN-NOH GRAIN CORP p 1642
1127 Hwy 190 E Service Rd 70433
Tel (985) 867-3500 SIC 5153

CROWLEY, LA

ACADIA PARISH SCHOOL DISTRICT p 13
2402 N Parkerson Ave 70526
Tel (337) 783-3664 SIC 8211

FRANCIS DRILLING FLUIDS LTD p 573
240 Jasmine Rd 70526
Tel (337) 783-8685 SIC 5169 1389 7353

LOUISIANA RICE MILL LLC p 880
4 S Avenue D 70526
Tel (337) 783-9777 SIC 2044

SHOP RITE INC p 1318
115 E 1st St 70526
Tel (337) 785-2924 SIC 5411

CUT OFF, LA

OFFSHORE MARINE CONTRACTORS INC p 1076
133 W 113th St 70345
Tel (985) 632-7927 SIC 1389

OFFSHORE SERVICE VESSELS LLC p 1076
16201 E Main St 70345
Tel (985) 601-4444 SIC 4491

DENHAM SPRINGS, LA

PLANTATION MANAGEMENT CO LLC p 1154
301 Veterans Blvd 70726
Tel (225) 664-6697 SIC 8051

DERIDDER, LA

▲ **AMERISAFE INC** p 83
2301 Highway 190 W 70634
Tel (337) 463-9052 SIC 6331

BEAUREGARD ELECTRIC COOPERATIVE INC p 166
1010 E 1st St 70634
Tel (800) 367-0275 SIC 4911

DONALDSONVILLE, LA

ASCENSION PARISH SCHOOLS p 116
1100 Webster St 70346
Tel (225) 257-2000 SIC 8211

ELTON, LA

COUSHATTA ALLIANCE p 383
1940 C C Bel Rd 70532
Tel (337) 584-1401 SIC 9131

EUNICE, LA

LOUISIANA CRANE & CONSTRUCTION LLC p 880
1045 Highway 190 70535
Tel (337) 550-6217 SIC 7389 7353 1623

SUNLAND CONSTRUCTION INC p 1403
2532 Aymond St 70535
Tel (337) 546-0241 SIC 1623

GALLIANO, LA

CROSBY TUGS LLC p 393
17771 Highway 3235 70354
Tel (985) 632-7575 SIC 4492

GRAND ISLE SHIPYARD INC p 629
18838 Highway 3235 70354
Tel (985) 475-5238 SIC 1389

GEISMAR, LA

LION COPOLYMER HOLDINGS LLC p 869
36191 Highway 30 70734
Tel (225) 673-8871 SIC 2891

LION ELASTOMER HOLDINGS LLC p 869
36191 Highway 30 70734
Tel (225) 673-8871 SIC 2822

GOLDEN MEADOW, LA

ABDON CALLAIS OFFSHORE LLC p 10
1300 N Alex Plisance Blvd 70357
Tel (985) 475-7111 SIC 4499

GONZALES, LA

▲ **CROWN CRAFTS INC** p 395
916 S Burnside Ave 70737
Tel (225) 647-9100 SIC 2211 2389

EATELCORP LLC p 473
913 S Burnside Ave 70737
Tel (225) 621-4300 SIC 5731

OUR LADY OF LAKE ASCENSION COMMUNITY HOSPITAL p 1098
1125 W Highway 30 70737
Tel (225) 647-5000 SIC 8062

SMITH TANK & STEEL INC p 1333
42422 Highway 30 70737
Tel (225) 644-8747 SIC 1541

GRAMBLING, LA

GRAMBLING STATE UNIVERSITY p 629
403 Main St 71245
Tel (318) 274-2558 SIC 8221 9411

GRAMERCY, LA

NORANDA ALUMINA LLC p 1047
1111 E Airline Hwy Us61 70052
Tel (225) 869-2100 SIC 3334

GRAY, LA

DANOS AND CUROLE MARINE CONTRACTORS LLC p 412
3878 W Main St 70359
Tel (985) 693-3313 SIC 1389

GREENWELL SPRINGS, LA

DIXIE ELECTRIC MEMBERSHIP CORP p 444
16262 Wax Rd 70739
Tel (225) 261-1221 SIC 4911

GRETNA, LA

ACME TRUCK LINE INC p 18
200 Westbank Expy 70053
Tel (504) 368-2510 SIC 4213 4212

JOHN W STONE OIL DISTRIBUTOR LLC p 789
87 1st St 70053
Tel (504) 366-3401 SIC 5172

PARISH OF JEFFERSON p 1115
200 Derbigny St 70053
Tel (504) 364-2600 SIC 9111

HAMMOND, LA

HOSPITAL SERVICE DISTRICT NO 1 OF TANGIPAHOA PARISH p 710
15770 Paul Vega Md Dr 70403
Tel (985) 230-6934 SIC 8062

NEILL CORP p 1024
303 S Pine St 70403
Tel (985) 345-1085 SIC 5087 5999

NORTH OAKS HEALTH SYSTEM FOUNDATION p 1053
15790 Paul Vega Md Dr 70403
Tel (985) 345-2700 SIC 6733

SOUTHEASTERN LOUISIANA UNIVERSITY p 1346
500 Ned Mcgehee Dr 70402
Tel (985) 549-2068 SIC 8221

HARAHAN, LA

BLESSEY ENTERPRISES INC p 189
1515 River Oaks Rd E 70123
Tel (504) 734-1156 SIC 4449

BLESSEY MARINE SERVICE INC p 189
1515 River Oaks Rd E 70123
Tel (504) 734-1156 SIC 4492

DONOVAN MARINE INC p 451
6316 Humphreys St 70123
Tel (504) 729-2520 SIC 5088

GIBBS CONSTRUCTION LLC p 611
5736 Citrus Blvd Ste 200 70123
Tel (504) 733-4336 SIC 1542 1541

IMPERIAL TRADING CO LLC p 734
701 Edwards Ave 70123
Tel (504) 733-1400 SIC 5194 5141 5145

INSULATIONS INC p 747
1101 Edwards Ave 70123
Tel (504) 733-5033 SIC 1799 1761 1741

INTRALOX LLC p 760
301 Plantation Rd 70123
Tel (504) 733-6739 SIC 3535

LAITRAM LLC p 838
220 Laitram Ln 70123
Tel (504) 733-6000
SIC 3535 3556 7359 3446 6719

NU-LITE ELECTRICAL WHOLESALERS LLC p 1066
850 Edwards Ave 70123
Tel (504) 733-3300 SIC 5063

X-CHEM INC p 1630
6141 River Rd 70123
Tel (504) 733-5806 SIC 5169

HARVEY, LA

CAMERON INC p 245
1036 Destrehan Ave 70058
Tel (504) 371-3000 SIC 1389

JEFFERSON PARISH PUBLIC SCHOOL SYSTEM p 782
501 Manhattan Blvd 70058
Tel (504) 349-7600 SIC 8211

JEFFERSON PARISH SCHOOL BOARD INC p 782
501 Manhattan Blvd 70058
Tel (504) 349-7803 SIC 8211

JEFFERSON PARISH SHERIFFS OFFICE p 782
1233 Westbank Expy 70058
Tel (504) 363-5500 SIC 9221 9223

LOUISIANA I GAMING LP p 880
4132 Peters Rd 70058
Tel (504) 366-7711 SIC 7999

RAY BRANDT NISSAN INC p 1209
4000 Lapalco Blvd 70058
Tel (504) 367-1666 SIC 5511 5521

RETIF OIL & FUEL L L C p 1228
1840 Jutland Dr 70058
Tel (504) 349-9000 SIC 5171

HAUGHTON, LA

EVERGREEN PRESBYTERIAN MINISTRIES INC p 514
2101 Highway 80 71037
Tel (318) 949-5500 SIC 8331 8361

HOLDEN, LA

FERRARA FIRE APPARATUS INC p 538
27855 James Chapel Rd N 70744
Tel (225) 567-7100 SIC 3711

FERRARA FIREFIGHTING EQUIPMENT INC p 538
27855 James Chapel Rd N 70744
Tel (225) 567-7100 SIC 5087

HOUMA, LA

BABEN MANAGEMENT LLC p 143
3400 Industrial Park 70363
Tel (985) 879-2487 SIC 5084 3599

BLAKE INTERNATIONAL USA RIGS LLC p 188
410 S Van Ave 70363
Tel (985) 274-2200 SIC 1381

■ **CARO FOODS INC** p 259
2324 Bayou Blue Rd 70364
Tel (985) 872-1483 SIC 5141

CENAC MARINE SERVICES LLC p 274
742 Highway 182 70364
Tel (985) 872-2413 SIC 4492

CHET MORRISON CONTRACTORS LLC p 295
9 Bayou Dularge Rd 70363
Tel (985) 868-1950
SIC 1623 3498 1629 1389

■ **GRAHAM MARINE INC** p 629
7910 Main St Ste 200 70360
Tel (985) 876-5400 SIC 4499

GULFSTREAM SERVICES INC p 647
103 Dickson Rd 70363
Tel (985) 868-0303 SIC 1382 7359

HOSPITAL SERVICE DISTRICT NO 1 p 709
8166 Main St 70360
Tel (985) 873-4141 SIC 8062

NORTH AMERICAN FABRICATORS LLC p 1050
367 Dickson Rd 70363
Tel (985) 917-2000 SIC 3731

OFFSHORE DRILLING CO p 1076
24 Concord Rd 70360
Tel (985) 876-6987 SIC 1381

PERFORMANCE ENERGY SERVICES LLC p 1135
132 Valhi Lagoon Xing 70360
Tel (985) 868-4895 SIC 1623 1389 7363

QUALITY ENERGY SERVICES INC p 1197
230 Menard Rd 70363
Tel (985) 850-0025 SIC 1389

■ **SEACOR MARINE LLC** p 1296
7910 Main St Ste 200 70360
Tel (985) 858-6427 SIC 4424

TERREBONNE PARISH CONSOLIDATED GOVERNMENT p 1439
8026 Main St Ste 300 70360
Tel (985) 873-6454 SIC 9111

TERREBONNE PARISH SCHOOL BOARD INC p 1439
201 Stadium Dr 70360
Tel (985) 876-7400 SIC 8211

TERREBONNE PARISH SCHOOLS p 1440
201 Stadium Dr 70360
Tel (985) 876-7400 SIC 8211

JEANERETTE, LA

MA PATOUT & SON LIMITED LLC p 891
3512 J Patout Burns Rd 70544
Tel (337) 276-4592 SIC 2061

JEFFERSON, LA

■ **EL INVESTMENT CO LLC** p 482
4809 Jefferson Hwy 70121
Tel (504) 576-4000 SIC 4911 4922

■ **ENTERGY GULF STATES LOUISIANA LLC** p 501
4809 Jefferson Hwy 70121
Tel (504) 576-4000 SIC 4911 4924

■ **ENTERGY LOUISIANA HOLDINGS INC** p 501
4809 Jefferson Hwy 70121
Tel (504) 840-2734 SIC 4911 4922

■ **ENTERGY LOUISIANA LLC** p 501
4809 Jefferson Hwy 70121
Tel (504) 576-4000 SIC 4911 4922

■ **ENTERGY UTILITY HOLDING CO LLC** p 502
4809 Jefferson Hwy 70121
Tel (504) 576-4000 SIC 4911 4922

JENNINGS, LA

LEEVAC SHIPYARDS JENNINGS LLC p 852
111 Bunge St 70546
Tel (337) 824-2210 SIC 3731

PORT AGGREGATES INC p 1161
314 N Main St 70546
Tel (337) 656-3224 SIC 5032 3273

■ **TALENS MARINE & FUEL LLC** p 1422
1707 Evangeline Hwy 70546
Tel (800) 256-3835 SIC 5172 7389

KENNER, LA

OCHSNER MEDICAL CENTER - KENNER LLC p 1073
180 W Esplanade Ave 70065
Tel (504) 468-8600 SIC 8062 8099

■ **TREASURE CHEST CASINO LLC** p 1475
5050 Williams Blvd 70065
Tel (504) 443-8000 SIC 7999

KROTZ SPRINGS, LA

■ **ALON REFINING KROTZ SPRINGS INC** p 59
E I 20 70750
Tel (337) 594-5300 SIC 2911

LA PLACE, LA

ALL STAR ELECTRIC INC p 51
1032 Bert St 70068
Tel (985) 618-1200 SIC 1731

BD LAPLACE LLC p 164
138 Highway 3217 70068
Tel (985) 652-4900 SIC 3312

LAFAYETTE, LA

ACADIAN AMBULANCE SERVICE INC p 14
130 E Kaliste Saloom Rd 70508
Tel (337) 291-3333 SIC 4119

ACADIANA HEALTH CARE OF LOUISIANA INC p 14
101 La Rue France Ste 300 70508
Tel (337) 232-5044 SIC 7363

AMERICAS PIZZA CO LLC p 81
201 Rue De Jean Ste 200 70508
Tel (337) 806-1100 SIC 5812

ANALYTIC STRESS RELIEVING INC p 88
3118 W Pinhook Rd Ste 202 70508
Tel (337) 237-8790 SIC 1389

ATC GROUP HOLDINGS LLC p 124
221 Rue De Jean Ste 300 70508
Tel (337) 324-8777
SIC 8711 8732 8731 8249 8748

ATC GROUP SERVICES LLC p 124
221 Rue De Jean Ste 200 70508
Tel (337) 234-8777
SIC 8711 8734 8731 8249 8748

C & C TECHNOLOGIES INC p 231
730 E Kaliste Saloom Rd 70508
Tel (337) 210-0000 SIC 8713

CAL-CHLOR CORP p 237
627 Jefferson St 70501
Tel (337) 264-1449 SIC 5169

COMMUNICATIONS CORP OF AMERICA p 347
700 John St Ste 300 70501
Tel (337) 237-1142 SIC 4832 4833

DIOCESE OF LAFAYETTE p 440
1408 Carmel Dr 70501
Tel (337) 261-5652 SIC 8661

DUPRE INVESTMENTS INC p 462
201 Energy Pkwy Ste 500 70508
Tel (337) 237-8471 SIC 4212 4213 4731

DUPRE LOGISTICS LLC p 462
201 Energy Pkwy Ste 500 70508
Tel (337) 237-8471 SIC 4213 4212

ECOSERV LLC p 476
207 Towncenter Pkwy Fl 2 70506
Tel (337) 984-4445 SIC 4959 7699

EUREST SUPPORT SERVICES p 512
207 Towncenter Pkwy 70506
Tel (337) 233-9153 SIC 5812

FRANKS CASING CREW & RENTAL TOOLS INC p 575
700 E Verot School Rd 70508
Tel (337) 233-0303 SIC 7353 1389

FUGRO CHANCE INC p 583
200 Dulles Dr 70506
Tel (337) 237-1300 SIC 8713

■ **IBERIABANK** p 726
200 W Congress St 70501
Tel (800) 682-3231 SIC 6036 6163

▲ **IBERIABANK CORP** p 726
200 W Congress St 70501
Tel (337) 521-4003 SIC 6022

JP OIL CO LLC p 795
1604 W Pinhook Rd Ste 300 70508
Tel (337) 234-1170 SIC 1311

LAFAYETTE CITY PARISH CONSOLIDATED GOVERNMENT p 837
705 W University Ave 70506
Tel (337) 291-8353 SIC 9111

LAFAYETTE CONSOLIDATED GOVERNMENT p 837
705 W University Ave 70506
Tel (337) 291-8200 SIC 9111

LAFAYETTE GENERAL HEALTH SYSTEM INC p 837
1214 Coolidge Blvd 70503
Tel (337) 289-8125 SIC 8062

LAFAYETTE GENERAL MEDICAL CENTER INC p 837
1214 Coolidge Blvd 70503
Tel (337) 289-7991 SIC 8062

LAFAYETTE GENERAL SURGICAL HOSPITAL LLC p 837
1000 W Pinhook Rd Ste 100 70503
Tel (337) 289-8095 SIC 8062

LAFAYETTE PARISH SCHOOL BOARD p 837
113 Chaplin Dr 70508
Tel (337) 521-7000 SIC 8211

LAFAYETTE PARISH SCHOOL SYSTEM p 838
113 Chaplin Dr 70508
Tel (337) 521-7000 SIC 8211

LEMOINE CO L L C p 855
214 Jefferson St Ste 200 70501
Tel (337) 896-7720 SIC 1542

▲ **LHC GROUP INC** p 860
901 Hugh Wallis Rd S 70508
Tel (337) 233-1307 SIC 8082 8322

LINEAR CONTROLS INC p 869
107 1/2 Commission Blvd 70508
Tel (337) 839-9702 SIC 5063

MARLIN ENERGY LLC p 909
3861 Ambassador Caffery P 70503
Tel (337) 769-0032 SIC 1311 1382

▲ **MIDSOUTH BANCORP INC** p 966
102 Versailles Blvd 70501
Tel (337) 237-8343 SIC 6021

■ **MIDSOUTH BANK NA** p 966
102 Versailles Blvd # 100 70501
Tel (337) 237-8343 SIC 6021

OUR LADY OF LORDES REGIONAL MEDICAL CENTER INC p 1098
4801 Ambssdor Cffery Pkwy 70508
Tel (337) 289-2000 SIC 8011 8021

OUR LADY OF LOURDES REGIONAL MEDICAL CENTER INC p 1098
4801 Ambssdor Cffery Pkwy 70508
Tel (337) 470-2000 SIC 8062

▲ **PETROQUEST ENERGY INC** p 1139
400 E Kaliste Saloom Rd # 6000 70508
Tel (337) 232-7028 SIC 1311

▲ **PHI INC** p 1142
2001 Se Evangeline Trwy 70508
Tel (337) 235-2452 SIC 4512 4522 4581

SCHUMACHER GROUP OF DELAWARE INC p 1291
200 Corporate Blvd # 201 70508
Tel (337) 237-1915 SIC 7363

SCHUMACHER GROUP OF LOUISIANA INC p 1291
200 Corporate Blvd # 201 70508
Tel (337) 237-1915 SIC 8741

SHORELINE ENERGY PARTNERS LP p 1318
400 E Kaliste Saloom Rd # 2600 70508
Tel (281) 872-0051 SIC 4911

SOUTHWEST LOUISIANA ELECTRIC MEMBERSHIP CORP p 1352
3420 Ne Evangeline Trwy 70507
Tel (337) 896-5384 SIC 4911

▲ **STONE ENERGY CORP** p 1391
625 E Kaliste Saloom Rd # 201 70508
Tel (337) 237-0410 SIC 1311 1382

STULLER INC p 1394
302 Rue Louis Xiv 70508
Tel (337) 262-7700 SIC 5094 3911

TIMCO SERVICES INC p 1454
1724 E Milton Ave 70508
Tel (337) 233-5185 SIC 1389

UNIVERSITY OF LOUISIANA AT LAFAYETTE p 1522
104 E University Ave 70503
Tel (337) 482-1000 SIC 8221

UV LOGISTICS ACQUISITION HOLDING CORP p 1537
4021 Abr Csy Py S 200 B A 70503
Tel (337) 291-6700 SIC 4213

UV LOGISTICS LLC p 1537
4021 Ambssdor Cffery Pkwy 70503
Tel (337) 837-4757 SIC 4213 1389

LAFITTE, LA

SEMCO LLC p 1302
186 Jean Lafitte Blvd 70067
Tel (504) 689-2054 SIC 3441 3731

LAKE CHARLES, LA

CALCASIEU PARISH PUBLIC SCHOOLS p 238
3310 Broad St 70615
Tel (337) 217-4000 SIC 8211

CALCASIEU PARISH SCHOOL BOARD p 238
3310 Broad St 70615
Tel (337) 217-4000 SIC 8211

CHRISTUS HEALTH SOUTHWESTERN LOUISIANA p 303
524 Dctor Mchael Dbkey Dr 70601
Tel (337) 436-2511 SIC 8062

CITY OF LAKE CHARLES p 316
326 Pujo St 70601
Tel (337) 491-1201 SIC 9111

GOLDEN NUGGET LLC p 621
2550 Golden Nugget Blvd 70601
Tel (337) 508-7777 SIC 7011

LAKE CHARLES MEMORIAL HOSPITAL p 838
1701 Oak Park Blvd 70601
Tel (337) 494-2121 SIC 8011

■ **PNK (LAKE CHARLES) LLC** p 1158
777 Ave Lauberge 70601
Tel (337) 395-7777 SIC 7011

SOLAR SUPPLY INC p 1338
1212 12th St 70601
Tel (337) 310-1000 SIC 5075 5078

SOUTHWEST LOUISIANA HOSPITAL ASSOCIATION p 1352
1701 Oak Park Blvd 70601
Tel (337) 494-2121 SIC 8062

SOUTHWEST LOUISIANA MEMORIAL FOUNDATION p 1352
1701 Oak Park Blvd 70601
Tel (337) 494-3204 SIC 8062

■ **ST CHARLES GAMING CO INC** p 1365
100 Lake St 70607
Tel (337) 430-0711 SIC 7011

SWLHS INC p 1413
1701 Oak Park Blvd 70601
Tel (337) 494-3204 SIC 5912

LAROSE, LA

NORTH AMERICAN SHIPBUILDING LLC p 1050
800 Industrial Park Rd 70373
Tel (985) 693-4072 SIC 3731

ODYSSEA MARINE HOLDINGS INC p 1075
11864 Highway 308 70373
Tel (985) 385-0189 SIC 1381

WORKPLACE STAFFING SOLUTIONS LLC p 1624
13055 Hwy 1 70373
Tel (985) 798-5111 SIC 7363 7361

LEESVILLE, LA

VERNON PARISH SCHOOL BOARD p 1551
201 Belview Rd 71446
Tel (337) 239-3401 SIC 8211

VERNON PARISH SCHOOL DISTRICT p 1551
201 Belview Rd 71446
Tel (337) 239-3401 SIC 8211

LIVINGSTON, LA

LIVINGSTON PARISH SCHOOL DISTRICT p 872
13909 Florida Blvd 70754
Tel (225) 686-7044 SIC 8211

LOCKPORT, LA

BOLLINGER SHIPYARDS LLC p 198
8365 Highway 308 70374
Tel (985) 532-2554 SIC 3731 3599

BOLLINGER SHIPYARDS LOCKPORT LLC p 198
8365 Highway 308 70374
Tel (985) 532-2554 SIC 3731

LULING, LA

ST CHARLES PARISH PUBLIC SCHOOLS p 1365
13855 River Rd 70070
Tel (985) 785-6289 SIC 7991

MANDEVILLE, LA

COMMCARE CORP p 344
950 W Causeway Approach C 70471
Tel (504) 324-8950 SIC 8059

DIVERSIFIED FOODS AND SEASONINGS LLC p 444
1115 N Causeway Blvd # 200 70471
Tel (985) 809-3600 SIC 2099 2034

F A RICHARD & ASSOCIATES INC p 522
1625 W Causeway Approach 70471
Tel (985) 624-8383 SIC 6411

MAX FOOTE CONSTRUCTION CO LLC p 922
225 Antibes St W Ste 3 70448
Tel (985) 624-8569 SIC 1629

MARKSVILLE, LA

TUNICA-BILOXI GAMING AUTHORITY p 1491
711 Paragon Pl 71351
Tel (318) 253-1946 SIC 7011 7999 5999

TUNICA-BILOXI TRIBAL ECONOMIC DEVELOPMENT CORP p 1491
164 Yuroni Rd 71351
Tel (318) 253-9767 SIC 5812

MARRERO, LA

HOSPITAL SERVICE DISTRICT 1 INC p 709
1101 Medical Center Blvd 70072
Tel (504) 347-5511 SIC 8062

RIVERSIDE FOOD DISTRIBUTORS LLC p 1238
7251 River Rd 70072
Tel (504) 328-7383 SIC 5142

MERAUX, LA

UNITED STATES ENVIRONMENTAL SERVICES LLC p 1513
2809 E Judge Perez Dr 70075
Tel (504) 279-9930 SIC 8744

METAIRIE, LA

ADVANTAGE MEDICAL PROFESSIONALS LLC p 26
3340 Severn Ave Ste 320 70002
Tel (504) 456-0073 SIC 7361 7363

BARRIERE CONSTRUCTION CO LLC p 157
1 Galleria Blvd Ste 1650 70001
Tel (504) 581-7283 SIC 1611 1629

BENSCO INC p 173
5800 Airline Dr 70003
Tel (210) 349-6200 SIC 5511

BURRUS INVESTMENT GROUP INC p 229
401 Veterans Memrl 70005
Tel (504) 455-7600 SIC 6799

COPELANDS OF NEW ORLEANS INC p 368
2601 Severn Ave 70002
Tel (504) 830-1000 SIC 5812 5813

CORE CONSTRUCTION SERVICES LLC p 369
3131 N I 10 Service Rd E # 401 70002
Tel (504) 733-2212 SIC 1542

EAST JEFFERSON GENERAL HOSPITAL p 470
4200 Houma Blvd 70006
Tel (504) 454-4000 SIC 8062

GRAY & CO INC p 632
3625 N I 10 Service Rd W 70002
Tel (504) 888-7790 SIC 6331

GULF COAST TEACHING FAMILY SERVICES INC p 646
2400 Edenborn Ave Ste 299 70001
Tel (504) 831-6561 SIC 8322

MCC GROUP L L C p 926
3001 17th St 70002
Tel (504) 833-8291 SIC 1711 1542 1731

PROJECT CONSULTING SERVICES INC p 1182
3300 W Esplanade Ave S 70002
Tel (504) 219-3426 SIC 1389

RAAM GLOBAL ENERGY CO p 1203
3838 N Causeway Blvd # 2800 70002
Tel (859) 253-1300 SIC 1311

SAZERAC CO INC p 1285
3850 N Causeway Blvd # 1695 70002
Tel (504) 831-9450 SIC 5182 2085

SOUTHERN EAGLE SALES & SERVICE LP p 1348
5300 Blair St 70003
Tel (504) 733-8656 SIC 5181

SOUTHERN EAGLE SALES MANAGEMENT LLC p 1348
5300 Blair St 70003
Tel (504) 733-8656 SIC 5181

MINDEN, LA

FIBREBOND CORP p 540
1300 Davenport Dr 71055
Tel (318) 377-1030 SIC 3272

MADDEN CONTRACTING CO LLC p 893
11288 Hwy 371 71055
Tel (318) 377-0927 SIC 1611 2951

MONROE, LA

ABELL CORP p 11
2500 Sterlington Rd 71203
Tel (318) 343-7565 SIC 5191 3089

ALLIED BUILDING STORES INC p 56
850 Kansas Ln 71203
Tel (318) 699-9100 SIC 5031

■ **CAROLINA TELEPHONE AND TELEGRAPH CO LLC** p 259
100 Centurylink Dr 71203
Tel (318) 388-9000 SIC 4813 8721 5065

■ **CENTEL CORP** p 275
100 Centurylink Dr 71203
Tel (318) 388-9000 SIC 4813 4812

CENTRAL OIL & SUPPLY CORP p 279
2300 Booth St 71201
Tel (318) 388-2602 SIC 5171 5541

■ **CENTRAL TELEPHONE CO** p 280
100 Centurylink Dr 71203
Tel (318) 361-5955 SIC 4813

▲ **CENTURYLINK INC** p 282
100 Centurylink Dr 71203
Tel (318) 388-9000 SIC 4813 4812

■ **CENTURYTEL HOLDINGS INC** p 282
100 Centurylink Dr 71203
Tel (318) 388-9000 SIC 4813

■ **CENTURYTEL HOLDINGS MISSOURI INC** p 282
100 Centurylink Dr 71203
Tel (318) 388-9000 SIC 4812

■ **CENTURYTEL OF NORTHWEST INC** p 283
100 Centurylink Dr 71203
Tel (318) 388-9000 SIC 4813 4812

■ **CENTURYTEL SERVICE GROUP LLC** p 283
100 Centurylink Dr 71203
Tel (318) 388-9500 SIC 8721

■ **CENTURYTEL.COM LLC** p 283
100 Centurylink Dr 71203
Tel (318) 388-9500 SIC 4813

CITY OF MONROE p 316
700 Washington St 71201
Tel (318) 329-2310 SIC 9111

■ EMBARQ CORP p 490
100 Centurylink Dr 71203
Tel (318) 388-9000 SIC 4813

■ EMBARQ FLORIDA INC p 490
100 Centurylink Dr 71203
Tel (318) 388-9000 SIC 4813

■ EMBARQ MID-ATLANTIC MANAGEMENT SERVICES INC p 490
100 Centurylink Dr 71203
Tel (318) 388-9000 SIC 4813

EVANS OIL CO LLC p 513
8450 Millhaven Rd 71203
Tel (318) 345-1502 SIC 5172

MONROE CITY SCHOOLS INC p 985
2006 Tower Dr 71201
Tel (318) 325-0601 SIC 8211

MONROE L BRFHH L C p 985
4864 Jackson St 71202
Tel (318) 330-7000 SIC 8062

OUACHITA PARISH SCHOOL SYSTEM p 1098
100 Bry St 71201
Tel (318) 432-5000 SIC 8211

■ QWEST COMMUNICATIONS INTERNATIONAL INC p 1201
100 Centurylink Dr 71203
Tel (318) 388-9000 SIC 4813 4822 4812

■ QWEST CORP p 1201
100 Centurylink Dr 71203
Tel (318) 388-9000 SIC 4813

SCOTT EQUIPMENT CO LLC p 1293
1000 M L King Jr Dr J 71203
Tel (318) 387-4160 SIC 7353 5082

SOUTHEAST FOODS INC p 1345
1001 N 11th St 71201
Tel (318) 388-1884 SIC 5411

ST FRANCIS MEDICAL CENTER INC p 1367
309 Jackson St 71201
Tel (318) 966-4000 SIC 8062

ST FRANCIS SPECIALTY HOSPITAL INC p 1367
309 Jackson St 71201
Tel (318) 966-4196 SIC 8062

MORGAN CITY, LA

B & G FOOD ENTERPRISES INC p 141
1430 Sandra St 70380
Tel (985) 384-3333 SIC 5812

B & G FOOD ENTERPRISES OF TEXAS LLC p 141
1430 Sandra St 70380
Tel (985) 384-3333 SIC 5812

▲ CONRAD INDUSTRIES INC p 358
1100 Brashear Ave Ste 200 70380
Tel (985) 702-0195 SIC 3731

INTERMOOR INC p 753
101 Youngswood Rd 70380
Tel (985) 385-3083 SIC 1381

■ PRODUCTION MANAGEMENT INDUSTRIES LLC p 1179
1204 Youngs Rd 70380
Tel (985) 631-3837 SIC 1389 8731 4789

NATCHITOCHES, LA

LOTT OIL CO INC p 879
1855 South Dr 71457
Tel (318) 356-5858 SIC 5171

NEW IBERIA, LA

AGGREKO LLC p 35
4610 W Admiral Doyle Dr 70560
Tel (337) 367-7884 SIC 5064 3822

ASRC ENERGY SERVICES OMEGA LLC p 119
4418 Pesson Rd 70560
Tel (337) 365-6028 SIC 1389 3533

■ BAYOU HOLDINGS OF NEW IBERIA LLC p 162
5200 Curtis Ln 70560
Tel (337) 369-3761 SIC 1389

■ BRISTOW US LLC p 214
4605 Industrial Dr 70560
Tel (337) 365-6771 SIC 4522

IBERIA PARISH SCHOOL DISTRICT p 726
1500 Jane St 70563
Tel (337) 685-4395 SIC 8211

PREMIERE INC p 1171
615 N Landry Dr 70563
Tel (337) 369-1000 SIC 5961

TOTAL SERVICE SUPPLY LP p 1463
513 Vortex Dr 70560
Tel (337) 365-5954 SIC 5085

VISCARDI INDUSTRIAL SERVICES LLC p 1561
815 Lucerne Dr 70563
Tel (337) 367-0824 SIC 1541

NEW ORLEANS, LA

ADAMS AND REESE LLP p 21
701 Poydras St Ste 4500 70139
Tel (504) 581-3234 SIC 8111

ADMINISTRATORS OF TULANE EDUCATIONAL FUND p 23
6823 Saint Charles Ave 70118
Tel (504) 865-5000 SIC 8221 8733

AECO INTERIORS OF NEW ORLEANS p 28
1836 Iberville St 70112
Tel (504) 301-9600 SIC 7389

ALL ABOARD AMERICA HOLDINGS INC p 50
2838 Touro St 70122
Tel (800) 356-6831
SIC 6719 4141 4131 4119 4111

ALTON OCHSNER MEDICAL FOUNDATION p 62
1516 Jefferson Hwy # 517 70121
Tel (504) 842-3700 SIC 8082

ARCHDIOCESE OF NEW ORLEANS INC p 105
7887 Walmsley Ave 70125
Tel (504) 861-9521 SIC 8211 8661

BOH BROS CONSTRUCTION CO LLC p 197
730 S Tonti St 70119
Tel (504) 821-2400
SIC 1611 1622 1629 1623

CANAL BARGE CO INC p 246
835 Union St Ste 300 70112
Tel (504) 581-2424 SIC 4449 4424 5171

CB&T HOLDING CORP p 268
1100 Poydras St Ste 1800 70163
Tel (504) 525-4381 SIC 6022

CH2M HILL - DYNETICS SYNERGY ALLIANCE LLC p 286
1515 Poydras St Ste 1550 70112
Tel (504) 593-9421 SIC 8744

CHILDRENS HOSPITAL p 299
200 Henry Clay Ave 70118
Tel (504) 899-9511 SIC 8069

CITY OF NEW ORLEANS p 317
1300 Perdido St Bsmt Fl2 70112
Tel (504) 658-4900 SIC 9111

COMMCARE CORP p 344
2755 Pan American Lf Ctr 70130
Tel (504) 324-8950 SIC 8093

COMMCARE LOUISIANA p 344
601 Poydras St 70130
Tel (504) 324-8950 SIC 8093

CONSOLIDATED COMPANIES INC p 359
918 Edwards Ave 70123
Tel (318) 869-3061 SIC 5141

CONTANDA LLC p 362
365 Canal St Ste 2900 70130
Tel (504) 525-9741 SIC 4226 2048

CRESCENT BANK & TRUST p 391
1100 Poydras St Ste 100 70163
Tel (504) 556-5950 SIC 6021

CRESCENT CROWN DISTRIBUTING LLC p 391
5900 Almonaster Ave 70126
Tel (504) 240-5900 SIC 5181

DOMINION EXPLORATION & PRODUCTION INC p 449
1250 Poydras St Ste 2000 70113
Tel (504) 593-7000 SIC 1382

DYNAMIC INDUSTRIES INC p 464
400 Poydras St Ste 1800 70130
Tel (504) 684-1305 SIC 3441

▲ ENTERGY CORP p 501
639 Loyola Ave Ste 300 70113
Tel (504) 576-4000 SIC 4931

■ ENTERGY NEW ORLEANS INC p 501
1600 Perdido St Bldg 505 70112
Tel (504) 670-3700 SIC 4931

■ ENTERGY NEW ORLEANS TRANSMISSION OWNER p 501
1600 Perdido St Bldg 505 70112
Tel (501) 228-2888 SIC 4931

■ ENTERGY NUCLEAR HOLDING CO p 501
639 Loyola Ave 70113
Tel (504) 576-4000 SIC 4911

■ ENTERGY SERVICES INC p 501
639 Loyola Ave Ste 300 70113
Tel (504) 576-4000 SIC 8741 8711

■ FIRST NBC BANK p 548
210 Baronne St Frnt 70112
Tel (504) 566-8000 SIC 6022

▲ FIRST NBC BANK HOLDING CO p 548
210 Baronne St 70112
Tel (504) 566-8000 SIC 6022

FIRSTRUST CORP p 551
909 Poydras St Ste 1700 70112
Tel (504) 584-5900 SIC 6022

GULF COAST BANK AND TRUST CO p 646
200 Saint Charles Ave 70130
Tel (504) 561-6100 SIC 6022

HAMMERMAN & GAINER INTERNATIONAL INC p 656
1010 Common St Ste 2600 70112
Tel (504) 681-6135 SIC 8742

HISTORIC RESTORATION INC p 696
812 Gravier St Apt 200 70112
Tel (504) 493-6129 SIC 6552

INTERIOR/EXTERIOR BUILDING SUPPLY LIMITED PARTNERSHIP p 753
727 S Cortez St 70119
Tel (504) 488-1998 SIC 5031

■ INTERNATIONAL-MATEX TANK TERMINALS p 757
321 Saint Charles Ave 70130
Tel (504) 586-8300 SIC 4226 1799

■ J RAY MCDERMOTT & CO INC p 772
1340 Poydras St Ste 1200 70112
Tel (504) 587-5000 SIC 1629 1389 1623

JAZZ CASINO CO L L C p 779
8 Canal St 70130
Tel (504) 525-6260 SIC 7011

JONES WALKER LLP p 792
201 Saint Charles Ave # 5200 70170
Tel (504) 582-8000 SIC 8111

JUDICIARY COURTS OF STATE OF LOUISIANA p 796
400 Royal St Ste 4200 70130
Tel (504) 310-2300 SIC 9211

LATTER & BLUM INC p 846
430 Notre Dame St 70130
Tel (504) 525-1311 SIC 6531

LOUISIANA CHILDRENS MEDICAL CENTER INC p 880
200 Henry Clay Ave 70118
Tel (504) 896-9581 SIC 8069

■ LOUISIANA COCA-COLA BOTTLING CO LIMITED p 880
5601 Citrus Blvd 70123
Tel (504) 818-7000 SIC 2086 5962

LOUISIANA DEPARTMENT OF MILITARY AFFAIRS p 880
6400 Saint Claude Ave 70117
Tel (504) 278-8071 SIC 9711 9451

LOYOLA UNIVERSITY NEW ORLEANS INC p 882
6363 Saint Charles Ave 70118
Tel (504) 865-2011 SIC 8221

MEDICAL CENTER OF LOUISIANA AT NEW ORLEANS p 936
1532 Tulane Ave 70112
Tel (504) 903-3000 SIC 8062

OCHSNER CLINIC FOUNDATION p 1073
1514 Jefferson Hwy 70121
Tel (504) 842-3000 SIC 8062 5947

OCHSNER CLINIC HEALTH SERVICES CORP p 1073
1514 Jefferson Hwy 70121
Tel (504) 842-4000 SIC 8011

OCHSNER COMMUNITY HOSPITALS p 1073
1514 Jefferson Hwy 70121
Tel (504) 842-3400 SIC 8062

OCHSNER FOUNDATION HOSPITAL p 1073
1514 Jefferson Hwy 70121
Tel (504) 842-4000 SIC 8062

OCHSNER HEALTH SYSTEM p 1073
1516 Jefferson Hwy 70121
Tel (504) 842-3483 SIC 8099

ORLEANS PARISH SCHOOL DISTRICT p 1095
3520 Gen Degaulle Dr # 5055 70114
Tel (504) 304-3520 SIC 8211

PAN-AMERICAN LIFE INSURANCE GROUP INC p 1110
601 Poydras St Ste 1000 70130
Tel (504) 566-1300 SIC 6311 7389

PAN-AMERICAN LIFE MUTUAL HOLDING CO p 1110
601 Poydras St Ste 1000 70130
Tel (877) 939-4550 SIC 6799

■ PENDLETON MEMORIAL METHODIST HOSPITAL p 1128
5620 Read Blvd 70127
Tel (504) 244-5100 SIC 8062

PHELPS DUNBAR LLP p 1141
365 Canal St Ste 2000 70130
Tel (504) 566-1311 SIC 8111

RECOVERY SCHOOL DISTRICT p 1215
1615 Poydras St Ste 400 70112
Tel (504) 373-6200 SIC 9411

REILY FOODS CO p 1221
400 Poydras St Fl 10 70130
Tel (504) 524-6131 SIC 2099 2095

REPUBLIC NATIONAL DISTRIBUTING CO LLC p 1225
809 Jefferson Hwy 70121
Tel (404) 696-9440 SIC 5182

SODEXO REMOTE SITES PARTNERSHIP p 1337
5749 Susitna Dr 70123
Tel (504) 733-5761 SIC 5812

SOUTHERN RECYCLING LLC p 1350
902 Julia St 70113
Tel (504) 636-7200 SIC 5093

SOUTHERN THEATRES LLC p 1350
935 Gravier St Ste 1200 70112
Tel (504) 297-1133 SIC 7832

■ STEWART ENTERPRISES INC p 1389
1333 S Clearview Pkwy 70121
Tel (504) 729-1400 SIC 7261 5087

▲ TIDEWATER INC p 1452
601 Poydras St Ste 1500 70130
Tel (504) 568-1010 SIC 4424 4493 4492

TOURO INFIRMARY p 1464
1401 Foucher St 70115
Tel (504) 897-7011 SIC 8062

TULANE UNIVERSITY HOSPITAL AND CLINIC p 1491
1415 Tulane Ave Fl 4 70112
Tel (504) 988-3516 SIC 8011

■ UNIVERSITY HEALTHCARE SYSTEM LC p 1519
1415 Tulane Ave 70112
Tel (504) 988-5263 SIC 8062

UNIVERSITY MEDICAL CENTER MANAGEMENT CORP p 1519
2000 Canal St 70112
Tel (504) 903-3000 SIC 8062

UNIVERSITY OF NEW ORLEANS p 1523
2000 Lakeshore Dr 70122
Tel (888) 514-4275 SIC 8221

UP PROFESSIONAL SOLUTIONS LLC p 1528
1100 Poydras St Ste 1300 70163
Tel (800) 245-8274 SIC 7361 7363

VINSON GUARD SERVICE INC p 1558
955 Howard Ave 70113
Tel (504) 525-0591 SIC 7381

WALTON CONSTRUCTION - A CORE CO LLC p 1575
2 Commerce Ct 70123
Tel (504) 733-2212 SIC 1541 1542

WEISER SECURITY SERVICES INC p 1588
3939 Tulane Ave 300 70119
Tel (504) 586-4712 SIC 7381

WHITNEY BANK p 1607
228 Saint Charles Ave # 228 70130
Tel (504) 586-7272 SIC 6021

WM B REILY & CO INC p 1620
640 Magazine St 70130
Tel (504) 539-5200
SIC 2095 2035 2079 5962 5963 2099

WOODWARD DESIGN + BUILD LLC p 1623
1000 S Jffrson Dvis Pkwy 70125
Tel (504) 822-6443 SIC 1541 1542

XAVIER UNIVERSITY OF LOUISIANA p 1631
1 Drexel Dr 70125
Tel (504) 520-7411 SIC 8221

OPELOUSAS, LA

IMPERIAL MANAGEMENT CORP p 734
4670 I 49 N Service Rd 70570
Tel (337) 942-5691 SIC 6331

OPELOUSAS GENERAL HEALTH SYSTEM p 1089
539 E Prudhomme St 70570
Tel (337) 948-3011 SIC 8062

ST LANDRY PARISH AIRPORT AUTHORITY p 1369
299 Hangar Rd 70570
Tel (337) 407-1551 SIC 4581

ST LANDRY PARISH SCHOOLS p 1369
1013 Creswell Ln 70570
Tel (337) 948-3657 SIC 8211

PINEVILLE, LA

CLECO CORPORATE HOLDINGS LLC p 325
2030 Donahue Ferry Rd 71360
Tel (318) 484-7400 SIC 4911

CLECO PARTNERS LP p 325
2030 Donahue Ferry Rd 71360
Tel (318) 484-7400 SIC 4911

CLECO POWER LLC p 325
2030 Donahue Ferry Rd 71360
Tel (318) 484-7400 SIC 4911

CREST INDUSTRIES p 392
4725 Highway 28 E 71360
Tel (318) 767-5530
SIC 3699 3612 3441 5063 2439

CREST OPERATIONS LLC p 392
4725 Highway 28 E 71360
Tel (318) 448-0274
SIC 3441 2439 3699 5063 3612

PONCHATOULA, LA

ELMER CANDY CORP p 489
401 N 5th St 70454
Tel (985) 386-6166 SIC 2066 2064

PORT ALLEN, LA

LYONS SPECIALTY CO LLC p 888
2800 La Highway 1 N 70767
Tel (225) 356-1319 SIC 5194 5145 5149

PETRIN CORP p 1139
1405 Commercial Dr 70767
Tel (225) 343-0471 SIC 1799 2952

PRAIRIEVILLE, LA

PCE CONSTRUCTORS INC p 1124
13544 Eads Rd 70769
Tel (225) 677-9100 SIC 1629

RESERVE, LA

DIVERSIFIED WELL LOGGING INC p 444
711 W 10th St 70084
Tel (985) 536-4143 SIC 1389

LOUISIANA MACHINERY CO LLC p 880
3799 W Airline Hwy 70084
Tel (985) 536-1121 SIC 5082 7699 7353

ST JOHN BAPTIST PARISH PUBLIC SCHOOLS p 1367
118 W 10th St 70084
Tel (985) 536-1106 SIC 8211

ROSELAND, LA

SMITTYS SUPPLY INC p 1334
63399 Highway 51 70456
Tel (985) 748-9687 SIC 5172 5531

RUSTON, LA

COMMUNITY TRUST FINANCIAL CORP p 350
1511 N Trenton St 71270
Tel (318) 255-2222 SIC 6712

FOREST HUNT PRODUCTS INC p 566
401 E Reynolds Dr 71270
Tel (318) 255-2245 SIC 2436 2421

HUNT GUILLOT & ASSOCIATES LLC p 719
603 E Reynolds Dr 71270
Tel (318) 255-6825 SIC 8711

LINCOLN BUILDERS INC p 866
1809 Nrthpinte Ln Ste 201 71270
Tel (318) 255-3822 SIC 1542

LINCOLN PARISH WILDLIFE FEDERATION p 867
410 S Farmerville St 71270
Tel (318) 255-1430 SIC 8211

LOUISIANA TECH UNIVERSITY p 880
1100 Hull Ave 71270
Tel (318) 257-3267 SIC 8221

SAINT FRANCISVILLE, LA

HOOD CONTAINER OF LOUISIANA LLC p 705
2105 Highway 964 70775
Tel (225) 336-2530 SIC 2621

SCHRIEVER, LA

K&B MACHINE WORKS LLC p 799
208 Rebeccas Pond Rd 70395
Tel (985) 868-6730 SIC 3599

ROMAN CATHOLIC CHURCH OF DIOCESE OF HOUMA THIBODAUX p 1248
2779 Highway 311 70395
Tel (985) 868-7720 SIC 8661

SCOTT, LA

ISLAND OPERATING CO INC p 766
108 Zachary Dr 70583
Tel (337) 262-0620 SIC 1389

SHREVEPORT, LA

ALLEGIANCE HEALTH MANAGEMENT INC p 53
504 Texas St Ste 200 71101
Tel (318) 226-8202 SIC 8741

ARKLATEX ENERGY SERVICES LLC p 110
6913 Westport Ave 71129
Tel (318) 688-9850 SIC 1389

BIOMEDICAL RESEARCH FOUNDATION OF NORTHWEST LOUISIANA p 184
2031 Kings Hwy 71103
Tel (318) 716-4100 SIC 8733 8732

BRAMMER ENGINEERING INC p 207
400 Texas St Ste 600 71101
Tel (318) 429-2345 SIC 1389

BRFHH SHREVEPORT LLC p 211
1541 Kings Hwy 71103
Tel (318) 675-5000 SIC 8062

CADDO PARISH COMMISSION p 236
525 Marshall St 71101
Tel (318) 226-6891 SIC 7361

CADDO PARISH PUBLIC SCHOOLS p 236
1961 Midway St 71108
Tel (318) 603-6300 SIC 8211

CADDO PARISH SCHOOL BOARD p 236
1961 Midway St 71108
Tel (318) 636-0210 SIC 8211

CHRISTUS HEALTH NORTHERN LOUISIANA p 303
1 Saint Mary Pl 71101
Tel (318) 681-4500 SIC 8069

CITY OF SHREVEPORT p 318
505 Travis St Ste 600 71101
Tel (318) 673-7900 SIC 9111

COMMUNITY CARE CENTER OF WESTWOOD LLC p 347
1 Westwood Circel 71109
Tel (318) 635-4444 SIC 8051

ELDORADO CASINO SHREVEPORT JOINT VENTURE p 484
451 Clyde Fant Pkwy 71101
Tel (877) 602-0711 SIC 7011

■ **FRYMASTER LLC** p 582
8700 Line Ave 71106
Tel (318) 865-1711 SIC 3589 5046

IVAN SMITH FURNITURE CO LLC p 769
5434 Technology Dr 71129
Tel (318) 688-1335 SIC 5712

MORRIS & DICKSON CO LLC p 990
410 Kay Ln 71115
Tel (318) 797-7900 SIC 5122

RED BALL OXYGEN CO INC p 1215
609 N Market St 71107
Tel (318) 425-6300
SIC 5084 5085 5169 5099 5531 5013

■ **RED RIVER ENTERTAINMENT OF SHREVEPORT** p 1216
315 Clyde Fant Pkwy 71101
Tel (318) 424-7777 SIC 7999

RED RIVER SPECIALTIES INC p 1216
1324 N Hearne Ave Ste 120 71107
Tel (318) 425-5944 SIC 5191

ROUNDTREE AUTOMOTIVE GROUP LLC p 1253
7607 Fern Ave Ste 401 71105
Tel (318) 798-6500 SIC 5511

ROUNDTREE OF SHREVEPORT LLC p 1253
910 Pierremont Rd Ste 312 71106
Tel (318) 798-6500 SIC 5511

SPORTS SOUTH LLC p 1360
1039 Kay Ln 71115
Tel (318) 797-4848 SIC 5091

VA HOSPITAL p 1538
510 E Stoner Ave 71101
Tel (318) 221-8411 SIC 8011

WILLIS-KNIGHTON MEDICAL CENTER p 1612
2600 Greenwood Rd 71103
Tel (318) 212-4000 SIC 8062

SLIDELL, LA

SPARTAN OFFSHORE DRILLING LLC p 1355
516 J F Smith Ave 70460
Tel (504) 885-7449 SIC 3533

SPARTAN OFFSHORE INTERMEDIATE LLC p 1355
516 J F Smith Ave 70460
Tel (504) 885-7449 SIC 3533

ST TAMMANY PARISH HOSPITAL SERVICE DISTRICT 2 p 1373
1001 Gause Blvd 70458
Tel (985) 280-2200 SIC 8062

SULPHUR, LA

BOLLINGER CALCASIEU LLC p 198
8086 Global Dr 70665
Tel (337) 583-7383 SIC 3731

HOLLY HILL HOUSE INC p 701
100 Kingston Rd 70663
Tel (337) 625-5843 SIC 8051

SENTRY SUPPLY INC p 1305
318 S Cities Service Hwy 70663
Tel (337) 625-2300 SIC 5085 5051

STINE LLC p 1390
2950 Ruth St 70665
Tel (337) 527-0121 SIC 5211

SUNSET, LA

LOUISIANA WHOLESALE DRUG CO INC p 880
2085 I 49 S Service Rd 70584
Tel (337) 662-1040 SIC 5122 5912

THIBODAUX, LA

GAUBERT OIL CO INC p 594
1201 Saint Patrick St 70301
Tel (800) 256-1250 SIC 5172 5411

HOSPITAL SERVICE DISTRICT 3 LAFOURCHE PARISH p 709
602 N Acadia Rd 70301
Tel (985) 493-4740 SIC 8062 8051 8082

LAFOURCHE PARISH SCHOOL BOARD INC p 838
805 E 7th St 70301
Tel (985) 446-5631 SIC 8211

LAFOURCHE PARISH SCHOOL DISTRICT p 838
805 E 7th St 70301
Tel (985) 446-5631 SIC 8211

ROUSES ENTERPRISES LLC p 1253
1301 Saint Mary St 70301
Tel (985) 447-5998 SIC 5411

WEST MONROE, LA

ADVANTAGE HUMAN RESOURCING INC p 26
401 Thomas Rd Ste 2 71292
Tel (318) 324-8060 SIC 7363

BANCROFT BAG INC p 150
425 Bancroft Blvd 71292
Tel (318) 387-2550 SIC 2674

GLENWOOD RESOLUTION AUTHORITY INC p 615
503 Mcmillan Rd 71291
Tel (318) 329-4200 SIC 8062

IASIS GLENWOOD REGIONAL MEDICAL CENTER LP p 726
503 Mcmillan Rd 71291
Tel (318) 329-4200 SIC 8011

WESTLAKE, LA

■ **ISLE OF CAPRI LAKE CHARLES** p 767
100 Westlake Ave 70669
Tel (337) 430-2400 SIC 7011

■ **KRONOS LOUISIANA INC** p 830
3300 Bayou Dinde Rd 70669
Tel (337) 882-1774 SIC 2816

LOUISIANA PIGMENT CO LP p 880
3300 Bayou Dinde Rd 70669
Tel (337) 882-7000 SIC 2816

WESTWEGO, LA

CORNERSTONE CHEMICAL CO p 371
10800 River Rd 70094
Tel (504) 431-9511 SIC 2822 2821

WHITE CASTLE, LA

CROWN ENTERPRISES LLC p 395
52410 Clarke Rd 70788
Tel (225) 545-3040 SIC 1541 1791 4212

WINNFIELD, LA

KISATCHIE CORP p 822
9258 Highway 84 71483
Tel (318) 628-4116 SIC 8741

WOODWORTH, LA

PERFOREX LLC p 1135
2663 E Coulee Crossing Rd 71485
Tel (318) 445-6799 SIC 0851

YOUNGSVILLE, LA

QUALITY CONSTRUCTION & PRODUCTION LLC p 1197
425 Griffin Rd 70592
Tel (337) 857-6000 SIC 1542

TRACO PRODUCTION SERVICES INC p 1468
425 Griffin Rd 70592
Tel (337) 857-6000 SIC 5082 1389

MAINE

AUBURN, ME

AUBURN SCHOOL DEPARTMENT p 130
60 Court St Fl 4 04210
Tel (207) 784-6431 SIC 8211

FORMED FIBER TECHNOLOGIES INC p 567
125 Allied Rd 04210
Tel (207) 784-1118 SIC 2824 3089 2823

■ **LEPAGE BAKERIES INC** p 856
11 Adamian Dr 04210
Tel (207) 783-9161 SIC 2051 5461

MAINE OXY-ACETYLENE SUPPLY CO p 898
22 Albiston Way 04210
Tel (207) 784-5788 SIC 5169 5084

AUGUSTA, ME

■ **CENTRAL MAINE POWER CO INC** p 279
83 Edison Dr 04336
Tel (207) 623-3521 SIC 4911

■ **CMP GROUP INC** p 329
83 Edison Dr 04336
Tel (207) 623-3521 SIC 4911

DEPARTMENT OF CORRECTIONS MAINE p 430
25 Tyson Dr 3rd Flr 04333
Tel (207) 287-2711 SIC 9223

EXECUTIVE OFFICE OF STATE OF MAINE p 518
1 Stathuse Stn 2nd Fl 236 04333
Tel (207) 287-3531 SIC 9111

HUTCHINS MOTORS INC p 721
187 Riverside Dr 04330
Tel (207) 622-3191 SIC 5511 5012

JEROME GROUP INC p 783
6 E Chestnut St 04330
Tel (207) 626-1496 SIC 8011 8062

MAINE COMMUNITY COLLEGE SYSTEM p 898
323 State St 04330
Tel (207) 629-4000 SIC 8222

MAINE DEPARTMENT OF HEALTH AND HUMAN SERVICES p 898
221 State St 04330
Tel (207) 287-1716 SIC 9441 9431

MAINE DEPARTMENT OF TRANSPORTATION p 898
16 State House Sta 04333
Tel (207) 624-3000 SIC 9621

MAINE MUNICIPAL ASSOCIATION p 898
60 Community Dr 04330
Tel (207) 621-2645 SIC 8611

MAINE STATE HOUSING AUTHORITY p 898
353 Water St 04330
Tel (207) 626-4600 SIC 6162

MAINE VETERANS HOMES p 898
460 Civic Center Dr 04330
Tel (207) 622-0075 SIC 8052

MAINEGENERAL HEALTH p 898
35 Medical Center Pkwy 04330
Tel (207) 626-1000 SIC 8062

MAINEGENERAL MEDICAL CENTER p 898
35 Medical Center Pkwy 04330
Tel (207) 626-1289 SIC 8062

ME DEPT OF BEHAVIORAL AND DEVELOPMENTAL SERVICES p 933
40 State House Sta 04333
Tel (207) 287-4200 SIC 9431

NRF DISTRIBUTORS INC p 1064
485 Old Belgrade Rd 04330
Tel (207) 622-4744 SIC 5023

STATE OF MAINE p 1381
1 State House Sta 04333
Tel (207) 549-7182 SIC 9111

BAILEYVILLE, ME

WOODLAND PULP LLC p 1623
144 Main St 04694
Tel (207) 427-3311 SIC 2611

BANGOR, ME

AFFILIATED HEALTHCARE SYSTEMS p 32
931 Union St 04401
Tel (207) 973-6720
SIC 5047 8071 8741 7322 6512

BANGOR BANCORP MHC p 150
3 State St 04401
Tel (207) 942-5211 SIC 6712

BANGOR SAVINGS BANK p 150
99 Franklin St 04401
Tel (207) 942-3300 SIC 6029

BHE HOLDINGS INC p 180
21 Telcom Dr 04401
Tel (207) 947-2414 SIC 4911

CROSS FINANCIAL CORP p 393
491 Main St 04401
Tel (207) 947-7345 SIC 6411

DEAD RIVER CO p 419
80 Exchange St Ste 3 04401
Tel (207) 947-8641
SIC 6512 5172 5983 5541 5411

DENNIS BEVERAGE CO p 428
101 Mecaw Rd 04401
Tel (207) 947-0321 SIC 5141 5113

EASTERN MAINE MEDICAL CENTER p 472
489 State St 04401
Tel (207) 973-7000 SIC 8062

EMERA MAINE p 491
21 Telcom Dr 04401
Tel (207) 945-5621 SIC 4911

HARTT TRANSPORTATION SYSTEMS INC p 666
262 Bomarc Rd 04401
Tel (207) 947-1106 SIC 4213

OCEAN INVESTMENTS CORP p 1073
700 Maine Ave 04401
Tel (207) 942-7000 SIC 5541 5411

ST JOSEPH HEALTHCARE FOUNDATION INC p 1368
360 Broadway 04401
Tel (207) 907-1000 SIC 8099

ST JOSEPH HOSPITAL p 1368
360 Broadway 04401
Tel (207) 262-1000 SIC 8062

UNIVERSITY OF MAINE SYSTEM p 1522
16 Central St 04401
Tel (207) 973-3300 SIC 8221

BAR HARBOR, ME

JACKSON LABORATORY p 774
600 Main St 04609
Tel (207) 288-6000 SIC 8733

BATH, ME

■ **BATH IRON WORKS CORP** p 159
700 Washington St Stop 1 04530
Tel (207) 443-3311 SIC 3731 8711

BELFAST, ME

WALDO COUNTY GENERAL HOSPITAL p 1572
118 Northport Ave 04915
Tel (207) 338-2500 SIC 8062

BELGRADE, ME

HAMMOND LUMBER CO p 656
2 Hammond Dr 04917
Tel (207) 495-3303 SIC 5211 2421 5031

BIDDEFORD, ME

SOUTHERN MAINE HEALTH CARE p 1349
1 Medical Center Dr 04005
Tel (207) 283-7000 SIC 8062

UNIVERSITY OF NEW ENGLAND p 1523
11 Hills Beach Rd 04005
Tel (207) 282-3025 SIC 8221 5942

BREWER, ME

DARLINGS p 412
96 Parkway S Unit 1 04412
Tel (207) 992-1720 SIC 5511 6411

EASTERN MAINE HEALTHCARE SYSTEMS p 472
43 Whiting Hill Rd # 500 04412
Tel (207) 973-7050 SIC 8621 8062

BRUNSWICK, ME

BOWDOIN COLLEGE p 204
5600 College Sta 04011
Tel (207) 725-3000 SIC 8221

MID COAST HOSPITAL p 962
123 Medical Center Dr 04011
Tel (207) 373-6000 SIC 8062

MID COAST-PARKVIEW HEALTH p 963
123 Medical Center Dr G 04011
Tel (207) 729-0181 SIC 8062 8082 8051

BURNHAM, ME

PRIDE MANUFACTURING CO LLC p 1174
10 N Main St 04922
Tel (207) 487-3322 SIC 2411 3949

CAMDEN, ME

■ **CAMDEN NATIONAL BANK (INC)** p 244
2 Elm St 04843
Tel (207) 236-8821 SIC 6022

▲ CAMDEN NATIONAL CORP p 245
2 Elm St 04843
Tel (207) 236-8821 SIC 6021 6733

CASCO, ME

HANCOCK LUMBER CO INC p 657
4 Edes Falls Rd 04015
Tel (207) 627-4201 SIC 5211 5031

DAMARISCOTTA, ME

MILES HEALTH CARE INC p 969
35 Miles St 04543
Tel (207) 563-1234 SIC 8741

DOVER FOXCROFT, ME

HIBBARD NURSING HOME INC p 690
1037 W Main St 04426
Tel (207) 564-8129 SIC 8052 8051

FALMOUTH, ME

TD BANKNORTH LEASING CORP p 1428
70 Gray Rd 04105
Tel (207) 317-4616 SIC 6712

FREEPORT, ME

L L BEAN INC p 834
15 Casco St 04033
Tel (207) 552-2000
SIC 5961 5621 5611 5941 5661 5948

LL BEAN INTERNATIONAL p 872
15 Casco St 04033
Tel (207) 865-4761 SIC 5961

GARDINER, ME

ASSOCIATED GROCERS OF MAINE INC p 120
190 Water St 04345
Tel (207) 596-0636
SIC 5141 5147 5148 5122

EVERETT J PRESCOTT INC p 514
32 Prescott St Libby Libby Hill 04345
Tel (207) 582-2006 SIC 5074

MAINE DRILLING AND BLASTING INC p 898
544 Brunswick Ave 04345
Tel (207) 582-4300 SIC 1629

PINE STATE TRADING CO p 1149
47 Market St 04345
Tel (207) 622-2345 SIC 5181 5194 5145

HAMPDEN, ME

R H FOSTER ENERGY LLC p 1202
110 Mecaw Rd 04444
Tel (207) 947-3835
SIC 5172 5541 5411 5983

KITTERY, ME

GREENPAGES INC p 638
33 Badgers Is W 03904
Tel (207) 439-7310 SIC 7379

LEWISTON, ME

CENTRAL MAINE HEALTH VENTURES INC p 279
300 Main St 04240
Tel (207) 795-0111
SIC 8049 8052 7322 8011

CENTRAL MAINE HEALTHCARE CORP p 279
300 Main St 04240
Tel (207) 795-0111 SIC 8062 8052 8049

CENTRAL MAINE MEDICAL CENTER INC p 279
300 Main St 04240
Tel (207) 795-0111 SIC 8062

GEIGER BROS p 597
70 Mount Hope Ave 04240
Tel (207) 755-2000
SIC 5199 3993 2752 2782 2789

NORTH COUNTRY ASSOCIATES INC p 1052
179 Lisbon St Ste 3 04240
Tel (207) 786-3554 SIC 8361

PRESIDENT & TRUSTEES OF BATES COLLEGE p 1172
2 Andrews Rd 04240
Tel (207) 786-6255 SIC 8221

SISTERS OF CHARITY HEALTH SYSTEMS p 1327
99 Campus Ave Ste 303 04240
Tel (207) 782-5424 SIC 8011

ST MARYS HEALTH SYSTEM p 1371
96 Campus Ave 04240
Tel (207) 777-8546
SIC 8062 8052 8051 8011 8361

ST MARYS REGIONAL MEDICAL CENTER p 1372
93 Campus Ave 04240
Tel (207) 777-8546
SIC 8062 8052 8051 8011 8361

V I P INC p 1538
12 Lexington St 04240
Tel (207) 784-5423 SIC 5531

WAHLCOMETROFLEX INC p 1571
29 Lexington St 04240
Tel (207) 784-2338 SIC 3441 3822 8711

LINCOLN, ME

LINCOLN PAPER AND TISSUE LLC p 867
50 Katadin Ave 04457
Tel (207) 794-0600 SIC 2621

MACHIAS, ME

MARSHALL NURSING SERVICES INC p 911
9 Beal St 04654
Tel (207) 255-3387 SIC 8051

MADAWASKA, ME

NEXFOR (USA) INC p 1040
82 Bridge Ave 04756
Tel (207) 728-3321 SIC 2621 2493

TWIN RIVERS PAPER CO CORP p 1495
82 Bridge Ave 04756
Tel (207) 523-2350 SIC 2621

TWIN RIVERS PAPER CO LLC p 1495
82 Bridge Ave 04756
Tel (207) 728-3321 SIC 2621

MADISON, ME

MADISON UPM p 894
1 Main St 04950
Tel (207) 696-3307 SIC 2621

MARS HILL, ME

■ SARGENT TRUCKING INC p 1282
64 Main St 04758
Tel (207) 429-8106 SIC 4213

NEW GLOUCESTER, ME

■ IBERDROLA USA MANAGEMENT CORP p 726
52 Farm View Dr 04260
Tel (207) 688-6300 SIC 5063

■ UIL HOLDINGS CORP p 1500
52 Farm View Dr 04260
Tel (203) 499-2000 SIC 4931 4924

OAKLAND, ME

FABIAN OIL INC p 523
15 Oak St 04963
Tel (207) 465-7958
SIC 5541 5983 5984 5411

ORONO, ME

UNIVERSITY OF MAINE AT ORONO p 1522
168 College Ave 04469
Tel (207) 581-1865 SIC 8221

PITTSFIELD, ME

CIANBRO COMPANIES p 305
1 Hunnewell Ave 04967
Tel (207) 487-3311
SIC 1629 1622 1542 1541 8742

CIANBRO CORP p 305
101 Cianbro Sq 04967
Tel (207) 487-3311
SIC 1622 1629 1542 1541 8742

PORTLAND, ME

■ BARBER FOODS p 154
56 Milliken St 04103
Tel (207) 482-5500 SIC 2015

CITY OF PORTLAND p 317
389 Congress St Rm 110 04101
Tel (207) 874-8665 SIC 9111

COUNCIL INTERNATIONAL STUDY PROGRAMS INC (ISP) p 374
300 Fore St Fl 2 04101
Tel (207) 553-4000 SIC 8211

DIOCESE OF PORTLAND SCHOOL OFFICE p 440
510 Ocean Ave 04103
Tel (207) 773-6471 SIC 8211

DIVERSIFIED BUSINESS COMMUNICATIONS p 444
121 Free St 04101
Tel (207) 842-5400
SIC 4833 4841 2721 7389

EMERY-WATERHOUSE CO p 492
7 Rand Rd 04102
Tel (207) 775-2371 SIC 5072

GOODWILL INDUSTRIES OF NORTHERN NEW ENGLAND p 625
75 Washington Ave Ste 300 04101
Tel (207) 774-6323 SIC 8331 2392

■ HUNTER PANELS LLC p 719
15 Franklin St Ste B2 04101
Tel (888) 746-1114 SIC 3086

■ K & R HOLDINGS INC p 798
400 Warren Ave 04103
Tel (207) 797-7950 SIC 5033 3089

MAINE EMPLOYERS MUTUAL INSURANCE CO p 898
261 Commercial St 04101
Tel (207) 791-3300 SIC 6331

MAINE MEDICAL CENTER p 898
22 Bramhall St 04102
Tel (207) 662-0111 SIC 8062 8071 6513

MAINE TURNPIKE AUTHORITY p 898
2360 Congress St Ste 1 04102
Tel (207) 842-4030 SIC 4785

MAINEHEALTH p 898
110 Free St 04101
Tel (207) 661-7001 SIC 8741

MARTINS POINT HEALTH CARE INC p 913
331 Veranda St Ste 1 04103
Tel (207) 774-5801 SIC 8093

MERCY HOSPITAL p 947
144 State St 04101
Tel (207) 879-3000 SIC 8062

MTM OLDCO INC p 998
1 City Ctr Fl 5 04101
Tel (207) 791-6650 SIC 2711

NICHOLS PORTLAND LLC p 1042
2400 Congress St 04102
Tel (207) 774-6121 SIC 3714 8711

PORTLAND HOTEL GARDEN INN p 1163
145 Jetport Blvd 04102
Tel (207) 828-1117 SIC 7011

PORTLAND PUBLIC SCHOOL DISTRICT p 1163
353 Cumberland Ave 04101
Tel (207) 874-8100 SIC 8211

PORTLAND WATER DISTRICT p 1163
225 Douglass St 04102
Tel (207) 761-8310 SIC 4941 4952 8741

ROMAN CATHOLIC BISHOP OF PORTLAND p 1248
510 Ocean Ave 04103
Tel (207) 773-6471 SIC 8052 8661

TD BANK US HOLDING CO p 1428
2 Portland Sq 04101
Tel (207) 761-8500 SIC 6022

■ UNUM LIFE INSURANCE CO OF AMERICA p 1528
2211 Congress St 04122
Tel (207) 575-2211 SIC 6321

WOODARD & CURRAN INC p 1622
41 Hutchins Dr 04102
Tel (800) 426-4262 SIC 8711 8748

PRESQUE ISLE, ME

AROOSTOOK MEDICAL CENTER INC p 112
140 Academy St 04769
Tel (207) 768-4000 SIC 8062 8011 8052

MMG INSURANCE CO p 979
44 Maysville Rd 04769
Tel (207) 764-6611 SIC 6331

READFIELD, ME

SCHOOL UNION 42 CSD 10 p 1290
45 Millard Harrison Dr 04355
Tel (207) 685-3336 SIC 8211

ROCKPORT, ME

PEN BAY MEDICAL CENTER p 1128
6 Glen Cove Dr 04856
Tel (207) 921-8000 SIC 8062 8082

PENOBSCOT BAY MEDICAL CENTER p 1131
6 Glen Cove Dr 04856
Tel (207) 230-6380 SIC 8062 8059

SACO, ME

SURE WINNER FOODS INC p 1408
2 Lehner Rd 04072
Tel (207) 282-1258 SIC 5143 4226 2024

SANFORD, ME

HENRIETTA D GOODALL HOSPITAL INC p 684
25 June St 04073
Tel (207) 324-4310 SIC 8062

SCARBOROUGH, ME

HANNAFORD BROS CO LLC p 658
145 Pleasant Hill Rd 04074
Tel (207) 883-2911 SIC 5411 5912

HANNAFORD BROTHERS CO p 658
145 Pleasant Hill Rd 04074
Tel (207) 883-2911 SIC 5411 6519

MARTINS FOODS OF S BURLINGTON INC p 913
145 Pleasant Hill Rd 04074
Tel (207) 883-2911 SIC 5411

PROGRESSIVE DISTRIBUTORS INC p 1181
145 Pleasant Hill Rd 04074
Tel (207) 883-2911 SIC 5122 5149 5199

SOUTH PARIS, ME

CN BROWN CO p 329
1 C N Brown Way 04281
Tel (207) 743-9212 SIC 5411 5541 5983

SOUTH PORTLAND, ME

■ FAIRCHILD SEMICONDUCTOR CORP p 524
82 Running Hill Rd 04106
Tel (207) 775-8100 SIC 3674

FIRST ATLANTIC CORP p 545
100 Waterman Dr Ste 401 04106
Tel (207) 874-2700 SIC 8741

RESIDENTIAL MORTGAGE SERVICES INC p 1226
24 Christopher Toppi Dr 04106
Tel (207) 675-3609 SIC 6162

T D BANKNORTH INSURANCE GROUP p 1419
75 John Roberts Rd Bldg C 04106
Tel (207) 239-3500 SIC 6411

▲ WEX INC p 1603
97 Darling Ave 04106
Tel (207) 773-8171 SIC 7389 7375

STANDISH, ME

TRUSTEES OF ST JOSEPHS COLLEGE p 1488
278 Whites Bridge Rd 04084
Tel (207) 892-6766 SIC 8221

STILLWATER, ME

SARGENT CORP p 1282
378 Bennoch Rd 04489
Tel (207) 827-4435 SIC 1629

SC HOLDINGS INC p 1285
378 Bennoch Rd 04489
Tel (207) 827-4435 SIC 1629

TURNER, ME

AUSTIN JACK DE COSTER p 133
Plains Rd 04282
Tel (207) 224-8222 SIC 0252 0213 0723

NORTON SOUND HEALTH CORP p 1061
790 Lower St 04282
Tel (907) 443-3311
SIC 8062 8051 8069 8093 8011

WATERVILLE, ME

COLBY COLLEGE p 335
4000 Mayflower Hl 04901
Tel (207) 859-4000 SIC 8221

MAINE GENERAL MEDICAL CENTER INC p 898
149 North St 04901
Tel (207) 872-4190 SIC 8011

MARDENS INC p 905
184 College Ave 04901
Tel (207) 873-6111 SIC 5311

PRESIDENT AND TRUSTEES OF COLBY COLLEGE p 1172
4120 Mayflower Hl 04901
Tel (207) 859-4127 SIC 6733

WATERVILLE OSTEOPATHIC HEALTH CARE (INC) p 1582
200 Kennedy Memorial Dr 04901
Tel (207) 873-0731 SIC 8069

WESTBROOK, ME

▲ IDEXX LABORATORIES INC p 729
1 Idexx Dr 04092
Tel (207) 556-0300 SIC 3826 2834 5047

MAINE BEHAVIORAL HEALTHCARE p 898
123 Andover Rd 04092
Tel (207) 761-2200 SIC 8062

OLYMPIA SPORT CENTER INC p 1083
5 Bradley Dr 04092
Tel (207) 854-2794 SIC 5941

OSC SPORTS INC p 1096
5 Bradley Dr 04092
Tel (207) 854-2794 SIC 5699 5661 5941

■ SYSCO NORTHERN NEW ENGLAND INC p 1417
55 Thomas Dr 04092
Tel (207) 871-0700
SIC 5141 5147 5148 5142

WOOLWICH, ME

REED & REED INC p 1217
275 River Rd 04579
Tel (207) 443-9747 SIC 1622 1629 1541

YORK, ME

STONEWALL KITCHEN LLC p 1391
2 Stonewall Ln 03909
Tel (207) 351-2713
SIC 2033 2035 2032 5149 5064

YORK HOSPITAL p 1637
15 Hospital Dr 03909
Tel (207) 351-2023
SIC 8062 8051 8069 7361

MARYLAND

ABERDEEN PROVING GRO, MD

TWENTIETH SUPPORT COMMAND p 1494
2400 21st St Bush Rver Rd 21010
Tel (410) 436-0330 SIC 9711

ACCOKEEK, MD

BERETTA USA CORP p 174
17601 Beretta Dr 20607
Tel (301) 283-2191 SIC 5091 3484

ADELPHI, MD

UNIVERSITY OF MARYLAND UNIVERSITY COLLEGE ALUMNI ASSOCIATION INC p 1522
3501 University Blvd E # 105 20783
Tel (301) 985-7122 SIC 8221

UNIVERSITY SYSTEM OF MARYLAND p 1527
3300 Metzerott Rd 20783
Tel (301) 445-2740 SIC 8221

ANNAPOLIS JUNCTION, MD

CG ENTERPRISES INC p 285
12001 Guilford Rd Ste 1 20701
Tel (301) 953-3366 SIC 1611 1623

▲ COLFAX CORP p 336
420 Natl Bus Pkwy Fl 5 20701
Tel (301) 323-9000 SIC 3561 3829 3625

CORMAN CONSTRUCTION INC p 370
12001 Guilford Rd 20701
Tel (301) 953-0900 SIC 1611 1622 1623

CUMMINS-WAGNER CO INC p 401
10901 Pump House Rd 20701
Tel (410) 792-4230 SIC 5046

MSTC INC p 997
10900 Pump House Rd Ste B 20701
Tel (240) 280-8064 SIC 8742 8748

PRAXIS ENGINEERINGTECHNOLOGIES INC p 1168
135 Natl Bus Pkwy 20701
Tel (301) 490-4299 SIC 7371

TAYLOR FARMS MARYLAND INC p 1427
9055 Junction Dr 20701
Tel (301) 617-2942 SIC 5431 0723

ANNAPOLIS, MD

■ AERONAUTICAL RADIO INC p 30
2551 Riva Rd 21401
Tel (410) 266-4000 SIC 4812 4899

ANNE ARUNDEL COUNTY BOARD OF EDUCATION p 92
2644 Riva Rd 21401
Tel (410) 222-5000 SIC 8211

ANNE ARUNDEL COUNTY PUBLIC SCHOOLS p 92
2644 Riva Rd 21401
Tel (410) 222-5000 SIC 8211

ANNE ARUNDEL MEDICAL CENTER INC p 92
2001 Medical Pkwy 21401
Tel (443) 481-1000 SIC 8062

ANNE ARUNDEL MEDICAL CENTER INC p 92
2001 Medical Pkwy 21401
Tel (443) 481-1000 SIC 8062 8093 6732

■ ARINC INC p 108
2551 Riva Rd 21401
Tel (410) 266-4000 SIC 8711 4899

■ ARINC RESEARCH CORP p 108
2551 Riva Rd 21401
Tel (410) 266-4000 SIC 8711

CAPITAL FOREST PRODUCTS INC p 249
111 Gibralter Ave 21401
Tel (410) 280-6102 SIC 5031

CCE/DFS INC p 270
201 Defense Hwy Ste 202 21401
Tel (410) 263-6422 SIC 1542 8711 8744

▲ CHESAPEAKE LODGINGTRUST p 295
1997 Annapolis Exch Pkwy 21401
Tel (410) 972-4140 SIC 6798

CIRI - STROUP INC p 308
1 Park Pl Ste 200 21401
Tel (410) 267-6111 SIC 7299

COMPTROLLER OF MARYLAND OFFICE OF p 352
80 Calvert St L1 21401
Tel (410) 260-7801 SIC 9311

COUNTY OF ANNE ARUNDEL p 376
44 Calvert St Ste 1 21401
Tel (410) 222-1166 SIC 9111

COURT OF APPEALS MARYLAND STATE p 383
580 Taylor Ave 21401
Tel (410) 260-1500 SIC 9211

EXECUTIVE OFFICE OF STATE OF MARYLAND p 518
100 State Cir 21401
Tel (410) 974-3901 SIC 9111

■ FTI LLC p 583
909 Commerce Rd 21401
Tel (410) 224-8770 SIC 8621

HOTEL ACQUISITION CO LLC p 710
1997 Annapolis Exch Pkwy 21401
Tel (410) 268-0515 SIC 8741 7011

MARYLAND DEPARTMENT OF NATURAL RESOURCES p 914
580 Taylor Ave Bldg E3 21401
Tel (410) 260-8100 SIC 9512

PHYSICIAN ENTERPRISE LLC p 1145
2001 Medical Pkwy 21401
Tel (443) 481-6554 SIC 8011

■ RADIO HOLDINGS INC p 1204
2551 Riva Rd 21401
Tel (410) 266-4000 SIC 8711 4899

STATE OF MARYLAND p 1381
45 Calvert St Ste 1 21401
Tel (410) 974-3901 SIC 9111

STATE OF MARYLANDTREASURERS OFFICE p 1382
80 Calvert St 21401
Tel (800) 974-0468 SIC 9311

■TELECOMMUNICATION SYSTEMS INC p 1434
275 West St 21401
Tel (410) 263-7616 SIC 7373 4899

THAYER LODGING GROUP INC p 1446
1997 Annapolis Exchange P 21401
Tel (410) 268-0515 SIC 6799 6726

TOWNE PARK LLC p 1466
1 Park Pl Ste 200 21401
Tel (410) 267-6111 SIC 7521 4119

UNITED ASSOCIATION p 1506
3 Park Pl Ste 300 21401
Tel (410) 269-2000 SIC 8641

UNITED ASSOCIATION OF JOURNEYMEN & APPRENTICES OF PLUMBING & PIPEFITTERS p 1506
3 Park Pl 21401
Tel (410) 269-2000 SIC 8631

ARNOLD, MD

ANNE ARUNDEL COMMUNITY COLLEGE p 92
101 College Pkwy 21012
Tel (410) 777-2222 SIC 8222

BALTIMORE, MD

1132 TRUST LLC p 1
1 E Chase St Ste 1132a 21202
Tel (410) 601-3042 SIC 8741

ABACUS CORP p 9
610 Gusryan St 21224
Tel (410) 633-1900 SIC 7381 7363 7349

AEGON DIRECT MARKETING SERVICES INC p 29
100 Light St Fl B1 21202
Tel (410) 685-5500 SIC 6311 8011

AGORA INC p 35
14 W Mount Vernon Pl 21201
Tel (410) 783-8499 SIC 2741 7331

ALBAN TRACTOR CO INC p 45
8531 Pulaski Hwy 21237
Tel (410) 686-7777 SIC 5082 5084 7699

AMERICAN OFFICE EQUIPMENT CO INC p 77
309 N Calvert St 21202
Tel (410) 539-7529 SIC 5021

AMERICAN TRADING AND PRODUCTION CORP p 80
1 South St Ste 2800 21202
Tel (410) 347-7150 SIC 6552

AMERITOX LIMITED PARTNERSHIP p 84
300 E Lombard St Ste 1610 21202
Tel (443) 220-0115 SIC 7374 8734 8731

ANNIE E CASEY FOUNDATION INC p 92
701 Saint Paul St 21202
Tel (410) 547-6600 SIC 8322 8361

AON RISK SERVICES INC OF MARYLAND p 95
500 E Pratt St 21202
Tel (410) 547-2800 SIC 6411

ARCHDIOCESES OF BALTIMORE p 105
320 Cathedral St Ste 1 21201
Tel (410) 547-5442 SIC 8211

ASPLUNDISH TREE EXPERT CO p 119
4070 North Point Rd 21222
Tel (443) 242-6666 SIC 0783

ASSOCIATED CATHOLIC CHARITIES INC p 120
320 Cathedral St 21201
Tel (410) 561-6363 SIC 8322

ATLANTIC FOREST PRODUCTS LLC p 126
240 W Dickman St 21230
Tel (410) 752-8092 SIC 5031

AWM LLC p 139
1800 Washington Blvd # 140 21230
Tel (916) 387-7317 SIC 5031

B GREEN & CO INC p 142
1300 S Monroe St Ste 1 21230
Tel (410) 783-7777 SIC 5141

BALTIMORE CITY PUBLIC SCHOOL SYSTEMS (INC) p 149
200 E North Ave 21202
Tel (410) 222-5000 SIC 8211

■ BALTIMORE GAS AND ELECTRIC CO p 149
110 W Fayette St 21201
Tel (410) 234-5000 SIC 4931

■ BALTIMORE SUN CO p 149
501 N Calvert St 21278
Tel (410) 539-7700 SIC 2711

BERGER GROUP HOLDINGS INC p 174
111 Market Pl 21202
Tel (410) 468-4054 SIC 8711 8732 8712

■ BGE HOME PRODUCTS AND SERVICES INC p 180
1409 Tangier Dr Ste A 21220
Tel (410) 918-5600 SIC 5722

BHS CORRUGATED - NORTH AMERICA INC p 180
9103 Yellow Brick Rd N 21237
Tel (410) 574-1550 SIC 5084 7699 3316

BON SECOURS BALTIMORE HEALTH CORP p 199
2000 W Baltimore St 21223
Tel (410) 362-3000 SIC 8062

BON SECOURS BALTIMORE HEALTH SYTEM p 199
2000 W Baltimore St 21223
Tel (410) 362-3000 SIC 8051

BON SECOURS HOSPITAL BALTIMORE INC p 199
2000 W Baltimore St 21223
Tel (410) 362-3000 SIC 8062

■ BRAVO HEALTH LLC p 209
3601 Odonnell St 21224
Tel (800) 235-9188 SIC 6321

BROADWAY SERVICES INC p 216
3709 E Monument St 21205
Tel (410) 563-6900
SIC 7349 7381 7521 6512 4119

BROWN ADVISORY HOLDINGS INC p 219
901 S Bond St Ste 400 21231
Tel (410) 537-5400 SIC 6282

BROWN ADVISORY LLC p 219
901 S Bond St Ste 400 21231
Tel (410) 537-5487 SIC 6211

CALLISONRTKL INC p 242
901 S Bond St 21231
Tel (410) 537-6000 SIC 8712

■ CALVERT CLIFFS NUCLEAR POWER PLANT INC p 243
750 E Pratt St 21202
Tel (410) 495-4600 SIC 4911

CAMPBELL & CO INC p 245
2850 Quarry Lake Dr # 302 21209
Tel (410) 413-2600 SIC 6221

CAMPBELL FUND TRUST p 245
2850 Quarry Lake Dr 21209
Tel (410) 413-2600 SIC 6221

CARE SOURCE LLC p 254
9114 Philadelphia Rd # 214 21237
Tel (410) 391-2627 SIC 7361

CARROLL INDEPENDENT FUEL LLC p 261
2700 Loch Raven Rd 21218
Tel (410) 235-1066 SIC 5172 5983

CATHOLIC RELIEF SERVICES - UNITED STATES CONFERENCE OF CATHOLIC BISHOPS p 267
228 W Lexington St 21201
Tel (410) 625-2220 SIC 8322

■ CENTERS FOR MEDICARE AND MEDICAID SERVICES p 276
7500 Sec Blvd Ms C31103 21244
Tel (410) 786-3000 SIC 9431

CENTRAL SERVICES OF ROMAN CATHOLIC ARCHBISHOP OF BALTIMORE (INC) p 280
320 Cathedral St 21201
Tel (410) 547-5555 SIC 8661

CHARLESTOWN COMMUNITY INC p 290
719 Maiden Choice Ln 21228
Tel (410) 737-8830 SIC 6513 8051

CHIMES DISTRICT OF COLUMBIA INC p 300
4815 Seton Dr 21215
Tel (410) 358-5193 SIC 8331

■ CITIFINANCIAL CREDIT CO p 310
300 Saint Paul St Fl 3 21202
Tel (410) 332-3000
SIC 6141 6162 7389 6331 6159 6022

CITY OF BALTIMORE p 313
100 Holliday St Ste 250 21202
Tel (410) 396-3835 SIC 9111

CLOVERLAND DAIRY LIMITED PARTNERSHIP p 328
2701 Loch Raven Rd 21218
Tel (410) 235-4477 SIC 2026

■ COMCAST CABLEVISION p 343
8031 Corporate Dr 21236
Tel (410) 931-4600 SIC 4841

COMILOG US INC p 344
610 Pittman Rd 21226
Tel (410) 789-8800 SIC 2819 3313 3356

COMMERCE LLC p 345
7603 Energy Pkwy 21226
Tel (410) 255-3500 SIC 5191 5072 5199

COMMUNITY COLLEGE OF BALTIMORE COUNTY p 348
7200 Sollers Point Rd 21222
Tel (443) 840-3620 SIC 8222

CONNECTION EDUCATION INC p 357
1001 Fleet St Fl 5 21202
Tel (443) 529-1000 SIC 6719

CONNECTIONS EDUCATION LLC p 357
1001 Fleet St Fl 5 21202
Tel (443) 529-1000 SIC 8299

CONSTELLATION ENERGY GROUP INC p 361
100 Constellation Way 21202
Tel (410) 470-2800 SIC 4911 4924 1711

■ CONSTELLATION ENERGY NUCLEAR GROUP LLC p 361
100 Constellation Way 200c 21202
Tel (410) 783-2800 SIC 4911

■ CONSTELLATION ENERGY RESOURCES LLC p 361
750 E Pratt St 21202
Tel (410) 470-2800 SIC 4911 4924

■ CONSTELLATION NEWENERGY INC p 361
1310 Point St Fl 9 21231
Tel (410) 783-2800 SIC 4911 8748

■ CONSTELLATION NUCLEAR SERVICES L L C p 361
39 W Lexington St 21201
Tel (410) 234-7950 SIC 4911

COUNTY OF BALTIMORE p 376
400 Washington Ave Rm 100 21204
Tel (410) 887-2008 SIC 9111

COWAN SYSTEMS LLC p 385
4555 Hollins Ferry Rd 21227
Tel (410) 247-0800 SIC 4213

CROWN CENTRAL PETROLEUM CORP p 395
1 N Charles St Ste 2100 21201
Tel (410) 539-7400 SIC 2911 5171 6794

D-S PIPE & STEEL SUPPLY LLC p 407
1301 Wicomico St Ste 3 21230
Tel (410) 837-1717 SIC 5085 5051

DANFOSS LLC p 411
11655 Crossroads Cir A 21220
Tel (410) 931-8250 SIC 3585 3625 3822

DLA PIPER LLP (US) p 445
6225 Smith Ave Ste 200 21209
Tel (410) 580-3000 SIC 8111

DOME CORP p 448
1101 E 33rd St Ste E100 21218
Tel (443) 997-3737 SIC 8741

E2 ACQUISITION CORP p 467
1430 Sparrows Point Blvd 21219
Tel (410) 388-3000 SIC 3325

EDGE ACQUISITION LLC p 477
1001 Fleet St 21202
Tel (410) 843-8000 SIC 8299 8748

EDUCATION AFFILIATES INC p 479
5026 Campbell Blvd 21236
Tel (410) 633-2929 SIC 8221

EDUCATION AFFILIATES LLC p 479
5204 Campbell Blvd Ste A 21236
Tel (410) 633-2929 SIC 8222 6211

■ ELLICOTT DREDGE ENTERPRISES LLC p 488
1611 Bush St 21230
Tel (410) 625-0808 SIC 3731

■ ELLICOTT DREDGES LLC p 488
1611 Bush St 21230
Tel (410) 625-0808 SIC 3731

ENVIRONMENT MARYLAND DEPARTMENT OF p 503
1800 Washington Blvd A 21230
Tel (410) 537-3000 SIC 9511

FAST FARE INC p 531
1 N Charles St 21201
Tel (410) 539-7400 SIC 5411 5541

■ FIDELITY & GUARANTY LIFE INSURANCE CO p 540
1001 Fleet St Fl 7 21202
Tel (410) 895-0100 SIC 6311

FIRST AUSA LIFE INSURANCE CO p 545
1111 N Charles St 21201
Tel (410) 576-4571 SIC 6311

FOREST HAVEN NURSING & CONVALE p 566
315 Ingleside Ave 21228
Tel (410) 747-7425 SIC 8051

FRANKLIN SQUARE HOSPITAL CENTER INC p 575
9000 Franklin Square Dr 21237
Tel (410) 933-2777 SIC 8062 8011

FREDERICK P WINNER LTD p 576
7001 Quad Ave 21237
Tel (410) 646-5500 SIC 5181 5182

GEORGE J FALTER CO p 606
3501 Benson Ave 21227
Tel (410) 646-3641
SIC 5194 5145 5141 5015

GOOD SAMARITAN HOSPITAL OF MD INC p 623
5601 Loch Raven Blvd 21239
Tel (443) 444-3780 SIC 8062 8741

GOUCHER COLLEGE p 626
1021 Dulaney Valley Rd 21204
Tel (410) 337-6000 SIC 8221

GREATER BALTIMORE MEDICAL CENTER INC p 635
6701 N Charles St 21204
Tel (410) 849-2000 SIC 8062 8011

GREATER BALTIMORE MEDICAL CENTER LAND CORP p 635
6701 N Charles St 21204
Tel (443) 849-2000 SIC 8062

H & S BAKERY INC p 649
601 S Caroline St 21231
Tel (410) 558-3050 SIC 2051

HARBOR HOSPITAL CENTER INC p 659
3001 S Hanover St 21225
Tel (410) 350-3200 SIC 8062

HARBOR HOSPITAL FOUNDATION INC p 659
3001 S Hanover St 21225
Tel (410) 350-2563 SIC 8062

HEALTHSOURCE DISTRIBUTORS LLC p 677
7200 Rutherford Rd # 150 21244
Tel (410) 653-1113 SIC 5122

HOLLY POULTRY INC p 701
2221 Berlin St 21230
Tel (410) 727-6210 SIC 5144 5147

HOPKINS JOHNS MEDICAL SERVICES CORP p 706
3100 Wyman Park Dr 21211
Tel (410) 338-3071 SIC 8011 8741

JENSEN HUGHES INC p 782
3610 Commerce Dr Ste 817 21227
Tel (410) 737-8677 *SIC* 8748 8711 8734

JHPIEGO CORP p 785
1615 Thames St Ste 310 21231
Tel (410) 537-1800 *SIC* 8299

JOHNS HOPKINS BAYVIEW MEDICAL CENTER INC p 790
4940 Eastern Ave 21224
Tel (410) 550-0100 *SIC* 8062 8051

JOHNS HOPKINS HEALTH SYS CORP p 790
600 N Wolfe St 21287
Tel (410) 955-5000 *SIC* 8062

JOHNS HOPKINS HOSPITAL p 790
1800 Orleans St 21287
Tel (410) 550-0730 *SIC* 8062

JOHNS HOPKINS MEDICINE INTERNATIONAL LLC p 790
600 N Wolfe St 21287
Tel (410) 955-1725 *SIC* 8062 8221

JOHNS HOPKINS UNIVERSITY p 790
3400 N Charles St 21218
Tel (410) 516-8000 *SIC* 8221

KENNEDY KRIEGER CHILDRENS HOSPITAL INC p 811
707 N Broadway 21205
Tel (443) 923-9400 *SIC* 8069

KENNEDY KRIEGER INSTITUTE INC p 811
707 N Broadway 21205
Tel (443) 923-9200 *SIC* 8069

LAFARGE MID-ATLANTIC LLC p 837
300 E Joppa Rd Ste 200 21286
Tel (410) 847-9445 *SIC* 3273 1422

LAUREATE EDUCATION INC p 847
650 S Exeter St Fl 7 21202
Tel (410) 843-6100 *SIC* 8299

▲ LEGG MASON INC p 853
100 International Dr 21202
Tel (410) 539-0000 *SIC* 6282 6211 6162

LIFEBRIDGE HEALTH INC p 864
2401 W Belvedere Ave 21215
Tel (410) 601-5653 *SIC* 8062

LOYOLA UNIVERSITY MARYLAND INC p 882
5000 York Rd Ste 200 21212
Tel (410) 617-2000 *SIC* 8221

LUPIN PHARMACEUTICALS INC p 886
111 S Calvert St Fl 21 21202
Tel (410) 576-2000 *SIC* 5122

LYON CONKLIN & CO INC p 888
4501 Hollins Ferry Rd # 140 21227
Tel (410) 540-4880 *SIC* 5075 5051

M-L HOLDINGS CO p 890
4601 Washington Blvd 21227
Tel (410) 242-6500 *SIC* 5082 6719

MARS SUPER MARKETS INC p 910
9627 Philadelphia Rd # 100 21237
Tel (410) 590-0500 *SIC* 5411

MARYLAND DEPARTMENT OF HEALTH & MENTAL HYGIENE p 914
201 W Preston St Fl 5 21201
Tel (410) 767-6500 *SIC* 9431

MARYLAND DEPARTMENT OF HUMAN RESOURCES p 914
311 W Saratoga St 21201
Tel (410) 767-7109 *SIC* 9441

MARYLAND DEPARTMENT OF JUVENILE SERVICES p 914
120 W Fayette St 21201
Tel (410) 230-3333 *SIC* 9223

MARYLAND ECONOMIC DEVELOPMENT CORP p 914
300 E Lombard St Ste 1000 21202
Tel (410) 727-8049 *SIC* 8742

MARYLAND GENERAL HOSPITAL INC p 915
827 Linden Ave 21201
Tel (410) 225-8000 *SIC* 8062

MARYLAND INSTITUTE p 915
1300 W Mount Royal Ave 21217
Tel (410) 383-2063 *SIC* 8221

MARYLAND STATE DEPARTMENT OF EDUCATION p 915
200 W Baltimore St 21201
Tel (410) 767-0462 *SIC* 9411

MARYLAND TRASPORTATION AUTHORITY p 915
2400 Ste 115 21224
Tel (410) 537-5710 *SIC* 4785

MEDSTAR GOOD SAMARITAN HOSPITAL p 939
5601 Loch Raven Blvd 21239
Tel (443) 444-4100 *SIC* 8062 8011

MERCY MEDICAL CENTER INC p 947
345 Saint Paul St 21202
Tel (410) 332-9000 *SIC* 8062 8011

MILES & STOCKBRIDGE PC p 969
100 Light St Fl 5 21202
Tel (410) 385-3671 *SIC* 8111

■ MILLENNIAL MEDIA INC p 970
2400 Boston St Ste 300 21224
Tel (410) 522-8705 *SIC* 7319 7371

MITCHELL BEVERAGE OF MARYLAND LLC p 977
7001 Quad Ave 21237
Tel (410) 646-5500 *SIC* 5181 5182

MORGAN STATE UNIVERSITY p 989
1700 E Cold Spring Ln 21251
Tel (443) 885-3015 *SIC* 8221

■ MRA SYSTEMS INC p 996
103 Chesapeake Park Plz 21220
Tel (410) 682-1500 *SIC* 3728

NATIONAL ASSOCIATION FOR ADVANCEMENT OF COLORED PEOPLE p 1009
4805 Mount Hope Dr 21215
Tel (410) 358-8900 *SIC* 8641

■ NATIONSBANK NA (INC) p 1017
100 S Charles St Ste 207 21201
Tel (410) 605-5000 *SIC* 6021 6531

NEW RIDGE ASSOCIATES INC p 1033
2700 Loch Raven Rd 21218
Tel (410) 859-3636 *SIC* 5411

NORTHEAST FOODS INC p 1054
601 S Caroline St 21231
Tel (410) 276-7254 *SIC* 2051 5149

NORTHEASTERN SUPPLY INC p 1055
8323 Pulaski Hwy 21237
Tel (410) 574-0010 *SIC* 5074

OAK CREST VILLAGE INC p 1070
8800 Walther Blvd Ste 1 21234
Tel (410) 665-2222 *SIC* 8051 8052 8059

■ ONEMAIN FINANCIAL GROUP LLC p 1087
100 Intl Dr 15000 21202
Tel (855) 663-6246 *SIC* 6141

■ ONEMAIN FINANCIAL HOLDINGS LLC p 1087
100 Intl Dr Ste 15000 21202
Tel (410) 332-3000 *SIC* 6162 6163

P FLANIGAN AND SONS INC p 1102
2444 Loch Raven Rd 21218
Tel (410) 467-5900 *SIC* 1611

PANDORA JEWELRY LLC p 1111
250 W Pratt St 21201
Tel (410) 309-0200 *SIC* 5094

PIMLICO RACING ASSOCIATION INC p 1148
5201 Park Heights Ave 21215
Tel (410) 542-9400 *SIC* 7948

PROMETRIC INC p 1183
1501 S Clinton St # 1200 21224
Tel (443) 455-8000 *SIC* 8748 8741

■ RAVEN POWER OPERATING LLC p 1209
1000 Brandon Shores Rd 21226
Tel (410) 255-3072 *SIC* 4911

RELIABLE CHURCHILL LLLP p 1221
1413 Tangier Dr 21220
Tel (410) 439-5000 *SIC* 5182

REMEDI SENIORCARE OF MARYLAND LLC p 1222
9006 Yellow Brick Rd 21237
Tel (443) 927-8400 *SIC* 5122

RIGGS COUNSELMAN MICHAELS & DOWNES INC p 1234
555 Fairmount Ave 21286
Tel (410) 339-7263 *SIC* 6411

ROSEMORE HOLDINGS INC p 1251
1 N Charles St Ste 2200 21201
Tel (410) 347-7090
SIC 2911 5171 5541 5411

ROSEMORE INC p 1251
1 N Charles St Ste 2200 21201
Tel (410) 347-7080 *SIC* 5541

RUBIN INSTITUTE FOR ADVANCED ORTHOPEDICS p 1257
2401 W Belvedere Ave 21215
Tel (410) 601-9000 *SIC* 8062

RUMMEL KLEPPER & KAHL LLP p 1257
81 Mosher St 21217
Tel (410) 728-2900
SIC 8711 8741 1623 8999 8713 1611

RUSSEL MOTOR CARS INC p 1259
6700 Baltimore Nat Pike 21228
Tel (410) 788-8400
SIC 5511 7538 7532 5521

SCHMIDT BAKING CO INC p 1287
7801 Fitch Ln 21236
Tel (410) 668-8200 *SIC* 2051

SHELTER DEVELOPMENT LLC p 1314
218 N Charles St Ste 220 21201
Tel (410) 962-0595 *SIC* 6552

SHEPHERD ELECTRIC CO INC p 1315
7401 Pulaski Hwy 21237
Tel (410) 866-6000 *SIC* 5063

SHEPPARD PRATT HEALTH SYSTEM INC p 1315
6501 N Charles St 21204
Tel (410) 938-3000 *SIC* 8741 8062

SINAI HOSPITAL OF BALTIMORE INC p 1326
2401 W Belvedere Ave 21215
Tel (410) 601-5678 *SIC* 8062

■ SOCIAL SECURITY ADMINISTRATION p 1336
6401 Security Blvd 21235
Tel (410) 965-8882 *SIC* 9441

ST AGNES HEALTHCARE INC p 1364
900 S Caton Ave 21229
Tel (667) 234-6000 *SIC* 8062

STATE OF MARYLAND p 1381
2901 Liberty Heights Ave 21215
Tel (410) 462-8300 *SIC* 8222

STERLING PARTNERS LLC p 1387
650 S Exeter St Ste 1000 21202
Tel (443) 703-1700 *SIC* 6211

STRUEVER BROS ECCLES & ROUSE INC p 1394
2400 Boston St Ste 404 21224
Tel (443) 573-4000 *SIC* 1542 1522

SYNAGRO TECHNOLOGIES INC p 1414
435 Williams Ct Ste 100 21220
Tel (800) 370-0035 *SIC* 4953

■T ROWE PRICE ASSOCIATES INC p 1420
100 E Pratt St 21202
Tel (410) 345-2000 *SIC* 6799

▲T ROWE PRICE GROUP INC p 1420
100 E Pratt St 21202
Tel (410) 345-2000 *SIC* 6282

TOWSON UNIVERSITY p 1466
8000 York Rd 21252
Tel (410) 704-2000 *SIC* 8221

TWO FARMS INC p 1495
3611 Roland Ave 21211
Tel (410) 889-0200 *SIC* 5411

▲ UNDER ARMOUR INC p 1502
1020 Hull St Ste 300 21230
Tel (410) 454-6428
SIC 2329 2353 2339 3021

UNION MEMORIAL HOSPITAL p 1504
201 E University Pkwy 21218
Tel (410) 554-2865 *SIC* 8062

UNIVERSITY OF MARYLAND p 1522
220 Arch St Fl 14 21201
Tel (410) 706-2929 *SIC* 8221 8299

UNIVERSITY OF MARYLAND BALTIMORE COUNTY p 1522
1000 Hilltop Cir 21250
Tel (410) 455-2695 *SIC* 8221

UNIVERSITY OF MARYLAND MEDICAL SYSTEM CORP p 1522
22 S Greene St 21201
Tel (410) 328-8667 *SIC* 8011

UNIVERSITY OF MARYLAND MIDTOWN HEALTH INC p 1522
827 Linden Ave 21201
Tel (410) 225-8000 *SIC* 8062

VENABLE LLP p 1547
750 E Pratt St Ste 900 21202
Tel (410) 244-7400 *SIC* 8111

WHITING-TURNER CONTRACTING CO p 1607
300 E Joppa Rd Ste 800 21286
Tel (410) 821-1100
SIC 1542 1541 1629 8741

WILLIAMS SCOTSMAN INC p 1611
901 S Bond St Ste 600 21231
Tel (410) 931-6000
SIC 1531 1541 5039 7359

WILLIAMS SCOTSMAN INTERNATIONAL INC p 1611
901 S Bond St Ste 600 21231
Tel (800) 782-1500 *SIC* 4225

WM T BURNETT HOLDING LLC p 1620
1500 Bush St 21230
Tel (410) 837-3000 *SIC* 2299 3086

YMCA OF CENTRAL MARYLAND INC p 1636
303 W Chesapeake Ave 21204
Tel (443) 322-9622 *SIC* 8641 8351

BEL AIR, MD

COUNTY OF HARFORD p 378
220 S Main St 21014
Tel (410) 638-3314 *SIC* 9111

HARFORD COUNTY BOARD OF EDUCATION (INC) p 661
102 S Hickory Ave 21014
Tel (410) 838-7300 *SIC* 8211

HARFORD COUNTY PUBLIC SCHOOL DISTRICT p 661
102 S Hickory Ave 21014
Tel (410) 838-7300 *SIC* 8211

HARFORD MUTUAL INSURANCE CO p 661
200 N Main St 21014
Tel (410) 879-2360 *SIC* 6331

UPPER CHESAPEAKE HEALTH FOUNDATION INC p 1529
520 Upper Chesapeake 40 Ste 405 21014
Tel (443) 643-1500 *SIC* 8062

UPPER CHESAPEAKE MEDICAL CENTER INC p 1529
500 Upper Chesapeake Dr 21014
Tel (443) 643-1000 *SIC* 8062

BELCAMP, MD

■ LIFOAM INDUSTRIES LLC p 865
9999 E 121st 21017
Tel (866) 770-3626 *SIC* 3086

SAFENET HOLDING CORP p 1266
4690 Millennium Dr 21017
Tel (410) 931-7500 *SIC* 7371

SAFENET INC p 1266
4690 Millennium Dr # 400 21017
Tel (410) 931-7500 *SIC* 7371

UNITED SOURCE ONE INC p 1511
4610 Mercedes Dr Ste 110 21017
Tel (410) 278-0800 *SIC* 5147 5087

BELTSVILLE, MD

■ AGRICULTURAL RESEARCH SERVICE p 36
5601 Sunnyside Ave 20705
Tel (301) 504-1147 *SIC* 9641

ALARM SECURITY GROUP LLC p 44
12301 Kiln Ct Ste A 20705
Tel (301) 623-4000 *SIC* 7382

ASRC AEROSPACE CORP p 119
7000 Muirkirk Meadows Dr # 100 20705
Tel (301) 837-5500
SIC 3812 7371 7373 5088

ASRC COMMUNICATIONS LTD p 119
7000 Muirkirk Meadows Dr 20705
Tel (301) 837-5500 *SIC* 4813

ASRC FEDERAL HOLDING CO LLC p 119
7000 Muirkirk Meadows Dr # 100 20705
Tel (301) 345-4500 *SIC* 7379

■ ATK SPACE SYSTEMS INC p 125
11310 Frederick Ave 20705
Tel (301) 595-5500 *SIC* 8711

DISTRICT PHOTO INC p 443
10501 Rhode Island Ave 20705
Tel (301) 595-5300 *SIC* 7384 5043 5946

JE RICHARDS INC p 781
10401 Tucker St 20705
Tel (301) 345-1300 *SIC* 1731

MANGANARO MIDATLANTIC LLC p 901
6405d Ammendale Rd 20705
Tel (301) 937-0580 *SIC* 1741 1742 1799

PRIMUS SOLUTIONS LLC p 1176
7000 Muirkirk Meadows Dr # 100 20705
Tel (301) 345-5500 *SIC* 7379

VOCUS INC p 1564
12051 Indian Creek Ct 20705
Tel (301) 459-2590 *SIC* 7371 7372

W E BOWERS & ASSOCIATES INC p 1568
12401a Kiln Ct Ste A 20705
Tel (800) 989-0011 *SIC* 1711

WE BOWERS INC p 1585
12401 Kiln Ct Ste A 20705
Tel (301) 419-2488 *SIC* 1711

BERLIN, MD

ATLANTIC GENERAL HOSPITAL CORP p 126
9733 Healthway Dr 21811
Tel (410) 641-1100 *SIC* 8062

PENNINSULA REGIONAL MEDICAL CENTER p 1130
10514 Racetrack Rd Ste C 21811
Tel (410) 641-8585 *SIC* 8011

BETHESDA, MD

ACACIA LIFE INSURANCE CO p 13
7315 Wisconsin Ave 1000w 20814
Tel (301) 280-1000
SIC 6311 6411 6035 6282 6211

▲ AGNC INVESTMENT CORP p 35
2 Bethesda Metro Ctr # 12 20814
Tel (301) 968-9315 *SIC* 6798

▲ AMERICAN CAPITAL LTD p 69
2 Bethesda Metro Ctr # 14 20814
Tel (301) 951-6122 *SIC* 6726

B F SAUL CO p 141
7501 Wisconsin Ave 20814
Tel (301) 986-6000 *SIC* 6531 6411

B F SAUL REAL ESTATE INVESTMENT TRUST p 141
7501 Wscnsin Ave Ste 1500 20814
Tel (301) 657-2619 *SIC* 6512 6513

BETHESDA INVESTMENT HOLDING CO INC p 178
10400 Auto Park Ave 20817
Tel (301) 469-6600
SIC 5511 7539 5013 5531

BF SAUL PROPERTY CO p 179
7501 Wisconsin Ave 20814
Tel (301) 986-6000
SIC 6531 6519 1542 1522

CENTERS FOR ADVANCED ORTHOPAEDICS LLC p 276
6707 Democracy Blvd # 504 20817
Tel (301) 637-8710 *SIC* 8011

▲ CENTRUS ENERGY CORP p 281
6901 Rockledge Dr Ste 800 20817
Tel (301) 564-3200 *SIC* 1094

■ CHEVY CHASE BANK FSB p 296
7501 Wisconsin Ave Fl 11 20814
Tel (240) 497-4101
SIC 6035 6411 6211 6519 6552 6719

CHINDEX INTERNATIONAL INC p 301
4340 East West Hwy # 1100 20814
Tel (301) 215-7777 *SIC* 5047 8062

CLARK CONSTRUCTION GROUP LLC p 322
7500 Old Georgetown Rd # 15 20814
Tel (301) 272-8100 *SIC* 1542 1611 1522

CLARK CONSTRUCTION LLC p 322
7500 Old Georgetown Rd # 1500 20814
Tel (301) 272-8337 *SIC* 1542

CLARK ENTERPRISES INC p 322
7500 Old Georgetown Rd # 7 20814
Tel (301) 657-7100
SIC 6552 4832 7359 1521 1542 6726

COAKLEY & WILLIAMS CONSTRUCTION INC p 331
7475 Wisconsin Ave # 900 20814
Tel (301) 963-5000 *SIC* 1542

■ COURTYARD MANAGEMENT CORP p 383
10400 Fernwood Rd 20817
Tel (301) 380-3000 *SIC* 7011

■ COVENTRY HEALTH CARE INC p 385
6720 Rockledge Dr 700b 20817
Tel (301) 581-0600 *SIC* 6324

CROSSROADS HOSPITALITY CO LLC p 394
6430 Rockland Dr 20817
Tel (301) 581-5900 *SIC* 7011

CYSTIC FIBROSIS FOUNDATION p 406
6931 Arlington Rd Fl 2 20814
Tel (301) 951-4422 *SIC* 8733 8399

DAI GLOBAL LLC p 408
7600 Wisconsin Ave # 200 20814
Tel (301) 771-7600 *SIC* 8748

▲ DIAMONDROCK HOSPITALITY CO p 437
3 Bethesda Metro Ctr # 1500 20814
Tel (240) 744-1150 *SIC* 6798

DIGITAL MANAGEMENT LLC p 439
6550 Rock Spring Dr Fl 7 20817
Tel (240) 223-4800 *SIC* 7371

▲ EAGLE BANCORP INC p 467
7830 Old Georgtwn Rd Fl 3 20814
Tel (301) 986-1800 *SIC* 6022

■ EAGLEBANK p 468
7830 Old Georgtwn Rd Fl 3 20814
Tel (301) 986-1800 *SIC* 6022

ECO GSI CONSTRUCTION AND MAINTENANCE LLC p 475
6917 Arlington Rd 20814
Tel (240) 832-8035 *SIC* 7349

ENVIVA PARTNERS LP p 504
7200 Wscnsin Ave Ste 1000 20814
Tel (301) 657-5660 *SIC* 2421

ESCAL INSTITUTE OF ADVANCED TECHNOLOGIES INC p 509
8120 Woodmont Ave Ste 310 20814
Tel (301) 951-0102 *SIC* 8732

EURO MOTORCARS INC p 512
7020 Arlington Rd 20814
Tel (888) 250-2987 *SIC* 5511

FIDELIS CYBERSECURITY INC p 540
4416 East West Hwy # 310 20814
Tel (617) 275-8800 *SIC* 7373

FIRST POTOMAC REALTY TRUST p 549
7600 Wisconsin Ave # 1100 20814
Tel (301) 986-9200 *SIC* 6798

GETWELLNETWORK INC p 609
7700 Old Georgetown Rd # 4 20814
Tel (240) 482-3200 *SIC* 7371

GIFT COLLECTION INC p 611
6905 Rockledge Dr Fl 1 20817
Tel (240) 694-4100 *SIC* 6512 5812

HENRY M JACKSON FOUNDATION FOR ADVANCEMENT OF MILITARY MEDICINE INC p 684
6720a Rockledge Dr # 100 20817
Tel (240) 694-2000 *SIC* 8099

HMSHOST CORP p 698
6905 Rockledge Dr Fl 1 20817
Tel (240) 694-4100
SIC 5812 5813 5994 5947

▲ HOST HOTELS & RESORTS INC p 710
6903 Rockledge Dr # 1500 20817
Tel (240) 744-1000 *SIC* 6798 7011

■ HOST HOTELS & RESORTS LP p 710
6903 Rockledge Dr # 1500 20817
Tel (240) 744-1000 *SIC* 6798 7011

HOST INTERNATIONAL INC p 710
6905 Rockledge Dr Fl 1 20817
Tel (240) 694-4100
SIC 5812 5813 5994 5947

HOST MARRIOTT SERVICES INC p 710
6711 Democracy Blvd 20817
Tel (240) 344-1000 *SIC* 7011

INTERNATIONAL BACCALAUREATE ORGANIZATION INC p 754
7501 Wisconsin Ave # 200 20814
Tel (301) 202-3000 *SIC* 8299

LASALLE HOTEL OPERATING PARTNERSHIP LP p 846
7550 Wisconsin Ave Fl 10 20814
Tel (301) 941-1500 *SIC* 8741

LASALLE HOTEL PROPERTIES p 846
7550 Wisconsin Ave # 100 20814
Tel (301) 941-1500 *SIC* 6798

▲ LOCKHEED MARTIN CORP p 873
6801 Rockledge Dr 20817
Tel (301) 897-6000
SIC 3761 3721 3663 3764 3812 3728

■ LOCKHEED MARTIN GLOBAL TELECOMMUNICATIONS LLC p 873
6560 Rock Spring Dr 20817
Tel (301) 571-7135 *SIC* 4813

■ LOCKHEED MARTIN INTEGRATED SYSTEMS INC p 873
6801 Rockledge Dr 20817
Tel (856) 486-5000 *SIC* 3812

LODGING RLJ TRUST L P p 874
3 Bethesda Metro Ctr # 1000 20814
Tel (301) 280-7777 *SIC* 7011

▲ MARRIOTT INTERNATIONAL INC p 910
10400 Fernwood Rd 20817
Tel (301) 380-3000 *SIC* 7011 6794 6531

■ MARRIOTT WORLDWIDE CORP p 910
10400 Fernwood Rd 20817
Tel (301) 634-5100 *SIC* 7011

■ MARRIOTT WORLDWIDE SALES AND MARKETING INC p 910
10400 Fernwood Rd 20817
Tel (301) 634-5100 *SIC* 8741

MILLER & LONG CO INC p 970
4824 Rugby Ave 20814
Tel (301) 657-8000 *SIC* 1771

▲ MTGE INVESTMENT CORP p 998
2 Bethesda Metro Ctr # 14 20814
Tel (301) 968-9220 *SIC* 6798

■ NATIONAL GEOSPATIAL-INTELLIGENCE AGENCY p 1012
4600 Sangamore Rd 20816
Tel (703) 262-4316 *SIC* 9711

■ NATIONAL INSTITUTES OF HEALTH p 1013
9000 Rockville Pike # 1 20892
Tel (301) 496-4000 *SIC* 8062 9431

PALISADES ASSOCIATES HOLDING INC p 1108
9140 Vendome Dr 20817
Tel (301) 469-7564 *SIC* 6719

PEBBLEBROOK HOTEL TRUST p 1126
7315 Wisconsin Ave 1100w 20814
Tel (240) 507-1300 *SIC* 6798

PERSEUS LLC p 1137
4350 East West Hwy # 202 20814
Tel (301) 652-3200 *SIC* 6799

■ RC MARRIOTT II INC p 1212
10400 Fernwood Rd 20817
Tel (301) 333-3333 *SIC* 7011

RED COATS INC p 1215
4520 East West Hwy # 200 20814
Tel (301) 654-4360 *SIC* 7349 7381

RENAISSANCE HOTEL OPERATING CO INC p 1223
10400 Fernwood Rd 20817
Tel (301) 380-3000 *SIC* 7011 8741 6794

■ RESIDENCE INN BY MARRIOTT LLC p 1226
10400 Fernwood Rd 20817
Tel (301) 380-3000 *SIC* 7011

RETAIL SERVICES & SYSTEMS INC p 1228
6600 Rockledge Dr Ste 150 20817
Tel (301) 795-1000 *SIC* 5921

RLJ LODGING TRUST p 1239
3 Bethesda Metro Ctr 20814
Tel (301) 280-7777 *SIC* 6798

▲ SAUL CENTERS INC p 1283
7501 Wisconsin Ave 1500e 20814
Tel (301) 986-6200 *SIC* 6798

SUBURBAN HOSPITAL HEALTHCARE SYSTEM INC p 1396
8600 Old Georgetown Rd 20814
Tel (301) 896-3100 *SIC* 8062

SUBURBAN HOSPITAL INC p 1396
8600 Old Georgetown Rd 20814
Tel (301) 896-3100 *SIC* 8062

■ TERRAFORM POWER INC p 1439
7550 Wisconsin Ave Fl 9 20814
Tel (240) 762-7700 *SIC* 4911

TRIBALCO LLC p 1479
4915 Saint Elmo Ave # 501 20814
Tel (301) 652-8450 *SIC* 8748

UNITED STATES ENRICHMENT CORP p 1513
6903 Rockledge Dr 20817
Tel (301) 564-3200 *SIC* 2819 2869

UNITED STATES SERVICE INDUSTRIES INC p 1514
4340 East West Hwy # 204 20814
Tel (202) 783-2030 *SIC* 7349

UNIVERSITY RESEARCH CO LLC p 1527
7200 Wisconsin Ave # 600 20814
Tel (301) 654-8338 *SIC* 8742 8748

▲ WALKER & DUNLOP INC p 1573
7501 Wisconsin Ave 1200e 20814
Tel (301) 215-5500 *SIC* 7389 8741

BOWIE, MD

▲ INOVALON HOLDINGS INC p 745
4321 Collington Rd # 100 20716
Tel (301) 809-4000 *SIC* 7371 7374 7372

INOVALON INC p 745
4321 Collington Rd # 100 20716
Tel (301) 262-3848 *SIC* 8733

MIL CORP p 968
4000 Mitchellville Rd R 20716
Tel (301) 805-8500
SIC 7371 7373 7374 7375 7376 8711

POWER SOLUTIONS LLC p 1165
17201 Melford Blvd Ste C 20715
Tel (301) 794-0330 *SIC* 1731

CAMBRIDGE, MD

■ CAMBRIDGE INTERNATIONAL HOLDINGS CORP p 244
105 Goodwill Rd 21613
Tel (410) 901-4979 *SIC* 3291

CAMBRIDGE INTERNATIONAL INC p 244
105 Goodwill Rd 21613
Tel (410) 228-3000 *SIC* 3496

CAPITOL HEIGHTS, MD

LONG FENCE CO INC p 876
8545 Edgeworth Dr 20743
Tel (301) 350-2400 *SIC* 1799

CATONSVILLE, MD

ERICKSON LIVING MANAGEMENT LLC p 507
701 Maiden Choice Ln 21228
Tel (410) 402-2097 *SIC* 8741

CENTREVILLE, MD

QUEEN ANNES COUNTY PUBLIC SCHOOLS p 1198
202 Chesterfield Ave 21617
Tel (410) 758-2403 *SIC* 8211

CHESTERTOWN, MD

DIXON VALVE & COUPLING CO p 445
800 High St 21620
Tel (410) 778-2000 *SIC* 3492 5085

DVCC INC p 463
800 High St 21620
Tel (410) 778-2000
SIC 3492 5085 3535 3321 3364

WASHINGTON COLLEGE p 1577
300 Washington Ave 21620
Tel (410) 778-2800 *SIC* 8221

CHEVERLY, MD

DIMENSIONS HEALTH CORP p 440
3001 Hospital Dr 20785
Tel (301) 618-2000 *SIC* 8062 8059

CHEVY CHASE, MD

ABACUS TECHNOLOGY CORP p 9
5404 Wscnsin Ave Ste 1100 20815
Tel (301) 907-8500 *SIC* 8742

ARLINGTON CAPITAL PARTNERS LP p 110
5425 Wisconsin Ave # 200 20815
Tel (202) 337-7500 *SIC* 6726 6211

BLACKSTREET CAPITAL MANAGEMENT LLC p 188
5425 Wisconsin Ave # 701 20815
Tel (240) 223-1330
SIC 6726 5149 5145 5961

■ GOVERNMENT EMPLOYEES INSURANCE CO INC p 627
5260 Western Ave 20815
Tel (301) 986-2500 *SIC* 6411

HOWARD HUGHES MEDICAL INSTITUTE INC p 713
4000 Jones Bridge Rd 20815
Tel (301) 215-8500 *SIC* 8733

JBG COMPANIES L L C p 779
4445 Willard Ave 20815
Tel (240) 333-3600 *SIC* 6799

JBG PROPERTIES INC p 779
4445 Willard Ave Ste 400 20815
Tel (240) 333-3600 *SIC* 6531 6552

MILLS CORP p 971
5425 Wisconsin Ave # 300 20815
Tel (301) 968-6000 *SIC* 6798

■ RITZ-CARLTON HOTEL CO LLC p 1237
4445 Willard Ave Ste 800 20815
Tel (301) 547-4700 *SIC* 7011

CHURCHVILLE, MD

DIXIE CONSTRUCTION CO INC p 444
260 Hopewell Rd 21028
Tel (410) 879-8055 *SIC* 1611 1623

CLARKSBURG, MD

PLEASANTS CONSTRUCTION INC p 1156
24024 Frederick Rd 20871
Tel (301) 428-0800 *SIC* 1794 1623 1611

THALES DEFENSE & SECURITY INC p 1446
22605 Gateway Center Dr 20871
Tel (240) 864-7000 *SIC* 3663

CLINTON, MD

MEDSTAR SOUTHERN MARYLAND HOSPITAL CENTER INC p 939
7503 Surratts Rd 20735
Tel (301) 868-8000 *SIC* 8062 8011

MONA ELECTRIC GROUP INC p 983
7915 Malcolm Rd Ste 400w 20735
Tel (301) 868-8400 *SIC* 1731

COCKEYSVILLE, MD

ADVANCE BUSINESS SYSTEMS & SUPPLY CO p 24
10755 York Rd 21030
Tel (410) 252-4800 *SIC* 5044

CRISTAL INORGANIC CHEMICALS US INC p 393
20 Wight Ave Ste 150 21030
Tel (410) 229-4400 *SIC* 2819

DANFORTH ASSOCIATES INC p 411
20 Wight Ave Ste 155 21030
Tel (781) 235-9100 *SIC* 6282

DIAMOND COMIC DISTRIBUTORS INC p 436
10150 York Rd Ste 300 21030
Tel (443) 318-8001 *SIC* 5192

WARD MACHINERY CO p 1575
10615 Beaver Dam Rd 21030
Tel (410) 584-7700 *SIC* 3554

COLLEGE PARK, MD

CBMC CAPITAL BUILDING MAINTENANCE CORP p 268
5018 College Ave 20740
Tel (301) 277-8000 *SIC* 7349

■ NATIONAL ARCHIVES AND RECORDS ADMINISTRATION p 1009
8601 Adelphi Rd Ste 4200 20740
Tel (301) 837-2000 *SIC* 9199

UNIVERSITY OF MARYLAND COLLEGE PARK p 1522
Patuxent Bldg 010 20742
Tel (301) 405-1000 *SIC* 8221

COLUMBIA, MD

AMBU INC p 65
6230 Old Dobbin Ln # 250 21045
Tel (410) 768-6464 *SIC* 5047

AMERICAN WOOD FIBERS INC p 81
9841 Broken Land Pkwy # 302 21046
Tel (410) 290-8700 *SIC* 2499

CERTIS USA LLC p 284
9145 Guilford Rd Ste 175 21046
Tel (301) 604-7340 *SIC* 5191 2879

COLUMBIA ASSOCIATION INC p 340
6310 Hillside Ct Ste 100 21046
Tel (410) 715-3000 *SIC* 8641

COLUMBIA BANCORP p 340
7168 Columbia Gateway Dr 21046
Tel (410) 872-9165 *SIC* 6029

CORPORATE OFFICE PROPERTIES TRUST p 372
6711 Columbia Gateway Dr 21046
Tel (443) 285-5400 *SIC* 6798

GEA NORTH AMERICA INC p 597
9165 Rumsey Rd 21045
Tel (410) 997-8700 *SIC* 7218

GEA PROCESS ENGINEERING INC p 597
9165 Rumsey Rd 21045
Tel (410) 772-5792 *SIC* 8711

GEA PT NORTH AMERICA INC p 597
9165 Rumsey Rd 21045
Tel (410) 997-8700 *SIC* 8748

▲ GP STRATEGIES CORP p 627
11000 Broken Land Pkwy # 200 21044
Tel (443) 367-9600 *SIC* 8742 8711 8748

HH MEDSTAR HEALTH INC p 689
5565 Sterrett Pl Ste 500 21044
Tel (410) 772-6500 *SIC* 8082

HOWARD COUNTY GENERAL HOSPITAL INC p 713
5755 Cedar Ln 21044
Tel (410) 740-7935 *SIC* 8062

INTERCONTINENTAL EXPORT IMPORT INC p 752
8815 Centre Park Dr # 400 21045
Tel (410) 674-5600 *SIC* 5162

■ KBRWYLE TECHNOLOGY SOLUTIONS LLC p 806
7000 Columbia Gateway Dr # 100 21046
Tel (410) 964-7000 *SIC* 4899 8711

L B & B ASSOCIATES INC p 833
9891 Broken Land Pkwy # 400 21046
Tel (301) 621-3944
SIC 8744 7338 4225 8742 8748 4581

LYRIC HEALTH CARE LLC p 888
7150 Columbia Gateway Dr J 21046
Tel (443) 539-2369 *SIC* 8059

MANIKEN LLC p 901
8621 Robert Fulton Dr # 100 21046
Tel (410) 290-1400 *SIC* 6512

MAXIM HEALTH SYSTEMS LLC p 922
7227 Lee Deforest Dr 21046
Tel (410) 910-1500 *SIC* 8011 8099

MAXIM HEALTHCARE SERVICES INC p 922
7227 Lee Deforest Dr 21046
Tel (410) 910-1500 *SIC* 8082

MEDSTAR HEALTH INC p 939
5565 Sterrett Pl Ste 500 21044
Tel (410) 772-6500
SIC 8741 8062 8082 8051 8011

■ MERIDIAN MEDICAL TECHNOLOGIES INC p 949
6350 Stevens Forest Rd 21046
Tel (443) 259-7800 *SIC* 3841

MERKLE GROUP INC p 950
7001 Columbia Gateway Dr 21046
Tel (443) 542-4000 *SIC* 7331

MERKLE INC p 950
7001 Columbia Gateway Dr 21046
Tel (443) 542-4000 *SIC* 8742

■ MICROS SYSTEMS INC p 962
7031 Columbia Gateway Dr # 1 21046
Tel (443) 285-6000
SIC 7373 7372 3577 3578

NIELSEN AUDIO INC p 1043
7000 Columbia Gateway Dr # 200 21046
Tel (410) 312-8000 *SIC* 8732 7372

OXFORD-COLUMBIA ASSOCIATES A MARYLAND LIMITED PARTNERSHIP p 1101
6531 Quiet Hours 21045
Tel (410) 381-1906 *SIC* 6513

PEAK-RYZEX INC p 1126
10330 Old Columbia Rd # 102 21046
Tel (410) 312-6000 *SIC* 7378 5045 7372

PLANNED SYSTEMS INTERNATIONAL INC p 1154
10632 Little Patuxent Pkw 21044
Tel (410) 964-8000 *SIC* 8742

■ ROUSE CO LP p 1253
10221 Wincopin Cir # 300 21044
Tel (410) 992-6000 *SIC* 6798 6512

S & W MANAGEMENT INC p 1261
7070 Oakland Mills Rd 21046
Tel (410) 720-6336 SIC 5812

SCIENCE AND ENGINEERING SERVICES LLC p 1292
6992 Columbia Gateway Dr # 200 21046
Tel (443) 539-0139 SIC 8711 8731 3826

SHIMADZU AMERICA INC p 1316
7102 Riverwood Dr 21046
Tel (410) 381-1227 SIC 5049 5047 5088

STRUCTURAL GROUP INC p 1394
10150 Old Columbia Rd 21046
Tel (410) 850-7000 SIC 1771

STRUCTURAL PRESERVATION SYSTEMS LLC p 1394
10150 Old Columbia Rd 21046
Tel (410) 850-7000 SIC 1771

STRUCTURAL TECHNOLOGIES LLC p 1394
10150 Old Columbia Rd 21046
Tel (410) 850-7000 SIC 1622 8711

SUMMIT HOLDING ONE CORP p 1399
10330 Old Columbia Rd 21046
Tel (410) 312-6000 SIC 6719

TENABLE NETWORK SECURITY INC p 1436
7021 Columbia Gateway Dr # 200 21046
Tel (410) 872-0555 SIC 7372 7371

UNIVERSITIES SPACE RESEARCH ASSOCIATION p 1518
7178 Columbia Gateway Dr 21046
Tel (410) 730-2656 SIC 8733

▲ W R GRACE & CO p 1569
7500 Grace Dr 21044
Tel (410) 531-4000
SIC 2819 3531 2899 2891 3479

■ W R GRACE & CO-CONN p 1569
7500 Grace Dr 21044
Tel (410) 531-4000
SIC 2819 3531 2899 2891 3479

■ WASTE MANAGEMENT OF MARYLAND INC p 1580
6994 Columbia Gateway Dr # 200 21046
Tel (410) 796-7010 SIC 4953 4212

CONOWINGO, MD

WILDCAT POINT GENERATION FACILITY p 1609
179 Old Mill Rd 21918
Tel (724) 422-2169 SIC 4911

CRISFIELD, MD

ALICE BYRD TAWES NURSING HOME INC p 50
201 Hall Hwy 21817
Tel (410) 968-1200 SIC 8051

CROFTON, MD

DAVCO ACQUISITION HOLDING INC p 415
1657 Crofton Blvd 21114
Tel (410) 721-3770 SIC 5812

DAVCO RESTAURANTS INC p 415
1657 Crofton Blvd 21114
Tel (410) 721-3770 SIC 5812

FORCE 3 LLC p 565
2151 Priest Bridge Dr # 7 21114
Tel (301) 261-0204 SIC 7373 5045 3571

CUMBERLAND, MD

ALLEGANY COUNTY PUBLIC SCHOOLS p 52
108 Washington St 21502
Tel (301) 759-2000 SIC 8211

BOARD OF EDUCATION OF ALLEGANY COUNTY MD INC p 195
108 Washington St 21502
Tel (301) 722-6013 SIC 8211

CARL BELT INC p 256
11521 Milnor Ave 21502
Tel (240) 362-0270 SIC 1542

■ MACRO RETAILING LLC p 893
10365 Mount Savage Rd Nw 21502
Tel (301) 722-6563 SIC 5661

SACRED HEART HOSPITAL OF SISTERS OF CHARITY INC p 1265
12500 Willowbrook Rd 21502
Tel (240) 964-7000 SIC 8062

WESTERN MARYLAND HEALTH SYSTEM p 1599
12500 Willowbrook Rd 21502
Tel (240) 964-7000 SIC 8062

WESTERN MARYLAND HEALTH SYSTEM REHAB p 1599
600 Memorial Ave 21502
Tel (301) 723-4200 SIC 8049 8093

DENTON, MD

CHOPTANK ELECTRIC COOPERATIVE INC p 302
24820 Meeting House Rd 21629
Tel (410) 479-0420 SIC 4911 1731

DISTRICT HEIGHTS, MD

FLIPPO CONSTRUCTION CO INC p 557
3820 Penn Belt Pl 20747
Tel (301) 967-6800 SIC 1623 1622

EASTON, MD

MEMORIAL HOSPITAL OF EASTON MD INC p 942
219 S Washington St 21601
Tel (410) 822-1000 SIC 8062

SEA WATCH INTERNATIONAL LTD p 1295
8978 Glebe Park Dr 21601
Tel (410) 822-7501 SIC 2092 2091

SHORE HEALTH SYSTEM INC p 1318
219 S Washington St 21601
Tel (410) 822-1000 SIC 8741

UNIVERSITY OF MARYLAND SHORE REGIONAL HEALTH INC p 1522
219 S Washington St 21601
Tel (410) 822-1000 SIC 8062

EDGEWOOD, MD

SMITHS DETECTION INC p 1334
2202 Lakeside Blvd 21040
Tel (410) 510-9100
SIC 3824 3823 3829 8731

ELKRIDGE, MD

CYBERCORE TECHNOLOGIES LLC p 404
6605 Business Pkwy 21075
Tel (410) 561-7177 SIC 5045

KANE CO p 802
6500 Kane Way 21075
Tel (410) 799-3200 SIC 4212

LEMEK LLC p 855
8184 Lark Brown Rd # 101 21075
Tel (443) 552-0700 SIC 5812

SAVAL FOODS CORP p 1284
6740 Dorsey Rd 21075
Tel (410) 379-5100 SIC 5141 2013

ELKTON, MD

■ ATK ELKTON LLC p 125
55 Thiokol Rd 21921
Tel (410) 392-6890 SIC 3764

CECIL COUNTY PUBLIC SCHOOLS p 272
201 Booth St 21921
Tel (410) 996-5400 SIC 8211

UNION HOSPITAL OF CECIL COUNTY HEALTH SERVICES INC p 1504
106 Bow St 21921
Tel (410) 392-7009 SIC 6324 8062

UNION HOSPITAL OF CECIL COUNTY INC p 1504
106 Bow St 21921
Tel (410) 620-3753 SIC 8062

ELLICOTT CITY, MD

FIELDSTONE MORTGAGE CO p 541
5094 Dorsey Hall Dr # 104 21042
Tel (410) 772-7217 SIC 6163

HOWARD COUNTY OF MARYLAND (INC) p 713
3430 Court House Dr # 100 21043
Tel (410) 313-2195 SIC 9111

HOWARD COUNTY PUBLIC SCHOOL SYSTEM p 713
10910 State Route 108 21042
Tel (410) 313-6600 SIC 8211

EMMITSBURG, MD

MOUNT SAINT MARYS UNIVERSITY INC p 994
16300 Old Emmitsburg Rd 21727
Tel (301) 447-3723 SIC 8221

FALLSTON, MD

ALLAN MYERS MD INC p 52
2011 Bel Air Rd 21047
Tel (410) 879-3055 SIC 1611 1623

FEDERALSBURG, MD

H & M BAY INC p 649
1800 Industrial Park Rd 21632
Tel (410) 754-8001 SIC 4731

TRI-GAS & OIL CO INC p 1477
3941 Federalsburg Hwy 21632
Tel (410) 754-2000 SIC 5172 5984 4731

FINKSBURG, MD

MACAULAY-BROWN INC p 891
1951 Polaris Rd 21048
Tel (937) 426-3421 SIC 8711

FOREST HILL, MD

GEMCRAFT HOMES GROUP INC p 598
2205 Commerce Rd Ste A 21050
Tel (410) 893-8458 SIC 1522

FORESTVILLE, MD

TRANSIT EMPLOYEE HEALTH & WELFARE PLAN p 1472
2701 Whitney Pl Ste B 20747
Tel (301) 568-2294 SIC 8099

FORT MEADE, MD

■ DEFENSE INFORMATION SYSTEMS AGENCY p 422
6910 Cooper Rd 20755
Tel (301) 225-1474 SIC 9711

■ DEFENSE MEDIA ACTIVITY p 422
6700 Taylor Ave 20755
Tel (301) 222-6000 SIC 9711

FORT WASHINGTON, MD

SAVE MORE INC p 1284
9405 Livingston Rd 20744
Tel (301) 372-1000 SIC 5531 5015

FREDERICK, MD

AVEMCO CORP p 136
8490 Progress Dr Ste 100 21701
Tel (301) 694-5700
SIC 6331 6321 6399 6411 7372

AVEMCO INSURANCE CO p 136
8490 Progress Dr Ste 100 21701
Tel (301) 694-5700 SIC 6321 6331

BANNER LIFE INSURANCE CO p 153
3275 Bennett Creek Ave 21704
Tel (301) 279-4800 SIC 6311 6411

BECHTEL NATIONAL INC p 167
5275 Westview Dr 21703
Tel (415) 768-1234 SIC 8711 1629 8742

BOARD OF EDUCATION OF FREDERICK COUNTY MD (INC) p 195
191 S East St 21701
Tel (301) 696-6850 SIC 8211

■ BUILDERS FIRSTSOURCE - ATLANTIC GROUP LLC p 225
5330 Spectrum Dr Ste L 21703
Tel (301) 631-2282 SIC 5031 5211

COUNTY OF FREDERICK p 378
355 Montevue Ln 101 21702
Tel (301) 600-9000 SIC 9111

■ FARMERS & MECHANICS BANK p 529
110 Thomas Johnson Dr # 100 21702
Tel (301) 694-4050 SIC 6021 6163

■ FIRST NATIONWIDE MORTGAGE CORP p 548
5280 Corporate Dr 21703
Tel (301) 791-8108 SIC 6163

FITZGERALD AUTO MALL INC p 553
114 Baughmans Ln 21702
Tel (301) 696-9200 SIC 5511

FOODPRO CORP p 564
321 E 5th St 21701
Tel (301) 663-3171
SIC 5142 5149 5148 5147 5143 5113

FREDERICK COMMUNITY COLLEGE p 576
7932 Opossumtown Pike 21702
Tel (301) 846-2400 SIC 8222

FREDERICK COUNTY PUBLIC SCHOOLS p 576
191 S East St 21701
Tel (301) 644-5000 SIC 8211

FREDERICK MEMORIAL HOSPITAL INC p 576
400 W 7th St 21701
Tel (240) 566-3300 SIC 8062

■ HOURGLASS HOLDINGS LLC p 711
8490 Progress Dr Ste 300 21701
Tel (301) 682-0600 SIC 1446

LANDCARE USA LLC p 842
5295 Westview Dr Ste 100 21703
Tel (301) 874-3300 SIC 0782

LEGAL & GENERAL AMERICA INC p 853
3275 Bennett Creek Ave 21704
Tel (800) 638-8428 SIC 6411 6311

■ LEIDOS BIOMEDICAL RESEARCH INC p 854
1050 Boyles St 21702
Tel (301) 846-5031 SIC 8733

MORGAN-KELLER INC p 989
70 Thomas Johnson Dr # 200 21702
Tel (301) 663-0626 SIC 1542 1541

NEW WAVE TECHNOLOGIES INC p 1033
4635 Wedgewood Blvd # 107 21703
Tel (301) 624-5300 SIC 5045

■ OVATIONS FOOD SERVICES LP p 1099
21 Stadium Dr 21703
Tel (301) 815-9935 SIC 5812

PLAMONDON ENTERPRISES INC p 1154
4991 New Design Rd # 109 21703
Tel (301) 695-5051 SIC 5812 7011

STULZ AIR TECHNOLOGY SYSTEM INC p 1395
1572 Tilco Dr 21704
Tel (301) 620-2033 SIC 3585

STULZ INVESTMENT CORP OF AMERICA p 1395
1572 Tilco Dr 21704
Tel (301) 620-2033 SIC 3822

■ U S SILICA CO p 1497
8490 Progress Dr Ste 300 21701
Tel (301) 682-0600 SIC 1446 1455 1459

▲ US SILICA HOLDINGS INC p 1533
8490 Progress Dr Ste 300 21701
Tel (301) 682-0600 SIC 1446

WELOCALIZE INC p 1591
241 E 4th St Ste 207 21701
Tel (301) 668-0330 SIC 7389

FRUITLAND, MD

ROMMEL HOLDINGS INC p 1249
103 E Main St 21826
Tel (410) 749-3600 SIC 5211 8741

FULTON, MD

PRESIDIO NETWORKED SOLUTIONS LLC p 1172
8161 Maple Lawn Blvd # 150 20759
Tel (301) 313-2000 SIC 7373

GAITHERSBURG, MD

ADVENTIST HEALTHCARE INC p 27
820 W Diamond Ave Ste 600 20878
Tel (301) 315-3030 SIC 8082 8059 8062

ASBURY ATLANTIC INC p 115
201 Russell Ave 20877
Tel (301) 216-4100 SIC 8059 8051

BG INTERMEDIATE CORP p 179
18227 Flower Hill Way 20879
Tel (301) 987-9200 SIC 0782 0781

BOLAND TRANE SERVICES INC p 198
30 W Watkins Mill Rd # 300 20878
Tel (240) 306-3000 SIC 5075

▲ BROADSOFT INC p 215
9737 Washingtonian Blvd # 350 20878
Tel (301) 977-9440 SIC 7372 7371 8748

CORPORATE FOOD SERVICES INC p 372
9801 Washington Blvd 20878
Tel (301) 987-4000 SIC 8741

▲ EMERGENT BIOSOLUTIONS INC p 492
400 Professional Dr # 400 20879
Tel (240) 631-3200 SIC 2834 2836

GXS GROUP INC p 649
9711 Washingtonian Blvd 20878
Tel (301) 340-4000 SIC 7372

GXS HOLDINGS INC p 649
100 Edison Park Dr 20878
Tel (301) 340-5370 SIC 6719

GXS INC p 649
9711 Washingtonian Blvd # 5 20878
Tel (301) 340-4000 SIC 7374

HEALTHWELL FOUNDATION p 678
9801 Washingtonian Blvd # 900 20878
Tel (800) 675-8416 SIC 8082

ICON DEVELOPMENT SOLUTIONS LLC p 727
820 W Diamond Ave Ste 100 20878
Tel (301) 944-6810 SIC 8733

■ INFORMATION NETWORK SYSTEMS INC p 742
700 N Frederick Ave 20879
Tel (301) 240-7000 SIC 7373 7363

JW HOME IMPROVEMENT LLC p 798
849 Quince Orch 20878
Tel (703) 899-3129 SIC 7299

■ LEIDOS ASPEN SYSTEMS CORP p 854
700 N Frederick Ave 20879
Tel (301) 240-7000 SIC 7374 7379 7389

■ LEIDOS GOVERNMENT SERVICES INC p 854
700 N Frederick Ave 20879
Tel (856) 486-5156
SIC 7379 7373 7374 7372

■ LEIDOS INTEGRATED TECHNOLOGY LLC p 854
700 N Frederick Ave 20879
Tel (301) 240-7000 SIC 8741

■ LEIDOS TECHNICAL SERVICES INC p 854
700 N Frederick Ave 20879
Tel (301) 240-7000 SIC 8731

■ LOCKHEED MARTIN SERVICES INC p 873
700 N Frederick Ave 20879
Tel (301) 240-7669 SIC 8711 8741 8742

■ LOCKHEED MARTIN SPACE OPERATIONS LLC p 873
700 N Frederick Ave 20879
Tel (301) 240-7000 SIC 4789

MDA INFORMATION SYSTEMS LLC p 933
820 W Diamond Ave Ste 300 20878
Tel (240) 833-8200 SIC 7371

MEDIMMUNE BIOLOGICS INC p 938
1 Medimmune Way 20878
Tel (301) 398-0000 SIC 8731

MEDIMMUNE LLC p 938
1 Medimmune Way 20878
Tel (301) 398-1200 SIC 2834

■ NATIONAL INSTITUTE OF STANDARDS & TECHNOLOGY p 1013
100 Bureau Dr Stop 1070 20899
Tel (301) 975-6478 SIC 9611

■ OAO CORP p 1071
700 N Frederick Ave 20879
Tel (301) 240-7000
SIC 7371 8711 3823 3559

OCIMUM BIOSOLUTIONS INC p 1074
50 W Watkins Mill Rd 20878
Tel (317) 228-0600 SIC 8731

SDH EDUCATION WEST LLC p 1295
9801 Washington Blvd 20878
Tel (301) 987-4000 SIC 8741

SIGMA-TAU PHARMACEUTICALS INC p 1321
9841 Wash Blvd Ste 500 20878
Tel (301) 948-1041 SIC 5122

SMO FINANCE CORP p 1334
9801 Washington Blvd 20878
Tel (301) 987-4000 SIC 8741

SODEXO AMERICA LLC p 1336
9801 Washington Blvd 20878
Tel (301) 987-4000 SIC 8741

SODEXO INC p 1337
9801 Washingtonian Blvd # 1 20878
Tel (301) 987-4000 SIC 5812 7349

SODEXO LAUNDRY SERVICES INC p 1337
9801 Washington Blvd 20878
Tel (301) 987-4000 SIC 8741

SODEXO MANAGEMENT INC p 1337
9801 Washingtonian Blvd 20878
Tel (301) 987-4000 SIC 8741 6552

SODEXO OPERATIONS LLC p 1337
9801 Washingtonian Blvd 20878
Tel (301) 987-4000 SIC 8741 5812 7349

SODEXO SERVICES OFTX LTD PARTNERSHIP p 1337
9801 Washington Blvd 20878
Tel (301) 987-4000 SIC 8741

SODEXOMAGIC LLC p 1337
9801 Washingtonian Blvd 20878
Tel (301) 987-4433 SIC 8742

■ SYTEX GROUP INC p 1419
700 N Frederick Ave 20879
Tel (301) 240-7000 SIC 4813

■ SYTEX INC p 1419
700 N Frederick Ave 20879
Tel (301) 240-7000 SIC 4813

UNITED COMMUNICATIONS GROUP LIMITED PARTNERSHIP p 1507
9737 Washingtonian Blvd # 500 20878
Tel (301) 287-2700 SIC 2721 7375

GAMBRILLS, MD

CHANEY ENTERPRISES LIMITED PARTNERSHIP p 288
2410 Evergreen Rd Ste 201 21054
Tel (410) 451-0197
SIC 3273 1442 5032 3429

KNOLLWOOD MANOR GENESIS ELDERCARE p 825
1221 Waugh Chapel Rd 21054
Tel (410) 987-1644 SIC 8051 8052

GERMANTOWN, MD

AC FIRST LLC p 13
20501 Seneca Meadows Pkwy 20876
Tel (817) 698-6860 SIC 8744

■ ACTERNA LLC p 19
20250 Century Blvd # 100 20874
Tel (301) 353-1550
SIC 3669 7379 3825 5065 3679 8734

■ AECOM GOVERNMENT SERVICES INC p 28
20501 Seneca Meadows Pkwy 20876
Tel (703) 921-1600
SIC 4959 4173 4581 7299

■ AECOM SPECIAL MISSIONS SERVICES INC p 28
20501 Seneca Meadows Pkwy 20876
Tel (412) 367-6060 SIC 8744

ASBURY ATLANTIC INC p 115
20030 Century Blvd 20874
Tel (301) 250-2100 SIC 7389

ASBURY COMMUNITIES INC p 115
20030 Century Blvd # 300 20874
Tel (301) 250-2100 SIC 8361

DRS DEFENSE SOLUTIONS LLC p 457
1 Milestone Center Ct 20876
Tel (240) 238-3900 SIC 3812

■ HUGHES COMMUNICATIONS INC p 717
11717 Exploration Ln 20876
Tel (301) 428-5500 SIC 4813 4899 3663

■ HUGHES NETWORK SYSTEMS LLC p 717
11717 Exploration Ln 20876
Tel (301) 428-5500 SIC 4899

▲ INTREXON CORP p 760
20374 Seneca Meadows Pkwy 20876
Tel (301) 556-9900 SIC 8731

■ JDSU ACTERNA HOLDINGS LLC p 781
1 Milestone Center Ct 20876
Tel (240) 404-1550 SIC 3825

■ URS FEDERAL SERVICES INC p 1530
20501 Seneca Meadows Pkwy # 300 20876
Tel (301) 944-3100 SIC 8711

URS FEDERAL SERVICES INTERNATIONAL INC p 1530
20501 Seneca Meadows Pkwy # 300 20876
Tel (301) 944-3100 SIC 8711

URS FEDERAL SUPPORT SERVICES INC p 1530
20501 Seneca Meadows Pkwy # 300 20876
Tel (301) 944-3100 SIC 8249 4581

URS FEDERAL TECHINCAL SERVICES INC p 1530
20501 Seneca Meadows Pkwy # 300 20876
Tel (301) 944-3100 SIC 8711

■ WABTEC RAILWAY ELECTRONICS INC p 1570
21200 Dorsey Mill Rd 20876
Tel (301) 515-2000
SIC 3825 3679 3743 3672

GLEN BURNIE, MD

BALTIMORE WASHINGTON MEDICAL SYSTEM INC p 149
301 Hospital Dr 21061
Tel (410) 787-4000 SIC 8062

JJ HAINES & CO LLC p 786
6950 Aviation Blvd 21061
Tel (410) 760-4040 SIC 5023

MCLEAN CONTRACTING CO p 931
6700 Mclean Way 21060
Tel (410) 553-6700
SIC 1622 1623 1629 3449

R E MICHEL CO LLC p 1202
1 Re Michel Dr 21060
Tel (410) 760-4000 SIC 5075 5078

■ VISIONTECHNOLOGIES INC p 1561
530 Mccormick Dr Ste G 21061
Tel (410) 424-2183 SIC 7373

GREENBELT, MD

BOZZUTO & ASSOCIATES INC p 205
6406 Ivy Ln Ste 700 20770
Tel (301) 220-0100 SIC 6513 1522 6552

BOZZUTO CONSTRUCTION CO INC p 205
6406 Ivy Ln Ste 700 20770
Tel (301) 220-0100 SIC 1522 1542

BOZZUTO CONTRACTING CO p 205
6406 Ivy Ln 20770
Tel (301) 220-0100 SIC 1521 1542

CHESAPEAKE HOSPITALITY LLC p 295
6404 Ivy Ln Ste 800 20770
Tel (301) 474-3307 SIC 7011

KNIGHT PROTECTIVE SERVICE INC p 824
6411 Ivy Ln Ste 320 20770
Tel (301) 808-4669 SIC 7381

MARYLAND HOSPITALITY INC p 915
6411 Ivy Ln Ste 510 20770
Tel (301) 474-3307 SIC 7011 8741 8742

MURRYS OF MARYLAND INC p 1002
7852 Walker Dr Ste 420 20770
Tel (888) 668-7797 SIC 5421

■ NASA/GODDARD SPACE FLIGHT CENTER p 1008
8800 Greenbelt Rd 20771
Tel (301) 286-2000 SIC 9661

OAOTECHNOLOGY SOLUTIONS INC p 1071
7500 Greenway Center Dr # 150 20770
Tel (301) 486-0400 SIC 7379

SGT INC p 1310
7701 Greenbelt Rd Ste 400 20770
Tel (301) 614-8600 SIC 7371 7373 7376

GWYNN OAK, MD

UNIVERSITY OF MARYLAND REHABILITATION INSTITUTE OF SOUTHERN MARYLAND p 1522
2200 Kernan Dr 21207
Tel (410) 448-2500 SIC 8069

HAGERSTOWN, MD

BRETHREN MUTUAL INSURANCE CO p 210
149 N Edgewood Dr 21740
Tel (800) 621-4264 SIC 6331 6411

C & T A CO INC p 231
11535 Hopewell Rd 21740
Tel (800) 458-3835
SIC 5541 5172 7359 7699

FIVES LANDIS CORP p 553
16778 Halfway Blvd 21740
Tel (301) 797-3400 SIC 3541

MERITUS HEALTH INC p 949
11116 Medical Campus Rd 21742
Tel (301) 790-8000 SIC 6321

MERITUS MEDICAL CENTER INC p 950
11116 Medical Campus Rd 21742
Tel (301) 797-2000 SIC 8062

■ PHOENIX COLOR CORP p 1144
18249 Phoenix Rd 21742
Tel (301) 733-0018 SIC 2732 3469 2796

TRIVERGENT HEALTH ALLIANCE MSO LLC p 1483
1800 Dual Hwy Ste 304 21740
Tel (301) 790-9130 SIC 8742

■ VERIZON MARYLAND LLC p 1550
1710 Undrpamd Way Ste 401 21740
Tel (301) 790-7135 SIC 4813 8721

WASHINGTON COUNTY BOARD OF EDUCATION p 1578
10435 Downsville Pike 21740
Tel (301) 766-2800 SIC 8211

WASHINGTON COUNTY ENDOWMENT FUND (INC) p 1578
251 E Antietam St 21740
Tel (301) 790-8102 SIC 8741

WASHINGTON COUNTY PUBLIC SCHOOLS p 1578
10435 Downsville Pike 21740
Tel (301) 766-2800 SIC 8211

HALETHORPE, MD

LIFESTAR RESPONSE CORP p 864
3710 Commerce Dr Ste 1006 21227
Tel (631) 289-1100 SIC 4119

HAMPSTEAD, MD

■ JOS A BANK CLOTHIERS INC p 793
500 Hanover Pike 21074
Tel (410) 239-2700 SIC 5611 5961

HANOVER, MD

AEROTEK INC p 31
7301 Parkway Dr 21076
Tel (410) 694-5100 SIC 7363 8748 8711

ALLEGIS GLOBAL SOLUTIONS INC p 53
7312 Parkway Dr 21076
Tel (410) 579-3000 SIC 7361

ALLEGIS GROUP INC p 53
7301 Parkway Dr 21076
Tel (410) 579-3000 SIC 7361

BFPE INTERNATIONAL INC p 179
7512 Connelley Dr 21076
Tel (410) 768-2200 SIC 1731 7382 7389

▲ CIENA CORP p 306
7035 Ridge Rd 21076
Tel (410) 694-5700 SIC 3661 7373

CONMED HEALTHCARE MANAGEMENT INC p 356
7250 Parkway Dr Ste 400 21076
Tel (410) 712-4760 SIC 8062

CONMED INC p 356
7250 Parkway Dr Ste 400 21076
Tel (410) 567-5520 SIC 8011

CONVERGENCE MARKETING INC p 364
7361 Coca Cola Dr Ste A 21076
Tel (443) 688-5100 SIC 8742

CORRECT RX PHARMACY SERVICES INC p 372
1352 Charwood Rd Ste C 21076
Tel (800) 636-0501 SIC 5122

DTLR INC p 458
1300 Mercedes Dr 21076
Tel (410) 850-5900 SIC 5611 5661

GILBERT FOODS LLC p 612
7251 Standard Dr 21076
Tel (410) 712-6000
SIC 5148 5147 5146 5142

HAYWARD BAKER INC p 670
7550 Teague Rd Ste 300 21076
Tel (410) 551-8200 SIC 1799

KELLER FOUNDATIONS LLC p 808
7550 Teague Rd Ste 300 21076
Tel (410) 551-8200 SIC 1799 8711

■ KEYW CORP p 816
7740 Milestone Pkwy # 400 21076
Tel (443) 733-1600 SIC 8711 8748

▲ KEYW HOLDING CORP p 816
7740 Milestone Pkwy # 400 21076
Tel (443) 733-1600
SIC 7373 7372 8731 7375

MARYLAND DEPARTMENT OF TRANSPORTATION p 914
7201 Corporate Center Dr 21076
Tel (410) 865-1037 SIC 8748 9621

MCKINNEY DRILLING CO LLC p 930
7550 Teague Rd Ste 300 21076
Tel (410) 874-1235 SIC 1794 5082

PHILLIPS CORP p 1144
7390 Coca Cola Dr Ste 200 21076
Tel (800) 878-4747 SIC 5084 7373 3542

RHEE BROS INC p 1231
7461 Coca Cola Dr 21076
Tel (410) 381-9000 SIC 5141

TEKSYSTEMS INC p 1433
7437 Race Rd 21076
Tel (410) 540-7700 SIC 7379 7376 7373

HAVRE DE GRACE, MD

HARFORD MEMORIAL HOSPITAL INC p 661
501 S Union Ave 21078
Tel (443) 843-5000 SIC 8062

HARFORD MEMORIAL HOSPITAL INC p 661
501 S Union Ave 21078
Tel (410) 939-2400 SIC 8062

HOLLYWOOD, MD

SMARTRONIX INC p 1332
44150 Smartronix Way 20636
Tel (301) 373-6000 SIC 7371 8731 7373

HUGHESVILLE, MD

MARYLAND SOUTHERN ELECTRIC COOPERATIVE INC p 915
15035 Burnt Store Rd 20637
Tel (301) 274-3111 SIC 4911

HUNT VALLEY, MD

■ AAI CORP p 8
124 Industry Ln 21030
Tel (410) 666-1400
SIC 3728 3769 7699 8711

ALTRADIUS CREDIT INSURANCE INC p 62
230 Schilling Cir Ste 240 21031
Tel (410) 568-3850 SIC 6351

CRISTAL p 392
20 Wight Ave Ste 100 21030
Tel (410) 229-4440
SIC 1241 3531 2816 2869 1321 3631

CRISTAL METALS INC p 393
20 Wight Ave Ste 100 21030
Tel (410) 229-4400 SIC 5051

CRISTAL USA INC p 393
20 Wight Ave Ste 150 21030
Tel (410) 229-4441 SIC 2816

DUNBAR ARMORED INC p 461
50 Schilling Rd 21031
Tel (410) 584-9800 SIC 7381

EDUCATE INC p 479
4 North Park Dr Ste 500 21030
Tel (410) 843-8000 SIC 8299

MEDICAL MUTUAL LIABILITY INSURANCE SOCIETY OF MARYLAND p 937
225 International Cir # 300 21030
Tel (410) 785-0050 SIC 6351

NORDIC CORP p 1048
11019 Mccormick Rd # 320 21031
Tel (410) 771-1880 SIC 5812

■ NOXELL CORP p 1064
11050 York Rd 21030
Tel (410) 785-7300 SIC 2844

▲ OMEGA HEALTHCARE INVESTORS INC p 1084
200 International Cir # 3500 21030
Tel (410) 427-1700 SIC 6798

PDP GROUP INC p 1125
10909 Mccormick Rd 21031
Tel (410) 584-2000 SIC 6411

PHARMACEUTICS INTERNATIONAL INC p 1141
10819 Gilroy Rd Ste 100 21031
Tel (410) 584-0001 SIC 2834 5122

SHERIDAN GROUP INC p 1315
11311 Mccormick Rd # 260 21031
Tel (410) 785-7277 SIC 2752 2732

▲ SINCLAIR BROADCAST GROUP INC p 1326
10706 Beaver Dam Rd 21030
Tel (410) 568-1500 SIC 4833

■ SINCLAIRTELEVISION GROUP INC p 1326
10706 Beaver Dam Rd 21030
Tel (410) 568-1500 SIC 4832

TECHTRONIC INDUSTRIES NORTH AMERICA INC p 1432
303 Intrntl Cir Ste 490 21030
Tel (443) 391-1541 SIC 5083 5251

■TESSCO INC p 1440
11126 Mccormick Rd 21031
Tel (410) 229-1000 SIC 5065

▲TESSCOTECHNOLOGIES INC p 1440
11126 Mccormick Rd 21031
Tel (410) 229-1000 SIC 5065

■ UNITED INDUSTRIAL CORP p 1509
124 Industry Ln 21030
Tel (410) 628-3500 SIC 8711

WEBB-MASON INC p 1586
10830 Gilroy Rd 21031
Tel (410) 785-1111 SIC 2752

HYATTSVILLE, MD

B FRANK JOY LLC p 142
5355 Kilmer Pl 20781
Tel (301) 779-9400 SIC 1623

CANADA DRY POTOMAC CORP p 246
3600 Pennsy Dr 20785
Tel (301) 773-5500 SIC 5149

GIANT FOOD LLC p 610
8301 Profess Pl Ste 115 20785
Tel (301) 341-4100 SIC 5411 6512 5912

IESI MD CORP p 730
2911 52nd Ave Ste A 20781
Tel (410) 768-1900 SIC 4953 4212

JESSUP, MD

BALTIMORE AIRCOIL CO INC p 149
7600 Dorsey Run Rd 20794
Tel (410) 799-6200 SIC 3585 3443

CA LINDMAN INC p 234
10401 Guilford Rd 20794
Tel (410) 724-0040 SIC 1542

■ CHERRY HILL CONSTRUCTION INC p 294
8211 Washington Blvd 20794
Tel (410) 799-3577 SIC 1611 1622

CLASS PRODUCE GROUP LLC p 323
8477 Dorsey Run Rd 20794
Tel (410) 799-5700 SIC 5148

ELITE SPICE INC p 487
7151 Montevideo Rd 20794
Tel (410) 796-1900 SIC 2099

KRONHEIM CO INC p 830
8201 Stayton Dr 20794
Tel (410) 724-3300 SIC 5182 5181

LANCASTER FOODS LLC p 841
7700 Conowingo Ave 20794
Tel (410) 799-0010 SIC 5148

NEXT DAY BLINDS CORP p 1040
8251 Preston Ct Ste B 20794
Tel (240) 568-8800
SIC 5023 2591 5719 1799

■ SYSCO BALTIMORE LLC p 1416
8000 Dorsey Run Rd 20794
Tel (410) 799-7000 SIC 5142 5149 5087

KENSINGTON, MD

BAKERY & CONFECTIONERY UNION & INDUSTRY INTERNATIONAL PENSION FUND p 147
10401 Conn Ave Ste 210 20895
Tel (301) 468-3700 SIC 6371

LA PLATA, MD

CHARLES COUNTY BOARD OF EDUCATION p 289
5980 Radio Station Rd 20646
Tel (301) 934-7224 SIC 8211

CHARLES COUNTY GOVERNMENT p 289
200 Baltimore St 20646
Tel (301) 645-0550 *SIC* 9111

CHARLES REGIONAL MEDICAL CENTER FOUNDATION INC p 289
5 Garrett Ave 20646
Tel (301) 609-4000 *SIC* 8062

CIVISTA MEDICAL CENTER INC p 320
5 Garrett Ave 20646
Tel (301) 609-4000 *SIC* 8062

COLLEGE OF SOUTHERN MARYLAND FOUNDATION INC p 337
8730 Mitchell Rd 20646
Tel (301) 934-2251 *SIC* 8351

DASH IN FOOD STORES INC p 413
6355 Crain Hwy 20646
Tel (301) 932-3600 *SIC* 5541 5411 6794

FACCHINA CONSTRUCTION CO INC p 523
102 Centennial St Ste 201 20646
Tel (240) 776-7000
SIC 1542 1799 1623 1611 1622 1629

FOUNDATION FOR PUBLIC SCHOOL CHILDREN OF CHARLES COUNTY INC p 571
5980 Radio Station Rd 20646
Tel (301) 932-6610 *SIC* 8211

SMO INC p 1334
6355 Crain Hwy 20646
Tel (301) 932-3600 *SIC* 5172

WILLS GROUP INC p 1613
6355 Crain Hwy 20646
Tel (301) 932-3600
SIC 5541 5983 5172 5411

LANDOVER, MD

▲ 2U INC p 2
8201 Corporate Dr Ste 900 20785
Tel (301) 892-4350 *SIC* 7372 8748 8299

ADAMS-BURCH LLC p 21
1901 Stanford Ct 20785
Tel (301) 276-2000 *SIC* 5046 5113 5087

■ AM BRIGGS INC p 63
1920 Stanford Ct 20785
Tel (301) 773-2175 *SIC* 5147 5144 5146

AW INDUSTRIES INC p 139
8415 Ardwick Ardmore Rd 20785
Tel (301) 322-1000 *SIC* 2515

CITADEL LAND INC p 309
1802 Brightseat Rd # 600 20785
Tel (301) 683-6498 *SIC* 6552

ELECTRICAL WHOLESALERS METRO DC INC p 485
6500a Sheriff Rd 20785
Tel (301) 333-5990 *SIC* 5063

■ K HOVNANIAN HOMES AT FAIRWOOD LLC p 798
1802 Brightseat Rd # 500 20785
Tel (301) 772-8900 *SIC* 1531 1522 1521

■ MARSHALS SERVICE UNITED STATES p 911
3601 Pennsy Dr 20785
Tel (202) 307-9001 *SIC* 9221

MMSP INC p 979
1920 Stanford Ct 20785
Tel (301) 773-2175
SIC 5143 5144 5146 5147

NATIONAL AUTOMATIC SPRINKLER INDUSTRY WELFARE FUND p 1010
8000 Corporate Dr 20785
Tel (301) 577-1700 *SIC* 8741 6371

NOVITEX GOVERNMENT SOLUTIONS LLC p 1063
8401 Corporate Dr Ste 420 20785
Tel (301) 731-4595 *SIC* 8744

P J K FOOD SERVICE CORP p 1102
3310 75th Ave 20785
Tel (301) 772-3333 *SIC* 5148

S FREEDMAN & SONS INC p 1262
3322 Pennsy Dr 20785
Tel (301) 322-6400 *SIC* 5113 5087

LANHAM, MD

■ COMCAST OF MARYLAND LLC p 343
9609 Annapolis Rd 20706
Tel (301) 306-5774 *SIC* 4841

DOCTORS HOSPITAL INC p 447
8118 Good Luck Rd 20706
Tel (301) 552-8118 *SIC* 8062

■ FOODARAMA INC (DE) p 564
4600 Forbes Blvd Ste 1 20706
Tel (301) 306-8600 *SIC* 5411

NATIONAL BOOK NETWORK INC p 1010
4501 Forbes Blvd Ste 200 20706
Tel (301) 459-8020 *SIC* 5192

ROWMAN & LITTLEFIELD PUBLISHING GROUP INC p 1253
4501 Forbes Blvd Ste 200 20706
Tel (301) 459-3366 *SIC* 2731 5192

SAFEWARE INC p 1266
4403 Forbes Blvd 20706
Tel (301) 683-1234 *SIC* 5084

■ SHOPPERS FOOD WAREHOUSE CORP p 1318
4600 Forbes Blvd 20706
Tel (301) 306-8600 *SIC* 5411

■ WA CHESTER LLC p 1569
4390 Parliament Pl Ste Q 20706
Tel (202) 466-1940 *SIC* 1731

LAUREL, MD

AES ELECTRICAL INC p 31
13335 Mid Atlantic Blvd 20708
Tel (301) 770-2060 *SIC* 1731

AIRECO SUPPLY INC p 40
8860 Gorman Rd 20723
Tel (301) 953-8800 *SIC* 5075 5078

BUCH CONSTRUCTION INC p 222
11292 Buch Way 20723
Tel (301) 369-3500 *SIC* 1542

CENTRAL WHOLESALERS INC p 281
13401 Konterra Dr 20707
Tel (800) 935-2947
SIC 5074 5063 5087 5072 5211 1799

COASTAL SUNBELT INC p 332
9001 Whiskey Bottom Rd 20723
Tel (410) 799-8000
SIC 5148 4214 0723 2099

JOHNS HOPKINS UNIVERSITY APPLIED PHYSICS LABORATORY LLC p 790
11100 Johns Hopkins Rd 20723
Tel (240) 228-5000 *SIC* 8731

LAUREL SAND & GRAVEL INC p 847
14504 Greenview Dr # 210 20708
Tel (410) 792-7234 *SIC* 1422 1442

TOWER FEDERAL CREDIT UNION p 1464
7901 Sandy Spring Rd # 102 20707
Tel (301) 490-6926 *SIC* 6163 6061

WASHINGTON SUBURBAN SANITARY COMMISSION (INC) p 1579
14501 Sweitzer Ln 20707
Tel (301) 206-8000 *SIC* 4941 4952

LAYTONSVILLE, MD

RUPPERT LANDSCAPE INC p 1258
23601 Laytonsville Rd 20882
Tel (301) 482-0300 *SIC* 0781 0783 0782

LEONARDTOWN, MD

BOARD OF EDUCATION OF ST MARYS COUNTY p 195
23160 Moakley St Ste 101 20650
Tel (301) 475-5511 *SIC* 8211

LEONARDTOWN SCHOOL DISTRICT p 856
P.O. Box 641 20650
Tel (301) 475-4250 *SIC* 8211

ST MARYS COUNTY PUBLIC SCHOOLS p 1371
23160 Moakley St Ste 101 20650
Tel (301) 475-5511 *SIC* 8211

ST MARYS HOSPITAL OF SAINT MARYS COUNTY INC p 1371
25500 Point Lookout Rd 20650
Tel (301) 475-8981 *SIC* 8062

LEXINGTON PARK, MD

J F TAYLOR INC p 771
21610 S Essex Dr 20653
Tel (301) 862-4744 *SIC* 8711

LINTHICUM HEIGHTS, MD

C-CARE LLC p 234
979 Corporate Blvd 21090
Tel (410) 850-0035 *SIC* 5122

SAPA EXTRUSIONS NORTH AMERICA LLC p 1281
999 Corporate Blvd # 100 21090
Tel (410) 487-4500 *SIC* 3354

STATE EMPLOYEES CREDIT UNION OF MARYLAND INC p 1380
971 Corporate Blvd # 100 21090
Tel (410) 487-7920 *SIC* 6062

LINTHICUM, MD

■ BOOZ ALLEN HAMILTON ENGINEERING SERVICES LLC p 200
900 Elkridge Landing Rd # 100 21090
Tel (703) 902-5000 *SIC* 8711

LUKE, MD

■ LUKE PAPER CO p 885
300 Pratt St 21540
Tel (301) 359-3311 *SIC* 2621

LUTHERVILLE TIMONIUM, MD

ALBERT S SMYTH CO INC p 46
2020 York Rd 21093
Tel (410) 252-6666 *SIC* 5944 5961

GRAY & SON INC p 632
430 W Padonia Rd 21093
Tel (410) 771-4311 *SIC* 1611 1623 1794

MID-ATLANTIC HEALTH CARE LLC p 963
1922 Greenspring Dr Ste 3 21093
Tel (410) 308-2300 *SIC* 8062

MOSAIC COMMUNITY SERVICES INC p 991
1925 Greenspring Dr 21093
Tel (410) 453-9553 *SIC* 8322 8093

■ PALL FILTRATION AND SEPARATIONS GROUP INC p 1108
2118 Greenspring Dr 21093
Tel (410) 252-0800 *SIC* 3569

LUTHERVILLE, MD

SAGE DINING SERVICES INC p 1267
1402 York Rd Ste 100 21093
Tel (410) 339-3950 *SIC* 5812

MARRIOTTSVILLE, MD

BON SECOURS HEALTH SYSTEM INC p 199
1505 Marriottsville Rd 21104
Tel (410) 442-5511 *SIC* 8062 8099

HARKINS BUILDERS INC p 661
2201 Warwick Way 21104
Tel (410) 750-2600 *SIC* 1522 1542

MILLERSVILLE, MD

TECH USA INC p 1431
8334 Veterans Hwy 21108
Tel (410) 584-9003 *SIC* 8742

NEWARK, MD

WORCESTER COUNTY PUBLIC SCHOOLS p 1624
6270 Worcester Hwy 21841
Tel (410) 632-5020 *SIC* 8211

NOTTINGHAM, MD

FIRST HOME MORTGAGE CORP p 547
5355 Nottingham Dr # 130 21236
Tel (877) 933-3100 *SIC* 6163

OCEAN CITY, MD

MAYOR AND CITY COUNCIL OF OCEAN CITY p 924
301 N Baltimore Ave 21842
Tel (410) 289-8221 *SIC* 9121

REAL HOSPITALITY GROUP LLC p 1213
12800 Hospitality Ln 21842
Tel (410) 213-1971 *SIC* 8741

ODENTON, MD

KEY IMPACT SALES & SYSTEMS INC p 814
1701 Crossroads Dr 21113
Tel (410) 381-1239 *SIC* 8742

OLNEY, MD

MONTGOMERY GENERAL HOSPITAL INC p 986
18101 Prince Philip Dr 20832
Tel (301) 774-8882 *SIC* 8062

▲ SANDY SPRING BANCORP INC p 1279
17801 Georgia Ave 20832
Tel (301) 774-6400 *SIC* 6411

■ SANDY SPRING BANK p 1279
17801 Georgia Ave 20832
Tel (301) 774-6400 *SIC* 6021

OWINGS MILLS, MD

BALTIMORE LIFE INSURANCE CO INC p 149
10075 Red Run Blvd # 175 21117
Tel (410) 581-6600 *SIC* 6311

CAREFIRST BLUECHOICE INC p 254
10455 Mill Run Cir 21117
Tel (202) 479-8000 *SIC* 6321 8011 6411

CAREFIRST INC p 254
10455 Mill Run Cir 21117
Tel (301) 805-5005 *SIC* 6324

CAREFIRST OF MARYLAND INC p 254
10455 Mill Run Cir 21117
Tel (410) 581-3000 *SIC* 6324

CLAMPETT INDUSTRIES LLC p 321
10461 Mill Run Cir # 1100 21117
Tel (410) 785-6200 *SIC* 8748 6531

DANIEL G SCHUSTER LLC p 411
3717 Crondall Ln Ste B 21117
Tel (410) 363-9620 *SIC* 5032 1771

EULER HERMES ACI HOLDING INC p 512
800 Red Brook Blvd # 400 21117
Tel (410) 753-0753 *SIC* 7322 6351 6719

EULER HERMES NORTH AMERICA INSURANCE CO p 512
800 Red Brook Blvd 21117
Tel (410) 753-0753 *SIC* 6351 6411

GROUP HOSPITALIZATION AND MEDICAL SERVICES INC p 641
10455 Mill Run Cir 21117
Tel (202) 479-8000 *SIC* 6324

LEN STOLER INC p 855
11275 Reisterstown Rd 21117
Tel (410) 581-7000 *SIC* 5511

▲ MEDIFAST INC p 938
3600 Crondall Ln 21117
Tel (410) 581-8042 *SIC* 2099 2023 8093

R & H MOTOR CARS LTD p 1201
9727 Reisterstown Rd 21117
Tel (410) 363-7793 *SIC* 5511 7538 5531

RAND WORLDWIDE INC p 1207
11201 Dlfeld Blvd Ste 112 21117
Tel (410) 581-8080 *SIC* 7372 7373

RAND WORLDWIDE SUBSIDIARY INC p 1207
11201 Dlfeld Blvd Ste 112 21117
Tel (877) 726-3243
SIC 7379 7373 5045 5734

WEINBERG HARRY & JEANETTE FOUNDATION INC p 1588
7 Park Center Ct 21117
Tel (410) 654-8500 *SIC* 8699

OXON HILL, MD

MELWOOD-WERNER HOUSING INC p 941
6188 Oxon Hill Rd 20745
Tel (301) 982-6207 *SIC* 7021

PASADENA, MD

DOUGLAS REALTY LLC p 452
8096 Edwin Raynor Blvd C 21122
Tel (410) 255-3690 *SIC* 6531

FUTURE CARE HEALTH AND MANAGEMENT OF HOMEWOOD INC p 585
8028 Ritchie Hwy Ste 210b 21122
Tel (410) 766-1995 *SIC* 8741

PIKESVILLE, MD

STATE POLICE MARYLAND p 1382
1201 Reisterstown Rd 21208
Tel (410) 653-4219 *SIC* 9221

POCOMOKE CITY, MD

■ SYSCO EASTERN MARYLAND LLC p 1417
33239 Costen Rd 21851
Tel (410) 677-5555 *SIC* 5141

POINT OF ROCKS, MD

CANAM STEEL CORP p 246
4010 Clay St 21777
Tel (301) 874-5141 *SIC* 3441 5051

POOLESVILLE, MD

BETHESDA-CHEVY CHASE CHAPTER IZAAK WALTON LEAGUE OF AMERICA p 178
20601 Izaak Walton Way 20837
Tel (301) 972-8913 *SIC* 8641

PRESTON, MD

CHOPTANK TRANSPORT INC p 302
3601 Choptank Rd 21655
Tel (410) 673-2240 *SIC* 4731

PRINCE FREDERICK, MD

CALVERT COUNTY PUBLIC SCHOOLS p 243
1305 Dares Beach Rd 20678
Tel (410) 535-1700 *SIC* 8211

CALVERT MEMORIAL HOSPITAL OF CALVERT COUNTY p 243
100 Hospital Rd 20678
Tel (410) 535-4000 *SIC* 8062

COUNTY OF CALVERT p 376
175 Main St 20678
Tel (410) 535-1600 *SIC* 9111

PRINCESS ANNE, MD

UNIVERSITY OF MARYLAND EASTERN SHORE p 1522
11868 Academic Oval 21853
Tel (410) 651-2200 *SIC* 8221

RANDALLSTOWN, MD

NORTHWEST HOSPITAL CENTER INC p 1060
5401 Old Court Rd 21133
Tel (410) 521-2200 *SIC* 8062

REISTERSTOWN, MD

R/C THEATRES MANAGEMENT CORP p 1203
231 W Cherry Hill Ct 21136
Tel (410) 526-4774 *SIC* 8741 7922 7832

RIVERDALE, MD

MARYLAND-NATIONAL CAPITAL PARK AND PLANNING COMMISSION p 915
6611 Kenilworth Ave # 103 20737
Tel (301) 454-1540 *SIC* 7999

■ USDA APHIS VETERINARY p 1534
4700 River Rd Unit 54 20737
Tel (301) 851-2873 *SIC* 9641

ROCKVILLE, MD

ACCESS INTELLIGENCE LLC p 15
9211 Corp Blvd Fl 4 20850
Tel (301) 354-2000 *SIC* 2741 2721

AMERICAN KIDNEY FUND INC p 75
11921 Rockville Pike # 300 20852
Tel (301) 881-3690 *SIC* 8399

APEX COMPANIES LLC p 96
15850 Crabbs Branch Way # 200 20855
Tel (301) 417-0200 *SIC* 8744 8748 8742

▲ ARGAN INC p 107
1 Church St Ste 201 20850
Tel (301) 315-0027 *SIC* 4813 1623 8748

AVENDRA LLC p 136
702 King Farm Blvd # 600 20850
Tel (301) 825-0500 *SIC* 8741

BAE SYSTEMS TECHNOLOGY SOLUTIONS & SERVICES INC p 144
520 Gaither Rd 20850
Tel (301) 738-4880 *SIC* 8711

BG HOLDING LLC p 179
2275 Res Blvd Ste 600 20850
Tel (301) 987-9200 *SIC* 0781 0782

BIORELIANCE CORP p 184
14920 Broschart Rd 20850
Tel (301) 738-1000 *SIC* 8734 8731

BRICKMAN ACQUISITION HOLDINGS INC p 211
2275 Res Blvd Ste 600 20850
Tel (240) 683-2000 *SIC* 0781

BRICKMAN GROUP HOLDINGS INC p 211
2275 Res Blvd Ste 700 20850
Tel (301) 987-9200 *SIC* 0782 4959
BRICKMAN PARENT LP p 211
2275 Res Blvd Ste 600 20850
Tel (240) 683-2000 *SIC* 0781
BRIGHTVIEW COMPANIES LLC p 213
2275 Research Blvd 20850
Tel (240) 683-2000 *SIC* 0781 0782
BRIGHTVIEW LANDSCAPES LLC p 213
2275 Res Blvd Ste 600 20850
Tel (301) 987-9200 *SIC* 0781 0782
■ **CATAMARAN HEALTH SOLUTIONS LLC** p 264
800 King Farm Blvd # 300 20850
Tel (301) 548-2900 *SIC* 5912 6411
CENTER FOR PAIN MANAGEMENT LLC p 276
11921 Rockville Pike # 505 20852
Tel (301) 881-7246 *SIC* 8011
CENTURY DISTRIBUTORS INC p 282
15710 Crabbs Branch Way 20855
Tel (301) 212-9100
SIC 5194 5145 5149 5113
▲ **CHOICE HOTELS INTERNATIONAL INC** p 302
1 Choice Hotels Cir 20850
Tel (301) 592-5000 *SIC* 7011 7373
■ **CLAIMS ADMINISTRATION CORP** p 321
15400 Calhoun Dr Ste 300 20855
Tel (301) 762-5806 *SIC* 6411
CLIENT NETWORK SERVICES INC p 326
2277 Research Blvd 20850
Tel (301) 634-4600 *SIC* 7371 7373 7379
COUNTY OF MONTGOMERY p 380
101 Monroe St Fl 15 20850
Tel (240) 777-8220 *SIC* 9111
DAVIS CONSTRUCTION CORP JAMES G p 416
12530 Parklawn Dr Ste 100 20852
Tel (301) 881-2990 *SIC* 1542
ENVELOPES UNLIMITED INC p 503
649 N Horners Ln 20850
Tel (301) 424-3300 *SIC* 2759 7331
FCN INC p 533
12315 Wilkins Ave 20852
Tel (301) 770-2925 *SIC* 8748
▲ **FEDERAL REALTY INVESTMENT TRUST** p 535
1626 E Jefferson St 20852
Tel (301) 998-8100 *SIC* 6798
FITZGERALD AUTOMALL p 553
11411 Rockville Pike 20852
Tel (301) 881-4000 *SIC* 5511
FORRESTER CONSTRUCTION CO p 568
12231 Parklawn Dr 20852
Tel (301) 816-1700 *SIC* 1542
GALI SERVICE INDUSTRIES INC p 589
12312 Wilkins Ave Ste 100 20852
Tel (301) 986-8890 *SIC* 7349
GROVE SHADY ADVENTIST HOSPITAL p 642
9901 Medical Center Dr 20850
Tel (240) 826-6000 *SIC* 8062
GRUNLEY CONSTRUCTION CO INC p 642
15020 Shady Ste 500 20850
Tel (240) 399-2000 *SIC* 1542
HBW PROPERTIES INC p 671
1055 1st St Ste 200 20850
Tel (301) 424-2900 *SIC* 1542 6512 6531
■ **HEALTH RESOURCES & SERVICES ADMINISTRATION** p 675
5600 Fishers Ln 20852
Tel (301) 443-5460 *SIC* 9431
HEBREW HOME OF GREATER WASHINGTON p 680
6121 Montrose Rd 20852
Tel (301) 881-0300 *SIC* 8051
HUMAN GENOME SCIENCES INC p 718
14200 Shady Grove Rd 20850
Tel (301) 309-8504 *SIC* 8731 2834
INFINITE COMPUTER SOLUTIONS INC p 740
15201 Diamondback Dr # 125 20850
Tel (301) 355-7760 *SIC* 7379 7371
INFOSYS PUBLIC SERVICES INC p 742
800 King Farm Blvd # 505 20850
Tel (301) 354-8600 *SIC* 7371 7374 8742
INTEGRATED SERVICE MANAGEMENT LLC p 749
12312 Wilkins Ave 20852
Tel (703) 480-2671 *SIC* 7349
JOHN C GRIMBERG CO INC p 787
3200 Tower Oaks Blvd Fl 3 20852
Tel (301) 881-5120 *SIC* 1542
JOHN J KIRLIN INC p 789
515 Dover Rd Ste 2100 20850
Tel (301) 424-3410 *SIC* 1711
JOHN J KIRLIN INC p 789
515 Dover Rd Ste 2200 20850
Tel (301) 424-3410 *SIC* 1711
KAISER FOUNDATION HEALTH PLAN OF MID-ATLANTIC STATES INC p 800
2101 E Jefferson St 20852
Tel (301) 816-2424 *SIC* 6324
▲ **MACROGENICS INC** p 893
9704 Medical Center Dr 20850
Tel (301) 251-5172 *SIC* 2834
MESO SCALE DISCOVERY LLC p 951
1601 Research Blvd 20850
Tel (240) 314-2600 *SIC* 3826
MICRO FOCUS (US) INC p 961
700 King Farm Blvd # 125 20850
Tel (301) 838-5000 *SIC* 7372
■ **MID ATLANTIC MEDICAL SERVICES LLC** p 962
800 King Farm Blvd # 600 20850
Tel (301) 990-3844 *SIC* 6324
MONTGOMERY COLLEGE p 986
900 Hungerford Dr 20850
Tel (240) 567-5000 *SIC* 8222
MONTGOMERY COUNTY PUBLIC SCHOOLS p 986
850 Hungerford Dr Rm 149 20850
Tel (301) 279-3617 *SIC* 8211
MONTGOMERY COUNTY PUBLIC SCHOOLS p 986
850 Hungerford Dr 20850
Tel (301) 517-5099 *SIC* 8621 8741
NATIONAL ELECTRICAL BENEFIT FUND p 1011
2400 Res Blvd Ste 500 20850
Tel (301) 556-4300 *SIC* 6371
■ **NUCLEAR REGULATORY COMMISSION UNITED STATES** p 1066
11555 Rockville Pike 20852
Tel (800) 368-5642 *SIC* 9631
OTSUKA AMERICA PHARMACEUTICAL INC p 1098
2440 Res Blvd Ste 500 20850
Tel (301) 990-0030 *SIC* 8733 8011 8731
PAY STAFF p 1122
700 King Farm Blvd # 300 20850
Tel (301) 527-0655 *SIC* 7363 8721
ROBERTS OXYGEN CO INC p 1242
15830 Redland Rd 20855
Tel (301) 315-9090 *SIC* 5085 5169 5047
SHAPIRO & DUNCAN INC p 1311
14620 Rothgeb Dr 20850
Tel (240) 453-0280 *SIC* 1711
SILVER DINER INC p 1323
12276 Rockville Pike 20852
Tel (301) 770-2828 *SIC* 5812
SPECIAL AGENTS MUTUAL BENEFIT ASSOCIATION INC p 1355
11301 Old Georgetown Rd 20852
Tel (301) 984-1440 *SIC* 6411
▲ **SUCAMPO PHARMACEUTICALS INC** p 1396
805 King Farm Blvd # 550 20850
Tel (301) 961-3400 *SIC* 2834
SUPERNUS PHARMACEUTICALS INC p 1407
1550 E Gude Dr 20850
Tel (301) 838-2500 *SIC* 2834
▲ **SYNUTRA INTERNATIONAL INC** p 1416
2275 Res Blvd Ste 500 20850
Tel (301) 840-3888 *SIC* 2023
UNITED STATES PHARMACOPOEIAL CONVENTION p 1514
12601 Twinbrook Pkwy 20852
Tel (301) 881-0666 *SIC* 8731 8734
US NUCLEAR REGULATORY COMMISSION p 1532
21 Church St 20850
Tel (301) 415-7000 *SIC* 9631
WESTAT INC p 1596
1600 Research Blvd 20850
Tel (301) 251-1500
SIC 8732 7371 7373 8741 8742 8999
WTS INTERNATIONAL INC p 1628
3200 Tower Oaks Blvd # 400 20852
Tel (301) 622-7800 *SIC* 7991 7992
ZENIMAX MEDIA INC p 1642
1370 Piccard Dr Ste 120 20850
Tel (301) 948-2200 *SIC* 7371

SALISBURY, MD

CATO INC p 267
1004 Parsons Rd 21801
Tel (410) 546-1215 *SIC* 5172
HOLT PAPER AND CHEMICAL CO INC p 702
31375 John Deere Dr 21804
Tel (410) 742-7577
SIC 5142 5087 5113 5147
LABINAL SALISBURY LLC p 836
600 Glen Ave 21804
Tel (410) 548-7800 *SIC* 3728
PENINSULA REGIONAL MEDICAL CENTER p 1129
100 E Carroll St 21801
Tel (410) 546-6400 *SIC* 8062
PERDUE AGRIBUSINESS LLC p 1134
6906 Zion Church Rd 21804
Tel (410) 543-3000 *SIC* 5159 3556
PERDUE FARMS INC p 1134
31149 Old Ocean City Rd 21804
Tel (410) 543-3000 *SIC* 2015 2075 4213
■ **PIEDMONT AIRLINES INC** p 1146
5443 Airport Terminal Rd 21804
Tel (410) 742-2996 *SIC* 4512
POHANKA OF SALISBURY INC p 1159
2015 N Salisbury Blvd 21801
Tel (410) 749-2301
SIC 5511 7513 7514 7538 7515
WICOMICO COUNTY PUBLIC SCHOOLS p 1608
2424 Northgate Dr Ste 100 21801
Tel (410) 677-4400 *SIC* 8211

SANDY SPRING, MD

HORIZON COACH LINES p 707
17810 Meeting House Rd # 200 20860
Tel (301) 260-2060 *SIC* 4141

SAVAGE, MD

ACME PAPER & SUPPLY CO INC p 18
8229 Sandy Ct 20763
Tel (410) 792-2333 *SIC* 5113 5087

SILVER SPRING, MD

AUTOMATED RESOURCE MANAGEMENT ASSOCIATES INC p 134
962 Wayne Ave Ste 320 20910
Tel (301) 587-7077 *SIC* 7379
CAPITAL DIGESTIVE CARE LLC p 249
12510 Prosperity Dr # 200 20904
Tel (240) 485-5203 *SIC* 8011
COMFORT CALIFORNIA INC p 344
10750 Columbia Pike # 300 20901
Tel (301) 592-3800 *SIC* 7011
COOPERATIVE HOUSING FOUNDATION CORP p 367
8601 Georgia Ave Ste 300 20910
Tel (301) 587-4700 *SIC* 8732
DB CONSULTING GROUP INC p 418
8401 Colesville Rd # 300 20910
Tel (301) 589-4020 *SIC* 8748
▲ **DISCOVERY COMMUNICATIONS INC** p 442
1 Discovery Pl 20910
Tel (240) 662-2000 *SIC* 4841 7812 7922
■ **DISCOVERY COMMUNICATIONS LLC** p 442
1 Discovery Pl 20910
Tel (240) 662-2000 *SIC* 4841
■ **FOOD & DRUG ADMINISTRATION** p 563
10903 Nh Ave Ste 2217 20903
Tel (301) 796-5000 *SIC* 9431
GENERAL CONFERENCE OF SEVENTH-DAY ADVENTISTS p 599
12501 Old Columbia Pike 20904
Tel (301) 680-6000 *SIC* 8661
GENGOTEX CORP p 603
12301 Old Columbia Pike 20904
Tel (240) 753-5497 *SIC* 7389
HOLY CROSS HEALTH INC p 702
1500 Forest Glen Rd 20910
Tel (301) 754-7000 *SIC* 8062
HOLY CROSS HOSPITAL p 702
2701 W 68th St 20910
Tel (301) 754-7000 *SIC* 8062 8011
JANJER ENTERPRISES INC p 777
12150 Tech Rd 20904
Tel (301) 625-5920 *SIC* 5812 8721 8741
MARIAM INC p 906
12210 Cherry Hill Rd 20904
Tel (888) 841-9679 *SIC* 5511
■ **NATIONAL OCEAN SERVICE** p 1014
1305 E West Hwy 20910
Tel (301) 713-3074 *SIC* 9511
■ **NATIONAL OCEANIC AND ATMOSPHERIC ADMINISTRATION** p 1014
1305 Ew Hwy Fl 10 20910
Tel (301) 713-3155 *SIC* 9611
■ **NATIONAL WEATHER SERVICE** p 1017
1325 E West Hwy 20910
Tel (609) 261-6600 *SIC* 9611
■ **OFFICE OF OCEANIC AND ATMOSPHERIC RESEARCH** p 1075
1315 E West Hwy Fl 11 20910
Tel (301) 713-2458 *SIC* 9511
■ **OFFICE OF REGULATORY AFFAIRS** p 1075
10903 Nh Ave Wo31 Rm 3528 20993
Tel (301) 796-8800 *SIC* 9431
▲ **RADIO ONE INC** p 1204
1010 Wayne Ave Ste 1400 20910
Tel (301) 429-3200 *SIC* 4832 4841 4813
RIDERWOOD VILLAGE INC p 1234
3150 Gracefield Rd 20904
Tel (301) 572-1300 *SIC* 8361
▲ **RLJ ENTERTAINMENT INC** p 1239
8515 Georgia Ave Ste 650 20910
Tel (301) 608-2115 *SIC* 7822
SOCIAL & SCIENTIFIC SYSTEMS INC p 1336
8757 Georgia Ave Ste 1200 20910
Tel (301) 628-3000 *SIC* 7374 7371
SUNBURST HOSPITALITY CORP p 1401
10750 Columbia Pike # 300 20901
Tel (301) 592-3800 *SIC* 8741 7011
TECHNOLOGY SERVICE CORP p 1432
962 Wayne Ave 20910
Tel (301) 576-2300 *SIC* 8711
UNION LABOR LIFE INSURANCE CO p 1504
8403 Colesville Rd # 1000 20910
Tel (202) 682-0900
SIC 6311 6321 6324 6371
▲ **UNITED THERAPEUTICS CORP** p 1514
1040 Spring St 20910
Tel (301) 608-9292 *SIC* 2834
■ **WESTERN PACIFIC REGIONAL FISHERY MANAGEMENT COUNCIL** p 1599
1315 E West Hwy 20910
Tel (301) 713-2239 *SIC* 9611

SPARKS GLENCOE, MD

KCI HOLDINGS INC p 806
936 Ridgebrook Rd 21152
Tel (410) 316-7800 *SIC* 8711 1799
KELLY & ASSOCIATES INSURANCE GROUP INC p 809
1 Kelly Way 21152
Tel (410) 527-3400 *SIC* 6411

SPARKS, MD

APEX TOOL GROUP LLC p 96
14600 York Rd Ste A 21152
Tel (410) 773-7800 *SIC* 3423
BC MOUNTAIN HOLDINGS INC p 163
14600 York Rd Ste A 21152
Tel (800) 763-1233 *SIC* 3423
ELEMENT VEHICLE MANAGEMENT SERVICES GROUP LLC p 486
940 Ridgebrook Rd 21152
Tel (410) 771-1900 *SIC* 6141
ELEMENT VEHICLE MANAGEMENT SERVICES LLC p 486
940 Ridgebrook Rd 21152
Tel (410) 771-1900 *SIC* 7513 7515
FIDELITY ENGINEERING CORP p 540
25 Loveton Cir 21152
Tel (410) 771-9400
SIC 1711 5063 1799 8711
■ **FILA USA INC** p 542
930 Ridgebrook Rd Ste 200 21152
Tel (410) 773-3000
SIC 5139 5131 5137 5611 5621 5632
JOHNSON MIRMIRAN & THOMPSON INC p 791
72 Loveton Cir 21152
Tel (410) 329-3100 *SIC* 8711
KCI TECHNOLOGIES INC p 806
936 Ridgebrook Rd 21152
Tel (410) 316-7800 *SIC* 8711
▲ **MCCORMICK & CO INC** p 927
18 Loveton Cir 21152
Tel (410) 771-7301
SIC 2099 2087 2038 2037
■ **PHH VEHICLE SALES INC** p 1142
940 Ridgebrook Rd 21152
Tel (800) 665-9744 *SIC* 7513
TRANS HEALTHCARE INC p 1470
930 Ridgebrook Rd 21152
Tel (410) 773-1000 *SIC* 8011 8051
TRIDENT USA HEALTH SERVICES LLC p 1480
930 Ridgebrook Rd Fl 3 21152
Tel (800) 786-8015 *SIC* 8734

STEVENSON, MD

JULIE VILLA COLLEGE p 797
1525 Greenspring Vly Rd 21153
Tel (410) 486-7000 *SIC* 8221
STEVENSON UNIVERSITY INC p 1388
1525 Greenspring Vly Rd 21153
Tel (410) 486-7000 *SIC* 8221

STEVENSVILLE, MD

■ **Z MARINE NORTH AMERICA LLC** p 1640
540 Thompson Creek Rd 21666
Tel (843) 376-3470 *SIC* 5091

SUITLAND, MD

■ **CENSUS BUREAU UNITED STATES** p 275
4600 Silver Hill Rd 20746
Tel (301) 763-2135 *SIC* 9611
DAR CARS DODGE INC p 412
5060 Auth Way 20746
Tel (301) 423-5111 *SIC* 5511
INTERNATIONAL MOTOR CARS INC p 756
5000 Auth Way 20746
Tel (301) 423-8400 *SIC* 5511 7538 5521

SYKESVILLE, MD

NEXION HEALTH INC p 1040
6937 Warfield Ave 21784
Tel (410) 552-4800 *SIC* 8051

TANEYTOWN, MD

EVAPCO INC p 513
5151 Allendale Ln 21787
Tel (410) 756-2600 *SIC* 3443 3585

TOWSON, MD

ATLANTIC AUTOMOTIVE CORP p 125
1 Olympic Pl Ste 1210 21204
Tel (410) 602-6177 *SIC* 5511 7538 7515
BALTIMORE COUNTY PUBLIC SCHOOLS p 149
6901 N Charles St 21204
Tel (410) 887-4554 *SIC* 8211
■ **BLACK & DECKER CORP** p 186
701 E Joppa Rd 21286
Tel (410) 716-3900
SIC 3546 3553 3541 3634 3452

CHESAPEAKE EMPLOYERS INSURANCE CO p 295
8722 Loch Raven Blvd 21286
Tel (410) 494-2000 *SIC* 6321

E4E INC p 467
502 Washington Ave # 200 21204
Tel (443) 275-1632 *SIC* 7389

LIVER AND PANCREAS CENTER UNIVERSITY OF MARYLAND ST JOSEPH MEDICAL CENTER p 871
7505 Osler Dr Ste 303 21204
Tel (410) 427-2024 *SIC* 8062

MARYLAND DEPT OF PUBLIC SAFETY & CORRECTIONAL SERVICES p 914
300 E Joppa Rd Ste 1000 21286
Tel (410) 339-5000 *SIC* 9223

PUBLISHERS CIRCULATION FULFILLMENT INC p 1190
502 Wshington Ave Ste 500 21204
Tel (410) 821-8614 *SIC* 5963

REMEDI SENIORCARE HOLDING CORP p 1222
1 Olympic Pl Ste 600 21204
Tel (443) 927-8400 *SIC* 6719

UNIVERSITY OF MARYLAND ST JOSEPH MEDICAL CENTER LLC p 1522
7601 Osler Dr 21204
Tel (410) 337-1000 *SIC* 8062

UPPER MARLBORO, MD

BRANCH GROUP INC p 207
1049 Prince Georges Blvd 20774
Tel (301) 249-5005 *SIC* 5063 5211

CAPITAL LIGHTING & SUPPLY LLC p 249
8511 Pepco Pl 20772
Tel (301) 909-6500 *SIC* 5063

COASTAL INTERNATIONAL SECURITY INC p 332
6101 Fallard Dr 20772
Tel (703) 339-0233 *SIC* 7381

COUNTY OF PRINCE GEORGES p 381
14741 Gvrnor Oden Bwie Dr 20772
Tel (301) 952-6000 *SIC* 9111

DPI SPECIALTY FOODS MID ATLANTIC INC p 454
1000 Prince Georges Blvd 20774
Tel (301) 430-2200 *SIC* 5149

MELWOOD HORTICULTURAL TRAINING CENTER INC p 941
5606 Dower House Rd 20772
Tel (301) 599-8000 *SIC* 8331 8322

MENDELSON HOLDING CO LTD INC p 943
8300 Pennsylvania Ave 20772
Tel (301) 420-6400 *SIC* 5411

P4 CORP p 1103
16001 Trade Zone Ave 20774
Tel (301) 218-7039 *SIC* 5087 5072

PRINCE GEORGES COMMUNITY COLLEGE p 1176
301 Largo Rd 20774
Tel (301) 336-6000 *SIC* 8221 8222

PRINCE GEORGES COUNTY PUBLIC SCHOOLS p 1176
14201 School Ln 20772
Tel (301) 952-6000 *SIC* 8211

THOS SOMERVILLE CO p 1450
16155 Trade Zone Ave 20774
Tel (301) 390-9575 *SIC* 5074 5075

WALDORF, MD

ADAMS COMMUNICATION & ENGINEERING TECHNOLOGY INC p 21
11637 Terrace Dr Ste 201 20602
Tel (301) 861-5000 *SIC* 7379

UNITED SITE SERVICES OF MARYLAND INC p 1511
3250 Old Washington Rd 20602
Tel (301) 396-8501 *SIC* 7349

WALKERSVILLE, MD

LONZA WALKERSVILLE INC p 877
8830 Biggs Ford Rd 21793
Tel (301) 898-7025 *SIC* 2836

WESTMINSTER, MD

BOARD OF EDUCATION OF CARROLL COUNTY p 195
125 N Court St 21157
Tel (410) 751-3000 *SIC* 8211

CARROLL COUNTY HEALTH SERVICES CORP p 261
200 Memorial Ave 21157
Tel (410) 848-3000 *SIC* 6324

CARROLL COUNTY PUBLIC SCHOOLS p 261
125 N Court St Ste 101 21157
Tel (410) 751-3128 *SIC* 8211

CARROLL HOSPITAL CENTER INC p 261
200 Memorial Ave 21157
Tel (410) 848-3000 *SIC* 8062

COMMISSIONERS OF CARROLL COUNTY p 345
225 N Center St 21157
Tel (410) 386-2400 *SIC* 9111

MIDATLANTIC FARM CREDIT p 964
45 Aileron Ct 21157
Tel (410) 848-1033 *SIC* 6159

WILLIAMSPORT, MD

HOMEWOOD RETIREMENT CENTERS OF UNITED CHURCH OF CHRIST INC p 704
16107 Elliott Pkwy 21795
Tel (301) 582-1626 *SIC* 8051 8361

■ POTOMAC EDISON CO p 1164
10802 Bower Ave 21795
Tel (800) 686-0011 *SIC* 4911

MASSACHUSETTS

ACTON, MA

HAARTZ CORP p 651
87 Hayward Rd 01720
Tel (978) 264-2600 *SIC* 3069 2295

▲ SEACHANGE INTERNATIONAL INC p 1296
50 Nagog Park 01720
Tel (978) 897-0100 *SIC* 3663 7822 7371

AGAWAM, MA

CONRAD FAFARD INC p 358
770 Silver St 01001
Tel (413) 786-4343 *SIC* 5191 2875

SPRINGFIELD WATER & SEWER COMMISSION p 1361
250 M St 01001
Tel (413) 787-6060 *SIC* 4941

SUN GRO HORTICULTURE DISTRIBUTION INC p 1400
770 Silver St 01001
Tel (413) 786-4343 *SIC* 1499 2875

SUNGROW HORTICULTURE CANADA INC p 1402
770 Silver St 01001
Tel (800) 732-8667 *SIC* 0782

TOWN OF AGAWAM p 1465
36 Main St 01001
Tel (413) 786-0400 *SIC* 9111

AMESBURY, MA

AMESBURY GROUP INC p 84
57 S Hunt Rd 01913
Tel (978) 834-3233
SIC 3053 3442 3086 2221 3089

MUNTERS CORP p 1001
79 Monroe St 01913
Tel (978) 241-1100
SIC 3585 3822 3569 3564

MUNTERS USA INC p 1001
79 Monroe St 01913
Tel (978) 241-1100 *SIC* 3585

AMHERST, MA

EMILY DICKINSON MUSEUM p 493
280 Main St 01002
Tel (413) 542-8161 *SIC* 8412

STAVROS CENTER FOR INDEPENDENT LIVING INC p 1383
210 Old Farm Rd 01002
Tel (413) 256-0473 *SIC* 8322

TRUSTEES OF AMHERST COLLEGE p 1487
103 Converse Hl 01002
Tel (413) 542-2000 *SIC* 8221

TRUSTEES OF HAMPSHIRE COLLEGE p 1488
893 West St 01002
Tel (413) 549-4600 *SIC* 8221

ANDOVER, MA

ANDOVER PUBLIC SCHOOLS p 90
50 Bartlet St 01810
Tel (978) 623-8519 *SIC* 8211

BAY STATE INSURANCE CO p 161
95 River Rd 01810
Tel (978) 475-3300 *SIC* 6331

CGI INFORMATION SYSTEMS & MANAGEMENT CONSULTANTS INC p 286
600 Federal St 01810
Tel (978) 946-3000 *SIC* 7374 3577 7373

■ DYNAMICS RESEARCH CORP p 464
2 Tech Dr 01810
Tel (978) 289-1500 *SIC* 7373 7379 8711

ENEL GREEN POWER NORTH AMERICA INC p 497
1 Tech Dr Ste 220 01810
Tel (978) 681-1900 *SIC* 4911

■ ENGILITY CORP p 499
35 New Engld Busctr Dr200 01810
Tel (978) 749-2100 *SIC* 8711

GENLYTE GROUP INC p 604
3000 Minuteman Rd 01810
Tel (781) 418-7900 *SIC* 3646 3645 3648

■ INDIGO AMERICA INC p 739
165 Dascomb Rd 1 01810
Tel (978) 474-2000 *SIC* 5049

MERRIMACK MUTUAL FIRE INSURANCE CO p 950
95 River Rd 01810
Tel (978) 475-3300 *SIC* 6331

▲ MKS INSTRUMENTS INC p 979
2 Tech Dr Ste 201 01810
Tel (978) 645-5500 *SIC* 3823 3491 3494

■ NAVISITE LLC p 1020
400 Minuteman Rd 01810
Tel (978) 682-8300 *SIC* 4813

PHILIPS ELECTRONICS NORTH AMERICA CORP p 1143
3000 Minuteman Rd Ms1203 01810
Tel (978) 687-1501
SIC 5064 3651 3674 3641 3645 5047

PHILIPS HOLDING USA INC p 1143
3000 Minuteman Rd Ste 109 01810
Tel (978) 687-1501
SIC 5064 3674 5045 5047 3641

PHILIPS MEDICAL SYSTEMS HSG p 1143
3000 Minuteman Rd 01810
Tel (978) 687-1501 *SIC* 3675 3676

SCHNEIDER AUTOMATION INC p 1287
800 Federal St Ste 1 01810
Tel (978) 794-0800 *SIC* 3822

SCHNEIDER ELECTRIC USA INC p 1288
800 Federal St 01810
Tel (978) 975-9600
SIC 3613 3643 3612 3823 3625 5063

STRAUMANN USA LLC p 1393
60 Minuteman Rd 01810
Tel (978) 747-2500 *SIC* 5047

TAC INC p 1421
1 High St 01810
Tel (978) 470-0555 *SIC* 3822

TOWN OF ANDOVER p 1465
36 Bartlet St 01810
Tel (978) 623-8225 *SIC* 9111

TRUSTEES OF PHILLIPS ACADEMY p 1488
180 Main St 01810
Tel (978) 749-4000 *SIC* 8211 8412

▲ VICOR CORP p 1555
25 Frontage Rd 01810
Tel (978) 470-2900 *SIC* 3679 3613

ARLINGTON, MA

TOWN OF ARLINGTON p 1465
730 Massachusetts Ave 02476
Tel (781) 316-3000 *SIC* 9111

ASHLAND, MA

■ KIDDE-FENWAL INC p 817
400 Main St 01721
Tel (508) 881-2000
SIC 3669 3823 3825 3822 3643 3625

ONPROCESS TECHNOLOGY INC p 1088
200 Homer Ave 01721
Tel (508) 520-2711 *SIC* 7379

ATHOL, MA

▲ L S STARRETT CO p 834
121 Crescent St 01331
Tel (978) 249-3551
SIC 3545 3423 3999 3425 3823

ATTLEBORO, MA

CITY OF ATTLEBORO p 313
77 Park St Ste 1 02703
Tel (508) 223-2222 *SIC* 9111

EMS ENGINEERED MATERIALS SOLUTIONS LLC p 495
39 Perry Ave 02703
Tel (508) 342-2100 *SIC* 3351

■ LEACH GARNER - A BERKSHIRE HATHAWAY CO p 850
49 Pearl St 02703
Tel (508) 222-7400 *SIC* 5094

PEP INDUSTRIES LLC p 1133
110 Frank Mossberg Dr 02703
Tel (508) 226-5600
SIC 3089 3351 3469 3471 3643 3841

PRECISION ENGINEERED PRODUCTS LLC p 1168
110 Frank Mossberg Dr 02703
Tel (508) 226-5600
SIC 3643 3469 3841 3471 3089 3351

SENSATA TECHNOLOGIES INC p 1304
529 Pleasant St 02703
Tel (508) 236-3800 *SIC* 3679

SENSATA TECHNOLOGIES INDIANA INC p 1304
529 Pleasant St 02703
Tel (508) 236-3245 *SIC* 3676 3625

STURDY MEMORIAL HOSPITAL INC p 1395
211 Park St 02703
Tel (508) 222-5200 *SIC* 8062 8011

SUPPLY NEW ENGLAND INC p 1407
123 East St 02703
Tel (508) 222-5555 *SIC* 5074

TRIMARK UNITED EAST INC p 1480
505 Collins St 02703
Tel (508) 399-6000
SIC 5046 5021 5113 5087

TRIMARK USA LLC p 1480
505 Collins St 02703
Tel (508) 399-2400 *SIC* 5021 5023

WABASH TECHNOLOGIES INC p 1570
529 Pleasant St 02703
Tel (260) 355-4100 *SIC* 3625 3676

AUBURN, MA

AMERICAN STEEL AND ALUMINUM CORP p 80
27 Elm St 01501
Tel (508) 832-9681 *SIC* 5051

AUBURNDALE, MA

ALLIANCE HEALTH INC p 54
134 Rumford Ave Ste 306 02466
Tel (617) 332-3366 *SIC* 8051

ATRIUS HEALTH INC p 129
275 Grove St Ste 3-300 02466
Tel (617) 559-8000 *SIC* 8099 8062

ATRIUS HEALTH INC p 129
275 Grove St Ste 3-300 02466
Tel (617) 559-8444 *SIC* 8011

C&W FACILITY SERVICES INC p 234
275 Grove St Ste 3-200 02466
Tel (617) 527-5222 *SIC* 7349 6531

DTZ GOVERNMENT SERVICES INC p 458
275 Grove St Ste 3-200 02466
Tel (617) 527-5222 *SIC* 7349

▲ TECHTARGET INC p 1432
275 Grove St Ste 1-150 02466
Tel (617) 431-9200 *SIC* 7375

AUBURN, MA

IMPERIAL DISTRIBUTORS INC p 734
33 Sword St 01501
Tel (508) 756-5156 *SIC* 5122

R H WHITE COMPANIES INC p 1202
41 Central St 01501
Tel (508) 832-3295
SIC 1629 7359 1522 1521

AVON, MA

CUMING CORP p 400
225 Bodwell St 02322
Tel (508) 580-2660 *SIC* 3533 3679

BABSON PARK, MA

BABSON COLLEGE p 143
231 Forest St 02457
Tel (781) 235-1200 *SIC* 8221

BEDFORD, MA

ACME PACKET INC p 18
100 Crosby Dr 01730
Tel (781) 328-4400 *SIC* 7372

▲ ANIKA THERAPEUTICS INC p 91
32 Wiggins Ave 01730
Tel (781) 457-9000 *SIC* 2836

▲ ASPEN TECHNOLOGY INC p 118
20 Crosby Dr 01730
Tel (781) 221-6400 *SIC* 7371 7372

CONTINENTAL RESOURCES INC p 363
175 Middlesex Tpke Ste 1 01730
Tel (781) 275-0850
SIC 5045 5065 7377 7359 7378 7629

F W WEBB CO p 522
160 Middlesex Tpke 01730
Tel (781) 272-6600 *SIC* 5074 5085 5075

IGLOO HOLDINGS CORP p 730
32 Crosby Dr 01730
Tel (781) 687-8500 *SIC* 6289 7375

IGLOO INTERMEDIATE CORP p 730
32 Crosby Dr 01730
Tel (781) 687-8500 *SIC* 6289 7375

INSTRUMENTATION LABORATORY CO p 747
180 Hartwell Rd 01730
Tel (800) 955-9525
SIC 3841 2819 8731 2835

■ INTERACTIVE DATA CORP p 751
32 Crosby Dr 01730
Tel (781) 687-8500 *SIC* 6289 7375

■ INTERACTIVE DATA PRICING AND REFERENCE DATA LLC p 751
32 Crosby Dr 01730
Tel (781) 687-8800 *SIC* 6022

▲ IROBOT CORP p 764
8 Crosby Dr 01730
Tel (781) 430-3000 *SIC* 3569 3731

MITRE CORP p 977
202 Burlington Rd 01730
Tel (781) 271-2000 *SIC* 8733 8711

■ NOVANTA CORP p 1062
125 Middlesex Tpke 01730
Tel (781) 266-5700 *SIC* 3699

▲ NOVANTA INC p 1062
125 Middlesex Tpke 01730
Tel (781) 266-5700 *SIC* 3699 3845

▲ PROGRESS SOFTWARE CORP p 1181
14 Oak Park Dr 01730
Tel (781) 280-4000 *SIC* 7372 7371

■ RAYTHEON LOGISTICS SUPPORT & TRAINING CO p 1211
180 Hartwell Rd 01730
Tel (310) 647-9438 *SIC* 3761

■ RSA SECURITY LLC p 1255
174 Middlesex Tpke 01730
Tel (781) 515-5000 *SIC* 3577 7372 7373

BELMONT, MA

MCLEAN HOSPITAL CORP p 931
115 Mill St 02478
Tel (617) 855-2000 *SIC* 8063

BEVERLY, MA

■ ALLIED WIRELESS COMMUNICATIONS CORP p 57
600 Cummings Ctr 01915
Tel (978) 619-1300 *SIC* 4813

▲ AMERICAN RENAL ASSOCIATES HOLDINGS INC p 78
500 Cummings Ctr Ste 6550 01915
Tel (978) 922-3080 *SIC* 8092

■ AMERICAN RENAL ASSOCIATES LLC p 78
500 Cummings Ctr Ste 6550 01915
Tel (978) 922-3080 *SIC* 8092

■ AMERICAN RENAL HOLDINGS INC p 78
500 Cummings Ctr Ste 6550 01915
Tel (978) 922-3080 *SIC* 8092

▲ ATN INTERNATIONAL INC p 128
500 Cummings Ctr Ste 2450 01915
Tel (978) 619-1300 *SIC* 4813 4812 1711

▲ AXCELIS TECHNOLOGIES INC p 140
108 Cherry Hill Dr 01915
Tel (978) 787-4000 *SIC* 3559 3829

CITY OF BEVERLY p 313
191 Cabot St Rm 1 01915
Tel (978) 922-2500 *SIC* 9121

ENDICOTT COLLEGE p 496
376 Hale St 01915
Tel (978) 927-0585 *SIC* 8221

ENDICOTT COLLEGE p 496
376 Hale St 01915
Tel (978) 927-0585 *SIC* 8221

KING CANNON INC p 820
60 River St 01915
Tel (978) 921-7438 *SIC* 5812

LEDGEWOOD HEALTH CARE CORP p 851
87 Herrick St 01915
Tel (978) 524-6100 *SIC* 8051

NORTHEAST HEALTH SYSTEMS INC p 1055
85 Herrick St 01915
Tel (978) 922-3000 *SIC* 8741

NORTHEAST HOSPITAL CORP p 1055
85 Herrick St 01915
Tel (978) 922-3000 *SIC* 8062

ORCHARD BRANDS CORP p 1093
138 Conant St Ste 3 01915
Tel (978) 998-3800 *SIC* 5621 5611 5719

■ OXFORD GLOBAL RESOURCES LLC p 1101
100 Cummings Ctr Ste 206c 01915
Tel (978) 236-1182 *SIC* 7363 8748

PETEDGE INC p 1138
100 Cummings Ctr Ste 307b 01915
Tel (978) 998-8100 *SIC* 5199

PETEDGE MASSACHUSETTS BUSINESS TRUST p 1138
100 Cummings Ctr Ste 307b 01915
Tel (978) 998-8100 *SIC* 5199

■ SENSITECH INC p 1305
800 Cummings Ctr Ste 258x 01915
Tel (978) 927-7033 *SIC* 3826 3823 3822

STEVEN LAVERTY p 1388
85 Herrick St 01915
Tel (978) 927-7880 *SIC* 8062

YMCA OF NORTH SHORE INC p 1636
245 Cabot St 01915
Tel (978) 922-0990
SIC 7021 8322 8351 7999 7032

BILLERICA, MA

■ AMERICAN SCIENCE AND ENGINEERING INC p 79
829 Middlesex Tpke 01821
Tel (978) 262-8700 *SIC* 7389 8734 7382

BILLERICA PUBLIC SCHOOLS p 182
365 Boston Rd 01821
Tel (978) 528-7900 *SIC* 8211

▲ BRUKER CORP p 220
40 Manning Rd 01821
Tel (978) 663-3660 *SIC* 3826 3844

■ BRUKER DALTONICS INC p 221
40 Manning Rd 01821
Tel (978) 667-9580 *SIC* 3826 5049

EMD MILLIPORE CORP p 491
290 Concord Rd 01821
Tel (781) 533-6000 *SIC* 3559 1541 3999

EMPIRIX INC p 494
600 Technology Park Dr # 1 01821
Tel (978) 313-7000 *SIC* 7371 8734

▲ ENTEGRIS INC p 501
129 Concord Rd 01821
Tel (978) 436-6500 *SIC* 3089 3081 3674

■ GE INFRASTRUCTURE SENSING INC p 596
1100 Technology Park Dr # 100 01821
Tel (978) 437-1000
SIC 3823 5084 3699 3674 3663 3625

GETRONICS USA INC p 609
290 Concord Rd 01821
Tel (978) 625-5000 *SIC* 7378 7373 7379

▲ INSULET CORP p 747
600 Technology Park Dr # 200 01821
Tel (978) 600-7000 *SIC* 3841

JOHNSON OHARE CO INC p 791
1 Progress Rd 01821
Tel (978) 663-9000 *SIC* 5141

MORPHOTRUST USA LLC p 990
296 Concord Rd Ste 300 01821
Tel (978) 215-2400 *SIC* 7374 8711

ORBOTECH INC p 1093
44 Manning Rd 01821
Tel (978) 667-6037 *SIC* 5065 3823 3674

PORTLAND GROUP INC p 1163
74 Salem Rd 01821
Tel (978) 262-1444 *SIC* 5074

SEURAT HOLDINGS INC p 1309
5 Fortune Dr 01821
Tel (877) 489-9449 *SIC* 3544 5084

TOWN OF BILLERICA p 1465
365 Boston Rd Ste 207 01821
Tel (978) 671-0928 *SIC* 9111

BOLTON, MA

FAI ELECTRONICS CORP p 524
41 Main St 01740
Tel (978) 779-3111 *SIC* 5065

FUTURE ELECTRONICS CORP p 585
41 Main St 01740
Tel (800) 444-0050 *SIC* 5065

BOSTON, MA

ABBEY LAFAYETTE p 9
2 Avenue De Lafayette 02111
Tel (617) 542-7373 *SIC* 6553

ABP CORP p 12
19 Fid Kennedy Ave 02210
Tel (617) 423-0629 *SIC* 5461 5812 2051

ABRY PARTNERS INC p 12
888 Boylston St Ste 1600 02199
Tel (617) 859-2959 *SIC* 4899 2741

ABRY PARTNERS LLC p 12
888 Boylston St Ste 1600 02199
Tel (617) 375-8800 *SIC* 6799

ABRY PARTNERS VI LP p 12
111 Huntington Ave Fl 30 02199
Tel (617) 859-2959 *SIC* 6722

ACTION FOR BOSTON COMMUNITY DEVELOPMENT INC p 19
178 Tremont St 02111
Tel (617) 357-6000 *SIC* 8399 8322

ADMINISTRATION AND FINANCE MASSACHUSETTS EXECUTIVE OFFICE FOR p 23
24 Beacon St Ste 373 02133
Tel (617) 727-2040 *SIC* 9199 9311

ADVENT INTERNATIONAL CORP p 27
75 State St Ste 2900 02109
Tel (617) 951-0555 *SIC* 6726

ADVENT INTERNATIONAL GPE VII LLC p 27
75 State St Fl 29 02109
Tel (617) 951-9493 *SIC* 6726

AEW CAPITAL MANAGEMENT LP p 32
2 Seaport Ln 02210
Tel (617) 951-0812 *SIC* 6282 6798

■ AIR WORLDWIDE CORP p 39
131 Dartmouth St Ste 401 02116
Tel (617) 267-6645 *SIC* 6411

ALLIED WORLD ASSURANCE CO (US) INC p 57
2 Liberty Sq Fl 11 02109
Tel (857) 288-6000 *SIC* 6411

▲ AMERICAN TOWER CORP p 80
116 Huntington Ave # 1100 02116
Tel (617) 375-7500 *SIC* 4813 3663

ANALYSIS GROUP INC p 88
111 Huntington Ave Fl 10 02199
Tel (617) 425-8000 *SIC* 8732

AQUENT LLC p 101
501 Boylston St Ste 3 02116
Tel (617) 535-5000 *SIC* 7361

ARBELLA INC p 102
101 Arch St Ste 1860 02110
Tel (617) 328-2800 *SIC* 6411

ARCLIGHT CAPITAL HOLDINGS LLC p 105
200 Clarendon St Fl 55 02116
Tel (617) 531-6300 *SIC* 6799

ARCLIGHT CAPITAL PARTNERS LLC p 105
200 Clarendon St Fl 55 02116
Tel (617) 531-6300 *SIC* 6799

ARNOLD WORLDWIDE LLC p 112
10 Summer St Ste 600 02110
Tel (617) 587-8000 *SIC* 7311 8743

■ ATC TOWER SERVICES LLC p 124
116 Huntington Ave # 1100 02116
Tel (617) 375-7500 *SIC* 4813 3663

ATG / USM HOLDINGS LLC p 124
101 Huntington Ave 02199
Tel (860) 257-3443 *SIC* 5999

AUDAX GROUP LP p 130
101 Huntington Ave # 2450 02199
Tel (617) 859-1500 *SIC* 6726 3646

BAIN & CO INC p 145
131 Dartmouth St Ste 901 02116
Tel (617) 572-2000 *SIC* 8742

BAIN CAPITAL LP p 145
200 Clarendon St 02116
Tel (617) 516-2000 *SIC* 6282

BAIN CAPITAL PARTNERS LLC p 145
200 Clarendon St 02116
Tel (617) 516-2000 *SIC* 6799

■ BANCBOSTON CAPITAL INC p 149
100 Federal St Ste 1m 02110
Tel (617) 434-2509 *SIC* 6799

BARINGS LLC p 155
470 Atlantic Ave Fl 9 02210
Tel (617) 225-3800 *SIC* 6282

BAY COVE HUMAN SERVICES INC p 160
66 Canal St 02114
Tel (617) 371-3000 *SIC* 8052 8093 8361

BEACON COMPANIES INC p 164
2 Center Plz Ste 700 02108
Tel (617) 574-1100 *SIC* 1522 6531 1542

BEACON HILL STAFFING GROUP LLC p 164
152 Bowdoin St 02108
Tel (617) 326-4000 *SIC* 7361

BEACON RESIDENTIAL MANAGEMENT LIMITED PARTNERSHIP p 165
2 Center Plz Ste 700 02108
Tel (617) 574-1100 *SIC* 6531

BERKLEE COLLEGE OF MUSIC INC p 175
1140 Boylston St 02215
Tel (617) 266-1400 *SIC* 8221

BERKSHIRE PARTNERS LLC p 175
200 Clarendon St Ste 3500 02116
Tel (617) 227-0050 *SIC* 6211 6726 8741

BETH ISRAEL DEACONESS MEDICAL CENTER INC p 177
330 Brookline Ave 02215
Tel (617) 667-7000 *SIC* 8062

BIDMC TELECOMMUNICATIONS p 181
1 Jimmy Fund Way 02115
Tel (617) 278-6351 *SIC* 4813

BLAUER MANUFACTURING CO INC p 189
20 Aberdeen St 02215
Tel (617) 536-6606 *SIC* 5099 3842 2337

BLUE CROSS AND BLUE SHIELD OF MASSACHUSETTS INC p 191
101 Huntington Ave # 1300 02199
Tel (617) 246-5000 *SIC* 6321 8741 6324

BMC PARTNERS LLP p 193
1 Federal St 02110
Tel (617) 951-8000 *SIC* 8111

▲ BOSTON BEER CO INC p 202
1 Design Center Pl # 850 02210
Tel (617) 368-5000 *SIC* 2082

■ BOSTON BEER CORP p 202
1 Design Center Pl # 850 02210
Tel (617) 368-5000 *SIC* 2082

■ BOSTON BREWING CO INC p 202
1 Design Center Pl # 850 02210
Tel (617) 368-5250 *SIC* 8741

■ BOSTON CO INC p 202
1 Boston Pl Ste 2100 02108
Tel (617) 722-7000 *SIC* 6022 6282

BOSTON CONSULTING GROUP INC p 202
1 Beacon St Fl 10 02108
Tel (617) 850-3700 *SIC* 8742

BOSTON FOUNDATION INC p 202
75 Arlington St Fl 10 02116
Tel (617) 338-1700 *SIC* 6733

BOSTON GLOBE LLC p 203
135 Wliam T Mrrssey Blvd 02125
Tel (617) 929-2684 *SIC* 2711

BOSTON MEDICAL CENTER CORP p 203
1 Boston Medical Ctr Pl # 1 02118
Tel (617) 414-5000 *SIC* 8062

BOSTON MEDICAL CENTER HEALTH PLAN INC p 203
2 Copley Pl Ste 600 02116
Tel (617) 748-6000 *SIC* 6324

■ BOSTON PRIVATE BANK & TRUST CO p 203
10 Post Office Sq Lbby F 02109
Tel (617) 912-1931 *SIC* 6022

▲ BOSTON PRIVATE FINANCIAL HOLDINGS INC p 203
10 Post Office Sq 02109
Tel (617) 912-1900 *SIC* 6022 6722 6282

■ BOSTON PROPERTIES INC p 203
800 Boylston St Ste 1900 02199
Tel (617) 236-3300 *SIC* 6798

■ BOSTON PROPERTIES LIMITED PARTNERSHIP p 203
800 Boylston St Ste 1900 02199
Tel (617) 236-3300 *SIC* 6798

BOSTON SAND & GRAVEL CO INC p 203
100 N Washington St Fl 2 02114
Tel (617) 227-9000 *SIC* 3273 1442

BOSTON SYMPHONY ORCHESTRA INC p 203
301 Massachusetts Ave 02115
Tel (617) 266-1492 *SIC* 7929

BOSTON UNIVERSITY p 203
590 Commonwealth Ave # 255 02215
Tel (617) 353-2000 *SIC* 8221

BRIGHAM AND WOMENS FAULKNER HOSPITAL INC p 212
1153 Centre St 02130
Tel (617) 983-7000 *SIC* 8062

BRIGHAM AND WOMENS HEALTH CARE INC p 212
75 Francis St 02115
Tel (617) 732-5500 *SIC* 8741

BRIGHAM AND WOMENS HOSPITAL INC p 212
75 Francis St 02115
Tel (617) 732-5500 *SIC* 8062

▲ BRIGHTCOVE INC p 213
290 Congress St Fl 4 02210
Tel (888) 882-1880 *SIC* 4813 7372

▲ BROOKLINE BANCORP INC p 218
131 Clarendon St 02116
Tel (617) 425-4600 *SIC* 6035

■ BROOKLINE BANK p 218
131 Clarendon St 02116
Tel (617) 425-4625 *SIC* 6036

▲ CABOT CORP p 235
2 Seaport Ln Ste 1300 02210
Tel (617) 345-0100
SIC 2895 3081 3084 2819 3339

■ CABOT INTERNATIONAL CAPITAL CORP p 235
2 Seaport Ln Ste 1300 02210
Tel (617) 345-0100 *SIC* 5169

CAMBRIDGE ASSOCIATES LLC p 244
125 High St Ste 1505 02110
Tel (617) 457-7500 *SIC* 6282

CARAT FUSION INC p 252
1 South Sta 300 02110
Tel (617) 449-4100 *SIC* 7319

▲ CARBONITE INC p 252
2 Avenue De Lafayette # 2 02111
Tel (617) 587-1100 *SIC* 7372 7374

CAREER PARTNERS INTERNATIONAL LLC p 254
125 Summer St Ste 1020 02110
Tel (919) 401-4260 *SIC* 8742

CAREGROUP INC p 255
375 Longwood Ave Fl 7 02215
Tel (617) 667-1715 *SIC* 8741

CB HOLDING CORP p 268
1 Congress St Ste 113 02114
Tel (617) 720-2994 *SIC* 6712

CCC ACQUISITION HOLDINGS INC p 269
200 Clarendon St Ste 4000 02116
Tel (617) 516-2000 *SIC* 6719 2821

CDM CONSTRUCTORS INC p 271
75 State St Ste 701 02109
Tel (617) 452-6000 *SIC* 1541 1623

CDM SMITH INC p 271
75 State St Ste 701 02109
Tel (617) 452-6000 *SIC* 8711

CENGAGE LEARNING HOLDINGS II INC p 275
20 Channel Ctr St 02210
Tel (617) 289-7700 *SIC* 2731

CENGAGE LEARNING INC p 275
20 Channel Ctr St 02210
Tel (617) 289-7700 *SIC* 2731

CHARLESBANK CAPITAL PARTNERS LLC p 289
200 Clarendon St Fl 54 02116
Tel (617) 619-5400 *SIC* 6211

CHARLIE BROWNS ACQUISITION CORP p 290
1 Congress St Ste 113 02114
Tel (201) 842-3612 *SIC* 5812

CHARLOTTE RUSSE ENTERPRISE INC p 290
75 State St 02109
Tel (617) 951-9400 *SIC* 5621

CHELSEA PETROLEUM PRODUCTS HOLDINGS LLC p 293
200 Clarendon St Fl 55 02116
Tel (617) 531-6300 *SIC* 6141

CHILDRENS HOSPITAL CORP p 299
300 Longwood Ave 02115
Tel (617) 355-6000 *SIC* 8069

CHILDRENS HOSPITAL PEDIATRIC ASSOCIATES INC p 300
20 Overland St Ste 2 02215
Tel (617) 919-2822 *SIC* 8011

■ CITIZENS BANK OF MASSACHUSETTS p 310
28 State St Fl 13 02109
Tel (617) 725-5900 *SIC* 6021

CITY OF BOSTON p 313
1 City Hall Sq Ste 242 02201
Tel (617) 635-4545 *SIC* 9111

CITY SPORTS INC p 320
77 N Washington St # 500 02114
Tel (617) 391-9100 *SIC* 5699

CITY YEAR INC p 320
287 Columbus Ave Ste 1 02116
Tel (617) 927-2500 *SIC* 8299

▲ CIVITAS SOLUTIONS INC p 320
313 Congress St Fl 6 02210
Tel (617) 790-4800 *SIC* 8082

CLINTON HEALTH ACCESS INITIATIVE INC p 327
383 Dorchester Ave # 400 02127
Tel (617) 774-0110 *SIC* 6732

CNL HOSPITALITY PROPERTIES II INC p 330
1 Post Office Sq Ste 3100 02109
Tel (617) 964-8389 *SIC* 6798

COMBINED JEWISH PHILANTHROPIES OF GREATER BOSTON INC p 343
126 High St Fl 2 02110
Tel (617) 457-8500 *SIC* 8399

COMMONWEALTH CARE ALLIANCE INC p 346
30 Winter St Fl 12 02108
Tel (617) 426-0600 *SIC* 8099 8011

COMMONWEALTH OF MASSACHUSETTS p 346
1 Ashburton Pl Fl 9 02108
Tel (617) 727-5000 SIC 9111

■ **COMMUNISPACE CORP** p 347
290 Congress St Fl 7 02210
Tel (617) 316-4000 SIC 4813

COMMUNITY INTERVENTION SERVICES INC p 349
500 Boylston St Ste 1350 02116
Tel (617) 262-8455 SIC 6719

CONNELL LIMITED PARTNERSHIP p 358
1 International Pl Fl 31 02110
Tel (617) 737-2700
SIC 3443 3444 3341 3544 6719

CONSOLIDATED EDISON MASTER RETIREE HEALTH VEBA TRUST FOR WEEKLY EES p 359
P.O. Box 5100 02206
Tel (617) 664-9564 SIC 6733

■ **CONVERSE INC** p 365
1 Love Joy Wharf 02114
Tel (978) 983-3300 SIC 5139 5661

COSI INC p 373
294 Washington St Ste 510 02108
Tel (857) 415-5000 SIC 5812 6794

COSTA FRUIT & PRODUCE CO p 374
18 Bunker Hill Indus Park 02129
Tel (617) 241-8007
SIC 5148 5143 5142 5141

COUNTY OF SUFFOLK p 382
1 City Hall Sq Ste 550 02201
Tel (617) 635-4000 SIC 9111

▲ **CRA INTERNATIONAL INC** p 388
200 Clarendon St 02116
Tel (617) 425-3000 SIC 8742

CREATIVE OFFICE INTERIORS INC p 390
1 Design Center Pl # 734 02210
Tel (617) 956-4100 SIC 5021

CRESA PARTNERS LLC p 391
200 State St Ste 13a 02109
Tel (617) 758-6000 SIC 8742 6531

DANA-FARBER CANCER INSTITUTE INC p 411
450 Brookline Ave 02215
Tel (617) 632-3000 SIC 8733 8069

DELAWARE NORTH COMPANIES INC -BOSTON p 424
100 Legends Way Ste 100 02114
Tel (617) 624-1000
SIC 5812 5994 6512 7311

DENTAQUEST VENTURES LLC p 429
465 Medford St Ste 150 02129
Tel (617) 886-1818 SIC 6324

DIGITAS INC p 439
33 Arch St Fl 8 02110
Tel (617) 369-8000 SIC 8742

DOUBLE EAGLE PARENT INC p 452
75 State St Fl 29 02109
Tel (617) 951-0555 SIC 6719

EAST BOSTON NEIGHBORHOOD HEALTH CENTER CORP p 470
10 Gove St 02128
Tel (617) 567-3600 SIC 8062

■ **EAST BOSTON SAVING BANK** p 470
10 Meridian St 02128
Tel (617) 567-1500 SIC 6029 6141

EASTERN BANK p 471
265 Franklin St Fl 2 02110
Tel (617) 897-1100 SIC 6036

EASTERN BANK CORP p 471
265 Franklin St Fl 2 02110
Tel (617) 897-1100 SIC 6036 6022 6282

▲ **EATON VANCE CORP** p 473
2 International Pl # 1400 02110
Tel (617) 482-8260 SIC 6282

■ **EATON VANCE MANAGEMENT INC** p 474
2 International Pl # 1400 02110
Tel (617) 482-8260 SIC 6282

EDWARDS WILDMAN PALMER LLP p 480
111 Huntington Ave 02199
Tel (617) 239-0100 SIC 8111

EMERSON COLLEGE p 492
120 Boylston St Ste 414 02116
Tel (617) 824-8500 SIC 8221

EMMANUEL COLLEGE (INC) p 493
400 Fenway 02115
Tel (617) 277-9340 SIC 8221

▲ **ENERNOC INC** p 498
1 Marina Park Dr Ste 400 02210
Tel (617) 224-9900 SIC 7371

■ **EVERGREEN INVESTMENT MANAGEMENT CO LLC** p 514
200 Berkeley St Ste 22 02116
Tel (617) 210-3200 SIC 6282

EXECUTIVE OFFICE OF COMMONWEALTH OF MASSACHUSETTS p 517
24 Beacon St Rm 360 02133
Tel (617) 727-3600 SIC 9111

EXECUTIVE OFFICE OF LABOR AND WORKFORCE DEVELOPMENT p 517
19 Staniford St 02114
Tel (617) 626-5680 SIC 9441

FACULTY PRACTICE FOUNDATION INC AND AFFILIATES p 524
660 Harrison Ave 02118
Tel (617) 638-8923 SIC 8011

FEDERAL HOME LOAN BANK OF BOSTON p 534
800 Boylston St Ste 900 02199
Tel (617) 292-9600 SIC 6111 6019

FEDERAL RESERVE BANK OF BOSTON p 535
600 Atlantic Ave 02210
Tel (617) 973-3000 SIC 6011

FIDELITY CAPITAL INVESTORS INC p 540
82 Devonshire St 02109
Tel (617) 563-7000 SIC 6282 6211

FIDELITY INV CHARITABLE GIFT FUND p 540
200 Seaport Blvd Ste 1 02210
Tel (617) 392-8679 SIC 5947

FIDELITY INVESTMENTS INSTITUTIONAL OPERATIONS CO INC p 540
245 Summer St Ste 1100 02210
Tel (617) 563-7000 SIC 6282 6211

FIDELITY MANAGEMENT & RESEARCH CO p 540
1 Federal St Fl 33 02110
Tel (603) 791-5000 SIC 6282

FIDELITY MANAGEMENT TRUST CO p 540
82 Devonshire St 02109
Tel (617) 563-7000 SIC 6282

FIDELITY WELFARE BENEFIT PLANS VEBA TRUST p 541
82 Devonshire St 02109
Tel (617) 563-1428 SIC 6411

FIDELITY/WTC INC p 541
82 Devonshire St 02109
Tel (617) 563-8300 SIC 6282

FIDESSA BUY-SIDE INC p 541
160 Federal St 02110
Tel (617) 235-1000 SIC 6726 8742

FIRST STATE MANAGEMENT GROUP INC p 549
141 Tremont St Ste 1200 02111
Tel (617) 526-7600 SIC 6311

FIRST STEP REALTY INC p 549
1620 Commonwealth Ave 02135
Tel (617) 264-4900 SIC 6531

FISH & RICHARDSON PC p 551
1 Marina Park Dr Ste 1700 02210
Tel (617) 542-5070 SIC 8111

FMR CORP p 562
82 Devonshire St 02109
Tel (617) 563-7000 SIC 6211

FMR LLC p 562
245 Summer St 02210
Tel (617) 563-7000
SIC 6282 6211 6799 6552 6531

■ **FOUNDATION FOR MARINE ANIMAL HUSBANDRY INC** p 571
222 Berkeley St 02116
Tel (617) 351-5072 SIC 0742

FOUNDATION OF MASSACHUSETTS EYE AND EAR INFIRMARY INC p 571
243 Charles St 02114
Tel (617) 523-7900 SIC 8069

FULD & CO INC p 584
131 Oliver St Fl 3 02110
Tel (617) 492-5900 SIC 8742

▲ **GENERAL ELECTRIC CO** p 600
41 Farnsworth St 02210
Tel (617) 443-3000
SIC 3511 3724 3632 3845

■ **GILLETTE CO** p 612
1 Gillette Park 02127
Tel (617) 421-7000
SIC 3421 3634 2844 3951 2899

■ **GILLETTE DE MEXICO INC** p 612
800 Boylston St 02199
Tel (617) 421-7000 SIC 3634

GOODWIN PROCTER LLP p 625
100 Northern Ave 02210
Tel (617) 570-1000 SIC 8111

GORDON BROTHERS GROUP LLC p 626
800 Boylston St Ste 27 02199
Tel (888) 424-1903 SIC 6722

GORTON SLADE & CO INC p 626
225 Southampton St 02118
Tel (617) 442-5800 SIC 5146

GRAND CIRCLE LLC p 629
347 Congress St 02210
Tel (617) 350-7500 SIC 4725

GRANTHAM MAYO VAN OTTERLOO & CO LLC p 631
40 Rowes Wharf Ste 600 02110
Tel (617) 330-7500 SIC 6282 6722

GREATER BOSTON FOOD BANK INC p 635
70 S Bay Ave 02118
Tel (617) 427-5200 SIC 8399

HANCOCK NATURAL RESOURCE GROUP INC p 657
197 Clarendon St 02116
Tel (617) 747-1600 SIC 6411

■ **HARBOR ELECTRIC ENERGY CO** p 659
800 Boylston St 02199
Tel (617) 424-2000 SIC 4911

HARVARD BUSINESS SCHOOL STUDENT ASSOCIATION INC p 666
Soldiers Fld 02163
Tel (617) 495-6000 SIC 8221

HARVARD MANAGEMENT CO INC p 666
600 Atlantic Ave Ste 15 02210
Tel (617) 720-6526 SIC 8741 6722

HARVARD MEDICAL FACULTY PHYSICIANS AT BETH ISRAEL DEACONESS MEDICAL CENTER INC p 666
375 Longwood Ave Ste 3 02215
Tel (617) 632-9755 SIC 8621

HEBREW REHABILITATION CENTER p 680
1200 Centre St 02131
Tel (617) 363-8000 SIC 8069

HELMSMAN MANAGEMENT SERVICES LLC p 682
175 Berkeley St 02116
Tel (857) 224-1970 SIC 6331

HERALD MEDIA HOLDINGS INC p 685
70 Fargo St Ste 600 02210
Tel (617) 423-4545 SIC 2711

HM PUBLISHING CORP p 697
222 Berkeley St 02116
Tel (617) 251-5000 SIC 2731

■ **HMH PUBLISHERS LLC** p 698
222 Berkeley St 02116
Tel (617) 351-5000 SIC 2731

HOMESITE GROUP INC p 704
1 Federal St Ste 400 02110
Tel (617) 832-1300 SIC 6411

▲ **HOUGHTON MIFFLIN HARCOURT CO** p 711
222 Berkeley St Fl 1-11 02116
Tel (617) 351-5000 SIC 3999 2731

■ **HOUGHTON MIFFLIN HARCOURT PUBLISHERS INC** p 711
222 Berkeley St Fl 1-11 02116
Tel (617) 351-5000 SIC 2731

■ **HOUGHTON MIFFLIN HARCOURT PUBLISHING CO** p 711
222 Berkeley St 02116
Tel (617) 351-5000 SIC 2731

HOUGHTON MIFFLIN HOLDING CO INC p 711
222 Berkeley St Fl 1-11 02116
Tel (617) 351-5000 SIC 2731

HOUGHTON MIFFLIN HOLDINGS INC p 711
222 Berkeley St Fl 1-11 02116
Tel (617) 351-5000 SIC 2731

■ **HST LESSEE BOSTON LLC** p 715
39 Dalton St 02199
Tel (617) 236-2000
SIC 7011 5812 7299 5813

■ **INDEPENDENT ADVERTISING INC** p 736
53 State St 02109
Tel (617) 437-1600
SIC 7311 7331 7389 8732

INTERNATIONAL DATA GROUP INC p 755
1 Exeter Plz Fl 15 02116
Tel (617) 534-1200 SIC 2721 8732 7389

IPROSPECT.COM INC p 763
1 South Sta Ste 300 02110
Tel (617) 449-4300 SIC 8742

▲ **IRON MOUNTAIN INC** p 764
1 Federal St Fl 7 02110
Tel (617) 535-4766
SIC 4226 8741 7375 6798

■ **IRON MOUNTAIN INFORMATION MANAGEMENT LLC** p 765
1 Federal St 02110
Tel (617) 357-4455 SIC 4226

■ **IRON MOUNTAIN/PACIFIC RECORDS MANAGEMENT INC** p 765
1 Federal St 02110
Tel (617) 357-4455 SIC 7382

■ **JACK MORTON WORLDWIDE INC** p 773
142 Berkeley St Ste 6 02116
Tel (617) 585-7000 SIC 8748 8742

JENZABAR INC p 783
101 Huntington Ave # 2200 02199
Tel (617) 492-9099 SIC 7372

JOHN HANCOCK CORPORATE TAX CREDIT FUND I LP p 788
200 Clarendon St 02116
Tel (617) 572-6000 SIC 7389

JOHN HANCOCK FINANCIAL SERVICES INC p 788
200 Clarendon St 02116
Tel (617) 572-6000
SIC 6311 6351 6411 6371 6321

JOHN HANCOCK MANULIFE p 788
197 Clarendon St Fl 4 02116
Tel (617) 663-3000 SIC 6411

JOHN HANCOCK SIGNATURE SERVICES INC p 789
101 Huntington Ave Fl 3 02199
Tel (617) 375-4708 SIC 6289 6282

JOHN R GRAHAM HEADACHE CENTER INC p 789
1153 Centre St 02130
Tel (617) 983-7243 SIC 8011 8062

JOHN SNOW INC p 789
44 Farnsworth St Fl 7 02210
Tel (617) 482-9485 SIC 8742

JOSLIN DIABETES CENTER INC p 794
1 Joslin Pl 02215
Tel (617) 732-2400 SIC 8011

JSI RESEARCH AND TRAINING INSTITUTE INC p 796
44 Farnsworth St Fl 7 02210
Tel (617) 482-9485 SIC 8742

LEE THOMAS H EQUITY FUND V LIMITED PARTNERSHIP p 852
100 Federal St Ste 3500 02110
Tel (617) 737-3261
SIC 3585 3444 3634 2431 3699

LEGAL SEA FOODS LLC p 853
1 Seafood Way 02210
Tel (617) 530-9000 SIC 5812 5146 5961

LEILA A MANKARIOUS p 854
243 Charles St 02114
Tel (617) 573-3413 SIC 8011

■ **LEXINGTON INSURANCE CO** p 859
99 High St Fl 23 02110
Tel (617) 330-1100 SIC 6331

LIBERTY INSURANCE CORP p 862
175 Berkeley St 02116
Tel (617) 357-9500 SIC 6331

LIBERTY INTERNATIONAL HOLDINGS INC p 862
175 Berkeley St 02116
Tel (617) 357-9500 SIC 6331

LIBERTY MUTUAL FIRE INSURANCE CO INC p 862
175 Berkeley St 02116
Tel (617) 357-9500 SIC 6331

LIBERTY MUTUAL GROUP INC p 862
175 Berkeley St 02116
Tel (617) 357-9500
SIC 6331 6321 6351 7389

LIBERTY MUTUAL HOLDING CO INC p 862
175 Berkeley St 02116
Tel (617) 357-9500 SIC 6331 6351 7389

LIBERTY MUTUAL HOLDING CORP p 862
175 Berkeley St 02116
Tel (617) 357-9500 SIC 6331

LIBERTY MUTUAL INSURANCE CO p 862
175 Berkeley St 02116
Tel (617) 357-9500
SIC 6331 6321 6351 7389

LIBERTY SPAIN INSURANCE GROUP LLC p 862
175 Berkeley St 02116
Tel (617) 357-9500 SIC 6311

LMHC MASSACHUSETTS HOLDINGS INC p 872
175 Berkeley St 02116
Tel (617) 357-9500
SIC 6331 6321 6351 7389

▲ **LOGMEIN INC** p 875
320 Summer St Ste 100 02210
Tel (781) 638-9050 SIC 7372 7379

LOOMIS SAYLES & CO LP p 877
1 Financial Ctr Fl 34 02111
Tel (617) 482-2451 SIC 6282

▲ **LPL FINANCIAL HOLDINGS INC** p 882
75 State St Ste 2401 02109
Tel (617) 423-3644 SIC 6211 6282 6091

LYONS GROUP LTD p 888
334 Boylston St Ste 501 02116
Tel (617) 262-2605 SIC 8741

M G H HEALTH SERVICES CORP p 889
55 Fruit St 02114
Tel (617) 724-0567
SIC 8082 8059 8071 8062

MASSACHUSETTS BAY COMMUTER RAILROAD CO LLC p 916
89 South St 02111
Tel (617) 222-8080 SIC 4011 4111

MASSACHUSETTS BAY TRANSPORTATION AUTHORITY p 916
Mbta 10 Park Plz Ste 3910 02116
Tel (617) 222-3106 SIC 9621

MASSACHUSETTS BOARD OF HIGHER EDUCATION SYSTEM p 916
1 Ashburton Pl Rm 1401 02108
Tel (617) 727-7785 SIC 9411

MASSACHUSETTS COMMUNITY COLLEGES p 916
15 Court Sq Ste 1100 02108
Tel (617) 542-2911 SIC 8222 9199

MASSACHUSETTS DEPARTMENT OF CHILDREN AND FAMILIES p 916
600 Washington St 02111
Tel (617) 748-2000 SIC 9111

MASSACHUSETTS DEPARTMENT OF ENVIRONMENTAL PROTECTION p 916
1 Winter St 02108
Tel (617) 292-5500 SIC 9511

MASSACHUSETTS DEPARTMENT OF PUBLIC SAFETY p 916
1 Ashburton Pl Rm 2133 02108
Tel (617) 727-7775 SIC 9221 9229 9223

MASSACHUSETTS DEPARTMENT OF REVENUE p 916
100 Cambridge St 02114
Tel (617) 626-2201 SIC 9311

MASSACHUSETTS DEPARTMENT OF TRANSPORTATION p 916
10 Park Plz Ste 4160 02116
Tel (857) 368-4636 SIC 9621

MASSACHUSETTS DEPT OF MENTAL HEALTH p 916
25 Staniford St 02114
Tel (617) 626-8000 SIC 9431

MASSACHUSETTS DEPT OF MENTAL RETARDATION p 916
500 Harrison Ave Ste 1r 02118
Tel (617) 727-5608 SIC 9431

MASSACHUSETTS DEPT OF PUBLIC HEALTH p 916
250 Washington St 02108
Tel (617) 624-6000 SIC 9431

MASSACHUSETTS DEPT OF TRANSITIONAL ASSISTANCE p 916
600 Washington St Fl 5 02111
Tel (617) 348-8500 SIC 9441

MASSACHUSETTS DEPT OF WORKFORCE DEVELOPMENT p 916
1 Ashburton Pl Rm 2112 02108
Tel (617) 626-7122 SIC 9651

MASSACHUSETTS EDUCATIONAL FINANCING AUTHORITY p 916
160 Federal St Fl 4 02110
Tel (617) 224-4800 SIC 6111

MASSACHUSETTS EXECUTIVE OFFICE OF ENERGY & ENVIRONMENTAL AFFAIRS p 916
100 Cambridge St Ste 900 02114
Tel (617) 626-1000 SIC 9511 9512 9641

MASSACHUSETTS EXECUTIVE OFFICE OF HEALTH AND HUMAN SERVICES p 916
1 Ashburton Pl Rm 1111 02108
Tel (617) 573-1600 SIC 9431 9441

MASSACHUSETTS EYE AND EAR ASSOCIATES INC p 916
243 Charles St 02114
Tel (617) 523-7900 SIC 8011

MASSACHUSETTS EYE AND EAR INFIRMARY p 917
243 Charles St 02114
Tel (617) 573-3499 SIC 8069

MASSACHUSETTS EYE AND EAR INFIRMARY & PHYSICIAN STAFF INC p 917
243 Charles St 02114
Tel (617) 573-3499 SIC 8069 8011

MASSACHUSETTS FINANCIAL SERVICES CO p 917
111 Huntington Ave 02199
Tel (617) 954-5000 SIC 6282 6211 6289

MASSACHUSETTS GENERAL HOSPITAL p 917
55 Fruit St 02114
Tel (617) 724-6454 SIC 8062 8011

MASSACHUSETTS GENERAL PHYSICIANS ORGANIZATION INC p 917
55 Fruit St 208 02114
Tel (617) 724-0578 SIC 8011

MASSACHUSETTS HIGHER EDUCATION ASSISTANCE CORP p 917
100 Cambridge St Ste 1600 02114
Tel (617) 728-4507 SIC 6111

MASSACHUSETTS PORT AUTHORITY p 917
1 Harborside Dr Ste 200s 02128
Tel (617) 561-1600
SIC 4581 4491 6799 6512 4785

MASSACHUSETTS SUPREME JUDICIAL COURT p 917
1 Pemberton Sq Ste 2500 02108
Tel (617) 557-1020 SIC 9211

MASSACHUSETTS TURNPIKE AUTHORITY p 917
10 Park Plz Ste 5170 02116
Tel (617) 248-2800 SIC 4785 9199

MASSACHUSETTS WATER RESOURCES AUTHORITY p 917
Charl Navy Yard 100 First 02129
Tel (617) 788-4917 SIC 1623

MASSACHUSETTS WATER RESOURCES AUTHORITY p 917
100 1st Ave 02129
Tel (617) 242-6000 SIC 9511

MCCOURT CONSTRUCTION CO INC p 927
60 K St 02127
Tel (617) 269-2330 SIC 1611 1622

MCPHS UNIVERSITY p 932
179 Longwood Ave 02115
Tel (617) 732-2132 SIC 8221

MEDICAL PROFESSIONAL MUTUAL INSURANCE CO p 937
1 Financial Ctr Fl 13 02111
Tel (800) 225-6168 SIC 6331

■ MELLON TRUST OF NEW ENGLAND NA p 941
1 Boston Pl Fl 8 02108
Tel (617) 722-7000 SIC 6733

■ MERCER HUMAN RESOURCE CONSULTING OF MASSACHUSETTS INC p 944
99 High St 02110
Tel (617) 450-6000 SIC 8742

■ METCALF & EDDY INC p 953
1 Federal St Ste 800 02110
Tel (781) 246-5200 SIC 8711

METSO USA INC p 957
133 Federal St Ste 302 02110
Tel (617) 369-7850 SIC 3554 5084

MFS INVESTMENT MANAGEMENT FOUNDATION INC p 958
111 Huntington Ave # 200 02199
Tel (800) 343-2829 SIC 6722

MILLENNIUM PARTNERS SPORTS CLUB MANAGEMENT LLC p 970
7 Water St Ste 200 02109
Tel (617) 476-8910 SIC 7991

MINTZ LEVIN COHN FERRIS GLOVSKY AND POPEO PC p 974
1 Financial Ctr Fl 39 02111
Tel (617) 348-4951 SIC 8111

MUSEUM OF FINE ARTS p 1002
465 Huntington Ave 02115
Tel (617) 369-3861 SIC 8412 5961 8299

NATIONAL FINANCIAL SERVICES LLC p 1012
200 Seaport Blvd Ste 630 02210
Tel (800) 471-0382 SIC 6211 6411 6282

NATIONAL MENTOR HOLDINGS INC p 1014
313 Congress St Fl 5 02210
Tel (617) 790-4800 SIC 8082 8361

NATIONAL MENTOR INC p 1014
313 Congress St Fl 5 02210
Tel (617) 790-4800 SIC 8361

NATIXIS GLOBAL ASSET MANAGEMENT LP p 1018
399 Boylston St 02116
Tel (617) 449-2100 SIC 6282 8742

NE MEDIA GROUP INC p 1022
135 William T Mrrssey Blvd 02125
Tel (617) 929-2000 SIC 2711

NEIGHBORHOOD HEALTH PLAN p 1024
253 Summer St Fl 5 02210
Tel (617) 772-5500 SIC 8011

NEPC LLC p 1026
255 State St Ste 600 02109
Tel (617) 314-3176 SIC 6411 6282

NEW BALANCE ATHLETICS INC p 1029
100 Guest St Fl 5 02135
Tel (617) 783-4000 SIC 8699

NEW ENGLAND BAPTIST HOSPITAL INC p 1030
125 Parker Hill Ave Ste 2 02120
Tel (617) 754-5000 SIC 8062

NEW ENGLAND DEACONESS HOSPITAL CORP p 1030
1 Deaconess Rd 02215
Tel (814) 777-4805 SIC 8062

NEW ENGLAND DEVELOPMENT INC p 1030
75 Park Plz Ste 3 02116
Tel (617) 965-8700 SIC 6552

■ NEW ENGLAND LIFE INSURANCE CO p 1030
501 Boylston St Ste 1 02116
Tel (617) 578-2000 SIC 6411

▲ NEWSTAR FINANCIAL INC p 1039
500 Boylston St Ste 1250 02116
Tel (617) 848-2500 SIC 6162

NMH INVESTMENT LLC p 1045
313 Congress St Fl 5 02210
Tel (617) 790-4800 SIC 8361

NORTHEAST INVESTORS TRUST p 1055
125 High St Ste 1801 02110
Tel (857) 263-8100 SIC 6722

NORTHEASTERN UNIVERSITY p 1055
360 Huntington Ave 02115
Tel (617) 373-2000 SIC 8221

■ NSTAR ELECTRIC & GAS CORP p 1065
800 Boylston St Ste 1700 02199
Tel (617) 424-2000 SIC 4922 4911

■ NSTAR ELECTRIC CO p 1065
800 Boylston St Ste 1700 02199
Tel (617) 424-2000 SIC 4911 4924

■ NSTAR LLC p 1065
800 Boylston St Ste 1700 02199
Tel (617) 424-2000 SIC 4911 4924

NTT DATA INTERNATIONAL SERVICES INC p 1066
100 City Sq 02129
Tel (800) 745-3263 SIC 7371 7372

OFFICE RESOURCES INC p 1076
263 Summer St 02210
Tel (617) 423-9100 SIC 5021

OLD MUTUAL (US) HOLDINGS INC p 1081
200 Clarendon St Fl 53 02116
Tel (617) 369-7300 SIC 6726

■ OMGEO LLC p 1084
55 Thomson Pl 02210
Tel (877) 664-3625 SIC 6211

OVERSEAS ADVENTURE TRAVEL p 1099
347 Congress St Ste 2 02210
Tel (800) 955-1925 SIC 4725

OXFAM AMERICA INC p 1100
226 Causeway St Fl 5 02114
Tel (617) 482-1211 SIC 8399

PARTHENON CAPITAL PARTNERS p 1118
1 Federal St Fl 21 02110
Tel (617) 960-4000 SIC 6211

PARTNERS HEALTHCARE SYSTEM INC p 1118
800 Boylston St Ste 1150 02199
Tel (617) 278-1000 SIC 8741

PARTNERS MEDICAL INTERNATIONAL INC p 1118
100 Cambridge St Fl 20 02114
Tel (617) 535-6400 SIC 8741

PIONEER INVESTMENT MANAGEMENT INC p 1150
60 State St 02109
Tel (617) 742-7825 SIC 6282

PIONEER INVESTMENT MANAGEMENT USA INC p 1151
60 State St Ste 700 02109
Tel (617) 742-7825 SIC 6722 6282

PLYMOUTH ROCK ASSURANCE CORP p 1157
695 Atlantic Ave Fl 7 02111
Tel (866) 353-6292 SIC 6331

PLYMOUTH ROCK CO INC p 1157
695 Atlantic Ave 02111
Tel (617) 720-1620 SIC 6331

PROMUTUAL GROUP INC p 1183
1 Financial Ctr Fl 13 02111
Tel (617) 330-1755 SIC 6321 8742

PUBLIC CONSULTING GROUP INC p 1189
148 State St Fl 10 02109
Tel (617) 426-2026 SIC 8742

PUTNAM INTERMEDIATE GOVERNMENT INCOME TRUST p 1193
1 Post Office Sq 02109
Tel (617) 292-1000 SIC 6211

PUTNAM INVESTMENTS p 1193
1 Post Office Sq 02109
Tel (617) 292-1000 SIC 6722 6282 6726

PUTNAM INVESTOR SERVICES INC p 1193
1 Post Office Sq Ste 500 02109
Tel (617) 292-1000 SIC 6289

PYRAMID ADVISORS LLC p 1193
1 Post Office Sq Ste 1950 02109
Tel (617) 202-2033 SIC 7011

QUALIFIED HOUSING TAX CREDITS LP V p 1196
101 Arch St Fl 16 02110
Tel (617) 439-3911 SIC 6211 6531

▲ RAPID7 INC p 1208
100 Summer St Fl 13 02110
Tel (617) 247-1717 SIC 7372

■ RED THREAD SPACES LLC p 1216
101 Seaport Blvd Ste 600 02210
Tel (617) 439-4900
SIC 5999 5021 8712 5198

RENAISSANCE WORLDWIDE INC p 1223
711 Boylston St 02116
Tel (617) 535-5000
SIC 7363 8742 7379 7361 8748 7371

RHODE ISLAND JOINT REINSURANCE ASSOC p 1232
2 Center Plz Ste 700 02108
Tel (617) 723-3800 SIC 6331

ROBERT N KARPP CO INC p 1241
480 E 1st St 02127
Tel (617) 269-5880 SIC 5031 1799

ROPES & GRAY LLP p 1250
800 Prudential Tower # 3600 02199
Tel (617) 951-7000 SIC 8111

RSC INSURANCE BROKERAGE INC p 1255
160 Federal St 02110
Tel (617) 330-5700 SIC 6411

RUELALA INC p 1257
20 Channel Ctr St 02210
Tel (617) 695-7300 SIC 5961

S D WARREN CO p 1262
255 State St Fl 4 02109
Tel (617) 423-7300
SIC 2679 2674 2672 2621

■ SAFETY INDEMNITY INSURANCE CO INC p 1266
20 Custom House St # 400 02110
Tel (617) 951-0600 SIC 6321

■ SAFETY INSURANCE CO p 1266
20 Custom House St # 400 02110
Tel (617) 951-0600 SIC 6331

▲ SAFETY INSURANCE GROUP INC p 1266
20 Custom House St # 400 02110
Tel (617) 951-0600 SIC 6331 6411

■ SANTANDER BANK NA p 1281
28 State St Fl 5 02109
Tel (617) 757-3410 SIC 6035

■ SANTANDER HOLDINGS USA INC p 1281
75 State St 02109
Tel (617) 346-7200 SIC 6021 6035

SAPIENT CORP p 1281
131 Dartmouth St Ste 301 02116
Tel (617) 621-0200
SIC 7373 7374 7371 8742

SCHOONER CAPITAL LLC p 1290
60 South St 02111
Tel (617) 963-5200 SIC 6159

SDW HOLDINGS CORP p 1295
255 State St Fl 7 02109
Tel (617) 423-5400 SIC 2621

SEVONE INC p 1309
800 Boylston St Bsmt 5 02199
Tel (617) 982-7700 SIC 7373

SG SEAFOOD HOLDINGS INC p 1310
225 Southampton St 02118
Tel (617) 442-5800 SIC 5146

SHARED TECHNOLOGY SERVICES GROUP INC p 1312
695 Atlantic Ave 02111
Tel (617) 720-1620 SIC 1521

SHAWMUT WOODWORKING & SUPPLY INC p 1313
560 Harrison Ave Ste 200 02118
Tel (617) 338-6200 SIC 1542

SIMMONS COLLEGE p 1324
300 Fenway 02115
Tel (617) 521-2000 SIC 8221

SMITH & WOLLENSKY RESTAURANT GROUP INC p 1333
260 Franklin St Ste 240 02110
Tel (617) 600-3500 SIC 5812

▲ STAG INDUSTRIAL INC p 1374
1 Federal St Fl 23 02110
Tel (617) 574-4777 SIC 6798

STANTEC ARCHITECTURE AND ENGINEERING PC p 1377
311 Summer St 02210
Tel (617) 234-3100 SIC 8712

■ STATE STREET BANK AND TRUST CO p 1383
1 Lincoln St Fl 1 02111
Tel (617) 786-3000 SIC 6022

▲ STATE STREET CORP p 1383
1 Lincoln St 02111
Tel (617) 786-3000 SIC 6022 6282

■ STATE STREET HOLDING CO LLC p 1383
225 Franklin St Lbby 1 02110
Tel (617) 664-1029 SIC 6082

STAVIS SEAFOODS INC p 1383
212 Northern Ave Ste 305 02210
Tel (617) 482-6349 SIC 5146

STEWARD HEALTH CARE SYSTEM LLC p 1388
500 Boylston St 02116
Tel (617) 419-4700 SIC 8082

STEWARD HOME CARE INC p 1388
500 Boylston St 02116
Tel (781) 551-5600 SIC 8082

STEWARD ST ELIZABETHS MEDICAL CENTER OF BOSTON INC p 1388
736 Cambridge St 02135
Tel (617) 789-3000 SIC 8062

STONE & WEBSTER OVERSEAS GROUP INC p 1391
45 Milk St Bsmt 02109
Tel (617) 778-7500 SIC 8742 8711

SUFFOLK CONSTRUCTION CO INC p 1396
65 Allerton St 02119
Tel (617) 445-3500 SIC 1542

SUFFOLK UNIVERSITY p 1396
120 Tremont St 02108
Tel (617) 573-8000 SIC 8221 8244

SUFFOLK UNIVERSITY p 1397
8 Ashburton Pl 02108
Tel (617) 573-8000 SIC 8221

SUFFOLK/KRAFT CONSTRUCTION CO LLC p 1397
65 Allerton St 02119
Tel (617) 445-3500 SIC 1542

SULLIVAN & MCLAUGHLIN COMPANIES INC p 1397
74 Lawley St 02122
Tel (617) 474-0500 SIC 1731

SUMMIT PARTNERS LP p 1399
222 Berkeley St Fl 18 02116
Tel (617) 824-1000 SIC 6799

TA ASSOCIATES p 1420
200 Clarendon St Ste 5600 02116
Tel (617) 574-6700 SIC 6799

TA ASSOCIATES MANAGEMENT LP p 1420
200 Clarendon St Fl 56 02116
Tel (617) 574-6700 SIC 6799

TAS-CSEMCB INC p 1425
736 Cambridge St 02135
Tel (617) 789-3149 SIC 8062

TEAMSTERS UNION 25 HEALTH SERVICES & INSURANCE PLAN p 1430
16 Sever St 02129
Tel (617) 241-9220 SIC 6371

▲ THL CREDIT INC p 1448
100 Federal St Fl 31 02110
Tel (800) 450-4424 SIC 6726

THL-NORTEK INVESTORS LLC p 1448
100 Federal St Ste 3100 02110
Tel (617) 227-1050
SIC 3585 3444 3634 2431

■ THOMAS BLACK CORP p 1448
20 Custom House St # 400 02110
Tel (617) 951-0600 SIC 6411

THOMAS H LEE ADVISORS II LP p 1448
100 Federal St 02110
Tel (617) 227-1050 SIC 6282

TRI VENTURES INC p 1477
711 Boylston St 02116
Tel (617) 535-5000 SIC 7363

TRUSTEES OF BOSTON UNIVERSITY p 1487
1 Silber Way 02215
Tel (617) 353-9550 SIC 8221

TUFTS MEDICAL CENTER INC p 1491
800 Washington St 02111
Tel (617) 636-5000
SIC 8062 7371 8742 8741

TUFTS MEDICAL CENTER PARENT INC p 1491
800 Washington St 02111
Tel (617) 636-5000 SIC 8062 7371

UG2 LLC p 1499
1 International Pl # 1402 02110
Tel (617) 279-8100 SIC 7349

UNIDINE CORP p 1503
1000 Washington St # 510 02118
Tel (617) 467-3700 SIC 8741

UNIVERSITY OF MASSACHUSETTS INC p 1523
1 Beacon St Fl 31 02108
Tel (617) 287-7000 SIC 8221 8733 8062

URC LLC p 1530
100 Charles Park Rd 02132
Tel (617) 323-9200 SIC 5812 5813 6794

VEOLIA ENERGY NORTH AMERICA HOLDINGS INC p 1548
53 State St Ste 14 02109
Tel (617) 849-6612 SIC 4939 4961

VEOLIA NORTH AMERICA LLC p 1548
53 State St Ste 14 02109
Tel (312) 552-2800 SIC 8711

VEOLIA WATER NORTH AMERICA-CENTRAL LLC p 1549
53 State St Ste 14 02109
Tel (617) 849-6600 SIC 4952 4941

■ **VERIZON NEW ENGLAND INC** p 1550
185 Franklin St 4th 02110
Tel (617) 743-9800 SIC 4813 8721

▲ **VERTEX PHARMACEUTICALS INC** p 1552
50 Northern Ave 02210
Tel (617) 341-6100 SIC 2834 8731

VIPER HOLDINGS CORP p 1558
200 Clarendon St Fl 54 02116
Tel (617) 619-5400 SIC 3669 3651

VPNE PARKING SOLUTIONS LLC p 1566
343 Congress St Ste 3300 02210
Tel (617) 451-1393 SIC 7521

WANG CENTER FOR PERFORMING ARTS INC p 1575
270 Tremont St 02116
Tel (617) 482-9393 SIC 7922

▲ **WAYFAIR INC** p 1584
4 Copley Pl Ste 700 02116
Tel (617) 532-6100 SIC 5961

■ **WAYFAIR LLC** p 1584
4 Copley Pl Ste 700 02116
Tel (617) 532-6100 SIC 5963 5712 5023

WDC DEVELOPMENT ASSOCIATES LP p 1585
6 Faneuil Hall Market Pl 02109
Tel (617) 742-4500 SIC 6552

WELLINGTON MANAGEMENT GROUP LLP p 1589
280 Congress St 02210
Tel (617) 951-5000 SIC 6282

WENTWORTH INSTITUTE OF TECHNOLOGY INC p 1592
550 Huntington Ave 02115
Tel (617) 989-4590 SIC 8221

WESTON PRESIDIO CAPITAL MANAGEMENT II LP p 1602
200 Clarendon St Fl 50 02116
Tel (617) 988-2500 SIC 6726

WESTON PRESIDIO INC p 1602
200 Clarendon St Ste 5000 02116
Tel (617) 988-2500
SIC 6799 3944 2519 3085

WGBH EDUCATIONAL FOUNDATION p 1604
1 Guest St 02135
Tel (617) 300-2000 SIC 7812 4833 4832

WHDH-TV INC p 1604
7 Bulfinch Pl 02114
Tel (617) 725-0777 SIC 4833

WHITE MOUNTAINS CAPITAL INC p 1606
265 Franklin St Ste 500 02110
Tel (617) 330-5310 SIC 6331

■ **WILLIAM GALLAGHER ASSOCIATES INSURANCE BROKERS INC** p 1610
470 Atlantic Ave Fl 13 02210
Tel (617) 261-6700 SIC 6411 8742

WINN MANAGEMENT CO LLC p 1616
6 Faneuil Hall Market Pl # 500 02109
Tel (617) 742-4501 SIC 6531

WINN WB MANAGEMENT CO LLC p 1616
6 Faneuil Hall Market Pl # 500 02109
Tel (617) 742-4500 SIC 6513

WINNCOMPANIES LLC p 1616
6 Faneuil Hall Market Pl 02109
Tel (617) 742-4500 SIC 6531

WINNRESIDENTIAL LIMITED PARTNERSHIP p 1616
6 Faneuil Hall Market Pl 02109
Tel (617) 742-4500 SIC 6513

WINNRESIDENTIAL LLC p 1617
6 Faneuil Hall Market Pl 02109
Tel (617) 742-4500 SIC 8741

YMCA OF GREATER BOSTON INC p 1636
316 Huntington Ave Ste 1 02115
Tel (617) 536-6950
SIC 8641 7991 8351 7032 8322

■ **ZIPCAR INC** p 1643
35 Thomson Pl 02210
Tel (617) 995-4231 SIC 7514

BOXBOROUGH, MA

EGENERA INC p 481
80 Central St Ste 300 01719
Tel (978) 206-6300 SIC 7373 1731 8741

LIGHTTOWER FIBER LLC p 865
80 Central St Ste 240 01719
Tel (978) 264-6000 SIC 4899

LTS BUYER LLC p 883
80 Central St 01719
Tel (978) 264-6001 SIC 4899

LTS GROUP HOLDINGS LLC p 883
80 Central St Ste 240 01719
Tel (978) 264-6001 SIC 3661

BRAINTREE, MA

▲ **ALTRA INDUSTRIAL MOTION CORP** p 62
300 Granite St Ste 201 02184
Tel (781) 917-0600
SIC 3568 5085 3542 3625

BRAINTREE HOTEL OPERATOR INC p 207
215 Wood Rd 02184
Tel (781) 380-3300 SIC 7011

BT CONFERENCING INC p 222
30 Braintree Hill Park # 301 02184
Tel (617) 801-6700 SIC 4813

DANIEL J QUIRK INC p 411
372 Quincy Ave 02184
Tel (781) 843-4800
SIC 5511 5013 5531 7538 5521 7515

▲ **HAEMONETICS CORP** p 652
400 Wood Rd 02184
Tel (781) 848-7100 SIC 3841 3845

MIB GROUP INC p 959
50 Braintree Hill Park # 400 02184
Tel (781) 751-6000 SIC 6411

RICHELIEU FOODS INC p 1233
222 Forbes Rd Ste 401 02184
Tel (781) 786-6800 SIC 2038

ROMAN CATHOLIC ARCHBISHOP OF BOSTON p 1248
66 Brooks Dr 02184
Tel (617) 254-0100 SIC 8661

SUBURBAN CONTRACT CLEANING INC p 1396
65 Bay State Dr Ste 4 02184
Tel (781) 356-4400 SIC 7349

SUPER PETROLEUM INC p 1405
25 Braintree Hill Park # 409 02184
Tel (781) 356-1960 SIC 5541

TAVISTOCK RESTAURANT GROUP p 1426
35 Braintree Hill Park # 1107 02184
Tel (781) 817-4400 SIC 5812

UNITED GROUP OPERATING COMPANIES LLC p 1508
175 Campanelli Dr 02184
Tel (781) 348-8000 SIC 5181 5182

BRIDGEWATER, MA

BRIDGEWATER STATE UNIVERSITY p 212
131 Summer St Rm 109 02325
Tel (508) 531-1000 SIC 8221 9199

CALLAHAN INC p 242
80 1st St 02324
Tel (508) 279-0012 SIC 1542

▲ **CHASE CORP** p 291
26 Summer St 02324
Tel (508) 819-4200 SIC 3644 3479 3672

BRIGHTON, MA

AMERICAN CLEANING CO INC p 70
94 Lincoln St 02135
Tel (617) 562-4000 SIC 7349

BRIGHTON MARINE HEALTH CENTER INC p 213
77 Warren St Fl 7 02135
Tel (617) 562-5222 SIC 6531

HARVARD BUSINESS SCHOOL PUBLISHING CORP p 666
20 Guest St Ste 700 02135
Tel (617) 783-7400 SIC 2721 2731 2741

NEW BALANCE INC p 1029
100 Guest St 02135
Tel (617) 783-4000 SIC 5139

BROCKTON, MA

BROCKTON HOSPITAL INC p 216
680 Centre St 02302
Tel (508) 941-7000 SIC 8062

CITY OF BROCKTON p 313
45 School St 02301
Tel (508) 580-7123 SIC 9111

CONCORD FOODS INC p 354
10 Minuteman Way 02301
Tel (508) 580-1700 SIC 2099 2045

HARBORONE BANK p 660
770 Oak St 02301
Tel (508) 895-1000 SIC 6036

MASSASOIT COMMUNITY COLLEGE p 917
1 Massasoit Blvd 02302
Tel (508) 588-9100 SIC 8222

OLD COLONY p 1080
320 Main St 02301
Tel (508) 583-2155
SIC 8641 7991 8351 7032 8322

SIGNATURE HEALTHCARE CORP p 1322
680 Centre St 02302
Tel (508) 941-7000 SIC 8062

SONEPAR DISTRIBUTION NEW ENGLAND INC p 1339
560 Oak St 02301
Tel (508) 998-8900 SIC 5063

TAS-CGSMC INC p 1425
235 N Pearl St 02301
Tel (508) 427-3000 SIC 8062

W B MASON CO INC p 1568
59 Center St 02301
Tel (781) 794-8800 SIC 5712 5943

BROOKLINE, MA

BROOKLINE SCHOOL DISTRICT p 218
333 Washington St 02445
Tel (617) 730-2401 SIC 8211

BROOKLINE TOWN OF (INC) p 218
333 Washington St 02445
Tel (617) 730-2000 SIC 9111

BURLINGTON, MA

■ **ARBOR NETWORKS INC** p 103
76 Blanchard Rd Ste 1 01803
Tel (781) 362-4300 SIC 4899

ASSOCIATED INDUSTRIES OF MASSACHUSETTS MUTUAL INSURANCE CO p 120
54 3rd Ave 01803
Tel (781) 221-1600 SIC 6331

ASSOCIATED INSURANCE MANAGEMENT LLC p 120
54 3rd Ave 01803
Tel (781) 221-1600 SIC 8741

▲ **AVID TECHNOLOGY INC** p 138
75 Network Dr 01803
Tel (978) 640-6789 SIC 3861 7372

CENTRA TECHNOLOGY INC p 277
25 Burlington Mall Rd # 504 01803
Tel (781) 272-7887 SIC 8748

CHARLES RIVER DEVELOPMENT INC p 289
700 District Ave Ste 400 01803
Tel (781) 238-0099 SIC 7371

CHARLES RIVER SYSTEMS INC p 289
700 District Ave Ste 400 01803
Tel (781) 238-0099 SIC 7371

▲ **CIRCOR INTERNATIONAL INC** p 308
30 Corporate Dr Ste 200 01803
Tel (781) 270-1200 SIC 3492

DECISION RESOURCES INC p 421
800 District Ave Ste 600 01803
Tel (781) 993-2500 SIC 8732 2721

■ **DEMANDWARE INC** p 427
5 Wall St Fl 2 01803
Tel (888) 553-9216 SIC 7371 7372

▲ **ENDURANCE INTERNATIONAL GROUP HOLDINGS INC** p 497
10 Corporate Dr Ste 300 01803
Tel (781) 852-3200 SIC 7372

■ **ENDURANCE INTERNATIONAL GROUP INC** p 497
10 Corporate Dr Ste 300 01803
Tel (866) 897-5421 SIC 8732

ENTEGEE INC p 501
70 Blanchard Rd Ste 102 01803
Tel (781) 221-5800 SIC 7363 5045

ENVIROBUSINESS INC p 503
21 B St 01803
Tel (781) 273-2500 SIC 8748

■ **GE IONICS INC** p 596
3 Burlington Woods Dr # 200 01803
Tel (781) 359-7000
SIC 3589 2086 4941 3559 2899 3823

HALEY & ALDRICH INC p 653
70 Blanchard Rd Ste 204 01803
Tel (617) 886-7400 SIC 8748 8711

INVENTIV GROUP HOLDINGS INC p 761
1 Van De Graaff Dr 01803
Tel (609) 951-6800 SIC 8742 8731

INVENTIV HEALTH CLINICAL SRE LLC p 761
1 Van De Graaff Dr 01803
Tel (800) 416-0555 SIC 5122

INVENTIV HEALTH INC p 761
1 Van De Graaff Dr 01803
Tel (800) 416-0555 SIC 8731

LAHEY CLINIC FOUNDATION INC p 838
41 Mall Rd 01805
Tel (781) 273-5100 SIC 8059

LAHEY CLINIC HOSPITAL INC p 838
41 Mall Rd 01805
Tel (781) 273-5100 SIC 8062

LAHEY CLINIC INC p 838
41 Mall Rd 01805
Tel (781) 744-5100 SIC 8062

LAHEY HEALTH SYSTEM INC p 838
41 Mall Rd 01805
Tel (781) 744-5100 SIC 8059

MASSACHUSETTS LABORERS HEALTH AND WELFARE FUND p 917
14 New England Exec Park 01803
Tel (781) 238-0700 SIC 6371

▲ **NUANCE COMMUNICATIONS INC** p 1066
1 Wayside Rd 01803
Tel (781) 565-5000 SIC 7372

ONE COMMUNICATIONS CORP p 1086
5 Wall St Fl 5 01803
Tel (781) 362-5700 SIC 4813

PHILIPS LIGHTING NORTH AMERICA CORP p 1143
3 Burlington Woods Dr # 4 01803
Tel (617) 423-9999 SIC 3646

■ **RANGE SYSTEMS ENGINEERING SUPPORT CO** p 1208
2 Wayside Rd 01803
Tel (781) 983-1396 SIC 8711

SOPHOS INC p 1341
3 Van De Graaff Dr Ste 2 01803
Tel (781) 494-5800 SIC 7371

■ **TRILLIUM SOFTWARE INC** p 1480
17 New England Executive 01803
Tel (978) 901-0000 SIC 7374

■ **VIECORE FEDERAL SYSTEMS DIVISION INC** p 1556
1 Wayside Rd 01803
Tel (781) 565-5000 SIC 7371

BYFIELD, MA

■ **LYNNFIELD DRUG INC** p 888
12 Kent Way Ste 120 01922
Tel (978) 499-1400 SIC 5912 5961

CAMBRIDGE, MA

ABT ASSOCIATES INC p 13
55 Wheeler St Ste 1a 02138
Tel (617) 492-7100 SIC 8732

▲ **AKAMAI TECHNOLOGIES INC** p 42
150 Broadway Ste 100 02142
Tel (617) 444-3000 SIC 7372 7374

▲ **ARIAD PHARMACEUTICALS INC** p 108
26 Landsdowne St Ste 175 02139
Tel (617) 494-0400 SIC 2836 8731

BAY STATE POOL SUPPLIES INC p 161
691 Concord Ave 02138
Tel (617) 547-9145 SIC 5169 5091

▲ **BIOGEN INC** p 184
225 Binney St 02142
Tel (617) 679-2000 SIC 2834 2836 8731

BOSTON CULINARY GROUP INC p 202
55 Cambridge Pkwy Ste 200 02142
Tel (617) 225-0005 SIC 5812 5145

BROAD INSTITUTE INC p 215
415 Main St 02142
Tel (617) 714-7000 SIC 8733

CAMBRIDGE FINANCIAL GROUP INC p 244
1374 Massachusetts Ave 02138
Tel (617) 864-8700 SIC 6036

CAMBRIDGE HOSPITAL p 244
1493 Cambridge St 02139
Tel (617) 665-1000 SIC 8062

CAMBRIDGE PUBLIC HEALTH COMMISSION p 244
1493 Cambridge St 02139
Tel (617) 665-1000 SIC 8062

CAMBRIDGE PUBLIC SCHOOLS p 244
159 Thorndike St 02141
Tel (617) 349-6400 SIC 8211

CHARLES STARK DRAPER LABORATORY INC p 289
555 Technology Sq 02139
Tel (617) 258-1000 SIC 8734

CITY OF CAMBRIDGE p 313
795 Massachusetts Ave 02139
Tel (617) 349-4260 SIC 9111

COUNTY OF MIDDLESEX p 380
40 Thorndike St 02141
Tel (617) 494-4113 SIC 9111

▲ **FORRESTER RESEARCH INC** p 568
60 Acorn Park Dr 02140
Tel (617) 613-6000 SIC 8732

■ **FOUNDATION MEDICINE INC** p 571
150 2nd St 02141
Tel (617) 418-2200 SIC 8069

▲ **GCP APPLIED TECHNOLOGIES INC** p 595
62 Whittemore Ave 02140
Tel (617) 876-1400 SIC 2819 2899

GENZYME CORP p 605
500 Kendall St 02142
Tel (617) 252-7500
SIC 2835 2834 8071 3842 2836 5122

HARVARD STUDENT AGENCIES INC p 666
67 Mount Auburn St 02138
Tel (617) 495-3030 SIC 7361

▲ **HUBSPOT INC** p 716
25 1st St Ste 200 02141
Tel (888) 482-7768 SIC 7372

IGATE AMERICAS INC p 730
1 Broadway Fl 13 02142
Tel (617) 914-8000 SIC 7371 7373

▲ **INFINITY PHARMACEUTICALS INC** p 741
784 Memorial Dr 02139
Tel (617) 453-1000 SIC 2834 8731

INTERSYSTEMS CORP p 758
1 Memorial Dr Ste 6 02142
Tel (617) 621-0600 SIC 7371

▲ **IRONWOOD PHARMACEUTICALS INC** p 765
301 Binney St 02142
Tel (617) 621-7722 SIC 2834 8731

LESLEY UNIVERSITY p 857
29 Everett St 02138
Tel (617) 868-9600 SIC 8221

LETS GO INC p 857
67 Mount Auburn St 02138
Tel (617) 495-9659 SIC 2741

MASSACHUSETTS INSTITUTE OF TECHNOLOGY p 917
77 Massachusetts Ave 02139
Tel (617) 253-1000 SIC 8221

MERRIMACK PHARMACEUTICALS INC p 950
1 Kendall Sq Ste B7201 02139
Tel (617) 441-1000 SIC 2834

MILLENNIUM PHARMACEUTICALS INC p 970
40 Landsdowne St 02139
Tel (617) 679-7000 SIC 8731

▲ MOMENTA PHARMACEUTICALS INC p 983
675 W Kendall St 02142
Tel (617) 491-9700 SIC 2834

MOUNT AUBURN HOSPITAL p 993
330 Mount Auburn St 02138
Tel (617) 492-3500 SIC 8062

NOVARTIS VACCINES AND DIAGNOSTICS INC p 1063
350 Massachusetts Ave 02139
Tel (617) 871-7000 SIC 2834 2835 2836

NOVELION THERAPEUTICS INC p 1063
1 Main St 800 02142
Tel (877) 764-3131 SIC 2834

▲ PEGASYSTEMS INC p 1127
1 Rogers St 02142
Tel (617) 374-9600 SIC 7379 7371 7372

PRESIDENT AND FELLOWS OF HARVARD COLLEGE p 1172
1350 Massachusetts Ave 02138
Tel (617) 496-4873 SIC 8221 8732 2721

QUICKBASE INC p 1199
150 Cambridgepark Dr # 500 02140
Tel (855) 725-2293 SIC 7372

■ RAYTHEON BBN TECHNOLOGIES CORP p 1210
10 Moulton St 02138
Tel (617) 873-3052 SIC 7371 7374 7373

TAPPET BROTHERS ASSOCIATES p 1424
5 John F Kennedy St # 304 02138
Tel (617) 876-6632 SIC 7922

THOMAS G GALLAGHER INC p 1448
109 Smith Pl 02138
Tel (617) 661-7000 SIC 1711

TOYOTA RESEARCH INSTITUTE INC p 1467
1 Kendall Sq Bldg 100 02139
Tel (857) 285-6160 SIC 8733

VINFEN CORP p 1558
950 Cambridge St 02141
Tel (617) 441-1800 SIC 8361 8331

CANTON, MA

ALL SEASONS SERVICES INC p 51
5 Campanelli Cir Ste 200 02021
Tel (781) 828-2345 SIC 5962 5812

BOSTON MUTUAL LIFE INSURANCE CO p 203
120 Royall St Ste 1 02021
Tel (781) 828-7000 SIC 6311

C H POWELL CO p 232
75 Shawmut Rd 02021
Tel (781) 302-7300 SIC 4731

■ CMRG APPAREL LLC p 329
555 Turnpike St 02021
Tel (781) 828-9300 SIC 5699 2389

COMPUTERSHARE INC p 353
250 Royall St 02021
Tel (781) 575-2000 SIC 6289 6211

▲ DESTINATION XL GROUP INC p 432
555 Turnpike St 02021
Tel (781) 828-9300 SIC 5699

▲ DUNKIN BRANDS GROUP INC p 461
130 Royall St 02021
Tel (781) 737-3000
SIC 5461 5499 6794 5812

■ DUNKIN BRANDS INC p 461
130 Royall St 02021
Tel (781) 737-5200 SIC 5461 5812

E M DUGGAN INC p 466
140 Will Dr 02021
Tel (781) 828-2292 SIC 1711

■ GRAVITY FINANCIAL LLC p 632
1 New Boston Dr Ste 7 02021
Tel (781) 828-7800 SIC 6282

INDEPENDENT PIPE & SUPPLY BUSINESS TRUST p 736
6 Whitman Rd 02021
Tel (781) 828-8500 SIC 5074

■ LOJACK CORP p 875
40 Pequot Way 02021
Tel (781) 302-4200 SIC 3699

■ NEEDHAM ELECTRIC SUPPLY CORP p 1024
5 Shawmut Rd 02021
Tel (781) 828-9494 SIC 5063 3648

ONEBEACON INSURANCE GROUP LLC p 1087
150 Royall St 02021
Tel (781) 332-7000 SIC 6331

ORGANOGENESIS INC p 1094
150 Dan Rd Ste 3 02021
Tel (781) 575-0198 SIC 2836

REEBOK INTERNATIONAL LTD p 1217
1895 J W Foster Blvd 02021
Tel (781) 401-5000
SIC 3149 3143 3144 2329 2339 5661

SPORTS LICENSED DIVISION OF ADIDAS GROUP LLC p 1360
1895 J W Foster Blvd 02021
Tel (781) 401-5000 SIC 2329

THOMPSON STEEL CO INC p 1449
120 Royall St Ste 2 02021
Tel (781) 828-8800 SIC 5051 3316

UNICOM ENGINEERING INC p 1502
25 Dan Rd 02021
Tel (781) 332-1000 SIC 3572 7372

YALE ELECTRICAL SUPPLY CO p 1634
55 Shawmut Rd 02021
Tel (781) 737-2500 SIC 5063

CARLISLE, MA

ASSURANCE TECHNOLOGY CORP p 121
84 South St 01741
Tel (978) 369-8848 SIC 8711 3629

CHARLESTOWN, MA

■ BEACON HOSPICE INC p 164
529 Main St Ste 126 02129
Tel (617) 242-4872 SIC 8051

DENTAL SERVICE OF MASSACHUSETTS INC p 429
465 Medford St Ste 150 02129
Tel (617) 886-1000 SIC 6324

■ SALESLINK CORP p 1272
425 Medford St 02129
Tel (617) 886-4800 SIC 7379 8744 7331

SPAULDING REHABILITATION HOSPITAL (SRH) VOLUNTEER SERVICES p 1355
300 1st Ave 02129
Tel (617) 952-5000 SIC 8069 8011

SPAULDING REHABILITATION HOSPITAL CORP p 1355
300 1st Ave 02129
Tel (617) 952-5000 SIC 8062

TREVI ICOS CORP p 1476
38 3rd Ave 02129
Tel (617) 241-4800 SIC 1629 1622

VISITING NURSE ASSOCIATION OF BOSTON p 1561
500 Rutherford Ave # 200 02129
Tel (617) 886-6463 SIC 8082

CHARLTON, MA

KARL STORZ ENDOVISION INC p 804
91 Carpenter Hill Rd 01507
Tel (508) 248-9011 SIC 3841

CHELMSFORD, MA

■ AECOM C&E INC p 28
250 Apollo Dr 01824
Tel (978) 905-2100 SIC 8711

■ AIRVANA LP p 41
250 Apollo Dr 01824
Tel (877) 855-4092 SIC 4899

▲ BROOKS AUTOMATION INC p 218
15 Elizabeth Dr 01824
Tel (978) 262-2400
SIC 3559 3563 3823 7699

BULL DATA SYSTEMS INC p 225
285 Billerica Rd Ste 200 01824
Tel (978) 294-6000 SIC 3571 3577 7378

BULL HN INFORMATION SYSTEMS INC p 225
285 Billerica Rd Ste 200 01824
Tel (978) 294-6000 SIC 5045 7373

ENSR INTL CORP p 501
250 Apollo Dr 01824
Tel (978) 589-3000 SIC 8748 8711

■ HITTITE MICROWAVE LLC p 697
2 Elizabeth Dr 01824
Tel (978) 250-3343 SIC 3674

KRONOS ACQUISITION CORP p 830
297 Billerica Rd 01824
Tel (978) 250-9800 SIC 7372 7373 6726

KRONOS INC p 830
297 Billerica Rd 01824
Tel (978) 250-9800 SIC 7372 7373

KRONOS PARENT CORP p 830
297 Billerica Rd 01824
Tel (978) 250-9800 SIC 7372 7373

▲ MERCURY SYSTEMS INC p 945
201 Riverneck Rd 01824
Tel (978) 256-1300 SIC 3672 7372

TOWN OF CHELMSFORD p 1465
50 Billerica Rd 01824
Tel (978) 250-5201 SIC 9111

ZOLL MEDICAL CORP p 1644
269 Mill Rd 01824
Tel (978) 421-9100 SIC 3845 7372

CHELSEA, MA

CITY OF CHELSEA p 314
500 Broadway Ste 1 02150
Tel (617) 466-4240 SIC 9111

DENNIS K BURKE INC p 428
284 Eastern Ave 02150
Tel (617) 884-7800 SIC 5172 5541

DIMARE BROTHERS INC p 440
84 New England Prod Ctr 02150
Tel (617) 889-3800 SIC 5148

KAYEM FOODS INC p 805
75 Arlington St 02150
Tel (781) 933-3115 SIC 2011 2013

CHESTNUT HILL, MA

■ GENERAL CINEMA CORP OF TEXAS p 599
1300 Boylston St 02467
Tel (617) 738-3513 SIC 7832

TRUSTEES OF BOSTON COLLEGE p 1487
140 Commonwealth Ave 02467
Tel (617) 552-8000 SIC 8221

CHICOPEE, MA

CITY OF CHICOPEE p 314
274 Front St 01013
Tel (413) 594-1490 SIC 9111

CONSUMER PRODUCT DISTRIBUTORS INC p 361
705 Meadow St 01013
Tel (413) 592-4141
SIC 5194 5141 7389 5145

MEDICAL WEST COMMUNITY HEALTH p 937
444 Montgomery St 01020
Tel (413) 598-7440 SIC 6324

■ TOP-FLITE GOLF CO p 1460
425 Meadow St 01013
Tel (413) 536-1200 SIC 5941

CLINTON, MA

■ NYPRO INC p 1069
101 Union St 01510
Tel (978) 365-8100
SIC 3089 3559 7389 8711

CONCORD, MA

BARRETT SOTHEBYS INTERNATIONAL REALTY p 157
33 Walden St 01742
Tel (978) 369-6453 SIC 6531

EMERSON HOSPITAL p 492
133 Old Rd To 9 Acre Cor 01742
Tel (978) 369-1400 SIC 8062

HAYES PUMP INC p 670
66 Old Powder Mill Rd I 01742
Tel (978) 369-8800 SIC 5084 3561

MANUFACTURERS SERVICES LIMITED p 903
300 Baker Ave Ste 106 01742
Tel (978) 287-5630
SIC 3571 3577 3572 3661 3663

WELCH FOODS INC A COOPERATIVE p 1588
300 Baker Ave Ste 101 01742
Tel (978) 371-1000 SIC 2033 2037

DALTON, MA

CRANE & CO INC p 388
30 South St 01226
Tel (617) 648-3714 SIC 2621 5943

DANVERS, MA

▲ ABIOMED INC p 11
22 Cherry Hill Dr 01923
Tel (978) 646-1400 SIC 3845

CLEANING SERVICE GROUP INC p 324
230 North St 01923
Tel (978) 750-8900 SIC 7349

CONSTRUCTION MANAGEMENT & BUILDERS INC p 361
75 Sylvan St Ste C103 01923
Tel (781) 246-9400 SIC 8741

COPYRIGHT CLEARANCE CENTER INC p 368
222 Rosewood Dr Fl 10 01923
Tel (978) 750-8400 SIC 6794 7375

ELIZA CORP p 487
75 Sylvan St Ste B205 01923
Tel (978) 921-2700 SIC 5045

■ GATEHOUSE MEDIA MASSACHUSETTS I INC p 593
75 Sylvan St Ste C105 01923
Tel (585) 598-0030 SIC 2711

GREENCORE US HOLDINGS p 637
222 Rosewood Dr Ste 240 01923
Tel (508) 586-8418 SIC 2043

GREENCORE USA INC p 637
222 Rosewood Dr Fl 4 01923
Tel (978) 716-2530 SIC 2099

HEALTH & EDUCATION SERVICES INC p 673
199 Rosewood Dr Ste 250 01923
Tel (978) 921-1293 SIC 8093

INTERNATIONAL CARS LTD INC p 754
382 Newbury St 01923
Tel (800) 514-1627 SIC 5511 5521

MARKETFARE FOODS LLC p 908
222 Rosewood Dr Fl 2 01923
Tel (978) 716-2530 SIC 5142

MEDTRONIC INTERVENTIONAL VASCULAR INC p 939
37a Cherry Hill Dr 01923
Tel (978) 777-0042 SIC 3841

NORTH AMERICAN FAMILY INSTITUTE INC p 1050
300 Rosewood Dr Ste 101 01923
Tel (978) 538-0286 SIC 8322

NORTHEAST ARC INC p 1054
64 Holten St 01923
Tel (978) 762-4878 SIC 8361 8322 8331

DEDHAM, MA

▲ ATLANTIC POWER CORP p 127
3 Allied Dr Ste 220 02026
Tel (617) 977-2400 SIC 4911 3621

DEDHAM MEDICAL ASSOCIATES INC p 421
1 Lyons St 02026
Tel (781) 329-1400 SIC 8011 8021

DELOPS INC p 425
600 Providence Hwy 02026
Tel (508) 697-7742 SIC 5812

MULBERRY CHILD CARE CENTERS INC p 999
990 Washington St Ste 104 02026
Tel (781) 320-9222 SIC 8351

PAPA GINOS HOLDINGS CORP p 1112
600 Providence Hwy 02026
Tel (781) 461-1200 SIC 5812 6794

PAPA GINOS INC p 1112
600 Providence Hwy 02026
Tel (781) 461-1200 SIC 5812

POINT GROUP HEALTH CARE GROUP & SENIOR LIVING CENTER INC p 1159
3 Allied Dr Ste 106 02026
Tel (781) 251-9001 SIC 8051 8741

RIVERSIDE COMMUNITY CARE INC p 1237
270 Bridge St Ste 301 02026
Tel (617) 969-4925 SIC 8322

DEERFIELD, MA

TRUSTEES OF DEERFIELD ACADEMY p 1487
7 Boyden Ln 01342
Tel (413) 772-0241 SIC 8211

DEVENS, MA

▲ AMERICAN SUPERCONDUCTOR CORP p 80
64 Jackson Rd 01434
Tel (978) 842-3000 SIC 3674 3621

■ PATTERSON VETERINARY SUPPLY INC p 1121
137 Barnum Rd 01434
Tel (978) 353-6000 SIC 5047

DRACUT, MA

BROX INDUSTRIES INC p 220
1471 Methuen St 01826
Tel (978) 454-9105
SIC 1442 1499 1611 1629 1794 2951

DUDLEY, MA

GENTEX OPTICS INC p 605
183 W Main St 01571
Tel (570) 282-8531 SIC 3851 3842

DUXBURY, MA

VERC ENTERPRISES INC p 1549
5 Chestnut St 02332
Tel (781) 934-7300 SIC 5541 7542

EAST LONGMEADOW, MA

CARTAMUNDI EAST LONGMEADOW LLC p 261
443 Shaker Rd 01028
Tel (413) 526-2000 SIC 3944 3999

SECURE ENERGY SOLUTIONS LLC p 1298
12 Somers Rd 14 01028
Tel (413) 733-2571 SIC 8711

EAST TAUNTON, MA

■ JORDANS FURNITURE INC p 793
450 Revolutionary Dr 02718
Tel (508) 828-4000 SIC 5712

EAST WALPOLE, MA

HOLLINGSWORTH & VOSE CO p 701
112 Washington St 02032
Tel (508) 850-2000
SIC 2621 3053 2297 2499

EAST WEYMOUTH, MA

BARTLETT NUCLEAR INC p 158
97 Libbey Industrial Pkwy # 400 02189
Tel (508) 746-6464 SIC 7389 8734

WEYMOUTH PUBLIC SCHOOLS p 1603
111 Middle St 02189
Tel (781) 337-7500 SIC 8211

EVERETT, MA

BOND BROTHERS INC p 199
145 Spring St 02149
Tel (617) 387-3400 SIC 1542

BOSTON COACH CORP p 202
69 Norman St Ste 13 02149
Tel (800) 672-7676 SIC 4119 8741

CITY OF EVERETT p 314
484 Broadway Rm 14 02149
Tel (617) 394-2270 SIC 9111

EVERETT PUBLIC SCHOOLS p 514
121 Vine St 02149
Tel (617) 394-2400 SIC 8211

FTM CORP p 583
69 Norman St Ste 13 02149
Tel (800) 672-7676 SIC 4111

MTG ACQUISITIONS LLC p 998
69 Norman St 02149
Tel (800) 922-0343 SIC 4789

FAIRHAVEN, MA

■ ACUSHNET CO p 20
333 Bridge St 02719
Tel (508) 979-2000 *SIC* 3949 3149 2381

■ ACUSHNET HOLDINGS CORP p 20
333 Bridge St 02719
Tel (800) 225-8500 *SIC* 3949

SOUTHCOAST PHYSICIANS GROUP INC p 1345
200 Mill Rd Ste 180 02719
Tel (508) 758-3781 *SIC* 8011

FALL RIVER, MA

■ AMERICAN DRYER CORP p 71
88 Currant Rd 02720
Tel (508) 678-9000 *SIC* 3582

BLOUNT FINE FOODS CORP p 190
630 Currant Rd 02720
Tel (774) 888-1300 *SIC* 2092 2038

CHARLTON MEMORIAL HOSPITAL INC p 290
363 Highland Ave 02720
Tel (508) 679-3131 *SIC* 8062

CITY OF FALL RIVER p 314
1 Government Ctr 02722
Tel (508) 324-2000 *SIC* 9111

DIOCESAN HEALTH FACILITIES OFFICE p 440
368 N Main St 02720
Tel (508) 679-8154 *SIC* 8051

DUROTEXTILES LLC p 463
110 Chace St 02724
Tel (508) 675-0102 *SIC* 2261 2262

■ ENTERPRISE PUBLISHING CO LLC p 502
10 Purchase St 02720
Tel (585) 598-0030 *SIC* 2711

FALL RIVER PUBLIC SCHOOLS p 526
417 Rock St 02720
Tel (508) 675-8420 *SIC* 8211

GOLD MEDAL BAKERY INC p 620
21 Penn St 02724
Tel (508) 679-8958 *SIC* 2051

ROMAN CATHOLIC DIOCESE OF FALL RIVER OFFICE OF AIDS MINISTR p 1248
47 Underwood St 02720
Tel (508) 235-1184 *SIC* 8661 8211

SOUTHCOAST HOSPITALS GROUP INC p 1345
363 Highland Ave 02720
Tel (508) 679-3131 *SIC* 8062

ST ANNES HEALTH CARE SYSTEM INC p 1364
795 Middle St 02721
Tel (508) 674-5741 *SIC* 8741

STEWARD ST ANNES HOSPITAL CORP p 1388
795 Middle St 02721
Tel (508) 674-5741 *SIC* 8062

TAS-SAHC INC p 1426
795 Middle St 02721
Tel (508) 674-5600 *SIC* 8062 8011

FALMOUTH, MA

FALMOUTH HOSPITAL ASSOCIATION INC p 526
100 Ter Heun Dr 02540
Tel (508) 548-5300 *SIC* 8062

FITCHBURG, MA

CITY OF FITCHBURG p 314
166 Boulder Dr Ste 108 01420
Tel (978) 345-9567 *SIC* 9111

SIMONDS INTERNATIONAL LLC p 1325
135 Intervale Rd 01420
Tel (978) 343-3731 *SIC* 3553

FOXBORO, MA

CORINTHIAN SCHOOLS INC p 370
124 Washington St Ste 101 02035
Tel (714) 427-3001 *SIC* 8249

DECOR HOLDINGS INC p 421
225 Foxboro Blvd 02035
Tel (508) 339-9151 *SIC* 5023

GPX INTERNATIONAL TIRE CORP p 628
124 Washington St Ste 101 02035
Tel (781) 321-3910 *SIC* 3011

INTERNATIONAL FOREST PRODUCTS LLC p 755
1 Patriot Pl 02035
Tel (508) 698-4600 *SIC* 0831

KRAFT GROUP LLC p 829
1 Patriot Pl 02035
Tel (508) 384-4230 *SIC* 2653

MICROFIBRES INC p 962
124 Washington St Ste 101 02035
Tel (401) 725-4883
SIC 2221 2295 5131 2262

ROBERT ALLEN GROUP INC p 1241
2 Hampshire St Ste 300 02035
Tel (508) 339-9151 *SIC* 5023

SHANGHAI FOXBORO CO p 1311
33 Commercial St 02035
Tel (508) 543-8750 *SIC* 3699

FRAMINGHAM, MA

▲ AMERESCO INC p 66
111 Speen St Ste 410 01701
Tel (508) 661-2200 *SIC* 8711 1731

BOSE CORP p 202
100 The Mountain 01701
Tel (508) 879-7330 *SIC* 3651 5731

CCL LABEL INC p 270
161 Worcester Rd Ste 504 01701
Tel (508) 872-4511 *SIC* 2759 3411 2671

■ CONCORD BUYING GROUP INC p 354
770 Cochituate Rd 01701
Tel (508) 390-4000 *SIC* 5651

CUMBERLAND FARMS INC p 400
100 Crossing Blvd 01702
Tel (508) 270-1400
SIC 5411 5541 5172 2086 2051 2026

HEARTWARE INTERNATIONAL INC p 679
500 Old Connecticut Path 01701
Tel (508) 739-0950 *SIC* 3841

■ HOMEGOODS INC p 703
770 Cochituate Rd 01701
Tel (508) 390-3199 *SIC* 5719

IDC RESEARCH INC p 728
5 Speen St 01701
Tel (508) 872-8200 *SIC* 8732

IDG COMMUNICATIONS INC p 729
5 Speen St 01701
Tel (508) 875-5000 *SIC* 2721 2731

J F WHITE CONTRACTING CO p 771
10 Burr St 01701
Tel (508) 879-4700 *SIC* 1622

LIFELINE SYSTEMS CO p 864
111 Lawrence St 01702
Tel (508) 988-1000 *SIC* 3669

■ MARMAXX OPERATING CORP p 909
770 Cochituate Rd 01701
Tel (508) 390-1000 *SIC* 5311 5651

■ MARSHALLS OF MA INC p 911
770 Cochituate Rd 01701
Tel (508) 390-1000 *SIC* 5651 5719

MASSACHUSETTS DEPARTMENT OF STATE POLICE p 916
470 Worcester Rd 01702
Tel (508) 820-2350 *SIC* 9221

■ PERINI MANAGEMENT SERVICES INC p 1136
73 Mount Wayte Ave 01702
Tel (508) 628-2000
SIC 1541 1542 1611 1629

PR EDUCATION LLC p 1166
111 Speen St 01701
Tel (508) 663-5050 *SIC* 8748 8299

■ STAPLES CONTRACT & COMMERCIAL INC p 1377
500 Staples Dr 01702
Tel (508) 253-5000 *SIC* 5943

▲ STAPLES INC p 1377
500 Staples Dr 01702
Tel (508) 253-5000
SIC 5943 5999 7513 5961 5712

■ STAPLES INTERNATIONAL INC p 1378
500 Staples Dr 01702
Tel (508) 253-5000
SIC 5943 5712 5044 5021 5112

▲ TJX COMPANIES INC p 1457
770 Cochituate Rd Ste 1 01701
Tel (508) 390-1000 *SIC* 5311 5651 5719

TOWN OF FRAMINGHAM p 1465
150 Concord St 01702
Tel (508) 532-5400 *SIC* 9111

■ VHS ACQUISITION SUBSIDIARY NUMBER 9 INC p 1553
115 Lincoln St 01702
Tel (508) 383-1000 *SIC* 8062

FRANKLIN, MA

BARRETT DISTRIBUTION CENTERS INC p 157
15 Freedom Way 02038
Tel (508) 528-1747 *SIC* 4225

■ GARELICK FARMS LLC p 592
1199 W Central St Ste 1 02038
Tel (508) 528-9000 *SIC* 2026

PIERCE ALUMINUM CO INC p 1147
34 Forge Pkwy 02038
Tel (508) 541-7007 *SIC* 5051

PLANSEE USA LLC p 1154
115 Constitution Blvd 02038
Tel (508) 553-3800 *SIC* 3499

PSE HOLDING CORP p 1188
115 Constitution Blvd 02038
Tel (508) 553-3800 *SIC* 8742

SPEEDLINE TECHNOLOGIES INC p 1358
16 Forge Pkwy 02038
Tel (508) 541-4867 *SIC* 3565 3569

SPORTS IMAGES INC p 1360
1000 Franklin Village Dr # 104 02038
Tel (508) 530-3225 *SIC* 5199

TEGRA MEDICAL LLC p 1432
9 Forge Pkwy 02038
Tel (508) 541-4200 *SIC* 3841

■ THERMO OPTEK CORP p 1447
27 Forge Pkwy 02038
Tel (508) 553-5100 *SIC* 3823

TOWN OF FRANKLIN p 1465
355 E Central St Ste 1 02038
Tel (508) 528-7900 *SIC* 9111

GARDNER, MA

ADVANCED CABLE TIES INC p 25
245 Suffolk Ln 01440
Tel (978) 630-3900 *SIC* 5063

HENRY HEYWOOD MEMORIAL HOSPITAL p 684
242 Green St 01440
Tel (978) 632-3420 *SIC* 8062

HEYWOOD HEALTHCARE INC p 688
242 Green St 01440
Tel (978) 632-3420 *SIC* 8741

GLOUCESTER, MA

GORTONS INC p 626
128 Rogers St 01930
Tel (978) 283-3000 *SIC* 2092 2091

NATIONAL FISH AND SEAFOOD INC p 1012
11 15 Parker St 01930
Tel (978) 282-7880 *SIC* 5146 2092

■ VARIAN SEMICONDUCTOR EQUIPMENT ASSOCIATES INC p 1544
35 Dory Rd 01930
Tel (978) 282-2000 *SIC* 5065 3674

GREENFIELD, MA

FRANKLIN BAYSTATE MEDICAL CENTER p 575
164 High St 01301
Tel (413) 773-0211 *SIC* 8062

GROTON, MA

■ NEW ENGLAND BUSINESS SERVICE INC p 1030
500 Main St 01471
Tel (978) 448-6111
SIC 2759 2771 5045 2653 3089 3069

GROVELAND, MA

A W CHESTERTON CO p 7
860 Salem St 01834
Tel (781) 438-7000
SIC 3053 2851 2992 2891 5169

HANOVER, MA

EXCEL MODULAR SCAFFOLD AND LEASING CORP p 516
720 Washington St Unit 5 02339
Tel (508) 830-1111 *SIC* 1799

▲ INDEPENDENT BANK CORP p 736
2036 Washington St 02339
Tel (781) 878-6100 *SIC* 6022

LINCHRIS HOTEL CORP p 866
269 Hanover St Ste 2 02339
Tel (781) 826-8824 *SIC* 7011

P A LANDERS INC p 1102
351 Winter St 02339
Tel (781) 826-8818 *SIC* 1611 1442

HANSCOM AFB, MA

MASSACHUSETTS NATIONAL GUARD p 917
2 Randolph Rd 01731
Tel (339) 202-3832 *SIC* 9711

HAVERHILL, MA

CITY OF HAVERHILL p 315
City Hl Rm 100 01830
Tel (978) 374-2300 *SIC* 9111

COUNTY BROADCASTING CO LLC p 375
30 How St 01830
Tel (603) 668-6400 *SIC* 4832

■ COVANTA HAVERHILL INC p 384
100 Recovery Way 01835
Tel (978) 372-6288 *SIC* 4953 1629 4931

DONUT MANAGEMENT INC p 451
3 Pluff Ave 01835
Tel (978) 664-2854 *SIC* 5461

GOLDEN FLEECE MANUFACTURING GROUP LLC p 620
25 Computer Dr 01832
Tel (978) 738-0855 *SIC* 2329

HINGHAM, MA

BUILDING 19 INC p 225
319 Lincoln St 02043
Tel (781) 749-6900 *SIC* 5311

RUSSELECTRIC INC p 1259
S Shore Park 02043
Tel (781) 749-6000 *SIC* 3613

TALBOTS INC p 1422
1 Talbots Dr Ste 1 02043
Tel (781) 749-7600
SIC 5621 5137 5632 5641

HOLLISTON, MA

CENTURY FIBER OPTICS p 282
79 Lowland St 01746
Tel (508) 429-2342 *SIC* 1731

▲ HARVARD BIOSCIENCE INC p 666
84 October Hill Rd Ste 10 01746
Tel (508) 893-8999 *SIC* 3821 3826

WAYNE J GRIFFIN ELECTRIC INC p 1584
116 Hopping Brook Rd 01746
Tel (508) 429-8830 *SIC* 1731

HOLYOKE, MA

ACCOUNTS PAYABLE MERCY ME p 15
1221 Main St Ste 108 01040
Tel (413) 539-2692 *SIC* 8011

CITY OF HOLYOKE p 315
536 Dwight St 01040
Tel (413) 322-5510 *SIC* 9111

DANIEL OCONNELLS SONS INC p 411
480 Hampden St 01040
Tel (413) 534-5667
SIC 1541 1542 1522 1611 1622 1629

HOLYOKE MEDICAL CENTER INC p 702
575 Beech St 01040
Tel (413) 534-2554 *SIC* 8062

HOLYOKE PUBLIC SCHOOLS p 702
57 Suffolk St Ste 101 01040
Tel (413) 534-2000 *SIC* 8211

ISO NEW ENGLAND INC p 767
1 Sullivan Rd 01040
Tel (413) 535-4000 *SIC* 8611

OCONNELL COMPANIES INC p 1074
480 Hampden St 01040
Tel (413) 534-0246 *SIC* 1541

VALLEY HEALTH SYSTEMS INC p 1540
575 Beech St 01040
Tel (413) 534-2500
SIC 8082 8093 8399 8741 8721

HOPKINTON, MA

■ CALIPER LIFE SCIENCES INC p 242
68 Elm St 01748
Tel (508) 435-9500 *SIC* 3826

■ EMC CORP p 490
176 South St 01748
Tel (508) 435-1000
SIC 3572 7372 7371 3577

■ EMC INTERNATIONAL HOLDINGS INC p 490
176 South St 01748
Tel (508) 435-1000 *SIC* 3572 3577

■ HUTCHINSON AEROSPACE & INDUSTRY INC p 721
82 South St 01748
Tel (508) 417-7000 *SIC* 3714 3061 3724

HUDSON, MA

■ INTEL MASSACHUSETTS INC p 750
75 Reed Rd 01749
Tel (978) 553-4000 *SIC* 3674

HYANNIS, MA

BOSTON-WYMAN INC p 203
110 Breeds Hill Rd Ste 8 02601
Tel (508) 778-5044 *SIC* 5812

CAPE COD HEALTHCARE INC p 248
27 Park St 02601
Tel (508) 862-5030 *SIC* 8062

CAPE COD HOSPITAL p 248
27 Park St 02601
Tel (508) 862-7575 *SIC* 8062 8011 8063

SHEPLEY WOOD PRODUCTS INC p 1315
216 Thornton Dr 02601
Tel (508) 862-6200 *SIC* 5031

TOWN OF BARNSTABLE p 1465
230 South St 02601
Tel (508) 862-4661 *SIC* 9111

IPSWICH, MA

EBSCO PUBLISHING INC p 474
10 Estes St 01938
Tel (978) 356-6500
SIC 2741 7375 2731 2721

UNITED PIPE & STEEL CORP p 1510
83 Turnpike Rd 01938
Tel (978) 356-9300 *SIC* 5074

KINGSTON, MA

L KNIFE & SON INC p 834
35 Elder Ave 02364
Tel (781) 585-2364 *SIC* 5181 5182

LAKEVILLE, MA

DENNISON LUBRICANTS INC p 428
102 Charles Eldridge Rd 02347
Tel (508) 946-0500 *SIC* 5172

OCEAN SPRAY INTERNATIONAL SALES INC p 1073
1 Ocean Spray Dr 02347
Tel (508) 946-1000 *SIC* 5149

LANCASTER, MA

RAND WHITNEY PACKAGING p 1207
580 Fort Pond Rd 01523
Tel (978) 870-1188 *SIC* 1541

LAWRENCE, MA

ABEL WOMACK INC p 11
1 International Way 01843
Tel (978) 989-9400 *SIC* 5084 7699

CITY OF LAWRENCE p 316
200 Common St 01840
Tel (978) 620-3010 *SIC* 9111

COMMUNITY DAY CARE CENTER OF LAWRENCE INC p 348
190 Hampshire St Ste 2 01840
Tel (978) 682-6628 SIC 8351

LAWRENCE GENERAL HOSPITAL p 848
1 General St 01841
Tel (978) 683-4000 SIC 8062

LAWRENCE SCHOOL DISTRICT p 848
233 Haverhill St 01840
Tel (978) 975-5905 SIC 8211

LGH CHARITABLE TRUST INC p 860
1 General St 01841
Tel (978) 683-4000 SIC 8082

▲ NXSTAGE MEDICAL INC p 1068
350 Merrimack St 01843
Tel (978) 687-4700 SIC 3845

POLARTEC LLC p 1159
46 Stafford St 01841
Tel (978) 685-6341 SIC 2299

LEE, MA

FITZPATRICK COMPANIES INC p 553
705 Pleasant St 01238
Tel (413) 298-1610 SIC 5714 5021 5023

RAY MURRAY INC p 1210
50 Limestone 01238
Tel (413) 243-7700 SIC 5085 5091

LEICESTER, MA

MILLBROOK DISTRIBUTION SERVICES INC p 970
88 Huntoon Memorial Hwy 01524
Tel (508) 892-8171
SIC 5122 5023 5072 5112 5049 5199

LEOMINSTER, MA

CENTRAL NEW ENGLAND HEALTHALLIANCE INC p 279
60 Hospital Rd 01453
Tel (978) 343-5000 SIC 8741

CITY OF LEOMINSTER p 316
25 West St Ste 5 01453
Tel (978) 534-7500 SIC 9111

HEALTH ALLIANCE WITH PHYSICIAN p 674
60 Hospital Rd 01453
Tel (978) 466-2000 SIC 6411

HEALTHALLIANCE HOSPITALS INC p 676
60 Hospital Rd 01453
Tel (978) 466-2000 SIC 8062

IMA DAIRY & FOOD USA INC p 733
7 New Lancaster Rd 01453
Tel (732) 343-7600 SIC 5083

MEXICHEM SPECIALTY COMPOUNDS INC p 957
170 Pioneer Dr 01453
Tel (978) 537-8071 SIC 3087 2899

MONSON COMPANIES INC p 985
154 Pioneer Dr 01453
Tel (978) 840-7007
SIC 5169 5172 2899 2842

LEXINGTON, MA

BIO-MEDICAL APPLICATIONS MANAGEMENT CO INC p 183
95 Hayden Ave 02421
Tel (781) 402-9000 SIC 8092

ELIOT COMMUNITY HUMAN SERVICES INC p 487
186 Bedford St 02420
Tel (781) 861-0890 SIC 8361 8322

HOME DIALYSIS OF MUHLENBERG COUNTY INC p 703
95 Hayden Ave 02421
Tel (781) 402-9000 SIC 7389

IBASIS INC p 726
10 Maguire Rd Ste 300 02421
Tel (781) 505-7500 SIC 4813

IMPRIVATA INC p 735
10 Maguire Rd Ste 125 02421
Tel (781) 674-2700 SIC 7372 7382

IPSWITCH INC p 764
83 Hartwell Ave 02421
Tel (781) 676-5700 SIC 5045

SEKISUI DIAGNOSTICS LLC p 1301
4 Hartwell Pl 02421
Tel (781) 652-7800 SIC 3841

SHIRE HUMAN GENETIC THERAPIES INC p 1317
300 Shire Way 02421
Tel (617) 349-0200 SIC 8731

SHIRE US INC p 1317
300 Shire Way 02421
Tel (781) 482-9222 SIC 5122

SHIRE-NPS PHARMACEUTICALS INC p 1317
300 Shire Way 02421
Tel (617) 349-0200 SIC 2834

TOWN OF LEXINGTON p 1465
1625 Massachusetts Ave 02420
Tel (781) 862-0500 SIC 9111

WATERMILL VENTURES LTD p 1582
1 Cranberry Hl 750 02421
Tel (781) 891-6660 SIC 6799

WINTERGREEN RESEARCH INC p 1617
6 Raymond St 02421
Tel (781) 863-5078 SIC 8748 8742

LITTLETON, MA

DOVER SADDLERY INC p 453
525 Great Rd 01460
Tel (978) 952-8062 SIC 5941

MIDDLESEX CORP p 965
1 Spectacle Pond Rd 01460
Tel (978) 742-4400 SIC 1611 1794 1622

LOWELL, MA

COBHAM DEFENSE ELECTRONIC SYSTEMS CORP p 332
1001 Pawtucket Blvd 01854
Tel (978) 779-7000 SIC 3812

COBHAM ELECTRONIC SYSTEMS INC p 332
1001 Pawtucket Blvd 01854
Tel (978) 442-4700 SIC 3812

▲ CSP INC p 398
175 Cabot St Ste 210 01854
Tel (978) 663-7598 SIC 3577 7372 7373

▲ ENTERPRISE BANCORP INC p 502
222 Merrimack St 01852
Tel (978) 459-9000 SIC 6022

■ ENTERPRISE BANK AND TRUST CO p 502
222 Merrimack St Fl 1 01852
Tel (978) 459-9000 SIC 6022

GN NETCOM INC p 619
900 Chelmsford St # 313 01851
Tel (800) 826-4656 SIC 3661

LOWELL CITY OF (INC) p 881
375 Merrimack St Rm 27 01852
Tel (978) 970-4200 SIC 9311

LOWELL GENERAL HOSPITAL p 881
295 Varnum Ave 01854
Tel (978) 937-6000 SIC 8062

▲ MACOM TECHNOLOGY SOLUTIONS HOLDINGS INC p 893
100 Chelmsford St 01851
Tel (978) 656-2500 SIC 3674

■ MACOM TECHNOLOGY SOLUTIONS INC p 893
100 Chelmsford St 01851
Tel (978) 656-2500 SIC 3663 3679

MADISON SECURITY GROUP INC p 894
31 Kirk St 01852
Tel (978) 459-5911 SIC 6289

PLUMCHOICE INC p 1157
900 Chelmsford St Ofc 1 01851
Tel (866) 811-3321 SIC 7378

SAINTS MEDICAL CENTER INC p 1271
1 Hospital Dr 01852
Tel (978) 458-1411 SIC 8051 8062

▲ TRC COMPANIES INC p 1475
650 Suffolk St 01854
Tel (978) 970-5600
SIC 7363 8734 7382 8748

WESTMINSTER PRESERVATION LP p 1601
1307 Pawtucket Blvd 01854
Tel (212) 506-5885 SIC 6531

LUDLOW, MA

EAST COAST TILE IMPORTS INC p 470
8 Stony Brook St Ste 1 01056
Tel (518) 344-7000 SIC 5032 8741

LYNN, MA

ELEMENT CARE INC p 486
37 Friend St 01902
Tel (781) 715-6608 SIC 8399

LYNNFIELD, MA

BABCOCK POWER INC p 143
6 Kimball Ln Ste 210 01940
Tel (978) 646-3300 SIC 3443 3569 3433

BRIDGEWELL INC p 212
471 Broadway 01940
Tel (781) 599-4240 SIC 8361 8093

HP HOOD LLC p 714
6 Kimball Ln Ste 400 01940
Tel (617) 887-8441 SIC 2026 2024 2022

INVESTORS CAPITAL HOLDINGS LLC p 761
6 Kimball Ln Ste 150 01940
Tel (781) 246-7982 SIC 6211 6282

NEW ENGLAND PETROLEUM LIMITED PARTNERSHIP p 1030
6 Kimball Ln Ste 400 01940
Tel (617) 660-7400 SIC 5172

LYNN, MA

KETTLE CUISINE LLC p 814
330 Lynnway Ste 405 01901
Tel (617) 409-1100 SIC 2032 2035

LYNN COMMUNITY HEALTH INC p 888
269 Union St 01901
Tel (781) 581-3900 SIC 8093

LYNN PUBLIC SCHOOLS p 888
100 Bennett St 01905
Tel (781) 593-1680 SIC 8211

MALDEN, MA

CAMBRIDGE HEALTH ALLIANCE PHYSICIANS ORGANIZATION INC p 244
350 Main St Ste 16 02148
Tel (617) 498-1000 SIC 8011

WASH DEPOT AUTO CENTERS LP p 1577
435 Eastern Ave 02148
Tel (781) 324-2000 SIC 7542 5541 5947

WASH DEPOT HOLDINGS INC p 1577
14 Summer St Ste 302 02148
Tel (781) 324-2000 SIC 7542 5541

WEST COAST DISTRIBUTING INC p 1594
350 Main St Fl 1 02148
Tel (781) 665-0300 SIC 4731 5148

WHIDDEN MEMORIAL HOSPITAL INC p 1605
350 Main St Ste 16 02148
Tel (781) 306-8872 SIC 8062

MANSFIELD, MA

BELKNAP WHITE GROUP INC p 169
111 Plymouth St 02048
Tel (508) 337-2700 SIC 5023

COVIDIEN LP p 385
15 Hampshire St 02048
Tel (508) 261-8000
SIC 3842 3841 3845 5122

HUB FOLDING BOX CO INC p 715
774 Norfolk St 02048
Tel (508) 339-0005 SIC 2657

NATIONAL LUMBER CO p 1014
245 Oakland St 02048
Tel (508) 337-8020 SIC 5211 2431

NELLCOR PURITAN BENNETT LLC p 1025
15 Hampshire St 02048
Tel (508) 261-8000 SIC 3845 3841

NEW ENGLAND CONTROLS INC p 1030
9 Oxford Rd 02048
Tel (508) 339-5522 SIC 5085

ONEBEACON INSURANCE CO p 1087
11 Norfolk St 02048
Tel (781) 332-7000 SIC 6411

SAMSONITE LLC p 1274
575 West St Ste 110 02048
Tel (508) 851-1400 SIC 5948 5199

MARION, MA

■ LOCKHEED MARTIN SIPPICAN INC p 873
7 Barnabas Rd 02738
Tel (508) 748-3399
SIC 3812 3826 3499 3672 3829 3845

■ POLARIS CONTRACT MANUFACTURING INC p 1159
15 Barnabas Rd 02738
Tel (508) 748-3399 SIC 3812

MARLBOROUGH, MA

APITECHNOLOGIES CORP p 96
400 Nickerson Rd 01752
Tel (855) 294-3800 SIC 3674

▲ BOSTON SCIENTIFIC CORP p 203
300 Boston Scientific Way 01752
Tel (508) 683-4000 SIC 3841 3842 3845

CITY OF MARLBOROUGH p 316
140 Main St Ofc 4 01752
Tel (508) 460-3775 SIC 9111

CIVIGENICS INC p 320
290 Donald Lynch Blvd # 301 01752
Tel (508) 486-9300 SIC 8741

COMMUNICATION TECHNOLOGY SERVICES LLC p 346
33 Locke Dr Ste 201 01752
Tel (508) 382-2700 SIC 1731

■ CYTYC CORP p 406
250 Campus Dr 01752
Tel (508) 263-2900 SIC 3841

DIGITAL EMPLOYEES FEDERAL CREDIT UNION p 439
220 Donald Lynch Blvd 01752
Tel (508) 263-6700 SIC 6061

■ GE HEALTHCARE BIO-SCIENCES CORP p 596
100 Results Way 01752
Tel (800) 526-3593 SIC 5122

■ GE HEALTHCARE INC p 596
100 Results Way 01752
Tel (800) 292-8514 SIC 5122 2833

▲ HOLOGIC INC p 702
250 Campus Dr 01752
Tel (508) 263-2900 SIC 3845 3844 3841

KAZ INC p 805
400 Donald Lynch Blvd # 300 01752
Tel (508) 490-7000 SIC 8082 2834 5047

KENS FOODS INC p 812
1 Dangelo Dr 01752
Tel (508) 229-1100 SIC 2033

■ MEDI-PHYSICS INC p 935
100 Results Way 01752
Tel (800) 526-3593 SIC 5122

RF1 HOLDING CO p 1231
400 Nickerson Rd 01752
Tel (855) 294-3800 SIC 3674 6719

■ ROHM AND HAAS ELECTRONIC MATERIALS LLC p 1247
455 Forest St 01752
Tel (508) 481-7950 SIC 2819 2869

SUNOVION PHARMACEUTICALS INC p 1403
84 Waterford Dr 01752
Tel (508) 481-6700 SIC 2834

WEB INDUSTRIES INC p 1586
377 Simarano Dr Ste 220 01752
Tel (508) 898-2988
SIC 2671 5162 3089 2269 3441

■ WEETABIX CO INC p 1587
500 Nickerson Rd Ste 150 01752
Tel (978) 365-1000 SIC 2043

MARSHFIELD, MA

TOWN OF MARSHFIELD p 1465
870 Moraine St 02050
Tel (781) 834-5552 SIC 9121

MAYNARD, MA

▲ ACACIA COMMUNICATIONS INC p 13
3 Mill And Main Pl # 400 01754
Tel (978) 938-4896 SIC 3674 8999

STRATUS TECHNOLOGIES INC p 1393
5 Mill Main Pl Ste 500 01754
Tel (978) 461-7000 SIC 7372

MEDFORD, MA

AGERO - CHECK p 34
1 Cabot Rd 02155
Tel (781) 393-9300 SIC 8699

AGERO INC p 34
1 Cabot Rd Ste 4 02155
Tel (781) 393-9300 SIC 8699

▲ CENTURY BANCORP INC p 282
400 Mystic Ave 02155
Tel (781) 393-4160 SIC 6022

■ CENTURY BANK AND TRUST CO p 282
400 Mystic Ave 02155
Tel (781) 393-4677 SIC 6022

CITY OF MEDFORD p 316
85 George P Hassett Dr 02155
Tel (781) 396-5500 SIC 9111

GENERAL INSULATION CO p 601
278 Mystic Ave Ste 209 02155
Tel (781) 391-2070 SIC 5033 7389

HALLMARK HEALTH CORP p 654
170 Governors Ave 02155
Tel (781) 979-3000 SIC 8741

MANAGEMENT SCIENCES FOR HEALTH INC p 900
200 Rivers Edge Dr 02155
Tel (617) 250-9500 SIC 8742

MEDWAY, MA

■ CYBEX INTERNATIONAL INC p 405
10 Trotter Dr 02053
Tel (508) 533-4300 SIC 3949

MICROGROUP INC p 962
7 Industrial Park Rd 02053
Tel (508) 533-4925
SIC 5051 3312 3498 3494 3492 3317

MELROSE, MA

HALLMARK HEALTH SYSTEM INC p 654
585 Lebanon St 02176
Tel (781) 979-3000 SIC 8741

METHUEN, MA

■ 3M TOUCH SYSTEMS INC p 3
501 Griffin Brook Dr 01844
Tel (978) 659-0053 SIC 3577

AGRI-MARK INC p 36
100 Milk St Ste 5 01844
Tel (978) 689-4442 SIC 2026 2022

CITY OF METHUEN p 316
41 Pleasant St 01844
Tel (978) 983-8505 SIC 9111

NRT BUS INC p 1064
55 Hampshire Rd 01844
Tel (978) 681-4100 SIC 4151

TAS-CHFH p 1425
70 East St 01844
Tel (978) 687-0156 SIC 8062

TAS-CVRHS INC p 1426
70 East St 01844
Tel (978) 687-0151 SIC 8062

MIDDLEBORO, MA

OCEAN SPRAY CRANBERRIES INC p 1073
1 Ocean Spray Dr 02349
Tel (508) 946-1000 SIC 2033 2034 2037

OCEAN SPRAY INTERNATIONAL INC p 1073
1 Ocean Spray Dr 02349
Tel (508) 946-1000 SIC 2037 2034 2033

■ SAGER ELECTRICAL SUPPLY CO INC p 1268
19 Leona Dr 02346
Tel (508) 923-6600 SIC 5065

MIDDLETON, MA

NORM THOMPSON OUTFITTERS INC p 1048
35 Village Rd Ste 500 01949
Tel (503) 614-4600 SIC 5961

MILFORD, MA

BARKER STEEL LLC p 155
55 Sumner St Ste 1 01757
Tel (508) 473-8484 SIC 3449

COMMONWEALTH OF MASSACHUSETTS DEPARTMENT OF CORRECTION p 346
50 Maple St Ste 3 01757
Tel (508) 233-6530 SIC 9121

CONSIGLI BUILDING GROUP INC p 358
72 Sumner St 01757
Tel (508) 473-2580 SIC 1542

CONSIGLI CONSTRUCTION CO INC p 359
72 Sumner St 01757
Tel (508) 473-2580 SIC 1541 1542

CONSUMER AUTO PARTS INC p 361
75 Fortune Blvd 01757
Tel (508) 634-0600 SIC 5531 5013

MILFORD REGIONAL HEALTHCARE FOUNDATION INC p 969
14 Prospect St 01757
Tel (508) 473-1190 SIC 6733 8082 8011

MILFORD REGIONAL MEDICAL CENTER INC p 969
14 Prospect St 01757
Tel (508) 473-1190 SIC 8062 8082

SOUTHWORTH-MILTON INC p 1353
100 Quarry Dr 01757
Tel (508) 634-3400 SIC 5082 7353

▲ WATERS CORP p 1582
34 Maple St 01757
Tel (508) 478-2000
SIC 3826 3829 7371 7372

■ WATERS TECHNOLOGIES CORP p 1582
34 Maple St 01757
Tel (508) 478-2000 SIC 3826 3829

MILTON, MA

BETH ISRAEL DEACONESS HOSPITAL - MILTON INC p 177
199 Reedsdale Rd 02186
Tel (617) 696-4600 SIC 8011

CURRY COLLEGE p 402
1071 Blue Hill Ave 02186
Tel (617) 333-0500 SIC 8221

NOT YOUR AVERAGE JOES INC p 1062
2 Granite Ave Ste 300 02186
Tel (774) 213-2800 SIC 5812

NATICK, MA

■ AMERICAN MEDICAL RESPONSE OF MASSACHUSETTS INC p 76
4 Tech Cir 01760
Tel (508) 650-5600 SIC 4119

▲ COGNEX CORP p 334
1 Vision Dr 01760
Tel (508) 650-3000 SIC 3823

FOREIGN MOTORS WEST INC p 566
253 N Main St 01760
Tel (508) 655-5350 SIC 5511 7538

MATHWORKS INC p 920
3 Apple Hill Dr 01760
Tel (508) 647-7000 SIC 7371 3823 8222

MIDDLESEX BANCORP MHC p 965
6 Main St 01760
Tel (508) 653-0300 SIC 6036

MIDDLESEX SAVINGS BANK p 965
6 Main St 01760
Tel (508) 653-0300 SIC 6036

PRINCETON REVIEW INC p 1177
24 Prime Park Way Ste 201 01760
Tel (800) 273-8439 SIC 8748 8299

TOWN OF NATICK p 1465
13 E Central St Ste 1 01760
Tel (508) 647-6410 SIC 9111

NEEDHAM HEIGHTS, MA

EXTREME REACH INC p 521
75 2nd Ave Ste 720 02494
Tel (781) 577-2016 SIC 7311

NEEDHAM, MA

CONTINENTAL WINGATE CO INC p 364
1 Charles River Pl 02494
Tel (781) 707-9000 SIC 6513 8051

CRESSON SECURE TREATMENT UNIT p 391
160 Gould St Ste 300 02494
Tel (781) 559-4900 SIC 8361

LILY TRANSPORTATION CORP p 866
145 Rosemary St Ste D3 02494
Tel (781) 247-1300 SIC 4213 4212

▲ PTC INC p 1189
140 Kendrick St 02494
Tel (781) 370-5000 SIC 7372 7373 7371

TOWN OF NEEDHAM p 1465
1471 Highland Ave 02492
Tel (781) 455-7500 SIC 9111

■ TRIPADVISOR INC p 1482
400 1st Ave 02494
Tel (781) 800-5000 SIC 4724 7374

■ TRIPADVISOR LLC p 1482
400 1st Ave 02494
Tel (781) 800-5000 SIC 7374

WINGATE HEALTH CARE HOLDINGS INC p 1616
63 Kendrick St 02494
Tel (781) 707-9000 SIC 8741

WINGATE HEALTH CARE INC p 1616
589 Highland Ave 02494
Tel (781) 707-9500 SIC 8741

NEW BEDFORD, MA

ACUSHNET RUBBER CO INC p 20
744 Belleville Ave 02745
Tel (508) 998-4000 SIC 3053 3061 2821

AEROVOX INC p 31
167 John Vertente Blvd 02745
Tel (508) 994-9661 SIC 3629 3675

■ ATI ALLEGHENY LUDLUM INC p 124
1357 E Rodney French Blvd 02744
Tel (508) 992-4067 SIC 3316

FRIENDLY FRUIT INC p 580
2301 Purchase St Unit 1 02746
Tel (508) 999-6408 SIC 5148 5149

HTP INC p 715
272 Duchaine Blvd 02745
Tel (508) 763-8071 SIC 5084 3443

NEW BEDFORD CITY OF (INC) p 1029
133 William St Unit 208 02740
Tel (508) 979-1400 SIC 9111

PLUMBERS SUPPLY CO p 1156
429 Church St 02745
Tel (508) 985-4966 SIC 5074 5084 5082

SAINT LUKES HOSPITAL OF NEW BEDFORD INC p 1270
101 Page St 02740
Tel (508) 997-1515 SIC 8062 8082 8093

SOUTHCOAST HEALTH SYSTEM INC p 1345
101 Page St 02740
Tel (508) 997-1515 SIC 8741 8062

SOUTHCOAST PHYSICIAN SERVICES INC p 1345
101 Page St 02740
Tel (508) 961-5555 SIC 8741

ZD USA HOLDINGS INC p 1641
744 Belleville Ave 02745
Tel (508) 998-4000 SIC 3053

NEWBURYPORT, MA

ANNA JAQUES HOSPITAL p 92
25 Highland Ave 01950
Tel (978) 463-1000 SIC 8062

DIANNES FINE DESSERT INC p 437
4 Graf Rd 01950
Tel (978) 463-3832 SIC 2024

■ NEWBURYPORT HOLDINGS INC p 1037
4 Middle St Ste 226 01950
Tel (781) 246-8234 SIC 7371

▲ UFP TECHNOLOGIES INC p 1499
100 Hale St 01950
Tel (978) 352-2200 SIC 3086

NEWTON, MA

CHELSEA INDUSTRIES INC p 293
46a Glen Ave 02459
Tel (617) 232-6060 SIC 6552

CITY OF NEWTON p 317
1000 Cmmwl Ave Newton Ctr 02459
Tel (617) 796-1200 SIC 9111

FIRST MARKET RESEARCH CORP p 547
99 Needham St Apt 1305 02461
Tel (617) 734-7080 SIC 8732

▲ FIVE STAR QUALITY CARE INC p 553
400 Centre St 02458
Tel (617) 796-8387 SIC 8051 8052

■ GALAXY INVESTMENT HOLDINGS INC p 589
38 Glen Ave 02459
Tel (617) 928-9300 SIC 4813 4812

GOVERNMENT PROPERTIES INCOME TRUST p 627
255 Washington St Ste 300 02458
Tel (617) 219-1440 SIC 6798

H C STARCK INC p 649
45 Industrial Pl 02461
Tel (617) 630-5800 SIC 3339 3356 3313

▲ HOSPITALITY PROPERTIES TRUST p 710
255 Washington St Ste 300 02458
Tel (617) 964-8389 SIC 6798

■ HPT TRS IHG-2 INC p 714
255 Washington St Ste 300 02458
Tel (617) 964-8389 SIC 7011

NEWTON PUBLIC SCHOOL DISTRICT p 1039
100 Walnut St 02460
Tel (617) 559-6000 SIC 8211

NEWTON WELLESLEY HOSPITAL CORP p 1039
2014 Washington St 02462
Tel (617) 243-6000 SIC 8062

NEWTON-WELLESLEY HEALTH CARE SYSTEM INC p 1039
2014 Washington St 02462
Tel (617) 243-6000 SIC 8741 7374 6512

NORTHLAND INVESTMENT CORP p 1057
2150 Washington St # 300 02462
Tel (617) 965-7100 SIC 6799 6411 6531

PR RESTAURANTS LLC p 1167
2150 Washington St # 125 02462
Tel (617) 581-6160 SIC 5461 5812

▲ RMR GROUP INC p 1239
255 Washington St Ste 300 02458
Tel (617) 928-1300 SIC 8742

SEABOARD FLOUR LLC p 1295
1320 Centre St Ste 200 02459
Tel (617) 928-6040 SIC 5046

SELECT INCOME REIT p 1301
255 Washington St Ste 300 02458
Tel (617) 796-8303 SIC 6798

SENIOR HOUSING PROPERTIES TRUST p 1304
255 Washington St Ste 300 02458
Tel (617) 796-8350 SIC 6798

■ SOFTBANK HOLDINGS INC p 1337
1188 Centre St Ste 2 02459
Tel (617) 928-9300 SIC 8741

SONESTA INTERNATIONAL HOTELS CORP p 1340
255 Washington St Ste 270 02458
Tel (770) 923-1775 SIC 7011

WT RICH CO INC p 1569
29 Crafts St Ste 300 02458
Tel (617) 467-6010 SIC 1541 1542

NORTH ADAMS, MA

CASCADE SCHOOL SUPPLIES INC p 262
1 Brown St 01247
Tel (413) 663-3716 SIC 5049

CRANE STATIONARY p 389
1466 Curran Hwy 01247
Tel (413) 664-2527 SIC 2621

CRANES PERSONAL DESIGN SERVICES p 389
1466 Curran Hwy 01247
Tel (413) 664-4321 SIC 7389 2796 2759

NORTH ANDOVER, MA

■ ASSOCIATED HOME CARE LLC p 120
991 Osgood St 01845
Tel (978) 682-0745 SIC 8082

CA COURTESY DEMOS INC p 234
85 Flagship Dr Ste C 01845
Tel (978) 296-2600 SIC 7389

EAGLE-TRIBUNE PUBLISHING CO p 468
100 Turnpike St 01845
Tel (978) 946-2000 SIC 2711

■ KEYW CORP p 816
250 Clark St 01845
Tel (978) 682-7767 SIC 7371 8713 7389

L-COM INC p 835
50 High St Fl 3 01845
Tel (800) 343-1455 SIC 3678 3577 3357

■ LSB CORP p 883
30 Massachusetts Ave # 8 01845
Tel (978) 725-7500 SIC 6022

MERRIMACK COLLEGE p 950
315 Turnpike St 01845
Tel (978) 837-5000 SIC 8221

POLYGON US CORP p 1160
15 Sharpners Pond Rd F 01845
Tel (800) 422-6379 SIC 1521

■ WATTS REGULATOR CO p 1583
815 Chestnut St 01845
Tel (978) 689-6000 SIC 3491 3494

▲ WATTS WATER TECHNOLOGIES INC p 1583
815 Chestnut St 01845
Tel (978) 688-1811 SIC 3491 3494

NORTH ATTLEBORO, MA

TOWN OF NORTH ATTLEBOROUGH p 1465
43 S Washington St 02760
Tel (508) 699-0100 SIC 9121

NORTH BILLERICA, MA

BOSTON AND MAINE CORP p 202
1700 Iron Horse Park 01862
Tel (978) 663-1130 SIC 3531

INTERSTATE ELECTRICAL SERVICES CORP p 758
70 Treble Cove Rd 01862
Tel (978) 667-5200 SIC 1731

▲ LANTHEUS HOLDINGS INC p 844
331 Treble Cove Rd 01862
Tel (978) 671-8001 SIC 2835 2834

LANTHEUS MEDICAL IMAGING INC p 844
331 Treble Cove Rd 01862
Tel (978) 671-8001 SIC 3841 2834

LANTHEUS MI INTERMEDIATE INC p 844
331 Treble Cove Rd 01862
Tel (978) 671-8001 SIC 3841 2834

PAN AM RAILWAYS INC p 1110
1700 Iron Horse Park 01862
Tel (978) 663-1129 SIC 4011

SCHAFER GOVERNMENT SERVICES LLC p 1286
101 Billerica Ave 01862
Tel (978) 256-2070 SIC 7389

SPRINGFIELD TERMINAL RAILWAY CO INC p 1361
1700 Iron Horse Park 01862
Tel (978) 663-1050 SIC 4011

NORTH CHELMSFORD, MA

COURIER CORP p 383
15 Wellman Ave 01863
Tel (978) 251-6000 SIC 2732 2731

■ RAVEN VENTURES LLC p 1209
15 Wellman Ave 01863
Tel (978) 251-6000 SIC 2731

NORTH DARTMOUTH, MA

TOWN OF DARTMOUTH p 1465
400 Slocum Rd 02747
Tel (508) 910-1800 SIC 9111

NORTH DIGHTON, MA

DRAKA CABLETEQ USA INC p 455
22 Joseph E Warner Blvd 02764
Tel (508) 822-5444 SIC 3357

NORTH EASTON, MA

STONEHILL COLLEGE INC p 1391
320 Washington St 02357
Tel (508) 565-1000 SIC 8221

NORTH GRAFTON, MA

WASHINGTON MILLS GROUP INC p 1578
20 N Main St 01536
Tel (508) 839-6511 SIC 3291

■ WYMAN-GORDON CO p 1629
244 Worcester St 01536
Tel (508) 839-8252
SIC 3463 3462 3324 3728 3317

NORTH READING, MA

EQUITY INTERNATIONAL INC p 507
54 Concord St 01864
Tel (978) 664-2712 SIC 5065

▲ TERADYNE INC p 1439
600 Riverpark Dr 01864
Tel (978) 370-2700 SIC 3825 3643 3674

NORTHAMPTON, MA

CITY OF NORTHAMPTON p 317
210 Main St Rm 4 01060
Tel (413) 587-1249 SIC 9111

COOLEY DICKINSON HEALTH CARE CORP p 366
30 Locust St 01060
Tel (413) 582-2000 SIC 8062

COOLEY DICKINSON HOSPITAL INC p 366
30 Locust St 01060
Tel (413) 582-2000 SIC 8062 8063 8069

COOLEY DICKINSON PHYSICIAN HOSPITAL ORGANIZATION INC p 366
30 Locust St 01060
Tel (413) 582-2343 SIC 8062

TRUSTEES OF SMITH COLLEGE p 1488
10 Elm St College Hall 01063
Tel (413) 585-2550 SIC 8221

NORTHBOROUGH, MA

▲ ASPEN AEROGELS INC p 118
30 Forbes Rd Bldg B 01532
Tel (508) 691-1111 SIC 2899

BERTUCCIS CORP p 176
155 Otis St Ste 3 01532
Tel (508) 351-2500 SIC 5812

THG CORP p 1447
70 Bearfoot Rd 01532
Tel (508) 393-7660
SIC 5085 5084 3569 3728 3625 3494

NORTON, MA

■ AUTOPART INTERNATIONAL INC p 135
192 Mansfield Ave 02766
Tel (781) 784-1111 SIC 5013 5531

CONVERTIBLE CASTLE INC p 365
308 E Main St 02766
Tel (800) 244-9350 SIC 5712

HORIZON BEVERAGE CO INC p 707
45 Commerce Way 02766
Tel (508) 587-1110 SIC 5181 5182

NORWELL, MA

■ CLEAN HARBORS ENVIRONMENTAL SERVICES INC p 324
42 Longwater Dr 02061
Tel (781) 792-5000 SIC 4953

▲ CLEAN HARBORS INC p 324
42 Longwater Dr 02061
Tel (781) 792-5000 SIC 4953

COMPUTER MERCHANT LTD p 353
95 Longwater Cir 02061
Tel (781) 878-1070 SIC 7379 7371

■ PARTYLITE WORLDWIDE LLC p 1119
600 Cordwainer Dr Ste 202 02061
Tel (508) 830-3100 SIC 5199

SOUTH SHORE MEDICAL CENTER INC p 1345
75 Washington St Ste 1 02061
Tel (781) 878-5200 SIC 8011

SULLIVAN INVESTMENT CO INC p 1397
41 Accord Park Dr 02061
Tel (781) 982-1550 SIC 5531 7534

SULLIVAN TIRE CO INC p 1397
41 Accord Park Dr 02061
Tel (781) 982-1550 SIC 5531 7538 5014

TCML BUSINESS TRUST p 1428
95 Longwater Cir 02061
Tel (781) 878-1070 SIC 8611

NORWOOD, MA

ADVANTAGE RESOURCING AMERICA INC p 26
220 Norwood Park S 02062
Tel (781) 251-8000 SIC 7361

▲ ANALOG DEVICES INC p 88
1 Technology Way 02062
Tel (781) 329-4700 SIC 3674

GALLERY AUTOMOTIVE GROUP LLC p 590
918 Providence Hwy 02062
Tel (877) 201-8871 SIC 5511 5012 7538

GZA GEOENVIRONMENTAL INC p 649
249 Vanderbilt Ave 02062
Tel (781) 278-3700 SIC 8711 8734

GZA GEOENVIRONMENTAL TECHNOLOGIES INC p 649
249 Vanderbilt Ave Unit 2 02062
Tel (781) 278-3700
SIC 8711 8999 1799 8744

HIRETHINKING INC p 695
220 Norwood Park S Ste 1 02062
Tel (781) 251-8000 *SIC* 7363

HOME MARKET FOODS INC p 703
140 Morgan Dr Ste 100 02062
Tel (781) 948-1500 *SIC* 2013

▲ NATIONAL AMUSEMENTS INC p 1009
846 University Ave 02062
Tel (781) 461-1600
SIC 7832 7833 4832 4833 4841

STEWARD NORWOOD HOSPITAL INC p 1388
800 Washington St Ste 1 02062
Tel (781) 769-4000 *SIC* 8062

TAS-CNH INC p 1425
800 Washington St Ste 1 02062
Tel (781) 769-4000 *SIC* 8062

TECHNICAL AID CORP p 1431
220 Norwood Park S Ste 2 02062
Tel (781) 251-8000 *SIC* 7363

TOWN OF NORWOOD p 1465
566 Washington St 02062
Tel (781) 762-1240 *SIC* 9121

▲ XCERRA CORP p 1631
825 University Ave 02062
Tel (781) 461-1000 *SIC* 3825 3429

ORLEANS, MA

CAPE COD FIVE CENTS SAVINGS BANK p 248
19 West Rd 02653
Tel (508) 240-0555 *SIC* 6036

OXFORD, MA

▲ IPG PHOTONICS CORP p 763
50 Old Webster Rd 01540
Tel (508) 373-1100 *SIC* 3699 3229 3674

PEABODY, MA

▲ ANALOGIC CORP p 88
8 Centennial Dr 01960
Tel (978) 326-4000 *SIC* 3825 3812

CARL ZEISS MICROSCOPY LLC p 256
1 Corporate Pl Ste 3 01960
Tel (978) 826-1500 *SIC* 5047 3826

CITY OF PEABODY p 317
24 Lowell St 01960
Tel (978) 532-3000 *SIC* 9111

■ FEI CO MEPD PEABODY p 537
1 Corporation Way Ste 2 01960
Tel (978) 538-6700 *SIC* 3559 3827 3699

IRC INC p 764
1 Corporation Way Ste 230 01960
Tel (781) 581-9800 *SIC* 8742

JEOL USA INC p 783
11 Dearborn Rd 01960
Tel (978) 535-5900 *SIC* 5049

▲ MERIDIAN BANCORP INC p 948
67 Prospect St 01960
Tel (617) 567-1500 *SIC* 6035

■ PCG PARENT CORP p 1124
4 Technology Dr 01960
Tel (978) 538-8000
SIC 5045 5065 4953 5093 7378

■ PCGTRADING LLC p 1124
4 Technology Dr 01960
Tel (978) 538-8000
SIC 5045 5065 4953 5093 7378

STAHL (USA) INC p 1374
13 Corwin St 01960
Tel (978) 531-0371 *SIC* 2891

TRU CORP p 1485
245 Lynnfield St 01960
Tel (978) 532-0775 *SIC* 3643 3678

TUV SUD AMERICA INC p 1493
10 Centennial Dr Fl 2a 01960
Tel (978) 573-2500 *SIC* 8734

WESTON & SAMPSON INC p 1602
5 Centennial Dr Ste 1 01960
Tel (978) 532-1900 *SIC* 8711 8748 4953

PITTSFIELD, MA

■ BERKSHIRE BANK p 175
24 North St 01201
Tel (413) 443-5601 *SIC* 6035

BERKSHIRE HEALTH SYSTEMS INC p 175
725 North St 01201
Tel (413) 447-2000 *SIC* 8062

▲ BERKSHIRE HILLS BANCORP INC p 175
24 North St 01201
Tel (413) 443-5601 *SIC* 6022 6411

BERKSHIRE LIFE INSURANCE CO OF AMERICA p 175
700 South St 01201
Tel (413) 395-4321 *SIC* 6321

BERKSHIRE MEDICAL CENTER INC p 175
725 North St 01201
Tel (413) 447-2000 *SIC* 8062

■ GENERAL DYNAMICS DEFENSE SYSTEMS INC p 600
100 Plastics Ave 01201
Tel (413) 494-1110 *SIC* 3812 3795 3625

PETRICCA INDUSTRIES INC p 1139
550 Cheshire Rd 01201
Tel (413) 499-1441
SIC 1611 1623 3273 3272 1442

PITTSFIELD PUBLIC SCHOOLS p 1152
269 1st St 01201
Tel (413) 395-0101 *SIC* 8211

SABIC INNOVATIVE PLASTICS US LLC p 1264
1 Plastics Ave 01201
Tel (413) 448-7110 *SIC* 5049

SABIC US HOLDINGS LP p 1264
1 Plastics Ave 01201
Tel (413) 448-7110 *SIC* 2821

PLYMOUTH, MA

BETH ISRAEL DEACONESS HOSPITAL - PLYMOUTH INC p 177
275 Sandwich St 02360
Tel (508) 746-2000 *SIC* 8082

JORDAN HEALTH SYSTEMS INC p 793
275 Sandwich St 02360
Tel (508) 830-2388 *SIC* 8741 8062

JORDAN HOSPITAL CLUB INC p 793
275 Sandwich St 02360
Tel (508) 830-2391 *SIC* 8062

■ PARTYLITE INC p 1119
59 Armstrong Rd 02360
Tel (203) 661-1926
SIC 2023 3999 3641 5199 5023

PLYMOUTH PUBLIC SCHOOLS p 1157
253 S Meadow Rd 02360
Tel (508) 830-4348 *SIC* 8211

TECH-ETCH INC p 1431
45 Aldrin Rd 02360
Tel (508) 747-0300 *SIC* 3469 3672 3479

VOLTA OIL CO INC p 1565
1 Roberts Rd Ste 2 02360
Tel (508) 747-3778 *SIC* 5172 1799

PLYMPTON, MA

■ SYSCO BOSTON LLC p 1416
99 Spring St 02367
Tel (781) 422-2300 *SIC* 5149

QUINCY, MA

AHOLD USA INC p 37
1385 Hancock St 02169
Tel (717) 249-4000 *SIC* 5411

ARBELLA MUTUAL INSURANCE CO p 102
1100 Crown Colony Dr 02169
Tel (617) 328-2800 *SIC* 6411 6331

ARBELLA PROTECTION INSURANCE CO INC p 102
1100 Crown Colony Dr 02169
Tel (617) 328-2800 *SIC* 6411

ARBELLA SERVICE CO INC p 102
1100 Crown Colony Dr 02169
Tel (617) 328-2800 *SIC* 8742

ATLANTIC BROADBAND FINANCE LLC p 126
1 Pine Hill Dr Ste 205 02169
Tel (617) 786-8800 *SIC* 4841 4813

ATLANTIC BROADBAND MANAGEMENT LLC p 126
1 Pine Hill Dr Ste 205 02169
Tel (617) 786-8800 *SIC* 4841

BAY STATE MILLING CO p 161
100 Congress St Ste 2 02169
Tel (617) 328-4423 *SIC* 2041

BOSTON FINANCIAL DATA SERVICES INC p 202
2000 Crown Colony Dr 02169
Tel (617) 483-5000 *SIC* 6211 6289 6282

CASHMAN DREDGING AND MARINE CONTRACTING CO LLC p 263
549 South St 02169
Tel (617) 890-0600 *SIC* 1629

CITY OF QUINCY p 317
1305 Hancock St 02169
Tel (617) 376-1000 *SIC* 9111

■ ENTERPRISE NEWSMEDIA LLC p 502
400 Crown Colony Dr 02169
Tel (585) 598-0030 *SIC* 2711

GRANITE CITY ELECTRIC SUPPLY CO INC p 631
19 Quincy Ave 02169
Tel (617) 472-6500 *SIC* 5063 5719

GRANITE TELECOMMUNICATIONS LLC p 631
100 Newport Avenue Ext # 1 02171
Tel (617) 933-5500 *SIC* 4813

J CALNAN & ASSOCIATES INC p 770
3 Batterymarch Park # 500 02169
Tel (617) 801-0200 *SIC* 8741 1542

J JILL GROUP INC p 771
4 Batterymarch Park 02169
Tel (617) 376-4300
SIC 5961 5621 5661 5632

JAY CASHMAN INC p 779
549 South St Bldg 19 02169
Tel (617) 890-0600 *SIC* 1629

JCI HOLDINGS LLC p 780
549 South St Bldg 19 02169
Tel (617) 890-0600 *SIC* 1629

JILL ACQUISITION LLC p 785
4 Batterymarch Park 02169
Tel (617) 376-4300 *SIC* 5961 5621

LEE KENNEDY CO INC p 851
122 Quincy Shore Dr Ste 1 02171
Tel (617) 825-6930 *SIC* 1542

MCMC LLC p 932
300 Crown Colony Dr # 203 02169
Tel (617) 375-7700 *SIC* 8742

QUINCY MUTUAL FIRE INSURANCE CO INC p 1200
57 Washington St 02169
Tel (617) 770-5100 *SIC* 6331 6411

QUINCY PUBLIC SCHOOLS p 1200
34 Coddington St 02169
Tel (617) 984-8700 *SIC* 8211

STOP & SHOP SUPERMARKET CO p 1391
1385 Hancock St 02169
Tel (717) 960-1700 *SIC* 5411

STOP & SHOP SUPERMARKET CO LLC p 1391
1385 Hancock St 02169
Tel (800) 767-7772 *SIC* 5411

RANDOLPH, MA

BREWSTER WALLPAPER CORP p 210
67 Pacella Park Dr 02368
Tel (781) 963-4800 *SIC* 5198

BURKE DISTRIBUTING CORP p 227
89 Teed Dr 02368
Tel (781) 767-6056 *SIC* 5181

EMERSON-SWAN INC p 492
300 Pond St Ste 1 02368
Tel (781) 986-2000 *SIC* 5084 5074

MAY INSTITUTE INC p 923
41 Pacella Park Dr 02368
Tel (781) 440-0400 *SIC* 8361

ROADLINK USA INC p 1240
1 Kelleway Dr 02368
Tel (888) 622-6076 *SIC* 4212

TOWN OF RANDOLPH p 1465
41 S Main St 02368
Tel (781) 961-0911 *SIC* 9121

READING, MA

VITALIZE CONSULTING SOLUTIONS INC p 1562
248 Main St Ste 101 01867
Tel (781) 670-1000 *SIC* 8082 7379

ROCKLAND, MA

EMD SERONO INC p 491
1 Technology Pl 02370
Tel (781) 982-9000 *SIC* 2834

■ ROCKLAND TRUST CO p 1245
288 Union St 02370
Tel (781) 878-6100 *SIC* 6022

TEDESCHI FOOD SHOPS INC p 1432
14 Howard St 02370
Tel (781) 878-8210 *SIC* 5411

TFS NEWCO LLC p 1445
14 Howard St 02370
Tel (781) 878-8210 *SIC* 5411

ROWLEY, MA

ELDER LIVING CONCEPTS INC p 484
51 Summer St 01969
Tel (978) 948-7383 *SIC* 8051

ROXBURY, MA

BOSTON PUBLIC SCHOOLS p 203
2300 Washington St 02119
Tel (617) 635-9000 *SIC* 8211

SALEM, MA

CITY OF SALEM p 318
93 Washington St 01970
Tel (978) 745-9595 *SIC* 9111

HARBOR MEDICAL GROUP p 660
55 Highland Ave Ste 102 01970
Tel (978) 741-9500 *SIC* 8011

NORTH SHORE MEDICAL CENTER INC p 1053
81 Highland Ave 01970
Tel (978) 741-1200 *SIC* 8062

NORTH SHORE PHYSICIANS GROUP INC p 1053
81 Highland Ave 01970
Tel (617) 724-9841 *SIC* 8011

NSMC HEALTHCARE INC p 1065
81 Highland Ave 01970
Tel (978) 354-2575 *SIC* 8099

SALEM FIVE BANCORP p 1272
210 Essex St 01970
Tel (978) 745-5555 *SIC* 6712

SALEM FIVE CENTS SAVINGS BANK p 1272
210 Essex St 01970
Tel (978) 745-5555 *SIC* 6022

SALEM HOSPITAL p 1272
81 Highland Ave 01970
Tel (978) 741-1200 *SIC* 8062

SALEM STATE UNIVERSITY p 1272
352 Lafayette St 01970
Tel (978) 542-6000 *SIC* 8221

SCITUATE, MA

TOWN OF SCITUATE p 1465
600 Chief Just Cshng Hghy 02066
Tel (781) 545-8700 *SIC* 9121

SEEKONK, MA

DF PRAY INC p 435
25 Anthony St 02771
Tel (508) 336-3366 *SIC* 1542 1541

SHIRLEY, MA

BEMIS ASSOCIATES INC p 171
1 Bemis Way 01464
Tel (978) 425-6761 *SIC* 2891 2851 3479

SHREWSBURY, MA

FLYNN PETROLEUM LLC p 562
307 Hartford Tpke 01545
Tel (508) 756-7693 *SIC* 5172

METSO FLOW CONTROL USA INC p 957
44 Bowditch Dr 01545
Tel (508) 852-0200 *SIC* 3592

SOMERSET, MA

NORTH ATLANTIC CORP p 1050
1255 Grand Army Hwy 02726
Tel (508) 324-7700 *SIC* 5031

SOMERVILLE, MA

■ BEACON SALES ACQUISITION INC p 165
50 Webster Ave 02143
Tel (877) 645-7663 *SIC* 5033 5031

■ CENTURY BANK AND TRUST CO p 282
102 Fellsway W 02145
Tel (617) 629-0929 *SIC* 6029

CITY OF SOMERVILLE p 318
93 Highland Ave 02143
Tel (617) 666-3311 *SIC* 9111

CITY OF SOMERVILLE p 318
42 Cross St 02145
Tel (617) 625-6600 *SIC* 9111

HERB CHAMBERS I-93 INC p 685
259 Mcgrath Hwy 02143
Tel (617) 666-4100 *SIC* 5511

INDEPENDENT ELECTRIC SUPPLY CORP p 736
41 Innerbelt Rd 02143
Tel (617) 625-5155 *SIC* 5063

M S WALKER INC p 890
20 3rd Ave 02143
Tel (617) 776-6700 *SIC* 5182

ROGERS FOAM CORP p 1246
20 Vernon St Ste 1 02145
Tel (617) 623-3010 *SIC* 3086

TRIUMVIRATE ENVIRONMENTAL INC p 1483
200 Innerbelt Rd 4 02143
Tel (617) 623-0109 *SIC* 4212

TRUSTEES OF TUFTS COLLEGE p 1488
169 Holland St Ste 318 02144
Tel (617) 628-5000 *SIC* 8221 2791 2752

SOUTH DEERFIELD, MA

■ YANKEE CANDLE CO INC p 1634
16 Yankee Candle Way 01373
Tel (413) 665-8306 *SIC* 3999 2899 5999

■ YANKEE CANDLE INVESTMENTS LLC p 1634
16 Yankee Candle Way 01373
Tel (413) 665-8306 *SIC* 3999 5999

■ YANKEE HOLDING CORP p 1635
16 Yankee Candle Way 01373
Tel (413) 665-8306 *SIC* 3999 2899

■ YCC HOLDINGS LLC p 1635
16 Yankee Candle Way 01373
Tel (413) 665-8306 *SIC* 3999 2899 5999

SOUTH HADLEY, MA

TRUSTEES OF MOUNT HOLYOKE COLLEGE p 1488
50 College St 01075
Tel (413) 538-2000 *SIC* 8221

SOUTH WEYMOUTH, MA

SOUTH SHORE HEALTH AND EDUCATIONAL CORP p 1345
55 Fogg Rd 02190
Tel (781) 340-8000 *SIC* 8062

SOUTH SHORE HOSPITAL INC p 1345
55 Fogg Rd 02190
Tel (781) 624-8000 *SIC* 8062 8049

SOUTHBOROUGH, MA

COMMONWEALTH ANNUITY & LIFE INSURANCE p 345
132 Turnpike Rd Ste 210 01772
Tel (508) 460-2400 *SIC* 6311

GYRUS ACMI LLC p 649
136 Turnpike Rd Ste 300 01772
Tel (508) 804-2600 *SIC* 3841 5047

IKASYSTEMS CORP p 731
134 Turnpike Rd Ste 200 01772
Tel (508) 251-3182 *SIC* 5045

SOUTHBORO MEDICAL GROUP INC p 1345
24-28 Newton St 01772
Tel (508) 481-5500 *SIC* 8011

SOUTHBRIDGE, MA

HARRINGTON MEMORIAL HOSPITAL INC p 663
100 South St Ste 1 01550
Tel (508) 765-9771 SIC 8062

SOUTHWICK, MA

WHALLEY COMPUTER ASSOCIATES INC p 1604
1 Whalley Way 01077
Tel (413) 569-4200 SIC 5045 7378

SPENCER, MA

FLEXCON CO INC p 556
1 Flexcon Industrial Park 01562
Tel (508) 885-8200 SIC 3081 2891

SPRINGFIELD, MA

BAYSTATE HEALTH INC p 162
759 Chestnut St 01199
Tel (413) 784-0000 SIC 8062 8221 8249

BAYSTATE HEALTH SYSTEM HEALTH SERVICES INC p 162
280 Chestnut St 01199
Tel (413) 794-9939
SIC 8741 8062 6324 6512

BAYSTATE MEDICAL PRACTICES INC p 162
759 Chestnut St 01199
Tel (413) 794-0000 SIC 8099

BEHAVIORAL HEALTH NETWORK INC p 168
417 Liberty St Ste 1 01104
Tel (413) 747-0705 SIC 8093 8322

BIG Y FOODS INC p 182
2145 Roosevelt Ave 01104
Tel (413) 784-0600 SIC 5411

CENTER FOR HUMAN DEVELOPMENT INC p 276
332 Birnie Ave 01107
Tel (413) 733-6624 SIC 8322

DENNIS GROUP INC p 428
1537 Main St Fl 2 01103
Tel (413) 787-1785 SIC 8711

▲ EVERSOURCE ENERGY p 515
300 Cadwell Dr 01104
Tel (413) 785-5871 SIC 4911 4924

HARRY GRODSKY & CO INC p 664
33 Shaws Ln 01104
Tel (413) 785-1947 SIC 1711

HEALTH NEW ENGLAND INC p 675
1 Monarch Pl Ste 1500 01144
Tel (413) 787-4000 SIC 6324

MARYLANE HOSPITAL p 915
759 Chestnut St 01199
Tel (413) 794-5436 SIC 8082

MASSACHUSETTS MUTUAL LIFE INSURANCE CO p 917
1295 State St 01111
Tel (413) 788-8411
SIC 6321 6324 6411 6282

MASSMUTUAL INTERNATIONAL LLC p 917
1295 State St 01111
Tel (413) 788-8411 SIC 6311

MASSMUTUAL MORTGAGE FINANCE LLC p 917
1295 State St 01111
Tel (413) 788-8411 SIC 6531

MERCY HOSPITAL INC p 947
271 Carew St 01104
Tel (413) 748-9000
SIC 8062 8071 8011 7219 8748

MERCY INPATIENT MEDICAL ASSOCIATES INC p 947
271 Carew St Ste 106 01104
Tel (413) 748-9000 SIC 8011 8322

PETER PAN BUS LINES INC p 1138
1776 Main St Ste 1 01103
Tel (413) 781-2900 SIC 4131

REPUBLICAN CO p 1226
1860 Main St 01103
Tel (413) 788-1000 SIC 2711

ROCKYS HARDWARE INC p 1245
40 Island Pond Rd 01118
Tel (413) 781-1650 SIC 5251

ROMAN CATHOLIC BISHOP OF SPRINGFIELD p 1248
65 Elliot St 01105
Tel (413) 732-3175 SIC 8661

■ SMITH & WESSON CORP p 1333
2100 Roosevelt Ave 01104
Tel (413) 781-8300
SIC 3484 3429 3999 5091

▲ SMITH & WESSON HOLDING CORP p 1333
2100 Roosevelt Ave 01104
Tel (800) 331-0852 SIC 3482

SPHS CORP p 1358
271 Carew St 01104
Tel (413) 748-9000 SIC 8741

SPRINGFIELD CITY OF (INC) p 1360
36 Court St 01103
Tel (413) 736-3111 SIC 9111

SPRINGFIELD COLLEGE p 1360
263 Alden St 01109
Tel (413) 748-3000 SIC 8221

SPRINGFIELD PUBLIC SCHOOLS p 1361
1550 Main St Fl 2 01103
Tel (413) 787-7100 SIC 8211

TITEFLEX CORP p 1456
603 Hendee St 01104
Tel (413) 271-8170 SIC 3052 3599

■ WESTERN MASSACHUSETTS ELECTRIC CO p 1599
300 Cadwell Dr 01104
Tel (413) 785-5871 SIC 4911

WESTERN NEW ENGLAND UNIVERSITY p 1599
1215 Wilbraham Rd 01119
Tel (413) 782-1243 SIC 8221

STOCKBRIDGE, MA

COUNTRY CURTAINS INC p 375
705 Pleasant St 01262
Tel (413) 243-1474 SIC 2391

STOUGHTON, MA

CEREBRAL PALSY OF MASSACHUSETTS INC p 283
600 Technology Center Dr 02072
Tel (800) 924-7570 SIC 8093

FRANKLIN SPORTS INC p 575
17 Campanelli Pkwy 02072
Tel (781) 344-1111 SIC 3949

GARBER BROS INC p 591
Kay Way Rr 139 02072
Tel (781) 341-0800
SIC 5194 5145 5141 5122

■ ITW ARK-LES CORP p 769
95 Mill St 02072
Tel (781) 297-6000 SIC 3643 3644

■ JC HIGGINS CORP p 780
70 Hawes Way 02072
Tel (781) 341-1500 SIC 1711

MEDICAL SPECIALTIES DISTRIBUTORS LLC p 937
800 Technology Center Dr # 3 02072
Tel (781) 344-6000 SIC 5047 7352

SUDBURY, MA

CAUSE FOR CHANGE LLC p 267
370 Hudson Rd 01776
Tel (617) 571-6990 SIC 5137

METHODS MACHINE TOOLS INC p 954
65 Union Ave 01776
Tel (978) 443-5388 SIC 5084

TOWN OF SUDBURY p 1465
322 Concord Rd 01776
Tel (978) 443-8891 SIC 9111

SUNDERLAND, MA

ALL STATES ASPHALT INC p 51
325 Amherst Rd 01375
Tel (413) 665-7021 SIC 5032

SUTTON, MA

ATLAS BOX AND CRATING CO INC p 127
223 Wrcster Prvdence Tpke 01590
Tel (508) 865-1155 SIC 2441 2448 2653

SWANSEA, MA

CARDIS DEPARTMENT STORE INC p 253
1 Furniture Way 02777
Tel (508) 379-7500 SIC 5712

TAUNTON, MA

CITY OF TAUNTON p 319
141 Oak St 02780
Tel (508) 821-1000 SIC 9111

MARTIGNETTI CORP p 912
500 John Hancock Rd 02780
Tel (781) 278-2000 SIC 5182 5921

MARTIGNETTI GROCERY CO INC p 912
500 John Hancock Rd 02780
Tel (781) 278-2000 SIC 5182

MORTON HOSPITAL AND MEDICAL CENTER INC p 991
88 Washington St 02780
Tel (508) 828-7000 SIC 6733 8062

NEW ENGLAND ICE CREAM CORP p 1030
555 Constitution Dr 02780
Tel (508) 824-0500 SIC 5084

PERKINS PAPER INC p 1136
630 John Hancock Rd 02780
Tel (508) 824-2800
SIC 5113 5149 5087 5046

TAUNTON MUNICIPAL LIGHTING PLANT p 1426
33 Weir St 02780
Tel (508) 824-5844 SIC 4911

TRIBE MEDITERRANEAN FOODS INC p 1479
100 Myles Standish Blvd # 1 02780
Tel (774) 961-0000 SIC 5141

UNITED LIQUORS LLC p 1510
500 John Hancock Rd 02780
Tel (781) 348-8000 SIC 5182 5181

TEWKSBURY, MA

■ AXYGEN BIOSCIENCE INC p 140
836 North St 01876
Tel (978) 442-2200 SIC 3089

DEMOULAS SUPER MARKETS INC p 428
875 East St 01876
Tel (978) 640-8100 SIC 5411

■ FISHER THERMO SCIENTIFIC CHEMICALS INC p 552
2 Radcliff Rd 01876
Tel (978) 521-6300 SIC 5169

GETRONICS US OPERATIONS INC p 609
100 Ames Pond Dr Ste 99 01876
Tel (978) 625-5000 SIC 7373

GRIFFIN GREENHOUSE SUPPLIES INC p 640
1619 Main St 01876
Tel (978) 851-4346 SIC 5191

MARKET BASKET PRODUCE INC p 908
875 East St 01876
Tel (978) 851-8000 SIC 5411

TRI-WIRE ENGINEERING SOLUTIONS INC p 1478
890 East St 01876
Tel (978) 640-6899 SIC 1623 8748

WELLPET LLC p 1589
200 Ames Pond Dr Ste 200 01876
Tel (877) 869-2971 SIC 2047

WORLDWIDE TECHSERVICES LLC p 1626
836 North St Unit 5 01876
Tel (978) 848-9000 SIC 7373 7375

TOPSFIELD, MA

AMERICAN HOLDCO LLC p 74
448 Boston St 01983
Tel (978) 561-3800 SIC 5146 4213

EAST COAST SEAFOOD INC p 470
448 Boston St 01983
Tel (978) 561-3800 SIC 5146

TOWNSEND, MA

STERILITE CORP p 1386
30 Scales Ln 01469
Tel (978) 597-1000 SIC 3089 4226

UPTON, MA

SINOHUB INC p 1326
3 Kensington Way 01568
Tel (508) 603-1085 SIC 3663

VINEYARD HAVEN, MA

MARTHAS VINEYARD MORTGAGE CO LLC p 912
107 Beach Rd Ste 101 02568
Tel (508) 696-1801 SIC 6163

WAKEFIELD, MA

AMERICAN DENTAL PARTNERS INC p 71
401 Edgewater Pl Ste 430 01880
Tel (781) 224-0880 SIC 8621 8742

■ EDGEWATER TECHNOLOGY p 477
200 Harvard Mill Sq # 210 01880
Tel (781) 246-3343 SIC 7371

▲ EDGEWATER TECHNOLOGY INC p 477
200 Harvard Mill Sq # 210 01880
Tel (781) 246-3343 SIC 7379 8742

▲ FRANKLIN STREET PROPERTIES CORP p 575
401 Edgewater Pl Ste 200 01880
Tel (781) 557-1300 SIC 6798

PRESS GANEY HOLDINGS INC p 1172
401 Edgewater Pl Ste 500 01880
Tel (781) 295-5000 SIC 8731

ROUNDTOWER NORTHEAST LLC p 1253
200 Quannapowitt Pkwy 01880
Tel (781) 621-8600 SIC 5734

XURA INC p 1633
200 Quannapowitt Pkwy 01880
Tel (781) 246-9000 SIC 7371

WALPOLE, MA

APOLLO SECURITY INTERNATIONAL INC p 97
2150 Bston Providence Hwy 02081
Tel (508) 660-1197 SIC 7381 8748

CALM INC p 242
102 Elm St 02081
Tel (508) 850-4100 SIC 6163

ISLAND OASIS FROZEN COCKTAIL CO INC p 766
141 Norfolk St 02081
Tel (508) 660-1177 SIC 5142

ROLLS-ROYCE MARINE NORTH AMERICA INC p 1247
110 Norfolk St 02081
Tel (508) 668-9610 SIC 3599 3446 3429

TOWN OF WALPOLE p 1465
135 School St 02081
Tel (508) 660-7289 SIC 9111

TOWN OF WALPOLE p 1465
135 School St 02081
Tel (508) 660-7353 SIC 7999

WALPOLE WOODWORKERS INC p 1574
767 East St 02081
Tel (508) 668-2800 SIC 2499

WALTHAM, MA

3DS ACQUISITION CORP p 2
175 Wyman St 02451
Tel (781) 810-5011 SIC 7371

ACTIFIO INC p 19
333 Wyman St Ste 30 02451
Tel (781) 790-7676 SIC 7374

▲ ALERE INC p 48
51 Sawyer Rd Ste 200 02453
Tel (781) 647-3900 SIC 2835 8071 8742

ALKERMES INC p 50
852 Winter St 02451
Tel (781) 609-6000 SIC 2834 8731

■ ALLIANCE ENERGY LLC p 54
800 South St Ste 500 02453
Tel (781) 674-7780 SIC 5411 5541

▲ AMAG PHARMACEUTICALS INC p 64
1100 Winter St Fl 3 02451
Tel (617) 498-3300 SIC 2834 2835

■ APOGENT TECHNOLOGIES INC p 97
81 Wyman St 02451
Tel (781) 622-1300 SIC 3821 3229 3843

B456 SYSTEMS INC p 143
200 West St 02451
Tel (617) 778-5700 SIC 3691

BENTLEY UNIVERSITY p 173
175 Forest St 02452
Tel (781) 891-2000 SIC 8221

BIO MEDICAL APPLICATIONS OF FLORIDA INC p 183
920 Winter St Ste A 02451
Tel (781) 699-9000 SIC 8092

BIO-MEDICAL APPLICATIONS OF CALIFORNIA INC p 183
920 Winter St 02451
Tel (781) 699-4404 SIC 8092

BIO-MEDICAL APPLICATIONS OF NORTH CAROLINA INC p 183
920 Winter St 02451
Tel (781) 699-4404 SIC 8092

BOSTON GAS CO p 203
40 Sylvan Rd 02451
Tel (781) 907-3646 SIC 4924 4922

BRANDEIS UNIVERSITY p 208
415 South St Ms110 02453
Tel (781) 736-8318 SIC 8221

C & J CLARK AMERICA INC p 231
60 Tower Rd 02451
Tel (617) 964-1222 SIC 3143 5139 5661

CAMBRIDGE COMPUTER SERVICES INC p 244
271 Waverley Oaks Rd # 301 02452
Tel (781) 250-3000
SIC 5045 7373 7371 7379

CARBON BLACK INC p 252
1100 Winter St Fl 4 02451
Tel (617) 393-7400 SIC 7371 7379

▲ CARE.COM INC p 254
77 4th Ave Ste 5 02451
Tel (781) 642-5900 SIC 4813

CIMPRESS USA INC p 307
275 Wyman St Ste 100 02451
Tel (866) 614-8002 SIC 2752

CITY OF WALTHAM p 319
610 Main St Fl 2 02452
Tel (781) 314-3000 SIC 9111

CLARKS AMERICAS INC p 322
60 Tower Rd 02451
Tel (617) 796-5000 SIC 5661 5139

COMMONWEALTH EQUITY SERVICES LLP p 346
29 Sawyer Rd Ste 2 02453
Tel (781) 398-0401 SIC 6211 6282 6221

■ CONSTANT CONTACT INC p 360
1601 Trapelo Rd Ste 329 02451
Tel (781) 472-8100 SIC 7373 4813 7331

■ CSC CONSULTING INC p 397
404 Wyman St Ste 355 02451
Tel (781) 890-7446 SIC 7373 7371 8742

CYS INVESTMENTS INC p 406
500 Totten Pond Rd Ste 6 02451
Tel (617) 639-0440 SIC 6798

DASSAULT SYSTEMES AMERICAS CORP p 413
175 Wyman St 02451
Tel (781) 810-3000 SIC 7371

DASSAULT SYSTEMES SOLIDWORKS CORP p 413
175 Wyman St 02451
Tel (781) 810-3000 SIC 7371

DDJ CAPITAL MANAGEMENT LLC p 419
130 Turner St Ste 600 02453
Tel (781) 283-8500 SIC 6282 5094 5812

DELAWARE LIFE HOLDINGS LLC p 424
1601 Trapelo Rd Ste 30 02451
Tel (877) 253-2323 SIC 6311

DYNATRACE LLC p 464
404 Wyman St Ste 500 02451
Tel (781) 530-1000 SIC 7372 5045

EDUCATION DEVELOPMENT CENTER INC p 479
43 Foundry Ave 02453
Tel (617) 969-7100 SIC 8732 2741

EPOCH SL III INC p 505
51 Sawyer Rd Ste 500 02453
Tel (781) 891-0777 SIC 8059 8051

EXCELITAS TECHNOLOGIES CORP p 516
200 West St 02451
Tel (781) 522-5910 SIC 3648 3845

EXCELITAS TECHNOLOGIES HOLDING CORP p 516
200 West St Ste E403 02451
Tel (781) 522-5914 SIC 3648 3845

EXCELITAS TECHNOLOGIES HOLDINGS LLC p 516
200 West St Ste E403 02451
Tel (781) 522-5900 SIC 3648

■ **FISHER SCIENTIFIC INTERNATIONAL LLC** p 552
81 Wyman St 02451
Tel (781) 622-1000
SIC 2869 3821 5169 5049

FRESENIUS MEDICAL CARE CARDIOVASCULAR RESOURCES INC p 578
920 Winter St Ste A 02451
Tel (781) 402-9000 SIC 8092 5047 8071

FRESENIUS MEDICAL CARE HOLDINGS INC p 578
920 Winter St 02451
Tel (781) 699-9000 SIC 3841 8092

FRESENIUS MEDICAL CARE NORTH AMERICA p 578
920 Winter St 02451
Tel (781) 699-4404 SIC 8092

FRESENIUS MEDICAL CARE NORTH AMERICA HOLDINGS LIMITED PARTNERSHIP p 578
920 Winter St Ste A 02451
Tel (781) 699-9000 SIC 3841

■ **GLOBAL COMPANIES LLC** p 616
800 South St Ste 500 02453
Tel (800) 542-0778 SIC 5172 5171

■ **GLOBAL ENERGY MARKETING LLC** p 616
800 South St Ste 500 02453
Tel (781) 894-8800 SIC 5172 4924

■ **GLOBAL OPERATING LLC** p 617
800 South St Ste 500 02453
Tel (800) 542-0778 SIC 4924 4911

▲ **GLOBAL PARTNERS LP** p 617
800 South St Ste 500 02453
Tel (781) 894-8800 SIC 5172 5171

GLOBAL PETROLEUM CORP p 617
800 South St Ste 500 02453
Tel (781) 894-6920 SIC 4924 5172 4911

HARRISON GLOBAL LLC p 664
224 Calvary St 02453
Tel (781) 863-2626 SIC 4119

HARVEST POWER INC p 666
200 5th Ave Fl 4b 02451
Tel (781) 314-9500 SIC 4953

HARVEY INDUSTRIES INC p 667
1400 Main St Fl 3 02451
Tel (781) 899-3500
SIC 5031 5033 3442 2431

HMG HOLDING CORP p 698
920 Winter St 02451
Tel (781) 699-9000 SIC 8741 6719

JANITRONICS INC p 777
29 Sawyer Rd Ste 11 02453
Tel (781) 647-5570 SIC 7349

JW CHILDS ASSOCIATES LP p 798
500 Totten Pond Rd Ste 6 02451
Tel (617) 753-1100 SIC 5812

■ **KEDS LLC** p 807
500 Totten Pond Rd Ste 1 02451
Tel (617) 824-6000 SIC 5139 5661

▲ **LIONBRIDGE TECHNOLOGIES INC** p 870
1050 Winter St Ste 2300 02451
Tel (781) 434-6000 SIC 7389 7374 7371

MASS ELECTRIC CONSTRUCTION CO p 916
400 Totten Pond Rd # 400 02451
Tel (781) 290-1000 SIC 1731 1623

MASSACHUSETTS ELECTRIC CO p 916
40 Sylvan Rd 02451
Tel (781) 907-1000 SIC 4911

MASSACHUSETTS MEDICAL SOCIETY INC p 917
860 Winter St 02451
Tel (781) 893-4610 SIC 2721 8621

■ **MODUSLINK CORP** p 981
1601 Trapelo Rd Ste 170 02451
Tel (781) 663-5000 SIC 7379 7389 5045

▲ **MODUSLINK GLOBAL SOLUTIONS INC** p 981
1601 Trapelo Rd Ste 170 02451
Tel (781) 663-5000 SIC 7379

NATIONAL GRID USA p 1013
40 Sylvan Rd 02451
Tel (781) 907-1000 SIC 4911

NATIONAL GRID USA SERVICE CO INC p 1013
40 Sylvan Rd 02451
Tel (800) 260-0054 SIC 4911 1311

NATIONAL MEDICAL CARE INC p 1014
920 Winter St Ste A 02451
Tel (781) 699-9000 SIC 8092

NETCRACKER TECHNOLOGY CORP p 1027
95 Sawyer Rd 02453
Tel (781) 419-3300 SIC 7372

NOVA BIOMEDICAL CORP p 1062
200 Prospect St 02453
Tel (781) 894-0800 SIC 2833 3826

NWN CORP p 1068
271 Waverley Oaks Rd # 302 02452
Tel (781) 472-3400 SIC 7373

OLYMPUS SCIENTIFIC SOLUTIONS AMERICAS CORP p 1083
48 Woerd Ave Ste 105 02453
Tel (781) 419-3900 SIC 5013

OLYMPUS SCIENTIFIC SOLUTIONS AMERICAS INC p 1083
48 Woerd Ave 02453
Tel (781) 419-3900 SIC 5084

OLYMPUS SCIENTIFIC SOLUTIONS TECHNOLOGIES INC p 1083
48 Woerd Ave 02453
Tel (781) 419-3900 SIC 5047

▲ **PAREXEL INTERNATIONAL CORP** p 1114
195 West St 02451
Tel (781) 487-9900 SIC 8731

■ **PAREXEL INTERNATIONAL LLC** p 1114
195 West St 02451
Tel (781) 487-9900 SIC 8731

■ **PERKINELMER HEALTH SCIENCES INC** p 1136
940 Winter St 02451
Tel (617) 482-9595 SIC 3821

▲ **PERKINELMER INC** p 1136
940 Winter St 02451
Tel (781) 663-6900 SIC 3826 3845

PRIVATE HEALTHCARE SYSTEMS INC p 1178
1100 Winter St Ste 2300 02451
Tel (781) 895-7500 SIC 6324

QINETIQ NORTH AMERICA INC p 1195
350 2nd Ave Bldg 1 02451
Tel (781) 684-4000 SIC 3812 8731

▲ **RAYTHEON CO** p 1211
870 Winter St 02451
Tel (781) 522-3000 SIC 3812 3663 3761

▲ **REPLIGEN CORP** p 1225
41 Seyon St Ste 100 02453
Tel (781) 250-0111 SIC 2836

ROCKET SOFTWARE INC p 1244
77 4th Ave Ste 101 02451
Tel (781) 577-4323 SIC 7371

SALARY.COM LLC p 1272
610 Lincoln St Ste 200 02451
Tel (781) 989-9488 SIC 7371 7375

SIMPSON GUMPERTZ & HEGER INC p 1325
41 Seyon St Ste 500 02453
Tel (781) 907-9000 SIC 8711

SOURCE CODE CORP p 1342
159 Overland Rd Ste 3 02451
Tel (781) 255-2022 SIC 5045

■ **STRIDE RITE CHILDRENS GROUP LLC** p 1393
500 Totten Pond Rd Ste 1 02451
Tel (617) 824-6000 SIC 5139 5661

■ **STRIDE RITE CORP** p 1393
500 Totten Pond Rd Ste 1 02451
Tel (617) 824-6000 SIC 5139 5661 3149

TELERIK INC p 1435
201 Jones Rd Ste 200 02451
Tel (888) 365-2779 SIC 5045

▲ **THERMO FISHER SCIENTIFIC INC** p 1447
168 3rd Ave 02451
Tel (781) 622-1000
SIC 3826 3845 3823 3629

■ **THERMO FISHER SCIENTIFIC WEST PALM HOLDINGS LLC** p 1447
168 3rd Ave 02451
Tel (781) 622-1000 SIC 3826

WARE, MA

KANZAKI SPECIALTY PAPERS INC p 803
20 Cummings St 01082
Tel (413) 967-6204 SIC 2672

WATERTOWN, MA

▲ **ATHENAHEALTH INC** p 124
311 Arsenal St Ste 14 02472
Tel (617) 402-1000 SIC 7372

■ **BRIGHT HORIZONS CHILDRENS CENTERS LLC** p 212
200 Talcott Ave 02472
Tel (617) 673-8000 SIC 8351

▲ **BRIGHT HORIZONS FAMILY SOLUTIONS INC** p 212
200 Talcott Ave 02472
Tel (617) 673-8000 SIC 8351

■ **BRIGHT HORIZONS FAMILY SOLUTIONS LLC** p 212
200 Talcott Ave 02472
Tel (617) 673-8000 SIC 8351

■ **DOBLE ENGINEERING CO** p 447
85 Walnut St 02472
Tel (617) 926-4900
SIC 3825 7359 3829 3826

ENANTA PHARMACEUTICALS INC p 495
500 Arsenal St 02472
Tel (617) 607-0800 SIC 2834 8731

JC CANNISTRARO LLC p 780
80 Rosedale Rd 02472
Tel (617) 926-0092 SIC 1711

PATHFINDER INTERNATIONAL p 1120
9 Galen St Ste 217 02472
Tel (617) 924-7200 SIC 8322

TUFTS ASSOCIATED HEALTH PLANS INC p 1491
705 Mount Auburn St 02472
Tel (617) 972-9400 SIC 6324

VANASSE HANGEN BRUSTLIN INC p 1543
101 Walnut St 02472
Tel (617) 924-1770 SIC 8711

WAYLAND, MA

CANDELA CORP p 247
530 Boston Post Rd 01778
Tel (949) 716-6670 SIC 3845

WEBSTER, MA

CITATION INSURANCE CO p 309
211 Main St 01570
Tel (508) 943-9000 SIC 6411

COMMERCE INSURANCE CO p 345
211 Main St 01570
Tel (508) 943-9000 SIC 6331

MAPFRE USA CORP p 903
211 Main St 01570
Tel (508) 943-9000 SIC 6331

WELLESLEY HILLS, MA

GULF OIL LIMITED PARTNERSHIP p 646
80 William St Ste 400 02481
Tel (339) 933-7200 SIC 5171 5172

WELLESLEY, MA

▲ **AMERICAN BILTRITE INC** p 69
57 River St Ste 302 02481
Tel (781) 237-6655
SIC 3069 2672 2241 3961 5094

■ **EAGLE INVESTMENT SYSTEMS LLC** p 468
45 William St Ste 200 02481
Tel (781) 943-2200
SIC 6722 6282 8721 7372

GROVE SERVICES (UKRAINE) LLC p 642
100 William St Ste 210 02481
Tel (617) 558-1991 SIC 5144

GROVE SERVICES INC p 642
100 William St Ste 210 02481
Tel (781) 772-1187 SIC 5141

HARVARD PILGRIM HEALTH CARE INC p 666
93 Worcester St 02481
Tel (781) 263-6000 SIC 6324

■ **PERKINELMER HOLDINGS INC** p 1136
940 Winter St 02481
Tel (781) 663-6900 SIC 3053

ROCHE BROS SUPERMARKETS INC p 1242
70 Hastings St Ste 1 02481
Tel (781) 235-9400 SIC 5411

SUN LIFE ASSURANCE CO OF CANADA (US) p 1400
1 Sun Life Park 02481
Tel (781) 237-6030 SIC 6311 6282

SUN LIFE FINANCIAL (US) SERVICES CO INC p 1400
1 Sun Life Executive Park 02481
Tel (781) 237-6030 SIC 6311

SUN LIFE OF CANADA (US) HOLDINGS INC p 1400
1 Sun Life Park 02481
Tel (781) 237-6030 SIC 6311

TOWN OF WELLESLEY p 1465
525 Washington St 02482
Tel (781) 431-1019 SIC 9111

WELLESLEY COLLEGE p 1589
106 Central St 02481
Tel (781) 283-1000 SIC 8221

WELLESLEY PUBLIC SCHOOLS p 1589
40 Kingsbury St 02481
Tel (781) 446-6200 SIC 8211

WEST BRIDGEWATER, MA

M & M TRANSPORT SERVICES INC p 888
643 Manley St 02379
Tel (508) 521-6201 SIC 4213 4212

NOONAN BROTHERS PETROLEUM PRODUCTS INC p 1047
415 West St 02379
Tel (508) 588-8026 SIC 5172

SHAWMUT CORP p 1313
208 Manley St 02379
Tel (508) 588-3300 SIC 2295

SHAWS HOLDINGS INC p 1313
750 W Center St 02379
Tel (508) 313-4000 SIC 5411

SHAWS SUPERMARKETS INC p 1313
750 W Center St 02379
Tel (508) 313-4000 SIC 5411

WEST SPRINGFIELD, MA

BALISE MOTOR SALES CO p 148
400 Riverdale St 01089
Tel (413) 733-8604 SIC 5511

■ **NEENAH NORTHEAST LLC** p 1024
70 Front St 01089
Tel (413) 533-0699 SIC 2631

UNITED FINANCIAL BANCORP INC p 1508
95 Elm St 01089
Tel (413) 787-1700 SIC 6035

WESTBOROUGH, MA

■ **BAY STATE GAS CO** p 161
4 Technology Dr 01581
Tel (508) 836-7000 SIC 4923

BEACON HOLDING INC p 164
25 Research Dr 01581
Tel (774) 512-7400 SIC 5399 5541

BJS WHOLESALE CLUB INC p 186
25 Research Dr 01581
Tel (774) 512-7400 SIC 5399

COGHLIN COMPANIES INC p 334
27 Otis St Ste 300 01581
Tel (508) 753-2354 SIC 3613

COLUMBIA ELECTRICAL CONTRACTORS INC p 340
27 Otis St Ste 300 01581
Tel (508) 366-8297 SIC 3613

CONSERVATION SERVICES GROUP INC p 358
50 Washington St Ste 3000 01581
Tel (508) 836-9500 SIC 8748

ECLINICAL WORKS LLC p 475
2 Technology Dr 01581
Tel (508) 366-8301 SIC 7371

ECLINICALWORKS LLC p 475
2 Technology Dr 01581
Tel (508) 475-0450 SIC 7371

EL HARVEY & SONS INC p 482
68 Hopkinton Rd 01581
Tel (508) 836-3000 SIC 4953

■ **ESOTERIX GENETIC LABORATORIES LLC** p 509
3400 Computer Dr 01581
Tel (508) 389-6650 SIC 8731 2835 8071

EXAGRID SYSTEMS INC p 516
2000 W Park Dr Ste 110 01581
Tel (508) 898-2872 SIC 5045

HEALTH PLANS INC p 675
1500 W Park Dr Ste 330 01581
Tel (508) 752-2480 SIC 6411

NEW ENGLAND ELECTRIC TRANSMISSION CORP p 1030
25 Research Dr 01581
Tel (617) 322-3091 SIC 4911

NEW ENGLAND POWER CO p 1030
25 Research Dr 01581
Tel (315) 460-3981 SIC 4911

■ **NORESCO INC** p 1048
1 Research Dr Ste 400c 01581
Tel (508) 614-1000
SIC 8711 8741 8748 4911 4924

■ **NORESCO LLC** p 1048
1 Research Dr Ste 400c 01581
Tel (508) 614-1000
SIC 8711 8741 8744 8748 4911 4924

SPECTRIS INC p 1357
117 Flanders Rd 01581
Tel (508) 768-6400
SIC 3674 3829 3826 3821

■ **SPRINGSTONE FINANCIAL LLC** p 1361
1700 W Park Dr Ste 310 01581
Tel (800) 630-1663 SIC 6282

UNITED SITE SERVICES INC p 1511
50 Washington St 1000 01581
Tel (508) 594-2655 SIC 4953

▲ **VIRTUSA CORP** p 1560
2000 W Park Dr Ste 300 01581
Tel (508) 389-7300 SIC 7371 7379

WESTFIELD, MA

■ **CALIBER CO** p 239
100 Springdale Rd 01085
Tel (413) 642-4260 SIC 3484

CITY OF WESTFIELD p 319
59 Court St Ste 1 01085
Tel (413) 572-6200 SIC 9111

JEN-COAT INC p 782
132 N Elm St 01085
Tel (413) 875-9861 SIC 3554

MESTEK INC p 951
260 N Elm St 01085
Tel (413) 568-9571
SIC 3585 3634 3549 3542 3354

PROLAMINA CORP p 1182
132 N Elm St 01085
Tel (413) 562-2315 SIC 2671 5199

■ **SAVAGE ARMS INC** p 1283
140 Apremont Way 01085
Tel (413) 642-4135 SIC 3484

■ **SAVAGE SPORTS CORP** p 1284
100 Springdale Rd 01085
Tel (413) 568-7001 SIC 3484

WESTFIELD PUBLIC SCHOOLS p 1601
94 N Elm St Ste 101 01085
Tel (413) 572-6403 SIC 8211

WESTFORD, MA

▲ **CYNOSURE INC** p 405
5 Carlisle Rd 01886
Tel (978) 256-4200 SIC 3845

▲ **KADANT INC** p 800
1 Technology Park Dr # 210 01886
Tel (978) 776-2000 SIC 3554 3321 2621

MACK TECHNOLOGIES INC p 892
27 Carlisle Rd 01886
Tel (978) 392-5500 SIC 3577 3571

▲ **NETSCOUT SYSTEMS INC** p 1027
310 Littleton Rd 01886
Tel (978) 614-4000 SIC 7373 3577

PUMA NORTH AMERICA INC p 1192
10 Lyberty Way 01886
Tel (978) 698-1000
SIC 5136 5139 8741 5137

▲ SONUS NETWORKS INC p 1340
4 Technology Park Dr 01886
Tel (978) 614-8100 *SIC* 7373

TOWN OF WESTFORD p 1465
55 Main St 01886
Tel (978) 692-5500 *SIC* 9111

WESTMINSTER, MA

SIMPLEX TIME RECORDER LLC p 1325
50 Technology Dr 01441
Tel (978) 731-2500 *SIC* 7382 3669 1711

W E AUBUCHON CO INC p 1568
95 Aubuchon Dr 01473
Tel (978) 874-0521
SIC 5251 5211 5231 5719

WESTON, MA

■ BIOGEN MA INC p 184
133 Boston Post Rd 02493
Tel (617) 679-2000 *SIC* 2836 8731

CORPORATE CONSULTING GROUP INC p 372
133 Boston Post Rd 15 02493
Tel (978) 461-8000 *SIC* 7371

MONSTER WORLDWIDE INC p 985
133 Boston Post Rd 02493
Tel (978) 461-8000 *SIC* 7311 7361

TOWN OF WESTON p 1465
11 Townhouse Rd 02493
Tel (781) 786-5070 *SIC* 9111

WESTWOOD, MA

■ GENERAL DYNAMICS NETWORK SYSTEMS INC p 600
101 Station Dr Apt 200 02090
Tel (781) 400-7669 *SIC* 8711

MEDICAL INFORMATION TECHNOLOGY INC p 937
Meditech Cir 02090
Tel (781) 821-3000 *SIC* 7372

TOWN OF WESTWOOD p 1465
580 High St 02090
Tel (781) 326-6450 *SIC* 9111

UNIVERSAL WILDE INC p 1518
26 Dartmouth St Ste 1 02090
Tel (781) 251-2700 *SIC* 2752

WEYMOUTH, MA

BARTLETT HOLDINGS INC p 157
97 Libbey Industrial Pkwy # 400 02189
Tel (800) 225-0385 *SIC* 1311

CAP GROUP INC p 248
77 Washington St 02188
Tel (781) 335-9650 *SIC* 5461

ELECTRO SWITCH BUSINESS TRUST p 485
775 Pleasant St Ste 1 02189
Tel (781) 335-1195 *SIC* 6733

ELECTRO SWITCH CORP p 485
775 Pleasant St Ste 1 02189
Tel (781) 335-1195 *SIC* 3613 3625

TOWN OF WEYMOUTH p 1465
75 Middle St 02189
Tel (781) 335-2000 *SIC* 9111

WILBRAHAM, MA

CONCORD ELECTRIC SUPPLY LIMITED p 354
2701 Boston Rd Ste 100 01095
Tel (413) 599-1750 *SIC* 5063

FREEZE OPERATIONS HOLDING CORP p 577
1855 Boston Rd 01095
Tel (413) 543-2445 *SIC* 5812 2024 5143

FRIENDLYS ICE CREAM LLC p 580
1855 Boston Rd 01095
Tel (413) 731-4000 *SIC* 2024 5812

■ FRIENDLYS MANUFACTURING AND RETAIL LLC p 580
1855 Boston Rd 01095
Tel (413) 731-4136 *SIC* 5812

FRIENDLYS RESTAURANTS LLC p 580
1855 Boston Rd 01095
Tel (413) 731-4000 *SIC* 5812

WILLIAMSTOWN, MA

PRESIDENT & TRUSTEES OF WILLIAMS COLLEGE p 1172
880 Main St Fl 1 01267
Tel (413) 597-4412 *SIC* 8221

WILMINGTON, MA

ACCELLENT ACQUISITION CORP p 14
100 Fordham Rd Bldg C 01887
Tel (978) 570-6900
SIC 3841 3317 3679 3315 3552 3089

ACCELLENT HOLDINGS CORP p 14
100 Fordham Rd 01887
Tel (978) 570-6900
SIC 3841 3679 3315 3552 3317 3089

■ ACCELLENT LLC p 14
100 Fordham Rd Bldg C 01887
Tel (978) 570-6900 *SIC* 3841 8711

AMERICAN FLORIST SUPPLY INC p 72
1 Progress Way 01887
Tel (978) 658-2400 *SIC* 6411

BROCKWAY-SMITH CO p 216
35 Upton Dr Ste 100 01887
Tel (978) 475-7100 *SIC* 5031

CASEPICK SYSTEMS LLC p 263
200 Research Dr 01887
Tel (978) 284-2800 *SIC* 3549

■ CHARLES RIVER LABORATORIES INC p 289
251 Ballardvale St 01887
Tel (978) 658-6000
SIC 8742 8734 8731 0279

▲ CHARLES RIVER LABORATORIES INTERNATIONAL INC p 289
251 Ballardvale St 01887
Tel (781) 222-6000 *SIC* 8731

D B ROBERTS INC p 406
30 Upton Dr Ste 3 01887
Tel (978) 988-5777 *SIC* 5065

HEILIND ELECTRONICS INC p 681
58 Jonspin Rd 01887
Tel (978) 658-7000 *SIC* 5065 3679 5063

KOCH MEMBRANE SYSTEMS INC p 825
850 Main St 01887
Tel (978) 694-7000 *SIC* 3569 3564

■ LAKE REGION MANUFACTURING INC p 839
100 Fordham Rd 01887
Tel (952) 361-2515 *SIC* 3841 3845

■ LAKE REGION MEDICAL INC p 839
100 Fordham Rd 01887
Tel (978) 570-6900 *SIC* 3841

LEDVANCE LLC p 851
200 Ballardvale St 01887
Tel (978) 570-3000 *SIC* 5063

■ MEDSOURCE TECHNOLOGIES HOLDINGS LLC p 939
100 Fordham Rd Bldg C 01887
Tel (978) 570-6900 *SIC* 3841 8711

NORTHERN NEW ENGLAND DISTRICT COUNCIL OF CARPENTERS INC p 1056
350 Fordham Rd 01887
Tel (800) 383-2759 *SIC* 8631

NORTHLAND INDUSTRIAL TRUCK CO INC p 1057
6 Jonspin Rd 01887
Tel (978) 658-5900 *SIC* 5084 7699 7359

OSRAM SYLVANIA INC p 1097
200 Ballardvale St # 305 01887
Tel (978) 570-3000
SIC 3646 3641 3647 3643 3297

PACIFIC PACKAGING PRODUCTS INC p 1105
24 Industrial Way 01887
Tel (978) 657-9100
SIC 5113 5199 5084 5162 2671 2653

▲ RUDOLPH TECHNOLOGIES INC p 1257
16 Jonspin Rd 01887
Tel (973) 691-1300 *SIC* 3823 3827

STANDARD ELECTRIC SUPPLY CO INC p 1376
14 Jewel Dr 01887
Tel (978) 658-5050 *SIC* 5063

SYLVANIA LIGHTING SERVICES CORP p 1414
200 Ballardvale St 01887
Tel (978) 570-3000 *SIC* 7349

TECOMET INC p 1432
115 Eames St 01887
Tel (978) 642-2400 *SIC* 3841 3444

■ TEXTRON SYSTEMS CORP p 1445
201 Lowell St 01887
Tel (978) 657-5111 *SIC* 3483 5088

▲ UNIFIRST CORP p 1503
68 Jonspin Rd 01887
Tel (978) 658-8888 *SIC* 7218 2326

WINCHESTER, MA

WINCHESTER HEALTHCARE MANAGEMENT INC p 1614
41 Highland Ave 01890
Tel (781) 756-2126 *SIC* 8741

WINCHESTER HOSPITAL p 1614
41 Highland Ave 01890
Tel (781) 729-9000 *SIC* 8062

WOBURN, MA

99 BOSTON INC p 4
160 Olympia Ave 01801
Tel (781) 933-8999 *SIC* 5812 5813

ADMIRAL METALS SERVICENTER CO INC p 23
11 Forbes Rd 01801
Tel (781) 933-8300 *SIC* 5051

ATLANTIC PLYWOOD CORP p 127
8 Roessler Rd 01801
Tel (781) 933-1932 *SIC* 5031 5198

BMH CORP p 194
11 Forbes Rd 01801
Tel (781) 933-8300 *SIC* 5051

CITY OF WOBURN p 319
10 Common St Ste 12 01801
Tel (781) 932-4400 *SIC* 9111

CUMMINGS FOUNDATION INC p 401
200 W Cummings Park 01801
Tel (781) 935-8000 *SIC* 8361 6512

EASTERN CONNECTION OPERATING INC p 472
60 Olympia Ave Ste 2 01801
Tel (800) 795-2872 *SIC* 4215

GEI CONSULTANTS INC p 597
400 Unicorn Park Dr Ste 8 01801
Tel (781) 721-4000 *SIC* 8711

KAMCO SUPPLY CORP OF BOSTON p 802
181 New Boston St 01801
Tel (508) 587-1500
SIC 5032 5031 5039 5023 5033

KRAFT POWER CORP p 829
199 Wildwood Ave 01801
Tel (781) 938-9100 *SIC* 5084 7699

MANGANARO INDUSTRIES INC p 901
52 Cummings Park 01801
Tel (781) 937-8880
SIC 1742 1741 1799 1743

▲ MONOTYPE IMAGING HOLDINGS INC p 985
600 Unicorn Park Dr 01801
Tel (781) 970-6000 *SIC* 7371 7372

RANDSTAD PROFESSIONALS US LP p 1208
150 Presidential Way Fl 4 01801
Tel (781) 213-1500 *SIC* 7361

RANDSTAD TECHNOLOGIES LP p 1208
150 Presidential Way # 300 01801
Tel (781) 938-1910 *SIC* 7361

ROHTSTEIN CORP p 1247
70 Olympia Ave 01801
Tel (781) 935-8300
SIC 5149 2099 2087 2062 2041 2033

SAVINGS BANK LIFE INSURANCE CO OF MASSACHUSETTS p 1284
1 Linscott Rd 01801
Tel (781) 938-3500 *SIC* 6311

▲ SKYWORKS SOLUTIONS INC p 1330
20 Sylvan Rd 01801
Tel (781) 376-3000 *SIC* 3674

VITASOY USA INC p 1563
57 Russell St 01801
Tel (781) 430-8988 *SIC* 5149 2099

WOODS HOLE, MA

WOOD HOLE OCEANAL GRAPHICS INSTITUTION INC p 1622
38 Water St 02543
Tel (508) 457-2620 *SIC* 8731 8733 8221

WOODS HOLE MARTHAS VINEYARD AND NANTUCKET STEAMSHIP AUTHORITY p 1623
1 Cowdry Rd 02543
Tel (508) 548-5011 *SIC* 4482

WOODS HOLE OCEANOGRAPHIC INSTITUTION p 1623
266 Woods Hole Rd 02543
Tel (508) 457-2000 *SIC* 8733

WORCESTER, MA

ALLEGRO MICROSYSTEMS LLC p 53
115 Ne Cutoff 01606
Tel (508) 853-5000 *SIC* 3674

■ ALLMERICA FINANCIAL LIFE INSURANCE AND ANNUITY p 58
440 Lincoln St 01653
Tel (508) 855-1000 *SIC* 6411 6211

ASCENTRIA CARE ALLIANCE p 116
14 E Worcester St Ste 300 01604
Tel (774) 343-3900 *SIC* 8322 8051 8361

ASSUMPTION COLLEGE p 121
500 Salisbury St 01609
Tel (508) 767-7000 *SIC* 8221

CITY OF WORCESTER p 319
455 Main St Rm 112 01608
Tel (508) 799-1049 *SIC* 9111

COGHLIN CONSTRUCTION SERVICES INC p 334
100 Prescott St Ste 3 01605
Tel (508) 793-0300 *SIC* 1731

COGHLIN ELECTRICAL CONTRACTORS INC p 334
100 Prescott St 01605
Tel (508) 793-0300 *SIC* 1731

COLLEGE OF HOLY CROSS p 336
1 College St 01610
Tel (508) 793-2011 *SIC* 8221

FALLON COMMUNITY HEALTH PLAN INC p 526
10 Chestnut St Ste 800 01608
Tel (508) 799-2100 *SIC* 6324

FIRST ALLMERICA FINANCIAL LIFE INSURANCE CO p 544
440 Lincoln St 01653
Tel (508) 855-1000 *SIC* 6411 6211 6324

■ HANOVER INSURANCE CO p 658
440 Lincoln St 01653
Tel (508) 853-7200 *SIC* 6331 6351

▲ HANOVER INSURANCE GROUP INC p 658
440 Lincoln St 01653
Tel (508) 855-1000 *SIC* 6331 6311

HUDSON-RPM DISTRIBUTORS LLC p 717
150 Blackstone River Rd # 6 01607
Tel (617) 328-9500 *SIC* 5192

■ OPUS INVESTMENT MANAGEMENT INC p 1091
440 Lincoln St 01653
Tel (508) 855-1000
SIC 6311 6321 6324 6351 6722

■ PAUL REVERE LIFE INSURANCE CO p 1121
1 Mercantile St 01608
Tel (508) 366-8707 *SIC* 6311 6321

POLAR CORP p 1159
1001 Southbridge St 01610
Tel (508) 753-6383 *SIC* 2086 5149

RAND-WHITNEY CONTAINER LLC p 1207
1 Agrand St 01607
Tel (508) 890-7000 *SIC* 2653 2631

RAND-WHITNEY GROUP LLC p 1207
1 Agrand St 01607
Tel (508) 791-2301 *SIC* 2653 2657 2631

RELIANT MEDICAL GROUP INC p 1222
630 Plantation St 01605
Tel (508) 368-5400 *SIC* 8011 7352 5912

RILEY POWER INC p 1235
5 Neponset St 01606
Tel (508) 852-7100
SIC 3569 3443 3433 1711 3564 3511

ROMAN CATHOLIC BISHOP OF WORCESTER p 1248
49 Elm St 01609
Tel (508) 791-7171 *SIC* 8661

■ SAINT VINCENT HOSPITAL LLC p 1271
123 Summer St 01608
Tel (508) 363-5000 *SIC* 8062

SAINT-GOBAIN ABRASIVES INC p 1271
1 New Bond St 01606
Tel (508) 795-5000
SIC 3291 3559 3545 3297 3082 2891

SAINT-GOBAIN CORP p 1271
1 New Bond St 01606
Tel (508) 795-5000 *SIC* 5945

SAINT-GOBAIN SEMICONDUCTOR COMPONENTS p 1271
1 New Bond St 01606
Tel (508) 795-5400 *SIC* 5085

SEVEN HILLS FOUNDATION INC p 1309
81 Hope Ave 01603
Tel (508) 755-2340 *SIC* 8211 8361

SPECTRUM HEALTH SYSTEMS INC p 1357
10 Mechanic St Ste 302 01608
Tel (508) 792-1508 *SIC* 8361 8093

TRUSTEES OF CLARK UNIVERSITY p 1487
950 Main St 01610
Tel (508) 793-7711 *SIC* 8221

UMASS MEMORIAL COMMUNITY HOSPITALS INC p 1501
119 Belmont St 01605
Tel (508) 334-1000 *SIC* 8062

UMASS MEMORIAL COMMUNITY MEDICAL GROUP INC p 1501
121 Lincoln St 01605
Tel (508) 757-7745 *SIC* 8011

UMASS MEMORIAL HEALTH CARE INC p 1501
365 Plantation St Ste 300 01605
Tel (508) 754-6026 *SIC* 8011

UMASS MEMORIAL HEALTH CARE INC AND AFFILIATES GROUP RETURN p 1501
306 Belmont St 120 01604
Tel (508) 334-5106 *SIC* 8748

UMASS MEMORIAL MEDICAL CENTER INC p 1501
55 Lake Ave N 01655
Tel (508) 334-1000 *SIC* 8062

■ UMASS MEMORIAL MEDICAL CENTER INC p 1501
119 Belmont St 01605
Tel (508) 334-1000 *SIC* 8062

■ UNUM INSURANCE CO p 1528
1 Mercantile St 01608
Tel (508) 366-8707 *SIC* 6311

VNA CARE NETWORK FOUNDATION INC p 1563
120 Thomas St 01608
Tel (508) 786-0693 *SIC* 8082

WORCESTER EPISCOPAL HOUSING CO LIMITED PARTNERSHIP p 1624
6 Wachusett St 01609
Tel (508) 757-1133 *SIC* 6513

WORCESTER POLYTECHNIC INSTITUTE p 1624
100 Institute Rd 01609
Tel (508) 831-5000 *SIC* 8221

WORCESTER PUBLIC SCHOOLS p 1624
20 Irving St 01609
Tel (508) 799-3116 *SIC* 8211

MICHIGAN

ADA, MI

ACCESS BUSINESS GROUP LLC p 14
7575 Fulton St E 49355
Tel (616) 787-6000
SIC 5169 2842 5122 2833 5136 5137

ALTICOR GLOBAL HOLDINGS INC p 62
7575 Fulton St E 49301
Tel (616) 787-1000
SIC 5169 5122 2833 5136 5137 5021

ALTICOR INC p 62
7575 Fulton St E 49355
Tel (616) 787-1000
SIC 5169 5122 2833 5136 5137 5021

AMWAY CORP p 87
7575 Fulton St E 49355
Tel (616) 787-6000 *SIC* 5963

AMWAY INTERNATIONAL INC p 87
7575 Fulton St E 49355
Tel (616) 787-1000
SIC 5169 5122 5099 5199 2099 2032

CORPORATE SECURITY SOLUTIONS INC p 372
8066 Fulton St E 49301
Tel (616) 248-3372 *SIC* 7382

SOLSTICE HOLDINGS INC p 1339
7575 Fulton St E 49355
Tel (616) 787-1000 *SIC* 4731

ADRIAN, MI

ADRIAN STEEL CO p 24
906 James St 49221
Tel (517) 265-6194 *SIC* 3496 3469

BRAZEWAY INC p 209
2711 E Maumee St 49221
Tel (517) 265-2121 *SIC* 3354 3353

GLEANER LIFE INSURANCE SOCIETY INC p 614
5200 W Us Highway 223 49221
Tel (517) 263-2244 *SIC* 6311

■ **MASCO BUILDER CABINET GROUP** p 915
5353 W Us Highway 223 49221
Tel (517) 264-9153 *SIC* 2434

■ **MERILLAT LP** p 949
5353 W Us Highway 223 49221
Tel (517) 263-0771 *SIC* 2434

PROMEDICA NORTH REGION INC p 1183
818 Riverside Ave 49221
Tel (517) 265-0390 *SIC* 8011

SOUTHEASTERN MICHIGAN RURAL ELECTRIC COOPERATIVE p 1346
1610 E Maumee St 49221
Tel (517) 263-1808 *SIC* 4911

WACKER BIOCHEM CORP p 1570
3301 Sutton Rd 49221
Tel (517) 264-8500 *SIC* 2899

WACKER CHEMICAL CORP p 1570
3301 Sutton Rd 49221
Tel (517) 264-8500 *SIC* 2869 5169

ALLEGAN, MI

L PERRIGO CO p 834
515 Eastern Ave 49010
Tel (269) 673-8451 *SIC* 2834

PERRIGO CO p 1137
515 Eastern Ave 49010
Tel (269) 673-8451 *SIC* 2834

ALLEN PARK, MI

AEES POWER SYSTEMS LIMITED PARTNERSHIP p 29
999 Republic Dr 48101
Tel (248) 489-4900 *SIC* 3694

BELLE TIRE DISTRIBUTORS INC p 170
1000 Enterprise Dr 48101
Tel (888) 462-3553 *SIC* 5531 5014

ALLENDALE, MI

GRAND VALLEY STATE UNIVERSITY p 630
1 Campus Dr 49401
Tel (616) 331-5000 *SIC* 8221

ALMA, MI

ETX HOLDINGS INC p 512
2000 Michigan Ave 48801
Tel (989) 463-1151
SIC 3585 3621 3714 5013 3089

ETX INC p 512
2000 Michigan Ave 48801
Tel (989) 463-1151 *SIC* 7549

GREAT LAKES PETROLEUM CORP p 634
6525 N Jerome Rd 48801
Tel (989) 463-4654 *SIC* 5172

MIDMICHIGAN MEDICAL CENTER-GRATIOT p 966
300 E Warwick Dr 48801
Tel (989) 463-1101 *SIC* 8062

ALPENA, MI

ALPENA REGIONAL MEDICAL CENTER p 60
1501 W Chisholm St 49707
Tel (989) 356-7390 *SIC* 8062

BESSER CO p 177
801 Johnson St 49707
Tel (989) 354-4508
SIC 3531 3559 3564 3443

DEVERE CONSTRUCTION CO INC p 433
1030 Devere Dr 49707
Tel (989) 356-4411
SIC 1542 1541 1629 8741

ALTO, MI

EMPLOYMENT TRADITIONS INC p 494
10045 E Rivershore Dr Se 49302
Tel (616) 891-9194 *SIC* 7363

MAGNA MIRRORS NORTH AMERICA LLC p 896
6151 Bancroft Ave Se 49302
Tel (616) 868-6122 *SIC* 3231 3442

SAND PRODUCTS CORP p 1278
13495 92nd St Se 49302
Tel (231) 722-6691 *SIC* 1446

ANN ARBOR, MI

▲ **AROTECH CORP** p 112
1229 Oak Valley Dr 48108
Tel (800) 281-0356 *SIC* 3691 3694

AVFUEL CORP p 137
47 W Ellsworth Rd 48108
Tel (734) 663-6466 *SIC* 5172

BUSCHS INC p 229
2240 S Main St 48103
Tel (734) 998-2666 *SIC* 5411

COUNTY OF WASHTENAW p 382
220 N Main St 48104
Tel (734) 222-4357 *SIC* 9111

▲ **DOMINOS PIZZA INC** p 449
30 Frank Lloyd Wright Dr 48105
Tel (734) 930-3030 *SIC* 5812 5149 6794

■ **DOMINOS PIZZA LLC** p 449
30 Frank Lloyd Wright Dr 48105
Tel (734) 930-3030
SIC 5812 6794 5046 5149 8741 2045

■ **DTE COAL SERVICES INC** p 458
414 S Main St Ste 600 48104
Tel (734) 913-2080 *SIC* 5052 4212

■ **DTE ENERGY RESOURCES INC** p 458
414 S Main St Ste 600 48104
Tel (734) 302-4800 *SIC* 4911 1389

■ **DTE ENERGY SERVICES INC** p 458
414 S Main St Ste 600 48104
Tel (734) 302-4800 *SIC* 4911

■ **DTE ENERGYTRADING INC** p 458
414 S Main St Ste 200 48104
Tel (734) 887-2000 *SIC* 4911 4923

EAST WEST INDUSTRIAL ENGINEERING CO p 471
1099 Highland Dr Ste D 48108
Tel (734) 971-6265 *SIC* 5085 5172

EDWARDS BROTHERS INC p 480
5411 Jackson Rd 48103
Tel (800) 722-3231 *SIC* 2732 2789

EDWARDS BROTHERS MALLOY INC p 480
5411 Jackson Rd 48103
Tel (734) 665-6113 *SIC* 2732

ERVIN INDUSTRIES INC p 508
3893 Research Park Dr 48108
Tel (734) 769-4600 *SIC* 3291 6159

ETAS INC p 511
3021 Miller Rd 48103
Tel (734) 997-9393 *SIC* 5049

■ **GELMAN SCIENCES INC** p 598
674 S Wagner Rd 48103
Tel (734) 665-0651
SIC 3821 3569 3564 3841 3845 3699

IHA HEALTH SERVICES CORP p 730
24 Frank Lloyd Wright Dr 48105
Tel (734) 747-6766 *SIC* 8011

■ **INFRA SOURCE INC** p 742
2311 Green Rd Ste D 48105
Tel (734) 434-2000 *SIC* 1521

INTEGRATED HEALTH ASSOCIATES INC p 749
24 Frank Lloyd Wright Dr 48105
Tel (734) 747-6766 *SIC* 8011

KAYDON CORP p 805
2723 S State St Ste 300 48104
Tel (734) 747-7025
SIC 3562 3569 3592 3053 3621 3679

MA INDUSTRIAL JV LLC p 891
5683 Hines Dr 48108
Tel (734) 585-9500 *SIC* 3585 3679 6719

■ **MASCO CABINETRY LLC** p 915
4600 Arrowhead Dr 48105
Tel (734) 205-4600 *SIC* 2434

MCKINLEY INC p 930
320 N Main St Ste 200 48104
Tel (734) 769-8520 *SIC* 6513

NSF INTERNATIONAL p 1065
789 N Dixboro Rd 48105
Tel (734) 769-8010 *SIC* 8731 8734

NSF INTERNATIONAL HOLDINGS p 1065
789 N Dixboro Rd 48105
Tel (734) 769-8010 *SIC* 6799

NSK AMERICAS INC p 1065
4200 Goss Rd 48105
Tel (734) 913-7500 *SIC* 3714 5013 5085

NSK CORP p 1065
4200 Goss Rd 48105
Tel (734) 913-7500
SIC 3714 5013 3594 3568 3562

NSK STEERING SYSTEMS AMERICA INC p 1065
4200 Goss Rd 48105
Tel (734) 913-7500 *SIC* 3714

OLAMETER CORP p 1080
4325 Concourse Dr 48108
Tel (734) 769-2600 *SIC* 7389

PROQUEST LLC p 1184
789 E Eisenhower Pkwy 48108
Tel (734) 761-4700 *SIC* 7375

PUBLIC SCHOOLS OF CITY ANN ARBOR p 1189
2555 S State St 48104
Tel (734) 994-2200 *SIC* 8211

REGENTS OF UNIVERSITY OF MICHIGAN p 1219
503 Thompson St 48109
Tel (734) 764-1817 *SIC* 8221

TECUMSEH PRODUCTS CO p 1432
5683 Hines Dr 48108
Tel (734) 585-9500 *SIC* 3585 3679

TERUMO CARDIOVASCULAR SYSTEMS CORP p 1440
6200 Jackson Rd 48103
Tel (734) 663-4145 *SIC* 3845 3841

THETFORD CORP p 1447
7101 Jackson Rd 48103
Tel (734) 769-6000
SIC 3632 3089 2842 2621 3431 2899

TRUCK HERO INC p 1485
5400 S State Rd 48108
Tel (734) 677-0444 *SIC* 3714

■ **TRUVEN HEALTH ANALYTICS INC** p 1489
100 Phoenix Dr 48108
Tel (734) 913-3000 *SIC* 8742

■ **TRUVEN HOLDING CORP** p 1489
100 Phoenix Dr Ste 100 48108
Tel (734) 913-3000 *SIC* 8742

UNIBAR SERVICES INC p 1502
4325 Concourse Dr 48108
Tel (734) 769-2600 *SIC* 1623

WASHTENAW COMMUNITY COLLEGE p 1580
4800 E Huron River Dr 48105
Tel (734) 973-3300 *SIC* 8222 8221

WASHTENAW INTERMEDIATE SCHOOL DISTRICT p 1580
1819 S Wagner Rd 48103
Tel (734) 994-8100 *SIC* 8211

■ **XPO CNW INC** p 1632
2211 Old Earhart Rd 48105
Tel (253) 926-2251 *SIC* 4213 4731 3715

■ **XPO ENTERPRISE SERVICES INC** p 1632
2211 Old Earhart Rd # 100 48105
Tel (734) 998-4200 *SIC* 4213

AUBURN HILLS, MI

ABB FLEXIBLE AUTOMATION INC p 9
1250 Brown Rd 48326
Tel (248) 391-9000 *SIC* 5084

AIRBOSS FLEXIBLE PRODUCTS CO p 39
2600 Auburn Ct 48326
Tel (248) 852-5500 *SIC* 3069 3714

ANDROID INDUSTRIES LLC p 91
2155 Executive Hills Dr 48326
Tel (248) 454-0500 *SIC* 5013

ANTOLIN INTERIORS USA INC p 94
1700 Atlantic Blvd 48326
Tel (248) 373-1749 *SIC* 3714

AUTOMOTIVE LIGHTING LLC p 134
3900 Automation Ave 48326
Tel (248) 418-3000 *SIC* 8711 3647

BENTELER AUTOMOTIVE CORP p 173
2650 N Opdyke Rd Ste B 48326
Tel (248) 364-7190 *SIC* 3714 3465 3999

BENTELER NORTH AMERICA CORP p 173
2650 N Opdyke Rd Ste B 48326
Tel (248) 377-9999 *SIC* 5051

■ **BORGWARNER EMISSIONS SYSTEMS OF MICHIGAN INC** p 201
3800 Automation Ave # 200 48326
Tel (248) 754-9600 *SIC* 3714

▲ **BORGWARNER INC** p 201
3850 Hamlin Rd 48326
Tel (248) 754-9200 *SIC* 3714

■ **BORGWARNER TORQTRANSFER SYSTEMS INC** p 201
3850 Hamlin Rd 48326
Tel (248) 754-9600 *SIC* 3714

■ **BORGWARNER TRANSMISSION SYSTEMS INC** p 201
3800 Automation Ave # 500 48326
Tel (248) 754-0200 *SIC* 3714

BROSE NORTH AMERICA INC p 218
3933 Automation Ave 48326
Tel (248) 339-4000 *SIC* 5015

COMMERCIAL CONTRACTING CORP p 345
4260 N Atlantic Blvd 48326
Tel (248) 209-0500 *SIC* 1541 1796

COMMERCIAL CONTRACTING GROUP INC p 345
4260 N Atlantic Blvd 48326
Tel (248) 209-0500 *SIC* 1796

CONTINENTAL AUTOMOTIVE SYSTEMS INC p 363
1 Continental Dr 48326
Tel (248) 393-5300 *SIC* 3714

CONTINENTAL STRUCTURAL PLASTICS HOLDINGS CORP p 363
255 Rex Blvd 48326
Tel (248) 237-7800 *SIC* 3089

CONTINENTAL STRUCTURAL PLASTICS INC p 363
255 Rex Blvd 48326
Tel (248) 237-7800 *SIC* 3089

CONTINENTAL TEVES INC p 363
1 Continental Dr 48326
Tel (248) 393-5300 *SIC* 3714

CSP HOLDING CORP p 398
255 Rex Blvd 48326
Tel (248) 237-7800 *SIC* 3089

■ **DOVER ENERGY INC** p 453
15 Corporate Dr 48326
Tel (248) 836-6700 *SIC* 3429

DURA AUTOMOTIVE SYSTEMS LLC p 462
1780 Pond Run 48326
Tel (248) 299-7500 *SIC* 3714

DURA OPERATING LLC p 462
1780 Pond Run 48326
Tel (248) 299-7500 *SIC* 3429 3714

FAURECIA AUTOMOTIVE SEATING LLC p 531
2800 High Meadow Cir 48326
Tel (248) 288-1000 *SIC* 8711

FAURECIA INTERIOR SYSTEMS INC p 531
2500 Executive Hills Dr 48326
Tel (248) 409-3500 *SIC* 5013 3999

FAURECIA USA HOLDINGS INC p 531
2800 High Meadow Cir 48326
Tel (248) 724-5100 *SIC* 3714

FCA NORTH AMERICA HOLDINGS LLC p 532
1000 Chrysler Dr 48326
Tel (248) 512-2950 *SIC* 3711 3714

FCA US LLC p 532
1000 Chrysler Dr 48326
Tel (248) 512-2950 *SIC* 3711 3714

FEV NORTH AMERICA INC p 539
4554 Glenmeade Ln 48326
Tel (248) 475-4761 *SIC* 8748 8743

GARDNER WHITE FURNITURE CO INC p 592
4445 N Atlantic Blvd 48326
Tel (586) 774-8853 *SIC* 5712

GEORGE P JOHNSON CO p 606
3600 Giddings Rd 48326
Tel (248) 475-2500 *SIC* 3993 7389

GKN DRIVELINE NORTH AMERICA INC p 613
2200 N Opdyke Rd 48326
Tel (248) 296-7000 *SIC* 3714 5013

GKN NORTH AMERICA INC p 613
2200 N Opdyke Rd 48326
Tel (248) 296-7200 *SIC* 3714 5013 7359

GKN SINTER METALS LLC p 613
2200 N Opdyke Rd 48326
Tel (248) 296-7832
SIC 3714 3568 3369 3366

GLOBAL AUTOMOTIVE SYSTEMS LLC p 615
1780 Pond Run 48326
Tel (248) 299-7230 *SIC* 3469

GRUPO ANTOLIN NORTH AMERICA INC p 643
1700 Atlantic Blvd 48326
Tel (248) 373-1437 *SIC* 8741 8711

GUARDIAN INDUSTRIES CORP p 645
2300 Harmon Rd 48326
Tel (248) 340-1800 *SIC* 3211

HENNIGES AUTOMOTIVE HOLDINGS INC p 683
2750 High Meadow Cir 48326
Tel (248) 340-4100 *SIC* 3069 2891 3714

HENNIGES AUTOMOTIVE SEALING SYSTEMS NORTH AMERICA INC p 683
2750 High Meadow Cir 48326
Tel (248) 340-4100 *SIC* 3053 2891 3714

HIROTEC AMERICA INC p 695
3000 High Meadow Cir 48326
Tel (248) 836-5100 *SIC* 3569

■ **HUTCHINSON FTS INC** p 722
1060 Centre Rd 48326
Tel (248) 589-7710
SIC 3714 3061 3567 3492 3443 3429

■ **HUTCHINSON SEALING SYSTEMS INC** p 722
1060 Centre Rd 48326
Tel (248) 375-3720 *SIC* 3069

INALFA ROOF SYSTEMS INC p 735
1370 Pacific Dr 48326
Tel (248) 371-3060 *SIC* 3714

LJ/HAH HOLDINGS CORP p 872
2750 High Meadow Cir 48326
Tel (248) 340-4100 *SIC* 2891 3714

MAGNA CARTOP SYSTEMS OF AMERICA INC p 895
2725 Commerce Pkwy 48326
Tel (248) 836-4500 *SIC* 2394

MORRELL INC p 990
3333 Bald Mountain Rd 48326
Tel (248) 373-1600
SIC 5084 5065 3621 3643 3559 3357

NEXLINK COMMUNICATIONS LLC p 1040
3355 Bald Mountain Rd # 10 48326
Tel (248) 409-2511 *SIC* 5065

NEXTEER AUTOMOTIVE CORP p 1040
1272 Doris Rd 48326
Tel (989) 757-5000 *SIC* 3714

OLD CARCO INTERNATIONAL CORP p 1080
1000 Chrysler Dr 48326
Tel (248) 576-5741 *SIC* 5012

PALACE SPORTS & ENTERTAINMENT LLC p 1108
6 Championship Dr 48326
Tel (248) 377-0165 *SIC* 7941 7922

PROJECT WORLDWIDE INC p 1182
3600 Giddings Rd 48326
Tel (248) 475-8863 *SIC* 7311

RECTICEL NORTH AMERICA INC p 1215
1653 Atlantic Blvd 48326
Tel (248) 393-2100 *SIC* 5169

■ **RGIS HOLDINGS LLC** p 1231
2000 Taylor Rd 48326
Tel (248) 651-2511 *SIC* 7389

■ **RGIS LLC** p 1231
2000 Taylor Rd 48326
Tel (248) 651-2511 *SIC* 7389

SCHLEGEL CORP p 1287
2750 High Meadow Cir 48326
Tel (248) 340-4100 *SIC* 5013 7539

SYNCREON AMERICA INC p 1414
2851 High Meadow Cir 48326
Tel (248) 377-4700 *SIC* 4731

SYNCREON HOLDINGS INC p 1415
2851 High Meadow Cir # 250 48326
Tel (248) 377-4700 *SIC* 3559

TI AUTOMOTIVE INC p 1452
1272 Doris Rd Ste 100 48326
Tel (248) 276-4721 *SIC* 5013 7538

TI AUTOMOTIVE LLC p 1452
2020 Taylor Rd 48326
Tel (248) 494-5000
SIC 3317 3312 3599 3052 3714 3585

TI GROUP AUTOMOTIVE SYSTEMS LLC p 1452
2020 Taylor Rd 48326
Tel (248) 296-8000
SIC 3317 3312 3599 3052 3714 3585

TK HOLDINGS INC p 1457
2500 Takata Dr 48326
Tel (248) 373-8040
SIC 2221 2399 2396 3714

▲ **UNIQUE FABRICATING INC** p 1505
800 Standard Pkwy 48326
Tel (248) 853-2333
SIC 3053 3086 3296 2671

UNITED SOLAR OVONIC LLC p 1511
3800 Lapeer Rd 48326
Tel (248) 475-0100 *SIC* 3674

WILLAN INC p 1610
2851 High Meadow Cir # 250 48326
Tel (248) 377-4700 *SIC* 3559

AUBURN, MI

■ **DOW CORNING CORP** p 453
2200 W Salzburg Rd 48611
Tel (989) 496-4000 *SIC* 2821 2869

BAD AXE, MI

GEMINI GROUP INC p 598
175 Thompson Rd Ste A 48413
Tel (989) 269-6272 *SIC* 8741 3089

BATTLE CREEK, MI

ASMO MAUNFACTURING INC p 118
500 Fritz Keiper Blvd 49037
Tel (269) 441-2040 *SIC* 3621 3089

BRONSON BATTLE CREEK HOSPITAL p 217
300 North Ave 49017
Tel (269) 966-8000 *SIC* 8062 8063 8051

DAVIS OIL CO p 416
1265 Columbia Ave E 49014
Tel (269) 965-2201 *SIC* 5541

DENSO AIR SYSTEMS MICHIGAN INC p 428
300 Fritz Keiper Blvd 49037
Tel (269) 962-9676 *SIC* 3714 3498

DENSO MANUFACTURING MICHIGAN INC p 429
1 Denso Rd 49037
Tel (269) 965-3322 *SIC* 5531

EPI PRINTERS INC p 505
5404 Wayne Rd 49037
Tel (800) 562-9733 *SIC* 2752

HI-LEX AMERICA INC p 689
5200 Wayne Rd 49037
Tel (269) 968-0781 *SIC* 3496 3357

II STANLEY CO INC p 731
1500 Hill Brady Rd 49037
Tel (269) 660-7777 *SIC* 5063 4911

JO GALLOUP CO p 786
130 Helmer Rd N 49037
Tel (269) 965-2303 *SIC* 5051 5085 5162

■ **KEEBLER CO** p 807
1 Kellogg Sq 49017
Tel (269) 961-2000 *SIC* 2052 2051

▲ **KELLOGG CO** p 808
1 Kellogg Sq 49017
Tel (269) 961-2000
SIC 2043 2041 2052 2051 2038

KELLOGG COMMUNITY COLLEGE FOUNDATION p 808
450 North Ave 49017
Tel (269) 965-4142 *SIC* 8222

■ **KELLOGG NORTH AMERICA CO** p 809
1 Kellogg Sq 49017
Tel (269) 961-2000 *SIC* 2052

■ **KELLOGG SALES CO** p 809
1 Kellogg Sq 49017
Tel (269) 961-2000 *SIC* 5149

■ **KELLOGG USA INC** p 809
1 Kellogg Sq 49017
Tel (269) 961-2000 *SIC* 2043

MC DONALDS OF CALHOUN INC p 925
806 Columbia Ave W 49015
Tel (269) 965-1402 *SIC* 5812 8742 6794

MUSASHI AUTO PARTS MICHIGAN INC p 1002
195 Brydges Dr 49037
Tel (269) 965-0057 *SIC* 3714

■ **POST FOODS LLC** p 1163
275 Cliff St 49014
Tel (269) 966-1000 *SIC* 2043

■ **SELECT SPECIALTY HOSPITAL-BATTLE CREEK INC** p 1301
300 North Ave 49017
Tel (269) 245-4675 *SIC* 8069

SYSTEX PRODUCTS CORP p 1419
300 Buckner Rd 49037
Tel (269) 964-8800 *SIC* 3089

TRMI INC p 1483
100 Hill Brady Rd 49037
Tel (269) 966-0800 *SIC* 3714 3643

TSK OF AMERICA INC p 1489
5200 Wayne Rd 49037
Tel (269) 968-0781 *SIC* 3357

W K KELLOGG FOUNDATION p 1568
1 Michigan Ave E 49017
Tel (269) 968-1611 *SIC* 8399

BAY CITY, MI

BAY REGIONAL MEDICAL CENTER p 161
1900 Columbus Ave 48708
Tel (989) 894-3000 *SIC* 8062

COUNTY OF BAY p 376
515 Center Ave Ste 401 48708
Tel (989) 895-4130 *SIC* 9111

FABIANO BROS INC p 523
1885 Bevanda Ct 48706
Tel (989) 509-0200 *SIC* 5181 5182

HOSPICE ADVANTAGE LLC p 708
401 Center Ave Ste 130 48708
Tel (989) 891-2200 *SIC* 8052 8082

MICHIGAN SUGAR CO p 961
122 Uptown Dr Unit 300 48708
Tel (989) 686-0161 *SIC* 2063

BEAR LAKE, MI

BLARNEY CASTLE OIL CO p 189
12218 West St 49614
Tel (231) 864-3111 *SIC* 5541 5411 5171

BEAVER ISLAND, MI

■ **ISLAND TELEPHONE CO** p 766
37940 King Hwy 49782
Tel (608) 831-1000 *SIC* 4813

BELDING, MI

BELCO INDUSTRIES INC p 169
9138 W Belding Rd 48809
Tel (616) 794-0410
SIC 3567 5084 3541 3535 3444

BELLEVILLE, MI

■ **ACTIVE AERO GROUP INC** p 19
2068 E St 48111
Tel (734) 547-7200 *SIC* 4522

■ **MURRAYS DISCOUNT AUTO STORES INC** p 1002
8080 Haggerty Rd 48111
Tel (734) 957-8080 *SIC* 5531

NEAPCO HOLDINGS LLC p 1023
6735 Haggerty Rd 48111
Tel (734) 447-1380
SIC 3568 3714 6719 6799

WELLINGTON INDUSTRIES INC p 1589
39555 S I 94 Servce Dr 48111
Tel (734) 942-1060 *SIC* 3465

BENTON HARBOR, MI

■ **GAST MANUFACTURING INC** p 593
2300 M 139 49022
Tel (269) 926-6171
SIC 3563 3594 3621 3566 3561

JVIS MANUFACTURING LLC p 798
1285 N Crystal Ave 49022
Tel (269) 927-8200 *SIC* 5015

■ **MAYTAG CORP** p 924
2000 N M 63 49022
Tel (269) 923-5000
SIC 3633 3631 3632 3639 3635 3581

▲ **WHIRLPOOL CORP** p 1605
2000 N M 63 49022
Tel (269) 923-5000
SIC 3633 3585 3632 3635

BERRIEN SPRINGS, MI

ANDREWS UNIVERSITY p 90
4150 Aministration Dr 49104
Tel (269) 471-7771 *SIC* 8221

BEVERLY HILLS, MI

SCHOOL DISTRICT OF CITY OF BIRMINGHAM p 1289
31301 Evergreen Rd 48025
Tel (248) 203-3000 *SIC* 8211

BIG RAPIDS, MI

FERRIS STATE UNIVERSITY p 538
1201 S State St 49307
Tel (231) 591-2000 *SIC* 8221

BINGHAM FARMS, MI

ARDEN COMPANIES INC p 106
30400 Telg Rd Ste 200 48025
Tel (248) 415-8500 *SIC* 2392

DETROIT TECHNOLOGIES INC p 433
32500 Telg Rd Ste 207 48025
Tel (248) 647-0400 *SIC* 3714

KRAMS ENTERPRISES INC p 829
30400 Telg Rd Ste 200 48025
Tel (248) 415-8500 *SIC* 2392

BIRMINGHAM, MI

BELFOR HOLDINGS INC p 169
185 Oakland Ave Ste 300 48009
Tel (248) 594-1144 *SIC* 6719

BELFOR USA GROUP INC p 169
185 Oakland Ave Ste 150 48009
Tel (248) 594-1144 *SIC* 1799

FRED LAVERY CO p 576
34602 Woodward Ave 48009
Tel (248) 645-5930 *SIC* 5511

GAS CITY LTD p 593
401 S Old Woodward Ave # 340 48009
Tel (815) 469-9000 *SIC* 5541 5411 5172

MAGNI GROUP INC p 896
390 Park St Ste 300 48009
Tel (248) 647-4500 *SIC* 2899 3479

QUESTOR MANAGEMENT CO LLC p 1199
101 Southfield Rd Fl 2 48009
Tel (248) 593-1930 *SIC* 8742

QUESTOR PARTNERS FUND II LP p 1199
101 Southfield Rd 2 48009
Tel (248) 593-1930 *SIC* 8742 2099

SAIC USA INC p 1268
322 N Old Woodward Ave # 3 48009
Tel (248) 267-9117 *SIC* 5013

SANCTUS LLC p 1278
348 E Maple Rd 48009
Tel (248) 594-2396 *SIC* 8741 7319 8742

US AUTO GROUP LIMITED p 1531
34602 Woodward Ave 48009
Tel (248) 645-5930 *SIC* 5511

BLOOMFIELD HILLS, MI

AJM PACKAGING CORP p 41
E-4111 Andover Rd 48302
Tel (248) 901-0040 *SIC* 2656 2674

BLOOMFIELD HILLS SCHOOL DISTRICT p 190
7273 Wing Lake Rd Ste A 48301
Tel (248) 341-5400 *SIC* 8211

FIRST INTERNATIONAL EXCHANGE GROUP (INC) p 547
6632 Telegraph Rd Ste 231 48301
Tel (248) 737-9300 *SIC* 8742

FRANK AMBROSE INC p 574
550 Hulet Dr Ste 103 48302
Tel (248) 655-2300 *SIC* 5111

OAKLAND COMMUNITY COLLEGE FOUNDATION p 1071
2480 Opdyke Rd 48304
Tel (248) 341-2000 *SIC* 8222

▲ **PENSKE AUTOMOTIVE GROUP INC** p 1131
2555 S Telegraph Rd 48302
Tel (248) 648-2500 *SIC* 5511

PENSKE CO LLC p 1131
2555 S Telegraph Rd 48302
Tel (248) 648-2000 *SIC* 3647

PENSKE CORP p 1131
2555 S Telegraph Rd 48302
Tel (248) 648-2000 *SIC* 5511 7538 7948

▲ **TAUBMAN CENTERS INC** p 1426
200 E Long Lake Rd # 300 48304
Tel (248) 258-6800 *SIC* 6798

▲ **TRIMAS CORP** p 1480
39400 Woodward Ave # 130 48304
Tel (248) 631-5450
SIC 3799 3714 3443 2672 3452 3545

V2SOFT INC p 1538
300 Enterprise Ct Ste 100 48302
Tel (248) 904-1705 *SIC* 7371

BLOOMFIELD, MI

ARCHDIOCESE OF DETROIT ED OFF p 105
3691 Lincoln Rd 48301
Tel (248) 646-2612 *SIC* 8211

BOYNE CITY, MI

GREAT LAKES ENERGY COOPERATIVE p 633
1323 Boyne Ave 49712
Tel (231) 582-6521 *SIC* 4911

LEXAMAR CORP p 859
100 Lexamar Dr 49712
Tel (231) 582-3163 *SIC* 3089

BOYNE FALLS, MI

BOYNE USA INC p 205
1 Boyne Mountain Rd 49713
Tel (231) 549-6000 *SIC* 7011 7992 7032

BRIGHTON, MI

BRIGHTON AREA SCHOOL DISTRICT p 213
125 S Church St 48116
Tel (810) 299-4000 *SIC* 8211

H H BARNUM CO p 650
7915 Lochlin Dr 48116
Tel (800) 695-3055 *SIC* 5084

HURON-CLINTON METROPOLITAN AUTHORITY p 721
13000 Highridge Dr 48114
Tel (810) 227-2757 *SIC* 9512

LOWRY HOLDING CO INC p 882
9420 Maltby Rd 48116
Tel (810) 229-7200
SIC 5045 2672 8742 7373 5044 5734

TG FLUID SYSTEMS USA CORP p 1446
100 Brighton Interior Dr 48116
Tel (810) 220-6161 *SIC* 3082 3089

BROWNSTOWN, MI

NWS MICHIGAN INC p 1068
17550 Allen Rd 48193
Tel (734) 324-3000 *SIC* 5182

BRUCE TWP, MI

L & L PRODUCTS INC p 833
160 Mclean 48065
Tel (586) 336-1600 *SIC* 3053

PLASTIC SYSTEMS LLC p 1155
15055 32 Mile Rd 48065
Tel (586) 336-9696 *SIC* 3089

ZEPHYROS INC p 1642
160 Mclean 48065
Tel (586) 336-1600 *SIC* 3053

BURTON, MI

BISHOP CONSTRUCTION INC p 185
3374 S Center Rd Ste C 48519
Tel (810) 744-4550 *SIC* 1521 1542

BYRON CENTER, MI

CENTER MANUFACTURING INC p 276
990 84th St Sw 49315
Tel (616) 878-3324 *SIC* 3499 3441

■ **GYPSUM SUPPLY CO** p 649
859 74th St Sw 49315
Tel (616) 583-9300 *SIC* 5032

JOMAR INVESTMENTS INC p 792
400 Gordon Indus Ct Sw 49315
Tel (616) 878-3633 *SIC* 5013

M & K TRUCK AND TRAILER INC p 888
8800 Byron Commerce Dr Sw 49315
Tel (616) 583-2100 *SIC* 5511 4212

MARTIN TRANSPORTATION SYSTEMS INC p 913
7300 Clyde Park Ave Sw 49315
Tel (616) 455-8850 *SIC* 4212

▲ **SPARTANNASH CO** p 1355
850 76th St Sw 49315
Tel (616) 878-2000 *SIC* 5141 5411 5912

CADILLAC, MI

AVON AUTOMOTIVE HOLDINGS INC p 139
603 7th St 49601
Tel (231) 775-6571 *SIC* 3061 3089

AVON RUBBER & PLASTICS INC p 139
503 8th St 49601
Tel (231) 779-6290 *SIC* 3089 3061

CADILLAC CASTING INC p 236
1500 4th Ave 49601
Tel (231) 779-9600 *SIC* 3714

REC BOAT HOLDINGS LLC p 1214
925 Frisbie St 49601
Tel (231) 775-1351 *SIC* 3732

WOLVERINE POWER SUPPLY COOPERATIVE INC p 1621
10125 W Watergate Rd 49601
Tel (231) 775-5700 *SIC* 4911

CALEDONIA, MI

ACRISURE LLC p 18
5664 Prairie Creek Dr Se 49316
Tel (800) 748-0351 *SIC* 7389

■ **ASPEN SURGICAL PRODUCTS INC** p 118
6945 Southbelt Dr Se 49316
Tel (616) 698-7100 *SIC* 5047

CALEDONIA FARMERS ELEVATOR CO INC p 238
146 E Main St Se 49316
Tel (616) 891-4150
SIC 5153 5169 5251 5261

FOREMOST AFFINITY SERVICES INC p 566
5600 Beechtree Ln Se 49316
Tel (616) 942-3000 *SIC* 6331

FOREMOST CORP OF AMERICA p 566
5600 Beechtree Ln Se 49316
Tel (616) 942-3000 *SIC* 6331

FOREMOST FINANCIAL SERVICES CORP p 566
5600 Beechtree Ln Se 49316
Tel (616) 956-3501 *SIC* 6331

FOREMOST INSURANCE CO p 566
5600 Beechtree Ln Se 49316
Tel (616) 942-3000 *SIC* 6331

FOREMOST LLOYDS OF TEXAS p 566
5600 Beechtree Ln Se 49316
Tel (616) 942-3000 *SIC* 6331

NETECH CORP p 1027
6355 E Paris Ave Se 49316
Tel (212) 324-4398 *SIC* 7379

CANTON, MI

AD TRANSPORT EXPRESS INC p 21
5601 Belleville Rd 48188
Tel (734) 397-7100 *SIC* 4213 4212

AERO COMMUNICATIONS HOLDING INC p 30
5711 Research Dr 48188
Tel (734) 467-8121 *SIC* 1623

AERO COMMUNICATIONS INC p 30
5711 Research Dr 48188
Tel (734) 467-8121 *SIC* 1623

CANTON WIND-DOWN CO p 247
5711 Research Dr 48188
Tel (734) 467-8121 *SIC* 1731

LOTUS INTERNATIONAL CO p 879
6880 Commerce Blvd 48187
Tel (734) 245-0140 *SIC* 8711 3651 1221

MATERIAL SCIENCES CORP p 919
6855 Commerce Blvd 48187
Tel (734) 207-4444 *SIC* 3479 3471

MICHIGAN PAVING AND MATERIALS CO p 961
2575 S Haggerty Rd # 100 48188
Tel (734) 397-2050 *SIC* 1522 1541 2911

SCHULER INC p 1290
7145 Commerce Blvd 48187
Tel (734) 207-7200 *SIC* 5084 3444 3599

SERVICE SOLUTIONS US LLC p 1307
7121 N Haggerty Rd 48187
Tel (734) 582-2382 *SIC* 8711

■ SYSCO DETROIT LLC p 1417
41600 Van Born Rd 48188
Tel (734) 397-7990 *SIC* 5087

YAZAKI INTERNATIONAL CORP p 1635
6801 N Haggerty Rd 4707e 48187
Tel (734) 983-1000 *SIC* 5013 3643

YAZAKI NORTH AMERICA INC p 1635
6801 N Haggerty Rd 48187
Tel (734) 983-1000 *SIC* 5013

CENTER LINE, MI

SODECIA USA AUTOMOTIVE CORP p 1336
24331 Sherwood 48015
Tel (586) 759-2200 *SIC* 3465

TRIANON INDUSTRIES CORP p 1478
24331 Sherwood 48015
Tel (586) 759-2200 *SIC* 3465 3544

CHARLOTTE, MI

▲ SPARTAN MOTORS INC p 1355
1541 Reynolds Rd 48813
Tel (517) 543-6400 *SIC* 3711 3714 7519

CHELSEA, MI

HATCH STAMPING CO LLC p 667
635 E Industrial Dr 48118
Tel (734) 475-8628 *SIC* 3465 3544

CHESTERFIELD, MI

BURTEK HOLDINGS INC p 229
50325 Patricia St 48051
Tel (586) 421-8000 *SIC* 7371 3812 8711

CLARKSTON, MI

AAA INSURANCE OF MICHIGAN p 7
6751 Dixie Hwy Ste 103 48346
Tel (248) 620-9120 *SIC* 6411

CLARKSTON COMMUNITY SCHOOLS p 322
6389 Clarkston Rd 48346
Tel (248) 623-5400 *SIC* 8211

GATEWAY COMMUNITY HEALTH p 593
7457 M E Cad Blvd Ste 200 48348
Tel (313) 262-5050 *SIC* 6324

CLAWSON, MI

ND INDUSTRIES INC p 1022
1000 N Crooks Rd 48017
Tel (248) 288-0000
SIC 3452 2851 5072 2891 3479

CLINTON TOWNSHIP, MI

21ST CENTURY NEWSPAPERS INC p 2
19176 Hall Rd Ste 200 48038
Tel (586) 469-4510 *SIC* 2711

CHIPPEWA VALLEY SCHOOLS (INC) p 301
19120 Cass Ave 48038
Tel (586) 723-2000 *SIC* 8211

COMPLETE PROTOTYPE SERVICES INC p 351
44783 Morley Dr 48036
Tel (586) 690-8897 *SIC* 3543 3714

HENRY FORD MACOMB HOSPITAL CORP p 684
15855 19 Mile Rd 48038
Tel (586) 263-2300 *SIC* 8062

LANSE CREUSE PUBLIC SCHOOLS p 844
24076 Frdrick Pankow Blvd 48036
Tel (586) 783-6300 *SIC* 8211

MACOMB INTERMEDIATE SCHOOL DISTRICT p 893
44001 Garfield Rd 48038
Tel (586) 228-3479 *SIC* 8211

MACOMB OAKLAND REGIONAL CENTER INC p 893
16200 19 Mile Rd 48038
Tel (586) 263-8700 *SIC* 8093

MORC REHABILITATION SERVICES p 988
16200 19 Mile Rd 48038
Tel (586) 739-5792 *SIC* 8322

■ TWEDDLE GROUP INC p 1494
24700 Maplehurst Dr 48036
Tel (586) 307-3700
SIC 2732 2791 2752 2759 2741 7371

COLDWATER, MI

ALLIANCE FOODS INC p 54
605 W Chicago Rd 49036
Tel (517) 278-2395 *SIC* 5411 5141

ASAMA COLDWATER MANUFACTURING INC p 115
180 Asama Pkwy 49036
Tel (517) 279-1090 *SIC* 3714

COMMERCE TOWNSHIP, MI

FKA DISTRIBUTING CO LLC p 553
3000 N Pontiac Trl 48390
Tel (248) 863-3000 *SIC* 3679 3634

■ VHS HURON VALLEY-SINAI HOSPITAL INC p 1554
1 William Carls Dr 48382
Tel (248) 937-3300 *SIC* 8062

WILLIAMS INTERNATIONAL CO LLC p 1611
2280 E West Maple Rd 48390
Tel (248) 624-5200 *SIC* 3724 3764

COOPERSVILLE, MI

ADMIRAL PETROLEUM CO p 23
785 W Randall St 49404
Tel (616) 837-6218
SIC 5541 5411 5194 5145

CORUNNA, MI

FORTERRA BRICK LLC p 569
3820 Serr Rd 48817
Tel (989) 743-3444 *SIC* 3251

COVERT, MI

■ ENTERGY NUCLEAR PALISADES LLC p 501
27780 Blue Star Hwy 49043
Tel (269) 764-2000 *SIC* 4911

DAFTER, MI

CLOVERLAND ELECTRIC COOPERATIVE INC p 328
2916 W M 28 49724
Tel (906) 635-6800 *SIC* 4911

DAVISON, MI

GENOVA PRODUCTS INC p 604
7034 E Court St 48423
Tel (810) 744-4500
SIC 3089 2891 2911 3494 3084 2952

DEARBORN, MI

AUTO CLUB GROUP p 133
1 Auto Club Dr 48126
Tel (313) 336-1234 *SIC* 8699

AUTO CLUB INSURANCE ASSOCIATION CO p 133
1 Auto Club Dr 48126
Tel (313) 336-1234 *SIC* 6331

BALLARD POWER SYSTEMS CORP p 148
15001 N Commerce Dr 48120
Tel (313) 583-5980 *SIC* 3621

CARHARTT INC p 255
5750 Mercury Dr 48126
Tel (313) 271-8460 *SIC* 2326 2329 2325

CHASE CASH & CARRY INC p 291
6661 Chase Rd 48126
Tel (313) 582-1200 *SIC* 5199

DEARBORN PUBLIC SCHOOLS p 420
18700 Audette St 48124
Tel (313) 827-3000 *SIC* 8211 8222

EDW C LEVY CO p 479
9300 Dix 48120
Tel (313) 429-2200 *SIC* 3295 5032 2951

■ FORD HOLDINGS LLC p 565
American Rd 48121
Tel (313) 845-5338 *SIC* 6552 6512

▲ FORD MOTOR CO p 565
1 American Rd 48126
Tel (313) 322-3000
SIC 3711 3713 3714 6153 6141 7515

■ FORD MOTOR CREDIT CO LLC p 565
1 American Rd 48126
Tel (313) 322-3000 *SIC* 6159 6141

■ FORD MOTOR LAND DEVELOPMENT CORP p 566
330 Town Center Dr # 1100 48126
Tel (313) 323-3100 *SIC* 6512 6552

GHAFARI ASSOCIATES LLC p 610
17101 Michigan Ave 48126
Tel (313) 271-6280 *SIC* 8711

HOLLINGSWORTH LOGISTICS MANAGEMENT LLC p 701
14225 W Warren Ave 48126
Tel (313) 768-1400 *SIC* 4225 4783

KENWAL STEEL CORP p 813
8223 W Warren Ave 48126
Tel (313) 739-1000 *SIC* 5051

LOGISTICS HOLLINGSWORTH GROUP LLC p 874
14225 W Warren Ave 48126
Tel (313) 768-1400 *SIC* 7389

OAKWOOD HEALTHCARE INC p 1071
18101 Oakwood Blvd 48124
Tel (313) 593-7000 *SIC* 8062

OAKWOOD METAL FABRICATING CO p 1071
1100 Oakwood Blvd 48124
Tel (313) 561-7740 *SIC* 5199 3714 3469

■ PERCEPTA LLC p 1134
290 Town Center Dr # 610 48126
Tel (866) 737-2378 *SIC* 7389

TEAMDETROIT LLC p 1430
550 Town Center Dr 48126
Tel (313) 615-2000 *SIC* 7311

■ WOLVERINE ADVANCED MATERIALS LLC p 1621
5850 Mercury Dr Ste 250 48126
Tel (313) 749-6100 *SIC* 3559 3694

DETROIT, MI

ALLIANCE HEALTH AND LIFE INSURANCE CO p 54
2850 W Grand Blvd Fl 5 48202
Tel (313) 872-8100 *SIC* 6311

▲ ALLY FINANCIAL INC p 59
500 Woodward Ave Fl 1 48226
Tel (866) 710-4623
SIC 6021 6153 6159 6311 6331 6162

■ ALLY INSURANCE HOLDINGS INC p 59
500 Woodward Ave Fl 1 48226
Tel (888) 737-8460 *SIC* 6331 6141

■ ALLY SERVICING LLC p 59
500 Woodward Ave Fl 1 48226
Tel (248) 948-7702 *SIC* 1389

▲ AMERICAN AXLE & MANUFACTURING HOLDINGS INC p 68
1 Dauch Dr 48211
Tel (313) 758-2000 *SIC* 3714 3711

■ AMERICAN AXLE & MANUFACTURING INC p 68
1 Dauch Dr 48211
Tel (313) 758-3600 *SIC* 3714

AON CONSULTING (MICHIGAN) INC p 94
400 Renaissance Ctr Lbby 48243
Tel (313) 393-7888 *SIC* 6411

BARBARA ANN KARMANOS CANCER INSTITUTE p 154
4100 John R St 48201
Tel (800) 527-6266 *SIC* 8733 8093

BARDEN COMPANIES INC p 155
400 Renaissance Ctr # 2400 48243
Tel (313) 496-2900 *SIC* 7371 7372

BLUE CROSS AND BLUE SHIELD OF MICHIGAN p 191
600 E Lafayette Blvd 48226
Tel (313) 225-9000 *SIC* 6321 6324

BOARD OF EDUCATION OF CITY OF DETROIT p 195
3011 W Grand Blvd Fl 6 48202
Tel (313) 873-7860 *SIC* 8211

BRIDGEWATER INTERIORS LLC p 212
4617 W Fort St 48209
Tel (313) 842-3300 *SIC* 5013 2531

CARAMAGNO FOODS CO p 252
14255 Dequindre St 48212
Tel (313) 869-8200 *SIC* 5141 5142

CARELINK NETWORK INC p 255
1333 Brewery Park Blvd 48207
Tel (313) 656-0000 *SIC* 8099

CITY OF DETROIT p 314
2 Woodward Ave Rm 1126 48226
Tel (313) 224-3400 *SIC* 9111

COMPUWARE CORP p 353
1 Campus Martius Fl 4 48226
Tel (313) 227-7300 *SIC* 7372 7371

COMPUWARE HOLDINGS LLC p 353
1 Campus Martius 48226
Tel (313) 227-7300 *SIC* 7371

COUNTY OF WAYNE p 382
500 Griswold St Fl 31 48226
Tel (313) 224-5952 *SIC* 9111

CRAIN COMMUNICATIONS INC p 388
1155 Gratiot Ave 48207
Tel (313) 446-6000 *SIC* 2721 2711

CW PROFESSIONAL SERVICES LLC p 404
150 W Jefferson Ave # 1200 48226
Tel (313) 416-1011 *SIC* 8748

DETROIT CITY SCHOOL DISTRICT p 433
3011 W Grand Blvd Fl 14 48202
Tel (313) 873-7553 *SIC* 8211

DETROIT DIESEL CORP p 433
13400 W Outer Dr 48239
Tel (313) 592-5000 *SIC* 3519 3714 7538

DETROIT DIESEL REMANUFACTURING CORP p 433
13400 W Outer Dr 48239
Tel (313) 592-5000 *SIC* 3519

DETROIT ENTERTAINMENT LLC p 433
2901 Grand River Ave 48201
Tel (313) 237-7711 *SIC* 7999

■ DETROIT NEWSPAPER PARTNERSHIP LP p 433
160 W Fort St 48226
Tel (313) 222-2300 *SIC* 2711

DEVON INDUSTRIAL GROUP p 434
535 Griswold St Ste 2050 48226
Tel (313) 965-3455 *SIC* 1541

DIVERSIFIED CHEMICAL TECHNOLOGIES INC p 444
15477 Woodrow Wilson St 48238
Tel (313) 867-5444
SIC 2891 2992 2899 2842 2841

■ DTE ELECTRIC CO p 458
1 Energy Plz 48226
Tel (313) 235-4000 *SIC* 4911

▲ DTE ENERGY CO p 458
1 Energy Plz 48226
Tel (313) 235-4000 *SIC* 4911 4923 1311

■ DTE GAS CO p 458
1 Energy Plz Rm 1600 48226
Tel (313) 235-4000 *SIC* 4924 4922

DYKEMA GOSSETT PLLC p 464
400 Renaissance Ctr 48243
Tel (313) 568-6800 *SIC* 8111 8742

■ FAYGO BEVERAGES INC p 532
3579 Gratiot Ave 48207
Tel (313) 925-1600 *SIC* 2086

FERROUS PROCESSING AND TRADING CO p 538
3400 E Lafayette St 48207
Tel (313) 582-2910 *SIC* 5093

FUTURENET GROUP INC p 586
12801 Auburn St 48223
Tel (313) 544-7117 *SIC* 1542 8748

■ GENERAL MOTORS CHINA INC p 601
300 Renaissance Ctr L1 48243
Tel (313) 556-5000 *SIC* 3714

▲ GENERAL MOTORS CO p 601
300 Renaissance Ctr L1 48243
Tel (313) 556-5000 *SIC* 3711 3714

■ GENERAL MOTORS HOLDINGS LLC p 601
300 Renaissance Ctr L1 48243
Tel (313) 556-5000 *SIC* 3711 3714

■ GENERAL MOTORS LLC p 601
300 Renaissance Ctr L1 48243
Tel (313) 556-5000 *SIC* 3711 3714

■ GM COMPONENTS HOLDINGS LLC p 618
300 Renaissance Ctr 48243
Tel (313) 556-5000 *SIC* 3711 3714

GRACE SINAI HOSPITAL p 628
6701 W Outer Dr 48235
Tel (313) 966-3333 *SIC* 8062

GREEKTOWN CASINO LLC p 636
555 E Lafayette Blvd 48226
Tel (313) 223-2999 *SIC* 5812 7011

GREEKTOWN SUPERHOLDINGS INC p 636
555 E Lafayette Blvd 48226
Tel (313) 223-2999 *SIC* 6719

HEALTH ALLIANCE PLAN OF MICHIGAN p 674
2850 W Grand Blvd 48202
Tel (313) 872-8100 *SIC* 6324 8011 8099

HENRY FORD HEALTH SYSTEM p 684
1 Ford Pl 48202
Tel (313) 916-2600 *SIC* 8062

HENRY FORD HEALTH SYSTEM p 684
1 Ford Pl 5f 48202
Tel (313) 876-1031 *SIC* 8699

HONIGMAN MILLER SCHWARTZ AND COHN LLP p 705
660 Woodward Ave Ste 2290 48226
Tel (313) 465-7000 *SIC* 8111

HUTZEL HOSPITAL p 722
3980 John R St 48201
Tel (313) 745-7555 *SIC* 8062

IDEAL CONTRACTING LLC p 729
2525 Clark St 48209
Tel (313) 843-8000
SIC 1542 1742 1771 1791

ILITCH HOLDINGS INC p 732
2211 Woodward Ave 48201
Tel (313) 983-6000 *SIC* 7941 7922 5812

INTEGRATED MANUFACTURING & ASSEMBLY LLC p 749
6501 E Nevada St 48234
Tel (734) 530-5600 *SIC* 2531

INTERNATIONAL UNION UNITED AUTOMOBILE AEROSPACE AND AGRICULTURAL IMPLEMENT WORKERS OF AM p 757
8000 E Jefferson Ave 48214
Tel (313) 926-5000 *SIC* 8631

JOHN E GREEN CO p 788
220 Victor St 48203
Tel (313) 868-2400 *SIC* 1711

LAGRASSO BROS INC p 838
5001 Bellevue St 48211
Tel (313) 579-1455 *SIC* 5148

LITTLE CAESAR ENTERPRISES INC p 870
2211 Woodward Ave 48201
Tel (313) 983-6000
SIC 5812 6794 5141 5046 8741

LUTHERAN SOCIAL SERVICES OF MICHIGAN p 886
8131 E Jefferson Ave 48214
Tel (313) 823-7700 *SIC* 8051 8322

MARTIN AND SNYDER PRODUCT SALES CO p 912
8880 Hubbell St 48228
Tel (313) 272-4900 *SIC* 5194 5145

■ **MGM GRAND DETROIT LLC** p 958
1777 3rd St 48226
Tel (313) 465-1777 SIC 7011 5812 7991

■ **MICHCON PIPELINE CO** p 960
500 Griswold St Fl 16th 48226
Tel (313) 256-5505 SIC 4922

■ **MICHIGAN BELL TELEPHONE CO** p 960
444 Michigan Ave 48226
Tel (313) 223-9900 SIC 4813 8721

MICHIGAN CONFERENCE OF TEAMSTERS WELFARE FUND p 960
2700 Trumbull St 48216
Tel (313) 964-2400 SIC 6371

MIDWEST STEEL INC p 968
2525 E Grand Blvd 48211
Tel (313) 873-2220 SIC 3441 1791

MILLER CANFIELD PADDOCK AND STONE PLC p 970
150 W Jefferson Ave # 2500 48226
Tel (313) 963-6420 SIC 8111

MOTOR CITY ELECTRIC CO p 992
9440 Grinnell St 48213
Tel (313) 567-5300 SIC 1731

MSX INTERNATIONAL INC p 997
500 Woodward Ave Ste 2150 48226
Tel (248) 829-6300
SIC 8748 7363 8742 8711

■ **NORTRU LLC** p 1061
515 Lycaste St 48214
Tel (313) 824-5840 SIC 4953 5169

OLYMPIA ENTERTAINMENT INC p 1083
2211 Woodward Ave 48201
Tel (313) 471-3200 SIC 7832

■ **OLYMPIC STEEL LAFAYETTE INC** p 1083
3600 Military St 48210
Tel (313) 894-4552 SIC 5051

PENSKE TRANSPORTATION HOLDINGS CORP p 1131
13400 W Outer Dr 48239
Tel (313) 592-7311 SIC 6799

PRESSURE VESSEL SERVICE INC p 1173
10900 Harper Ave 48213
Tel (313) 921-1200
SIC 5169 2819 2899 4953 3535

PVS CHEMICAL SOLUTIONS INC p 1193
10900 Harper Ave 48213
Tel (313) 921-1200 SIC 5169

PVS-NOLWOOD CHEMICALS INC p 1193
10900 Harper Ave 48213
Tel (313) 921-1200 SIC 5169

QUICKEN LOANS INC p 1199
1050 Woodward Ave 48226
Tel (734) 805-5000 SIC 6162

RIGGIO DISTRIBUTION CO p 1234
7939 Lafayette Blvd 48209
Tel (313) 841-7911 SIC 5148

ROCKBRIDGE GROWTH EQUITY LLC p 1243
1078 Woodward Ave 48226
Tel (313) 373-7000 SIC 6282

ROMAN CATHOLIC ARCHDIOCESE OF DETROIT p 1248
12 State St 48226
Tel (313) 237-5800 SIC 8661

SACHSE CONSTRUCTION AND DEVELOPMENT CO LLC p 1264
1528 Woodward Ave Ste 600 48226
Tel (313) 481-8200 SIC 1542 1522

SHERWOOD FOOD DISTRIBUTORS LLC p 1316
12499 Evergreen Ave 48228
Tel (313) 659-7300
SIC 5147 5144 5146 5142 5143

SMITHGROUP COMPANIES INC p 1334
500 Griswold St Fl 1700 48226
Tel (313) 442-8351 SIC 8712 8711

SOAVE ENTERPRISES LLC p 1336
3400 E Lafayette St 48207
Tel (313) 567-7000 SIC 6719

STRATEGIC STAFFING SOLUTIONS LC p 1392
645 Griswold St Ste 2900 48226
Tel (888) 738-3261 SIC 8742

SUBURBAN MOBILITY AUTHORITY FOR REGIONAL TRANSPORATION p 1396
535 Griswold St Ste 600 48226
Tel (313) 223-2100 SIC 4111

TITLE SOURCE INC p 1456
662 Woodward Ave 48226
Tel (888) 848-5355 SIC 6541

TOTAL HEALTH CARE INC p 1463
3011 W Grand Blvd # 1600 48202
Tel (313) 871-2000 SIC 8011

TPG HOLDINGS LLC p 1467
719 Griswold St Ste 2100 48226
Tel (313) 496-3500 SIC 7349

UAW PUBLIC RELATIONS p 1498
8000 E Jefferson Ave 48214
Tel (313) 926-5291 SIC 8743

UNIVERSITY OF DETROIT MERCY p 1521
4001 W Mcnichols Rd 48221
Tel (313) 993-6000 SIC 8221

URBAN SCIENCE APPLICATIONS INC p 1530
400 Renaissance Ctr # 2900 48243
Tel (313) 259-9900 SIC 8742

■ **VHS CHILDRENS HOSPITAL OF MICHIGAN INC** p 1553
3901 Beaubien St 48201
Tel (313) 745-5437 SIC 8069

■ **VHS DETROIT RECEIVING HOSPITAL INC** p 1553
4201 Saint Antoine St 48201
Tel (313) 745-3000 SIC 8093 8069 8062

■ **VHS HARPER-HUTZEL HOSPITAL INC** p 1554
3980 John R St 48201
Tel (313) 745-8040 SIC 8062

■ **VHS OF MICHIGAN INC** p 1554
3990 John R St 48201
Tel (313) 745-1250 SIC 8062

■ **VHS SINAI-GRACE HOSPITAL INC** p 1554
6071 W Outer Dr 48235
Tel (313) 966-3300 SIC 8062

VISION INFORMATION TECHNOLOGIES INC p 1561
3031 W Grand Blvd Ste 600 48202
Tel (313) 664-5650 SIC 7363 7379

VISIONIT SUPPLIES AND SERVICES INC p 1561
3031 W Grand Blvd Ste 600 48202
Tel (313) 664-5650 SIC 3577 3955 5734

WALBRIDGE ALDINGER LLC p 1572
777 Woodward Ave Ste 300 48226
Tel (313) 963-8000 SIC 1541 1542 8741

WALBRIDGE GROUP INC p 1572
777 Woodward Ave Ste 300 48226
Tel (313) 963-8000 SIC 1542

WALBRIDGE INDUSTRIAL PROCESS LLC p 1572
777 Woodward Ave Ste 300 48226
Tel (313) 963-8000 SIC 1796

WALBRIDGE INTERNATIONAL LLC p 1572
777 Woodward Ave Fl 3 48226
Tel (313) 963-8000 SIC 8741

WAYNE COUNTY AIRPORT AUTHORITY p 1584
1 Detroit Metro Airport 48242
Tel (734) 247-7364 SIC 4581

WAYNE STATE UNIVERSITY p 1584
656 W Kirby 4200 Faculty 48202
Tel (313) 577-2230 SIC 8221

WOLVERINE PACKING CO p 1621
2535 Rivard St 48207
Tel (313) 259-7500 SIC 5147 2011 5142

YOUNG MENS CHRISTIAN ASSOCIATION OF METROPOLITAN DETROIT p 1638
1401 Broadway St Ste A 48226
Tel (313) 267-5300 SIC 7999 8641

DEXTER, MI

PALADIN BRANDS GROUP INC p 1108
2800 Zeeb Rd 48130
Tel (319) 378-3696 SIC 3531

SWEEPSTER ATTACHMENTS LLC p 1411
2800 Zeeb Rd 48130
Tel (734) 996-9116 SIC 3589 3991

DIMONDALE, MI

MICHIGAN DEPARTMENT OF STATE POLICE p 961
7150 Harris Dr 48821
Tel (517) 241-1075 SIC 9221

DUNDEE, MI

AGGREGATE INDUSTRIES p 34
6211 N Ann Arbor Rd 48131
Tel (734) 529-5876
SIC 3273 2951 1442 1411 1771 5211

HOLCIM (US) INC p 700
6211 N Ann Arbor Rd 48131
Tel (734) 529-4278 SIC 3241 3272

EAST JORDAN, MI

EJ AMERICAS LLC p 482
301 Spring St 49727
Tel (231) 536-2261 SIC 6719 3321

EJ GROUP INC p 482
301 Spring St 49727
Tel (231) 536-2261 SIC 3321

EJ USA INC p 482
301 Spring St 49727
Tel (800) 874-4100 SIC 3321

EAST LANSING, MI

MICHIGAN EDUCATION SPECIAL SERVICES ASSOCIATION p 961
1475 Kendale Blvd 48823
Tel (517) 332-2581 SIC 6411 6321

MICHIGAN STATE UNIVERSITY p 961
426 Auditorium Rd Rm 301 48824
Tel (517) 355-5029 SIC 8221

MICHIGAN STATE UNIVERSITY FEDERAL CREDIT UNION p 961
3777 West Rd 48823
Tel (517) 333-2424 SIC 6061

EAST TAWAS, MI

PLASTIC TRIM INTERNATIONAL INC p 1155
935 Aulerich Rd 48730
Tel (248) 259-7468 SIC 3465

EASTPOINTE, MI

EAST DETROIT PUBLIC SCHOOLS p 470
24685 Kelly Rd 48021
Tel (586) 445-4400 SIC 8211

EDWARDSBURG, MI

■ **NORTH AMERICAN FOREST PRODUCTS LIQUIDATION INC** p 1050
27263 May St 49112
Tel (269) 663-8500 SIC 2421 5031

ELK RAPIDS, MI

BURNETTE FOODS INC p 228
701 S Us Highway 31 49629
Tel (231) 264-8116 SIC 2033

ERIE, MI

BENORE LOGISTIC SYSTEMS INC p 173
2500 E Erie Rd 48133
Tel (734) 848-2046 SIC 4225

ESCANABA, MI

ENGINEERED MACHINED PRODUCTS INC p 499
3111 N 28th St 49829
Tel (906) 786-8404
SIC 3519 3714 3568 3599 3561

ESCANABA PAPER CO p 509
7100 County Rd 426 49829
Tel (906) 786-1660 SIC 2611 2621 2672

FARMINGTON HILLS, MI

ACCESSPOINT LLC p 15
28800 Orchard Lake Rd # 200 48334
Tel (248) 504-6539 SIC 8742

ACO INC p 18
27555 Farmington Rd # 100 48334
Tel (248) 471-0100 SIC 5251

AEES INC p 29
36555 Corp Dr Ste 300 48331
Tel (248) 489-4700 SIC 3679

AJK ENTERPRISES INC p 41
30833 Northwestern Hwy 48334
Tel (248) 932-9000 SIC 6411

AKEBONO BRAKE CORP p 42
34385 W 12 Mile Rd 48331
Tel (248) 489-7400 SIC 3714

AMERISURE INC p 84
26777 Halsted Rd Lbby 48331
Tel (248) 615-9000 SIC 6411

AMERISURE INSURANCE CO p 84
26777 Halsted Rd Lbby 48331
Tel (248) 615-9000 SIC 6331

AMERISURE MUTUAL INSURANCE CO p 84
26777 Halsted Rd Lbby 48331
Tel (248) 615-9000 SIC 6331

ANSARA RESTAURANT GROUP INC p 93
23925 Industrial Park Dr 48335
Tel (248) 848-9099 SIC 5812 5813

AUTONEUM NORTH AMERICA INC p 135
38555 Hills Tech Dr 48331
Tel (570) 784-4100 SIC 3714

BEZTAK CO (INC) p 179
31731 Northwstrn Hwy 25 Ste 250 W 48334
Tel (248) 855-5400 SIC 6552

BOSCH AUTOMOTIVE MOTOR SYSTEMS CORP p 202
38000 Hills Tech Dr 48331
Tel (248) 553-9000 SIC 3714

BOTSFORD GENERAL HOSPITAL p 203
28050 Grand River Ave 48336
Tel (248) 471-8000 SIC 8062

BURNS & WILCOX LTD p 228
120 Kaufm Finan Cente 30 48334
Tel (248) 932-9000 SIC 6331 6411

CAMACO LLC p 243
37000 W 12 Mile Rd 48331
Tel (248) 442-6800 SIC 3565 3499

DAIFUKU WEBB HOLDING CO p 408
34375 W 12 Mile Rd 48331
Tel (248) 553-1000 SIC 3695

DAIMLER PURCHASING COORDINATION CORP p 408
36455 Corporate Dr 48331
Tel (248) 991-6700 SIC 5012 5013

DOMESTIC LINEN SUPPLY AND LAUNDRY CO p 448
30555 Northwestern Hwy 48334
Tel (248) 737-2000 SIC 7213

ELECTRO-MATIC VENTURES INC p 485
23409 Industrial Park Ct 48335
Tel (248) 478-1182 SIC 5063 3674

ENCORE REHABILITATION SERVICES LLC p 496
33533 W 12 Mile Rd # 290 48331
Tel (248) 865-1177 SIC 8093 8049

EXHIBIT WORKS INC p 519
27777 Inkster Rd Ste 200 48334
Tel (734) 525-9010 SIC 7389

FIVES INC p 553
23400 Halsted Rd 48335
Tel (248) 477-0800 SIC 3549

GALE GROUP INC p 589
27500 Drake Rd 48331
Tel (248) 699-4253 SIC 7375

H W KAUFMAN FINANCIAL GROUP INC p 651
30833 Northwestern Hwy 48334
Tel (248) 932-9000 SIC 6141 6719

HAPPYS PIZZA CO p 659
30201 Orchrd Lke Rd 200 48334
Tel (248) 358-8888 SIC 5812

HCL GLOBAL SYSTEMS INC p 672
24543 Indoplex Cir # 220 48335
Tel (248) 473-0720 SIC 7379 7371

HINO MOTORS MANUFACTURING USA INC p 695
37777 Interchange Dr 48335
Tel (248) 442-9077 SIC 5013

HIRAIN TECHNOLOGIES USA INC p 695
37632 Hills Tech Dr 48331
Tel (248) 839-1309 SIC 5013 8711

INNOVATION VENTURES LLC p 744
38955 Hills Tech Dr Ste 1 48331
Tel (248) 960-1700 SIC 5149

JERVIS B WEBB CO p 783
34375 W 12 Mile Rd 48331
Tel (248) 553-1000
SIC 3535 3536 3462 3537 3613

KURABE AMERICA CORP p 832
37735 Interchange Dr 48335
Tel (248) 939-5803 SIC 7699 7549

MAHLE INDUSTRIES INC p 897
23030 Mahle Dr 48335
Tel (248) 305-8200 SIC 3714

MELODY FOODS INC p 941
30777 Northwestern Hwy # 300 48334
Tel (248) 851-6990
SIC 5143 2026 5149 5145

MERCEDES-BENZ FINANCIAL SERVICES USA LLC p 944
36455 Corporate Dr 48331
Tel (248) 991-6700 SIC 6159

MINACS GROUP USA INC p 972
34115 W 12 Mile Rd 48331
Tel (248) 553-8355 SIC 7389 8742

NK STEEL LLC p 1045
31731 Northwstrn Hwy 15 Ste 157 W 48334
Tel (248) 865-9000 SIC 5051

ORLEANS INTERNATIONAL INC p 1095
30600 Northwestern Hwy # 300 48334
Tel (248) 855-5556 SIC 5142

P & C GROUP I INC p 1102
37000 W 12 Mile Rd 48331
Tel (248) 442-6800 SIC 3499 3465

▲ **RAMCO-GERSHENSON PROPERTIES TRUST** p 1207
31500 Northwestern Hwy 48334
Tel (248) 350-9900 SIC 6798 6519

RIDE CONTROL LLC p 1234
39300 Country Club Dr 48331
Tel (248) 247-7600 SIC 3714

ROGER ZATKOFF CO p 1246
23230 Industrial Park Dr 48335
Tel (248) 478-2400 SIC 5085 5072 3053

ROUTEONE LLC p 1253
31500 Nrthwstrn Hwy 200 48334
Tel (866) 768-8301 SIC 6141 7379

STAR CUTTER CO p 1378
23461 Industrial Park Dr 48335
Tel (248) 474-8200
SIC 3545 3479 3546 3541

TACHI-S ENGINEERING USA INC p 1421
23227 Commerce Dr 48335
Tel (248) 478-5050 SIC 2531 8711

TD AUTO FINANCE LLC p 1428
27777 Inkster Rd 48334
Tel (248) 427-6800 SIC 6153 5511

VILLAGE GREEN HOLDING LLC p 1557
30833 Northwestern Hwy # 300 48334
Tel (248) 851-9600 SIC 6719

VILLAGE GREEN MANAGEMENT CLEARING CO p 1557
30833 Northwestern Hwy 48334
Tel (248) 851-9600 SIC 6531

WW GROUP INC p 1629
28555 Orchard Lake Rd # 100 48334
Tel (248) 553-8555 SIC 7299

ZIEGER HEALTH CARE CORP p 1643
28050 Grand River Ave 48336
Tel (248) 471-8000 SIC 8062

FARMINGTON, MI

FARMINGTON PUBLIC SCHOOL DISTRICT p 530
32500 Shiawassee Rd 48336
Tel (248) 489-3300 SIC 8211

MAHLE AFTERMARKET INC p 897
23030 Mahle Dr 48335
Tel (248) 347-9700 SIC 5013

FENTON, MI

CREATIVE FOAM CORP p 390
300 N Alloy Dr 48430
Tel (574) 546-4238
SIC 3061 3089 3053 3086 3069

FLAT ROCK, MI

AUTOALLIANCE MANAGEMENT CO p 133
1 International Dr 48134
Tel (734) 782-7800 SIC 3711

■ **FORD FLAT ROCK ASSEMBLY PLANT** p 565
1 International Dr 48134
Tel (734) 782-7800 SIC 5013 3711

FLINT, MI

A I FLINT LLC p 5
4444 W Maple Ave 48507
Tel (810) 732-8760 SIC 3714

BAKER COLLEGE p 145
1050 W Bristol Rd 48507
Tel (810) 767-7600 SIC 8222 8221

CITIZENS BANK p 310
328 S Saginaw St Lbby 48502
Tel (810) 766-7500 SIC 6022 6159 6162

COUNTY OF GENESEE p 378
1101 Beach St Fl 3 48502
Tel (810) 257-3040 SIC 9111

▲ **DIPLOMAT PHARMACY INC** p 441
4100 S Saginaw St Ste A 48507
Tel (888) 720-4450 SIC 5912

E L HOLLINGSWORTH & CO p 466
3039 Airpark Dr N 48507
Tel (810) 233-7331 SIC 4212 4213

GENESEE INTERMEDIATE SCHOOL DISTRICT p 602
2413 W Maple Ave 48507
Tel (810) 591-4400 SIC 8211

HEALTHPLUS INSURANCE CO p 677
2050 S Linden Rd 48532
Tel (810) 230-2000 SIC 6321

HEALTHPLUS OF MICHIGAN INC p 677
2050 S Linden Rd 48532
Tel (810) 230-2000 SIC 6324

HEALTHPLUS PARTNERS INC p 677
2050 S Linden Rd 48532
Tel (810) 230-2192 SIC 8748

HURLEY MEDICAL CENTER p 721
1 Hurley Plz 48503
Tel (810) 257-9000 SIC 8062

MCLAREN HEALTH CARE CORP p 931
G3235 Beecher Rd Ste B 48532
Tel (810) 342-1100 SIC 8062

MCLAREN REGIONAL MEDICAL CENTER p 931
401 S Ballenger Hwy 48532
Tel (810) 342-2000 SIC 8062

MOTT CHARLES STEWART FOUNDATION INC p 993
503 S Saginaw St Ste 1200 48502
Tel (810) 238-5651 SIC 6732

OAKLEY INDUSTRIES SUB ASSEMBLY DIVISION INC p 1071
4333 Matthew 48507
Tel (810) 720-4444 SIC 3714

PIONEER STATE MUTUAL INSURANCE CO p 1151
1510 N Elms Rd 48532
Tel (810) 733-2300 SIC 6411

REPUBLIC BANK p 1225
328 S Saginaw St Lbby 48502
Tel (810) 257-2506 SIC 6022 6163 6029

SCHOOL DISTRICT OF CITY OF FLINT p 1289
923 E Kearsley St 48503
Tel (810) 760-1000 SIC 8211

SHIVELY BROTHERS INC p 1317
2919 S Grand Traverse St 48507
Tel (810) 232-7401 SIC 5084 5085

US FENCE INC p 1531
3200 Rbert T Longway Blvd 48506
Tel (810) 235-0400 SIC 2499

WGS GLOBAL SERVICES LC p 1604
6350 Taylor Dr 48507
Tel (810) 239-4947 SIC 3711

FOWLERVILLE, MI

ASAHI KASEI PLASTICS (AMERICA) INC p 115
1 Thermofil Way 48836
Tel (517) 223-2000 SIC 2821

ASAHI KASEI PLASTICS NORTH AMERICA INC p 115
1 Thermofil Way 48836
Tel (517) 223-2000 SIC 2821

VENTRA FOWLERVILLE LLC p 1548
8887 W Grand River Rd 48836
Tel (517) 223-5900 SIC 5013

FRANKENMUTH, MI

FRANKENMUTH MUTUAL INSURANCE CO INC p 574
1 Mutual Ave 48787
Tel (989) 652-6121 SIC 6331

STAR OF WEST MILLING CO p 1378
121 E Tuscola St 48734
Tel (330) 673-2941 SIC 2041 5153 5191

FREMONT, MI

GERBER LIFE INSURANCE CO p 608
1311 Mmroneck Ave Ste 350 49412
Tel (800) 704-2180 SIC 6311 6321

GARDEN CITY, MI

GARDEN CITY HOSPITAL p 591
6245 Inkster Rd 48135
Tel (734) 458-3300 SIC 8062

GARDEN CITY HOSPITAL FOUNDATION p 591
6245 Inkster Rd Ste 210 48135
Tel (734) 458-4421 SIC 8741 7389

GAYLORD, MI

JOHNSON OIL CO OF GAYLORD p 791
507 S Otsego Ave 49735
Tel (989) 732-6014 SIC 5171 5541 5983

OTSEGO MEMORIAL HOSPITAL ASSOCIATION p 1097
825 N Center Ave 49735
Tel (989) 731-2100 SIC 8062

GLADSTONE, MI

FOREST BESSE PRODUCTS INC p 566
933 N 8th St 49837
Tel (906) 428-3113 SIC 5031 5099

GRAND BLANC, MI

DORTCH ENTERPRISES LLC p 451
8487 Retreat Dr 48439
Tel (810) 771-4500 SIC 5812

GENESYS HEALTH SYSTEM p 603
1 Genesys Pkwy 48439
Tel (810) 606-5710 SIC 8062

GENESYS REGIONAL MEDICAL CENTER p 603
1 Genesys Pkwy 48439
Tel (810) 606-5000 SIC 8062

GRAND BLANC COMMUNITY SCHOOLS p 629
11920 S Saginaw St 48439
Tel (810) 591-6000 SIC 8211

IRB MEDICAL EQUIPMENT LLC p 764
1000 Health Park Blvd B 48439
Tel (810) 953-0760 SIC 5047 7389

SERRA AUTOMOTIVE INC p 1306
3118 E Hill Rd 48439
Tel (810) 695-1451 SIC 5511 8742

GRAND HAVEN, MI

GHSP INC p 610
1250 S Beechtree St 49417
Tel (248) 588-5095 SIC 3714

HARBOR INDUSTRIES INC p 659
14130 172nd Ave 49417
Tel (616) 842-5330 SIC 2541 3993

JOST INTERNATIONAL CORP p 794
1770 Hayes St 49417
Tel (616) 846-7700 SIC 3715

JSJ CORP p 796
700 Robbins Rd 49417
Tel (616) 842-6350
SIC 3465 3469 3366 3089 3086 2522

SHAPE CORP p 1311
1900 Hayes St 49417
Tel (616) 846-8700 SIC 3449 3089

GRAND RAPIDS, MI

ADAC PLASTICS INC p 21
5920 Tahoe Dr Se 49546
Tel (616) 957-0311 SIC 3089

ADVANCE PACKAGING CORP p 24
4459 40th St Se 49512
Tel (616) 949-6610 SIC 2653 3412

AGILITY HEALTH LLC p 35
607 Dewey Ave Nw Ste 300 49504
Tel (616) 356-5000 SIC 8049

AIS CONSTRUCTION EQUIPMENT SERVICE CORP p 41
600 44th St Sw 49548
Tel (616) 538-2400 SIC 5082

ALLIANCE BEVERAGE DISTRIBUTING LLC p 54
4490 60th St Se 49512
Tel (616) 241-5022 SIC 5181

AMERICAN SEATING CO p 79
401 Amrcan Seating Ctr Nw 49504
Tel (616) 732-6600 SIC 2522 2531

■ **AMPHENOL BORISCH TECHNOLOGIES INC** p 86
4511 East Paris Ave Se 49512
Tel (616) 554-9820 SIC 3679 3599

AUTO-WARES GROUP INC p 133
440 Kirtland St Sw 49507
Tel (616) 243-2125 SIC 3559

AWI HOLDINGS INC p 139
440 Kirtland St Sw 49507
Tel (616) 243-2125 SIC 5013 5531

BARFLY VENTURES LLC p 155
35 Oakes St Sw Ste 400 49503
Tel (616) 965-9780 SIC 5812

BETHANY CHRISTIAN SERVICES p 178
901 Eastern Ave Ne 49503
Tel (616) 224-7550 SIC 8322

BETHANY CHRISTIAN SERVICES USA LLC p 178
901 Eastern Ave Ne 49503
Tel (616) 224-7610 SIC 8322

BISSELL HOMECARE INC p 185
2345 Walker Ave Nw 49544
Tel (616) 453-4451 SIC 3635

BISSELL INC p 185
2345 Walker Ave Nw 49544
Tel (616) 453-4451 SIC 3589 2842 3635

BLACKFORD CAPITAL LLC p 187
190 Monroe Ave Nw Ste 6 49503
Tel (616) 233-3101 SIC 6726

BOUMA CORP p 204
4101 Roger B Chaffee Mem 49548
Tel (616) 538-3600 SIC 1542 1752 1742

BOUMA GROUP INC p 204
4101 Roger B Chaffee Mem 49548
Tel (616) 538-3600 SIC 1542 1752 1742

CALVIN COLLEGE p 243
3201 Burton St Se 49546
Tel (616) 526-6000 SIC 8661

CASCADE ENGINEERING INC p 262
3400 Innovation Ct Se 49512
Tel (616) 975-4800 SIC 3089

CHALLENGE MFG CO p 287
3200 Fruit Ridge Ave Nw 49544
Tel (616) 735-6500 SIC 3465

CITY OF GRAND RAPIDS p 315
300 Monroe Ave Nw Unit 1 49503
Tel (616) 456-3000 SIC 9111

■ **COUNTRY FRESH LLC** p 375
2555 Buchanan Ave Sw 49548
Tel (616) 243-0173 SIC 2026 2024 2097

CRYSTAL FLASH LIMITED PARTNERSHIP OF MICHIGAN p 396
1754 Alpine Ave Nw 49504
Tel (616) 363-4851 SIC 5172 5984

DATA STRATEGY LLC p 413
4020 E Beltline Ave Ne # 201 49525
Tel (616) 281-5566 SIC 5045

DAVENPORT EDUCATIONAL SYSTEMS INC p 415
6191 Kraft Ave Se 49512
Tel (616) 698-7111 SIC 8221

DAVENPORT UNIVERSITY p 415
6191 Kraft Ave Se 49512
Tel (616) 698-7111 SIC 8221

DEMATIC CORP p 428
507 Plymouth Ave Ne 49505
Tel (678) 695-4500 SIC 3535 1796 8711

DISPLAY PACK INC p 443
1340 Monroe Ave Nw Ste 1 49505
Tel (616) 451-3061 SIC 3089 2759 7389

ETNA DISTRIBUTORS LLC p 511
529 32nd St Se 49548
Tel (616) 245-4373 SIC 5074

EXIT 76 CORP p 519
2696 Chicago Dr Sw 49519
Tel (616) 534-2181 SIC 5812

FAMILY CHRISTIAN STORES LLC p 526
5300 Patterson Ave Se 49530
Tel (616) 554-8700
SIC 5942 5735 5947 5699 8741

FASTENERS INC p 531
640 44th St Sw Ste 1 49548
Tel (616) 241-3448 SIC 5072

■ **FIFTH THIRD BANK** p 541
1 Vandenberg Ctr Nw 49503
Tel (616) 653-5900 SIC 6022

FIRSTRONIC LLC p 551
1655 Michigan St Ne 49503
Tel (616) 456-9220 SIC 3559

FOREST HILLS PUBLIC SCHOOLS p 566
6590 Cascade Rd Se 49546
Tel (616) 493-8800 SIC 8211

GILL CORP p 612
706 Bond Ave Nw 49503
Tel (859) 625-5284
SIC 3469 3312 3495 3493 3496 3465

GILL HOLDING CO INC p 612
5271 Plainfield Ave Ne 49525
Tel (616) 559-2700 SIC 3465 3544

GILL INDUSTRIES INC p 612
5271 Plainfield Ave Ne 49525
Tel (616) 559-2700 SIC 3465 3544

GRAD INC p 628
4001 3 Mile Rd Nw 49534
Tel (616) 676-5969
SIC 5141 5194 5145 5122 5113 5411

GRAND RAPIDS PUBLIC SCHOOLS p 630
1331 Franklin St Se 49506
Tel (616) 819-2000 SIC 8211

GRANITE HOLDINGS INC p 631
2580 28th St Sw 49519
Tel (616) 532-2375 SIC 5169

HART & COOLEY INC p 664
5030 Corp Exch Blvd Se 49512
Tel (616) 656-8200 SIC 3446 3822

HAVILAND ENTERPRISES INC p 668
421 Ann St Nw 49504
Tel (616) 361-6691 SIC 5169

HAVILAND PRODUCTS CO p 668
421 Ann St Nw 49504
Tel (616) 361-6691 SIC 5169 2819

HOLLAND HOME p 700
2100 Raybrook St Se # 300 49546
Tel (616) 235-5000 SIC 8361 8051

HOPE NETWORK p 706
3075 Orchard Vista Dr Se # 100 49546
Tel (616) 301-8000 SIC 8331

■ **HUTCHINSON ANTIVIBRATION SYSTEMS INC** p 722
460 Fuller Ave Ne 49503
Tel (616) 459-4541 SIC 3069 3061

■ **HUTCHINSON CORP** p 722
460 Fuller Ave Ne 49503
Tel (616) 459-4541 SIC 3069 3011

▲ **INDEPENDENT BANK CORP** p 736
4200 E Beltline Ave Ne 49525
Tel (616) 527-5820 SIC 6022

INTEGRITY BUSINESS SOLUTIONS LLC p 750
4740 Talon Ct Se Ste 8 49512
Tel (616) 656-6010 SIC 5112

IRWIN SEATING CO p 766
3251 Fruit Ridge Ave Nw 49544
Tel (616) 784-2621 SIC 2531

IRWIN SEATING HOLDING CO p 766
3251 Fruit Ridge Ave Nw 49544
Tel (616) 574-7400 SIC 2531 7641

J & H OIL CO p 769
2696 Chicago Dr Sw 49519
Tel (616) 534-2181 SIC 5172 5013

JASPER WELLER LLC p 778
1500 Gezon Pkwy Sw 49509
Tel (616) 724-2000 SIC 7538 5013

KAMPS INC p 802
2900 Peach Ridge Ave Nw 49534
Tel (616) 453-9676 SIC 2448 2499

KENT COUNTY CMH AUTHORITY p 812
790 Fuller Ave Ne 49503
Tel (616) 336-3765 SIC 8069

KENT COUNTY OF (INC) p 812
300 Monroe Ave Nw Unit 1 49503
Tel (616) 632-7580 SIC 9111

KENT INTERMEDIATE SCHOOL DISTRICT p 812
2930 Knapp St Ne 49525
Tel (616) 364-1333 SIC 8211

KENTWOOD PUBLIC SCHOOLS p 813
5820 Eastern Ave Se 49508
Tel (616) 455-4400 SIC 8211

KNAPE & VOGT MANUFACTURING CO p 824
2700 Oak Industrial Dr Ne 49505
Tel (616) 459-3311 SIC 2542 2541 3429

■ **L-3 COMMUNICATIONS AVIONICS SYSTEMS INC** p 834
5353 52nd St Se 49512
Tel (616) 977-6837 SIC 3812

LACKS ENTERPRISES INC p 837
5460 Cascade Rd Se 49546
Tel (616) 949-6570 SIC 3089

LACKS EXTERIOR SYSTEMS LLC p 837
5460 Cascade Rd Se 49546
Tel (616) 949-6570 SIC 3089

LACKS INDUSTRIES INC p 837
5460 Cascade Rd Se 49546
Tel (616) 949-6570 SIC 3089

LAKE MICHIGAN CREDIT UNION p 839
4027 Lake Dr Se Ste 100 49546
Tel (616) 242-9790 SIC 6062

LIMSON TRADING INC p 866
1300 Gezon Pkwy Sw 49509
Tel (616) 530-3110 SIC 5141

LRR FOOD INC p 882
850 76th St Sw 49518
Tel (810) 629-1383 SIC 5411 5921

LUMBERMENS INC p 885
4433 Stafford Ave Sw 49548
Tel (616) 261-3200 SIC 5033 5031 5198

MAGIC STEEL CORP p 895
4242 Clay Ave Sw Ste 2 49548
Tel (616) 532-4071 SIC 5051

MAGIC STEEL SALES LLC p 895
4242 Clay Ave Sw Ste 2 49548
Tel (616) 532-4071 SIC 5051

MAGNA MIRRORS OF AMERICA INC p 896
5085 Kraft Ave Se 49512
Tel (616) 942-0163 SIC 3231 3647 3827

MARY FREE BED REHABILITATION HOSPITAL p 914
235 Wealthy St Se 49503
Tel (616) 242-0300 SIC 8069 8093

MEIJER COMPANIES LTD p 940
2929 Walker Ave Nw 49544
Tel (616) 453-6711 SIC 5311 5411 5912

MEIJER DISTRIBUTION INC p 940
2929 Walker Ave Nw 49544
Tel (616) 453-6711 SIC 5141

MEIJER INC p 940
2929 Walker Ave Nw 49544
Tel (616) 453-6711 SIC 5411 5311

▲ **MERCANTILE BANK CORP** p 943
310 Leonard St Nw 49504
Tel (616) 406-3000 SIC 6022

■ **MERCANTILE BANK OF MICHIGAN** p 943
310 Leonard St Nw 49504
Tel (616) 406-3000 SIC 6022

▲ **MERITAGE HOSPITALITY GROUP INC** p 949
45 Ottawa Ave Sw Ste 600 49503
Tel (616) 776-2600 SIC 5812 6794

■ **MICHIGAN OFFICE SOLUTIONS INC** p 961
2859 Walkent Dr Nw 49544
Tel (616) 459-1161 SIC 5044 5045 7629

MICHIGAN SPORTING GOODS DISTRIBUTORS INC p 961
3070 Shaffer Ave Se 49512
Tel (616) 942-2600 SIC 5941

MIDWEST CASE MANAGEMENT INC p 967
2905 Lucerne Dr Se # 102 49546
Tel (616) 957-7796 SIC 8331

MORRISON INDUSTRIES INC p 990
1825 Monroe Ave Nw 49505
Tel (616) 447-3838 *SIC* 5084 7699 7359

NATIONAL HERITAGE ACADEMIES INC p 1013
3850 Broadmoor Ave Se # 201 49512
Tel (877) 223-6402 *SIC* 8211 8741

NEAL MAST AND SON INC p 1023
1780 4 Mile Rd Nw 49544
Tel (616) 784-3323 *SIC* 5193

NOTIONS MARKETING CORP p 1062
1500 Buchanan Ave Sw 49507
Tel (616) 243-8424 *SIC* 5131 5199 5092

OLIVER PRODUCTS CO p 1082
445 6th St Nw 49504
Tel (616) 456-7711 *SIC* 5084 5199 3053

OLIVER-TOLAS HEALTHCARE PACKAGING LLC p 1082
445 6th St Nw 49504
Tel (616) 456-7711 *SIC* 2672

OPEN SYSTEMS TECHNOLOGIES DE LLC p 1089
605 Seward Ave Nw Ste 101 49504
Tel (616) 574-3500 *SIC* 7379

PINE REST CHRISTIAN MENTAL HEALTH SERVICES p 1149
300 68th St Se 49548
Tel (616) 455-5000 *SIC* 8063

PRIDGEON & CLAY INC p 1174
50 Cottage Grove St Sw 49507
Tel (616) 241-5675 *SIC* 3714 3465

PRIORITY HEALTH MANAGED BENEFITS INC p 1177
1231 E Beltline Ave Ne 49525
Tel (616) 942-0954 *SIC* 6324

RANIR LLC p 1208
4701 East Paris Ave Se 49512
Tel (616) 698-8880 *SIC* 3843 3991

RIDGEVIEW INDUSTRIES INC p 1234
3093 Northridge Dr Nw 49544
Tel (616) 453-8636 *SIC* 3469 7692

ROCKFORD CONSTRUCTION CO p 1244
601 1st St Nw 49504
Tel (616) 285-6933 *SIC* 1542

ROMAN CATHOLIC DIOCESE OF GRAND RAPIDS p 1248
360 Division Ave S 49503
Tel (616) 243-0491 *SIC* 8661

ROSKAM BAKING CO p 1251
4880 Corp Exch Blvd Se 49512
Tel (616) 574-5757 *SIC* 2051 2043 7389

ROTHBURY FARMS INC p 1252
3061 Shaffer Ave Se 49512
Tel (616) 574-5757 *SIC* 5149 2051 2043

SEI INC p 1300
3854 Broadmoor Ave Se # 101 49512
Tel (616) 698-2221 *SIC* 7378

SELKIRK CORP p 1302
5030 Corp Exch Blvd Se 49512
Tel (616) 656-8200 *SIC* 3444

■ SPARTAN STORES FUEL LLC p 1355
850 76th St Sw 49518
Tel (616) 878-2000 *SIC* 5541 5411

SPECTRUM HEALTH HOSPITALS p 1357
100 Michigan St Ne Mc-498 49503
Tel (616) 391-1774
SIC 8062 6351 8082 6331

SPECTRUM HEALTH PRIMARY CARE PARTNERS DBA p 1357
1840 Wealthy St Se 49506
Tel (616) 774-7322 *SIC* 8011

SPECTRUM HEALTH SYSTEM p 1357
100 Michigan St Ne 49503
Tel (616) 391-1774 *SIC* 8062

▲ STEELCASE INC p 1384
901 44th St Se 49508
Tel (616) 247-2710
SIC 2522 2521 3648 8748

STILES MACHINERY INC p 1389
3965 44th St Se 49512
Tel (616) 698-7500 *SIC* 5084

SUPER SERVICE HOLDINGS LLC p 1405
6000 Clay Ave Sw 49548
Tel (616) 530-8551 *SIC* 4213

SUPER SERVICE LLC p 1405
6000 Clay Ave Sw 49548
Tel (616) 530-8558 *SIC* 4213

■ SYSCO GRAND RAPIDS LLC p 1417
3700 Sysco Ct Se 49512
Tel (616) 956-0700 *SIC* 5141 5087

TRIANGLE ASSOCIATES INC p 1478
3769 3 Mile Rd Nw 49534
Tel (616) 453-3950 *SIC* 1542 1541

TRUE TEXTILES INC p 1486
5300 Corprte Grv Dr Se 49512
Tel (616) 301-7540 *SIC* 2221

TWINLAB HOLDINGS INC p 1495
3133 Orchard Vista Dr Se 49546
Tel (616) 464-5000
SIC 2833 2834 5149 2721

▲ UNIVERSAL FOREST PRODUCTS INC p 1516
2801 E Beltline Ave Ne 49525
Tel (616) 364-6161 *SIC* 2421 1796

VAN ANDEL INSTITUTE p 1542
333 Bostwick Ave Ne 49503
Tel (616) 234-5000 *SIC* 8733

VAN ANDEL RESEARCH INSTITUTE p 1542
333 Bostwick Ave Ne 49503
Tel (616) 234-5000 *SIC* 8733

VAN DYK MORTGAGE CORP p 1542
2449 Camelot Ct Se 49546
Tel (616) 940-3000 *SIC* 6162 6163

VAN MANEN PETROLEUM INC p 1542
0-305 Lake Michigan Dr Nw 49534
Tel (616) 453-6344 *SIC* 5172

VENTRA GRAND RAPIDS 5 LLC p 1548
3075 Breton Rd Se 49512
Tel (616) 949-6303 *SIC* 3465

WEGE FOUNDATION p 1587
99 Monroe Ave Nw Ste 902 49503
Tel (616) 957-0480 *SIC* 8699

■ WEN OHIO LLC p 1591
3310 Eagle Park Dr Ne 49525
Tel (616) 988-8751 *SIC* 5812

WILLIAMS DISTRIBUTING CO p 1611
658 Richmond St Nw 49504
Tel (616) 771-0505 *SIC* 5075

■ WM LIMITED PARTNERSHIP - 1998 p 1620
45 Ottawa Ave Sw Ste 600 49503
Tel (616) 776-2600 *SIC* 5812

WOLVERINE BUILDING GROUP INC p 1621
4045 Barden St Se 49512
Tel (616) 281-6236 *SIC* 1541 1542

GRANDVILLE, MI

HUMPHREY COMPANIES LLC p 718
2851 Prairie St Sw 49418
Tel (616) 530-1717
SIC 3537 3714 3089 5023 5162

GROSSE POINTE FARMS, MI

BON SECOURS COTTAGE HEALTH SERVICES p 199
159 Kercheval Ave 48236
Tel (313) 640-1000 *SIC* 8062

▲ SAGA COMMUNICATIONS INC p 1267
73 Kercheval Ave 48236
Tel (313) 886-7070 *SIC* 4832 4833

■ SAGA COMMUNICATIONS OF ILLINOIS LLC p 1267
73 Kercheval Ave Ste 201 48236
Tel (313) 886-7070 *SIC* 4832

■ SAGA COMMUNICATIONS OF NEW ENGLAND INC p 1267
73 Kercheval Ave Ste 201 48236
Tel (313) 886-7070 *SIC* 4832

GROSSE POINTE SHORES, MI

EDSEL & ELEANOR FORD HOUSE p 479
1100 Lake Shore Rd 48236
Tel (313) 884-4222 *SIC* 8412

GROSSE POINTE, MI

GROSSE POINTE PUBLIC SCHOOL SYSTEM p 641
389 Saint Clair St 48230
Tel (313) 432-3000 *SIC* 8211

HARRISON TOWNSHIP, MI

YANFENG USA AUTOMOTIVE TRIM SYSTEMS INC p 1634
42150 Executive Dr 48045
Tel (586) 354-2101 *SIC* 2396

HART, MI

■ GRAY & CO p 632
3325 W Polk Rd 49420
Tel (231) 873-5628 *SIC* 2033

HASTINGS, MI

FLEXFAB HORIZONS INTERNATIONAL INC p 556
102 Cook Rd 49058
Tel (269) 945-4700
SIC 3599 3052 3053 2822

FLEXFAB LLC p 556
1699 W M 43 Hwy 49058
Tel (269) 945-2433 *SIC* 3599 3052 2822

HASTINGS MUTUAL INSURANCE CO p 667
404 E Woodlawn Ave 49058
Tel (800) 442-8277 *SIC* 6411

SUPPLY NETWORK INC p 1407
210 N Industrial Park Rd 49058
Tel (269) 945-9501 *SIC* 5087

VIKING CORP p 1556
210 Industrial Park Dr 49058
Tel (269) 945-9501 *SIC* 3499

HAZEL PARK, MI

CAPITAL SALES CO p 250
1471 E 9 Mile Rd 48030
Tel (248) 542-4400 *SIC* 5141 7311

HAZEL PARK PUBLIC SCHOOL DISTRICT p 671
1620 E Elza Ave 48030
Tel (248) 658-5217 *SIC* 8211

HEMLOCK, MI

■ HEMLOCK SEMICONDUCTOR OPERATIONS LLC p 682
12334 Geddes Rd 48626
Tel (989) 642-5201 *SIC* 3295

HIGHLAND PARK, MI

DIALOGDIRECT INC p 436
13700 Oakland St 48203
Tel (313) 957-5100 *SIC* 8742

DIALOGDIRECT LLC p 436
13700 Oakland St 48203
Tel (313) 957-5100 *SIC* 6799 8742

GREAT LAKES WINE & SPIRITS LLC p 634
373 Victor St 48203
Tel (313) 278-5400 *SIC* 5182 2084

WOLPIN CO p 1621
1600 Modern St 48203
Tel (586) 757-4900 *SIC* 5181

HIGHLAND, MI

HURON VALLEY BOARD OF EDUCATION p 721
2390 S Milford Rd 48357
Tel (248) 684-8000 *SIC* 8211

HURON VALLEY SCHOOLS p 721
2390 S Milford Rd 48357
Tel (248) 684-8000 *SIC* 8211

HILLSDALE, MI

BEACON HILL PRESERVATION LIMITED DIVIDEND HOUSING ASSOCIATION LIMITED PARTNERSHIP p 164
32 E Carleton Rd 49242
Tel (517) 437-2177 *SIC* 6513

HILLSDALE COLLEGE p 694
33 E College St 49242
Tel (517) 437-7341 *SIC* 8221 8211

HOLLAND, MI

BRENNER OIL CO p 210
12948 Quincy St 49424
Tel (616) 399-9742 *SIC* 5172 4212

HAWORTH INC p 670
1 Haworth Ctr 49423
Tel (616) 393-3000 *SIC* 2522 2521

HAWORTH INTERNATIONAL LTD p 670
1 Haworth Ctr 49423
Tel (616) 393-3000 *SIC* 2522 2521

HOLLAND COMMUNITY HOSPITAL AUXILIARY INC p 700
602 Michigan Ave 49423
Tel (616) 748-9346 *SIC* 8062

HOPE COLLEGE p 706
141 E 12th St 49423
Tel (616) 395-7000 *SIC* 8221

JR AUTOMATION TECHNOLOGIES LLC p 795
13365 Tyler St 49424
Tel (616) 399-2168 *SIC* 3549

JR TECHNOLOGY GROUP LLC p 795
13365 Tyler St 49424
Tel (616) 399-2168 *SIC* 3549

LAKESHORE HEALTH PARTNERS p 840
3235 N Wellness Dr 120b 49424
Tel (616) 399-9522 *SIC* 8062

LEON INTERIORS INC p 856
88 E 48th St 49423
Tel (616) 531-7970 *SIC* 3089 3714 3086

LIGHTHOUSE INSURANCE GROUP INC p 865
877 E 16th St 49423
Tel (616) 392-6900
SIC 6411 6331 6321 6311

LOUIS PADNOS IRON AND METAL CO p 879
185 W 8th St 49423
Tel (616) 396-6521 *SIC* 5093 4491 3599

MOTUS LLC p 993
88 E 48th St 49423
Tel (616) 422-7479 *SIC* 3465

PRINCE MANUFACTURING CORP p 1176
36 W 8th St Ste 250 49423
Tel (616) 494-5374 *SIC* 1611 3613 5013

THERMOTRON INDUSTRIES INC p 1447
291 Kollen Park Dr 49423
Tel (616) 392-1491 *SIC* 3569

■ TOTAL LOGISTICS ONLINE LLC p 1463
10717 Adams St Ste 200 49423
Tel (800) 333-5599 *SIC* 7513

■ USF HOLLAND LLC p 1535
700 S Waverly Rd 49423
Tel (616) 395-5000 *SIC* 4213

WEST OTTAWA PUBLIC SCHOOLS p 1595
1138 136th Ave 49424
Tel (616) 738-5700 *SIC* 8211

WEST OTTAWA SCHOOLS p 1595
1138 136th Ave 49424
Tel (616) 738-5710 *SIC* 8211

HOLLY, MI

MAGNA ELECTRONICS INC p 896
10410 N Holly Rd 48442
Tel (810) 606-0444 *SIC* 3672 3679

PICO ENTERPRISES INC p 1146
4150 Grange Hall Rd 48442
Tel (248) 328-5000 *SIC* 8742

HOLT, MI

DAKKOTA INTEGRATED SYSTEMS LLC p 409
1875 Holloway Dr 48842
Tel (517) 694-6500 *SIC* 3711

PARTNERS BOOK DISTRIBUTING INC p 1118
2325 Jarco Dr 48842
Tel (517) 694-3205 *SIC* 5192

TULIP US HOLDINGS INC p 1491
1489 Cedar St 48842
Tel (517) 694-2300 *SIC* 3842

HOUGHTON LAKE, MI

MIDMICHIGAN HEALTH SERVICES p 966
9249 W Lake City Rd 48629
Tel (989) 422-5148 *SIC* 8011

HOUGHTON, MI

MICHIGAN TECHNOLOGICAL UNIVERSITY p 961
1400 Townsend Dr 49931
Tel (906) 487-1885 *SIC* 8221

HOWELL, MI

■ CITIZENS INSURANCE CO OF AMERICA p 311
808 N Highlander Way 48843
Tel (517) 546-2160 *SIC* 6331

■ CITIZENS INSURANCE CO OF MIDWEST p 311
808 N Highlander Way 48843
Tel (517) 546-2160 *SIC* 6331

HOWELL PUBLIC SCHOOLS p 713
411 N Highlander Way 48843
Tel (517) 548-6200 *SIC* 8211

THAI SUMMIT AMERICA CORP p 1446
1480 Mcpherson Park Dr 48843
Tel (517) 548-4900 *SIC* 3465

HUDSONVILLE, MI

FAMILY FARE INC p 526
3030 Corporate Grove Dr 49426
Tel (616) 896-5910 *SIC* 5411

LAMAR CONSTRUCTION CO p 841
4404 Central Pkwy 49426
Tel (616) 662-2933 *SIC* 1542 1541

ROYAL TECHNOLOGIES CORP p 1254
3765 Quincy St 49426
Tel (616) 669-3393 *SIC* 3089

INTERLOCHEN, MI

OMNI UNITED (USA) INC p 1085
5350 Birch Point Dr 49643
Tel (231) 943-9804 *SIC* 3011

IONIA, MI

■ INDEPENDENT BANK CORP p 736
230 W Main St 48846
Tel (616) 527-2400 *SIC* 6022

VENTRA IONIA MAIN LLC p 1548
14 Beardsley St 48846
Tel (616) 597-3220 *SIC* 3469 3089 5198

IRON MOUNTAIN, MI

CCI SYSTEMS INC p 270
105 Kent St 49801
Tel (906) 774-6621 *SIC* 5065

CHAMPION INC p 287
180 Traders Mine Rd 49801
Tel (906) 779-2300
SIC 8741 1542 5063 5082 3273 3272

DICKINSON COUNTY HEALTHCARE SYSTEM p 438
1721 S Stephenson Ave 49801
Tel (906) 774-1313 *SIC* 8062

IRON RIVER, MI

KRIST OIL CO p 830
303 Selden Rd 49935
Tel (906) 265-6144 *SIC* 5541 5411

JACKSON, MI

ALRO STEEL CORP p 61
3100 E High St 49203
Tel (517) 787-5500 *SIC* 5085 5162

▲ CMS ENERGY CORP p 329
1 Energy Plaza Dr 49201
Tel (517) 788-0550
SIC 4931 4911 4924 4922

■ CMS ENTERPRISES CO p 329
1 Energy Plaza Dr 49201
Tel (517) 788-0550 *SIC* 1382 4911

■ CONSUMERS ENERGY CO p 362
1 Energy Plaza Dr 49201
Tel (517) 788-0550 *SIC* 4931 4911 4924

DAWN EQUIPMENT CO INC p 416
2021 Micor Dr 49203
Tel (517) 789-4500 *SIC* 5046 3556

DAWN FOOD PRODUCTS INC p 416
3333 Sargent Rd 49201
Tel (517) 789-4400 *SIC* 2045 5046 3556

DAWN FOODS INC p 416
3333 Sargent Rd 49201
Tel (517) 789-4400
SIC 2053 2045 3556 5046 6719

GERDAU MACSTEEL INC p 608
5591 Morrill Rd 49201
Tel (517) 782-0415 *SIC* 3316 3312

HENRY FORD ALLEGIANCE HEALTH GROUP p 684
205 N East Ave 49201
Tel (517) 788-4800 SIC 8741 8721
J STANTON DAVID & ASSOCIATES INC p 772
714 W Michigan Ave 49201
Tel (517) 784-4094 SIC 5812
JACKSON PUBLIC SCHOOLS p 774
522 Wildwood Ave 49201
Tel (517) 841-2200 SIC 8211
MELLING TOOL CO p 941
2620 Saradan Dr 49202
Tel (517) 787-8172
SIC 3451 3714 3625 3568 3561 3494
MIRAMED GLOBAL SERVICES INC p 974
255 W Michigan Ave 49201
Tel (866) 544-6647 SIC 8742
POLLYS FOOD SERVICE INC p 1160
1821 Spring Arbor Rd 49203
Tel (517) 787-5228 SIC 5411 5921
TAC MANUFACTURING INC p 1421
4111 County Farm Rd 49201
Tel (517) 789-7000 SIC 3714 3625
W A FOOTE MEMORIAL HOSPITAL p 1568
205 N East Ave 49201
Tel (517) 788-4800 SIC 8062
WAY BAKERY p 1584
2100 Enterprise St 49203
Tel (517) 787-6720 SIC 2051

JONESVILLE, MI

MARTINREA JONESVILLE LLC p 913
260 Gaige St 49250
Tel (517) 849-2195 SIC 3465
NYLONCRAFT OF MICHIGAN INC p 1069
1640 E Chicago Rd 49250
Tel (517) 849-9911 SIC 3089

KALAMAZOO, MI

BORGESS HEALTH ALLIANCE INC p 201
1521 Gull Rd 49048
Tel (269) 226-7000 SIC 8062
BORGESS MEDICAL CENTER p 201
1521 Gull Rd 49048
Tel (269) 226-7000 SIC 8062
BORROUGHS CORP p 201
3002 N Burdick St 49004
Tel (800) 748-0227 SIC 5044
BRONSON HEALTH CARE GROUP INC p 217
301 John St 49007
Tel (269) 341-6000 SIC 8741
BRONSON MANAGEMENT SERVICES CORP p 217
1 Healthcare Plz 49007
Tel (269) 341-6000 SIC 8082
BRONSON METHODIST HOSPITAL INC p 217
601 John St Ste E-012 49007
Tel (269) 341-7654 SIC 8062
BRONSON PEDIATRIC NEUROLOGY SERVICE p 217
601 John St Ste M-460 49007
Tel (269) 341-8383 SIC 8011
BRONSON PHYSICIAN SERVICES INC p 217
601 John St Ste W002 49007
Tel (269) 341-6000 SIC 8011
CITY OF KALAMAZOO p 315
241 W South St 49007
Tel (269) 337-8047 SIC 9111
CKL CORP p 320
3825 Emerald Dr 49001
Tel (269) 382-4200 SIC 5181 5182 5149
CONSUMERS CONCRETE CORP p 362
3508 S Sprinkle Rd 49001
Tel (269) 342-0136 SIC 3273 3271 5032
COUNTY OF KALAMAZOO p 379
201 W Kalamazoo Ave # 101 49007
Tel (269) 384-8305 SIC 9111
FABRI-KAL CORP p 523
600 Plastics Pl 49001
Tel (269) 385-5050 SIC 3089
■ **FLOWSERVE FSD CORP** p 560
2100 Factory St 49001
Tel (269) 226-3954 SIC 3053
GREENLEAF HOSPITALITY GROUP INC p 638
100 W Michigan Ave # 100 49007
Tel (269) 567-7691 SIC 7011 5813
KALAMAZOO COLLEGE p 801
1200 Academy St 49006
Tel (269) 337-7000 SIC 8221
KALAMAZOO PUBLIC SCHOOL DISTRICT p 801
1220 Howard St 49008
Tel (269) 337-0113 SIC 8211
KALAMAZOO VALLEY COMMUNITY COLLEGE p 801
6767 W O Ave 49009
Tel (269) 488-4400 SIC 8222
LANDSCAPE FORMS INC p 843
7800 E Michigan Ave 49048
Tel (269) 381-0396
SIC 2531 2522 2511 2449 3648
POCH STAFFING INC p 1158
5555 Gull Rd Ste 300 49048
Tel (810) 229-2033 SIC 7363
SCHUPAN & SONS INC p 1291
2619 Miller Rd 49001
Tel (269) 382-0000 SIC 5093 5051 3341
STAFFORD-SMITH INC p 1374
3414 S Burdick St 49001
Tel (269) 343-1240 SIC 5046 5078
TOTAL PLASTICS RESOURCES LLC p 1463
2810 N Burdick St Ste A 49004
Tel (269) 344-0009 SIC 3083 5162
WESTERN MICHIGAN UNIVERSITY p 1599
1903 W Michigan Ave 49008
Tel (269) 387-1000 SIC 8221

KALKASKA, MI

BECKMAN PRODUCTION SERVICES INC p 167
3786 Beebe Rd Ne 49646
Tel (231) 258-9524 SIC 1382

KAWKAWLIN, MI

R ROESE CONTRACTING CO INC p 1202
2674 S Huron Rd 48631
Tel (989) 684-5121 SIC 1623

KENTWOOD, MI

■ **AUTOCAM CORP** p 134
4180 40th St Se 49512
Tel (616) 698-0707
SIC 3714 3572 3841 5084
CORVAC COMPOSITES LLC p 373
4450 36th St Se 49512
Tel (616) 281-4026 SIC 3559
MICRON HOLDINGS INC p 962
4436 Broadmoor Ave Se 49512
Tel (616) 698-0707 SIC 3714
TITAN HOLDINGS INC p 1456
4436 Broadmoor Ave Se 49512
Tel (616) 698-0707 SIC 3714

LAKE ORION, MI

LAKE ORION COMMUNITY SCHOOLS p 839
315 N Lapeer St 48362
Tel (248) 693-5400 SIC 8211

LANSING, MI

ACCIDENT FUND HOLDINGS INC p 15
200 N Grand Ave 48933
Tel (866) 206-5851 SIC 6331
AUTO-OWNERS INSURANCE CO p 133
6101 Anacapri Blvd 48917
Tel (517) 323-1200 SIC 6331
AUTO-OWNERS LIFE INSURANCE CO p 133
6101 Anacapri Blvd 48917
Tel (517) 323-1200 SIC 6411 6331
CAPITOL BANCORP LTD p 250
200 N Washington Sq 48933
Tel (517) 487-6555 SIC 6021
CHRISTMAN CO p 303
208 N Capitol Ave Fl 4 48933
Tel (517) 482-1488
SIC 8741 1542 1541 1629
CITY OF LANSING p 316
124 W Michigan Ave Fl 5 48933
Tel (517) 483-4433 SIC 9111
DART CONTAINER OF MICHIGAN LLC p 413
3120 Sovereign Dr Ste 4b 48911
Tel (888) 327-8001 SIC 3086
DEMMER CORP p 428
1600 N Larch St Ste 1 48906
Tel (517) 321-3600
SIC 3795 3812 3544 3465 3441
DEPARTMENT OF CORRECTIONS MICHIGAN p 430
206 E Michigan Ave 48933
Tel (517) 373-0720 SIC 9223
DEPARTMENT OF STATE MICHIGAN p 430
430 W Allegan St 48933
Tel (517) 373-2510 SIC 9199
DIOCESE OF LANSING p 440
228 N Walnut St 48933
Tel (517) 342-2440 SIC 8661
EDWARD W SPARROW HOSPITAL ASSOCIATION p 480
1215 E Michigan Ave 48912
Tel (517) 364-1000 SIC 8062
■ **EMERGENT BIODEFENSE OPERATIONS LANSING LLC** p 492
3500 N Martin Luther King 48906
Tel (517) 327-1500 SIC 2836 2834
EXECUTIVE OFFICE OF STATE OF MICHIGAN p 518
Romne Bldg 111 S Cap 48933
Tel (517) 373-3400 SIC 9111
FARM BUREAU GENERAL INSURANCE CO OF MICHIGAN p 528
7373 W Saginaw Hwy 48917
Tel (517) 323-7000 SIC 6411
FARM BUREAU MUTUAL INSURANCE CO OF MICHIGAN p 528
7373 W Saginaw Hwy 48917
Tel (517) 323-7000 SIC 6331
GRANGER ASSOCIATES INC p 630
16980 Wood Rd 48906
Tel (517) 372-2800 SIC 4953 1794 6552
GRANGER CONSTRUCTION CO INC p 631
6267 Aurelius Rd 48911
Tel (517) 393-1670 SIC 1542 1541
INGHAM REGIONAL MEDICAL CENTER p 743
401 W Greenlawn Ave 48910
Tel (517) 975-7800 SIC 8062
JACKSON NATIONAL LIFE INSURANCE CO INC p 774
1 Corporate Way 48951
Tel (517) 381-5500
SIC 6311 6282 6211 6411
JUDICIARY COURTS OF STATE OF MICHIGAN p 797
925 W Ottawa St 48915
Tel (517) 373-0120 SIC 9211
LANSING COMMUNITY COLLEGE p 844
610 N Capitol Ave 48933
Tel (517) 483-1957 SIC 8222
LANSING L MPT L C p 844
3140 Spanish Oak Dr Ste A 48911
Tel (517) 316-1013 SIC 3714
LANSING MALL LIMITED PARTNERSHIP p 844
5330 W Saginaw Hwy 48917
Tel (517) 321-0145 SIC 6512 7311
■ **LANSING MPS INC** p 844
5800 W Grand River Ave 48906
Tel (517) 323-9000
SIC 2759 2731 2761 3089 2671
LANSING SCHOOL DISTRICT p 844
519 W Kalamazoo St 48933
Tel (517) 755-1000 SIC 8211
LEGISLATIVE OFFICE OF MICHIGAN p 853
George Romney Building 48933
Tel (517) 373-3400 SIC 9121
MICHIGAN DEPARTMENT OF COMMUNITY HEALTH p 960
201 Townsend St Fl 7 48933
Tel (517) 241-1193 SIC 9431
MICHIGAN DEPARTMENT OF ENVIRONMENTAL QUALITY p 961
525 W Allegan St 48933
Tel (517) 284-6700 SIC 9511
MICHIGAN DEPARTMENT OF HEALTH & HUMAN SERVICES p 961
201 Townsend St 48933
Tel (517) 373-3740 SIC 9431 9441
MICHIGAN DEPARTMENT OF HUMAN SERVICES p 961
235 S Grand Ave 48933
Tel (517) 373-2000 SIC 9441 8249
MICHIGAN DEPARTMENT OF INFORMATION TECHNOLOGY p 961
111 S Capitol Ave 48933
Tel (517) 241-2000 SIC 9111
MICHIGAN DEPARTMENT OF MILITARY AND VETERANS AFFAIRS p 961
3411 N Martin Luther King 48906
Tel (517) 481-8083 SIC 9711 9451
MICHIGAN DEPARTMENT OF NATURAL RESOURCES p 961
525 W Allegan St 48933
Tel (517) 284-5936 SIC 9512
MICHIGAN DEPARTMENT OF TREASURY p 961
430 W Allegan St 48933
Tel (517) 373-3223 SIC 9311
MICHIGAN FARM BUREAU FINANCIAL CORP p 961
7373 W Saginaw Hwy 48917
Tel (517) 323-7000 SIC 6311 6331
MICHIGAN HEALTH ENDOWMENT FUND p 961
330 Marshall St Ste 200 48912
Tel (517) 374-0031 SIC 8099
■ **MPS HOLDCO INC** p 995
5800 W Grand River Ave 48906
Tel (517) 886-2526 SIC 6719
MUNICIPAL EMPLOYEES RETIREMENT SYSTEM OF MICHIGAN p 1000
1134 Municipal Way 48917
Tel (517) 703-9030 SIC 6371
▲ **NEOGEN CORP** p 1025
620 Lesher Pl 48912
Tel (517) 372-9200 SIC 2835 3841 2836
OWNERS INSURANCE CO p 1100
6101 Anacapri Blvd 48917
Tel (517) 323-1200 SIC 6411 6331
PECKHAM VOCATIONAL INDUSTRIES INC p 1126
3510 Capitol City Blvd 48906
Tel (517) 316-4000
SIC 8331 2396 2311 2331 2339 2326
PHYSICIANS HEALTH PLAN OF MID-MICHIGAN INC p 1145
1400 E Michigan Ave 48912
Tel (517) 364-8400 SIC 8011 6321
QUALITY DAIRY CO p 1197
111 W Mount Hope Ave 3a 48910
Tel (517) 319-4100 SIC 5451 5411
SENIOR RELATED WORLD LLC p 1304
5600 Mall Dr W 48917
Tel (517) 321-5058 SIC 6513
SPARROW HEALTH SYSTEM p 1354
1215 E Michigan Ave 48912
Tel (517) 364-1000 SIC 8062 7991
STATE OF MICHIGAN p 1382
111 S Capitol Ave 48933
Tel (517) 373-3400 SIC 9111

LAPEER, MI

ALBAR INDUSTRIES INC p 45
780 Whitney Dr 48446
Tel (810) 667-0150 SIC 3089
LAPEER REGIONAL MEDICAL CENTER p 845
1375 N Main St 48446
Tel (810) 667-5500 SIC 8062
MCLAREN LAPEER REGION p 931
1375 N Main St 48446
Tel (810) 667-5580 SIC 8069
ZF CHASSIS COMPONENTS LLC p 1642
3300 John Conley Dr 48446
Tel (810) 245-2000 SIC 3714

LIVONIA, MI

A123 SYSTEMS LLC p 7
39000 7 Mile Rd 48152
Tel (734) 772-0300 SIC 5063 3691
AAA LIFE INSURANCE CO p 7
17900 N Laurel Park Dr 48152
Tel (734) 779-2600 SIC 6311
ACRO SERVICE CORP p 18
39209 6 Mile Rd Ste 250 48152
Tel (734) 591-1100 SIC 7363 7371
ACRO STAFFING INC p 18
39209 W Six Ste 250 48152
Tel (734) 542-4204 SIC 7363
ALTA EQUIPMENT CO INC p 61
13211 Merriman Rd 48150
Tel (248) 449-6700 SIC 3537 5084
AMERICAN COMMUNITY MUTUAL INSURANCE CO p 70
39201 7 Mile Rd 48152
Tel (734) 591-9000 SIC 6321 6311
ANCHOR STAFFING INC p 89
39209 6 Mile Rd Ste 250 48152
Tel (734) 591-1100 SIC 7363
ARCH GLOBAL PRECISION LLC p 104
12955 Inkster Rd 48150
Tel (734) 266-6900 SIC 5049 3399
ARISTEO CONSTRUCTION CO p 108
12811 Farmington Rd 48150
Tel (734) 427-9111 SIC 1541
ARISTEO INSTALLATION LLC p 108
12811 Farmington Rd 48150
Tel (734) 427-9111 SIC 1541
CONTRACTORS STEEL CO p 364
36555 Amrhein Rd 48150
Tel (734) 464-4000 SIC 5051
GENERIC DRUG HOLDINGS INC p 602
31778 Enterprise Dr 48150
Tel (734) 743-6000 SIC 8734 5122 5047
■ **HARVARD DRUG GROUP L L C** p 666
17177 N Laurel Park Dr # 233 48152
Tel (734) 525-8700 SIC 5122 5047 8734
HOWARD TERNES PACKAGING CO p 713
35275 Industrial Rd 48150
Tel (734) 793-4130 SIC 4783 6512 6552
KELSEY-HAYES CO p 809
12001 Tech Center Dr 48150
Tel (734) 812-6979 SIC 3714
KEY PLASTICS LLC p 814
19575 Victor Pkwy Ste 400 48152
Tel (248) 449-6100 SIC 3089 7389
KING VENTURE INC p 820
17800 N Laurel Park Dr 48152
Tel (248) 357-6182 SIC 5812
LIVONIA PUBLIC SCHOOL DISTRICT p 872
15125 Farmington Rd 48154
Tel (734) 744-2500 SIC 8211
LUCASVARITY AUTOMOTIVE HOLDING CO p 884
12001 Tech Center Dr 48150
Tel (734) 855-2600 SIC 3714
MAIPF p 898
17456 N Laurel Park Dr # 130 48152
Tel (734) 464-1100 SIC 6331
MARKET STRATEGIES INC p 908
17430 College Pkwy 48152
Tel (734) 542-7600 SIC 8742 8732
■ **MCKESSON PHARMACY SYSTEMS LLC** p 930
30881 Schoolcraft Rd 48150
Tel (734) 421-0260 SIC 7372 5122
MERCY HEALTH SERVICES-IOWA CORP p 946
20555 Victor Pkwy 48152
Tel (734) 343-1000 SIC 8011
■ **MICHIGAN DAIRY LLC** p 960
29601 Industrial Rd 48150
Tel (734) 367-5390 SIC 5143
NYX LLC p 1069
36111 Schoolcraft Rd 48150
Tel (734) 462-2385
SIC 3089 3714 3565 2671
PHILLIPS SERVICE INDUSTRIES INC p 1144
11878 Hubbard St 48150
Tel (734) 853-5000 SIC 7699 7694 7629
PSP STORES LLC p 1188
17197 N Laurel Park Dr 48152
Tel (734) 793-6600 SIC 5999
QUALITY METALCRAFT INC p 1197
33355 Glendale St 48150
Tel (734) 261-6700
SIC 3544 3465 3469 3444

RAM CONSTRUCTION SERVICES OF MICHIGAN INC p 1206
13800 Eckles Rd 48150
Tel (734) 464-3800 SIC 1799 1541 1542

ROCK HOLDINGS INC p 1243
20555 Victor Pkwy 48152
Tel (313) 373-7700 SIC 6719

ROUSH ENTERPRISES INC p 1253
12447 Levan Rd 48150
Tel (734) 779-7006
SIC 8711 3714 7948 8734

ROUSH INDUSTRIES INC p 1253
12447 Levan Rd 48150
Tel (734) 779-7006 SIC 8734 8711

SCHOOLCRAFT COLLEGE p 1290
18600 Haggerty Rd 48152
Tel (734) 462-4400 SIC 8222

ST MARY HOSPITAL OF LIVONIA p 1371
36475 5 Mile Rd 48154
Tel (734) 655-4800 SIC 8062 8051

■ STEMCO PRODUCTS INC p 1385
37770 Amrhein Rd 48150
Tel (734) 416-8911 SIC 3714 3465

STENCO CONSTRUCTION CO LLC p 1385
12741 Farmington Rd 48150
Tel (734) 427-8843 SIC 1541

■ TOWER AUTOMOTIVE HOLDINGS USA LLC p 1464
17672 N Laurel Park Dr 400e 48152
Tel (248) 675-6000 SIC 3465

■ TOWER AUTOMOTIVE OPERATIONS USA I LLC p 1464
17672 N Laurel Park Dr 400e 48152
Tel (248) 675-6000 SIC 3465

▲ TOWER INTERNATIONAL INC p 1464
17672 N Laurel Park Dr 48152
Tel (248) 675-6000 SIC 3465 3441

TRINITY CONTINUING CARE SERVICES - INDIANA INC p 1481
17410 College Pkwy # 200 48152
Tel (734) 542-8300 SIC 8051

TRINITY HEALTH CORP p 1481
20555 Victor Pkwy 48152
Tel (734) 343-1000 SIC 8741 8062

TRINITY HEALTH-MICHIGAN p 1481
20555 Victor Pkwy 48152
Tel (810) 985-1500 SIC 8062

TRINITY SENIOR LIVING COMMUNITIES p 1482
17410 College Pkwy # 200 48152
Tel (734) 542-8300 SIC 8361

TRW AUTOMOTIVE INC p 1489
12025 Tech Center Dr 48150
Tel (734) 266-2600 SIC 3714

TRW AUTOMOTIVE US LLC p 1489
12001 Tech Center Dr 48150
Tel (734) 855-2600 SIC 3679 3469 3089

USA SELLER CO LLC p 1534
17197 N Laurel Park Dr # 402 48152
Tel (734) 793-6600 SIC 5999

VALASSIS COMMUNICATIONS INC p 1539
19975 Victor Pkwy 48152
Tel (734) 591-3000 SIC 7319 7331 7372

VALASSIS INTERNATIONAL INC p 1539
19975 Victor Pkwy 48152
Tel (734) 591-3000
SIC 8743 3993 2759 2752

VIRGINIA TILE CO p 1560
28320 Plymouth Rd 48150
Tel (248) 476-7850 SIC 5032 5023

WORKFORCE SOFTWARE LLC p 1624
38705 7 Mile Rd Ste 300 48152
Tel (734) 542-4100 SIC 7372 7371

ZF TRW AUTOMOTIVE HOLDINGS CORP p 1642
12001 Tech Center Dr 48150
Tel (734) 855-2600 SIC 3714 3711

LUDINGTON, MI

INDIAN SUMMER COOPERATIVE INC p 738
3958 W Chauvez Rd Ste 1 49431
Tel (231) 845-6248
SIC 2033 0723 4213 2035

OPTION ENERGY LLC p 1090
5481 N Whitetail Ln 49431
Tel (269) 329-4317
SIC 4924 1311 4931 1711

SRS INDUSTRIES LLC p 1363
5175 W 6th St 49431
Tel (231) 845-5101 SIC 3354

MACOMB, MI

BAKER INDUSTRIES INC p 146
16936 Enterprise Dr 48044
Tel (586) 286-4900 SIC 3544

REHMANN LLC p 1220
1500 W Big Beaver Rd 48044
Tel (866) 799-9580 SIC 8748 8721

MADISON HEIGHTS, MI

CNI ENTERPRISES INC p 330
1451 E Lincoln Ave 48071
Tel (248) 586-3300 SIC 2396

CTA ACOUSTICS INC p 399
25211 Dequindre Rd 48071
Tel (248) 544-2580 SIC 3714

EFTEC NORTH AMERICA LLC p 481
31601 Research Park Dr 48071
Tel (248) 526-4565
SIC 2891 8731 3296 2899 2851

FICOSA NORTH AMERICA CORP p 540
30870 Stephenson Hwy 48071
Tel (248) 307-2230 SIC 5531

■ FLUID ROUTING SOLUTIONS INC p 561
30000 Stephenson Hwy 48071
Tel (248) 228-8900 SIC 5013

GALCO INDUSTRIAL ELECTRONICS INC p 589
26010 Pinehurst Dr 48071
Tel (248) 542-9090 SIC 5065

IONBOND LLC p 762
1823 E Whitcomb Ave 48071
Tel (248) 398-9100 SIC 3398 3479

KAR NUT PRODUCTS CO p 804
1200 E 14 Mile Rd Ste A 48071
Tel (248) 588-1903 SIC 5145 2068

LOUIS T OLLESHEIMER & SON INC p 880
605 E 12 Mile Rd 48071
Tel (248) 544-3900 SIC 5033 5082

MCNAUGHTON-MCKAY ELECTRIC CO p 932
1357 E Lincoln Ave 48071
Tel (248) 399-7500 SIC 5065 5063

NETLINK SOFTWARE GROUP AMERICA INC p 1027
999 Tech Row 48071
Tel (248) 204-8803 SIC 7379 7371

NICA INC p 1042
1451 E Lincoln Ave 48071
Tel (248) 586-3300 SIC 2396

OAKLAND HOSPITAL p 1071
27351 Dequindre Rd 48071
Tel (248) 967-7000 SIC 8062

QUALIS AUTOMOTIVE LLC p 1196
29380 John R Rd 48071
Tel (248) 740-1668 SIC 5013 7539

SHANNON PRECISION FASTENER LLC p 1311
31600 Stephenson Hwy 48071
Tel (248) 589-9670 SIC 3452

UNIVERSAL TRIM INC p 1518
1451 E Lincoln Ave 48071
Tel (248) 586-3300
SIC 3714 3199 3089 3429

MANCHESTER, MI

AMCOR RIGID PLASTICS USA LLC p 66
10521 M 52 48158
Tel (734) 428-9741 SIC 3085

MARTINREA INDUSTRIES INC p 913
10501 Mi State Road 52 48158
Tel (734) 428-2400
SIC 3714 3317 3089 3544

MARQUETTE, MI

MARQUETTE GENERAL HOSPITAL INC p 910
420 W Magnetic St 49855
Tel (906) 228-9440 SIC 8062

NORTHERN MICHIGAN UNIVERSITY p 1056
1401 Presque Isle Ave 49855
Tel (906) 227-1000 SIC 8221

UPPER PENINSULA HEALTH PLAN LLC p 1529
853 W Washington St 49855
Tel (906) 225-7500 SIC 6321 6411

UPPER PENINSULA POWER CO INC p 1529
1002 Harbor Hills Dr 49855
Tel (906) 232-1444 SIC 4911

MARSHALL, MI

■ BORGWARNER THERMAL SYSTEMS INC p 201
1507 S Kalamazoo Ave 49068
Tel (269) 781-1228 SIC 3625

ELLA E M BROWN CHARITABLE CIRCLE p 488
200 N Madison St 49068
Tel (269) 781-4271 SIC 8062 8049

WALTERS-DIMMICK PETROLEUM INC p 1574
1620 S Kalamazoo Ave 49068
Tel (269) 781-4654
SIC 5541 5411 6512 5172 5171 5983

MARYSVILLE, MI

SMR AUTOMOTIVE MIRROR INTERNATIONAL USA INC p 1334
1855 Busha Hwy 48040
Tel (810) 364-4141 SIC 3231

SMR AUTOMOTIVE SYSTEMS USA INC p 1334
1855 Busha Hwy 48040
Tel (810) 364-4141 SIC 3231

SMR AUTOMOTIVE TECHNOLOGY HOLDINGS USA PARTNERS LLP p 1334
1855 Busha Hwy 48040
Tel (810) 364-4141 SIC 3231

ZF AXLE DRIVES MARYSVILLE LLC p 1642
2900 Busha Hwy 48040
Tel (810) 989-8702 SIC 3711

MASON, MI

COUNTY OF INGHAM p 378
Ingham County Court House 48854
Tel (517) 676-7206 SIC 9111

DART CONTAINER CORP p 412
500 Hogsback Rd 48854
Tel (800) 248-5960 SIC 3086

DART CONTAINER CORP OF GEORGIA p 412
500 Hogsback Rd 48854
Tel (517) 676-3800 SIC 3089

DART CONTAINER CORP OF KENTUCKY p 413
500 Hogsback Rd 48854
Tel (517) 676-3800 SIC 2821 3086

DART ENERGY CORP p 413
600 Dart Rd 48854
Tel (517) 676-2900 SIC 1311 1382

GESTAMP MASON LLC p 609
200 E Kipp Rd 48854
Tel (517) 244-8800
SIC 3398 5013 3714 3711 3465

MATTAWAN, MI

MPI RESEARCH INC p 995
54943 N Main St 49071
Tel (269) 668-3336 SIC 8731

MENDON, MI

TH PLASTICS INC p 1446
106 E Main St 49072
Tel (269) 496-8495 SIC 3089

MENOMINEE, MI

■ ANCHOR COUPLING INC p 89
5520 13th St 49858
Tel (906) 863-2672 SIC 3429

L E JONES CO p 834
1200 34th Ave 49858
Tel (906) 863-1043 SIC 3592 3545

MIDDLEVILLE, MI

HPS LLC p 714
3275 N M 37 Hwy 49333
Tel (269) 795-3308 SIC 7389

MIDLAND, MI

■ CHEMICAL BANK AND TRUST CO p 293
333 E Main St 48640
Tel (989) 631-9200 SIC 6022

▲ CHEMICAL FINANCIAL CORP p 293
235 E Main St 48640
Tel (989) 839-5350 SIC 6022

▲ DOW CHEMICAL CO p 453
2030 Dow Ctr 48674
Tel (989) 636-1000
SIC 2821 3081 3086 2812 2879

■ DOW CORNING SILICON ENERGY SYSTEMS INC p 453
2200 Salzburg St 48640
Tel (989) 496-4000 SIC 6719

DOW HERBERT H & GRACE A FOUNDATION p 453
1809 Eastman Ave 48640
Tel (989) 631-2677 SIC 6732

■ DOW HOLDINGS LLC p 453
2030 Dow Ctr 48674
Tel (989) 636-1000 SIC 8748

MIDLAND PUBLIC SCHOOL DISTRICT p 966
600 E Carpenter St 48640
Tel (989) 923-5001 SIC 8211

MIDMICHIGAN HEALTH p 966
4000 Wellness Dr 48670
Tel (989) 839-3000 SIC 8741

MIDMICHIGAN MEDICAL CENTER-MIDLAND p 966
4000 Wellness Dr 48670
Tel (989) 839-3000 SIC 8062

NORTHWOOD UNIVERSITY p 1061
4000 Whiting Dr 48640
Tel (800) 622-9000 SIC 8221

■ ROFAN SERVICES INC p 1246
2030 Dow Ctr 48674
Tel (989) 636-6943 SIC 7359

THREE RIVERS CORP p 1450
3069 E Vantage Point Dr 48642
Tel (989) 631-9726 SIC 1542 1541

MILFORD, MI

P M GROUP INC p 1102
1050 Corporate Office Dr 48381
Tel (248) 529-2000 SIC 6531 1522 6552

MONROE, MI

BACKYARD PRODUCTS LLC p 143
1000 Ternes Dr 48162
Tel (734) 242-6900 SIC 2452 2511

BACKYARD STORAGE SOLUTIONS LLC p 143
1000 Ternes Dr 48162
Tel (734) 242-6900 SIC 2452

■ ENGLAND INC p 499
1 La Z Boy Dr 48162
Tel (734) 242-1444 SIC 2512

▲ LA-Z-BOY INC p 836
1 La Z Boy Dr 48162
Tel (734) 242-1444 SIC 2512 2511 5712

■ LZB MANUFACTURING INC p 888
1 Lazboy Dr 48162
Tel (734) 242-1444 SIC 2512

MERCY MEMORIAL HOSPITAL CORP p 948
718 N Macomb St 48162
Tel (734) 240-8400 SIC 8062

MIDWAY PRODUCTS GROUP INC p 967
1 Lyman E Hoyt Dr 48161
Tel (734) 241-7242 SIC 8741 3469

NATIONAL GALVANIZING LP p 1012
1500 Telb St 48162
Tel (734) 243-1882
SIC 3312 3316 3471 3341 5051

■ PULLMAN CO p 1191
1 International Dr 48161
Tel (734) 243-8000 SIC 3714 3715 3061

SOURCE CAPITAL BACKYARD LLC p 1342
1000 Ternes Dr 48162
Tel (734) 242-6900 SIC 2511 2452

■ TWB CO LLC p 1494
1600 Nadeau Rd 48162
Tel (734) 289-6400 SIC 3465

ZHONGDING SEALING PARTS (USA) INC p 1643
400 Detroit Ave 48162
Tel (734) 241-8870 SIC 3069

MOUNT CLEMENS, MI

24/7 BAIL AGENCY INC p 2
Elizabeth Rd 48043
Tel (866) 322-2245 SIC 7389

COUNTY OF MACOMB p 379
120 N Main St 48043
Tel (586) 469-5260 SIC 9111

HENRY FORD MACOMB HOSPITALS p 684
215 North Ave 48043
Tel (586) 466-9310 SIC 8062

MOUNT CLEMENS REGIONAL MEDICAL CENTER p 993
1000 Harrington St 48043
Tel (586) 493-8000 SIC 8062

MOUNT PLEASANT, MI

AMERICAN MITSUBA CORP p 76
2945 Three Leaves Dr 48858
Tel (989) 779-4962 SIC 3714

BELLEHOFF CORP p 170
405 S Mission St 48858
Tel (989) 772-2902 SIC 5812

CENTRAL MICHIGAN UNIVERSITY p 279
1200 S Franklin St 48859
Tel (989) 774-4000
SIC 8221 5942 4833 4832 5812

■ DELFIELD CO LLC p 424
980 S Isabella Rd 48858
Tel (989) 773-7981 SIC 3589

MILAN SUPPLY CO p 968
7125 E Pickard Rd 48858
Tel (989) 773-9938 SIC 5082

NORTHWIND INVESTMENTS INC p 1061
109 E Broadway St 48858
Tel (989) 772-2600 SIC 5812

SAGINAW CHIPPEWA INDIAN TRIBE p 1268
7070 E Broadway Rd 48858
Tel (989) 775-4000 SIC 5812

SUMMIT-REED CITY INC p 1399
1315 S Mission Rd 48858
Tel (989) 772-2028 SIC 1311

MUSKEGON, MI

BRUNSWICK BOWLING PRODUCTS LLC p 221
525 W Laketon Ave 49441
Tel (231) 725-3300 SIC 3949

COUNTY OF MUSKEGON p 380
990 Terrace St 49442
Tel (231) 724-6520 SIC 9111

FAMILY FARM & HOME INC p 526
900 3rd St Ste 302 49440
Tel (231) 722-8335
SIC 5999 5261 5149 5611 5211 5091

■ GE AVIATION MUSKEGON p 595
2034 Latimer Dr 49442
Tel (231) 777-2685 SIC 3724

HACKLEY HOSPITAL p 652
1700 Clinton St 49442
Tel (231) 728-4950 SIC 8062

MERCY GENERAL HEALTH PARTNERS p 946
1500 E Sherman Blvd 49444
Tel (231) 728-4032 SIC 8062

NEWKIRK ELECTRIC ASSOCIATES INC p 1037
1875 Roberts St 49442
Tel (231) 722-1691 SIC 1731 1629 8711

PORT CITY GROUP INC p 1162
1985 E Laketon Ave 49442
Tel (231) 777-3941 SIC 3542 3089

SAF-HOLLAND INC p 1265
1950 Industrial Blvd 49442
Tel (231) 773-3271 SIC 5013

SAF-HOLLAND INC p 1265
1950 Industrial Blvd 49442
Tel (231) 773-3271
SIC 3714 3715 3568 3537 3452

WEBB CHEMICAL SERVICE CORP p 1586
2708 Jarman St 49444
Tel (231) 733-2181 SIC 5169

WESCO INC p 1593
1460 Whitehall Rd 49445
Tel (231) 719-4300
SIC 5411 5541 5145 5149

NEW BOSTON, MI

L & W INC p 833
17757 Woodland Dr 48164
Tel (734) 397-6300
SIC 3469 3465 3441 3429

NEW HUDSON, MI

■ CUMMINS BRIDGEWAY LLC p 401
21810 Clessie Ct 48165
Tel (248) 573-1600 SIC 5084 7538 3519

K & S PROPERTY INC p 798
21810 Clessie Ct 48165
Tel (248) 573-1600 SIC 5084 3519

TNG WORLDWIDE INC p 1458
29683 Wk Smith Dr Stet 48165
Tel (248) 347-7700 SIC 5099 5087

NILES, MI

AACOA EXTRUSIONS INC p 8
2005 Mayflower Rd 49120
Tel (269) 697-6063 SIC 3354

B&R OIL CO INC p 142
2147 S 3rd St 49120
Tel (269) 687-9642 SIC 5172

MODINEER CO p 981
2190 Industrial Dr 49120
Tel (269) 683-2550 SIC 3469 3599 3544

NATIONAL-STANDARD LLC p 1017
1631 Lake St 49120
Tel (269) 683-9902 SIC 3315 3496

NORTHVILLE, MI

AISIN WORLD CORP OF AMERICA p 41
15300 Centennial Dr 48168
Tel (734) 453-5551 SIC 5013

▲ GENTHERM INC p 605
21680 Haggerty Rd Ste 101 48167
Tel (248) 504-0500 SIC 3714

NORTHVILLE PUBLIC SCHOOL DISTRICT p 1059
501 W Main St 48167
Tel (248) 349-3400 SIC 8211

ZF NORTH AMERICA INC p 1642
15811 Centennial Dr 48168
Tel (734) 416-6200 SIC 3714 5013

NORTON SHORES, MI

■ CANNON-MUSKEGON CORP p 247
2875 Lincoln St 49441
Tel (231) 759-2831
SIC 3313 3341 3339 3312

HARBOR GROUP INC p 659
1115 E Broadway Ave 49444
Tel (231) 739-7152 SIC 5051

HARBOR STEEL AND SUPPLY CORP p 660
1115 E Broadway Ave 49444
Tel (231) 739-7152 SIC 5051

HINES CORP p 695
1218 E Pontaluna Rd Ste B 49456
Tel (231) 799-6240
SIC 3443 3823 3589 3531 3535 5082

NICHOLS PAPER & SUPPLY CO p 1042
1391 Judson Rd 49456
Tel (231) 799-2120 SIC 5113 5087

■ PRATT & WHITNEY COMPONENT SOLUTIONS INC p 1167
4905 Stariha Dr 49441
Tel (231) 798-8464 SIC 5088

NOVI, MI

■ AMGRAM CASSELL-EAST LLC p 85
40020 Grand River Ave 48375
Tel (248) 615-6025 SIC 8322

■ BRASSCRAFT MANUFACTURING CO p 208
39600 Orchard Hill Pl 48375
Tel (248) 305-6000 SIC 3432

CHILDRENS COURTYARD INC p 299
21333 Haggerty Rd Ste 300 48375
Tel (248) 697-9000 SIC 8351

CHILDTIME CHILDCARE INC p 300
21333 Haggerty Rd Ste 300 48375
Tel (248) 697-9000 SIC 8351

■ COOPER-STANDARD AUTOMOTIVE INC p 367
39550 Orchard Hill Pl 48375
Tel (248) 596-5900 SIC 3714

▲ COOPER-STANDARD HOLDINGS INC p 367
39550 Orchard Hill Pl 48375
Tel (248) 596-5900 SIC 3714

■ DIGITAL LEASH LLC p 439
39500 High Pointe Blvd # 250 48375
Tel (877) 775-3274 SIC 6331 6411

EBERSPAECHER NORTH AMERICA INC p 474
29101 Haggerty Rd 48377
Tel (248) 994-7010 SIC 3714

FRANK W KERR CO p 574
43155 W 9 Mile Rd Ste 1 48375
Tel (248) 349-5000 SIC 5122

■ HARMAN BECKER AUTOMOTIVE SYSTEMS INC p 662
30001 Cabot Dr 48377
Tel (248) 785-2361 SIC 3931 3812

HENRY FORD MEDICAL CENTER p 684
39450 W 12 Mile Rd 48377
Tel (248) 661-7393 SIC 8011

HEPHAESTUS HOLDINGS INC p 685
39475 W 13 Mile Rd # 105 48377
Tel (248) 479-2700 SIC 3462 3463

INTERNATIONAL TRANSMISSION CO p 757
27175 Energy Way 48377
Tel (248) 374-7100 SIC 4911

IOCHPE HOLDINGS LLC p 762
39500 Orchard Hill Pl # 500 48375
Tel (734) 737-5000 SIC 3714

ITC HOLDINGS CORP p 767
27175 Energy Way 48377
Tel (248) 946-3000 SIC 4911

KONGSBERG AUTOMOTIVE INC p 827
27275 Haggerty Rd Ste 610 48377
Tel (248) 468-1300 SIC 3714

KONGSBERG HOLDING III INC p 827
27275 Haggerty Rd Ste 610 48377
Tel (248) 468-1300 SIC 3714

LA PETITE ACADEMY INC p 835
21333 Haggerty Rd Ste 300 48375
Tel (877) 861-5078 SIC 8351

LA PETITE HOLDINGS CORP p 835
21333 Haggerty Rd Ste 300 48375
Tel (248) 697-9000 SIC 8351

LEARNING CARE GROUP (US) INC p 850
21333 Haggerty Rd Ste 300 48375
Tel (248) 697-9000 SIC 8351

LEARNING CARE GROUP INC p 850
21333 Haggerty Rd Ste 300 48375
Tel (248) 697-9000 SIC 8351 8299

LEE STEEL CORP p 851
45525 Grand River Ave 48374
Tel (855) 533-7833 SIC 5051

LPA INVESTMENT LLC p 882
21333 Haggerty Rd Ste 300 48375
Tel (866) 244-5384 SIC 8351

MACALLISTER MACHINERY CO INC p 891
24800 Novi Rd 48375
Tel (248) 349-4800 SIC 5082

MAGNA SEATING OF AMERICA INC p 896
39600 Lewis Dr Ste 216 48377
Tel (248) 553-8094 SIC 3714

MAXION WHEELS p 922
39500 Orchard Hill Pl # 500 48375
Tel (734) 737-5000 SIC 3714

MAXION WHEELS USA LLC p 922
39500 Orchard Hill Pl # 500 48375
Tel (734) 737-5000 SIC 3714

METALSA STRUCTURAL PRODUCTS INC p 953
29545 Hudson Dr 48377
Tel (248) 669-3704 SIC 3714

MICHIGAN MILK PRODUCERS ASSOCIATION p 961
41310 Bridge St 48375
Tel (248) 474-6672
SIC 5143 2023 2021 8611 2026

MTU AMERICA INC p 998
39525 Mackenzie Dr 48377
Tel (248) 560-8000 SIC 3519

NATIONAL FOOD GROUP INC p 1012
46820 Magellan Dr Ste A 48377
Tel (734) 453-4544 SIC 5142

NEW JERNBERG SALES INC p 1031
39475 W 13 Mile Rd # 105 48377
Tel (248) 479-2699 SIC 5051

NHK INTERNATIONAL CORP p 1041
46855 Magellan Dr Ste 200 48377
Tel (248) 926-0111 SIC 8711

PREH INC p 1170
28850 Cabot Dr Ste 1300 48377
Tel (248) 381-3800 SIC 5013

PRESTOLITE ELECTRIC HOLDING INC p 1173
30120 Hudson Dr 48377
Tel (248) 313-3807 SIC 3621 3694

PRESTOLITE ELECTRIC INC p 1173
30120 Hudson Dr 48377
Tel (585) 492-1700 SIC 3621 3694

PRESTOLITE ELECTRIC LLC p 1173
30120 Hudson Dr 48377
Tel (248) 313-3807
SIC 3643 3824 3621 3625 3694

RESIDEX LLC p 1226
46495 Humboldt Dr 48377
Tel (855) 737-4339
SIC 5191 7342 0781 0782

▲ STONERIDGE INC p 1391
39675 Mackenzie Dr # 400 48377
Tel (330) 856-2443 SIC 3714 3679 3625

SUMITOMO BAKELITE NORTH AMERICA INC p 1398
46820 Magellan Dr Ste C 48377
Tel (248) 313-7000 SIC 2821

■ SUMMIT HEALTH INC p 1399
27175 Haggerty Rd 48377
Tel (248) 799-8303 SIC 8099 8741

TA DELAWARE INC p 1420
17672 N Laure Park Dr Ste 48377
Tel (248) 675-6000 SIC 3469

TATA TECHNOLOGIES INC p 1426
41050 W 11 Mile Rd 48375
Tel (248) 426-1482 SIC 8711

TUTOR TIME LEARNING CENTERS LLC p 1493
21333 Haggerty Rd Ste 300 48375
Tel (248) 697-9000 SIC 8351

OAK PARK, MI

EATON STEEL CORP p 473
10221 Capital St 48237
Tel (248) 398-3434 SIC 5051 3312

OKEMOS, MI

DELTA DENTAL PLAN OF MICHIGAN INC p 426
4100 Okemos Rd 48864
Tel (517) 349-6000 SIC 6324

LEONA GROUP L L C p 856
2125 University Park Dr # 250 48864
Tel (517) 333-9030 SIC 8742

RSI LOGISTICS INC p 1256
2419 Science Pkwy 48864
Tel (517) 349-7713 SIC 8742 4231

WESTON SOLUTIONS OF MICHIGAN INC p 1602
2501 Jolly Rd Ste 100 48864
Tel (517) 381-5920 SIC 8748

ORCHARD LAKE, MI

KONVISSER CUSTOM SOFTWARE p 827
5109 Deer Run Cir 48323
Tel (248) 682-0717 SIC 7371

ORION, MI

POWERS DISTRIBUTING CO INC p 1166
3700 Giddings Rd 48359
Tel (248) 393-3700 SIC 5181

OWOSSO, MI

MEMORIAL HEALTH CARE INC p 941
826 W King St 48867
Tel (989) 725-8101 SIC 8641 5947

MEMORIAL HOSPITAL p 942
826 W King St 48867
Tel (989) 723-5211 SIC 8062

PARMA, MI

MICHIGAN AUTOMOTIVE COMPRESSOR INC p 960
2400 N Dearing Rd 49269
Tel (517) 622-7000
SIC 3585 3714 3568 3563

PETOSKEY, MI

HEALTHSHARE INC p 677
416 Connable Ave 49770
Tel (231) 487-4803 SIC 8741 8062

MCLAREN NORTHERN MICHIGAN p 931
416 Connable Ave 49770
Tel (800) 248-6777 SIC 8062

PIGEON, MI

COOPERATIVE ELEVATOR CO p 367
7211 E Michigan Ave 48755
Tel (989) 453-4500
SIC 5172 5191 5541 5261 5153

HURON CASTING INC p 721
7050 Hartley St 48755
Tel (989) 453-3933 SIC 3325 3369

PLAINWELL, MI

HARDINGS MARKET-WEST INC p 661
211 E Bannister St Ste E 49080
Tel (269) 427-8003 SIC 5411

PLYMOUTH, MI

ABSOPURE WATER CO LLC p 13
8845 General Dr 48170
Tel (313) 898-1200 SIC 5499 5149

ADIENT HOLDING MEXICO LLC p 22
49200 Halyard Dr 48170
Tel (414) 220-8900 SIC 6719

ADIENT INC p 22
49200 Halyard Dr 48170
Tel (414) 220-8900 SIC 6719

ADIENT US LLC p 22
49200 Halyard Dr 48170
Tel (734) 254-5000 SIC 3714

ASP MD HOLDINGS INC p 118
47659 Halyard Dr 48170
Tel (734) 207-6200 SIC 5013

BREMBO NORTH AMERICA INC p 209
47765 Halyard Dr 48170
Tel (734) 416-1275 SIC 3714 5013

BURROUGHS INC p 228
41100 Plymouth Rd 48170
Tel (734) 737-4000 SIC 5049

BURROUGHS PAYMENT SYSTEMS INC p 228
41100 Plymouth Rd 48170
Tel (734) 737-4000 SIC 5049

■ CEQUENT PERFORMANCE PRODUCTS INC p 283
47912 Halyard Dr Ste 100 48170
Tel (734) 656-3000 SIC 3799 3714

DAY INTERNATIONAL GROUP INC p 417
14909 N Beck Rd 48170
Tel (734) 781-4600 SIC 3069

EP MANAGEMENT CORP p 504
801 W Ann Arbor Trl # 220 48170
Tel (313) 749-5500
SIC 3692 3661 2834 3674 3691

FLINT GROUP NORTH AMERICA CORP p 557
14909 N Beck Rd 48170
Tel (734) 781-4600 SIC 2893

FLINT GROUP US LLC p 557
14909 N Beck Rd 48170
Tel (734) 781-4600 SIC 2865 2893

FREUDENBERG NORTH AMERICA LIMITED PARTNERSHIP p 579
47774 W Anchor Ct 48170
Tel (734) 354-5505
SIC 2821 3714 3053 3061

FREUDENBERG-NOK GENERAL PARTNERSHIP p 579
47690 E Anchor Ct 48170
Tel (734) 451-0020
SIC 2821 3714 3053 3061

HELLA CORPORATE CENTER USA INC p 681
43811 Plymouth Oaks Blvd 48170
Tel (586) 232-4788
SIC 3625 5013 5088 3822 3585 3429

HELLA ELECTRONICS CORP p 681
43811 Plymouth Oaks Blvd 48170
Tel (734) 414-0900 SIC 3625 3714

HOOVER UNIVERSAL INC p 706
49200 Halyard Dr 48170
Tel (734) 454-0994 SIC 2531

INTERTEC SYSTEMS LLC p 759
45000 Helm St Ste 200 48170
Tel (734) 254-3268 SIC 3714

JCIM US LLC p 780
45000 Helm St Ste 200 48170
Tel (734) 254-3100 SIC 3089

JOHNSON ELECTRIC AUTOMOTIVE INC p 791
47660 Halyard Dr 48170
Tel (734) 392-1022 SIC 5013 8731 8742

JOHNSON ELECTRIC NORTH AMERICA INC p 791
47660 Halyard Dr 48170
Tel (734) 392-5300
SIC 5063 3625 3674 8711

JTEKT NORTH AMERICA INC p 796
47771 Halyard Dr 48170
Tel (734) 454-1500 SIC 5013

LINK GROUP INC p 869
43855 Plymouth Oaks Blvd 48170
Tel (734) 453-0800 SIC 5013

LOC PERFORMANCE PRODUCTS INC p 872
13505 N Haggerty Rd 48170
Tel (734) 453-2300 SIC 3541

MD INVESTORS CORP p 933
47659 Halyard Dr 48170
Tel (734) 207-6200 SIC 6799

MEBILODDE OF PLYMOUTH p 934
395 W Ann Arbor Trl 48170
Tel (734) 453-3983 SIC 8051

■ METALDYNE LLC p 952
47659 Halyard Dr 48170
Tel (734) 207-6200 SIC 3714

MOBIS NORTH AMERICA LLC p 980
46501 Commerce Dr 48170
Tel (248) 426-5577 SIC 5013 8731

MPG p 995
47659 Halyard Dr 48170
Tel (734) 207-6200 SIC 3499

PLASTIPAK HOLDINGS INC p 1155
41605 Ann Arbor Rd E 48170
Tel (734) 455-3600 SIC 3089

PLASTIPAK PACKAGING INC p 1155
41605 Ann Arbor Rd E 48170
Tel (734) 455-3600 SIC 3089

PLYMOUTH-CANTON COMMUNITY SCHOOLS p 1157
454 S Harvey St 48170
Tel (734) 416-2700 SIC 8211

POWERTEAM SERVICES LLC p 1166
477 S Main St 48170
Tel (919) 372-8614 SIC 1623 1629

■ PROGRESSIVE MICHIGAN INSURANCE CO p 1181
46333 Five Mile Rd 100 48170
Tel (734) 456-5742 SIC 6411

■ ROFIN-SINAR TECHNOLOGIES INC p 1246
40984 Concept Dr 48170
Tel (734) 416-0206 SIC 3699

TECHNOTRIM INC p 1432
49200 Halyard Dr 48170
Tel (734) 254-6600 SIC 2399

TRAM INC p 1469
47200 Port St 48170
Tel (734) 254-8500 SIC 3714 3643

VARROC LIGHTING SYSTEMS INC p 1545
47828 Halyard Dr 48170
Tel (734) 446-4400 SIC 3751

YANFENG US AUTOMOTIVE INTERIOR SYSTEMS I LLC p 1634
45000 Helm St 48170
Tel (414) 524-1200 *SIC* 2531

PONTIAC, MI

ABC APPLIANCE INC p 10
1 W Silverdome Indus Park 48342
Tel (248) 335-4222
SIC 5722 5731 5999 5065 5064 5063

COUNTY OF OAKLAND p 380
1200 N Telegraph Rd Ste 1 48341
Tel (248) 858-1000 *SIC* 9111

GONZALEZ CONTRACT SERVICES INC p 623
1670 Highwood E 48340
Tel (248) 548-6010 *SIC* 7361

IRVIN AUTOMOTIVE PRODUCTS INC p 765
2600 Centerpoint Pkwy 48341
Tel (248) 451-4100 *SIC* 3429 2396

JAC HOLDING CORP p 773
3937 Campus Dr 48341
Tel (248) 874-1800 *SIC* 3089

JAC PRODUCTS INC p 773
3937 Campus Dr 48341
Tel (248) 874-1800 *SIC* 3089 3714

LEE CONTRACTING INC p 851
631 Cesar E Chavez Ave 48342
Tel (888) 833-8776 *SIC* 1731 1542 1541

MCLAREN OAKLAND p 931
50 N Perry St 48342
Tel (248) 338-5000 *SIC* 8062

METALWORKING LUBRICANTS CO p 953
25 W Silverdome Indus Par 48342
Tel (248) 332-3500
SIC 5172 2869 2843 2992

OAKLAND PHYSICIANS MEDICAL CENTER LLC p 1071
461 W Huron St 48341
Tel (248) 857-7200 *SIC* 8062

SCHOOL DISTRICT OF CITY OF PONTIAC p 1289
47200 Woodward Ave 48342
Tel (248) 451-6800 *SIC* 8211

ST JOSEPH MERCY OAKLAND p 1368
44405 Woodward Ave 48341
Tel (248) 858-3000 *SIC* 8062

ST JOSEPH MERCY OAKLAND HOSPITAL p 1368
44405 Woodward Ave 48341
Tel (248) 858-6186 *SIC* 8062

PORT HURON, MI

AFX INDUSTRIES LLC p 33
1411 3rd St Ste G 48060
Tel (810) 966-4650 *SIC* 3111 5531

CONTINENTAL ENERGY SYSTEMS LLC p 363
1411 3rd St Ste A 48060
Tel (800) 624-2019 *SIC* 4924

DUNN PAPER HOLDINGS INC p 461
218 Riverview St 48060
Tel (810) 984-5521 *SIC* 2621 2672

DUNN PAPER INC p 461
218 Riverview St 48060
Tel (810) 984-5521 *SIC* 2671 2672

E B EDDY PAPER INC p 466
1700 Washington Ave 48060
Tel (810) 982-0191 *SIC* 2621

MCLAREN PORT HURON p 931
1221 Pine Grove Ave 48060
Tel (810) 987-5000 *SIC* 5912

PORT HURON AREA SCHOOL DISTRICT p 1162
2720 Riverside Dr 48060
Tel (810) 984-3101 *SIC* 8211

SEMCO ENERGY INC p 1302
1411 3rd St Ste A 48060
Tel (810) 987-2200 *SIC* 4924

SEMCO HOLDING CORP p 1302
1411 3rd St Ste A 48060
Tel (810) 987-2200 *SIC* 4924

WILLOW ENTERPRISES INC p 1613
1221 Pine Grove Ave 48060
Tel (810) 987-2064 *SIC* 8082 5999

PORTAGE, MI

AMERIFIRST FINANCIAL CORP p 82
950 Trade Centre Way # 400 49002
Tel (269) 324-4240 *SIC* 6162

KENDALL ELECTRIC INC p 810
5101 S Sprinkle Rd 49002
Tel (800) 632-5422 *SIC* 5063 7629 5084

MANN + HUMMEL INC p 902
6400 S Sprinkle Rd 49002
Tel (269) 329-3900 *SIC* 3559 3585

MANN + HUMMEL USA INC p 902
6400 S Sprinkle Rd 49002
Tel (269) 329-3900 *SIC* 3089 3714

PORTAGE PUBLIC SCHOOLS p 1162
8107 Mustang Dr 49002
Tel (269) 323-6800 *SIC* 8211

▲ STRYKER CORP p 1394
2825 Airview Blvd 49002
Tel (269) 385-2600 *SIC* 3841 3842 2599

SUMMIT POLYMERS INC p 1399
6715 S Sprinkle Rd 49002
Tel (269) 324-9330 *SIC* 3089

W SOULE & CO p 1569
7125 S Sprinkle Rd 49002
Tel (269) 324-7001 *SIC* 1711 3444

WOLVERINE PIPE LINE CO p 1621
8075 Creekside Dr Ste 210 49024
Tel (269) 323-2491 *SIC* 4613

REDFORD, MI

PISTON AUTOMOTIVE LLC p 1152
12723 Telegraph Rd Ste 1 48239
Tel (313) 541-8674 *SIC* 3714

■ TROY DESIGN & MANUFACTURING CO p 1485
12675 Berwyn 48239
Tel (313) 592-2300 *SIC* 3465

REED CITY, MI

POWER LINE SUPPLY CO p 1165
420 S Roth St Ste A 49677
Tel (231) 832-2297 *SIC* 5063

UTILITY SUPPLY AND CONSTRUCTION CO p 1537
420 S Roth St Ste A 49677
Tel (231) 832-2297
SIC 2411 2491 2631 5063

REMUS, MI

BANDIT INDUSTRIES INC p 150
6750 W Millbrook Rd 49340
Tel (989) 561-2270 *SIC* 3531 5082

ROCHESTER HILLS, MI

A RAYMOND CORPORATE NORTH AMERICA INC p 6
2350 Austin Ave Ste 200 48309
Tel (248) 853-2500 *SIC* 5085 3469 6719

A RAYMOND TINNERMAN AUTOMOTIVE INC p 6
3091 Research Dr 48309
Tel (248) 260-2121 *SIC* 5085 3469

ARCHDIOCESE OF DETROIT ED OFF p 105
2633 John R Rd 48307
Tel (248) 299-3798 *SIC* 8211

FANUC AMERICA CORP p 527
3900 W Hamlin Rd 48309
Tel (248) 377-7000
SIC 3559 3548 3569 3542

FLEXTRONICS AUTOMOTIVE USA INC p 556
2120 Austin Ave 48309
Tel (248) 853-5724 *SIC* 3625 3714 3643

LETICA CORP p 857
52585 Dequindre Rd 48307
Tel (248) 652-0557 *SIC* 2656 3089

M P I INTERNATIONAL INC p 889
2129 Austin Ave 48309
Tel (608) 764-5416 *SIC* 3462 3714 3469

NEWCOR INC p 1037
715 South Blvd E Ste 101 48307
Tel (248) 537-0014 *SIC* 3714

PARI ROBOTICS INC p 1114
2930 Technology Dr 48309
Tel (248) 377-4447 *SIC* 5084

PRECISION PARTS HOLDINGS INC p 1168
2129 Austin Ave 48309
Tel (248) 853-9010 *SIC* 3465 3469 3544

TECHNICAL TRAINING INC p 1431
3903 W Hamlin Rd 48309
Tel (248) 853-5550 *SIC* 8742 8999

TRICO PRODUCTS CORP p 1479
3255 W Hamlin Rd 48309
Tel (248) 371-1700
SIC 3714 3069 3082 8734 8731

▲ WABCO HOLDINGS INC p 1570
2770 Research Dr Fl 1 48309
Tel (248) 270-9299 *SIC* 3714

WEBASTO ROOF SYSTEMS INC p 1586
1757 Northfield Dr 48309
Tel (800) 860-7866 *SIC* 3714 3441 3469

WRIGHT & FILIPPIS INC p 1627
2845 Crooks Rd 48309
Tel (248) 829-8292 *SIC* 7352 5999

ROCHESTER, MI

■ ALLEGAN METROPOLITAN TITLE AGENCY p 52
400 Water St Ste 100 48307
Tel (248) 656-8686 *SIC* 6361

CRITTENTON HOSPITAL MEDICAL CENTER p 393
1101 W University Dr 48307
Tel (248) 652-5000 *SIC* 8062 8011

CRITTENTON HOSPITAL MEDICAL CENTER FOUNDATION p 393
1101 W University Dr 48307
Tel (248) 652-5000 *SIC* 8741 8062

EMPLOYEES ONLY INC p 494
805 Oakwood Dr Ste 100 48307
Tel (248) 276-0950 *SIC* 5812

OAKLAND UNIVERSITY p 1071
2200 N Squirrel Rd 48309
Tel (248) 370-2100 *SIC* 8221

ROCHESTER COMMUNITY SCHOOLS p 1243
501 W University Dr 48307
Tel (248) 726-3000 *SIC* 8211

ROCKFORD, MI

ROCKFORD PUBLIC SCHOOLS p 1244
350 N Main St 49341
Tel (616) 863-6320 *SIC* 8211

▲ WOLVERINE WORLD WIDE INC p 1621
9341 Courtland Dr Ne 49351
Tel (616) 866-5500
SIC 3143 3149 3144 3111

ROMULUS, MI

RKA PETROLEUM COMPANIES INC p 1239
28340 Wick Rd 48174
Tel (734) 946-2199 *SIC* 5172

TRANSPORTATION SERVICES INC p 1473
18165 Telegraph Rd 48174
Tel (734) 282-4444 *SIC* 4213

UNITED ROAD SERVICES INC p 1511
10701 Middlebelt Rd 48174
Tel (734) 946-3232 *SIC* 4213

URS MIDWEST INC p 1530
10701 Middlebelt Rd 48174
Tel (888) 278-2793 *SIC* 4731

ROSEBUSH, MI

■ MEARS GROUP INC p 934
4500 N Mission Rd 48878
Tel (989) 433-2929 *SIC* 1623 8711

ROSEVILLE, MI

ALL STATE FASTENER CORP p 51
15460 E 12 Mile Rd 48066
Tel (586) 773-5400 *SIC* 5072

LAKE COURT MEDICAL SUPPLIES INC p 839
27733 Groesbeck Hwy 48066
Tel (800) 860-3130 *SIC* 5047

RCO ENGINEERING INC p 1212
29200 Calahan Rd 48066
Tel (586) 774-0100
SIC 3714 3089 3365 7361 3325 2531

ROYAL OAK, MI

ASP HHI HOLDINGS INC p 118
2727 W 14 Mile Rd 48073
Tel (248) 597-3800 *SIC* 3462

BARRICK ENTERPRISES INC p 157
4338 Delemere Blvd 48073
Tel (248) 549-3737 *SIC* 5541

BEAUMONT HEALTH p 166
3601 W 13 Mile Rd 48073
Tel (248) 898-5000 *SIC* 8062

FORM HHITECH LLC p 567
2727 W 14 Mile Rd 48073
Tel (248) 597-3800 *SIC* 3462

■ HHI FORGING LLC p 689
2727 W 14 Mile Rd 48073
Tel (248) 284-2900 *SIC* 3462

HHI FORMTECH INDUSTRIES LLC p 689
2727 W 14 Mile Rd 48073
Tel (248) 597-3800 *SIC* 3463

■ HHI GROUP HOLDINGS LLC p 689
2727 W 14 Mile Rd 48073
Tel (248) 284-2900 *SIC* 7549

WILLIAM BEAUMONT HOSPITAL p 1610
3601 W 13 Mile Rd 48073
Tel (248) 898-5000 *SIC* 8062

SAGINAW, MI

CARAVAN FACILITIES MANAGEMENT LLC p 252
1400 Weiss St Ste 1 48602
Tel (989) 239-2126 *SIC* 7349

COVENANT MEDICAL CENTER INC p 384
1447 N Harrison St 48602
Tel (989) 583-0000 *SIC* 8062

DURO-LAST INC p 463
525 E Morley Dr 48601
Tel (800) 248-0280 *SIC* 2295

GARBER MANAGEMENT GROUP INC p 591
999 S Washington Ave # 1 48601
Tel (989) 790-9090 *SIC* 5511

HSS LLC p 715
5310 Hampton Pl Ste B 48604
Tel (989) 777-2983 *SIC* 8741 8742 7389

MAHAR TOOL SUPPLY CO INC p 897
112 Williams St 48602
Tel (989) 799-5530 *SIC* 5085

MEANS INDUSTRIES INC p 934
3715 E Washington Rd 48601
Tel (989) 754-1433 *SIC* 3714 3465

MERRILL TOOL HOLDING CO p 950
400 Florence St 48602
Tel (989) 791-6676
SIC 3443 3599 8734 8711 3724

MORLEY COMPANIES INC p 989
1 Morley Plz 48603
Tel (989) 791-2550 *SIC* 8742 4724

SAGINAW CONTROL & ENGINEERING INC p 1268
95 Midland Rd 48638
Tel (989) 799-6871 *SIC* 3699 3444

ST MARYS MEDICAL CENTER OF SAGINAW INC p 1372
800 S Washington Ave 48601
Tel (989) 907-8000 *SIC* 8062

STANDARD ELECTRIC CO p 1376
2650 Trautner Dr 48604
Tel (989) 497-2100 *SIC* 5063

WOLGAST CORP p 1621
4835 Towne Centre Rd # 203 48604
Tel (989) 233-5228 *SIC* 1542 1541

SAINT CLAIR SHORES, MI

FISHER & CO INC p 551
33300 Fisher Dr 48082
Tel (586) 746-2000 *SIC* 2531

NGS AMERICAN INC p 1041
27575 Harper Ave 48081
Tel (586) 552-4656 *SIC* 6411 8741

SAINT CLAIR, MI

BIEWER LUMBER LLC p 181
812 S Riverside Ave 48079
Tel (810) 326-3930 *SIC* 2491

JOHN A BIEWER LUMBER CO p 787
812 S Riverside Ave 48079
Tel (810) 329-4789 *SIC* 2491

SAINT JOHNS, MI

SUNTREE-OXFORD ASSOCIATES LIMITED DIVIDEND HOUSING ASSOCIATION p 1405
1100 Sunview Dr 48879
Tel (989) 224-8910 *SIC* 6513

SAINT JOSEPH, MI

LAKELAND HOSPITALS AT NILES AND ST JOSEPH INC p 840
1234 Napier Ave 49085
Tel (800) 968-0115 *SIC* 8062

LAKELAND MEDICAL HEALTH CENTER p 840
1234 Napier Ave 49085
Tel (269) 982-4935 *SIC* 8099

LAKELAND REGIONAL HEALTH SYSTEM p 840
1234 Napier Ave 49085
Tel (269) 983-8300 *SIC* 8741

LECO CORP p 851
3000 Lakeview Ave 49085
Tel (269) 983-5531
SIC 4493 3821 3826 3825 3823 3264

MICHIGAN PIZZA HUT INC p 961
2053 Niles Rd 49085
Tel (269) 983-3888 *SIC* 5812

PRI MAR PETROLEUM INC p 1173
1207 Broad St 49085
Tel (269) 983-7314 *SIC* 5411 5172

TURFIX LLC p 1492
2228 Mount Curve Ave 49085
Tel (888) 495-3195 *SIC* 0782

UNITED FEDERAL CREDIT UNION p 1508
2807 S State St 49085
Tel (888) 982-1400 *SIC* 6061 6163

SALINE, MI

FAURECIA INTERIOR SYSTEMS SALINE LLC p 531
7700 E Michigan Ave 48176
Tel (734) 429-0030 *SIC* 5013

PRODUCTION SERVICES MANAGEMENT INC p 1180
1255 Beach Ct 48176
Tel (734) 677-0454 *SIC* 5085

SARANAC, MI

HERBRUCK POULTRY RANCH INC p 685
6425 Grand River Ave 48881
Tel (616) 642-9421 *SIC* 0252

SAULT SAINTE MARIE, MI

CHIPPEWA COUNTY WAR MEMORIAL HOSPITAL INC p 301
500 Osborn Blvd 49783
Tel (906) 635-4460 *SIC* 8062 8051

ROMULUS KEWADIN CASINO LLC p 1249
2186 Shunk Rd 49783
Tel (906) 632-0530 *SIC* 7011

SAULT SAINTE MARIE TRIBE OF CHIPPEWA INDIANS p 1283
523 Ashmun St 49783
Tel (906) 635-6050 *SIC* 9131

SHELBY TOWNSHIP, MI

JK & T WINGS INC p 786
13405 W Star Dr Ste 2 48315
Tel (586) 781-0591 *SIC* 8741

JVIS INTERNATIONAL LLC p 798
52048 Shelby Pkwy 48315
Tel (586) 739-9542 *SIC* 3089

JVIS USA LLC p 798
52048 Shelby Pkwy 48315
Tel (586) 884-5700 *SIC* 3089

STRESS CON INDUSTRIES INC p 1393
50500 Design Ln 48315
Tel (586) 731-1628 *SIC* 3272

US FARATHANE HOLDINGS CORP p 1531
11650 Park Ct 48315
Tel (248) 754-7000 *SIC* 3089

SHELBY, MI

PETERSON FARMS INC p 1138
3104 W Baseline Rd 49455
Tel (231) 861-6333 *SIC* 2037 0723

SOUTH HAVEN, MI

TRELLEBORG AUTOMOTIVE USA INC p 1476
400 Aylworth Ave 49090
Tel (269) 637-2116 *SIC* 3061 3625

TRELLEBORG CORP p 1476
200 Veterans Blvd Ste 3 49090
Tel (269) 639-9891
SIC 3341 1021 1044 1031 4226 1041

VIBRACOUSTIC NORTH AMERICA L P p 1555
400 Aylworth Ave 49090
Tel (269) 637-2116
SIC 2821 3714 3053 3061

SOUTH LYON, MI

MICHIGAN SEAMLESS TUBE LLC p 961
400 Mcmunn St 48178
Tel (248) 486-0100 *SIC* 3317

SOUTH LYON COMMUNITY SCHOOLS p 1344
345 S Warren St 48178
Tel (248) 573-8127 *SIC* 8211

SOUTHFIELD, MI

■ **ABC GROUP HOLDINGS INC** p 10
24133 Northwestern Hwy 48075
Tel (248) 352-3706 *SIC* 3089

ABC INOAC EXTERIOR SYSTEMS LLC p 10
24175 Northwestern Hwy 48075
Tel (248) 619-6057 *SIC* 5013

ALTIMETRIK CORP p 62
1000 Town Ctr Ste 700 48075
Tel (248) 281-2500 *SIC* 7371

■ **AMERITECH PUBLISHING INC** p 84
23500 Northwestern Hwy 48075
Tel (800) 996-4609 *SIC* 2741

ARCADIA SERVICES INC p 103
20750 Civic Center Dr # 100 48076
Tel (248) 352-7530 *SIC* 7363 8082

ASSOCIATED COMMUNITY SERVICES INC p 120
23800 W 10 Mile Rd # 200 48033
Tel (248) 352-2600 *SIC* 7389

ATWELL LLC p 130
2 Towne Sq Ste 700 48076
Tel (248) 447-2000
SIC 8999 8713 8748 8711

BARTECH GROUP INC p 157
27777 Franklin Rd Ste 600 48034
Tel (201) 970-0605 *SIC* 7363

BARTON MALOW CO p 158
26500 American Dr 48034
Tel (248) 436-5000 *SIC* 8741

BARTON MALOW ENTERPRISES INC p 158
26500 American Dr 48034
Tel (248) 436-5000 *SIC* 8741 1542 1541

BLUE CARE NETWORK OF MICHIGAN p 191
20500 Civic Center Dr 48076
Tel (248) 799-6400 *SIC* 6324

BRANDMOTION LLC p 208
21518 Bridge St 48033
Tel (734) 619-1250 *SIC* 5013

C A MUER CORP p 232
400 Galleria Ofc Ctr 48034
Tel (248) 226-9400 *SIC* 5812

CHASSIX INC p 291
300 Galleria Officentre 48034
Tel (248) 728-8642 *SIC* 3714

COMAU LLC p 343
21000 Telegraph Rd 48033
Tel (248) 353-8888 *SIC* 3548 3829 3545

■ **COMERICA INSURANCE SERVICES INC** p 344
20700 Civic Center Dr # 290 48076
Tel (248) 603-3600 *SIC* 6021

CONCORD INTERNATIONAL INC p 354
300 Galleria Officentre # 501 48034
Tel (248) 728-8642 *SIC* 3465

▲ **CREDIT ACCEPTANCE CORP** p 390
25505 W 12 Mile Rd # 2300 48034
Tel (248) 353-2700 *SIC* 6141

DENSO INTERNATIONAL AMERICA INC p 428
24777 Denso Dr 48033
Tel (248) 350-7500 *SIC* 3714 5013

DIVERSIFIED MACHINE INC p 444
300 Galleria Officentre # 501 48034
Tel (248) 728-8642 *SIC* 3465

▲ **DIVERSIFIED RESTAURANT HOLDINGS INC** p 444
27680 Franklin Rd 48034
Tel (248) 223-9160 *SIC* 5812 5813 6794

■ **DONER PARTNERS LLC** p 450
25900 Northwestern Hwy 48075
Tel (248) 354-9700 *SIC* 7311

DURR SYSTEMS INC p 463
26801 Northwestern Hwy 48033
Tel (248) 450-2000 *SIC* 3559 3567

DURR–INC p 463
26801 Northwestern Hwy 48033
Tel (734) 459-6800 *SIC* 3559 3567

■ **EAGLE OTTAWA LLC** p 468
21557 Telegraph Rd 48033
Tel (248) 364-7400 *SIC* 3111 2399 2396

EPITEC INC p 505
24800 Denso Dr Ste 150 48033
Tel (248) 353-6800
SIC 7371 7379 7373 8748 8711

■ **FEDERAL-MOGUL CORP** p 536
27300 W 11 Mile Rd 48034
Tel (248) 354-7700
SIC 3559 3462 3812 3674 3694

■ **FEDERAL-MOGUL HOLDINGS CORP** p 536
27300 W 11 Mile Rd 48034
Tel (248) 354-7700
SIC 3462 3559 3694 3812 3674 3714

■ **FEDERAL-MOGUL PISTON RINGS INC** p 536
26555 Northwestern Hwy 48033
Tel (248) 354-7700 *SIC* 3592 3053 3369

■ **FEDERAL-MOGUL PRODUCTS INC** p 536
26555 Northwestern Hwy 48033
Tel (248) 354-7700 *SIC* 3714

FIRST MERCURY FINANCIAL CORP p 548
26600 Telegraph Rd 48033
Tel (248) 358-4010 *SIC* 6331

FIRST MERCURY INSURANCE CO p 548
26600 Telegraph Rd 48033
Tel (248) 358-4010 *SIC* 6331

GDI FACILITY SERVICES INC p 595
24300 Southfield Rd # 220 48075
Tel (248) 483-3170 *SIC* 7349

GDI SERVICES INC p 595
24300 Southfield Rd # 220 48075
Tel (248) 483-3170 *SIC* 7349

GOLDEN OPTICAL CORP p 621
19800 W 8 Mile Rd 48075
Tel (248) 354-7100 *SIC* 5995 6794

GREAT EXPRESSIONS DENTAL CENTERS PC p 633
28626 Telegraph Rd 48034
Tel (248) 203-2330 *SIC* 8021 8741

GREDE FOUNDRIES INC p 636
4000 Town Ctr Ste 500 48075
Tel (248) 440-9500 *SIC* 3321

■ **GREDE HOLDINGS LLC** p 636
1 Towne Sq Ste 550 48076
Tel (248) 440-9500 *SIC* 3321

■ **GREDE II LLC** p 636
4000 Town Ctr Ste 500 48075
Tel (248) 522-4500 *SIC* 3321

■ **GREDE LLC** p 636
1 Towne Sq Ste 550 48076
Tel (248) 440-9500 *SIC* 3321

GST AUTOLEATHER INC p 643
20 Oak Hollow St Ste 300 48033
Tel (248) 436-2300 *SIC* 3111

GU-YOUNGTECH CO LTD p 644
26555 Evergreen Rd 48076
Tel (248) 701-6663 *SIC* 5013

GUARDIAN GUARD SERVICES INC p 645
18000 W 8 Mile Rd 48075
Tel (248) 423-1000 *SIC* 7381

HANTZ GROUP INC p 659
26200 American Dr Ste 500 48034
Tel (248) 304-2855 *SIC* 6282

HARTMAN AND TYNER INC p 666
24700 W 12 Mile Rd 48034
Tel (248) 352-2010 *SIC* 6513 6531

INTERNATIONAL AUTOMOTIVE COMPONENTS GROUP NORTH AMERICA HOLDINGS INC p 754
28333 Telegraph Rd 48034
Tel (248) 455-7000 *SIC* 5013

INTERNATIONAL AUTOMOTIVE COMPONENTS GROUP NORTH AMERICA INC p 754
28333 Telegraph Rd 48034
Tel (248) 455-7000 *SIC* 3089 5013

▲ **LEAR CORP** p 850
21557 Telegraph Rd 48033
Tel (248) 447-1500
SIC 3714 2531 2396 3643

■ **LEAR OPERATIONS CORP** p 850
21557 Telegraph Rd 48033
Tel (248) 447-1500 *SIC* 3089

MEADOWBROOK INC p 934
26255 American Dr 48034
Tel (248) 358-1100 *SIC* 6411

MEADOWBROOK INSURANCE GROUP INC p 934
26255 American Dr 48034
Tel (248) 358-1100 *SIC* 6411 6211

▲ **METALDYNE PERFORMANCE GROUP INC** p 952
1 Towne Sq Ste 550 48076
Tel (248) 727-1800 *SIC* 3714

■ **MOTORS INSURANCE CORP** p 993
300 Galleria Officentre # 201 48034
Tel (248) 263-6000 *SIC* 6331

PETERSON AMERICAN CORP p 1138
21200 Telegraph Rd 48033
Tel (248) 799-5400 *SIC* 3495

PLANTE & MORAN PLLC p 1154
27400 Northwestern Hwy # 300 48034
Tel (248) 223-3247 *SIC* 8721 8742

PLANTE MORAN PC p 1154
27400 Northwestern Hwy # 300 48034
Tel (248) 352-2500 *SIC* 8721

■ **PRESTOLITE WIRE LLC** p 1173
200 Galleria Officentre 48034
Tel (248) 355-4422 *SIC* 3694

PROVIDENCE HOSPITAL p 1186
16001 W 9 Mile Rd 48075
Tel (248) 849-3000 *SIC* 8062

R L POLK & CO p 1202
26933 Northwestern Hwy 48033
Tel (248) 728-7000 *SIC* 8742

REAL ESTATE ONE INC p 1213
25800 Northwestern Hwy # 100 48075
Tel (248) 208-2900 *SIC* 6531

SOUTHFIELD PUBLIC SCHOOL DISTRICT p 1351
24661 Lahser Rd 48033
Tel (248) 746-8500 *SIC* 8211

STEFANINI INC p 1385
27335 W 11 Mile Rd 48033
Tel (248) 357-2866 *SIC* 7379

▲ **SUN COMMUNITIES INC** p 1400
27777 Franklin Rd Ste 200 48034
Tel (248) 208-2500 *SIC* 6798 2451

▲ **SUPERIOR INDUSTRIES INTERNATIONAL INC** p 1406
26600 Telg Rd Ste 400 48033
Tel (248) 352-7300 *SIC* 3714

TECHNOSOFT CORP p 1432
28411 Northwestern Hwy # 640 48034
Tel (248) 603-2600 *SIC* 7379

THYSSENKRUPP INDUSTRIAL SERVICES NA INC p 1451
22355 W 11 Mile Rd 48033
Tel (248) 233-5600 *SIC* 4225 4731

THYSSENKRUPP MATERIALS NA INC p 1451
22355 W 11 Mile Rd 48033
Tel (248) 233-5600
SIC 5051 5162 3444 8741

TIBA LLC p 1452
29600 Southfield Rd 200 48076
Tel (248) 633-6067 *SIC* 8742

UC HOLDINGS INC p 1498
300 Galleria Officentre 48034
Tel (248) 728-8642 *SIC* 3465 3714

VESCO OIL CORP p 1552
16055 W 12 Mile Rd 48076
Tel (800) 527-5358 *SIC* 5172

SOUTHGATE, MI

ST JAMES INC p 1367
18500 Walnut St 48195
Tel (734) 285-4911 *SIC* 3714 3711 3465

SPRING LAKE, MI

JSJ FURNITURE CORP p 796
17237 Van Wagoner Rd 49456
Tel (616) 847-6534 *SIC* 2521

STANDISH, MI

FORWARD CORP p 570
219 N Front St 48658
Tel (989) 846-4501
SIC 5411 5541 5172 5812

STERLING HEIGHTS, MI

ACUMENT GLOBAL TECHNOLOGIES INC p 20
6125 18 Mile Rd 48314
Tel (586) 254-3900 *SIC* 3965 5072

ADMINISTRATIVE EMPLOYER SERVICES INC p 23
13900 Lakeside Cir 200 48313
Tel (586) 997-3377 *SIC* 8742

BETA STEEL LLC p 177
6300 Hughes Dr 48312
Tel (586) 698-9200 *SIC* 5051

CIRAULO BROTHERS BUILDING CO p 308
7670 19 Mile Rd 48314
Tel (586) 731-3670 *SIC* 5031 5211 1761

CONTI CORP p 362
6417 Center Dr Ste 120 48312
Tel (586) 274-4800 *SIC* 1731 1711

CONTINENTAL DISTRIBUTORS INC p 363
35710 Mound Rd 48310
Tel (586) 268-3835 *SIC* 5962 5812

■ **E & R INDUSTRIAL SALES INC** p 465
40800 Enterprise Dr 48314
Tel (586) 795-2400 *SIC* 5085

FONTANA AMERICA INC p 563
6125 18 Mile Rd 48314
Tel (586) 997-5600 *SIC* 5085

■ **GENERAL DYNAMICS LAND SYSTEMS INC** p 600
38500 Mound Rd 48310
Tel (586) 825-4000 *SIC* 5088 8711

IWKA HOLDING CORP p 769
6600 Center Dr 48312
Tel (586) 795-2000
SIC 3549 5084 7371 8711

KEY SAFETY RESTRAINT SYSTEMS INC p 814
7000 19 Mile Rd 48314
Tel (586) 726-3800 *SIC* 3714 3674 3679

KEY SAFETY SYSTEMS INC p 814
7000 19 Mile Rd 48314
Tel (586) 726-3800 *SIC* 2399 3714

KUKA SYSTEMS NORTH AMERICA LLC p 831
6600 Center Dr 48312
Tel (586) 795-2000 *SIC* 3549

MACOMB GROUP INC p 893
6600 15 Mile Rd 48312
Tel (586) 274-4100 *SIC* 5085

MAYCO INTERNATIONAL LLC p 923
42400 Merrill Rd 48314
Tel (586) 803-6000 *SIC* 3089

MEADE GROUP INC p 933
6951 19 Mile Rd 48314
Tel (586) 803-6250 *SIC* 5511

MILLIKEN MILLWORK INC p 971
6361 Sterling Dr N 48312
Tel (586) 264-0950 *SIC* 5031

RONCELLI INC p 1249
6471 Metropolitan Pkwy 48312
Tel (586) 264-2060 *SIC* 1541 8711

STONEBRIDGE INDUSTRIES INC p 1391
42400 Merrill Rd 48314
Tel (586) 323-0348 *SIC* 3496 3462 3451

US HEALTH HOLDINGS LTD p 1532
8220 Irving Rd 48312
Tel (586) 693-4400 *SIC* 6411

UTICA COMMUNITY SCHOOLS p 1537
11303 Greendale Dr 48312
Tel (586) 797-1000 *SIC* 8211

VCST INC p 1545
13854 Lakeside Cir 201 48313
Tel (586) 685-1747 *SIC* 8742

STURGIS, MI

MORGAN OLSON LLC p 988
1801 S Nottawa St 49091
Tel (269) 659-0200 *SIC* 3713

STURGIS MOLDED PRODUCTS CO p 1395
70343 Clark Rd 49091
Tel (269) 651-9381 *SIC* 3089 3544

SUTTONS BAY, MI

GRAND TRAVERSE BAND ECONOMIC DEVELOPMENT CORP p 630
2331 N West Bay Shore Dr 49682
Tel (231) 534-8000 *SIC* 7011 7993 5812

GRAND TRAVERSE BAND LLC p 630
2605 N West Bay Shore Dr 49682
Tel (231) 534-7750 *SIC* 9131

SWARTZ CREEK, MI

HOUGEN MANUFACTURING INC p 711
3001 Hougen Dr 48473
Tel (810) 635-7111
SIC 5084 3545 3546 3541

TAYLOR, MI

ATLAS OIL CO p 128
24501 Ecorse Rd 48180
Tel (313) 292-5500 *SIC* 5172 5171

COMMERCIAL GROUP INC p 345
12801 Universal Dr 48180
Tel (313) 931-6100
SIC 5085 5051 3496 3537 3534

DEARBORN MID-WEST CO LLC p 420
20334 Superior Rd 48180
Tel (734) 288-4400 *SIC* 3535

DETROIT CITY DAIRY p 433
21405 Trolley Indus Dr 48180
Tel (313) 295-6300
SIC 5143 5141 5147 5149

■ **MASCO BUILDING PRODUCTS CORP** p 915
21001 Van Born Rd 48180
Tel (313) 274-7400 *SIC* 3429 3639 3644

▲ **MASCO CORP** p 915
21001 Van Born Rd 48180
Tel (313) 274-7400
SIC 2434 3432 3088 3429 1742

PAINTERS SUPPLY AND EQUIPMENT CO p 1108
25195 Brest 48180
Tel (734) 946-8119 *SIC* 5198 5231

PRUDENTIAL SECURITY INC p 1187
20600 Eureka Rd Ste 900 48180
Tel (734) 286-6000 *SIC* 7381

SUGAR AMERICANE REFINING LLC p 1397
21010 Trolley Indus Dr 48180
Tel (313) 299-1300 *SIC* 2062

TAYLOR SCHOOL DISTRICT p 1427
23033 Northline Rd 48180
Tel (734) 374-1200 *SIC* 8211

TECUMSEH, MI

LENAWEE STAMPING CORP p 855
1200 E Chicago Blvd 49286
Tel (517) 423-2400 *SIC* 3465

TEMPERANCE, MI

ROLLED ALLOYS INC p 1247
125 W Sterns Rd 48182
Tel (800) 521-0332
SIC 5051 3369 3341 3317 2899 2851

THREE RIVERS, MI

ARMSTRONG INTERNATIONAL INC p 111
816 Maple St 49093
Tel (269) 273-1415 *SIC* 3491

■ JOHNSON KADANT INC p 791
805 Wood St 49093
Tel (269) 278-1715
SIC 3494 8711 1389 3052 1099

TRAVERSE CITY, MI

CHERRY CENTRAL COOPERATIVE INC p 294
1771 N Us Highway 31 S 49685
Tel (231) 946-1860 *SIC* 2033

HAGERTY INSURANCE AGENCY INC p 652
141 Rvers Edge Dr Ste 200 49684
Tel (231) 947-6868 *SIC* 6411

HOSPITALITY WEST LLC p 710
745 S Garfield Ave Ste A 49686
Tel (231) 941-5052 *SIC* 5812

LAKE HARLEYSVILLE STATES INSURANCE CO p 839
600 E Front St Ste 200 49686
Tel (231) 946-6390 *SIC* 6331

MUNSON HEALTHCARE p 1000
1105 Sixth St 49684
Tel (800) 252-2065 *SIC* 8062

MUNSON MEDICAL CENTER p 1000
1105 Sixth St 49684
Tel (231) 935-6000 *SIC* 8062

NORTH BAY PRODUCE INC p 1051
1771 N Us Highway 31 S 49685
Tel (231) 946-1941 *SIC* 5148

OILGEAR CO p 1079
1424 International Dr 49686
Tel (231) 929-1660 *SIC* 3594 3492 3593

TRAVERSE CITY AREA PUBLIC SCHOOLS p 1475
412 Webster St 49686
Tel (231) 933-1700 *SIC* 8211

TRENTON, MI

FRITZ ENTERPRISES INC p 580
1650 W Jefferson Ave 48183
Tel (734) 692-4231 *SIC* 5093

HURON VALLEY STEEL CORP p 721
1650 W Jefferson Ave 48183
Tel (734) 479-3500 *SIC* 5093 3341 3559

TROY, MI

AJAX PAVING INDUSTRIES INC p 41
1957 Crooks Rd A 48084
Tel (248) 244-3300
SIC 1611 2951 3273 3272

ALTAIR ENGINEERING INC p 61
1820 E Big Beaver Rd 48083
Tel (248) 614-2400 *SIC* 8711

AMERICAN SPECIALTY RETAILING GROUP INC p 79
5607 New King Dr Ste 125 48098
Tel (248) 674-4991 *SIC* 5661 5941 5699

■ ARVINMERITOR EXHAUST SYSTEMS INC p 114
2135 W Maple Rd 48084
Tel (248) 435-1000 *SIC* 5013

■ ARVINMERITOR OE LLC p 114
2135 W Maple Rd 48084
Tel (248) 435-1000 *SIC* 3714

■ ASSET ACCEPTANCE CAPITAL CORP p 119
320 E Big Beaver Rd 48083
Tel (800) 505-5166 *SIC* 6153 7322

ASSET ACCEPTANCE HOLDINGS LLC p 119
320 E Big Beaver Rd 48083
Tel (586) 939-9600 *SIC* 6141

ASSET ACCEPTANCE LLC p 119
320 E Big Beaver Rd 48083
Tel (586) 939-9600 *SIC* 6141

BNP MEDIA INC p 194
2401 W Big Beaver Rd # 700 48084
Tel (248) 362-3700 *SIC* 2721

CADILLAC PRODUCTS INC p 236
5800 Crooks Rd Ste 100 48098
Tel (248) 813-8200
SIC 3714 3081 2673 3089

CADILLAC PRODUCTS PACKAGING CO p 236
5800 Crooks Rd 48098
Tel (248) 879-5000 *SIC* 3081

CAPITAL FOR MERCHANTS LLC p 249
250 Stephenson Hwy 48083
Tel (248) 269-6000 *SIC* 6153

CARLEX GLASS OF INDIANA INC p 257
1209 E Big Beaver Rd 48083
Tel (586) 365-4900 *SIC* 3211

CEI LIQUIDATION ESTATES p 273
755 W Big Beaver Rd 48084
Tel (248) 614-8200 *SIC* 2451 5271

CHAMPION ENTERPRISES HOLDINGS LLC p 287
755 W Big Beaver Rd 48084
Tel (248) 614-8200 *SIC* 1521

CHAMPION HOME BUILDERS INC p 287
755 W Big Beaver Rd # 1000 48084
Tel (248) 614-8200 *SIC* 1521 2451

CHICL LLC p 298
1708 Northwood Dr 48084
Tel (859) 294-5590 *SIC* 3641

CHINA AUTOMOTIVE SYSTEMS INC p 301
2546 Elliott Dr 48083
Tel (248) 577-0353 *SIC* 5812

COSMA AMERICA HOLDINGS INC p 373
750 Tower Dr 48098
Tel (248) 524-5300 *SIC* 3714

COSMA INTERNATIONAL OF AMERICA INC p 373
750 Tower Dr 48098
Tel (248) 631-1100 *SIC* 3714

CRESTMARK BANK p 392
5480 Corporate Dr 48098
Tel (248) 641-5100 *SIC* 6022

DAYCO INC p 417
1650 Research Dr Ste 200 48083
Tel (716) 689-4972
SIC 3641 3646 3643 3625 3613

DAYCO PRODUCTS LLC p 417
1650 Research Dr Ste 200 48083
Tel (248) 404-6500 *SIC* 3568

DELPHI AUTOMOTIVE LLP p 425
5725 Delphi Dr 48098
Tel (248) 813-2494 *SIC* 5065 5012

DELPHI AUTOMOTIVE SYSTEMS LLC p 425
5725 Delphi Dr 48098
Tel (248) 813-2000 *SIC* 3714

DELPHI CORP p 425
5725 Delphi Dr 48098
Tel (248) 813-2000 *SIC* 3714

DELPHI HOLDINGS LLC p 425
5725 Delphi Dr 48098
Tel (248) 813-2000 *SIC* 3714

DIALOGUE MARKETING INC p 436
800 Tower Dr Ste 200 48098
Tel (800) 523-5867 *SIC* 7389

DIEOMATIC INC p 438
750 Tower Dr Mail 7000 Mail Code 48098
Tel (319) 668-2031 *SIC* 3714

DPH HOLDINGS CORP p 454
5725 Delphi Dr 48098
Tel (248) 813-2000 *SIC* 3714

DPH LLC p 454
5725 Delphi Dr 48098
Tel (248) 813-2000 *SIC* 3714

DPH-DAS GLOBAL (HOLDINGS) LLC p 454
5725 Delphi Dr 48098
Tel (248) 813-2000 *SIC* 3714

DPH-DAS LLC p 454
5725 Delphi Dr 48098
Tel (248) 813-2000 *SIC* 3714

DRIVESOL WORLDWIDE HOLDING CORP p 456
1104 W Maple Rd 48084
Tel (248) 729-2222 *SIC* 5013

DUNHAMS ATHLEISURE CORP p 461
5607 New King Dr Ste 125 48098
Tel (248) 674-4991
SIC 5699 5661 5941 5961

EMPIRE ELECTRONICS INC p 493
214 E Maple Rd 48083
Tel (248) 585-8130 *SIC* 3679

ENERGY CONVERSION DEVICES INC p 497
1441 E Maple Rd Ste 301 48083
Tel (248) 293-8772 *SIC* 3674

▲ FLAGSTAR BANCORP INC p 554
5151 Corporate Dr 48098
Tel (248) 312-2000 *SIC* 6035

■ FLAGSTAR BANK FSB p 554
5151 Corporate Dr 48098
Tel (248) 312-2000 *SIC* 6035

GESTAMP NORTH AMERICA INC p 609
2701 Troy Center Dr # 150 48084
Tel (248) 743-3400 *SIC* 5013

HANSONS WINDOWS AND SIDING OF LANSING LLC p 659
977 E 14 Mile Rd 48083
Tel (248) 681-9202 *SIC* 1751

HHJ HOLDINGS LIMITED p 689
1957 Crooks Rd A 48084
Tel (248) 652-9716 *SIC* 1611 2951

HOLLYWOOD HOLDING CO LLC p 701
2670 W Maple Rd 48084
Tel (248) 643-0309 *SIC* 5921 5141 5411

▲ HORIZON GLOBAL CORP p 707
2600 W Big Beaver Rd # 555 48084
Tel (248) 593-8820 *SIC* 3714 3711 5531

HP PELZER AUTOMOTIVE SYSTEMS INC p 714
1175 Crooks Rd 48084
Tel (248) 280-1010 *SIC* 3061 2273

HSP EPI ACQUISITION LLC p 715
1401 Crooks Rd Ste 150 48084
Tel (248) 404-1520 *SIC* 2731

HTC GLOBAL SERVICES INC p 715
3270 W Big Beaver Rd # 100 48084
Tel (248) 786-2500 *SIC* 7379

ICONMA LLC p 728
850 Stephenson Hwy 48083
Tel (248) 583-1930 *SIC* 7363

INERGY AUTOMOTIVE SYSTEMS (USA) LLC p 740
2710 Bellingham Dr # 400 48083
Tel (248) 743-5700 *SIC* 3714

INOAC USA INC p 745
1515 Equity Dr Ste 200 48084
Tel (248) 619-7031 *SIC* 3085 3714

INTEVA PRODUCTS LLC p 759
1401 Crooks Rd 48084
Tel (248) 655-8886 *SIC* 3714 5085

KAMAX LP p 801
500 W Long Lake Rd 48098
Tel (248) 879-0200 *SIC* 3452

■ KAUTEX INC p 805
750 Stephenson Hwy 48083
Tel (248) 616-5100 *SIC* 3714

▲ KELLY SERVICES INC p 809
999 W Big Beaver Rd 48084
Tel (248) 362-4444 *SIC* 7363

KRESGE FOUNDATION p 829
3215 W Big Beaver Rd 48084
Tel (248) 643-9630 *SIC* 6732

MAGNA EXTERIORS OF AMERICA INC p 896
750 Tower Dr 48098
Tel (248) 631-1100 *SIC* 3714 3544 8711

MAGNA INTERNATIONAL OF AMERICA INC p 896
750 Tower Dr 7000 48098
Tel (248) 729-2400 *SIC* 3714

MAGNA POWERTRAIN OF AMERICA INC p 896
1870 Technology Dr 48083
Tel (248) 597-7811 *SIC* 5013

MAGNA POWERTRAIN USA INC p 896
1870 Technology Dr 48083
Tel (248) 680-4900 *SIC* 3714

MAHLE BEHR MANUFACTURING MANAGEMENT INC p 897
2700 Daley Dr 48083
Tel (248) 735-3623 *SIC* 5013 3714

MAHLE BEHR USA INC p 897
2700 Daley Dr 48083
Tel (248) 743-3700 *SIC* 3714

MARTINREA AUTOMOTIVE-STRUCTURES (USA) INC p 913
2800 Livernois Rd Ste 450 48083
Tel (248) 823-5700 *SIC* 3714

▲ MERITOR INC p 949
2135 W Maple Rd 48084
Tel (248) 435-1000
SIC 3714 3493 3625 3465

MERITOR WABCO VEHICLE CONTROL SYSTEMS p 949
2135 W Maple Rd 48084
Tel (248) 273-4698 *SIC* 5013

METAVATION LLC p 953
900 Wilshire Dr Ste 270 48084
Tel (248) 351-1000 *SIC* 3714

N S INTERNATIONAL LTD p 1005
600 Wilshire Dr 48084
Tel (248) 251-1600 *SIC* 5013

■ NBD SERVICE CORP p 1021
1235 E Big Beaver Rd 48083
Tel (248) 680-2600 *SIC* 7389

NOBLE INTERNATIONAL LTD p 1046
840 W Long Lake Rd # 601 48098
Tel (248) 519-0700 *SIC* 3714

NORTH AMERICAN BANCARD LLC p 1049
250 Stephenson Hwy 48083
Tel (800) 226-2273 *SIC* 6153

NTVB MEDIA INC p 1066
209 Park Dr 48083
Tel (248) 583-4190 *SIC* 2752

OLGAS KITCHEN INC p 1082
2125 Butterfield Dr # 301 48084
Tel (248) 362-0001 *SIC* 5812

■ OPPENHEIMER & CO INC p 1090
3310 W Big Beaver Rd # 205 48084
Tel (248) 637-8300 *SIC* 6211

PEERLESS STEEL CO p 1127
2450 Austin Dr 48083
Tel (248) 528-3200 *SIC* 5051

PLASTIC OMNIUM AUTO EXTERIORS LLC p 1155
2710 Bellingham Dr # 400 48083
Tel (248) 458-0700 *SIC* 3089

PLEX SYSTEMS INC p 1156
900 Tower Dr Ste 1400 48098
Tel (248) 391-8001 *SIC* 7374

POPULUS GROUP LLC p 1161
850 Stephenson Hwy 48083
Tel (248) 581-1100 *SIC* 7363

■ PROCTOR FINANCIAL INC p 1179
5225 Crooks Rd 48098
Tel (248) 269-5700 *SIC* 6411

QUAD ELECTRONICS INC p 1195
379 Executive Dr 48083
Tel (800) 969-9220 *SIC* 5063

■ QUEST DIAGNOSTICS INC p 1199
1947 Technology Dr 100 48083
Tel (248) 364-1324 *SIC* 8071

RAPID GLOBAL BUSINESS SOLUTIONS INC p 1208
1200 Stephenson Hwy 48083
Tel (248) 589-1135 *SIC* 8711 7371 7361

■ REXAIR HOLDINGS INC p 1230
50 W Big Beavr Rd Ste 350 48084
Tel (248) 643-7222 *SIC* 3635

■ REXAIR LLC p 1230
50 W Big Beaver Rd # 350 48084
Tel (248) 643-7222 *SIC* 3635

ROSS MORTGAGE CORP p 1252
2075 W Big Beaver Rd # 700 48084
Tel (248) 968-1800 *SIC* 6162

SECO HOLDING CO INC p 1298
2805 Bellingham Dr 48083
Tel (248) 528-5200 *SIC* 3545

SECOTOOLS LLC p 1298
2805 Bellingham Dr 48083
Tel (248) 528-5200 *SIC* 5084 3545

SELECTCARE INC p 1301
2401 W Big Beaver Rd 48084
Tel (248) 358-2560 *SIC* 6324 8741

SRG GLOBAL INC p 1363
800 Stephenson Hwy 48083
Tel (586) 757-7800
SIC 3089 3571 3494 2522 3826 3825

SRG GLOBAL INC p 1363
800 Stephenson Hwy 48083
Tel (248) 509-1100 *SIC* 2396

SUBURBAN MOTORS CO INC p 1396
1810 Maplelawn Dr 48084
Tel (248) 643-0070 *SIC* 5511

▲ SYNTEL INC p 1416
525 E Big Beaver Rd # 300 48083
Tel (248) 619-2800 *SIC* 7371 7372 8748

TALMER BANK AND TRUST p 1423
2301 W Big Beaver Rd # 525 48084
Tel (248) 649-2301 *SIC* 6022

THYSSENKRUPP AUTOMOTIVE SALES & TECHNICAL CENTER INC p 1451
3155 W Big Beaver Rd # 260 48084
Tel (248) 530-2902 *SIC* 5013 3714

TOYODA GOSEI NORTH AMERICA CORP p 1466
1400 Stephenson Hwy 48083
Tel (248) 280-2100 *SIC* 3069 3089

TROY SCHOOL DISTRICT p 1485
475 First St 48098
Tel (248) 823-4000 *SIC* 8211

TYDE GROUP WORLDWIDE LLC p 1496
5700 Crooks Rd Ste 207 48098
Tel (248) 879-7656 *SIC* 3592

UNITED SHORE FINANCIAL SERVICES LLC p 1511
1414 E Maple Rd Fl 5 48083
Tel (248) 647-8590 *SIC* 6282

UNIVERSITY PHYSICIAN GROUP p 1527
540 E Cnfield St Ste 1241 48083
Tel (877) 978-3627 *SIC* 8399

UTICA ENTERPRISES INC p 1537
5750 New King Dr Ste 200 48098
Tel (586) 726-4300
SIC 3548 3549 3545 8711 3541 3544

VALEO INC p 1539
150 Stephenson Hwy 48083
Tel (248) 619-8300 *SIC* 3714

VALEO NORTH AMERICA INC p 1539
150 Stephenson Hwy 48083
Tel (248) 619-8300 *SIC* 3714

VALEO RADAR SYSTEMS INC p 1539
150 Stephenson Hwy 48083
Tel (248) 619-8300 *SIC* 5731 3714

VALEO SWITCHES & DETECTION SYSTEMS INC p 1539
150 Stephenson Hwy 48083
Tel (248) 619-8300 *SIC* 3714

WABASH INTERMEDIATE HOLDING CORP p 1570
3155 W Big Beaver Rd # 209 48084
Tel (248) 220-5400 *SIC* 6719

WOODBRIDGE HOLDINGS INC p 1622
1515 Equity Dr 48084
Tel (248) 288-0100 *SIC* 2531 3086

UBLY, MI

PEPRO ENTERPRISES INC p 1134
2147 Leppek Rd 48475
Tel (989) 658-3200 *SIC* 3089

UTICA, MI

MNP CORP p 980
44225 Utica Rd 48317
Tel (586) 254-1320
SIC 3452 5051 5072 3714

VAN BUREN TWP, MI

HANON SYSTEMS USA LLC p 658
1 Village Center Dr 48111
Tel (734) 710-5000 *SIC* 3714 3585 3699

▲ VISTEON CORP p 1562
1 Village Center Dr 48111
Tel (800) 847-8366 *SIC* 3714

VERMONTVILLE, MI

CITIZENS LLC p 311
870 S Main St 49096
Tel (517) 726-0514
SIC 5191 5153 5999 2041

WALLED LAKE, MI

LAKE WALLED CONSOLIDATED SCHOOL DISTRICT p 839
850 Ladd Rd Bldg D 48390
Tel (248) 956-2000 *SIC* 8211

WARREN, MI

ANGELO IAFRATE CONSTRUCTION CO p 91
26300 Sherwood Ave 48091
Tel (586) 756-1070 *SIC* 1623 1794 1611

ART VAN FURNITURE INC p 113
6500 E 14 Mile Rd 48092
Tel (586) 939-2100 *SIC* 5712

BIG BOY RESTAURANTS INTERNATIONAL LLC p 181
4199 Marcy St 48091
Tel (586) 759-6000 *SIC* 5812 2099

CENTRAL TRANSPORT INTERNATIONAL INC p 280
12225 Stephens Rd 48089
Tel (586) 467-0100 *SIC* 4212 4213

CENTURION p 281
12225 Stephens Rd 48089
Tel (586) 939-7000 *SIC* 4213 4212 4581

CG LIQUIDATION INC p 285
2111 Walter P Reuther Dr 48091
Tel (586) 575-9800 *SIC* 3479 3471

CITY OF WARREN p 319
1 City Sq Ste 215 48093
Tel (586) 574-4500 *SIC* 9111

COLD HEADING CO p 335
21777 Hoover Rd 48089
Tel (586) 497-7000 *SIC* 3452 8711

COUNTRYSIDE FOODS LLC p 375
26661 Bunert Rd 48089
Tel (586) 447-3500 *SIC* 5141 2099

CROWN GROUP CO p 395
2111 Walter Reuther Dr 48091
Tel (586) 575-9800 *SIC* 3479

DETROIT-MACOMB HOSPITAL CORP p 433
28000 Dequindre Rd 48092
Tel (313) 499-3000 *SIC* 8062

FIVE BROTHERS MORTGAGE CO SERVICES AND SECURING INC p 553
12220 E 13 Mile Rd 48093
Tel (586) 772-7600 *SIC* 6162

FLEX-N-GATE LLC p 555
5663 E 9 Mile Rd 48091
Tel (800) 398-1496 *SIC* 5162

GUARDIAN AUTOMOTIVE CORP p 645
23751 Amber Ave 48089
Tel (586) 757-7800 *SIC* 3089 3465

LINC LOGISTICS CO p 866
12755 E 9 Mile Rd 48089
Tel (586) 467-1500 *SIC* 8742

LIPARI FOODS OPERATING CO LLC p 870
26661 Bunert Rd 48089
Tel (586) 447-3500 *SIC* 5146 5145 5149

■ **LOGISTICS INSIGHT CORP** p 874
12755 E 9 Mile Rd 48089
Tel (586) 467-1500 *SIC* 8742

MACOMB COMMUNITY COLLEGE p 893
14500 E 12 Mile Rd 48088
Tel (586) 445-7306 *SIC* 8221

MADISON ELECTRIC CO p 894
31855 Van Dyke Ave 48093
Tel (586) 825-0200 *SIC* 5063 3679

PASLIN CO p 1119
25303 Ryan Rd 48091
Tel (586) 758-0200 *SIC* 3548 3544 3545

PRODUCTION TOOL SUPPLY CO LLC p 1180
8655 E 8 Mile Rd 48089
Tel (586) 755-2200 *SIC* 5085 5084

PROPER GROUP INTERNATIONAL INC p 1183
13870 E 11 Mile Rd 48089
Tel (586) 779-8787 *SIC* 3089

SET ENTERPRISES INC p 1308
30500 Van Dyke Ave # 701 48093
Tel (586) 573-3600
SIC 7389 3465 3544 3312

ST JOHN HOSPITAL AND MEDICAL CENTER p 1367
28000 Dequindre Rd 48092
Tel (313) 343-4000 *SIC* 8062

ST JOHN MACOMB-OAKLAND HOSPITAL p 1367
28000 Dequindre Rd 48092
Tel (586) 753-0094 *SIC* 8062

ST JOHN PROVIDENCE HEALTH SYSTEM p 1367
28000 Dequindre Rd 48092
Tel (586) 753-0500 *SIC* 8062

U S MANUFACTURING CORP p 1497
28201 Van Dyke Ave 48093
Tel (586) 467-1600 *SIC* 3714 3462 3356

■ **UNIVERSAL DEDICATED INC** p 1516
12755 E 9 Mile Rd 48089
Tel (800) 233-9445 *SIC* 4214

▲ **UNIVERSAL LOGISTICS HOLDINGS INC** p 1517
12755 E 9 Mile Rd 48089
Tel (586) 920-0100 *SIC* 4213

VITRAN EXPRESS INC p 1563
12225 Stephens Rd 48089
Tel (317) 803-4000 *SIC* 4213

WARREN CONSOLIDATED SCHOOLS p 1576
31300 Anita Dr 48093
Tel (586) 825-2400 *SIC* 8211

WASHINGTON, MI

TRW VEHICLE SAFETY SYSTEMS INC p 1489
4505 26 Mile Rd 48094
Tel (734) 855-2600 *SIC* 3714

WATERFORD, MI

OAKLAND SCHOOLS INC p 1071
2111 Pontiac Lake Rd 48328
Tel (248) 209-2000 *SIC* 8211

WATERFORD SCHOOL DISTRICT p 1582
501 N Cass Lake Rd 48328
Tel (248) 682-7800 *SIC* 8211

WATERVLIET, MI

LANE AUTOMOTIVE INC p 843
8300 Lane Dr 49098
Tel (269) 463-4113 *SIC* 5013 5531

WAYNE, MI

COMMUNITY LIVING SERVICES INC p 349
35425 W Michigan Ave # 1 48184
Tel (734) 467-7600 *SIC* 8322

RUSH TRUCKING CORP p 1259
35160 E Michigan Ave 48184
Tel (734) 641-1711 *SIC* 4213

WIMSATT BUILDING MATERIALS CORP p 1614
36340 Van Born Rd 48184
Tel (734) 722-3460 *SIC* 5033 8742

WEBBERVILLE, MI

OAK LANE GOLF COURSE INC p 1070
800 N Main St 48892
Tel (517) 521-3900 *SIC* 7992 5812

WEST BLOOMFIELD, MI

SINGH MANAGEMENT CO INC p 1326
7125 Orchard Lake Rd # 200 48322
Tel (248) 865-1600 *SIC* 6531 6513 8742

WEST BLOOMFIELD SCHOOL DISTRICT p 1594
5810 Commerce Rd 48324
Tel (248) 865-6420 *SIC* 8211

WESTLAND, MI

GT TECHNOLOGIES INC p 644
5859 E Executive Dr 48185
Tel (734) 467-8371
SIC 8711 3714 3545 3089

SPECTRUM COMMUNITY SERVICES p 1357
28303 Joy Rd 48185
Tel (734) 453-8804 *SIC* 8361

SPECTRUM HUMAN SERVICES INC p 1357
28303 Joy Rd 48185
Tel (734) 458-8736 *SIC* 8361

WAYNE-WESTLAND COMMUNITY SCHOOLS p 1584
36745 Marquette St 48185
Tel (734) 419-2000 *SIC* 8211

WHITEHALL, MI

■ **HOWMET HOLDINGS CORP** p 713
1 Misco Dr 49461
Tel (231) 894-5686
SIC 3324 3542 5051 3479

WILLIAMSTON, MI

CENTURION MEDICAL PRODUCTS CORP p 281
100 Centurion Way 48895
Tel (517) 546-5400 *SIC* 3842 2759 2671

WILLIAMSTON PRODUCTS INC p 1612
845 Progress Ct 48895
Tel (517) 655-2131 *SIC* 3089

WILSON, MI

HANNAHVILLE INDIAN COMMUNITY p 658
N14911 Hannahville Rd B 1 49896
Tel (906) 466-2932 *SIC* 9111

WINN, MI

MORBARK LLC p 988
8507 S Winn Rd 48896
Tel (989) 866-2381
SIC 3599 3553 3549 3523

WIXOM, MI

GENERAL RV CENTER INC p 602
25000 Assembly Park Dr 48393
Tel (248) 349-0900 *SIC* 5561

J&B MEDICAL SUPPLY CO INC p 772
50496 Pontiac Trl Ste 500 48393
Tel (800) 737-0045 *SIC* 5047

KIEKERT USA INC p 817
46941 Liberty Dr 48393
Tel (248) 960-4100 *SIC* 3714

MAC VALVES INC p 891
30569 Beck Rd 48393
Tel (248) 624-7700 *SIC* 3492 3494 3491

MOELLER MFG CO LLC p 982
30100 Beck Rd 48393
Tel (248) 960-3999 *SIC* 3724 3728

NGK SPARK PLUGS (USA) INC p 1041
46929 Magellan 48393
Tel (248) 926-6900 *SIC* 3643 3264

REVSPRING INC p 1229
29241 Beck Rd 48393
Tel (248) 567-7300 *SIC* 7371 7375

■ **WASTE MANAGEMENT OF MICHIGAN INC** p 1580
48797 Alpha Dr Ste 100 48393
Tel (586) 574-2760 *SIC* 4953

WYANDOTTE, MI

ARROW MOTOR & PUMP INC p 113
629 Cent St 48192
Tel (734) 285-7860
SIC 7694 5063 7699 5084

HENRY FORD WYANDOTTE HOSPITAL p 684
2333 Biddle Ave 48192
Tel (734) 246-6000 *SIC* 8062

WYOMING, MI

BEHLER-YOUNG CO p 168
4900 Clyde Park Ave Sw 49509
Tel (616) 531-3400 *SIC* 5075 5051 5074

GORDON FOOD SERVICE INC p 626
1300 Gezon Pkwy Sw 49509
Tel (888) 437-3663
SIC 5149 5142 5147 5146 5144 5143

GRAND RAPIDS FOAMTECHNOLOGIES INC p 630
2788 Remico St Sw 49519
Tel (616) 726-1677 *SIC* 5199

MARKET DAY LLC p 908
1300 Gezon Pkwy Sw 49509
Tel (630) 285-1470 *SIC* 5141

METROPOLITAN HOSPITAL p 956
5900 Byron Center Ave Sw 49519
Tel (616) 252-7200 *SIC* 8062 8069

MICHIGAN TURKEY PRODUCERS COOPERATIVE INC p 961
2140 Chicago Dr Sw 49519
Tel (616) 245-2221 *SIC* 2015

PURITY CYLINDER GASES INC p 1192
2580 28th St Sw 49519
Tel (616) 532-2375
SIC 5085 7359 5999 7699

WELLER AUTO PARTS INC p 1589
2525 Chicago Dr Sw 49519
Tel (616) 538-5000 *SIC* 5013 5015 5531

YPSILANTI, MI

BOSAL INDUSTRIES-GEORGIA INC p 201
1476 Seaver Way 48197
Tel (734) 547-7022 *SIC* 3714

EASTERN MICHIGAN UNIVERSITY p 472
202 Welch Hall 48197
Tel (734) 487-2031 *SIC* 8221

KALITTA AIR LLC p 801
818 Willow Run Airport 48198
Tel (734) 484-0088 *SIC* 4513

NATIONAL CONSTRUCTION ENTERPRISES INC p 1011
5075 Carpenter Rd 48197
Tel (734) 434-1600 *SIC* 8741

ZEELAND, MI

■ **E C AVIATION SERVICES INC** p 466
600 N Centennial St 49464
Tel (616) 772-1800 *SIC* 4522

EMPIRE CO LLC p 493
8181 Logistics Dr 49464
Tel (616) 772-7272 *SIC* 5031 2431

▲ **GENTEX CORP** p 604
600 N Centennial St 49464
Tel (616) 772-1800 *SIC* 3231 3714 3669

▲ **HERMAN MILLER INC** p 687
855 E Main Ave 49464
Tel (616) 654-3000
SIC 2521 2522 2541 2542 2531

HOWARD MILLER CO p 713
860 E Main Ave 49464
Tel (616) 772-9131 *SIC* 3873 3829 3823

ODL INC p 1074
215 E Roosevelt Ave 49464
Tel (616) 772-9111 *SIC* 2431

STONE PLASTICS AND MANUFACTURING INC p 1391
8245 Riley St Ste 100 49464
Tel (616) 748-9740 *SIC* 5162 3089

MINNESOTA

ALBANY, MN

WELLS CONCRETE PRODUCTS CO p 1589
210 Inspiration Ln 56307
Tel (800) 658-7049 *SIC* 3272 3273

ALBERT LEA, MN

MAYO CLINIC HEALTH SYSTEM-ALBERT LEA AND AUSTIN p 924
404 W Fountain St 56007
Tel (507) 373-2384
SIC 8062 8069 8051 8063 8011

■ **STREATER LLC** p 1393
411 S 1st Ave 56007
Tel (800) 527-4197 *SIC* 2542 2541

ALEXANDRIA, MN

ALEXANDRIA EXTRUSION CO p 49
401 County Road 22 Nw 56308
Tel (320) 762-7657 *SIC* 3354

DOUGLAS MACHINE INC p 452
3404 Iowa St 56308
Tel (320) 763-6587 *SIC* 3565

HENRYS FOODS INC p 684
234 Mckay Ave N 56308
Tel (320) 763-3194
SIC 5194 5145 5111 5113 5141

REM CENTRAL LAKES INC p 1222
1802 Autumn Dr Nw 56308
Tel (320) 759-5650 *SIC* 8011

■ **RURAL CELLULAR CORP** p 1258
4133 Iowa St Ste 200 56308
Tel (320) 808-2111 *SIC* 4812 5999

ANOKA, MN

ANOKA-HENNEPIN SCHOOL DIST NO 11 p 92
2727 N Ferry St 55303
Tel (763) 506-1000 *SIC* 8211

BAKERY CRAFTS LLC p 147
3500 Thurston Ave 100 55303
Tel (513) 942-0862 *SIC* 5046 5149 2064

COUNTY OF ANOKA p 376
2100 3rd Ave 55303
Tel (763) 421-4760 *SIC* 9111

DECOPAC INC p 421
3500 Thurston Ave Ste 200 55303
Tel (763) 574-0091 *SIC* 5999

HOFFMAN ENCLOSURES INC p 699
2100 Hoffman Way 55303
Tel (763) 421-2240
SIC 3444 3699 3613 3469 3053

PENTAIR TECHNICAL PRODUCTS p 1132
2100 Hoffman Way 55303
Tel (763) 323-8200 *SIC* 3585 3443

■ **VISTA OUTDOOR SALES LLC** p 1562
1 Vista Way 55303
Tel (763) 323-2414 *SIC* 3482 3069

APPLE VALLEY, MN

UPONOR NORTH AMERICA INC p 1529
5925 148th St W 55124
Tel (952) 891-2000 *SIC* 8742 3312

ARDEN HILLS, MN

FRANDSEN FINANCIAL CORP p 574
4388 Round Lake Rd W 55112
Tel (651) 242-5700 *SIC* 6022 6712

LAND OLAKES INC p 842
4001 Lexington Ave N 55126
Tel (651) 375-2222 *SIC* 2879

NOTT CO p 1062
4480 Round Lake Rd W 55112
Tel (651) 415-3400
SIC 5084 5085 3492 3053

VENTURE SOLUTIONS INC p 1548
1170 Grey Fox Rd 55112
Tel (651) 494-1740 *SIC* 2759

AUSTIN, MN

▲ **HORMEL FOODS CORP** p 708
1 Hormel Pl 55912
Tel (507) 437-5611 *SIC* 2011 2013 2032

■ **HORMEL FOODS CORPORATE SERVICES LLC** p 708
1 Hormel Pl 55912
Tel (507) 437-5611 *SIC* 5147

MAYO CLINIC HEALTH SYSTEM-AUSTIN p 924
1000 1st Dr Nw 55912
Tel (507) 433-7351 *SIC* 8399

QUALITY PORK PROCESSORS INC p 1197
711 Hormel Century Pkwy 55912
Tel (507) 434-6300 *SIC* 2011

AVON, MN

BLATTNER ENERGY INC p 189
392 County Road 50 56310
Tel (320) 356-7351 *SIC* 1731

COLUMBIA GEAR CORP p 340
530 County Road 50 56310
Tel (440) 838-4700 *SIC* 3566 3462

BAGLEY, MN

TEAM INDUSTRIES BAGLEY-AUDUBON INC p 1430
105 Park Ave Nw 56621
Tel (218) 694-3550 *SIC* 3599 8711 3714

TEAM INDUSTRIES INC p 1430
105 Park Ave Nw 56621
Tel (218) 694-3550 *SIC* 3599 8711 3714

BAXTER, MN

NOR-SON INC p 1047
7900 Hastings Rd 56425
Tel (218) 828-1722 *SIC* 1521 1542 1541

BAYPORT, MN

ANDERSEN CORP p 89
100 4th Ave N 55003
Tel (651) 264-5150 *SIC* 2431 3231

ANDERSEN DISTRIBUTION INC p 89
100 4th Ave N 55003
Tel (651) 264-5150 *SIC* 5031

BELGRADE, MN

FEEDCO p 537
521 Wells St 56312
Tel (320) 254-8294 *SIC* 5999

BELLE PLAINE, MN

MINNESOTA AVIATION LLC p 973
805 Enterprise Dr E Ste H 56011
Tel (651) 681-3900 *SIC* 6719

BEMIDJI, MN

JOHANNESONS INC p 787
2301 Johanneson Dr Nw 56601
Tel (218) 751-9644 *SIC* 5411

SANFORD HEALTH OF NORTHERN MINNESOTA p 1279
1300 Anne St Nw 56601
Tel (218) 751-5430 *SIC* 8082

BIG LAKE, MN

MINNESOTA LIMITED LLC p 973
18640 200th St Nw 55309
Tel (763) 262-7000 *SIC* 1623

BLAINE, MN

■ **AVEDA CORP** p 136
4000 Pheasant Ridge Dr Ne 55449
Tel (763) 783-4250 *SIC* 2844 7231

BLOOMINGTON, MN

ADVANCED BIOENERGY LLC p 25
8000 Norman Center Dr # 610 55437
Tel (763) 226-2701 *SIC* 2869

■ **CAPITAL SAFETY INC** p 250
7900 Intl Dr Ste 405 55425
Tel (612) 216-5800 *SIC* 3842

CHIN LEEANN INC p 301
3600 American Blvd W # 52 55431
Tel (952) 896-3606 *SIC* 5812

■ **CYPRESS SEMICONDUCTOR (MINNESOTA) INC** p 405
2401 E 86th St 55425
Tel (952) 851-5200 *SIC* 3674

EDMENTUM INC p 478
5600 W 83rd St 3008200 55437
Tel (800) 447-5286 *SIC* 7372

GN HEARING CARE CORP p 619
8001 E Bloomington Fwy 55420
Tel (800) 248-4327 *SIC* 3842

■ **HARMON INC** p 662
7900 Xerxes Ave S # 1800 55431
Tel (952) 944-5700 *SIC* 5039

HEALTHPARTNERS INC p 677
8170 33rd Ave S 55425
Tel (952) 883-6000 *SIC* 8011

HOLIDAY COMPANIES p 700
4567 American Blvd W 55437
Tel (952) 830-8700 *SIC* 5541 5411 5172

HOLIDAY STATIONSTORES INC p 700
4567 American Blvd W 55437
Tel (952) 830-8700 *SIC* 5541 5411

INDEPENDENT SCHOOL DISTRICT 271 p 737
1350 W 106th St 55431
Tel (952) 681-6400 *SIC* 8211

INTERNATIONAL OPERATING ENGINEERS UNION 49 HEALTH AND WELFARE FUND p 756
3001 Metro Dr Ste 500 55425
Tel (952) 854-0795 *SIC* 8631

ISTATE TRUCK INC p 767
2601 American Blvd E 55425
Tel (952) 854-2044 *SIC* 5084

LAMEX FOODS INC p 841
8500 Normandale Ste 1150 55437
Tel (952) 844-0585 *SIC* 5144 5147

POLAR SEMICONDUCTOR LLC p 1159
2800 E Old Shakopee Rd 55425
Tel (952) 876-3000 *SIC* 3674

QUALITY BICYCLE PRODUCTS INC p 1196
6400 W 105th St 55438
Tel (952) 941-9391 *SIC* 5091

SCHWANS CONSUMER BRANDS INC p 1291
8500 Normandale Lake Blvd 55437
Tel (952) 346-0100 *SIC* 5142

SFM MUTUAL INSURANCE CO p 1310
3500 Amrcn Blvd W Ste 700 55431
Tel (952) 838-4200 *SIC* 6331

▲ **TORO CO** p 1461
8111 Lyndale Ave S 55420
Tel (952) 888-8801
SIC 3523 3524 3494 3645

BRAINERD, MN

BRAINERD PUBLIC SCHOOLS p 207
804 Oak St 56401
Tel (218) 454-6900 *SIC* 8211

D & J PRINTING INC p 406
3323 Oak St 56401
Tel (218) 829-2877 *SIC* 2752 2789 2732

INDEPENDENT SCHOOL DISTRICT 181 p 737
804 Oak St 56401
Tel (218) 454-6900 *SIC* 8211

ST JOSEPHS MEDICAL CENTER p 1369
523 N 3rd St 56401
Tel (218) 829-2861 *SIC* 8062

BREWSTER, MN

MINNESOTA SOYBEAN PROCESSORS p 974
121 Zeh Ave 56119
Tel (507) 842-6677 *SIC* 5153 2075

NEW VISION CO-OP p 1033
38438 210th St 56119
Tel (507) 842-2001 *SIC* 5153

BROOKLYN PARK, MN

ABRA AUTO BODY & GLASS LP p 12
7225 Northland Dr N # 210 55428
Tel (651) 487-2470 *SIC* 6794 7532

■ **AM RETAIL GROUP INC** p 63
7401 Boone Ave N 55428
Tel (763) 391-4000 *SIC* 3199

DIVERSIFIED DISTRIBUTION SYSTEMS LLC p 444
7351 Boone Ave N 55428
Tel (612) 813-5200 *SIC* 5112

EGAN CO p 481
7625 Boone Ave N 55428
Tel (763) 595-4358
SIC 1711 1731 3444 7623 1793

GLS COMPANIES p 618
6845 Winnetka Cir 55428
Tel (763) 535-7277 *SIC* 2752

NILFISK INC p 1043
9435 Winnetka Ave N 55445
Tel (800) 334-1083 *SIC* 3589 5087

■ **WILSONS HOUSE OF SUEDE INC** p 1614
7401 Boone Ave N 55428
Tel (763) 391-4000 *SIC* 5699 5948

WILSONS LEATHER EXPERTS INC p 1614
7401 Boone Ave N 55428
Tel (763) 391-4000 *SIC* 5699 5948

WURTH ADAMS NUT & BOLT CO p 1628
9485 Winnetka Ave N 55445
Tel (763) 424-3374 *SIC* 5072

BUFFALO, MN

CENTRA SOTA COOPERATIVE p 277
805 Highway 55 E 55313
Tel (763) 682-2557
SIC 5191 2875 5171 5153

BURNSVILLE, MN

AMES CONSTRUCTION INC p 84
14420 County Road 5 55306
Tel (952) 435-7106
SIC 1611 1041 1021 1794

APOTHECARY PRODUCTS LLC p 97
11750 12th Ave S 55337
Tel (800) 328-2742 *SIC* 2834 5122 3069

BOSCH SECURITY SYSTEMS INC p 202
12000 Portland Ave 55337
Tel (952) 884-4051 *SIC* 1731 3669 3679

BURNSVILLE EAGAN SAVAGE INDEPENDENT SCHOOL DISTRICT 191 p 228
100 River Ridge Ct 55337
Tel (952) 707-2000 *SIC* 8211

BURNSVILLE-EAGAN-SAVAGE BOARD OF EDUCATION p 228
100 River Ridge Ct 55337
Tel (952) 707-2000 *SIC* 8211

DATA LISTING SERVICES LLC p 413
11351 Rupp Dr 55337
Tel (952) 948-5488 *SIC* 7389

DATA SALES CO INC p 413
3450 W Burnsville Pkwy 55337
Tel (952) 890-8838 *SIC* 5045 7377

FORCE AMERICA INC p 565
501 Cliff Rd E Ste 100 55337
Tel (952) 707-1300 *SIC* 5084 3568

■ **FRONTIER COMMUNICATIONS CORP** p 581
14450 Burnhaven Dr 55306
Tel (952) 435-3133 *SIC* 4813

■ **FRONTIER COMMUNICATIONS OF MINNESOTA INC** p 581
1405 W 150th St 55306
Tel (952) 898-6422 *SIC* 4813

■ **GOODRICH CORP** p 624
14300 Judicial Rd 55306
Tel (952) 892-4000 *SIC* 5088

INNOVATIVE OFFICE SOLUTIONS LLC p 745
151 Cliff Rd E Ste 40 55337
Tel (952) 808-9900 *SIC* 5112 5021

MACKIN BOOK CO p 892
3505 County Road 42 W 55306
Tel (952) 895-9540 *SIC* 5192

MONGOLIAN OPERATING CO LLC p 984
200 E Travelers Trl # 235 55337
Tel (952) 288-2363 *SIC* 5812 6794

NESS ELECTRONICS INC p 1026
1800 E 121st St 55337
Tel (651) 251-5700 *SIC* 5065

NORTHERN TOOL & EQUIPMENT CATALOG CO INC p 1057
2800 Southcross Dr W 55306
Tel (952) 894-9510 *SIC* 5961

NORTHERN TOOL & EQUIPMENT CO INC p 1057
2800 Southcross Dr W 55306
Tel (952) 894-9510 *SIC* 5961 5251

NXTRANET CORP p 1068
1500 Mcandrews Rd W 55337
Tel (952) 808-5554 *SIC* 7371

■ **ROSEMOUNT AEROSPACE INC** p 1251
14300 Judicial Rd 55306
Tel (952) 892-4000 *SIC* 3812

TELEX COMMUNICATIONS HOLDINGS INC p 1435
12000 Portland Ave 55337
Tel (877) 863-4166 *SIC* 3663 3669 3679

CANNON FALLS, MN

■ **CANNON EQUIPMENT LLC** p 247
324 Washington St W 55009
Tel (507) 263-6426 *SIC* 5085

CARLTON, MN

FOND DU LAC RESERVATION p 563
1785 Highway 210 55718
Tel (218) 879-4593 *SIC* 9131

CENTER CITY, MN

HAZELDEN BETTY FORD FOUNDATION p 671
15251 Pleasant Valley Rd 55012
Tel (651) 213-4000 *SIC* 8361 2731

CHAMPLIN, MN

DECO INC p 421
11156 Zealand Ave N 55316
Tel (763) 576-9572 *SIC* 7381

CHANHASSEN, MN

BERGQUIST CO p 174
18930 W 78th St 55317
Tel (952) 835-2322
SIC 5731 5063 3645 3646 2822

DIRECT SOURCE INC p 441
8176 Mallory Ct 55317
Tel (952) 934-8000 *SIC* 5046 5045

INSTANT WEB LLC p 747
7951 Powers Blvd 55317
Tel (952) 474-0961 *SIC* 7331

INSTANT WEB LLC p 747
7951 Powers Blvd 55317
Tel (952) 474-0961 *SIC* 7331

INSULATION DISTRIBUTORS INC p 747
8303 Audubon Rd 55317
Tel (952) 279-6400 *SIC* 5033

LIFE TIME FITNESS INC p 864
2902 Corporate Pl 55317
Tel (952) 229-7543 *SIC* 7997

LTF HOLDINGS INC p 883
2902 Corporate Pl 55317
Tel (952) 380-0303 *SIC* 6719

NORTHCOTT HOSPITALITY INTERNATIONAL LLC p 1054
250 Lake Dr E 55317
Tel (952) 294-5100 *SIC* 7011 5812

■ **ROSEMOUNT INC** p 1251
8200 Market Blvd 55317
Tel (952) 906-8888
SIC 3823 3824 3545 5084 3829

UNITED MAILING INC p 1510
1001 Park Rd 55317
Tel (952) 474-0961 *SIC* 7331 2759 8732

CHASKA, MN

APEX INTERNATIONAL MFG INC p 96
134 Columbia Ct 55318
Tel (952) 227-3000 *SIC* 2844

CIRCLE PINES, MN

NORTH AMERICAN COMPOSITES CO p 1049
300 Apollo Dr 55014
Tel (651) 766-6892 *SIC* 5162

CLEARBROOK, MN

ALPHA OIL & GAS SERVICES INC p 60
453 Tower St Nw 56634
Tel (218) 776-2278 *SIC* 5172 1623 1522

CLEARWATER, MN

■ **TELCOM CONSTRUCTION INC** p 1433
2218 200th St E 55320
Tel (320) 558-9485 *SIC* 1623

CLOQUET, MN

BEST OIL CO p 177
30 N 8th St 55720
Tel (218) 879-0201
SIC 5171 5172 5013 5983 5541 5411

DIAMOND BRANDS INC p 436
1800 Cloquet Ave 55720
Tel (218) 879-6700 *SIC* 2499

COLD SPRING, MN

COLD SPRING GRANITE CO INC p 335
17482 Granite West Rd 56320
Tel (320) 685-3621 *SIC* 3281 1741 3366

COTTAGE GROVE, MN

SOUTH WASHINGTON COUNTY SCHOOLS ISD 833 p 1345
7362 E Point Douglas Rd S 55016
Tel (651) 458-6300 *SIC* 8211

TRADEHOME SHOE STORES INC p 1468
8300 97th St S 55016
Tel (651) 459-8600 *SIC* 5661

WERNER ELECTRIC VENTURES LLC p 1592
7450 95th St S 55016
Tel (651) 458-3701 *SIC* 5063 5084 5085

COTTONWOOD, MN

NORTH STAR GENERAL INSURANCE CO p 1054
269 Barstad Rd S 56229
Tel (507) 423-6262 *SIC* 6411

NORTH STAR MUTUAL INSURANCE CO INC p 1054
269 Barstad Rd S 56229
Tel (507) 423-6262 *SIC* 6411

CROSBY, MN

CUYUNA RANGE HOSPITAL INC p 403
320 E Main St 56441
Tel (218) 546-7000 *SIC* 8062 8051

DELANO, MN

LANDSCAPE STRUCTURES INC p 843
601 7th St S 55328
Tel (763) 972-3391 *SIC* 3949 2531

DETROIT LAKES, MN

■ **BTD MANUFACTURING INC** p 222
1111 13th Ave Se 56501
Tel (218) 847-4446 *SIC* 3469 3544

ST MARYS REGIONAL HEALTH CENTER p 1372
1027 Washington Ave 56501
Tel (218) 847-5611 *SIC* 8062 8051

DEXTER, MN

WAPSIPINICON WIND PROJECT LLC p 1575
234 Industrial Park Dr 55926
Tel (760) 329-1437 *SIC* 4911

DODGE CENTER, MN

■ **MCNEILUS COMPANIES INC** p 932
524 E Highway St 55927
Tel (507) 374-6321 *SIC* 3713

MCNEILUS STEEL INC p 932
702 2nd Ave Se 55927
Tel (507) 374-6336 *SIC* 5051

■ **MCNEILUS TRUCK AND MANUFACTURING INC** p 932
524 County Rd 34 E 55927
Tel (614) 868-0760
SIC 3713 3531 3537 3272

DULUTH, MN

ADVANSTAR HOLDINGS CORP p 26
131 W 1st St 55802
Tel (218) 740-7200 *SIC* 7389 2721 7331

▲ **ALLETE INC** p 53
30 W Superior St 55802
Tel (218) 279-5000
SIC 4931 4924 4941 1231 6552

BELLISIO FOODS INC p 171
525 S Lake Ave Ste 201 55802
Tel (218) 723-5555 *SIC* 2038

BENEDICTINE HEALTH SYSTEM p 172
503 E 3rd St Ste 400 55805
Tel (218) 786-2370 *SIC* 8059

DIVERSIFIED MOTEL PROPERTIES LIMITED PARTNERSHIP p 444
2305 W Superior St 55806
Tel (218) 723-8433 *SIC* 6512

DULUTH CLINIC LTD p 460
400 E 3rd St 55805
Tel (218) 786-3600 *SIC* 8011

ESSENTIA HEALTH p 510
502 E 2nd St 55805
Tel (218) 786-8376 *SIC* 8062 8051

INDEPENDENT SCHOOL DISTRICT 709 p 737
215 N 1st Ave E 55802
Tel (218) 336-8700 *SIC* 8211

JAMAR CO p 776
4701 Mike Colalillo Dr 55807
Tel (218) 628-1027
SIC 1711 1761 1742 5033 7699 3444

LUIGINOS INC p 884
1325 Port Terminal Rd 55802
Tel (218) 722-1427 *SIC* 4222 4225

■ **MAURICES INC** p 921
425 W Superior St 55802
Tel (218) 727-8431 *SIC* 5621

S M D C ST MARYS DULUTH CLINIC HEALTH SYSTEM HOSPICE & PALLIATIVE CARE p 1262
407 E 3rd St 55805
Tel (218) 786-4020 *SIC* 8062

SMDC MEDICAL CENTER p 1332
502 E 2nd St 55805
Tel (218) 726-4000 *SIC* 8062

ST LOUIS COUNTY OF (INC) p 1369
100 N 5th Ave W Rm 320 55802
Tel (218) 726-2340 *SIC* 9131

ST LUKES HOSPITAL OF DULUTH p 1370
915 E 1st St 55805
Tel (218) 726-5555 *SIC* 8062 8011

ST MARYS DULUTH CLINIC HEALTH SYSTEM p 1371
400 E 3rd St 55805
Tel (218) 786-8364 *SIC* 8093 8011 8062

ST MARYS MEDICAL CENTER p 1371
407 E 3rd St 55805
Tel (218) 786-4000 *SIC* 8062 8082 8351

TEACHERS RETIREMENT FUND p 1429
625 E Central Entrance 55811
Tel (218) 722-2894 *SIC* 8631

UNITED PIPING INC p 1510
4510 Airport Rd 55811
Tel (218) 727-7676 *SIC* 1623

UNIVERSITY OF MINNESOTA DULUTH p 1523
1049 University Dr 55812
Tel (218) 726-8000 *SIC* 8221

EAGAN, MN

APPLIED POWER PRODUCTS INC p 100
1240 Trapp Rd 55121
Tel (651) 452-2250 *SIC* 5085

BAY & BAY TRANSPORTATION SERVICES INC p 160
2905 W Svc Rd Ste 2000 55121
Tel (651) 480-7961 *SIC* 4731

CAPITOL SALES CO INC p 251
1245 Trapp Rd Ste 130 55121
Tel (651) 688-6830 *SIC* 5064 5065 8742

CH HOLDINGS USA INC p 286
2770 Blue Waters Rd # 100 55121
Tel (651) 796-6100 *SIC* 1791

CONVERGEONE HOLDINGS CORP p 365
3344 Highway 149 55121
Tel (651) 994-6800 *SIC* 4813 5999 1731

CONVERGEONE INC p 365
3344 Highway 149 55121
Tel (651) 994-6800 *SIC* 4813 5999 1731

ELLIOTT AUTO SUPPLY CO INC p 488
1380 Corporate Center Cur 55121
Tel (651) 454-4100 *SIC* 5013

MENDOTA INSURANCE CO p 943
2805 Dodd Rd Ste 300 55121
Tel (800) 422-0792 *SIC* 6331

■ MESABA AVIATION INC p 951
1000 Blue Gentian Rd # 200 55121
Tel (651) 367-5000 *SIC* 4512

MILLER MANUFACTURING CO p 970
2910 Waters Rd Ste 150 55121
Tel (651) 982-5100 *SIC* 1542 5199

MN AIRLINES LLC p 979
1300 Corporate Ctr Curv 55121
Tel (651) 681-3900 *SIC* 4512

NORCRAFT HOLDINGS LP p 1047
950 Blue Gentian Rd 55121
Tel (800) 297-0661 *SIC* 2434

PRIME THERAPEUTICS LLC p 1175
1305 Corporate Center Dr 55121
Tel (612) 777-4000 *SIC* 8741 6411 2834

SCANTRON CORP p 1286
1313 Lone Oak Rd 55121
Tel (651) 683-6000
SIC 3577 7372 2752 3575 2761

■ STREAM GLOBAL SERVICES INC p 1393
3285 Northwood Cir # 120 55121
Tel (651) 288-2979 *SIC* 7389

■ THOMSON REUTERS (LEGAL) INC p 1450
610 Opperman Dr 55123
Tel (651) 687-7000 *SIC* 2731

■ THOMSON REUTERS APPLICATIONS INC p 1450
610 Opperman Dr 55123
Tel (651) 687-7000 *SIC* 7374

TRANSPORT CORP OF AMERICA INC p 1472
1715 Yankee Doodle Rd # 100 55121
Tel (651) 686-2500 *SIC* 4213

■ WEST PUBLISHING CORP p 1595
610 620 Opperman Dr 55123
Tel (651) 687-7000 *SIC* 7375

EAST GRAND FORKS, MN

L GARY HART ASSOCIATED p 834
13381 440th Ave Sw 56721
Tel (520) 297-3237 *SIC* 8733

VIGEN CONSTRUCTION INC p 1556
42247 180th St Sw 56721
Tel (218) 773-1159 *SIC* 1541

EDEN PRAIRIE, MN

■ ALLIANT HOLDINGS LLC p 55
7480 Flying Cloud Dr 55344
Tel (952) 351-3000
SIC 3764 3812 3483 3482 3489

AMERICAN BAPTIST HOMES OF MIDWEST p 68
14850 Scenic Heights Rd 55344
Tel (952) 941-3175 *SIC* 8051 8361 8052

■ ANAGRAM INTERNATIONAL INC p 88
7700 Anagram Dr 55344
Tel (952) 949-5600 *SIC* 3069

ARTESYN NORTH AMERICA LLC p 114
7575 Market Place Dr 55344
Tel (952) 392-6500 *SIC* 3679 7629

AVI SYSTEMS INC p 137
9675 W 76th St Ste 200 55344
Tel (952) 949-3700
SIC 5065 7622 8748 1799

■ BIOSCRIP PHARMACY INC p 184
10050 Crosstown Cir # 300 55344
Tel (952) 979-3600 *SIC* 5912

BLUESTEM BRANDS INC p 193
7075 Flying Cloud Dr 55344
Tel (952) 656-4037 *SIC* 5961

BLUESTEM GROUP INC p 193
7505 Flying Cloud Dr 55344
Tel (952) 656-3700 *SIC* 6799 7389

BRAAS CO p 206
7970 Wallace Rd 55344
Tel (952) 937-8902 *SIC* 5084

■ C H ROBINSON INTERNATIONAL INC p 232
14701 Charlson Rd 55347
Tel (952) 683-2800 *SIC* 4731

CAPMARK FINANCE INC p 251
7075 Flying Cloud Dr 55344
Tel (215) 328-4622 *SIC* 6162

CARDINAL GLASS INDUSTRIES INC p 253
775 Prrie Ctr Dr Ste 200 55344
Tel (952) 229-2600 *SIC* 3231 3211

■ CH ROBINSON CO INC p 286
14701 Charlson Rd 55347
Tel (952) 937-7896 *SIC* 4731

▲ CH ROBINSON WORLDWIDE INC p 286
14701 Charlson Rd 55347
Tel (952) 937-8500 *SIC* 4731

CHERNE CONTRACTING CORP p 294
9855 W 78th St Ste 400 55344
Tel (952) 944-4300 *SIC* 1629

■ CIGNA BEHAVIORAL HEALTH INC p 306
11095 Viking Dr Ste 350 55344
Tel (952) 996-2000 *SIC* 6324

■ COMPELLENT TECHNOLOGIES INC p 351
12982 Valley View Rd 55344
Tel (952) 294-3300 *SIC* 3571 3695

▲ DATALINK CORP p 414
10050 Crosstown Cir # 500 55344
Tel (952) 944-3462 *SIC* 5045 7371 7373

DAVISCO FOODS INTERNATIONAL INC p 416
704 Mainstreet 55343
Tel (952) 914-0400 *SIC* 2023 2022

DOUGLAS CORP p 452
9650 Valley View Rd 55344
Tel (800) 806-6113 *SIC* 3089 2759

E A SWEEN CO p 466
16101 W 78th St 55344
Tel (952) 937-9440 *SIC* 2099 5142

EATON HYDRAULICS LLC p 473
14615 Lone Oak Rd 55344
Tel (952) 937-9800
SIC 3089 3052 3568 3492 3594 3728

EDEN PRAIRIE SCHOOLS p 477
8100 School Rd 55344
Tel (952) 975-7000 *SIC* 8211

ELIM CARE INC p 487
7485 Office Ridge Cir 55344
Tel (952) 259-4500 *SIC* 8051 8322

▲ EVINE LIVE INC p 515
6740 Shady Oak Rd 55344
Tel (952) 943-6000 *SIC* 5961

■ GELCO CORP p 598
3 Capital Dr 55344
Tel (952) 828-1000 *SIC* 6159

GRAIN MILLERS INC p 629
10400 Viking Dr Ste 301 55344
Tel (952) 829-8821 *SIC* 2041 5084

HELP/SYSTEMS LLC p 682
6455 City West Pkwy 55344
Tel (952) 933-0609 *SIC* 7372

KROLL ONTRACK LLC p 830
9023 Columbine Rd 55347
Tel (952) 937-5161 *SIC* 7374 7372

LIFETOUCH CHURCH DIRECTORIES AND PORTRAITS INC p 865
11000 Viking Dr Ste 400 55344
Tel (952) 826-4000 *SIC* 7221 2741

LIFETOUCH INC p 865
11000 Viking Dr 55344
Tel (952) 826-4000 *SIC* 7221 7812 2741

LIFETOUCH NATIONAL SCHOOL STUDIOS INC p 865
11000 Viking Dr Ste 300 55344
Tel (952) 826-4000 *SIC* 7221

LIFETOUCH PORTRAIT STUDIOS INC p 865
11000 Viking Dr 55344
Tel (952) 826-4335 *SIC* 7221

LOGIC PD INC p 874
6201 Bury Dr 55346
Tel (952) 646-1191 *SIC* 3672 8711

LONG TERM CARE GROUP INC p 876
11000 Prairie Lakes Dr 55344
Tel (952) 516-6800 *SIC* 6411

METROPOLITAN MECHANICAL CONTRACTORS INC p 956
7450 Flying Cloud Dr 55344
Tel (952) 941-7010 *SIC* 1711 8711

MILESTONE AV TECHNOLOGIES LLC p 969
6436 City West Pkwy 55344
Tel (952) 236-7231 *SIC* 3669

MILK SPECIALTIES CO p 969
7500 Flying Cloud Dr # 500 55344
Tel (952) 942-7310 *SIC* 2026 2834 5149

▲ MTS SYSTEMS CORP p 998
14000 Technology Dr 55344
Tel (952) 937-4000 *SIC* 3829 3825

NORTEK AIR SOLUTIONS LLC p 1049
13200 Pioneer Trl Ste 150 55347
Tel (952) 358-6600 *SIC* 3585

■ OPTUM INC p 1090
11000 Optum Cir 55344
Tel (952) 936-1300 *SIC* 6324

■ OPTUMHEALTH HOLDINGS LLC p 1090
13625 Technology Dr 55344
Tel (763) 595-3200 *SIC* 6324 8741 6411

■ OPTUMINSIGHT INC p 1091
11000 Optum Cir 55344
Tel (952) 833-7100
SIC 7371 7375 8742 8741

PHILLIPS & TEMRO INDUSTRIES INC p 1143
9700 W 74th St 55344
Tel (952) 941-9700 *SIC* 3714

■ PULTE HOMES OF MINNESOTA LLC p 1192
7500 Office Ridge Cir 55344
Tel (952) 936-7833 *SIC* 1521

■ SPECIALTY BENEFITS LLC p 1356
11000 Optum Cir 55344
Tel (866) 427-6845 *SIC* 6321

STARKEY LABORATORIES INC p 1379
6600 Washington Ave S 55344
Tel (952) 941-6401 *SIC* 3842

STRATASYS INC p 1392
7665 Commerce Way 55344
Tel (800) 801-6491 *SIC* 3577

■ SUPERMARKET OPERATORS OF AMERICA INC p 1407
11840 Valley View Rd 55344
Tel (952) 828-4000 *SIC* 5411 4225

■ SUPERVALU HOLDINGS INC p 1407
11840 Valley View Rd 55344
Tel (952) 828-4000 *SIC* 5411

▲ SUPERVALU INC p 1407
11840 Valley View Rd 55344
Tel (952) 828-4000 *SIC* 5411 5141

■ SUPERVALU TRANSPORTATION INC p 1407
11840 Valley View Rd 55344
Tel (952) 828-4000 *SIC* 4213

UNIVITA HEALTH HOLDINGS INC p 1528
11000 Prairie Lakes Dr # 600 55344
Tel (952) 516-6800 *SIC* 8082

VIKING FOREST PRODUCTS LLC p 1557
7615 Smetana Ln Ste 140 55344
Tel (952) 941-6512 *SIC* 5031 5051

VOLUNTEERS OF AMERICA CARE FACILITIES p 1565
7530 Market Place Dr 55344
Tel (952) 941-0305 *SIC* 8322

VOLUNTEERS OF AMERICA NATIONAL SERVICES p 1565
7530 Market Place Dr 55344
Tel (952) 941-0305 *SIC* 8051 8052

WUNDERLICH-MALEC ENGINEERING INC p 1628
6101 Blue Circle Dr 55343
Tel (952) 933-3222 *SIC* 8711

EDINA, MN

EQUUS COMPUTER SYSTEMS INC p 507
7725 Washington Ave S 55439
Tel (612) 617-6200 *SIC* 3571

JERRYS ENTERPRISES INC p 783
5125 Vernon Ave S 55436
Tel (952) 922-8335 *SIC* 5411 5812 5251

▲ REGIS CORP p 1220
7201 Metro Blvd 55439
Tel (952) 947-7777 *SIC* 7231 7299 6794

SCHOENECKERS INC p 1288
7630 Bush Lake Rd 55439
Tel (952) 835-4800 *SIC* 8742 7361

SUNOPTA FOODS INC p 1403
7301 Ohms Ln Ste 600 55439
Tel (952) 820-2518 *SIC* 5149

SUNOPTA INGREDIENTS INC p 1403
7301 Ohms Ln Ste 600 55439
Tel (831) 685-6506 *SIC* 5159

ELK RIVER, MN

CRETEX COMPANIES INC p 392
311 Lowell Ave Nw 55330
Tel (763) 441-2121 *SIC* 3272 3089 3841

ELK RIVER AREA SCHOOL DISTRICT 728 p 487
815 Highway 10 55330
Tel (763) 241-3400 *SIC* 8211

ELK RIVER MACHINE CO p 487
828 4th St Nw 55330
Tel (763) 441-1581 *SIC* 3599

■ TESCOM CORP p 1440
12616 Industrial Blvd Nw 55330
Tel (763) 441-6330 *SIC* 3491 3625 3494

EXCELSIOR, MN

BEP/LYMAN LLC p 174
520 3rd St Ste 200 55331
Tel (952) 470-3600 *SIC* 5031 5211

FAIRMONT, MN

■ AVERY WEIGH-TRONIX LLC p 137
1000 Armstrong Dr 56031
Tel (507) 238-4461 *SIC* 3596 5083

ROSENS DIVERSIFIED INC p 1251
1120 Lake Ave 56031
Tel (507) 238-4201
SIC 2011 8748 5149 2879

ROSENS INC p 1251
1120 Lake Ave 56031
Tel (507) 238-4201 *SIC* 5191

FARIBAULT, MN

ABC BUS COMPANIES INC p 10
1506 30th St Nw 55021
Tel (507) 334-1871 *SIC* 5012 4173 5599

ABC BUS INC p 10
1506 30th St Nw 55021
Tel (507) 334-1871 *SIC* 5012 4173

BLUESTREAM PROFESSIONAL SERVICES LLC p 193
3305 Highway 60 W 55021
Tel (678) 355-6200 *SIC* 1731

KGP TELECOMMUNICATIONS INC p 816
3305 Highway 60 W 55021
Tel (507) 334-2268 *SIC* 5065

MET-CON CONSTRUCTION INC p 952
15760 Acorn Trl 55021
Tel (507) 332-2266 *SIC* 1541 1542 5251

FARMINGTON, MN

DAKOTA ELECTRIC ASSOCIATION p 409
4300 220th St W 55024
Tel (651) 463-6212 *SIC* 8611

FARMINGTON AREA PUBLIC SCHOOLS p 530
20655 Flagstaff Ave 55024
Tel (651) 463-5001 *SIC* 8211

FERGUS FALLS, MN

LAKE REGION HEALTHCARE CORP p 839
712 S Cascade St 56537
Tel (218) 736-8000 *SIC* 8062

OTTER TAIL AG ENTERPRISES LLC p 1098
24096 170th Ave 56537
Tel (218) 998-4301 *SIC* 2869

▲ OTTER TAIL CORP p 1098
215 S Cascade St 56537
Tel (218) 739-8200
SIC 4911 3084 5047 2099 1731

■ OTTER TAIL ENERGY SERVICES CO INC p 1098
224 E Washington Ave 56537
Tel (218) 739-8888 *SIC* 4932

■ OTTER TAIL POWER CO p 1098
215 S Cascade St 56537
Tel (218) 739-8200 *SIC* 4911

■ OTTER TAIL POWER CO p 1098
215 S Cascade St 56537
Tel (218) 739-8200 *SIC* 3699 4953 6531

FOREST LAKE, MN

INDEPENDENT SCHOOL DISTRICT 831 p 737
6100 210th St N 55025
Tel (651) 982-8100 *SIC* 8211

GLENWOOD, MN

FAST GLOBAL SOLUTIONS INC p 531
20631 State Highway 55 56334
Tel (320) 634-5126 *SIC* 3537 3565 3523

GOLDEN VALLEY, MN

AMERICAN PHOENIX INC p 77
5500 Wayzata Blvd # 1010 55416
Tel (763) 591-5035 *SIC* 3069

LIBERTY CARTON CO p 861
870 Louisiana Ave S 55426
Tel (763) 540-9600 *SIC* 2653

■ OPTUMHEALTH CARE SOLUTIONS INC p 1090
6300 Olson Memorial Hwy 55427
Tel (877) 801-3507 *SIC* 6324 7374 8999

GOODHUE, MN

AG PARTNERS COOP p 33
1st And Bdwy Way 55027
Tel (651) 345-3328 *SIC* 5153 5191

GRAND RAPIDS, MN

BLANDIN PAPER CO p 189
115 Sw 1st St 55744
Tel (218) 327-6200 *SIC* 2621 2672

L AND M SUPPLY INC p 833
1200 E Us Highway 169 55744
Tel (218) 326-9451 *SIC* 5251 5331 5013

MAGNETATION LLC p 896
102 Ne 3rd St Ste 120 55744
Tel (218) 398-0079 *SIC* 1011

GRANITE FALLS, MN

FAGEN INC p 524
501 Highway 212 W 56241
Tel (320) 564-3324 *SIC* 1541 1731 1711

GRANITE FALLS ENERGY LLC p 631
15045 Highway 23 Se 56241
Tel (320) 564-3100 *SIC* 2869 2085 2046

PROJECT VIKING LLC p 1182
501 Highway 212 W 56241
Tel (320) 564-3324 *SIC* 1321

HAMEL, MN

LORAM MAINTENANCE OF WAY INC p 878
3900 Arrowhead Dr 55340
Tel (763) 478-6014 *SIC* 3743

HANLEY FALLS, MN

FARMERS CO-OPERATIVE ELEVATOR CO p 529
1972 510th St 56245
Tel (507) 768-3448 *SIC* 0723

HASTINGS, MN

COUNTY OF DAKOTA p 377
1590 Highway 55 55033
Tel (651) 437-3191 *SIC* 9111

POLKA DOT DAIRY INC p 1160
110 17th St E 55033
Tel (651) 438-2793 *SIC* 5143

SMEAD MANUFACTURING CO INC p 1332
600 Smead Blvd 55033
Tel (651) 437-4111
SIC 2675 7372 2789 2759 2752 2542

HERMANTOWN, MN

CIRRUS DESIGN CORP p 308
4515 Taylor Cir 55811
Tel (218) 727-2737 *SIC* 3721

CIRRUS INDUSTRIES INC p 309
4515 Taylor Cir 55811
Tel (218) 727-2737 *SIC* 3721

MINERS INC p 973
5065 Miller Trunk Hwy 55811
Tel (218) 729-5882 *SIC* 5411

HERON LAKE, MN

HERON LAKE BIOENERGY LLC p 687
91246 390th Ave 56137
Tel (507) 793-0077 *SIC* 1321 2869

HIBBING, MN

ESSAR PROJECTS (USA) LLC p 510
555 W 27th St 55746
Tel (218) 263-3331 *SIC* 1542

RANGE REGIONAL HEALTH SERVICES p 1208
750 E 34th St 55746
Tel (218) 262-4881 *SIC* 8062

HOLDINGFORD, MN

POLAR TANK TRAILERS p 1159
12810 County Road 17 56340
Tel (417) 862-5526 *SIC* 3443 3715

HOLLOWAY, MN

WESTERN CONSOLIDATED COOPERATIVE p 1597
520 County Road 9 56249
Tel (320) 394-2171 *SIC* 5153 4221 2875

HOPKINS, MN

AMERICAN MEDICAL SYSTEMS HOLDINGS INC p 76
10700 Bren Rd W 55343
Tel (952) 930-6000 *SIC* 3842

AMERIPRIDE SERVICES INC p 83
10801 Wayzata Blvd # 100 55305
Tel (800) 750-4628 *SIC* 7213 7218

▲ APPLIANCE RECYCLING CENTERS OF AMERICA INC p 99
175 Jackson Ave N Ste 102 55343
Tel (952) 930-9000 *SIC* 5722 4953

CARLSON HOTELS MANAGEMENT CORP p 258
701 Tower Carlson Pkwy 55305
Tel (763) 212-5000 *SIC* 6794 6531 6552

■ COLLABORATIVE CARE HOLDINGS LLC p 336
9900 Bren Rd E 55343
Tel (952) 936-1300 *SIC* 6324

EXPRESSPOINT TECHNOLOGY SERVICES INC p 521
10900 Wayzata Blvd # 800 55305
Tel (763) 543-6000
SIC 5045 7379 7699 8741 7389 7378

INDEPENDENT SCHOOL DISTRICT 270 p 737
1001 Highway 7 55305
Tel (952) 988-4000 *SIC* 8211

INFORMATION PROVIDERS INC p 742
33 10th Ave S Ste 301 55343
Tel (952) 938-1400 *SIC* 6411

JACOBS INDUSTRIES INC p 775
8096 Excelsior Blvd 55343
Tel (612) 339-9500
SIC 2841 2087 2099 2844 5084 6794

OSMONICS INC p 1097
5951 Clearwater Dr 55343
Tel (952) 933-2277
SIC 3569 3589 3561 3824 3823 3089

■ OVATIONS INC p 1099
9900 Bren Rd E Ste 300w 55343
Tel (952) 936-1300 *SIC* 6324

POLAR CORP p 1159
1015 W St Germain St 42 Ste 420 55305
Tel (612) 430-6401 *SIC* 3443 5012 7699

SYNGENTA SEEDS INC p 1415
11055 Wayzata Blvd 55305
Tel (612) 656-8600
SIC 2074 2075 2076 5191

TONKA BAY EQUITY PARTNERS LLC p 1460
301 Carlson Pkwy Ste 325 55305
Tel (952) 345-2030 *SIC* 6799

WCE OIL FIELD SERVICES LLC p 1585
601 Carlson Pkwy Ste 110 55305
Tel (701) 356-7303 *SIC* 1389

HUTCHINSON, MN

HUTCHINSON HEALTH CARE p 722
1095 Highway 15 S 55350
Tel (320) 234-5000 *SIC* 8082

HUTCHINSON TECHNOLOGY INC p 722
40 W Highland Park Dr Ne 55350
Tel (320) 587-3797 *SIC* 3679 8731

INVER GROVE HEIGHTS, MN

AGRILIANCE LLC p 36
5500 Cenex Dr 55077
Tel (651) 481-2031 *SIC* 5083

CENEX INC p 275
5500 Cenex Dr 55077
Tel (800) 232-3639
SIC 1311 2911 4613 4922 4789 4213

CHS COOPERATIVES p 304
5500 Cenex Dr Ste 1 55077
Tel (651) 355-6000 *SIC* 5211

▲ CHS INC p 304
5500 Cenex Dr 55077
Tel (651) 355-6000
SIC 5153 5191 2075 1311 2911 4613

GERTEN GREENHOUSES & GARDEN CENTER INC p 609
5500 Blaine Ave 55076
Tel (651) 450-1501 *SIC* 5261 5193

RIVER COUNTRY COOPERATIVE p 1237
9072 Cahill Ave 55076
Tel (651) 451-1151 *SIC* 5171 5172 5191

■ TEMCO LLC p 1436
5500 Cnex Dr Mail Stn 370 Mail Station 55077
Tel (651) 355-6471 *SIC* 5153

TRAVEL TAGS INC p 1473
5842 Carmen Ave 55076
Tel (651) 450-1201 *SIC* 2396 3999 2752

LAKE CRYSTAL, MN

TRUCK BODIES & EQUIPMENT INTERNATIONAL INC p 1485
52182 Ember Rd 56055
Tel (507) 726-2728 *SIC* 3713 4953

LAKEVILLE, MN

■ ELAN NUTRITION INC p 483
21325 Hamburg Ave 55044
Tel (616) 940-6000 *SIC* 2099

■ HEARTH & HOME TECHNOLOGIES LLC p 678
7571 215th St W 55044
Tel (952) 985-6000 *SIC* 3429 4925

IMPERIAL PLASTICS INC p 734
21320 Hamburg Ave 55044
Tel (952) 469-4951 *SIC* 3089

LAKEVILLE AREA PUBLIC SCHOOLS p 840
8670 210th St W 55044
Tel (952) 232-2000 *SIC* 8211

MIDWEST VETERINARY SUPPLY INC p 968
21467 Holyoke Ave 55044
Tel (952) 894-4350 *SIC* 5122 5047

■ MOM BRANDS CO LLC p 983
20802 Kensington Blvd 55044
Tel (952) 322-8000 *SIC* 2043

■ POST FOODS LLC p 1163
20802 Kensington Blvd 55044
Tel (973) 658-2457 *SIC* 2041

RAILWORKS TRACK SYSTEMS INC p 1205
8485 210th St W 55044
Tel (212) 502-7900 *SIC* 1629

RYT-WAY ACQUISITION CO LLC p 1261
21850 Grenada Ave 55044
Tel (952) 469-1417 *SIC* 7389 2023 3565

RYT-WAY INDUSTRIES LLC p 1261
21850 Grenada Ave 55044
Tel (952) 469-1417 *SIC* 7389 2023

RYT-WAY MIDCO LLC p 1261
21850 Grenada Ave 55044
Tel (952) 469-1417 *SIC* 7389 2023 3565

■ VERDUN LLC p 1549
8860 207th St W 55044
Tel (952) 469-5424 *SIC* 3567

LAMBERTON, MN

HIGHWATER ETHANOL LLC p 692
24500 Us Highway 14 56152
Tel (507) 752-6160 *SIC* 2869

MEADOWLAND FARMERS COOP p 934
25861 Us Highway 14 56152
Tel (507) 752-7335 *SIC* 5153 5191 0723

LE CENTER, MN

GENESIS p 602
1273 W Derrynane St 56057
Tel (507) 357-6868 *SIC* 7359

LE SUEUR, MN

CAMBRIA CO LLC p 244
31496 Cambria Ave 56058
Tel (507) 665-5003 *SIC* 5211 3429

LE SUEUR INC p 850
1409 Vine St 56058
Tel (507) 665-6204
SIC 3363 3089 3544 3369

LESTER PRAIRIE, MN

LESTER BUILDING SYSTEMS LLC p 857
1111 2nd Ave S 55354
Tel (320) 395-5212 *SIC* 2452

LINDSTROM, MN

PLASTIC PRODUCTS CO INC p 1155
30355 Akerson St 55045
Tel (651) 257-5980 *SIC* 3089

LINO LAKES, MN

DISTRIBUTION ALTERNATIVES INC p 443
435 Park Ct 55014
Tel (651) 636-9167 *SIC* 5122 5912

LITCHFIELD, MN

FIRST DISTRICT ASSOCIATION p 546
101 S Swift Ave 55355
Tel (320) 693-3236 *SIC* 2023 2022 2026

SPARBOE FARMS INC p 1354
23577 Mn Hwy 22 55355
Tel (320) 693-7241 *SIC* 2015

SPARBOE FOODS LLC p 1354
23577 Minnesota Hwy 22 55355
Tel (320) 593-9600 *SIC* 2015

LITTLE CANADA, MN

SLUMBERLAND INC p 1331
3060 Centerville Rd 55117
Tel (651) 482-7500 *SIC* 5712

LITTLE FALLS, MN

UNITY FAMILY HEALTHCARE p 1515
815 2nd St Se 56345
Tel (320) 632-5441 *SIC* 8062

MANKATO, MN

AGSTAR FINANCIAL SERVICES ACA p 36
1921 Premier Dr 56001
Tel (507) 387-4174 *SIC* 6111

ENVENTIS CORP p 503
221 E Hickory St 56001
Tel (507) 387-1151 *SIC* 4813

INDEPENDENT SCHOOL DISTRICT NO 77 p 737
10 Civic Center Plz 56001
Tel (507) 387-3167 *SIC* 8211

MAYO CLINIC HEALTH SYSTEM -ST JAMES p 923
1025 Marsh St 56001
Tel (507) 625-4031 *SIC* 8082

MAYO CLINIC HEALTH SYSTEM-MANKATO p 924
1025 Marsh St 56001
Tel (507) 625-4031 *SIC* 8062

MINNESOTA STATE UNIVERSITY MANKATO p 974
620 South Rd 56001
Tel (507) 389-1866 *SIC* 8221 9199

MTU ONSITE ENERGY CORP p 998
100 Power Dr 56001
Tel (507) 625-7973 *SIC* 3621

OPERATING ENGINEERS LOCAL 49 p 1089
308 Lundin Blvd 56001
Tel (507) 625-3670 *SIC* 8631

RIDLEY USA INC p 1234
111 W Cherry St Ste 500 56001
Tel (507) 388-9400 *SIC* 2048

TONY DOWNS FOODS CO p 1460
54934 210th Ln 56001
Tel (507) 375-3111 *SIC* 2015 2099

MAPLE GROVE, MN

CARL ZEISS INDUSTRIAL METROLOGY LLC p 256
6250 Sycamore Ln N 55369
Tel (763) 533-9990 *SIC* 3545 3825

CS MCCROSSAN INC p 397
7865 Jefferson Hwy 55369
Tel (763) 425-4167 *SIC* 1611 1622 1799

DATA RECOGNITION CORP p 413
13490 Bass Lake Rd 55311
Tel (763) 268-2000 *SIC* 8732 2752

GREAT RIVER ENERGY p 634
12300 Elm Creek Blvd N 55369
Tel (763) 445-5000 *SIC* 4911

INDEPENDENT SCHOOL DISTRICT 279 p 737
11200 93rd Ave N 55369
Tel (763) 391-7000 *SIC* 8211

MAAX US CORP p 891
7767 Elm Creek Blvd N # 310 55369
Tel (877) 438-6229 *SIC* 3088

MAPLE GROVE HOSPITAL CORP p 903
9875 Hospital Dr 55369
Tel (763) 581-1000 *SIC* 8062

MIDWEST HARDWOOD CORP p 967
9540 83rd Ave N 55369
Tel (763) 425-8700 *SIC* 5031 2421

▲ NORTECH SYSTEMS INC p 1049
7550 Meridian Cir N # 150 55369
Tel (952) 345-2244 *SIC* 3674 3679

TILLER CORP p 1453
7200 Hemlock Ln N Ste 200 55369
Tel (763) 424-5400 *SIC* 1442 2951

UPSHER-SMITH LABORATORIES INC p 1529
6701 Evenstad Dr N 55369
Tel (763) 315-2000 *SIC* 2834

▲ VASCULAR SOLUTIONS INC p 1545
6464 Sycamore Ct N 55369
Tel (763) 656-4300 *SIC* 3841

MAPLE LAKE, MN

BERNATELLOS PIZZA INC p 176
200 Congress St W 55358
Tel (320) 963-6191 *SIC* 2038

MP NEXLEVEL LLC p 995
500 County Road 37 55358
Tel (320) 963-2400 *SIC* 1623

MAPLE PLAIN, MN

▲ PROTO LABS INC p 1185
5540 Pioneer Creek Dr 55359
Tel (763) 479-3680 *SIC* 3089

MAPLEWOOD, MN

■ 3M INTERAMERICA INC p 2
2501 Old Hudson Rd 55144
Tel (651) 733-1110
SIC 5113 5085 5065 5084 5122 8741

MARSHALL, MN

RUNNING SUPPLY INC p 1258
901 Highway 59 56258
Tel (507) 532-9566 *SIC* 5999

SCHWAN FOOD CO p 1291
115 W College Dr 56258
Tel (507) 532-3274 *SIC* 2038 2024 2037

SCHWANS HOME SERVICE INC p 1291
115 W College Dr 56258
Tel (507) 532-3274 *SIC* 5411

SFC GLOBAL SUPPLY CHAIN INC p 1310
115 W College Dr 56258
Tel (507) 532-3274 *SIC* 2045 2038

TURKEY VALLEY FARMS LLC p 1492
112 S 6th St 56258
Tel (507) 337-3100 *SIC* 2015

MEDINA, MN

OPEN SYSTEMS INTERNATIONAL INC p 1089
4101 Arrowhead Dr 55340
Tel (763) 551-0559 *SIC* 7371 5734

▲ POLARIS INDUSTRIES INC p 1159
2100 Highway 55 55340
Tel (763) 542-0500
SIC 3799 3751 3714 5699

ROCKLER COMPANIES INC p 1245
4365 Willow Dr 55340
Tel (763) 478-8201 *SIC* 5251 5961 2721

MENDOTA HEIGHTS, MN

CEMSTONE PRODUCTS CO p 274
2025 Centr Poin Blvd Ste 300 55120
Tel (651) 688-9292 *SIC* 3273 5032 1442

DUNGARVIN GROUP INC p 461
1444 Northland Dr Ste 200 55120
Tel (651) 699-6050 *SIC* 7389

RESTAURANT TECHNOLOGIES INC p 1228
2250 Pilot Knob Rd # 100 55120
Tel (651) 796-1600 *SIC* 5149 3631

TWIN CITY CONCRETE PRODUCTS CO INC p 1495
2025 Centre Pointe Blvd # 300 55120
Tel (651) 688-9116
SIC 5032 3273 3255 1442

MENDOTA, MN

MID-STATES DISTRIBUTING CO INC p 963
1370 Mendota Hts Rd 55150
Tel (651) 280-4300
SIC 5072 5013 5191 5091 5092 5136

MINNEAPOLIS, MN

ABBOTT NORTHWESTERN HOSPITAL p 9
800 E 28th St 55407
Tel (612) 863-4000 *SIC* 8062

ABILITY NETWORK INC p 11
100 N 6th St Ste 900a 55403
Tel (612) 460-4301 *SIC* 7379

ACTIVAR INC p 19
7808 Creekridge Cir # 200 55439
Tel (952) 944-3533
SIC 2542 3479 3442 3429 3089

ADOLFSON & PETERSON INC p 24
6701 W 23rd St 55426
Tel (952) 544-1561 *SIC* 1542

AEG MANAGEMENT TWN LLC p 29
600 1st Ave N Ste Sky 55403
Tel (612) 673-1300 *SIC* 7941

AGMOTION INC p 35
730 2nd Ave S Ste 700 55402
Tel (612) 486-3800 *SIC* 5153

AIMIA PROPRIETARY LOYALTY US INC p 38
100 N 6th St Ste 700b 55403
Tel (763) 445-3000 *SIC* 8741

ALLIANZ LIFE INSURANCE CO OF NORTH AMERICA p 56
5701 Golden Hills Dr 55416
Tel (763) 765-6500 *SIC* 6311

ALLINA HEALTH SYSTEM p 57
2925 Chicago Ave 55407
Tel (612) 262-5000 *SIC* 8062 8741 8011

■ **AMERICAN ENTERPRISE INVESTMENT SERVICES INC** p 71
70400 Axp Financial Ctr 55474
Tel (612) 671-3131 *SIC* 8742

■ **AMERIPRISE CERTIFICATE CO** p 83
1099 Ameriprise Fincl Ctr 55474
Tel (612) 671-3131 *SIC* 6726

▲ **AMERIPRISE FINANCIAL INC** p 83
55 Ameriprise Fincl Ctr 55474
Tel (612) 671-3131
SIC 6282 7389 6411 6311

ANALYSTS INTERNATIONAL CORP p 88
7700 France Ave S Ste 200 55435
Tel (952) 835-5900 *SIC* 7371 7379

AON BENFIELD INC p 94
5600 W 83rd St Ste 1100 55437
Tel (866) 280-3720 *SIC* 6321

AP MIDWEST LLC p 95
6701 W 23rd St 55426
Tel (952) 544-1561 *SIC* 1542

▲ **APOGEE ENTERPRISES INC** p 97
4400 W 78th St Ste 520 55435
Tel (952) 835-1874 *SIC* 3231

▲ **ARCTIC CAT INC** p 106
500 N 3rd St 55401
Tel (763) 354-1800
SIC 3799 2329 2339 3732

ATMOSPHERE COMMERCIAL INTERIORS LLC p 128
81 S 9th St Ste 350 55402
Tel (612) 343-0868 *SIC* 5021 5023 7389

ATTERRO INC p 129
730 2nd Ave S Ste 520 55402
Tel (612) 373-2600 *SIC* 7363 7361

AUGSBURG COLLEGE p 131
2211 Riverside Ave 55454
Tel (612) 330-1000 *SIC* 8221

AUGUSTANA CARE p 131
1007 E 14th St 55404
Tel (612) 238-5101 *SIC* 6513 8051

BACHMANS INC p 143
6010 Lyndale Ave S 55419
Tel (612) 861-7600
SIC 5992 5261 0181 5193 7359

BANNER ENGINEERING CORP p 153
9714 10th Ave N 55441
Tel (763) 544-3164 *SIC* 3674

BARR ENGINEERING CO p 156
4300 Marketpointe Dr # 200 55435
Tel (952) 832-2600 *SIC* 8711

BELLISIO FOODS FOODSERVICE p 171
1201 Hennepin Ave 55403
Tel (952) 469-2000 *SIC* 5141

■ **BERKLEY RISK ADMINISTRATION CO LLC** p 175
222 S 9th St Ste 2700 55402
Tel (612) 766-3000 *SIC* 6411 3052 3432

■ **BEST BUY ENTERPRISE SERVICES INC** p 177
7601 Penn Ave S 55423
Tel (612) 291-1000 *SIC* 8742

▲ **BIO-TECHNE CORP** p 183
614 Mckinley Pl Ne 55413
Tel (612) 379-8854 *SIC* 2835 8731

BOARD OF PENSIONS OF EVANGELICAL LUTHERAN CHURCH IN AMERICA p 195
800 Marquette Ave # 1050 55402
Tel (612) 333-7651 *SIC* 6371

BORDER FOODS INC p 201
5425 Boone Ave N 55428
Tel (763) 559-7338 *SIC* 5812

BRAUN INTERTEC CORP p 209
11001 Hampshire Ave S 55438
Tel (952) 995-2000 *SIC* 8711 8734

▲ **BUFFALO WILD WINGS INC** p 224
5500 Wayzata Blvd # 1600 55416
Tel (952) 593-9943 *SIC* 5812 6794

BUREAU OF ENGRAVING INC p 226
6465 Wayzata Blvd Ste 240 55426
Tel (612) 788-1000 *SIC* 2752 8249

C&N ETHANOL MARKETING LLC p 234
8011 34th Ave S Ste 350 55425
Tel (888) 263-8357 *SIC* 8742

CALABRIO INC p 238
400 1st Ave N Ste 300 55401
Tel (763) 592-4600 *SIC* 5045 7371

▲ **CAPELLA EDUCATION CO** p 248
225 S 6th St Fl 9 55402
Tel (888) 227-3552 *SIC* 8221

■ **CAPELLA UNIVERSITY INC** p 248
225 S 6th St Fl 9 55402
Tel (612) 339-8650 *SIC* 8221

CARIBOU COFFEE CO INC p 256
3900 Lake Breeze Ave 55429
Tel (763) 592-2200 *SIC* 5812 5499 6794

CARLSON HOTELS LIMITED PARTNERSHIP p 257
Carlson Parkway 701 Twr St Carlson Parkw 55459
Tel (763) 212-1000
SIC 6794 7011 5812 5813

■ **CATERPILLAR PAVING PRODUCTS INC** p 265
9401 85th Ave N 55445
Tel (763) 425-4100 *SIC* 3531

CATHOLIC ELDERCARE COMMUNITY FOUNDATION INC p 266
817 Main St Ne 55413
Tel (612) 379-1370 *SIC* 8051

CERIDIAN HCM HOLDING INC p 283
3311 E Old Shakopee Rd 55425
Tel (952) 853-8100 *SIC* 6719 7374

CERIDIAN LLC p 283
3311 E Old Shakopee Rd 55425
Tel (952) 853-8100 *SIC* 8721

CHILDRENS HOSPITALS AND CLINICS OF MINNESOTA p 300
2525 Chicago Ave 55404
Tel (612) 813-6000 *SIC* 8069

CHURCHILL COMPANIES p 305
333 S 7th St Ste 3100 55402
Tel (612) 673-6700 *SIC* 3211 3824 5083

CITY OF MINNEAPOLIS p 316
350 S 5th St Ste 325m 55415
Tel (612) 673-3000 *SIC* 9111

CLIFTONLARSONALLEN LLP p 326
220 S 6th St Ste 300 55402
Tel (612) 376-4620 *SIC* 8742 7371 8721

COLOPLAST CORP p 338
1601 W River Rd 55411
Tel (612) 337-7800 *SIC* 3842 2844 5047

COMMODITY SPECIALISTS CO p 345
920 2nd Ave S Ste 850 55402
Tel (612) 330-9889 *SIC* 5191

■ **CONWED PLASTICS LLC** p 365
2810 Weeks Ave Se 55414
Tel (612) 623-1700 *SIC* 3089

COVIDIEN HOLDING INC p 385
710 Medtronic Pkwy 55432
Tel (508) 261-8000 *SIC* 3842

■ **CUMMINS POWER GENERATION INC** p 401
1400 73rd Ave Ne 55432
Tel (763) 574-5000 *SIC* 3621 3519

CURLYS FOODS INC p 402
5201 Eden Ave Ste 370 55436
Tel (612) 920-3400 *SIC* 2011

DAIKIN APPLIED AMERICAS INC p 408
13600 Industrial Pk Blvd 55441
Tel (763) 553-5330 *SIC* 5075 3585

DAIN RAUSCHER INC p 408
60 S 6th St Ste 700 55402
Tel (704) 377-4300 *SIC* 6211

DAMICO & PARTNERS INC p 410
211 N 1st St Ste 175 55401
Tel (612) 317-4223 *SIC* 8741

DAMICO HOLDING CO p 410
275 Market St Ste 117 55405
Tel (612) 374-1776 *SIC* 5812

DESIGN READY CONTROLS INC p 432
9325 Winnetka Ave N 55445
Tel (763) 565-3000 *SIC* 5084 3613 3561

DOLAN LLC p 447
222 S 9th St Ste 2300 55402
Tel (612) 317-9420
SIC 7375 2741 2711 2752

▲ **DONALDSON CO INC** p 450
1400 W 94th St 55431
Tel (952) 887-3131
SIC 3599 3569 3714 3564

DORSEY & WHITNEY LLP p 451
50 S 6th St Ste 1500 55402
Tel (612) 340-2600 *SIC* 8111

EARLY BLOOM LEARNING p 469
17805 County Road 6 55447
Tel (763) 449-0600 *SIC* 8351

EATON CORP p 473
505 Hghway 169 N Ste 1200 55441
Tel (763) 595-7777 *SIC* 5084

EBENEZER SOCIETY p 474
2722 Park Ave 55407
Tel (612) 874-3460 *SIC* 8051 8741

EBERSEN INC p 474
7401 Central Ave Ne Ste 2 55432
Tel (763) 572-2661
SIC 4911 1521 6211 1382 4731 8711

ECM PUBLISHERS INC p 475
4095 Coon Rapids Blvd Nw 55433
Tel (763) 712-2400
SIC 2711 2741 7319 2789 2752

ECMC GROUP INC p 475
111 Washington Ave S # 1400 55401
Tel (651) 325-3652 *SIC* 6111

EDUCATIONAL CREDIT MANAGEMENT CORP p 479
111 Wshngton Ave Ste 1400 55401
Tel (651) 221-0566 *SIC* 6111

ELECTRIC MACHINERY CO INC p 484
800 Central Ave Ne 55413
Tel (612) 378-8000 *SIC* 3621

■ **ELLERBE BECKET INC** p 488
800 Lasalle Ave Fl 5 55402
Tel (612) 376-2000 *SIC* 8712 8711

■ **ENDEAVOR AIR INC** p 496
7500 Airline Dr 55450
Tel (901) 348-4100 *SIC* 4512

■ **ENVENTIS TELECOM INC** p 503
2950 Xenium Ln N Ste 138 55441
Tel (763) 577-3900 *SIC* 4813

FAIRVIEW HEALTH SERVICES p 525
2450 Riverside Ave 55454
Tel (612) 672-6300 *SIC* 8062

FAIRVIEW PHARMACY SERVICES LLC p 525
711 Kasota Ave Se 55414
Tel (612) 672-5200 *SIC* 5912 5122

FARIBAULT FOODS INC p 528
222 S 9th St Ste 3380 55402
Tel (612) 333-6461 *SIC* 2099 2032 2033

FASTENTECH INC p 531
8500 Normandale Lake Blvd 55437
Tel (952) 921-2090 *SIC* 3452

FEDERAL RESERVE BANK OF MINNEAPOLIS p 535
90 Hennepin Ave 55401
Tel (612) 204-5000 *SIC* 6011

FLOW CONTROL US HOLDING CORP p 560
5500 Wayzata Blvd 55416
Tel (763) 545-1730 *SIC* 3561

FOUNDATION HOLDINGS INC p 571
3311 E Old Shakopee Rd 55425
Tel (952) 853-8100 *SIC* 8641 8721

GDG HOLDINGS INC p 595
2901 E 78th St 55425
Tel (952) 854-2044 *SIC* 5084

■ **GEEK SQUAD INC** p 597
1213 Washington Ave N 55401
Tel (952) 544-0377 *SIC* 7379

▲ **GENERAL MILLS INC** p 601
1 General Mills Blvd 55426
Tel (763) 764-7600
SIC 2099 2041 2045 2064 2024

■ **GENERAL MILLS OPERATIONS LLC** p 601
1 General Mills Blvd 55426
Tel (763) 764-7600 *SIC* 4221

GN US HOLDINGS INC p 619
8001 E Bloomington Fwy 55420
Tel (952) 769-8000 *SIC* 3842

GOLDEN VALLEYTCA A LLC p 621
9393 Wayzata Blvd 55426
Tel (763) 744-9393 *SIC* 5511

GOLDNER HAWN JOHNSON & MORRISON INC p 622
3700 Wells Fargo Ctr # 90 55402
Tel (612) 338-5912 *SIC* 6211

GOODIN CO p 624
2700 N 2nd St 55411
Tel (612) 588-7811 *SIC* 5074 5075

▲ **GRACO INC** p 628
88 11th Ave Ne 55413
Tel (612) 623-6000
SIC 3561 3594 3563 3491 3823 3569

■ **GRANITE CITY FOOD & BREWERY LTD** p 631
3500 Amrcn Blvd W Ste 450 55431
Tel (952) 215-0660 *SIC* 5812 5813

GREATER TWIN CITIES UNITED WAY p 636
404 S 8th St Ste 100 55404
Tel (612) 340-7400 *SIC* 8322

GRIFFITHS CORP p 640
2717 Niagara Ln N 55447
Tel (763) 557-8935
SIC 3544 3469 3444 3451

GRIFFITHS HOLDING CORP p 640
2717 Niagara Ln N 55447
Tel (763) 557-8935 *SIC* 3544 3469

GYRUS ACMI LP p 649
9600 Louisiana Ave N 55445
Tel (763) 416-3000 *SIC* 3841

H ENTERPRISES INTERNATIONAL INC p 650
120 S 6th St Ste 2300 55402
Tel (612) 343-8293 *SIC* 5032 8611 5211

HAIRSTYLISTS MANAGEMENT SYSTEMS INC p 653
12700 Industrial Park Blv 55441
Tel (763) 550-1332 *SIC* 7231

HALDEMAN-HOMME INC p 653
430 Industrial Blvd Ne 55413
Tel (612) 331-4880 *SIC* 5021 5211 5084

HAMMEL GREEN AND ABRAHAMSON INC p 656
420 N 5th St Ste 100 55401
Tel (612) 758-4000 *SIC* 8712 8711

HAYS GROUP INC p 670
80 S 8th St Ste 700 55402
Tel (612) 347-8377 *SIC* 6411

HEALTH FITNESS CORP p 675
1700 W 82nd St Ste 200 55431
Tel (800) 639-7913 *SIC* 8099 7991

HEALTH PARTNERS INC p 675
8170 33rd Ave S 55425
Tel (952) 883-6000 *SIC* 8062

■ **HEALTHLAND INC** p 677
1600 Utica Ave S Ste 300 55416
Tel (612) 787-3120 *SIC* 7373 5045

HENNEPIN COUNTY p 683
300 S 6th St 55487
Tel (612) 348-3000 *SIC* 9111

HENNEPIN HEALTHCARE SYSTEM INC p 683
701 Park Ave 55415
Tel (612) 873-3000 *SIC* 8062 5912

HIGHJUMP SOFTWARE INC p 691
5600 W 83rd St Ste 600 55437
Tel (952) 947-4088 *SIC* 7371

HIRSHFIELDS INC p 696
725 2nd Ave N Ste 1 55405
Tel (612) 377-3910 *SIC* 5198 5231 2851

HITCHCOCK INDUSTRIES INC p 697
8701 Harriet Ave S 55420
Tel (952) 881-1000
SIC 3365 3364 3544 3369

HOM FURNITURE INC p 703
10301 Woodcrest Dr Nw 55433
Tel (763) 767-3600 *SIC* 5712

■ **HOMESERVICES OF AMERICA INC** p 704
333 S 7th St Fl 27 55402
Tel (612) 336-5900 *SIC* 6351 6361

HUNT ELECTRIC CORP p 719
7900 Chicago Ave S 55420
Tel (651) 646-2911 *SIC* 1731

INDEPENDENT SCHOOL DISTRICT 273 p 737
5701 Normandale Rd 55424
Tel (952) 848-3900 *SIC* 8211

INDEPENDENT SCHOOL DISTRICT 281 p 737
4148 Winnetka Ave N 55427
Tel (763) 504-8000 *SIC* 8211

INDEPENDENT SCHOOL DISTRICT NO 271 p 737
1350 W 106th St 55431
Tel (952) 681-6400 *SIC* 8211

■ **INTEGRIS METALS CORP** p 749
455 85th Ave Nw 55433
Tel (763) 717-9000 *SIC* 5051

■ **INTERNATIONAL DAIRY QUEEN INC** p 755
7505 Metro Blvd Ste 500 55439
Tel (952) 830-0200 *SIC* 5812

INTERSTATE COMPANIES INC p 758
2501 American Blvd E 55425
Tel (952) 854-2044 *SIC* 7538 8711 5085

INTERSTATE POWER SYSTEMS INC p 758
2901 E 78th St 55425
Tel (952) 854-2044 *SIC* 5084

INVESTMENT RARITIES INC p 761
7850 Metro Pkwy Ste 121 55425
Tel (952) 853-0700 *SIC* 5999

■ **JOSTENS INC** p 794
3601 Minnesota Dr Ste 400 55435
Tel (952) 830-3300 *SIC* 3911 2759 2741

KATUN CORP p 804
10951 Bush Lake Rd # 100 55438
Tel (952) 941-9505 *SIC* 5112

■ **KEYSTONE AUTOMOTIVE INDUSTRIES MN INC** p 815
3615 Marshall St Ne 55418
Tel (612) 789-1919 *SIC* 5013 3312 3465

KNUTSON CONSTRUCTION SERVICES INC p 825
7515 Wayzata Blvd 55426
Tel (763) 546-1400 *SIC* 1542 1541

KNUTSON HOLDINGS INC p 825
7515 Wayzata Blvd 55426
Tel (763) 546-1400 *SIC* 1542 1541

■ **KORN FERRY HAY GROUP INC** p 828
33 S 6th St Ste 4900 55402
Tel (612) 339-0927 *SIC* 8742

KURT MANUFACTURING CO INC p 832
5280 Main St Ne 55421
Tel (763) 572-1500
SIC 3499 3545 3363 3728 3842 3365

LAB HOLDINGS INC p 836
8500 Normandale Lake Blvd # 1750 55437
Tel (612) 607-1700 *SIC* 8734 8731

LE JEUNE STEEL CO p 849
118 W 60th St 55419
Tel (612) 861-3321 *SIC* 3441

LLP ROBINS KAPLAN p 872
800 Lasalle Ave Ste 2800 55402
Tel (612) 349-8500 *SIC* 8111

LUBRICATION TECHNOLOGIES INC p 884
900 Mendelssohn Ave N 55427
Tel (763) 545-0707 *SIC* 5172 5169

LUND FOOD HOLDINGS INC p 885
4100 W 50th St Ste 100 55424
Tel (952) 927-3663 *SIC* 5411

LUNDS INC p 886
4100 W 50th St Ste 100 55424
Tel (952) 927-3663 *SIC* 5411

LUTHER HOLDING CO p 886
3701 Alabama Ave S 55416
Tel (763) 593-5755
SIC 5511 7515 7513 6512 6552 5611

LYNDALE TERMINAL CO p 887
4567 American Blvd W 55437
Tel (952) 830-8700 *SIC* 5311 5411 5541

M A MORTENSON CO p 889
700 Meadow Ln N 55422
Tel (763) 522-2100 *SIC* 1542 1629

M A MORTENSON COMPANIES INC p 889
700 Meadow Ln N 55422
Tel (763) 522-2100 *SIC* 1542 1629

MACKAY MITCHELL ENVELOPE CO LLC p 892
2100 Elm St Se 55414
Tel (612) 331-9311 *SIC* 2677

MC KNIGHT FOUNDATION p 925
710 S 2nd St Ste 400 55401
Tel (612) 333-4220 *SIC* 6732

■ MCKESSON MEDICAL-SURGICAL MEDIMART INC p 930
8121 10th Ave N 55427
Tel (763) 595-6000 *SIC* 5047 5999

■ MEDIVATORS INC p 938
14605 28th Ave N 55447
Tel (763) 553-3300
SIC 3841 3842 3845 3589

MEDTRONIC INC p 939
710 Medtronic Pkwy 55432
Tel (763) 514-4000 *SIC* 3845 3842 3841

MEDTRONIC USA INC p 939
710 Medtronic Pkwy 55432
Tel (763) 514-4000 *SIC* 3841 5047

MEDTRONIC WORLD TRADE CORP p 939
710 Medtronic Pkwy 55432
Tel (763) 574-4000 *SIC* 5047

METAL-MATIC INC p 952
629 2nd St Se 55414
Tel (612) 928-2856 *SIC* 3317

METRO SALES INC p 955
1640 E 78th St 55423
Tel (612) 861-4000
SIC 5044 5112 5065 7359

METROPOLITAN AIRPORTS COMMISSION p 955
6040 28th Ave S 55450
Tel (612) 726-8100 *SIC* 4581

MIDCONTINENT COMMUNICATIONS p 964
3600 Minnesota Dr Ste 700 55435
Tel (952) 844-2600 *SIC* 4841 4813

MIDCONTINENT MEDIA INC p 964
3600 Minnesota Dr Ste 700 55435
Tel (952) 844-2600 *SIC* 4841

MIDCOUNTRY BANK p 964
Investors Bldg 7 Ste 103 55402
Tel (952) 843-5200 *SIC* 6035

MINCO PRODUCTS INC p 972
7300 Commerce Ln Ne 55432
Tel (763) 571-3121 *SIC* 3672 3823 3829

MINNEAPOLIS FOUNDATION p 973
80 S 8th St Ste 800 55402
Tel (612) 672-3878 *SIC* 6732

MINNEAPOLIS PUBLIC SCHOOL DISTRICT p 973
1250 W Broadway Ave 55411
Tel (612) 668-0200 *SIC* 8211

MINNESOTA MUNICIPAL POWER AGENCY p 973
220 S 6th St Ste 1300 55402
Tel (612) 349-6868 *SIC* 4911

■ MINTER-WEISMAN CO p 974
1035 Nathan Ln N Ste A 55441
Tel (763) 545-3706
SIC 5194 5149 5145 5013 5122

MIRACLE-EAR INC p 974
5000 Cheshire Pkwy N # 1 55446
Tel (763) 268-4000 *SIC* 5999

MMIC GROUP INC p 979
7701 France Ave S Ste 500 55435
Tel (952) 838-6700 *SIC* 6719

MOBILESOFT TECHNOLOGY INC p 980
100 Washington Ave S 55401
Tel (612) 460-4700 *SIC* 7371

■ MONEYGRAM PAYMENT SYSTEMS INC p 984
1550 Utica Ave S Ste 100 55416
Tel (952) 591-3000 *SIC* 6099 7389

MOREYS SEAFOOD INTERNATIONAL LLC p 988
742 Decatur Ave N 55427
Tel (763) 541-0129 *SIC* 5146 2091

■ MOSAIC CROP NUTRITION LLC p 991
3033 Campus Dr 55441
Tel (763) 577-2700 *SIC* 2874 1474

■ MOSAIC GLOBAL HOLDINGS INC p 991
3033 Campus Dr Ste E490 55441
Tel (763) 577-2700
SIC 2874 1474 1475 2875 2819

■ NASH-FINCH CO p 1008
7600 France Ave S Ste 200 55435
Tel (952) 832-0534
SIC 5141 5148 5142 5147 5411

NATH COMPANIES INC p 1009
900 American Blvd E # 300 55420
Tel (952) 853-1400 *SIC* 5812

NATH MINNESOTA FRANCHISE GROUP INC p 1009
900 E 79th St Ste 300 55420
Tel (952) 853-1400 *SIC* 5812 8741

NATIONAL MARROW DONOR PROGRAM INC p 1014
500 N 5th St 55401
Tel (612) 627-5800 *SIC* 8099 8742

NCS PEARSON INC p 1022
5601 Green Valley Dr # 220 55437
Tel (952) 681-3000
SIC 3577 7372 7374 8748 7379

NEW HORIZON ENTERPRISES INC p 1031
3405 Annapolis Ln N # 100 55447
Tel (763) 557-1111 *SIC* 8351

NEWSCYCLE SOLUTIONS INC p 1039
7900 Intl Dr Ste 800 55425
Tel (651) 639-0662 *SIC* 7371

■ NEXTIRAONE LLC p 1040
5050 Lincoln Dr Ste 300 55436
Tel (952) 352-4410
SIC 5065 7629 1731 5999 4813 4841

■ NORSTAN COMMUNICATIONS INC p 1049
5050 Lincoln Dr Ste 300 55436
Tel (952) 935-9002 *SIC* 5065 1731 7629

■ NORSTAN INC p 1049
5050 Lincoln Dr Ste 300 55436
Tel (952) 352-4000
SIC 7389 3661 8748 7379

NORTH CENTRAL EQUITY LLC p 1051
60 S 6th St Ste 2535 55402
Tel (612) 465-0260 *SIC* 6799 4813

NORTH MEMORIAL HEALTH CARE p 1053
3300 Oakdale Ave N 55422
Tel (763) 520-5200 *SIC* 8062 8011

NORTH RIDGE SKILLED LLC p 1053
5430 Boone Ave N 55428
Tel (763) 592-3000 *SIC* 6513 8051

NORTH STAR RESOURCE GROUP p 1054
2701 University Ave Se # 300 55414
Tel (612) 617-6000 *SIC* 6411

■ NORTHERN STATES POWER CO p 1057
414 Nicollet Mall 55401
Tel (612) 330-5500 *SIC* 4931

NORTHLAND ALUMINUM PRODUCTS INC p 1057
5005 Highway 7 55416
Tel (952) 924-8505 *SIC* 3089 3479

NORTHWEST AIRLINES INC p 1059
7500 Airline Dr 55450
Tel (404) 715-2600 *SIC* 4512 4513 4522

■ NORWEST VENTURE CAPITAL MANAGEMENT INC p 1061
80 S 8th St Ste 3600 55402
Tel (612) 215-1600 *SIC* 6799

■ NUCLEAR MANAGEMENT CO LLC p 1066
414 Nicollet Mall 55401
Tel (612) 330-5500 *SIC* 8741 8999

■ OLD REPUBLIC NATIONAL TITLE HOLDING CO p 1081
400 2nd Ave S 55401
Tel (612) 371-1111 *SIC* 6361

■ OLD REPUBLIC NATIONAL TITLE INSURANCE CO p 1081
400 2nd Ave S 55401
Tel (612) 371-1111 *SIC* 6361

OMNI WORKSPACE CO LLC p 1085
1300 Washington Ave N # 200 55411
Tel (612) 627-1600 *SIC* 7641 4212 4226

OPEN ACCESS TECHNOLOGY INTERNATIONAL INC p 1089
3660 Technology Dr 55418
Tel (763) 201-2000 *SIC* 7371 8711

PACE ANALYTICAL SERVICES LLC p 1103
1800 Elm St Se 55414
Tel (612) 607-6369 *SIC* 8734 8748 8731

PADDOCK LABORATORIES LLC p 1107
3940 Quebec Ave N 55427
Tel (763) 546-4676 *SIC* 2834

PARK CONSTRUCTION CO p 1115
1481 81st Ave Ne 55432
Tel (763) 786-9800 *SIC* 1611 1622 1629

PARK NICOLLET CLINIC p 1115
3800 Park Nicollet Blvd 55416
Tel (952) 993-3123 *SIC* 8011 5912 5999

PARSONS ELECTRIC LLC p 1118
5960 Main St Ne 55432
Tel (763) 571-8000 *SIC* 1731 7382 8711

PENTAIR INC p 1132
5500 Wayzata Blvd Ste 600 55416
Tel (763) 545-1730
SIC 3491 3559 4971 3589

■ PEPSI AMERICAS INC p 1134
60 S 6th St 55402
Tel (612) 661-4000 *SIC* 2086

PETTERS AVIATION LLC p 1140
431 S 7th St Ste 2530 55415
Tel (612) 238-7780 *SIC* 4581

PINNACLE AIRLINES CORP p 1149
7500 Airline Dr 55450
Tel (800) 603-4594 *SIC* 4512

▲ PIPER JAFFRAY COMPANIES p 1151
800 Nicollet Mall Ste 800 55402
Tel (612) 303-6000 *SIC* 6211

POHLAD COMPANIES p 1159
60 S 6th St Ste 3700 55402
Tel (612) 661-3700
SIC 8742 7929 6531 5013 7549 7379

PREMIUM WATERS INC p 1171
2100 Summer St Ne Ste 200 55413
Tel (612) 379-4141 *SIC* 2086

PROCESS DISPLAYS LLC p 1179
7108 31st Ave N 55427
Tel (763) 541-1245
SIC 2541 2542 2599 2675 2752 2759

PRODUCTIVITY INC p 1180
15150 25th Ave N 55447
Tel (763) 476-8600 *SIC* 5085 5084

QUADION HOLDINGS LLC p 1196
1100 Xenium Ln N Ste 1 55441
Tel (952) 927-1400 *SIC* 3069 3089

■ QUADION LLC p 1196
1100 Xenium Ln N Ste 1 55441
Tel (952) 927-1400 *SIC* 3069 3089

RAINEY ROAD HOLDINGS INC p 1205
15600 37th Ave N Ste 100 55446
Tel (763) 541-1410 *SIC* 6712

RBC CAPITAL MARKETS CORP p 1211
60 S 6th St Ste 700 55402
Tel (612) 371-2711 *SIC* 7374

RBC CAPITAL MARKETS LLC p 1211
60 S 6th St Ste 700 55402
Tel (612) 371-2711
SIC 6211 6512 6513 6282

RBC DAIN RAUSCHER LENDING SERVICES INC p 1211
60 S 6th Strreet 55402
Tel (612) 371-2941 *SIC* 6282

REGENTS OF UNIVERSITY OF MINNESOTA p 1219
600 Mcnamara Alumni # 200 55455
Tel (612) 625-5000 *SIC* 8221

REGIONS HOSPITAL p 1220
8170 33rd Ave S 55425
Tel (952) 883-6280 *SIC* 8062

REID ENTERPRISES INC p 1220
8000 Penn Ave S 55431
Tel (952) 238-4300 *SIC* 5511

■ RELIASTAR LIFE INSURANCE CO p 1222
20 Washington Ave S 55401
Tel (612) 372-5432 *SIC* 6311 6321 6324

■ RESEARCH AND DIAGNOSTIC SYSTEMS INC p 1226
614 Mckinley Pl Ne 55413
Tel (612) 379-2956
SIC 8733 2833 8731 3829 3625

RIVERLAND AG CORP p 1237
1660 Highway 100 S # 350 55416
Tel (952) 746-6800 *SIC* 5153 4221

■ RIVERSOURCE LIFE INSURANCE CO p 1238
1099 Ameriprise Fincl Ctr 55474
Tel (612) 671-3131 *SIC* 6311 6321

■ RJF AGENCIES INC p 1239
7225 Northland Dr N 55428
Tel (763) 746-8000 *SIC* 6411

RMS CO p 1239
8600 Evergreen Blvd Nw 55433
Tel (763) 786-1520 *SIC* 3841

ROBERT A WILLIAMS ENTERPRISES p 1241
3701 Central Ave Ne 55421
Tel (763) 788-1113 *SIC* 5541 6519

ROOM & BOARD INC p 1249
4600 Olson Memorial Hwy 55422
Tel (763) 588-7525 *SIC* 5712

RUST CONSULTING INC p 1260
625 Marquette Ave Ste 900 55402
Tel (612) 359-2000 *SIC* 8741 8111

RYAN COMPANIES US INC p 1260
50 S 10th St Ste 300 55403
Tel (612) 492-4000
SIC 1542 1541 6552 6512 1522

SATELLITE SHELTERS INC p 1283
2530 Xenium Ln N Ste 150 55441
Tel (763) 553-1900 *SIC* 1542 7353

SCHOLARSHIP AMERICA INC p 1288
7900 Intl Dr Ste 500 55425
Tel (800) 537-4180 *SIC* 8399

▲ SELECT COMFORT CORP p 1301
9800 59th Ave N 55442
Tel (763) 551-7000 *SIC* 2515

■ SELECT COMFORT RETAIL CORP p 1301
9800 59th Ave N 55442
Tel (763) 551-7000 *SIC* 5712

SENIOR TEALWOOD LIVING p 1304
7400 W 109th St 55438
Tel (952) 888-2923 *SIC* 8051 8741

SENTAGE CORP p 1305
801 12th Ave N 55411
Tel (412) 431-3353 *SIC* 8072

SMITHS MEDICAL MD INC p 1334
6000 Nathan Ln N Ste 100 55442
Tel (651) 633-2556 *SIC* 3841 3586 3561

SONUS-USA INC p 1340
5000 Cheshire Pkwy N # 1 55446
Tel (763) 268-4065 *SIC* 5999

SOO LINE RAILROAD CO p 1341
120 S 6th St Ste 900 55402
Tel (800) 234-0013 *SIC* 4011

SOURCECORP LEGAL INC p 1342
625 Marquette Ave Ste 880 55402
Tel (612) 359-2822 *SIC* 8748

SPANLINK COMMUNICATIONS INC p 1354
5940 Golden Hills Dr 55416
Tel (763) 971-2000 *SIC* 7373 7371

SPELL CAPITAL PARTNERS FUND III FOR QUALIFIED PURCHASERS LP p 1358
222 S 9th St Ste 2880 55402
Tel (612) 371-9650 *SIC* 6799

SPELL CAPITAL PARTNERS LLC p 1358
222 S 9th St Ste 2880 55402
Tel (612) 371-9650 *SIC* 3599 3469 3444

▲ SPS COMMERCE INC p 1362
333 S 7th St Ste 1000 55402
Tel (612) 435-9400 *SIC* 7374 7372

SPS COMPANIES INC p 1362
6363 Highway 7 55416
Tel (952) 929-1377 *SIC* 5074 5075 3498

ST THERESE HOME INC p 1373
8000 Bass Lake Rd 55428
Tel (763) 531-5000 *SIC* 8051

STAN KOCH & SONS TRUCKING INC p 1375
4200 Dahlberg Dr Ste 100 55422
Tel (763) 302-5400 *SIC* 4213 4731

STAR TRIBUNE MEDIA CO LLC p 1378
650 3rd Ave S Ste 1300 55488
Tel (612) 673-4000 *SIC* 2711

■ SUPERCUTS INC p 1406
7201 Metro Blvd 55439
Tel (952) 947-7777 *SIC* 7231

SYNICO STAFFING LLC p 1415
3033 Excelsior Blvd # 495 55416
Tel (612) 926-6000 *SIC* 7363

■ TARGET CAPITAL CORP p 1425
1000 Nicollet Mall 55403
Tel (612) 304-6073 *SIC* 6282

▲ TARGET CORP p 1425
1000 Nicollet Mall 55403
Tel (612) 304-6073 *SIC* 5311 5411

■ TARGET STORES INC p 1425
1000 Nicollet Mall 55403
Tel (612) 304-6073 *SIC* 5411 5311 5461

■ TCF NATIONAL BANK p 1428
1405 Xenium Ln N Ste 180 55441
Tel (612) 661-8450 *SIC* 6021 6159

▲ TENNANT CO p 1437
701 Lilac Dr N 55422
Tel (763) 540-1200 *SIC* 3589 3635

THERMO KING CORP p 1447
314 W 90th St 55420
Tel (952) 887-2200 *SIC* 3585

THIELE TECHNOLOGIES INC p 1448
315 27th Ave Ne 55418
Tel (612) 782-1200 *SIC* 3565

THRIVENT FINANCIAL FOR LUTHERANS FOUNDATION p 1451
625 4th Ave S 55415
Tel (920) 734-5721
SIC 6311 6321 8742 6411 6211

■ TORO LLC p 1462
8111 Lyndale Ave S 55420
Tel (952) 887-8041 *SIC* 3524 5083

■ TORO MANUFACTURING CORP p 1462
8111 Lyndale Ave S 55420
Tel (952) 888-8801 *SIC* 3084

TWIN CITY FAN COMPANIES LTD p 1495
5959 Trenton Ln N 55442
Tel (763) 551-7500 *SIC* 3564 5084

UCARE MINNESOTA p 1498
500 Stinson Blvd 55413
Tel (612) 676-6500 *SIC* 6324

UNITED SUGARS CORP p 1514
8000 W 78th St Ste 300 55439
Tel (952) 896-0131 *SIC* 5149

UNITED WAY OF MINN AREA p 1515
404 S 8th St Ste 100 55404
Tel (612) 340-7400 *SIC* 8399

UNIVERSAL HOSPITAL SERVICES INC p 1517
6625 W 78th St Ste 300 55439
Tel (952) 893-3200 *SIC* 7352

UNIVERSITY OF MINNESOTA PHYSICIANS p 1523
720 Washington Ave Se # 200 55414
Tel (612) 884-0600 *SIC* 8011

▲ US BANCORP p 1531
800 Nicollet Mall # 1500 55402
Tel (651) 466-3000
SIC 6021 6022 6162 6091 6159 6411

■ US BANCORP INFORMATION SERVICES INC p 1531
800 Nicollet Mall 55402
Tel (651) 466-3000 *SIC* 6411

US COMMODITIES LLC p 1531
730 2nd Ave S Ste 700 55402
Tel (612) 486-3800 *SIC* 5191 6221

▲ VALSPAR CORP p 1542
1101 S 3rd St 55415
Tel (612) 851-7000 *SIC* 2851

VIKING ELECTRIC SUPPLY INC p 1557
451 Industrial Blvd Ne # 2 55413
Tel (612) 627-1234 *SIC* 5063

■ VISANT CORP p 1560
3601 Minnesota Dr Ste 400 55435
Tel (914) 595-8200
SIC 3911 2741 2389 7221

■ VISANT HOLDING CORP p 1561
3601 Minnesota Dr Ste 400 55435
Tel (914) 595-8200
SIC 2741 2759 3911 6719

W D LARSON COMPANIES LTD INC p 1568
10700 Lyndale Ave S Ste A 55420
Tel (952) 888-4934
SIC 5012 5013 7538 6159

■ WACHOVIA PREFERRED FUNDING CORP p 1570
90 S 7th St Fl 13 55402
Tel (855) 825-1437 SIC 6798

WAGNER HOLDINGS INC p 1571
1770 Fernbrook Ln N 55447
Tel (763) 553-7000 SIC 3563 3559

WALKER METHODIST p 1573
3737 Bryant Ave S 55409
Tel (612) 827-5931 SIC 8361

WALMAN OPTICAL CO p 1573
801 12th Ave N Ste 1 55411
Tel (612) 520-6000 SIC 5048 3851

WEIS BUILDERS INC p 1588
7645 Lyndale Ave S # 300 55423
Tel (612) 243-5000 SIC 1522 1541 1542

■ WELLS FARGO BUSINESS CREDIT INC p 1590
730 2nd Ave S Fl 8 55402
Tel (612) 673-8500 SIC 6021 6141

■ WELLS FARGO FOUNDATION MINNESOTA p 1590
N 9305-192 55479
Tel (612) 667-1234 SIC 6021

■ WELLS FARGO FUNDING INC p 1590
2701 Wells Fargo Way Fl 5 55467
Tel (800) 328-5074 SIC 6162

■ WELLS FARGO INSURANCE SERVICES OF MINNESOTA INC p 1590
400 Highway 169 S Ste 800 55426
Tel (952) 563-0600 SIC 6411

■ WELLS FARGO SERVICES INC p 1591
255 2nd Ave S 55401
Tel (612) 667-1234 SIC 7374

WESTERN NATIONAL MUTUAL INSURANCE CO INC p 1599
5350 W 78th St 55439
Tel (952) 835-5350 SIC 6331

WHOLESALE PRODUCE SUPPLY LLC p 1607
752 Kasota Cir Se 55414
Tel (612) 378-2025 SIC 5148

WOLTERS KLUWER FINANCIAL SERVICES INC p 1621
100 S 5th St Ste 700 55402
Tel (612) 656-7700 SIC 7371

▲ XCEL ENERGY INC p 1631
414 Nicollet Mall 55401
Tel (612) 330-5500 SIC 4911 4922

■ XCEL ENERGY SERVICES INC p 1631
414 Nicollet Mall Fl 7 55401
Tel (612) 330-5500 SIC 4931

XERXES CORP p 1631
7901 Xerxes Ave S Ste 201 55431
Tel (952) 887-1890 SIC 3089 3443 3088

YOUNG MENS CHRISTIAN ASSOCIATION OF GREATER TWIN CITIES p 1638
2125 E Hennepin Ave 55413
Tel (612) 465-0450 SIC 8641

ZIEGLER INC p 1643
901 W 94th St 55420
Tel (952) 888-4121 SIC 5082 5084

MINNETONKA, MN

■ AMERICAN MEDICAL SYSTEMS LLC p 76
10700 Bren Rd W 55343
Tel (952) 930-6000 SIC 3842 3841

■ ASSOCIATED FINANCIAL GROUP LLC p 120
12600 Whitewater Dr # 100 55343
Tel (952) 945-0200 SIC 6411

B4 TRAVEL GROUP INC p 143
701 Carlson Pkwy 55305
Tel (763) 212-5000 SIC 4724

CARLSON HOLDINGS INC p 257
701 Carlson Pkwy 55305
Tel (763) 212-5000
SIC 7011 5812 6794 7389 4724

CARLSON INC p 258
701 Carlson Pkwy 55305
Tel (763) 212-5000
SIC 7011 5812 6794 8742 8743 7389

CARLSON WAGONLIT TRAVEL INC p 258
701 Carlson Pkwy 55305
Tel (763) 212-1000 SIC 4724

▲ COMMUNICATIONS SYSTEMS INC p 347
10900 Red Circle Dr 55343
Tel (952) 996-1674
SIC 3661 3577 3663 8748

■ CRYSTAL FARMS REFRIGERATED DISTRIBUTION CO p 396
301 Carlson Pkwy Ste 400 55305
Tel (952) 672-8260 SIC 5143 5144

CULLIGAN SOFT WATER SERVICE CO p 400
6030 Culligan Way 55345
Tel (952) 933-7200 SIC 5999 7389

DAVID AND LILY PENN INC p 415
10201 Wayzata Blvd 55305
Tel (763) 746-0410 SIC 5014

▲ DIGI INTERNATIONAL INC p 438
11001 Bren Rd E 55343
Tel (952) 912-3444
SIC 3577 3575 7374 7371

DIGITAL RIVER INC p 439
10380 Bren Rd W 55343
Tel (952) 253-1234 SIC 4813

▲ FAMOUS DAVES OF AMERICA INC p 527
12701 Whitewater Dr # 200 55343
Tel (952) 294-1300 SIC 5812 6794

▲ G&K SERVICES INC p 587
5995 Opus Pkwy Ste 500 55343
Tel (952) 912-5500 SIC 7218 7213 7219

MEDICA HEALTH PLANS p 936
401 Carlson Pkwy 55305
Tel (952) 992-3056 SIC 8011

■ METRAHEALTH CARE MANAGEMENT CORP p 954
9900 Bren Rd E 55343
Tel (952) 936-1300 SIC 6321 6311

■ MFI HOLDING CORP p 958
301 Carlson Pkwy Ste 400 55305
Tel (952) 258-4000 SIC 6719 0252

■ MG WALDBAUM CO p 958
301 Carlson Pkwy Ste 400 55305
Tel (952) 258-4000 SIC 2015 5153 5191

■ MICHAEL FOODS GROUP INC p 960
301 Carlson Pkwy Ste 400 55305
Tel (952) 258-4000
SIC 0252 2015 5144 5143 5148 6719

■ MICHAEL FOODS INC p 960
301 Carlson Pkwy Ste 400 55305
Tel (507) 237-4600
SIC 0252 2015 5144 5143 5148 5499

■ MICHAEL FOODS OF DELAWARE INC p 960
301 Carlson Pkwy Ste 400 55305
Tel (952) 258-4000
SIC 0252 2015 5144 5143 5148 2024

MINNETONKA INDEPENDENT SCHOOL DISTRICT 276 p 974
5621 County Road 101 55345
Tel (952) 401-5000 SIC 8211

MINNWEST CORP p 974
14820 Highway 7 Ste 200 55345
Tel (952) 230-9800 SIC 6022

OPUS DESIGN BUILD LLC p 1091
10350 Bren Rd W 55343
Tel (952) 656-4444 SIC 1522 1541

OPUS HOLDING LLC p 1091
10350 Bren Rd W 55343
Tel (952) 656-4444 SIC 6531

■ PEOPLENET COMMUNICATIONS CORP p 1132
4400 Baker Rd 55343
Tel (952) 908-6200 SIC 7373 3663 4812

PINE RIVER CAPITAL MANAGEMENT LP p 1149
601 Carlson Pkwy Ste 330 55305
Tel (612) 238-3300 SIC 6722

POLAROID CONSUMER ELECTRONICS INTERNATIONAL LLC p 1159
4400 Baker Rd Ste 900 55343
Tel (952) 936-5000 SIC 5199

RADISSON HOTELS INTERNATIONAL INC p 1204
701 Carlson Pkwy 55305
Tel (763) 212-5000
SIC 7011 6794 6552 6531 8742 7389

■ ST JUDE MEDICAL CARDIOVASCULAR DIVISION p 1369
14901 Deveau Pl 55345
Tel (952) 933-4700 SIC 3841 3842

TAHER INC p 1421
5570 Smetana Dr 55343
Tel (952) 945-0505 SIC 5812

TAYLOR-WHARTON INTERNATIONAL LLC p 1427
5600 Rowland Rd Ste 170 55343
Tel (717) 763-5060 SIC 3443 3491

■ UNITED HEALTHCARE SERVICES INC p 1509
9700 Health Care Ln 55343
Tel (952) 936-1300 SIC 6321

▲ UNITEDHEALTH GROUP INC p 1515
9900 Bren Rd E Ste 300w 55343
Tel (952) 936-1300 SIC 6324 6411 6321

MONTEVIDEO, MN

■ SL-MONTEVIDEO TECHNOLOGY INC p 1331
2002 Black Oak Ave 56265
Tel (320) 269-5583 SIC 3625

MONTICELLO, MN

CARGILL KITCHEN SOLUTIONS INC p 255
206 W 4th St 55362
Tel (763) 271-5600 SIC 2015

MOORHEAD, MN

■ AEV INC p 31
3030 24th Ave S 56560
Tel (218) 284-9518 SIC 1731

AMERICAN CRYSTAL SUGAR CO p 70
101 3rd St N 56560
Tel (218) 236-4326 SIC 2063 7359

CONCORDIA COLLEGE CORP p 355
901 8th St S 56562
Tel (218) 299-4000 SIC 8299

■ PRIMORIS AV ENERGY & ELECTRICAL CONSTRUCTION CORP p 1176
3030 24th Ave S 56560
Tel (218) 284-9500 SIC 1731 1623

MORA, MN

ENGINEERED POLYMERS CORP p 499
1020 Maple Ave E 55051
Tel (320) 679-3232 SIC 3086 3089

MORGAN, MN

HARVEST LAND COOPERATIVE p 666
711 Front St W 56266
Tel (507) 249-3196 SIC 5153 5191 0253

MORRIS, MN

ST FRANCIS HEALTH SERVICES OF MORRIS INC p 1366
801 Nevada Ave 56267
Tel (320) 589-2004 SIC 8741

SUPERIOR INDUSTRIES INC p 1406
315 State Highway 28 56267
Tel (320) 589-2406 SIC 3535

NEW BRIGHTON, MN

BELL LUMBER & POLE CO p 170
778 1st St Nw 55112
Tel (651) 633-4334 SIC 5099 2411

NEW HOPE, MN

ATRENNE INTEGRATED SOLUTIONS INC p 129
9210 Science Center Dr 55428
Tel (763) 533-3533 SIC 8711 5065

LIBERTY DIVERSIFIED INTERNATIONAL INC p 861
5600 Highway 169 N 55428
Tel (763) 536-6600
SIC 2653 2631 5112 2542 3089 5961

NEW LONDON, MN

■ MID-STATE TELEPHONE CO p 963
7902 Chapin Dr Ne 56273
Tel (320) 354-7805 SIC 4813

NEW PRAGUE, MN

■ CHART INC p 290
407 7th St Nw 56071
Tel (952) 758-4484 SIC 3443 3842

NEW ULM, MN

ASSOCIATED MILK PRODUCERS INC p 121
315 N Brdwy St 56073
Tel (507) 354-8295
SIC 2023 2022 2021 2024 2026 5143

J & R SCHUGEL TRUCKING INC p 770
2026 N Broadway St 56073
Tel (800) 359-2900 SIC 4213

NEWPORT, MN

BAILEY NURSERIES INC p 145
1325 Bailey Rd 55055
Tel (651) 459-9744 SIC 5193

NORTH BRANCH, MN

FRANDSEN CORP p 574
5481 Saint Croix Trl # 200 55056
Tel (651) 407-5700 SIC 8742

NORTH MANKATO, MN

CAPSTONE DIGITAL LLC p 251
1710 Roe Crest Dr 56003
Tel (507) 385-8280 SIC 2731

CARLSON CRAFT INC p 257
1750 Tower Blvd 56003
Tel (507) 625-5011 SIC 2759

COMMERCIAL PRINT GROUP INC p 345
1750 Northway Dr 56003
Tel (507) 625-2828 SIC 7313

CORPORATE GRAPHICS INTERNATIONAL INC p 372
1885 Northway Dr 56003
Tel (507) 625-4400 SIC 2752

COUGHLAN COMPANIES INC p 374
1710 Roe Crest Dr 56003
Tel (507) 345-8100 SIC 7361 1741

■ KATO ENGINEERING INC p 804
2075 Howard Dr W 56003
Tel (507) 345-2716 SIC 3621 3643 3625

NAVITOR INC p 1020
1725 Roe Crest Dr 56003
Tel (507) 625-2828 SIC 2759

OCCASIONS GROUP INC p 1072
1725 Roe Crest Dr 56003
Tel (208) 359-1000 SIC 2759

PRECISION PRESS INC p 1168
2020 Lookout Dr 56003
Tel (507) 625-7155 SIC 2678 2752

TAYLOR CORP p 1427
1725 Roe Crest Dr 56003
Tel (507) 625-2828
SIC 8742 2752 2677 2759

NORTHFIELD, MN

CANNON VALLEY COOPERATIVE p 247
1500 Highway 3 S 55057
Tel (507) 645-9556
SIC 5541 5171 1711 5191 5153 5211

CARLETON COLLEGE p 257
1 N College St 55057
Tel (507) 222-4000 SIC 8221

■ MCLANE MINNESOTA INC p 931
1111 5th St W 55057
Tel (507) 664-3000 SIC 5141

MULTEK FLEXIBLE CIRCUITS INC p 999
1150 Sheldahl Rd 55057
Tel (507) 663-8000 SIC 3672

NORTHFIELD HOSPITAL & SKILLED NURSING p 1057
2000 North Ave 55057
Tel (507) 646-1000 SIC 8062

ST OLAF COLLEGE p 1372
1520 Saint Olaf Ave 55057
Tel (507) 786-2222 SIC 8221

NORWOOD, MN

BONGARDS CREAMERIES p 200
13200 County Road 51 55368
Tel (952) 466-5521
SIC 2023 2022 5451 2021

OAKDALE, MN

DEDICATED LOGISTICS INC p 421
2900 Granada Ln N 55128
Tel (651) 631-5918 SIC 4213 4212 4225

▲ IMATION CORP p 733
1099 Helmo Ave N Ste 250 55128
Tel (651) 704-4000 SIC 3695 3572

OGEMA, MN

WHITE EARTH BAND OF CHIPPEWA INDIANS p 1606
35500 Eagleview Rd 56569
Tel (800) 950-3248 SIC 9131

OSSEO, MN

■ 3 WIRE GROUP INC p 2
101 Broadway St W Ste 300 55369
Tel (763) 488-3000 SIC 5078

OWATONNA, MN

CENTRAL VALLEY COOPERATIVE p 280
900 30th Pl Nw 55060
Tel (507) 451-1230 SIC 5191 5171 5541

FEDERATED LIFE INSURANCE CO p 536
121 E Park Sq 55060
Tel (507) 455-5200 SIC 6311

FEDERATED MUTUAL INSURANCE CO p 536
121 E Park Sq 55060
Tel (507) 455-5200 SIC 6331 6321 6311

FEDERATED SERVICE INSURANCE CO p 536
121 E Park Sq 55060
Tel (507) 455-5200 SIC 6331

MAYO CLINIC HEALTH SYSTEM—OWATONNA p 923
2200 Nw 26th St 55060
Tel (507) 451-1120 SIC 8011

TRUTH HARDWARE CORP p 1489
700 W Bridge St 55060
Tel (507) 451-5620 SIC 2431 3442 3429

■ VIRACON INC p 1558
800 Park Dr 55060
Tel (507) 451-9555 SIC 3211

WENGER CORP p 1592
555 Park Dr 55060
Tel (507) 455-4100 SIC 2541 3446

PERHAM, MN

ARVIG ENTERPRISES INC p 114
150 2nd St Sw Ste 100 56573
Tel (218) 346-4227 SIC 4813 4841

BARREL OFUN SNACK FOODS CO LLC p 157
400 Lakeside Dr 56573
Tel (218) 346-7000 SIC 2096

EAST OTTER TAIL TELEPHONE CO p 470
150 2nd Ave Sw 56573
Tel (218) 346-5500 SIC 4813

KLN ENTERPRISES INC p 823
400 Lakeside Dr 56573
Tel (218) 346-7000 SIC 2047 2064

TUFFYS PET FOODS INC p 1491
245 1st Ave N 56573
Tel (218) 346-7500 SIC 2047

PLAINVIEW, MN

PLAINVIEW MILK PRODUCTS COOPERATIVE p 1154
130 2nd St Sw 55964
Tel (507) 534-3872 SIC 2023 2021

PLYMOUTH, MN

■ ALLIANT TECHSYSTEMS OPERATIONS LLC p 55
4700 Nathan Ln N 55442
Tel (952) 351-3000 SIC 3484

ALLIED INTERSTATE LLC p 56
12755 Hwy 55 Ste 300 55441
Tel (973) 630-5720 *SIC* 7322

AMPLIFON (USA) INC p 86
5000 Cheshire Pkwy N 55446
Tel (763) 268-4000 *SIC* 3842

BEDIVERE INSURANCE CO p 168
605 Hwy 169th N Ste 800 55441
Tel (952) 852-2431
SIC 6331 6282 6159 7389

BUHLER INC p 224
13105 12th Ave N 55441
Tel (763) 847-9900
SIC 3556 3542 3535 3564

▲ CHRISTOPHER & BANKS CORP p 303
2400 Xenium Ln N 55441
Tel (763) 551-5000 *SIC* 5621 5632 5961

■ CHRISTOPHER & BANKS INC p 303
2400 Xenium Ln N 55441
Tel (763) 551-5000 *SIC* 5621

EV3 ENDOVASCULAR INC p 513
3033 Campus Dr Ste W550 55441
Tel (763) 398-7000 *SIC* 3841

J H LARSON ELECTRICAL CO p 771
10200 51st Ave N Ste B 55442
Tel (763) 545-1717 *SIC* 5063 5074 5075

■ MOS HOLDINGS INC p 991
3033 Campus Dr Ste E490 55441
Tel (763) 577-2700
SIC 2874 1475 2819 1094 1481

▲ MOSAIC CO p 991
3033 Campus Dr Ste E490 55441
Tel (800) 918-8270 *SIC* 2874 1475

NEXUS p 1041
505 Highway 169 N Ste 500 55441
Tel (763) 551-8640 *SIC* 8322 8361

▲ ONEBEACON INSURANCE GROUP LTD p 1087
605 Highway 169 N Ste 800 55441
Tel (952) 852-2431 *SIC* 6331

ONVOY LLC p 1088
10300 6th Ave N 55441
Tel (763) 230-2036 *SIC* 4813

SILVER BAY REALTY TRUST CORP p 1323
3300 Fernbrook Ln N 55447
Tel (952) 358-4400 *SIC* 6798 6531 1521

SMITHS MEDICAL ASD INC p 1334
6000 Nathan Ln N Ste 100 55442
Tel (763) 383-3000 *SIC* 3842

■ STERILMED INC p 1386
5010 Cheshire Pkwy N # 2 55446
Tel (888) 541-0078 *SIC* 5047

THREE RIVERS PARK DISTRICT p 1450
3000 Xenium Ln N 55441
Tel (763) 559-9000 *SIC* 7999

THRIFTY DRUG STORES INC p 1451
6055 Nathan Ln N Ste 200 55442
Tel (763) 513-4300 *SIC* 5912

▲ TILE SHOP HOLDINGS INC p 1453
14000 Carlson Pkwy 55441
Tel (763) 852-2988 *SIC* 5211 5961 2891

TILE SHOP INC p 1453
14000 Carlson Pkwy 55441
Tel (763) 541-9720 *SIC* 5713 5023

TRAVEL LEADERS GROUP LLC p 1473
3033 Campus Dr Ste W320 55441
Tel (763) 744-3700 *SIC* 4724

TURCK INC p 1492
3000 Campus Dr 55441
Tel (763) 553-9224 *SIC* 3625

UNITED HARDWARE DISTRIBUTING CO p 1509
5005 Nathan Ln N 55442
Tel (763) 559-1800 *SIC* 5251

UNITRON HEARING INC p 1515
14755 27th Ave N 55447
Tel (763) 744-3300 *SIC* 3842

■ US FOODS CULINARY EQUIPMENT & SUPPLIES LLC p 1531
5353 Nathan Ln N 55442
Tel (763) 268-1200 *SIC* 5087

PRINSBURG, MN

DUININCK INC p 460
408 6th St 56281
Tel (320) 978-6011 *SIC* 1629 1611

PRINSBURG FARMERS CO-OP p 1177
404 Railroad Ave 56281
Tel (320) 978-8100 *SIC* 5153 5191 0253

PRIOR LAKE, MN

SHAKOPEE MDEWAKANTON SIOUX COMMUNITY p 1311
2330 Sioux Trl Nw 55372
Tel (952) 445-8900 *SIC* 7999

SMSC GAMING ENTERPRISE p 1334
2400 Mystic Lake Blvd 55372
Tel (952) 445-9000 *SIC* 7999 7011

RAMSEY, MN

CONNEXUS ENERGY p 358
14601 Ramsey Blvd Nw 55303
Tel (763) 323-2600 *SIC* 4911

LENS VISION-EASE CORP p 856
7000 Sunwood Dr Nw 55303
Tel (763) 576-3930 *SIC* 3851

NAU COUNTRY INSURANCE CO p 1019
7333 Sunwood Dr Nw 55303
Tel (763) 323-0175 *SIC* 6331

RED WING, MN

■ D B INDUSTRIES INC p 406
3833 Sala Way 55066
Tel (651) 388-8282 *SIC* 5099 5084 7352

MAYO CLINIC HEALTH SYSTEM - RED WING p 923
701 Hewitt Blvd 55066
Tel (651) 267-5000 *SIC* 8062

RED WING REGIONAL HOME HEALTH p 1216
1407 W 4th St 55066
Tel (651) 385-3410 *SIC* 8082 8011

RED WING SHOE CO INC p 1216
314 Main St 55066
Tel (651) 388-8211
SIC 3143 3149 3144 3111 5661 3021

REDWOOD FALLS, MN

FARMERS UNION INDUSTRIES LLC p 530
590 W Park Rd 56283
Tel (507) 637-5210 *SIC* 2048 2047

RENVILLE, MN

CO-OP COUNTRY FARMERS ELEVATOR p 330
340 Dupont Ave Ne 56284
Tel (320) 329-8377 *SIC* 5153 5191

SOUTHERN MINNESOTA BEET SUGAR COOPERATIVE p 1349
83550 County Road 21 56284
Tel (320) 329-8305 *SIC* 2063

RICHFIELD, MN

▲ BEST BUY CO INC p 177
7601 Penn Ave S 55423
Tel (612) 291-1000
SIC 5731 5734 5735 5712 5722

■ BEST BUY STORES LP p 177
7601 Penn Ave S 55423
Tel (612) 291-3979 *SIC* 5961

■ BUY BEST PURCHASING LLC p 230
7601 Penn Ave S 55423
Tel (612) 291-1000 *SIC* 5065

ROCHESTER, MN

ACADEMY OF OUR LADY OF LOURDES INC p 13
1001 14th St Nw Ste 100 55901
Tel (507) 282-7441 *SIC* 8661

COUNTY OF OLMSTED p 380
151 4th St Se Ste 11 55904
Tel (507) 328-6001 *SIC* 9111

CRENLO CAB PRODUCTS INC p 391
1600 4th Ave Nw 55901
Tel (507) 289-3371
SIC 2522 3531 2542 3713 3469 3444

GREEN-WAY COOPERATIVE SERVICE CO p 637
3520 E River Rd Ne 55906
Tel (507) 289-4086 *SIC* 5541 5171 5191

INDEPENDENT SCHOOL DISTRICT #535 p 737
615 7th St Sw 55902
Tel (507) 328-3000 *SIC* 8211

LTX INC p 883
1515 Industrial Dr Nw 55901
Tel (507) 282-6715 *SIC* 4213

MAYO CLINIC p 923
200 1st St Sw 55905
Tel (507) 284-2511
SIC 8011 8062 8071 8733 8221

MAYO CLINIC p 923
200 1st St Sw 55905
Tel (507) 284-2511
SIC 8062 8733 8071 8011

MAYO FOUNDATION FOR MEDICAL EDUCATION AND RESEARCH p 924
200 1st St Sw 55905
Tel (507) 284-2511 *SIC* 8741

NUSS TRUCK GROUP INC p 1067
6500 Highway 63 S 55904
Tel (507) 288-9488 *SIC* 5511 5531

OLMSTED MEDICAL CENTER p 1083
210 9th St Se Ste 1 55904
Tel (507) 288-3443 *SIC* 8062

REICHEL FOODS INC p 1220
3706 Enterprise Dr Sw 55902
Tel (507) 289-7264
SIC 2011 5812 2013 0723

ROCHESTER METHODIST HOSPITAL AUXILIARY INC p 1243
1216 2nd St Sw 55902
Tel (507) 255-5123 *SIC* 8062

SAINT MARYS HOSPITAL p 1270
1216 2nd St Sw 55902
Tel (507) 255-5123 *SIC* 8062

SOUTHERN MINNESOTA MUNICIPAL POWER AGENCY p 1349
500 1st Ave Sw 55902
Tel (507) 285-0478 *SIC* 4911

ROCKFORD, MN

SKYBRIDGE AMERICAS INC p 1330
7600 69th Ave 55373
Tel (763) 477-7600 *SIC* 8742

WRIGHT-HENNEPIN COOPERATIVE ELECTRIC ASSOCIATION p 1627
6800 Electric Dr 55373
Tel (763) 477-3000 *SIC* 4911

WRIGHT-HENNEPIN SECURITY CORP p 1627
6800 Electric Dr 55373
Tel (763) 477-3664
SIC 1731 1711 7382 5063 4911

ROCKVILLE, MN

SJ LOUIS CONSTRUCTION INC p 1328
1351 Broadway St W 56369
Tel (320) 685-4164 *SIC* 1623

ROGERS, MN

ARCHWAY MARKETING HOLDINGS INC p 105
19850 S Diamond Lake Rd 55374
Tel (763) 428-3300 *SIC* 8742

ARCHWAY MARKETING SERVICES INC p 105
19850 S Diamond Lake Rd 55374
Tel (763) 428-3300 *SIC* 8742 4225

HARDRIVES INC p 661
14475 Quiram Dr Ste 1 55374
Tel (763) 428-8886 *SIC* 1611 2951

VEIT & CO INC p 1547
14000 Veit Pl 55374
Tel (763) 428-2242 *SIC* 1611 1795 4953

ROSEAU, MN

NORTHERN RESOURCES COOPERATIVE p 1056
1504 Center St W 56751
Tel (218) 463-1805
SIC 5191 5172 5251 5541

ROSEMOUNT, MN

BAY & BAY TRANSFER CO INC p 160
3686 140th St E 55068
Tel (800) 273-0366 *SIC* 4213 4212

■ MINNESOTA ENERGY RESOURCES CORP p 973
2665 145th St W 55068
Tel (651) 322-8900 *SIC* 4924

ROSEMOUNT-APPLE VALLEY-EAGAN SCHOOL BOARD p 1251
3455 153rd St W 55068
Tel (651) 423-7700 *SIC* 8211

ROSEMOUNT-APPLE VALLEY-EAGAN SCHOOL DISTRICT p 1251
3455 153rd St W 55068
Tel (651) 423-7700 *SIC* 8211

ROSEVILLE, MN

AVIANDS LLC p 137
1751 County Road B W # 300 55113
Tel (651) 631-0940 *SIC* 8742

CERNX MN LLC p 284
2355 Highway 36 W Ste 400 55113
Tel (320) 372-7400
SIC 4212 7389 4731 4222

▲ HAWKINS INC p 670
2381 Rosegate 55113
Tel (612) 331-6910 *SIC* 5169 5074 2899

PRESBYTERIAN HOMES AND SERVICES p 1171
2845 Hamline Ave N # 200 55113
Tel (651) 631-6100 *SIC* 8361

ROUND LAKE, MN

FARLEYS & SATHERS CANDY CO INC p 528
1 Sather Plz 56167
Tel (507) 945-8181 *SIC* 5145

RUSH CITY, MN

BEVERLY ENTERPRISES - MINNESOTA LLC p 179
650 Ramer Ave S 55069
Tel (320) 358-4765 *SIC* 8051

SAINT CLOUD, MN

ANDERSON TRUCKING SERVICE INC p 90
725 Opportunity Dr 56301
Tel (320) 255-7400 *SIC* 4213

■ APPERTS INC p 98
900 Highway 10 S 56304
Tel (320) 251-3200
SIC 5142 5141 5411 5421 2013

AUTOMOTIVE PARTS HEADQUARTERS INC p 134
2959 Clearwater Rd 56301
Tel (320) 252-5411 *SIC* 5013

CENTRACARE CLINIC p 277
1200 6th Ave N 56303
Tel (320) 240-2829 *SIC* 8011

CENTRACARE HEALTH SYSTEM p 277
1406 6th Ave N 56303
Tel (320) 656-7020 *SIC* 8062

COBORNS INC p 333
1921 Coborn Blvd 56301
Tel (320) 252-4222 *SIC* 5411 5541 5921

CONSUMER DIRECTIONS INC p 361
425 E Saint Germain St # 200 56304
Tel (320) 420-3423 *SIC* 7361 8721

DEE SPEE DELIVERY SERVICE INC p 421
4101 Clearwater Rd 56301
Tel (320) 251-6697 *SIC* 4212

GILLELAND CHEVROLET CADILLAC INC p 612
3019 W Division St 56301
Tel (320) 281-4290 *SIC* 5511 5531 7538

GNP CO p 619
4150 2nd St S Ste 200 56301
Tel (320) 251-3570 *SIC* 2015

GOLDEN PUMP POULTRY INC p 621
4150 2nd St S Ste 200 56301
Tel (320) 240-6234 *SIC* 2015 0251

JFC LLC p 785
4150 2nd St S Ste 200 56301
Tel (320) 251-3570 *SIC* 2015 0251

MARCO TECHNOLOGIES LLC p 905
4510 Heatherwood Rd 56301
Tel (320) 259-3000
SIC 7371 4813 7313 7812

MINNESOTA STATE COLLEGES AND UNIVERSITIES p 974
720 4th Ave S 56301
Tel (320) 308-0121 *SIC* 8221 9199

NAHAN PRINTING INC p 1006
7000 Saukview Dr 56303
Tel (320) 217-7700 *SIC* 2759 2752

NEW FLYER OF AMERICA INC p 1030
6200 Glenn Carlson Dr 56301
Tel (320) 203-0576 *SIC* 3713 3711

PAN-O-GOLD BAKING CO p 1110
444 E Saint Germain St 56304
Tel (320) 251-9361 *SIC* 5149 2051

PSC CUSTOM LP p 1188
1015 W Saint Germain St # 420 56301
Tel (320) 746-2255 *SIC* 7539 5012

SIMONSON PROPERTIES CO p 1325
2455 12th St Se 56304
Tel (320) 252-9385 *SIC* 5211

ST CLOUD AREA SCHOOL DISTRICT p 1365
1000 44th Ave N Ste 100 56303
Tel (320) 253-9333 *SIC* 8211

ST CLOUD HOSPITAL p 1365
1406 6th Ave N 56303
Tel (320) 251-2700 *SIC* 8062

STEARNS BANK NATIONAL ASSOCIATION p 1384
4191 2nd St S 56301
Tel (320) 253-6607 *SIC* 6021

■ SYSCO WESTERN MINNESOTA INC p 1418
900 Highway 10 S 56304
Tel (320) 251-3200
SIC 5141 5142 5143 5144 5145 5146

■ WOODCRAFT INDUSTRIES INC p 1622
525 Lincoln Ave Se 56304
Tel (320) 656-2345 *SIC* 2434 2431 2426

SAINT JOSEPH, MN

ASPHALT SURFACE TECHNOLOGIES CORP p 118
8348 Ridgewood Rd 56374
Tel (320) 363-8500 *SIC* 1611 4959

SAINT LOUIS PARK, MN

AGSPRING IDAHO LLC p 36
600 Highway 169 S Ste 720 55426
Tel (952) 956-6720 *SIC* 5153

PARK NICOLLET METHODIST HOSPITAL p 1115
6500 Excelsior Blvd 55426
Tel (952) 993-5000 *SIC* 8062

SAINT MICHAEL, MN

J & B GROUP INC p 769
13200 43rd St Ne 55376
Tel (763) 497-3913 *SIC* 6719 5963

J & B WHOLESALE DISTRIBUTING INC p 769
13200 43rd St Ne 55376
Tel (763) 497-3913
SIC 5147 5144 5142 5143 5148

SAINT PAUL, MN

▲ 3M CO p 2
3m Center Bldg 22011w02 55144
Tel (651) 733-1110
SIC 3841 3842 3291 2842 2672 2891

3M EMPLOYEES WELFARE BENEFITS ASSOCIATION TRUST II p 2
3m Center Bldg 224 55144
Tel (651) 737-3201 *SIC* 6733

■ 3M INNOVATIVE PROPERTIES CO p 2
3m Center Bldg 2253s06 55144
Tel (651) 733-8904 *SIC* 8111

A P I INC p 6
1100 Old Highway 8 Nw 55112
Tel (651) 636-4320 *SIC* 1742 5033

ALLIANCE HEALTH CARE INC p 54
2260 Cliff Rd 55122
Tel (651) 895-8030 *SIC* 8082

AMERICAN SECURITY LLC p 79
1717 University Ave W 55104
Tel (651) 644-1155 *SIC* 7381

■ ANNS HOUSE OF NUTS INC p 92
380 Sint Pter St Ste 1000 55102
Tel (651) 348-4100 *SIC* 2068 2064

ANTEA USA INC p 93
5910 Rice Creek Pkwy 55126
Tel (651) 639-9449 *SIC* 8748

API GROUP INC p 96
1100 Old Highway 8 Nw 55112
Tel (651) 636-4320
SIC 1711 1742 7699 1799

ARCHDIOCESE OF SAINT PAUL AND MINNEAPOLIS p 105
226 Summit Ave 55102
Tel (651) 291-4400 *SIC* 8661

ARCTIC GLACIER USA HOLDINGS LLC p 106
1654 Marthaler Ln 55118
Tel (651) 455-0410 *SIC* 2097

ARCTIC GLACIER USA INC p 106
1654 Marthaler Ln 55118
Tel (204) 784-5873 *SIC* 2097

ATLAS STAFFING INC p 128
189 7th Pl E 55101
Tel (651) 222-5894 *SIC* 7363 7361

AWARE INTEGRATED INC p 139
3535 Blue Cross Rd 55122
Tel (651) 662-8000 *SIC* 6324

BANYAN INCENTIVES p 153
4875 White Bear Pkwy 55110
Tel (651) 426-1667 *SIC* 2759

BATTMANN HOLDINGS INC p 160
2480 Long Lake Rd 55113
Tel (651) 639-2800 *SIC* 4214

BCBSM INC p 163
3535 Blue Cross Rd 55122
Tel (651) 662-8000 *SIC* 6321 6324

BELTMANN GROUP INC p 171
2480 Long Lake Rd 55113
Tel (651) 639-2800 *SIC* 4213 4214

BERGER TRANSFER & STORAGE INC p 174
2950 Long Lake Rd 55113
Tel (651) 639-2260 *SIC* 4731 4213 4214

BEST BRANDS CORP p 177
111 Cheshire Ln Ste 100 55121
Tel (952) 404-7500
SIC 5149 2045 2053 2052 2051

BETHEL UNIVERSITY p 178
3900 Bethel Dr 55112
Tel (651) 638-6400 *SIC* 8221

BETHESDA HEALTHEAST HOSPITAL p 178
559 Capitol Blvd Fl 6 55103
Tel (651) 232-2000 *SIC* 8062 8741 8069

BIX PRODUCE CO LLC p 185
1415 L Orient St 55117
Tel (651) 487-8000 *SIC* 5148 5143

BREMER FINANCIAL CORP p 210
380 Sint Peter St Ste 500 55102
Tel (800) 908-2265 *SIC* 6022 6712

■ CARDIAC PACEMAKERS INC p 252
4100 Hamline Ave N 55112
Tel (651) 638-4000 *SIC* 3845

▲ CARDIOVASCULAR SYSTEMS INC p 253
1225 Old Highway 8 Nw 55112
Tel (651) 259-1600 *SIC* 3841

CATHOLIC UNITED FINANCIAL p 267
3499 Lexington Ave N 55126
Tel (651) 490-0170 *SIC* 8641 6411

CENTURY COLLEGE p 282
3300 Century Ave N 55110
Tel (651) 779-3300 *SIC* 8222 9199

CITY OF SAINT PAUL p 318
15 Kellogg Blvd W Ste 390 55102
Tel (651) 266-8500 *SIC* 9111

COLWELL INDUSTRIES INC p 343
1611 County Road B W # 315 55113
Tel (612) 340-0365 *SIC* 2752

COMPUTYPE INC p 353
2285 County Road C W 55113
Tel (651) 633-0633
SIC 2759 2672 2679 3565 3577 2671

CORVAL GROUP INC p 373
1633 Eustis St 55108
Tel (651) 645-0451 *SIC* 8742

COUNTY OF RAMSEY p 381
15 Kellogg Blvd W Ste 270 55102
Tel (651) 266-8044 *SIC* 9111

■ DECARE DENTAL LLC p 420
3560 Delta Dental Dr 55122
Tel (800) 371-6561 *SIC* 6324 8621

DEPARTMENT OF CORRECTIONS MINNESOTA p 430
1450 Energy Park Dr # 200 55108
Tel (651) 361-7200 *SIC* 9223

DEPARTMENT OF HEALTH MINNESOTA p 430
625 Robert St N 55155
Tel (651) 201-5000 *SIC* 9431

DEPARTMENT OF REVENUE MINNESOTA p 430
600 Robert St N 55101
Tel (651) 556-3000 *SIC* 9311

DITECH FINANCIAL LLC p 443
345 Sint Peter St Ste 300 55102
Tel (651) 293-4800 *SIC* 6162

▲ ECOLAB INC p 476
370 Wabasha St N 55102
Tel (800) 232-6522 *SIC* 2841 2842 7342

■ ECOWATER SYSTEMS LLC p 476
1890 Woodlane Dr 55125
Tel (651) 731-7401 *SIC* 5074 3589

ECUMEN p 476
3530 Lexington Ave N Fl 2 55126
Tel (651) 766-4300 *SIC* 8051

EMPI INC p 493
599 Cardigan Rd 55126
Tel (651) 415-9000 *SIC* 3845

ENCLOS CORP p 495
2770 Blue Waters Rd # 100 55121
Tel (651) 796-6100 *SIC* 1741

ERGOTRON INC p 507
1181 Trapp Rd Ste 100 55121
Tel (651) 681-7600 *SIC* 7373 3577

EXECUTIVE OFFICE OF STATE OF MINNESOTA p 518
75 Rev Doc Martin Luther 55155
Tel (651) 201-3400 *SIC* 9111

FARM CREDIT FOUNDATIONS WELFARE BENEFITS p 528
30 7th St E 55101
Tel (651) 282-8347 *SIC* 6159

■ FLAGSTONE FOODS INC p 554
380 Sint Pter St Ste 1000 55102
Tel (651) 348-4100 *SIC* 5411 2068

FOURCROWN INC p 572
434 Hale Ave N Ste 160 55128
Tel (651) 714-0030 *SIC* 5812

GANDER MOUNTAIN CO p 590
180 5th St E Ste 1300 55101
Tel (651) 325-4300 *SIC* 5941

■ GCS SYSTEMS INC p 595
370 Wabasha St N 55102
Tel (651) 293-2134 *SIC* 5046 7699

GEODIGM CORP p 605
1740 Prior Ave N 55113
Tel (952) 556-5657 *SIC* 8731

GG MCGUIGGAN CORP p 610
1085 Snelling Ave N 55108
Tel (651) 646-4544 *SIC* 2679 3993 2752

GILLETTE CHILDRENS SPECIALTY HEALTHCARE p 612
200 University Ave E 55101
Tel (651) 291-2848 *SIC* 8069

GOODWILL INDUSTRIES INC p 624
553 Fairview Ave N 55104
Tel (651) 379-5800
SIC 4953 8331 8322 5932 4226

■ GUIDANT SALES LLC p 645
4100 Hamline Ave N 55112
Tel (800) 949-9459
SIC 3841 3845 5047 8733

HAMLINE UNIVERSITY p 656
1536 Hewitt Ave 55104
Tel (651) 523-2015 *SIC* 8221

HARRIS CONTRACTING CO p 663
909 Montreal Cir 55102
Tel (651) 602-6500 *SIC* 1711

▲ HB FULLER CO p 671
1200 Willow Lake Blvd 55110
Tel (651) 236-5900 *SIC* 2891 2899

HEALTHEAST CARE INC p 676
559 Capitol Blvd 55103
Tel (651) 232-2300 *SIC* 8741 8721

HEALTHEAST CARE SYSTEM p 677
1700 University Ave W # 5 55104
Tel (651) 232-5353 *SIC* 8741 8062 7389

HEALTHEAST COMPANIES INC p 677
1700 University Ave W 55104
Tel (651) 232-2300 *SIC* 8082 8051 8011

HEALTHEAST ST JOHNS HOSPITAL p 677
1575 Beam Ave 55109
Tel (651) 232-7000 *SIC* 8062

HEALTHEAST ST JOSEPHS HOSPITAL p 677
45 10th St W 55102
Tel (651) 232-3000 *SIC* 8062

HMO MINNESOTA p 698
3535 Blue Cross Rd 55122
Tel (952) 456-8434 *SIC* 8011

HUBBARD BROADCASTING INC p 716
3415 University Ave W 55114
Tel (651) 642-4656 *SIC* 4833 7812 4832

I C SYSTEM INC p 725
444 Highway 96 E 55127
Tel (651) 483-8201 *SIC* 7322

■ IMATION ENTERPRISES CORP p 733
1099 Helmo Ave N Ste 250 55128
Tel (651) 704-4000 *SIC* 3695 3845 5112

IND SCHOOL DIST 621 p 735
350 Highway 96 W 55126
Tel (651) 621-6000 *SIC* 8211 8742

INDEPENDENT SCHOOL DIST 625 p 737
360 Colborne St 55102
Tel (651) 767-8100 *SIC* 8299

INDEPENDENT SCHOOL DISTRICT 622 p 737
2520 12th Ave E 55109
Tel (651) 748-7622 *SIC* 8211

INDEPENDENT SCHOOL DISTRICT 623 (INC) p 737
1251 County Road B2 W 55113
Tel (651) 635-1600 *SIC* 8211

INTERPLASTIC CORP p 757
1225 Willow Lake Blvd 55110
Tel (651) 481-6860 *SIC* 2821

JOHNSON BROTHERS LIQUOR CO p 790
1999 Shepard Rd 55116
Tel (651) 649-5800 *SIC* 5182 5149

JUDICIARY COURTS OF STATE OF MINNESOTA p 797
25 Rev Dr Mlk Jr Blvd 55155
Tel (651) 297-7650 *SIC* 9211

■ JUPITER HOLDINGS INC p 797
1285 Northland Dr 55120
Tel (952) 681-3005 *SIC* 6331

KEMPS LLC p 810
1270 Energy Ln 55108
Tel (651) 379-6500 *SIC* 2026 2024

LAMPERT YARDS INC p 841
1850 Como Ave 55108
Tel (651) 695-3600
SIC 5211 1521 2439 2426

LEGISLATIVE OFFICE OF STATE OF MINNESOTA p 853
100 Rev Dr M L King Jr Bl 55155
Tel (651) 296-2146 *SIC* 9121

LUTHERAN SOCIAL SERVICE OF MINNESOTA p 886
2485 Como Ave 55108
Tel (651) 642-5990 *SIC* 8322

MAC ARTHUR CO p 891
2400 Wycliff St 55114
Tel (651) 646-2773 *SIC* 5033 3448

MACALESTER COLLEGE p 891
200 Amherst St 55105
Tel (651) 698-8650 *SIC* 8299

MACALESTER COLLEGE p 891
1600 Grand Ave 55105
Tel (651) 696-6000 *SIC* 8221

MARSDEN HOLDING LLC p 910
2124 University Ave W 55114
Tel (651) 641-1717 *SIC* 1731

MCGOUGH CONSTRUCTION CO INC p 929
2737 Fairview Ave N 55113
Tel (651) 633-5050 *SIC* 1541 1542

MERRILL COMMUNICATIONS LLC p 950
1 Merrill Cir 55108
Tel (651) 646-4501 *SIC* 7374 7389

MERRILL CORP p 950
1 Merrill Cir 55108
Tel (651) 646-4501 *SIC* 7389 8111 8999

MERRILL/GLOBAL INC p 950
1 Merrill Cir Ste 1433 55108
Tel (651) 646-4501 *SIC* 2759 2752 2791

METROPOLITAN COUNCIL MINNESOTA p 955
390 Robert St N 55101
Tel (651) 602-1629 *SIC* 9532

MIDWEST SIGN & SCREEN PRINTING SUPPLY CO INC p 968
45 Maryland Ave E 55117
Tel (651) 489-9999 *SIC* 5084 5063

MIDWEST STAFFING GROUP INC p 968
162 Pennsylvania Ave W 55103
Tel (651) 641-0442 *SIC* 7363

MINNESOTA DEPARTMENT OF EMPLOYMENT AND ECONOMIC DEVELOPMENT p 973
332 Minnesota St Ste E200 55101
Tel (651) 259-7114 *SIC* 9441

MINNESOTA DEPARTMENT OF HUMAN SERVICES p 973
540 Cedar St 55164
Tel (651) 431-2000 *SIC* 9441

MINNESOTA DEPARTMENT OF NATURAL RESOURCES p 973
500 Lafayette Rd N 55155
Tel (651) 296-6157 *SIC* 9512

MINNESOTA DEPARTMENT OF PUBLIC SAFETY p 973
445 Minnesota St 55101
Tel (651) 201-7000 *SIC* 9229

MINNESOTA DEPARTMENT OF TRANSPORTATION p 973
395 John Ireland Blvd 55155
Tel (651) 296-3000 *SIC* 9621

MINNESOTA LIFE INSURANCE CO p 973
400 And 401 Robert St N 55101
Tel (478) 314-3189 *SIC* 6311

MINNESOTA MUTUAL COMPANIES INC p 973
400 Robert St N Ste A 55101
Tel (651) 665-3500 *SIC* 6311

MINNESOTA PUBLIC RADIO AMERICAN PUBLIC MEDIA p 974
480 Cedar St 55101
Tel (651) 290-1446 *SIC* 4832

MINNESOTA STATE COLLEGES AND UNIVERSITIES p 974
30 7th St E Ste 350 55101
Tel (651) 296-8012 *SIC* 8221 9411

■ NORCRAFT COMPANIES INC p 1047
950 Blue Gentian Rd # 200 55121
Tel (800) 297-0661 *SIC* 2434

■ NORCRAFT COMPANIES LP p 1047
950 Blue Gentian Rd # 200 55121
Tel (651) 234-3300 *SIC* 2434

NORTH SAINT PAUL MAPLEWOOD & OAKDALE SCHOOL DISTRICT 622 p 1053
2520 12th Ave E 55109
Tel (651) 748-7420 *SIC* 8211

NORTHERN AIR CORP p 1055
1001 Labore Industrial Ct B 55110
Tel (651) 490-9868 *SIC* 1711

NORTHERN CONTOURS INC p 1056
1355 Mendota Heights Rd # 100 55120
Tel (651) 695-1698 *SIC* 3083 1751 2435

■ NORTHFIELD INSURANCE CO p 1057
385 Washington St 55102
Tel (651) 310-4100 *SIC* 6331

■ NORTHLAND CO p 1057
385 Washington St 55102
Tel (800) 328-5972 *SIC* 6331 6162 6531

■ NORTHLAND INSURANCE CO p 1057
385 Washington St 55102
Tel (651) 310-4100 *SIC* 6331

OLD DUTCH FOODS INC p 1080
2375 Terminal Rd 55113
Tel (651) 633-8810 *SIC* 2096

OTTO BREMER FOUNDATION p 1098
30 7th St E Ste 2900 55101
Tel (651) 227-8036 *SIC* 6732 6022

▲ PATTERSON COMPANIES INC p 1121
1031 Mendota Heights Rd 55120
Tel (651) 686-1600
SIC 5047 5112 7372 7699 2834

■ PATTERSON DENTAL SUPPLY INC p 1121
1031 Mendota Heights Rd 55120
Tel (651) 686-1600 *SIC* 5047

PEDIATRIC RHEUMATOLOGY p 1127
200 University Ave E 55101
Tel (651) 229-3892 *SIC* 8011 8062

POWER/MATION DIVISION INC p 1165
1310 Energy Ln 55108
Tel (651) 605-3300
SIC 5085 5065 5084 5045 8742 7549

■ Q3 CONTRACTING INC p 1194
3066 Spruce St 55117
Tel (651) 224-2424 *SIC* 1623 7699 3669

RATNER STEEL SUPPLY CO p 1209
2500 County Road B W 1a 55113
Tel (219) 787-6700 *SIC* 5051 7389

REGIONS HOSPITAL p 1220
640 Jackson St 55101
Tel (651) 254-3456 *SIC* 8062

REGIONS HOSPITAL FOUNDATION p 1220
640 Jackson St 55101
Tel (651) 254-3456 *SIC* 8062

■ RTI REMMELE ENGINEERING INC p 1256
10 Old Highway 8 Sw 55112
Tel (651) 635-4100
SIC 3728 3569 3812 3761 3842

SAINT PAUL FOUNDATION INC p 1270
101 5th St E Ste 2400 55101
Tel (651) 224-5463 *SIC* 8641 8399

SCHWING AMERICA INC p 1291
5900 Centerville Rd 55127
Tel (651) 429-0999 *SIC* 3531 3561 3999

SCOTTISH RITE TEMPLE p 1294
200 Plato Blvd E 55107
Tel (651) 222-2676 *SIC* 8641

■ SEBESTA INC p 1298
1450 Energy Park Dr # 300 55108
Tel (651) 634-0775 *SIC* 8711

SECOND HARVEST HEARTLAND p 1298
1140 Gervais Ave 55109
Tel (651) 484-5117 *SIC* 8322

SECURIAN FINANCIAL GROUP INC p 1298
400 Robert St N Ste A 55101
Tel (651) 665-3500 *SIC* 7389 6399

SENIOR CARE COMMUNITIES INC p 1304
161 Saint Anthony Ave # 825 55103
Tel (651) 287-6408 *SIC* 8059

SHAW-LUNDQUIST ASSOCIATES INC p 1313
2757 W Service Rd 55121
Tel (651) 454-0670 *SIC* 1542 1541

SHORT-ELLIOTT-HENDRICKSON INC p 1318
3535 Vadnais Center Dr # 200 55110
Tel (651) 490-2000 *SIC* 8711 8712

SMYTH COMPANIES LLC p 1335
1085 Snelling Ave N 55108
Tel (651) 646-4544
SIC 2679 2752 3993 7389 5084 7699

SPECIALTY MFG CO p 1356
5858 Centerville Rd 55127
Tel (651) 653-0599 *SIC* 3494

ST CATHERINE UNIVERSITY p 1365
2004 Randolph Ave 55105
Tel (651) 690-6000 *SIC* 8221

■ ST JUDE MEDICAL ATG INC p 1369
1 Lillehei Plz 55117
Tel (651) 756-2000 *SIC* 3842

▲ ST JUDE MEDICAL INC p 1369
1 Saint Jude Medical Dr 55117
Tel (651) 756-2000 *SIC* 3845 3842 3841

■ ST JUDE MEDICAL SC INC p 1369
1 Lillehei Plz 55117
Tel (651) 483-2000 *SIC* 5047

ST PAUL ELECTRICAL ADMINISTRATIVE SERVICES CORP p 1372
1330 Conway St Ste 130 55106
Tel (651) 772-8746 *SIC* 6733

■ ST PAUL FIRE AND MARINE INSURANCE CO p 1372
385 Washington St 55102
Tel (651) 221-7911
SIC 6331 6351 6321 6411

■ **ST PAUL GUARDIAN INSURANCE CO** p 1372
385 Washington St 55102
Tel (651) 221-7911 SIC 6331

■ **ST PAUL SURPLUS LINES INSURANCE CO** p 1372
385 Washington St 55102
Tel (651) 310-7911 SIC 6331

ST PAUL TEACHERS RETMNT FUND ASSN p 1372
1619 Dayton Ave Ste 309 55104
Tel (651) 642-2550 SIC 6371

STATE OF MINNESOTA p 1382
116 Veteran Service Bld 55155
Tel (218) 828-2400 SIC 9111

SUMMIT FIRE PROTECTION CO p 1398
575 Minnehaha Ave W 55103
Tel (651) 288-0777 SIC 1711

■ **SYSCO ASIAN FOODS INC** p 1416
1300 L Orient St 55117
Tel (651) 558-2400 SIC 5149

■ **SYSCO MINNESOTA INC** p 1417
2400 County Road J 55112
Tel (763) 785-9000 SIC 5141 5812 5813

TENACIOUS HOLDINGS INC p 1437
1021 Bandana Blvd E # 220 55108
Tel (651) 642-9889 SIC 5099

TIERNEY BROTHERS INC p 1453
1771 Energy Park Dr 55108
Tel (612) 331-5500 SIC 5049 5043 3651

TRAVELERS INSURANCE COMPANIES p 1474
385 Washington St 55102
Tel (651) 310-7911 SIC 6411

TRUSTEES OF HAMLINE UNIVERSITY OF MINNESOTA p 1488
1536 Hewitt Ave Ms-Ai775 55104
Tel (651) 523-2800 SIC 8221

TSI INC p 1489
500 Cardigan Rd 55126
Tel (651) 483-0900
SIC 3579 3829 3823 3845 3825

UNITED HOSPITAL INC p 1509
333 Smith Ave N 55102
Tel (651) 241-8000 SIC 8011

UNITED SUBCONTRACTORS INC p 1514
445 Minnesota St Ste 2500 55101
Tel (651) 225-6300
SIC 1742 1796 1542 1522

UNIVERSAL COOPERATIVES INC p 1516
1300 Corporate Ctr Curv 55121
Tel (651) 239-1000 SIC 2879 5169 2298

UNIVERSITY OF NORTHWESTERN - ST PAUL p 1524
3003 Snelling Ave N 55113
Tel (651) 631-5100 SIC 8221

UNIVERSITY OF ST THOMAS p 1525
2115 Summit Ave 55105
Tel (651) 962-5000 SIC 8221 2741 2721

UPONOR INC p 1529
5925 148th St W 55124
Tel (952) 891-2000 SIC 3084 3567 3433

VOMELA SPECIALTY CO p 1565
274 Fillmore Ave E 55107
Tel (651) 228-2200 SIC 7336 2396 2752

■ **WELLS FARGO EQUIPMENT FINANCE INC** p 1590
2345 Rice St Ste 230 55113
Tel (612) 667-9876 SIC 6159

■ **WEST SERVICES INC** p 1595
610 Opperman Dr 55123
Tel (651) 687-5882 SIC 2721

■ **WESTROCK MINNESOTA CORP** p 1603
2250 Wabash Ave 55114
Tel (612) 641-4938 SIC 2631

WINFIELD SOLUTIONS LLC p 1616
1080 County Road F W 55126
Tel (651) 481-2222 SIC 5191

WINGS FINANCIAL CREDIT UNION p 1616
14985 Glazier Ave Ste 100 55124
Tel (952) 997-8000 SIC 6061 6282

WOODWINDS HEALTH CAMPUS p 1624
1925 Woodwinds Dr 55125
Tel (651) 232-0100 SIC 8069

SAINT PETER, MN

GUSTAVUS ADOLPHUS COLLEGE p 648
800 W College Ave 56082
Tel (507) 933-7508 SIC 8221

ST PETER PUBLIC SCHOOL DISTRICT p 1372
100 Lincoln Dr Ste 229 56082
Tel (507) 934-5703 SIC 8211

SARTELL, MN

DEZURIK INC p 435
250 Riverside Ave N 56377
Tel (320) 259-2000 SIC 3491

SAUK RAPIDS, MN

GATR OF SAUK RAPIDS INC p 594
218 Stearns Dr 56379
Tel (320) 251-7356 SIC 5511

■ **KNIFE RIVER CORP - NORTH CENTRAL** p 824
4787 Shadowwood Dr Ne 56379
Tel (320) 251-9472
SIC 1611 1442 3273 2951

SAVAGE, MN

FABCON COMPANIES LLC p 523
6111 Highway 13 W 55378
Tel (952) 890-4444 SIC 3272 1771

FABCON INC p 523
6111 Highway 13 W 55378
Tel (952) 890-4444 SIC 3272 1771

ROAD MACHINERY & SUPPLIES CO p 1240
5633 Highway 13 W 55378
Tel (952) 895-9595 SIC 5082

SOO LINE CORP p 1341
14327 Huntington Ave 55378
Tel (952) 895-5277 SIC 4011

SHAKOPEE, MN

BREWERS SUPPLY GROUP INC p 210
800 1st Ave W 55379
Tel (952) 224-1380 SIC 5149

COKEM INTERNATIONAL LTD p 335
3880 4th Ave E 55379
Tel (952) 358-6000 SIC 5092

CYBERPOWER SYSTEMS (USA) INC p 405
4241 12th Ave E Ste 400 55379
Tel (952) 403-9500 SIC 3679

ENTRUST DATACARD CORP p 503
1187 Park Pl 55379
Tel (952) 933-1223
SIC 3579 3089 7373 7372

IMAGINE PRINT SOLUTIONS INC p 733
1000 Valley Park Dr 55379
Tel (952) 903-4400 SIC 2759

ST FRANCIS REGIONAL MEDICAL CENTER p 1367
1455 Saint Francis Ave 55379
Tel (952) 428-3000 SIC 8062

SHOREVIEW, MN

▲ **DELUXE CORP** p 427
3680 Victoria St N 55126
Tel (651) 483-7111 SIC 2782 2761 7389

MOUNDS VIEW PUBLIC SCHOOL DISTRICT p 993
350 Highway 96 W 55126
Tel (651) 621-6017 SIC 8211

PAR SYSTEMS INC p 1113
707 County Road E W 55126
Tel (651) 484-7261 SIC 8742

PURINA ANIMAL NUTRITION LLC p 1192
1080 County Road F W 55126
Tel (651) 375-5500 SIC 5191

SLEEPY EYE, MN

CHRISTENSEN FARMS & FEEDLOTS INC p 302
23971 County Road 10 56085
Tel (507) 794-5310 SIC 0213

SOUTH SAINT PAUL, MN

LONG PRAIRIE PACKING CO INC p 876
100 Bridgepoint Curv # 249 55075
Tel (651) 552-8230 SIC 2011

TWIN CITY BAGEL INC p 1494
130 Hardman Ave S 55075
Tel (651) 554-0200 SIC 2051

WATEROUS CO p 1582
125 Hardman Ave S 55075
Tel (651) 450-5000
SIC 3491 3561 3494 3321

SPRING PARK, MN

WENDY WEIHE STORLIE INC p 1592
4032 Shoreline Dr Ste 2 55384
Tel (952) 548-9306 SIC 2079 2077

ST LOUIS PARK, MN

JAPS-OLSON CO p 778
7500 Excelsior Blvd 55426
Tel (952) 932-9393
SIC 2752 7331 2791 2759

PARK NICOLLET HEALTH SERVICES p 1115
3800 Park Nicollet Blvd 55416
Tel (952) 993-3123 SIC 8011

STAPLES, MN

LAKEWOOD HEALTH SYSTEM p 840
49725 County 83 56479
Tel (218) 894-1515 SIC 8062 8051

STEWARTVILLE, MN

ROCHESTER MEDICAL CORP p 1243
1 Rochester Medical Dr Nw 55976
Tel (507) 533-9600 SIC 3841

STILLWATER, MN

■ **CUB FOODS INC** p 399
421 3rd St S 55082
Tel (651) 439-7200 SIC 5411

DIASORIN INC p 437
1951 Northwestern Ave S 55082
Tel (651) 439-9710 SIC 2835 5047

INDEPENDENT SCHOOL DISTRICT 834 p 737
1875 Greeley St S 55082
Tel (651) 351-8340 SIC 8211

STILLWATER MEDICAL GROUP p 1390
927 Churchill St W 55082
Tel (952) 883-6048 SIC 8011

THIEF RIVER FALLS, MN

DIGI-KEY CORP p 439
701 Brooks Ave S 56701
Tel (800) 344-4539 SIC 5065

SANFORD MEDICAL CENTER THIEF RIVER FALLS p 1279
120 Labree Ave S Ste A 56701
Tel (218) 681-4240 SIC 8062

TRIMONT, MN

NU WAY COOPERATIVE (INC) p 1066
440 Highway 4 S 56176
Tel (507) 639-2311
SIC 5191 5171 5541 2875

TRUMAN, MN

WATONWAN FARM SERVICE INC p 1583
233 W Ciro St 56088
Tel (507) 776-1244 SIC 5153 5191 5172

VADNAIS HEIGHTS, MN

KNOWLANS SUPER MARKETS INC p 825
111 County Road F E 55127
Tel (651) 483-9242 SIC 5411

WACONIA, MN

ELKAY WOOD PRODUCTS CO p 488
1 Medallion Way 55387
Tel (952) 442-5171 SIC 2434

MEDALLION CABINETRY INC p 935
1 Medallion Way Ste 10501 55387
Tel (952) 442-5171 SIC 2434

RIDGEVIEW MEDICAL CENTER p 1234
500 S Maple St 55387
Tel (952) 442-2191 SIC 8062

WADENA, MN

DAVIS RUSS WHOLESALE INC p 416
266 4th St Ne 56482
Tel (218) 631-3078 SIC 5148

WAITE PARK, MN

STERLING PARK HEALTH CARE CENTER p 1387
142 1st St N 56387
Tel (320) 252-9595 SIC 8051

WARROAD, MN

MARVIN LUMBER AND CEDAR CO p 914
Hwy 11 & W Lake St 56763
Tel (218) 386-1430 SIC 2431

WAYZATA, MN

CARGILL INC p 255
15407 Mcginty Rd W 55391
Tel (952) 742-7575
SIC 5153 2075 2046 2048 2011 2015

NORTHERN OIL AND GAS INC p 1056
315 Manitoba Ave Ste 200 55391
Tel (952) 476-9800 SIC 1311

▲ **TCF FINANCIAL CORP** p 1428
200 Lake St E 55391
Tel (952) 745-2760 SIC 6021

WAYZATA INDEPENDENT SCHOOL DISTRICT 284 p 1584
210 County Road 101 N 55391
Tel (763) 745-5000 SIC 8211

▲ **WAYZATA INVESTMENT PARTNERS LLC** p 1584
701 Lake St E Ste 300 55391
Tel (952) 345-0700 SIC 6799

WELCH, MN

PRAIRIE ISLAND INDIAN COMMUNITY p 1167
5636 Sturgeon Lake Rd 55089
Tel (800) 554-5473 SIC 7999 5812 7011

TREASURE ISLAND RESORT AND CASINO p 1475
5734 Sturgeon Lake Rd 55089
Tel (651) 388-6300 SIC 7999 7011 5812

WHEATON, MN

COOP WHEATON-DUMONT ELEVATOR INC p 366
6587 Us Highway 75 56296
Tel (320) 563-8152 SIC 5153 5191

WHITE BEAR LAKE, MN

■ **CUMMINS NPOWER LLC** p 401
1600 Buerkle Rd 55110
Tel (800) 642-0085
SIC 5084 5063 7538 3519

INDEPENDENT SCHOOL DISTRICT 624 (INC) p 737
4855 Bloom Ave 55110
Tel (651) 407-7500 SIC 8211

WILSON TOOL INTERNATIONAL INC p 1614
12912 Farnham Ave N 55110
Tel (651) 286-6000 SIC 3542 3544

WILLMAR, MN

AFFILIATED COMMUNITY MEDICAL CENTERS PA p 32
101 Willmar Ave Sw 56201
Tel (320) 231-5000 SIC 8011

ALLIANCE ENERGY SERVICES LLC p 54
1405 Highway 12 E 56201
Tel (320) 875-2641 SIC 5172

■ **JENNIE-O TURKEY STORE INC** p 782
2505 Willmar Ave Sw 56201
Tel (320) 235-2622 SIC 2015 0253

■ **JENNIE-O TURKEY STORE INTERNATIONAL INC** p 782
2505 Willmar Ave Sw 56201
Tel (320) 235-2622 SIC 2015

PRINSCO INC p 1177
1717 16th St Ne Fl 3 56201
Tel (320) 978-4116 SIC 3084

RICE MEMORIAL HOSPITAL p 1232
301 Becker Ave Sw 56201
Tel (320) 235-4543 SIC 8062

TORGERSON PROPERTIES INC p 1461
103 15th Ave Nw Ste 200 56201
Tel (320) 235-7207 SIC 7011 5812 5813

WEST CENTRAL DISTRIBUTION LLC p 1594
2700 Trott Ave Sw 56201
Tel (320) 235-8518 SIC 5191

WEST CENTRAL STEEL INC p 1594
110 19th St Nw 56201
Tel (320) 235-4070 SIC 5051

WILLMAR POULTRY CO INC p 1612
1800 Technology Dr Ne 56201
Tel (320) 235-8850 SIC 0254 0253

WILLMAR POULTRY FARMS INC p 1613
3939 1st Ave W 56201
Tel (320) 235-8870 SIC 0253 2048

WINDOM, MN

STAPLES OIL CO INC p 1378
1680 N Redding Ave 56101
Tel (507) 831-4450 SIC 5411

WINONA, MN

DIOCESE OF WINONA FOUNDATION p 441
55 W Sanborn St 55987
Tel (507) 454-4643 SIC 8661

▲ **FASTENAL CO** p 531
2001 Theurer Blvd 55987
Tel (507) 454-5374
SIC 5085 5072 5063 5169 5198

MILLER WASTE MILLS INC p 971
580 E Front St 55987
Tel (507) 454-6906 SIC 3087 2821

PEERLESS INDUSTRIAL GROUP INC p 1127
1416 E Sanborn St 55987
Tel (507) 457-9100 SIC 3496

RTP INTERNATIONAL HOLDINGS INC p 1256
580 E Front St 55987
Tel (507) 454-6900 SIC 2299

SAINT MARYS UNIVERSITY OF MINNESOTA p 1270
700 Terrace Hts 8 55987
Tel (507) 457-1436 SIC 8221

WATKINS INC p 1582
150 Liberty St 55987
Tel (507) 457-3300 SIC 2087 2841

WINCRAFT INC p 1615
960 E Mark St 55987
Tel (507) 454-5510
SIC 3499 2399 3089 3961 3999 3069

WINONA HEALTH p 1617
855 Mankato Ave 55987
Tel (507) 454-3650 SIC 8062 8051

WINONA HEALTH SERVICES p 1617
859 Mankato Ave 55987
Tel (507) 454-3650 SIC 8062 8051

WINONA STATE UNIVERSITY FOUNDATION p 1617
175 W Mark St 55987
Tel (507) 457-5000 SIC 8221 9199

WINSTED, MN

MILLERBERND MANUFACTURING CO p 971
622 6th St S 55395
Tel (320) 485-2111 SIC 3312

WINTHROP, MN

UNITED FARMERS COOPERATIVE p 1508
705 E 4th St 55396
Tel (507) 237-2281
SIC 5153 5191 5983 5083

WOODBURY, MN

HALL ENTERPRISES INC p 654
731 Bielenberg Dr Ste 108 55125
Tel (651) 552-4905 SIC 4731

KOWALSKI COMPANIES INC p 828
8505 Valley Creek Rd 55125
Tel (651) 578-8800 SIC 5411

PIONEER POWER INC p 1151
2500 Ventura Dr 55125
Tel (651) 488-5561 SIC 1711

WORTHINGTON, MN

BEDFORD INDUSTRIES INC p 168
1659 Rowe Ave 56187
Tel (507) 376-4136 SIC 2671 2759

WYOMING, MN

ROSENBAUER MINNESOTA LLC p 1251
5181 260th St 55092
Tel (651) 462-1000 SIC 3713 7699 3711

ROSENBAUER MOTORS LLC p 1251
5181 260th St 55092
Tel (651) 408-9304 SIC 6719

MISSISSIPPI

ABERDEEN, MS

EUTAW CONSTRUCTION CO INC p 513
109 W Commerce St 39730
Tel (662) 369-7121 SIC 1611 1623 1794

AMORY, MS

U F I TRANSPORTATION LLC p 1497
60063 Puckett Dr 38821
Tel (662) 257-1811 SIC 5021

BALDWYN, MS

HANCOCK FABRICS INC p 656
1 Fashion Way 38824
Tel (662) 365-6000 SIC 5949

BATESVILLE, MS

DUNLAP & KYLE CO INC p 461
280 Eureka St 38606
Tel (662) 563-7601 SIC 5014 5531 5013

GRAVES OIL CO p 632
226 Pearson St 38606
Tel (662) 563-4604 SIC 5171 5541 5411

BAY ST LOUIS, MS

PSL-NORTH AMERICA LLC p 1188
13092 Sea Plane Road Bay 39520
Tel (228) 533-7779 SIC 3312

BELZONI, MS

BANKPLUS p 152
202 E Jackson St 39038
Tel (601) 898-8300 SIC 6022

CITIZENS FINANCIAL CORP p 311
202 E Jackson St 39038
Tel (662) 746-6811 SIC 6022 6021 6141

BILOXI, MS

■ **BEAU RIVAGE RESORTS INC** p 166
875 Beach Blvd 39530
Tel (228) 386-7111 SIC 7011

■ **BILOXI HMA LLC** p 182
150 Reynoir St 39530
Tel (228) 432-1571 SIC 8062

■ **BILOXI REGIONAL MEDICAL CENTER INC** p 183
150 Reynoir St 39530
Tel (228) 432-1571 SIC 8062

CLC OF BILOXI LLC p 323
2279 Atkinson Rd 39531
Tel (228) 388-1805 SIC 8051

IMPERIAL PALACE OF MISSISSIPPI LLC p 734
850 Bayview Ave 39530
Tel (228) 432-3243
SIC 7011 5812 5813 7832

■ **RIVERBOAT CORP OF MISSISSIPPI** p 1237
151 Beach Blvd 39530
Tel (228) 435-5400 SIC 7011

TENIX HOLDINGS INC p 1437
925 Tommy Munro Dr Ste J 39532
Tel (228) 594-6800 SIC 8748

BOONEVILLE, MS

LONGWOOD COMMUNITY LIVING CENTER p 877
200 Long St 38829
Tel (662) 728-6234 SIC 8051

BRANDON, MS

COMMUNITY BANCSHARES OF MISSISSIPPI INC p 347
1255 W Government St 39042
Tel (601) 825-4323 SIC 6712

DENMISS LLC p 428
1368 Old Fannin Rd # 100 39047
Tel (601) 919-1757 SIC 6211 6531

ON-SITE FUEL SERVICE INC p 1086
1089 Old Fannin Rd Ste A 39047
Tel (601) 353-4142 SIC 5983

RANKIN COUNTY SCHOOL DISTRICT ASSOCIATION OF EDUCATIONAL OFFICE PERSONNEL INC p 1208
1220 Apple Park Pl 39042
Tel (601) 825-5590 SIC 8211

BROOKHAVEN, MS

■ **MCLANE/SOUTHERN INC** p 931
2104 Mfrs Blvd Ne 39601
Tel (601) 833-6761 SIC 5141

BURNSVILLE, MS

MISSISSIPPI SILICON LLC p 976
80 County Road 210 38833
Tel (662) 696-2600 SIC 3339

CANTON, MS

JACKIES INTERNATIONAL INC p 773
1554 W Peace St 39046
Tel (601) 855-0146 SIC 5812 7011

CHARLESTON, MS

SAYLE OIL CO INC p 1285
410 W Main St 38921
Tel (800) 844-8120 SIC 5541 5171 5411

CHOCTAW, MS

MISSISSIPPI BAND OF CHOCTAW INDIANS p 975
101 Industrial Rd 39350
Tel (601) 650-1845 SIC 9131

CLINTON, MS

■ **ENTERGY ENTERPRISES INC** p 501
905 Highway 80 E 39056
Tel (601) 925-6504 SIC 4931

COLUMBIA, MS

BUCKLEY TRANSPORT LOGISTICS INC p 223
197 Airport Rd 39429
Tel (601) 731-6309 SIC 4213

SOUTHERN TIRE MART LLC p 1350
800 Us 98 39429
Tel (601) 424-3200 SIC 7534 5014

TL WALLACE CONSTRUCTION INC p 1457
4025 Highway 35 N 39429
Tel (601) 736-4525 SIC 1611 4212 8322

YAK MAT LLC p 1634
2438 Highway 98 E 39429
Tel (601) 876-2427 SIC 5211 5099

COLUMBUS, MS

4- COUNTY ELECTRIC POWER ASSOCIATION p 3
5265 S Frontage Rd 39701
Tel (662) 327-8900 SIC 4911

BAPTIST MEMORIAL HOSPITAL-GOLDEN TRIANGLE INC p 154
2520 5th St N 39705
Tel (662) 244-1000 SIC 8062

■ **MICROTEK MEDICAL INC** p 962
512 N Lehmberg Rd 39702
Tel (662) 327-1863 SIC 3841

■ **STEEL DYNAMICS COLUMBUS LLC** p 1384
1945 Airport Rd 39701
Tel (662) 245-4200 SIC 3325

CORINTH, MS

CORINTHIAN INC p 370
41 Henson Rd 38834
Tel (662) 287-7835 SIC 2512

LITCO PETROLEUM INC p 870
323 Highway 72 W 38834
Tel (662) 287-1471 SIC 5541 5172 5411

MAGNOLIA REGIONAL HEALTH CENTER FOUNDATION INC p 896
611 Alcorn Dr 38834
Tel (662) 293-1000 SIC 8062

CRYSTAL SPRINGS, MS

COPIAH COMMUNITY CARE CENTER LLC p 368
806 W Georgetown St 39059
Tel (601) 892-1880 SIC 8051

ECRU, MS

AMERICAN FURNITURE MANUFACTURING INC p 73
604 Pontotoc County Indu 38841
Tel (662) 489-2633 SIC 2519

ELLISVILLE, MS

JONES COUNTY SCHOOL DISTRICT p 792
5204 Highway 11 N 39437
Tel (601) 649-5201 SIC 8211 9411

FALKNER, MS

HILL BROTHERS CONSTRUCTION CO INC p 693
20831 Highway 15 38629
Tel (662) 837-3041
SIC 1611 1622 1541 1542

FLORENCE, MS

HEMPHILL CONSTRUCTION CO INC p 682
1858 Highway 49 S 39073
Tel (601) 932-2060 SIC 1623 1542

FLOWOOD, MS

ERGON ASPHALT & EMULSIONS INC p 507
2829 Lakeland Dr Ste 2000 39232
Tel (601) 933-3000 SIC 5172 2951

ERGON INC p 507
2829 Lakeland Dr Ste 2000 39232
Tel (601) 933-3000
SIC 2911 4213 4449 4613 5171 5172

■ **HOME HEALTH CARE AFFILIATES INC** p 703
106 Riverview Dr 39232
Tel (601) 362-7801 SIC 8082

JACKSON PAPER CO p 774
4400 Mangum Dr 39232
Tel (800) 844-5449 SIC 5111 5113 5087

KLUMB LUMBER CO p 823
1080 River Oaks Dr Sa200 39232
Tel (601) 932-6070 SIC 5031

KOCH FOODS INC p 825
1300 W Higgins Rd 39232
Tel (601) 732-8911 SIC 5144

■ **NUCOR STEEL JACKSON INC** p 1066
3630 Fourth St 39232
Tel (601) 939-1623 SIC 3312

PUCKETT MACHINERY CO p 1190
100 Caterpillar Dr 39232
Tel (601) 969-6000
SIC 5082 5084 5063 7699

■ **RIVER OAKS HOSPITAL LLC** p 1237
1030 River Oaks Dr 39232
Tel (601) 932-1030 SIC 8062

FULTON, MS

F L CRANE AND SONS INC p 522
508 S Spring St 38843
Tel (662) 862-2172 SIC 1542

GAUTIER, MS

SINGING RIVER HEALTH SYSTEM p 1326
2101 Highway 90 39553
Tel (228) 497-7900 SIC 8062

GOLDEN, MS

GOLDEN MANUFACTURING CO INC p 621
125 Highway 366 38847
Tel (662) 454-3428
SIC 2311 2325 2321 2326

GREENVILLE, MS

DELTA REGIONAL MEDICAL CENTER p 427
1400 E Union St 38703
Tel (662) 378-3783 SIC 8062

FARMERS GRAIN TERMINAL INC p 529
1977 Harbor Front Rd 38701
Tel (662) 332-0987 SIC 5153

GREENVILLE PUBLIC SCHOOLS INC p 638
412 S Main St 38701
Tel (662) 334-7000 SIC 8211 9411

RETZER RESOURCES INC p 1229
1215 S Main St 38701
Tel (662) 335-7138 SIC 5812

GREENWOOD, MS

GREENWOOD LEFLORE HOSPITAL p 639
1401 River Rd 38930
Tel (662) 459-7000 SIC 8062

STAPLE COTTON CO-OPERATIVE ASSOCIATION p 1377
214 W Market St 38930
Tel (662) 453-6231 SIC 5159 4221 6159

■ **VIKING RANGE LLC** p 1557
111 W Front St 38930
Tel (662) 455-1200 SIC 3631 5064

GRENADA, MS

■ **ADVANCED DISTRIBUTOR PRODUCTS LLC** p 25
1995 Air Industrial Pk Rd 38901
Tel (662) 229-3000 SIC 3585

COMMUNITY CARE CENTER OF GRENADA LLC p 347
1950 Grandview Dr 38901
Tel (662) 226-9554 SIC 8051

LUVATA GRENADA LLC p 887
3984 Highway 51 S 38901
Tel (662) 226-3421 SIC 3621 3585

GULFPORT, MS

■ **ANDERSON COMPANIES INC** p 89
11400 Reichold Rd 39503
Tel (228) 896-4000 SIC 1542 1541 1522

BAILEY LUMBER & SUPPLY CO p 145
813 E Pass Rd 39507
Tel (228) 896-6071 SIC 5211 5031

GRAND CASINOS INC p 629
3300 W Beach Blvd 39501
Tel (228) 314-2100 SIC 7011

GULF COAST SHIPYARD GROUP INC p 646
13085 Seaway Rd 39503
Tel (228) 276-1051 SIC 3731

GULFPORT MEMORIAL HOSPITAL EMR p 647
4500 13th St 39501
Tel (228) 867-4000 SIC 8062

GULFSIDE CASINO PARTNERSHIP DBA p 647
3300 W Beach Blvd 39501
Tel (228) 832-5374 SIC 7011

▲ **HANCOCK HOLDING CO** p 657
2510 14th St 39501
Tel (228) 868-4000 SIC 6022

HARRISON COUNTY SCHOOL DISTRICT p 664
11072 Highway 49 39503
Tel (228) 539-5956 SIC 8211

MEMORIAL HOSPITAL AUXILIARY INC p 942
4500 13th St 39501
Tel (228) 867-4000 SIC 8062

■ **MISSISSIPPI POWER CO** p 975
2992 W Beach Blvd 39501
Tel (228) 864-1211 SIC 4911

NEWMAN LUMBER CO p 1038
11367 Reichold Rd 39503
Tel (228) 604-2178 SIC 5031

■ **ROY ANDERSON CORP** p 1254
11400 Reichold Rd 39503
Tel (228) 896-4000 SIC 1542 1541 1522

RPM PIZZA LLC p 1255
15384 5th St 39503
Tel (228) 832-4000 SIC 5812

■ **WHITNEY BANK** p 1607
1 Hancock Plz Fl 7 39501
Tel (228) 868-4000 SIC 6022

GUNTOWN, MS

AUTO PARTS MANUFACTURING MISSISSIPPI INC p 133
100 Tab Way 38849
Tel (662) 365-3082 SIC 3089 3465

HM RICHARDS INC p 697
120 H M Richards Way 38849
Tel (662) 365-9485 SIC 2512

HATTIESBURG, MS

CHAIN ELECTRIC CO p 286
1308 1/2 W Pine St 39401
Tel (601) 545-3800 SIC 1731

CHANNEL CONTROL MERCHANTS LLC p 288
6892 U S Highway 49 39402
Tel (601) 268-7555 SIC 5331

COOPERATIVE ENERGY A MISSISSIPPI ELECTRIC COOPERATIVE p 367
7037 U S Highway 49 39402
Tel (601) 579-0215 SIC 4911

FORREST GENERAL HEALTH SERVICES INC p 568
6051 U S Highway 49 39401
Tel (601) 288-7000 SIC 8062 8063 8069

FORREST GENERAL HEALTH SERVICES INC p 568
6051 U S Highway 49 39401
Tel (601) 288-7000 SIC 8062

FORREST GENERAL HOSPITAL p 568
1414 S 28th Ave 39402
Tel (601) 288-2500 SIC 8082 8093

HATTIESBURG CLINIC PROFESSIONAL ASSOCIATION p 668
415 S 28th Ave 200 39401
Tel (601) 264-6000 SIC 8011

HOOD COMPANIES INC p 705
623 N Main St Ste 300 39401
Tel (601) 582-1545 SIC 3086 2952 6719

HOOD CONTAINER CORP p 705
623 N Main St Ste 100 39401
Tel (601) 582-1545 SIC 2673

HOOD DISTRIBUTION INC p 705
15 Professional Pkwy # 8 39402
Tel (601) 264-2962 SIC 8741

HOOD INDUSTRIES INC p 705
15 Professional Pkwy # 8 39402
Tel (601) 264-2962 SIC 2436 2421 5031

LAMAR COMMUNITY CARE CENTER LLC p 841
37 Hillcrest Dr Ofc 39402
Tel (601) 264-0058 SIC 8051

MERCHANTS CO p 944
1100 Edwards St 39401
Tel (601) 353-2461 SIC 5141

TATUM DEVELOPMENT CORP p 1426
11 Parkway Blvd 39401
Tel (601) 544-6043
SIC 5141 5084 4924 3443

UNIVERSITY OF SOUTHERN MISSISSIPPI p 1525
118 College Dr 39406
Tel (601) 266-1000 SIC 8221

WESLEY HEALTH SYSTEM LLC p 1593
5001 Hardy St 39402
Tel (601) 268-8000
SIC 8051 8062 8082 8011

HORN LAKE, MS

JT SHANNON LUMBER CO INC p 796
2200 Cole Rd 38637
Tel (662) 393-3765 SIC 5031 3559 2421

HOUSTON, MS

FRANKLIN CORP p 575
600 Franklin Dr 38851
Tel (662) 456-5771 SIC 2512

INDIANOLA, MS

GRESHAM PETROLEUM CO p 639
415 Pershing Ave 38751
Tel (662) 887-2160 SIC 5171 5984

ISOLA, MS

CONSOLIDATED CATFISH COMPANIES LLC p 359
299 South St 38754
Tel (662) 962-3101 SIC 2092

ITTA BENA, MS

AMERICAS CATCH INC p 81
46623 County Road 523 38941
Tel (662) 254-7207 SIC 2092 0273

HEARTLAND CATFISH CO INC p 679
55001 Highway 82 W 38941
Tel (662) 254-7100 SIC 2092

SCOTT PETROLEUM CORP p 1293
102 Main St 38941
Tel (662) 254-9024 SIC 5171 5984 5411

JACKSON, MS

BLUE CROSS & BLUE SHIELD OF MISSISSIPPI A MUTUAL INSURANCE CO p 191
3545 Lakeland Dr 39232
Tel (601) 932-3704 SIC 6324

BOARD OF TRUSTEES OF STATE INSTITUTIONS OF HIGHER LEARNING p 196
3825 Ridgewood Rd 39211
Tel (601) 432-6198 SIC 8611

▲ CAL-MAINE FOODS INC p 238
3320 W Woodrow Wilson Ave 39209
Tel (601) 948-6813 SIC 0252

CITY OF JACKSON p 315
219 S President St 39201
Tel (601) 960-1111 SIC 9111

DEPARTMENT OF CORRECTIONS MISSISSIPPI p 430
633 N State St Ste 208 39202
Tel (601) 359-5600 SIC 9223

DEWEY CORP p 434
5500 Highway 80 W 39209
Tel (601) 922-8331 SIC 4213 6719

▲ EASTGROUP PROPERTIES INC p 473
190 E Capitol St Ste 400 39201
Tel (601) 354-3555 SIC 6798

■ ENTERGY MISSISSIPPI INC p 501
308 E Pearl St 39201
Tel (601) 368-5000 SIC 4911

■ ENTERGY NUCLEAR GENERATION CO p 501
1340 Echelon Pkwy Ste 100 39213
Tel (601) 368-5000 SIC 4911

■ ENTERGY OPERATIONS INC p 501
1340 Echelon Pkwy Ste 100 39213
Tel (601) 366-2727 SIC 4911

EXECUTIVE OFFICE OF STATE OF MISSISSIPPI p 518
550 High St 39201
Tel (601) 359-3100 SIC 9111

G S & L ENTERPRISES INC p 587
408 Highway 49 S 39218
Tel (601) 939-1000 SIC 5012 5082

HEALTH MISSISSIPPI ORGANIZATION INC p 675
570 E Woodrow Wilson Ave 39216
Tel (601) 576-7400 SIC 8099

■ JACKSON HMA LLC p 774
1850 Chadwick Dr 39204
Tel (601) 376-1000 SIC 8011

JACKSON PUBLIC SCHOOL DISTRICT LEASE CORP INC p 774
662 S President St 39201
Tel (601) 960-8921 SIC 8211

JACKSON STATE UNIVERSITY p 774
1400 J R Lynch St Ste 206 39217
Tel (601) 979-2121 SIC 8221

KLLM TRANSPORT SERVICES LLC p 823
135 Riverview Dr 39218
Tel (601) 939-2545 SIC 4213

LAMPTON-LOVE INC p 841
2829 Lakeland Dr Ste 1505 39232
Tel (601) 933-3400 SIC 5171

MILITARY DEPARTMENT MISSISSIPPI p 969
1410 Riverside Dr 39202
Tel (601) 313-6209 SIC 9711

MILLER TRANSPORTATION SERVICES INC p 971
5500 Highway 80 W 39209
Tel (601) 856-6526 SIC 4231

MILLER TRANSPORTERS EMPLOYEES p 971
5500 Highway 80 W 39209
Tel (601) 922-8331 SIC 6141

MILLER TRANSPORTERS INC p 971
5500 Highway 80 W 39209
Tel (601) 922-8331 SIC 4731

MINACT INC p 972
5220 Keele St 39206
Tel (601) 362-1631 SIC 8331 8742

MISSISSIPPI ACTION FOR PROGRESS INC p 975
1751 Morson Rd 39209
Tel (601) 923-4100 SIC 8099 8211

MISSISSIPPI BAPTIST HEALTH SYSTEMS INC p 975
1225 N State St Ofc 39202
Tel (601) 968-1000 SIC 8741 8721 8069

MISSISSIPPI BAPTST MEDICAL CENTER INC p 975
1225 N State St 39202
Tel (601) 968-1000 SIC 8062 8069 8051

MISSISSIPPI DEPARTMENT OF HUMAN SERVICES p 975
750 N State St 39202
Tel (601) 359-5131 SIC 9441

MISSISSIPPI DEPARTMENT OF MENTAL HEALTH p 975
239 N Lamar St Ste 1101 39201
Tel (601) 359-1288 SIC 9431

MISSISSIPPI DEPARTMENT OF PUBLIC SAFETY p 975
1900 E Woodrow Wilson Ave 39216
Tel (601) 987-1212 SIC 9229 9221

MISSISSIPPI DEPARTMENT OF TRANSPORTATION p 975
401 N West St 39201
Tel (601) 359-7001 SIC 9621

MISSISSIPPI FARM BUREAU MUTUAL INSURANCE CO INC p 975
6311 Ridgewood Rd 39211
Tel (601) 957-3200 SIC 6331

MMI HOTEL GROUP INC p 979
1000 Red Fern Pl 39232
Tel (601) 936-3666 SIC 7011

MS SUPREME COURT p 996
450 High St Ste 300 39201
Tel (601) 359-3694 SIC 9211

NEEL-SCHAFFER INC p 1024
125 S Congress St # 1100 39201
Tel (601) 948-3071 SIC 8711

SOUTHERN FARM BUREAU LIFE INSURANCE CO INC p 1348
1401 Livingston Ln 39213
Tel (601) 981-7422 SIC 6411

SOUTHERN STATES UTILITY TRAILER SALES INC p 1350
550 Highway 49 S 39218
Tel (601) 939-9000 SIC 5012

ST DOMINIC HEALTH SERVICES INC p 1366
969 Lakeland Dr 39216
Tel (601) 200-2000
SIC 8741 8093 8069 8062

ST DOMINIC-JACKSON MEMORIAL HOSPITAL p 1366
969 Lakeland Dr 39216
Tel (601) 200-6776 SIC 8062

STA-HOME HEALTH & HOSPICE INC p 1374
406 Briarwood Dr Ste 200 39206
Tel (601) 956-5100 SIC 8082

STATE OF MISSISSIPPI p 1382
501 N West St 39201
Tel (601) 359-3100 SIC 9111

STEEL SERVICE CORP p 1384
2260 Flowood Dr 39232
Tel (601) 939-9222
SIC 3441 1791 3496 3443

STUART C IRBY CO p 1394
815 Irby Dr 39201
Tel (601) 960-7346 SIC 5063

■ SYSCO JACKSON LLC p 1417
4400 Milwaukee St 39209
Tel (601) 354-1701 SIC 5142

■ SYSTEM ENERGY RESOURCES INC p 1418
1340 Echelon Pkwy Ste 100 39213
Tel (601) 368-5000 SIC 4911

▲ TRUSTMARK CORP p 1488
248 E Capitol St Ste 704 39201
Tel (601) 208-5111 SIC 6021

■ TRUSTMARK NATIONAL BANK p 1488
248 E Capitol St Ste 704 39201
Tel (601) 208-5111 SIC 6021

UNIVERSITY NEUROSURGEONS PLLC p 1519
2500 N State St 39216
Tel (601) 984-5700 SIC 8062

UNIVERSITY OF MISSISSIPPI MEDICAL CENTER RESEARCH DEVELOPMENT p 1523
2500 N State St 39216
Tel (601) 984-1000 SIC 8062

■ WASTE MANAGEMENT OF MISSISSIPPI INC p 1581
1450 Country Club Dr 39209
Tel (601) 922-9647 SIC 4953

WATSON QUALITY FORD INC p 1583
6130 I 55 N 39211
Tel (601) 956-7000 SIC 5511

WAVERLEY GROUP INC p 1584
460 Briarwood Dr Ste 410 39206
Tel (601) 956-1013 SIC 8051

KILN, MS

COAST ELECTRIC POWER ASSOCIATION p 331
18020 Highway 603 39556
Tel (228) 363-7000 SIC 4911

KOSCIUSKO, MS

IVEY MECHANICAL CO LLC p 769
514 N Wells St 39090
Tel (662) 289-8601 SIC 1711

M & F FIRST CORP p 888
134 W Washington St 39090
Tel (662) 289-5121 SIC 6022

LAUREL, MS

BOOTS SMITH OILFIELD SERVICES LLC p 200
2501 Airport Dr 39440
Tel (601) 649-1220 SIC 1623

CLC OF LAUREL LLC p 323
1036 West Dr 39440
Tel (601) 425-3191 SIC 8051

▲ SANDERSON FARMS INC p 1278
127 Flynt Rd 39443
Tel (601) 649-4030 SIC 0251 2015

■ SANDERSON FARMS INC (FOODS DIVISION) p 1278
127 Flynt Rd 39443
Tel (601) 649-4030 SIC 2038 2092

■ SANDERSON FARMS INC (PROCESSING DIVISION) p 1278
127 Flynt Rd 39443
Tel (601) 649-4030 SIC 2015

■ SANDERSON FARMS INC (PRODUCTION DIVISION) p 1278
127 Flynt Rd 39443
Tel (601) 425-2552 SIC 0251

SOUTH CENTRAL REGIONAL MEDICAL CENTER p 1343
1220 Jefferson St 39440
Tel (601) 426-4000 SIC 8062

WEST QUALITY FOOD SERVICE INC p 1595
220 N 16th Ave 39440
Tel (601) 428-4791 SIC 5812

LOUISVILLE, MS

TAYLOR GROUP INC p 1427
650 N Church Ave 39339
Tel (662) 773-3421 SIC 7699 5999

TAYLOR HOLDINGS INC p 1427
650 N Church Ave 39339
Tel (662) 773-3421 SIC 5051

TAYLOR MACHINE WORKS INC p 1427
650 N Church Ave 39339
Tel (662) 773-3421 SIC 3537

LUCEDALE, MS

SINGING RIVER ELECTRIC POWER ASSOCIATION p 1326
11187 Old 63 S 39452
Tel (601) 947-4211 SIC 4911

MADISON, MS

HOOD PACKAGING CORP p 705
25 Woodgreen Pl 39110
Tel (601) 853-7260 SIC 2674

■ L-3 COMMUNICATIONS VERTEX AEROSPACE LLC p 835
555 Industrial Dr S 39110
Tel (601) 856-2274 SIC 4581 5088

SYSTEMS ELECTRO COATING LLC p 1419
253 Old Jackson Rd 39110
Tel (601) 407-2340 SIC 3479

VSS LLC p 1567
382 Galleria Pkwy Ste 400 39110
Tel (601) 853-8550 SIC 5045 7373

MCCOMB, MS

BUFFALO SERVICES INC p 224
747 S Broadway St 39648
Tel (601) 684-7702
SIC 5172 5411 6519 4212

MAGNOLIA ELECTRIC POWER ASSOCIATION p 896
3012 Highway 98 E 39648
Tel (601) 876-5671 SIC 4911

SOUTHWEST MISSISSIPPI REGIONAL MEDICAL CENTER p 1352
215 Marion Ave 39648
Tel (601) 249-5500 SIC 8062

MERIDIAN, MS

ANDERSON REGIONAL MEDICAL CENTER p 90
2124 14th St 39301
Tel (601) 553-6000 SIC 8062

ATLAS ROOFING CORP p 128
802 Highway 19 N Ste 190 39307
Tel (601) 484-8900 SIC 3086 2952

EAST MISSISSIPPI ELECTRIC POWER ASSN INC p 470
2128 Highway 39 N 39301
Tel (601) 581-8600 SIC 4911

LAUDERDALE COUNTY SCHOOL DISTRICT p 847
410 Constitution Ave Fl 3 39301
Tel (601) 482-9746 SIC 8211

MERIDIAN PUBLIC SCHOOL DISTRICT p 949
1019 25th Ave 39301
Tel (601) 483-6271 SIC 8211

MID SOUTH LUMBER INC p 963
1115 C St 39301
Tel (601) 483-4389 SIC 2411

MITCHELL DISTRIBUTING CO INC p 977
100 James E Chaney Dr 39307
Tel (601) 482-6161 SIC 5181

PEAVEY ELECTRONICS CORP p 1126
5022 Hartley Peavey Dr 39305
Tel (601) 486-1383 SIC 3931

PROGRESSIVE PIPELINE CONSTRUCTION LLC p 1182
12340 Qitman Meridian Hwy 39301
Tel (601) 693-8777 SIC 1623

PROGRESSIVE PIPELINE HOLDINGS LLC p 1182
12340 Qitman Meridian Hwy 39301
Tel (601) 693-8777 SIC 6719 1623

RUSH HEALTH SYSTEMS INC p 1258
1314 19th Ave 39301
Tel (601) 703-9607 SIC 8741

RUSH MEDICAL FOUNDATION p 1258
1314 19th Ave 39301
Tel (601) 483-0011 SIC 8062

RUSH SERVICE CO INC p 1258
1314 19th Ave 39301
Tel (601) 483-0011 SIC 8741 7371

SOUTHEASTERN VENTURES INC p 1347
4803 29th Ave Ste B 39305
Tel (601) 693-0900 SIC 1799

SOUTHERN ELECTRIC SUPPLY CO INC p 1348
301 46th Ct 39305
Tel (601) 693-4141 SIC 5063

SOUTHERN PIPE & SUPPLY CO INC p 1350
4330 Highway 39 N 39301
Tel (601) 693-2911 SIC 5074 1711 1623

STRUCTURAL STEEL HOLDING INC p 1394
6210 Saint Louis St 39307
Tel (601) 483-5381 SIC 3441 3443 4213

YTG LLC p 1640
6222 Saint Louis St 39307
Tel (601) 483-2384 SIC 1731

MISSISSIPPI STATE, MS

MISSISSIPPI STATE UNIVERSITY p 976
245 Barr Ave Mcrthur Hl Mcarthur Hall 39762
Tel (662) 325-2302 SIC 8221

MORTON, MS

KOCH FOODS OF MISSISSIPPI LLC p 825
4688 Highway 80 39117
Tel (601) 732-8911 SIC 2015

MOSELLE, MS

SOUTHERN HENS INC p 1348
327 Moselle Seminary Rd 39459
Tel (601) 582-2262 SIC 3556

NATCHEZ, MS

■ CALLON OFFSHORE PRODUCTION INC p 242
200 N Canal St 39120
Tel (601) 442-1601 SIC 1311 1382

▲ CALLON PETROLEUM CO p 242
200 N Canal St 39120
Tel (601) 442-1601 SIC 1311

■ CALLON PETROLEUM OPERATING CO p 242
200 N Canal St 39120
Tel (601) 442-1601 SIC 1311

FREDERICKS OF HOLLYWOOD INC p 576
71 Homochitto St 39120
Tel (323) 466-5151 SIC 5632 5961

JORDAN CARRIERS INC p 793
170 Highway 61 S 39120
Tel (601) 446-8899 SIC 4213

NEW ALBANY, MS

ALBANY INDUSTRIES INC p 45
504 N Glenfield Rd 38652
Tel (662) 534-9800 SIC 2512

DIVERSITY-VUTEQ LLC p 444
2300 Munsford Dr 38652
Tel (662) 534-9250 SIC 3089

NEW AUGUSTA, MS

LEAF RIVER CELLULOSE LLC p 850
157 Buck Creek Rd 39462
Tel (601) 964-8411 SIC 2676

OCEAN SPRINGS, MS

BLOSSMAN COMPANIES INC p 190
809 Washington Ave 39564
Tel (228) 875-2261 SIC 5984 5722

JACKSON COUNTY BOARD OF EDUCATION p 773
4700 Col Vickery Rd 39565
Tel (228) 826-1757 SIC 8211

OLIVE BRANCH, MS

LANDAU UNIFORMS INC p 842
8410 W Sandidge Rd 38654
Tel (662) 895-7200 SIC 2326 2337 2339

MCCLATCHY MEDICAL CENTER p 926
7235 Hacks Cross Rd 38654
Tel (662) 893-7878 SIC 8011

NORTHCENTRAL MISSISSIPPI ELECTRIC POWER ASSOCIATION (INC) p 1054
4600 Northcentral Way 38654
Tel (800) 325-8925 SIC 4911

OXFORD, MS

BAPTIST MEMORIAL HOSPITAL - NORTH MISSISSIPPI INC p 154
2301 S Lamar Blvd 38655
Tel (662) 232-8100 SIC 8062

PASCAGOULA, MS

COUNTY OF JACKSON p 378
2902c Shortcut Rd 39567
Tel (228) 769-3258 SIC 9111

■ HUNTINGTON INGALLS INDUSTRIES INTERNATIONAL SHIPBUILDING INC p 720
1000 Access Rd 39567
Tel (228) 935-1122 SIC 3731

MISSISSIPPI PHOSPHATES CORP p 975
601 Industrial Rd 39581
Tel (228) 762-3210 SIC 2874

PASCAGOULA SCHOOL DISTRICT p 1119
1006 Communy Ave 39567
Tel (228) 938-6491 SIC 8211

SIGNAL INTERNATIONAL LLC p 1322
601 Bayou Casotte Pkwy 39581
Tel (228) 762-0010 SIC 7699 3731 3441

VT HALTER MARINE INC p 1567
900 Bayou Casotte Pkwy 39581
Tel (228) 696-6888 SIC 3731

PERKINSTON, MS

MISSISSIPPI GULF COAST COMMUNITY COLLEGE p 975
51 Main St 39573
Tel (601) 928-5211 SIC 8222

PETAL, MS

ELTM LP p 489
1374 Highway 11 39465
Tel (601) 583-9991 SIC 5172

PHILADELPHIA, MS

CHOCTAW RESORT DEVELOPMENT ENTERPRISE p 302
Highway 16 W 39350
Tel (866) 447-3275 SIC 7011

PEARL RIVER RESORT p 1126
13541 Highway 16 W 39350
Tel (601) 663-4438 SIC 5812 8641

W G YATES & SONS CONSTRUCTION CO p 1568
1 Gully Ave 39350
Tel (904) 714-1376
SIC 1542 1541 2339 1611 5211 1731

YATES COMPANIES INC p 1635
1 Gully Ave 39350
Tel (601) 656-5411
SIC 1542 1541 1611 5211 1731

PITTSBORO, MS

CALHOUN COUNTY SCHOOL DISTRICT p 238
119 W Main St 38951
Tel (662) 412-3152 SIC 8211

PONTOTOC, MS

SOUTHERN MOTION INC p 1349
298 Henry Southern Dr 38863
Tel (662) 488-4007 SIC 2512

PURVIS, MS

LAMAR CO SCHOOL SYSTEM p 841
424 Martin Luther King Dr 39475
Tel (601) 794-1030 SIC 8211

PINE BELT OIL CO INC p 1148
343 Highway 589 39475
Tel (601) 794-5900 SIC 5172

RAYMOND, MS

HINDS COMMUNITY COLLEGE DISTRICT PUBLIC IMPROVEMENT CORP p 695
501 E Main St 39154
Tel (601) 857-5261 SIC 8222 8221

RICHLAND, MS

APAC-MISSISSIPPI INC p 95
101 Riverview Dr 39218
Tel (601) 376-4000
SIC 1611 1771 3531 5032 2951

FIRST CHOICE MEDICAL SUPPLY LLC p 545
127 Interstate Dr 39218
Tel (800) 809-4556 SIC 5047

■ IRBY CONSTRUCTION CO p 764
318 Old Highway 49 S 39218
Tel (601) 709-4729 SIC 1623 1731

KLLM INC p 823
135 Riverview Dr 39218
Tel (601) 932-8616 SIC 4213

STRIBLING EQUIPMENT LLC p 1393
408 Highway 49 S 39218
Tel (601) 939-1000 SIC 5082 7353

TOTAL TRANSPORTATION OF MISSISSIPPI LLC p 1463
125 Riverview Dr 39218
Tel (601) 936-2104 SIC 4213

RIDGELAND, MS

BANCPLUS CORP p 150
1068 Highland Colony Pkwy 39157
Tel (601) 898-8300 SIC 6712

BROWN BOTTLING GROUP INC p 219
591 Highland Colony Pkwy 39157
Tel (601) 607-3011 SIC 5149

CELLULAR SOUTH INC p 274
1018 Highland Pkwy # 330 39157
Tel (855) 277-4732 SIC 4812

FIRST HERITAGE CREDIT CORP p 547
605 Crescent Blvd Ste 101 39157
Tel (601) 952-0635 SIC 6141

GKR SYSTEMS INC p 613
860 Centre St 39157
Tel (601) 956-5440 SIC 5045 7373

HORNE LLP p 708
1020 Highland Colony Pkwy # 400 39157
Tel (601) 948-0940 SIC 8721 8742

LOUISIANA EXTENDED CARE CENTERS INC p 880
763 Avery Blvd N 39157
Tel (601) 956-8884 SIC 8051 8052

MADISON COUNTY SCHOOL DISTRICT p 894
476 Highland Colony Pkwy 39157
Tel (601) 879-3000 SIC 8211

MAGNOLIA MANAGEMENT CORP p 896
763 Avery Blvd N 39157
Tel (601) 956-8884 SIC 8051

MCCLAIN SONICS INC p 926
425 Christine Dr 39157
Tel (601) 914-3401 SIC 5812

MMC MATERIALS INC p 979
1052 Highland Colony Pkwy # 201 39157
Tel (601) 898-4000 SIC 3273

P C YOUNGWILLIAMS p 1102
141 Township Ave Ste 200 39157
Tel (601) 990-3100 SIC 8111

SOUTHERN FARM BUREAU CASUALTY INSURANCE CO p 1348
1800 E County Line Rd 39157
Tel (601) 957-3200 SIC 6411

TELAPEX INC p 1433
1018 Highland Pkwy # 500 39157
Tel (601) 355-1522 SIC 4812 4813

TELLUS OPERATING GROUP LLC p 1435
602 Crescent Pl Ste 100 39157
Tel (601) 898-7444 SIC 1311

ROBINSONVILLE, MS

■ BL DEVELOPMENT CORP p 186
13615 Old Highway 61 N 38664
Tel (662) 357-3097 SIC 7011

■ BOYD TUNICA INC p 205
1477 Csno Strip Res Blvd 38664
Tel (662) 363-0711 SIC 7011

MAJESTIC MISSISSIPPI LLC p 899
711 Lucky Ln 38664
Tel (662) 363-5825 SIC 7011

■ OLYMPIA BALLYS LIMITED PARTNERSHIP p 1083
1450 Ballys Blvd 38664
Tel (662) 357-1500
SIC 7999 7011 5813 5812

RIH ACQUISITIONS MS I LLC p 1235
1100 Casino Strip Resort 38664
Tel (662) 363-7777 SIC 7999

RIH ACQUISITIONS MS II LLC p 1235
1450 Ballys Blvd 38664
Tel (800) 382-2559 SIC 7999

■ ROBINSON PROPERTY GROUP LIMITED PARTNERSHIP p 1242
1021 Casino Center Dr 38664
Tel (662) 357-5500 SIC 7011 5813 5812

■ TUNICA ROADHOUSE CORP p 1491
13615 Old Highway 61 N 38664
Tel (662) 363-4900
SIC 7999 7011 5813 5812

SALTILLO, MS

BAUHAUS FURNITURE GROUP LLC p 160
1 Bauhaus Dr 38866
Tel (662) 869-2664 SIC 2512

SYNTRON MATERIAL HANDLING LLC p 1416
2730 Highway 145 38866
Tel (662) 869-5711 SIC 3532

SANDY HOOK, MS

DIXIE MAT AND HARDWOOD CO p 444
236 Herring Rd 39478
Tel (601) 876-2427 SIC 2448 2426

SOUTHAVEN, MS

BAPTIST MEMORIAL HOSPITAL-DESOTO INC p 154
7601 Southcrest Pkwy 38671
Tel (662) 772-4000 SIC 8062

STARKVILLE, MS

C C CLARK INC p 232
501 Academy Rd 39759
Tel (662) 323-4317 SIC 5149 2086

CADENCE FINANCIAL CORP p 236
301 E Main St 39759
Tel (662) 323-1341 SIC 6021

STARKVILLE OKTIBBEHA CONSOLIDATED SCHOOL DISTRICT p 1379
401 Greensboro St 39759
Tel (662) 324-4050 SIC 8211

TAYLORSVILLE, MS

■ REMY REMAN LLC p 1223
214 Fellowship Rd 39168
Tel (601) 785-9504 SIC 3714

SOUTHERN PINE ELECTRIC POWER ASSOCIATION p 1350
110 Risher St 39168
Tel (601) 785-6511 SIC 4911

TUPELO, MS

■ BANCORPSOUTH BANK p 150
201 S Spring St 38804
Tel (662) 680-2000 SIC 6022

▲ BANCORPSOUTH INC p 150
201 S Spring St 38804
Tel (662) 680-2000 SIC 6022

■ BANCORPSOUTH INSURANCE SERVICES INC p 150
201 W Main St Fl 2 38804
Tel (662) 680-2000 SIC 6411

COMMUNITY ELDERCARE SERVICES LLC p 348
2844 Traceland Dr 38801
Tel (662) 680-7300 SIC 8741

JESCO INC p 783
2020 Mccullough Blvd 38801
Tel (662) 842-3240 SIC 1541

LFI WIND DOWN INC p 860
5380 Highway 145 S 38801
Tel (662) 566-7211 SIC 2512

NORTH MISSISSIPPI HEALTH SERVICES INC p 1053
830 S Gloster St 38801
Tel (662) 377-3000 SIC 8741

NORTH MISSISSIPPI MEDICAL CENTER INC p 1053
830 S Gloster St 38801
Tel (662) 377-3000 SIC 8062 8051 8082

R & D MARKETING LLC p 1201
4110 Westside Dr 38801
Tel (662) 620-2828 SIC 5147

■ RENASANT BANK p 1223
209 Troy St 38804
Tel (662) 680-1001 SIC 6022 6162

▲ RENASANT CORP p 1223
209 Troy St 38804
Tel (662) 680-1001 SIC 6029 6411

TUPELO PUBLIC SCHOOL DISTRICT p 1492
72 S Green St 38804
Tel (662) 841-8850 SIC 8211

UNITED FURNITURE INDUSTRIES INC p 1508
5380 Highway 145 S 38801
Tel (662) 447-4000 SIC 2512

UNIVERSITY, MS

UNIVERSITY OF MISSISSIPPI p 1523
113 Falkner 38677
Tel (662) 915-6538 SIC 8221

VANCLEAVE, MS

JACKSON COUNTY SCHOOL DISTRICT p 773
4700 Colonel Vickrey Rd 39565
Tel (228) 826-1757 SIC 8211

VICKSBURG, MS

■ AMERISTAR CASINO VICKSBURG INC p 83
4116 Washington St 39180
Tel (601) 638-1000 SIC 7999 7011 5812

ANDERSON-TULLY CO p 90
1725 N Washington St 39183
Tel (601) 629-3283 SIC 2421 0811

HERITAGE HOUSE NURSING CENTER p 686
3103 Wisconsin Ave 39180
Tel (601) 883-9911 SIC 8049

■ RIVER REGION BEHAVIORAL HEALTH p 1237
1111 N Frontage Rd 39180
Tel (601) 619-3838 SIC 8062

VICKSBURG HEALTHCARE LLC p 1555
2100 Highway 61 N 39183
Tel (601) 883-4287 SIC 8062

WAYNESBORO, MS

CLARK OIL CO INC p 322
720 Station St 39367
Tel (601) 735-4847 SIC 5541 5172

KELLEY BROTHERS CONTRACTORS INC p 808
401 County Farm Rd 39367
Tel (601) 735-2541 SIC 1389 1382 1381

MAR-JAC POULTRY MS LLC p 904
261 Marshall Durbin Dr 39367
Tel (601) 735-3132 SIC 2048

T K STANLEY INC p 1419
6739 Highway 184 39367
Tel (601) 735-2855 SIC 1389

WEST POINT, MS

SOUTHERN IONICS INC p 1349
180 W Broad St 39773
Tel (662) 494-3055 SIC 2819

YAZOO CITY, MS

CLAY FARMS p 323
85 Cypress Ln 39194
Tel (662) 836-7629 SIC 0191

MISSISSIPPI AG CO p 975
441 Haley Barbour Pkwy 39194
Tel (662) 746-6208 SIC 5083

MISSOURI

ARNOLD, MO

FOX C-6 SCHOOL DISTRICT p 572
745 Jeffco Blvd 63010
Tel (636) 296-8000 SIC 8211

MEDART INC p 935
124 Manufacturers Dr 63010
Tel (636) 282-2300 SIC 5084 5088

SINCLAIR & RUSH INC p 1326
123 Manufacturers Dr 63010
Tel (636) 282-6800 SIC 3089

BALLWIN, MO

AEGIS CORP p 29
614 Dartmouth Terrace Ct 63011
Tel (636) 273-1011
SIC 3699 4812 3812 3444 2326

ANCHOR PACKAGING INC p 89
13515 Barrett Parkway Dr # 100 63021
Tel (314) 394-3701 SIC 3086

BILFINGER INDUSTRIAL SERVICES INC p 182
15933 Clayton Rd Ste 305 63011
Tel (636) 391-4500
SIC 1541 1731 1796 8711 8744

COMMUNITY CARE CENTERS INC p 347
312 Solley Dr Rear 63021
Tel (636) 394-3000 SIC 8051

EASTER SEALS MIDWEST p 471
13545 Barrett Parkway Dr 63021
Tel (314) 394-7026
SIC 8361 8331 8322 8052

BATTLEFIELD, MO

RUSSELL CELLULAR INC p 1259
5624 S Hwy Ff 65619
Tel (417) 886-7542 SIC 4812

BELTON, MO

SAFE FLEET HOLDINGS LLC p 1266
6800 E 163rd St 64012
Tel (816) 318-8000 SIC 3089 3448

BLUE SPRINGS, MO

BLUE SPRINGS R-IV SCHOOL DISTRICT p 192
1801 Nw Vesper St 64015
Tel (816) 224-1300 SIC 8211

DURVET INC p 463
100 Se Magellan Dr 64014
Tel (816) 229-9101 SIC 5122

FIKE CORP p 542
704 Sw 10th St 64015
Tel (816) 229-3405
SIC 3494 3569 3444 2899

ST MARYS REGIONAL REHAB CENTER p 1372
201 Nw R D Mize Rd 64014
Tel (816) 228-5900 SIC 8093

BOLIVAR, MO

CITIZENS MEMORIAL HOSPITAL DISTRICT p 311
1500 N Oakland Ave 65613
Tel (417) 326-6000 SIC 8011

CITIZENS MEMORIAL HOSPITAL DISTRICT OF POLK COUNTY p 311
1500 N Oakland Ave 65613
Tel (417) 326-6000 SIC 8062 8011 8082

TETERS FLORAL PRODUCTS INC p 1441
1425 S Lillian Ave 65613
Tel (800) 333-7178 SIC 5193

BOURBON, MO

PARAMOUNT APPAREL INTERNATIONAL INC p 1114
1 Paramount Dr 65441
Tel (573) 732-4411 SIC 2353

PARAMOUNT HOLDING INC p 1114
1 Paramount Dr 65441
Tel (573) 732-4411 SIC 2353

BRANSON WEST, MO

MIKE STUART ENTERPRISES INC p 968
18565 Business 13 65737
Tel (417) 272-8064 SIC 5122

BRANSON, MO

SKAGGS COMMUNITY HOSPITAL ASSOCIATION p 1329
251 Skaggs Rd 65616
Tel (417) 335-7000
SIC 8062 8082 8011 7352 8051

TRI-LAKES PETROLEUM CO LLC p 1477
943 E State Highway 76 65616
Tel (417) 334-3940 SIC 5172

BRIDGETON, MO

DAUGHTERS OF CHARITY SERVICES OF ST LOUIS p 414
12303 De Paul Dr 63044
Tel (314) 344-6000
SIC 8062 8051 8063 8069

■ DEALS-NOTHING OVER A DOLLAR LLC p 420
12100 St Charles Rock Rd 63044
Tel (314) 291-5081 SIC 5311

HUNTER ENGINEERING CO INC p 719
11250 Hunter Dr 63044
Tel (314) 731-3020 SIC 3559

HUSSMANN CORP p 721
12999 St Charles Rock Rd 63044
Tel (314) 291-2000 SIC 3585

HUSSMANN INTERNATIONAL INC p 721
12999 St Charles Rock Rd 63044
Tel (314) 291-2000 SIC 3585 5963

NESHER PHARMACEUTICALS (USA) LLC p 1026
13910 St Charles Rock Rd 63044
Tel (314) 209-4700 SIC 2834

TRANS STATES AIRLINES INC p 1470
11495 Navaid Rd 340 63044
Tel (314) 222-4300 SIC 4512

ZOLTEK COMPANIES INC p 1644
3101 Mckelvey Rd 63044
Tel (314) 291-5110 SIC 3624

BRUNSWICK, MO

AGRI SERVICES OF BRUNSWICK LLC p 36
Hwy 24 W 65236
Tel (660) 549-3351 SIC 5153 5191

CABOOL, MO

B&C HOLDING CO LLC p 142
351 Peabody Ave 65689
Tel (417) 962-2300 SIC 4212 4213

MILK TRANSPORT SERVICES LP p 969
910 Shelton Dr 65689
Tel (417) 962-2373 SIC 4213 4212

WESTERN DAIRY TRANSPORT LLC p 1598
910 Shelton Dr 65689
Tel (417) 962-2300 SIC 4212 4213

CALIFORNIA, MO

BURGERS OZARK COUNTRY CURED HAMS INC p 227
32819 Highway 87 65018
Tel (573) 796-3134
SIC 5147 5812 2015 2013

CAMERON, MO

N W ELECTRIC POWER COOPERATIVE INC p 1005
1001 W Grand Ave 64429
Tel (816) 632-2121 SIC 4911

CANTON, MO

AYERS OIL CO p 140
401 N 4th St 63435
Tel (573) 288-4464
SIC 5171 5411 5541 5172

CAPE GIRARDEAU, MO

CAPE ELECTRICAL SUPPLY LLC p 248
489 Kell Farm Dr 63701
Tel (573) 431-1838 SIC 3699 5063

DELTA COMPANIES INC p 426
114 S Silver Springs Rd 63703
Tel (573) 334-5261 SIC 2951 1611

FRANCIS SAINT MEDICAL CENTER p 573
211 Saint Francis Dr 63703
Tel (573) 331-3000 SIC 8062

MIDAMERICA HOTELS CORP p 964
105 S Mount Auburn Rd 63703
Tel (573) 334-0546 SIC 5812

PLAZA TIRE SERVICE INC p 1156
2075 Corporate Cir 63703
Tel (573) 334-5036 SIC 5014 5531 7538

PYRAMID HOMEMAKER SERVICES INC p 1193
18 N Main St 63701
Tel (573) 339-1864 SIC 7363

SOUTHEAST MISSOURI HOSPITAL ASSOCIATION p 1346
1701 Lacey St 63701
Tel (573) 334-4822 SIC 8062

SOUTHEAST MISSOURI STATE UNIVERSITY p 1346
1 University Plz 63701
Tel (573) 651-2000 SIC 8221

SOUTHEAST MISSOURI STATE UNIVERSITY p 1346
1 University Plz 63701
Tel (573) 651-2000 SIC 8351

TRI-COUNTY GROUP XV INC p 1477
1912 Independence St 63703
Tel (573) 339-1864 SIC 8082

CARTHAGE, MO

■ EBV EXPLOSIVES ENVIRONMENTAL CO p 474
4174 County Road 180 64836
Tel (417) 624-0212 SIC 4953

H E WILLIAMS INC p 650
831 W Fairview Ave 64836
Tel (417) 358-4065 SIC 3646

▲ LEGGETT & PLATT INC p 853
1 Leggett Rd 64836
Tel (417) 358-8131
SIC 2515 2514 3495 2392 2542 3363

CHESTERFIELD, MO

ABENGOA BIOENERGY US HOLDING LLC p 11
16150 Main Circle Dr # 300 63017
Tel (478) 254-7183 SIC 2869

▲ AEGION CORP p 29
17988 Edison Ave 63005
Tel (636) 530-8000 SIC 1623

AMDOCS INC p 66
1390 Timberlake Manor Pkw 63017
Tel (314) 212-7000 SIC 7372 7371 7373

ANDY MARK INC p 91
18081 Chstrfld Aprt Rd 63005
Tel (636) 532-4433 SIC 3555 3565

BOOMERANG TUBE LLC p 200
14567 North Outer 40 Rd # 500 63017
Tel (636) 534-5555 SIC 3317

BULL MOOSE TUBE CO p 225
1819 Clarkson Rd Ste 100 63017
Tel (636) 537-1249 SIC 3317

■ CONTINENTAL CEMENT CO LLC p 363
16100 Swingley Ridge Rd 63017
Tel (636) 532-7440 SIC 3241 4953

CPC LOGISTICS INC p 387
14528 South Outer 40 Rd # 210 63017
Tel (314) 542-2266 SIC 4731

CROWN PACKAGING CORP p 395
17854 Chstrfld Aprt Rd 63005
Tel (636) 681-8000
SIC 5113 5169 5131 5084

DELMAR GARDENS ENTERPRISES INC p 425
14805 North Outer 40 Rd # 300 63017
Tel (636) 733-7000 SIC 8741

DIERBERGS INC p 438
16690 Swingley Ridge Rd # 300 63017
Tel (636) 532-8884 SIC 5411 5992

DIERBERGS MARKETS INC p 438
16690 Swingley Ridge Rd # 300 63017
Tel (636) 532-8884 SIC 5411

DIERBERGS OFALLON LLC p 438
16690 Swingley Ridge Rd 63017
Tel (636) 532-8884 SIC 5411

▲ EDGEWELL PERSONAL CARE CO p 477
1350 Tmberlake Manor Pkwy 63017
Tel (314) 594-1900
SIC 3421 2844 2676 3069

■ EDGEWELL PERSONAL CARE LLC p 478
1350 Timberlake Mano 63017
Tel (314) 594-1900 SIC 2844

EXPERITEC INC p 520
504 Trade Center Blvd 63005
Tel (636) 681-1500 SIC 5085 5084

HARBISON CORP p 659
15450 South Outer 40 Rd # 120 63017
Tel (314) 727-8200 SIC 3089

■ INSITUFORM TECHNOLOGIES LLC p 746
17988 Edison Ave 63005
Tel (636) 530-8000 SIC 1623

KELLWOOD CO LLC p 809
600 Kellwood Pkwy Ste 200 63017
Tel (314) 576-3100 SIC 5136 5137

MC BRIDE & SON HOMES INC p 925
16091 Swingley Ridge Rd 63017
Tel (636) 537-2000 SIC 1521

MCBRIDE & SON ENTERPRISES INC p 926
16091 Swingley Ridge Rd # 300 63017
Tel (636) 537-2000 SIC 1522 1542

MERCY HEALTH p 946
14528 South Outer 40 Rd # 100 63017
Tel (314) 579-6100 SIC 8062

MERCY HEALTH CENTER INC p 946
14528 South Outer 40 Rd # 100 63017
Tel (405) 755-1515 SIC 8062

■ MERCY HEALTH PLANS INC p 946
14528 South Outer 40 Rd # 100 63017
Tel (314) 214-2384 SIC 6324

MISSOURI HIGHER EDUCATION LOAN AUTHORITY p 976
633 Spirit Dr 63005
Tel (636) 733-3700 SIC 6111

■ MITEK INDUSTRIES INC p 977
16023 Swinly Rdg 63017
Tel (314) 434-1200 SIC 8711 8748

■ MITEK USA INC p 977
16023 Swingley Ridge Rd 63017
Tel (314) 434-1200
SIC 3443 3429 3542 8711 5051 5085

OPAA FOOD MANAGEMENT INC p 1089
100 Chesterfield Business 63005
Tel (636) 812-0777 SIC 5812

PARKWAY SCHOOL DISTRICT p 1117
455 N Woods Mill Rd 63017
Tel (314) 415-8100 SIC 8211

PARKWAY SCHOOL DISTRICT PARENT-TEACHERS ORGANIZATION COUNCIL p 1117
455 N Woods Mill Rd 63017
Tel (314) 415-8100 SIC 8641

PREMIUM RETAIL SERVICES INC p 1171
618 Spirit Dr Ste 200 63005
Tel (636) 728-0592 SIC 8742

PRETIUM HOLDING LLC p 1173
15450 South Outer 40 Rd 63017
Tel (314) 727-8200 SIC 6719

PRETIUM PACKAGING LLC p 1173
15450 S Outer Forty Dr St Ste 120 63017
Tel (314) 727-8200 SIC 3089

R G BRINKMANN CO p 1202
16650 Chstrfield Grove Rd 63005
Tel (636) 537-9700 SIC 1542

▲ REINSURANCE GROUP OF AMERICA INC p 1221
16600 Swingley Ridge Rd 63017
Tel (636) 736-7000 SIC 6311 6321 6411

ROSE INTERNATIONAL INC p 1250
16401 Swingley Ridge Rd 63017
Tel (636) 812-4000 SIC 7371 8748

■ SILGAN PLASTICS LLC p 1323
14515 North Outer 40 Rd # 210 63017
Tel (800) 274-5426 SIC 3085 3089

ST LUKES EPISCOPAL-PRESBYTERIAN HOSPITALS p 1370
232 S Woods Mill Rd 63017
Tel (314) 434-1500 SIC 8062

ST LUKES HEALTH CORP p 1370
232 S Woods Mill Rd 63017
Tel (314) 434-1500 SIC 8741

TLC VISION (USA) CORP p 1457
16305 Swingley Ridge Rd # 300 63017
Tel (636) 534-2300 SIC 8011

■ VICTOR TECHNOLOGIES GROUP INC p 1555
16253 Swingley Ridge Rd # 200 63017
Tel (636) 728-3000
SIC 3541 3423 3613 3443 3621 3548

■ VICTOR TECHNOLOGIES HOLDINGS INC p 1555
16052 Swingley Ridge Rd # 300 63017
Tel (636) 728-3000 SIC 3541

VOLT SYSTEMS LLC p 1565
618 Spirit Dr 63005
Tel (636) 393-8658 SIC 7379

WATERWAY GAS & WASH CO p 1582
727 Goddard Ave 63005
Tel (636) 537-1111 SIC 5541 7542

CHILLICOTHE, MO

MIDWEST QUALITY GLOVES INC p 967
835 Industrial Rd 64601
Tel (660) 646-2165 SIC 5199 3151

CLINTON, MO

COMPASS HEALTH INC p 351
1800 Community 64735
Tel (660) 885-8131
SIC 8011 8069 8093 8361

COLE CAMP, MO

■ GOOD SAMARITAN NURSING HOME p 623
403 W Main St 65325
Tel (660) 668-4515 SIC 8052

COLUMBIA, MO

ALLIANCE WATER RESOURCES INC p 55
206 S Keene St 65201
Tel (573) 874-8080 SIC 4941 4952

APAC-MISSOURI INC p 95
1591 E Prathersville Rd 65202
Tel (573) 449-0886 SIC 1611

BOONE HOSPITAL CENTER p 200
1600 E Broadway 65201
Tel (573) 815-8000 SIC 8062

COLUMBIA CITY OF (INC) p 340
701 E Broadway 65201
Tel (573) 874-7457 SIC 9111

COLUMBIA COLLEGE p 340
1001 Rogers St 65216
Tel (573) 875-8700 SIC 8221

COLUMBIA MUTUAL INSURANCE CO INC p 341
2102 Whitegate Dr 65202
Tel (573) 474-6193 SIC 6331

COLUMBIA PUBLIC SCHOOLS p 341
1818 W Worley St 65203
Tel (573) 214-3400 SIC 8211

EMERY SAPP & SONS INC p 492
2301 Interstate 70 Dr Nw 65202
Tel (573) 445-8331 SIC 1622 1629 1611

JOE MACHENS FORD INC p 787
1911 W Worley St 65203
Tel (573) 445-4411 SIC 5511

LANDMARK BANK NATIONAL ASSOCIATION p 842
801 E Broadway 65201
Tel (573) 449-3911 SIC 6021

MBS TEXTBOOK EXCHANGE INC p 925
2711 W Ash St 65203
Tel (573) 445-2243 SIC 5192

MFA INC p 957
201 Ray Young Dr 65201
Tel (573) 874-5111
SIC 2875 2048 5191 5153

MFA OIL CO p 957
1 Ray Young Dr 65201
Tel (573) 442-0171 SIC 7549 5541

MISSOURI EMPLOYERS MUTUAL INSURANCE CO p 976
101 N Keene St 65201
Tel (573) 499-9714 SIC 6331

MISSOURI JOINT MUNICIPAL ELECTRIC UTILITY COMMISSION p 976
1808 Interstate 70 Dr Sw 65203
Tel (573) 445-3279 SIC 4911

SHELTER MUTUAL INSURANCE CO p 1315
1817 W Broadway 65218
Tel (573) 445-8441 SIC 6331 6311

UNIVERSITY OF MISSOURI HEALTH CARE p 1523
1 Hospital Dr 65201
Tel (573) 882-4141 SIC 8062

UNIVERSITY OF MISSOURI SYSTEM p 1523
321 University Hall 65211
Tel (573) 882-2712 SIC 8221

CRYSTAL CITY, MO

MERCY HOSPITAL JEFFERSON p 947
1400 Hwy 61 S 63019
Tel (636) 933-1000 SIC 8062

CUBA, MO

WALLIS OIL CO p 1573
106 E Washington St 65453
Tel (573) 885-2277 SIC 5541 5171

EAGLEVILLE, MO

SHELTON WHOLESALE INC p 1315
24073 24th St 64442
Tel (660) 867-3354 SIC 5092

EARTH CITY, MO

BELTSERVICE CORP p 171
4143 Rider Trl N 63045
Tel (314) 344-8500 SIC 3052

BEN HUR CONSTRUCTION CO p 172
3783 Rider Trl S 63045
Tel (314) 298-8007
SIC 1542 1791 1541 3441

EARTHGRAINS BAKERY GROUP INC p 469
3470 Rider Trl S 63045
Tel (314) 291-5480 SIC 2051

IDX CORP p 729
1 Rider Trail Plaza Dr 63045
Tel (314) 739-4120 SIC 2542

INTERFACE SECURITY SYSTEMS LLC p 752
3773 Corporate Centre Dr 63045
Tel (314) 595-0100 SIC 4813

LAIRD TECHNOLOGIES INC p 838
3481 Rider Trl S 63045
Tel (636) 898-6000 SIC 3469 3663

MIDWEST MEDICAL SUPPLY CO LLC p 967
13400 Lakefront Dr 63045
Tel (314) 291-2900 SIC 5047

■ MORAN FOODS LLC p 988
100 Corporate Office Dr 63045
Tel (314) 592-9100 SIC 5141 5411

■ SAVE-A-LOT FOOD STORES LTD p 1284
100 Corporate Office Dr 63045
Tel (314) 592-9261 SIC 5411

SLBS MANAGEMENT INC p 1331
3201 Rider Trl S 63045
Tel (314) 874-0400 SIC 5181

■ UNITED INDUSTRIES CORP p 1509
1 Rider Trl Ste 300 63045
Tel (314) 738-0375 SIC 2879 3691

WESTERN OIL INC p 1599
3553 Rider Trl S 63045
Tel (314) 738-9900
SIC 5541 5411 7542 4225

ELLISVILLE, MO

COOPER BUSSMANN LLC p 366
114 Old State Rd 63021
Tel (636) 527-1324 SIC 3613 3699 3643

EUREKA, MO

ROCKWOOD SCHOOL DISTRICT R-6 (INC) p 1245
111 E North St 63025
Tel (636) 733-2000 SIC 8211

ROTO-DIE CO INC p 1252
800 Howerton Ln 63025
Tel (636) 587-3600 SIC 3544 3555 3312

EXCELSIOR SPRINGS, MO

■ AMERICAN ITALIAN PASTA CO p 75
1000 Italian Way 64024
Tel (816) 502-6000 SIC 2099

ONMEDIA COMMUNICATIONS CO INC p 1088
115 N Industrial Park Rd 64024
Tel (913) 491-4030 SIC 4841

FARMINGTON, MO

FIRST STATE COMMUNITY BANK INC p 549
201 E Columbia St 63640
Tel (573) 756-4547 SIC 6022

U S TOOL GRINDING INC p 1497
2000 Progress Dr 63640
Tel (573) 431-3856 SIC 3541 3545

FENTON, MO

BUTLER SUPPLY INC p 230
965 Horan Dr 63026
Tel (636) 349-9000 *SIC* 5063

ENVIRONMENTAL RESTORATION LLC p 503
1666 Fabick Dr 63026
Tel (636) 227-7477 *SIC* 8744

ERB EQUIPMENT CO INC p 507
200 Erb Industrial Dr 63026
Tel (636) 349-0200 *SIC* 5082 7353 5084

GRIMCO INC p 640
1585 Fencorp Dr 63026
Tel (636) 305-0088
SIC 3469 2759 3993 3429 3312

HARVEST SPORTING GROUP INC p 667
2219 Hitzert Ct 63026
Tel (314) 378-8905 *SIC* 5091

JOHN FABICK TRACTOR CO p 788
1 Fabick Dr 63026
Tel (636) 343-5900 *SIC* 5082 7699

JOYCE MEYER MINISTRIES INC p 794
700 Grace Pkwy 63026
Tel (636) 349-0303 *SIC* 8661

MARITZ HOLDINGS INC p 907
1375 N Highway Dr 63099
Tel (636) 827-4000
SIC 4725 8748 8732 4899

MARITZ LLC p 907
1375 N Highway Dr 63099
Tel (636) 827-4000
SIC 4725 8748 8732 4899

MARITZ TRAVEL CO p 907
1395 N Highway Dr 63026
Tel (636) 827-4000 *SIC* 4724

MARITZCX RESEARCH LLC p 907
1355 N Highway Dr 63026
Tel (636) 827-4000 *SIC* 8732

NOOTER/ERIKSEN INC p 1047
1509 Ocello Dr 63026
Tel (636) 651-1000 *SIC* 5075

SACHS ELECTRIC CO p 1264
1572 Larkin Williams Rd 63026
Tel (636) 532-2000 *SIC* 1731

SPORTSMANS SUPPLY INC p 1360
2219 Hitzert Ct 63026
Tel (636) 600-9301 *SIC* 5091

SWANK AUDIO VISUALS LLC p 1411
639 Gravois Bluffs Blvd E 63026
Tel (636) 680-9000 *SIC* 7359

TACONY CORP p 1421
1760 Gilsinn Ln 63026
Tel (636) 349-3000 *SIC* 3634

U-GAS INC p 1497
895 Bolger Ct 63026
Tel (636) 343-9770 *SIC* 5541

UNIGROUP INC p 1503
1 Premier Dr 63026
Tel (636) 305-5000 *SIC* 4213 7513 5087

■ **VANLINER GROUP INC** p 1544
1 Premier Dr 63026
Tel (636) 343-9889 *SIC* 6411 8742

FESTUS, MO

JEFFERSON MEMORIAL COMMUNITY FOUNDATION 145 p 782
1450 Parkway W 63028
Tel (636) 638-1400 *SIC* 8641

FLORISSANT, MO

FERGUSON REORGANIZED SCHOOL DISTRICT R-2 p 538
1005 Waterford Dr 63033
Tel (314) 506-9000 *SIC* 8211

HAZELWOOD SCHOOL DISTRICT p 671
15955 New Halls Ferry Rd 63031
Tel (314) 953-5000 *SIC* 8211

FREDERICKTOWN, MO

PENSE BROTHERS DRILLING CO INC p 1131
800 Newberry St 63645
Tel (573) 783-3011 *SIC* 1081 1381

TOWN AND COUNTRY GROCERS OF FREDERICKTOWN MISSOURI INC p 1464
208 Lincoln Dr 63645
Tel (573) 783-6477 *SIC* 5411

FREEBURG, MO

QUAKER WINDOW PRODUCTS CO p 1196
504 Highway 63 S 65582
Tel (800) 347-0438 *SIC* 3442

GRANDVIEW, MO

▲ **NASB FINANCIAL INC** p 1008
12498 S Us Highway 71 64030
Tel (816) 765-2200 *SIC* 6035

■ **NORTH AMERICAN SAVINGS BANK FSB** p 1050
12498 S Us Highway 71 64030
Tel (816) 765-2200 *SIC* 6035

PETERSON MANUFACTURING CO p 1138
4200 E 135th St 64030
Tel (816) 765-2000
SIC 3647 4111 3089 3714

RUSKIN CO p 1259
3900 Doctor Greaves Rd 64030
Tel (816) 761-7476 *SIC* 3822 3446 3585

U S TOY CO INC p 1497
13201 Arrington Rd 64030
Tel (816) 761-5900 *SIC* 5049 5092 5945

■ **WESTROCK DISPENSING SYSTEMS INC** p 1602
11901 Grandview Rd 64030
Tel (816) 986-6000 *SIC* 3089

HANNIBAL, MO

HANNIBAL REGIONAL HOSPITAL INC p 658
6000 Hospital Dr 63401
Tel (573) 248-1300 *SIC* 8062

HARRISONVILLE, MO

MATERIAL PACKAGING CORP p 919
23018 S State Route 291 64701
Tel (816) 380-4473 *SIC* 3241

HAZELWOOD, MO

ACLARA METERS LLC p 17
945 Hornet Dr 63042
Tel (800) 297-2728 *SIC* 5045

ACLARA TECHNOLOGIES LLC p 17
945 Hornet Dr 63042
Tel (314) 895-6400
SIC 3824 3825 3829 7371 7373

ARD MALLINCKRODT INC p 106
675 Jmes S Mcdonnell Blvd 63042
Tel (714) 786-4200 *SIC* 2834

BEHLMANN AUTOMOTIVE HOLDING CO INC p 168
820 Jmes S Mcdonnell Blvd 63042
Tel (314) 895-1600 *SIC* 5511

COMMUNITY WHOLESALE TIRE DIS INC p 350
9124 Pershall Rd 63042
Tel (314) 241-3737 *SIC* 5014

MALLINCKRODT LLC p 900
675 Jmes S Mcdonnell Blvd 63042
Tel (314) 654-2000
SIC 3841 3829 2834 2833

METER READINGS HOLDING LLC p 953
945 Hornet Dr 63042
Tel (561) 394-0550
SIC 3824 3825 3829 7371 7373

UNITED SEATING & MOBILITY LLC p 1511
975 Hornet Dr 63042
Tel (314) 731-7867 *SIC* 5047

HIGH RIDGE, MO

DOBBS TIRE & AUTO CENTERS INC p 447
1983 Brennan Plz 63049
Tel (636) 677-2101 *SIC* 5531

INDEPENDENCE, MO

■ **ALLIED WASTE SERVICES OF INDEPENDENCE** p 57
1220 S Brookside Ave 64052
Tel (816) 254-1470 *SIC* 4953

BURD & FLETCHER CO p 226
5151 E Geospace Dr 64056
Tel (816) 257-0291 *SIC* 2657 2752 6512

CENTERPOINT MEDICAL CENTER OF INDEPENDENCE LLC p 276
19600 E 39th St S 64057
Tel (816) 698-8846 *SIC* 8062

CITY OF INDEPENDENCE p 315
111 E Maple Ave 64050
Tel (816) 325-7000 *SIC* 9111

CONSOLIDATED LIBRARY DISTRICT NO 3 p 360
15616 E Us Highway 24 64050
Tel (816) 836-8175 *SIC* 8231

INDEPENDENCE SCHOOL BOARD OF EDUCATION p 736
201 N Forest Ave 64050
Tel (816) 521-5300 *SIC* 8211

INDEPENDENCE SCHOOL DISTRICT p 736
201 N Forest Ave Ste 30 64050
Tel (816) 521-5300 *SIC* 8211

LAKE ATK CITY AMMUNITION p 838
101 N M 7 Hwy 64056
Tel (816) 796-7101 *SIC* 3761

MCKEEVER ENTERPRISES INC p 930
4216 S Hocker Dr 64055
Tel (816) 478-3095 *SIC* 5411

■ **REHABILITATION CENTER OF INDEPENDENCE LLC** p 1220
1800 S Swope Dr 64057
Tel (816) 257-2566 *SIC* 8051

JACKSON, MO

MONDI JACKSON LLC p 984
14591 State Highway 177 63755
Tel (573) 335-4900 *SIC* 2671

RHC HOLDING CORP p 1231
281 Lotus Dr 63755
Tel (573) 204-0373 *SIC* 6719

JEFFERSON CITY, MO

CAPITAL REGION MEDICAL CENTER p 250
1125 Madison St 65101
Tel (573) 632-5000 *SIC* 8062

CENTRAL BANCOMPANY INC p 277
238 Madison St 65101
Tel (573) 634-1234 *SIC* 6712

CENTRAL CAPITAL MARKETS p 277
238 Madison St 65101
Tel (573) 634-1330 *SIC* 6022 6211

CENTRAL ELECTRIC POWER COOPERATIVE INC p 278
2106 Jefferson St 65109
Tel (573) 634-2454 *SIC* 4911

CENTRAL TRUST BANK p 280
238 Madison St 65101
Tel (573) 634-1302 *SIC* 6022

DEPARTMENT OF CORRECTIONS MISSOURI p 430
2729 Plaza Dr 65109
Tel (573) 751-2389 *SIC* 9223

DEPARTMENT OF REVENUE MISSOURI p 430
301 W High St 65101
Tel (573) 751-4450 *SIC* 9311

EXECUTIVE OFFICE OF STATE OF MISSOURI p 518
201 W Capitol Ave Rm 216 65101
Tel (573) 751-1851 *SIC* 9111

JEFFERSON CITY PUBLIC SCHOOLS p 781
315 E Dunklin St 65101
Tel (573) 659-3000 *SIC* 8211

JUDICIARY COURTS OF STATE OF MISSOURI p 797
207 High St 65101
Tel (573) 751-4144 *SIC* 9211

LEARFIELD COMMUNICATIONS INC p 850
505 Hobbs Rd 65109
Tel (573) 893-7200 *SIC* 4832 4841

LEGISLATIVE OFFICE OF STATE OF MISSOURI p 853
201 W Capitol Ave 65101
Tel (573) 751-3829 *SIC* 9121

MENU MAKER FOODS INC p 943
913 Big Horn Dr 65109
Tel (573) 893-3000
SIC 5141 5087 2011 5149

MISSOURI CONSOLIDATED HEALTH CARE PLAN p 976
832 Weathered Rock Ct 65101
Tel (573) 751-8881 *SIC* 6321

MISSOURI DEPARTMENT OF CONSERVATION p 976
2901 W Truman Blvd 65109
Tel (573) 751-4115 *SIC* 9512

MISSOURI DEPARTMENT OF ECONOMIC DEVELOPMENT p 976
301 W High St 65101
Tel (573) 751-4962 *SIC* 9611

MISSOURI DEPARTMENT OF ELEMENTARY AND SECONDARY EDUCATION p 976
205 Jefferson St 65101
Tel (573) 751-4212 *SIC* 9411

MISSOURI DEPARTMENT OF HEALTH AND SENIOR SERVICES p 976
920 Wildwood Dr 65109
Tel (573) 751-6014 *SIC* 9431

MISSOURI DEPARTMENT OF MENTAL HEALTH p 976
1706 E Elm St 65101
Tel (573) 751-4122 *SIC* 9431

MISSOURI DEPARTMENT OF NATURAL RESOURCES p 976
1101 Riverside Dr 65101
Tel (573) 751-3443 *SIC* 9512

MISSOURI DEPARTMENT OF PUBLIC SAFETY p 976
1101 Riverside Dr 4w 65101
Tel (573) 751-4905 *SIC* 9229

MISSOURI DEPARTMENT OF SOCIAL SERVICES p 976
221 W High St Ste 240 65101
Tel (573) 751-4815 *SIC* 9441 8322

MISSOURI DEPARTMENT OF TRANSPORTATION p 976
105 W Capitol Ave 65101
Tel (573) 751-2551 *SIC* 9621

MISSOURI OFFICE OF ADMINISTRATION p 976
201 W Capitol Ave Rm125 65101
Tel (573) 751-1851 *SIC* 9199

STATE OF MISSOURI p 1382
201 W Capitol Ave Rm 216 65101
Tel (573) 751-3222 *SIC* 9111

VETERANS COMMISSION MISSOURI p 1553
205 Jefferson St Fl 12 65101
Tel (573) 751-3779 *SIC* 9451

JOPLIN, MO

CONTRACT FREIGHTERS INC p 364
4701 E 32nd St 64804
Tel (417) 623-5229 *SIC* 4213

EAGLEPICHER TECHNOLOGIES LLC p 468
C & Porter Sts 64802
Tel (417) 623-8000
SIC 3691 3629 3599 2892

▲ **EMPIRE DISTRICT ELECTRIC CO** p 493
602 S Joplin Ave 64801
Tel (417) 625-5100 *SIC* 4911 4941

FREEMAN HEALTH SYSTEM p 577
1102 W 32nd St 64804
Tel (417) 347-1111 *SIC* 8062 8069

■ **HEARTLAND PET FOODS MANUFACTURING INC** p 679
8101 E 32nd St 64804
Tel (417) 952-1400 *SIC* 2048

JASPER PRODUCTS LLC p 778
3877 E 27th St 64804
Tel (417) 206-3333 *SIC* 5149

JOPLIN SCHOOL p 793
310 W 8th St 64801
Tel (417) 625-5200 *SIC* 8211

MERCY HOSPITAL JOPLIN p 947
100 Mercy Way 64804
Tel (417) 781-2727 *SIC* 8062

TAMKO BUILDING PRODUCTS INC p 1423
220 W 4th St 64801
Tel (417) 624-6644 *SIC* 2952

TRI-STATE MOTOR TRANSIT CO INC p 1478
8141 E 7th St 64801
Tel (800) 234-8768 *SIC* 4213 4731

KANSAS CITY, MO

A ZAHNER CO p 7
1400 E 9th St 64106
Tel (816) 474-8882 *SIC* 1799 1761

AMERICAN CENTURY COMPANIES INC p 70
430 W 7th St 64105
Tel (816) 531-5575 *SIC* 6282

AMERICAN CENTURY INVESTMENT MANAGEMENT INC p 70
4500 Main St 64111
Tel (816) 531-5575 *SIC* 6722 6282

AMERICAN CENTURY SERVICES CORP p 70
4500 Main St 64111
Tel (816) 531-5575 *SIC* 7374 8741

AMERICO LIFE INC p 81
300 W 11th St 64105
Tel (816) 391-2000 *SIC* 6311 6321 6331

■ **AMERISTAR CASINO KANSAS CITY INC** p 83
3200 Ameristar Dr 64161
Tel (816) 414-7000 *SIC* 7011 7999

■ **APPLEBEES INTERNATIONAL INC** p 99
8140 Ward Pkwy Ste 300 64114
Tel (913) 890-0100 *SIC* 5812 6794

ARROW TRUCK SALES INC p 113
3200 Manchester Trfy L-70 64129
Tel (816) 923-5000 *SIC* 5521 5012

ASPEN PRODUCTS INC p 118
4231 Clary Blvd 64130
Tel (816) 921-0234 *SIC* 2674

ASURION PROTECTION SERVICES LLC p 123
8880 Ward Pkwy Fl 5 64114
Tel (816) 237-3000 *SIC* 6411

■ **BAPTIST-LUTHERAN MEDICAL CENTER** p 154
6601 Rockhill Rd 64131
Tel (816) 276-7000 *SIC* 8062 8731

BARTLETT AGRI ENTERPRISES INC p 157
4900 Main St Ste 1200 64112
Tel (816) 753-6300 *SIC* 5153 5154 2041

BEAUTY BRANDS LLC p 166
4600 Madison Ave Ste 400 64112
Tel (816) 531-2266 *SIC* 5999 7231

BIRCH TELECOM INC p 185
2323 Grand Blvd Ste 925 64108
Tel (816) 300-3000 *SIC* 4813 7375 4812

■ **BLOCK FINANCIAL CORP** p 189
4400 Main St 64111
Tel (816) 753-6900 *SIC* 8741

BLOUNT INTERNATIONAL INC p 190
10331 Nw Transcon Dr 64153
Tel (816) 231-5007 *SIC* 5083 3524 3469

BLUE CROSS AND BLUE SHIELD OF KANSAS CITY p 191
2301 Main St 64108
Tel (816) 395-2222 *SIC* 6321

BLUESCOPE BUILDINGS NORTH AMERICA INC p 193
1540 Genessee St 64102
Tel (816) 245-6000 *SIC* 1542

BLUESCOPE CONSTRUCTION INC p 193
1540 Genessee St 64102
Tel (816) 245-6000 *SIC* 1542

BLUESCOPE STEEL NORTH AMERICA CORP p 193
1540 Genessee St 64102
Tel (816) 968-1700 *SIC* 1542 3448

BRADKEN INC p 206
12200 N Ambassador Dr # 647 64163
Tel (816) 270-0700 *SIC* 3325 3321 3312

■ **BROADRIDGE CUSTOMER COMMUNICATIONS CENTRAL LLC** p 215
2600 Southwest Blvd 64108
Tel (816) 221-1234 *SIC* 7331

■ **BROADRIDGE CUSTOMER COMMUNICATIONS LLC** p 215
2600 Southwest Blvd 64108
Tel (816) 221-1234
SIC 7389 2759 7374 7331 2752 7336

BURNS & MCDONNELL ENGINEERING CO INC p 228
9400 Ward Pkwy 64114
Tel (816) 333-9400 *SIC* 1382 8711

BURNS & MCDONNELL INC p 228
9400 Ward Pkwy 64114
Tel (816) 333-9400 *SIC* 8711 8741

■ CAPITAL ELECTRIC CONSTRUCTION CO INC p 249
600 Broadway Blvd Ste 600 64105
Tel (816) 472-9500 *SIC* 1731

CARONDELET HEALTH p 260
1000 Carondelet Dr 64114
Tel (816) 942-4400 *SIC* 8082

CARONDELET PHYSICIAN SERVICES INC p 260
1000 Carondelet Dr 64114
Tel (816) 943-2679 *SIC* 8011

CATHOLIC DIOCESE OF KANSAS CITY-ST JOSEPH p 266
850 Main St 64105
Tel (816) 756-1850
SIC 8661 8211 8351 8361 6553

■ CBI-KANSAS INC p 268
1000 Walnut St Fl 700 64106
Tel (816) 234-2000 *SIC* 6021

CECO CONCRETE CONSTRUCTION DELAWARE LLC p 272
10100 N Ambassador Dr 64153
Tel (816) 459-7000 *SIC* 1542 1522

▲ CERNER CORP p 284
2800 Rock Creek Pkwy 64117
Tel (816) 201-1024 *SIC* 7373

■ CERNER DHT INC p 284
2800 Rock Creek Pkwy 64117
Tel (816) 221-1024 *SIC* 8742 7372 7371

CHILDREN INTERNATIONAL p 298
2000 E Red Bridge Rd 64131
Tel (816) 943-3722 *SIC* 8322

CHILDRENS MERCY HOSPITAL FOUNDATION p 300
2401 Gillham Rd 64108
Tel (816) 234-3000 *SIC* 8641

CIMARRON LUMBER AND SUPPLY CO p 307
4000 Main St 64111
Tel (816) 756-3000 *SIC* 5031

CLARK RICHARDSON AND BISKUP CONSULTING ENGINEERS INC p 322
1251 Nw Briarcliff Pkwy # 500 64116
Tel (816) 880-9800 *SIC* 8711

CLARKSON CONSTRUCTION CO INC p 322
4133 Gardner Ave 64120
Tel (816) 483-5444 *SIC* 1611

CNL HOLDINGS LLC p 330
430 W 7th St Ste 219001 64105
Tel (407) 650-1000 *SIC* 6519

CNS CORP p 330
500 E 9th St 64106
Tel (816) 842-6300 *SIC* 6211 6311 4724

COGENT INC p 334
318 Brdwy St 64105
Tel (816) 221-0650 *SIC* 5084 5082 7359

▲ COMMERCE BANCSHARES INC p 344
1000 Walnut St 64106
Tel (816) 234-2000 *SIC* 6022 6311 6162

■ COMMERCE BANK p 345
1000 Walnut St Fl 700 64106
Tel (816) 234-2000 *SIC* 6022

COMMUNITY FOUNDATION OF WYANDOTTE COUNTY p 348
1055 Broadway Blvd # 150 64105
Tel (816) 842-0944 *SIC* 8699

COSENTINO ENTERPRISES INC p 373
8700 E 63rd St 64133
Tel (913) 749-1500 *SIC* 5411

COSENTINO GROUP II INC p 373
8700 E 63rd St 64133
Tel (816) 358-2270 *SIC* 5411

CRESTWOOD EQUITY PARTNERS LP p 392
2 Brush Creek Blvd Ste 20 64112
Tel (816) 842-8181 *SIC* 5172

CST INDUSTRIES INC p 398
903 E 104th St Ste 900 64131
Tel (913) 621-3700 *SIC* 3443

CUSTOMTRUCK & EQUIPMENT LLC p 403
7701 Independence Ave 64125
Tel (816) 241-4888 *SIC* 3713

■ CYPRESS MEDIA LLC p 405
1729 Grand Blvd 64108
Tel (816) 234-4141 *SIC* 2711

DAIRY FARMERS OF AMERICA INC p 408
10220 N Ambassador Dr 64153
Tel (816) 801-6455
SIC 2026 2023 2021 2022 5083 2024

DELAVAL INC p 423
11100 N Congress Ave 64153
Tel (816) 891-7700
SIC 5083 3523 2842 0241

DICKINSON FINANCIAL CORP II p 438
1111 Main St Ste 1600 64105
Tel (816) 472-5244 *SIC* 6712

▲ DST SYSTEMS INC p 458
333 W 11th St 64105
Tel (816) 435-1000
SIC 7374 7371 7331 7372

EPR PROPERTIES p 505
909 Walnut St Ste 200 64106
Tel (816) 472-1700 *SIC* 6798

EWING MARION KAUFFMAN FOUNDATION p 516
4801 Rockhill Rd 64110
Tel (816) 932-1000 *SIC* 8699

FAIRBANKS SCALES INC p 524
821 Locust St 64106
Tel (816) 471-0231 *SIC* 3596

FANCOR INC p 527
821 Locust St 64106
Tel (816) 471-0231 *SIC* 3596 7699 5046

FARMLAND FOODS INC p 530
11500 Nw Ambassa Ste 500 64153
Tel (816) 243-2700 *SIC* 2011

■ FCSTONE GROUP INC p 533
1251 Nw Briarcliff Pkwy 64116
Tel (816) 410-7120 *SIC* 6221

FEDERAL RESERVE BANK OF KANSAS CITY (INC) p 535
1 Memorial Dr 64198
Tel (816) 881-2000 *SIC* 6011

FELLOWSHIP OF CHRISTIAN ATHLETES p 537
8701 Leeds Rd 64129
Tel (816) 921-0909 *SIC* 8661

FELLOWSHIP OF CHRISTIAN ATHLETES p 537
8701 Leeds Rd 64129
Tel (816) 921-0909 *SIC* 8661

FINANCIAL HOLDING CORP p 542
1055 Broadway Blvd Fl 11 64105
Tel (816) 391-2000 *SIC* 6411 6311 6153

FOLEY CO p 563
7501 E Front St 64120
Tel (816) 241-3335 *SIC* 1623 1711 1541

FORRESTT JONES & CO INC p 568
3130 Brdwy Blvd 64111
Tel (816) 756-1060 *SIC* 6411

■ FREIGHTQUOTE.COM INC p 577
901 Carondelet Dr 64114
Tel (913) 642-4700 *SIC* 4731

GARNEY COMPANIES INC p 592
1333 Nw Vivion Rd 64118
Tel (816) 741-4600 *SIC* 1623 1629

GARNEY HOLDING CO p 592
1333 Nw Vivion Rd 64118
Tel (816) 741-4600 *SIC* 1623 1611 1629

GORDON MCCOWN CONSTRUCTION LLC p 626
422 Admiral Blvd 64106
Tel (816) 960-1111 *SIC* 1542

▲ GREAT PLAINS ENERGY INC p 634
1200 Main St 64105
Tel (816) 556-2200 *SIC* 4911

■ GREAT PLAINS ENERGY SERVICES INC p 634
1201 Walnut St 64106
Tel (816) 556-2200 *SIC* 4911

GREAT SOUTHERN LIFE INSURANCE CO p 634
300 W 11th St 64105
Tel (816) 391-2000 *SIC* 6311

GREATER HORIZONS p 635
1055 Broadway Blvd # 130 64105
Tel (816) 842-0944 *SIC* 8399

GREATER KANSAS CITY COMMUNITY FOUNDATION AND AFFILIATED TRUSTS p 635
1055 Broadway Blvd # 130 64105
Tel (816) 842-0944 *SIC* 6732 7941

■ H&R BLOCK BANK p 651
1 H And R Block Way 64105
Tel (888) 687-4722 *SIC* 6035

■ H&R BLOCK GROUP INC p 651
4400 Main St 64111
Tel (816) 854-3000 *SIC* 6211 8721 8742

▲ H&R BLOCK INC p 651
1 H&R Block Way 64105
Tel (816) 854-3000 *SIC* 7291 6794

HALDEX BRAKE PRODUCTS CORP p 653
10930 N Pomona Ave 64153
Tel (816) 891-2470 *SIC* 3714

HALDEX INC p 653
10930 N Pomona Ave 64153
Tel (816) 891-2470 *SIC* 3714 3594

HALLMARK CARDS INC p 654
2501 Mcgee St 64108
Tel (816) 274-5111 *SIC* 2771

HALLMARK MARKETING CO LLC p 654
2501 Mcgee St 64108
Tel (816) 274-5111 *SIC* 5947 2542 7389

HALLMARK RETAIL LLC p 655
2440 Pershing Rd Ste 200 64108
Tel (816) 274-5878 *SIC* 5947

HARVESTERS - COMMUNITY FOOD NETWORK p 667
3801 Topping Ave 64129
Tel (816) 231-3173 *SIC* 8322

■ HELZBERGS DIAMOND SHOPS INC p 682
1825 Swift Ave 64116
Tel (816) 842-7780 *SIC* 5944

HICKMAN MILLS C-1 SCHOOL DISTRICT p 690
9000 Old Santa Fe Rd 64138
Tel (816) 316-7000 *SIC* 8211

HNTB CORP p 698
715 Kirk Dr 64105
Tel (816) 472-1201 *SIC* 8711 8712

HNTB HOLDINGS LTD p 698
715 Kirk Dr 64105
Tel (816) 472-1201 *SIC* 8712 8711

▲ HOSTESS BRANDS INC p 710
1 E Armour Blvd 64111
Tel (816) 701-4600 *SIC* 2051 5461

■ HOSTESS BRANDS LLC p 710
1 E Armour Blvd 64111
Tel (816) 701-4600 *SIC* 2051

■ HOSTESS HOLDINGS LP p 710
1 E Armour Blvd 64111
Tel (816) 701-4600 *SIC* 5461

HUNT MIDWEST ENTERPRISES INC p 719
8300 Ne Underground Dr # 100 64161
Tel (816) 455-2500 *SIC* 6552 1422 6211

HUSCH BLACKWELL LLP p 721
4801 Main St Ste 1000 64112
Tel (816) 983-8000 *SIC* 8111

INERGY HOLDINGS LP p 740
2 Brush Creek Blvd # 200 64112
Tel (816) 842-8181 *SIC* 5172 6719

■ INERGY PROPANE LLC p 740
2 Brush Creek Blvd # 200 64112
Tel (816) 842-8181 *SIC* 5984 5172

■ INVESTORS FIDUCIARY TRUST CO p 761
801 Pennsylvania Ave 64105
Tel (816) 871-4100 *SIC* 6722 6733 6282

IPFS CORP p 763
1055 Broadway Blvd Fl 11 64105
Tel (816) 627-0500 *SIC* 6153

ISS WORLDWIDE p 767
1225 E 18th St 64108
Tel (816) 421-8088 *SIC* 7349 7381

JACK COOPER TRANSPORT CO INC p 773
1100 Walnut St Ste 2400 64106
Tel (816) 983-4000 *SIC* 4213 7389

JACKSON COUNTY p 773
415 E 12th St 64106
Tel (816) 881-3333 *SIC* 9111

JE DUNN CONSTRUCTION CO p 781
1001 Locust St 64106
Tel (816) 474-8600 *SIC* 1542

JE DUNN CONSTRUCTION GROUP INC p 781
1001 Locust St 64106
Tel (816) 474-8600 *SIC* 1542

JUNIOR COLLEGE DISTRICT OF METROPOLITAN KANSAS CITY MISSOURI p 797
3200 Broadway Blvd 64111
Tel (816) 604-1000 *SIC* 8222

K-STATE-MRI BIODEFENSE COALITION LLC p 799
425 Volker Blvd 64110
Tel (816) 753-7600 *SIC* 6794

KANSAS CITY LIFE INSURANCE CO p 802
3520 Broadway Blvd 64111
Tel (816) 753-7000 *SIC* 6311 6411

■ KANSAS CITY POWER & LIGHT CO p 802
1200 Main St Ste 114 64105
Tel (816) 556-2200 *SIC* 4911

KANSAS CITY PUBLIC SCHOOLS p 802
2901 Troost Ave 64109
Tel (816) 418-7000 *SIC* 8211

▲ KANSAS CITY SOUTHERN p 802
427 W 12th St 64105
Tel (816) 983-1303 *SIC* 4011

■ KANSAS CITY SOUTHERN RAILWAY CO p 802
427 W 12th St 64105
Tel (816) 983-1303 *SIC* 4011 4213

■ KCP&L GREATER MISSOURI OPERATIONS CO p 806
1200 Main St Fl 30 64105
Tel (816) 556-2200 *SIC* 4911

KCR INTERNATIONAL TRUCKS INC p 806
7700 Ne 38th St 64161
Tel (816) 455-1833
SIC 5511 5531 7538 7513

KCS HOLDINGS LLC p 806
8001 Nw 106th St 64153
Tel (515) 266-4100 *SIC* 6719

KISSICK CONSTRUCTION CO INC p 822
8131 Indiana Ave 64132
Tel (816) 363-5530
SIC 1541 1623 1771 1794

LATHROP & GAGE LLP p 846
2345 Grand Blvd Ste 2200 64108
Tel (816) 292-2000 *SIC* 8111

LOCKTON INC p 873
444 W 47th St Ste 900 64112
Tel (816) 960-9000 *SIC* 6411

MARK ONE ELECTRIC CO INC p 907
909 Troost Ave 64106
Tel (816) 842-7023 *SIC* 1731

■ MASTIC HOME EXTERIORS INC p 918
2600 Grand Blvd Ste 900 64108
Tel (816) 426-8200 *SIC* 3081 3089

MERCY CHILDRENS HOSPITAL p 945
2401 Gillham Rd 64108
Tel (816) 234-3000 *SIC* 8069

MHC KENWORTH - KANSAS CITY p 959
1524 N Corrington Ave 64120
Tel (816) 483-7035 *SIC* 5012

MIDAMERICA CARE FOUNDATION INC p 964
7611 State Line Rd 64114
Tel (816) 444-0900 *SIC* 8051 8052

MIDAMERICA DIVISION INC p 964
903 E 104th St Ste 500 64131
Tel (816) 508-4000 *SIC* 8741

MIDWAY FORD TRUCK CENTER INC p 967
7601 Ne 38th St 64161
Tel (816) 455-3000 *SIC* 5511 7538

■ MIDWEST DIVISION RMC LLC p 967
2316 E Meyer Blvd 64132
Tel (816) 276-4000 *SIC* 8062

MILBANK MANUFACTURING CO p 968
4801 Deramus Ave 64120
Tel (816) 483-5314 *SIC* 3825 3444

MISSOURI CITY OF KANSAS CITY p 976
414 E 12th St Ste 105 64106
Tel (816) 513-1313 *SIC* 9111

MISSOURI VALLEY LINE CONTRUCTORS p 976
7505 Nw Tffany Sprng Pkwy 64153
Tel (816) 891-9066 *SIC* 8742 8631

MIX HOLDINGS INC p 978
2501 Mc Gee Traffic Way 64108
Tel (816) 274-5111
SIC 3952 3951 3295 3944

MMC CONTRACTORS NATIONAL INC p 979
13800 Wyandotte St 64145
Tel (816) 215-3422 *SIC* 1711

MRIGLOBAL p 996
425 Volker Blvd 64110
Tel (816) 753-7600 *SIC* 8731 6794

MSS LIQUIDATION CORP p 997
1716 Guinotte Ave 64120
Tel (816) 842-4290 *SIC* 5085 3545

MYERS AND STAUFFER LC p 1004
700 W 47th St Ste 1100 64112
Tel (816) 945-5300 *SIC* 8721

NATIONAL ASSOCIATION OF INSURANCE COMMISSIONERS p 1009
1100 Walnut St Ste 1500 64106
Tel (816) 842-3600 *SIC* 8621

■ NATIONAL BEEF PACKING CO LLC p 1010
12200 N Ambassador Dr # 101 64163
Tel (800) 449-2333 *SIC* 2011

■ NBH BANK p 1021
1111 Main St Ste 100 64105
Tel (816) 471-9800 *SIC* 6022

NEWPORT TELEVISION LLC p 1038
460 Nichols Rd Ste 250 64112
Tel (816) 751-0200 *SIC* 7922

NORTH KANSAS CITY SCHOOL DISTRICT NO 74 p 1053
2000 Ne 46th St 64116
Tel (816) 413-5000 *SIC* 8211

■ NOVASTAR MORTGAGE LLC p 1063
2114 Central St Ste 600 64108
Tel (816) 237-7000 *SIC* 6162

OLD HB INC p 1081
3101 Mercier St Ste 422 64111
Tel (816) 502-4000 *SIC* 2051 5461

OZARK KENWORTH INC p 1101
1524 N Corrington Ave 64120
Tel (816) 483-7035 *SIC* 5012

OZARK NATIONAL LIFE INSURANCE CO p 1101
500 E 9th St 64106
Tel (314) 664-4389 *SIC* 6311 6321

■ PAR ELECTRICAL CONTRACTORS INC p 1112
4770 N Belleview Ave # 300 64116
Tel (816) 474-9340 *SIC* 1623

PARK HILL SCHOOL DISTRICT p 1115
7703 Nw Barry Rd 64153
Tel (816) 359-4040 *SIC* 8211

PAXTON WOOD SOURCE INC p 1122
6311 Saint John Ave 64123
Tel (816) 483-7000
SIC 5031 2431 5211 5072

PLY GEM PRIME HOLDINGS INC p 1157
2600 Grand Blvd Ste 900 64108
Tel (888) 975-9436 *SIC* 2431

PLY GEM SIDING GROUP p 1157
2600 Grand Blvd 64108
Tel (816) 426-8200 *SIC* 3272

POLSINELLI PC p 1160
900 W 48th Pl Ste 900 64112
Tel (816) 753-1000 *SIC* 8111

POPULOUS HOLDINGS INC p 1161
4800 Main St Ste 300 64112
Tel (816) 221-1500 *SIC* 1542

REGAL SUPPLY CO p 1218
111 E 10th Ave 64116
Tel (816) 421-6290 *SIC* 5162

RUSSELL STOVER CHOCOLATES LLC p 1259
4900 Oak St 64112
Tel (816) 842-9240 *SIC* 2064 5441

SAINT LUKES HEALTH SYSTEM INC p 1270
901 E 104th St 64131
Tel (816) 932-2000 *SIC* 8062

SAINT LUKES HOSPITAL OF KANSAS CITY p 1270
4401 Wornall Rd 64111
Tel (816) 932-2000
SIC 8062 8742 8011 6512 8082 7322

SCHENCK PROCESS LLC p 1286
7901 Nw 107th Ter 64153
Tel (816) 891-9300 *SIC* 5084

SHOOK HARDY & BACON LLP p 1318
2555 Grand Blvd 64108
Tel (816) 474-6550 *SIC* 8111

ST JOSEPH MEDICAL CENTER p 1368
1000 Carondelet Dr 64114
Tel (816) 942-4400 *SIC* 8062

ST LUKES HOSPITAL OF KANSAS CITY p 1370
4401 Wornall Rd 64111
Tel (816) 932-2000 *SIC* 8062

STINSON LEONARD STREET LLP p 1390
1201 Walnut St Ste 2900 64106
Tel (816) 842-8600 *SIC* 8111

STOWERS INSTITUTE FOR MEDICAL RESEARCH p 1392
1000 E 50th St 64110
Tel (816) 926-4000 *SIC* 8733

STOWERS RESOURCE MANAGEMENT INC p 1392
1000 E 50th St 64110
Tel (816) 926-4000 *SIC* 8741

TENSION ENVELOPE CORP p 1438
819 E 19th St 64108
Tel (816) 471-3800 *SIC* 2677

TNEMEC CO INC p 1458
6800 Corporate Dr 64120
Tel (816) 483-3400 *SIC* 2851

TRANSYSTEMS CORP p 1473
2400 Pershing Rd Ste 400 64108
Tel (816) 329-8700 *SIC* 8711

TRUMAN MEDICAL CENTER INC p 1486
2301 Holmes St 64108
Tel (816) 404-1000 *SIC* 8062

U S ENGINEERING CO p 1497
3433 Roanoke Rd 64111
Tel (816) 753-6969 *SIC* 1711

■ **UMB BANK NATIONAL ASSOCIATION** p 1501
1010 Grand Blvd Fl 3 64106
Tel (816) 842-2222 *SIC* 6021

▲ **UMB FINANCIAL CORP** p 1501
1010 Grand Blvd 64106
Tel (816) 860-7930 *SIC* 6021

UNITED FIDELITY LIFE INSURANCE CO INC p 1508
1055 Broadway Blvd Ste Ph 64105
Tel (816) 391-2000 *SIC* 6311

UTILITY ONE SOURCE LP p 1537
7701 Independence Ave 64125
Tel (312) 316-9520 *SIC* 3713

VC999 PACKAGING SYSTEMS INC p 1545
419 E 11th Ave 64116
Tel (816) 472-8999 *SIC* 5084 3565

VETERANS OF FOREIGN WARS OF UNITED STATES p 1553
406 W 34th St Fl 11 64111
Tel (816) 756-3390 *SIC* 8641

VML INC p 1563
250 Nw Richards Rd # 255 64116
Tel (816) 283-0700 *SIC* 7311 7373 8742

VSMA INC p 1566
1540 Genessee St 64102
Tel (816) 968-3000 *SIC* 1542

WEST PLAINS LLC p 1595
11500 N Ambassador Dr # 250 64153
Tel (816) 270-4000 *SIC* 5153 4221

WESTERN EXTRALITE CO p 1598
1470 Liberty St 64102
Tel (816) 421-8404 *SIC* 5063

YARCO CO INC p 1635
7920 Ward Pkwy 64114
Tel (816) 561-4240 *SIC* 6552 6531

YOUNG MENS CHRISTIAN ASSOCIATION OF GREATER KANSAS CITY p 1638
3100 Broadway Blvd # 1020 64111
Tel (816) 561-9622 *SIC* 8641 7993 7991

KEARNEY, MO

■ **VARIFORM INC** p 1545
303 W Major St 64060
Tel (919) 677-3900 *SIC* 3089 1521 3444

KENNETT, MO

BAKER IMPLEMENT CO p 146
915 Homecrest St 63857
Tel (573) 888-4646 *SIC* 5083 7699

KINGSVILLE, MO

STAHL SPECIALTY CO p 1374
111 E Pacific St 64061
Tel (816) 597-3322
SIC 5051 3544 3365 3567 3369

KIRKSVILLE, MO

A T STILL UNIVERSITY OF HEALTH SCIENCES p 6
800 W Jefferson St 63501
Tel (660) 626-2121 *SIC* 8221

LAKE SAINT LOUIS, MO

MEDICAL TRANSPORTATION MANAGEMENT INC p 937
16 Hawk Ridge Cir Ste 120 63367
Tel (636) 561-5686 *SIC* 4119

NATIONAL INFORMATION SOLUTIONS COOPERATIVE INC p 1013
1 Innovation Cir 63367
Tel (636) 755-2300 *SIC* 7374

LEBANON, MO

BREECH REGIONAL MEDICAL CENTER p 209
100 Hospital Dr 65536
Tel (417) 533-6026 *SIC* 8011

DETROIT TOOL METAL PRODUCTS CO p 433
949 Bethel Rd 65536
Tel (417) 532-2142 *SIC* 3469 3444

DURHAM CO p 462
722 Durham Rd 65536
Tel (417) 532-7121 *SIC* 3644 3643 3613

INDEPENDENT STAVE CO LLC p 737
1078 S Jefferson Ave 65536
Tel (417) 588-4151 *SIC* 2449 5947 2499

ISCO HOLDING CO INC p 766
1078 S Jefferson Ave 65536
Tel (417) 588-4151 *SIC* 2449

MERCY HOSPITAL LEBANON p 947
100 Hospital Dr 65536
Tel (417) 533-6100 *SIC* 8062

LEES SUMMIT, MO

GOVERNMENT EMPLOYEES HEALTH ASSOCIATION INC p 627
310 Ne Mulberry St 64086
Tel (816) 257-5500 *SIC* 6321

LEES SUMMIT R-7 SCHOOL DISTRICT p 852
301 Ne Tudor Rd 64086
Tel (816) 986-1000 *SIC* 8211

LIBERTY, MO

CONTINENTAL DISC CORP p 363
3160 W Heartland Dr 64068
Tel (816) 792-1500
SIC 3491 3498 7699 3494

LIBERTY 53 SCHOOL DISTRICT p 861
8 Victory Ln Ste 100 64068
Tel (816) 736-5300 *SIC* 8211

NEW LIBERTY HOSPITAL DISTRICT OF CLAY COUNTY MISSOURI p 1032
2525 Glenn Hendren Dr 64068
Tel (816) 781-7200 *SIC* 8062 8051

LOUISIANA, MO

ABEL OIL CO p 11
10406 Highway 79 63353
Tel (573) 754-5595 *SIC* 5171 5411

MALTA BEND, MO

MID-MISSOURI ENERGY LLC p 963
15311 N Saline 65 Hwy 65339
Tel (660) 595-0144 *SIC* 2869

MARBLE HILL, MO

CRADER EQUIPMENT CO p 388
808 Highway 34 W 63764
Tel (573) 238-2675 *SIC* 5083 5084

KAISER MIDWEST INC p 800
808 Highway 34 W 63764
Tel (573) 238-2675 *SIC* 5083 5084

MARCELINE, MO

WALSWORTH PUBLISHING CO INC p 1574
306 N Kansas Ave 64658
Tel (660) 376-3543 *SIC* 2741 2752

MARSHALL, MO

CENTRAL MISSOURI AGRISERVICE LLC p 279
211 N Lyon Ave 65340
Tel (660) 886-7880 *SIC* 2875 2048 5251

MARSHFIELD, MO

SHO-ME POWER ELECTRIC COOPERATIVE p 1317
301 W Jackson St 65706
Tel (417) 859-2615 *SIC* 4911

MARYLAND HEIGHTS, MO

ARIZON COMPANIES INC p 108
11880 Dorsett Rd 63043
Tel (314) 739-0037
SIC 3585 1711 2394 1541 1542 8611

BUCKEYE INTERNATIONAL INC p 223
2700 Wagner Pl 63043
Tel (314) 291-1900 *SIC* 2842

■ **COLDWELL BANKER GUNDAKER REAL ESTATE SCHOOL** p 335
2458 Old Dorsett Rd 63043
Tel (314) 298-5000 *SIC* 6531

D & D DISTRIBUTORS LLLP p 406
2340 Millpark Dr 63043
Tel (314) 429-9100 *SIC* 5182 5149

DASH MULTI-CORP INC p 413
2500 Adie Rd 63043
Tel (314) 432-3200
SIC 2821 3069 6512 5169 7359

FRED WEBER INC p 576
2320 Creve Coeur Mill Rd 63043
Tel (314) 344-0070
SIC 1611 1442 3272 1622 1542

FROST ELECTRIC SUPPLY CO p 581
2429 Schuetz Rd 63043
Tel (314) 567-4004 *SIC* 5063

HARRAHS MARYLAND HEIGHTS OPERATING CO INC p 663
777 Casino Center Dr 63043
Tel (314) 770-8100 *SIC* 7011 5813 5812

HYDROMAT INC p 723
11600 Adie Rd 63043
Tel (314) 432-0070 *SIC* 5084

J D STREETT & CO INC p 771
144 Weldon Pkwy 63043
Tel (314) 432-6600
SIC 5171 5541 7389 5172

■ **MAGELLAN HEALTHCARE INC** p 895
14100 Magellan Plz 63043
Tel (410) 953-1000 *SIC* 6324

■ **SENSORYEFFECTS INC** p 1305
13723 Rverport Dr Ste 201 63043
Tel (314) 291-5444 *SIC* 2087

■ **ST LOUIS GAMING VENTURES LLC** p 1369
777 Casino Center Dr 63043
Tel (314) 770-7629 *SIC* 7999 7011

▲ **SUNEDISON INC** p 1402
13736 Rverport Dr Ste 180 63043
Tel (314) 770-7300 *SIC* 3674

SUNEDISON INTERNATIONAL LLC p 1402
13736 Rverport Dr Ste 180 63043
Tel (443) 909-7200 *SIC* 4911

TELCOBUY.COM LLC p 1433
60 Weldon Pkwy 63043
Tel (314) 569-7000 *SIC* 5065

■ **UNITED HEALTHCARE OF MIDWEST INC** p 1509
13655 Riverport Dr 63043
Tel (314) 592-7000 *SIC* 8741 6324

WORLD WIDE TECHNOLOGY INC p 1625
60 Weldon Pkwy 63043
Tel (314) 569-7000 *SIC* 5045 5065 8741

MEXICO, MO

MEXICO PLASTIC CO p 957
2000 W Boulevard St 65265
Tel (573) 581-4128 *SIC* 2673 3089 2655

SPARTAN LIGHT METAL PRODUCTS LLC p 1355
2510 Lakeview Rd 65265
Tel (573) 581-2272
SIC 3363 3364 3369 3365

MOBERLY, MO

MID-AM BUILDING SUPPLY INC p 963
1615 Omar Bradley Rd 65270
Tel (660) 263-2140 *SIC* 5031

ORSCHELN FARM AND HOME LLC p 1096
1800 Overcenter Dr 65270
Tel (800) 577-2580
SIC 5251 5999 5945 5731

MONETT, MO

3D CORPORATE SOLUTIONS LLC p 2
601 13th St 65708
Tel (417) 236-9602 *SIC* 5199 5149 2048

EFCO CORP p 480
1000 County Rd 65708
Tel (800) 221-4169 *SIC* 3442 3449

FRIEND TIRE CO p 580
11 Indl Dr 65708
Tel (800) 950-8473 *SIC* 5014

▲ **JACK HENRY & ASSOCIATES INC** p 773
663 W Highway 60 65708
Tel (417) 235-6652 *SIC* 7373

NEOSHO, MO

NUTRA BLEND LLC p 1067
3200 2nd St 64850
Tel (417) 451-6111 *SIC* 2048

OPAL FOODS LLC p 1089
1100 Blair Ave 64850
Tel (417) 455-5000 *SIC* 0252

NEW MADRID, MO

NORANDA ALUMINUM INC p 1047
St Jude Industrial Park 63869
Tel (573) 643-2361
SIC 3353 3354 3334 3714

NORTH KANSAS CITY, MO

C & C PRODUCE INC p 231
1100 Atlantic Ave 64116
Tel (816) 241-4425 *SIC* 5148

■ **HARRAHS NORTH KANSAS CITY LLC** p 663
1 Riverboat Dr 64116
Tel (816) 472-7777 *SIC* 7999

HENRY WURST INC p 684
1331 Saline St 64116
Tel (816) 701-0825 *SIC* 2752 7331

NORTH KANSAS CITY HOSPITAL p 1052
2800 Clay Edwards Dr 64116
Tel (816) 691-2000 *SIC* 8062

PAS TECHNOLOGIES INC p 1119
1234 Atlantic Ave 64116
Tel (816) 556-5113 *SIC* 7699 1389

WAGNER INDUSTRIES INC p 1571
1201 E 12th Ave 64116
Tel (816) 421-3520 *SIC* 4225 4214 4731

O FALLON, MO

BISTATE BISTRO ASSOCIATES LP p 185
4 Boston Crest Ct 63366
Tel (636) 537-9777 *SIC* 5812

■ **CITIMORTGAGE INC** p 310
1000 Technology Dr 63368
Tel (636) 261-2484 *SIC* 6162

■ **FIRST COLLATERAL SERVICES INC** p 545
1000 Technology Dr 63368
Tel (813) 604-8143 *SIC* 6162

FT ZUMWALT R-II SCHOOL DISTRICT p 582
555 E Terra Ln 63366
Tel (636) 240-2072 *SIC* 8211

■ **HERNDON AEROSPACE & DEFENSE LLC** p 687
3801 Lloyd King Dr 63368
Tel (314) 739-7400 *SIC* 5088

■ **HERNDON PRODUCTS LLC** p 687
3801 Lloyd King Dr 63368
Tel (314) 739-7400 *SIC* 5088

NORTEK GLOBAL HVAC LLC p 1049
8000 Phoenix Pkwy 63368
Tel (636) 561-7300 *SIC* 3585 3567 3433

PROGRESS WEST HEALTHCARE CENTER p 1181
2 Progress Point Ct 63368
Tel (636) 344-1000 *SIC* 8062

SAK CONSTRUCTION LLC p 1271
864 Hoff Rd 63366
Tel (636) 674-9104 *SIC* 1623 1622

TRUE MANUFACTURING CO INC p 1486
2001 E Terra Ln 63366
Tel (636) 240-2400 *SIC* 3585

■ **TW TELECOM MANAGEMENT CO LLC** p 1494
2342 Technology Dr 63368
Tel (636) 625-7000 *SIC* 4813

OSAGE BEACH, MO

LAKE REGIONAL HEALTH SYSTEM p 839
54 Hospital Dr 65065
Tel (573) 348-8000 *SIC* 8062

PALMYRA, MO

CHESTER BROSS CONSTRUCTION CO p 295
6739 County Road 423 63461
Tel (573) 221-5958 *SIC* 1611 1629

PARK HILLS, MO

PROFFER WHOLESALE PRODUCE INC p 1180
920 5th St 63601
Tel (573) 431-0625 *SIC* 5148 4213

PARKVILLE, MO

PARK UNIVERSITY p 1116
8700 Nw River Park Dr 64152
Tel (816) 741-2000 *SIC* 8221

PERRYVILLE, MO

BUCHHEIT ENTERPRISES INC p 222
33 Pcr 540 63775
Tel (573) 547-1010
SIC 4213 4212 5251 4225

CENTRAL STATES WHOLESALE & DISTRIBUTION INC p 280
33 Pcr 540 63775
Tel (573) 547-4260 *SIC* 5031

CITIZENS ELECTRIC CORP p 311
1500 Rand Ave 63775
Tel (877) 876-3511 *SIC* 4911

MARY LEE PACKAGING CORP p 914
615 Saint Marys Rd 63775
Tel (573) 547-1705
SIC 2043 2099 3089 2098

ROBINSON MECHANICAL CONTRACTORS INC p 1242
2411 Walters Ln 63775
Tel (573) 547-8397 *SIC* 1629 1711

TG MISSOURI CORP p 1446
2200 Plattin Rd 63775
Tel (573) 547-1041 *SIC* 5531

PLEASANT VALLEY, MO

CENTRAL POWER SYSTEMS & SERVICES LLC p 280
9200 Liberty Dr 64068
Tel (816) 781-8070 *SIC* 5013 7629

POINT LOOKOUT, MO

SCHOOL OF OZARKS p 1290
100 Opportunity Ave 65726
Tel (417) 239-1900 *SIC* 8221

POPLAR BLUFF, MO

BLACKWELL BALDWIN CHEVROLET GEO OLDSMOBILE CADILLAC INC p 188
621 S Westwood Blvd 63901
Tel (573) 785-0893 *SIC* 5511

CEDAR GATE PHASE II p 272
2350 Kanell Blvd 63901
Tel (573) 785-3443 *SIC* 8051

GREGORY LOGISTICS INC p 639
2844 Fair St 63901
Tel (573) 785-1088 *SIC* 4213 4212

■ LUCY LEE HOSPITAL INC p 884
2620 N Westwood Blvd 63901
Tel (573) 785-7721 *SIC* 8062

■ POPLAR BLUFF REGIONAL MEDICAL CENTER p 1161
3100 Oak Grove Rd 63901
Tel (573) 686-4111 *SIC* 8093

POPLAR BLUFF REGIONAL MEDICAL CENTER INC p 1161
3100 Oak Grove Rd 63901
Tel (573) 785-7721 *SIC* 8062

PRO-AM INC p 1178
2350 Kanell Blvd 63901
Tel (573) 785-0858 *SIC* 8051 8741

PUXICO, MO

HOLLOWAY DISTRIBUTING INC p 701
210 E Owen Ave 63960
Tel (573) 222-6255 *SIC* 5145 5194 5149

RAYTOWN, MO

CONSOLIDATED SCHOOL DISTRICT 2 (INC) p 360
6608 Raytown Rd 64133
Tel (816) 268-7000 *SIC* 8211

DEACONESS LONG TERM CARE OF MO INC p 419
8540 Blue Ridge Blvd 64138
Tel (816) 380-3319 *SIC* 8051

DYNAMIC FASTENER SERVICE INC p 464
9911 E 53rd St 64133
Tel (816) 358-9898 *SIC* 5072

ELECTRICAL CORP OF AMERICA INC p 485
7320 Arlington Ave 64133
Tel (816) 737-3206 *SIC* 1731

REEDS SPRING, MO

■ GREAT SOUTHERN BANK p 634
14309 State Highway 13 65737
Tel (417) 888-5880 *SIC* 6021 4724 6712

RICHMOND, MO

RAY CARROLL COUNTY GRAIN GROWERS INC p 1209
807 W Main St 64085
Tel (816) 776-2291 *SIC* 5171 5191 5153

RIVERSIDE, MO

MARTINREA RIVERSIDE LLC p 913
5233 Nw 41st St 64150
Tel (816) 587-0875 *SIC* 3465

■ MISSOURI GAMING CO p 976
777 Nw Argosy Pkwy 64150
Tel (816) 746-3171 *SIC* 7999 7011

NORTHPOINT DEVELOPMENT LLC p 1057
4825 Nw 41st St Ste 500 64150
Tel (816) 888-7380 *SIC* 6552 6531

ROGERSVILLE, MO

ROSWIL INC p 1252
1878 S State Highway 125 65742
Tel (417) 667-7530 *SIC* 5411

ROLLA, MO

PHELPS COUNTY REGIONAL MEDICAL CENTER p 1141
1000 W 10th St 65401
Tel (573) 364-8899 *SIC* 8062

SAINT ANN, MO

PATTONVILLE SCHOOL DISTRICT p 1121
11097 St Charles Rock Rd 63074
Tel (314) 213-8500 *SIC* 8211

SAINT CHARLES, MO

▲ AMERICAN RAILCAR INDUSTRIES INC p 78
100 Clark St 63301
Tel (636) 940-6000 *SIC* 3743 8742

■ AMERISTAR CASINO ST CHARLES INC p 83
1 Ameristar Blvd 63301
Tel (636) 949-7777 *SIC* 7999 7011

AROGAS INC p 112
1821 Sherman Dr Ste 200 63303
Tel (636) 947-0255 *SIC* 5172

DISTRIBUTION MANAGEMENT INC p 443
5 Research Park Dr 63304
Tel (636) 300-4000 *SIC* 5112

FRANCIS HOWELL SCHOOL DISTRICT p 573
4545 Central School Rd 63304
Tel (636) 851-4000 *SIC* 8211

FRANCIS HOWELL SCHOOL DISTRICT EDUCATIONAL FACILITIES AUTHORITY p 573
4545 Central School Rd 63304
Tel (636) 851-4000 *SIC* 8699

INTEGRITY SOLUTION SERVICES INC p 750
20 Corporate Hills Dr 63301
Tel (636) 530-7985 *SIC* 8748 7322

LINDENWOOD UNIVERSITY p 868
209 S Kingshighway St 63301
Tel (636) 949-2000 *SIC* 8221

▲ LMI AEROSPACE INC p 872
411 Fountain Lakes Blvd 63301
Tel (636) 946-6525 *SIC* 3728

NOVUS INTERNATIONAL INC p 1063
20 Research Park Dr 63304
Tel (314) 576-8886 *SIC* 0752

ROYAL CANIN USA INC p 1254
500 Fountain Lakes Blvd # 100 63301
Tel (636) 724-1692 *SIC* 2047 0752

SSM HEALTH ST JOSEPH HOSPITAL-ST CHARLES p 1364
300 1st Capitol Dr 63301
Tel (636) 947-5000 *SIC* 8062

SUPPLIES NETWORK INC p 1407
5 Research Park Dr 63304
Tel (636) 300-4001 *SIC* 5112

■ SYSCO ST LOUIS LLC p 1418
3850 Mueller Rd 63301
Tel (636) 940-9230
SIC 5141 5149 5146 5143 5142

SAINT CLAIR, MO

PLAZE INC p 1156
105 Bolte Ln 63077
Tel (630) 543-7600 *SIC* 5169 2819

SAINT JOSEPH, MO

B FOUR CORP p 142
3734 Pear St 64503
Tel (913) 321-4223 *SIC* 5912

BOEHRINGER INGELHEIM VETMEDICA INC p 197
2621 N Belt Hwy 64506
Tel (800) 325-9167 *SIC* 2836 2834 5191

HEARTLAND HEALTH p 679
5325 Faraon St 64506
Tel (816) 271-6000 *SIC* 8062 7322 8721

HEARTLAND REGIONAL MEDICAL CENTER p 679
5325 Faraon St 64506
Tel (816) 271-6000 *SIC* 8062

HERZOG CONTRACTING CORP p 688
600 S Riverside Rd 64507
Tel (816) 233-9001 *SIC* 1629 1611 4953

HILLYARD INC p 694
302 N 4th St 64501
Tel (816) 233-1321 *SIC* 5169 5087

MIDWEST SCRAP MANAGEMENT INC p 967
4501 Packers Ave 64504
Tel (816) 214-9204 *SIC* 5093

MISSOURI WESTERN STATE UNIVERSITY p 976
4525 Downs Dr 64507
Tel (816) 271-4464 *SIC* 8221

■ NATIONAL BEEF LEATHERS LLC p 1010
205 Florence Rd 64504
Tel (816) 236-1603 *SIC* 3111

NEWS-PRESS & GAZETTE CO INC p 1039
825 Edmond St 64501
Tel (816) 271-8500 *SIC* 2711

ST JOSEPH SCHOOL DISTRICT p 1368
925 Felix St 64501
Tel (816) 671-4000 *SIC* 8211

SYSTEMS & SERVICES TECHNOLOGIES INC p 1418
4315 Pickett Rd 64503
Tel (800) 392-8308 *SIC* 7374

TRIUMPH FOODS LLC p 1483
5302 Stockyards Expy 64504
Tel (816) 396-2700 *SIC* 2011

VEDCO INC p 1546
5503 Corporate Dr 64507
Tel (816) 238-8840 *SIC* 5047

SAINT LOUIS, MO

4M BUILDING SOLUTIONS INC p 3
2827 Clark Ave 63103
Tel (314) 535-2100 *SIC* 7349

AB MAURI FOOD INC p 9
4240 Duncan Ave Ste 150 63110
Tel (314) 392-0800 *SIC* 2052

■ ABM INDUSTRIES INC p 12
500 S Ewing Ave Ste A 63103
Tel (314) 241-1975 *SIC* 7349

AIH FLINTCO LLC p 38
8800 Page Ave 63114
Tel (314) 733-2000 *SIC* 1389 1522

AIRPORT TERMINAL SERVICES FOREIGN HOLDINGS CORP p 40
111 West Port Plz Ste 400 63146
Tel (314) 739-1900 *SIC* 4581

AIRPORT TERMINAL SERVICES INC p 40
111 West Port Plz Ste 400 63146
Tel (314) 739-1900 *SIC* 4581

ALAMO RENTAL (US) INC p 44
600 Corporate Park Dr 63105
Tel (314) 512-5000 *SIC* 7514

ALBERICI CONSTRUCTORS INC p 46
8800 Page Ave 63114
Tel (314) 733-2000 *SIC* 1541 1542 1622

ALBERICI CORP p 46
8800 Page Ave 63114
Tel (314) 733-2000
SIC 1541 1542 1622 1629

ALBERICI GROUP INC p 46
8800 Page Ave 63114
Tel (314) 733-2000 *SIC* 1541 1542 1622

ALPHA PACKAGING HOLDINGS INC p 60
1555 Page Industrial Blvd 63132
Tel (314) 427-4300 *SIC* 3085

ALPHA PLASTICS INC p 60
1555 Page Industrial Blvd 63132
Tel (314) 427-4300 *SIC* 3085

ALTER TRADING CORP p 62
700 Office Pkwy 63141
Tel (314) 872-2400 *SIC* 5093

▲ AMEREN CORP p 66
1901 Chouteau Ave 63103
Tel (314) 621-3222 *SIC* 4911 4931 4923

■ AMEREN SERVICES CO p 66
1901 Chouteau Ave 63103
Tel (314) 621-3222 *SIC* 8741

AMERICAN RESIDENTIAL SERVICES OF INDIANA INC p 78
10403 Baur Blvd Ste E 63132
Tel (314) 812-6000
SIC 1711 1731 1799 5722

ANHEUSER BUSCH INVESTMENT p 91
1 Busch Pl 63118
Tel (314) 577-2000 *SIC* 2082

ANHEUSER-BUSCH COMPANIES LLC p 91
1 Busch Pl 63118
Tel (314) 632-6777 *SIC* 2082 3411 7996

ANHEUSER-BUSCH INTERNATIONAL INC p 91
1 Busch Pl 63118
Tel (314) 577-2000 *SIC* 5181

ANHEUSER-BUSCH LLC p 91
1 Busch Pl 63118
Tel (314) 632-6777 *SIC* 5181 2082

ANSIRA PARTNERS INC p 93
2300 Locust St 63103
Tel (314) 783-2300 *SIC* 7389 7331

APEX HOLDING CO p 96
8235 Forsyth Blvd Ste 400 63105
Tel (314) 889-9600 *SIC* 6792 4412 4226

APEX OIL CO INC p 96
8235 Forsyth Blvd Ste 400 63105
Tel (314) 889-9600 *SIC* 4412 5084

■ APPLE JV HOLDING CORP p 98
8000 W Florissant Ave 63136
Tel (314) 553-2000
SIC 3644 3643 3613 3446 3699

▲ ARCH COAL INC p 104
1 Cityplace Dr Ste 300 63141
Tel (314) 994-2700 *SIC* 1221 1222

■ ARCH WESTERN RESOURCES LLC p 104
1 Cityplace Dr Ste 300 63141
Tel (314) 994-2700 *SIC* 1221

ARCHDIOCESE OF ST LOUIS p 105
20 Archbishop May Dr 63119
Tel (314) 633-2222 *SIC* 8661

ARCHWAY SALES LLC p 105
4155 Manchester Ave 63110
Tel (314) 533-4662 *SIC* 5169

ARCO NATIONAL CONSTRUCTION CO p 105
900 N Rock Hill Rd 63119
Tel (314) 963-0715 *SIC* 1541

ARCTURIS INC p 106
720 Olive St Ste 200 63101
Tel (314) 206-7100 *SIC* 8712 7389

ASCENSION HEALTH p 116
4600 Edmundson Rd 63134
Tel (314) 733-8000 *SIC* 8099

ASCENSION HEALTH ALLIANCE p 116
4600 Edmundson Rd 63134
Tel (314) 733-8000 *SIC* 5912

ASCENSION HEALTH INSURANCE LTD p 116
4600 Edmundson Rd 63134
Tel (314) 733-8000 *SIC* 6411

ASCENSION HEALTH WELFARE BENEFITS TRUST p 116
11775 Borman Dr Ste 200 63146
Tel (314) 733-8648 *SIC* 6733

AUTOMOBILE CLUB OF MISSOURI p 134
12901 N 40 Dr 63141
Tel (314) 523-7350 *SIC* 8699 4724

BALDWIN TECHNOLOGY CO INC p 147
8040 Forsyth Blvd 63105
Tel (314) 726-2152 *SIC* 3555

BARNES HOSPITAL (INC) p 156
Barnes Hospital Plz 63110
Tel (314) 362-5000 *SIC* 8062

BARNES-JEWISH HOSPITAL p 156
216 S Kingshwy Blvd 140 63110
Tel (314) 747-3000 *SIC* 8062

BARNES-JEWISH HOSPITAL p 156
1 B J Hospital Plaza Dr 63110
Tel (314) 747-3000 *SIC* 8062

BARNES-JEWISH WEST COUNTY HOSPITAL p 156
12634 Olive Blvd 63141
Tel (314) 996-8000 *SIC* 8062

BARRY-WEHMILLER COMPANIES INC p 157
8020 Forsyth Blvd 63105
Tel (314) 862-8000
SIC 3565 3535 3554 8711

BARRY-WEHMILLER GROUP INC p 157
8020 Forsyth Blvd 63105
Tel (314) 862-8000
SIC 3565 3535 3554 8711

■ BELDEN 1993 LLC p 169
1 N Brentwood Blvd # 1500 63105
Tel (314) 854-8000 *SIC* 3357

▲ BELDEN INC p 169
1 N Brentwood Blvd # 1500 63105
Tel (314) 854-8000 *SIC* 3357

BETHESDA HEALTH GROUP INC p 178
1630 Des Peres Rd Ste 290 63131
Tel (314) 800-1900 *SIC* 8052

■ BG RETAIL LLC p 180
8300 Maryland Ave 63105
Tel (314) 854-4000 *SIC* 5661

BI-STATE DEVELOPMENT AGENCY OF MISSOURI-ILLINOIS METROPOLITAN DISTRICT (INC) p 181
211 N Broadway Ste 700 63102
Tel (314) 982-1400 *SIC* 4111 4581

BJC HEALTH SYSTEM p 186
4901 Forest Park Ave 63108
Tel (314) 286-2000 *SIC* 8741

BLUE CROSS AND BLUE SHIELD OF MISSOURI INC p 191
1831 Chestnut St 63103
Tel (314) 923-4444 *SIC* 6321

BODINE ALUMINUM INC p 197
2100 Walton Rd 63114
Tel (314) 423-8200 *SIC* 3363

■ BOEING SERVICE CO p 197
6200 J S Mcdonnell Blvd 63134
Tel (972) 705-8000 *SIC* 8741 8711

BOXES OF ST LOUIS INC p 205
1833 Knox Ave 63139
Tel (314) 781-2600 *SIC* 2653

BREADS OF WORLD LLC p 209
2127 Innerbelt Business C 63114
Tel (314) 965-3304 *SIC* 5812 5461

■ BREMNER FOOD GROUP INC p 210
800 Market St Ste 2900 63101
Tel (314) 877-7000 *SIC* 2052

BRYAN CAVE LLP p 221
1 Metropolitan Sq 63102
Tel (314) 259-2000 *SIC* 8111

▲ BUILD-A-BEAR WORKSHOP INC p 224
1954 Innerbelt Bus Ctr Dr 63114
Tel (314) 423-8000 *SIC* 5945 6794

BUNGE MILLING INC p 225
11720 Borman Dr 63146
Tel (314) 292-2000 *SIC* 2041 2075

BUNGE NORTH AMERICA FOUNDATION p 226
11720 Borman Dr 63146
Tel (314) 872-3030
SIC 2075 2079 2048 2834

BUNGE NORTH AMERICA INC p 226
11720 Borman Dr 63146
Tel (314) 292-2000 *SIC* 5153

BUNZL DISTRIBUTION CALIFORNIA LLC p 226
1 Cityplace Dr Ste 200 63141
Tel (888) 997-5959 *SIC* 5113

BUNZL DISTRIBUTION MIDCENTRAL INC p 226
11434 Moog Dr 63146
Tel (314) 569-2800 *SIC* 5199

BUNZL DISTRIBUTION USA LLC p 226
1 Cityplace Dr Ste 200 63141
Tel (314) 997-5959 *SIC* 5131

BUNZL INDUSTRIAL INC p 226
1 Cityplace Dr Ste 200 63141
Tel (314) 997-5959 *SIC* 3089

BUNZL INTERNATIONAL SERVICES INC p 226
1 Cityplace Dr Ste 200 63141
Tel (314) 997-5959 *SIC* 5131

BUNZL USA HOLDINGS LLC p 226
1 Cityplace Dr Ste 200 63141
Tel (314) 997-5959 *SIC* 5162 5113

BUNZL USA INC p 226
1 Cityplace Dr Ste 200 63141
Tel (314) 997-5959 *SIC* 5113 5162 5085

BUSCH AGRICULTURAL RESOURCES LLC p 229
3636 S Geyer Rd Fl 2 63127
Tel (314) 577-2000
SIC 2044 2083 0181 5153

C HAGER & SONS HINGE MANUFACTURING CO p 232
139 Victor St 63104
Tel (314) 772-4400 *SIC* 3429

C L SMITH CO INC p 232
1311 S 39th St 63110
Tel (314) 771-1202 *SIC* 5085

▲ CALERES INC p 238
8300 Maryland Ave 63105
Tel (314) 854-4000 *SIC* 5661 5139

■ CARBOLINE CO p 252
2150 Schuetz Rd 63146
Tel (314) 644-1000 *SIC* 2851

CARPENTERS HEALTH & WELFARE TRUST FUND OF ST LOUIS p 260
1419 Hampton Ave 63139
Tel (314) 644-4802 *SIC* 8631

▲ CASS INFORMATION SYSTEMS INC p 263
12444 Powerscort Dr # 550 63131
Tel (314) 506-5500 *SIC* 7389 7374 6029

CASSIDY TURLEY COMMERCIAL REAL ESTATE SERVICES INC p 264
7700 Forsyth Blvd Ste 900 63105
Tel (314) 862-7100 *SIC* 6531

CATHOLIC CHARITIES OF ST LOUIS p 266
4445 Lindell Blvd 63108
Tel (314) 367-5500 *SIC* 8699 8322

■ CC VIII HOLDINGS LLC p 269
12405 Powerscourt Dr 63131
Tel (314) 543-2411 *SIC* 4841

■ CCH II LLC p 270
12405 Powerscourt Dr 63131
Tel (314) 965-0555 *SIC* 4841

■ CCO HOLDINGS LLC p 270
12405 Powerscourt Dr 63131
Tel (314) 965-0555 *SIC* 4841 4813 7389

■ CCO NR HOLDINGS LLC p 270
12405 Powerscourt Dr 63131
Tel (314) 965-0555 *SIC* 4841

▲ CENTENE CORP p 275
7700 Forsyth Blvd Ste 800 63105
Tel (314) 725-4477 *SIC* 6324 8011 8099

CENTRAL FREIGHT MANAGEMENT LLC p 278
11500 Olive Blvd Ste 276 63141
Tel (314) 428-9900 *SIC* 4213

CEQUEL COMMUNICATIONS HOLDINGS LLC p 283
520 Maryville Centre Dr 63141
Tel (314) 965-0500 *SIC* 4841

CEQUEL COMMUNICATIONS LLC p 283
520 Maryville Centre Dr # 300 63141
Tel (314) 965-2020 *SIC* 4813 4841

CEQUEL CORP p 283
520 Maryville Centre Dr # 300 63141
Tel (314) 315-9400 *SIC* 4841 4813

CEQUEL DATA CENTERS LP p 283
520 Maryville Centre Dr # 300 63141
Tel (314) 965-2020 *SIC* 7374

CHARLES L CRANE AGENCY CO p 289
100 N Broadway Ste 900 63102
Tel (314) 241-8700 *SIC* 6411

■ CHARTER COMMUNICATIONS ENTERTAINMENT II LLC p 290
12405 Powerscourt Dr 63131
Tel (314) 965-0555 *SIC* 4841

■ CHARTER COMMUNICATIONS HOLDING CO LLC p 290
12405 Powerscourt Dr 63131
Tel (314) 965-0555 *SIC* 4841

■ CHARTER COMMUNICATIONS HOLDINGS LLC p 290
12405 Powerscourt Dr 63131
Tel (314) 543-2480 *SIC* 4841 4813

■ CHARTER COMMUNICATIONS LLC p 291
12405 Powerscourt Dr 63131
Tel (314) 288-3478 *SIC* 8748

■ CHARTER COMMUNICATIONS OPERATING LLC p 291
12405 Powerscourt Dr 63131
Tel (314) 965-0555 *SIC* 4841

CHRISTIAN HOSPITAL NORTHEAST - NORTHWEST p 303
11133 Dunn Rd 63136
Tel (314) 355-2300 *SIC* 8062 8322

CHRISTIAN HOSPITAL NORTHEAST SURGERY CENTER p 303
11133 Dunn Rd 63136
Tel (314) 355-2300 *SIC* 8742 8049 5912

CIC GROUP INC p 306
530 Maryville Centre Dr 63141
Tel (314) 682-2900 *SIC* 7692 3542 8741

CITY OF ST LOUIS p 318
1200 Market St Rm 212 63103
Tel (314) 622-3201 *SIC* 9121

CLUB EXCHANGE CORP p 328
12901 N 40 Dr 63141
Tel (314) 523-6976 *SIC* 6331

CODE 3 INC p 333
10986 N Warson Rd 63114
Tel (314) 996-2721 *SIC* 3669 3648

COIN ACCEPTORS INC p 335
300 Hunter Ave 63124
Tel (314) 725-0100 *SIC* 3581

COLOR ART INTEGRATED INTERIORS LLC p 338
1325 N Warson Rd 63132
Tel (314) 432-3000
SIC 5021 7641 5999 5712 5099 2521

■ COMMONWEALTH MUTUAL p 346
12115 Lackland Rd 63146
Tel (314) 644-1255 *SIC* 6411

■ COMPUTATIONAL SYSTEMS INC p 352
8000 W Florissant Ave 63136
Tel (314) 553-2000 *SIC* 3829

CONCORDIA HEALTH PLAN p 355
1333 S Kirkwood Rd 63122
Tel (314) 965-9917 *SIC* 6411

CONCRETE STRATEGIES LLC p 355
2199 Innerbelt Bus Ctr Dr 63114
Tel (314) 595-6300 *SIC* 1791 1799

CORIZON LLC p 370
12647 Olive Blvd Ste 400 63141
Tel (314) 919-8501 *SIC* 8011

CORRIGAN BROTHERS INC p 373
3545 Gratiot St 63103
Tel (314) 771-6200 *SIC* 1711 1761 1623

COUNTY OF ST LOUIS p 382
41 S Central Ave 63105
Tel (314) 615-7016 *SIC* 9111

■ COVENTRY HEALTH CARE OF MISSOURI INC p 385
550 Maryville Centre Dr # 300 63141
Tel (314) 506-1700 *SIC* 6324

■ CRANE MERCHANDISING SYSTEMS INC p 389
2043 Wdlnd Pkwy Ste 102 63146
Tel (314) 298-3500 *SIC* 3589 5087

CRAWFORD GROUP INC p 389
600 Corporate Park Dr 63105
Tel (314) 512-5000 *SIC* 7514 7515

CRESCENT PARTS & EQUIPMENT CO INC p 391
5121 Manchester Ave 63110
Tel (314) 647-5511 *SIC* 5075

CSI LEASING INC p 398
9990 Old Olive Street Rd # 101 63141
Tel (314) 997-4934 *SIC* 7377 5045

■ D & K HEALTHCARE RESOURCES LLC p 406
8235 Forsyth Blvd 63105
Tel (888) 727-3485 *SIC* 5122

DANIEL & HENRY CO p 411
1001 Highlands Plaza Dr W # 500 63110
Tel (314) 421-1525 *SIC* 6411

DAUGHERTY SYSTEMS INC p 414
3 Cityplace Dr Ste 400 63141
Tel (314) 432-8200
SIC 7379 7371 8742 7373 7372

DAUGHTERS OF CHARITY PROVINCE OF ST LOUISE p 414
4330 Olive St 63108
Tel (314) 533-4770 *SIC* 8661 5912

DAVE SINCLAIR FORD WEST p 415
7466 S Lindbergh Blvd 63125
Tel (314) 892-2600
SIC 5511 7538 5521 5012

DELTA DENTAL OF MISSOURI p 426
12399 Gravois Rd Fl 2 63127
Tel (314) 656-3000 *SIC* 6324 6321

■ DES PERES HOSPITAL INC p 431
2345 Dougherty Ferry Rd 63122
Tel (314) 966-9100 *SIC* 8062

DOE RUN RESOURCES CORP p 447
1801 Park 270 Dr Ste 300 63146
Tel (314) 453-7100 *SIC* 1031 1021 3339

DRURY DEVELOPMENT CORP p 457
721 Emerson Rd Ste 200 63141
Tel (314) 423-6698 *SIC* 6512 1542 5812

DRURY HOTELS CO LLC p 457
721 Emerson Rd Ste 400 63141
Tel (314) 429-2255 *SIC* 7011

■ DUCOMMUN LABARGE TECHNOLOGIES INC p 459
689 Craig Rd 200 63141
Tel (314) 997-0800 *SIC* 3812 3699

DUKE MFG PROPERTIES LLC p 460
2224 N 10th St 63102
Tel (800) 735-3853 *SIC* 3589 3556

EAN HOLDINGS LLC p 468
600 Corporate Park Dr 63105
Tel (314) 512-5000 *SIC* 7514 7515

ECI HOLDING INC p 475
1 Cityplace Dr Ste 450 63141
Tel (314) 692-4204 *SIC* 3643

EDWARD D JONES & CO LP p 479
12555 Manchester Rd 63131
Tel (314) 515-2000 *SIC* 6211

ELDER MANUFACTURING CO INC p 484
999 Executive Parkway Dr # 300 63141
Tel (314) 469-1120 *SIC* 2321 2361 2253

ELECTRICAL COMPONENTS INTERNATIONAL INC p 485
1 Cityplace Dr Ste 450 63141
Tel (314) 692-4204 *SIC* 3679

■ EMERSON ELECTRIC (US) HOLDING CORP p 492
850 Library Ave Ste 204c 63136
Tel (314) 553-2000 *SIC* 3824

▲ EMERSON ELECTRIC CO p 492
8000 W Florissant Ave 63136
Tel (314) 553-2000
SIC 3823 3491 3621 3585 3679

■ EMERSON ELECTRIC OVERSEAS FINANCE CORP p 492
8000 W Florissant Ave 63136
Tel (314) 553-2000 *SIC* 6153

■ EMERSON PROCESS MANAGEMENT VALVE AUTOMATION INC p 492
8000 W Florissant Ave 63136
Tel (314) 553-2000 *SIC* 3594 3593

■ EMERSUB 14 LLC p 492
8000 W Florissant Ave 63136
Tel (314) 553-2000 *SIC* 3823

■ ENERGIZER BATTERY INC p 497
533 Maryville Univ Dr 63141
Tel (314) 985-2000 *SIC* 3691

■ ENERGIZER BRANDS LLC p 497
533 Maryville Univ Dr 63141
Tel (314) 985-2000 *SIC* 5063

▲ ENERGIZER HOLDINGS INC p 497
533 Maryville Univ Dr 63141
Tel (314) 985-2000 *SIC* 3691

■ ENTERPRISE BANK & TRUST p 502
150 N Meramec Ave Ste 300 63105
Tel (314) 725-5500 *SIC* 6022

▲ ENTERPRISE FINANCIAL SERVICES CORP p 502
150 N Meramec Ave Ste 350 63105
Tel (314) 725-5500 *SIC* 6022

ENTERPRISE FLEET MANAGEMENT INC p 502
2600 S Hanley Rd Ste 460 63144
Tel (314) 256-5100 *SIC* 7515 7514

ENTERPRISE HOLDINGS INC p 502
600 Corporate Park Dr 63105
Tel (314) 512-5000 *SIC* 7514 7515

■ ESCO TECHNOLOGIES HOLDING LLC p 509
9900 Clayton Rd Ste A 63124
Tel (314) 213-7200
SIC 3825 3492 3812 3711 3663

▲ ESCO TECHNOLOGIES INC p 509
9900 Clayton Rd Ste A 63124
Tel (314) 213-7200 *SIC* 3669 3569 3825

▲ EXPRESS SCRIPTS HOLDING CO p 520
1 Express Way 63121
Tel (314) 996-0900 *SIC* 5912 5961

■ EXPRESS SCRIPTS INC p 520
1 Express Way 63121
Tel (314) 996-0900 *SIC* 5961

■ FALCON CABLE COMMUNICATIONS LLC p 526
12405 Powerscourt Dr 63131
Tel (314) 965-0555 *SIC* 4841

FEDERAL INTERNATIONAL INC p 535
7935 Clayton Rd Ste A 63117
Tel (314) 721-3377 *SIC* 3086 7389

FEDERAL RESERVE BANK OF ST LOUIS p 535
1421 Dr Martin Luther 63106
Tel (314) 444-8444 *SIC* 6011

FIRST BANK p 545
11901 Olive Blvd Stop 1 63141
Tel (314) 995-8700 *SIC* 6036

FIRST BANKS INC p 545
135 N Meramec Ave 63105
Tel (314) 854-4600 *SIC* 6021

■ FLEISHMAN-HILLARD INC p 555
200 N Broadway 63102
Tel (314) 982-1700 *SIC* 8743

▲ FORESIGHT ENERGY LP p 566
211 N Broadway Ste 2600 63102
Tel (314) 932-6160 *SIC* 1221

FORSYTH BALDWIN LLC p 568
8040 Forsyth Blvd 63105
Tel (314) 726-2152 *SIC* 6722

FORSYTH CAPITAL INVESTORS LLC p 568
8040 Forsyth Blvd 63105
Tel (314) 726-2152 *SIC* 6722

FRENCH-GERLEMAN ELECTRIC CO p 578
2023 Westport Center Dr 63146
Tel (314) 569-3122 *SIC* 5063

FURNITURE BRANDS INTERNATIONAL INC p 585
1 N Brentwood Blvd # 700 63105
Tel (314) 863-1100 *SIC* 2511 2512 2515

FUSION PERFORMANCE MARKETING LLC p 585
1928 Locust St 63103
Tel (314) 576-7500 *SIC* 8742

▲ FUTUREFUEL CORP p 586
8235 Forsyth Blvd 4 63105
Tel (314) 854-8385 *SIC* 2819

G K N AEROSPACE NORTH AMERICA INC p 587
142 Js Mcdonnell Blvd 63135
Tel (314) 264-3000 *SIC* 3812 3728

G P & W INC p 587
600 Mason Ridge Center Dr # 2 63141
Tel (314) 682-3500 *SIC* 5172

GATEWAY REGION YOUNG MENS CHRISTIAN ASSOCIATION p 594
326 S 21st St Ste 400 63103
Tel (314) 436-1177 *SIC* 8641 8741 8322

■ GENERAL AMERICAN LIFE INSURANCE CO p 599
13045 Tesson Ferry Rd 63128
Tel (314) 843-8700 *SIC* 6411 6311

■ GENERAL AMERICAN MUTUAL HOLDING CO p 599
700 Market St 63101
Tel (314) 231-1700 *SIC* 6311

GL GROUP INC p 613
5111 Southwest Ave 63110
Tel (314) 647-0600 *SIC* 5192 2789

GLASS GALLERY LTD p 614
10300 Lake Bluff Dr 63123
Tel (314) 416-4200 *SIC* 5947 5199

GRAYBAR ELECTRIC CO INC p 632
34 N Meramec Ave 63105
Tel (314) 573-9200 *SIC* 5063 5065

GROSSMAN IRON AND STEEL CO p 641
5 N Market St 63102
Tel (314) 231-9423 *SIC* 5093

GUARANTEE ELECTRICAL CO p 644
3405 Bent Ave 63116
Tel (314) 772-5400 *SIC* 1731

HARBOUR GROUP LTD p 660
7701 Forsyth Blvd Ste 600 63105
Tel (314) 727-5550 *SIC* 3823

HARDEES RESTAURANTS LLC p 660
100 N Broadway Ste 1200 63102
Tel (314) 259-6200 *SIC* 5812

HBE CORP p 671
11330 Olive Blvd 63141
Tel (314) 567-9000 *SIC* 1542 8742

HERMANN COMPANIES INC p 687
7701 Forsyth Blvd # 1000 63105
Tel (314) 863-9200 *SIC* 3086

HIMAGINE SOLUTIONS INC p 695
600 Emerson Rd Ste 225 63141
Tel (314) 627-5135 *SIC* 8741 7361

HOK GROUP INC p 699
10 S Broadway Ste 200 63102
Tel (314) 421-2000 *SIC* 8711 8712 8742

HOK INC p 699
10 S Broadway Ste 200 63102
Tel (314) 421-2000 *SIC* 0781 8712 8711

HOUSE OF TOOLS AND ENGINEERING INC p 711
2021 Congressional Dr 63146
Tel (314) 731-4444 *SIC* 5084

▲ HUTTIG BUILDING PRODUCTS INC p 722
555 Maryville University 63141
Tel (314) 216-2600 *SIC* 5031 5033

ICE CREAM SPECIALTIES INC p 727
8419 Hanley Industrial Ct 63144
Tel (314) 962-2550 *SIC* 2024

ICL NORTH AMERICA INC p 727
622 Emerson Rd Ste 500 63141
Tel (314) 983-7500 *SIC* 2819

ICL PERFORMANCE PRODUCTS LP p 727
622 Emerson Rd Ste 500 63141
Tel (314) 983-7500 *SIC* 2819

■ ILLINOIS POWER RESOURCES LLC p 732
1901 Chouteau Ave 63103
Tel (314) 554-4110 *SIC* 4911

INDOFF INC p 739
11816 Lackland Rd Ste 200 63146
Tel (314) 997-1122 *SIC* 5021 5044 5084

INTERSTATE CLEANING CORP p 758
1566 N Warson Rd 63132
Tel (314) 428-0566 *SIC* 7349

▲ ISLE OF CAPRI CASINOS INC p 767
600 Emerson Rd Ste 300 63141
Tel (314) 813-9200 *SIC* 7011 7948

ITALGRANI USA INC p 767
7900 Van Buren St 63111
Tel (314) 638-1447 *SIC* 2041 5153

J H BERRA HOLDING CO INC p 771
5091 Baumgartner Rd 63129
Tel (314) 487-5617 *SIC* 6552

J S LEASING CO INC p 772
1441 Hampton Ave 63139
Tel (314) 647-7529 *SIC* 7359

■ JACOBS FACILITIES INC p 775
501 N Broadway 63102
Tel (314) 335-4000
SIC 8712 8711 8713 8741 1542 1541

JIH TRUCKING LLC p 785
1041 Camelot Gardens Dr 63125
Tel (314) 487-7159 *SIC* 4212 4213

JOHN M QUALY p 789
701 Market St Ste 1070 63101
Tel (314) 231-3931 *SIC* 6411 6311

JONES FINANCIAL COMPANIES LLLP p 792
12555 Manchester Rd 63131
Tel (314) 515-2000 *SIC* 6211 6411 6163

JOST CHEMICAL CO p 794
8150 Lackland Rd 63114
Tel (314) 428-4300 *SIC* 2834 2819

JUNIOR COLLEGE DISTRICT OF ST LOUIS p 797
300 S Broadway 63102
Tel (314) 206-2150 *SIC* 8222

▲ KATY INDUSTRIES INC p 805
11840 Westline Industrial 63146
Tel (314) 656-4321 *SIC* 3589 2673

KCI CONSTRUCTION CO p 806
10315 Lake Bluff Dr 63123
Tel (314) 894-8888 *SIC* 1542 1611 1629

KEEFE GROUP LLC p 807
10880 Linpage Pl 63132
Tel (314) 963-8700 *SIC* 7389

KELLY MITCHELL GROUP INC p 809
8229 Maryland Ave 63105
Tel (314) 727-1700 *SIC* 7371 7373

KIRKWOOD R-VII SCHOOL DISTRICT p 822
11289 Manchester Rd 63122
Tel (314) 213-6100 *SIC* 8211

KORTE CONSTRUCTION CO p 828
5700 Oakland Ave Ste 275 63110
Tel (314) 231-3700 *SIC* 1541 1542

L KEELEY CONSTRUCTION CO p 834
500 S Ewing Ave Ste G 63103
Tel (314) 421-5933 *SIC* 1541 1611 1623

■ LACLEDE GAS CO p 837
700 Market St 63101
Tel (314) 342-0878 *SIC* 4924

LIEBEL-FLARSHEIM CO LLC p 863
1034 S Brentwood Blvd 63117
Tel (314) 654-8625 *SIC* 1541

LINCOLN INDUSTRIAL CORP p 867
5148 N Hanley Rd 63134
Tel (314) 679-4200
SIC 3569 3559 3561 3714

LIONMARK CONSTRUCTION COMPANIES LLC p 870
1620 Woodson Rd 63114
Tel (314) 991-2180 SIC 1611 2951 1622

LOHR DISTRIBUTING CO INC p 875
1100 S 9th St 63104
Tel (314) 436-8299 SIC 5181

LOU FUSZ AUTOMOTIVE NETWORK INC p 879
925 N Lindbergh Blvd 63141
Tel (314) 997-3400 SIC 5511 5531 5521

LOU FUSZ MOTOR CO p 879
10329 Old Olive Street Rd 63141
Tel (314) 994-1500 SIC 5511 7514

LUTHERAN CHURCH - MISSOURI SYNOD p 886
1333 S Kirkwood Rd 63122
Tel (314) 965-9000 SIC 8661

LUTHERAN SENIOR SERVICES p 886
1150 Hanley Industrial Ct 63144
Tel (314) 968-9313 SIC 8361

MAJOR BRANDS INC p 899
6701 Southwest Ave 63143
Tel (314) 645-1843 SIC 5182 5181

MAR-CONE APPLIANCE PARTS CO p 904
1 Cityplace Dr Ste 400 63141
Tel (877) 993-9196 SIC 5064

MC INDUSTRIAL INC p 925
3117 S Big Bend Blvd 63143
Tel (314) 646-4100 SIC 1541

MCCARTHY BUILDING COMPANIES INC p 926
1341 N Rock Hill Rd 63124
Tel (314) 968-3300 SIC 1542 1541

MCCARTHY HOLDINGS INC p 926
1341 N Rock Hill Rd 63124
Tel (314) 968-3300 SIC 1542 1541

MCCARTHY STRAUB JV I p 926
1341 N Rock Hill Rd 63124
Tel (314) 646-4189 SIC 1542

MEDICAL WEST RESPIRATORY SVCS LLC p 937
9301 Dielman Indus Dr 63132
Tel (314) 993-8100 SIC 5047 8082

MEHLVILLE R-IX SCHOOL DISTRICT p 940
3120 Lemay Ferry Rd 63125
Tel (314) 892-5000 SIC 8211

MERCY HOSPITALS EAST COMMUNITIES p 947
615 S New Ballas Rd 63141
Tel (417) 820-2000 SIC 8062

MERCY MEDICAL GROUP p 948
12800 Corporate Hill Dr 63131
Tel (888) 700-7171 SIC 8011

MERS/MISSOURI GOODWILL INDUSTRIES p 951
1727 Locust St 63103
Tel (314) 241-3464 SIC 8331

METAL CONTAINER CORP p 952
3636 S Geyer Rd Ste 400 63127
Tel (314) 577-2000 SIC 3411

METAL EXCHANGE CORP p 952
111 West Port Plz Ste 350 63146
Tel (314) 542-7250 SIC 3334 5093

METROPOLITAN ST LOUIS SEWER DISTRICT p 956
2350 Market St Ste 300 63103
Tel (314) 768-6200 SIC 4952

MID-CONTINENT PAPER AND DISTRIBUTING CO INC p 963
11809 Borman Dr 63146
Tel (314) 989-0894 SIC 5113

■ **MIDDENDORF MEAT CO LLC** p 964
3737 N Broadway 63147
Tel (314) 241-4800
SIC 5147 5141 5148 5146 5113 2011

MIDWEST GERIATRIC MANAGEMENT LLC p 967
477 N Lindbergh Blvd # 310 63141
Tel (314) 631-3000 SIC 8741

MIDWEST PETROLEUM CO p 967
6760 Southwest Ave 63143
Tel (314) 647-5550 SIC 5541

MILLMAN LUMBER CO p 971
9264 Manchester Rd 63144
Tel (314) 961-6195 SIC 5031

MISSISSIPPI LIME CO p 975
3870 S Lindbergh Blvd # 200 63127
Tel (314) 543-6300
SIC 3274 2819 2879 1422

MISSISSIPPI VALLEY BANCSHARES INC p 976
13205 Manchester Rd 63131
Tel (314) 543-3512 SIC 6022 6712

MISSOURI BAPTIST MEDICAL CENTER p 976
3015 N Ballas Rd 63131
Tel (314) 996-5000 SIC 8062

MISSOURI FOUNDATION FOR HEALTH p 976
415 S 18th St Ste 400 63103
Tel (314) 345-5500 SIC 8399

MISSOURI PETROLEUM PRODUCTS CO LLC p 976
1620 Woodson Rd 63114
Tel (314) 219-7305 SIC 5033 1611 2951

▲ **MONSANTO CO** p 985
800 N Lindbergh Blvd 63167
Tel (314) 694-1000 SIC 2879 0181

MURPHY CO MECHANICAL CONTRACTORS AND ENGINEERS p 1001
1233 N Price Rd 63132
Tel (314) 997-6600 SIC 1711

NAG LLC p 1006
1260 Andes Blvd 63132
Tel (314) 214-2700 SIC 5149

NESTLE PURINA PETCARE CO p 1027
901 Chouteau Ave 63102
Tel (314) 982-1000 SIC 2047

■ **NEW STAR HOLDINGS INTERNATIONAL INC** p 1033
10 Sunnen Dr 63143
Tel (800) 264-7827 SIC 3589

NIDEC AMERICAS HOLDING CORP p 1043
8050 W Florissant Ave 63136
Tel (314) 595-8000 SIC 3625 3594 6719

NIDEC MOTOR CORP p 1043
8050 W Florissant Ave 63136
Tel (314) 595-8000 SIC 3625 3594

■ **NIES/ARTCRAFT INC** p 1043
3049 Chouteau Ave 63103
Tel (314) 951-0400 SIC 2752

NISA INVESTMENT ADVISORS INC p 1044
101 S Hanley Rd Ste 1700 63105
Tel (314) 721-1900 SIC 6722 6282

NOOTER CONSTRUCTION CO p 1047
1500 S 2nd St 63104
Tel (314) 621-6000 SIC 1541

NOOTER CORP p 1047
1500 S 2nd St 63104
Tel (314) 421-7200
SIC 3443 3479 1796 8711 7699 1542

NU WAY CONCRETE FORMS INC p 1066
4190 Hoffmeister Ave 63125
Tel (573) 893-8786
SIC 5032 5051 5072 7359

▲ **OLIN CORP** p 1082
190 Carondelet Plz # 1530 63105
Tel (314) 480-1400
SIC 2812 2819 2821 2842 2869 2891

■ **OLIN SUNBELT II INC** p 1082
190 Carondelet Plz # 1530 63105
Tel (314) 480-1400 SIC 2812

■ **OUTSOURCE GROUP INC** p 1099
3 Cityplace Dr Ste 690 63141
Tel (314) 692-6500 SIC 7322

PACKAGING CONCEPTS INC p 1106
9832 Evergreen Indus Dr 63123
Tel (314) 329-9700 SIC 5113 2674 2671

▲ **PANERA BREAD CO** p 1111
3630 S Geyer Rd Ste 100 63127
Tel (314) 984-1000 SIC 5812 5461 6794

■ **PARADISE BAKERY & CAFES INC** p 1113
3630 S Geyer Rd Ste 400 63127
Tel (480) 889-5347 SIC 5812

PARIC CORP p 1114
77 West Port Plz Ste 250 63146
Tel (636) 561-9500 SIC 1542 1541

PASTA HOUSE CO p 1120
700 N New Ballas Rd 63141
Tel (314) 535-6644 SIC 5812 5813

PAULO PRODUCTS CO p 1121
5711 W Park Ave 63110
Tel (314) 647-7500
SIC 3471 3398 8734 3567

PAYNECREST ELECTRIC INC p 1122
10411 Baur Blvd 63132
Tel (314) 996-0400 SIC 1731

PEABODY COAL CO p 1125
701 Market St 63101
Tel (314) 342-3400 SIC 1222 1221

PEABODY COALSALES LLC p 1125
701 Market St Fl 9 63101
Tel (314) 342-3400 SIC 5052

PEABODY ENERGY CORP p 1125
701 Market St 63101
Tel (314) 342-3400 SIC 1221 1222

PEABODY HOLDING CO LLC p 1125
701 Market St Ste 700 63101
Tel (314) 342-3400
SIC 1221 1222 5052 2873 6719

PEABODY INVESTMENTS CORP p 1125
701 Market St 63101
Tel (314) 342-3400 SIC 6211

PEABODY NATURAL RESOURCES CO p 1125
701 Market St Ste 700 63101
Tel (314) 342-3400 SIC 1221

▲ **PERFICIENT INC** p 1135
555 Maryville Univ Dr 6 63141
Tel (314) 529-3600 SIC 7371

■ **PETROLITE CORP** p 1139
369 Marshall Ave 63119
Tel (314) 961-3500
SIC 3559 2999 2899 2821 2911

■ **POLYONE DESIGNED STRUCTURES AND SOLUTIONS LLC** p 1160
11650 Lkeside Crossing Ct 63105
Tel (888) 721-4242 SIC 5199

▲ **POST HOLDINGS INC** p 1163
2503 S Hanley Rd 63144
Tel (314) 644-7600
SIC 2015 2034 2038 2041 2099

■ **PRECOAT METALS** p 1169
1310 Papin St Ste 300 63103
Tel (314) 436-7010 SIC 3479

PRESIDENT CASINOS INC p 1172
1000 N Lnor K Sllvan Blvd 63102
Tel (314) 622-3000 SIC 6799

PRINCIPIA CORP p 1177
13201 Clayton Rd 63131
Tel (314) 434-2100 SIC 8211 8221

PROVISION LIVING LLC p 1187
1630 Des Peres Rd Ste 310 63131
Tel (314) 238-3800 SIC 6531

PUBLIC SAFETY EQUIPMENT INC p 1189
10986 N Warson Rd 63114
Tel (314) 426-2700 SIC 3647 3669

PULITZER INC p 1191
900 N Tucker Blvd 63101
Tel (314) 340-8000 SIC 2711 4833 4832

■ **PULITZER INC** p 1191
900 N Tucker Blvd 63101
Tel (314) 340-8000 SIC 2711

PURINA MILLS LLC p 1192
555 Maryvle Univ Dr 200 63141
Tel (877) 454-7094 SIC 2048 2047

QRS INC p 1195
345 Marshall Ave Ste 301 63119
Tel (314) 963-8000 SIC 4953

■ **RAWLINGS SPORTING GOODS CO INC** p 1209
510 Maryville University 63141
Tel (866) 678-4327 SIC 3949 5091

■ **REHABCARE HOSPITAL HOLDINGS LLC** p 1220
7733 Forsyth Blvd # 2300 63105
Tel (800) 677-1238 SIC 8093

ROBERT FAMILY HOLDINGS INC p 1241
12430 Tesson Ferry Rd 63128
Tel (314) 821-5665
SIC 2671 3572 3491 3498 7699 3494

ROYAL VENDORS INC p 1254
300 Hunter Ave Fl 2 63124
Tel (304) 728-7056 SIC 3581

S M WILSON & CO p 1262
2185 Hampton Ave 63139
Tel (314) 645-9595 SIC 1541 1542

SAFETY NATIONAL CASUALTY CORP p 1266
1832 Schuetz Rd 63146
Tel (314) 995-5300 SIC 6331

SAINT LOUIS UNIVERSITY p 1270
1 N Grand Blvd 63103
Tel (314) 977-2500 SIC 8221

SBI INC p 1285
8500 Valcour Ave 63123
Tel (314) 615-2000
SIC 5199 5122 7334 5084

SCHAEFFER MFG CO p 1286
102 Barton St 63104
Tel (314) 865-4100 SIC 2992 2879

SCHNUCK MARKETS INC p 1288
11420 Lackland Rd 63146
Tel (314) 994-9900
SIC 5411 5912 5812 7841

SCOTTRADE BANK p 1294
12800 Corp Hill Dr 63131
Tel (314) 965-1555 SIC 6035

SCOTTRADE INC p 1294
12800 Corporate Hill Dr 63131
Tel (314) 965-1555 SIC 6211

■ **SENSIENT COLORS LLC** p 1304
2515 N Jefferson Ave 63106
Tel (314) 889-7600 SIC 2816

SHAPIRO SALES CO p 1312
9666 Olive Blvd Ste 500 63132
Tel (314) 381-9300 SIC 5093 4953

SHAUGHNESSY-KNIEP-HAWE-PAPER CO p 1312
2355 Ball Dr 63146
Tel (314) 810-8100 SIC 5111

■ **SHOP N SAVE WAREHOUSE FOODS INC** p 1318
10461 Manchester Rd 63122
Tel (314) 984-0322 SIC 5411

SIGMA - ALDRICH CO LLC p 1321
3050 Spruce St 63103
Tel (314) 771-5765 SIC 2899 5169

SIGMA CHEMICAL CORP p 1321
3050 Spruce St 63103
Tel (314) 771-5765 SIC 2836 2869

SIGMA-ALDRICH CORP p 1321
3050 Spruce St 63103
Tel (314) 771-5765 SIC 2899 5169 8099

SIGNATURE MEDICAL GROUP INC p 1322
12639 Old Tesson Rd # 115 63128
Tel (314) 849-0311 SIC 8011

SLAY TRANSPORTATION CO INC p 1331
1441 Hampton Ave 63139
Tel (314) 647-7529 SIC 4213

SMI-FUEL LLC p 1333
11420 Lackland Rd 63146
Tel (314) 994-9900 SIC 5172

■ **SOLAE LLC** p 1337
4300 Duncan Ave 63110
Tel (314) 659-3000 SIC 2075 2076

■ **SOLUTIA INC** p 1339
575 Maryville Centre Dr 63141
Tel (423) 229-2000
SIC 2824 2821 3081 2869

SPARTECH CORP p 1355
120 S Central Ave # 1700 63105
Tel (314) 721-4242 SIC 3081 2821 3089

SPECIAL SCHOOL DISTRICT OF ST LOUIS COUNTY p 1356
12110 Clayton Rd 63131
Tel (314) 989-8100 SIC 8211

▲ **SPIRE INC** p 1359
700 Market St 63101
Tel (314) 342-0500 SIC 4924

SSM CARDINAL GLENNON CHILDRENS HOSPITAL p 1364
1465 S Grand Blvd 63104
Tel (314) 577-5600 SIC 8069

SSM HEALTH CARE CORP p 1364
10101 Woodfield Ln # 100 63132
Tel (314) 994-7800
SIC 8062 8082 8011 8051

ST ANTHONYS MEDICAL CENTER p 1364
10010 Kennerly Rd 63128
Tel (314) 525-1000 SIC 8062

ST JOHNS MERCY HEALTH CARE p 1367
645 Maryville Centre Dr # 100 63141
Tel (314) 364-2400 SIC 8741

ST LOUIS CHILDRENS HOSPITAL p 1369
1 Childrens Pl 63110
Tel (314) 454-6000 SIC 8069

ST LOUIS COMMUNITY COLLEGE p 1369
5600 Oakland Ave 63110
Tel (314) 644-9100 SIC 8222

ST LOUIS ELECTRIC SUPPLY INC p 1369
6801 Hoffman Ave 63139
Tel (314) 645-9000 SIC 5063 5719

■ **ST LOUIS POST-DISPATCH LLC** p 1369
900 N Tucker Blvd 63101
Tel (314) 340-8000 SIC 2711

ST LOUIS PUBLIC SCHOOLS p 1370
801 N 11th St 63101
Tel (314) 231-3720 SIC 8211

ST MARYS HEALTH CENTER p 1371
6420 Clayton Rd 63117
Tel (228) 233-4998 SIC 8099

■ **STAR INTERNATIONAL HOLDINGS INC** p 1378
10 Sunnen Dr 63143
Tel (314) 781-2777 SIC 3589

▲ **STIFEL FINANCIAL CORP** p 1389
501 N Broadway 63102
Tel (314) 342-2000 SIC 6211 6719

■ **STIFEL NICOLAUS & CO INC** p 1389
501 N Broadway 63102
Tel (314) 342-2000 SIC 6211

STUPP BROS INC p 1395
3800 Weber Rd 63125
Tel (314) 638-5000 SIC 3441 3317 6022

SUMNER GROUP INC p 1399
6717 Waldemar Ave 63139
Tel (314) 633-8000 SIC 5044 7699 5112

SUNNEN PRODUCTS CO p 1403
7910 Manchester Rd 63143
Tel (314) 781-2100 SIC 3549 3541

SWAN SURFACES LLC p 1411
515 Olive St Ste 900 63101
Tel (314) 231-8148 SIC 2541 5722 3431

SYSTEMS DRS SUSTAINMENT INC p 1418
201 Evans Ln 63121
Tel (314) 553-4000
SIC 3715 3537 3812 3829 3769

■ **TALX CORP** p 1423
11432 Lackland Rd 63146
Tel (314) 214-7000 SIC 7373 7379 7389

TECH L ENTERPRISES INC p 1431
7701 Forsyth Blvd Ste 600 63105
Tel (314) 727-5550 SIC 5063

THOMPSON COBURN LLP p 1449
505 N 7th St Ste 2700 63101
Tel (314) 552-6000 SIC 8111

TIAA-CREF TRUST CO FSB p 1452
1 Metropolitan Sq 63102
Tel (314) 588-9738 SIC 7389 6282

TIERPOINT LLC p 1453
520 Maryville Centre Dr # 300 63141
Tel (314) 594-1300 SIC 7374

TIERPOINT SPOKANE ONE & TWO LLC p 1453
520 Maryville Centre Dr 63141
Tel (314) 315-9372 SIC 6719

■ **TOTAL FILTRATION SERVICES INC** p 1463
2071 Congressional Dr 63146
Tel (314) 202-3635 SIC 7699

■ **TREEHOUSE PRIVATE BRANDS INC** p 1475
800 Market St 63101
Tel (314) 877-7300
SIC 2043 2052 2068 2035

TRIAD CATALOG CO LLC p 1478
1100 N Lindbergh Blvd 63132
Tel (314) 812-5200 SIC 5961

TRICORBRAUN INC p 1479
6 Cityplace Dr Ste 100 63141
Tel (314) 569-3633 SIC 5085

TRIDENT STEEL CORP p 1480
12825 Flushing Meadows Dr # 110 63131
Tel (314) 822-0500 SIC 5051

TROVERCO INC p 1485
727 N 1st St 63102
Tel (800) 468-3354 SIC 2099 5149

TSI HOLDING CO p 1489
999 Exectve Pkwy Dr # 202 63141
Tel (314) 628-6000 *SIC* 5094 5051

■ TUBULAR STEEL INC p 1490
1031 Executive Parkway Dr 63141
Tel (314) 851-9200 *SIC* 5051

■ UNION ELECTRIC CO p 1504
1901 Chouteau Ave 63103
Tel (314) 621-3222 *SIC* 4931

■ UNION ELECTRIC DEVELOPMENT CORP p 1504
1901 Chouteau Ave 63103
Tel (618) 234-3523 *SIC* 4911 4924

■ UNION NATIONAL LIFE INSURANCE CO p 1504
12115 Lackland Rd 63146
Tel (877) 710-5081 *SIC* 6311

UNITED INDUSTRIES INC p 1509
55 Produce Row 63102
Tel (314) 621-9440 *SIC* 5148

■ UNITED INSURANCE CO OF AMERICA p 1509
12115 Lackland Rd 63146
Tel (314) 819-4300 *SIC* 6411 6321 6331

UNIVERSITY OF MISSOURI AT SAINT LOUIS p 1523
1 University Blvd 63121
Tel (314) 516-5000 *SIC* 8221

■ UTILIMAP CORP p 1537
10025 Office Center Ave 63128
Tel (636) 533-0472 *SIC* 7389

VATTEROTT EDUCATIONAL CENTERS INC p 1545
7730 Carondelet Ave # 400 63105
Tel (314) 264-1500 *SIC* 8249

VECTRA CO p 1546
120 S Central Ave Ste 200 63105
Tel (314) 797-8600 *SIC* 2819

VERNON L GOEDECKE CO INC p 1551
812 E Taylor Ave 63147
Tel (314) 652-1810 *SIC* 5082 5085

VI-JON INC p 1554
8515 Page Ave 63114
Tel (314) 427-1000 *SIC* 2869 2844

■ VIASYSTEMS GROUP INC p 1554
101 S Hanley Rd Ste 400 63105
Tel (314) 727-2087 *SIC* 3672 3694

■ VIASYSTEMS INC p 1554
520 Maryville Centre Dr # 400 63141
Tel (314) 727-2087 *SIC* 3672

VILLA LIGHTING SUPPLY INC p 1557
2929 Chouteau Ave 63103
Tel (314) 531-2600 *SIC* 5063

VJCS HOLDINGS INC p 1563
8515 Page Ave 63114
Tel (314) 427-1000 *SIC* 6719 2844

WASHINGTON UNIVERSITY p 1579
1 Brookings Dr 63130
Tel (314) 935-8566 *SIC* 8221

WATLOW ELECTRIC MANUFACTURING CO p 1582
12001 Lackland Rd 63146
Tel (314) 878-4600 *SIC* 3699

WATLOW ELECTRIC MANUFACTURING HOLDINGS CO p 1582
12001 Lackland Rd 63146
Tel (314) 878-4600 *SIC* 6719

WEBSTER UNIVERSITY p 1587
470 E Lockwood Ave 63119
Tel (314) 968-6900 *SIC* 8221

■ WELLS FARGO ADVISORS LLC p 1590
1 N Jefferson Ave 63103
Tel (314) 955-3000 *SIC* 6211

WESTERN CONSTRUCTION GROUP INC p 1597
1637 N Warson Rd 63132
Tel (314) 427-1637
SIC 1799 1761 1741 1771

WESTERN DIESEL SERVICES INC p 1598
1100 Research Blvd 63132
Tel (314) 868-8620 *SIC* 5084 7538

WESTERN WATERPROOFING CO INC p 1600
1637 N Warson Rd 63132
Tel (314) 427-5461
SIC 1799 1761 1741 1771

WHELAN SECURITY CO p 1605
1699 S Hanley Rd Ste 350 63144
Tel (314) 644-3227 *SIC* 7382

WIESE HOLDING CO p 1608
1445 Woodson Rd 63132
Tel (314) 997-4444 *SIC* 5084 7359

WIESE MATERIAL HANDLING INC p 1608
1435 Woodson Rd 63132
Tel (314) 997-4210 *SIC* 5084

WILLERT HOME PRODUCTS INC p 1610
4044 Park Ave 63110
Tel (314) 772-2822
SIC 3089 2869 2879 2842

WINTER GARDEN PRESERVATION LP p 1617
5708 Kingsbury Pl 63112
Tel (314) 361-0251 *SIC* 6513

▲ WORLD POINT TERMINALS LP p 1625
8235 Forsyth Blvd Ste 400 63105
Tel (314) 889-9660 *SIC* 5171

WORLD WIDE TECHNOLOGY HOLDING CO INC p 1625
60 Weldon Pkwy 63101
Tel (314) 919-1400 *SIC* 5045 5065 8748

■ XTRA COMPANIES INC p 1633
7911 Forsyth Blvd Ste 600 63105
Tel (636) 207-6761 *SIC* 7513

■ XTRA CORP p 1633
7911 Forsyth Blvd Ste 600 63105
Tel (314) 719-0300 *SIC* 7359

■ XTRA LEASE LLC p 1633
7911 Forsyth Blvd Ste 600 63105
Tel (800) 325-1453 *SIC* 7513

■ XTRA LLC p 1633
7911 Forsyth Blvd Ste 600 63105
Tel (314) 719-0400 *SIC* 7513

SAINT PETERS, MO

BARNES-JEWISH ST PETERS HOSPITAL INC p 156
10 Hospital Dr 63376
Tel (636) 916-9000 *SIC* 8062

PROGRESSIVE BALLOONS INC p 1181
3100 Industrial Park Pl W 63376
Tel (636) 240-0444 *SIC* 5092

■ SUN EDISON p 1400
501 Pearl Dr 63376
Tel (636) 474-5000 *SIC* 3674

SUNEDISON INTERNATIONAL INC p 1402
501 Pearl Dr 63376
Tel (636) 474-5000 *SIC* 3559

WAINWRIGHT INDUSTRIES INC p 1571
114 Piper Hill Dr Ste 201 63376
Tel (636) 327-8292 *SIC* 3469 3728 3544

WOODBRIDGE CORP p 1622
11 Cermak Blvd 63376
Tel (636) 970-1002 *SIC* 2439

SALEM, MO

TOWN AND COUNTRY SUPER MARKET INC p 1464
1104 E Highway 32 65560
Tel (573) 729-2325 *SIC* 5411

SCOTT CITY, MO

HAVCO WOOD PRODUCTS LLC p 668
3200 E Outer Rd 63780
Tel (573) 334-0611 *SIC* 2426

SEDALIA, MO

PROENERGY SERVICES LLC p 1180
2001 Proenergy Blvd 65301
Tel (660) 829-5100 *SIC* 1629

WATERLOO HOLDINGS INC p 1582
1500 Waterloo Dr 65301
Tel (660) 826-0960 *SIC* 3429 6719

WATERLOO HOLDINGS LLC p 1582
1500 Waterloo Dr 65301
Tel (660) 826-0960 *SIC* 6719

WATERLOO INDUSTRIES INC p 1582
1500 Waterloo Dr 65301
Tel (660) 826-0960 *SIC* 3429

SIKESTON, MO

CIRCLE B ENTERPRISES HOLDING CO INC p 308
731 N Main St Ste 106 63801
Tel (573) 471-1276 *SIC* 8059

FOOD GIANT SUPERMARKETS INC p 564
120 Industrial Dr 63801
Tel (573) 471-3500 *SIC* 5411

HEALTH FACILITIES MANAGEMENT CORP p 674
731 N Main St 63801
Tel (573) 471-1276 *SIC* 6531

HEALTH SYSTEMS INC p 676
1220 N Main St 63801
Tel (573) 481-9625 *SIC* 6321 8011 8322

MISSOURI DELTA MEDICAL CENTER p 976
1008 N Main St 63801
Tel (573) 471-1600 *SIC* 8062

RH MONTGOMERY PROPERTIES INC p 1231
214 N Scott St 63801
Tel (573) 471-1113 *SIC* 6512

SIKESTON BOARD OF MUNICIPAL UTILITIES p 1322
107 E Malone Ave 63801
Tel (573) 471-5000 *SIC* 4911 1623

TELECOMMUNICATIONS MANAGEMENT LLC p 1434
1 Montgomery Plz Fl 4 63801
Tel (573) 481-2420 *SIC* 4899

SMITHVILLE, MO

SAINT LUKES NORTHLAND HOME CARE p 1270
601 S Us Highway 169 64089
Tel (816) 532-3700
SIC 8062 8051 8069 8063

SPRINGFIELD, MO

ALTERNATIVE OPPORTUNITIES INC p 62
1111 S Glenstone Ave 3-100 65804
Tel (417) 869-8911 *SIC* 8322

■ AMERICAN NATIONAL PROPERTY AND CASUALTY CO p 77
1949 E Snshine Corp Cntre 65804
Tel (417) 887-0220 *SIC* 6411

■ AMERICAN NATIONAL PROPERTY AND CASUALTY INSURANCE CO p 77
1949 E Snshine Corp Cntre 65899
Tel (417) 887-0220 *SIC* 6411

ASSOCIATED ELECTRIC COOPERATIVE INC p 120
2814 S Golden Ave 65807
Tel (417) 881-1204 *SIC* 4911

ATRIUM HOTELS INC p 129
300 S John Q Hammons Pkwy # 900 65806
Tel (417) 864-4300 *SIC* 7011

BASS PRO GROUP LLC p 159
2500 E Kearney St 65898
Tel (417) 873-5000 *SIC* 5941

BASS PRO LLC p 159
2500 E Kearney St 65898
Tel (417) 873-5000
SIC 5961 5941 5551 5661

BKD LLP p 186
910 E Saint Louis St # 400 65806
Tel (417) 865-8701 *SIC* 8721

CITY OF SPRINGFIELD p 318
840 N Boonville Ave 65802
Tel (417) 864-1000 *SIC* 9111

CITY UTILITIES OF SPRINGFIELD MO p 320
301 E Central St 65802
Tel (417) 863-9000 *SIC* 4924 4941

■ COMMERCE BANK (MO) p 345
1345 E Battlefield St 65804
Tel (417) 869-5411 *SIC* 6021

COMMUNITY COLLEGE DISTRICT OF CENTRAL SW MO p 348
1001 E Chestnut Expy 65802
Tel (417) 447-7500 *SIC* 8222 8221

CONVOY OF HOPE p 365
330 S Patterson Ave # 100 65802
Tel (417) 823-8998 *SIC* 8322

DAIRICONCEPTS LP p 408
3253 E Chestnut Expy 65802
Tel (417) 829-3400 *SIC* 2022

DIGITAL MONITORING PRODUCTS INC p 439
2500 N Partnership Blvd 65803
Tel (417) 831-9362 *SIC* 3669

▲ GREAT SOUTHERN BANCORP INC p 634
1451 E Battlefield St 65804
Tel (417) 887-4400 *SIC* 6022

HAMMONS INC p 656
300 S John Q Hammons Pkwy # 900 65806
Tel (417) 864-4300 *SIC* 7011

HEALTHCARE SERVICES OF OZARKS INC p 676
3660 S National Ave 65807
Tel (417) 882-4170 *SIC* 7363 8082

HILAND DAIRY FOODS CO LLC p 692
1133 E Kearney St 65803
Tel (417) 862-9311
SIC 2026 2024 2037 5143

HUTCHENS INDUSTRIES INC p 721
215 N Patterson Ave 65802
Tel (417) 862-5012 *SIC* 3714

INTERNAL MEDICINE GROUP FREMONT p 754
1965 S Fremont Ave # 350 65804
Tel (417) 820-3128 *SIC* 8011

JOHN Q HAMMONS HOTELS MANAGEMENT LLC p 789
300 S John Q Hammons Pkwy # 900 65806
Tel (471) 864-7333 *SIC* 7011

JOHN Q HAMMONS RVOC TR 12281989 p 789
300 S John Q Hammons Pkwy # 9 65806
Tel (417) 864-4300 *SIC* 7011 6733

LEO JOURNAGAN CONSTRUCTION CO INC p 856
3003 E Chestnut Expy 65802
Tel (417) 869-7222 *SIC* 1422 1611 1623

LESTER E COX MEDICAL CENTER p 857
305 S National Ave # 500 65802
Tel (417) 269-6000 *SIC* 8011

LESTER E COX MEDICAL CENTERS p 857
1423 N Jefferson Ave 65802
Tel (417) 269-3000 *SIC* 8062 8069

LOREN COOK CO p 878
2015 E Dale St 65803
Tel (417) 869-6474 *SIC* 3564

MEEK LUMBERYARD INC p 939
1311 E Woodhurst Dr 65804
Tel (417) 521-2801 *SIC* 5211

MERCY HEALTH SPRINGFIELD COMMUNITIES p 946
1235 E Cherokee St 65804
Tel (417) 885-2000 *SIC* 8062

MERCY HOSPITAL SPRINGFIELD p 947
1235 E Cherokee St 65804
Tel (417) 820-2000 *SIC* 8062 8011

MISSOURI STATE UNIVERSITY p 976
901 S National Ave 65897
Tel (417) 836-5000 *SIC* 8221 8211

NEW PRIME INC p 1033
2740 N Mayfair Ave 65803
Tel (800) 321-4552 *SIC* 4213

NORTHSTAR BATTERY CO LLC p 1058
4000 E Continental Way 65803
Tel (417) 575-8200 *SIC* 3692

■ OREILLY AUTO ENTERPRISES LLC p 1094
233 S Patterson Ave 65802
Tel (417) 862-6708 *SIC* 5531

▲ OREILLY AUTOMOTIVE INC p 1094
233 S Patterson Ave 65802
Tel (417) 862-6708 *SIC* 5531 5013

■ OREILLY AUTOMOTIVE STORES INC p 1094
233 S Patterson Ave 65802
Tel (417) 862-6708 *SIC* 5013 5531

■ OZARK AUTOMOTIVE DISTRIBUTORS INC p 1101
233 S Patterson Ave 65802
Tel (417) 862-6708 *SIC* 5013

■ OZARK PURCHASING LLC p 1101
233 S Patterson Ave 65802
Tel (417) 862-6708 *SIC* 7389

OZARKS COCA-COLA/DR PEPPER BOTTLING CO p 1101
1777 N Packer Rd 65803
Tel (417) 865-9900 *SIC* 2086 5149

OZARKS COMMUNITY HOSPITAL INC p 1101
2828 N National Ave 65803
Tel (417) 837-4000 *SIC* 8062

▲ PAUL MUELLER CO p 1121
1600 W Phelps St 65802
Tel (417) 831-3000 *SIC* 3443 3556 3523

POSITRONIC INDUSTRIES INC p 1163
423 N Campbell Ave 65806
Tel (417) 866-2322 *SIC* 3678

REDNECK INC p 1217
2100 N West Byp 65803
Tel (417) 864-5210 *SIC* 5013 5561 5012

RESTAURANT SYSTEMS INC p 1228
3880 W Battlefield St 65807
Tel (417) 887-5929 *SIC* 5812

SOUTHERN MISSOURI CONTAINERS INC p 1349
3131 E Division St 65802
Tel (417) 831-2685 *SIC* 2671 2653

SPORTSMANS DISTRIBUTION CO p 1360
2500 E Kearney St 65898
Tel (417) 873-5000 *SIC* 4225

SPRINGFIELD GROCER CO p 1361
2415 W Battlefield St 65807
Tel (417) 883-4230 *SIC* 5142 5141 5149

SPRINGFIELD REMANUFACTURING CORP p 1361
650 N Broadview Pl 65802
Tel (417) 862-3501
SIC 3519 3714 3713 3561

SPRINGFIELD SCHOOL DISTRICT R12 p 1361
1359 E Saint Louis St 65802
Tel (417) 523-0000 *SIC* 8211

SRC AUTOMOTIVE INC p 1363
4431 W Calhoun St 65802
Tel (417) 829-2400 *SIC* 5012

SRC HOLDINGS CORP p 1363
531 S Union Ave 65802
Tel (417) 862-2337 *SIC* 3519 3714

ST JOHNS CLINIC INC p 1367
1235 E Cherokee St 65804
Tel (417) 820-2000 *SIC* 8062

■ TIMKEN SMO LLC p 1455
2601 W Battlefield St 65807
Tel (866) 773-2926 *SIC* 3451 3714

TRACKER MARINE LLC p 1468
2500 E Kearney St 65898
Tel (417) 873-5900 *SIC* 3732

TRADITIONAL BAKERY INC p 1469
2040 W Vista St 65807
Tel (417) 889-8282 *SIC* 5461 5812

STRAFFORD, MO

LARSON GROUP p 845
3026 N Mulroy Rd 65757
Tel (417) 865-5355 *SIC* 3713

PETERBILT OF SPRINGFIELD INC p 1138
3026 N Mulroy Rd 65757
Tel (417) 865-5355 *SIC* 5511 5012

TCSI-TRANSLAND INC p 1428
1601 W Old Route 66 65757
Tel (417) 864-5710 *SIC* 4213

SUGAR CREEK, MO

■ AUDUBON MATERIALS LLC p 131
15100 E Crtney Athrton Rd 64058
Tel (816) 257-4040 *SIC* 2891

■ CENTRAL PLAINS CEMENT CO LLC p 279
15100 E Crtney Athrton Rd 64058
Tel (816) 257-4028 *SIC* 8741

SULLIVAN, MO

FIDELITY COMMUNICATIONS CO p 540
64 N Clark St 63080
Tel (800) 392-8070 *SIC* 4841 4813

TOWN AND COUNTRY, MO

■ SAVVIS COMMUNICATIONS CORP p 1284
1 Solutions Pkwy 63017
Tel (314) 628-7000 *SIC* 4813 7375

SAVVIS INC p 1284
1 Solutions Pkwy 63017
Tel (314) 628-7000
SIC 7373 7379 4813 7375

TROY, MO

CUIVRE RIVER ELECTRIC COOPERATIVE INC p 400
1112 E Cherry St 63379
Tel (636) 528-8261 SIC 4911

TROY R-III SCHOOL DISTRICT p 1485
951 W College St 63379
Tel (636) 462-6098 SIC 8211

UNION, MO

PTI UNION LLC p 1189
1310 Stylemaster Dr 63084
Tel (636) 583-8664 SIC 5122

■ **SILGAN PLASTIC FOOD CONTAINERS CORP** p 1323
710 W Park Rd 63084
Tel (636) 583-5550 SIC 3086

WARRENSBURG, MO

UNIVERSITY OF CENTRAL MISSOURI p 1520
415 E Clark St 213 64093
Tel (660) 543-4233 SIC 8221

WASHINGTON, MO

CG POWER SYSTEMS USA INC p 285
1 Pauwels Dr 63090
Tel (636) 239-6783 SIC 3612

MERCY HOSPITAL WASHINGTON p 947
901 E 5th St Ste 222 63090
Tel (636) 239-8000 SIC 8062

WEBB CITY, MO

CARDINAL SCALE MANUFACTURING CO p 253
203 E Daugherty St 64870
Tel (417) 673-4631 SIC 3596

WELDON SPRING, MO

PII INC p 1147
17 Research Park Dr # 100 63304
Tel (636) 685-1047 SIC 2311 2326

WENTZVILLE, MO

■ **CENTURYTEL OF MISSOURI LLC** p 283
1151 Century Tel Dr 63385
Tel (636) 332-3011 SIC 4813

WENTZVILLE R-IV SCHOOL DISTRICT p 1592
1 Campus Dr 63385
Tel (636) 327-3800 SIC 8211

WEST PLAINS, MO

OZARKS MEDICAL CENTER p 1101
1100 N Kentucky Ave 65775
Tel (417) 256-9111 SIC 8062

WILDWOOD, MO

▲ **PEAK RESORTS INC** p 1126
17409 Hidden Valley Dr 63025
Tel (636) 938-7474 SIC 7992 7999 7011

WILLOW SPRINGS, MO

G W FOODS INC p 587
2041 Railroad Ave 65793
Tel (417) 469-4000 SIC 5411

WRIGHT CITY, MO

DOREL HOME FURNISHINGS INC p 451
410 E 1st St S 63390
Tel (636) 745-3351 SIC 2511

MONTANA

ANACONDA, MT

AWARE INC p 139
205 E Park Ave 59711
Tel (406) 563-5229 SIC 8361 8331

BELGRADE, MT

ROCKY MOUNTAIN SUPPLY INC p 1245
350 Jackrabbit Ln Stop 1 59714
Tel (406) 388-4008
SIC 5171 5191 5541 5411

BILLINGS, MT

2 M CO INC p 1
5249 Holiday Ave 59101
Tel (406) 245-1490
SIC 5084 5083 5074 5051

BALLARD PETROLEUM HOLDINGS LLC p 148
845 12th St W 59102
Tel (406) 259-8790 SIC 1311

BILLINGS CLINIC p 182
2800 10th Ave N 59101
Tel (406) 657-4000 SIC 8062

BILLINGS SCHOOL DISTRICT 2 p 182
415 N 30th St 59101
Tel (406) 281-5000 SIC 8211

COP CONSTRUCTION LLC p 368
242 S 64th St W 59106
Tel (406) 656-4632 SIC 1622 1629

CTA INC p 399
13 N 23rd St 59101
Tel (406) 248-7455 SIC 8711 8712

ELECTRICAL CONSULTANTS INC p 485
3521 Gabel Rd Ste A 59102
Tel (406) 259-9933 SIC 8711

EPC SERVICES CO p 504
3521 Gabel Rd Ste B 59102
Tel (406) 294-8544 SIC 1731 8711

▲ **FIRST INTERSTATE BANCSYSTEM INC** p 547
401 N 31st St 59101
Tel (406) 255-5390 SIC 6022

■ **FIRST INTERSTATE BANK** p 547
401 N 31st St Bsmt 59101
Tel (406) 255-5000 SIC 6022

■ **JTL GROUP INC** p 796
4014 Hesper Rd 59106
Tel (406) 655-2010 SIC 1611

KAMPGROUNDS OF AMERICA INC p 802
550 N 31st St Ste 400 59101
Tel (406) 248-8135 SIC 6794 7033

MONTANA STATE UNIVERSITY-BILLINGS p 986
1500 University Dr 59101
Tel (406) 657-2011 SIC 4832 5942 8221

PAYNEWEST INSURANCE INC p 1122
3289 Gabel Rd 59102
Tel (406) 238-1900 SIC 6411

SOUTHERN MONTANA ELECTRIC GENERATION AND TRANSMISSION COOPERATIVE INC p 1349
7250 Entryway Dr 59101
Tel (406) 294-9527 SIC 4911

ST VINCENT HEALTHCARE p 1373
1233 N 30th St 59101
Tel (406) 657-7000 SIC 8062

■ **SYSCO MONTANA INC** p 1417
1509 Monad Rd 59101
Tel (406) 247-1100 SIC 5149 5142 5141

■ **TALEN MONTANA LLC** p 1422
303 N 28th St Ste 400 59101
Tel (406) 237-6900 SIC 4911

TIRE GUYS INC p 1455
1401 Industrial Ave 59101
Tel (406) 245-4006 SIC 5531

WAGGONERS TRUCKING p 1571
5220 Midland Rd 59101
Tel (406) 248-1919 SIC 4213

■ **WESTMORELAND MINING LLC** p 1602
490 N 31st St Ste 308 59101
Tel (719) 442-2600 SIC 1241

BLACK EAGLE, MT

MOUNTAIN VIEW CO-OP p 994
2200 Old Havre Hwy 59414
Tel (406) 453-5900
SIC 5541 5153 2875 5191

BOZEMAN, MT

BARNARD CONSTRUCTION CO INC p 155
701 Gold Ave 59715
Tel (406) 586-1995
SIC 1623 1629 1611 1622

BOZEMAN DEACONESS HEALTH SERVICES p 205
915 Highland Blvd 59715
Tel (406) 585-5000 SIC 8062 8059

GALLATIN COUNTY REST HOME p 589
1221 Durston Rd 59715
Tel (406) 582-3300 SIC 8051

MONTANA STATE UNIVERSITY INC p 986
901 W Garfield St 59717
Tel (406) 994-4361 SIC 8221

RANCH AND HOME SUPPLY LLC p 1207
2311 N 7th Ave 59715
Tel (406) 586-8466
SIC 5699 5191 5531 5251

BUTTE, MT

NORTHWESTERN ENERGY p 1060
11 E Park St 59701
Tel (406) 497-3000 SIC 4911

REC ADVANCED SILICON MATERIALS LLC p 1214
119140 Rick Jones Way 59750
Tel (406) 496-9898 SIC 3339

ST JAMES HEALTHCARE INC p 1367
400 S Clark St 59701
Tel (406) 723-2484 SIC 8062

TOWN PUMP INC p 1465
600 S Main St 59701
Tel (406) 497-6700
SIC 5541 5411 7993 6512 5812

COLSTRIP, MT

■ **WESTERN ENERGY CO** p 1598
148 Rosebud Ln 59323
Tel (406) 748-5100 SIC 1221

CROW AGENCY, MT

CROW TRIBE OF INDIANS p 394
Hwy 212 & 87 59022
Tel (406) 638-3700 SIC 9131

GREAT FALLS, MT

BENEFIS HOSPITALS INC p 173
1101 26th St S 59405
Tel (406) 455-5000 SIC 8062 8051

DA DAVIDSON & CO p 407
8 3rd St N 59401
Tel (406) 727-4200 SIC 6211

DA DAVIDSON COMPANIES p 407
8 3rd St N 59401
Tel (406) 727-4200 SIC 6211 6733 8741

FRINGE BENEFIT RESOURCES p 580
1730 Alder Dr 59404
Tel (406) 268-1721 SIC 6411

GREAT FALLS PUBLIC SCHOOLS DIST1 p 633
1100 4th St S 59405
Tel (406) 268-6052 SIC 8211

PACIFIC HIDE & FUR DEPOT p 1104
5 River Dr S 59405
Tel (406) 771-7222 SIC 5051 5093

SLETTEN CONSTRUCTION CO p 1331
1000 25th St N Ste 4 59401
Tel (406) 761-7920 SIC 1541 1542 1611

SLETTEN INC p 1331
1000 25th St N Ste 4 59401
Tel (406) 761-7920 SIC 1542 1541 1611

TRANSPORT LEASING CO LLP p 1472
1901 Benefis Ct 59405
Tel (406) 727-7500 SIC 7513

TRANSYSTEMS LLC p 1473
1901 Benefis Ct 59405
Tel (406) 727-7500 SIC 4212

HAVRE, MT

HAVRE SCHOOL DISTRICT 16-A p 668
425 6th St 59501
Tel (406) 265-4356 SIC 8211

HELENA, MT

COONEY CONVALESCENT HOME p 366
2555 E Broadway St 59601
Tel (406) 447-1651 SIC 8059 8051

DEPARTMENT OF CORRECTIONS MONTANA p 430
5 S Last Chance Gulch 59601
Tel (406) 444-3930 SIC 9223

DEPARTMENT OF REVENUE MONTANA p 430
125 N Roberts St Fl 34 59601
Tel (406) 444-2460 SIC 9311

DICK ANDERSON CONSTRUCTION INC p 437
3424 E Us Highway 12 59601
Tel (406) 443-3225 SIC 1542 1622 1611

EXECUTIVE OFFICE OF STATE OF MONTANA p 518
State Capitol Rm 204 59620
Tel (406) 444-3111 SIC 9111

■ **HERITAGE OPERATING LP** p 686
754 River Rock Dr 59602
Tel (406) 442-9759 SIC 5984 5172

MERGENTHALER TRANSFER & STORAGE CO INC p 948
1414 N Montana Ave 59601
Tel (406) 442-9470 SIC 4213 4214 7538

MONTANA DEPARTMENT OF PUBLIC HEALTH AND HUMAN SERVICES p 986
111 N Sanders St Rm 6 59601
Tel (406) 444-4228 SIC 9431

MONTANA DEPARTMENT OF TRANSPORTATION p 986
2701 Prospect Ave 59601
Tel (406) 444-6201 SIC 9621

MONTANA DEPT OF JUSTICE p 986
215 N Sanders St 59601
Tel (406) 444-2026 SIC 9222

MONTANA STATE FUND p 986
855 Front St 59601
Tel (406) 444-6500 SIC 6331

MONTANA UNIVERSITY SYSTEM p 986
2500 E Broadway St 59601
Tel (406) 444-6570 SIC 8221

ROMAN CATHOLIC BISHOP OF HELENA MONTANA p 1248
515 N Ewing St 59601
Tel (406) 442-5820
SIC 8661 8211 8221 2741

ST PETERS HOSPITAL p 1372
2475 E Broadway St 59601
Tel (406) 442-2480 SIC 8062

KALISPELL, MT

AON NATIONAL FLOOD SERVICES INC p 95
555 Corporate Dr 59901
Tel (406) 756-8656 SIC 6331

■ **CENTURYTEL OF IDAHO INC** p 283
290 N Main St 59901
Tel (703) 363-8774 SIC 4813

CITYSERVICEVALCON LLC p 320
640 W Montana St 59901
Tel (406) 755-4321 SIC 5172 5983

FLATHEAD ELECTRIC COOPERATIVE INC p 554
2510 Us Highway 2 E 59901
Tel (406) 751-4483 SIC 4911

▲ **GLACIER BANCORP INC** p 613
49 Commons Loop 59901
Tel (406) 756-4200 SIC 6022

■ **GLACIER BANK** p 614
202 Mn St 59901
Tel (406) 756-4200 SIC 6022

KALISPELL REGIONAL HEALTHCARE SYSTEM p 801
310 Sunnyview Ln 59901
Tel (406) 752-8991
SIC 8051 8011 4522 7352

KALISPELL REGIONAL MEDICAL CENTER INC p 801
310 Sunnyview Ln 59901
Tel (406) 752-5111 SIC 8062

■ **SEMITOOL INC** p 1303
655 W Reserve Dr 59901
Tel (406) 752-2107 SIC 3559

LAUREL, MT

TOWN AND COUNTRY SUPPLY ASSOCIATION p 1464
18 8th Ave 59044
Tel (406) 628-6314
SIC 5984 5191 5411 5999

LEWISTOWN, MT

SPORTS INC p 1360
333 2nd Ave N 59457
Tel (406) 538-3496 SIC 5091

MILES CITY, MT

OFTEDAL CONSTRUCTION INC p 1076
434 Highway 59 N 59n 59301
Tel (406) 232-5911 SIC 1629 3273 1611

STOCKMAN BANK OF MONTANA p 1390
700 Main St 59301
Tel (406) 234-8420 SIC 6022

STOCKMAN FINANCIAL CORP p 1390
700 Main St 59301
Tel (406) 234-8420 SIC 6022

MISSOULA, MT

■ **ALLEGIANCE BENEFIT PLAN MANAGEMENT INC** p 52
2806 S Grfield St Ste 101 59801
Tel (406) 523-3122 SIC 6324

BLACKFOOT TELEPHONE COOPERATIVE INC p 187
1221 N Russell St 59808
Tel (406) 541-2121 SIC 4813

CMC MISSOULA INC p 329
2827 Fort Missoula Rd 59804
Tel (406) 728-4100 SIC 8062 8361

ENVIROCON INC p 503
101 International Dr 59808
Tel (406) 523-1150 SIC 1795

MISSOULA COUNTY PUBLIC SCHOOLS p 976
215 S 6th St W 59801
Tel (406) 728-2400 SIC 8299 8211

MODERN MACHINERY CO INC p 981
101 International Dr 59808
Tel (406) 523-1100 SIC 5082

MONTANA RAIL LINK INC p 986
101 International Dr 59808
Tel (406) 523-1500 SIC 4011

NIGHTINGALE NURSING SERVICE INC p 1043
3301 Great Northrn Ave203 Ste 203 59808
Tel (406) 541-1700 SIC 8082

NORTHWEST NEWS CO INC p 1060
1701 Rankin St 59808
Tel (406) 721-7801 SIC 5192

NUTRAMED INC p 1068
1001 S 3rd St W 59801
Tel (406) 273-5493 SIC 5149

PROVIDENCE CORP p 1185
500 W Broadway St 59802
Tel (406) 543-7271 SIC 6719

ST PATRICK HOSPITAL AND HEALTH SCIENCES CENTER p 1372
500 W Broadway St 59802
Tel (406) 543-7271 SIC 8062

ST PATRICK HOSPITAL CORP p 1372
500 W Broadway St 59802
Tel (406) 543-7271 SIC 8062

STERLING GROUP INC p 1387
3010 Santa Fe Ct 59808
Tel (406) 251-5788 SIC 8741

UNIVERSITY OF MONTANA p 1523
32 Campus Dr Main Hall 59812
Tel (406) 243-6670 SIC 8221

WASHINGTON CORPS p 1577
101 International Dr 59808
Tel (406) 523-1300
SIC 5082 7353 4213 8741

WATKINS AND SHEPARD TRUCKING INC p 1582
N6400 Hwy 10 W 59801
Tel (406) 532-6121 SIC 4213 8299

PABLO, MT

CONFEDERATED SALISH & KOOTENAI TRIBES INC p 355
42487 Complex Blvd 59855
Tel (406) 675-2700 SIC 7011

SHERIDAN, MT

TOBACCO ROOT MOUNTAINS CARE CENTER p 1458
326 Madison St 59749
Tel (406) 842-5418 SIC 8051

SIDNEY, MT

MITCHELLS OILFIELD SERVICE INC p 977
409 N Central Ave 59270
Tel (406) 482-4927 SIC 1389 3273

UPPER MISSOURI G & T ELECTRIC CO-OPERATIVE INC p 1529
111 2nd Ave Sw 59270
Tel (406) 433-4100 SIC 4911

THREE FORKS, MT

WHEAT MONTANA FARMS INC p 1604
10778 Us Highway 287 59752
Tel (406) 285-3614 SIC 5149 0111

VALIER, MT

SWANK ENTERPRISES p 1411
615 Pondera Ave 59486
Tel (406) 279-3241 SIC 1542 5211

NEBRASKA

ALLIANCE, NE

WESTERN COOPERATIVE CO INC p 1598
724 W 3rd St 69301
Tel (308) 762-3291 SIC 5172 5541 5191

ARCADIA, NE

TROTTER INC p 1484
300 Railway 68815
Tel (308) 789-6200 SIC 5191 5153 5172

AURORA, NE

AURORA COOPERATIVE ELEVATOR CO p 132
2225 Q St 68818
Tel (402) 694-2106 SIC 5153 5191

HERITAGE GROUP INC p 686
1101 12th St 68818
Tel (402) 694-3136 SIC 6029

NEDELCO INC p 1023
1001 12th St 68818
Tel (402) 694-5101 SIC 4813

BATTLE CREEK, NE

BATTLE CREEK FARMERS COOPERATIVE NON-STOCK p 160
83755 Highway 121 68715
Tel (402) 675-2375
SIC 5153 5191 5172 5541 5411

BEATRICE, NE

SOUTHEAST NEBRASKA COOPERATIVE CO p 1346
403 S 3rd St 68310
Tel (402) 228-3458 SIC 5191 5153 2048

BELLEVUE, NE

BELLEVUE PUBLIC SCHOOLS p 170
2600 Arboretum Dr 68005
Tel (402) 293-4000 SIC 8299 8748 8211

■TD AMERITRADE INC p 1428
1005 N Ameritrade Pl 68005
Tel (402) 970-7000 SIC 6211

BLAIR, NE

NEBRASKA-IOWA SUPPLY CO INC p 1023
1160 Lincoln St 68008
Tel (402) 426-2171 SIC 5172

BOYS TOWN, NE

FATHER FLANAGANS BOYS HOME p 531
14086 Mother Theresa Ln 68010
Tel (402) 498-1111 SIC 8361

BRAINARD, NE

FRONTIER COOPERATIVE CO p 581
211 S Lincoln St 68626
Tel (402) 545-2811 SIC 5153 5191

BRUNSWICK, NE

J E MEURET GRAIN CO INC p 771
101 N Franklin St 68720
Tel (402) 842-2515 SIC 5153

COLUMBUS, NE

BEHLEN MFG CO p 168
4025 E 23rd St 68601
Tel (402) 564-3111
SIC 3523 3448 4213 3556 3496 3443

BEHLEN MKTG CO p 168
4025 E 23rd St 68601
Tel (402) 564-3111 SIC 3523 3448 4213

COOP HUSKER p 366
2468 33rd Ave 68601
Tel (402) 564-2704 SIC 5153 5191

■ DALE VISHAY ELECTRONICS LLC p 409
1122 23rd St 68601
Tel (605) 665-9301
SIC 3676 3679 3677 3678

LOUP RIVER PUBLIC POWER DISTRICT p 881
2404 15th St 68601
Tel (402) 564-3171 SIC 4911

MEAD HOLDING CO INC p 933
2218 11th St 68601
Tel (402) 564-5225 SIC 6719 5211

NEBRASKA ELECTRIC GENERATION & TRANSMISSION COOPERATIVE INC p 1023
2472 18th Ave 68601
Tel (402) 564-8142 SIC 4911

NEBRASKA PUBLIC POWER DISTRICT p 1023
1414 15th St 68601
Tel (402) 564-8561 SIC 4911

NPP LLC p 1064
4860 33rd Ave 68601
Tel (402) 564-9464 SIC 0213

COZAD, NE

PAULSEN INC p 1122
1116 E Highway 30 69130
Tel (308) 784-3333 SIC 1611 1542 3273

DORCHESTER, NE

FARMERS COOPERATIVE p 529
208 W Depot St 68343
Tel (402) 946-4631 SIC 5153 5191 5172

EDISON, NE

AG VALLEY COOPERATIVE NON-STOCK p 34
72133 State Hwy 136 68936
Tel (308) 927-3681 SIC 5153 5191

ELKHORN, NE

■ ACI WORLDWIDE CORP p 17
6060 Coventry Dr 68022
Tel (402) 390-7600 SIC 7372 5045

■ CSG SYSTEMS INC p 397
18020 Burt St 68022
Tel (402) 431-7000 SIC 7374

ELKHORN SCHOOL DISTRICT 010 p 488
20650 Glenn St 68022
Tel (402) 289-2579 SIC 8211

PINNACLE BANCORP INC p 1149
1801 Burt St 68022
Tel (402) 697-8666 SIC 6022 6712

VETTER HEALTH SERVICES INC p 1553
20220 Harney St 68022
Tel (402) 895-3932 SIC 8052

ELMWOOD, NE

GREENWOOD FARMERS COOPERATIVE p 639
304 S 3rd St 68349
Tel (402) 994-2585 SIC 5191

MIDWEST FARMERS COOPERATIVE p 967
304 S 3rd St 68349
Tel (402) 994-2585 SIC 5153 5191 5541

FAIRBURY, NE

LAMBERT VET SUPPLY LLC p 841
714 5th St 68352
Tel (402) 729-3044 SIC 5047

FRANKLIN, NE

SOUTHERN POWER DISTRICT p 1350
101 16th Ave 68939
Tel (308) 425-6217 SIC 4911

FREMONT, NE

FREMONT HEALTH p 577
450 E 23rd St 68025
Tel (402) 727-3795 SIC 8062 8051

GOTHENBURG, NE

ALL POINTS COOPERATIVE p 51
120 8th St 69138
Tel (308) 537-7141 SIC 5153 5191 5541

GRAND ISLAND, NE

BOSSELMAN ENERGY INC p 202
3123 W Stolley Park Rd B 68801
Tel (308) 381-6900 SIC 5172

BOSSELMAN INC p 202
3123 W Stolley Park Rd 68801
Tel (308) 381-2800
SIC 5541 5411 5812 7011 5172 5084

CHIEF INDUSTRIES INC p 298
3942 W Old Highway 30 68803
Tel (308) 389-7200
SIC 3448 2451 3523 2869 3442

DIAMOND PLASTICS CORP p 437
1212 Johnstown Rd 68803
Tel (765) 287-9234 SIC 3084

GLOBAL INDUSTRIES INC p 617
1804 E 4th St 68801
Tel (800) 247-6621
SIC 7992 3589 3444 5084 5083 3535

HALL COUNTY SCHOOL DISTRICT 2 p 654
123 S Webb Rd 68803
Tel (308) 385-5886 SIC 8211 9411

HORNADY MANUFACTURING CO p 708
3625 W Old Potash Hwy 68803
Tel (308) 382-1390 SIC 3482 3559 3483

KRIZ-DAVIS CO p 830
2400 W 3rd St 68803
Tel (308) 382-2230 SIC 5063

KWS INC p 833
3048 W Stolley Park Rd 68801
Tel (308) 382-1053 SIC 5812

SAINT FRANCIS MEDICAL CENTER INC p 1269
2620 W Faidley Ave 68803
Tel (308) 384-4600 SIC 8062 8069

SOUTHERN NEBRASKA RURAL PUBLIC POWER DISTRICT p 1349
4550 W Husker Hwy 68803
Tel (402) 725-3370 SIC 4911

TOBA INC p 1458
2621 W Us Highway 30 68803
Tel (308) 389-5987
SIC 5148 5194 5145 5141

HASTINGS, NE

COOPERATIVE PRODUCERS INC p 367
265 N Showboat Blvd 68901
Tel (402) 463-5148 SIC 2048 5153

DUTTON-LAINSON CO p 463
451 W 2nd St 68901
Tel (402) 463-6702
SIC 3531 5999 5063 5074

MARY LANNING MEMORIAL HOSPITAL ASSOCIATION p 914
715 N Saint Joseph Ave 68901
Tel (402) 463-4521 SIC 8062

T-L IRRIGATION CO p 1420
151 E Hwy 6 And Ab Rd 68901
Tel (402) 462-4128
SIC 3523 3561 3479 7359

IMPERIAL, NE

FRENCHMAN VALLEY FARMERS COOPERATIVE INC p 578
202 Broadway 69033
Tel (308) 882-3220 SIC 5153 5191 5541

JACKSON, NE

SIOUXLAND ETHANOL LLC p 1326
1501 Knox Blvd 68743
Tel (402) 632-2676 SIC 2869 2083

KEARNEY, NE

■ BALDWIN FILTERS INC p 147
4400 Highway 30 E 68847
Tel (800) 822-5394 SIC 3714 3564

▲ BUCKLE INC p 223
2407 W 24th St 68845
Tel (308) 236-8491
SIC 5661 5632 5621 5611

CASH-WA DISTRIBUTING CO OF KEARNEY INC p 263
401 W 4th St 68845
Tel (308) 237-3151 SIC 5149 5046 5194

GOOD SAMARITAN HOSPITAL p 623
4503 2nd Ave Ste 209 68847
Tel (308) 865-2009 SIC 8062

GOOD SAMARITAN HOSPITAL KEARNEY NEBRASKA p 623
10 E 31st St 68847
Tel (308) 865-7997 SIC 8062

LA VISTA, NE

ROTELLAS ITALIAN BAKERY INC p 1252
6949 S 108th St 68128
Tel (402) 592-6600 SIC 2051

LEXINGTON, NE

NEBRASKALAND TIRE INC p 1023
Hwy 283 & Hwy I 80 68850
Tel (308) 324-2338 SIC 5531 5541 5411

LINCOLN, NE

AMERITAS HOLDING CO p 84
5900 O St 68510
Tel (402) 467-1122 SIC 6311

AMERITAS LIFE INSURANCE CORP p 84
5900 O St 68510
Tel (402) 467-1122 SIC 6371 6311 6211

AMERITAS MUTUAL HOLDING CO p 84
5900 O St 68510
Tel (402) 467-1122 SIC 6311

ASG INC p 116
1526 K St 68508
Tel (402) 476-6500 SIC 6321 6311

ASSURITY SECURITY GROUP INC p 122
1526 K St 68508
Tel (402) 476-6500 SIC 6321 6311

B & R STORES INC p 141
4554 W St 68503
Tel (402) 423-9602 SIC 5411

■ BLACK HILLS/NEBRASKA GAS UTILITY CO LLC p 187
1600 Windhoek Dr 68512
Tel (402) 437-1705 SIC 4924

BOARD OF REGENTS OF UNIVERSITY OF NEBRASKA p 195
3835 Holdrege St 68503
Tel (402) 472-2111 SIC 8221

BRYAN HEALTH p 221
1600 S 48th St 68506
Tel (402) 481-1111 SIC 8062

BRYAN HEALTH WEST CAMPUS p 221
2300 S 16th St 68502
Tel (402) 475-1011 SIC 8062

BRYAN MEDICAL CENTER p 221
1600 S 48th St 68506
Tel (402) 481-3190 SIC 8062

CELERION HOLDINGS INC p 273
621 Rose St 68502
Tel (402) 476-2811 SIC 8731

CELERION INC p 273
621 Rose St 68502
Tel (402) 476-2811 SIC 8731

CHI NEBRASKA p 296
555 S 70th St 68510
Tel (402) 219-8000 SIC 8741

CITY OF LINCOLN p 316
555 S 10th St Rm B115 68508
Tel (402) 441-7511 SIC 9111

COMMONWEALTH ELECTRIC CO OF MIDWEST p 346
1901 Y St Ste 100 68503
Tel (402) 473-2214 SIC 1731

CONCORD HOSPITALITY INC p 354
1701 Windhoek Dr 68512
Tel (402) 421-2551 SIC 5812 7011 7311

CONCORD NEIGHBORHOOD CORP p 355
1701 Windhoek Dr 68512
Tel (402) 421-2551 SIC 5812

COUNTY OF LANCASTER p 379
555 S 10th St Rm 110 68508
Tel (402) 441-4944 SIC 9111

CRETE CARRIER CORP p 392
400 Nw 56th St 68528
Tel (402) 475-9521 SIC 4213 4212 6512

DUNCAN AVIATION INC p 461
3701 Aviation Rd 68524
Tel (402) 479-1616
SIC 7699 5088 4522 4512

FARMLAND FOODS INC p 530
200 S 2nd St 68508
Tel (402) 475-6700 SIC 2013

GROWTH MANAGEMENT CORP p 642
3201 Pioneers Blvd # 112 68502
Tel (402) 488-8500 SIC 5812 5411

HORIZON FOOD SERVICE INC p 707
6101 S 58th St Ste B 68516
Tel (402) 421-6400 SIC 5812

HORIZON HOLDINGS INC p 707
6101 S 58th St Ste B 68516
Tel (402) 421-6400 SIC 5812

INDUSTRIAL ACOUSTICS CO INC p 739
233 S 13th St Ste 1100 68508
Tel (718) 931-8000 SIC 3448 1742

■ INFORMATION TECHNOLOGY INC p 742
1345 Old Cheney Rd 68512
Tel (402) 423-2682
SIC 5045 7373 7374 7371

KAWASAKI MOTORS MANUFACTURING CORP USA p 805
6600 Nw 27th St 68524
Tel (402) 476-6600 SIC 3751 5571

LANDSCAPES UNLIMITED LLC p 843
1201 Aries Dr 68512
Tel (402) 423-6653 SIC 1629

LI-COR INC p 861
4647 Superior St 68504
Tel (402) 467-3576 SIC 3826

LINCOLN ELECTRIC SYSTEM p 867
1040 O St 68508
Tel (402) 475-4211 SIC 4911

LINCOLN HEXAGON INC p 867
5150 Nw 40th St 68524
Tel (402) 470-5000 SIC 3714

LINCOLN INDUSTRIES INC p 867
600 W E St 68522
Tel (402) 475-3671 SIC 3471 3441

LINCOLN PUBLIC SCHOOLS INC p 868
5905 O St 68510
Tel (402) 436-1000 SIC 8211

■ LINCOLN SYSCO INC p 868
900 King Bird Rd 68521
Tel (402) 423-1031
SIC 5148 5142 5143 5141 5087 5113

MADONNA REHABILITATION HOSPITAL p 894
5401 South St 68506
Tel (402) 413-3000 SIC 8051

MUNICIPAL ENERGY AGENCY OF NEBRASKA (INC) p 1000
8377 Glynoaks Dr 68516
Tel (402) 474-4759 SIC 4911

▲ NATIONAL RESEARCH CORP p 1015
1245 Q St Ste 100 68508
Tel (402) 475-2525 SIC 8732

NBC ACQUISITION CORP p 1021
4700 S 19th St 68512
Tel (402) 421-7300 SIC 5192 5942

NBC HOLDINGS CORP p 1021
4700 S 19th St 68512
Tel (402) 421-7300 SIC 5192 6719

NEBCO INC p 1023
1815 Y St 68508
Tel (402) 434-1212
SIC 5999 3273 3272 3271 1442 4013

NEBRASKA BOOK CO INC p 1023
4700 S 19th St 68512
Tel (402) 421-7300 *SIC* 5942 5192 5961

NEBRASKA BOOK HOLDINGS INC p 1023
4700 S 19th St 68512
Tel (402) 421-0500
SIC 6719 5942 5192 5961

NEBRASKA BOOK INTERMEDIATE HOLDINGS INC p 1023
4701 S 19th St 68512
Tel (402) 421-7300
SIC 6719 5942 5192 5961

NEBRASKA DEPARTMENT OF ADMINISTRATIVE SERVICES p 1023
1526 K St Ste 250 68508
Tel (402) 471-2331 *SIC* 9199

NEBRASKA INDUSTRAIL COMPETITIVENESS SERVICE p 1023
8800 O St 68520
Tel (402) 437-2535 *SIC* 9199

▲ NELNET INC p 1025
121 S 13th St Ste 100 68508
Tel (402) 458-2370 *SIC* 6141 7389

■ NELNET STUDENT LOAN CORP-1 p 1025
121 S 13th St Ste 301 68508
Tel (402) 458-2370 *SIC* 6111

OLSSON ASSOCIATES INC p 1083
601 P St 68508
Tel (402) 474-6311 *SIC* 8711

PCE INC p 1124
1711 Yolande Ave 68521
Tel (402) 474-4690 *SIC* 3089 3644 3088

PHYSICIAN NETWORK p 1145
2000 Q St Fl 5th 68503
Tel (402) 421-0896 *SIC* 8011

RITCHIE BROS AUCTIONEERS (AMERICA) INC p 1236
4000 Pine Lake Rd 68516
Tel (402) 421-3631 *SIC* 7389

SAINT ELIZABETH REGIONAL MEDICAL CENTER p 1269
555 S 70th St 68510
Tel (402) 219-5200 *SIC* 8062 8082

SAMPSON CONSTRUCTION CO INC p 1274
3730 S 14th St 68502
Tel (308) 865-1375 *SIC* 1542 1541

SECURITY FINANCIAL LIFE INSURANCE CO p 1299
4000 Pine Lake Rd 68516
Tel (402) 434-9500 *SIC* 6311

SNYDER INDUSTRIES INC p 1336
6940 O St Ste 100 68510
Tel (402) 465-1206 *SIC* 3089

SOUTHEAST COMMUNITY COLLEGE AREA p 1345
301 S 68th Street Pl 68510
Tel (402) 323-3400 *SIC* 8222

STATE OF NEBRASKA p 1382
1445 K St Oom 2316 68509
Tel (402) 471-2311 *SIC* 9111

■ TELEDYNE ISCO INC p 1434
4700 Superior St 68504
Tel (402) 464-0231 *SIC* 3823 3826

TO HAAS TIRE CO INC p 1458
1415 W Commerce Way 68521
Tel (402) 434-3434 *SIC* 5014 5531 7539

UNION BANK AND TRUST CO p 1504
3643 S 48th St 68506
Tel (402) 488-0941
SIC 6111 6029 6162 6021 6035 6022

UNIVERSITY OF NEBRASKA FOUNDATION p 1523
1010 Lincoln Mall Ste 300 68508
Tel (402) 458-1100 *SIC* 7389

LOUP CITY, NE

ROSE LANE HOME p 1250
1005 N 8th St 68853
Tel (308) 745-0303 *SIC* 8051 6411

NEBRASKA CITY, NE

■ ELSTER AMERICAN METER CO LLC p 489
2221 Industrial Rd 68410
Tel (402) 873-8200 *SIC* 3829

NORFOLK, NE

ADVANCE SERVICES INC p 25
112 S Birch St 68701
Tel (402) 371-5733 *SIC* 7361

AFFILIATED FOODS MIDWEST COOPERATIVE INC p 32
1301 W Omaha Ave 68701
Tel (402) 371-0555 *SIC* 5141 5142

REHABILITATION THERAPIST p 1220
1500 Koenigstein Ave 68701
Tel (402) 644-7396 *SIC* 8093

SUPERTEL HOSPITALITY MANAGEMENT INC p 1407
1800 W Pswalk Ave Ste 200 68701
Tel (402) 371-2520 *SIC* 7011

NORTH PLATTE, NE

NORTH PLATTE NEBRASKA HOSPITAL CORP p 1053
601 W Leota St 69101
Tel (308) 534-9310 *SIC* 8062 8082

TODD HLAVATY MD p 1458
601 W Leota St 69101
Tel (308) 535-7405 *SIC* 8011

OMAHA, NE

AG PROCESSING INC p 33
12700 W Dodge Rd 68154
Tel (402) 496-7809 *SIC* 4221

AG PROCESSING INC A COOPERATIVE p 33
12700 W Dodge Rd 68154
Tel (402) 496-7809
SIC 5153 2075 2048 5999 0254

AGP GRAIN LTD p 35
12700 W Dodge Rd 68154
Tel (402) 496-7809 *SIC* 5153

AIRLITE PLASTICS CO p 40
6110 Abbott Dr 68110
Tel (402) 341-7300 *SIC* 3089

ALEGENT HEALTH - IMMANUEL MEDICAL CENTER p 48
6901 N 72nd St 68122
Tel (402) 572-2121 *SIC* 8062 8051 8351

ALEGENT HEALTH- BERGAN MERCY HEALTH SYSTEM p 48
7500 Mercy Rd 68124
Tel (402) 398-6060 *SIC* 8062

ALLIED OIL & TIRE CO p 56
2209 S 24th St 68108
Tel (402) 344-4343 *SIC* 5014 5172

▲ AMCON DISTRIBUTING CO INC p 65
7405 Irvington Rd 68122
Tel (402) 331-3727
SIC 5194 5141 5145 5113 5122

AMERICAN NATIONAL BANK p 76
8990 W Dodge Rd Ste 1 68114
Tel (402) 399-5000 *SIC* 6021

■ APPLIED UNDERWRITERS INC p 100
10805 Old Mill Rd 68154
Tel (402) 342-4900
SIC 6331 8721 8741 8742

ARCHBISHOP BERGAN MERCY AUXILIARY p 104
7500 Mercy Rd 68124
Tel (402) 398-6199 *SIC* 5947

ARCHBISHOP BERGAN MERCY HOSPITAL p 104
7500 Mercy Rd 68124
Tel (402) 398-6060 *SIC* 8062 8051

■ ASPEN HOLDINGS INC p 118
222 S 15th St Ste 1500n 68102
Tel (402) 926-0099 *SIC* 6719

BAKERS SUPERMARKETS INC p 146
4509 S 143rd St Ste 4 68137
Tel (402) 397-4321 *SIC* 5411

▲ BALLANTYNE STRONG INC p 148
11422 Miracle Hills Dr # 300 68154
Tel (402) 453-4444 *SIC* 3861 3648

▲ BERKSHIRE HATHAWAY INC p 175
3555 Farnam St Ste 1440 68131
Tel (402) 346-1400
SIC 6331 6321 4911 4924 6531 5963

■ BH MEDIA GROUP HOLDINGS INC p 180
Omaha World Herald Bldg 1 68102
Tel (402) 444-1000 *SIC* 2711 7379

■ BH MEDIA GROUP INC p 180
Omaha Wrld Hrld Bldg 1314 68102
Tel (402) 444-1000 *SIC* 2711 7379

■ BHSF INC p 180
1440 Kiewit Plz 68131
Tel (402) 346-1400
SIC 3635 3563 2731 3715

BLUE CROSS & BLUE SHIELD OF NEBRASKA p 191
1919 Aksarben Dr 68180
Tel (402) 982-7000 *SIC* 6324 6311

BROOKESTONE VILLAGE INC p 217
4330 S 144th St 68137
Tel (402) 614-4000 *SIC* 8051

BUCKS INC p 223
5001 Dodge St 68132
Tel (402) 558-9860 *SIC* 5541

BUILDERS SUPPLY CO INC p 225
5701 S 72nd St 68127
Tel (402) 331-4500 *SIC* 5211 5031

■ CALENERGY OPERATING CORP p 238
1111 S 103rd St Fl 4 68124
Tel (402) 398-7200 *SIC* 3621

CARLSON SYSTEMS HOLDINGS INC p 258
10840 Harney St 68154
Tel (402) 593-5300 *SIC* 5085 5199

CASSLING DIAGNOSTIC IMAGING INC p 264
13808 F St 68137
Tel (402) 334-5000 *SIC* 5047 7699

CATHOLIC MUTUAL RELIEF SOCIETY OF AMERICA p 267
10843 Old Mill Rd 68154
Tel (402) 551-8765 *SIC* 6351

CHILDRENS FAMILY SUPPORT CENTER p 299
8200 Dodge St 68114
Tel (402) 955-8117 *SIC* 8069

CHILDRENS HOSPITAL & MEDICAL CENTER p 299
8200 Dodge St 68114
Tel (402) 955-5400 *SIC* 8069

CITY OF OMAHA p 317
1819 Farnam St Rm 300 68183
Tel (402) 444-5000 *SIC* 9111

■ COLUMBIA INSURANCE CO p 341
3024 Harney St 68131
Tel (402) 536-3000 *SIC* 6331

■ CONAGRA GROCERY PRODUCTS CO LLC p 354
11 Conagra Dr 68102
Tel (630) 857-1000
SIC 2033 2079 2099 2032 2066 5149

CREIGHTON ALEGENT CLINIC p 391
12809 W Dodge Rd 68154
Tel (402) 343-4343 *SIC* 8062

■ CREIGHTON ALEGENT HEALTH p 391
601 N 30th St 68131
Tel (402) 449-4000 *SIC* 8062

CREIGHTON ALEGENT HEALTH p 391
12809 W Dodge Rd 68154
Tel (402) 343-4300 *SIC* 5912

CREIGHTON UNIVERSITY p 391
2500 California Plz 68178
Tel (402) 280-2900 *SIC* 8221

■ CUMMINS CENTRAL POWER LLC p 401
10088 S 136th St 68138
Tel (402) 551-7678
SIC 5084 7538 5999 3519

CUTCHALL MANAGEMENT CO INC p 403
13305 Birch Dr Ste 201 68164
Tel (402) 558-3333 *SIC* 5812

DATA SYSTEMS INC p 414
6515 S 118th St Ste 100 68137
Tel (402) 597-6477 *SIC* 5044

DOUGLAS COUNTY NEBRASKA p 452
Omaha Douglas Civic Cente 68183
Tel (402) 444-7025 *SIC* 9111

■ DRIVERS MANAGEMENT LLC p 456
14507 Frontier Rd 68138
Tel (402) 895-6640 *SIC* 7363

DRM INC p 456
5324 N 134th Ave 68164
Tel (402) 573-1216 *SIC* 5812

DULTMEIER SALES LIMITED LIABILITY CO p 460
13808 Industrial Rd 68137
Tel (402) 333-1444 *SIC* 5083 5084

E MAIL SOLUTIONS INC p 466
12111 Emmet St 68164
Tel (402) 496-2223 *SIC* 4822

ELECTION SYSTEMS & SOFTWARE LLC p 484
11208 John Galt Blvd 68137
Tel (402) 593-0101 *SIC* 3577

ELIASON & KNUTH COMPANIES INC p 487
13324 Chandler Rd 68138
Tel (402) 896-1614 *SIC* 1742 5032

ELLIOTT EQUIPMENT CO p 488
4427 S 76th Cir 68127
Tel (402) 592-4500 *SIC* 3531

ENERFO USA INC p 497
16934 Frances St Ste 105 68130
Tel (402) 401-6300 *SIC* 6221

FARM CREDIT SERVICES OF AMERICA PCA/FLCA p 528
5015 S 118th St 68137
Tel (800) 884-3276 *SIC* 6159

FASTENER HOLDINGS INC p 531
10840 Harney St 68154
Tel (402) 593-5300 *SIC* 6719

FBG SERVICE CORP p 532
407 S 27th Ave 68131
Tel (402) 346-4422 *SIC* 7349

■ FIRST DATA RESOURCES LLC p 546
6855 Pacific St 68106
Tel (303) 967-8000 *SIC* 7374 7389 7375

■ FIRST DATA TECHNOLOGIES INC p 546
6902 Pine St 68106
Tel (402) 222-5679 *SIC* 7374

FIRST NATIONAL BANK OF OMAHA INC p 548
1620 Dodge St 68197
Tel (402) 341-0500 *SIC* 6021

FIRST NATIONAL OF ILLINOIS INC p 548
1620 Dodge St 68102
Tel (402) 991-6131 *SIC* 6021

FIRST NATIONAL OF NEBRASKA INC p 548
1620 Dodge St 68197
Tel (402) 341-0500 *SIC* 6022 6141 7371

■ FIRSTCOMP INSURANCE CO p 550
222 S 15th St Ste 1500n 68102
Tel (888) 500-3344 *SIC* 6411

FORD ATCHLEY INC p 565
3633 N 72nd St 68134
Tel (402) 571-8801 *SIC* 5511

G4S SECURE INTEGRATION LLC p 588
1299 Farnam St Ste 1300 68102
Tel (402) 233-7700 *SIC* 1623 7382

GAVILON AGRICULTURE HOLDINGS CO p 594
1331 Capitol Ave 68102
Tel (402) 889-4000 *SIC* 5153 5191

GAVILON AGRICULTURE INVESTMENT INC p 594
1331 Capitol Ave 68102
Tel (402) 889-4000 *SIC* 5153 5191

GAVILON GRAIN LLC p 594
1331 Capitol Ave 68102
Tel (402) 889-4000
SIC 6221 5153 4221 4226

GAVILON GROUP LLC p 594
1331 Capitol Ave 68102
Tel (402) 889-4000 *SIC* 5153 5191

GAVILON HOLDINGS LLC p 594
1331 Capitol Ave 68102
Tel (402) 889-4000 *SIC* 6719

GAVILON INTERMEDIATE HOLDINGS LLC p 594
1331 Capitol Ave 68102
Tel (402) 889-4000 *SIC* 6722

GODFATHERS PIZZA INC p 619
2808 N 108th St 68164
Tel (402) 391-1452 *SIC* 5812 6794

GORDMANS INC p 625
1926 S 67th St 68106
Tel (402) 691-4000 *SIC* 5311

■ GORDMANS STORES INC p 625
1926 S 67th St 68106
Tel (402) 691-4000 *SIC* 5651 5963

GREATER OMAHA PACKING CO INC p 635
3001 L St 68107
Tel (402) 731-1700 *SIC* 2011 5147

▲ GREEN PLAINS INC p 637
450 Regency Pkwy Ste 400 68114
Tel (402) 884-8700 *SIC* 2869 2046

HAWKINS CONSTRUCTION CO p 669
2516 Deer Park Blvd 68105
Tel (402) 342-4455 *SIC* 1542 1611 1541

■ HAYNEEDLE INC p 670
9394 W Dodge Rd Ste 300 68114
Tel (402) 715-3000
SIC 5943 5719 5945 5947

HDR ARCHITECTURE INC p 673
8404 Indian Hills Dr 68114
Tel (402) 399-1000 *SIC* 8711

HDR ENGINEERING INC p 673
8404 Indian Hills Dr 68114
Tel (402) 399-1000 *SIC* 8742 8711

HDR INC p 673
8404 Indian Hills Dr 68114
Tel (402) 399-1000
SIC 8712 8711 8742 8748 4789

HOCKENBERGS EQUIPMENT AND SUPPLY CO INC p 699
7002 F St 68117
Tel (402) 339-8900 *SIC* 5046

KIEWIT BUILDING GROUP INC p 817
302 S 36th St Ste 500 68131
Tel (402) 977-4500 *SIC* 1521

KIEWIT CORP p 817
3555 Farnam St Ste 1000 68131
Tel (402) 342-2052
SIC 1542 1541 1611 1622 1629

KIEWIT INDUSTRIAL GROUP INC p 817
3555 Farnam St 68131
Tel (402) 342-2052 *SIC* 1629

KIEWIT INFRASTRUCTURE CO p 817
Kiewit Plz 68131
Tel (402) 342-2052
SIC 1541 1542 1629 1622 1522

KIEWIT INFRASTRUCTURE GROUP INC p 817
3555 Farnam St 68131
Tel (402) 342-2052 *SIC* 1611 1622

KIEWIT INFRASTRUCTURE SOUTH CO p 817
Kiewit Plz No 1044 68131
Tel (402) 342-2052 *SIC* 1622 1611

KIEWIT INFRASTRUCTURE WEST CO p 817
4004 S 60th St 68117
Tel (402) 342-2052
SIC 1611 1629 1541 1622 1623

KIEWIT MINING GROUP INC p 817
Kiewit Plz 68131
Tel (402) 342-2052 *SIC* 1241

KIEWIT OFFSHORE SERVICES LTD p 817
Kiewit Plz 68131
Tel (402) 342-2052 *SIC* 3441

KUTAK ROCK LLP p 832
1650 Farnam St Fl 2 68102
Tel (402) 346-6000 *SIC* 8111

LEO A DALY CO p 856
8600 Indian Hills Dr 68114
Tel (808) 521-8889 *SIC* 8712

LEO A DALY/BURNS & MCCONNELL JOINT VENTURE p 856
8600 Indian Hills Dr 68114
Tel (402) 391-8111 *SIC* 8712 8711

▲ LINDSAY CORP p 868
2222 N 111th St 68164
Tel (402) 829-6800 *SIC* 3523 3599 3443

■ LINDSAY MANUFACTURING LLC p 868
2222 N 111th St 68164
Tel (402) 829-6800
SIC 3523 3599 3499 3443

LOZIER CORP p 882
6336 John J Pershing Dr 68110
Tel (402) 457-8000 *SIC* 2541 2542

LOZIER STORE FIXTURES LLC p 882
6336 John J Pershing Dr 68110
Tel (402) 457-8000 *SIC* 5046

LYMAN-RICHEY CORP p 887
4315 Cuming St 68131
Tel (402) 556-3600
SIC 3273 1442 3271 5211 5032

MALNOVE HOLDING CO INC p 900
13434 F St 68137
Tel (402) 330-1100 *SIC* 2657

MARIANNA INDUSTRIES INC p 906
11222 I St Ste A 68137
Tel (402) 593-0211 *SIC* 5122 2844 7231

METROPOLITAN COMMUNITY COLLEGE p 955
5300 N 30th St 68111
Tel (402) 457-2400 *SIC* 8222

METROPOLITAN UTILITIES DISTRICT p 956
1723 Harney St 68102
Tel (402) 554-6666 *SIC* 4932

MILLARD LUMBER INC p 970
12900 I St 68137
Tel (402) 896-2800 *SIC* 5031 5211

MILLARD PUBLIC SCHOOLS p 970
5606 S 147th St 68137
Tel (402) 715-8200 *SIC* 8211

MILLARD REFRIGERATED SERVICES LLC p 970
13030 Pierce St 68144
Tel (402) 896-6600 *SIC* 4222

MILLER ELECTRIC CO p 970
2501 Saint Marys Ave 68105
Tel (402) 341-6479 *SIC* 1731

MOSAIC p 991
4980 S 118th St 68137
Tel (402) 896-3884 *SIC* 8361 8741

MUTUAL OF OMAHA BANK p 1003
3333 Farnam St Ste 10 68131
Tel (402) 351-5118 *SIC* 6035

MUTUAL OF OMAHA HEALTH PLANS INC p 1003
3301 Dodge St 68131
Tel (402) 342-7600 *SIC* 6411

MUTUAL OF OMAHA INSURANCE CO p 1003
Mutual Of Omaha Plaza 68175
Tel (402) 342-7600 *SIC* 6311 6211 8748

MUTUAL OF OMAHA MARKETING CORP p 1003
3301 Dodge St 68131
Tel (402) 342-7600 *SIC* 6722

■ NATIONAL INDEMNITY CO (INC) p 1013
1314 Douglas St Ste 1400 68102
Tel (402) 916-3000 *SIC* 6331 6411 6311

■ NATIONAL LIABILITY & FIRE INSURANCE CO p 1014
3024 Harney St 68131
Tel (402) 536-3000 *SIC* 6411

NEBRASKA BEEF LTD p 1023
4501 S 36th St 68107
Tel (402) 734-6823 *SIC* 2011

■ NEBRASKA FURNITURE MART INC p 1023
700 S 72nd St 68114
Tel (402) 397-6100
SIC 5712 5713 5722 5731 5734 5946

NEBRASKA MEDICAL CENTER p 1023
987400 Nebraska Med Ctr 68198
Tel (402) 552-2000 *SIC* 8062

NEBRASKA METHODIST HEALTH SYSTEM INC p 1023
8511 W Dodge Rd 68114
Tel (402) 354-2176 *SIC* 8062

NEBRASKA METHODIST HOSPITAL INC p 1023
8303 Dodge St 68114
Tel (402) 354-4540 *SIC* 8062

NEBRASKA ORTHOPAEDIC HOSPITAL LLC p 1023
2808 S 143rd Plz 68144
Tel (402) 637-0600 *SIC* 8069

■ NGL CRUDE LOGISTICS LLC p 1041
1299 Farnam St Ste 120 68102
Tel (402) 889-4000 *SIC* 6221 5153

NMC GROUP INC p 1045
11002 Sapp Brothers Dr 68138
Tel (402) 891-8600 *SIC* 5082 5084

NO FRILLS SUPERMARKETS INC OF OMAHA p 1046
11163 Mill Valley Rd 68154
Tel (402) 399-9244 *SIC* 5411

■ NORTHERN NATURAL GAS CO p 1056
1111 S 103rd St 68124
Tel (877) 654-0646
SIC 4226 4922 4923 4925

OMAHA COMMUNITY FOUNDATION p 1083
302 S 36th St Ste 100 68131
Tel (402) 342-3458 *SIC* 8399 8733

OMAHA PUBLIC POWER DISTRICT p 1083
444 S 16th St 68102
Tel (402) 636-2000 *SIC* 4911

OMAHA PUBLIC SCHOOLS p 1083
3215 Cuming St 68131
Tel (402) 557-2120 *SIC* 8211

OMAHA STEAKS INTERNATIONAL INC p 1083
11030 O St 68137
Tel (402) 597-3000 *SIC* 5142 8741

OMAHA TRUCK CENTER INC p 1083
10550 I St 68127
Tel (402) 592-2440 *SIC* 5511

■ OMAHA WORLD-HERALD CO p 1084
1314 Douglas St Ste 700 68102
Tel (402) 444-1000 *SIC* 2711 7331

■ ORIENTAL TRADING CO INC p 1094
5455 S 90th St 68127
Tel (402) 596-1200 *SIC* 5199 4813

■ OTC DIRECT INC p 1097
4206 S 108th St 68137
Tel (402) 331-5511 *SIC* 5961

■ OTC WORLDWIDE HOLDINGS INC p 1097
4206 S 108th St 68137
Tel (800) 348-6483 *SIC* 4813

PAMIDA BRANDS HOLDING LLC p 1110
8800 F St 68127
Tel (402) 493-4765 *SIC* 5331 5912

■ PAYFLEX HOLDINGS INC p 1122
10802 Farnam Dr Ste 100 68154
Tel (800) 284-4885 *SIC* 6411

■ PAYFLEX SYSTEMS USA INC p 1122
10802 Farnam Dr Ste 100 68154
Tel (402) 345-0666 *SIC* 6411

PETER KIEWIT SONS INC p 1138
3555 Farnam St Ste 1000 68131
Tel (402) 342-2052
SIC 1611 1622 1711 1542 1629 1221

PHYSICIANS CLINIC INC p 1145
8601 W Dodge Rd Ste 216 68114
Tel (402) 354-1700 *SIC* 8011 8031

PHYSICIANS LIFE INSURANCE CO p 1145
2600 Dodge St 68131
Tel (402) 633-1000 *SIC* 6311

PHYSICIANS MUTUAL INSURANCE CO p 1145
2600 Dodge St 68131
Tel (402) 633-1000 *SIC* 6321 6311

■ PITNEY BOWES PRESORT SERVICES INC p 1152
10110 I St 68127
Tel (402) 339-6500 *SIC* 7389

PROKARMA INC p 1182
222 S 15th St Ste 505n 68102
Tel (877) 527-6226 *SIC* 7379

QUALITY PORK INTERNATIONAL INC p 1197
10404 F Plz 68127
Tel (402) 339-1911 *SIC* 2011

REID PLASTICS INC p 1221
10861 Mill Valley Rd 68154
Tel (402) 934-2400 *SIC* 3085 2821 3089

RITE WAY INVESTMENTS INC p 1236
8400 I St 68127
Tel (402) 331-6400 *SIC* 5172 5541 5411

ROBERT B DAUGHERTY FOUNDATION INC p 1241
1 Valmont Plz 68154
Tel (402) 933-4663 *SIC* 8641

ROBERTS DAIRY CO LLC p 1242
2901 Cuming St 68131
Tel (402) 344-4321 *SIC* 2026 5812

SAPP BROS INC p 1281
9915 S 148th St 68138
Tel (402) 895-7038 *SIC* 5812

SAPP BROS TRAVEL CENTERS INC p 1281
9915 S 148th St 68138
Tel (402) 895-2202 *SIC* 5541

SCOULAR CO p 1294
2027 Dodge St Ste 200 68102
Tel (402) 342-3500 *SIC* 5153

SERGEANTS PET CARE PRODUCTS INC p 1306
10077 S 134th St 68138
Tel (402) 938-7000 *SIC* 2834 5199 2048

SHARED SERVICE SYSTEMS INC p 1312
1725 S 20th St 68108
Tel (402) 536-5300
SIC 5047 5142 7211 5149 5113 7218

SHERWOOD FOUNDATION p 1316
3555 Farnam St 68131
Tel (402) 341-1717 *SIC* 8641

SHOPKO p 1318
8800 F St 68127
Tel (402) 339-2400 *SIC* 5331 5912

SIGNAL 88 FRANCHISE GROUP INC p 1322
3880 S 149th St Ste 102 68144
Tel (877) 498-8494 *SIC* 7381

SIGNAL 88 LLC p 1322
3880 S 149th St Ste 102 68144
Tel (877) 498-8494 *SIC* 7381

SILVERSTONE GROUP INC p 1324
11516 Miracle Hills Dr # 100 68154
Tel (402) 964-5400
SIC 6371 6311 8742 6411

SIMMONDS RESTAURANT MANAGEMENT INC p 1324
3730 S 149th St Ste 107 68144
Tel (402) 493-2300 *SIC* 5812

SITEL CORP p 1327
5601 N 103rd St 68134
Tel (402) 963-6810 *SIC* 7389

SKO GROUP HOLDING LLC p 1330
8800 F St 68127
Tel (920) 429-2211 *SIC* 6719

SOLUTIONARY INC p 1339
9420 Underwood Ave # 300 68114
Tel (402) 361-3000 *SIC* 7379

SUN GORDMANS LLC p 1400
1926 S 67th St 68106
Tel (402) 691-4000 *SIC* 5651

SUSAN THOMPSON BUFFETT FOUNDATION p 1409
222 Kiewit Plz 68131
Tel (402) 943-1300 *SIC* 8641

■ TD AMERITRADE CLEARING INC p 1428
200 S 108th Ave 68154
Tel (402) 331-2744 *SIC* 6211

▲ TD AMERITRADE HOLDING CORP p 1428
200 S 108th Ave 68154
Tel (402) 331-7856 *SIC* 6211

TELVENT DTN LLC p 1435
9110 W Dodge Rd Ste 100 68114
Tel (402) 390-2328 *SIC* 7375

TENASKA BROWNSVILLE PARTNERS LLC p 1437
14302 Fnb Pkwy 68154
Tel (402) 691-9500 *SIC* 4911

TENASKA CAPITAL MANAGEMENT LLC p 1437
14302 Fnb Pkwy 68154
Tel (402) 691-9571 *SIC* 8742

TENASKA ENERGY INC p 1437
14302 Fnb Pkwy 68154
Tel (402) 691-9500
SIC 4911 4924 4939 8742

TENASKA FRONTIER PARTNERS LTD p 1437
14302 Fnb Pkwy 68154
Tel (402) 691-9500 *SIC* 4911

TENASKA INC p 1437
14302 Fnb Pkwy 68154
Tel (402) 691-9500
SIC 4924 4911 4939 8742

TENASKA MARKETING VENTURES p 1437
14302 Fnb Pkwy 68154
Tel (402) 758-6100 *SIC* 4924

TENASKA PENNSYLVANIA PARTNERS LLC p 1437
14302 Fnb Pkwy 68154
Tel (402) 691-9581 *SIC* 4911

TRANSWOOD CARRIERS INC p 1473
2565 Saint Marys Ave 68105
Tel (402) 346-8092 *SIC* 4213 4212 7513

TRANSWOOD INC p 1473
2565 Saint Marys Ave 68105
Tel (402) 346-8092 *SIC* 4212 4213

TRAVEL AND TRANSPORT INC p 1473
2120 S 72nd St Ste 120 68124
Tel (402) 399-4500 *SIC* 4724

▲ UNION PACIFIC CORP p 1504
1400 Douglas St 68179
Tel (402) 544-5000 *SIC* 4011

■ UNION PACIFIC RAILROAD CO INC p 1504
1400 Douglas St 68179
Tel (402) 544-5000 *SIC* 4011

UNITED OF OMAHA LIFE INSURANCE CO p 1510
Mutual Of Omaha Plaza 68175
Tel (402) 342-7600 *SIC* 6311 6321 6324

UNIVERSITY OF NEBRASKA MEDICAL CENTER p 1523
42nd And Emile 68105
Tel (402) 559-4000 *SIC* 8011

UNMC PHYSICIANS p 1528
988101 Nebraska Med Ctr 68198
Tel (402) 559-9700 *SIC* 8011

▲ VALMONT INDUSTRIES INC p 1541
1 Valmont Plz Ste 500 68154
Tel (402) 963-1000
SIC 3441 3399 3317 3523 3612

VIRGINIA TENASKA PARTNERS L P p 1560
14302 Fnb Pkwy 68154
Tel (402) 691-9500 *SIC* 4911

WAITT MEDIA INC p 1571
1125 S 103rd St Ste 425 68124
Tel (402) 697-8000 *SIC* 6726

WARREN DISTRIBUTION INC p 1577
727 S 13th St 68102
Tel (402) 341-9397 *SIC* 2992

■ WELLS FARGO BANK NEBRASKA NA p 1590
1919 Douglas St 68102
Tel (402) 536-2022 *SIC* 6021

▲ WERNER ENTERPRISES INC p 1592
14507 Frontier Rd 68138
Tel (402) 895-6640 *SIC* 4213

▲ WEST CORP p 1594
11808 Miracle Hills Dr 68154
Tel (402) 963-1200
SIC 7389 7372 4813 7374

WEST CUSTOMER MANAGEMENT GROUP LLC p 1594
11808 Miracle Hills Dr 68154
Tel (402) 571-7700 *SIC* 7389

■ WEST INTERACTIVE CORP p 1594
11650 Miracle Hills Dr 68154
Tel (402) 963-1200 *SIC* 7389

■ WEST IP COMMUNICATIONS INC p 1594
11808 Miracle Hills Dr 68154
Tel (402) 963-1200 *SIC* 4813

■ WEST REVENUE GENERATION SERVICES LLC p 1595
11808 Miracle Hills Dr 68154
Tel (800) 232-0900 *SIC* 7389

WESTSIDE COMMUNITY SCHOOL DISTRICT 66 p 1603
909 S 76th St 68114
Tel (402) 390-2100 *SIC* 8211

WOODMEN INSURANCE AGENCY INC p 1623
1700 Farnam St Ste 840 68102
Tel (402) 342-1890 *SIC* 6311

WOODMEN OF WORLD LIFE INSURANCE SOCIETY AND/OR OMAHA WOODMEN LIFE INSURANCE SOCIETY p 1623
1700 Farnam St Ste 840 68102
Tel (402) 342-1890 *SIC* 6311

XL FOUR STAR BEEF INC p 1632
3435 Gomez Ave 68107
Tel (402) 731-3370 *SIC* 2011

ONEILL, NE

CENTRAL VALLEY AG COOPERATIVE NONSTOCK p 280
415 E Highway 20 68763
Tel (402) 336-1263 *SIC* 5191

■ GREEN PLAINS ATKINSON LLC p 637
49131 Highway 20 68763
Tel (402) 315-1658 *SIC* 2869

■ J & J SANITATION INC p 770
87181 494th Ave 68763
Tel (402) 336-3011 *SIC* 4953

PAPILLION, NE

INFOGROUP INC p 741
1020 E 1st St 68046
Tel (402) 836-4500 *SIC* 7331

PAPILLION-LAVISTA PUBLIC SCHOOLS p 1112
420 S Washington St 68046
Tel (402) 537-6244 *SIC* 8211

PLAINVIEW, NE

HUSKER AG LLC p 721
54048 Highway 20 68769
Tel (402) 582-4446 *SIC* 2869

HUSKER AG MARKETING INC p 721
54048 Highway 20 68769
Tel (402) 582-4446 *SIC* 8742

SCHUYLER, NE

ALEGENT HEALTH MEMORIAL HOSPITAL p 48
104 W 17th St 68661
Tel (402) 352-2441 *SIC* 8062

SCOTTSBLUFF, NE

KELLEY BEAN CO INC p 808
2407 Circle Dr 69361
Tel (308) 635-6438 *SIC* 5153 2034

PANHANDLE COOPERATIVE ASSOCIATION p 1111
401 S Beltline Hwy W 69361
Tel (308) 632-5301 *SIC* 5541 0721

REGIONAL WEST HEALTH SERVICES INC p 1219
4021 Avenue B 69361
Tel (308) 635-3711 *SIC* 8741

REGIONAL WEST MEDICAL CENTER p 1219
4021 Avenue B 69361
Tel (308) 635-3711 *SIC* 8062

SIDNEY, NE

▲ CABELAS INC p 234
1 Cabelas Dr 69162
Tel (308) 254-5505 *SIC* 5961 5941

■ WORLDS FOREMOST BANK p 1626
1 Cabelas Dr 69162
Tel (402) 323-4300 *SIC* 6099

SNYDER, NE

SMEAL FIRE APPARATUS CO p 1332
610 W 4th St 68664
Tel (402) 568-2224 *SIC* 3711

SOUTH SIOUX CITY, NE

■ GREAT WEST CASUALTY p 634
1100 W 29th St 68776
Tel (402) 494-2411 *SIC* 6331

■ GREAT WEST CASUALTY CO p 634
1100 W 29th St 68776
Tel (402) 494-2411 *SIC* 6331

ULYSSES, NE

COLEEN M MCCORMICK p 336
415 Center St Dakota Pl 68669
Tel (402) 549-2778 *SIC* 8748 6799

VALLEY, NE

VALMONT INDUSTRIES INC p 1542
7002 N 288th St 68064
Tel (402) 359-2201 *SIC* 3523

WINNEBAGO, NE

HO-CHUNK INC p 698
1 Mission Dr 68071
Tel (402) 878-4135 *SIC* 5172

WINNEBAGO TRIBE OF NEBRASKA p 1616
100 Bluff Ave 68071
Tel (402) 878-3100 *SIC* 7011

NEVADA

CARSON CITY, NV

CARSON TAHOE REGIONAL HEALTHCARE p 261
1600 Medical Pkwy 89703
Tel (775) 445-8000 *SIC* 8062

COMPLETE MILLWORK SERVICES INC p 351
4909 Goni Rd Ste A 89706
Tel (775) 246-0485 *SIC* 5031

DREAM MARRIAGE GROUP INC p 455
2533 N Carson St Ste 3988 89706
Tel (310) 200-8875 *SIC* 8322

EXECUTIVE OFFICE OF STATE OF NEVADA p 518
101 N Carson St 89701
Tel (775) 684-5670 *SIC* 9111

JUDICIARY COURTS OF STATE OF NEVADA p 797
201 S Carson St Ste 201 89701
Tel (775) 684-1700 *SIC* 9211

NEVADA DEPARTMENT OF CORRECTIONS p 1028
5500 Snyder Ave Bldg 89 89701
Tel (775) 887-3285 *SIC* 9223

NEVADA DEPARTMENT OF HEALTH AND HUMAN SERVICES p 1028
4126 Tech Way Ste 100 89706
Tel (775) 684-4000 *SIC* 9431

NEVADA DEPARTMENT OF MOTOR VEHICLES p 1028
555 Wright Way 89711
Tel (775) 684-4549 *SIC* 9621

NEVADA DEPARTMENT OF PUBLIC SAFETY p 1028
555 Wright Way 89701
Tel (775) 684-4556 *SIC* 9229

NEVADA DEPARTMENT OF TRANSPORTATION p 1028
1263 S Stewart St 89712
Tel (775) 888-7440 *SIC* 9621

STATE OF NEVADA p 1382
101 N Carson St Ste 1 89701
Tel (775) 684-5670 *SIC* 9111

SWIFT COMMUNICATIONS INC p 1412
580 Mallory Way 89701
Tel (775) 850-7676 *SIC* 2711

ELKO, NV

BARRICK GOLDSTRIKE MINES INC p 157
905 W Main St 89801
Tel (775) 748-1001 *SIC* 1041

ELKO COUNTY SCHOOL DISTRICT p 488
850 Elm St 89801
Tel (775) 738-5196 *SIC* 8211

FALLON, NV

A & K EARTH MOVERS INC p 4
515 Windmill Dr 89406
Tel (775) 825-1636 *SIC* 1611 1542

FERNLEY, NV

FORTIFIBER CORP p 569
300 Industrial Dr 89408
Tel (800) 773-4777 *SIC* 2671

HENDERSON, NV

CASHMAN EQUIPMENT CO p 263
3300 Saint Rose Pkwy 89052
Tel (702) 649-8777
SIC 5084 5063 7353 7699

CITY OF HENDERSON p 315
240 S Water St 89015
Tel (702) 267-2323 *SIC* 9111

FINDLAY AUTOMOTIVE INC p 543
310 N Gibson Rd 89014
Tel (702) 558-8888 *SIC* 5511

GLOBAL PACIFIC PRODUCE INC p 617
11500 S Eastern Ave # 160 89052
Tel (702) 898-8051 *SIC* 5148

GREEN VALLEY RANCH GAMING LLC p 637
2300 Paseo Verde Pkwy 89052
Tel (702) 617-7777 *SIC* 7011

LV GAMING VENTURES LLC p 887
12300 Las Vegas Blvd S 89044
Tel (702) 797-1000 *SIC* 7011 7991

■ **LVGV LLC** p 887
12300 Las Vegas Blvd S 89044
Tel (702) 797-1000 *SIC* 7011 7991

MARNELL SHER GAMING LLC p 909
12300 Las Vegas Blvd S 89044
Tel (702) 797-1000 *SIC* 7011

MITSUBISHI CEMENT CORP p 977
151 Cassia Way 89014
Tel (702) 932-3900 *SIC* 3297 5032

OMICS GROUP INC p 1084
2360 Corp Cir Ste 400 89074
Tel (888) 843-8169 *SIC* 2721

PERRY JOHNSON & ASSOCIATES INC p 1137
1489 W Warm Springs Rd 89014
Tel (800) 803-6330 *SIC* 7338

PROFICIO MORTGAGE VENTURES LLC p 1180
2225 Village Walk Dr # 200 89052
Tel (407) 476-2400 *SIC* 6162

▲ **SPECTRUM PHARMACEUTICALS INC** p 1357
11500 S Estrn Ave Ste 240 89052
Tel (702) 835-6300 *SIC* 2834

SUNSET STATION HOTEL AND CASINO p 1404
1301 W Sunset Rd 89014
Tel (702) 547-7777 *SIC* 7011 5962 7389

WALLBOARD SYSTEMS HAWAII p 1573
696 Turtlewood Pl 89052
Tel (702) 233-3654 *SIC* 1742

WESTCARE FOUNDATION INC p 1596
1711 Whitney Mesa Dr # 100 89014
Tel (702) 385-3330 *SIC* 8322 8611

WINCO FOODS p 1614
80 N Stephanie St 89074
Tel (702) 558-5366 *SIC* 5411

INCLINE VILLAGE, NV

▲ **PDL BIOPHARMA INC** p 1124
932 Southwood Blvd 89451
Tel (775) 832-8500 *SIC* 2836

JEAN, NV

PRIMADONNA CO LLC p 1174
31900 Las Vegas Blvd S 89019
Tel (702) 386-7867 *SIC* 7011

PRIMM VALLEY RESORT AND CASINO p 1176
31900 Las Vegas Blvd S 89019
Tel (702) 679-5160 *SIC* 7011

LAS VEGAS, NV

640 LAS VEGAS HEALTHCARE AND REHABIL p 3
2832 S Maryland Pkwy 89109
Tel (702) 735-5848 *SIC* 8051

■ **ACE GAMING LLC** p 16
8918 Spanish Ridge Ave 89148
Tel (702) 401-5931 *SIC* 7011

AFFINITY GAMING p 32
3755 Breakthrough Way # 300 89135
Tel (702) 341-2400 *SIC* 7011

AFFINITY GAMING FINANCE CORP p 32
3755 Breakthrough Way # 300 89135
Tel (702) 341-2400 *SIC* 7011 7999

AHERN RENTALS INC p 36
1401 Mineral Ave 89106
Tel (702) 362-0623 *SIC* 7353

ALLADDIN GAMING LLC p 51
3667 Las Vegas Blvd S 89109
Tel (702) 785-5555 *SIC* 7011

■ **ALLEGIANT AIR LLC** p 53
1201 N Town Center Dr # 110 89144
Tel (702) 505-8888 *SIC* 4512

▲ **ALLEGIANT TRAVEL CO** p 53
1201 N Town Center Dr 89144
Tel (702) 851-7300 *SIC* 4512 4724

AMERICAN CASINO & ENTERTAINMENT PROPERTIES LLC p 69
2000 Las Vegas Blvd S 89104
Tel (702) 383-5242 *SIC* 7011

AMERICAN WEST HOMES INC p 81
250 Pilot Rd Ste 140 89119
Tel (702) 736-6434 *SIC* 6552

AMERISTAR CASINOS INC p 83
3773 Howard Hughes Pkwy # 490 89169
Tel (702) 567-7000 *SIC* 7011

ARCATA ASSOCIATES INC p 104
2588 Fire Mesa St Ste 110 89128
Tel (702) 642-9500 *SIC* 8711

ARISTOCRAT TECHNOLOGIES INC p 108
7230 Amigo St 89119
Tel (702) 270-1000 *SIC* 5099

ARIZONA CHARLIES INC p 108
740 S Decatur Blvd 89107
Tel (702) 258-5200 *SIC* 7011 5812 5813

■ **ARK LAS VEGAS RESTAURANT CORP** p 109
3790 Las Vegas Blvd S 89109
Tel (702) 207-4498 *SIC* 5812

ARM STRONG GROUP LLC p 110
3960 Howard Hughes Pkwy 89169
Tel (702) 948-8960 *SIC* 5169

■ **BALLY GAMING INC** p 148
6601 Bermuda Rd 89119
Tel (702) 532-7700 *SIC* 3999

■ **BALLY GAMING INTERNATIONAL INC** p 148
6601 Bermuda Rd 89119
Tel (702) 584-7700 *SIC* 3999

■ **BALLY TECHNOLOGIES INC** p 148
6601 Bermuda Rd 89119
Tel (770) 420-2388
SIC 3999 7999 7993 7372

BANK OF NEVADA p 151
2700 W Sahara Ave Ste 100 89102
Tel (702) 248-4200 *SIC* 6022

BASELINEAGENT INC p 158
3960 Howard Hughes Pkwy # 500 89169
Tel (813) 435-6244 *SIC* 7941

BEAL BANK USA p 165
1970 Vlg Ctr Cir Ste 1 89134
Tel (702) 242-8846 *SIC* 6036

BOARD OF REGENTS NEVADA SYSTEM OF HIGHER EDUCATION p 195
4505 S Maryland Pkwy 89154
Tel (702) 895-4727 *SIC* 8221 9411

■ **BOMBARD ELECTRIC LLC** p 199
3570 W Post Rd 89118
Tel (702) 263-3570 *SIC* 1731

BONANZA BEVERAGE CO p 199
6333 Ensworth St 89119
Tel (702) 361-4166 *SIC* 5181

BOULDER STATION INC p 204
4111 Boulder Hwy 89121
Tel (702) 432-7777 *SIC* 7011 7389

▲ **BOYD GAMING CORP** p 205
3883 Howard Flr 9 89169
Tel (702) 792-7200 *SIC* 7011

BRAD HENRY FRIEDMUTTER & ASSOCIATES LTD p 206
4022 Dean Martin Dr 89103
Tel (702) 736-7477 *SIC* 8712 7389

BRADY INDUSTRIES INC p 207
7055 Lindell Rd 89118
Tel (702) 876-3990
SIC 5169 5087 5999 5023 5064

▲ **CAESARS ACQUISITION CO** p 237
1 Caesars Palace Dr 89109
Tel (702) 407-6000 *SIC* 7011

▲ **CAESARS ENTERTAINMENT CORP** p 237
1 Caesars Palace Dr 89109
Tel (702) 407-6000 *SIC* 7011 7999

■ **CAESARS ENTERTAINMENT OPERATING CO INC** p 237
1 Caesars Palace Dr 89109
Tel (702) 407-6000 *SIC* 7999

■ **CAESARS GROWTH PARTNERS LLC** p 237
1 Caesars Palace Dr 89109
Tel (702) 407-6586 *SIC* 7011

■ **CAESARS LICENSE CO LLC** p 237
3645 Las Vegas Blvd S 89109
Tel (702) 739-4111 *SIC* 7999

■ **CAESARS PALACE CORP** p 237
3570 Las Vegas Blvd S 89109
Tel (702) 731-7110 *SIC* 7011

■ **CAESARS WORLD INC** p 237
3570 Las Vegas Blvd S 89109
Tel (702) 731-7110
SIC 7011 7999 5812 6552 5611 5621

■ **CALIFORNIA HOTEL AND CASINO** p 240
12 E Ogden Ave 89101
Tel (702) 385-1222 *SIC* 7011

CALTROL INC p 243
1385 Pama Ln Ste 111 89119
Tel (702) 966-1800 *SIC* 5084

CANNERY CASINO RESORTS LLC p 247
9107 W Russell Rd 89148
Tel (702) 507-5700 *SIC* 7011

CHINA ENERGY CORP p 301
6130 Elton Ave 89107
Tel (702) 998-8146 *SIC* 7011

■ **CIRCUS CIRCUS CASINOS INC** p 308
2880 Las Vegas Blvd S 89109
Tel (702) 734-0410 *SIC* 7011

CIRQUE DU SOLEIL AMERICA INC p 308
980 Kelly Johnson Dr 2nd 89119
Tel (702) 352-0200 *SIC* 7929

CITADEL BROADCASTING CO p 309
7201 W Lake Mead Blvd # 400 89128
Tel (702) 804-5200 *SIC* 4832

CITY CENTER HOLDINGS LLC p 312
3950 Las Vegas Blvd S 89119
Tel (702) 632-9800 *SIC* 6719

CITY OF LAS VEGAS p 316
495 S Main St 89101
Tel (702) 229-6321 *SIC* 9111

CLARK COUNTY SCHOOL DIST p 322
5101 Obannon Dr Apt 233 89146
Tel (702) 799-1042 *SIC* 8211

CLARK COUNTY SCHOOL DISTRICT p 322
5100 W Sahara Ave 89146
Tel (702) 799-5000 *SIC* 8211

■ **COAST HOTELS & CASINOS INC** p 331
4500 W Tropicana Ave 89103
Tel (702) 367-7111 *SIC* 7011

■ **COAST HOTELS AND CASINOS INC** p 331
4500 W Tropicana Ave 89103
Tel (702) 365-7111 *SIC* 7011

COLONY RESORTS LVH ACQUISITIONS LLC p 338
3000 Paradise Rd 89109
Tel (702) 732-5111 *SIC* 7011

▲ **CONSUMER PORTFOLIO SERVICES INC** p 361
3800 Howard Hughes Pkwy 89169
Tel (949) 753-6800 *SIC* 6141

COUNTY OF CLARK p 377
500 S Grand Central Pkwy # 6 89155
Tel (702) 455-3530 *SIC* 9111

CREDIT ONE BANK NATIONAL ASSOCIATION p 390
585 Pilot Rd 89119
Tel (702) 269-3900 *SIC* 6021

CREDIT ONE FINANCIAL p 390
585 Pilot Rd 89119
Tel (702) 269-1000 *SIC* 6021

CREEL PRINTING & PUBLISHING CO INC p 391
6330 W Sunset Rd 89118
Tel (702) 735-8161 *SIC* 2752

■ **DESERT PALACE INC** p 432
1 Caesars Palace Dr 89109
Tel (702) 407-6269 *SIC* 7011

■ **DESERT SPRINGS HOSPITAL MEDICAL CENTER** p 432
2075 E Flamingo Rd 89119
Tel (702) 733-8800 *SIC* 8062

DIAMOND RESORTS CORP p 437
10600 W Charleston Blvd 89135
Tel (702) 684-8000 *SIC* 7041 6141 8741

DIAMOND RESORTS HOLDINGS LLC p 437
10600 W Charleston Blvd 89135
Tel (877) 787-0906 *SIC* 7011 6141 8741

DIAMOND RESORTS INTERNATIONAL INC p 437
10600 W Charleston Blvd 89135
Tel (702) 798-8840 *SIC* 7011

DIAMOND RESORTS MANAGEMENT INC p 437
10600 W Charleston Blvd 89135
Tel (702) 240-9712 *SIC* 7011

E-T-T LLC p 467
3440 W Russell Rd 89118
Tel (877) 736-5388 *SIC* 7993

■ **EG&G SPECIAL PROJECTS INC** p 481
811 Grier Dr Ste A 89119
Tel (702) 492-7800 *SIC* 8741

▲ **EVERI HOLDINGS INC** p 515
7250 S Tenaya Way Ste 100 89113
Tel (800) 833-7110 *SIC* 7389

■ **EVERI PAYMENTS INC** p 515
7250 S Tenaya Way Ste 100 89113
Tel (702) 855-3000 *SIC* 7389 6099

EXX INC p 521
1350 E Flamingo Rd 689 89119
Tel (248) 409-1070
SIC 3621 3669 3714 3944

FITZGERALDS GAMING CORP p 553
301 Fremont St Fl 12 89101
Tel (702) 388-2400 *SIC* 7011

FITZGERALDS LAS VEGAS INC p 553
301 Fremont St 89101
Tel (702) 388-2224 *SIC* 7011

FLETCHER JONES LAS VEGAS INC p 555
7300 W Sahara Ave 89117
Tel (702) 739-9800 *SIC* 5511

FP HOLDINGS LP p 573
4321 W Flamingo Rd 89103
Tel (702) 942-7777 *SIC* 7011

▲ **FULL HOUSE RESORTS INC** p 584
4670 S Fort Apache Rd # 190 89147
Tel (702) 221-7800 *SIC* 7011 7993

GAUGHAN SOUTH LLC p 594
9777 Las Vegas Blvd S 89183
Tel (702) 796-7111 *SIC* 7011

GET FRESH SALES INC p 609
6745 Escondido St 89119
Tel (702) 897-8522 *SIC* 5148

■ **GLOBAL EXPERIENCE SPECIALISTS INC** p 616
7000 Lindell Rd 89118
Tel (702) 515-5500 *SIC* 7389

GO WIRELESS INC p 619
9970 W Cheyenne Ave # 100 89129
Tel (702) 853-6200 *SIC* 5999

▲ **GOLDEN ENTERTAINMENT INC** p 620
6595 S Jones Blvd 89118
Tel (702) 893-7777 *SIC* 7999

■ **GOLDEN NUGGET FINANCE CORP** p 621
129 Fremont St 89101
Tel (702) 385-7111 *SIC* 7011

GOLDEN NUGGET INC p 621
129 Fremont St 89101
Tel (702) 385-7111 *SIC* 5812 7011

GORDON BIERSCH BREWING CO p 626
10801 W Charleston Blvd # 600 89135
Tel (702) 221-4475 *SIC* 5813

GPX CORP p 628
300 S 4th St Ste 1100 89101
Tel (702) 386-4789 *SIC* 7389

HAKKASAN HOLDINGS LLC p 653
6385 S Rainbow Blvd # 800 89118
Tel (702) 212-8804 *SIC* 8741

HARD ROCK HOTEL HOLDINGS LLC p 660
4455 Paradise Rd 89169
Tel (702) 693-5000 *SIC* 7011

HARD ROCK HOTEL INC p 660
4455 Paradise Rd 89169
Tel (702) 693-5000 *SIC* 7011

■ **HEALTH PLAN OF NEVADA INC** p 675
2720 N Tenaya Way 89128
Tel (702) 242-7300 *SIC* 8011

HEALTHCARE PARTNERS NEVADA LLC p 676
700 E Warm Springs Rd # 230 89119
Tel (702) 932-8500 *SIC* 8011

HRHH GAMING SENIOR MEZZ LLC p 714
4455 Paradise Rd 89169
Tel (702) 693-5026 *SIC* 7999

HRHH HOTEL/CASINO LLC p 714
4455 Paradise Rd 89169
Tel (702) 693-5000 *SIC* 7011

■ **HUGHES CORP** p 717
10801 W Charleston Blvd # 300 89135
Tel (702) 791-4000 *SIC* 6552

IKE GAMING INC p 731
600 Fremont St 89101
Tel (702) 385-5200 SIC 7011

INTERMOUNTAIN WEST COMMUNICATIONS CO p 754
701 S 9th St 89101
Tel (702) 642-3333 SIC 4833

INTERNATIONAL GAME TECHNOLOGY INC p 755
7900 W Sunset Rd 89113
Tel (702) 669-7777 SIC 7999

INTERNATIONAL MARKET CENTERS INC p 756
475 S Grand Central Pkwy 89106
Tel (702) 599-9621 SIC 6798

INTERNATIONAL MARKET CENTERS LP p 756
495 S Grand Central Pkwy 89106
Tel (702) 599-9621 SIC 8741

JT3 LLC p 796
821 Grier Dr 89119
Tel (702) 492-2100 SIC 8711

JUST LIKE SUGAR INC p 797
2020 Pama Ln 89119
Tel (702) 483-6777 SIC 2869

KALDI MANAGEMENT INC p 801
4824 Winterset Dr Ste 100 89130
Tel (702) 340-7283 SIC 6099

KB FRAMERS LLC p 805
5795 Rogers St 89118
Tel (702) 873-9451 SIC 1751 1521

KONAMI GAMING INC p 827
585 Konami Cir 89119
Tel (702) 616-1400 SIC 5092 3999

LAS VEGAS CONVENTION & VISITORS AUTHORITY p 845
3150 Paradise Rd 89109
Tel (702) 892-0711 SIC 7389

LAS VEGAS PAVING CORP p 845
4420 S Decatur Blvd 89103
Tel (702) 251-5800 SIC 1611 1629 8711

LAS VEGAS RESORT HOLDINGS LLC p 845
2535 Las Vegas Blvd S 89109
Tel (702) 761-7702 SIC 7011

▲ LAS VEGAS SANDS CORP p 845
3355 Las Vegas Blvd S 89109
Tel (702) 414-1000 SIC 7011

■ LAS VEGAS SANDS LLC p 845
3355 Las Vegas Blvd S 89109
Tel (702) 414-1000 SIC 7011

LAS VEGAS VALLEY WATER DISTRICT p 845
1001 S Valley View Blvd 89107
Tel (702) 870-2011 SIC 4941

LAS-CAL CORP p 846
3225 S Rainbow Blvd # 102 89146
Tel (702) 880-5818 SIC 5812

MAJESTIC STAR CASINO LLC p 899
5524 S Fort Apache Rd # 120 89148
Tel (702) 386-0226 SIC 7011

MALCO ENTERPRISES OF NEVADA INC p 899
7120 Haven St 89119
Tel (702) 736-1212 SIC 5521 7514 7513

■ MANDALAY RESORT GROUP p 901
3950 Las Vegas Blvd S 89119
Tel (702) 693-7120 SIC 7011 7999 7996

MARSHALL RETAIL GROUP LLC p 911
3755 W Sunset Rd Ste A 89118
Tel (702) 385-5233
SIC 5661 5621 5641 5611

MARTIN-HARRIS CONSTRUCTION LLC p 913
3030 S Highland Dr 89109
Tel (702) 385-5257 SIC 1541 1542

■ MERILLAT INDUSTRIES INC p 949
865 Pilot Rd 89119
Tel (702) 897-9800 SIC 3999

■ MGM GRAND HOTEL LLC p 958
3799 Las Vegas Blvd S 89109
Tel (702) 891-1111 SIC 7011

▲ MGM RESORTS INTERNATIONAL p 958
3600 Las Vegas Blvd S 89109
Tel (702) 693-7120 SIC 7011

■ MH INC p 958
3950 Las Vegas Blvd S 89119
Tel (702) 693-7120 SIC 7011

MIDJIT MARKET INC p 965
1580 S Jones Blvd 89146
Tel (702) 216-2154 SIC 5541 5141

■ MIRAGE CASINO-HOTEL p 974
3400 Las Vegas Blvd S 89109
Tel (702) 791-7111 SIC 7011

■ MIRAGE RESORTS INC p 974
3400 Las Vegas Blvd S 89109
Tel (702) 791-7111 SIC 7011

MOUNTAINVIEW HOSPITAL INC p 994
3100 N Tenaya Way 89128
Tel (702) 255-5000 SIC 8062 8011 4119

NASSIRI INC p 1009
2035 Helm Dr 89119
Tel (702) 837-7332 SIC 5136 5137

NEVADA BEVERAGE CO p 1028
3940 W Tropicana Ave 89103
Tel (702) 739-9998 SIC 5181

▲ NEVADA GOLD & CASINOS INC p 1028
133 E Warm Springs Rd # 102 89119
Tel (702) 685-1000 SIC 7011

■ NEVADA POWER CO p 1028
6226 W Sahara Ave 89146
Tel (702) 402-5000 SIC 4911

NEVADA PROPERTY 1 LLC p 1028
3708 Las Vegas Blvd S 89109
Tel (702) 698-7000 SIC 7011

NEVADA STATE BANK p 1028
750 E Warm Springs Rd # 240 89119
Tel (702) 855-4575 SIC 6022

NEVADA YELLOW CAB CORP p 1029
5225 W Post Rd 89118
Tel (702) 873-8012 SIC 4121

■ NEW CASTLE CORP p 1029
3850 Las Vegas Blvd S 89109
Tel (702) 597-7777 SIC 5812 7011

■ NEW YORK - NEW YORK HOTEL & CASINO LLC p 1033
3790 Las Vegas Blvd S 89109
Tel (702) 740-6969 SIC 7011 7996

NEW-COM INC p 1036
6600 Amelia Earhart Ct B 89119
Tel (702) 642-3331 SIC 7353

NORTH AMERICAN KIOSK LLC p 1050
3930 Howard Hughes Pkwy # 500 89169
Tel (702) 691-2948 SIC 8741

NOS COMMUNICATIONS INC p 1062
250 Pilot Rd Ste 300 89119
Tel (702) 547-8000 SIC 8748 4813

■ NV ENERGY INC p 1068
6226 W Sahara Ave 89146
Tel (702) 402-5000 SIC 4911 4924

PA MEADOWS LLC p 1103
9107 W Russell Rd 89148
Tel (702) 856-5158 SIC 7999

PALACE STATION HOTEL & CASINO INC p 1108
2411 W Sahara Ave 89102
Tel (702) 367-2411 SIC 7011

■ PARBALL CORP p 1114
3655 Las Vegas Blvd S 89109
Tel (702) 967-4111
SIC 7011 7999 6512 7521 7211

■ PARIS LAS VEGAS p 1115
3655 Las Vegas Blvd S 89109
Tel (702) 946-7000 SIC 7011

PENTA BUILDING GROUP INC p 1131
181 E Warm Springs Rd 89119
Tel (702) 614-1678 SIC 1542

PHILCOR TV & ELECTRONIC LEASING INC p 1143
4200 Spring Mountain Rd 89102
Tel (702) 367-0400 SIC 5063 5065

PINNACLE ENTERTAINMENT INC p 1149
3980 Howard Hughes Pkwy 89169
Tel (702) 541-7777 SIC 7999 7011

PLAZA HOTEL & CASINO LLC p 1156
1 S Main St 89101
Tel (702) 386-2110 SIC 7011

PREMIER IMAGE CORP p 1170
635 Trade Center Dr 89119
Tel (702) 263-3500 SIC 5399

■ QUEST DIAGNOSTICS INC p 1199
4230 Burnham Ave 89119
Tel (702) 733-7866 SIC 8071 8731

■ RAMPARTS INC p 1207
3900 Las Vegas Blvd S 89119
Tel (702) 262-4000 SIC 7011

REBEL OIL CO INC p 1214
2200 Highland Dr 89102
Tel (702) 382-5866 SIC 5171 5411

RED ROCK RESORTS INC p 1216
1505 S Pavilion Center Dr 89135
Tel (702) 495-3000 SIC 7011

■ REPUBLIC SILVER STATE DISPOSAL INC p 1225
770 E Sahara Ave Ste 400 89104
Tel (702) 735-5151 SIC 4953

RIMINI STREET INC p 1235
3993 Howard Hughes Pkwy 89169
Tel (702) 839-9671 SIC 7379 7373

■ RIO HOTEL & CASINO INC p 1236
3700 W Flamingo Rd 89103
Tel (702) 777-7777 SIC 7011 7997

■ RIO PROPERTIES INC p 1236
3700 W Flamingo Rd 89103
Tel (702) 777-7777 SIC 7011 5812

RIVIERA HOLDINGS CORP p 1239
2901 Las Vegas Blvd S 89109
Tel (702) 794-9237 SIC 7011

RUFFIN ACQUISITION LLC p 1257
3300 Las Vegas Blvd S 89109
Tel (800) 944-7444 SIC 8732

SAGEBRUSH ENTERPRISES INC p 1267
4730 S Fort Apache Rd 89147
Tel (702) 873-5338
SIC 1522 1542 7992 6799

■ SAM-WILL INC p 1274
200 Fremont St 89101
Tel (702) 385-3232 SIC 7011

SANTA FE STATION INC p 1280
4949 N Rancho Dr 89130
Tel (702) 658-4900 SIC 7011

▲ SCIENTIFIC GAMES CORP p 1292
6650 El Camino Rd 89118
Tel (702) 897-7150 SIC 7999 7373

■ SHFL ENTERTAINMENT INC p 1316
6650 El Camino Rd 89118
Tel (702) 897-7150 SIC 3999 3949 3944

■ SIERRA HEALTH AND LIFE INSURANCE CO INC p 1320
2720 N Tenaya Way 89128
Tel (702) 242-7700 SIC 6311

■ SIERRA HEALTH SERVICES INC p 1320
2720 N Tenaya Way 89128
Tel (702) 242-7000
SIC 6324 6311 8082 8741 8093

SILVERTON CASINO LLC p 1324
3333 Blue Diamond Rd 89139
Tel (702) 263-7777 SIC 7011 7299 5813

SOUTHERN NEVADA WATER AUTHORITY p 1349
100 N City Pkwy Ste 700 89106
Tel (702) 862-3400 SIC 4941

▲ SOUTHWEST GAS CORP p 1352
5241 Spring Mountain Rd 89150
Tel (702) 876-0711 SIC 4923 1623 1389

SPRING VALLEY HOSPITAL MEDICAL CENTER p 1360
5400 S Rainbow Blvd 89118
Tel (702) 853-3000 SIC 8011

■ SPRING VALLEY MEDICAL CENTER INC p 1360
5400 S Rainbow Blvd 89118
Tel (702) 853-3000 SIC 8062

STARVING STUDENTS INC p 1379
6220 Kimberly Ave Ste 2 89122
Tel (702) 900-4002 SIC 4214 4213

STATION CASINOS INC p 1383
4949 N Rancho Dr 89130
Tel (702) 658-4900 SIC 7011

STATION CASINOS INC p 1383
1505 S Pavilion Center Dr 89135
Tel (702) 495-3000 SIC 8741 7993 7011

STATION CASINOS LLC p 1383
1505 S Pavilion Center Dr 89135
Tel (702) 495-3000 SIC 7011

STATION VOTECO LLC p 1383
1505 S Pavilion Center Dr 89135
Tel (702) 495-3000 SIC 7011

STEPHENS MEDIA LLC p 1386
1111 W Bonanza Rd 89106
Tel (702) 383-0211 SIC 2711

STERNSCHNUPPE LLC p 1388
3325 W Sunset Rd Ste E 89118
Tel (702) 458-6797 SIC 3612

STRATOSPHERE GAMING LLC p 1392
2000 Las Vegas Blvd S 89104
Tel (702) 380-7777 SIC 7011

STRATOSPHERE LLC p 1393
2000 Las Vegas Blvd S 89104
Tel (702) 380-7777 SIC 7011 7999

■ SUMMERLIN HOSPITAL MEDICAL CENTER LLC p 1398
657 N Town Center Dr 89144
Tel (702) 233-7000 SIC 8062 8011

■ SUNRISE HOSPITAL AND MEDICAL CENTER LLC p 1404
3186 S Maryland Pkwy 89109
Tel (702) 731-8080 SIC 8062

SWITCH LTD p 1413
7135 S Decatur Blvd 89118
Tel (702) 444-4000 SIC 4899

T H ONE INC p 1419
3773 Howard Hughes Pkwy 350n 89169
Tel (702) 734-3700 SIC 6719

TEACHERS HEALTH TRUST p 1429
2950 E Rochelle Ave 89121
Tel (702) 866-6133 SIC 6733

TEAM FORD LLC p 1430
5445 Drexel Rd 89130
Tel (702) 395-5100 SIC 5511

TERRIBLE HERBST INC p 1440
5195 Las Vegas Blvd S 89119
Tel (702) 597-6296 SIC 5541

TOWBIN AUTOMOTIVE ENTERPRISES INC p 1464
5550 W Sahara Ave 89146
Tel (702) 253-7000 SIC 5511 7514

TRAX INTERNATIONAL CORP p 1475
8337 W Sunset Rd Ste 250 89113
Tel (702) 216-4455
SIC 7373 8711 7376 8742 8744

TREASURE ISLAND LLC p 1475
3300 Las Vegas Blvd S 89109
Tel (702) 894-7111 SIC 7011 7231

TROPICANA ENTERTAINMENT HOLDINGS LLC p 1484
3930 Howard Hughes Pkwy 89169
Tel (702) 589-3900 SIC 7011

■ TROPICANA ENTERTAINMENT INC p 1484
8345 W Sunset Rd Ste 300 89113
Tel (702) 589-3900 SIC 7011 7999

TROPICANA ENTERTAINMENT LLC p 1484
3930 Howard Hughes Pkwy # 400 89169
Tel (702) 589-3900 SIC 7011

■ TROPICANA LAS VEGAS INC p 1484
3801 Las Vegas Blvd S 89109
Tel (702) 739-2222 SIC 7011

■ TROPICANA ST LOUIS LLC p 1484
3930 Howard Hughes Pkwy # 4 89169
Tel (702) 589-3900 SIC 7011

UHS SUMMERLIN RECEIVING p 1500
657 N Town Center Dr 89144
Tel (702) 233-7000 SIC 8211

UNIVERSITY MEDICAL CENTER OF SOUTHERN NEVADA p 1519
1800 W Charleston Blvd 89102
Tel (702) 383-2000 SIC 8062

UNIVERSITY OF NEVADA LAS VEGAS p 1523
4505 S Maryland Pkwy 89154
Tel (702) 895-3011 SIC 8221

UNIVERSITY OF NEVADA LAS VEGAS p 1523
4505 S Maryland Pkwy 89154
Tel (702) 895-3354 SIC 8221 9411

USAA SAVINGS BANK p 1534
3773 Howard Hughes Pkwy 89169
Tel (702) 862-8891 SIC 6036

■ VALLEY HEALTH SYSTEM LLC p 1540
620 Shadow Ln 89106
Tel (702) 388-4000 SIC 8062 8011

VAOPTO LLC p 1544
5178 W Patrick Ln 89118
Tel (702) 979-3582 SIC 3674

■ VENETIAN CASINO RESORT LLC p 1547
3355 Las Vegas Blvd S 89109
Tel (702) 414-1000
SIC 7011 5812 5813 7299

■ VICTORIA PARTNERS p 1555
3770 Las Vegas Blvd S 89109
Tel (888) 529-4828
SIC 7011 5812 7299 5813

WALTERS BAYER AUTOMOTIVE GROUP LLC p 1574
2030 E Flamingo Rd # 290 89119
Tel (702) 450-8001 SIC 5012

WALTERS GROUP p 1574
2030 E Flamingo Rd # 290 89119
Tel (702) 450-8001 SIC 6798

■ WELLS FARGO BANK NEVADA NA p 1590
3300 W Sahara Ave Frnt 89102
Tel (702) 765-3593 SIC 6021

WESTGATE LAS VEGAS RESORT LLC p 1601
3000 Paradise Rd 89109
Tel (702) 732-5111 SIC 7011

WESTGATE LVH LLC p 1601
3000 Paradise Rd 89109
Tel (702) 732-5111 SIC 7011

WHITTLESEA BLUE CAB CO p 1607
2000 Industrial Rd 89102
Tel (702) 384-6111 SIC 4121

■ WYNN LAS VEGAS LLC p 1630
3131 Las Vegas Blvd S 89109
Tel (702) 770-7555 SIC 7011

■ WYNN RESORTS HOLDINGS LLC p 1630
3131 Las Vegas Blvd S 89109
Tel (702) 770-7555 SIC 7011

▲ WYNN RESORTS LIMITED p 1630
3131 Las Vegas Blvd S 89109
Tel (702) 770-7555 SIC 7011

XPRESS HOLDINGS INC p 1633
3993 Howard Hughes Pkwy # 250 89169
Tel (702) 866-6001 SIC 6719 4213

■ ZAPPOS.COM INC p 1641
400 Stewart Ave Ste A 89101
Tel (702) 943-7777
SIC 5661 4813 5632 5611

LAUGHLIN, NV

AMERICAN CASINO & ENTERTAINMENT PROPERTIES LLC p 70
1900 S Casino Dr 89029
Tel (702) 298-5111 SIC 6512 7011

DONALD J LAUGHLIN p 450
1650 S Casino Dr Pmb 500 89029
Tel (702) 298-2535 SIC 7993 5812

■ HARRAHS LAUGHLIN LLC p 663
2900 S Casino Dr 89029
Tel (702) 298-4600 SIC 7011 5812

LAUGHLIN RECREATIONAL ENTERPRISES INC p 847
1650 S Casino Dr 89029
Tel (702) 298-2535 SIC 6512

MARNELL GAMING LLC p 909
2100 S Casino Dr 89029
Tel (702) 298-4000 SIC 7999

RIVER PALMS RESORT CASINO p 1237
2121 S Casino Dr 89029
Tel (702) 298-2242 SIC 7011

TROPICANA EXPRESS INC p 1484
2121 S Casino Dr 89029
Tel (702) 299-0306 SIC 7011

MINDEN, NV

■ BENTLY NEVADA INC p 173
1631 Bently Pkwy S 89423
Tel (775) 782-3611 SIC 3829

NORTH LAS VEGAS, NV

AGGREGATE INDUSTRIES-SWR INC p 35
3101 E Craig Rd 89030
Tel (702) 281-9696 SIC 1611 5032

BECHTEL NEVADA CORP p 167
2621 Losee Rd 89030
Tel (702) 295-1000 SIC 8711 1629

CITY OF NORTH LAS VEGAS p 317
2250 Las Vegas Blvd N # 100 89030
Tel (702) 633-1007 *SIC* 9111

COLLEGE OF SOUTHERN NEVADA FOUNDATION INC p 337
3200 E Cheyenne Ave 89030
Tel (702) 651-4000 *SIC* 8222

■ E & H DISTRIBUTING LLC p 465
1685 W Cheyenne Ave 89032
Tel (702) 636-3663
SIC 5113 5141 5142 5149

EPIC RESORTS - SCOTTSDALE LINKS RESORT LLC p 505
3865 W Cheyenne Ave 89032
Tel (610) 992-0100 *SIC* 7011

JIM L SHETAKIS DISTRIBUTING CO p 785
3840 Civic Center Dr A 89030
Tel (702) 940-3663 *SIC* 5141 5046

MISSION OF NEVADA INC p 975
1 W Mayflower Ave 89030
Tel (702) 639-2500 *SIC* 7213

NATIONAL SECURITY TECHNOLOGIES LLC p 1016
2621 Losee Rd 89030
Tel (702) 295-1000 *SIC* 8711 1629

REAL PROPERTY SERVICES CORP p 1214
9960 W Chynne Ave Ste 110 89030
Tel (702) 313-3700 *SIC* 6531 6211

TEXAS GAMBLING HALL & HOTEL INC p 1443
2101 Texas Star Ln 89032
Tel (702) 631-1000 *SIC* 7011 7999 5812

TEXAS STATION GAMBLING HALL & HOTEL INC p 1444
2101 Texas Star Ln 89032
Tel (702) 631-1000 *SIC* 7011 7993

■ VA SOUTHERN NEVADA HEALTHCARE SYSTEM p 1538
6900 Pecos Rd 89086
Tel (702) 791-9000 *SIC* 8051 9451

VISTA NORTH HOSPITAL INC p 1562
1409 E Lake Mead Blvd 89030
Tel (702) 649-7711 *SIC* 8062

PAHRUMP, NV

VALLEY ELECTRIC ASSOCIATION INC p 1540
800 E Highway 372 89048
Tel (775) 727-5312 *SIC* 4911

RENO, NV

ADAMS AND ASSOCIATES INC p 21
10395 Double R Blvd 89521
Tel (775) 348-0900 *SIC* 8748

▲ AMERCO p 66
5555 Kietzke Ln Ste 100 89511
Tel (775) 688-6300 *SIC* 7513 7519 4226

ARGONAUT GOLD INC p 107
9600 Prototype Ct 89521
Tel (775) 284-4422 *SIC* 1081 1041

ARMAND AGRA INC p 110
1330 Capital Blvd 89502
Tel (775) 322-4073 *SIC* 0291 5147

BELLA FOUR BAKERY INC p 170
1150 Trademark Dr Ste 101 89521
Tel (775) 883-2253 *SIC* 2064 5461

■ CC-RENO LLC p 269
500 N Sierra St 89503
Tel (775) 328-9469 *SIC* 7011

■ CHARLES SCHWAB BANK NATIONAL ASSOCIATION p 289
5190 Neil Rd Ste 100 89502
Tel (775) 689-6800 *SIC* 6021

■ CIRCUS AND ELDORADO JOINT VENTURE LLC p 308
407 N Virginia St 89501
Tel (777) 329-4777 *SIC* 7011

CITY OF RENO p 317
1 E 1st St Fl 1 89501
Tel (775) 334-2020 *SIC* 9111

CLEARCAPITAL.COM INC p 324
300 E 2nd St Ste 1405 89501
Tel (775) 470-5656 *SIC* 6531

■ CLP HOLDINGS CORP p 328
10539 Prof Cir St 200 89521
Tel (775) 321-8000 *SIC* 7363 7361

COUNTY OF WASHOE p 382
1001 E 9th St Bldg A 89512
Tel (775) 328-2552 *SIC* 9311

DIRECTORS INVESTMENT GROUP INC p 442
955 S Virginia St Ste 116 89502
Tel (775) 329-3311 *SIC* 6311

▲ ELDORADO RESORTS INC p 484
100 W Liberty St Ste 1150 89501
Tel (775) 328-0100 *SIC* 7011

ELDORADO RESORTS LLC p 484
345 N Virginia St 89501
Tel (775) 786-5700 *SIC* 7011 5812 5813

■ EMPLOYERS GROUP INC p 494
9790 Gateway Dr 89521
Tel (775) 327-6000 *SIC* 6331

▲ EMPLOYERS HOLDINGS INC p 494
10375 Professional Cir 89521
Tel (888) 682-6671 *SIC* 6331

■ EMPLOYERS INSURANCE CO OF NEVADA p 494
10375 Professional Cir 89521
Tel (775) 327-2700 *SIC* 6331

EP MINERALS LLC p 504
9785 Gateway Dr Ste 1000 89521
Tel (775) 824-7600 *SIC* 1481

GLASS MTN PUMICE INC p 614
3400 Kauai Ct Ste 206 89509
Tel (775) 826-3399 *SIC* 5032

■ GOLDEN ROAD MOTOR INN INC p 621
3800 S Virginia St 89502
Tel (775) 335-4521
SIC 7011 5812 5813 7299

GRAND SIERRA RESORT CORP p 630
2500 2nd St 89595
Tel (800) 501-2651 *SIC* 7011

HAT LIMITED PARTNERSHIP p 667
63 Keystone Ave Ste 202 89503
Tel (775) 328-6020 *SIC* 7363

HYCROFT MINING CORP p 723
9790 Gateway Dr Ste 200 89521
Tel (775) 358-4455 *SIC* 1041 1044

INTERNATIONAL GAME TECHNOLOGY p 755
9295 Prototype Dr 89521
Tel (775) 448-7777 *SIC* 3999 5099

IT CONVERGENCE p 767
5370 Kietzke Ln Ste 200 89511
Tel (415) 675-7935 *SIC* 8742

ITS LOGISTICS LLC p 768
620 Spice Islands Dr 89501
Tel (775) 358-5300 *SIC* 4731 4225

■ JOHN DEERE CAPITAL CORP p 788
10587 Double R Blvd # 100 89521
Tel (775) 786-5527 *SIC* 6153

MEI-GSR HOLDINGS LLC p 940
2500 2nd St 89595
Tel (775) 789-2000 *SIC* 7011

■ MODEL DAIRY LLC p 981
500 Gould St 89502
Tel (775) 788-7900 *SIC* 2026 5143

▲ MONARCH CASINO & RESORT INC p 983
3800 S Virginia St 89502
Tel (775) 335-4600 *SIC* 7011

■ NEVADA BELL TELEPHONE CO p 1028
645 E Plumb Ln B128 89502
Tel (775) 333-3124 *SIC* 4813

NEVADA SYSTEM OF HIGHER EDUCATION p 1028
2601 Enterprise Rd 89512
Tel (775) 784-4901 *SIC* 8221 9411

■ ORMAT NEVADA INC p 1095
6225 Neil Rd 89511
Tel (775) 356-9029 *SIC* 4939

▲ ORMAT TECHNOLOGIES INC p 1095
6225 Neil Rd 89511
Tel (775) 356-9029 *SIC* 4911 3511

PEPPERMILL CASINOS INC p 1134
90 W Grove St Ste 600 89509
Tel (775) 689-8900 *SIC* 7011 7999

PRIME HEALTHCARE SERVICES - RENO LLC p 1175
235 W 6th St 89503
Tel (775) 770-3000 *SIC* 8062

QCH INC p 1194
241 Ridge St Fl 4 89501
Tel (510) 226-1000 *SIC* 5045

RECREATIONAL ENTERPRISES INC p 1215
345 N Virginia St 89501
Tel (775) 786-5700
SIC 7011 7999 5813 5812

RENO DISPOSAL CO p 1224
100 Vassar St 89502
Tel (775) 329-8822 *SIC* 4953

RENOWN HEALTH p 1224
1155 Mill St 89502
Tel (775) 982-4100 *SIC* 8062

RENOWN REGIONAL MEDICAL CENTER p 1224
1155 Mill St 89502
Tel (775) 982-4100 *SIC* 8062

RENOWN SOUTH MEADOWS MEDICAL CENTER p 1224
1155 Mill St 89502
Tel (775) 982-4404 *SIC* 8099

SAINT MARYS HEALTH CARE CORP p 1270
235 W 6th St 89503
Tel (775) 770-3000 *SIC* 8062

SIERRA DEVELOPMENT CO p 1320
38 E 2nd St 89501
Tel (775) 323-1046 *SIC* 7011

■ SIERRA PACIFIC POWER CO p 1321
6100 Neil Rd Ste 100 89511
Tel (775) 834-4011
SIC 4911 4924 4941 4971

▲ TAHOE RESOURCES INC p 1421
5310 Kietzke Ln Ste 200 89511
Tel (775) 825-8574
SIC 1021 1041 1044 1031 1311

■ U-HAUL CO OF MAINE INC p 1498
1325 Airmotive Way # 100 89502
Tel (775) 688-6300 *SIC* 7513

UNITED CONSTRUCTION CO p 1507
5300 Mill St 89502
Tel (775) 858-8090 *SIC* 1541 1542

UNIVERSITY OF NEVADA RENO p 1523
1664 N Virginia St 89557
Tel (775) 784-1110 *SIC* 8221 9411

WASHOE COUNTY SCHOOL DISTRICT p 1580
425 E 9th St 89512
Tel (775) 348-0200 *SIC* 8211

WHITTLESEA-BELL p 1607
100 Sunshine Ln 89502
Tel (775) 785-3533 *SIC* 8721

SPARKS, NV

JENSEN ENTERPRISES INC p 782
825 Steneri Way 89431
Tel (775) 352-2700 *SIC* 3272

■ NORTHERN NEVADA MEDICAL CENTER LP p 1056
2375 E Prater Way 89434
Tel (775) 331-7000
SIC 8062 8093 8071 8049 8011

Q AND D CONSTRUCTION INC p 1194
1050 S 21st St 89431
Tel (775) 353-1104 *SIC* 1623

SCOLARIS WAREHOUSE MARKETS INC p 1292
950 Holman Way 89431
Tel (775) 355-8568 *SIC* 5411

SIERRA NEVADA CORP p 1320
444 Salomon Cir 89434
Tel (775) 331-0222 *SIC* 3728 3812

SPARKS NUGGET INC p 1354
1100 Nugget Ave 89431
Tel (775) 356-3300 *SIC* 7011

THOLL FENCE INC p 1448
800 Glendale Ave 89431
Tel (775) 358-8680 *SIC* 1799

WESTERN NEVADA SUPPLY CO p 1599
950 S Rock Blvd 89431
Tel (775) 359-5800 *SIC* 5074 5083

STATELINE, NV

■ HARVEYS CASINO RESORTS p 667
Hwy 50 & Stateline Ave 89449
Tel (775) 588-2411 *SIC* 7011

YERINGTON, NV

LYON COUNTY SCHOOL DISTRICT p 888
25 Joe Parr Way 89447
Tel (775) 463-3006 *SIC* 8211

NEW HAMPSHIRE

AUBURN, NH

■ INSTALLED BUILDING PRODUCTS LLC p 747
62 King St 03032
Tel (603) 645-1604
SIC 1761 5021 5719 2515

BARRINGTON, NH

TURBOCAM INC p 1492
607 Calef Hwy 03825
Tel (603) 749-6066 *SIC* 3599

BEDFORD, NH

■ 25 RIDGEWOOD ROAD OPERATIONS LLC p 2
25 Ridgewood Rd 03110
Tel (603) 623-8805 *SIC* 8051

■ CHARTIS US INC p 291
1 Executive Park Dr 03110
Tel (603) 645-7000 *SIC* 6331

COCA-COLA BOTTLING CO OF NORTHERN NEW ENGLAND INC p 333
1 Executive Park Dr # 330 03110
Tel (603) 627-7871 *SIC* 2086

BELMONT, NH

ALL METALS INDUSTRIES INC p 51
4 Higgins Dr 03220
Tel (603) 267-7023 *SIC* 5051

PIKE INDUSTRIES INC p 1148
3 Eastgate Park Dr 03220
Tel (603) 527-5100 *SIC* 1611 2951 3295

BOW, NH

■ PITCO FRIALATOR INC p 1152
553 Route 3a 03304
Tel (603) 225-6684 *SIC* 3589

CLAREMONT, NH

NATIONAL FIELD REPRESENTATIVES INC p 1012
136 Maple Ave 03743
Tel (603) 543-5210 *SIC* 7389 1799

RED RIVER COMPUTER CO INC p 1216
21 Water St Ste 500 03743
Tel (603) 298-5293 *SIC* 7379

CONCORD, NH

AUTOMOTIVE SUPPLY ASSOCIATES INC p 134
129 Manchester St 03301
Tel (603) 225-4000
SIC 5013 7539 5531 5169 5015

CAPITAL REGION HEALTH CARE CORP p 250
250 Pleasant St 03301
Tel (603) 225-2711
SIC 8741 8062 8051 8093 8082

CHUBB AMERICA SERVICE CORP p 304
1 Granite Pl 03301
Tel (603) 224-7741 *SIC* 8741

COMMUNITY COLLEGE SYSTEM OF NEW HAMPSHIRE p 348
26 College Dr 03301
Tel (603) 230-3500 *SIC* 8222

CONCORD GENERAL MUTUAL INSURANCE CO p 354
4 Bouton St 03301
Tel (603) 224-4086 *SIC* 6331

CONCORD HOSPITAL INC p 354
250 Pleasant St 03301
Tel (603) 227-7000 *SIC* 8062

DELTA DENTAL PLAN OF NEW HAMPSHIRE INC p 426
1 Delta Dr 03301
Tel (800) 537-1715 *SIC* 6324 8021

EXECUTIVE OFFICE OF STATE OF NEW HAMPSHIRE p 518
107 N Main St Rm 208 03301
Tel (603) 271-2121 *SIC* 9111

GRANITE GROUP WHOLESALERS LLC p 631
6 Storrs St 03301
Tel (603) 224-1901 *SIC* 5075 5074

GRANITE GROUP WHOLESALERS LLC p 631
6 Storrs St 03301
Tel (603) 545-3345 *SIC* 5074 5075

■ LINCOLN FINANCIAL SECURITIES CORP p 867
1 Granite Pl 03301
Tel (603) 226-5000 *SIC* 6722

NEW HAMPSHIRE DEPARTMENT OF TRANSPORTATION p 1030
7 Hazen Dr 03301
Tel (603) 271-3734 *SIC* 9621

NEW HAMPSHIRE DEPT OF CORRECTIONS p 1030
105 Pleasant St Fl 4 03301
Tel (603) 271-4053 *SIC* 9223

NEW HAMPSHIRE DEPT OF HEALTH AND HUMAN SERVICES p 1030
129 Pleasant St 03301
Tel (603) 271-4688 *SIC* 9431 9441

NEW HAMPSHIRE STATE POLICE p 1030
33 Hazen Dr 03305
Tel (603) 223-8500 *SIC* 9221 9229

RUGBY ACQUISITION p 1257
1 Pillsbury St Ste 302 03301
Tel (603) 369-4710 *SIC* 5031

RUGBY IPD CORP p 1257
1 Pillsbury St Ste 302 03301
Tel (603) 369-4710 *SIC* 5031

STATE OF NEW HAMPSHIRE p 1382
64 South St 03301
Tel (603) 271-1110 *SIC* 9111

UNIVERSITY SYSTEM OF NEW HAMPSHIRE p 1527
5 Chenell Dr Ste 301 03301
Tel (603) 862-1800 *SIC* 8221

DERRY, NH

■ PARKLAND MEDICAL CENTER p 1116
1 Parkland Dr 03038
Tel (603) 432-1500 *SIC* 8062

DOVER, NH

DMI TECHNOLOGY CORP p 446
1 Progress Dr 03820
Tel (603) 742-3330 *SIC* 3625 3621

ELECTROCRAFT INC p 485
1 Progress Dr 03820
Tel (603) 742-3330 *SIC* 3625 3621

MEASURED PROGRESS INC p 934
100 Education Way 03820
Tel (603) 749-9102 *SIC* 8732

WENTWORTH-DOUGLASS HOSPITAL p 1592
789 Central Ave 03820
Tel (603) 742-5252 *SIC* 8062

DURHAM, NH

GOSS INTERNATIONAL AMERICAS LLC p 626
121 Technology Dr 03824
Tel (603) 749-6600 *SIC* 7699 3555

EXETER, NH

■ ANVIL INTERNATIONAL LLC p 94
2 Holland Way 03833
Tel (603) 418-2800
SIC 3498 3321 3317 3494 3429

BAUER HOCKEY INC p 160
100 Domain Dr Ste 1 03833
Tel (603) 430-2111 *SIC* 3949

CONTINENTAL MICROWAVE AND TOOL CO INC p 363
11 Continental Dr 03833
Tel (603) 775-5200 *SIC* 3679

CORE PHYSICIANS LLC p 369
7 Holland Way Fl 1 03833
Tel (603) 580-7939 *SIC* 8062

EXETER HOSPITAL INC p 519
5 Alumni Dr 03833
Tel (603) 778-7311 *SIC* 8062

EXETER SCHOOL DISTRICT p 519
24 Front St Ste 111 03833
Tel (603) 778-7772 *SIC* 8211

PERFORMANCE SPORTS GROUP LTD p 1135
100 Domain Dr 03833
Tel (603) 610-5802 *SIC* 3949

PHILLIPS EXETER ACADEMY p 1144
20 Main St 03833
Tel (603) 772-4311 *SIC* 8211

SCHOOL ADMINISTRATIVE UNIT 16 p 1288
30 Linden St 03833
Tel (603) 775-8400 *SIC* 8211

FARMINGTON, NH

■ UNION TELEPHONE CO p 1505
7 Central St 03835
Tel (603) 859-3700 *SIC* 4813

GREENLAND, NH

COLE HAAN LLC p 335
150 Ocean Rd 03840
Tel (207) 846-2500 *SIC* 5651 5632

HAMPTON, NH

FOSS HOLDINGS LLC p 570
11 Merrill Industrial Dr A1 03842
Tel (603) 929-6000 *SIC* 2297

FOSS MANUFACTURING CO LLC p 570
11 Merrill Industrial Dr A1 03842
Tel (603) 929-6000 *SIC* 2297

SHIPSTON GROUP US INC p 1317
363 Exeter Rd 03842
Tel (603) 929-6811 *SIC* 8741

■ TSI GROUP INC p 1489
94 Tide Mill Rd 03842
Tel (603) 964-0296
SIC 3599 3398 3443 3444

▲ UNITIL CORP p 1515
6 Liberty Ln W 03842
Tel (603) 772-0775 *SIC* 4911 4924

■ WASTE MANAGEMENT OF MASSACHUSETTS INC p 1580
4 Liberty Ln W 03842
Tel (603) 929-3000 *SIC* 4953 8748

■ WHEELABRATOR ENVIRONMENTAL SYSTEMS INC p 1604
4 Liberty Ln W 03842
Tel (603) 929-3000 *SIC* 4953 4911

HANOVER, NH

DARTMOUTH COLLEGE p 413
6193 Hinman 03755
Tel (603) 646-2191 *SIC* 8231

HYPERTHERM INC p 724
21 Great Hollow Rd 03755
Tel (603) 643-3441 *SIC* 3541

TRUSTEES OF DARTMOUTH COLLEGE p 1487
20 Lebanon St 03755
Tel (603) 646-1110 *SIC* 8221

HOOKSETT, NH

GREAT STATE BEVERAGES INC p 634
1000 Quality Dr 03106
Tel (603) 644-2337 *SIC* 5181 5149 5145

■ HEALTHSOURCE INC p 677
2 College Park Dr 03106
Tel (603) 268-7000 *SIC* 6324 8741 8011

MERCHANTS AUTOMOTIVE GROUP INC p 944
1278 Hooksett Rd 03106
Tel (603) 669-4100 *SIC* 5521 7515

POULTRY PRODUCTS CO INC p 1164
11 Bemis Rd 03106
Tel (603) 668-7414 *SIC* 5144

POULTRY PRODUCTS CO OF NEW ENGLAND INC p 1164
11 Bemis Rd 03106
Tel (603) 263-1600 *SIC* 5147 5149

PRO CON INC p 1178
1359 Hooksett Rd Ste 16 03106
Tel (603) 623-8811 *SIC* 1542 1541

REGENCY MORTGAGE CORP p 1219
26 Londonderry Tpke 03106
Tel (603) 669-5626 *SIC* 6162

STEBBINS ENTERPRISES INC p 1384
1359 Hooksett Rd 03106
Tel (603) 623-8811 *SIC* 1542 1541

HUDSON, NH

ATRIUM MEDICAL CORP p 129
5 Wentworth Dr 03051
Tel (603) 880-1433 *SIC* 3842 3841

PRESSTEK LLC p 1173
55 Executive Dr 03051
Tel (603) 595-7000 *SIC* 3555 3577 3861

■ VECTRON INTERNATIONAL INC p 1546
267 Lowell Rd Ste B 03051
Tel (603) 598-0070 *SIC* 3671

KEENE, NH

C&S WHOLESALE GROCERS INC p 234
7 Corporate Dr 03431
Tel (603) 354-7000
SIC 5141 5147 5143 5142 5122 5145

CHESHIRE MEDICAL CENTER p 295
580 Court St 03431
Tel (603) 354-5400 *SIC* 8062

■ CORNING NETOPTIX p 371
69 Island St Ste T 03431
Tel (603) 357-7662 *SIC* 3827 3851 3826

LIBERTY-USA CORP p 863
62 Maple Ave 03431
Tel (603) 352-3221 *SIC* 6411

■ MARKEM-IMAJE CORP p 908
150 Congress St 03431
Tel (603) 352-1130 *SIC* 2893

■ MPB CORP p 995
7 Optical Ave 03431
Tel (603) 352-0310 *SIC* 3562 6061

NATIONAL GRANGE MUTUAL INSURANCE CO p 1012
55 West St 03431
Tel (603) 358-6517 *SIC* 6411

NETHERLANDS INSURANCE CO p 1027
62 Maple Ave 03431
Tel (603) 352-3221 *SIC* 6411

PEERLESS INSURANCE CO p 1127
62 Maple Ave 03431
Tel (603) 352-3221 *SIC* 6331

SOUTHERN FAMILY MARKETS LLC p 1348
7 Corporate Dr 03431
Tel (973) 605-6381 *SIC* 5411

LACONIA, NH

AAVID CORP p 9
1 Aavid Cir 03246
Tel (603) 528-3400 *SIC* 3679

AAVID THERMALLOY LLC p 9
1 Aavid Cir 03246
Tel (603) 528-3400 *SIC* 3679

LRGHEALTHCARE p 882
80 Highland St 03246
Tel (603) 524-3211 *SIC* 8062

SMITHS TUBULAR SYSTEMS-LACONIA INC p 1334
93 Lexington Dr 03246
Tel (603) 524-2064
SIC 3463 3498 8734 7692 3441 3398

LEBANON, NH

DARTMOUTH-HITCHCOCK MEDICAL CENTER p 413
1 Medical Center Dr 03756
Tel (603) 650-5000 *SIC* 8062 8011 8051

DARTMOUTH-HITCHCOCK MEDICAL CENTER p 413
1 Medical Center Dr 03756
Tel (603) 650-5150 *SIC* 8021

MARY HITCHCOCK MEMORIAL HOSPITAL p 914
1 Medical Center Dr 03756
Tel (603) 650-5000 *SIC* 8062

MAXIFACIAL DENTAL SURGERY p 922
1 Medical Center Dr 03756
Tel (603) 650-5000 *SIC* 8011

NEW ENGLAND ALLIANCE FOR HEALTH LLC p 1029
1 Medical Center Dr 03756
Tel (603) 653-1223 *SIC* 8742

■ TIMKEN US LLC p 1455
336 Mechanic St 03766
Tel (603) 443-5217 *SIC* 3562

LITTLETON, NH

LITTLETON HOSPITAL ASSOCIATION p 871
600 Saint Johnsbury Rd 03561
Tel (603) 444-9000 *SIC* 8062

LONDONDERRY, NH

BOSCH THERMOTECHNOLOGY CORP p 202
50 Wentworth Ave 03053
Tel (603) 552-1100 *SIC* 5075

ECCO USA INC p 475
16 Delta Dr 03053
Tel (603) 537-7300 *SIC* 5139 5661

■ L-3 COMMUNICATIONS CORP p 834
9 Akira Way 03053
Tel (603) 626-4800 *SIC* 3827

LIBERTY ENERGY UTILITIES (NEW HAMPSHIRE) CORP p 861
15 Buttrick Rd 03053
Tel (905) 287-2061 *SIC* 1311

LIBERTY UTILITIES (ENERGYNORTH NATURAL GAS) CORP p 863
15 Buttrick Rd 03053
Tel (603) 328-2700 *SIC* 4924

WALLBOARD SUPPLY CO - US LBM LLC p 1573
527 Mammoth Rd 03053
Tel (603) 434-4597 *SIC* 5032

MANCHESTER, NH

■ BURNDY AMERICAS INC p 228
47 E Industrial Pk Dr 03109
Tel (603) 647-5000 *SIC* 3643 5063

■ BURNDY LLC p 228
47 E Industrial Park Dr 03109
Tel (603) 626-3730 *SIC* 3643 5063

CATHOLIC MEDICAL CENTER p 267
100 Mcgregor St 03102
Tel (603) 663-6888 *SIC* 8062

CATHOLIC MEDICAL CENTER PHYSICIAN PRACTICE ASSOCIATES p 267
100 Mcgregor St 03102
Tel (603) 668-3545 *SIC* 8062 8011

CITY OF MANCHESTER p 316
1 City Hall Plz 03101
Tel (603) 624-6460 *SIC* 9111

EASTER SEAL NEW HAMPSHIRE INC p 471
555 Auburn St 03103
Tel (603) 623-8863
SIC 8331 8399 4119 8322

ELLIOT HEALTH SYSTEM p 488
1 Elliot Way 03103
Tel (603) 663-1600 *SIC* 8062

ELLIOT HOSPITAL OF CITY OF MANCHESTER p 488
1 Elliot Way 03103
Tel (603) 669-5300 *SIC* 8062

GLOBAL PLASTICS LP p 617
99 Middle St Ste 1 03101
Tel (800) 417-4605 *SIC* 2821

INTEGRATED DEICING SERVICES LLC p 749
175 Ammon Dr 03103
Tel (603) 647-1717 *SIC* 3728 4581

KALWALL CORP p 801
1111 Candia Rd 03109
Tel (603) 627-3861 *SIC* 3089 3083

MCDEVITT TRUCKS INC p 927
1 Mack Ave 03103
Tel (800) 370-6225 *SIC* 5012 5013 7538

NEW HAMPSHIRE CATHOLIC CHARITIES INC p 1030
215 Myrtle St 03104
Tel (603) 669-3030
SIC 8322 8059 8331 8661 8361

NORTHERN NEW ENGLAND BENEFIT TRUST p 1056
51 Goffstown Rd Ste 2 03102
Tel (603) 669-4771 *SIC* 6371

■ PUBLIC SERVICE CO OF NEW HAMPSHIRE p 1189
780 North Commercial St 03101
Tel (603) 669-4000 *SIC* 4911

ROMAN CATHOLIC BISHOP OF MANCHESTER p 1248
153 Ash St 03104
Tel (603) 669-3100 *SIC* 8661

SAINT ANSELM COLLEGE p 1268
100 Saint Anselm Dr 03102
Tel (603) 641-7000 *SIC* 8221

SOUTHERN NEW HAMPSHIRE UNIVERSITY p 1349
2500 N River Rd 03106
Tel (603) 668-2211 *SIC* 8221

ST JOSEPH RESIDENCE INC p 1368
495 Mammoth Rd 03104
Tel (603) 668-6011 *SIC* 8059

SUMMIT PACKAGING SYSTEMS INC p 1399
400 Gay St 03103
Tel (603) 669-5410 *SIC* 3499 3089

SURGE RESOURCES INC p 1408
920 Candia Rd 03109
Tel (603) 623-0007 *SIC* 8742 7361 7363

TIG HOLDINGS INC p 1453
250 Commercial St # 5000 03101
Tel (603) 656-2200 *SIC* 6331

TIG INSURANCE CO p 1453
250 Commercial St # 5000 03101
Tel (603) 656-2200 *SIC* 6331

TIG INSURANCE GROUP p 1453
250 Commercial St # 5000 03101
Tel (603) 656-2200 *SIC* 6331

VELCRO INC p 1547
95 Sundial Ave 03103
Tel (603) 669-4880 *SIC* 2241

VELCRO USA INC p 1547
95 Sundial Ave 03103
Tel (603) 669-4880 *SIC* 2241 3965

WINDWARD PETROLEUM INC p 1616
1064 Goffs Falls Rd 03103
Tel (603) 222-2900 *SIC* 5531

MERRIMACK, NH

BROOKSTONE CO INC p 218
1 Innovation Way 03054
Tel (866) 576-7337
SIC 5947 5399 5331 5961

BROOKSTONE HOLDINGS CORP p 218
1 Innovation Way 03054
Tel (603) 880-9500 *SIC* 5947 5961

BROOKSTONE INC p 218
1 Innovation Way 03054
Tel (603) 880-9500 *SIC* 5961 5947

CAMP SYSTEMS INTERNATIONAL INC p 245
11 Continental Blvd Ste C 03054
Tel (603) 595-0030 *SIC* 7374

CELESTICA LLC p 273
11 Continental Blvd # 103 03054
Tel (603) 657-3001 *SIC* 3679

GT ADVANCED TECHNOLOGIES INC p 644
243 Daniel Webster Hwy 03054
Tel (603) 883-5200 *SIC* 3674

GTAT CORP p 644
243 Daniel Webster Hwy 03054
Tel (603) 883-5200 *SIC* 3674 3567

KOLLSMAN INC p 826
220 Daniel Webster Hwy 03054
Tel (603) 889-2500 *SIC* 3812 3629

■ NASHUA CORP p 1008
59 Daniel Webster Hwy A 03054
Tel (603) 880-1100
SIC 2672 2754 2679 2621 2782

▲ PC CONNECTION INC p 1123
730 Milford Rd 03054
Tel (603) 683-2000 *SIC* 5961

■ PC CONNECTION SALES CORP p 1123
730 Milford Rd 03054
Tel (603) 423-2000 *SIC* 5961 5045

MILFORD, NH

HITCHINER MANUFACTURING CO INC p 697
594 Elm St 03055
Tel (603) 673-1100 *SIC* 3324

■ MARMON UTILITY LLC p 909
53 Old Wilton Rd 03055
Tel (603) 673-2040 *SIC* 3357

NASHUA, NH

■ AMPHENOL PRINTED CIRCUITS INC p 86
91 Northeastern Blvd 03062
Tel (603) 324-4500
SIC 3679 3678 3672 3357

BAE SYSTEMS INFORMATION AND ELECTRONIC SYSTEMS INTEGRATION INC p 144
65 Spit Brook Rd 03060
Tel (603) 885-4321 *SIC* 3812

■ CONWAY TECHNOLOGY GROUP LLC p 365
10 Capitol St 03063
Tel (603) 889-1665
SIC 5044 5065 7699 7359

FOUNDATION MEDICAL PARTNERS IN p 571
8 Prospect St 03060
Tel (603) 577-2000 *SIC* 8099

■ GENERAL DYNAMICS GLOBAL IMAGING TECHNOLOGIES INC p 600
24 Simon St 03060
Tel (603) 864-6300 *SIC* 3827 3861

NASHUA SCHOOL DISTRICT p 1008
141 Ledge St 03060
Tel (603) 966-1000 *SIC* 8211

NORTHPOINT PROPERTY MANAGEMENT LLC p 1058
55 Lake St Ste 4 03060
Tel (603) 594-2300 *SIC* 8641 6531

PFEIFFER VACUUM INC p 1140
24 Trafalgar Sq 03063
Tel (603) 578-6500 *SIC* 3561

SCHOOL ADMINISTRATIVE UNIT 42 p 1289
141 Ledge St 03060
Tel (603) 966-1000 *SIC* 8211

SKILLSOFT CORP p 1330
107 Northeastern Blvd 03062
Tel (603) 821-3715 *SIC* 7372

SOUTHERN NEW HAMPSHIRE MEDICAL CENTER p 1349
8 Prospect St 03060
Tel (603) 577-2000 *SIC* 8062 8011

SSI INVESTMENTS I LIMITED p 1364
107 Northeastern Blvd 03062
Tel (603) 324-3000 *SIC* 7372

SSI INVESTMENTS II LIMITED p 1364
107 Northeastern Blvd 03062
Tel (603) 324-3000 *SIC* 7372

ST JOSEPH HOSPITAL p 1368
172 Kinsley St 03060
Tel (603) 882-3000 *SIC* 8062

ST JOSEPHS HOSPITAL CORPORATE SERVICES p 1369
172 Kinsley St 03060
Tel (603) 882-3000 *SIC* 6719

NEW IPSWICH, NH

HUTTER CONSTRUCTION CORP p 722
810 Turnpike Rd 03071
Tel (603) 878-2300 *SIC* 1541 1542

NEWINGTON, NH

■ ESSENTIAL POWER NEWINGTON ENERGY LLC p 510
200 Shattuck Way 03801
Tel (603) 766-1880 *SIC* 4911

▲ PLANET FITNESS INC p 1154
26 Fox Run Rd 03801
Tel (603) 750-0001 *SIC* 7991

SIG SAUER INC p 1321
72 Pease Blvd 03801
Tel (603) 610-3000 *SIC* 3484 7999

TYCO ELECTRONICS INTEGRATED CABLE SYSTEMS LLC p 1496
100 Piscataqua Dr 03801
Tel (603) 436-6100 *SIC* 3357

PELHAM, NH

WAKEFIELD THERMAL SOLUTIONS INC p 1572
33 Bridge St 03076
Tel (603) 635-2800 *SIC* 3354

PEMBROKE, NH

ASSOCIATED GROCERS OF NEW ENGLAND INC p 120
11 Cooperative Way 03275
Tel (603) 223-6710 *SIC* 5141

PETERBOROUGH, NH

NEW HAMPSHIRE BALL BEARINGS INC p 1030
175 Jaffrey Rd 03458
Tel (603) 924-3311 *SIC* 3562

PITTSFIELD, NH

GLOBE HOLDING CO LLC p 618
37 Loudon Rd 03263
Tel (603) 435-8323 *SIC* 6519

GLOBE MANUFACTURING CO-OK LLC p 618
37 Loudon Rd 03263
Tel (603) 435-8323 *SIC* 3842

PLAINFIELD, NH

DON HENRY JR & SONS p 450
Rr Box 12a 03781
Tel (603) 298-8551 *SIC* 7349

PLAISTOW, NH

TIMBERLANE REGIONAL SAU p 1454
30 Greenough Rd 03865
Tel (603) 382-6119 *SIC* 8211

PLYMOUTH, NH

NEW HAMPSHIRE ELECTRIC COOPERATIVE INC p 1030
579 Tenney Mountain Hwy 03264
Tel (603) 536-8824 *SIC* 4911

PORTSMOUTH, NH

AMADEUS HOSPITALITY AMERICAS INC p 64
75 Nh Ave Ste 300 03801
Tel (603) 436-7500 *SIC* 7371

▲ BOTTOMLINE TECHNOLOGIES (DE) INC p 204
325 Corporate Dr Ste 300 03801
Tel (603) 436-0700 *SIC* 7372

COLWEN MANAGEMENT INC p 343
230 Commerce Way Ste 200 03801
Tel (603) 897-6100 *SIC* 8742 7389

■ ERIE SCIENTIFIC LLC p 508
20 Post Rd 03801
Tel (603) 430-6859
SIC 3231 3821 3229 3221 3211

■ HCA HEALTH SERVICES OF NEW HAMPSHIRE INC p 671
333 Borthwick Ave 03801
Tel (603) 436-0600 *SIC* 8062 8063

HIGH LINER FOODS (USA) INC p 690
1 Highliner Ave 03801
Tel (603) 431-6865 *SIC* 2092

HIGHLANDS FUEL DELIVERY LLC p 691
190 Commerce Way 03801
Tel (603) 559-8700 *SIC* 5172 5541 1389

IRVING OIL TERMINALS INC p 765
190 Commerce Way 03801
Tel (603) 559-8736 *SIC* 5171

LONZA BIOLOGICS INC p 877
101 International Dr 03801
Tel (603) 610-4500 *SIC* 2834

MARGARITAS MANAGEMENT GROUP INC p 905
200 Griffin Rd Ste 1 03801
Tel (603) 430-8905 *SIC* 5812

NMTI HOLDINGS INC p 1045
75 Nh Ave 03801
Tel (603) 427-5794 *SIC* 7371

PORTSMOUTH CHEVROLET INC p 1163
549 Us Highway 1 Byp 03801
Tel (603) 436-5010 *SIC* 5511

ROCKINGHAM ELECTRICAL SUPPLY CO INC p 1244
437 Shattuck Way 03801
Tel (603) 436-7731 *SIC* 5063

SPECIALTY HOSPITAL OF AMERICA LLC p 1356
155 Fleet St 03801
Tel (603) 570-4888 *SIC* 8062

■ SPRAGUE OPERATING RESOURCES LLC p 1360
185 International Dr 03801
Tel (603) 431-1000 *SIC* 5172 5052 5171

▲ SPRAGUE RESOURCES LP p 1360
185 International Dr 03801
Tel (800) 225-1560 *SIC* 5172 4922

STAFF HUNTERS p 1374
1 Nh Ave Ste 125 03801
Tel (603) 766-4909 *SIC* 7361

WHEELABRATOR TECHNOLOGIES INC p 1604
100 Aboretum Dr Ste 310 03801
Tel (603) 929-3156 *SIC* 4953

ROCHESTER, NH

▲ ALBANY INTERNATIONAL CORP p 45
216 Airport Dr 03867
Tel (518) 445-2200
SIC 2221 3496 2399 2899 3089

CVC HOLDING CO INC p 404
28 Industrial Way 03867
Tel (603) 332-2080 *SIC* 5984

FRISBIE MEMORIAL HOSPITAL p 580
11 Whitehall Rd 03867
Tel (603) 332-5211 *SIC* 8062

SALEM, NH

APOLLO PROFESSIONAL SOLUTIONS INC p 97
29 Stiles Rd Ste 302 03079
Tel (866) 277-3343 *SIC* 7363

■ ENTERASYS NETWORKS INC p 501
9 Northstern Blvd Ste 300 03079
Tel (603) 952-5000
SIC 3577 7373 3357 5045

■ HADCO CORP p 652
12a Manor Pkwy 03079
Tel (603) 421-3400 *SIC* 3672

▲ STANDEX INTERNATIONAL CORP p 1376
11 Keewaydin Dr 03079
Tel (603) 893-9701 *SIC* 3585 3549 3675

VENTION MEDICAL ADVANCED COMPONENTS INC p 1548
29 Northwestern Dr 03079
Tel (603) 327-0600 *SIC* 3082 3069 3083

WORLDCOM EXCHANGE INC p 1625
43 Northwestern Dr 03079
Tel (603) 893-0900 *SIC* 7373 5045 7379

SEABROOK, NH

■ NEXTERA ENERGY SEABROOK LLC p 1040
626 Lafayette Rd 03874
Tel (603) 474-3808 *SIC* 4911

■ NORTH ATLANTIC ENERGY CORP p 1050
626 Lafayette Rd 03874
Tel (603) 474-9521 *SIC* 4911

■ NORTH ATLANTIC ENERGY SERVICE CORP p 1051
626 Lafayette Rd 03874
Tel (603) 474-9521 *SIC* 4924

STRATHAM, NH

LINDT & SPRUNGLI (USA) INC p 868
1 Fine Chocolate Pl 03885
Tel (603) 778-8100 *SIC* 2066 5149 5441

TIMBERLAND LLC p 1454
200 Domain Dr 03885
Tel (603) 772-9500
SIC 3143 3144 2386 2329 2321 2325

NEW JERSEY

ALLENDALE, NJ

LEICA CAMERA INC p 854
1 Pearl Ct Unit A 07401
Tel (201) 995-0051 *SIC* 5043

LONZA AMERICA INC p 877
90 Boroline Rd Ste 1 07401
Tel (201) 316-9200 *SIC* 8731

LONZA INC p 877
90 Boroline Rd Ste 1 07401
Tel (201) 316-9200 *SIC* 2899 2869 2819

PROMOTION IN MOTION INC p 1183
25 Commerce Dr 07401
Tel (201) 962-8530
SIC 2064 5441 5145 2066

ALLENTOWN, NJ

ALLENTOWN INC p 53
165 Route 526 08501
Tel (609) 259-7951 *SIC* 3444 3496 5162

ATLANTIC CITY, NJ

ADAMAR GARAGE CORP p 21
Brighton Avenue Boardwalk 08401
Tel (609) 340-4000 *SIC* 6162

ATLANTIC CITY BOARD OF EDUCATION p 126
1300 Atlantic Ave Ste 500 08401
Tel (609) 343-7200 *SIC* 8211

ATLANTIC CITY PUBLIC SCHOOL p 126
1300 Atlantic Ave 08401
Tel (609) 343-0086 *SIC* 8211

ATLANTIC CITY SHOWBOAT INC p 126
801 Boardwalk 08401
Tel (609) 343-4000 *SIC* 7011

ATLANTICARE REGIONAL MEDICAL CENTER INC p 127
1925 Pacific Ave 08401
Tel (609) 345-4000 *SIC* 8062

■ BALLYS PARK PLACE INC p 149
1900 Pacific Ave 08401
Tel (609) 340-2000 *SIC* 7011

■ BALLYS PARK PLACE INC p 149
1721 Boardwalk 08401
Tel (609) 340-2000 *SIC* 6512 5812

■ CAESARS NEW JERSEY INC p 237
2100 Pacific Ave 08401
Tel (609) 348-4411 *SIC* 7011

CALVI ELECTRIC CO p 243
14 S California Ave Ste 1 08401
Tel (609) 345-0151 *SIC* 1731

CITY OF ATLANTIC CITY (INC) p 313
1301 Bacharach Blvd 08401
Tel (609) 347-5300 *SIC* 9111

COUNTY OF ATLANTIC p 376
1333 Atlantic Ave 08401
Tel (609) 345-6700 *SIC* 9111

DGMB CASINO LLC p 435
1133 Boardwalk 08401
Tel (800) 772-9000 *SIC* 7011

FLAGSHIP RESORT DEVELOPMENT CORP p 554
60 N Maine Ave 08401
Tel (609) 347-3524 *SIC* 6531 7011

■ HARRAHS ATLANTIC CITY OPERATING CO LLC p 663
777 Harrahs Blvd 08401
Tel (609) 441-5000 *SIC* 7011

MARINA ASSOCIATES LTD p 906
777 Harrahs Blvd 08401
Tel (609) 441-5000 *SIC* 7011 5812

MARINA CLUB CONDOMINIUM p 906
655 Absecon Blvd Ste B 08401
Tel (609) 348-0040 *SIC* 6513

MARINA DISTRICT DEVELOPMENT CO LLC p 906
1 Borgata Way 08401
Tel (609) 317-1000 *SIC* 7011

MARINA DISTRICT FINANCE CO INC p 906
1 Borgata Way 08401
Tel (609) 317-1000 *SIC* 7011

RAMADA NEW JERSEY HOLDINGS CORP p 1206
Brighton Ave Boardwalk 08401
Tel (609) 340-4000 *SIC* 7011

RESORTS CASINO HOTEL p 1227
1133 Boardwalk 08401
Tel (609) 344-6000 *SIC* 7011

REVEL ENTERTAINMENT GROUP LLC p 1229
500 Boardwalk 08401
Tel (609) 340-0003 *SIC* 7011

SHOWBOAT INC p 1319
801 Boardwalk 08401
Tel (609) 343-4000 *SIC* 7011

■ TROPICANA ATLANTIC CITY CORP p 1484
2831 Boardwalk 08401
Tel (609) 340-4000 *SIC* 7011

TROPICANA ENTERTAINMENT INC p 1484
2831 Brighton Ave 08401
Tel (609) 340-4000 *SIC* 7011

TRUMP ENTERTAINMENT RESORTS INC p 1487
1000 Boardwalk 08401
Tel (609) 449-5534 *SIC* 7011 7999

TRUMP TAJ MAHAL ASSOCIATES LLC p 1487
1000 Boardwalk 08401
Tel (609) 345-4045 *SIC* 7011

TRUMP TAJ MAHAL REALTY CORP p 1487
1000 Boardwalk 08401
Tel (609) 449-1000 *SIC* 6512

AVENEL, NJ

BRADCO SUPPLY CORP p 206
34 Engelhard Ave 07001
Tel (732) 382-3400 *SIC* 5033 5211

DANA TRANSPORT SYSTEM INC p 411
210 Essex Ave E 07001
Tel (732) 750-9100 *SIC* 4213 7513

PRIDE SOLVENTS & CHEMICAL CO OF NEW JERSEY INC p 1174
211 Randolph Ave 07001
Tel (732) 499-0123 *SIC* 5169

SAVINO DEL BENE USA INC p 1284
34 Engelhard Ave 07001
Tel (347) 960-5568 *SIC* 3799 4731

BARRINGTON, NJ

EDMUND OPTICS INC p 478
101 E Gloucester Pike 08007
Tel (856) 547-3488 *SIC* 3211 5961

BASKING RIDGE, NJ

ARLA FOODS INC p 110
106 Allen Rd Ste 401 07920
Tel (908) 604-6551 *SIC* 5143

■ BARNES & NOBLE COLLEGE BOOKSELLERS LLC p 155
120 Mountainview Blvd A 07920
Tel (908) 991-2665 *SIC* 5942 5943 5947

▲ BARNES & NOBLE EDUCATION INC p 156
120 Mountainview Blvd A 07920
Tel (908) 991-2665 *SIC* 5942

■ CELLCO PARTNERSHIP p 273
1 Verizon Way 07920
Tel (908) 306-7000 *SIC* 4812 5999 5065

FEDWAY ASSOCIATES INC p 537
505 Martinsville Rd Fl 1 07920
Tel (973) 624-6444 *SIC* 5182

■ GTE WIRELESS INC p 644
1 Verizon Way 07920
Tel (908) 559-7000 *SIC* 4813

MATHESON TRI-GAS INC p 919
150 Allen Rd Ste 302 07920
Tel (908) 991-9200 *SIC* 2813 5084

MITSUBISHI HITACHI POWER SYSTEMS AMERICA-ENERGY AND ENVIRONMENT LTD p 977
645 Martinsville Rd 07920
Tel (908) 542-9101 *SIC* 8711

NEW JERSEY PROPERTY LIABILITY INSURANCE GUARANTY ASSOCIATION p 1031
222 Mount Airy Rd 07920
Tel (908) 953-9533 *SIC* 6411

TORRENT PHARMA INC p 1462
150 Allen Rd Ste 102 07920
Tel (269) 544-2299 *SIC* 2834

■ VERIZON CORPORATE SERVICES GROUP INC p 1550
295 N Maple Ave 07920
Tel (908) 559-7000 *SIC* 4813

■ VERIZON WIRELESS INC p 1551
1 Verizon Way 07920
Tel (908) 559-2000 *SIC* 4812

BAYONNE, NJ

BAYONNE MEDICAL CENTER INC p 162
29th Street At Ave E 07002
Tel (201) 858-5000 *SIC* 8062

BAYONNE SCHOOL DISTRICT p 162
669 Avenue A 07002
Tel (201) 858-5814 *SIC* 8211

BOOKAZINE CO INC p 200
75 Hook Rd 07002
Tel (201) 339-7777 *SIC* 5192 2741

CITY OF BAYONNE p 313
630 Avenue C 07002
Tel (201) 858-6046 *SIC* 9111

GEL SPICE CO INC p 598
48 Hook Rd 07002
Tel (201) 339-0700 *SIC* 2099 5149

GEL SPICE CO LLC p 598
48 Hook Rd 07002
Tel (201) 339-0700 *SIC* 2099

HADDAD APPAREL GROUP LTD p 652
90 E 5th St Ste 1 07002
Tel (201) 356-2000 *SIC* 5137

HADDAD ORGANIZATION LTD p 652
90 E 5th St Ste 1 07002
Tel (201) 339-0665 *SIC* 6531

KENOVER MARKETING CORP p 812
72 Hook Rd 07002
Tel (718) 369-4600 *SIC* 5141

BEDMINSTER, NJ

■ AT&T COMMUNICATIONS AMERICAS INC p 123
900 Us Highway 202 206 07921
Tel (404) 861-9188 *SIC* 5065

■ AT&T CORP p 123
1 At&T Way 07921
Tel (800) 403-3302 *SIC* 4813 4822 7375

CEGEDIM INC p 272
1425 Us Highway 206 07921
Tel (908) 443-2000 *SIC* 7371 7372

▲ GAIN CAPITAL HOLDINGS INC p 589
135 Route 202 206 07921
Tel (908) 731-0700 *SIC* 6211 6221

GL CAPITAL PARTNERS LLC p 613
350 Main St Ste 8 07921
Tel (928) 526-2735 *SIC* 6159

■ PEAPACK-GLADSTONE BANK p 1126
500 Hills Dr Ste 300 07921
Tel (908) 234-0700 *SIC* 6022

▲ PEAPACK-GLADSTONE FINANCIAL CORP p 1126
500 Hills Dr Ste 300 07921
Tel (908) 234-0700 *SIC* 6029

PREMIER HEALTHCARE EXCHANGE CORP p 1170
2 Crossroads Dr Ste 101b 07921
Tel (908) 658-3535 *SIC* 7372

BELLEVILLE, NJ

CLARA MAASS MEDICAL CENTER (INC) p 321
1 Clara Maass Dr 07109
Tel (973) 450-2000 *SIC* 8062

BELLMAWR, NJ

EMR (USA HOLDINGS) INC p 495
143 Harding Ave Ste 1 08031
Tel (856) 365-7500 *SIC* 6719

BELMAR, NJ

■ NJR ENERGY SERVICES CO p 1045
1415 Wyckoff Rd 07719
Tel (732) 938-1273 *SIC* 4924

BELVIDERE, NJ

COUNTY OF WARREN p 382
165 County Road 519 Ste 1 07823
Tel (908) 475-6500 *SIC* 9111

BERKELEY HEIGHTS, NJ

■ **AIG CLAIM SERVICES INC** p 37
100 Connell Dr Ste 2100 07922
Tel (973) 402-2800 *SIC* 6411 8111

CONNELL CO p 357
200 Connell Dr Ste 4100 07922
Tel (908) 673-3700
SIC 6552 6512 7359 5082

■ **HEWLETT-PACKARD FINANCIAL SERVICES CO** p 688
200 Connell Dr Ste 5000 07922
Tel (908) 288-9315 *SIC* 6159 7389

PALISADES SAFETY INSURANCE AGENCY INC p 1108
200 Connell Dr 07922
Tel (908) 790-7800 *SIC* 6321

SALONCENTRIC INC p 1273
50 Connell Dr 07922
Tel (212) 984-4000 *SIC* 5122

SUMMIT MEDICAL GROUP PA p 1399
1 Diamond Hill Rd 07922
Tel (908) 277-8880 *SIC* 8099 8011

BERLIN, NJ

AC MOORE ARTS & CRAFTS INC p 13
130 A C Moore Dr 08009
Tel (856) 768-4930 *SIC* 5945

AC MOORE INC p 13
130 A C Moore Dr 08009
Tel (856) 768-4930 *SIC* 5945

BIRMINGHAM, NJ

LANXESS SYBRON CHEMICALS INC p 844
200 Birmingham Rd 08011
Tel (609) 893-1100 *SIC* 2843 2899 3589

BLACKWOOD, NJ

CAMDEN COUNTY COLLEGE p 244
200 College Dr 08012
Tel (856) 227-7200 *SIC* 8222

■ **CLASSIC AUTO GROUP INC** p 323
Black Horse Pike Rr 555 08012
Tel (856) 629-1900 *SIC* 5511

GLOUCESTER TOWNSHIP BOARD OF EDUCATION p 618
17 Erial Rd 08012
Tel (856) 227-1400 *SIC* 8211

GLOUCESTER TOWNSHIP PUBLIC SCHOOLS p 618
17 Erial Rd 08012
Tel (856) 227-1400 *SIC* 8211

REFAC OPTICAL GROUP p 1217
1 Harmon Dr 08012
Tel (856) 228-1000 *SIC* 3827

RELIABLE TIRE DISTRIBUTORS INC p 1221
805 N Black Horse Pike 08012
Tel (800) 342-3426 *SIC* 5014

BLOOMFIELD, NJ

ATLANTIC TRACK & TURNOUT CO p 127
400 Broadacres Dr Ste 415 07003
Tel (973) 748-5885 *SIC* 5088

DEWBERRY ENGINEERS INC p 434
200 Broadacres Dr Ste 410 07003
Tel (973) 338-9100 *SIC* 8711

LEGENDS HOSPITALITY LLC p 853
400 Bradacrest Dr Ste 200 07003
Tel (973) 707-2800 *SIC* 7929

LUMMUS OVERSEAS CORP p 885
1515 Broad St 07003
Tel (973) 893-1515 *SIC* 8711 1629 8741

WORLD FINER FOODS LLC p 1625
1455 Broad St Ste 4 07003
Tel (973) 338-0300 *SIC* 5149

BOONTON, NJ

MERSEN USA BN CORP p 951
400 Myrtle Ave 07005
Tel (973) 334-0700 *SIC* 3624

BRANCHBURG, NJ

BRIDGEWATER WHOLESALERS INC p 212
210 Industrial Pkwy 08876
Tel (908) 526-7555 *SIC* 2431 5031

DANCKER SELLEW & DOUGLAS INC p 411
291 Evans Way 08876
Tel (908) 429-1200 *SIC* 5021 5063 5049

FERREIRA CONSTRUCTION CO INC p 538
31 Tannery Rd 08876
Tel (908) 534-8655 *SIC* 1611

FURINO & SON INC p 585
66 Columbia Rd 08876
Tel (908) 756-7736 *SIC* 1541 1542

LIFECELL CORP p 864
1 Millennium Way 08876
Tel (908) 947-1100 *SIC* 2836

MARCOLIN USA EYEWEAR CORP p 905
3140 Rte 22 08876
Tel (800) 345-8482 *SIC* 5099 5048

MARCOLIN USA INC p 905
3140 Us Highway 22 08876
Tel (480) 951-7174 *SIC* 5048

■ **RATHGIBSON NORTH BRANCH LLC** p 1209
100 Aspen Hill Rd 08876
Tel (908) 253-3260 *SIC* 3317

SCHUTZ CONTAINER SYSTEMS INC p 1291
200 Aspen Hill Rd 08876
Tel (908) 429-1637 *SIC* 2655

SCHUTZ CORP p 1291
200 Aspen Hill Rd 08876
Tel (908) 526-6161 *SIC* 2655

BRANCHVILLE, NJ

■ **SELECTIVE INSURANCE CO OF AMERICA** p 1302
40 Wantage Ave 07890
Tel (973) 948-3000 *SIC* 6411 6351

▲ **SELECTIVE INSURANCE GROUP INC** p 1302
40 Wantage Ave 07890
Tel (973) 948-3000 *SIC* 6331

BRICK, NJ

BRICK TOWNSHIP BOARD OF EDUCATION p 211
101 Hendrickson Ave 08724
Tel (732) 785-3000 *SIC* 8211

BRICK TOWNSHIP PUBLIC SCHOOL BOARD p 211
101 Hendrickson Ave 08724
Tel (732) 785-3000 *SIC* 8211

TRYKO PARTNERS LLC p 1489
575 Route 70 Fl 2 08723
Tel (732) 961-9991 *SIC* 6531 8051

BRIDGEPORT, NJ

■ **XYLEM DEWATERING SOLUTIONS INC** p 1633
84 Floodgate Rd 08014
Tel (410) 243-4900 *SIC* 7353 3561 5084

BRIDGETON, NJ

CUMBERLAND MUTUAL FIRE INSURANCE CO (INC) p 400
633 Shiloh Pike 08302
Tel (856) 451-4050 *SIC* 6331 6411

INSPIRA MEDICAL CENTERS INC p 746
333 Irving Ave 08302
Tel (856) 575-4500 *SIC* 8062

SEABROOK BROTHERS & SONS INC p 1296
85 Finley Rd 08302
Tel (856) 455-8080 *SIC* 2037

BRIDGEWATER, NJ

AKZO NOBEL SPG LLC p 43
10 Finderne Ave Ste A 08807
Tel (908) 685-5000 *SIC* 2841

AMNEAL PHARMACEUTICALS LLC p 86
400 Crossing Blvd Fl 3 08807
Tel (631) 952-0214 *SIC* 2834 3999

AVENTIS INC p 136
55 Corporate Dr 08807
Tel (800) 981-2491 *SIC* 2834

BRIDGEWATER-RARITAN REGIONAL SCHOOL DISTRICT p 212
836 Newmans Ln 08807
Tel (908) 685-2777 *SIC* 8211

BRIDGEWATER-RARITAN REGIONAL SCHOOL DISTRICT p 212
836 Newmans Ln 08807
Tel (908) 685-2777 *SIC* 8211

BROTHER INTERNATIONAL CORP p 219
200 Crossing Blvd 08807
Tel (908) 704-1700
SIC 5044 3579 3559 5084 5064 5065

CONVATEC INC p 364
1160 Rte 22 Ste 201 08807
Tel (908) 904-2500 *SIC* 3841

DENDREON PHARMACEUTICALS INC p 428
400 Somerset Corp Blvd # 500 08807
Tel (908) 927-1400 *SIC* 2834

ICI AMERICA INC p 727
10 Finderne Ave 08807
Tel (908) 203-2800
SIC 2821 3081 2869 2843 2865

ICI AMERICAN HOLDINGS LLC p 727
10 Finderne Ave 08807
Tel (908) 203-2800
SIC 2851 2821 3081 2869 2843 2865

IGATE CORP p 730
100 Somerset Corp Blvd # 5000 08807
Tel (908) 219-8050 *SIC* 7371 7374 7389

IGATE TECHNOLOGIES INC p 730
100 Somerset Corp Blvd # 5000 08807
Tel (908) 219-8050 *SIC* 7371

■ **IMCLONE SYSTEMS LLC** p 733
440 Us Highway 22 08807
Tel (908) 541-8000 *SIC* 2836 2834

INDOPCO INC p 739
10 Finderne Ave Ste A 08807
Tel (908) 685-5000
SIC 2891 2046 2821 2869 2899 2099

LINDE GAS NORTH AMERICA LLC p 868
200 Somerset Corp Blvd # 7000 08807
Tel (908) 464-8100 *SIC* 2813

LINDE GAS USA LLC p 868
200 Somset Cor B Ste 7000 08807
Tel (908) 464-8100 *SIC* 2813 5084

LINDE LLC p 868
200 Somerset Corporate Bl 08807
Tel (908) 464-8100
SIC 2813 3569 3561 3823

LINDE NORTH AMERICA INC p 868
200 Somerset Corporate Bl 08807
Tel (908) 464-8100
SIC 2813 3569 3559 3561 3511 3823

MEDICIS PHARMACEUTICAL CORP p 937
700 Us Highway 202/206 08807
Tel (866) 246-8245 *SIC* 2834

■ **NATIONAL STARCH AND CHEMICAL HOLDING CORP** p 1016
10 Finderne Ave 08807
Tel (908) 685-5000 *SIC* 2891 2046 2869

RYAN AUTOMOTIVE LLC p 1260
1120 Us Highway 22 Bldg 2 08807
Tel (732) 650-1550 *SIC* 5511

SALIX PHARMACEUTICALS LTD p 1273
400 Somerset Corp Blvd 08807
Tel (919) 862-1000 *SIC* 2834

SANOFI US SERVICES INC p 1280
55 Corporate Dr 08807
Tel (336) 407-4994 *SIC* 2834

SANOFI-AVENTIS US LLC p 1280
55 Corporate Dr 08807
Tel (908) 981-5000 *SIC* 5122 2834

SANOFI-SYNTHELABO INC p 1280
55 Corporate Dr 08807
Tel (908) 981-5000 *SIC* 8011

▲ **SYNCHRONOSS TECHNOLOGIES INC** p 1414
200 Crossing Blvd Fl 8 08807
Tel (866) 620-3940 *SIC* 7371 4813

TRIGEN LABORATORIES LLC p 1480
400 Crossing Blvd 08807
Tel (732) 721-0070 *SIC* 2834

VALEANT PHARMACEUTICALS INTERNATIONAL CORP p 1539
400 Somerset Corp Blvd 08807
Tel (908) 927-1400 *SIC* 2834

ZENTRY LLC p 1642
200 Crossing Blvd Fl 8 08807
Tel (866) 620-3940 *SIC* 7371

BROWNS MILLS, NJ

DEBORAH HEART AND LUNG CENTER p 420
200 Trenton Rd 08015
Tel (609) 893-6611 *SIC* 8062

BURLINGTON, NJ

BURLINGTON COAT FACTORY HOLDINGS INC p 227
1830 N Route 130 08016
Tel (609) 387-7800
SIC 5651 5632 5719 5947 5712

■ **BURLINGTON COAT FACTORY HOLDINGS LLC** p 227
1830 N Route 130 08016
Tel (609) 387-7800 *SIC* 5311

■ **BURLINGTON COAT FACTORY INVESTMENTS HOLDINGS INC** p 227
1830 N Route 130 08016
Tel (609) 387-7800 *SIC* 5311

■ **BURLINGTON COAT FACTORY REALTY OF MORROW INC** p 227
1830 N Route 130 08016
Tel (609) 387-7800 *SIC* 5651

■ **BURLINGTON COAT FACTORY WAREHOUSE CORP** p 227
1830 N Route 130 # 2006 08016
Tel (609) 387-7800 *SIC* 5311

■ **BURLINGTON COAT FACTORY WAREHOUSE OF MONMOUTH INC** p 228
1830 N Route 130 08016
Tel (609) 387-7800 *SIC* 5651

▲ **BURLINGTON STORES INC** p 228
2006 Route 130 08016
Tel (609) 387-7800 *SIC* 5311 5961

COMPASSIONATE CARE HOSPICE OF CENTRAL NEW JERSEY LLC p 351
261 Connecticut Dr Ste 1 08016
Tel (609) 267-1178 *SIC* 8082

■ **LUXURY LINENS OF NASHVILLE INC** p 887
1830 N Route 130 08016
Tel (609) 387-7800 *SIC* 5719

MCCOLLISTERS TRANSPORTATION GROUP INC p 927
1800 N Route 130 08016
Tel (609) 386-0600 *SIC* 4213 4212

MILK INDUSTRY MANAGEMENT CORP p 969
4 Manhattan Dr 08016
Tel (609) 747-9542 *SIC* 5143

QUALITY PACKAGING SPECIALISTS INTERNATIONAL LLC p 1197
5 Cooper St 08016
Tel (609) 239-0503 *SIC* 7389 3565

CAMDEN, NJ

CAMDEN CITY BOARD OF EDUCATION FOUNDATION INC p 244
201 N Front St 08102
Tel (856) 966-2000 *SIC* 8211

CAMDEN CITY PUBLIC SCHOOLS p 244
201 N Front St 08102
Tel (856) 966-2000 *SIC* 8211

■ **CAMPBELL SALES CO** p 245
1 Campbell Pl 08103
Tel (856) 342-4800 *SIC* 8743

▲ **CAMPBELL SOUP CO** p 245
1 Campbell Pl 08103
Tel (856) 342-4800
SIC 2032 2038 2033 2052 2051 2096

CATAPULT LEARNING LLC p 265
2 Aquarium Dr Ste 100 08103
Tel (856) 831-7909 *SIC* 8299

CATELLI BROS INC p 265
50 Ferry Ave 08103
Tel (856) 869-9293 *SIC* 5147

CITY OF CAMDEN p 313
520 Marke St City Hall 4t 08101
Tel (856) 757-7200 *SIC* 9111

COOPER HEALTH CARE p 366
1 Cooper Plz Ste 504 08103
Tel (856) 342-2000 *SIC* 8741

COOPER HEALTH SYSTEM p 366
1 Cooper Plz 08103
Tel (856) 342-2000 *SIC* 8062

COUNTY OF CAMDEN p 376
520 Market St Fl 11 08102
Tel (856) 225-5000 *SIC* 9111

DELAWARE RIVER PORT AUTHORITY p 424
2 Riverside Dr Ste 603 08103
Tel (856) 968-2000 *SIC* 4111 4785

DIOCESE OF CAMDEN NEW JERSEY p 440
631 Market St 08102
Tel (856) 756-7900 *SIC* 2711 8661

OUR LADY OF LOURDES HEALTH CARE SERVICES INC p 1098
1600 Haddon Ave 08103
Tel (856) 757-3500 *SIC* 8741

OUR LADY OF LOURDES MEDICAL CENTER INC p 1098
1600 Haddon Ave 08103
Tel (856) 757-3500 *SIC* 8062

VIRTUA-WEST JERSEY HEALTH SYSTEM INC p 1560
1000 Atlantic Ave 08104
Tel (856) 246-3000 *SIC* 8062

CAPE MAY COURT HOUSE, NJ

CAPE HEALTH SYSTEM INC p 248
2 Stone Harbor Blvd 08210
Tel (609) 463-2000 *SIC* 8741

CAPE REGIONAL MEDICAL CENTER INC p 248
2 Stone Harbor Blvd 08210
Tel (609) 463-2000 *SIC* 8062

COUNTY OF CAPE MAY p 376
4 Moore Rd 08210
Tel (609) 465-1125 *SIC* 9111

CAPE MAY, NJ

ATLANTIC CAPES FISHERIES INC p 126
985 Ocean Dr 08204
Tel (609) 884-3000 *SIC* 5146

CARLSTADT, NJ

ALLIED BEVERAGE GROUP LLC p 56
600 Washington Ave 07072
Tel (201) 842-6200 *SIC* 5182

ARCHBROOK LAGUNA LLC p 104
350 Starke Rd Ste 400 07072
Tel (201) 372-0304 *SIC* 5045 5065

GENERAL TRADING CO INC p 602
455 16th St 07072
Tel (201) 935-7717 *SIC* 5141

H BETTI INDUSTRIES INC p 649
303 Paterson Plank Rd 07072
Tel (201) 438-1300 *SIC* 5046 5091 7699

THUMANN INC p 1451
670 Dell Rd Ste 1 07072
Tel (201) 935-3636 *SIC* 2013

TRISH MCEVOY LTD p 1482
430 Commerce Blvd 07072
Tel (201) 559-9234 *SIC* 5122

UNION GRAPHICS INC p 1504
350 Michele Pl 07072
Tel (201) 372-1000 *SIC* 6719

CARNEYS POINT, NJ

LASSONDE PAPPAS AND CO INC p 846
1 Collins Dr Ste 200 08069
Tel (856) 455-1000 *SIC* 2033

PAPPAS LASSONDE HOLDINGS INC p 1112
1 Collins Dr Ste 200 08069
Tel (856) 455-1000 *SIC* 2033 6719

CARTERET, NJ

BERJE INC p 174
700 Blair Rd 07008
Tel (973) 748-8980 *SIC* 5169 2869

NU-WORLD CORP p 1066
300 Milik St 07008
Tel (732) 541-6300 *SIC* 2844

PIPELINE SUPPLY INC p 1151
100 Middlesex Ave Ste 1 07008
Tel (908) 436-1100 *SIC* 5074

PORKY PRODUCTS INC p 1161
400 Port Carteret Dr 07008
Tel (732) 541-0200
SIC 5147 5146 5144 5143

SKANSKA KOCH INC p 1329
400 Roosevelt Ave 07008
Tel (732) 969-1700 *SIC* 1622

TOLL GLOBAL FORWARDING (AMERICAS) INC p 1459
800 Federal Blvd Ste 3 07008
Tel (732) 750-9000 SIC 4789 4731

TOLL GLOBAL FORWARDING SCS (USA) INC p 1459
800 Federal Blvd Ste 2 07008
Tel (732) 750-9000 SIC 4731 8741

TRIDEC AQUISITION CO INC p 1479
800 Federal Blvd 07008
Tel (732) 750-9000 SIC 6719

WHITE ROSE INC p 1606
380 Middlesex Ave 07008
Tel (732) 541-5555
SIC 5141 5143 5142 5122 7311 8721

CEDAR KNOLLS, NJ

OLD RAZOR CO LLC p 1081
240 Cedar Knolls Rd 07927
Tel (973) 753-3000 SIC 3421

CHATHAM, NJ

CLEARVIEW CINEMA GROUP INC p 324
97 Main St Ste A 07928
Tel (973) 377-4646 SIC 7832

ESCADA US SUBCO LLC p 509
26 Main St 07928
Tel (212) 852-5300
SIC 5137 5621 5632 5099

PREFERRED FREEZER SERVICES INC p 1169
1 Main St Fl 3 07928
Tel (973) 820-4040 SIC 4222

STRATEGIC INDUSTRIES LLC p 1392
26 Main St Ste 200 07928
Tel (732) 512-0195
SIC 3724 3499 3451 3083 3111

CHERRY HILL, NJ

ADELPHIA METALS I LIMITED LIABILITY CO p 22
1930 Marlton Pike E M66 08003
Tel (856) 988-8889 SIC 5051

AMERIQUEST BUSINESS SERVICES INC p 83
457 Haddonfield Rd # 220 08002
Tel (800) 608-0809 SIC 7389

AMERIQUEST INC p 83
457 Haddonfield Rd # 220 08002
Tel (630) 925-7681 SIC 7374

BANCROFT NEUROHEALTH A NEW JERSEY NONPROFIT CORP p 150
1255 Caldwell Rd 08034
Tel (856) 348-1183 SIC 8361 8299 8211

BANCROFT REHABILITATION SERVICES A NEW JERSEY NONPROFIT CORP p 150
1255 Caldwell Rd 08034
Tel (856) 348-1183 SIC 8322

■ BIRDS EYE FOODS INC p 185
121 Woodcrest Rd 08003
Tel (585) 383-1850
SIC 2037 2096 2052 2038 2035

CHERRY HILL PUBLIC SCHOOL DISTRICT p 294
315 Roosevelt Dr 08002
Tel (856) 667-1220 SIC 8211

FOULKE MANAGEMENT CORP p 571
1708 Marlton Pike W 08002
Tel (856) 665-9000 SIC 5511

J&J STAFFING RESOURCES INC p 772
1814 Marlton Pike E # 210 08003
Tel (856) 751-5050 SIC 7363

N J PROTOCALL INC p 1005
1 Mall Dr Ste 100 08002
Tel (856) 667-9003 SIC 7363

NATIONAL DISTRIBUTION CENTERS LP p 1011
1515 Burnt Mill Rd 08003
Tel (856) 691-7000 SIC 4225

NATIONAL FREIGHT INC p 1012
1515 Burnt Mill Rd 08003
Tel (856) 691-7000 SIC 7513 4213

■ NEW JERSEY AMERICAN WATER CO p 1031
131 Woodcrest Rd 08003
Tel (856) 310-2206 SIC 4941

NFI INDUSTRIES INC p 1041
1515 Burnt Mill Rd 08003
Tel (856) 691-7000
SIC 4213 4212 8741 4225 4214 4783

NFI INTERACTIVE LOGISTICS LLC p 1041
1515 Burnt Mill Rd 08003
Tel (856) 857-1324 SIC 4731 8742

ONTIME STAFFING LLC p 1086
535 Route 38 Ste 412 08002
Tel (866) 333-3007 SIC 7361

■ PEAK FINANCE HOLDINGS LLC p 1126
121 Woodcrest Rd 08003
Tel (856) 969-7100
SIC 2038 2092 2099 2045

RIGGS DISTLER & CO INC p 1234
4 Esterbrook Ln 08003
Tel (856) 433-6000 SIC 1731

SOVEREIGN DISTRIBUTORS INC p 1353
2030 Springdale Rd 08003
Tel (856) 489-4996 SIC 5713

SUBARU OF AMERICA INC p 1395
2235 Rte 70 W 08002
Tel (856) 488-8500
SIC 5012 5013 7515 8732

TD BANK NA p 1428
1701 Marlton Pike E # 200 08003
Tel (856) 751-2739 SIC 6021

TD EQUIPMENT FINANCE INC p 1429
1006 Astoria Blvd 08003
Tel (856) 470-5741 SIC 6021

CHESTER, NJ

FRENCHS FOOD CO LLC p 578
4 Mill Ridge Ln 07930
Tel (973) 404-2600 SIC 2035

CINNAMINSON, NJ

EMSL ANALYTICAL INC p 495
200 Route 130 N 08077
Tel (856) 858-4800 SIC 8734

HOEGANAES CORP p 699
1001 Taylors Ln 08077
Tel (856) 303-0366 SIC 3312 3399

■ QUICKIE MANUFACTURING CORP p 1199
1150 Taylors Ln Ste 2 08077
Tel (856) 829-7900 SIC 2392 3991

CLARK, NJ

DSV AIR & SEA HOLDING INC p 458
100 Walnut Ave Ste 405 07066
Tel (732) 850-8000 SIC 4731

NB VENTURES INC p 1021
100 Walnut Ave Ste 304 07066
Tel (732) 382-6565 SIC 8742

UTI UNITED STATES INC p 1536
100 Walnut Ave Ste 405 07066
Tel (732) 850-8000 SIC 4731

WORLDWIDE INFORMATION SYSTEMS LLC p 1626
360 Central Ave 2051 07066
Tel (908) 272-9430 SIC 7371

CLAYTON, NJ

REVERE INDUSTRIES LLC p 1229
838 N Delsea Dr 08312
Tel (856) 881-3600 SIC 3497 3089

CLEMENTON, NJ

BERAT CORP p 174
1230 Blckwood Clmenton Rd 08021
Tel (856) 627-6501 SIC 5411

CLIFTON, NJ

BOWLES CORPORATE SERVICES INC p 204
335 Broad St 07013
Tel (973) 773-0699 SIC 7381 7389 7361

■ CENTRAL LEWMAR LLC p 279
261 River Rd 07014
Tel (973) 405-2300 SIC 5111 5199

CLIFTON BOARD OF EDUCATION INC p 326
745 Clifton Ave 07013
Tel (973) 470-2300 SIC 8211 8741

■ ITT CORP p 768
77 River Rd 07014
Tel (973) 284-0123 SIC 3812

METROPOLITAN FOODS INC p 955
174 Delawanna Ave 07014
Tel (973) 672-9400
SIC 5142 5149 2099 5141

PASSAIC METAL & BUILDING SUPPLIES CO p 1119
5 Central Ave Ste 1 07011
Tel (973) 546-9000
SIC 5033 5031 5051 5075 3444 3296

ROMAN CATHOLIC DIOCESE OF PATERSON (INC) p 1249
777 Valley Rd 07013
Tel (973) 777-8818 SIC 8211 8661

■ SCHER CHEMICALS INC p 1286
Industrial West 07012
Tel (973) 471-1300 SIC 2869

TWININGS NORTH AMERICA INC p 1495
777 Passaic Ave Ste 230 07012
Tel (973) 591-0600 SIC 2099

COLLINGSWOOD, NJ

IMPERIAL PARKING (US) LLC p 734
900 Haddon Ave Ste 333 08108
Tel (856) 854-7111 SIC 7521

IMPERIAL PARKING CORP p 734
900 Haddon Ave Ste 333 08108
Tel (856) 854-7111 SIC 7521

CRANBURY, NJ

AMSPEC LLC p 87
1249 S River Rd Ste 204 08512
Tel (908) 925-7333 SIC 8734 7389

ANTRONIX INC p 94
440 Forsgate Dr 08512
Tel (609) 860-0160 SIC 3663 5063

C R P INDUSTRIES INC p 233
35 Commerce Dr 08512
Tel (609) 578-4100 SIC 5013 5085 5063

HBC HOLDINGS LLC p 671
324a Half Acre Rd 08512
Tel (609) 860-9990 SIC 5072 5087 5074

▲ INNOPHOS HOLDINGS INC p 744
259 Prospect Plains Rd A 08512
Tel (609) 495-2495 SIC 2874 2819

■ INNOPHOS INC p 744
259 Prospect Plains Rd A 08512
Tel (609) 495-2495 SIC 2819

■ INNOPHOS INVESTMENTS II INC p 744
259 Prospect Plains Rd 08512
Tel (609) 495-2495 SIC 2874 2819

■ KOS PHARMACEUTICALS INC p 828
1 Cedarbrook Dr 08512
Tel (609) 495-0500 SIC 2834

MGL AMERICAS INC p 958
1249 S River Rd Ste 102 08512
Tel (609) 235-9632 SIC 7379 7371

■ QUADRANT 4 CONSULTING INC p 1196
1246 S River Rd Ste 102 08512
Tel (609) 799-3762 SIC 7379

SOLVAY HOLDING INC p 1339
8 Cedarbrook Dr 08512
Tel (609) 860-4000
SIC 2819 2812 2865 2869

SUN PHARMACEUTICAL INDUSTRIES INC p 1400
270 Prospect Plains Rd 08512
Tel (609) 495-2800 SIC 2834

WORLD AND MAIN (CRANBURY) LLC p 1624
324a Half Acre Rd 08512
Tel (609) 860-9990 SIC 5072 5087 5074

WORLD AND MAIN LLC p 1624
324a Half Acre Rd 08512
Tel (609) 860-9990 SIC 1711 3429

CRANFORD, NJ

AKRIMAX PHARMACEUTICALS LLC p 42
11 Commerce Dr Ste 103 07016
Tel (908) 372-0506 SIC 2834

EII INC p 481
530 South Ave E 07016
Tel (908) 276-1000 SIC 1731

METALICO INC p 952
135 Dermody St 07016
Tel (908) 497-9610 SIC 3449

NEWARK GROUP INC p 1037
20 Jackson Dr 07016
Tel (908) 276-4000 SIC 2679 2631

SIMPSON & BROWN INC p 1325
119 North Ave W 07016
Tel (908) 276-2776 SIC 1629 1771

WEEKS MARINE INC p 1587
4 Commerce Dr Fl 2 07016
Tel (908) 272-4010 SIC 1629

CREAM RIDGE, NJ

SIGMA CORP p 1321
700 Goldman Dr 08514
Tel (609) 758-0800 SIC 5074 5199

SIGMA INTERNATIONAL GROUP INC p 1321
700 Goldman Dr 08514
Tel (609) 758-0800 SIC 3494

DAYTON, NJ

AUROBINDO PHARMA USA INC p 131
6 Wheeling Rd 08810
Tel (732) 839-9400 SIC 5122

CENTRAL MILLS INC p 279
473 Ridge Rd 08810
Tel (732) 329-0032
SIC 2329 2339 2369 2322 2341 2321

CREST FURNITURE INC p 392
30 Tower Rd 08810
Tel (732) 355-9200 SIC 5712

DIRECT CABINET SALES - US LBM LLC p 441
180 Herrod Blvd 08810
Tel (908) 587-9577 SIC 5031 5064

LOCCITANE INC p 873
120 Herrod Blvd 08810
Tel (212) 696-9098 SIC 5999

PIRAMAL GLASS - USA INC p 1151
329 Herrod Blvd 08810
Tel (856) 293-6400 SIC 3221

SUNSHINE BOUQUET CO p 1404
3 Chris Ct Ste A 08810
Tel (732) 274-2900 SIC 5193 3999

■ TELEPORT COMMUNICATIONS GROUP INC (DEL CORP) p 1435
429 Ridge Rd 08810
Tel (732) 392-2000 SIC 4813

DELAIR, NJ

SHAPES/ARCH HOLDINGS LLC p 1311
9000 River Rd 08110
Tel (856) 662-5500 SIC 3354 3365

DELRAN, NJ

BILLOWS ELECTRIC SUPPLY CO INC p 182
1813 Underwood Blvd 08075
Tel (215) 332-9700
SIC 5063 3679 3621 3643 3644

SEA GULL LIGHTING PRODUCTS LLC p 1295
1829 Underwood Blvd Ste 2 08075
Tel (856) 764-0500 SIC 3645

DENVILLE, NJ

PRIME HEALTHCARE SERVICES - SAINT CLARES LLC p 1175
25 Pocono Rd 07834
Tel (973) 625-6000 SIC 8062

SAINT CLARES HOSPITAL INC p 1268
25 Pocono Rd 07834
Tel (973) 625-6000 SIC 8062

DOVER, NJ

CASIO AMERICA INC p 263
570 Mount Pleasant Ave 07801
Tel (973) 361-5400
SIC 5044 5045 5094 5099

CASIO HOLDINGS INC p 263
570 Mount Pleasant Ave 07801
Tel (973) 361-5400 SIC 5044

DOVER GENERAL HOSPITAL & MEDICAL CENTER (INC) p 453
400 W Blackwell St 07801
Tel (973) 989-3000 SIC 8062

TOTOWA PEDIATRICS p 1463
400 W Blackwell St 07801
Tel (973) 989-3645 SIC 8011

EAST BRUNSWICK, NJ

■ ARICENT US INC p 108
1 Tower Center Blvd Fl 18 08816
Tel (732) 514-6654 SIC 7371

EAST BRUNSWICK BOARD OF EDUCATION (INC) p 470
760 State Route 18 08816
Tel (732) 613-6700 SIC 8211

EAST BRUNSWICK PUBLIC SCHOOLS p 470
760 Highway 18 08816
Tel (732) 613-6700 SIC 8211

EASTER SEALS NEW JERSEY p 471
25 Kennedy Blvd Ste 600 08816
Tel (732) 257-6662 SIC 8322

MAUSER USA LLC p 921
35 Cotters Ln 08816
Tel (732) 353-7100 SIC 3412 2655

MCCARTER & ENGLISH LLP p 926
2 Tower Center Blvd Fl 11 08816
Tel (732) 393-1900 SIC 8111

WIPRO LLC p 1618
2 Tower Center Blvd # 2200 08816
Tel (732) 509-1664 SIC 7371

EAST HANOVER, NJ

CONSOLIDATED SERVICE DISTRIBUTORS INC p 360
905 Murray Rd 07936
Tel (908) 687-5800 SIC 5145 5194

FOREMOST GROUPS INC p 566
906 Murray Rd Ste 2 07936
Tel (973) 428-0400 SIC 5074 5021

NOVARTIS PHARMACEUTICALS CORP p 1062
1 Health Plz 07936
Tel (862) 778-8300 SIC 3826

PAPER MART INC p 1112
151 Ridgedale Ave 07936
Tel (973) 884-2505 SIC 5111

WARNOCK AUTOMOTIVE GROUP INC p 1576
175 State Route 10 07936
Tel (973) 884-2100
SIC 5511 7515 5012 5013

EAST MILLSTONE, NJ

LIFE SCIENCES RESEARCH INC p 864
Mettlers Rd 08875
Tel (732) 649-9961 SIC 8731

LION HOLDINGS INC p 869
Mettlers Rd 08875
Tel (732) 649-9961 SIC 8731

EAST ORANGE, NJ

CITY OF EAST ORANGE p 314
44 City Hall Plz 07018
Tel (973) 266-5140 SIC 9111

EAST ORANGE GENERAL HOSPITAL (INC) p 470
300 Central Ave 07018
Tel (973) 672-8400 SIC 8062

EAST ORANGE SCHOOL DISTRICT p 470
199 4th Ave 07017
Tel (862) 233-7300 SIC 8211 9111

ESSEX VALLEY HEALTHCARE INC p 510
300 Central Ave 07018
Tel (973) 672-8400 SIC 8741

EAST RUTHERFORD, NJ

AEGIS INSURANCE SERVICES INC p 29
1 Meadowlands Plz Ste 300 07073
Tel (201) 508-2600 SIC 6411

ALLIED BUILDING PRODUCTS CORP p 56
15 E Union Ave 07073
Tel (201) 507-8400 SIC 5031 5033

▲ CAMBREX CORP p 244
1 Meadowlands Plz # 1510 07073
Tel (201) 804-3000 SIC 2834

HUDSON GROUP (HG) INC p 716
1 Meadowlands Plz 07073
Tel (201) 939-5050 SIC 2731

JOYCE LESLIE INC p 794
186 Paterson Ave Ste 102 07073
Tel (201) 804-7800 SIC 3087

KID BRANDS INC p 817
1 Meadowlands Plz Ste 803 07073
Tel (201) 405-2400 SIC 2399 3944

MWW GROUP LLC p 1004
1 Meadowlands Plz Ste 600 07073
Tel (201) 507-9500 SIC 8743

NEAD ELECTRIC INC p 1023
187 E Union Ave 07073
Tel (201) 460-5200 SIC 1731

NEAD ORGANIZATION INC p 1023
187 E Union Ave 07073
Tel (201) 460-5200 SIC 1731

OLDCASTLE DISTRIBUTION INC p 1082
15 E Union Ave 07073
Tel (201) 507-8400 SIC 5031 5032

EAST WINDSOR, NJ

ELEMENTIS GLOBAL LLC p 486
469 Old Trenton Rd 08512
Tel (609) 443-2000 SIC 2899

ELEMENTIS SPECIALTIES INC p 486
469 Old Trenton Rd 08512
Tel (609) 443-2000
SIC 2851 8731 2899 2865 2816

SHISEIDO AMERICA INC p 1317
366 Prnctn Hightstown Rd 08520
Tel (609) 371-5800 SIC 5122 2844

EATONTOWN, NJ

D & S CONSULTANTS INC p 406
40 Christopher Way 07724
Tel (732) 389-2140 SIC 8711

E WALSH MANAGEMENT CORP p 467
45 Main St 07724
Tel (732) 443-8100 SIC 5999 8082

EMPIRE TECHNOLOGIES LLC p 494
246 Industrial Way W # 1 07724
Tel (732) 625-3200 SIC 5065 1731 5999

EUROHEALTH (USA) INC p 512
401 Industrial Way W 07724
Tel (732) 542-1191 SIC 6719

INDUSTRIAL CONTROLS DISTRIBUTORS LLC p 739
17 Christopher Way 07724
Tel (732) 918-9000 SIC 5075 5074

TYCO ELECTRONICS SUBSEA COMMUNICATIONS LLC p 1496
250 Industrial Way W 07724
Tel (732) 578-7000
SIC 3661 5063 7373 1731 8999

WEST-WARD PHARMACEUTICALS CORP p 1596
401 Industrial Way W 07724
Tel (732) 542-1191 SIC 2834

YORK TELECOM CORP p 1637
81 Corbett Way 07724
Tel (732) 413-6000 SIC 3669 3651

EDISON, NJ

AARHUSKARLSHAMN USA INC p 8
499 Thornall St Ste 5 08837
Tel (973) 344-1300 SIC 2079

AEROGROUP INTERNATIONAL INC p 30
201 Meadow Rd 08817
Tel (732) 985-6900 SIC 5139 5661

AIR SAFETY EQUIPMENT INC p 39
1601 State Route 27 08817
Tel (732) 591-9412 SIC 4581

ARGENT ASSOCIATES INC p 107
140 Fieldcrest Ave 08837
Tel (732) 512-9009 SIC 4225

BEACH TRADING CO INC p 164
80 Carter Dr 08817
Tel (800) 572-3224 SIC 3861 5731

BIOCON INC p 183
125 May St 08837
Tel (732) 661-0202 SIC 8731

BIRLASOFT INC p 185
399 Thornall St Ste 8 08837
Tel (732) 287-5000 SIC 7371

C & A MARKETING INC p 231
114 Tived Ln E 08837
Tel (201) 881-1900
SIC 5065 8742 7384 5946 7359 7221

■ CHASE MANHATTAN MORTGAGE CORP p 291
343 Thornall St Ste 7 08837
Tel (732) 205-0600 SIC 6162

COMMUNITY HOSPITAL GROUP INC p 349
98 James St Ste 400 08820
Tel (732) 321-7000 SIC 8062 8069

CONTI ENTERPRISES INC p 362
2045 Lincoln Hwy 08817
Tel (732) 520-5000 SIC 1611 1622 1623

CONTROL ENVIRONMENTAL SERVICES INC p 364
737 New Durham Rd Ste 1 08817
Tel (732) 548-5272 SIC 0782

CREDIT-BASED ASSET SERVICING AND SECURITIZATION LLC p 391
333 Thornall St Ste 602 08837
Tel (212) 850-7700 SIC 8732

DGL GROUP LTD p 435
195 Raritan Center Pkwy 08837
Tel (718) 499-1000 SIC 5731 5065

DI GIORGIO CORP p 436
160 Fieldcrest Ave Ste A 08837
Tel (718) 470-1744 SIC 5149

DR LEONARDS HEALTHCARE CORP p 454
100 Nixon Ln 08837
Tel (732) 572-0900 SIC 5961

EDISON TOWNSHIP PUBLIC SCHOOLS p 478
312 Pierson Ave 08837
Tel (732) 452-4900 SIC 8211

GENERAL PLUMBING SUPPLY INC p 601
980 New Durham Rd 08817
Tel (732) 248-1000 SIC 5075 5074

HACKENSACK MERIDIAN HEALTH INC p 652
343 Thornall St 08837
Tel (732) 751-7500 SIC 8062

J F K JOHNSON REHABILITION INSTITUTE p 771
65 James St 08820
Tel (732) 321-7070 SIC 8093

JFK HEALTH SYSTEM INC p 785
80 James St 08820
Tel (732) 321-7000 SIC 8062

JM HUBER CORP p 786
499 Thornall St Ste 8 08837
Tel (732) 603-3630
SIC 0811 1311 1455 2493 2819

JPC ENTERPRISES INC p 795
47 Brunswick Ave 08817
Tel (732) 750-1900 SIC 5113

LARSEN & TOUBRO INFOTECH LIMITED p 845
2035 State Route 27 # 3000 08817
Tel (732) 248-6111 SIC 7379

▲ MACK-CALI REALTY CORP p 892
343 Thornall St 08837
Tel (732) 590-1000 SIC 6798

MIDDLESEX COUNTY COLLEGE p 965
2600 Woodbridge Ave 08837
Tel (732) 548-6000
SIC 8222 9111 8221 8211

MUSCULOSKELETAL TRANSPLANT FOUNDATION INC p 1002
125 May St 08837
Tel (732) 661-0202 SIC 8099

NANDANSONS INTERNATIONAL INC p 1007
55 Mayfield Ave 08837
Tel (908) 561-2400 SIC 5122

NEW JERSEY CARPENTERS PENSION FUND p 1031
91 Fieldcrest Ave 08837
Tel (732) 417-3900 SIC 6371

NEW YORK SHIPPING ASSOCIATION INC p 1036
333 Thornall St Ste 3a 08837
Tel (732) 452-7800 SIC 8611

NJ CARPENTERS CATASTROPHIC HEALTH FUND p 1045
P.O. Box 7818 08818
Tel (732) 417-3900 SIC 8631

■ ORACLE FINANCIAL SERVICES SOFTWARE INC p 1091
399 Thornall St Ste 6 08837
Tel (732) 623-0399 SIC 5045

PXRE CORP p 1193
379 Thornall St Ste 2 08837
Tel (973) 321-3590 SIC 6331 6324 6321

PXRE REINSURANCE CO p 1193
379 Thornall St Ste 2 08837
Tel (732) 906-9157 SIC 6331

RAND DIRECT INC p 1207
112 Truman Dr 08817
Tel (732) 985-0800 SIC 7389

RCG GLOBAL SERVICES INC p 1212
379 Thornall St Ste 14 08837
Tel (732) 744-3500 SIC 8748

SAKAR INTERNATIONAL INC p 1271
195 Carter Dr 08817
Tel (732) 248-1306 SIC 5043

TEKMARK GLOBAL SOLUTIONS LLC p 1433
100 Metroplex Dr Ste 102 08817
Tel (732) 572-5400 SIC 7379 7371 7363

TRIGYN TECHNOLOGIES INC p 1480
100 Metroplex Dr Ste 101 08817
Tel (732) 777-0050 SIC 7371 7379

UBI LIQUIDATING CORP p 1498
300 Nixon Ln 08837
Tel (201) 319-9093
SIC 5621 5641 5651 5137 5632

ZSL INC p 1644
85 State Route 27 08820
Tel (877) 800-0975 SIC 7379

EGG HARBOR TOWNSHIP, NJ

ATLANTIC COUNTY UTILITIES AUTHORITY p 126
6700 Delilah Rd 08234
Tel (609) 272-6950 SIC 4953 4952

ATLANTICARE HEALTH SYSTEM INC p 127
2500 English Creek Ave 08234
Tel (609) 407-2300 SIC 8071 8082

EGG HARBOR TOWNSHIP BOARD OF EDUCATION INC p 481
13 Swift Ave 08234
Tel (609) 646-7911 SIC 8211

SPENCER GIFTS HOLDINGS INC p 1358
6826 Black Horse Pike 08234
Tel (609) 645-3300 SIC 5947

SPENCER GIFTS LLC p 1358
6826 Black Horse Pike 08234
Tel (609) 645-3300 SIC 5947 5944

SPENCER SPIRIT HOLDINGS INC p 1358
6826 Black Horse Pike 08234
Tel (609) 645-3300 SIC 5699 6719

SPIRIT HALLOWEEN SUPER STORES LLC p 1359
6826 Black Horse Pike 08234
Tel (609) 645-5691 SIC 5311

ELIZABETH, NJ

ACTAVIS ELIZABETH LLC p 19
200 Elmora Ave 07202
Tel (908) 527-9100 SIC 2834

AFI FOOD SERVICE DISTRIBUTORS INC p 33
1 Ikea Dr 07201
Tel (908) 629-1800 SIC 5141

ALPHA WIRE CORP p 60
711 Lidgerwood Ave 07202
Tel (908) 259-2613 SIC 5063 3082 3357

ATALANTA CORP p 123
1 Atlanta Plz Ste 3 07206
Tel (908) 351-8000 SIC 5143 5149 5142

CARL F EWIG INC p 256
529 Dowd Ave 07201
Tel (908) 248-9001 SIC 5088

CITY OF ELIZABETH p 314
50 Winfield Scott Plz 07201
Tel (908) 820-4111 SIC 9111

CLEAN VENTURE INC p 324
201 S 1st St 07206
Tel (908) 355-5800
SIC 4225 4212 4953 8748

COUNTY OF UNION p 382
10 Elizabeth Ave 07206
Tel (908) 659-7407 SIC 9111

ELIZABETH PUBLIC SCHOOLS p 487
500 N Broad St 07208
Tel (908) 436-5010 SIC 8211

HAYWARD INDUSTRIES INC p 670
620 Division St 07201
Tel (908) 351-5400
SIC 3589 3561 3423 3494 3569 3089

INTER-CITY TIRE & AUTO CENTER INC p 751
777 Dowd Ave 07201
Tel (908) 354-5533 SIC 5531 5013 7538

NEW ENGLAND MOTOR FREIGHT INC p 1030
1-71 North Ave E 07201
Tel (908) 965-0100 SIC 4213

ELIZABETHPORT, NJ

■ PAPETTIS HYGRADE EGG PRODUCTS INC p 1112
1 Papetti Plz 07206
Tel (908) 282-7900 SIC 2015

ELIZABETH, NJ

SAFEWAY CONTRACTING INC p 1267
107 Trumbull St 07206
Tel (212) 627-8050 SIC 5411

TRINITAS REGIONAL MEDICAL CENTER p 1481
225 Williamson St 07202
Tel (908) 351-0714 SIC 8062

TRUE WORLD FOODS NEW YORK LLC p 1486
32-34 Papetti Plz 07206
Tel (908) 351-9090 SIC 5146

ELMWOOD PARK, NJ

■ BIO-REFERENCE LABORATORIES INC p 183
481 Edward H Ross Dr 07407
Tel (201) 791-2600 SIC 8071 8734

CBA INDUSTRIES INC p 268
669 River Dr Ste 101 07407
Tel (201) 587-1717 SIC 5192

CORBAN ENERGY GROUP CORP p 368
418 Falmouth Ave 07407
Tel (201) 509-8555 SIC 1623 3443 5085

■ CRYOVAC INC p 396
200 Riverfront Blvd 07407
Tel (201) 791-7600 SIC 3086

EMDEON CORP p 491
669 River Dr Ste 240 07407
Tel (201) 703-3400 SIC 7373 3089

KEYENCE CORP OF AMERICA p 815
669 River Dr Ste 403 07407
Tel (201) 930-0100 SIC 3825 5084 3674

MARCAL MANUFACTURING LLC p 904
1 Market St 07407
Tel (201) 703-6225 SIC 2676

MARCAL PAPER MILLS LLC p 905
1 Market St 07407
Tel (201) 791-0852 SIC 2676

■ SEALED AIR CORP (US) p 1296
200 Riverfront Blvd # 301 07407
Tel (201) 791-7600
SIC 2673 2671 3087 3086 3089

SOUNDVIEW PAPER HOLDINGS LLC p 1342
1 Market St 07407
Tel (201) 796-4000 SIC 2676 2656

ENGLEWOOD CLIFFS, NJ

ALBERTO-CULVER CO p 46
800 Sylvan Ave 07632
Tel (708) 681-2668 SIC 2844 2842 2099

ALLIANCE SHIPPERS INC p 55
516 Sylvan Ave 07632
Tel (201) 227-0400 SIC 4731

AVIO INC p 138
270 Sylvan Ave Ste 130 07632
Tel (201) 816-2720 SIC 3724

COFCO (USA) INC p 334
910 Sylvan Ave Fl 1 07632
Tel (201) 568-6788 SIC 5153

▲ CONNECTONE BANCORP INC p 357
301 Sylvan Ave 07632
Tel (201) 816-8900 SIC 6022

CONOPCO INC p 358
700 Sylvan Ave 07632
Tel (201) 894-2727
SIC 2035 2038 2086 2024 2844 2841

ET BROWNE DRUG CO INC p 511
440 Sylvan Ave 07632
Tel (201) 894-9020 SIC 2844

FERRARI NORTH AMERICA INC p 538
250 Sylvan Ave 07632
Tel (201) 816-2600 SIC 5511 5012

LG CHEM AMERICA INC p 860
910 Sylvan Ave 07632
Tel (201) 816-2000 SIC 5099 5169 5199

LG ELECTRONICS USA INC p 860
1000 Sylvan Ave 07632
Tel (201) 816-2000 SIC 5064 3651

NEXXAR GROUP INC p 1041
580 Sylvan Ave Ste Ma 07632
Tel (201) 477-6045 SIC 6099

REMA FOODS INC p 1222
140 Sylvan Ave Ste 200 07632
Tel (201) 947-1000 SIC 5142 5149 5141

UNILEVER BESTFOODS NORTH AMERICA p 1503
800 Sylvan Ave 07632
Tel (201) 894-4000
SIC 2046 2034 2035 2098 2099 2051

UNILEVER MANUFACTURING (US) INC p 1503
800 Sylvan Ave 07632
Tel (800) 298-5018 SIC 2844 2099

UNILEVER UNITED STATES INC p 1503
700 Sylvan Ave 07632
Tel (201) 894-4000
SIC 2035 2086 2024 2038 2844 2841

ENGLEWOOD, NJ

■ CONNECTONE BANK p 357
301 Sylvan Ave Ste 1 07632
Tel (201) 816-8900 SIC 6022

ENGLEWOOD HOSPITAL AND MEDICAL CENTER FOUNDATION INC p 499
350 Engle St 07631
Tel (201) 894-3000 SIC 8062 8011

ERMENEGILDO ZEGNA CORP p 508
100 W Forest Ave Ste A 07631
Tel (201) 816-0921 SIC 5136 5611

HARCO INDUSTRIES INC USA p 660
333 S Van Brunt St 07631
Tel (201) 894-8941 SIC 5947

SUPREME OIL CO INC p 1408
66 Grand Ave Ste 201 07631
Tel (201) 408-0800 SIC 5149 2079

UFCW NATIONAL HEALTH AND WELFARE FUND p 1499
66 Grand Ave Ste A 07631
Tel (201) 569-8802 SIC 6371

WORMSER CORP p 1626
150 Coolidge Ave 07631
Tel (800) 666-9676 SIC 5085 5199

ENGLISHTOWN, NJ

FREEHOLD REGIONAL HIGH SCHOOL DISTRICT p 576
11 Pine St 07726
Tel (732) 792-7300 SIC 8211

MANALAPAN-ENGLISHTOWN REGIONAL SCHOOL DISTRICT p 900
54 Main St 07726
Tel (732) 786-2500 SIC 8211

EWING, NJ

CENLAR CAPITAL CORP p 275
425 Phillips Blvd 08618
Tel (609) 883-3900 SIC 6035

CENLAR FSB p 275
425 Phillips Blvd 08618
Tel (609) 883-3900 SIC 6035

▲ CHURCH & DWIGHT CO INC p 305
500 Charles Ewing Blvd 08628
Tel (609) 806-1200
SIC 2841 2812 2842 2844 2819

COLLEGE OF NEW JERSEY p 337
2000 Pennington Rd 08618
Tel (609) 771-2495 *SIC* 8221

HORIZON NJ HEALTH p 707
210 Silvia St 08628
Tel (609) 718-9001 *SIC* 6321

NEW JERSEY DEPT OF TRANSPORTATION p 1031
1035 Parkway Ave Fl 2 08618
Tel (609) 530-3855 *SIC* 9621

NEW JERSEY MANUFACTURERS INSURANCE CO p 1031
301 Sullivan Way 08628
Tel (609) 883-1300 *SIC* 6331

NEW JERSEY RE-INSURANCE CO p 1031
301 Sullivan Way 08628
Tel (609) 883-1300 *SIC* 6311 6331

NEW JERSEY TRANSPORTATION TRUST FUND AUTHORITY p 1032
1035 Parkway Ave 08618
Tel (609) 530-2035 *SIC* 8611

▲ UNIVERSAL DISPLAY CORP p 1516
375 Phillips Blvd Ste 1 08618
Tel (609) 671-0980 *SIC* 3674

■ WASTE MANAGEMENT OF NEW JERSEY INC p 1581
107 Silvia St 08628
Tel (609) 434-5200 *SIC* 3087

FAIR HAVEN, NJ

■ MASCO CONTRACTOR SERVICES EAST INC p 915
612 River Rd 07704
Tel (732) 933-4433 *SIC* 1742

FAIR LAWN, NJ

COLUMBIA BANK p 340
19-01 State Rt 208 07410
Tel (201) 796-3600 *SIC* 6035

JACK DANIELS MOTORS INC p 773
16-01 Mcbride Ave 07410
Tel (201) 796-8500 *SIC* 5511

KUIKEN BROTHERS CO INC p 831
6-02 Fair Lawn Ave 07410
Tel (201) 796-2082 *SIC* 5211 5031 3272

RADVISION INC p 1205
17-17 State Rt 208 # 300 07410
Tel (201) 689-6300 *SIC* 5065

SANDVIK INC p 1279
17-02 Nevins Rd 07410
Tel (201) 794-5000
SIC 3316 3317 3356 3315 3545 3533

FAIRFIELD, NJ

ACUATIVE CORP p 20
30 Two Bridges Rd Ste 240 07004
Tel (862) 926-5600 *SIC* 7373 5065 1731

ALDO US INC p 48
180 Passaic Ave 07004
Tel (888) 818-2536 *SIC* 5611

AMERICAN HUTS INC p 74
350 Passaic Ave 07004
Tel (973) 808-9525 *SIC* 5812

ARTHUR SCHUMAN INC p 114
40 New Dutch Ln 07004
Tel (973) 227-0030 *SIC* 2022

■ CHARLES RIVER LABORATORIES SA USA INC p 289
30 Two Bridges Rd Ste 200 07004
Tel (919) 245-3114 *SIC* 8731

DATASCOPE CORP p 414
15 Law Dr 07004
Tel (973) 244-6100 *SIC* 3845

DIALECTIC DISTRIBUTION LLC p 436
1275 Bloomfield Ave # 66 07004
Tel (973) 870-0250 *SIC* 5065

ERA RIZZO REALTY LLC p 507
244 Us Highway 46 Ste 6 07004
Tel (973) 575-1155 *SIC* 6531

FUJITSU GENERAL AMERICA INC p 584
353 Us Highway 46 07004
Tel (973) 575-0380 *SIC* 3585

JASON INDUSTRIAL INC p 778
340 Kaplan Dr 07004
Tel (973) 227-4904 *SIC* 5084 3052

■ KEARNY BANK p 807
120 Passaic Ave 07004
Tel (973) 244-4500 *SIC* 6022

■ KEARNY BANK p 807
120 Passaic Ave 07004
Tel (973) 244-4500 *SIC* 6035

▲ KEARNY FINANCIAL CORP p 807
120 Passaic Ave 07004
Tel (973) 244-4500 *SIC* 6035

KEARNY MHC p 807
120 Passaic Ave 07004
Tel (973) 244-4500 *SIC* 6035

KMM TELECOMMUNICATIONS INC p 824
9 Law Dr Ste 13 07004
Tel (844) 566-8488 *SIC* 7629 4225

■ KYOCERA DOCUMENT SOLUTIONS AMERICA INC p 833
225 Sand Rd 07004
Tel (973) 808-8444 *SIC* 5044 5084 5065

MIDDLE ATLANTIC PRODUCTS INC p 964
300 Fairfield Rd 07004
Tel (973) 839-1011 *SIC* 3444

MUSEUM CO INC p 1002
695 Us Highway 46 Ste 400 07004
Tel (973) 575-4446 *SIC* 5947

POMPTONIAN INC p 1161
3 Edison Pl Ste 5 07004
Tel (973) 882-8070 *SIC* 5812

SCHRATTER FOODS INC p 1290
333 Fairfield Rd Ste 2 07004
Tel (973) 461-2400 *SIC* 5143 5149

TELQUEST INTERNATIONAL CORP p 1435
26 Commerce Rd Ste B 07004
Tel (973) 808-4588 *SIC* 5065

FAR HILLS, NJ

UNITED STATES GOLF ASSOCIATION p 1513
77 Liberty Corner Rd 07931
Tel (908) 234-2300 *SIC* 8699

FLANDERS, NJ

SIEMENS MEDICAL SOLUTIONS DIAGNOSTICS p 1320
62 Flanders Bartley Rd 07836
Tel (973) 927-2828 *SIC* 3826

FLEMINGTON, NJ

HUNTERDON MEDICAL CENTER (INC) p 719
2100 Wescott Dr 08822
Tel (908) 788-6100 *SIC* 8062

JOHANNA FOODS INC p 787
20 Johanna Farms Rd 08822
Tel (908) 788-2200 *SIC* 2033 2026

FLORENCE, NJ

CREAM-O-LAND DAIRIES LLC p 390
529 Cedar Ln 08518
Tel (609) 499-3601 *SIC* 5143

CREAM-O-LAND DAIRY INC p 390
529 Cedar Ln 08518
Tel (609) 499-3601 *SIC* 5143 5149

FLORHAM PARK, NJ

ASCO POWER TECHNOLOGIES LP p 116
50-60 Hanover Rd 07932
Tel (973) 966-2000 *SIC* 3699

■ ASCO VALVE INC p 116
50-60 Hanover Rd 07932
Tel (973) 966-2437
SIC 3443 3491 3492 3625 5063

■ AUTOMATIC SWITCH CO p 134
50-60 Hanover Rd 07932
Tel (973) 966-2000
SIC 3491 3625 3677 3674 3613 3492

BASF CORP p 158
100 Park Ave 07932
Tel (973) 245-6000
SIC 2869 2819 2899 2843 2834 2879

BASFIN CORP p 158
100 Campus Dr Ste 301 07932
Tel (973) 245-6000
SIC 2869 2819 2899 2843 2879 2834

BURRELLES INFORMATION SERVICES LLC p 228
30b Vreeland Rd 07932
Tel (973) 992-6600 *SIC* 7389

DAMCO DISTRIBUTION SERVICES INC p 410
180 Park Ave Ste 105 07932
Tel (973) 514-5000 *SIC* 4214 4225

DAMCO USA INC p 410
180 Park Ave Ste 105 07932
Tel (973) 514-5000 *SIC* 4412 4491 4731

GERBER PRODUCTS CO p 608
12 Vreeland Rd Fl 2 07932
Tel (973) 593-7500
SIC 2023 2043 2037 2052 2086 2091

■ GLOBAL CROSSING NORTH AMERICA INC p 616
200 Park Ave Ste 300 07932
Tel (973) 937-0100 *SIC* 4813

■ GLOBAL CROSSING NORTH AMERICAN HOLDINGS INC p 616
200 Park Ave Ste 300 07932
Tel (973) 937-0100 *SIC* 4813

LAPP HOLDING NA INC p 845
29 Hanover Rd 07932
Tel (973) 660-9700 *SIC* 3355

LAPP USA LLC p 845
29 Hanover Rd 07932
Tel (973) 660-9700 *SIC* 5063 3678

MAERSK INC p 894
180 Park Ave Ste 105 07932
Tel (973) 514-5000 *SIC* 4731 4491 4412

NESTLE HEALTHCARE NUTRITION INC p 1026
12 Vreeland Rd Fl 2 07932
Tel (952) 848-6000 *SIC* 2099 2032

PCS WIRELESS LLC p 1124
11 Vreeland Rd 07932
Tel (973) 805-7400 *SIC* 5065 5999

PWC STRATEGY& (US) LLC p 1193
300 Campus Dr Ste 100 07932
Tel (973) 630-6791 *SIC* 8742

SHIONOGI PHARMA INC p 1317
300 Campus Dr Ste 300 07932
Tel (678) 427-5359 *SIC* 2834

TROY CORP p 1485
8 Vreeland Rd 07932
Tel (973) 443-4200 *SIC* 2869

VDM METALS USA LLC p 1546
306 Columbia Tpke 07932
Tel (973) 437-1664 *SIC* 3313

■ ZOETIS LLC p 1644
100 Campus Dr 07932
Tel (800) 601-1357 *SIC* 2834

■ ZOETIS P&U LLC p 1644
100 Campus Dr 07932
Tel (973) 822-7000 *SIC* 5159 0742 8734

■ ZOETIS PRODUCTS LLC p 1644
100 Campus Dr Ste 3 07932
Tel (973) 660-5000 *SIC* 2833 2834

FORT LEE, NJ

AJINOMOTO NORTH AMERICA INC p 41
400 Kelby St 07024
Tel (201) 292-3200
SIC 5142 5169 2869 2899

AMERICAN BANKNOTE CORP p 68
2200 Fletcher Ave Ste 501 07024
Tel (201) 592-3400 *SIC* 2759 2752 2621

CARE ONE LLC p 254
173 Bridge Plz N 07024
Tel (201) 242-4000 *SIC* 8051 8052

DAICEL AMERICA HOLDINGS INC p 408
1 Parker Plz 07024
Tel (201) 461-4466 *SIC* 8741

DAINIPPON SUMITOMO PHARMA AMERICA HOLDINGS INC p 408
1 Bridge Plz N Ste 510 07024
Tel (201) 592-2050 *SIC* 2834

▲ EMPIRE RESOURCES INC p 493
2115 Linwood Ave Ste 200 07024
Tel (201) 944-2200 *SIC* 5051

HANSOL AMERICA INC p 658
400 Kelby St Ste 6 07024
Tel (201) 461-6661 *SIC* 5113

HANWA AMERICAN CORP p 659
Parker Plz 400 Kelby St F 07024
Tel (201) 363-4500
SIC 5051 5172 5031 5084 5146

INNOVACARE SERVICES CO LLC p 744
173 Bridge Plz N 07024
Tel (201) 969-2300
SIC 6324 8011 8741 8742

KEDRION BIOPHARMA INC p 807
400 Kelby St Ste 11 07024
Tel (201) 242-8900 *SIC* 8099

▲ PIONEER POWER SOLUTIONS INC p 1151
400 Kelby St Ste 12 07024
Tel (212) 867-0700 *SIC* 3612

WICKED FASHIONS INC p 1608
222 Bridge Plz S 07024
Tel (201) 242-5909 *SIC* 5137 5136

WIND TURBINE AND ENERGY CABLES CORP p 1615
1 Bridge Plz N Ste 260 07024
Tel (201) 242-9906 *SIC* 5063

FRANKLIN LAKES, NJ

▲ BECTON DICKINSON AND CO p 167
1 Becton Dr 07417
Tel (201) 847-6800
SIC 3841 3842 3829 3826 3821

■ MEDCO HEALTH SOLUTIONS INC p 935
100 Parsons Pond Dr 07417
Tel (201) 269-3400 *SIC* 5961

VALIDUS SPECIALTY INC p 1540
400 Parsons Pond Dr 07417
Tel (201) 847-8600 *SIC* 6331

FRANKLINVILLE, NJ

C&H INDUSTRIAL SERVICES INC p 234
542 Penny St 08322
Tel (856) 875-8152 *SIC* 7349 1542

FREEHOLD, NJ

CENTRASTATE HEALTHCARE SYSTEM INC p 281
901 W Main St 07728
Tel (732) 431-2000 *SIC* 8099 8741

CENTRASTATE MEDICAL CENTER INC p 281
901 W Main St 07728
Tel (732) 431-2000 *SIC* 8062

COUNTY OF MONMOUTH p 380
1 E Main St 07728
Tel (732) 431-7000 *SIC* 9111

FOODARAMA SUPERMARKETS INC p 564
922 State Route 33 Bldg 1 07728
Tel (732) 462-3120 *SIC* 5411 5261 5921

INTERNATIONAL VITAMIN CORP p 757
500 Halls Mill Rd 07728
Tel (951) 361-1120 *SIC* 2834 5149 8099

SAKER HOLDINGS CORP p 1271
922 State Route 33 Bldg 1 07728
Tel (732) 462-4700 *SIC* 5411 5261 5921

SAKER SHOPRITES INC p 1271
922 Hwy 33 Bldg 1 07728
Tel (732) 462-4700 *SIC* 5411

GALLOWAY, NJ

STOCKTON UNIVERSITY p 1390
101 Vera King Farris Dr 08205
Tel (609) 652-1776 *SIC* 8221

GIBBSTOWN, NJ

MYCONE DENTAL SUPPLY CO INC p 1004
480 S Democrat Rd 08027
Tel (856) 663-4700 *SIC* 5047 3843 2844

THAYER DISTRIBUTION p 1446
333 Swedesboro Ave 08027
Tel (800) 999-4271 *SIC* 5145

GLASSBORO, NJ

ROWAN UNIVERSITY p 1253
201 Mullica Hill Rd 08028
Tel (856) 256-4000 *SIC* 8221

ROWAN UNIVERSITY/RUTGERS-CAMDEN BOARD OF GOVERNORS p 1253
201 Mullica Hill Rd 08028
Tel (856) 256-4121 *SIC* 8221

GLEN ROCK, NJ

B D AMERICAN CO p 141
25 De Boer Dr 07452
Tel (201) 689-1200 *SIC* 5182

GLENDORA, NJ

US VISION INC p 1533
1 Harmon Dr 08029
Tel (856) 227-8339 *SIC* 5995 3827

USV OPTICAL INC p 1536
1 Harmon Dr Glen Oaks 08029
Tel (856) 228-1000 *SIC* 5995 3851

GREEN BROOK, NJ

BRAVO BUILDING SERVICES INC p 209
29 King George Rd 08812
Tel (732) 465-0707 *SIC* 7349

HACKENSACK, NJ

BERGEN RECORD CORP p 174
150 River St 07601
Tel (201) 646-4000 *SIC* 2711

CARE FINDERS TOTAL CARE LLC p 254
171 Main St Ste 2 07601
Tel (201) 342-5122 *SIC* 8082

COUNTY OF BERGEN p 376
1 Bergen County Plz Ste 1 07601
Tel (201) 336-6000 *SIC* 9111

CYBER CITY TELESERVICES MARKETING INC p 404
401 Hackensack Ave Fl 3 07601
Tel (201) 487-1616 *SIC* 7389

EMERGING POWER INC p 492
200 Holt St 07601
Tel (201) 441-3590 *SIC* 5063

HACKENSACK CITY SCHOOL DISTRICT p 652
191 2nd St 07601
Tel (201) 646-8000 *SIC* 8211

HACKENSACK UNIVERSITY HEALTH NETWORK INC p 652
30 Prospect Ave 07601
Tel (551) 996-2000 *SIC* 8062

HACKENSACK UNIVERSITY MEDICAL CENTER p 652
30 Prospect Ave Ste 1 07601
Tel (201) 996-2000 *SIC* 8062

HACKNSCK HSPTL EMPLYS FDRL CRDT UN (INC) p 652
241 Moore St 07601
Tel (201) 996-2000 *SIC* 6061

▲ INNODATA INC p 744
3 University Plz 07601
Tel (201) 371-8000 *SIC* 7374

J FLETCHER CREAMER & SON INC p 771
101 E Broadway 07601
Tel (201) 488-9800
SIC 1623 1611 1771 1622 1629

LOSURDO FOODS INC p 879
20 Owens Rd 07601
Tel (201) 343-6680
SIC 5141 2022 2033 2045

MACROMEDIA INC p 893
150 River St 07601
Tel (201) 646-4000 *SIC* 2711 2721

STEVE SELVIN ASSOCIATES INC p 1388
207 Union St 07601
Tel (201) 488-3332 *SIC* 5136 5137

TECHNOLOGY SUPPLIER LLC p 1432
81 Hobart St 07601
Tel (201) 500-8050 *SIC* 7389

UNIMAVEN INC p 1503
74 Green St 07601
Tel (201) 500-8050 *SIC* 4225

VISION PROMOTIONS INC p 1561
81 Hobart St 07601
Tel (908) 333-4213 *SIC* 7311

HACKETTSTOWN, NJ

ASTRODYNE CORP p 122
36 Newburgh Rd 07840
Tel (908) 850-5088 *SIC* 3625 3621 3613

HACKETTSTOWN COMMUNITY HOSPITAL (INC) p 652
651 Willow Grove St Ste A 07840
Tel (908) 852-5100 *SIC* 8062

MARS CHOCOLATE NORTH AMERICA LLC p 910
800 High St 07840
Tel (908) 852-1000 *SIC* 2064 2066

TRANSISTOR DEVICES INC p 1471
36 Newburgh Rd 07840
Tel (908) 850-1595
SIC 3612 3625 3672 3812 3829

HADDONFIELD, NJ

UM HOLDING CO p 1501
56 N Haddon Ave Ste 300 08033
Tel (856) 354-2200 *SIC* 8099

HAMILTON, NJ

DAMCO SOLUTIONS INC p 410
3240 E Estate St Ext 08619
Tel (609) 632-0350 *SIC* 7371

ROBERT WOOD JOHNSON UNIVERSITY HOSPITAL AT HAMILTON p 1242
1 Hamilton Health Pl # 2 08690
Tel (609) 586-7900 *SIC* 8062

ROSETTA LLC p 1251
100 American Metro Blvd # 201 08619
Tel (609) 689-6100 *SIC* 8742

HAMMONTON, NJ

■ SOUTH JERSEY GAS CO p 1344
1 S Jersey Plz 08037
Tel (609) 561-9000 *SIC* 4923 4924 4922

▲ SOUTH JERSEY INDUSTRIES INC p 1344
1 S Jersey Plz 08037
Tel (609) 561-9000 *SIC* 4911 4922 4924

UNIVERSAL SUPPLY CO LLC p 1517
582 S Egg Harbor Rd 08037
Tel (609) 561-3000 *SIC* 5033 5031

HAMPTON, NJ

AMEC FOSTER WHEELER NORTH AMERICA CORP p 66
Perryville Corporate Pk 5 08827
Tel (908) 713-2891
SIC 3433 3443 3532 3569

FOSTER WHEELER INC p 570
53 Frontage Rd 08827
Tel (908) 730-4000 *SIC* 7389

FOSTER WHEELER ZACK INC p 571
53 Frontage Rd 08827
Tel (908) 730-4000
SIC 8711 1629 3569 4931

HANCOCKS BRIDGE, NJ

■ PSEG NUCLEAR LLC p 1188
80 Park Plz 08038
Tel (856) 339-1002 *SIC* 3462

HASBROUCK HEIGHTS, NJ

LOVING CARE AGENCY INC p 881
611 Rte 46 W Ste 200 07604
Tel (201) 403-9300 *SIC* 8011 8082

NATIONAL MUSIC RACK INC p 1014
440a Boulevard Apt 1 07604
Tel (201) 641-8188 *SIC* 5099

HAWTHORNE, NJ

▲ CCOM GROUP INC p 270
275 Wagaraw Rd 07506
Tel (973) 427-8224 *SIC* 5074 5075

CHURCHILL CORPORATE SERVICES INC p 305
56 Utter Ave 07506
Tel (973) 636-9400 *SIC* 6513 7389

HIGHLAND LAKES, NJ

HIGHLAND LAKES COUNTRY CLUB & COMMUNITY ASSOCIATION p 691
2240 Lakeside Dr W 07422
Tel (973) 764-4366 *SIC* 7997

HIGHLAND PARK, NJ

KAPLAN AT OLD BRIDGE INC p 803
433 River Rd 08904
Tel (732) 846-5900 *SIC* 6552

HIGHTSTOWN, NJ

COFACE NORTH AMERICA INC p 334
Suite 3 Bldg 100 08520
Tel (609) 469-0400 *SIC* 6411

HILLSBOROUGH, NJ

HILLSBOROUGH TOWNSHIP BOARD OF EDUCATION p 694
379 S Branch Rd 08844
Tel (908) 431-6600 *SIC* 8211

HILLSBOROUGH TOWNSHIP SCHOOL DISTRICT p 694
379 S Branch Rd 08844
Tel (908) 431-6600 *SIC* 8211

MERCK PATIENT ASSISTANCE PROGRAM INC p 945
2 Clerico Ln Apt 201 08844
Tel (908) 423-1000 *SIC* 8699

HILLSDALE, NJ

FORNAZOR INTERNATIONAL INC A NEW JERSEY CORP p 568
455 Hillsdale Ave 07642
Tel (201) 664-4000
SIC 0119 2034 2044 2045 2075 4449

HILLSIDE, NJ

COMMUNITY FOOD BANK OF NEW JERSEY INC p 348
31 Evans Terminal 07205
Tel (908) 355-3663 *SIC* 8322

FRANK M GARGIULO & SON INC p 574
535 Sweetland Ave Ste 1 07205
Tel (908) 233-8222 *SIC* 5148

NATIONAL ENTERTAINMENT COLLECTIBLES ASSOCIATION INC p 1011
603 Sweetland Ave 07205
Tel (908) 686-3300 *SIC* 5199

HOBOKEN, NJ

FRANCISCAN HEALTH SYSTEMS OF NEW JERSEY INC p 573
308 Willow Ave 07030
Tel (201) 418-1000 *SIC* 8741

HOBOKEN UNIVERSITY MEDICAL CENTER p 699
308 Willow Ave 07030
Tel (201) 418-1000 *SIC* 8062

HUDSON HEALTHCARE INC p 716
308 Willow Ave 07030
Tel (201) 418-1000 *SIC* 8062

HUMC HOLDCO LLC p 718
308 Willow Ave 07030
Tel (201) 418-1000 *SIC* 6211

HUMC OPCO LLC p 718
308 Willow Ave 07030
Tel (201) 418-1000 *SIC* 8062

■ JET.COM INC p 784
221 River St Fl 8 07030
Tel (844) 538-2255 *SIC* 4813

▲ JOHN WILEY & SONS INC p 789
111 River St Ste 2000 07030
Tel (201) 748-6000 *SIC* 2731 2721

▲ NEWELL BRANDS INC p 1037
221 River St 07030
Tel (201) 610-6600
SIC 3089 3469 2591 3951 3999 3546

SHIPCO TRANSPORT INC p 1317
80 Washington St 07030
Tel (973) 457-3300 *SIC* 8742 4731

SSNYC INC p 1364
80 Washington St 07030
Tel (201) 216-1500 *SIC* 4731 6512

STEVENS INSTITUTE OF TECHNOLOGY (INC) p 1388
1 Castle Point Ter 07030
Tel (201) 216-5000 *SIC* 8221

SUMITOMO MITSUI TRUST BANK (USA) INC p 1398
111 River St 07030
Tel (201) 595-8900 *SIC* 6021

■ WILEY PUBLISHING INC p 1609
111 River St 07030
Tel (201) 748-6000 *SIC* 2731

ZUEGG USA CORP p 1644
50 Harrison St Ste 214b 07030
Tel (201) 222-0291 *SIC* 5149

HOLMDEL, NJ

BAYSHORE COMMUNITY HEALTH SERVICES INC p 162
727 N Beers St 07733
Tel (732) 739-5900 *SIC* 8062 8741

BAYSHORE COMMUNITY HOSPITAL p 162
727 N Beers St 07733
Tel (732) 739-5900 *SIC* 8062

CARE ONE AT HOLMDEL LLC p 254
188 State Route 34 07733
Tel (732) 946-4200 *SIC* 8322

CEI HOLDINGS INC p 273
2182 State Route 35 07733
Tel (732) 888-7788
SIC 2844 7389 4225 5122

COSMETIC ESSENCE LLC p 373
2182 Hwy 35 07733
Tel (732) 888-7788 *SIC* 2844 7389 4225

▲ VONAGE HOLDINGS CORP p 1565
23 Main St 07733
Tel (732) 528-2600 *SIC* 4813

HOWELL, NJ

HOWELL TOWNSHIP BOARD OF EDUCATION p 713
200 Sqnkum Yellowbrook Rd 07731
Tel (732) 751-2480 *SIC* 8211

IRVINGTON, NJ

IRVINGTON PUBLIC SCHOOLS p 765
1 University Pl Fl 4 07111
Tel (973) 399-6800 *SIC* 8211

ISELIN, NJ

ANSELL HEALTHCARE PRODUCTS LLC p 93
111 Wood Ave S Ste 210 08830
Tel (732) 345-5400
SIC 3069 3842 2822 2326

ANSELL PROTECTIVE PRODUCTS LLC p 93
111 Wood Ave S Ste 210 08830
Tel (732) 345-5400 *SIC* 3842 3069

BASF CATALYSTS LLC p 158
25 Middlesex Tpke 08830
Tel (732) 205-5000
SIC 2819 2816 5094 3339

DIRECT ENERGY BUSINESS MARKETING LLC p 441
194 Wood Ave S Fl 2 08830
Tel (732) 516-7500 *SIC* 8742

DOMINO FOODS INC p 449
99 Wood Ave S Ste 901 08830
Tel (732) 590-1173 *SIC* 5149

EPCOS INC p 504
485b Route 1 S Ste 200 08830
Tel (732) 906-4300
SIC 3679 3546 5065 3671

GEODIS WILSON USA INC p 605
485c Us Highway 1 S # 410 08830
Tel (732) 362-0600 *SIC* 4731 4412 4225

H & M INTERNATIONAL TRANSPORTATION INC p 649
485b Us Highway 1 S # 110 08830
Tel (732) 510-4640 *SIC* 4731 8741 4225

HEXAWARE TECHNOLOGIES INC p 688
101 Wood Ave S Ste 600 08830
Tel (609) 409-6950 *SIC* 7379

HOMEBRIDGE FINANCIAL SERVICES INC p 703
194 Wood Ave S Fl 9 08830
Tel (201) 498-9300 *SIC* 6162

IESI NY CORP p 730
99 Wood Ave S Ste 1001 08830
Tel (201) 443-3000 *SIC* 4953

MACDONALD MOTT GROUP INC p 892
111 Wood Ave S Ste 5 08830
Tel (973) 379-3400 *SIC* 8711

MAIDENFORM p 897
485 Us Highway 1 S 08830
Tel (732) 621-2216 *SIC* 2341

■ MAIDENFORM BRANDS INC p 897
485 Us Highway 1 S 08830
Tel (888) 573-0299 *SIC* 2341 2342 5621

MAIDENFORM INC p 897
485f Us Highway 1 S # 120 08830
Tel (732) 621-2500 *SIC* 2341 2342

▲ MIDDLESEX WATER CO p 965
1500 Ronson Rd 08830
Tel (732) 634-1500 *SIC* 4941 1623

■ PROVIDENT BANK p 1186
100 Wood Ave S Ste 119 08830
Tel (800) 448-7768 *SIC* 6036 6029

SIEMENS FINANCIAL SERVICES INC p 1320
170 Wood Ave S Fl 1 08830
Tel (609) 954-2489 *SIC* 6159

VELOCITA WIRELESS LLC p 1547
70 Wood Ave S Ste 202 08830
Tel (848) 248-4722 *SIC* 4899 4812

JACKSON, NJ

JACKSON TOWNSHIP SCHOOL DISTRICT p 774
151 Don Connor Blvd 08527
Tel (732) 833-4600 *SIC* 8211

NEKTOVA GROUP LIMITED LIABILITY CO p 1025
534 Whitesville Rd 08527
Tel (732) 835-2303 *SIC* 5065

JAMESBURG, NJ

ARGIX DIRECT INC p 107
100 Middlesex Center Blvd 08831
Tel (732) 536-9173 *SIC* 4213 4225

JERSEY CITY, NJ

AMERICAN INSTITUTE OF CERTIFIED PUBLIC ACCOUNTANTS FOUNDATION p 75
201 Plaza Three Harborsid 07311
Tel (903) 823-2727 *SIC* 8399

ARCH INSURANCE GROUP INC p 104
Harborside 3 210 Hudson S 07311
Tel (201) 743-4000 *SIC* 6331 6351

ATLANTIC COAST MEDIA GROUP LLC p 126
100 Town Square Pl Fl 6 07310
Tel (201) 942-3400 *SIC* 5961 5999

AVEPOINT INC p 137
3 Plaza Ten 07311
Tel (201) 793-1111 *SIC* 7371

AXON SOLUTIONS INC p 140
1 Evertrust Plz Ste 501 07302
Tel (201) 680-7000 *SIC* 8742

▲ BEL FUSE INC p 169
206 Van Vorst St 07302
Tel (201) 432-0463
SIC 3679 3674 3613 3677

C SCEC-USA INC p 233
525 Washington Blvd Fl 31 07310
Tel (201) 876-2788 *SIC* 8742

CAREPOINT HEALTH MANAGEMENT ASSOCIATES LLC p 255
10 Exchange Pl Fl 15 07302
Tel (201) 795-8554 *SIC* 8062

■ CEQUENT UK LTD p 283
123 Town Square Pl 07310
Tel (734) 656-3078 *SIC* 4789 3714 5531

CHARLES KOMAR & SONS INC p 289
16 E 34th St Fl 10 07308
Tel (212) 725-1500 *SIC* 2341 2384 5137

CHRIST HOSPITAL p 302
176 Palisade Ave 07306
Tel (201) 795-8200 *SIC* 8062

CHRIST HOSPITAL HEALTH SERVICES CORP p 302
176 Palisade Ave 07306
Tel (201) 795-8200 *SIC* 6719

CITY OF JERSEY CITY p 315
280 Grove St 07302
Tel (201) 547-5000 *SIC* 9111

COUNTY OF HUDSON p 378
567 Pavonia Ave Fl 4 07306
Tel (201) 795-6000 *SIC* 9111 9223

DAN-DEE INTERNATIONAL LIMITED p 410
106 Harbor Dr 07305
Tel (201) 332-7600 *SIC* 5092

DATAPIPE INC p 414
10 Exchange Pl 07302
Tel (201) 792-1918 *SIC* 7374

DB SERVICES NEW JERSEY INC p 418
100 Plaza One 07311
Tel (201) 593-4183 *SIC* 8744

DG3 GROUP AMERICA INC p 435
100 Burma Rd 07305
Tel (201) 793-5000 *SIC* 2752

DG3 HOLDINGS LLC p 435
100 Burma Rd 07305
Tel (201) 793-5000 *SIC* 2752

DG3 NORTH AMERICA INC p 435
100 Burma Rd 07305
Tel (201) 793-5000 *SIC* 2752

EDISONLEARNING INC p 478
Harborside Financial Center 2910 07311
Tel (201) 630-2600 *SIC* 8211

EVERGREEN SHIPPING AGENCY (AMERICA) CORP p 515
1 Evertrust Plz 07302
Tel (201) 761-3000 *SIC* 4731

FABUWOOD CABINETRY CORP p 523
99 Caven Point Rd 07305
Tel (201) 432-6555 *SIC* 2434

FORBES MANAGEMENT CO INC p 565
499 Washington Blvd Fl 9 07310
Tel (212) 620-2200 *SIC* 6722

FRANKLIN CREDIT HOLDING CORP p 575
101 Hudson St Fl 25 07302
Tel (201) 604-1800 *SIC* 6163 6162

FRED ALGER MANAGEMENT INC p 575
600 Plaza One 07311
Tel (201) 547-3600 *SIC* 6282 6211 6799

FUNDTECH CORP p 585
30 Montgomery St Ste 501 07302
Tel (201) 324-0203 *SIC* 7372 7371

GOYA FOODS INC p 627
350 County Rd 07307
Tel (201) 348-4900 *SIC* 5142

HUDSON HOSPITAL OPCO LLC p 716
176 Palisade Ave 07306
Tel (201) 795-8200 *SIC* 8062

ICAP CAPITAL MARKETS LLC p 726
1100 Plaza Five 07311
Tel (212) 732-6900 *SIC* 6099

ICAP SERVICES NORTH AMERICA LLC p 726
1100 Plaza Five Fl 12 07311
Tel (212) 341-9900 *SIC* 6211

IJKG LLC p 731
714 Bergen Ave 07306
Tel (201) 858-5000 *SIC* 8741

IJKG OPCO LLC p 731
714 Bergen Ave 07306
Tel (201) 858-5000 *SIC* 8741

IMPERIAL BAG & PAPER CO LLC p 734
255 Us Highway 1 And 9 07306
Tel (201) 437-7440 *SIC* 5087

■ INSURANCE SERVICES OFFICE INC p 748
545 Washington Blvd Fl 12 07310
Tel (201) 469-2000 *SIC* 7375

IPC SYSTEMS HOLDINGS CORP p 763
1500 Plaza Ten Fl 15 07311
Tel (201) 253-2000 *SIC* 5045 4813

IPC SYSTEMS INC p 763
Harborside Fincl 2nd St 07311
Tel (201) 253-2000 *SIC* 3661

IPFS CORP p 763
101 Hudson St Fl 33 07302
Tel (201) 557-4625 *SIC* 6311

ISO SERVICES INC p 767
545 Washington Blvd Fl 12 07310
Tel (201) 469-2000 *SIC* 7375

JERSEY CITY BOARD OF EDUCATION (INC) p 783
346 Claremont Ave 07305
Tel (201) 915-6202 *SIC* 8211

JERSEY CITY INCINERATOR AUTHORITY p 783
501 State Rt 440 07305
Tel (201) 432-4645 *SIC* 4953 0782 4212

JERSEY CITY MEDICAL CENTER INC p 783
355 Grand St 07302
Tel (201) 915-2000 SIC 8062

JERSEY CITY PUBLIC SCHOOLS p 783
346 Claremont Ave 07305
Tel (201) 915-6202 SIC 8211

▲ KCG HOLDINGS INC p 806
545 Washington Blvd 07310
Tel (201) 222-9400 SIC 6211 6282

■ KNIGHT CAPITAL AMERICAS LP p 824
545 Washington Blvd Ste 1 07310
Tel (800) 544-7508 SIC 6211

■ KNIGHT CAPITAL GROUP INC p 824
545 Washington Blvd Ste 1 07310
Tel (201) 222-9400 SIC 6211 6282

KOMAR INTIMATES LLC p 827
90 Hudson St 07302
Tel (212) 725-1500 SIC 5621

KUEHNE + NAGEL INC p 831
10 Exchange Pl Fl 19 07302
Tel (201) 413-5500 SIC 4731

KUEHNE + NAGEL INVESTMENT INC p 831
10 Exchange Pl Fl 19 07302
Tel (201) 413-5500 SIC 4731

LIBERTY HEALTHCARE SYSTEM INC p 862
355 Grand St 07302
Tel (318) 251-9458 SIC 8062

LORD ABBETT & CO LLC p 878
90 Hudson St Fl 10 07302
Tel (201) 827-2000 SIC 6282

NEW JERSEY CITY UNIVERSITY p 1031
2039 Kennedy Blvd 07305
Tel (201) 200-2000 SIC 8221

NEWYORK LIFE INVESTMENT MANAGEMENT LLC p 1035
30 Hudson St 07302
Tel (973) 394-3000 SIC 6799

OPERA SOLUTIONS LLC p 1089
10 Exchange Pl Fl 11 07302
Tel (646) 520-4320 SIC 7371

■ PERSHING LLC p 1137
95 Chrstopher Columbus Dr 07302
Tel (201) 413-2078 SIC 6211

PORT AUTHORITY TRANS-HUDSON CORP p 1162
1 Path Plz 07306
Tel (201) 239-3500 SIC 4111

■ PORTS AMERICA INC p 1163
525 Washington Blvd 07310
Tel (732) 635-3899 SIC 4491

PRINCETON INFORMATION LTD p 1177
100 Plaza Ten Ste 1101h 07311
Tel (201) 604-9900 SIC 7374 7379

▲ PROVIDENT FINANCIAL SERVICES INC p 1186
239 Washington St 07302
Tel (732) 590-9200 SIC 6035

PROXIMO SPIRITS INC p 1187
333 Washington St Ste 401 07302
Tel (201) 204-1720 SIC 5182

■ QUIDSI INC p 1199
10 Exchange Pl Fl 25 07302
Tel (973) 509-5444 SIC 5137

▲ RAND LOGISTICS INC p 1207
333 Washington St Ste 201 07302
Tel (212) 863-9427 SIC 4789 4492

REDI GLOBAL TECHNOLOGIES LLC p 1216
30 Hudson St 07302
Tel (212) 357-3840 SIC 6211

ST PETERS UNIVERSITY p 1372
2641 John F Kennedy Blvd 07306
Tel (201) 761-6000 SIC 8221

STAR SNACKS CO LLC p 1378
105 Harbor Dr 07305
Tel (201) 200-9820 SIC 2068

■ SYSCO METRO NEWYORK LLC p 1417
20 Theodore Conrad Dr 07305
Tel (201) 451-0997
SIC 5141 5144 5142 5147 5087

TOTAL AMERICAN SERVICES INC p 1462
100 Town Square Pl # 401 07310
Tel (206) 626-3500
SIC 2911 4612 5541 2895

TOWER GROUP INC p 1464
800 Plaza Two 8 07311
Tel (212) 655-2000 SIC 6411

U S TECH SOLUTIONS INC p 1497
10 Exchange Pl Ste 1820 07302
Tel (201) 524-9600 SIC 7379 7372

UBS FINANCIAL SERVICES INC p 1498
499 Washington Blvd 07310
Tel (201) 318-5900 SIC 6211

▲ VERISK ANALYTICS INC p 1549
545 Washington Blvd 07310
Tel (201) 469-2000 SIC 7375

■ VF SPORTSWEAR INC p 1553
545 Wshngton Blvd Fl 8 07310
Tel (212) 541-5757
SIC 2329 2384 5136 5137 5611 6794

WELL LUCK CO INC p 1589
104 Harbor Dr Ste 1 07305
Tel (201) 434-1177 SIC 5149

KEARNY, NJ

DESSERT SERVICE INC p 432
630 Belleville Tpke 07032
Tel (201) 246-7292 SIC 5142

KEARNY PUBLIC SCHOOLS p 807
100 Davis Ave 07032
Tel (201) 955-5000 SIC 8211

KUEHNE CHEMICAL CO INC p 831
86 N Hackensack Ave 07032
Tel (973) 589-0700 SIC 2819 4226 2812

PHARMACHEM LABORATORIES INC p 1141
265 Harrison Tpke 07032
Tel (201) 246-1000 SIC 2099 2834

ST GEORGE WAREHOUSE OF DELAWARE INC p 1367
5 Logistics Dr 07032
Tel (973) 578-8400 SIC 6719

KEASBEY, NJ

SHOP-RITE SUPERMARKETS INC p 1318
5000 Riverside Dr 08832
Tel (908) 527-3300 SIC 5411

WAKEFERN FOOD CORP p 1572
5000 Riverside Dr 08832
Tel (908) 527-3300
SIC 5141 5149 5411 4213 2026

KENILWORTH, NJ

■ CUBIST PHARMACEUTICALS LLC p 399
2000 Galloping Hill Rd 07033
Tel (908) 740-4000 SIC 2834

KENECO INC p 810
123 N 8th St 07033
Tel (908) 241-3700 SIC 3535

▲ MERCK & CO INC p 945
2000 Galloping Hill Rd 07033
Tel (908) 740-4000
SIC 2834 2836 2844 5122

■ MERCK SHARP & DOHME CORP p 945
2000 Galloping Hill Rd 07033
Tel (908) 740-4000 SIC 2834 8741

ONE DIVERSIFIED LLC p 1086
37 Market St 07033
Tel (908) 245-4833
SIC 5099 7373 4899 8711

KINGSTON, NJ

TRAP ROCK INDUSTRIES INC p 1473
460 River Rd 08528
Tel (609) 924-0300
SIC 3273 3272 1429 1611

LAKEWOOD, NJ

AMERICAN PRIDE PAPER & PLASTIC LLC p 78
601 Prospect St 08701
Tel (732) 367-4444 SIC 5162

J KNIPPER AND CO INC p 771
1 Healthcare Way 08701
Tel (732) 905-7878 SIC 8742

KIMBALL MEDICAL CENTER INC p 818
600 River Ave 08701
Tel (732) 363-1900 SIC 8062

LAKEWOOD BOARD OF EDUCATION (INC) p 840
200 Ramsey Ave 08701
Tel (732) 730-1606 SIC 8211

MADISON TITLE AGENCY LLC p 894
1125 Ocean Ave Ste 1 08701
Tel (732) 905-9400 SIC 6411

PINE BELT ENTERPRISES INC p 1148
1088 Route 88 08701
Tel (732) 363-2900 SIC 5511 7537 5531

RENAISSANCE LAKEWOOD LLC p 1223
1200 Paco Way 08701
Tel (732) 367-9000 SIC 2834 2844 2675

LAWRENCEVILLE, NJ

BENECARD SERVICES INC p 172
3131 Princeton Pike 2-B103 08648
Tel (609) 219-0400 SIC 6411

ETOWN CORP p 512
989 Lenox Dr Ste 224 08648
Tel (609) 512-9400 SIC 4941

JOSEPH JINGOLI & SON INC p 793
100 Lenox Dr Ste 100 08648
Tel (609) 896-3111 SIC 1541

LAWRENCEVILLE SCHOOL p 848
2500 Main St 08648
Tel (609) 896-0400 SIC 8211

RIDER UNIVERSITY A NEW JERSEY NON-PROFIT CORP p 1234
2083 Lawrenceville Rd 08648
Tel (609) 896-5000 SIC 8221

LEBANON, NJ

CONSTRUCTION SPECIALTIES INC p 361
3 Werner Way Ste 100 08833
Tel (908) 236-0800
SIC 3446 3354 3443 3272 3585

LEDGEWOOD, NJ

RONETCO SUPERMARKETS INC p 1249
1070 Us Highway 46 Ste 1 07852
Tel (973) 927-8300 SIC 5411 5921

LEONARDO, NJ

MIDDLETOWN TOWNSHIP BOARD OF EDUCATION p 965
834 Leonardville Rd Fl 2 07737
Tel (732) 671-3850 SIC 8211

LEONIA, NJ

INFOCROSSING INC p 741
2 Christie Hts 07605
Tel (201) 840-4700 SIC 7374

KULITE SEMICONDUCTOR PRODUCTS INC p 832
1 Willow Tree Rd 07605
Tel (201) 461-0900 SIC 3728 3829

WIPRO DATA CENTER AND CLOUD SERVICES INC p 1618
2 Christie Hts 07605
Tel (201) 840-4772 SIC 7379

LIBERTY CORNER, NJ

EVEREST REINSURANCE CO p 514
477 Martinsville Rd 07938
Tel (908) 604-3000 SIC 6331

EVEREST REINSURANCE HOLDINGS INC p 514
477 Martinsville Rd 07938
Tel (908) 604-3000 SIC 6411 6331 6321

TREVCON CONSTRUCTION CO INC p 1476
30 Church St 07938
Tel (908) 580-0200 SIC 1629 1623

LINCOLN PARK, NJ

UNGERER & CO INC p 1502
4 Bridgewater Ln 07035
Tel (973) 628-0600 SIC 0119

UNGERER INDUSTRIES INC p 1502
4 Bridgewater Ln 07035
Tel (973) 628-0600 SIC 2899 2844 2087

LINCROFT, NJ

BROOKDALE COMMUNITY COLLEGE INC p 217
765 Newman Springs Rd 07738
Tel (732) 842-1900 SIC 8222

LINDEN, NJ

INFINEUM USA LP p 740
1900 E Linden Ave 07036
Tel (908) 474-0100 SIC 5169

MAXIMUM QUALITY FOODS INC p 922
3351 Tremley Point Rd # 2 07036
Tel (908) 474-0003 SIC 5141

ROUND-THE-WORLD LOGISTICS (USA) CORP p 1253
333 Cantor Ave Unit C 07036
Tel (908) 862-3535 SIC 8999

S BERTRAM INC p 1262
3401 Tremley Point Rd 07036
Tel (908) 862-8200 SIC 5143 5141

TURTLE & HUGHES INC p 1493
1900 Lower Rd 07036
Tel (732) 574-3600 SIC 5063 5085

LINWOOD, NJ

CLOFINE DAIRY PRODUCTS INC p 327
1407 New Rd 08221
Tel (609) 653-1000 SIC 5143 5149

LITTLE FALLS, NJ

▲ CANTEL MEDICAL CORP p 247
150 Clove Rd Ste 36 07424
Tel (973) 890-7220 SIC 3841 3589

LITTLE FERRY, NJ

DASSAULT FALCON JET CORP p 413
200 Riser Rd 07643
Tel (201) 440-6700 SIC 5088 3721

LIVINGSTON, NJ

■ AIG TECHNOLOGIES INC p 38
2 Peach Tree Hill Rd 07039
Tel (973) 597-0285 SIC 8742 6411 7374

BRIAD CORP p 211
78 Okner Pkwy 07039
Tel (973) 597-6433 SIC 5812

BRIAD MAIN STREET INC p 211
78 Okner Pkwy 07039
Tel (973) 597-6433 SIC 5812

BRIAD RESTAURANT GROUP LLC p 211
78 Okner Pkwy 07039
Tel (973) 597-6433 SIC 5812

■ CIT FINANCE LLC p 309
1 Cit Dr 07039
Tel (973) 740-5000 SIC 6159

■ CIT FINANCIAL USA INC p 309
1 Cit Dr 07039
Tel (973) 740-5000 SIC 6159

■ CIT GROUP (NJ) LLC p 309
1 Cit Dr 07039
Tel (973) 740-5000 SIC 8741

■ CIT SMALL BUSINESS LENDING CORP p 309
1 Cit Dr 07039
Tel (973) 740-5000 SIC 6036

FORMOSA PLASTICS CORP USA p 568
9 Peach Tree Hill Rd 07039
Tel (973) 994-7674 SIC 2821 2812

INTEPLAST GROUP CORP p 750
9 Peach Tree Hill Rd 07039
Tel (973) 994-8000 SIC 2673

ISS TMC SERVICES INC p 767
81 Dorsa Ave 07039
Tel (973) 740-0032 SIC 6512 7349 7699

NAN YA PLASTICS CORP AMERICA p 1007
9 Peach Tree Hill Rd 07039
Tel (973) 992-1775 SIC 2824 2869 3083

NAN YA PLASTICS CORP USA p 1007
9 Peach Tree Hill Rd 07039
Tel (973) 992-1775 SIC 3081

SAINT BARNABAS REALTY DEVELOP CORP p 1268
94 Old Short Hills Rd 07039
Tel (732) 923-8072 SIC 6531

SPINIELLO COMPANIES p 1358
354 Eisenhower Pkwy # 1200 07039
Tel (973) 808-8383 SIC 1623

ST BARNABAS MEDICAL CTR p 1365
94 Old Short Hills Rd # 1 07039
Tel (973) 322-5000 SIC 8062

TRINITY PLASTICS INC p 1481
9 Peach Tree Hill Rd 07039
Tel (973) 994-8018 SIC 2673 3081

VERITEXT LEGAL SOLUTIONS p 1550
290 W Mount Pleasant Ave 07039
Tel (973) 410-4040 SIC 6719 7338

LODI, NJ

ATLANTIC DETROIT DIESEL ALLISON LLC p 126
180 Route 17 South 07644
Tel (201) 489-5800 SIC 5084 7538 7389

DWL INTERNATIONAL TRADING INC p 463
65 Industrial Rd 07644
Tel (973) 916-9958 SIC 5023 5046

LOGAN TOWNSHIP, NJ

■ ALBERTS ORGANICS INC p 46
1155 Commerce Blvd 08085
Tel (800) 899-5944 SIC 5149 5148

VERONI USA INC p 1551
1110 Commerce Blvd # 200 08085
Tel (609) 970-0320 SIC 2011

LONG BRANCH, NJ

J F KIELY CONSTRUCTION CO INC p 771
700 Mcclellan St 07740
Tel (732) 222-4400 SIC 1623 7353

MONMOUTH MEDICAL CENTER INC p 984
300 2nd Ave 07740
Tel (732) 222-5200 SIC 8062

LONG VALLEY, NJ

FRAZIER INDUSTRIAL CO p 575
91 Fairview Ave 07853
Tel (908) 876-3001 SIC 3441 2542

LYNDHURST, NJ

AERO OPCO LLC p 30
125 Chubb Ave Fl 5 07071
Tel (201) 508-4500 SIC 5621 5611

ALPHA INDUSTRIES MANAGEMENT INC p 60
Page And Schuyler Ave 07071
Tel (201) 933-6000 SIC 2673

ARGO TURBOSERVE CORP p 107
160 Chubb Ave Ste 102 07071
Tel (201) 804-6200 SIC 5084

GRAND SUPERCENTER INC p 630
300 Chubb Ave 07071
Tel (201) 507-9900 SIC 5141

NEW JERSEY SPORTS & EXPOSITION AUTHORITY p 1031
1 Dekorte Park Plz 07071
Tel (201) 460-1700 SIC 8641 7941 6512

OMEGA PLASTICS CORP p 1084
Page & Schuyler Ave Ste 5 07071
Tel (201) 933-1270 SIC 2673

■ RALPH LAUREN RETAIL INC p 1206
9 Polito Ave Fl 5 07071
Tel (888) 475-7674 SIC 5651 5661 5719

SIKA CORP p 1322
201 Polito Ave 07071
Tel (201) 933-8800
SIC 2891 2899 2851 2821 3272

WACOAL AMERICA INC p 1570
1 Wacoal Plz 07071
Tel (201) 933-8400 SIC 2342 2341

WACOAL INTERNATIONAL CORP p 1571
1 Wacoal Plz 07071
Tel (201) 933-8400 SIC 2341

MADISON, NJ

DREW UNIVERSITY p 455
36 Madison Ave 07940
Tel (973) 408-3000 SIC 8221

■ NRT COMMERCIAL UTAH LLC p 1064
175 Park Ave 07940
Tel (973) 407-6880 SIC 6531

▲ QUEST DIAGNOSTICS INC p 1199
3 Giralda Farms 07940
Tel (973) 520-2700 SIC 8071 2835

■ REALOGY GROUP LLC p 1214
175 Park Ave 07940
Tel (973) 407-2000
SIC 6531 6794 7389 6541

▲ **REALOGY HOLDINGS CORP** p 1214
175 Park Ave 07940
Tel (973) 407-2000
SIC 6531 6794 7389 6541

■ **REALOGY INTERMEDIATE HOLDINGS LLC** p 1214
175 Park Ave 07940
Tel (973) 407-0000
SIC 6531 6794 7389 6541

■ **WYETH HOLDINGS LLC** p 1629
5 Giralda Farms 07940
Tel (973) 660-5000 *SIC* 2834 2836

MAHWAH, NJ

▲ **ASCENA RETAIL GROUP INC** p 115
933 Macarthur Blvd 07430
Tel (551) 777-6700 *SIC* 5621 5632

D & M HOLDINGS US INC p 406
100 Corporate Dr 07430
Tel (201) 762-6500 *SIC* 5065 3651

DIALAMERICA MARKETING INC p 436
960 Macarthur Blvd 07430
Tel (201) 327-0200 *SIC* 7389

■ **DRESS BARN INC** p 455
933 Macarthur Blvd 07430
Tel (800) 373-7722 *SIC* 5621 5632

GLENMARK PHARMACEUTICALS INC USA p 615
750 Corporate Dr 07430
Tel (201) 684-8000 *SIC* 5122

HABAND CO LLC p 651
1 International Blvd # 800 07495
Tel (570) 383-3226 *SIC* 5961 5611

HEALTHSTAR COMMUNICATIONS INC p 678
1000 Wyckoff Ave Ste 202 07430
Tel (201) 560-5370 *SIC* 7372 7311 6719

■ **HOWMEDICA OSTEONICS CORP** p 713
325 Corporate Dr 07430
Tel (201) 831-5000 *SIC* 3842 5047

HUDSON UNITED BANK p 717
1000 Macarthur Blvd 07430
Tel (201) 236-2600 *SIC* 6141 6022

INSERRA SUPERMARKETS INC p 745
20 Ridge Rd Ste 1 07430
Tel (201) 529-5900 *SIC* 5411 5735

JAGUAR CARS INC p 776
555 Macarthur Blvd 07430
Tel (201) 818-8500 *SIC* 5012 5013

MARCRAFT CLOTHES INC p 905
301 Island Rd 07430
Tel (201) 828-2085 *SIC* 5136

MINDRAY DS USA INC p 972
800 Macarthur Blvd 07430
Tel (201) 995-8000 *SIC* 3845 2835 3841

RADWARE INC p 1205
575 Corporate Dr Ste 205 07430
Tel (201) 512-9771 *SIC* 8731

RAMAPO COLLEGE OF NEW JERSEY p 1206
505 Ramapo Valley Rd 07430
Tel (201) 684-7500 *SIC* 8221

SEIKO CORP OF AMERICA p 1301
1111 Macarthur Blvd # 101 07430
Tel (201) 529-3316 *SIC* 5094

SHARP ELECTRONICS CORP p 1312
1 Sharp Plz Ste 1 07495
Tel (201) 529-8200
SIC 5044 5064 3651 3631 3861 3674

SINGER SUPERMARKETS INC p 1326
20 Ridge Rd 07430
Tel (201) 529-5900 *SIC* 5411 5912

TD BANKNORTH NATIONAL ASSOCIATION p 1429
1000 Macarthur Blvd 07430
Tel (201) 236-2680 *SIC* 6029

THERMWELL PRODUCTS CO INC p 1447
420 State Rt 17 07430
Tel (201) 684-4400 *SIC* 3442

MANAHAWKIN, NJ

SOUTHERN OCEAN COUNTY HEALTH SYSTEM INC p 1350
1140 Route 72 W 08050
Tel (609) 597-6011 *SIC* 8062

MANALAPAN, NJ

CAREER NETWORK AFFILIATES INC p 254
38 Ivanhoe Dr 07726
Tel (732) 972-3000 *SIC* 7361

MAPLE SHADE, NJ

EASTERN LIFT TRUCK CO INC p 472
549 E Linwood Ave 08052
Tel (856) 779-8880 *SIC* 5084 7699 7359

HOLMAN AUTOMOTIVE GROUP INC p 701
244 E Kings Hwy 08052
Tel (856) 663-5200 *SIC* 5511

HOLMAN ENTERPRISES INC p 701
244 E Kings Hwy 08052
Tel (856) 662-1042 *SIC* 5511

■ **STONCOR GROUP INC** p 1391
1000 E Park Ave 08052
Tel (800) 257-7953 *SIC* 2851

MAPLEWOOD, NJ

BOARD OF EDUCATION OF SOUTH ORANGE-MAPLEWOOD p 195
525 Academy St 07040
Tel (973) 378-9613 *SIC* 8211

RICCIARDI BROS INC p 1232
1915 Springfield Ave 07040
Tel (973) 762-3830 *SIC* 5198 5231

MARLBORO, NJ

MARLBORO TOWNSHIP BOARD OF EDUCATION p 909
1980 Township Dr 07746
Tel (732) 972-2000 *SIC* 8211

MARLTON, NJ

CONNER STRONG & BUCKELEW COMPANIES INC p 358
401 Route 73 N Ste 300 08053
Tel (877) 861-3220 *SIC* 6411

GLOBAL INDUSTRIES INC p 616
17 W Stow Rd 08053
Tel (856) 596-3390 *SIC* 2522 5021

INTERSTATE REALTY MANAGEMENT CO INC p 758
3 E Stow Rd 08053
Tel (856) 596-0500 *SIC* 6531 6513

SURETY TITLE CO LLC p 1408
11 Eves Dr Ste 150 08053
Tel (856) 988-8900 *SIC* 6361 6541

VIRTUA HEALTH INC p 1560
303 Lippincott Dr 08053
Tel (888) 847-8823 *SIC* 8062 8399

VIRTUA MEDICAL GROUP PA p 1560
301 Lippincott Dr 08053
Tel (856) 355-0340 *SIC* 8099 8082

MATAWAN, NJ

OLD BRIDGE TOWNSHIP BOARD OF EDUCATION p 1080
4207 Hwy 516 07747
Tel (732) 566-1000 *SIC* 8211

TATA COMMUNICATIONS (US) INC p 1426
90 Matawan Rd Ste 300 07747
Tel (732) 888-6700 *SIC* 4813

MAYS LANDING, NJ

HAMILTON TOWNSHIP SCHOOL DISTRICT p 655
1876 Dr Dennis Foreman Dr 08330
Tel (609) 476-6300 *SIC* 8211

MAYWOOD, NJ

MYRON CORP p 1005
205 Maywood Ave 07607
Tel (201) 843-6464 *SIC* 5199

MEDFORD, NJ

DUBELL LUMBER CO p 459
148 Route 70 08055
Tel (609) 654-4143 *SIC* 5031 5211

■ **HADDON HOUSE FOOD PRODUCTS INC** p 652
250 Old Marlton Pike 08055
Tel (609) 654-7901 *SIC* 5149

METUCHEN, NJ

FRANCO MANUFACTURING CO INC p 574
555 Prospect St 08840
Tel (732) 494-0503
SIC 2269 2392 2211 5023 5131

MIDDLESEX, NJ

COREPHARMA LLC p 369
215 Wood Ave 08846
Tel (732) 356-0318 *SIC* 2834

MIDDLETOWN, NJ

■ **AT&T SERVICES INC** p 123
200 S Laurel Ave 07748
Tel (732) 420-3131 *SIC* 3669

FOOD CIRCUS SUPER MARKETS INC p 564
853 State Route 35 07748
Tel (732) 671-2220 *SIC* 5411

MIDDLETOWN TOWNSHIP SCHOOL DISTRICT p 965
834 Leonardville Rd 07748
Tel (732) 671-3850 *SIC* 8211

MILLBURN, NJ

ELIE TAHARI LTD p 487
16 Bleeker St 07041
Tel (973) 671-6300
SIC 2331 2339 2335 2337 5621 5611

MILLVILLE, NJ

AMCOR PHARMACEUTICAL PACKAGING USA LLC p 66
625 Sharp St N 08332
Tel (856) 327-1540 *SIC* 3221 3085

ARC INTERNATIONAL NORTH AMERICA INC p 103
601 S Wade Blvd 08332
Tel (856) 825-5620 *SIC* 5023 2821

DURAND GLASS MANUFACTURING CO INC p 462
901 S Wade Blvd 08332
Tel (856) 327-1850 *SIC* 3229 3269 5023

MILLVILLE BOARD OF EDUCATION p 971
110 N 3rd St 08332
Tel (856) 293-2000 *SIC* 8211

MILLVILLE PUBLIC SCHOOLS p 971
110 N 3rd St 08332
Tel (856) 293-2000 *SIC* 8211

NIPRO PHARMAPACKAGING AMERICAS CORP p 1044
1200 N 10th St 08332
Tel (856) 825-1400 *SIC* 3221

MONMOUTH JUNCTION, NJ

BUNZL NEW JERSEY INC p 226
27 Distribution Way 08852
Tel (732) 821-7000 *SIC* 5113 5169

BUTH-NA-BODHAIGE INC p 230
77 Deans Rhode Hall Rd 08852
Tel (732) 348-2152 *SIC* 5999

■ **FACTIVA INC** p 523
4300 N Rt 1 820 Ridge Rd 08852
Tel (609) 627-2000 *SIC* 7375

HIGH GRADE BEVERAGE p 690
891 Georges Rd 08852
Tel (732) 821-7600 *SIC* 5181

SOUTH BRUNSWICK TOWNSHIP BOARD OF EDUCATION p 1343
4 Executive Dr 08852
Tel (732) 297-7800 *SIC* 8211

■ **SYSCO GUEST SUPPLY LLC** p 1417
4301 Us Highway 1 Ste 300 08852
Tel (609) 514-9696
SIC 5122 2844 5131 5139 7011 8741

TRIS PHARMA INC p 1482
2033 Rte 130 Ste D 08852
Tel (732) 940-2800 *SIC* 8731

MONROE TOWNSHIP, NJ

APPLIANCE DEALERS COOPERATIVE INC p 99
2 Matrix Dr 08831
Tel (609) 235-1000 *SIC* 5064

BRACCO DIAGNOSTICS INC p 206
259 Prospect Plains Rd 08831
Tel (609) 514-2200 *SIC* 2835

BRACCO USA INC p 206
259 Prospect Plains Rd 08831
Tel (609) 514-2200 *SIC* 2835

MONROE TOWNSHIP BOARD OF EDUCATION p 985
423 Buckelew Ave 08831
Tel (732) 521-2111 *SIC* 8211

W CAMPBELL SUPPLY CO LLC p 1585
1015 Cranbury S River Rd 08831
Tel (732) 287-8884 *SIC* 5012

MONTCLAIR, NJ

HACKENSACKUMC MOUNTAINSIDE p 652
1 Bay Ave 07042
Tel (973) 429-6000 *SIC* 8062

MONTCLAIR BOARD OF EDUCATION (INC) p 986
22 Valley Rd 07042
Tel (973) 509-4000 *SIC* 8211

MONTCLAIR PUBLIC SCHOOLS p 986
22 Valley Rd 07042
Tel (973) 509-4000 *SIC* 8211

MONTVALE, NJ

▲ **AEP INDUSTRIES INC** p 29
95 Chestnut Ridge Rd 07645
Tel (201) 641-6600 *SIC* 3081 2821

■ **BENJAMIN MOORE & CO** p 173
101 Paragon Dr 07645
Tel (201) 573-9600 *SIC* 2851 5231

EIGHT OCLOCK COFFEE CO p 481
155 Chestnut Ridge Rd # 2 07645
Tel (201) 571-9214 *SIC* 5149 2095

FLIGHT CENTRE TRAVEL GROUP (USA) INC p 556
5 Paragon Dr Ste 200 07645
Tel (201) 934-3500 *SIC* 4512

FLIGHT CENTRE USA HOLDING CORP p 556
5 Paragon Dr Ste 200 07645
Tel (201) 312-6855 *SIC* 4724

GANTRADE CORP p 591
210 Summit Ave Ste B5 07645
Tel (201) 573-1955 *SIC* 5169

GOTHAM TECHNOLOGY GROUP LLC p 626
1 Paragon Dr Ste 200 07645
Tel (201) 802-9600 *SIC* 5045 7361 5932

GREAT ATLANTIC & PACIFIC TEA CO INC p 633
2 Paragon Dr 07645
Tel (201) 573-9700 *SIC* 5411

PATHMARK STORES INC p 1120
2 Paragon Dr 07645
Tel (866) 443-7374 *SIC* 5411

PENTAX OF AMERICA INC p 1132
3 Paragon Dr 07645
Tel (201) 391-4229 *SIC* 5047

US CABLE OF COASTAL-TEXAS LP p 1531
28 W Grand Ave Ste 6 07645
Tel (201) 930-9000 *SIC* 4841

WALDBAUM INC p 1572
2 Paragon Dr 07645
Tel (201) 571-4132 *SIC* 5411

WINEBOW INC p 1616
75 Chestnut Ridge Rd # 1 07645
Tel (201) 445-0620 *SIC* 5182

MOONACHIE, NJ

CONTENT CRITICAL SOLUTIONS INC p 362
121 Moonachie Ave 07074
Tel (201) 528-2777 *SIC* 7379

PRESIDENT CONTAINER INC p 1172
200 W Commercial Ave 07074
Tel (201) 933-7500 *SIC* 2653

TUBE LIGHT CO INC p 1490
300 E Park St 07074
Tel (201) 641-6660 *SIC* 5046 5085

MOORESTOWN, NJ

BAYADA HOME HEALTH CARE INC p 161
290 Chester Ave 08057
Tel (856) 231-1000 *SIC* 8082

CLONDALKIN PHARMA & HEALTHCARE LLC p 327
1224 N Church St 08057
Tel (856) 439-1700 *SIC* 5122 8361

▲ **DESTINATION MATERNITY CORP** p 432
232 Strawbridge Dr # 100 08057
Tel (856) 291-9700 *SIC* 5621

NICOLE CRAFTS LLC p 1043
14 Sbar Blvd 08057
Tel (856) 234-8220 *SIC* 5092

OPEX CORP p 1089
305 Commerce Dr 08057
Tel (856) 727-1100 *SIC* 3579

PRO-TECH ENERGY SOLUTIONS LLC p 1178
215 Executive Dr 08057
Tel (856) 437-6220 *SIC* 1711

SBARS INC p 1285
14 Sbar Blvd 08057
Tel (856) 234-8220 *SIC* 5092

SIMCO LOGISTICS INC p 1324
101 Commerce Dr 08057
Tel (856) 813-2300 *SIC* 5143

MORRIS PLAINS, NJ

ABSCO LTD CORP p 12
2740 Rte 10 E Ste 205 07950
Tel (973) 402-2148
SIC 6351 6411 6211 6282

■ **BIOSCRIP INFUSION SERVICES LLC** p 184
102 The American Rd 07950
Tel (973) 597-0444 *SIC* 5047

■ **HONEYWELL INC** p 705
115 Tabor Rd 07950
Tel (973) 455-2000
SIC 3823 3812 3669 3491 3699 3822

▲ **HONEYWELL INTERNATIONAL INC** p 705
115 Tabor Rd 07950
Tel (973) 455-2000
SIC 3724 3812 3585 2824 2821 3714

WEICHERT CO p 1587
1625 State Route 10 07950
Tel (973) 984-1400 *SIC* 6531

MORRISTOWN, NJ

ADVOCARE LLC p 28
25 Lindsley Dr Ste 205 07960
Tel (973) 993-8777 *SIC* 8011

AHS HOSPITAL CORP p 37
465 South St 07960
Tel (973) 660-3100 *SIC* 8062 8249

ARCH REINSURANCE CO p 104
445 South St Ste 220 07960
Tel (973) 898-9575 *SIC* 6411

ARTECH INFORMATION SYSTEMS LLC p 114
360 Mount Kemble Ave # 2 07960
Tel (973) 998-2500 *SIC* 7371 7379

ATLANTIC HEALTH p 126
200 South St 07960
Tel (973) 683-0104 *SIC* 8011

ATLANTIC HEALTH SYSTEM INC p 126
475 South St 07960
Tel (973) 660-3100 *SIC* 8249 8062

CAPSUGEL INC p 251
412 Mount Kemble Ave 200c 07960
Tel (862) 242-1700 *SIC* 2834

CCA CIVIL INC p 269
445 South St Ste 310 07960
Tel (862) 701-7200 *SIC* 1611

COLAS INC p 335
163 Madison Ave Ste 500 07960
Tel (973) 290-9082 *SIC* 1611 1622 2951

COLLABERA INC p 336
25 Airport Rd 07960
Tel (973) 889-5200 *SIC* 7371

COLLABERA TECHNOLOGIES p 336
25 Airport Rd 07960
Tel (973) 889-5200 *SIC* 7371

COUNTY OF MORRIS p 380
Court St 07960
Tel (973) 285-6010 *SIC* 9111

■ **COVANTA ARC LLC** p 384
445 South St 07960
Tel (862) 345-5000 *SIC* 4953

■ **COVANTA ENERGY GROUP INC** p 384
445 South St 07960
Tel (862) 345-5000
SIC 1541 1629 4953 4931

■ **COVANTA ENERGY LLC** p 384
445 South St Ste 400 07960
Tel (862) 345-5000 *SIC* 4953 4911

▲ **COVANTA HOLDING CORP** p 384
445 South St 07960
Tel (862) 345-5000 *SIC* 4953 4911

■ **COVANTA SYSTEMS INC** p 384
445 South St 07960
Tel (862) 345-5000 *SIC* 4953

CRUM & FORSTER HOLDINGS CORP p 396
305 Madison Ave 07960
Tel (973) 490-6600 *SIC* 6331 6321 6351

CRUM & FORSTER INC p 396
305 Madison Ave 07960
Tel (973) 490-6600
SIC 6311 6321 6331 6411

FAIRFAX INC p 524
305 Madison Ave 07960
Tel (973) 490-6600 *SIC* 6411

■ **HONEYWELL SPECIALTY WAX & ADDITIVES INC** p 705
101 Columbia Rd 07960
Tel (973) 455-2000 *SIC* 2999 5169

LOUIS BERGER AND ASSOCIATES INC p 879
412 Mount Kemble Ave 07960
Tel (973) 407-1000 *SIC* 8711

LOUIS BERGER GROUP INC p 879
412 Mount Kemble Ave 07960
Tel (973) 407-1000 *SIC* 8748 8712 8711

■ **MAJESCO** p 898
412 Mount Kemble Ave 110c 07960
Tel (973) 461-5200 *SIC* 7372 7371

MC ELROY DEUTSCH MULVANEY & CARPERNTER LLP p 925
1300 Mount Kemble Ave 07960
Tel (973) 993-8100 *SIC* 8111

NORTH RIVER INSURANCE CO p 1053
305 Madison Ave 07960
Tel (973) 490-6600 *SIC* 6331

OLYMPUS HOLDINGS LLC p 1083
67 E Park Pl Ste 475 07960
Tel (973) 889-9100 *SIC* 4911

OLYMPUS POWER LLC p 1083
67 E Park Pl Ste 4 07960
Tel (973) 889-9100 *SIC* 4911

PANALPINA INC p 1111
1776 On The Green 67 07960
Tel (973) 683-9000 *SIC* 4731

▲ **PERNIX THERAPEUTICS HOLDINGS INC** p 1136
10 N Park Pl Ste 201 07960
Tel (800) 793-2145 *SIC* 2834

PROSIGHT SPECIALTY INSURANCE GROUP INC p 1184
412 Mount Kemble Ave 300c 07960
Tel (973) 532-1900 *SIC* 6351 6331

SCHINDLER ELEVATOR CORP p 1287
20 Whippany Rd 07960
Tel (973) 397-6500 *SIC* 3534 7699 1796

SCHINDLER ENTERPRISES INC p 1287
20 Whippany Rd 07960
Tel (973) 397-6500 *SIC* 3534 7699 1796

TYCOM LIMITED p 1496
10 Park Ave 07960
Tel (973) 753-3040 *SIC* 3643 1623

UNITED STATES FIRE INSURANCE CO p 1513
305 Madison Ave 07960
Tel (973) 490-6600 *SIC* 6331

VILLA PIZZA INC p 1557
3 South St 07960
Tel (973) 285-4800 *SIC* 5812

MOUNT ARLINGTON, NJ

AERC.COM INC p 30
111 Howard Blvd Ste 108 07856
Tel (973) 691-3200 *SIC* 4953

MOUNT HOLLY, NJ

COUNTY OF BURLINGTON p 376
49 Rancocas Rd 08060
Tel (609) 265-5000 *SIC* 9199

NEW CENTURY TRANSPORTATION INC p 1029
45 E Park Dr 08060
Tel (609) 265-1110 *SIC* 4213

RRERF REGENCY PARK LLC p 1255
64 Regency Dr 08060
Tel (856) 848-6700 *SIC* 6531

VIRTUA MEMORIAL HOSPITAL BURLINGTON COUNTY INC p 1560
175 Madison Ave 08060
Tel (609) 267-0700 *SIC* 8062

MOUNT LAUREL, NJ

■ **ADMIRAL INSURANCE CO** p 23
1000 Howard Blvd Ste 300 08054
Tel (856) 429-9200 *SIC* 6331 6411 6324

■ **ADP FINANCIAL INFORMATION SERVICES INC** p 24
110 W Park Dr 08054
Tel (856) 787-8000 *SIC* 7374

AMERICAN NEIGHBOURHOOD MORTGAGE ACCEPTANCE CO LLC p 77
700 E Gate Dr Ste 400 08054
Tel (856) 252-1506 *SIC* 6162

AUTOMOTIVE RENTALS INC p 134
4001 Leadenhall Rd 08054
Tel (856) 778-1500 *SIC* 7513 7515 7549

BRANDYWINE SENIOR LIVING MANAGEMENT LLC p 208
525 Fellowship Rd Ste 360 08054
Tel (856) 778-6100 *SIC* 8361 8051

CANON FINANCIAL SERVICES INC p 247
158 Gaither Dr Ste 200 08054
Tel (856) 813-1000 *SIC* 6159 7389

CMW HOLDCO INC p 329
20000 Horizon Way Ste 600 08054
Tel (267) 443-2547 *SIC* 7313

FREEDOM MORTGAGE CORP p 576
907 Pleasant Valley Ave # 3 08054
Tel (866) 759-8624 *SIC* 6162

■ **FULTON BANK OF NEW JERSEY** p 584
533 Fellowship Rd Ste 250 08054
Tel (856) 787-1997 *SIC* 6029 6163

JOHNSON & TOWERS INC p 790
2021 Briggs Rd 08054
Tel (856) 234-6990
SIC 5084 5013 7699 7538 5085

KENNEDY CULVERT & SUPPLY CO p 811
125 6th Ave Ste 100 08054
Tel (856) 813-5000 *SIC* 5085

▲ **MARLIN BUSINESS SERVICES CORP** p 909
300 Fellowship Rd 08054
Tel (888) 479-9111 *SIC* 7389 7359 6022

■ **METROLOGIC INSTRUMENTS INC** p 955
534 Fellowship Rd 08054
Tel (856) 228-8100 *SIC* 3577 3699

OKI DATA AMERICAS INC p 1079
2000 Bishops Gate Blvd 08054
Tel (856) 235-2600 *SIC* 5045

PENNY PLATE LLC p 1131
14000 Horizon Way Ste 300 08054
Tel (856) 429-7583 *SIC* 3411 3556

▲ **PHH CORP** p 1142
1 Mortgage Way 08054
Tel (856) 917-1744 *SIC* 6531 8741

■ **PHH MORTGAGE CORP** p 1142
1 Mortgage Way 08054
Tel (866) 946-0081 *SIC* 6162

PMC GROUP INC p 1157
1288 Route 73 Ste 401 08054
Tel (856) 533-1866 *SIC* 3089 2812

■ **REALOGY SERVICES GROUP LLC** p 1214
3001 Leadenhall Rd 08054
Tel (856) 914-8500 *SIC* 6531 6211

ROOSEVELT PAPER CO p 1249
1 Roosevelt Dr 08054
Tel (856) 303-4100 *SIC* 2679

ROUST CORP p 1253
3000 Atrium Way Ste 265 08054
Tel (856) 273-6980 *SIC* 5181 2085 5182

SENIOR BRANDYWINE CARE INC p 1303
525 Fellowship Rd Ste 360 08054
Tel (856) 813-2000 *SIC* 8741 8322 8051

■ **SL INDUSTRIES INC** p 1330
520 Fellowship Rd A114 08054
Tel (856) 727-1500 *SIC* 3679 3643

SODASTREAM USA INC p 1336
200 E Park Dr Ste 600 08054
Tel (800) 763-2258 *SIC* 2087 3585

▲ **SUN BANCORP INC** p 1400
350 Fellowship Rd Ste 101 08054
Tel (856) 691-7700 *SIC* 6029

TEKNION LLC p 1433
350 Fellowship Rd Ste 100 08054
Tel (856) 552-5750 *SIC* 5021

■ **TITLE RESOURCE GROUP LLC** p 1456
3001 Leadenhall Rd 08054
Tel (856) 914-8500 *SIC* 6541 6211

UFCW LOCAL 152 HEALTH & WELFARE FUND p 1499
27 Roland Ave Ste 100 08054
Tel (856) 793-2500 *SIC* 8099

WE R WIRELESS INC p 1585
520 Fellowship Rd E508 08054
Tel (443) 735-7500 *SIC* 5999

MOUNTAINSIDE, NJ

BUGABOO CREEK HOLDINGS INC p 224
1450 Us Highway 22 Ste 4 07092
Tel (908) 518-1800 *SIC* 5812

CHILDRENS SPECIALIZED HOSPITAL INC p 300
150 New Providence Rd # 1 07092
Tel (888) 244-5373 *SIC* 8069 8093

NEPTUNE, NJ

■ **ASBURY PARK PRESS INC** p 115
3600 Route 66 07753
Tel (732) 922-6000 *SIC* 2711 2752

MERIDIAN HOSPITALS CORP p 948
1945 Route 33 07753
Tel (732) 751-7500 *SIC* 8062

NETCONG, NJ

CSS INC p 398
35 Love Ln 07857
Tel (973) 364-1118 *SIC* 5199

NEW BRUNSWICK, NJ

DEPUY INC p 431
1 Johnson And Johnson Plz 08901
Tel (732) 524-0400 *SIC* 3842

GDB INTERNATIONAL INC p 595
1 Home News Row 08901
Tel (732) 246-3001
SIC 2851 5162 5111 5093

▲ **JOHNSON & JOHNSON** p 790
1 Johnson And Johnson Plz 08933
Tel (732) 524-0400
SIC 2676 2844 3841 3842 2834

JOHNSON & JOHNSON PATIENT ASSISTANCE FOUNDATION INC p 790
1 Johnson And Johnson Plz 08933
Tel (732) 524-1394 *SIC* 8699

MIDDLESEX COUNTY OF (INC) p 965
75 Bayard St 08901
Tel (732) 745-3000 *SIC* 9111

NEW BRUNSWICK PUBLIC SCHOOLS p 1029
268 Baldwin St 08901
Tel (732) 745-5300 *SIC* 8211

PLAINFIELD TOBACCO AND CANDY CO INC p 1153
25 Van Dyke Ave 08901
Tel (732) 296-8900 *SIC* 5194 5145

ROBERT WOOD JOHNSON UNIVERSITY HOSPITAL p 1241
1 Robert Wood Johnson Pl 08901
Tel (732) 828-3000 *SIC* 8062

RUTGER STATE UNIVERSITY p 1260
Asb 3 Rutgers Pl 08901
Tel (732) 932-4370 *SIC* 8221

SAINT PETERS UNIVERSITY HOSPITAL INC p 1270
254 Easton Ave 08901
Tel (732) 745-8600 *SIC* 8062

NEW GRETNA, NJ

VIKING YACHT CO p 1557
On The Bass Riv Rr 9 08224
Tel (609) 296-6000 *SIC* 3732

NEW MILFORD, NJ

CURTIS CIRCULATION CO p 402
730 River Rd Ste 2 07646
Tel (201) 634-7400 *SIC* 5192

NEW PROVIDENCE, NJ

ALCATEL-LUCENT USA INC p 47
600 Mountain Ave Ste 700 07974
Tel (908) 582-3275 *SIC* 7372 3674

BOC GROUP INC p 196
575 Mountain Ave 07974
Tel (908) 665-2400
SIC 2813 3569 3559 3561 3511 3823

▲ **C R BARD INC** p 233
730 Central Ave 07974
Tel (908) 277-8000 *SIC* 3841 3845 3842

■ **CHEMETALL US INC** p 293
675 Central Ave 07974
Tel (908) 464-6900 *SIC* 2842 2899 2851

LUCENT TECHNOLOGIES INTERNATIONAL INC p 884
600 Mountain Ave 700 07974
Tel (908) 582-8500 *SIC* 5065

NEWARK, NJ

BLACKSTONE GROUP LLC p 188
570 Broad St Ste 1606 07102
Tel (973) 624-6300 *SIC* 1542 1522 1541

CITY OF NEWARK NEW JERSEY p 317
920 Broad St 07102
Tel (973) 733-3934 *SIC* 9111

COUNTY OF ESSEX p 378
465 Martn L King Jr Blvd 07102
Tel (973) 621-4454 *SIC* 9111

ESSEX COUNTY WELFARE BOARD INC p 510
18 Rector St Ste 9 07102
Tel (973) 733-3326 *SIC* 8322 8399

FAPS INC p 528
371 Craneway St 07114
Tel (973) 589-5656 *SIC* 3499 3711 7538

GATEWAY SECURITY INC p 594
604 Market St 608 07105
Tel (973) 465-8006 *SIC* 7381

▲ **GENIE ENERGY LTD** p 603
550 Broad St 07102
Tel (973) 438-3500 *SIC* 4911 4924 4931

H & GL FUNDS OF NJ p 649
700 Raymond Blvd 07105
Tel (973) 589-5056 *SIC* 8699

HEAVY & GENERAL CONSTRUCTION LABORERS UNION LOCAL NO 472 p 679
700 Raymond Blvd 07105
Tel (973) 589-5050 *SIC* 8631

HORIZON HEALTHCARE PLAN HOLDING p 707
3 Penn Plz E Ste 15-D 07105
Tel (973) 466-4000 *SIC* 8011

HORIZON HEALTHCARE SERVICES INC p 707
3 Penn Plz E Ste 1 07105
Tel (973) 466-4000 *SIC* 6324 6411 6321

HOUSING AUTHORITY OF CITY OF NEWARK p 711
500 Broad St 07102
Tel (973) 273-6000 *SIC* 9531

▲ **IDT CORP** p 729
550 Broad St 07102
Tel (973) 438-1000 *SIC* 4813

■ **IDT DOMESTIC TELECOM INC** p 729
520 Broad St 07102
Tel (973) 438-1000 *SIC* 4813

INTERNATIONAL FIDELITY INSURANCE CO p 755
1111 Raymond Blvd Fl 20 07102
Tel (973) 286-7911 *SIC* 6351

LIME ENERGY CO p 866
4 Gateway Ctr Fl 4 07102
Tel (201) 416-2575 *SIC* 1711 8711

MATTHEW BENDER & CO INC p 920
744 Broad St Fl 8 07102
Tel (518) 487-3000 *SIC* 2731

MITSUBISHI INTERNATIONAL POLYMERTRADE CORP p 978
2 Penn Plz E Fl 11 07105
Tel (732) 357-2000 *SIC* 5169

NEW COMMUNITY CORP p 1029
233 W Market St 07103
Tel (973) 623-2800 *SIC* 8399

NEW JERSEY INSTITUTE OF TECHNOLOGY (INC) p 1031
323 Dr Martin Luth 07102
Tel (973) 596-3000 *SIC* 8221

NEW JERSEY TRANSIT BUS OPERATIONS INC p 1031
1 Penn Plz E 07105
Tel (973) 491-7000 *SIC* 4131 4111

NEW JERSEY TRANSIT CORP p 1031
1 Penn Plz E 07105
Tel (973) 491-7000 *SIC* 4111 4131

NEWARK BETH ISRAEL MEDICAL CENTER INC p 1036
201 Lyons Ave 07112
Tel (973) 926-7000 *SIC* 8062

NEWARK MORNING LEDGER CO p 1037
1 Gateway Ctr Ste 1100 07102
Tel (973) 392-4141 *SIC* 2711

NEWARK PUBLIC SCHOOLS p 1037
2 Cedar St Ste 1 07102
Tel (973) 733-7333 *SIC* 8211

PANASONIC CORP OF NORTH AMERICA p 1111
2 Riverfront Plz Ste 200 07102
Tel (201) 348-7000
SIC 5064 5045 5065 5044 5084 5063

PASSAIC VALLEY SEWERAGE COMMISSION p 1119
600 Wilson Ave 07105
Tel (973) 344-1800 *SIC* 4952

■ **PGIM INC** p 1140
655 Broad St 07102
Tel (973) 802-6791 *SIC* 6411 6799 6282

■ **PORT NEWARK CONTAINER TERMINAL LLC** p 1162
241 Calcutta St 07114
Tel (973) 522-2200 *SIC* 4491

PRIME HEALTHCARE SERVICES - ST MICHAELS LLC p 1175
111 Central Ave 07102
Tel (973) 877-5000 *SIC* 8062

■ **PRUCO LIFE INSURANCE CO** p 1187
213 Washington St 07102
Tel (973) 802-6000 *SIC* 6311 6411

■ **PRUCO LIFE INSURANCE CO OF NEW JERSEY** p 1187
213 Washington St 07102
Tel (973) 802-6000 *SIC* 6311

■ **PRUCO SECURITIES LLC** p 1187
751 Broad St 07102
Tel (800) 235-7637
SIC 6321 6331 6211 6282 8071

▲ **PRUDENTIAL FINANCIAL INC** p 1187
751 Broad St 07102
Tel (973) 802-6000
SIC 6311 6321 6331 6211 6552

■ **PRUDENTIAL HOLDINGS LLC** p 1187
751 Broad St 07102
Tel (973) 802-6000 *SIC* 6282 6321 6324

■ **PRUDENTIAL INSURANCE CO OF AMERICA** p 1187
751 Broad St 07102
Tel (973) 802-6000
SIC 6311 6371 6282 6722

PRUDENTIAL WELFARE BENEFITS TRUST p 1187
751 Broad St Fl 18 07102
Tel (973) 802-7490 *SIC* 6733

■ **PSEG ENERGY HOLDINGS LLC** p 1188
80 Park Plz Ste 3 07102
Tel (973) 430-7000 *SIC* 6153 6512

■ **PSEG FOSSIL LLC** p 1188
80 Park Plz Ste 3 07102
Tel (973) 430-7000 *SIC* 4911

■ **PSEG POWER LLC** p 1188
80 Park Plz T-9 07102
Tel (973) 430-7000 *SIC* 4911

■ **PSEG SERVICES CORP** p 1188
80 Park Plz Ste 3 07102
Tel (973) 430-7000 *SIC* 8611

■ **PUBLIC SERVICE ELECTRIC AND GAS CO INC** p 1190
80 Park Plz Ste 3 07102
Tel (973) 430-7000 *SIC* 4931

▲ **PUBLIC SERVICE ENTERPRISE GROUP INC** p 1190
80 Park Plz 07102
Tel (973) 430-7000 *SIC* 4931 4911 4924

RAB FOOD GROUP p 1203
80 Avenue K 07105
Tel (201) 553-1100 *SIC* 5411

ROMAN CATHOLIC ARCHDIOCESE OF NEWARK p 1248
171 Clifton Ave 07104
Tel (973) 497-4000 *SIC* 8661

SAINT MICHAELS MEDICAL CENTER INC p 1270
111 Center Ter 07114
Tel (973) 877-5000 *SIC* 8062

SALSON LOGISTICS INC p 1273
888 Doremus Ave 07114
Tel (973) 986-0200 *SIC* 4213

TMCI HOLDINGS INC p 1457
80 Avenue K 07105
Tel (201) 553-1100
SIC 5122 5023 5072 5112 5049 5199

TROY CHEMICAL CORP INC p 1485
1 Avenue L 07105
Tel (973) 443-4200 *SIC* 5169

UNIVERSITY HOSPITAL p 1519
150 Bergen St Ste 1 07103
Tel (973) 972-4300 *SIC* 8062

UNIVERSITY OF MEDICINE AND DENTISTRY OF NJ (INC) p 1523
150 Bergen St 07103
Tel (973) 972-4400 *SIC* 8221 9411

UNIVERSITY PHYSICIAN ASSOCIATES OF NEW JERSEY INC p 1527
30 Bergen St Ste 1 07107
Tel (973) 972-5004 *SIC* 8221 8011

US WIRE & CABLE CORP p 1533
1 Flexon Plz 07114
Tel (973) 824-5530 *SIC* 3052 3315

■ **VERIZON NEW JERSEY INC** p 1550
540 Broad St 07102
Tel (973) 649-9900 *SIC* 4813 8721

■ **WELCO-CGI GAS TECHNOLOGIES LLC** p 1588
425 Avenue P 07105
Tel (973) 589-8795
SIC 5085 5169 5999 5984

WUHL SHAFMAN & LIEBERMAN INC p 1628
52 Cornelia St Ste 62 07105
Tel (973) 589-3513 *SIC* 5148

YOUTH CONSULTATION SERVICE (INC) p 1639
284 Broadway 07104
Tel (973) 482-2774 *SIC* 8093 8361 8211

NEWFIELD, NJ

MB INDUSTRIES INC p 925
560 Salem Ave 08344
Tel (609) 970-1503 *SIC* 5051

NEWFOUNDLAND, NJ

■ **LAKELAND BANK** p 839
2717 Route 23 07435
Tel (973) 697-2040 *SIC* 6022

NEWTON, NJ

NEW JERSEY HERALD p 1031
2 Spring St 07860
Tel (973) 383-1500 *SIC* 2711

NEWTON MEMORIAL HOSPITAL INC p 1039
175 High St 07860
Tel (973) 383-2121 *SIC* 8062

NORTH JERSEY HEALTH CARE CORP p 1052
175 High St 07860
Tel (973) 383-2121 *SIC* 8741

THORLABS INC p 1450
56 Sparta Ave 07860
Tel (973) 579-7227 *SIC* 3826

NORTH ARLINGTON, NJ

G P JOHNSTON INC p 587
322 Belleville Tpke 07031
Tel (201) 991-7400 *SIC* 5065

NORTH BERGEN, NJ

618 MAIN CLOTHING CORP p 3
5601 W Side Ave Ste 2 07047
Tel (201) 319-1400 *SIC* 5621

A & M (2015) LLC p 4
5901 W Side Ave Ste 500 07047
Tel (201) 868-6220 *SIC* 5621

DYNAMIC INTERNATIONAL USA INC p 464
2501 71st St 07047
Tel (973) 344-6300 *SIC* 4214

■ **LCI HOLDINGS INC** p 849
5901 W Side Ave 07047
Tel (201) 295-6300
SIC 5651 5136 5137 5094 5122 5944

NATIONAL RETAIL SYSTEMS INC p 1015
2820 16th St 07047
Tel (201) 330-1900 *SIC* 7363

NATIONAL RETAIL TRANSPORTATION INC p 1016
2820 16th St 07047
Tel (201) 866-0462 *SIC* 4213

PALISADES GENERAL HOSPITAL GIFT SHOP p 1108
7600 River Rd 07047
Tel (201) 854-5123 *SIC* 5947

PALISADES MEDICAL CENTER INC p 1108
7600 River Rd 07047
Tel (201) 854-5000 *SIC* 8062

PAT LAFRIEDA MEAT PURVEYORS INC p 1120
3701 Tonnelle Ave 07047
Tel (201) 537-8210 *SIC* 5147

TEXTILES FROM EUROPE INC p 1445
5901 W Side Ave Fl 6 07047
Tel (212) 213-1828 *SIC* 5131

■ **VITAMIN SHOPPE INDUSTRIES INC** p 1562
2101 91st St 07047
Tel (201) 868-5959 *SIC* 5961

■ **VS HERCULES LLC** p 1566
2101 91st St 07047
Tel (201) 868-5959 *SIC* 2834

VS PARENT INC p 1566
2101 91st St 07047
Tel (201) 868-5959 *SIC* 5961 5499

NORTH BRUNSWICK, NJ

BARI HOME CORP p 155
1215 Livingston Ave Ste 4 08902
Tel (973) 713-0591 *SIC* 2273

BIOLIFE PLASMA SERVICES LP p 184
203 N Center Dr 08902
Tel (732) 422-4200 *SIC* 5122

NORTH BRUNSWICK TOWNSHIP BOARD OF EDUCATION p 1051
300 Old Georges Rd 08902
Tel (732) 289-3000 *SIC* 8211

PRO TAPES & SPECIALTIES INC p 1178
621 Us Highway 1 Unit A 08902
Tel (732) 346-0900 *SIC* 5113 2675

SILVER LINE BUILDING PRODUCTS LLC p 1324
1 Silverline Dr 08902
Tel (732) 435-1000 *SIC* 3089 3442

NORTHVALE, NJ

GEA MECHANICAL EQUIPMENT US INC p 597
100 Fairway Ct 07647
Tel (201) 767-3900 *SIC* 5084 7699

GEA WESTFALIA SEPARATOR INC p 597
100 Fairway Ct 07647
Tel (201) 767-3900 *SIC* 5083 5084 3523

NASSAU LENS CO INC p 1009
160 Legrand Ave 07647
Tel (201) 767-8033 *SIC* 5048

NORWOOD, NJ

MITSUI FOODS INC p 978
35 Maple St 07648
Tel (201) 750-0500 *SIC* 5142 5149 5499

PHOENIX AROMAS HOLDINGS LLC p 1144
355 Chestnut St 07648
Tel (201) 784-6100 *SIC* 5169

NUTLEY, NJ

■ **HOFFMANN-LA ROCHE INC** p 699
340 Kingsland St 07110
Tel (973) 235-5000 *SIC* 2834 8733

ROCHE EMPLOYEE WELFARE BENEFIT TRUST p 1243
340 Kingsland St 07110
Tel (973) 235-5000 *SIC* 6733

■ **ROCHE LABORATORIES INC** p 1243
340 Kingsland St 07110
Tel (973) 235-5000 *SIC* 8071

OAK RIDGE, NJ

▲ **LAKELAND BANCORP INC** p 839
250 Oak Ridge Rd 07438
Tel (973) 697-2000 *SIC* 6022

OAKLAND, NJ

AMERLUX LLC p 84
178 Bauer Dr 07436
Tel (973) 882-5010 *SIC* 3646

TOPCON AMERICA CORP p 1461
111 Bauer Dr 07436
Tel (201) 599-5117 *SIC* 3845

TOPCON MEDICAL SYSTEMS INC p 1461
111 Bauer Dr 07436
Tel (201) 599-5100
SIC 3841 3826 3827 3829 3851 5049

OLD BRIDGE, NJ

AMBOY BANCORPORATION p 65
3590 Us Highway 9 08857
Tel (732) 591-8700 *SIC* 6021

AMBOY BANK p 65
3590 Us Highway 9 08857
Tel (732) 721-4200 *SIC* 6021

OLDWICK, NJ

AM BEST CO INC p 63
1 Ambest Rd 08858
Tel (908) 439-2200 *SIC* 2731 2721 2732

ORADELL, NJ

BURNS & ROE GROUP INC p 228
800 Kinderkamack Rd Ste 1 07649
Tel (201) 265-2000 *SIC* 8711

HUNTINGTON LEARNING CORP p 720
496 Kinderkamack Rd G01 07649
Tel (201) 261-8400 *SIC* 8299

ORANGE, NJ

CITY OF ORANGE TOWNSHIP p 317
29 N Day St 07050
Tel (973) 266-4000 *SIC* 9111

PALMYRA, NJ

CALLAHAN CHEMICAL CO p 242
S Broad St & Filmore Ave 08065
Tel (856) 786-7900 *SIC* 5169

PARAMUS, NJ

▲ **ALEXANDERS INC** p 49
210 E Rte 4 07652
Tel (201) 587-8541 *SIC* 6798

BERGEN COMMUNITY COLLEGE p 174
400 Paramus Rd Ste A330-C 07652
Tel (201) 447-7100 *SIC* 8222

BERGEN REGIONAL MEDICAL CENTER LP p 174
230 E Ridgewood Ave 07652
Tel (201) 967-4000 *SIC* 8062

BLINDS TO GO (US) INC p 189
101 E State Rt 4 07652
Tel (201) 441-9260 *SIC* 2591

COACH USA INC p 331
160 S Route 17 N 07652
Tel (201) 225-7500 *SIC* 4725 4111 4121

HANJIN SHIPPING AMERICA LLC p 657
80 E State Rt 4 Ste 490 07652
Tel (201) 291-4600 *SIC* 4449

HANJIN SHIPPING CO LTD p 657
80 E Rte 4 Ste 490 07652
Tel (201) 291-4600 *SIC* 4499

HUDSON CITY BANCORP INC p 716
W80 Century Rd 07652
Tel (201) 967-1900 *SIC* 6035

HUDSON CITY SAVINGS BANK p 716
80 W Century Rd 07652
Tel (201) 967-1900 *SIC* 6035 6163

LOVING HANDS LTD p 881
676 Winters Ave Ste 1 07652
Tel (201) 265-3523 *SIC* 7363 8082

■ **METAL IMPROVEMENT CO LLC** p 952
80 E State Rt 4 Ste 310 07652
Tel (201) 843-7800 *SIC* 3398

▲ **MOVADO GROUP INC** p 995
650 From Rd Ste 375 07652
Tel (201) 267-8000 *SIC* 3873 3915 7631

N A SUEZ p 1005
461 From Rd Ste F 07652
Tel (201) 767-9300 *SIC* 4941

NICE SYSTEMS INC p 1042
461 From Rd Ste 103 07652
Tel (201) 964-2600
SIC 7372 7382 1731 8741

PARAMUS BOARD OF EDUCATION INC p 1114
145 Spring Valley Rd 07652
Tel (201) 261-7800 *SIC* 8211

SUEZ ENVIRONNEMENT p 1396
461 From Rd Ste 400 07652
Tel (201) 767-9300 *SIC* 4941

SUEZ TREATMENT SOLUTIONS INC p 1396
461 From Rd Ste 400 07652
Tel (804) 756-7600 *SIC* 3589

SUEZ WATER INC p 1396
461 From Rd Ste 400 07652
Tel (201) 767-9300 *SIC* 6719 4941 4952

SUEZ WATER NEW JERSEY INC p 1396
461 From Rd Ste 400 07652
Tel (201) 767-9300 *SIC* 4941

URS CORP p 1530
Mack Ctr Ii Mack Ctr Dr 07652
Tel (201) 262-7000 *SIC* 8711 8748

PARK RIDGE, NJ

■ **HERTZ INTERNATIONAL LTD** p 687
225 Brae Blvd 07656
Tel (201) 307-2000 *SIC* 7514 7515 7513

■ **HERTZ INVESTORS INC** p 687
225 Brae Blvd 07656
Tel (201) 307-2000
SIC 7514 7515 7513 7359 5521 6794

■ **HERTZ LOCAL EDITION CORP** p 688
225 Brae Blvd 07656
Tel (201) 307-2000 *SIC* 7514

PARSIPPANY, NJ

ACTAVIS LLC p 19
400 Interpace Pkwy 07054
Tel (862) 261-7000 *SIC* 2834 5122

ACTAVIS PHARMA INC p 19
400 Interpace Pkwy Ste A1 07054
Tel (862) 261-7000 *SIC* 2834

■ **AETNA HEALTH INC (NJ)** p 31
9 Entin Rd 07054
Tel (973) 244-3500 *SIC* 6324 6321

ALLERGAN INC p 53
400 Interpace Pkwy Bldg D 07054
Tel (862) 261-7000 *SIC* 2834 3841

AMERICAN FINANCIAL RESOURCES INC p 72
9 Sylvan Way Ste 310 07054
Tel (973) 983-5626 *SIC* 6163

■ **ASCENSIA DIABETES CARE US INC** p 116
5 Woodhollow Rd 07054
Tel (973) 560-6500 *SIC* 5047 2835 3841

ATLAS COPCO NORTH AMERICA LLC p 128
7 Campus Dr Ste 200 07054
Tel (973) 397-3400 *SIC* 3312

ATLAS COPCO USA HOLDINGS INC p 128
7 Campus Dr Ste 200 07054
Tel (973) 397-3432 *SIC* 6722 6159 7699

▲ **AVIS BUDGET GROUP INC** p 138
6 Sylvan Way Ste 1 07054
Tel (973) 496-4700 *SIC* 7514 7513 6794

■ **AVIS GROUP HOLDINGS LLC** p 138
6 Sylvan Way Ste 1 07054
Tel (973) 496-4328 *SIC* 7514

■ **AVIS RENT A CAR SYSTEM INC** p 138
6 Sylvan Way Ste 1 07054
Tel (973) 496-3500 *SIC* 7514

AVIS RENTAL CAR SYSTEMS p 138
6 Sylvan Way Ste 1 07054
Tel (973) 496-3000 *SIC* 7514

▲ **B&G FOODS INC** p 142
4 Gatehall Dr Ste 110 07054
Tel (973) 401-6500
SIC 2013 2032 2033 2035 2099

■ **BUDGET RENT A CAR SYSTEM INC** p 224
6 Sylvan Way Ste 1 07054
Tel (973) 496-3500 *SIC* 7514

■ **BUDGET TRUCK RENTAL LLC** p 224
6 Sylvan Way Ste 1 07054
Tel (973) 496-3500 *SIC* 7514

CHEMTRADE CHEMICALS CORP p 293
90 E Halsey Rd Ste 301 07054
Tel (973) 515-0900 *SIC* 2819

CHEMTRADE CHEMICALS US LLC p 293
90 E Halsey Rd 07054
Tel (973) 515-0900 *SIC* 2812

CHEMTRADE GCC HOLDING CO p 293
90 E Halsey Rd 07054
Tel (973) 515-0900 *SIC* 6719 2819

CHEMTRADE SOLUTIONS LLC p 293
90 E Halsey Rd 07054
Tel (973) 515-0900 *SIC* 5169 2819

COMPUTER HORIZONS CORP p 353
2001 Us Highway 46 # 310 07054
Tel (973) 257-5030 *SIC* 7373

DAIICHI SANKYO INC p 408
2 Hilton Ct Ste 1 07054
Tel (973) 359-2600 *SIC* 5122 8731

■ **DELAWARE CITY REFINING CO LLC** p 423
1 Sylvan Way Ste 2 07054
Tel (320) 834-6000 *SIC* 1629

DIALOGIC INC p 436
4 Gatehall Dr 07054
Tel (973) 967-6000 *SIC* 3661 3577 7371

■ **DOLCE INTERNATIONAL HOLDINGS INC** p 448
22 Sylvan Way 07054
Tel (201) 307-8700 *SIC* 7011 8741

■ **DOLCE INTERNATIONAL HOSPITALITY LLC** p 448
22 Sylvan Way 07054
Tel (201) 307-8700 *SIC* 7011

DPI NEWCO LLC p 454
45 Waterview Blvd 07054
Tel (973) 257-8113 *SIC* 2834

DSM FOOD SPECIALTIES USA INC p 458
45 Waterview Blvd 07054
Tel (973) 257-1063 *SIC* 5149

DSM HOLDING CO USA INC p 458
45 Waterview Blvd 07054
Tel (973) 257-1063
SIC 2891 2816 3089 3083 5169

■ **EARTHCOLOR INC** p 469
249 Pomeroy Rd 07054
Tel (973) 884-1300 *SIC* 2752 2759

■ **EBI LLC** p 474
399 Jefferson Rd 07054
Tel (973) 299-9300 *SIC* 5047

■ **ELECTRO-BIOLOGY INC** p 485
100 Interpace Pkwy Ste 1 07054
Tel (973) 299-9022 *SIC* 3841

EVONIK CORP p 515
299 Jefferson Rd 07054
Tel (973) 929-8000
SIC 2819 2869 2851 2816

EVONIK CYRO LLC p 515
299 Jefferson Rd 07054
Tel (973) 929-8000 *SIC* 2821

FERRING PHARMACEUTICALS INC p 538
100 Interpace Pkwy 07054
Tel (973) 796-1600 *SIC* 2834 5122

FOREST PHARMACEUTICALS INC p 567
400 Interpace Pkwy Ste A1 07054
Tel (862) 261-7000 *SIC* 2834

FOX HILL HOLDINGS INC p 572
99 Cherry Hill Rd 07054
Tel (212) 734-1525 SIC 6411

G HOLDINGS INC p 587
1 Campus Dr 07054
Tel (973) 628-3000 SIC 2869 2843 3295

GAF CORP p 589
1 Campus Dr 07054
Tel (973) 628-3000 SIC 3444 3634

GENTEK INC p 604
90 E Halsey Rd Ste 301 07054
Tel (973) 515-0900
SIC 2869 2819 2844 3714 3496

■ **GLOBAL AEROSPACE INC** p 615
1 Sylvan Way Ste 3 07054
Tel (973) 490-8500 SIC 6411

HUDSON NEWS DISTRIBUTORS LLC p 717
701 Jefferson Rd 07054
Tel (201) 867-3600 SIC 5192

IMS HEALTH INC p 735
100 Ims Dr 07054
Tel (203) 448-4600 SIC 7379

■ **INNOVEX INC** p 745
10 Waterview Blvd Ste 100 07054
Tel (973) 257-4500 SIC 8734 8999 7374

KINGS SUPER MARKETS INC p 820
700 Lanidex Plz Ste 2 07054
Tel (973) 463-6300 SIC 5411

LANGAN ENGINEERING AND ENVIRONMENTAL SERVICES INC p 844
300 Kimball Dr 07054
Tel (201) 794-6900 SIC 8711

LANGAN ENGINEERING ENVIRONMENTAL SURVEYING AND LANDSCAPE ARCHITECTURE DPC p 844
300 Kimball Dr Ste 4 07054
Tel (973) 560-4900
SIC 8711 8748 1389 0781

▲ **MEDICINES CO** p 937
8 Sylvan Way 07054
Tel (973) 290-6000 SIC 2834

▲ **PACIRA PHARMACEUTICALS INC** p 1106
5 Sylvan Way Ste 300 07054
Tel (973) 254-3560 SIC 2834

PARSIPPANY-TROY HILLS TOWNSHIP SCHOOL DISTRICT p 1117
292 Parsippany Rd 07054
Tel (973) 263-7200 SIC 8211 9111

■ **PBF ENERGY CO LLC** p 1123
1 Sylvan Way Ste 2 07054
Tel (973) 455-7500 SIC 2911

▲ **PBF ENERGY INC** p 1123
1 Sylvan Way Ste 2 07054
Tel (973) 455-7500 SIC 2911

■ **PBF HOLDING CO LLC** p 1123
1 Sylvan Way Ste 2 07054
Tel (888) 661-8949 SIC 2911 2992

■ **PBF LOGISTICS LP** p 1123
1 Sylvan Way Ste 2 07054
Tel (973) 455-7500 SIC 4612

■ **PINNACLE FOODS FINANCE LLC** p 1149
399 Jefferson Rd 07054
Tel (973) 541-6620
SIC 2038 2092 2099 2045

■ **PINNACLE FOODS GROUP LLC** p 1149
399 Jefferson Rd 07054
Tel (856) 969-7100
SIC 2038 2092 2099 2045

▲ **PINNACLE FOODS INC** p 1149
399 Jefferson Rd 07054
Tel (973) 541-6620 SIC 2038 2035

PNY TECHNOLOGIES INC p 1158
100 Jefferson Rd 07054
Tel (973) 515-9700 SIC 3572

RB MANUFACTURING LLC p 1211
399 Interpace Pkwy 07054
Tel (973) 404-2600 SIC 2035 2842

RECKITT BENCKISER (NORTH AMERICA) INC p 1214
399 Interpace Pkwy # 101 07054
Tel (973) 404-2600 SIC 2035 2842

RECKITT BENCKISER LLC p 1214
399 Interpace Pkwy # 101 07054
Tel (973) 404-2600 SIC 2035 2842

■ **RESORT CONDOMINIUMS INTERNATIONAL LLC** p 1227
1 Sylvan Way 07054
Tel (973) 753-6667 SIC 7011

SAFILO AMERICA INC p 1267
801 Jefferson Rd 07054
Tel (973) 952-2800 SIC 5048 5099 5091

SAFILO USA INC p 1267
801 Jefferson Rd 07054
Tel (973) 952-2800 SIC 5048

SECURITAS HOLDINGS INC p 1298
9 Campus Dr Ste 1 07054
Tel (973) 267-5300 SIC 7381

SECURITAS SECURITY SERVICES USA INC p 1299
9 Campus Dr 07054
Tel (973) 267-5300 SIC 7381

SECURITAS SERVICES INC p 1299
9 Campus Dr Ste 1 07054
Tel (973) 267-5300 SIC 7381

SKANSKA USA BUILDING INC p 1329
389 Interpace Pkwy Ste 5 07054
Tel (973) 753-3500 SIC 1541 1542 8741

■ **SKYLINE STEEL LLC** p 1330
8 Woodhollow Rd Ste 102 07054
Tel (973) 428-6100 SIC 3317 5051

SOS SECURITY INC p 1341
1915 Us Highway 46 Ste 1 07054
Tel (973) 402-6600 SIC 7381

SOS SECURITY LLC p 1341
1915 Us Highway 46 07054
Tel (973) 402-6600 SIC 7381

SOUTHERN CALIFORNIA RISK MANAGEMENT ASSOCIATES INC p 1347
99 Cherry Hill Rd Ste 102 07054
Tel (973) 541-1330 SIC 6411

STANDARD INDUSTRIES INC p 1376
1 Campus Dr 07054
Tel (973) 628-3000 SIC 2493

STRATEGIC PRODUCTS AND SERVICES LLC p 1392
300 Littleton Rd Ste 200 07054
Tel (973) 540-0600 SIC 5999

SUN CHEMICAL CORP p 1400
35 Waterview Blvd Ste 100 07054
Tel (973) 404-6000 SIC 2893 2865

■ **SUPER 8 WORLDWIDE INC** p 1405
22 Sylvan Way Fl 3 07054
Tel (850) 973-3331 SIC 6794

■ **TETRA TECH EC INC** p 1441
6 Century Dr Ste 3 07054
Tel (973) 630-8000 SIC 8748

TRAVELPORT INC p 1474
6 Campus Dr Ste 1 07054
Tel (770) 563-7400 SIC 4724

TRAVELPORT LLC p 1474
6 Campus Dr Ste 1 07054
Tel (770) 563-7400 SIC 7375

UNIMET METAL SUPPLY INC p 1503
150 Lackawanna Ave 07054
Tel (973) 673-5700 SIC 3324

WARNER CHILCOTT (US) LLC p 1576
400 Interpace Pkwy 07054
Tel (862) 261-7000 SIC 2834

WESTERN WORLD INSURANCE CO p 1600
300 Kimball Dr Ste 500 07054
Tel (201) 847-8600 SIC 6351

WESTERN WORLD INSURANCE GROUP INC p 1600
300 Kimball Dr Ste 500 07054
Tel (201) 847-8600 SIC 6331

■ **WYNDHAM HOTEL GROUP LLC** p 1629
22 Sylvan Way 07054
Tel (973) 753-6000 SIC 7011

WYNDHAM INTERNATIONAL INC p 1630
22 Sylvan Way 07054
Tel (973) 753-6000 SIC 7011 8741

▲ **WYNDHAM WORLDWIDE CORP** p 1630
22 Sylvan Way 07054
Tel (973) 753-6000
SIC 7011 8741 7389 6531

YORK RISK SERVICES GROUP INC p 1637
1 Upper Pond Bldg F 07054
Tel (973) 404-1200 SIC 6411

▲ **ZOETIS INC** p 1644
10 Sylvan Way Ste 105 07054
Tel (973) 822-7000 SIC 2834 5122

PASSAIC, NJ

BOARD OF EDUCATION OF CITY OF PASSAIC INC p 195
101 Passaic Ave 07055
Tel (973) 470-5244 SIC 8211

PASSAIC CITY PUBLIC SCHOOLS p 1119
101 Passaic Ave 07055
Tel (973) 470-5500 SIC 8211

PRIME HEALTHCARE SERVICES - ST MARYS PASSAIC LLC p 1175
350 Boulevard 07055
Tel (973) 365-4300 SIC 8062

ST MARY HEALTH CORP p 1370
211 Pennington Ave 07055
Tel (973) 470-3000 SIC 8741

PATERSON, NJ

COUNTY OF PASSAIC p 380
401 Grand St Ste 1 07505
Tel (973) 881-4405 SIC 9111

PASSAIC COUNTY COMMUNITY COLLEGE (INC) p 1119
1 College Blvd 07505
Tel (973) 684-6868 SIC 8222 8221

PATERSON CITY OF (INC) p 1120
155 Market St Fl 2 07505
Tel (973) 321-1350 SIC 9111

PATERSON PUBLIC SCHOOL DISTRICT p 1120
90 Delaware Ave 07503
Tel (973) 321-0980 SIC 8211

ST JOSEPHS HEALTHCARE SYSTEM INC p 1368
703 Main St 07503
Tel (973) 754-4500 SIC 8062

ST JOSEPHS HOSPITAL AND MEDICAL CENTER p 1368
703 Main St 07503
Tel (973) 754-2000 SIC 8062

PAULSBORO, NJ

ARAMSCO INC p 102
1480 Grandview Ave 08066
Tel (856) 686-7700
SIC 5085 5084 5136 5139

■ **MOBIL RESEARCH AND DEVELOPMENT CORP** p 980
600 Billingsport Rd 08066
Tel (856) 224-2134 SIC 2911

■ **PAULSBORO REFINING CO LLC** p 1122
800 Jenkins Blvd 08066
Tel (973) 455-7500 SIC 2911

PEAPACK, NJ

■ **GREENSTONE LLC** p 638
100 Rte 206 N 07977
Tel (800) 447-3360 SIC 5122

■ **PHARMACIA & UPJOHN INC** p 1141
100 Route 206 N 07977
Tel (908) 901-8000 SIC 2834 2833

PEMBERTON, NJ

PEMBERTON TOWNSHIP SCHOOL DISTRICT p 1128
1 Egbert St 08068
Tel (609) 893-8141 SIC 8211

PENNINGTON, NJ

MERRILL LYNCH INSURANCE GROUP INC p 950
1700 American Blvd 08534
Tel (609) 274-5351 SIC 6311

ZYDUS PHARMACEUTICALS USA INC p 1645
73 Route 31 N 08534
Tel (609) 730-1900 SIC 2834

PENNS GROVE, NJ

■ **MCLANE NEW JERSEY** p 931
742 Courses Landing Rd 08069
Tel (856) 351-6200 SIC 5141 5149

PENNSAUKEN, NJ

■ **AIRBORNE SYSTEMS NORTH AMERICA INC** p 39
5800 Magnolia Ave 08109
Tel (856) 663-1275 SIC 2426 3429

AMERICAN FURNITURE RENTALS INC p 73
720 Hylton Rd 08110
Tel (856) 406-1200 SIC 7359 5712

ARETT SALES CORP p 107
9285 Commerce Hwy 08110
Tel (856) 751-1224 SIC 5191

AUDIO AND VIDEO LABS INC p 130
7905 N Crescent Blvd 08110
Tel (856) 663-9030
SIC 3652 5099 7389 3651

DATWYLER PHARMA PACKAGING USA REALTY INC p 414
9012 Pennsauken Hwy 08110
Tel (856) 663-2202 SIC 5047 3841

FORMAN MILLS INC p 567
1070 Thomas Busch Mem Hwy 08110
Tel (856) 486-1447 SIC 5699

FOULKROD ASSOCIATES p 571
8275 N Crescent Blvd 08110
Tel (856) 662-6767 SIC 3411 5149

▲ **J & J SNACK FOODS CORP** p 770
6000 Central Hwy 08109
Tel (856) 665-9533
SIC 2053 2087 2086 2024 2052 2051

PEPSI-COLA & NATIONAL BRAND BEVERAGES LTD (INC) p 1134
8275 N Crescent Blvd 08110
Tel (856) 665-6200 SIC 2086

■ **RCM TECHNOLOGIES (USA) INC** p 1212
2500 Mcclellan Ave # 350 08109
Tel (856) 356-4500 SIC 8742 7379 8711

▲ **RCM TECHNOLOGIES INC** p 1212
2500 Mcclellan Ave # 350 08109
Tel (856) 356-4500
SIC 8711 8748 7373 8049 7363

TEAMSTERS HEALTH AND WELFARE FUND OF PHILADELPHIA AND VICINITY p 1430
6981 N Park Dr Ste 400 08109
Tel (856) 382-2400 SIC 8631

PENNSVILLE, NJ

SIEGFRIED USA HOLDING INC p 1320
33 Industrial Park Rd 08070
Tel (856) 678-3601 SIC 2834

PERTH AMBOY, NJ

ENGLERT INC p 499
1200 Amboy Ave 08861
Tel (800) 364-5378 SIC 3444 5033

F M SYLVAN INC p 522
1001 State St 08861
Tel (732) 826-7474 SIC 1711

PERTH AMBOY PUBLIC SCHOOLS p 1137
178 Barracks St 08861
Tel (732) 376-6200 SIC 8211

RARITAN BAY MEDICAL CENTER A NEW JERSEY NONPROFIT CORP p 1209
530 New Brunswick Ave 08861
Tel (732) 442-3700 SIC 8062

SYLVAN FM HOLDING LLC p 1413
1001 State St 08861
Tel (732) 826-7474 SIC 1711

TROPICAL CHEESE INDUSTRIES INC p 1484
452 Fayette St 08861
Tel (732) 442-4898 SIC 2022 5143

PHILLIPSBURG, NJ

WARREN ST LUKES HOSPITAL INC p 1577
185 Roseberry St 08865
Tel (908) 859-6700 SIC 8062 8093

PINE BROOK, NJ

ALVOGEN GROUP INC p 63
10 Bloomfield Ave 07058
Tel (973) 796-3400 SIC 2834

ALVOGEN INC p 63
10 Bloomfield Ave Ste 3 07058
Tel (973) 796-3400 SIC 2834

ALVOGEN PHARMA US INC p 63
10 Bloomfield Ave 07058
Tel (973) 796-3400 SIC 3559

WESTPORT CORP p 1602
331 Changebridge Rd Ste 3 07058
Tel (973) 575-0110 SIC 5948 5199

PISCATAWAY, NJ

AARON AND CO INC p 8
30 Turner Pl 08854
Tel (732) 752-8200 SIC 5074 5075

AEQUOR TECHNOLOGIES INC p 30
377 Hoes Ln Ste 300 08854
Tel (732) 494-4999 SIC 7371

ARBEE ASSOCIATES p 102
1531 S Washington Ave # 3 08854
Tel (908) 686-3900 SIC 5021

AS AMERICA INC p 115
1 Centennial Ave Ste 101 08854
Tel (732) 980-3000 SIC 3261 3432

BINSKY & SNYDER LLC p 183
281 Centennial Ave Ste 1 08854
Tel (732) 885-0700 SIC 1711 8711

DIOCESE OF METUCHEN INC p 440
146 Metlars Ln 08854
Tel (732) 562-1990 SIC 8661

EDGEWOOD PROPERTIES INC p 478
1260 Stelton Rd 08854
Tel (732) 985-1900 SIC 6552 6531

EDUCATIONAL SERVICES COMMISSION OF NEW JERSEY p 479
1660 Stelton Rd 08854
Tel (732) 777-9848 SIC 9411

FERRARO FOODS INC p 538
287 S Randolphville Rd 08854
Tel (732) 424-3400 SIC 5149 5812

FOLEY INC p 563
855 Centennial Ave 08854
Tel (732) 885-5555 SIC 5082 7699 7353

FRANCIS E PARKER MEMORIAL HOME INC p 573
1421 River Rd 08854
Tel (732) 545-8330 SIC 8741

HELM AMERICA CORP p 682
1110 Centennial Ave Ste 2 08854
Tel (732) 981-1160
SIC 5169 5122 5191 4231 4226

HELM US CORP p 682
1110 Centennial Ave Ste 2 08854
Tel (732) 981-1116 SIC 5169

INGERSOLL-RAND US TRANE HOLDINGS CORP p 742
1 Centennial Ave Ste 101 08854
Tel (732) 652-7100 SIC 3585

MARLABS INC p 909
1 Corporate Pl S Fl 3 08854
Tel (732) 694-1000 SIC 7371

■ **POLARIS CONSULTING & SERVICES LTD** p 1159
20 Corporate Pl S 08854
Tel (732) 590-8100 SIC 7371

■ **QUALCARE ALLIANCE NETWORKS INC** p 1196
30 Knightsbridge Rd # 530 08854
Tel (732) 562-0833 SIC 6324

QUALITY COMPUTER ACCESSORIES INC p 1196
70 Ethel Rd W Ste 1 08854
Tel (732) 572-2719
SIC 5063 5051 3315 3644

RUTGERS STATE UNIVERSITY p 1260
96 Davidson Rd 08854
Tel (732) 932-4636 SIC 8221

SCHOLES ELECTRIC & COMMUNICATIONS p 1288
1021 Centennial Ave 08854
Tel (732) 562-1900 SIC 1731

SIVANTOS INC p 1328
10 Constitution Ave 08854
Tel (732) 562-6600 SIC 3842

SYNECHRON INC p 1415
1 Corporate Pl S Ste 200 08854
Tel (732) 562-0088 SIC 8748

TELCORDIA TECHNOLOGIES INC p 1433
444 Hoes Ln 08854
Tel (732) 699-6800 *SIC* 7371 7373 8742

TR BRYANT ASSOCIATES INC p 1468
377 Hoes Ln 08854
Tel (732) 981-0440 *SIC* 7363 7361

TRANE INC p 1469
1 Centennial Ave Ste 101 08854
Tel (732) 652-7100 *SIC* 3585

TRANE US INC p 1469
1 Centennial Ave Ste 101 08854
Tel (732) 652-7100 *SIC* 3585

PLAINFIELD, NJ

MUHLENBERG REGIONAL MEDICAL CENTER INC p 999
Park Ave & Randolph Rd 07060
Tel (908) 668-2000 *SIC* 8062

PLAINFIELD PUBLIC SCHOOL DISTRICT p 1153
1200 Myrtle Ave 07063
Tel (908) 731-4200 *SIC* 8211

PLAINSBORO, NJ

COMPUNNEL SOFTWARE GROUP INC p 352
103 Morgan Ln Ste 102 08536
Tel (609) 606-9010 *SIC* 7371

FIRMENICH INC p 544
250 Plainsboro Rd 08536
Tel (609) 452-1000 *SIC* 2899 2869

■ INTEGRA LIFESCIENCES CORP p 748
311 Enterprise Dr 08536
Tel (609) 275-2700 *SIC* 3841

▲ INTEGRA LIFESCIENCES HOLDINGS CORP p 748
311 Enterprise Dr 08536
Tel (609) 275-0500 *SIC* 3841 2836 3842

MEDICAL CENTER AT PRINCETON NEW JERSEY p 936
1 Plainsboro Rd 08536
Tel (609) 497-4000 *SIC* 8062

NITYO INFOTECH CORP p 1045
666 Plainsboro Rd Ste 210 08536
Tel (609) 799-5959 *SIC* 7379

NOVO NORDISK INC p 1063
800 Scudders Mill Rd 08536
Tel (609) 987-5800 *SIC* 2834

NOVO-NORDISK OF NORTH AMERICA INC p 1063
800 Scudders Mill Rd 08536
Tel (609) 987-5800
SIC 8741 8733 5122 2833 2834

PRINCETON HEALTHCARE SYSTEM A NEW JERSEY NONPROFIT CORP p 1177
1 Plainsboro Rd 08536
Tel (609) 497-4000 *SIC* 8741

PRINCETON HEALTHCARE SYSTEM HOLDING INC p 1177
1 Plainsboro Rd 08536
Tel (609) 497-4190 *SIC* 6733

POINT PLEASANT BEACH, NJ

NORKUS ENTERPRISES INC p 1048
505 Richmond Ave 08742
Tel (732) 899-8485 *SIC* 5411

POMONA, NJ

ATLANTICARE REGIONAL MEDICAL CENTER p 127
65 W Jimmie Leeds Rd 08240
Tel (609) 652-1000 *SIC* 8062

POMPTON PLAINS, NJ

CHILTON HOSPITAL p 300
97 W Parkway 07444
Tel (973) 831-5000 *SIC* 8062

WIRELESS NETWORK GROUP INC p 1618
220 W Parkway Ste 10a 07444
Tel (973) 831-4015 *SIC* 1623

PRINCETON JUNCTION, NJ

▲ MISTRAS GROUP INC p 976
195 Clarksville Rd Ste 2 08550
Tel (609) 716-4000
SIC 8711 7372 3829 3825

WEST WINDSOR-PLAINSBORO REGIONAL BOARD OF EDUCATION p 1596
321 Village Rd E 08550
Tel (609) 716-5000 *SIC* 8211

PRINCETON, NJ

■ ABBOTT POINT OF CARE INC p 9
400 College Rd E 08540
Tel (609) 454-9000 *SIC* 3841

■ ARMKEL LLC p 111
469 N Harrison St 08540
Tel (609) 683-5900 *SIC* 2844 2835

BERLITZ CORP p 175
7 Roszel Rd Fl 3 08540
Tel (207) 828-3768 *SIC* 8299 8748

BERLITZ LANGUAGES (UNITED STATES) INC p 175
7 Roszel Rd Fl 3 08540
Tel (609) 759-5371 *SIC* 8299 7389 2731

CHEMICAL RESOURCES INC p 293
103 Carnegie Ctr Ste 100 08540
Tel (609) 520-0000 *SIC* 5162 5169 2865

COMMUNITY OPTIONS INC p 349
16 Farber Rd 08540
Tel (609) 951-9900 *SIC* 8322

■ COVANCE INC p 383
210 Carnegie Ctr Ste 106 08540
Tel (609) 452-4440
SIC 8731 8734 8733 8732

▲ DERMA SCIENCES INC p 431
214 Carnegie Ctr Ste 300 08540
Tel (609) 514-4744 *SIC* 3842 2211 2834

DR REDDYS LABORATORIES INC p 455
107 College Rd E Ste 100 08540
Tel (908) 203-4900 *SIC* 5122 3089

EDUCATIONAL TESTING SERVICE INC p 479
660 Rosedale Rd 08540
Tel (609) 921-9000 *SIC* 8748 8732

■ GENON AMERICAS GENERATION LLC p 604
211 Carnegie Ctr 08540
Tel (609) 524-4500 *SIC* 4911

■ GENON ENERGY INC p 604
804 Carnegie Ctr 08540
Tel (609) 524-4500 *SIC* 4911

■ GENON ENERGY SERVICES LLC p 604
211 Carnegie Ctr 08540
Tel (609) 524-4500 *SIC* 4911

■ GENON MID-ATLANTIC LLC p 604
211 Carnegie Ctr 08540
Tel (609) 524-4500 *SIC* 4911

■ HEARTLAND PAYMENT SYSTEMS LLC p 679
300 Carnegie Ctr Ste 300 08540
Tel (609) 683-3831 *SIC* 7389 8721

INVENTIV HEALTH CLINICAL INC p 761
504 Carnegie Ctr 08540
Tel (609) 514-9400 *SIC* 8731

■ LOUISIANA GENERATING LLC p 880
211 Carnegie Ctr 08540
Tel (609) 524-4500 *SIC* 4911

MATHEMATICA INC p 919
600 Alexander Park # 100 08540
Tel (609) 799-3535 *SIC* 8732

MATHEMATICA POLICY RESEARCH INC p 919
600 Alexander Park 08540
Tel (609) 799-3535 *SIC* 8732

MIELE INC p 968
9 Independence Way 08540
Tel (609) 419-9898 *SIC* 5064

■ MUNICH HEALTH NORTH AMERICA INC p 1000
555 College Rd E 08540
Tel (609) 243-4200 *SIC* 6331

■ MUNICH RE AMERICA BROKERS INC p 1000
685 College Rd E 08540
Tel (609) 243-4900 *SIC* 6321 6311

■ MUNICH RE AMERICA CORP p 1000
555 College Rd E 08540
Tel (609) 243-4200 *SIC* 6331

■ MUNICH REINSURANCE AMERICA INC p 1000
555 College Rd E 08540
Tel (609) 243-4200 *SIC* 6331 6311

■ MUNICH-AMERICAN HOLDING CORP p 1000
555 College Rd E 08540
Tel (609) 243-4876 *SIC* 6331

NASSAU BROADCASTING PARTNERS LP p 1008
619 Alexander Rd Ste 300 08540
Tel (609) 452-9696 *SIC* 4832

NAVITAS INC p 1020
502 Carnegie Ctr Ste 100 08540
Tel (609) 720-1002 *SIC* 7379

NEOSTRATA CO INC p 1026
307 College Rd E 08540
Tel (609) 520-0715 *SIC* 5122

▲ NRG ENERGY INC p 1064
804 Carnegie Ctr 08540
Tel (609) 524-4500 *SIC* 4911

■ NRG NORTHEAST GENERATING LLC p 1064
211 Carnegie Ctr 08540
Tel (609) 524-4500 *SIC* 4911

■ NRG POWER MARKETING LLC p 1064
804 Carnegie Ctr 08540
Tel (609) 524-4500 *SIC* 4911 4924

■ NRG YIELD INC p 1064
804 Carnegie Ctr 08540
Tel (609) 524-4500 *SIC* 4911

ORC INTERNATIONAL INC p 1093
902 Carnegie Ctr Ste 220 08540
Tel (609) 452-5400 *SIC* 8732

PRINCETON PUBLIC SCHOOLS INC p 1177
25 Valley Rd 08540
Tel (609) 806-4204 *SIC* 8211

RANBAXY INC p 1207
600 College Rd E Ste 2100 08540
Tel (609) 720-9200 *SIC* 8741

RANBAXY PHARMACEUTICALS INC p 1207
600 College Rd E Ste 2100 08540
Tel (609) 720-9200 *SIC* 2834 5122

RCN TELECOM SERVICES LLC p 1212
650 College Rd E Ste 3100 08540
Tel (609) 452-8197 *SIC* 4841 7375 4813

■ ROCKWOOD HOLDINGS INC p 1245
100 Overlook Ctr Ste 101 08540
Tel (609) 514-0300 *SIC* 2819 2816

■ ROCKWOOD SPECIALTIES CONSOLIDATED INC p 1245
100 Overlook Ctr Ste 101 08540
Tel (609) 514-0300 *SIC* 5169

■ ROCKWOOD SPECIALTIES GROUP INC p 1245
100 Overlook Ctr Ste 101 08540
Tel (609) 514-0300 *SIC* 5169 2899

SANDOZ INC p 1278
100 College Rd W 08540
Tel (609) 627-8500 *SIC* 2834 5122

SENIOR PHS LIVING INC p 1304
13 Roszel Rd Ste C120 08540
Tel (609) 426-6802 *SIC* 8361 8052 8051

SES AMERICOM INC p 1308
4 Research Way 08540
Tel (609) 987-4000 *SIC* 4899

SES GLOBAL- AMERICAS INC p 1308
4 Research Way 08540
Tel (609) 987-4000 *SIC* 4899

SIEMENS CORPORATE RESEARCH INC p 1320
755 College Rd E 08540
Tel (609) 734-6500 *SIC* 8731 7373

SOLVAY USA INC p 1339
504 Carnegie Ctr 08540
Tel (609) 860-4000
SIC 2899 2869 2821 2087 2865

TECHNICOLOR USA INC p 1431
4 Research Way 08540
Tel (317) 587-3000 *SIC* 3651 3861 3661

TOTE INC p 1463
14 Nassau St Ste 3 08542
Tel (609) 454-3651 *SIC* 4731

TRAC INTERMODAL LLC p 1468
750 College Rd E 08540
Tel (609) 452-8900 *SIC* 7359 3715 5012

TRISTRATA INC p 1483
307 College Rd E 08540
Tel (609) 520-0715 *SIC* 5122

TRUSTEES OF PRINCETON UNIVERSITY p 1488
1 Nassau Hall 08544
Tel (609) 258-3000 *SIC* 8221

TYCO INTERNATIONAL MANAGEMENT CO LLC p 1496
9 Roszel Rd Ste 2 08540
Tel (609) 720-4200
SIC 3999 1711 1731 3669 3491

VATAMERICA LP p 1545
344 Nassau St 08540
Tel (609) 430-4960 *SIC* 8741

WITHUMSMITH+BROWN PC p 1619
506 Carnegie Ctr Ste 400 08540
Tel (609) 520-1188 *SIC* 8721

RAHWAY, NJ

P & J FUEL INC p 1102
2456 Saint Georges Ave 07065
Tel (732) 382-5100 *SIC* 5172

ROBERT WOOD JOHNSON UNIVERSITY HOSPITAL AT RAHWAY p 1242
865 Stone St 07065
Tel (732) 381-4200 *SIC* 8062

RAMSEY, NJ

ERASE INC p 507
107 Myrtle Ave 27 07446
Tel (201) 760-0189 *SIC* 8748

GLATT AIR TECHNIQUES INC p 614
20 Spear Rd 07446
Tel (201) 825-6308 *SIC* 5084

KONICA MINOLTA BUSINESS SOLUTIONS USA INC p 827
100 Williams Dr 07446
Tel (201) 825-4000 *SIC* 5044 5045

KONICA MINOLTA HOLDINGS USA INC p 827
100 Williams Dr 07446
Tel (201) 825-4000
SIC 5043 5065 5044 5047

OKONITE CO p 1080
102 Hilltop Rd 07446
Tel (201) 825-0300 *SIC* 3357 3315 3355

PRESTIGE OF BERGEN INC p 1173
50 Williams Dr 07446
Tel (201) 825-2700 *SIC* 5511 5521 5012

WURTH GROUP OF NORTH AMERICA INC p 1628
93 Grant St 07446
Tel (201) 818-8877 *SIC* 5013 5099 5072

WURTH USA INC p 1628
93 Grant St 07446
Tel (201) 825-2710 *SIC* 5013

RANCOCAS, NJ

INDEL INC p 736
10 Indel Ave 08073
Tel (609) 267-9000
SIC 3567 3548 3822 3541 3563

PEMBERTON FABRICATORS INC p 1128
30 Indel Ave 08073
Tel (609) 267-0922 *SIC* 3444 3824

RANDOLPH, NJ

COUNTY COLLEGE OF MORRIS p 375
214 Center Grove Rd 07869
Tel (973) 328-5000 *SIC* 8222

FARREN INTERNATIONAL LLC p 530
1578 Sussex Tpke 07869
Tel (800) 253-3203 *SIC* 4213 1796 6719

RARITAN, NJ

■ JANSSEN RESEARCH & DEVELOPMENT LLC p 777
920 Us Highway 202 08869
Tel (908) 704-4000 *SIC* 2834 8731

ORTHO-CLINICAL DIAGNOSTICS INC p 1096
1001 Us Highway 202 08869
Tel (908) 218-8000 *SIC* 2835 2834

RED BANK, NJ

HIGH POINT SAFETY AND INSURANCE MANAGEMENT CORP p 691
331 Newman Springs Rd # 304 07701
Tel (732) 978-6000 *SIC* 6411

▲ HOVNANIAN ENTERPRISES INC p 713
110 W Front St 07701
Tel (732) 747-7800
SIC 1521 1531 1522 6162 6361

INNOCOR FOAM TECHNOLOGIES LLC p 744
200 Schulz Dr Ste 2 07701
Tel (732) 263-0800 *SIC* 3086

INNOCOR INC p 744
200 Schulz Dr Ste 2 07701
Tel (844) 824-9348 *SIC* 2515 2392 3069

■ K HOVNANIAN COMPANIES OF NEW YORK INC p 798
10 Rte 35 07701
Tel (732) 747-7800 *SIC* 6531

■ K HOVNANIAN DEVELOPMENTS OF NEW JERSEY INC p 798
10 State Route 35 07701
Tel (732) 747-7800 *SIC* 1531

■ K HOVNANIAN DEVELOPMENTS OF NEW YORK INC p 798
10 State Route 35 07701
Tel (732) 747-7800 *SIC* 1531

■ K HOVNANIAN HOLDINGS NJ LLC p 798
110 W Front St 07701
Tel (732) 747-7800 *SIC* 6552

MASER CONSULTING PA p 915
331 Newman Springs Rd # 203 07701
Tel (732) 383-1950 *SIC* 8711 8742 8713

PACIFIC DUNLOP HOLDINGS (USA) LLC p 1104
200 Schulz Dr 07701
Tel (732) 345-5400 *SIC* 3069 3691

PACIFIC DUNLOP INVESTMENTS (USA) INC p 1104
200 Schulz Dr 07701
Tel (732) 345-5400 *SIC* 3069 3842

RIVERVIEW MEDICAL HOSPITAL p 1238
1 Riverview Plz 07701
Tel (732) 741-2700 *SIC* 8093

SUTHERLAND ASSET MANAGEMENT CORP p 1409
2 Bridge Ave Ste 322 07701
Tel (732) 978-7518 *SIC* 6162

TORCON INC p 1461
328 Newman Springs Rd # 5 07701
Tel (732) 704-9800 *SIC* 1542

VISITING NURSE ASSOCIATION OF CENTRAL JERSEY INC p 1561
176 Riverside Ave 07701
Tel (732) 747-1204 *SIC* 8082

RIDGEFIELD PARK, NJ

SAMSUNG C&T AMERICA INC p 1275
105 Challenger Rd Fl 3 07660
Tel (201) 229-4000 *SIC* 5169 6799 8742

SAMSUNG ELECTRONICS AMERICA INC p 1275
85 Challenger Rd 07660
Tel (201) 229-4000 *SIC* 5064 5065 5045

SAMSUNG OPTO-ELECTRONICS AMERICA INC p 1275
100 Challenger Rd Ste 700 07660
Tel (201) 325-2612 *SIC* 5043 7699 3861

SAMSUNG SDS AMERICA INC p 1275
100 Challenger Rd 07660
Tel (201) 229-4456 *SIC* 7372 7371

SPECIALTY RX INC p 1356
2 Bergen Tpke 07660
Tel (908) 241-6337 *SIC* 5122

RIDGEFIELD, NJ

UNITED ENVELOPE LLC p 1508
65 Railroad Ave Ste 1a 07657
Tel (201) 699-5800 *SIC* 2759 2677

RIDGEWOOD, NJ

VALLEY HEALTH SYSTEM INC p 1540
223 N Van Dien Ave 07450
Tel (201) 447-8000 *SIC* 8062 8099

VALLEY HOSPITAL INC p 1541
223 N Van Dien Ave 07450
Tel (201) 447-8000 *SIC* 8062

RINGOES, NJ

REAGENT CHEMICAL & RESEARCH INC p 1213
115 Rte 202 08551
Tel (908) 284-2800 SIC 3949 2819

RIVERDALE, NJ

CAMFIL USA INC p 245
1 N Corporate Dr 07457
Tel (973) 616-7300 SIC 3564 3569

ROCHELLE PARK, NJ

AVENUE STORES LLC p 137
365 W Passaic St Ste 230 07662
Tel (201) 845-0880 SIC 5621

GLASS GARDENS INC p 614
220 W Passaic St 07662
Tel (201) 843-1424 SIC 5411 5921

▲ ORBCOMM INC p 1092
395 W Passaic St Ste 3 07662
Tel (703) 433-6361 SIC 4899 8748

UNITED RETAIL GROUP INC p 1511
365 W Passaic St Ste 205 07662
Tel (201) 845-0880 SIC 5621

UNITED RETAIL GROUP INC p 1511
365 W Passaic St Ste 12 07662
Tel (201) 845-0880 SIC 5621

ROCKAWAY, NJ

ALLAN INDUSTRIES INC p 51
270 Us Highway 46 Ste E 07866
Tel (973) 586-9400 SIC 1521 7349 1799

MORETRENCH AMERICAN CORP p 988
100 Stickle Ave 07866
Tel (262) 652-4444 SIC 1629

■ PA ACQUISITION CORP p 1103
25 Green Pond Rd Ste 1 07866
Tel (973) 453-8600 SIC 5947 7389

■ PARTY CITY CORP p 1119
25 Green Pond Rd Ste 1 07866
Tel (973) 453-8600 SIC 6794 5947 7299

TATA CHEMICALS NORTH AMERICA INC p 1426
100 Enterprise Dr Ste 701 07866
Tel (973) 599-5500 SIC 2812

TITANIUM INDUSTRIES INC p 1456
18 Green Pond Rd Ste 1 07866
Tel (973) 983-1185 SIC 5051 3542 3462

WARNER CHILCOTT CORP p 1576
100 Enterprise Dr Ste 280 07866
Tel (862) 261-7000 SIC 2834 6719

ROCKLEIGH, NJ

CRESTRON ELECTRONICS INC p 392
15 Volvo Dr 07647
Tel (201) 767-3400
SIC 3571 3651 1731 3663 3499 3669

TAKASAGO INTERNATIONAL CORP (USA) p 1421
4 Volvo Dr 07647
Tel (201) 767-9001 SIC 2844

TRUE WORLD HOLDINGS LLC p 1486
24 Link Dr 07647
Tel (201) 750-0024 SIC 5146

VOLVO CARS OF NORTH AMERICA LLC p 1565
1 Volvo Dr 07647
Tel (201) 768-7300
SIC 5511 5013 6159 7515 3714

ROSELAND, NJ

■ A D P FOUNDATION p 5
1 Adp Blvd Ste 1 07068
Tel (973) 994-5000 SIC 8641

■ ADP ATLANTIC LLC p 24
1 Adp Blvd Ms420 07068
Tel (605) 809-4388 SIC 8721

AMANO USA HOLDINGS INC p 64
140 Harrison Ave 07068
Tel (973) 403-1900
SIC 3589 2842 3579 3559 5169 5087

ANNIN & CO p 92
105 Eisenhower Pkwy # 203 07068
Tel (973) 228-9400 SIC 2399

▲ AUTOMATIC DATA PROCESSING INC p 134
1 Adp Blvd Ste 1 07068
Tel (973) 974-5000 SIC 7374

BARRETT INDUSTRIES CORP p 157
3 Becker Farm Rd Ste 307 07068
Tel (973) 533-1001
SIC 1611 2951 4213 1799 1794

BARRETT PAVING MATERIALS INC p 157
3 Becker Farm Rd Ste 307 07068
Tel (973) 533-1001
SIC 1611 2951 4213 1799 1794

BOBST NORTH AMERICA INC p 196
146 Harrison Ave 07068
Tel (973) 226-8000 SIC 5084

CGI AMS p 285
75 Livingston Ave Ste 202 07068
Tel (972) 788-0400
SIC 7379 8748 7374 7371

■ CITI INVESTOR SERVICES INC p 310
105 Eisenhower Pkwy Ste 2 07068
Tel (973) 461-2500 SIC 6411 7374

CRUMP GROUP INC p 396
105 Eisenhower Pkwy Fl 4 07068
Tel (973) 461-2100 SIC 6411

LOWENSTEIN SANDLER LLP p 881
65 Livingston Ave Ste 2 07068
Tel (973) 597-2500 SIC 8111

MACK-CALI REALTY L P p 892
4 Becker Farm Rd Ste 104 07068
Tel (973) 577-2472 SIC 6798

MATAN B SETER FOUNDATION INC p 919
65 Livingston Ave 07068
Tel (973) 597-2510 SIC 8699

ROSELLE, NJ

PAMARCO TECHNOLOGIES LLC p 1110
235 E 11th Ave 07203
Tel (908) 241-1200 SIC 3555

RONELL INDUSTRIES INC p 1249
298 Cox St 07203
Tel (908) 245-5255 SIC 7349 2842

ROSENHAYN, NJ

F&S PRODUCE CO INC p 522
913 Bridgeton Ave 08352
Tel (856) 453-0316
SIC 0723 2099 2032 0181

RUTHERFORD, NJ

SGS NORTH AMERICA INC p 1310
301 Route 17 07070
Tel (201) 508-3000
SIC 8734 7389 8071 4499 4785

SGS US HOLDING INC p 1310
201 Route 17 07070
Tel (201) 508-3000 SIC 8734 6719 7389

SADDLE BROOK, NJ

■ ARROW FASTENER CO LLC p 113
271 Mayhill St 07663
Tel (201) 843-6900
SIC 3579 3315 3452 3542 2891 3586

DIAZ FOODS p 437
4 Rosol Ln 07663
Tel (404) 629-3616 SIC 2038

HITOUCH BUSINESS SERVICES LLC p 697
74 Kenny Pl 07663
Tel (201) 636-9900 SIC 5112 5021 5149

MALT PRODUCTS CORP p 900
88 Market St 07663
Tel (201) 845-4420 SIC 2083 2087

TINGUE BROWN & CO p 1455
535 N Midland Ave 07663
Tel (201) 796-4490 SIC 5087 3089 2394

SALEM, NJ

MANNINGTON MILLS INC p 902
75 Mannington Mills Rd 08079
Tel (856) 935-3000
SIC 3996 3253 2273 2435

SAYREVILLE, NJ

GERDAU AMERISTEEL SAYREVILLE INC p 608
N Crossman Rd 08872
Tel (732) 721-6600 SIC 3312

MIDDLESEX COUNTY UTILITIES AUTHORITY INC p 965
2571 Main St 08872
Tel (732) 721-3800 SIC 4952

SABERT CORP p 1264
2288 Main St 08872
Tel (800) 722-3781 SIC 3089

SECAUCUS, NJ

▲ CHILDRENS PLACE INC p 300
500 Plaza Dr Ste 400 07094
Tel (201) 558-2400 SIC 5641 5651

COMMAND WEB OFFSET CO INC p 344
100 Castle Rd 07094
Tel (201) 863-8100 SIC 2752 2732

CONTROL BUILDING SERVICES INC p 364
333 Meadowlands Pkwy Fl 1 07094
Tel (201) 864-1900 SIC 7349 0782

CORY JOSEPH HOLDING LLC p 373
150 Mdwlands Pkwy Fl 3 07094
Tel (201) 795-1000 SIC 4212

COSCO CONTAINER LINES AMERICAS INC p 373
100 Lighting Way Fl 3 07094
Tel (201) 422-0500 SIC 4731

DAFFYS INC p 408
Daffys Way 07094
Tel (201) 902-0800 SIC 5651

DELTA GALIL USA INC p 427
1 Harmon Plz Fl 5 07094
Tel (201) 392-9098 SIC 2341

E & J LAWRENCE CORP p 465
85 Metro Way 07094
Tel (201) 210-5577 SIC 5651

EYEA LLLP p 522
200 Plaza Dr Ste 2222 07094
Tel (201) 872-2200 SIC 8721

FABER COE & GREGG INC p 523
550 Madowlands Pkwy Ste 2 07094
Tel (201) 330-1515 SIC 5994 5499 5813

FERRAGAMO U S A INC p 538
700 Castle Rd 07094
Tel (201) 553-6100
SIC 5139 5136 5137 5621 5632

▲ FRESHPET INC p 579
400 Plaza Dr Fl 1 07094
Tel (201) 520-4000 SIC 2047

HARTZ MOUNTAIN CORP p 666
400 Plaza Dr Ste 400 07094
Tel (201) 271-4800 SIC 5199 3999

HARTZ MOUNTAIN INDUSTRIES INC p 666
400 Plaza Dr Ste 400 07094
Tel (201) 348-1200 SIC 6531

MHA LLC p 958
55 Meadowlands Pkwy 07094
Tel (201) 392-3200 SIC 8062

■ MIKASA INC p 968
1 Century Way 07094
Tel (866) 645-2721 SIC 5023 5099 5719

NATIONAL BASKETBALL ASSOCIATION INC p 1010
100 Plaza Dr Fl 3 07094
Tel (212) 407-8000 SIC 7941

NORTHSTAR TRAVEL MEDIA LLC p 1059
100 Lighting Way Ste 200 07094
Tel (201) 902-2000 SIC 2721 4789 4724

NYK GROUP AMERICAS INC p 1069
300 Lighting Way Ste 500 07094
Tel (201) 330-3000
SIC 4412 4731 4011 4491 7519

NYK LINE (NORTH AMERICA) INC p 1069
300 Lighting Way 4th 07094
Tel (201) 330-3000
SIC 4412 4731 4213 4011 7519 4491

ROSE BRAND WIPERS INC p 1250
4 Emerson Ln 07094
Tel (201) 809-1730 SIC 5049 2399

S S K CONSTRUCTORS JV p 1262
150 Meadowlands Pkwy Fl 3 07094
Tel (201) 867-5070 SIC 1622

SCHIAVONE CONSTRUCTION CO LLC p 1287
150 Meadowlands Pkwy # 2 07094
Tel (201) 867-5070 SIC 1622 1629

SEKISUI AMERICA CORP p 1301
666 5th St Fl 12t 07094
Tel (201) 423-7960 SIC 3086

SYMS CORP p 1414
1 Syms Way 07094
Tel (201) 902-9600 SIC 5651 5661

▲ VITAMIN SHOPPE INC p 1562
300 Harmon Meadow Blvd # 2 07094
Tel (201) 868-5959 SIC 5961 5499

■ XEROX HR SOLUTIONS LLC p 1631
200 Plaza Dr Nj 07094
Tel (201) 902-2300 SIC 8742

YUSEN LOGISTICS (AMERICAS) INC p 1640
300 Lighting Way Ste 600 07094
Tel (201) 553-3800 SIC 4724 4731

ZT GROUP INTL INC p 1644
333 Meadowlands Pkwy Fl 2 07094
Tel (201) 559-1000 SIC 7379

SEWAREN, NJ

WOROCO MANAGEMENT LLC p 1626
40 Woodbridge Ave Ste 3 07077
Tel (732) 855-7720 SIC 5172

SEWELL, NJ

DELAWARE VALLEY FLORAL GROUP INC p 424
520 Mantua Blvd 08080
Tel (800) 676-1212 SIC 5193 4213 4214

DELAWARE VALLEY WHOLESALE FLORIST INC p 424
520 Mantua Blvd 08080
Tel (856) 468-7000 SIC 5193

■ K-TRON INTERNATIONAL INC p 799
590 Woodbury Glassboro Rd 08080
Tel (856) 589-0500 SIC 3532 3535

RAY ANGELINI INC p 1209
105 Blckwood Barnsboro Rd 08080
Tel (856) 228-5566 SIC 1731 1711 8741

WASHINGTON TOWNSHIP BOARD OF EDUCATION p 1579
206 E Holly Ave 08080
Tel (856) 589-6644 SIC 8211

WASHINGTON TOWNSHIP PUBLIC SCHOOL DISTRICT p 1579
206 E Holly Ave 08080
Tel (856) 589-6644 SIC 8211

SHAMONG, NJ

LENAPE REGIONAL HIGH SCHOOL DISTRICT p 855
93 Willow Grove Rd 08088
Tel (609) 268-2588 SIC 8211

SHORT HILLS, NJ

CORPORATE TRADE INC p 372
51 John F Kennedy Pkwy 07078
Tel (973) 218-2551 SIC 7389

▲ DUN & BRADSTREET CORP p 461
103 Jfk Pkwy 07078
Tel (973) 921-5500 SIC 7323

■ DUN & BRADSTREET INC p 461
103 Jfk Pkwy 07078
Tel (973) 921-5500 SIC 7323

■ DUN & BRADSTREET INTERNATIONAL LTD p 461
103 Jfk Pkwy 07078
Tel (973) 921-5500 SIC 7323 8741

ENERGY CAPITAL PARTNERS II LLC p 497
51 John F Kennedy Pkwy # 200 07078
Tel (973) 671-6100 SIC 6799 4953 8711

ENERGY CAPITAL PARTNERS III LLC p 497
51 John F Kennedy Pkwy 07078
Tel (973) 671-6100 SIC 5211

GARDEN HOMES INC p 591
820 Morris Tpke Ste 301 07078
Tel (973) 467-5000 SIC 1531 6531

GARDEN PROPERTIES CORP p 591
820 Morris Tpke 07078
Tel (973) 467-5000 SIC 6531

▲ INVESTORS BANCORP INC p 761
101 Jfk Pkwy Ste 3 07078
Tel (973) 924-5100 SIC 6035

INVESTORS BANCORP MHC p 761
101 Jfk Pkwy Ste 3 07078
Tel (973) 376-5100 SIC 6036

■ INVESTORS BANK p 761
101 John F Kennedy Pkwy # 3 07078
Tel (973) 376-5100 SIC 6036

SHREWSBURY, NJ

METALLIX REFINING INC p 952
59 Avenue At The Cmn # 201 07702
Tel (732) 936-0050 SIC 3339

▲ WAYSIDE TECHNOLOGY GROUP INC p 1584
1157 Shrewsbury Ave 07702
Tel (732) 389-8950 SIC 5045 7373 7379

SKILLMAN, NJ

■ JOHNSON & JOHNSON CONSUMER INC p 790
199 Grandview Rd 08558
Tel (908) 874-1000 SIC 2834

SOMERS POINT, NJ

SHORE MEMORIAL HEALTH FOUNDATION INC p 1318
100 Medical Center Way 08244
Tel (609) 653-3500 SIC 8062

SHORE MEMORIAL HOSPITAL p 1318
100 Medical Center Way 08244
Tel (609) 653-3500 SIC 8062

SOMERS RELATED POINT LLC p 1339
50 Mays Landing Rd # 226 08244
Tel (609) 927-0441 SIC 7299 6531

SOMERSET, NJ

AUTOMANN INC p 134
850 Randolph Rd 08873
Tel (201) 529-4996 SIC 5013 3715

■ CARDINAL HEALTH SYSTEMS INC p 253
14 Schoolhouse Rd 08873
Tel (732) 537-6544 SIC 7372 2834

▲ CATALENT INC p 264
14 Schoolhouse Rd 08873
Tel (732) 537-6200 SIC 2834

■ CATALENT PHARMA SOLUTIONS INC p 264
14 Schoolhouse Rd 08873
Tel (732) 537-6200 SIC 2834 3841

EKORNES INC p 482
615 Pierce St 08873
Tel (732) 302-0097 SIC 5021

FERRERO U S A INC p 538
600 Cottontail Ln 08873
Tel (732) 764-9300 SIC 5145 2064

FRANKLIN TOWNSHIP BOARD OF EDUCATION p 575
1755 Amwell Rd 08873
Tel (732) 873-2400 SIC 8211

FRANKLIN TOWNSHIP PUBLIC SCHOOL DISTRICT OF SOMERSET p 575
1755 Amwell Rd 08873
Tel (732) 873-2400 SIC 8211

GAFFNEY-KROESE ELECTRICAL SUPPLY CORP p 589
50 Randolph Rd 08873
Tel (732) 885-9000 SIC 5063 5084 5085

GENLYTE THOMAS GROUP LLC p 604
200 Franklin Pk Sq Dr 08875
Tel (800) 825-5844 SIC 3646

HEALTH PRODUCTS RESEARCH INC p 675
500 Atrium Dr Ste 100 08873
Tel (908) 534-4148 SIC 8742 8732

MEDA PHARMACEUTICALS INC p 935
265 Davidson Ave Ste 400 08873
Tel (732) 564-2200 SIC 2834

▲ MEDICAL TRANSCRIPTION BILLING CORP p 937
7 Clyde Rd 08873
Tel (732) 873-5133 SIC 7372

NOVEL LABORATORIES INC p 1063
400 Campus Dr 08873
Tel (908) 603-6000 SIC 2834

PHARMSCRIPT LLC p 1141
150 Pierce St 08873
Tel (908) 389-1818 SIC 5122

■ **PTS INTERMEDIATE HOLDINGS LLC** p 1189
14 Schoolhouse Rd 08873
Tel (732) 537-6200 SIC 2834

RARITAN INC p 1209
400 Cottontail Ln 08873
Tel (732) 764-8886 SIC 3612 3577

ROTOR CLIP CO INC p 1252
187 Davidson Ave 08873
Tel (732) 469-7707 SIC 3429

SHI INTERNATIONAL CORP p 1316
290 Davidson Ave 08873
Tel (732) 764-8888 SIC 7371 7374

STAR MICRONICS AMERICA INC p 1378
65 Clyde Rd Ste G 08873
Tel (732) 623-5500 SIC 5065 5045

TERUMO AMERICAS HOLDING INC p 1440
2101 Cottontail Ln 08873
Tel (732) 302-4900 SIC 3841

VALOR GROUP LLC p 1542
245 Belmont Dr 08873
Tel (732) 357-2426 SIC 5043

VENTIV HEALTH INC p 1548
200 Cottontail Ln Ste J 08873
Tel (732) 537-4800 SIC 8742

VILLAGE OFFICE SUPPLY INC p 1557
600 Apgar Dr 08873
Tel (908) 526-0600 SIC 5112

SOMERVILLE, NJ

COUNTY OF SOMERSET p 382
20 Grove St 08876
Tel (908) 231-7000 SIC 9111

■ **ETHICON INC** p 511
Us Route 22 08876
Tel (732) 524-0400 SIC 3842

HAMON CORP p 656
58 E Main St 08876
Tel (908) 333-2000
SIC 1629 3564 3499 5084

■ **JOHNSON & JOHNSON MEDICAL INC** p 790
Us Rt 22 08876
Tel (908) 218-0707 SIC 3842

SOMERSET HEALTH CARE CORP p 1339
110 Rehill Ave 08876
Tel (908) 685-2200 SIC 8093 8011

SOMERSET MEDICAL CENTER p 1339
110 Rehill Ave 08876
Tel (908) 685-2200 SIC 8062

SOUTH AMBOY, NJ

■ **DCH AUTO GROUP (USA) INC** p 418
955 Route 9 N 08879
Tel (732) 727-9168
SIC 5511 7515 6512 6514

SOUTH HACKENSACK, NJ

DAZIAN LLC p 418
18 Central Blvd 07606
Tel (877) 232-9426 SIC 5131

DORAS NATURALS INC p 451
21 Empire Blvd 07606
Tel (201) 229-0500 SIC 5149

ICON EYEWEAR INC p 727
5 Empire Blvd 07606
Tel (201) 330-9333 SIC 5099

NATUREX INC p 1019
375 Huyler St 07606
Tel (201) 440-5000 SIC 2833

SOUTH ORANGE, NJ

MYERS GROUP L L C p 1004
74 Blanchard Rd 07079
Tel (973) 761-6414 SIC 3111

SETON HALL UNIVERSITY p 1308
400 S Orange Ave 07079
Tel (973) 761-9000 SIC 8221

SOUTH PLAINFIELD, NJ

BETT-A-WAY TRAFFIC SYSTEMS INC p 178
110 Sylvania Pl 07080
Tel (908) 222-2500 SIC 4731

BINDER MACHINERY CO INC p 183
2820 Hamilton Blvd 07080
Tel (908) 561-9000
SIC 5082 5084 7353 7699

BRENNTAG SPECIALTIES INC p 210
1000 Coolidge St 07080
Tel (800) 732-0562 SIC 5169 2816 2899

G & W LABORATORIES INC p 586
111 Coolidge St 07080
Tel (908) 753-2000 SIC 2834

KSI TRADING CORP p 831
100a Wade Ave 07080
Tel (908) 754-7154 SIC 5013

PETRA SYSTEMS INC p 1139
1 Cragwood Rd Ste 303 07080
Tel (908) 462-5200 SIC 5074 3671

TUMI HOLDINGS INC p 1491
1001 Durham Ave Ste 1b 07080
Tel (908) 756-4400 SIC 3161 3172 5948

TUMI INC p 1491
1001 Durham Ave Ste 1b 07080
Tel (908) 756-4400 SIC 5199 5948 3161

VENTION MEDICAL INC p 1548
6 Century Ln 07080
Tel (908) 561-0717 SIC 3841

WARE INDUSTRIES INC p 1575
400 Metuchen Rd 07080
Tel (908) 757-9000 SIC 3444

SOUTH RIVER, NJ

R & S PARTS AND SERVICE INC p 1201
7 Brick Plant Rd Ste C 08882
Tel (732) 525-5938 SIC 5531

SPARTA, NJ

HIGH POINT SOLUTIONS INC p 691
5 Gail Ct 07871
Tel (973) 940-0040 SIC 5045 7373

SPRINGFIELD, NJ

JMK AUTO SALES INC p 786
391-399 Rt 22 E 07081
Tel (973) 379-7744 SIC 7538 5511

OPERATING ENGINEERS LOCAL NO 825 WELFARE FUND p 1089
65 Springfield Ave Ste 2 07081
Tel (973) 921-1661 SIC 8711

PARTNERS PHARMACY LLC p 1118
50 Lawrence Rd 07081
Tel (908) 931-9111 SIC 5122

▲ **VILLAGE SUPER MARKET INC** p 1557
733 Mountain Ave 07081
Tel (973) 467-2200 SIC 5411

STRATFORD, NJ

KENNEDY HEALTH CARE FOUNDATION INC p 811
18 E Laurel Rd 08084
Tel (856) 661-5100
SIC 6733 4119 8051 6531 7361 8721

SUMMIT, NJ

▲ **CELGENE CORP** p 273
86 Morris Ave 07901
Tel (908) 673-9000 SIC 2834

HOSOKAWA MICRON INTERNATIONAL INC p 708
10 Chatham Rd 07901
Tel (908) 273-6360 SIC 3559

OLAM HOLDINGS PARTNERSHIP p 1080
25 Union Pl Fl 2 07901
Tel (908) 988-1960 SIC 8741

OVERLOOK HOSPITAL ASSOCIATION p 1099
99 Beauvoir Ave 07901
Tel (908) 522-2000 SIC 8621

UNION HOSPITAL p 1504
99 Beauvoir Ave 07901
Tel (973) 740-0607 SIC 8062

SWEDESBORO, NJ

ARTHUR H THOMAS CO p 114
1654 High Hill Rd 08085
Tel (856) 467-2000 SIC 3821 5049

GLOBAL TRADING ENTERPRISES LLC p 617
504 Sharptown Rd 08085
Tel (856) 223-9966 SIC 5147

POWELL ELECTRONICS INC p 1165
200 Commodore Dr 08085
Tel (856) 241-8000 SIC 3678

RASTELLI BROTHERS INC p 1209
300 Heron Dr 08085
Tel (856) 803-1100 SIC 5147 5421 2011

■ **VISTAR MIDATLANTIC** p 1562
1109 Commerce Blvd 100 08085
Tel (856) 294-0500 SIC 5145

WELLSHIRE FARMS INC p 1591
509 Woodstown Rd 08085
Tel (877) 467-2331 SIC 5149

TEANECK, NJ

ACTION ENVIRONMENTAL GROUP INC p 19
300 Frank W Burr Blvd 07666
Tel (212) 564-7600 SIC 4953

AURAMET TRADING LLC p 131
300 Frank W Burr Blvd # 24 07666
Tel (201) 905-5000 SIC 3339

▲ **BFI CO LLC** p 179
300 Frank W Burr Blvd # 21 07666
Tel (201) 329-7300 SIC 6211

▲ **COGNIZANT TECHNOLOGY SOLUTIONS CORP** p 334
500 Frank W Burr Blvd 07666
Tel (201) 801-0233 SIC 7371 7379 7372

FAIRLEIGH DICKINSON UNIVERSITY p 525
1000 River Rd 07666
Tel (800) 338-8803 SIC 8221

HANWHA HOLDINGS (USA) INC p 659
300 Frank W Burr Blvd # 52 07666
Tel (609) 655-2500 SIC 5169 5013 5084

HOLY NAME MEDICAL CENTER INC p 702
718 Teaneck Rd 07666
Tel (201) 833-3000 SIC 8062

KUMON NORTH AMERICA INC p 832
300 Frank W Burr Blvd # 6 07666
Tel (201) 928-0444 SIC 8299

NESS TECHNOLOGIES INC p 1026
300 Frank W Burr Blvd 07666
Tel (201) 488-7222 SIC 7371

NIPPON PAINT (USA) INC p 1044
300 Frank W Burr Blvd # 10 07666
Tel (201) 692-1111 SIC 2851

■ **PHIBRO ANIMAL HEALTH CORP** p 1142
300 Frank W Burr Blvd 07666
Tel (201) 329-7300
SIC 2819 5169 2899 2834

POSCO DAEWOO AMERICA CORP p 1163
300 Frank W Burr Blvd 07666
Tel (201) 591-8000
SIC 5131 5051 5169 5015

UNIVISION TELEVISION GROUP INC p 1528
500 Frank W Burr Blvd # 20 07666
Tel (201) 287-4141 SIC 4833

TETERBORO, NJ

A & E STORES INC p 4
1000 Huyler St 07608
Tel (201) 393-0600
SIC 5621 8721 4226 7389

PARTY RENTAL LTD p 1119
275 North St 07608
Tel (201) 727-4700 SIC 7359

SUPERIOR PRINTING INK CO INC p 1407
100 North St 07608
Tel (201) 478-5600 SIC 2893 2851

SWIFT ELECTRICAL SUPPLY CO p 1412
100 Hollister Rd Unit C1 07608
Tel (201) 462-0900 SIC 5063

SYMRISE INC p 1414
300 North St 07608
Tel (201) 462-5559 SIC 2869

THOROFARE, NJ

ARAMSCO HOLDINGS INC p 102
1480 Grand View Ave 08086
Tel (856) 686-7700
SIC 5085 5136 5084 5139

J AMBROGI FOOD DISTRIBUTION INC p 770
1400 Metropolitan Ave 08086
Tel (856) 845-0377 SIC 5141

TINTON FALLS, NJ

AASKI TECHNOLOGY INC p 8
1 Radar Way 07724
Tel (732) 493-1700 SIC 8711

▲ **COMMVAULT SYSTEMS INC** p 350
1 Commvault Way 07724
Tel (732) 870-4000 SIC 7373 7372 7376

HATTERAS PRESS INC p 668
56 Park Rd 07724
Tel (732) 935-9800 SIC 2752 2796

TDK-LAMBDA AMERICAS INC p 1429
405 Essex Rd 07753
Tel (732) 922-9300 SIC 3629

TITUSVILLE, NJ

■ **JANSSEN PHARMACEUTICALS INC** p 777
1125 Trnton Harbourton Rd 08560
Tel (609) 730-2000 SIC 2833 2834

TOMS RIVER, NJ

BOARD OF EDUCATION OF TOMS RIVER SCHOOLS (INC) p 195
1144 Hooper Ave Ste 304 08753
Tel (732) 505-5500 SIC 8211

COMMUNITY MEDICAL CENTER INC p 349
99 Route 37 W 08755
Tel (732) 557-8000 SIC 8062

COMMUNITY SURGICAL SUPPLY OF TOMS RIVER INC p 350
1390 Rte 37 W 08755
Tel (732) 349-2990 SIC 5047 7352 5912

COUNTY OF OCEAN p 380
101 Hooper Ave 08753
Tel (732) 929-2101 SIC 9111

HEYCO PRODUCTS INC p 688
1800 Industrial Way 08755
Tel (732) 286-4336 SIC 3351 3679

MIDJERSEY DISPOSAL INC p 965
1298 Industrial Way 08755
Tel (732) 341-6100 SIC 4212 4953

■ **OCEANFIRST BANK** p 1073
975 Hooper Ave 08753
Tel (732) 240-4500 SIC 6035

▲ **OCEANFIRST FINANCIAL CORP** p 1073
975 Hooper Ave 08753
Tel (732) 240-4500 SIC 6035

PERLMART INC p 1136
954 Route 166 Ste 1 08753
Tel (732) 341-0700 SIC 5411 5912

TOMS RIVER REGIONAL SCHOOLS p 1460
1144 Hooper Ave Ste 304 08753
Tel (732) 505-5500 SIC 8211 8741

TOTOWA, NJ

BC INTERNATIONAL GROUP INC p 163
922 Riverview Dr 07512
Tel (973) 826-1140 SIC 5632

HMP SERVICES HOLDING INC p 698
721 Union Blvd 07512
Tel (973) 812-0400 SIC 5084 5199

PRECISION CUSTOM COATINGS LLC p 1168
200 Maltese Dr 07512
Tel (973) 785-4390 SIC 2295

SPIRAL BINDING CO INC p 1359
1 Maltese Dr 07512
Tel (973) 256-0666
SIC 2789 3083 5112 2891

STAR STAINLESS SCREW CO p 1378
30 W End Rd 07512
Tel (973) 256-2300 SIC 5072

TRENTON, NJ

BAI BRANDS LLC p 145
1800 E State St Ste 153 08609
Tel (609) 586-0500 SIC 2086

BOARD OF EDUCATION OF CITY OF TRENTON (INC) p 195
108 N Clinton Ave 08609
Tel (609) 656-4900 SIC 8211

■ **BREYUT CONVALESCENT CENTER INC** p 210
2240 Whthrse Mrcrville Rd 08619
Tel (609) 586-7500 SIC 8051 8069

CAPITAL HEALTH SYSTEM INC p 249
750 Brunswick Ave 08638
Tel (609) 394-6000 SIC 8062

■ **CHARTERX INC** p 291
18 W Piper Ave 08628
Tel (800) 579-1694 SIC 4512

CITY OF TRENTON p 319
319 E State St 08608
Tel (609) 989-3030 SIC 9111

COMMERCE & ECONOMIC GROWTH COMMISSION NEW JERSEY p 344
20 W State St 08608
Tel (609) 292-1800 SIC 9611

CONGOLEUM CORP p 356
3500 Quakerbridge Rd 08619
Tel (609) 584-3000 SIC 3081 5713 8741

COUNTY OF MERCER p 379
640 S Broad St 08611
Tel (609) 989-6502 SIC 9111

DIOCESE OF TRENTON p 441
701 Lawrenceville Rd 08648
Tel (609) 406-7400 SIC 8661

EXECUTIVE OFFICE OF STATE OF NEW JERSEY p 518
125 W State St 08608
Tel (609) 292-6000 SIC 9111

▲ **FIRST BANK OF NEW JERSEY** p 545
2465 Kuser Rd 08690
Tel (609) 528-4400 SIC 6029 6021

FIRST CHOICE BANK p 545
669 Whitehead Rd 08648
Tel (609) 454-0338 SIC 6021

HAMILTON TOWNSHIP BOARD OF EDUCATION p 655
90 Park Ave 08690
Tel (609) 631-4100 SIC 8211

HAMILTON TOWNSHIP SCHOOL DISTRICT p 655
90 Park Ave 08690
Tel (609) 631-4100 SIC 8211

HEAVY & GENERAL LABORERS LOCAL 472 & 172 FUNDS OF NJ p 679
604 Us Highway 206 08610
Tel (609) 291-9197 SIC 8631

HIBBERT CO p 690
400 Pennington Ave 08618
Tel (609) 392-0478 SIC 7331 7389

■ **HUTCHINSON INDUSTRIES INC** p 722
460 Southard St 08638
Tel (609) 394-1010 SIC 3069

JUDICIARY COURTS OF STATE OF NEW JERSEY p 797
25 Market St 08611
Tel (609) 984-0627 SIC 9211

MEADOWGATE TECHNOLOGIES LLC p 934
171 Jersey St Ste 1 08611
Tel (609) 393-3618 SIC 5045 8711

MERCER COUNTY COMMUNITY COLLEGE p 944
1200 Old Trenton Rd 08690
Tel (609) 586-4800 SIC 8222

NEW JERSEY COMMISSION ON HIGHER EDUCATION p 1031
20 W State St Fl 7 08608
Tel (609) 292-4310 SIC 9411

NEW JERSEY DEPARTMENT OF ENVIRONMENTAL PROTECTION p 1031
401 E State St 08608
Tel (609) 292-2885 SIC 9512 9511

NEW JERSEY DEPARTMENT OF HEALTH p 1031
369 S Warren St 08608
Tel (609) 292-6915 SIC 9431

NEW JERSEY DEPARTMENT OF HUMAN SERVICES p 1031
222 S Warren St 08608
Tel (609) 292-3717 SIC 9441

NEW JERSEY DEPARTMENT OF LABOR AND WORKFORCE DEVELOPMENT p 1031
1 John Fitch Plz Fl 13 08611
Tel (609) 292-2323 SIC 9651

NEW JERSEY DEPARTMENT OF TREASURY p 1031
125 W State St 08608
Tel (609) 292-6748 SIC 9311

NEW JERSEY DEPT OF COMMUNITY AFFAIRS p 1031
101 S Broad St 08608
Tel (609) 292-6420 SIC 9441

NEW JERSEY DEPT OF LAW & PUBLIC SAFETY p 1031
25 Market St Fl 8 08611
Tel (609) 292-4925 SIC 9222 9221

NEW JERSEY EDUCATION ASSOCIATION INC p 1031
180 W State St 08608
Tel (609) 599-4561 SIC 8621

NEW JERSEY HOUSING AND MORTGAGE FINANCE AGENCY CJ p 1031
637 S Clinton Ave 08611
Tel (609) 278-7400 SIC 6162 9199

NEW JERSEY SCHOOLS DEVELOPMENT AUTHORITY p 1031
32 E Front St 08608
Tel (609) 943-5955 SIC 1542

NJ DEPARTMENT OF CORRECTIONS p 1045
Stuyvsant Av Whttlesey Rd Whittlesey 08618
Tel (609) 292-2162 SIC 9223

ST FRANCIS MEDICAL CENTER p 1366
601 Hamilton Ave 08629
Tel (609) 599-5000 SIC 8062

STATE DEPARTMENT OF COMMUNITY AFFAIRS p 1380
101 S Broad St 08608
Tel (609) 292-6420 SIC 9441

STATE OF NEW JERSEY p 1382
125 W State St 08608
Tel (609) 396-4657 SIC 9111

TRENTON PUBLIC SCHOOL DISTRICT p 1476
108 N Clinton Ave 08609
Tel (609) 656-4900 SIC 8211

TURNERSVILLE, NJ

KENNEDY UNIVERSITY HOSPITAL INC p 811
435 Hurffvl Cross Keys Rd 08012
Tel (856) 582-2500 SIC 8221

TWP WASHINTON, NJ

■ ORITANI BANK p 1095
370 Pascack Rd 07676
Tel (201) 664-5400 SIC 6036

▲ ORITANI FINANCIAL CORP p 1095
370 Pascack Rd 07676
Tel (201) 664-5400 SIC 6022

UNION, NJ

ADVANCED BEVERAGE INC p 25
1835 Burnet Ave Ste 2 07083
Tel (908) 686-3666 SIC 5962

AMERICAN CARGO EXPRESS INC p 69
2345 Vauxhall Rd 07083
Tel (908) 351-3400 SIC 4789

▲ BED BATH & BEYOND INC p 167
650 Liberty Ave 07083
Tel (908) 688-0888 SIC 5719 5947 5999

■ BED N BATH STORES INC p 167
650 Liberty Ave Ste 2 07083
Tel (908) 688-0888 SIC 6719

BOARD OF EDUCATION OF TOWNSHIP OF UNION p 195
2369 Morris Ave 07083
Tel (908) 810-0492 SIC 8211

■ CHRISTMAS TREE SHOPS INC p 303
650 Liberty Ave 07083
Tel (908) 688-0888 SIC 5331

■ COMCAST CABLEVISION OF NEW JERSEY INC p 343
800 Rahway Ave 07083
Tel (908) 206-8640 SIC 4841 1731 7375

DARTAGNAN INC p 413
600 Green Ln 07083
Tel (973) 344-0565
SIC 5147 5148 5149 2011

■ ELIZABETHTOWN GAS CO p 487
1 Elizabethtown Plz 07083
Tel (908) 289-5000 SIC 4932 4924

KEAN UNIVERSITY REALTY FOUNDATION INC p 807
1000 Morris Ave Ste 1 07083
Tel (908) 527-2000 SIC 8221

MINDLANCE INC p 972
1095 Morris Ave Unit 101a 07083
Tel (201) 386-5400 SIC 8742

PAIGE ELECTRIC CO LP p 1108
1160 Springfield Rd 07083
Tel (908) 687-7810 SIC 5063 3699

PEERLESS BEVERAGE CO p 1127
1000 Floral Ave 07083
Tel (908) 351-0101 SIC 5181

■ PIVOTAL UTILITY HOLDINGS INC p 1152
1085 Morris Ave Ste 1 07083
Tel (908) 289-5000 SIC 4924

TIMCO INC p 1454
2285 Us Highway 22 W 07083
Tel (908) 964-1600 SIC 5511

USI SERVICES GROUP INC p 1535
51 Progress St 07083
Tel (973) 376-6000 SIC 7349

UPPER SADDLE RIVER, NJ

CLIFFORD PAPER INC p 326
600 E Crescent Ave # 301 07458
Tel (201) 934-5115 SIC 5111

MINWAX GROUP INC p 974
10 Montinview Rd Ste N300 07458
Tel (201) 818-7500 SIC 2851

PEARSON EDUCATION INC p 1126
1 Lake St 07458
Tel (201) 236-7000 SIC 7371

VINELAND, NJ

DANDREA PRODUCE INC p 411
3665 N Mill Rd 08360
Tel (856) 205-1830 SIC 5148

FALASCA MECHANICAL INC p 526
3329 N Mill Rd 08360
Tel (856) 794-2010 SIC 1711

GERRESHEIMER GLASS INC p 609
537 Crystal Ave 08360
Tel (856) 692-3600 SIC 3221

INSPIRA HEALTH NETWORK INC p 746
2950 College Dr Ste 2d 08360
Tel (856) 641-8680 SIC 8741 8062

KIMBLE CHASE LIFE SCIENCE AND RESEARCH PRODUCTS LLC p 818
1022 Spruce St 08360
Tel (865) 717-2600 SIC 3231

MCCOLLISTERS TRANSPORTATION SYSTEMS OF NEW JERSEY p 927
1344 N West Blvd 08360
Tel (800) 257-9595 SIC 4213 4225 4214

OMNI BAKING CO LLC p 1084
2621 Freddy Ln Bldg 7 08360
Tel (856) 205-1485 SIC 2051

RIGGINS INC p 1234
3938 S Main Rd 08360
Tel (856) 825-7600 SIC 5171

■ SUN NATIONAL BANK p 1400
226 W Landis Ave Ste 1 08360
Tel (800) 786-9066 SIC 6021

VINELAND BOARD OF EDUCATION p 1557
625 E Plum St 08360
Tel (856) 207-6229 SIC 8211

VINELAND PUBLIC SCHOOLS p 1558
625 E Plum St 08360
Tel (856) 794-6700 SIC 8211

VOORHEES, NJ

■ AMERICAN INDUSTRIAL WATER LLC p 74
1025 Laurel Oak Rd 08043
Tel (856) 346-8200 SIC 1629

■ AMERICAN INTERNATIONAL WATER SERVICES CO p 75
1025 Laurel Oak Rd 08043
Tel (856) 346-8200 SIC 4941

▲ AMERICAN WATER WORKS CO INC p 81
1025 Laurel Oak Rd 08043
Tel (856) 346-8200 SIC 4941 1629 1623

HALE TRAILER BRAKE & WHEEL INC p 653
Cooper Rd Rr 73 08043
Tel (800) 232-6535 SIC 5511 7539 5531

KENNEDY HEALTH SYSTEM INC p 811
1099 White Horse Rd 08043
Tel (856) 566-5200 SIC 8062

KENNEDY MEMORIAL HOSPITAL UNIVERSITY MEDICAL CENTER INC p 811
1099 White Horse Rd Fl 3 08043
Tel (856) 566-2000 SIC 8062

TATEM BROWN FAMILY PRACTICE p 1426
2225 E Evesham Rd Ste 101 08043
Tel (856) 795-7075 SIC 8011

UNITED STATES COLD STORAGE INC p 1512
201 Laurel Rd Ste 400 08043
Tel (856) 354-8181 SIC 2097 4222

WALL TOWNSHIP, NJ

AIR CRUISERS CO LLC p 38
1747 State Route 34 07727
Tel (732) 681-3527
SIC 2531 3069 3728 2399

■ CENTENNIAL PUERTO RICO OPERATIONS CORP p 275
3349 State Route 138 A 07719
Tel (732) 556-2200 SIC 4812

DIALIGHT CORP p 436
1501 State Route 34 07727
Tel (732) 919-3119 SIC 3679 3674

GROUNDWATER AND ENVIRONMENTAL SERVICES INC p 641
1599 Rte 34 Ste 1 07727
Tel (800) 220-3068 SIC 8748

HANSON AGGREGATES WRP INC p 659
1333 Campus Pkwy 07753
Tel (972) 653-5500
SIC 3281 3272 2951 1442

JAG COMPANIES INC p 776
1433 State Route 34 Ste 5 07727
Tel (732) 557-6100
SIC 1623 1622 1629 1611

K-C INTERNATIONAL LLC p 799
1800 Rte 34 Ste 401 07719
Tel (732) 202-9500 SIC 5093

■ NEW JERSEY NATURAL GAS CO p 1031
1415 Wyckoff Rd 07727
Tel (732) 938-1000 SIC 4924

▲ NEW JERSEY RESOURCES CORP p 1031
1415 Wyckoff Rd 07727
Tel (732) 938-1480 SIC 4924

NORTHEAST REMSCO CONSTRUCTION INC p 1055
1433 State Route 34 Ste 6 07727
Tel (732) 557-6100
SIC 1623 1622 1629 1611

RALPH CLAYTON & SONS LLC p 1206
1355 Campus Pkwy 07753
Tel (732) 363-1995 SIC 5032

ROXBORO HOLDINGS INC p 1254
1501 State Route 34 07727
Tel (732) 919-3119
SIC 3643 3679 3993 3823 3674

SENIOR SPRINGPOINT LIVING INC p 1304
4814 Outlook Dr Ste 201 07753
Tel (609) 987-8900 SIC 8059 8741

STUDENT TRANSPORTATION OF AMERICA INC p 1394
3349 Hwy 138 07719
Tel (732) 280-4200 SIC 4151

WWRD US LLC p 1629
1330 Campus Pkwy 07753
Tel (732) 938-5800 SIC 5023

ZODIAC US CORP p 1644
1747 State Route 34 07727
Tel (732) 681-3527 SIC 3728

WALLINGTON, NJ

FARMLAND DAIRIES LLC p 530
520 Main Ave 07057
Tel (973) 777-2500 SIC 5143 2026 2023

WANAQUE, NJ

NORTH JERSEY DISTRICT WATER SUPPLY COMMISSION p 1052
1 F A Orechio Dr 07465
Tel (973) 831-6212 SIC 4971 4941

WARREN, NJ

ADVANTEDGE HEALTHCARE SOLUTIONS INC p 27
30 Technology Dr Ste 1n 07059
Tel (908) 279-8111 SIC 8742

CHUBB & SON INC p 304
15 Mountainview Rd 07059
Tel (908) 903-2000 SIC 6399

CHUBB CAPITAL CORP p 304
15 Mountainview Rd 07059
Tel (908) 903-2000 SIC 6321

CHUBB CORP p 304
15 Mountainview Rd 07059
Tel (908) 903-2000 SIC 6331

CHUBB GROUP OF INSURANCE COMPANIES p 304
15 Mountainview Rd 07059
Tel (908) 903-2000 SIC 6331

FEDERAL INSURANCE CO p 535
15 Mountainview Rd 07059
Tel (908) 903-2000 SIC 6411

GLAXOSMITHKLINE CONSUMER HEALTHCARE LP p 614
184 Libery Corner Rd 07059
Tel (251) 591-4188 SIC 5122

GSK CONSUMER HEALTHCARE p 643
184 Liberty Corner Rd # 2 07059
Tel (973) 503-8000 SIC 2834

HORIZON GROUP USA INC p 707
45 Technology Dr 07059
Tel (908) 810-1111 SIC 5092

JNET COMMUNICATIONS LLC p 786
25 Independence Blvd # 103 07059
Tel (203) 951-6400 SIC 4899 1731

MITSUI SUMITOMO INSURANCE CO OF AMERICA p 978
15 Independence Blvd 1100a 07059
Tel (908) 604-2900 SIC 6331

P C BOHLER ENGINEERING p 1102
35 Technology Dr Ste 5 07059
Tel (908) 222-0023 SIC 8711

PAULUS SOKOLOWSKI & SARTOR ENGINEERING A PROFESSIONAL CORP p 1122
67b Mountain Blvd Ext 07059
Tel (732) 560-9700 SIC 8711 8748 8712

■ VIRGIN MOBILE USA INC p 1558
10 Independence Blvd # 200 07059
Tel (908) 607-4000 SIC 4812

WASHINGTON, NJ

ALBEA AMERICAS INC p 46
191 State Route 31 N 07882
Tel (908) 689-3000 SIC 3312

WATCHUNG, NJ

COWORX STAFFING SERVICES LLC p 386
1375 Plainfield Ave Ste 1 07069
Tel (908) 757-5300 SIC 7361 8721

WAYNE, NJ

BMCA HOLDINGS CORP p 194
1361 Alps Rd 07470
Tel (973) 628-3000 SIC 2493

BP LUBRICANTS USA INC p 205
1500 Valley Rd 07470
Tel (973) 633-2200 SIC 2992

ELRAC LLC p 489
1550 Route 23 07470
Tel (973) 709-2499
SIC 7514 7515 5511 5521

G-I HOLDINGS INC p 587
1361 Alps Rd 07470
Tel (973) 628-3000 SIC 2869 2843 3295

HAIER AMERICA CO LLC p 653
1800 Valley Rd 07470
Tel (973) 617-1800 SIC 5064

HAIER AMERICA TRADING LLC p 653
1800 Valley Rd 07470
Tel (973) 617-1800 SIC 5064

IDEAVILLAGE PRODUCTS CORP p 729
155 Route 46 W Fl 4 07470
Tel (973) 826-8400 SIC 5961

■ INTERNATIONAL SPECIALTY PRODUCTS INC p 757
1361 Alps Rd 07470
Tel (859) 815-3333
SIC 2869 2821 2843 2842 2899

ISP CHEMICALS INC p 767
1361 Alps Rd 07470
Tel (973) 628-4000 SIC 2869

KBWB OPERATIONS-RICE LLC p 806
1120 Alps Rd 07470
Tel (973) 339-8899 SIC 8051 8361

KONICA MINOLTA HEALTHCARE AMERICAS INC p 827
411 Newark Pompton Tpke 07470
Tel (973) 633-1500 SIC 5047 3861 3845

MANE USA INC p 901
60 Demarest Dr 07470
Tel (973) 633-5533 SIC 2869

MAQUET CARDIOVASCULAR US SALES LLC p 904
45 Barbour Pond Dr 07470
Tel (201) 995-8700 SIC 5047

MAQUET INC p 904
45 Barbour Pond Dr 07470
Tel (973) 709-7000 SIC 5047

SILVER STAR SOLUTIONS-KNIGHT PROTECTIVE SERVICE-JOINT VENTURE LLC p 1324
59 Osceola Rd 07470
Tel (201) 847-9148 SIC 7381

ST JOSEPHS WAYNE HOSPITAL INC p 1369
224 Hamburg Tpke 07470
Tel (973) 942-6900 SIC 8062

TOYS "R" US INC p 1467
1 Geoffrey Way 07470
Tel (973) 617-3500
SIC 5945 5734 5999 5735 5641 5941

TOYS "R" US PROPERTY CO II LLC p 1467
1 Geoffrey Way 07470
Tel (973) 617-3500 SIC 6512

TOYS "R" US-DELAWARE INC p 1467
1 Geoffrey Way 07470
Tel (973) 617-3500 SIC 5945 5999 5641

▲ VALLEY NATIONAL BANCORP p 1541
1455 Valley Rd Ste 3 07470
Tel (973) 305-8800 SIC 6021

■ VALLEY NATIONAL BANK p 1541
1455 Valley Rd Ste 3 07470
Tel (973) 696-4020 SIC 6021 6162

VNB MORTGAGE SERVICES INC p 1563
1720 Rte 23 07470
Tel (973) 696-2813 SIC 6021

WAYNE PUBLIC LIBRARY INC p 1584
461 Valley Rd 07470
Tel (973) 694-4272 SIC 8231

WAYNE TOWNSHIP BOARD OF EDUCATION p 1584
50 Nellis Dr 07470
Tel (973) 633-3000 SIC 8211

WAYNE TOWNSHIP PUBLIC SCHOOLS p 1584
50 Nellis Dr 07470
Tel (973) 633-3000 SIC 8211

WILLIAM PATERSON UNIVERSITY p 1610
300 Pompton Rd 07470
Tel (973) 720-2000 SIC 8221

WEEHAWKEN, NJ

HANOVER DIRECT INC p 658
1200 Harbor Blvd Fl 9 07086
Tel (201) 863-7300
SIC 5712 5961 7389 2211 2221

SWATCH GROUP U S INC p 1411
1200 Harbor Blvd Fl 7 07086
Tel (201) 271-1400
SIC 5063 3625 5094 3873

WEST CALDWELL, NJ

COMMUNITY EDUCATION CENTERS INC p 348
35 Fairfield Pl 07006
Tel (973) 226-2900 SIC 8744

LTS LOHMANN THERAPY SYSTEMS CORP p 883
21 Henderson Dr 07006
Tel (973) 575-5170 SIC 2834

R & R MARKETING LLC p 1201
10 Patton Dr 07006
Tel (973) 228-5100 SIC 5182

RICOH AMERICAS HOLDINGS INC p 1233
5 Dedrick Pl 07006
Tel (973) 882-2000 SIC 5044 5065 5043

RICOH CORP p 1233
5 Dedrick Pl 07006
Tel (973) 882-2000 SIC 5065

RLB FOOD DISTRIBUTORS LP p 1239
2 Dedrick Pl Cn2285 07006
Tel (973) 575-9526 SIC 5148 5141

VITAQUEST INTERNATIONAL LLC p 1563
8 Henderson Dr 07006
Tel (973) 575-9200
SIC 2834 5149 5122 8742

WEST DEPTFORD, NJ

ALBERT TIRE CO p 46
39 Phoenix Dr 08086
Tel (856) 663-0574 SIC 5014

CENTO FINE FOODS INC p 277
100 Cento Blvd 08086
Tel (856) 853-7800 SIC 5141

CHECKPOINT SYSTEMS INC p 292
101 Wolf Dr 08086
Tel (856) 848-1800 SIC 3699 3812 3663

WEST LONG BRANCH, NJ

MONMOUTH UNIVERSITY p 984
400 Cedar Ave 07764
Tel (732) 571-3400 SIC 8221

WEST NEW YORK, NJ

JID TRANSPORTATION LLC p 785
158 61st St Apt 2 07093
Tel (201) 362-0841 SIC 3713 4212 7363

WEST NEW YORK SCHOOL DISTRICT p 1595
6028 Broadway 07093
Tel (201) 553-4000 SIC 8211

WEST ORANGE, NJ

BARNABAS HEALTH INC p 155
95 Old Short Hills Rd 07052
Tel (973) 322-4018 SIC 8082 8099

BARNABAS RWJ HEALTH INC p 155
95 Old Short Hills Rd 07052
Tel (973) 322-4000 SIC 8399

■ KESSLER INSTITUTE FOR REHABILITATION INC p 814
1199 Pleasant Valley Way 07052
Tel (973) 731-3600 SIC 8069 8093

■ KESSLER REHABILITATION CORP p 814
1199 Pleasant Valley Way 07052
Tel (973) 731-3600 SIC 8062

▲ LINCOLN EDUCATIONAL SERVICES CORP p 866
200 Executive Dr Ste 340 07052
Tel (973) 736-9340 SIC 8222

■ LINCOLN TECHNICAL INSTITUTE INC p 868
200 Executive Dr Ste 340 07052
Tel (718) 246-4001 SIC 8222

■ PATIENT CARE INC p 1120
300 Executive Dr Ste 175 07052
Tel (973) 243-6299 SIC 8082

SAINT BARNABAS CORP p 1268
95 Old Short Hills Rd 07052
Tel (973) 322-5000 SIC 8062 8082

WEST WINDSOR, NJ

WEST WINDSOR-PLAINSBORO REGIONAL SCHOOL DISTRICT p 1596
321 Village Rd E 08550
Tel (609) 716-5000 SIC 8211

WESTAMPTON, NJ

OAKS INTEGRATED CARE INC p 1071
770 Woodlane Rd Ste 23 08060
Tel (609) 267-5928 SIC 8322

PARIS CORP OF NEW JERSEY p 1115
800 Highland Dr 08060
Tel (609) 265-9200 SIC 5112 2752 5063

WESTFIELD, NJ

ATLANTIC CONTAINER LINE AB p 126
50 Cardinal Dr 07090
Tel (908) 518-5300 SIC 4412

ROMARK LOGISTICS LLC p 1249
822 South Ave W 07090
Tel (908) 789-2800 SIC 4225 4789 2631

WESTVILLE, NJ

BROWNS SUPER STORES INC p 220
700 Delsea Dr 08093
Tel (856) 933-7000 SIC 5411

CORNELL & CO INC p 370
224 Cornell Ln 08093
Tel (856) 742-1900 SIC 1542 1541

WHARTON, NJ

CUSTOMIZED DISTRIBUTION SERVICES INC p 403
20 Harry Shupe Blvd 07885
Tel (973) 366-5090 SIC 4225

TRI-COASTAL DESIGN GROUP INC p 1477
40 Harry Shupe Blvd 07885
Tel (973) 560-0300 SIC 5137 5199

WHIPPANY, NJ

800-JR CIGAR INC p 4
301 State Route 10 07981
Tel (973) 884-9555 SIC 5194 5993 5961

BAYER HEALTHCARE LLC p 161
100 Bayer Blvd 07981
Tel (862) 404-3000
SIC 2834 8731 3845 3841

BAYER HEALTHCARE PHARMACEUTICALS INC p 161
100 Bayer Blvd 07981
Tel (862) 404-3000 SIC 2834 3841

BERLIN SCHERING INC p 175
100 Bayer Blvd 07981
Tel (862) 404-3000 SIC 2834 3841

■ BOLLINGER INC p 198
200 Jefferson Park 07981
Tel (800) 526-1379 SIC 6411

■ BREEZE-EASTERN LLC p 209
35 Melanie Ln 07981
Tel (973) 602-1001 SIC 3728 3563 3531

CORE TECHNOLOGY SOLUTIONS LIMITED LIABILITY CO p 369
80 S Jefferson Rd 07981
Tel (973) 588-4533 SIC 7379 7373

DREW MARINE GROUP INC p 455
100 S Jefferson Rd # 204 07981
Tel (973) 526-5700 SIC 8999 5169

DREW MARINE PARTNERS LP p 455
100 S Jefferson Rd # 102 07981
Tel (973) 526-5700 SIC 5169

DREW MARINE USA INC p 455
100 S Jefferson Rd # 204 07981
Tel (973) 526-5700 SIC 5169

HERLEY-CTI INC p 686
9 Whippany Rd 07981
Tel (973) 884-2580 SIC 3679

■ IMAGE SOLUTIONS INC p 733
100 S Jefferson Rd # 300 07981
Tel (973) 560-0404 SIC 7374

NATIONAL EXCHANGE CARRIER ASSOCIATION p 1011
80 S Jefferson Rd Ste 1 07981
Tel (800) 228-8398 SIC 7389 8611

STAR-LO ELECTRIC INC p 1378
32 S Jefferson Rd 07981
Tel (973) 515-0500 SIC 1731

STEPHEN GOULD CORP p 1386
35 S Jefferson Rd 07981
Tel (973) 428-1500 SIC 2631 2759

■ SUBURBAN PROPANE LP p 1396
240 State Route 10 07981
Tel (973) 887-5300 SIC 5983

▲ SUBURBAN PROPANE PARTNERS LP p 1396
240 Route 10 W 07981
Tel (973) 887-5300
SIC 5984 5172 4939 1711

■ WHIPPANY ACTUATION SYSTEMS LLC p 1605
110 Algonquin Pkwy 07981
Tel (973) 428-9898 SIC 3625 3728

WHITEHOUSE STATION, NJ

MERCK AND CO INC EMPLOYEE BENEFITS TRUST p 945
1 Merck Dr 08889
Tel (908) 423-1000 SIC 6411

■ MERCK HOLDINGS LLC p 945
1 Merck Dr 08889
Tel (908) 423-1000 SIC 2834 6712

■ MERCK SHARP & DOHME (IA) LLC p 945
1 Merck Dr 08889
Tel (908) 423-1000 SIC 5122

QUICK CHEK CORP p 1199
3 Old Highway 28 08889
Tel (908) 534-2200 SIC 5411

WHITEHOUSE, NJ

READINGTON FARMS INC p 1213
12 Mill Rd 08888
Tel (908) 534-2121 SIC 2026

WILLINGBORO, NJ

LOURDES MEDICAL CENTER OF BURLINGTON COUNTY p 881
218 Sunset Rd 08046
Tel (609) 835-2900 SIC 8062

LOURDES MEDICAL CENTER OF BURLINGTON COUNTY A NEW JERSEY NONPROFIT CORP p 881
218 Sunset Rd 08046
Tel (609) 835-2900 SIC 8062

RADWELL INTERNATIONAL INC p 1205
1 Millenium Dr 08046
Tel (609) 288-9393 SIC 5065 7629

WOOD RIDGE, NJ

CERTECH INC p 284
1 Park Pl W 07075
Tel (201) 842-6800 SIC 3364

REDDY RAW INC p 1216
1 Ethel Blvd Ste 1 07075
Tel (201) 804-7633 SIC 5142 5141

WOODBRIDGE, NJ

BESSEMER GROUP INC p 176
100 Woodbridge Center Dr 07095
Tel (732) 694-5500 SIC 6282

NEW JERSEY TURNPIKE AUTHORITY INC p 1032
581 Mack Cali Bldg Main 07095
Tel (732) 750-5300 SIC 4785

▲ NORTHFIELD BANCORP INC p 1057
581 Main St 07095
Tel (732) 499-7200 SIC 6035

WOODBRIDGE TOWNSHIP BOARD OF EDUCATION (INC) p 1622
428 School St 07095
Tel (732) 750-3200 SIC 8211

WOODBRIDGE TOWNSHIP SCHOOL DISTRICT p 1622
428 School St 07095
Tel (732) 750-3200 SIC 8211

WOODBURY, NJ

GLOUCESTER COUNTY NEW JERSEY (INC) p 618
2 S Broad St 08096
Tel (856) 853-3200 SIC 9111

INSPIRA MEDICAL CENTERS INC p 746
509 N Broad St 08096
Tel (856) 845-0100 SIC 8062

UNDERWOOD MEMORIAL HOSPITAL INC p 1502
509 N Broad St 08096
Tel (856) 845-0100 SIC 8062

WOODCLIFF LAKE, NJ

BMW (US) HOLDING CORP p 194
300 Chestnut Ridge Rd 07677
Tel (201) 307-4000 SIC 5511

BMW OF NORTH AMERICA LLC p 194
300 Chestnut Ridge Rd 07677
Tel (201) 307-4000
SIC 5013 3751 5012 3711

EISAI CORP OF NORTH AMERICA p 482
100 Tice Blvd 07677
Tel (201) 692-1100 SIC 5169 8731

EISAI INC p 482
100 Tice Blvd 07677
Tel (919) 941-6920 SIC 2834

LEE HECHT HARRISON LLC p 851
50 Tice Blvd Ste 115 07677
Tel (201) 930-9333 SIC 8742 8741

ROLLS-ROYCE MOTOR CARS NA LLC p 1247
300 Chestnut Ridge Rd 07677
Tel (201) 307-4117 SIC 3711

SYNCSORT INC p 1415
50 Tice Blvd Ste 250 07677
Tel (877) 700-0970 SIC 7371

WALLENIUS WILHELMSEN LOGISTICS AMERICAS LLC p 1573
188 Broadway Ste 1 07677
Tel (201) 307-1300 SIC 4412

WWL VEHICLE SERVICES AMERICAS INC p 1629
188 Broadway Ste 1 07677
Tel (201) 505-5100 SIC 4225 5531 7549

WOODLAND PARK, NJ

CYTEC INDUSTRIES INC p 406
5 Garret Mountain Plz 07424
Tel (973) 357-3100
SIC 2899 2821 2672 2851 2823 2819

KEARFOTT CORP p 807
1150 Mcbride Ave Ste 1 07424
Tel (973) 785-6000 SIC 3812

NORTH JERSEY MEDIA GROUP INC p 1052
1 Garret Mountain Plz # 201 07424
Tel (201) 646-4000 SIC 2711 4813

NEW MEXICO

ALAMOGORDO, NM

OTERO COUNTY HOSPITAL ASSOCIATION INC p 1097
2669 Scenic Dr 88310
Tel (575) 439-6100 SIC 8062

ALBUQUERQUE, NM

ABQ HEALTH PARTNERS LLC p 12
5400 Gibson Blvd Se 87108
Tel (505) 254-6500 SIC 8011

ALBUQUERQUE BERNALILLO COUNTY WATER UTILITY AUTHORITY p 47
1 Civic Plz Nw Fl 10 87102
Tel (505) 768-2907 SIC 4941

ALBUQUERQUE PUBLIC SCHOOL DISTRICT p 47
6400 Uptown Blvd Ne 87110
Tel (505) 880-3700 SIC 8211

AMERICAN RV CENTERS LLC p 78
14303 Central Ave Nw 87121
Tel (505) 293-1983 SIC 5561

APPLIED RESEARCH ASSOCIATES INC p 100
4300 San Mateo Blvd Ne A220 87110
Tel (505) 883-3636 SIC 8731 8748

ARA HOLDINGS INC p 102
4300 San Mateo Blvd Ne 87110
Tel (505) 881-8074 SIC 6719

BROKEN ARROW COMMUNICATIONS INC p 216
8316 Corona Loop Ne 87113
Tel (505) 877-2100 SIC 4899 1623

CENTRAL NEW MEXICO COMMUNITY COLLEGE p 279
525 Buena Vista Dr Se 87106
Tel (505) 224-4511 SIC 8249 8222

CITY OF ALBUQUERQUE p 312
400 Marquette Ave Nw 87102
Tel (505) 768-3000 SIC 9111

COUNTY OF BERNALILLO p 376
1 Civic Plz Nw Fl 10 87102
Tel (505) 468-7240 SIC 9111

■ CVI LASER LLC p 404
200 Dorado Pl Se 87123
Tel (505) 296-9541 SIC 3827 3851 3826

DELTA DENTAL PLAN OF NEW MEXICO INC p 426
2500 La Blvd Ne Ste 600 87110
Tel (505) 883-4777 SIC 6324

DELTA GROUP ELECTRONICS INC p 427
4521a Osuna Rd Ne 87109
Tel (505) 883-7674 SIC 3643 3679

DESERT FUELS INC p 432
4421 Irving Blvd Nw Ste A 87114
Tel (505) 750-3835 SIC 5172 5171

EL ENCANTO INC p 482
2001 4th St Sw 87102
Tel (505) 243-2722 SIC 2038 2099

ERNEST HEALTH INC p 508
7770 Jefferson St Ne # 320 87109
Tel (505) 856-5300 SIC 8069

EXCEL STAFFING COMPANIES LLC p 516
2100 Osuna Rd Ne Ste 100 87113
Tel (505) 262-1871 SIC 7361 7363

■ HARBORSIDE HEALTHCARE ADVISORS LIMITED PARTNERSHIP p 660
101 Sun Ave Ne 87109
Tel (505) 821-1216 SIC 8051

■ HBR KENTUCKY LLC p 671
101 Sun Ave Ne 87109
Tel (505) 821-3355 SIC 8051

JAYNES COMPANIES p 779
2906 Broadway Blvd Ne 87107
Tel (505) 345-8591 SIC 1611

JAYNES CORP p 779
2906 Broadway Blvd Ne 87107
Tel (505) 345-8591 SIC 1542 1541

LAGUNA DEVELOPMENT CORP p 838
14500 Central Ave Sw I40 87121
Tel (505) 352-7877 SIC 7011 5411

LOVELACE BIOMEDICAL & ENVIRONMENTAL RESEARCH INSTITUTE p 881
2425 Ridgecrest Dr Se 87108
Tel (505) 348-9400 SIC 8733

LOVELACE HEALTH SYSTEM INC p 881
4101 Indian School Rd Ne # 110 87110
Tel (800) 808-7363 SIC 8062

LPG ENTERPRISES INC p 882
12854 Eastridge Dr Ne 87112
Tel (505) 299-4155 SIC 5812

MALOOF DISTRIBUTING LLC p 900
701 Comanche Rd Ne 87107
Tel (505) 345-1218 SIC 5181 5149

MELLOY BROTHERS ENTERPRISES INC p 941
7707 Lomas Blvd Ne 87110
Tel (505) 265-8721 SIC 5511

NEW MEXICO GAS CO p 1032
7120 Wyoming Blvd Ne # 20 87109
Tel (505) 697-3803 SIC 4924 4922

NEW MEXICO GAS INTERMEDIATE INC p 1032
7201 Wyoming Blvd Ne 87109
Tel (505) 697-3827 SIC 4924

NEW MEXICO MUTUAL CASUALTY CO p 1032
3900 Singer Blvd Ne 87109
Tel (800) 788-8851 SIC 6331

■ OPTIM ENERGY TWIN OAKS LP p 1090
Alvarado Sq Ms-Z110 87158
Tel (505) 241-2821 SIC 4911

■ OSO BIOPHARMACEUTICAL MANUFACTURING LLC p 1097
4401 Alexander Blvd Ne 87107
Tel (505) 923-1500 SIC 2834

▲ PNM RESOURCES INC p 1158
414 Silver Ave Sw Fl 4 87102
Tel (505) 241-2700 SIC 4911 4922 4924

■ PNMR SERVICES CO p 1158
414 Silver Ave Sw Fl 4 87102
Tel (505) 241-2700 SIC 7539

PREMIER DISTRIBUTING CO p 1170
4321 Yale Blvd Ne 87107
Tel (575) 524-1661 SIC 5181 5149

PRESBYTERIAN HEALTHCARE SERVICES p 1171
9521 San Mateo Blvd Ne 87113
Tel (505) 923-5700 SIC 8062

■ PUBLIC SERVICE CO OF NEW MEXICO p 1190
414 Silver Ave Sw Fl 4 87102
Tel (505) 241-2700 SIC 4911

RINCHEM CO INC p 1235
5131 Masthead St Ne 87109
Tel (505) 998-4300 *SIC* 4789 4225

RIO GRANDE INC p 1235
7500 Bluewater Rd Nw 87121
Tel (505) 839-3550 *SIC* 5094 5049 3915

ROSE L BRAND & ASSOCIATES PC p 1250
7301 Jefferson St Ne 87109
Tel (505) 833-3036 *SIC* 8111

ROSES SOUTHWEST PAPERS INC p 1251
1701 2nd St Sw 87102
Tel (505) 842-0134 *SIC* 2676 2674 2621

■ **SANDIA CORP** p 1278
1515 Eubank Blvd Se 87123
Tel (505) 284-4784 *SIC* 8733

■ **SHG SERVICES INC** p 1316
101 Sun Ave Ne 87109
Tel (505) 468-4973 *SIC* 7363

SOLAERO TECHNOLOGIES CORP p 1338
10420 Res Rd Se Bldg 1 87123
Tel (505) 332-5000 *SIC* 3679 3674

SOUTH VALLEY CARE CENTER p 1345
1629 Bowe Ln Sw 87105
Tel (505) 877-2200 *SIC* 8051 8059

SUMMIT ELECTRIC SUPPLY CO INC p 1398
2900 Stanford Dr Ne 87107
Tel (505) 346-2900 *SIC* 5063

■ **SUNBRIDGE HEALTHCARE LLC** p 1401
101 Sun Ave Ne 87109
Tel (505) 821-3355 *SIC* 8052 8051

■ **SUNBRIDGE RETIREMENT CARE ASSOCIATES INC** p 1401
101 Sun Ave Ne 87109
Tel (505) 821-3355 *SIC* 6513 3842

■ **SYSCO NEW MEXICO LLC** p 1417
601 Comanche Rd Ne 87107
Tel (505) 761-1200 *SIC* 5141

T L C CO INC p 1419
5000 Edith Blvd Ne 87107
Tel (505) 761-9696 *SIC* 1711

TRICORE REFERENCE LABORATORIES p 1479
1001 Woodward Pl Ne 87102
Tel (505) 938-8999 *SIC* 8071

UNITED STATES DEPARTMENT OF ENERGY ALBUQUERQUE OFFICE p 1512
1515 Eubank Blvd Se 87123
Tel (505) 845-0011 *SIC* 9611

UNIVERSITY OF NEW MEXICO p 1523
1800 Roma Blvd Ne 87131
Tel (505) 277-0732 *SIC* 8221

■ **WELLS FARGO BANK NEW MEXICO NA** p 1590
200 Lomas Blvd Nw Ste 100 87102
Tel (505) 765-5000 *SIC* 6021

■ **WELLS FARGO INC** p 1590
200 Lomas Blvd Nw Ste 100 87102
Tel (505) 353-5000 *SIC* 6021

YEAROUT MECHANICAL INC p 1635
8501 Washington St Ne 87113
Tel (505) 884-0994 *SIC* 1711

ARTESIA, NM

■ **HOLLYFRONTIER NAVAJO REFINING LLC** p 701
501 E Main St 88210
Tel (575) 748-3311 *SIC* 2911 2951

MACK ENERGY CORP p 892
11344 Lovington Hwy 88210
Tel (575) 748-1288 *SIC* 1311 2911

YATES PETROLEUM CORP p 1635
105 S 4th St 88210
Tel (575) 748-1471 *SIC* 1311

AZTEC, NM

AZTEC WELL SERVICING CO p 140
300 Legion Rd 87410
Tel (505) 334-6194 *SIC* 1381 4213

BELEN, NM

AMBERCARE CORP p 65
420 N Main St 87002
Tel (505) 861-0060
SIC 8082 8361 5047 7352

■ **BELEN MEADOWS HEALTHCARE AND REHABILITATION CENTER LLC** p 169
1831 Camino Del Llano 87002
Tel (505) 864-1600 *SIC* 8051

CARLSBAD, NM

■ **CARLSBAD MEDICAL CENTER LLC** p 257
2430 W Pierce St 88220
Tel (575) 887-4100 *SIC* 8062

FORREST TIRE CO INC p 568
414 S Canal St 88220
Tel (575) 887-3567 *SIC* 5531 5014

■ **INTREPID POTASH-NEW MEXICO LLC** p 760
1996 Potash Mines Rd 88220
Tel (575) 887-5591 *SIC* 1474

CHURCH ROCK, NM

NAVAJO NATION GAMING ENTERPRISE p 1019
249 E Nm State Hwy 118 87311
Tel (505) 905-7100 *SIC* 8748

CLOVIS, NM

ALLSUP ENTERPRISES INC p 58
2112 N Thornton St 88101
Tel (575) 769-2311
SIC 5411 5541 4832 6519 5171

ALLSUPS CONVENIENCE STORES INC p 58
2112 N Thornton St 88101
Tel (575) 769-2311 *SIC* 5411 5541

CITY OF CLOVIS BOARD OF EDUCATION SCHOOL DISTRICT 1 p 314
1009 N Main St 88101
Tel (575) 769-4300 *SIC* 8211

CLOVIS MUNICIPAL SCHOOL DISTRICT p 328
1009 N Main St 88101
Tel (575) 769-4300 *SIC* 8211

ENMR TELEPHONE COOPERATIVE p 500
7111 N Prince St 88101
Tel (575) 389-5100 *SIC* 4813

SOUTHWEST CHEESE CO LLC p 1351
1141 Cr N Ste 4 88101
Tel (575) 742-9200 *SIC* 5143 2022

ESPANOLA, NM

AKAL SECURITY INC p 42
7 Infinity Loop 87532
Tel (505) 753-7832 *SIC* 7381

LOS ALAMOS NATIONAL LABORATORY FOUNDATION p 878
1112 Plaza Del Norte 87532
Tel (505) 753-8890 *SIC* 8699

EUNICE, NM

■ **B & H MAINTENANCE AND CONSTRUCTION INC** p 141
S Loop 207 88231
Tel (575) 394-2588 *SIC* 1623

LOUISIANA ENERGY SERVICES LLC p 880
275 Andrews Hwy 88231
Tel (575) 394-4646 *SIC* 1094

FARMINGTON, NM

FARMINGTON MUNICIPAL SCHOOLS p 530
2001 N Dustin Ave 87401
Tel (505) 324-9840 *SIC* 8211

NAVAJO AGRICULTURAL PRODUCTS INDUSTRY p 1019
10086 Nm Hwy 371 87499
Tel (505) 326-2730 *SIC* 0191

■ **PEAK MEDICAL FARMINGTON LLC** p 1126
806 W Maple St 87401
Tel (505) 325-2910 *SIC* 8051

PROCESS EQUIPMENT & SERVICE CO INC p 1179
5680 Us 64 87401
Tel (505) 327-2222
SIC 3443 5084 7699 3533

SAN JUAN REGIONAL MEDICAL CENTER INC p 1277
801 W Maple St 87401
Tel (505) 609-2000 *SIC* 8062

GALLUP, NM

GALLUP-MC KINLEY COUNTY PUBLIC SCHOOL DISTRICT 1 (INC) p 590
700 Boardman Dr 87301
Tel (505) 722-7711 *SIC* 8211

HOBBS, NM

HOBBS MUNICIPAL SCHOOLS p 699
1515 E Sanger St 88240
Tel (575) 433-0100 *SIC* 8211

MPS ENTERPRISES INC p 995
1224 W Broadway Pl 88240
Tel (432) 563-3332 *SIC* 5169

NOVA MUD INC p 1062
5800 Nova 88240
Tel (575) 393-8786 *SIC* 5169

ISLETA, NM

PUEBLO OF ISLETA p 1190
Tribal Rd 40 Bldg 117-A 87022
Tel (505) 869-3111 *SIC* 9111

LAS CRUCES, NM

B & B CONSULTANTS INC p 141
750 N 17th St 88005
Tel (575) 524-8998 *SIC* 5812

CITY OF LAS CRUCES p 316
700 N Main St 88001
Tel (575) 541-2000 *SIC* 9111

■ **LAS CRUCES MEDICAL CENTER LLC** p 845
4311 E Lohman Ave 88011
Tel (575) 556-7600 *SIC* 8062

LAS CRUCES PUBLIC SCHOOLS p 845
505 S Main St Ste 249 88001
Tel (575) 527-5893 *SIC* 8211

MEMORIAL MEDICAL CENTER INC p 942
2450 S Telshor Blvd 88011
Tel (575) 522-8641 *SIC* 8062

MEMORIAL MEDICAL CENTER INC p 942
2450 S Telshor Blvd 88011
Tel (575) 522-8641 *SIC* 8011

MVT SERVICES LLC p 1003
3590 W Picacho Ave 88007
Tel (915) 791-4000 *SIC* 4213

NEW MEXICO STATE UNIVERSITY p 1032
2850 Weddell St Rm 210 88003
Tel (575) 646-0111 *SIC* 8221

■ **PEAK MEDICAL LAS CRUCES LLC** p 1126
2905 Missouri Ave 88011
Tel (575) 522-0404 *SIC* 8051

■ **PHC-LAS CRUCES INC** p 1141
2450 S Telshor Blvd 88011
Tel (575) 522-8641 *SIC* 8062

LOS ALAMOS, NM

LOS ALAMOS NATIONAL SECURITY LLC p 878
105 Central Park Sq 87544
Tel (877) 723-4101 *SIC* 8748

LOS LUNAS, NM

RAKS BUILDING SUPPLY INC p 1206
108 Carson Dr Se 87031
Tel (505) 865-1100 *SIC* 5031 5211 5072

MESCALERO, NM

INN OF MOUNTAIN GODS RESORT AND CASINO p 744
287 Carrizo Canyon Rd 88340
Tel (575) 464-7777 *SIC* 7999 7011

MESCALERO APACHE HOUSING AUTHORITY p 951
101 Central Ave 88340
Tel (575) 464-9245 *SIC* 9531

MESCALERO APACHE TRIBE p 951
108 Old Mescalero Blvd 88340
Tel (575) 464-4494 *SIC* 9131

PUEBLO OF ACOMA, NM

ACOMA BUSINESS ENTERPRISES p 18
I 40 Exit 102 87034
Tel (888) 759-2489 *SIC* 6719 5154

RIO RANCHO, NM

RIO RANCHO PUBLIC SCHOOLS p 1236
500 Laser Rd Ne 87124
Tel (505) 896-0667 *SIC* 8211

ROSWELL, NM

NEXT PHASE INC p 1040
1410 S Main St 88203
Tel (575) 624-9999 *SIC* 8082

■ **PEAK MEDICAL ROSWELL LLC** p 1126
3200 Mission Arch Dr 88201
Tel (575) 624-2583 *SIC* 8051

■ **ROSWELL HOSPITAL CORP** p 1252
405 W Country Club Rd 88201
Tel (575) 622-8170 *SIC* 8062

ROSWELL INDEPENDENT SCHOOL DISTRICT (INC) p 1252
300 N Kentucky Ave 88201
Tel (575) 627-2500 *SIC* 8211

SANTA FE, NM

BOARD OF EDUCATION OF CITY OF SANTA FE (INC) p 195
610 Alta Vista St 87505
Tel (505) 467-2000 *SIC* 8211

CITY OF SANTA FE p 318
200 Lincoln Ave 87501
Tel (505) 955-6532 *SIC* 9111

CORRECTIONS DEPARTMENT NEW MEXICO p 373
4337 State Highway 14 87508
Tel (505) 827-8793 *SIC* 9223

GOVERNORS OFFICE NEW MEXICO p 627
490 Old Santa Fe Trl # 400 87501
Tel (505) 476-2200 *SIC* 9111

NEW MEXICO DEPARTMENT OF CHILDREN YOUTH AND FAMILIES p 1032
1120 Paseo De Peralta 87501
Tel (505) 827-7602 *SIC* 9441

NEW MEXICO DEPARTMENT OF FINANCE & ADMINISTRATION p 1032
Bataan Memorial Bldg 180 87501
Tel (505) 827-4985 *SIC* 9311

NEW MEXICO DEPARTMENT OF HEALTH p 1032
1190 S Saint Francis Dr 87505
Tel (505) 827-2613 *SIC* 9431

NEW MEXICO DEPARTMENT OF HUMAN SERVICES p 1032
2009 S Pacheco St 87505
Tel (505) 827-7750 *SIC* 9441

NEW MEXICO DEPARTMENT OF PUBLIC SAFETY p 1032
4491 Cerrillos Rd 87507
Tel (505) 827-9000 *SIC* 9229

NEW MEXICO DEPARTMENT OF TAXATION AND REVENUE p 1032
1100 S Saint Francis Dr 87505
Tel (505) 827-0700 *SIC* 9311

NEW MEXICO DEPARTMENT OF TRANSPORTATION p 1032
1120 Cerrillos Rd 87505
Tel (505) 827-5100 *SIC* 9621

NEW MEXICO DEPT OF MILITARY AFFAIRS p 1032
47 Bataan Blvd 87508
Tel (505) 474-1200 *SIC* 9711

PRESBYTERIAN MEDICAL SERVICES INC p 1171
1422 Paseo De Peralta # 1 87501
Tel (505) 982-5565 *SIC* 8011

SANTA FE COMMUNITY COLLEGE p 1280
6401 S Richards Ave 87508
Tel (505) 428-1000 *SIC* 8222 8221

SANTA FE PUBLIC SCHOOLS p 1280
610 Alta Vista St 87505
Tel (505) 467-2000 *SIC* 8211

ST VINCENT HOSPITAL p 1373
455 Saint Michaels Dr 87505
Tel (505) 983-3361 *SIC* 8062

STATE OF NEW MEXICO p 1382
237 Don Gaspar Ave 87501
Tel (505) 827-3000 *SIC* 9111

THORNBURG INVESTMENT MANAGEMENT p 1450
2300 N Ridgetop Rd 87506
Tel (505) 984-0200 *SIC* 6211

TMST INC p 1458
125 Lincoln Ave Ste 100 87501
Tel (505) 989-1900 *SIC* 6531 6798

SHIPROCK, NM

CENTRAL CONSOLIDATED SCHOOL DIST 22 p 278
U S Hwy 64 87420
Tel (505) 368-4984 *SIC* 8211

NAVAJO ENGINEERING & CONSTRUCTION AUTHORITY p 1019
1 Uranium Blvd 87420
Tel (505) 368-5151 *SIC* 1611 1623

SILVER CITY, NM

GILA REGIONAL MEDICAL CENTER p 611
1313 E 32nd St 88061
Tel (575) 538-4000 *SIC* 8093 8062

SOCORRO, NM

NEW MEXICO INSTITUTE OF MINING AND TECHNOLOGY p 1032
801 Leroy Pl 87801
Tel (575) 835-5312 *SIC* 8221

SUNLAND PARK, NM

GADSDEN INDEPENDENT SCHOOL DISTRICT p 589
4950 Mcnutt Rd 88063
Tel (575) 882-6200 *SIC* 8211

T OR C, NM

NEW MEXICO STATE VETERANS HOME p 1032
922 S Broadway St 87901
Tel (575) 894-4200 *SIC* 8051

WATERFLOW, NM

B H P MINERALS INTERNATIONAL INC p 142
300 W Arrington Ste 101 87421
Tel (505) 598-4200 *SIC* 1481

NEW YORK

ADAMS, NY

FUCCILLO AUTOMOTIVE GROUP INC p 583
10524 Us Route 11 13605
Tel (315) 232-4117 *SIC* 5511

AKRON, NY

WHITING DOOR MFG CORP p 1607
113 Cedar St 14001
Tel (716) 542-5427 *SIC* 3714

ALBANY, NY

ALBANY CITY SCHOOL DISTRICT p 45
1 Academy Park 12207
Tel (518) 475-6000 *SIC* 8211

ALBANY MEDICAL CENTER p 45
43 New Scotland Ave 12208
Tel (518) 262-3125 *SIC* 8062

ALBANY MEDICAL CENTER HOSPITAL p 45
43 New Scotland Ave 12208
Tel (518) 262-3125 *SIC* 8062 8249

ALBANY MEDICAL COLLEGE p 45
47 New Scotland Ave 12208
Tel (518) 262-6008 *SIC* 8249

▲ **ALBANY MOLECULAR RESEARCH INC** p 45
26 Corporate Cir 12203
Tel (518) 512-2000 *SIC* 2836 8731

■ **ALO ACQUISITION LLC** p 59
26 Corporate Cir 12203
Tel (518) 464-0279 *SIC* 2833 5122 8733

■ **AMERICAN FAMILY LIFE ASSURANCE CO OF NY (INC)** p 72
22 Corporate Woods Blvd 12211
Tel (518) 438-0764 *SIC* 6321

ATTORNEY GENERAL NEW YORK STATE p 129
The Capitol 12224
Tel (518) 776-2000 SIC 9222

BBL LLC p 163
302 Washington Ave 12203
Tel (518) 452-8200
SIC 1542 1541 1521 1622 8741

CAPITAL DISTRICT PHYSICIANS HEALTH PLAN INC p 249
500 Patroon Creek Blvd 12206
Tel (518) 641-3700 SIC 8011

CAPITAL REGION BOCES p 250
900 Watervliet Shaker Rd # 102 12205
Tel (518) 862-4924 SIC 8211

CATHOLIC CHARITIES OF DIOCESE OF ALBANY p 266
40 N Main Ave Ste 1 12203
Tel (518) 453-6650 SIC 8322

CENTER FOR DISABILITY SERVICES INC p 275
314 S Manning Blvd 12208
Tel (518) 437-5506
SIC 8351 8093 8361 8099

CENTER RESIDENCE CORP p 276
314 S Manning Blvd 12208
Tel (518) 437-5700 SIC 8322

CENTRAL TOWERS PRESERVATION LP p 280
400 Central Ave Ste 1 12206
Tel (518) 438-6834 SIC 6513

CHA CONSULTING INC p 286
3 Winners Cir Ste 301 12205
Tel (518) 453-4500 SIC 8711

CHA HOLDINGS INC p 286
3 Winners Cir 12205
Tel (518) 453-4500 SIC 8711

CITY OF ALBANY p 312
24 Eagle St Rm 102 12207
Tel (518) 434-5100 SIC 9111

CIVIL SERVICE EMPLOYEES ASSOCIATION INC p 320
143 Washington Ave 12210
Tel (518) 257-1000 SIC 8631

CLOUGH HARBOUR & ASSOCIATES LLP p 327
3 Winners Cir Ste 100 12205
Tel (518) 453-4500 SIC 8711

COLLEGE OF SAINT ROSE p 337
432 Western Ave 12203
Tel (518) 454-5111 SIC 8221

▲ COMMERCEHUB INC p 345
201 Fuller Rd Fl 6 12203
Tel (518) 810-0700 SIC 7372

CONVERGENCE TECHNOLOGIES INC p 365
80 State St 12207
Tel (914) 697-7669 SIC 7373

COUNTY OF ALBANY p 376
112 State St Rm 900 12207
Tel (518) 447-7130 SIC 9111

DORMITORY AUTHORITY - STATE OF NEW YORK p 451
515 Broadway Ste 100 12207
Tel (518) 257-3000 SIC 8611

EDEN PARK MANAGEMENT INC p 477
22 Holland Ave 12209
Tel (518) 729-5230 SIC 8051

EDUCATION DEPARTMENT NEW YORK STATE p 479
89 Washington Ave 12234
Tel (518) 474-3852 SIC 8299 9411

EXCELSIOR COLLEGE p 517
7 Columbia Cir 12203
Tel (518) 464-8500 SIC 8221

EXECUTIVE OFFICE OF STATE OF NEW YORK p 518
Executive Chamber Capitol 12224
Tel (518) 474-8390 SIC 9111

■ FLEET/NORSTAR EMPLOYEES BENEFIT SERVICES INC p 555
1 Peter Kiernan Plz 12207
Tel (518) 956-1007 SIC 6282

LEGISLATIVE OFFICE STATE OF NY p 853
State Capital Bldg 12248
Tel (518) 455-4100 SIC 9121

M+W US INC p 890
201 Fuller Rd Ste 400 12203
Tel (518) 266-3400 SIC 1542 8711

MEMORIAL HOSPITAL p 942
600 Northern Blvd 12204
Tel (518) 471-3221 SIC 8062

MOMENTIVE PERFORMANCE MATERIALS HOLDINGS INC p 983
22 Corporate Woods Blvd 12211
Tel (518) 533-4600 SIC 2869 3479

NEW YORK DEPARTMENT OF CORRECTIONS AND COMMUNITY SUPERVISION p 1035
1220 Washngtn Ave Bldg 2 12226
Tel (518) 457-8126 SIC 8322 9223

NEW YORK DEPARTMENT OF ENVIRONMENTAL CONSERVATION p 1035
625 Broadway 12207
Tel (518) 402-8545 SIC 9512

NEW YORK DEPARTMENT OF HEALTH p 1035
Empire State Plaza 12237
Tel (518) 474-2011 SIC 9431

NEW YORK DEPARTMENT OF TRANSPORTATION p 1035
50 Wolf Rd Ste 5 12205
Tel (518) 457-4445 SIC 9621

NEW YORK OFFICE OF ALCOHOLISM & SUBSTANCE ABUSE SERVICES p 1035
1450 Western Ave 12203
Tel (518) 457-2061 SIC 9431

NEW YORK OFFICE OF TEMPORARY & DISABILITY ASSISTANCE p 1035
40 N Pearl St Ste 100 12207
Tel (518) 426-2950 SIC 9441

NEW YORK STATE DEPARTMENT OF MOTOR VEHICLES p 1036
6 Empire State Plz Rm 321 12223
Tel (518) 474-0835 SIC 9621

NEW YORK STATE DIVISION OF CRIMINAL JUSTICE SERVICES p 1036
80 S Swan St 12210
Tel (518) 457-9896 SIC 9211

NEW YORK STATE DIVISION OF HOUSING AND COMMUNITY RENEWAL p 1036
38-40 State St 12207
Tel (518) 473-2517 SIC 9531

NEW YORK STATE ENVIRONMENTAL FACILITIES CORP p 1036
625 Broadway 12207
Tel (518) 486-9267 SIC 8742

NEW YORK STATE INDUSTRIES FOR DISABLED INC p 1036
11 Columbia Cir 12203
Tel (518) 463-9706 SIC 8322

NEW YORK STATE OFFICE OF MENTAL HEALTH p 1036
44 Holland Ave 12208
Tel (518) 474-4403 SIC 9431

NEW YORK STATE OFFICE OF STATE COMPTROLLER p 1036
110 State St 12207
Tel (518) 474-4044 SIC 9311

NORTHEAST HEALTH p 1054
600 Northern Blvd 12204
Tel (518) 471-3229 SIC 8741

NORTHEAST HEALTH INC p 1054
315 S Manning Blvd 12208
Tel (518) 292-6200 SIC 8059 8322

NYS POLICE INVESTIGATORS ASSOCIATION EMERGENCY ASSISTANCE FUND INC p 1069
11 N Pearl St Ste 1202 12207
Tel (518) 436-0120 SIC 8631

PEOPLE WITH DEVELOPMENTAL DISABILITIES NEW YORK STATE OFFICE FOR p 1132
44 Holland Ave 12208
Tel (518) 473-1997 SIC 9431

PUBLIC SERVICE COMMISSION NEW YORK STATE p 1190
3 Empire State Plz 20th 12223
Tel (518) 474-7080 SIC 9441

■ RECORD TOWN INC p 1215
38 Corporate Cir 12203
Tel (518) 452-1242 SIC 5735

RESEARCH FOUNDATION FOR STATE UNIVERSITY OF NEW YORK p 1226
35 State St 12207
Tel (518) 434-7000 SIC 8733

ROMAN CATHOLIC DIOCESE OF ALBANY INC p 1248
40 N Main Ave Ste 4 12203
Tel (518) 453-6600 SIC 8661

SOUTH COLONIE CENTRAL SCHOOLS DISTRICT p 1344
102 Loralee Dr 12205
Tel (518) 869-6481 SIC 8211

ST PETERS HEALTH PARTNERS p 1372
315 S Manning Blvd 12208
Tel (518) 525-1550 SIC 8062

ST PÈTERS HEALTH PARTNERS p 1372
315 S Manning Blvd 12208
Tel (518) 525-1111 SIC 8062

STATE ASSEMBLY NEW YORK p 1380
1 Enterprise Dr 12204
Tel (518) 455-4100 SIC 9121

STATE EMPLOYEES FEDERAL CREDIT UNION p 1380
575 Broadway 12207
Tel (518) 452-8183 SIC 6061

STATE EMPLOYEES FEDERAL CREDIT UNION p 1380
700 Patroon Creek Blvd 12206
Tel (518) 452-8183 SIC 6061

STATE POLICE NEW YORK p 1382
1220 Washngtn Ave Bldg 22 12226
Tel (518) 457-6721 SIC 9221

STATE UNIVERSITY OF NEW YORK p 1383
353 Broadway 12246
Tel (518) 320-1100 SIC 8221 9411

STEIN FIBERS LTD p 1385
4 Computer Dr W Ste 200 12205
Tel (518) 489-5700 SIC 2824

TAXATION AND FINANCE DEPARTMENT NEW YORK STATE p 1426
W A Harriman Campus Bldg 12227
Tel (518) 457-2244 SIC 9311

THRUWAY AUTHORITY OF NEW YORK STATE p 1451
200 Southern Blvd 12209
Tel (518) 436-2700 SIC 4785 4499

▲ TRANS WORLD ENTERTAINMENT CORP p 1470
38 Corporate Cir 12203
Tel (518) 452-1242
SIC 5735 5731 5734 7841 5961

UNIFIED COURT SYSTEM OF NEW YORK STATE p 1503
20 Eagle St 12207
Tel (518) 455-7700 SIC 9211

UNIVERSITY AT ALBANY p 1518
1400 Washington Ave 12222
Tel (518) 442-3300 SIC 8221 9411

AMHERST, NY

▲ ALLIED MOTION TECHNOLOGIES INC p 56
495 Commerce Dr Ste 3 14228
Tel (716) 242-8634 SIC 3621 3825

■ AMERICAN PRECISION INDUSTRIES INC p 77
45 Hazelwood Dr 14228
Tel (716) 691-9100
SIC 3677 3621 3625 3443

EMPLOYER SERVICES CORP p 494
20 Pineview Dr Ste 3 14228
Tel (716) 691-4455 SIC 7363 8721

FIRSTSOURCE ADVANTAGE LLC p 551
205 Bryant Woods S 14228
Tel (716) 564-4400 SIC 7322

INTERNATIONAL IMAGING MATERIALS INC p 755
310 Commerce Dr 14228
Tel (716) 691-6333 SIC 3955 3555

IVOCLAR VIVADENT INC p 769
175 Pineview Dr 14228
Tel (716) 691-0010 SIC 5047 8021

■ MERITAIN HEALTH INC p 949
300 Corporate Pkwy 100s 14226
Tel (716) 319-5500 SIC 8741

MIDDLE ATLANTIC WAREHOUSE DISTRIBUTOR INC p 964
20 Hazelwood Dr Ste 100 14228
Tel (716) 531-9200 SIC 5013

NORTHTOWN AUTOMOTIVE COMPANIES INC p 1059
1135 Millersport Hwy 14226
Tel (716) 836-4600 SIC 5511

STAMPEDE PRESENTATION PRODUCTS INC p 1375
55 Woodridge Dr 14228
Tel (716) 635-9474 SIC 5065

AMITYVILLE, NY

ALBERT KEMPERLE INC p 46
8400 New Horizons Blvd 11701
Tel (631) 841-1241 SIC 5013

B & G ELECTRICAL CONTRACTORS OF NY INC p 141
7100 New Horizons Blvd 11701
Tel (631) 669-6000 SIC 1731

BELLCO DRUG CORP p 170
5500 New Horizons Blvd 11701
Tel (631) 789-6900 SIC 5122 5047

■ EDO LLC p 478
1500 New Horizons Blvd 11701
Tel (631) 630-4000
SIC 3812 3728 3663 3679

GKN AEROSPACE MONITOR INC p 613
1000 New Horizons Blvd 11701
Tel (562) 619-8558 SIC 3728 3769

■ HI-TECH PHARMACAL CO INC p 689
369 Bayview Ave 11701
Tel (631) 789-8228 SIC 2834

LONG ISLAND HOME p 876
400 Sunrise Hwy 11701
Tel (631) 264-4000
SIC 8063 8051 8099 8011

▲ NAPCO SECURITY TECHNOLOGIES INC p 1007
333 Bayview Ave 11701
Tel (631) 842-9400
SIC 3669 3699 3429 1731 7373

AMSTERDAM, NY

ALPIN HAUS SKI SHOP INC p 60
4850 State Highway 30 12010
Tel (518) 843-4400 SIC 5561 5551 5941

AMSTERDAM PRINTING & LITHO INC p 87
166 Wallins Corners Rd 12010
Tel (518) 842-6000 SIC 3993 2752 2761

BEECH-NUT NUTRITION CO p 168
1 Nutritious Pl 12010
Tel (518) 839-0300 SIC 2032

CV HOLDINGS LLC p 404
1030 Riverfront Ctr 12010
Tel (518) 627-0051 SIC 5162 3089

HILL & MARKES INC p 693
1997 State Highway 5s 12010
Tel (518) 842-2410 SIC 5087 5113

ST MARYS HEALTHCARE p 1371
427 Guy Park Ave Ste 1 12010
Tel (518) 842-1900 SIC 8062

ANNANDALE ON HUDSON, NY

BARD COLLEGE p 155
30 Campus Rd 12504
Tel (845) 758-7518 SIC 8221

BARD COLLEGE PUBLICATIONS p 155
Annandale Rd 12504
Tel (845) 758-7417 SIC 8999 2759 5311

ARCADE, NY

■ PIONEER CREDIT RECOVERY INC p 1150
26 Edward St 14009
Tel (585) 492-1234 SIC 7322

ARDSLEY, NY

▲ ACORDA THERAPEUTICS INC p 18
420 Saw Mill River Rd 10502
Tel (914) 347-4300 SIC 2834 8731 2836

ARGYLE, NY

ADIRONDACK SCENIC INC p 23
439 County Route 45 Ste 1 12809
Tel (518) 638-8000 SIC 2599

ARMONK, NY

■ IBM CREDIT LLC p 726
1 North Castle Dr 10504
Tel (914) 765-1900 SIC 6153 6159

■ IBM WORLD TRADE CORP p 726
1 New Orchard Rd Ste 1 10504
Tel (914) 765-1900
SIC 3571 3577 7377 7379

INTER-WIRE PRODUCTS INC p 751
355 Main St Ste 2 10504
Tel (914) 273-6633 SIC 5051

▲ INTERNATIONAL BUSINESS MACHINES CORP p 754
1 New Orchard Rd Ste 1 10504
Tel (914) 499-1900
SIC 7379 7371 3571 3572 3674

LIFE RE CORP p 863
175 King St 10504
Tel (914) 828-8500 SIC 6311 6321

PRODUCTION RESOURCE GROUP LLC p 1179
200 Business Park Dr # 109 10504
Tel (212) 589-5400 SIC 3999 7922

SR CORPORATE SOLUTIONS AMERICA HOLDING CORP p 1362
175 King St 10504
Tel (914) 828-8000 SIC 6331 6311

SWISS REINSURANCE AMERICA CORP p 1413
175 King St 10504
Tel (914) 828-8000 SIC 6331

TRINITY PACKAGING CORP p 1481
357 Main St 10504
Tel (914) 273-4111 SIC 2673 2679

■ VISANT SECONDARY HOLDINGS CORP p 1561
357 Main St 10504
Tel (914) 595-8200 SIC 2741

ASTORIA, NY

CHARMER INDUSTRIES INC p 290
1950 48th St 11105
Tel (718) 726-2500 SIC 5182

EXCAVATORS 731 PROPERTY CORP p 516
3411 35th Ave 11106
Tel (718) 706-0720 SIC 6512

GOODWILL INDUSTRIES OF GREATER NEW YORK INC p 624
421 27th Ave 11102
Tel (718) 728-5400 SIC 8331

MAX FINKELSTEIN INC p 922
2840 31st St 11102
Tel (718) 274-8900 SIC 5014 5531

AUBURN, NY

AUBURN COMMUNITY HOSPITAL p 130
17 Lansing St 13021
Tel (315) 255-7011 SIC 8062 8051

D & W DIESEL INC p 406
1503 Clark Street Rd 13021
Tel (315) 253-5300 SIC 5013 5531

JOHNSTON PAPER CO INC p 791
2 Eagle Dr 13021
Tel (315) 253-8435 SIC 5113 5084

■ NUCOR STEEL AUBURN INC p 1066
25 Quarry Rd 13021
Tel (315) 253-4561 SIC 3312

BABYLON, NY

ACA INDUSTRIES INC p 13
385 W Main St 11702
Tel (631) 587-2485 SIC 7349

GREENMAN-PEDERSEN INC p 638
325 W Main St Bldg 1 11702
Tel (631) 587-5060 SIC 8711

NORTH BABYLON UNION FREE SCHOOL DISTRICT p 1051
5 Jardine Pl 11703
Tel (631) 321-3209 SIC 8211 8741

BALDWIN, NY

BALDWIN UNION FREE SCHOOL DISTRICT p 147
960 Hastings St 11510
Tel (516) 377-9312 *SIC* 8211

BALDWINSVILLE, NY

GYPSUM EXPRESS LTD p 649
8280 Sixty Rd 13027
Tel (315) 638-2201 *SIC* 4212 4213

■ MCLANE/EASTERN INC p 931
2828 Mclane Rd 13027
Tel (315) 638-7500 *SIC* 5141

BALLSTON SPA, NY

BALLSTON SPA CENTRAL SCHOOL DISTRICT p 148
70 Malta Ave 12020
Tel (518) 884-7195 *SIC* 8211

COUNTY OF SARATOGA p 381
25 W High St 12020
Tel (518) 884-4742 *SIC* 9111

CURTIS LUMBER CO INC p 402
885 State Route 67 12020
Tel (518) 885-5311 *SIC* 5211

NORTH AMERICAN INDUSTRIAL SERVICES INC p 1050
1240 Saratoga Rd 12020
Tel (518) 885-1820 *SIC* 7349

STEWARTS SHOPS CORP p 1389
2907 State Route 9 12020
Tel (518) 581-1201 *SIC* 5411

BARKER, NY

SOMERSET OPERATING CO LLC p 1339
7725 Lake Rd 14012
Tel (716) 795-9501 *SIC* 4911

BATAVIA, NY

GENESEE COUNTY OF (INC) p 602
15 Main St 14020
Tel (585) 344-2550 *SIC* 9111

▲ GRAHAM CORP p 629
20 Florence Ave 14020
Tel (585) 343-2216 *SIC* 3563 3585 3443

O-AT-KA MILK PRODUCTS COOPERATIVE INC p 1070
700 Ellicott St 14020
Tel (585) 343-0536 *SIC* 2023 2021 2026

UNITED MEMORIAL MEDICAL CENTER p 1510
127 North St 14020
Tel (585) 343-6030 *SIC* 8062 8049 8011

BATH, NY

HILLSIDES CHILDRENS CENTER p 694
24 Liberty St 14810
Tel (607) 776-7480 *SIC* 8322

BAY SHORE, NY

1550 BAYSHORE CORP p 1
1550 5th Ave 11706
Tel (631) 206-7100 *SIC* 5149

BAY SHORE UNION FREE SCHOOL DISTRICT p 161
75 Perkal St 11706
Tel (631) 968-1100 *SIC* 8211

BIMBO FOODS BAKERIES INC p 183
40 Harold Ct 11706
Tel (631) 273-6000 *SIC* 2051

DAVID PEYSER SPORTSWEAR INC p 415
88 Spence St 11706
Tel (631) 231-7788 *SIC* 2329

DYNE DURO NATIONAL CORP p 465
81 Spence St 11706
Tel (631) 249-9000 *SIC* 3585

ENTENMANNS INC p 501
1724 5th Ave 11706
Tel (631) 273-6000 *SIC* 2051

■ REMY USA INDUSTRIES LLC p 1223
215 Candlewood Rd 11706
Tel (631) 969-2222 *SIC* 5012

ROCKETTECH FUEL CORP p 1244
20 Corbin Ave 11706
Tel (516) 810-8947 *SIC* 1311

SOUTHSIDE HOSPITAL p 1351
301 E Main St 11706
Tel (631) 968-3000 *SIC* 8062

BAYPORT, NY

BLACKMAN PLUMBING SUPPLY CO INC p 188
900 Sylvan Ave 11705
Tel (631) 823-4300 *SIC* 5074 5075

WENNER BREAD PRODUCTS INC p 1592
33 Rajon Rd 11705
Tel (800) 869-6262 *SIC* 2051 2053 5461

BAYSIDE, NY

NEW YORK CITY GEOGRAPHIC DISTRICT 26 p 1034
6115 Oceania St 11364
Tel (718) 631-6982 *SIC* 8211

PERSONAL TOUCH HOME CARE p 1137
22215 Northern Blvd Fl 3 11361
Tel (718) 468-4747 *SIC* 8082

BEDFORD HILLS, NY

NATURES TREES INC p 1019
550 Bedford Rd 10507
Tel (914) 241-4999
SIC 0783 0782 0781 1629

BELLE HARBOR, NY

AFTERDARKK MEDIA SOLUTIONS LLC p 33
271 Beach 135th St 11694
Tel (347) 244-6619 *SIC* 7374

BELLPORT, NY

BROOKHAVEN MEMORIAL HOSPITAL p 217
656 Bourdois Ave 11713
Tel (631) 654-7770 *SIC* 8062

▲ PERFUMANIA HOLDINGS INC p 1135
35 Sawgrass Dr Ste 2 11713
Tel (631) 866-4100 *SIC* 5122 5999

PROS CHOICE BEAUTY CARE INC p 1184
35 Sawgrass Dr Ste 4 11713
Tel (631) 803-3200 *SIC* 5122

QUALITY KING DISTRIBUTORS INC p 1197
35 Sawgrass Dr Ste 3 11713
Tel (631) 439-2000 *SIC* 5122

■ QUALITY KING FRAGRANCE INC p 1197
35 Sawgrass Dr Ste 1 11713
Tel (631) 866-4100 *SIC* 5122

BERGEN, NY

LIBERTY PUMPS INC p 862
7000 Appletree Ave 14416
Tel (800) 543-2550 *SIC* 3561

BETHPAGE, NY

ADULTS AND CHILDREN WITH LEARNING AND DEVELOPMENTAL DISABILITIES INC p 24
807 S Oyster Bay Rd 11714
Tel (516) 681-4500 *SIC* 8322 8331

BBHI HOLDINGS LLC p 163
1111 Stewart Ave 11714
Tel (516) 803-2300 *SIC* 6719

BEST YET MARKET INC p 177
1 Lexington Ave 11714
Tel (516) 570-5300 *SIC* 5411

BETHPAGE FEDERAL CREDIT UNION INC p 178
899 S Oyster Bay Rd 11714
Tel (516) 349-6700 *SIC* 6061

BETHPAGE UNION FREE SCHOOL DISTRICT p 178
10 Cherry Ave 11714
Tel (516) 644-4100 *SIC* 8211

■ BRESNAN BROADBAND HOLDINGS LLC p 210
1111 Stewart Ave 11714
Tel (516) 803-2300 *SIC* 1623

■ BRESNAN COMMUNICATIONS LLC p 210
1111 Stewart Ave 11714
Tel (516) 803-2300 *SIC* 4841

CABLEVISION SYSTEMS CORP p 235
1111 Stewart Ave 11714
Tel (516) 803-2300 *SIC* 4841

CABLEVISION SYSTEMS LONG ISLAND CORP p 235
1111 Stewart Ave 11714
Tel (516) 803-2300 *SIC* 4841

CCG HOLDINGS LLC p 270
1111 Stewart Ave 11714
Tel (516) 803-2300 *SIC* 7832

COMFORCE TELECOM INC p 344
999 Stewart Ave 11714
Tel (516) 437-3300 *SIC* 7363

CSC HOLDINGS LLC p 397
1111 Stewart Ave 11714
Tel (516) 803-2300 *SIC* 4841 4813

EPISCOPAL HEALTH SERVICES INC p 505
700 Hicksville Rd Ste 210 11714
Tel (516) 349-6100 *SIC* 8062 8051

KING KULLEN GROCERY CO INC p 820
185 Central Ave 11714
Tel (516) 733-7100 *SIC* 5411

KRAVET FABRICS INC p 829
225 Central Ave S 11714
Tel (516) 293-2000 *SIC* 2392

KRAVET INC p 829
225 Cent Ave S 11714
Tel (516) 293-2000 *SIC* 5131 5198 2392

PRO CORP p 1178
999 Stewart Ave Ste 100 11714
Tel (516) 437-3300 *SIC* 7363 7361

PRO UNLIMITED GLOBAL SOLUTIONS INC p 1178
999 Stewart Ave Ste 100 11714
Tel (516) 437-3300 *SIC* 7363 7361

WSNCHS NORTH INC p 1628
4295 Hempstead Tpke 11714
Tel (516) 579-6000 *SIC* 8062

BINGHAMTON, NY

BINGHAMTON UNIVERSITY p 183
4400 Vestal Pkwy 13902
Tel (607) 777-2000 *SIC* 8221 9411

BOTNICK/5 VENTURES INC p 203
159 Front St 163 13905
Tel (607) 723-8971 *SIC* 5511 7218

BROOME COUNTY p 218
60 Hawley St 13901
Tel (607) 778-2452 *SIC* 9111

BROOME-TIOGA BOARD OF COOPERATIVE EDUCATIONAL SERVICES p 218
435 Glenwood Rd 13905
Tel (607) 763-3618 *SIC* 8299

■ BW ELLIOTT MANUFACTURING CO LLC p 230
11 Beckwith Ave 13901
Tel (607) 772-0404 *SIC* 3568 3492 3531

COLUMBIAN MUTUAL LIFE INSURANCE CO INC p 342
4704 Vestal Pkwy E 13902
Tel (607) 724-2472 *SIC* 6411

CROWLEY FOODS INC p 394
93 Pennsylvania Ave 13903
Tel (800) 637-0019 *SIC* 2026 2024

FELCHAR MANUFACTURING CORP p 537
196 Corporate Dr 13904
Tel (607) 723-3106 *SIC* 3678 3089 3621

I3 ELECTRONICS INC p 725
100 Eldredge St 13901
Tel (607) 238-7077 *SIC* 3672

KOST TIRE DISTRIBUTORS INC p 828
200 Holleder Pkwy 13904
Tel (607) 723-9471 *SIC* 5014 5531 7538

LOURDES HOSPITAL p 881
169 Riverside Dr 13905
Tel (607) 798-5111 *SIC* 8062

MIRABITO HOLDINGS INC p 974
49 Court St Ste 1 13901
Tel (607) 561-2700
SIC 5172 4925 5541 5411 5983

NEW YORK STATE ELECTRIC & GAS CORP p 1036
18 Link Dr 13904
Tel (607) 762-7200 *SIC* 4911 4924 4923

OUR LADY OF LOURDES MEMORIAL HOSPITAL INC p 1098
169 Riverside Dr 13905
Tel (607) 798-5111 *SIC* 8062

SECURITY MUTUAL LIFE INSURANCE CO OF NEW YORK p 1299
100 Court St 13901
Tel (607) 723-3551 *SIC* 6311 6321

UMH NY CORP p 1501
10 Acre Pl 13904
Tel (607) 775-6400 *SIC* 8059 8051 8741

UNITED HEALTH SERVICES HOSPITAL INC p 1509
10-42 Mitchell Ave 13903
Tel (607) 762-2200 *SIC* 8062

UNITED HEALTH SERVICES INC p 1509
10-42 Mitchell Ave 13903
Tel (607) 762-3024 *SIC* 8062 8051

BLAUVELT, NY

OAK BEVERAGES INC p 1070
1 Flower Ln 10913
Tel (718) 652-8555 *SIC* 5181

BOHEMIA, NY

CONNETQUOT CENTRAL SCHOOL DISTRICT OF ISLIP p 358
780 Ocean Ave 11716
Tel (631) 244-2203 *SIC* 8211

CONSTANCE FOOD GROUP INC p 360
545 Johnson Ave Ste 10 11716
Tel (631) 582-1144 *SIC* 5149 5141

■ DATA DEVICE CORP p 413
105 Wilbur Pl 11716
Tel (631) 567-5600 *SIC* 3577 3674 3677

■ ILC HOLDINGS INC p 731
105 Wilbur Pl 11716
Tel (631) 567-5600 *SIC* 3674

■ ILC INDUSTRIES LLC p 731
105 Wilbur Pl 11716
Tel (631) 567-5600 *SIC* 3674

J & B RESTAURANT PARTNERS OF LONG ISLAND LLC p 769
4000 Veterans Memorial Hw 11716
Tel (631) 218-9067 *SIC* 5812

MED SERVICES INC p 935
100 Knickerbocker Ave C 11716
Tel (631) 218-6450 *SIC* 3845 7699

PRECISION-AIRE INC p 1169
2100 Artic Ave Unit 9 11716
Tel (631) 563-8280 *SIC* 1711

■ REXALL SUNDOWN INC p 1230
110 Orville Dr 11716
Tel (631) 567-9500 *SIC* 5961 5122 2833

SARTORIUS STEDIM NORTH AMERICA INC p 1282
5 Orville Dr Ste 200 11716
Tel (631) 254-4249 *SIC* 5085

VWRE HOLDINGS INC p 1567
105 Orville Dr 11716
Tel (631) 567-9500 *SIC* 6719 5499

WHELANS INTERNATIONAL CO INC p 1605
163 Keyland Ct 11716
Tel (631) 244-6962 *SIC* 7349

BRENTWOOD, NY

BRENTWOOD UNION FREE SCHOOL DISTRICT p 210
52 3rd Ave 11717
Tel (631) 434-2335 *SIC* 8211

PETLAND DISCOUNTS INC p 1138
355 Crooked Hill Rd 11717
Tel (631) 273-6363 *SIC* 5999

US NONWOVENS CORP p 1532
100 Emjay Blvd 11717
Tel (631) 952-0100 *SIC* 2842

BREWSTER, NY

ACE ENDICO CORP p 16
80 International Blvd 10509
Tel (914) 347-3131 *SIC* 5141 5142 5148

BRIARCLIFF MANOR, NY

AGERA ENERGY LLC p 34
555 Pleasantville Rd 107s 10510
Tel (844) 692-4372 *SIC* 4911

AGERA HOLDINGS LLC p 34
555 Pleasantville Rd 107s 10510
Tel (914) 236-1405 *SIC* 4911

SAW MILL CAPITAL LLC p 1284
555 Pleasantville Rd 220s 10510
Tel (914) 741-2426 *SIC* 6726 6282

USI SERVICE CORP p 1535
555 Plsntvlle Rd Ste 160s 10510
Tel (914) 747-6300 *SIC* 6411

BRIARWOOD, NY

SAMARITAN DAYTOP VILLAGE INC p 1274
13802 Queens Blvd Fl 1 11435
Tel (718) 206-2000 *SIC* 8322 8093

UNITED WELFARE FUND p 1515
13850 Queens Blvd 11435
Tel (718) 658-4848 *SIC* 6371

BRIDGEHAMPTON, NY

▲ BRIDGE BANCORP INC p 211
2200 Montauk Hwy 11932
Tel (631) 537-1000 *SIC* 6021

■ BRIDGEHAMPTON NATIONAL BANK p 211
2200 Montauk Hwy 11932
Tel (631) 602-3005 *SIC* 6021

BRONX, NY

ACACIA NETWORK INC p 13
300 E 175th St 10457
Tel (718) 299-1100 *SIC* 8399

AFFINITY HEALTH PLAN INC p 32
1776 Eastchester Rd # 202 10461
Tel (718) 794-7700 *SIC* 6324

ALBERT EINSTEIN COLLEGE OF MEDICINE p 46
1300 Morris Park Ave 10461
Tel (718) 430-2000 *SIC* 8221

ALBERT EINSTEIN COLLEGE OF MEDICINE INC p 46
1300 Morris Park Ave 10461
Tel (718) 920-6758 *SIC* 8249

BALDOR SPECIALTY FOODS INC p 147
155 Food Center Dr Ste 1 10474
Tel (718) 860-9100 *SIC* 5141

BETH ABRAHAM HEALTH SERVICES p 177
2540 Barker Ave Ofc 10467
Tel (718) 519-5831 *SIC* 8059 8351 8082

BRONX LEBANON HOSPITAL CENTER (INC) p 217
1276 Fulton Ave 10456
Tel (718) 590-1800 *SIC* 8062

CALVARY HOSPITAL INC p 243
1740 Eastchester Rd 10461
Tel (718) 518-2000 *SIC* 8069

CENTERLIGHT HEALTHCARE INC p 276
1250 Waters Pl Ste 602 10461
Tel (347) 640-6000 *SIC* 8051 8082 8322

■ DAIRYLAND USA CORP p 409
1250 Waters Pl Ste 704 10461
Tel (718) 842-8700 *SIC* 5141

DARRIGO BROS CO OF NEW YORK INC p 412
315 Nyc Terminal Mkt 10474
Tel (718) 991-5900 *SIC* 5148

E ARMATA INC p 466
114 Nyc Term Mkt 10474
Tel (718) 991-5600 *SIC* 5148

EUGENIO MARIA DEHOSTOS COMMUNITY COLLEGE p 512
500 Grand Concourse 10451
Tel (718) 518-4444 *SIC* 8222

FANCY FOODS INC p 527
Hunts Pt Cooperative Mkt 10474
Tel (718) 617-3000 *SIC* 5144 5147

FORDHAM UNIVERSITY p 566
441 E Fordham Rd 10458
Tel (718) 817-1000 *SIC* 8221

HEBREW HOME FOR AGED AT RIVERDALE p 680
5901 Palisade Ave 10471
Tel (718) 581-1000 *SIC* 8059

HERBERT H LEHMAN COLLEGE p 685
250 Bedford Park Blvd W 10468
Tel (718) 960-8261 *SIC* 8221

JEWISH HOME AND HOSPITAL p 784
100 W Kingsbridge Rd # 100 10468
Tel (718) 579-0420 SIC 6513 6531

LANCE INVESTIGATION SERVICE INC p 841
1438 Boston Rd 10460
Tel (718) 893-1400 SIC 7381 1731

LINCOLN MEDICAL AND MENTAL HEALTH CENTER p 867
234 E 149th St 10451
Tel (718) 579-5000 SIC 8062

LOEHMANNS HOLDINGS INC p 874
2500 Halsey St Frnt 1 10461
Tel (718) 409-2000 SIC 5621 5661 3171

LOEHMANNS INC p 874
2500 Halsey St 10461
Tel (718) 409-2000 SIC 5621

MANHATTAN BEER DISTRIBUTORS LLC p 901
955 E 149th St 10455
Tel (718) 292-9300 SIC 5181

MANHATTAN COLLEGE CORP p 901
4513 Mnhttan College Pkwy 10471
Tel (718) 862-8000 SIC 8221

MONTEFIORE MEDICAL CENTER p 986
111 E 210th St 10467
Tel (718) 920-4321 SIC 8062

NATHEL & NATHEL INC p 1009
357 Nyc Term Mkt C 10474
Tel (718) 991-6050 SIC 5148

NEBRASKALAND INC p 1023
355 Food Center Dr Ste G4 10474
Tel (718) 842-0700 SIC 5147

NEW YORK BOTANICAL GARDEN p 1034
2900 Southern Blvd 10458
Tel (718) 817-8779 SIC 8422 8299

NEW YORK CITY GEOGRAPHIC DISTRICT 10 p 1034
1 Fordham Plz Rm 835 10458
Tel (718) 741-5852 SIC 8211

NEW YORK CITY GEOGRAPHIC DISTRICT 12 p 1034
1970 W Farms Rd 10460
Tel (718) 328-2310 SIC 8211

NEW YORK CITY GEOGRAPHIC DISTRICT 7 p 1034
501 Courtland Ave 10451
Tel (718) 742-6500 SIC 8211

NEW YORK CITY GEOGRAPHIC DISTRICT 8 p 1034
601 Stickball Blvd 10473
Tel (718) 828-6653 SIC 8211

NEW YORK CITY GEOGRAPHIC DISTRICT 9 p 1034
250 E 164th St 10456
Tel (718) 741-3157 SIC 8211

NEW YORK GEOGRAPHIC DISTRICT 11 p 1035
2750 Throop Ave 10469
Tel (718) 519-2620 SIC 8211

PAPER ENTERPRISES INC p 1112
770 E 132nd St 10454
Tel (718) 402-1200 SIC 5113 5087

PERRIGO NEW YORK INC p 1137
1700 Bathgate Ave 10457
Tel (718) 960-9900 SIC 2834

QUALITY HOME BRANDS HOLDINGS LLC p 1197
125 Rose Feiss Blvd 10454
Tel (718) 292-2024 SIC 3645 5063

REGIONAL AID FOR INTERIM NEEDS INC p 1219
811 Morris Park Ave 10462
Tel (718) 892-5520 SIC 8322

RIVERBAY CORP p 1237
2049 Bartow Ave 10475
Tel (718) 320-3300 SIC 6513

RIVERDALE CENTER FOR NURSING AND REHABILITATION LLC p 1237
3220 Henry Hudson Pkwy 10463
Tel (718) 514-2000 SIC 8051

S & J SHEET METAL SUPPLY INC p 1261
608 E 133rd St 10454
Tel (718) 993-0460 SIC 5033 3444

S KATZMAN PRODUCE INC p 1262
Row A 153 157 Hnts Pt Mkt 10474
Tel (718) 991-4700 SIC 5148

ST BARNABAS COMMUNITY ENTERPRISES p 1365
4422 3rd Ave 10457
Tel (718) 960-6100 SIC 8062

ST BARNABAS HOSPITAL p 1365
4422 3rd Ave 10457
Tel (718) 960-9000 SIC 8062

SULTANA DISTRIBUTION SERVICES INC p 1397
600 Food Center Dr 10474
Tel (718) 842-4674 SIC 5145 5149

BRONXVILLE, NY

LAWRENCE HOSPITAL CENTER p 848
55 Palmer Ave 10708
Tel (914) 787-1000 SIC 8062

BRONX, NY

VISTA FOOD EXCHANGE INC p 1562
355 Food Center Dr B101 10474
Tel (718) 542-4401
SIC 5144 5147 5146 5148 5143

WEST SIDE FOODS INC p 1595
355 Food Center Dr A23 10474
Tel (718) 842-8500 SIC 5141

WILDLIFE CONSERVATION SOCIETY p 1609
2300 Southern Blvd 10460
Tel (718) 220-5144 SIC 8422 8641

BROOKHAVEN, NY

AMNEAL PHARMACEUTICALS OF NEW YORK LLC p 86
50 Horseblock Rd 11719
Tel (631) 952-0214 SIC 2834 5122

BROOKLYN, NY

1 STOP ELECTRONICS CENTER INC p 1
1100 Coney Island Ave 11230
Tel (718) 249-1211 SIC 5722 5021

A F SUPPLY CORP p 5
942 Lafayette Ave 11221
Tel (212) 243-5400 SIC 5074

A G M DECO INC p 5
741 Myrtle Ave 11205
Tel (718) 624-6200 SIC 3442

AIJJ ENTERPRISES INC p 38
1000 Pennsylvania Ave 11207
Tel (718) 485-3000 SIC 5621

AMERICAN STOCK TRANSFER & TRUST CO LLC p 80
6201 15th Ave 11219
Tel (718) 921-8200 SIC 6289

AMERICAN TRANSIT INSURANCE CO INC p 80
1 Metrotech Ctr Fl 7 11201
Tel (212) 857-8200 SIC 6321 6331 6311

AMPLIFY EDUCATION INC p 86
55 Washington St Ste 900 11201
Tel (212) 213-8177 SIC 7371 8299

ATTENTIVE HOME CARE AGENCY INC p 129
3131 Coney Island Ave 11235
Tel (718) 843-8430 SIC 8082

BAYSIDE FUEL OIL CORP p 162
1776 Shore Pkwy 11214
Tel (718) 622-2900 SIC 5171

BAYSIDE FUEL OIL DEPOT CORP p 162
1776 Shore Pkwy 11214
Tel (718) 372-9800 SIC 5171

BEECHWOOD MOUNTAIN LLC p 168
500 Broadway Ste A 11211
Tel (718) 418-3205 SIC 5021

BOGOPA ENTERPRISES INC p 197
650 Fountain Ave 11208
Tel (718) 346-6500 SIC 5141

BOGOPA SERVICE CORP p 197
650 Fountain Ave 11208
Tel (718) 257-7801 SIC 5411 4225 5149

BROOKDALE HOSPITAL CENTER HOUSING CO INC p 217
1 Brookdale Plz 11212
Tel (718) 240-5000 SIC 8062

BROOKDALE HOSPITAL CENTER HOUSING CO INC p 217
10101 Avenue D 11236
Tel (718) 240-5000 SIC 8082

BROOKDALE HOSPITAL MEDICAL CENTER p 217
1 Brookdale Plz 11212
Tel (718) 240-5000 SIC 8011 8062

BROOKDALE UNIVERSITY HOSPITAL & MEDICAL CENTER p 217
1 Brookdale Plz 11212
Tel (718) 240-5000 SIC 8011 6324

BROOKLYN DEVELOPMENT CENTER p 218
888 Fountain Ave 11239
Tel (718) 642-6002 SIC 8051

BROOKLYN HOSPITAL CENTER p 218
121 Dekalb Ave 11201
Tel (718) 250-8000 SIC 8062

BROOKLYN LAW SCHOOL p 218
250 Joralemon St 11201
Tel (718) 625-2200 SIC 8221

BROOKLYN PUBLIC LIBRARY p 218
280 Cadman Plz W 11201
Tel (718) 230-2100 SIC 8231

BRUCE SUPPLY CORP p 220
8805 18th Ave 11214
Tel (718) 259-4900 SIC 5074

CABS HOME ATTENDANTS SERVICE INC p 235
44 Varet St 11206
Tel (718) 388-0220 SIC 8082

CAMBA INC p 243
1720 Church Ave Ste 2 11226
Tel (718) 287-2600 SIC 8399

CATHOLIC CHARITIES DIOCESE OF BROOKLYN & QUEENS p 265
191 Joralemon St 11201
Tel (718) 722-6000 SIC 8322 8361

CATHOLIC CHARITIES NEIGHBORHOOD SERVICES INC p 265
191 Joralemon St 11201
Tel (718) 722-6000 SIC 8059 8322

CERTIFIED LUMBER CORP p 284
Isack Rosenberg 470 Kent 11211
Tel (718) 387-1233 SIC 5031 5211

COMPOSTELA FUND OF ROMAN CATHOLIC DIOCESE OF BROOKLYN NEW YORK p 352
75 Greene Ave 11238
Tel (718) 623-5231 SIC 6722

CUMBERLAND PACKING CORP p 400
2 Cumberland St 11205
Tel (718) 858-4200 SIC 2869

▲ DIME COMMUNITY BANCSHARES INC p 440
209 Havemeyer St 11211
Tel (718) 782-6200 SIC 6035

■ DIME COMMUNITY BANK p 440
209 Havemeyer St 11211
Tel (718) 782-6200 SIC 6035

DK MAGAZINES CORP p 445
24 Meadow St 11206
Tel (718) 417-3573 SIC 5199

DOLLAR PHONE CORP p 448
34 Franklin Ave Ste 220 11205
Tel (718) 889-1100 SIC 4813

ELDERPLAN INC p 484
6323 7th Ave Ste 3 11220
Tel (800) 353-3765 SIC 6324

EMPIRE MERCHANTS LLC p 493
16 Bridgewater St 11222
Tel (718) 383-5500 SIC 5182

▲ ETSY INC p 512
117 Adams St 11201
Tel (718) 855-7955 SIC 5961 5947 7319

EXTECH BUILDING MATERIALS INC p 521
87 Bowne St 11231
Tel (718) 852-7090 SIC 5082 5033 5031

FASHION GALLERY INC p 531
1000 Pennsylvania Ave 11207
Tel (718) 485-3000 SIC 5699

GETYOURPERFUME.COM INC p 609
700 Columbia St Bldg 302 11231
Tel (888) 264-2899 SIC 5999

GLANTZ HOLDINGS INC p 614
16 Court St Ste 3000 11241
Tel (502) 271-5560 SIC 5046

GLOBAL SWITCHING INC p 617
34 Franklin Ave Ste 220 11205
Tel (718) 889-1100 SIC 4813

H SCHRIER & CO INC p 650
4901 Glenwood Rd 11234
Tel (718) 258-7500 SIC 5141

HEARTSHARE HUMAN SERVICES OF NY ROMAN CATHOLIC DIOCESE OF BROOKLYN p 679
12 Metrotech Ctr Fl 29 11201
Tel (718) 422-4200 SIC 8322

HSCB FOUNDATION INC p 715
450 Clarkson Ave 11203
Tel (718) 270-3041 SIC 8699

IMPREMEDIA LLC p 735
1 Metrotech Ctr Fl 18 11201
Tel (212) 807-4785 SIC 2711

INFINITY CLASSICS INTERNATIONAL INC p 741
1368 38th St 11218
Tel (718) 851-2577 SIC 5139

INTERFAITH MEDICAL CENTER p 752
1545 Atlantic Ave 11213
Tel (718) 613-4000 SIC 8062

JAZZY ELECTRONICS CORP p 779
1600 63rd St 11204
Tel (718) 236-8000 SIC 6512 5064 3651

JEWISH CHILD CARE ASSOCIATION OF NEW YORK p 784
858 E 29th St 11210
Tel (917) 808-4800 SIC 8361 8399

■ JP MORGAN CLEARING CORP p 794
1 Metrotech Ctr N Lbby 4 11201
Tel (212) 272-1000 SIC 6289 6211

KAMCO SUPPLY CORP p 801
80 21st St 11232
Tel (718) 840-1700 SIC 5031 5033

KEYSPAN CORP p 815
1 Metrotech Ctr Fl 1 11201
Tel (718) 403-1000 SIC 4924

KINGSBROOK JEWISH MEDICAL CENTER INC p 820
585 Schenectady Ave Ste 2 11203
Tel (718) 604-5000 SIC 8062

L & R DISTRIBUTORS INC p 833
9301 Avenue D 11236
Tel (718) 272-2100 SIC 5122 5131

L I C H CORP p 834
339 Hicks St 11201
Tel (718) 780-1000 SIC 8062 8092 5912

LINROC COMMUNITY SERVICES CORP p 869
Linden Blvd At Brookdale 11212
Tel (718) 240-5656 SIC 8741

LONG ISLAND COLLEGE HOSPITAL INC p 876
450 Clarkson Ave 11203
Tel (718) 780-1000 SIC 8062 9431

MAIMONIDES MEDICAL CENTER p 897
4802 10th Ave 11219
Tel (718) 581-0598 SIC 8062

MAKERBOT INDUSTRIES LLC p 899
1 Metrotech Ctr Fl 21 11201
Tel (347) 334-6800 SIC 3621 3625 5084

MARAMONT CORP p 904
5600 1st Ave 11220
Tel (718) 439-8900 SIC 2099 8322

METROPOLITAN JEWISH HEALTH SYSTEM INC p 956
6323 7th Ave Ste 2 11220
Tel (718) 621-3600 SIC 8322

METROPOLITAN JEWISH HOME CARE INC p 956
6323 7th Ave Ste 2 11220
Tel (718) 921-7742 SIC 8082

NATIONAL GRID ENERGY CORP p 1013
1 Metrotech Ctr Fl 1 11201
Tel (718) 403-2000 SIC 8748

NATIONAL GRID SERVICES INC p 1013
1 Metrotech Ctr Fl 1 11201
Tel (718) 403-2000 SIC 4924

NEW 5-7-9 AND BEYOND INC p 1029
1000 Pennsylvania Ave 11207
Tel (718) 485-3000 SIC 5621

NEW YORK CITY GEOGRAPHIC DISTRICT 13 p 1034
355 Park Pl 11238
Tel (718) 636-3204 SIC 8211

NEW YORK CITY GEOGRAPHIC DISTRICT 14 p 1034
215 Heyward St 11206
Tel (718) 302-7600 SIC 8211

NEW YORK CITY GEOGRAPHIC DISTRICT 15 p 1034
131 Livingston St Rm 301 11201
Tel (718) 935-4317 SIC 8211

NEW YORK CITY GEOGRAPHIC DISTRICT 17 p 1034
1224 Park Pl 11213
Tel (718) 221-4372 SIC 8211

NEW YORK CITY GEOGRAPHIC DISTRICT 19 p 1034
335 Adams St 11201
Tel (718) 923-5124 SIC 8211

NEW YORK CITY GEOGRAPHIC DISTRICT 20 p 1034
415 89th St 11209
Tel (718) 759-3942 SIC 8211

NEW YORK CITY GEOGRAPHIC DISTRICT 21 p 1034
501 West Ave 11224
Tel (718) 714-2502 SIC 8211

NEW YORK CITY GEOGRAPHIC DISTRICT 22 p 1034
5619 Flatlands Ave 11234
Tel (718) 968-6117 SIC 8211

NEW YORK CITY GEOGRAPHIC DISTRICT 23 p 1034
1665 Saint Marks Ave 11233
Tel (718) 922-4794 SIC 8211

NEW YORK COMMUNITY HOSPITAL p 1035
2525 Kings Hwy 11229
Tel (718) 692-5300 SIC 8062

NEW YORK GEOGRAPHIC DISTRICT 18 p 1035
1106 E 95th St 11236
Tel (718) 566-6008 SIC 8211

NEW YORK METHODIST HOSPITAL p 1035
506 6th St 11215
Tel (718) 780-3000 SIC 8062

NEW YUNG WAH TRADING LLC p 1036
311 Richardson St 11222
Tel (718) 388-3322 SIC 5141

NYU LUTHERAN MEDICAL CENTER p 1069
150 55th St 11220
Tel (718) 630-7000 SIC 8062 8621

PEERLESS IMPORTERS INC p 1127
16 Bridgewater St 11222
Tel (718) 383-5500 SIC 5182

PHOENIX BEVERAGES INC p 1144
2 Atlantic Ave Pier 7 11201
Tel (718) 609-7200 SIC 5181

PHOENIX HOUSE FOUNDATION INC p 1145
50 Jay St 11201
Tel (646) 505-2000 SIC 8361

POLYTECHNIC INSTITUTE OF NEW YORK UNIVERSITY p 1160
6 Metrotech Ctr 11201
Tel (718) 260-3600 SIC 8221

PRATT INSTITUTE p 1167
200 Willoughby Ave 11205
Tel (718) 636-3600 SIC 8221

PREFERRED HOME CARE INC p 1169
1267 57th St Ste 1p 11219
Tel (718) 841-8000 SIC 8059

RAINBOW USA INC p 1205
1000 Pennsylvania Ave 11207
Tel (718) 485-3000 SIC 5621

ROBERT W WILSON CHARITABLE TRUST p 1241
520 83rd St 11209
Tel (718) 748-6113 SIC 8699

ROMAN CATHOLIC DIOCESE OF BROOKLYN p 1248
310 Prospect Park W 11215
Tel (718) 399-5900 SIC 8661

S J FUEL CO INC p 1262
601 Union St 11215
Tel (718) 855-6060 SIC 5983 1711

SCIENTIFIC COMPONENTS CORP p 1292
13 Neptune Ave 11235
Tel (718) 934-4500 SIC 3679

SPECIAL TOUCH HOME HEALTH CARE SERVICES INC p 1356
2091 Coney Island Ave 11223
Tel (718) 627-1122 SIC 8082

ST JOSEPHS COLLEGE NEW YORK p 1368
245 Clinton Ave 11205
Tel (718) 940-5300 SIC 8221

ST NICHOLAS LOCAL DEVELOPMENT CORP p 1372
11 Catherine St 11211
Tel (718) 388-2233 SIC 8322

STARRETT CITY ASSOCIATES LP p 1379
1230 Pa Ave Ste 1 11239
Tel (718) 240-4112 SIC 6513

STARRETT CITY INC p 1379
1230 Pa Ave Ste 1 11239
Tel (718) 642-8700 SIC 6513

SUNSET PARK HEALTH COUNCIL INC p 1404
150 55th St Ste 1 11220
Tel (718) 630-7000 SIC 8099

SUNY DOWNSTATE MEDICAL CENTER p 1405
450 Clarkson Ave 11203
Tel (718) 270-1000 SIC 8221 9411

TOM CHEITORAH INSTITUTE p 1459
1372 47th St 11219
Tel (718) 438-3061 SIC 8733

TRANSCARE CORP p 1471
1 Metrotech Ctr Fl 20 11201
Tel (718) 251-4600 SIC 4119

UB DISTRIBUTORS LLC p 1498
1213 Grand St 11211
Tel (718) 497-2407 SIC 5181

US HISPANIC MEDIA INC p 1532
1 Metrotech Ctr Fl 18 11201
Tel (212) 885-8000 SIC 2711

VICE GROUP HOLDING INC p 1555
49 S 2nd St 11249
Tel (718) 599-3101 SIC 8748 7812

VICE MEDIA LLC p 1555
49 S 2nd St 11249
Tel (718) 732-8142 SIC 7922

VICTORY MEMORIAL HOSPITAL p 1556
699 92nd St 11228
Tel (718) 567-1234 SIC 8062 8051

■ WASTE MANAGEMENT OF NEW YORK LLC p 1581
123 Varick Ave 11237
Tel (718) 533-5100 SIC 4953

WHITE GLOVE PLACEMENT INC p 1606
630 Flushing Ave Fl 2 11206
Tel (718) 387-8181 SIC 7349

WOODHULL MEDICAL & MENTAL HEALTH CENTER AUXILIARY INC p 1623
760 Broadway Rm 3cc27 11206
Tel (718) 963-8467 SIC 8062

WYCKOFF HEIGHTS MEDICAL CENTER p 1629
374 Stockholm St 11237
Tel (718) 963-7272 SIC 8062

YELED VYALDA EARLY CHILDHOOD CENTER INC p 1635
1312 38th St 11218
Tel (718) 686-3700 SIC 8351

BUFFALO, NY

ACCUMED TECHNOLOGIES INC p 16
160 Bud Mil Dr Ste 1 14206
Tel (716) 853-1800 SIC 5047

API HEAT TRANSFER CO p 96
2777 Walden Ave Ste 1 14225
Tel (716) 684-6700 SIC 3443

API HEAT TRANSFER INC p 96
2777 Walden Ave Ste 1 14225
Tel (716) 684-6700 SIC 5084

AURUBIS BUFFALO INC p 132
70 Sayre St 14207
Tel (716) 879-6700 SIC 3351

B & L WHOLESALE SUPPLY INC p 141
70 Hartford St 14206
Tel (716) 853-2600 SIC 5033 5031

■ BRACOR INC p 206
346 Delaware Ave 14202
Tel (716) 856-7500 SIC 8082 8071 7361

BUFFALO CITY SCHOOL DISTRICT p 224
65 Niagara Sq Rm 712 14202
Tel (716) 816-3500 SIC 8211

BUFFALO HOSPITAL SUPPLY CO INC p 224
4039 Genesee St Ste 100 14225
Tel (716) 626-9400 SIC 5047

BUFFALO ORLANDO I LLC p 224
570 Delaware Ave 14202
Tel (716) 886-0211 SIC 8741

BUFFALO VILLAGE ASSOC 190 CAROLINA BUF p 224
190 Carolina St 14201
Tel (716) 847-6313 SIC 6513

CANISIUS COLLEGE p 247
2001 Main St 14208
Tel (716) 883-7000 SIC 8221

CATHOLIC HEALTH SYSTEM INC p 266
144 Genesee St Fl 1 14203
Tel (716) 862-2400
SIC 8741 8062 5999 8051

CHOCOLAT FREY USA LTD p 301
3500 Genesee St 14225
Tel (716) 340-0880 SIC 5145

CITY OF BUFFALO p 313
65 Niagara Sq Rm 201 14202
Tel (716) 851-4200 SIC 9111

▲ COMPUTER TASK GROUP INC p 353
800 Delaware Ave 14209
Tel (716) 882-8000 SIC 7371 7379 7361

COUNTY OF ERIE p 378
95 Franklin St Rm 1603 14202
Tel (716) 858-8500 SIC 9111

CROSSROADS ARENA LLC p 394
1 Seymour H Knox Iii Plz 14203
Tel (716) 855-4100 SIC 7389

DELAWARE NORTH COMPANIES GAMING & ENTERTAINMENT INC p 424
250 Delaware Ave Ste 3 14202
Tel (716) 858-5000 SIC 7948

DELAWARE NORTH COMPANIES INC p 424
250 Delaware Ave 14202
Tel (716) 858-5000
SIC 5461 7011 7993 7999

DELAWARE NORTH COMPANIES PARKS & RESORTS INC p 424
250 Delaware Ave Ste 3 14202
Tel (716) 858-5000 SIC 7011

DELAWARE NORTH COMPANIES SPORTSERVICE INC p 424
250 Delaware Ave 14202
Tel (716) 858-5000 SIC 5812

DELAWARE NORTH COMPANIES TRAVEL HOSPITALITY SERVICES INC p 424
250 Delaware Ave Ste 3 14202
Tel (716) 858-5000 SIC 5812 5947 5813

DELTA-SONIC CARWASH SYSTEMS INC p 427
570 Delaware Ave 14202
Tel (716) 874-5668 SIC 5461 7542

DERRICK CORP p 431
590 Duke Rd 14225
Tel (716) 683-9010 SIC 3533

DIVAL SAFETY EQUIPMENT INC p 443
1721 Niagara St 14207
Tel (716) 874-9060
SIC 5099 8748 8734 5047 5136 5661

DNC LANDMARK HOLDINGS LLC p 446
40 Fountain Plz 14202
Tel (716) 858-5000 SIC 5812

DUNN TIRE LLC p 461
475 Cayuga Rd Ste 500 14225
Tel (716) 683-3910 SIC 5531 5014

ELLICOTT DEVELOPMENT OF BUFFALO LLC p 488
295 Main St Rm 210 14203
Tel (716) 854-0060 SIC 1522 1542 6531

ELMWOOD SQUARE PRESERVATION LP p 489
505 Elmwood Ave 14222
Tel (716) 881-6662 SIC 6531

ERIE COMMUNITY COLLEGE p 508
121 Ellicott St 14203
Tel (716) 842-2770 SIC 5942 8222

ERIE COUNTY MEDICAL CENTER CORP p 508
462 Grider St 14215
Tel (716) 898-3000 SIC 8062

ERIE COUNTY WATER AUTHORITY p 508
295 Main St Rm 350 14203
Tel (716) 849-8484 SIC 4941

■ FEDEX TRADE NETWORKS TRANSPORT & BROKERAGE INC p 537
128 Dearborn St 14207
Tel (716) 879-1300 SIC 4731

■ FIRST NIAGARA BANK NATIONAL ASSOCIATION p 548
726 Exchange St Ste 618 14210
Tel (716) 625-7500 SIC 6021

FIRST NIAGARA FINANCIAL GROUP INC p 548
726 Exchange St Ste 618 14210
Tel (716) 819-5500 SIC 6411

■ FIRST NIAGARA RISK MANAGEMENT INC p 548
726 Exchange St Ste 900 14210
Tel (716) 819-5500 SIC 6411

FIRSTSOURCE SOLUTIONS USA INC p 551
205 Bryant Woods S 14228
Tel (716) 564-4400 SIC 8741

▲ GIBRALTAR INDUSTRIES INC p 611
3556 Lake Shore Rd # 100 14219
Tel (716) 826-6500
SIC 3499 3316 3441 3398

GRAPHIC CONTROLS ACQUISITION CORP p 631
400 Exchange St 14204
Tel (716) 853-7500 SIC 2752 2679

GRAPHIC CONTROLS HOLDINGS INC p 631
400 Exchange St 14204
Tel (716) 853-7500 SIC 2752 2679 6719

HAMISTER GROUP LLC p 655
10 Lafayette Sq Ste 1900 14203
Tel (716) 839-4000 SIC 7011 8052 8741

HANES SUPPLY INC p 657
55 James E Casey Dr 14206
Tel (716) 826-2636
SIC 5085 5082 3496 1799

HART HOTELS INC p 665
617 Dingens St Ste 4 14206
Tel (716) 893-6551 SIC 7011

HEALTHNOW NEW YORK INC p 677
257 W Genesee St 14202
Tel (716) 887-6900 SIC 6324 6411

HSBC NORTH AMERICA INC p 715
1 Hsbc Ctr Ste 1 14203
Tel (716) 841-2424
SIC 6021 6035 6221 6091 6211

INDEPENDENT HEALTH CORP p 736
511 Farber Lakes Dr Ste 2 14221
Tel (716) 631-3001 SIC 6324

KALEIDA HEALTH p 801
726 Exchange St 14210
Tel (716) 859-8000 SIC 8062

KENMORE-TONAWANDA UNION FREE SCHOOL DISTRICT p 810
1500 Colvin Blvd 14223
Tel (716) 874-8400 SIC 8211

KNIA HOLDINGS INC p 824
110 Hopkins St 14220
Tel (914) 241-7430 SIC 6719

LABOR MANAGEMENT HEALTHCARE FU p 836
3786 Broadway St 14227
Tel (716) 601-7980 SIC 8011

LACTALIS AMERICAN GROUP INC p 837
2376 S Park Ave 14220
Tel (716) 823-6262 SIC 2022

LAWLEY SERVICE INC p 847
361 Delaware Ave 14202
Tel (716) 849-8618 SIC 6411

▲ M&T BANK CORP p 890
1 M&T Plz Fl 5 14203
Tel (716) 635-4000 SIC 6022

■ M&TMORTGAGE CORP p 890
1 Fountain Plz 14203
Tel (716) 842-5445 SIC 6162

■ MANUFACTURERS AND TRADERS TRUST CO p 903
1 M And T Plz 14203
Tel (716) 842-4200 SIC 6022

MARRANO CORP p 910
2730 Transit Rd 14224
Tel (716) 675-1200 SIC 1521

MARTIN ATTEA p 912
1509 Clinton St 14206
Tel (716) 822-0378 SIC 5064 5722

■ MATERION ADVANCED MATERIALS TECHNOLOGIES AND SERVICES INC p 919
2978 Main St 14214
Tel (800) 327-1355 SIC 3339

MERCHANTS INSURANCE GROUP p 945
250 Main St 14202
Tel (716) 849-3333 SIC 6331

MERCHANTS MUTUAL INSURANCE CO p 945
240 Main St 14202
Tel (716) 849-3333 SIC 6331

MERCY HOSPITAL OF BUFFALO p 947
565 Abbott Rd 14220
Tel (716) 826-7000 SIC 8062

MILLARD FILLMORE HOSPITALS p 969
100 High St D1-588 14203
Tel (716) 859-5960 SIC 8062

MULTISORB TECHNOLOGIES INC p 1000
325 Harlem Rd 14224
Tel (716) 824-8900 SIC 2819

NATIONAL HEALTH CARE AFFILIATES INC p 1013
10 Lafayette Sq Ste 1900 14203
Tel (716) 839-4000 SIC 8082 8052

NEW ERA CAP CO INC p 1030
160 Delaware Ave 14202
Tel (716) 604-9000 SIC 2353

NIAGARA FRONTIER HOCKEY LP p 1042
111 Eight Ave 14203
Tel (716) 855-4160 SIC 7941

NIAGARA FRONTIER TRANSPORTATION AUTHORITY p 1042
181 Ellicott St Ste 1 14203
Tel (716) 855-7300 SIC 4111 4581

PARKVIEW HEALTH SERVICES OF NEW YORK LLC p 1117
1770 Colvin Blvd 14223
Tel (716) 876-2323 SIC 5912

PII HOLDINGS INC p 1147
2150 Elmwood Ave 14207
Tel (716) 876-9951 SIC 3089 3822 6719

PROTECTIVE INDUSTRIES INC p 1185
2150 Elmwood Ave 14207
Tel (716) 876-9951 SIC 3089 3822

PYRAMID WALDEN CO LP p 1194
1 Walden Galleria 14225
Tel (315) 422-7000 SIC 6512

RICH PRODUCTS CORP p 1232
1 Robert Rich Way 14213
Tel (716) 878-8422
SIC 2053 2092 2023 2099

ROBERTS-GORDON LLC p 1242
1250 William St 14206
Tel (716) 852-4400 SIC 3675 3433

ROSWELL PARK CANCER INSTITUTE p 1252
Elm And Carlton St 14263
Tel (716) 845-2300 SIC 8733

SCHMITT SALES INC p 1287
2101 Saint Ritas Ln 14221
Tel (716) 639-1500 SIC 5172 5541

SISTERS OF CHARITY HOSPITAL OF BUFFALO p 1327
144 Genesee St 14203
Tel (716) 828-3723 SIC 8661

SISTERS OF CHARITY HOSPITAL OF BUFFALO NEW YORK p 1327
2157 Main St 14214
Tel (716) 862-1000 SIC 8062

■ SUNLIGHT US CO INC p 1403
3556 Lake Shore Rd # 100 14219
Tel (716) 826-6500
SIC 3499 3316 3441 3398

SUNY UNIVERSITY AT BUFFALO p 1405
501 Capen Hall 14260
Tel (716) 645-2901 SIC 8221 9411

SUPERMARKET MANAGEMENT INC p 1407
460 Niagara St Ste 1 14201
Tel (716) 853-5787 SIC 5411

SWEETWORKS INC p 1412
3500 Genesee St 14225
Tel (716) 634-4545 SIC 2066 2067 2064

▲ SYNACOR INC p 1414
40 La Riviere Dr Ste 300 14202
Tel (716) 853-1362 SIC 7371 7374

TRIPIFOODS INC p 1482
1427 William St 14206
Tel (716) 853-7400
SIC 5141 5194 5145 5143 5142 5122

U B FOUNDATION ACTIVITIES INC p 1497
101 Center For Tommorrow 14260
Tel (716) 645-3013 SIC 6732

UNIVERA COMMUNITY HEALTH CARE p 1516
205 Park Club Ln Fl 2 14221
Tel (585) 454-1700 SIC 6321

UNIVERSITY AT BUFFALO p 1518
501 Capen Hall 14260
Tel (716) 645-2000 SIC 8221

UPSTATE NIAGARA COOPERATIVE INC p 1530
25 Anderson Rd 14225
Tel (716) 892-3156 SIC 2026

VALU HOME CENTERS INC p 1542
45 S Rossler Ave 14206
Tel (716) 824-4150 SIC 5211

■ WILMINGTON TRUST CORP p 1613
1 M And T Plz Ste 1 14203
Tel (302) 651-1000 SIC 6712

CALVERTON, NY

MILLER ENVIRONMENTAL GROUP INC p 970
538 Edwards Ave 11933
Tel (631) 369-4900 SIC 4959

RIVERHEAD BUILDING SUPPLY CORP p 1237
250 David Ct 11933
Tel (631) 727-1400 SIC 5031 5211

CAMDEN, NY

CAMDEN WIRE CO INC p 245
12 Masonic Ave 13316
Tel (315) 245-3800 SIC 3351 3357

INTERNATIONAL WIRE GROUP p 757
12 Masonic Ave 13316
Tel (315) 245-3800 SIC 3351

INTERNATIONAL WIRE GROUP INC p 757
12 Masonic Ave 13316
Tel (315) 245-2000 SIC 3357

OMEGA WIRE INC p 1084
12 Masonic Ave 13316
Tel (315) 245-3800 SIC 3351

CANANDAIGUA, NY

■ CANANDAIGUA NATIONAL BANK & TRUST CO p 246
72 S Main St 14424
Tel (585) 394-4260 SIC 6021

▲ CANANDAIGUA NATIONAL CORP p 246
72 S Main St 14424
Tel (585) 394-4260 SIC 6021

■ CONSTELLATION BRANDS US OPERATIONS INC p 361
235 N Bloomfield Rd 14424
Tel (585) 396-7600 SIC 2084

COUNTY OF ONTARIO p 380
20 Ontario St 14424
Tel (585) 396-4400 SIC 9111

FF THOMPSON HEALTH SYSTEM INC p 539
350 Parrish St 14424
Tel (585) 396-6000 SIC 8741 8069

FREDERICK FERRIS THOMPSON HOSPITAL p 576
350 Parrish St 14424
Tel (585) 396-6000 SIC 8062 8011

CANASTOTA, NY

NICE N EASY GROCERY SHOPPES INC p 1042
7840 Oxbow Rd 13032
Tel (315) 397-2802 SIC 5411 5541

CANTON, NY

ST LAWRENCE COUNTY p 1369
48 Court St 13617
Tel (315) 379-2276 SIC 9111

ST LAWRENCE UNIVERSITY p 1369
23 Romoda Dr 13617
Tel (315) 229-5011 *SIC* 8221 7011

CARLE PLACE, NY

▲ **1-800-FLOWERS.COM INC** p 1
1 Old Country Rd Ste 500 11514
Tel (516) 237-6000 *SIC* 5992 5961 5947

CARMEL, NY

PUTNAM HOSPITAL CENTER FOUNDATION INC p 1193
670 Stoneleigh Ave 10512
Tel (845) 279-5711 *SIC* 8062

PUTNAM HOSPITAL CENTER HOME HEALTH AGENCY PRIVATE DUTY CARE SERVICE INC p 1193
670 Stoneleigh Ave 10512
Tel (845) 279-5711 *SIC* 8062

CAZENOVIA, NY

MARQUARDT SWITCHES INC p 910
2711 Us Route 20 13035
Tel (315) 655-8050 *SIC* 3625 3613

CENTER MORICHES, NY

KURT WEISS GREENHOUSES INC p 832
95 Main St 11934
Tel (631) 878-2500 *SIC* 0181 5193

CENTEREACH, NY

MIDDLE COUNTRY CENTRAL SCHOOL DISTRICT p 964
8 43rd St 11720
Tel (631) 285-8000 *SIC* 8211

CENTRAL ISLIP, NY

CENTRAL ISLIP UNION FREE SCHOOL DISTRICT p 279
50 Wheeler Rd 11722
Tel (631) 348-5112 *SIC* 8211

GRAPHIC PAPER INC p 632
31 Windsor Pl 11722
Tel (631) 761-9700 *SIC* 5111

CENTRAL VALLEY, NY

MONROE-WOODBURY CENTRAL SCHOOL DISTRICT p 985
278 Route 32 10917
Tel (845) 460-6200 *SIC* 8211

CHAPPAQUA, NY

CHAPPAQUA CENTRAL SCHOOL DISTRICT INC p 288
70 Roaring Brook Rd 10514
Tel (914) 238-7200 *SIC* 8211

CHATHAM, NY

■ **SONOCO-CRELLIN INTERNATIONAL INC** p 1340
87 Center St 12037
Tel (518) 392-2000 *SIC* 3089

CHEEKTOWAGA, NY

■ **FLUID HANDLING LLC** p 561
175 Standard Pkwy 14227
Tel (716) 897-2800 *SIC* 3561

TOWN OF CHEEKTOWAGA p 1465
3301 Broadway St 14227
Tel (716) 686-3400 *SIC* 9111

CHESTNUT RIDGE, NY

CREATIVE MANAGEMENT SERVICES LLC p 390
3 Alpine Ct 10977
Tel (845) 578-1651 *SIC* 7389

PAR PHARMACEUTICAL COMPANIES INC p 1113
1 Ram Ridge Rd 10977
Tel (845) 573-5500 *SIC* 2834

PAR STERILE PRODUCTS LLC p 1113
1 Ram Ridge Rd 10977
Tel (845) 573-5500 *SIC* 2834

■ **TELEDYNE LECROY INC** p 1434
700 Chestnut Ridge Rd 10977
Tel (845) 425-2000 *SIC* 3825 3829

CHITTENANGO, NY

CPP-SYRACUSE INC p 387
901 E Genesee St 13037
Tel (315) 687-0014 *SIC* 3324 3369 3356

CLARENCE, NY

JOHN W DANFORTH CO p 789
4770 Bickert Dr 14031
Tel (716) 832-1940 *SIC* 1711

MEDIMA LLC p 938
5727 Strickler Rd 14031
Tel (716) 741-0400 *SIC* 3339 3313

CLIFTON PARK, NY

BAST HATFIELD INC p 159
1399 Vischers Ferry Rd 12065
Tel (518) 373-2000 *SIC* 1542 1541 8741

SHENENDEHOWA CENTRAL SCHOOL DISTRICT p 1315
5 Chelsea Pl 12065
Tel (518) 881-0600 *SIC* 8211

CLIFTON SPRINGS, NY

GW LISK CO INC p 648
2 South St 14432
Tel (315) 462-2611 *SIC* 3679 4119 3492

CLINTON, NY

HAMILTON COLLEGE p 655
198 College Hill Rd 13323
Tel (315) 859-4727 *SIC* 8221

INDIUM CORP OF AMERICA p 739
34 Robinson Rd 13323
Tel (800) 446-3486 *SIC* 3356

CLYDE, NY

■ **ADVANCED ATOMIZATION TECHNOLOGIES LLC** p 25
124 Columbia St 14433
Tel (315) 923-2341 *SIC* 3724

COBLESKILL, NY

COBLESKILL STONE PRODUCTS INC p 333
112 Rock Rd 12043
Tel (518) 234-0221 *SIC* 1422

COHOES, NY

MOHAWK FINE PAPERS INC p 982
465 Saratoga St 12047
Tel (518) 237-1740 *SIC* 2672 2621

COLD SPRING HARBOR, NY

COLD SPRING HARBOR LABORATORY ASSOCIATION INC p 335
1 Bungtown Rd 11724
Tel (516) 367-8446
SIC 8733 2731 2741 8249

COLLEGE POINT, NY

CANADA DRY BOTTLING CO OF NEW YORK LP p 246
11202 15th Ave 11356
Tel (718) 358-2000 *SIC* 5149

INTERPLEX INDUSTRIES INC p 757
1434 110th St Ste 301 11356
Tel (718) 961-6212
SIC 3471 3825 3674 3469

JETRO CASH AND CARRY ENTERPRISES LLC p 784
1524 132nd St 11356
Tel (718) 939-6400
SIC 5142 5046 5181 5147 5411

JETRO HOLDINGS LLC p 784
1506 132nd St 11356
Tel (718) 762-8700 *SIC* 5149 5141 5812

JRD HOLDINGS INC p 795
1524 132nd St 11356
Tel (718) 762-8700
SIC 5141 5142 5147 5181 5194

PEPSI-COLA BOTTLING CO OF NEW YORK INC p 1134
11402 15th Ave Ste 5 11356
Tel (718) 392-1000 *SIC* 2086

RD FOOD SERVICES LLC p 1212
1524 132nd St 11356
Tel (718) 961-4356
SIC 5141 5148 5142 5113 5046 5087

RESTAURANT DEPOT LLC p 1228
1524 132nd St 11356
Tel (718) 762-8700
SIC 5147 5141 5142 5181 5194

COLLIERSVILLE, NY

JETT INDUSTRIES INC p 784
121 Willow Ln 13747
Tel (607) 433-2100 *SIC* 1611 1623

COMMACK, NY

■ **CARR BUSINESS SYSTEMS INC** p 260
500 Commack Rd Unit 110 11725
Tel (631) 249-9880 *SIC* 5044 7699

ROSALIND AND JOSEPH GURWIN JEWISH GERIATRIC CENTER OF LONG ISLAND INC p 1250
68 Hauppauge Rd 11725
Tel (631) 499-6500 *SIC* 8059

UNIVERSAL PACKAGING SYSTEMS INC p 1517
6080 Jericho Tpke 11725
Tel (631) 543-2277
SIC 2844 7389 3565 2671

CONKLIN, NY

MAINES PAPER & FOOD SERVICE INC p 898
101 Broome Corporate Pkwy 13748
Tel (607) 779-1200
SIC 5142 5113 5141 5087 5147 5146

MEIER SUPPLY CO INC p 940
275 Broome Corporate Pkwy 13748
Tel (607) 797-7700 *SIC* 5075 5078

UI ACQUISITION HOLDING CO p 1500
33 Broome Corporate Pkwy 13748
Tel (607) 779-7522 *SIC* 3559

UI HOLDING CO p 1500
33 Broome Corporate Pkwy 13748
Tel (607) 779-7522 *SIC* 3559

UNIVERSAL INSTRUMENTS CORP p 1517
33 Broome Corporate Pkwy 13748
Tel (800) 842-9732 *SIC* 3559

COOPERSTOWN, NY

MARY IMOGENE BASSETT HOSPITAL p 914
1 Atwell Rd 13326
Tel (607) 547-3456 *SIC* 8011 8062 5999

COPIAGUE, NY

FEDERATION EMPLOYMENT AND GUIDANCE SERVICE INC p 536
445 Oak St 11726
Tel (212) 366-8040 *SIC* 8399

CORFU, NY

YANCEYS FANCY INC p 1634
857 Main Rd 14036
Tel (585) 599-4448 *SIC* 5143

CORNING, NY

CORNING HOSPITAL p 371
1 Guthrie Dr 14830
Tel (607) 937-7200 *SIC* 8062

▲ **CORNING INC** p 371
1 Riverfront Plz 14831
Tel (607) 974-9000
SIC 3229 3357 3661 3674

■ **CORNING INTERNATIONAL CORP** p 371
1 Riverfront Plz 14831
Tel (607) 974-9000 *SIC* 3229 5945

■ **CORNING RESEARCH & DEVELOPMENT CORP** p 371
1 Riverfront Plz 14831
Tel (607) 974-9000 *SIC* 8731

■ **CORNING VITRO CORP** p 371
1 Riverfront Plz 14830
Tel (607) 974-8605 *SIC* 3229 3469

CORONA, NY

NEW YORK CITY GEOGRAPHIC DISTRICT 24 p 1034
9850 50th Ave 11368
Tel (718) 592-3357 *SIC* 7336

CORTLAND, NY

INTERTEK TESTING SERVICES NA INC p 759
3933 Us Route 11 13045
Tel (607) 753-6711 *SIC* 8734

MARIETTA CORP p 906
37 Huntington St 13045
Tel (607) 753-6746 *SIC* 2844 2834 2541

MARIETTA HOLDING CORP INC p 906
37 Huntington St 13045
Tel (607) 753-6746 *SIC* 6719 2841

P C CORTLAND PATHOLOGY p 1102
134 Homer Ave 13045
Tel (607) 756-3500 *SIC* 8071

■ **PALL TRINITY MICRO CORP** p 1108
3643 State Route 281 13045
Tel (607) 753-6041 *SIC* 3677

SUIT-KOTE CORP p 1397
1911 Lorings Crossing Rd 13045
Tel (607) 753-1100 *SIC* 2951 1611

SUNY COLLEGE AT CORTLAND p 1405
38 Cheney Hall 13045
Tel (607) 753-2011 *SIC* 8221 9411

CORTLANDT MANOR, NY

HUDSON VALLEY HOSPITAL CENTER p 717
1980 Crompond Rd 10567
Tel (914) 737-9000 *SIC* 8062

COXSACKIE, NY

EMPIRE MERCHANTS NORTH LLC p 493
16 Houghtaling Rd 12051
Tel (518) 731-5200 *SIC* 5182

CUBA, NY

EMPIRE CHEESE INC p 493
4520 County Road 6 14727
Tel (585) 968-1552 *SIC* 2022

DE WITT, NY

▲ **COMMUNITY BANK SYSTEM INC** p 347
5790 Widewaters Pkwy # 1 13214
Tel (315) 445-2282 *SIC* 6021

DEER PARK, NY

■ **COMMERCIAL ENVELOPE MANUFACTURING CO INC** p 345
900 Grand Blvd 11729
Tel (631) 242-2500 *SIC* 2677 5112

INTER-COUNTY BAKERS INC p 751
1095 Long Island Ave A 11729
Tel (631) 957-1350 *SIC* 5142

DEPEW, NY

HARLEQUIN DISTRIBUTION CENTER p 661
3010 Walden Ave 14043
Tel (716) 684-1800 *SIC* 5192

■ **HARLEQUIN SALES CORP** p 661
3010 Walden Ave 14043
Tel (716) 684-1800 *SIC* 5192

■ **HOWDEN NORTH AMERICA INC** p 713
2475 George Urban Blvd # 100 14043
Tel (803) 741-2700 *SIC* 3564 3568

■ **OSMOSE HOLDINGS INC** p 1097
2475 George Urban Blvd # 160 14043
Tel (716) 882-5905 *SIC* 2491

■ **PCB GROUP INC** p 1123
3425 Walden Ave 14043
Tel (716) 684-0001 *SIC* 3679 3823

■ **PCB PIEZOTRONICS INC** p 1123
3425 Walden Ave 14043
Tel (716) 684-0001 *SIC* 3829 3679

SEFAR INC p 1300
111 Calumet St 14043
Tel (716) 683-4050
SIC 5131 5051 5084 3496 2297 2221

DEPOSIT, NY

■ **DEPOSIT TELEPHONE CO INC** p 431
87 Front St 13754
Tel (607) 467-2111 *SIC* 4813

DIX HILLS, NY

WESTERN SUFFOLK BOCES SECOND SUPERVISORY DISTRICT SUFFOLK COUNTY p 1600
507 Deer Park Rd 11746
Tel (631) 549-4900 *SIC* 8211

DOBBS FERRY, NY

MERCY COLLEGE p 946
555 Broadway Frnt 10522
Tel (914) 455-2650 *SIC* 8221

ST JOHNS RIVERSIDE HOSPITAL DOBBS FERRY PAVILION p 1368
128 Ashford Ave 10522
Tel (914) 693-0700 *SIC* 8062

DUNKIRK, NY

CLIFFSTAR LLC p 326
1 Cliffstar Dr 14048
Tel (716) 366-6100 *SIC* 2033 2086

FFC HOLDING CORP AND SUBSIDIARIES p 539
1 Ice Cream Dr 14048
Tel (716) 366-5400 *SIC* 2024

FIELDBROOK FOODS CORP p 541
1 Ice Cream Dr 14048
Tel (716) 366-5400 *SIC* 2024

EAST AMHERST, NY

WILLIAMSVILLE CENTRAL SCHOOL DISTRICT p 1612
Administratiion Center 10 Er Stratiion Cent 14051
Tel (716) 626-8050 *SIC* 8211

EAST AURORA, NY

▲ **ASTRONICS CORP** p 122
130 Commerce Way 14052
Tel (716) 805-1599 *SIC* 3728 3647

■ **FISHER-PRICE INC** p 552
636 Girard Ave 14052
Tel (716) 687-3000 *SIC* 5092 5945 3944

EAST ELMHURST, NY

SKANSKA USA CIVIL INC p 1329
7520 Astoria Blvd Ste 200 11370
Tel (718) 340-0777 *SIC* 1611

SKANSKA USA CIVIL NORTHEAST INC p 1329
7520 Astoria Blvd Ste 200 11370
Tel (718) 340-0811 *SIC* 1622

EAST HAMPTON, NY

COOK MARAN & ASSOCIATES INC p 366
461 Pantigo Rd 11937
Tel (631) 324-1440 *SIC* 6321

EAST MEADOW, NY

HIBU INC p 690
90 Merrick Ave Ste 530 11554
Tel (516) 730-1900 *SIC* 2741

NASSAU HEALTH CARE CORP p 1008
2201 Hempstead Tpke 11554
Tel (516) 572-0123 *SIC* 8062

EAST NORTHPORT, NY

COMMACK UNION FREE SCHOOL DISTRICT 10 p 344
480 Clay Pitts Rd 11731
Tel (631) 912-2000 *SIC* 8211

EAST PATCHOGUE, NY

BROOKHAVEN MEMORIAL HOSPITAL MEDICAL CENTER INC p 217
101 Hospital Rd 11772
Tel (631) 654-7100 *SIC* 8062

EAST ROCHESTER, NY

VAN BORTEL FORD INC p 1542
71 Marsh Rd 14445
Tel (585) 586-4415 *SIC* 5531 7539

EAST SETAUKET, NY

TRITEC BUILDING CO INC p 1483
45 Research Way Ste 100 11733
Tel (631) 751-0300 SIC 6552 8742

EAST SYRACUSE, NY

ADVANCE/NEWHOUSE COMMUNICATIONS PARTNERSHIP p 25
5823 Widewaters Pkwy 13057
Tel (315) 438-4100 SIC 4841

ANAREN INC p 88
6635 Kirkville Rd 13057
Tel (315) 432-8909 SIC 3679

ASPEN DENTAL MANAGEMENT INC p 118
281 Sanders Creek Pkwy 13057
Tel (315) 454-6000 SIC 8021 8072 6794

DUMAC BUSINESS SYSTEMS INC p 461
19 Corporate Cir Ste 1 13057
Tel (315) 463-1010 SIC 5045 7699 3578

INFICON INC p 740
2 Technology Pl 13057
Tel (315) 434-1149 SIC 3823 3812

■ PPC BROADBAND INC p 1166
6176 E Molloy Rd 13057
Tel (315) 431-7200 SIC 8748

SAAB SENSIS CORP p 1263
85 Collamer Crossings 13057
Tel (315) 445-0550 SIC 3699 7371 3728

TIME WARNER INC p 1454
6005 Fair Lakes Rd 13057
Tel (315) 234-1000 SIC 5063

TRACEY ROAD EQUIPMENT INC p 1468
6803 Manlius Center Rd 13057
Tel (315) 437-1471
SIC 5082 5012 7353 7699 5013

EAST YAPHANK, NY

CLARE ROSE INC p 321
100 Rose Executive Blvd 11967
Tel (631) 475-2337 SIC 5181

EDGEWOOD, NY

CPI AEROSTRUCTURES INC p 387
91 Heartland Blvd 11717
Tel (631) 586-5200 SIC 3728

KELTA INC p 809
141 Rodeo Dr 11717
Tel (631) 789-5000 SIC 3089 3643 3661

KINPLEX CORP p 821
200 Heartland Blvd 11717
Tel (631) 242-4800 SIC 3589

EDMESTON, NY

NEW YORK CENTRAL MUTUAL FIRE INSURANCE CO p 1034
1899 Central Plz E 13335
Tel (607) 965-8321 SIC 6331

TOWN OF EDMESTON p 1465
607965 6th W St 13335
Tel (607) 965-9823 SIC 9111

EDWARDS, NY

EDWARDS TELEPHONE CO INC p 480
159 Main St 13635
Tel (315) 562-9913 SIC 1731 4813

ELLICOTTVILLE, NY

WIN-SUM SKI CORP p 1614
6557 Holiday Valley Rd 14731
Tel (716) 699-2345 SIC 7011 7997 6531

ELMA, NY

▲ MOOG INC p 987
400 Jamison Rd Plant26 14059
Tel (716) 652-2000
SIC 3812 3492 3625 3769 3728 3841

SENECA MORTGAGE SERVICING LLC p 1303
611 Jamison Rd Ste 1201 14059
Tel (716) 204-3601 SIC 6162

ELMHURST, NY

ELMHURST HOSPITAL CENTER p 489
7901 Broadway 11373
Tel (718) 334-2424 SIC 8062

ELMIRA, NY

ARNOT HEALTH INC p 112
600 Roe Ave 14905
Tel (607) 737-4231 SIC 8062

CITY SCHOOL DISTRICT OF CITY OF ELMIRA NY p 319
951 Hoffman St 14905
Tel (607) 735-3000 SIC 8211

COUNTY OF CHEMUNG p 377
320 E Market St 14901
Tel (607) 737-2925 SIC 9111

CREATIVE ORTHOTICS & PROSTHETICS INC p 390
1300 College Ave Ste 1 14901
Tel (607) 734-7215 SIC 3842 5999 5047

▲ HARDINGE INC p 661
1 Hardinge Dr 14902
Tel (607) 734-2281
SIC 3541 3545 3553 3549

HILLIARD CORP p 693
100 W 4th St 14901
Tel (607) 733-7121 SIC 3564 3569 3823

OGDEN ARNOT MEDICAL CENTER p 1076
600 Roe Ave 14905
Tel (607) 737-4100 SIC 8011

ST JOSEPHS HOSPITAL p 1368
555 Saint Josephs Blvd 14901
Tel (607) 733-6541 SIC 8062

ELMSFORD, NY

■ AMSCAN HOLDINGS INC p 87
80 Grasslands Rd Ste 3 10523
Tel (914) 345-2020
SIC 5947 2679 3089 3069 6794

■ AMSCAN INC p 87
80 Grasslands Rd Ste 3 10523
Tel (914) 345-2020
SIC 2656 3089 5113 2676

■ CENTRAL COCA-COLA BOTTLING CO INC p 277
555 Taxter Rd Ste 550 10523
Tel (914) 789-1100 SIC 5149 2086 8741

■ MOTTS LLP p 993
55 Hunter Ln 10523
Tel (972) 673-8088 SIC 2033 5149 2087

■ NEXTEL OF NEW YORK INC p 1040
565 Taxter Rd Ste 450 10523
Tel (914) 421-2800 SIC 4812

▲ PARTY CITY HOLDCO INC p 1119
80 Grasslands Rd 10523
Tel (914) 345-2020
SIC 5947 5963 5199 6794

■ PARTY CITY HOLDINGS INC p 1119
80 Grasslands Rd 10523
Tel (973) 453-8600 SIC 5947 6794

■ PC INTERMEDIATE HOLDINGS INC p 1123
80 Grasslands Rd 10523
Tel (914) 345-2020 SIC 7389

RELIABLE AUTOMATIC SPRINKLER CO INC p 1221
103 Fairview Pk Dr Ste 1 10523
Tel (914) 829-2042 SIC 3569

SCHOTT CORP p 1290
555 Taxter Rd Ste 470 10523
Tel (914) 831-2200
SIC 3211 3829 3221 3229

SCHOTT NORTH AMERICA INC p 1290
555 Taxter Rd Ste 470 10523
Tel (914) 831-2200 SIC 5099

TWOS CO INC p 1495
500 Saw Mill River Rd 10523
Tel (914) 664-2277 SIC 5199 5023 5094

ENDICOTT, NY

■ AMPHENOL INTERCONNECT PRODUCTS CORP p 86
20 Valley St 13760
Tel (607) 754-4444 SIC 3679

BAE SYSTEMS CONTROLS INC p 144
1098 Clark St 13760
Tel (607) 770-2000 SIC 3812

GAULT CHEVROLET CO INC p 594
2205 North St 13760
Tel (607) 748-8244 SIC 5511 5012

VISIONS FEDERAL CREDIT UNION p 1561
24 Mckinley Ave 13760
Tel (607) 754-7900 SIC 6061

FAIRPORT, NY

BOARD OF COOPERATIVE EDUCATIONAL SERVICES FIRST SUPERVISORY DISTRICT OF MONROE COUNTY p 195
41 Oconnor Rd 14450
Tel (585) 377-4660 SIC 8211

BOSCH SECURITY SYSTEMS INC p 202
130 Perinton Pkwy 14450
Tel (585) 223-4060
SIC 3669 3699 3826 3825 3823 3625

FLOUR CITY BAGELS INC p 560
585 Moseley Rd Ste 3 14450
Tel (585) 223-0450 SIC 5461 2051

LIDESTRI FOODS INC p 863
815 Whitney Rd W 14450
Tel (585) 377-7700 SIC 3221 2033

MANNING & NAPIER ADVISORS LLC p 902
290 Woodcliff Dr Ste 300 14450
Tel (800) 551-0224 SIC 6282 8742 7375

▲ MANNING & NAPIER INC p 902
290 Woodcliff Dr Ste 300 14450
Tel (585) 325-6880 SIC 6282 8742 6722

MONROE 1 BOCES EDUCATIONAL FOUNDATION INC p 985
41 Oconnor Rd 14450
Tel (585) 377-4660 SIC 8299

■ PAETEC COMMUNICATIONS INC p 1107
600 Willowbrook Office Pa 14450
Tel (585) 340-2500 SIC 4813 7375 7372

■ PAETEC HOLDING CORP p 1107
1 Paetec Plz 14450
Tel (585) 340-2500 SIC 4813

■ QUALITROL CO LLC p 1196
1385 Fairport Rd 14450
Tel (586) 643-3717 SIC 3825

FALCONER, NY

JAMESTOWN CONTAINER CORP p 777
14 Deming Dr 14733
Tel (716) 665-4623 SIC 2653 3086

MAPLEVALE FARMS INC p 904
2063 Allen Street Ext 14733
Tel (716) 355-4114 SIC 5141

MRC BEARINGS INC p 996
1 Maroco St 14733
Tel (716) 661-2600 SIC 3562

TRUCK-LITE CO INC p 1485
310 E Elmwood Ave 14733
Tel (716) 665-6214 SIC 3648 3647

TRUCK-LITE CO LLC p 1485
310 E Elmwood Ave 14733
Tel (716) 665-6214 SIC 3647

ZAHM & MATSON INC p 1641
1756 Lindquist Dr 14733
Tel (716) 665-3110 SIC 5261 5999

FAR ROCKAWAY, NY

PENINSULA GENERAL NURSING HOME CORP p 1129
5015 Beach Channel Dr 11691
Tel (718) 734-2000 SIC 8051

ROCKAWAY HOME ATTENDANT SERVICES INC p 1243
1603 Central Ave 100 11691
Tel (718) 327-1850 SIC 8082 8361

ST JOHNS EPISCOPAL HOSPITAL p 1367
327 Beach 19th St 11691
Tel (718) 869-7000 SIC 8062

FARMINGDALE, NY

A J RICHARD & SONS INC p 5
150 Price Pkwy 11735
Tel (631) 843-4300 SIC 5722 5731

ALCOTT GROUP INC p 47
71 Executive Blvd Ste 1 11735
Tel (631) 420-0100 SIC 7363

COLORADO PRIME OF PENNSYLVANIA INC p 339
1 Michael Ave 11735
Tel (631) 694-1111 SIC 5421 5722

CRESCENT PACKING CORP p 391
1970 New Hwy 11735
Tel (631) 253-0700 SIC 5147

■ CURTISS-WRIGHT FLOW CONTROL CORP p 402
1966 Broadhollow Rd Ste E 11735
Tel (631) 293-3800 SIC 3491 3494

DADDARIO & CO INC p 408
595 Smith St 11735
Tel (631) 439-3300 SIC 3931

FERRANDINO & SON INC p 538
71 Carolyn Blvd 11735
Tel (866) 571-4609
SIC 1542 0781 3531 7299

HAROLD LEVINSON ASSOCIATES INC p 662
21 Banfi Plz N 11735
Tel (631) 962-2400 SIC 5194 5145

ICON CENTRAL LABORATORIES INC p 727
123 Smith St 11735
Tel (631) 777-8833 SIC 8071 8734

ISHAN INTERNATIONAL INC p 766
500 Smith St 11735
Tel (631) 618-3000 SIC 5065

LEGEND HEALTH SYSTEMS INC p 853
1111 Broadhollow Rd # 319 11735
Tel (631) 630-4713 SIC 5912

MARJAM SUPPLY CO INC p 907
885 Conklin St 11735
Tel (631) 249-4900 SIC 5211 5031

NATIONAL ELECTRONICS INC p 1011
500 Smith St 11735
Tel (631) 683-8000 SIC 5065

P C RICHARD & SON LONG ISLAND CORP p 1102
150 Price Pkwy 11735
Tel (631) 843-4300 SIC 5722 5731 5064

PC RICHARD & SON INC p 1123
150 Price Pkwy 11735
Tel (631) 843-4300
SIC 5722 5064 7629 7623

PC RICHARD & SON LLC p 1123
150 Price Pkwy 11735
Tel (631) 843-4300 SIC 5999

POSILLICO CIVIL INC p 1163
1750 New Hwy 11735
Tel (631) 249-1872 SIC 1611 1542

■ TELEPHONICS CORP p 1435
815 Broadhollow Rd 11735
Tel (631) 755-7000
SIC 3669 3661 3679 3812 3663

FARMINGVILLE, NY

TOWN OF BROOKHAVEN p 1465
1 Independence Hl Frnt 11738
Tel (631) 451-6680 SIC 9111

FISHKILL, NY

CENTRAL PURCHASING CORP p 280
205 Old Route 9 12524
Tel (845) 896-6291 SIC 5074 5075

FLORAL PARK, NY

FJC SECURITY SERVICES INC p 553
275 Jericho Tpke 11001
Tel (516) 328-6000 SIC 7381

SEWANHAKA CENTRAL HIGH SCHOOL DISTRICT p 1309
77 Landau Ave 11001
Tel (516) 488-9810 SIC 8211

FLUSHING, NY

BLUE GOLD EQUITIES LLC p 192
6818 Main St 11367
Tel (718) 268-6469 SIC 5411 5311

CRYSTAL WINDOW & DOOR SYSTEMS LTD p 397
3110 Whitestone Expy 11354
Tel (718) 961-7300
SIC 5031 3442 3231 3211 2431 1751

DAHUA ELECTRONICS CORP p 408
13412 59th Ave 11355
Tel (718) 886-2188 SIC 3676

■ FLIGHTSAFETY INTERNATIONAL INC p 556
Marine Air Terminal 11371
Tel (718) 565-4100 SIC 7363

■ FLUSHING BANK p 561
220 Rxr Plz 11354
Tel (718) 512-2929 SIC 6035 6163

FLUSHING HOSPITAL AND MEDICAL CENTER p 561
4500 Parsons Blvd 11355
Tel (718) 670-5000 SIC 8062

HOUSE OF SPICES (INDIA) INC p 711
12740 Willets Point Blvd 11368
Tel (718) 507-4900
SIC 5149 2099 5153 2033 2024

JUDLAU CONTRACTING INC p 797
2615 Ulmer St 11354
Tel (718) 554-2320 SIC 1611 1623

NEWYORK-PRESBYTERIAN/QUEENS p 1039
5645 Main St 11355
Tel (718) 670-2000 SIC 8062

OHL USA INC p 1078
2615 Ulmer St 11354
Tel (718) 554-2320 SIC 8711

PSCH INC p 1188
14202 20th Ave Rm 301 11351
Tel (718) 559-0516 SIC 8361 8331 8093

TULLY CONSTRUCTION CO INC p 1491
12750 Northern Blvd 11368
Tel (718) 446-7000 SIC 1611

UNITY ELECTRIC CO INC p 1515
6545 Fresh Meadow Ln 11365
Tel (718) 539-4300 SIC 1731

UNITY INTERNATIONAL GROUP INC p 1515
6545 Fresh Meadow Ln 11365
Tel (718) 539-4300 SIC 1731

FONDA, NY

KASSON & KELLER INC p 804
60 School St 12068
Tel (518) 853-3421
SIC 3442 3089 1521 3231

KEYMARK CORP p 815
1188 Cayadutta St 12068
Tel (518) 853-3421 SIC 3354 3479 3471

FOREST HILLS, NY

ELITELUCK.COM INC p 487
10510 62nd Rd Apt 1d 11375
Tel (718) 938-1203 SIC 7311

FOREST HILLS HOSPITAL p 566
10201 66th Rd 11375
Tel (718) 830-4000 SIC 8062

HEALTH ACQUISITION CORP p 674
7000 Austin St Ste 2 11375
Tel (718) 657-2966 SIC 8082

FORT EDWARD, NY

IRVING CONSUMER PRODUCTS INC p 765
1 Eddy St 12828
Tel (518) 747-4151 SIC 2621

FRANKFORT, NY

NORTHERN SAFETY CO INC p 1056
232 Industrial Park Dr 13340
Tel (315) 793-4900 SIC 5099

FREDONIA, NY

■ CARRIAGE HOUSE COMPANIES INC p 260
196 Newton St 14063
Tel (716) 672-4321
SIC 2099 2033 2035 2087

SUNY COLLEGE AT FREDONIA p 1405
280 Central Ave 14063
Tel (716) 673-3111 SIC 8221 9411

FREEPORT, NY

EMO-TRANS INC p 493
135 Guy Lombardo Ave 11520
Tel (516) 867-6800 SIC 4731

FREEPORT UNION FREE SCHOOL DISTRICT p 577
235 N Ocean Ave 11520
Tel (516) 867-5200 SIC 8211

KARPELES FREIGHT SERVICES INC p 804
150 Albany Ave 11520
Tel (516) 377-3000 *SIC* 4731

OKIN-WALLACK CORP p 1079
65 S Columbus Ave 11520
Tel (516) 379-0449 *SIC* 5074

SCHENKER INC p 1286
150 Albany Ave 11520
Tel (516) 377-3000 *SIC* 4731 4225

FRESH MEADOWS, NY

ELECTRICAL EMPLOYERS SELF INSURANCE SAFETY PLAN p 485
15811 Jewel Ave 11365
Tel (718) 591-2000 *SIC* 6311

GARDEN CITY, NY

ADELPHI UNIVERSITY p 22
1 S Ave Lvh 310 310 Lvh 11530
Tel (516) 877-3000 *SIC* 8221

■ **BUY BUY BABY INC** p 230
895 E Gate Blvd Ste 2 11530
Tel (516) 507-3400 *SIC* 5641 5999 2023

CAMPUS COURSE PAKS INC p 246
1 South Ave Fl 1 11530
Tel (516) 877-3967 *SIC* 2731

▲ **LIFETIME BRANDS INC** p 864
1000 Stewart Ave 11530
Tel (516) 683-6000 *SIC* 3421 5023 5719

MAPFRE INSURANCE CO p 903
901 Franklin Ave 11530
Tel (516) 564-8000 *SIC* 6411

MORTGAGE SOURCE LLC p 991
600 Old Country Rd Rm 210 11530
Tel (516) 487-3111 *SIC* 6162

NASSAU BOCES SCHOOL DISTRICT p 1008
71 Clinton Rd Ste 100 11530
Tel (516) 396-2500 *SIC* 8211

NASSAU COMMUNITY COLLEGE p 1008
1 Education Dr 11530
Tel (516) 572-7501 *SIC* 8222 9411

QUEENS-LONG ISLAND MEDICAL GROUP PC p 1198
1000 Zeckendorf Blvd B 11530
Tel (516) 542-5500 *SIC* 8011

GARNERVILLE, NY

HAVERSTRAW STONY POINT CENTRAL SCHOOL DISTRICT INC p 668
65 Chapel St 10923
Tel (845) 942-3053 *SIC* 8211

GENEVA, NY

FINGER LAKES REGIONAL HEALTH SYSTEM INC p 543
196 North St 14456
Tel (315) 787-4000 *SIC* 8051

GENEVA GENERAL HOSPITAL p 603
196 North St 14456
Tel (315) 787-4000 *SIC* 8062

HOBART AND WILLIAM SMITH COLLEGES p 698
300 Pulteney St 14456
Tel (315) 781-3337 *SIC* 8221

HOBART AND WILLIAM SMITH COLLEGES p 698
327 Pulteney St 14456
Tel (315) 781-3337 *SIC* 8221

GETZVILLE, NY

ASPIRE OF WESTERN NEW YORK INC p 118
2356 N Forest Rd 14068
Tel (716) 505-5500 *SIC* 8322

BRYANT & STRATTON COLLEGE INC p 221
2410 N Forest Rd Ste 101 14068
Tel (716) 250-7500 *SIC* 8244

▲ **COLUMBUS MCKINNON CORP** p 342
205 Crosspoint Pkwy 14068
Tel (716) 689-5400
SIC 3536 3496 3535 3537

■ **SPX FLOW TECHNOLOGY SYSTEMS INC** p 1362
105 Crosspoint Pkwy 14068
Tel (716) 692-3000 *SIC* 3556 8742

GLEN COVE, NY

GLEN COVE HOSPITAL p 614
101 Saint Andrews Ln 11542
Tel (516) 674-7300 *SIC* 8062

SCO FAMILY OF SERVICES p 1292
1 Alexander Pl 11542
Tel (516) 671-1253 *SIC* 8322

GLEN HEAD, NY

■ **FIRST NATIONAL BANK OF LONG ISLAND** p 548
10 Glen Head Rd 11545
Tel (516) 671-4900 *SIC* 6021

▲ **FIRST OF LONG ISLAND CORP** p 548
10 Glen Head Rd 11545
Tel (516) 671-4900 *SIC* 6021

NASSAU ASSOCIATION FOR HELP OF RETARDED CHILDREN INC p 1008
189 Wheatley Rd 11545
Tel (516) 626-1000 *SIC* 8093 8322

NASSAU COUNTY A H R C p 1008
189 Wheatley Rd 11545
Tel (516) 626-1000 *SIC* 8331 8322

GLENMONT, NY

■ **FARM FAMILY HOLDINGS INC** p 529
344 Route 9w 12077
Tel (518) 431-5000 *SIC* 6331

GLENS FALLS, NY

▲ **ARROW FINANCIAL CORP** p 113
250 Glen St 12801
Tel (518) 745-1000 *SIC* 6021

BARTON MINES CO LLC p 158
6 Warren St 12801
Tel (518) 798-5462 *SIC* 1499 3291 5085

GENPAK LLC p 604
68 Warren St 12801
Tel (518) 798-9511 *SIC* 5113

GLENS FALLS HOSPITAL p 615
100 Park St 12801
Tel (518) 926-1000 *SIC* 8011 8062 8221

■ **GLENS FALLS NATIONAL BANK & TRUST CO** p 615
250 Glen St 12801
Tel (518) 793-4121 *SIC* 6021

GREAT PACIFIC ENTERPRISES (US) INC p 634
68 Warren St 12801
Tel (518) 761-2593 *SIC* 3089

■ **NAVILYST MEDICAL INC** p 1020
10 Glens Fls Technical Pa 12801
Tel (800) 833-9973 *SIC* 3841

GLENVILLE, NY

▲ **TRUSTCO BANK CORP N Y** p 1487
5 Sarnowski Dr 12302
Tel (518) 377-3311 *SIC* 6022

GLOVERSVILLE, NY

■ **CITIZENS TELECOMMUNICATIONS CO OF NEW YORK INC** p 311
137 Harrison St 12078
Tel (518) 773-6466 *SIC* 4813

HANDWEAR SALES INC p 657
74 Bleecker St 12078
Tel (518) 725-8641
SIC 3151 3949 2253 3021

NATHAN LITTAUER HOSPITAL ASSOCIATION p 1009
99 E State St 12078
Tel (518) 725-8621 *SIC* 8051 8062 8011

TAYLOR MADE GROUP HOLDINGS INC p 1427
66 Kingsboro Ave 12078
Tel (518) 725-0681 *SIC* 3429

TAYLOR MADE GROUP LLC p 1427
66 Kingsboro Ave 12078
Tel (518) 725-0681 *SIC* 3429 3231

GOSHEN, NY

BLASER SWISSLUBE HOLDING CORP p 189
31 Hatfield Ln 10924
Tel (845) 294-3200 *SIC* 2992

COUNTY OF ORANGE p 380
265 Main St 10924
Tel (845) 291-2480 *SIC* 9121

KONICA MINOLTA SUPPLIES MANUFACTURING USA INC p 827
51 Hatfield Ln 10924
Tel (845) 294-8400 *SIC* 3861

ORANGE-ULSTER BOCES INC p 1092
53 Gibson Rd 10924
Tel (845) 291-0100 *SIC* 8211

GOUVERNEUR, NY

KPH HEALTHCARE SERVICES INC p 828
29 E Main St 13642
Tel (315) 287-3600 *SIC* 5912

GRAND ISLAND, NY

CANNON CORP p 247
2170 Whitehaven Rd 14072
Tel (716) 773-6800 *SIC* 8712

SAINT-GOBAIN ADFORS AMERICA INC p 1271
1795 Baseline Rd 14072
Tel (716) 775-3900 *SIC* 2297

GREAT NECK, NY

AMERICAN INDUSTRIAL CLEANING CO INC p 74
10 Chelsea Pl 11021
Tel (516) 482-8424 *SIC* 7349

BUTLER CAPITAL CORP p 230
60 Cuttermill Rd Ste 214 11021
Tel (212) 980-0606 *SIC* 6211

DASTECH INTERNATIONAL INC p 413
10 Cuttermill Rd Ste 400 11021
Tel (516) 466-7676 *SIC* 5169

FIRST QUALITY ENTERPRISES INC p 549
80 Cuttermill Rd Ste 500 11021
Tel (516) 829-3030 *SIC* 5149

FIRST QUALITY PRODUCTS INC p 549
80 Cuttermill Rd Ste 500 11021
Tel (516) 829-4949 *SIC* 2676

FLEXTRADE SYSTEMS INC p 556
111 Great Neck Rd Ste 314 11021
Tel (516) 627-8993 *SIC* 7372

GREAT NECK PUBLIC SCHOOLS p 634
345 Lakeville Rd 11020
Tel (516) 441-4001 *SIC* 8211

LAURAND ASSOCIATES INC p 847
11 Grace Ave Ste 405 11021
Tel (516) 829-8821 *SIC* 5051

SHELTERPOINT GROUP INC p 1315
600 Northern Blvd Ste 310 11021
Tel (516) 829-8100 *SIC* 6411

WILLIAM H KOPKE JR INC p 1610
1000 Nthrn Blvd Ste 200 11021
Tel (516) 328-6800 *SIC* 5148

GREAT RIVER, NY

NATIONAL RESPONSE CORP p 1015
3500 Sunrise Hwy 11739
Tel (631) 224-9141 *SIC* 4959 8999

GREENE, NY

RAYMOND CONSOLIDATED CORP p 1210
22 S Canal St 13778
Tel (800) 235-7200 *SIC* 3537

RAYMOND CORP p 1210
22 S Canal St 13778
Tel (607) 656-2311 *SIC* 3537 3535 7359

GREENVALE, NY

LONG ISLAND UNIVERSITY p 876
700 Northern Blvd 11548
Tel (516) 299-2535 *SIC* 8221

SLANT/FIN CORP p 1331
100 Forest Dr 11548
Tel (516) 484-2600 *SIC* 3433 3443

GREENWICH, NY

FORT MILLER GROUP INC p 569
688 Wilbur Ave 12834
Tel (518) 695-5000 *SIC* 3272 3441

FORT MILLER SERVICE CORP p 569
688 Wilbur Ave 12834
Tel (518) 695-5000
SIC 3272 3271 5211 1799

GUILDERLAND CENTER, NY

GUILDERLAND CENTRAL SCHOOL DISTRICT p 646
8 School Rd 12085
Tel (518) 456-6200 *SIC* 8211

HALFMOON, NY

NFRASTRUCTURE TECHNOLOGIES LLC p 1041
5 Enterprise Ave 12065
Tel (518) 664-3899 *SIC* 7373

■ **SYSCO ALBANY LLC** p 1416
1 Liebich Ln 12065
Tel (518) 877-3200 *SIC* 5149 5963

HALL, NY

SEEDWAY LLC p 1300
1734 Railroad Pl 14463
Tel (585) 526-6391 *SIC* 5261

HAMBURG, NY

BAILLIE LUMBER CO LP p 145
4002 Legion Dr 14075
Tel (800) 950-2850 *SIC* 5211

FRONTIER CENTRAL SCHOOL DISTRICT p 581
5120 Orchard Ave 14075
Tel (716) 926-1710 *SIC* 8211

HAMILTON, NY

COLGATE UNIVERSITY p 336
13 Oak Dr 13346
Tel (315) 228-1000 *SIC* 8221

HAMMONDSPORT, NY

MERCURY AIRCRAFT INC p 945
8126 County Route 88 14840
Tel (607) 569-4200 *SIC* 3469 3444

HARRIMAN, NY

METROPLEX HOLDINGS INC p 955
15 Commerce Dr S 10926
Tel (845) 781-5000 *SIC* 6512 5149 5087

HARRIS, NY

CENTER FOR DISCOVERY INC p 275
641 Old Route 17 12742
Tel (845) 794-1400 *SIC* 8361

HARRISON, NY

APPLE-METRO INC p 99
550 Mmaroneck Ave Ste 204 10528
Tel (914) 777-2331 *SIC* 5812

CASE PAPER CO INC p 263
500 Mamaroneck Ave Fl 2 10528
Tel (914) 899-3500 *SIC* 5111

CITICORP NORTH AMERICA INC p 310
450 Mamaroneck Ave Ste A 10528
Tel (914) 899-7000 *SIC* 6153 6159

DIVERSIFIED RETIREMENT CORP p 444
440 Mamaroneck Ave 10528
Tel (914) 627-3000 *SIC* 6282

RUSAL AMERICA CORP p 1258
500 Mmaroneck Ave Ste 102 10528
Tel (914) 670-5771 *SIC* 5051

TRANSAMERICA FINANCIAL LIFE INSURANCE CO p 1470
440 Mamaroneck Ave 10528
Tel (319) 355-8511 *SIC* 6311

HAUPPAUGE, NY

ADVANCED ACOUSTIC CONCEPTS LLC p 25
425 Oser Ave Unit 1 11788
Tel (631) 273-5700 *SIC* 5088

AMERICAN CAPITAL PARTNERS LLC p 69
205 Oser Ave 11788
Tel (631) 851-0918 *SIC* 6282

COMPANION LIFE INSURANCE CO p 350
888 Veterans Hwy Ste 515 11788
Tel (866) 371-8905 *SIC* 6311

CONTRACT PHARMACAL CORP p 364
135 Adams Ave 11788
Tel (631) 231-4610 *SIC* 2834

COUNTY OF SUFFOLK p 382
100 Veterans Hwy 11788
Tel (631) 853-4000 *SIC* 9111

CUSTOM COMPUTER SPECIALISTS INC p 403
70 Suffolk Ct Ste 100 11788
Tel (800) 598-8989 *SIC* 7379 7373 7378

DURALEE FABRICS LTD p 462
49 Wireless Blvd Ste 150 11788
Tel (631) 273-8800 *SIC* 5199

FESTO CORP p 539
395 Moreland Rd 11788
Tel (800) 993-3786
SIC 5085 3593 3566 3492

GLOBECOMM SYSTEMS INC p 618
45 Oser Ave 11788
Tel (631) 231-9800 *SIC* 3663 4813

HAUPPAUGE UNION FREE SCHOOL DISTRICT p 668
495 Hoffman Ln Ste 1 11788
Tel (631) 265-3630 *SIC* 8211

INVAGEN PHARMACEUTICALS INC p 760
7 Oser Ave Ste 4 11788
Tel (631) 231-3233 *SIC* 2834 5122

MULLER MARTINI CORP p 999
456 Wheeler Rd 11788
Tel (631) 582-4343 *SIC* 5084 7699

PREMIER UTILITY SERVICES LLC p 1171
100 Marcus Blvd Ste 1 11788
Tel (631) 758-7038 *SIC* 1623

RELIANCE COMMUNICATIONS LLC p 1221
555 Wireless Blvd 11788
Tel (631) 952-4800 *SIC* 5065 5999

SPELLMAN HIGH VOLTAGE ELECTRONICS CORP p 1358
475 Wireless Blvd 11788
Tel (631) 630-3000 *SIC* 3612

SPOTLESS PLASTICS (USA) INC p 1360
100 Motor Pkwy Ste 155 11788
Tel (631) 951-9000 *SIC* 3089

■ **STANDARD MICROSYSTEMS CORP** p 1376
80 Arkay Dr Ste 100 11788
Tel (631) 435-6000 *SIC* 3674

TEACHERS FEDERAL CREDIT UNION p 1429
100 Hauppauge 11788
Tel (631) 698-7000 *SIC* 6061

TRANSFIRST INC p 1471
1393 Veterans Hwy 307s 11788
Tel (631) 840-6900 *SIC* 7389

■ **VOXX ACCESSORIES CORP** p 1566
3502 Wodview Trce Ste 220 11788
Tel (631) 231-7750 *SIC* 5099

■ **VOXX ELECTRONICS CORP** p 1566
150 Marcus Blvd 11788
Tel (631) 231-7750 *SIC* 5065 5731

HAWTHORNE, NY

ALLSTAR MARKETING GROUP LLC p 58
2 Skyline Dr 10532
Tel (914) 347-7827 *SIC* 5023

TARO PHARMACEUTICALS USA INC p 1425
3 Skyline Dr Ste 120 10532
Tel (914) 345-9000 *SIC* 5122

HEMPSTEAD, NY

DANS SUPREME SUPER MARKETS INC p 412
474 Fulton Ave Fl 3 11550
Tel (516) 483-2400 *SIC* 5411

HEMPSTEAD UNION FREE SCHOOL DISTRICT p 682
185 Peninsula Blvd 11550
Tel (516) 292-7001 *SIC* 8211

HOFSTRA UNIVERSITY p 699
100 Hofstra University 11549
Tel (516) 463-6600 *SIC* 8221

STATE WIDE INSURANCE CO INC p 1383
20 Main St 11550
Tel (516) 564-8000 *SIC* 6331

TOWN OF HEMPSTEAD p 1465
1 Washington St 11550
Tel (516) 489-5000 *SIC* 9111

HENRIETTA, NY

MONROE TRACTOR & IMPLEMENT CO INC p 985
1001 Lehigh Station Rd 14467
Tel (585) 334-3867 *SIC* 5082 5083 7353

REGIONAL INTERNATIONAL CORP p 1219
1007 Lehigh Station Rd 14467
Tel (585) 359-2011
SIC 5013 5012 7539 7538 5531

RUSH-HENRIETTA CENTRAL SCHOOL DISTRICT p 1259
2034 Lehigh Station Rd 14467
Tel (585) 359-5000 *SIC* 8211

HICKSVILLE, NY

AUTHENTIC LIFESTYLE PRODUCTS LLC p 133
485 S Broadway Ste 11 11801
Tel (212) 354-2170 *SIC* 5399

AVA PORK PRODUCTS INC p 135
383 W John St Unit A 11801
Tel (516) 750-1500 *SIC* 5147

FAMILY AIDES INC p 526
120 W John St B 11801
Tel (516) 681-2300 *SIC* 8082

FLEXFIT LLC p 556
350 Karin Ln Unit A 11801
Tel (516) 932-8800 *SIC* 2353

HICKSVILLE UNION FREE SCHOOL DISTRICT (INC) p 690
200 Division Ave 11801
Tel (516) 733-6600 *SIC* 8211

KEYSPAN GAS EAST CORP p 815
175 Old Country Rd 11801
Tel (718) 403-1000 *SIC* 4924

NASSAU CANDY DISTRIBUTORS INC p 1008
530 W John St 11801
Tel (516) 433-7100 *SIC* 5145

NATIONAL GRID CORPORATE SERVICES LLC p 1013
175 E Old Country Rd 11801
Tel (718) 403-2000
SIC 4924 4911 1311 4922

NATIONAL GRID GENERATION LLC p 1013
175 E Old Country Rd 11801
Tel (631) 755-6650 *SIC* 4924

SAM ASH MEGASTORES LLC p 1273
278 Duffy Ave Unit A 11801
Tel (516) 932-6400 *SIC* 5736

SAM ASH MUSIC CORP p 1273
278 Duffy Ave Unit A 11801
Tel (516) 932-6400 *SIC* 5099 5736

SAM ASH MUSIC CORP p 1273
278 Duffy Ave Unit A 11801
Tel (516) 932-6400
SIC 5736 5731 5734 5961 7359 8741

SLEEPYS LLC p 1331
1000 S Oyster Bay Rd 11801
Tel (516) 861-8800 *SIC* 5712

SLEEPYS REORGANIZATION INC p 1331
1000 S Oyster Bay Rd 11801
Tel (516) 861-8800 *SIC* 5712

SLOMINS INC p 1331
125 Lauman Ln 11801
Tel (516) 932-7000 *SIC* 5983 1731 1711

HIGHLAND FALLS, NY

RELATED COMPANIES L P p 1221
40 W Point Hwy 10928
Tel (845) 446-4966 *SIC* 6531

HILLBURN, NY

RAMAPO CENTRAL SCHOOL DISTRICT p 1206
45 Mountain Ave 10931
Tel (845) 357-7783 *SIC* 8211

HOGANSBURG, NY

ST REGIS MOHAWK EDUCATION AND COMMUNITY FUND INC p 1372
412 State Route 37 13655
Tel (518) 358-2272 *SIC* 7929

HOLBROOK, NY

FUTURE TECH ENTERPRISE INC p 585
101 Colin Dr Unit 8 11741
Tel (631) 472-5500 *SIC* 7373

VITAMIN WORLD INC p 1562
4320 Veterans Mem Hwy 11741
Tel (631) 567-9500 *SIC* 5499

HOLLIS, NY

NEW YORK CITY GEOGRAPHIC DISTRICT 29 p 1034
22214 Jamaica Ave 11423
Tel (718) 217-7740 *SIC* 8211

HOLTSVILLE, NY

BURMAX CO INC p 228
28 Barretts Ave 11742
Tel (631) 447-8700 *SIC* 5087 7231

DI CARLO DISTRIBUTORS INC p 436
1630 N Ocean Ave 11742
Tel (800) 342-2756 *SIC* 5142 5141 5143

J KINGS FOOD SERVICE PROFESSIONALS INC p 771
700 Furrows Rd 11742
Tel (631) 289-8401
SIC 5149 5143 5144 5142 5148

LANDMARK FOOD CORP p 843
865 Waverly Ave 11742
Tel (631) 654-4500
SIC 5142 5141 5148 5147

■ SYMBOL TECHNOLOGIES LLC p 1414
1 Zebra Plz 11742
Tel (631) 737-6851 *SIC* 4812

■ TELXON CORP p 1435
1 Zebra Plz 11742
Tel (631) 738-2400 *SIC* 3571 7373 3663

HOPEWELL JUNCTION, NY

BRYANSTON GROUP INC p 221
1886 State Route 52 52 12533
Tel (845) 223-3603 *SIC* 7011

GLOBALFOUNDRIES US 2 LLC p 617
2070 Route 52 12533
Tel (408) 582-8140 *SIC* 3674

WAPPINGERS CENTRAL SCHOOL DISTRICT p 1575
25 Corporate Park Rd 12533
Tel (845) 298-5000 *SIC* 8211

HORNELL, NY

ALSTOM USA INC p 61
1 Transit Dr 14843
Tel (607) 324-4595 *SIC* 3321 7699

HUDSON, NY

COLUMBIA MEMORIAL HOSPITAL p 341
71 Prospect Ave 12534
Tel (518) 828-7601 *SIC* 8062 8051

GINSBERGS INSTITUTIONAL FOODS INC p 612
29 Ginsburg Ln 12534
Tel (518) 828-4004
SIC 5148 5147 5142 5141 5143

TACONIC BIOSCIENCES INC p 1421
1 Hudson City Ctr 12534
Tel (609) 860-0806 *SIC* 0279

HUNTINGTON STATION, NY

■ AMERICAN TECHNICAL CERAMICS CORP p 80
1 Norden Ln 11746
Tel (631) 622-4700 *SIC* 3672 3675

SOUTH HUNTINGTON UNION FREE SCHOOL DISTRICT p 1344
60 Weston St 11746
Tel (631) 425-5300 *SIC* 8211

HUNTINGTON, NY

ABOFFS INC p 12
33 Gerard St Ste 204 11743
Tel (631) 427-2008 *SIC* 5198 5231

HUNTINGTON HOSPITAL AUXILIARY p 720
270 Park Ave 11743
Tel (631) 351-2257 *SIC* 5947 5499 8322

HUNTINGTON HOSPITAL DOLAN FAMILY HEALTH CENTER INC p 720
270 Park Ave 11743
Tel (631) 351-2000 *SIC* 8062

KLEET LUMBER CO INC p 823
777 Park Ave 11743
Tel (631) 427-7060 *SIC* 5031

TOWN OF HUNTINGTON p 1465
100 Main St 11743
Tel (631) 351-3177 *SIC* 9111

HYDE PARK, NY

CULINARY INSTITUTE OF AMERICA p 400
1946 Campus Dr 12538
Tel (845) 452-9600 *SIC* 8221

INWOOD, NY

MARK GOLDEN MAINTENANCE LTD INC p 907
420 Doughty Blvd Ste 4 11096
Tel (516) 239-3400 *SIC* 7349 5087

IRVING, NY

TLC HEALTH NETWORK p 1457
845 Route 5 And 20 14081
Tel (716) 951-7000 *SIC* 8062 8069

IRVINGTON, NY

EILEEN FISHER INC p 481
2 Bridge St Ste 230 10533
Tel (914) 591-5700 *SIC* 2339

NATURAL MARKETS FOOD GROUP p 1018
1 Bridge St Ste 2 10533
Tel (914) 472-7900 *SIC* 5499

ISLAND PARK, NY

HALLEN CONSTRUCTION CO INC p 654
4270 Austin Blvd 11558
Tel (516) 432-8300 *SIC* 1623

ISLANDIA, NY

ARCSERVE (USA) LLC p 106
1 Ca Plz 11749
Tel (866) 576-9742 *SIC* 7372

WHITSONS FOOD SERVICE CORP p 1607
1800 Motor Pkwy 11749
Tel (631) 424-2700 *SIC* 5812

ISLIP TERRACE, NY

EAST ISLIP UNION FREE SCHOOL DISTRICT 3 p 470
1 Craig B Gariepy Ave 11752
Tel (631) 224-2000 *SIC* 8211

ITHACA, NY

■ BORGWARNER MORSETEC INC p 201
800 Warren Rd 14850
Tel (607) 257-6700 *SIC* 3714 3462 3568

CAYUGA MEDICAL CENTER AT ITHACA INC p 268
101 Dates Dr 14850
Tel (607) 274-4011 *SIC* 8062

■ CBORD GROUP INC p 269
950 Danby Rd Ste 100c 14850
Tel (607) 257-2410 *SIC* 7372 5045

CORNELL UNIVERSITY p 370
308 Duffield Hall 14853
Tel (607) 254-4636 *SIC* 8221 8011

ITHACA CITY SCHOOL DISTRICT p 768
400 Lake St 14850
Tel (607) 274-2201 *SIC* 8211

ITHACA COLLEGE p 768
953 Danby Rd 14850
Tel (607) 274-3011 *SIC* 8221

ONGWEOWEH CORP p 1088
767 Warren Rd 14850
Tel (607) 266-7070 *SIC* 8741 4953

▲ TOMPKINS FINANCIAL CORP p 1460
The Cmns 14851
Tel (607) 273-3210 *SIC* 6022

■ TOMPKINS TRUST CO p 1460
110 N Tioga St 14850
Tel (607) 257-1909 *SIC* 6733

JAMAICA, NY

ARCH-AUTO PARTS CORP p 104
17008 Jamaica Ave 11432
Tel (718) 657-9600 *SIC* 5013 5531

BARTLETT DAIRY INC p 157
9004 161st St Ste 609 11432
Tel (718) 658-2299 *SIC* 5143 5141

BOLLORE LOGISTICS USA INC p 198
15010 132nd Ave 11434
Tel (718) 276-3907 *SIC* 4731

CARGO AIRPORT SERVICES USA LLC p 255
Cargo Bldg 261 N Boundary 11430
Tel (718) 244-0900 *SIC* 4789

DERLE FARMS INC p 431
15602 Liberty Ave 11433
Tel (718) 257-2040 *SIC* 5143

GABRIELLI TRUCK SALES LTD p 588
15320 S Conduit Ave 11434
Tel (718) 977-7348 *SIC* 5511 5531 7538

INTEGRATED AIRLINE SERVICES INC p 749
1639 W 23rd St Ste 240 11430
Tel (718) 880-3453 *SIC* 4581

JAMAICA HOSPITAL p 776
8900 Van Wyck Expy Fl 4n 11418
Tel (718) 206-6290 *SIC* 8062

JAMAICA HOSPITAL MEDICAL CENTER p 776
8900 Van Wyck Expy 11418
Tel (718) 206-6000 *SIC* 8011

LONG ISLAND RAIL ROAD CO p 876
9027 Sutphin Blvd 11435
Tel (718) 558-4704 *SIC* 4111

MEDISYS HEALTH NETWORK INC p 938
8900 Van Wyck Expy 11418
Tel (718) 206-6000 *SIC* 8741

MEDISYS JAMAICA HOSPITAL & MEDICAL CENTER p 938
8900 Van Wyck Expy 11418
Tel (718) 206-6000 *SIC* 8062

NEW YORK CITY GEOGRAPHIC DISTRICT 28 p 1034
9027 Sutphin Blvd Rm 24 11435
Tel (718) 557-2618 *SIC* 8211

NYRA INC p 1069
11000 Rockaway Blvd Ste 1 11420
Tel (718) 641-4700 *SIC* 7948

Q INTERNATIONAL COURIER INC p 1194
17528 148th Ave 11434
Tel (718) 995-3616 *SIC* 7389

QUEENS BOROUGH PUBLIC LIBRARY p 1198
8911 Merrick Blvd 11432
Tel (718) 990-0700 *SIC* 8231

ST JOHNS UNIVERSITY NEW YORK p 1368
8000 Utopia Pkwy 11439
Tel (718) 990-6161 *SIC* 8221

STEUBEN FOODS INC p 1388
15504 Liberty Ave 11433
Tel (718) 291-3333 *SIC* 2032 2026

TERMINAL ONE GROUP ASSOCIATION LP p 1439
Jfk International Airport 11430
Tel (718) 751-1700 *SIC* 4581

JAMESTOWN, NY

BUSH INDUSTRIES INC p 229
1 Mason Dr 14701
Tel (716) 665-2000 *SIC* 2511 2521

ED SHULTS CHEVROLET INC p 476
300 Fluvanna Ave 14701
Tel (716) 484-7151 *SIC* 5511

OCCUPATIONAL HEALTH SERVICE p 1072
207 Foote Ave 14701
Tel (716) 664-8165 *SIC* 8011 8062

RESOURCE CENTER p 1227
200 Dunham Ave 14701
Tel (716) 661-4829
SIC 8093 6513 6512 8052

TITANX ENGINE COOLING INC p 1456
2258 Allen Street Ext 14701
Tel (716) 665-7129 *SIC* 3714

TRINITY BIOTECH INC p 1481
2823 Girts Rd 14701
Tel (800) 325-3424 *SIC* 5047

WCA GROUP INC p 1585
207 Foote Ave 14701
Tel (716) 487-0141 *SIC* 8062 4119

WOMANS CHRISTIAN ASSOCIATION OF JAMESTOWN N Y p 1621
207 Foote Ave 14701
Tel (716) 487-0141
SIC 8062 8063 8093 8069

JERICHO, NY

BAMBERGER POLYMERS CORP p 149
2 Jericho Plz Ste 109 11753
Tel (516) 622-3600 *SIC* 5162

BAMBERGER POLYMERS INC p 149
2 Jericho Plz Ste 109 11753
Tel (516) 622-3600 *SIC* 5162

CABLEVISION LIGHTPATH INC p 235
200 Jericho Quadrangle 11753
Tel (516) 803-2300 *SIC* 4841

■ CLOPAY AMES TRUE TEMPER HOLDING CORP p 327
100 Jericho Quadrangle # 224 11753
Tel (516) 938-5544 *SIC* 3423 3799 3524

CONTINENTAL CONCESSION SUPPLIES INC p 363
575 Jericho Tpke Ste 300 11753
Tel (516) 739-8777 *SIC* 5145

DARBY DENTAL SUPPLY LLC p 412
300 Jericho Quadrangle Ll 11753
Tel (516) 688-6252 *SIC* 5047

▲ GETTY REALTY CORP p 609
2 Jericho Plz Ste 110 11753
Tel (516) 478-5400 *SIC* 6798

GP HARMON RECYCLING LLC p 627
2 Jericho Plz Ste 200 11753
Tel (516) 997-3400 *SIC* 5093

KINTETSU WORLD EXPRESS (USA) INC p 821
1 Jericho Plz Ste 100 11753
Tel (516) 933-7100 *SIC* 4731

▲ NATHANS FAMOUS INC p 1009
1 Jericho Plz Fl 2 11753
Tel (516) 338-8500 *SIC* 5812 6794

NORTH SHORE LIJ HEALTH SYSTEM FEDERAL CREDIT UNION p 1053
350 Jericho Tpke Ste 103 11753
Tel (516) 301-3040 *SIC* 6061

SCHONFELD SECURITIES LLC p 1288
2 Jericho Plz Ste 300 11753
Tel (646) 735-3180 *SIC* 6211

SPRINGFIELD LLC p 1361
100 Jericho Quadrangle # 340 11753
Tel (516) 861-6250 *SIC* 2221

TUNNEL HILL PARTNERS LP p 1491
390 N Broadway Ste 220 11753
Tel (516) 806-6232 *SIC* 4953

■ WEIGHT WATCHERS NORTH AMERICA INC p 1588
300 Jericho Quadrangle # 350 11753
Tel (516) 390-1400 *SIC* 8093

JOHNSTOWN, NY

FAGE USA DAIRY INDUSTRY INC p 524
1 Opportunity Dr 12095
Tel (518) 762-5912 *SIC* 2026

FAGE USA HOLDINGS p 524
1 Opportunity Dr 12095
Tel (518) 762-5912 *SIC* 2026 5143

FULTON COUNTY A R C p 584
465 N Perry St 12095
Tel (518) 762-0024 *SIC* 8331 8361

NYSARC INC FULTON COUNTY CHAPTER p 1069
465 N Perry St 12095
Tel (518) 773-7931 *SIC* 8641

KATONAH, NY

NORTH AMERICAN COMMUNICATIONS INC p 1049
7 Edgemont Rd 10536
Tel (914) 273-8620 *SIC* 7331

KEESEVILLE, NY

■ FRONTIER COMMUNICATIONS OF AUSABLE VALLEY INC p 581
310 Front St 12944
Tel (518) 834-7211 SIC 4813

KENMORE, NY

KENMORE MERCY HOSPITAL p 810
2950 Elmwood Ave Fl 6 14217
Tel (716) 447-6100 SIC 8062 8059 8011

KEW GARDENS, NY

BROADBAND TELECOM INC p 215
8002 Kew Gardens Rd # 1040 11415
Tel (718) 261-0148 SIC 4813

KINGS PARK, NY

UTOPIA HOME CARE INC p 1537
60 E Main St 11754
Tel (631) 544-6005 SIC 8082 8093

KINGSTON, NY

CITY SCHOOL DISTRICT KINGSTON NY p 319
61 Crown St 12401
Tel (845) 339-3000 SIC 8211

COUNTY OF ULSTER p 382
244 Fair St 12401
Tel (845) 340-3000 SIC 9111

HEALTHALLIANCE HOSPITAL BROADWAY CAMPUS p 676
396 Broadway 12401
Tel (845) 331-3131 SIC 8062

HEALTHALLIANCE HOSPITAL MARYS AVENUE CAMPUS p 676
105 Marys Ave 12401
Tel (845) 338-2500 SIC 8062 8051

KIRKWOOD, NY

WILLOW RUN FOODS INC p 1613
1006 Us Route 11 13795
Tel (607) 338-5221
SIC 5142 5149 5147 5113 5148 5087

LA FAYETTE, NY

BYRNE DAIRY INC p 231
2394 Us Route 11 13084
Tel (315) 475-2121 SIC 2026 2024

LACKAWANNA, NY

BAKER HALL p 146
780 Ridge Rd 14218
Tel (716) 828-9515 SIC 8361 8211 8322

LAGRANGEVILLE, NY

ARLINGTON CENTRAL SCHOOL DISTRICT p 110
144 Todd Hill Rd 12540
Tel (845) 486-4460 SIC 8211

HEALTH QUEST SYSTEMS INC p 675
1351 Route 55 Ste 200 12540
Tel (845) 475-9500 SIC 8741

LAKE KATRINE, NY

HEALTH ALLIANCE INC p 674
741 Grant Ave 12449
Tel (845) 334-3151 SIC 8062

LAKE RONKONKOMA, NY

SACHEM CENTRAL SCHOOL DISTRICT AT HOLBROOK p 1264
51 School St 11779
Tel (631) 471-1336 SIC 8211

LAKE SUCCESS, NY

■ ASTORIA BANK p 122
1 Astoria Federal Plz 11042
Tel (516) 535-9000 SIC 6035

LANCASTER, NY

AMERICAN SALES CO LLC p 79
4201 Walden Ave 14086
Tel (716) 686-7000 SIC 5199 5122

▲ ECOLOGY AND ENVIRONMENT INC p 476
368 Pleasant View Dr 14086
Tel (716) 684-8060 SIC 8748 8734 8711

LANCASTER CENTRAL SCHOOLS DISTRICT p 841
177 Central Ave 14086
Tel (716) 686-3200 SIC 8211 9411

SAMUEL SON & CO INC p 1275
4334 Walden Ave 14086
Tel (716) 681-4200 SIC 5085 5051

SEALING DEVICES INC p 1296
4400 Walden Ave 14086
Tel (716) 684-7600 SIC 5085 3069 3053

LARCHMONT, NY

DAGOSTINO SUPERMARKETS INC p 408
1385 Boston Post Rd Ste 1 10538
Tel (914) 833-4000 SIC 5411

LATHAM, NY

▲ ANGIODYNAMICS INC p 91
14 Plaza Dr 12110
Tel (518) 795-1400 SIC 3841

AYCO CAFE p 140
25 British American Blvd 12110
Tel (518) 782-5080 SIC 5812

BETTE & CRING LLC p 178
22 Century Hill Dr # 201 12110
Tel (518) 213-1010
SIC 1541 1542 1622 1611

CG POWER USA INC p 285
7 Century Hill Dr 12110
Tel (518) 452-7718 SIC 8711

COMBINED LIFE INSURANCE CO OF NEW YORK INC p 343
11 British American Blvd # 2 12110
Tel (518) 220-9333 SIC 6321 6311

COMMUNITY CARE PHYSICIANS PC p 347
711 Troy Schenectady Rd # 201 12110
Tel (518) 783-3110 SIC 8011

CURRIER MCCABE & ASSOCIATES INC p 402
700 Troy Schenectady Rd 12110
Tel (518) 783-9003 SIC 7371 7379

LATHAM INTERNATIONAL INC p 846
787 Watervliet Shaker Rd 12110
Tel (518) 783-7776 SIC 3086 3081

LATHAM MANUFACTURING CORP p 846
787 Watervliet Shaker Rd 12110
Tel (518) 783-7776
SIC 3086 3081 3083 3949

LATHAM POOL PRODUCTS INC p 846
787 Watervliet Shaker Rd 12110
Tel (518) 951-1000 SIC 3949

MECHANICAL DYNAMICS & ANALYSIS LTD p 934
19 British American Blvd 12110
Tel (518) 399-3616 SIC 8711 7699

NEW YORK DIVISION OF MILITARY AND NAVAL AFFAIRS p 1035
330 Old Niskayuna Rd 12110
Tel (518) 786-4500 SIC 9711

NEW YORK STATE UNITED TEACHERS p 1036
800 Troy Schenectady Rd 12110
Tel (518) 213-6000 SIC 8631

NORTH COLONIE CENTRAL SCHOOL DISTRICT p 1052
91 Fiddlers Ln 12110
Tel (518) 785-8591 SIC 8211

NYSARC INC p 1069
29 British American Blvd # 2 12110
Tel (518) 439-8311
SIC 8361 8322 8093 8331

PAMAL BROADCASTING LTD p 1110
6 Johnson Rd 12110
Tel (518) 786-6600 SIC 4832

PHILIPS MEDICAL SYSTEMS MR INC p 1143
450 Old Niskayuna Rd 12110
Tel (518) 782-1122 SIC 3845 3674 3679

▲ PLUG POWER INC p 1156
968 Albany Shaker Rd 12110
Tel (518) 782-7700 SIC 2679

PROTECTIVE INDUSTRIAL PRODUCTS INC p 1185
968 Albany Shaker Rd 12110
Tel (518) 861-0133 SIC 5085

LAWRENCE, NY

JOHN P PICONE INC p 789
31 Garden Ln 11559
Tel (516) 239-1600
SIC 1611 1622 1623 1629

LAWRENCE UNION FREE SCHOOL DISTRICT p 848
195 Broadway 11559
Tel (516) 295-7000 SIC 8211

LE ROY, NY

TOWNSEND OIL CORP p 1466
64 Main St 14482
Tel (585) 768-8188 SIC 5171 5983

LEVITTOWN, NY

BESTCARE INC p 177
3000 Hempstead Tpke # 205 11756
Tel (516) 731-3535 SIC 8082

LEWISTON, NY

MOUNT ST MARYS HOSPITAL OF NIAGARA FALLS p 994
5300 Military Rd 14092
Tel (716) 297-4800 SIC 8062

LINDENHURST, NY

LINDENHURST UNION FREE SCHOOL DISTRICT p 868
350 Daniel St 11757
Tel (631) 226-6441 SIC 8211

LITTLE FALLS, NY

BURROWS PAPER CORP p 229
501 W Main St Ste 1 13365
Tel (315) 823-2300
SIC 2621 2671 2611 2679

LITTLE NECK, NY

E GLUCK CORP p 466
6015 Little Neck Pkwy 11362
Tel (718) 784-0700 SIC 3873 5094

LITTLE VALLEY, NY

COUNTY OF CATTARAUGUS p 376
303 Court St 14755
Tel (716) 938-9111 SIC 9111

LIVERPOOL, NY

AMERICAN FOOD & VENDING CORP p 72
124 Metropolitan Park Dr 13088
Tel (315) 457-9950 SIC 5962 5812

JGB ENTERPRISES INC p 785
115 Metropolitan Dr 13088
Tel (315) 451-2770 SIC 3052 5085 3429

LIVERPOOL CENTRAL SCHOOL DISTRICT p 871
195 Blackberry Rd 13090
Tel (315) 622-7148 SIC 8211

■ LOCKHEED MARTIN GLOBAL INC p 873
497 Electronics Pkwy # 5 13088
Tel (315) 456-2982 SIC 3812

RAYMOURS FURNITURE CO INC p 1210
7248 Morgan Rd 13090
Tel (315) 453-2500 SIC 5712

LOCKPORT, NY

COUNTY OF NIAGARA p 380
175 Hawley St 14094
Tel (716) 439-7085 SIC 9111

REID COMPANIES INC p 1220
100 W Genesee St 14094
Tel (716) 434-2885 SIC 5541

REID PETROLEUM CORP p 1221
100 W Genesee St 14094
Tel (716) 434-2885 SIC 5541 5172

LONG ISLAND CITY, NY

ABCO REFRIGERATION SUPPLY CORP p 10
4970 31st St 11101
Tel (718) 937-9000 SIC 5078

ANAYA GEMS INC p 88
3100 47th Ave Unit 5 11101
Tel (718) 391-7400 SIC 5094 3911

■ CITICORP CREDIT SERVICES INC p 310
One Court Square 25th Flr 11120
Tel (718) 248-3192 SIC 7389

■ CITICORP SELECT INVESTMENTS INC p 310
1 Court Sq Fl 24 11101
Tel (212) 559-1000 SIC 6282

E-J ELECTRIC INSTALLATION CO INC p 467
4641 Vernon Blvd 11101
Tel (718) 786-9400 SIC 1731

FRESH DIRECT HOLDINGS INC p 578
2330 Borden Ave 11101
Tel (718) 433-0982 SIC 5499 4813

HARDWARE SPECIALTY CO INC p 661
4875 36th St 11101
Tel (718) 361-9320 SIC 5063 5085

■ JANOVIC-PLAZA INC p 777
3035 Thomson Ave 11101
Tel (718) 392-3999
SIC 5198 5231 5023 5719

▲ JETBLUE AIRWAYS CORP p 784
2701 Queens Plz N 11101
Tel (718) 286-7900 SIC 4512

MAJOR AUTOMOTIVE COMPANIES INC p 899
4340 Northern Blvd 11101
Tel (718) 625-6753 SIC 5511

MAJOR WORLD CHEVROLET LLC p 899
4340 Northern Blvd 11101
Tel (718) 937-3700
SIC 5511 7515 7538 5521

MANA PRODUCTS INC p 900
3202 Queens Blvd Fl 6 11101
Tel (718) 361-2550 SIC 2844 5122

MECCA ELECTRONICS INDUSTRIES INC p 934
1016 44th Dr 11101
Tel (718) 361-9001 SIC 5092

MECHOSHADE SYSTEMS INC p 934
4203 35th St 11101
Tel (718) 729-2020 SIC 2591

■ METLIFE INVESTORS DISTRIBUTION CO p 954
1 Met Life Plz 11101
Tel (212) 578-2211 SIC 6411

■ METROPOLITAN LIFE INSURANCE CO (INC) p 956
2701 Queens Plz N Ste 1 11101
Tel (212) 578-2211
SIC 6411 6324 6331 6321 6531

MICHAEL C FINA CO INC p 960
3301 Hunters Point Ave 11101
Tel (212) 557-2500 SIC 5094 5947

MZ BERGER & CO INC p 1005
2976 Northern Blvd Fl 4 11101
Tel (718) 472-7500 SIC 5094 3873

NESPRESSO USA INC p 1026
2401 44th Rd Fl 12 11101
Tel (800) 562-1465 SIC 5149 5046 5499

NEW YORK CITY GEOGRAPHIC DISTRICT 30 p 1034
2811 Queens Plz N 11101
Tel (718) 391-8323 SIC 8211

NEW YORK CITY SCHOOL CONSTRUCTION AUTHORITY p 1034
3030 Thomson Ave Fl 3 11101
Tel (718) 472-8000 SIC 1542

NEW YORK PAVING INC p 1035
3718 Railroad Ave 11101
Tel (718) 482-0780 SIC 1611

NIPPON EXPRESS USA INC p 1044
2401 44th Rd Fl 14 11101
Tel (212) 758-6100 SIC 4731 4225

NOUVEAU ELEVATOR INDUSTRIES INC p 1062
4755 37th St 11101
Tel (718) 349-4700 SIC 7699 1796

RESEARCH FOUNDATION OF CITY UNIVERSITY OF NEW YORK p 1226
2 Court Sq 11101
Tel (212) 417-8587 SIC 8221

■ SIRONA DENTAL SYSTEMS INC p 1327
3030 47th Ave Ste 500 11101
Tel (718) 482-2011
SIC 8021 3313 3843 3841

▲ STANDARD MOTOR PRODUCTS INC p 1376
3718 Northern Blvd # 600 11101
Tel (718) 392-0200
SIC 3714 3694 3585 3564 3052

STEINWAY AND SONS p 1385
1 Steinway Pl 11105
Tel (718) 721-2600 SIC 3931 5736

STEINWAY INC p 1385
1 Steinway Pl 11105
Tel (718) 721-2600 SIC 3931 5736

▲ STEVEN MADDEN LTD p 1388
5216 Barnett Ave 11104
Tel (718) 446-1800
SIC 3143 3144 3149 5632

UNITED NATIONS FEDERAL CREDIT UNION p 1510
2401 44th Rd 11101
Tel (347) 686-6000 SIC 6061

UTF TRUCKING INC p 1536
2330 Borden Ave 11101
Tel (718) 928-1000 SIC 4212

LORRAINE, NY

TOWN OF LORRAINE p 1465
20876 County Route 189 13659
Tel (315) 232-4676 SIC 9111

LOUDONVILLE, NY

SIENA COLLEGE p 1320
515 Loudon Rd 12211
Tel (518) 783-2300 SIC 8221

LYNBROOK, NY

FUN STATION ASSOCIATES INC p 585
40 Rocklyn Ave 11563
Tel (516) 599-7757 SIC 7299 7999

PAR PLUMBING CO INC p 1113
60 N Prospect Ave 11563
Tel (516) 887-4000 SIC 1711

PEARL ARTIST & CRAFT SUPPLY CORP p 1126
185 Merrick Rd 11563
Tel (954) 564-5700 SIC 5999 5199

LYONS, NY

COUNTY OF WAYNE p 383
9 Pearl St Rm 1 14489
Tel (315) 946-5400 SIC 9111

MAMARONECK, NY

MAMARONECK UNION FREE SCHOOL DISTRICT p 900
1000 W Boston Post Rd 10543
Tel (914) 220-3000 SIC 8211

MANHASSET, NY

AJB VENTURES INC p 41
10 Walter Ln 11030
Tel (516) 365-6690 SIC 6321

APPLE BANK FOR SAVINGS p 98
1395 Northern Blvd 11030
Tel (516) 627-1800 SIC 6036

MORSTAN GENERAL INSURANCE AGENCY INC p 991
600 Community Dr 11030
Tel (516) 488-4747 SIC 6411

NORTH SHORE UNIVERSITY HOSPITAL p 1053
300 Community Dr 11030
Tel (516) 562-0100 SIC 8062 8011

MANLIUS, NY

L& JG STICKLEY INC p 834
1 Stickley Dr 13104
Tel (315) 682-5500 SIC 2511 2519

MANORVILLE, NY

INDEPENDENT TRANSPORTERS OF HANDICAPPED INC p 737
221 N Sunrise Service Rd 11949
Tel (631) 878-9270 SIC 8361 4729

MARGARETVILLE, NY

CITIHOPE INTERNATIONAL INC p 310
629 Main St Ste 2 12455
Tel (845) 586-6202 SIC 8322

MARION, NY

▲ SENECA FOODS CORP p 1303
3736 S Main St 14505
Tel (315) 926-8100 SIC 2033 2037

MASPETH, NY

BIG GEYSER INC p 181
5765 48th St 11378
Tel (718) 821-2200 SIC 5149

DAVIS & WARSHOW INC p 416
5722 49th St 11378
Tel (718) 937-9500 SIC 5074

J & J FARMS CREAMERY INC p 769
5748 49th St Ste 1 11378
Tel (718) 821-1200 SIC 5143 5149

WEEKS-LERMAN GROUP LLC p 1587
5838 Page Pl 11378
Tel (718) 803-4700
SIC 5112 5021 2752 5044

MASSAPEQUA, NY

MASSAPEQUA UNION FREE SCHOOL DISTRICT p 917
4925 Merrick Rd 11758
Tel (516) 308-5900 SIC 8211

RECCO HOME CARE SERVICE INC p 1214
524 Hicksville Rd 11758
Tel (516) 798-6688 SIC 8082

MAYVILLE, NY

COUNTY OF CHAUTAUQUA p 377
3 N Erie St 14757
Tel (716) 753-7111 SIC 9121

MEDFORD, NY

EASTERN WHOLESALE FENCE CO INC p 473
274 Middle Island Rd 11763
Tel (631) 698-0900
SIC 5039 5031 5051 3496

GERSHOW RECYCLING CORP p 609
71 Peconic Ave 11763
Tel (631) 289-6188 SIC 4953

INTERCOUNTY APPLIANCE CORP p 752
10 National Blvd 11763
Tel (631) 543-6900 SIC 5064

MEDIACOM PARK, NY

MEDIACOM BROADBAND LLC p 936
1 Mediacom Way 10918
Tel (845) 443-2600 SIC 4841

MEDIACOM COMMUNICATIONS CORP p 936
1 Mediacom Way 10918
Tel (877) 847-6221 SIC 4841 4813

MEDIACOM LLC p 936
1 Mediacom Way 10918
Tel (845) 443-2600 SIC 4841

MEDINA, NY

■ SIGMA INTERNATIONAL GENERAL MEDICAL APPARATUS LLC p 1321
711 Park Ave 14103
Tel (585) 798-3901 SIC 3841

MELVILLE, NY

ADECCO EMPLOYMENT SERVICES INC p 22
175 Broadhollow Rd 11747
Tel (631) 844-7100 SIC 7363 7361

ADECCO INC p 22
175 Broadhollow Rd # 200 11747
Tel (631) 391-5776 SIC 6719

■ ADI CORPORATE p 22
263 Old Country Rd 11747
Tel (800) 233-6261 SIC 5063 5085

ADO STAFFING INC p 23
175 Broadhollow Rd 11747
Tel (631) 844-7800 SIC 7363 6794

AJILON LLC p 41
175 Broadhollow Rd 11747
Tel (631) 844-7800 SIC 7379 8742 7374

■ ALL POINTS CAPITAL CORP p 51
275 Broadhollow Rd 11747
Tel (631) 531-2800 SIC 6035 6159

AMBASSADOR BOOK SERVICE INC p 65
445 Broadhollow Rd 11747
Tel (631) 770-1010 SIC 5192

ANALYSIS & DESIGN APPLICATION CO LTD p 88
60 Broadhollow Rd 11747
Tel (631) 549-2300 SIC 7371

CANON SOLUTIONS AMERICA INC p 247
1 Canon Park 11747
Tel (631) 330-5000 SIC 7389

CANON USA INC p 247
1 Canon Park 11747
Tel (516) 328-5000
SIC 5044 5065 5045 3861 3577 5043

■ CAPITAL ONE BANK p 250
275 Broadhollow Rd 11747
Tel (631) 844-1376 SIC 6022

▲ COMTECH TELECOMMUNICATIONS CORP p 353
68 S Service Rd Ste 230 11747
Tel (631) 962-7000 SIC 3663

CONSUMER HOME MORTGAGE INC p 361
115 Broadhollow Rd 11747
Tel (631) 547-6840 SIC 6163

ESSELTE HOLDINGS INC p 510
48 S Service Rd Ste 400 11747
Tel (631) 675-5700
SIC 2675 2782 3579 2672 3953 3596

EVO MERCHANT SERVICES LLC p 515
515 Broadhollow Rd # 100 11747
Tel (516) 479-9000 SIC 7389

EVO PAYMENTS INTERNATIONAL LLC p 515
515 Broadhollow Rd # 100 11747
Tel (800) 227-3794 SIC 8721

FOUGERA PHARMACEUTICALS INC p 571
60 Baylis Rd 11747
Tel (631) 454-7677
SIC 2834 2851 2821 3479 3829

GLOBAL FACILITY MANAGEMENT & CONSTRUCTION INC p 616
525 Broadhollow Rd # 100 11747
Tel (866) 213-2337 SIC 8744

▲ HENRY SCHEIN INC p 684
135 Duryea Rd 11747
Tel (631) 843-5500 SIC 5047 5122 7372

KORG USA INC p 828
316 S Service Rd 11747
Tel (631) 390-6500 SIC 5099

LEVITON MANUFACTURING CO INC p 858
201 N Service Rd 11747
Tel (631) 812-6000
SIC 3643 3613 3357 3674 3694 3678

LLOYD STAFFING INC p 872
445 Broadhollow Rd # 119 11747
Tel (631) 777-7600 SIC 7363

MARCHON EYEWEAR INC p 905
201 Old Country Rd Fl 3 11747
Tel (631) 756-8530 SIC 5048

▲ MSC INDUSTRIAL DIRECT CO INC p 996
75 Maxess Rd 11747
Tel (516) 812-2000
SIC 5084 5085 5063 5072

NEPTUNE HOLDING US CORP p 1026
6 Corporate Center Dr 11747
Tel (516) 803-2265 SIC 7313 7929

NEWSDAY LLC p 1039
235 Pinelawn Rd 11747
Tel (631) 843-4050 SIC 2711

NIC HOLDING CORP p 1042
225 Brd Hllow Rd Ste 212w 11747
Tel (631) 753-4200 SIC 5172

NIKON AMERICAS INC p 1043
1300 Walt Whitman Rd Fl 2 11747
Tel (631) 547-4200 SIC 5043 5084

NIKON INC p 1043
1300 Walt Whitman Rd Fl 2 11747
Tel (631) 547-4200 SIC 5043 5049

■ NU HORIZONS ELECTRONICS CORP p 1066
70 Maxess Rd 11747
Tel (631) 396-5000 SIC 5065

▲ PARK ELECTROCHEMICAL CORP p 1115
48 S Service Rd Ste 300 11747
Tel (631) 465-3600 SIC 3672 3674

POLY-PAK INDUSTRIES INC p 1160
125 Spagnoli Rd 11747
Tel (631) 293-6767 SIC 2673 2677

SAGE PARTS PLUS INC p 1267
30 Hub Dr Ste 1 11747
Tel (631) 501-1300 SIC 5088 3812 3537

SBARRO HOLDINGS LLC p 1285
401 Broadhollow Rd Ll10 11747
Tel (631) 715-4100 SIC 5812 6794

SBARRO INC p 1285
401 Broadhollow Rd Ll10 11747
Tel (631) 715-4100 SIC 5812 6794

■ SID TOOL CO INC p 1319
75 Maxess Rd 11747
Tel (516) 812-2000 SIC 5085 5084

STAR MULTI CARE SERVICES INC p 1378
115 Broadhollow Rd # 275 11747
Tel (631) 423-6689 SIC 8082 7361

■ TNT USA INC p 1458
68 S Service Rd Ste 340 11747
Tel (631) 712-6700 SIC 4513

■ TOPS SLT INC p 1461
225 Broadhollow Rd # 300 11747
Tel (631) 675-5700 SIC 2675

■ VERINT ACQUISITION LLC p 1549
330 S Service Rd Ste 108 11747
Tel (631) 962-9600 SIC 7371

▲ VERINT SYSTEMS INC p 1549
175 Broadhollow Rd # 100 11747
Tel (631) 962-9600 SIC 7382 7372

VYTRA HEALTH PLANS LONG ISLAND INC p 1568
395 N Service Rd Ste 110 11747
Tel (631) 694-4000 SIC 6324

MENANDS, NY

ALBANY STEEL INC p 45
566 Broadway Ste 2 12204
Tel (518) 436-4851 SIC 5051 3441

HEALTH RESEARCH INC p 675
150 Broadway Ste 560 12204
Tel (518) 431-1200 SIC 8733

RESEARCH FOD FOR MTAL HY INC p 1226
150 Broadway Ste 301 12204
Tel (518) 474-5661 SIC 8733

STATE OF NEW YORK p 1382
800 N Pearl St 12204
Tel (518) 473-6790 SIC 9111

MIDDLETOWN, NY

■ LOCAL MEDIA GROUP INC p 873
40 Mulberry St 10940
Tel (845) 341-1100 SIC 2711 7313

ORANGE REGIONAL MEDICAL CENTER p 1092
707 E Main St 10940
Tel (845) 343-2424 SIC 8062

MILLWOOD, NY

MAVIS TIRE SUPPLY LLC p 922
358 Saw Mill River Rd # 17 10546
Tel (914) 984-2500 SIC 5014 5531

SOMERSET TIRE SERVICE INC p 1339
358 Saw Mill River Rd # 5 10546
Tel (732) 356-8500
SIC 5531 5014 5013 7538

MINEOLA, NY

COUNTY OF NASSAU p 380
1550 Franklin Ave 11501
Tel (516) 571-3131 SIC 9111

GREAT NECK SAW MANUFACTURERS INC p 634
165 E 2nd St 11501
Tel (800) 457-0600 SIC 5072

INTERBORO MANAGEMENT INC p 751
155 Mineola Blvd 11501
Tel (516) 213-0286 SIC 6411

RAYTECH CORP ASBESTOS PERSONAL INJURY SETTLEMENT TRUST p 1210
190 Willis Ave 11501
Tel (516) 747-0300 SIC 3499

VASS PIPE & STEEL CO INC p 1545
158 3rd St Ste 2 11501
Tel (516) 741-8398 SIC 5051 3317

WINTHROP-UNIVERSITY HOSPITAL (INC) p 1617
259 1st St 11501
Tel (516) 663-0333 SIC 8062

MODEL CITY, NY

MODERN DISPOSAL SERVICES INC p 981
4746 Model City Rd 14107
Tel (716) 692-1272 SIC 4953

MONSEY, NY

NORTHERN SERVICES GROUP INC p 1056
2000 Fountainview Dr 10952
Tel (845) 356-9880 SIC 8059

MONTEBELLO, NY

▲ STERLING BANCORP p 1386
400 Rella Blvd 10901
Tel (845) 369-8040 SIC 6021

■ STERLING NATIONAL BANK p 1387
400 Rella Blvd Fl 3 10901
Tel (845) 369-8040 SIC 6035

MONTICELLO, NY

SULLIVAN COUNTY p 1397
100 North St 12701
Tel (845) 794-3000 SIC 9111

MONTOUR FALLS, NY

WELLIVER MCGUIRE INC p 1589
250 N Genesee St 14865
Tel (704) 454-5500 SIC 1542 1541

MOUNT KISCO, NY

CAREMOUNT MEDICAL PC p 255
110 S Bedford Rd 10549
Tel (914) 241-1050 SIC 8011

CURTIS INSTRUMENTS INC p 402
200 Kisco Ave 10549
Tel (914) 666-2971 SIC 3825 3824 3629

KOHLBERG & CO LLC p 826
111 Radio Circle Dr 10549
Tel (914) 241-7430 SIC 6726 6211

KOHLBERG SPORTS GROUP INC p 826
111 Radio Circle Dr 10549
Tel (914) 241-7430 SIC 3949

KOHLBERG TE INVESTORS VII-B LP p 826
111 Radio Circle Dr 10549
Tel (914) 241-7430 SIC 6799

KPLT HOLDINGS INC p 828
111 Radio Circle Dr 10549
Tel (914) 241-7430 SIC 6719

NORTHERN WESTCHESTER HOSPITAL ASSOCIATION p 1057
400 E Main St 10549
Tel (914) 666-1200 SIC 8062

OHI PARENT INC p 1077
111 Radio Circle Dr 10549
Tel (914) 241-7430 SIC 8641

PREMIER COLLECTION p 1170
299 Kisco Ave 10549
Tel (877) 360-9162 SIC 5511

MOUNT VERNON, NY

COMMODORE CONSTRUCTION CORP p 345
602 S 3rd Ave 10550
Tel (914) 663-4394 SIC 1542

DOROTHEA HOPFER SCHOOL OF NURSING p 451
53 Valentine St 10550
Tel (914) 361-6221 SIC 8099

■ GREENSTAR SERVICES CORP p 638
30 N Macquesten Pkwy 10550
Tel (914) 776-8000 SIC 1521

MT VERNON CITY SCHOOL DISTRICT p 997
165 N Columbus Ave 10553
Tel (914) 665-5000 SIC 8211

WDF INC p 1585
30 N Macquesten Pkwy 10550
Tel (914) 776-8000 SIC 1711

MOUNTAINVILLE, NY

AMAZING SAVINGS HOLDING LLC p 64
20 Industry Dr 10953
Tel (845) 534-1000 SIC 5399

NANUET, NY

ROCKLAND BAKERY INC p 1244
94 Demarest Mill Rd W 10954
Tel (845) 623-5800 SIC 2051

NEW BERLIN, NY

PREFERRED MUTUAL INSURANCE CO p 1169
1 Preferred Way 13411
Tel (607) 847-6161 SIC 6331

NEW CITY, NY

COUNTY OF ROCKLAND p 381
11 New Hempstead Rd # 100 10956
Tel (845) 638-5122 SIC 9111

NEW HAMPTON, NY

▲ BALCHEM CORP p 147
52 Sunrise Park Rd 10958
Tel (845) 326-5600 SIC 2869 2899

NEW HARTFORD, NY

EXPANSION STRATEGIES INC p 519
17 Rollingwood Dr 13413
Tel (315) 793-3137 SIC 8742

FAXTON ST LUKES HEALTH CARE p 532
8411 Seneca Tpke Ste 1 13413
Tel (315) 724-0659 SIC 8011

GRAPHIC ARTS MUTUAL INSURANCE CO INC p 631
180 Genesee St 13413
Tel (315) 734-2000 SIC 6331

GU MARKETS LLC p 644
4350 Middle Settlement Rd 13413
Tel (315) 793-9226 SIC 5411

▲ PAR TECHNOLOGY CORP p 1113
8383 Seneca Tpke Ste 2 13413
Tel (315) 738-0600 SIC 7372 7832

■ PARTECH INC p 1118
8383 Seneca Tpke Ste 2 13413
Tel (315) 738-0600 SIC 7373

UTICA MUTUAL INSURANCE CO p 1537
180 Genesee St 13413
Tel (315) 734-2000 SIC 6331 6311

UTICA NATIONAL INSURANCE GROUP p 1537
180 Genesee St 13413
Tel (315) 734-2000 SIC 6331 6411

NEW HYDE PARK, NY

ASSOCIATED GLOBAL SYSTEMS INC p 120
3333 New Hyde Park Rd # 207 11042
Tel (516) 627-8910 SIC 4731

▲ ASTORIA FINANCIAL CORP p 122
1 Astoria Bank Plz 11042
Tel (516) 327-3000 SIC 6035

ATC HEALTHCARE SERVICES INC p 124
1983 Marcus Ave Ste E122 11042
Tel (516) 345-9928 SIC 7363

ATC STAFFING SERVICES INC p 124
1983 Marcus Ave Ste E122 11042
Tel (516) 326-1396 SIC 7361 8093 8011

▲ BROADRIDGE FINANCIAL SOLUTIONS INC p 215
5 Dakota Dr Ste 300 11042
Tel (516) 472-5400 SIC 7374 7372

■ BROADRIDGE OUTPUT SOLUTIONS INC p 215
5 Dakota Dr Ste 300 11042
Tel (516) 472-5400 SIC 7374

DEALERTRACK INC p 420
1111 Marcus Ave Ste M04 11042
Tel (516) 734-3600 SIC 7374

DEALERTRACK TECHNOLOGIES INC p 420
1111 Marcus Ave Ste M04 11042
Tel (516) 734-3600 SIC 7373

DESIGNATRONICS INC p 432
2101 Jericho Tpke Ste 1 11040
Tel (516) 328-3300
SIC 3824 3559 3545 3625 3462

DITTMAN AND GREER INC p 443
270 Park Ave 11040
Tel (860) 347-4655 SIC 5063

▲ HAIN CELESTIAL GROUP INC p 653
1111 Marcus Ave Ste 100 11042
Tel (516) 587-5000
SIC 2023 2034 2096 2086 2844

HERRICKS UNION FREE SCHOOL DISTRICT p 687
999 Herricks Rd Ste B 11040
Tel (516) 305-8903 SIC 8211

JAMAICA BEARINGS CO INC p 776
1700 Jericho Tpke Ste 1 11040
Tel (516) 326-1350 SIC 5085 5088

▲ KIMCO REALTY CORP p 818
3333 New Hyde Park Rd # 100 11042
Tel (516) 869-9000 SIC 6798

LONG ISLAND JEWISH MEDICAL CENTER p 876
27005 76th Ave 11040
Tel (516) 465-2600 SIC 8062 8063 8069

▲ NEWTEK BUSINESS SERVICES INC p 1039
1981 Marcus Ave Ste C130 11042
Tel (212) 356-9500 SIC 6153 7374 4813

NORTH SHORE-LONG ISLAND JEWISH HEALTH SYSTEM LABORATORIES p 1054
10 Nevada Dr 11042
Tel (516) 719-1000 SIC 8734

NORTHWELL HEALTH INC p 1059
2000 Marcus Ave 11042
Tel (516) 321-6000 SIC 8082 8062

PARKER JEWISH INSTITUTE FOR HEALTH CARE AND REHABILITATION FOUNDATION p 1116
27111 76th Ave 11040
Tel (516) 247-6500 SIC 8051 8082 8069

PARKERJEWISH GERIATRIC INSTITUTE p 1116
27111 76th Ave 11040
Tel (718) 289-2100 SIC 7389

PROHEALTH CARE ASSOCIATES LLP p 1182
1 Dakota Dr 11042
Tel (516) 622-6000 SIC 8011

TRANSERVICE LEASE CORP p 1471
5 Dakota Dr 11042
Tel (800) 645-8018
SIC 7699 7539 4212 7353

TRANSERVICE LOGISTICS INC p 1471
5 Dakota Dr Ste 209 11042
Tel (800) 645-8018 SIC 4212

NEW ROCHELLE, NY

BEL-AQUA POOL SUPPLY INC p 169
20 Commerce Dr 10801
Tel (914) 235-2200 SIC 5091

CITY SCHOOL DISTRICT OF NEW ROCHELLE (INC) p 320
515 North Ave 10801
Tel (914) 576-4243 SIC 8211

IONA COLLEGE (INC) p 762
715 North Ave 10801
Tel (914) 633-2000 SIC 8221

LGS SPECIALTY SALES LTD p 860
1 Radisson Plz Fl 10 10801
Tel (718) 542-2200 SIC 5141 5148

MONTEFIORE NEW ROCHELLE HOSPITAL p 986
16 Guion Pl 10801
Tel (914) 632-5000 SIC 8062

NRHMC INC p 1064
16 Guion Pl 10801
Tel (914) 632-5000 SIC 8062 8721

SOUND SHORE HEALTH SYSTEM INC p 1342
16 Guion Pl 10801
Tel (914) 632-5000 SIC 8062

SOUND SHORE MEDICAL CENTER OF WESTCHESTER p 1342
16 Guion Pl 10801
Tel (914) 632-5000 SIC 8062

NEW WINDSOR, NY

LBM ADVANTAGE INC p 849
555 Hudson Valley Ave # 200 12553
Tel (845) 564-4900 SIC 5031

■ LSI LIGHTRON INC p 883
500 Hudson Valley Ave 12553
Tel (845) 562-5500 SIC 3646 5063

VERLA INTERNATIONAL LTD p 1551
463 Temple Hill Rd 12553
Tel (845) 561-2440 SIC 2844

NEW YORK, NY

11 PENNTV LLC p 1
11 Penn Plz Fl 2 10001
Tel (212) 324-8506 SIC 4841

1199 SEIU NATIONAL BENEFIT FUND p 1
330 W 42nd St Fl 8 10036
Tel (646) 473-6300 SIC 6371

1199 SEIU NATIONAL BENEFIT FUND FOR HEALTH AND HUMAN SERVICE EMPLOYEES p 1
P.O. Box 842 10108
Tel (646) 473-6020 SIC 6733

1199SEIU UNITED HEALTH CARE WORKERS EAST p 1
310 W 43rd St 10036
Tel (212) 582-1890 SIC 8631

■ 21ST CENTURY FOX AMERICA INC p 1
1211 Ave Of The Americas 10036
Tel (212) 852-7000
SIC 2752 2721 4833 7812

21ST CENTURY ONCOLOGY INVESTMENTS LLC p 2
245 Park Ave Fl 41 10167
Tel (239) 931-7275 SIC 6282

2328 ONTWELFTH LLC p 2
2328 12th Ave 10027
Tel (212) 234-3883 SIC 5411

488 PERFORMANCE GROUP INC p 3
18 E 41st St Fl 13 10017
Tel (212) 758-4385 SIC 8742

95TH IH ASSOCIATES LLC p 4
238 E 95th St 10128
Tel (212) 996-0646 SIC 6531

■ A C S HUMAN RESOURCES SOLUTIONS INC p 5
112 W 34th St Ste 605 10120
Tel (212) 685-7981 SIC 8742 6282

A T I C MANAGEMENT CORP DE CORP p 6
275 7th Ave Fl 3 10001
Tel (212) 857-8200 SIC 6411

A&ETELEVISION NETWORKS LLC p 7
235 E 45th St Frnt C 10017
Tel (212) 210-1400 SIC 4841

AB STABLE LLC p 9
301 Park Ave 10022
Tel (212) 355-3000 SIC 7011

■ ABC HOLDING CO INC p 10
77 W 66th St Rm 100 10023
Tel (212) 456-7777 SIC 4833

ABC HOME FURNISHINGS INC p 10
888 Brdwy Fl 4 10003
Tel (212) 473-3000 SIC 5712 5719 5023

■ ABC INC p 10
77 W 66th St Rm 100 10023
Tel (212) 456-7777
SIC 4833 4832 7812 6794 2711 2721

▲ ABM INDUSTRIES INC p 12
1 Liberty Plz Fl Con1 10006
Tel (212) 297-0200
SIC 7349 7521 7381 8711

■ ABM ONSITE SERVICES INC p 12
1 Liberty Plz Fl 7 10006
Tel (212) 497-0600
SIC 7349 7381 7521 8711

ACCESS INDUSTRIES INC p 14
730 5th Ave Fl 20 10019
Tel (212) 247-6400 SIC 6211

ACCESS STAFFING LLC p 15
360 Lexington Ave Fl 8 10017
Tel (212) 687-5440 SIC 7361

ACCESSORY CORP p 15
575 8th Ave Fl 16 10018
Tel (212) 391-8607 SIC 3089 5199

ACCOR BUSINESS AND LEISURE NORTH AMERICA INC p 15
245 Park Ave 10167
Tel (972) 360-9000 SIC 7011

ACF INDUSTRIES HOLDING CORP p 17
767 5th Ave 10153
Tel (212) 702-4363
SIC 3743 4741 4789 6799

ACN HOLDINGS INC p 18
85 Broad St 10004
Tel (646) 654-5000 SIC 8732

ACNIELSEN CORP p 18
85 Broad St 10004
Tel (646) 654-5000 SIC 8732

ACQUISITION HOLDINGS SUBSIDIARY I LLC p 18
1177 Ave Of The Americas 10036
Tel (212) 715-8000 SIC 6799

ACT COMMODITIES INC p 19
437 Madison Ave Fl 19c 10022
Tel (415) 741-2290 SIC 6221

ACTIMIZE INC p 19
1359 Broadway Fl 5 10018
Tel (212) 643-4600 SIC 7371

ADMINISTRATIVETRIALS & HEARINGS OFFICE OF (OATH) p 23
100 Church St Fl 12 10007
Tel (844) 628-4692 SIC 9111

ADRIANNA PAPELL LLC p 24
500 7th Ave Fl 10a 10018
Tel (212) 695-5244 SIC 5137

ADVANCE MAGAZINE PUBLISHERS INC p 24
1 World Trade Ctr Fl 28 10007
Tel (212) 286-2860 SIC 2721

ADVANSTAR INC p 26
641 Lexington Ave Fl 8 10022
Tel (212) 951-6600 SIC 2721 7389 8742

ADVANTAGECARE PHYSICIANS PC p 27
441 9th Ave Fl 8 10001
Tel (646) 680-1563 SIC 8011

ADVENTITY INC p 27
444 Park Ave S Ste 1202 10016
Tel (212) 404-2468 SIC 7375 8742 8732

ADVISOR GROUP INC p 28
1 World Financial Ctr 10281
Tel (866) 673-1550 SIC 6311

AEA INVESTORS LP p 28
666 5th Ave Fl 36 10103
Tel (212) 644-5900 SIC 6282 6211

■ AECOM USA INC p 29
605 3rd Ave 10158
Tel (212) 973-2900 SIC 8748

AEGIS LIFESTYLE INC p 29
32 Aveune Of The Americas 10013
Tel (212) 366-3400 SIC 7311 7389 8743

AEGIS MEDIA AMERICAS INC p 29
150 E 42nd St 10017
Tel (212) 591-9122 SIC 4899

AEON USA INC p 29
1 Penn Plz Fl 36 10119
Tel (212) 946-8780
SIC 5621 5961 2211 2391

▲ AEROPOSTALE INC p 30
100 W 33rd St Ste 1100 10001
Tel (646) 485-5410 SIC 5621 5611

AFI PARTNERS LLC p 33
158 Mercer St Frnt 2 10012
Tel (212) 938-0016 SIC 6719

AFTRA HEALTH & RETIREMENT FUND (INC) p 33
261 Madison Ave Fl 7 10016
Tel (212) 499-4800 SIC 6371 8111

AFTRA HEALTH FUND p 33
261 Madison Ave Fl 8 10016
Tel (212) 499-4800 SIC 8099

AG MORTGAGE INVESTMENTTRUST INC p 33
245 Park Ave Fl 26 10167
Tel (212) 692-2000 SIC 6798

AG SUPERMARKET HOLDINGS LLC p 34
245 Park Ave 10167
Tel (212) 692-2000 SIC 5411

AGE GROUP LTD p 34
2 Park Ave Fl 18 10016
Tel (212) 213-9500 SIC 5137

AGT CRUNCH ACQUISITION LLC p 36
22 W 19th St Ste 3l 10011
Tel (212) 993-0300 SIC 7991

AI ENTERTAINMENT HOLDINGS LLC p 37
730 5th Ave Fl 20 10019
Tel (212) 247-6400 SIC 2731

AI FRIEDMAN LP p 37
44 W 18th St Fl 4 10011
Tel (212) 243-9000 SIC 5199 5945

■ AIG CAPITAL CORP p 37
70 Pine St Fl 11 10270
Tel (908) 679-3150 SIC 6411 6799

■ AIG FUNDING INC p 37
70 Pine St Fl 50 10270
Tel (212) 770-7000 SIC 6411 6153

■ AIG GLOBAL ASSET MANAGEMENT HOLDINGS CORP p 37
111 8th Ave 10011
Tel (212) 709-6100 SIC 6722 6411

■ AIG GLOBAL INVESTMENT CORP p 37
175 Water St Fl 18 10038
Tel (212) 770-7000 SIC 6722 6411

■ AIG GLOBAL REAL ESTATE INVESTMENT CORP p 37
32 Old Slip Fl 28 10005
Tel (646) 857-2300 SIC 6512 6411

■ AIG HIGHSTAR CAPITAL LP p 38
277 Park Ave Fl 45 10172
Tel (646) 857-8700 SIC 6722 4491

■ AIG PROPERTY CASUALTY CO p 38
70 Pine St Fl 1 10005
Tel (800) 551-0824 SIC 6411

■ AIG PROPERTY CASUALTY INC p 38
175 Water St Fl 5 10038
Tel (212) 458-5000 SIC 6331 6321 6311

AIP LLC p 38
330 Madison Ave Fl 28 10017
Tel (212) 627-2360 SIC 6799

AIP/AEROSPACE HOLDINGS LLC p 38
330 Madison Ave Fl 28 10017
Tel (212) 916-8142 SIC 3721 6799

AIR INDIA LIMITED p 38
570 Lexington Ave Rm 1401 10022
Tel (212) 407-1400 SIC 7363

■ AIU INSURANCE CO p 41
175 Water St Fl 24 10038
Tel (212) 770-7000 SIC 6331 6321

ALBEA COSMETICS AMERICA INC p 46
595 Madison Ave Fl 10 10022
Tel (212) 371-5100
SIC 3089 3911 5162 5051

▲ ALCOA CORP p 47
390 Park Ave Fl 12 10022
Tel (212) 518-5400
SIC 3355 3363 3297 2819

ALFRED DUNNER INC p 49
1411 Broadway Fl 24 10018
Tel (212) 478-4300 SIC 2337 2331 2339

ALFRED P SLOAN FOUNDATION p 50
45 Rockefeller Plz # 2200 10111
Tel (212) 649-1649 SIC 6732

ALIXPARTNERS LLP p 50
909 3rd Ave Fl 30 10022
Tel (212) 490-2500 SIC 7311

▲ ALJ REGIONAL HOLDINGS INC p 50
244 Madison Ave 10016
Tel (212) 883-0083 SIC 6719

ALL MARKET INC p 51
250 Park Ave S Fl 7 10003
Tel (212) 206-0763 SIC 5499

■ ALLEGHANY CAPITAL CORP p 52
7 Times Square Tower 10036
Tel (212) 752-1356 SIC 3944

▲ ALLEGHANY CORP p 52
7 Times Sq Tower 10036
Tel (212) 752-1356 SIC 6331 6411 6531

■ ALLEGHANY INSURANCE HOLDINGS LLC p 52
7 Times Sq Tower Fl 17 10152
Tel (212) 752-1356 SIC 6331

■ ALLIANCEBERNSTEIN CORP p 55
1345 Ave Of The Americas 10105
Tel (212) 969-1000 SIC 6282

■ ALLIANCEBERNSTEIN HOLDING LP p 55
1345 Ave Of The Americas 10105
Tel (212) 969-1000 SIC 6282

■ ALLIANCEBERNSTEIN LP p 55
1345 Ave Of The Americas 10105
Tel (212) 969-1000 SIC 6282

ALLIED AVIATION SERVICES INC p 56
462 7th Ave Fl 17 10018
Tel (212) 868-3870 SIC 5172

ALLIED HEALTHCARE INTERNATIONAL INC p 56
245 Park Ave Fl 39 10167
Tel (212) 750-0064 SIC 8082 8049

ALLOY INC p 58
151 W 26th St Fl 11 10001
Tel (609) 655-8878
SIC 8743 8742 7331 7312

ALLOY MEDIA HOLDINGS LLC p 58
19 W 44th St Fl 18 10036
Tel (212) 784-2010 SIC 8743

ALM MEDIA HOLDINGS INC p 59
120 Broadway Fl 5 10271
Tel (212) 457-9400
SIC 2721 2711 2741 2731 7389

ALM MEDIA LLC p 59
120 Broadway Fl 5 10271
Tel (212) 457-9400
SIC 2721 2711 2741 2731 7389

ALMOD DIAMONDS LTD p 59
592 5th Ave Fl 9 10036
Tel (212) 764-6900 SIC 5094

ALVAREZ & MARSAL CORPORATE PERFORMANCE IMPROVEMENT LLC p 63
600 Madison Ave Fl 8 10022
Tel (212) 759-4433 SIC 8748 8742

ALVAREZ & MARSAL INC p 63
600 Madison Ave Fl 8 10022
Tel (212) 759-4433 SIC 8742

AMALGAMATED BANK p 64
275 7th Ave Lbby 2 10001
Tel (212) 895-8988 SIC 6022

▲ AMBAC FINANCIAL GROUP INC p 65
1 State St Fl 15 10004
Tel (212) 658-7470 SIC 6211

▲ AMC NETWORKS INC p 65
11 Penn Plz 10001
Tel (212) 324-8500 SIC 4841

AMEREX GROUP INC p 66
512 Fashion Ave Fl 9 10018
Tel (212) 221-3151 SIC 5137 5136

■ AMERICAN BROADCASTING COMPANIES INC p 69
77 W 66th St Rm 100 10023
Tel (212) 456-7777 SIC 4833

AMERICAN CIVIL LIBERTIES UNION FOUNDATION INC p 70
125 Broad St Fl 18 10004
Tel (212) 549-2500 SIC 8699

AMERICAN EUROPEAN GROUP INC p 72
605 3rd Ave Fl 9 10158
Tel (212) 355-3310 SIC 6331

▲ AMERICAN EXPRESS CO p 72
200 Vesey St 10285
Tel (212) 640-2000
SIC 6141 7389 6282 6099 6311 6211

■ AMERICAN EXPRESS CREDIT CORP p 72
200 Vesey St 10285
Tel (866) 572-4944 SIC 6153

■ AMERICAN EXPRESSTRAVEL RELATED SERVICES CO INC p 72
200 Vesey St 10285
Tel (212) 640-2000 SIC 4724

■ AMERICAN HOME ASSURANCE CO INC p 74
70 Pine St Fl 1 10005
Tel (212) 770-7000 SIC 6331 7371

AMERICAN INDUSTRIAL ACQUISITION CORP p 74
250 Park Ave Fl 7 10177
Tel (212) 572-4853 SIC 6211 6153

AMERICAN INDUSTRIAL PARTNERS CAPITAL FUND IV (PARALLEL) LP p 74
330 Madison Ave Fl 28 10017
Tel (212) 627-2360 SIC 6726

▲ AMERICAN INTERNATIONAL GROUP INC p 75
175 Water St Rm 1800 10038
Tel (212) 770-7000
SIC 6331 6321 6311 6324 6411 6282

AMERICAN JEWISH JOINT DISTRIBUTION COMMITTEE INC p 75
711 3rd Ave Rm 901 10017
Tel (212) 687-6200 *SIC* 8699

AMERICAN MANAGEMENT ASSOCIATION INTERNATIONAL p 75
1601 Broadway Fl 7 10019
Tel (212) 586-8100
SIC 8299 2731 8621 7812 2721

AMERICAN MARKETING ENTERPRISES INC p 75
Empir State Bldg 350fl 10018
Tel (646) 839-7000 *SIC* 5137

AMERICAN MUSEUM OF NATURAL HISTORY p 76
Central Park W At 79th St 10024
Tel (212) 769-5000 *SIC* 8412 8221

■ AMERICAN REALTY CAPITAL HEALTHCARE TRUST INC p 78
1065 Ave Of The Amer # 23 10018
Tel (212) 415-6500 *SIC* 6798

AMERICAN REALTY CAPITAL OPERATING PARTNERSHIP II LP p 78
405 Park Ave Fl 15 10022
Tel (212) 415-6500 *SIC* 6733

AMERICAN ROLAND FOOD CORP p 78
71 W 23rd St Ste 1500 10010
Tel (800) 221-4030 *SIC* 5149

▲ AMERICAN SECURITIES LLC p 79
299 Park Ave Fl 34 10171
Tel (212) 476-8000 *SIC* 6799

AMERICAN SOCIETY FOR PREVENTION OF CRUELTY TO ANIMALS (INC) p 79
424 E 92nd St 10128
Tel (212) 876-7700 *SIC* 8699

AMERICAN SOCIETY FOR TECHNION-ISRAEL INSTITUTE OF TECHNOLOGY INC p 79
55 E 59th St Fl 14 10022
Tel (212) 407-6300 *SIC* 8399

AMERICAN SOCIETY OF COMPOSERS AUTHORS AND PUBLISHERS p 79
1 Lincoln Plz Fl 6 10023
Tel (212) 621-6000 *SIC* 8621

AMERICAN UNIVERSITY IN CAIRO p 81
420 5th Ave Fl 3 10018
Tel (212) 730-8800 *SIC* 8221

AMERICAN UNIVERSITY OF BEIRUT INC p 81
3 Dag Hammarskjold Plz # 8 10017
Tel (212) 583-7600 *SIC* 8221

■ AMERIGROUP NEW YORK LLC p 82
360 W 31st St Fl 5 10001
Tel (212) 372-6900 *SIC* 6324

AMHERST PIERPONT SECURITIES LLC p 85
245 Park Ave Fl 15 10167
Tel (203) 428-2500 *SIC* 6211

■ AMIC HOLDINGS INC p 85
485 Madison Ave Fl 14 10022
Tel (212) 355-4141 *SIC* 6321 6411

AMIDA CARE INC p 85
225 W 34th St Fl 2 10122
Tel (646) 757-7000 *SIC* 6324

▲ AMTRUST FINANCIAL SERVICES INC p 87
59 Maiden Ln Fl 43 10038
Tel (212) 220-7120 *SIC* 6331

ANAREN HOLDING CORP p 88
590 Madison Ave Fl 41 10022
Tel (212) 415-6700 *SIC* 3663

ANDREW W MELLON FOUNDATION p 90
140 E 62nd St 10065
Tel (212) 838-8400 *SIC* 7389

ANGEL HOLDINGS LLC p 91
245 Park Ave 10167
Tel (212) 692-2000 *SIC* 6282

ANGELO GORDON & CO LP p 91
245 Park Ave Fl 24 10167
Tel (212) 692-2000 *SIC* 6282

■ ANN INC p 92
7 Times Sq Bsmt Sb4 10036
Tel (212) 541-3300 *SIC* 5621 5632 5661

▲ ANNALY CAPITAL MANAGEMENT INC p 92
1211 Ave Of The Americas 10036
Tel (212) 696-0100 *SIC* 6798

■ ANNTAYLOR INC p 92
7 Times Sq 10036
Tel (212) 541-3300 *SIC* 5621 5632 5661

■ ANNTAYLOR RETAIL INC p 92
7 Times Sq 10036
Tel (212) 541-3300 *SIC* 5621 5632 5661

ANVIL HOLDINGS INC p 94
228 E 45th St Fl 4 10017
Tel (843) 774-8211 *SIC* 5137

ANZ LIMITED PARTNERSHIP p 94
1177 Ave Of The Americas 10036
Tel (212) 801-9800 *SIC* 6081

■ AOL INC p 94
770 Broadway Fl 4 10003
Tel (212) 652-6400 *SIC* 7374

AP CARIB HOLDING LTD p 95
9 W 57th St Fl 43 10019
Tel (212) 515-3202 *SIC* 8741 8748 7379

APAX PARTNERS LP p 96
601 Lexington Ave Fl 53 10022
Tel (212) 753-6300 *SIC* 6282

APAX PARTNERS OF NEW YORK p 96
601 Lexington Ave Fl 53 10022
Tel (212) 419-2447
SIC 6282 5399 5199 5812 5813

APOLLO COMMERCIAL REAL ESTATE FINANCE INC p 97
9 W 57th St Fl 43 10019
Tel (212) 515-3200 *SIC* 6798

▲ APOLLO GLOBAL MANAGEMENT LLC p 97
9 W 57th St Fl 43 10019
Tel (212) 515-3200 *SIC* 6726 6282 6799

▲ APOLLO INVESTMENT CORP p 97
9 W 57th St Fl 43 10019
Tel (212) 515-3450 *SIC* 6726

■ APOLLO MANAGEMENT HOLDINGS LP p 97
9 W 57th St Fl 43 10019
Tel (212) 515-3200 *SIC* 8741

■ APOLLO MANAGEMENT LP p 97
9 W 57th St Fl 43 10019
Tel (212) 515-3200 *SIC* 6799 6531

APOLLO RESIDENTIAL MORTGAGE INC p 97
9 W 57th St Fl 43 10019
Tel (212) 515-3200 *SIC* 6798

APPLE REIT SIX INC p 99
345 Park Ave 10154
Tel (804) 344-8121 *SIC* 6798

APPNEXUS INC p 100
28 W 23rd St Fl 4 10010
Tel (646) 825-6460 *SIC* 4813

AQUILINE CAPITAL PARTNERS LLC p 102
535 Madison Ave Fl 24 10022
Tel (212) 624-9500 *SIC* 6799

■ ARAMIS INC p 102
767 5th Ave 10153
Tel (212) 572-4200 *SIC* 5122 2844

■ ARCADE INC p 103
1700 Broadway Fl 25 10019
Tel (212) 541-2600 *SIC* 2752

ARCH CAPITAL GROUP (US) INC p 104
1 Liberty Plz Fl 53 10006
Tel (212) 651-6500 *SIC* 6311 6321

ARCHDIOCESE OF NEW YORK p 105
1011 1st Ave 10022
Tel (212) 371-1000 *SIC* 8661

▲ ARCONIC INC p 106
390 Park Ave 10022
Tel (212) 836-2674 *SIC* 3334 3353 1099

■ AREA PROPERTY PARTNERS L P p 106
245 Park Ave Fl 44 10167
Tel (212) 515-3400 *SIC* 6799

▲ ARES CAPITAL CORP p 107
245 Park Ave Fl 44 10167
Tel (212) 750-7300 *SIC* 6726

ARES COMMERCIAL REAL ESTATE CORP p 107
245 Park Ave Fl 42 10167
Tel (212) 750-7300 *SIC* 6798

ARETEC GROUP INC p 107
405 Park Ave Fl 12 10022
Tel (866) 904-2988 *SIC* 6211 6282 6722

ARGOS HOLDINGS INC p 107
650 Madison Ave Fl 15 10022
Tel (212) 891-2880 *SIC* 0752

▲ ARK RESTAURANTS CORP p 109
85 5th Ave 10003
Tel (212) 206-8800 *SIC* 5812 5813

ARLEE HOME FASHIONS INC p 110
261 5th Ave Fl Mezz 10016
Tel (212) 213-0425 *SIC* 2392

ARLON FOOD AND AGRICULTURE PARTNERS LP p 110
277 Park Ave 10172
Tel (212) 207-5200 *SIC* 6799

ARSENAL CAPITAL PARTNERS LP p 113
100 Park Ave Fl 31 10017
Tel (212) 771-1717 *SIC* 6722

ARTISTIC FRAME CORP p 114
979 3rd Ave Ste 1705 10022
Tel (212) 289-2100 *SIC* 2426 5021

ARUP AMERICAS INC p 114
77 Water St 10005
Tel (212) 896-3000 *SIC* 8711

ASHER ALADJEM p 117
403 E 34th St Fl 3 10016
Tel (212) 263-8360 *SIC* 8011

ASI SYSTEM INTEGRATION INC p 117
48 W 37th St Fl 4 10018
Tel (212) 695-7970 *SIC* 7379

ASP BLADE INTERMEDIATE HOLDINGS INC p 118
299 Park Ave Fl 34 10171
Tel (212) 476-8000 *SIC* 3531 3523 6719

ASSET CHURCHILL MANAGEMENT LLC p 119
430 Park Ave Ste 701 10022
Tel (212) 478-9207 *SIC* 6799

ASSOCIATED PRESS p 121
450 W 33rd St Fl 16 10001
Tel (212) 621-1500 *SIC* 7383 4822

▲ ASSURANT INC p 121
28 Liberty St Fl 41 10005
Tel (212) 859-7000 *SIC* 6311 6399 6331

ASSURED GUARANTY CORP p 122
31 W 52nd St Fl 26 10019
Tel (212) 974-0100 *SIC* 6411

ASSURED GUARANTY US HOLDINGS INC p 122
31 W 52nd St Fl 26 10019
Tel (212) 974-0100 *SIC* 6311

ATERIAN INVESTMENT PARTNERS LP p 124
11 E 44th St Rm 1803 10017
Tel (212) 547-2806 *SIC* 3398

■ ATLANTIC AVIATION FBO HOLDINGS LLC p 126
600 5th Ave Fl 21 10020
Tel (212) 548-6538 *SIC* 4581 4785 1731

AUTHENTIC BRANDS GROUP LLC p 133
1411 Broadway Fl 4 10018
Tel (212) 760-2410 *SIC* 6794

AVENUE CAPITAL GROUP LLC p 136
399 Park Ave Fl 6 10022
Tel (212) 878-3500 *SIC* 6282 6159

AVISTA CAPITAL HOLDINGS LP p 138
65 E 55th St Fl 18 10022
Tel (212) 593-6900 *SIC* 6799

▲ AVON PRODUCTS INC p 139
777 3rd Ave 10017
Tel (212) 282-5000
SIC 2844 3961 5961 5023 5137

AWC LIQUIDATING CO p 139
1407 Brdwy Ste 400 10018
Tel (212) 221-1177
SIC 5112 5199 3873 5094

■ AXA ADVISORS LLC p 139
1290 Ave Of Amrcs Fl Cnc1 10104
Tel (212) 554-1234 *SIC* 7389

■ AXA EQUITABLE LIFE INSURANCE CO p 139
1290 Avenue Of The Americ 10104
Tel (212) 554-1234 *SIC* 6311 6411 6282

■ AXA FINANCIAL INC p 139
1290 Ave Of The Am Fl Con 10104
Tel (212) 554-1234
SIC 6311 6211 6552 6531 6371 6221

AXEL JOHNSON INC p 140
155 Spring St Fl 6 10012
Tel (646) 291-2445 *SIC* 5171

AXELON SERVICES CORP p 140
44 Wall St Fl 18 10005
Tel (877) 711-8700 *SIC* 7379

B & H FOTO & ELECTRONICS CORP p 141
420 9th Ave 10001
Tel (212) 239-7500 *SIC* 5946 5731 5961

BACK TO SCHOOL ACQUISITION LLC p 143
540 Madison Ave Fl 25 10022
Tel (212) 339-8500 *SIC* 8222

BAHA INDUSTRIES CORP p 145
462 7th Ave Fl 15 10018
Tel (212) 273-1921 *SIC* 8748

BAKERCORP INTERNATIONAL HOLDINGS INC p 146
320 Park Ave 10022
Tel (212) 386-7480 *SIC* 7359

BANK LEUMI LE-ISRAEL CORP p 151
579 5th Ave Lbby 1 10017
Tel (917) 542-2343 *SIC* 6022

BANK LEUMI USA p 151
579 5th Ave Frnt A 10017
Tel (917) 542-2343 *SIC* 6022 7359

■ BANK OF AMERICA PVT WEALTH MANAGEMENT p 151
114 W 47th St Ste C-1 10036
Tel (800) 878-7878
SIC 6282 6022 6099 6733

■ BANK OF NEW YORK MELLON p 151
225 Liberty St 10281
Tel (212) 495-1784
SIC 6153 6211 6282 6082

▲ BANK OF NEW YORK MELLON CORP p 151
225 Liberty St 10281
Tel (212) 495-1784 *SIC* 6022

▲ BANKRATE INC p 152
1675 Broadway Fl 2 10019
Tel (917) 368-8600 *SIC* 7389

BANORTE USA CORP p 153
540 Madison Ave Fl 36 10022
Tel (212) 484-5200 *SIC* 6029

BAR-ILAN UNIVERSITY IN ISRAEL p 154
160 E 56th St Fl 5 10022
Tel (212) 906-3900 *SIC* 8399

BARCLAYS CAPITAL INC p 155
745 7th Ave 10019
Tel (212) 526-7000 *SIC* 6211

BARCLAYS CAPITAL REAL ESTATE HOLDINGS INC p 155
1301 Ave Of The Americas 10019
Tel (212) 581-1628 *SIC* 6162

BARCLAYS GROUP US INC p 155
745 7th Ave 10019
Tel (212) 412-4000 *SIC* 6712

BARCLAYS USA INC p 155
200 Park Ave Fl 3w 10166
Tel (212) 412-4000 *SIC* 6211

BARNARD COLLEGE p 155
3009 Broadway Frnt 1 10027
Tel (212) 854-7732 *SIC* 8221

■ BARNES & NOBLE BOOKSELLERS INC p 155
1166 Ave Of Amer 18 10036
Tel (212) 403-2580
SIC 5942 5994 5999 5735

▲ BARNES & NOBLE INC p 156
122 5th Ave Fl 2 10011
Tel (212) 633-3300 *SIC* 5942 5961 5945

■ BARNES & NOBLE PURCHASING INC p 156
122 5th Ave Fl 2 10011
Tel (212) 633-4068 *SIC* 5192

BARNEYS INC p 156
575 5th Ave Fl 11 10017
Tel (212) 450-8700
SIC 5611 5621 5632 5932 5947 6794

BARNEYS NEW YORK INC p 156
575 5th Ave Fl 11 10017
Tel (212) 450-8700 *SIC* 5651

BARR & BARR INC p 156
460 W 34th St Fl 10 10001
Tel (212) 563-2330 *SIC* 1542 1541

BASIN HOLDINGS US LLC p 159
200 Park Ave Fl 58 10166
Tel (212) 695-7376 *SIC* 3533

BAUSCH & LOMB HOLDINGS INC p 160
450 Lexington Ave 10017
Tel (585) 338-6000 *SIC* 3851 2834

BBC WORLDWIDE AMERICAS INC p 163
1120 Ave Of The Amrcas 10036
Tel (212) 705-9300 *SIC* 4833

■ BBDO WORLDWIDE INC p 163
1285 Ave Of The Amer 10019
Tel (212) 459-5000 *SIC* 7311

BEAR PARENT INC p 165
9 W 57th St Ste 3100 10019
Tel (212) 796-8500 *SIC* 5311

■ BEAR STEARNS COMPANIES LLC p 165
383 Madison Ave 10179
Tel (212) 272-2000
SIC 6211 6282 6221 6099 6091 6289

■ BEE CEE INC p 168
30 Rockefeller Plz Fl 31 10112
Tel (212) 664-4444 *SIC* 4833

BEHRMAN CAPITAL LP p 168
126 E 56th St Fl 27 10022
Tel (212) 980-5419 *SIC* 6799

BERGDORF GOODMAN INC p 174
754 5th Ave 10019
Tel (800) 558-1855 *SIC* 5621 5632 5611

BERTELSMANN INC p 176
1745 Broadway Fl 20 10019
Tel (212) 782-1000
SIC 2731 2721 7819 3652 6512

BERTELSMANN PUBLISHING GROUP INC p 176
1540 Broadway Fl 24 10036
Tel (212) 782-1000 *SIC* 2731 2721

BESSEMER TRUST CO NA p 176
45 Rockefeller Plz 600b 10111
Tel (212) 708-9100 *SIC* 6022

BETH ISRAEL MEDICAL CENTER p 177
First Ave 16th St 10003
Tel (212) 420-2806 *SIC* 8062 8063

▲ BGC PARTNERS INC p 180
499 Park Ave 10022
Tel (212) 610-2200 *SIC* 6211

BILLIONTOWER INTL LLC p 182
989 6th Ave Fl 8 10018
Tel (212) 220-0608 *SIC* 2326 5136

BKH ACQUISITION HOLDCO I LLC p 186
150 E 58th St Bsmt 10155
Tel (787) 474-7762 *SIC* 6799

■ BLACKHAWK PARENT LLC p 187
345 Park Ave 10154
Tel (212) 583-5000 *SIC* 6798 6531

▲ BLACKROCK CAPITAL INVESTMENT CORP p 188
40 E 52nd St 10022
Tel (212) 810-5800 *SIC* 6211

■ BLACKROCK FINANCIAL MANAGEMENT INC p 188
40 E 52nd St Fl 2 10022
Tel (212) 810-5300 *SIC* 6282

■ BLACKROCK HOLDCO 2 INC p 188
40 E 52nd St 10022
Tel (212) 754-5300 *SIC* 6282

▲ BLACKROCK INC p 188
55 E 52nd St Fl 11 10055
Tel (212) 810-5300 *SIC* 6282 6211

■ BLACKSTONE CAPITAL PARTNERS V LP p 188
345 Park Ave 10154
Tel (212) 583-5000 *SIC* 6719

■ BLACKSTONE GROUP HOLDINGS LLC p 188
345 Park Ave Ste 1100 10154
Tel (212) 583-5000 *SIC* 6211

▲ BLACKSTONE GROUP L P p 188
345 Park Ave Ste 1100 10154
Tel (212) 583-5000 *SIC* 6282 6211

BLACKSTONE MORTGAGE TRUST INC p 188
345 Park Ave Fl 42 10154
Tel (212) 655-0220 *SIC* 6798

BLACKSTONE REAL ESTATE PARTNERS VI LP p 188
345 Park Ave 10154
Tel (212) 583-5000 *SIC* 8741 6531

BLISS WORLD LLC p 189
200 Vesey St Fl 25 10281
Tel (212) 931-6383 *SIC* 5999

BLOOMBERG FAMILY FOUNDATION INC p 189
909 3rd Ave 10022
Tel (212) 205-0100 *SIC* 8699

BLOOMBERG LP p 190
731 Lexington Ave Fl Ll2 10022
Tel (212) 318-2000 *SIC* 7383

BLOOMBERG TRADEBOOK LLC p 190
731 Lexington Ave 10022
Tel (212) 617-7070 *SIC* 6211

■ **BLOOMINGDALES INC** p 190
1000 3rd Ave 10022
Tel (212) 705-2000 *SIC* 5311 2389

BLUE APRON INC p 190
5 Crosby St 10013
Tel (888) 278-4349 *SIC* 5961

BLUE STAR JETS LLC p 192
880 3rd Ave Fl 11 10022
Tel (212) 446-9037 *SIC* 7389

BLUETEE CORP p 192
387 Park Ave S Fl 5 10016
Tel (212) 598-0880
SIC 3533 3589 5093 3715 3823 5051

BLUE WOLF CAPITAL FUND II LP p 192
1 Liberty Plz Fl 52 10006
Tel (212) 488-1340 *SIC* 6726

■ **BLUE WOLF GROUP LLC** p 192
11 E 26th St Fl 21 10010
Tel (866) 455-9653 *SIC* 7372

BMO CAPITAL MARKETS CORP p 194
3 Times Sq 10036
Tel (212) 885-4000 *SIC* 7389

■ **BNP PARIBAS ASSET MANAGEMENT INC** p 194
200 Park Ave Rm 4520 10166
Tel (212) 681-3000 *SIC* 6726

■ **BNP PARIBAS NORTH AMERICA INC** p 194
787 7th Ave Fl 27 10019
Tel (212) 841-2000 *SIC* 6211

■ **BNP PARIBAS SECURITIES CORP** p 194
787 7th Ave Fl 27 10019
Tel (212) 841-3000 *SIC* 6211

■ **BORDERFREE INC** p 201
292 Madison Ave 10017
Tel (212) 299-3500 *SIC* 8742 4731 7312

BORO OF MANHATTAN COMMUNITY CO p 201
199 Chambers St 10007
Tel (212) 220-8000 *SIC* 8231

BOWLMOR AMF CORP p 204
222 W 44th St 10036
Tel (212) 777-2214 *SIC* 7933

BP PRUDHOE BAY ROYALTY TRUST INC p 206
101 Barclay St 10007
Tel (212) 815-6908 *SIC* 6733

BRAIFORM ENTERPRISES INC p 207
237 W 35th St Ste 504 10001
Tel (800) 738-7396 *SIC* 3089

BRAVADO INTERNATIONAL GROUP MERCHANDISING SERVICES INC p 209
1755 Broadway Fl 2 10019
Tel (212) 445-3400
SIC 5136 5137 5611 5621

BRE RETAIL CENTERS HOLDINGS LP p 209
345 Park Ave 10154
Tel (212) 583-5000 *SIC* 6513 6722

BRE SELECT HOTELS CORP p 209
345 Park Ave 10154
Tel (212) 583-5000 *SIC* 6722

BRE SPADE VOTECO LLC p 209
345 Park Ave Fl 42 10154
Tel (212) 583-5000 *SIC* 6799

BREAKTHRU BEVERAGE GROUP LLC p 209
60 E 42nd St Ste 1915 10165
Tel (212) 699-7000 *SIC* 5182

BREF HR LLC p 209
250 Vesey St Fl 15 10281
Tel (212) 417-7265 *SIC* 7011

BREF HR MANAGEMENT LLC p 209
250 Vesey St Fl 11 10281
Tel (212) 417-7265 *SIC* 7011

BRERA CAPITAL PARTNERS LLC p 210
244 5th Ave 10001
Tel (212) 230-5495 *SIC* 6799

BRIGHTPOINT HEALTH p 213
71 W 23rd St Fl 8 10010
Tel (718) 681-8700 *SIC* 8099

▲ **BRISTOL-MYERS SQUIBB CO** p 214
345 Park Ave Bsmt Lc3 10154
Tel (212) 546-4000 *SIC* 2834

BRIXMOR LLC p 215
450 Lexington Ave Fl 13 10017
Tel (212) 869-3000 *SIC* 6798

BRIXMOR PROPERTY GROUP INC p 215
450 Lexington Ave Fl 13 10017
Tel (212) 869-3000 *SIC* 6798

BROADCAST MEDIA PARTNERS HOLDINGS INC p 215
605 3rd Ave Fl 12 10158
Tel (212) 455-5200 *SIC* 4833 4813 7389

BROADCAST MUSIC INC p 215
250 Greenwich St 10007
Tel (212) 220-3000 *SIC* 6794

BROADSTONE GROUP INC p 215
156 W 56th St Ste 1604 10019
Tel (212) 333-2100 *SIC* 6552 7011 8741

BROOKFIELD ASSET MANAGEMENT (US) INC p 217
Brookfield Pl 250 Vesey S 10281
Tel (212) 417-7000 *SIC* 8741

BROOKFIELD ASSET MANAGEMENT INC p 217
3 World Financial Ctr 10281
Tel (212) 417-7000 *SIC* 8741

BROOKS BROTHERS GROUP INC p 218
346 Madison Ave 10017
Tel (212) 309-7765 *SIC* 5651 5632

BROOKS BROTHERS INC p 218
346 Madison Ave 10017
Tel (212) 682-8800 *SIC* 5611 5621 5651

BROOKWOOD COMPANIES INC p 218
485 Madison Ave Frnt 5 10022
Tel (212) 551-0100 *SIC* 5131

BROWN BROTHERS HARRIMAN & CO p 219
140 Brdwy 10005
Tel (212) 483-1818 *SIC* 6091 6211

BRUCKMANN ROSSER SHERRILL & CO INC p 220
126 E 56th St Fl 29 10022
Tel (212) 521-3700 *SIC* 6726

BTF/CFI INC p 222
144 W 38th St 10018
Tel (212) 993-0300
SIC 6794 7991 5621 5411

■ **BUCK CONSULTANTS LLC** p 222
485 Lexington Ave Fl 10 10017
Tel (212) 330-1000 *SIC* 8742 6282 2741

BUFFALO INVESTORS CORP p 224
1 Wall Street Ct Apt 980 10005
Tel (212) 702-4363 *SIC* 3743 4741

BUILDING MAINTENANCE SERVICE LLC p 225
11 Penn Plz 10001
Tel (212) 714-0004 *SIC* 7349

BULOVA CORP p 225
350 5th Ave Fl 29 10118
Tel (212) 497-1875 *SIC* 5094

BUSINESS DEVELOPMENT CORP OF AMERICA p 229
405 Park Ave Fl 15 10022
Tel (212) 415-6500 *SIC* 8748

C I B C OPPENHEIMER HOLDINGS INC p 232
425 Lexington Ave Fl 5 10017
Tel (212) 856-4000 *SIC* 6211

C P C HOME ATTENDANT PROGRAM p 233
40 Worth St Fl 13 10013
Tel (212) 219-8100 *SIC* 8999

CT CORP SYSTEM p 233
111 8th Ave Fl 13 10011
Tel (212) 894-8940 *SIC* 8111

C V STARR & CO INC p 233
90 Park Ave Fl 7 10016
Tel (212) 230-5050 *SIC* 6719

▲ **CA INC** p 234
520 Madison Ave Fl 22 10022
Tel (800) 225-5224 *SIC* 7372 8742

CACHE INC p 235
256 W 38th St Fl 3 10018
Tel (212) 575-3200 *SIC* 5632 5621 5961

CACHE OF VIRGINIA INC p 235
256 W 38th St Fl 3 10018
Tel (212) 840-4226 *SIC* 5632 5621

CADWALADER WICKERSHAM & TAFT LLP p 236
200 Liberty St 10281
Tel (212) 504-6000 *SIC* 8111

CALCEUS TOPCO INC p 238
601 Lexington Ave 10022
Tel (212) 753-6300 *SIC* 6719

CALCEUS TOPCO LP p 238
601 Lexington Ave 10022
Tel (212) 753-6300 *SIC* 6719

■ **CALVIN KLEIN INC** p 243
205 W 39th St Lbby 2 10018
Tel (212) 719-2600
SIC 5651 5137 5136 5611 5621 6794

■ **CALVIN KLEIN JEANSWEAR CO** p 243
205 W 39th St Lbby 2 10018
Tel (212) 292-9290 *SIC* 5611 5621

CAMBRIDGE INFORMATION GROUP INC p 244
888 7th Ave Ste 1701 10106
Tel (301) 961-6700 *SIC* 2741

CAN CAPITAL INC p 246
414 W 14th St Fl 3 10014
Tel (914) 725-9301 *SIC* 6153

CANADIAN IMPERIAL HOLDINGS INC p 246
425 Lexington Ave Bsmt C2 10017
Tel (212) 856-4000 *SIC* 6719

CANON BUSINESS PROCESS SERVICES INC p 247
460 W 34th St Fl 6 10001
Tel (212) 502-2100 *SIC* 8741

CANTOR FITZGERALD & CO INC p 248
110 E 59th St Fl 5 10022
Tel (212) 938-5000 *SIC* 6211

CANTOR FITZGERALD SECURITIES CORP p 248
499 Park Ave 10022
Tel (212) 938-5000 *SIC* 6211

CAP GEMINI AMERICA INC p 248
623 5th Ave Fl 33 10022
Tel (917) 934-8000 *SIC* 7379

CAPGEMINI NORTH AMERICA INC p 249
623 5th Ave Fl 33 10022
Tel (212) 314-8000 *SIC* 7379

CAPGEMINI US LLC p 249
623 5th Ave Fl 33 10022
Tel (917) 934-8000 *SIC* 8748

■ **CAPITAL IQ INC** p 249
55 Water St Fl 49 10041
Tel (212) 438-8736 *SIC* 8742

▲ **CAPITAL ON DECK INC** p 250
1400 Broadway Fl 25 10018
Tel (888) 269-4246 *SIC* 6153

CAPITAL-MERCURY APPAREL LTD p 250
1385 Broadway Rm 1800 10018
Tel (212) 704-4800 *SIC* 2321 2331

■ **CAPLEASE INC** p 251
1065 Avenue Of The Americ 10018
Tel (212) 217-6300 *SIC* 6798

CARAT USA INC p 252
150 E 42nd St 10017
Tel (212) 591-9100 *SIC* 7319

CAREY WATERMARK INVESTORS INC p 255
50 Rockefeller Plz 10020
Tel (212) 492-1100 *SIC* 6798 7011

CARNEGIE HALL CORP p 258
881 Sventh Ave At 57th St 10019
Tel (212) 903-9600 *SIC* 7922 6531

CARPENTERS WELFARE BENEFIT FUND OF NEW YORK CITY (INC) p 260
395 Hudson St Fl 9 10014
Tel (212) 366-7300 *SIC* 6371

CASTLE HARLAN PARTNERS III LP p 264
150 E 58th St Fl 38 10155
Tel (212) 644-8600
SIC 5812 6282 6211 8732

CASTLE HARLAN PARTNERS IV LP p 264
150 E 58th St Fl 38 10155
Tel (212) 644-8600 *SIC* 6799 6719

CATHOLIC GUARDIAN SERVICES p 266
1011 1st Ave Fl 10 10022
Tel (212) 371-1011 *SIC* 8322 8361

CATHOLIC MEDICAL MISSION BOARD INC p 267
100 Wall St Fl 9 10005
Tel (212) 242-7757 *SIC* 8011

CAYRE GROUP LTD p 268
1407 Broadway Fl 41 10018
Tel (212) 789-7000 *SIC* 5137

■ **CB RICHARD ELLIS REAL ESTATE SERVICES LLC** p 268
200 Park Ave Fl 19 10166
Tel (212) 984-8000 *SIC* 6531 6162

■ **CBS BROADCASTING INC** p 269
51 W 52nd St 10019
Tel (212) 975-4321 *SIC* 4833 4832 7812

■ **CBS CORP** p 269
51 W 52nd St Bsmt 1 10019
Tel (212) 975-4321
SIC 4833 4832 7312 2731

■ **CBS RADIO INC** p 269
1271 Ave Of The Amer 44 10020
Tel (212) 314-9200 *SIC* 4832 7312

CCMP CAPITAL ADVISORS LP p 270
277 Park Ave Fl 27 10172
Tel (212) 600-9600 *SIC* 6726

CCMP CAPITAL INVESTORS III LP p 270
245 Park Ave Fl 16 10167
Tel (212) 600-9600 *SIC* 6799

CDPQ US INC p 271
1211 6th Ave Ste 3001 10036
Tel (212) 596-6300 *SIC* 6799

CELEBRITY INTERNATIONAL INC p 273
10 W 33rd St Rm 910 10001
Tel (212) 279-1616 *SIC* 5137

CENIBRA INC p 275
335 Madison Ave Fl 23 10017
Tel (212) 818-8242 *SIC* 2611 5159

CENTERBRIDGE CAPITAL PARTNERS LP p 276
375 Park Ave Fl 12 10152
Tel (212) 672-5000 *SIC* 6799

CENTERBRIDGE PARTNERS LP p 276
375 Park Ave Fl 13 10152
Tel (212) 672-5000 *SIC* 6282 6211

CENTRE LANE PARTNERS LLC p 281
60 E 42nd St Ste 1250 10165
Tel (646) 843-0710 *SIC* 6799

CENTRE PARTNERS MANAGEMENT LLC p 281
825 3rd Ave Fl 40 10022
Tel (212) 332-5800 *SIC* 6726 5112

CENTURY 21 DEPARTMENT STORES LLC p 281
22 Cortland St 10007
Tel (212) 227-9092 *SIC* 5311

CENTURY 21 INC p 281
21 Cortlandt St 10007
Tel (212) 227-9092 *SIC* 6531

■ **CERBERUS ABP INVESTOR LLC** p 283
299 Park Ave 10171
Tel (212) 891-2100 *SIC* 5031 5211

▲ **CERBERUS CAPITAL MANAGEMENT LP** p 283
875 3rd Ave 10022
Tel (212) 891-2100
SIC 6722 6726 5031 5211

■ **CERBERUS LP LLC** p 283
875 3rd Ave Fl 11 10022
Tel (212) 891-2100 *SIC* 7389 7374

■ **CERBERUS PARTNERS LP** p 283
450 Park Ave Fl 28 10022
Tel (212) 421-2600 *SIC* 6726

CHADBOURNE & PARKE LLP p 286
1301 Ave Of The Americas 10019
Tel (212) 408-5100 *SIC* 8111

CHANEL INC p 288
9 W 57th St Fl 44 10019
Tel (212) 688-5055
SIC 5632 2844 5122 5944 5961 5999

CHAPIN SCHOOL p 288
100 E End Ave 10028
Tel (212) 744-2335 *SIC* 8211

CHARTERHOUSE GROUP INC p 291
535 Madison Ave Fl 28 10022
Tel (212) 584-3200 *SIC* 8741 6799 6282

CHELSEY DIRECT LLC p 293
110 E 59th St 10022
Tel (201) 863-7300 *SIC* 5961 5947 5611

CHF INDUSTRIES INC p 296
1 Park Ave Fl 9 10016
Tel (212) 951-7800 *SIC* 5023 2221

CHILDRENS AID SOCIETY p 298
711 3rd Ave Rm 700 10017
Tel (212) 949-4800 *SIC* 8322

▲ **CHIMERA INVESTMENT CORP** p 300
520 Madison Ave Rm 3200 10022
Tel (646) 454-3759 *SIC* 6798

CHINA INDUSTRIAL STEEL INC p 301
110 Wall St Fl 11 10005
Tel (646) 328-1502 *SIC* 3312

CHINA NORTH EAST PETROLEUM HOLDINGS LIMITED p 301
445 Park Ave Ste 900 10022
Tel (212) 307-3568 *SIC* 1311

CHINESE AMERICAN PLANNING p 301
1 York St Fl 2 10013
Tel (212) 219-8100 *SIC* 8322

CHINOS HOLDINGS INC p 301
770 Broadway 10003
Tel (212) 209-2500
SIC 5961 5621 5611 5632 6794

CHINOS INTERMEDIATE HOLDINGS B INC p 301
770 Broadway 10003
Tel (212) 209-2500
SIC 5961 5621 5611 5632 6794

CHOICE LOGISTICS INC p 302
1 Whitehall St Fl 12 10004
Tel (917) 344-4000 *SIC* 4731

CHRISTIES INC p 303
20 Rockefeller Plz 10020
Tel (212) 636-2000 *SIC* 7389

CHUBB GROUP HOLDINGS INC p 304
1133 Ave Of The Americas 10036
Tel (212) 827-4400 *SIC* 6411

CHURCH PENSION GROUP SERVICES CORP p 305
19 E 34th St Fl 3 10016
Tel (212) 592-1800
SIC 6371 6321 6311 6331 2731

CI CAPITAL PARTNERS LLC p 305
500 Park Ave Fl 8 10022
Tel (212) 752-1850 *SIC* 6726

CIBC DELAWARE HOLDINGS INC p 306
300 Madison Ave Bsmt C2 10017
Tel (212) 856-4000 *SIC* 6211

CIBC WORLD MARKETS CORP p 306
425 Lexington Ave Bsmt C2 10017
Tel (212) 667-7000 *SIC* 6211 6311 6531

■ **CIFC CORP** p 306
250 Park Ave Ste 400 10177
Tel (212) 624-1200 *SIC* 6722

■ **CIFC LLC** p 306
250 Park Ave Ste 400 10177
Tel (212) 624-1200 *SIC* 6722

▲ **CINEDIGM CORP** p 307
902 Broadway Fl 9 10010
Tel (212) 206-8600 *SIC* 7384 7389 7371

CIRCLE PEAK CAPITAL MANAGEMENT LLC p 308
1325 Ave Of The Americas 10019
Tel (646) 230-8812 *SIC* 2053 6799

▲ **CIT GROUP INC** p 309
11 W 42nd St Fl 7 10036
Tel (212) 461-5200
SIC 6022 6162 6159 6141

■ **CIT GROUP/COMMERCIAL SERVICES INC** p 309
11 W 42nd St Fl 11 10036
Tel (212) 461-5200 *SIC* 6153

■ **CITIBANK NA** p 310
399 Park Ave Bsmt 1 10022
Tel (212) 559-1000
SIC 6021 6153 6091 6099 6162

■ **CITIGROUP FINANCIAL PRODUCTS INC** p 310
388 Greenwich St 10013
Tel (212) 816-6000 *SIC* 6211

■ CITIGROUP GLOBAL MARKETS HOLDINGS INC p 310
388 Greenwich St 10013
Tel (212) 816-6000 *SIC* 6211

■ CITIGROUP GLOBAL MARKETS INC p 310
388 Greenwich St Fl 18 10013
Tel (212) 816-6000 *SIC* 6211 6221 6282

▲ CITIGROUP INC p 310
399 Park Ave 10022
Tel (212) 559-1000
SIC 6021 6141 6331 6311 6321

■ CITIGROUP VENTURE CAPITAL INTERNATIONAL DE CORP p 310
731 Lexington Ave Fl 21 10022
Tel (212) 559-5099 *SIC* 6799

CITY HARVEST INC p 312
6 E 32nd St Fl 5 10016
Tel (646) 412-0600 *SIC* 8322

CITY OF NEW YORK p 317
City Hl 10007
Tel (212) 788-3000 *SIC* 9111

CITY UNIVERSITY OF NEW YORK p 320
230 W 41st St Fl 10 10036
Tel (212) 397-5600 *SIC* 8221

CLARENDON NATIONAL INSURANCE CO (MD CORP) p 321
411 5th Ave Fl 5 10016
Tel (212) 790-9700
SIC 6321 1542 1541 7011

CLARINS USA INC p 321
1 Park Ave Fl 19 10016
Tel (212) 223-2956 *SIC* 5122

CLARION CAPITAL PARTNERS LLC p 321
527 Madison Ave Fl 10 10022
Tel (212) 821-0111 *SIC* 6799

■ CLARION PARTNERS LLC p 322
230 Park Ave Fl 12 10169
Tel (212) 883-2500 *SIC* 6722

CLARK FOUNDATION p 322
1 Rockefeller Plz Fl 31 10020
Tel (212) 977-6900 *SIC* 6732

CLAYTON DUBILIER & RICE FUND V LIMITED PARTNERSHIP p 323
375 Park Ave Fl 18 10152
Tel (212) 407-5200
SIC 3825 3661 3812 3577 3575 7372

CLAYTON DUBILIER & RICE INC p 323
375 Park Ave Fl 18 10152
Tel (212) 407-5200 *SIC* 6799 3589 5812

CLAYTON DUBILIER & RICE LLC p 323
375 Park Ave Fl 18 10152
Tel (212) 407-5200 *SIC* 6719 6726 6211

CLEARING HOUSE PAYMENTS CO L L C p 324
1114 Avenue Of The Americ 10036
Tel (212) 612-9200 *SIC* 6099

CLEARY GOTTLIEB STEEN & HAMILTON LLP p 325
1 Liberty Plz Fl 43 10006
Tel (212) 225-2000 *SIC* 8111

CLIFFORD CHANCE US LLP p 326
31 W 52nd St Fl 3 10019
Tel (212) 878-8000 *SIC* 8111

CLOTHESLINE HOLDINGS INC p 327
399 Park Ave Fl 15 10022
Tel (212) 607-8450 *SIC* 6719

CLP PB LLC p 328
250 W 57th St Fl 15 10107
Tel (212) 340-8100 *SIC* 2721

■ CMGRP INC p 329
909 3rd Ave 10022
Tel (212) 445-8000
SIC 8743 7311 7319 8742

CMP I OWNER-T LLC p 329
399 Park Ave Fl 18 10022
Tel (212) 547-2609 *SIC* 7011

▲ COACH INC p 330
10 Hudson Yards 10001
Tel (212) 594-1850
SIC 3171 3172 2387 3143 3144

COACH STORES INC p 331
516 W 34th St Bsmt 5 10001
Tel (212) 643-9727
SIC 3171 3161 3172 2387 5137 5099

COFACE NORTH AMERICA HOLDING CO p 334
1350 Broadway Rm 615 10018
Tel (212) 389-6500 *SIC* 6331

COGR INC p 334
200 Park Ave Fl 20 10166
Tel (212) 370-5600 *SIC* 8742

▲ COHEN & STEERS INC p 334
280 Park Ave Fl 10w 10017
Tel (212) 832-3232 *SIC* 6282

COHNREZNICK LLP p 335
1301 Ave Of The Americas 10019
Tel (212) 297-0400 *SIC* 8721

COLER GOLDWATER SPECIALTY HOSPITAL & NURSING FACILITY p 336
900 Main St 10044
Tel (212) 848-6000 *SIC* 8069 8051

▲ COLGATE-PALMOLIVE CO p 336
300 Park Ave Fl 5 10022
Tel (212) 310-2000
SIC 2844 3991 2841 2842 2047

COLLECTION XIIX LTD p 336
1370 Broadway Fl 17 10018
Tel (212) 686-8990 *SIC* 2339

COLLEGE ENTRANCE EXAMINATION BOARD p 336
250 Vesey St 10281
Tel (212) 713-8000 *SIC* 8299 8221 2732

COLUMBIA LAKE ACQUISITION HOLDINGS INC p 341
9 W 57th St Fl 43 10019
Tel (212) 515-3450 *SIC* 6719

■ COMCAST SPOTLIGHT p 343
5 Times Sq 10036
Tel (212) 278-8156 *SIC* 7311

■ COMEDY PARTNERS p 344
345 Hudson St Fl 9 10014
Tel (212) 767-8600 *SIC* 4841

COMMERZBANK AG p 345
225 Liberty St Fl 31 10281
Tel (212) 266-7200 *SIC* 6029

COMMUNITY FUNDS INC p 348
2 Park Ave Fl 24 10016
Tel (212) 686-0010 *SIC* 6732

COMPUTER GENERATED SOLUTIONS INC p 352
200 Vesey St Fl 27 10281
Tel (212) 408-3800
SIC 7373 7379 7371 8243

COMPUTERSHARE INVESTOR SERVICES LLC p 353
1290 Ave Of The Americas 10104
Tel (312) 588-4700 *SIC* 6289 6211 6282

COMVERSE INC p 353
810 7th Ave Fl 32 10019
Tel (212) 739-1060 *SIC* 7371

COMVERSETECHNOLOGY INC p 353
810 7th Ave 10019
Tel (212) 739-1000 *SIC* 7372 7371

CONDE NAST INTERNATIONAL INC p 355
1 World Trade Ctr 10007
Tel (212) 286-2860 *SIC* 2721

CONDOR 3 CORP p 355
120 Broadway Ste 31 10271
Tel (212) 655-2000 *SIC* 6331

CONFERENCE ON JEWISH MATERIAL CLAIMS AGAINST GERMANY INC p 356
1359 Broadway Rm 2000 10018
Tel (646) 536-9100 *SIC* 8699

CONNAUGHT GROUP LTD p 356
423 W 55th St Fl 3 10019
Tel (212) 315-4486 *SIC* 5137

■ CONSOLIDATED EDISON CO OF NEW YORK INC p 359
4 Irving Pl 10003
Tel (212) 460-4600 *SIC* 4911 4924 4961

▲ CONSOLIDATED EDISON INC p 359
4 Irving Pl 10003
Tel (212) 460-4600 *SIC* 4931

■ CONTINENTAL CORP p 363
111 8th Ave 10011
Tel (212) 440-3000
SIC 6331 6351 6321 6159 8741 6411

CONTINENTAL GRAIN CO p 363
767 5th Ave Fl 15 10153
Tel (212) 207-5930 *SIC* 2015 2041

CONVERGEX GROUP LLC p 365
1633 Broadway Ste 1300 10019
Tel (212) 468-7500 *SIC* 6211

CORAL REEF CAPITAL GROUP LLC p 368
757 3rd Ave 10017
Tel (646) 599-9680 *SIC* 6799 1081

■ CORCORAN GROUP INC p 368
660 Madison Ave Fl 11 10065
Tel (212) 355-3550 *SIC* 6531

CORE STAFFING SERVICES INC p 369
40 Wall St Ste 1600 10005
Tel (212) 766-1222 *SIC* 7361

CORINTHIAN CAPITAL GROUP LLC p 370
601 Lexington Ave Rm 5901 10022
Tel (212) 920-2300 *SIC* 6211

■ CORPORATE PROPERTY ASSOCIATES 15 INC p 372
50 Rockefeller Plz 10020
Tel (212) 492-1100 *SIC* 6798

CORPORATE PROPERTY ASSOCIATES 16 - GLOBAL INC p 372
50 Rockefeller Plz Fl 2 10020
Tel (212) 492-1100 *SIC* 6798

CORPORATE PROPERTY ASSOCIATES 17 - GLOBAL INC p 372
50 Rockefeller Plz Fl 2 10020
Tel (212) 492-1100 *SIC* 6798

CORPORATE PROPERTY INVESTORS p 372
305 E 47th St 10017
Tel (212) 421-8200 *SIC* 6798

CORPORATE RESOURCE SERVICES INC p 372
160 Broadway Rm 1300 10038
Tel (646) 443-2380 *SIC* 7363 8742

CORPORATE RISK HOLDINGS LLC p 372
600 3rd Ave Fl 4 10016
Tel (212) 896-2001
SIC 6719 8748 7375 7389

■ COTY INC p 374
350 5th Ave Ste 2700 10118
Tel (212) 389-7300 *SIC* 2844

■ COTY US LLC p 374
350 5th Ave Fl C1700 10118
Tel (212) 389-7000 *SIC* 2844

COUNTRY-WIDE INSURANCE CO p 375
40 Wall St Fl 13 10005
Tel (212) 514-7000 *SIC* 6411

COURT SQUARE CAPITAL LIMITED p 383
55 E 52nd St Rm 3400 10055
Tel (212) 752-6110 *SIC* 8743 6162

COURT SQUARE CAPITAL PARTNERS LP p 383
55 E 52nd St Rm 3400 10055
Tel (212) 752-6110 *SIC* 6799 2731 2721

COVENANT HOUSE p 384
5 Penn Plz Ste 201 10001
Tel (212) 727-4000 *SIC* 8322 8361

■ COWEN AND CO LLC p 385
599 Lexington Ave Fl 19 10022
Tel (646) 562-1000 *SIC* 6211

▲ COWEN GROUP INC p 385
599 Lexington Ave 10022
Tel (212) 845-7900 *SIC* 6211 6722

■ COWEN HOLDINGS INC p 385
599 Lexington Ave Fl 26 10022
Tel (212) 562-1000 *SIC* 6211 6159

CPA 17 LIMITED PARTNERSHIP p 387
50 Rockefeller Plz 10020
Tel (212) 492-1100 *SIC* 8742

CPS 1 REALTY LP p 387
768 5th Ave 10019
Tel (212) 759-3000 *SIC* 7011 7299 5812

CPX INTERACTIVE HOLDINGS LLC p 388
1441 Broadway Fl 18 10018
Tel (646) 863-8309 *SIC* 7313

CRAVATH SWAINE & MOORE LLP p 389
825 8th Ave Lbby L 10019
Tel (212) 474-1000 *SIC* 8111

CREDIT AGRICOLE AMERICA SERVICES INC p 390
1301 Ave Of The Americas 10019
Tel (212) 261-7000 *SIC* 6159

CREDIT AGRICOLE GLOBALPARTNERS INC p 390
1301 Ave Of The Americas 10019
Tel (212) 261-7000 *SIC* 6211

CREDIT SUISSE (USA) INC p 390
11 Madison Ave Frnt 1 10010
Tel (212) 325-2000 *SIC* 6211 6282 6799

CREDIT SUISSE ASSET MANAGEMENT LLC p 390
11 Madison Ave Bsmt 1b 10010
Tel (212) 325-2000 *SIC* 6211

CREDIT SUISSE HOLDINGS (USA) INC p 390
11 Madison Ave Bsmt 1b 10010
Tel (646) 935-0299 *SIC* 6712

CREDIT SUISSE SECURITIES (USA) LLC p 391
11 Madison Ave Bsmt 1b 10010
Tel (212) 325-2000 *SIC* 6211

CRESTVIEW PARTNERS LP p 392
667 Madison Ave Fl 10 10065
Tel (212) 906-0700 *SIC* 6211

CRUNCH LLC p 396
220 W 19th St 10011
Tel (212) 993-0300 *SIC* 7991 6794

CRYSTAL FRANK & CO INC p 397
32 Old Slip 10005
Tel (212) 344-2444 *SIC* 6411

CTPARTNERS EXECUTIVE SEARCH INC p 399
1166 Avenue Of The Amrcs 10036
Tel (212) 588-3500 *SIC* 7361

■ CURRENEX INC p 402
1230 Ave Of 10020
Tel (212) 340-1780 *SIC* 6099

CUSHMAN & WAKEFIELD HOLDINGS INC p 402
1290 Ave Of The Americas 10104
Tel (212) 841-7500 *SIC* 6531 8742 8732

D E SHAW INVESTMENTS LP p 407
1166 Avenue Of The Americ 10036
Tel (212) 478-0000 *SIC* 6211

D E SHAW LAMINAR PORTFOLIOS LLC p 407
120 W 45th St Fl 22 10036
Tel (212) 478-0000 *SIC* 6282 2392 5945

D L J MERCHANT BANKING PARTNERS I I LP p 407
11 Madison Ave 10010
Tel (212) 325-2000 *SIC* 6211

DAILY NEWS LP p 408
4 New York Plz Fl 6 10004
Tel (212) 210-2100 *SIC* 2711

DAIWA CAPITAL MARKETS AMERICA HOLDINGS INC p 409
32 Old Slip Fl 14 10005
Tel (212) 612-7000 *SIC* 6211

DAKOTA PARENT INC p 409
9 W 57th St Fl 43 10019
Tel (212) 515-3200 *SIC* 6719

DANUBE PRIVATE HOLDINGS II LLC p 412
601 Lexington Ave 10022
Tel (212) 231-0095 *SIC* 7371

■ DAS HOLDINGS INC p 413
437 Madison Ave 10022
Tel (212) 415-3700 *SIC* 7311

DATA VISION COMPUTER VIDEO INC p 414
50 W 23rd St 10010
Tel (212) 689-1111 *SIC* 5045 5961

DATAART SOLUTIONS INC p 414
475 Park Ave S Fl 15 10016
Tel (212) 378-4108 *SIC* 7371

DAVID YURMAN ENTERPRISES LLC p 415
24 Vestry St 10013
Tel (212) 896-1550 *SIC* 3911

DAVIS POLK & WARDWELL LLP p 416
450 Lexington Ave Fl 10 10017
Tel (212) 450-4000 *SIC* 8111

■ DAVIS ZIFF PUBLISHING INC p 416
28 E 28th St Fl 10 10016
Tel (212) 503-3500 *SIC* 2721 2731 7371

DAYCO GLOBAL HOLDING CORP p 417
111 8th Ave 10011
Tel (716) 689-4972 *SIC* 6719

DB USA CORP p 418
60 Wall St 10005
Tel (212) 250-2500 *SIC* 6141 6153

■ DDB WORLDWIDE COMMUNICATIONS GROUP INC p 419
437 Madison Ave Fl 11 10022
Tel (212) 415-2000 *SIC* 7311

DEAN & DE LUCA BRANDS INC p 420
560 Broadway Frnt 2 10012
Tel (212) 226-6800 *SIC* 5499 5812 2099

DEAN & DELUCA INC p 420
560 Broadway Frnt 2 10012
Tel (212) 226-6800
SIC 5499 5812 5961 2099

DEBEVOISE & PLIMPTON LLP p 420
919 3rd Ave Lbby 2 10022
Tel (212) 909-6000 *SIC* 8111

DELIAS INC p 424
50 W 23rd St 10010
Tel (212) 590-6200 *SIC* 5632 5611

DELOITTE & TOUCHE LLP p 425
30 Rockefeller Plz # 4350 10112
Tel (212) 492-4000 *SIC* 8721

DELOITTE CONSULTING LLP p 425
30 Rockefeller Plz 10112
Tel (212) 492-4000 *SIC* 8742

DELOITTE FINANCIAL ADVISORY SERVICES LLP p 425
30 Rockefeller Plz 10112
Tel (212) 492-4000 *SIC* 8721

DELOITTE LLP p 425
30 Rockefeller Plz 10112
Tel (212) 492-4000 *SIC* 8742 8721

DELOITTE SERVICES LP p 425
1633 Broadway Fl 35 10019
Tel (212) 492-2000 *SIC* 8721

DELTA ENTERPRISE CORP p 427
114 W 26th St Fl 11 10001
Tel (212) 736-7000 *SIC* 5021 5099

DEPARTMENT OF ECONOMIC AND SOCIAL AFFAIRS p 430
Secretariat Bldg Unitedn 10003
Tel (212) 963-1707 *SIC* 9721

▲ DEPOSITORY TRUST & CLEARING CORP p 431
55 Water St Ste Conc3 10041
Tel (212) 855-1000 *SIC* 6289 6211 7389

■ DEPOSITORY TRUST CO INC p 431
55 Water St Ste Conc4 10041
Tel (212) 855-1000 *SIC* 6289

■ DESIGNTEX GROUP INC p 432
200 Varick St Fl 8 10014
Tel (212) 886-8100 *SIC* 5131

■ DEUTSCH INC p 433
6 E 78th St 10075
Tel (212) 981-7600 *SIC* 7311

DEUTSCHE BANK AMERICAS HOLDING CORP p 433
60 Wall St 10005
Tel (212) 250-2500 *SIC* 6141 6153 6211

DEUTSCHE BANK SECURITIES INC p 433
60 Wall St Bsmt 1 10005
Tel (212) 250-2500 *SIC* 6211 6036

DEUTSCHE BANK TRUST CO AMERICAS p 433
60 Wall St Bsmt 1 10005
Tel (212) 250-2500 *SIC* 6021 6211

DEUTSCHE BANK US FINANCIAL MARKETS HOLDING CORP p 433
60 Wall St Bsmt 1 10005
Tel (212) 250-2500 *SIC* 6211

DEWITT STERN GROUP INC p 434
420 Lexington Ave Rm 2700 10170
Tel (212) 867-3550 *SIC* 6411

DEXIA CREDIT LOCAL (INC) p 434
445 Park Ave Fl 8 10022
Tel (212) 515-7000 *SIC* 6082

DHARM INTERNATIONAL LLC p 435
15 W 47th St Ste 506 10036
Tel (212) 398-7777 *SIC* 5094

DHG MANAGEMENT CO LLC p 435
551 5th Ave Fl 10 10176
Tel (212) 465-3700 *SIC* 8741

▲ DHI GROUP INC p 435
1040 Avenue Of The Amrcas 10018
Tel (212) 725-6550 *SIC* 7361 4813 7375

DIAMLINK INC p 436
25 W 45th St Ste 1406 10036
Tel (212) 704-0777 *SIC* 5094

DIAMOND CASTLE HOLDINGS LLC p 436
280 Pk Ave Fl 25 E Tower 10017
Tel (212) 300-1900 *SIC* 7353 7699 5082

DIESEL USA INC p 438
220 W 19th St Fl 5 10011
Tel (212) 755-9200
SIC 5137 5136 5621 5632 5611

DIGITAL FIRST MEDIA LLC p 439
20 W 33rd St Fl 7 10001
Tel (212) 257-7212 *SIC* 2711

DILIGENT CORP p 439
1385 Brdwy Fl 19 10018
Tel (212) 741-8181 *SIC* 7372

DIMENSION DATA NORTH AMERICA INC p 440
1 Penn Plz Ste 1600 10119
Tel (212) 613-1220 *SIC* 7373

DISTRICT COUNCIL 37 BENEFITS FUND TRUST p 443
125 Barclay St Bsmt B 10007
Tel (917) 716-2097 *SIC* 6371

DISTRICT COUNCIL 37 HEALTH & SECURITY PLAN TRUST p 443
125 Barclay St 10007
Tel (212) 815-1305 *SIC* 8699

DNP CORP USA p 446
335 Madison Ave Fl 3 10017
Tel (212) 503-1060 *SIC* 5111

DONALD J FAGER & ASSOCIATES INC p 450
2 Park Ave Fl 25 10016
Tel (212) 576-9800 *SIC* 6411

DONNA KARAN CO LLC p 450
240 W 40th St 10018
Tel (212) 789-1500
SIC 2335 2337 2331 2339 2311 2325

DONNA KARAN INTERNATIONAL INC p 450
240 W 40th St 10018
Tel (212) 789-1500
SIC 2335 2337 2331 2339 2321 2325

■ DONNELLEY FINANCIAL LLC p 451
55 Water St Lowr L1 10041
Tel (212) 425-0298 *SIC* 2752

DORAL FINANCIAL CORP p 451
200 Park Ave Ste 1700 10166
Tel (646) 632-3700
SIC 6029 6162 6035 6211 6411

■ DOW JONES & CO INC p 453
1211 Avenue Of The Americ 10036
Tel (609) 627-2999 *SIC* 2711 2721

■ DOW JONES AER CO INC p 453
1211 Av Of The Am Lwr C3r 10036
Tel (212) 416-2000 *SIC* 2721

DR JAYS INC p 454
15 W 37th St Fl 11 10018
Tel (212) 239-3355 *SIC* 5611 5661

DRA ADVISORS LLC p 455
220 E 42nd St Fl 27 10017
Tel (212) 697-4740 *SIC* 6282

DRAGADOS USA INC p 455
810 7th Ave Fl 9 10019
Tel (212) 779-0900 *SIC* 1611

■ DREYFUS CORP p 456
200 Park Ave Fl 7east 10166
Tel (212) 922-6000 *SIC* 6211 6282

■ DREYFUS SERVICE ORGANIZATION INC p 456
200 Park Ave 10166
Tel (212) 922-6000 *SIC* 6211

DSJS INC p 458
16 W 36th St Rm 901 10018
Tel (212) 564-9326 *SIC* 5199

■ DUANE READE INC p 459
40 Wall St Fl 22 10005
Tel (212) 273-5700 *SIC* 5912

■ DUANE READE SHAREHOLDERS LLC p 459
40 Wall St Fl 22 10005
Tel (212) 273-5700 *SIC* 5912

DUCON TECHNOLOGIES INC p 459
5 Penn Plz Ste 2403 10001
Tel (631) 694-1700 *SIC* 3537 3564

DUFF & PHELPS CORP p 459
55 E 52nd St Fl 31 10055
Tel (212) 871-2000 *SIC* 6282 6211

DUFF & PHELPS LLC p 459
55 E 52nd St Fl 31 10055
Tel (212) 871-2000 *SIC* 8742

DURST ORGANIZATION INC p 463
1 Bryant Park Fl 49 10036
Tel (212) 257-6600 *SIC* 6512

E S SUTTON INC p 467
1400 Broadway Fl 26 10018
Tel (212) 944-9494 *SIC* 5137

▲ E TRADE FINANCIAL CORP p 467
1271 Ave Of The Americas 10020
Tel (646) 521-4300 *SIC* 6211 6035

E-LO SPORTSWEAR LLC p 467
500 Fashion Ave 10018
Tel (862) 902-5225 *SIC* 5137 5621

ECONOMIST NEWSPAPER GROUP INC p 476
750 3rd Ave Fl 5 10017
Tel (212) 541-0500 *SIC* 2721 7313 5963

ED & F MAN HOLDINGS INC p 476
33 Whitehall St Broad 10004
Tel (212) 618-2802 *SIC* 5149

EDUCATIONAL ALLIANCE INC p 479
197 E Brdwy 10002
Tel (646) 654-1297 *SIC* 8399

EISNERAMPER LLP p 482
750 3rd Ave 10017
Tel (212) 949-8700 *SIC* 8742 8721

ELIAS BEN INDUSTRIES CORP p 487
550 Fashion Ave Fl 12 10018
Tel (212) 354-8300 *SIC* 5137 5136

ELITE INVESTIGATIONS LTD p 487
538 W 29th St 10001
Tel (212) 629-3131 *SIC* 7381

ELLIOTT ASSOCIATES LP p 488
712 5th Ave Fl 36 10019
Tel (212) 586-9431 *SIC* 6282 1382

ELSEVIER INC p 489
230 Park Ave Fl 7 10169
Tel (212) 633-3773 *SIC* 2741

EMBLEMHEALTH INC p 490
55 Water St Ste Conc1 10041
Tel (646) 447-5000 *SIC* 6324

EMIGRANT SAVINGS BANK p 493
5 E 42nd St Fl 5 10017
Tel (212) 850-4000
SIC 6036 6311 6512 6514

EMPIRE OFFICE INC p 493
105 Madison Ave Fl 15 10016
Tel (212) 607-5500 *SIC* 5021

EMPIRE STATE REALTY TRUST INC p 493
60 E 42nd St 10165
Tel (212) 687-8700 *SIC* 6798

ENDURANCE ASSURANCE CORP p 496
750 3rd Ave Fl 1819 10017
Tel (212) 471-2800 *SIC* 6351

ENDURANCE SERVICES LIMITED p 497
750 3rd Ave 210 10017
Tel (212) 471-2800 *SIC* 6411

ENER-G GROUP INC p 497
1261 Broadway Fl 6 10001
Tel (917) 281-0020 *SIC* 8711

ENER1 INC p 497
1540 Broadway Fl 25c 10036
Tel (212) 920-3500 *SIC* 3691

ENLIGHTEN AIR INC p 500
23 E 81st St Apt 10 10028
Tel (917) 656-1248 *SIC* 3728

ENSEMBLE PARENT LLC p 500
345 Park Ave 10154
Tel (212) 583-5000 *SIC* 7363 8741

ENVIRONMENTAL DEFENSE FUND INC p 503
257 Park Ave S Fl 17 10010
Tel (212) 505-2100 *SIC* 8641 8748

▲ ENZO BIOCHEM INC p 504
527 Madison Ave Rm 901 10022
Tel (212) 583-0100 *SIC* 8071 8731

EOS PARTNERS LP p 504
320 Park Ave Rm 900 10022
Tel (212) 832-5800 *SIC* 6211

EQUINOX HOLDINGS INC p 506
895 Broadway Fl 3 10003
Tel (212) 677-0180 *SIC* 7991

EQUINOX-76TH STREET INC p 506
895 Broadway Fl 3 10003
Tel (212) 677-0180 *SIC* 7991

▲ EQUITY ONE INC p 507
410 Park Ave Ste 1220 10022
Tel (212) 796-1760 *SIC* 6798

ERNST & YOUNG LLP p 508
5 Times Sq Fl Conlv1 10036
Tel (212) 773-3000 *SIC* 8721

■ ESPN HOLDING CO INC p 509
77 W 66th St 10023
Tel (212) 916-9200 *SIC* 4841

▲ ESTEE LAUDER COMPANIES INC p 511
767 5th Ave Fl 37 10153
Tel (212) 572-4200 *SIC* 2844

■ ESTEE LAUDER INC p 511
767 5th Ave Fl 37 10153
Tel (212) 572-4200 *SIC* 2844 5999

■ ESTEE LAUDER INTERNATIONAL INC p 511
767 5th Ave Bsmt 1 10153
Tel (212) 572-4200 *SIC* 2844

ETHICAL CULTURE FIELDSTON SCHOOL p 511
33 Central Park W 10023
Tel (212) 712-6220 *SIC* 8211

ETRALI NORTH AMERICA LLC p 512
1500 Broadway Ste 708 10036
Tel (212) 418-9328 *SIC* 5045 7378 1731

EUREKA BROADBAND CORP p 512
39 Broad St Fl 19 10004
Tel (212) 404-5000 *SIC* 4822

EURO RSCG LATINO p 512
350 Hudson St Fl 6 10014
Tel (212) 345-6383 *SIC* 7311

EUROMONEY US HOLDINGS LP p 512
225 Park Ave S Fl 7 10003
Tel (212) 224-3300 *SIC* 6719

EUROPEAN UNION DELEGATION TO UNITED NATION p 513
666 3rd Ave Fl 31 10017
Tel (212) 401-0117 *SIC* 9721

EVERCORE LP p 514
55 E 52nd St Fl 35 10055
Tel (212) 857-3100 *SIC* 6282 6211

▲ EVERCORE PARTNERS INC p 514
55 E 52nd St Fl 35 10055
Tel (212) 857-3100 *SIC* 6282 6211

EVERCORE PARTNERS SERVICES EAST LLC p 514
55 E 52nd St 10055
Tel (212) 857-3100 *SIC* 2711

EVERGREEN CAPITAL LP p 514
21st Fl 551 5th Ave 10176
Tel (914) 400-4277 *SIC* 6211

▲ EVERYDAY HEALTH INC p 515
345 Hudson St Rm 1600 10014
Tel (646) 728-9500 *SIC* 8099 7319

EWT HOLDINGS I CORP p 516
666 5th Ave Fl 36 10103
Tel (212) 644-5900 *SIC* 8748

EWT HOLDINGS III CORP p 516
666 5th Ave Fl 36 10103
Tel (212) 644-5900
SIC 3589 3823 3826 4941 5051

EXCELLED SHEEPSKIN & LEATHER COAT CORP p 516
1400 Brdwy Fl 31 10018
Tel (212) 594-5843
SIC 2386 3172 2337 2311

EXHALE ENTERPRISES INC p 519
250 W 57th St Ste 1901 10107
Tel (212) 300-2310 *SIC* 7991

▲ EXLSERVICE HOLDINGS INC p 519
280 Park Ave Fl 38 10017
Tel (212) 277-7100 *SIC* 7389

■ EXLSERVICE.COM LLC p 519
280 Park Ave 10017
Tel (212) 277-7100 *SIC* 7389

EXPRESS TRADE CAPITAL INC p 520
1410 Broadway Fl 26 10018
Tel (212) 997-0155 *SIC* 6153 4731

F SCHUMACHER & CO p 522
875 Ave Of The Amrcs 14 10001
Tel (212) 213-7900 *SIC* 5131 2299

▲ FAB HOLDINGS I LP p 523
250 Park Ave Fl 4 10177
Tel (212) 624-1200 *SIC* 6798

FACTORYOUTLETSTORE LLC p 524
1407 Broadway Rm 700 10018
Tel (646) 367-6141 *SIC* 5722 5064

FAIRCHILD PUBLICATIONS INC p 524
475 5th Ave 10017
Tel (212) 630-4000 *SIC* 2721 2711 2731

FAIRFIELD-MAXWELL LTD p 525
60 E 42nd St Fl 55 10165
Tel (212) 297-9030
SIC 8741 4731 5172 4412

FAIRWAY GROUP HOLDINGS CORP p 525
2284 12th Ave 10027
Tel (646) 616-8000 *SIC* 5411

FALCONHEAD CAPITAL LLC p 526
645 Madison Ave Fl 9 10022
Tel (212) 634-3304 *SIC* 6722 3812

FALCONHEAD CAPITAL PARTNERS II LP p 526
450 Park Ave Bsmt 10022
Tel (212) 634-3304 *SIC* 6722 7221 7335

FAREPORTAL INC p 528
135 W 50th St Ste 500 10020
Tel (646) 738-7813 *SIC* 7379

FASHION ACCESSORY BAZAAR LLC p 531
15 W 34th St Fl 2 10001
Tel (212) 947-9001 *SIC* 5199 5112

FASHION AVENUE KNITS INC p 531
525 Fashion Ave Fl 4 10018
Tel (718) 456-9000 *SIC* 5137

FASHION INSTITUTE OF TECHNOLOGY p 531
7th Ave 27th St Rm C908 10001
Tel (212) 217-7999 *SIC* 8222 9411

FCB INTERNATIONAL LLC p 532
100 W 23rd St Frnt 10011
Tel (212) 885-3000 *SIC* 7311

■ FCB WORLDWIDE INC p 532
100 W 33rd St Fl 5 10001
Tel (212) 885-3000 *SIC* 7311 8743

FDG ASSOCIATES LLC p 533
605 3rd Ave Fl 15 10158
Tel (212) 940-6864 *SIC* 7389

FEDCAP REHABILITATION SERVICES INC p 533
633 3rd Ave Fl 6 10017
Tel (212) 727-4200 *SIC* 8093

FEDERAL HOME LOAN BANK OF NEW YORK p 534
101 Park Ave Fl 5 10178
Tel (212) 441-6616 *SIC* 6111

FEDERAL RESERVE BANK OF NEW YORK p 535
33 Liberty St 10045
Tel (212) 720-6130 *SIC* 6011

FEINBERG GRADUATE SCHOOL OF WEIZMANN INSTITUTE OF SCIENCE p 537
633 3rd Ave Fl 20 10017
Tel (212) 895-7900 *SIC* 6411

FENWAY PARTNERS LLC p 537
152 W 57th St Fl 5927 10019
Tel (212) 698-9400 *SIC* 6211

FGIC CORP p 539
125 Park Ave Fl 5 10017
Tel (212) 312-3000 *SIC* 6411 7389

FIAT USA INC p 539
375 Park Ave Ste 2703 10152
Tel (212) 355-2600
SIC 3714 8741 3535 5012 5013 5082

■ FIDELITY NATIONAL TITLE INSURANCE CO OF NEW YORK p 541
1 Pak Ave Ste 1402 10016
Tel (904) 854-8100 *SIC* 6361

FIDESSA CORP p 541
17 State St Fl 18 10004
Tel (212) 269-9000 *SIC* 7371

■ FIDUCIARY TRUST CO INTERNATIONAL p 541
280 Park Ave 10017
Tel (212) 632-3000 *SIC* 6099

FILMED ENTERTAINMENT INC p 542
1 Penn Plz Fl 5 10119
Tel (212) 596-2000 *SIC* 5961

FINANCIAL GUARANTY INSURANCE CO p 542
521 5th Ave Fl 15 10175
Tel (212) 312-3000 *SIC* 6351

FINANCIAL SECURITY ASSURANCE HOLDINGS LTD p 542
31 W 52nd St 10019
Tel (212) 826-0100 *SIC* 6351

FINANCIAL SECURITY ASSURANCE INTERNATIONAL INC p 542
350 Park Ave Fl 13 10022
Tel (212) 826-0100 *SIC* 6351

■ FIRST AMERICAN TITLE INSURANCE CO OF NEW YORK p 544
666 3rd Ave Fl 5 10017
Tel (646) 487-5640 *SIC* 6361

FIRST ATLANTIC CAPITAL LTD p 545
135 E 57th St Rear 10022
Tel (212) 750-0300 *SIC* 6799

FIRST CHINESE PRESBYTERIAN COMMUNITY AFFAIRS HOME ATTENDANT CORP p 545
30 Broad St Ste 602 10004
Tel (212) 226-4910 *SIC* 8051

▲ FIRST DATA CORP p 546
225 Liberty St Fl 29 10281
Tel (800) 735-3362 *SIC* 7389 6099 6153

FIRST EAGLE INVESTMENT MANAGEMENT LLC p 546
1345 Ave Of The Americas 10105
Tel (212) 698-3300 *SIC* 6282

FIRST INVESTORS CORP p 547
40 Wall St Fl 10 10005
Tel (212) 858-8000 *SIC* 6282 6211

FIRSTMARK CAPITAL LLC p 551
100 5th Ave Fl 3 10011
Tel (212) 792-2200 *SIC* 6282

FITCH GROUP INC p 552
33 Whitehall St 10004
Tel (212) 908-0500 *SIC* 6289

FITCH RATINGS INC p 552
33 Whitehall St 10004
Tel (212) 612-7726 *SIC* 6289

FITZGERALD CANTOR L P p 553
499 Park Ave 10022
Tel (212) 938-5000 *SIC* 6211

FLAVORS HOLDINGS INC p 555
35 E 62nd St 10065
Tel (212) 572-8677 *SIC* 2869 6712

FLOW TRADERS US LLC p 560
1140 Avenue Of Americas 10036
Tel (917) 210-5000 *SIC* 6799

FOCUS FINANCIAL PARTNERS LLC p 562
825 3rd Ave Fl 27 10022
Tel (646) 519-2456 *SIC* 6799

FOJP SERVICE CORP p 563
28 E 28th St Fl 14 10016
Tel (212) 891-0700 *SIC* 8741

▲ FOOT LOCKER INC p 564
330 W 34th St 10001
Tel (212) 720-3700
SIC 5661 5941 5961 6794

■ FOOT LOCKER RETAIL INC p 564
112 W 34th St Frnt 1 10120
Tel (212) 465-9041 *SIC* 5661 5699

■ FOOT LOCKER SPECIALTY INC p 564
112 W 34th St Lbby 1 10120
Tel (212) 720-3700 *SIC* 5632 5961 7311

FORD FOUNDATION p 565
320 E 43rd St Fl 4 10017
Tel (212) 573-5370 *SIC* 6732

■ FOREST ELECTRIC CORP p 566
1375 Broadway Fl 7 10018
Tel (212) 318-1500 *SIC* 1731 7349

FOREST LABORATORIES LLC p 566
909 3rd Ave Fl 23 10022
Tel (212) 421-7850 *SIC* 2834 5122

FORESTERS FINANCIAL SERVICES p 567
40 Wall St Fl 10 10005
Tel (212) 858-8000
SIC 6036 6211 6282 6311 8742 6153

FOREX CAPITAL MARKETS LLC p 567
55 Water St Fl 50 10041
Tel (646) 355-0839 *SIC* 6211

FORREST SOLUTIONS INC p 568
19 W 44th St Fl 9 10036
Tel (212) 986-3600 *SIC* 7361

FORSTMANN LITTLE & CO p 568
767 5th Ave Fl 4 10153
Tel (212) 355-5656 *SIC* 7991 6211

▲ FORTRESS INVESTMENT GROUP LLC p 570
1345 Avenue 10105
Tel (212) 798-6100 *SIC* 6282

▲ FORTRESS TRANSPORTATION AND INFRASTRUCTURE INVESTORS LLC p 570
1345 Ave Of The Americas 10105
Tel (212) 798-6100 *SIC* 4789

FOUNDERS EQUITY INC p 571
711 5th Ave Ste 501 10022
Tel (212) 829-0900 *SIC* 6211

FOWNES BROTHERS & CO INC p 572
16 E 34th St Fl 5 10016
Tel (212) 683-0150
SIC 3151 2381 5136 5137 3949

■ FOX BUSINESS NETWORK p 572
1211 Avenue Of The 10036
Tel (212) 601-7000 *SIC* 7389

■ FOX ENTERTAINMENT GROUP INC p 572
1211 Ave Of The Americas 10036
Tel (212) 852-7000 *SIC* 7812 4841

■ FOX NEWS NETWORK LLC p 572
1211 Avenue Of The Americ 10036
Tel (212) 301-3000 *SIC* 7812

FRAGOMEN DEL REY BERNSEN & LOEWY LLP p 573
7 Hanover Sq Ste 800 10004
Tel (732) 862-5000 *SIC* 8111

FREE COUNTRY LTD p 576
1071 6th Ave Fl 9 10018
Tel (212) 719-4596 *SIC* 5136 5137

FRENKEL BENEFITS LLC p 578
350 Hudson St Fl 4 10014
Tel (212) 488-0200 *SIC* 6411

FRIED FRANK HARRIS SHRIVER & JACOBSON LLP p 579
1 New York Plz Fl 27 10004
Tel (212) 859-8000 *SIC* 8111

■ FRONTIER CALIFORNIA INC p 581
140 West St 10007
Tel (212) 395-1000
SIC 4813 6519 8721 5065 1731 7629

FUEL SYSTEMS SOLUTIONS INC p 583
780 3rd Ave Fl 25 10017
Tel (646) 502-7170 *SIC* 3714 3592 7363

FULLBEAUTY BRANDS INC p 584
1 New York Plz Fl 13 10004
Tel (212) 613-9500 *SIC* 5961 7389 5611

FULLBEAUTY BRANDS LP p 584
1 New York Plz Fl 13 10004
Tel (212) 613-9500 *SIC* 5961

▲ FUSION TELECOMMUNICATIONS INTERNATIONAL INC p 585
420 Lexington Ave Rm 1718 10170
Tel (212) 201-2400 *SIC* 7372 4813

FX ALLIANCE INC p 586
3 Times Sq 10036
Tel (646) 268-9900 *SIC* 6231 6211

▲ FXCM INC p 586
55 Water St Fl 50 10041
Tel (646) 432-2986 *SIC* 6211 6099

FXDIRECTDEALER LLC p 586
7 World Trade Ctr 32nd 10007
Tel (212) 266-0700 *SIC* 6099

▲ G-III APPAREL GROUP LTD p 588
512 7th Ave Fl 35 10018
Tel (212) 403-0500
SIC 2337 2339 2311 2329 2386 5136

■ G-III LEATHER FASHIONS INC p 588
512 Fashion Ave Fl 35 10018
Tel (212) 403-0500 *SIC* 5199

GAMECHANGE SOLAR LLC p 590
152 W 57th St Fl 17 10019
Tel (212) 359-0200 *SIC* 5074

GARAGE MANAGEMENT CO LLC p 591
770 Lexington Ave Rm 1102 10065
Tel (212) 888-7400 *SIC* 5511

■ GARAN INC p 591
200 Madison Ave Fl 4 10016
Tel (212) 563-1292
SIC 2361 2369 2331 2339 2321

GARRISON INVESTMENT GROUP LP p 592
1290 Avenue Of The Americ 10104
Tel (212) 372-9500 *SIC* 6282

GBG ACCESSORIES GROUP LLC p 594
350 5th Ave Lbby 9 10118
Tel (646) 839-7000 *SIC* 5137

GBG USA INC p 594
350 5th Ave Lbby 9 10118
Tel (646) 839-7083 *SIC* 5139 5137 5136

GBG WEST LLC p 594
350 5th Ave Fl 5 10118
Tel (646) 839-7000 *SIC* 2339

GCE INTERNATIONAL INC p 595
1385 Broadway Fl 21 10018
Tel (212) 704-4800
SIC 2253 2389 2331 5137 5136

GELLER & CO LLC p 598
909 3rd Ave Fl 15 10022
Tel (212) 583-6000 *SIC* 8742 8721

▲ GENCO SHIPPING & TRADING LTD p 598
299 Park Ave Rm 1200 10171
Tel (646) 443-8550 *SIC* 4412

GENER8 MARITIME INC p 599
299 Park Ave Fl 2 10171
Tel (212) 763-5600 *SIC* 4412

GENERAL ATLANTIC SERVICE CO LLC p 599
55 E 52nd St Fl 32 10055
Tel (203) 629-8600 *SIC* 8742

GENESIS CORP p 602
950 3rd Ave Ste 2702 10022
Tel (212) 688-5522 *SIC* 7379 8742

GENISYS SOFTWARE LTD p 604
1345 Ave Of The Americas 10105
Tel (732) 635-7132 *SIC* 7371 7372 5734

GENNX360 CAPITAL PARTNERS LP p 604
590 Madison Ave Fl 27 10022
Tel (212) 257-6772 *SIC* 6282

GENPACT LIMITED p 604
1155 Avenue Of The Americ 10036
Tel (212) 896-6600 *SIC* 8741 7372

GEORGE G SHARP INC p 606
160 Broadway 10038
Tel (212) 732-2800 *SIC* 3731 4225 8712

GEORGE WASHINGTON CARVER ACADEMY p 606
45 Broadway Fl 17 10006
Tel (404) 841-2305 *SIC* 8299

GERSON LEHRMAN GROUP INC p 609
60 E 42nd St Fl 3 10165
Tel (212) 223-0839 *SIC* 6282

GF INVESTORS LLC p 609
60 E 42nd St Rm 4510 10165
Tel (212) 457-1138 *SIC* 1742

■ GFI GROUP INC p 610
55 Water St 10041
Tel (212) 968-4100 *SIC* 6211

GFI MANAGEMENT SERVICES INC p 610
50 Brdwy 140 Brdwy 41 10004
Tel (212) 668-1444 *SIC* 6513 6512

GFK CUSTOM RESEARCH LLC p 610
200 Liberty St Fl 4 10281
Tel (212) 240-5300 *SIC* 8732

■ GH BASS & CO p 610
200 Madison Ave 10016
Tel (212) 381-3900
SIC 3144 3143 3149 5661

GILBERT GLOBAL EQUITY CAPITAL LLC p 612
767 5th Ave Fl 15 10153
Tel (212) 584-6200 *SIC* 8741

GILDAN APPAREL USA INC p 612
48 W 38th St Fl 8 10018
Tel (212) 476-0341 *SIC* 2253 2331

GILT GROUPE HOLDINGS INC p 612
2 Park Ave Fl 4 10016
Tel (877) 445-8692 *SIC* 5611

GILT GROUPE INC p 612
250 Vesey St Fl 21 10281
Tel (877) 280-0545 *SIC* 5961

GIORGIO ARMANI CORP p 612
450 W 15th St 3 10011
Tel (212) 209-3500
SIC 5136 5137 5122 5611 5621 5632

GIRL SCOUTS OF UNITED STATES OF AMERICA p 613
420 5th Ave Fl 13 10018
Tel (212) 852-8000
SIC 8641 5137 6794 2721

GLOBAL BRANDS HOLDING GROUP LLC p 615
350 5th Ave 10118
Tel (646) 839-7000 *SIC* 5136 5137 5139

GLOBAL CAPITAL RESOURCES GROUP LLC p 616
1201 Broadway Ste 608 10001
Tel (646) 221-1898 *SIC* 6722

GLOBAL DATA PUBLICATIONS INC p 616
441 Lexington Ave Fl 3 10017
Tel (646) 395-5460 *SIC* 7379 8732 8748

GLOBAL REINSURANCE CORP OF AMERICA p 617
125 Broad St Lbby 5 10004
Tel (212) 754-7500 *SIC* 6321

GMA ACCESSORIES INC p 618
1 E 33rd St Fl 9 10016
Tel (212) 684-3344 *SIC* 5137 5139

GMACCH INVESTOR LLC p 619
9 W 57th St 10019
Tel (212) 750-8300 *SIC* 6799

GODIVA CHOCOLATIER INC p 619
333 W 34th St Fl 6 10001
Tel (212) 984-5900
SIC 2066 5149 5441 2064

GOLDBERG LINDSAY & CO LLC p 620
630 5th Ave Fl 30 10111
Tel (212) 651-1100 *SIC* 6799 8711 8712

■ GOLDMAN SACHS & CO p 622
200 West St Bldg 200 10282
Tel (212) 346-5440
SIC 6211 6221 6282 6153

■ GOLDMAN SACHS (ASIA) LLC p 622
200 West St Bldg 200 10282
Tel (212) 902-1000 *SIC* 6211 6282 6722

■ GOLDMAN SACHS BANK USA p 622
200 West St 10282
Tel (212) 902-1000 *SIC* 6022

■ GOLDMAN SACHS BANK USA HOLDINGS LLC p 622
200 West St Bldg 200 10282
Tel (212) 357-2882 *SIC* 6029

■ GOLDMAN SACHS BDC INC p 622
200 West St Bldg 200 10282
Tel (212) 902-1000 *SIC* 6726

GOLDMAN SACHS CHARITABLE GIFT FUND p 622
200 West St Fl 29 10282
Tel (212) 902-4223 *SIC* 5947

GOLDMAN SACHS FOUNDATION p 622
375 Park Ave Ste 1002 10152
Tel (212) 902-6875 *SIC* 8748

▲ GOLDMAN SACHS GROUP INC p 622
200 West St Bldg 200 10282
Tel (212) 902-1000 *SIC* 6211 6282

GOOD SHEPHERD SERVICES p 623
305 7th Ave Fl 9 10001
Tel (212) 243-7070 *SIC* 8322

GOODE PARTNERS LLC p 624
767 3rd Ave Fl 22 10017
Tel (646) 722-9450 *SIC* 6282

GOULD PAPER CORP p 626
99 Park Ave Fl 10 10016
Tel (212) 301-0000 *SIC* 5113 5111 3523

GOULD PAPER CORP p 626
99 Park Ave Fl 10 10016
Tel (212) 301-0000 *SIC* 5111 2759

GOVERNORS ISLAND CORP p 627
10 South St Frnt Slip7 10004
Tel (212) 440-2200 *SIC* 6733

GRACE HOLMES INC p 628
770 Broadway Fl 11 10003
Tel (212) 209-2500 *SIC* 5611 5621

GRACE I W2007 LLC p 628
85 Broad St Fl 15 10004
Tel (212) 902-1000 *SIC* 7011

GRAMERCY PROPERTY TRUST p 629
521 5th Ave Fl 30 10175
Tel (212) 297-1000 *SIC* 6798

GRAMERCY PROPERTY TRUST INC p 629
521 5th Ave Fl 30 10175
Tel (212) 297-1000 *SIC* 6798

■ GRAND SLAM HOLDINGS LLC p 630
345 Park Ave Bsmt Lb4 10154
Tel (212) 583-5000 *SIC* 3842

GREATER NEW YORK MUTUAL INSURANCE CO p 635
200 Madison Ave Frnt 2 10016
Tel (212) 683-9700 *SIC* 6411

GREEN LIGHT CAPITAL INC p 637
140 E 45th St Fl 24 10017
Tel (212) 922-9370 *SIC* 6726

GREENBERG TRAURIG LLP p 637
200 Park Ave Fl 39 10166
Tel (212) 801-9200 *SIC* 8111

▲ GREENHILL & CO INC p 638
300 Park Ave Fl 23 10022
Tel (212) 389-1500 *SIC* 6211

GREENWICH VILLAGE FISH CO INC p 639
2135 Broadway 10023
Tel (631) 324-9190 *SIC* 5146

GREY GLOBAL GROUP LLC p 639
200 5th Ave Bsmt B 10010
Tel (212) 546-2000 *SIC* 7311

▲ GRIFFON CORP p 640
712 5th Ave Fl 18 10019
Tel (212) 957-5000
SIC 3442 2431 1751 1799 3083 3663

GRISTEDES FOODS INC p 641
800 3rd Ave Fl 5 10022
Tel (212) 956-5770 *SIC* 5411

GROUP HEALTH INC p 641
441 9th Ave Frnt 10001
Tel (212) 615-0000 *SIC* 6324

GROUP M WORLDWIDE LLC p 642
498 7th Ave 10018
Tel (212) 297-7000 *SIC* 7319

GRUNER + JAHR USA GROUP INC p 642
1745 Broadway Fl 16 10019
Tel (866) 323-9336 *SIC* 2721 2754

■ GSO CAPITAL PARTNERS LP p 643
345 Park Ave Ste 1100 10154
Tel (212) 583-5000 *SIC* 6722 7389

■ GTE CORP p 644
140 West St 10007
Tel (212) 395-1000
SIC 4813 4812 3661 3663 4899 2741

GUARDIAN INSURANCE & ANNUITY CO INC p 645
7 Hanover Sq 10004
Tel (212) 598-8000 *SIC* 6311 6371

GUARDIAN LIFE INSURANCE CO OF AMERICA p 645
7 Hanover Sq Fl 14 10004
Tel (212) 598-8000
SIC 6311 6371 6324 6321 6722 6282

GUARDIAN SERVICE INDUSTRIES INC p 645
161 Ave Of The Amer 10013
Tel (212) 645-9500 *SIC* 7349

GUCCI AMERICA INC p 645
195 Broadway Fl 12 10007
Tel (212) 750-5220
SIC 5632 5948 5661 5611 5621 5137

GUGGENHEIM PARTNERS LLC p 645
330 Madison Ave Rm 201 10017
Tel (212) 739-0700 *SIC* 8742

GUILDNET INC p 646
15 W 65th St 10023
Tel (212) 769-6200 *SIC* 8011

■ GUY CARPENTER & CO LLC p 648
1166 Ave Of The Americas 10036
Tel (917) 937-3000 *SIC* 6411 8742 8732

H & M HENNES & MAURITZ LP p 649
110 5th Ave Fl 11 10011
Tel (212) 564-9922 *SIC* 5651

HACHETTE BOOK GROUP INC p 652
1290 Ave Of The Americas 10104
Tel (800) 759-0190 *SIC* 2731 5192

HACHETTE DISTRIBUTION INC p 652
60 E 42nd St Ste 1940 10165
Tel (212) 477-7373 *SIC* 5192 5994 5947

HADASSAH MEDICAL RELIEF ASSOCIATION INC p 652
40 Wall St 10005
Tel (212) 355-7900 *SIC* 8322

HAIGHTS CROSS COMMUNICATIONS INC p 653
136 Madison Ave Fl 8 10016
Tel (212) 209-0500 *SIC* 2731

HAKS ENGINEERS ARCHITECTS AND LAND SURVEYORS PC p 653
40 Wall St Fl 11 10005
Tel (212) 747-1997 *SIC* 8712 8711 8713

HAMMOND KENNEDY WHITNEY & CO INC p 656
420 Lexington Ave Rm 402 10170
Tel (212) 867-1010 *SIC* 7389

HANKY PANKY LTD p 658
373 Park Ave S Fl 12 10016
Tel (212) 725-4996 *SIC* 5137

HANRAHANMEYERS ARCHITECTS LLP p 658
6 Maiden Ln Rm 510 10038
Tel (212) 989-6026 *SIC* 8712

■ HARBINGER OM LLC p 659
450 Park Ave Fl 27 10022
Tel (212) 906-8555 *SIC* 6726

HARLAN CASTLE INC p 661
150 E 58th St Fl 38 10155
Tel (212) 644-8600 *SIC* 6726

HARLEM CHILDRENS ZONE INC p 661
35 E 125th St 10035
Tel (212) 534-0700 *SIC* 8299

HARLEM HOSPITAL CENTER p 661
506 Malcolm X Blvd 10037
Tel (212) 939-1000 *SIC* 8062

■ HARPERCOLLINS PUBLISHERS LLC p 663
195 Broadway Fl 2 10007
Tel (212) 207-7000 *SIC* 5942 2731

HARTREE PARTNERS LP p 666
1185 Avenue Of The Americ 10036
Tel (212) 536-8915 *SIC* 6221 5172

HARTZ GROUP INC p 666
667 Madison Ave Fl 24 10065
Tel (212) 308-3336
SIC 6512 6552 6531 6159

HARVEST PARTNERS LP p 666
280 Park Ave Fl 25w 10017
Tel (212) 599-6300 *SIC* 6799 7349

HAVAS HEALTH INC p 668
200 Madison Ave 10016
Tel (212) 532-1000 *SIC* 7311

HAVAS NORTH AMERICA INC p 668
200 Hudson St 10013
Tel (212) 886-2000 *SIC* 7311 5963

HAZEN AND SAWYER DPC p 671
498 Fashion Ave Fl 11 10018
Tel (212) 539-7000 *SIC* 8711

■ HBO SERVICES INC p 671
1100 Ave Of The Am Frnt 3 10036
Tel (212) 512-1000 *SIC* 7822

▲ HC2 HOLDINGS INC p 671
450 Park Ave Fl 30 10022
Tel (212) 235-2690 *SIC* 4813 3325 8731

HDS RETAIL NORTH AMERICA LP p 673
60 E 42nd St Rm 3410 10165
Tel (212) 477-7373 *SIC* 5994

■ HEALTH PLUS PREPAID HEALTH SERVICES PLAN INC p 675
9 Pine St Fl 14 10005
Tel (718) 532-1011 *SIC* 6321 6324 8741

HEALTHCARE TRUST INC p 676
405 Park Ave Fl 15 10022
Tel (215) 449-3638 *SIC* 6798

HEALTHFIRST HEALTH PLAN OF NEW JERSEY INC p 677
25 Broadway Fl 9 10004
Tel (212) 801-6000 *SIC* 6321

HEALTHFIRST PHSP INC p 677
100 Church St Fl 17 10007
Tel (212) 801-6000 *SIC* 6321

HEARST CORP p 678
300 W 57th St Fl 42 10019
Tel (212) 649-2000
SIC 2721 2731 2711 4832 4833 7383

HEARST HOLDINGS INC p 678
300 W 57th St 10019
Tel (212) 649-2000 *SIC* 2721 4841

HEARST TELEVISION INC p 678
300 W 57th St 10019
Tel (212) 887-6800 *SIC* 4833

HEINZEL IMPORT & EXPORT INC p 681
220 E 42nd St Rm 3010 10017
Tel (212) 953-3200 *SIC* 5111

HELMSLEY ENTERPRISES INC p 682
230 Park Ave Rm 659 10169
Tel (212) 679-3600 *SIC* 6513 8742 1522

HELMSLEY-NOYES CO LLC p 682
230 Park Ave Rm 659 10169
Tel (212) 679-6772 *SIC* 6531

HELP USA INC p 682
115 E 13th St 10003
Tel (212) 400-7000 SIC 6513 8322
HELP USA INC AND AFFILIATES p 682
115 E 13th St 10003
Tel (212) 400-7000 SIC 8322
HENRY MODELL & CO INC p 684
498 7th Ave Fl 20 10018
Tel (212) 822-1000
SIC 5941 5661 5611 5621 5641 5961
HERAEUS METALS NEW YORK LLC p 685
540 Madison Ave 10022
Tel (212) 752-2181 SIC 5094
▲ HESS CORP p 688
1185 Ave Of The Americas 10036
Tel (212) 997-8500
SIC 1311 2911 5171 5541 4911
■ HESS OIL VIRGIN ISLAND CORP p 688
1185 Ave Of The Amer 39 10036
Tel (212) 997-8500 SIC 2911
■ HESS TRADING CORP p 688
1185 Ave Of The Americas 10036
Tel (212) 997-8500 SIC 5199
HF MANAGEMENT SERVICES LLC p 688
100 Church St Fl 18 10007
Tel (212) 801-6000 SIC 8741
■ HFC PRESTIGE INTERNATIONAL US LLC p 689
350 5th Ave 10118
Tel (212) 389-7800
SIC 2844 2676 3421 2842 2841
HH LIQUIDATING CORP p 689
110 E 59th St Fl 34 10022
Tel (646) 282-2500
SIC 3624 2999 3356 3339
HHC FOUNDATION OF NEW YORK CITY INC p 689
160 Water St Fl 10 10038
Tel (646) 458-2810 SIC 6321
■ HIGHBRIDGE CAPITAL MANAGEMENT LLC p 691
40 W 57th St Fl 33 10019
Tel (212) 287-5496 SIC 6211
HIGHCREST INVESTORS LLC p 691
Icahn Associates Corp 767 10153
Tel (212) 702-4323
SIC 3743 4741 4789 4813
HILL AND KNOWLTON STRATEGIES LLC p 693
466 Lexington Ave Frnt 4 10017
Tel (212) 885-0300 SIC 8743 8748
HILTON HOTELS HOLDINGS CORP p 695
345 Park Ave 10154
Tel (212) 583-5000 SIC 7011 6794
■ HILTON NEW YORK p 695
1335 Ave Of The Americas 10019
Tel (212) 586-7000 SIC 6512
HIS INTERNATIONAL CORP p 696
34 W 33rd St Fl 2 10001
Tel (212) 594-4250 SIC 5137
HIS INTERNATIONAL GROUP LLC p 696
34 W 33rd St Fl 2 10001
Tel (212) 967-3990 SIC 5136
HISCOX INC p 696
520 Madison Ave Rm 3200 10022
Tel (914) 273-7400 SIC 6411
■ HISTORIC TW INC p 696
75 Rockefeller Plz 10019
Tel (212) 484-8000
SIC 3652 6794 2741 7812 4841 2721
HK DESIGNS INC p 697
535 5th Ave Fl 18 10017
Tel (212) 201-0755 SIC 5094
HKI SUPPORT INC p 697
352 Park Ave S 10010
Tel (212) 532-0544 SIC 8699
HMAN INTERMEDIATE HOLDINGS CORP p 697
245 Park Ave Fl 16 10167
Tel (513) 851-4900 SIC 6719 5072 7699
HMX LLC p 698
125 Park Ave Fl 7 10017
Tel (212) 682-9073 SIC 2211
HOCHTIEF USA INC p 699
375 Hudson St Fl 6 10014
Tel (212) 229-6000
SIC 1542 1541 1522 8741 8742 6799
HOLTZBRINCK PUBLISHERS LLC p 702
175 5th Ave 10010
Tel (646) 307-5151 SIC 2731
■ HOME BOX OFFICE INC p 703
1100 Avenue Of The Americ 10036
Tel (212) 512-1000 SIC 4841 7812
HORIZON MEDIA INC p 707
75 Varick St Ste 1404 10013
Tel (212) 220-5000 SIC 7319
HOSPITAL FOR SPECIALTY SURGERY p 709
535 E 70th St Fl 6 10021
Tel (212) 606-1469 SIC 8011 8062
▲ HRG GROUP INC p 714
450 Park Ave Fl 29 10022
Tel (212) 906-8555
SIC 3691 3634 3999 6311
HUB INTERNATIONAL GROUP NORTHEAST INC p 716
5 Bryant Park Fl 4 10018
Tel (212) 338-2000 SIC 6411
▲ HUDSON GLOBAL INC p 716
1325 Avenue Of The Americ 10019
Tel (212) 351-7300 SIC 7361 7363
HUDSON HOTEL BAR p 716
356 W 58th St 10019
Tel (212) 554-6000 SIC 7011
HUDSON INSURANCE CO p 716
100 William St Fl 5 10038
Tel (212) 978-2800 SIC 6311
HUDSON LEASECO LLC p 716
356 W 58th St 10019
Tel (212) 247-2353 SIC 6719
HUGHES HUBBARD & REED LLP p 717
1 Battery Park 10004
Tel (212) 837-6000 SIC 8111
HUGO BOSS USA INC p 717
55 Water St Fl 48 10041
Tel (212) 940-0600
SIC 2311 2325 2337 5136 5611 6794
HUMANSCALE CORP p 718
11 E 26th St Fl 8 10010
Tel (212) 725-4749 SIC 3577 2521
HUNTER ROBERTS CONSTRUCTION GROUP LLC p 719
55 Water St Fl 51 10041
Tel (212) 321-6800 SIC 8742 1542
HVB AMERICA INC p 722
150 E 42nd St Fl 29 10017
Tel (212) 672-6000 SIC 6082
▲ IAC/INTERACTIVECORP p 725
555 W 18th St 10011
Tel (212) 314-7300 SIC 7372 7375 5961
IATSE NATIONAL HEALTH AND WELFARE FUND p 726
55 W 39th St Fl 5 10018
Tel (212) 580-9092 SIC 8011
■ ICAHN ENTERPRISES HOLDINGS LP p 726
767 5th Ave Fl 17 10153
Tel (212) 702-4300
SIC 6512 5719 6211 5093
▲ ICAHN ENTERPRISES LP p 726
767 5th Ave Ste 4700 10153
Tel (212) 702-4300
SIC 6722 3714 7999 3743 5093 6531
ICAHN SCHOOL OF MEDICINE AT MOUNT SINAI p 726
1 Gustave L Levy Pl 10029
Tel (212) 241-6500 SIC 8249
ICC CHEMICAL CORP p 727
460 Park Ave Fl 7 10022
Tel (212) 521-1700 SIC 5169 5122 5162
ICC INDUSTRIES INC p 727
460 Park Ave Fl 7 10022
Tel (212) 521-1700
SIC 2821 2869 2911 2899 3081 2834
▲ ICONIX BRAND GROUP INC p 728
1450 Broadway Fl 3 10018
Tel (212) 730-0030 SIC 6794 3143 3144
ICROSSING INC p 728
300 W 57th St Fl 20f 10019
Tel (212) 649-3900 SIC 8742 7311
ICV PARTNERS p 728
810 7th Ave Ste 3501 10019
Tel (212) 455-9600 SIC 6282 6211
IDEA NUOVA INC p 729
302 5th Ave Fl 5 10001
Tel (212) 643-0680 SIC 5021
■ IEH FM HOLDINGS LLC p 730
767 5th Ave Ste 4700 10153
Tel (212) 702-4300
SIC 3462 3559 3694 3812 3674
IFM GLOBAL INFRASTRUCTURE FUND p 730
114 W 47th St Fl 26 10036
Tel (212) 784-2260 SIC 6799 1623
IGNITIONONE INC p 730
200 Park Ave Fl 27 10166
Tel (888) 744-6483 SIC 7319
IHI INC p 731
150 E 52nd St Fl 24 10022
Tel (212) 599-8100
SIC 5099 8732 8711 5084
■ IHP I OWNER JV LLC p 731
399 Park Ave 10022
Tel (212) 547-2640 SIC 8741
INCEPTION PARENT INC p 735
9 W 57th St Fl 43 10019
Tel (212) 515-3200 SIC 6726
INDEPENDENCE CARE SYSTEMS INC p 736
257 Park Ave S Fl 2 10010
Tel (212) 584-2500 SIC 8322 6324
INFOR INC p 741
641 Ave Of The Americas # 4 10011
Tel (646) 336-1700 SIC 7371 7372
INFOR LUX BOND CO p 741
641 Ave Of The Americas 10011
Tel (646) 336-1700 SIC 7371 7372 8748
INFORMATION BUILDERS INC p 741
2 Penn Plz Fl 28 10121
Tel (212) 736-4433 SIC 7373 6794
■ INSIGHT COMMUNICATIONS CO INC p 746
810 7th Ave 10019
Tel (917) 286-2300 SIC 4841 4813
INSIGHT COMMUNICATIONS OF KENTUCKY LP p 746
810 7th Ave Fl 28 10019
Tel (917) 286-2300 SIC 4841
■ INSIGHT MIDWEST LP p 746
810 7th Ave Fl 28 10019
Tel (917) 286-2300 SIC 4841
INSTINET CORP p 747
1095 Avenue Of The 10036
Tel (212) 310-9500 SIC 6211 7379
INSTINET GROUP LLC p 747
Worldwide Plz 309 W 49th 10019
Tel (212) 310-9500 SIC 6231
INSTITUTE FOR COMMUNITY LIVING INC p 747
125 Broad St 10004
Tel (212) 385-3030 SIC 8052
INSTITUTE FOR FAMILY HEALTH p 747
2006 Madison Ave 10035
Tel (212) 633-0800 SIC 8011
INSTITUTE OF ELECTRICAL AND ELECTRONICS ENGINEERS INC p 747
3 Park Ave Fl 17 10016
Tel (212) 419-7900 SIC 8621
INSTITUTE OF INTERNATIONAL EDUCATION INC p 747
809 United Nations Plz 10017
Tel (212) 883-8200 SIC 8299
INSURANCE FUND NEW YORK STATE p 748
199 Church St Fl 13 10007
Tel (212) 587-7390 SIC 9199
INTEGRO LTD p 750
1 State St Fl 9 10004
Tel (212) 295-8000 SIC 6411
INTEGRO USA INC p 750
1 State St Fl 9 10004
Tel (212) 295-8000 SIC 6411
INTELLIRISK MANAGEMENT CORP p 750
335 Madison Ave Fl 27 10017
Tel (646) 274-3030 SIC 7322
▲ INTER PARFUMS INC p 751
551 5th Ave 10176
Tel (212) 983-2640 SIC 2844
■ INTERBRAND CORP p 751
130 5th Ave Fl 4 10011
Tel (212) 798-7500 SIC 8742 7336
■ INTERFINANCIAL INC p 752
28 Liberty St Fl 41 10005
Tel (212) 859-7000 SIC 6719
INTERNATIONAL CENTRE FOR DISPUTE RESOLUTION p 754
120 Brdwy Fl 21 10271
Tel (212) 484-4181 SIC 7389
INTERNATIONAL COSMETICS & PERFUMES p 755
30 W 21st St Fl 7 10010
Tel (212) 643-0011 SIC 5122
▲ INTERNATIONAL FLAVORS & FRAGRANCES INC p 755
521 W 57th St 10019
Tel (212) 765-5500 SIC 2869 2844 2087
INTERNATIONAL HOTEL MANAGEMENT SERVICES INC p 755
2 E 61st St 10065
Tel (212) 838-8000 SIC 7011
INTERNATIONAL RESCUE COMMITTEE INC p 756
122 E 42nd St Fl 12 10168
Tel (212) 551-3000 SIC 8322
■ INTERNATIONAL SECURITIES EXCHANGE HOLDINGS INC p 756
60 Broad St Fl 26 10004
Tel (212) 943-2400 SIC 6231
INTERNATIONAL SECURITIES EXCHANGE LLC p 756
60 Broad St Fl 26 10004
Tel (212) 943-2400 SIC 6231
▲ INTERPUBLIC GROUP OF COMPANIES INC p 757
909 3rd Ave Fl 7 10022
Tel (212) 704-1200 SIC 7311 8742
INTERSECTION MEDIA HOLDINGS INC p 757
10 Hudson Yards Fl 26 10001
Tel (212) 644-6200 SIC 7312 6719
▲ INTL FCSTONE INC p 759
708 3rd Ave Rm 1500 10017
Tel (212) 485-3500 SIC 6282 6211 6289
▲ INTRALINKS HOLDINGS INC p 760
150 E 42nd St Fl 8 10017
Tel (212) 543-7700 SIC 7372 7382
■ INTRALINKS INC p 760
150 E 42nd St Fl 8 10017
Tel (212) 543-7700 SIC 4899 7375
INVESTCORP INTERNATIONAL HOLDINGS INC p 761
280 Park Ave Fl 36 10017
Tel (212) 599-4700 SIC 6282
INVESTCORP INTERNATIONAL INC p 761
280 Park Ave Fl 36 10017
Tel (212) 599-4700 SIC 6531
INVESTCORP SERVICES INC p 761
280 Park Ave Fl 36 10017
Tel (212) 599-4700 SIC 6282
▲ INVESTMENT TECHNOLOGY GROUP INC p 761
165 Broadway 10006
Tel (212) 588-4000 SIC 6211
INVIVA INC p 762
434 Hudson St Apt 2 10014
Tel (212) 741-9322 SIC 6411
IPC/RAZOR LLC p 763
277 Park Ave Fl 39 10172
Tel (212) 551-4500 SIC 3541
IPREO HOLDINGS LLC p 763
1359 Broadway Fl 2 10018
Tel (212) 849-5000 SIC 8748
IPREO LLC p 763
1359 Broadway Fl 2 10018
Tel (212) 849-5000 SIC 8748
IPSOFT INC p 764
17 State St Fl 14 10004
Tel (888) 477-6388
SIC 7376 7363 7374 8742
IPSOS AMERICA INC p 764
1271 Ave Of The 10020
Tel (212) 265-3200 SIC 8742
IQOR HOLDINGS INC p 764
1 Progress Plz 10017
Tel (866) 657-2057 SIC 7374
IRON WORK 40 361 & 417 HLTH FND p 765
451 Park Ave S 10016
Tel (212) 684-1586 SIC 1791
IRONSHORE SERVICES INC p 765
1 State St Fl 8 10004
Tel (646) 826-6600 SIC 6411
IRVING PLACE CAPITAL LLC p 765
745 5th Ave Fl 7 10151
Tel (212) 551-4500 SIC 5999 5099
ISABELLA GERIATRIC CENTER INC p 766
515 Audubon Ave 10040
Tel (212) 342-9200 SIC 8051
ISRAEL BIRTHRIGHT FOUNDATION p 767
33 E 33rd St Fl 7 10016
Tel (212) 457-0036 SIC 8641
ISRAEL DISCOUNT BANK OF NEW YORK p 767
511 5th Ave 10017
Tel (212) 551-8500 SIC 6022
▲ ISTAR INC p 767
1114 Ave Of The Americas 10036
Tel (212) 930-9400 SIC 6798
■ ITG INC p 768
1 Liberty Plz Fl 4 10006
Tel (212) 588-4000 SIC 6211
ITHAKA HARBORS INC p 768
2 Rector St Fl 18 10006
Tel (212) 500-2600 SIC 7379
ITOCHU INTERNATIONAL INC p 768
1251 Avenue Of The Americ 10020
Tel (212) 818-8000
SIC 5131 5084 5065 5051 5153 5141
ITOCHU PROMINENT USA LLC p 768
1411 Broadway Fl 7 10018
Tel (212) 827-5707 SIC 5199
ITRIA LLC p 768
333 7th Ave Fl 18 10001
Tel (212) 644-4555 SIC 6531
J CREW INC p 770
770 Broadway Fl 14 10003
Tel (212) 209-8010 SIC 5961 5621 5611
J CREW OPERATING CORP p 770
770 Brdwy Fl 11 & 12 10003
Tel (212) 209-2500
SIC 5961 5621 5611 5661 5632 6794
■ J P MORGAN ASSET MANAGEMENT INC p 772
270 Park Ave Fl 12 10017
Tel (212) 270-6000 SIC 6211 6282
J P MORGAN CHASE FOUNDATION p 772
270 Park Ave Fl 6 10017
Tel (212) 270-6000 SIC 8699
J WALTER THOMPSON CO LLC p 772
466 Lexington Ave Ste 6r 10017
Tel (212) 210-7000 SIC 7311
J WALTER THOMPSON USA LLC p 772
466 Lexington Ave Ste 6r 10017
Tel (212) 210-7000 SIC 7311
■ JA HOLDING INC p 773
650 5th Ave Fl 20 10019
Tel (212) 586-9140 SIC 5136
JACHS NY LLC p 773
359 Broadway Fl 3 10013
Tel (212) 334-4380 SIC 5136
JACKTHREADS INC p 774
568 Broadway Rm 607 10012
Tel (646) 786-1980 SIC 5136
JACMEL JEWELRY INC p 775
1385 Broadway Fl 8 10018
Tel (718) 349-4300 SIC 3911
JACQUES MORET INC p 775
1411 Broadway Fl 8 10018
Tel (212) 354-2400 SIC 2339 5137
JANE STREET GROUP LLC p 777
250 Vesey St 10281
Tel (646) 759-6000 SIC 6211
JASPER PARENT LLC p 778
9 W 57th St Ste 3100 10019
Tel (212) 796-8500 SIC 6211
JAY FRANCO & SONS INC p 779
295 5th Ave Ste 312 10016
Tel (212) 679-3022 SIC 5023 2211

JCREW GROUP INC p 780
770 Broadway Fl 11 10003
Tel (212) 209-2500
SIC 5961 5621 5611 5632

JDRF INTERNATIONAL p 781
26 Broadway 10004
Tel (212) 785-9500 SIC 8399 8733

JEANJER LLC p 781
1400 Broadway Fl 15 10018
Tel (212) 944-1330
SIC 2331 2337 2339 2369

■ JEFFERIES GROUP LLC p 781
520 Madison Ave 10022
Tel (212) 284-2550 SIC 6211

■ JEFFERIES LLC p 781
520 Madison Ave Fl 10 10022
Tel (212) 284-2300 SIC 6211

JEWISH AGENCY FOR ISRAEL INC p 784
111 8th Ave Fl 11 10011
Tel (212) 284-6900 SIC 8399

JEWISH BOARD OF FAMILY AND CHILDRENS SERVICES INC p 784
135 W 50th St Fl 6 10020
Tel (212) 582-9100 SIC 8361 8322

JEWISH COMMUNAL FUND p 784
575 Madison Ave Ste 703 10022
Tel (212) 752-8277 SIC 6732

JEWISH FEDERATIONS OF NORTH AMERICA INC p 784
25 Broadway Fl 17 10004
Tel (212) 284-6500 SIC 8399

JEWISH HOME LIFECARE HARRY AND JEANETTE WEINBERG CAMPUS BRONX p 784
120 W 106th St 10025
Tel (212) 870-5000 SIC 8051

JEWISH HOME LIFECARE MANHATTAN p 784
120 W 106th St 10025
Tel (212) 870-5000 SIC 8361 7521

JF LEHMAN & CO INC p 785
110 E 59th St Fl 27 10022
Tel (212) 634-0100 SIC 6722

JIMLAR CORP p 785
350 5th Ave Lbby 8 10118
Tel (212) 475-0787 SIC 5139

JLL PARTNERS FUND IV LP p 786
450 Lexington Ave Fl 31 10017
Tel (212) 286-8600 SIC 6722

JLL PARTNERS INC p 786
450 Lexington Ave Fl 31 10017
Tel (212) 286-8600 SIC 6799 6099

JOBSON MEDICAL INFORMATION LLC p 787
440 9th Ave Fl 14 10001
Tel (212) 274-7000 SIC 2721 2741

JOHN GORE ORGANIZATION INC p 788
1619 Broadway Fl 9 10019
Tel (917) 421-5400 SIC 7922

JOHN VARVATOS ENTERPRISES INC p 789
26 W 17th St Fl 12 10011
Tel (212) 812-8000 SIC 5136

JONATHAN ADLER ENTERPRISES LLC p 792
333 Hudson St Fl 7 10013
Tel (212) 645-2802 SIC 5023

JONES GROUP INC p 792
1411 Broadway Fl 15 10018
Tel (212) 642-3860
SIC 5632 5137 5139 5661 5641

JONES HOLDINGS LLC p 792
1411 Brdwy 10018
Tel (215) 785-4000 SIC 5137

JORDACHE ENTERPRISES INC p 793
1400 Broadway Rm 1404b 10018
Tel (212) 643-8400
SIC 2339 2325 2369 2331 2321 2361

JORDACHE LIMITED p 793
1400 Broadway Rm 1404b 10018
Tel (212) 944-1330 SIC 5137 5136 6153

JORDAN CO L P p 793
399 Park Ave Fl 30 10022-
Tel (212) 572-0800 SIC 6726

■ JOTALY INC p 794
1385 Broadway Fl 12 10018
Tel (212) 886-6000 SIC 3911

JOURNAL REGISTER CO p 794
5 Hanover Sq Fl 25 10004
Tel (212) 257-7212 SIC 2711

■ JP MORGAN INVESTMENT MANAGEMENT INC p 794
270 Park Ave Fl 12 10017
Tel (212) 483-2323 SIC 6722

■ JP MORGAN SECURITIES LLC p 795
383 Madison Ave Fl 9 10179
Tel (212) 272-2000 SIC 6211 6282 6289

JPB FOUNDATION p 795
9 W 57th St Ste 3800 10019
Tel (212) 364-6266 SIC 8641

▲ JPMORGAN CHASE & CO p 795
270 Park Ave Fl 38 10017
Tel (212) 270-6000
SIC 6021 6211 6162 6141

JPMORGAN CHASE VEBA TRUST FOR RETIREE p 795
1 Chase Manhattan Plz 10005
Tel (212) 552-2992 SIC 6733

JRM CONSTRUCTION MANAGEMENT LLC p 795
242 W 36th St Rm 901 10018
Tel (212) 545-0500 SIC 1542

JT MAGEN & CO INC p 796
44 W 28th St Fl 11 10001
Tel (212) 790-4200 SIC 1542

JUILLIARD SCHOOL p 797
60 Lincoln Center Plz 10023
Tel (212) 799-5000
SIC 8299 7911 5942 8221

K2 INTELLIGENCE LLC p 799
845 3rd Ave Fl 15 10022
Tel (212) 694-7000 SIC 6411

KABLE MEDIA SERVICES INC p 800
14 Wall St Ste 4c 10005
Tel (212) 705-4600 SIC 5192 7389

KALTEX AMERICA INC p 801
350 5th Ave Ste 7100 10118
Tel (212) 971-0575 SIC 2339 2325

KALTEX NORTH AMERICA INC p 801
350 5th Ave Ste 7100 10118
Tel (212) 894-3200 SIC 2392

KANEMATSU USA INC p 802
500 5th Ave Fl 29 10110
Tel (212) 704-9400
SIC 5084 5051 5065 5153

KANTAR MEDIA INTELLIGENCES INC p 803
11 Madison Ave Fl 12 10010
Tel (800) 497-8450 SIC 7313

■ KAPLAN K12 LEARNING SERVICES LLC p 803
395 Hudson St Fl 4 10014
Tel (888) 527-5268 SIC 8299

KASPER GROUP LLC p 804
1412 Broadway Fl 5 10018
Tel (212) 354-4311 SIC 2335

▲ KATE SPADE & CO p 804
2 Park Ave Fl 8 10016
Tel (212) 354-4900
SIC 2331 5651 5136 5137 5961

■ KATE SPADE LLC p 804
2 Park Ave Fl 8 10016
Tel (201) 295-6000 SIC 5137 5632

■ KATZ MEDIA GROUP INC p 805
125 W 55th St Fl 11 10019
Tel (212) 315-0956 SIC 7313

■ KATZ MILLENNIUM SALES & MARKETING INC p 805
125 W 55th St Frnt 3 10019
Tel (212) 424-6000 SIC 7313

KAYE SCHOLER LLP p 805
250 W 55th St Fl 4 10019
Tel (212) 836-8000 SIC 8111

KBF AMSTERDAM PARTNERS p 806
189 W 89th St 10024
Tel (212) 712-2661 SIC 6531

■ KBW LLC p 806
787 7th Ave Fl 4 10019
Tel (212) 887-7777 SIC 6211

KCP HOLDCO INC p 806
603 W 50th St 10019
Tel (212) 265-1500
SIC 3143 3171 5661 5632 5611

KDDI AMERICA INC p 806
825 3rd Ave Fl 3 10022
Tel (212) 295-1200
SIC 4813 7375 7374 8743

KEARNEY-NATIONAL INC p 807
565 5th Ave Fl 4 10017
Tel (212) 661-4600
SIC 3679 3694 3714 3625

■ KEEFE BRUYETTE & WOODS INC p 807
787 7th Ave Fl 4 10019
Tel (212) 887-7777 SIC 6211

KELLEY DRYE & WARREN LLP p 808
101 Park Ave Fl 30 10178
Tel (212) 808-7800 SIC 8111

KENNER & CO INC p 811
437 Madison Ave Ste 3601 10022
Tel (212) 319-2300 SIC 6211

KENNETH COLE PRODUCTIONS INC p 811
603 W 50th St 10019
Tel (212) 265-1500
SIC 3143 3144 3171 5661 5632 5611

KERING AMERICAS INC p 813
3 E 57th St 10022
Tel (212) 238-3010 SIC 8742

■ KETCHUM INC p 814
1285 Avenue Of The Americ 10019
Tel (646) 935-3900 SIC 8743

KIND LLC p 819
1372 Broadway Frnt 3 10018
Tel (855) 884-5463 SIC 5141

KINDERHOOK INDUSTRIES LLC p 819
521 5th Ave Fl 34 10175
Tel (212) 201-6780 SIC 6799

KING TELESERVICES LLC p 820
48 Wall St Fl 23 10005
Tel (718) 238-7924 SIC 7389

■ KINNEY SYSTEM INC p 821
60 Madison Ave Fl 7 10010
Tel (212) 889-2056 SIC 7521 8742

KIRSHENBAUM BOND SENECAL & PARTNERS LLC p 822
160 Varick St Fl 4 10013
Tel (646) 336-9400 SIC 7311

▲ KKR & CO LP p 822
9 W 57th St Ste 4200 10019
Tel (212) 750-8300 SIC 6282 6799

■ KKR FUND HOLDINGS LP p 822
9 W 57th St Fl 41 10019
Tel (212) 230-9742 SIC 6798

KKR MILLENNIUM GP LLC p 822
9 W 57th St Ste 4150 10019
Tel (212) 750-8300 SIC 2515

KOBE STEEL USA HOLDINGS INC p 825
535 Madison Ave Fl 5 10022
Tel (212) 751-9400 SIC 3542 3089

■ KOHLBERG KRAVIS ROBERTS & CO LP p 826
9 W 57th St Ste 4200 10019
Tel (212) 750-8300 SIC 6726

KOP KLINE PLAZA LLC p 827
450 Lexington Ave Fl 13 10017
Tel (212) 661-9890 SIC 6512

KPI CAPITAL HOLDINGS INC p 828
437 Madison Ave Fl 36 10022
Tel (479) 443-1455 SIC 6719 3363 3312

KPI HOLDINGS INC p 828
437 Madison Ave Fl 36 10022
Tel (479) 443-1455 SIC 6719 3363 3312

KPMG LLP p 828
345 Park Ave Lowr Ll4 10154
Tel (212) 758-9700 SIC 8721

KPS CAPITAL PARTNERS LP p 829
485 Lexington Ave Fl 31 10017
Tel (212) 338-5100
SIC 3541 6722 3545 5084

KRAMER LEVIN NAFTALIS & FRANKEL LLP p 829
1177 Ave Of The Americas 10036
Tel (212) 715-9236 SIC 8111

KROLL LLC p 830
600 3rd Ave Fl 4 10016
Tel (212) 593-1000
SIC 7381 8742 8748 7389

KUSHNER COMPANIES INC p 832
666 5th Ave Fl 15 10103
Tel (212) 527-7000
SIC 1521 6513 6531 6512 1522 1531

■ L-3 COMMUNICATIONS CORP p 834
600 3rd Ave 10016
Tel (212) 697-1111
SIC 3812 3663 3669 3679 3769

▲ L-3 COMMUNICATIONS HOLDINGS INC p 835
600 3rd Ave 10016
Tel (212) 697-1111
SIC 3663 3669 3679 3812 3769

LACTALIS DELI INC p 837
77 Water St Fl Mezz 10005
Tel (212) 758-6666 SIC 5143 2022

▲ LADDER CAPITAL CORP p 837
345 Park Ave Fl 8 10154
Tel (212) 715-3170 SIC 6798 6162

LAFAYETTE 148 INC p 837
148 Lafayette St Fl 2 10013
Tel (646) 708-7010 SIC 5137

LAGARDERE NORTH AMERICA INC p 838
60 E 42nd St Ste 1940 10165
Tel (212) 477-7373 SIC 2721

LAVAZZA PREMIUM COFFEES CORP p 847
120 Wall St Fl 27 10005
Tel (212) 725-8800 SIC 5149

LAZ-MD HOLDINGS LLC p 848
30 Rockefeller Plz 10112
Tel (212) 632-6000 SIC 6211 6221

LAZARD ASSET MANAGEMENT LLC p 848
30 Rockefeller Plz Fl 57 10112
Tel (212) 632-1890 SIC 6351

LAZARD FRERES & CO LLC p 849
30 Rockefeller Plz 10112
Tel (212) 632-6000 SIC 6211

LAZARD GROUP LLC p 849
30 Rockefeller Plz 10112
Tel (212) 632-6000 SIC 6282 6211

LEBANESE AMERICAN UNIVERSITY p 850
211 E 46th St Fl 3 10017
Tel (212) 203-4333 SIC 8221

LEBHAR-FRIEDMAN INC p 850
150 W 30th St Fl 19 10001
Tel (212) 756-5000 SIC 2721 2711

LEFRAK ORGANIZATION INC p 852
40 W 57th St Fl 23 10019
Tel (212) 707-6600 SIC 6513 6512

LEGAL AID SOCIETY p 853
199 Water St Frnt 3 10038
Tel (212) 577-3346 SIC 8111

LEGENDS HOSPITALITY MANAGEMENT LIMITED LIABILITY CO p 853
61 Broadway Ste 2400 10006
Tel (646) 977-8521 SIC 8741 8744 8742

LEND LEASE (US) INC p 855
250 Civic Center Dr 10166
Tel (212) 592-6700 SIC 6799 6552

LEND LEASE AMERICAS INC p 855
200 Park Ave Fl 9 10166
Tel (212) 592-6700 SIC 1542 1541

LENDLEASE (US) CONSTRUCTION HOLDINGS INC p 855
200 Park Ave Fl 9 10166
Tel (212) 592-6700 SIC 1542 1541 8742

LENDLEASE (US) CONSTRUCTION INC p 855
200 Park Ave Fl 9 10166
Tel (212) 592-6700
SIC 1541 1542 1522 8741 8742

LENDLEASE (US) CONSTRUCTION LMB INC p 855
200 Park Ave Fl 9 10166
Tel (212) 592-6700
SIC 1522 1541 1542 8741 8742

LENOX HILL HOSPITAL p 856
210 E 64th St Fl 4 10065
Tel (212) 472-8872 SIC 8062

LEONA M AND HARRY B HELMSLEY CHARITABLE TRUST p 856
230 Park Ave 10169
Tel (212) 679-3600 SIC 6733

■ LERNER NEW YORK HOLDING INC p 857
450 W 33rd St Fl 3 10001
Tel (212) 736-1222 SIC 5621

■ LERNER NEW YORK INC p 857
330 W 34th St Fl 7 10001
Tel (212) 884-2000 SIC 5621

LETTIRE CONSTRUCTION CORP p 857
334 E 110th St 336 10029
Tel (212) 996-6640 SIC 1531

▲ LEUCADIA NATIONAL CORP p 858
520 Madison Ave Bsmt A 10022
Tel (212) 460-1900
SIC 6798 6211 1382 2011 2426

LEVY GROUP INC p 858
1333 Broadway Fl 9 10018
Tel (212) 398-0707 SIC 2337 2385

LEXINGTON REALTY TRUST p 859
1 Penn Plz Ste 4015 10119
Tel (212) 692-7200 SIC 6798

LF MENS GROUP LLC p 860
1359 Broadway Fl 21 10018
Tel (646) 839-7000 SIC 5136

LF SOURCING SPORTSWEAR LLC p 860
1359 Broadway Fl 18 10018
Tel (646) 943-8505 SIC 5611

LHH CORP p 860
100 E 77th St 10075
Tel (212) 434-2000 SIC 8062

LIBERTY INTERNATIONAL UNDERWRITERS USA p 862
55 Water St Fl 23 10041
Tel (212) 208-4100 SIC 6331

LIFESPIRE INC p 864
1 Whitehall St Fl 9 10004
Tel (212) 741-0100 SIC 8322

LIFETIME ENTERTAINMENT SERVICES LLC p 864
235 E 45th St 10017
Tel (212) 424-7000 SIC 4841

LIGHTHOUSE GUILD INTERNATIONAL INC p 865
15 W 65th St 10023
Tel (212) 769-6200 SIC 8322 8042

LIGHTSTONE GROUP LLC p 865
460 Park Ave Rm 1300 10022
Tel (212) 616-9969 SIC 6531

LIGHTYEAR CAPITAL LLC p 865
9 W 57th St 10019
Tel (212) 328-0555 SIC 6726

LINCOLNSHIRE MANAGEMENT INC p 868
780 3rd Ave Rm 4000 10017
Tel (212) 319-3633 SIC 6211 7389 3599

LINDSAY GOLDBERG LLC p 868
630 5th Ave Fl 30 10111
Tel (212) 651-1100 SIC 6799

■ LIVE NATION WORLDWIDE INC p 871
220 W 42nd St 10036
Tel (917) 421-5100 SIC 7922

▲ LIVEPERSON INC p 871
475 10th Ave Fl 5 10018
Tel (212) 609-4200 SIC 7371 4813

LOCAL 94 94A 94B HEALTH & BENEFIT TRUST FUND IUOE AFL-CIO p 872
331 W 44th St 337 10036
Tel (212) 541-9880 SIC 8631

LOCCITANE INC p 873
1430 Broadway Fl 2 10018
Tel (212) 333-4880 SIC 5122 5999 5961

▲ LOEWS CORP p 874
667 Madison Ave Fl 7 10065
Tel (212) 521-2000
SIC 6331 6311 1381 4922 7011

■ LOEWS HOTELS HOLDING CORP p 874
667 Madison Ave 10065
Tel (212) 521-2000 SIC 7011

LOGICALIS INC p 874
1 Penn Plz Ste 5130 10119
Tel (212) 596-7160 SIC 5045

LOGICALIS US HOLDINGS INC p 874
1 Penn Plz 10119
Tel (212) 596-7160 SIC 5045

▲ LORAL SPACE & COMMUNICATIONS INC p 878
565 5th Ave 10017
Tel (212) 697-1105 SIC 3663 4899

■ LORAL SPACECOM CORP p 878
565 5th Ave Fl 19 10017
Tel (212) 697-1105 SIC 3663

LORD & TAYLOR LLC p 878
424 5th Ave 10018
Tel (212) 391-3344
SIC 5621 5611 5632 5999

LOREAL USA INC p 878
10 Hudson Yards Fl 30 10001
Tel (212) 818-1500 *SIC* 5122 2844

LOTTE HOTEL NEW YORK PALACE LLC p 879
455 Madison Ave 10022
Tel (212) 888-7000 *SIC* 7011

LOUIS GLICK DIAMOND CORP p 879
810 7th Ave Fl 28 10019
Tel (212) 259-0300 *SIC* 5094 3911

LOUISE PARIS LTD p 880
1407 Broadway Rm 1405 10018
Tel (212) 354-5411 *SIC* 5137

LUCENT JEWELERS INC p 884
1200 Ave Of Americas 10036
Tel (212) 869-2820 *SIC* 5094

LUDWIG INSTITUTE FOR CANCER RESEARCH p 884
666 3rd Ave Fl 28 10017
Tel (212) 450-1500 *SIC* 8733

LUKOIL AMERICAS CORP p 885
505 5th Ave Fl 9 10017
Tel (212) 421-4141 *SIC* 1311

LVI HOLDING CORP p 887
80 Broad St Fl 3 10004
Tel (212) 951-3660 *SIC* 1799

LVI PARENT CORP p 887
370 7th Ave Ste 1803 10001
Tel (212) 951-3660 *SIC* 1795

LVMH MOET HENNESSY LOUIS VUITTON INC p 887
19 E 57th St 10022
Tel (212) 931-2700 *SIC* 5948 5199

M & F WORLDWIDE CORP p 888
35 E 62nd St 10065
Tel (212) 572-8600 *SIC* 5149 8741 2782

M/L BOVIS HOLDINGS LTD p 890
200 Park Ave Fl 9 10166
Tel (212) 592-6700
SIC 1522 1541 1542 8741 8742

MACANDREWS & FORBES HOLDINGS INC p 891
35 E 62nd St 10065
Tel (212) 572-8600 *SIC* 7819

MACANDREWS & FORBES INC p 891
38 E 63rd St 10065
Tel (212) 688-9000
SIC 2844 2087 2121 7819 2721 2731

MACMILLAN HOLDINGS LLC p 892
175 5th Ave 10010
Tel (646) 307-5151 *SIC* 2721 2731

MACMILLAN PUBLISHERS INC p 892
175 5th Ave Ste 400 10010
Tel (646) 307-5151 *SIC* 2731 5192

MACMILLAN PUBLISHING GROUP LLC p 893
175 5th Ave 10010
Tel (212) 674-5151 *SIC* 2731 5192

MACQUARIE CAPITAL (USA) INC p 893
125 W 55th St Frnt 3 10019
Tel (212) 231-1000 *SIC* 6211

MACQUARIE HOLDINGS (USA) INC p 893
125 W 55th St Fl 8 10019
Tel (212) 231-1000 *SIC* 6211

▲ **MACQUARIE INFRASTRUCTURE CORP** p 893
125 W 55th St 10019
Tel (212) 231-1000
SIC 5172 4581 4785 7521 4932

MACQUARIE INFRASTRUCTURE PARTNERS II INTERNATIONAL LP p 893
125 W 55th St 10019
Tel (212) 231-1310 *SIC* 6282

■ **MACYS MERCHANDISING CORP** p 893
151 W 34th St 10001
Tel (212) 695-4400 *SIC* 5311

■ **MACYS MERCHANDISING GROUP INC** p 893
11 Penn Plz Fl 10 10001
Tel (646) 429-6000 *SIC* 5699 5399

MADISON INDUSTRIES INC p 894
295 5th Ave Ste 512 10016
Tel (212) 679-5110 *SIC* 2392 5023

MADISON SQUARE GARDEN CO p 894
2 Penn Plz Fl 15 10121
Tel (212) 465-6000 *SIC* 7941

MAFCO CONSOLIDATED GROUP INC p 895
35 E 62nd St 10065
Tel (212) 572-8600 *SIC* 2121 2131 2869

MAGAZINE PUBLISHERS OF AMERICA p 895
810 7th Ave Fl 24 10019
Tel (212) 872-3700 *SIC* 8611

MAGNA CARTA COMPANIES INC p 895
1 Park Ave Fl 15 10016
Tel (212) 591-9500 *SIC* 6331

MAJOR LEAGUE BASEBALL ENTERPRISES INC p 899
245 Park Ave 10167
Tel (212) 931-7500 *SIC* 4833 8699

MAJOR LEAGUE BASEBALL PROPERTIES INC p 899
245 Park Ave Fl 34 10167
Tel (212) 931-7800 *SIC* 6794 4833 8748

MAMIYE BROTHERS INC p 900
1385 Brdwy Fl 18 10018
Tel (212) 279-4150 *SIC* 5137

■ **MANAGEMENT SHIP LLC GENCO** p 900
299 Park Ave Fl 12 10171
Tel (646) 443-8550 *SIC* 8748

MANAGEMENT-ILA MANAGED HEALTH CARE TRUST FUND p 900
111 Broadway Fl 5 10006
Tel (212) 766-5700 *SIC* 8741

MANHATTAN AND BRONX SURFACE TRANSIT OPERATING AUTHORITY p 901
2 Broadway 10004
Tel (718) 694-1000 *SIC* 4111

MANHATTAN PSYCHIATRIC CENTER p 901
1 Wards Is Ofc 2 10035
Tel (646) 672-6767 *SIC* 8063

MARATHON ASSET MANAGEMENT LP p 904
1 Bryant Park Fl 38 10036
Tel (212) 500-3000 *SIC* 6282

MARCUM LLP p 905
750 3rd Ave Fl 11 10017
Tel (212) 485-5500 *SIC* 8721

MARK FOODS INC p 907
20 W 22nd St Ste 901 10010
Tel (212) 255-6048 *SIC* 5146

▲ **MARKETAXESS HOLDINGS INC** p 908
299 Park Ave Fl 10 10171
Tel (212) 813-6000 *SIC* 6211

MARKIT GROUP LIMITED p 908
620 8th Ave Fl 35 10018
Tel (212) 931-4900 *SIC* 7374

MARKIT NORTH AMERICA INC p 909
620 8th Ave Fl 35 10018
Tel (212) 931-4900 *SIC* 6289

MARKS PANETH LLP p 909
685 3rd Ave Fl 4 10017
Tel (212) 503-8800 *SIC* 8721

▲ **MARSH & MCLENNAN COMPANIES INC** p 910
1166 Avenue Of The Americ 10036
Tel (212) 345-5000 *SIC* 6411 6282 8742

■ **MARSH LLC** p 911
1166 Avenue Of The Americ 10036
Tel (212) 345-5000 *SIC* 6411 6282 8742

■ **MARSH USA INC** p 911
1166 Ave Of The Americas 10036
Tel (212) 345-6000
SIC 6411 6331 6351 6282

■ **MARTHA STEWART LIVING OMNIMEDIA INC** p 912
601 W 26th St Rm 900 10001
Tel (212) 827-8000
SIC 2721 2731 4813 7812

MARUBENI AMERICA CORP p 913
375 Lexington Ave 10017
Tel (212) 450-0100
SIC 5131 5084 5012 5169 5172 5094

MARUBENI AUTO & CONSTRUCTION MACHINERY (AMERICA) INC p 913
450 Lexington Ave 10017
Tel (212) 450-0447 *SIC* 5082 7353 7699

MARUBENI POWER SERVICES INC p 913
375 Lexington Ave 10017
Tel (212) 450-0640 *SIC* 1629 4911 8711

MARUBENI-ITOCHU STEEL AMERICA INC p 913
150 E 42nd St Fl 7 10017
Tel (212) 660-6000 *SIC* 5051

■ **MARVEL ENTERTAINMENT LLC** p 913
135 W 50th St Fl 7 10020
Tel (212) 576-4000
SIC 2721 6794 3944 7929

MASON TENDER DISTRICT COUNCIL TRUST FUND p 916
520 8th Ave Rm 600 10018
Tel (212) 452-9700 *SIC* 6371

MASON TENDERS DISTRICT COUNCIL GREATER NEW YORK p 916
520 8th Ave Rm 650 10018
Tel (212) 452-9400 *SIC* 8631

MATLINPATTERSON ATA HOLDINGS LLC p 920
520 Madison Ave Fl 35 10022
Tel (212) 651-9500 *SIC* 4581

MATLINPATTERSON GLOBAL ADVISERS LLC p 920
520 Madison Ave Fl 35 10022
Tel (212) 651-9500 *SIC* 6733

MAVERIK LACROSSE LLC p 922
535 W 24th St Fl 5 10011
Tel (516) 213-3050 *SIC* 3949

MAXIM GROUP LLC p 922
405 Lexington Ave Fl 2 10174
Tel (212) 895-3500 *SIC* 6211

MAXMARA USA INC p 922
555 Madison Ave Fl 10 10022
Tel (212) 536-6200 *SIC* 5621

MAXUS COMMUNICATIONS LLC p 923
498 Fashion Ave 10018
Tel (212) 297-8300 *SIC* 8999

MAYBELLINE INC p 923
575 5th Ave Bsmt Fl 10017
Tel (212) 885-1310 *SIC* 2844 2841

MC ROBERTS CORP p 925
87 Nassau St 10038
Tel (212) 425-2500 *SIC* 7381

MCALLISTER BROTHERS INC p 925
17 Battery Pl Ste 1200 10004
Tel (212) 269-3200 *SIC* 4424

MCALLISTER TOWING AND TRANSPORTATION CO INC p 925
17 Battery Pl Ste 1200 10004
Tel (212) 269-3200 *SIC* 4492

■ **MCCANN WORLDGROUP LLC** p 926
622 3rd Ave Ste 3 10017
Tel (646) 865-5000 *SIC* 7311 7319

■ **MCCANN-ERICKSON USA INC** p 926
622 3rd Ave Fl 16 10017
Tel (646) 865-2000 *SIC* 8732 7311

MCGRAW-HILL GLOBAL EDUCATION HOLDINGS LLC p 929
2 Penn Plz Fl 20 10121
Tel (646) 766-2000 *SIC* 2731

MCGRAW-HILL GLOBAL EDUCATION LLC p 929
2 Penn Plz Fl 20 10121
Tel (646) 766-2000 *SIC* 8299

MCGRAW-HILL SCHOOL EDUCATION HOLDINGS LLC p 929
2 Penn Plz Fl 20 10121
Tel (646) 766-2000 *SIC* 2731

MCGRAW-HILL SCHOOL EDUCATION LLC p 929
2 Penn Plz Fl 20 10121
Tel (646) 766-2060 *SIC* 2731

MCKINSEY & CO INC p 930
55 E 52nd St Fl 21 10055
Tel (212) 446-7000 *SIC* 8742

MCROBERTS PROTECTIVE AGENCY INC p 932
42 Broadway Ste 1836 10004
Tel (732) 886-0990 *SIC* 7381 1731

▲ **MDC PARTNERS INC** p 933
745 5th Ave Fl 19 10151
Tel (646) 429-1800 *SIC* 7311 8748

MDI HOLDINGS LLC p 933
399 Park Ave Fl 14 10022
Tel (212) 559-1127
SIC 2899 2842 2874 2992 2752 3577

MDRC p 933
16 E 34th St Fl 19 10016
Tel (212) 532-3200 *SIC* 8641 8733

MEADOWS OFFICE SUPPLY CO INC p 934
885 3rd Ave Fl 29 10022
Tel (212) 741-0333 *SIC* 5021

MEDECINS SANS FRONTIERES USA INC p 935
333 7th Ave Fl 2 10001
Tel (212) 679-6800 *SIC* 8399 7363

MEDIA PLANNING GROUP USA LLC p 936
200 Hudson St 10013
Tel (646) 587-5000 *SIC* 7319

■ **MEDIABRANDS WORLDWIDE INC** p 936
100 W 33rd St 10001
Tel (212) 605-7000 *SIC* 7319 7311

MEDIAMATH INC p 936
4 World Trade Ctr 10007
Tel (646) 840-4200 *SIC* 7379

MEDIAOCEAN LLC p 936
45 W 18th St 10011
Tel (212) 633-8100 *SIC* 7371 7311

▲ **MEDIDATA SOLUTIONS INC** p 937
350 Hudson St Fl 9 10014
Tel (212) 918-1800 *SIC* 7372

MEDITERRANEAN SHIPPING CO (USA) INC p 938
420 5th Ave Fl 8 10018
Tel (212) 764-8280 *SIC* 4731

MEDLEY CAPITAL CORP p 938
375 Park Ave Fl 33 10152
Tel (212) 759-0777 *SIC* 6726

MEE APPAREL LLC p 939
501 10th Ave Fl 7 10018
Tel (917) 262-1000 *SIC* 2329

MEMORIAL HOSPITAL FOR CANCER AND ALLIED DISEASES p 942
1275 York Ave 10065
Tel (212) 639-2000 *SIC* 8069

MEMORIAL SLOAN-KETTERING CANCER CENTER p 942
1275 York Ave 10065
Tel (212) 639-2000 *SIC* 8069

MERCEDES-BENZ MANHATTAN INC p 944
770 11th Ave 10019
Tel (212) 629-1600 *SIC* 5511

■ **MERCER (US) INC** p 944
1166 Ave Of The Americ 10036
Tel (212) 345-7000 *SIC* 8742

■ **MERCER HEALTH & BENEFITS LLC** p 944
1166 Ave Of The Americas 10036
Tel (212) 345-7000 *SIC* 8742

■ **MERCER INC** p 944
1166 Avenue Of The Americ 10036
Tel (212) 345-7000 *SIC* 8748

■ **MERCER INVESTMENT CONSULTING INC** p 944
1166 Ave Of The Americas 10036
Tel (212) 345-7000 *SIC* 6282

MERCHANT CASH AND CAPITAL LLC p 944
460 Park Ave S Fl 10 10016
Tel (212) 545-3180 *SIC* 6153 7389

MERLIN ENTERTAINMENTS GROUP US LLC p 950
234 W 42nd St Frnt 4 10036
Tel (212) 512-9604 *SIC* 7996

■ **MERRILL LYNCH GROUP INC** p 950
4 World Financial Ctr # 4 10080
Tel (646) 855-5000 *SIC* 6282 6162

■ **MERRILL LYNCH INTERNATIONAL INC** p 950
4 Wrld Fncl Ctr Fl 12 10281
Tel (646) 855-5000 *SIC* 6211

■ **MERRILL LYNCH INVESTMENT MANAGEMENT INC** p 950
225 Liberty St Fl C1056 10281
Tel (212) 449-1000 *SIC* 6211 6282

■ **MERRILL LYNCH PIERCE FENNER & SMITH INC** p 950
111 8th Ave 10011
Tel (800) 637-7455 *SIC* 6211 6411

MERYL DIAMOND LTD p 951
1375 Broadway Fl 9 10018
Tel (212) 730-0333 *SIC* 2339 2389

METALMARK CAPITAL LLC p 952
1177 Ave Of The Americas 10036
Tel (212) 823-1900 *SIC* 6726

■ **METLIFE GROUP INC** p 954
1095 Ave Of The Americas 10036
Tel (800) 638-5433 *SIC* 6411

▲ **METLIFE INC** p 954
200 Park Ave Fl 1200 10166
Tel (212) 578-9500 *SIC* 6311 6321 6331

METRO-NORTH COMMUTER RAILROAD CO INC p 955
420 Lexington Ave 10170
Tel (212) 878-7000 *SIC* 4013 4111

METROMEDIA CO p 955
810 Seventh Ave Fl 29 10019
Tel (212) 606-4437
SIC 5812 6794 4813 4911

METROPLUS HEALTH PLAN INC p 955
160 Water St Fl 3 10038
Tel (212) 788-3648 *SIC* 6324

METROPOLITAN HOSPITAL CENTER ASSOCIATION INC p 956
1901 1st Ave 10029
Tel (212) 423-6262 *SIC* 8062

■ **METROPOLITAN INSURANCE & ANNUITY CO** p 956
1 Madison Ave Lbby 10010
Tel (212) 578-2211 *SIC* 6411

METROPOLITAN LUMBER p 956
617 11th Ave 10036
Tel (212) 246-9090 *SIC* 5031 5211 5251

METROPOLITAN MUSEUM OF ART p 956
1000 5th Ave 10028
Tel (212) 535-7710 *SIC* 8412 5999

METROPOLITAN OPERA ASSOCIATION INC p 956
Lincoln Ctr 10023
Tel (212) 799-3100 *SIC* 7922

METROPOLITAN TRANSPORTATION AUTHORITY p 956
2 Broadway Bsmt B 10004
Tel (212) 878-7000 *SIC* 4111

MF GLOBAL HOLDINGS LTD p 957
142 W 57th St Ste 401 10019
Tel (646) 568-8114 *SIC* 6211

MF GLOBAL HOLDINGS USA INC p 957
717 5th Ave Fl 11 10022
Tel (212) 589-6200 *SIC* 6211

MFA FINANCIAL INC p 957
350 Park Ave Fl 20 10022
Tel (212) 207-6400 *SIC* 6798

MICHAEL J FOX FOUNDATION FOR PARKINSONS RESEARCH p 960
498 Fashion Ave 10018
Tel (212) 509-0995 *SIC* 7389

MICHAEL KORS (USA) INC p 960
11 W 42nd St Fl 20 10036
Tel (212) 201-8100 *SIC* 5137 5651 5621

▲ **MIDAS MEDICI GROUP HOLDINGS INC** p 964
445 Park Ave Frnt 5 10022
Tel (212) 792-0920 *SIC* 7372

MIDOCEAN US ADVISOR LP p 966
320 Park Ave Fl 16 10022
Tel (212) 497-1400 *SIC* 8742

MILBANK TWEED HADLEY & MCCLOY LLP p 969
28 Liberty St Fl 47 10005
Tel (212) 530-5000 *SIC* 8111

MILL-RUN TOURS INC p 969
424 Madison Ave Fl 12 10017
Tel (212) 486-9840 *SIC* 4724 4725

MILLWARD BROWN LLC p 971
11 Madison Ave Ste 1200 10010
Tel (212) 548-7200 *SIC* 8732

MIMEO.COM INC p 972
3 Park Ave Fl 22 10016
Tel (212) 847-3000 *SIC* 2759

MINDSHARE USA LLC p 972
498 Fashion Ave 10018
Tel (212) 297-7000 *SIC* 7319

MINDSINSYNC INC p 972
276 5th Ave Rm 505 10001
Tel (212) 228-1828 *SIC* 5023

▲ MINERALSTECHNOLOGIES INC p 973
622 3rd Ave Fl 38 10017
Tel (212) 878-1800
SIC 3295 2819 3274 1411 3281 5032

MISTRAL EQUITY PARTNERS LP p 976
650 5th Ave Fl 31 10019
Tel (212) 616-9600 *SIC* 6211

MISYS INTERNATIONAL BANKING SYSTEMS INC p 976
1180 Avenue Of The Amer 10036
Tel (914) 428-7200 *SIC* 7378 7372

MITSUBISHI CORP (AMERICAS) p 977
655 3rd Ave 10017
Tel (212) 605-2000
SIC 5051 5172 5141 5153 5169 5084

MITSUBISHI GAS CHEMICAL AMERICA INC p 977
655 3rd Ave Fl 24 10017
Tel (212) 687-9030 *SIC* 5169 8742

MITSUBISHI INTERNATIONAL CORP p 978
655 3rd Ave Ste 800 10017
Tel (212) 605-2000
SIC 5051 5172 5141 5153 5169 5084

MITSUBISHI RAYON AMERICA INC p 978
655 3rd Ave Fl 15 10017
Tel (212) 223-3043 *SIC* 5169

MITSUI & CO (USA) INC p 978
200 Park Ave Fl 35 10166
Tel (212) 878-4000
SIC 5051 5094 5084 5153 5172 5169

MITSUI SUMITOMO INSURANCE CO OF AMERICA p 978
560 Lexington Ave Fl 20 10022
Tel (212) 446-3600 *SIC* 6331

MIZUHO BANK LTD p 978
1251 Ave Of The Americas 10020
Tel (212) 282-3000 *SIC* 6022 6082 7359

MIZUHO SECURITIES USA INC p 978
320 Park Ave Fl 12 10022
Tel (212) 282-3000 *SIC* 6211

MKTG INC p 979
32 Avenue Of The Americas # 20 10013
Tel (212) 366-3481 *SIC* 8742

MKTG INC p 979
32 Avenue Of The Americas # 20 10013
Tel (212) 366-3400 *SIC* 7311 7389 8743

MLB ADVANCED MEDIA LP p 979
75 9th Ave Fl 5 10011
Tel (212) 485-3444 *SIC* 4841 7313 7929

MMETRO.COM LLC p 979
568 Broadway Rm 507 10012
Tel (646) 786-1938 *SIC* 7371

MMS USA INVESTMENTS INC p 979
41 Madison Ave 10010
Tel (212) 463-2000 *SIC* 7311

▲ MOELIS & CO p 981
399 Park Ave Fl 5 10022
Tel (212) 883-3800 *SIC* 6282

■ MOELIS & CO LLC p 981
399 Park Ave Fl 5 10022
Tel (212) 883-3800 *SIC* 6733 6282

MOELIS CAPITAL PARTNERS LLC p 982
399 Park Ave Fl 5 10022
Tel (212) 883-3800 *SIC* 6726

MOET HENNESSY USA INC p 982
85 10th Ave Fl 2 10011
Tel (212) 888-7575
SIC 0172 2844 6153 5182 5122

■ MOMENTUM-NA INC p 983
250 Hudson St Fl 2 10013
Tel (646) 638-5400 *SIC* 8743 7311 8732

MONOMOY CAPITAL PARTNERS LLC p 984
142 W 57th St Fl 17 10019
Tel (212) 699-4000 *SIC* 6371

MONOMOY CAPITAL PARTNERS LP p 984
142 W 57th St Fl 17 10019
Tel (212) 699-4000 *SIC* 6799

MONTCLAIR STATE UNIVERSITY p 986
825 8th Ave Fl 14 10019
Tel (973) 655-4000 *SIC* 8221

■ MONY GROUP INC p 987
1740 Broadway Ste 202 10019
Tel (212) 708-2000 *SIC* 6411

MONY LIFE INSURANCE CO p 987
1740 Broadway 10019
Tel (800) 487-6669
SIC 6411 6321 6211 6282 6531

■ MOODYS ANALYTICS INC p 987
250 Greenwich St 7w 10007
Tel (415) 874-6368 *SIC* 7323

▲ MOODYS CORP p 987
250 Greenwich St 10007
Tel (212) 553-0300 *SIC* 7323 6282

■ MOODYS INVESTORS SERVICE INC p 987
250 Greenwich St 10007
Tel (212) 553-0300 *SIC* 7323

▲ MORGAN STANLEY p 988
1585 Broadway 10036
Tel (212) 761-4000 *SIC* 6211 6282

■ MORGAN STANLEY & CO LLC p 989
1585 Broadway 10036
Tel (212) 761-4000 *SIC* 6211

■ MORGAN STANLEY CAPITAL GROUP INC p 989
1585 Broadway 10036
Tel (212) 761-4000 *SIC* 6221

■ MORGAN STANLEY DEAN WITTER & CO p 989
1585 Broadway Lowr B 10036
Tel (212) 761-4000 *SIC* 6211

■ MORGAN STANLEY INVESTMENT MANAGEMENT INC p 989
1585 Broadway 10036
Tel (888) 454-3965 *SIC* 6282

■ MORGAN STANLEY MORTGAGE CAPITAL HOLDINGS LLC p 989
1585 Broadway Lowr B 10036
Tel (212) 761-4000 *SIC* 6162

■ MORGAN STANLEY SMITH BARNEY HOLDINGS LLC p 989
1585 Broadway 10036
Tel (212) 761-4000 *SIC* 6211

▲ MORGANS HOTEL GROUP CO p 989
475 10th Ave Fl 11 10018
Tel (212) 277-4100 *SIC* 7011

MORGANS HOTEL GROUP MANAGEMENT LLC p 989
475 10th Ave Fl 11 10018
Tel (212) 277-4100 *SIC* 7011

MOSBY HOLDINGS CORP p 992
125 Park Ave 10017
Tel (212) 309-8100 *SIC* 2741 8999

MOUNT SINAI HEALTH SYSTEM INC p 994
150 E 42nd St Bsmt 2 10017
Tel (646) 605-4750 *SIC* 8011

MOUNT SINAI HOSPITAL p 994
1 Gustave L Levy Pl Fl 12 10029
Tel (212) 241-6500 *SIC* 8062

MPHASIS CORP p 995
460 Park Ave S Rm 1101 10016
Tel (212) 686-6655 *SIC* 7371

▲ MSCI INC p 996
250 Greenwich St Fl 49 10007
Tel (212) 804-3900
SIC 7389 7371 6282 8742

▲ MSG NETWORKS INC p 997
11 Penn Plz 10001
Tel (212) 465-6400
SIC 4841 7922 7941 4832

MSG SPORTS & ENTERTAINMENT LLC p 997
2 Penn Plz Fl 15 10121
Tel (212) 465-6000 *SIC* 7941

■ MSGN HOLDINGS LP p 997
4 Penn Plz 10121
Tel (212) 465-6000 *SIC* 4832 7922

MSIG HOLDINGS (AMERICAS) INC p 997
560 Lexington Ave Fl 20 10022
Tel (212) 446-3600 *SIC* 8741 6331

MSIP-SSCC HOLDINGS LLC p 997
1585 Broadway 10036
Tel (270) 852-5000 *SIC* 4923

■ MTV NETWORKS INC p 998
1515 Broadway Fl 31 10036
Tel (212) 258-8000 *SIC* 4833

MUFG AMERICAS HOLDINGS CORP p 999
1251 Ave Of The Americas 10020
Tel (212) 782-5911 *SIC* 6021

■ MULTI PACKAGING SOLUTIONS INC p 999
150 E 52nd St Ste 2800 10022
Tel (646) 885-0005
SIC 2759 2731 2761 3089 5092 2671

▲ MULTI PACKAGING SOLUTIONS INTERNATIONAL LIMITED p 999
150 E 52nd St Fl 28 10022
Tel (646) 885-0005 *SIC* 2657

MULTIPLAN INC p 999
115 5th Ave Fl 7 10003
Tel (212) 780-2000 *SIC* 8742

MUNICIPAL CREDIT UNION p 1000
2 Lafayette St Frnt D 10007
Tel (212) 238-3300 *SIC* 6062

MUSEUM OF MODERN ART p 1002
11 W 53rd St 10019
Tel (212) 708-9400 *SIC* 8412 5942

MUTUAL OF AMERICA CORP p 1003
320 Park Ave Fl 5 10022
Tel (212) 224-1147 *SIC* 6311 7389

MUTUAL OF AMERICA LIFE INSURANCE CO p 1003
320 Park Ave Fl 5 10022
Tel (212) 224-1600 *SIC* 6311

MYSTIC APPAREL LLC p 1005
1333 Broadway Fl 6 10018
Tel (212) 279-2466 *SIC* 5021 5137

■ N Y MCG INC p 1006
1 Battery Park Plz Fl 26 10004
Tel (212) 972-3600 *SIC* 6163

NAGASE AMERICA CORP p 1006
546 5th Ave Fl 16 10036
Tel (212) 703-1340
SIC 5169 5162 5122 5065 5047

NAMDAR INC p 1007
800 3rd Ave Fl 5 10022
Tel (212) 956-5770 *SIC* 5411

NARS COSMETICS INC p 1007
900 3rd Ave Fl 6 10022
Tel (212) 941-0890 *SIC* 5122

■ NASDAQ CORPORATE SOLUTIONS LLC p 1008
1 Liberty Plz Ste 4900 10006
Tel (212) 231-5369 *SIC* 6231

▲ NASDAQ INC p 1008
1 Liberty Plz Ste 4900 10006
Tel (212) 401-8700 *SIC* 6231 8742

■ NATHAN & LEWIS SECURITIES INC p 1009
260 Madison Ave Ste 11 10016
Tel (212) 413-4553 *SIC* 6211

NATIONAL AUDUBON SOCIETY INC p 1010
225 Varick St Fl 7 10014
Tel (212) 979-3000 *SIC* 8641 2721

NATIONAL CONVENTION SERVICES LLC p 1011
145 W 30th St Rm 200 10001
Tel (212) 947-8255 *SIC* 7389

NATIONAL FOOTBALL LEAGUE INC p 1012
345 Park Ave Bsmt Lc1 10154
Tel (212) 450-2000 *SIC* 7941

▲ NATIONAL GENERAL HOLDINGS CORP p 1012
59 Maiden Ln Fl 38 10038
Tel (212) 380-9500 *SIC* 6411

NATIONAL GENERAL INSURANCE p 1012
59 Maiden Ln Fl 38 10038
Tel (212) 380-9477 *SIC* 6411

■ NATIONAL HOLDINGS CORP p 1013
410 Park Ave Fl 14 10022
Tel (212) 417-8000 *SIC* 6719

NATIONAL MULTIPLE SCLEROSIS SOCIETY p 1014
733 3rd Ave Fl 3 10017
Tel (212) 463-9791 *SIC* 8322

NATIONAL RESTAURANTS MANAGEMENT INC p 1015
560 5th Ave Fl 3 10036
Tel (212) 563-7440 *SIC* 5812 6531

NATIONAL RESTAURANTS MANAGEMENT INC p 1015
604 5th Ave Fl 5 10020
Tel (212) 563-7440 *SIC* 5812

■ NATIONAL UNION FIRE INSURANCE CO OF PITTSBURGH PA p 1016
70 Pine St Fl 50 10005
Tel (631) 692-4545 *SIC* 6331

NATURAL RESOURCES DEFENSE COUNCIL INC p 1018
40 W 20th St 10011
Tel (212) 727-2700 *SIC* 8641

NATURE AMERICA INC p 1018
1 New York Plz Ste 4500 10004
Tel (212) 726-9200 *SIC* 2721

■ NAUTICA RETAIL USA INC p 1019
40 W 57th St Fl 3 10019
Tel (212) 541-5990 *SIC* 5611

NAVILLUSTILE INC p 1020
633 3rd Ave Fl 17 10017
Tel (212) 750-1808 *SIC* 1741 1771 1743

■ NBC INTERNATIONAL LTD p 1021
30 Rockefeller Plz Fl 2 10112
Tel (212) 664-4444 *SIC* 7822

■ NBC NEWS WORLDWIDE LLC p 1021
30 Rockefeller Plz Fl 2 10112
Tel (212) 664-4444
SIC 4832 4833 4841 6021 6531 7383

■ NBC UNIVERSAL LLC p 1021
1221 Avenue Of The Americ 10020
Tel (212) 664-4444 *SIC* 4833 8111

■ NBC UNIVERSITY LLC p 1021
30 Rockefeller Plz Fl 51 10112
Tel (212) 664-4444
SIC 4832 4833 4841 6021 6531 7383

■ NBCUNIVERSAL MEDIA LLC p 1021
30 Rockefeller Plz Fl 2 10112
Tel (212) 664-4444
SIC 4841 4833 7812 7996

ND PROPERTIES INC p 1022
730 3rd Ave Ste 15485 10017
Tel (800) 842-2252 *SIC* 6512

NEUBERGER & BERMAN PARTNERS FUND INC p 1028
605 3rd Ave Fl 21 10158
Tel (212) 476-8800 *SIC* 6722

NEUBERGER BERMAN GROUP LLC p 1028
605 3rd Ave Fl 21 10158
Tel (212) 476-9000 *SIC* 6282 6211 6722

NEUBERGER BERMAN LLC p 1028
605 3rd Ave Fl 21 10158
Tel (212) 476-9000 *SIC* 6282 6211 6722

NEVADA MEZZ 1 LLC p 1028
60 Wall St 10005
Tel (702) 314-3265 *SIC* 7011

■ NEW AVON LLC p 1029
777 3rd Ave Fl 8 10017
Tel (212) 282-8500 *SIC* 2844 5122 5999

■ NEW HAMPSHIRE INSURANCE CO p 1030
70 Pine St Fl 23 10005
Tel (212) 770-7000 *SIC* 6331

▲ NEW MEDIA INVESTMENT GROUP INC p 1032
1345 Avenue Of The Americ 10105
Tel (212) 479-3160 *SIC* 2711 7373

NEW MOUNTAIN CAPITAL I LLC p 1032
787 7th Ave Fl 49 10019
Tel (212) 720-0300 *SIC* 6726

NEW MOUNTAIN CAPITAL LLC p 1032
787 7th Ave Fl 49 10019
Tel (212) 720-0300 *SIC* 6726

NEW MOUNTAIN FINANCE CORP p 1032
787 7th Ave Fl 48 10019
Tel (212) 720-0300 *SIC* 6726

NEW OMAHA HOLDINGS LP p 1032
9 W 57th St Ste 4200 10019
Tel (212) 750-8300 *SIC* 6712

NEW PARTNERS INC p 1032
1250 Broadway Fl 10 10001
Tel (212) 609-7700 *SIC* 8082

▲ NEW RESIDENTIAL INVESTMENT CORP p 1033
1345 Ave Americas 10105
Tel (212) 798-3150 *SIC* 6798

NEW SCHOOL p 1033
66 W 12th St 10011
Tel (212) 229-5600 *SIC* 8221

NEW SENIOR INVESTMENT GROUP INC p 1033
1345 Avenue Of The Americ 10105
Tel (212) 479-3140 *SIC* 6726

NEW WATER STREET CORP p 1033
55 Water St Ste Conc6 10041
Tel (212) 422-1320 *SIC* 6531

▲ NEWYORK & CO INC p 1033
330 W 34th St Fl 9 10001
Tel (212) 884-2000 *SIC* 5621

NEWYORK AND PRESBYTERIAN HOSPITAL p 1034
525 E 68th St 10065
Tel (212) 746-5454 *SIC* 8062 8011

NEWYORK BLOOD CENTER INC p 1034
310 E 67th St 10065
Tel (212) 570-3010 *SIC* 8099 2836

NEWYORK CITY BOARD OF EDUCATION p 1034
52 Chambers St Ste 320 10007
Tel (212) 374-5141 *SIC* 8211

NEWYORK CITY DEPT OF EDUCATION p 1034
52 Chambrs St Twd Crthse Tweed Courthouse 10007
Tel (212) 374-6000 *SIC* 8732

NEWYORK CITY GEOGRAPHIC DISTRICT 1 p 1034
166 Essex St 10002
Tel (212) 353-2948 *SIC* 8211

NEWYORK CITY GEOGRAPHIC DISTRICT 2 p 1034
333 7th Ave Fl 7 10001
Tel (212) 356-3815 *SIC* 8211

NEWYORK CITY GEOGRAPHIC DISTRICT 3 p 1034
501 W 165th St 10032
Tel (212) 678-5857 *SIC* 8211

NEWYORK CITY GEOGRAPHIC DISTRICT 4 p 1034
319 E 117th St 10035
Tel (212) 831-4981 *SIC* 8211

NEWYORK CITY GEOGRAPHIC DISTRICT 5 p 1034
425 W 123rd St 10027
Tel (212) 769-7500 *SIC* 8211

NEWYORK CITY GEOGRAPHIC DISTRICT 6 p 1034
4360 Broadway Rm 527 10033
Tel (212) 521-3757 *SIC* 8211

NEWYORK CITY HEALTH AND HOSPITALS CORP p 1034
125 Worth St Rm 514 10013
Tel (212) 788-3321 *SIC* 8062 8069 8093

NEWYORK CITY HOUSING AUTHORITY p 1034
250 Broadway 10007
Tel (212) 306-3000 *SIC* 9531

NEWYORK CITYTRANSIT AUTHORITY p 1034
2 Broadway 10004
Tel (718) 330-1234 *SIC* 4111

NEWYORK COMMUNITYTRUST AND COMMUNITY FUNDS INC p 1035
909 3rd Ave Fl 22 10022
Tel (212) 686-0010 *SIC* 6732

NEWYORK CONVENTION CENTER OPERATING CORP p 1035
655 W 34th St 10001
Tel (212) 216-2000 *SIC* 7389

NEWYORK DOWNTOWN HOSPITAL p 1035
170 William St 10038
Tel (212) 312-5000 *SIC* 8062

NEWYORK EYE AND EAR INFIRMARY IPA INC p 1035
310 E 14th St 10003
Tel (212) 979-4000 *SIC* 8069

NEWYORK FOUNDLING HOSPITAL p 1035
590 Ave Of The Americas # 1 10011
Tel (212) 633-9300 *SIC* 8361 8399

NEWYORK HOTELTRADES COUNCIL & HOTEL ASSOC OF NEWYORK p 1035
305 W 44th St 10036
Tel (212) 586-6400 *SIC* 8011

NEWYORK HOTELTRADES COUNCIL AND HOTEL ASSOC OF NYC INC HEALTH BENEFITS FUND p 1035
305 W 44th St 10036
Tel (212) 586-6400 *SIC* 8631

NEWYORK INTERCONNECT L L C p 1035
530 5th Ave Fl 6 10036
Tel (212) 382-5300 *SIC* 7311

NEW YORK LIFE INSURANCE CO p 1035
51 Madison Ave Bsmt 1b 10010
Tel (212) 576-7000 *SIC* 6311 6321 6282

NEW YORK MEDIA LLC p 1035
75 Varick St 10013
Tel (212) 508-0700 *SIC* 2721

■ **NEW YORK MERCANTILE EXCHANGE INC** p 1035
1 N End Ave Frnt 10282
Tel (212) 299-2000 *SIC* 6221

NEW YORK MORTGAGE TRUST INC p 1035
275 Madison Ave Fl 32 10016
Tel (212) 792-0107 *SIC* 6798 6163

NEW YORK PRESBYTERIAN HOSPITAL WEILL CORNELL UNIVERSITY MEDICAL CENTER p 1036
525 E 68th St 10065
Tel (212) 746-1754 *SIC* 8011

NEW YORK PUBLIC LIBRARY p 1036
5th Ave & 42nd St 10018
Tel (212) 592-7400 *SIC* 8231

NEW YORK PUBLIC LIBRARY ASTOR LENOX AND TILDEN FOUNDATIONS p 1036
188 Madison Ave 10016
Tel (212) 592-7403 *SIC* 8231

NEW YORK REIT INC p 1036
405 Park Ave Fl 14 10022
Tel (212) 415-6500 *SIC* 6531

NEW YORK SOCIETY FOR RELIEF OF RUPTURED AND CRIPPLED MAINTAINING HOSPITAL FOR p 1036
535 E 70th St 10021
Tel (212) 606-1000 *SIC* 8069

NEW YORK STATE COURT OFFICERS ASSOCIATION SECURITY BENEFIT FUND p 1036
321 Broadway Ste 600 10007
Tel (212) 608-1124 *SIC* 6371

■ **NEW YORK STOCK EXCHANGE LLC** p 1036
11 Wall St Fl 6 10005
Tel (212) 656-3000 *SIC* 6231

▲ **NEW YORK TIMES CO** p 1036
620 8th Ave 10018
Tel (212) 556-1234
SIC 2711 4832 4833 7383 7375

NEW YORK UNIVERSITY p 1036
70 Washington Sq S 10012
Tel (212) 998-1212 *SIC* 8221

NEW YORK UNIVERSITY p 1036
250 Park Ave S Fl 6 10003
Tel (212) 998-5813 *SIC* 8621

NEW YORK UNIVERSITY MEDICAL CENTER p 1036
550 1st Ave 10016
Tel (646) 929-7870 *SIC* 8011

NEW YORK-PRESBYTERIAN FUND INC p 1036
525 E 68th St 10065
Tel (212) 297-4356 *SIC* 8011

NEWBAY MEDIA LLC p 1037
28 E 28th St Fl 12 10016
Tel (212) 378-0400 *SIC* 4833

▲ **NEWCASTLE INVESTMENT CORP** p 1037
1345 Avenue Of America Flr 46 10105
Tel (212) 798-6100 *SIC* 6798

■ **NEWMARK & CO REAL ESTATE INC** p 1038
125 Park Ave 10017
Tel (212) 372-2000 *SIC* 6531

▲ **NEWS CORP** p 1039
1211 Ave Of The Americas 10036
Tel (212) 416-3400 *SIC* 2711 2731 7375

NEXTSOURCE INC p 1041
1040 Avenue Of The Americ 10018
Tel (212) 736-5870 *SIC* 7363 8741

NFP CORP p 1041
340 Madison Ave Fl 21 10173
Tel (212) 301-4000 *SIC* 6411 7389 6282

NHL ENTERPRISES INC p 1042
1185 Ave Of The Americas 10036
Tel (212) 789-2000 *SIC* 7941

NIELSEN CO p 1043
85 Broad St Bsmt 10004
Tel (646) 654-5000 *SIC* 7389

NIELSEN CO US LLC p 1043
85 Broad St 10004
Tel (646) 654-5000 *SIC* 8732

NINE WEST FOOTWEAR CORP p 1044
1411 Broadway Fl 20 10018
Tel (800) 999-1877
SIC 3144 3171 5661 5632 5139

NIPPON STEEL & SUMITOMO METAL USA INC p 1044
1251 Ave Of The Ave Fl 23 10020
Tel (212) 486-7150 *SIC* 5051 5084

■ **NL HOLDING CORP (DEL)** p 1045
260 Madison Ave Ste 11 10016
Tel (212) 354-8800 *SIC* 6211 6411

NM Z PARENT INC p 1045
787 7th Ave Fl 49 10019
Tel (212) 720-0300
SIC 6726 2841 2879 2842

NOMURA HOLDING AMERICA INC p 1047
309 W 49th St 10019
Tel (212) 667-9300 *SIC* 6211

NOMURA SECURITIES INTERNATIONAL INC p 1047
Worldwide Plaza 309 W 49t 10019
Tel (212) 667-9000 *SIC* 6211

▲ **NORTHSTAR ASSET MANAGEMENT GROUP INC** p 1058
399 Park Ave Fl 18 10022
Tel (212) 547-2600 *SIC* 8741 6531 6282

NORTHSTAR GROUP HOLDINGS LLC p 1059
370 7th Ave Ste 1803 10001
Tel (212) 951-3660 *SIC* 1795

NORTHSTAR GROUP SERVICES INC p 1059
370 7th Ave Ste 1803 10001
Tel (212) 951-3660 *SIC* 1795 1799

NORTHSTAR HEALTHCARE INCOME INC p 1059
399 Park Ave Fl 18 10022
Tel (212) 547-2600 *SIC* 6798

NORTHSTAR REALTY EUROPE CORP p 1059
399 Park Ave Fl 18 10022
Tel (212) 547-2600 *SIC* 6798

NORTHSTAR REALTY FINANCE CORP p 1059
399 Park Ave Fl 18 10022
Tel (212) 319-8801 *SIC* 6798

▲ **NORTHSTAR REALTY FINANCE CORP** p 1059
399 Park Ave Fl 18 10022
Tel (212) 547-2600 *SIC* 6798

NOVO FOUNDATION p 1063
535 5th Ave Fl 33 10017
Tel (212) 808-5400 *SIC* 8641

■ **NRG TEXAS LLC** p 1064
521 5th Ave Fl 30 10175
Tel (713) 795-6000 *SIC* 4911

NTT AMERICA INC p 1065
757 3rd Ave Ste 1400 10017
Tel (212) 661-0810 *SIC* 4813

NTT DATA INTERNATIONAL LLC p 1066
45 W 36th St Fl 7 10018
Tel (212) 355-5585 *SIC* 7374

NURTURE INC p 1067
40 Fulton St Fl 17 10038
Tel (212) 374-2779 *SIC* 5137

NYC DISTRICT COUNCIL OF CARPENTERS WELFARE FUND p 1069
395 Hudson St Lbby 3 10014
Tel (212) 366-7300 *SIC* 6371

NYLIFE LLC p 1069
51 Madison Ave 10010
Tel (212) 576-7000
SIC 6282 6211 6733 6153

■ **NYMEX HOLDINGS INC** p 1069
1 N End Ave Rm 1215 10282
Tel (212) 299-2000 *SIC* 6231

■ **NYNEX INFORMATION SOLUTIONS GROUP INC** p 1069
1095 Ave Of The Amer Fl 7 10036
Tel (212) 395-1000 *SIC* 8732 7371 7379

■ **NYP HOLDINGS INC** p 1069
1211 Avenue Of The Amer 10036
Tel (212) 997-9272 *SIC* 2711

NYSARC p 1069
252 W 29th St Rm 700 10001
Tel (212) 780-2500 *SIC* 8322

NYSARC INC p 1069
83 Maiden Ln 10038
Tel (212) 780-2635 *SIC* 8099

■ **NYSE EURONEXT HOLDINGS LLC** p 1069
11 Wall St 10005
Tel (212) 656-3000 *SIC* 6231

■ **NYSE GROUP INC** p 1069
11 Wall St 10005
Tel (212) 656-3000 *SIC* 6231 6289

NYU p 1069
120 Sullivan St Apt 1b 10012
Tel (212) 998-1212 *SIC* 8221

NYU HOSPITAL FOR JOINT DISEASES p 1069
301 E 17th St Fl 14 10003
Tel (212) 598-6000 *SIC* 8069

NYU HOSPITALS CENTER p 1069
550 1st Ave 10016
Tel (212) 263-7300 *SIC* 8062

OAK HILL CAPITAL PARTNERS III LP p 1070
65 E 55th St Fl 32 10022
Tel (212) 527-8400
SIC 5812 5813 7999 7993

OAK HILL CAPITAL PARTNERS LP p 1070
65 E 55th St Fl 32 10022
Tel (212) 527-8400 *SIC* 7379

OCC NATIONAL BANK EXAMINERS p 1072
111 Wall St Bsmt 1 10005
Tel (212) 527-1020 *SIC* 7389

OCH-ZIFF CAPITAL MANAGEMENT GROUP LLC p 1073
9 W 57th St 10019
Tel (212) 790-0000 *SIC* 6282

▲ **OCIP HOLDING LLC** p 1074
660 Madison Ave Fl 19 10065
Tel (646) 589-6180 *SIC* 2861 2873

ODYSSEY INVESTMENT PARTNERS LLC p 1075
590 Madison Ave Fl 39 10022
Tel (212) 351-7900 *SIC* 6211

OEP CAPITAL ADVISORS LP p 1075
510 Madison Ave Fl 19 10022
Tel (212) 277-1552 *SIC* 6726

OGILVY & MATHER WORLDWIDE INC p 1076
636 11th Ave 10036
Tel (212) 237-4000
SIC 7311 7812 7375 8742

OGILVY GROUP LLC p 1076
636 11th Ave 10036
Tel (212) 237-4000
SIC 7311 8743 8748 7336 7361 8732

OGILVY PUBLIC RELATIONS WORLDWIDE INC p 1076
636 11th Ave 10036
Tel (212) 880-5200 *SIC* 8743 8999

■ **OMD USA LLC** p 1084
195 Broadway 10007
Tel (212) 590-7100 *SIC* 7311

▲ **OMNICOM GROUP INC** p 1085
437 Madison Ave 10022
Tel (212) 415-3600 *SIC* 7311

■ **OMNICOM MEDIA GROUP** p 1085
195 Broadway Fl 12 10007
Tel (212) 590-7100 *SIC* 7311

OMX (US) INC p 1085
140 Broadway Fl 25 10005
Tel (646) 428-2800 *SIC* 7372

ONE EQUITY PARTNERS LLC p 1086
320 Park Ave Fl 18 10022
Tel (212) 794-3434 *SIC* 6726 8748

▲ **ONE GROUP HOSPITALITY INC** p 1086
411 W 14th St Fl 3 10014
Tel (212) 277-5301 *SIC* 5812

ONE ROCK CAPITAL PARTNERS LLC p 1086
30 Rockefeller Plz # 5400 10112
Tel (212) 605-6000 *SIC* 6282

ONEX INVESTMENT CORP p 1088
712 5th Ave Fl 40 10019
Tel (212) 582-2211 *SIC* 6799 6282

OPEN SOCIETY INSTITUTE p 1089
224 W 57th St Frnt 1 10019
Tel (212) 548-0600 *SIC* 8399

■ **OPPENHEIMER & CO INC** p 1090
85 Broad St Bldg 85 10004
Tel (212) 668-8000 *SIC* 6211

OPPENHEIMER FUNDS p 1090
2 Wrld Fncl Ctr Ste 1100 10281
Tel (212) 323-0200 *SIC* 6289 6282

▲ **OPPENHEIMER HOLDINGS INC** p 1090
85 Broad St 10004
Tel (212) 668-8000 *SIC* 6211 6712 6722

OPPENHEIMERFUNDS INC p 1090
2 Wrld Fncl Ctr Fl 14 10281
Tel (303) 768-3200 *SIC* 6282 6289

■ **ORAL COLGATE PHARMACEUTICALS INC** p 1091
300 Park Ave Fl 3 10022
Tel (212) 310-2000 *SIC* 5122 2834

ORIENT EXPRESS HOTELS INC p 1094
441 Lexington Ave Rm 504 10017
Tel (212) 302-5055
SIC 7011 3743 5947 6552

■ **ORIGINS NATURAL RESOURCES INC** p 1094
767 5th Ave Fl 38 10153
Tel (212) 572-4200 *SIC* 5122

OSCAR DE LA RENTA LLC p 1096
11 W 42nd St Fl 24 10036
Tel (212) 282-0500 *SIC* 5137

OTG EXP INC p 1097
352 Park Ave S Fl 10 10010
Tel (212) 776-1478 *SIC* 5812

▲ **OUTFRONT MEDIA INC** p 1099
405 Lexington Ave Fl 17 10174
Tel (212) 297-6400 *SIC* 7312 7319 6798

■ **OUTFRONT MEDIA LLC** p 1099
405 Lexington Ave 10174
Tel (212) 297-6400 *SIC* 7312

■ **OUTSOURCE PARTNERS INTERNATIONAL INC** p 1099
280 Park Ave Rm 3801w 10017
Tel (212) 752-2439 *SIC* 8721 8748

▲ **OVERSEAS SHIPHOLDING GROUP INC** p 1099
600 3rd Ave 10016
Tel (212) 953-4100 *SIC* 4412 4424

OXFORD UNIVERSITY PRESS LLC p 1101
198 Madison Ave Fl 8 10016
Tel (212) 726-6000 *SIC* 2731 5961

P KAUFMANN INC p 1102
3 Park Ave 10016
Tel (212) 292-2200
SIC 5131 5714 5712 2262

P O I ACQUISITION I INC p 1102
375 Park Ave Ste 1202 10152
Tel (212) 418-1700 *SIC* 6799

P&MCS HOLDING LLC p 1102
150 E 58th St 10155
Tel (212) 644-8600 *SIC* 5812

PACE UNIVERSITY p 1103
1 Pace Plz 10038
Tel (212) 346-1956 *SIC* 8221

PAINTING INDUSTRY INSURANCE FUND p 1108
45 W 14th St Fl 5 10011
Tel (212) 255-2950 *SIC* 6411

PALLADIUM EQUITY PARTNERS III LP p 1108
1270 Ave Of The 10020
Tel (212) 218-5150 *SIC* 6211 6799

PALLADIUM EQUITY PARTNERS IV LP p 1108
1270 Ave Of The Americas 10020
Tel (212) 218-5150 *SIC* 6411

PAPER CUT CLOTHING LLC p 1112
499 7th Ave Frnt 2 10018
Tel (917) 475-9356 *SIC* 5137

■ **PARAMOUNT COMMUNICATIONS ACQUISITION CORP** p 1114
1515 Broadway Lbby 10036
Tel (212) 258-6000 *SIC* 6719

PARAMOUNT GROUP INC p 1114
1633 Broadway Ste 1801 10019
Tel (212) 974-1450 *SIC* 6552 6531

■ **PARIBAS PROPERTIES INC** p 1114
787 7th Ave Fl 33 10019
Tel (212) 841-3000
SIC 6211 6221 6799 8742

PARIGI GROUP LTD p 1114
20 W 33rd St Fl 12 10001
Tel (212) 736-0688 *SIC* 5137

PARSONS BRINCKERHOFF GROUP LLC p 1117
1 Penn Plz 2nd 10119
Tel (212) 465-5000 *SIC* 8742 8711 8741

PARSONS BRINCKERHOFF INC p 1117
1 Penn Plz Ste 200 10119
Tel (212) 465-5000 *SIC* 8711 8748

PATRIARCH PARTNERS LLC p 1120
1 Broadway Fl 5 10004
Tel (212) 825-0550 *SIC* 8741

PATRIOT INTERMEDIATE HOLDINGS B CORP p 1120
340 Madison Ave 10173
Tel (212) 301-4000 *SIC* 6719

PAUL WEISS RIFKIND WHARTON & GARRISON LLP p 1121
1285 Ave Of The Americas 10019
Tel (212) 373-3000 *SIC* 8111 8748

PEAK HOLDINGS LLC p 1126
345 Park Ave Fl 30 10154
Tel (212) 583-5000
SIC 2038 2092 2099 2045

PEARSON EDUCATION HOLDINGS INC p 1126
330 Hudson St Fl 9 10013
Tel (201) 236-6716 *SIC* 2731

PEARSON INC p 1126
1330 Hudson St 10013
Tel (212) 641-2400 *SIC* 2711 2731

PEM HOLDING CO INC p 1128
800 3rd Ave Fl 40 10022
Tel (212) 446-9300 *SIC* 6211 3429 3621

PENGUIN GROUP (USA) LLC p 1128
375 Hudson St Bsmt 1 10014
Tel (212) 367-0200 *SIC* 2731

PENGUIN RANDOM HOUSE LLC p 1128
1745 Broadway 10019
Tel (212) 782-9000 *SIC* 2731

PENNANTPARK INVESTMENT CORP p 1129
590 Madison Ave Fl 15 10022
Tel (212) 905-1000 *SIC* 6726

PENTON MEDIA INC p 1132
1166 Avenue Of The Americ 10036
Tel (212) 204-4200
SIC 2721 7389 7313 7375

PEOPLE CARE HOLDINGS INC p 1132
116 W 32nd St Fl 15 10001
Tel (212) 631-7300 *SIC* 8082

PEOPLE CARE INC p 1132
116 W 32nd St Fl 15 10001
Tel (212) 631-7300 *SIC* 8082

PERELLA WEINBERG PARTNERS GROUP LP p 1135
767 5th Ave Fl 3 10153
Tel (212) 287-3200 *SIC* 6282

PERKINS EASTMAN ARCHITECTS DPC p 1136
115 5th Ave Fl 3 10003
Tel (212) 353-7200 *SIC* 8712 8742 7389

PERMIRA ADVISERS LLC p 1136
320 Park Ave Fl 33 10022
Tel (212) 386-7480 *SIC* 6282

PERNOD RICARD USA LLC p 1136
250 Park Ave Ste 17a 10177
Tel (914) 848-4800 *SIC* 2085

▲ **PFIZER INC** p 1140
235 E 42nd St 10017
Tel (212) 733-2323 *SIC* 2834 2833

▲ **PHILIP MORRIS INTERNATIONAL INC** p 1143
120 Park Ave Fl 6 10017
Tel (917) 663-2000 *SIC* 2111

PHYSICIAN AFFILIATE GROUP OF NEW YORK PC p 1145
55 W 125th St Rm 1002 10027
Tel (646) 672-3651 *SIC* 8011

PILLSBURY WINTHROP SHAW PITTMAN LLP p 1148
1540 Broadway Fl 9 10036
Tel (212) 858-1000 *SIC* 8111

PILOT GROUP LP p 1148
1270 Ave Of The Americas 10020
Tel (212) 486-4446 *SIC* 4833

PINEBRIDGE INVESTMENTS LLC p 1149
399 Park Ave Fl 4 10022
Tel (646) 857-8000 *SIC* 8741

■ **PJT PARTNERS HOLDINGS LP** p 1153
280 Park Ave Fl 15w 10017
Tel (212) 364-7800 SIC 6282

▲ **PJT PARTNERS INC** p 1153
280 Park Ave Fl 16 10017
Tel (212) 364-7800 SIC 6282 6153

PLANNED PARENTHOOD FEDERATION OF AMERICA INC p 1154
123 William St Fl 10 10038
Tel (212) 541-7800 SIC 8093

PLATINUM PARTNERS VALUE ARBITRAGE FUND LP p 1155
250 W 55th St Fl 14 10019
Tel (212) 581-0500 SIC 6726

PLAZA CONSTRUCTION LLC p 1155
1065 Avenue Of The Americ 10018
Tel (212) 849-4800 SIC 1542 8741

PLUS ONE HOLDINGS INC p 1157
77 Water St Fl 15 10005
Tel (212) 269-2896 SIC 6719

PM BEEF HOLDINGS LLC p 1157
810 7th Ave Fl 29 10019
Tel (507) 831-2761 SIC 5144 5147 2011

PMI GROUP INC p 1157
350 5th Ave 10118
Tel (925) 658-7878 SIC 6351 6211

PMI MORTGAGE INSURANCE CO p 1157
350 5th Ave 10118
Tel (925) 658-7878 SIC 6351 6331

PMX AGENCY INC p 1158
5 Hanover Sq Fl 6 10004
Tel (212) 387-0300 SIC 8742

PORT AUTHORITY OF NEW YORK & NEW JERSEY p 1162
4 World Trade Ctr 150 10007
Tel (212) 435-7000
SIC 4581 4785 6512 4491 4111

PQ NEW YORK INC p 1166
50 Broad St Fl 12 10004
Tel (212) 359-9000 SIC 5812

PR NEWSWIRE ASSOCIATION LLC p 1167
350 Hudson St Fl 3 10014
Tel (800) 776-8090 SIC 7383

PRADA USA CORP p 1167
609 W 51st St 10019
Tel (212) 307-9300
SIC 5136 5137 5139 5661 5632 8741

PREMIER & COMPANIES INC p 1170
460 W 34th St Fl 5 10001
Tel (212) 947-1365 SIC 5112

PRESIDIO INC p 1172
1 Penn Plz Ste 2832 10119
Tel (212) 324-4398 SIC 7373

PRESIDIO INTERNATIONAL INC p 1172
450 W 15th St 4 10011
Tel (212) 462-1100 SIC 5651 7379

PRET A MANGER (USA) LIMITED p 1173
853 Broadway Ste 700 10003
Tel (646) 728-0505 SIC 5812

PRICEWATERHOUSECOOPERS LLP p 1174
300 Madison Ave Fl 24 10017
Tel (646) 471-4000 SIC 8721 8742

PRIDE CAPITAL PARTNERS LLC p 1174
420 Lexington Ave Rm 2903 10170
Tel (212) 235-5300 SIC 7373

PRIME SECURITY SERVICES BORROWER LLC p 1175
9 W 57th St Fl 43 10019
Tel (212) 515-3200
SIC 6799 7382 3699 7381

PRINCE MINERAL HOLDING CORP p 1176
21 W 46th St Fl 14th 10036
Tel (646) 747-4222 SIC 2819

PRINCE MINERALS LLC p 1176
21 W 46th St Fl 14 10036
Tel (646) 747-4222 SIC 3295 3356

PRITCHARD INDUSTRIES INC p 1178
1120 Ave Of The Amrcs 17r 10036
Tel (212) 382-2295 SIC 7349

PROGRESSIVE HOME HEALTH SERVICES INC p 1181
225 W 34th St Fl 9 10122
Tel (212) 273-5500 SIC 8059

PROJECT OHR INC p 1182
80 Maiden Ln Fl 10 10038
Tel (718) 853-2700 SIC 8322 8742

PROJECT ORBIS INTERNATIONAL INC p 1182
520 8th Ave Rm 1101 10018
Tel (646) 674-5500 SIC 8699

PROSKAUER ROSE LLP p 1184
11 Times Sq Fl 17 10036
Tel (212) 969-3000 SIC 8111

▲ **PROSPECT CAPITAL CORP** p 1184
10 E 40th St Fl 42 10016
Tel (212) 448-0702 SIC 6726

PROSPERITY LIFE INSURANCE GROUP p 1184
650 Madison Ave Fl 26 10022
Tel (212) 223-5627 SIC 6311

■ **PRUDENTIAL SECURITIES GROUP INC** p 1187
199 Water St 10038
Tel (212) 778-1000 SIC 6722

PSILOS GROUP MANAGERS LLC p 1188
1 Liberty Plz Ste 2301 10006
Tel (212) 242-8844 SIC 6799 8059

PUBLIC HEALTH SOLUTIONS p 1189
40 Worth St Fl 5 10013
Tel (646) 619-6400 SIC 8733

PUBLICIS INC p 1190
1675 Broadway Fl 2 10019
Tel (212) 279-5000 SIC 7311

▲ **PVH CORP** p 1193
200 Madison Ave Bsmt 1 10016
Tel (212) 381-3500
SIC 2321 2331 2253 3143 5621 5611

PWC STRATEGY& (US) LLC p 1193
101 Park Ave Fl 18 10178
Tel (212) 697-1900 SIC 8742

PX HOLDING CORP p 1193
35 E 62nd St 10065
Tel (212) 688-9000 SIC 7359 3861 3648

▲ **PZENA INVESTMENT MANAGEMENT INC** p 1194
320 Park Ave Fl 8 10022
Tel (212) 355-1600 SIC 6722

QBE HOLDINGS INC p 1194
88 Pine St 10005
Tel (212) 422-1212 SIC 6321 6411

QBE INSURANCE CORP p 1194
88 Pine St Fl 16 10005
Tel (212) 422-1212 SIC 6311 6321

QUAKER EQUITIES LTD p 1196
257 Park Ave S Fl 7 10010
Tel (212) 473-1510 SIC 5182

QUALITY BUILDING SERVICES CORP p 1196
801 2nd Ave Fl 8 10017
Tel (212) 883-0009 SIC 7349

R SISKIND & CO INC p 1202
1385 Broadway Fl 24 10018
Tel (212) 840-0880 SIC 5137 5136

■ **R/GA MEDIA GROUP INC** p 1203
450 W 33rd St Fl 12 10001
Tel (212) 946-4000
SIC 7374 7336 7375 7311

RADIANZ AMERICAS INC p 1204
620 8th Ave Fl 46 10018
Tel (212) 205-1800 SIC 4813

RAG & BONE HOLDINGS LLC p 1205
425 W 13th St Ofc 2 10014
Tel (212) 982-3992 SIC 5621

RAILWORKS CORP p 1205
5 Penn Plz 10001
Tel (212) 502-7900 SIC 1629

RAKUTEN MARKETING LLC p 1206
215 Park Ave S Fl 9 10003
Tel (646) 943-8200 SIC 8742 7375

▲ **RALPH LAUREN CORP** p 1206
650 Madison Ave Fl C1 10022
Tel (212) 318-7000
SIC 2325 2321 2253 2323 2311 2329

RANDA CORP p 1207
417 5th Ave Fl 11 10016
Tel (212) 768-8800 SIC 2323 2389

RANDOM HOUSE LLC p 1208
1745 Broadway Frnt 3 10019
Tel (212) 782-9000 SIC 5942 2731

RATP DEV USA LLC p 1209
295 Madison Ave Fl 29 10017
Tel (646) 927-0201 SIC 4151

RAV INVESTIGATIVE & SECURITIES SERVICES LTD p 1209
347 W 36th St 10018
Tel (212) 447-7777 SIC 6211

RBC CAPITAL MARKETS LLC p 1211
200 Vesey St Fl 6 10281
Tel (212) 858-7000 SIC 6211

RBC USA HOLDCO CORP p 1211
3 World Financial Ctr 10281
Tel (212) 858-7200 SIC 6712 6021 6022

RDA HOLDING CO p 1212
750 3rd Ave 10017
Tel (914) 238-1000
SIC 2721 2731 5961 2741

■ **READE DUANE HOLDINGS INC** p 1213
40 Wall St Fl 22 10005
Tel (212) 273-5700 SIC 5912

RECKSON OPERATING PARTNERSHIP LP p 1214
420 Lexington Ave 10170
Tel (212) 594-2700 SIC 6531

RED APPLE GROUP INC p 1215
800 3rd Ave Fl 5 10022
Tel (212) 956-5803 SIC 5461 5541 5411

REDI HOLDINGS LLC p 1216
80 Pine St Fl 27 10005
Tel (212) 419-9696 SIC 6211

RELATED COMPANIES INC p 1221
511 W 33rd St Rm 200 10001
Tel (212) 801-1000 SIC 6552 6531

RELATED COMPANIES L P p 1221
60 Columbus Cir 10023
Tel (212) 421-5333 SIC 6552 6531

RELATED MANAGEMENT CORP p 1221
423 W 55th St 10019
Tel (212) 319-1200 SIC 6531

RELX INC p 1222
230 Park Ave 10169
Tel (212) 309-8100
SIC 2721 2731 7389 7374 8748

REMY COINTREAU USA INC p 1222
1290 Ave Of The Americas 10104
Tel (646) 277-2307 SIC 5182

RENAISSANCE JEWELRY NEW YORK INC p 1223
3 E 54th St Ste 603 10022
Tel (212) 986-7287 SIC 5094

RENAISSANCE TECHNOLOGIES LLC p 1223
800 3rd Ave Fl 33 10022
Tel (212) 821-1502 SIC 6722 6282

RENAL RESEARCH INSTITUTE LLC p 1223
315 E 62nd St Fl 4 10065
Tel (212) 360-6579 SIC 8092

RENCO GROUP INC p 1223
1 Rockefeller Plz Fl 29 10020
Tel (212) 541-6000
SIC 3312 3316 2514 2511 3171 3496

RESEARCH FOUNDATION OF CITY UNIVERSITY OF NEW YORK p 1226
230 W 41st St Fl 7 10036
Tel (212) 417-8300 SIC 8733

RESEARCH FOUNDATION OF CITY UNIVERSITY OF NEW YORK p 1226
50 W 40th St 10018
Tel (212) 417-8557 SIC 8221

▲ **RESOURCE CAPITAL CORP** p 1227
712 5th Ave Fl 12 10019
Tel (212) 506-3870 SIC 6798

RESTAURANT ASSOCIATES CORP p 1228
132 W 31st St Rm 601 10001
Tel (212) 613-5500 SIC 5812

RESTAURANT ASSOCIATES LLC p 1228
132 W 31st St Rm 601 10001
Tel (212) 613-5500 SIC 5812

RESURGENCE ASSET MANAGEMENT LLC p 1228
1185 Av Of The Amer Fl 18 10036
Tel (212) 710-5001
SIC 6282 2865 2821 2869 2861 2819

REUNITED LLC p 1229
1385 Broadway Fl 22 10018
Tel (646) 439-7576 SIC 5137 5136

■ **REUTERS AMERICA LLC** p 1229
3 Times Sq 10036
Tel (646) 223-4000 SIC 7383

REV HOLDINGS INC p 1229
466 Lexington Ave Fl 21 10017
Tel (212) 527-4000
SIC 2844 3421 5122 5199 5999

REVAL.COM INC p 1229
420 5th Ave Fl 5 10018
Tel (212) 393-1313 SIC 7371

■ **REVLON CONSUMER PRODUCTS CORP** p 1229
1 New York Plz 10004
Tel (212) 527-4000 SIC 2844 3421

REVLON HOLDINGS INC p 1229
237 Park Ave 10017
Tel (212) 527-4000
SIC 2844 3421 5122 5199 5999

▲ **REVLON INC** p 1229
1 New York Plz 10004
Tel (212) 527-4000 SIC 2844

■ **REVLON REAL ESTATE CORP** p 1229
466 Lexington Ave Fl 13 10017
Tel (212) 527-4000
SIC 5122 2844 3421 5199 5999

■ **RG PARENT LLC** p 1231
264 W 40th St Fl 10 10018
Tel (212) 869-8001 SIC 5611

RGI GROUP INC p 1231
625 Madison Ave Frnt 4 10022
Tel (212) 527-4000
SIC 2844 3421 5122 5199 5999

RHONE CAPITAL LLC p 1232
45 Rockefeller Plz # 2710 10111
Tel (212) 218-6700 SIC 6799

RHONE GROUP LLC p 1232
630 5th Ave Ste 2710 10111
Tel (212) 218-6700 SIC 6282

■ **RICHLINE GROUP INC** p 1233
1385 Broadway Fl 12 10018
Tel (212) 886-6000 SIC 5094 3911

RIPPLEWOOD ADVISORS LLC p 1236
920 Broadway Fl 6 10010
Tel (212) 218-2705 SIC 6799

RIPPLEWOOD HOLDINGS LLC p 1236
1 Rockefeller Plz Fl 10 10020
Tel (212) 218-2705 SIC 7389 6211

RIPPLEWOOD INVESTMENTS LLC p 1236
920 Broadway Fl 6 10010
Tel (212) 218-2705 SIC 6282

■ **RISKMETRICS GROUP INC** p 1236
1 Chase Manhattan Plz F 10005
Tel (212) 981-7475 SIC 8742

RIVERSIDE PARTNERS LLC p 1238
45 Rockefeller Plz # 400 10111
Tel (212) 265-6575 SIC 6799

RIVERSIDE RESEARCH INSTITUTE p 1238
156 William St Fl 9 10038
Tel (212) 563-4545 SIC 8733

ROBECO USA INC p 1241
909 3rd Ave 10022
Tel (212) 908-9500 SIC 6282

■ **ROBERT GRAHAM DESIGNS LLC** p 1241
264 W 40th St Fl 10 10018
Tel (212) 869-8001 SIC 5137 5136

ROBERTSON FOUNDATION p 1242
101 Park Ave Fl 48 10178
Tel (212) 984-5714 SIC 8699

ROBIN HOOD FOUNDATION p 1242
826 Broadway Fl 9 10003
Tel (212) 227-6601 SIC 8699 8322

ROCKEFELLER FOUNDATION p 1244
420 5th Ave Fl 22 10018
Tel (212) 869-8500 SIC 8699

ROCKEFELLER GROUP INC p 1244
1221 Ave Of The Am Flr 17 10020
Tel (212) 282-2000 SIC 6531 7389

ROCKEFELLER GROUP INTERNATIONAL INC p 1244
1221 Avenue Of The Americ 10020
Tel (212) 282-2000 SIC 6512 6552 4813

ROCKEFELLER UNIVERSITY p 1244
1230 York Ave 10065
Tel (212) 327-8078 SIC 8733 8221 8062

ROCKROSE DEVELOPMENT CORP p 1245
15 E 26th St Fl 7 10010
Tel (212) 847-3700 SIC 6552

ROGOSIN INSTITUTE INC p 1246
505 E 70th St Fl 2 10021
Tel (212) 746-1551 SIC 8733 8399

ROLAND FOODS LLC p 1247
71 W 23rd St 10010
Tel (212) 741-8290 SIC 5149

ROLEX INDUSTRIES INC p 1247
665 5th Ave Fl 6 10022
Tel (212) 758-7700 SIC 5094 7631 6512

ROOSEVELT MANAGEMENT CO LLC p 1249
1540 Broadway Ste 1500 10036
Tel (212) 704-4106 SIC 8741

ROSA MEXICANO MIAMI LLC p 1250
846 7th Ave Fl 4 10019
Tel (212) 397-0666 SIC 5812

ROSENTHAL & ROSENTHAL INC p 1251
1370 Broadway 10018
Tel (212) 356-1400 SIC 6153

ROTHSCHILD INC p 1252
1251 Avenue Of The Americ 10020
Tel (212) 403-3500 SIC 6282 6211

ROTHSCHILD NORTH AMERICA INC p 1252
1251 Ave Of The Ave Fl 51 10020
Tel (212) 403-3500
SIC 6211 6159 8742 6221 6282 8741

ROUSE PROPERTIES LLC p 1253
1114 Avenue Of The Americ 10036
Tel (212) 608-5108 SIC 6799

ROYAL ALLIANCE ASSOCIATES INC p 1254
1 Wrld Fncl Ctr Fl 14 10281
Tel (212) 786-0235 SIC 6211

RR ACQUISITION HOLDING LLC p 1255
1345 Avenue Of The Americ 10105
Tel (212) 479-7116 SIC 4011

RUDER FINN GROUP INC p 1257
301 E 57th St 10022
Tel (212) 593-5838 SIC 8743 6799 8741

RUDER FINN INC p 1257
425 E 53rd St 10022
Tel (212) 593-6400 SIC 8743 7311 2752

RUN INC p 1258
375 Hudson St Fl 8 10014
Tel (212) 244-3200 SIC 7311 7319

RUSSELL REYNOLDS ASSOCIATES INC p 1259
200 Park Ave Fl 23 10166
Tel (212) 309-1089 SIC 7361

RWL WATER LLC p 1260
767 5th Ave Ste 4200 10153
Tel (212) 572-5700 SIC 1629

▲ **S&P GLOBAL INC** p 1263
55 Water St Ste Conc2 10041
Tel (212) 438-1000 SIC 7323 6282

SAATCHI & SAATCHI ADVERTISING GROUP INC p 1263
355 Park Ave S 10010
Tel (212) 229-6403 SIC 7311

SABIN ROBBINS CONVERTING CO LLC p 1264
455 E 86th St Apt 5e 10028
Tel (513) 874-5270 SIC 5111

SAFE SKIES LLC p 1266
954 3rd Ave Ste 504 10022
Tel (888) 632-5027 SIC 3429

SAFRA NATIONAL BANK OF NEW YORK p 1267
546 5th Ave 10036
Tel (212) 382-9200 SIC 6021

SAFWAY HOLDINGS LLC p 1267
280 Park Ave Fl 38 10017
Tel (212) 351-7900 SIC 7359 5082 1799

SAGARD CAPITAL PARTNERS LP p 1267
280 Park Ave Fl 3ny 10017
Tel (203) 629-6700 SIC 6799

SAINT VINCENTS CATHOLIC MEDICAL CENTERS OF NEW YORK p 1271
5 Penn Plz Ste 900 10001
Tel (212) 356-4792 SIC 8062

SAKS & CO p 1271
611 5th Ave 10022
Tel (212) 753-4000 SIC 5621 5311 5651

SAKS FIFTH AVENUE LLC p 1271
12 E 49th St Fl 2 10017
Tel (212) 940-5013 SIC 5311

SAKS INC p 1271
12 E 49th St Fl 2 10017
Tel (212) 940-5305
SIC 5311 5611 5621 5641

SALONCENTRIC INC p 1273
575 5th Ave 10017
Tel (800) 282-2843 SIC 5087

SANDLER ONEILL & PARTNERS LP p 1278
1251 Ave Of Americas 6t 10020
Tel (212) 466-7800 SIC 6211

SARATOGA LIGHTING HOLDINGS LLC p 1282
535 Madison Ave Fl 4 10022
Tel (212) 906-7800
SIC 3641 3645 3646 3648

SAUMIL DIAM LLC p 1283
15 W 47th St Ste 1707 10036
Tel (212) 575-3655 SIC 5094

SAVILLS AMERICA LIMITED p 1284
399 Park Ave Fl 11 10022
Tel (212) 326-1000 SIC 6531 6799

SAVILLS STUDLEY INC p 1284
399 Park Ave Fl 11 10022
Tel (212) 326-1000 SIC 6531 6799

SCHNEIDER MILLS INC p 1288
1430 Broadway Rm 1202 10018
Tel (212) 768-7500 SIC 2221

▲ SCHOLASTIC CORP p 1288
557 Broadway Lbby 1 10012
Tel (212) 343-6100
SIC 2731 2721 7372 7812 6794 7311

■ SCHOLASTIC INC p 1288
557 Broadway Lbby 1 10012
Tel (800) 724-6527
SIC 2731 2721 7372 7812

SCHOOL OF VISUAL ARTS INC p 1290
209 E 23rd St Frnt 1 10010
Tel (212) 592-2000 SIC 8221 5734 5999

SCHRODER US HOLDINGS INC p 1290
875 3rd Ave Fl 21 10022
Tel (212) 641-3800
SIC 6282 6719 6211 6799

SCHULTE ROTH & ZABEL LLP p 1290
919 3rd Ave Frnt 2 10022
Tel (212) 756-2000 SIC 8111

SCOR REINSURANCE CO p 1293
199 Water St Fl 21 10038
Tel (212) 884-9000 SIC 6331

SCOR US CORP p 1293
199 Water St Fl 21 10038
Tel (212) 884-9667 SIC 6411

■ SEABURY & SMITH (DELAWARE) INC p 1296
1166 Ave Of The Americas 10036
Tel (212) 345-9049
SIC 6411 6331 6321 6311

SEGAL GROUP INC p 1300
333 W 34th St 10001
Tel (212) 251-5000 SIC 8742

SENECA MORTGAGE INVESTMENTS LP p 1303
375 Park Ave Ste 3401 10152
Tel (888) 601-6718 SIC 6799 6719

SENIOR HEALTH PARTNERS INC p 1304
100 Church St Fl 17 10007
Tel (646) 273-4610 SIC 6321

SENTINEL CAPITAL PARTNERS LLC p 1305
330 Madison Ave Fl 27 10017
Tel (212) 688-3100 SIC 5812

▲ SEQUENTIAL BRANDS GROUP INC p 1306
5 Bryant Park Fl 30 10001
Tel (646) 564-2577 SIC 7389

SERVICES FOR UNDERSERVED INC p 1308
305 7th Ave Fl 10 10001
Tel (212) 633-6900 SIC 8322

SESAME WORKSHOP p 1308
1 Lincoln Plz Fl 2 10023
Tel (212) 595-3456 SIC 7812 2731

▲ SFX ENTERTAINMENT INC p 1310
902 Broadway Fl 8 10010
Tel (646) 561-6400 SIC 7929

SG AMERICAS SECURITIES HOLDINGS LLC p 1310
245 Park Ave Fl 5 10167
Tel (212) 278-6000 SIC 6211

SG AMERICAS SECURITIES LLC p 1310
245 Park Ave 10167
Tel (212) 278-6000 SIC 6211

SH GROUP INC p 1310
1515 Broadway 10036
Tel (212) 921-2300 SIC 8748 8711 1542

SHACKLEFORDS CONSTRUCTION & CONTRACTING LTD p 1310
303 Lexington Ave 10016
Tel (646) 771-4470
SIC 1522 1542 1541 7389

▲ SHAKE SHACK INC p 1310
24 Union Sq E Fl 5 10003
Tel (646) 747-7200 SIC 5812

SHEARMAN & STERLING LLP p 1313
599 Lexington Ave Fl 16 10022
Tel (212) 848-4000 SIC 8111

SHELLPOINT PARTNERS LLC p 1314
140 E 45th St Fl 37 10017
Tel (212) 850-7700 SIC 6162 7389

SHISEIDO AMERICAS CORP p 1317
900 3rd Ave Fl 15 10022
Tel (212) 805-2300 SIC 2844 5122

SHOPWELL INC p 1318
42 W 39th St Fl 18 10018
Tel (212) 915-2202 SIC 5411

SHOREGROUP INC p 1318
460 W 35th St 10001
Tel (212) 736-2915 SIC 7373

SHUBERT FOUNDATION INC p 1319
234 W 44th St Fl 6 10036
Tel (212) 944-3777 SIC 8699 6512

SHUBERT ORGANIZATION INC p 1319
234 W 44th St Fl 6 10036
Tel (212) 944-3700 SIC 6512 7922

SHUTTERSTOCK INC p 1319
350 5th Ave Fl 21 10118
Tel (646) 766-1855 SIC 7374 7335

▲ SIGNATURE BANK p 1322
565 5th Ave Fl 8r 10017
Tel (646) 822-1500 SIC 6029 7389

SILVERPEAK REAL ESTATE PARTNERS LP p 1324
909 3rd Ave Fl 30 10022
Tel (212) 716-2000 SIC 6531

■ SIMON & SCHUSTER INC p 1324
1230 Ave Of The Americas 10020
Tel (212) 698-7000
SIC 2731 2741 7372 8732

SIMONS FOUNDATION INC p 1325
160 5th Ave Fl 7 10010
Tel (646) 654-0066 SIC 8399

SIMPLICITY CREATIVE GROUP INC p 1325
261 Madison Ave Fl 4 10016
Tel (212) 686-7676
SIC 2241 2221 2396 2298

SIMPSON THACHER & BARTLETT LLP p 1325
425 Lexington Ave Fl 15 10017
Tel (212) 455-2000 SIC 8111 6531

SIMS GROUP USA HOLDINGS CORP p 1326
16 W 22nd St Fl 10 10010
Tel (212) 604-0710 SIC 5093

SINGER WORLDWIDE LLC p 1326
295 Madison Ave Fl 6 10017
Tel (615) 213-0880 SIC 5064

SIRIS CAPITAL GROUP LLC p 1326
601 Lexington Ave Rm 5901 10022
Tel (212) 231-0095 SIC 6799

SIRIUS AMERICA INSURANCE CO p 1326
140 Broadway Fl 32 10005
Tel (212) 312-2500 SIC 6331

■ SIRIUS XM HOLDINGS INC p 1327
1221 Avenue Of Americas Flr 36 10020
Tel (212) 584-5100 SIC 4832

■ SIRIUS XM RADIO INC p 1327
1221 Avenue Of The Americ 10020
Tel (212) 584-5100 SIC 4832

SK CAPITAL PARTNERS II LP p 1328
400 Park Ave Ste 820 10022
Tel (212) 826-2700 SIC 6799

SK CAPITAL PARTNERS LP p 1328
400 Park Ave Ste 820 10022
Tel (212) 826-2700 SIC 6211

SK TITAN HOLDINGS LLC p 1329
400 Park Ave 10022
Tel (212) 826-2700 SIC 6799

SKADDEN ARPS SLATE MEAGHER & FLOM LLP p 1329
4 Times Sq Fl 24 10036
Tel (212) 735-3000 SIC 8111

SKANSKA INC p 1329
350 5th Ave Fl 32 10118
Tel (917) 438-4500 SIC 8741 1542

SKANSKA USA INC p 1329
350 5th Ave Fl 32 10118
Tel (917) 438-4500 SIC 8741 1542

SKY ACQUISITION LLC p 1330
345 Park Ave 10154
Tel (212) 583-5000 SIC 6799

SL GREEN OPERATING PARTNERSHIP LP p 1330
420 Lexington Ave Rm 1800 10170
Tel (212) 594-2700 SIC 6798

▲ SL GREEN REALTY CORP p 1330
420 Lexington Ave Rm 1824 10170
Tel (212) 594-2700 SIC 6798

SLOAN-KETTERING INSTITUTE FOR CANCER RESEARCH p 1331
1275 York Ave 10065
Tel (212) 639-2000 SIC 8733

SMILE TRAIN INC p 1333
41 Madison Ave Ste 2801 10010
Tel (212) 689-9199 SIC 8699

■ SMITH BARNEY CONSULTING CORP p 1333
388 Greenwich St Ofc 1 10013
Tel (212) 816-6000 SIC 7389

SNOW PHIPPS GROUP LLC p 1336
667 Madison Ave Fl 18 10065
Tel (212) 508-3300 SIC 6799

SOJITZ CORP OF AMERICA p 1337
1120 Ave Of The 10036
Tel (212) 704-6500
SIC 5065 5084 5169 5051 5099 5052

SOLAR CAPITAL LTD p 1338
500 Park Ave Fl 3 10022
Tel (212) 993-1670 SIC 6799

SOLOMON R GUGGENHEIM FOUNDATION p 1338
1071 5th Ave 10128
Tel (212) 423-3500 SIC 8412

SOLOMON-PAGE GROUP LLC p 1338
260 Madison Ave Fl 3 10016
Tel (212) 403-6100 SIC 7361

SOLVATION INC p 1339
885 3rd Ave Fl 34 10022
Tel (212) 888-5500 SIC 6153 1611 3272

SOMPO AMERICA INSURANCE SERVICES LLC p 1339
777 3rd Ave Fl 24 10017
Tel (212) 416-1200 SIC 6331

SONY BROADBAND ENTERTAINMENT CORP p 1340
550 Madison Ave Fl 6 10022
Tel (212) 833-6800
SIC 3652 7812 5734 7832 5735

SONY CORP OF AMERICA p 1341
25 Madison Ave Fl 27 10010
Tel (212) 833-8000
SIC 3695 3652 3651 3577 3572

SONY MUSIC ENTERTAINMENT INC p 1341
25 Madison Ave Fl 19 10010
Tel (212) 833-8500 SIC 3652 5064

SONY MUSIC HOLDINGS INC p 1341
550 Madison Ave Fl 16 10022
Tel (212) 833-8000 SIC 3652 5099 2741

SOROS FUND MANAGEMENT LLC p 1341
250 W 55th St Fl 28 10019
Tel (212) 872-1054 SIC 6282

SOS INTERNATIONAL LLC p 1341
40 Fulton St Fl 26 10038
Tel (212) 742-2410
SIC 3724 8711 7389 8732

SOS INTERNATIONAL LTD p 1341
40 Fulton St Fl 26 10038
Tel (212) 742-2410 SIC 7389

▲ SOTHEBYS p 1341
1334 York Ave 10021
Tel (212) 606-7000 SIC 6531 6111 5921

SOULCYCLE INC p 1342
609 Greenwich St Fl Grnd 10014
Tel (212) 787-7685 SIC 7991

SOURCE MEDIA INC p 1342
1 State St Fl 26 10004
Tel (212) 803-8200 SIC 2721

SOUTHPORT LANE MANAGEMENT LLC p 1351
350 Madison Ave Fl 21 10017
Tel (212) 729-3247 SIC 6799

SPARTAN SECURITY SERVICES INC p 1355
417 5th Ave Fl 9 10016
Tel (212) 251-7888 SIC 7381

■ SPECIALTY MINERALS INC p 1356
622 3rd Ave Fl 38 10017
Tel (212) 878-1800
SIC 2819 5032 1422 5169 2899

■ SPF HOLDINGS II LLC p 1358
9 W 57th St Ste 4200 10019
Tel (212) 750-8300
SIC 2033 5149 6719 2099

▲ SPH GROUP HOLDINGS LLC p 1358
590 Madison Ave Fl 32 10022
Tel (212) 520-2300 SIC 3339 3011 3312

■ SPH GROUP INC p 1358
590 Madison Ave 10022
Tel (212) 520-2300 SIC 6141

■ SPH SERVICES INC p 1358
590 Madison Ave Fl 32 10022
Tel (212) 520-2300 SIC 6141

SPRINKLR INC p 1361
29 W 35th St Fl 7 10001
Tel (917) 933-7800 SIC 8742 7372

SQUARESPACE INC p 1362
225 Varick St Fl 12 10014
Tel (646) 580-3456 SIC 7371

SSCG GROUP LLC p 1363
220 E 42nd St 10017
Tel (212) 907-4300 SIC 7311

ST LUKES-ROOSEVELT HOSPITAL CENTER p 1370
1111 Amsterdam Ave 10025
Tel (212) 523-4000 SIC 8062

STABILIS CAPITAL MANAGEMENT LP p 1374
767 5th Ave Fl 12 10153
Tel (212) 256-8970 SIC 6211

▲ STAFFING 360 SOLUTIONS INC p 1374
641 Lexington Ave 10022
Tel (646) 507-5710 SIC 7363

■ STANDARD & POORS FINANCIAL SERVICES LLC p 1375
55 Water St Fl 49 10041
Tel (212) 438-2000 SIC 6282

■ STANDARD & POORS SECURITIES EVALUATIONS INC p 1375
55 Water St Fl 44 10041
Tel (212) 438-3388 SIC 7323 6289

STANDARD AMERICAS INC p 1375
520 Madison Ave Fl 28 10022
Tel (212) 407-5000 SIC 6081 6082

STANDARD CHARTERED HOLDINGS INC p 1375
1095 Ave Of The Americas 10036
Tel (212) 667-0700 SIC 6221 6211 6531

STANDARD CHARTERED INTERNATIONAL (USA) LTD p 1375
200 Vesey St 10285
Tel (212) 640-2000 SIC 6082 6021 6099

■ STANLEY MORGAN DOMESTIC HOLDINGS INC p 1377
1585 Broadway Lowr B 10036
Tel (212) 761-4000 SIC 6021

STANTEC CONSULTING SERVICES INC p 1377
50 W 23rd St Fl 8 10010
Tel (212) 366-5600 SIC 8731 8711 1541

STARK CARPET CORP p 1379
979 3rd Ave Fl 11 10022
Tel (844) 407-8275 SIC 5099 5131 5021

STARR COMPANIES p 1379
399 Park Ave Rm 1700 10022
Tel (646) 227-6300 SIC 6321

STARR INDEMNITY & LIABILITY CO p 1379
399 Park Ave Rm 1700 10022
Tel (646) 227-6300 SIC 6321

STARR INSURANCE HOLDINGS INC p 1379
399 Park Ave Rm 1702 10022
Tel (646) 227-6300 SIC 6282 6411

STARR INTERNATIONAL CO INC p 1379
399 Park Ave Fl 8 10022
Tel (646) 227-6300 SIC 6531

STARR TECHNICAL RISKS AGENCY INC p 1379
90 Park Ave Fl 9 10016
Tel (646) 227-6301 SIC 6331

STARRETT CORP p 1379
70 E 55th St Fl 7 10022
Tel (212) 350-9909 SIC 6552

■ STARSUPPLY PETROLEUM LLC p 1379
55 Water St 10041
Tel (212) 968-2920 SIC 5172

▲ STEEL PARTNERS HOLDINGS LP p 1384
590 Madison Ave Rm 3202 10022
Tel (212) 520-2300
SIC 3479 3497 1381 6141

STEEL PARTNERS II LP p 1384
590 Madison Ave Rm 3202 10022
Tel (212) 758-3232 SIC 5191 2874

STEINWAY MUSICAL INSTRUMENTS INC p 1385
1133 Ave Of The Am Fl 33 10036
Tel (781) 894-9770 SIC 3931

STEMCOR USA INC p 1385
2 Park Ave Rm 1600 10016
Tel (212) 563-0262 SIC 5051 8711

STERLING BANCORP p 1386
650 5th Ave Ste 2406 10019
Tel (212) 757-3300 SIC 6021

STERLING ENTERTAINMENT ENTERPRISES LLC p 1387
75 Rockefeller Plz Fl 29 10019
Tel (212) 485-4400 SIC 4833

STERLING INFOSYSTEMS INC p 1387
1 State St Fl Plaza24 10004
Tel (800) 899-2272 SIC 7375 7381

STERLING NATIONAL BANK p 1387
650 5th Ave Fl 4 10019
Tel (212) 757-3300 SIC 6021

■ STERLING PUBLISHING CO INC p 1387
1166 Avenue Of The Flr 17 10036
Tel (212) 532-7160 SIC 5192 2731

■ STEWART TITLE INSURANCE CO p 1389
300 E 42nd St Fl 10 10017
Tel (212) 922-0050 SIC 6361

STONE SOURCE LLC p 1391
215 Park Ave S Fl 7 10003
Tel (212) 979-6400 SIC 5032

STRIVECTIN OPERATING CO INC p 1394
601 W 26th St Rm 1505 10001
Tel (212) 220-3400 SIC 8743

STROOCK & STROOCK & LAVAN LLP p 1394
180 Maiden Ln Fl 17 10038
Tel (212) 806-5400 SIC 8111

STROZ FRIEDBERG LLC p 1394
32 Avenue Of The Americas # 1 10013
Tel (212) 981-6540 SIC 7379

STRUCTURE TONE INC p 1394
330 W 34th St Fl 11 10001
Tel (212) 481-6100 SIC 8741

STUART WEITZMAN INC p 1394
50 W 57th St Fl 10 10019
Tel (212) 582-9500 SIC 5661

STUART WEITZMAN RETAIL STORES LLC p 1394
625 Madison Ave Frnt 3 10022
Tel (212) 582-6388 SIC 7389 3171 5999

STUDIO 3 PARTNERS LLC p 1394
1515 Broadway Rm 43 10036
Tel (212) 846-4004 SIC 4841

STV INC p 1395
225 Park Ave S Fl 5 10003
Tel (212) 529-2722 SIC 8711 8712 8741

SUCCESS ACADEMY CHARTER SCHOOLS INC p 1396
95 Pine St Fl 6 10005
Tel (646) 597-4641 SIC 8741

SUGAR FOODS CORP p 1397
950 3rd Ave Fl 21 10022
Tel (212) 753-6900
SIC 2869 2023 2099 2068 7389

SULLIVAN & CROMWELL LLP p 1397
125 Broad St Fl 35 10004
Tel (212) 558-4000 SIC 8111

SUMITOMO CORP OF AMERICAS p 1398
300 Madison Ave 10017
Tel (212) 207-0700
SIC 5051 5172 5084 5063 5141

SUMITOMO MITSUI FINANCE AND LEASING CO LTD p 1398
277 Park Ave Fl 15 10172
Tel (212) 224-4000 *SIC* 7389

SUNBELT BEVERAGE CO LLC p 1401
60 E 42nd St Ste 1915 10165
Tel (212) 699-7000 *SIC* 5182

SUNHAM HOME FASHIONS LLC p 1402
136 Madison Ave Fl 16 10016
Tel (212) 695-1218 *SIC* 2392

SUNTORY INTERNATIONAL CORP p 1405
600 3rd Ave Fl 21 10016
Tel (212) 891-6600
SIC 5149 2084 2086 5499 5812

SURDNA FOUNDATION INC p 1408
330 Madison Ave Fl 30 10017
Tel (212) 557-0010 *SIC* 6732 8742

SUS - MENTAL HEALTH PROGRAMS INC p 1409
305 7th Ave Fl 7 10001
Tel (212) 633-6900 *SIC* 8699

SW GROUP LLC p 1410
9 E 40th St Fl Mezz 10016
Tel (646) 688-2608 *SIC* 5311

SW MERGER ACQUISITION CORP p 1410
245 Park Ave 10167
Tel (212) 648-2355 *SIC* 4941 4952

SW RETAIL GROUP LLC p 1411
9 E 40th St Fl Mezz 10016
Tel (646) 688-2608 *SIC* 5311

SWISS POST SOLUTIONS INC p 1412
10 E 40th St Fl 9 10016
Tel (212) 204-0900 *SIC* 8744

SWISS POST US HOLDINGS INC p 1412
10 E 40th St Fl 9 10016
Tel (212) 204-0900 *SIC* 6719

SYCAMORE PARTNERS LLC p 1413
9 W 57th St Ste 3100 10019
Tel (212) 796-8500 *SIC* 6552

SYCAMORE PARTNERS MANAGEMENT LP p 1413
9 W 57th St Ste 3100 10019
Tel (212) 796-8500 *SIC* 6211

SYMPHONYTALENT LLC p 1414
45 Rockefeller Plz # 659 10111
Tel (212) 999-9000 *SIC* 7372 7361

SYNCORA GUARANTEE INC p 1414
135 W 50th St Fl 20 10020
Tel (212) 478-3400 *SIC* 6399

SYSKA HENNESSY GROUP INC p 1418
1515 Broadway Fl 14 10036
Tel (212) 921-2300 *SIC* 8711

T2 COMPUTING INC p 1420
119 W 23rd St Ste 206 10011
Tel (212) 220-9600 *SIC* 7373 7379

TAILWIND MANAGEMENT LP p 1421
485 Lexington Ave Rm 2300 10017
Tel (212) 271-3800 *SIC* 6799

▲TAKE-TWO INTERACTIVE SOFTWARE INC p 1422
622 Broadway Fl 6 10012
Tel (646) 536-2842 *SIC* 7371 7372

TAKEDA AMERICA HOLDINGS INC p 1422
767 3rd Ave 10017
Tel (212) 421-6954 *SIC* 5122 5169 2819

■TARGET SOURCING SERVICES CORP p 1425
500 Fashion 7th Ave Fl 5a 10018
Tel (800) 440-0680 *SIC* 7389

TATA AMERICA INTERNATIONAL CORP p 1426
101 Park Ave Rm 2603 10178
Tel (212) 557-8038 *SIC* 7379

TAXI HOLDINGS CORP p 1426
390 Park Ave 10022
Tel (212) 318-9800 *SIC* 5812 6794

■TBWA CHIAT/DAY INC p 1427
488 Madison Ave Fl 7 10022
Tel (212) 804-1000 *SIC* 7311 8743

■TBWA WORLDWIDE INC p 1427
488 Madison Ave 10022
Tel (212) 804-1000 *SIC* 7311

TEACH FOR AMERICA INC p 1429
25 Broadway Fl 12 10004
Tel (212) 279-2080 *SIC* 7361

TEACHERS COLLEGE COLUMBIA UNIVERSITY p 1429
525 W 120th St 10027
Tel (212) 678-3000 *SIC* 8221

TEACHERS INSURANCE AND ANNUITY ASSOCIATION OF AMERICA p 1429
730 3rd Ave Ste 2a 10017
Tel (212) 490-9000 *SIC* 6311

TEACHERS INSURANCE AND ANNUITY ASSOCIATION-COLLEGE RETIREMENT EQUITIES FUND p 1429
730 3rd Ave Ste 2a 10017
Tel (212) 490-9000 *SIC* 6311

TEIJIN HOLDINGS USA INC p 1433
600 Lexington Ave Fl 27 10022
Tel (212) 308-8744 *SIC* 5131

TEKSERVE CORP p 1433
119 W 23rd St Frnt 1 10011
Tel (212) 929-3645 *SIC* 7378 5734

TELECOM ITALIA SPARKLE OF NORTH AMERICA INC p 1434
622 3rd Ave Fl 38 10017
Tel (212) 310-9000 *SIC* 4813

■TELESECTOR RESOURCES GROUP INC p 1435
140 West St 10007
Tel (212) 395-1000 *SIC* 8742

■TELEVISION FOOD NETWORK GP p 1435
75 9th Ave 10011
Tel (212) 366-0509 *SIC* 4841

■TELX LLC p 1435
1 State St Fl 21 10004
Tel (212) 480-9049 *SIC* 4899

TEMCO SERVICE INDUSTRIES INC p 1436
417 5th Ave Fl 9 10016
Tel (212) 889-6353 *SIC* 7349 7342 6289

TENEX CAPITAL MANAGEMENT LP p 1437
60 E 42nd St Rm 5230 10165
Tel (212) 457-1138 *SIC* 6722

TERENCE CARDINAL COOKE HEALTH CARE CENTER p 1439
1249 5th Ave 10029
Tel (212) 360-1000 *SIC* 8051

TERRA HOLDINGS LLC p 1439
770 Lexington Ave Rm 301 10065
Tel (212) 508-7200 *SIC* 6531

TERRA-GEN POWER LLC p 1439
1095 Avenue Of The Americ 10036
Tel (646) 829-3900 *SIC* 4911

THERACARE OF NEW YORK INC p 1447
116 W 32nd St Fl 8 10001
Tel (212) 564-2350 *SIC* 8093 7361

THIRD POINT LLC p 1448
390 Park Ave Fl 18 10022
Tel (212) 715-3880 *SIC* 6799

THIRTEEN PRODUCTIONS LLC p 1448
825 8th Ave Fl 14 10019
Tel (212) 560-2000 *SIC* 4833

THOMAS PUBLISHING CO LLC p 1449
5 Penn Plz Fl 9 10001
Tel (212) 695-0500
SIC 2741 2721 7374 7331

■THOMSON REUTERS (MARKETS) LLC p 1450
3 Times Sq Lbby Mailroom 10036
Tel (646) 223-4000 *SIC* 7375

■THOMSON REUTERS CORP p 1450
3 Times Sq Lbby Mailroom 10036
Tel (646) 223-4000
SIC 2741 8111 7372 7383

THOR EQUITIES LLC p 1450
25 W 39th St Fl 11 10018
Tel (212) 529-5055 *SIC* 6531 6211 6282

THORNTONTOMASETTI INC p 1450
51 Madison Ave Fl 19 10010
Tel (917) 661-7800 *SIC* 8711 8712

THREE CITIES RESEARCH INC p 1450
37 W 20th St Ste 908 10011
Tel (212) 838-9660 *SIC* 6282

TIAA REAL ESTATE ACCOUNT p 1452
730 3rd Ave 10017
Tel (212) 490-9000 *SIC* 6531

TIAA-CREF INDIVIDUAL & INSTITUTIONAL SERVICES LLC p 1452
730 3rd Ave Ste 2a 10017
Tel (212) 490-9000 *SIC* 6211

▲TIFFANY & CO p 1453
200 5th Ave Bsmt 2 10010
Tel (212) 755-8000
SIC 5944 5094 5719 5943 5999 5961

▲TIME INC p 1454
225 Liberty St Ste C2 10281
Tel (212) 522-1212 *SIC* 2721

▲TIME WARNER INC p 1454
1 Time Warner Ctr Bsmt B 10019
Tel (212) 484-8000
SIC 4841 7812 2731 2721

TINICUM CAPITAL PARTNERS II LP p 1455
800 3rd Ave Fl 40 10022
Tel (212) 446-9300 *SIC* 6211 3429 3621

▲TIPTREE FINANCIAL INC p 1455
780 3rd Ave Fl 21 10017
Tel (212) 446-1400
SIC 6162 6282 6311 6798

■TIPTREE OPERATING CO LLC p 1455
780 3rd Ave Rm 2103 10017
Tel (212) 446-1410 *SIC* 8082

■TISHMAN CONSTRUCTION CORP p 1455
100 Park Ave Fl 5 10017
Tel (212) 708-6800 *SIC* 8741 1611

■TISHMAN REALTY & CONSTRUCTION CO INC p 1456
100 Park Ave Fl 5 10017
Tel (212) 708-6800 *SIC* 8741 6552

TISHMAN SPEYER PROPERTIES LP p 1456
45 Rockefeller Plz Conc1 10111
Tel (212) 715-0300 *SIC* 6531 6552

■TITLEVEST AGENCY OF NEW YORK INC p 1456
44 Wall St Fl 10 10005
Tel (212) 757-5800 *SIC* 6361

TLB HOLDINGS LLC p 1457
9 W 57th St 10019
Tel (212) 796-8555
SIC 5961 5661 5632 5641 5621

TMP WORLDWIDE ADVERTISING & COMMUNICATIONS LLC p 1457
125 Broad St Fl 10 10004
Tel (646) 613-2000 *SIC* 7311

TNC (US) HOLDINGS INC p 1458
770 Broadway Fl 8 10003
Tel (646) 654-5500
SIC 8732 2721 2732 2741

TOKIO MARINE AMERICA p 1458
230 Park Ave Fl 2 10169
Tel (212) 297-6600 *SIC* 6411

TOMEN AMERICA INC p 1459
805 3rd Ave Fl 16 10022
Tel (212) 355-3600
SIC 5153 5169 5031 5131 2261

■TOMMY HILFIGER USA INC p 1459
601 W 26th St Rm 500 10001
Tel (212) 840-8888
SIC 5611 5632 5641 5136 5137 5139

TOPPS CO INC p 1461
1 Whitehall St Fl 4 10004
Tel (212) 376-0300
SIC 5145 5092 5112 2064

TORAY HOLDING (USA) INC p 1461
461 5th Ave Fl 9 10017
Tel (212) 697-8150 *SIC* 2821

TORCHLIGHT INVESTORS LLC p 1461
475 5th Ave Fl 10 10017
Tel (212) 883-2800 *SIC* 6722 6282

TORY BURCH LLC p 1462
11 W 19th St Fl 7 10011
Tel (212) 683-2323 *SIC* 5621

TOSHIBA AMERICA INC p 1462
1251 Ave Of Ameri Ste 4100 10020
Tel (212) 596-0600
SIC 3651 3631 5064 5075 3571 3661

TOSHIBA AMERICA INFORMATION SYSTEMS INC p 1462
1251 Ave Of The Ste 4110 10020
Tel (949) 583-3000
SIC 3571 3577 3572 3661 5045

TOSHIBA NUCLEAR ENERGY HOLDINGS (US) INC p 1462
1251 Ave Of Amrcs 400 Ste 4100 10020
Tel (212) 596-0600
SIC 8711 3829 3823 2819

TOURO COLLEGE p 1464
500 7th Ave Fl 5 10018
Tel (646) 565-6000 *SIC* 8221

TOWER INSURANCE CO OF NEW YORK p 1464
120 Broadway Ste 31 10271
Tel (212) 655-2000 *SIC* 6411

TOWERBROOK CAPITAL PARTNERS LP p 1464
65 E 55th St Fl 27 10022
Tel (212) 699-2200 *SIC* 6282

TOWERS WATSON DELAWARE HOLDINGS INC p 1464
335 Madison Ave Fl 20 10017
Tel (212) 309-3400 *SIC* 8742 8999

TOWN RESIDENTIAL LLC p 1465
33 Irving Pl Frnt 1 10003
Tel (212) 557-6500 *SIC* 6531

▲TOWN SPORTS INTERNATIONAL HOLDINGS INC p 1466
5 Penn Plz Fl 4 10001
Tel (212) 246-6700 *SIC* 7991 7997

■TOWN SPORTS INTERNATIONAL INC p 1466
5 Penn Plz Fl 4 10001
Tel (212) 246-6700 *SIC* 7997 7991

TOYOTA MOTOR NORTH AMERICA INC p 1467
601 Lexington Ave Fl 49 10022
Tel (212) 751-3053 *SIC* 5511 5012 3711

TOYOTA TSUSHO AMERICA INC p 1467
805 3rd Ave Fl 17 10022
Tel (212) 355-3600
SIC 5051 5013 4225 6331 5153

■TRADEWEB MARKETS LLC p 1469
1177 Avenues Of The Am 10036
Tel (646) 430-6000 *SIC* 6211

TRADITION (NORTH AMERICA) INC p 1469
255 Greenwich St Fl 4 10007
Tel (212) 791-4500 *SIC* 6211

TRAMMO INC p 1469
1 Rockefeller Plz Fl 9 10020
Tel (212) 223-3200 *SIC* 5191 5172 5169

■TRANSATLANTIC HOLDINGS INC p 1470
80 Pine St Fl 9 10005
Tel (212) 365-2200 *SIC* 6331

■TRANSATLANTIC REINSURANCE CO p 1471
1 Liberty Plz Fl 17 10006
Tel (212) 365-2200 *SIC* 6331

TRANSPERFECT GLOBAL INC p 1472
3 Park Ave Fl 39 10016
Tel (212) 689-5555 *SIC* 7389 7371 8748

TRANSPERFECT TRANSLATIONS INTERNATIONAL INC p 1472
3 Park Ave Fl 39 10016
Tel (212) 689-5555 *SIC* 7389 8748 8111

▲TRAVELERS COMPANIES INC p 1474
485 Lexington Ave 10017
Tel (917) 778-6000 *SIC* 6331 6351 6321

TRAVELEX CURRENCY SERVICES INC p 1474
122 E 42nd St Rm 2800 10168
Tel (212) 363-6206 *SIC* 6099

▲TRAVELZOO INC p 1475
590 Madison Ave Rm 3700 10022
Tel (212) 484-4900 *SIC* 7313 7373

TRAXYS NORTH AMERICA LLC p 1475
825 3rd Ave Fl 9 10022
Tel (212) 918-8000 *SIC* 6111 7389

▲TREMOR VIDEO INC p 1476
1501 Broadway Fl 8 10036
Tel (646) 723-5300 *SIC* 7311

TRI-STATE EMPLOYMENT SERVICE INC p 1477
160 Broadway Fl 15 10038
Tel (212) 346-7960 *SIC* 7361

TRIANGLE PRIVATE HOLDINGS I LLC p 1478
601 Lexington Ave Fl 59 10022
Tel (212) 231-0095 *SIC* 6719

TRIBOROUGH BRIDGE & TUNNEL AUTHORITY p 1479
Robert Moses Bldg Randal 10035
Tel (212) 360-3000 *SIC* 4785

TRIDENT PRIVATE HOLDINGS I LLC p 1479
601 Lexington Ave 59thf 10022
Tel (212) 231-0095 *SIC* 4813 7374

TRIMARAN FUND MANAGEMENT LLC p 1480
1325 Ave Of The Flr 34 10019
Tel (212) 616-3700 *SIC* 6211

TRINITY EPISCOPAL SCHOOL CORP p 1481
139 W 91st St 10024
Tel (212) 873-1650 *SIC* 8211

TRIUMPH APPAREL CORP p 1483
530 Fashion Ave Ste M1 10018
Tel (212) 302-2606 *SIC* 2331

■TRUE NORTH COMMUNICATIONS INC p 1486
1114 Ave Of The Americas 10036
Tel (212) 704-1200 *SIC* 7311

TRUMP ORGANIZATION INC p 1487
725 5th Ave Bsmt A 10022
Tel (212) 832-2000 *SIC* 6531 7922 6794

TRUSTED MEDIA BRANDS INC p 1487
750 3rd Ave Fl 3 10017
Tel (914) 238-1000
SIC 2721 2731 5961 2741

TRUSTEES OF COLUMBIA UNIVERSITY IN CITY OF NEW YORK p 1487
116th And Bdwy Way 10027
Tel (212) 854-9970 *SIC* 8221 8062

TRUSTEES OF COLUMBIA UNIVERSITY IN CITY OF NEW YORK p 1487
630 W 168th St Fl 4 10032
Tel (212) 305-2862 *SIC* 8221 8733 8062

TRZ HOLDINGS II INC p 1489
3 World Financial Ctr 10281
Tel (212) 693-8150 *SIC* 6798

TULLETT PREBON AMERICAS CORP p 1491
199 Water St Fl 17 10038
Tel (212) 208-2000 *SIC* 6211 7373

TURKISH AIRLINES INC p 1492
350 5th Ave Ste 7510 10118
Tel (800) 874-8875 *SIC* 4512

TURN ON PRODUCTS INC p 1492
270 W 38th St Rm 1200 10018
Tel (212) 764-2121 *SIC* 2339 2331

TURNER CONSTRUCTION CO INC p 1492
375 Hudson St Fl 6 10014
Tel (212) 229-6000
SIC 1542 1541 1522 8741 8742

TURNER CORP p 1492
375 Hudson St Rm 700 10014
Tel (212) 229-6000
SIC 1542 1541 1522 8742

TURNER INTERNATIONAL INDUSTRIES INC p 1493
375 Hudson St Fl 6 10014
Tel (212) 229-6000 *SIC* 8741 8712 1542

TV GUIDE MAGAZINE LLC p 1493
50 Rockefeller Plz Fl 14 10020
Tel (212) 852-7500 *SIC* 2721

▲TWENTY-FIRST CENTURY FOX INC p 1494
1211 Ave Of The Americas 10036
Tel (212) 852-7000 *SIC* 4833 4841

▲TWO HARBORS INVESTMENT CORP p 1495
590 Madison Ave Fl 3600 10022
Tel (612) 629-2500 *SIC* 6798

TZELL TRAVEL LLC p 1497
119 W 40th St Fl 14 10018
Tel (212) 944-2121 *SIC* 4724

UBM INC p 1498
2 Penn Plz 10121
Tel (212) 600-3000
SIC 2721 2711 8732 2741

UBM LLC p 1498
2 Penn Plz Fl 15 10121
Tel (516) 562-5085
SIC 2721 2711 7319 7389

UBS FINANCIAL SERVICES INC p 1498
1285 Ave Of The Americas 10019
Tel (212) 713-2000 *SIC* 6211 6282

UBS REAL ESTATE SECURITIES INC p 1498
1285 Av Of Amrc Fl Sconc1 10019
Tel (212) 713-2000 *SIC* 6211

UFX HOLDING I CORP p 1499
55 E 52nd St Fl 35 10055
Tel (212) 644-5900 *SIC* 3299

UFX HOLDING II CORP p 1499
55 E 52nd St Fl 35 10055
Tel (212) 644-5900 *SIC* 3299

UHS HOLDCO INC p 1500
383 Madison Ave Fl 40 10179
Tel (212) 272-2000 *SIC* 7352 5047

UNCN HOLDINGS INC p 1502
320 Park Ave Ste 2500 10022
Tel (212) 893-9500 *SIC* 8011

UNIFRAX HOLDING CO p 1503
55 E 52nd St Fl 35 10055
Tel (212) 644-5900 *SIC* 3299

UNIPEC AMERICA INC p 1505
410 Park Ave Ste 610 10022
Tel (212) 759-5085 *SIC* 5172

UNITED BROTHERHOOD OF CARPENTERS AND RESILIENT FLOOR COVERERS LOCAL 2287 p 1506
395 Hudson St Fl 8 10014
Tel (212) 929-2940 *SIC* 8631

UNITED CEREBRAL PALSY ASSOCIATIONS OF NEW YORK STATE INC p 1507
330 W 34th St Fl 15 10001
Tel (212) 947-5770 *SIC* 8059

UNITED CEREBRAL PALSY OF NEW YORK CITY INC p 1507
80 Maiden Ln Fl 8 10038
Tel (212) 683-6700 *SIC* 8322

UNITED CHARITIES p 1507
633 3rd Ave Fl 10 10017
Tel (212) 614-5393 *SIC* 6512

UNITED FEDERATION OF TEACHERS WELFARE FUND p 1508
52 Broadway Lowr 10004
Tel (212) 539-0500 *SIC* 6371

UNITED JEWISH APPEAL-FEDERATION OF JEWISH PHILANTHROPIES OF NEW YORK CHARITABLE FUND LLC p 1509
130 E 59th St Fl 3 10022
Tel (212) 980-1000 *SIC* 8399

UNITED NATIONS p 1510
405 E 42nd St Bsmt 1 10017
Tel (212) 963-1234 *SIC* 9721

UNITED NATIONS DEVELOPMENT PROGRAMME p 1510
1 United Nations Plz Fl 3 10017
Tel (212) 906-5000 *SIC* 9721

UNITED NATIONS MINE ACTION SERVICE p 1510
1 United Nations Plz Fl 6 10017
Tel (212) 963-3768 *SIC* 8699

UNITED NATIONS POPULATION FUND p 1510
605 3rd Ave 10158
Tel (212) 297-5000 *SIC* 9611

UNITED STATES FUND FOR UNICEF p 1513
125 Maiden Ln Fl 11 10038
Tel (800) 367-5437 *SIC* 8399

UNITED STATES FUND FOR UNICEF IN KIND ASSISTANCE CORP p 1513
125 Maiden Ln Fl 10 10038
Tel (212) 686-5522 *SIC* 8399

■ UNIVERSAL MCCANN WORLDWIDE INC p 1517
100 W 33rd St Fl 5 10001
Tel (212) 494-4700 *SIC* 7319

UNIVISION COMMUNICATIONS INC p 1527
605 3rd Ave Fl 12 10158
Tel (212) 455-5200 *SIC* 4833

UNIVISION HOLDINGS INC p 1527
605 3rd Ave Fl 12 10158
Tel (212) 455-5200 *SIC* 4833 4813 7389

▲ URBAN EDGE PROPERTIES p 1530
888 7th Ave Ste 602 10106
Tel (212) 956-2556 *SIC* 6798

US NEWS & WORLD REPORT INC p 1532
4 New York Plz Fl 6 10004
Tel (212) 716-6800 *SIC* 2721

USA CABLE INC p 1534
30 Rockefeller Plz Conc28 10112
Tel (212) 413-5000 *SIC* 4841

USABLENET INC p 1534
142 W 57th St Fl 7 10019
Tel (212) 965-5388 *SIC* 4813

■ USL SEPARATE ACCOUNT USL VL-R p 1535
1 World Fin Ctr 10281
Tel (800) 874-8743 *SIC* 6311 6321

UTAIR - HELICOPTER SERVICES LTD p 1536
420 Lexington Ave Rm 300 10170
Tel (212) 297-6207 *SIC* 4513

UTRECHT - AMERICA HOLDINGS INC p 1537
245 Park Ave Fl 36 10167
Tel (212) 916-7800 *SIC* 6022

UTTAM GALVA NORTH AMERICA INC p 1537
1500 Broadway Fl 16 10036
Tel (917) 722-8177 *SIC* 5051

▲ VARONIS SYSTEMS INC p 1545
1250 Broadway Fl 29 10001
Tel (877) 292-8767 *SIC* 7372

VELO HOLDINGS INC p 1547
320 Park Ave Fl 18 10022
Tel (212) 277-1500 *SIC* 7389

VEOLIA ES WASTE-TO-ENERGY INC p 1548
1 Penn Plz Ste 4401 10119
Tel (212) 947-5824 *SIC* 4953

VERITAS CAPITAL FUND II L P p 1549
590 Madison Ave Ste 3501 10022
Tel (212) 415-6700 *SIC* 8742 7374

VERITAS CAPITAL MANAGEMENT LLC p 1549
9 W 57th St Fl 29 10019
Tel (212) 415-6700 *SIC* 6799

▲ VERIZON COMMUNICATIONS INC p 1550
1095 Ave Of The Americas 10036
Tel (212) 395-1000 *SIC* 4813 4812 4841

■ VERIZON NEW YORK INC p 1550
140 West St 10007
Tel (212) 395-1000 *SIC* 4813 7359

VERONIS SUHLER & ASSOCIATES INC p 1551
55 E 52nd St Fl 33 10055
Tel (212) 935-4990 *SIC* 6211

VERSO PAPER MANAGEMENT LP p 1552
60 W 42nd Ste 1942 10165
Tel (212) 599-2700 *SIC* 2621

VESTAR CAPITAL PARTNERS INC p 1552
245 Park Ave Rm 4100 10167
Tel (212) 351-1600 *SIC* 6799

VEXOS INC p 1553
60 E 42nd St Ste 1400 10165
Tel (646) 843-0710 *SIC* 7371

VI(Z)RT INC p 1554
352 7th Ave Fl 14 10001
Tel (212) 560-0708 *SIC* 7819

▲ VIACOM INC p 1554
1515 Broadway 10036
Tel (212) 258-6000 *SIC* 4841 7812

■ VIACOM SONGS INC p 1554
1515 Broadway Lbby 10036
Tel (212) 258-6000
SIC 6531 6519 7359 7941 7812 2731

VICTORY CAPITAL HOLDINGS INC p 1555
667 Madison Ave Fl 10 10065
Tel (212) 906-0746 *SIC* 6282 6722

VIDACARE INC p 1556
248 W 35th St Fl 7 10001
Tel (917) 637-3780 *SIC* 6321

VILLAGE CARE OF NEW YORK INC p 1557
120 Broadway Ste 2840 10271
Tel (212) 337-5816 *SIC* 8741 8322

VILLAGE CENTER FOR CARE p 1557
120 Broadway Ste 2840 10271
Tel (212) 367-3748 *SIC* 8051 8082 8322

▲ VINCE HOLDING CORP p 1557
500 5th Ave Ste 20 10110
Tel (212) 515-2600 *SIC* 5632 5611 5621

■ VINCE LLC p 1557
500 5th Ave Ste 20 10110
Tel (212) 515-2600 *SIC* 5137 5136

VIRGIN MEDIA HOLDINGS INC p 1558
65 Bleecker St Fl 6 10012
Tel (212) 966-2310 *SIC* 4812 4813 4841

▲ VIRTU FINANCIAL INC p 1560
900 3rd Ave Fl 29 10022
Tel (212) 418-0100 *SIC* 6211

VIRTU FINANCIAL LLC p 1560
645 Madison Ave Fl 16 10022
Tel (212) 418-0100 *SIC* 6799

VISITING NURSE SERVICE OF NEW YORK p 1561
5 Penn Plz Ste 1201 10001
Tel (212) 609-6100 *SIC* 8082

VISITING NURSE SERVICE OF NEW YORK HOME CARE p 1561
107 E 70th St 10021
Tel (212) 484-3950 *SIC* 8082

VISITING NURSE SERVICE OF NEW YORK HOME CARE II p 1561
5 Penn Plz Fl 12 10001
Tel (212) 609-5716 *SIC* 8082

VISITING NURSE SERVICE OF NEW YORK HOSPICE CARE p 1561
5 Penn Plz Ste 1201 10001
Tel (212) 609-5716 *SIC* 8082

VITECH SYSTEMS GROUP INC p 1563
401 Park Ave S Fl 12 10016
Tel (212) 868-0900 *SIC* 7371

VIVENDI HOLDING I LLC p 1563
1755 Broadway Fl 2 10019
Tel (212) 572-7000 *SIC* 7812 7389

■ VIVENDI UNIVERSAL ENTERTAINMENT LLLP p 1563
30 Rockefeller Plz 10112
Tel (212) 664-4444
SIC 7812 3652 2741 5947 5944 5961

VNS CHOICE p 1563
5 Penn Plz Ste 1201 10001
Tel (212) 609-5600 *SIC* 8082

VNS CHOICE COMMUNITY CARE p 1563
5 Penn Plz Fl 12 10001
Tel (212) 609-5716 *SIC* 8699

VNU MARKETING INFORMATION INC p 1564
770 Broadway Fl 15 10003
Tel (646) 654-5011
SIC 8732 6282 7374 5045

VOIP GUARDIAN LLC p 1564
405 E 56th St Apt 3g 10022
Tel (212) 421-0888 *SIC* 6153

VOIP GUARDIAN PARTNERS I LLC p 1564
405 E 56th St Apt 3g 10022
Tel (212) 421-0888 *SIC* 6411

▲ VOLT INFORMATION SCIENCES INC p 1564
1133 Avenue Of The Americ 10036
Tel (212) 704-2400 *SIC* 7363 4813 4899

VOLT MANAGEMENT CORP p 1565
1133 Ave Of The Americas 10036
Tel (212) 704-2400 *SIC* 7363

VOLUNTEERS OF AMERICA - GREATER NEW YORK INC p 1565
340 W 85th St 10024
Tel (212) 873-2600 *SIC* 8399

VONTOBEL ASSET MANAGEMENT INC p 1565
1540 Broadway Fl 38 10036
Tel (212) 415-7000 *SIC* 6282

VORNADO REALTY TRUST p 1565
888 7th Ave Fl 44 10106
Tel (212) 894-7000 *SIC* 6798

▲ VOYA FINANCIAL INC p 1566
230 Park Ave Fl 14 10169
Tel (212) 309-8200
SIC 6311 6411 6282 6211 7389

VSM INVESTORS LLC p 1566
245 Park Ave Fl 41 10167
Tel (212) 351-1600 *SIC* 3842 2599 2515

VSS-AHC CONSOLIDATED HOLDINGS CORP p 1567
350 Park Ave Fl 7 10022
Tel (212) 935-4990 *SIC* 7389 2721 7331

▲ VSS-CAMBIUM HOLDINGS III LLC p 1567
55 E 52nd St Fl 33 10055
Tel (212) 308-2281 *SIC* 6726

▲ W P CAREY INC p 1569
50 Rockefeller Plz Fl 2 10020
Tel (212) 492-1100 *SIC* 6531 6282

W W NORTON & CO INC p 1569
500 5th Ave Fl 6 10110
Tel (212) 354-5500 *SIC* 2731 5192

W2007/ACEP MANAGERS VOTECO LLC p 1569
85 Broad St 10004
Tel (212) 902-1000 *SIC* 7011 7999

WACHTELL LIPTON ROSEN & KATZ p 1570
51 W 52nd St Fl 29 10019
Tel (212) 403-1000 *SIC* 8111

WALL STREET SYSTEMS SERVICES CORP p 1573
1345 Ave Of The 10105
Tel (212) 809-7200 *SIC* 7371

WALLACE FOUNDATION p 1573
5 Penn Plz Fl 7 10001
Tel (212) 251-9700 *SIC* 6732

WARBURG PINCUS LLC p 1575
450 Lexington Ave 10017
Tel (212) 878-0600 *SIC* 6799 6211

WARBURG PINCUS PRIVATE EQUITY VIII LP p 1575
450 Lexington Ave 10017
Tel (212) 878-0600 *SIC* 6799

■ WARNACO GROUP INC p 1576
501 Fashion Ave 10018
Tel (212) 287-8000
SIC 2322 2329 2339 2369 2342 2341

■ WARNACO INC p 1576
501 Fashion Ave Fl 14 10018
Tel (212) 287-8000
SIC 2342 2341 2321 2329 2322 2323

■ WARNER COMMUNICATIONS INC p 1576
1 Time Warner Ctr 10019
Tel (212) 484-8000 *SIC* 7812 4841 7389

WARNER MUSIC GROUP CORP p 1576
1633 Broadway 10019
Tel (212) 275-2000 *SIC* 3652 6794

WARNER MUSIC INC p 1576
75 Rockefeller Plz Bsmt 1 10019
Tel (212) 275-2000 *SIC* 3652 2741

WARNER-ELEKTRA-ATLANTIC CORP p 1576
1633 Broadway Lowr 2c01 10019
Tel (212) 275-2000 *SIC* 7389

WASSERSTEIN & CO LP p 1580
1185 Avenue Of The Americ 10036
Tel (212) 702-5600 *SIC* 6799 2721 2741

WASSERSTEIN COSMOS CO-INVEST LP p 1580
1301 Ave Of The Americas 10019
Tel (212) 702-5600 *SIC* 6799

WASSERSTEIN HOLDINGS LLC p 1580
1301 Avenue Of The Americ 10019
Tel (212) 702-5600 *SIC* 6799 2721 2741

WEA INTERNATIONAL INC p 1585
75 Rockefeller Plz 10019
Tel (212) 275-1300 *SIC* 3652

▲ WEBMD HEALTH CORP p 1586
395 Hudson St 10014
Tel (212) 624-3700 *SIC* 7375 4813

■ WEBMD LLC p 1586
395 Hudson St Lbby 3 10014
Tel (212) 624-3700 *SIC* 7375

▲ WEIGHT WATCHERS INTERNATIONAL INC p 1588
675 Ave Americas Fl 6 10010
Tel (212) 589-2700 *SIC* 7299 7991

WEIL GOTSHAL & MANGES LLP p 1588
767 5th Ave Fl Conc1 10153
Tel (212) 310-8000 *SIC* 8111

WEISERMAZARS LLP p 1588
135 W 50th St 10020
Tel (212) 812-7000 *SIC* 8721

■ WELLCHOICE INC p 1589
1 Liberty Pl 10038
Tel (212) 476-1000 *SIC* 6321

■ WELLS FARGO CAPITAL FINANCE LLC p 1590
100 Park Ave Fl 3 10017
Tel (212) 840-2000 *SIC* 6162 7389

WELLSPRING CAPITAL MANAGEMENT LLC p 1591
390 Park Ave Fl 5 10022
Tel (212) 318-9800 *SIC* 5812

WELLSPRING CAPITAL PARTNERS III LP p 1591
390 Park Ave Fl 5 10022
Tel (212) 318-9800
SIC 5812 5813 7999 7993

WELLSPRING DISTRIBUTION INC p 1591
390 Park Ave Fl 5 10022
Tel (212) 318-9800 *SIC* 6794 5812

WELSH CARSON ANDERSON & STOWE VI LP p 1591
320 Park Ave Fl 25 10022
Tel (212) 893-9500 *SIC* 6799

WELSPUN USA INC p 1591
295 Textile Bldg 5th Ave 10016
Tel (212) 620-2000 *SIC* 5131

WENDEL NORTH AMERICA LLC p 1591
152 W 57th St Fl 55 10019
Tel (212) 557-5100 *SIC* 6211

WENNER MEDIA LLC p 1592
1290 Ave Of The Amer Fl 2 10104
Tel (212) 484-1616 *SIC* 2721

■ WESTINGHOUSE CBS HOLDING CO INC p 1601
51 W 52nd St Bsmt 1 10019
Tel (212) 975-4321 *SIC* 4833

■ WESTPOINT HOME LLC p 1602
28 E 28th St Rm 8 10016
Tel (212) 930-2074 *SIC* 2211 2221

■ WESTPOINT INTERNATIONAL INC p 1602
28 E 28th St Bsmt 2 10016
Tel (212) 930-2044 *SIC* 2211

■ WESTWOOD ONE INC p 1603
220 W 42nd St Fl 4 10036
Tel (212) 967-2888 *SIC* 4832 7922

WHITE & CASE LLP p 1605
1155 Avenue Of The Americ 10036
Tel (212) 819-8200 *SIC* 8111

■ WHITEHALL STREET INTERNATIONAL REAL ESTATE LIMITED PARTNERSHIP 2001 p 1606
85 Broad St 10004
Tel (212) 902-1000 *SIC* 6719

WHITNEY MUSEUM OF AMERICAN ART p 1607
99 Gansevoort St 10014
Tel (212) 570-3600 *SIC* 8412

WICKS COMMUNICATIONS & MEDIA PARTNERS III LP p 1608
405 Park Ave Ste 702 10022
Tel (212) 838-2100 *SIC* 6799

WICKS GROUP OF COMPANIES LLC (DE CORP) p 1608
400 Park Ave Fl 12a 10022
Tel (212) 838-2100 *SIC* 6211 6282

WIESNER PRODUCTS INC p 1608
1333 Brdwy Fl 6 10018
Tel (212) 279-2466 *SIC* 5139 2252

WILLIAMS LEA INC p 1611
381 Park Ave S Fl 5 10016
Tel (212) 351-9000 *SIC* 8741

WILLIS NORTH AMERICA INC p 1612
200 Liberty St Fl 7 10281
Tel (212) 915-8888
SIC 6411 8742 8999 8748

WILLIS OF NEW YORK INC p 1612
335 Madison Ave Fl 20 10017
Tel (212) 938-2439 *SIC* 6411

WILLIS OF NEW YORK INC p 1612
200 Liberty St 10281
Tel (212) 915-8888 *SIC* 6411

WILLKIE FARR & GALLAGHER LLP p 1612
787 7th Ave Fl 2 10019
Tel (212) 728-8000 *SIC* 8111

WILSON ELSER MOSKOWITZ EDELMAN & DICKER LLP p 1613
150 E 42nd St Fl 23 10017
Tel (212) 490-3000 *SIC* 8111

WIND HOTELS HOLDINGS INC p 1615
345 Park Ave 10154
Tel (212) 583-5000 *SIC* 7011 8741

▲ WISDOMTREE INVESTMENTS INC p 1619
245 Park Ave Fl 35 10167
Tel (212) 801-2080 *SIC* 7389

WLR RECOVERY ASSOCIATES II LLC p 1620
1166 Ave Of The Americas 10036
Tel (212) 826-1100 *SIC* 6719

WLR RECOVERY FUND II LP p 1620
1166 6th Ave 10036
Tel (212) 278-9821 *SIC* 6719 3714

WMG ACQUISITION CORP p 1620
75 Rockefeller Plz 10019
Tel (212) 275-2000 *SIC* 2782 2741 7929

WMG HOLDING CO INC p 1620
75 Rockefeller Plz 10019
Tel (212) 275-2000 *SIC* 3652 2741

WMG HOLDINGS CORP p 1620
75 Rockefeller Plz Fl 18 10019
Tel (212) 275-2000 *SIC* 7929

WNET p 1620
825 8th Ave Fl 14 10019
Tel (212) 560-2000 *SIC* 4833

WORKMAN PUBLISHING CO INC p 1624
225 Varick St Fl 9 10014
Tel (212) 254-5900 *SIC* 2731

WORLD CULTURAL ORGANIZATION INC p 1625
1330 Avenue Ste 23 10019
Tel (212) 653-0657 *SIC* 8399

■ **WPIX LLC** p 1627
80 State St 10017
Tel (212) 949-1100 *SIC* 4833

WPP CLAPTON SQUARE LLC p 1627
100 Park Ave Fl 4 10017
Tel (212) 632-2200 *SIC* 7311

WPP GROUP HOLDINGS LLC p 1627
100 Park Ave Fl 4 10017
Tel (212) 632-2200 *SIC* 7311

WPP GROUP US INVESTMENTS INC p 1627
100 Park Ave 10017
Tel (212) 632-2200 *SIC* 7311

WPP GROUP USA INC p 1627
100 Park Ave Fl 4 10017
Tel (212) 632-2200 *SIC* 7311

WPP GROUP USA INC p 1627
100 Park Ave 10017
Tel (212) 632-2200 *SIC* 7311

WS MIDWAY HOLDINGS INC p 1628
390 Park Ave Fl 6 10022
Tel (212) 318-9800
SIC 5812 5813 7999 7993

WSP USA CORP p 1628
1 Penn Plz 250w 10119
Tel (914) 747-1120 *SIC* 8711 8732

WSP USA HOLDINGS INC p 1628
512 7th Ave Fl 13 10018
Tel (212) 532-9600 *SIC* 8711 8732

■ **WYETH LLC** p 1629
235 E 42nd St 10017
Tel (973) 660-5000 *SIC* 2834 2836

XAXIS INC p 1631
132 W 31st St Fl 9 10001
Tel (212) 629-7173 *SIC* 7319 7313

XAXIS LLC p 1631
132 W 31st St Fl 9 10001
Tel (646) 259-4200 *SIC* 7311

▲ **XO GROUP INC** p 1632
195 Broadway Fl 25 10007
Tel (212) 219-8555 *SIC* 7299

XSTELOS CORP p 1633
45 Rockefeller Plz # 2260 10111
Tel (201) 934-2000 *SIC* 5661

YESHIVA UNIVERSITY p 1636
500 W 185th St 10033
Tel (212) 960-5400 *SIC* 8221

■ **YODLE WEB.COM INC** p 1636
330 W 34th St Fl 18 10001
Tel (877) 276-5104 *SIC* 4813

YOUNG & RUBICAM INC p 1637
3 Columbus Cir Fl 8 10019
Tel (212) 210-3000 *SIC* 8742

YOUNG ADULT INSTITUTE INC p 1638
460 W 34th St Fl 11 10001
Tel (212) 563-7474 *SIC* 8059 8361 8011

YOUNG BROADCASTING LLC p 1638
599 Lexington Ave 10022
Tel (517) 372-8282 *SIC* 4833

YOUNG MENS CHRISTIAN ASSOCIATION OF GREATER NEW YORK p 1638
5 W 63rd St Fl 6 10023
Tel (212) 630-9600
SIC 8641 7991 8351 7032 8322

Z CAPITAL GROUP LLC p 1640
1330 Avenue Of The Americ 10019
Tel (212) 595-8400 *SIC* 6722

ZAR GROUP LLC p 1641
1375 Broadway Fl 12 10018
Tel (212) 944-2510 *SIC* 2339

ZENITH MEDIA SERVICES INC p 1642
299 W Houston St Fl 11 10014
Tel (212) 989-3034 *SIC* 7319

ZETA INTERACTIVE CORP p 1642
185 Madison Ave 10016
Tel (212) 967-5055 *SIC* 8742

ZGS INC p 1643
456 W 55th St 10019
Tel (212) 586-1620 *SIC* 5063

■ **ZIFF DAVIS LLC** p 1643
28 E 28th St Fl 11-R 10016
Tel (212) 503-3500 *SIC* 7319

ZOCDOC INC p 1643
568 Broadway Fl 9 10012
Tel (866) 962-3621 *SIC* 8011 8099

ZURICH FINANCE (USA) INC p 1645
1 Liberty Plz Ste 2800 10006
Tel (917) 534-4500 *SIC* 6211

NEWARK, NY

▲ **IEC ELECTRONICS CORP** p 730
105 Norton St 14513
Tel (315) 331-7742 *SIC* 3672 3679

■ **MCDOWELL RESEARCH CO INC** p 928
2000 Technology Pkwy 14513
Tel (315) 332-7100 *SIC* 3669

NEWARK-WAYNE COMMUNITY HOSPITAL p 1037
1200 Driving Park Ave 14513
Tel (315) 332-2022 *SIC* 8062

WAYNE NEWARK COMMUNITY HOSPITAL p 1584
1250 Driving Park Ave 14513
Tel (315) 332-2244 *SIC* 8062

NEWBURGH, NY

CAMBRIDGE PETROLEUM HOLDING INC p 244
31 S Plank Rd Unit 105 12550
Tel (516) 542-4900
SIC 5983 5541 5984 5172 5074

NEWBURGH CITY SCHOOL DISTRICT p 1037
124 Grand St 12550
Tel (845) 563-3400 *SIC* 8211

ST LUKES CORNWALL HOSPITAL p 1370
70 Dubois St 12550
Tel (845) 561-4400 *SIC* 8062

TRIPLE A SUPPLIES INC p 1482
50 Jeanne Dr 12550
Tel (845) 566-4200 *SIC* 5169

■ **WAREXTERMINALS CORP** p 1575
1 S Water St 12550
Tel (845) 561-4000 *SIC* 5172

NIAGARA FALLS, NY

CASCADES CONTAINERBOARD PACKAGING INC p 263
4001 Packard Rd 14303
Tel (716) 285-3681 *SIC* 2631 2653

CITY OF NIAGARA FALLS p 317
745 Main St 14301
Tel (716) 286-4310 *SIC* 9111

CITY SCHOOL DISTRICT OF CITY OF NIAGARA FALLS p 320
630 66th St 14304
Tel (716) 286-4211 *SIC* 8211

GHD SERVICES INC p 610
2055 Niagara Falls Blvd 14304
Tel (716) 297-6150 *SIC* 8748

NIAGARA FALLS MEMORIAL MEDICAL CENTER INC p 1042
621 10th St 14301
Tel (716) 278-4000 *SIC* 8062

SAINT GOBAIN GRAINS & POWDERS p 1269
6600 Walmore Rd 14304
Tel (716) 731-8200 *SIC* 3221 3269 2891

SAINT-GOBAIN STRUCTURAL CERAMICS p 1271
23 Acheson Dr 14303
Tel (716) 278-6233 *SIC* 3255

SEVENSON ENVIRONMENTAL SERVICES INC p 1309
2749 Lockport Rd 14305
Tel (716) 284-0431 *SIC* 4959 1795

NIAGARA UNIVERSITY, NY

NIAGARA UNIVERSITY p 1042
5795 Lewiston Rd 14109
Tel (716) 285-1212 *SIC* 8221

NORTH SYRACUSE, NY

MOHAWK CUSTOMS & SHIPPING CORP p 982
123 Air Cargo Rd 13212
Tel (315) 455-3003 *SIC* 4731

NORTH SYRACUSE CENTRAL SCHOOL DISTRICT p 1054
5355 W Taft Rd 13212
Tel (315) 218-2100 *SIC* 8211

RICCELLI ENTERPRISES INC p 1232
6131 E Taft Rd 13212
Tel (315) 433-5115 *SIC* 4213

SRC INC p 1363
7502 Round Pond Rd 13212
Tel (315) 452-8000 *SIC* 8733

NORTH TONAWANDA, NY

IRR SUPPLY CENTERS INC p 765
908 Niagara Falls Blvd # 125 14120
Tel (716) 692-1600 *SIC* 5074

SOLVAIRA SPECIALTIES INC p 1339
50 Bridge St 14120
Tel (716) 693-4040 *SIC* 2823 2299

SUPERIOR LUBRICANTS CO INC p 1406
32 Ward Rd 14120
Tel (716) 693-8412 *SIC* 5172 5013

NORWICH, NY

CHOBANI LLC p 301
147 State Highway 320 13815
Tel (607) 337-1246 *SIC* 2026

▲ **NBT BANCORP INC** p 1021
52 S Broad St 13815
Tel (607) 337-2265 *SIC* 6021

■ **NBT BANK NA** p 1021
52 S Broad St 13815
Tel (607) 337-2265 *SIC* 6021

NYACK, NY

ATHENE ANNUITY & LIFE ASSURANCE CO OF NEW YORK p 124
69 Lydecker St 10960
Tel (845) 358-2300 *SIC* 6311

D &Y CHEESES INC p 406
20 N Broadway Ste 5 10960
Tel (845) 353-4570 *SIC* 7389

NOVA CORP INC p 1062
1 Main St 10960
Tel (201) 567-4404 *SIC* 1541 8748

NYACK HOSPITAL FOUNDATION INC p 1068
160 N Midland Ave 10960
Tel (845) 348-2000 *SIC* 8062 8011 8082

PRESIDENTIAL LIFE CORP p 1172
69 Lydecker St 10960
Tel (845) 358-2300 *SIC* 6311

OAKDALE, NY

DOWLING COLLEGE INC p 453
150 Idle Hour Blvd 11769
Tel (631) 244-3000 *SIC* 8221

NYLSI INC p 1069
3984 Sunrise Hwy 11769
Tel (631) 589-9000 *SIC* 5511

SUFFOLK COUNTY WATER AUTHORITY INC p 1396
4060 Sunrise Hwy 11769
Tel (631) 563-0255 *SIC* 4941

OAKFIELD, NY

■ **M&T BANK NATIONAL ASSOCIATION** p 890
48 Main St 14125
Tel (800) 528-6532 *SIC* 8611

OCEANSIDE, NY

AIR STREAM CORP p 39
3400 Lawson Blvd 11572
Tel (516) 763-1600 *SIC* 5141 5148

SOUTH NASSAU COMMUNITIES HOSPITAL INC p 1344
1 Healthy Way 11572
Tel (516) 632-3000 *SIC* 8062

OGDENSBURG, NY

ANSEN CORP p 93
100 Chimney Point Dr 13669
Tel (315) 393-3573 *SIC* 3672

CLAXTON MEDICAL PC p 323
214 King St 13669
Tel (315) 393-1559 *SIC* 8011

OLD BETHPAGE, NY

FAMILY RESIDENCES & ESSENTIAL ENTERPRISES INC p 527
191 Bethpage Sweet Holw 11804
Tel (516) 870-1600 *SIC* 8399

OLD WESTBURY, NY

NEW YORK INSTITUTE OF TECHNOLOGY INC p 1035
Northern Blvd 11568
Tel (516) 686-7530 *SIC* 8221

OLEAN, NY

CUTCO CORP p 403
1116 E State St 14760
Tel (716) 372-3111 *SIC* 5963 3421

DRESSER-RAND CO p 455
500 Paul Clark Dr 14760
Tel (716) 375-3000 *SIC* 3563 3511 3621

OLEAN GENERAL HOSPITAL p 1082
515 Main St 14760
Tel (716) 373-2600 *SIC* 8062

UPPER ALLEGHENY HEALTH SYSTEM INC p 1529
130 S Union St Ste 300 14760
Tel (716) 375-6975 *SIC* 8062

ONEIDA, NY

ONEIDA HEALTH CARE CENTER p 1087
321 Genesee St 13421
Tel (315) 361-2342 *SIC* 8062

ONEIDA HEALTH SYSTEMS INC p 1087
321 Genesee St 13421
Tel (315) 363-6000 *SIC* 8062 8051

ONEIDA INDIAN NATION p 1087
2037 Dream Catcher Plz 13421
Tel (315) 829-8900 *SIC* 5812

ONEIDA LTD p 1087
163 Kenwood Ave 13421
Tel (315) 361-3000
SIC 5046 5719 5023 5094

ONEONTA, NY

SPRINGBROOK NY INC p 1360
105 Campus Dr 13820
Tel (607) 286-7171 *SIC* 8211

SUNY COLLEGE AT ONEONTA p 1405
108 Ravine Pkwy 13820
Tel (607) 436-3500 *SIC* 8221 9411

ORANGEBURG, NY

API INDUSTRIES INC p 96
2 Glenshaw St 10962
Tel (845) 365-2200 *SIC* 2673 3081

ARC-COM FABRICS INC p 103
33 Ramland Rd S 10962
Tel (845) 365-1100 *SIC* 5131

DAIKIN AMERICA INC p 408
20 Olympic Dr 10962
Tel (845) 365-9500 *SIC* 3081 2821

NICE-PAK PRODUCTS INC p 1042
2 Nice Pak Park 10962
Tel (845) 365-2772 *SIC* 2621 7389 2676

PROFESSIONAL DISPOSABLES INC p 1180
2 Nice Pak Park 10962
Tel (845) 365-1700 *SIC* 2676 7389 2621

ORCHARD PARK, NY

CARLETON TECHNOLOGIES INC p 257
10 Cobham Dr 14127
Tel (716) 662-0006 *SIC* 3728

COBHAM HOLDINGS (US) INC p 332
10 Cobham Dr 14127
Tel (716) 662-0006 *SIC* 3679 3812

COBHAM HOLDINGS INC p 332
10 Orchard Park Dr 14127
Tel (716) 662-0006 *SIC* 3679 3812

COBHAM MANAGEMENT SERVICES INC p 332
10 Cobham Dr 14127
Tel (716) 662-0006 *SIC* 3568

CURBELL INC p 402
7 Cobham Dr 14127
Tel (716) 667-3377 *SIC* 5162 3669 3842

CURBELL PLASTICS INC p 402
7 Cobham Dr 14127
Tel (716) 667-3377 *SIC* 5162

■ **ITT ENIDINE INC** p 768
7 Centre Dr 14127
Tel (716) 662-1900 *SIC* 3724 3714 3593

MCGARD LLC p 929
3875 California Rd 14127
Tel (716) 662-8980 *SIC* 5072

OSSINING, NY

OSSINING UNION FREE SCHOOL DISTRICT p 1097
400 Executive Blvd 10562
Tel (914) 941-7700 *SIC* 8211

SAFE ENVIRONMENT BUSINESS SOLUTIONS INC p 1266
8 Revolutionary Rd 10562
Tel (914) 741-1000 *SIC* 7381

OSWEGO, NY

AUXILIARY SERVICES STATE UNIVERSITY COLLEGE AT OSWEGO INC p 135
7060 Route 104 13126
Tel (315) 312-2106
SIC 5812 5942 5962 5441

COUNTY OF OSWEGO p 380
46 E Bridge St 13126
Tel (315) 349-8393 *SIC* 9111

OSWEGO HOSPITAL INC p 1097
110 W 6th St 13126
Tel (315) 349-5511 *SIC* 8062 8063

SUNY COLLEGE AT OSWEGO p 1405
702 Culkin Hall 13126
Tel (315) 312-2222 *SIC* 8221 9411

OWEGO, NY

BEN WEITSMAN AND SON INC p 172
15 W Main St 13827
Tel (607) 687-2780 *SIC* 5051 5093 3341

WEITSMAN SHREDDING p 1588
15 W Main St 13827
Tel (607) 687-2780 *SIC* 5051 5093 5099

OXFORD, NY

BLUEOX CORP p 193
38 N Canal St 13830
Tel (607) 843-2583 *SIC* 5172 5411 5541

OYSTER BAY, NY

TOWN OF OYSTER BAY p 1465
54 Audrey Ave 11771
Tel (516) 624-6498 *SIC* 9199

OZONE PARK, NY

■ **FIVE STAR ELECTRIC CORP** p 553
10132 101st St 11416
Tel (718) 641-5000 *SIC* 1731

NEW YORK CITY GEOGRAPHIC DISTRICT 27 p 1034
8201 Rockaway Blvd 11416
Tel (718) 642-5861 *SIC* 8211

NORTHPOINT MORTGAGE CORP p 1057
10002 101st Ave 11416
Tel (718) 641-7000 *SIC* 6162

PALMYRA, NY

■ GARLOCK SEALING TECHNOLOGIES LLC p 592
1666 Division St 14522
Tel (315) 597-4811 *SIC* 3053 3585 3714

PATCHOGUE, NY

BOARD OF COOPERATIVE EDUCATIONAL SERVICES p 195
201 Sunrise Hwy W 11772
Tel (631) 289-2200 *SIC* 8249

PATTERSON, NY

CARMEL CENTRAL SCHOOL DISTRICT p 258
81 South St 12563
Tel (845) 878-2094 *SIC* 8211

PEARL RIVER, NY

ACTIVE MEDIA SERVICES INC p 20
1 Blue Hill Plz Ste 1705 10965
Tel (845) 735-1700 *SIC* 7319 4731 4789

HOLT CONSTRUCTION CORP p 702
50 E Washington Ave 10965
Tel (845) 735-4054 *SIC* 1541 8742

HUNTER DOUGLAS INC p 719
1 Blue Hill Plz Ste 1569 10965
Tel (845) 664-7000 *SIC* 2591 3444 5084

■ ORANGE AND ROCKLAND UTILITIES INC p 1091
1 Blue Hill Plz Ste 20 10965
Tel (845) 352-6000
SIC 4924 4911 1311 6552

■ ROCKLAND ELECTRIC CO p 1244
1 Blue Hill Plz Ste 20 10965
Tel (845) 352-6000 *SIC* 4911

UNITED STATES INFORMATION SYSTEMS INC p 1513
35 W Jefferson Ave 10965
Tel (845) 358-7755 *SIC* 1731

PEEKSKILL, NY

HUDSON RIVER HEALTHCARE INC p 717
1200 Brown St Ste 12 10566
Tel (914) 734-8800 *SIC* 8011

PELHAM, NY

COMPONENT ASSEMBLY SYSTEMS INC p 351
620 Fifth Ave Ste 1 10803
Tel (212) 567-5737 *SIC* 1751 1742

PETERSBURG, NY

TONOGA INC p 1460
136 Coon Brook Rd 12138
Tel (518) 658-3202 *SIC* 2295 3629

PHELPS, NY

WADHAMS ENTERPRISES INC p 1571
369 Bostwick Rd 14532
Tel (800) 334-1314 *SIC* 4212 4213

PINE CITY, NY

DALRYMPLE HOLDING CORP p 410
2105 S Broadway 14871
Tel (607) 737-6200
SIC 3273 1611 1442 1622 3281

PITTSFORD, NY

■ CONCENTRIX CORP p 354
3750 Monroe Ave 14534
Tel (585) 218-5300 *SIC* 7379 7331 7311

■ GATEHOUSE MEDIA LLC p 593
175 Sullys Trl Ste 300 14534
Tel (585) 598-0030 *SIC* 2711 7311 2759

MONROE PLAN FOR MEDICAL CARE INC p 985
1120 Pittsford Victor Rd 14534
Tel (585) 244-5550 *SIC* 6324

PITTSFORD CENTRAL SCHOOL DISTRICT p 1152
75 Barker Rd 14534
Tel (585) 267-1800 *SIC* 8211

SUTHERLAND GLOBAL SERVICES INC p 1409
1160 Pittsford Victor Rd A 14534
Tel (585) 586-5757 *SIC* 8742

PLAINVIEW, NY

AEROFLEX HOLDING CORP p 30
35 S Service Rd 11803
Tel (516) 694-6700 *SIC* 3674

AEROFLEX INC p 30
35 S Service Rd 11803
Tel (516) 694-6700
SIC 3812 3621 3677 3674 3496 3827

AEROFLEX PLAINVIEW INC p 30
35 S Service Rd 11803
Tel (516) 694-6700
SIC 3679 3621 3674 3827

COINMACH CORP p 335
303 Sunnyside Blvd # 70 11803
Tel (516) 349-8555
SIC 7215 7359 5087 5064 7211 8741

COINMACH SERVICE CORP p 335
303 Sunnyside Blvd # 70 11803
Tel (516) 349-8555 *SIC* 3633 5087

CSC SERVICEWORKS HOLDINGS INC p 397
303 Sunnyside Blvd # 70 11803
Tel (516) 349-8555 *SIC* 3633 5087

CSC SERVICEWORKS INC p 397
303 Sunnyside Blvd # 70 11803
Tel (516) 349-8555 *SIC* 3633 5087

CULINART INC p 400
175 Sunnyside Blvd # 200 11803
Tel (516) 437-2700 *SIC* 5812

DAVIS VISION INC p 416
159 Express St 11803
Tel (210) 245-2200 *SIC* 8011

IMOBILE LLC p 734
207 Terminal Dr 11803
Tel (516) 433-9300 *SIC* 5999

LANCER INSURANCE CO p 842
1 Fairchild Ct Ste 200 11803
Tel (541) 472-0950 *SIC* 6331

▲ NEULION INC p 1028
1600 Old Country Rd 11803
Tel (516) 622-8300 *SIC* 4841 7372

PLAINVIEW HOSPITAL p 1154
888 Old Country Rd 11803
Tel (516) 719-2200 *SIC* 8062

PLAINVIEW-OLD BETHPAGE CENTRAL SCHOOL DISTRICT p 1154
106 Washington Ave 11803
Tel (516) 937-6300 *SIC* 8211

SPIN HOLDCO INC p 1358
303 Sunnyside Blvd # 70 11803
Tel (516) 349-8555 *SIC* 3633 5087

▲ VEECO INSTRUMENTS INC p 1546
1 Terminal Dr 11803
Tel (516) 677-0200 *SIC* 3559

■ VEECO PROCESS EQUIPMENT INC p 1546
1 Terminal Dr 11803
Tel (516) 677-0200 *SIC* 3569

WALLACE EANNACE ASSOCIATES INC p 1573
50 Newtown Rd 11803
Tel (516) 454-9300 *SIC* 5074

WE TRANSPORT INC p 1585
75 Commercial St 11803
Tel (516) 349-8200 *SIC* 4151

PLATTSBURGH, NY

CHAMPLAIN VALLEY PHYSICIANS HOSPITAL p 287
75 Beekman St 12901
Tel (518) 561-2000 *SIC* 8062

COMMUNITY PROVIDERS INC p 350
75 Beekman St 12901
Tel (518) 561-2000 *SIC* 8062 8741 6512

INTRAPAC (PLATTSBURGH) INC p 760
4 Plant St 12901
Tel (518) 561-2030 *SIC* 5199 3565

PREVOST CAR US INC p 1173
260 Banker Rd 12901
Tel (518) 957-2052 *SIC* 3711

UNIVERSITY OF VERMONT CHAMPLAIN VALLEY PHYSICIANS HOSPITAL p 1526
75 Beekman St 12901
Tel (518) 561-2000 *SIC* 8062 8051

PLEASANT VALLEY, NY

CONSIGLI CONSTRUCTION NY LLC p 359
199 West Rd Ste 100 12569
Tel (845) 635-1121 *SIC* 1542

PLEASANTVILLE, NY

ZWILLING JA HENCKELS LLC p 1645
270 Marble Ave 10570
Tel (914) 749-3440 *SIC* 5023 5719

PORT CHESTER, NY

NERIS BAKERY PRODUCTS INC p 1026
31 Pearl St 37 10573
Tel (914) 937-3235 *SIC* 5149 5461 2051

PARSONS & WHITTEMORE ENTERPRISES CORP p 1117
4 International Dr # 300 10573
Tel (914) 937-9009 *SIC* 2611

SOUTHPORT MEWS HOUSING PRESERVATION p 1351
50 S Main St 10573
Tel (914) 937-1681 *SIC* 6513

STRAUSS PAPER CO INC p 1393
10 Slater St 10573
Tel (914) 937-0004 *SIC* 5113

PORT JEFF STA, NY

MARYHAVEN CENTER OF HOPE INC p 914
51 Terryville Rd 11776
Tel (631) 474-4120 *SIC* 8322 7389

PORT JEFFERSON, NY

JOHN T MATHER MEMORIAL HOSPITAL OF PORT JEFFERSON NEW YORK INC p 789
75 N Country Rd 11777
Tel (631) 476-2738 *SIC* 8062

ST CHARLES CORP p 1365
200 Belle Terre Rd 11777
Tel (631) 474-6260 *SIC* 8741

ST CHARLES HOSPITAL AND REHABILITATION CENTER p 1365
200 Belle Terre Rd 11777
Tel (631) 474-6000 *SIC* 8062 8011

PORT JERVIS, NY

BON SECOURS COMMUNITY HOSPITAL p 199
160 E Main St 12771
Tel (845) 858-7000 *SIC* 8062

KLG USA LLC p 823
20 W King St 12771
Tel (845) 856-5311 *SIC* 2844 7389 2834

KOLMAR LABORATORIES INC p 827
20 W King St 12771
Tel (845) 856-5311 *SIC* 2844

PJ HOUSING PRESERVATION LP p 1153
230 Jersey Ave 12771
Tel (845) 856-7677 *SIC* 6513

PORT WASHINGTON, NY

4004 INC p 3
12 Harbor Park Dr 11050
Tel (516) 829-4730 *SIC* 5699

▲ ACETO CORP p 17
4 Tri Harbor Ct 11050
Tel (516) 627-6000 *SIC* 5122 5169

ALMOND JEWELERS INC p 59
16 S Maryland Ave 11050
Tel (516) 933-6000 *SIC* 3911

▲ CEDAR REALTY TRUST INC p 272
44 S Bayles Ave Ste 304 11050
Tel (516) 767-6492 *SIC* 6798

DEJANA INDUSTRIES INC p 422
30 Sagamore Hill Dr 11050
Tel (516) 944-3100 *SIC* 4959

■ GLOBAL EQUIPMENT CO INC p 616
11 Harbor Park Dr 11050
Tel (516) 608-7000 *SIC* 5085

LUXOTTICA US HOLDINGS CORP p 887
12 Harbor Park Dr 11050
Tel (516) 484-3800
SIC 5048 5099 5995 5999

MODEL MODEL HAIR FASHION INC p 981
83 Harbor Rd 11050
Tel (516) 944-7777 *SIC* 5087

NPD GROUP INC p 1064
900 W Shore Rd 11050
Tel (516) 625-0700 *SIC* 8732

PAINT APPLICATOR CORP OF AMERICA p 1108
7 Harbor Park Dr 11050
Tel (516) 284-3000 *SIC* 5072 5198

■ PALL CORP p 1108
25 Harbor Park Dr 11050
Tel (516) 484-5400
SIC 3569 3599 3714 2834 3841

PUBLISHERS CLEARING HOUSE LLC p 1190
382 Channel Dr 11050
Tel (516) 883-5432 *SIC* 5961 8742

SAFAVIEH INC p 1265
40 Harbor Park Dr 11050
Tel (516) 945-1900 *SIC* 2273 5712

SANDATA HOLDINGS INC p 1278
26 Harbor Park Dr 11050
Tel (516) 484-4400 *SIC* 7374 7373

SHAKE-N-GO FASHION INC p 1310
85 Harbor Rd 11050
Tel (516) 944-7777 *SIC* 3999

▲ SYSTEMAX INC p 1418
11 Harbor Park Dr 11050
Tel (516) 608-7000 *SIC* 5961 5046

TWEEZERMAN INTERNATIONAL LLC p 1494
2 Tri Harbor Ct 11050
Tel (516) 676-7772 *SIC* 5087

■ WESCO INTEGRATED SUPPLY INC p 1593
36 Harbor Park Dr 11050
Tel (516) 484-6070 *SIC* 5085

POTSDAM, NY

CANTON-POTSDAM HOSPITAL p 248
50 Leroy St 13676
Tel (315) 265-3300 *SIC* 8062

CLARKSON UNIVERSITY p 322
8 Clarkson Ave 13676
Tel (315) 268-6400 *SIC* 8733

POUGHKEEPSIE, NY

ADAMS FAIRACRE FARMS INC p 21
765 Dutchess Tpke 12603
Tel (845) 454-4330 *SIC* 5411 5261 5199

CENTRAL HUDSON GAS & ELECTRIC CORP p 278
284 South Ave Dept 100 12601
Tel (845) 452-2700 *SIC* 4911 4924 4932

CH ENERGY GROUP INC p 286
284 South Ave 12601
Tel (845) 452-2000 *SIC* 4911 4924

DKM LTD p 445
2515 South Rd 12601
Tel (212) 661-4600 *SIC* 6211

DUTCHESS COMMUNITY COLLEGE p 463
53 Pendell Rd 12601
Tel (845) 431-8000 *SIC* 8222 9411

DUTCHESS COUNTY OF (INC) p 463
626 Dutchess Tpke 12603
Tel (845) 486-2000 *SIC* 9111

DUTCHESS EDUCATIONAL HEALTH INSURAN p 463
5 Boces Rd 12601
Tel (845) 486-4800 *SIC* 8211

DYSON-KISSNER-MORAN CORP p 465
2515 South Rd Ste 5 12601
Tel (212) 661-4600 *SIC* 3433 3625 3699

H O PENN MACHINERY CO INC p 650
122 Noxon Rd 12603
Tel (845) 452-1200 *SIC* 5082 5084

HASTINGS HEALTH SYSTEMS INC p 667
241 North Rd 12601
Tel (845) 471-2000 *SIC* 8741 8062

HEALTH QUEST p 675
45 Reade Pl 12601
Tel (845) 454-8500 *SIC* 8099

HUDSON VALLEY FEDERAL CREDIT UNION p 717
137 Boardman Rd 12603
Tel (845) 463-3011 *SIC* 6061

MARIST COLLEGE p 907
3399 North Rd 12601
Tel (845) 575-3000 *SIC* 8221

MARSHALL & STERLING ENTERPRISES INC p 911
110 Main St Ste 4 12601
Tel (845) 454-0800 *SIC* 6411

MIDHUDSON REGIONAL HOSPITAL OF WESTCHESTER MEDICAL CENTER p 965
241 North Rd 12601
Tel (845) 483-5000 *SIC* 8062 8322

ST FRANCIS HOSPITAL POUGHKEEPSIE NEW YORK p 1366
241 North Rd 12601
Tel (845) 483-5000
SIC 8062 8069 8011 8351

VASSAR BROTHERS HOSPITAL p 1545
45 Reade Pl 12601
Tel (845) 454-8500 *SIC* 8062

VASSAR COLLEGE p 1545
124 Raymond Ave Box 12 12604
Tel (845) 437-7000 *SIC* 8221

VASSER BROTHERS MEDICAL CENTER p 1545
45 Reade Pl 12601
Tel (845) 454-8500 *SIC* 8062

PULASKI, NY

FELIX SCHOELLER NORTH AMERICA INC p 537
179 County Route 2a 13142
Tel (315) 298-5133 *SIC* 2679

FULTON BOILER WORKS INC p 584
3981 Port St 13142
Tel (315) 298-5121 *SIC* 3443

PURCHASE, NY

AFFINION GROUP HOLDINGS LLC p 32
1 Manhattanville Rd # 201 10577
Tel (203) 956-1000 *SIC* 8611

APOLLO INVESTMENT FUND VI LP p 97
1 Manhattanville Rd # 201 10577
Tel (914) 694-8000 *SIC* 6726

APOLLO MANAGEMENT V LP p 97
1 Manhattanville Rd # 201 10577
Tel (914) 467-6510 *SIC* 5051 3272 3354

■ APOLLO SVF MANAGEMENT LP p 97
1 Manhattanville Rd # 201 10577
Tel (914) 694-8000 *SIC* 6726

■ APOLLO VALUE MANAGEMENT LP p 97
2 Mnhttnvlle Rd Fl 2 10577
Tel (914) 694-8000 *SIC* 6726

■ ATLAS AIR INC p 127
2000 Westchester Ave 10577
Tel (914) 701-8000 *SIC* 4512

▲ ATLAS AIR WORLDWIDE HOLDINGS INC p 127
2000 Westchester Ave 10577
Tel (914) 701-8000 *SIC* 4522 4512 7359

ATOS IT SOLUTIONS AND SERVICES INC p 128
2500 Westchester Ave Fl 3 10577
Tel (914) 881-3000 *SIC* 7379

CENTRAL NATIONAL GOTTESMAN INC p 279
3 Manhattanville Rd # 301 10577
Tel (914) 696-9000 *SIC* 5111 5099

CENTRAL NATIONAL PULP & PAPER SALES INC p 279
3 Manhattanville Rd 10577
Tel (914) 696-9000 *SIC* 2611

HAMLET HOLDING LLC p 656
2 Manhattanville Rd 10577
Tel (914) 694-8000 *SIC* 7011 7999

HITACHI CABLE AMERICA INC p 696
2 Manhattanville Rd # 301 10577
Tel (914) 694-9200 *SIC* 3052

HITACHI METALS AMERICA LTD p 697
2 Manhattanville Rd # 301 10577
Tel (914) 694-9200
SIC 3264 3577 3365 5051 3321 3559

HUDSONS BAY TRADING CO LP p 717
3 Manhattanville Rd 10577
Tel (914) 694-4444 *SIC* 5311

INTEGRAMED AMERICA INC p 749
2 Manhattanville Rd 10577
Tel (914) 253-8000 *SIC* 8093

INTEGRAMED HOLDING CORP p 749
2 Manhattanville Rd 10577
Tel (914) 253-8000 SIC 6719

LIGHTING HOLDINGS INTERNATIONAL LLC p 865
4 Manhattanville Rd 10577
Tel (845) 306-1850
SIC 3641 5719 5063 4225 3643 3229

▲ MASTERCARD INC p 918
2000 Purchase St 10577
Tel (914) 249-2000 SIC 7389

■ MASTERCARD INTERNATIONAL INC p 918
2000 Purchase St 10577
Tel (914) 249-2000 SIC 7389 6099

▲ MBIA INC p 925
1 Manhattanville Rd # 301 10577
Tel (914) 273-4545 SIC 6351

■ MORGAN STANLEY SMITH BARNEY LLC p 989
2000 Westchester Ave 10577
Tel (914) 225-5510 SIC 6211

▲ PEPSICO INC p 1134
700 Anderson Hill Rd 10577
Tel (914) 253-2000
SIC 2096 2087 2086 2037 2052 2043

TAL INTERNATIONAL CONTAINER CORP p 1422
100 Manhattanville Rd # 13 10577
Tel (914) 251-9000 SIC 7359

TAL INTERNATIONAL GROUP INC p 1422
100 Manhattanville Rd # 13 10577
Tel (914) 251-9000 SIC 7359 5085 4412

WESTCHESTER MEDICAL GROUP PC p 1597
2700 Wstchstr Ave Ste 200 10577
Tel (914) 682-0700 SIC 8011

QUEENSBURY, NY

GREAT ESCAPE AMUSEMENT PARK p 633
1172 State Route 9 12804
Tel (518) 792-3500 SIC 7996

KEENA STAFF INC p 807
2 Progress Blvd 12804
Tel (518) 793-9825 SIC 7361 7363

REGO PARK, NY

7MOD2 LLC p 4
6565 Wetherole St Apt 3j 11374
Tel (347) 581-3742 SIC 8712

NEW YORK STATE CATHOLIC HEALTH PLAN INC p 1036
9525 Queens Blvd Fl 8 11374
Tel (888) 343-3547 SIC 8011

RENSSELAER, NY

■ AMRI RENSSELAER INC p 86
33 Riverside Ave 12144
Tel (518) 433-7700 SIC 5169

NEW YORK INDEPENDENT SYSTEM OPERATOR INC p 1035
10 Krey Blvd 12144
Tel (518) 356-6000 SIC 4911

RETSOF, NY

AMERICAN ROCK SALT CO LLC p 78
3846 Retsof Rd 14539
Tel (585) 991-6878 SIC 1479 5169

RHINEBECK, NY

NORTHERN DUTCHESS HOSPITAL p 1056
6511 Spring Brook Ave 12572
Tel (845) 876-3001 SIC 8062

RICHMOND HILL, NY

INTERNATIONAL UNION OF OPERATING ENGINEERS LOCAL 30 p 757
11506 Myrtle Ave 11418
Tel (718) 847-8484 SIC 8631 6512

RUBIES COSTUME CO INC p 1257
12008 Jamaica Ave 11418
Tel (718) 846-1008 SIC 2389 7299

VIP HEALTH CARE SERVICES INC p 1558
11612 Myrtle Ave 11418
Tel (718) 849-2300 SIC 8082

RIDGEWOOD, NY

CACTUS HOLDINGS INC p 236
4705 Metropolitan Ave 11385
Tel (718) 417-3770
SIC 5411 5147 5144 5146 5148 5143

RIDGEWOOD SAVINGS BANK p 1234
7102 Forest Ave Ste 1 11385
Tel (718) 240-4800 SIC 6036

WESTERN BEEF RETAIL INC p 1597
4705 Metropolitan Ave 11385
Tel (718) 417-3770 SIC 5411

RIFTON, NY

COMMUNITY PRODUCTS LLC p 350
2032 Route 213 St 12471
Tel (845) 658-8799 SIC 3842 2511 3844

RIVERHEAD, NY

CENTRAL SUFFOLK HOSPITAL p 280
1300 Roanoke Ave 11901
Tel (631) 548-6000 SIC 8062

PECONIC BAY PRIMARY MEDICAL CARE PC p 1127
1300 Roanoke Ave 11901
Tel (631) 288-6622 SIC 8011

SPIRENT INC p 1359
303 Griffing Ave 11901
Tel (631) 208-0680 SIC 3699

ROCHESTER, NY

5LINX ENTERPRISES INC p 3
1 S Clinton Ave Ste 800 14604
Tel (585) 334-2600 SIC 7389

■ ACC CORP p 14
400 West Ave Ste 3 14611
Tel (585) 987-3000 SIC 4813

ADMAR SUPPLY CO INC p 23
1950 Brghtn Hnrietta Town 14623
Tel (585) 272-9390 SIC 5082

AMERICAN PACKAGING CORP p 77
777 Driving Park Ave 14613
Tel (585) 254-9500
SIC 2673 3497 2671 2754 2674

■ ARNOLD MAGNETIC TECHNOLOGIES CORP p 112
770 Linden Ave 14625
Tel (585) 385-9010 SIC 3264 3499

BAUSCH & LOMB INC p 160
1400 N Goodman St 14609
Tel (585) 338-6000 SIC 3851 2834 3841

BELL CO LLC p 170
1340 Lexington Ave 14606
Tel (585) 277-1000 SIC 1541 1542

BIRDS EYE HOLDINGS INC p 185
90 Linden Park 14625
Tel (585) 383-1850
SIC 2033 2013 2035 2096

BLUE CROSS & BLUE SHIELD OF ROCHESTER p 191
165 Court St 14647
Tel (585) 454-1700 SIC 6324

CARESTREAM HEALTH INC p 255
150 Verona St 14608
Tel (585) 627-1800 SIC 8011 7374

CENTURY MOLD CO INC p 282
25 Vantage Point Dr 14624
Tel (585) 352-8600 SIC 3089 3544

CITY OF ROCHESTER p 318
400 Dewey Ave 14613
Tel (585) 428-6755 SIC 9111

CONIFER REALTY LLC p 356
1000 University Ave # 500 14607
Tel (585) 324-0500 SIC 6531

COUNTY OF MONROE p 380
39 W Main St Ste 110 14614
Tel (585) 428-5301 SIC 9111

DORSCHEL REALTY CORP p 451
3817 W Henrietta Rd 14623
Tel (585) 475-1700 SIC 5511 7538 7549

■ EASTMAN KODAK CO p 473
343 State St 14650
Tel (585) 724-4000 SIC 3861 3577 7384

EJ DEL MONTE CORP p 482
909 Linden Ave Ste 1 14625
Tel (585) 586-3121
SIC 6552 8741 6512 6799 7011

ESL FEDERAL CREDIT UNION p 509
225 Chestnut St 14604
Tel (585) 336-1000 SIC 6061

EXCELLUS HEALTH PLAN INC p 517
165 Court St 14647
Tel (585) 454-1700 SIC 6321

FIRTH RIXSON INC p 551
181 Mckee Rd 14611
Tel (585) 328-1383 SIC 3462

FLOWER CITY PRINTING INC p 560
1725 Mount Read Blvd 14606
Tel (585) 663-9000 SIC 2657 2752

FUCCILLO HYUNDAI OF GREECE INC p 583
3975 W Ridge Rd 14626
Tel (585) 720-9000 SIC 5511 5531

GENESEE REGION HOME CARE ASSOCIATION INC p 602
165 Court St 14647
Tel (585) 238-4399 SIC 8699

GENESEE REGION HOME CARE ASSOCIATION INC p 602
3111 Winton Rd S 14623
Tel (585) 214-1000 SIC 8082

GENESEE VALLEY GROUP HEALTH ASSOCIATION p 602
800 Carter St 14621
Tel (585) 338-1400 SIC 8011

GETINGE USA INC p 609
1777 E Henrietta Rd 14623
Tel (585) 475-1400 SIC 3842 3841

GLEASON CORP p 614
1000 University Ave 14607
Tel (585) 473-1000 SIC 3541 3829

GLEASON WORKS p 614
1000 University Ave 14607
Tel (585) 473-1000
SIC 3714 3728 3566 3541 3829 3469

GLICK LLC p 615
415 W Main St 14608
Tel (716) 235-1595 SIC 6719

■ GLOBAL CROSSING BANDWIDTH INC p 616
200 Meridian Centre Blvd # 130 14618
Tel (212) 920-8201 SIC 4813 7373 7374

GRAYWOOD COMPANIES INC p 633
1390 Mount Read Blvd 14606
Tel (585) 254-7000
SIC 3541 3545 3544 3398

GREATER ROCHESTER INDEPENDENT PRACTICE ASSOCIATION INC p 636
100 Kings Hwy S Ste 2500 14617
Tel (585) 922-1500 SIC 8011

GREECE CENTRAL SCHOOL DISTRICT p 636
750 Maiden Ln 14615
Tel (585) 966-2000 SIC 8211

HAHN AUTOMOTIVE WAREHOUSE INC p 653
415 W Main St 14608
Tel (585) 235-1595 SIC 5013

HIGH FALLS OPERATING CO LLC p 690
445 Saint Paul St 14605
Tel (585) 546-1030 SIC 2082

HIGHLAND HOSPITAL OF ROCHESTER p 691
1000 South Ave 14620
Tel (585) 473-2200 SIC 8062

HILLSIDE FAMILY OF AGENCIES p 694
1183 Monroe Ave 14620
Tel (585) 256-7500 SIC 8361 8322 8093

HILLSIDE FAMILY OF AGENCIES p 694
1183 Monroe Ave 14620
Tel (585) 256-7500 SIC 8322

HOME PROPERTIES INC p 703
300 Clinton Sq 14604
Tel (585) 546-4900 SIC 6798

HOME PROPERTIES LIMITED PARTNERSHIP p 703
850 Clinton Sq 14604
Tel (585) 546-4900 SIC 6513

HORIZON SOLUTIONS LLC p 707
175 Josons Dr 14623
Tel (585) 274-8235 SIC 5063 5085

HUDSON HOTELS CORP p 716
400 Linden Oaks Ste 120 14625
Tel (585) 419-4000 SIC 7011 8741

HURLEY OF AMERICA INC p 721
803 Linden Ave Ste 3 14625
Tel (781) 438-7830 SIC 7349 7382

KESSLER FAMILY LLC p 814
410 White Spruce Blvd 14623
Tel (585) 424-5277 SIC 5812

■ KIT ZELLER INC p 822
1000 University Ave # 800 14607
Tel (585) 254-8840 SIC 5063

KODAK ALARIS INC p 826
2400 Mount Read Blvd # 1175 14615
Tel (585) 290-2891 SIC 3861

LECHASE CONSTRUCTION SERVICES LLC p 850
205 Indigo Creek Dr 14626
Tel (585) 254-3510 SIC 1541 1542

LIFETIME ASSISTANCE INC p 864
425 Paul Rd 14624
Tel (585) 247-2255 SIC 8322 6512

LIFETIME HEALTHCARE INC p 864
165 Court St 14647
Tel (585) 454-1700 SIC 6324 6321

MARKIT INC p 909
250 Mill St Ste 303 14614
Tel (585) 777-4018 SIC 8742

▲ MONRO MUFFLER BRAKE INC p 985
200 Holleder Pkwy 14615
Tel (585) 647-6400
SIC 7539 7533 7534 7549

MONROE COMMUNITY COLLEGE p 985
1000 E Henrietta Rd 14623
Tel (585) 292-2000 SIC 8222 9411

MONROE COMMUNITY HOSPITAL (INC) p 985
435 E Henrietta Rd 14620
Tel (585) 760-6500 SIC 8051

■ NALGE NUNC INTERNATIONAL CORP p 1007
75 Panorama Creek Dr 14625
Tel (585) 586-8800
SIC 3089 3949 3821 3085 3083

NATIONWIDE PRECISION PRODUCTS CORP p 1018
200 Tech Park Dr 14623
Tel (585) 272-7100 SIC 3356

NIXON PEABODY LLP p 1045
1300 Clinton Sq 14604
Tel (585) 263-1000 SIC 8111

NORTH AMERICAN BREWERIES INC p 1049
445 Saint Paul St 14605
Tel (585) 546-1030 SIC 2082

PALMER FAMILY OF COMPANIES INC p 1109
900 Jefferson Rd Ste 1000 14623
Tel (585) 424-3210 SIC 6719

PALMER FISH CO INC p 1109
900 Jefferson Rd Ste 1000 14623
Tel (585) 424-3210
SIC 5146 5147 5142 2013

PARK RDG APOTHECARIES p 1115
89 Genesee St 14611
Tel (585) 368-3928 SIC 5912

PARK RIDGE NURSING HOME INC p 1115
1555 Long Pond Rd 14626
Tel (585) 723-7205 SIC 8051

▲ PAYCHEX INC p 1122
911 Panorama Trl S 14625
Tel (585) 385-6666 SIC 8721 7363

PEACE OF CHRIST ROMAN CATHOLIC PARISH p 1125
25 Empire Blvd 14609
Tel (585) 288-5000 SIC 8661

PENFIELD CENTRAL SCHOOL DISTRICT INC p 1128
2590 Atlantic Ave 14625
Tel (585) 249-5700 SIC 8211

■ PFAUDLER INC p 1140
1000 West Ave 14611
Tel (585) 464-5663 SIC 3559

PIKE CO INC p 1147
1 Circle St 14607
Tel (585) 271-5256 SIC 1542

QUALITY VISION INTERNATIONAL INC p 1197
850 Hudson Ave 14621
Tel (585) 544-0400 SIC 3827

RESOURCES MANAGEMENT INC p 1227
1931 Buffalo Rd 14624
Tel (585) 426-8000 SIC 8741

ROCHESTER CITY SCHOOL DISTRICT p 1243
131 W Broad St 14614
Tel (585) 262-8100 SIC 8211

ROCHESTER DRUG CO-OPERATIVE INC p 1243
50 Jetview Dr 14624
Tel (585) 271-7220 SIC 5122

■ ROCHESTER GAS AND ELECTRIC CORP p 1243
89 East Ave 14649
Tel (800) 295-7323 SIC 4911 4924

ROCHESTER GENERAL HEALTH SYSTEM p 1243
1425 Portland Ave 14621
Tel (585) 922-4000 SIC 8741 8093 8059

ROCHESTER GENERAL HOSPITAL INC p 1243
1425 Portland Ave 14621
Tel (585) 922-4101 SIC 8062

ROCHESTER INSTITUTE OF TECHNOLOGY (INC) p 1243
1 Lomb Memorial Dr 14623
Tel (585) 475-2411 SIC 8221

ROCHESTER MIDLAND CORP p 1243
155 Paragon Dr 14624
Tel (585) 336-2200 SIC 2842 2676 2899

ROCHESTER-GENESEE REGIONAL TRANSPORTATION AUTHORITY p 1243
1372 E Main St 14609
Tel (585) 654-0200 SIC 4111

RU SYSTEM INC p 1256
100 Kings Hwy S 14617
Tel (585) 922-1053 SIC 8062

SCHLEGEL SYSTEMS INC p 1287
1555 Jefferson Rd 14623
Tel (585) 427-7200 SIC 3053 3089 3069

ST ANNS HOME FOR AGED p 1364
287 Flower City Park # 2 14615
Tel (585) 697-6086 SIC 8051

ST JOHN FISHER COLLEGE p 1367
3690 East Ave Ofc 14618
Tel (585) 385-8000 SIC 8221

SUPERIOR PLUS ENERGY SERVICES INC p 1407
1870 Winton Rd S Ste 200 14618
Tel (585) 328-3930 SIC 5171 5983

▲ TRANSCAT INC p 1471
35 Vantage Point Dr 14624
Tel (585) 352-7777 SIC 5049 7699

UA (UNITED ASSOCIATION) LOCAL 13 OF JOURNEY MAN AND A PREMISES OF PLUMBING p 1498
1850 Mount Read Blvd 14615
Tel (585) 338-2360 SIC 8631

UNITY HEALTH SYSTEM p 1515
89 Genesee St 14611
Tel (585) 723-7000 SIC 8062

UNITY HEALTH SYSTEM FOUNDATION p 1515
1555 Long Pond Rd 14626
Tel (585) 723-7050 SIC 6733

UNITY HOSPITAL OF ROCHESTER p 1515
89 Genesee St 14611
Tel (585) 723-7000 SIC 8062

UNIVERSITY OF ROCHESTER p 1525
601 Elmwood Ave 14642
Tel (585) 275-5000 SIC 8221

V & J NATIONAL AND UNITED ENTERPRISES LLC p 1538
1425 Mount Read Blvd # 1 14606
Tel (585) 458-8140 SIC 5812

V & J NATIONAL ENTERPRISES LLC p 1538
1425 Mount Read Blvd # 1 14606
Tel (585) 458-8140 SIC 5812

V P SUPPLY CORP p 1538
3445 Winton Pl Ste 101 14623
Tel (585) 272-0110 SIC 5074

VISION BUICK GMC LLC p 1561
800 Panorama Trl S 14625
Tel (585) 586-6940 SIC 5511

WEGMANS FOOD MARKETS INC p 1587
1500 Brooks Ave 14624
Tel (585) 328-2550 *SIC* 5411

WRIGHT WISNER DISTRIBUTING CORP p 1627
3165 Brghtn Hnrietta Twn 14623
Tel (585) 427-2880 *SIC* 5181 5149

XEROX CAPITAL SERVICES LLC p 1631
100 S Clinton Ave Fl 18 14604
Tel (585) 423-3805 *SIC* 6211

XMH-HFI INC p 1632
1155 N Clinton Ave 14621
Tel (585) 467-7240 *SIC* 2311 2325

ROCKVILLE CENTRE, NY

AMERICAN UNIVERSITY OF GREECE p 81
53 N Park Ave Ste 50 11570
Tel (516) 766-2718 *SIC* 8222

CATHOLIC HEALTH SYSTEM OF LONG ISLAND INC p 266
992 N Village Ave 11570
Tel (516) 705-3700 *SIC* 8062

CHS SERVICES INC p 304
992 N Village Ave 11570
Tel (516) 705-1935 *SIC* 8741

MERCY MEDICAL CENTER p 947
1000 N Village Ave 11570
Tel (516) 562-6907 *SIC* 8062

MOLLOY COLLEGE p 983
1000 Hempstead Ave Unit 1 11570
Tel (516) 678-5733 *SIC* 8221

PARTS AUTHORITY INC p 1118
495 Merrick Rd 11570
Tel (516) 678-3900 *SIC* 5013 5015 5531

ROME, NY

BIRNIE BUS SERVICE INC p 185
248 Otis St 13441
Tel (315) 336-3950
SIC 4151 4119 4141 4111

ROME CITY SCHOOL DISTRICT p 1249
409 Bell Rd S 13440
Tel (315) 338-6500 *SIC* 8211

ROME MEMORIAL HOSPITAL INC p 1249
1500 N James St 13440
Tel (315) 338-7000 *SIC* 8062 8051

SOVENA USA INC p 1353
1 Olive Grove St 13441
Tel (315) 797-7070 *SIC* 5149

RONKONKOMA, NY

ACME BUS CORP p 17
3355 Vtrans Mem Hwy Ste C 11779
Tel (631) 471-4600 *SIC* 4151

■ ALPHABET HOLDING CO INC p 60
2100 Smithtown Ave 11779
Tel (631) 200-2000
SIC 2833 5122 5499 5961

J & B RESTAURANT PARTNERS OF LONG ISLAND INC p 769
3385 Vtrans Mem Hwy Ste A 11779
Tel (631) 218-9067 *SIC* 5812

▲ LAKELAND INDUSTRIES INC p 840
3555 Vtrans Mem Hwy Ste C 11779
Tel (631) 981-9700 *SIC* 3842 2389

MORRIS ROTHENBERG & SON INC p 990
3015 Veterans Mem Hwy 11779
Tel (631) 585-9446
SIC 5199 5091 5139 5136

■ NATURES BOUNTY INC p 1019
2100 Smithtown Ave 11779
Tel (631) 580-6137 *SIC* 2834

■ NBTY INC p 1021
2100 Smithtown Ave 11779
Tel (631) 200-2000
SIC 2833 5122 5499 5961

PERFUME CENTER OF AMERICA INC p 1135
2020 Ocean Ave 11779
Tel (516) 348-1127 *SIC* 5122

PERFUME WORLDWIDE INC p 1135
2020 Ocean Ave Unit A 11779
Tel (516) 575-2499 *SIC* 5122 5999

PRIDE PRODUCTS CORP p 1174
4333 Veterans Mem Hwy 11779
Tel (631) 737-4444
SIC 5113 5122 5023 5072 5199

SOURCE-RAY INC p 1342
50 Fleetwood Ct 11779
Tel (631) 244-8200 *SIC* 5047

ROSLYN, NY

ADMINISTRATORS FOR PROFESSIONS INC p 23
1800 N Blvd 11576
Tel (516) 365-6690 *SIC* 6321

NORTHWEST CO LLC p 1059
49 Bryant Ave 11576
Tel (516) 484-6996 *SIC* 2211

PHYSICIANS RECIPROCAL INSURERS p 1146
1800 Northern Blvd 11576
Tel (516) 365-6690 *SIC* 6321

ROSLYN UNION FREE SCHOOL DISTRICT p 1251
300 Harbor Hill Rd 11576
Tel (516) 801-5000 *SIC* 8211

ST FRANCIS HOSPITAL ROSLYN NEW YORK p 1366
100 Port Washington Blvd 11576
Tel (516) 627-3813 *SIC* 8069

RUSH, NY

OPTIMATION TECHNOLOGY INC p 1090
50 High Tech Dr 14543
Tel (585) 321-2300 *SIC* 8711

SEALAND CONTRACTORS CORP p 1296
85 High Tech Dr 14543
Tel (704) 522-1102 *SIC* 1622 1611 1623

RYE BROOK, NY

BROADVIEW NETWORKS HOLDINGS INC p 215
800 Westchester Ave Ste N 10573
Tel (914) 922-7000 *SIC* 4813 4899

BROADVIEW NETWORKS INC p 215
800 Westchester Ave N501 10573
Tel (914) 922-7000 *SIC* 4813

FIRST SECURITY BENEFIT LIFE INSURANCE AND ANNUITY CO OF NEW YORK p 549
800 Westchester Ave N641 10573
Tel (914) 697-4748 *SIC* 6411

FLIK INTERNATIONAL CORP p 557
2 International Dr Fl 2 10573
Tel (914) 935-5300 *SIC* 8742 5812

FRAMACO INTERNATIONAL INC p 573
800 Westchester Ave S430 10573
Tel (914) 633-6600 *SIC* 8741

LEUKEMIA & LYMPHOMA SOCIETY INC p 858
3 International Dr # 200 10573
Tel (914) 949-5213
SIC 8699 8399 8322 8011 8733 8621

MITSUI CHEMICALS AMERICA INC p 978
800 Westchester Ave N607 10573
Tel (914) 253-0777
SIC 2821 2865 3082 8731 5169 6159

PARACO GAS CORP p 1113
800 Westchester Ave S604 10573
Tel (800) 647-4427 *SIC* 1321

PARACO GAS OF NEW YORK INC p 1113
800 Westchester Ave 10573
Tel (914) 250-3740 *SIC* 4925

PORT CHESTER-RYE UNION FREE SCHOOL DISTRICT p 1162
113 Bowman Ave 10573
Tel (914) 934-7900 *SIC* 8211

PRECISION VALVE CORP p 1169
800 Westchester Ave 10573
Tel (914) 969-6500 *SIC* 3499 0273 5085

WESTCHESTER BOCES SCHOOL DISTRICT p 1596
17 Berkley Dr 10573
Tel (914) 937-6107 *SIC* 8211

▲ XYLEM INC p 1633
1 International Dr 10573
Tel (914) 323-5700 *SIC* 3561

RYE, NY

▲ ACADIA REALTY TRUST p 13
411 Theodore Fremd Ave # 300 10580
Tel (914) 288-8100 *SIC* 6798

DUNES POINT CAPITAL LLC p 461
411 Theodore Fremd Ave # 125 10580
Tel (914) 967-1390 *SIC* 6799

GABELLI & CO INC p 588
1 Corporate Ctr 10580
Tel (914) 921-3700 *SIC* 6211 6282

■ GABELLI FUNDS LLC p 588
1 Corporate Ctr 10580
Tel (914) 921-5105 *SIC* 6726 3993

GABELLI GROUP CAPITAL PARTNERS INC p 588
555 Theodore Fremd Ave C300 10580
Tel (914) 921-3700 *SIC* 6211 6282

GABELLI SECURITIES INC p 588
1 Corporate Ctr 401 10580
Tel (914) 921-3700 *SIC* 6211

■ GAMCO ASSET MANAGEMENT INC p 590
401 Theodore Fremd Ave 10580
Tel (914) 921-5000 *SIC* 6282

▲ GAMCO ASSET MANAGEMENT INC p 590
1 Corporate Ctr 10580
Tel (914) 921-3700 *SIC* 6282

GREENBRIAR EQUITY GROUP LLC p 637
555 Theodore Fremd Ave A201 10580
Tel (914) 925-9600 *SIC* 4789 6799

LICT CORP p 863
401 Theodore Fremd Ave 10580
Tel (914) 921-8821 *SIC* 4813 4841 4833

■ QUOIN LLC p 1201
555 Theodore Fremd Ave B302 10580
Tel (914) 967-9400 *SIC* 3089

SAINT JAMES, NY

NISSAN SMITHTOWN INC p 1044
535 Middle Country Rd 11780
Tel (631) 361-9696 *SIC* 5511

SALAMANCA, NY

SENECA NATION OF INDIANS p 1303
90 Ohiyo Way 14779
Tel (716) 945-1790 *SIC* 9131

SANBORN, NY

EDWARDS VACUUM LLC p 480
6416 Inducon Dr W 14132
Tel (800) 848-9800 *SIC* 3563

RAPTIM INTERNATIONAL TRAVEL INC p 1209
6420 Inducon Dr W Ste A 14132
Tel (716) 754-2946 *SIC* 4724

SARANAC LAKE, NY

ADIRONDACK MEDICAL CENTER p 23
2233 State Route 86 12983
Tel (518) 891-4141 *SIC* 8062

SARATOGA SPRINGS, NY

■ AYCO CO L P p 140
321 Broadway 12866
Tel (518) 886-4000
SIC 6411 6282 8742 7291

NEW COUNTRY MOTOR CAR GROUP INC p 1029
358 Broadway Ste 403 12866
Tel (518) 583-4896 *SIC* 8741 5511

SARATOGA CARE INC p 1282
211 Church St Ste 1 12866
Tel (518) 587-3222 *SIC* 8062 8741

SARATOGA HOSPITAL p 1282
211 Church St 12866
Tel (518) 587-3222 *SIC* 8062 8051

SARATOGA SPRINGS CITY SCHOOL DISTRICT p 1282
3 Blue Streak Blvd 12866
Tel (518) 583-4708 *SIC* 8211

SKIDMORE COLLEGE p 1329
815 N Broadway 12866
Tel (518) 580-5000 *SIC* 8221

SCARSDALE, NY

A G HOME HEALTH LLC p 5
700 White Plains Rd # 275 10583
Tel (914) 722-9000 *SIC* 6282

NATIONAL HOME HEALTH CARE CORP p 1013
700 White Plains Rd Ste 2 10583
Tel (914) 722-9000 *SIC* 8082 7361

SCHENECTADY, NY

ADIRONDACK BEVERAGE CO INC p 22
701 Corporation Park 12302
Tel (518) 370-3621 *SIC* 2086

CALLANAN INDUSTRIES INC p 242
1245 Kings Rd Ste 1 12303
Tel (518) 374-2222 *SIC* 3272 2951

CB&I FEDERAL SERVICES LLC p 268
2401 River Rd 12309
Tel (518) 557-2518 *SIC* 8744

CONTEC LLC p 362
1011 State St 12307
Tel (518) 382-8150 *SIC* 5065 7629

COUNTY OF SCHENECTADY p 381
620 State St 12305
Tel (518) 285-8435 *SIC* 9111

DMN MANAGEMENT SERVICES LLC p 446
26 N Broadway 12305
Tel (518) 346-9640 *SIC* 8051

DSM NUTRITIONAL PRODUCTS LLC p 458
2105 Technology Dr 12308
Tel (518) 372-5155 *SIC* 2834 2836

ELLIS HOSPITAL p 488
1101 Nott St 12308
Tel (518) 243-4000 *SIC* 8062 8051

■ GE POWER & WATER p 596
1 River Rd Bldg 5-419 12345
Tel (518) 385-2211 *SIC* 7382 5063

GOLUB CORP p 622
461 Nott St 12308
Tel (518) 355-5000 *SIC* 5411

KAPL INC p 803
2401 River Rd 12309
Tel (877) 527-5522 *SIC* 8731

MVP HEALTH PLAN INC p 1003
625 State St 12305
Tel (518) 370-4793 *SIC* 8011

PRICE CHOPPER OPERATING CO INC p 1174
501 Duanesburg Rd 12306
Tel (518) 379-1600 *SIC* 5411

PRICE CHOPPER OPERATING CO OF CONNECTICUT INC p 1174
501 Duanesburg Rd 12306
Tel (518) 861-5099 *SIC* 5411

PRICE CHOPPER OPERATING CO OF VERMONT INC p 1174
501 Duanesburg Rd 12306
Tel (518) 355-5000 *SIC* 5411

SI GROUP INC p 1319
2750 Balltown Rd 12309
Tel (518) 347-4200 *SIC* 2865 3087 2851

■ TRUSTCO BANK p 1487
1 Sarnowski Dr 12302
Tel (518) 344-7510 *SIC* 6022

TRUSTEES OF UNION COLLEGE IN TOWN OF SCHENECTADY IN STATE OF NEW YORK p 1488
807 Union St 12308
Tel (518) 388-6630 *SIC* 8221

WORLDWIDE DIGITAL CO LLC p 1626
1023 State St 12307
Tel (518) 382-8000 *SIC* 5065

SELDEN, NY

SUFFOLK COUNTY COMMUNITY COLLEGE p 1396
533 College Rd 11784
Tel (631) 451-4110 *SIC* 8222 9411

SELKIRK, NY

SECURITY PLUMBING & HEATING SUPPLY CO p 1299
196 Maple Ave 12158
Tel (518) 767-2226 *SIC* 5074

SENECA FALLS, NY

■ GOULDS PUMPS INC p 627
240 Fall St 13148
Tel (315) 568-2811 *SIC* 3561 5084

■ ITT GOULDS PUMPS INC p 768
240 Fall St 13148
Tel (914) 641-2129 *SIC* 3561 5084

SETAUKET, NY

ODYSSEY GROUP OF COMPANIES p 1075
11 Overlook Way 11733
Tel (631) 751-8400
SIC 7373 3577 7371 1731

SHIRLEY, NY

LUITPOLD PHARMACEUTICALS INC p 884
5 Ramsey Rd 11967
Tel (631) 924-4000 *SIC* 2834

SHRUB OAK, NY

LAKELAND CENTRAL SCHOOL DISTRICT OF SHRUB OAK INC p 839
1086 E Main St 10588
Tel (914) 245-1700 *SIC* 8211

SIDNEY, NY

■ AMPHENOL AEROSPACE FRANCE INC p 86
191 Delaware Ave 13838
Tel (800) 678-0141 *SIC* 5065

SKANEATELES FALLS, NY

ALLYN WELCH HOLDINGS INC p 59
4341 State Street Rd 13153
Tel (315) 685-4100 *SIC* 3841

■ HAND HELD PRODUCTS INC p 657
700 Visions Dr 13153
Tel (315) 554-6000
SIC 3577 3571 3663 3578

■ WELCH ALLYN INC p 1588
4341 State Street Rd 13153
Tel (315) 685-4100 *SIC* 3841 2835 3827

SKANEATELES, NY

TESSY PLASTICS CORP p 1441
700 Visions Dr 13152
Tel (315) 689-3924 *SIC* 3089 3549

SLEEPY HOLLOW, NY

PHELPS MEMORIAL HOSPITAL ASSOCIATION p 1141
701 N Broadway 10591
Tel (914) 366-3000 *SIC* 8062

SMITHTOWN, NY

DEVELOPMENTAL DISABILITIES INSTITUTE INC p 433
99 Hollywood Dr 11787
Tel (631) 366-2900 *SIC* 8211 8052

SCOPE INC p 1293
100 Lawrence Ave Ste 105 11787
Tel (631) 360-0800 *SIC* 8299

SMITHTOWN CENTRAL SCHOOL DISTRICT p 1334
26 New York Ave Unit 1 11787
Tel (631) 382-2000 *SIC* 8211

ST CATHERINE OF SIENA MEDICAL CENTER p 1365
50 Route 25a 11787
Tel (631) 862-3000 *SIC* 8062

STRATEGIC SECURITY CORP p 1392
4 Higbie Dr 11787
Tel (212) 509-0547 *SIC* 7381

SOMERS, NY

BEST PLUMBING SUPPLY INC p 177
49 Route 138 10589
Tel (914) 232-2020 *SIC* 5074 5999

■ GENERAL CINEMA BEVERAGES OF OHIO INC p 599
1 Pepsi Way Ste 1 10589
Tel (914) 767-6000 *SIC* 2086

SOUTH OZONE PARK, NY

NEW YORK RACING ASSOCIATION INC p 1036
11000 Rockaway Blvd Ste 1 11420
Tel (718) 641-4700 *SIC* 7948

SOUTHAMPTON, NY

SOUTHAMPTON HOSPITAL ASSOCIATION p 1345
240 Meeting House Ln 11968
Tel (631) 726-8200 *SIC* 8062

SPENCERPORT, NY

BOARD OF COOP EDUC SERVICES OF 2ND SUPERVISORY DISTRICT OF MONROE & ORLEANS COUNTIES p 194
3599 Big Ridge Rd 14559
Tel (585) 352-2412 *SIC* 8211

SPRING VALLEY, NY

EAST RAMAPO CENTRAL SCHOOL DISTRICT p 470
105 S Madison Ave 10977
Tel (845) 577-6000 *SIC* 8211

LIPTIS PHARMACEUTICALS USA INC p 870
110 Red Schoolhouse Rd 10977
Tel (845) 627-0260 *SIC* 2834

PAR PHARMACEUTICAL COMPANIES INC p 1113
1 Ram Ridge Rd 10977
Tel (201) 802-4000 *SIC* 2834

PAR PHARMACEUTICAL INC p 1113
1 Ram Ridge Rd 10977
Tel (845) 425-7100 *SIC* 2834

SPRINGFIELD GARDENS, NY

ARAMEX NEW YORK LTD p 102
18221 150th Ave 11413
Tel (718) 553-8740 *SIC* 4513

STATEN ISLAND, NY

ADCO ELECTRICAL CORP p 21
201 Edward Curry Ave 10314
Tel (718) 494-4400 *SIC* 1731

AMBOY BUS CO INC p 65
7 North St 10302
Tel (718) 442-7000 *SIC* 4151

ATLANTIC EXPRESS OF PENNSYLVANIA INC p 126
7 North St 10302
Tel (718) 442-7000 *SIC* 4151 4142

ATLANTIC EXPRESS TRANSPORTATION GROUP INC p 126
7 North St 10302
Tel (718) 442-7000 *SIC* 4151 4141 5012

▲ COFFEE HOLDING CO INC p 334
3475 Victory Blvd Ste 4 10314
Tel (718) 832-0800 *SIC* 2095 5149 5499

ISLAND COMPUTER PRODUCTS INC p 766
20 Clifton Ave 10305
Tel (718) 556-6700
SIC 5045 7373 7379 7378

KEY FOOD STORES CO-OPERATIVE INC p 814
1200 South Ave 10314
Tel (718) 370-4200 *SIC* 5141

NEW YORK CITY GEOGRAPHIC DISTRICT 31 p 1034
715 Ocean Ter Rm 129 10301
Tel (718) 420-5667 *SIC* 8211

NORTHFIELD SAVINGS BANK p 1057
1731 Victory Blvd 10314
Tel (718) 448-1000 *SIC* 6036

REINAUER TRANSPORTATION COMPANIES LLC p 1221
1983 Richmond Ter 10302
Tel (718) 816-8167 *SIC* 4449 4492

RICHMOND MEDICAL CENTER p 1233
355 Bard Ave 10310
Tel (718) 818-1234 *SIC* 8062

STATEN ISLAND UNIVERSITY HOSPITAL p 1383
475 Seaview Ave 10305
Tel (718) 226-9000 *SIC* 8062

STELLA ORTON HOME CARE AGENCY INC p 1385
3155 Amboy Rd Ste 1 10306
Tel (718) 987-4300 *SIC* 8082

WAGNER COLLEGE p 1571
1 Campus Rd 10301
Tel (718) 390-3100 *SIC* 8221

STONY BROOK, NY

CLINICAL PRACTICE MANAGEMENT PLAN p 326
Suny At Stony Brk Hsc 11790
Tel (631) 444-2055 *SIC* 8741

STONY BROOK UNIVERSITY p 1391
100 Nicolls Rd 11794
Tel (631) 632-6000 *SIC* 8221 9411

THREE VILLAGE CENTRAL SCHOOL DISTRICT p 1450
100 Suffolk Ave 11790
Tel (631) 730-4000 *SIC* 8211

SUFFERN, NY

BON SECOURS CHARITY HEALTH SYSTEM INC p 199
255 Lafayette Ave 10901
Tel (845) 368-5000 *SIC* 8099

GOOD SAMARITAN REGIONAL MEDICAL CENTER p 623
255 Lafayette Ave 10901
Tel (845) 368-5000 *SIC* 8062

SUNNYSIDE, NY

SUNNYSIDE HOME CARE PROJECT INC p 1403
4331 39th St Ste A 11104
Tel (718) 784-6173 *SIC* 8361 8322

SYOSSET, NY

ISOCHEM NORTH AMERICA INC p 767
6800 Jericho Tpke 120w 11791
Tel (516) 393-5915 *SIC* 5169

LIRO ENGINEERS INC p 870
3 Aerial Way 11791
Tel (516) 938-5476 *SIC* 1522

PAY-O-MATIC CORP p 1122
160 Oak Dr 11791
Tel (516) 496-4900 *SIC* 6099 7381 7999

PETRO VM INC p 1139
2188 Kirby Ln 11791
Tel (516) 921-7190 *SIC* 5172

SWSNY INC p 1413
345 Underhill Blvd 11791
Tel (516) 921-9005 *SIC* 5182

SYOSSET CENTRAL SCHOOL DISTRICT p 1416
99 Pell Ln 11791
Tel (516) 364-5600 *SIC* 8211

SYRACUSE, NY

■ CARROLS CORP p 261
968 James St 13203
Tel (315) 424-0513 *SIC* 5812

■ CARROLS LLC p 261
968 James St 13203
Tel (315) 424-0513 *SIC* 5812

▲ CARROLS RESTAURANT GROUP INC p 261
968 James St 13203
Tel (315) 424-0513 *SIC* 5812 6794

CATHOLIC CHARITIES OF ROMAN CATHOLIC DIOCESE OF SYRACUSE NY p 266
240 E Onondaga St 13202
Tel (315) 470-1450 *SIC* 8661

CITY ELECTRIC CO INC p 312
501 W Genesee St 13204
Tel (315) 474-7841 *SIC* 5063 5085

CITY OF SYRACUSE p 319
233 E Wshngtn St Ste 231 13202
Tel (315) 448-8005 *SIC* 9111

■ COMMUNITY BANK N A p 347
5790 Widewaters Pkwy # 1 13214
Tel (315) 445-2282 *SIC* 6021

COOPER CROUSE-HINDS LLC p 366
1201 Wolf St 13208
Tel (315) 477-7000 *SIC* 3699

COUNTY OF ONONDAGA p 380
1000 Erie Blvd W 13204
Tel (315) 435-8683 *SIC* 9111

COYNE INTERNATIONAL ENTERPRISES CORP p 387
140 Cortland Ave 13202
Tel (315) 475-1626 *SIC* 7218

CROUSE HEALTH HOSPITAL INC p 394
736 Irving Ave 13210
Tel (315) 470-7111 *SIC* 8062

CROUSE HEALTH SYSTEM INC p 394
736 Irving Ave 13210
Tel (315) 470-7521 *SIC* 8062

CROUSE HOSPITAL AUXILIARY INC p 394
736 Irving Ave 13210
Tel (315) 470-7111 *SIC* 8062

CRUCIBLE INDUSTRIES LLC p 396
575 State Fair Blvd 13209
Tel (800) 365-1180 *SIC* 3312

EMPIRE VISION CENTER INC p 494
2921 Erie Blvd E 13224
Tel (315) 446-3145 *SIC* 5995

ERIE MATERIALS INC p 508
500 Factory Ave 13208
Tel (315) 455-7434 *SIC* 5033 5031

FELDMEIER EQUIPMENT INC p 537
6800 Townline Rd 13211
Tel (315) 823-2000 *SIC* 3443

FIESTA RESTAURANT GROUP INC p 541
968 James St 13203
Tel (315) 424-0513 *SIC* 5812

G & C FOOD DISTRIBUTORS & BROKERS INC p 586
3407 Walters Rd 13209
Tel (315) 422-3191 *SIC* 5147 5146 4222

GRANT CADARET & CO INC p 631
1 Lincoln Rd Fl 5 13212
Tel (315) 471-2191 *SIC* 6211

HERALD NEWSPAPERS CO INC p 685
220 S Warren St 13202
Tel (315) 470-0011 *SIC* 2711

LE MOYNE COLLEGE p 849
1419 Salt Springs Rd 13214
Tel (315) 445-4100 *SIC* 8221

LORETTO HEALTH AND REHABILITATION CENTER p 878
700 E Brighton Ave 13205
Tel (315) 469-1991 *SIC* 8322

N Y STEAMSTER HEALTH PENSION & RETIREMENT FUND p 1006
151 Northern Concourse 13212
Tel (315) 455-9790 *SIC* 8631

NIAGARA MOHAWK HOLDINGS INC p 1042
300 Erie Blvd W 13202
Tel (315) 474-1511 *SIC* 4911 4924

NIAGARA MOHAWK POWER CORP p 1042
300 Erie Blvd W 13202
Tel (315) 474-1511 *SIC* 4911 4924

OBRIEN & GERE LIMITED p 1072
333 W Washington St # 400 13202
Tel (315) 437-6100 *SIC* 8711 8741

OCONNELL ELECTRIC CO INC p 1074
7001 Performance Dr 13212
Tel (585) 924-2176 *SIC* 1731

ONONDAGA COMMUNITY COLLEGE p 1088
4585 W Seneca Tpke 13215
Tel (315) 498-2622 *SIC* 8222 9411

ONONDAGA-CORTLAND-MADISON BOCES p 1088
6820 Thompson Rd 13211
Tel (315) 433-8300 *SIC* 8211

PASS & SEYMOUR INC p 1119
50 Boyd Ave 13209
Tel (315) 468-6211 *SIC* 3643 5731

PETR-ALL PETROLEUM CONSULTING CORP p 1139
7401 Round Pond Rd 13212
Tel (315) 446-0125 *SIC* 5172 5411

POMCO INC p 1160
2425 James St 13206
Tel (315) 432-9171 *SIC* 6411

PYRAMID MANAGEMENT GROUP INC p 1193
4 Clinton Sq 13202
Tel (315) 422-7000 *SIC* 6531 6512

RIVER VALLEY FOODS INC p 1237
5881 Court Street Rd # 2 13206
Tel (315) 437-4636 *SIC* 5142

■ SENECA DATA DISTRIBUTORS INC p 1303
6040 Tarbell Rd Ste 103 13206
Tel (315) 433-1160 *SIC* 5045

ST JOSEPHS HOSPITAL HEALTH CENTER p 1369
301 Prospect Ave 13203
Tel (315) 448-5113 *SIC* 8062

STAFF LEASING OF CENTRAL NEW YORK INC p 1374
149 Northern Concourse # 3 13212
Tel (315) 641-3600 *SIC* 7363 8721

STATE UNIVERSITY OF NEW YORK HEALTH SCIENCE CENTER AT SYRACUSE p 1383
750 E Adams St 13210
Tel (315) 464-5540 *SIC* 8011 8062

SUNY UPSTATE MEDICAL UNIVERSITY p 1405
750 E Adams St Ste Wh 13210
Tel (315) 464-5540 *SIC* 8011

SYRACUSE CITY SCHOOL DISTRICT p 1416
725 Harrison St 13210
Tel (315) 435-4499 *SIC* 8211

SYRACUSE UNIVERSITY p 1416
900 S Crouse Ave Ste 620 13244
Tel (315) 443-1870 *SIC* 8221

■ SYSTEMS MADE SIMPLE INC p 1419
149 Northern Concourse # 1 13212
Tel (315) 455-3200 *SIC* 7371 8742

TEAMSTERS NEW YORK STATE CONFERENCE p 1430
151 Northern Concourse # 1 13212
Tel (315) 455-9790 *SIC* 6722

UPSTATE UNIVERSITY MEDICAL ASSOCIATES AT SYRACUSE INC p 1530
750 E Adams St 13210
Tel (315) 464-7087 *SIC* 8221 9411 8231

TARRYTOWN, NY

AMPACET CORP p 86
660 White Plains Rd # 360 10591
Tel (914) 631-6600 *SIC* 3087

DB US CORP p 418
120 White Plains Rd 10591
Tel (914) 366-7200 *SIC* 4789 4731

DB US HOLDING CORP p 418
120 White Plains Rd 10591
Tel (914) 366-7203 *SIC* 4731

FUJICOLOR PROCESSING INC p 583
120 White Plains Rd # 400 10591
Tel (914) 220-4700 *SIC* 7384

HITACHI AMERICA LTD p 696
50 Prospect Ave 10591
Tel (914) 332-5800
SIC 5084 5065 3577 5063 5045 3651

HUDSON HEALTH PLAN INC p 716
303 S Broadway Ste 321 10591
Tel (800) 339-4557 *SIC* 6321

MONTEFIORE HEALTH SYSTEM INC p 986
555 S Broadway 10591
Tel (718) 920-8239 *SIC* 8062

NOVARTIS CORP p 1062
520 White Plains Rd 10591
Tel (212) 307-1122
SIC 2834 2879 2032 2865

▲ PRESTIGE BRANDS HOLDINGS INC p 1173
660 White Plains Rd 10591
Tel (914) 524-6800 *SIC* 2834 2841

■ PRESTIGE BRANDS INC p 1173
660 White Plains Rd 10591
Tel (914) 524-6810 *SIC* 5149 5087

▲ REGENERON PHARMACEUTICALS INC p 1219
777 Old Saw Mill River Rd # 10 10591
Tel (914) 847-7000 *SIC* 2834

SCHENKER (BAX) HOLDING CORP p 1286
120 White Plains Rd 10591
Tel (914) 366-7200 *SIC* 4731

SIEMENS HEALTHCARE DIAGNOSTICS INC p 1320
511 Benedict Ave 10591
Tel (914) 631-8000 *SIC* 5047

WESTCON GROUP INC p 1597
520 White Plains Rd # 200 10591
Tel (914) 829-7000 *SIC* 5045

WESTCON GROUP NORTH AMERICA INC p 1597
520 White Plains Rd # 200 10591
Tel (914) 829-7000 *SIC* 5045

THORNWOOD, NY

CARL ZEISS INC p 256
1 Zeiss Dr 10594
Tel (914) 747-1800
SIC 3827 5049 3829 5084 3826

CARL ZEISS MICROSCOPY LLC p 256
1 Zeiss Dr 10594
Tel (914) 747-1800 *SIC* 5049

TONAWANDA, NY

FIRST SOURCE LLC p 549
100 Pirson Pkwy 14150
Tel (716) 877-0800 *SIC* 5499 2064

JWD GROUP INC p 798
300 Colvin Woods Pkwy 14150
Tel (716) 832-1940 *SIC* 1711 1629 1623

LIVINGSTON INTERNATIONAL INC p 871
670 Young St 14150
Tel (716) 692-3100 *SIC* 4731

MUELLER SERVICES INC p 998
63 Main St 14150
Tel (716) 691-4344 *SIC* 6331

NOCO INC p 1046
2440 Sheridan Dr Ste 202 14150
Tel (716) 833-6626
SIC 2992 6719 5172 4924

NOCO NATURAL GAS LLC p 1046
2440 Sheridan Dr 14150
Tel (716) 614-1152 *SIC* 5171

SUMITOMO RUBBER USA LLC p 1398
80 State St 14150
Tel (716) 879-8200 *SIC* 5531

■ UNIFRAX I LLC p 1503
600 Rverwalk Pkwy Ste 120 14150
Tel (716) 768-6500 *SIC* 3299

TROY, NY

ENLARGED CITY SCHOOL DISTRICT OF TROY p 500
2920 5th Ave 12180
Tel (518) 328-5005 *SIC* 8211

HUDSON VALLEY COMMUNITY COLLEGE p 717
80 Vandenburgh Ave Ste 1 12180
Tel (518) 629-4822 *SIC* 8222 9411

RENSSELAER COUNTY p 1224
1600 7th Ave Ste 3 12180
Tel (518) 270-2626 *SIC* 9111

RENSSELAER POLYTECHNIC INSTITUTE p 1224
110 8th St 12180
Tel (518) 276-6000 *SIC* 8221

SAMARITAN HOSPITAL OF TROY NEW YORK p 1274
2215 Burdett Ave 12180
Tel (518) 271-3300 *SIC* 8062

SETON HEALTH SYSTEM INC p 1308
1300 Massachusetts Ave 12180
Tel (518) 268-5000 *SIC* 8062 8011

TUXEDO PARK, NY

M SPIEGEL & SONS OIL CORP p 890
10 E Village Rd 10987
Tel (845) 351-4700 *SIC* 5172 5983

UNIONDALE, NY

ARBOR REALTY TRUST INC p 103
333 Earle Ovington Blvd # 900 11553
Tel (516) 506-4200 *SIC* 6798

▲ FLUSHING FINANCIAL CORP p 561
220 Rxr Plz 11556
Tel (718) 961-5400 *SIC* 6035

FORTUNOFF FINE JEWELRY AND SILVERWARE INC p 570
70 Charles Lindbergh Blvd 11553
Tel (516) 222-7879 *SIC* 5944 5719

HEALTHPLEX INC p 677
333 Earle Ovington Blvd # 300 11553
Tel (516) 542-2200 *SIC* 6324

LONG ISLAND ELECTRIC UTILITY SERVCO LLC p 876
333 Earle Ovington Blvd 11553
Tel (516) 719-9810 *SIC* 4911

LONG ISLAND POWER AUTHORITY p 876
333 Earle Ovington Blvd # 403 11553
Tel (516) 222-7700 *SIC* 4911

OPENLINK FINANCIAL LLC p 1089
1502 Rxr Plz Fl 15w 11556
Tel (516) 227-6600 *SIC* 7371 7372 8742

RXR REALTY p 1260
625 Rxr Plz 11556
Tel (516) 506-6000 *SIC* 6798

SUMMIT SECURITY SERVICES INC p 1399
390 Rxr Plz Lobbyl 11556
Tel (516) 240-2400 *SIC* 7381

TDK USA CORP p 1429
455 Rxr Plz 11556
Tel (516) 535-2600 *SIC* 3679 8741

UNIONDALE UNION FREE SCHOOL DISTRICT p 1505
933 Goodrich St 11553
Tel (516) 560-8957 *SIC* 8211

UPTON, NY

BROOKHAVEN SCIENCE ASSOCIATES LLC p 217
2 Center St 11973
Tel (631) 344-8000 *SIC* 8733

UTICA, NY

▲ CONMED CORP p 356
525 French Rd Ste 3 13502
Tel (315) 797-8375 *SIC* 3845 3841

COUNTY OF ONEIDA p 380
800 Park Ave Ste 5 13501
Tel (315) 798-5780 *SIC* 9111

ECR INTERNATIONAL INC p 476
2201 Dwyer Ave 13501
Tel (315) 797-1310 *SIC* 3433 3443

FAXTON-ST LUKES HEALTHCARE p 532
1656 Champlin Ave 13502
Tel (315) 624-6000 *SIC* 8062

MOHAWK VALLEY HEALTH SYSTEM p 982
1656 Champlin Ave 13502
Tel (315) 624-5116 *SIC* 8062

RESOURCE CENTER FOR INDEPENDENT LIVING (INC) p 1227
401 Columbia St 13502
Tel (315) 797-4642 *SIC* 8399

RIGHT LIGHT ENERGY SERVICES LLC p 1234
811 Court St Ste 214 13502
Tel (315) 723-2329 *SIC* 8748

RLE CORP p 1239
1301 Broad St 13501
Tel (315) 724-4189 *SIC* 5141

ST ELIZABETH MEDICAL CENTER p 1366
2209 Genesee St 13501
Tel (315) 798-8100 *SIC* 8062

UPSTATE CEREBRAL PALSY INC p 1529
1020 Mary St 13501
Tel (315) 724-6907 *SIC* 8322

UTICA CITY SCHOOL DISTRICT p 1537
106 Memorial Pkwy 13501
Tel (315) 792-2222 *SIC* 8211

VALHALLA, NY

BOSTON CHILDRENS HEALTH PHYSICIANS LLP p 202
40 Sunshine Cottage Rd 10595
Tel (914) 594-2100 *SIC* 8011

■ CES RETAIL ENERGY SUPPLY LLC p 284
100 Summit Lake Dr # 410 10595
Tel (914) 286-7000 *SIC* 4924

■ CONSOLIDATED EDISON SOLUTIONS INC p 359
100 Summit Lake Dr # 410 10595
Tel (914) 286-7000 *SIC* 4924 4911 8748

FUJIFILM HOLDINGS AMERICA CORP p 583
200 Summit Lake Dr Fl 2 10595
Tel (914) 789-8100 *SIC* 5043 5065

FUJIFILM NORTH AMERICA CORP p 583
200 Summit Lake Dr Fl 2 10595
Tel (914) 789-8100
SIC 7384 5043 5065 3695 2673 3861

NEW YORK MEDICAL COLLEGE (INC) p 1035
40 Sunshine Cottage Rd 10595
Tel (914) 594-4100 *SIC* 8221

USI INC p 1535
200 Summit Lake Dr # 350 10595
Tel (914) 747-6300 *SIC* 6411

USI INSURANCE SERVICES LLC p 1535
200 Summit Lake Dr 10595
Tel (914) 749-8500 *SIC* 6411

■ VTB HOLDINGS INC p 1567
100 Summit Lake Dr 10595
Tel (914) 345-2255 *SIC* 3651

WESTCHESTER COMMUNITY COLLEGE p 1596
75 Grasslands Rd 10595
Tel (914) 606-6600 *SIC* 8222 9411

WESTCHESTER COUNTY HEALTH CARE CORP p 1596
100 Woods Rd 10595
Tel (914) 493-7000 *SIC* 8062

VALLEY STREAM, NY

ALNOR OIL CO INC p 59
70 E Sunrise Hwy Ste 418 11581
Tel (516) 561-6146 *SIC* 5199

FRANKLIN HOSPITAL p 575
900 Franklin Ave 11580
Tel (516) 256-6000 *SIC* 8062 8051

NATIONAL HEALTH CARE ASSOCIATES INC p 1013
20 E Sunrise Hwy Unit 1 11581
Tel (516) 705-4800 *SIC* 8741

▲ NEW YORK HEALTH CARE INC p 1035
20 E Sunrise Hwy Ste 201 11581
Tel (718) 375-6700 *SIC* 2834 8082

TRIANGLE SERVICES INC p 1478
10 5th St Ste 200 11581
Tel (516) 561-1700
SIC 7349 4581 1799 7382

VERNON, NY

■ VERNON TELEPHONE CO INC p 1551
1 Curtis Rd 13476
Tel (608) 831-1000 *SIC* 4813

VERONA, NY

MADISON-ONEIDA COUNTY BOCES (INC) p 894
4937 Spring Rd 13478
Tel (315) 361-5500 *SIC* 8211

VESTAL, NY

GREAT AMERICAN INDUSTRIES INC p 633
300 Plaza Dr 13850
Tel (607) 729-9331
SIC 3086 5031 5074 3442 3069 5091

NATIONAL PIPE & PLASTICS INC p 1015
3421 Vestal Rd 13850
Tel (607) 729-9381 *SIC* 3084

PUBLIC LOAN CO INC p 1189
300 Plaza Dr 13850
Tel (607) 584-5274 *SIC* 6153

VICTOR, NY

▲ CONSTELLATION BRANDS INC p 360
207 High Point Dr # 100 14564
Tel (585) 678-7100
SIC 2084 5182 5181 2082 2085 2087

■ COOPERVISION INC p 367
209 High Point Dr 14564
Tel (585) 385-6810 *SIC* 3851

VOORHEESVILLE, NY

ATLAS COPCO COMPTEC LLC p 127
46 School Rd 12186
Tel (518) 765-3344 *SIC* 3563

WALDEN, NY

AMPAC PAPER LLC p 86
30 Coldenham Rd 12586
Tel (845) 778-5511 *SIC* 2674 2621 5162

WANTAGH, NY

TRANSCARE NEW YORK INC p 1471
3305 Jerusalem Ave # 201 11793
Tel (718) 763-8888 *SIC* 4119

WAPPINGERS FALLS, NY

KEEN LIVE INC p 807
2789 W Main St Ste 4 12590
Tel (845) 790-0813 *SIC* 7336

LAERDAL MEDICAL CORP p 837
167 Myers Corners Rd 12590
Tel (845) 297-7770 *SIC* 5047 3845 3841

WARNERS, NY

■ SYSCO SYRACUSE LLC p 1418
2508 Warners Rd 13164
Tel (315) 672-7000 *SIC* 5141

WARSAW, NY

▲ FINANCIAL INSTITUTIONS INC p 542
220 Liberty St 14569
Tel (585) 786-1100 *SIC* 6021 7389

■ FIVE STAR BANK p 553
220 Liberty St 14569
Tel (585) 786-3131 *SIC* 6022

WATERFORD, NY

MOMENTIVE PERFORMANCE MATERIALS INC p 983
260 Hudson River Rd 12188
Tel (518) 237-3330 *SIC* 2869 3479 3679

MPM HOLDINGS INC p 995
260 Hudson River Rd 12188
Tel (518) 237-3330 *SIC* 2869 3479 3679

MPM INTERMEDIATE HOLDINGS INC p 995
260 Hudson River Rd 12188
Tel (518) 237-3330 *SIC* 2869 3479 3679

MPM SILICONES LLC p 995
260 Hudson River Rd 12188
Tel (518) 233-3330 *SIC* 2869

WATERTOWN, NY

COUNTY OF JEFFERSON p 378
175 Arsenal St Rm 2 13601
Tel (315) 785-3055 *SIC* 9111

KNORR BRAKE HOLDING CORP p 825
748 Starbuck Ave 13601
Tel (315) 786-5356 *SIC* 3743 5013

KNORR BRAKE TRUCK SYSTEMS CO p 825
748 Starbuck Ave 13601
Tel (315) 786-5200 *SIC* 3743

PURCELL CONSTRUCTION CORP p 1192
566 Coffeen St 13601
Tel (315) 782-1050 *SIC* 1542 1541 1522

RENZI BROS INC p 1224
901 Rail Dr 13601
Tel (315) 755-5610 *SIC* 5141

SAMARITAN MEDICAL CENTER p 1274
830 Washington St 13601
Tel (315) 785-4000 *SIC* 8062 5047

STEBBINS ENGINEERING AND MANUFACTURING CO p 1384
363 Eastern Blvd 13601
Tel (315) 782-3000 *SIC* 1799 3443

WAYNES FOOD MARKET INC p 1584
235 E Division St 13601
Tel (315) 493-2854 *SIC* 5411

WAYLAND, NY

■ GUNLOCKE CO L L C p 647
1 Gunlocke Dr 14572
Tel (585) 728-5111 *SIC* 2521

WEBSTER, NY

WEBSTER CENTRAL SCHOOL DISTRICT p 1587
119 South Ave 14580
Tel (585) 265-6500 *SIC* 8211

WELLSVILLE, NY

ARVOS HOLDING LLC p 114
3020 Truax Rd 14895
Tel (585) 596-2501 *SIC* 3494

ARVOS INC p 115
3020 Truax Rd 14895
Tel (585) 593-2700 *SIC* 3443

OTIS EASTERN SERVICE LLC p 1097
2971 Andover Rd 14895
Tel (585) 593-4760 *SIC* 1623 1389

WEST BABYLON, NY

LINZER PRODUCTS CORP p 869
248 Wyandanch Ave 11704
Tel (631) 253-3333 *SIC* 5198 3991

WEST BABYLON UNION FREE SCHOOL DISTRICT p 1593
10 Farmingdale Rd 11704
Tel (631) 321-3143 *SIC* 8211

WEST HEMPSTEAD, NY

NWL HOLDINGS INC p 1068
111 Hempstead Tpke 11552
Tel (516) 489-3300 *SIC* 6712

WEST HENRIETTA, NY

CAREER SYSTEMS DEVELOPMENT CORP p 254
75 Thruway Park Dr # 100 14586
Tel (585) 334-8080 *SIC* 8741 8331

HAMMER PACKAGING CORP p 656
200 Lucius Gordon Dr 14586
Tel (585) 424-3880 *SIC* 2759

HENRIETTA BUILDING SUPPLIES INC p 683
1 Riverton Way 14586
Tel (585) 334-2365 *SIC* 5031

LAHR CONSTRUCTION CORP p 838
75 Thruway Park Dr Ste 1 14586
Tel (585) 334-4490 *SIC* 1521 1541

LEWIS TREE SERVICE INC p 859
300 Lucius Gordon Dr 14586
Tel (585) 436-3208 *SIC* 0783

WAVODYNE THERAPEUTICS INC p 1584
150 Lucius Gordon Dr 14586
Tel (954) 632-6630 *SIC* 2834

WEST ISLIP, NY

GOOD SAMARITAN HOSPITAL MEDICAL CENTER p 623
1000 Montauk Hwy 11795
Tel (631) 376-3000 *SIC* 8062 8051 8092

WEST NYACK, NY

GENERAL BEARING CORP p 599
44 High St 10994
Tel (845) 358-6000 *SIC* 3562

SALVATION ARMY p 1273
440 W Nyack Rd Ofc 10994
Tel (845) 620-7200 *SIC* 8661

TILCON NEW YORK INC p 1453
162 Old Mill Rd 10994
Tel (845) 358-4500 *SIC* 1429

WEST POINT, NY

■ UNITED STATES MILITARY ACADEMY p 1513
646 Swift Rd 10996
Tel (845) 938-2523 *SIC* 9711

WEST SENECA, NY

ERIE 1 BOARD OF COOPERATIVE EDUCATIONAL SERVICES p 508
355 Harlem Rd 14224
Tel (716) 821-7000 *SIC* 8211

WEST SENECA CENTRAL SCHOOL DISTRICT p 1595
1397 Orchard Park Rd # 1 14224
Tel (716) 677-3100 *SIC* 8211

WESTERN NEW YORK DEVELOPMENTAL DISABILITIES SERVICES OFFICE p 1599
1200 East And West Rd 14224
Tel (716) 517-2000 *SIC* 9431

WESTBURY, NY

EAST MEADOW UFSD (INC) p 470
718 The Plain Rd Ste 1 11590
Tel (516) 478-5730 *SIC* 8211

ERGONOMIC GROUP INC p 507
609 Cantiague Rock Rd # 3 11590
Tel (516) 746-7777
SIC 5045 7373 7374 7376 7379

■ NEW YORK COMMERCIAL BANK p 1034
615 Merrick Ave 11590
Tel (800) 535-2269 *SIC* 6022

▲ NEW YORK COMMUNITY BANCORP INC p 1034
615 Merrick Ave 11590
Tel (516) 683-4100 *SIC* 6036

■ NEW YORK COMMUNITY BANK p 1035
615 Merrick Ave 11590
Tel (516) 203-0010 *SIC* 6036

NORTH SHORE-LONG ISLAND JEWISH HEALTH CARE p 1053
972 Brush Hollow Rd 5th 11590
Tel (516) 876-6611 *SIC* 8099

■ NORTHEAST RECYCLING CORP p 1055
1198 Prospect Ave 11590
Tel (516) 937-0900 *SIC* 4953 4212

OERLIKON METCO (US) INC p 1075
1101 Prospect Ave 11590
Tel (516) 334-1300 *SIC* 3399 5084 3479

P & L DEVELOPMENT LLC p 1102
200 Hicks St 11590
Tel (516) 986-1700 *SIC* 2834

■ ST CLAIRE FLORAL CO INC p 1365
1600 Stewart Ave 11590
Tel (516) 237-6000 *SIC* 7389

WESTBURY UNION FREE SCHOOL DISTRICT p 1596
2 Hitchcock Ln 11568
Tel (516) 876-5000 *SIC* 8211

WESTFIELD, NY

NATIONAL GRAPE CO-OPERATIVE ASSOCIATION INC p 1012
80 State St 14787
Tel (716) 326-5200 *SIC* 2033 2037

WHITE PLAINS, NY

■ ABOVENET INC p 12
360 Hamilton Ave 10601
Tel (866) 859-6971 *SIC* 4813

AMALGAMATED NATIONAL HEALTH FUND p 64
333 Westchester Ave N101 10604
Tel (914) 367-5000 *SIC* 8631

AMERICAN CANCER SOCIETY EASTERN DIVISION INC p 69
2 Lyon Pl 10601
Tel (914) 949-4800 *SIC* 8322

APS HEALTHCARE BETHESDA INC p 100
44 S Broadway Ste 1200 10601
Tel (800) 305-3720 *SIC* 8099

APS HEALTHCARE INC p 100
44 S Broadway Ste 1200 10601
Tel (914) 288-4700 *SIC* 8099

APS HEALTHCARE NORTHWEST INC p 100
44 S Broadway Ste 1200 10601
Tel (800) 305-3720 *SIC* 8099

ARCADIS CE INC p 103
44 S Broadway Ste 1500 10601
Tel (914) 694-2100 *SIC* 8711 8731

■ BOTTLING GROUP LLC p 203
1111 Westchester Ave 10604
Tel (800) 789-2626 *SIC* 2086

■ BOTTLING GROUP LLC p 203
1111 Westchester Ave 10604
Tel (914) 767-6000 *SIC* 2086

BUNGE GLOBAL MARKETS INC p 225
50 Main St 10606
Tel (914) 684-3300 *SIC* 5153 5159

BYRAM HEALTHCARE CENTERS INC p 231
120 Bloomingdale Rd # 301 10605
Tel (914) 286-2000 *SIC* 5999 5047

CAMPGROUP LLC p 246
4 New King St Ste 130 10604
Tel (914) 997-2177 *SIC* 7032

COMBE INC p 343
1101 Westchester Ave 10604
Tel (914) 694-5454 *SIC* 2841 2834

COUNTY OF WESTCHESTER p 383
148 Martine Ave 10601
Tel (914) 995-2000 *SIC* 9111

DANNON CO INC p 412
100 Hillside Ave Fl 3 10603
Tel (914) 872-8400 SIC 2026

DANONE NORTH AMERICA LLC p 412
100 Hillside Ave 10603
Tel (212) 441-1000 SIC 5149

FORTISTAR LLC p 569
1 N Lexington Ave Ste 620 10601
Tel (914) 421-4900 SIC 4911

GREAT-WEST LIFE & ANNUITY INSURANCE CO OF NEW YORK p 635
50 Main St 10606
Tel (914) 682-3611 SIC 6411

■ HANDY & HARMAN p 657
1133 Westchester Ave N-222 10604
Tel (914) 461-1300
SIC 3356 3399 3341 3317 3315

■ HANDY & HARMAN GROUP LTD p 657
1133 Westchester Ave N-222 10604
Tel (914) 461-1300 SIC 3462

■ HANDY & HARMAN LTD p 657
1133 Westchester Ave N-222 10604
Tel (914) 461-1300 SIC 3339 3011 3312

HEINEKEN USA INC p 681
360 Hamilton Ave Ste 1103 10601
Tel (914) 681-4100 SIC 5181

HH BENFIELD ELECTRIC SUPPLY CO INC p 689
25 Lafayette Ave 10603
Tel (914) 948-6660 SIC 5063

HOP ENERGY HOLDINGS INC p 706
4 W Red Oak Ln Ste 310 10604
Tel (914) 304-1300 SIC 5983

HOP ENERGY LLC p 706
4 W Red Oak Ln Ste 310 10604
Tel (914) 304-1300 SIC 5983

INNOVATIVE RESOURCE GROUP LLC p 745
44 S Broadway Ste 1200 10601
Tel (800) 305-3720 SIC 8099

ITOCHU CHEMICALS AMERICA INC p 768
360 Hamilton Ave Fl 6 10601
Tel (914) 333-7800 SIC 5169

ITT FLUID TECHNOLOGY CORP p 768
1133 Westcstr Ave N100 Ste N 10604
Tel (914) 641-2000 SIC 3494 3594 3561

▲ ITT INC p 768
1133 Westchester Ave N-100 10604
Tel (914) 641-2000
SIC 3594 3625 3823 3812

■ ITT LLC p 768
1133 Westchester Ave N-100 10604
Tel (914) 641-2000
SIC 3594 3625 3823 3812

■ KINRO MANUFACTURING INC p 821
200 Mmaroneck Ave Ste 301 10601
Tel (817) 483-7791 SIC 3442

KRASDALE FOODS INC p 829
65 W Red Oak Ln Ste 2 10604
Tel (914) 694-6400 SIC 5141

LEWIS P C JACKSON p 859
1133 Weschester Ave 10604
Tel (914) 872-8060 SIC 8111

MARCH OF DIMES FOUNDATION p 905
1275 Mamaroneck Ave 10605
Tel (914) 428-7100 SIC 8399

■ MARSH & MCLENNAN AGENCY LLC p 910
360 Hamilton Ave Ste 930 10601
Tel (914) 397-1600 SIC 6411

MARUBENI SPECIALTY CHEMICALS INC p 913
10 Bank St Ste 740 10606
Tel (914) 428-8900 SIC 5169

MITSUI PLASTICS INC p 978
11 Martine Ave Ste 1175 10606
Tel (914) 287-6800 SIC 5162

NEW YORK POWER AUTHORITY p 1035
123 Main St 10601
Tel (914) 681-6200 SIC 4911

PEARSON LONGMAN LLC p 1126
10 Bank St Ste 1030 10606
Tel (212) 641-2400 SIC 2731 2711

PECKHAM INDUSTRIES INC p 1126
20 Haarlem Ave Ste 200 10603
Tel (914) 949-2000 SIC 2951

PENTEGRA SERVICES INC p 1132
701 Westchester Ave 320e 10604
Tel (800) 872-3473 SIC 6371

■ PEPSI-COLA BOTTLING GROUP p 1134
1111 Westchester Ave 10604
Tel (914) 767-6000 SIC 2086

■ PEPSI-COLA METROPOLITAN BOTTLING CO INC p 1134
1111 Westchester Ave 10604
Tel (914) 767-6000 SIC 2086 2087

PERK-UP INC p 1136
399 Knollwood Rd Ste 309 10603
Tel (914) 580-3200
SIC 5113 5149 2673 3411 2674 2035

S & K DISTRIBUTION LLC p 1261
535 Old Tarrytown Rd 10603
Tel (914) 948-6363 SIC 5031 2952 5033

SABRA DIPPING CO LLC p 1264
777 Westchester Ave Fl 3 10604
Tel (914) 372-3900 SIC 2035

■ SHERATON CORP p 1315
1111 Westchester Ave 10604
Tel (800) 328-6242 SIC 7011 8741 6794

▲ SPAR GROUP INC p 1354
333 Westchester Ave S204 10604
Tel (914) 332-4100 SIC 7389 8732

■ SPAR MARKETING FORCE INC p 1354
333 Westc Ave South Build 10604
Tel (914) 332-4100 SIC 8742

STARFIRE HOLDING CORP p 1379
445 Hamilton Ave Ste 1210 10601
Tel (914) 614-7000 SIC 3743 4741 4789

■ STEEL EXCEL INC p 1384
1133 Westchester Ave N-222 10604
Tel (914) 461-1300 SIC 1389 7353 7032

TRIBORO QUILT MANUFACTURING CORP p 1479
172 S Broadway Ste 100 10605
Tel (914) 428-7551 SIC 5023 5999

ULYSSES CAREMARK HOLDING CORP p 1501
44 S Broadway Fl 12f 10601
Tel (914) 934-5200 SIC 6311 6321

UNITED STATES TENNIS ASSOCIATION INC p 1514
70 W Red Oak Ln Fl 1 10604
Tel (914) 696-7000 SIC 8699

▲ UNIVERSAL AMERICAN CORP p 1516
44 S Broadway Ste 1200 10601
Tel (914) 934-5200 SIC 6311 6321 6324

UNLIMITED CARE INC p 1528
333 Westchester Ave G02 10604
Tel (914) 428-4300 SIC 8059 8011

WESTIN HOTELS LIMITED PARTNERSHIP p 1601
1111 Westchester Ave 10604
Tel (617) 532-4600 SIC 7011

WHITE PLAINS HOSPITAL MEDICAL CENTER p 1606
41 E Post Rd 10601
Tel (914) 681-0600 SIC 8062

WHITE PLAINS PUBLIC SCHOOLS p 1606
5 Homeside Ln 10605
Tel (914) 422-2000 SIC 8211

WHITESBORO, NY

TURBINE ENGINE COMPONENTS TECHNOLOGIES - UTICA CORP p 1492
2 Halsey Rd 13492
Tel (315) 768-8070
SIC 3724 3511 3429 3842 3769

WHITESTONE, NY

■ KINRAY INC p 821
15235 10th Ave 11357
Tel (718) 767-1234 SIC 5122

WILLIAMSON, NY

JAMES FORD OF WILLIAMSON LLC p 776
3923 Route 104 14589
Tel (800) 246-2000 SIC 5511

WILLIAMSVILLE, NY

INDEPENDENT HEALTH ASSOCIATION INC p 736
511 Farber Lakes Dr Ste 2 14221
Tel (716) 631-3001 SIC 6324

LACKAWANNA PRODUCTS CORP p 837
8545 Main St Ste 1 14221
Tel (716) 633-1940 SIC 5191 5153

▲ LIFE STORAGE INC p 864
6467 Main St 14221
Tel (716) 633-1850 SIC 6798

▲ NATIONAL FUEL GAS CO p 1012
6363 Main St 14221
Tel (716) 857-7000
SIC 4924 4922 1311 1382

■ NATIONAL FUEL GAS DISTRIBUTION CORP p 1012
6363 Main St 14221
Tel (716) 857-7000 SIC 4925

■ NATIONAL FUEL GAS SUPPLY CORP p 1012
6363 Main St 14221
Tel (716) 857-7000 SIC 4924

PEOPLE INC p 1132
1219 N Forest Rd 14221
Tel (716) 817-7400 SIC 8361

■ SOVRAN ACQUISITION LIMITED PARTNERSHIP p 1353
6467 Main St 14221
Tel (716) 633-1850 SIC 6798

SUPERIOR WORKFORCE SOLUTIONS INC p 1407
250 International Dr 14221
Tel (716) 631-8310 SIC 7363

TOPS HOLDING II CORP p 1461
6363 Main St 14221
Tel (716) 635-5000 SIC 5411

TOPS HOLDING LLC p 1461
6363 Main St 14221
Tel (716) 635-5000 SIC 5411

TOPS MARKETS LLC p 1461
6363 Main St 14221
Tel (716) 635-5000
SIC 5411 5141 5147 5148 5122 5912

TOPS PT LLC p 1461
6363 Main St 14221
Tel (716) 635-5000 SIC 5411

TUXEDO JUNCTION INC p 1493
120 Earhart Dr 14221
Tel (716) 633-2400 SIC 5136 5699 7299

WILSON FARMS INC p 1613
1780 Wehrle Dr Ste 110 14221
Tel (716) 204-4300 SIC 5199

WILLSBORO, NY

NYCO MINERALS INC p 1069
803 Mountain View Dr 12996
Tel (518) 963-4262
SIC 1499 5052 3295 3291

WOODBURY, NY

ARIZONA BEVERAGES USA LLC p 108
60 Crossways Park Dr W 11797
Tel (516) 812-0300 SIC 5149

AZ METRO DISTRIBUTORS LLC p 140
60 Crossways Park Dr W # 400 11797
Tel (516) 812-0300 SIC 5064

CARDWORKS INC p 254
101 Crossways Park Dr W 11797
Tel (516) 576-0404 SIC 7322 7389

CARDWORKS LP p 254
101 Crossways Park Dr W 11797
Tel (516) 576-0404 SIC 7389

JENNIFER CONVERTIBLES INC p 782
335 Crossways Park Dr 11797
Tel (516) 496-1900 SIC 5712 6794 5021

LACKMANN FOOD SERVICE INC p 837
303 Crossways Park Dr 11797
Tel (516) 364-2300 SIC 5812

LEVITZ FURNITURE CORP p 858
300 Crossways Park Dr 11797
Tel (516) 682-0481 SIC 5712

NORTHERN VIDEO SYSTEMS INC p 1057
135 Cronyways Park Dr Ste 101 11797
Tel (516) 941-2800 SIC 5065

OVERSEAS MILITARY SALES CORP - OMSC LTD p 1099
175 Crossways Park Dr W 11797
Tel (516) 921-2800 SIC 5511

PORT ROYAL SALES LTD p 1162
95 Froehlich Farm Blvd # 200 11797
Tel (516) 921-8383 SIC 5149

RAYTECH CORP p 1210
97 Froehlich Farm Blvd 11797
Tel (718) 259-7388 SIC 3499

■ SERVICE BY AIR INC p 1307
222 Crossways Park Dr 11797
Tel (800) 243-5545 SIC 4731

■ STERLING & STERLING LLC p 1386
135 Crossways Park Dr # 300 11797
Tel (516) 487-0300 SIC 6411

TRI-ED DISTRIBUTION INC p 1477
135 Crossways Park Dr # 101 11797
Tel (516) 941-2800 SIC 5065

TRI-NORTHERN SECURITY DISTRIBUTION INC p 1477
135 Crossways Park Dr # 101 11797
Tel (516) 941-2800 SIC 5065

WIN-HOLT EQUIPMENT CORP p 1614
20 Crossways Park Dr N # 205 11797
Tel (516) 222-0335 SIC 2099

WOODSIDE, NY

ACE WIRE & CABLE CO INC p 16
7201 51st Ave 11377
Tel (718) 458-9200 SIC 5063

WOODSTOCK, NY

■ ROTRON INC p 1252
55 Hasbrouck Ln 12498
Tel (845) 679-2401 SIC 3564

WYNANTSKILL, NY

CASCADES TISSUE GROUP - NEW YORK INC p 263
148 Hudson River Rd 12198
Tel (518) 238-1900 SIC 2679

YAPHANK, NY

■ MAHARAM FABRIC CORP p 897
74 Horseblock Rd 11980
Tel (631) 582-3434 SIC 5131 7389

YONKERS, NY

A & A MAINTENANCE ENTERPRISE INC p 4
965 Midland Ave 10704
Tel (914) 969-0009
SIC 7349 1721 1542 4959 0782

AMERICAN SUGAR REFINING INC p 80
1 Federal St 10705
Tel (800) 729-4840 SIC 2062

ASR GROUP INTERNATIONAL INC p 119
1 Federal St 10705
Tel (914) 963-2400 SIC 2062

CITY OF YONKERS p 319
40 S Broadway Ste 1 10701
Tel (914) 377-6000 SIC 9111

CONSUMERS UNION OF UNITED STATES INC p 362
101 Truman Ave 10703
Tel (914) 378-2000 SIC 2741 2721 7389

CREATIVE SOLUTIONS GROUP INC p 390
555 Tuckahoe Rd 10710
Tel (914) 771-4200 SIC 3993

FISK TELECOM LLC p 552
1091 Yonkers Ave 10704
Tel (914) 476-2073 SIC 4813

HUDSON VALLEY BANK p 717
21 Scarsdale Rd 10707
Tel (914) 961-6100 SIC 6029

HUDSON VALLEY HOLDING CORP p 717
21 Scarsdale Rd 10707
Tel (914) 961-6100 SIC 6022

ITR INDUSTRIES INC p 768
441 Saw Mill River Rd 10701
Tel (914) 964-7063
SIC 3431 3429 3446 3088

JAC VANDENBERG INC p 773
100 Corporate Dr Ste 155 10701
Tel (914) 964-5900 SIC 5148

KIMBER MFG INC p 818
1 Lawton St 10705
Tel (914) 964-0771 SIC 3599

NATIONS ROOF EAST LLC p 1017
255 Lake Ave 10701
Tel (914) 423-6171 SIC 1761

NATIONS ROOF OF NEW YORK LLC p 1017
70 Saint Casimir Ave 10701
Tel (914) 509-7020 SIC 1761

POP DISPLAYS USA LLC p 1161
555 Tuckahoe Rd 10710
Tel (914) 771-4200 SIC 5046

RIVERSIDE HEALTH CARE SYSTEM INC p 1238
967 N Broadway 10701
Tel (914) 964-4444 SIC 8062

SOHEL DISTRIBUTORS NY LLC p 1337
1091 Yonkers Ave 10704
Tel (914) 476-2073 SIC 4812

ST JOSEPHS HOSPITAL YONKERS p 1369
127 S Broadway 10701
Tel (914) 378-7000 SIC 8062 8011

WALLICO MAINTENANCE GROUP LLC p 1573
965 Midland Ave 10704
Tel (914) 595-0664 SIC 7349

YONKERS CITY SCHOOL DISTRICT p 1637
1 Larkin Ctr Fl 3 10701
Tel (914) 376-8000 SIC 8211 9111

YONKERS CONTRACTING CO INC p 1637
969 Midland Ave 10704
Tel (914) 965-1500 SIC 1611

YONKERS RACING CORP p 1637
810 Yonkers Ave 10704
Tel (914) 968-4200 SIC 7948

NORTH CAROLINA

ABERDEEN, NC

LEE ELECTRICAL CONSTRUCTION INC p 851
12828 Us Highway 15 501 28315
Tel (910) 944-9728 SIC 1731

MCMURRAY FABRICS INC p 932
105 Vann Pl 28315
Tel (910) 944-2128 SIC 2257

ADVANCE, NC

DONNIE SHONOBI BRAND NAME TRADEMARK COLLECTION CORP p 451
160 Town Park Dr 27006
Tel (336) 940-5682 SIC 5699 7389

AHOSKIE, NC

JERNIGAN OIL CO INC p 783
415 Main St E 27910
Tel (252) 332-2131 SIC 5411 5171

ALBEMARLE, NC

AMERICAN FIBER & FINISHING INC p 72
225 N Depot St 28001
Tel (704) 983-6102
SIC 2211 3842 2844 2392

LUTHERAN HOME ALBEMARLE PROPERTY INC p 886
24724 S Business 52 28001
Tel (704) 982-8191 SIC 6531

MONARCH p 983
350 Pee Dee Ave Ste 101 28001
Tel (704) 986-1500
SIC 8322 8049 8331 8052

STANLY COUNTY SCHOOLS p 1377
1000 N 1st St Ste 4 28001
Tel (704) 961-3000 SIC 8211

STANLY COUNTY SCHOOLS EDUCATIONAL FOUNDATION INC p 1377
1000 N 1st St Ste 4 28001
Tel (704) 983-5151 SIC 8399

STANLY HEALTH SERVICES INC p 1377
301 Yadkin St 28001
Tel (704) 982-3888 SIC 8741

STANLY REGIONAL MEDICAL CENTER p 1377
301 Yadkin St 28001
Tel (704) 982-3888 SIC 8062

APEX, NC

PETROLIANCE LLC p 1139
1009 Schieffelin Rd 27502
Tel (919) 387-9810 SIC 5171

ARCHDALE, NC

HAFELE AMERICA CO p 652
3901 Cheyenne Dr 27263
Tel (336) 434-2322 SIC 5072

■ HUBBELL INDUSTRIAL CONTROLS INC p 716
4301 Cheyenne Dr 27263
Tel (336) 434-2800 SIC 3625

ARDEN, NC

GUTHY-RENKER FULFILLMENT SERVICES LLC p 648
1845 Brevard Rd 28704
Tel (828) 684-4300 SIC 7389 7374

■ MEDICAL ACTION INDUSTRIES INC p 936
25 Heywood Rd 28704
Tel (631) 231-4600 SIC 3842

ASHEBORO, NC

ACME - MCCRARY CORP p 17
159 North St 27203
Tel (336) 625-2161 SIC 2251

ASHEBORO ELASTICS CORP p 117
150 N Park St 27203
Tel (336) 629-2626 SIC 2221 2241

■ COMMUNITYONE BANK NATIONAL ASSOCIATION p 350
101 Sunset Ave 27203
Tel (336) 625-4012 SIC 6712 6021

KLAUSSNER CORP p 823
405 Lewallen Rd 27205
Tel (888) 732-5948 SIC 2512

KLAUSSNER FURNITURE INDUSTRIES INC p 823
405 Lewallen Rd 27205
Tel (336) 625-6174 SIC 2512

PRESTIGE FABRICATORS INC p 1173
905 Nc Highway 49 S 27205
Tel (336) 626-4595 SIC 3069

PUGH OIL CO INC p 1191
701 Mcdowell Rd 27205
Tel (336) 629-2061
SIC 5172 5983 5541 5411 5149

RANDOLPH COUNTY BOARD OF EDUCATION p 1207
2222 S Fayetteville St C 27205
Tel (336) 318-6100 SIC 8211

RANDOLPH HOSPITAL INC p 1207
364 White Oak St 27203
Tel (336) 625-5151 SIC 8062

TECHNIMARK LLC p 1431
180 Commerce Pl 27203
Tel (336) 498-4171 SIC 3089 5199

TECHNIMARK REYNOSA LLC p 1431
180 Commerce Pl 27203
Tel (336) 498-4171 SIC 3089

ASHEVILLE, NC

ASHEVILLE NURSING AND REHAB CENTER p 117
91 Victoria Rd 28801
Tel (828) 255-0076 SIC 8099

BILTMORE CO p 183
1 Lodge St 28803
Tel (828) 225-6776 SIC 7999 5947 5812

BUNCOMBE COUNTY SCHOOL DISTRICT p 225
175 Bingham Rd 28806
Tel (828) 251-0499 SIC 8211

CAROLINA RHA/NORTH MR INC p 259
1200 Rdgfeld Blvd Ste 270 28806
Tel (828) 322-4200 SIC 8744

COMMUNITY CAREPARTNERS INC p 347
68 Sweeten Creek Rd 28803
Tel (828) 274-2400 SIC 8322 8093

COUNTY OF BUNCOMBE p 376
200 College St Ste 300 28801
Tel (828) 250-4100 SIC 9111

GROVE PARK INN RESORT INC p 642
290 Macon Ave 28804
Tel (828) 252-2711
SIC 7011 5812 5813 7992 7991 7299

▲ HOMETRUST BANCSHARES INC p 704
10 Woodfin St 28801
Tel (828) 259-3939 SIC 6035

MB HAYNES CORP p 925
187 Deaverview Rd 28806
Tel (828) 254-6141
SIC 1542 1623 1711 7382

MISSION HEALTH SYSTEM INC p 975
509 Biltm Ave Aka Hwy 25 28801
Tel (828) 213-1111 SIC 8062

MISSION HEALTH SYSTEM INC p 975
400 Ridgefield Ct 28806
Tel (828) 257-7004 SIC 8062

MISSION HOSPITAL INC p 975
509 Biltmore Ave 28801
Tel (828) 213-1111 SIC 8062

NORTH AMERICAN ROOFING SERVICES INC p 1050
41 Dogwood Rd 28806
Tel (828) 687-7767 SIC 1761

OMNI GROVE PARK LLC p 1084
290 Macon Ave 28804
Tel (828) 252-2711
SIC 7299 5812 7011 5813 7992 7991

RHA HEALTH SERVICES INC p 1231
17 Church St 28801
Tel (828) 232-6844 SIC 8741

SILVER-LINE PLASTICS CORP p 1324
900 Riverside Dr 28804
Tel (828) 252-8755 SIC 3084

■ THERMO FISHER SCIENTIFIC (ASHVILLE) LLC p 1447
28 Schenck Pkwy Ste 400 28803
Tel (828) 658-2711
SIC 3585 3826 3821 3829

U C A HOLDINGS INC p 1497
1 W Pack Sq Ste 305 28801
Tel (828) 210-8120 SIC 6719

UNIVERSITY OF NORTH CAROLINA AT ASHEVILLE p 1523
1 University Hts 28804
Tel (828) 232-5009 SIC 8221

BATTLEBORO, NC

■ MCLANE/CAROLINA INC p 931
7253 Nc 48 27809
Tel (252) 972-2500 SIC 5141 5142 5149

BEAUFORT, NC

CARTERET COUNTY BOARD OF EDUCATION (INC) p 262
107 Safrit Dr 28516
Tel (252) 728-4583 SIC 8211

BELMONT, NC

IDG USA LLC p 729
2100 The Oaks Pkwy 28012
Tel (704) 398-5600 SIC 5085 5084

INDUSTRIAL DISTRIBUTION GROUP INC p 740
2100 The Oaks Pkwy 28012
Tel (704) 398-5600 SIC 5084 7699

WILBERT INC p 1608
2001 Oaks Pkwy 28012
Tel (704) 247-3850 SIC 5162 3272

BLACK MOUNTAIN, NC

▲ INGLES MARKETS INC p 743
2913 Us Highway 70 28711
Tel (828) 669-2941
SIC 5411 5912 5541 2026 6512

BOLIVIA, NC

BRUNSWICK COUNTY BOARD OF EDUCATION p 221
35 Referendum Dr Ne 28422
Tel (910) 253-2900 SIC 8211

BRUNSWICK COUNTY SCHOOLS p 221
35 Referendum Dr Ne 28422
Tel (910) 253-2900 SIC 8211

BRUNSWICK NOVANT MEDICAL CENTER p 221
240 Hospital Dr Ne 28422
Tel (336) 277-1120 SIC 8011

BOONE, NC

APPALACHIAN REGIONAL HEALTHCARE SYSTEM INC p 98
336 Deerfield Rd 28607
Tel (828) 262-4100 SIC 8062

APPALACHIAN STATE UNIVERSITY INC p 98
438 Academy St Rm 340 28608
Tel (828) 262-2000 SIC 8221

CMD SALES LLC p 329
355 Industrial Park Dr 28607
Tel (828) 355-7121 SIC 1791

FFC LIMITED PARTNERSHIP p 539
166 Southgate Dr Ste 10 28607
Tel (828) 262-1811 SIC 5812

SAMARITANS PURSE p 1274
801 Bamboo Rd 28607
Tel (828) 262-1980 SIC 8322 6732

TAR HEEL CAPITAL CORP NO 2 p 1424
166 Southgate Dr Ste 10 28607
Tel (828) 264-4221 SIC 5812

WATAUGA MEDICAL CENTER INC p 1581
336 Deerfield Rd 28607
Tel (828) 262-4100 SIC 8062 8011

BROWNS SUMMIT, NC

BONSET AMERICA CORP p 200
6107 Corporate Park Dr 27214
Tel (336) 375-0234 SIC 3081

DIXIE SERVANTAGE SALES INC p 445
5920 Summit Ave 27214
Tel (336) 375-7500 SIC 5083

MORRISETTE PAPER CO INC p 990
5925 Summit Ave 27214
Tel (336) 375-1515 SIC 5113 5111 5087

SHAMROCK ENVIRONMENTAL CORP p 1311
6106 Corporate Park Dr 27214
Tel (336) 375-1989
SIC 4953 4212 8748 7699

BUIES CREEK, NC

CAMPBELL UNIVERSITY INC p 246
148 Main St 27506
Tel (910) 893-1240 SIC 8221

BURGAW, NC

FOUR COUNTY ELECTRIC MEMBERSHIP CORP p 571
1822 Nc Highway 53 W 28425
Tel (910) 259-2361 SIC 4911

PENDER COUNTY SCHOOLS p 1128
925 Penderlea Hwy 28425
Tel (910) 259-2187 SIC 8211

BURLINGTON, NC

ALAMANCE FOODS INC p 43
840 Plantation Dr 27215
Tel (336) 226-6392
SIC 2026 2899 2024 2086

ALAMANCE REGIONAL MEDICAL CENTER INC p 44
1240 Huffman Mill Rd 27215
Tel (336) 538-7000 SIC 8062

ALAMANCE-BURLINGTON SCHOOL DISTRICT p 44
1712 Vaughn Rd 27217
Tel (336) 570-6060 SIC 8211

BURLINGTON MOTORS INC p 228
660 Huffman Mill Rd 27215
Tel (336) 584-1701 SIC 5511

CAROLINA BIOLOGICAL SUPPLY CO p 259
2700 York Rd 27215
Tel (336) 584-0381
SIC 5049 2836 3829 3826 3821

CHANDLER CONCRETE INC p 288
1006 S Church St 27215
Tel (336) 272-6127 SIC 3273

CITY OF BURLINGTON p 313
425 S Lexington Ave 27215
Tel (336) 222-5060 SIC 9111

FIRST FINANCIAL INSURANCE CO INC p 547
238 International Rd 27215
Tel (336) 586-2500 SIC 6331

GLEN RAVEN INC p 614
1831 N Park Ave 27217
Tel (336) 227-6211
SIC 2221 2281 2261 2211

HUNT ELECTRIC SUPPLY CO p 719
1213 Maple Ave 27215
Tel (336) 229-5351 SIC 5063 5211

INTERNATIONAL FINANCIAL GROUP INC p 755
238 International Rd 27215
Tel (336) 586-2500 SIC 6331

■ LABORATORY CORP OF AMERICA p 836
358 S Main St Ste 458 27215
Tel (336) 229-1127 SIC 8071

▲ LABORATORY CORP OF AMERICA HOLDINGS p 836
358 S Main St 27215
Tel (336) 229-1127 SIC 8071

STAR FOOD PRODUCTS INC p 1378
2050 Willow Spring Ln A 27215
Tel (336) 227-4079 SIC 5147 2099

■ TAPCO UNDERWRITERS INC p 1424
3060 S Church St 27215
Tel (336) 584-8892 SIC 6411

TRI VANTAGE LLC p 1477
1831 N Park Ave 27217
Tel (800) 786-1876
SIC 5199 5088 5099 5091 2394

TRIANGLE GRADING & PAVING INC p 1478
1521 Huffman Mill Rd 27215
Tel (336) 584-1745 SIC 1611 1794

■ UFP MID-ATLANTIC LLC p 1499
5631 S Nc Highway 62 27215
Tel (336) 226-9356 SIC 2439

BUTNER, NC

CAROLINA SUNROCK LLC p 259
1001 W B St 27509
Tel (919) 575-4502
SIC 1429 3273 2951 1411

CENTRAL REGIONAL HOSPITAL p 280
300 Veazey Dr 27509
Tel (919) 575-7211 SIC 8062 9431

MURDOCH CENTER FOUNDATION INC p 1001
1600 E C St 27509
Tel (919) 575-1000 SIC 8699

CAMP LEJEUNE, NC

MORALE WELFARE RECREATION ACTIVITY p 988
1401 West Rd 28547
Tel (910) 451-2861
SIC 5311 5812 8322 7999 9711

CANDLER, NC

CAROLINA ADVENTIST RETIREMENT SYSTEMS INC p 259
95 Holcombe Cove Rd 28715
Tel (828) 667-9851 SIC 8052 8051 8082

CANTON, NC

BLUE RIDGE PAPER PRODUCTS INC p 192
41 Main St 28716
Tel (828) 454-0676 SIC 2621

CARRBORO, NC

ORANGE WATER AND SEWER AUTHORITY p 1092
400 Jones Ferry Rd 27510
Tel (919) 960-6142 SIC 4941 4952

CARTHAGE, NC

MOORE COUNTY BOARD OF EDUCATION p 987
5227 Us 15 501 Hwy 28327
Tel (910) 947-2976 SIC 8211

MOORE COUNTY SCHOOLS p 987
5277 Hwy 15 501 S 28327
Tel (910) 947-2976 SIC 8211

PINELAKE HEALTH & REHAB p 1149
801 Pinehurst Ave 28327
Tel (910) 947-5155 SIC 8051

CARY, NC

ABB HOLDINGS INC p 9
12040 Regency Pkwy # 200 27518
Tel (919) 856-2360 SIC 3612

ABB INC p 9
12040 Regency Pkwy # 200 27518
Tel (919) 856-2360
SIC 8711 3612 3511 5063 3613 3625

BUHLER AEROGLIDE CORP p 224
100 Aeroglide Dr 27511
Tel (919) 278-2925 SIC 3556 3585 3567

CARY OIL CO INC p 262
110 Mackenan Dr Ste 300 27511
Tel (919) 462-1100 SIC 5172 5171

COC PROPERTIES INC p 333
110 Mackenan Dr Ste 300 27511
Tel (919) 462-1100 SIC 6512 5541 5411

DEX ONE CORP p 434
1001 Winstead Dr Ste 100 27513
Tel (919) 297-1600 SIC 2741 8732

GK HOLDINGS INC p 613
9000 Regency Pkwy Ste 500 27518
Tel (800) 268-7737 SIC 6719

GLOBAL KNOWLEDGETRAINING LLC p 617
9000 Regency Pkwy Ste 400 27518
Tel (919) 388-1064 SIC 8243

LOPAREX LLC p 877
1255 Crescent Green # 400 27518
Tel (919) 678-7700 SIC 2672

LORD CORP p 878
111 Lord Dr 27511
Tel (877) 275-5673
SIC 2891 3724 3728 2851

NORTH CAROLINA INSURANCE UNDERWRITING ASSOCIATION p 1051
5651 Dillard Dr 27518
Tel (919) 821-1299 SIC 6331

PANTRY INC p 1112
305 Gregson Dr 27511
Tel (919) 774-6700 SIC 5541 5411

▲ PLY GEM HOLDINGS INC p 1157
5020 Weston Pkwy Ste 400 27513
Tel (919) 677-3900 SIC 2431 2952

■ PLY GEM INDUSTRIES INC p 1157
5020 Weston Pkwy Ste 400 27513
Tel (919) 677-3900 SIC 2431

PRECISION WALLS INC p 1169
1230 Ne Maynard Rd 27513
Tel (919) 832-0380 SIC 1743 1742 1799

SAS INSTITUTE INC p 1282
100 Sas Campus Dr 27513
Tel (919) 677-8000 SIC 8243 7372

SIEMENS POWERTRANSMISSION & DISTRIBUTION INC p 1320
110 Macalyson Ct 27511
Tel (919) 463-8702 SIC 3613 3625

■ SPECTRASITE COMMUNICATIONS LLC p 1357
400 Regency Forest Dr # 300 27518
Tel (919) 468-0112
SIC 4812 8748 1623 3661 4813 4899

TOWN OF CARY p 1465
316 N Academy St 27513
Tel (919) 469-4048 SIC 9111

TRANS WORLD RADIO p 1470
300 Gregson Dr 27511
Tel (919) 460-9597 SIC 4832

VANTAGESOUTH BANK p 1544
1005 High House Rd 27513
Tel (919) 460-7770 SIC 6022

WAKE COUNTY PUBLIC SCHOOL SYSTEM p 1571
5625 Dillard Dr 27518
Tel (919) 431-7343 SIC 8211

CHADBOURN, NC

WAYNE BAILEY INC p 1584
490 Old Hwy 74 28431
Tel (910) 654-5163 SIC 5148 0139

CHAPEL HILL, NC

ADVANCED SPORTS ENTERPRISES INC p 26
1 Performance Way 27517
Tel (919) 933-9113 SIC 5091

CHAPEL HILL-CARRBORO CITY SCHOOL SYSTEM p 288
750 S Merritt Mill Rd 27516
Tel (919) 967-8211 *SIC* 8211

DIVI HOTELS MARKETING INC p 444
6320 Quadrangle Dr # 210 27517
Tel (919) 419-3484 *SIC* 7011 7999 6531

FORESTLAND GROUP LLC p 567
1512 E Franklin St # 104 27514
Tel (919) 929-2497 *SIC* 6282

INTRAHEALTH INTERNATIONAL INC p 760
6340 Quadrangle Dr # 200 27517
Tel (919) 313-9100 *SIC* 8011

▲ INVESTORS TITLE CO p 762
121 N Columbia St 27514
Tel (919) 968-2200 *SIC* 6361 6351

■ INVESTORS TITLE INSURANCE CO p 762
121 N Columbia St 27514
Tel (919) 968-2200 *SIC* 6361

JAMES RIVER GROUP INC p 777
1414 Raleigh Rd Ste 405 27517
Tel (919) 883-4171 *SIC* 6411

KENAN TRANSPORT LLC p 810
100 Europa Dr Ste 170 27517
Tel (919) 967-8221 *SIC* 4212 4213

PERFORMANCE DIRECT INC p 1135
1 Performance Way 27517
Tel (919) 933-9113 *SIC* 5961 5941

UNIVERSITY OF NORTH CAROLINA p 1523
910 Raleigh Rd 27514
Tel (919) 962-1000 *SIC* 8221

UNIVERSITY OF NORTH CAROLINA AT CHAPEL HILL p 1523
104 Airport Dr 27599
Tel (919) 962-1370 *SIC* 8221

UNIVERSITY OF NORTH CAROLINA HOSPITALS p 1524
101 Manning Dr Bldg 2 27514
Tel (919) 966-5111 *SIC* 8062

CHARLOTTE, NC

AKIMA CORP p 42
11405 N Community House R 28277
Tel (704) 552-0082 *SIC* 8744

▲ ALBEMARLE CORP p 46
4350 Congress St Ste 700 28209
Tel (980) 299-5700
SIC 2821 2834 2819 2899 2812 2869

ALLEN TATE CO INC p 53
6700 Fairview Rd 28210
Tel (704) 365-6910 *SIC* 6411

ALLIANCE DEVELOPMENT GROUP LLC p 54
301 S Tryon St Ste 1500 28282
Tel (704) 973-2950 *SIC* 5812 6552

ALLIED STAFF AUGMENTATION PARTNERS INC p 57
7421 Carmel Executive Par 28226
Tel (980) 219-8477 *SIC* 8711

AMERICAN CITY BUSINESS JOURNALS INC p 70
120 W Morehead St Ste 400 28202
Tel (704) 973-1000 *SIC* 2711 2721

AMERICAN PRODUCT DISTRIBUTORS INC p 78
8350 Arrowridge Blvd 28273
Tel (704) 522-9411
SIC 5111 5112 5047 5044 5085 5087

AMWINS GROUP INC p 87
4725 Piedmont Row Dr # 600 28210
Tel (704) 749-2700 *SIC* 6411 8748

APM TERMINALS NORTH AMERICA INC p 97
9300 Arrowpoint Blvd 28273
Tel (704) 571-2768 *SIC* 4491

AREVA INC p 107
7207 Ibm Dr 28262
Tel (704) 805-2000
SIC 3823 3829 8711 5085 3561 2819

ARROWOOD INDEMNITY CO p 113
3600 Arco Corporate Dr 28273
Tel (704) 522-2000 *SIC* 6331

ARROWPOINT CAPITAL CORP p 113
3600 Arco Corporate Dr 28273
Tel (704) 522-2000 *SIC* 6331

ASC CONSTRUCTION EQUIPMENT USA INC p 115
9115 Harris Corners Pkwy # 450 28269
Tel (704) 494-8100 *SIC* 5082

ASHTEAD US HOLDINGS INC p 117
401 S Tryon St 28202
Tel (803) 578-5811 *SIC* 7353 7359 5082

■ ATI PRODUCTS INC p 124
5100 W W T Harris Blvd H 28269
Tel (800) 438-0660 *SIC* 5083 5084 5085

■ AVINTIV INC p 138
9335 Harris Corners Pkwy 28269
Tel (704) 697-5100 *SIC* 2297

■ AVINTIV SPECIALTY MATERIALS INC p 138
9335 Harris Corners Pkwy 28269
Tel (704) 697-5100 *SIC* 2297 2392

▲ BABCOCK & WILCOX ENTERPRISES INC p 143
13024 Ballantyne Corporat 28277
Tel (704) 625-4900 *SIC* 3621 3829

BAHAKEL SPORTS INC p 145
1 Television Pl 28205
Tel (704) 372-4434 *SIC* 4833 4832

BAKER & TAYLOR ACQUISITIONS CORP p 145
2550 W Tyvola Rd Ste 300 28217
Tel (704) 998-3100 *SIC* 2731

BAKER & TAYLOR FULFILLMENT INC p 145
2550 W Tyvola Rd Ste 300 28217
Tel (704) 998-3154
SIC 5192 5045 7822 5065

BAKER & TAYLOR HOLDINGS LLC p 145
2550 W Tyvola Rd Ste 300 28217
Tel (704) 998-3100
SIC 5192 7822 5065 5045

BAKER & TAYLOR LLC p 145
2550 W Tyvola Rd Ste 300 28217
Tel (704) 998-3100
SIC 5192 7822 5065 5045 5099

BALL INC p 148
4201 Congress St Ste 340 28209
Tel (704) 551-1500 *SIC* 3411

■ BANC OF AMERICA MORTGAGE CAPITAL CORP p 149
100 N Tryon St Ste 4700 28202
Tel (800) 876-4496 *SIC* 6411

▲ BANK OF AMERICA CORP p 151
100 N Tryon St Ste 220 28202
Tel (704) 386-5681
SIC 6021 6022 6211 6091 6162 6159

■ BANK OF AMERICA MORTGAGE SECURITIES INC p 151
101 S Tryon St Ste 1000 28280
Tel (704) 386-5681 *SIC* 6162 6163

BANK OF AMERICA N A p 151
401 N Tryon St Ste 300 28202
Tel (800) 432-1000 *SIC* 6021

■ BANK OF AMERICA NATIONAL ASSOCIATION p 151
101 S Tryon St 28280
Tel (704) 386-5681 *SIC* 6021

BARLOWORLD HANDLING LLC p 155
7621 Little Ave Ste 201 28226
Tel (704) 588-1300 *SIC* 5084

BARNHARDT MANUFACTURING CO p 156
1100 Hawthorne Ln 28205
Tel (704) 376-0380 *SIC* 0131 3086

BELK FINANCE CO INC p 169
2801 W Tyvola Rd 28217
Tel (704) 357-1000 *SIC* 8741

BELK INC p 169
2801 W Tyvola Rd 28217
Tel (704) 357-1000 *SIC* 5311

BILLY GRAHAM EVANGELISTIC ASSN p 182
1 Billy Graham Pkwy 28201
Tel (704) 401-2432 *SIC* 8661

BJ HOLDINGS CORP p 185
9432 Southern Pine Blvd 28273
Tel (704) 527-2675 *SIC* 5812 6794

BLYTHE CONSTRUCTION INC p 193
2911 N Graham St 28206
Tel (704) 375-8474 *SIC* 1611 1622 2951

BLYTHE DEVELOPMENT CO p 193
1415 E Westinghouse Blvd 28273
Tel (704) 588-0023 *SIC* 1611

BOJANGLES HOLDINGS INC p 198
9432 Southern Pine Blvd 28273
Tel (704) 527-2675 *SIC* 5812

▲ BOJANGLES INC p 198
9432 Southern Pine Blvd 28273
Tel (704) 527-2675 *SIC* 5812

■ BOJANGLES RESTAURANTS INC p 198
9432 Southern Pine Blvd 28273
Tel (704) 527-2675 *SIC* 5812 6794

BONSAL AMERICAN INC p 200
625 Griffith Rd Ste 100 28217
Tel (704) 525-1621
SIC 3272 1442 3253 2899

BOSCH REXROTH CORP p 202
14001 S Lakes Dr 28273
Tel (847) 645-3600 *SIC* 3594

BTAC ACQUISITION LLC p 222
2550 W Tyvola Rd Ste 300 28217
Tel (704) 998-3100
SIC 5192 7822 5065 5045

BTAC HOLDING CORP p 222
2550 W Tyvola Rd Ste 300 28217
Tel (704) 998-3100
SIC 5192 7822 5065 5045

■ BWXT INVESTMENT CO p 231
11525 N Community House 28277
Tel (704) 625-4900
SIC 3511 3443 3564 1629 1541 7699

CAMPUS CREST COMMUNITIES INC p 246
2100 Rexford Rd Ste 300 28211
Tel (704) 496-2500 *SIC* 6798 6552 6531

CAMSO USA INC p 246
306 Forsyth Hall Dr 28273
Tel (704) 374-9700 *SIC* 5531 5014

▲ CAPITAL BANK FINANCIAL CORP p 249
4725 Piedmont Row Dr 28210
Tel (704) 554-5901 *SIC* 6021

■ CARLISLE CORP p 257
11605 N Community Hse Rd 28277
Tel (704) 501-1100
SIC 2952 2899 3011 2295 3089 3577

CAROLINA FOODS INC p 259
1807 S Tryon St 28203
Tel (704) 333-9812 *SIC* 2051

CAROLINA HANDLING LLC p 259
3101 Piper Ln 28208
Tel (704) 357-6273 *SIC* 5084

CAROLINA MOTOR CLUB INC p 259
6600 Aaa Dr 28212
Tel (704) 377-3600 *SIC* 8699 4724

CAROLINA RESTAURANT GROUP INC p 259
8040 Arrowridge Blvd # 100 28273
Tel (704) 525-3434 *SIC* 5812

CAROLINA TRACTOR & EQUIPMENT CO INC p 259
9000 Statesville Rd 28269
Tel (704) 596-6700
SIC 5082 5084 5013 7353 7359 7629

CAROLINA WHOLESALE GROUP INC p 259
425 E Arrowhead Dr 28213
Tel (704) 598-8101 *SIC* 5044

CAROLINAS MEDICAL CENTER AT HOME LLC p 259
1000 Blythe Blvd 28203
Tel (704) 355-3165 *SIC* 8062

CAROUSEL CAPITAL CO LLC p 260
201 N Tryon St Ste 2450 28202
Tel (704) 372-2040 *SIC* 6211

■ CARRIER ENTERPRISE LLC p 261
4300 Golf Acres Dr 28208
Tel (704) 394-7311 *SIC* 5075

▲ CATO CORP p 267
8100 Denmark Rd 28273
Tel (704) 554-8510
SIC 5621 5632 5137 5699 5311 5641

■ CCBCC OPERATIONS LLC p 269
4100 Coca Cola Plz 28211
Tel (704) 364-8728 *SIC* 2086

CDA INC p 270
8500 S Tryon St 28273
Tel (704) 504-1877 *SIC* 5099 3652

CELGARD LLC p 273
13800 S Lakes Dr 28273
Tel (704) 588-5310 *SIC* 2821 3081

CENTRAL PIEDMONT COMMUNITY COLLEGE p 279
1201 Elizabeth Ave 28204
Tel (704) 330-2722 *SIC* 8222 9411

CHARLOTTE CATH HIGH p 290
7702 Pneville Matthews Rd 28226
Tel (704) 543-1127 *SIC* 8211

■ CHARLOTTE OBSERVER PUBLISHING CO p 290
550 S Caldwell St 28202
Tel (704) 358-5000 *SIC* 2711 4813

CHARLOTTE PIPE AND FOUNDRY CO p 290
2109 Randolph Rd 28207
Tel (704) 372-5030 *SIC* 3084 3089 3321

CHARLOTTE-MECKLENBURG HOSPITAL AUTHORITY p 290
1000 Blythe Blvd 28203
Tel (704) 355-2000
SIC 8062 8069 8063 8051 8011

CHARLOTTE-MECKLENBURG SCHOOL DISTRICT p 290
600 E 4th St 28202
Tel (980) 343-6372 *SIC* 8211

CHICAGO BRIDGE & IRON CO p 297
128 S Tryon St Ste 400 28202
Tel (704) 331-6200 *SIC* 8731

■ CHICOPEE INC p 298
9335 Harr Corn Pkwy Ste 3 28269
Tel (704) 697-5100 *SIC* 2297

CHILDRESS KLEIN PROPERTIES INC p 300
301 S College St Ste 2800 28202
Tel (704) 342-9000 *SIC* 6552 6512 6531

CITY OF CHARLOTTE p 313
600 E 4th St 28202
Tel (704) 336-7600 *SIC* 9111

CLARIANT CORP p 321
4000 Monroe Rd 28205
Tel (704) 331-7000 *SIC* 2869 2819

CLARIANT PLASTICS & COATINGS USA INC p 321
4000 Monroe Rd 28205
Tel (704) 331-7000 *SIC* 2869 2819

CLASSIC GRAPHICS LLC p 323
8335 Classic Dr 28262
Tel (704) 597-9015 *SIC* 2752

COATS & CLARK INC p 332
3430 Toringdon Way # 301 28277
Tel (704) 329-5800
SIC 2284 2281 3364 3089 2241 3965

COATS AMERICAN INC p 332
3430 Toringdon Way # 301 28277
Tel (704) 329-5800 *SIC* 2284

COATS NORTH AMERICA DE REPUBLICA DOMINICANA INC p 332
3430 Toringdon Way # 301 28277
Tel (800) 242-8095
SIC 2284 2281 3364 3089 2241 3965

▲ COCA-COLA BOTTLING CO CONSOLIDATED p 333
4100 Coca Cola Plz # 100 28211
Tel (704) 557-4400 *SIC* 2086

■ COGENTRIX ENERGY POWER MANAGEMENT LLC p 334
9405 Arrowpoint Blvd 28273
Tel (704) 525-3800 *SIC* 4911

COINMACH HOLDINGS LLC p 335
1017 E Morehead St # 100 28204
Tel (704) 375-1947 *SIC* 7215

COINMACH LAUNDRY CORP p 335
1017 E Morehead St # 100 28204
Tel (704) 375-1947 *SIC* 7215

■ COLTEC INDUSTRIES INC p 339
5605 Carnegie Blvd # 500 28209
Tel (704) 731-1500 *SIC* 3053 3519 3089

COMMUNITYONE BANCORP p 350
1017 E Morehead St # 200 28204
Tel (336) 626-8300 *SIC* 6021

COMPASS GROUP USA INC p 351
2400 Yorkmont Rd 28217
Tel (704) 329-4000 *SIC* 5812

COMPASS GROUP USA INVESTMENTS LLP p 351
2400 Yorkmont Rd 28217
Tel (704) 328-4000 *SIC* 6726

COMPASS HOLDINGS INC p 351
2400 Yorkmont Rd 28217
Tel (704) 328-4000 *SIC* 5812 5962

CONCRETE SUPPLY HOLDINGS INC p 355
3823 Raleigh St 28206
Tel (704) 372-2930 *SIC* 3273

■ CONSOLIDATED THEATRES INC p 360
5970 Fairview Rd Ste 600 28210
Tel (704) 554-1695 *SIC* 7832 5441

COUNTY OF MECKLENBURG p 379
600 E 4th St 28202
Tel (704) 336-2108 *SIC* 9111

CRESCENT RESOURCES LLC p 391
227 W Trade St Ste 1000 28202
Tel (980) 321-6000 *SIC* 6552

CROWDER CONSTRUCTION CO INC p 394
6425 Brookshire Blvd 28216
Tel (800) 849-2966 *SIC* 1622 1629 1623

CROWDER CONSTRUCTORS INC p 394
6425 Brookshire Blvd 28216
Tel (704) 372-3541 *SIC* 1623

■ CURTISS-WRIGHT CONTROLS INC p 402
15801 Brixham Hill Ave # 200 28277
Tel (704) 869-4600 *SIC* 3728

▲ CURTISS-WRIGHT CORP p 402
13925 Balntyn Corp Pl 28277
Tel (704) 869-4600 *SIC* 3491 3621 3812

DAISY CHAIN DESIGNS p 409
2743 Goneaway Rd 28210
Tel (704) 517-8591 *SIC* 7389

DAK AMERICAS LLC p 409
5925 Carnegie Blvd # 500 28209
Tel (704) 940-7500 *SIC* 2821

DARAMIC LLC p 412
11430 N Cmnity Hse Rd # 350 28277
Tel (704) 587-8599 *SIC* 3069 2499 3269

■ DIVERSEY INC p 443
2415 Cascade Pointe Blvd 28208
Tel (262) 631-4001 *SIC* 2842

DIXON HUGHES GOODMAN LLP p 445
4350 Congress St Ste 900 28209
Tel (704) 367-7760 *SIC* 8721

DRIVEN BRANDS INC p 456
440 S Church St Ste 700 28202
Tel (704) 337-8855 *SIC* 7533

■ DUKE ENERGY BUSINESS SERVICES LLC p 460
526 S Church St Ec-03t 28202
Tel (704) 594-6200 *SIC* 4911 4922

▲ DUKE ENERGY CORP p 460
550 S Tryon St 28202
Tel (704) 382-3853 *SIC* 4911 4924 4931

■ DUKE ENERGY CORPORATE SERVICES INC p 460
526 S Church St 28202
Tel (704) 594-6200 *SIC* 4911

■ DUKE ENERGY OHIO INC p 460
400 S Tryon 28285
Tel (704) 382-3853
SIC 4911 4922 4924 4931

■ DUKE ENERGY REGISTRATION SERVICES INC p 460
526 S Church St 28202
Tel (704) 594-6200 *SIC* 4922

■ DUKE ENERGY SERVICES INC p 460
526 S Church St 28202
Tel (704) 594-6200 *SIC* 4911

DYNACAST INTERNATIONAL INC p 464
14045 Ballantyne Ste 400 28277
Tel (704) 927-2790 *SIC* 3364

E MASON ROBERT & ASSOCIATES INC p 466
1726 N Graham St 28206
Tel (704) 375-4465 *SIC* 5085 7699

EASTERN METAL SUPPLY OF NORTH CAROLINA INC p 472
2925 Stewart Creek Blvd 28216
Tel (704) 391-2266 *SIC* 5051

EASTWOOD CONSTRUCTION LLC p 473
2857 Westport Rd 28208
Tel (704) 399-4663 *SIC* 1521

EDIFICE INC p 478
1401 W Morehead St Ste A 28208
Tel (704) 332-0900 *SIC* 1542

ELECTROLUX HOME CARE PRODUCTS INC p 485
10200 David Taylor Dr 28262
Tel (980) 236-2000 *SIC* 5064

ELECTROLUX HOME PRODUCTS INC p 485
10200 David Taylor Dr 28262
Tel (980) 236-2000 SIC 5064

ELECTROLUX NORTH AMERICA INC p 485
10200 David Taylor Dr 28262
Tel (980) 236-2000
SIC 3631 3585 3632 3633 3635 3639

■ **EMPIRE DISTRIBUTORS OF NORTH CAROLINA INC** p 493
13833 Carowinds Blvd 28273
Tel (704) 588-9463 SIC 5182 5181

▲ **ENPRO INDUSTRIES INC** p 500
5605 Carnegie Blvd # 500 28209
Tel (704) 731-1500 SIC 3053 3519 3089

ENVIRONAMICS INC p 503
13935 S Point Blvd 28273
Tel (704) 376-3613 SIC 1542

ENVIRONMENTAL FILTRATION TECHNOLOGIES LLC p 503
4404a Chesapeake Dr 28216
Tel (704) 399-7441
SIC 3569 5085 3564 3444 3469 3561

■ **ESA 2007 OPERATING LESSEE LLC** p 509
11525 N Cmnity Hse Rd R 28277
Tel (980) 345-1600 SIC 7011

■ **ESA MANAGEMENT LLC** p 509
11525 N Community House R 28277
Tel (980) 345-1600 SIC 8741

■ **ESH HOSPITALITY INC** p 509
11525 N Community Hse Rd 28277
Tel (980) 345-1600 SIC 6798

EUROPA SPORTS PRODUCTS INC p 513
11401 Granite St Ste H 28273
Tel (704) 405-2022 SIC 5122 5149 5941

■ **EVEREN CAPITAL CORP** p 514
301 S College St 28202
Tel (704) 374-6565 SIC 6211

EXECUSOURCE INC p 517
5925 Carnegie Blvd # 350 28209
Tel (704) 483-9800 SIC 8742

▲ **EXTENDED STAY AMERICA INC** p 521
11525 N Community House 28277
Tel (980) 345-1600 SIC 7011

▲ **FAIRPOINT COMMUNICATIONS INC** p 525
521 E Morehead St Ste 500 28202
Tel (704) 344-8150 SIC 4813 4812 4899

FAISON ENTERPRISES INC p 526
121 W Trade St Fl 27 28202
Tel (704) 972-2500 SIC 6799

FALFURRIAS CAPITAL PARTNERS LP p 526
100 N Tryon St Ste 4100 28202
Tel (704) 371-3220 SIC 6726

FIREBIRDS INTERNATIONAL LLC p 543
13850 Balntyn Corp Pl # 450 28277
Tel (704) 944-5180 SIC 5812

FONTEM US INC p 563
1100 S Tryon St Ste 300 28203
Tel (888) 207-4588 SIC 2111 5993

FORTERRA BRICK LLC p 569
7400 Carmel Exec Park 2 28226
Tel (704) 341-8750 SIC 3251

FOUNDATION FOR CAROLINAS p 571
220 N Tryon St 28202
Tel (704) 973-4500 SIC 8399

FURNITURE DISTRIBUTORS INC p 585
4524 South Blvd 28209
Tel (704) 523-3424 SIC 5712 5713 5722

■ **GOLDEN WEST FINANCIAL CORP** p 621
301 S College St 28202
Tel (704) 374-6565 SIC 6035

■ **GOODRICH CORP** p 624
4 Coliseum Ctr 2730 W 28217
Tel (704) 423-7000 SIC 7372 3724 3728

HENDRICK AUTOMOTIVE GROUP p 683
6000 Monroe Rd Ste 100 28212
Tel (704) 568-5550 SIC 5511

HEPACO LLC p 685
2711 Burch Dr 28269
Tel (704) 598-9787 SIC 4959

■ **HORIZON LINES HOLDING CORP** p 707
2550 W Tyvola Rd Ste 530 28217
Tel (704) 973-7000 SIC 4731 6512

HORIZON LINES LLC p 707
2550 W Tyvola Rd Ste 530 28217
Tel (877) 678-7447
SIC 4424 4783 4731 4412

HUBER + SUHNER INC p 716
8530 Steele Creek Place D 28273
Tel (704) 790-7300
SIC 3679 3678 3357 5065

HUBER ENGINEERED WOODS LLC p 716
10925 David Taylor Dr 28262
Tel (704) 547-0671 SIC 2493

HUSQVARNA CONSUMER OUTDOOR PRODUCTS NA INC p 721
9335 Harris Corners Pkwy P 28269
Tel (704) 597-5000 SIC 3524

■ **HVM LLC** p 722
11525 N Community House 28277
Tel (980) 345-1600 SIC 7011

HYOSUNG HOLDINGS USA INC p 724
15801 Prixham Hll Ave 5 Ste 575 28277
Tel (704) 790-6100 SIC 2299 2296

HYOSUNG USA INC p 724
15801 Brixham Hill Ave # 575 28277
Tel (704) 790-6136 SIC 2221 2296 5199

INDUSTRIAL PIPING INC p 740
212 S Tryon St Ste 1050 28281
Tel (704) 588-1100 SIC 3599 3569

INSOURCE PERFORMANCE SOLUTIONS LLC p 746
5601 77 Center Dr Ste 240 28217
Tel (704) 643-3232 SIC 7363

JELD-WEN INC p 782
440 S Church St Ste 400 28202
Tel (800) 535-3936 SIC 3442 5031 2421

JOERNS HEALTHCARE LLC p 787
2430 Whit Park Dr Ste 100 28273
Tel (704) 499-6000 SIC 5047

JOHN M BELK EDUCATIONL ENDOWMENT p 789
4201 Congress St Ste 470 28209
Tel (704) 357-1000 SIC 8699

JOHNS LONE STAR DISTRIBUTION GP LLC p 790
11401 Granite St 28273
Tel (214) 340-0718 SIC 5122 5149

■ **KAVO DENTAL TECHNOLOGIES LLC** p 805
11729 Fruehauf Dr 28273
Tel (888) 275-5286 SIC 5047

LANDDESIGN INC p 842
223 N Graham St 28202
Tel (704) 333-0325 SIC 0781

▲ **LENDINGTREE INC** p 855
11115 Rushmore Dr 28277
Tel (704) 541-5351 SIC 6163 6531

LIBERTY N & R CTR OF MECKLENBURG p 862
3700 Shamrock Dr 28215
Tel (704) 940-8367 SIC 8051

LIFTONE LLC p 865
440 E Westinghouse Blvd 28273
Tel (704) 588-1300 SIC 5084

LINCOLN HARRIS LLC p 867
4725 Piedmont Row Dr 28210
Tel (704) 331-0917 SIC 6531 6552

LWIN FAMILY CO p 887
11949 Steele Creek Rd 28273
Tel (704) 926-2200 SIC 5146

MAGELLAN AIRCRAFT SERVICES LLLP p 895
2345 Township Rd Ste B 28273
Tel (704) 504-9204 SIC 5088

MAGELLAN AVIATION GROUP LLLP p 895
2345 Township Rd Ste B 28273
Tel (704) 504-9204 SIC 5088

■ **MARLEY CO LLC** p 909
13515 Balntyn Corp Pl 28277
Tel (704) 752-4400
SIC 3443 3433 3586 3561 3634

■ **MATSON ALASKA INC** p 920
2550 W Tyvola Rd 28217
Tel (704) 973-7000 SIC 4424 4731 4412

MCGRANN PAPER CORP p 929
3800 Arco Corprt Dr # 350 28273
Tel (800) 240-9455 SIC 5111 2752

MEDCATH CORP p 935
10800 Sikes Pl Ste 200 28277
Tel (704) 815-7700 SIC 8099 8062

MEDCATH INC p 935
10800 Sikes Pl Ste 200 28277
Tel (704) 815-7700 SIC 8069 8093 8742

MERCHANDISING CORP OF AMERICA INC p 944
11121 Carmel Commons Blvd # 455 28226
Tel (704) 944-4600 SIC 8748

MERCY MEDICAL SERVICE INC p 948
2001 Vail Ave 28207
Tel (704) 379-5000 SIC 8011

■ **METLIFE INSURANCE CO USA** p 954
11225 N Community Hse Rd 28277
Tel (980) 949-3626
SIC 6411 6321 6331 6324

MIDREX TECHNOLOGIES INC p 966
2725 Water Ridge Pkwy # 100 28217
Tel (704) 373-1600 SIC 8711

MOORE & VAN ALLEN PLLC p 987
100 N Tryon St Ste 4700 28202
Tel (704) 331-1000 SIC 8111

MOSS SUPPLY CO p 992
5001 N Graham St 28269
Tel (704) 596-8717 SIC 3442

MURATA MACHINERY USA HOLDINGS INC p 1001
2120 Queen City Dr 28208
Tel (704) 394-8331 SIC 3542 3552 5065

MURATA MACHINERY USA INC p 1001
2120 Queen City Dr 28208
Tel (704) 875-9280 SIC 5084 5085 3542

NEW NGC INC p 1032
2001 Rexford Rd 28211
Tel (704) 365-7300 SIC 2679

NGC INDUSTRIES LLC p 1041
2001 Rexford Rd 28211
Tel (704) 365-7300 SIC 2679

NOVANT MEDICAL GROUP INC p 1062
200 Hawthorne Ln 28204
Tel (704) 384-4966 SIC 8011

▲ **NUCOR CORP** p 1066
1915 Rexford Rd Ste 400 28211
Tel (704) 366-7000
SIC 3312 3441 3448 3452 5093

OBRIEN & GERE/ CROWDER JOINT VENTURE p 1072
6425 Brookshire Blvd 28216
Tel (704) 372-3541 SIC 1542

OCTAPHARMA PLASMA INC p 1074
10644 Westlake Dr 28273
Tel (704) 654-4600 SIC 2836

OFFICE ENVIRONMENTS INC p 1075
11407 Granite St Ste B 28273
Tel (704) 714-7200 SIC 5021 7641 7389

OTTO ENVIRONMENTAL SYSTEMS (NC) LLC p 1098
12700 General Dr 28273
Tel (704) 588-9191 SIC 3537

OTTO INDUSTRIES NORTH AMERICA INC p 1098
12700 General Dr 28273
Tel (704) 588-9191 SIC 3537

PAMLICO CAPITAL MANAGEMENT LP p 1110
150 N College St Ste 2400 28202
Tel (704) 374-6100 SIC 6799

■ **PANENERGY CORP** p 1111
526 S Church St 28202
Tel (704) 594-6200
SIC 4922 1321 2813 5172 4911 4613

■ **PARK STERLING BANK** p 1116
1043 E Morehead St # 201 28204
Tel (704) 370-2444 SIC 6036

▲ **PARK STERLING CORP** p 1116
1043 E Morehead St # 111 28204
Tel (704) 716-2134 SIC 6022

PARSONS ENVIRONMENT & INFRASTRUCTURE GROUP INC p 1118
4701 Hedgemore Dr 28209
Tel (704) 529-6246 SIC 8711

PEAK 10 INC p 1125
8910 Lenox Pointe Dr G 28273
Tel (704) 264-1010 SIC 4813

■ **PGI NONWOVEN/CHICOPEE INC** p 1140
9335 Harris Corners Pkwy 28269
Tel (704) 697-5100 SIC 2297 2392

PHT INTERNATIONAL INC p 1145
8133 Ardrey Kell Rd # 204 28277
Tel (704) 246-3480 SIC 5169

■ **PIEDMONT COCA-COLA BOTTLING PARTNERSHIP** p 1146
4115 Coca Cola Plz 28211
Tel (704) 551-4400 SIC 2086

■ **PIEDMONT NATURAL GAS CO INC** p 1147
4720 Piedmont Row Dr # 100 28210
Tel (704) 364-3120 SIC 4924 4923 4925

PIEDMONT PLASTICS INC p 1147
5010 W Wt Harris Blvd 28269
Tel (704) 597-8200 SIC 3081 3082 5162

POLYPORE INTERNATIONAL LP p 1160
11430 N Community House R 28277
Tel (704) 587-8409 SIC 3691

POOL BUILDERS SUPPLY OF CAROLINAS INC p 1161
1124 Central Ave 28204
Tel (704) 375-7573 SIC 5091 5999

POSITEC TOOL CORP p 1163
10130 Perimeter Pkwy # 300 28216
Tel (704) 599-3711 SIC 5072 6719

POSITEC USA INC p 1163
10130 Perimeter Pkwy # 300 28216
Tel (704) 599-3711 SIC 5072

PP HOLDING CORP p 1166
13800 S Lakes Dr 28273
Tel (704) 587-8409 SIC 3081 3089

PREMIER HEALTHCARE ALLIANCE LP p 1170
13034 Balntyn Corp Pl 28277
Tel (704) 357-0022 SIC 8741

■ **PREMIER HEALTHCARE SOLUTIONS INC** p 1170
13034 Balntyn Corp Pl 28277
Tel (704) 357-0022 SIC 8741

▲ **PREMIER INC** p 1170
13034 Balntyn Corp Pl 28277
Tel (704) 357-0022 SIC 8742 7375

PRESBYTERIAN HEALTH SERVICES CORP p 1171
200 Hawthorne Ln 28204
Tel (704) 384-4000 SIC 8062

PRESBYTERIAN HOSPITAL p 1171
200 Hawthorne Ln 28204
Tel (704) 384-4000 SIC 8062

PRESBYTERIAN-ORTHOPEDIC HOSPITAL p 1171
1901 Randolph Rd 28207
Tel (704) 316-2000 SIC 8069

PRESTIGE FARMS INC p 1173
7120 Orr Rd 28213
Tel (704) 596-2824 SIC 5144

QUAD-C JH HOLDINGS INC p 1195
2430 Whitehall Park Dr 28273
Tel (800) 826-0270 SIC 5047

RACK ROOM SHOES INC p 1203
8310 Technology Dr 28262
Tel (704) 547-9200 SIC 5661

RAYCOM SPORTS NETWORK INC p 1210
1900 W Morehead St 28208
Tel (704) 378-4400
SIC 6311 6321 6324 6411 4832 4833

RE COMMUNITY HOLDINGS II INC p 1212
809 W Hill St 28208
Tel (704) 697-2000 SIC 4953

RECOMMUNITY CORP p 1214
809 W Hill St Ste E 28208
Tel (860) 289-8480 SIC 4953

RECOMMUNITY RECYCLING p 1214
1007 Amble Dr 28206
Tel (704) 598-8595 SIC 4953

■ **RED CLASSIC TRANSIT LLC** p 1215
1800 Continental Blvd # 400 28273
Tel (980) 275-5721 SIC 4731

REGULUS INTEGRATED SOLUTIONS LLC p 1220
9645-L Part Blvd 28216
Tel (704) 904-8759
SIC 2752 7389 3861 2759

RODGERS BUILDERS INC p 1246
5701 N Sharon Amity Rd 28215
Tel (704) 537-6044 SIC 1542 1541

ROMAN CATHOLIC DIOCESE OF CHARLOTTE p 1248
1123 S Church St 28203
Tel (704) 370-6299 SIC 8661

■ **RUDDICK OPERATING CO LLC** p 1257
301 S Tryon St Ste 1800 28282
Tel (704) 372-5404 SIC 5411 2284

S BAUCOM NURSERY CO p 1262
10020 John Russell Rd 28213
Tel (704) 596-3220 SIC 0181 5193

■ **S-L SNACKS NATIONAL LLC** p 1263
13024 Ballantyne Pl 350 28273
Tel (704) 554-1421 SIC 2052

■ **S-L SNACKS NC LLC** p 1263
13024 Balntyn Corp Pl 28277
Tel (717) 632-4477 SIC 2052

SCHAEFER SYSTEMS INTERNATIONAL INC p 1286
10021 Westlake Dr 28273
Tel (704) 944-4500
SIC 3089 5046 5084 5099 7372

■ **SCORPIO ACQUISITION CORP** p 1293
9335 Harris Corners Pkwy 28269
Tel (704) 697-5100 SIC 2297

▲ **SEALED AIR CORP** p 1296
8215 Forest Point Blvd # 100 28273
Tel (980) 221-3235
SIC 2673 2671 3087 3086 3089

SECOND HARVEST FOOD BANK OF METROLINA INC p 1298
500 Spratt St Ste B 28206
Tel (704) 376-1785 SIC 8699

SENIOR LIVING COMMUNITES LLC p 1304
3530 Toringdon Way # 204 28277
Tel (704) 246-1620 SIC 8052

SGL CARBON LLC p 1310
10130 Perimeter Pkwy # 500 28216
Tel (704) 593-5100 SIC 3624

■ **SHARK ACQUISITION SUB II LLC** p 1312
13515 Balntyn Corp Pl 28277
Tel (704) 554-1421 SIC 2099

SHELCO LLC p 1314
2320 Cascade Pointe Blvd # 100 28208
Tel (704) 367-5600 SIC 1541 1542

SHOW PROS ENTERTAINMENT SERVICES INC p 1318
514 Springbrook Rd Ste A 28217
Tel (704) 525-3784 SIC 7363 7361

SMITHTURF & IRRIGATION LLC p 1333
4355 Golf Acres Dr 28208
Tel (704) 393-8873 SIC 5083

SMS SYSTEMS MAINTENANCE SERVICES INC p 1334
10420 Harris Oak Blvd C 28269
Tel (704) 921-1620 SIC 7378

▲ **SNYDERS-LANCE INC** p 1336
13515 Balntyn Corp Pl 28277
Tel (704) 554-1421
SIC 2052 2064 2068 2096 5145

▲ **SONIC AUTOMOTIVE INC** p 1340
4401 Colwick Rd 28211
Tel (704) 566-2400 SIC 5511 7538

▲ **SONIC FINANCIAL CORP** p 1340
5401 E Independence Blvd 28212
Tel (704) 536-5600 SIC 7948 6321 6311

SOUTHEAST INDUSTRIAL EQUIPMENT INC p 1346
12200 Steele Creek Rd 28273
Tel (704) 363-6432 SIC 7353 7359 5084

SOUTHERN PUMP & TANK CO LLC p 1350
4800 N Graham St 28269
Tel (704) 596-4373 SIC 5084 1799

SPANGLER COMPANIES INC p 1354
1110 E Morehead St 28204
Tel (704) 372-4500 SIC 6799

■ **SPECTRA ENERGY CAPITAL LLC** p 1356
526 S Church St 28202
Tel (704) 594-6200 SIC 4922

▲ **SPX CORP** p 1362
13320a Balntyn Corp Pl 28277
Tel (980) 474-3700
SIC 3443 3599 3829 3559 3545

▲ **SPX FLOW INC** p 1362
13320 Balntyn Corp Pl 28277
Tel (704) 752-4400 SIC 3556

STEAM GENERATING TEAM LLC p 1384
7207 Ibm Dr 3a 28262
Tel (704) 805-2810 SIC 1796

STEELFAB INC p 1384
8623 Old Dowd Rd 28214
Tel (704) 394-5376 *SIC* 3441 3449

STERITECH GROUP INC p 1386
6701 Carmel Rd Ste 300 28226
Tel (704) 544-1900 *SIC* 7342 8721

STORK UNITED CORP p 1392
3201 Rotary Dr 28269
Tel (704) 598-7171 *SIC* 5084 3552 3556

SWISHER HYGIENE INC p 1412
4725 Piedmont Row Dr # 400 28210
Tel (704) 364-7707 *SIC* 5169

■ **TECHNETICS GROUP LLC** p 1431
5605 Carnegie Blvd # 500 28209
Tel (704) 731-1500 *SIC* 3053 3351

TIAA CREF INVESTMENT MANAGEMENT LLC p 1452
8500 Andrew Carnegie Blvd 28262
Tel (704) 595-1000 *SIC* 6726 6722

TOSHIBA AMERICA ENERGY SYSTEMS CORP p 1462
3545 Whitehall Park Dr # 500 28273
Tel (704) 548-7777 *SIC* 3674

TOSHIBA AMERICA NUCLEAR ENERGY CORP p 1462
3545 Whitehall Park Dr # 500 28273
Tel (704) 548-7777 *SIC* 3443 5211

■ **TOWN & COUNTRY FORD INC** p 1464
5401 E Independence Blvd 28212
Tel (704) 536-5600
SIC 5511 7538 7532 5521

TROPICAL NUT & FRUIT CO p 1484
1100 Continental Blvd 28273
Tel (704) 588-0400
SIC 5149 5145 2099 2068

TRUSTHOUSE SERVICES GROUP INC p 1488
4135 Southstream Blvd # 250 28217
Tel (704) 424-1071 *SIC* 5812

UNIVERSAL MARITIME SERVICE CORP p 1517
9300 Arrowpoint Blvd 28273
Tel (704) 571-2768 *SIC* 4491

UNIVERSITY OF NORTH CAROLINA AT CHARLOTTE p 1523
9201 University City Blvd 28223
Tel (704) 687-5727 *SIC* 8221

US GREENFIBER LLC p 1532
5500 77 Center Dr Ste 100 28217
Tel (704) 379-0640 *SIC* 2679

■ **US LEC COMMUNICATIONS LLC** p 1532
6801 Morrison Blvd 28211
Tel (704) 319-1000 *SIC* 4813

VELOCITY TECHNOLOGY SOLUTIONS INC p 1547
1901 Roxborough Rd 4 28211
Tel (646) 884-6600 *SIC* 7373

■ **WACHOVIA BANK NATIONAL ASSOCIATION** p 1570
301 S Tryon St 28282
Tel (704) 335-5878 *SIC* 6021

■ **WACHOVIA INVESTMENT HOLDINGS LLC** p 1570
201 S College St Ste 500 28244
Tel (704) 374-2584 *SIC* 6211

■ **WACHOVIA MORTGAGE CORP** p 1570
201 S College St Fl 16 28244
Tel (704) 374-6161 *SIC* 6162 6411

WASTEQUIP LLC p 1581
6525 Morrison Blvd # 300 28211
Tel (704) 366-7140 *SIC* 3443 3537

WASTEQUIP MANUFACTURING CO LLC p 1581
1901 Roxborough Rd # 300 28211
Tel (704) 366-7140 *SIC* 3443

WECTEC GLOBAL PROJECT SERVICES INC p 1587
128 S Tryon St Ste 1000 28202
Tel (980) 859-6837 *SIC* 1731 8712

■ **WELLS FARGO SECURITIES LLC** p 1591
301 S Tryon St 28282
Tel (312) 920-9177 *SIC* 6211

WINN-DIXIE CHARLOTTE INC p 1616
2401 Nevada Blvd 28273
Tel (704) 587-4000
SIC 5411 8741 5141 4226 4222

WURTH WOOD GROUP INC p 1628
4250 Golf Acres Dr 28208
Tel (704) 394-9479 *SIC* 5211 5031

YOUNG MEN S CHRISTIAN ASSOCIATION OF GREATER CHARLOTTE p 1638
400 E Morehead St 28202
Tel (704) 716-6200 *SIC* 7032 8641

YOUNGS TRUCK CENTER INC p 1639
3880 Jeff Adams Dr 28206
Tel (704) 597-0551 *SIC* 5511 7513 7532

CHEROKEE, NC

EASTERN BAND OF CHEROKEE INDIANS p 471
88 Council House Loop 28719
Tel (828) 497-2771 *SIC* 9131

TRIBAL CASINO GAMING ENTERPRISES p 1479
777 Casino Dr 28719
Tel (877) 811-0777 *SIC* 7011

CLAREMONT, NC

DRAKA HOLDINGS USA INC p 455
2512 Penny Rd 28610
Tel (828) 459-8550 *SIC* 3357

■ **SAGEBRUSH INC** p 1268
112 Main St 28610
Tel (828) 459-0821 *SIC* 5812

CLAYTON, NC

NOVO NORDISK PHARMACEUTICAL INDUSTRIES INC p 1063
3612 Powhatan Rd 27527
Tel (919) 550-2200 *SIC* 2833

URGENT CARES OF AMERICA HOLDINGS LLC p 1530
935 Shotwell Rd Ste 108 27520
Tel (919) 550-0821 *SIC* 6719 8011

CLEMMONS, NC

■ **BAHNSON HOLDINGS INC** p 145
4731 Commercial Park Ct 27012
Tel (336) 760-3111
SIC 8711 1711 3585 3564

■ **BAHNSON INC** p 145
4731 Commercial Park Ct 27012
Tel (336) 760-3111 *SIC* 8711 1711

PETRALEX USA INC p 1139
4740 Coml Pk Ct Ste 2 27012
Tel (336) 778-1049 *SIC* 2396

CLINTON, NC

PRESTAGE FARMS INC p 1173
4651 Taylors Bridge Hwy 28328
Tel (910) 596-5700 *SIC* 0213 0253

SAMPSON-BLADEN OIL CO INC p 1274
510 Commerce St 28328
Tel (910) 592-4177 *SIC* 5171 5411 5983

UNITED ENERGY INC p 1508
932 N Hwy 421 28328
Tel (919) 785-1904 *SIC* 5541 5411

CLYDE, NC

HAYWOOD REGIONAL MEDICAL CENTER p 671
262 Leroy George Dr 28721
Tel (828) 456-7311 *SIC* 8062

COLFAX, NC

BALTEK INC p 149
5240 National Center Dr 27235
Tel (336) 398-1900 *SIC* 2436

ENDURA PRODUCTS INC p 496
8817 W Market St 27235
Tel (336) 668-2472 *SIC* 3429

CONCORD, NC

CABARRUS COUNTY SCHOOL p 234
4401 Old Airport Rd 28025
Tel (704) 786-6191 *SIC* 8211

CARDINAL LOGISTICS HOLDINGS LLC p 253
5333 Davidson Hwy 28027
Tel (972) 228-7300 *SIC* 4213 4731

CARDINAL LOGISTICS MANAGEMENT CORP p 253
5333 Davidson Hwy 28027
Tel (704) 786-6125 *SIC* 4213

CARDINAL LOGISTICS MANAGEMENT INC p 253
5333 Davidson Hwy 28027
Tel (704) 786-6125 *SIC* 4212 4213 1541

CAROLINAS MEDICAL CENTER NORTHEAST p 259
920 Church St N 28025
Tel (704) 783-3000 *SIC* 8062 8221

COUNTY OF CABARRUS p 376
65 Church St S 28025
Tel (704) 920-2107 *SIC* 9111

DNP IMAGINGCOMM AMERICA CORP p 446
4524 Enterprise Dr Nw 28027
Tel (704) 784-8100 *SIC* 3955

FORTILINE INC p 569
7025 Northwinds Dr Nw 28027
Tel (704) 788-9800 *SIC* 5085

FORTILINE LLC p 569
7025 Northwinds Dr Nw 28027
Tel (704) 788-9800 *SIC* 3317 5085

■ **FUN-TEES INC** p 585
4735 Corp Dr Nw Ste 100 28027
Tel (704) 788-3003 *SIC* 2321 2361 2331

S & D COFFEE INC p 1261
300 Concord Pkwy S 28027
Tel (704) 782-3121 *SIC* 2095 5149 2086

S&D COFFEE HOLDING CO p 1263
300 Concord Pkwy S 28027
Tel (704) 782-3121
SIC 6719 2095 5149 2086

SHOE SHOW INC p 1317
2201 Trinity Church Rd 28027
Tel (704) 782-4143 *SIC* 5661

■ **SPEEDWAY MOTORSPORTS INC** p 1358
5555 Concord Pkwy S 28027
Tel (704) 455-3239 *SIC* 7948

CONOVER, NC

■ **GENERAL DYNAMICS SATCOM TECHNOLOGIES INC** p 600
1700 Cable Dr Ne 28613
Tel (704) 462-7330 *SIC* 3663

LEE INDUSTRIES INC p 851
210 4th St Sw 28613
Tel (828) 464-8318 *SIC* 2512

CORNELIUS, NC

TT OF LAKE NORMAN LLC p 1489
20700 Torrence Chapel Rd 28031
Tel (704) 896-3800 *SIC* 5511

CULLOWHEE, NC

WESTERN CAROLINA UNIVERSITY p 1597
565 H F Robinson 28723
Tel (828) 227-7211 *SIC* 8221

DALLAS, NC

ROCHLING ENGINEERED PLASTICS LIMITED PARTNERSHIP p 1243
903 Gastonia Tech Pkwy 28034
Tel (704) 922-7814 *SIC* 3081 3082

DAVIDSON, NC

CIVITAS MEDIA LLC p 320
130 Harbour Place Dr # 300 28036
Tel (704) 897-6020 *SIC* 2711

INGERSOLL-RAND CO p 742
800 Beaty St Ste B 28036
Tel (704) 655-4000
SIC 3561 3429 3546 3563 3531

TRUSTEES OF DAVIDSON COLLEGE p 1487
209 Ridge Rd 28035
Tel (704) 894-2000 *SIC* 8221

DOBSON, NC

SURRY COUNTY SCHOOL DISTRICT p 1409
209 N Crutchfield St 27017
Tel (336) 386-8211 *SIC* 8211

DUNN, NC

ARC3 GASES INC p 103
1636 Us Highway 301 S 28334
Tel (910) 892-4016
SIC 2813 5084 5169 7359 7692

HARNETT HEALTH SYSTEM INC p 662
800 Tilghman Dr 28334
Tel (910) 892-1000 *SIC* 8062

MACHINE & WELDING SUPPLY CO p 892
1660 Us Highway 301 S 28334
Tel (910) 892-4016 *SIC* 5084 5169

SOUTH RIVER ELECTRIC MEMBERSHIP CORP p 1345
17494 Us Highway 421 S 28334
Tel (910) 892-8071 *SIC* 4911

WARREN OIL CO INC p 1577
2340 Us Highway 301 N 28334
Tel (910) 892-6456
SIC 5172 5171 3826 2911

DURHAM, NC

ACCORD HEALTHCARE INC p 15
1009 Slater Rd Ste 210b 27703
Tel (919) 941-7878 *SIC* 5122

AMERICAN INSTITUTE OF CERTIFIED PUBLIC ACCOUNTANTS p 75
220 Leigh Farm Rd 27707
Tel (919) 402-0682 *SIC* 8299 8621 2721

AW NORTH CAROLINA INC p 139
4112 Old Oxford Rd 27712
Tel (919) 620-5500 *SIC* 3714

BAYER CROPSCIENCE LP p 161
2 Tw Alexander Dr 27709
Tel (919) 549-2000 *SIC* 2879 5191

BELL AND HOWELL LLC p 169
3791 S Alston Ave 27713
Tel (919) 767-4401 *SIC* 3579

BIOMERIEUX INC p 184
100 Rodolphe St 27712
Tel (919) 620-2000
SIC 3845 8071 3841 3826

BKRY PHYSICIAN GROUP INC p 186
1000 Park Forty Plz # 500 27713
Tel (919) 383-0355 *SIC* 8741 8742

BLUE CROSS AND BLUE SHIELD NORTH CAROLINA p 191
4615 University Dr 27707
Tel (919) 489-7431 *SIC* 6324

■ **BURTS BEES INC** p 229
210 W Pettigrew St 27701
Tel (919) 998-5200 *SIC* 2844 5122 5087

CITY OF DURHAM p 314
101 City Hall Plz 27701
Tel (919) 560-4333 *SIC* 9111

■ **CONSTELLA GROUP LLC** p 360
2605 Meridian Pkwy # 200 27713
Tel (919) 544-8500
SIC 7371 8742 7375 8748 8731 8071

COUNTY OF DURHAM p 377
200 E Main St Ste 235 27701
Tel (919) 560-0035 *SIC* 9111

▲ **CREE INC** p 391
4600 Silicon Dr 27703
Tel (919) 407-5300 *SIC* 3674 3672

DPX HOLDINGS INC p 454
4307 Emperor Blvd Ste 140 27703
Tel (919) 226-3200 *SIC* 6799

DUKE CLINICAL RESEARCH INSTITUTE p 460
2400 Pratt St 27705
Tel (919) 668-8725 *SIC* 8071

DUKE UNIVERSITY p 460
2200 W Main St Ste 710 27705
Tel (919) 684-3030 *SIC* 8221

DUKE UNIVERSITY HEALTH SYSTEM INC p 460
2301 Erwin Rd 27705
Tel (919) 684-8111 *SIC* 8062

DURHAM COUNTY HOSPITAL CORP p 462
3643 N Roxboro St 27704
Tel (919) 470-4000 *SIC* 8062

DURHAM PUBLIC SCHOOLS p 463
511 Cleveland St 27701
Tel (919) 560-2000 *SIC* 8211

■ **EAST COAST METAL DISTRIBUTORS LLC** p 470
1313 S Briggs Ave 27703
Tel (919) 598-5030 *SIC* 5075

EASTERN CAROLINA ORGANICS LLC p 472
2210 E Pettigrew St 27703
Tel (919) 542-3264 *SIC* 0723

FAMILY HEALTH INTERNATIONAL INC p 527
359 Blackwell St Ste 200 27701
Tel (919) 544-7040 *SIC* 8733

FUEL USA LLC p 583
1 Stoneglen Ct 27712
Tel (434) 525-1615 *SIC* 5411

GRIFOLS THERAPEUTICS INC p 640
79 Tw Alexander Dr 27709
Tel (919) 316-6300 *SIC* 2836

I KESTREL ACQUISITION CORP p 725
1035 Swabia Ct 27703
Tel (919) 990-7500
SIC 2821 2822 2869 2899 2891 2851

IMPLUS FOOTCARE LLC p 735
2001 Tw Alexander Dr 27709
Tel (919) 544-7900 *SIC* 5139

■ **KENDLE INTERNATIONAL LLC** p 810
3201 Beechleaf Ct 27703
Tel (919) 876-9300 *SIC* 8731

MEASUREMENT INC p 934
423 Morris St 27701
Tel (919) 683-2413
SIC 2752 8748 2791 2789 2759

NORTH CAROLINA CENTRAL UNIVERSITY p 1051
1801 Fayetteville St 27707
Tel (919) 530-6100 *SIC* 8221

NORTH CAROLINA MUTUAL WHOLESALE DRUG CO p 1051
816 Ellis Rd 27703
Tel (919) 596-2151 *SIC* 5122

PARATA SYSTEMS LLC p 1114
2600 Meridian Pkwy 27713
Tel (919) 433-4400 *SIC* 3826 8733

PATHEON INC p 1120
4815 Emperor Blvd Ste 300 27703
Tel (919) 226-3200 *SIC* 2834

■ **PBM GRAPHICS INC** p 1123
3700 S Miami Blvd 27703
Tel (919) 544-6222 *SIC* 2752

QUALEX INC p 1196
4020 Stirrup Creek Dr # 100 27703
Tel (919) 484-3500 *SIC* 7384

▲ **QUINTILES IMS HOLDINGS INC** p 1200
4820 Emperor Blvd 27703
Tel (919) 998-2000 *SIC* 8731

■ **QUINTILES INC** p 1200
4820 Emperor Blvd 27703
Tel (919) 998-2000 *SIC* 8731

■ **QUINTILES TRANSNATIONAL CORP** p 1200
4820 Emperor Blvd 27703
Tel (919) 998-2000 *SIC* 8732 8731 8999

REICHHOLD HOLDINGS US INC p 1220
1035 Swabia Ct 27703
Tel (919) 990-7500
SIC 2821 2822 2891 3089 5169 5162

REICHHOLD INDUSTRIES INC p 1220
1035 Swabia Ct 27703
Tel (919) 990-7500 *SIC* 2821

REICHHOLD LIQUIDATION INC p 1220
1035 Swabia Ct 27703
Tel (919) 990-7500
SIC 2821 2822 2869 2899 2891 2851

REICHHOLD LLC 2 p 1220
1035 Swabia Ct 27703
Tel (919) 990-7500 *SIC* 2821 2851

RESEARCH TRIANGLE INSTITUTE INC p 1226
3040 Cornwallis Rd 27709
Tel (919) 541-6000 *SIC* 8732 8731

SQUARE 1 BANK p 1362
406 Blackwell St Ste 240 27701
Tel (919) 314-3040 *SIC* 6021

SQUARE 1 FINANCIAL INC p 1362
406 Blackwell St Ste 240 27701
Tel (866) 355-0468 *SIC* 6022 6799

STERLING GROUP PHYSICIAN SERVICES LLC p 1387
1000 Park Forty Plz # 500 27713
Tel (919) 383-0355 *SIC* 8741 8742

STIEFEL LABORATORIES INC p 1389
20 Tw Alexander Dr 27709
Tel (888) 784-3335 *SIC* 5122 2834

TALECRIS PLASMA RESOURCES INC p 1422
79 Tw Alexander Dr 4101 27709
Tel (817) 921-1886 *SIC* 8099

TOSHIBA GLOBAL COMMERCE SOLUTIONS INC p 1462
3901 S Miami Blvd 27703
Tel (984) 444-7153 *SIC* 8742 7375

EAST FLAT ROCK, NC

■ GE LIGHTING SYSTEMS LLC p 596
3010 Spartanburg Hwy 28726
Tel (828) 693-2000 *SIC* 5063

EDEN, NC

GILDAN ACTIVEWEAR (EDEN) INC p 612
602 E Meadow Rd 27288
Tel (336) 623-9555 *SIC* 5136 5311

ROCKINGHAM COUNTY SCHOOLS p 1244
511 Harrington Hwy 27288
Tel (336) 627-2600 *SIC* 8211

EDENTON, NC

BRITTHAVEN OF EDENTON INC p 214
1341 Paradise Rd 27932
Tel (252) 482-7481 *SIC* 8051 8052

JIMBOS JUMBOS INC p 785
185 Peanut Dr 27932
Tel (252) 482-2193 *SIC* 5159

VIDANT MEDICAL GROUP LLC p 1556
104 Mark Dr 27932
Tel (252) 482-5171 *SIC* 8099

ELIZABETH CITY, NC

ALBEMARLE HOSPITAL AUTHORITY p 46
1144 N Road St 27909
Tel (252) 338-0101 *SIC* 8062

ELIZABETHTOWN, NC

CAMPBELL RENTALS LLC p 245
418 Peanut Plant Rd 28337
Tel (910) 862-7657 *SIC* 5171 5411 5541

ELKIN, NC

HUGH CHATHAM MEMORIAL HOSPITAL INC p 717
180 Parkwood Dr 28621
Tel (336) 835-3722 *SIC* 8062 8051 8361

ELON, NC

ELON UNIVERSITY p 489
100 Campus Dr 27244
Tel (336) 278-2000 *SIC* 8221

ENGINEERED CONTROLS INTERNATIONAL LLC p 499
100 Rego Dr 27244
Tel (336) 449-7707 *SIC* 3491

ENKA, NC

LOW & BONAR INC p 881
1301 Sand Hill Rd 28728
Tel (828) 665-5000
SIC 5199 3296 2899 2297 2221

FAYETTEVILLE, NC

CAPE FEAR VALLEY MEDICAL CENTER p 248
1638 Owen Dr 28304
Tel (910) 615-4000 *SIC* 8011

CAROLINA HEALTHCARE CENTER OF CUMBERLAND LP p 259
4600 Cumberland Rd 28306
Tel (910) 429-1690 *SIC* 8741 8051

CITY OF FAYETTEVILLE p 314
433 Hay St 28301
Tel (910) 433-1990 *SIC* 9111

COUNTY OF CUMBERLAND p 377
117 Dick St 28301
Tel (910) 678-7740 *SIC* 9111

CUMBERLAND COUNTY HOSPITAL SYSTEM INC p 400
1638 Owen Dr 28304
Tel (910) 609-4000 *SIC* 8062

CUMBERLAND COUNTY SCHOOLS p 400
2465 Gillespie St 28306
Tel (910) 678-2300 *SIC* 8211

FAYETTEVILLE PUBLISHING CO INC p 532
458 Whitfield St 28306
Tel (910) 486-2741
SIC 2711 2791 2759 2752

FAYETTEVILLE STATE UNIVERSITY p 532
1200 Murchison Rd 28301
Tel (910) 672-1111 *SIC* 8221

FAYETTEVILLE TECHNICAL COMMUNITY COLLEGE FOUNDATION INC p 532
2201 Hull Rd 28303
Tel (910) 678-8400 *SIC* 8222 9411

LIL THRIFT FOOD MARTS INC p 866
1007 Arsenal Ave 28305
Tel (910) 433-4490 *SIC* 5541 5411

MANN+HUMMEL PUROLATOR FILTERS LLC p 902
3200 Natal St 28306
Tel (910) 425-4181 *SIC* 3569

■ MJ SOFFE LLC p 978
1 Soffe Dr 28312
Tel (910) 435-3138
SIC 2339 2329 2369 2321

PUBLIC WORKS COMMISSION OF CITY OF FAYETTEVILLE p 1190
955 Old Wilmington Rd 28301
Tel (910) 223-4005 *SIC* 4911 4941

FLETCHER, NC

BLUE RIDGE METALS CORP p 192
180 Mills Gap Rd 28732
Tel (828) 687-2525 *SIC* 3399 3315

DERROUGH AND TALLEY INC p 431
145 Cane Cr Ind P Rd 15 28732
Tel (828) 281-4800 *SIC* 5499

EARTH FARE INC p 469
220 Continuum Dr 28732
Tel (828) 281-4800 *SIC* 5499

FOREST CITY, NC

RUTHERFORD COUNTY SCHOOLS p 1260
382 W Main St 28043
Tel (828) 288-2200 *SIC* 8211

RUTHERFORD ELECTRIC MEMBERSHIP CORP p 1260
186 Hudlow Rd 28043
Tel (704) 245-1621 *SIC* 4911

FORT BRAGG, NC

■ ARMY FORCES COMMAND UNITED STATES p 112
4700 Knox St 28310
Tel (910) 570-7200 *SIC* 9711

■ ARMY RESERVE COMMAND UNITED STATES p 112
4710 Knox St 28310
Tel (910) 570-8472 *SIC* 9711

FRANKLINTON, NC

NOVOZYMES NORTH AMERICA INC p 1063
77 Perry Chapel Church Rd 27525
Tel (919) 494-2014 *SIC* 2869

FUQUAY VARINA, NC

BOB BARKER CO INC p 196
134 N Main St 27526
Tel (800) 235-8586
SIC 5131 5122 2392 5136 3441

FIDELITY BANCSHARES (NC) INC p 540
100 S Main St 27526
Tel (919) 552-2242 *SIC* 6712

FREIGHT HANDLERS INC p 577
310 N Judd Pkwy Ne 27526
Tel (919) 552-3157 *SIC* 4731 7363

GARNER, NC

BUTTERBALL LLC p 230
1 Butterball Ln 27529
Tel (919) 255-7900 *SIC* 2015

GASTONIA, NC

CAROMONT HEALTH INC p 259
2525 Court Dr 28054
Tel (704) 834-2000 *SIC* 8741 8093

CAROMONT MEDICAL GROUP INC p 260
2525 Court Dr 28054
Tel (704) 671-7483 *SIC* 7363

CAROMONT OCCUPATIONAL MEDICINE LLC p 260
2525 Court Dr 28054
Tel (704) 834-2000 *SIC* 8099

CAROMONT REGIONAL MEDICAL CENTER p 260
2525 Court Dr 28054
Tel (704) 333-9033 *SIC* 8062

GASTON COUNTY p 593
128 W Main Ave 28052
Tel (704) 866-3100 *SIC* 9111

GASTON COUNTY SCHOOL DISTRICT p 593
943 Osceola St 28054
Tel (704) 866-6100 *SIC* 8211

INDUSTRIAL FABRICATORS INC p 740
4328 York Hwy 28052
Tel (704) 864-5026 *SIC* 3441

MANN+HUMMEL FILTRATION TECHNOLOGY GROUP INC p 902
1 Wix Way 28054
Tel (704) 869-3300 *SIC* 3714 5013

MANN+HUMMEL FILTRATION TECHNOLOGY HOLDINGS INC p 902
1 Wix Way 28054
Tel (704) 869-3300 *SIC* 3714

MANN+HUMMEL FILTRATION TECHNOLOGY INTERMEDIATE HOLDINGS INC p 902
1 Wix Way 28054
Tel (704) 869-3300 *SIC* 3714

MANN+HUMMEL FILTRATION TECHNOLOGY US LLC p 902
1 Wix Way 28054
Tel (704) 869-3300 *SIC* 3714

PARKDALE AMERICA LLC p 1116
531 Cotton Blossom Cir 28054
Tel (704) 864-8761 *SIC* 2281

PARKDALE MILLS INC p 1116
531 Cotton Blossom Cir 28054
Tel (704) 864-8761 *SIC* 2281 2844 2241

■ PUBLIC SERVICE CO OF NORTH CAROLINA INC p 1190
800 Gaston 800 Gas 28056
Tel (704) 864-6731 *SIC* 4924

STABILUS INC p 1374
1201 Tulip Dr 28052
Tel (704) 865-7444 *SIC* 3493

STABLE HOLDCO INC p 1374
1201 Tulip Dr 28052
Tel (704) 866-7140 *SIC* 3493

UNITED OIL OF CAROLINAS INC p 1510
1627 Spencer Mountain Rd 28054
Tel (704) 824-3561 *SIC* 5172

US COTTON LLC p 1531
531 Cotton Blossom Cir 28054
Tel (216) 676-6400 *SIC* 2844 2241

GOLDSBORO, NC

AP EMISSIONS TECHNOLOGIES LLC p 95
300 Dixie Trl 27530
Tel (919) 580-2000 *SIC* 3714

BRITTHAVEN OF GOLDSBORO INC p 214
2401 Wayne Memorial Dr 27534
Tel (919) 736-2121 *SIC* 8051 8052

CROSCILL HOME LLC p 393
1500 N Carolina St 27530
Tel (919) 735-7111 *SIC* 5023 3431

■ FRANKLIN BAKING CO LLC p 574
500 W Grantham St 27530
Tel (919) 735-0344 *SIC* 2051

GOLDSBORO MILLING CO p 622
938 Millers Chapel Rd 27534
Tel (919) 778-3130 *SIC* 2048

MAXWELL FOODS LLC p 923
938 Millers Chapel Rd 27534
Tel (919) 778-3130 *SIC* 0213

PDNC LLC p 1125
402 Commerce Ct 27534
Tel (919) 778-3000
SIC 5142 5141 5147 5148 5431

SOUTHCO DISTRIBUTING CO p 1345
2201 S John St 27530
Tel (919) 735-8012 *SIC* 5194 5141 5131

SSC GOLDSBORO OPERATING CO LLC p 1363
1700 Wayne Memorial Dr 27534
Tel (919) 731-2805 *SIC* 8051

TA LOVING CO p 1420
400 Patetown Rd 27530
Tel (919) 734-8400 *SIC* 1541 1542 1623

UCHIYAMA MANUFACTURING AMERICA LLC p 1499
494 Arrington Bridge Rd 27530
Tel (919) 731-2364 *SIC* 5085 3714 3053

WAYNE COUNTY PUBLIC SCHOOLS FOUNDATION INC p 1584
2001 Royall Ave 27534
Tel (919) 705-6117 *SIC* 8211

WAYNE HEALTH CORP p 1584
2700 Wayne Memorial Dr 27534
Tel (919) 736-1110 *SIC* 8741

WAYNE MEMORIAL HOSPITAL INC p 1584
2700 Wayne Memorial Dr 27534
Tel (919) 736-1110 *SIC* 8062

GRAHAM, NC

C P BUCKNER STEEL ERECTION INC p 233
4732 S Nc Highway 54 27253
Tel (336) 376-8888 *SIC* 1791 7353

COUNTY OF ALAMANCE p 376
124 W Elm St 27253
Tel (336) 228-1312 *SIC* 9111

GREENSBORO, NC

AC CORP p 13
301 Creek Ridge Rd 27406
Tel (336) 273-4472
SIC 1711 1731 3556 3823 3625 3535

APAC-ATLANTIC INC p 95
300 S Benbow Rd 27401
Tel (336) 412-6800
SIC 1611 1771 3531 5032

■ ASBURY AUTOMOTIVE NORTH CAROLINA LLC p 115
3633c W Wendover Ave 27407
Tel (336) 851-3500 *SIC* 5511

BATTLEGROUND RESTAURANT GROUP INC p 160
1337 Winstead Pl 27408
Tel (336) 272-9355 *SIC* 5812

BELL PARTNERS INC p 170
300 N Greene St Ste 1000 27401
Tel (336) 232-1900 *SIC* 6513

BGF INDUSTRIES INC p 180
3802 Robert Porcher Way 27410
Tel (843) 537-3172
SIC 2221 3624 2241 2295

BRADY SALES AND SERVICE INC p 207
1915 N Church St 27405
Tel (336) 378-0670 *SIC* 5075

BRADY TRANE SERVICE INC p 207
1915 N Church St 27405
Tel (919) 781-0458 *SIC* 5075 1711 7623

BURLINGTON INDUSTRIES LLC p 228
804 Green Valley Rd # 300 27408
Tel (336) 379-6220
SIC 2231 2211 2221 2273 2262 2261

CAFFEY DISTRIBUTING CO INC p 237
8749 W Market St 27409
Tel (336) 668-0877 *SIC* 5181

CAMCO MANUFACTURING INC p 244
121 Landmark Dr 27409
Tel (336) 668-7661 *SIC* 3949

CENTER FOR CREATIVE LEADERSHIP INC p 275
1 Leadership Pl 27410
Tel (336) 288-7210 *SIC* 8299 2731

CENTRAL CAROLINA FARM & MOWER INC p 277
801 E Wendover Ave 27405
Tel (336) 574-4400 *SIC* 5261 5082

CITY OF GREENSBORO p 315
300 W Washington St 27401
Tel (336) 373-2002 *SIC* 9111

COLUMBIA FOREST PRODUCTS INC p 340
7900 Triad Center Dr # 200 27409
Tel (336) 605-0429 *SIC* 2435

CONE DENIM LLC p 355
804 Green Valley Rd # 300 27408
Tel (336) 379-6220 *SIC* 2211

COUNTY OF GUILFORD p 378
301 W Market St 27401
Tel (336) 641-3836 *SIC* 9111

CROSS TECHNOLOGIES INC p 394
4400 Piedmont Pkwy 27410
Tel (336) 856-6000 *SIC* 5084 3492

D H GRIFFIN WRECKING CO INC p 407
4716 Hilltop Rd 27407
Tel (336) 855-7030 *SIC* 1795 5093

■ ELANCO US INC p 483
3200 Northline Ave # 300 27408
Tel (877) 352-6261 *SIC* 2834

■ ENVIRONMENTAL AIR SYSTEMS LLC p 503
521 Banner Ave 27401
Tel (336) 273-1975 *SIC* 1711

EPES CARRIERS INC p 504
3400 Edgefield Ct 27409
Tel (336) 668-3358 *SIC* 4213

EPES LOGISTICS SERVICES INC p 504
538 N Regional Rd 27409
Tel (336) 665-1553 *SIC* 4731

EPES TRANSPORT SYSTEM INC p 504
3400 Edgefield Ct 27409
Tel (336) 668-3358 *SIC* 4213

EVONIK STOCKHAUSEN LLC p 516
2401 Doyle St 27406
Tel (336) 333-3500 *SIC* 2869 2899

FRESH MARKET INC p 579
628 Green Valley Rd # 500 27408
Tel (336) 272-1338 *SIC* 5411

GCA SERVICES GROUP OF NORTH CAROLINA INC p 595
1 Centerview Dr Ste 109 27407
Tel (336) 294-9411 *SIC* 7349 7363

GENEVA HOLDINGS INC p 603
8015 Piedmont Triad Pkwy 27409
Tel (336) 275-9936 *SIC* 5084 5063

GET YOU FOUND ONLINE MARKETING INC p 609
301 S Elm St Ste 401 27401
Tel (336) 790-6735 *SIC* 8742

■ GILBARCO INC p 612
7300 W Friendly Ave 27410
Tel (336) 547-5000 *SIC* 3586

GREENSBORO AUTO AUCTION INC p 638
3907 W Wendover Ave 27407
Tel (336) 299-7777 *SIC* 5012

GUARANTEED SUPPLY CO p 644
1211 Rotherwood Rd 27406
Tel (336) 273-3491 *SIC* 5032 5031

GUILFORD COUNTY SCHOOL SYSTEM p 646
712 N Eugene St 27401
Tel (336) 370-8100 *SIC* 8211

GUILFORD HEALTH CARE CENTER INC p 646
2041 Willow Rd 27406
Tel (336) 272-9700 *SIC* 8051

HAECO USA HOLDINGS INC p 652
623 Radar Rd 27410
Tel (336) 668-4410 *SIC* 4581

HAMS RESTAURANTS INC p 656
3017 W Gate City Blvd # 2 27403
Tel (336) 851-4800 *SIC* 5812 5813

HOFFMAN & HOFFMAN INC p 699
3816 Patterson St 27407
Tel (336) 292-8777 *SIC* 5075

HONDA AIRCRAFT CO INC p 704
6430 Ballinger Rd 27410
Tel (336) 662-0246 *SIC* 3728

INTERNATIONAL TEXTILE GROUP INC p 757
804 Green Valley Rd # 300 27408
Tel (336) 379-6299
SIC 3714 3496 2211 2231 2221 2273

ITG BRANDS LLC p 768
714 Green Valley Rd 27408
Tel (336) 335-7000 *SIC* 2111

ITG HOLDINGS INC p 768
804 Green Valley Rd # 300 27408
Tel (336) 379-6220
SIC 2211 2231 2221 2273 2262 2261

JAMES M PLEASANTS CO INC p 776
603 Diamond Hill Ct 27406
Tel (336) 275-3152
SIC 5075 3585 3561 3494

■ KAY CHEMICAL CO p 805
8300 Capital Dr 27409
Tel (336) 668-7290 *SIC* 2842

KAYSER-ROTH CORP p 805
102 Corporate Center Blvd 27408
Tel (336) 852-2030
SIC 2252 2251 5961 8741 3842

KOURY CORP p 828
2275 Vanstory St Ste 200 27403
Tel (336) 299-9200 *SIC* 6512 6513

■ LINCOLN NATIONAL LIFE INSURANCE CO p 867
100 N Greene St 27401
Tel (336) 691-3000 *SIC* 6411 6321 6324

LORILLARD TOBACCO CO LLC p 878
714 Green Valley Rd 27408
Tel (336) 335-6600 *SIC* 2111

MACK TRUCKS INC p 892
7825 National Service Rd 27409
Tel (336) 291-9001
SIC 3711 3714 5012 6141 6153 7538

MARKET AMERICA INC p 908
1302 Pleasant Ridge Rd 27409
Tel (336) 605-0040 *SIC* 5199

MARKET AMERICA WORLDWIDE INC p 908
1302 Pleasant Ridge Rd 27409
Tel (336) 605-0040 *SIC* 5199

MEAT AND SEAFOOD SOLUTIONS LLC p 934
3500 Old Battleground Rd 27410
Tel (336) 545-3827 *SIC* 5146 5147

MOSES CONE-WESLEY LONG COMMUNITY HEALTH FOUNDATION INC p 992
1200 N Elm St 27401
Tel (336) 832-9555 *SIC* 8699

MOSES H CONE MEMORIAL HOSPITAL p 992
1200 N Elm St 27401
Tel (336) 832-7000 *SIC* 8062

MOSES H CONE MEMORIAL HOSPITAL OPERATING CORP p 992
1200 N Elm St 27401
Tel (336) 832-7000 *SIC* 8062

NEWBRIDGE BANCORP p 1037
1501 Highwoods Blvd # 400 27410
Tel (336) 369-0900 *SIC* 6022

NEWBRIDGE BANK p 1037
1501 Highwoods Blvd 27410
Tel (336) 248-6500 *SIC* 6022

NORTH CAROLINA AGRICULTURAL AND TECHNICAL STATE UNIVERSITY p 1051
1601 E Marke St Dowdy Bld 27411
Tel (336) 334-7684 *SIC* 8221

NOUVEAU VERRE HOLDINGS INC p 1062
3802 Robert Porcher Way 27410
Tel (336) 545-0011
SIC 2221 3624 2241 2295

NS FLEXIBLES LLC p 1064
2619 Phoenix Dr 27406
Tel (336) 292-9911 *SIC* 2671 7336 2759

NVH INC p 1068
3802 Robert Porcher Way 27410
Tel (336) 545-0011
SIC 2221 3624 2241 2295

PIEDMONT EXPRESS INC p 1147
7343 W Friendly Ave 27410
Tel (336) 855-7300 *SIC* 4729 4731

POMEGRANATE HOLDINGS INC p 1160
628 Green Valley Rd # 500 27408
Tel (336) 272-1338 *SIC* 5411

PRECISION FABRICS GROUP INC p 1168
301 N Elm St Ste 600 27401
Tel (336) 510-8000 *SIC* 2262 2221

▲ QORVO INC p 1195
7628 Thorndike Rd 27409
Tel (336) 664-1233 *SIC* 3825 3674

■ QORVO US INC p 1195
7628 Thorndike Rd 27409
Tel (336) 664-1233 *SIC* 3674

R H BARRINGER DISTRIBUTING CO INC p 1202
1620 Fairfax Rd 27407
Tel (336) 854-0555 *SIC* 5181

RF MICRO DEVICES INC p 1231
7628 Thorndike Rd 27409
Tel (336) 664-1233 *SIC* 3674

SAMET CORP p 1274
309 Gallimore Dairy Rd # 102 27409
Tel (336) 544-2600 *SIC* 1541 1542

SDM&R INC p 1295
3625 N Elm St 27455
Tel (336) 272-7161 *SIC* 6321

SNIDER TIRE INC p 1335
200 E Meadowview Rd 27406
Tel (336) 691-5480 *SIC* 5531 7534

■ SOLSTAS LAB PARTNERS GROUP LLC p 1338
4380 Federal Dr Ste 100 27410
Tel (336) 664-6100 *SIC* 8071

SOUTHERN FOODS INC p 1348
3500 Old Battlegrd Rd A 27410
Tel (336) 545-3800
SIC 5147 5143 5146 5148 5142

STARR ELECTRIC CO INC p 1379
6 Battleground Ct 27408
Tel (336) 275-0241 *SIC* 1731

SUNSTATES SECURITY LLC p 1404
7011 Albert Pick Rd Ste B 27409
Tel (336) 664-6944 *SIC* 7381

SYNGENTA CROP PROTECTION LLC p 1415
410 S Swing Rd 27409
Tel (336) 632-6000 *SIC* 0721

▲ TANGER FACTORY OUTLET CENTERS INC p 1424
3200 Northline Ave # 360 27408
Tel (336) 292-3010 *SIC* 6798

■ TANGER PROPERTIES LIMITED PARTNERSHIP p 1424
3200 Northline Ave # 360 27408
Tel (336) 292-3010 *SIC* 6798

TAS HOLDING INC p 1425
623 Radar Rd 27410
Tel (336) 668-4410 *SIC* 4581 5088

TENCARVA MACHINERY CO LLC p 1437
1115 Pleasant Ridge Rd 27409
Tel (336) 665-1435 *SIC* 5084

TIMCO AVIATION SERVICES INC p 1454
623 Radar Rd 27410
Tel (336) 668-4410 *SIC* 4581 5088

TRIAD INTERNATIONAL MAINTENANCE CORP p 1478
623 Radar Rd 27410
Tel (336) 668-4410 *SIC* 4581

▲ UNIFI INC p 1503
7201 W Friendly Ave 27410
Tel (336) 294-4410 *SIC* 2281 2282 2221

■ UNIFI MANUFACTURING INC p 1503
7201 W Friendly Ave 27410
Tel (336) 294-4410 *SIC* 2281

■ UNITED GUARANTY CORP p 1509
230 N Elm St Ste 1200 27401
Tel (336) 373-0232 *SIC* 6351

■ UNITED GUARANTY INSURANCE CO p 1509
230 N Elm St Ste 1200 27401
Tel (336) 373-0232 *SIC* 6351

■ UNITED GUARANTY RESIDENTIAL INSURANCE CO p 1509
230 N Elm St 27401
Tel (336) 373-0232 *SIC* 6351

■ UNITEDHEALTHCARE OF NORTH CAROLINA INC p 1515
2307 W Cone Blvd Ste 200 27408
Tel (336) 540-2000 *SIC* 6324

UNIVERSITY OF NORTH CAROLINA AT GREENSBORO INVESTMENT FUND INC p 1523
1202 Spring Garden St 27412
Tel (336) 334-5000 *SIC* 8221

▲ VF CORP p 1553
105 Corp Ctr Blvd 27408
Tel (336) 424-6000
SIC 2325 2321 2329 2339 2331 2369

■ VF JEANSWEAR LIMITED PARTNERSHIP p 1553
400 N Elm St 27401
Tel (336) 332-3400
SIC 2325 2339 2331 2329

■ VF SERVICES LLC p 1553
105 Corporate Center Blvd 27408
Tel (336) 424-6000 *SIC* 2211

VNA HOLDING INC p 1563
7825 National Service Rd 27409
Tel (336) 393-4890
SIC 6159 3713 5012 5013

VOLVO GROUP NORTH AMERICA LLC p 1565
7900 National Service Rd 27409
Tel (336) 393-2000 *SIC* 3713 5012 5013

VOLVO TRUCKS NORTH AMERICA INC p 1565
7900 National Service Rd 27409
Tel (336) 393-2000 *SIC* 3713 5012 5013

WESLEY LONG COMMUNITY HEALTH SERVICES INC p 1593
501 N Elam Ave 27403
Tel (336) 832-1000 *SIC* 8062

GREENVILLE, NC

ABC PHONES OF NORTH CAROLINA INC p 10
1290 E Arlington Blvd B 27858
Tel (252) 317-0388 *SIC* 5999

ASMO GREENVILLE OF NORTH CAROLINA INC p 118
1125 Sugg Pkwy 27834
Tel (252) 754-1000 *SIC* 3594

ASSOCIATED HYGIENIC PRODUCTS LLC p 120
1029 Old Creek Rd 27834
Tel (770) 476-3594 *SIC* 2676

BILL CLARK HOMES LLC p 182
200 E Arlington Blvd A 27858
Tel (252) 355-5805 *SIC* 1522

COASTAL AGROBUSINESS INC p 331
3702 Evans St 27834
Tel (252) 756-1126 *SIC* 5191 3523

DELCOR INC p 424
834 Rivit St 27834
Tel (252) 321-8868 *SIC* 1711

DPI NEWCO LLC p 454
5900 Martin Luther King 27834
Tel (252) 758-3436 *SIC* 2834

DSM PHARMACEUTICALS INC p 458
5900 M L King Jr Hwy 27834
Tel (252) 758-3436 *SIC* 2834

EAST CAROLINA HEALTH INC p 470
2100 Stantonsburg Rd 27834
Tel (252) 847-6156 *SIC* 8099

EAST CAROLINA UNIVERSITY p 470
E Fifth St 27858
Tel (252) 328-6131 *SIC* 8221

GREENFIELD PLACE LLC p 638
2575 W 5th St 27834
Tel (252) 830-9100 *SIC* 8051 8052 8059

■ HYSTER-YALE GROUP INC p 724
1400 Sullivan Dr 27834
Tel (252) 931-5100 *SIC* 3537

■ MAYNE PHARMA INC p 923
1240 Sugg Pkwy 27834
Tel (252) 752-3800 *SIC* 5122 2834

PENCO PRODUCTS INC p 1128
1820 Stonehenge Dr 27858
Tel (252) 917-5287 *SIC* 2599 2542

PITT COUNTY MEMORIAL HOSPITAL INC p 1152
2100 Stantonsburg Rd 27834
Tel (252) 847-4100 *SIC* 8062

PITT COUNTY SCHOOLS p 1152
1717 W 5th St 27834
Tel (252) 830-4200 *SIC* 8211

TRIEST AG GROUP INC p 1480
1101 Industrial Blvd 27834
Tel (252) 758-4263 *SIC* 8748

UHS PHYSICIANS LLC p 1500
2100 Stantonsburg Rd 27834
Tel (252) 847-6809 *SIC* 8211

UNIVERSITY HEALTH SYSTEMS OF EASTERN CAROLINA INC p 1519
2100 Stantonsburg Rd 27834
Tel (252) 847-4451 *SIC* 8062

GRIMESLAND, NC

■ INTERNATIONAL BROADCASTING BUREAU p 754
3919 Voa Site B Rd 27837
Tel (252) 758-2171 *SIC* 9199

HAMLET, NC

RICHMOND COUNTY SCHOOL DISTRICT p 1233
118 Vance St 28345
Tel (910) 582-5860 *SIC* 8211

HAMPTONVILLE, NC

■ LYDALL THERMAL/ACOUSTICAL INC p 887
1243 Buck Shoals Rd 27020
Tel (336) 468-8522 *SIC* 3441

HENDERSON, NC

■ PROGRESS ENERGY SERVICE CO LLC p 1180
602 Raleigh Rd 27536
Tel (919) 508-5400 *SIC* 4911

VANCE COUNTY BOARD OF EDUCATION p 1543
1724 Graham Ave 27536
Tel (252) 492-2127 *SIC* 8211

VARIETY STORES INC p 1544
218 S Garnett St 27536
Tel (252) 430-2600 *SIC* 5331

VARIETY WHOLESALERS INC p 1545
218 S Garnett St 27536
Tel (252) 430-2600 *SIC* 5331

HENDERSONVILLE, NC

FLETCHER HOSPITAL INC p 555
100 Hospital Dr 28792
Tel (828) 684-8501 *SIC* 8062

HENDERSON COUNTY BOARD OF PUBLIC EDUCATION p 682
414 4th Ave W 28739
Tel (828) 697-4510 *SIC* 8211

HENDERSON COUNTY HOSPITAL CORP p 682
800 N Justice St 28791
Tel (828) 698-7191 *SIC* 8062 8051 8082

HENDERSON COUNTY SCHOOLS p 682
414 4th Ave W 28739
Tel (828) 697-4733 *SIC* 8211

■ KYOCERA INDUSTRIAL CERAMICS CORP p 833
100 Industrial Park Rd 28792
Tel (828) 693-0241 *SIC* 5065 5013 5085

MANUAL WOODWORKERS & WEAVERS INC p 903
3737 Howard Gap Rd 28792
Tel (828) 692-7333 *SIC* 2392

WORTH BON INC p 1626
40 Francis Rd 28792
Tel (828) 697-2216
SIC 2331 5621 2339 2335 2337 8741

HICKORY, NC

ALEX LEE INC p 48
120 4th St Sw 28602
Tel (828) 725-4424
SIC 5141 5142 5147 5148 5194 5411

BUMGARNER OIL CO INC p 225
2004 Highland Ave Ne 28601
Tel (828) 322-4377 *SIC* 5172 5983

CATAWBA VALLEY MEDICAL CENTER INC p 265
810 Fairgrove Church Rd 28602
Tel (828) 326-3000 *SIC* 8062

CENTURY FURNITURE LLC p 282
401 11th St Nw 28601
Tel (828) 267-8739 *SIC* 2511 2512

■ COMMSCOPE CONNECTIVITY LLC p 346
1100 Commscope Pl Se 28602
Tel (828) 324-2200 *SIC* 4899

■ COMMSCOPE CONNECTIVITY SOLUTIONS LLC p 346
1100 Commscope Pl Se 28602
Tel (828) 324-2200
SIC 3661 3357 3643 8999

▲ COMMSCOPE HOLDING CO INC p 346
1100 Commscope Pl Se 28602
Tel (828) 324-2200 *SIC* 3663 4899

■ COMMSCOPE INC OF NORTH CAROLINA p 346
1100 Commscope Pl Se 28602
Tel (828) 324-2200
SIC 3663 3357 3679 3812 3699

■ CORNING OPTICAL COMMUNICATIONS LLC p 371
800 17th St Nw 28601
Tel (828) 901-5000 *SIC* 3661

CV INDUSTRIES INC p 404
401 11th St Nw 28601
Tel (828) 328-1851 *SIC* 2511 2512 2211

■ FRYE REGIONAL MEDICAL CENTER INC p 582
420 N Center St Ste 20 28601
Tel (828) 315-5000 *SIC* 8062

■ HICKORY BUSINESS FURNITURE LLC p 690
900 12th Street Dr Nw 28601
Tel (828) 322-1169 *SIC* 2521 2299

HICKORY SPRINGS MANUFACTURING CO p 690
235 2nd Ave Nw 28601
Tel (828) 328-2201
SIC 3069 3495 2514 5072 2399

■ INSTITUTION FOOD HOUSE INC p 747
543 12th Street Dr Nw 28601
Tel (800) 800-0434 *SIC* 5141 5142

KOHLER INTERIORS FURNITURE CO p 826
1105 22nd St Se 28602
Tel (828) 624-7000 *SIC* 2511 5021

MERCHANTS DISTRIBUTORS LLC p 944
5005 Alex Lee Blvd 28601
Tel (828) 725-4424
SIC 5141 5142 5147 5148 5194 5122

NEXANS USA INC p 1039
39 2nd St Nw 28601
Tel (828) 323-2660 *SIC* 3357 3661 3678

PEPSI-COLA BOTTLING CO OF HICKORY NC INC p 1134
2401 14th Avenue Cir Nw 28601
Tel (828) 322-8090 *SIC* 5149 2086

RHF INVESTMENTS INC p 1231
401 11th St Nw 28601
Tel (828) 326-8350 *SIC* 6799

■ RPM WOOD FINISHES GROUP INC p 1255
2220 Hwy 70 Se Ste 100 28602
Tel (828) 261-0325 *SIC* 2851

SHERRILL FURNITURE CO INC p 1316
2405 Highland Ave Ne 28601
Tel (828) 322-2640 *SIC* 2512 2511

SHURTAPE TECHNOLOGIES INC p 1319
1506 Highland Ave Ne 28601
Tel (828) 322-2700 *SIC* 2672

SHURTAPE TECHNOLOGIES LLC p 1319
1712 8th Street Dr Se 28602
Tel (828) 322-2700 *SIC* 2672

SNYDER PAPER CORP p 1336
250 26th Street Dr Se 28602
Tel (828) 328-2501 *SIC* 5199 5085

STM INDUSTRIES INC p 1390
1985 Tate Blvd Se Ste 2 28602
Tel (828) 322-2700 *SIC* 2672

TRANSPORTATION INSIGHT LLC p 1472
310 Main Avenue Way Se 28602
Tel (828) 485-5000 *SIC* 8742

UNITED BEVERAGES OF NORTH CAROLINA LLC p 1506
105 9th St Nw 28601
Tel (828) 322-1933 *SIC* 5181

VON DREHLE CORP p 1565
612 3rd Ave Ne Ste 200 28601
Tel (828) 322-1805 *SIC* 2621 2676

▲ WORLDTEX INC p 1626
990 3rd Ave Se 28602
Tel (828) 322-2242 *SIC* 2241

HIDDENITE, NC

CRAFTMASTER FURNITURE INC p 388
221 Craftmaster Rd 28636
Tel (828) 632-9786 *SIC* 2512

HIGH POINT, NC

ADVANCED HOME CARE INC p 25
4001 Piedmont Pkwy 27265
Tel (336) 878-8950 SIC 8082 5999

▲ BNC BANCORP p 194
3980 Premier Dr Ste 210 27265
Tel (336) 476-9200 SIC 6021

CAROLINA CONTAINER CO p 259
909 Prospect St 27260
Tel (336) 883-7146 SIC 5999

CITY OF HIGH POINT p 315
211 S Hamilton St 27260
Tel (336) 883-3289 SIC 9111

CORNERSTONE HEALTH CARE PA p 371
1701 Westchester Dr # 850 27262
Tel (336) 802-2700 SIC 8741 8099

▲ CULP INC p 400
1823 Eastchester Dr 27265
Tel (336) 889-5161 SIC 2221

HERITAGE HOME GROUP LLC p 686
1925 Eastchester Dr 27265
Tel (314) 863-1100 SIC 2511 2512 2515

HFI WIND DOWN INC p 689
1925 Eastchester Dr 27265
Tel (336) 888-4800 SIC 2511 2512

HIGH POINT REGIONAL HEALTH p 691
601 N Elm St 27262
Tel (336) 878-6000 SIC 8062

HIGH POINT UNIVERSITY p 691
1 University Pkwy 27268
Tel (336) 841-9000 SIC 8221

HOME CARE OF CENTRAL CAROLINA INC p 703
4001 Piedmont Pkwy 27265
Tel (336) 878-8822 SIC 8082

KAO SPECIALTIES AMERICAS LLC p 803
243 Woodbine St 27260
Tel (336) 878-4230 SIC 5169

MARSH FURNITURE CO p 911
1001 S Centennial St 27260
Tel (336) 884-7363 SIC 2434 5712 2421

MICKEY TRUCK BODIES INC p 961
1305 Trinity Ave 27260
Tel (336) 882-6806
SIC 3713 7532 3711 3715

NATUZZI AMERICAS INC p 1019
130 W Commerce Ave 27260
Tel (336) 887-8300 SIC 5021

NORTH STATE COMMUNICATIONS LLC p 1054
111 Hayden Pl 27260
Tel (336) 886-3600 SIC 4813

NORTH STATE TELECOMMUNICATIONS CORP p 1054
111 N Main St 27260
Tel (336) 472-6048 SIC 4813

NORTH STATE TELEPHONE CO p 1054
111 N Main St 27260
Tel (336) 886-3660 SIC 4813

PATHEON SOFTGELS INC p 1120
4125 Premier Dr 27265
Tel (336) 812-8700 SIC 2834

PIEDMONT CHEMICAL INDUSTRIES INC p 1146
331 Burton Ave 27262
Tel (336) 885-5131 SIC 2841 2843

SAMSON INVESTMENT HOLDING INC p 1274
2575 Penny Rd 27265
Tel (336) 449-4600 SIC 2512

TFI WIND DOWN INC p 1445
1925 Eastchester Dr 27265
Tel (336) 472-4000 SIC 2511 2512

THOMAS BUILT BUSES INC p 1448
1408 Courtesy Rd 27260
Tel (336) 889-4871 SIC 3711 3713

UNIVERSAL FURNITURE LIMITED p 1517
2575 Penny Rd 27265
Tel (336) 822-8888 SIC 2511 2512

VRUSH INDUSTRIES INC p 1566
118 N Wrenn St 27260
Tel (336) 886-7700
SIC 5045 5021 7379 3469 5712 7375

■ XPO LOGISITCS SUPPLY CHAIN HOLDING CO p 1632
4035 Piedmont Pkwy 27265
Tel (336) 232-4100 SIC 4731

■ XPO LOGISTICS SUPPLY CHAIN INC p 1633
4035 Piedmont Pkwy 27265
Tel (336) 232-4100 SIC 4731

■ XPO LOGISTICS WORLDWIDE GOVERNMENT SERVICES LLC p 1633
4035 Piedmont Pkwy 27265
Tel (844) 742-5976
SIC 4731 4225 4213 8741

■ XPO LOGISTICS WORLDWIDE LLC p 1633
4035 Piedmont Pkwy 27265
Tel (415) 486-2660 SIC 4731 4512 4213

■ XPO SUPPLY CHAIN INC p 1633
4035 Piedmont Pkwy 27265
Tel (336) 232-4100 SIC 4731

HIGHLANDS, NC

APPAREL BRANDS INC p 98
434 Carolina Way 28741
Tel (828) 526-0167 SIC 2325 2337 8721

HILLSBOROUGH, NC

ORANGE COUNTY SCHOOLS p 1092
200 E King St 27278
Tel (919) 732-8126 SIC 8211

SPORTS ENDEAVORS INC p 1359
431 Us Highway 70a E 27278
Tel (919) 644-6800 SIC 5941

THALLE CONSTRUCTION CO INC p 1446
900 Nc Highway 86 N 27278
Tel (919) 245-1490
SIC 1611 1622 1623 1629

HOBBSVILLE, NC

CA PERRY & SON TRANSIT INC p 234
4033 Virginia Rd 27946
Tel (252) 221-4463 SIC 4213 4212

HOPE MILLS, NC

COASTAL AUTO TRANSPORT LLC p 331
4928 Us Highway 301 S 28348
Tel (910) 429-9902 SIC 4212

CONTAMINANT CONTROL INC p 362
3434 Black And Decker Rd 28348
Tel (910) 484-6841 SIC 4959

HUDSON, NC

■ KINCAID FURNITURE CO INC p 819
240 Pleasant Hill Rd 28638
Tel (828) 728-3261 SIC 2511 2512

HUNTERSVILLE, NC

AMERICAN TIRE DISTRIBUTORS HOLDINGS INC p 80
12200 Herbert Wayne Ct # 150 28078
Tel (704) 992-2000 SIC 5014 5013

AMERICAN TIRE DISTRIBUTORS INC p 80
12200 Herbert Wayne Ct # 150 28078
Tel (704) 992-2000 SIC 5014 5013

DURAFIBER TECHNOLOGIES (DFT) ENTERPRISES INC p 462
13620 Reese Blvd E # 400 28078
Tel (704) 912-3770 SIC 2824

DURAFIBER TECHNOLOGIES (DFT) HOLDINGS II LLC p 462
13620 Reese Blvd E # 400 28078
Tel (704) 912-3700 SIC 2824

DURAFIBER TECHNOLOGIES (DFT) INC p 462
13620 Reese Blvd E # 400 28078
Tel (704) 912-3700 SIC 2824

DURAFIBER TECHNOLOGIES (DFT) OPERATIONS LLC p 462
13620 Reese Blvd E # 400 28078
Tel (704) 912-3770 SIC 2824

FORBO SIEGLING LLC p 565
12201 Vanstory Dr 28078
Tel (704) 948-0800 SIC 3052 3535

■ IRWIN INDUSTRIAL TOOL CO p 765
8935 N Pointe Exec Pk Dr 28078
Tel (704) 987-4555 SIC 3423 3545 3421

METROLINA GREENHOUSES INC p 955
16400 Hntrsvle Concrd Rd 28078
Tel (704) 659-9400 SIC 0181

PLAYPOWER INC p 1155
11515 Vanstory Dr Ste 100 28078
Tel (704) 875-6550 SIC 3949

TERRYS TIRE TOWN INC p 1440
12200 Herbert Wayne Ct 28078
Tel (330) 821-5022 SIC 5014 5531

INDIAN TRAIL, NC

RADIATOR SPECIALTY CO INC p 1204
600 Radiator Rd 28079
Tel (704) 688-2302 SIC 2899

JACKSON, NC

HAMPTON WOODS HEALTH & REHABILITATION CENTER p 656
200 Hmpton Wods Cmplex Rd 27845
Tel (252) 534-0131 SIC 8051 8052

JACKSONVILLE, NC

BRITTHAVEN OF ONSLOW INC p 214
1839 Onslow Dr 28540
Tel (910) 455-3610 SIC 8051 8052

COUNTY OF ONSLOW p 380
4024 Richlands Hwy 28540
Tel (910) 455-1750 SIC 9111

EVOKE NEUROSCIENCE INC p 515
200 Valencia Dr Ste 109 28546
Tel (910) 353-1760 SIC 3845

JONES-ONSLOW ELECTRIC MEMBERSHIP CORP p 793
259 Western Blvd 28546
Tel (910) 353-1940 SIC 4911

■ KEYSTONE AMERICA INC p 815
2685 Henderson Dr 28546
Tel (910) 347-2595 SIC 7261

ONSLOW COUNTY HOSPITAL AUTHORITY p 1088
317 Western Blvd 28546
Tel (910) 577-2345 SIC 8062

ONSLOW COUNTY SCHOOLS INC p 1088
200 Broadhurst Rd 28540
Tel (910) 455-2211 SIC 8211

ONSLOW MEMORIAL HOSPITAL INC p 1088
241 New River Dr 28540
Tel (910) 577-4703 SIC 8062

PLATINUM CORRAL LLC p 1155
521 New Bridge St 28540
Tel (910) 347-3971 SIC 5812

JAMESTOWN, NC

FURNITURELAND SOUTH INC p 585
5635 Riverdale Dr 27282
Tel (336) 822-3000 SIC 5712

HIGHLAND CONTAINERS INC p 691
3520 Dillon Rd 27282
Tel (336) 887-5400 SIC 2653

JEFFERSON, NC

JAMES R VANNOY & SONS CONSTRUCTION CO INC p 777
1608 Us Highway 221 N 28640
Tel (336) 846-7191 SIC 1542 1541 1799

KANNAPOLIS, NC

EI LLC p 481
2865 N Cannon Blvd 28083
Tel (704) 939-4300 SIC 2834 2844

KENANSVILLE, NC

AG PROVISION LLC p 33
277 Faison W Mcgowan Rd 28349
Tel (910) 296-0302 SIC 5191

DUPLIN COUNTY BOARD OF EDUCATION p 462
315 N Main St 28349
Tel (910) 293-4218 SIC 8211

KERNERSVILLE, NC

DEERE-HITACHI CONSTRUCTION MACHINERY CORP p 422
1000 Deere Hitachi Rd 27284
Tel (336) 996-8100 SIC 3531

GRASS AMERICA INC p 632
1202 Nc Highway 66 S 27284
Tel (336) 996-4041 SIC 3429

HIGHLAND INDUSTRIES INC p 691
1350 Bridgeport Dr Ste 1 27284
Tel (336) 992-7500 SIC 2221

JOMARSHE INVESTMENT GROUP INC p 792
1617 Nc Highway 66 S # 201 27284
Tel (336) 992-0200 SIC 6531

S & N COMMUNICATIONS INC p 1261
636 Gralin St 27284
Tel (336) 992-5420 SIC 1623 1731

ZEN HRO INC p 1642
110 Hepler St Ste E 27284
Tel (877) 569-8660 SIC 7363 8742

KINGS MOUNTAIN, NC

BUCKEYE FIRE EQUIPMENT CO p 223
110 Kings Rd 28086
Tel (704) 739-7415 SIC 3569

FIRESTONE FIBERS & TEXTILES CO LLC p 544
100 Firestone Ln 28086
Tel (704) 734-2110 SIC 5531

■ ROCKWOOD LITHIUM INC p 1245
348 Holiday Inn Dr 28086
Tel (704) 739-2501 SIC 2819

KINSTON, NC

AFFORDABLE CARE INC p 32
1400 Industrial Dr 28504
Tel (252) 527-6121 SIC 8741

BRITTHAVEN INC p 214
1435 Highway 258n 28504
Tel (252) 939-4131 SIC 8051 8059

HARVEY FERTILIZER AND GAS CO p 667
303 Bohannon Rd 28501
Tel (252) 526-4150 SIC 5191 2873 2875

HILLCO LTD p 693
1435 Hwy 258 N 28504
Tel (252) 523-9094
SIC 8051 8059 5047 5122

KINSTON NEUSE CORP p 821
2000 Dobbs Farm Rd 28504
Tel (252) 522-3088 SIC 3537

LENOIR COUNTY BOARD OF EDUCATION INC p 855
2017 W Vernon Ave 28504
Tel (252) 527-1109 SIC 8211

LENOIR COUNTY PUBLIC SCHOOLS p 855
2017 W Vernon Ave 28504
Tel (252) 527-1109 SIC 8211

LENOIR MEMORIAL HOSPITAL INC p 856
100 Airport Rd 28501
Tel (252) 522-7000 SIC 8062

MALLARD OIL CO p 899
1502 Dr Martin Luther 28501
Tel (252) 527-0364 SIC 5171 5983 5984

KNIGHTDALE, NC

WAKE STONE CORP p 1572
6821 Knightdale Blvd 27545
Tel (919) 266-1100 SIC 1423

LA GRANGE, NC

COOPER CROUSE- HINDS LLC p 366
4758 Washington St 28551
Tel (252) 566-3014 SIC 3069 3643

HOWELL CHILD CARE CENTER INC p 713
3738 Howell Day Care Rd 28551
Tel (252) 566-9011 SIC 8361 8052

RHA/HOWELL CARE CENTERS INC p 1231
3738 Howell Day Care Rd 28551
Tel (252) 566-9011 SIC 8361 8052

LAURINBURG, NC

SCOTLAND COUNTY SCHOOL SYSTEM p 1293
322 S Main St 28352
Tel (910) 276-1138 SIC 8211

SCOTLAND HEALTH CARE SYSTEM p 1293
500 Lauchwood Dr 28352
Tel (910) 291-7000 SIC 8062 8011 8082

SCOTLAND MEMORIAL HOSPITAL INC p 1293
500 Lauchwood Dr 28352
Tel (910) 291-7680 SIC 8062

LENOIR, NC

BERNHARDT FURNITURE CO INC p 176
1839 Morganton Blvd Sw 28645
Tel (828) 758-9811
SIC 2511 2512 2521 2522

BERNHARDT INDUSTRIES INC p 176
1839 Morganton Blvd Sw 28645
Tel (828) 758-9811
SIC 2511 2521 2512 2522

BFI WIND DOWN INC p 179
815 Visionary St 28645
Tel (828) 759-8000 SIC 5712 2512

BLUE RIDGE ELECTRIC MEMBERSHIP CORP p 192
1216 Blowing Rock Blvd 28645
Tel (828) 758-2383 SIC 4911

CALDWELL COUNTY SCHOOLS p 238
1914 Hickory Blvd Sw 28645
Tel (828) 728-8407 SIC 8211

CALDWELL MEMORIAL HOSPITAL INC p 238
321 Mulberry St Sw 28645
Tel (828) 757-5577 SIC 8062

FAIRFIELD CHAIR CO p 524
1331 Harper Ave Sw 28645
Tel (828) 758-5571 SIC 2512 2511

LEXINGTON, NC

DAVIDSON COUNTY BOARD OF EDUCATION p 416
250 County School Rd 27292
Tel (336) 249-6704 SIC 8211

DAVIDSON COUNTY SCHOOLS p 416
250 County School Rd 27292
Tel (336) 249-8181 SIC 8211

DAVIDSON HEALTH CARE INC p 416
250 Hospital Dr 27292
Tel (336) 248-5161 SIC 5912 8062

LILLINGTON, NC

HARNETT COUNTY BOARD OF EDUCATION p 662
1008 S 11th St 27546
Tel (910) 893-8151 SIC 8211

HARNETT COUNTY SCHOOLS p 662
1008 11th St 27546
Tel (910) 893-8151 SIC 8211

LINCOLNTON, NC

CAROLINAS MEDICAL CENTER-LINCOLN p 259
433 Mcalister Rd 28092
Tel (980) 212-2000 SIC 8062

LINCOLN COUNTY SCHOOL DISTRICT p 866
353 N Generals Blvd 28092
Tel (704) 732-2261 SIC 8211

TENOWO INC p 1438
1968 Kawai Rd 28092
Tel (704) 732-3525 SIC 2297

LUCAMA, NC

SCOTT FARMS INC p 1293
7965a Simpson Rd 27851
Tel (919) 284-4030
SIC 0132 0115 0116 0161 0139

LUMBERTON, NC

PUBLIC SCHOOLS OF ROBESON COUNTY p 1189
410 Caton Rd 28360
Tel (910) 671-6000 SIC 8211

SOUTH EASTERN REGIONAL MEDICAL INC p 1344
300 W 27th St 28358
Tel (910) 671-5543 SIC 5947

SOUTHEASTERN REGIONAL MEDICAL CENTER p 1347
300 W 27th St 28358
Tel (910) 671-5000 SIC 8062

MADISON, NC

BRITTHAVEN OF MADISON INC p 214
1721 Bald Hill Loop 27025
Tel (336) 548-9658 SIC 8051 8052

■ **FGI OPERATING CO LLC** p 539
870 Remington Dr 27025
Tel (336) 548-8700 SIC 3484 3482

■ **REMINGTON ARMS CO LLC** p 1222
870 Remington Dr 27025
Tel (336) 548-8700 SIC 3482 3484

■ **REMINGTON OUTDOOR CO INC** p 1222
870 Remington Dr 27025
Tel (336) 548-8700 SIC 5099 3949

MAIDEN, NC

CAROLINA MILLS INC p 259
618 N Carolina Ave 28650
Tel (828) 428-9911
SIC 2281 2211 2221 2257 2511 2512

▲ **T AIR INC** p 1419
3524 Airport Rd 28650
Tel (828) 464-8741 SIC 4512 3728 7699

MARION, NC

MC DOWELL COUNTY BOARD OF EDUCATION (INC) p 925
334 S Main St 28752
Tel (828) 652-4535 SIC 8211

MATTHEWS, NC

CENTURY CONTRACTORS INC p 282
5100 Smith Farm Rd 28104
Tel (704) 821-8050 SIC 1541

CHAMBERS EXPRESS TRUCKING INC p 287
2132 Bluebonnet Ln 28104
Tel (704) 292-2916 SIC 4212

CONBRACO INDUSTRIES INC p 354
701 Matthews Mint Hill Rd 28105
Tel (704) 841-6000 SIC 3625 3494

■ **FAMILY DOLLAR SERVICES INC** p 526
10401 Monroe Rd 28105
Tel (704) 847-6961 SIC 5331

■ **FAMILY DOLLAR STORES INC** p 526
10401 Monroe Rd 28105
Tel (704) 847-6961 SIC 5331

■ **FAMILY DOLLAR STORES OF LOUISIANA INC** p 526
10401 Monroe Rd 28105
Tel (704) 847-6961 SIC 5331

■ **FAMILY DOLLAR STORES OF MISSOURI INC** p 526
10401 Monroe Rd 28105
Tel (704) 847-6961 SIC 5331

■ **FAMILY DOLLAR STORES OF VIRGINIA INC** p 526
10401 Old Monroe St 28105
Tel (704) 847-6961 SIC 5331

■ **HARRIS TEETER LLC** p 664
701 Crestdale Rd 28105
Tel (704) 844-3100 SIC 5411

■ **HARRIS TEETER SUPERMARKETS INC** p 664
701 Crestdale Rd 28105
Tel (704) 844-3100 SIC 5411

PRESBYTERIAN MEDICAL CARE CORP p 1171
1500 Mtthews Twnship Pkwy 28105
Tel (704) 384-6500 SIC 8062

SELLETHICS MARKETING GROUP INC p 1302
941 Matthews Mint Hill Rd 28105
Tel (704) 847-4450 SIC 5141

MC ADENVILLE, NC

PHARR YARNS LLC p 1141
100 Main St 28101
Tel (704) 824-3551 SIC 2281 2282 2824

MC LEANSVILLE, NC

REPLACEMENTS LTD p 1224
1089 Knox Rd 27301
Tel (336) 697-3000 SIC 5961

MEBANE, NC

ARCATECH SYSTEMS LLC p 104
1151 Holmes Rd 27302
Tel (919) 442-5200 SIC 5049

KINGSDOWN INC p 821
126 W Holt St 27302
Tel (919) 563-3531 SIC 2515

■ **LIGGETT GROUP LLC** p 865
100 Maple Ln 27302
Tel (919) 304-7700 SIC 2111

■ **WALTER KIDDE PORTABLE EQUIPMENT INC** p 1574
1016 Corporate Park Dr 27302
Tel (919) 563-5911 SIC 3999

MILLS RIVER, NC

FLAVOR 1ST GROWERS & PACKERS LLC p 555
331 Banner Farm Rd 28759
Tel (828) 890-3630 SIC 5148

UPM RAFLATAC INC p 1528
400 Broadpointe Dr 28759
Tel (828) 651-4800 SIC 2672 3083

VAN WINGERDEN INTERNATIONAL INC p 1543
4112 Haywood Rd 28759
Tel (828) 696-4500 SIC 5193

MOCKSVILLE, NC

ACCUMED CORP p 16
155 Boyce Dr 27028
Tel (800) 278-6796 SIC 3841

AVGOL AMERICA INC p 137
178 Avgol Dr 27028
Tel (336) 751-5007 SIC 2297

MONROE, NC

ASSA ABLOY ENTRANCE SYSTEMS US INC p 119
1900 Airport Rd 28110
Tel (704) 290-5520 SIC 3699 1796 3442

CAROLINA MEDICAL CENTER UNION p 259
600 Hospital Dr 28112
Tel (704) 283-3100 SIC 8062

GREINER BIO-ONE NORTH AMERICA INC p 639
4238 Capital Dr 28110
Tel (704) 261-7883 SIC 5047

■ **IMO INDUSTRIES INC** p 734
1710 Airport Rd 28110
Tel (704) 289-6511 SIC 3561 3714 3829

MCGEE BROTHERS CO INC p 929
4608 Carriker Rd 28110
Tel (704) 753-4582 SIC 1741 1521

MONROE HARDWARE CO INC p 985
101 N Sutherland Ave 28110
Tel (704) 289-3121 SIC 5072 5083

SCOTT TECHNOLOGIES INC p 1294
4320 Goldmine Rd 28110
Tel (800) 247-7257 SIC 3842 3728 3569

UNION COUNTY BOARD OF EDUCATION p 1504
400 N Church St 28112
Tel (704) 296-9898 SIC 8211

UNION COUNTY PUBLIC SCHOOLS p 1504
400 N Church St 28112
Tel (704) 296-9898 SIC 8211

UNION ELECTRIC MEMBERSHIP CORP p 1504
1525 N Rocky River Rd 28110
Tel (704) 220-1408 SIC 4911

UNION MEMORIAL REGIONAL MEDICAL CENTER INC p 1504
600 Hospital Dr 28112
Tel (980) 993-3100 SIC 8062 8011

UNION REGIONAL MEDICAL CENTER p 1505
600 Hospital Dr 28112
Tel (704) 283-3100 SIC 8011

YALE SECURITY INC p 1634
1902 Airport Rd 28110
Tel (704) 283-2101 SIC 3429 3466

MOORESVILLE, NC

BESTCO HOLDINGS INC p 177
288 Mazeppa Rd 28115
Tel (704) 664-4300 SIC 2064

BESTCO INC p 177
288 Mazeppa Rd 28115
Tel (704) 664-4300 SIC 2023

CLAREMONT RESTAURANT GROUP LLC p 321
129 Fast Ln 28117
Tel (704) 660-5939 SIC 5812

INTRAPAC INTERNATIONAL CORP p 760
136 Fairview Rd Ste 320 28117
Tel (704) 360-8910 SIC 3085 3221

LAKE NORMAN REGIONAL MEDICAL CENTRE p 839
171 Fairview Rd 28117
Tel (704) 660-4000 SIC 8062

LKN COMMUNICATIONS INC p 872
134 Medical Park Rd # 105 28117
Tel (704) 260-3323 SIC 4813

▲ **LOWES COMPANIES INC** p 881
1000 Lowes Blvd 28117
Tel (704) 758-1000
SIC 5211 5031 5722 5064

■ **MOORESVILLE HOSPITAL MANAGEMENT ASSOCIATES LLC** p 987
170 Medical Park Rd # 208 28117
Tel (704) 660-4000 SIC 8062

SUNENERGY1 LLC p 1402
192 Raceway Dr 28117
Tel (704) 662-0375 SIC 1711

MOREHEAD CITY, NC

ALLEGIANCE SECURITY GROUP LLC p 53
2900 Arendell St Ste 18 28557
Tel (252) 247-1138 SIC 7381

BIG ROCK SPORTS LLC p 182
158 Little Nine Rd 28557
Tel (252) 808-3500 SIC 5091

CARTERET COUNTY GENERAL HOSPITAL CORP p 262
3500 Arendell St 28557
Tel (252) 808-6000 SIC 8093 8062

HENRYS TACKLE LLC p 684
158 Little Nine Rd 28557
Tel (252) 726-6186 SIC 5091

SSA HOLDINGS II LLC p 1363
1207 Arendell St Ste C 28557
Tel (252) 808-3185 SIC 7381

■ **SSA SECURITY INC** p 1363
5447 Hwy 70 W Ste 200 28557
Tel (252) 808-3185 SIC 7381

MORGANTON, NC

BLUE RIDGE HEALTHCARE HOSPITALS INC p 192
2201 S Sterling St 28655
Tel (828) 580-5000 SIC 8062

BLUE RIDGE HEALTHCARE SYSTEM INC p 192
2201 S Sterling St 28655
Tel (828) 580-5580 SIC 8062

BURKE COUNTY PUBLIC SCHOOLS p 227
700 E Parker Rd 28655
Tel (828) 437-4770 SIC 8211

DHHS-BROUGHTON HOSPITAL p 435
1000 S Sterling St 28655
Tel (828) 433-2516 SIC 5122

■ **HANESBRANDS DIRECT LLC** p 657
450 W Hanes Mill Rd 28655
Tel (336) 519-8080 SIC 8742

J IVERSON RIDDLE DEVELOPMENT CENTER p 771
300 Enola Rd 28655
Tel (828) 433-2800 SIC 8211

MORRISVILLE, NC

▲ **ALLIANCE ONE INTERNATIONAL INC** p 54
8001 Aerial Center Pkwy # 100 27560
Tel (919) 379-4300 SIC 5159

▲ **CHANNELADVISOR CORP** p 288
3025 Carringtn Ml Blvd # 500 27560
Tel (919) 228-4700 SIC 7372

■ **COVENTRY HEALTH CARE OF CAROLINAS INC** p 385
2801 Slater Rd Ste 200 27560
Tel (919) 337-1800 SIC 6324

FREUDENBERG IT LP p 579
601 Keystone Park Dr # 600 27560
Tel (919) 321-0254 SIC 7371

FUJIFILM DIOSYNTH BIOTECHNOLOGIES USA INC p 583
101 J Morris Commons Ln # 300 27560
Tel (919) 337-4400 SIC 2836

HANSON AGGREGATES EAST LLC p 658
3131 Rdu Center Dr 27560
Tel (919) 380-2500 SIC 3531 5032

LENOVO (UNITED STATES) INC p 856
1009 Think Pl 27560
Tel (919) 294-2500 SIC 3571

LENOVO HOLDING CO INC p 856
1009 Think Pl 27560
Tel (919) 294-0600 SIC 3571

LUIHN FOOD SYSTEMS INC p 884
2950 Gateway Centre Blvd 27560
Tel (919) 850-0558 SIC 5812

▲ **MAXPOINT INTERACTIVE INC** p 923
3020 Carrington Mill Blvd 27560
Tel (800) 916-9960 SIC 7311 8711

MICROLEASE INC p 962
9221 Globe Center Dr # 105 27560
Tel (866) 520-0200 SIC 7359

NNE PHARMAPLAN INC p 1045
3005 Carrington Mill Blvd 27560
Tel (919) 481-3765 SIC 8711

■ **NOVELLA CLINICAL INC** p 1063
1700 Perimeter Park Dr 27560
Tel (919) 484-1921 SIC 8731

REGED INC p 1218
2100 Gateway Centre Blvd # 200 27560
Tel (919) 653-5200 SIC 6411

SCIQUEST INC p 1292
3020 Carrington Mill Blvd # 100 27560
Tel (919) 659-2100 SIC 7372

SCIQUEST PARENT LLC p 1292
3020 Carrington Mill Blvd 27560
Tel (919) 659-2100 SIC 7372

TECAN US GROUP INC p 1430
9401 Globe Center Dr # 140 27560
Tel (919) 361-5200 SIC 5047 3841

TEKELEC GLOBAL INC p 1433
5200 Paramount Pkwy 27560
Tel (919) 460-5500 SIC 3661 3825 7371

■ **TELEFLEX MEDICAL INC** p 1434
3015 Carrington Mill Blvd 27560
Tel (919) 544-8000 SIC 3842

TITAN PRIVATE HOLDINGS I LLC p 1456
5200 Paramount Pkwy 27560
Tel (919) 460-5500 SIC 3661 3825 7371

TRIMACO LLC p 1480
2300 Gateway Centre Blvd # 200 27560
Tel (919) 674-3476
SIC 2851 2621 2672 2679 2394

MOUNT AIRY, NC

▲ **INSTEEL INDUSTRIES INC** p 747
1373 Boggs Dr 27030
Tel (336) 786-2141 SIC 3315

■ **INSTEEL WIRE PRODUCTS CO** p 747
1373 Boggs Dr 27030
Tel (336) 719-9000 SIC 3315

NEIGHBORS STORES INC p 1024
1314 Old Highway 601 27030
Tel (336) 789-5561 SIC 5541 5411

PIKE CORP p 1147
100 Pike Way 27030
Tel (336) 789-2171 SIC 1731 8711

PIKE ELECTRIC LLC p 1148
100 Pike Way 27030
Tel (336) 789-2171 SIC 1731 8711

PIKE ENTERPRISES LLC p 1148
100 Pike Way 27030
Tel (336) 789-2171 SIC 8741

PIONEER PARENT INC p 1151
100 Pike Way 27030
Tel (336) 789-2171 SIC 1731 8711

RENFRO CORP p 1224
661 Linville Rd 27030
Tel (336) 719-8000 SIC 2252

SMITH-ROWE LLC p 1333
639 Old Us 52 S 27030
Tel (336) 789-8221 SIC 1622

MOUNT HOLLY, NC

AMERICAN & EFIRD LLC p 67
22 American St 28120
Tel (704) 827-4311 SIC 2284

MOUNT OLIVE, NC

MOUNT OLIVE PICKLE CO INC p 994
1 Cucumber Blvd 28365
Tel (919) 658-2535 SIC 2035

SOUTHERN BANCSHARES (NC) INC p 1347
116 E Main St 28365
Tel (919) 658-7000 SIC 6022

MOUNT PLEASANT, NC

TUSCARORA YARNS INC p 1493
8760 Franklin St E 28124
Tel (704) 436-6527 SIC 2281

MOYOCK, NC

CONSTELLIS HOLDINGS LLC p 361
850 Puddin Ridge Rd 27958
Tel (252) 435-2488 SIC 6719

NASHVILLE, NC

NASH-ROCKY MOUNT SCHOOLS p 1008
930 Eastern Ave 27856
Tel (252) 459-5220 SIC 8211

NEW BERN, NC

BRITTHAVEN OF NEW BERN INC p 214
2600 Old Cherry Point Rd 28560
Tel (252) 637-4730 SIC 8051

CAROLINAEAST MEDICAL CENTER p 259
2000 Neuse Blvd 28560
Tel (252) 633-8111 SIC 8062

CRAVEN COUNTY SCHOOL DISTRICT p 389
3600 Trent Rd 28562
Tel (252) 514-6300 SIC 8211

HATTERAS YACHTS INC p 668
110 N Glenburnie Rd 28560
Tel (252) 633-3101 SIC 3732

MAOLA MILK AND ICE CREAM CO LLC p 903
305 Avenue C 28560
Tel (252) 638-1131 SIC 2026 2024

NEW LONDON, NC

FIBER COMPOSITES LLC p 539
181 Random Dr 28127
Tel (704) 463-7120 SIC 2899

GENE WHITLEY KELLY p 598
44439 Fish Camp Rd 28127
Tel (704) 984-0811 SIC 5031

NEWTON GROVE, NC

HOG SLAT INC p 699
206 Fayetteville St 28366
Tel (866) 464-7528
SIC 1542 3272 3523 0213

NEWTON, NC

CATAWBA COUNTY SCHOOLS p 265
10 E 25th St 28658
Tel (828) 464-8333 SIC 8211

COUNTY OF CATAWBA p 376
100 Southwest Blvd Bldg A 28658
Tel (828) 465-8200 SIC 9111

GKN DRIVELINE NEWTON LLC p 613
1848 Gkn Way 28658
Tel (828) 428-1591 SIC 3462 3714

MCCREARY MODERN INC p 927
2564 S Us 321 Hwy 28658
Tel (828) 464-6465 SIC 2512

NORTH WILKESBORO, NC

ECMD INC p 475
2 Grandview St 28659
Tel (336) 667-5976 SIC 2431 5031

GARDNER GLASS PRODUCTS INC p 592
301 Elkin Hwy 28659
Tel (336) 651-9300 SIC 3231

■ **L G SOURCING INC** p 834
1605 Curtis Bridge Rd 28659
Tel (866) 578-0563 SIC 5023 5031 2499

WILKES COUNTY BOARD OF EDUCATION p 1609
613 Cherry St 28659
Tel (336) 667-1121 SIC 8211

WILKES COUNTY SCHOOLS p 1609
613 Cherry St 28659
Tel (336) 667-1121 SIC 8211

WRMC HOSPITAL OPERATING CORP p 1628
1370 W D St 28659
Tel (336) 651-8100 SIC 8062

PINE HALL, NC

WIELAND COPPER PRODUCTS LLC p 1608
3990 Us 311 Hwy N 27042
Tel (336) 445-4500 SIC 3351

PINEHURST, NC

APPLIED RESEARCH ASSOCIATES INC p 100
11 Villiage Club Ct 28374
Tel (910) 246-2030 SIC 8711 8731

FIRSTCAROLINACARE INSURANCE CO p 550
42 Memorial Dr 28374
Tel (910) 715-8100 SIC 6324

FIRSTHEALTH MOORE REGIONAL MEDICAL CENTER p 550
110 Page Rd 28374
Tel (910) 715-1077 SIC 8062

FIRSTHEALTH OF CAROLINAS INC p 550
155 Memorial Dr 28374
Tel (910) 715-1000
SIC 8062 8093 8051 8021 7991 7219

MOORE REGIONAL HOSPITAL p 987
20 Page Dr 28374
Tel (910) 295-7888 SIC 8062

PINEHURST LLC p 1149
80 Carolina Vista Dr 28374
Tel (910) 295-6811
SIC 7011 7997 7992 5813 5812

PINEVILLE, NC

BUILDING CENTER INC p 225
10201 Industrial Dr 28134
Tel (704) 889-8182 SIC 5031 2431

RAEFORD, NC

HOUSE OF RAEFORD FARMS INC p 711
1000 E Central Ave 28376
Tel (910) 289-6900 SIC 2015

RALEIGH, NC

ABB POWERT & D CO INC p 9
940 Main Campus Dr # 400 27606
Tel (919) 856-3806 SIC 3612

AL SMITH CO INC p 43
2511 Wake Forest Rd 27609
Tel (919) 839-7481 SIC 5511 5521

ALFRED WILLIAMS & CO p 50
410 S Salisbury St # 200 27601
Tel (919) 832-9570 SIC 5021

ALLIANCE HOSPITALITY MANAGEMENT LLC p 54
215 N Boylan Ave 27603
Tel (919) 791-1801 SIC 7011

■ ALLSCRIPTS HEALTHCARE LLC p 58
8529 Six Forks Rd 27615
Tel (919) 847-8102 SIC 7372

AMERICAN WELDING & GAS INC p 81
4900 Falls Of Neuse Rd 27609
Tel (406) 969-1444 SIC 3548

APHC INC p 96
421 Fayetteville St # 600 27601
Tel (919) 677-2000 SIC 8711

APPLE GOLD INC p 98
164 Wind Chime Ct 27615
Tel (919) 846-2577 SIC 5812

ARGOS READY MIX (CAROLINAS) CORP p 107
3610 Bush St 27609
Tel (919) 790-1520 SIC 3273

BAKER ROOFING CO p 146
517 Mercury St 27603
Tel (919) 828-2975 SIC 1761 1799

BANDWIDTH.COM INC p 150
900 Main Campus Dr # 400 27606
Tel (800) 808-5150 SIC 4813

■ BB&T INSURANCE SERVICES INC p 163
3605 Glenwood Ave Ste 190 27612
Tel (919) 716-9907 SIC 6411

BJT INC p 186
2233 Capital Blvd 27604
Tel (919) 828-3842 SIC 5182 5149 5181

■ BMC EAST LLC p 193
8020 Arco Corp Dr Ste 400 27617
Tel (919) 431-1000
SIC 5211 2431 5031 5713 5251

■ BUSINESS TELECOM LLC p 229
4300 Six Forks Rd Ste 500 27609
Tel (919) 863-7000 SIC 4813 4812

■ CAPITAL BANK CORP p 249
333 Fayetteville St 27601
Tel (919) 645-0868 SIC 6022

CAPITAL FORD INC p 249
4900 Capital Blvd 27616
Tel (919) 790-4600 SIC 5511

CAPITOL BROADCASTING CO INC p 250
2619 Western Blvd 27606
Tel (919) 890-6000
SIC 4833 4832 4841 8732

CAPTIVE-AIRE SYSTEMS INC p 252
4641 Paragon Park Rd # 104 27616
Tel (919) 882-2410 SIC 3444

CITY OF RALEIGH p 317
222 W Hargett St 27601
Tel (919) 996-3000 SIC 9111

CLANCY & THEYS CONSTRUCTION CO INC p 321
516 W Cabarrus St 27603
Tel (919) 834-3601 SIC 1542 1541

COASTAL FEDERAL CREDIT UNION p 331
1000 Saint Albans Dr 27609
Tel (919) 420-8000 SIC 6061

CONCORD HOSPITALITY ENTERPRISES CO p 354
11410 Common Oaks Dr 27614
Tel (919) 455-2900 SIC 7011

COUNTY OF WAKE p 382
300 S Salisbury St # 4800 27601
Tel (919) 856-6160 SIC 9111

DILLON SUPPLY CO p 440
440 Civic Blvd 27610
Tel (919) 838-4200
SIC 5084 5085 5051 5074 5072

■ DUKE ENERGY CAROLINAS LLC p 460
410 S Wilmington St 27601
Tel (704) 382-3853 SIC 4911

■ DUKE ENERGY PROGRESS LLC p 460
410 S Wilmington St 27601
Tel (704) 382-3853 SIC 4911

DUKE HEALTH RALEIGH HOSPITAL GUILD p 460
3400 Wake Forest Rd 27609
Tel (919) 954-3000 SIC 8062

EASTER SEALS UCP NORTH CAROLINA & VIRGINIA INC p 471
5171 Glenwood Ave Ste 400 27612
Tel (919) 832-3787 SIC 8322

ELECTRICAL EQUIPMENT CO INC p 485
1440 Diggs Dr 27603
Tel (919) 828-5411 SIC 5063 7699

■ ELSTER AMERICAN METER CO LLC p 489
208 S Rogers Ln 27610
Tel (800) 257-9754 SIC 3824 3613

■ ELSTER SOLUTIONS LLC p 489
208 S Rogers Ln 27610
Tel (919) 212-4800 SIC 3825

EXECUTIVE OFFICE OF STATE OF NORTH CAROLINA p 518
20301 Mail Svc Ctr 27699
Tel (919) 814-2000 SIC 9111

FHA/RALEIGH INC p 539
9101 Glenwood Ave 27617
Tel (919) 787-0099 SIC 5511 5521 5012

▲ FIRST CITIZENS BANCSHARES INC p 545
4300 Six Forks Rd 27609
Tel (919) 716-7000 SIC 6022

■ FIRST-CITIZENS BANK & TRUST CO p 550
4300 Six Forks Rd 27609
Tel (919) 716-7000 SIC 6035

■ FLORIDA PROGRESS CORP p 559
410 S Wilmington St 27601
Tel (919) 546-6111
SIC 1221 4911 4011 4449

FOOD BANK OF CENTRAL & EASTERN NORTH CAROLINA INC p 564
1924 Capital Blvd 27604
Tel (919) 875-0707 SIC 8322

G4S COMPLIANCE & INVESTIGATIONS INC p 588
910 Paverstone Dr 27615
Tel (800) 927-0456 SIC 6411

■ GENERAL PARTS INC p 601
2635 E Millbrook Rd Ste C 27604
Tel (919) 573-3000 SIC 5013 5531

■ GENERAL PARTS INTERNATIONAL INC p 601
2635 E Millbrook Rd Ste B 27604
Tel (919) 573-3000 SIC 5013

■ GENWORTH MORTGAGE INSURANCE CORP p 605
8325 Six Forks Rd 27615
Tel (919) 846-4100 SIC 6351 8741

GOLDEN CORRAL CORP p 620
5151 Glenwood Ave Ste 300 27612
Tel (919) 781-9310 SIC 5812

GREEN APPLE LLC p 636
164 Wind Chime Ct 27615
Tel (919) 846-2577 SIC 5812

GREGORY POOLE EQUIPMENT CO p 639
4807 Beryl Rd 27606
Tel (919) 828-0641 SIC 5082

▲ HIGHWOODS PROPERTIES INC p 692
3100 Smoketree Ct Ste 600 27604
Tel (919) 872-4924 SIC 6798

■ HIGHWOODS REALTY LIMITED PARTNERSHIP p 692
3100 Smoketree Ct Ste 600 27604
Tel (919) 872-4924 SIC 6519 6531 6798

HOL-DAV INC p 700
5839 Capital Blvd 27616
Tel (888) 240-7435 SIC 5511 5012

▲ INC RESEARCH HOLDINGS INC p 735
3201 Beechleaf Ct Ste 600 27604
Tel (919) 876-9300 SIC 8731

■ INC RESEARCH LLC p 735
3201 Beechleaf Ct Ste 600 27604
Tel (919) 876-9300 SIC 8731

INVESTORS MANAGEMENT CORP p 761
801 N West St 27603
Tel (919) 653-7499 SIC 5812 8741

JF ACQUISITION LLC p 785
1330 Saint Marys St # 210 27605
Tel (757) 857-5700 SIC 5084 1799 7299

JUDICIARY COURTS OF STATE OF NORTH CAROLINA p 797
2 E Morgan St 27601
Tel (919) 733-3723 SIC 9211

■ KDITRANSITION CO INC p 806
3220 Spring Forest Rd 27616
Tel (412) 828-1884 SIC 5912

KIMLEY-HORN AND ASSOCIATES INC p 818
421 Fayetteville St # 600 27601
Tel (919) 677-2000 SIC 8711

▲ KKR PRA INVESTORS LP p 822
4130 Parklake Ave Ste 400 27612
Tel (919) 786-8200 SIC 6722 6726

LEITH INC p 854
5607 Capital Blvd 27616
Tel (919) 876-5432
SIC 5511 7515 7513 5012

LONG BEVERAGE INC p 876
10500 World Trade Blvd 27617
Tel (919) 481-2738 SIC 5181 5149

LUCOR INC p 884
790 Pershing Rd 27608
Tel (919) 828-9511 SIC 7549

MAKHTESHIM AGAN OF NORTH AMERICA INC p 899
3120 Highwoods Blvd # 100 27604
Tel (919) 256-9300 SIC 2879

MARLIN HOLDCO LP p 909
3301 Benson Dr Ste 601 27609
Tel (919) 325-3000 SIC 4953

▲ MARTIN MARIETTA MATERIALS INC p 912
2710 Wycliff Rd 27607
Tel (919) 781-4550
SIC 1423 1422 1442 3295 3297

MAYVIEW CONVALESCENT HOME INC p 924
513 E Whitaker Mill Rd 27608
Tel (919) 828-2348 SIC 8051

MCKIM & CREED PA p 930
1730 Varsity Dr Ste 500 27606
Tel (919) 233-8091 SIC 8711 8713

MCM CORP p 932
702 Oberlin Rd Ste 300 27605
Tel (919) 833-1600 SIC 6331

MERZ NORTH AMERICA INC p 951
6501 Six Forks Rd 27615
Tel (919) 582-8000 SIC 3841

MORGANITE INDUSTRIES INC p 989
4000 Westchase Blvd # 170 27607
Tel (919) 821-1253
SIC 3674 3255 3699 3264 3299 3624

NATIONAL CANCER COALITION LLC p 1010
225 Hillsborough St # 280 27603
Tel (919) 821-2182 SIC 8099

NATIONAL COATINGS & SUPPLIES INC p 1010
4900 Falls Of Neuse Rd 27609
Tel (919) 573-2900 SIC 5013

NATIONAL GUARD NORTH CAROLINA p 1013
1636 Gold Star Dr 27607
Tel (919) 664-6000 SIC 9711

NC HEALTH AND HUMAN SERVICES p 1021
3006 Mail Service Ctr 27699
Tel (252) 208-4000 SIC 8211

NC MEDICAL SOCIETY HEALTH p 1021
700 Spring Forest Rd # 400 27609
Tel (919) 878-7513 SIC 8621

NEW APPLE INC p 1029
170 Wind Chime Ct 27615
Tel (919) 870-0513 SIC 5812

■ NEWS AND OBSERVER PUBLISHING CO p 1039
215 S Mcdowell St 27601
Tel (919) 829-4500
SIC 2711 2741 2721 2752

NORTH CAROLINA COMMUNITY COLLEGE SYSTEM p 1051
200 W Jones St 27603
Tel (919) 807-7100 SIC 8222 9411

NORTH CAROLINA DEPARTMENT OF AGRICULTURE & CONSUMER SERVICES p 1051
2 W Edenton St 27601
Tel (919) 707-3000 SIC 9641

NORTH CAROLINA DEPARTMENT OF CRIME CONTROL AND PUBLIC SAFETY p 1051
512 N Salisbury St 27604
Tel (919) 825-2720 SIC 9221

NORTH CAROLINA DEPARTMENT OF ENVIRONMENTAL QUALITY p 1051
217 W Jones St Ste 5103 27603
Tel (877) 623-6748 SIC 9512

NORTH CAROLINA DEPARTMENT OF HEALTH & HUMAN SERVICES p 1051
2025 Mail Service Ctr 27699
Tel (919) 733-4534 SIC 9441

NORTH CAROLINA DEPARTMENT OF JUSTICE p 1051
114 W Edenton St 27603
Tel (919) 779-8213 SIC 9222

NORTH CAROLINA DEPARTMENT OF PUBLIC SAFETY p 1051
512 N Salisbury St 27604
Tel (919) 733-2126 SIC 9223

NORTH CAROLINA DEPARTMENT OF REVENUE p 1051
501 N Wilmington St 27604
Tel (877) 252-3052 SIC 9311

NORTH CAROLINA DEPARTMENT OF TRANSPORTATION p 1051
1 S Wilmington St 27601
Tel (919) 707-2500 SIC 9621

NORTH CAROLINA DIVISION OF ADULT PROBATION AND PAROLE p 1051
4000 Wake Forest Rd 27609
Tel (919) 850-2900 SIC 9223

NORTH CAROLINA DIVISION OF HIGHWAYS p 1051
1 S Wilmington St 27601
Tel (919) 733-7384 SIC 9621

NORTH CAROLINA DIVISION OF PRISONS p 1051
831 W Morgan St 27603
Tel (919) 838-4000 SIC 9223

NORTH CAROLINA EASTERN MUNICIPAL POWER AGENCY p 1051
1427 Meadow Wood Blvd 27604
Tel (919) 760-6000 SIC 4911

NORTH CAROLINA ELECTRIC MEMBERSHIP CORP p 1051
3400 Sumner Blvd 27616
Tel (919) 872-0800 SIC 4911

NORTH CAROLINA FARM BUREAU INSURANCE AGENCY INC p 1051
5301 Glenwood Ave 27612
Tel (919) 782-1705 SIC 6331 6411 6311

NORTH CAROLINA PARTNERSHIP FOR CHILDREN INC p 1051
1100 Wake Forest Rd 27604
Tel (919) 821-7999 SIC 8399

NORTH CAROLINA STATE UNIVERSITY p 1051
2701 Sullivan Dr Ste 240 27695
Tel (919) 515-2011 SIC 8221

OCCIDENTAL FIRE & CASUALTY CO OF NORTH CAROLINA p 1072
702 Oberlin Rd Ste 300 27605
Tel (919) 833-1600 SIC 6331

PANTHER SUMMIT INDUSTRIES INC p 1111
4807 Beryl Rd 27606
Tel (919) 828-0641 SIC 5082 5084 4931

PEPSI BOTTLING VENTURES LLC p 1134
4141 Parklake Ave Ste 600 27612
Tel (919) 865-2300 SIC 5149 2086

■ PRA HEALTH SCIENCES INC p 1167
4130 Parklake Ave Ste 400 27612
Tel (919) 786-8200 SIC 8731

■ PRA INTERNATIONAL OPERATIONS INC p 1167
4130 Parklake Ave Ste 400 27612
Tel (919) 786-8200 SIC 8731

■ PROGRESS ENERGY INC p 1180
410 S Wilmington St 27601
Tel (704) 382-3853 SIC 4911

RBC BANCORPORATION (USA) p 1211
301 Fayetteville St 27601
Tel (252) 454-4400 SIC 6712 6022

▲ RED HAT INC p 1215
100 E Davie St 27601
Tel (919) 754-3700 SIC 7372

■ REPUBLIC AUTOMOTIVE PARTS SALES INC p 1225
2635 E Millbrook Rd 27604
Tel (919) 573-3000 SIC 5013 5531

REPUBLIC WIRELESS INC p 1226
900 Main Campus Dr 27606
Tel (877) 913-0894 SIC 4812

REX HEALTHCARE INC p 1230
4420 Lake Boone Trl 27607
Tel (919) 784-3100 SIC 8082 8011 8062

REX HOSPITAL INC p 1230
4420 Lake Boone Trl 27607
Tel (919) 784-3100 SIC 8062

S&ME INC p 1263
3201 Spring Forest Rd 27616
Tel (919) 872-2660 SIC 8711

SALIX PHARMACEUTICALS INC p 1273
8540 Colonnade Center Dr # 401 27615
Tel (919) 862-1000 SIC 2834

SENSUS (BERMUDA 2) LTD p 1305
8601 Six Forks Rd 27615
Tel (919) 845-4000 SIC 3824 3363 3491

SENSUS USA INC p 1305
8601 Six Forks Rd Ste 700 27615
Tel (919) 845-4000
SIC 3824 3363 2891 3491

SET AND SERVICE RESOURCES LLC p 1308
8303 Six Forks Rd Ste 207 27615
Tel (919) 787-5571 SIC 7361

■ SOUTHERN INDUSTRIAL CONSTRUCTORS INC p 1349
6101 Triangle Dr 27617
Tel (919) 782-4600
SIC 1629 1799 1731 1796 1791 7353

STATE EMPLOYEES CREDIT UNION p 1380
119 N Salisbury St 27603
Tel (919) 839-5000 SIC 6062

STATE OF NORTH CAROLINA p 1382
20301 Mail Service Ctr 27699
Tel (919) 715-1411 SIC 9111

STOCK BUILDING SUPPLY HOLDINGS LLC p 1390
8020 Arco Corp Dr Ste 400 27617
Tel (919) 431-1000
SIC 5211 2431 5031 5713 5251

SUNROCK GROUP HOLDINGS CORP p 1404
200 Horizon Dr Ste 100 27615
Tel (919) 747-6400
SIC 1429 3273 2951 1411

▲ TRIANGLE CAPITAL CORP p 1478
3700 Glenwood Ave Ste 530 27612
Tel (919) 719-4770 SIC 7389

UMICORE USA INC p 1501
3600 Glenwood Ave Ste 250 27612
Tel (919) 874-7171
SIC 5052 5051 5093 5169 3339

VANTAGESOUTH BANCSHARES INC p 1544
3600 Glenwood Ave Ste 300 27612
Tel (919) 659-9000 SIC 6022

WAKE TECHNICAL COMMUNITY COLLEGE FOUNDATION INC p 1572
9101 Fayetteville Rd 27603
Tel (919) 866-5000 SIC 8222 9411

WAKEMED p 1572
3000 New Bern Ave G100 27610
Tel (919) 350-8000 SIC 8062

WASTE INDUSTRIES LLC p 1580
3301 Benson Dr Ste 601 27609
Tel (919) 325-3000 SIC 4953

WASTE INDUSTRIES USA INC p 1580
3301 Benson Dr Ste 601 27609
Tel (919) 325-3000 SIC 4953 3443

▲ WILLIAMS INDUSTRIES INC p 1611
1128 Tyler Farms Dr 27603
Tel (919) 604-1746
SIC 3441 1531 1541 3315 1791

▲ YADKIN FINANCIAL CORP p 1633
3600 Glenwood Ave Ste 300 27612
Tel (919) 659-9000 SIC 6022

YORK PROPERTIES INC OF RALEIGH p 1637
1900 Cameron St 27605
Tel (919) 821-1350 SIC 6552 6531

RANDLEMAN, NC

HUGHES FURNITURE INDUSTRIES INC p 717
952 S Stout Rd 27317
Tel (336) 498-8700 SIC 2512 7641 2426

RED SPRINGS, NC

LUMBEE RIVER ELECTRIC MEMBERSHIP CORP p 885
605 E 4th Ave 28377
Tel (910) 843-7932 SIC 4911

REIDSVILLE, NC

ALBAAD USA INC p 45
129 S Technology Dr 27320
Tel (336) 634-0091 SIC 2844

EDEN OIL CO INC p 477
2507 Richardson Dr 27320
Tel (336) 349-8228 SIC 5171 5983

ROANOKE RAPIDS, NC

HALIFAX REGIONAL MEDICAL CENTER INC p 654
250 Smith Church Rd 27870
Tel (215) 994-4000 SIC 8062 8011

NEW DIXIE OIL CORP p 1029
1501 Marshall St 27870
Tel (252) 537-4118 SIC 5983

ROCKY MOUNT, NC

AUTUMN CORP p 135
451 N Winstead Ave 27804
Tel (252) 443-6265 SIC 8059 8051

BARNHILL CONTRACTING CO INC p 156
800 Tiffany Blvd Ste 200 27804
Tel (252) 823-1021 SIC 1771 1541

BAY FOODS INC p 161
1021 Noell Ln 27804
Tel (252) 937-2000 SIC 5812

BODDIE-NOELL ENTERPRISES INC p 197
1021 Noell Ln 27804
Tel (252) 937-2000 SIC 5812 6552

EAGLE TRANSPORT CORP p 468
300 S Wesleyan Blvd # 200 27804
Tel (252) 937-2464 SIC 4213

ECPH MANAGEMENT INC p 476
2317 Professional Dr 27804
Tel (252) 443-4028 SIC 5812

GUARDIAN CORP p 645
3801 Sunset Ave Ste A 27804
Tel (252) 443-4101 SIC 5812

ILCO UNICAN HOLDING CORP p 731
400 Jeffreys Rd 27804
Tel (252) 446-3321 SIC 3429

JAY GROUP LTD p 779
1450 Atlantic Ave 27801
Tel (252) 442-2139 SIC 5139

KABA ILCO CORP p 799
400 Jeffreys Rd 27804
Tel (252) 446-3321 SIC 3429

KINEXO p 820
800 Tiffany Blvd Ste 300 27804
Tel (252) 407-2000 SIC 5141

■ MEADOWBROOK MEAT CO INC p 934
2641 Meadowbrook Rd 27801
Tel (252) 985-7200
SIC 5147 5113 5149 5142

NASH HEALTH CARE SYSTEMS p 1008
2460 Curtis Ellis Dr 27804
Tel (252) 962-8000 SIC 8011 8741

NHCS INC p 1041
2416 Professional Dr 27804
Tel (252) 962-8585 SIC 8062 8063

ROSE HILL, NC

MURPHY FARMS LLC p 1001
600 Rte Hwy A 28458
Tel (910) 289-6439 SIC 0213

NASH JOHNSON & SONS FARMS INC p 1008
3385 S Us Highway 117 28458
Tel (910) 289-3113
SIC 2015 0254 0253 0251 2048

ROSEBORO, NC

DUBOSE STEEL INC OF NORTH CAROLINA p 459
767 Dr Mlk Jr Blvd 28382
Tel (910) 525-4161 SIC 5051

RUTHERFORDTON, NC

TRELLEBORG COATED SYSTEMS US INC p 1476
715 Railroad Ave 28139
Tel (864) 576-1210
SIC 2295 2221 2394 2396 2211

SAINT PAULS, NC

PRESTAGE FOODS INC p 1173
4470 Hwy 20 E 28384
Tel (910) 865-6611 SIC 2015

SALISBURY, NC

B V HEDRICK GRAVEL & SAND CO p 142
120 1/2 N Church St 28144
Tel (704) 633-5982
SIC 1442 7359 6512 3273 1541 1542

COUNTY OF ROWAN p 381
130 W Innes St Ste 120 28144
Tel (704) 636-0361 SIC 9111

DELHAIZE AMERICA LLC p 424
2110 Executive Dr 28147
Tel (704) 633-8250 SIC 5411

FOOD LION LLC p 564
2110 Executive Dr 28147
Tel (704) 633-8250 SIC 5411

FRESHOUSE II LLC p 579
311 Long Meadow Dr 28147
Tel (704) 630-6950 SIC 5148

GLOBAL CONTACT SERVICES LLC p 616
118b S Main St B 28144
Tel (704) 647-9672 SIC 7319 7389

GOLD TOE MORETZ HOLDINGS CORP p 620
2121 Heilig Rd 28146
Tel (828) 464-0751 SIC 5136 5137 5699

LUTHERAN SERVICES FOR AGING INC p 886
1416 S Martin Luther 28144
Tel (704) 637-2870 SIC 8051 8052 8059

MCKENZIE SPORTS PRODUCTS LLC p 930
1910 Saint Luke Church Rd 28146
Tel (704) 279-7985 SIC 3949 3423

ROWAN HEALTH SERVICES CORP p 1253
612 Mocksville Ave 28144
Tel (704) 210-5000 SIC 8062

ROWAN REGIONAL MEDICAL CENTER INC p 1253
612 Mocksville Ave 28144
Tel (704) 210-5000 SIC 8062

SALISBURY SCHOOL ROWAN SYSTEM p 1272
500 N Main St 28144
Tel (704) 630-6026 SIC 8211

SANFORD, NC

FRONTIER SPINNING MILLS HOLDING CORP p 581
1823 Boone Trail Rd 27330
Tel (919) 776-9940 SIC 2281

FRONTIER SPINNING MILLS INC p 581
1823 Boone Trail Rd 27330
Tel (919) 777-2689 SIC 2281

GRP INC p 642
1823 Boone Trail Rd 27330
Tel (919) 776-9940 SIC 2281

JT DAVENPORT & SONS INC p 772
1144 Broadway Rd 27332
Tel (919) 774-9444 SIC 5199

LEE COUNTY OF (INC) p 851
106 Hillcrest Dr 27330
Tel (919) 718-4600 SIC 9111

LEE COUNTY SCHOOLS p 851
106 Gordon St 27330
Tel (919) 774-6226 SIC 8211

MAGNETI MARELLI POWERTRAIN USA LLC p 896
2101 Nash St 27330
Tel (919) 776-4111 SIC 3714 3592

PENTAIR WATER POOL AND SPA INC p 1132
1620 Hawkins Ave 27330
Tel (919) 774-4151
SIC 3589 3561 3569 3648

■ PHILOSOPHY INC p 1144
1400 Broadway Rd 27332
Tel (602) 794-8500 SIC 5122 2844

SANFORD CONTRACTORS INC p 1279
628 Rocky Fork Church Rd 27332
Tel (919) 775-7882
SIC 1611 1622 1629 6552 1794 1623

SANTRONICS INC p 1281
3010 Lee Ave 27332
Tel (919) 775-1223 SIC 3679 3674

STATIC CONTROL COMPONENTS INC p 1383
3010 Lee Ave 27332
Tel (919) 774-3808 SIC 3629

STATIC CONTROL IC-DISC INC p 1383
3010 Lee Ave 27332
Tel (919) 774-3808 SIC 7389

SEVERN, NC

MEHERRIN AGRICULTURAL & CHEMICAL CO p 940
413 Main St 27877
Tel (252) 585-1744 SIC 5159 5191 5145

SHELBY, NC

CLEVELAND COUNTY HEALTHCARE SYSTEM p 325
201 E Grover St 28150
Tel (900) 487-3000 SIC 8062 8051

CLEVELAND COUNTY SCHOOLS p 325
400 W Marion St 28150
Tel (704) 476-8000 SIC 8211

■ HURST JAWS OF LIFE INC p 721
711 N Post Rd 28150
Tel (704) 487-6961 SIC 3569 3561 3594

IMC-METALSAMERICA LLC p 733
135 Old Boiling Sprng Rd 28152
Tel (704) 482-8200 SIC 3331

■ PPG INDUSTRIES FIBER GLASS PRODUCTS INC p 1166
940 Washburn Switch Rd 28150
Tel (704) 434-2261 SIC 3229

SCHLETTER INC p 1287
1001 Commerce Center Dr 28150
Tel (704) 595-4200 SIC 3441 3999

SMITHFIELD, NC

BRITTHAVEN OF SMITHFIELD INC p 214
515 Barbour Rd 27577
Tel (919) 934-6017 SIC 8051 8052

COUNTY OF JOHNSTON p 379
207 E Johnston St 27577
Tel (919) 989-5100 SIC 9111

JOHNSTON COUNTY SCHOOLS p 791
2320 Us Highway 70 Bus E 27577
Tel (919) 934-6031 SIC 8211

JOHNSTON MEMORIAL HOSPITAL CORP p 791
509 N Brightleaf Blvd 27577
Tel (919) 934-8171 SIC 8062

SNOW HILL, NC

BRITTHAVEN OF SNOW HILL INC p 214
1304 Se 2nd St 28580
Tel (252) 747-8126 SIC 8051 8052

SOUTHERN PINES, NC

DIRECT SAT TV LLC p 441
1930 N Poplar St Ste 21 28387
Tel (910) 693-3000 SIC 4841

▲ FIRST BANCORP p 545
300 Sw Broad St 28387
Tel (910) 246-2500 SIC 6022

STANLEY, NC

BLUM INC p 193
7733 Old Plank Rd 28164
Tel (704) 827-1345 SIC 3429

SUNTERRACE CASUAL FURNITURE INC p 1405
2369 Chrles Rper Jnes Hwy 28164
Tel (704) 263-1967 SIC 2519

STATESVILLE, NC

3A COMPOSITES USA INC p 2
3480 Taylorsville Hwy 28625
Tel (704) 872-8974
SIC 3334 2679 3081 3449

AMESBURY ACQUISITION HOLDINGS (2) INC p 84
2061 Sherrill Dr 28625
Tel (704) 924-8586 SIC 3272

ASMO NORTH AMERICA LLC p 118
470 Crawford Rd 28625
Tel (704) 872-2319 SIC 3089 3621

ASMO NORTH CAROLINA INC p 118
470 Crawford Rd 28625
Tel (704) 878-6663 SIC 3519 3621

ENERGYUNITED ELECTRIC MEMBERSHIP CORP p 498
567 Mocksville Hwy 28625
Tel (704) 873-5241 SIC 4911

HEXPOL COMPOUNDING NC INC p 688
280 Crawford Rd 28625
Tel (704) 872-1585 SIC 3069 3087 2891

IREDELL MEMORIAL HOSPITAL INC p 764
557 Brookdale Dr 28677
Tel (704) 873-5661 SIC 8062 8051

IREDELL-STATESVILLE SCHOOLS p 764
549 N Race St 28677
Tel (704) 872-8931 SIC 8211

▲ KEWAUNEE SCIENTIFIC CORP p 814
2700 W Front St 28677
Tel (704) 873-7202 SIC 3821 2599

■ STATESVILLE HMA LLC p 1383
218 Old Mocksville Rd 28625
Tel (704) 873-0281 SIC 8051 8063 8062

THARPE CO INC p 1446
149 Crawford Rd 28625
Tel (704) 872-5231 SIC 5199

THARPEROBBINS CO INC p 1446
149 Crawford Rd 28625
Tel (704) 872-5231 SIC 3911

TOTER LLC p 1463
841 Meacham Rd 28677
Tel (800) 424-0422
SIC 3089 3536 3469 3412 2821

■ YADKIN BANK p 1633
325 E Front St 28677
Tel (704) 924-8815 SIC 6022

SUPPLY, NC

BRUNSWICK ELECTRIC MEMBERSHIP CORP p 221
795 Ocean Hwy W 28462
Tel (910) 754-4391 SIC 4911

SWEPSONVILLE, NC

HONDA POWER EQUIPMENT MFG INC p 704
3721 Nc Hwy 119 27359
Tel (336) 578-5300 SIC 3524

SYLVA, NC

■ HRH OF NC INC p 714
68 Hospital Rd 28779
Tel (828) 586-7000 SIC 8062

WESTCARE HEALTH CORP p 1596
68 Hospital Rd 28779
Tel (828) 586-7100 SIC 8011

WESTCARE HEALTH SYSTEM p 1596
68 Hospital Rd 28779
Tel (828) 586-7000 SIC 8069

TARBORO, NC

EDGECOMBE COUNTY SCHOOLS p 477
2311 N Main St 27886
Tel (252) 641-2600 SIC 8211

KEIHIN CAROLINA SYSTEM TECHNOLOGY LLC p 807
4047 Mcnair Rd 27886
Tel (252) 641-6750 SIC 3694 3625 3714

PARKWAY AG CENTER INC p 1117
2801 Industrial Pkwy 27886
Tel (252) 823-5778 SIC 5191

TARBORO NURSING CARE p 1424
911 Western Blvd 27886
Tel (252) 823-2041 SIC 8051

TAYLORSVILLE, NC

ATLANTIC COAST MERCHANDISING LLC p 126
599 Wood Hollow Rd 28681
Tel (910) 300-9231 SIC 8742 7389

MITCHELL GOLD CO p 977
135 One Comfortable Pl 28681
Tel (828) 632-9200 SIC 2512

THOMASVILLE, NC

■ BANK OF NORTH CAROLINA p 151
831 Julian Ave 27360
Tel (336) 476-9200 SIC 6022

BRITTHAVEN OF DAVIDSON INC p 214
706 Pineywood Rd 27360
Tel (336) 475-9116 SIC 8051 8052

ENNIS PAINT INC p 500
115 Todd Ct 27360
Tel (800) 331-8118 SIC 2851 3953

LEXINGTON FURNITURE INDUSTRIES INC p 859
1300 National Hwy 27360
Tel (336) 474-5300 SIC 2512

NORDFAB LLC p 1048
150 Transit Ave 27360
Tel (336) 821-0829 SIC 3443

▲ OLD DOMINION FREIGHT LINE INC p 1080
500 Old Dominion Way 27360
Tel (336) 889-5000 SIC 4213 4212 4731

■ **UNILIN FLOORING NC LLC** p 1503
550 Cloniger Dr 27360
Tel (336) 313-4000 *SIC* 2421 2426

TRINITY, NC

■ **OHIO MATTRESS CO LICENSING AND COMPONENTS GROUP** p 1077
1 Office Parkway Rd 27370
Tel (336) 861-3500 *SIC* 2515 6794

■ **SEALY CORP** p 1296
1 Office Parkway Rd 27370
Tel (336) 861-3500 *SIC* 2515

■ **SEALY INC** p 1296
1 Office Parkway Rd 27370
Tel (336) 861-3500 *SIC* 8741

■ **SEALY MATTRESS CO** p 1297
1 Office Parkway Rd 27370
Tel (336) 861-3500 *SIC* 2515

■ **SEALY MATTRESS MANUFACTURING CO INC** p 1297
1 Office Parkway Rd 27370
Tel (336) 861-3500 *SIC* 2515

TROUTMAN, NC

AMERICAN STAINLESS TUBING INC p 79
129 Honeycutt Rd 28166
Tel (704) 878-8823 *SIC* 3317

CASE FARMS LLC p 263
385 Pilch Rd 28166
Tel (704) 528-4501 *SIC* 2015 8731

CASE FARMS PROCESSING INC p 263
385 Pilch Rd 28166
Tel (704) 528-4501 *SIC* 2015

CASE FOODS INC p 263
385 Pilch Rd 28166
Tel (704) 528-4501 *SIC* 2015

TROY, NC

■ **FIRST BANK** p 545
341 N Main St 27371
Tel (910) 576-6171 *SIC* 6022

VALDESE, NC

VALDESE WEAVERS LLC p 1539
1000 Perkins Rd Se 28690
Tel (828) 874-2181 *SIC* 2211 2221

WAKE FOREST, NC

1-800-PACK-RAT LLC p 1
11640 Northpark Dr 200 27587
Tel (202) 362-0101 *SIC* 5932

BODY SHOP INC p 197
5036 One World Way 27587
Tel (919) 554-4900 *SIC* 5999 6794 2844

■ **POWERSECURE INC** p 1166
1609 Heritage Commerce Ct 27587
Tel (919) 556-3056 *SIC* 7373

■ **POWERSECURE INTERNATIONAL INC** p 1166
1609 Heritage Commerce Ct 27587
Tel (919) 556-3056 *SIC* 3629 4931

WARSAW, NC

MURPHY-BROWN LLC p 1001
2822 W Nc 24 Hwy 28398
Tel (910) 293-3434 *SIC* 0213

WASHINGTON, NC

BEAUFORT COUNTY BOARD OF EDUCATION p 166
321 Smaw Rd 27889
Tel (252) 946-6593 *SIC* 8211

BEAUFORT COUNTY SCHOOLS p 166
321 Smaw Rd 27889
Tel (252) 946-6593 *SIC* 8211

FLANDERS CORP p 554
531 Flanders Filter Rd 27889
Tel (252) 946-8081 *SIC* 3564

NATIONAL SPINNING CO INC p 1016
1481 W 2nd St 27889
Tel (252) 975-7111 *SIC* 2281

PRECISIONAIRE INC p 1169
531 Flanders Filter Rd 27889
Tel (252) 946-8081 *SIC* 3564

RIDGEWOOD MANOR INC p 1234
1624 Highland Dr 27889
Tel (252) 946-9570 *SIC* 8051 8052

VT HACKNEY INC p 1567
911 W 5th St 27889
Tel (252) 946-6521 *SIC* 3713

WAYNESVILLE, NC

HAYWOOD COUNTY PUBLIC SCHOOLS INC p 671
1230 N Main St 28786
Tel (828) 456-2400 *SIC* 8211

WEAVERVILLE, NC

BRIAN CENTER REHAB p 211
78 Weaver Blvd 28787
Tel (828) 645-4297 *SIC* 8059

WELCOME, NC

WALKER AND ASSOCIATES INC p 1573
7129 Old Hwy 52 27374
Tel (336) 731-6391
SIC 4813 5065 8731 8711 3572 3571

WALKER GROUP INC p 1573
7129 Old Hwy 52 27374
Tel (336) 731-6391
SIC 4813 8748 5065 8711

WEST END, NC

SANDHILL CENTER LME/MCO p 1278
1120 7 Lakes Dr 27376
Tel (910) 673-9111 *SIC* 8011

WHITAKERS, NC

■ **CONSOLIDATED DIESEL INC** p 359
9377 N Us Highway 301 27891
Tel (252) 437-6611 *SIC* 3519

WHITEVILLE, NC

COLUMBUS COUNTY BOARD OF EDUCATION p 342
817 Washington St 28472
Tel (910) 642-5168 *SIC* 8211

COLUMBUS REGIONAL HEALTHCARE SYSTEM p 342
500 Jefferson St 28472
Tel (910) 642-8011 *SIC* 8062

S BLACK TIRE SERVICE INC p 1262
30 Bitmore Rd 28472
Tel (910) 642-4123 *SIC* 5531 5014

WHITSETT, NC

LENOVO US FULFILLMENT CENTER LLC p 856
6540 Franz Warner Pkwy 27377
Tel (919) 294-0477 *SIC* 3571

WILKESBORO, NC

BRITTHAVEN OF WILKESBORO INC p 214
1016 Fletcher St 28697
Tel (336) 667-9261 *SIC* 8051

■ **LOWES HOME CENTERS LLC** p 881
1605 Curtis Bridge Rd 28697
Tel (336) 658-4000
SIC 5211 5031 5722 5064

WILLIAMSTON, NC

MARTIN COUNTY BOARD OF EDUCATION p 912
300 N Watts St 27892
Tel (252) 792-1575 *SIC* 8211

WILMINGTON, NC

ALCAMI CAROLINAS CORP p 47
2320 Scientific Park Dr 28405
Tel (910) 254-7000 *SIC* 2834 8734 8731

ALCAMI CORP p 47
2320 Scientific Park Dr 28405
Tel (910) 254-7000 *SIC* 2834

ALCAMI HOLDINGS LLC p 47
2320 Scientific Park Dr 28405
Tel (910) 254-7000 *SIC* 2834 8731 8734

APPLIED BIOSCIENCE INTERNATIONAL LLC p 99
3151 S 17th St 28412
Tel (910) 251-0081 *SIC* 8731

ATLANTIC CORP p 126
806 N 23rd St 28405
Tel (910) 343-0624 *SIC* 2671

ATLANTIC CORP OF WILMINGTON INC p 126
806 N 23rd St 28405
Tel (910) 343-0624 *SIC* 5113 2621 2679

■ **BLUE WATER FINANCE & INSURANCE** p 192
5041 New Cntre Dr Ste 212 28403
Tel (877) 934-9393 *SIC* 7389

CAPE FEAR COMMUNITY COLLEGE p 248
411 N Front St 28401
Tel (910) 362-7000 *SIC* 8222 9411

CENAMA INC p 274
1410 Commwl Dr Ste 202 28403
Tel (910) 395-5300 *SIC* 5411

CHEMTEX INTERNATIONAL INC p 293
1979 Eastwood Rd 28403
Tel (910) 509-4400 *SIC* 8711 8731

CITY OF WILMINGTON p 319
305 Chestnut St 28401
Tel (910) 341-7800 *SIC* 9111

COASTAL BEVERAGE CO INC p 331
301 Harley Dr 28405
Tel (910) 799-3011 *SIC* 5181

COASTAL REHABILITATION HOSPITAL p 332
2131 S 17th St 28401
Tel (910) 343-7845 *SIC* 8093

COUNTY OF NEW HANOVER p 380
230 Govt Ctr Dr 125 28403
Tel (910) 798-7187 *SIC* 9111

■ **GE-HITACHI NUCLEAR ENERGY AMERICA LLC** p 597
3901 Castle Hayne Rd 28401
Tel (910) 819-5073 *SIC* 2819

■ **GUILFORD MILLS INC** p 646
1001 Military Cutoff Rd # 300 28405
Tel (910) 794-5810 *SIC* 2258 2399

LIBERTY HOMECARE GROUP LLC p 862
2334 S 41st St 28403
Tel (910) 815-3122 *SIC* 8082

LIVE OAK BANCSHARES INC p 871
1741 Tiburon Dr 28403
Tel (910) 790-5867 *SIC* 6022

LIVE OAK BANKING CO p 871
1741 Tiburon Dr 28403
Tel (910) 790-5867 *SIC* 6153

LONGLEY SUPPLY CO p 877
2018 Oleander Dr 28403
Tel (910) 762-7793 *SIC* 5074 5063 5075

MEGACORP LOGISTICS LLC p 939
7040 Wrightsville Ave 28403
Tel (910) 332-0820 *SIC* 4731

NEW HANOVER COUNTY BLACK LEADERSHIP CONFERENCE p 1030
6410 Carolina Beach Rd 28412
Tel (910) 763-5431 *SIC* 8211

NEW HANOVER COUNTY SCHOOLS p 1030
6410 Carolina Beach Rd 28412
Tel (910) 254-4206 *SIC* 8211

NEW HANOVER REGIONAL MEDICAL CENTER INC p 1030
2131 S 17th St 28401
Tel (910) 343-7001 *SIC* 8062

PHARMACEUTICAL PRODUCT DEVELOPMENT LLC p 1141
929 N Front St 28401
Tel (910) 251-0081 *SIC* 8731

PORT CITY JAVA INC p 1162
101 Portwatch Way 28412
Tel (910) 796-6646 *SIC* 6719

PPD DEVELOPMENT LP p 1166
929 N Front St 28401
Tel (910) 251-0081 *SIC* 8731

PPD DEVELOPMENT LP p 1166
929 N Front St 28401
Tel (910) 251-0081 *SIC* 8731

PPD INTERNATIONAL HOLDINGS INC p 1166
929 N Front St 28401
Tel (910) 251-0081 *SIC* 2834

REEDS JEWELERS INC p 1217
2525 S 17th St 28401
Tel (910) 350-3100 *SIC* 5944

UNIVERSITY OF NORTH CAROLINA WILMINGTON p 1524
601 S College Rd 28403
Tel (910) 962-7209 *SIC* 8221

WILMINGTON HEALTH PLLC p 1613
1202 Medical Center Dr 28401
Tel (910) 341-3300 *SIC* 8011

WILSON, NC

BARNES MOTOR & PARTS CO INC p 156
2728 Forest Hills Rd Sw 27893
Tel (252) 243-2161 *SIC* 5531

BRITTHAVEN OF WILSON INC p 214
403 Crestview Ave Sw 27893
Tel (252) 237-0724 *SIC* 8051 8052

HEALTH CARE FOUNDATION OF WILSON p 674
2505a Nash St Nw 27896
Tel (252) 281-2105 *SIC* 8062

INTERIM HOME HEALTHCARE CO p 752
2526 Ward Blvd 27893
Tel (252) 243-7808 *SIC* 8082

■ **KIDDE TECHNOLOGIES INC** p 817
4200 Airport Dr Nw 27896
Tel (252) 237-7004 *SIC* 3728

S T WOOTEN CORP p 1263
3801 Black Creek Rd Se 27893
Tel (252) 637-4294 *SIC* 1611 3273 1623

SPC MECHANICAL CORP p 1355
1908 Baldree Rd S 27893
Tel (252) 237-9035 *SIC* 3494 1711 3444

WATSON ELECTRICAL CONSTRUCTION CO LLC p 1583
1500 Charleston St Se 27893
Tel (252) 237-7511 *SIC* 1731

WILSON COUNTY SCHOOLS p 1613
117 Tarboro St Ne 27893
Tel (252) 399-7700 *SIC* 8211

WINGATE, NC

WINGATE UNIVERSITY p 1616
220 N Camden Rd 28174
Tel (704) 233-8000 *SIC* 8221

WINSTON SALEM, NC

A T WILLIAMS OIL CO p 6
5446 University Pkwy 27105
Tel (336) 767-9883 *SIC* 6719

■ **ALLIANCE DISPLAY AND PACKAGING CO** p 54
5921 Grassy Creek Blvd 27105
Tel (336) 661-1700 *SIC* 2653

AMARR CO p 64
165 Carriage Ct 27105
Tel (336) 744-5100
SIC 2431 3442 5031 5211

AUTO SUPPLY CO INC p 133
3740 N Patterson Ave 27105
Tel (336) 661-6113 *SIC* 5013

■ **BB&T CAPITAL TRUST IV** p 163
200 W 2nd St Ste 1800 27101
Tel (336) 733-2000 *SIC* 6021

▲ **BB&T CORP** p 163
200 W 2nd St Ste 260 27101
Tel (336) 733-2000
SIC 6021 6311 6035 6211

■ **BB&T INSURANCE HOLDINGS INC** p 163
200 W 2nd St 27101
Tel (336) 733-2500 *SIC* 6021

BEKAERT TEXTILES USA INC p 169
240 Business Park Dr 27107
Tel (336) 747-4900 *SIC* 5021 2211

BEVERAGE-AIR CORP p 178
3779 Champion Blvd 27105
Tel (336) 245-6400 *SIC* 5078

■ **BRANCH BANKING AND TRUST CO** p 207
200 W 2nd St 27101
Tel (336) 733-2000 *SIC* 6022 6021

BRANCH BANKING AND TRUST CO HEALTH CARE PLAN p 207
P.O. Box 1215 27102
Tel (336) 733-2411 *SIC* 6733

BUDD GROUP INC p 223
2325 S Stratford Rd 27103
Tel (336) 765-9324 *SIC* 0781 7349

CITY OF WINSTON-SALEM p 319
101 N Main St 27101
Tel (336) 727-8000 *SIC* 9111

COOK & BOARDMAN GROUP LLC p 365
3916 Westpoint Blvd 27103
Tel (336) 768-8872 *SIC* 2431

COTTON PARENT INC p 374
370 Knollwood St 27103
Tel (336) 726-8876 *SIC* 5461

COUNTY OF FORSYTH p 378
201 N Chestnut St 27101
Tel (336) 703-2050 *SIC* 9111

COVILLE INC p 385
8065 N Point Blvd Ste O 27106
Tel (336) 759-0115 *SIC* 5131

DEBBIES STAFFING SERVICES INC p 420
4431 Cherry St Ste 50 27105
Tel (336) 744-2393 *SIC* 7363

E G FORREST CO p 466
1023 N Chestnut St 27101
Tel (336) 723-9151 *SIC* 5142 5141

FORSYTH MEDICAL CENTER FOUNDATION p 568
3333 Silas Creek Pkwy 27103
Tel (336) 277-1120 *SIC* 8062

FORSYTH MEMORIAL HOSPITAL INC p 568
3333 Silas Creek Pkwy 27103
Tel (336) 277-1120 *SIC* 8062

FORSYTH TECHNICAL COMMUNITY COLLEGE INC p 568
2100 Silas Creek Pkwy 27103
Tel (336) 723-0371 *SIC* 8222 9411

GOODWILL INDUSTRIES OF NORTHWEST NORTH CAROLINA INC p 625
2701 University Pkwy 27105
Tel (336) 724-3621 *SIC* 5932 8331

■ **HANES COMPANIES INC** p 657
815 Buxton St 27101
Tel (336) 747-1600 *SIC* 2262 2261 2297

▲ **HANESBRANDS INC** p 657
1000 E Hanes Mill Rd 27105
Tel (336) 519-8080
SIC 2253 2342 2341 2322 2252 2251

HATTERAS FINANCIAL CORP p 668
751 W 4th St Ste 400 27101
Tel (336) 760-9347 *SIC* 6798

INMAR INC p 744
635 Vine St 27101
Tel (800) 765-1277 *SIC* 7389

K & W CAFETERIAS INC p 798
1391 Plaza West Dr 27103
Tel (336) 760-0526 *SIC* 5812

KRISPY KREME DOUGHNUT CORP p 830
259 S Stratford Rd 27103
Tel (336) 724-2484 *SIC* 5461 2051

KRISPY KREME DOUGHNUTS INC p 830
370 Knollwood St Ste 500 27103
Tel (336) 726-8876 *SIC* 5461 5149 2051

■ **LIBERTY HARDWARE MFG CORP** p 861
140 Business Park Dr 27107
Tel (336) 769-4077 *SIC* 5072

LOWES FOODS LLC p 881
1381 Old Mill Cir Ste 200 27103
Tel (336) 659-2429 *SIC* 5411

■ **MAIDENFORM LLC** p 897
1000 E Hanes Mill Rd 27105
Tel (336) 519-8080 *SIC* 5137

■ **NATIONAL GENERAL MANAGEMENT CORP** p 1012
5630 University Pkwy 27105
Tel (336) 435-3164 *SIC* 6411

NOVANT HEALTH INC p 1062
3333 Silas Creek Pkwy 27103
Tel (336) 718-5000 *SIC* 6324

NOVANT HEALTH INC p 1062
2085 Frontis Plaza Blvd 27103
Tel (336) 277-1120 *SIC* 8062

ORACLE FLEXIBLE PACKAGING INC p 1091
220 Polo Rd 27105
Tel (336) 777-4695 *SIC* 2672

PARRISH TIRE CO p 1117
5130 Indiana Ave 27106
Tel (336) 767-0202 *SIC* 5014 5531 7534

PARTNERS NATIONAL HEALTH PLANS OF NORTH CAROLINA INC p 1118
5660 University Pkwy 27105
Tel (336) 760-4822 SIC 6324

PINE HALL BRICK CO INC p 1149
2701 Shorefair Dr 27105
Tel (336) 721-7500 SIC 3251 5032

▲ PRIMO WATER CORP p 1176
101 N Cherry St Ste 501 27101
Tel (336) 331-4000 SIC 5149 3585 5141

QUALITY OIL CO LLC p 1197
1540 Silas Creek Pkwy 27127
Tel (336) 722-3441 SIC 5983 5541 7011

■ R J REYNOLDS TOBACCO CO p 1202
401 N Main St 27101
Tel (336) 741-5000 SIC 2131

■ R J REYNOLDS TOBACCO HOLDINGS INC p 1202
401 N Main St 27101
Tel (336) 741-5000 SIC 2111

■ REPUBLIC MORTGAGE INSURANCE CO INC p 1225
101 N Cherry St Ste 101 27101
Tel (336) 661-0015 SIC 6351

RESOURCE CO INC p 1227
1292 S Stratford Rd 27103
Tel (336) 896-1000 SIC 7363 7361

▲ REYNOLDS AMERICAN INC p 1230
401 N Main St 27101
Tel (336) 741-2000 SIC 2111 2121 2131

ROYCE TOO LLC p 1254
3330 Healy Dr Ste 200 27103
Tel (212) 356-1627 SIC 5137 5136

SALEM CARRIERS INC p 1272
175 Charlois Blvd 27103
Tel (336) 768-6800 SIC 4213 4212

SALEM HOLDING CO p 1272
175 Charlois Blvd 27103
Tel (336) 768-6800 SIC 7513 4213

SALEM LEASING CORP p 1272
175 Charlois Blvd 27103
Tel (336) 768-6800 SIC 7513

SALEM WINSTON FORSYTH COUNTY SCHOOLS p 1272
475 Corporate Square Dr 27105
Tel (336) 748-4000 SIC 8211

■ SONOCO DISPLAY & PACKAGING LLC p 1340
555 Aureole St 27107
Tel (336) 784-0445 SIC 3086

SSC WINSTON-SALEM OPERATING CO LLC p 1363
4911 Brian Center Ln 27106
Tel (336) 744-5674 SIC 8051

STANTEC ARCHITECTURE INC p 1377
301 N Main St Ste 2452 27101
Tel (336) 714-7413 SIC 8712 7389

W R VERNON PRODUCE CO p 1569
1035 N Cherry St 27101
Tel (336) 725-9741 SIC 5148

WAKE FOREST BAPTIST MEDICAL CENTER p 1571
Medical Center Blvd 27157
Tel (336) 716-2011 SIC 8062

WAKE FOREST BAPTIST MEDICAL CENTER p 1571
Medical Center Blvd 27157
Tel (336) 748-8843 SIC 8062

WAKE FOREST UNIVERSITY p 1571
1834 Wake Forest Rd 27109
Tel (336) 758-5000 SIC 8221

WILCOHESS LLC p 1608
5446 University Pkwy 27105
Tel (336) 767-6280 SIC 5461 5812 5541

WILLIAM PRINCE HOSPITAL p 1611
2085 Frontis Plaza Blvd 27103
Tel (336) 718-2803 SIC 8699

WINSTON-SALEM INDUSTRIES FOR BLIND INC p 1617
7730 N Point Blvd 27106
Tel (336) 759-0551
SIC 2515 3021 2392 2253 2394 3851

WINSTON-SALEM STATE UNIVERSITY FOUNDATION INC p 1617
601 S Martin Lut 27110
Tel (336) 750-2000 SIC 8221

WINSTON-SALEM/FORSYTH COUNTY SCHOOLS p 1617
4801 Bethania Station Rd 27105
Tel (336) 727-2635 SIC 8211 9111

WOMBLE CARLYLE SANDRIDGE & RICE LLP p 1621
1 W 4th St 27101
Tel (336) 721-3600 SIC 8111

YMCA OF NORTHWEST NORTH CAROLINA p 1636
301 N Main St Ste 1900 27101
Tel (336) 777-8055
SIC 8641 7991 8351 7032 8322

WINTERVILLE, NC

PITT COMMUNITY COLLEGE p 1152
1986 Pitt Tech Dr 28590
Tel (252) 321-4200 SIC 8222

■ ROBERTS CO FIELD SERVICES INC p 1242
133 Forlines Rd 28590
Tel (252) 355-9353 SIC 1541

YADKINVILLE, NC

TRIAD GROUP INC p 1478
623 W Main St 27055
Tel (336) 679-8852 SIC 8051 5047 7374

TRIAD MEDICAL SERVICES INC p 1478
623 W Main St 27055
Tel (336) 679-8852 SIC 8082

YADKIN NURSING CARE CENTER INC p 1633
903 W Main St 27055
Tel (336) 679-8863 SIC 8082 8051

YOUNGSVILLE, NC

■ WEAVEXX LLC p 1586
14101 Capital Blvd 27596
Tel (919) 556-7235 SIC 2221

▲ XERIUM TECHNOLOGIES INC p 1631
14101 Capital Blvd 27596
Tel (919) 526-1400 SIC 2221 3069

ZEBULON, NC

NOEL GROUP LLC p 1046
501 Nmc Dr 27597
Tel (919) 269-6500 SIC 3086

NOMACORC LLC p 1047
400 Vintage Park Dr 27597
Tel (919) 460-2200 SIC 3089

NORTH DAKOTA

ARTHUR, ND

ARTHUR COMPANIES INC p 114
429 Main St 58006
Tel (701) 967-8312 SIC 5153

BELFIELD, ND

MBI ENERGY LOGISTICS LLC p 925
12980 35th St Sw 58622
Tel (701) 575-8242 SIC 4731

MISSOURI BASIN WELL SERVICE INC p 976
12980 35th St Sw 58622
Tel (701) 575-8242 SIC 4213 1389

BEULAH, ND

■ COTEAU PROPERTIES CO p 374
204 County Road 15 58523
Tel (701) 873-2281 SIC 1221

BISMARCK, ND

BASIN ELECTRIC POWER COOPERATIVE p 158
1717 E Interstate Ave 58503
Tel (701) 223-0441 SIC 4911 1311

BILFINGER WESTCON INC p 182
7401 Yukon Dr 58503
Tel (701) 222-0076 SIC 1542

■ CENTENNIAL ENERGY HOLDINGS INC p 275
Schuchart Bldg 918e 58501
Tel (701) 222-7900 SIC 1382 8748 1221

■ CENTENNIAL ENERGY RESOURCES LLC p 275
1200 W Century Ave 58503
Tel (701) 530-1000 SIC 4911

CHALLENGER INDUSTRIES INC p 287
2005 N Kavaney Dr Ste A 58501
Tel (701) 255-1665 SIC 5085

DAKOTA COAL CO p 409
1717 E Interstate Ave 58503
Tel (701) 223-0441 SIC 6519 7353 3274

DAKOTA GASIFICATION CO INC p 409
1717 E Interstate Ave 58503
Tel (701) 223-0441 SIC 2873 5169 1311

EXECUTIVE OFFICE OF STATE OF NORTH DAKOTA p 518
600 E Boulevard Ave 58505
Tel (701) 328-2680 SIC 9111

KLJ SOLUTIONS CO p 823
4585 Coleman St 58503
Tel (701) 355-8400 SIC 8711 8713

■ KNIFE RIVER CORP p 824
1150 W Century Ave 58503
Tel (701) 530-1400 SIC 1442 3273 1221

■ MDU CONSTRUCTION SERVICES GROUP INC p 933
1150 W Century Ave 58503
Tel (701) 530-1000 SIC 4911

▲ MDU RESOURCES GROUP INC p 933
1200 W Century Ave 58503
Tel (701) 530-1000
SIC 4911 4924 4922 1221 1442 1311

MIDWEST MOTOR EXPRESS INC p 967
5015 E Main Ave 58501
Tel (701) 223-1880 SIC 4212

MILLER INSULATION CO INC p 970
3520 E Century Ave 58503
Tel (701) 258-4323 SIC 1742 1542

NORTH DAKOTA DEPARTMENT OF HUMAN SERVICES p 1052
600 E Boulevard Ave # 325 58505
Tel (701) 872-2081 SIC 9441

NORTH DAKOTA DEPARTMENT OF MILITARY AFFAIRS p 1052
30 Fraine Barracks Ln 58504
Tel (701) 333-2079 SIC 9711

NORTH DAKOTA DEPT OF TRANSPORTATION p 1052
608 E Boulevard Ave 58505
Tel (701) 328-2500 SIC 9621

NORTH DAKOTA UNIVERSITY SYSTEM FOUNDATION p 1052
600 E Boulevard Ave # 215 58505
Tel (701) 328-2960 SIC 8221

RDO CONSTRUCTION EQUIPMENT CO p 1212
2000 Industrial Dr 58501
Tel (701) 223-5798 SIC 5082 5084 7353

SANFORD BISMARCK p 1279
300 N 7th St 58501
Tel (701) 323-6000 SIC 8011 8062

ST ALEXIUS MEDICAL CENTER p 1364
900 E Broadway Ave 58501
Tel (701) 530-7000 SIC 8062

STATE OF NORTH DAKOTA p 1382
600 E Boulevard Ave # 101 58505
Tel (701) 328-4905 SIC 9111

TRI-ENERGY COOPERATIVE p 1477
219 N 20th St 58501
Tel (701) 223-8707 SIC 5812 5541 5251

UNITED ENERGY CORP p 1508
919 S 7th St Ste 405 58504
Tel (701) 255-7970 SIC 1311

■ WASTE MANAGEMENT OF NORTH DAKOTA INC p 1581
7007 15th St Nw 58503
Tel (701) 223-2295 SIC 4953

■ WBI ENERGY TRANSMISSION INC p 1585
1250 W Century Ave 58503
Tel (701) 530-1601 SIC 4922 1311

■ WBI HOLDINGS INC p 1585
1250 W Century Ave 58503
Tel (701) 530-1600 SIC 4922 1311

WESTCON INC p 1597
7401 Yukon Dr 58503
Tel (701) 222-0076 SIC 1541 3498 8741

WORKERS SAFETY INSURANCE p 1624
1600 E Century Ave Ste 1 58503
Tel (701) 328-3800 SIC 9441

CARRINGTON, ND

■ DAKOTA GROWERS PASTA CO INC p 409
1 Pasta Ave 58421
Tel (701) 652-2855 SIC 2098

CASSELTON, ND

MAPLE RIVER GRAIN & AGRONOMY LLC p 904
1630 1st Ave S 58012
Tel (701) 347-4465 SIC 5153 5191

DEVILS LAKE, ND

LEEVERS FOODS PARTNERSHIP LLP p 852
501 4th St Se 58301
Tel (701) 662-8646 SIC 5411

DICKINSON, ND

ALLIED RESOURCES LLC p 57
387 15th St W 366 58601
Tel (800) 677-1142 SIC 1389

FISHER SAND & GRAVEL CO p 552
3020 Energy Dr 58601
Tel (701) 456-9184 SIC 1442 3532 5084

KADRMAS LEE & JACKSON INC p 800
1463 I94 Business Loop E 58601
Tel (701) 355-8400 SIC 8711 8713

WYOMING CASING SERVICE INC p 1630
198 40th St E 58601
Tel (701) 225-8521 SIC 1389

ENDERLIN, ND

PLAINS GRAIN & AGRONOMY LLC p 1153
109 3rd Ave 58027
Tel (701) 437-2565 SIC 5153 5191 5171

FAIRMOUNT, ND

FARMERS UNION OIL OF SOUTHERN VALLEY p 530
100 S Front St 58030
Tel (701) 474-5440
SIC 5171 5191 5541 5251

FARMERS UNION OIL OF SOUTHERN VALLEY p 530
107 S Front St 58030
Tel (701) 474-5882 SIC 5999

FARGO, ND

AGCOUNTRY FARM CREDIT SERVICES ACA p 34
1900 44th St S 58103
Tel (701) 235-9858 SIC 6029

BELL BANK p 170
3100 13th Ave S 58103
Tel (701) 298-1500 SIC 6022

BORDER STATES ELECTRIC SUPPLY OF MINNESOTA INC p 201
105 25th St N 58102
Tel (701) 258-6060 SIC 5063

BORDER STATES ELECTRIC SUPPLY OF TEXAS INC p 201
105 25th St N 58102
Tel (701) 293-5834 SIC 5063

BORDER STATES INDUSTRIES INC p 201
105 25th St N 58102
Tel (701) 293-5834 SIC 5063

BUTLER MACHINERY CO p 230
3401 33rd St S 58104
Tel (701) 298-1700 SIC 5082 7353 7699

CASS COUNTY ELECTRIC COOP INC p 263
3312 42nd St S Ste 200 58104
Tel (701) 356-4400 SIC 4911

COLE PAPERS INC p 335
1300 38th St N 58102
Tel (800) 800-8090
SIC 5113 5111 5169 5023 5112 5049

DAKOTA SUPPLY GROUP INC p 409
2601 3rd Ave N 58102
Tel (701) 237-9440 SIC 5063

EIDE BAILLY LLP p 481
4310 17th Ave S 58103
Tel (701) 239-8500 SIC 8721

ESSENTIA HEALTH LLC p 510
1702 University Dr S 58103
Tel (701) 364-8900 SIC 8011

FARGO ASSEMBLY CO p 528
3300 7th Ave N 58102
Tel (701) 298-3803 SIC 3643

FARGO SCHOOL DISTRICT NO 1 p 528
415 4th St N 58102
Tel (701) 446-1000 SIC 8211

FORUM COMMUNICATIONS CO p 570
101 5th St N 58102
Tel (701) 235-7311 SIC 2711 4833 4832

INNOVIS HEALTH LLC p 745
1702 University Dr S 58103
Tel (701) 364-8000 SIC 8093

MCCORMICK INC p 927
4000 12th Ave N 58102
Tel (701) 277-1225 SIC 1611 1629 1623

NORIDIAN HEALTHCARE SOLUTIONS LLC p 1048
900 42nd St S 58103
Tel (701) 277-6500 SIC 6324

NORIDIAN MUTUAL INSURANCE CO p 1048
4510 13th Ave S 58121
Tel (701) 282-1100 SIC 8399 6321 6324

NORTH DAKOTA STATE UNIVERSITY p 1052
1919 University Dr N # 102 58102
Tel (701) 231-7015 SIC 8221

NORTH DAKOTA UNIVERSITY SYSTEM p 1052
2000 44th St S Ste 301 58103
Tel (701) 231-6326 SIC 8221

NORTHERN IMPROVEMENT CO p 1056
4000 12th Ave N 58102
Tel (701) 277-1225 SIC 1611 1629

■ NORTHERN PIPE PRODUCTS INC p 1056
1302 39th St N 58102
Tel (701) 282-7655 SIC 3084

RD OFFUTT CO p 1212
700 7th St S 58103
Tel (701) 526-9670 SIC 0134 2038

RDO AGRICULTURE EQUIPMENT CO p 1212
700 7th St S 58103
Tel (701) 239-8730 SIC 5083

RDO EQUIPMENT CO p 1212
700 7th St S 58103
Tel (701) 239-8700
SIC 5083 5082 5084 7699 7359 7353

RDO HOLDINGS CO p 1212
700 7th St S 58103
Tel (701) 239-8700 SIC 5083 5082

RED RIVER COMMODITIES INC p 1216
501 42nd St N 58102
Tel (701) 282-2600 SIC 5153 5145 5149

S-N-GO STORES INC p 1263
2701 University Dr S 58103
Tel (701) 235-7531 SIC 5541 5411

SANFORD p 1279
801 Broadway N 58102
Tel (701) 234-6000 SIC 8062 8011 8051

SANFORD CLINIC NORTH p 1279
737 Broadway N 58102
Tel (701) 234-2000 SIC 5912

SANFORD CLINIC NORTH p 1279
801 Broadway N 58102
Tel (701) 234-2000 SIC 8741 8721

SANFORD MEDICAL CENTER FARGO p 1279
720 4th St N 58122
Tel (701) 234-6000 SIC 8062

SANFORD NORTH p 1279
801 Broadway N 58102
Tel (701) 234-2000 SIC 8011

SCHEELS ALL SPORTS INC p 1286
4550 15th Ave S 58103
Tel (701) 364-0572
SIC 5661 5941 5699 5251 5261

SHAZZAM INC p 1313
1001 25th St N 58102
Tel (701) 237-3330 SIC 6719

■ SPECIALTY COMMODITIES INC p 1356
1530 47th St N 58102
Tel (701) 282-8222 SIC 5149 5153

STATE BANKSHARES INC p 1380
3100 13th Ave S 58103
Tel (701) 298-1500 SIC 6022

SWANSON HEALTH PRODUCTS INC p 1411
4075 40th Ave S 58104
Tel (701) 356-2700 SIC 5499 2834

TMI HOSPITALITY LP p 1457
4850 32nd Ave S 58104
Tel (701) 235-1060 *SIC* 7011

■ US BANK NATIONAL ASSOCIATION ND p 1531
4325 17th Ave S 58125
Tel (701) 461-0346 *SIC* 6021

VANITY SHOP OF GRAND FORKS INC p 1543
1001 25th St N 58102
Tel (701) 282-0486 *SIC* 5621

■ VARISTAR CORP p 1545
4334 18th Ave S Ste 200 58103
Tel (701) 232-6414
SIC 6719 4899 1623 5047 1731 4213

WW WALLWORK INC p 1629
900 35th St N 58102
Tel (701) 282-6700 *SIC* 5511 5012 5013

FORT TOTTEN, ND

LAKE SPIRIT TRIBE p 839
816 3rd Ave N 58335
Tel (701) 766-1270
SIC 9131 0191 2394 2298 7999

FULLERTON, ND

FULLERTON FARMERS ELEVATOR p 584
202 Minneapolis Ave 58441
Tel (701) 375-7881 *SIC* 5153 5191

GRAND FORKS, ND

ACME ELECTRIC MOTOR INC p 17
1705 13th Ave N 58203
Tel (701) 746-2823
SIC 5084 5063 5082 5072 5251 5211

ALERUS FINANCIAL NATIONAL ASSN p 48
2300 S Columbia Rd 58201
Tel (701) 795-3200 *SIC* 6021

ALTRU HEALTH SYSTEM p 63
1200 S Columbia Rd 58201
Tel (701) 780-5000
SIC 7352 8011 8062 8063

BLACK GOLD FARMS p 186
4320 18th Ave S 58201
Tel (701) 792-3414 *SIC* 0134 0191

BLACK GOLD POTATO SALES INC p 186
4320 18th Ave S 58201
Tel (701) 248-3788 *SIC* 5141

GRAND FORKS PUBLIC SCHOOLS p 629
2400 47th Ave S 58201
Tel (701) 746-2200 *SIC* 8211

LM WIND POWER BLADES (ND) INC p 872
1580 S 48th St 58201
Tel (701) 780-9910 *SIC* 3511 3621

MINNKOTA POWER COOPERATIVE INC p 974
1822 Mill Rd 58203
Tel (701) 795-4000 *SIC* 4911

NODAK ELECTRIC COOPERATIVE INC p 1046
4000 32nd Ave S 58201
Tel (701) 746-4461 *SIC* 4911

NORTH DAKOTA MILL & ELEVATOR ASSOCIATION INC p 1052
1823 Mill Rd 58203
Tel (701) 795-7000 *SIC* 2052 2041

RYDELL CO p 1260
2700 S Washington St 58201
Tel (701) 780-1380 *SIC* 5511

STRATA CORP p 1392
1600 N 48th St 58203
Tel (701) 775-4205
SIC 1611 3273 1442 5032

UNIVERSITY OF NORTH DAKOTA p 1524
264 Centennial Dr 58202
Tel (701) 777-2015 *SIC* 8221

HANKINSON, ND

■ HANKINSON RENEWABLE ENERGY LLC p 658
9230 County Road 1 58041
Tel (701) 242-9420 *SIC* 2869

JAMESTOWN, ND

CAVENDISH FARMS INC p 267
5855 3rd St Se 58401
Tel (701) 252-5222 *SIC* 5142 2099

MANDAN, ND

CLOVERDALE FOODS CO p 328
3015 34th St Nw 58554
Tel (701) 663-9511 *SIC* 2013 5147

MISSOURI VALLEY PETROLEUM INC p 976
1722 Mandan Ave 58554
Tel (701) 663-5091 *SIC* 5172 3443

MINOT, ND

APPLE CORE ENTERPRISES INC p 98
1400 31st Ave Sw 58701
Tel (701) 838-2822 *SIC* 5812

CENTRAL POWER ELECTRIC COOPERATIVE INC p 280
525 20th Ave Sw 58701
Tel (701) 852-4407 *SIC* 4911

FARSTAD OIL INC p 530
100 27th St Ne 58703
Tel (701) 852-1194 *SIC* 5172

INVESTORS REAL ESTATE TRUST p 761
1400 31st Ave Sw Ste 60 58701
Tel (701) 837-4738 *SIC* 6798

MINOT PUBLIC SCHOOLS p 974
215 2nd St Se 58701
Tel (701) 420-7503 *SIC* 8211

SPF ENERGY INC p 1358
100 27th St Ne 58703
Tel (701) 852-1194 *SIC* 5541 5411

SUPERPUMPER INC p 1407
100 27th St Ne 58703
Tel (701) 852-0061 *SIC* 5541 5411

TRINITY HEALTH p 1481
1 Burdick Expy W 58701
Tel (701) 857-5260 *SIC* 8011 8051 8062

WESTLIE MOTOR CO p 1601
500 S Broadway 58701
Tel (701) 852-1354 *SIC* 7513 5511

NECHE, ND

NORTHDALE OIL INC p 1054
448 Main Ave 58265
Tel (218) 773-4345 *SIC* 5171

NEW TOWN, ND

UNITED PRAIRIE COOPERATIVE p 1511
307 Main St 58763
Tel (701) 627-3636 *SIC* 5191

PEMBINA, ND

MOTOR COACH INDUSTRIES INC p 992
552 W Stutsman St 58271
Tel (701) 825-6234 *SIC* 3711

RICHARDTON, ND

RED TRAIL ENERGY LLC p 1216
3682 Highway 8 58652
Tel (701) 974-3308 *SIC* 2869 2085

STANLEY, ND

FARMERS UNION OIL CO OF STANLEY p 530
8149 Highway 2 58784
Tel (701) 628-2322
SIC 5172 5251 5541 5411

TAYLOR, ND

CHS INC p 304
3645 98th Ave Sw 58656
Tel (701) 483-6781 *SIC* 5153 5191

UNDERWOOD, ND

■ FALKIRK MINING CO p 526
2801 1st St Sw 58576
Tel (701) 442-5751 *SIC* 1221

WAHPETON, ND

MINN-DAK FARMERS COOPERATIVE INC p 973
7525 Red River Rd 58075
Tel (701) 642-8411 *SIC* 2099

■ PRIMEWOOD INC p 1175
2217 9th St N 58075
Tel (701) 642-2727 *SIC* 2434 2431

WATFORD CITY, ND

■ BADLANDS POWER FUELS LLC p 144
3711 4th Ave Ne 58854
Tel (701) 842-3618 *SIC* 2869

FIRST INTERNATIONAL BANK AND TRUST p 547
100 N Main St 58854
Tel (701) 232-1700 *SIC* 6022

MCKENZIE ELECTRIC COOPERATIVE INC p 930
908 4th Ave Ne 58854
Tel (701) 842-2311 *SIC* 4911

WEST FARGO, ND

CLARK EQUIPMENT CO p 322
250 E Beaton Dr 58078
Tel (701) 241-8700 *SIC* 3599 3531

E W WYLIE CORP p 467
1520 2nd Ave Nw 58078
Tel (701) 277-7540 *SIC* 4213

GATEWAY BUILDING SYSTEMS INC p 593
2138 Main Ave W 58078
Tel (701) 293-7202 *SIC* 1542 5083

INDUSTRIAL BUILDERS INC p 739
1307 County Road 17 N 58078
Tel (701) 282-4977
SIC 1629 1622 1542 1611 1623

SERVICE OIL INC p 1307
1718 Main Ave E 58078
Tel (701) 277-1050 *SIC* 5541 5411

▲ TITAN MACHINERY INC p 1456
644 E Beaton Dr 58078
Tel (701) 356-0130 *SIC* 5251 5082

TRUENORTH STEEL INC p 1486
702 13th Ave E 58078
Tel (701) 373-7781 *SIC* 3443 3444 3441

■ WANZEK CONSTRUCTION INC p 1575
2028 2nd Ave Nw 58078
Tel (701) 282-6171
SIC 1542 1623 1622 1799 1541 1629

WEST FARGO SCHOOL DISTRICT 6 p 1594
207 Main Ave W 58078
Tel (701) 356-2000 *SIC* 8211

WILLISTON, ND

HORIZON RESOURCES p 707
317 2nd St W 58801
Tel (701) 572-2171
SIC 5172 5541 5411 5191

MOUNTRAIL-WILLIAMS ELECTRIC COOPERATIVE p 994
218 58th St W 58801
Tel (701) 577-3765 *SIC* 4911

OHIO

ADA, OH

OHIO NORTHERN UNIVERSITY p 1078
525 S Main St Unit 1 45810
Tel (419) 772-2000 *SIC* 8221

AKRON, OH

ACTIONLINK LLC p 19
2279 Romig Rd 44320
Tel (888) 737-8757 *SIC* 8748

AIRBORN ELECTRONICS INC p 39
2230 Picton Pkwy 44312
Tel (330) 245-2630 *SIC* 5065

AKROCHEM CORP p 42
3770 Embassy Pkwy 44333
Tel (330) 535-2100 *SIC* 5169

AKRON CITY HOSPITAL INC p 42
525 E Market St 44304
Tel (330) 253-5046 *SIC* 8062

■ AKRON COCA-COLA BOTTLING CO p 42
1560 Triplett Blvd 44306
Tel (330) 784-2653 *SIC* 5149

AKRON GENERAL HEALTH SYSTEM p 42
1 Akron General Ave 44307
Tel (330) 344-6000 *SIC* 8741

AKRON GENERAL MEDICAL CENTER INC p 42
1 Akron General Ave 44307
Tel (330) 344-6000
SIC 8062 8011 8322 8221

AKRON PUBLIC SCHOOLS p 42
70 N Broadway St 44308
Tel (330) 761-1661 *SIC* 8211

BRIDGESTONE PROCUREMENT HOLDINGS USA INC p 211
381 W Wilbeth Rd 44301
Tel (337) 882-1200 *SIC* 2822

BRIDGESTONE RESEARCH LLC p 211
1655 S Main St 44301
Tel (330) 379-7570 *SIC* 8731

CHESTNUT HOLDINGS INC p 295
670 W Market St 44303
Tel (330) 849-6503
SIC 3053 5014 5013 3714

CHILDRENS HOSPITAL MEDICAL CENTER OF AKRON p 299
1 Perkins Sq 44308
Tel (330) 543-1000 *SIC* 8069

CITY OF AKRON p 312
166 S High St Rm 502 44308
Tel (330) 375-2720 *SIC* 9111

■ CLEVELAND ELECTRIC ILLUMINATING CO p 325
76 S Main St 44308
Tel (800) 589-3101 *SIC* 4911

COUNTRY PURE FOODS INC p 375
681 W Waterloo Rd 44314
Tel (330) 753-2293 *SIC* 2033 2037 2086

COUNTY OF SUMMIT p 382
650 Dan St 44310
Tel (330) 643-2500 *SIC* 9111

FAMOUS DISTRIBUTION INC p 527
2620 Ridgewood Rd Ste 200 44313
Tel (330) 762-9621
SIC 5074 5075 5085 5023

FAMOUS ENTERPRISES INC p 527
2620 Ridgewood Rd Ste 200 44313
Tel (330) 762-9621
SIC 5075 5031 5074 7699

FAMOUS INDUSTRIES INC p 527
2620 Ridgewood Rd Ste 200 44313
Tel (330) 535-1811 *SIC* 5074 3444 5065

FIRESTONE POLYMERS LLC p 544
381 W Wilbeth Rd 44301
Tel (330) 379-7000 *SIC* 3069

▲ FIRSTENERGY CORP p 550
76 S Main St Bsmt 44308
Tel (800) 736-3402 *SIC* 4911

■ FIRSTENERGY GENERATION LLC p 550
76 S Main St 44308
Tel (800) 633-4766 *SIC* 4911

■ FIRSTENERGY NUCLEAR OPERATING CO p 550
76 S Main St Bsmt 44308
Tel (800) 646-0400 *SIC* 4911

■ FIRSTENERGY SOLUTIONS CORP p 550
76 S Main St Bsmt 44308
Tel (800) 736-3402 *SIC* 4911

FIRSTMERIT BANK NATIONAL ASSOCIATION p 551
106 S Main St Fl 5 44308
Tel (330) 384-7201 *SIC* 6021

FIRSTMERIT CORP p 551
Iii Cascade Plz Fl 7 44308
Tel (330) 996-6300 *SIC* 6021

FRED W ALBRECHT GROCERY CO p 576
2700 Gilchrist Rd Ste A 44305
Tel (330) 733-2861 *SIC* 5411

GLAUS PYLE SCHOMER BURNS & DEHAVEN INC p 614
520 S Main St Ste 2531 44311
Tel (330) 572-2100 *SIC* 8711 8712

GOJO INDUSTRIES INC p 620
1 Gojo Plz Ste 500 44311
Tel (330) 255-6000 *SIC* 2842 3586 2844

▲ GOODYEAR TIRE & RUBBER CO p 625
200 E Innovation Way 44316
Tel (330) 796-2121
SIC 3011 3052 7534 7538 7539 5013

HARWICK STANDARD DISTRIBUTION CORP p 667
60 S Seiberling St 44305
Tel (330) 798-9300 *SIC* 5169

HASCO MEDICAL INC p 667
810 Moe Dr 44310
Tel (214) 302-0930 *SIC* 5999 8082

HEIDMAN INC p 680
500 Grant St 44311
Tel (330) 535-8400 *SIC* 5812

HOLLAND OIL CO p 700
1485 Marion Ave 44313
Tel (330) 835-1815 *SIC* 5541 5172 5411

HYGENIC CORP p 723
1245 Home Ave 44310
Tel (330) 633-8460 *SIC* 3069 3061

INFOCISION MANAGEMENT CORP p 741
325 Springside Dr 44333
Tel (330) 668-1400 *SIC* 7389

■ JERSEY CENTRAL POWER & LIGHT CO p 783
76 S Main St 44308
Tel (800) 736-3402 *SIC* 4911

KENMORE CONSTRUCTION CO INC p 810
700 Home Ave 44310
Tel (330) 762-8936 *SIC* 1611 5032

MATURE SERVICES INC p 921
415 S Portage Path 44320
Tel (330) 253-4597 *SIC* 8322

MEGGITT AIRCRAFT BRAKING SYSTEMS CORP p 940
1204 Massillon Rd 44306
Tel (330) 796-4400 *SIC* 3728

■ METROPOLITAN EDISON CO p 955
76 S Main St 44308
Tel (800) 736-3402 *SIC* 4911

▲ MYERS INDUSTRIES INC p 1004
1293 S Main St 44301
Tel (330) 253-5592
SIC 3089 3086 3069 3052 5013 5014

■ MYERS TIRE SUPPLY DISTRIBUTION INC p 1004
1293 S Main St 44301
Tel (330) 253-5592 *SIC* 5531

NATURAL COUNTRY FARMS INC p 1018
681 W Waterloo Rd 44314
Tel (330) 753-2293 *SIC* 2033 2037 2086

■ OHIO EDISON CO p 1077
76 S Main St Bsmt 44308
Tel (800) 736-3402 *SIC* 4911

ORIANA HOUSE INC p 1094
885 E Buchtel Ave 44305
Tel (330) 535-8116 *SIC* 8322 9111

■ PENNSYLVANIA ELECTRIC CO p 1130
76 S Main St Bsmt 44308
Tel (800) 545-7741 *SIC* 4911

■ PENNSYLVANIA POWER CO INC p 1130
76 S Main St Bsmt 44308
Tel (800) 720-3600 *SIC* 4911

PHYSICIANS WEIGHT LOSS CENTERS OF AMERICA INC p 1146
395 Springside Dr 44333
Tel (330) 666-7952 *SIC* 5141 5122 6794

QUALITY MOLD INC p 1197
2200 Massillon Rd 44312
Tel (330) 645-6653 *SIC* 3544

RIVER VALLEY PAPER CO p 1237
120 E Mill St Ste 337 44308
Tel (330) 535-1001 *SIC* 5113

SUMMA HEALTH SYSTEM p 1398
95 Arch St Ste G50 44304
Tel (330) 375-3000 *SIC* 8062

SUMMA INSURANCE CO INC p 1398
10 N Main St 44308
Tel (800) 996-8411 *SIC* 6321 6311

■ TOLEDO EDISON CO p 1458
76 S Main St Bsmt 44308
Tel (800) 447-3333 *SIC* 4911

UNIVERSITY OF AKRON p 1519
302 Buchtel Mall 44325
Tel (330) 972-7111 *SIC* 8221

VAN DEVERE INC p 1542
300 W Market St 44303
Tel (330) 253-6137 *SIC* 5511 7515

ALLIANCE, OH

ALLIANCE CITIZENS HEALTH ASSOCIATION p 54
200 E State St 44601
Tel (330) 596-6000 *SIC* 8062

ALLIANCE COMMUNITY HOSPITAL p 54
200 E State St 44601
Tel (330) 596-6000 *SIC* 8062

ALLIANCE TOWERS LLC p 55
350 S Arch Ave Apt 106 44601
Tel (330) 823-1063 *SIC* 6513

MAC MANUFACTURING INC p 891
14599 Commerce St Ne 44601
Tel (330) 823-9900 *SIC* 3715 5012

MAC TRAILER MANUFACTURING INC p 891
14599 Commerce St Ne 44601
Tel (330) 823-9900
SIC 3715 5012 5013 5015 7539

AMELIA, OH

■ **AMERICAN MODERN HOME INSURANCE CO** p 76
7000 Midland Blvd 45102
Tel (513) 943-7100 *SIC* 6331

■ **AMERICAN MODERN INSURANCE GROUP INC** p 76
7000 Midland Blvd 45102
Tel (513) 943-7100 *SIC* 6411 6321

■ **MIDLAND CO** p 965
7000 Midland Blvd 45102
Tel (513) 947-5503 *SIC* 6331 4449

■ **MIDLAND-GUARDIAN CO** p 966
7000 Midland Blvd 45102
Tel (513) 943-7100 *SIC* 6311 6331

ARCHBOLD, OH

MBC HOLDINGS INC p 925
1613 S Defiance St 43502
Tel (419) 445-1015 *SIC* 1622 1611

SAUDER MANUFACTURING CO p 1283
930 W Barre Rd 43502
Tel (419) 445-7670 *SIC* 2531

SAUDER WOODWORKING CO p 1283
502 Middle St 43502
Tel (419) 446-3828 *SIC* 2519 5021

ASHLAND, OH

BALL BOUNCE AND SPORT INC p 148
1 Hedstrom Dr 44805
Tel (419) 759-3838 *SIC* 5092 5091 3089

■ **CHARLES RIVER LABORATORIES ASHLAND LLC** p 289
1407 George Rd 44805
Tel (419) 282-8700 *SIC* 8733

■ **CRL SAFETY ASSESSMENT INC** p 393
1407 George Rd 44805
Tel (419) 952-0553 *SIC* 8734

PENTAIR FLOW TECHNOLOGIES LLC p 1132
1101 Myers Pkwy 44805
Tel (419) 289-1144 *SIC* 3561

TOWN AND COUNTRY CO-OP INC p 1464
813 Clark Ave 44805
Tel (419) 281-2153 *SIC* 5541 5261 5999

ZANESVILLE COMMUNITY SCHOOL p 1641
401 College Ave 44805
Tel (419) 289-5125 *SIC* 8221

ASHTABULA, OH

ASHTABULA COUNTY MEDICAL CENTER p 117
2420 Lake Ave 44004
Tel (440) 997-2262 *SIC* 8062

MOLDED FIBER GLASS COMPANIES p 982
2925 Mfg Pl 44004
Tel (440) 997-5851 *SIC* 3089

ASHVILLE, OH

COLUMBUS INDUSTRIES INC p 342
2938 State Route 752 43103
Tel (740) 983-2552 *SIC* 3569

ATHENS, OH

OHIO UNIVERSITY p 1078
1 Ohio University 45701
Tel (740) 593-1000 *SIC* 8221

OHIO UNIVERSITY FOUNDATION p 1078
Hdl Center Ste 218 Rm 168 45701
Tel (740) 593-1901 *SIC* 7389

SHELTERING ARMS HOSPITAL FOUNDATION INC p 1315
55 Hospital Dr 45701
Tel (740) 592-9300 *SIC* 8062

AURORA, OH

PARTSSOURCE INC p 1119
777 Lena Dr 44202
Tel (330) 562-9900 *SIC* 5047

ROVISYS CO p 1253
1455 Danner Dr 44202
Tel (330) 562-8600 *SIC* 8711

TECHNICAL CONSUMER PRODUCTS INC p 1431
325 Campus Dr 44202
Tel (800) 324-1496 *SIC* 5063

AVON LAKE, OH

MEXICHEM SPECIALTY RESINS INC p 957
33653 Walker Rd 44012
Tel (440) 930-1435 *SIC* 2822 2821

▲ **POLYONE CORP** p 1160
33587 Walker Rd 44012
Tel (440) 930-1000
SIC 2821 3087 5162 3081

AVON, OH

A J ROSE MFG CO p 5
38000 Chester Rd 44011
Tel (216) 631-4645 *SIC* 3465 3568 3469

FREEMAN MANUFACTURING & SUPPLY CO p 577
1101 Moore Rd 44011
Tel (440) 934-1902
SIC 5084 3087 3543 2821

JENNE INC p 782
33665 Chester Rd 44011
Tel (440) 835-0040 *SIC* 7371 7382

MAROON GROUP LLC p 910
1390 Jaycox Rd 44011
Tel (440) 937-1000 *SIC* 5169

SHURTECH BRANDS LLC p 1319
32150 Just Imagine Dr 44011
Tel (440) 937-7000 *SIC* 2671

BARBERTON, OH

ARIS HORTICULTURE INC p 108
115 3rd St Se 44203
Tel (330) 745-2143 *SIC* 0181

■ **BABCOCK & WILCOX CO** p 143
20 S Van Buren Ave 44203
Tel (330) 753-4511
SIC 1629 1711 3443 7699 8741 3822

■ **BABCOCK & WILCOX CONSTRUCTION CO INC** p 143
74 Robinson Ave 44203
Tel (330) 860-6301 *SIC* 1629

CHRISTIAN HEALTHCARE MINISTRIES INC p 302
127 Hazelwood Ave 44203
Tel (330) 848-1511 *SIC* 8011

CHRISTIAN HEALTHCARE MINISTRIES INC p 302
127 Hazelwood Ave 44203
Tel (800) 791-6225 *SIC* 8661

PREFERRED COMPOUNDING CORP p 1169
1020 Lambert St 44203
Tel (330) 798-4790 *SIC* 3069

■ **S A COMUNALE CO INC** p 1261
2900 Newpark Dr 44203
Tel (330) 706-3040 *SIC* 1711

SUMMA BARBERTON CITIZENS HOSPITAL p 1398
155 5th St Ne 44203
Tel (330) 615-3000 *SIC* 8062

BATAVIA, OH

COUNTY OF CLERMONT p 377
177 E Main St 45103
Tel (513) 732-7980 *SIC* 9111

MI 2009 INC p 959
4165 Half Acre Rd 45103
Tel (513) 536-2000 *SIC* 3559

■ **MILACRON MARKETING CO LLC** p 968
4165 Half Acre Rd 45103
Tel (513) 536-2000 *SIC* 3541

■ **MILACRON PLASTICS TECHNOLOGIES GROUP LLC** p 968
4165 Half Acre Rd 45103
Tel (513) 536-2000 *SIC* 3544

▲ **MULTI-COLOR CORP** p 999
4053 Clough Woods Dr 45103
Tel (513) 381-1480 *SIC* 2759 2679 2672

SISTERS OF MERCY OF CLERMONT COUNTY OHIO INC p 1327
3000 Hospital Dr 45103
Tel (513) 732-8200 *SIC* 8062 8011

BEACHWOOD, OH

ALERIS INTERNATIONAL INC p 48
25825 Science Park Dr # 400 44122
Tel (216) 910-3400 *SIC* 3355 3354

ALERIS ROLLED PRODUCTS INC p 48
25825 Science Park Dr # 400 44122
Tel (216) 910-3400 *SIC* 3341

▲ **DDR CORP** p 419
3300 Enterprise Pkwy 44122
Tel (216) 755-5500 *SIC* 6798

EZRA HEALTH CARE INC p 522
23258 Fernwood Dr 44122
Tel (440) 498-3000 *SIC* 8051

KIRTLAND CAPITAL PARTNERS LP p 822
3201 Entp Pkwy Ste 200 44122
Tel (216) 593-0100
SIC 5051 3312 3498 3494 3492 3317

MCM CAPITAL PARTNERS p 932
25201 Chagrin Blvd # 360 44122
Tel (216) 514-1840 *SIC* 6211

NICHOLS ALUMINUM LLC p 1042
25825 Science Park Dr # 400 44122
Tel (216) 910-3400 *SIC* 3355 3354

OHIO VALLEY RESOURCES INC p 1078
29325 Chagrin Blvd # 300 44122
Tel (216) 765-1240 *SIC* 1241

▲ **OMNOVA SOLUTIONS INC** p 1085
25435 Harvard Rd 44122
Tel (216) 682-7000
SIC 2819 2211 3069 3081

■ **PCC AIRFOILS LLC** p 1123
3401 Entp Pkwy Ste 200 44122
Tel (216) 831-3590 *SIC* 3369

■ **REAL ALLOY HOLDING INC** p 1213
3700 Park East Dr Ste 300 44122
Tel (216) 755-8800 *SIC* 3341 3313 3334

■ **REAL ALLOY RECYCLING INC** p 1213
3700 Park East Dr Ste 300 44122
Tel (216) 755-8900 *SIC* 3341

■ **REAL ALLOY SPECIALTY PRODUCTS INC** p 1213
3700 Park East Dr Ste 300 44122
Tel (216) 755-8836 *SIC* 3355

■ **TREMCO INC** p 1476
3735 Green Rd 44122
Tel (216) 292-5000
SIC 2891 2952 1761 1752 2851 2842

BEAVERCREEK, OH

DRS ICAS LLC p 457
2601 Mission Point Blvd 45431
Tel (937) 429-7408 *SIC* 3812

MACAULAY-BROWN INC p 891
4021 Executive Dr 45430
Tel (937) 426-3421 *SIC* 8711 8733

WOOLPERT INC p 1624
4454 Idea Center Blvd 45430
Tel (937) 461-5660 *SIC* 8711

WRIGHT-PATT CREDIT UNION INC p 1627
3560 Pentagon Blvd 45431
Tel (937) 912-7000 *SIC* 6062

WRIGHT-PATT FINANCIAL GROUP LTD p 1627
2455 Presidential Dr 45324
Tel (937) 912-7000 *SIC* 7389

BEDFORD HEIGHTS, OH

AMERICAN SPRING WIRE CORP p 79
26300 Miles Rd 44146
Tel (216) 292-4620
SIC 3272 3315 3316 3339 3624

BEDFORD, OH

BEN VENUE LABORATORIES INC p 172
300 Northfield Rd 44146
Tel (800) 989-3320 *SIC* 2834

DAVES SUPERMARKET INC p 415
5300 Richmond Rd 44146
Tel (216) 361-5130 *SIC* 5411

BELLBROOK, OH

HEALTH CARE INDUSTRIES CORP p 674
4195 Sugarcreek Dr 45305
Tel (937) 848-2973 *SIC* 8051 8052

BELLEFONTAINE, OH

ACUSPORT CORP p 20
1 Hunter Pl 43311
Tel (937) 593-7010 *SIC* 5091

MARY RUTAN HOSPITAL p 914
205 E Palmer Rd 43311
Tel (937) 592-4015 *SIC* 8062

BELMONT, OH

STINGRAY ENERGY SERVICES p 1390
42739 National Rd 43718
Tel (405) 648-4177 *SIC* 1389

BEREA, OH

BALDWIN WALLACE UNIVERSITY p 147
275 Eastland Rd 44017
Tel (440) 826-2900 *SIC* 8221

OHIO TURNPIKE AND INFRASTRUCTURE COMMISSION p 1078
682 Prospect St 44017
Tel (440) 234-2081 *SIC* 4785

OHIOGUIDESTONE p 1078
434 Eastland Rd 44017
Tel (440) 234-2006
SIC 8322 8361 8351 8051

STANDBY SCREW MACHINE PRODUCTS CO p 1376
1122 W Bagley Rd 44017
Tel (440) 243-8200 *SIC* 3451

BERLIN, OH

CHRISTIAN AID MINISTRIES p 302
4464 State Rte 39 E 44610
Tel (330) 893-2428 *SIC* 8661 5999 5947

BEVERLY, OH

APPALACHIAN RESPITE CARE LTD p 98
501 Pinecrest Dr 45715
Tel (740) 984-4262 *SIC* 8051

BLACKLICK, OH

ATRIUM BUYING CORP p 129
1010 Jackson Hole Dr # 100 43004
Tel (740) 966-8200 *SIC* 5137

EDUCATION UNLIMITED OF OHIO INC p 479
8216 Kennedy Rd 43004
Tel (614) 451-1309 *SIC* 8211

BLUE ASH, OH

▲ **ADVANCEPIERRE FOODS HOLDINGS INC** p 26
9987 Carver Rd 45242
Tel (800) 969-2747 *SIC* 2099 2013

■ **ADVANCEPIERRE FOODS INC** p 26
9987 Carver Rd Ste 500 45242
Tel (513) 874-8741 *SIC* 2013 2015

BELCAN ENGINEERING GROUP LLC p 169
10200 Anderson Way 45242
Tel (513) 891-0972 *SIC* 8711

BELCAN LLC p 169
10200 Anderson Way 45242
Tel (513) 891-0972 *SIC* 7363 8711

BELCAN SERVICES GROUP LIMITED PARTNERSHIP p 169
10200 Anderson Way 45242
Tel (513) 891-0972 *SIC* 7363

BERENFIELD CONTAINERS INC p 174
4555 Lake Forest Dr # 205 45242
Tel (513) 618-3780 *SIC* 3412 2655

BEVERAGES HOLDINGS LLC p 178
10300 Alliance Rd Ste 500 45242
Tel (513) 483-3300 *SIC* 2086 2037

CANDLE-LITE CO LLC p 247
10521 Millington Ct Ste B 45242
Tel (513) 563-1113 *SIC* 3999

DUGAN & MEYERS CONSTRUCTION CO p 460
11110 Kenwood Rd 45242
Tel (513) 891-4300 *SIC* 1541 1542 1522

DUGAN & MEYERS INTERESTS INC p 460
11110 Kenwood Rd 45242
Tel (513) 891-4300 *SIC* 1541 1542 1522

EMPIRE MARKETING STRATEGIES INC p 493
11243 Cornell Park Dr 45242
Tel (513) 793-6241 *SIC* 5141

EQUIPMENT DEPOT OHIO INC p 506
4331 Rossplain Dr 45236
Tel (513) 891-0600 *SIC* 5084

■ **ETHICON ENDO-SURGERY INC** p 511
4545 Creek Rd 45242
Tel (513) 337-7000 *SIC* 3841

F+W MEDIA INC p 523
10151 Carver Rd Ste 200 45242
Tel (513) 531-2690 *SIC* 2731 2721

■ **FECHHEIMER BROTHERS CO** p 533
4545 Malsbary Rd 45242
Tel (513) 793-7819
SIC 2311 2337 2339 5699

FEINTOOL US OPERATIONS INC p 537
11280 Cornell Park Dr 45242
Tel (513) 247-0110 *SIC* 3469 3465

FOOD FOLKS & FUN INC p 564
4354 Glendale Milford Rd 45242
Tel (513) 769-4386 *SIC* 5812

■ **HAMILTON MUTUAL INSURANCE CO** p 655
11311 Cornell Park Dr # 500 45242
Tel (513) 221-6010 *SIC* 6331

▲ **LSI INDUSTRIES INC** p 883
10000 Alliance Rd 45242
Tel (513) 793-3200 *SIC* 3648 3993 3663

LUMINEX HOME DECOR & FRAGRANCE HOLDING CORP p 885
10521 Millington Ct 45242
Tel (513) 563-1113 *SIC* 5023 2844

MATTHEW 25 MINISTRIES INC p 920
11060 Kenwood Rd 45242
Tel (513) 793-6256 *SIC* 8399

▲ **MILACRON HOLDINGS CORP** p 968
10200 Alliance Rd Ste 200 45242
Tel (513) 487-5000 *SIC* 3544

■ **MILACRON LLC** p 968
10200 Alliance Rd Ste 200 45242
Tel (513) 487-5000 *SIC* 3549 2899

NIGHTINGALE HOLDINGS LLC p 1043
4700 Ashwood Dr Ste 200 45241
Tel (513) 489-7100 *SIC* 8051

OMYA INC p 1085
9987 Carver Rd Ste 300 45242
Tel (513) 387-4600 *SIC* 2819

OMYA INDUSTRIES INC p 1085
9987 Carver Rd Ste 300 45242
Tel (513) 387-4600 *SIC* 1422

RELADYNE I LLC p 1221
9395 Kenwood Rd Ste 104 45242
Tel (513) 489-6000 *SIC* 5171 5172

RELADYNE INC p 1221
9395 Kenwood Rd Ste 104 45242
Tel (513) 489-6000 *SIC* 2992

REQ/JQH HOLDINGS INC p 1226
4243 Hunt Rd Ste 2 45242
Tel (513) 891-1066 *SIC* 8741 6552

RIGHT HUMAN RESOURCE CONSULTANTS INC p 1234
4445 Lake Forest Dr # 470 45242
Tel (513) 733-1313 *SIC* 8742 7361

■ **SHRED-IT US JV LLC** p 1319
11311 Cornell Park Dr # 125 45242
Tel (513) 245-8659 *SIC* 7389

■ **SHRED-IT USA LLC** p 1319
11311 Cornell Park Dr # 125 45242
Tel (513) 699-0845 *SIC* 3589

SUNNY DELIGHT BEVERAGE CO p 1403
10300 Alliance Rd Ste 500 45242
Tel (513) 483-3300 *SIC* 2086

TRUSTAFF MANAGEMENT INC p 1487
4675 Cornell Rd 45241
Tel (513) 272-3999 *SIC* 8741

VIUS SERVICES CORP p 1563
9395 Kenwood Rd Ste 200 45242
Tel (513) 731-3590 *SIC* 7349 8741 3714

WORNICK CO p 1626
4700 Creek Rd 45242
Tel (800) 860-4555 *SIC* 2032

WORNICK HOLDING CO INC p 1626
4700 Creek Rd 45242
Tel (513) 794-9800 *SIC* 2032

BLUFFTON, OH

DTR INDUSTRIES INC p 458
320 Snider Rd 45817
Tel (419) 358-2121
SIC 3052 3069 3829 3714

GROB SYSTEMS INC p 641
1070 Navajo Dr 45817
Tel (419) 358-9015 *SIC* 3535 7699

BOARDMAN, OH

ST ELIZABETH BOARDMAN HEALTH CENTER p 1366
8401 Market St 44512
Tel (330) 729-4580 *SIC* 8099 8062

BOTKINS, OH

KOENIG EQUIPMENT INC p 826
15213 State Route 274 45306
Tel (937) 693-5000 *SIC* 5999 0782

BOWLING GREEN, OH

ARGO-HYTOS INC p 107
1835 N Research Dr 43402
Tel (419) 353-6070 *SIC* 5084

BETCO CORP p 177
400 Van Camp Rd 43402
Tel (419) 241-2156 *SIC* 6719

BOWLING GREEN STATE UNIVERSITY p 204
110 Mcfall Ctr 43403
Tel (419) 372-2311 *SIC* 8221

PRINCIPLE BUSINESS ENTERPRISES INC p 1177
20189 Pine Lake Rd 43402
Tel (419) 352-1551 *SIC* 2676 3142

WOOD COUNTY HOSPITAL ASSOC p 1622
960 W Wooster St 43402
Tel (419) 354-8900 *SIC* 8062

WOOD COUNTY OHIO p 1622
1 Court House Sq 43402
Tel (419) 354-9100 *SIC* 9111

BRECKSVILLE, OH

EFG HOLDINGS INC p 480
10217 Brecksville Rd 44141
Tel (812) 717-2544 *SIC* 3452

ELGIN FASTENER GROUP LLC p 486
10217 Brecksville Rd 44141
Tel (812) 717-2544 *SIC* 3399 3452

HOUSE OF LA ROSE CLEVELAND INC p 711
6745 Southpointe Pkwy 44141
Tel (440) 746-7500 *SIC* 5181

INDUSTRIAL MANUFACTURING CO LLC p 740
8223 Brecksville Rd Ste 1 44141
Tel (440) 838-4700 *SIC* 2542 3728 3566

■ **LUBRIZOL ADVANCED MATERIALS INC** p 884
9911 Brecksville Rd 44141
Tel (216) 447-5000
SIC 2899 2891 3088 2834 3629

TRUE NORTH ENERGY LLC p 1486
10346 Brecksville Rd 44141
Tel (877) 245-9336 *SIC* 5541 5172

BREWSTER, OH

BREWSTER CHEESE CO p 210
800 Wabash Ave S 44613
Tel (330) 767-3492 *SIC* 2022

WHEELING & LAKE ERIE RAILWAY CO p 1605
100 1st St Se 44613
Tel (330) 767-3401 *SIC* 4011

WHEELING CORP p 1605
100 1st St Se 44613
Tel (330) 767-3401 *SIC* 1629 4011

BROADVIEW HEIGHTS, OH

OHIO MACHINERY CO p 1077
3993 E Royalton Rd 44147
Tel (440) 526-6200
SIC 7513 6159 7699 5082 7353

BROOKLYN HEIGHTS, OH

TOWLIFT INC p 1464
1395 Valley Belt Rd 44131
Tel (216) 749-6800 *SIC* 5084 7699 7359

BROOKLYN, OH

VICTORY CAPITAL MANAGEMENT INC p 1555
4900 Tiedeman Rd Fl 4 44144
Tel (216) 898-2400 *SIC* 6282

BROOKPARK, OH

J & R ASSOCIATES p 770
14803 Holland Rd 44142
Tel (440) 250-4080 *SIC* 1542 8361 6514

BROOKVILLE, OH

GREEN TOKAI CO LTD p 637
55 Robert Wright Dr 45309
Tel (937) 833-5444 *SIC* 3714 3069

PROVIMI NORTH AMERICA INC p 1186
10 Collective Way 45309
Tel (937) 770-2400 *SIC* 2048 5191

BRUNSWICK, OH

MACK INDUSTRIES INC p 892
1321 Industrial Pkwy N # 500 44212
Tel (330) 460-7005 *SIC* 3272 1771

TURF CARE SUPPLY CORP p 1492
50 Pearl Rd Ste 200 44212
Tel (877) 220-1014 *SIC* 2873

BUCYRUS, OH

OHIO MUTUAL INSURANCE CO p 1077
1725 Hopley Ave 44820
Tel (419) 562-3011 *SIC* 6411 6331

BURTON, OH

BFG SUPPLY CO LLC p 179
14500 Kinsman Rd 44021
Tel (440) 834-1883 *SIC* 5191 5261

HEXPOL COMPOUNDING LLC p 688
14330 Kinsman Rd 44021
Tel (440) 834-4644 *SIC* 3087 2821

HEXPOL HOLDING INC p 688
14330 Kinsman Rd 44021
Tel (440) 834-4644 *SIC* 6719

BYESVILLE, OH

DETROIT DIESEL REMANUFACTURING-EAST INC p 433
60703 Country Club Rd 43723
Tel (740) 439-7701 *SIC* 3519

CAMBRIDGE, OH

HARTLEY CO p 666
319 Wheeling Ave 43725
Tel (740) 432-2328 *SIC* 5541 5172

SOUTHEASTERN OHIO REGIONAL MEDICAL CENTER p 1346
1341 Clark St 43725
Tel (740) 439-3561 *SIC* 8062

CANAL FULTON, OH

AVALON FOODSERVICE INC p 135
1 Avalon Dr 44614
Tel (330) 854-4551
SIC 5142 5149 5169 5113 8322 5812

CANAL WINCHESTER, OH

HFI LLC p 689
59 Gender Rd 43110
Tel (614) 491-0700
SIC 2396 2821 3714 3429 3086

NIFCO AMERICA CORP p 1043
8015 Dove Pkwy 43110
Tel (614) 920-6800 *SIC* 3089

TS TRIM INDUSTRIES INC p 1489
6380 Canal St 43110
Tel (614) 837-4114
SIC 5013 3465 3714 3083

CANFIELD, OH

AGLAND CO-OP INC p 35
364 Lisbon St 44406
Tel (330) 533-5551 *SIC* 5153

CANTON, OH

50 X 20 HOLDING CO INC p 3
2715 Wise Ave Nw 44708
Tel (330) 478-4500 *SIC* 1521

AULTCARE CORP p 131
2600 6th St Sw 44710
Tel (330) 363-6360 *SIC* 6324

AULTCARE INSURANCE CO p 131
2600 6th St Sw 44710
Tel (330) 363-6360 *SIC* 6321

AULTMAN HEALTH FOUNDATION p 131
2600 6th St Sw 44710
Tel (330) 452-9911 *SIC* 8011

AULTMAN HOSPITAL p 131
2600 6th St Sw 44710
Tel (330) 452-9911 *SIC* 8062 8069 8221

BEAVER EXCAVATING CO p 166
2000 Beaver Place Ave Sw 44706
Tel (330) 478-2151
SIC 1794 1611 1771 1623

BIOTECH MEDICAL INC p 184
7800 Whipple Ave Nw 44767
Tel (330) 494-5504 *SIC* 5047

CANTON CITY SCHOOL DISTRICT p 247
305 Mckinley Ave Nw 44702
Tel (330) 438-2500 *SIC* 8211

CANTON DROP FORGE INC p 247
4575 Southway St Sw 44706
Tel (330) 477-4511
SIC 3462 3463 3356 3312

CITY OF CANTON p 313
218 Cleveland Ave Sw 44702
Tel (330) 438-4300 *SIC* 9111

COLUMBIA-CSA/HS GREATER CANTON AREA HEALTHCARE SYSTEMS LP p 342
1320 Mercy Dr Nw 30 44708
Tel (330) 489-1000 *SIC* 8062

CORDIER GROUP HOLDINGS INC p 369
4575 Southway St Sw 44706
Tel (330) 477-4511 *SIC* 3462

COUNTY OF STARK p 382
110 Central Plz S Ste 240 44702
Tel (330) 451-7371 *SIC* 9111

COUNTY OF STARK p 382
110 Central Plz S Ste 240 44702
Tel (330) 451-7999 *SIC* 9199

DIEBOLD SELF SERVICE SYSTEMS p 438
5995 Mayfair Rd 44720
Tel (330) 490-5099 *SIC* 3578

DLHBOWLES INC p 445
2422 Leo Ave Sw 44706
Tel (330) 478-2503 *SIC* 8711 3089 3082

FISHER FOODS MARKETING INC p 552
4855 Frank Ave Nw 44720
Tel (330) 433-1180 *SIC* 5411 8741

HOSPITALISTS MANAGEMENT GROUP LLC p 710
4535 Dressler Rd Nw 44718
Tel (866) 464-7497 *SIC* 8741

■ **KITCHENAID INC** p 822
101 E Maple St 44720
Tel (330) 499-9200 *SIC* 5064

KOYO BEARINGS NORTH AMERICA LLC p 828
4895 Dressler Rd Nw Ste B 44718
Tel (330) 994-0890 *SIC* 3562

M K MORSE CO p 889
1101 11th St Se 44707
Tel (330) 453-8187 *SIC* 3425

MERCY MEDICAL CENTER INC p 947
1320 Mercy Dr Nw 44708
Tel (330) 489-1000 *SIC* 8062

OHIO GRATINGS INC p 1077
5299 Southway St Sw 44706
Tel (330) 477-6707
SIC 3446 3444 3441 3312

REPUBLIC STEEL INC p 1225
2633 8th St Ne 44704
Tel (330) 438-5435 *SIC* 3312

REPUBLIC STORAGE SYSTEMS LLC p 1226
1038 Belden Ave Ne 44705
Tel (330) 438-5800 *SIC* 2542 3441

STARK TRUSS CO INC p 1379
109 Miles Ave Sw 44710
Tel (330) 478-2100 *SIC* 5031 2439

▲ **TIMKENSTEEL CORP** p 1455
1835 Dueber Ave Sw 44706
Tel (330) 471-7000 *SIC* 3312

UNIVERSAL COMMERCE LLC p 1516
3939 Everhard Rd Nw 44709
Tel (800) 504-8105 *SIC* 5722

CARDINGTON, OH

CARDINGTON YUTAKA TECHNOLOGIES INC p 253
575 W Main St 43315
Tel (419) 864-8777 *SIC* 3714

CAREY, OH

VAUGHN INDUSTRIES LLC p 1545
1201 E Findlay St 43316
Tel (419) 396-3900 *SIC* 1731 1711

CEDARVILLE, OH

CEDARVILLE UNIVERSITY p 272
251 N Main St 45314
Tel (937) 766-7700 *SIC* 8221

CELINA, OH

CELINA ALUMINUM PRECISION TECHNOLOGY INC p 273
7059 Staeger Rd 45822
Tel (419) 586-2278 *SIC* 3592

CELINA MUTUAL INSURANCE CO p 273
1 Insurance Sq 45822
Tel (419) 586-5181 *SIC* 6331

MERCER LANDMARK INC p 944
426 W Market St 45822
Tel (419) 628-3093 *SIC* 5153 5999

MIDWEST LOGISTICS SYSTEMS LTD p 967
7021 State Route 703 45822
Tel (419) 584-1414 *SIC* 4213 4212

CHAGRIN FALLS, OH

TARKETT INC p 1425
16910 Munn Rd 44023
Tel (800) 899-8916 *SIC* 3069

CHARDON, OH

BEST SAND CORP p 177
11830 Ravenna Rd 44024
Tel (440) 285-3132 *SIC* 1446 1442

TECHNISAND INC p 1431
11833 Ravenna Rd 44024
Tel (440) 285-3132 *SIC* 1442

UNIVERSITY HOSPITALS GEAUGA MEDICAL CENTER p 1519
13207 Ravenna Rd 44024
Tel (440) 285-6000 *SIC* 8062

CHESTERLAND, OH

FAIRMOUNT MINERALS LLC p 525
8834 Mayfield Rd Ste A 44026
Tel (269) 926-9450 *SIC* 1446

FAIRMOUNT SANTROL HOLDINGS INC p 525
8834 Mayfield Rd Ste A 44026
Tel (800) 255-7263 *SIC* 1446

FAIRMOUNT SANTROL INC p 525
8834 Mayfield Rd Ste A 44026
Tel (440) 214-3200 *SIC* 2891

HF GROUP LLC p 688
8844 Mayfield Rd 44026
Tel (440) 729-2445 *SIC* 2732

CHILLICOTHE, OH

ADENA HEALTH SYSTEM p 22
272 Hospital Rd 45601
Tel (740) 779-7360 *SIC* 8062

HORIZON TELCOM INC p 707
68 E Main St 45601
Tel (740) 772-8200 *SIC* 4813

■ **KITCHEN COLLECTION LLC** p 822
71 E Water St 45601
Tel (740) 773-9150 *SIC* 5719

CINCINNATI, OH

AAA ALLIED GROUP INC p 7
15 W Central Pkwy 45202
Tel (513) 762-3100 *SIC* 4724 8699

▲ **AGILYSYS INC** p 35
425 Walnut St Ste 1800 45202
Tel (770) 810-7800 *SIC* 5045

ALLIED CASH HOLDINGS LLC p 56
7755 Montgomery Rd # 400 45236
Tel (305) 371-3141 *SIC* 6099

▲ **AMERICAN FINANCIAL GROUP INC** p 72
301 E 4th St 45202
Tel (513) 579-2121 *SIC* 6331 6311 6321

AMPAC HOLDINGS LLC p 86
12025 Tricon Rd 45246
Tel (513) 671-1777
SIC 2673 2677 3081 2674 6719

AMPAC PACKAGING LLC p 86
12025 Tricon Rd 45246
Tel (513) 671-1777 *SIC* 2673

ARCHDIOCESE OF CINCINNATI p 105
100 E 8th St Fl 8 45202
Tel (513) 421-3131 *SIC* 8661 8211

AXCESS FINANCIAL SERVICES INC p 140
7755 Montgomery Rd # 400 45236
Tel (513) 336-7735 *SIC* 6141

BARDES CORP p 155
4730 Madison Rd 45227
Tel (513) 533-6200 *SIC* 3643

BELFLEX STAFFING NETWORK LLC p 169
11591 Goldcoast Dr 45249
Tel (513) 488-8588 *SIC* 7361 7363

BELTING CO OF CINCINNATI p 171
5500 Ridge Ave 45213
Tel (513) 621-9050 *SIC* 5085 5063

BETHESDA HOSPITAL INC p 178
619 Oak St 45206
Tel (513) 569-6100 *SIC* 8062

BETHESDA INC p 178
619 Oak St 7n 45206
Tel (513) 569-6400 *SIC* 8062

■ **BIORX LLC** p 184
7167 E Kemper Rd 45249
Tel (866) 442-4679
SIC 5122 8748 2834 5047 8051

BISTRO MANAGEMENT INC p 185
5803 Mariemont Ave 45227
Tel (513) 271-2349 *SIC* 5812

BUDCO GROUP INC p 223
1100 Gest St 45203
Tel (513) 621-6111 *SIC* 7359

BUFFALO WINGS & RINGS LLC p 224
564 Old State Route 74 # 3 45244
Tel (513) 831-9464 *SIC* 5812

CAROCO INC p 259
8635 Colerain Ave 45251
Tel (513) 385-1244 *SIC* 5812

▲ **CECO ENVIRONMENTAL CORP** p 272
4625 Red Bank Rd Ste 200 45227
Tel (513) 458-2600 *SIC* 3564

■ **CECO GROUP INC** p 272
4625 Red Bank Rd Ste 200 45227
Tel (513) 458-2600
SIC 8711 3564 8734 3443 3444 1761

CHAMPION OPCO LLC p 287
12121 Champion Way 45241
Tel (513) 924-4858 *SIC* 3089 1761 3442

▲ CHEMED CORP p 293
255 E 5th St Ste 2600 45202
Tel (513) 762-6690 *SIC* 8082 1711 7699

CHILDRENS HOSPITAL MEDICAL CENTER p 299
3333 Burnet Ave 45229
Tel (513) 636-4200
SIC 8733 8011 8069 8731

CHILLICOTHE LONG TERM CARE INC p 300
7265 Kenwood Rd Ste 300 45236
Tel (513) 793-8804 *SIC* 8051

CHRIST HOSPITAL p 302
2139 Auburn Ave 45219
Tel (513) 585-2000 *SIC* 8062

■ CIMCOOL INDUSTRIAL PRODUCTS LLC p 307
3000 Disney St 45209
Tel (888) 246-2665 *SIC* 5169

▲ CINCINNATI BELL INC p 307
221 E 4th St Ste 700 45202
Tel (513) 397-9900
SIC 4813 7373 7374 7379

■ CINCINNATI BELL TECHNOLOGY SOLUTIONS INC p 307
4600 Montgomery Rd # 400 45212
Tel (513) 841-2287 *SIC* 7379 5734

■ CINCINNATI BELL TELEPHONE CO p 307
209 W 7th St Fl 1 45202
Tel (513) 565-9402 *SIC* 4813

CINCINNATI PUBLIC SCHOOLS p 307
2651 Burnet Ave 45219
Tel (513) 363-0000 *SIC* 8211

CINCINNATI STATE TECHNICAL AND COMMUNITY COLLEGE p 307
3520 Central Pkwy 45223
Tel (513) 569-1500 *SIC* 8222

CINCOM SYSTEMS INC p 307
55 Merchant St Ste 100 45246
Tel (513) 612-2300 *SIC* 7373

■ CINERGY CORP p 308
139 E 4th St 45202
Tel (513) 421-9500 *SIC* 4911 4924

■ CINERGY POWER GENERATION SERVICES LLC p 308
139 E 4th St 45202
Tel (513) 421-9500 *SIC* 4911

▲ CINTAS CORP p 308
6800 Cintas Blvd 45262
Tel (513) 459-1200
SIC 7218 2337 2326 5084

■ CINTAS R US INC p 308
6800 Cintas Blvd 45262
Tel (513) 459-1200 *SIC* 7218

CITY OF CINCINNATI p 314
801 Plum St Rm 246 45202
Tel (513) 352-3221 *SIC* 9111

CLARKE POWER SERVICES INC p 322
3133 E Kemper Rd 45241
Tel (513) 771-2200 *SIC* 5084

CNG FINANCIAL CORP p 330
7755 Montgomery Rd # 400 45236
Tel (513) 336-7735 *SIC* 6099

CNG FINANCIAL CORP p 330
7755 Montgomery Rd # 400 45236
Tel (513) 336-7735 *SIC* 6282

CNG HOLDINGS INC p 330
7755 Montgomery Rd # 400 45236
Tel (513) 336-7735 *SIC* 6719

▲ CONVERGYS CORP p 365
201 E 4th St 45202
Tel (513) 723-7000 *SIC* 7374 7373

■ CONVERGYS CUSTOMER MANAGEMENT GROUP INC p 365
201 E 4th St Bsmt 45202
Tel (513) 723-6104 *SIC* 7389 8732

COUNTY OF HAMILTON p 378
138 E Court St Rm 607 45202
Tel (513) 946-4400 *SIC* 9111

■ DAVID J JOSEPH CO p 415
300 Pike St Fl 3 45202
Tel (513) 621-8770 *SIC* 5093

DCS SANITATION MANAGEMENT INC p 419
7864 Camargo Rd 45243
Tel (513) 891-4980 *SIC* 7349 7342

DE FOXX & ASSOCIATES INC p 419
324 W 9th St Fl 5 45202
Tel (513) 621-5522 *SIC* 8742 8741

DEACONESS LONG TERM CARE OF MISSOURI INC p 419
330 Straight St Ste 310 45219
Tel (513) 487-3600
SIC 8059 8361 8052 8051

DEVICOR MEDICAL PRODUCTS INC p 434
300 E Business Way Fl 5 45241
Tel (513) 864-9000 *SIC* 3841

DINSMORE & SHOHL LLP p 440
255 E 5th St Ste 1900 45202
Tel (513) 977-8200 *SIC* 8111

■ DJJ HOLDING CORP p 445
300 Pike St 45202
Tel (513) 621-8770 *SIC* 5093 5088 4741

DUBOIS CHEMICALS p 459
3630 E Kemper Rd 45241
Tel (800) 438-2647 *SIC* 2842

■ DUKE ENERGY BECKJORD LLC p 460
139 E 4th St 45202
Tel (513) 287-2561 *SIC* 4911

■ DYNEGY COMMERCIAL ASSET MANAGEMENT LLC p 465
139 E 4th St 45202
Tel (704) 382-5460 *SIC* 4924 4911

▲ E W SCRIPPS CO p 467
312 Walnut St Ste 2800 45202
Tel (513) 977-3000
SIC 4841 2711 4833 7375

EASY WAY LEISURE CORP p 473
8950 Rossash Rd 45236
Tel (513) 731-5640 *SIC* 2392

■ EMCOR FACILITIES SERVICES INC p 491
15 W Voorhees St 45215
Tel (888) 846-9462 *SIC* 8744

EMERY OLEOCHEMICALS LLC p 492
4900 Este Ave 45232
Tel (513) 762-2500 *SIC* 2899

ENERFAB INC p 497
4955 Spring Grove Ave 45232
Tel (513) 641-0500
SIC 3443 1629 1541 1711 3479

EP BOLLINGER LLC p 504
2664 Saint Georges Ct 45233
Tel (513) 941-1101 *SIC* 2821

FEDERAL HOME LOAN BANK OF CINCINNATI p 534
600 Atrium Two # 2 45201
Tel (513) 852-7500 *SIC* 6019

▲ FIFTH THIRD BANCORP p 541
38 Fountain Square Plz 45202
Tel (800) 972-3030 *SIC* 6022

■ FIFTH THIRD BANK p 541
38 Fountain Square Plz 45202
Tel (800) 972-3030 *SIC* 6022

▲ FIRST FINANCIAL BANCORP p 546
255 E 5th St Ste 700 45202
Tel (877) 322-9530 *SIC* 6021

FIRST GROUP INVESTMENT PARTNERSHIP p 547
600 Vine St Ste 1200 45202
Tel (513) 241-2200
SIC 7513 4212 4213 4225 4151 4111

FIRST SERVICES INC p 549
600 Vine St Ste 1200 45202
Tel (513) 241-2200 *SIC* 8741 7539

FIRST STUDENT INC p 549
600 Vine St Ste 1400 45202
Tel (513) 241-2200 *SIC* 4151

FIRST TRANSIT INC p 550
600 Vine St Ste 1400 45202
Tel (513) 241-2200 *SIC* 8741 7539 8742

FIRST VEHICLE SERVICES INC p 550
600 Vine St Ste 1400 45202
Tel (513) 241-2200 *SIC* 7549

FIRSTGROUP AMERICA INC p 550
600 Vine St Ste 1400 45202
Tel (513) 241-2200
SIC 4151 4111 4119 4131 4141 8744

FIRSTGROUP USA INC p 550
600 Vine St Ste 1400 45202
Tel (513) 241-2200
SIC 7513 4212 4213 4225 4151 4111

FOREST HILLS SCHOOL DISTRICT p 566
7550 Forest Rd 45255
Tel (513) 231-3335 *SIC* 8211

FORMICA CORP p 567
10155 Reading Rd 45241
Tel (513) 786-3400 *SIC* 2541 2679

FORT WASHINGTON INVESTMENT ADVISORS INC p 569
303 Broadway St Ste 1100 45202
Tel (513) 361-7600 *SIC* 6282

■ FRISCHS OHIO INC p 580
2800 Gilbert Ave 45206
Tel (513) 961-2660 *SIC* 5812

FRISCHS RESTAURANTS INC p 580
2800 Gilbert Ave 45206
Tel (513) 961-2660 *SIC* 5812

FROST BROWN TODD LLC p 581
3300 Grt Amrcn Towe 301e 45202
Tel (513) 651-6800 *SIC* 8111

G & J PEPSI-COLA BOTTLERS INC p 586
9435 Waterstone Blvd # 390 45249
Tel (513) 785-6060 *SIC* 2086

GAMBLE ELIZABETH DEACONESS HOME ASSOCIATION (INC) p 590
2139 Auburn Ave 45219
Tel (513) 751-4224 *SIC* 8062 8082

■ GE AIRCRAFT ENGINES HOLDINGS INC p 595
1 Neumann Way 45215
Tel (513) 243-8251 *SIC* 7699

■ GE AVIATION SYSTEMS LLC p 595
1 Neumann Way 45215
Tel (513) 243-2000 *SIC* 3812

■ GE ENGINE SERVICES LLC p 596
1 Neumann Way 45215
Tel (513) 243-2000 *SIC* 7699

■ GENERAL ELECTRIC INTERNATIONAL INC p 600
191 Rosa Parks St 45202
Tel (513) 813-9133 *SIC* 8711

■ GENERAL ELECTRIC INTERNATIONAL OPERATIONS CO INC p 600
191 Rosa Parks St 45202
Tel (513) 813-9133 *SIC* 7389

GIVAUDAN FLAVORS AND FRAGRANCES INC p 613
1199 Edison Dr 45216
Tel (513) 948-8000 *SIC* 2869 2087

GIVAUDAN FLAVORS CORP p 613
1199 Edison Dr 45216
Tel (513) 948-8000 *SIC* 2869 2087

GIVAUDAN FRAGRANCES CORP p 613
1199 Edison Dr Ste 1-2 45216
Tel (513) 948-3428 *SIC* 2869

GIVAUDAN ROURE (UNITED STATES) INC p 613
1199 Edison Dr 45216
Tel (513) 948-8000 *SIC* 2869 2087

GOETTLE HOLDING CO INC p 619
12071 Hamilton Ave 45231
Tel (513) 825-8100
SIC 1799 1629 1771 1794

GOLD MEDAL PRODUCTS CO p 620
10700 Medallion Dr 45241
Tel (513) 769-7676
SIC 3556 3589 5145 3581

GOOD SAMARITAN HOSPITAL OF CINCINNATI p 623
375 Dixmyth Ave 45220
Tel (513) 569-6251 *SIC* 8062 8082 8011

GRAETERS MANUFACTURING CO p 628
1175 Regina Graeter Way 45216
Tel (513) 721-3323
SIC 2024 2051 2064 2066

■ GREAT AMERICAN FINANCIAL RESOURCES INC p 633
250 E 5th St Ste 1000 45202
Tel (513) 333-5300 *SIC* 6371

■ GREAT AMERICAN HOLDING INC p 633
301 E 4th St 45202
Tel (513) 369-3000 *SIC* 6719

■ GREAT AMERICAN INSURANCE CO p 633
301 E 4th St Ste 2800 45202
Tel (513) 369-5000 *SIC* 6331

GREATER CINCINNATI FOUNDATION p 635
200 W 4th St Fl 1 45202
Tel (513) 241-2880 *SIC* 6732

HABEGGER CORP p 651
4995 Winton Rd 45232
Tel (513) 853-6644 *SIC* 5075

HALMA HOLDINGS INC p 655
11500 Northlake Dr # 306 45249
Tel (513) 772-5501 *SIC* 3826

HAMILTON COURT JUSTICE OFFICE p 655
1000 Sycamore St Ste 110 45202
Tel (513) 946-6400 *SIC* 9229

HICKMAN WILLIAMS & CO p 690
250 E 5th St Ste 300 45202
Tel (513) 621-1946
SIC 5051 5052 5169 5085 5084

HILLMAN COMPANIES INC p 693
10590 Hamilton Ave 45231
Tel (513) 851-4900 *SIC* 5072 7699

HILLMAN GROUP INC p 693
10590 Hamilton Ave 45231
Tel (513) 851-4900 *SIC* 5072

HILLTOP BASIC RESOURCES INC p 694
1 W 4th St Ste 1100 45202
Tel (513) 651-5000 *SIC* 1442 3273

HMAN GROUP HOLDINGS INC p 697
10590 Hamilton Ave 45231
Tel (513) 851-4900 *SIC* 6719 5072 7699

HMAN INTERMEDIATE II HOLDINGS CORP p 697
10590 Hamilton Ave 45231
Tel (513) 851-4900 *SIC* 5072 7699

HOBSONS INC p 699
50 E Business Way Ste 300 45241
Tel (513) 891-5444 *SIC* 8741

HOME CITY ICE CO p 703
6045 Bridgetown Rd Ste 1 45248
Tel (513) 574-1800 *SIC* 2097

ILSCO CORP p 733
4730 Madison Rd 45227
Tel (513) 533-6200
SIC 3643 3369 3451 3678 3544 3469

INTEGRITY LIFE INSURANCE CO p 750
400 Broadway St 45202
Tel (513) 362-8000 *SIC* 6311

■ INTER AMERICAN PRODUCTS INC p 750
1240 State Ave 45204
Tel (800) 645-2233
SIC 2095 2099 2033 2079 2087 2022

ITELLIGENCE INC p 768
10856 Reed Hartman Hwy 45242
Tel (513) 956-2000 *SIC* 7379

JEWISH HOSPITAL CINCINNATI INC p 784
3200 Burnet Ave 45229
Tel (513) 569-2367 *SIC* 8031

JEWISH HOSPITAL LLC p 784
4777 E Galbraith Rd 45236
Tel (513) 686-3000 *SIC* 8062

JEWISH HOSPITAL OF CINCINNATI INC p 785
4777 E Galbraith Rd 45236
Tel (513) 686-3000 *SIC* 8062

K - O - I WAREHOUSE INC p 798
2701 Spring Grove Ave 45225
Tel (513) 357-2400 *SIC* 5013

KAO USA INC p 803
2535 Spring Grove Ave 45214
Tel (513) 421-1400 *SIC* 2844 2841

KDM SIGNS INC p 807
10450 Medallion Dr 45241
Tel (513) 769-1932 *SIC* 2759 3993

KGBO HOLDINGS INC p 816
4289 Ivy Pointe Blvd 45245
Tel (513) 831-2600 *SIC* 4731

KINGS FORD INC p 820
9555 Kings Auto Mall Rd 45249
Tel (513) 683-0220 *SIC* 5511

KLOSTERMAN BAKING CO p 823
4760 Paddock Rd 45229
Tel (513) 242-5667 *SIC* 2051

KOI ENTERPRISES INC p 826
2701 Spring Grove Ave 45225
Tel (513) 357-2400 *SIC* 5013 5531

■ KPS LLC p 829
1014 Vine St 45202
Tel (513) 762-4000 *SIC* 5141

▲ KROGER CO p 830
1014 Vine St Ste 1000 45202
Tel (513) 762-4000
SIC 5411 5912 5541 5944

■ KROGER LIMITED PARTNERSHIP I p 830
1014 Vine St Ste 1000 45202
Tel (513) 762-4000 *SIC* 5411

■ L-3 FUZING AND ORDNANCE SYSTEMS INC p 835
3975 Mcmann Rd 45245
Tel (513) 943-2000 *SIC* 3483

LAIDLAW TRANSIT SERVICES INC p 838
600 Vine St Ste 1400 45202
Tel (513) 241-2200 *SIC* 4131

LAROSAS INC p 845
2334 Boudinot Ave 45238
Tel (513) 347-5660
SIC 5812 6794 5141 5921

■ LOYAL AMERICAN LIFE INSURANCE CO p 882
250 E 5th St Fl 8 45202
Tel (800) 633-6752 *SIC* 6311

■ MACYS CORPORATE SERVICES INC p 893
7 W 7th St Ste 1100 45202
Tel (513) 579-7000 *SIC* 5311

■ MACYS FLORIDA STORES LLC p 893
7 W 7th St Fl 17 45202
Tel (513) 579-7000 *SIC* 5311

▲ MACYS INC p 893
7 W 7th St 45202
Tel (513) 579-7000 *SIC* 5311

■ MACYS RETAIL HOLDINGS INC p 893
7 W 7th St Ste 1100 45202
Tel (513) 579-7000 *SIC* 5311

■ MACYS WEST STORES INC p 893
7 W 7th St Fl 17 45202
Tel (513) 579-7000 *SIC* 5311

■ MACYS.COM INC p 893
7 W 7th St 45202
Tel (513) 579-7000 *SIC* 5961 5311

■ MEDPACE ACQUISITION INC p 938
5375 Medpace Way 45227
Tel (513) 579-9911 *SIC* 8741

▲ MEDPACE HOLDINGS INC p 938
5375 Medpace Way 45227
Tel (513) 579-9911 *SIC* 2834 8731

■ MEDPACE INC p 938
5375 Medpace Way 45227
Tel (513) 579-9911 *SIC* 8731 5122 5047

■ MEDPACE INTERMEDIATECO INC p 938
5375 Medpace Way 45227
Tel (513) 579-9911 *SIC* 8741

MERCY FRANCISCAN HOSPITAL MT AIRY p 946
2446 Kipling Ave 45239
Tel (513) 853-5101 *SIC* 8741 8062

MERCY HEALTH p 946
1701 Mercy Health Pl 45237
Tel (513) 639-2800 *SIC* 8062

MERCY HEALTH ANDERSON HOSPITAL p 946
7500 State Rd 45255
Tel (513) 624-4500 *SIC* 8062

MERCY HEALTH PARTNERS p 946
1701 Mercy Health Pl 45237
Tel (513) 952-5000 *SIC* 8062

▲ MERIDIAN BIOSCIENCE INC p 948
3471 River Hills Dr 45244
Tel (513) 271-3700 *SIC* 2835 2834

MESSER CONSTRUCTION CO p 951
5158 Fishwick Dr 45216
Tel (513) 242-1541 *SIC* 1542 1541 1522

MEYER TOOL INC p 957
3055 Colerain Ave 45225
Tel (513) 681-7362 *SIC* 3724 3599

■ MILACRON INTERMEDIATE HOLDINGS INC p 968
3010 Disney St 45209
Tel (513) 536-2000 *SIC* 5962 8741

■ MILLSTONE COFFEE INC p 971
1 Procter And Gamble Plz 45202
Tel (513) 983-1100 *SIC* 2095

MORRELL JOHN & CO p 990
805 E Kemper Rd 45246
Tel (513) 782-3800 *SIC* 2011

MUELLER ROOFING DISTRIBUTORS INC p 998
327 E Wyoming Ave 45215
Tel (513) 679-8540 *SIC* 5033 5099

MV RESIDENTIAL CONSTRUCTION INC p 1003
9349 Waterstone Blvd # 200 45249
Tel (513) 588-1000 SIC 1522

■ NEIGHBORCARE HOLDINGS INC p 1024
201 E 4th St Ste 900 45202
Tel (513) 719-2600 SIC 8741

■ NEIGHBORCARE INC p 1024
201 E 4th St Ste 900 45202
Tel (513) 719-2600
SIC 5122 5912 5047 7389

■ NEIGHBORCARE PHARMACY SERVICES INC p 1024
201 E 4th St Ste 900 45202
Tel (513) 719-2600 SIC 5912

■ NEIGHBORCARE SERVICES CORP p 1024
201 E 4th St Ste 900 45202
Tel (513) 719-2600 SIC 5122

NEXGEN ENTERPRISES INC p 1040
3274 Spring Grove Ave 45225
Tel (513) 618-0300 SIC 5032

NORTHWEST LOCAL SCHOOL DISTRICT p 1060
3240 Banning Rd 45239
Tel (513) 923-1000 SIC 8211

NOVELART MANUFACTURING CO p 1063
2121 Section Rd 45237
Tel (513) 351-7700 SIC 5141 5145 5194

OHIO VALLEY FLOORING INC p 1078
5555 Murray Ave 45227
Tel (513) 271-3434 SIC 5023

■ OMNICARE INC p 1085
900 Omnicare Ctr 45202
Tel (513) 719-2600
SIC 5122 5047 8082 8741

■ OMNICARE MANAGEMENT CO p 1085
201 E 4th St Ste 900 45202
Tel (513) 719-1535 SIC 8741

PARKING CO OF AMERICA INC p 1116
250 W Court St Ste 200e 45202
Tel (513) 241-0415 SIC 7521

PARSEC INC p 1117
1100 Gest St 45203
Tel (513) 621-6111 SIC 4789

PAYCOR INC p 1122
4811 Montgomery Rd 45212
Tel (513) 381-0505 SIC 8721

■ PENNSYLVANIA CO INC p 1130
1 E 4th St 45202
Tel (513) 579-2121 SIC 6321

PHILLIPS EDISON - ARC SHOPPING CENTER REIT INC p 1144
11501 Northlake Dr Fl 1 45249
Tel (513) 554-1110 SIC 6512

PHILLIPS EDISON-ARC GROCERY CENTER REIT II INC p 1144
11501 Northlake Dr 45249
Tel (513) 554-1110 SIC 6798

PRINCETON CITY SCHOOL DISTRICT p 1177
3900 Cottingham Dr 45241
Tel (513) 864-1000 SIC 8211

PROAMPAC HOLDINGS INC p 1178
12025 Tricon Rd 45246
Tel (513) 671-1777 SIC 6722

PROAMPAC INTERMEDIATE INC p 1178
12025 Tricon Rd 45246
Tel (513) 671-1777 SIC 6722

PROAMPAC LLC p 1178
12025 Tricon Rd 45246
Tel (513) 671-1777 SIC 2671

▲ PROCTER & GAMBLE CO p 1179
1 Procter And Gamble Plz 45202
Tel (513) 983-1100
SIC 2844 2676 3421 2842 2841

■ PROCTER & GAMBLE DISTRIBUTING LLC p 1179
1 Procter And Gamble Plz 45202
Tel (513) 983-1100
SIC 5169 5122 5149 5113 5137

■ PROCTER & GAMBLE FAR EAST INC p 1179
1 Procter And Gamble Plz 45202
Tel (513) 983-1100 SIC 2842 2844 2676

■ PROCTER & GAMBLE MANUFACTURING CO p 1179
1 Procter And Gamble Plz 45202
Tel (513) 983-1100
SIC 2841 2079 2099 2844 2045

■ PROCTER & GAMBLE PAPER PRODUCTS CO p 1179
1 Procter And Gamble Plz 45202
Tel (513) 983-1100 SIC 2676

PROCTER AND GAMBLE RETIREE BENEFIT TRUST p 1179
2 Procter And Gamble Plz 45202
Tel (513) 698-4501 SIC 6733

PROFILL HOLDINGS LLC p 1180
255 W Crescentville Rd 45246
Tel (513) 742-4000
SIC 5199 5136 5137 6798

PROVIDENCE HOSPITAL p 1186
2446 Kipling Ave 45239
Tel (513) 853-5000 SIC 8062

QUEBECOR WORLD JOHNSON & HARDIN CO p 1198
3600 Red Bank Rd 45227
Tel (614) 326-0299 SIC 2759 2752 2732

QUEST GLOBAL SERVICES-NA INC p 1199
11499 Chester Rd Ste 600 45246
Tel (513) 648-4900 SIC 8731 8711

RESTAURANT MANAGEMENT INC p 1228
300 Main St 45202
Tel (513) 362-8900 SIC 5812

RICHARDS ELECTRIC SUPPLY CO INC p 1232
4620 Reading Rd 45229
Tel (513) 242-8800 SIC 5063

RIVERFRONT STEEL INC p 1237
10310 S Medallion Dr 45241
Tel (513) 769-9999 SIC 5051

■ ROTO-ROOTER DEVELOPMENT CO p 1252
255 E 5th St Ste 2600 45202
Tel (513) 762-6690 SIC 7699 1711

■ ROTO-ROOTER SERVICES CO p 1252
2500 Chemed Ctr 255e5th 45202
Tel (513) 762-6690 SIC 7699 1711

RUMPKE CONSOLIDATED COMPANIES INC p 1258
10795 Hughes Rd 45251
Tel (800) 582-3107 SIC 4953

RUMPKE OF INDIANA INC p 1258
3800 Struble Rd 45251
Tel (513) 851-0122 SIC 4953

RUMPKE OF KENTUCKY INC p 1258
10795 Hughes Rd 45251
Tel (513) 851-0122 SIC 4953

RUMPKE OF OHIO INC p 1258
3800 Struble Rd 45251
Tel (513) 851-0122 SIC 4953 4212

RUMPKE TRANSPORTATION CO LLC p 1258
10795 Hughes Rd 45251
Tel (513) 851-0122
SIC 3561 5084 7537 4953

RUMPKE WASTE INC p 1258
10795 Hughes Rd 45251
Tel (513) 851-0122 SIC 4953

SENCO BRANDS INC p 1303
4270 Ivy Pointe Blvd # 300 45245
Tel (513) 388-2000 SIC 3546

SIBCY CLINE INC p 1319
8044 Montgomery Rd # 300 45236
Tel (513) 984-4100 SIC 6531

SIMS-LOHMAN INC p 1326
6325 Este Ave 45232
Tel (513) 651-3510 SIC 5031 2435

SMYTH AUTOMOTIVE INC p 1335
4275 Mt Carmel Tobasco Rd 45244
Tel (513) 528-2800 SIC 5013 5531

SOUTHWEST OHIO REGIONAL TRANSIT AUTHORITY p 1352
602 Main St Ste 1100 45202
Tel (513) 621-4455 SIC 4111

ST BERNARD SOAP CO p 1365
5177 Spring Grove Ave 45217
Tel (513) 242-2227 SIC 2841

STAFFMARK HOLDINGS INC p 1374
201 E 4th St Ste 800 45202
Tel (513) 651-1111 SIC 7361 7363

STAFFMARK INVESTMENT LLC p 1374
201 E 4th St Ste 800 45202
Tel (513) 651-3600 SIC 7361

STAND ENERGY CORP p 1375
1077 Celestial St Ste 110 45202
Tel (513) 621-1113 SIC 4924

STANDARD TEXTILE CO INC p 1376
1 Knollcrest Dr 45237
Tel (513) 761-9255
SIC 2389 2326 2337 2211 2391 5136

STERLING MEDICAL CORP p 1387
411 Oak St 45219
Tel (513) 984-1800 SIC 8741

■ SYSCO CINCINNATI LLC p 1416
10510 Evendale Dr 45241
Tel (513) 563-6300
SIC 5144 5149 5143 5113

■ TAMBRANDS SALES CORP p 1423
1 Procter And Gamble Plz 45202
Tel (513) 983-1100 SIC 2676

THOMAS J DYER CO p 1448
5240 Lester Rd 45213
Tel (513) 321-8100 SIC 1711

TOTAL QUALITY LOGISTICS LLC p 1463
4289 Ivy Pointe Blvd 45245
Tel (513) 831-2600 SIC 4731

TP MECHANICAL CONTRACTORS INC p 1467
1500 Kemper Meadow Dr 45240
Tel (513) 851-8881 SIC 6552

TRIHEALTH INC p 1480
619 Oak St 45206
Tel (513) 569-6111 SIC 8741

TRIHEALTH PHYSICIAN INSTITUTE p 1480
619 Oak St 45206
Tel (513) 569-5126 SIC 8011

UC HEALTH LLC p 1498
3200 Burnet Ave 45229
Tel (513) 585-6000 SIC 8741

UNION CENTRAL LIFE INSURANCE CO p 1504
1876 Waycross Rd 45240
Tel (866) 696-7478 SIC 6311 6321

UNION SAVINGS BANK p 1505
8534 E Kemper Rd Fl 1 45249
Tel (513) 489-1955 SIC 6036

UNITED DAIRY FARMERS INC p 1507
3955 Montgomery Rd 45212
Tel (513) 396-8700
SIC 5411 5143 2026 2024 5541 5451

■ UNITED STATES DEPT OF ENERGY OHIO FIELD OFFICE p 1513
250 E 5th St Ste 500 45202
Tel (513) 246-0500 SIC 9611

UNIVERSITY OF CINCINNATI p 1520
2600 Clifton Ave 45220
Tel (513) 556-6000 SIC 8221

UNIVERSITY OF CINCINNATI MEDICAL CENTER LLC p 1521
234 Goodman St 45219
Tel (513) 584-1000 SIC 8062

■ US BANK NATIONAL ASSOCIATION p 1531
425 Walnut St Fl 1 45202
Tel (513) 632-4234 SIC 6021

VALLEY ASPHALT CORP p 1540
11641 Mosteller Rd 45241
Tel (513) 771-0820 SIC 1611 2951

VALLEY INTERIOR SYSTEMS INC p 1541
2203 Fowler St 45206
Tel (513) 961-0400 SIC 1742

VEGA AMERICAS INC p 1546
4170 Rosslyn Dr Ste A 45209
Tel (513) 272-0131 SIC 3823

■ VIGOR ACQUISITION CORP p 1556
1014 Vine St 45202
Tel (513) 762-4000 SIC 5411

WARNER CHILCOTT PHARMACEUTICALS INC p 1576
1 Procter And Gamble Plz 45202
Tel (513) 983-1100 SIC 2834

WCM HOLDINGS INC p 1585
1150 Canal Rd 45241
Tel (513) 705-2100 SIC 5099 2381 3842

WEST CLERMONT LOCAL SCHOOL DISTRICT p 1594
4350 Aicholtz Rd Ste 220 45245
Tel (513) 943-5000 SIC 8211

WESTERN & SOUTHERN FINANCIAL GROUP INC p 1597
400 Broadway St 45202
Tel (866) 832-7719 SIC 6211

WESTERN & SOUTHERN LIFE INSURANCE CO p 1597
400 Broadway St 45202
Tel (513) 629-1800 SIC 6211

WESTERN & SOUTHERN MUTUAL HOLDING CO p 1597
400 Broadway St 45202
Tel (866) 832-7719 SIC 6211

XAVIER UNIVERSITY p 1630
3800 Victory Pkwy Unit 1 45207
Tel (513) 961-0133 SIC 8221

XTEK INC p 1633
11451 Reading Rd 45241
Tel (513) 733-7800
SIC 3568 3547 3398 3312

YOUNG MENS CHRISTIAN ASSOCIATION OF GREATER CINCINNATI p 1638
1105 Elm St 45202
Tel (513) 651-2100 SIC 8641

CLEVELAND HEIGHTS, OH

PRIMERATURF INC p 1175
2065 Lamberton Rd 44118
Tel (216) 397-9716 SIC 5191

CLEVELAND, OH

A W S INC p 7
1275 Lakeside Ave E 44114
Tel (216) 861-0250
SIC 8331 7374 7334 7331

AEROQUIP-VICKERS INC p 30
1111 Superior Ave E 44114
Tel (216) 523-5000
SIC 3052 3492 3429 3069 3585 3728

AIRGAS MERCHANT GASES LLC p 40
6055 Rckside Woods Blvd N 44131
Tel (800) 242-0105 SIC 5169

ALBERT M HIGLEY CO p 46
2926 Chester Ave 44114
Tel (216) 404-5783 SIC 1542 1541

ALCAN CORP p 47
6060 Parkland Blvd 44124
Tel (440) 460-3307
SIC 3351 3355 3496 3357

ALERIS CORP p 48
25825 Science Park Dr # 400 44122
Tel (216) 910-3400 SIC 3355 3354

ALERIS ROLLED PRODUCTS LLC p 48
25825 Science Park Dr # 400 44122
Tel (216) 910-3400 SIC 3355

ALL ERECTION & CRANE RENTAL CORP p 51
4700 Acorn Dr 44131
Tel (216) 524-6550 SIC 7353 7359

AMERICAN BREAD CO LLC p 69
8905 Lake Ave Fl 2 44102
Tel (216) 961-6767 SIC 7389

AMERICAN GREETINGS CORP p 73
1 American Rd 44144
Tel (216) 252-7300
SIC 2771 2679 2656 2678

AMERIMARK DIRECT LLC p 82
6864 Engle Rd 44130
Tel (440) 826-1900 SIC 4226 5961 7331

AMERIMARK HOLDINGS LLC p 82
6864 Engle Rd 44130
Tel (440) 325-2000 SIC 5961 4226 7331

■ AMTRUST NORTH AMERICA INC p 87
800 Superior Ave E # 2100 44114
Tel (216) 328-6100 SIC 6331 6411

ANGSTROM GRAPHICS INC p 91
4437 E 49th St 44125
Tel (216) 271-5300 SIC 2721 2754 2752

ANTIOCH PRESERVATION LP p 94
8920 Carnegie Ave 44106
Tel (216) 721-6100 SIC 6513

AON RISK SERVICES NORTHEAST INC p 95
1660 W 2nd St 44113
Tel (216) 621-8100 SIC 6411

APPLE AMERICAN LIMITED PARTNERSHIP OF OHIO p 98
8905 Lake Ave 44102
Tel (216) 961-6767 SIC 5812

APPLE AMERICAN LP OF INDIANA p 98
8905 Lake Ave Fl 2 44102
Tel (216) 961-6767 SIC 5812

■ APPLIED INDUSTRIAL TECHNOLOGIES - CA LLC p 99
1 Applied Plz 44115
Tel (216) 426-4000 SIC 5063

■ APPLIED INDUSTRIAL TECHNOLOGIES - DIXIE INC p 99
1 Applied Plz 44115
Tel (216) 426-4000 SIC 5172 5169

▲ APPLIED INDUSTRIAL TECHNOLOGIES INC p 99
1 Applied Plz 44115
Tel (216) 426-4000 SIC 5085 5169 7699

ARCELORMITTAL CLEVELAND LLC p 104
3060 Eggers Ave 44105
Tel (216) 429-6000 SIC 3312

AREA TEMPS INC p 106
1228 Euclid Ave Ste 1115 44115
Tel (216) 781-5350 SIC 7363

ARROW INTERNATIONAL INC p 113
9900 Clinton Rd 44144
Tel (216) 961-3500 SIC 3944

AT HOLDINGS CORP p 123
23555 Euclid Ave 44117
Tel (216) 692-6000 SIC 3724 3728 6512

AUSTIN BUILDING AND DESIGN INC p 132
6095 Parkland Blvd # 100 44124
Tel (440) 544-2600
SIC 1541 1542 8742 8711 8712

AUSTIN POWDER CO p 133
25800 Science Park Dr # 300 44122
Tel (216) 464-2400 SIC 2892

AUSTIN POWDER HOLDINGS CO p 133
25800 Science Park Dr # 300 44122
Tel (216) 464-2400 SIC 2892

AUXILIARY BOARD OF FAIRVIEW GENERAL HOSPITAL p 135
18101 Lorain Ave 44111
Tel (216) 476-7000 SIC 8062

■ AVIATION TECHNOLOGIES INC p 138
1301 E 9th St Ste 3000 44114
Tel (216) 706-2960
SIC 3643 3678 3679 3728 3812 3648

BAKER & HOSTETLER LLP p 145
127 Public Sq Ste 2000 44114
Tel (216) 621-0200 SIC 8111

BASF CONSTRUCTION CHEMICALS LLC p 158
23700 Chagrin Blvd 44122
Tel (216) 831-5500 SIC 2899 2851 1799

BDI INC p 164
8000 Hub Pkwy 44125
Tel (216) 642-9100 SIC 1389

BEARING DISTRIBUTORS INC p 165
8000 Hub Pkwy 44125
Tel (216) 642-9100 SIC 5085

■ BLOOM LAKE IRON ORE MINE LTD p 189
200 Public Sq 44114
Tel (216) 694-5700 SIC 1011

CARLTON CARDS RETAIL INC p 258
1 American Rd 44144
Tel (216) 252-7300 SIC 5947 5943

CASE WESTERN RESERVE UNIVERSITY p 263
10900 Euclid Ave 44106
Tel (216) 368-2000 SIC 8221

CATHOLIC DIOCESE OF CLEVELAND p 266
1404 E 9th St Ste 201 44114
Tel (216) 696-6525 SIC 8661

CAVALIERS HOLDINGS LLC p 267
1 Center Ct 44115
Tel (216) 420-2000 SIC 7941 6512

CAVALIERS OPERATING CO LLC p 267
1 Center Ct 44115
Tel (216) 420-2000 SIC 7941

▲ CBIZ INC p 268
6050 Oak Tree Blvd # 500 44131
Tel (216) 447-9000 SIC 8742 7389 7363

CENTURY INTERMEDIATE HOLDING CO p 282
1 American Rd 44144
Tel (216) 252-7300
SIC 2771 2679 2656 2678

▲ CHART INDUSTRIES INC p 290
1 Infinity Corp Ctr Dr # 300 44125
Tel (440) 753-1490 SIC 3559 3569 3443

■ CHARTER ONE BANK NATIONAL ASSOCIATION p 291
1215 Superior Ave E # 245 44114
Tel (216) 277-5326 SIC 6021

CHEMICAL SOLVENTS INC p 293
3751 Jennings Rd 44109
Tel (216) 741-9310
SIC 5169 7349 3471 2992

CITY OF CLEVELAND p 314
601 Lakeside Ave E Rm 210 44114
Tel (216) 664-2000 SIC 9111

CLEVELAND CLINIC FOUNDATION p 325
9500 Euclid Ave 44195
Tel (216) 636-8335 SIC 8062 8011 8741

CLEVELAND CLINIC HEALTH SYSTEM-WESTERN REGION p 325
18101 Lorain Ave 44111
Tel (216) 476-7000 SIC 8741

CLEVELAND FOUNDATION p 325
1422 Euclid Ave Ste 1300 44115
Tel (216) 861-3810 SIC 6732

CLEVELAND MUNICIPAL SCHOOL DISTRICT p 325
1111 Superior Ave E # 1800 44114
Tel (216) 838-0000 SIC 8211 8399

CLEVELAND STATE UNIVERSITY p 325
2121 Euclid Ave 44115
Tel (216) 687-2000 SIC 8221

■ CLEVELAND SYSCO INC p 326
4747 Grayton Rd 44135
Tel (216) 201-3000 SIC 5149

CLEVELAND WATER DEPARTMENT p 326
5953 Deering Ave 44130
Tel (216) 664-3168 SIC 4941

▲ CLIFFS NATURAL RESOURCES INC p 326
200 Public Sq Ste 3300 44114
Tel (216) 694-5700 SIC 1011

COLUMBIA NATIONAL GROUP INC p 341
6600 Grant Ave 44105
Tel (216) 883-4972 SIC 5051 5093 1542

■ COMEX NORTH AMERICA INC p 344
101 W Prospect Ave # 1020 44115
Tel (303) 307-2100
SIC 2851 8742 5198 5231

CONSOLIDATED PRECISION PRODUCTS CORP p 360
1621 Euclid Ave Ste 1850 44115
Tel (909) 595-2252 SIC 3365 3324

CONTAINERPORT GROUP INC p 362
1340 Depot St Ste 103 44116
Tel (440) 333-2009 SIC 3715

COUNTY OF CUYAHOGA p 377
1215 W 3rd St 44113
Tel (216) 443-7022 SIC 9121

CROWNE GROUP LLC p 396
127 Public Sq Ste 5110 44114
Tel (216) 589-0198 SIC 3559 8711

CSA ST JOHN MINISTRIES p 397
29000 Center Ridge Rd 44145
Tel (440) 835-8000 SIC 5947

CUYAHOGA COMMUNITY COLLEGE p 403
700 Carnegie Ave 44115
Tel (216) 987-6000 SIC 8222

CUYAHOGA METROPOLITAN HOUSING AUTHORITY p 403
8120 Kinsman Rd 44104
Tel (216) 348-5000 SIC 9532

DAWSON INSURANCE INC p 417
1340 Depot St Ste 300 44116
Tel (440) 333-9000 SIC 6411

DEALER TIRE LLC p 419
3711 Chester Ave 44114
Tel (216) 432-0088 SIC 5014

DMD MANAGEMENT INC p 446
12380 Plaza Dr 44130
Tel (216) 898-8399 SIC 8741

DONLEYS INC p 450
5430 Warner Rd 44125
Tel (216) 524-6800 SIC 1542

■ DRIVE INSURANCE HOLDINGS INC p 456
6300 Wilson Mills Rd 44143
Tel (440) 461-5000 SIC 6331 6351

EATON AEROSPACE LLC p 473
1000 Eaton Blvd 44122
Tel (216) 523-5000 SIC 3812

EATON CORP p 473
1000 Eaton Blvd 44122
Tel (216) 523-5000
SIC 3625 3714 3594 3559 3571

EATON INDUSTRIAL CORP p 473
23555 Euclid Ave 44117
Tel (216) 692-5456 SIC 3724 3728

EATON USEV HOLDING CO INC p 473
1111 Suprr Eatn Ctr 173 44114
Tel (216) 523-5000 SIC 3592

EATON-AEROQUIP LLC p 474
1000 Eaton Blvd 44122
Tel (216) 523-5000
SIC 3052 3492 3429 3069 3585 3728

EMPIRE IRON MINING PARTNERSHIP p 493
1100 Superior Ave E Fl 15 44114
Tel (216) 694-5700 SIC 1011

ENPROTECH CORP p 500
4259 E 49th St 44125
Tel (216) 206-0080 SIC 5084

■ EUCLID CHEMICAL CO p 512
19218 Redwood Rd 44110
Tel (800) 321-7628 SIC 2899 4213

FAIRVIEW HOSPITAL p 525
18101 Lorain Ave 44111
Tel (216) 476-7000 SIC 8062 8011

FC CONTINENTAL LANDLORD LLC p 532
50 Public Sq Ste 1360 44113
Tel (216) 621-6060 SIC 6531

FEDERAL RESERVE BANK OF CLEVELAND p 535
1455 E 6th St 44114
Tel (216) 579-2000 SIC 6011

■ FIFTH THIRD BANK OF NORTHEASTERN OHIO p 542
600 Superior Ave E Fl 5 44114
Tel (216) 274-5533 SIC 6021

FIVES NORTH AMERICAN COMBUSTION INC p 553
4455 E 71st St 44105
Tel (216) 271-6000 SIC 3567

FLIGHT SERVICES & SYSTEMS INC p 556
5005 Rockside Rd Ste 940 44131
Tel (216) 328-0090 SIC 7389

FLORAL SPECIALTIES INC p 557
20601 Aurora Rd 44146
Tel (216) 475-2302 SIC 5992

FOREST CITY COMMERCIAL MANAGEMENT INC p 566
50 Public Sq Ste 1410 44113
Tel (216) 621-6060 SIC 6531

FOREST CITY ENTERPRISES LP p 566
50 Public Sq Ste 1100 44113
Tel (216) 621-6060 SIC 6512 6513 6552

FOREST CITY PROPERTIES LLC p 566
50 Public Sq Ste 1360 44113
Tel (216) 621-6060 SIC 6512 6513

FOREST CITY REALTY TRUST INC p 566
50 Public Sq 44113
Tel (216) 621-6060 SIC 6798

GARLAND CO INC p 592
3800 E 91st St 44105
Tel (216) 641-7500 SIC 2952 2851

GARLAND INDUSTRIES INC p 592
3800 E 91st St 44105
Tel (216) 641-7500 SIC 2952 6512 8712

GCA SERVICES GROUP INC p 595
1350 Euclid Ave Ste 1500 44115
Tel (216) 535-4900 SIC 7349

■ GENERAL ALUMINUM MFG CO p 599
6065 Parkland Blvd 44124
Tel (440) 947-2000 SIC 3365 3369

GREAT LAKES PETROLEUM CO p 633
4500 Renaissance Pkwy 44128
Tel (216) 478-0501 SIC 5171

GREATER CLEVELAND REGIONAL TRANSIT AUTHORITY p 635
1240 W 6th St 44113
Tel (216) 566-5100 SIC 4111

GUNTON CORP p 648
26150 Richmond Rd 44146
Tel (216) 831-2420 SIC 5031

H LEFF ELECTRIC CO p 650
4700 Spring Rd 44131
Tel (216) 325-0941 SIC 5063

HEALTHSPAN INTEGRATED CARE p 678
1001 Lakeside Ave E # 1200 44114
Tel (216) 621-5600 SIC 8011

HIBBING TACONITE CO (A JOINT VENTURE) p 690
200 Public Sq Ste 3300 44114
Tel (216) 694-5700 SIC 1011

HILLCREST EGG & CHEESE CO p 693
2735 E 40th St 44115
Tel (216) 361-4625
SIC 5143 5142 5147 5144 5149 5148

HOSPICE OF WESTERN RESERVE INC p 709
17876 Saint Clair Ave 44110
Tel (216) 383-2222 SIC 8059

HUSQVARNA US HOLDING INC p 721
20445 Emerald Pkwy 44135
Tel (216) 898-1800 SIC 3582

▲ HYSTER-YALE MATERIALS HANDLING INC p 724
5875 Landerbrook Dr # 300 44124
Tel (440) 449-9600 SIC 3537

I & M J GROSS CO p 724
14300 Ridge Rd Ste 100 44133
Tel (440) 237-1681 SIC 1522

INFOTELECOM HOLDINGS LLC p 742
75 Erieview Plz Fl 4 44114
Tel (216) 373-4811 SIC 4813 7373

INTERNATIONAL MANAGEMENT GROUP (OVERSEAS) LLC p 756
1360 E 9th St Ste 100 44114
Tel (216) 522-1200 SIC 7941 7999 7922

INTERSTATE DIESEL SERVICE INC p 758
5300 Lakeside Ave E 44114
Tel (216) 881-0015 SIC 5013 3714

ITL CORP p 768
23925 Commerce Park 44122
Tel (216) 831-3140 SIC 2421 2426

JAMES B OSWALD CO p 776
1100 Superior Ave E # 1500 44114
Tel (216) 367-8787 SIC 6411

JEWISH FEDERATION OF CLEVELAND p 784
25701 Science Park Dr 44122
Tel (216) 593-2900 SIC 8399

JONES DAY LIMITED PARTNERSHIP p 792
901 Lakeside Ave E Ste 2 44114
Tel (216) 586-3939 SIC 8111

JOSHEN PAPER & PACKAGING CO p 794
5800 Grant Ave 44105
Tel (216) 441-5600 SIC 5113 5169

■ KAR PRODUCTS p 804
1301 E 9th St Ste 700 44114
Tel (216) 416-7200 SIC 5013 5084 5072

KEN-MAC METALS INC p 810
17901 Englewood Dr 44130
Tel (440) 891-1480 SIC 5051

■ KEYBANC CAPITAL MARKETS INC p 815
800 Superior Ave E # 1400 44114
Tel (800) 553-2240 SIC 6021 6211

■ KEYBANK EB MANAGED GUARANTEED INVESTMENT CONTRACT FUND p 815
127 Public Sq 44114
Tel (216) 689-3000 SIC 6722

■ KEYBANK NATIONAL ASSOCIATION p 815
127 Public Sq Ste 5600 44114
Tel (800) 539-2968 SIC 6021 6022 6159

▲ KEYCORP p 815
127 Public Sq 44114
Tel (216) 689-3000 SIC 6021 6141 6211

KIRBY SALES CO INC p 821
1920 W 114th St 44102
Tel (216) 228-2400 SIC 3635

L D KICHLER CO p 834
7711 E Pleasant Valley Rd 44131
Tel (216) 573-1000 SIC 3645 3648 3641

■ LESCO INC p 857
1385 E 36th St 44114
Tel (216) 706-9250 SIC 5191 5083 5261

▲ LINCOLN ELECTRIC HOLDINGS INC p 867
22801 Saint Clair Ave 44117
Tel (216) 481-8100 SIC 3548

LINSALATA CORP p 869
5900 Landerbrook Dr # 280 44124
Tel (440) 684-1400 SIC 5013

LUTHERAN MEDICAL CENTER (INC) p 886
1730 W 25th St 44113
Tel (216) 696-4300 SIC 8062 8011 8069

MAJESTIC STEEL USA INC p 899
31099 Chagrin Blvd # 150 44124
Tel (440) 786-2666 SIC 5051

MARC GLASSMAN INC p 904
5841 W 130th St 44130
Tel (216) 265-7700 SIC 5331

MARYMOUNT HOSPITAL INC p 915
9500 Euclid Ave 44195
Tel (216) 581-0500
SIC 8062 8063 8051 8082

MAYFIELD CITY SCHOOL DISTRICT p 923
1101 Som Center Rd 44124
Tel (440) 995-6800 SIC 8211

MAZZELLA HOLDING CO INC p 924
21000 Aerospace Pkwy 44142
Tel (513) 772-4466
SIC 5051 5085 5088 5072

MCPC INC p 932
1801 Superior Ave E # 300 44114
Tel (440) 238-0102 SIC 5045

MEDICAL MUTUAL OF OHIO p 937
2060 E 9th St Frnt Ste 44115
Tel (216) 687-7000 SIC 6324

MENORAH PARK CENTER FOR SENIOR LIVING BET MOSHAV ZEKENIM HADATI p 943
27100 Cedar Rd 44122
Tel (216) 831-6500 SIC 8051 6513 8322

MENTOR REM p 943
9775 Rockside Rd Ste 200 44125
Tel (216) 642-5339 SIC 8211

METROHEALTH MEDICAL CENTER p 955
2500 Metrohealth Dr 44109
Tel (216) 778-7800 SIC 8062

METROHEALTH SYSTEM p 955
2500 Metrohealth Dr 44109
Tel (216) 398-6000 SIC 8062

MIDDOUGH INC p 965
1901 E 13th St Ste 400 44114
Tel (216) 367-6000 SIC 8711 8712

■ MIDLAND TITLE SECURITY INC p 966
1111 Superior Ave E # 700 44114
Tel (216) 241-6045 SIC 6361

MILLCRAFT GROUP LLC p 970
6800 Grant Ave 44105
Tel (216) 441-5500 SIC 5111 5113 2679

MILLCRAFT PAPER CO p 970
6800 Grant Ave 44105
Tel (216) 441-5505 SIC 5111 5113

MORGANS FOODS INC p 989
4829 Galaxy Pkwy Ste S 44128
Tel (216) 359-9000 SIC 5812

MORGANS RESTAURANT OF PENNSYLVANIA INC p 989
24200 Chagrin Blvd # 126 44122
Tel (216) 360-7500 SIC 5812

MORGENTHALER MANAGEMENT PARTNERS VI LLC p 989
50 Public Sq Ste 2700 44113
Tel (216) 416-7500
SIC 1731 5065 7622 7373 5999

MORRISON PRODUCTS INC p 990
16900 S Waterloo Rd 44110
Tel (216) 486-4000 SIC 3564

MORTGAGE INFORMATION SERVICES INC p 991
4877 Galaxy Pkwy Ste I 44128
Tel (216) 514-7480 SIC 6361 6531

▲ NACCO INDUSTRIES INC p 1006
5875 Landerbrook Dr # 300 44124
Tel (440) 229-5151
SIC 3634 1221 5719 3631

■ NASA GLENN RESEARCH CENTER p 1007
21000 Brookpark Rd 44135
Tel (216) 433-4000 SIC 9661

NCS HEALTHCARE INC p 1022
3201 Entp Pkwy Ste 220 44122
Tel (216) 514-3350
SIC 5122 8093 8049 8082 8742 5912

■ NES INVESTMENT CO p 1026
6140 Parkland Blvd 44124
Tel (440) 461-6000
SIC 5065 5085 5169 5013

NESCO INC p 1026
6140 Parkland Blvd # 110 44124
Tel (440) 461-6000
SIC 3535 3541 3544 8711 6531

NORTHEAST OHIO REGIONAL SEWER DISTRICT p 1055
3900 Euclid Ave 44115
Tel (216) 881-6600 SIC 4959

NORTHERN FROZEN FOODS INC p 1056
21500 Alexander Rd 44146
Tel (440) 439-0600 SIC 5142 5149 5147

NORTHERN STAMPING CO p 1056
6600 Chapek Pkwy 44125
Tel (216) 883-8888 SIC 3465 3469

■ NORTHSHORE MINING CO p 1058
1100 Superior Ave E # 1500 44114
Tel (216) 694-5700 SIC 1011 4931

NRP CONTRACTORS LLC p 1064
5309 Transportation Blvd 44125
Tel (216) 475-8900 SIC 1521 1522

NRP HOLDINGS LLC p 1064
5309 Transportation Blvd 44125
Tel (216) 475-8900 SIC 1531

OATEY CO p 1072
4700 W 160th St 44135
Tel (216) 267-7100 SIC 3444

OATEY SUPPLY CHAIN SERVICES INC p 1072
20600 Emerald Pkwy 44135
Tel (216) 267-7100 SIC 5074

■ OHIO BELL TELEPHONE CO p 1077
45 Erieview Plz 44114
Tel (216) 822-3439 SIC 4813 8721

OHIO CARPENTERS PENSION FUND p 1077
3611 Chester Ave 44114
Tel (330) 652-3475 SIC 6722

▲ OLYMPIC STEEL INC p 1083
22901 Millcreek Blvd # 650 44122
Tel (216) 292-3800 SIC 5051

ORLANDO BAKING CO p 1095
7777 Grand Ave 44104
Tel (216) 361-1872 SIC 2051

PARK CORP p 1115
6200 Riverside Dr 44135
Tel (216) 267-4870
SIC 3547 1711 3443 5084 6512 7999

▲ PARK-OHIO HOLDINGS CORP p 1116
6065 Parkland Blvd Ste 1 44124
Tel (440) 947-2000
SIC 3462 3069 3567 3363 3631 3524

■ PARK-OHIO INDUSTRIES INC p 1116
6065 Parkland Blvd Ste 1 44124
Tel (440) 947-2000
SIC 3462 3069 3567 3363 3524

▲ PARKER-HANNIFIN CORP p 1116
6035 Parkland Blvd 44124
Tel (216) 896-3000
SIC 3594 3593 3492 3569 3053 3829

PENTON BUSINESS MEDIA INC p 1132
1100 Superior Ave E Fl 8 44114
Tel (216) 696-7000 SIC 2741 7379

PHILIPS MEDICAL SYSTEMS (CLEVELAND) INC p 1143
595 Miner Rd 44143
Tel (440) 247-2652
SIC 3844 5047 5137 3842 3821 3699

PLAIN DEALER PUBLISHING CO p 1153
4800 Tiedeman Rd 44144
Tel (216) 999-5000 SIC 2711

■ PNC BANK NATIONAL ASSOCIATION p 1158
1900 E 9th St Lowr Ll1 44114
Tel (877) 762-2000 SIC 6021

■ PPG INDUSTRIES OHIO INC p 1166
3800 W 143rd St 44111
Tel (216) 671-0050 SIC 2851

PRESRITE CORP p 1172
3665 E 78th St 44105
Tel (216) 441-5990 SIC 3462

PRINCE & IZANT CO p 1176
12999 Plaza Dr 44130
Tel (216) 362-7000
SIC 5051 3398 3351 3341 3339 2899

■ PROGRESSIVE AGENCY INC p 1181
6300 Wilson Mills Rd 44143
Tel (440) 461-5000 SIC 6331

■ **PROGRESSIVE AMERICAN INSURANCE CO** p 1181
6300 Wilson Mills Rd 44143
Tel (440) 461-5000 *SIC* 6331

■ **PROGRESSIVE BAYSIDE INSURANCE CO** p 1181
6300 Wilson Mills Rd 44143
Tel (440) 395-4460 *SIC* 6311

■ **PROGRESSIVE CHOICE INSURANCE CO** p 1181
6300 Wilson Mills Rd 44143
Tel (440) 461-5000 *SIC* 6331

■ **PROGRESSIVE DIRECT INSURANCE CO** p 1181
6300 Wilson Mills Rd 44143
Tel (440) 461-5000 *SIC* 6331

■ **PROGRESSIVE HAWAII INSURANCE CORP** p 1181
6300 Wilson Mills Rd 44143
Tel (440) 461-5000 *SIC* 6411

■ **PROGRESSIVE MARATHON INSURANCE CO INC** p 1181
6300 Wilson Mills Rd 44143
Tel (888) 223-3558 *SIC* 6331

■ **PROGRESSIVE MAX INSURANCE CO** p 1181
6300 Wilson Mills Rd 44143
Tel (440) 461-5000 *SIC* 6331 6411

■ **PROGRESSIVE NORTHWESTERN INSURANCE CO** p 1181
6300 Wilson Mills Rd 44143
Tel (440) 461-5000 *SIC* 6331

■ **PROGRESSIVE PREFERRED INSURANCE CO** p 1182
6300 Wilson Mills Rd 44143
Tel (216) 464-8000 *SIC* 6331

■ **PROGRESSIVE PREMIER INSURANCE CO OF ILLINOIS** p 1182
6300 Wilson Mills Rd W33 44143
Tel (440) 461-5000 *SIC* 6411

■ **PROGRESSIVE SELECT INSURANCE CO** p 1182
6300 Wilson Mills Rd 44143
Tel (440) 461-5000 *SIC* 6331

■ **PROGRESSIVE SPECIALTY INSURANCE CO** p 1182
6300 Wilson Mills Rd 44143
Tel (440) 461-5000 *SIC* 6331

PUBCO CORP p 1189
3830 Kelley Ave 44114
Tel (216) 881-5300 *SIC* 3531 6512 3955

REALTY ONE INC p 1214
800 W Saint Clair Ave 44113
Tel (216) 328-2500 *SIC* 6531

RESILIENCE CAPITAL PARTNERS LLC p 1226
25101 Chagrin Blvd # 350 44122
Tel (216) 292-0200 *SIC* 7389

ROYAL APPLIANCE MFG CO p 1254
7005 Cochran Rd 44139
Tel (440) 996-2000 *SIC* 5064

S S KEMP & CO p 1262
4567 Willow Pkwy 44125
Tel (216) 271-7062 *SIC* 5046

SAFEGUARD PROPERTIES LLC p 1266
7887 Safeguard Cir 44125
Tel (216) 739-2900 *SIC* 8741 7382 7381

SAFEGUARD PROPERTIES MANAGEMENT LLC p 1266
7887 Hub Pkwy 44125
Tel (216) 739-2900 *SIC* 1522

■ **SHERWIN-WILLIAMS AUTOMOTIVE FINISHES CORP** p 1316
4440 Warrensville Ctr Rd 44128
Tel (216) 332-8330 *SIC* 5231 2851

▲ **SHERWIN-WILLIAMS CO** p 1316
101 W Prospect Ave # 1020 44115
Tel (216) 566-2000 *SIC* 5231 2851

▲ **SIFCO INDUSTRIES INC** p 1321
970 E 64th St 44103
Tel (216) 881-8600 *SIC* 3724 3462 3471

SISTERS OF CHARITY OF ST AUGUSTINE HEALTH SYSTEM INC p 1327
2475 E 22nd St 44115
Tel (216) 696-5560 *SIC* 8661 8733

SOUTHWEST COMMUNITY HEALTH SYSTEMS (INC) p 1351
18697 Bagley Rd 44130
Tel (440) 816-8000 *SIC* 8062

SOUTHWEST GENERAL HEALTH CENTER p 1352
18697 Bagley Rd 44130
Tel (440) 816-8000 *SIC* 8062

SQUIRE PATTON BOGGS (US) LLP p 1362
4900 Key Tower 127 Pub Sq 44114
Tel (216) 479-8500 *SIC* 8111

ST VINCENT CHARITY MEDICAL CENTER p 1373
2351 E 22nd St 44115
Tel (216) 861-6200 *SIC* 8062

STATE INDUSTRIAL PRODUCTS CORP p 1381
5915 Landerbrook Dr # 300 44124
Tel (877) 747-6986
SIC 2841 5072 2842 2992 2952 2899

STEIN INC p 1385
1929 E Royalton Rd Ste C 44147
Tel (440) 526-9301 *SIC* 3399 3312 5084

STEVENS ENGINEERS & CONSTRUCTORS INC p 1388
7850 Freeway Cir Ste 100 44130
Tel (440) 234-7888 *SIC* 1541 1711 8711

SUMMA HOLDINGS INC p 1398
8223 Brecksville Rd # 100 44141
Tel (440) 838-4700
SIC 2542 3462 3569 7359 3728

■ **SUPPLY TECHNOLOGIES LLC** p 1407
6065 Parkland Blvd Ste 1 44124
Tel (440) 947-2100 *SIC* 5085 3452 3469

SWIGER COIL SYSTEMS LTD p 1412
4677 Manufacturing Ave 44135
Tel (216) 362-7500 *SIC* 3621 3677

■ **T A HOLDINGS CORP** p 1419
24601 Center Ridge Rd # 200 44145
Tel (440) 808-9100 *SIC* 5541

TENABLE PROTECTIVE SERVICES INC p 1437
2423 Payne Ave 44114
Tel (216) 361-0002 *SIC* 7381

■ **TFS FINANCIAL CORP** p 1445
7007 Broadway Ave 44105
Tel (216) 441-6000 *SIC* 6035

■ **THIRD FEDERAL SAVINGS AND LOAN ASSOCIATION OF CLEVELAND** p 1448
7007 Broadway Ave 44105
Tel (800) 844-7333 *SIC* 6035

THOMPSON HINE LLP p 1449
127 Public Sq 44114
Tel (216) 566-5500 *SIC* 8111

TILDEN MINING CO LC p 1453
1100 Superior Ave E 44114
Tel (216) 694-5278 *SIC* 1011

▲ **TRANSDIGM GROUP INC** p 1471
1301 E 9th St Ste 3000 44114
Tel (216) 706-2960 *SIC* 3728 5088

■ **TRANSDIGM INC** p 1471
4223 Monticello Blvd 44121
Tel (216) 706-2939
SIC 5088 3563 3625 3492 3691 3491

TRANSPORTATION UNLIMITED INC p 1473
3740 Carnegie Ave Ste 101 44115
Tel (216) 426-0088 *SIC* 7363 4213 4212

TRANSTAR HOLDING CO p 1473
5900 Landerbrook Dr Bsmt 44124
Tel (440) 684-1400 *SIC* 3444 3281 2952

TRANSTAR INDUSTRIES INC p 1473
7350 Young Dr 44146
Tel (440) 232-5100 *SIC* 5013

■ **UNITED FINANCIAL CASUALTY CO INC** p 1508
6300 Wilson Mills Rd 44143
Tel (440) 461-5000 *SIC* 6331

■ **UNITED TACONITE LLC** p 1514
1100 Superior Ave E # 1500 44114
Tel (218) 744-7800 *SIC* 1011

UNIVERSITY HOSPITALS HEALTH SY p 1519
11100 Euclid Ave 44106
Tel (216) 844-4663 *SIC* 8062

UNIVERSITY HOSPITALS OF CLEVELAND p 1519
11100 Euclid Ave 44106
Tel (216) 844-1000 *SIC* 8062 8069

■ **URS FEDERAL SERVICES INTERNATIONAL INC** p 1530
1300 E 9th St Ste 500 44114
Tel (301) 944-3100 *SIC* 8711

VALLEY FORD TRUCK INC p 1540
5715 Canal Rd 44125
Tel (216) 524-2400
SIC 5013 5511 5521 5531 5012

VOCATIONAL GUIDANCE SERVICES INC p 1564
2239 E 55th St 44103
Tel (216) 431-7800 *SIC* 8331

WAXMAN INDUSTRIES INC p 1584
24460 Aurora Rd 44146
Tel (440) 439-1830
SIC 5072 5074 3494 3491 3432

WEINBERG CAPITAL GROUP INC p 1588
5005 Rockside Rd Ste 1140 44131
Tel (216) 503-8307 *SIC* 6799

WELTMAN WEINBERG & REIS CO LPA p 1591
323 W Lkeside Ave Ste 200 44113
Tel (216) 685-1000 *SIC* 8111

WIRELESS CENTER INC p 1618
1925 Saint Clair Ave Ne 44114
Tel (216) 503-3777 *SIC* 4812

WORLD SHIPPING INC p 1625
1340 Depot St Ste 200 44116
Tel (440) 356-7676 *SIC* 4213 4731

ZENITH SYSTEMS LLC p 1642
5055 Corbin Dr 44128
Tel (216) 587-9510 *SIC* 1731

CLYDE, OH

REVERE PLASTICS SYSTEMS GROUP LLC p 1229
401 Elm St 43410
Tel (419) 547-6918 *SIC* 3089

REVERE PLASTICS SYSTEMS LLC p 1229
401 Elm St 43410
Tel (419) 547-6918 *SIC* 3089

COLUMBIANA, OH

ENVELOPE 1 INC p 503
41969 State Route 344 44408
Tel (330) 482-3900 *SIC* 2677

COLUMBUS, OH

2CHECKOUT.COM INC p 2
855 Grandview Ave Ste 110 43215
Tel (614) 921-2449 *SIC* 5961

ADB SAFEGATE AMERICAS LLC p 21
977 Gahanna Pkwy 43230
Tel (614) 861-1304 *SIC* 3648 3812

■ **AEP GENERATING CO** p 29
1 Riverside Plz Ste 1600 43215
Tel (614) 223-1000 *SIC* 4911

■ **AEP POWER MARKETING INC** p 29
1 Riverside Plz Fl 1 43215
Tel (614) 716-1000 *SIC* 4911

■ **AEP TEXAS CENTRAL CO** p 29
1 Riverside Plz 43215
Tel (614) 716-1000 *SIC* 4911

AIRNET SYSTEMS INC p 40
7250 Star Check Dr 43217
Tel (614) 409-4900 *SIC* 4522 4731

ALLIED MINERAL PRODUCTS INC p 56
2700 Scioto Pkwy 43221
Tel (614) 876-0244 *SIC* 3297

■ **ALPINE INSULATION I LLC** p 60
495 S High St Ste 50 43215
Tel (614) 221-3399 *SIC* 5033 5211

AMERICAN COMMERCE INSURANCE CO p 70
3590 Twin Creeks Dr 43204
Tel (614) 272-6951 *SIC* 6331 6351

▲ **AMERICAN ELECTRIC POWER CO INC** p 71
1 Riverside Plz Fl 1 43215
Tel (614) 716-1000 *SIC* 4911

■ **AMERICAN ELECTRIC POWER SERVICE CORP** p 71
1 Riverside Plz Fl 1 43215
Tel (614) 716-1000
SIC 4911 8711 8713 8721

AMERICAN HEALTH NETWORK INC p 73
2500 Corporate Exchange D 43231
Tel (614) 794-4500 *SIC* 8011

AMERICAN MUNICIPAL POWER INC p 76
1111 Schrock Rd Ste 100 43229
Tel (614) 540-1111 *SIC* 4911

AMERICAN SIGNATURE INC p 79
4300 E 5th Ave 43219
Tel (614) 449-6107 *SIC* 7389

■ **APPALACHIAN POWER CO** p 98
1 Riverside Plz 43215
Tel (614) 716-1000 *SIC* 4911

ARC INDUSTRIES INC OF FRANKLIN COUNTY OHIO p 103
2879 Johnstown Rd 43219
Tel (614) 475-6440 *SIC* 8331

ATLAS INDUSTRIAL CONTRACTORS LLC p 128
5275 Sinclair Rd 43229
Tel (614) 841-4500 *SIC* 1731 3498 1796

ATTORNEY GENERAL OF OHIO p 129
30 E Broad St Fl 17 43215
Tel (614) 466-6963 *SIC* 9222

AUTOMOTIVE DISTRIBUTORS CO INC p 134
2981 Morse Rd 43231
Tel (614) 476-1315 *SIC* 5013

■ **BANC ONE SERVICES CORP** p 149
1111 Polaris Pkwy Ste B3 43240
Tel (614) 248-5800 *SIC* 7389

BATTELLE LIBRARY p 159
505 King Ave 43201
Tel (614) 424-6302 *SIC* 8733

BATTELLE MEMORIAL INSTITUTE INC p 159
505 King Ave 43201
Tel (614) 424-6424 *SIC* 8731

▲ **BIG LOTS INC** p 181
300 Phillipi Rd 43228
Tel (614) 278-6800 *SIC* 5331

■ **BIG LOTS STORES INC** p 181
300 Phillipi Rd 43228
Tel (614) 278-6800 *SIC* 5331

▲ **BRAVO BRIO RESTAURANT GROUP INC** p 209
777 Goodale Blvd Ste 100 43212
Tel (614) 326-7944 *SIC* 5812

■ **BROADSTREET PARTNERS INC** p 215
580 N 4th St Ste 450 43215
Tel (614) 993-3009 *SIC* 6211

BUCKEYE POWER INC p 223
6677 Busch Blvd 43229
Tel (614) 781-0573 *SIC* 8611 4911

BURGESS & NIPLE INC p 227
5085 Reed Rd 43220
Tel (502) 254-2344 *SIC* 8711 8712

CAMERON MITCHELL RESTAURANTS LLC p 245
515 Park St 43215
Tel (614) 621-3663 *SIC* 8741 5812

CBC COMPANIES INC p 268
250 E Broad St Fl 21 43215
Tel (614) 222-4343 *SIC* 7322

CENTRIC FINANCIAL GROUP LLC p 281
4016 Townsfair Way # 202 43219
Tel (614) 824-6100 *SIC* 6311 6282 6321

CITY OF COLUMBUS p 314
90 W Broad St Rm B33 43215
Tel (614) 645-7671 *SIC* 9111

■ **CLOSEOUT DISTRIBUTION INC** p 327
300 Phillipi Rd 43228
Tel (614) 278-6800 *SIC* 5092

■ **COLUMBIA ENERGY GROUP** p 340
200 Civic Center Dr 43215
Tel (614) 460-4683 *SIC* 4922 1311 1731

■ **COLUMBIA GAS OF OHIO INC** p 340
290 W Nationwide Blvd # 114 43215
Tel (614) 460-6000 *SIC* 4924

■ **COLUMBIA GAS TRANSMISSION LLC** p 340
200 Cizzic Ctr Dr 43216
Tel (614) 460-6000 *SIC* 4922

COLUMBUS ASSOCIATION FOR PERFORMING ARTS p 342
55 E State St 43215
Tel (614) 469-1045 *SIC* 6512

COLUMBUS DISTRIBUTING CO p 342
4949 Freeway Dr E 43229
Tel (614) 846-1000 *SIC* 5181

COLUMBUS EQUIPMENT CO p 342
2323 Performance Way 43207
Tel (614) 437-0352 *SIC* 5082 7353

COLUMBUS PUBLIC SCHOOL DISTRICT p 342
270 E State St Fl 3 43215
Tel (614) 365-5000 *SIC* 8211 8299

COLUMBUS REGIONAL AIRPORT AUTHORITY p 342
4600 Intl Gtwy Ste 2 43219
Tel (614) 239-4015 *SIC* 4581

■ **COLUMBUS SOUTHERN POWER CO** p 342
1 Riverside Plz 43215
Tel (614) 716-1000 *SIC* 4911

COLUMBUS STATE COMMUNITY COLLEGE p 342
550 E Spring St 43215
Tel (614) 287-2400 *SIC* 8222 8221

COLUMBUS STEEL CASTINGS CO p 342
2211 Parsons Ave 43207
Tel (614) 444-2121 *SIC* 3325

COLUMBUS WEST-WARD INC p 342
1809 Wilson Rd 43228
Tel (614) 276-4000 *SIC* 2834

CONTINENTAL OFFICE FURNITURE CORP p 363
2601 Silver Dr 43211
Tel (614) 262-5010 *SIC* 5021 1752

CONTINENTAL REAL ESTATE COMPANIES p 363
150 E Broad St Ste 200 43215
Tel (614) 221-1800 *SIC* 1542 1541

■ **CORE AUTOMOTIVE TECHNOLOGIES LLC** p 369
800 Manor Park Dr 43228
Tel (614) 870-5000 *SIC* 3714 5521

▲ **CORE MOLDING TECHNOLOGIES INC** p 369
800 Manor Park Dr 43228
Tel (614) 870-5000 *SIC* 3089

CORPORATE FINANCE ASSOCIATES OF COLUMBUS INC p 372
671 Camden Yard Ct 43235
Tel (614) 457-9219 *SIC* 8742 7389 6211

CORTES NP ACQUISITION CORP p 373
1050 Dearborn Dr 43085
Tel (614) 888-0246 *SIC* 3679 3585

CRANE GROUP CO p 389
330 W Spring St Ste 200 43215
Tel (614) 754-3000 *SIC* 8741

CRANE GROUP COMPANIES LIMITED p 389
2141 Fairwood Ave 43207
Tel (614) 443-4891 *SIC* 3089

CRANEL INC p 389
8999 Gemini Pkwy Ste A 43240
Tel (614) 431-8000 *SIC* 5045

■ **CSC DISTRIBUTION INC** p 397
300 Phillipi Rd 43228
Tel (614) 278-6800 *SIC* 5092

DAMONS INTERNATIONAL INC p 410
4645 Executive Dr 43220
Tel (614) 442-7900 *SIC* 6794 8741 5812

DEPARTMENT OF HEALTH OHIO p 430
246 N High St 43215
Tel (614) 466-3543 *SIC* 9431

▲ **DIAMOND HILL INVESTMENT GROUP INC** p 436
325 John H Mcconnell Blvd # 200 43215
Tel (614) 255-3333 *SIC* 6282

DIAMOND INNOVATIONS INC p 437
6325 Huntley Rd 43229
Tel (614) 438-2000 *SIC* 3291

DISPATCH PRINTING CO p 443
62 E Broad St 43215
Tel (614) 461-5000 *SIC* 4833

DLZ CORP p 445
6121 Huntley Rd 43229
Tel (614) 888-0040 *SIC* 1623 8713 8712

DOCTORS OHIOHEALTH CORP p 447
5100 W Broad St 43228
Tel (614) 544-5424 *SIC* 8062 8011

DONATOS PIZZERIA LLC p 450
935 Taylor Station Rd 43230
Tel (614) 864-2444 *SIC* 5812

▲ DSW INC p 458
810 Dsw Dr 43219
Tel (614) 237-7100 *SIC* 5661

■ DSW SHOE WAREHOUSE INC p 458
4314 E 5th Ave 43219
Tel (614) 237-7100 *SIC* 5661

ELECTRONIC CLASSROOM OF TOMORROW p 485
3700 S High St Ste 95 43207
Tel (888) 326-8395 *SIC* 8211

ELFORD INC p 486
1220 Dublin Rd 43215
Tel (614) 488-4000 *SIC* 1542 1541 8741

ERNIE GREEN INDUSTRIES INC p 508
2030 Dividend Dr 43228
Tel (614) 219-1423
SIC 3714 3089 3471 3469

EXECUTIVE OFFICE STATE OF OHIO p 518
30 E Broad St 43215
Tel (614) 466-3555 *SIC* 9111

▲ EXPRESS INC p 520
1 Express Dr 43230
Tel (614) 474-4001 *SIC* 5621 5632 5611

■ EXPRESS LLC p 520
1 Express Dr 43230
Tel (614) 474-4001 *SIC* 5621 5611

■ EXPRESS TOPCO LLC p 520
1 Express Dr 43230
Tel (614) 474-4001 *SIC* 5621 5611

FAMILY MEDICINE NORTH INC p 527
1930 Crown Park Ct # 130 43235
Tel (614) 457-1793 *SIC* 8011

FCX PERFORMANCE INC p 533
3000 E 14th Ave 43219
Tel (614) 324-6050 *SIC* 5084 5085 3494

■ FIFTH THIRD BANK OF COLUMBUS OH p 542
21 E State St Fl 4 43215
Tel (614) 744-7553 *SIC* 6022

FISHEL CO p 551
1366 Dublin Rd 43215
Tel (614) 274-8100 *SIC* 1623 1731 8711

■ FORTUNE BRANDS WINDOWS INC p 570
3948 Townsfair Way # 200 43219
Tel (614) 532-3500 *SIC* 1751 5211

FRANKLIN COUNTY BOARD OF COMMISSIONERS p 575
373 S High St Fl 26 43215
Tel (614) 525-3322 *SIC* 9111

FST LOGISTICS INC p 582
1727 Georgesville Rd 43228
Tel (614) 529-7900 *SIC* 4212

GARDNER INC p 592
3641 Interchange Rd 43204
Tel (614) 351-1325 *SIC* 5084 6512

GEO BYERS SONS HOLDING INC p 605
427 S Hamilton Rd 43213
Tel (614) 228-5111 *SIC* 5511

GEORGE J IGEL & CO INC p 606
2040 Alum Creek Dr 43207
Tel (614) 445-8421 *SIC* 1794 1623 6552

GERMAIN TOYOTA p 608
4250 Morse Xing 43219
Tel (239) 592-5550 *SIC* 5511

GLIMCHER REALTY TRUST p 615
180 E Broad St Fl 20 43215
Tel (614) 621-9000 *SIC* 6512

GRANGE MUTUAL CASUALTY CO p 630
671 S High St 43206
Tel (614) 445-2900 *SIC* 6331

■ HEXION HOLDINGS LLC p 688
180 E Broad St 43215
Tel (614) 225-4000 *SIC* 6719

■ HEXION INC p 688
180 E Broad St Fl 26 43215
Tel (614) 225-4000 *SIC* 2821

■ HEXION LLC p 688
180 E Broad St Fl 26 43215
Tel (614) 225-4000 *SIC* 2821 2899

HIGHLIGHTS FOR CHILDREN INC p 692
1800 Watermark Dr 43215
Tel (614) 486-0631 *SIC* 2721

HILLIARD CITY SCHOOL DISTRICT p 693
2140 Atlas St 43228
Tel (614) 921-7000 *SIC* 8211

HOMETOWN URGENT CARE p 704
2400 Corp Exchange Dr # 102 43231
Tel (614) 505-7633 *SIC* 8062

▲ HUNTINGTON BANCSHARES INC p 720
41 S High St 43215
Tel (614) 480-8300 *SIC* 6021

■ HUNTINGTON NATIONAL BANK p 720
17 S High St Fl 1 43215
Tel (614) 480-4293 *SIC* 6029

HY-TEK MATERIAL HANDLING INC p 722
2222 Rickenbacker Pkwy W 43217
Tel (614) 497-2500
SIC 5084 5013 7538 7513 1796

IBP CORP HOLDINGS INC p 726
495 S High St Ste 50 43215
Tel (614) 692-6360 *SIC* 1742 6719

■ INDIANA MICHIGAN POWER CO p 738
1 Riverside Plz 43215
Tel (614) 716-1000 *SIC* 4911

▲ INSTALLED BUILDING PRODUCTS INC p 746
495 S High St Ste 50 43215
Tel (614) 221-3399 *SIC* 1522 5033 5211

■ INSTALLED BUILDING PRODUCTS LLC p 746
495 S High St Ste 50 43215
Tel (614) 221-3399 *SIC* 1742 5211 1761

■ INTIMATE BRANDS HOLDING LLC p 759
3 Limited Pkwy 43230
Tel (614) 415-7000 *SIC* 5632

■ INTIMATE BRANDS INC p 759
3 Limited Pkwy 43230
Tel (614) 415-7000 *SIC* 5632

JMAC INC p 786
200 W Nationwide Blvd # 1 43215
Tel (614) 436-2418
SIC 3325 5198 7999 5511 8741

JOBSOHIO p 787
41 S High St 43215
Tel (614) 224-6446 *SIC* 7361

■ JPMORGAN CHASE BANK NATIONAL ASSOCIATION p 795
1111 Polaris Pkwy 43240
Tel (614) 436-3055
SIC 6022 6099 6799 6211 6162 7389

■ JPMORGAN INVESTMENT ADVISORS INC p 795
1111 Polaris Pkwy 43240
Tel (614) 248-5800 *SIC* 6282

KAPPA KAPPA GAMMA FOUNDATION p 803
530 E Town St 43215
Tel (614) 228-6515 *SIC* 8641

KOKOSING CONSTRUCTION CO INC p 826
886 Mckinley Ave 43222
Tel (614) 228-1029
SIC 1611 1622 1629 1542 1541 1623

▲ L BRANDS INC p 833
3 Limited Pkwy 43230
Tel (614) 415-7000
SIC 5632 5961 5621 5999

■ L BRANDS STORE DESIGN & CONSTRUCTION INC p 834
3 Ltd Pkwy 43230
Tel (614) 415-7000 *SIC* 1542

▲ LANCASTER COLONY CORP p 841
37 W Broad St Ste 500 43215
Tel (614) 224-7141 *SIC* 2035 2038

■ LANE BRYANT INC p 843
3344 Morse Xing 43219
Tel (614) 476-9281 *SIC* 5621

LIEBERT CORP p 863
1050 Dearborn Dr 43085
Tel (614) 888-0246 *SIC* 3585 3613 7629

LIEBERT NORTH AMERICA INC p 863
1050 Dearborn Dr 43085
Tel (614) 888-0246 *SIC* 3699 3585

LIQUI-BOX CORP p 870
480 Schrock Rd Ste G 43229
Tel (804) 325-1400
SIC 2673 3585 3089 3081 5149

LOEB ELECTRIC CO p 874
1800 E 5th Ave Ste A 43219
Tel (614) 294-6351 *SIC* 5063

LUXURY HOME FURNISHINGS LLC p 887
130 S Merkle Rd 43209
Tel (661) 631-0299 *SIC* 5712

▲ M/I HOMES INC p 890
3 Easton Oval Ste 500 43219
Tel (614) 418-8000 *SIC* 1531 6162

■ MAST INDUSTRIES INC p 917
2 Limited Pkwy 43230
Tel (614) 415-7000 *SIC* 5137 5136

■ MAST LOGISTICS SERVICES INC p 917
2 Limited Pkwy 43230
Tel (614) 415-7500 *SIC* 5113

MCNAUGHTON-MCKAY ELECTRIC CO OF OHIO INC p 932
2255 Citygate Dr 43219
Tel (614) 476-2800 *SIC* 5063

▲ METTLER-TOLEDO INTERNATIONAL INC p 957
1900 Polaris Pkwy Fl 6 43240
Tel (614) 438-4511
SIC 3596 3821 3826 3823

■ METTLER-TOLEDO LLC p 957
1900 Polaris Pkwy Fl 6 43240
Tel (614) 438-4511
SIC 3596 5049 7699 3821 3823 3826

MGF SOURCING US LLC p 958
4200 Regent St Ste 205 43219
Tel (614) 904-3269 *SIC* 5137 5136

MIDWEST MOTOR SUPPLY CO p 967
4800 Roberts Rd 43228
Tel (800) 233-1294 *SIC* 3965 3399 8742

MILBANK INSURANCE CO p 968
518 E Broad St 43215
Tel (614) 464-5000 *SIC* 6411

MOMENTIVE PERFORMANCE MATERIALS INC p 983
180 E Broad St 43215
Tel (614) 986-2495 *SIC* 2821 2869

MOTORISTS COMMERCIAL MUTUAL INSURANCE CO p 993
471 E Broad St Bsmt 43215
Tel (614) 225-8211 *SIC* 6331

MOTORISTS LIFE INSURANCE CO p 993
471 E Broad St Ste 200 43215
Tel (614) 225-8211 *SIC* 6311

MOTORISTS MUTUAL INSURANCE CO p 993
471 E Broad St Ste 200 43215
Tel (614) 225-8211 *SIC* 6331

MOUNT CARMEL EAST HOSPITAL p 993
6001 E Broad St 43213
Tel (614) 234-6000 *SIC* 8062

MOUNT CARMEL HEALTH p 993
793 W State St 43222
Tel (614) 234-5000 *SIC* 8062

MOUNT CARMEL HEALTH PLAN MEDIG p 993
6150 E Broad St 43213
Tel (614) 546-3138 *SIC* 8099

MOUNT CARMEL HEALTH SYSTEM p 993
793 W State St 43222
Tel (614) 234-5000 *SIC* 8062

MOUNT CARMEL HEALTH SYSTEM p 993
6150 E Broad St 43213
Tel (614) 234-6000 *SIC* 8062

N WASSERSTROM & SONS INC p 1005
2300 Lockbourne Rd 43207
Tel (614) 737-8543 *SIC* 3556 5046 3444

NATIONAL CHURCH RESIDENCES p 1010
2333 N Bank Dr 43220
Tel (614) 451-2151
SIC 6531 6513 8051 8059

NATIONWIDE BANK p 1017
3 Nationwide Plz 43215
Tel (800) 882-2822 *SIC* 6035

NATIONWIDE CHILDRENS HOSPITAL p 1017
700 Childrens Dr 43205
Tel (614) 722-3040 *SIC* 8069

NATIONWIDE CORP p 1017
1 Nationwide Plz 43215
Tel (614) 249-7111 *SIC* 6411 6321

NATIONWIDE FINANCIAL INSTITUTION DISTRIBUTORS AGENCY INC p 1017
1 W Nationwide Blvd 2-0501 43215
Tel (614) 249-6825 *SIC* 6211

NATIONWIDE FINANCIAL SERVICES INC p 1017
1 Nationwide Plz 43215
Tel (614) 249-7111 *SIC* 6311 6411 8742

NATIONWIDE INSURANCE CO OF FLORIDA p 1018
2 Nationwide Plz 43215
Tel (614) 249-7111 *SIC* 6411

NATIONWIDE LIFE AND ANNUITY INSURANCE CO p 1018
1 W Nationwide Blvd # 100 43215
Tel (614) 249-7111 *SIC* 6411

NATIONWIDE LIFE INSURANCE CO p 1018
1 Nationwide Plz 43215
Tel (877) 669-6877 *SIC* 6411

NATIONWIDE MUTUAL FIRE INSURANCE CO p 1018
1 W Nationwide Blvd # 100 43215
Tel (614) 249-7111 *SIC* 6411

NATIONWIDE MUTUAL INSURANCE CO p 1018
1 Nationwide Plz 43215
Tel (614) 249-7111
SIC 6331 6311 6321 6531

■ NETJETS AVIATION INC p 1027
4111 Bridgeway Ave 43219
Tel (614) 239-5500 *SIC* 4522

■ NETJETS INC p 1027
4111 Bridgeway Ave 43219
Tel (614) 239-5500 *SIC* 4522 5088 7359

■ NETJETS SALES INC p 1027
4111 Bridgeway Ave 43219
Tel (614) 239-5500 *SIC* 5088 4522

NEW SBARRO INTERMEDIATE HOLDINGS INC p 1033
1328 Dublin Rd 43215
Tel (614) 769-9911 *SIC* 6719

NIAGARA HEALTH CORP p 1042
6150 E Broad St 43213
Tel (614) 898-4000 *SIC* 8741 8062

ODW LOGISTICS INC p 1074
1580 Williams Rd 43207
Tel (614) 497-1660 *SIC* 4225 4226

OHIO BUREAU OF WORKERS COMPENSATION p 1077
30 W Spring St Fl 2-29 43215
Tel (614) 644-6292 *SIC* 6331 9199

OHIO BUSINESS DEVELOPMENT COALITION p 1077
41 S High St Ste 3625 43215
Tel (614) 469-1044 *SIC* 8611

OHIO DEPARTMENT OF ADMINISTRATIVE SERVICES p 1077
30 E Broad St Fl 39 43215
Tel (614) 466-6511 *SIC* 9199

OHIO DEPARTMENT OF DEVELOPMENTAL DISABILITIES p 1077
30 E Broad St Fl 13 43215
Tel (614) 728-5544 *SIC* 9441

OHIO DEPARTMENT OF JOB AND FAMILY SERVICES p 1077
30 E Broad St Fl 32 43215
Tel (614) 466-6282 *SIC* 9441

OHIO DEPARTMENT OF MENTAL HEALTH p 1077
30 E Broad St Fl 8 43215
Tel (614) 466-2337 *SIC* 8052

OHIO DEPARTMENT OF MENTAL HEALTH AND ADDICTION SERVICES p 1077
30 E Broad St Fl 11 43215
Tel (614) 466-2337 *SIC* 9431

OHIO DEPARTMENT OF NATURAL RESOURCES p 1077
2045 Morse Rd Bldg D-3 43229
Tel (614) 265-6875 *SIC* 9512

OHIO DEPARTMENT OF PUBLIC SAFETY p 1077
1970 W Broad St Fl 5 43223
Tel (614) 466-3383 *SIC* 9229

OHIO DEPARTMENT OF REHABILITATION AND CORRECTION p 1077
770 W Broad St 43222
Tel (614) 752-1233 *SIC* 9223

OHIO DEPARTMENT OF TAXATION p 1077
30 E Broad St Fl 22 43215
Tel (614) 466-3020 *SIC* 9311

OHIO DEPARTMENT OF TRANSPORTATION p 1077
1980 W Broad St 43223
Tel (614) 466-7170 *SIC* 9621

OHIO ENVIRONMENTAL PROTECTION AGENCY p 1077
50 W Town St Ste 700 43215
Tel (614) 644-3020 *SIC* 9511

OHIO NATIONAL GUARD p 1077
2825 W Dblin Granville Rd 43235
Tel (614) 336-7000 *SIC* 9711

OHIO OPERATING ENGINEERS HEALTH & WELFARE FUND p 1078
1180 Dublin Rd 43215
Tel (614) 488-0708 *SIC* 6371

■ OHIO POWER CO p 1078
1 Riverside Plz 43215
Tel (614) 716-1000 *SIC* 4911

OHIO PRESBYTERIAN RETIREMENT SERVICES (INC) p 1078
1001 Kingsmill Pkwy 43229
Tel (614) 888-7800 *SIC* 8361

OHIO PUBLIC EMPLOYEES RETIREMENT SYSTEM p 1078
277 E Town St 43215
Tel (614) 228-8471 *SIC* 6371 9441

OHIO STATE UNIVERSITY p 1078
Student Acade Servi Bldg 43210
Tel (614) 292-6446 *SIC* 8221 5812

OHIO STATE UNIVERSITY FOUNDATION p 1078
364 W Lane Ave Ste B 43201
Tel (614) 292-6261 *SIC* 8641

OHIO STATE UNIVERSITY WEXNER MEDICAL CENTER p 1078
1492 E Broad St 43205
Tel (614) 293-8000 *SIC* 8741

OHIO TRANSMISSION CORP p 1078
1900 Jetway Blvd 43219
Tel (614) 342-6247 *SIC* 5084 5085

OHIOHEALTH CORP p 1078
180 E Broad St 43215
Tel (614) 788-8860
SIC 8049 8062 8082 8051

OLEN CORP p 1082
4755 S High St 43207
Tel (614) 491-1515 *SIC* 1442

PALMER-DONAVIN MANUFACTURING CO p 1109
3210 Centerpoint Dr 43212
Tel (614) 486-0975 *SIC* 5033

PARKING SOLUTIONS INC p 1116
353 W Nationwide Blvd 43215
Tel (614) 469-7000 *SIC* 7299

PEDIATRIC ACADEMIC ASSOCIATION p 1127
700 Childrens Dr 43205
Tel (614) 722-2459 *SIC* 8621

PERSONAL SERVICE INSURANCE CO p 1137
2760 Airport Dr Ste 130 43219
Tel (800) 282-9416 *SIC* 6331

PHYSICIANS OF OHIO STATE UNIVERSITY p 1146
700 Ackerman Rd Ste 360 43202
Tel (614) 263-2450 *SIC* 8621

PLASKOLITE LLC p 1155
1770 Joyce Ave 43219
Tel (614) 294-3281 *SIC* 2821

PLASTIC SUPPLIERS INC p 1155
2450 Marilyn Ln 43219
Tel (614) 471-9100 *SIC* 3081

POWER DISTRIBUTORS LLC p 1165
3700 Paragon Dr 43228
Tel (614) 876-3533 *SIC* 5084

PRESTRESS SERVICES INDUSTRIES LLC p 1173
250 N Hartford Ave 43222
Tel (859) 299-0461 *SIC* 3272

PUBLIC EMPLOYEE DEFERRED COMPENSATION OHIO p 1189
257 E Town St Ste 457 43215
Tel (614) 466-7245 *SIC* 8721 9311

■ **PUBLIC SERVICE CO OF OKLAHOMA** p 1190
1 Riverside Plz 43215
Tel (614) 716-1000 *SIC* 4911

REAL LIVING INC p 1213
77 E Nationwide Blvd 43215
Tel (614) 221-7400 *SIC* 6531

RED CAPITAL GROUP LLC p 1215
10 W Broad St Ste 1510 43215
Tel (614) 857-1400 *SIC* 6282

RED ROOF INNS INC p 1216
605 S Front St Ste 150 43215
Tel (614) 744-2600 *SIC* 7011

■ **RETAIL VENTURES SERVICES INC** p 1228
4150 E 5th Ave 43219
Tel (614) 238-4105 *SIC* 5661

ROSEMARK PAPER INC p 1250
1845 Progress Ave 43207
Tel (614) 443-0303 *SIC* 5111 5199

ROXANE LABORATORIES INC p 1253
1809 Wilson Rd 43228
Tel (614) 276-4000 *SIC* 2834

SAFE AUTO INSURANCE CO p 1265
4 Easton Oval 43219
Tel (614) 231-0200 *SIC* 6411

SAFE AUTO INSURANCE GROUP INC p 1265
4 Easton Oval 43219
Tel (614) 231-0200 *SIC* 6331 6411

SAFELITE FULFILLMENT INC p 1266
7400 Safelite Way 43235
Tel (614) 210-9747 *SIC* 5231

SAFELITE GLASS CORP p 1266
7400 Safelite Way 43235
Tel (614) 210-9000 *SIC* 3231

SAFELITE GROUP INC p 1266
7400 Safelite Way 43235
Tel (614) 210-9000 *SIC* 7536 3231 6411

SAFELITE SOLUTIONS LLC p 1266
7400 Safelite Way 43235
Tel (614) 210-9000 *SIC* 8742

SALO INC p 1273
960 Checkrein Ave Ste A 43229
Tel (614) 436-9404 *SIC* 8082

SB CAPITAL ACQUISITIONS LLC p 1285
4010 E 5th Ave 43219
Tel (614) 443-4080 *SIC* 5399

SB CAPITAL GROUP LLC p 1285
4300 E 5th Ave 43219
Tel (516) 829-2400 *SIC* 7389

SBARRO LLC p 1285
1328 Dublin Rd Ste 21 43215
Tel (614) 769-9911 *SIC* 5812

SCHOOL EMPLOYEES RETIREMENT SYSTEM OF OHIO p 1290
300 E Broad St Ste 100 43215
Tel (614) 222-5853 *SIC* 6371 9441

SCHOTTENSTEIN STORES CORP p 1290
4300 E 5th Ave 43219
Tel (614) 221-9200
SIC 5311 5712 5912 5999

■ **SCIOTO DOWNS INC** p 1292
6000 S High St 43207
Tel (614) 295-4700 *SIC* 7948

SCOTTSDALE INSURANCE CO p 1294
1 Nationwide Plz 13207 43215
Tel (480) 365-4000 *SIC* 6411

SECRETARY OF STATE OHIO p 1298
180 E Broad St Fl 16 43215
Tel (614) 466-2655 *SIC* 9111 9611

■ **SOUTHWESTERN ELECTRIC POWER CO** p 1353
1 Riverside Plz 43215
Tel (614) 716-1000 *SIC* 4911

■ **STATE AUTO FINANCIAL CORP** p 1380
518 E Broad St 43215
Tel (614) 464-5000 *SIC* 6331

■ **STATE AUTO PROPERTY AND CASUALTY INSURANCE CO** p 1380
518 E Broad St 43215
Tel (614) 464-5000 *SIC* 6331

▲ **STATE AUTOMOBILE MUTUAL INSURANCE CO INC** p 1380
518 E Broad St 43215
Tel (614) 464-5000 *SIC* 6331 6411 6351

STATE OF OHIO p 1382
30 E Broad St Fl 40 43215
Tel (614) 466-3455 *SIC* 9111

STATE OF OHIO p 1382
30 W Spring St Fl 5 43215
Tel (614) 466-8660 *SIC* 9441

STATE OF OHIO OFFICE OF BUDGET AND MANAGEMENT STATE ACCOUNTING p 1382
30 E Broad St 43215
Tel (614) 466-4034 *SIC* 9311

STATE OF OHIO OFFICE OF BUDGET AND MANAGEMENT STATE ACCOUNTING p 1382
30 E Broad St Fl 34 43215
Tel (614) 466-4034 *SIC* 9511

STATE TEACHERS RETIREMENT SYSTEM OF OHIO p 1383
275 E Broad St 43215
Tel (614) 227-4090 *SIC* 6371

STERLING PAPER CO p 1387
1845 Progress Ave 43207
Tel (614) 443-0303 *SIC* 5111 5199

■ **SYSCO CENTRAL OHIO INC** p 1416
2400 Harrison Rd 43204
Tel (614) 272-0658 *SIC* 5141 5142

THIRTY-ONE GIFTS LLC p 1448
3425 Morse Xing 43219
Tel (614) 414-4300 *SIC* 5947

■ **TMARZETTI CO** p 1457
1105 Schrock Rd Fl 3 43229
Tel (614) 846-2232 *SIC* 2035 2098

TRI-W GROUP INC p 1478
835 Goodale Blvd 43212
Tel (614) 228-5000 *SIC* 3694 7538 7537

■ **UNITED HEALTHCARE OF OHIO INC** p 1509
9200 Worthington Rd 43085
Tel (614) 410-7000 *SIC* 6324

UNITED PRODUCERS INC p 1511
8351 N High St Ste 250 43235
Tel (614) 433-2150 *SIC* 5154

VALUE CITY FURNITURE INC p 1542
4300 E 5th Ave 43219
Tel (888) 751-8552 *SIC* 5712

VOIGT & SCHWEITZER LLC p 1564
987 Buckeye Park Rd 43207
Tel (614) 449-8281 *SIC* 3479

VORYS SATER SEYMOUR AND PEASE LLP p 1566
52 E Gay St 43215
Tel (614) 464-6400 *SIC* 8111

▲ **WASHINGTON PRIME GROUP INC** p 1578
180 E Broad St 43215
Tel (614) 621-9000 *SIC* 6798

WASSERSTROM CO p 1580
477 S Front St 43215
Tel (614) 737-8472
SIC 5087 3566 5021 5046 5112 5719

WHITE CASTLE SYSTEM INC p 1606
555 W Goodale St 43215
Tel (614) 228-5781
SIC 5812 5142 2051 2013

■ **WP GLIMCHER INC** p 1627
180 E Broad St Fl 21 43215
Tel (614) 621-9000 *SIC* 6798

YACHIYO OF AMERICA INC p 1633
2285 Walcutt Rd 43228
Tel (614) 876-3220 *SIC* 3089 3465 3714

YOUNG MENS CHRISTIAN ASSOCIATION OF CENTRAL OHIO p 1638
40 W Long St 43215
Tel (614) 224-1142 *SIC* 8641

CONCORD TOWNSHIP, OH

RANPAK CORP p 1208
7990 Auburn Rd 44077
Tel (440) 354-4445 *SIC* 2621

CONNEAUT, OH

CASCADE OHIO INC p 262
1209 Maple Ave 44030
Tel (440) 593-5800 *SIC* 2431 3442

COSHOCTON, OH

■ **OXFORD MINING CO INC** p 1101
544 Chestnut St 43812
Tel (740) 622-6302 *SIC* 1221

■ **OXFORD MINING CO-KENTUCKY LLC** p 1101
544 Chestnut St 43812
Tel (740) 622-6302 *SIC* 1221

CROTON, OH

OHIO FRESH EGGS LLC p 1077
11212 Croton Rd 43013
Tel (740) 893-7200 *SIC* 5144 2015

CUYAHOGA FALLS, OH

AMERICHEM INC p 81
2000 Americhem Way 44221
Tel (330) 929-4213
SIC 2865 2851 2819 2816

AMH HOLDINGS II INC p 85
3773 State Rd 44223
Tel (330) 929-1811 *SIC* 3355

AMH HOLDINGS LLC p 85
3773 State Rd 44223
Tel (330) 929-1811 *SIC* 3355 3444

ASSOCIATED MATERIALS HOLDINGS LLC p 120
3773 State Rd 44223
Tel (330) 929-1811
SIC 3089 5033 5031 5063 3442

ASSOCIATED MATERIALS LLC p 121
3773 State Rd 44223
Tel (330) 929-1811
SIC 3089 5033 5031 3442

CITY OF CUYAHOGA FALLS p 314
2310 2nd St 44221
Tel (330) 971-8230 *SIC* 9111

CUYAHOGA FALLS GENERAL HOSPITAL p 403
1900 23rd St 44223
Tel (330) 971-7000 *SIC* 8062

CUYAHOGA VALLEY CHRISTIAN ACADEMY ENDOWMENT FUND p 403
4687 Wyoga Lake Rd 44224
Tel (330) 929-0575 *SIC* 8211

GENTEK BUILDING PRODUCTS INC p 604
3773 State Rd 44223
Tel (800) 548-4542 *SIC* 3444 3089

■ **OHIO CVS STORES LLC** p 1077
641 Graham Rd 44221
Tel (330) 922-1298 *SIC* 5912

PNEUMATIC SCALE CORP p 1158
10 Ascot Pkwy 44223
Tel (330) 923-0491 *SIC* 3565 3569 3535

PROSPECT MOLD & DIE CO p 1184
1100 Main St 44221
Tel (330) 929-3311 *SIC* 5084 3544

DAYTON, OH

AD INDUSTRIES INC p 21
6450 Poe Ave Ste 109 45414
Tel (303) 744-1911
SIC 3634 3564 3535 3714 3088 3089

ADAMS-ROBINSON ENTERPRISES INC p 21
2735 Needmore Rd 45414
Tel (937) 274-5318 *SIC* 1541

ATS ASSEMBLY AND TEST INC p 129
313 Mound St 45402
Tel (937) 222-3030 *SIC* 3599

BETA LASERMIKE INC p 177
8001 Technology Blvd 45424
Tel (937) 233-9935 *SIC* 3545

■ **BROWER INSURANCE AGENCY LLC** p 219
409 E Monu Ave Ste 400 45402
Tel (937) 228-4135 *SIC* 6411

CARESOURCE MANAGEMENT GROUP CO p 255
230 N Main St 45402
Tel (937) 224-3300 *SIC* 6321

CHEMGROUP INC p 293
2600 Thunderhawk Ct 45414
Tel (937) 898-5566 *SIC* 5169

CHILDRENS MEDICAL CENTER TOLEDO p 300
1 Childrens Plz 45404
Tel (937) 641-3000 *SIC* 8069

CITY OF DAYTON p 314
101 W 3rd St 45402
Tel (937) 333-3333 *SIC* 9111

CORBUS LLC p 368
1129 Miamisbrg Cntrvle Rd Ste 45449
Tel (937) 226-7724 *SIC* 8741 7373

COUNTY OF MONTGOMERY p 380
451 W 3rd St Fl 4 45422
Tel (937) 225-4000 *SIC* 9111

COX MEDIA GROUP OHIO INC p 386
1611 S Main St 45409
Tel (937) 225-2000 *SIC* 2711

DAYTON BOARD OF EDUCATION p 417
156 Grant St 45404
Tel (937) 226-1084 *SIC* 8211

DAYTON CHILDRENS HOSPITAL p 417
1 Childrens Plz 45404
Tel (937) 641-3000 *SIC* 8069

DAYTON FREIGHT LINES INC p 417
6450 Poe Ave Ste 311 45414
Tel (937) 264-4060 *SIC* 4213 4212

DAYTON LAMINA CORP p 417
500 Progress Rd 45449
Tel (937) 859-5111 *SIC* 3544 6719

DAYTON OSTEOPATHIC HOSPITAL p 418
405 W Grand Ave 45405
Tel (937) 762-1629 *SIC* 8062

■ **DAYTON POWER AND LIGHT CO** p 418
1065 Woodman Dr 45432
Tel (937) 224-6000 *SIC* 4911 4931

DAYTON PROGRESS CORP p 418
500 Progress Rd 45449
Tel (937) 859-5111
SIC 3544 3545 3495 3493

DAYTON-PHOENIX GROUP INC p 418
1619 Kuntz Rd 45404
Tel (937) 496-3900 *SIC* 3621 3743

■ **DPL INC** p 454
1065 Woodman Dr 45432
Tel (937) 331-4063 *SIC* 4911

DRT HOLDINGS INC p 457
618 Greenmount Blvd 45419
Tel (937) 298-7391 *SIC* 6719

DUNCAN OIL CO p 461
849 Factory Rd 45434
Tel (937) 426-5945
SIC 5172 5411 5983 1542

ERNST ENTERPRISES INC p 508
3361 Successful Way 45414
Tel (937) 233-5555 *SIC* 3273

FOUNDATION FOR COMMUNITY BLOOD CENTER/COMMUNITY TISSUE SERVICES p 571
349 S Main St 45402
Tel (937) 461-3450 *SIC* 8099

FUYAO GLASS AMERICA INC p 586
2801 W Stroop Rd 45439
Tel (937) 626-4092 *SIC* 7536

G Z K INC p 587
660 Fame Rd 45449
Tel (937) 461-7500 *SIC* 5812

■ **GLOBE MOTORS INC** p 618
2275 Stanley Ave 45404
Tel (334) 983-3542 *SIC* 3621

GOOD SAMARITAN HOSPITAL p 623
2222 Philadelphia Dr 45406
Tel (937) 278-2612 *SIC* 8062

GOSIGER INC p 626
108 Mcdonough St 45402
Tel (937) 228-5174 *SIC* 5084

JOHN A BECKER CO p 787
1341 E 4th St 45402
Tel (937) 226-1341 *SIC* 5063

KETTERING ADVENTIST HEALTHCARE p 814
3535 Southern Blvd 45429
Tel (937) 298-4331 *SIC* 8741

KETTERING CITY SCHOOL DISTRICT p 814
3750 Far Hills Ave 45429
Tel (937) 499-1400 *SIC* 8211

LAU INDUSTRIES INC p 846
4509 Springfield St 45431
Tel (937) 476-6500 *SIC* 3564

LION APPAREL INC p 869
7200 Poe Ave Ste 400 45414
Tel (937) 898-1949 *SIC* 2311

LION GROUP INC p 869
7200 Poe Ave Ste 400 45414
Tel (937) 898-1949 *SIC* 6719

MAHLE BEHR DAYTON LLC p 897
1600 Webster St 45404
Tel (937) 369-2900 *SIC* 3714

MED AMERICA HEALTH SYSTEMS CORP p 934
1 Wyoming St 45409
Tel (937) 223-6192 *SIC* 8062 8741 8082

■ **METLIFE AUTO & HOME INSURANCE AGENCY INC** p 954
9797 Springboro Pike 45448
Tel (815) 266-5301 *SIC* 6411

MIAMI VALLEY HOSPITAL p 959
1 Wyoming St 45409
Tel (937) 208-8000 *SIC* 8062

MILLER-VALENTINE OPERATIONS INC p 971
137 N Main St Ste 900 45402
Tel (937) 293-0900 *SIC* 6552 6531

MISUMI INVESTMENT USA CORP p 976
500 Progress Rd 45449
Tel (937) 859-5111 *SIC* 6719 3544

■ **MORNING PRIDE MFG LLC** p 989
1 Innovation Ct 45414
Tel (937) 264-2662 *SIC* 3842 2326

MV COMMERCIAL CONSTRUCTION LLC p 1003
137 N Main St Ste 900 45402
Tel (937) 293-0900 *SIC* 1541

PREMIER HEALTH PARTNERS p 1170
110 N Main St 45402
Tel (937) 499-9596 *SIC* 8082

▲ **REX AMERICAN RESOURCES CORP** p 1229
7720 Paragon Rd 45459
Tel (937) 276-3931 *SIC* 2869 6531

SAMARITAN HEALTH PARTNERS p 1274
2222 Philadelphia Dr 45406
Tel (937) 208-8400 *SIC* 8062

SHOOK CONSTRUCTION CO p 1318
4977 Northcutt Pl 45414
Tel (937) 276-6666 *SIC* 1629 1542 8741

SHOOK NATIONAL CORP p 1318
4977 Northcutt Pl 45414
Tel (937) 276-6666
SIC 8741 1542 1629 1541

SHORE TO SHORE INC p 1318
8170 Washington Vlg Dr 45458
Tel (937) 866-1908 *SIC* 2679 2241

SINCLAIR COMMUNITY COLLEGE p 1326
444 W 3rd St 45402
Tel (937) 512-2525 *SIC* 8222 8221

SOIN INTERNATIONAL LLC p 1337
1129 Miamsbg Ctrvl Rd 1 Ste 45449
Tel (937) 427-7646 *SIC* 8741

SRC LIQUIDATION LLC p 1363
600 Albany St 45417
Tel (937) 221-1000
SIC 2761 2672 2677 2759

STANDARD REGISTER INC p 1376
600 Albany St 45417
Tel (937) 221-1000 *SIC* 8742

STRATACACHE INC p 1392
2 Emmet St Ste 200 45405
Tel (937) 224-0485 *SIC* 5734 4822

STRESS CARE/BRIDGES p 1393
405 W Grand Ave 45405
Tel (937) 723-3200 *SIC* 8069

UNIVERSITY OF DAYTON p 1521
300 College Park Ave 45469
Tel (937) 229-2919 *SIC* 8221 8733

VOSS AUTO NETWORK INC p 1566
766 Mmsburg Cnterville Rd 45459
Tel (937) 428-2400
SIC 5511 7538 7515 7513 5521 5012

WFSR HOLDINGS LLC p 1604
220 E Monument Ave 45402
Tel (877) 735-4966
SIC 2752 2754 2759 2761 2789 2791

WORKFLOWONE LLC p 1624
220 E Monument Ave 45402
Tel (877) 735-4966
SIC 2754 2791 4225 4731 2752 2759

WRIGHT STATE UNIVERSITY p 1627
3640 Colonel Glenn Hwy 45435
Tel (937) 775-3333 *SIC* 8221

YOUNG MENS CHRISTIAN ASSOCIATION OF GREATER DAYTON p 1638
118 W St Ste 300 45402
Tel (937) 223-5201
SIC 8641 7991 8351 7032 8322

DEFIANCE, OH

CHIEF SUPER MARKET INC p 298
705 Deatrick St 43512
Tel (419) 782-0950 SIC 5411

DEFIANCE METAL PRODUCTS CO p 422
21 Seneca St 43512
Tel (419) 784-5332 SIC 3465 3443 3544

▲ FIRST DEFIANCE FINANCIAL CORP p 546
601 Clinton St 43512
Tel (419) 782-5015
SIC 6035 6331 6321 6311

■ FIRST FEDERAL BANK OF MIDWEST p 546
601 Clinton St Ste 1 43512
Tel (419) 782-5015 SIC 6035

DELAWARE, OH

AFTERMARKET PARTS CO LLC p 33
3229 Sawmill Pkwy 43015
Tel (888) 333-6224 SIC 5013

■ CONTAINER LIFE CYCLE MANAGEMENT LLC p 362
425 Winter Rd 43015
Tel (740) 549-6087 SIC 5093

COUNTY OF DELAWARE p 377
101 N Sandusky St 43015
Tel (740) 368-1800 SIC 9111

GRADY MEMORIAL HOSPITAL p 628
561 W Central Ave 43015
Tel (740) 615-1000 SIC 8062

▲ GREIF INC p 639
425 Winter Rd 43015
Tel (740) 549-6000
SIC 2653 2449 2655 3412 3089 2674

■ GREIF PACKAGING LLC p 639
366 Greif Pkwy 43015
Tel (740) 549-6000 SIC 3086

■ GREIF USA LLC p 639
366 Greif Pkwy 43015
Tel (740) 549-6000 SIC 5093

■ KROGER CO p 830
2000 Nutter Farms Ln 43015
Tel (740) 657-2124 SIC 5411

OHIO WESLEYAN UNIVERSITY p 1078
61 S Sandusky St 43015
Tel (800) 922-8953 SIC 8221

DELPHOS, OH

K & M TIRE INC p 798
965 Spencerville Rd 45833
Tel (419) 695-1061 SIC 5014 7538 5531

LAKEVIEW FARMS LLC p 840
1600 Gressel Dr 45833
Tel (419) 695-9925 SIC 2026 2099 2022

DERWENT, OH

BI-CON SERVICES INC p 180
10901 Clay Pike Rd 43733
Tel (740) 685-2542 SIC 1623 3498 3443

DOVER, OH

DOVER CHEMICAL CORP p 453
3676 Davis Rd Nw 44622
Tel (330) 343-7711 SIC 2819 2869 2899

KIMBLE CO p 818
3596 State Route 39 Nw 44622
Tel (330) 343-1226 SIC 1221

KIMBLE COMPANIES INC p 818
3596 State Route 39 Nw 44622
Tel (330) 343-5665 SIC 4953

UNION HOSPITAL ASSOCIATION p 1504
659 Boulevard St 44622
Tel (330) 343-3311 SIC 8062 8011

DUBLIN, OH

AMERICAN HEALTH FOUNDATION INC p 73
5920 Venture Dr Ste 100 43017
Tel (614) 798-5110 SIC 8741

ASK CHEMICALS LP p 118
495 Metro Pl S Ste 250 43017
Tel (614) 763-0384 SIC 2899

BOUNDTREE MEDICAL LLC p 204
5000 Tuttle Crossing Blvd 43016
Tel (614) 760-5000 SIC 5047

BUCKEYE CHECK CASHING INC p 223
6785 Bobcat Way Ste 200 43016
Tel (614) 798-5900 SIC 6099

■ BUTLER ANIMAL HEALTH HOLDING CO LLC p 230
400 Metro Pl N Ste 100 43017
Tel (614) 761-9095 SIC 5122 5149 5047

■ BUTLER ANIMAL HEALTH SUPPLY LLC p 230
400 Metro Pl N Ste 100 43017
Tel (855) 724-3461 SIC 5122 5149 5047

■ CARDINAL HEALTH 100 INC p 253
7000 Cardinal Pl 43017
Tel (614) 757-5000 SIC 5122 5047

■ CARDINAL HEALTH 301 LLC p 253
7000 Cardinal Pl 43017
Tel (614) 757-5000 SIC 5047

■ CARDINAL HEALTH 414 LLC p 253
7000 Cardinal Pl 43017
Tel (614) 757-5000 SIC 2834 2835

▲ CARDINAL HEALTH INC p 253
7000 Cardinal Pl 43017
Tel (614) 757-5000
SIC 5122 5047 8741 3842

CHECKSMART FINANCIAL CO p 292
6785 Bobcat Way Ste 200 43016
Tel (614) 798-5900 SIC 6099

COMMUNITY CHOICE FINANCIAL INC p 347
6785 Bobcat Way 43016
Tel (614) 798-5900 SIC 6799

COMPMANAGEMENT INC p 351
6377 Emerald Pkwy 43016
Tel (614) 376-5300 SIC 6411

DELTA DENTAL PLAN OF OHIO INC p 426
5600 Blazer Pkwy Ste 150 43017
Tel (614) 776-2300 SIC 6324

DOMINION HOLDING CORP p 449
4900 Tuttle Crossing Blvd 43016
Tel (614) 356-5000 SIC 1521

DOMINION HOMES INC p 449
4900 Tuttle Crossing Blvd 43016
Tel (614) 356-5000 SIC 1521

DUBLIN CITY SCHOOLS p 459
7030 Coffman Rd 43017
Tel (614) 764-5913 SIC 8211

FRANK GATES COMPANIES INC p 574
5000 Bradenton Ave 43017
Tel (614) 793-8000 SIC 8742 6411

FRANK GATES SERVICE CO p 574
5000 Bradenton Ave # 100 43017
Tel (614) 793-8000 SIC 8742

HBD INDUSTRIES INC p 671
5200 Upper Metro Pl # 110 43017
Tel (614) 526-7000
SIC 3052 3621 3566 3564 3812

INTERSTATE GAS SUPPLY INC p 758
6100 Emerald Pkwy 43016
Tel (614) 659-5000 SIC 1311

MITSUBISHI INTERNATIONAL FOOD INGREDIENTS INC p 978
5080 Tuttle Crossing Blvd 43016
Tel (614) 652-1111 SIC 5169

OCLC ONLINE COMPUTER LIBRARY CENTER INCORPORATE p 1074
6565 Kilgour Pl 43017
Tel (614) 764-6000 SIC 7375

■ PACER TRANSPORTATION SOLUTIONS INC p 1103
5165 Emerald Pkwy 43017
Tel (614) 923-1400 SIC 4731

PCCW TELESERVICES (US) INC p 1124
5200 Rings Rd 43017
Tel (614) 652-6300 SIC 7389 7299

PEERLESS-WINSMITH INC p 1127
5200 Upper Metro Pl # 110 43017
Tel (614) 526-7000
SIC 3621 3566 3634 3812 3559

■ SAFETY SOLUTIONS INC p 1266
6161 Shamrock Ct 43016
Tel (614) 799-9900 SIC 5084 5136 5139

SARNOVA INC p 1282
5000 Tuttle Crossing Blvd 43016
Tel (614) 760-5000 SIC 5999 5047

STANLEY STEEMER INTERNATIONAL INC p 1377
5800 Innovation Dr 43016
Tel (614) 764-2007
SIC 7217 3635 6794 5713

STERLING COMMERCE LLC p 1387
4600 Lakehurst Ct 43016
Tel (614) 798-2192 SIC 7372

■ SYGMA NETWORK INC p 1413
5550 Blazer Pkwy Ste 300 43017
Tel (614) 734-2500 SIC 5149

THOMAS FIVE LTD p 1448
5131 Post Rd Ste 203 43017
Tel (614) 764-9495 SIC 5812

UNITED RETIREMENT PLAN CONSULTANTS INC p 1511
545 Metro Pl S Ste 240 43017
Tel (614) 923-8822 SIC 6411 6282

▲ WENDYS CO p 1592
1 Dave Thomas Blvd 43017
Tel (614) 764-3100 SIC 5812 6794

■ WENDYS INTERNATIONAL LLC p 1592
1 Dave Thomas Blvd 43017
Tel (614) 764-3100 SIC 5812

■ WENDYS OF DENVER INC p 1592
4288 W Dblin Granville Rd 43017
Tel (614) 764-3100 SIC 5812

■ WENDYS OF NE FLORIDA INC p 1592
4288 W Dblin Granville Rd 43017
Tel (614) 764-3100 SIC 5812

■ WENDYS OLD FASHIONED HAMBURGERS OF NEW YORK LLC p 1592
4288 W Dblin Granville Rd 43017
Tel (614) 764-3100 SIC 5812

■ WENDYS RESTAURANTS LLC p 1592
1 Dave Thomas Blvd 43017
Tel (614) 764-3100 SIC 5812 6794

■ XPO INTERMODAL INC p 1632
5165 Emerald Pkwy 300 43017
Tel (614) 923-1400 SIC 4731

EAST LIBERTY, OH

HONDA LOGISTICS NORTH AMERICA INC p 704
11590 Township Road 298 43319
Tel (937) 642-0335 SIC 4226

MIDWEST EXPRESS INC p 967
11590 Township Road 298 43319
Tel (937) 642-0335 SIC 4226

EAST LIVERPOOL, OH

HILL INTERNATIONAL TRUCKS NA LLC p 693
47866 Y And O Rd 43920
Tel (330) 386-6440 SIC 5511 5531 7538

EASTLAKE, OH

GOULD ELECTRONICS INC p 626
34929 Curtis Blvd Ste 100 44095
Tel (440) 953-5000
SIC 3825 3497 3613 3691 3674

EATON, OH

HENNY PENNY CORP p 683
1219 Us Route 35 45320
Tel (937) 456-8400 SIC 3589

NEATON AUTO PRODUCTS MANUFACTURING INC p 1023
975 S Franklin St 45320
Tel (937) 456-7103 SIC 3714

EDON, OH

EDON FARMERS COOPERATIVE ASSOCIATION p 478
205 S Michigan St 43518
Tel (419) 272-2121 SIC 5153 5191

ELYRIA, OH

ALL AMERICAN SPORTS CORP p 51
669 Sugar Ln 44035
Tel (440) 366-8225 SIC 7699

BENDIX COMMERCIAL VEHICLE SYSTEMS LLC p 172
901 Cleveland St 44035
Tel (440) 329-9000 SIC 5013 8711

COMPREHENSIVE HEALTH CARE OF OHIO INC p 352
630 E River St 44035
Tel (440) 329-7500 SIC 8741

COUNTY OF LORAIN p 379
226 Middle Ave 44035
Tel (440) 329-5201 SIC 9111

ELYRIA CITY SCHOOL DISTRICT p 490
42101 Griswold Rd 44035
Tel (440) 284-8000 SIC 8211

ELYRIA FOUNDRY CO LLC p 490
120 Filbert St 44035
Tel (440) 322-4657
SIC 3321 3369 3325 2821

EMH REGIONAL MEDICAL CENTER p 492
630 E River St 44035
Tel (440) 329-7500 SIC 8062

▲ INVACARE CORP p 760
1 Invacare Way 44035
Tel (440) 329-6000 SIC 3842 2514 2813

LORAIN COUNTY COMMUNITY COLLEGE DISTRICT p 878
1005 Abbe Rd N 44035
Tel (440) 365-5222 SIC 8222

MULTILINK INC p 999
580 Ternes Ln 44035
Tel (440) 366-6966 SIC 5063 3829

NELSON STUD WELDING INC p 1025
7900 W Ridge Rd 44035
Tel (440) 329-0400 SIC 3452 3548

■ RIDGE TOOL CO p 1234
400 Clark St 44035
Tel (440) 323-5581
SIC 3541 3423 3547 3546

■ RIDGE TOOL MANUFACTURING CO p 1234
400 Clark St 44035
Tel (440) 323-5581
SIC 3541 3423 3547 3546 3545 3469

ENON, OH

■ SPEEDWAY LLC p 1358
500 Speedway Dr 45323
Tel (937) 864-3000 SIC 5411 5541 2869

EUCLID, OH

B H C SERVICES INC p 142
26250 Euclid Ave Ste 901 44132
Tel (216) 289-5300 SIC 8082

EUCLID HOSPITAL p 512
18901 Lake Shore Blvd 44119
Tel (216) 531-9000 SIC 8062

■ LINCOLN ELECTRIC CO p 866
22801 Saint Clair Ave 44117
Tel (216) 481-8100 SIC 3548

■ LINCOLN ELECTRIC INTERNATIONAL HOLDING CO p 867
22801 Saint Clair Ave 44117
Tel (216) 481-8100 SIC 3548

FAIRBORN, OH

ALI INDUSTRIES INC p 50
747 E Xenia Dr 45324
Tel (937) 878-3946 SIC 3291

I SUPPLY CO p 725
1255 Spangler Rd 45324
Tel (937) 878-5240 SIC 5087 5113

MORRIS FURNITURE CO INC p 990
2377 Commerce Center Blvd 45324
Tel (937) 874-7100 SIC 5731 5722 5712

FAIRFIELD, OH

▲ CINCINNATI FINANCIAL CORP p 307
6200 S Gilmore Rd 45014
Tel (513) 870-2000 SIC 6311 6411

■ CINCINNATI INDEMINTY CO p 307
6200 S Gilmore Rd 45014
Tel (513) 870-2000 SIC 6331

■ CINCINNATI INSURANCE CO p 307
6200 S Gilmore Rd 45014
Tel (513) 870-2000
SIC 6311 6331 6321 6211

■ CINCINNATI LIFE INSURANCE CO p 307
6200 S Gilmore Rd 45014
Tel (513) 870-2000 SIC 6311

FAIRFIELD CITY SCHOOL DISTRICT (INC) p 524
4641 Bach Ln 45014
Tel (513) 829-6300 SIC 8211

MERCY HAMILTON HOSPITAL p 946
3000 Mack Rd 45014
Tel (513) 603-8600 SIC 8062

OHIO CASUALTY CORP p 1077
9450 Seward Rd 45014
Tel (513) 603-2400 SIC 6331

OHIO CASUALTY INSURANCE CO p 1077
9450 Seward Rd 45014
Tel (800) 843-6446 SIC 6331 6311

PACIFIC MANUFACTURING OHIO INC p 1105
8955 Seward Rd 45011
Tel (513) 860-3900 SIC 3714 3469

SKYLINE CHILI INC p 1330
4180 Thunderbird Ln 45014
Tel (513) 874-1188
SIC 5812 2038 6794 5149 2032

TAKUMI STAMPING INC p 1422
8585 Seward Rd 45011
Tel (513) 642-0081 SIC 3469

FAIRLAWN, OH

▲ A SCHULMAN INC p 6
3637 Ridgewood Rd 44333
Tel (330) 666-3751 SIC 2821

BEKAERT CORP p 169
3200 W Market St Ste 303 44333
Tel (330) 867-3325 SIC 3315

BEKAERT NORTH AMERICA MANAGEMENT CORP p 169
3200 W Market St Ste 303 44333
Tel (330) 867-3325 SIC 3315

BUCKEYE CORRUGATED INC p 223
822 Kumho Dr Ste 400 44333
Tel (330) 576-0590 SIC 2653

■ CITADEL INTERMEDIATE HOLDINGS LLC p 309
3637 Ridgewood Rd 44333
Tel (330) 666-3751 SIC 5162

■ CITADEL PLASTICS HOLDINGS INC p 309
3637 Ridgewood Rd 44333
Tel (330) 666-3751 SIC 6719

FIRST COMMUNICATIONS LLC p 546
3340 W Market St 44333
Tel (330) 835-2323 SIC 4813

FORD MONTROSE INC p 565
3960 Medina Rd 44333
Tel (330) 666-0711
SIC 5511 5521 7515 7513 7538 7532

■ HPC HOLDINGS LLC p 714
3637 Ridgewood Rd 44333
Tel (330) 666-3751 SIC 2821 2655

KOROSEAL INTERIOR PRODUCTS LLC p 828
3875 Embassy Pkwy Ste 110 44333
Tel (330) 668-7600 SIC 3081 3089 3069

MARKS & MORGAN JEWELERS INC p 909
375 Ghent Rd 44333
Tel (330) 668-5000 SIC 5944

RESERVE GROUP MANAGEMENT CO p 1226
3560 W Market St Ste 300 44333
Tel (330) 665-6706 SIC 8741

RJF INTERNATIONAL CORP p 1239
3875 Embassy Pkwy Ste 110 44333
Tel (330) 668-2069 SIC 3081 3089 3069

SIGNET JEWELERS LIMITED p 1322
375 Ghent Rd 44333
Tel (330) 668-5785 SIC 5944

STERLING INC p 1387
375 Ghent Rd 44333
Tel (216) 867-1230 SIC 5944

STERLING JEWELERS INC p 1387
375 Ghent Rd 44333
Tel (330) 668-5000 SIC 3423

FINDLAY, OH

■ AUTOLIV NISSIN BRAKE SYSTEMS AMERICA LLC p 134
2001 Industrial Dr 45840
Tel (419) 425-6725 SIC 3714

BLANCHARD VALLEY HEALTH SYSTEM p 188
1900 S Main St 45840
Tel (419) 423-4500 SIC 8741 7349

BLANCHARD VALLEY REGIONAL HEALTH CENTER p 188
1900 S Main St 45840
Tel (419) 423-4500 SIC 8062

BRIDGESTONE APM CO p 211
2030 Production Dr 45840
Tel (419) 423-9552 SIC 3061

▲ COOPER TIRE & RUBBER CO INC p 367
701 Lima Ave 45840
Tel (419) 423-1321 SIC 3011

DANBY PRODUCTS INC p 411
1800 Production Dr 45840
Tel (519) 837-0920 SIC 5064

G S WIRING SYSTEMS INC p 587
1801 Production Dr 45840
Tel (419) 423-7111 SIC 3714 5013

GSW MANUFACTURING INC p 644
1801 Production Dr 45840
Tel (419) 423-7111 SIC 3714 3694

■ HANCOR HOLDING CORP p 657
401 Olive St 45840
Tel (419) 422-6521 SIC 3084

KUSS FILTRATION INC p 832
2150 Industrial Dr 45840
Tel (419) 423-9040 SIC 3569

LEGACY FARMERS COOPERATIVE p 852
6566 County Road 236 45840
Tel (419) 423-2611
SIC 5153 5191 5984 2875 2048 2041

LUKE THEIS ENTERPRISES INC p 885
14120 State Route 568 45840
Tel (419) 422-2040 SIC 1542 1541 1521

■ MARATHON PETROLEUM CO LP p 904
539 S Main St 45840
Tel (419) 422-2121 SIC 5172 2951 2865

▲ MARATHON PETROLEUM CORP p 904
539 S Main St 45840
Tel (419) 422-2121 SIC 2911 5172

■ MARATHON PETROLEUM SUPPLY LLC p 904
539 S Main St 45840
Tel (419) 422-2121 SIC 2911

■ MARATHON PIPE LINE LLC p 904
539 S Main St Ste 7614 45840
Tel (419) 422-2121 SIC 4612 4613

▲ MPLX LP p 995
200 E Hardin St 45840
Tel (419) 672-6500 SIC 4612 4613

NATIONAL LIME AND STONE CO p 1014
551 Lake Cascade Pkwy 45840
Tel (419) 422-4341
SIC 1422 1442 3273 1423 1499

NEEDLER ENTERPRISES INC p 1024
317 W Main Cross St 45840
Tel (419) 422-8090 SIC 5411

NISSIN BRAKE OHIO INC p 1044
1901 Industrial Dr 45840
Tel (419) 420-3800 SIC 3714

ROKI AMERICA CO LTD p 1247
2001 Production Dr 45840
Tel (419) 424-9713 SIC 3714

SANOH AMERICA INC p 1280
1849 Industrial Dr 45840
Tel (419) 425-2600 SIC 3498

UNIVERSITY OF FINDLAY p 1521
1000 N Main St 45840
Tel (419) 422-8313 SIC 8221

FORT RECOVERY, OH

V H COOPER & CO INC p 1538
2321 State Route 49 45846
Tel (419) 375-4116 SIC 0253 2015 2011

FOSTORIA, OH

ROPPE HOLDING CO p 1250
1602 N Union St 44830
Tel (419) 435-8546 SIC 3089 3069

FRANKLIN FURNACE, OH

BIG SANDY DISTRIBUTION INC p 182
8375 Gallia Pike 45629
Tel (740) 574-2113 SIC 4225

FREDERICKTOWN, OH

FT PRECISION INC p 582
9731 Mount Gilead Rd 43019
Tel (740) 694-1500 SIC 3714

FREMONT, OH

ATLAS INDUSTRIES INC p 128
1750 E State St 43420
Tel (419) 355-1000 SIC 3599

BECK SUPPLIERS INC p 167
1000 N Front St 43420
Tel (419) 332-5527
SIC 5171 5541 5411 5984 1542

CROWN BATTERY MANUFACTURING CO p 395
1445 Majestic Dr 43420
Tel (419) 332-0563 SIC 3691

MOSSER CONSTRUCTION INC p 992
122 S Wilson Ave 43420
Tel (419) 334-3801 SIC 1541 1542

SIERRA LOBO INC p 1320
102 Pinnacle Dr 43420
Tel (419) 332-7101 SIC 8711

STYLE CREST ENTERPRISES INC p 1395
2450 Enterprise St 43420
Tel (419) 355-8586 SIC 3089 5075

STYLE CREST INC p 1395
2450 Enterprise St 43420
Tel (419) 332-7369 SIC 3089 5075

WMOG INC p 1620
122 S Wilson Ave 43420
Tel (419) 334-3801 SIC 1541 7359 1611

GALION, OH

GALION COMMUNITY HOSPITAL p 589
269 Portland Way S 44833
Tel (419) 468-4841 SIC 8062 8051

GALLIPOLIS, OH

HOLZER CONSOLIDATED HEALTH SYSTEMS INC p 703
100 Jackson Pike 45631
Tel (740) 446-5060 SIC 8062

HOLZER HEALTH SYSTEM p 703
100 Jackson Pike 45631
Tel (740) 446-5000 SIC 8062

HOLZER HOSPITAL FOUNDATION INC p 703
100 Jackson Pike 45631
Tel (740) 446-5000 SIC 8062

GIRARD, OH

AIM LEASING CO p 38
1500 Trumbull Ave 44420
Tel (330) 759-0438
SIC 7513 7538 4212 5983

OMNI MANOR INC p 1085
101 W Liberty St 44420
Tel (330) 545-1550 SIC 8051

GRANVILLE, OH

DENISON UNIVERSITY p 428
100 W College St 43023
Tel (740) 587-0810 SIC 8221

■ HOLOPHANE CORP p 702
3825 Columbus Rd Bldg A 43023
Tel (866) 759-1577 SIC 3646 3648

GREENVILLE, OH

FALCON PACKAGING LLC p 526
1359 Sater St 45331
Tel (937) 547-9800 SIC 7389 4225

GROVE CITY, OH

GRAND AERIE OF FRATERNAL ORDER OF EAGLES p 629
1623 Gateway Cir 43123
Tel (614) 883-2200 SIC 8641

MID-OHIO FOODBANK p 963
3960 Brookham Dr 43123
Tel (614) 317-9400 SIC 8322

SOUTH- WESTERN CITY SCHOOL DISTRICT p 1345
3805 Marlane Dr 43123
Tel (614) 801-3000 SIC 8211

TIGERPOLY MANUFACTURING INC p 1453
6231 Enterprise Pkwy 43123
Tel (614) 871-0045
SIC 3089 3714 3621 3061

TOSOH AMERICA INC p 1462
3600 Gantz Rd 43123
Tel (614) 539-8622
SIC 5169 3564 5047 5052

GROVEPORT, OH

BLUE LINE DISTRIBUTION p 192
2250 Spiegel Dr Ste P 43125
Tel (614) 497-9610 SIC 5141

FARO SERVICES INC p 530
7070 Pontius Rd 43125
Tel (614) 497-1700 SIC 4225 4731

RICART PROPERTIES INC p 1232
4255 S Hamilton Rd 43125
Tel (614) 836-6680 SIC 5511

TRILOGY FULFILLMENT LLC p 1480
6600 Alum Creek Dr 43125
Tel (614) 491-0553 SIC 8742

HAMILTON, OH

BUTLER COUNTY OF OHIO p 230
315 High St Fl 6 45011
Tel (513) 887-3278 SIC 9121

BUTLER TECHNOLOGY & CAREER DEVELOPMENT SCHOOLS p 230
3603 Hmlton Middletown Rd 45011
Tel (513) 868-1911 SIC 8211

CARINGTON HEALTH SYSTEMS p 256
8200 Beckett Park Dr 45011
Tel (513) 682-2700 SIC 8741 8051

■ FIRST FINANCIAL BANK NATIONAL ASSOCIATION p 546
300 High St Side 45011
Tel (513) 867-4700 SIC 6021

FORT HAMILTON HOSPITAL p 568
630 Eaton Ave 45013
Tel (513) 867-2000 SIC 8062

FORT HAMILTON-HUGHES HEALTHCARE CORP p 568
630 Eaton Ave 45013
Tel (513) 867-2000 SIC 8741

GOVERNMENT SERVICE CENTER p 627
315 High St Fl 10 45011
Tel (513) 887-3000 SIC 9199

HAMILTON CITY SCHOOL DISTRICT p 655
533 Dayton St 45011
Tel (513) 887-5000 SIC 8211

MATANDY STEEL & METAL PRODUCTS LLC p 919
1200 Central Ave 45011
Tel (513) 887-5274
SIC 5051 3312 3444 3399

HANNIBAL, OH

ORMET CORP p 1095
43840 State Rte 7 43931
Tel (740) 483-1381 SIC 3334

ORMET PRIMARY ALUMINUM CORP p 1095
43840 State Rt 7 43931
Tel (740) 483-1381 SIC 3334 3297

HARRISON, OH

■ CAMPBELL HAUSFELD LLC p 245
100 Production Dr 45030
Tel (513) 367-4811 SIC 3563 3546 3548

CINCINNATI INC p 307
7420 Kilby Rd 45030
Tel (513) 367-7100 SIC 3549

F & M MAFCO INC p 522
9149 Dry Fork Rd 45030
Tel (513) 367-2151
SIC 5085 5072 7353 5082

HUBERT CO LLC p 716
9555 Dry Fork Rd 45030
Tel (513) 367-8600 SIC 5046

JTM PROVISIONS CO INC p 796
200 Sales Ave 45030
Tel (513) 367-4900 SIC 2013 2051

HARTVILLE, OH

SCOTT PROCESS SYSTEMS INC p 1293
1160 Sunnyside St Sw 44632
Tel (330) 877-2350 SIC 3498

HEATH, OH

ENGLEFIELD INC p 499
447 James Pkwy 43056
Tel (740) 928-8215 SIC 5541

HEBRON, OH

HERITAGE SPORTSWEAR INC p 686
102 Reliance Dr 43025
Tel (740) 928-7771 SIC 5136 5137

MPW INDUSTRIAL SERVICES GROUP INC p 996
9711 Lancaster Rd 43025
Tel (740) 927-8790 SIC 7349 8744 3589

MPW INDUSTRIAL SERVICES INC p 996
9711 Lancaster Rd 43025
Tel (800) 827-8790 SIC 7349

HIGHLAND HEIGHTS, OH

NORMAN NOBLE INC p 1049
5507 Avion Park Dr 44143
Tel (216) 761-5387 SIC 3599

THINGS REMEMBERED INC p 1448
5500 Avion Park Dr 44143
Tel (440) 473-2000 SIC 7389 5947

HILLIARD, OH

▲ ADVANCED DRAINAGE SYSTEMS INC p 25
4640 Trueman Blvd 43026
Tel (614) 658-0050 SIC 3084 3086

BMW FINANCIAL SERVICES NA LLC p 194
5550 Britton Pkwy 43026
Tel (614) 718-6900 SIC 6159

■ HANCOR INC p 657
4640 Trueman Blvd 43026
Tel (614) 658-0050
SIC 3084 3088 3089 3083

JD EQUIPMENT INC p 780
3979 Parkway Ln 43026
Tel (614) 527-8800 SIC 5999 5083

MICRO ELECTRONICS INC p 961
4119 Leap Rd 43026
Tel (614) 850-3000 SIC 5045 5734

HILLSBORO, OH

HIGHLAND COUNTY COMMUNITY ACTION ORGANIZATION INC p 691
1487 N High St Ste 500 45133
Tel (937) 393-3060 SIC 8322

N C B SAVINGS BANK FSB p 1005
139 S High St Ste 1 45133
Tel (937) 393-4246 SIC 6035

HIRAM, OH

GREAT LAKES CHEESE CO INC p 633
17825 Great Lakes Pkwy 44234
Tel (440) 834-2500 SIC 5143 2022

HOLLAND, OH

MIDWEST TAPE LLC p 968
1417 Timber Wolf Dr 43528
Tel (419) 868-9370
SIC 7822 5099 8741 7389 5961 7374

HUDSON, OH

AMERICAN ENDOWMENT FOUNDATION p 71
1521 Georgetown Rd # 104 44236
Tel (330) 655-7552 SIC 8699 8733

ARHAUS LLC p 108
51 E Hines Hill Rd 44236
Tel (440) 439-7700 SIC 5712

■ FEDEX SUPPLY CHAIN SERVICES INC p 537
5455 Darrow Rd 44236
Tel (800) 588-3020
SIC 8742 4213 8741 4731

■ GRAPHIC COMMUNICATIONS HOLDINGS INC p 631
5700 Darrow Rd Ste 110 44236
Tel (330) 650-5522 SIC 5111 7389

HOUSE OF FABRICS INC p 711
5555 Darrow Rd 44236
Tel (330) 656-2600 SIC 5949 5945 5722

JO-ANN STORES HOLDINGS INC p 787
5555 Darrow Rd 44236
Tel (888) 739-4120 SIC 5945 5949 5947

JO-ANN STORES LLC p 787
5555 Darrow Rd 44236
Tel (330) 656-2600 SIC 5945 5949 5947

LITTLE TIKES CO p 871
2180 Barlow Rd 44236
Tel (330) 650-3000 SIC 3944 2519

NEEDLE HOLDINGS INC p 1024
5555 Darrow Rd 44236
Tel (330) 656-2600 SIC 5945

NORANDEX BUILDING MATERIALS DISTRIBUTION INC p 1047
300 Executive Park Ste 100 44236
Tel (330) 656-8924 SIC 5033 5031

WBC GROUP LLC p 1585
6333 Hudson Crossing Pkwy 44236
Tel (800) 472-4221 SIC 5122 5047 3843

HURON, OH

DISTRICT PETROLEUM PRODUCTS INC p 443
1814 River Rd 44839
Tel (419) 433-8373 SIC 5541 5171 5172

HURON HEALTH CARE CENTER INC p 721
1920 Cleveland Rd W 44839
Tel (419) 433-4990 SIC 8051

INDEPENDENCE, OH

ALCAN PRIMARY PRODUCTS CORP p 47
6055 Rockside Woods Blvd 44131
Tel (440) 460-3300 SIC 3334

APPLE AMERICAN GROUP LLC p 98
6200 Oak Tree Blvd # 250 44131
Tel (216) 525-2775 SIC 5812

C & K INDUSTRIAL SERVICES INC p 231
5617 E Schaaf Rd 44131
Tel (216) 642-0055 SIC 4959 7349

DENTALCARE PARTNERS INC p 429
6200 Oak Tree Blvd # 200 44131
Tel (216) 584-1000 SIC 8021

GRAFTECH HOLDINGS INC p 628
6100 Oak Tree Blvd # 300 44131
Tel (216) 676-2000 SIC 1499 3624

GRAFTECH INTERNATIONAL HOLDINGS INC p 628
6100 Oak Tree Blvd # 300 44131
Tel (216) 676-2000 SIC 3624

GRAFTECH INTERNATIONAL LTD p 628
6100 Oak Tree Blvd # 300 44131
Tel (216) 676-2000 SIC 3624

INDEPENDENCE EXCAVATING INC p 736
5720 E Schaaf Rd 44131
Tel (216) 524-1700
SIC 1629 1794 1611 1771 1795

INDY EQUIPMENT INDEPENDENCE RECYCLING INC p 740
6220 E Schaaf Rd 44131
Tel (216) 524-0999 SIC 3531

■ INTELLINEX LLC p 750
6000 Fredom Sq Dr Ste 100 44131
Tel (216) 685-6000 SIC 4813

MIDLAND FOOD SERVICES LLC p 965
6200 Rockside Woods Blvd # 315 44131
Tel (216) 524-2251 SIC 5812

NATIONS LENDING CORP p 1017
4 Summit Park Dr Ste 200 44131
Tel (440) 842-4817 SIC 6162 6163

■ OLD REPUBLIC TITLE CO OF NORTHERN OHIO LLC p 1081
6480 Rckside Woods Blvd S 44131
Tel (216) 524-5700 SIC 6411 6162 6211

POLYMER ADDITIVES HOLDINGS INC p 1160
7500 E Pleasant Valley Rd 44131
Tel (216) 875-7200 *SIC* 5169 2899

POLYMER ADDITIVES INC p 1160
7500 E Pleasant Valley Rd 44131
Tel (216) 875-7200 *SIC* 5169 2899

ROLTA ADVIZEX TECHNOLOGIES LLC p 1248
6480 S Rockside Woods 44131
Tel (216) 901-1818 *SIC* 7373

JACKSON CENTER, OH

■ **AIRSTREAM INC** p 40
419 W Pike St 45334
Tel (937) 596-6111
SIC 3716 3792 3714 3713 3711

JACKSON, OH

WATERLOO COAL CO INC p 1582
3675 Dixon Run Rd 45640
Tel (740) 286-5633 *SIC* 1221 1411 1459

JEFFERSON, OH

ASHTABULA COUNTY COMMISSIONERS p 117
25 W Jefferson St 44047
Tel (440) 576-3649 *SIC* 9121

COUNTY OF ASHTABULA p 376
25 W Jefferson St 44047
Tel (440) 576-3783 *SIC* 9111

JOHNSTOWN, OH

TECHNICAL RUBBER CO INC p 1431
200 E Coshocton St 43031
Tel (740) 967-9015 *SIC* 3011 5014 2891

TRILLIUM FARM HOLDINGS LLC p 1480
10513 Croton Rd 43031
Tel (740) 893-7200 *SIC* 5499

KALIDA, OH

UNVERFERTH MANUFACTURING CO INC p 1528
601 S Broad St 45853
Tel (419) 532-3121 *SIC* 3523

KENT, OH

■ **AMETEK TECHNICAL & INDUSTRIAL PRODUCTS INC** p 84
100 E Erie St Ste 130 44240
Tel (330) 677-3754 *SIC* 3621 5063 3566

AREA WIDE PROTECTIVE INC p 106
826 Overholt Rd 44240
Tel (330) 644-0655 *SIC* 3669

AWP INC p 139
826 Overholt Rd 44240
Tel (330) 644-0655 *SIC* 7381

CARTER LUMBER INC p 262
601 Tallmadge Rd 44240
Tel (330) 673-6100 *SIC* 5211

CARTER-JONES COMPANIES INC p 262
601 Tallmadge Rd 44240
Tel (330) 673-6100 *SIC* 5211 5031 6552

CARTER-JONES LUMBER CO p 262
601 Tallmadge Rd 44240
Tel (330) 673-6100 *SIC* 5211 5031

DAVEY TREE EXPERT CO p 415
1500 N Mantua St 44240
Tel (330) 673-9511
SIC 0783 0782 0811 0181

KENT STATE UNIVERSITY p 812
1500 Horning Rd 44242
Tel (330) 672-3000 *SIC* 8221

MAC LTT INC p 891
1400 Fairchild Ave 44240
Tel (330) 474-3795 *SIC* 3569

■ **SCHNELLER LLC** p 1288
6019 Powdermill Rd 44240
Tel (330) 676-7183 *SIC* 2295

KETTERING, OH

ACCO BRANDS USA LLC p 15
4751 Hempstead Station Dr 45429
Tel (937) 495-6323 *SIC* 5943

KETTERING MEDICAL CENTER p 814
3535 Southern Blvd 45429
Tel (937) 298-4331 *SIC* 8062

REYNOLDS AND REYNOLDS CO p 1230
1 Reynolds Way 45430
Tel (937) 485-2000 *SIC* 7373 6159

KIMBOLTON, OH

SALT FORK RESORT CLUB INC p 1273
74978 Broadhead Rd 43749
Tel (740) 498-8116 *SIC* 7011 7997

LAGRANGE, OH

STACI CORP p 1374
110 Commerce Dr 44050
Tel (440) 355-5102 *SIC* 3672

LAKEWOOD, OH

FERRY CAP & SET SCREW CO p 538
13300 Bramley Ave 44107
Tel (216) 649-7400 *SIC* 3452

IMCD US LLC p 733
14725 Detroit Ave Ste 300 44107
Tel (216) 228-8900 *SIC* 5169

LAKEWOOD HOSPITAL ASSOCIATION p 840
14519 Detroit Ave 44107
Tel (216) 529-7160 *SIC* 8062

LANCASTER, OH

ANCHI INC p 89
1115 W 5th Ave 43130
Tel (740) 653-2527 *SIC* 3231

ANCHOR HOCKING LLC p 89
519 N Pierce Ave 43130
Tel (740) 681-6478
SIC 3229 3089 3411 3221

■ **DIAMOND POWER INTERNATIONAL INC** p 437
2600 E Main St 43130
Tel (740) 687-6500 *SIC* 3564

EVERYWARE GLOBAL INC p 515
519 N Pierce Ave 43130
Tel (740) 687-2500 *SIC* 3469 3089

FAIRFIELD MEDICAL CENTER p 525
401 N Ewing St 43130
Tel (740) 687-8000 *SIC* 8062 7352 5999

GHP II LLC p 610
1115 W 5th Ave 43130
Tel (740) 687-2500
SIC 3229 3089 3411 3221

SOUTH CENTRAL POWER CO INC p 1343
2780 Coonpath Rd Ne 43130
Tel (740) 653-4422 *SIC* 4911

LEBANON, OH

ADVICS MANUFACTURING OHIO INC p 28
1650 Kingsview Dr 45036
Tel (513) 934-0023 *SIC* 3714

ADVICS NORTH AMERICA INC p 28
1650 Kingsview Dr 45036
Tel (513) 696-5450
SIC 8731 8742 5013 5531

COUNTY OF WARREN p 382
406 Justice Dr Rm 323 45036
Tel (513) 695-1242 *SIC* 9111

FORD LEBANON INC p 565
770 Columbus Ave 45036
Tel (513) 932-1010 *SIC* 5511 5521 7538

MANE INC p 901
2501 Henkle Dr 45036
Tel (513) 248-9876 *SIC* 2087 2099

MASTERS PHARMACEUTICAL INC p 918
3600 Pharma Way 45036
Tel (513) 354-2690 *SIC* 5122

LEIPSIC, OH

■ **CRABAR/GBF INC** p 388
68 Vine St 45856
Tel (419) 943-2141 *SIC* 2752

LEWIS CENTER, OH

ABRASIVE TECHNOLOGY INC p 12
8400 Green Meadows Dr N 43035
Tel (740) 548-4100 *SIC* 3291

ATS SYSTEMS OREGON INC p 129
425 Enterprise Dr 43035
Tel (541) 738-0932 *SIC* 3569 5084

AUTOMATION TOOLING SYSTEMS INC p 134
425 Enterprise Dr 43035
Tel (614) 781-8063 *SIC* 3569

MULTI-PLASTICS INC p 999
7770 N Central Dr 43035
Tel (740) 548-4894 *SIC* 5162

OLENTANGY LOCAL SCHOOL DISTRICT p 1082
814 Shanahan Rd Ste 100 43035
Tel (740) 657-4050 *SIC* 8211

TRIPLET TRANSPORT INC p 1482
704 Radio Dr 43035
Tel (740) 657-3244 *SIC* 4731

LIBERTY TWP, OH

LAKOTA LOCAL SCHOOL DISTRICT p 840
5572 Princeton Rd 45011
Tel (513) 874-5505 *SIC* 8211

LITHKO CONTRACTING LLC p 870
5353 Hmlton Middletown Rd 45011
Tel (513) 863-5100 *SIC* 1771

LIMA, OH

ALL YEAR SERVICES LLC p 51
270 Amherst Rd 45806
Tel (419) 296-1699 *SIC* 6531

AMERICAN TRIM LLC p 80
1005 W Grand Ave 45801
Tel (419) 228-1145 *SIC* 3469

COUNTY OF ALLEN p 376
301 N Main St 45801
Tel (419) 228-3700 *SIC* 9111

HCF MANAGEMENT INC p 672
1100 Shawnee Rd 45805
Tel (419) 999-2010 *SIC* 8051 6513

LIMA MEMORIAL HOSPITAL p 866
1001 Bellefontaine Ave 45804
Tel (419) 228-3335 *SIC* 8062

LIMA MEMORIAL JOINT OPERATING CO p 866
1001 Belelfontaine Ave 45804
Tel (419) 228-5165 *SIC* 8062

LIMA REFINING CO p 866
1150 S Metcalf St 45804
Tel (419) 226-2300 *SIC* 2911

■ **METOKOTE CORP** p 954
1340 Neubrecht Rd 45801
Tel (419) 996-7800 *SIC* 3479

QUALITOR INC p 1196
1840 Mccullough St 45801
Tel (248) 204-8600 *SIC* 3714 5013

RUDOLPH FOODS CO INC p 1257
6575 Bellefontaine Rd 45804
Tel (909) 383-7463 *SIC* 2096 2099

SPHERION OF LIMA INC p 1358
216 N Elizabeth St 45801
Tel (419) 224-8367 *SIC* 7363

ST RITAS MEDICAL CENTER p 1373
730 W Market St 45801
Tel (419) 227-3361 *SIC* 8062 7352

SUPERIOR METAL PRODUCTS INC p 1406
1005 W Grand Ave 45801
Tel (419) 228-1145 *SIC* 3469 3429

VIRTUAL TECHNOLOGIES GROUP p 1560
3820 S Dixie Hwy 45806
Tel (419) 991-4694 *SIC* 5045

LOGAN, OH

BAZELL OIL CO INC p 163
14371 State Route 328 43138
Tel (740) 385-5420 *SIC* 5172 5983

LONDON, OH

CREAMER METAL PRODUCTS INC p 390
77 S Madison Rd 43140
Tel (740) 852-1752 *SIC* 3523

STANLEY ELECTRIC US CO INC p 1377
420 E High St 43140
Tel (740) 852-5200 *SIC* 3647 3694 3089

LORAIN, OH

COMMUNITY HEALTH PARTNERS REGIONAL FOUNDATION p 348
3700 Kolbe Rd 44053
Tel (440) 960-4000 *SIC* 8062

COMMUNITY HEALTH PARTNERS REGIONAL HEALTH SYSTEM p 348
3700 Kolbe Rd 44053
Tel (440) 960-4000 *SIC* 8062

COMMUNITY HEALTH PARTNERS REGIONAL MEDICAL CENTER p 348
3700 Kolbe Rd 44053
Tel (440) 960-4000 *SIC* 8011

EMERSON NETWORK POWER ENERGY SYSTEMS NORTH AMERICA INC p 492
1510 Kansas Ave 44052
Tel (440) 288-1122 *SIC* 3661 3644 7629

LORAIN CITY SCHOOL DISTRICT p 878
2350 Pole Ave 44052
Tel (440) 233-2232 *SIC* 8211

LORAIN COUNTY AUTOMOTIVE SYSTEMS INC p 878
7470 Industrial Pkwy Dr 44053
Tel (440) 960-7470 *SIC* 3714

LOUISVILLE, OH

BIERY CHEESE CO p 181
6544 Paris Ave 44641
Tel (330) 875-3381 *SIC* 2022

LOVELAND, OH

INDIANA INSURANCE CO p 738
6281 Tri Ridge Blvd # 1 45140
Tel (816) 216-5313 *SIC* 6331

WASHING SYSTEMS LLC p 1577
167 Commerce Dr 45140
Tel (800) 272-1974 *SIC* 5169 2841

MACEDONIA, OH

TRADESMEN INTERNATIONAL LLC p 1469
9760 Shepard Rd 44056
Tel (440) 349-3432 *SIC* 7361

MALVERN, OH

■ **COLFOR MANUFACTURING INC** p 336
3255 Alliance Rd Nw 44644
Tel (330) 863-0404 *SIC* 3462 3599 3463

MANSFIELD, OH

COUNTY OF RICHLAND p 381
50 Park Ave E Ste 3 44902
Tel (419) 774-5501 *SIC* 9111

CRANE PLUMBING LLC p 389
41 Cairns Rd 44903
Tel (419) 522-4211 *SIC* 3261 3431 3088

D & S CREATIVE COMMUNICATIONS INC p 406
140 Park Ave E 44902
Tel (419) 524-6699
SIC 7311 2752 2791 2789

▲ **GORMAN-RUPP CO** p 626
600 S Airport Rd 44903
Tel (419) 755-1011 *SIC* 3561 3594

JAY INDUSTRIES INC p 779
150 Longview Ave E 44903
Tel (419) 524-3778 *SIC* 2531 3089

MEDCENTRAL HEALTH SYSTEM p 935
335 Glessner Ave 44903
Tel (419) 526-8000 *SIC* 8062

NEWMAN TECHNOLOGY INC p 1038
100 Cairns Rd 44903
Tel (419) 525-1856 *SIC* 3714 3751

■ **THERM-O-DISC INC** p 1447
1320 S Main St 44907
Tel (419) 525-8500 *SIC* 3822 3823

MAPLE HEIGHTS, OH

■ **EAST OHIO GAS CO** p 470
19701 Libby Rd 44137
Tel (800) 362-7557 *SIC* 4923

■ **HSN IMPROVEMENTS LLC** p 715
16501 Rockside Rd 44137
Tel (216) 662-6553 *SIC* 5961

MARIETTA, OH

MARIETTA ERAMET INC p 906
16705 State Route 7 45750
Tel (740) 374-1000 *SIC* 3313

MARIETTA MEMORIAL HOSPITAL INC p 906
401 Matthew St 45750
Tel (740) 374-1400 *SIC* 8062 8069

PAR MAR OIL CO p 1113
114 Westview Ave Unit A 45750
Tel (740) 373-7406 *SIC* 5411

▲ **PEOPLES BANCORP INC** p 1132
138 Putnam St 45750
Tel (740) 373-3155 *SIC* 6021

■ **PEOPLES BANK** p 1132
138 Putnam St 45750
Tel (740) 373-3155 *SIC* 6035

■ **PEOPLES BANKING AND TRUST CO** p 1132
138 Putnam St 45750
Tel (740) 373-3155 *SIC* 6022

PIONEER PIPE INC p 1151
2021 Hanna Rd 45750
Tel (740) 376-2400
SIC 3498 1711 3443 3441 3312

MARION, OH

CENTRAL OHIO FARMERS CO-OP INC p 279
730 Bellefontaine Ave 43302
Tel (740) 383-2158 *SIC* 5153 5261

MARION GENERAL HOSPITAL INC p 907
1000 Mckinley Park Dr 43302
Tel (740) 383-8400 *SIC* 8062

MARION INDUSTRIES INC p 907
999 Kellogg Pkwy 43302
Tel (740) 223-0075 *SIC* 3714

UNITED CHURCH HOMES INC p 1507
170 E Center St 43302
Tel (740) 382-4885 *SIC* 8051

US YACHIYO INC p 1533
1177 Kellogg Pkwy 43302
Tel (740) 223-3134 *SIC* 3795

WYANDOT INC p 1629
135 Wyandot Ave 43302
Tel (740) 383-4031 *SIC* 2096

MARTINS FERRY, OH

UNITED DAIRY INC p 1507
300 N 5th St 43935
Tel (740) 633-1451 *SIC* 2026 2024

MARYSVILLE, OH

HONDA ENGINEERING NORTH AMERICA INC p 704
24000 Honda Pkwy 43040
Tel (937) 642-5000 *SIC* 3544

HONDA OF AMERICA MFG INC p 704
24000 Honda Pkwy 43040
Tel (937) 642-5000 *SIC* 3711

■ **HYPONEX CORP** p 724
14111 Scottslawn Rd 43040
Tel (937) 644-0011 *SIC* 2873 2875

MEMORIAL HOSPITAL OF UNION COUNTY p 942
500 London Ave 43040
Tel (937) 644-6115 *SIC* 8062

■ **SCOTTS CO LLC** p 1294
14111 Scottslawn Rd 43040
Tel (937) 644-0011
SIC 2873 2874 2879 0782 2499 3524

▲ **SCOTTS MIRACLE-GRO CO** p 1294
14111 Scottslawn Rd 43040
Tel (937) 644-0011 *SIC* 3542 0782 7342

MASON, OH

▲ **ATRICURE INC** p 129
7555 Innovation Way 45040
Tel (513) 755-4100 *SIC* 3841

■ **CINTAS CORP NO 1** p 308
6800 Cintas Blvd 45040
Tel (513) 459-1200
SIC 7213 5136 5137 7549

■ **CINTAS CORP NO 2** p 308
6800 Cintas Blvd 45040
Tel (513) 459-1200 *SIC* 5084

■ **CINTAS CORP NO 3** p 308
6800 Cintas Blvd 45040
Tel (513) 459-1200 *SIC* 7218

■ **CINTAS-RUS LP** p 308
6800 Cintas Blvd 45040
Tel (513) 459-1200 *SIC* 7218

■ **CLOPAY BUILDING PRODUCTS CO INC** p 327
8585 Duke Blvd 45040
Tel (513) 770-4800 *SIC* 2431 3442 2436

■ **CLOPAY CORP** p 327
8585 Duke Blvd 45040
Tel (800) 282-2260
SIC 3081 3442 2431 1796

■ **CLOPAY PLASTIC PRODUCTS CO INC** p 327
8585 Duke Blvd 45040
Tel (513) 770-4800 *SIC* 3081

DOWN-LITE INTERNATIONAL INC p 453
8153 Duke Blvd 45040
Tel (513) 229-3696 *SIC* 2392 5719

FUJITEC AMERICA INC p 583
7258 Innovation Way 45040
Tel (513) 755-6100 *SIC* 3534

IAMS CO p 725
8700 S Masn Montgomery Rd 45040
Tel (800) 675-3849 *SIC* 2047 2048

INTELLIGRATED INC p 750
7901 Innovation Way 45040
Tel (866) 936-7300 *SIC* 3535

■ **INTELLIGRATED SYSTEMS INC** p 750
7901 Innovation Way 45040
Tel (866) 936-7300 *SIC* 3535 5084 7371

■ **INTELLIGRATED SYSTEMS LLC** p 750
7901 Innovation Way 45040
Tel (513) 701-7300 *SIC* 3535 5084 7371

■ **INTELLIGRATED SYSTEMS OF OHIO LLC** p 750
7901 Innovation Way 45040
Tel (513) 701-7300 *SIC* 3535 5084 3537

■ **L-3 COMMUNICATIONS CINCINNATI ELECTRONICS CORP** p 834
7500 Innovation Way 45040
Tel (513) 573-6100 *SIC* 3812 3769 3823

LUXOTTICA RETAIL NORTH AMERICA INC p 887
4000 Luxottica Pl 45040
Tel (513) 765-6000 *SIC* 5995

■ **MACYS CREDIT AND CUSTOMER SERVICES INC** p 893
9111 Duke Blvd 45040
Tel (513) 398-5221 *SIC* 7389 7322 6141

MAKINO INC p 899
7680 Innovation Way 45040
Tel (513) 573-7200 *SIC* 3541

MITSUBISHI ELECTRIC AUTOMOTIVE AMERICA INC p 977
4773 Bethany Rd 45040
Tel (513) 573-6614 *SIC* 3694 3651 3714

■ **PORTION PAC INC** p 1163
7325 Snider Rd 45040
Tel (513) 398-0400 *SIC* 2033 2035

PRASCO LLC p 1167
6125 Commerce Ct 45040
Tel (513) 204-1100 *SIC* 5122

SKILLED CARE PHARMACY INC p 1329
6175 Hi Tek Ct 45040
Tel (513) 459-7626 *SIC* 5122

SUNGLASS HUT TRADING LLC p 1402
4000 Luxottica Pl 45040
Tel (513) 765-4001 *SIC* 5995

MASSILLON, OH

ARE ACCESSORIES LLC p 106
400 Nave Rd Se 44646
Tel (330) 830-7800 *SIC* 3713

ARE INC p 106
400 Nave Rd Sw 44646
Tel (330) 830-7800
SIC 3713 3714 3792 5013

CAMPBELL OIL CO p 245
7977 Hills & Dales Rd Ne 44646
Tel (330) 833-8555 *SIC* 5171

■ **DHSC LLC** p 435
875 8th St Ne 44646
Tel (330) 832-8761 *SIC* 8062

FRESH MARK INC p 578
1888 Southway St Se 44646
Tel (330) 834-3669 *SIC* 2013 5147 2011

MANCAN INC p 901
48 1st St Nw 44647
Tel (330) 832-4595 *SIC* 7361

■ **MASSILLON HEALTH SYSTEM LLC** p 917
400 Austin Ave Nw 44646
Tel (330) 837-7200 *SIC* 8062

SHEARERS FOODS LLC p 1313
100 Lincoln Way E 44646
Tel (330) 834-4030 *SIC* 2096 5145

SNACK ALLIANCE INC p 1335
100 Lincoln Way E 44646
Tel (330) 767-3426 *SIC* 2096

MAUMEE, OH

▲ **ANDERSONS INC** p 90
480 W Dussel Dr 43537
Tel (419) 893-5050
SIC 5153 0723 5191 2874 4789 4741

■ **BUCKEYE DISCOUNT INC** p 223
1020 Ford St 43537
Tel (419) 893-9401 *SIC* 5912

CHECKER NOTIONS CO INC p 292
400 W Dussel Dr Ste B 43537
Tel (419) 893-3636 *SIC* 5131 5092

■ **DANA AUTOMOTIVE SYSTEMS GROUP LLC** p 410
3939 Technology Dr 43537
Tel (419) 887-3000 *SIC* 3714

■ **DANA DRIVESHAFT PRODUCTS LLC** p 410
3939 Technology Dr 43537
Tel (419) 887-3000 *SIC* 3714

■ **DANA HEAVY VEHICLE SYSTEMS GROUP LLC** p 410
3939 Technology Dr 43537
Tel (419) 887-3000 *SIC* 3714

▲ **DANA INC** p 410
3939 Technology Dr 43537
Tel (419) 887-3000
SIC 3714 3053 3593 3492

■ **DANA LIGHT AXLE MANUFACTURING LLC** p 410
3939 Technology Dr 43537
Tel (419) 887-3000 *SIC* 3714

■ **DANA LIMITED** p 410
3939 Technology Dr 43537
Tel (630) 697-3783
SIC 3714 3053 3593 3492

■ **DANA SEALING PRODUCTS LLC** p 411
3939 Technology Dr 43537
Tel (419) 887-3000 *SIC* 3714

KELLERMEYER BERGENSONS SERVICES LLC p 808
1575 Henthorne Dr 43537
Tel (419) 867-4300 *SIC* 7349

OHIO VIRTUAL ACADEMY p 1078
1690 Woodlands Dr Ste 200 43537
Tel (419) 482-0948 *SIC* 8211

SPARTAN CHEMICAL CO INC p 1355
1110 Spartan Dr 43537
Tel (419) 897-5551 *SIC* 2842

ST LUKES HOSPITAL p 1370
5901 Monclova Rd 43537
Tel (419) 893-5911 *SIC* 8062 5912

SYLVANIA FRANCISCAN HEALTH p 1414
1715 Indian Wood Cir # 200 43537
Tel (419) 882-8373 *SIC* 8062 8741

■ **THERMA-TRU CORP** p 1447
1750 Indian Wood Cir # 100 43537
Tel (419) 891-7400 *SIC* 3442

MAYFIELD HEIGHTS, OH

▲ **FERRO CORP** p 538
6060 Parkland Blvd # 250 44124
Tel (216) 875-5600
SIC 3479 2816 2851 3399 2821 2834

■ **MATERION BRUSH INC** p 919
6070 Parkland Blvd Ste 1 44124
Tel (216) 486-4200
SIC 3351 3356 3264 3339 3341 3674

▲ **MATERION CORP** p 919
6070 Parkland Blvd Ste 1 44124
Tel (216) 486-4200
SIC 3339 3351 3356 3341 3674

ONX ACQUISITION LLC p 1088
5910 Landerbrook Dr # 250 44124
Tel (440) 569-2300 *SIC* 7372 7379

PARK PLACE TECHNOLOGIES LLC p 1115
5910 Landerbrook Dr # 300 44124
Tel (877) 778-8707 *SIC* 7378

■ **TMW SYSTEMS INC** p 1458
6085 Parkland Blvd 44124
Tel (216) 831-6606 *SIC* 7372

MAYFIELD VILLAGE, OH

▲ **PREFORMED LINE PRODUCTS CO** p 1169
660 Beta Dr 44143
Tel (440) 461-5200 *SIC* 3644 3661

■ **PROGRESSIVE CASUALTY INSURANCE CO** p 1181
6300 Wilson Mills Rd 44143
Tel (440) 461-5000
SIC 6331 6351 6411 6321

▲ **PROGRESSIVE CORP** p 1181
6300 Wilson Mills Rd 44143
Tel (440) 461-5000 *SIC* 6331 6351

MC ARTHUR, OH

TWIN MAPLES NURSING HOME p 1495
31054 State Route 93 45651
Tel (740) 596-5955 *SIC* 8051 8052

MC CONNELSVILLE, OH

RIVERSIDE CARE CENTER LLC p 1237
856 Riverside Dr S 43756
Tel (740) 962-5303 *SIC* 8051

MCCONNELSVILLE, OH

MIBA BEARINGS US LLC p 959
5037 N State Route 60 Nw 43756
Tel (740) 962-4242 *SIC* 3799

MEDINA, OH

■ **CORRPRO COMPANIES INC** p 373
1055 W Smith Rd 44256
Tel (330) 723-5082 *SIC* 3699 8711

COUNTY OF MEDINA p 379
144 N Brdwy St Rm 201 44256
Tel (330) 722-9208 *SIC* 9111

DISCOUNT DRUG MART INC p 442
211 Commerce Dr 44256
Tel (330) 725-2340
SIC 5912 5331 5411 5451 5122 8082

■ **FRICTION PRODUCTS CO** p 579
920 Lake Rd 44256
Tel (330) 725-4941 *SIC* 3728 3714

MARCOR ENTERPRISES INC p 905
190 Highland Dr 44256
Tel (330) 722-7974 *SIC* 7363

MEDINA CITY SCHOOL DISTRICT p 938
739 Weymouth Rd 44256
Tel (330) 725-8831 *SIC* 8211

MEDINA HOSPITAL p 938
1000 E Washington St 44256
Tel (330) 725-1000 *SIC* 8062

■ **PANTHER PREMIUM LOGISTICS INC** p 1111
84 Medina Rd 44256
Tel (800) 685-0657 *SIC* 4213 4212

PREMIUM TRANSPORTATION STAFFING INC p 1171
190 Highland Dr 44256
Tel (330) 722-7974 *SIC* 7291 7363

■ **REPUBLIC POWDERED METALS INC** p 1225
2628 Pearl Rd 44256
Tel (330) 225-3192
SIC 2851 2891 3069 2899 2865 2842

▲ **RPM INTERNATIONAL INC** p 1255
2628 Pearl Rd 44256
Tel (330) 273-5090
SIC 2851 2891 3069 2899 2865 2842

SANDRIDGE FOOD CORP p 1278
133 Commerce Dr 44256
Tel (330) 725-2348 *SIC* 2099

WOLFF BROS SUPPLY INC p 1621
6078 Wolff Rd 44256
Tel (330) 725-3451 *SIC* 5063 5074 5075

MENTOR, OH

BUYERS PRODUCTS CO p 230
9049 Tyler Blvd 44060
Tel (440) 974-8888 *SIC* 5013 3714

CLEVELAND CONSTRUCTION INC p 325
8620 Tyler Blvd 44060
Tel (513) 398-8900 *SIC* 1542 1742 1752

▲ **GAS NATURAL INC** p 593
8470 Station St 44060
Tel (440) 974-3770
SIC 4924 4911 5172 5984

LAKE HOSPITAL SYSTEMS p 839
7956 Tyler Blvd 44060
Tel (440) 255-6400 *SIC* 8062

MENTOR EXEMPTED VILLAGE SCHOOL DISTRICT p 943
6451 Center St 44060
Tel (440) 255-4444 *SIC* 8211

POLYCHEM CORP p 1160
6277 Heisley Rd 44060
Tel (440) 357-1500 *SIC* 2671

SOURCEONE HEALTHCARE TECHNOLOGIES INC p 1342
8020 Tyler Blvd 44060
Tel (440) 701-1200 *SIC* 5047

STERIS CORP p 1386
5960 Heisley Rd 44060
Tel (440) 354-2600 *SIC* 3841 3842 3845

STERIS ISOMEDIX OPERATIONS INC p 1386
5960 Heisley Rd 44060
Tel (440) 354-2600 *SIC* 8734

WILLOUGHBY SUPPLY CO p 1613
7433 Clover Ave 44060
Tel (440) 942-7939 *SIC* 5033

MIAMISBURG, OH

AIRTRON INC p 41
9260 Marketpl Dr 45342
Tel (937) 898-0826 *SIC* 1711

ALLIANCE PHYSICIANS INC p 55
2110 Leiter Rd 45342
Tel (937) 558-9070 *SIC* 8011

DANIS BUILDING CONSTRUCTION CO p 411
3233 Newmark Dr 45342
Tel (937) 228-1225 *SIC* 1542 1541

DAYTON SUPERIOR CORP p 418
1125 Byers Rd 45342
Tel (937) 866-0711
SIC 3315 3452 3462 3089 2899

DIRECT ENERGY US HOME SERVICES INC p 441
9260 Marketplace Dr 45342
Tel (937) 898-0826 *SIC* 1711

■ **ESKO-GRAPHICS INC** p 509
8535 Gander Creek Dr 45342
Tel (937) 454-1721 *SIC* 5084 7372

EVENFLO CO INC p 513
225 Byers Rd 45342
Tel (937) 415-3300 *SIC* 3944 2519

INNOMARK COMMUNICATIONS LLC p 744
3005 W Tech Blvd 45342
Tel (513) 285-1040 *SIC* 7319

LEXISNEXIS GROUP p 859
9443 Springboro Pike 45342
Tel (937) 865-6800 *SIC* 7375 2741

■ **NATIONAL CITY MORTGAGE INC** p 1010
3232 Newmark Dr 45342
Tel (937) 910-1200 *SIC* 6162

■ **NEWPAGE CORP** p 1038
8540 Gander Creek Dr 45342
Tel (877) 855-7243 *SIC* 2621 2611

NEWPAGE ENERGY SERVICES LLC p 1038
8540 Gander Creek Dr 45342
Tel (877) 855-7243 *SIC* 2672 2621 2611

■ **NEWPAGE GROUP INC** p 1038
8540 Gander Creek Dr 45342
Tel (937) 242-9500 *SIC* 2671

■ **NEWPAGE HOLDING CORP** p 1038
8540 Gander Creek Dr 45342
Tel (877) 855-7243 *SIC* 2621 2672 2611

OCM LLC p 1074
4500 Lyons Rd 45342
Tel (937) 247-2700 *SIC* 2711

SOGETI USA LLC p 1337
10100 Innovation Dr # 200 45342
Tel (937) 291-8100 *SIC* 7379

TECHNICOTE INC p 1431
222 Mound Ave 45342
Tel (800) 358-4448 *SIC* 2672

▲ **TERADATA CORP** p 1439
10000 Innovation Dr 45342
Tel (866) 548-8348
SIC 3571 3572 7372 7371

■ **TERADATA OPERATIONS INC** p 1439
10000 Innovation Dr 45342
Tel (937) 242-4030 *SIC* 3571

ULLIMAN SCHUTTE CONSTRUCTION LLC p 1500
9111 Springboro Pike 45342
Tel (937) 247-0375 *SIC* 1629

MIDDLEBURG HEIGHTS, OH

BARRETTE OUTDOOR LIVING INC p 157
7830 Freeway Cir 44130
Tel (440) 891-0790 *SIC* 3315

COMPASS HEALTH BRANDS CORP p 351
6753 Engle Rd Ste A 44130
Tel (800) 947-1728 *SIC* 5047

INTERLAKE STEAMSHIP CO p 753
7300 Engle Rd 44130
Tel (440) 260-6900 *SIC* 4432

MIDDLEFIELD, OH

HC COMPANIES INC p 671
15150 Madison Rd 44062
Tel (440) 632-3333 *SIC* 5211

■ **MASCO CABINETRY MIDDLEFIELD LLC** p 915
15535 S State Ave 44062
Tel (440) 632-5333 *SIC* 2434

WESTERN RESERVE FARM COOPERATIVE INC p 1600
16003 E High St 44062
Tel (440) 632-0271 *SIC* 5191 5983 5211

MIDDLETOWN, OH

ATRIUM MEDICAL CENTER p 129
1 Medical Center Dr 45005
Tel (937) 499-9596 *SIC* 8099

ATRIUM MEDICAL CENTER p 129
1 Medical Center Dr 45005
Tel (513) 424-2111 *SIC* 8062

COHEN BROTHERS INC p 335
1723 Woodlawn Ave 45044
Tel (513) 422-3696
SIC 5093 3441 3341 3312

HIGHTOWERS PETROLEUM CO INC p 692
3577 Commerce Dr 45005
Tel (513) 423-4272 *SIC* 5172

MILAN, OH

COLES ENERGY INC p 336
3619 St Rt 113 E 44846
Tel (419) 499-1120 *SIC* 5172 5411 5541

MILFORD, OH

AMERICAN NURSING CARE INC p 77
1700 Edison Dr Ste 300 45150
Tel (513) 576-0262 *SIC* 8051

■ **BUCKHORN INC** p 223
55 W Techne Center Dr A 45150
Tel (513) 831-4402 *SIC* 3089

CHI HEALTH AT HOME p 296
1700 Edison Dr Ste 300 45150
Tel (513) 576-0262 *SIC* 7363 8093

LYKINS COMPANIES INC p 887
5163 Wlfpn Plsnt Hl Rd 45150
Tel (513) 831-8820 *SIC* 5172 4213 5411

LYKINS OIL CO p 887
5163 Wlfpn Plsnt Hl Rd 45150
Tel (513) 831-8820 *SIC* 5172 5983

MILFORD EXEMPTED VILLAGE SCHOOL DISTRICT p 969
777 Garfield Ave 45150
Tel (513) 576-4175 *SIC* 8211

MILLERSBURG, OH

CHRISTIAN AID MINISTRIES p 302
4464 State Route 39 44654
Tel (330) 893-2428 *SIC* 8322 5999

COBLENTZ DISTRIBUTING INC p 333
3850 State Route 39 44654
Tel (800) 543-6848 *SIC* 5143 5451

MINSTER, OH

NIDEC MINSTER CORP p 1043
240 W 5th St 45865
Tel (419) 628-2331 *SIC* 3542 3568

■ **PRECISION STRIP INC** p 1169
86 S Ohio St 45865
Tel (419) 501-1347 *SIC* 7389

MONROE, OH

BAKER CONCRETE CONSTRUCTION INC p 146
900 N Garver Rd 45050
Tel (513) 539-4000 *SIC* 1771 1611

DECEUNINCK NORTH AMERICA LLC p 421
351 N Garver Rd 45050
Tel (513) 539-5466 *SIC* 3082

OHIO PIZZA PRODUCTS INC p 1078
201 Lawton Ave 45050
Tel (937) 294-6969 *SIC* 5149

MONTGOMERY, OH

OHIO NATIONAL FINANCIAL SERVICES INC p 1077
1 Financial Way Ste 100 45242
Tel (513) 794-6100 *SIC* 6311

OHIO NATIONAL LIFE ASSURANCE CORP p 1077
1 Financial Way Ste 100 45242
Tel (513) 794-6100 *SIC* 6411

OHIO NATIONAL LIFE INSURANCE CO p 1078
1 Financial Way Ste 100 45242
Tel (513) 794-6100 *SIC* 6331

OHIO NATIONAL MUTUAL HOLDINGS INC p 1078
1 Financial Way Ste 100 45242
Tel (513) 794-6100 *SIC* 6311

MONTPELIER, OH

■ **CHASE BRASS AND COPPER CO LLC** p 291
14212 Selwyn Dr 43543
Tel (419) 485-3193 *SIC* 3351

CK TECHNOLOGIES LLC p 320
1701 Magda Dr 43543
Tel (419) 485-1110 *SIC* 3089 3999

MORAINE, OH

DAYTON HEIDELBERG DISTRIBUTING CO p 417
3601 Dryden Rd 45439
Tel (937) 222-8692 *SIC* 5181

■ **DMAX LTD** p 445
3100 Dryden Rd 45439
Tel (937) 425-9700 *SIC* 3519

■ **ELDER-BEERMAN STORES CORP** p 484
3155 Elbee Rd Ste 201 45439
Tel (937) 296-2700 *SIC* 5311 5661 7389

INTERNATIONAL COMMUNICATIONS EXCHANGE CORP p 755
4033 Ellery Ave 45439
Tel (937) 296-9605 *SIC* 8748 7379

KIDS IN NEED FOUNDATION p 817
3055 Kettering Blvd # 119 45439
Tel (937) 296-1230 *SIC* 8641

■ **L M BERRY AND CO** p 834
3170 Kettering Blvd 45439
Tel (937) 296-2121 *SIC* 7311 2741

LASTAR INC p 846
3555 Kettering Blvd 45439
Tel (937) 224-0639 *SIC* 3678

NOLAND CO p 1046
3110 Kettering Blvd 45439
Tel (937) 396-7980
SIC 5074 5075 5063 5085

WINSUPPLY INC p 1617
3110 Kettering Blvd 45439
Tel (937) 294-5331 *SIC* 1542 5074 5085

MOSCOW, OH

DYNEGY ZIMMER LLC p 465
1781 Us Rte 52 45153
Tel (713) 767-0483 *SIC* 1731

MOUNT HOPE, OH

GMI HOLDINGS INC p 619
1 Door Dr 44660
Tel (330) 821-5360 *SIC* 3699 3635

HRH DOOR CORP p 714
1 Door Dr 44660
Tel (850) 208-3400 *SIC* 3442 2431

MOUNT STERLING, OH

KEIHIN THERMAL TECHNOLOGY OF AMERICA INC p 808
10500 Oday Harrison Rd 43143
Tel (740) 869-3000 *SIC* 5013 3714

MOUNT VERNON, OH

ARIEL CORP p 108
35 Blackjack Road Ext 43050
Tel (740) 397-0311 *SIC* 3563

KNOX COMMUNITY HOSPITAL p 825
1330 Coshocton Ave 43050
Tel (740) 393-9000 *SIC* 8062

ROLLS-ROYCE ENERGY SYSTEMS INC p 1247
105 N Sandusky St 43050
Tel (740) 393-8888 *SIC* 3511 5084 8711

NAVARRE, OH

ALFRED NICKLES BAKERY INC p 50
26 Main St N 44662
Tel (330) 879-5635 *SIC* 2051

NELSONVILLE, OH

ED MAP INC p 476
296 S Harper St Ste 1 45764
Tel (740) 753-3439 *SIC* 5192

HOCKING TECHNICAL COLLEGE p 699
3301 Hocking Pkwy 45764
Tel (740) 753-3591 *SIC* 8222 8249 8221

■ **LEHIGH OUTFITTERS LLC** p 853
39 E Canal St 45764
Tel (740) 753-1951 *SIC* 5661 5139

▲ **ROCKY BRANDS INC** p 1245
39 E Canal St 45764
Tel (740) 753-1951
SIC 3143 3144 2329 2331 2339 2389

NEW ALBANY, OH

■ **A&F TRADEMARK INC** p 7
6301 Fitch Path 43054
Tel (614) 283-6500 *SIC* 5611

▲ **ABERCROMBIE & FITCH CO** p 11
6301 Fitch Path 43054
Tel (614) 283-6500
SIC 5611 5621 5641 5632 5651 5961

■ **ABERCROMBIE & FITCH HOLDING CORP** p 11
6301 Fitch Path 43054
Tel (614) 283-6500 *SIC* 5611

■ **ABERCROMBIE & FITCH MANAGEMENT CO** p 11
6301 Fitch Path 43054
Tel (614) 283-6500 *SIC* 5611

■ **ABERCROMBIE & FITCH STORES INC** p 11
6301 Fitch Path 43054
Tel (614) 283-6500 *SIC* 5611

■ **ABERCROMBIE & FITCH TRADING CO** p 11
6301 Fitch Path 43054
Tel (614) 283-6500
SIC 5136 5137 5641 5621 5611

AXIUM PLASTICS LLC p 140
9005 Smiths Mill Rd 43054
Tel (614) 706-5955 *SIC* 3089

■ **BEF FOODS INC** p 168
8111 Smiths Mill Rd 43054
Tel (800) 272-7675 *SIC* 5963

▲ **BOB EVANS FARMS INC** p 196
8111 Smiths Mill Rd 43054
Tel (614) 491-2225
SIC 5812 2011 2099 2035

■ **BOB EVANS FARMS LLC** p 196
8111 Smiths Mill Rd 43054
Tel (614) 491-2225 *SIC* 5812

▲ **COMMERCIAL VEHICLE GROUP INC** p 345
7800 Walton Pkwy 43054
Tel (614) 289-5360 *SIC* 3714 3231

DESCO CORP p 432
7795 Walton Pkwy Ste 175 43054
Tel (614) 888-8855
SIC 3442 3825 3643 3531 3429

■ **JMH TRADEMARK INC** p 786
6301 Fitch Path 43054
Tel (614) 283-6500 *SIC* 5611

LIMITED STORES LLC p 866
7775 Walton Pkwy Ste 400 43054
Tel (614) 289-2200 *SIC* 5621 5941 5632

MOUNT CARMEL NEW ALBANY SURGICAL HOSPITAL p 993
7333 Smiths Mill Rd 43054
Tel (614) 775-6600 *SIC* 8062

MXD GROUP INC p 1004
7795 Walton Pkwy Ste 400 43054
Tel (614) 895-1959 *SIC* 4214 4213

■ **NATIONAL SEATING CO** p 1016
7800 Walton Pkwy 43054
Tel (219) 872-7295 *SIC* 2392

RE/MAX CONSULTANT GROUP p 1212
6650 Walnut St 43054
Tel (614) 855-2822 *SIC* 6531

■ **TRIM SYSTEMS OPERATING CORP** p 1480
7800 Walton Pkwy 43054
Tel (614) 289-5360 *SIC* 3714

■ **TWEEN BRANDS INC** p 1494
8323 Walton Pkwy 43054
Tel (614) 775-3500 *SIC* 5641

■ **TWEEN BRANDS SERVICE CO** p 1494
8323 Walton Pkwy 43054
Tel (614) 775-3500 *SIC* 5137

NEW BREMEN, OH

CROWN EQUIPMENT CORP p 395
44 S Washington St 45869
Tel (419) 629-2311 *SIC* 5084

NEW CONCORD, OH

PENDAFORM CO p 1128
200 S Friendship Dr 43762
Tel (740) 826-5000 *SIC* 3089

NEW FRANKLIN, OH

CLINTON ALUMINUM ACQUISITION LLC p 327
6270 Van Buren Rd 44216
Tel (330) 882-6743 *SIC* 5051

NEW LONDON, OH

KENT SPORTING GOODS CO INC p 812
433 Park Ave 44851
Tel (419) 929-7021 *SIC* 3949

NEW PHILADELPHIA, OH

■ **GRADALL INDUSTRIES INC** p 628
406 Mill Ave Sw 44663
Tel (330) 339-2211 *SIC* 3537 3531

LAUREN INTERNATIONAL LTD p 847
2228 Reiser Ave Se 44663
Tel (330) 339-3373 *SIC* 3069

NEWARK, OH

■ **ALLTEL COMMUNICATIONS CORP** p 59
66 N 4th St 43055
Tel (740) 349-8551 *SIC* 4813 4812

ANOMATIC CORP p 92
1650 Tamarack Rd 43055
Tel (740) 522-2203 *SIC* 3471 3469 2396

COUNTY OF LICKING p 379
20 S 2nd St 43055
Tel (740) 670-5040 *SIC* 9111

■ **GOLF GALAXY GOLFWORKS INC** p 622
4820 Jacksontown Rd 43056
Tel (740) 328-4193
SIC 5091 2731 3949 5941

LICKING MEMORIAL HEALTH SYSTEMS p 863
1320 W Main St 43055
Tel (740) 348-4000 *SIC* 8741 6411

LICKING MEMORIAL HOSPITAL p 863
1320 W Main St 43055
Tel (740) 348-4137 *SIC* 8062

NEWARK CITY SCHOOLS p 1036
621 Mount Vernon Rd 43055
Tel (740) 670-7000 *SIC* 8211

■ **PARK NATIONAL BANK** p 1115
50 N 3rd St 43055
Tel (740) 349-8451 *SIC* 6021

▲ **PARK NATIONAL CORP** p 1115
50 N 3rd St 43055
Tel (740) 349-8451 *SIC* 6021

NEWBURGH HEIGHTS, OH

■ **HOWMET CASTINGS & SERVICES INC** p 713
1616 Harvard Ave 44105
Tel (216) 641-4400 *SIC* 3324

■ **HOWMET CORP** p 713
1616 Harvard Ave 44105
Tel (800) 242-9898
SIC 3324 3542 5051 3479

NEWBURY, OH

KINETICO INC p 820
10845 Kinsman Rd 44065
Tel (440) 564-9111 *SIC* 3589 5074

KUHNLE BROTHERS INC p 831
14905 Cross Creek Pkwy 44065
Tel (440) 564-7168 *SIC* 4213 4212

NEY, OH

NEY OIL CO INC p 1041
145 S Water St 43549
Tel (419) 658-2324 *SIC* 5171

NILES, OH

■ **RMI TITANIUM CO LLC** p 1239
1000 Warren Ave 44446
Tel (330) 652-9952
SIC 3399 3356 1741 3533

NORTH CANTON, OH

ASC INDUSTRIES INC p 115
2100 International Pkwy 44720
Tel (330) 899-0340 *SIC* 3714

▲ **DIEBOLD INC** p 438
5995 Mayfair Rd 44720
Tel (330) 490-4000 *SIC* 3578 3699 3499

DISTTECH INC p 443
4366 Mount Pleasant St Nw 44720
Tel (800) 969-5419 *SIC* 4213

■ **FANNIE MAY CONFECTIONS BRANDS INC** p 527
5353 Lauby Rd 44720
Tel (330) 494-0833 *SIC* 5441 2066

FLOWER FACTORY INC p 560
5655 Whipple Ave Nw 44720
Tel (330) 494-7978 *SIC* 5199

FRED OLIVIERI CONSTRUCTION CO p 576
6315 Promway Ave Nw 44720
Tel (330) 494-1007 *SIC* 1542

GBS CORP p 595
7233 Freedom Ave Nw 44720
Tel (330) 494-5330
SIC 5045 5112 2675 2672 2761 2759

KENAN ADVANTAGE GROUP INC p 810
4366 Mount Pleasant St Nw 44720
Tel (877) 999-2524 *SIC* 4213 4212

■ **PREMIER BANK & TRUST NATIONAL ASSOCIATION** p 1170
600 S Main St 44720
Tel (330) 499-1900 *SIC* 6733 6029

PROVANTAGE LLC p 1185
7576 Freedom Ave Nw 44720
Tel (330) 494-3781
SIC 5961 5719 5734 5045

STARK STATE COLLEGE p 1379
6200 Frank Ave Nw 44720
Tel (330) 494-6170 *SIC* 8222

SUAREZ CORP INDUSTRIES p 1395
7800 Whipple Ave Nw 44720
Tel (330) 494-5504 *SIC* 5961 5944

TESTAMERICA ENVIRONMENTAL SERVICES LLC p 1441
4101 Shuffel St Nw 44720
Tel (330) 497-9396 *SIC* 8734

TESTAMERICA HOLDINGS INC p 1441
4101 Shuffel St Nw 44720
Tel (330) 497-9396 *SIC* 8734

TESTAMERICA LABORATORIES INC p 1441
4101 Shuffel St Nw 44720
Tel (800) 456-9396 *SIC* 8734

▲ **TIMKEN CO** p 1454
4500 Mount Pleasant St Nw 44720
Tel (234) 262-3000 *SIC* 3562

■ **TIMKEN CORP** p 1455
4500 Mount Pleasant St Nw 44720
Tel (330) 471-3378 *SIC* 5085 5051

TSG RESOURCES INC p 1489
339 E Maple St Ste 110 44720
Tel (330) 498-8107 *SIC* 8742

NORTH KINGSVILLE, OH

■ **PREMIX INC** p 1171
3365 E Center St 44068
Tel (440) 224-2181 *SIC* 3089 2821

NORTH OLMSTED, OH

FORTNEY & WEYGANDT INC p 570
31269 Bradley Rd 44070
Tel (440) 716-4000 *SIC* 1541 1542

PALMER HOLLAND INC p 1109
25000 Country Club Blvd # 444 44070
Tel (440) 686-2300 *SIC* 5169

R L FORTNEY MANAGEMENT INC p 1202
31269 Bradley Rd 44070
Tel (440) 716-4000 *SIC* 1542

NORTH RIDGEVILLE, OH

INVACARE CORP (TW) p 760
39400 Taylor Pkwy 44035
Tel (440) 329-6000 *SIC* 3842

KELLEX CORP p 808
33390 Liberty Pkwy 44039
Tel (440) 327-4428 *SIC* 5021

NORTHWOOD, OH

BUCKEYE CABLEVISION INC p 223
2700 Oregon Rd 43619
Tel (419) 724-9802 *SIC* 4841

NORPLAS INDUSTRIES INC p 1049
7825 Caple Blvd 43619
Tel (419) 662-3317 *SIC* 3469

NORTH AMERICAN SCIENCE ASSOCIATES INC p 1050
6750 Wales Rd 43619
Tel (419) 666-9455 *SIC* 8731 8734

PRESCRIPTION SUPPLY INC p 1171
2233 Tracy Rd 43619
Tel (419) 661-6600 *SIC* 5122

NORWALK, OH

FISHER-TITUS MEDICAL CENTER p 552
272 Benedict Ave 44857
Tel (419) 668-8101 *SIC* 8052 8062

NEW HORIZONS BAKING CO INC p 1031
211 Woodlawn Ave 44857
Tel (419) 668-8226 *SIC* 2051

NORWALK AREA HEALTH SYSTEMS INC p 1061
272 Benedict Ave 44857
Tel (419) 668-8101 *SIC* 8062 8051

OAKWOOD, OH

COOPER HATCHERY INC p 366
22348 Road 140 45873
Tel (419) 594-3325
SIC 0254 0253 2015 5153 2048

DOROTHY LANE MARKET INC p 451
2710 Far Hills Ave 45419
Tel (937) 299-3561 *SIC* 5411

OBERLIN, OH

GREEN CIRCLE GROWERS INC p 636
51051 Us Highway 20 44074
Tel (440) 775-1411 *SIC* 0181

OBERLIN COLLEGE p 1072
173 W Lorain St 44074
Tel (440) 775-8121 *SIC* 8221

OBETZ, OH

COLUMBUS FAIR AUTO AUCTION INC p 342
4700 Groveport Rd 43207
Tel (614) 497-2000 *SIC* 5012 5521

OLMSTED TWP, OH

VITA-MIX CORP p 1562
8615 Usher Rd 44138
Tel (440) 235-4840 *SIC* 5961 3556

OREGON, OH

MERCY HEALTH - ST CHARLES HOSPITAL LLC p 946
2600 Navarre Ave 43616
Tel (419) 696-7200 *SIC* 8062

■TOLEDO REFINING CO LLC p 1459
1819 Woodville Rd 43616
Tel (419) 698-6600 *SIC* 1629

ORRVILLE, OH

■ FOLGER COFFEE CO p 563
1 Strawberry Ln 44667
Tel (800) 937-9745 *SIC* 2095

■ INTERNATIONAL MULTIFOODS CORP p 756
1 Strawberry Ln 44667
Tel (330) 682-3000
SIC 5145 5149 5143 2048 2041

▲ J M SMUCKER CO p 771
1 Strawberry Ln 44667
Tel (330) 682-3000
SIC 2099 2033 2023 2087 2035

JARRETT LOGISTICS SYSTEMS INC p 778
1347 N Main St 44667
Tel (330) 682-0099 *SIC* 8742 4731

SMITHFOODS ORRVILLE INC p 1334
1381 Dairy Ln 44667
Tel (330) 683-8710 *SIC* 2026 2024

OXFORD, OH

MIAMI UNIVERSITY p 959
501 E High St 45056
Tel (513) 529-1809 *SIC* 8221

PAINESVILLE, OH

COUNTY OF LAKE p 379
8 N State St Ste 215 44077
Tel (440) 350-2500 *SIC* 9111

LAKE HEALTH TRIPOINT MEDICAL CENTER p 839
7590 Auburn Rd 44077
Tel (440) 375-8100 *SIC* 8062

R W SIDLEY INC p 1203
436 Casement Ave 44077
Tel (440) 352-9343 *SIC* 1771 3299

RICERCA BIOSCIENCES LLC p 1232
7528 Auburn Rd 44077
Tel (440) 357-3300 *SIC* 8731

PARMA, OH

■ APPLIED MAINTENANCE SUPPLIES & SOLUTIONS LLC p 99
12420 Plaza Dr 44130
Tel (216) 433-7700 *SIC* 5085

PARMA CITY SCHOOL DISTRICT p 1117
5311 Longwood Ave 44134
Tel (440) 842-5300 *SIC* 8211

PARMA COMMUNITY GENERAL HOSPITAL p 1117
7007 Powers Blvd 44129
Tel (440) 743-3000 *SIC* 8062

PROGRESSIVE QUALITY CARE INC p 1182
5553 Broadview Rd 44134
Tel (216) 661-6800 *SIC* 7389

PATASKALA, OH

COUGHLIN CHEVROLET INC p 374
9000 Broad St Sw 43062
Tel (740) 964-9191
SIC 5511 5012 7538 7532 5531

PERRYSBURG, OH

B P L CORP p 142
27476 Holiday Ln 43551
Tel (419) 874-1933 *SIC* 5812

BENNETT ENTERPRISES INC p 173
27476 Holiday Ln 43551
Tel (419) 874-1933 *SIC* 7011 5812

■ BPREX HEALTHCARE BROOKVILLE INC p 206
1899 N Wilkinson Way 43551
Tel (847) 541-9700 *SIC* 3089

MASTER CHEMICAL CORP p 918
501 W Boundary St 43551
Tel (419) 874-7902 *SIC* 2992 3559

OWENS COMMUNITY COLLEGE p 1100
30335 Oregon Rd 43551
Tel (567) 661-7000 *SIC* 8222

■ OWENS-BROCKWAY GLASS CONTAINER INC p 1100
1 Michael Owens Way 43551
Tel (567) 336-8449 *SIC* 3221

■ OWENS-BROCKWAY PACKAGING INC p 1100
1 Michael Owens Way 43551
Tel (567) 336-5000 *SIC* 3221

■ OWENS-ILLINOIS GROUP INC p 1100
1 Michael Owens Way 43551
Tel (567) 336-5000 *SIC* 3221

▲ OWENS-ILLINOIS INC p 1100
1 Michael Owens Way 43551
Tel (567) 336-5000 *SIC* 3221

PERRYSVILLE, OH

MANSFIELD PLUMBING PRODUCTS LLC p 903
150 E 1st St 44864
Tel (419) 938-5211
SIC 3261 3463 3088 3431 3432 5074

PICKERINGTON, OH

PICKERINGTON LOCAL SCHOOL DISTRICT p 1146
90 N East St 43147
Tel (614) 833-2110 *SIC* 8211

PIKETON, OH

FLUOR-BWXT PORTSMOUTH LLC p 561
1862 Shyville Rd Ste 216 45661
Tel (866) 706-6992 *SIC* 1795

INDIANA-KENTUCKY ELECTRIC CORP p 739
3932 Us Rte 23 45661
Tel (740) 289-7200 *SIC* 4911

OHIO VALLEY ELECTRIC CORP p 1078
3932 Us Rte 23 45661
Tel (740) 289-7200 *SIC* 4911

WASTREN ADVANTAGE INC p 1581
1571 Shyville Rd 45661
Tel (970) 254-1277 *SIC* 4959 8744 8711

PIQUA, OH

■ CRANE PUMPS & SYSTEMS INC p 389
420 3rd St 45356
Tel (937) 773-2442 *SIC* 3561

MIAMI VALLEY STEEL SERVICE INC p 959
201 Fox Dr 45356
Tel (937) 773-7127 *SIC* 5051

TAILWIND TECHNOLOGIES INC p 1421
1 Propeller Pl 45356
Tel (937) 778-4200 *SIC* 3356

TRUPOINTE COOPERATIVE INC p 1487
215 Looney Rd 45356
Tel (937) 575-6780 *SIC* 5153 5191

PLAIN CITY, OH

SELECT SIRES INC p 1301
11740 U S 42 N 43064
Tel (614) 873-4683 *SIC* 0751

PORTSMOUTH, OH

GLOCKNER CHEVROLET CO p 618
4368 Us Route 23 45662
Tel (740) 353-2161 *SIC* 5013 5172 5511

OSCO INDUSTRIES INC p 1096
734 11th St 45662
Tel (740) 354-3183 *SIC* 3321

PORTSMOUTH HOSPITAL CORP p 1163
1901 Argonne Rd 45662
Tel (740) 991-4000 *SIC* 8011

SOUTHERN OHIO MEDICAL CENTER p 1350
1805 27th St 45662
Tel (740) 354-5000 *SIC* 8062

RAVENNA, OH

COUNTY OF PORTAGE p 381
449 S Meridian St Fl 7 44266
Tel (330) 297-3561 *SIC* 9111

ROBINSON HEALTH SYSTEM INC p 1242
6847 N Chestnut St 44266
Tel (330) 297-0811 *SIC* 8062 8011

SIRNA & SONS INC p 1327
7176 State Route 88 44266
Tel (330) 298-2222 *SIC* 5148

REYNOLDSBURG, OH

AMERICANA DEVELOPMENT INC p 81
7095 Americana Pkwy 43068
Tel (614) 866-9803 *SIC* 6552

■ BATH & BODY WORKS LLC p 159
7 Limited Pkwy E 43068
Tel (614) 856-6000 *SIC* 5999 2844

DAIFUKU AMERICA CORP p 408
6700 Tussing Rd 43068
Tel (614) 863-1888 *SIC* 5084

DEPARTMENT OF COMMERCE OHIO p 429
6606 Tussing Rd 43068
Tel (614) 644-2223 *SIC* 9611

TS TECH AMERICAS INC p 1489
8458 E Broad St 43068
Tel (614) 575-4100 *SIC* 5099

TS TECH USA CORP p 1489
8400 E Broad St 43068
Tel (614) 577-1088 *SIC* 3714

■ VICTORIAS SECRET DIRECT HOLDING LLC p 1555
5 Limited Pkwy E 43068
Tel (614) 577-7111 *SIC* 5961

■ VICTORIAS SECRET DIRECT LLC p 1555
5 Limited Pkwy E 43068
Tel (614) 577-7111 *SIC* 5961 5632 5621

■ VICTORIAS SECRET STORES LLC p 1555
4 Limited Pkwy E 43068
Tel (614) 577-7111 *SIC* 5632 5621

■ WHITE BARN CANDLE CO p 1606
7 Limited Pkwy E 43068
Tel (614) 856-6000 *SIC* 5199

RICHFIELD, OH

EAGLE FAMILY FOODS GROUP LLC p 468
4020 Kinross Lakes Pkwy 44286
Tel (330) 382-3725 *SIC* 2023

■ ELEMENT14 US HOLDINGS INC p 486
4180 Highlander Pkwy 44286
Tel (330) 523-4280 *SIC* 5065 3429

■ NATIONAL INTERSTATE CORP p 1013
3250 Interstate Dr 44286
Tel (330) 659-8900 *SIC* 6331 6411

■ NATIONAL INTERSTATE INSURANCE CO p 1013
3250 Interstate Dr 44286
Tel (330) 659-8900 *SIC* 6331

■ PREMIER FARNELL CORP p 1170
4180 Highlander Pkwy 44286
Tel (216) 525-4300 *SIC* 3451

■ PREMIER FARNELL HOLDING INC p 1170
4180 Highlander Pkwy 44286
Tel (330) 523-4273 *SIC* 5065 3429

■ SNAP-ON BUSINESS SOLUTIONS INC p 1335
4025 Kinross Lakes Pkwy 44286
Tel (330) 659-1600 *SIC* 2741

WMK LLC p 1620
4199 Kinross Lakes Pkwy # 300 44286
Tel (234) 312-2000 *SIC* 5511 7532

RICHMOND HEIGHTS, OH

ASSOCIATED ESTATES REALTY CORP p 120
1 Aec Pkwy 44143
Tel (216) 261-5000 *SIC* 6798 1531

DIRECTIONAL CAPITAL LLC p 441
355 Richmond Rd Ste 8 44143
Tel (216) 261-3000 *SIC* 6722

FLIGHT OPTIONS INC p 556
26180 Curtiss Wright Pkwy 44143
Tel (216) 261-3880 *SIC* 4581

TRANZONIC COMPANIES p 1473
26301 Curtiss Wright Pkwy # 200 44143
Tel (216) 535-4300
SIC 2676 2211 2326 2842 2273 2262

TZ ACQUISITION CORP p 1496
26301 Curtiss Wright Pkwy 44143
Tel (216) 535-4300
SIC 2676 2211 2326 2842 2262

RIDGEVILLE CORNERS, OH

ALEX PRODUCTS INC p 49
19911 County Rd T 43555
Tel (419) 267-5240 *SIC* 3599

RUSSELLS POINT, OH

HONDA TRANSMISSION MANUFACTURING OF AMERICA INC p 705
6964 State Route 235 N 43348
Tel (937) 843-5555 *SIC* 3714

SABINA, OH

NEW SABINA INDUSTRIES INC p 1033
12555 Us Highway 22 And 3 45169
Tel (937) 584-2433 *SIC* 3714

SAINT CLAIRSVILLE, OH

HEALTH PLAN OF UPPER OHIO VALLEY INC p 675
52160 National Rd E 43950
Tel (740) 695-3585 *SIC* 6324 8082

MURRAY ENERGY CORP p 1001
46226 National Rd W 43950
Tel (740) 338-3100 *SIC* 1222

OHIO VALLEY COAL CO p 1078
46226 National Rd W 43950
Tel (740) 926-1351 *SIC* 1241

OHIO VALLEY TRANSLOADING CO INC p 1078
46226 National Rd W 43950
Tel (740) 795-4967 *SIC* 1241

RIESBECK FOOD MARKETS INC p 1234
48661 National Rd W 43950
Tel (740) 695-7050 *SIC* 5411

SAINT MARYS, OH

AAP ST MARYS CORP p 8
1100 Mckinley Rd 45885
Tel (419) 394-7840 *SIC* 3714

JTD HEALTH SYSTEMS INC p 796
200 Saint Clair Ave 45885
Tel (419) 394-3335 *SIC* 8741

SETEX INC p 1308
1111 Mckinley Rd 45885
Tel (419) 394-7800 *SIC* 2531

SAINT PARIS, OH

KTH PARTS INDUSTRIES INC p 831
1111 State Route 235 N 43072
Tel (937) 663-5941 *SIC* 3714

SALEM, OH

SALEM COMMUNITY HOSPITAL p 1272
1995 E State St 44460
Tel (330) 332-1551 *SIC* 8062 8051

VENTRA SALEM LLC p 1548
800 Pennsylvania Ave 44460
Tel (330) 337-8002 *SIC* 5013

SANDUSKY, OH

▲ CEDAR FAIR LP p 272
1 Cedar Point Dr 44870
Tel (419) 626-0830 *SIC* 7996

FIRELANDS REGIONAL HEALTH SYSTEM p 543
1111 Hayes Ave 44870
Tel (419) 557-7400 *SIC* 8062

J H ROUTH PACKING CO p 771
4413 W Bogart Rd 44870
Tel (419) 626-2251 *SIC* 2011

■ KINGS DOMINION LLC p 820
1 Cedar Point Dr 44870
Tel (419) 626-0830 *SIC* 7996

KYKLOS BEARING INTERNATIONAL LLC p 833
2509 Hayes Ave 44870
Tel (419) 627-7000 *SIC* 3714

LMN DEVELOPMENT LLC p 872
7000 Kalahari Dr 44870
Tel (419) 433-7200 *SIC* 7011 7996 5091

■ MAGNUM MANAGEMENT CORP p 897
1 Cedar Point Dr 44870
Tel (419) 627-2334 *SIC* 4785 6552 7996

SANDUSKY NEWSPAPERS INC p 1278
314 W Market St 44870
Tel (419) 625-5500 *SIC* 4832 2711 2752

THORWORKS INDUSTRIES INC p 1450
2520 Campbell St 44870
Tel (419) 626-4375
SIC 2851 3531 2952 2951 2891 2816

SEVEN HILLS, OH

■ AMT WARRANTY CORP p 87
5800 Lombardo Ctr Ste 150 44131
Tel (212) 220-7120 *SIC* 6399

SHAKER HEIGHTS, OH

SHELBURNE CORP p 1314
20001 Shelburne Rd 44118
Tel (216) 321-9177
SIC 3443 3823 3544 3769

UNIVERSITY HOSPITALS HEALTH SYSTEM INC p 1519
3605 Warrensville Ctr Rd 44122
Tel (216) 767-8900 *SIC* 8062 8011 8741

SHARON CENTER, OH

RUHLIN CO p 1257
6931 Ridge Rd 44274
Tel (330) 239-2800
SIC 1542 1541 1622 1611

SHARONVILLE, OH

CHESTER WEST HOLDINGS INC p 295
11500 Canal Rd 45241
Tel (800) 647-1900
SIC 3842 5136 5099 5137 2381

DCP HOLDING CO p 418
100 Crowne Point Pl 45241
Tel (513) 554-1100 *SIC* 6324

DUBOIS CHEMICALS INC p 459
3630 E Kemper Rd 45241
Tel (800) 438-2647 *SIC* 2869

SHEFFIELD VILLAGE, OH

MD AUTO GROUP LLC p 933
5013 Detroit Rd 44054
Tel (440) 934-6001 *SIC* 5511

SHELBY, OH

ARCELORMITTAL TUBULAR PRODUCTS SHELBY LLC p 104
132 W Main St 44875
Tel (419) 347-2424 *SIC* 3317 3321

SIDNEY, OH

DICKMAN SUPPLY INC p 438
1991 St Marys Ave 45365
Tel (937) 492-6166 *SIC* 5063 5084

■ EMERSON CLIMATE TECHNOLOGIES INC p 492
1675 Campbell Rd 45365
Tel (937) 498-3011 *SIC* 3585

FERGUSON CONSTRUCTION CO INC p 538
400 Canal St 45365
Tel (937) 498-2381 *SIC* 1541 1542

FRESHWAY FOODS INC p 579
601 Stolle Ave 45365
Tel (937) 498-4664 *SIC* 5148 2099

HOLLOWAY SPORTSWEAR INC p 701
2633 Campbell Rd 45365
Tel (937) 497-7575 *SIC* 2329 2339 2392

MAMA ROSAS LLC p 900
1910 Fair Rd 45365
Tel (937) 498-4511 SIC 5141 5142

NK PARTS INDUSTRIES INC p 1045
777 S Kuther Rd 45365
Tel (937) 498-4651 SIC 5013 1796 4731

NORCOLD INC p 1047
600 S Kuther Rd 45365
Tel (937) 497-3080 SIC 3632

SHELBY COUNTY MEMORIAL HOSPITAL ASSOCIATION p 1314
915 Michigan St 45365
Tel (937) 498-2311 SIC 8062

WILSON MEMORIAL HOSPITAL p 1613
915 Michigan St 45365
Tel (937) 498-2311 SIC 8062

SOLON, OH

ADVANCED LIGHTING TECHNOLOGIES INC p 26
7905 Cochran Rd Ste 300 44139
Tel (440) 519-0500
SIC 3641 3645 3646 3648

■ **AIRBORNE ACQUISITION INC** p 39
30500 Aurora Rd Ste 100 44139
Tel (216) 438-6111 SIC 6726

BIRD TECHNOLOGIES GROUP INC p 185
30303 Aurora Rd 44139
Tel (440) 248-1200 SIC 3825 3669

■ **CARLISLE BRAKE & FRICTION INC** p 257
6180 Cochran Rd 44139
Tel (440) 528-4000 SIC 3751

■ **CEQUENT CONSUMER PRODUCTS INC** p 283
29000 Aurora Rd Ste 2 44139
Tel (440) 498-0001 SIC 5531 3714

CLEVELAND STEEL CONTAINER CORP p 326
30310 Emerald Valley Pkwy 44139
Tel (440) 349-8000 SIC 3412

CORE-MARK OHIO p 369
30300 Emerald Valley Pkwy 44139
Tel (650) 589-9445 SIC 5194

DOTS LLC p 452
30300 Emerald Valley Pkwy 44139
Tel (440) 349-7900 SIC 5621

ERICO INTERNATIONAL CORP p 507
31700 Solon Rd 44139
Tel (440) 349-2630 SIC 3441

GARDINER SERVICE CO p 592
31200 Bainbridge Rd Ste 1 44139
Tel (440) 349-5588 SIC 5075 1711 7623

HDT GLOBAL INC p 673
30500 Aurora Rd Ste 100 44139
Tel (216) 438-6111 SIC 8711

HOOVER INC p 706
7005 Cochran Rd 44139
Tel (330) 499-9200 SIC 5064

HUNTER DEFENSE TECHNOLOGIES INC p 719
30500 Aurora Rd Ste 100 44139
Tel (216) 438-6111
SIC 3433 3569 3822 8331 8711 3549

INTERDESIGN INC p 752
30725 Solon Indus Pkwy 44139
Tel (440) 248-0136 SIC 5023

KANAN ENTERPRISES INC p 802
31900 Solon Rd 44139
Tel (440) 248-8484 SIC 2068 2034

■ **KEITHLEY INSTRUMENTS INC** p 808
28775 Aurora Rd 44139
Tel (440) 248-0400 SIC 3825 3823 7371

MRI SOFTWARE LLC p 996
28925 Fountain Pkwy 44139
Tel (800) 327-8770 SIC 7374 7371 6531

NESTLE PREPARED FOODS CO p 1027
5750 Harper Rd 44139
Tel (440) 248-3600 SIC 2038 5411 2037

PIPELINE PACKAGING CORP p 1151
30310 Emerald Valley Pkwy 44139
Tel (440) 349-3200 SIC 5099

ROBBINS CO p 1241
29100 Hall St Ste 100 44139
Tel (440) 248-3303 SIC 3535 3541 3531

SAINT-GOBAIN PERFORMANCE PLASTICS CORP p 1271
31500 Solon Rd 44139
Tel (440) 836-6900 SIC 3089 3053

STOUFFER CORP p 1392
30003 Bainbridge Rd 44139
Tel (440) 349-5757 SIC 2038

SUPERIOR BEVERAGE GROUP LTD p 1406
31031 Diamond Pkwy 44139
Tel (440) 703-4580 SIC 5149 5499

SWAGELOK CO p 1411
29500 Solon Rd 44139
Tel (440) 248-4600 SIC 3494 3491 3599

TARKETT USA INC p 1425
30000 Aurora Rd 44139
Tel (440) 543-8916 SIC 3253

TTI FLOOR CARE NORTH AMERICA INC p 1489
7005 Cochran Rd 44139
Tel (440) 996-2000 SIC 5072 3825

SOUTH CHARLESTON, OH

YAMADA NORTH AMERICA INC p 1634
9000 Clmbus Cincinnati Rd 45368
Tel (937) 462-7111 SIC 3714

SOUTH POINT, OH

MCNATIONAL INC p 932
502 2nd St E 45680
Tel (740) 377-4391 SIC 3731 7699 4491

SPENCERVILLE, OH

OHIO DECORATIVE PRODUCTS LLC p 1077
220 S Elizabeth St 45887
Tel (419) 647-9033
SIC 3086 3369 3471 3363

SPRINGBORO, OH

BROTHERS TRADING CO INC p 219
400 Victory Ln 45066
Tel (937) 746-1010 SIC 5141 5122 5149

KELCHNER INC p 808
50 Advanced Dr 45066
Tel (937) 704-9890 SIC 1794 1389

MIAMI-LUKEN INC p 959
265 S Pioneer Blvd 45066
Tel (937) 743-7775 SIC 5122

NATIONS ROOF OF OHIO LLC p 1017
275 S Pioneer Blvd 45066
Tel (937) 439-4160 SIC 1761

PIONEER AUTOMOTIVE TECHNOLOGIES INC p 1150
100 S Pioneer Blvd 45066
Tel (937) 746-2293 SIC 5013 3714 3651

SPRINGFIELD, OH

BOARD OF DIRECTORS OF WITTENBERG COLLEGE p 195
200 W Ward St 45504
Tel (937) 327-6231 SIC 8221

CENTRAL FIRE PROTECTION CO INC p 278
583 Selma Rd 45505
Tel (937) 322-0713 SIC 7389

COMMUNITY MERCY FOUNDATION p 349
1 S Limestone St Ste 700 45502
Tel (937) 328-7000 SIC 8641

COMMUNITY MERCY HEALTH PARTNERS p 349
100 Medical Center Dr 45504
Tel (937) 523-6670 SIC 8062

COUNTY OF CLARK p 377
50 E Columbia St Fl 5 45502
Tel (937) 521-2005 SIC 9111

INTERNATIONAL TRUCK AND ENGINE CORP p 757
6125 Urbana Rd 45502
Tel (937) 390-4045 SIC 4212

KCI HOLDING USA INC p 806
4401 Gateway Blvd 45502
Tel (937) 525-5533 SIC 3536

KONECRANES INC p 827
4401 Gateway Blvd 45502
Tel (937) 525-5533 SIC 3536

MMH AMERICAS INC p 979
4401 Gateway Blvd 45502
Tel (414) 764-6200 SIC 3536 5084 6719

MMH HOLDINGS INC p 979
4401 Gateway Blvd 45502
Tel (937) 525-5533 SIC 3536 5084

MORRIS MATERIAL HANDLING INC p 990
4401 Gateway Blvd 45502
Tel (937) 525-5520 SIC 3625 3443 7699

SPRINGFIELD BOARD OF EDUCATION p 1360
1500 W Jefferson St 45506
Tel (937) 505-2800 SIC 8211

SPRINGFIELD CITY SCHOOL DISTRICT p 1360
1500 W Jefferson St 45506
Tel (937) 505-2800 SIC 8211

TRI-STATE FOREST PRODUCTS INC p 1477
2105 Sheridan Ave 45505
Tel (937) 323-6325 SIC 5031

STEUBENVILLE, OH

DIOCESE OF STEUBENVILLE CATHOLIC CHARITIES p 441
422 Washington St Ste 1 43952
Tel (740) 282-3631 SIC 8661

FRANCISCAN UNIVERSITY OF STEUBENVILLE p 574
1235 University Blvd 43952
Tel (740) 283-3771 SIC 8221

JACK A ALLEN INC p 773
2105 Old State Route 7 43952
Tel (740) 282-4531
SIC 5172 5983 5541 5411

TRINITY HEALTH SYSTEM p 1481
380 Summit Ave 43952
Tel (740) 283-7000 SIC 8062 8011

TRINITY HOSPITAL HOLDING CO p 1481
380 Summit Ave 43952
Tel (740) 264-8000 SIC 8062 8741

TRINITY MEDICAL CENTER WEST p 1481
4000 Johnson Rd 43952
Tel (740) 264-8000 SIC 8062

STOW, OH

AUDIO-TECHNICA US INC p 131
1221 Commerce Dr 44224
Tel (330) 686-2600 SIC 5065 5731

ELECTROMOTIVE INC p 485
4880 Hudson Dr 44224
Tel (330) 688-6494 SIC 3679 3677

■ **MATCO TOOLS CORP** p 919
4403 Allen Rd 44224
Tel (330) 929-4949
SIC 5251 5072 3469 3423 5013

MORGAN ADHESIVES CO LLC p 988
4560 Darrow Rd 44224
Tel (330) 688-1111
SIC 2891 3565 2672 2823

NATIONAL MACHINE CO p 1014
4880 Hudson Dr 44224
Tel (330) 688-6494 SIC 3599 3492

P3 INFRASTRUCTURE INC p 1103
3105 Preakness Dr 44224
Tel (330) 686-1129 SIC 7389

STREETSBORO, OH

AUTOMATED PACKAGING SYSTEMS INC p 134
10175 Philipp Pkwy 44241
Tel (330) 528-2000 SIC 3081 3565

DELTA SYSTEMS INC p 427
1734 Frost Rd 44241
Tel (330) 626-2811 SIC 3613 3625

SOFT-LITE LLC p 1337
10250 Philipp Pkwy 44241
Tel (330) 528-3400 SIC 3089

STEP2 CO LLC p 1386
10010 Aurora Hudson Rd 44241
Tel (866) 429-5200 SIC 3089 3944 3423

STRONGSVILLE, OH

AKZO NOBEL COATINGS INC p 42
8220 Mohawk Dr 44136
Tel (440) 297-5100 SIC 2851 5198 2821

AKZO NOBEL PAINTS LLC p 42
8381 Pearl Rd 44136
Tel (440) 297-8000 SIC 2851 2891

ATLANTIC TOOL & DIE CO INC p 127
19963 Progress Dr 44149
Tel (440) 238-6931 SIC 3469 3544

■ **DARICE INC** p 412
13000 Darice Pkwy 82 44149
Tel (440) 238-9150 SIC 5945 5193 5999

■ **LAMRITE WEST INC** p 841
14225 Pearl Rd 44136
Tel (440) 238-7318 SIC 5999 5199 5092

STRUTHERS, OH

ASTRO SHAPES INC p 122
65 Main St 44471
Tel (330) 755-1414 SIC 3354 3086

SUGARCREEK, OH

PROVIA DOOR INC p 1185
2150 State Route 39 44681
Tel (330) 852-4711 SIC 3442 5031

SUNBURY, OH

AMERICAN SHOWA INC p 79
707 W Cherry St 43074
Tel (740) 965-1133 SIC 3714

OHASHI TECHNICA USA INC p 1077
111 Burrer Dr 43074
Tel (740) 965-5115 SIC 5013 5072 3452

SWANTON, OH

■ **EXPRESS HOLDING LLC** p 520
11431 W Airport Svc Rd 43558
Tel (614) 474-4001 SIC 5621 5611

SYLVANIA, OH

FLOWER HOSPITAL p 560
5200 Harroun Rd 43560
Tel (419) 824-1444 SIC 8062

ICE INDUSTRIES INC p 727
3810 Herr Rd 43560
Tel (419) 842-3612 SIC 3469

SYLVANIA CITY SCHOOL DISTRICT p 1413
4747 N Hlland Sylvania Rd 43560
Tel (419) 824-8500 SIC 8211

SYMMES TWP, OH

■ **VANTIV HOLDING LLC** p 1544
8500 Governors Hill Dr 45249
Tel (513) 358-6192 SIC 7374

▲ **VANTIV INC** p 1544
8500 Governors Hill Dr 45249
Tel (513) 900-5250 SIC 7389

■ **VANTIV LLC** p 1544
8500 Governors Hill Dr 45249
Tel (877) 713-5964 SIC 7374

THORNVILLE, OH

SHELLY CO p 1314
80 Park Dr 43076
Tel (740) 246-6315 SIC 1611

SHELLY MATERIALS INC p 1314
80 Park Dr 43076
Tel (740) 246-6315
SIC 1422 1442 2951 4492

TIFFIN, OH

CONCORDANCE HEALTHCARE SOLUTIONS LLC p 355
85 Shaffer Park Dr 44883
Tel (419) 455-2153 SIC 5047

M & B ASPHALT CO INC p 888
1525 W Seneca Cnty Rd 42 44883
Tel (419) 992-4235
SIC 1429 2951 1611 2952 1771

NATIONAL MACHINERY LLC p 1014
161 Greenfield St 44883
Tel (419) 447-5211 SIC 3542

NM GROUP GLOBAL LLC p 1045
161 Greenfield St 44883
Tel (419) 447-5211 SIC 3542 3599 6799

SENECA MEDICAL LLC p 1303
85 Shaffer Park Dr 44883
Tel (419) 447-0236 SIC 5047

TIPP CITY, OH

AFTER HOURS FAMILY CARE INC p 33
450 N Hyatt St Ste 204 45371
Tel (937) 667-2614 SIC 8011

TOLEDO, OH

BLOCK COMMUNICATIONS INC p 189
405 Madison Ave Ste 2100 43604
Tel (419) 724-6212 SIC 4841 4833 2711

BOSTWICK-BRAUN CO p 203
7349 Crossleigh Ct 43617
Tel (419) 259-3600
SIC 5072 5084 5063 5083 5023

■ **BPREX PLASTIC PACKAGING INC** p 206
1 Seagate Ste 10 43604
Tel (419) 247-5000 SIC 3221 3089

■ **BREWER HOLDCO INC** p 210
4500 Dorr St 43615
Tel (419) 247-2800 SIC 6798

CANBERRA CORP p 246
3610 N Hlland Sylvania Rd 43615
Tel (419) 724-4300 SIC 2842

CAPITAL TIRE INC p 250
1001 Cherry St 43608
Tel (419) 241-5111 SIC 5014

CENTAUR INC p 275
2401 Front St 43605
Tel (419) 469-8000 SIC 3312 3316 3999

CITY OF TOLEDO p 319
1 Government Ctr Ste 2050 43604
Tel (419) 245-1050 SIC 9111

COUNTY OF LUCAS p 379
1 Government Ctr Ste 600 43604
Tel (419) 213-4406 SIC 9111

DECORATIVE PANELS INTERNATIONAL INC p 421
2900 Hill Ave 43607
Tel (419) 535-5921 SIC 2435

DIOCESE OF TOLEDO p 441
1933 Spielbusch Ave 43604
Tel (419) 244-6711 SIC 8661

DUNBAR MECHANICAL INC p 461
2806 N Reynolds Rd 43615
Tel (734) 856-6601 SIC 1711

FAMILY HEALTH PLAN INC p 527
2200 Jefferson Ave Fl 6 43604
Tel (419) 241-6501 SIC 6324 8011

FAURECIA AUTOMOTIVE HOLDINGS INC p 531
543 Matzinger Rd 43612
Tel (419) 727-5000 SIC 3714

FAURECIA EXHAUST SYSTEMS LLC p 531
543 Matzinger Rd 43612
Tel (419) 727-5000 SIC 3714 5013

■ **FIFTH THIRD BANK OF NORTHWESTERN OHIO NA** p 542
1 Seagate Ste 2200 43604
Tel (419) 259-7820 SIC 6021

GRAHAM PACKAGING PLASTIC PRODUCTS INC p 629
1 Seagate Ste 10 43604
Tel (717) 849-8500 SIC 3089

■ **HCR MANOR CARE INC** p 672
333 N Summit St Ste 103 43604
Tel (419) 252-5743 SIC 8051

■ **HCR MANORCARE MEDICAL SERVICES OF FLORIDA LLC** p 672
333 N Summit St Ste 100 43604
Tel (419) 252-5500 SIC 8051

■ **HEARTLAND EMPLOYMENT SERVICES LLC** p 679
333 N Summit St 43604
Tel (419) 252-5743 SIC 7361

■ **HEARTLAND HEALTHCARE SERVICES LLC** p 679
4755 South Ave 43615
Tel (419) 535-8435 SIC 8011

HEIDTMAN STEEL PRODUCTS INC p 681
2401 Front St 43605
Tel (419) 691-4646 SIC 3316 3312

■ **HUNTINGTON INSURANCE INC** p 720
519 Madison Ave 43604
Tel (419) 720-7900 SIC 6411

HYLANT GROUP INC p 724
811 Madison Ave Fl 11 43604
Tel (419) 255-1020 *SIC* 6411

■ IMPACT PRODUCTS LLC p 734
2840 Centennial Rd 43617
Tel (419) 841-2891
SIC 5084 5087 2392 3089

■ IN HOME HEALTH LLC p 735
333 N Summit St 43604
Tel (419) 252-5500 *SIC* 8082

JOB 1 USA p 787
701 Jefferson Ave Ste 202 43604
Tel (419) 255-5005 *SIC* 7381 7363 7361

KINGSTON HEALTHCARE CO p 821
1 Seagate Ste 1960 43604
Tel (419) 247-2880 *SIC* 8059 8741

■ LIBBEY GLASS INC p 861
300 Madison Ave Fl 4 43604
Tel (419) 325-2100 *SIC* 3229 3231

▲ LIBBEY INC p 861
300 Madison Ave 43604
Tel (419) 325-2100 *SIC* 3229 3262

LOTT INDUSTRIES INC p 879
3350 Hill Ave 43607
Tel (419) 534-4980 *SIC* 8331 8741

MAGNA MODULAR SYSTEMS INC p 896
1800 Nathan Dr 43611
Tel (419) 324-3387 *SIC* 3714

■ MANOR CARE INC p 902
333 N Summit St Ste 103 43604
Tel (419) 252-5500 *SIC* 8051 8082 8062

■ MANOR CARE OF AMERICA INC p 902
333 N Summit St Ste 103 43604
Tel (419) 252-5500 *SIC* 8051 8062 8082

MEDICAL UNIVERSITY OF OHIO p 937
3000 Arlington Ave 43614
Tel (419) 383-4000 *SIC* 8062 8221

MERCY HEALTH ST VINCENT MED LLC p 946
2213 Cherry St 43608
Tel (419) 251-3232 *SIC* 8062

MERCY HEALTH SYSTEM - NORTHERN REGION p 946
2200 Jefferson Ave 43604
Tel (419) 251-1359 *SIC* 8062

NZR RETAIL OF TOLEDO INC p 1070
4820 Monroe St 43623
Tel (419) 724-0005 *SIC* 5172

▲ OWENS CORNING p 1100
1 Owens Corning Pkwy 43659
Tel (419) 248-8000
SIC 3296 2952 3229 3089

■ OWENS CORNING SALES LLC p 1100
1 Owens Corning Pkwy 43659
Tel (419) 248-8000
SIC 3296 2952 3229 3089 1761

PILKINGTON HOLDINGS INC p 1148
811 Madison Ave Fl 1 43604
Tel (419) 247-3731 *SIC* 3211

PILKINGTON NORTH AMERICA INC p 1148
811 Madison Ave Fl 1 43604
Tel (419) 247-4955 *SIC* 3211

PINEWOOD PLACE APARTMENTS p 1149
1210 Collingwood Blvd 43604
Tel (419) 243-1413 *SIC* 6513

PROMEDICA HEALTH SYSTEMS INC p 1183
1801 Richards Rd 43607
Tel (419) 469-3800
SIC 8062 6324 8351 8741

RIVERSIDE MERCY HOSPITAL p 1238
3404 W Sylvania Ave 43623
Tel (419) 407-2663 *SIC* 8062

RUMPF CORP p 1258
701 Jefferson Ave Ste 201 43604
Tel (419) 255-5005 *SIC* 7361 7363 7381

SSOE INC p 1364
1001 Madison Ave Ste A 43604
Tel (419) 255-3830
SIC 8711 8712 8742 1541 7389

ST ANNE MERCY HOSPITAL p 1364
3404 W Sylvania Ave 43623
Tel (419) 407-2663 *SIC* 8062

TOLEDO CLINIC INC p 1458
4235 Secor Rd 43623
Tel (419) 473-3561 *SIC* 8011

TOLEDO HOSPITAL p 1458
2142 N Cove Blvd 43606
Tel (419) 291-4000 *SIC* 8011 8062

TOLEDO MOLDING & DIE INC p 1459
1429 Coining Dr 43612
Tel (419) 470-3950 *SIC* 3089 3544

TOLEDO PUBLIC SCHOOLS p 1459
1609 N Summit St 43604
Tel (419) 729-8200 *SIC* 8211

TSL LTD p 1489
5217 Monroe St Ste A1 43623
Tel (419) 843-3200 *SIC* 7363

UNIVERSITY OF TOLEDO p 1526
2801 W Bancroft St 43606
Tel (419) 530-4636 *SIC* 8221

▲ WELLTOWER INC p 1591
4500 Dorr St 43615
Tel (419) 247-2800 *SIC* 6798

YARK AUTOMOTIVE GROUP INC p 1635
6019 W Central Ave 43615
Tel (419) 841-7771 *SIC* 5511 7515

YOUNG MENS CHRISTIAN ASSOCIATION OF GREATER TOLEDO p 1638
1500 N Superior St Fl 2 43604
Tel (419) 729-8135
SIC 8641 7991 8351 7032 8322

TROY, OH

COUNTY OF MIAMI p 379
201 W Main St 45373
Tel (937) 440-5900 *SIC* 9111

EARHART PETROLEUM INC p 468
1494 Lytle Rd 45373
Tel (937) 335-2928 *SIC* 5172 5541 5983

F&P AMERICA MFG INC p 522
2101 Corporate Dr 45373
Tel (937) 339-0212 *SIC* 3714

■ HOBART BROTHERS CO p 698
101 Trade Sq E 45373
Tel (937) 332-5439 *SIC* 3548 3537

■ HOBART CORP p 698
701 S Ridge Ave 45374
Tel (937) 332-3000
SIC 3589 3556 3596 3585 3321

■ ITW FOOD EQUIPMENT GROUP LLC p 769
701 S Ridge Ave 45374
Tel (937) 332-3000 *SIC* 5046 3556

REMEDI SENIORCARE OF OHIO LLC p 1222
962 S Dorset Rd 45373
Tel (800) 232-4239 *SIC* 5122

UPPER VALLEY MEDICAL CENTER p 1529
3130 N County Road 25a 45373
Tel (937) 440-4000 *SIC* 8011 8062

TWINSBURG, OH

■ ASSURAMED INC p 121
1810 Summit Commerce Park 44087
Tel (330) 963-6998 *SIC* 5047

■ ENVISION PHARMACEUTICAL SERVICES LLC p 504
2181 E Aurora Rd Ste 201 44087
Tel (330) 405-8080 *SIC* 6411

EXPERIENT INC p 520
2500 E Enterprise Pkwy 44087
Tel (330) 425-8333 *SIC* 8742

FACIL NORTH AMERICA INC p 523
2242 Pinnacle Pkwy # 100 44087
Tel (330) 487-2500 *SIC* 5072 3452 5085

H B CHEMICAL CORP p 649
1665 Enterprise Pkwy 44087
Tel (330) 920-8023 *SIC* 5199

HITACHI MEDICAL SYSTEMS AMERICA INC p 697
1959 Summit Commerce Park 44087
Tel (330) 425-1313 *SIC* 5047

LEXINGTON RUBBER GROUP INC p 859
1700 Highland Rd 44087
Tel (330) 425-8472 *SIC* 3069

PEPPERL + FUCHS INC p 1134
1600 Enterprise Pkwy 44087
Tel (330) 425-3555
SIC 5065 3625 3822 3674

Q HOLDING CO p 1194
1700 Highland Rd 44087
Tel (330) 425-8472 *SIC* 3061

■ RGH ENTERPRISES INC p 1231
1810 Summit Commerce Park 44087
Tel (330) 963-6998 *SIC* 5999 5047 8011

UNIONTOWN, OH

■ FEDEX CUSTOM CRITICAL INC p 536
1475 Boettler Rd 44685
Tel (234) 310-4090 *SIC* 4213

SECURITAS ELECTRONIC SECURITY INC p 1298
1790 Graybill Rd Ste 100 44685
Tel (855) 331-0359 *SIC* 7382

UNIVERSITY HEIGHTS, OH

CLEVELAND HEIGHTS BOARD OF EDUCATION p 325
2155 Miramar Blvd 44118
Tel (216) 371-7171 *SIC* 8299

CLEVELAND HEIGHTS UNIVERSITY HEIGHTS CITY SCHOOLS p 325
2155 Miramar Blvd 44118
Tel (216) 371-7171 *SIC* 8211

JOHN CARROLL UNIVERSITY p 788
1 John Carroll Blvd 44118
Tel (216) 397-1886 *SIC* 8221

URBANA, OH

CHAMPAIGN RESIDENTIAL SERVICES INC p 287
1150 Scioto St Ste 201 43078
Tel (937) 653-1320 *SIC* 8361

■ GRIMES AEROSPACE CO p 640
550 State Route 55 43078
Tel (937) 484-2000
SIC 3728 3647 3646 3645 3577 3571

VALLEY CITY, OH

MTD CONSUMER GROUP INC p 997
5965 Grafton Rd 44280
Tel (330) 225-2600 *SIC* 3524

MTD HOLDINGS INC p 997
5965 Grafton Rd 44280
Tel (330) 225-2600
SIC 3524 3544 3469 6141

MTD PRODUCTS INC p 997
5965 Grafton Rd 44280
Tel (330) 225-2600 *SIC* 3524

■ SHILOH CORP p 1316
880 Steel Dr 44280
Tel (330) 558-2600 *SIC* 3469 3544

▲ SHILOH INDUSTRIES INC p 1316
880 Steel Dr 44280
Tel (330) 558-2600 *SIC* 3465 3469 3544

VAN WERT, OH

ALL AMERICA INSURANCE CO INC p 51
800 S Washington St 45891
Tel (419) 238-1010 *SIC* 6411

CENTRAL MUTUAL INSURANCE CO p 279
800 S Washington St 45891
Tel (419) 238-1010 *SIC* 6331

VANDALIA, OH

■ PSA AIRLINES INC p 1188
3400 Terminal Rd 45377
Tel (937) 454-1116 *SIC* 4512

VERSAILLES, OH

MIDMARK CORP p 966
60 Vista Dr 45380
Tel (937) 526-3662
SIC 3648 3842 3843 2542 3841

VIENNA, OH

■ LATROBE SPECIALTY METALS DISTRIBUTION INC p 846
1551 Vienna Pkwy 44473
Tel (330) 609-5137 *SIC* 5051 3312

MILLWOOD INC p 971
3708 International Blvd 44473
Tel (330) 393-4400 *SIC* 3565 4731

WADSWORTH, OH

CORNWELL QUALITY TOOLS CO p 371
667 Seville Rd 44281
Tel (330) 336-3506 *SIC* 5085 3423 6794

ROHRER CORP p 1247
717 Seville Rd 44281
Tel (330) 335-1541 *SIC* 3089 2675

SOPREMA INC p 1341
310 Quadral Dr 44281
Tel (330) 334-0066 *SIC* 5033

WALBRIDGE, OH

■ GREAT LAKES WINDOW INC p 634
30499 Tracy Rd 43465
Tel (419) 666-5555 *SIC* 3089 5211

LYDEN OIL CO p 887
30692 Tracy Rd 43465
Tel (419) 666-1948 *SIC* 5172

RUDOLPH LIBBE INC p 1257
6494 Latcha Rd 43465
Tel (419) 241-5000 *SIC* 1541 1542

RUDOLPH/LIBBE COMPANIES INC p 1257
6494 Latcha Rd 43465
Tel (419) 241-5000 *SIC* 1541 1542

WALNUT CREEK, OH

DUTCHMAN HOSPITALITY GROUP INC p 463
4985 State Rte 515 44687
Tel (330) 893-2926 *SIC* 5812

WAPAKONETA, OH

PETERSON CONSTRUCTION CO p 1138
18817 State Route 501 45895
Tel (419) 941-2233 *SIC* 1542 1629

WARREN, OH

ANDERSON AND DUBOSE INC p 89
5300 Tod Ave Sw 44481
Tel (440) 248-8800 *SIC* 5142 5141

AVI FOOD SYSTEMS INC p 137
2590 Elm Rd Ne 44483
Tel (330) 372-6000 *SIC* 5962 5812 8742

CADLE LIMITED LIABILITY CO p 236
3900 E Market St 44484
Tel (330) 856-3176 *SIC* 5812

COUNTY OF TRUMBULL p 382
160 High St Nw 44481
Tel (330) 675-2420 *SIC* 9111

COVELLI ENTERPRISES INC p 384
3900 E Market St Ste 1 44484
Tel (330) 856-3176 *SIC* 5812

FORUM HEALTH p 570
1350 E Market St 302 44483
Tel (330) 841-9011 *SIC* 8741 8011

SANESE SERVICES INC p 1279
2590 Elm Rd Ne 44483
Tel (614) 436-1234 *SIC* 5962 5812 7389

ST JOSEPH RIVERSIDE HOSPITAL p 1368
667 Eastland Ave Se 44484
Tel (330) 841-4000 *SIC* 8062

WARRENSVILLE HEIGHTS, OH

HEINENS INC p 681
4540 Richmond Rd 44128
Tel (216) 475-2300 *SIC* 5411

■ SPECIAL METALS CORP p 1356
4832 Richmond Rd Ste 100 44128
Tel (216) 755-3030 *SIC* 3356

WARREN, OH

TRUMBULL INDUSTRIES INC p 1487
400 Dietz Rd Ne 44483
Tel (330) 393-6624 *SIC* 5074 5085 5064

TRUMBULL MEMORIAL HOSPITAL p 1487
1350 E Market St 44483
Tel (330) 841-9011 *SIC* 8062 8049

TRUMBULL MEMORIAL HOSPITAL FOUNDATION p 1487
1350 E Market St 44483
Tel (330) 841-9376 *SIC* 8011

WARREN FABRICATING CORP p 1577
3240 Mahoning Ave Nw 44483
Tel (330) 847-0596
SIC 3441 3599 3547 3532 3444 3443

WARREN STEEL HOLDINGS LLC p 1577
4000 Mahoning Ave Nw 44483
Tel (330) 847-0487 *SIC* 3567

WASHINGTON COURT HOU, OH

YUSA CORP p 1640
151 Jamison Rd Sw 43160
Tel (740) 335-0335 *SIC* 3069

WATERFORD, OH

GLOBE METALLURGICAL INC p 618
County Road 32 45786
Tel (740) 984-2361 *SIC* 3339 3313 2819

WELLINGTON, OH

FOREST CITY TECHNOLOGIES INC p 566
299 Clay St 44090
Tel (440) 647-2115 *SIC* 3053

WEST CHESTER, OH

■ AK STEEL CORP p 41
9227 Centre Pointe Dr 45069
Tel (513) 425-4200 *SIC* 3312

▲ AK STEEL HOLDING CORP p 41
9227 Centre Pointe Dr 45069
Tel (513) 425-5000 *SIC* 3312

AMERICAN MORTGAGE SERVICE CO p 76
7324 Kingsgate Way Ste C 45069
Tel (513) 452-4120 *SIC* 6162

CEDAR ELECTRONICS HOLDINGS CORP p 272
5440 W Chester Rd 45069
Tel (513) 870-8500 *SIC* 3812 5088

CHASE INDUSTRIES INC p 291
10021 Commerce Park Dr 45246
Tel (513) 860-5565 *SIC* 3442

CHESTER WEST MEDICAL CENTER p 295
7700 University Dr 45069
Tel (513) 298-3000 *SIC* 8062

■ CINMAR LLC p 308
5566 W Chester Rd 45069
Tel (513) 603-1000 *SIC* 5961 5023 5712

CLARKWESTERN DIETRICH BUILDING SYSTEMS LLC p 322
9100 Centre Pointe Dr # 210 45069
Tel (513) 870-1100 *SIC* 3444 8711 3081

CONTECH ENGINEERED SOLUTIONS INC p 362
9025 Centre Pointe Dr # 400 45069
Tel (513) 645-7000
SIC 3444 3084 3317 3441 3443

CONTECH ENGINEERED SOLUTIONS LLC p 362
9025 Ctr Pinte Dr Ste 400 45069
Tel (513) 645-7000
SIC 3444 3084 3317 3441 3443

CONTINGENT NETWORK SERVICES LLC p 364
4400 Port Union Rd 45011
Tel (513) 616-5773 *SIC* 7379 7373

COOPER & CO INC p 366
10179 Commerce Park Dr 45246
Tel (513) 671-6067 *SIC* 5944

■ CORNERSTONE BRANDS INC p 371
5568 W Chester Rd 45069
Tel (513) 603-1000 *SIC* 5961

DRAKE REHAB WEST CHESTER p 455
7700 University Ct # 1600 45069
Tel (513) 475-7454 *SIC* 8049

FLOTURN INC p 560
4236 Thunderbird Ln 45014
Tel (513) 860-8040 *SIC* 3599

G R B INC p 587
6392 Gano Rd 45069
Tel (800) 628-9195 *SIC* 5113

HWZ DISTRIBUTION GROUP LLC p 722
40 W Crescentville Rd 45246
Tel (513) 618-0300 *SIC* 5032

MISA METALS INC p 974
9050 Centre Pointe Dr 45069
Tel (212) 660-6000 *SIC* 5051

MMTF LOGISTICS LLC p 979
8080 Beckett Center Dr 45069
Tel (513) 860-2871 SIC 4731

PIERRE HOLDING CORP p 1147
9990 Prnceton Glendale Rd 45246
Tel (513) 874-8741 SIC 2013 2015 2051

PMCO LLC p 1157
9220 Glades Dr 45011
Tel (513) 825-7626 SIC 2679

SKIDMORE SALES & DISTRIBUTING CO INC p 1329
9889 Cincinnati Dayton Rd 45069
Tel (513) 755-4200 SIC 5149 5169

STOROPACK INC p 1392
4758 Devitt Dr 45246
Tel (513) 874-0314 SIC 5199 3086 2671

TOTES ISOTONER HOLDINGS CORP p 1463
9655 International Blvd 45246
Tel (513) 682-8200
SIC 2381 3151 2211 3021 5699

TSS TECHNOLOGIES INC p 1489
8800 Global Way 45069
Tel (513) 772-7000 SIC 3599 8711

■ **ZARTIC LLC** p 1641
9990 Prnceton Glendale Rd 45246
Tel (513) 874-8741 SIC 2013 2015

WEST JEFFERSON, OH

JEFFERSON INDUSTRIES CORP p 781
6670 State Route 29 43162
Tel (614) 879-5300 SIC 3711

WEST MANSFIELD, OH

HERITAGE COOPERATIVE INC p 686
11177 Township Road 133 43358
Tel (419) 294-2371
SIC 5153 5261 4925 4932

WESTERVILLE, OH

■ **CHERYL & CO** p 295
646 Mccorkle Blvd 43082
Tel (614) 776-1500 SIC 2052

CORNA KOKOSING CONSTRUCTION CO p 370
6235 Westerville Rd 43081
Tel (614) 901-8844 SIC 1541 1542 8741

EMERSON NETWORK POWER LIEBERT SERVICES INC p 492
610 Executive Campus Dr 43082
Tel (614) 841-6400 SIC 7378

EXEL HOLDINGS (USA) INC p 518
570 Polaris Pkwy Ste 110 43082
Tel (614) 865-8500 SIC 4226 4213

EXEL INC p 518
570 Polaris Pkwy 43082
Tel (614) 865-8500 SIC 4213 4225 4581

EXEL NORTH AMERICAN LOGISTICS INC p 518
570 Players Pkwy 43081
Tel (800) 272-1052 SIC 4731

■ **HARRINGTON HEALTH SERVICES INC** p 663
780 Brooksedge Plaza Dr 43081
Tel (614) 212-7000 SIC 6411

HELIOS p 681
250 Progressive Way 43082
Tel (614) 794-3300 SIC 6411

KOKOSING INC p 826
6235 Wstrville Rd Ste 200 43081
Tel (614) 212-5700 SIC 1611

LAUREL HEALTH CARE CO p 847
8181 Worthington Rd Uppr 43082
Tel (614) 794-8800 SIC 8741

LAUREL HEALTH CARE CO OF NORTH WORTHTINGTON p 847
8181 Worthington Rd 43082
Tel (614) 794-8800 SIC 8059 8741

MCGRAW/KOKOSING INC p 929
101 Clark Blvd 43081
Tel (614) 212-5700 SIC 1541 1542

PROGRESSIVE ENTERPRISES HOLDINGS INC p 1181
250 Progressive Way 43082
Tel (614) 794-3300 SIC 8742

SAINT ANNS HOSPITAL AUXILIARY p 1268
500 S Cleveland Ave 43081
Tel (614) 769-4459
SIC 5947 5621 5611 5992 5441

■ **STANLEY INDUSTRIAL & AUTOMOTIVE LLC** p 1377
505 N Cleveland Ave 43082
Tel (614) 755-7000
SIC 3429 3546 3423 3452

WESTERVILLE CITY SCHOOL DISTRICT p 1600
936 Eastwind Dr Ste 200 43081
Tel (614) 797-5700 SIC 8211

WESTFIELD CENTER, OH

OHIO FARMERS INSURANCE CO p 1077
1 Park Cir 44251
Tel (800) 243-0210 SIC 6411 6331

WESTFIELD BANCORP INC p 1601
2 Park Cir 44251
Tel (330) 887-8112 SIC 6163

WESTFIELD INSURANCE CO p 1601
1 Park Cir 44251
Tel (800) 243-0210 SIC 6411 6331

WESTLAKE, OH

ALUMINUM LINE PRODUCTS CO p 63
24460 Sperry Cir 44145
Tel (440) 835-8880 SIC 5051 3365 3999

■ **ENERGIZER MANUFACTURING INC** p 497
25225 Detroit Rd 44145
Tel (440) 835-7866 SIC 3691

ERIE LAKE ELECTRIC INC p 508
25730 1st St 44145
Tel (440) 835-5565 SIC 1731

HYLAND SOFTWARE INC p 724
28500 Clemens Rd 44145
Tel (440) 788-5000 SIC 7372

JTEKT NORTH AMERICA CORP p 796
29570 Clemens Rd 44145
Tel (440) 835-1000 SIC 5085 3562

MISSION BROADCASTING INC p 975
30400 Detroit Rd Ste 304 44145
Tel (440) 526-2227 SIC 4833

▲ **NORDSON CORP** p 1048
28601 Clemens Rd 44145
Tel (440) 892-1580 SIC 3563

■ **SCOTT FETZER CO** p 1293
28800 Clemens Rd 44145
Tel (440) 892-3000 SIC 7699

SEA-LAND CHEMICAL CO p 1295
821 Westpoint Pkwy 44145
Tel (440) 871-7887 SIC 5169

SHAMROCK COMPANIES INC p 1311
24090 Detroit Rd 44145
Tel (440) 899-9510
SIC 5112 5199 7336 7389 2754 2395

ST JOHN MEDICAL CENTER p 1367
29000 Center Ridge Rd 44145
Tel (440) 835-8000 SIC 8062

■ **TA OPERATING LLC** p 1420
24601 Center Ridge Rd # 200 44145
Tel (440) 808-9100
SIC 5541 7538 5812 5411 6794

■ **TRAVELCENTERS OF AMERICA INC** p 1474
24601 Center Ridge Rd # 200 44145
Tel (440) 808-9100
SIC 5541 7538 5812 5411

▲ **TRAVELCENTERS OF AMERICA LLC** p 1474
24601 Center Ridge Rd # 200 44145
Tel (440) 808-9100 SIC 5541 5812 7538

VSM SEWING INC p 1566
31000 Viking Pkwy 44145
Tel (440) 808-6550 SIC 5064

WICKLIFFE, OH

GTM SERVICE INC p 644
1366 Rockefeller Rd 44092
Tel (440) 944-5099 SIC 5013

■ **LUBRIZOL CORP** p 884
29400 Lakeland Blvd 44092
Tel (440) 943-4200 SIC 2899 2869

WILLARD, OH

DENN-OHIO LLC p 428
1002 Armstrong Dr 44890
Tel (419) 544-4030 SIC 5812

WILLOUGHBY, OH

LAKE COUNTY COMMUNITY COLLEGE DISTRICT p 838
7700 Clocktower Dr 44094
Tel (440) 525-7000 SIC 8222

MAROUS BROTHERS CONSTRUCTION INC p 910
1702 Joseph Lloyd Pkwy 44094
Tel (440) 951-3904 SIC 1521 1751

WILLOUGHBY-EASTLAKE CITY SCHOOLS p 1613
37047 Ridge Rd 44094
Tel (440) 946-5000 SIC 8211

WILMINGTON, OH

■ **ABX AIR INC** p 13
145 Hunter Dr 45177
Tel (937) 382-5591
SIC 4513 5088 4581 8299

▲ **AIR TRANSPORT SERVICES GROUP INC** p 39
145 Hunter Dr 45177
Tel (937) 382-5591 SIC 4513

FERNO-WASHINGTON INC p 538
70 Weil Way 45177
Tel (877) 733-0911 SIC 5047

R & L CARRIERS INC p 1201
600 Gilliam Rd 45177
Tel (937) 382-1494 SIC 4213

R & L TRANSFER INC p 1201
600 Gilliam Rd 45177
Tel (937) 382-1494 SIC 4213

RCHP - WILMINGTON LLC p 1212
610 W Main St 45177
Tel (937) 382-6611 SIC 8062 8361

WINCHESTER, OH

WINCHESTER PLACE NURSING & REHABILITATION CENTER p 1614
36 Lehman Dr 45697
Tel (614) 834-2273 SIC 8051

WOODVILLE, OH

LUCKEY FARMERS INC p 884
1200 W Main St 43469
Tel (419) 849-2711 SIC 5153

WOOSTER, OH

■ **AKRON BRASS CO** p 42
343 Venture Blvd 44691
Tel (330) 264-5678 SIC 3647 3699

■ **AKRON BRASS HOLDING CORP** p 42
343 Venture Blvd 44691
Tel (330) 264-5678 SIC 3647 3699 6719

■ **ARTIFLEX MANUFACTURING LLC** p 114
1425 E Bowman St 44691
Tel (330) 262-2015 SIC 3465 3469

BUEHLER FOOD MARKETS INC p 224
1401 Old Mansfield Rd 44691
Tel (330) 264-4355 SIC 5411

CITY OF WOOSTER p 319
538 N Market St 44691
Tel (330) 263-5200 SIC 9111

E&H FAMILY GROUP INC p 467
1401 Old Mansfield Rd 44691
Tel (330) 264-4355 SIC 5411

KEN MILLER SUPPLY INC p 810
1537 Blachleyville Rd 44691
Tel (330) 264-9146 SIC 5084

KOKOSING CONSTRUCTION INC p 826
1516 Timken Rd 44691
Tel (330) 263-4168 SIC 1611

LUK CLUTCH SYSTEMS LLC p 884
3401 Old Airport Rd 44691
Tel (330) 264-4383 SIC 3714 3568 3566

LUK TRANSMISSION SYSTEMS LLC p 885
3401 Old Airport Rd 44691
Tel (330) 264-4383 SIC 3714 3566

LUK USA LLC p 885
3401 Old Airport Rd 44691
Tel (330) 264-4383 SIC 3714

PORTS PETROLEUM CO INC p 1163
1337 Blachleyville Rd 44691
Tel (330) 264-1885 SIC 5172 5983 5541

SANTMYER OIL CO INC p 1281
3000 Old Airport Rd 44691
Tel (330) 262-6501
SIC 5172 5983 4212 5531

SEAMAN CORP p 1297
1000 Venture Blvd 44691
Tel (330) 262-1111 SIC 2221

TEKFOR INC p 1433
3690 Long Rd 44691
Tel (330) 202-7420 SIC 3462

WESTERN RESERVE GROUP p 1600
1685 Cleveland Rd 44691
Tel (330) 262-9060 SIC 6331

WWST CORP LLC p 1629
186 S Hillcrest Dr 44691
Tel (330) 264-5122 SIC 4833

WORTHINGTON, OH

FILLMORE HOSPITALITY LLC p 542
250 W Old Wilson Bridge R 43085
Tel (614) 781-1420 SIC 7041

KLINGBEIL CAPITAL MANAGEMENT LLC p 823
500 W Wilson Bridge Rd 43085
Tel (614) 396-4919 SIC 6799 8741

MEDVET ASSOCIATES INC p 939
300 E Wilson Bridge Rd # 100 43085
Tel (614) 846-5800 SIC 0742

Q N P CORP p 1194
979 High St 43085
Tel (614) 846-0371 SIC 5511

WORTHINGTON CITY SCHOOLS p 1626
200 E Wilson Bridge Rd # 200 43085
Tel (614) 450-6000 SIC 8211

■ **WORTHINGTON CYLINDER CORP** p 1626
200 W Old Wlson Bridge Rd 43085
Tel (614) 840-3210 SIC 3443

▲ **WORTHINGTON INDUSTRIES INC** p 1626
200 W Old Wlson Bridge Rd 43085
Tel (614) 438-3210
SIC 3316 3449 3443 3325

■ **WORTHINGTON INDUSTRIES INC** p 1626
200 W Old Wilson Bridge Rd 43085
Tel (614) 438-3077 SIC 3316

WSHNGTN CT HS, OH

SUGAR CREEK PACKING CO p 1397
2101 Kenskill Ave 43160
Tel (740) 335-7440 SIC 2013 2011

XENIA, OH

GREENE COUNTY p 638
35 Greene St 45385
Tel (937) 562-5006 SIC 9111

YELLOW SPRINGS, OH

ANTIOCH UNIVERSITY p 94
900 Dayton St 45387
Tel (937) 769-1370 SIC 8221

YOUNGSTOWN, OH

AMERICAN BULK COMMODITIES INC p 69
8063 Southern Blvd 44512
Tel (330) 758-0841
SIC 4212 7532 6531 7363

BJ ALAN CO p 185
555 Mrtin Lther King Blvd 44502
Tel (330) 746-1064 SIC 5092

COMPREHENSIVE LOGISTICS CO INC p 352
4944 Belmont Ave Ste 202 44505
Tel (800) 734-0372 SIC 4225 4731

CONSTELLATIONS ENTERPRISE LLC p 361
1775 Logan Ave 44505
Tel (330) 740-8208 SIC 8741

EXAL CORP p 516
1 Performance Pl 44502
Tel (330) 744-9505 SIC 3411 3354

FALCON TRANSPORT CO p 526
4944 Belmont Ave 44505
Tel (330) 793-1345 SIC 4213

FORGE INDUSTRIES INC p 567
4450 Market St 44512
Tel (330) 782-8301
SIC 5085 3566 3599 3531 6411 7699

MAHONING COUNTY p 897
21 W Boardman St Ste 200 44503
Tel (330) 740-2130 SIC 9121

MERCY HEALTH YOUNGSTOWN LLC p 946
1044 Belmont Ave 44504
Tel (330) 746-7211 SIC 8062 8071

MODERN BUILDERS SUPPLY INC p 981
302 Mcclurg Rd 44512
Tel (330) 729-2690
SIC 5032 3089 3446 3442

PENNSYLVANIA TOOL SALES & SERVICE INC p 1130
625 Bev Rd 44512
Tel (330) 758-0845 SIC 7699 5085 5084

ROMAN CATHOLIC DIOCESE OF YOUNGSTOWN p 1249
144 W Wood St 44503
Tel (330) 744-8451 SIC 8661

ROTH BROS INC p 1252
3847 Crum Rd 44515
Tel (330) 793-5571 SIC 1711 1761

SCHWEBEL BAKING CO p 1291
965 E Midlothian Blvd 44502
Tel (330) 783-2860 SIC 2051

TURNING TECHNOLOGIES LLC p 1493
255 W Federal St 44503
Tel (330) 746-3015 SIC 7372

▲ **UNITED COMMUNITY FINANCIAL CORP** p 1507
275 W Federal St 44503
Tel (330) 742-0500 SIC 6036

V AND V APPLIANCE PARTS INC p 1538
27 W Myrtle Ave 44507
Tel (330) 743-5144 SIC 5064

VALLOUREC STAR LP p 1541
2669 M L K J Blvd 44510
Tel (330) 742-6300 SIC 3317

YOUNGSTOWN CITY SCHOOLS p 1639
20 W Wood St 44503
Tel (330) 744-6900 SIC 8211

YOUNGSTOWN STATE UNIVERSITY INC p 1639
1 University Plz 44555
Tel (330) 941-3000 SIC 8221

ZANESVILLE, OH

BETHESDA HOSPITAL ASSOCIATION INC p 178
2951 Maple Ave 43701
Tel (740) 454-4000 SIC 8062 8063 8082

GENESIS HEALTHCARE SYSTEM p 603
2951 Maple Ave 43701
Tel (740) 454-5000 SIC 8082

GENESIS HEALTHCARE SYSTEM p 603
2951 Maple Ave 43701
Tel (740) 454-4000 SIC 8062

MATTINGLY FOODS INC p 921
302 State St 43701
Tel (740) 454-0136 SIC 5149 5142 5141

PSC HOLDINGS INC p 1188
109 Graham St 43701
Tel (740) 454-6253 SIC 1389

SHELLY AND SANDS INC p 1314
3570 S River Rd 43701
Tel (740) 453-0721 SIC 1611 1442 2951

ZANDEX HEALTH CARE CORP p 1641
1122 Taylor St 43701
Tel (740) 454-1400 SIC 8052 8059 8051

ZANDEX INC p 1641
1122 Taylor St 43701
Tel (740) 454-1400 SIC 8052 8051

OKLAHOMA

ADA, OK

CHICKASAW NATION p 298
520 Arlington St 74820
Tel (580) 436-2603 SIC 9131

CHICKASAW NATION HEADQUARTERS ADMINISTRATION p 298
520 Arlington St 74820
Tel (580) 310-6403 *SIC* 9131

FLEX-N-GATE OKLAHOMA LLC p 556
1 General St 74820
Tel (580) 272-6700 *SIC* 3714

LEGALSHIELD p 853
1 Prepaid Way 74820
Tel (323) 325-3198 *SIC* 8111

ALTUS, OK

WCR ENTERPRISES INC p 1585
111 Sequoyah Ln Ste 7 73521
Tel (580) 482-4203 *SIC* 8052 8051

ANADARKO, OK

WESTERN FARMERS ELECTRIC COOPERATIVE p 1598
701 Ne 7th St 73005
Tel (405) 247-3351 *SIC* 4911

ANTLERS, OK

ANTLERS PUBLIC SCHOOLS p 94
219 Ne A St 74523
Tel (580) 298-5504 *SIC* 8211

ARDMORE, OK

MERCY HOSPITAL ARDMORE INC p 947
1011 14th Ave Nw 73401
Tel (580) 223-5400 *SIC* 8062

SAMUEL ROBERTS NOBLE FOUNDATION INC p 1275
2510 Sam Noble Pkwy 73401
Tel (580) 226-2178 *SIC* 8733

BARTLESVILLE, OK

JANE PHILLIPS MEDICAL CENTER p 777
3450 E Frank Phllips Blvd 74006
Tel (918) 338-3730 *SIC* 8011

JANE PHILLIPS MEMORIAL MEDICAL CENTER INC p 777
3500 E Frank Phllips Blvd 74006
Tel (918) 333-7200 *SIC* 8062

PHILLIPS JANE HEALTH CARE FOUNDATION INC p 1144
3500 E Frank Phllips Blvd 74006
Tel (918) 333-7200 *SIC* 8062

BETHANY, OK

INTERNATIONAL PENTECOSTAL HOLINESS CHURCH p 756
7300 Nw 39th Expy 73008
Tel (405) 787-7110 *SIC* 8661

BLACKWELL, OK

SHEPHERD OIL CO LLC p 1315
1831 S Main St 74631
Tel (580) 363-4280 *SIC* 5411 5172

BRISTOW, OK

RAINBOW HEALTHCARE CENTER INC p 1205
111 E Washington Ave 74010
Tel (918) 367-2246 *SIC* 8052 8051

BROKEN ARROW, OK

A G EQUIPMENT CO p 5
3401 W Albany St 74012
Tel (918) 250-7386 *SIC* 3563 5084

ADMIRAL EXPRESS INC p 23
1823 N Yellowood Ave 74012
Tel (918) 249-4000 *SIC* 5112 5021 5943

BLACKHAWK INDUSTRIAL DISTRIBUTION INC p 187
1501 Sw Expressway Dr 74012
Tel (918) 663-3252 *SIC* 5085 3561 5084

BROKEN ARROW ELECTRIC SUPPLY INC p 216
2350 W Vancouver St 74012
Tel (918) 258-3581 *SIC* 5063

BROKEN ARROW INDEPENDENT SCHOOL p 217
701 S Main St 74012
Tel (918) 259-5700 *SIC* 8211

CYMSTAR LLC p 405
1700 W Albany St Ste 500 74012
Tel (918) 251-8100 *SIC* 3699 3728

DMD INC p 446
1309 W Detroit St 74012
Tel (918) 250-5521 *SIC* 7361

ZEECO USA LLC p 1641
22151 E 91st St S 74014
Tel (918) 258-8551 *SIC* 3433

CATOOSA, OK

CHEROKEE NATION BUSINESSES LLC p 294
777 W Cherokee St Bldg 2 74015
Tel (918) 384-7474 *SIC* 3728 5085 5088

CHEROKEE NATION ENTERTAINMENT LLC p 294
777 W Cherokee St 74015
Tel (918) 458-1696
SIC 7999 7011 7948 5541 5993

PACESETTER CLAIMS SERVICE INC p 1103
2871 N Highway 167 74015
Tel (918) 665-8887 *SIC* 6411

CHECOTAH, OK

G L N INC p 587
207 S Broadway St 74426
Tel (918) 473-2369 *SIC* 5411

CHICKASHA, OK

LIVINGSTON MACHINERY CO p 871
5201 S Highway 81 73018
Tel (405) 224-5056
SIC 5083 5999 7699 5261

CLAREMORE, OK

AHS CLAREMORE REGIONAL HOSPITAL LLC p 37
1202 N Muskogee Pl 74017
Tel (918) 341-2556 *SIC* 8062

AXH AIR-COOLERS LLC p 140
401 E Lowry Rd 74017
Tel (918) 283-9200 *SIC* 3443

RCB BANK SERVICE INC p 1212
300 W Patti Page Blvd 74017
Tel (918) 341-6150 *SIC* 6022

CLEVELAND, OK

CLEVELAND INTEGRITY SERVICES INC p 325
370669 E Old Highway 64 74020
Tel (918) 358-5735 *SIC* 7389

CLINTON, OK

DOMINO FOOD AND FUEL INC p 449
Hwy 183 S 73601
Tel (580) 323-0341 *SIC* 5411

ELMER SMITH OIL CO p 489
Hwy 183 S 73601
Tel (580) 323-2929 *SIC* 5171 5411

COLEMAN, OK

SUNDOWNER TRAILERS INC p 1402
9805 Ok Highway 48 S 73432
Tel (580) 937-4255 *SIC* 3715

COLLINSVILLE, OK

FRANCES STREITEL - SOUTH p 573
2300 W Broadway St 74021
Tel (918) 371-2545 *SIC* 8051

DUNCAN, OK

COUNTRY CLUB CARE p 375
1904 N Hwy 81 73533
Tel (580) 255-4600 *SIC* 8059

DUNCAN REGIONAL HOSPITAL INC p 461
1407 N Whisenant Dr 73533
Tel (580) 252-5300 *SIC* 8062

O-TEX PUMPING LLC p 1070
7045 N Highway 81 73533
Tel (580) 255-3111 *SIC* 1389

DURANT, OK

CHOCTAW ARCHIVING ENTERPRISE p 301
2101 W Arkansas St 74701
Tel (580) 920-1501 *SIC* 8711 4226

CHOCTAW MANAGEMENT SERVICES ENTERPRISE p 301
2101 W Arkansas St 74701
Tel (580) 924-8280 *SIC* 8099 8011 8031

CHOCTAW NATION OF OKLAHOMA p 302
529 N 16th Ave 74701
Tel (580) 924-8280 *SIC* 9131

DURANT BANCORP INC p 462
1400 W Main St 74701
Tel (580) 924-2211 *SIC* 6022

■ DURANT HMA INC p 462
1800 W University Blvd 74701
Tel (580) 924-3080 *SIC* 8062

FIRST UNITED BANK AND TRUST CO p 550
1400 W Main St 74701
Tel (580) 924-2211 *SIC* 6022 6163 6021

STEPHENSON WHOLESALE CO INC p 1386
230 S 22nd Ave 74701
Tel (580) 920-0125
SIC 5194 5145 5143 5142 5141 5113

EDMOND, OK

ADFITECH INC p 22
3001 Technology Dr 73013
Tel (800) 880-0456 *SIC* 6162

CREST DISCOUNT FOODS INC p 392
2200 W 15th And Santa Fe 73013
Tel (405) 733-2330 *SIC* 5411

EATERIES INC p 473
1220 S Santa Fe Ave 73003
Tel (480) 347-3800 *SIC* 5812 5813 6794

EDMOND PUBLIC SCHOOLS p 478
1001 W Danforth Rd 73003
Tel (405) 340-2800 *SIC* 8211

LIFE COVENANT CHURCH INC p 863
4600 E 2nd St 73034
Tel (405) 680-5433 *SIC* 8661

OKLAHOMA MUNICIPAL POWER AUTHORITY p 1079
2701 W I 35 Frontage Rd 73013
Tel (405) 340-5047 *SIC* 4911

PETRA INDUSTRIES LLC p 1139
2101 S Kelly Ave 73013
Tel (405) 216-2100 *SIC* 5065

■ REMY POWER PRODUCTS LLC p 1223
3400 S Kelly Ave 73013
Tel (405) 475-9800 *SIC* 5063

UNIMARK LLC p 1503
3540 S Boulevard Ste 205 73013
Tel (405) 285-8670 *SIC* 4924

UNIVERSITY OF CENTRAL OKLAHOMA p 1520
100 N University Dr 73034
Tel (405) 974-2000 *SIC* 8221

EL RENO, OK

MATHENA INC p 919
3900 S Hwy 81 Service Rd 73036
Tel (405) 422-3600 *SIC* 3699 3822

ELK CITY, OK

G & G STEAM SERVICE INC p 586
120 W 12th St 73644
Tel (580) 225-4254 *SIC* 1389

HUTCHINSON OIL CO INC p 722
515 S Main St 73644
Tel (580) 225-0301 *SIC* 5171 5541

ENID, OK

■ ADVANCE FOOD CO INC p 24
221 W Oxford Ave 73701
Tel (800) 969-2747 *SIC* 2013 2015 2099

ATWOOD DISTRIBUTING LP p 130
500 S Garland Rd 73703
Tel (580) 233-3702
SIC 5261 5251 5531 5311

GROENDYKE TRANSPORT INC p 641
2510 Rock Island Blvd 73701
Tel (580) 234-4663 *SIC* 4213

JOHNSTON ENTERPRISES INC p 791
411 W Chestnut Ave 73701
Tel (580) 233-5800 *SIC* 5153 5191

MARSAU ENTERPRISES INC p 910
1209 N 30th St 73701
Tel (580) 233-3910 *SIC* 1389

■ METALS USA PLATES AND SHAPES SOUTHCENTRAL INC p 953
101 E Illinois Ave 73701
Tel (580) 233-0411 *SIC* 5051

■ ST MARYS REGIONAL MEDICAL CENTER p 1372
305 S 5th St 73701
Tel (580) 233-6100 *SIC* 8011

W B JOHNSTON GRAIN CO p 1568
411 W Chestnut Ave 73701
Tel (580) 233-5800
SIC 5153 5191 4491 4213 0111 0211

WARD PETROLEUM CORP p 1575
502 S Fillmore St 73703
Tel (580) 234-3229 *SIC* 4923

FORT GIBSON, OK

FORT GIBSON NURSING HOME p 568
205 E Poplar St 74434
Tel (918) 478-2456 *SIC* 8052

GUTHRIE, OK

GOLDEN AGE NURSING HOME OF GUTHRIE INC p 620
419 E Oklahoma Ave 73044
Tel (405) 282-6285 *SIC* 8051 8361

OKLAHOMA ROOF MASTERS INC p 1080
601 Evergreen Dr 73044
Tel (405) 814-6440
SIC 1761 1541 4731 4212 4213

GUYMON, OK

■ SEABOARD FARMS INC p 1295
424 N Main St Ste 200 73942
Tel (580) 338-1470 *SIC* 0213 2011

HEAVENER, OK

K & C LLC p 798
204 W 1st St 74937
Tel (918) 653-2464 *SIC* 8059

HENNESSEY, OK

R & D MAINTENANCE SERVICES INC p 1201
409 N Main St 73742
Tel (405) 853-7108 *SIC* 1629

HENRYETTA, OK

FOUNTAIN VIEW MANOR INC p 571
107 E Barclay St 74437
Tel (918) 652-7021 *SIC* 8051

HOOKER, OK

TRI-COUNTY ELECTRIC COOPERATIVE INC p 1477
995 Mile 46 Rd 73945
Tel (580) 652-2418 *SIC* 4911

INOLA, OK

INOLA HEALTH CARE CENTER INC p 745
400 N Broadway 74036
Tel (918) 543-8800 *SIC* 8011

JAY, OK

GRAND UNION HEALTHCARE LLC p 630
226 E Monore St 74346
Tel (918) 253-4500 *SIC* 8059

JENKS, OK

GATEWAY MORTGAGE GROUP LLC p 594
244 S Gateway Pl 74037
Tel (918) 712-9000 *SIC* 6163

JENKS PUBLIC SCHOOLS p 782
205 E B St 74037
Tel (918) 299-4415 *SIC* 8211

■ TULSA WINCH INC p 1491
11135 S James Ave 74037
Tel (918) 298-8300 *SIC* 5084 3566 3531

KINGFISHER, OK

PIONEER TELEPHONE COOPERATIVE INC p 1151
108 E Robberts Ave 73750
Tel (405) 375-4111 *SIC* 5999

LAWTON, OK

A&S ASSET RECOVERY INC p 7
608 Sw D Ave Ste 6 73501
Tel (855) 692-2786 *SIC* 7389

CAREY JOHNSON OIL CO INC p 255
701 Sw F Ave 73501
Tel (580) 595-8300 *SIC* 5171

COMANCHE COUNTY HOSPITAL AUTHORITY p 343
3401 W Gore Blvd 73505
Tel (580) 355-8620 *SIC* 8062

LAWTON PUBLIC SCHOOL DISTRICT I-008 p 848
753 Nw Fort Sill Blvd 73507
Tel (580) 357-6900 *SIC* 8211

LEXINGTON, OK

LEXINGTON NURSING HOME INC p 859
632 Se 3rd St 73051
Tel (405) 527-6531 *SIC* 8052

MADILL, OK

OKLAHOMA STEEL & WIRE CO INC p 1080
Hwy 70 S 73446
Tel (580) 795-7311 *SIC* 3496

MARLOW, OK

■ CESI CHEMICAL INC p 284
1004 S Plainsman Rd 73055
Tel (580) 658-6608 *SIC* 2087

WILCO MACHINE & FAB INC p 1608
1326 S Broadway St 73055
Tel (580) 658-6993 *SIC* 3533

MCALESTER, OK

MITCHELL MANOR CONVALESCENT HOME INC p 977
315 W Electric Ave 74501
Tel (918) 423-4661 *SIC* 8051 8059

MIDWEST CITY, OK

■ MIDWEST REGIONAL MEDICAL CENTER LLC p 967
2825 Parklawn Dr 73110
Tel (405) 610-4411 *SIC* 8011 8062

MOORE, OK

MOORE INDEPENDENT SCHOOL DISTRICT NO 2 p 987
1500 Se 4th St 73160
Tel (405) 735-4200 *SIC* 8211

MUSKOGEE, OK

ACME ENGINEERING AND MANUFACTURING CORP p 18
1820 N York St 74403
Tel (918) 682-7791 *SIC* 3564

BROADWAY MANOR NURSING HOME p 216
1622 E Broadway St 74403
Tel (918) 683-2851 *SIC* 8052 8051

CITY OF MUSKOGEE FOUNDATION p 316
120 N 3rd St 74401
Tel (918) 577-6562 *SIC* 8641

EASTGATE VILLAGE RETIREMENT CENTER p 473
3500 Haskell Blvd 74403
Tel (918) 682-3191 *SIC* 8052 8051

MUSKOGEE REGIONAL MEDICAL CENTER LLC p 1002
300 Rockefeller Dr 74401
Tel (918) 682-5501 *SIC* 8062

YAFFE COMPANIES INC p 1633
1200 S G St 74403
Tel (918) 687-7543 *SIC* 5093 5051

MUSTANG, OK

MUSTANG PUBLIC SCHOOLS p 1003
906 S Heights Dr 73064
Tel (405) 376-2461 *SIC* 8211

NORMAN, OK

CHICKASAW NATION INDUSTRIES INC p 298
2600 John Saxon Blvd # 100 73071
Tel (405) 253-8200 SIC 6719

HAMMER CONSTRUCTION INC p 656
4320 Adams Rd 73069
Tel (405) 310-3160 SIC 1389 1794

HARRISON GYPSUM LLC p 664
1550 Double C Dr 73069
Tel (405) 366-9500 SIC 1499 4213

HITACHI COMPUTER PRODUCTS (AMERICA) INC p 696
1800 E Imhoff Rd 73071
Tel (405) 360-5500 SIC 3577 3572 7379

INDEPENDENT SCHOOL DISTRICT I-29 p 737
131 S Flood Ave 73069
Tel (405) 364-1339 SIC 8211

MCCOYTREE SURGERY CO p 927
3201 Broce Dr 73072
Tel (405) 579-6000 SIC 0783

NORMAN REGIONAL HOSPITAL AUTHORITY p 1049
901 N Porter Ave 73071
Tel (405) 307-1000 SIC 8062

NORMANYORK INTERNATIONAL p 1049
5005 York Dr 73069
Tel (405) 364-4040 SIC 5075

OKLAHOMA ELECTRIC CO-OPERATIVE INC p 1079
242 24th Ave Nw 73069
Tel (405) 321-2024 SIC 4911 2721

UNIVERSITY OF OKLAHOMA p 1524
2800 Venture Dr 73069
Tel (405) 325-2000 SIC 8221

UNIVERSITY OF OKLAHOMA FOUNDATION INC p 1524
100 W Timberdell Rd Rm 1 73019
Tel (405) 321-1174 SIC 6211

OKLAHOMA CITY, OK

21C OKC LLC p 1
900 W Main St 73106
Tel (502) 882-6243 SIC 7011

7-ELEVEN LLC p 3
2021 S Macarthur Blvd 73128
Tel (405) 682-5711 SIC 5411 5541

■ ACCESS PERMIAN MIDSTREAM LLC p 15
525 Central Park Dr # 1005 73105
Tel (877) 413-1023 SIC 4922

ACCORD HUMAN RESOURCES INC p 15
210 Park Ave Ste 1200 73102
Tel (405) 232-9888 SIC 8742

ADDISON GROUP L L C p 22
901 N Lincoln Blvd # 305 73104
Tel (405) 235-6700 SIC 7361 8742

ALLIANCE STEEL INC p 55
3333 S Council Rd 73179
Tel (405) 745-7500 SIC 3448

■ ALSATE EXPLORATION INC p 61
1601 Nw Expwy St Ste 400 73118
Tel (405) 753-5500 SIC 1382

■ AMERICAN CELLULAR CORP p 70
14201 Wireless Way 73134
Tel (405) 529-8500 SIC 4812

AMERICAN ENERGY PARTNERS LP p 71
301 Nw 63rd St Ste 600 73116
Tel (405) 418-8000 SIC 1311

AMERICAN FARMERS & RANCHERS MUTUAL INSURANCE CO p 72
4400 Will Rogers Pkwy 73108
Tel (405) 218-5400 SIC 6331

AMERICAN FIDELITY ASSURANCE CO p 72
9000 Cameron Pkwy 73114
Tel (405) 523-2000 SIC 6321 6311

AMERICAN FIDELITY CORP p 72
2000 Classen Ctr Blvd 73106
Tel (405) 523-2000 SIC 6321 6311

AMERICAN FIDELITY GENERAL AGENCY INC p 72
9000 Cameron Pkwy 73114
Tel (405) 523-2000 SIC 6321 6311

■ AMERICAN MERCURY INSURANCE CO p 76
7301 Nw Expressway # 200 73132
Tel (405) 621-6509 SIC 6411 6331

AMITY CARE LLC p 85
4350 Will Rogers Pkwy 73108
Tel (405) 943-1144 SIC 8741

API ENTERPRISES INC p 96
4901 S I 35 Service Rd 73129
Tel (713) 580-4800 SIC 2673

ARCHER PRESSURE PUMPING LLC p 105
4500 Se 59th St 73135
Tel (405) 285-5812 SIC 1381

ASCENT RESOURCES LLC p 116
3501 Nw 63rd St 73116
Tel (405) 608-5544 SIC 1382 6719

■ ATC DRIVETRAIN LLC p 124
9901 W Reno Ave 73127
Tel (405) 350-3600 SIC 3714 4731

BALON CORP p 149
3245 S Hattie Ave 73129
Tel (405) 677-3321 SIC 3491 3494 5085

■ BANCFIRST p 149
101 N Broadway Ave # 1110 73102
Tel (405) 270-1000 SIC 6022

▲ BANCFIRST CORP p 149
101 N Broadway Ave # 1110 73102
Tel (405) 270-1086 SIC 6022

▲ BLUEKNIGHT ENERGY PARTNERS LP p 193
201 Nw 10th St Ste 200 73103
Tel (405) 278-6400 SIC 4612 4226

BOARD OF REGENTS OF UNIVERSITY OF OKLAHOMA-OU PHYSICIANS p 195
1122 Ne 13th St St236 73117
Tel (405) 271-1515 SIC 8011

BOB MOORE AUTO GROUP LLC p 196
101 N Robinson Ave # 820 73102
Tel (405) 605-2350 SIC 5511

BOB MOORE CADILLAC INC p 196
13020 Broadway Ext 73114
Tel (888) 876-9554 SIC 5511

■ BOEING AEROSPACE OPERATIONS INC p 197
6001 S Air Depot Blvd 73135
Tel (405) 622-6000 SIC 8711 8249

BRAUMS INC p 208
3000 Ne 63rd St 73121
Tel (405) 478-1656 SIC 5411 5812

BROWNE BOTTLING CO INC p 220
2712 Tealwood Dr 73120
Tel (405) 232-1158 SIC 2086

CAMERON ENTERPRISES A LIMITED PARTNERSHIP p 245
9000 Cameron Pkwy 73114
Tel (405) 523-2000 SIC 6733

CAPITAL DISTRIBUTING LLC p 249
421 N Portland Ave 73107
Tel (405) 521-1511 SIC 5181

■ CARLISLE FOODSERVICE PRODUCTS INC p 257
4711 E Hefner Rd 73131
Tel (405) 528-3011 SIC 3089 3269

CEDAR CREEK CORP p 272
450 N Macarthur Blvd 73127
Tel (405) 917-8300 SIC 5039

CEDAR CREEK HOLDINGS INC p 272
450 N Macarthur Blvd 73127
Tel (405) 917-8300 SIC 5031 5082

CEDAR CREEK LLC p 272
450 N Macarthur Blvd 73127
Tel (405) 917-8300 SIC 5031

CENTURY LLC p 282
1000 Century Blvd 73110
Tel (405) 732-2226 SIC 5091 3949

CHAPARRAL ENERGY INC p 288
701 Cedar Lake Blvd 73114
Tel (405) 478-8770 SIC 1311 1382

CHAPARRAL ENERGY LLC p 288
701 Cedar Lake Blvd 73114
Tel (405) 478-8770 SIC 1311 1382

▲ CHESAPEAKE ENERGY CORP p 295
6100 N Western Ave 73118
Tel (405) 848-8000 SIC 1311

■ CHESAPEAKE OPERATING LLC p 295
6100 N Western Ave 73118
Tel (405) 848-8000 SIC 1311 1389 4212

CITY OF OKLAHOMA CITY p 317
100 N Walker Ave 73102
Tel (405) 297-2506 SIC 9111

CLEARWATER ENTERPRISES LLC p 324
5637 N Classen Blvd 73118
Tel (405) 842-9200 SIC 4924

■ CLIMATE MASTER INC p 326
7300 Sw 44th St 73179
Tel (405) 745-6000 SIC 3585

■ CMITEREX CORP p 329
9528 W I 40 Service Rd 73128
Tel (405) 787-6020
SIC 3531 3715 3596 3541 3444 2951

COMMUNITY HOSPITAL LLC p 349
3100 Sw 89th St 73159
Tel (405) 602-8100 SIC 8062

■ COMPRESSCO INC p 352
1313 Se 25th St 73129
Tel (405) 677-0221 SIC 3533

COMPSOURCE MUTUAL INSURANCE CO p 352
1901 N Walnut Ave 73105
Tel (405) 232-7663 SIC 6331

▲ CONTINENTAL RESOURCES INC p 363
20 N Broadway 73102
Tel (405) 234-9000 SIC 1311

COUNTY OF OKLAHOMA p 380
320 Robert S Kerr Ave # 505 73102
Tel (405) 270-0082 SIC 9111

CRESCENT SERVICES LLC p 391
5721 Nw 132nd St 73142
Tel (405) 603-1200 SIC 1389

D & M CARRIERS LLC p 406
8125 Sw 15th St 73128
Tel (405) 491-2800 SIC 4213

■ DEACONESS HEALTH SYSTEM LLC p 419
5501 N Portland Ave 73112
Tel (405) 604-6000
SIC 8062 8051 8011 8361

DELTA DENTAL PLAN OF OKLAHOMA p 426
16 Nw 63rd St Ste 301 73116
Tel (405) 607-2100 SIC 6411

DEPT OF CORRECTIONS OKLAHOMA p 431
3400 N Mtn Lthr Kng Ave 73111
Tel (405) 425-2500 SIC 9223

▲ DEVON ENERGY CORP p 434
333 W Sheridan Ave 73102
Tel (405) 235-3611 SIC 1311 1382

■ DEVON ENERGY INTERNATIONAL CO p 434
20 N Broadway Ave # 1500 73102
Tel (405) 235-3611 SIC 2911

■ DEVON ENERGY PRODUCTION CO LP p 434
333 W Sheridan Ave 73102
Tel (405) 235-3611 SIC 1311 5172

■ DEVON GAS SERVICES LP p 434
333 W Sheridan Ave 73102
Tel (405) 235-3611 SIC 4922

■ DEVON OEI OPERATING INC p 434
20 N Broadway 73102
Tel (405) 235-3611
SIC 4922 4924 1311 4613

■ DOBSON COMMUNICATIONS CORP p 447
14201 Wireless Way 73134
Tel (405) 529-8500 SIC 4812

DOLESE BROS CO p 448
20 Nw 13th St 73103
Tel (405) 235-2311 SIC 3273 1422 1442

■ EL DORADO CHEMICAL CO INC p 482
16 S Pennsylvania Ave 73107
Tel (405) 235-4546 SIC 2819 2875 2892

■ ENABLE MIDSTREAM PARTNERS LP p 495
211 N Robinson Ave S410 73102
Tel (405) 525-7788 SIC 4922 4612 4619

■ ENABLE MISSISSIPPI RIVER TRANSMISSION LLC p 495
211 N Robinson Ave N950 73102
Tel (405) 557-5271 SIC 4619

■ ENABLE OKLAHOMA INTRASTATE TRANSMISSION LLC p 495
211 N Robinson Ave N950 73102
Tel (405) 525-7788
SIC 4922 1321 4923 2911

EVERETT HOSPITAL p 514
1200 Everett Dr 73104
Tel (405) 271-4700 SIC 8062

EXECUTIVE OFFICE OF STATE OF OKLAHOMA p 518
2300 N Lincoln Blvd 73105
Tel (405) 521-2342 SIC 9111

EXPRESS SERVICES INC p 520
9701 Boardwalk Blvd 73162
Tel (405) 840-5000 SIC 7363 6794 7361

FEED CHILDREN INC p 537
333 N Meridian Ave 73107
Tel (800) 627-4556 SIC 8661 8699 4832

FORD AUDIO-VIDEO SYSTEMS LLC p 565
4800 W Interstate 40 73128
Tel (405) 946-9966 SIC 1731 8711

▲ FOUNDATION HEALTHCARE INC p 571
13900 N Portland Ave # 200 73134
Tel (405) 608-1700 SIC 8062 8011 8093

FRONTIER DRILLING LLC p 581
1608 Nw Epwy Ste 102 73118
Tel (405) 745-7700 SIC 1381

■ GLOBE LIFE & ACCIDENT INSURANCE CO p 618
204 N Robinson Ave 73102
Tel (972) 540-6542 SIC 6311 6321

■ GREAT PLAINS COCA COLA BOTTLING CO p 634
600 N May Ave 73107
Tel (405) 280-2000 SIC 2086

GREAT PLAINS OILFIELD RENTAL LLC p 634
777 Nw 63rd St 73116
Tel (405) 608-7777 SIC 5084

▲ GULFPORT ENERGY CORP p 647
14313 N May Ave Ste 100 73134
Tel (405) 848-8807 SIC 1311

HAC INC p 652
390 Ne 36th St 73105
Tel (405) 290-3000 SIC 5411

HASKELL LEMON CONSTRUCTION CO p 667
3800 Sw 10th St 73108
Tel (405) 947-6069
SIC 5032 1611 3272 2951

■ HCA HEALTH SERVICES OF OKLAHOMA INC p 671
700 Ne 13th St 73104
Tel (405) 271-6035 SIC 8062

HEALTH DEPARTMENT OKLAHOMA STATE p 674
1000 Ne 10th St 73117
Tel (405) 271-5600 SIC 9431

HEALTHCARE PARTNERS INVESTMENTS LLC p 676
14024 Quail Pointe Dr 73134
Tel (405) 424-6677 SIC 8093

HOB-LOB LTD p 698
7707 Sw 44th St 73179
Tel (405) 745-1100
SIC 5945 5999 5949 5947

HOBBY LOBBY STORES INC p 699
7707 Sw 44th St 73179
Tel (855) 329-7060 SIC 5945

HUNZICKER BROTHERS INC p 721
501 N Virginia Ave 73106
Tel (405) 239-7771 SIC 5063

INDEPENDENT SCHOOL DISTRICT 52 p 737
7217 Se 15th St 73110
Tel (405) 737-4461 SIC 8211

INSURICA p 748
5100 N Classen Blvd # 300 73118
Tel (405) 556-2205 SIC 6411

INTEGRIS AMBULATORY CARE CORP p 749
5300 N Independence Ave 73112
Tel (405) 949-6026 SIC 8062

INTEGRIS BAPTIST MEDICAL CENTER INC p 749
3300 Nw Expressway 73112
Tel (405) 949-3011 SIC 8062

INTEGRIS HEALTH INC p 749
3300 Nw Expwy Bldg C32 73112
Tel (405) 949-6066 SIC 8062

INTEGRIS HEALTH INC p 749
5300 N Independence Ave # 280 73112
Tel (405) 949-6026 SIC 8099

INTEGRIS PHYSICIANS SERVICES INC p 749
5300 N Independence Ave # 260 73112
Tel (405) 951-2529 SIC 8742

INTEGRIS RURAL HEALTHCARE OF OKLAHOMA INC p 749
3300 Nw Expwy 73112
Tel (405) 951-2277 SIC 8062 6513

INTERBANK INC p 751
4921 N May Ave 73112
Tel (580) 928-5511 SIC 6712

JASCO PRODUCTS CO LLC p 778
10 E Memorial Rd Bldg B 73114
Tel (405) 752-0710 SIC 5065 5064

KIRBY - SMITH MACHINERY INC p 821
6715 W Reno Ave 73127
Tel (888) 861-0219 SIC 7353 5082 7692

■ LARIAT SERVICES INC p 845
123 Robert S Kerr Ave 73102
Tel (405) 753-5500 SIC 1382

LEGEND ENERGY SERVICES LLC p 853
5801 Broadway Ext Ste 210 73118
Tel (405) 600-1264 SIC 1389

■ LITTLE GIANT PUMP CO LLC p 871
301 N Macarthur Blvd 73127
Tel (405) 947-2511 SIC 3561

LOCKE SUPPLY CO p 873
1300 Se 82nd St 73149
Tel (405) 635-3230
SIC 5063 5074 5075 1711

LOPEZ FOODS INC p 877
6016 Nw 120th Ct 73162
Tel (405) 603-7500 SIC 2013 2011

LOVESTRAVEL STOPS & COUNTRY STORES INC p 881
10601 N Pennsylvania Ave 73120
Tel (405) 302-6500 SIC 5541 5411 5947

■ LSB CHEMICAL LLC p 883
16 S Pennsylvania Ave 73107
Tel (405) 235-4546 SIC 2819 2873 2892

▲ LSB INDUSTRIES INC p 883
16 S Pennsylvania Ave 73107
Tel (405) 235-4546
SIC 3822 3585 3567 2873

M & D INDUSTRIES CORP p 888
2701 W I 44 Service Rd # 102 73112
Tel (405) 942-2936 SIC 5812

M-D BUILDING PRODUCTS INC p 890
4041 N Santa Fe Ave 73118
Tel (405) 528-4411 SIC 3442

▲ MAMMOTH ENERGY PARTNERS LP p 900
4727 Gaillardia Pkwy # 200 73142
Tel (405) 265-4600 SIC 1389 1381

MARDEL INC p 905
7727 Sw 44th St 73179
Tel (405) 745-1300 SIC 5999 5943

MATHIS BROS OKLAHOMA CITY LLC p 920
3434 W Reno Ave 73107
Tel (405) 943-3434 SIC 7991

MAXCESS INTERNATIONAL CORP p 922
222 W Memorial Rd 73114
Tel (405) 755-1600 SIC 3554 3565 6719

MAXCESS INTERNATIONAL HOLDING CORP p 922
222 W Memorial Rd 73114
Tel (405) 755-1600 SIC 3554 3565 6719

MCBRIDE CLINIC ORTHOPEDIC HOSPITAL LLC p 926
9600 Broadway Ext 73114
Tel (405) 486-2515 SIC 8069

MERCY CLINIC OKLAHOMA COMMUNITIES INC p 945
4300 W Memorial Rd 73120
Tel (405) 936-5213 SIC 8011

MERIDIAN DRILLING CO LLC p 948
11500 S Meridian Ave 73173
Tel (405) 691-1202 SIC 1381 1799 5084

MID-WEST HOSE & SPECIALTY INC p 964
3312 S I 35 Service Rd 73129
Tel (405) 670-6718 SIC 5085

MIDFIRST BANK p 965
501 Nw Grand Blvd 73118
Tel (405) 767-7000 SIC 6035

MIDLAND FINANCIAL CO p 965
501 Nw Grand Blvd Ste 180 73118
Tel (405) 840-7600 SIC 6035 6162 6531

■ **MIDLANDS MANAGEMENT CORP** p 966
3817 Nw Expwy Ste 1000 73112
Tel (405) 840-0074 SIC 6411 6331 6321

MIDWEST CITY PUBLIC SCHOOLS I-52 p 967
7217 Se 15th St 73110
Tel (405) 737-4461 SIC 8211

MTM RECOGNITION CORP p 998
3201 Se 29th St 73115
Tel (405) 609-6900
SIC 3911 3873 2499 2389 3499 2791

MUSEUM OF BIBLE INC p 1002
7507 Sw 44th St 73179
Tel (405) 996-4900 SIC 8412

MUSKET CORP p 1002
10601 N Pennsylvania Ave 73120
Tel (713) 332-5726 SIC 5172

MUSTANG FUEL CORP p 1002
9800 N Oklahoma Ave 73114
Tel (405) 884-2092 SIC 1311 4923

NORTH AMERICAN INSURANCE AGENCY INC p 1050
5101 Classen Cir 73118
Tel (405) 523-2100 SIC 6411

NORTH AMERICAN TIE & TIMBER LLC p 1050
6406 N Santa Fe Ave Ste B 73116
Tel (405) 848-1800 SIC 5099

NORTHWEST BUILDING SUPPLY INC p 1059
5535 Nw 5th St 73127
Tel (405) 946-0500 SIC 5033 5031 5211

▲ **OGE ENERGY CORP** p 1076
321 N Harvey Ave 73102
Tel (405) 553-3000 SIC 4911 4922 4925

OKLAHOMA CITY ENVIRONMENTAL ASSISTANCE TRUST p 1079
200 N Walker Ave Ste 302 73102
Tel (405) 297-2424 SIC 8611

OKLAHOMA CITY PUBLIC SCHOOLS p 1079
900 N Klein Ave 73106
Tel (405) 587-0000 SIC 8211

OKLAHOMA CITY UNIVERSITY p 1079
2501 N Blackwelder Ave 73106
Tel (405) 208-5000 SIC 8221

OKLAHOMA DEPARTMENT OF COMMERCE p 1079
900 N Stiles Ave 73104
Tel (405) 815-6552 SIC 9611

OKLAHOMA DEPARTMENT OF MENTAL HEALTH AND SUBSTANCE ABUSE SERVICES p 1079
1200 Ne 13th St 73117
Tel (405) 522-3878 SIC 8399 9431

OKLAHOMA DEPARTMENT OF TRANSPORTATION p 1079
200 Ne 21st St 73105
Tel (405) 521-2631 SIC 9621

OKLAHOMA DEPT OF HUMAN SERVICES p 1079
2400 N Lincoln Blvd 73105
Tel (405) 521-3646 SIC 9431 9441

OKLAHOMA DEPT OF MILITARY p 1079
3501 Ne Military Cir 73111
Tel (405) 228-5000 SIC 9111

OKLAHOMA DEPT OF PUBLIC SAFETY p 1079
3600 N Martin Luther Knl 73111
Tel (405) 425-2424 SIC 9229

OKLAHOMA DEPT OF TOURISM AND RECREATION p 1079
120 N Robinson Ave # 600 73102
Tel (405) 230-8300 SIC 9611

OKLAHOMA FARM BUREAU MUTUAL INSURANCE CO p 1079
2501 N Stiles Ave 73105
Tel (405) 523-2300 SIC 6331 6351

■ **OKLAHOMA GAS AND ELECTRIC CO** p 1079
321 N Harvey Ave 73102
Tel (405) 553-3000 SIC 4911

OKLAHOMA HEART HOSPITAL LLC p 1079
4050 W Memorial Rd 73120
Tel (405) 608-3200 SIC 8069

OKLAHOMA HEART HOSPITAL SOUTH LLC p 1079
5200 E I 240 Service Rd 73135
Tel (405) 628-6000 SIC 8062

OKLAHOMA OFFICE OF MANAGEMENT AND ENTERPRISE SERVICES p 1080
2300 N Lincoln Blvd # 122 73105
Tel (405) 521-2141 SIC 9311

OKLAHOMA PUBLISHING CO OF OKLAHOMA p 1080
9000 N Brdwy 73114
Tel (405) 475-3311
SIC 2711 1311 6512 7375 2752

OKLAHOMA SECRETARY OF ENERGY & ENVIRONMENT p 1080
204 N Robinson Ave # 1010 73102
Tel (405) 522-7099 SIC 9511

OKLAHOMA TURNPIKE AUTHORITY p 1080
3500 N Martin Luther 73111
Tel (405) 425-3600 SIC 4785

PANHANDLE OILFIELD SERVICE COMPANIES INC p 1111
14000 Quail Springs Pkwy # 300 73134
Tel (405) 608-5330
SIC 1389 7389 3498 4212 5082 1794

▲ **PAYCOM SOFTWARE INC** p 1122
7501 W Memorial Rd 73142
Tel (405) 722-6900 SIC 8721 7371 7372

PHARMA CORR LLC p 1141
6705 Camille Ave 73149
Tel (405) 670-1400 SIC 5122

POSTROCK ENERGY CORP p 1164
210 Park Ave Ste 2750 73102
Tel (405) 600-7704 SIC 1311

■ **QUEST ENERGY PARTNERS LP** p 1199
210 Park Ave Ste 2750 73102
Tel (405) 600-7704 SIC 1382

QUIBIDS HOLDINGS LLC p 1199
1601 Nw Expwy St Ste 1500 73118
Tel (405) 253-3883 SIC 5961

RIVER ROCK ENERGY LLC p 1237
211 N Robinson Ave S1525 73102
Tel (405) 606-7481 SIC 1382

ROSE STATE COLLEGE p 1250
6420 Se 15th St 73110
Tel (405) 733-7673 SIC 8222

▲ **SANDRIDGE ENERGY INC** p 1278
123 Robert S Kerr Ave 73102
Tel (405) 429-5500 SIC 1311

SEVENTY SEVEN ENERGY INC p 1309
777 Nw 63rd St 73116
Tel (405) 608-7777 SIC 1389

SEVENTY SEVEN OPERATING LLC p 1309
777 Nw 63rd St 73116
Tel (405) 608-7777 SIC 3533 1389

SHEET METAL WORKERS LOCAL 124 p 1313
3717 Nw 63rd St Ste 100 73116
Tel (405) 848-4848 SIC 6371

▲ **SONIC CORP** p 1340
300 Johnny Bench Dr 73104
Tel (405) 225-5000 SIC 5812 6794

■ **SONIC INDUSTRIES SERVICES INC** p 1340
300 Johnny Bench Dr # 400 73104
Tel (405) 225-5000 SIC 6794 5812

SOUTH OKLAHOMA CITY HOSPITAL CORP p 1344
4401 S Western Ave 73109
Tel (405) 636-7000 SIC 8741

SOUTHWEST ELECTRIC CO p 1351
6503 Se 74th St 73135
Tel (800) 364-4445 SIC 3825 3612

SOUTHWEST MEDICAL CENTER OF OKLAHOMA p 1352
4401 S Western Ave 73109
Tel (405) 636-7000 SIC 8062

SSM HEALTH CARE OF OKLAHOMA INC p 1364
1000 N Lee Ave 73102
Tel (405) 272-7000 SIC 8062

STATE OF OKLAHOMA p 1382
421 Nw 13th St Ste 220 73103
Tel (405) 521-2342 SIC 7361

■ **STINGER WELLHEAD PROTECTION INC** p 1390
4301 Will Rogers Pkwy # 600 73108
Tel (405) 702-6575 SIC 1389

T & W TIRE LLC p 1419
25 N Council Rd 73127
Tel (405) 787-6711 SIC 5531

■ **THRIFTY RENT-A-CAR SYSTEM INC** p 1451
14501 Hertz Quail Spgs 73134
Tel (918) 665-3930 SIC 7515 7514 7513

■ **THRU TUBING SOLUTIONS INC** p 1451
11515 S Portland Ave 73170
Tel (405) 692-1900 SIC 1389

THUNDERBIRD RESOURCES EQUITY INC p 1451
9400 Broadway Ext Ste 600 73114
Tel (405) 600-0711 SIC 1311

TIMBERLAKE CONSTRUCTION CO INC p 1454
7613 N Classen Blvd 73116
Tel (405) 840-2521 SIC 1542 1541

TINKER FEDERAL CREDIT UNION p 1455
4140 W I 40 Service Rd 73108
Tel (405) 732-0324 SIC 6061

TRONOX LLC p 1484
3301 Nw 150th St 73134
Tel (405) 775-5000 SIC 2819 2816

TRONOX US HOLDINGS INC p 1484
3301 Nw 150th St 73134
Tel (405) 775-5000 SIC 2816 2819 5198

TRONOX WORLDWIDE LLC p 1484
3301 Nw 150th St 73134
Tel (405) 775-5000 SIC 2819 2816

UAMS EYE CENTER p 1498
921 Ne 13th St 73104
Tel (405) 456-1000 SIC 8011

■ **UE MANUFACTURING LLC** p 1499
10000 Nw 2nd St 73127
Tel (405) 947-3321 SIC 5084

UNION BANK p 1504
4921 N May Ave 73112
Tel (405) 949-7200 SIC 6022

■ **UNITED ENGINES LLC** p 1508
5555 W Reno Ave 73127
Tel (800) 955-3321
SIC 5013 5084 7538 7537

■ **UNITED HOLDINGS LLC** p 1509
5 N Mccormick St Ste 200 73127
Tel (405) 947-3321
SIC 5084 5013 7538 7537 3441

W H BRAUM INC p 1568
3000 Ne 63rd St 73121
Tel (405) 478-1656 SIC 5451 5812

WARREN POWER & MACHINERY LP p 1577
4501 W Reno Ave 73127
Tel (405) 947-6771 SIC 5082

WESTERN FLYER EXPRESS LLC p 1598
5204 W I 40 Service Rd 73128
Tel (405) 946-7289 SIC 4231

WORLD TRADING CO INC p 1625
6754 Melrose Ln 73127
Tel (405) 787-1982 SIC 2299

WWSC HOLDINGS CORP p 1629
1730 W Reno Ave 73106
Tel (405) 235-3621 SIC 7389

WWSC HOLDINGS LLC p 1629
1730 W Reno Ave 73106
Tel (405) 235-3621 SIC 3441

OKMULGEE, OK

MUSCOGEE CREEK NATION p 1002
1008 E Eufaula St 74447
Tel (918) 756-8700 SIC 9131

OWASSO, OK

NATIONAL STEAK PROCESSORS INC p 1016
301 E 5th Ave 74055
Tel (918) 274-8787 SIC 2013 2015

PARK HILL, OK

GREENLEAF NURSERY CO p 638
28406 Highway 82 74451
Tel (918) 457-5172 SIC 0181

PAULS VALLEY, OK

PAULS VALLEY HOSPITAL AUTHORITY p 1122
100 Valley Dr 73075
Tel (405) 238-5501 SIC 6324 8062

PERRY, OK

CHARLES MACHINE WORKS INC p 289
1959 W Fir St 73077
Tel (580) 572-3344
SIC 3531 3541 3829 3546

PERRY GREEN VALLEY NURSING HOME INC p 1137
1103 Birch St 73077
Tel (580) 336-2285 SIC 8051

POCOLA, OK

POCOLA NURSING CENTER p 1158
200 Home St 74902
Tel (918) 436-2228 SIC 8052

PONCA CITY, OK

EVANS & ASSOCIATES ENTERPRISES INC p 513
3320 N 14th St 74601
Tel (580) 765-6693
SIC 5032 2951 1442 1611 3273 1311

POTEAU, OK

SOUTHERN STAR INC p 1350
306 Kerr Ave 74953
Tel (918) 647-8383 SIC 4841

PRYOR, OK

ORCHIDS PAPER PRODUCTS CO p 1093
4826 Hunt St 74361
Tel (918) 825-0616 SIC 2676

■ **PRYOR CHEMICAL CO** p 1187
4463 Hunt St 74361
Tel (918) 825-3383 SIC 2873

RAE CORP p 1205
4492 Hunt St 74361
Tel (918) 825-7222 SIC 3585

SALLISAW, OK

OKLAHOMA NURSING HOMES LTD p 1079
210 E Choctaw Ave 74955
Tel (918) 775-4439 SIC 8051

SAND SPRINGS, OK

SHEFFIELD STEEL CORP p 1314
2300 S State Highway 97 74063
Tel (918) 245-1335 SIC 3312

▲ **WEBCO INDUSTRIES INC** p 1586
9101 W 21st St 74063
Tel (918) 245-2211 SIC 3312 5051

SAPULPA, OK

JCT HOLDING CO LLC p 780
19007 W Highway 33 74066
Tel (918) 227-1600 SIC 4213

JOHN CHRISTNER TRUCKING LLC p 788
19007 W Highway 33 74066
Tel (918) 248-3300 SIC 4213

PARAGON INDUSTRIES INC p 1113
3378 W Highway 117 74066
Tel (918) 291-4459 SIC 3317

SEMINOLE, OK

SEMINOLE SCHOOL DISTRICT I01 p 1302
617 Timmons St 74868
Tel (405) 382-5085 SIC 8211

SHAWNEE, OK

CITIZEN POTAWATOMI NATION p 310
1601 Gordon Cooper Dr 74801
Tel (405) 275-3121
SIC 7992 5411 7011 8412

GEORG FISCHER CENTRAL PLASTICS LLC p 606
39605 Independence St 74804
Tel (405) 273-6302 SIC 3089

STILLWATER, OK

■ **BANK SNB** p 152
608 S Main St 74074
Tel (405) 372-2230 SIC 6021 6163

DW-NATIONAL STANDARD-STILLWATER LLC p 463
3602 N Perkins Rd 74075
Tel (405) 377-5050 SIC 3315

■ **FLIR DETECTION INC** p 557
1024 S Innovation Way 74074
Tel (703) 678-2111 SIC 3826

HORIZON ENERGY SERVICES LLC p 707
203 E 80th St 74074
Tel (405) 533-4800 SIC 1381

MUSTANG HEAVY HAUL LLC p 1002
4905 S Perkins Rd 74074
Tel (405) 743-0085 SIC 1381

OKLAHOMA STATE UNIVERSITY p 1080
401 Whitehurst Hall 74078
Tel (405) 744-5892 SIC 8221

OKLAHOMA STATE UNIVERSITY FOUNDATION p 1080
400 S Monroe St 74074
Tel (405) 385-5100 SIC 8611

▲ **SOUTHWEST BANCORP INC** p 1351
608 S Main St 74074
Tel (405) 742-1800 SIC 6021

STILLWATER MEDICAL CENTER AUTHORITY p 1389
1323 W 6th Ave 74074
Tel (405) 372-1480 SIC 8062

STILLWATER MEDICAL PHYSICIAN CLINIC p 1390
1815 W 6th Ave 74074
Tel (405) 743-7300 SIC 8011

STILLWATER MILLING CO LLC p 1390
512 E 6th Ave 74074
Tel (405) 372-2766 SIC 2048 5999

TINKER FEDERAL CREDIT UNION p 1455
5101 W 6th Ave 74074
Tel (405) 707-7440 SIC 6062

WESTHAVEN NURSING HOME INC p 1601
1215 S Western Rd 74074
Tel (405) 743-1140 SIC 8051

STONEWALL, OK

■ **MID-AMERICA TELEPHONE INC** p 963
110 W 5th St 74871
Tel (608) 831-1000 SIC 4813

STROUD, OK

SERVICE KING MANUFACTURING INC p 1307
2100 W Hgwy 66 74079
Tel (918) 968-2899 SIC 3533

SULPHUR, OK

CALLAWAY NURSING HOME p 242
1300 W Lindsay Ave 73086
Tel (580) 622-2416 SIC 8059

CHICKASAW HOLDING CO p 298
124 W Vinita Ave 73086
Tel (580) 622-2111 SIC 4813 7371 5065

TAHLEQUAH, OK

CHEROKEE NATION p 294
17675 S Muskogee Ave 74464
Tel (918) 453-5000 SIC 9131

NORTHEASTERN STATE UNIVERSITY p 1055
600 N Grand Ave 74464
Tel (918) 456-5511 SIC 8221

REASORS LLC p 1214
200 W Choctaw St 74464
Tel (918) 456-1472 SIC 5411

TAHLEQUAH HOSPITAL AUTHORITY p 1421
1400 E Downing St 74464
Tel (918) 456-0641 SIC 8062

TAHLEQUAH MEDICAL GROUP LLC p 1421
1400 E Downing St 74464
Tel (918) 456-0641 SIC 8011 8062

TULSA, OK

▲ **AAON INC** p 8
2425 S Yukon Ave 74107
Tel (918) 583-2266 SIC 3585

AHS HILLCREST MEDICAL CENTER LLC p 37
1120 S Utica Ave 74104
Tel (918) 579-1000 SIC 8062

AHS OKLAHOMA HEALTH SYSTEM LLP p 37
110 W 7th St Ste 2540 74119
Tel (918) 579-1000
SIC 8062 8069 7352 6512 7389 5999

AHS SOUTHCREST HOSPITAL LLC p 37
8801 S 101st East Ave 74133
Tel (918) 294-4000 *SIC* 8062

AHS TULSA REGIONAL MEDICAL CENTER LLC p 37
744 W 9th St P252 74127
Tel (918) 587-2561 *SIC* 8062

■ ALLIANCE COAL LLC p 54
1717 S Boulder Ave # 400 74119
Tel (918) 295-7600 *SIC* 1221 1222

▲ ALLIANCE HOLDINGS GP LP p 54
1717 S Boulder Ave # 400 74119
Tel (918) 295-1415 *SIC* 1221 1222

ALLIANCE RESOURCE HOLDINGS INC p 55
1717 S Boulder Ave Fl 6 74119
Tel (918) 295-7600 *SIC* 1221 1222

■ ALLIANCE RESOURCE OPERATING PARTNERS LP p 55
1717 S Boulder Ave # 600 74119
Tel (918) 295-7600 *SIC* 1221

▲ ALLIANCE RESOURCE PARTNERS LP p 55
1717 S Boulder Ave # 400 74119
Tel (918) 295-7600 *SIC* 1221 1222 1241

AMERISTAR PERIMETER SECURITY USA INC p 83
1555 N Mingo Rd 74116
Tel (918) 835-0898 *SIC* 3089 3446 1799

■ ANCHOR DRILLING FLUIDS USA INC p 89
2431 E 61st St Ste 710 74136
Tel (918) 583-7701 *SIC* 5169

APAC-OKLAHOMA INC p 95
4150 S 100th East Ave # 300 74146
Tel (918) 438-2020 *SIC* 1611

ASPHALT AND FUEL SUPPLY LLC p 118
4200 E Skelly Dr Ste 600 74135
Tel (918) 488-1339 *SIC* 5172

B & M OIL CO INC p 141
5731 S 49th West Ave 74107
Tel (918) 445-0725 *SIC* 5171

BAMA COMPANIES INC p 149
2745 E 11th St 74104
Tel (918) 592-0778 *SIC* 2053 2041 2051

BAMA FROZEN DOUGH LLC p 149
2435 N Lewis Ave 74110
Tel (918) 732-2600 *SIC* 5142

BANK EQUIPMENT SYSTEMS INC p 150
8086 S Yale Ave Ste 103 74136
Tel (918) 630-4133 *SIC* 7382

BANK OF OKLAHOMA FINANCIAL CORP p 152
6424 E 41st St 74135
Tel (918) 619-1578 *SIC* 6022

BERENDSEN FLUID POWER INC p 174
401 S Boston Ave Ste 1200 74103
Tel (918) 592-3781 *SIC* 5084

■ BH MEDIA GROUP HOLDINGS INC p 180
315 S Boulder Ave 74103
Tel (918) 583-2161 *SIC* 2711

▲ BOK FINANCIAL CORP p 198
320 S Boston Ave 74103
Tel (918) 588-6000 *SIC* 6021

■ BOKF NATIONAL ASSOCIATION p 198
1 One Williams Ctr Bsmt 1 74172
Tel (918) 588-6000 *SIC* 6021

BORETS US INC p 201
1600 N Garnett Rd 74116
Tel (918) 439-7000 *SIC* 3533

■ CAPROCK PIPELINE CO p 251
100 W 5th St Ste Ll 74103
Tel (918) 588-7900 *SIC* 4922

CCC PARTS CO p 270
420 S 145th East Ave 74108
Tel (918) 838-9797 *SIC* 5531

CCI CORP p 270
420 S 145th East Ave 74108
Tel (918) 743-6005 *SIC* 5531

CENTRAL SECURITY GROUP INC p 280
2448 E 81st St Ste 4300 74137
Tel (918) 491-3151 *SIC* 7382

CITGO INVESTMENT CO p 309
6100 S Yale Ave Ste 1200 74136
Tel (918) 254-6062 *SIC* 2911

CITY OF TULSA p 319
175 E 2nd St Ste 15129 74103
Tel (918) 596-2100 *SIC* 9111

COMMUNITY CARE HMO INC p 347
218 W 6th St Ste 700 74119
Tel (918) 594-5200 *SIC* 6324

COMMUNITYCARE MANAGED HEALTHCARE PLANS OF OKLAHOMA INC p 350
218 W 6th St 74119
Tel (918) 594-5200 *SIC* 6324

COMPREHENSIVE MEDICAL CARE AFFILIATES INC p 352
218 W 6th St 704 74119
Tel (918) 594-5202 *SIC* 6324

CONTINUUM ENERGY LLC p 364
1323 E 71st St Ste 300 74136
Tel (918) 492-2840 *SIC* 4923

CONTINUUM ENERGY SERVICES LLC p 364
1323 E 71st St Ste 300 74136
Tel (918) 492-2840 *SIC* 4923

CONTINUUM MIDSTREAM LLC p 364
1323 E 71st St Ste 300 74136
Tel (918) 492-2840 *SIC* 4922

COUNTY OF TULSA p 382
500 S Denver Ave 74103
Tel (918) 596-5000 *SIC* 9111

CROSBY GROUP LLC p 393
2801 Dawson Rd 74110
Tel (918) 834-4611 *SIC* 3462 3429

CROSBY US ACQUISITION CORP p 393
2801 Dawson Rd 74110
Tel (918) 834-4611 *SIC* 3629

▲ CYPRESS ENERGY PARTNERS LP p 405
5727 S Lewis Ave Ste 300 74105
Tel (918) 748-3900 *SIC* 1389 7389

■ DOLLAR RENT A CAR INC p 448
5330 E 31st St Ste 100 74135
Tel (918) 669-3000 *SIC* 7514

■ DOLLAR THRIFTY AUTOMOTIVE GROUP INC p 448
5330 E 31st St 74135
Tel (918) 660-7700 *SIC* 6794 7514

■ DOVER ARTIFICIAL LIFT SYSTEMS LLC p 453
15 E 5th St Ste 1421 74103
Tel (918) 396-0558 *SIC* 1389

ENOVATION CONTROLS LLC p 500
5311 S 122nd East Ave 74146
Tel (918) 317-4100
SIC 3625 3714 3694 8711

F & M BANK & TRUST CO p 522
1330 S Harvard Ave 74112
Tel (918) 744-1330 *SIC* 6022

FABRICUT INC p 523
9303 E 46th St 74145
Tel (918) 622-7700 *SIC* 5199

FKI INDUSTRIES INC p 554
2801 Dawson Rd 74110
Tel (918) 834-4611
SIC 3429 3536 3535 3496 3569 3823

FLINTCO LLC p 557
1624 W 21st St 74107
Tel (918) 587-8451 *SIC* 1541 1542

GAFP INC p 589
1555 N Mingo Rd 74116
Tel (918) 835-0898 *SIC* 3315

GBK CORP p 594
6733 S Yale Ave 74136
Tel (918) 494-0000 *SIC* 1311

GDH CONSULTING INC p 595
4200 E Skelly Dr Ste 650 74135
Tel (918) 392-1600 *SIC* 7379 7361 7371

GEORGE KAISER FAMILY FOUNDATION p 606
7030 S Yale Ave Ste 600 74136
Tel (918) 392-1612 *SIC* 8641

▲ HELMERICH & PAYNE INC p 682
1437 S Boulder Ave # 1400 74119
Tel (918) 742-5531 *SIC* 1381 1389 6512

■ HELMERICH & PAYNE INTERNATIONAL DRILLING CO INC p 682
1437 S Boulder Ave # 1400 74119
Tel (918) 742-5531 *SIC* 1381

■ IC BUS OF OKLAHOMA LLC p 726
2322 N Mingo Rd 74116
Tel (918) 833-4000 *SIC* 3711 3713

INDEPENDENT SCHOOL DISTRICT 1 OF TULSA COUNTY p 737
3027 S New Haven Ave 74114
Tel (918) 746-6800 *SIC* 8211

INDEPENDENT SCHOOL DISTRICT 9 TULSA COUNTY OK p 737
8506 E 61st St 74133
Tel (918) 357-4321 *SIC* 8211

INDUSTRIAL PIPING SPECIALISTS INC p 740
606 N 145th East Ave 74116
Tel (918) 437-9100 *SIC* 5051 5085

INTERNATIONAL CHEMICAL CO p 754
1887 E 71st St 74136
Tel (918) 496-7711 *SIC* 5191

JANEPHILLIPS HEALTH CROP p 777
1923 S Utica Ave 74104
Tel (918) 273-3102 *SIC* 8062

JOHN ZINK CO LLC p 790
11920 E Apache St 74116
Tel (918) 234-1800 *SIC* 3823

KAISER-FRANCIS OIL CO p 800
6733 S Yale Ave 74136
Tel (918) 494-0000 *SIC* 1382 1311

LAKEWOOD MIDSTREAM LLC p 840
6655 S Lewis Ave Ste 200 74136
Tel (918) 392-9356 *SIC* 4932

▲ LAREDO PETROLEUM INC p 845
15 W 6th St Ste 1800 74119
Tel (918) 513-4570 *SIC* 1311

LATSHAW DRILLING & EXPLORATION CO p 846
4500 S 129th East Ave # 150 74134
Tel (918) 355-4380 *SIC* 1381

LINDE ENGINEERING NORTH AMERICA INC p 868
6100 S Yale Ave Ste 1200 74136
Tel (918) 477-1200 *SIC* 3567 8711

LINDE HOLDINGS LLC p 868
6100 S Yale Ave Ste 1200 74136
Tel (918) 477-1200 *SIC* 8711

LINDE PROCESS PLANTS INC p 868
6100 S Yale Ave Ste 1200 74136
Tel (918) 477-1200 *SIC* 3444 8711 1629

■ MAGELLAN MIDSTREAM HOLDINGS GP LLC p 895
1 One Williams Ctr Bsmt 2 74172
Tel (918) 574-7000 *SIC* 4613

▲ MAGELLAN MIDSTREAM PARTNERS LP p 895
1 Williams Ctr Bsmt 2 74172
Tel (918) 574-7000 *SIC* 5171 4613

■ MAGELLAN PIPELINE CO LP p 895
1 Williams Ctr 74172
Tel (918) 574-7000 *SIC* 4613

■ MAGELLAN TERMINALS HOLDINGS LP p 895
1 One Williams Ctr Bsmt 2 74172
Tel (918) 574-7000 *SIC* 5171

MANHATTAN CONSTRUCTION CO p 901
5601 S 122nd East Ave 74146
Tel (918) 583-6900 *SIC* 1542

MANHATTAN CONSTRUCTION GROUP INC p 901
5601 S 122nd East Ave 74146
Tel (918) 878-3341 *SIC* 1542

MANHATTAN ROAD & BRIDGE CO p 901
5601 S 122nd East Ave 74146
Tel (918) 583-6900 *SIC* 1622

■ MATRIX NORTH AMERICAN CONSTRUCTION INC p 920
5100 E Skelly Dr Ste 700 74135
Tel (918) 838-8822 *SIC* 1731 1623 1629

■ MATRIX PDM ENGINEERING INC p 920
5100 E Skelly Dr Ste 800 74135
Tel (918) 624-6300 *SIC* 1542 1623 8711

▲ MATRIX SERVICE CO p 920
5100 E Skelly Dr Ste 700 74135
Tel (918) 838-8822
SIC 1542 1623 7349 8711

■ MATRIX SERVICE INC p 920
5100 E Skelly Dr Ste 700 74135
Tel (918) 838-8822
SIC 1623 1629 1799 7699

MAZZIOS LLC p 924
4441 S 72nd East Ave 74145
Tel (918) 663-8880 *SIC* 5812 6794

MCGRAW DAVISSON STEWART INC p 929
4105 S Rockford Ave 74105
Tel (918) 592-6000 *SIC* 6531

MELTON TRUCK LINES INC p 941
808 N 161st East Ave 74116
Tel (918) 234-1000 *SIC* 4213

METRO BUILDERS SUPPLY INC p 954
5313 S Mingo Rd 74146
Tel (918) 622-7692 *SIC* 5064

▲ MID-CON ENERGY PARTNERS LP p 963
2431 E 61st St Ste 850 74136
Tel (972) 479-5980 *SIC* 1311

■ MID-CONTINENT CASUALTY CO p 963
1437 S Boulder Ave # 200 74119
Tel (918) 587-7221 *SIC* 6331

MIDCON INVESTORS INC p 964
401 S Boston Ave Ste 3600 74103
Tel (918) 587-7325 *SIC* 5084

▲ MIDSTATES PETROLEUM CO INC p 966
321 S Boston Ave Ste 1000 74103
Tel (918) 947-8550 *SIC* 1311

MILL CREEK LUMBER & SUPPLY CO INC p 969
6974 E 38th St 74145
Tel (405) 671-3540
SIC 3442 1771 5031 5211

MURPHY ENERGY CORP p 1001
2250 E 73rd St Ste 600 74136
Tel (918) 743-7979 *SIC* 5172

NADEL AND GUSSMAN LLC p 1006
15 E 5th St Ste 3300 74103
Tel (918) 583-3333 *SIC* 1311

NATIONAL RENTAL (US) INC p 1015
6929 N Lakewood Ave # 100 74117
Tel (918) 401-6000 *SIC* 7514

NATIONAL TRUCK PARTS OF MIDWEST INC p 1016
1901 N Sheridan Rd 74115
Tel (918) 836-0151 *SIC* 5531

NAVICO INC p 1020
4500 S 129th East Ave # 200 74134
Tel (918) 437-6881 *SIC* 3812

■ NEWFIELD EXPLORATION MID-CONTINENT INC p 1037
101 E 2nd St 74103
Tel (918) 582-2690 *SIC* 1311

▲ NGL ENERGY PARTNERS LP p 1041
6120 S Yale Ave Ste 805 74136
Tel (918) 481-1119 *SIC* 5172 5984

■ NGL SUPPLY LLC p 1041
6120 S Yale Ave Ste 805 74136
Tel (918) 481-1119 *SIC* 5172

NONNIS FOODS LLC p 1047
3920 E Pine St 74115
Tel (918) 621-1200 *SIC* 2052 2053

NORDAM GROUP INC p 1047
6911 Whirlpool Dr 74117
Tel (918) 878-4000 *SIC* 3728 3724

OKLAHOMA STATE UNIVERSITY MEDICAL TRUST p 1080
744 W 9th St 74127
Tel (918) 599-1000 *SIC* 8062

OKLAHOMA SURGICAL HOSPITAL LLC p 1080
2408 E 81st St Ste 900 74137
Tel (918) 477-5000 *SIC* 8062

OMNI AIR INTERNATIONAL LLC p 1084
3303 N Sheridan Rd Hngar19 74115
Tel (918) 836-5393 *SIC* 4522

▲ ONE GAS INC p 1086
15 E 5th St 74103
Tel (918) 947-7000 *SIC* 1311 4924

■ ONEOK FIELD SERVICES CO LLC p 1087
100 W 5th St Ste Ll 74103
Tel (918) 588-7000 *SIC* 1321

▲ ONEOK INC p 1087
100 W 5th St Ste Ll 74103
Tel (918) 588-7000
SIC 4922 4924 1311 1321 5172

▲ ONEOK PARTNERS LP p 1087
100 W 5th St Ste Ll 74103
Tel (918) 588-7000
SIC 4922 1321 1381 4925

■ ONEOK ROCKIES MIDSTREAM LLC p 1087
100 W 5th St Ste Ll 74103
Tel (918) 588-7000 *SIC* 1311

ORAL ROBERTS UNIVERSITY p 1091
7777 S Lewis Ave 74171
Tel (918) 495-6161 *SIC* 8221

■ ORS NASCO INC p 1096
907 S Detroit Ave Ste 500 74120
Tel (918) 781-5300 *SIC* 5085 5084

OSAGE NATION GAMING ENTERPRISE p 1096
1121 W 36th St 74127
Tel (918) 699-7710 *SIC* 7999

PACER ENERGY MARKETING LLC p 1103
823 S Detroit Ave Ste 300 74120
Tel (918) 398-2713 *SIC* 5172

PDV HOLDING INC p 1125
6100 S Yale Ave 74136
Tel (918) 495-4000
SIC 2911 2992 5171 4213

PENNWELL CORP p 1131
1421 S Sheridan Rd 74112
Tel (918) 835-3161
SIC 2721 2731 2741 7389

PINNACLE PACKAGING CO INC p 1150
1203 E 33rd St Ste 200 74105
Tel (918) 744-5400 *SIC* 7389

PRECISE MACHINING & MANUFACTURING LLC p 1168
12716 E Pine St 74116
Tel (918) 438-3121 *SIC* 3728

QUIKTRIP CORP p 1200
4705 S 129th East Ave 74134
Tel (918) 615-7700
SIC 5411 5541 5172 2099 5141 6512

RAMSEY INDUSTRIES INC p 1207
4707 N Mingo Rd 74117
Tel (918) 438-2760 *SIC* 3531 3536

ROBERTS TRUCK CENTER OF OKLAHOMA LLC p 1242
1023 N Garnett Rd 74116
Tel (918) 438-2000 *SIC* 3713

ROSE ROCK MIDSTREAM LP p 1250
6120 S Yale Ave Ste 1500 74136
Tel (918) 524-7700 *SIC* 1311 4612

ROSS GROUP CONSTRUCTION CORP p 1251
510 E 2nd St 74120
Tel (918) 878-2838 *SIC* 1542

ROYAL MFG CO LP p 1254
516 S 25th West Ave 74127
Tel (918) 584-2671 *SIC* 2992 2911

S&R COMPRESSION LLC p 1263
4234 S Jackson Ave 74107
Tel (918) 447-1947 *SIC* 5046

SAINT FRANCIS HEALTH SYSTEM INC p 1269
6161 S Yale Ave 74136
Tel (918) 494-2200 *SIC* 8011

SAINT FRANCIS HOSPITAL INC p 1269
6161 S Yale Ave 74136
Tel (918) 502-2050 *SIC* 8062 7352 5999

SAINT FRANCIS HOSPITAL SOUTH LLC p 1269
10501 E 91st St 74133
Tel (918) 307-6000 *SIC* 8062

SAMSON ENERGY CO LLC p 1274
110 W 7th St Ste 2000 74119
Tel (918) 879-0279 *SIC* 1389 1741

SAMSON INVESTMENT CO p 1274
2 W 2nd St Ste 1500 74103
Tel (918) 583-1791 *SIC* 1311 7353 5082

SAMSON RESOURCES CO p 1274
2 W 2nd St Ste 1500 74103
Tel (918) 583-1791 *SIC* 1311 2911

SAMSON RESOURCES CORP p 1274
2 W 2nd St Ste 1600 74103
Tel (918) 591-1791 *SIC* 1311

SANGUINE GAS EXPLORATION LLC p 1279
110 W 7th St Ste 2700 74119
Tel (918) 494-6070 *SIC* 1311

■ SEMGAS LP p 1302
6120 S Yale Ave Ste 700 74136
Tel (918) 524-7100 *SIC* 4923

▲ SEMGROUP CORP p 1302
6120 S Yale Ave Ste 700 74136
Tel (918) 524-8100
SIC 1389 4612 5171 2951

SILICONE SPECIALTIES INC p 1323
430 S Rockford Ave 74120
Tel (918) 587-5567 *SIC* 5072

SOUTHWESTERN REGIONAL MEDICAL CENTER INC p 1353
10109 E 79th St 74133
Tel (918) 286-5000 *SIC* 8069

SPECTRUM PAINT CO INC p 1357
15247 E Skelly Dr 74116
Tel (918) 836-9911 *SIC* 5198 5231

ST JOHN HEALTH SYSTEM INC p 1367
1923 S Utica Ave 74104
Tel (918) 744-2180
SIC 7991 6512 7389 8361 8071 8062

ST JOHN MEDICAL CENTER INC p 1367
1923 S Utica Ave 74104
Tel (918) 744-2828 *SIC* 8062

T D WILLIAMSON INC p 1419
6120 S Yale Ave Ste 1700 74136
Tel (918) 493-9494 *SIC* 7389

■ TARGA PIPELINE MID-CONTINENT HOLDINGS LLC p 1425
110 W 7th St Ste 2300 74119
Tel (918) 574-3500 *SIC* 4922

■ TARGA PIPELINE MID-CONTINENT LLC p 1425
110 W 7th St Ste 2300 74119
Tel (918) 574-3500 *SIC* 1389

■ THRIFTY INC p 1451
5310 E 31st St Ste 100 74135
Tel (918) 665-3930
SIC 6794 7515 7514 7513

■ TRIUMPH AEROSTRUCTURES - TULSA LLC p 1483
3330 N Mingo Rd 74116
Tel (615) 361-2061 *SIC* 3728 3999

TULSA COMMUNITY COLLEGE FOUNDATION p 1491
6111 E Skelly Dr Ste 200 74135
Tel (918) 595-7000 *SIC* 8222

TULSA COMMUNITY FOUNDATION p 1491
7030 S Yale Ave Ste 600 74136
Tel (918) 494-8823 *SIC* 8733

▲ UNIT CORP p 1506
8200 S Unit Dr 74132
Tel (918) 493-7700 *SIC* 1381 1382 1311

■ UNIT DRILLING CO p 1506
8200 S Unit Dr 74132
Tel (918) 493-7700 *SIC* 1381

■ UNIT PETROLEUM CO p 1506
8200 S Unit Dr 74132
Tel (918) 493-7700 *SIC* 1311

UNITED STATES BEEF CORP p 1512
4923 E 49th St 74135
Tel (918) 665-0740 *SIC* 5812

UNIVERSITY OF TULSA p 1526
800 S Tucker Dr 74104
Tel (918) 631-2000 *SIC* 8221

VANGUARD CAR RENTAL USA INC p 1543
6929 N Lakewood Ave # 100 74117
Tel (918) 401-6000 *SIC* 7514

WALVOIL FLUID POWER CORP p 1575
4111 N Garnett Rd 74116
Tel (918) 858-7100 *SIC* 5085

WAREHOUSE MARKET INC p 1575
6207 S Peoria Ave Ste A 74136
Tel (918) 749-4732 *SIC* 5411

WARREN CLINIC INC p 1576
6161 S Yale Ave 74136
Tel (918) 488-6000 *SIC* 8011

WHITLOCK PACKAGING CORP p 1607
6655 S Lewis Ave Ste 105 74136
Tel (918) 524-4029 *SIC* 2033

WILLBROS DOWNSTREAM LLC p 1610
4300 E 36th St N 74115
Tel (918) 556-3600 *SIC* 8711

▲ WILLIAMS COMPANIES INC p 1611
1 Williams Ctr 74172
Tel (918) 573-2000
SIC 4922 4924 1311 1321

■ WILLIAMS ENERGY SERVICES LLC p 1611
1 One Williams Ctr Bsmt 2 74172
Tel (918) 573-2000 *SIC* 4923 5172

■ WILLIAMS FIELD SERVICES CO LLC p 1611
1 Williams Ctr 74172
Tel (918) 573-2000 *SIC* 1311

■ WILLIAMS FIELD SERVICES GROUP LLC p 1611
1 One Williams Ctr 74172
Tel (918) 573-2000 *SIC* 4925

■ WILLIAMS OLEFINS LLC p 1611
1 One Williams Ctr Bsmt 2 74172
Tel (918) 573-2000 *SIC* 4922

WILLIAMS PARTNERS LP p 1611
1 Williams Ctr Bsmt 2 74172
Tel (918) 573-2000 *SIC* 4922 1321 4925

▲ WILLIAMS PARTNERS LP p 1611
1 Williams Ctr 74172
Tel (918) 573-2000 *SIC* 1311 4922

WILLIAMS PARTNERS OPERATING LLC p 1611
1 Williams Ctr 74172
Tel (918) 573-2000 *SIC* 4923

WOODARD TECHNOLOGY & INVESTMENTS LLC p 1622
10205 E 61st St Ste D 74133
Tel (918) 270-7000 *SIC* 5045

▲ WPX ENERGY INC p 1627
3500 One Williams Ctr 74172
Tel (855) 979-2012 *SIC* 1311

VINITA, OK

GRAND RIVER DAM AUTHORITY p 630
226 W Dwain Willis Ave 74301
Tel (918) 256-5545 *SIC* 4911 1629

KAMO ELECTRIC COOPERATIVE INC p 802
500 S Kamo Dr 74301
Tel (918) 256-5551 *SIC* 4911

WAGONER, OK

■ UNARCO INDUSTRIES LLC p 1502
400 Se 15th St 74467
Tel (918) 485-9531 *SIC* 3496

WARNER, OK

COUNTRYSIDE ESTATES INC p 375
Hwy 64 E 74469
Tel (918) 463-5143 *SIC* 8052

WARR ACRES, OK

■ HERTZ TECHNOLOGIES INC p 688
5601 Nw Expressway 73132
Tel (405) 280-4983 *SIC* 7514

PUTNAM CITY SCHOOL DISTRICT I-001 OKLAHOMA COUNTY p 1193
5401 Nw 40th St 73122
Tel (405) 495-5200 *SIC* 8211

PUTNAM CITY SCHOOLS p 1193
5401 Nw 40th St 73122
Tel (405) 495-5200 *SIC* 8211

WATONGA, OK

WHEELER BROTHERS GRAIN CO LLC p 1605
501 Russworm Dr 73772
Tel (580) 623-7223 *SIC* 5153

WEATHERFORD, OK

CASEDHOLE SOLUTIONS INC p 263
1720 N Airport Rd 73096
Tel (580) 772-8900 *SIC* 1389

WOODWARD, OK

BEAVER EXPRESS SERVICE LLC p 166
4310 Oklahoma Ave 73801
Tel (580) 256-6460 *SIC* 4213

SOUTHERN HOSPITALITY INC p 1348
3202 1st St 73801
Tel (580) 256-7600 *SIC* 7011

■ WOODWARD HEALTH SYSTEMS LLC p 1623
900 17th St 73801
Tel (580) 256-2820 *SIC* 8062

WYANDOTTE, OK

■ WYANDOTTE TELEPHONE CO p 1629
5 N Main 74370
Tel (918) 678-8992 *SIC* 4813

OREGON

ALBANY, OR

ALBANY GENERAL HOSPITAL p 45
1046 6th Ave Sw 97321
Tel (541) 812-4000 *SIC* 8062 8741

ALBANY GENERAL HOSPITAL LIFELINE p 45
1046 W 6th St 97321
Tel (541) 812-4000 *SIC* 8062

COASTAL FARM HOLDINGS INC p 331
1355 Goldfish Farm Rd Se 97322
Tel (541) 967-3450 *SIC* 5999

GREATER ALBANY PUBLIC SCHOOL DISTRICT 8 J p 635
718 7th Ave Sw 97321
Tel (541) 967-4501 *SIC* 8211

OFD FOODS INC p 1075
525 25th Ave Sw 97322
Tel (541) 926-6001
SIC 2013 2015 2091 2032 2023

SAMARITAN ALBANY GENERAL HOSPITAL p 1274
1046 6th Ave Sw 97321
Tel (541) 812-4732 *SIC* 8062

ARLINGTON, OR

■ CHEMICAL WASTE MANAGEMENT OF NORTHWEST INC p 293
17629 Cedar Springs Ln 97812
Tel (541) 454-2030 *SIC* 4953

ASTORIA, OR

COLUMBIA LUTHERAN CHARITIES p 341
2111 Exchange St 97103
Tel (503) 325-4321 *SIC* 8062

AURORA, OR

COLUMBIA HELICOPTERS INC p 340
14452 Arndt Rd Ne 97002
Tel (503) 678-7510 *SIC* 7699 2411 4522

BAY CITY, OR

TILLAMOOK COUNTRY SMOKER INC p 1453
8250 Warren Ave 97107
Tel (503) 377-2222 *SIC* 5147

BEAVERTON, OR

AMERICAN INTERNATIONAL FOREST PRODUCTS LLC p 75
5560 Sw 107th Ave 97005
Tel (503) 641-1611 *SIC* 5031

BEAVERTON SCHOOL DISTRICT p 166
16550 Sw Merlo Rd 97003
Tel (503) 591-8000 *SIC* 8211

CARR CHEVROLET INC p 260
15005 Sw Tualatin Vly 97003
Tel (503) 644-2161 *SIC* 5511

■ CASCADE MICROTECH INC p 262
9100 Sw Gemini Dr 97008
Tel (503) 601-1000 *SIC* 3825 3674 7372

COMP-VIEW INC p 350
10035 Sw Arctic Dr 97005
Tel (503) 641-8439 *SIC* 5043

KAIZEN RESTAURANTS INC p 801
16500 Nw Bethany Ct # 150 97006
Tel (214) 221-7599 *SIC* 5812

KNIGHT FOUNDATION p 824
1 Sw Bowerman Dr 97005
Tel (503) 671-3500 *SIC* 8699

LANPHERE ENTERPRISES INC p 844
12505 Sw Brdwy St 97005
Tel (503) 643-5577 *SIC* 5571 5511 5261

LEUPOLD & STEVENS INC p 858
14400 Nw Greenbrier Pkwy 97006
Tel (503) 526-1400 *SIC* 3827

▲ NIKE INC p 1043
1 Sw Bowerman Dr 97005
Tel (503) 671-6453
SIC 3021 2329 2339 5139 5661 5136

■ NIKE INTERNATIONAL LTD p 1043
1 Sw Bowerman Dr 97005
Tel (503) 671-6750 *SIC* 5139 5136 5137

■ NIKE RETAIL SERVICES INC p 1043
1 Sw Bowerman Dr 97005
Tel (503) 671-6453 *SIC* 5661 5699

■ NIKE USA INC p 1043
1 Sw Bowerman Dr 97005
Tel (503) 671-6453 *SIC* 7941

OWEN STEPHENS PRODUCTIONS LLC p 1100
1304 Sw 176th Ter 97003
Tel (503) 810-0812 *SIC* 3861

PACIFIC OFFICE AUTOMATION INC p 1105
14747 Nw Greenbrier Pkwy 97006
Tel (503) 641-2000 *SIC* 5044

PLAID PANTRIES INC p 1153
10025 Sw Allen Blvd 97005
Tel (503) 646-4246 *SIC* 5411

PLANAR SYSTEMS INC p 1154
1195 Nw Compton Way 97006
Tel (503) 748-1100 *SIC* 3679

PLATT ELECTRIC SUPPLY INC p 1155
10605 Sw Allen Blvd 97005
Tel (503) 641-6121 *SIC* 5063

RESERS FINE FOODS INC p 1226
15570 Sw Jenkins Rd 97006
Tel (503) 643-6431 *SIC* 2099 5141

SERENA SOFTWARE INC p 1306
2345 Nw Amberbrook Dr # 200 97006
Tel (650) 481-3400 *SIC* 7372

SHARIS MANAGEMENT CORP p 1312
9400 Sw Gemini Dr 97008
Tel (503) 605-4299 *SIC* 5812

■ TEKTRONIX INC p 1433
14150 Sw Karl Braun Dr 97005
Tel (800) 833-9200 *SIC* 3825

TOUCHMARK LIVING CENTERS INC p 1463
5150 Sw Griffith Dr 97005
Tel (503) 646-5186 *SIC* 8051

VANGUARD EMS INC p 1543
3725 Sw Hocken Ave 97005
Tel (503) 644-4808 *SIC* 3672 3679

VTECH COMMUNICATIONS INC p 1567
9590 Sw Gemini Dr Ste 120 97008
Tel (503) 596-1200 *SIC* 5065 5064

BEND, OR

■ AE SOLAR ENERGY INC p 28
20720 Brinson Blvd 97701
Tel (541) 312-3832 *SIC* 3674

■ BANK OF CASCADES p 151
1100 Nw Wall St 97703
Tel (541) 617-3500 *SIC* 6022

BEND-LAPINE SCHOOLS p 172
520 Nw Wall St 97703
Tel (541) 383-6000 *SIC* 8211

▲ CASCADE BANCORP p 262
1100 Nw Wall St 97703
Tel (541) 617-3500 *SIC* 6022

LES SCHWAB TIRE CENTERS OF PORTLAND INC p 857
20900 Cooley Rd 97701
Tel (541) 447-4136 *SIC* 5531

LES SCHWAB TIRE CENTERS OF WASHINGTON INC p 857
20900 Cooley Rd 97701
Tel (541) 447-4136 *SIC* 5531

LES SCHWAB WAREHOUSE CENTER INC p 857
20900 Cooley Rd 97701
Tel (541) 447-4136 *SIC* 5014 7534 5531

ST CHARLES HEALTH SYSTEM INC p 1365
2500 Ne Neff Rd 97701
Tel (541) 382-4321 *SIC* 8062 8011

BOARDMAN, OR

CALBEE NORTH AMERICA LLC p 238
72600 Lewis & Clark Dr 97818
Tel (541) 481-6550 *SIC* 5145

COLUMBIA RIVER PROCESSING INC p 341
79588 Rippee Rd 97818
Tel (541) 481-3770 *SIC* 2022

BORING, OR

INTERNATIONAL GARDEN PRODUCTS INC p 755
30590 Se Kelso Rd 97009
Tel (503) 663-1698 *SIC* 0181

J FRANK SCHMIDT & SON CO p 771
9500 Se 327th Ave 97009
Tel (503) 663-4128 *SIC* 0783 2875

VANPORT MANUFACTURING INC p 1544
28590 Se Wally Rd 97009
Tel (503) 663-4447 *SIC* 2421 5099

CANBY, OR

WILLAMETTE EGG FARMS LLC p 1609
31348 S Highway 170 97013
Tel (503) 651-0000 *SIC* 5144

WILSON CONSTRUCTION CO p 1613
1190 Nw 3rd Ave 97013
Tel (503) 263-6882 *SIC* 1623

CARLTON, OR

LAUGHLIN-CARTRELL INC p 847
12850 Ne Hendricks Rd 97111
Tel (503) 852-7151 *SIC* 5191

CLACKAMAS, OR

DULCICH INC p 460
16797 Se 130th Ave 97015
Tel (503) 226-2200 *SIC* 5146 2092

INTERNATIONAL BUILDING MATERIALS LLC p 754
14421 Se 98th Ct 97015
Tel (503) 650-9663 *SIC* 5031

PACIFIC SEA FOOD CO INC p 1106
16797 Se 130th Ave 97015
Tel (503) 905-4500 *SIC* 5146 5142

■ PECO INC p 1127
11241 Se Highway 212 97015
Tel (503) 233-6401
SIC 3089 3822 3364 3363

STRUCTURED COMMUNICATION SYSTEMS INC p 1394
12901 Se 97th Ave Ste 400 97015
Tel (503) 513-9979 *SIC* 7373 5045

VIGOR WORKS LLC p 1556
9700 Se Lawnfield Rd 97015
Tel (503) 653-6300 *SIC* 3441

■ WARN INDUSTRIES INC p 1575
12900 Se Capps Rd 97015
Tel (503) 722-1200 *SIC* 3714 3531

COOS BAY, OR

BAY AREA HEALTH DISTRICT p 160
1775 Thompson Rd 97420
Tel (541) 269-8111 *SIC* 8062 8082

CORVALLIS, OR

CORVALLIS CLINIC P C p 373
3680 Nw Samaritan Dr 97330
Tel (541) 754-1150 *SIC* 8011 5912

GOOD SAMARITAN HOSPITAL CORVALLIS p 623
3600 Nw Samaritan Dr 97330
Tel (541) 757-5111 *SIC* 8062

INTERCOMMUNITY HEALTH PLANS INC p 752
3600 Nw Samaritan Dr 97330
Tel (541) 757-5111 *SIC* 8099

OREGON STATE UNIVERSITY p 1094
308 Kerr Adm Bldg 97331
Tel (541) 737-1000 *SIC* 8221

OREGON STATE UNIVERSITY FOUNDATION INC p 1094
850 Sw 35th St 97333
Tel (541) 737-4218 *SIC* 6732

OREGON UNIVERSITY SYSTEM p 1094
P.O. Box 488 97339
Tel (541) 737-0827 *SIC* 8221

SAMARITAN HEALTH SERVICES p 1274
990 Nw Circle Blvd # 201 97330
Tel (541) 768-4773 *SIC* 8099

SAMARITAN HEALTH SERVICES INC p 1274
3600 Nw Samaritan Dr 97330
Tel (541) 757-5111 *SIC* 8741 8062

STAHLBUSH ISLAND FARMS INC p 1374
3122 Se Stahlbush Is 97333
Tel (541) 753-8942 *SIC* 2037 0161

COTTAGE GROVE, OR

COAST FORK NURSING CENTER INC p 331
515 Grant Ave 97424
Tel (541) 942-5528 *SIC* 8051

DALLAS, OR

MEDURI FARMS INC p 939
12375 Smithfield Rd 97338
Tel (503) 623-0308 *SIC* 2035

DILLARD, OR

RLC INDUSTRIES CO p 1239
10599 Old Hwy 99 S 97432
Tel (541) 679-3311 *SIC* 2493 2436 2421

DUFUR, OR

AZURE FARMS INC p 141
79709 Dufur Valley Rd 97021
Tel (971) 200-8350 *SIC* 5149 0723 2099

EUGENE, OR

BARTELS PACKING INC p 157
706 Oscar St 97402
Tel (541) 344-4177 *SIC* 2011

BI-MART ACQUISITION CORP p 180
220 Seneca Rd 97402
Tel (541) 344-0681 *SIC* 5912 5399

BI-MART CORP p 180
220 S Seneca Rd 97402
Tel (541) 344-0681 *SIC* 5399

CITY OF EUGENE p 314
99 W 10th Ave Ste 310 97401
Tel (541) 682-5010 *SIC* 9111

COUNTY OF LANE p 379
125 E 8th Ave 97401
Tel (541) 682-4203 *SIC* 9111

DATALOGIC ADC INC p 414
959 Terry St 97402
Tel (541) 683-5700 *SIC* 3577

DATALOGIC HOLDINGS INC p 414
959 Terry St 97402
Tel (541) 683-5700 *SIC* 3577

EMERGING ACQUISITIONS LLC p 492
3592 W 5th Ave 97402
Tel (541) 485-0999 *SIC* 3535

EUGENE SCHOOL DISTRICT 4J p 512
200 N Monroe St 97402
Tel (541) 790-7600 *SIC* 8211

EUGENE WATER & ELECTRIC BOARD p 512
500 E 4th Ave 97401
Tel (541) 685-7000 *SIC* 4931 9641

FARWEST STEEL CORP p 530
2000 Henderson Ave 97403
Tel (541) 686-2000 *SIC* 5051

INDUSTRIAL FINISHES & SYSTEMS INC p 740
3455 W 1st Ave 97402
Tel (541) 485-1503 *SIC* 5085 5198

JERRYS BUILDING MATERIALS INC p 783
2600 Highway 99 N 97402
Tel (541) 689-1911 *SIC* 5211

KENDALL AUTOMOTIVE GROUP INC p 810
1400 Executive Pkwy # 400 97401
Tel (541) 335-4000 *SIC* 5511

KEZI INC p 816
2975 Chad Dr 97408
Tel (541) 485-5611 *SIC* 4833 6512 4813

LANE COMMUNITY COLLEGE p 843
4000 E 30th Ave 97405
Tel (541) 463-3000 *SIC* 8222

MAJOR EAGLE INC p 899
2350 W Broadway 97402
Tel (541) 345-8421
SIC 5181 5141 5194 5142

MARKET OF CHOICE INC p 908
2580 Willakenzie Rd 97401
Tel (541) 345-3349 *SIC* 5411

MCDONALD WHOLESALE CO p 927
2350 W Broadway 97402
Tel (541) 345-8421 *SIC* 5141

MURPHY CO p 1001
2350 Prairie Rd 97402
Tel (541) 461-4545 *SIC* 2435 2436

ORGANICALLY GROWN CO p 1094
1800 Prairie Rd Ste B 97402
Tel (541) 689-5320 *SIC* 5148

PAPE GROUP INC p 1112
355 Goodpasture Island Rd # 300 97401
Tel (541) 334-3400
SIC 5084 5082 7699 6141 5599 4581

PAPE MACHINERY INC p 1112
355 Goodpasture Island Rd 97401
Tel (541) 683-5073 *SIC* 5082

PAPE MATERIAL HANDLING INC p 1112
355 Goodpasture Island Rd 97401
Tel (541) 683-5073 *SIC* 5084

PMD RESTAURANTS LLC p 1157
2117 Elkhorn Dr 97408
Tel (541) 684-7655 *SIC* 5812

SENECA SAWMILL CO p 1303
90201 Highway 99 N 97402
Tel (541) 689-1011 *SIC* 2421

SHAMROCK BUILDING MATERIALS INC p 1311
4725 Village Plaza Loop # 201 97401
Tel (877) 426-2341 *SIC* 5031 5051

UNIVERSITY OF OREGON p 1524
1585 E 13th Ave 97403
Tel (541) 346-1000 *SIC* 8221

UNIVERSITY OF OREGON FOUNDATION p 1524
1720 E 13th Ave Ste 410 97403
Tel (541) 302-0300 *SIC* 8699

WESTERN PNEUMATICS INC p 1599
110 N Seneca Rd 97402
Tel (541) 461-2600 *SIC* 3535 3553 5099

WILDISH LAND CO p 1609
3600 Wildish Ln 97408
Tel (541) 485-1700 *SIC* 1611 1542

WILLAMETTE VALLEY CO p 1609
1075 Arrowsmith St 97402
Tel (541) 484-9621
SIC 5085 2851 2891 5169

FAIRVIEW, OR

CASCADE CORP p 262
2201 Ne 201st Ave 97024
Tel (503) 669-6300 *SIC* 3537 3531

LEATHERS ENTERPRISES INC p 850
255 Depot St 97024
Tel (503) 661-1244 *SIC* 5541 6519

REYNOLDS SCHOOL DISTRICT 7 (INC) p 1231
1204 Ne 201st Ave 97024
Tel (503) 492-4921 *SIC* 8211

FOREST GROVE, OR

PACIFIC UNIVERSITY p 1106
2043 College Way 97116
Tel (503) 357-6151 *SIC* 8221

TUALITY HOME HEALTH INC p 1490
1809 Maple St 97116
Tel (503) 357-2737 *SIC* 8082

GLENDALE, OR

SWANSON GROUP INC p 1411
2695 Glendale Valley Rd 97442
Tel (541) 832-1121 *SIC* 2421 2436 4522

SWANSON GROUP MFG LLC p 1411
2695 Glendale Valley Rd 97442
Tel (541) 832-1121 *SIC* 2435

GRANTS PASS, OR

FIRE MOUNTAIN GEMS & BEADS INC p 543
1 Fire Mountain Way 97526
Tel (541) 956-7700 *SIC* 5094

THREE RIVERS COMMUNITY HOSPITAL AND HEALTH CENTER p 1450
500 Sw Ramsey Ave 97527
Tel (541) 472-7000 *SIC* 8062

GRESHAM, OR

GRESHAM-BARLOW SCHOOL DISTRICT p 639
1331 Nw Eastman Pkwy 97030
Tel (503) 618-2470 *SIC* 8211

LEGACY MOUNT HOOD MEDICAL CENTER p 852
24800 Se Stark St 97030
Tel (503) 674-1122 *SIC* 8062 5912

MT HOOD COMMUNITY COLLEGE DISTRICT FOUNDATION INC p 997
26000 Se Stark St 97030
Tel (503) 491-6422 *SIC* 8222 8221

HALSEY, OR

DLF PICKSEED USA INC p 445
175 W H St 97348
Tel (541) 369-2251 *SIC* 5191

SMITH SEED SERVICES LLC p 1333
26890 Powerline Rd 97348
Tel (541) 369-2831 *SIC* 5191

HARRISBURG, OR

S B INC p 1262
32921 Diamond Hill Dr 97446
Tel (541) 995-7751 *SIC* 4213 4731

HERMISTON, OR

HERMISTON FOODS INC p 687
2250 S Highway 395 97838
Tel (541) 567-8448 *SIC* 2037

■ **MARLETTE HOMES** p 909
400 W Elm Ave 97838
Tel (541) 567-5546 *SIC* 3999

RIVER POINT FARMS LLC p 1237
115 W Hermiston Ave # 240 97838
Tel (541) 567-4781 *SIC* 0723

UMATILLA ELECTRIC COOPERATIVE p 1501
750 W Elm Ave 97838
Tel (541) 567-6414 *SIC* 4911

HILLSBORO, OR

CLEAN WATER SERVICES p 324
2550 Sw Hillsboro Hwy 97123
Tel (503) 681-3600 *SIC* 4952

COUNTY OF WASHINGTON p 382
155 N 1st Ave Ste 300 97124
Tel (503) 846-8685 *SIC* 9111

EPSON PORTLAND INC p 506
3950 Nw Aloclek Pl 97124
Tel (503) 645-1118 *SIC* 3577

FARMERS INSURANCE p 529
23175 Nw Bennett St 97124
Tel (503) 372-2000 *SIC* 6411

■ **FEI CO** p 537
5350 Ne Dawson Creek Dr 97124
Tel (503) 726-7500 *SIC* 3826

HILLSBORO SCHOOL DISTRICT 1J p 694
3083 Ne 49th Pl 97124
Tel (503) 640-8403 *SIC* 8211

MACKENZIE MOTOR CO p 892
4151 Se Tualatin Vly Hwy 97123
Tel (503) 693-1133 *SIC* 5511 5521

MORGAN INDUSTRIAL INC p 988
23810 Nw Huffman St 97124
Tel (503) 647-7474 *SIC* 1796 4213

PARR LUMBER CO p 1117
5630 Nw Century Blvd 97124
Tel (503) 614-2500
SIC 5031 5211 5072 5251

▲ **RADISYS CORP** p 1204
5435 Ne Dawson Creek Dr 97124
Tel (503) 615-1100 *SIC* 3825 7374 7372

SOLARWORLD AMERICAS INC p 1338
25300 Nw Evergreen Rd 97124
Tel (503) 844-3400 *SIC* 3674

SOLARWORLD INDUSTRIES AMERICA LP p 1338
25300 Nw Evergreen Rd 97124
Tel (805) 482-6800 *SIC* 3674

STANCORP MORTGAGE INVESTORS LLC p 1375
19225 Nw Tanasbourne Dr 97124
Tel (503) 321-7785 *SIC* 6311

■ **TRIQUINT SALES & DESIGN INC** p 1482
2300 Ne Brookwood Pkwy 97124
Tel (503) 615-9000 *SIC* 3825

TUALITY HEALTHCARE p 1490
335 Se 8th Ave 97123
Tel (503) 681-1111 *SIC* 8062

TUALITY HEALTHCARE FOUNDATION INC p 1490
335 Se 8th Ave 97123
Tel (503) 681-1850
SIC 8082 7374 6512 5999 7359

TUALITY HOSPITAL INC p 1490
335 Se 8th Ave 97123
Tel (503) 681-1111 *SIC* 8062

WILLAMETTE DENTAL MANAGEMENT CORP p 1609
6950 Ne Campus Way 97124
Tel (503) 952-2000 *SIC* 8021

JUNCTION CITY, OR

GUARANTY RV INC p 644
20 Highway 99 S 97448
Tel (541) 998-2333 *SIC* 5561 5511

KLAMATH FALLS, OR

ED STAUB & SONS PETROLEUM INC p 476
1301 Esplanade Ave 97601
Tel (541) 887-8900 *SIC* 5172 5541 5411

KLAMATH FALLS INTERCOMMUNITY HOSPITAL AUTHORITY p 823
2865 Daggett Ave 97601
Tel (541) 883-6150 *SIC* 6162

MERLE WEST MEDICAL CENTER p 950
2865 Daggett Ave 97601
Tel (541) 882-6311 *SIC* 5912

SKY LAKES MEDICAL CENTER FOUNDATION INC p 1330
2865 Daggett Ave 97601
Tel (541) 882-6311 *SIC* 8062

LA GRANDE, OR

CERTIFIED PERSONNEL SERVICE AGENCY INC p 284
10201 N Mcalister Rd 97850
Tel (541) 963-6678 *SIC* 7361

NORTHWOOD INVESTMENTS CORP p 1061
59948 Downs Rd 97850
Tel (541) 962-6274 *SIC* 3792

NORTHWOOD MANUFACTURING INC p 1061
59948 Downs Rd 97850
Tel (541) 962-6274 *SIC* 3792

LAKE OSWEGO, OR

BIOTRONIK INC p 184
6024 Jean Rd Ste C8 97035
Tel (503) 635-3594 *SIC* 5047

▲ **GREENBRIER COMPANIES INC** p 637
1 Centerpointe Dr Ste 200 97035
Tel (503) 684-7000 *SIC* 3743 4789

■ **GUNDERSON RAIL SERVICES LLC** p 647
1 Centerpointe Dr Ste 200 97035
Tel (503) 684-7000 *SIC* 3743

HARVEST MANAGEMENT SUB LLC p 666
5885 Meadows Rd Ste 500 97035
Tel (503) 370-7070 *SIC* 8361

LUMBER PRODUCTS AN OREGON CORP p 885
5200 Meadows Rd Ste 150 97035
Tel (503) 692-3322 *SIC* 5031

NAVEX GLOBAL INC p 1020
5500 Meadows Rd Ste 500 97035
Tel (971) 250-4100 *SIC* 8748

NESS HOLDING CO p 1026
4550 Kruse Way Ste 350 97035
Tel (503) 240-0400 *SIC* 5141

LEBANON, OR

ENTEK INTERNATIONAL LLC p 501
250 Hansard Ave 97355
Tel (541) 259-3901 *SIC* 3089

MID-VALLEY HEALTHCARE INC p 963
525 N Santiam Hwy 97355
Tel (541) 258-2101
SIC 8062 8051 8011 8082

MADRAS, OR

BRIGHT WOOD CORP p 213
335 Nw Hess St 97741
Tel (541) 475-2234 *SIC* 2431

MCMINNVILLE, OR

■ **CASCADE STEEL ROLLING MILLS INC** p 262
3200 Ne Highway 99w 97128
Tel (503) 472-4181 *SIC* 3312

EVERGREEN AVIATION GROUND LOGISTICS ENTERPRISE INC p 514
3850 Three Mile Ln 97128
Tel (503) 472-9361 *SIC* 4581

EVERGREEN HOLDINGS INC p 514
3850 Ne Three Mile Ln 97128
Tel (503) 472-0011 *SIC* 4522 4513 4215

EVERGREEN INTERNATIONAL AVIATION INC p 514
3850 Ne Three Mile Ln 97128
Tel (503) 472-0011 *SIC* 4522 4513 4215

OREGON MUTUAL INSURANCE CO INC p 1093
400 Ne Baker St 97128
Tel (503) 472-2141 *SIC* 6331

WILLAMETTE VALLEY MEDICAL CENTER p 1610
2700 Se Stratus Ave 97128
Tel (503) 472-6131 *SIC* 8062

YAMHILL COUNTY CARE ORGANIZATION INC p 1634
807 Ne 3rd St 97128
Tel (503) 434-7339 *SIC* 8011

MEDFORD, OR

ASANTE p 115
2825 E Barnett Rd 97504
Tel (541) 789-7000 *SIC* 8069

ASANTE ROGUE REGIONAL MEDICAL CENTER p 115
2825 E Barnett Rd 97504
Tel (541) 608-4900 *SIC* 8062

C & K MARKET INC p 231
850 Ohare Pkwy Ste 100 97504
Tel (541) 469-3113 *SIC* 5411

COUNTY OF JACKSON p 378
10 S Oakdale Ave 97501
Tel (541) 774-6001 *SIC* 9111

■ **HARRY & DAVID HOLDINGS INC** p 664
2500 S Pacific Hwy 97501
Tel (541) 864-2362 *SIC* 5961 1541

■ **HARRY AND DAVID LLC** p 664
2500 S Pacific Hwy 97501
Tel (541) 864-2500 *SIC* 5961 5947

INTRANSIT INC p 760
3525 Excel Dr 97504
Tel (541) 773-3993 *SIC* 4731

▲ **LITHIA MOTORS INC** p 870
150 N Bartlett St 97501
Tel (541) 776-6401
SIC 5511 5531 5013 7539

MEDFORD SCHOOL DISTRICT 549C p 935
815 S Oakdale Ave 97501
Tel (541) 842-3621 *SIC* 8211

NAUMES INC p 1019
2 W Barnett St 97501
Tel (541) 772-6268 *SIC* 0175 0723 4222

PACIFIC RETIREMENT SERVICES INC p 1105
1 W Main St Ste 303 97501
Tel (541) 857-7777 *SIC* 8741 8051

PROVIDENCE MEDFORD MEDICAL CENTER p 1186
1111 Crater Lake Ave 97504
Tel (541) 732-5000 *SIC* 8322

THUNDERBIRD SHERMS MARKET INC p 1451
730 S Grape St 97501
Tel (541) 857-0850 *SIC* 5411

MILWAUKIE, OR

ALPINE FOOD DISTRIBUTING INC p 60
2400 Se Mailwell Dr 97222
Tel (503) 905-5201 *SIC* 5142 5149

NORTH CLACKAMAS SCHOOLS p 1052
12400 Se Freeman Way # 100 97222
Tel (503) 353-6001 *SIC* 8211

OECO HOLDINGS LLC p 1075
4607 Se International Way 97222
Tel (503) 659-5999 *SIC* 3679 5065

OECO LLC p 1075
4607 Se International Way 97222
Tel (503) 659-5999
SIC 3679 5065 4911 3621 3694

PROVIDENCE MILWAUKIE HOSPITAL INC p 1186
10150 Se 32nd Ave 97222
Tel (503) 513-8300 *SIC* 8062

MOUNT ANGEL, OR

WILCO FARMERS p 1608
200 Industrial Way Ne 97362
Tel (503) 845-6122 *SIC* 5541

NEWBERG, OR

A-DEC DENTAL UK LTD p 7
2601 Crestview Dr 97132
Tel (503) 538-9471 *SIC* 5047

A-DEC INC p 7
2601 Crestview Dr 97132
Tel (503) 538-9471 *SIC* 3843

CHEHALEM HEALTH & REHAB CENTER p 293
1900 Fulton St 97132
Tel (503) 538-2108 *SIC* 8099

GEORGE FOX UNIVERSITY p 606
414 N Meridian St 97132
Tel (503) 538-8383 *SIC* 8221

NEWPORT, OR

CENTRAL LINCOLN PEOPLES UTILITY DISTRICT JATC INC p 279
2129 N Coast Hwy 97365
Tel (541) 265-3211 *SIC* 4911

OREGON CITY, OR

CLACKAMAS COMMUNITY COLLEGE FOUNDATION p 321
19600 Molalla Ave 97045
Tel (503) 594-6100 *SIC* 8222

COUNTY OF CLACKAMAS p 377
2051 Kaen Rd 97045
Tel (503) 655-8459 *SIC* 9199

OREGON CITY SCHOOL DISTRICT 62 p 1093
1417 12th St 97045
Tel (503) 785-8000 *SIC* 8211

WILLAMETT FALLS HOSPITAL p 1609
1500 Division St 97045
Tel (503) 650-6765 *SIC* 8062

PORTLAND, OR

A CARING DOCTOR (TEXAS) PC p 5
8000 Ne Tillamook St 97213
Tel (503) 922-5000 *SIC* 0742 5047

A CARING DOCTOR MINNESOTA PA p 5
8000 Ne Tillamook St 97213
Tel (503) 922-5000 *SIC* 0742 5047

AAS HOLDING CO p 8
2401 Ne Argyle St 97211
Tel (503) 284-3314 *SIC* 5147 5142 5141

ACME CONSTRUCTION SUPPLY CO INC p 17
330 Se Salmon St 97214
Tel (503) 239-5230 *SIC* 5072

ADIDAS AMERICA INC p 22
5055 N Greeley Ave 97217
Tel (971) 234-2300
SIC 5139 5136 5137 3021 2339

ADIDAS NORTH AMERICA INC p 22
5055 N Greeley Ave 97217
Tel (971) 234-2300 *SIC* 2329

AJINOMOTO NORTH AMERICA HOLDINGS INC p 41
7124 N Marine Dr 97203
Tel (503) 505-5783
SIC 5142 6719 2038 2037

ALBERTINA KERR CENTERS p 46
424 Ne 22nd Ave 97232
Tel (503) 239-8101 *SIC* 8052 8361 8093

ANDERSEN CONSTRUCTION CO p 89
6712 N Cutter Cir 97217
Tel (503) 283-6712 *SIC* 1542 1541

■ AVANGRID RENEWABLES HOLDINGS INC p 136
1125 Nw Couch St Ste 700 97209
Tel (503) 796-7000 *SIC* 4932 4931

■ AVANGRID RENEWABLES LLC p 136
1125 Nw Couch St Ste 700 97209
Tel (503) 796-7179 *SIC* 4932 4931

■ AVB INC p 136
5209 Se International Way 97222
Tel (503) 335-8077 *SIC* 2051 2052

■ BENSON INDUSTRIES INC p 173
1650 Nw Naito Pkwy # 250 97209
Tel (503) 226-7611
SIC 5031 1793 3231 3211

BLOUNT INC p 190
4909 Se International Way 97222
Tel (503) 653-8881
SIC 3546 3568 7699 3495

BLOUNT INTERNATIONAL INC p 190
4909 Se International Way 97222
Tel (503) 653-8881 *SIC* 3531 3523

■ BONNEVILLE POWER ADMINISTRATION p 200
905 Ne 11th Ave 97232
Tel (503) 230-3000 *SIC* 9631

BOYD COFFEE CO p 205
19730 Ne Sandy Blvd 97230
Tel (503) 666-4545
SIC 2095 5499 5141 3634 2099

CAMBIA HEALTH SOLUTIONS INC p 243
100 Sw Market St 97201
Tel (503) 225-5336 *SIC* 6321 6411 6324

CAREOREGON INC p 255
315 Sw 5th Ave Ste 900 97204
Tel (503) 416-4100 *SIC* 8621

CARSON OIL CO INC p 261
3125 Nw 35th Ave 97210
Tel (503) 829-5441 *SIC* 5172

CASCADIA BEHAVIORAL HEALTHCARE INC p 263
847 Ne 19th Ave Ste 100 97232
Tel (503) 238-0769
SIC 8322 8093 8063 8361

CDC OREGON INC p 270
3601 Nw Yeon Ave 97210
Tel (503) 289-9600 *SIC* 5182 5181 5149

CH2M HILL INDUSTRIAL DESIGN & CONSTRUCTION INC p 286
2020 Sw 4th Ave Fl 3 97201
Tel (503) 224-6040
SIC 8711 8712 8741 7699

CHILDRENS CREATIVE LEARNING CENTERS LLC p 299
650 Ne Holladay St # 1400 97232
Tel (503) 872-1300 *SIC* 8351

CITY OF PORTLAND p 317
1221 Sw 4th Ave Rm 340 97204
Tel (503) 823-4120 *SIC* 9111

■ COFFEE BEAN INTERNATIONAL INC p 334
9120 Ne Alderwood Rd 97220
Tel (503) 227-4490 *SIC* 5149

COHO DISTRIBUTING LLC p 335
6840 N Cutter Cir 97217
Tel (503) 289-9600 *SIC* 5182

COLUMBIA FOREST PRODUCTS CORP p 340
222 Sw Columbia St # 610 97201
Tel (503) 224-5300 *SIC* 2435

COLUMBIA GRAIN INC p 340
1300 Sw 5th Ave Ste 2929 97201
Tel (503) 224-8624 *SIC* 5153

COLUMBIA HOUSING/PNC INSTITUTIONAL FUND XX LIMITED PARTNERSHIP p 341
121 Sw Morrison St # 1300 97204
Tel (503) 808-1300 *SIC* 6099

COLUMBIA PLYWOOD CORP p 341
222 Sw Columbia St # 1575 97201
Tel (503) 224-5300 *SIC* 2435

▲ COLUMBIA SPORTSWEAR CO p 341
14375 Nw Science Park Dr 97229
Tel (503) 985-4000
SIC 2329 2339 3021 2353 3949

■ COLUMBIA SPORTSWEAR USA CORP p 341
14375 Nw Science Park Dr 97229
Tel (503) 985-4000
SIC 5137 5136 2329 2339 3021 2353

COLUMBIA STEEL CASTING CO INC p 342
10425 N Bloss Ave 97203
Tel (503) 286-0685 *SIC* 3325

CONSUMER CELLULAR INC p 361
12447 Sw 69th Ave 97223
Tel (503) 675-8988 *SIC* 4812

COUNTY OF MULTNOMAH p 380
501 Se Hawthorne Blvd # 100 97214
Tel (503) 988-3511 *SIC* 9111

▲ CRAFT BREW ALLIANCE INC p 388
929 N Russell St 97227
Tel (503) 331-7270 *SIC* 2082

CROSS POINT NW LLC p 393
6803 Se Jhnson Creek Blvd 97206
Tel (503) 594-2800 *SIC* 5012

DAIMLER TRUCKS NORTH AMERICA LLC p 408
4747 N Channel Ave 97217
Tel (503) 745-8011 *SIC* 3711 4789

DAIMLER TRUCKS REMARKETING CORP p 408
4747 N Channel Ave 97217
Tel (503) 745-8000 *SIC* 6153

DAVID DOUGLAS SCHOOL DISTRICT p 415
11300 Ne Halsey St # 100 97220
Tel (503) 252-2900 *SIC* 8211

DAVID EVANS AND ASSOCIATES INC p 415
2100 Sw River Pkwy 97201
Tel (503) 223-6663 *SIC* 8711 8713 8741

DEPAUL INDUSTRIES p 430
4950 Ne Martin Luther Ki 97211
Tel (503) 281-1289 *SIC* 7361 8331

DOLAN NORTHWEST LLC p 447
1919 Nw 19th Ave 97209
Tel (503) 221-1919 *SIC* 5063 5719

DON RASMUSSEN CO p 450
720 Ne Grand Ave 97232
Tel (503) 230-7700 *SIC* 5511

DUCK DELIVERY PRODUCE INC p 459
8448 Ne 33rd Dr Ste 120 97211
Tel (503) 288-9380 *SIC* 5148 4212

EC CO p 474
2121 Nw Thurman St 97210
Tel (503) 224-3511
SIC 1731 7694 5063 5084

▲ ELECTRO SCIENTIFIC INDUSTRIES INC p 485
13900 Nw Science Park Dr 97229
Tel (503) 641-4141 *SIC* 3826

ELMERS RESTAURANTS INC p 489
8338 Ne Alderwood Rd 97220
Tel (503) 252-1485 *SIC* 6794 5812

ENDEAVOUR CAPITAL FUND LIMITED PARTNERSHIP p 496
920 Sw 6th Ave Ste 1400 97204
Tel (503) 223-2721 *SIC* 4213 4731 6799

ENERGY TRUST OF OREGON INC p 498
421 Sw Oak St Ste 300 97204
Tel (866) 368-7878 *SIC* 8699

ERICKSON INC p 507
5550 Sw Mcdam Ave Ste 200 97239
Tel (503) 505-5800
SIC 7363 4581 3721 7359 5599 3728

ESCO CORP p 509
2141 Nw 25th Ave 97210
Tel (360) 690-0074
SIC 3535 3545 3325 3531

FAMILYCARE INC p 527
825 Ne Multnomah St # 300 97232
Tel (503) 222-2880 *SIC* 8082

FAMILYCARE MEDICAL CLINICS INC p 527
825 Ne Multnomah St # 300 97232
Tel (503) 222-3205 *SIC* 6411

FCTG HOLDINGS INC p 533
10250 Sw Greenburg Rd # 200 97223
Tel (503) 246-8500 *SIC* 5031

FOREST CITY TRADING GROUP LLC p 566
10250 Sw Greenburg Rd # 200 97223
Tel (503) 246-8500 *SIC* 5031

FORTIS CONSTRUCTION INC p 569
1705 Sw Taylor St Ste 200 97205
Tel (503) 459-4477 *SIC* 1542 1611

■ FRED MEYER INC p 576
3800 Se 22nd Ave 97202
Tel (503) 232-8844
SIC 5411 5311 5912 5211 5731 5944

■ FRED MEYER JEWELERS INC p 576
3800 Se 22nd Ave 97202
Tel (503) 232-8844 *SIC* 5944

■ FRED MEYER STORES INC p 576
3800 Se 22nd Ave 97202
Tel (503) 232-8844
SIC 5211 5411 5912 5731 5944

FRONTIER MANAGEMENT LLC p 581
7420 Sw Bridgeprt Rd 10 Ste 105 97224
Tel (503) 443-1818 *SIC* 8741

■ GAS CONNECTION LLC p 593
9801 Se 82nd Ave 97086
Tel (503) 771-1750 *SIC* 5984 5722

GOODWILL INDUSTRIES OF COLUMBIA WILLAMETTE p 624
1943 Se 6th Ave 97214
Tel (503) 238-6100 *SIC* 8331

■ GRAPHIC ARTS CENTER INC p 631
2000 Nw Wilson St 97209
Tel (503) 224-7777 *SIC* 2752

GREAT NORTHERN STAFF ADMINISTRATORS LLC p 634
6915 Sw Mcdam Ave Ste 245 97219
Tel (503) 972-1944 *SIC* 6411

GRIFFITH RUBBER MILLS p 640
2625 Nw Indul St 97210
Tel (503) 226-6971 *SIC* 3061 3069

■ GUNDERSON LLC p 647
4350 Nw Front Ave 97210
Tel (503) 972-5700 *SIC* 3743

HAMPTON INVESTMENT CO p 656
9600 Sw Barnes Rd Ste 200 97225
Tel (503) 297-7691 *SIC* 5031 2435 2426

HAMPTON LUMBER MILLS INC p 656
9600 Sw Barnes Rd Ste 200 97225
Tel (503) 297-7691 *SIC* 2421

HAMPTON LUMBER SALES CO p 656
9600 Sw Barnes Rd Ste 200 97225
Tel (503) 297-7691 *SIC* 5031 2421 7389

HAMPTON RESOURCES INC p 656
9600 Sw Barnes Rd Ste 200 97225
Tel (503) 297-7691 *SIC* 5031 2421 0811

HANNA ANDERSSON LLC p 658
608 Ne 19th Ave 97232
Tel (503) 242-0920 *SIC* 5641 5621 5719

HARDER MECHANICAL CONTRACTORS INC p 660
2148 Ne Mlk Blvd 97212
Tel (503) 281-1112 *SIC* 1711 7389

HARRIS SOUP CO p 664
17711 Ne Riverside Pkwy 97230
Tel (503) 257-7687 *SIC* 2092 2099

HARRISON ELECTRICAL WORKERS TRUSTS p 664
1220 Sw Morrison St # 300 97205
Tel (503) 224-0048 *SIC* 6733

HEALTH SHARE OF OREGON p 676
2121 Sw Broadway Ste 200 97201
Tel (503) 416-2172 *SIC* 8099

HERBERT MALARKEY ROOFING CO p 685
3131 N Columbia Blvd 97217
Tel (503) 283-1191 *SIC* 2952

HOFFMAN CORP p 699
805 Sw Broadway Ste 2100 97205
Tel (503) 221-8811
SIC 8741 1541 1542 1623 1629

IDC CONSTRUCTION MANAGEMENT INC p 728
2020 Sw 4th Ave Ste 300 97201
Tel (503) 224-6040 *SIC* 8741

JOHNSTONE SUPPLY INC p 791
11632 Ne Ainsworth Cir 97220
Tel (503) 256-3663
SIC 5075 5085 5063 5064

JUBITZ CORP p 796
33 Ne Middlefield Rd 97211
Tel (503) 283-1111
SIC 5541 4789 5014 7011

KAISER FOUNDATION HEALTH PLAN OF NORTHWEST p 800
500 Ne Multnomah St # 100 97232
Tel (503) 813-2440 *SIC* 6324

■ KC DISTANCE LEARNING INC p 806
830 Ne Holladay St # 100 97232
Tel (503) 731-5427 *SIC* 8299

KEEN INC p 807
515 Nw 13th Ave 97209
Tel (503) 402-1520 *SIC* 5139 5661

KENNEDY WIEDEN INC p 811
224 Nw 13th Ave 97209
Tel (503) 937-7000 *SIC* 7311

KERR PACIFIC CORP p 813
1211 Sw 6th Ave 97204
Tel (503) 221-1301 *SIC* 5141 2041

KINDERCARE EDUCATION LLC p 819
650 Ne Holladay St # 1400 97232
Tel (503) 872-1300 *SIC* 8299

KINDERCARE LEARNING CENTERS LLC p 819
650 Ne Holladay St # 1400 97232
Tel (503) 872-1300 *SIC* 8351

LACROSSE FOOTWEAR INC p 837
17634 Ne Airport Way 97230
Tel (503) 262-0110 *SIC* 3021

▲ LATTICE SEMICONDUCTOR CORP p 846
111 Sw 5th Ave Ste 700 97204
Tel (503) 268-8000 *SIC* 3674

LEATHERMAN TOOL GROUP INC p 850
12106 Ne Ainsworth Cir 97220
Tel (503) 253-7826 *SIC* 3421

LEGACY EMANUEL HOSPITAL & HEALTH CENTER p 852
2801 N Gantenbein Ave 97227
Tel (503) 413-2200 *SIC* 8062

LEGACY GOOD SAMARITAN HOSPITAL AND MEDICAL CENTER p 852
1015 Nw 22nd Ave 97210
Tel (503) 413-7711 *SIC* 8069

LEGACY HEALTH p 852
1919 Nw Lovejoy St 97209
Tel (503) 415-5600 *SIC* 8011

LEGACY VISITING NURSE ASSOCIATION p 852
815 Ne Davis St 97232
Tel (503) 220-1000 *SIC* 8399 5999 8082

LEWIS & CLARK COLLEGE p 858
0615 Sw Palatine Hill Rd 97219
Tel (503) 768-7000 *SIC* 8221

LIBERTY NORTHWEST INSURANCE CORP p 862
650 Ne Holladay St 97232
Tel (503) 239-5800 *SIC* 6331

LIFEWISE HEALTH PLAN OF OREGON p 865
2020 Sw 4th Ave Ste 1000 97201
Tel (503) 295-6707 *SIC* 6321

MARKET INDUSTRIES LTD p 908
110 N Marine Dr 97217
Tel (503) 283-2405 *SIC* 4731 4213

MARKET TRANSPORT LTD p 908
110 N Marine Dr 97217
Tel (503) 283-3279 *SIC* 4213

MARQUIS COMPANIES I INC p 910
725 Se 202nd Ave 97233
Tel (503) 665-3118 *SIC* 8741

MCCALL OIL AND CHEMICAL CORP p 926
5480 Nw Front Ave 97210
Tel (503) 221-6400 *SIC* 5172

MCCORMICK & SCHMICK HOLDING CORP p 927
720 Sw Washington St # 550 97205
Tel (800) 552-6379 *SIC* 5812

MCMENAMINS INC p 932
430 N Killingsworth St 97217
Tel (503) 223-0109 *SIC* 5813 5812

MEDICAL MANAGEMENT INTERNATIONAL INC p 937
8000 Ne Tillamook St 97213
Tel (503) 922-5000 *SIC* 0742 5047

MERCY CORPS p 946
45 Sw Ankeny St 97204
Tel (503) 796-6800 *SIC* 8322

METRO METALS NORTHWEST INC p 955
5611 Ne Columbia Blvd 97218
Tel (503) 287-8861 *SIC* 5093

MILES MARINE INC p 969
5555 N Channel Ave 97217
Tel (503) 247-1777 *SIC* 3731

MILLER PAINT CO INC p 971
12812 Ne Whitaker Way 97230
Tel (503) 255-0190 *SIC* 2851 5231

MODA HEALTH PLAN INC p 980
601 Sw 2nd Ave 97204
Tel (503) 228-6554 *SIC* 6321

MOTOSPORT INC p 993
15353 Sw Sequoia Pkwy # 140 97224
Tel (503) 783-5600 *SIC* 5571

MULBERRY CHILDCARE CENTERS INC p 999
650 Ne Holladay St # 1400 97232
Tel (503) 872-1300 *SIC* 8351

NEW SEASONS MARKET LLC p 1033
1300 Se Stark St Ste 401 97214
Tel (503) 292-1987 *SIC* 5411

NMHG HOLDING CO p 1045
650 Ne Holladay St # 1600 97232
Tel (503) 721-6000 *SIC* 3537 5084

NORTH PACIFIC INSURANCE CO p 1053
1 Liberty Ctr 97232
Tel (503) 239-5800 *SIC* 6331

NORTHWEST EVALUATION ASSOCIATION p 1059
121 Nw Everett St 97209
Tel (503) 624-1951 *SIC* 8299 8748

▲ NORTHWEST NATURAL GAS CO p 1060
220 Nw 2nd Ave 97209
Tel (503) 226-4211 *SIC* 4924

NORTHWEST STAFFING RESOURCES INC p 1060
851 Sw 6th Ave Ste 300 97204
Tel (503) 323-9190 *SIC* 7363 7361

OIA GLOBAL LOGISTICS-SCM INC p 1078
2100 Sw Rver Pkwy Ste 800 97201
Tel (503) 736-5900 *SIC* 4731

■ ON ELECTRIC GROUP INC p 1086
1709 Se 3rd Ave 97214
Tel (503) 234-9900 *SIC* 1731 3613

ONPOINT COMMUNITY CREDIT UNION p 1088
2701 Nw Vaughn St Ste 800 97210
Tel (503) 228-8255 *SIC* 6062

OREGON COMMUNITY FOUNDATION p 1093
1221 Sw Ymhill St Ste 100 97205
Tel (503) 227-6846 *SIC* 8399 2741

OREGON DENTAL SERVICE p 1093
601 Sw 2nd Ave Ste 900 97204
Tel (503) 228-6554 *SIC* 6324

OREGON HEALTH & SCIENCE UNIVERSITY p 1093
3181 Sw Sam Jackson Pk Rd 97239
Tel (503) 494-8311 *SIC* 8221 8069

OREGON HEALTH & SCIENCE UNIVERSITY FOUNDATION INC p 1093
1121 Sw Salmon St Ste 100 97205
Tel (503) 228-1730
SIC 8399 6091 8733 6732

OREGON INTERNATIONAL AIR FREIGHT CO INC p 1093
2100 Sw Rver Pkwy Ste 800 97201
Tel (503) 736-5900 *SIC* 4731

OREGON METAL SLITTERS INC p 1093
7227 N Leadbetter Rd 97203
Tel (503) 286-0300 *SIC* 5051 7389

OREGONIAN PUBLISHING CO LLC p 1094
1500 Sw 1st Ave Ste 500 97201
Tel (503) 221-8327 *SIC* 2711

OSF INTERNATIONAL INC p 1096
0715 Sw Bancroft St 97239
Tel (503) 222-5375 *SIC* 5812 6794

OTAK INC p 1097
808 Sw 3rd Ave Ste 220 97204
Tel (503) 274-5445
SIC 0781 8712 8711 8713 8742 8999

P C NORTHWEST PERMANENTE p 1102
500 Ne Multnomah St # 100 97232
Tel (877) 313-3424 *SIC* 8082

PACIFIC NORTHWEST GENERATING COOPERATIVE p 1105
711 Ne Halsey St 97232
Tel (503) 288-1234 *SIC* 4911

■ PACIFICORP p 1106
825 Ne Multnomah St # 300 97232
Tel (503) 813-5645 *SIC* 4911

PAMPLIN COMMUNICATIONS CORP p 1110
6605 Se Lake Rd 97222
Tel (503) 546-5100 *SIC* 4899

PAPER PRODUCTS MARKETING (USA) INC p 1112
4380 Sw Mcdam Ave Ste 370 97239
Tel (503) 227-6615 *SIC* 5111 5113

■ PCC STRUCTURALS INC p 1123
4600 Se Harney Dr 97206
Tel (503) 777-3881
SIC 3728 3842 3511 3824

PENDLETON WOOLEN MILLS INC p 1128
220 Nw Broadway 97209
Tel (503) 226-4801 *SIC* 2337

PERFORMANCE WAREHOUSE CO p 1135
9440 N Whitaker Rd 97217
Tel (503) 417-5302 *SIC* 5013

PORT OF PORTLAND p 1162
7200 Ne Airport Way 97218
Tel (503) 944-7000 *SIC* 4491 4512

PORTLAND ADVENTIST MEDICAL CENTER p 1163
10123 Se Market St 97216
Tel (503) 257-2500 *SIC* 8062

PORTLAND CLINIC LLP p 1163
800 Sw 13th Ave 97205
Tel (503) 221-0161 *SIC* 8011

PORTLAND COMMUNITY COLLEGE FOUNDATION INC p 1163
12000 Sw 49th Ave 97219
Tel (971) 722-6111 *SIC* 8222

▲ PORTLAND GENERAL ELECTRIC CO p 1163
121 Sw Salmon St 97204
Tel (503) 464-8000 *SIC* 4911 4922

PORTLAND PUBLIC SCHOOLS p 1163
501 N Dixon St 97227
Tel (503) 916-2000 *SIC* 8211

PORTLAND STATE UNIVERSITY p 1163
1600 Sw 4th Ave Ste 730 97201
Tel (503) 725-4444 *SIC* 8221

■ PRECISION CASTPARTS CORP p 1168
4650 Sw Mcdam Ave Ste 300 97239
Tel (503) 946-4800
SIC 3324 3369 3724 3511 3519

PRECOA LLC p 1169
13221 Sw 68th Pkwy # 100 97223
Tel (503) 244-7755 *SIC* 6311

PROVIDENCE HEALTH PLAN p 1186
10126 Sw Park Way 97225
Tel (503) 574-5000 *SIC* 6324

PROVIDENCE HEALTH SYSTEM-OREGON p 1186
4805 Ne Glisan St 97213
Tel (503) 215-6111 *SIC* 8062

R B PAMPLIN CORP p 1201
805 Sw Brdwy Ste 2400 97205
Tel (503) 248-1133
SIC 2211 2392 2361 2369

R&H CONSTRUCTION CO p 1203
1530 Sw Taylor St 97205
Tel (503) 228-7177 *SIC* 1542 1522

REED INSTITUTE p 1217
3203 Se Woodstock Blvd 97202
Tel (503) 771-1112 *SIC* 8222

REGENCE BLUECROSS BLUESHIELD OF OREGON p 1218
100 Sw Market St 97201
Tel (503) 225-5336 *SIC* 6321

■ RENTRAK CORP p 1224
7700 Ne Ambassador Pl # 300 97220
Tel (503) 284-7581 *SIC* 7372

RODDA PAINT CO p 1246
6107 N Marine Dr Ste 3 97203
Tel (503) 521-4300
SIC 2851 5198 5023 5231 5719

ROMAN CATHOLIC ARCHBISHOP OF PORTLAND IN OREGON AND SUCCESSORS A CORP SOLE p 1248
2838 E Burnside St 97214
Tel (503) 234-5334 *SIC* 8661

RONTONKIN CHEVROLET CO p 1249
122 Ne 122nd Ave 97230
Tel (503) 255-4100 *SIC* 5511

RONTONKIN IMPORTS INC p 1249
9655 Sw Canyon Rd 97225
Tel (503) 292-0662 *SIC* 5511

SAPA PROFILES INC p 1281
7933 Ne 21st Ave 97211
Tel (503) 285-0404 *SIC* 3354 3471

▲ SCHNITZER STEEL INDUSTRIES INC p 1288
299 Sw Clay St Ste 350 97201
Tel (503) 224-9900
SIC 5093 3312 3449 3441 3433 5015

SERVICE STEEL INC p 1307
5555 N Channel Ave Bldg 2 97217
Tel (503) 224-9500 *SIC* 5051 3711

SHELTER PRODUCTS INC p 1315
1490 Se Gideon St Ste 100 97202
Tel (503) 872-3600 *SIC* 5031

SHILO MANAGEMENT CORP p 1316
11600 Sw Shilo Ln 97225
Tel (503) 641-6565 *SIC* 8741

SILTRONIC CORP p 1323
7200 Nw Front Ave 97210
Tel (503) 243-2020 *SIC* 3674

■ SOREL CORP p 1341
14375 Nw Science Park Dr 97229
Tel (503) 978-2300 *SIC* 5699

SPADA PROPERTIES INC p 1354
8448 Ne 33rd Dr Ste 100 97211
Tel (503) 288-8300 *SIC* 5148

ST VINCENT MEDICAL CENTER EAST PAVILION LOBBY GIFT SHOP p 1373
9205 Sw Barnes Rd 97225
Tel (503) 216-2100 *SIC* 8062

STANCORP FINANCIAL GROUP INC p 1375
1100 Sw 6th Ave 97204
Tel (971) 321-7000 *SIC* 6311 6321

STANDARD INSURANCE CO p 1376
920 Sw 6th Ave Ste 1100 97204
Tel (971) 321-7000 *SIC* 6311 6321 6411

STARPLEX CORP p 1379
12722 Ne Airport Way 97230
Tel (503) 222-5957 *SIC* 7381 7363 7999

STIMSON LUMBER CO p 1390
520 Sw Yamhill St Ste 700 97204
Tel (503) 222-1676 *SIC* 2421 2493 2411

STOEL RIVES LLP p 1390
760 Sw 9th Ave Ste 3000 97205
Tel (503) 224-3380 *SIC* 8111

TEC EQUIPMENT INC p 1430
750 Ne Columbia Blvd 97211
Tel (503) 285-7667 *SIC* 5511 7538 7549

TEMP-CONTROL MECHANICAL CORP p 1436
4800 N Channel Ave 97217
Tel (503) 285-9851 *SIC* 1711 3444 1731

TIRE FACTORY INC p 1455
6102 N Marine Dr 97203
Tel (503) 283-6494 *SIC* 5014

TRI-COUNTY METROPOLITAN TRANSPORTATION DISTRICT OF OREGON p 1477
1800 Sw 1st Ave Ste 300 97201
Tel (503) 238-7433 *SIC* 4111

■ TRIPWIRE INC p 1482
101 Sw Main St Ste 1500 97204
Tel (503) 276-7500 *SIC* 7371

TUMAC LUMBER CO INC p 1491
805 Sw Broadway Ste 1500 97205
Tel (503) 721-7696 *SIC* 5031 5159

▲ UMPQUA HOLDINGS CORP p 1502
1 Sw Columbia St Ste 1200 97258
Tel (503) 727-4100 *SIC* 6035 6022

UNITED SALAD CO p 1511
8448 Ne 33rd Dr Ste 100 97211
Tel (503) 288-8300 *SIC* 5148 0175 2033

UNITED STATES BAKERY p 1512
315 Ne 10th Ave 97232
Tel (503) 232-2191 *SIC* 2051 5461

UNIVERSITY OF PORTLAND p 1524
5000 N Willamette Blvd 97203
Tel (503) 943-7337 *SIC* 8221

UTI (US) HOLDINGS INC p 1536
400 Sw 6th Ave Ste 906 97204
Tel (503) 953-1300 *SIC* 4731

VA PORTLAND HEALTH CARE SYSTEM p 1538
3710 Sw Us Vtrans Hosp Rd 97239
Tel (503) 273-5048 *SIC* 8062 8742

VESTA CORP p 1552
11950 Sw Garden Pl 97223
Tel (503) 639-0235 *SIC* 3559 3578

VESTAS-AMERICAN WIND TECHNOLOGY INC p 1552
1417 Sw Naito Pkwy # 100 97201
Tel (503) 327-2000 *SIC* 3523 3511 5084

VIGOR FAB LLC p 1556
5555 N Channel Ave 97217
Tel (503) 247-1777 *SIC* 3731

VIGOR INDUSTRIAL LLC p 1556
5555 N Channel Ave # 71 97217
Tel (503) 247-1777 *SIC* 3731 3599 6531

VIGOR MARINE LLC p 1556
5555 N Channel Ave # 71 97217
Tel (503) 247-1804 *SIC* 3731

■ WALLACE THEATER HOLDINGS INC p 1573
919 Sw Taylor St Ste 800 97205
Tel (503) 221-7090 *SIC* 7832

WALSH CONSTRUCTION CO p 1574
2905 Sw 1st Ave 97201
Tel (503) 228-1190 *SIC* 1522 1542

WALTER E NELSON CO p 1574
5937 N Cutter Cir 97217
Tel (503) 285-3037 *SIC* 5169 5087

■ WASTE MANAGEMENT OF OREGON INC p 1581
5330 Ne Skyport Way 97218
Tel (503) 249-8078 *SIC* 4953

WEBTRENDS INC p 1587
555 Sw Oak St Ste 300 97204
Tel (503) 294-7025 *SIC* 7372

WEST ONE AUTOMOTIVE GROUP INC p 1595
2046 Nw Irving St 97209
Tel (503) 222-1335 *SIC* 7514

WESTERN BOXED MEATS DISTRIBUTORS p 1597
2401 Ne Argyle St 97211
Tel (503) 284-3314 *SIC* 5147 5142

WESTERN FAMILY FOODS INC p 1598
6700 Sw Sandburg St 97223
Tel (503) 639-6300 *SIC* 5141 5142

WFG NATIONAL TITLE INSURANCE CO INC p 1603
12909 Sw 68th Pkwy # 350 97223
Tel (503) 387-3636 *SIC* 6361

WILLISTON FINANCIAL GROUP LLC p 1612
12909 Sw 68th Pkwy # 350 97223
Tel (503) 387-3636 *SIC* 6361

WRIGHT BUSINESS FORMS INC p 1627
18440 Ne San Rafael St 97230
Tel (503) 661-2525 *SIC* 2761

■ XPO ENTERPRISE SERVICES INC p 1632
1717 Nw 21st Ave 97209
Tel (503) 450-2000 *SIC* 8721

YOSHIDAS INC p 1637
8440 Ne Alderwood Rd A 97220
Tel (503) 731-3702 *SIC* 5149 8741

ZIMMER GUNSUL FRASCA ARCHITECTS LLP p 1643
1223 Sw Washington St # 200 97205
Tel (503) 224-3860 *SIC* 8712 8748 7389

PRINEVILLE, OR

LES SCHWAB TIRE CENTERS OF IDAHO INC p 857
646 Nw Madras Hwy 97754
Tel (541) 447-4136 *SIC* 5531

REDMOND, OR

SAINT CHARLES MEDICAL CENTER REDMOND p 1268
1253 Nw Canal Blvd 97756
Tel (541) 548-8131 *SIC* 8011

ROSEBURG, OR

COW CREEK BAND OF UMPQUA TRIBE OF INDIANS p 385
2371 Ne Stephens St 97470
Tel (541) 957-8945 *SIC* 9131 6321 7999

MERCY MEDICAL CENTER INC p 947
2700 Nw Stewart Pkwy 97471
Tel (541) 673-0611 *SIC* 8062

■ UMPQUA BANK p 1501
445 Se Main St 97470
Tel (541) 440-3961 *SIC* 6021

SALEM, OR

CITY COUNTY INSURANCE SERVICES p 312
1212 Court St Ne 97301
Tel (503) 763-3800 *SIC* 6411 8111

CITY OF SALEM p 318
555 Liberty St Se Rm 230 97301
Tel (503) 588-6255 *SIC* 9111 9224 9221

COLSON & COLSON GENERAL CONTRACTOR INC p 339
2260 Mcgilchrist St Se # 100 97302
Tel (503) 586-7401 *SIC* 1522 1542

COUNTY OF MARION p 379
451 Division St Ne Ste 1 97301
Tel (503) 588-5212 *SIC* 9121

DEPARTMENT OF EMPLOYMENT OREGON p 430
875 Union St Ne 97311
Tel (503) 947-1470 *SIC* 9441

DEPARTMENT OF MILITARY OREGON p 430
1776 Militia Way Se 97301
Tel (503) 584-3910 *SIC* 9711

DRIVER & MOTOR VEHICLE SERVICES OREGON p 456
1905 Lana Ave Ne 97314
Tel (503) 945-5000 *SIC* 9621

EPIC AVIATION LLC p 505
3841 Fairview Indust 15 97302
Tel (503) 362-3633 *SIC* 5172

EXECUTIVE OFFICE OF STATE OF OREGON p 518
900 Court St Ne 97301
Tel (503) 378-3111 *SIC* 9111

JET INDUSTRIES INC p 783
1935 Silverton Rd Ne 97301
Tel (503) 363-2334 *SIC* 1711 1731

JUDICIARY COURTS OF STATE OF OREGON p 797
1163 State St 97301
Tel (503) 986-5555 *SIC* 9211

■ KETTLE FOODS INC p 814
3125 Kettle Ct Se 97301
Tel (503) 364-0399 *SIC* 2096

MAYTRUCKING CO p 923
4185 Brooklake Rd Ne 97303
Tel (503) 393-7030 *SIC* 4213

MCGRATHS PUBLICK FISH HOUSE LLC p 929
1935 Davcor St Se 97302
Tel (503) 399-8456 *SIC* 5812

MID VALLEY IPA INC p 963
2995 Ryan Dr Se Ste 200 97301
Tel (503) 371-7701 *SIC* 8011

NORPAC FOODS INC p 1049
3225 25th St Se 97302
Tel (503) 480-2100 *SIC* 2037 2033 2038

■ ONITY INC p 1088
4001 Fairview Indus Dr Se 97302
Tel (503) 581-9101 *SIC* 5072

OREGON DEPARTMENT OF ADMINISTRATIVE SERVICES p 1093
155 Cottage St Ne Ste U50 97301
Tel (503) 378-8344 *SIC* 9199

OREGON DEPARTMENT OF CONSUMER AND BUSINESS SERVICES p 1093
350 Winter St Ne 97301
Tel (503) 378-4100 *SIC* 9651 9311

OREGON DEPARTMENT OF CORRECTIONS p 1093
2575 Center St Ne 97301
Tel (503) 945-9090 *SIC* 9223

OREGON DEPARTMENT OF FISH AND WILDLIFE p 1093
4034 Fairview Indus Dr Se 97302
Tel (503) 947-6000 *SIC* 9512

OREGON DEPARTMENT OF HUMAN SERVICES p 1093
500 Summer St Ne Dept 4 97301
Tel (503) 945-5944 *SIC* 9431 9441

OREGON DEPARTMENT OF JUSTICE p 1093
1162 Court St Ne 97301
Tel (503) 378-4320 SIC 9222

OREGON DEPARTMENT OF STATE POLICE p 1093
255 Capitol St Ne Fl 4 97310
Tel (503) 378-3720 SIC 9221

OREGON DEPARTMENT OF TRANSPORTATION p 1093
355 Capitol St Ne Ms21 97301
Tel (503) 378-5849 SIC 9621

OREGON DIVISION OF ADULT & FAMILY SERVICES p 1093
500 Summer St Ne 97301
Tel (503) 945-5601 SIC 9441

REGENCE HMO OREGON INC p 1218
201 High St Se 97301
Tel (503) 364-4868 SIC 6321

ROTH IGA FOODLINER INC p 1252
4895 Indian School Rd Ne 97305
Tel (503) 393-7684 SIC 5411

SAIF CORP p 1268
400 High St Se 97312
Tel (503) 373-8000 SIC 6321 8111 6331

SALEM HEALTH p 1272
890 Oak St Se 97301
Tel (503) 561-5200 SIC 8062

SALEM-KEIZER SCHOOL DISTRICT 24J p 1272
2450 Lancaster Dr Ne # 100 97305
Tel (503) 399-3000 SIC 8211

STATE OF OREGON p 1382
900 Court St Ne Ste 160 97301
Tel (503) 378-3111 SIC 9111

SUPERIORTIRE SERVICE INC p 1407
4230 27th Ct Se 97302
Tel (503) 585-1955 SIC 5014 7534 3011

TRUITT BROS INC p 1486
1105 Front St Ne 97301
Tel (503) 365-2837 SIC 3556

WILLAMETTE UNIVERSITY p 1609
900 State St 97301
Tel (503) 370-6728 SIC 8221

SHERWOOD, OR

ALLIED SYSTEMS CO p 57
21433 Sw Oregon St 97140
Tel (503) 625-2560 SIC 3531 3537 3536

SILVERTON, OR

SILVERTON HEALTH p 1324
342 Fairview St 97381
Tel (503) 873-1500 SIC 8062

SILVERTON HOSPITAL NETWORK p 1324
342 Fairview St 97381
Tel (503) 873-1782 SIC 8062

SPRINGFIELD, OR

HAMILTON CONSTRUCTION CO p 655
2213 S F St 97477
Tel (541) 746-2426 SIC 1622 3441

■ **MCKENZIE-WILLAMETTE REGIONAL MEDICAL CENTER ASSOCIATES LLC** p 930
1460 G St 97477
Tel (541) 726-4400 SIC 8062

MCKINSEY WILLIAMETTE p 930
1460 G St 97477
Tel (541) 741-4600 SIC 8011 8062

PACIFICSOURCE HEALTH PLANS p 1106
110 International Way 97477
Tel (541) 686-1242 SIC 6321

ROSBORO LLC p 1250
2509 Main St 97477
Tel (541) 746-8411
SIC 2436 2421 2439 3441 2435

ROSEBURG FOREST PRODUCTS CO p 1250
3660 Gateway St Ste A 97477
Tel (541) 679-3311
SIC 2436 2421 2493 5031 5211 0811

SPRINGFIELD SCHOOL DISTRICT 19 p 1361
525 Mill St 97477
Tel (541) 726-3331 SIC 8211

SPRINGFIELD UTILITY BOARD (INC) p 1361
250 A St 97477
Tel (541) 746-8451 SIC 4931 4941

TIMBER PRODUCTS CO LIMITED PARTNERSHIP p 1454
305 S 4th St 97477
Tel (541) 747-4577
SIC 2436 2435 5031 2493

STAYTON, OR

SLAYDEN CONSTRUCTION GROUP INC p 1331
500 Willamette Ave 97383
Tel (503) 769-1969 SIC 1542

TANGENT, OR

■ **KNIFE RIVER CORP - NORTHWEST** p 824
32260 Old Highway 34 97389
Tel (541) 928-6491 SIC 1611 3273

THE DALLES, OR

MID-COLUMBIA MEDICAL CENTER p 963
1700 E 19th St 97058
Tel (541) 296-1111 SIC 8062 8011

TIGARD, OR

BRIDGEWELL RESOURCES LLC p 212
10200 Sw Greenburg Rd # 500 97223
Tel (503) 872-3566
SIC 5031 5039 5153 5159

CONSOLIDATED SUPPLY CO p 360
7337 Sw Kable Ln 97224
Tel (503) 620-7050 SIC 5074 5085

■ **HEALTH NET HEALTH PLAN OF OREGON INC** p 675
13221 Sw 68th Pkwy Ste 20 97223
Tel (503) 213-5000 SIC 6324 8011

MEDICAL TEAMS INTERNATIONAL p 937
14150 Sw Milton Ct 97224
Tel (503) 624-1000 SIC 8099 8399

TIGARD-TUALATIN SCHOOL DISTRICT p 1453
6960 Sw Sandburg St 97223
Tel (503) 431-4000 SIC 8211

WESTERN FAMILY HOLDING CO p 1598
6700 Sw Sandburg St 97223
Tel (503) 639-6300
SIC 5141 5142 5199 5122 5149

WESTERN PARTITIONS INC p 1599
8300 Sw Hunziker St 97223
Tel (503) 620-1600 SIC 1742

TILLAMOOK, OR

TILLAMOOK COUNTY CREAMERY ASSOCIATION p 1453
4185 Highway 101 N 97141
Tel (503) 842-4481 SIC 2022 2024 2021

TUALATIN, OR

AIREFCO INC p 40
18755 Sw Teton Ave 97062
Tel (503) 692-3210 SIC 5075

▲ **CUI GLOBAL INC** p 400
20050 Sw 112th Ave 97062
Tel (503) 612-2300 SIC 3824 8711

HUNTAIR INC p 719
19855 Sw 124th Ave 97062
Tel (503) 639-0113 SIC 3585

ICHOR SYSTEMS INC p 727
9660 Sw Herman Rd 97062
Tel (503) 625-2251 SIC 3559 5984

■ **INTERNATIONAL LINE BUILDERS INC** p 755
19020 Sw Cipole Rd Ste A 97062
Tel (503) 692-0193 SIC 1623

KAI USA LTD p 800
18600 Sw Teton Ave 97062
Tel (503) 682-1966 SIC 3421

LEGACY MERIDIAN PARK HOSPITAL p 852
19300 Sw 65th Ave 97062
Tel (503) 692-1212 SIC 8062 8011

PACIFIC FOODS OF OREGON INC p 1104
19480 Sw 97th Ave 97062
Tel (503) 692-9666 SIC 2033 2099 2086

■ **USF REDDAWAY INC** p 1535
7720 Sw Mohawk St Bldg H 97062
Tel (503) 650-1286 SIC 4213

WEST LINN-WILSONVILLE SCHOOL DISTRICT 3JT p 1595
22210 Sw Stafford Rd 97062
Tel (503) 673-7000 SIC 8211

WARM SPRINGS, OR

CONFEDERATED TRIBES OF WARM SPRINGS RESERVATION OF OREGON p 356
1233 Veterans St 97761
Tel (541) 553-1161 SIC 7011 4832 0811

WESTON, OR

SMITH FROZEN FOODS INC p 1333
101 Depot St 97886
Tel (541) 566-3515 SIC 2037

WILSONVILLE, OR

AVAMERE HEALTH SERVICES LLC p 136
25115 Sw Parkway Ave A 97070
Tel (503) 570-3405
SIC 8741 8051 8052 8093

COLLINS PINE CO p 337
29190 Sw Town Center Loop 97070
Tel (503) 227-1219
SIC 2421 2426 5211 4911 4013

COLLINS TIMBER CO LLC p 337
29100 Sw Town Ctr Loop W 97070
Tel (503) 227-1219 SIC 2493

▲ **FLIR SYSTEMS INC** p 557
27700 Sw Parkway Ave 97070
Tel (503) 498-3547 SIC 3812 3826

G I JOES INC p 587
9805 Sw Boeckman Rd 97070
Tel (503) 682-2242
SIC 5941 5699 5531 5999

HOLLYWOOD ENTERTAINMENT CORP p 701
9275 Sw Peyton Ln 97070
Tel (503) 214-4600 SIC 7841

▲ **MENTOR GRAPHICS CORP** p 943
8005 Sw Boeckman Rd 97070
Tel (503) 685-7000 SIC 7373

MOVIE GALLERY INC p 995
9275 Sw Peyton Ln 97070
Tel (503) 570-1700 SIC 7841 5735

■ **NTP DISTRIBUTION INC** p 1065
27150 Sw Kinsman Rd 97070
Tel (503) 570-2154 SIC 5013

OREGON PACIFIC BUILDING PRODUCTS (CALIF) INC p 1093
30170 Sw Ore Pac Ave 97070
Tel (503) 685-5499 SIC 5031

OREPAC HOLDING CO p 1094
30170 Sw Orepac Ave 97070
Tel (503) 682-5050 SIC 5031

PRECISION INTERCONNECT LLC p 1168
10025 Sw Freeman Dr 97070
Tel (503) 620-9400 SIC 3679

■ **SYSCO PORTLAND INC** p 1418
26250 Sw Parkway Ctr Dr 97070
Tel (503) 682-8700 SIC 5141 5046

WOODBURN, OR

BRUCE PACKING CO INC p 220
380 S Pacific Hwy 99e 97071
Tel (503) 874-3000 SIC 2013

JDB INC p 781
380 S Pacific Hwy 97071
Tel (503) 874-3000 SIC 2015 2013

UFP WOODBURN LLC p 1499
2895 Progress Way 97071
Tel (503) 226-6240 SIC 5031

PENNSYLVANIA

ABINGTON, PA

ABINGTON MEMORIAL HOSPITAL INC p 11
1200 Old York Rd 19001
Tel (215) 481-2000 SIC 8062

ABINGTON SCHOOL DISTRICT p 11
970 Highland Ave 19001
Tel (215) 884-4700 SIC 8211

ADAMSTOWN, PA

BOLLMAN HAT CO p 198
110 E Main St 19501
Tel (717) 484-4361 SIC 2353 5136

ALBURTIS, PA

SURE FIT INC p 1408
8000 Quarry Rd Ste C 18011
Tel (610) 264-7300 SIC 5023

ALIQUIPPA, PA

CRONIMET CORP p 393
1 Pilarsky Way 15001
Tel (724) 375-5004 SIC 5093 5051 3312

ALLENTOWN, PA

AGERE SYSTEMS INC p 34
1110 American Pkwy Ne 18109
Tel (610) 712-1000 SIC 3663

▲ **AIR PRODUCTS AND CHEMICALS INC** p 39
7201 Hamilton Blvd 18195
Tel (610) 481-4911
SIC 2813 2842 2891 3569

ALCO INDUSTRIES INC p 47
1275 Glenlivet Dr Ste 100 18106
Tel (610) 666-0930
SIC 2879 2851 2842 2873

AMCOR PET PACKAGING USA INC p 66
6974 Schantz Rd 18106
Tel (610) 871-9000 SIC 3089

BUTZ ENTERPRISES INC p 230
840 Hamilton St 18101
Tel (610) 395-6871 SIC 8741

CITY OF ALLENTOWN p 313
435 Hamilton St 18101
Tel (610) 437-7546 SIC 9111

COMPUTER AID INC p 352
1390 Ridgeview Dr Ste 300 18104
Tel (610) 530-5000 SIC 7371

COUNTY OF LEHIGH p 379
17 S 7th St 18101
Tel (610) 782-3000 SIC 9111

CREDIT CARD PROCESSING USA INC p 390
2202 N Irving St 18109
Tel (908) 790-1777 SIC 7389

▲ **CROSSAMERICA PARTNERS LP** p 394
515 Hamilton St Ste 200 18101
Tel (610) 625-8000 SIC 5172

DIAKON p 436
798 Hausman Rd Ste 300 18104
Tel (610) 682-1262 SIC 8322

DIOCESE OF ALLENTOWN p 440
4029 W Tilghman St Ste 3 18104
Tel (610) 437-0755 SIC 8661

■ **FISHER CLINICAL SERVICES INC** p 552
7554 Schantz Rd 18106
Tel (610) 391-0800 SIC 5122

GOOD SHEPHERD REHABILITATION HOSPITAL INC p 623
850 S 5th St 18103
Tel (610) 776-3100
SIC 8361 8051 8093 8069

GT&S INC p 644
5275 Tilghman St 18104
Tel (610) 398-2211
SIC 4925 5169 5084 5085 2813 5172

■ **H T LYONS INC** p 650
7165 Ambassador Dr 18106
Tel (610) 530-2600 SIC 1711

HOSPITAL CENTRAL SERVICES INC p 709
2171 28th St Sw 18103
Tel (610) 791-2222 SIC 8741

IDEAL CONCEPTS INC p 729
667 Union Blvd 18109
Tel (610) 740-0000 SIC 8742

LEHIGH VALLEY HEALTH NETWORK INC p 854
1247 S Cedar Crest Blvd 18103
Tel (610) 402-8000 SIC 8062

LEHIGH VALLEY HEALTH SERVICES INC p 854
2166 S 12th St 18103
Tel (610) 791-3682 SIC 4813 8741 8721

LEHIGH VALLEY HOSPITAL INC p 854
1200 S Cedar Crest Blvd 18103
Tel (610) 402-8000 SIC 8062

LEHIGH VALLEY PHYSICIANS GROUP p 854
1605 N Cedar Crest Blvd # 110 18104
Tel (610) 439-7500 SIC 8011

LEHIGH VALLEY RESTAURANT GROUP INC p 854
6802a Hamilton Blvd 18106
Tel (610) 481-0436 SIC 5812

MARCON & BOYER INC p 905
645 Hamilton St Ste 300 18101
Tel (610) 866-5959
SIC 3448 1742 1743 1799

■ **MORNING CALL LLC** p 989
101 N 6th St 18101
Tel (610) 820-6500 SIC 2752 2711

MUHLENBERG COLLEGE p 999
2400 Chew St 18104
Tel (484) 664-3100 SIC 8221

NATIONAL PENN BANCSHARES INC p 1015
645 Hamilton St Ste 1100 18101
Tel (800) 822-3321 SIC 6331

■ **NATIONAL PENN BANK** p 1015
645 Hamilton St Ste 900 18101
Tel (610) 705-9101 SIC 6021

PARKLAND SCHOOL DISTRICT AUTHORITY p 1116
1210 Springhouse Rd 18104
Tel (610) 351-5503 SIC 8211

PENN TREATY NETWORK AMERICA INSURANCE CO p 1129
3440 Lehigh St Ste 4 18103
Tel (800) 362-0700 SIC 6321

■ **PETROLEUM MARKETERS INC** p 1139
645 Hamilton St Ste 500 18101
Tel (540) 772-4900 SIC 5983 5411

▲ **PPL CORP** p 1166
2 N 9th St 18101
Tel (610) 774-5151 SIC 4911 4924

■ **PPL ELECTRIC UTILITIES CORP** p 1166
2 N 9th St 18101
Tel (610) 774-5151 SIC 4911

■ **PPL SERVICES CORP** p 1166
2 N 9th St 18101
Tel (610) 774-5151 SIC 6289 4911

■ **PRAXAIR DISTRIBUTION MID-ATLANTIC LLC** p 1167
5275 Tilghman St 18104
Tel (610) 398-2211 SIC 4925 3548

PRIMO NO 1 IN PRODUCE INC p 1176
2100 Hoover Ave 18109
Tel (610) 264-5000 SIC 5148

SACRED HEART HEALTH CARE SYSTEM INC p 1265
421 Chew St 18102
Tel (610) 776-4900 SIC 8741 5912

SACRED HEART HOSPITAL OF ALLENTOWN p 1265
421 Chew St 18102
Tel (610) 776-4500 SIC 8062 8011

SCHOOL DISTRICT OF CITY OF ALLENTOWN p 1289
31 S Penn St 18102
Tel (484) 765-4001 SIC 8211

SHEPHERD GOOD REHABILITATION NETWORK p 1315
850 S 5th St 18103
Tel (610) 776-3100 SIC 8051 8361 8322

STOCKTON COGEN (I) INC p 1390
7201 Hamilton Blvd 18195
Tel (610) 481-4911 SIC 4911

▲ **TALEN ENERGY CORP** p 1422
835 Hamilton St Ste 150 18101
Tel (888) 211-6011 SIC 4911

■ **TALEN ENERGY MARKETING LLC** p 1422
835 Hamilton St Ste 150 18101
Tel (610) 774-5151 SIC 4911

■ **TALEN ENERGY SERVICES GROUP LLC** p 1422
2 N 9th St 18101
Tel (610) 774-4005 SIC 4911

TALEN ENERGY SERVICES HOLDINGS LLC p 1422
835 Hamilton St 18101
Tel (610) 774-5151 SIC 4911 1711 3625

■ **TALEN ENERGY SUPPLY LLC** p 1422
835 Hamilton St Ste 150 18101
Tel (888) 211-6011 SIC 4911

■TALEN GENERATION LLC p 1422
835 Hamilton St Ste 150 18101
Tel (610) 774-6418 *SIC* 4911

■TAMINCO US LLC p 1423
7540 Windsor Dr Ste 411 18195
Tel (610) 366-6730 *SIC* 2869 5169

■ UGI CENTRAL PENN GAS INC p 1499
2 N 9th St 18101
Tel (610) 796-3499 *SIC* 4924

■ VERSUM MATERIALS US LLC p 1552
1919 Vultee St 18103
Tel (610) 481-3706 *SIC* 2842 2891 3569

WOOD CO p 1622
6081 Hamilton Blvd 18106
Tel (610) 366-5204 *SIC* 5812

ALTOONA, PA

ALTOONA AREA SCHOOL DISTRICT INC p 62
1415 6th Ave 16602
Tel (814) 946-8211 *SIC* 8211

BLAIR MEDICAL ASSOCIATES p 188
1414 9th Ave 16602
Tel (814) 944-0202 *SIC* 8011 8043

DEGOL ORGANIZATION L P p 422
3229 Pleasant Valley Blvd 16602
Tel (814) 941-7777
SIC 5031 5033 5211 5023 5713

HITE CO p 697
3101 Beale Ave 16601
Tel (814) 944-6121 *SIC* 5063

IDA TOWER p 728
1010 12th St 16601
Tel (814) 944-4055 *SIC* 6513

LEONARD S FIORE INC p 856
5506 6th Ave Rear 16602
Tel (814) 946-3686 *SIC* 1542

LEXINGTON HOLDINGS INC p 859
620 Howard Ave 16601
Tel (814) 946-2204 *SIC* 8741

SEVEN D WHOLESALE OF PA LP p 1309
3229 Pleasant Valley Blvd 16602
Tel (814) 941-7777 *SIC* 5031

SHEETZ INC p 1313
5700 6th Ave 16602
Tel (814) 946-3611 *SIC* 5411

UPMC ALTOONA p 1528
620 Howard Ave 16601
Tel (814) 889-2011 *SIC* 8062

WARD TRANSPORT & LOGISTICS CORP p 1575
1436 Ward Trucking Dr 16602
Tel (814) 944-0803 *SIC* 4214

WARD TRUCKING LLC p 1575
1436 Ward Trucking Dr 16602
Tel (814) 944-0803 *SIC* 4213 4214

YOUR BUILDING CENTERS INC p 1639
2607 Beale Ave 16601
Tel (814) 944-5098 *SIC* 5251

AMBLER, PA

BERKADIA COMMERCIAL MORTGAGE LLC p 174
323 Norristown Rd Ste 300 19002
Tel (215) 328-3200 *SIC* 6162

BRADFORD-WHITE CORP p 206
725 Talamore Dr 19002
Tel (215) 641-9400 *SIC* 3433 1711

■ CHAPEL STEEL CORP p 288
590 N Bethlehem Pike 19002
Tel (215) 793-0899 *SIC* 5051

WISSAHICKON SCHOOL DISTRICT p 1619
601 Knight Rd 19002
Tel (215) 619-8000 *SIC* 8211

ANNVILLE, PA

AIR NATIONAL GUARD PENNSYLVANIA p 39
215 S O 47 Bldg 17003
Tel (717) 861-8667 *SIC* 9711

PA DEPARTMENT OF MILITARY AND VETERANS AFFAIRS p 1103
47 Bldg S-O 17003
Tel (717) 861-8500 *SIC* 9711 9451

■TVC COMMUNICATIONS LLC p 1494
800 Airport Rd 17003
Tel (717) 838-3790 *SIC* 3663 2298

VETERANS AFFAIRS PENNSYLVANIA BUREAU FOR p 1552
0 47 Ftig Bldg S 17003
Tel (717) 861-8901 *SIC* 9451

ARDMORE, PA

HAJOCA CORP p 653
127 Coulter Ave 19003
Tel (610) 649-1430 *SIC* 5074

MERION LOWER SCHOOL DISTRICT INC p 949
301 E Montgomery Ave 19003
Tel (610) 645-1983 *SIC* 8211

ASHLAND, PA

TRI-STATE ENVELOPE CORP p 1477
20th Market St 17921
Tel (570) 875-0433 *SIC* 2677

ATGLEN, PA

J D ECKMAN INC p 770
4781 Lower Valley Rd 19310
Tel (610) 593-5300 *SIC* 1611

ATLASBURG, PA

ALEX E PARIS CONTRACTING CO INC p 48
1595 Smith Township State 15004
Tel (724) 947-2235 *SIC* 1623 1629

AUDUBON, PA

ALMAC PHARMA SERVICES LLC p 59
2661 Audubon Rd 19403
Tel (610) 666-9500 *SIC* 2834

▲ GLOBUS MEDICAL INC p 618
2560 Gen Armistead Ave 19403
Tel (610) 930-1800 *SIC* 3841

AVOCA, PA

JACK WILLIAMS TIRE CO INC p 773
700 Rocky Glen Rd 18641
Tel (570) 457-5000 *SIC* 5531 5014

AVONDALE, PA

BASCIANI FOODS INC p 158
8876 Gap Newport Pike 19311
Tel (610) 268-3610 *SIC* 5148

BALA CYNWYD, PA

■ ABE ENTERCOM HOLDINGS LLC p 10
401 E City Ave Ste 809 19004
Tel (404) 239-7211 *SIC* 6411

AMERICAN INSURANCE SERVICE INC p 75
3 Bala Plz E Ste 300 19004
Tel (610) 664-1500 *SIC* 6411 6331

CONNECT AMERICA.COM LLC p 356
1 Belmont Ave Fl 9 19004
Tel (610) 356-3307 *SIC* 5065 5999

DIAMOND STATE INSURANCE CO p 437
3 Bala Plz E Ste 300 19004
Tel (610) 664-1500 *SIC* 6331 6411

▲ ENTERCOM COMMUNICATIONS CORP p 501
401 E City Ave Ste 809 19004
Tel (610) 660-5610 *SIC* 4832

■ ENTERCOM RADIO LLC p 501
401 E City Ave Ste 409 19004
Tel (610) 660-5610 *SIC* 4832

GLOBAL INDEMNITY GROUP INC p 616
3 Bala Plz Ste 300 19004
Tel (610) 664-1500 *SIC* 6351

HOTWIRE COMMUNICATIONS LLC p 710
1 Belmont Ave Ste 1100 19004
Tel (800) 355-5668 *SIC* 4813

KEYSTONE SHIPPING CO p 816
1 Bala Plz Ste 600 19004
Tel (610) 617-6800 *SIC* 4731 4412 4424

L F DRISCOLL CO LLC p 834
401 E City Ave Ste 500 19004
Tel (610) 668-0950 *SIC* 8741

MAGUIRE INSURANCE AGENCY INC p 897
1 Bala Plz Ste LI34 19004
Tel (610) 617-7900 *SIC* 6411

PAPERWORKS INDUSTRIES INC p 1112
40 Monument Rd Ste 200 19004
Tel (215) 984-7000 *SIC* 2653

PEGASUS MEDIA & COMMUNICATIONS INC p 1127
225 E City Ave Ste 200 19004
Tel (610) 934-7000 *SIC* 4833 4841

PEGASUS TOWERS INC p 1127
225 E City Ave Ste 200 19004
Tel (610) 934-7000 *SIC* 4833

PHILADELPHIA CONSOLIDATED HOLDING CORP p 1142
1 Bala Plz Ste 100 19004
Tel (610) 617-7900 *SIC* 6331

PHILADELPHIA INDEMNITY INSURANCE CO p 1142
1 Bala Plz Ste 100 19004
Tel (610) 642-8400 *SIC* 6411

PHILADELPHIA INSURANCE CO p 1143
231 Sint Asphs Rd Ste 100 19004
Tel (877) 438-7459 *SIC* 6331 6411

PUROLITE CORP p 1193
150 Monument Rd Ste 202 19004
Tel (610) 668-9090 *SIC* 2821

SIG STRUCTURED PRODUCTS LLLP p 1321
401 E City Ave Ste 220 19004
Tel (610) 617-2600 *SIC* 6231

SUSQUEHANNA INTERNATIONAL GROUP LLP p 1409
401 E City Ave Ste 220 19004
Tel (610) 617-2600 *SIC* 6211

TOKIO MARINE SPECIALTY INSURANCE CO p 1458
1 Bala Plz Ste 100 19004
Tel (610) 206-7822 *SIC* 6411

UNITED NATIONAL INSURANCE CO p 1510
3 Bala Plz E Ste 300 19004
Tel (610) 664-1500 *SIC* 6331

BATH, PA

GIRARDS GARAGE DOOR SERVICES p 613
5962 Keystone Dr 18014
Tel (610) 837-4738 *SIC* 7699

BEAVER FALLS, PA

HERITAGE VALLEY HEALTH SYSTEM INC p 686
2580 Constitution Blvd 15010
Tel (724) 728-7000 *SIC* 8741 8062

■ MCCARLS INC p 926
1413 9th Ave 15010
Tel (724) 843-5660 *SIC* 1711

BEAVER, PA

COUNTY OF BEAVER p 376
810 3rd St 15009
Tel (724) 728-5700 *SIC* 9111

BEDFORD, PA

CYCLING SPORTS GROUP INC p 405
16 Trowbridge Dr 15522
Tel (203) 749-7000 *SIC* 3751 2329

ROCKLAND INC p 1244
152 Weber Ln 15522
Tel (814) 623-1115 *SIC* 3531

BELLE VERNON, PA

GUTTMAN ENERGY INC p 648
200 Speers Rd 15012
Tel (724) 489-5199 *SIC* 8731 5172

WESTMORELAND WASTE LLC p 1602
111 Conner Ln 15012
Tel (724) 929-7694 *SIC* 4953

BELLWOOD, PA

MARTIN OIL CO p 913
528 N 1st St 16617
Tel (814) 742-8438
SIC 5983 5171 5541 5411

WOLF FURNITURE ENTERPRISES INC p 1621
1620 N Tuckahoe St 16617
Tel (814) 742-4380
SIC 5712 5713 5722 5731 5719

BENSALEM, PA

AIRLINE HYDRAULICS CORP p 40
3557 Progress Dr 19020
Tel (610) 758-9400 *SIC* 5085 5084

■ CATHERINES INC p 265
3750 State Rd 19020
Tel (215) 245-9100 *SIC* 5632 5621

■ CATHERINES STORES CORP p 265
3750 State Rd 19020
Tel (551) 777-6700 *SIC* 5632 5621

■ CHARMING SHOPPES INC p 290
3750 State Rd 19020
Tel (215) 245-9100 *SIC* 5961 5632 5621

■ CHARMING SHOPPES OF DELAWARE INC p 290
3750 State Rd 19020
Tel (215) 245-9100 *SIC* 5621 8741

GILES & RANSOME INC p 612
2975 Galloway Rd 19020
Tel (215) 639-4300 *SIC* 5082 5084 7353

HADCO METAL TRADING CO LLC p 652
555 State Rd 19020
Tel (215) 695-2705 *SIC* 5051

▲ HEALTHCARE SERVICES GROUP INC p 676
3220 Tillman Dr Ste 300 19020
Tel (215) 639-4274 *SIC* 8059 7349 8049

INTERNATIONAL TURF INVESTMENT CO INC p 757
3001 Street Rd 19020
Tel (215) 639-9000 *SIC* 7948

NATIONAL REFRIGERATION & AIR CONDITIONING PRODUCTS INC p 1015
539 Dunksferry Rd 19020
Tel (215) 244-1400 *SIC* 3585 5075

ORLEANS HOMEBUILDERS INC p 1095
3333 Street Rd Ste 101 19020
Tel (215) 245-7500 *SIC* 1531 1521

RICHLIEU ASSOCIATES p 1233
3338 Richlieu Rd 19020
Tel (215) 639-2800 *SIC* 6513

SUMMIT SERVICES GROUP INC p 1399
3220 Tillman Dr Ste 300 19020
Tel (215) 639-4274 *SIC* 7213 7349

BENTON, PA

BENTON FOUNDRY INC p 173
5297 State Route 487 17814
Tel (570) 925-6711 *SIC* 3321

BERWICK, PA

WISE FOODS INC p 1619
228 Rasely St 18603
Tel (888) 759-4401 *SIC* 2096

BERWYN, PA

ACCT HOLDINGS LLC p 16
1235 Westlakes Dr Ste 160 19312
Tel (610) 695-0500 *SIC* 4813

ADVANCED CALL CENTER TECHNOLOGIES LLC p 25
1235 Westlakes Dr Ste 160 19312
Tel (610) 695-0500 *SIC* 7389

▲ AMETEK INC p 84
1100 Cassatt Rd 19312
Tel (610) 647-2121
SIC 3621 3823 3824 3825

CHIC AND SIMPLE LLC p 297
573 Lancaster Ave 19312
Tel (610) 636-0686 *SIC* 5932

MELMARK INC p 941
2600 Wayland Rd 19312
Tel (610) 353-1726 *SIC* 8211 8361

MINUTE TRANSFER INC p 974
1055 Westlakes Dr Ste 300 19312
Tel (215) 987-3711 *SIC* 7629

MODULAR SPACE CORP p 981
1200 W Swedesford Rd Fl 2 19312
Tel (610) 232-1200 *SIC* 7359 1542

MONETARY MANAGEMENT OF CA INC p 984
1436 Lancaster Ave 19312
Tel (610) 296-3400 *SIC* 6099

NATIONWIDE LIFE INSURANCE CO OF AMERICA p 1018
1000 Chesterbrook Blvd 19312
Tel (610) 407-1717 *SIC* 6411 6211 6719

PEGASUS COMMUNICATIONS HOLDINGS INC p 1127
1055 Westlakes Dr Ste 300 19312
Tel (302) 651-8300 *SIC* 4833 4841

PREPAY NATION LLC p 1171
1055 Westlakes Dr Ste 300 19312
Tel (215) 987-3711 *SIC* 7389

S A TRINSEO p 1261
1000 Chesterbrook Blvd 19312
Tel (610) 240-3200 *SIC* 2821

TRINSEO LLC p 1482
1000 Chesterbrook Blvd # 300 19312
Tel (610) 240-3200 *SIC* 2821

■TRIUMPH AEROSPACE SYSTEMS GROUP INC p 1483
899 Cassatt Rd Ste 210 19312
Tel (610) 251-1000 *SIC* 3728

▲TRIUMPH GROUP INC p 1483
899 Cassatt Rd Ste 210 19312
Tel (610) 251-1000 *SIC* 3728 3724 3812

TRIUMPH STRUCTURES - EAST TEXAS p 1483
899 Cassatt Rd Ste 210 19312
Tel (610) 251-1000 *SIC* 3324

TYCO ELECTRONICS CORP p 1496
1050 Westlakes Dr 19312
Tel (717) 986-7275 *SIC* 3678 3643

VERTEX INC p 1552
1041 Old Cassatt Rd 19312
Tel (610) 640-4200 *SIC* 7372

BETHLEHEM, PA

B BRAUN MEDICAL INC p 141
824 12th Ave 18018
Tel (610) 691-5400 *SIC* 3841

B BRAUN OF AMERICA INC p 141
824 12th Ave 18018
Tel (610) 691-5400 *SIC* 6719 3841

BETHLEHEM AREA SCHOOL DISTRICT p 178
1516 Sycamore St 18017
Tel (610) 807-5571 *SIC* 8211

BUZZI UNICEM USA INC p 230
100 Brodhead Rd Ste 230 18017
Tel (610) 882-5000 *SIC* 3241

EIGHTH & EATON PROFESSIONAL BUILDING LP p 481
801 Ostrum St 18015
Tel (610) 954-4000 *SIC* 8062

FLS US HOLDINGS INC p 561
2040 Avenue C 18017
Tel (610) 264-6011
SIC 3559 3554 3549 3532 3535

FLSMIDTH INC p 561
2040 Avenue C 18017
Tel (610) 264-6011 *SIC* 5084

GEO W KISTLER INC p 605
2210 City Line Rd 18017
Tel (610) 266-7100
SIC 5063 7382 5087 7389

HYDAC TECHNOLOGY CORP p 723
2260 City Line Rd 2280 18017
Tel (205) 520-1220 *SIC* 3492

JUST BORN INC p 797
1300 Stefko Blvd 18017
Tel (610) 867-7568 *SIC* 2064

LEHIGH UNIVERSITY p 854
27 Memorial Dr W Unit 8 18015
Tel (610) 758-3000 *SIC* 8221

■ MINTEQ INTERNATIONAL INC p 974
35 Highland Ave 18017
Tel (724) 794-3000 *SIC* 3297

NORTHAMPTON COMMUNITY COLLEGE p 1054
3835 Green Pond Rd 18020
Tel (610) 861-5300 *SIC* 8222

▲ ORASURE TECHNOLOGIES INC p 1092
220 E 1st St 18015
Tel (610) 882-1820 *SIC* 2835

RC LONESTAR INC p 1212
100 Brodhead Rd Ste 230 18017
Tel (610) 882-5000 *SIC* 6719

RECEIVABLE MANAGEMENT SERVICES CORP p 1214
240 Emery St 18015
Tel (484) 242-4000 *SIC* 7322

RECEIVABLE MANAGEMENT SERVICES INTERNATIONAL INC p 1214
240 Emery St 18015
Tel (484) 242-4000 *SIC* 7322

ROADLINK USA NATIONAL LLC p 1240
1240 Win Dr 18017
Tel (215) 333-4444 *SIC* 4212

SAINT LUKES HOSPITAL OF BETHLEHEM PENNSYLVANIA p 1270
801 Ostrum St 18015
Tel (484) 526-4000 *SIC* 8062 8249

■ **SANDS BETHWORKS GAMING LLC** p 1278
77 Sands Blvd 18015
Tel (877) 726-3777 *SIC* 7011

SERVICE ELECTRIC CABLETV INC p 1307
2200 Avenue A Ste 101 18017
Tel (610) 865-9100 *SIC* 4841 6719

SERVICE TIRE TRUCK CENTER INC p 1307
2255 Avenue A 18017
Tel (610) 691-8473 *SIC* 7534 5531

ST LUKES HEALTH NETWORK INC p 1370
801 Ostrum St 18015
Tel (610) 954-4000 *SIC* 8062

ST LUKES HOSPITAL & HEALTH NETWORK INC p 1370
801 Ostrum St 18015
Tel (484) 526-4000 *SIC* 8741

ST LUKES PHYSICIAN GROUP INC p 1370
801 Ostrum St Ste 1 18015
Tel (610) 954-4990 *SIC* 8741

BLOOMING GLEN, PA

GLEN BLOOMING CONTRACTORS INC p 614
901 Minsi Trl 18911
Tel (215) 257-9400 *SIC* 1611 1794

BLOOMSBURG, PA

BLOOMSBURG UNIVERSITY FOUNDATION INC p 190
400 E 2nd St 17815
Tel (570) 389-4000 *SIC* 8221 9411

SEKISUI POLYMER INNOVATIONS LLC p 1301
6685 Low St 17815
Tel (570) 387-6997 *SIC* 2821

BLOSSBURG, PA

WARD MANUFACTURING LLC p 1575
117 Gulick St 16912
Tel (570) 638-2131 *SIC* 3321 3322 3498

BLUE BALL, PA

M H EBY INC p 889
1194 Main St 17506
Tel (800) 292-4752 *SIC* 3713 5012

BLUE BELL, PA

AMERICAN INDEPENDENT INSURANCE CO INC p 74
1400 Union Meeting Rd # 250 19422
Tel (610) 832-4940 *SIC* 6331 6411

■ **AMERICAN PETROLEUM TANKERS PARENT LLC** p 77
1777 Sentry Pkwy W 19422
Tel (215) 367-1804 *SIC* 4491 4424

C&D TECHNOLOGIES INC p 233
1400 Union Meeting Rd # 110 19422
Tel (215) 619-7815
SIC 3612 3691 3613 3692 3674

CORRECTIONAL MEDICAL CARE INC p 372
980 Harvest Dr Ste 202 19422
Tel (215) 542-5800 *SIC* 6324 8742

FAMILY DINING INC p 526
1780 Swede Rd 19422
Tel (610) 277-4200 *SIC* 5812

HENKELS & MCCOY GROUP INC p 683
985 Jolly Rd 19422
Tel (215) 283-7600 *SIC* 1623

HENKELS & MCCOY INC p 683
985 Jolly Rd 19422
Tel (215) 283-7600 *SIC* 1623

KENCREST SERVICES p 810
960 Harvest Dr Ste 100a 19422
Tel (610) 825-9360 *SIC* 8361 8322 8351

MONTGOMERY COUNTY COMMUNITY COLLEGE p 986
340 Dekalb Pike 19422
Tel (215) 641-6300 *SIC* 8222

PEIRCE-PHELPS INC p 1128
516 Township Line Rd 19422
Tel (215) 879-7000 *SIC* 5075

■ **PENNSYLVANIA MANUFACTURERS ASSOCIATION INSURANCE CO** p 1130
380 Sentry Pkwy 19422
Tel (610) 397-5000 *SIC* 6331

■ **PENNSYLVANIA MANUFACTURERS INDEMNITY CO** p 1130
380 Sentry Pkwy 19422
Tel (610) 397-5000 *SIC* 6331

■ **PMA COMPANIES INC** p 1157
380 Sentry Pkwy Ste 200 19422
Tel (610) 397-5298 *SIC* 6331

U S RESTAURANTS INC p 1497
1780 Swede Rd 19422
Tel (610) 277-4200 *SIC* 5812

▲ **UNISYS CORP** p 1506
801 Lakeview Dr Ste 100 19422
Tel (215) 986-4011
SIC 7373 7378 7379 3571 3572

■ **UNITED BIOSOURCE LLC** p 1506
920 Harvest Dr Ste 200 19422
Tel (215) 591-2880 *SIC* 8731

UNITEK USA LLC p 1515
1777 Sentry Pkwy W # 302 19422
Tel (267) 464-1700 *SIC* 8742 8741

BOOTHWYN, PA

HUFF PAPER CO p 717
10 Crk Pky Namns Crk Ctr Namns Crk Cntr 19061
Tel (610) 497-5100 *SIC* 5113

OFFICE BASICS INC p 1075
22 Creek Cir 19061
Tel (610) 471-1000 *SIC* 5112

BOWMANSVILLE, PA

READING EQUIPMENT & DISTRIBUTION LLC p 1213
1363 Bowmansville Rd 17507
Tel (717) 445-6746 *SIC* 5531 7532

BOYERTOWN, PA

BOYERTOWN AREA SCHOOL DISTRICT p 205
911 Montgomery Ave 19512
Tel (610) 367-6031 *SIC* 8211

DRUG PLASTICS AND GLASS CO INC p 457
1 Bottle Dr 19512
Tel (610) 367-5000 *SIC* 3085

BRADFORD, PA

AMERICAN REFINING GROUP INC p 78
77 N Kendall Ave 16701
Tel (814) 368-1200 *SIC* 5171 2911

W R CASE & SONS CUTLERY CO p 1569
50 Owens Way 16701
Tel (800) 523-6350 *SIC* 3421

ZIPCORP INC p 1643
33 Barbour St 16701
Tel (814) 368-2700 *SIC* 3999 5172

ZIPPO MANUFACTURING CO INC p 1643
33 Barbour St 16701
Tel (814) 368-2700
SIC 3914 3993 5172 3999 3421 3172

BREINIGSVILLE, PA

CYOPTICS INC p 405
9999 Hamilton Blvd # 250 18031
Tel (484) 397-2000 *SIC* 3827

SAMUEL ADAMS PENNSYLVANIA BREWERY CO p 1275
7880 Penn Dr 18031
Tel (610) 391-4700 *SIC* 2082

WESTPORT AXLE p 1602
650 Boulder Dr Ste 100a 18031
Tel (610) 366-2900 *SIC* 5015

BRIDGEVILLE, PA

ANDERSON EQUIPMENT CO p 90
1000 Washington Pike 15017
Tel (412) 343-2300
SIC 5082 7699 7353 5531

DEVELOPMENT DIMENSIONS INTERNATIONAL INC p 433
1225 Washington Pike 15017
Tel (412) 257-0600 *SIC* 8742

■ **MAXIM CRANE WORKS HOLDINGS INC** p 922
1225 Wash Pike Ste 100 15017
Tel (412) 504-0200 *SIC* 7353 7359

■ **MAXIM CRANE WORKS LP** p 922
1225 Wash Pike Ste 100 15017
Tel (412) 504-0200 *SIC* 7353

UHDE CORP OF AMERICA p 1500
1370 Wash Pike Ste 510 15017
Tel (412) 257-8277 *SIC* 8711 7299

▲ **UNIVERSAL STAINLESS & ALLOY PRODUCTS INC** p 1517
600 Mayer St Ste 2 15017
Tel (412) 257-7600 *SIC* 3312

BRISTOL, PA

CHINA LENOX INC p 301
1414 Radcliffe St 19007
Tel (267) 525-7800 *SIC* 3263

■ **CUMMINS POWER SYSTEMS LLC** p 401
2727 Ford Rd 19007
Tel (215) 785-6005
SIC 5084 5063 7538 7629 3519

JAG FOOTWEAR ACCESSORIES AND RETAIL CORP p 776
180 Rittenhouse Cir 19007
Tel (215) 785-4000 *SIC* 5621

KASPER ASL LTD p 804
180 Rittenhouse Cir 19007
Tel (215) 785-4000 *SIC* 2337

LENOX HOLDINGS INC p 856
1414 Radcliffe St Fl 1 19007
Tel (267) 525-7800
SIC 3229 3161 5719 5948

LOWER BUCKS HOSPITAL p 881
501 Bath Rd 19007
Tel (215) 785-9200 *SIC* 8062

LUMBERMEN ASSOCIATES INC p 885
2101 Hunter Rd 19007
Tel (215) 785-4600 *SIC* 5031

MELR INC p 941
250 Rittenhouse Cir 19007
Tel (215) 785-4000 *SIC* 5621

MODERN GROUP LTD p 981
2501 Durham Rd 19007
Tel (215) 943-9100 *SIC* 5084 7353 7699

MODERN HANDLING EQUIPMENT CO p 981
2501 Durham Rd Ste G 19007
Tel (215) 943-9100 *SIC* 5084 7353

NINE WEST HOLDINGS INC p 1044
180 Rittenhouse Cir 19007
Tel (215) 785-4000 *SIC* 2337

SDI INC p 1295
1414 Radcliffe St Ste 300 19007
Tel (215) 633-1900
SIC 7374 7389 8711 8748

TELSTAR NORTH AMERICA INC p 1435
1504 Grundy Ln 19007
Tel (215) 826-0770 *SIC* 3565

BRODHEADSVILLE, PA

PLEASANT VALLEY SCHOOL DISTRICT p 1156
2233 Route 115 Ste 100 18322
Tel (570) 402-1000 *SIC* 8211

BRYN MAWR, PA

▲ **AQUA AMERICA INC** p 101
762 W Lancaster Ave 19010
Tel (610) 527-8000 *SIC* 4941 4952

■ **AQUA PENNSYLVANIA INC** p 101
762 W Lancaster Ave 19010
Tel (610) 525-1400
SIC 4941 8741 4971 1623

ARCHDIOCESE OF PHILADELPHIA p 105
222 N 17th St 19010
Tel (215) 587-3500 *SIC* 8322

▲ **BRYN MAWR BANK CORP** p 221
801 W Lancaster Ave 19010
Tel (610) 525-1700 *SIC* 6022

BRYN MAWR COLLEGE p 221
101 N Merion Ave 19010
Tel (610) 526-5000 *SIC* 8221

BRYN MAWR HOSPITAL p 221
130 S Bryn Mawr Ave 19010
Tel (610) 526-3620 *SIC* 8742

■ **BRYN MAWR TRUST CO** p 221
801 W Lancaster Ave 19010
Tel (610) 581-4819 *SIC* 6022

DELTA-T GROUP INC p 427
950 E Haverford Rd # 200 19010
Tel (610) 527-0830 *SIC* 7363

MAIN LINE HOSPITALS INC p 897
130 S Bryn Mawr Ave 19010
Tel (610) 526-3000 *SIC* 8062

MAIN LINE SERVICES p 897
950 E Haverford Rd # 110 19010
Tel (484) 337-8480 *SIC* 8011

RIDDLE MEMORIAL HOSPITAL p 1234
950 E Haverford Rd 19010
Tel (484) 337-8480 *SIC* 8062

BURNHAM, PA

STANDARD STEEL LLC p 1376
500 N Walnut St 17009
Tel (717) 242-4615 *SIC* 3312 3462

BUSHKILL, PA

RESORTS GROUP INC p 1227
Rr 209 18324
Tel (570) 588-6661 *SIC* 7011 6552

BUTLER, PA

ARMSTRONG GROUP OF COMPANIES INC p 111
1 Armstrong Pl 16001
Tel (724) 283-0925 *SIC* 4813

ARMSTRONG HOLDINGS INC p 111
1 Armstrong Pl 16001
Tel (724) 283-0925 *SIC* 1731 5999 7382

ARMSTRONG UTILITIES INC p 111
1 Armstrong Pl 16001
Tel (724) 283-0925 *SIC* 4841

BUTLER HEALTH SYSTEM INC p 230
1 Hospital Way 16001
Tel (724) 283-6666 *SIC* 8062

BUTLER HEALTHCARE PROVIDERS p 230
1 Hospital Way 16001
Tel (724) 283-6666 *SIC* 8062

HUNTER TRUCK SALES & SERVICE INC p 719
480 Pittsburgh Rd 16002
Tel (724) 586-5770 *SIC* 5511 5531 7538

■ **MARMON DISTRIBUTION SERVICES INC** p 909
225 E Cunningham St 16001
Tel (724) 283-3000 *SIC* 5051 4213

■ **MARMON/KEYSTONE LLC** p 909
225 E Cunningham St 16001
Tel (724) 283-3000 *SIC* 5051 4213

PEOPLES TWP LLC p 1133
205 N Main St 16001
Tel (724) 287-2751 *SIC* 4924

QUALITY LIFE SERVICES p 1197
612 N Main St Ste A 16001
Tel (724) 431-0770 *SIC* 5912 8051

CABOT, PA

CONCORDIA LUTHERAN MINISTRIES p 355
134 Marwood Rd 16023
Tel (724) 352-1571 *SIC* 8051

PENN UNITED TECHNOLOGIES INC p 1129
799 N Pike Rd 16023
Tel (724) 352-1507 *SIC* 3544 2819

CAMP HILL, PA

■ **AMES COMPANIES INC** p 84
465 Railroad Ave 17011
Tel (717) 737-1500 *SIC* 3423 3799 3524

FLEMING GANNETT INC p 555
207 Senate Ave 17011
Tel (717) 763-7211 *SIC* 8711

GANNETT FLEMING AFFILIATES INC p 590
207 Senate Ave 17011
Tel (717) 763-7211 *SIC* 8711 7374 6512

■ **HARCO INC** p 660
30 Hunter Ln 17011
Tel (717) 761-2633 *SIC* 5912

▲ **HARSCO CORP** p 664
350 Poplar Church Rd 17011
Tel (717) 763-7064
SIC 7359 7353 5082 3443 3585 4789

HEMPT BROS INC p 682
205 Creek Rd 17011
Tel (717) 774-2911
SIC 1611 3273 2951 1442 0212

HOLY SPIRIT HOSPITAL OF SISTERS OF CHRISTIAN CHARITY p 702
503 N 21st St 17011
Tel (717) 763-2100 *SIC* 8062

■ **MAXI DRUG INC** p 922
30 Hunter Ln 17011
Tel (717) 761-2633 *SIC* 5912

RAM INDUSTRIAL SERVICES LLC p 1206
2850 Appleton St Ste D 17011
Tel (717) 737-7810 *SIC* 5063 7629

▲ **RITE AID CORP** p 1236
30 Hunter Ln 17011
Tel (717) 761-2633 *SIC* 5912 7384 5963

■ **RITE AID OF KENTUCKY INC** p 1236
30 Hunter Ln 17011
Tel (717) 761-2633 *SIC* 5912

■ **RITE AID OF MARYLAND INC** p 1236
30 Hunter Ln 17011
Tel (717) 761-2633 *SIC* 5912

■ **RITE AID OF MICHIGAN INC** p 1236
30 Hunter Ln 17011
Tel (717) 761-2633 *SIC* 5912

■ **RITE AID OF NEW JERSEY INC** p 1236
30 Hunter Ln 17011
Tel (717) 761-2633 *SIC* 5912

■ **RITE AID OF NEW YORK INC** p 1236
30 Hunter Ln 17011
Tel (717) 761-2633 *SIC* 5912

■ **RITE AID OF OHIO INC** p 1236
30 Hunter Ln 17011
Tel (717) 761-2633 *SIC* 5912

■ **RITE AID OF PENNSYLVANIA INC** p 1236
30 Hunter Ln 17011
Tel (717) 761-2633 *SIC* 5912

■ **RITE AID OF SOUTH CAROLINA INC** p 1236
30 Hunter Ln 17011
Tel (717) 761-2633 *SIC* 5912

■ **RITE AID OF VIRGINIA INC** p 1236
30 Hunter Ln 17011
Tel (717) 761-2633 *SIC* 5912

■ **RITE AID OF WEST VIRGINIA INC** p 1236
30 Hunter Ln 17011
Tel (717) 761-2633 *SIC* 5912

CANONSBURG, PA

ANDRITZ INC p 91
500 Technology Dr 15317
Tel (724) 597-7801 *SIC* 3554 8711 7389

▲ **ANSYS INC** p 93
2600 Ansys Dr 15317
Tel (724) 746-3304 *SIC* 7372

AQUATECH INTERNATIONAL LLC p 101
1 Four Coins Dr 15317
Tel (724) 746-5300 *SIC* 3589

CCTM1 LLC p 270
2000 Corporate Dr 15317
Tel (724) 416-2000 *SIC* 4813

CENTIMARK CORP p 277
12 Grandview Cir 15317
Tel (724) 743-7777 *SIC* 1761

CNX COAL RESOURCES LP p 330
1000 Consol Energy Dr 15317
Tel (724) 485-4009 *SIC* 1241

■ **CNX GAS CORP** p 330
1000 Consol Energy Dr 15317
Tel (724) 485-4000 *SIC* 1311

■ **COLUMBIA GAS OF PENNSYLVANIA INC** p 340
121 Champion Way Ste 100 15317
Tel (724) 416-6300 *SIC* 4924

CONE MIDSTREAM PARTNERS LP p 355
1000 Consol Energy Dr 15317
Tel (724) 485-4000 SIC 4922

▲ CONSOL ENERGY INC p 359
1000 Consol Energy Dr 15317
Tel (724) 485-4000 SIC 1221 1222 1311

■ CONSOL ENERGY SALES CO p 359
1000 Consol Energy Dr 15317
Tel (724) 485-4000 SIC 5052

■ CONSOL PENNSYLVANIA COAL CO LLC p 359
1000 Consol Energy Dr 15317
Tel (724) 485-4000 SIC 1311 1222

CONSOLIDATION COAL CO INC p 360
1000 Consol Energy Dr 15317
Tel (740) 338-3100 SIC 1221

CROWN ATLANTIC CO LLC p 395
200 Corporate Dr 15317
Tel (724) 416-2000 SIC 1623

■ CROWN CASTLE USA INC p 395
2000 Corporate Dr 15317
Tel (724) 416-2000 SIC 4813

■ CROWN COMMUNICATION LLC p 395
2000 Corporate Dr 15317
Tel (724) 746-3600 SIC 4812

DRA TAGGART LLC p 455
4000 Town Center Way # 200 15317
Tel (724) 754-9800 SIC 5052

KVAERNER NORTH AMERICAN CONSTRUCTION INC p 832
701 Technology Dr 15317
Tel (724) 416-6900 SIC 1542 8741

LIGHTHOUSE ELECTRIC CO INC p 865
1957 Route 519 15317
Tel (724) 873-3500 SIC 1731

MYLAN INC p 1004
1000 Mylan Blvd 15317
Tel (724) 514-1800 SIC 2834

NICHOLSON CONSTRUCTION CO p 1042
2400 Ansys Dr Ste 303 15317
Tel (412) 221-4500 SIC 1629 1771 1799

PENNSYLVANIA TRANSFORMER TECHNOLOGY INC p 1130
30 Curry Ave Ste 2 15317
Tel (724) 873-2100 SIC 3612 5063 3677

PIPING AND EQUIPMENT p 1151
1001 Consol Energy Dr 15317
Tel (724) 514-3990 SIC 3317

PR SITE DEVELOPMENT LLC p 1167
2000 Corporate Dr 15317
Tel (724) 416-2000 SIC 4899

PRIMETALS TECHNOLOGIES USA HOLDINGS INC p 1175
501 Technology Dr 15317
Tel (724) 514-8500 SIC 5084 6719

■ RANGE RESOURCES - APPALACHIA LLC p 1208
3000 Town Center Blvd 15317
Tel (724) 743-6700 SIC 1382

▲ RICE ENERGY INC p 1232
2200 Rice Dr 15317
Tel (724) 271-7200 SIC 1311

▲ RICE MIDSTREAM PARTNERS LP p 1232
400 Woodcliff Dr 15317
Tel (724) 746-6720 SIC 4922

SOLETANCHE INC p 1338
2400 Ansys Dr Ste 303 15317
Tel (412) 221-4500 SIC 1771

VITAC CORP p 1562
101 Hillpointe Dr Ste 200 15317
Tel (724) 514-4000 SIC 4899 7819

CARBONDALE, PA

OSPREY RIDGE HEALTHCARE CENTER INC p 1097
45 N Scott St 18407
Tel (570) 282-1099 SIC 8051 8052

CARLISLE, PA

■ CARLISLE CONSTRUCTION MATERIALS LLC p 257
1285 Ritner Hwy 17013
Tel (717) 245-7000
SIC 2952 3069 5031 2899 2891

■ CARLISLE HMA INC p 257
361 Alexander Spring Rd 17015
Tel (717) 249-1212 SIC 8062

■ CARLISLE HMA LLC p 257
361 Alexander Spring Rd 17015
Tel (717) 243-1900 SIC 8062

DAILY EXPRESS INC p 408
1072 Harrisburg Pike 17013
Tel (717) 243-5757 SIC 4213

DICKINSON COLLEGE p 438
College & Louther St 17013
Tel (717) 245-1010 SIC 8221

GIANT FOOD STORES LLC p 610
1149 Harrisburg Pike 17013
Tel (717) 249-4000 SIC 5411

KEEN TRANSPORT INC p 807
1951 Harrisburg Pike 17015
Tel (717) 243-6885 SIC 4213

CARNEGIE, PA

▲ AMPCO-PITTSBURGH CORP p 86
726 Bell Ave Ste 301 15106
Tel (412) 456-4400
SIC 3312 3561 3351 3353

ARDAGH METAL PACKAGING USA INC p 106
600 N Bell Ave Ste 200 15106
Tel (412) 923-1080 SIC 3565

■ BFI WASTE SERVICES OF PENNSYLVANIA LLC p 179
73 Noblestown Rd Ste A 15106
Tel (412) 429-2600 SIC 4953

■ UNION ELECTRIC STEEL CORP p 1504
726 Bell Ave 15106
Tel (412) 429-7655 SIC 3325 3398 3312

CENTER VALLEY, PA

AVANTOR PERFORMANCE MATERIALS HOLDINGS LLC p 136
3477 Corp Pkwy Ste 200 18034
Tel (610) 573-2600 SIC 2819

AVANTOR PERFORMANCE MATERIALS INC p 136
3477 Corp Pkwy Ste 200 18034
Tel (610) 573-2600 SIC 2819

DESALES UNIVERSITY p 431
2755 Station Ave 18034
Tel (610) 282-1100 SIC 8221

OLYMPUS AMERICA INC p 1083
3500 Corporate Pkwy 18034
Tel (484) 896-5000
SIC 5047 5043 5064 3827 3695 3572

OLYMPUS CORP OF AMERICAS p 1083
3500 Corp Pkwy 18034
Tel (484) 896-5000
SIC 5047 5043 5064 3827 3695 3572

CHADDS FORD, PA

FLAGSHIP CREDIT ACCEPTANCE LLC p 554
3 Christy Dr Ste 203 19317
Tel (610) 717-1916 SIC 7389

HAAN CORP p 651
225 Wilmington W Chester 19317
Tel (717) 209-7000 SIC 5064

CHALFONT, PA

SERVICE CHAMP INC p 1307
180 New Britain Blvd 18914
Tel (215) 822-8500 SIC 5013

CHAMBERSBURG, PA

CHAMBERSBURG HOSPITAL p 287
112 N 7th St 17201
Tel (717) 267-3000 SIC 8062

DAVID H MARTIN EXCAVATING INC p 415
4961 Cumberland Hwy 17202
Tel (717) 264-1312 SIC 1623 1794 1711

MARTINS FAMOUS PASTRY SHOPPE INC p 913
1000 Potato Roll Ln 17202
Tel (717) 263-9580 SIC 2051

NURSERY SUPPLIES INC p 1067
1415 Orchard Dr 17201
Tel (717) 263-7780 SIC 3089

SUMMIT HEALTH p 1398
112 N 7th St 17201
Tel (717) 267-3000 SIC 8099

CHARLEROI, PA

LEE SUPPLY CO INC p 851
305 1st St 15022
Tel (724) 483-3543 SIC 5082 5084

VALLEY TIRE CO INC p 1541
15 Mckean Ave 15022
Tel (724) 489-4483
SIC 5531 7539 5014 7534

CHESTER SPRINGS, PA

PENNTANK LINES INC p 1129
300 Lionville Station Rd 19425
Tel (484) 713-1500 SIC 4213

TREVDAN INC p 1476
1031 Pottstown Pike 19425
Tel (610) 458-9860 SIC 5031

CHESTERBROOK, PA

1&1 INTERNET INC p 1
701 Lee Rd Ste 300 19087
Tel (877) 461-2631 SIC 7374 4813 4822

▲ AMERISOURCEBERGEN CORP p 83
1300 Morris Dr Ste 100 19087
Tel (610) 727-7000 SIC 5122 5047

■ AMERISOURCEBERGEN DRUG CORP p 83
1300 Morris Dr Ste 100 19087
Tel (610) 727-7000 SIC 5122

■ AMERISOURCEBERGEN SERVICES CORP p 83
1300 Morris Dr Ste 100 19087
Tel (610) 727-7000
SIC 5122 5047 5199 8721

CROTHALL HEALTHCARE INC p 394
1500 Liberty Ridge Dr # 210 19087
Tel (610) 576-5100 SIC 8742

CROTHALL SERVICES GROUP p 394
1500 Liberty Ridge Dr # 210 19087
Tel (610) 576-5100 SIC 7349

■ LIFESCAN INC p 864
965 Chesterbrook Blvd 19087
Tel (800) 227-8862 SIC 2835 3841

■ PLANCO FINANCIAL SERVICES INC p 1154
1500 Liberty Ridge Dr # 100 19087
Tel (610) 695-9500 SIC 6211 6311

SHIRE PHARMACEUTICALS LLC p 1317
1200 Morris Dr 19087
Tel (484) 595-8800 SIC 3826

CHESTER, PA

■ CHESTER DOWNS AND MARINA LLC p 295
777 Harrahs Blvd 19013
Tel (484) 490-1800 SIC 7011

CHESTER WATER AUTHORITY p 295
415 Welsh St 19013
Tel (610) 876-8181 SIC 4941

CROZER-CHESTER MEDICAL CENTER p 396
1 Medical Center Blvd 19013
Tel (610) 447-2000 SIC 8011

CROZER-KEYSTONE HEALTH NETWORK p 396
2602 W 9th St 19013
Tel (610) 497-7400 SIC 8059

KAMCO BUILDING SUPPLY CORP OF PENNSYLVANIA p 801
1100 Township Line Rd 19013
Tel (610) 364-1356 SIC 5031

POWER HOME REMODELING GROUP LLC p 1165
2501 Seaport Dr Lbby 1 19013
Tel (610) 874-5000 SIC 1751 1761

WIDENER UNIVERSITY p 1608
1 University Pl 19013
Tel (610) 499-4000 SIC 8221

CHESWICK, PA

■ CURTISS-WRIGHT ELECTRO-MECHANICAL CORP p 402
1000 Wright Way 15024
Tel (724) 275-5000 SIC 3561 3621 3511

ECM TRANSPORT LLC p 475
1 Rich Hill Rd 15024
Tel (724) 339-8800 SIC 4214 4213

TANDEM HEALTH CARE OF CHESWICK INC p 1424
3876 Saxonburg Blvd 15024
Tel (412) 767-4998 SIC 8051

CLAIRTON, PA

JEFFERSON HOSPITAL p 781
565 Coal Valley Rd 15025
Tel (412) 267-6024 SIC 8062 8063 8069

CLARKS SUMMIT, PA

ALLIED SERVICES FOUNDATION INC p 57
100 Abington Executive Pa 18411
Tel (570) 348-1407 SIC 8093 8361

CLAYSBURG, PA

NPC INC p 1064
13710 Dunnings Hwy 16625
Tel (814) 239-8787 SIC 2752 2789 2759

SHEETZ DISTRIBUTION SERVICES LLC p 1313
242 Sheetz Way 16625
Tel (814) 239-1600 SIC 5411

CLEARFIELD, PA

■ CNB BANK p 330
1 S 2nd St 16830
Tel (814) 765-4577 SIC 6022

▲ CNB FINANCIAL CORP p 330
1 S 2nd St 16830
Tel (814) 765-9621 SIC 6022

CLIFTON HEIGHTS, PA

CAPP INC p 251
201 Marple Ave 19018
Tel (610) 394-1100 SIC 5084 3699

COATESVILLE, PA

ARCELORMITTAL PLATE LLC p 104
139 Modena Rd 19320
Tel (610) 383-2000 SIC 3312

CHESTER COUNTY INTERMEDIATE UNIT 24 (INC) p 295
1525 E Lincoln Hwy 19320
Tel (610) 383-7400 SIC 8211

■ COATESVILLE HOSPITAL CORP p 332
201 Reeceville Rd 19320
Tel (610) 383-8000 SIC 8062

SIKORSKY GLOBAL HELICOPTERS INC p 1322
110 Stewart Huston Dr 19320
Tel (610) 644-4430 SIC 3721

COLLEGEVILLE, PA

ALLIED WIRE & CABLE INC p 57
101 Kestrel Dr 19426
Tel (484) 928-6700 SIC 5063

DFI HOLDINGS LLC p 435
3179 Deer Creek Rd 19426
Tel (610) 584-5836 SIC 6719

■ FIS DATA SYSTEMS INC p 551
200 Campus Dr 19426
Tel (484) 582-2000 SIC 7374 7372

■ FIS SYSTEMS INTERNATIONAL INC p 551
200 Campus Dr 19426
Tel (484) 582-2000 SIC 7372

■ QUEST DIAGNOSTICS CLINICAL LABORATORIES INC p 1199
1201 S Collegeville Rd 19426
Tel (610) 454-6000 SIC 8071

■ SUPERIOR TUBE CO INC p 1407
3900 Germantown Pike 19426
Tel (610) 489-5200 SIC 3317 3498

■ WYETH PHARMACEUTICALS INC p 1629
500 Arcola Rd 19426
Tel (484) 865-5000 SIC 5122 8731

COLMAR, PA

▲ DORMAN PRODUCTS INC p 451
3400 E Walnut St 18915
Tel (215) 997-1800 SIC 3714 3231 3965

■ RB DISTRIBUTION INC p 1211
3400 E Walnut St 18915
Tel (215) 997-1800 SIC 3714 3231

CONCORDVILLE, PA

LA FRANCE CORP p 835
1 Lafrance Way 19331
Tel (610) 361-4300
SIC 3089 3364 3993 5013 7389

SOUTHCO INC p 1345
210 N Brinton Lake Rd 19331
Tel (610) 459-4000 SIC 3965

TOUCHPOINT INC p 1463
210 N Brinton Lake Rd 19331
Tel (610) 459-4000 SIC 6512 3452

CONESTOGA, PA

■ TURKEY HILL LP p 1492
2601 River Rd 17516
Tel (717) 872-5461 SIC 2026 2024

CONSHOHOCKEN, PA

■ ALLIANCE CONSULTING GLOBAL HOLDINGS INC p 54
181 Washington St Ste 350 19428
Tel (610) 234-4301 SIC 7371

ALLIED SECURITY HOLDINGS LLC p 57
161 Washington St Ste 600 19428
Tel (484) 351-1300 SIC 7381 7382

ALLIED SECURITY LLC p 57
161 Washington St 19428
Tel (610) 239-1100 SIC 7381

ALLIEDBARTON AEROSPACE AND DEFENSE SERVICES LLC p 57
161 Washington St Ste 600 19428
Tel (484) 351-1300 SIC 7381 7382

ALLIEDBARTON SECURITY SERVICES LLC p 57
8 Tower Bridge 161 Wshgtn 19428
Tel (610) 239-1100 SIC 7381

AMERICAN HOMECARE SUPPLY LLC p 74
101 W Elm St Ste 210 19428
Tel (484) 530-0880 SIC 5999 7352

■ CRITICAL HOMECARE SOLUTIONS HOLDINGS INC p 393
2 Tower Brg 2 Tower Bridge 19428
Tel (610) 825-2061 SIC 8082

■ CRITICAL HOMECARE SOLUTIONS INC p 393
1 Fayette St 19428
Tel (720) 697-5200 SIC 8082

DAVIDS BRIDAL INC p 415
1001 Washington St 19428
Tel (610) 943-5000 SIC 5621

E AARON ENTERPRISES INC p 466
161 Wshington St Fl 11 19428
Tel (610) 940-0800 SIC 5111

FIRSTRUST SAVINGS BANK p 551
15 E Ridge Pike Ste 400 19428
Tel (610) 941-9898 SIC 6036

IKEA NORTH AMERICA SERVICES LLC p 731
420 Alan Wood Rd 19428
Tel (610) 834-0180 SIC 6794 5712

INDEPENDENT INSURANCE INVESTMENTS INC p 736
1000 River Rd Ste 300 19428
Tel (610) 832-4940 SIC 6331 6411

JOHN TEMPLETON FOUNDATION p 789
300 Conshohocken State Rd # 500 19428
Tel (610) 941-2828 SIC 8699

KYNETIC LLC p 833
225 Washington St 19428
Tel (484) 534-8100 SIC 8741 5961

MERCY CATHOLIC MEDICAL CENTER OF SOUTHEASTERN PENNSYLVANIA p 945
1 W Elm St 19428
Tel (610) 567-6725 SIC 8062

MERCY HEALTH FOUNDATION OF SOUTHEASTERN PENNSYLVANIA p 946
1 W Elm St Ste 100 19428
Tel (610) 567-6000 SIC 8062

MERCY HEALTH SYSTEM OF SOUTHEASTERN PENNSYLVANIA p 946
1 W Elm St Ste 100 19428
Tel (610) 567-6000 SIC 8062

NEW HORIZONS WORLDWIDE INC p 1031
100 4 Falls Corporate Ctr # 408 19428
Tel (888) 236-3625 SIC 6794 8243

▲ QUAKER CHEMICAL CORP p 1196
901 E Hector St 19428
Tel (610) 832-4000
SIC 2992 2899 2869 2891

RUMSEY ELECTRIC CO p 1258
15 Colwell Ln 19428
Tel (610) 832-9000 SIC 5063

SHARP CORP p 1312
22-23 Carland Rd 19428
Tel (610) 395-5800 SIC 7389

SMG HOLDINGS INC p 1332
300 Cnshohckn State Rd # 450 19428
Tel (610) 729-7900 SIC 6512 8742 7922

SPECTAGUARD ACQUISITION LLC p 1356
161 Washington St Ste 600 19428
Tel (484) 351-1300 SIC 7381

SPECTAGUARD HOLDING CORP p 1356
161 Washington St Ste 600 19428
Tel (610) 239-1100 SIC 7381

SUMMERWOOD CORP p 1398
14 Balligomingo Rd 19428
Tel (610) 260-1500 SIC 5812

SUPERIOR GROUP INC p 1406
100 Front St Ste 525 19428
Tel (610) 397-2040
SIC 5051 3357 3317 3491 3469 7389

TMG HEALTH INC p 1457
100 Four Falls Corporate 19428
Tel (610) 878-9111 SIC 6321

UNIVERSAL PROTECTION SERVICE LLC p 1517
161 Washington St Ste 600 19428
Tel (704) 334-4751 SIC 7381

UTILITY LINE SERVICES INC p 1537
1302 Conshohocken Rd # 100 19428
Tel (484) 685-3489 SIC 1623

VICTREX USA INC p 1556
300 Conshohocken State Rd # 120 19428
Tel (484) 342-6001 SIC 5084

COOPERSBURG, PA

LUTRON ELECTRONICS CO INC p 886
7200 Suter Rd 18036
Tel (610) 282-3800 SIC 3625

CORAOPOLIS, PA

ALLEGHENY VALLEY SCHOOL p 52
1996 Ewings Mill Rd 15108
Tel (412) 299-7777 SIC 8361

AMERICAN BRIDGE CO p 69
1000 American Bridge Way 15108
Tel (412) 631-1000 SIC 1791 8711 1622

AMERICAN BRIDGE HOLDING CO p 69
1000 American Bridge Way 15108
Tel (412) 631-1000 SIC 1791 1542

■ CENTRIA INC p 281
1005 Beaver Grade Rd # 2 15108
Tel (412) 299-8000
SIC 3444 1761 3564 3449

■ DICKS MERCHANDISING & SUPPLY CHAIN INC p 438
345 Court St 15108
Tel (724) 723-3400 SIC 5941

▲ DICKS SPORTING GOODS INC p 438
345 Court St 15108
Tel (724) 273-3400 SIC 5941 5699

ELKEM HOLDING INC p 488
Airport Office Park Bldg 15108
Tel (412) 299-7200 SIC 3313

■ FEDEX GROUND PACKAGE SYSTEM INC p 536
1000 Fed Ex Dr 15108
Tel (412) 269-1000 SIC 4213

GLOBAL INDUSTRIAL TECHNOLOGIES INC p 616
1305 Chrrington Pkwy Moon 15108
Tel (412) 375-6600
SIC 3297 3255 1459 3546 3272 3589

■ GOLF GALAXY INC p 622
345 Court St 15108
Tel (724) 273-3400 SIC 5941

HARBISON-WALKER REFRACTORIES CO p 659
1305 Cherrington Pkwy 15108
Tel (412) 375-6600 SIC 3255 3297

■ MASTECH DIGITAL TECHNOLOGIES INC p 918
1305 Cherrington Pkwy 15108
Tel (412) 787-2100 SIC 7371

NEH INC p 1024
Airport Ofc Pk Bl 2 400 R 15108
Tel (412) 299-7200 SIC 3313 6719

NORTH AMERICAN REFRACTORIES CO p 1050
1305 Cherrington Pkwy # 100 15108
Tel (412) 375-6600 SIC 3297 3255

■ RTI INTERNATIONAL METALS INC p 1256
5th Fl 1550 Crplis Hts Rd 15108
Tel (412) 893-0026 SIC 3356 3441

COUDERSPORT, PA

CHARLES COLE MEMORIAL HOSPITAL p 289
1001 E 2nd St 16915
Tel (814) 274-9300 SIC 7352 8069 8051

CRANBERRY TOWNSHIP, PA

AESYNT INC p 31
500 Cranberry Woods Dr # 400 16066
Tel (724) 741-8000 SIC 7373

■ EXCO RESOURCES (PA) LLC p 517
260 Executive Dr Ste 100 16066
Tel (724) 720-2500
SIC 1382 1381 1311 8741 6211

IPEG INC p 763
200 W Kensinger Dr # 100 16066
Tel (724) 584-5500 SIC 3559

MANHEIM REMARKETING INC p 901
21095 Route 19 16066
Tel (724) 452-5555 SIC 5012

■ MILLENNIUM PHARMACY SYSTEMS LLC p 970
100 E Kensinger Dr # 500 16066
Tel (724) 940-2490 SIC 5912

■ MINE SAFETY APPLIANCES CO LLC p 973
1000 Cranberry Woods Dr 16066
Tel (724) 776-8600
SIC 3842 3826 3823 3648 3829

▲ MSA SAFETY INC p 996
1000 Cranberry Woods Dr 16066
Tel (724) 776-8600
SIC 3842 3826 3823 3648 3829

PITTSBURGH LOGISTICS SYSTEMS INC p 1152
3120 Unionville Rd Ste 110 16066
Tel (724) 814-5100 SIC 4731

SMS TECHNICAL SERVICES LLC p 1334
210 W Kensinger Dr # 300 16066
Tel (724) 553-3420 SIC 3569 7539

■ TRACO DELAWARE INC p 1468
71 Progress Ave 16066
Tel (724) 776-7000
SIC 3442 3211 3444 3448 3354 7992

■ TRI CITY ALUMINUM CO p 1476
71 Progress Ave 16066
Tel (724) 799-8917 SIC 3442 3354 7992

TSB NUCLEAR ENERGY USA GROUP INC p 1489
1000 Westinghouse Dr 16066
Tel (412) 374-4111 SIC 3823 3559

WESTINGHOUSE ELECTRIC CO LLC p 1601
1000 Westinghouse Dr 16066
Tel (412) 374-2020
SIC 3829 8711 3823 2819

CROYDON, PA

GEORGE S COYNE CHEMICAL CO INC p 606
3015 State Rd 19021
Tel (215) 785-4500 SIC 5169

CURWENSVILLE, PA

LEZZER HOLDINGS INC p 860
311 Schofield St 16833
Tel (814) 236-0220 SIC 5211

LEZZER LUMBER INC p 860
311 Schofield St 16833
Tel (814) 236-0220 SIC 5211

DALLAS, PA

■ COMMONWEALTH TELEPHONE CO LLC p 346
100 Cte Dr Ste 2 18612
Tel (570) 631-4555 SIC 4813

■ COMMONWEALTH TELEPHONE ENTERPRISES INC p 346
100 Cte Dr Ste 2 18612
Tel (570) 631-2700 SIC 4813

METZ CULINARY MANAGEMENT INC p 957
2 Woodland Dr 18612
Tel (570) 675-8100 SIC 5461

MISERICORDIA UNIVERSITY p 975
301 Lake St 18612
Tel (570) 674-6400 SIC 8221

OFFSET PAPERBACK MFRS INC p 1076
2211 Memorial Hwy 18612
Tel (570) 675-5261 SIC 2731 2752

S&S CULINARY MANAGEMENT LLC p 1263
2 Woodland Dr 18612
Tel (570) 675-8100 SIC 5812

DALLASTOWN, PA

DALLASTOWN AREA SCHOOL DISTRICT p 410
700 New School Ln 17313
Tel (717) 244-4021 SIC 8211

■ GICHNER SYSTEMS GROUP INC p 611
490 E Locust St 17313
Tel (717) 246-5430 SIC 3795

TRI-BORO CONSTRUCTION SUPPLIES INC p 1477
465 E Locust St 17313
Tel (717) 246-3095 SIC 5082 3496 5251

DANBORO, PA

PENN ENGINEERING & MANUFACTURING CORP p 1129
5190 Old Easton Rd 18916
Tel (215) 766-8853 SIC 3429 3549 8711

DANVILLE, PA

FABTEX INC p 523
111 Woodbine Ln 17821
Tel (570) 275-7500
SIC 5072 2221 5023 2512 2392 2391

GEISINGER CLINIC p 597
100 N Academy Ave 17822
Tel (570) 271-6211 SIC 8011 8733

GEISINGER HEALTH PLAN p 597
100 N Academy Ave 17822
Tel (570) 271-8778 SIC 8011

GEISINGER HEALTH SYSTEM FOUNDATION p 597
100 N Academy Ave 17822
Tel (570) 271-6461 SIC 8741 6512 7699

GEISINGER MEDICAL CENTER p 597
100 N Academy Ave 17822
Tel (570) 271-6211 SIC 8062

GEISINGER SYSTEM SERVICES p 597
100 N Academy Ave 17822
Tel (570) 271-6211 SIC 8741 8082

DARBY, PA

MERCY FITZGERALD HOSPITAL p 946
1500 Lansdowne Ave Ste 1 19023
Tel (610) 237-4000 SIC 8062

DENVER, PA

■ COVANCE RESEARCH PRODUCTS INC p 384
310 Swamp Bridge Rd 17517
Tel (717) 336-4921 SIC 0279 2836 2834

HIGH CONCRETE GROUP LLC p 690
125 Denver Rd 17517
Tel (717) 336-9300 SIC 1791 3272

DEVON, PA

DECISIONONE CORP p 421
426 W Lancaster Ave 19333
Tel (610) 296-6000 SIC 7378

DILLSBURG, PA

ECICONSTRUCTION LLC p 475
124 W Church St 17019
Tel (717) 638-3000 SIC 1542

EICHELBERGER CONSTRUCTION INC p 481
124 W Church St 17019
Tel (717) 638-2000 SIC 1542

LOBAR INC p 872
1 Old Mill Rd 17019
Tel (717) 432-9728
SIC 1541 1542 8741 1629 1731 7371

PRESBYTERIAN HOMES INC p 1171
1 Trinity Dr E Ste 201 17019
Tel (717) 697-2255 SIC 8361

DOUGLASSVILLE, PA

STV ARCHITECTS INC p 1395
205 W Welsh Dr 19518
Tel (610) 385-8200 SIC 8711

STV CONSTRUCTION INC p 1395
205 W Welsh Dr 19518
Tel (610) 385-8200 SIC 8741

STV GROUP INC p 1395
205 W Welsh Dr 19518
Tel (610) 385-8200 SIC 8712 8711

DOWNINGTOWN, PA

CRJKK INC p 393
450 Acorn Ln 19335
Tel (610) 518-4000 SIC 5045

DOPACO INC p 451
461 Boot Rd 19335
Tel (610) 269-6048
SIC 2657 2656 3089 3792

DOWNINGTOWN AREA SCHOOL DISTRICT p 453
540 Trestle Pl 19335
Tel (610) 269-8460 SIC 8211

KM2 SOLUTIONS LLC p 824
112 Christine Dr 19335
Tel (610) 213-1408 SIC 8742

DOYLESTOWN, PA

ANTHONY & SYLVAN POOLS CORP p 94
3739 N Eastern Rd 18901
Tel (215) 489-5600 SIC 1799 5999

BIOCLINICA INC p 183
2005 S Easton Rd Ste 304 18901
Tel (267) 757-3000 SIC 8734

BUCKS COUNTY INTERMEDIATE UNIT 22 p 223
705 N Shady Retreat Rd 18901
Tel (215) 348-2940 SIC 8651

BUCKS COUNTY OF p 223
55 E Court St Fl 5 18901
Tel (215) 348-6424 SIC 9111

CALKINS MEDIA INC p 242
333 N Broad St 18901
Tel (215) 949-4000 SIC 2711

CENTRAL BUCKS SCHOOL DISTRICT p 277
20 Weldon Dr 18901
Tel (267) 893-2000 SIC 8351

DOYLESTOWN HOSPITAL HEALTH AND WELLNESS CENTER INC p 454
595 W State St 18901
Tel (215) 345-2200 SIC 8051 8062

FRED BEANS FORD INC p 575
876 N Easton Rd 18902
Tel (888) 903-2085
SIC 5511 7513 5521 5012

PENN COLOR INC p 1129
400 Old Dublin Pike 18901
Tel (215) 345-6364 SIC 2865 2816

SICOM SYSTEMS INC p 1319
4434 Progress Meadow Dr 18902
Tel (215) 489-2500 SIC 5045 3578 7379

DRESHER, PA

ASCENSUS INC p 116
200 Dryden Rd E Ste 1000 19025
Tel (215) 648-8000 SIC 6371

DREXEL HILL, PA

DELAWARE COUNTY MEMORIAL HOSPITAL p 423
501 N Lansdowne Ave 19026
Tel (610) 284-8100 SIC 8062

UPPER DARBY SCHOOL DISTRICT (INC) p 1529
4611 Bond Ave 19026
Tel (610) 789-7200 SIC 8211

DU BOIS, PA

DUBOIS REGIONAL MEDICAL CENTER INC p 459
100 Hospital Ave 15801
Tel (814) 371-2200 SIC 8093 8011

GASBARRE PRODUCTS INC p 593
590 Division St 15801
Tel (814) 371-3015 SIC 3542 3567 3544

DUNCANSVILLE, PA

HOSS'S STEAK & SEA HOUSE INC p 710
170 Patchway Rd 16635
Tel (814) 695-7600 SIC 5812 5146 5046

IMLERS POULTRY LP p 734
1887 Route 764 16635
Tel (814) 943-5563
SIC 5144 5147 5141 5142

ST PRODUCTS LLC p 1372
200 Oliphant Dr 16635
Tel (814) 693-6000 SIC 3351

VALUE DRUG CO p 1542
195 Theater Dr 16635
Tel (814) 944-9316 SIC 5122

DUNMORE, PA

GERTRUDE HAWK CHOCOLATES INC p 609
9 Keystone Industrial Par 18512
Tel (570) 342-7556 SIC 2064 2066

DUQUESNE, PA

AMERICAN TEXTILE CO INC p 80
10 N Linden St 15110
Tel (412) 948-1020 SIC 5719 2392

EAGLEVILLE, PA

STREAMLIGHT INC p 1393
30 Eagleville Rd Ste 1 19403
Tel (610) 631-0600 SIC 3648

EAST BUTLER, PA

CONSOLIDATED GLASS HOLDINGS INC p 359
500 Grant Ave Ste 201 16029
Tel (866) 412-6977
SIC 5039 3211 6719 1793

EAST EARL, PA

CONESTOGA WOOD SPECIALTIES CORP p 355
245 Reading Rd 17519
Tel (717) 445-6701 SIC 2431 2521 2434

MARTIN LIMESTONE INC p 912
3580 Division Hwy 17519
Tel (717) 335-4500
SIC 3273 3271 1611 1422 8741 5211

EAST GREENVILLE, PA

▲ KNOLL INC p 824
1235 Water St 18041
Tel (215) 679-7991 SIC 2521 2522 2299

EAST NORRITON, PA

EINSTEIN MEDICAL CENTER MONTGOMERY p 482
559 W Germantown Pike 19403
Tel (484) 622-1000 SIC 8011

HIGHPOINT SOLUTIONS LLC p 692
301 E Germantown Pike # 1 19401
Tel (610) 233-2700 SIC 7371

MERCY SUBURBAN HOSPITAL p 948
2701 Dekalb Pike 19401
Tel (215) 748-9000 SIC 8062

MONTGOMERY HOSPITAL p 986
559 W Germantown Pike 19403
Tel (215) 456-7890 SIC 8062

EAST STROUDSBURG, PA

AMERICAS BUSINESS SOLUTION LLC p 81
1070 Coolbaugh Rd 18302
Tel (718) 308-1331 SIC 8741 8742

BUSHKILL GROUP INC p 229
1008 Sand Hill Creek Rd 18302
Tel (570) 588-6661 SIC 7011

EAST STROUDSBURG AREA SCHOOL DISTRICT p 471
50 Vine St 18301
Tel (570) 424-8500 SIC 8211

EAST STROUDSBURG UNIVERSITY p 471
200 Prospect St Ste 1 18301
Tel (570) 422-3211 SIC 8221 9411

POCONO HEALTH SYSTEM p 1158
206 E Brown St 18301
Tel (570) 421-4000 SIC 8062

POCONO MEDICAL CENTER p 1158
206 E Brown St 18301
Tel (570) 421-4000 SIC 8062

VIGON INTERNATIONAL INC p 1556
127 Airport Rd 18301
Tel (570) 476-4172 SIC 2869 5149 2077

EASTON, PA

BROWN-DAUB INC p 220
3903 Hecktown Rd 18045
Tel (610) 253-3521 SIC 5511

COLONIAL INTERMEDIATE UNIT 20 p 337
6 Danforth Dr 18045
Tel (610) 252-5550 SIC 8211

COUNTY OF NORTHAMPTON p 380
669 Washington St 18042
Tel (610) 559-3000 SIC 9111

CRAYOLA LLC p 389
1100 Church Ln 18040
Tel (610) 253-6271
SIC 3952 3951 3295 3944

EMPLOYEE BENEFIT TR OF EASTERN PA p 494
6 Danforth Dr 18045
Tel (610) 515-6412 SIC 6351 8699 6321

FOLLETT CORP p 563
801 Church Ln 18040
Tel (610) 252-7301 SIC 3585

LAFAYETTE COLLEGE p 837
730 High St 18042
Tel (610) 330-5000 SIC 8221

LEHIGH BLUE PRINT CO INC p 853
2000 Butler St 18042
Tel (610) 253-3303 SIC 7334

MCS INDUSTRIES INC p 932
2280 Newlins Mill Rd 18045
Tel (610) 253-6268
SIC 2499 3089 3499 3993 3231

MOLDED ACOUSTICAL PRODUCTS OF EASTON INC p 982
3 Danforth Dr 18045
Tel (610) 253-7135 SIC 3296

■ **NORTHAMPTON HOSPITAL CORP** p 1054
250 S 21st St 18042
Tel (610) 250-4000 SIC 8062

PHILLIPS FEED SERVICE INC p 1144
3747 Hecktown Rd 18045
Tel (610) 250-2099 SIC 5199

ST LUKES HOSPITAL - ANDERSON CAMPUS p 1370
1872 St Lukes Blvd 18045
Tel (484) 503-3000 SIC 8062

VICTAULIC CO p 1555
4901 Kesslersville Rd 18040
Tel (610) 559-3300
SIC 3321 3491 3494 5085

EAU CLAIRE, PA

TRI-STATE GARDEN SUPPLY INC p 1477
And Sandy Pt Rd Rr 38 16030
Tel (724) 867-1711 SIC 5191

EBENSBURG, PA

MCANENY BROTHERS INC p 926
470 Industrial Park Rd 15931
Tel (814) 472-9800
SIC 5141 5147 5148 5194 5113 5142

EDDYSTONE, PA

DELPHINUS ENGINEERING INC p 425
1510 Chester Pike Ste 380 19022
Tel (610) 874-9160 SIC 8711

EIGHTY FOUR, PA

84 LUMBER CO p 4
1019 Route 519 15330
Tel (724) 228-8820
SIC 2431 2439 5031 5211

ELIZABETHTOWN, PA

ELIZABETHTOWN COLLEGE p 487
1 Alpha Dr 17022
Tel (717) 361-1000 SIC 8221

MASONIC VILLAGES OF GRAND LODGE OF PENNSYLVANIA p 916
1 Masonic Dr 17022
Tel (717) 367-1121 SIC 8361

MESSICK FARM EQUIPMENT INC p 951
187 Merts Dr 17022
Tel (800) 222-3373 SIC 5083 5082

MUSICIANS LIVEORG p 1002
77 Brookfield Dr 17022
Tel (717) 413-3265 SIC 5736 5961 7389

ELIZABETHVILLE, PA

RITESCREEN CO LLC p 1237
4314 State Route 209 17023
Tel (717) 362-7483 SIC 3442 2431

ELLWOOD CITY, PA

ELLWOOD GROUP INC p 489
600 Commercial Ave 16117
Tel (724) 752-3680 SIC 3312 3462

ELVERSON, PA

SINGER EQUIPMENT CO INC p 1326
150 S Twin Valley Rd 19520
Tel (610) 387-6400 SIC 5046

WHITFORD WORLDWIDE CO p 1606
47 Park Ave 19520
Tel (610) 286-3500 SIC 2891

EMMAUS, PA

■ **BUCKEYE PIPE LINE CO L P** p 223
5002 Buckeye Rd 18049
Tel (484) 232-4000 SIC 4613

EAST PENN SCHOOL DISTRICT p 470
800 Pine St 18049
Tel (610) 966-8300 SIC 8211

RODALE INC p 1246
400 S 10th St 18049
Tel (800) 848-4735 SIC 2721 2731

EPHRATA, PA

■ **D&E COMMUNICATIONS INC** p 407
124 E Main St Fl 6 17522
Tel (717) 733-4101 SIC 4813 4841

EPHRATA COMMUNITY HOSPITAL INC p 504
169 Martin Ave 17522
Tel (717) 721-5883 SIC 8062

FOUR SEASONS PRODUCE INC p 572
400 Wabash Rd 17522
Tel (717) 721-2800 SIC 5148

ERIE, PA

ALLIANCE PLASTICS INC p 55
3123 Station Rd 16510
Tel (814) 899-7671 SIC 5162 5065

ALSTOM SIGNALING OPERATION LLC p 61
2901 E Lake Rd Bldg 122 16531
Tel (800) 825-3178
SIC 3669 5088 3672 3663

AMTHOR STEEL INC p 87
1717 Gaskell Ave 16503
Tel (814) 452-4700 SIC 3441

BAYFRONT REGIONAL DEVELOPMENT CORP p 161
201 State St 16550
Tel (814) 877-7000 SIC 8011

CA CURTZE CO p 234
1717 E 12th St 16511
Tel (814) 452-2281 SIC 5141 5147 5142

CATHOLIC DIOCESE OF ERIE p 266
429 E Grandview Blvd 16504
Tel (814) 824-1111 SIC 8661

COUNTRY FAIR INC p 375
2251 E 30th St 16510
Tel (814) 898-1111 SIC 5411 5541

COUNTY OF ERIE p 378
140 W 6th St Erie 16501
Tel (814) 451-6000 SIC 9111

DR GERTRUDE A BARBER CENTER INC p 454
100 Barber Pl 16507
Tel (814) 453-7661 SIC 8361 8211

ERIE FAMILY LIFE INSURANCE CO INC p 508
100 Erie Insurance Pl 16530
Tel (814) 870-2000 SIC 6331

ERIE INSURANCE EXCHANGE ACTIVITIES ASSOCIATION INC p 508
100 Erie Insurance Pl 16530
Tel (800) 458-0811 SIC 6331

▲ **ERIE INSURANCE GROUP EMPLOYEES** p 508
100 Erie Insurance Pl 16530
Tel (814) 870-2000 SIC 6411 8741

ERIEZ MANUFACTURING CO p 508
2200 Asbury Rd 16506
Tel (814) 835-6000 SIC 3559

GANNON UNIVERSITY p 591
109 University Sq 16541
Tel (814) 871-7000 SIC 8221

HAMOT HEALTH FOUNDATION p 656
201 State St 16550
Tel (814) 877-7020 SIC 8741 8062 6514

LAKE ERIE COLLEGE OF OSTEOPATHIC MEDICINE INC p 839
1858 W Grandview Blvd 16509
Tel (814) 866-3986 SIC 8221

LOGISTICS PLUS INC p 875
1406 Peach St Ste 3 16501
Tel (814) 461-7600 SIC 4731

MERCYHURST UNIVERSITY p 948
501 E 38th St 16546
Tel (814) 824-2000
SIC 8221 8243 8742 8299

MILLCREEK TOWNSHIP SCHOOL DISTRICT p 970
3740 W 26th St 16506
Tel (814) 835-5300 SIC 8211 9111

PATTERSON-ERIE CORP p 1121
1250 Tower Ln Ste 1 16505
Tel (814) 455-8031 SIC 5812 6531 4522

PLASTEK INDUSTRIES INC p 1155
2425 W 23rd St 16506
Tel (814) 878-4400 SIC 3089

■ **PRESQUE ISLE DOWNS INC** p 1172
8199 Perry Hwy 16509
Tel (814) 860-8999 SIC 7011

SAINT VINCENT HEALTH CENTER INC p 1271
232 W 25th St 16544
Tel (814) 452-5000 SIC 8062

SAINT VINCENT HEALTH SYSTEM p 1271
232 W 25th St 16544
Tel (814) 452-5000 SIC 8741 8011

SCHOOL DISTRICT OF CITY OF ERIE p 1289
148 W 21st St 16502
Tel (814) 874-6000 SIC 8211

SCOTTS PEEK N PEAK LLC p 1294
2225 Downs Dr 16509
Tel (814) 868-9518 SIC 7011 7992

UPMC HAMOT p 1528
201 State St 16550
Tel (814) 877-6000 SIC 8062

EXETER, PA

■ **KEYSTONE AUTOMOTIVE HOLDINGS INC** p 815
44 Tunkhannock Ave 18643
Tel (570) 655-4514 SIC 5013 5531

■ **KEYSTONE AUTOMOTIVE OPERATIONS INC** p 815
44 Tunkhannock Ave 18643
Tel (570) 655-4514 SIC 5531 5013

■ **KEYSTONE AUTOMOTIVE WAREHOUSE** p 815
44 Tunkhannock Ave 18643
Tel (570) 655-4514 SIC 5013

PRIDE MOBILITY PRODUCTS CORP p 1174
182 Susquehanna Ave 18643
Tel (570) 655-5574 SIC 3842 3799 3751

EXPORT, PA

DURA-BOND INDUSTRIES INC p 462
2658 Puckety Dr 15632
Tel (724) 327-0280 SIC 3441 3479

FS-ELLIOTT CO LLC p 582
5710 Mellon Rd 15632
Tel (724) 387-3200 SIC 3563

OERLIKON USA HOLDING INC p 1075
5700 Mellon Rd 15632
Tel (303) 273-9700
SIC 3563 3823 3699 3479 3599 5084

EXTON, PA

ANALYTICAL GRAPHICS INC p 88
220 Valley Creek Blvd 19341
Tel (610) 981-8000 SIC 7372

BENTLEY SYSTEMS INC p 173
685 Stockton Dr 19341
Tel (610) 458-5000 SIC 7372 7373

CITADEL FEDERAL CREDIT UNION INC p 309
520 Eagleview Blvd 19341
Tel (610) 380-6000 SIC 6061

INTERNET PIPELINE INC p 757
222 Valley Creek Blvd # 300 19341
Tel (484) 348-6555 SIC 7372

NASH KENSEY CORP p 1008
735 Pennsylvania Dr 19341
Tel (484) 713-2100 SIC 3841

▲ **OMEGA FLEX INC** p 1084
451 Creamery Way 19341
Tel (610) 524-7272 SIC 3599 3429

PEOPLES BENEFIT LIFE INSURANCE CO p 1132
300 Eagleview Blvd 19341
Tel (610) 648-5000 SIC 6311 6321

PHYSIOTHERAPY ASSOCIATES INC p 1146
855 Springdale Dr Ste 200 19341
Tel (610) 644-7824 SIC 8049 8093

PHYSIOTHERAPY CORP p 1146
855 Springdale Dr Ste 200 19341
Tel (610) 644-7824 SIC 8049

PHYSIOTHERAPY-BMI INC p 1146
855 Springdale Dr Ste 200 19341
Tel (610) 644-7824 SIC 8049

■ **TITANIUM METALS CORP** p 1456
224 Valley Creek Blvd # 200 19341
Tel (610) 968-1300 SIC 3356

TW METALS INC p 1494
760 Constitution Dr # 204 19341
Tel (610) 458-1300 SIC 1761

▲ **WEST PHARMACEUTICAL SERVICES INC** p 1595
530 Herman O West Dr 19341
Tel (610) 594-2900
SIC 3069 3466 2673 3085 3089

WETHERILL ASSOCIATES INC p 1603
411 Eagleview Blvd # 100 19341
Tel (484) 875-6600 SIC 5013

WOLFINGTON BODY CO INC p 1621
N Off Pa Tpk Exit Rr 100 19341
Tel (610) 458-8501 SIC 3711 3713 5012

XL ENVIRONMENTAL INC p 1632
505 Eagleview Blvd # 100 19341
Tel (800) 327-1414 SIC 6411 8748

FAIRLESS HILLS, PA

ABINGTON RELDAN METALS LLC p 11
550 Old Bordentown Rd 19030
Tel (267) 316-2000 SIC 3339

STRICK CORP p 1393
225 Lincoln Hwy 19030
Tel (215) 949-3600
SIC 3715 2426 3713 3537

FAIRVIEW, PA

SPECTRUM CONTROL INC p 1357
8061 Avonia Rd 16415
Tel (814) 474-2207
SIC 3677 3663 3612 3676

SPECTRUM MICROWAVE INC p 1357
8061 Avonia Rd 16415
Tel (814) 474-4300 SIC 3679

FARRELL, PA

FARRELL AREA SCHOOL DISTRICT p 530
1600 Roemer Blvd 16121
Tel (724) 346-6585 SIC 8211

NLMK PENNSYLVANIA LLC p 1045
15 Roemer Blvd 16121
Tel (724) 983-6464 SIC 3316 3356 3312

FEASTERVILLE TREVOSE, PA

ADVERTISING SPECIALTY INSTITUTE INC p 27
4800 E Street Rd Ste 100a 19053
Tel (215) 953-4000 SIC 2721 7372

ALPHA SHIRT CO p 60
6 Neshaminy Interplex Dr # 6 19053
Tel (215) 291-0300 SIC 5136 5137

CEI GROUP INC p 272
4850 E Street Rd Ste 200 19053
Tel (215) 364-5600 SIC 6411 7532

GAMESA TECHNOLOGY CORP INC p 590
1150 Northbrook Dr # 300 19053
Tel (215) 710-3100 SIC 6719 3621

■ **GE INFRASTRUCTURE SENSING** p 596
4636 Somerton Rd 19053
Tel (617) 926-1749
SIC 3589 2086 4941 3559 2899 3823

KENNEDY AUTOMOTIVE GROUP INC p 811
620 Bustleton Pike 19053
Tel (215) 357-6600 SIC 5511

OLIVER-TOLAS HEALTHCARE PACKAGING INC p 1082
905 Pennsylvania Blvd 19053
Tel (215) 322-7900 SIC 2671

STONEMOR GP LLC p 1391
3600 Horizon Blvd Ste 100 19053
Tel (215) 826-2947 SIC 6553

FINLEYVILLE, PA

W G TOMKO INC p 1568
2559 State Route 88 15332
Tel (724) 348-2000 SIC 1711

FLEETWOOD, PA

FLEETWOOD AREA SCHOOL DISTRICT p 555
801 N Richmond St 19522
Tel (610) 944-8111 SIC 8211

FOLCROFT, PA

AMERICAN EXPEDITING CO p 72
801 Primos Ave 19032
Tel (484) 540-8180 SIC 4215 4513

FOLSOM, PA

RIDLEY SCHOOL DISTRICT AUTHORITY p 1234
901 Morton Ave Unit A 19033
Tel (610) 534-1900 SIC 8211

FOMBELL, PA

VEKA HOLDINGS INC p 1547
100 Veka Dr 16123
Tel (724) 452-1000 SIC 3089

VEKA INC p 1547
100 Veka Dr 16123
Tel (800) 654-5589 SIC 3089

FORT WASHINGTON, PA

COVENTRY FIRST LLC p 384
7111 Valley Green Rd 19034
Tel (877) 836-8300 SIC 6311

COVENTRY GROUP INC p 384
7111 Valley Green Rd # 320 19034
Tel (215) 233-5100 SIC 6311

■ GMAC MORTGAGE SECURITIES INC p 619
1100 Virginia Dr 19034
Tel (215) 682-1000 SIC 6211

KAPPA MEDIA GROUP INC p 803
40 Skippack Pike 19034
Tel (215) 643-5800 SIC 2721 2741 5111

▲ KULICKE AND SOFFA INDUSTRIES INC p 832
1005 Virginia Dr 19034
Tel (215) 784-6000 SIC 3674

LARON PHARMA INC p 845
500 Office Center Dr # 400 19034
Tel (267) 575-1470 SIC 2834 5122

LINCOLN INVESTMENT PLANNING LLC p 867
601 Office Center Dr # 200 19034
Tel (215) 887-8111 SIC 6211 6282

MONTGOMERY CAPITAL INC p 986
7111 Valley Green Rd 19034
Tel (877) 836-8300 SIC 8322

▲ NUTRISYSTEM INC p 1068
600 Office Center Dr 19034
Tel (215) 706-5300 SIC 5961

PETROCHOICE HOLDINGS INC p 1139
1300 Virginia Dr Ste 405 19034
Tel (267) 705-2015 SIC 5172

RESEARCH PHARMACEUTICAL SERVICES INC p 1226
520 Virginia Dr 19034
Tel (215) 540-0700 SIC 8099

SEVERN TRENT SERVICES INC p 1309
220 Gibraltar Rd Ste 200 19034
Tel (215) 646-9201 SIC 8748 3589

TRANSWORLD SYSTEMS INC p 1473
500 Virginia Dr Ste 514 19034
Tel (703) 757-0977 SIC 7322

FRANKLIN, PA

IA CONSTRUCTION CORP p 725
24 Gibb Rd 16323
Tel (814) 432-3184
SIC 1611 2951 1622 1623

FREDERICKSBURG, PA

FARMERS PRIDE INC p 530
154 W Main St 17026
Tel (717) 865-6626 SIC 2015

SECHLER FAMILY FOODS INC p 1298
154 W Main St 17026
Tel (717) 865-6626 SIC 2015

FREEPORT, PA

OBERG INDUSTRIES INC p 1072
2301 Silverville Rd 16229
Tel (724) 295-2121 SIC 3469 3545

FRIEDENS, PA

PBS COALS INC p 1123
1576 Stoystown Rd 15541
Tel (814) 443-4668 SIC 1221

GETTYSBURG, PA

GETTYSBURG COLLEGE p 609
300 N Washington St 17325
Tel (717) 337-6000 SIC 8221

GETTYSBURG HOSPITAL p 609
147 Gettys St 17325
Tel (717) 334-2121 SIC 8062

GIBSONIA, PA

■ NORTH PITTSBURGH SYSTEMS INC p 1053
4008 Gibsonia Rd 15044
Tel (724) 443-9600 SIC 4813 5065

GLASSPORT, PA

EARTH SUPPORT SERVICES INC p 469
25 Allegheny Sq 15045
Tel (412) 664-7788 SIC 1241

MILL SERVICES CORP p 969
12 Monongahela Ave 15045
Tel (412) 678-6141
SIC 3295 1422 8742 3341

TMS INTERNATIONAL CORP p 1457
12 Monongahela Ave 15045
Tel (412) 678-6141
SIC 3312 4731 3399 7359 4213

TMS INTERNATIONAL HOLDING CORP p 1457
12 Monongahela Ave 15045
Tel (412) 678-6141
SIC 3312 4731 3399 7359 4213

TMS INTERNATIONAL LLC p 1458
12 Monongahela Ave 15045
Tel (412) 678-6141
SIC 3312 4731 3399 7359 4213

GLEN ROCK, PA

ADHESIVES RESEARCH INC p 22
400 Seaks Run Rd 17327
Tel (717) 235-7979 SIC 2891

RAILNET DR INC p 1205
100 School St Apt B 17327
Tel (717) 817-1472 SIC 4011

GLENSIDE, PA

ARCADIA UNIVERSITY p 103
450 S Easton Rd 19038
Tel (215) 572-2900 SIC 8221

GLASGOW INC p 614
104 Willow Grove Ave 19038
Tel (215) 884-8800 SIC 2951 1611 1623

RGS INC p 1231
527 N Easton Rd 19038
Tel (215) 885-5400 SIC 5511

GRANTVILLE, PA

MOUNTAINVIEW THOROUGHBRED RACING ASSOCIATION LLC p 994
777 Hollywood Blvd 17028
Tel (717) 469-2211 SIC 7999

GRATZ, PA

MI WINDOWS AND DOORS INC p 959
650 W Market St 17030
Tel (717) 365-3300 SIC 3089 3442

GREENCASTLE, PA

GROVE INVESTORS INC p 642
1542 Buchanan Trl E 17225
Tel (717) 597-8121 SIC 3531

GREENSBURG, PA

■ ALLEGHENY ENERGY INC p 52
800 Cabin Hill Dr 15601
Tel (724) 837-3000 SIC 4911

■ ALLEGHENY ENERGY SERVICE CORP p 52
800 Cabin Hill Dr 15601
Tel (724) 837-3000 SIC 4911

■ ALLEGHENY ENERGY SUPPLY CO LLC p 52
800 Cabin Hill Dr 15601
Tel (724) 837-3000 SIC 4911

EXCELA HEALTH HOLDING CO INC p 516
532 W Pittsburgh St 15601
Tel (724) 832-4000
SIC 8062 8093 5999 7363 7322 8361

HEMPFIELD AREA SCHOOL DISTRICT p 682
4347 State Route 136 15601
Tel (724) 834-2590 SIC 8211

■ OLD REPUBLIC INSURANCE CO p 1081
133 Oakland Ave 15601
Tel (724) 838-5400 SIC 6411 6321 6311

POLYMER ENTERPRISES INC p 1160
4731 State Route 30 # 401 15601
Tel (724) 838-2340 SIC 3069 3011

ROMAN CATHOLIC DIOCESE OF GREENSBURG p 1248
723 E Pittsburgh St 15601
Tel (724) 837-0901 SIC 8661

SCOTT ELECTRIC CO p 1293
1000 S Main St 15601
Tel (800) 442-8045 SIC 5063

SCOTT ENTERPRISES INC p 1293
1000 S Main St 15601
Tel (814) 868-9500 SIC 8741

■ WEST PENN POWER CO p 1595
800 Cabin Hill Dr 15601
Tel (724) 837-3000 SIC 4911

WESTMORELAND COUNTY COURTHOUSE p 1602
2 N Main St Ste 101 15601
Tel (724) 830-3752 SIC 9121

WESTMORELAND REGIONAL HOSPITAL p 1602
532 W Pittsburgh St 15601
Tel (724) 832-4000 SIC 8062

GREENVILLE, PA

■ FIRST NATIONAL BANK OF PENNSYLVANIA p 548
166 Main St 16125
Tel (724) 588-6770 SIC 6021

NEW WERNER HOLDING CO INC p 1033
93 Werner Rd 16125
Tel (724) 588-2000
SIC 3499 3355 3089 3446 2499 6512

OLD LADDER CO p 1081
93 Werner Rd 16125
Tel (888) 523-3371
SIC 3446 3089 3334 3444 3499

U P M C HORIZON p 1497
110 N Main St 16125
Tel (724) 588-2100 SIC 8062

WERNER CO p 1592
93 Werner Rd 16125
Tel (724) 588-2000
SIC 3499 3355 3089 3446 2499

WERNER HOLDING CO (PA) INC p 1593
93 Werner Rd 16125
Tel (888) 523-3371
SIC 3499 3355 3089 3446 2499

GROVE CITY, PA

ESSEX BROKERAGE p 510
57 Center Church Rd 16127
Tel (724) 748-3126 SIC 4731

US INVESTIGATIONS SERVICES LLC p 1532
125 Lincoln Ave 16127
Tel (724) 458-1750 SIC 7381

HANOVER TOWNSHIP, PA

BEKINS A-1 MOVERS INC p 169
125 Stewart Rd 18706
Tel (570) 793-2586 SIC 4213

HANOVER, PA

HANOVER FOODS CORP p 658
1486 York St 17331
Tel (717) 632-6000
SIC 2033 2032 2037 2038 2099

HANOVER HEALTH CORP INC p 658
300 Highland Ave 17331
Tel (717) 637-3711 SIC 8062 8011 5912

HANOVER HOSPITAL INC p 658
300 Highland Ave 17331
Tel (717) 637-3711 SIC 8062

■ PCA CORRUGATED AND DISPLAY LLC p 1123
148 Penn St 17331
Tel (717) 632-4727 SIC 2653 5113

R H SHEPPARD CO INC p 1202
101 Philadelphia St 17331
Tel (717) 637-3751 SIC 3714 3321 3594

■ S-L DISTRIBUTION CO INC p 1263
1250 York St 17331
Tel (717) 632-4477 SIC 5145

■ S-L SNACKS REAL ESTATE INC p 1263
1250 York St 17331
Tel (717) 632-4477 SIC 2052 2096

UTZ QUALITY FOODS LLC p 1537
900 High St 17331
Tel (800) 367-7629 SIC 2096 2052 2099

HARLEYSVILLE, PA

DEACON INDUSTRIAL SUPPLY CO INC p 419
1510 Gehman Rd 19438
Tel (215) 256-1715 SIC 5074 5085

HARLEYSVILLE GROUP INC p 662
355 Maple Ave 19438
Tel (215) 256-9773 SIC 6331 6411

HARLEYSVILLE MUTUAL INSURANCE CO p 662
355 Maple Ave 19438
Tel (215) 256-5000 SIC 6311 6331

HARMONY, PA

■ SYSCO PITTSBURGH LLC p 1417
1 Whitney Dr 16037
Tel (724) 452-2100
SIC 5142 5149 5148 5023 5113 5046

HARRISBURG, PA

44 NEW ENGLAND MANAGEMENT CO p 3
450 Friendship Rd 17111
Tel (717) 412-5500 SIC 7011

ADMINISTRATIVE OFFICE OF PENNSYLVANIA COURTS p 23
601 Commonwealth Ave # 1500 17120
Tel (717) 231-3300 SIC 9211

ALLEGHENY ELECTRIC COOP INC p 52
212 Locust St Ste 500 17101
Tel (717) 233-5704 SIC 4911 8741

AMERICAN EDUCATIONAL SERVICES CORP p 71
1200 N 7th St 17102
Tel (717) 720-2700 SIC 6111

ARMY NATIONAL GUARD PENNSYLVANIA p 112
14th & Calder St 17103
Tel (717) 787-5113 SIC 9711

CAPITAL BLUE CROSS p 249
2500 Elmerton Ave 17177
Tel (717) 541-7000 SIC 6321

CENTRAL DAUPHIN SCHOOL DISTRICT AUTHORITY p 278
600 Rutherford Rd 17109
Tel (717) 540-4606 SIC 8211

CIESCO INC p 306
109 Miller Ln 17110
Tel (717) 232-5825
SIC 5032 5033 5169 5039

CLARK RESOURCES INC p 322
321 N Front St 17101
Tel (717) 230-8861 SIC 8741

CLEVELAND BROTHERS HOLDINGS INC p 325
5300 Paxton St 17111
Tel (717) 564-2121
SIC 7353 5082 5084 7629

COMMONWEALTH CHARTER ACADEMY p 346
4050 Crums Mill Rd # 303 17112
Tel (717) 651-7200 SIC 8211

COMMONWEALTH OF PENNSYLVANIA p 346
238 Main Capitol Building 17120
Tel (717) 787-5962 SIC 9111

COUNTY OF DAUPHIN p 377
Market & Front Sts 17101
Tel (717) 780-6300 SIC 9111

■ CRUMP LIFE INSURANCE SERVICES INC p 396
4135 N Front St 17110
Tel (717) 657-2740 SIC 6411

D & H DISTRIBUTING CO p 406
2525 N 7th St 17110
Tel (717) 236-8001
SIC 5045 5065 5064 5063 5044

DEPARTMENT OF HEALTH PENNSYLVANIA p 430
625 Forster St 17120
Tel (717) 787-6325 SIC 9431

DEPT OF EDUCATION PENNSYLVANIA p 431
333 Market St 17101
Tel (717) 787-5820 SIC 9411

EXECUTIVE OFFICE OF COMMONWEALTH OF PENNSYLVANIA p 517
225 Capitol Bldg 17120
Tel (717) 787-5962 SIC 9111

FEESERS INC p 537
5561 Grayson Rd 17111
Tel (717) 248-9658 SIC 5141

FIVE STAR INTERNATIONAL LLC p 553
1810 S 19th St 17104
Tel (717) 986-1500 SIC 5511 7538 5013

GOODWILL KEYSTONE AREA p 625
1150 Goodwill Dr 17101
Tel (610) 777-7875 SIC 8331

HARRISBURG AREA COMMUNITY COLLEGE FOUNDATION p 664
1 Hacc Dr 17110
Tel (717) 780-2300 SIC 8222

HARRISBURG NEWS CO p 664
980 Briarsdale Rd 17109
Tel (717) 561-8377 SIC 5192

HARRISBURG SCHOOL DISTRICT INC p 664
1601 State St 17103
Tel (717) 703-4000 SIC 8211

HERSHA HOSPITALITY MANAGEMENT LP p 687
44 Hersha Dr Fl 1 17102
Tel (717) 412-5500 SIC 7011

HERSHA HOSPITALITY TRUST p 687
44 Hersha Dr 17102
Tel (717) 236-4400 SIC 6798

HERSHEY CREAMERY CO p 687
301 S Cameron St 17101
Tel (717) 238-8134 SIC 2024

HOUSE OF REPRESENTATIVES PENNSYLVANIA p 711
Main Capitol Bldg Rm 132 17120
Tel (717) 787-3607 SIC 9121

KEYSTONE HUMAN SERVICES p 815
124 Pine St 17101
Tel (717) 232-7509 SIC 8322

KEYSTONE PEER REVIEW ORGANIZATION INC p 816
777 E Park Dr 17111
Tel (717) 564-8288 SIC 8099

KEYSTONE SERVICE SYSTEMS INC p 816
124 Pine St 17101
Tel (717) 232-7509 SIC 8361

LEGISLATIVE OFFICE OF COMMONWEALTH OF PENNSYLVANIA p 853
Main Capitol Bldg Rm 225 17120
Tel (717) 787-5962 SIC 9121

LIQUOR CONTROL BOARD PENNSYLVANIA p 870
Nw Office Bldg 910 17124
Tel (717) 787-7963 SIC 9651

■ MC CLURE CO INC p 925
4101 N 6th St 17110
Tel (717) 232-9743 SIC 1711

METRO BANCORP INC p 954
3801 Paxton St 17111
Tel (888) 937-0004 SIC 6022

NEW WORLD PASTA CO p 1033
85 Shannon Rd 17112
Tel (717) 526-2200 SIC 2098

▲ OLLIES BARGAIN OUTLET HOLDINGS INC p 1082
6295 Allentown Blvd Ste 1 17112
Tel (717) 657-2300 SIC 5399 5311

■ OLLIES BARGAIN OUTLET INC p 1082
6295 Allentown Blvd Ste 1 17112
Tel (717) 657-8243 SIC 6799

■ OLLIES HOLDINGS INC p 1082
6295 Allentown Blvd Ste 1 17112
Tel (717) 657-2300 SIC 6799

PA EMPLOYEES BENEFIT TRUST FUND (INC) p 1103
150 S 43rd St Ste 1 17111
Tel (717) 561-4750 SIC 6411

PENN NATIONAL HOLDING CORP p 1129
2 N 2nd St Ste 2 17101
Tel (717) 234-4941 SIC 6712

PENNSY SUPPLY INC p 1130
1001 Paxton St 17104
Tel (717) 233-4511
SIC 1422 2951 3273 4212 5032

PENNSYLVANIA DEPARTMENT OF CONSERVATION & NATURAL RESOURCES p 1130
400 Market St Fl 7 17101
Tel (717) 787-2869 SIC 9512

PENNSYLVANIA DEPARTMENT OF HUMAN SERVICES p 1130
625 Forster St 17120
Tel (717) 787-2600 *SIC* 9441

PENNSYLVANIA DEPARTMENT OF LABOR & INDUSTRY p 1130
Labor/Industry Bldg Fl 17 17120
Tel (717) 787-5279 *SIC* 9651

PENNSYLVANIA DEPARTMENT OF REVENUE p 1130
1147 Strawberry Sq 17128
Tel (717) 787-6300 *SIC* 9311

PENNSYLVANIA DEPT OF ENVIRONMENTAL PROTECTION p 1130
400 Market St 17101
Tel (717) 787-1319 *SIC* 9511

PENNSYLVANIA DEPT OF STATE POLICE p 1130
1800 Elmerton Ave 17110
Tel (717) 783-5599 *SIC* 9221

PENNSYLVANIA DEPT OF TRANSPORTATION p 1130
400 North St Fl 8 17120
Tel (717) 787-6875 *SIC* 9621

PENNSYLVANIA HIGHER EDUCATION ASSISTANCE AGENCY p 1130
1200 N 7th St 17102
Tel (717) 720-2700 *SIC* 9411

PENNSYLVANIA NATIONAL MUTUAL CASUALTY INSURANCE CO p 1130
2 N 2nd St Ste 2 17101
Tel (717) 230-8200 *SIC* 6331

PENNSYLVANIA STATE EMPLOYEES CREDIT UNION p 1130
1500 Elmerton Ave 17110
Tel (800) 237-7328 *SIC* 6062 9199

PERLITE INSTITUTE INC p 1136
2207 Forest Hills Dr 17112
Tel (717) 238-9723 *SIC* 5045

PINNACLE HEALTH HOSPITAL p 1149
4300 Londonderry Rd 17109
Tel (717) 782-3131 *SIC* 8062

PINNACLE HEALTH HOSPITALS p 1150
409 S 2nd St Ste 1c 17104
Tel (717) 782-5678 *SIC* 8062

PINNACLE HEALTH MEDICAL SERVICES p 1150
409 S 2nd St Ste 2b 17104
Tel (717) 231-8341 *SIC* 8011 8063

PINNACLE HEALTH SYSTEM p 1150
409 S 2nd St Ste 2b 17104
Tel (717) 231-8010 *SIC* 8741 8062

PSECU SERVICES INC p 1188
1 Credit Union Pl Ste 1 17110
Tel (800) 237-7238 *SIC* 8742

PUBLIC SCHOOL EMPLOYEES RETIREMENT SYSTEM p 1189
5 N 5th St 17101
Tel (717) 720-4734 *SIC* 6371 9441

QUANDEL CONSTRUCTION GROUP INC p 1198
3003 N Front St Ste 203 17110
Tel (717) 657-0909
SIC 1542 1541 1629 8741

QUANDEL ENTERPRISES INC p 1198
3003 N Front St Ste 203 17110
Tel (717) 657-0909 *SIC* 1542 1629 8741

ROMAN CATHOLIC DIOCESE OF HARRISBURG p 1249
4800 Union Deposit Rd 17111
Tel (717) 657-4804 *SIC* 8661 8211

SCHAEDLER/YESCO DISTRIBUTION INC p 1286
3982 Paxton St 17111
Tel (717) 843-9991 *SIC* 5063

STABLER COMPANIES INC p 1374
635 Lucknow Rd 17110
Tel (717) 236-9307
SIC 5032 3089 7359 3531 1611 3648

STATE SYSTEM OF HIGHER EDUCATION OF COMMONWEALTH OF PENNSYLVANIA p 1383
2986 N 2nd St 17110
Tel (717) 720-4000 *SIC* 9411

■ TRANSCORE HOLDINGS INC p 1471
3721 Tecport Dr 17111
Tel (717) 561-5812 *SIC* 7373

■ TRANSCORE LP p 1471
3721 Tecport Dr Ste 102 17111
Tel (615) 988-8960 *SIC* 1731

TRANSTECK INC p 1473
4303 Lewis Rd 17111
Tel (717) 564-6151 *SIC* 5511

TYCO ELECTRONICS BLANKET p 1496
100 Amp Dr 17106
Tel (717) 810-2598 *SIC* 5023

UNITED CONCORDIA COMPANIES INC p 1507
4401 Deer Path Rd 17110
Tel (717) 260-6800 *SIC* 6324

UNITED CONCORDIA LIFE AND HEALTH INSURANCE CO p 1507
4401 Deer Path Rd 17110
Tel (717) 260-7081 *SIC* 7389

VALENTI MID-ATLANTIC MANAGEMENT LLC p 1539
1 Rutherford Rd Ste 100 17109
Tel (717) 652-7822 *SIC* 8741

YOUTH ADVOCATE PROGRAMS INC p 1639
2007 N 3rd St 17102
Tel (717) 232-7580 *SIC* 8322

HATBORO, PA

BENJAMIN FOODS LLC p 173
1001 S York Rd 19040
Tel (215) 437-5000 *SIC* 5141 8741

■ CEI HOLDING CO p 273
334 S Warminster Rd 19040
Tel (215) 734-1400 *SIC* 1629

■ CLEAN EARTH HOLDINGS INC p 323
334 S Warminster Rd 19040
Tel (215) 734-1400 *SIC* 4959

■ CLEAN EARTH INC p 323
334 S Warminster Rd 19040
Tel (215) 734-1400 *SIC* 4959

HATFIELD, PA

CLEMENS FAMILY CORP p 325
2700 Clemens Rd 19440
Tel (800) 523-5291
SIC 0213 2011 4222 8661

CLEMENS FOOD GROUP LLC p 325
2700 Clemens Rd 19440
Tel (215) 368-2500 *SIC* 2011 2013

DENTAL IMAGING TECHNOLOGIES CORP p 429
2800 Crystal Dr 19440
Tel (215) 997-5666 *SIC* 3843 5047

HAVERFORD, PA

CORP OF HAVERFORD COLLEGE p 371
370 Lancaster Ave 19041
Tel (610) 896-1000 *SIC* 8221

HAVERTOWN, PA

HAVERFORD TOWNSHIP SCHOOL DISTRICT p 668
50 E Eagle Rd 19083
Tel (610) 853-5900 *SIC* 8211

HAZLE TOWNSHIP, PA

FORBO FLOORING INC p 565
8 Maplewood Dr 18202
Tel (570) 459-0771 *SIC* 5023

HAZLETON AREA SCHOOL DISTRICT p 671
1515 W 23rd St 18202
Tel (570) 459-3111 *SIC* 8211

HAZLETON, PA

DEANGELO BROTHERS LLC p 420
100 N Conahan Dr 18201
Tel (570) 459-5800 *SIC* 0782

NORTHEASTERN PENNSYLVANIA HEALTH CORP p 1055
700 E Broad St 18201
Tel (570) 501-4000 *SIC* 8062

HERMITAGE, PA

INTERSTATE CHEMICAL CO INC p 758
2797 Freedland Rd 16148
Tel (724) 981-3771 *SIC* 5169 2819

HERSHEY, PA

AMERICAN CANCER SOCIETY EAST CENTRAL DIVISION INC p 69
Sipe Ave Rr 422 17033
Tel (717) 533-6144 *SIC* 8733

COUNTRY MEADOWS ASSOCIATES p 375
830 Cherry Dr 17033
Tel (717) 533-2474 *SIC* 8051 8059 8741

GEORGE M LEADER FAMILY CORP p 606
830 Cherry Dr 17033
Tel (800) 322-3441 *SIC* 8051

▲ HERSHEY CO p 687
100 Crystal A Dr 17033
Tel (717) 534-4200 *SIC* 2066 2064 2099

HERSHEY ENTERTAINMENT & RESORTS CO p 687
27 W Chocolate Ave # 100 17033
Tel (717) 534-3131 *SIC* 7011 7996

MILTON HERSHEY SCHOOL p 972
1201 Homestead Ln 17033
Tel (717) 520-2000 *SIC* 8211

MILTON HERSHEY SCHOOL & SCHOOL TRUST p 972
711 Crest Ln 17033
Tel (717) 520-1100 *SIC* 8211

MILTON S HERSHEY MEDICAL CENTER p 972
500 University Dr 17033
Tel (717) 531-8521 *SIC* 8011

PENN STATE MILTON S HERSHEY MEDICAL CENTER p 1129
500 University Dr 17033
Tel (717) 531-5337 *SIC* 8062 8733 8211

■ PENNSYLVANIA - AMERICAN WATER CO p 1130
800 W Hershey Park Dr 17033
Tel (717) 533-5000 *SIC* 4941

HOLLIDAYSBURG, PA

DIOCESE OF ALTOONA-JOHNSTOWN p 440
927 S Logan Blvd 16648
Tel (814) 695-5579 *SIC* 8661

MCLANAHAN CORP p 930
200 Wall St 16648
Tel (814) 695-9807
SIC 3532 3321 3599 3523

HOLLSOPPLE, PA

NORTH AMERICAN HOGANAS CO p 1050
111 Hoganas Way 15935
Tel (814) 479-3500 *SIC* 3399

NORTH AMERICAN HOGANAS HOLDINGS INC p 1050
111 Hoganas Way 15935
Tel (814) 479-2551 *SIC* 3462

HOMESTEAD, PA

ALLEGHENY INTERMEDIATE UNIT 3 FOUNDATION p 52
475 E Waterfront Dr 15120
Tel (412) 394-5700 *SIC* 8211

EATN PARK HOSPITALITY GROUP INC p 473
285 E Waterfront Dr # 200 15120
Tel (412) 461-2000 *SIC* 8741

GAI CONSULTANTS INC p 589
385 E Waterfront Dr Fl 1 15120
Tel (412) 476-2000 *SIC* 8711

HONESDALE, PA

WAYNE MEMORIAL HOSPITAL p 1584
601 Park St 18431
Tel (570) 253-8100 *SIC* 8062

HONEY BROOK, PA

M SIMON ZOOK CO p 890
4960 Horseshoe Pike 19344
Tel (800) 327-4406 *SIC* 5149 2048 4013

HORSHAM, PA

APAC CUSTOMER SERVICES INC p 95
507 Prudential Rd 19044
Tel (215) 441-3000 *SIC* 8741

ARNOLD FOODS CO INC p 112
255 Business Center Dr # 200 19044
Tel (215) 672-8010 *SIC* 2051 5149

BBU INC p 163
255 Business Center Dr # 200 19044
Tel (215) 347-5500 *SIC* 2051

BIMBO BAKERIES USA INC p 183
255 Business Center Dr # 200 19044
Tel (215) 347-5500 *SIC* 2051

CAPMARK BANK p 251
116 Welsh Rd 19044
Tel (801) 569-4606 *SIC* 6022

EGS FINANCIAL CARE INC p 481
507 Prudential Rd 19044
Tel (877) 217-4423 *SIC* 7322

ELEMENT FLEET MANAGEMENT (US) CORP p 486
655 Business Center Dr 19044
Tel (267) 960-4000 *SIC* 6159

GATEWAY FUNDING DIVERSIFIED MORTGAGE SERVICES LP p 593
300 Welsh Rd 19044
Tel (215) 591-0222 *SIC* 6162

■ GMAC MORTGAGE GROUP LLC p 618
4 Walnut Grove Dr 19044
Tel (215) 682-1000 *SIC* 6211

■ GMAC MORTGAGE LLC p 618
4 Walnut Grove Dr 19044
Tel (215) 682-1000 *SIC* 6162

GRUNDY WORLDWIDE INC p 642
400 Horsham Rd Ste 150 19044
Tel (888) 647-8639 *SIC* 6331

HORNOR TOWNSEND & KENT INC p 708
600 Dresher Rd 19044
Tel (215) 957-7300 *SIC* 6211

INTERNATIONAL MILL SERVICE INC p 756
1155 Bus Ctr Dr Ste 200 19044
Tel (215) 956-5500
SIC 3295 3341 1422 8742

■ JANSSEN BIOTECH INC p 777
800 Ridgeview Dr 19044
Tel (610) 651-6000 *SIC* 2834 2835

NECTAR ACQUISITION CORP p 1023
410 Horsham Rd Frnt 19044
Tel (215) 442-9000 *SIC* 8732

OROGRAIN BAKERIES MANUFACTURING INC p 1095
255 Business Center Dr 19044
Tel (518) 463-2221 *SIC* 2051

PARTNERS SPECIALTY GROUP LLC p 1118
100 Tournament Dr Ste 214 19044
Tel (484) 322-0400 *SIC* 6411

PENN MUTUAL LIFE INSURANCE CO p 1129
600 Dresher Rd 19044
Tel (215) 956-8000 *SIC* 6311

■ QUEST DIAGNOSTICS INC p 1199
900 Business Center Dr 19044
Tel (866) 697-8378 *SIC* 8071

REED TECHNOLOGY AND INFORMATION SERVICES INC p 1217
7 Walnut Grove Dr 19044
Tel (215) 441-6400 *SIC* 2791

STROEHMANN BAKERIES LC p 1394
255 Business Center Dr # 200 19044
Tel (215) 672-8010 *SIC* 2051 5461

■ TELERX MARKETING INC p 1435
723 Dresher Rd 19044
Tel (215) 347-5700 *SIC* 7389 8742

▲ TOLL BROTHERS INC p 1459
250 Gibraltar Rd 19044
Tel (215) 938-8000 *SIC* 1521 1522

HOUSTON, PA

■ CATERPILLAR GLOBAL MINING AMERICA LLC p 265
2045 W Pike St 15342
Tel (724) 743-1200 *SIC* 3532 7629

HUMMELSTOWN, PA

■ DRAYER PHYSICAL THERAPY INSTITUTE LLC p 455
8205 Presidents Dr Fl 2 17036
Tel (717) 220-2100 *SIC* 8049

HUNTINGDON VALLEY, PA

HOLY REDEEMER HEALTH SYSTEM INC p 702
667 Welsh Rd Ste 300 19006
Tel (215) 938-0180 *SIC* 8082

HOLY REDEEMER HEALTHCARE SYSTEM p 702
667 Welsh Rd Ste 300 19006
Tel (215) 938-0180 *SIC* 8099

LAMI PRODUCTS INC p 841
860 Welsh Rd 19006
Tel (215) 947-5333 *SIC* 5199

HUNTINGDON, PA

MUTUAL BENEFIT INSURANCE CO p 1003
409 Penn St 16652
Tel (814) 643-3000 *SIC* 6331

IMMACULATA, PA

SISTERS SERVANTS OF IMMACULATE HEART OF MARY INC p 1327
1140 King Rd 19345
Tel (610) 647-2160 *SIC* 8661

IMPERIAL, PA

GOLDEN TRIANGLE CONSTRUCTION CO INC p 621
8555 Old Strubenville Pik 15126
Tel (724) 828-2800 *SIC* 1623 1611

MARONDA INC p 910
11 Timberglen Dr 15126
Tel (724) 695-1200 *SIC* 6552 1521

INDIANA, PA

DIAMOND DRUGS INC p 436
645 Kolter Dr 15701
Tel (724) 349-1111 *SIC* 5912 5999

■ FIRST COMMONWEALTH BANK p 545
601 Philadelphia St 15701
Tel (724) 349-7220 *SIC* 6021

▲ FIRST COMMONWEALTH FINANCIAL CORP p 546
601 Philadelphia St 15701
Tel (724) 349-7220 *SIC* 6021

INDIANA HEALTHCARE CORP p 738
835 Hospital Rd 15701
Tel (724) 357-7000 *SIC* 8741

INDIANA HOSPITAL p 738
823 Hospital Rd 15701
Tel (724) 357-7125 *SIC* 8741

INDIANA REGIONAL MEDICAL CENTER p 738
835 Hospital Rd 15701
Tel (724) 357-7000 *SIC* 8062 8011

INDIANA UNIVERSITY OF PENNSYLVANIA p 739
1011 S Dr Room 201 Sutton 15705
Tel (724) 357-2200 *SIC* 8221 9411

INTERSTATE GAS MARKETING INC p 758
2018 S 6th St 15701
Tel (724) 465-7958 *SIC* 4925 5172

■ S & T BANK p 1261
800 Philadelphia St 15701
Tel (724) 349-1800 *SIC* 6022

▲ S&T BANCORP INC p 1263
800 Philadelphia St 15701
Tel (800) 325-2265 *SIC* 6022

INDIANOLA, PA

BAYER MEDICAL CARE INC p 161
1 Bayer Dr 15051
Tel (724) 940-6800 *SIC* 3841

INTERCOURSE, PA

HOOBER INC p 705
3452 Old Philadelphia Pike 17534
Tel (717) 768-8231 *SIC* 5999 7699 5083

IRWIN, PA

IRWIN BUILDERS SUPPLY CORP p 765
10249 Garnet Ln 15642
Tel (724) 863-5200 *SIC* 5031 5211

NUTRITION INC p 1068
580 Wendel Rd Ste 100 15642
Tel (724) 978-2100 *SIC* 5812 2099

SHUSTERS BUILDERS SUPPLIES INC p 1319
2920 Clay Pike 15642
Tel (724) 446-7000 SIC 5031 5211

IVYLAND, PA

ASHFIELD HEALTHCARE LLC p 117
1 Ivybrook Blvd Ste 110 18974
Tel (215) 347-6400 SIC 8742

MILTON ROY LLC p 972
201 Ivyland Rd 18974
Tel (215) 441-0800 SIC 3561 3586 3826

JACKSON CENTER, PA

INTERNATIONAL TIMBER AND VENEER LLC p 757
75 Mcquiston Dr 16133
Tel (724) 662-0880 SIC 2435 5031

JEANNETTE, PA

ELLIOTT CO p 488
901 N 4th St 15644
Tel (724) 527-2811 SIC 3563 3511

GEORGE DELALLO CO INC p 606
6390 Route 30 15644
Tel (724) 925-2222 SIC 5149

JENKINTOWN, PA

ARSENS HOME CARE INC p 113
101 Washington Ln Ste G6 19046
Tel (215) 663-8090 SIC 8082

NATIONAL PHILANTHROPIC TRUST p 1015
165 Township Line Rd # 1200 19046
Tel (215) 277-3010 SIC 7389

RAF INDUSTRIES INC p 1205
165 Township Line Rd # 2100 19046
Tel (215) 572-0738 SIC 8742 3564

■ **SPS TECHNOLOGIES LLC** p 1362
301 Highland Ave 19046
Tel (215) 572-3000
SIC 3452 3423 3499 3264 3679 3341

JERSEY SHORE, PA

JERSEY SHORE STEEL CO p 783
70 Maryland Ave 17740
Tel (570) 753-3000 SIC 3312

JOHNSTOWN, PA

CONCURRENT TECHNOLOGIES CORP p 355
100 Ctc Dr 15904
Tel (814) 266-2874 SIC 8711

■ **CONEMAUGH HEALTH INITIATIVES INC** p 355
1020 Franklin St 15905
Tel (814) 534-9000 SIC 8741 8721

■ **CONEMAUGH HEALTH SYSTEM INC** p 355
1086 Franklin St 15905
Tel (814) 534-9000 SIC 8062 8741

CROWN HOLDING CO p 395
Pasquerilla Plz 15901
Tel (814) 536-4441 SIC 6512

DRS LAUREL TECHNOLOGIES p 457
246 Airport Rd 15904
Tel (814) 534-8900 SIC 3672 3315

GALLIKER DAIRY CO p 590
143 Donald Ln 15904
Tel (814) 266-8702 SIC 2026 2086 2024

■ **JOHNSTOWN AMERICA CORP** p 791
17 Johns St 15901
Tel (814) 533-5000 SIC 3743

LAUREL HOLDINGS INC p 847
111 Roosevelt Blvd 15906
Tel (814) 533-5777
SIC 4941 5063 3599 4724 7349

LEE REGIONAL HEALTH SYSTEM INC p 851
132 Walnut St Ste 3 15901
Tel (814) 533-0751 SIC 8399

NEWSPAPER HOLDING INC p 1039
425 Locust St 15901
Tel (814) 532-5102 SIC 2711

JONESTOWN, PA

PPC LUBRICANTS INC p 1166
305 Micro Dr 17038
Tel (717) 865-9993 SIC 5172

KENNETT SQUARE, PA

■ **AMERGEN ENERGY CO LLC** p 66
200 Exelon Way 19348
Tel (215) 841-4000 SIC 4911

CHATHAM FINANCIAL CORP p 291
235 Whitehorse Ln Frnt 19348
Tel (610) 925-3120 SIC 8742

EVERFAST INC p 514
203 Gale Ln 19348
Tel (610) 444-9700 SIC 5023

■ **EXELON GENERATION CO LLC** p 519
300 Exelon Way 19348
Tel (215) 841-4000 SIC 4911

■ **FC-GEN ACQUISITION INC** p 532
101 E State St 19348
Tel (610) 444-6350 SIC 8361 8051 8099

■ **GENESIS ELDER CARE REHABILATION SERVICES INC** p 602
101 E State St 19348
Tel (610) 925-4598 SIC 8049 8093

■ **GENESIS ELDERCARE NATIONAL CENTERS INC** p 602
101 E State St 19348
Tel (610) 444-6350 SIC 8051 8361

■ **GENESIS HEALTHCARE CORP** p 603
101 E State St 19348
Tel (610) 444-6350 SIC 8051 8361

▲ **GENESIS HEALTHCARE INC** p 603
101 E State St 19348
Tel (610) 444-6350
SIC 8051 8052 8059 8361

■ **GENESIS HEALTHCARE LLC** p 603
101 E State St 19348
Tel (610) 444-6350 SIC 8051 8099

KAOLIN MUSHROOM FARMS INC p 803
649 W South St 19348
Tel (610) 444-4800 SIC 0182

SOUTH MILL MUSHROOM SALES INC p 1344
649 W South St 19348
Tel (610) 444-4800 SIC 5148

KING OF PRUSSIA, PA

AGORA CYBER CHARTER SCHOOL p 35
590 N Gulph Rd 19406
Tel (610) 230-0775 SIC 8211

AMERICAN MANUFACTURING CORP p 75
555 Croton Rd Ste 200 19406
Tel (610) 962-3770 SIC 8748

■ **AMERIGAS INC** p 82
460 N Gulph Rd Ste 100 19406
Tel (610) 337-7000
SIC 5984 5172 5722 2911 2813

▲ **AMERIGAS PARTNERS LP** p 82
460 N Gulph Rd Ste 100 19406
Tel (610) 337-7000 SIC 5984 5172

■ **AMERIGAS PROPANE INC** p 82
460 N Gulph Rd Ste 100 19406
Tel (610) 337-7000 SIC 5984

■ **AMERIGAS PROPANE LP** p 82
460 N Gulph Rd Ste 100 19406
Tel (610) 337-7000 SIC 5984

ARKEMA DELAWARE INC p 110
900 First Ave 19406
Tel (610) 205-7000
SIC 2812 2819 2869 2891 2899 2992

ARKEMA INC p 110
900 First Ave 19406
Tel (610) 205-7000 SIC 2812

BORO DEVELOPERS INC p 201
400 Feheley Dr Ste B 19406
Tel (610) 272-7400 SIC 1542

■ **CARDCONNECT LLC** p 252
1000 Continental Dr # 300 19406
Tel (484) 581-2200 SIC 7389

CI&T INC p 305
630 Freedom Bus Ctr Dr # 300 19406
Tel (610) 482-4810 SIC 7371

CLINICAL CARE ASSOCIATES OF UNIVERSITY OF PENNSYLVANIA HEALTH SYSTEM p 326
2200 Renaissance Blvd # 320 19406
Tel (800) 789-7366 SIC 8011

COLONIAL ELECTRIC SUPPLY CO p 337
201 W Church Rd Ste 100 19406
Tel (610) 312-8100 SIC 5065

CSL BEHRING LLC p 398
1020 1st Ave 19406
Tel (610) 878-4000 SIC 2836

DATABANK IMX LLC p 414
620 Freedom Business Ctr 19406
Tel (610) 233-0251 SIC 7374 5044

DIRECTSAT USA LLC p 442
2010 Renaissance Blvd 19406
Tel (267) 464-1700 SIC 1731

EPIC RESORTS LLC p 505
1150 1st Ave Ste 900 19406
Tel (610) 992-0100 SIC 7011

FIRST QUALITY RETAIL SERVICES LLC p 549
601 Allendale Rd 19406
Tel (610) 265-5000 SIC 3822

GDI SERVICES INC p 595
780 5th Ave Ste 115 19406
Tel (610) 584-0888 SIC 7349

■ **GSI COMMERCE INC** p 643
935 1st Ave 19406
Tel (610) 491-7000 SIC 5961 7371 7379

MATRIX LLC p 920
780 5th Ave Ste 115 19406
Tel (607) 766-0700 SIC 7349

MDS PHARMA SERVICES (US) INC p 933
2200 Rnpance Blvd Ste 400 19406
Tel (610) 239-7900 SIC 8734

MEDRISK INC p 938
2701 Renaissance Blvd 19406
Tel (610) 768-5812 SIC 6411

NTP MARBLE INC p 1065
201 W Church Rd Ste 300 19406
Tel (610) 994-2222 SIC 5032

ONEILL PROPERTIES GROUP LP p 1087
2701 Renaissance Blvd # 4 19406
Tel (610) 337-5560 SIC 6552

PROCURIAN LLC p 1179
211 S Gulph Rd Ste 500 19406
Tel (484) 690-5000 SIC 7389 8748

PROMPTCARE COMPANIES INC p 1183
741 3rd Ave 19406
Tel (610) 278-1623 SIC 8093

QUALTEK USA LLC p 1198
1150 1st Ave Ste 600 19406
Tel (484) 804-4540 SIC 8741

QUENCH USA INC p 1198
780 5th Ave Ste 200 19406
Tel (888) 554-2782 SIC 5078

RADIAL INC p 1204
935 1st Ave 19406
Tel (610) 491-7000
SIC 3149 5139 5091 5136 5137 7375

RITTENHOUSE BOOK DISTRIBUTORS INC p 1237
511 Feheley Dr 19406
Tel (800) 345-6425 SIC 5192

■ **SUGARTOWN WORLDWIDE LLC** p 1397
800 3rd Ave 19406
Tel (610) 878-5550
SIC 2339 2361 5136 5611

SUPPLYFORCE.COM LLC p 1408
700 American Ave Ste 300 19406
Tel (866) 776-8289 SIC 5085

THEOREM CLINICAL RESEARCH INC p 1446
1016 W 9th Ave Ste 300 19406
Tel (484) 679-2400 SIC 8731 8071 2834

■ **TITAN PROPANE LLC** p 1456
460 N Gulph Rd Ste 100 19406
Tel (610) 337-7000 SIC 5984 5172

▲ **UGI CORP** p 1499
460 N Gulph Rd Ste 100 19406
Tel (610) 337-1000 SIC 4932

UGI EUROPE INC p 1499
460 N Gulph Rd 19406
Tel (610) 337-1000 SIC 1321

■ **UHS OF DELAWARE INC** p 1500
367 S Gulph Rd 19406
Tel (610) 768-3300 SIC 8062

UNITED PHOSPHORUS INC p 1510
630 Freedom Business Ctr 19406
Tel (610) 491-2800 SIC 5191

UNITEK GLOBAL SERVICES INC p 1515
2010 Renaissance Blvd 19406
Tel (267) 464-1700
SIC 1731 8741 8742 8711

▲ **UNIVERSAL HEALTH SERVICES INC** p 1517
367 S Gulph Rd 19406
Tel (610) 768-3300
SIC 8062 8063 8093 8011 8741

KITTANNING, PA

ARMSTRONG COUNTY MEMORIAL HOSPITAL p 111
1 Nolte Dr 16201
Tel (724) 543-8500 SIC 8062 8011

ROSEBUD MINING CO p 1250
301 Market St 16201
Tel (724) 545-6222 SIC 1222 1221

SNYDER ASSOCIATED COMPANIES INC p 1336
1 Glade Park Dr 16201
Tel (724) 548-8101 SIC 1442 3281 1222

KOPPEL, PA

IPSCO KOPPEL TUBULARS LLC p 764
6403 6th Ave 16136
Tel (724) 847-6389 SIC 3312

KREAMER, PA

WOOD-MODE INC p 1622
1 Second St 17833
Tel (570) 374-2711 SIC 2434

KULPSVILLE, PA

CMI HOLDING CORP p 329
1555 Bustard Rd 19443
Tel (215) 361-9000 SIC 5411 6512

TWEED GREENE & CO INC p 1494
2075 Detwiler Rd 19443
Tel (215) 256-9521 SIC 3053

KUTZTOWN, PA

PALRAM AMERICAS INC p 1110
9735 Commerce Cir 19530
Tel (610) 285-9918 SIC 5162

LAFAYETTE HILL, PA

NATIONAL LABEL CO p 1014
2025 Joshua Rd 19444
Tel (610) 825-3250
SIC 2672 2679 2759 2671

NHS HUMAN SERVICES INC p 1042
620 Germantown Pike 19444
Tel (610) 260-4600 SIC 8093 8059 8082

NHS PENNSYLVANIA p 1042
620 Germantown Pike 19444
Tel (610) 238-4403 SIC 8699 8299

PHILADELPHIA PRESBYTERY HOMES INC p 1143
2000 Joshua Rd 19444
Tel (610) 834-1001 SIC 8361 8052 8051

LAKE ARIEL, PA

TEAM BIONDI LLC p 1429
248 Easton Tpke 18436
Tel (570) 503-7087 SIC 3537

LANCASTER, PA

AMERIGREEN ENERGY INC p 82
1650 Manheim Pike Ste 201 17601
Tel (717) 945-1392 SIC 5172

▲ **ARMSTRONG FLOORING INC** p 111
2500 Columbia Ave 17603
Tel (717) 672-9611 SIC 3996 2426

■ **ARMSTRONG HARDWOOD FLOORING CO** p 111
2500 Columbia Ave 17603
Tel (717) 672-9611 SIC 2426

■ **ARMSTRONG WOOD PRODUCTS INC** p 111
2500 Columbia Ave 17603
Tel (800) 233-3823 SIC 2426

▲ **ARMSTRONG WORLD INDUSTRIES INC** p 111
2500 Columbia Ave Bldg 5b 17603
Tel (717) 397-0611 SIC 3646 3296

AUNTIE ANNES INC p 131
48-50 W Chestnut St # 200 17603
Tel (717) 435-1435 SIC 6794 2051 5461

BURNHAM HOLDINGS INC p 228
1241 Harrisburg Ave 17603
Tel (717) 390-7800 SIC 3433

CLARK ASSOCIATES INC p 322
2205 Old Philadelphia Pike 17602
Tel (717) 392-7550 SIC 5046 7623

■ **CLARK FILTER INC** p 322
3649 Hempland Rd 17601
Tel (717) 285-5941 SIC 3564 3714

COUNTY OF LANCASTER p 379
150 N Queen St Ste 712 17603
Tel (717) 299-8262 SIC 9111

DAY & ZIMMERMANN NPS INC p 417
1827 Freedom Rd Ste 101 17601
Tel (717) 299-3754 SIC 7361

DUTCH GOLD HONEY INC p 463
2220 Dutch Gold Dr 17601
Tel (717) 393-1716 SIC 2099 5149

■ **EASTERN INSURANCE HOLDINGS INC** p 472
25 Race Ave 17603
Tel (717) 239-1641 SIC 6311 6331

EUROFINS LANCASTER LABORATORIES INC p 512
2425 New Holland Pike 17601
Tel (717) 656-2300 SIC 8731 8734

FRANKLIN AND MARSHALL COLLEGE p 574
415 Harrisburg Ave 17603
Tel (717) 291-3911 SIC 8221

■ **FULTON BANK NATIONAL ASSOCIATION** p 584
1 Penn Sq Ste 1 17602
Tel (717) 581-3166 SIC 6022

▲ **FULTON FINANCIAL CORP** p 584
1 Penn Sq Ste 1 17602
Tel (717) 291-2411 SIC 6021

GRAHAM PACKAGING CO INC p 629
700 Indian Springs Dr # 100 17601
Tel (717) 849-8500 SIC 5199 3089 5162

GRAHAM PACKAGING CO LP p 629
700 Indian Springs Dr # 100 17601
Tel (717) 849-8500 SIC 3089

GRAHAM PACKAGING HOLDINGS CO p 629
700 Indian Springs Dr # 100 17601
Tel (717) 849-8500 SIC 3089

H & F GULF INC p 649
1834 Lincoln Hwy E 17602
Tel (717) 392-6793 SIC 5014 5531

HERLEY INDUSTRIES INC p 686
3061 Industry Dr 17603
Tel (717) 397-2777 SIC 7382

HIGH INDUSTRIES INC p 690
1853 William Penn Way 17601
Tel (717) 293-4444
SIC 1791 3272 5051 3441

HIGH STEEL STRUCTURES LLC p 691
1915 Old Philadelphia Pike 17602
Tel (717) 299-5211 SIC 1541

HORST GROUP INC p 708
320 Granite Run Dr 17601
Tel (717) 560-1919 SIC 1542 1541 6531

INTERFACE PERFORMANCE MATERIALS INC p 752
216 Wohlsen Way 17603
Tel (717) 390-1886 SIC 3053

IREX CORP p 764
120 N Lime St 17602
Tel (717) 397-3633 SIC 1799

JAY GROUP INC p 779
700 Indian Springs Dr 17601
Tel (717) 285-6200
SIC 5961 7389 7331 7319 5199

KALAS MFG INC p 801
167 Greenfield Rd 17601
Tel (717) 335-2360 SIC 3357 3694

■ **KERR GROUP LLC** p 813
1846 Charter Ln Ste 209 17601
Tel (812) 424-2904 SIC 3089

KUNZLER & CO INC p 832
652 Manor St 17603
Tel (717) 299-6301 SIC 2011 2013

LANCASTER GENERAL HEALTH p 841
555 N Duke St 17602
Tel (717) 290-5511 SIC 8062

LANCASTER GENERAL HOSPITAL p 841
555 N Duke St 17602
Tel (717) 544-5511 SIC 8062

LANCASTER-LEBANON INTERMEDIATE UNIT 13 (INC) p 841
1020 New Holland Ave 17601
Tel (717) 606-1600 SIC 8299

LNP MEDIA GROUP INC p 872
8 W King St 17603
Tel (717) 291-8811 SIC 2711 2752

NORTH LIME HOLDINGS CORP p 1053
120 N Lime St 17602
Tel (717) 397-3633 SIC 1799

■ **ROSE CITY HMA LLC** p 1250
250 College Ave 17603
Tel (717) 291-8211 SIC 8062

SCHOOL DISTRICT OF LANCASTER p 1289
251 S Prince St 17603
Tel (717) 299-2700 SIC 8211

SUPERIOR PLUS CONSTRUCTION PRODUCTS CORP p 1406
1650 Manheim Pike Ste 202 17601
Tel (717) 569-3900 SIC 5039 5033

TWOTON INC p 1495
1743 Rohrerstown Rd 17601
Tel (717) 569-5791 SIC 5812

WOHLSEN CONSTRUCTION CO INC p 1620
548 Steel Way 17601
Tel (717) 299-2500 SIC 1542 1541 8741

LANDISVILLE, PA

GE RICHARDS GRAPHIC SUPPLIES CO INC p 596
928 Links Ave 17538
Tel (717) 892-4620 SIC 5084 5045

LANGHORNE, PA

CLEARPEO LLC p 324
2080 Cabot Blvd W Ste 202 19047
Tel (215) 701-9400 SIC 7363

■ **CRESTVIEW NORTH INC** p 392
262 Tollgate Rd 19047
Tel (215) 968-4650 SIC 8051

EASTERN WAREHOUSE DISTRIBUTORS INC p 472
355 S Flowers Mill Rd 19047
Tel (215) 741-4228 SIC 5013

FORD MCCAFFERTY SALES INC p 565
1939 E Lincoln Hwy 19047
Tel (215) 945-8000
SIC 5511 5531 7538 7514 5521 5012

■ **INFRA-METALS CO** p 742
580 Middletown Blvd D100 19047
Tel (215) 741-1000 SIC 5051

■ **METALS USA PLATES AND SHAPES NORTHEAST LP** p 953
50 Cabot Blvd E 19047
Tel (267) 580-2100 SIC 5051

NESHAMINY SCHOOL DISTRICT p 1026
2001 Old Lincoln Hwy 19047
Tel (215) 809-6562 SIC 8211

REEDMAN CHEVROLET INC p 1217
Rr 1 19047
Tel (215) 757-4961
SIC 5511 5531 7538 5521

ST MARY MEDICAL CENTER p 1371
1201 Langhorne Newtown Rd 19047
Tel (215) 710-2000 SIC 8062

WOODS SERVICES INC p 1623
40 Martin Gross Dr 19047
Tel (215) 750-4000 SIC 8322 8211

LANSDALE, PA

COBHAM ADVANCED ELECTRONIC SOLUTIONS INC p 332
305 Richardson Rd 19446
Tel (215) 996-2000 SIC 3812

CONSOLIDATED SERVICES GROUP INC p 360
1555 Bustard Rd Ste 100 19446
Tel (215) 661-0500 SIC 6411

CRYSTAL INC - PMC p 397
601 W 8th St 19446
Tel (267) 649-7330 SIC 2899 2842

PENN NORTH SCHOOL DISTRICT p 1129
401 E Hancock St 19446
Tel (215) 368-0400 SIC 8211

SKF USA INC p 1329
890 Forty Foot Rd 19446
Tel (267) 436-6000 SIC 3562 3053 3829

TYCO FIRE PRODUCTS LP p 1496
1400 Pennbrook Pkwy 19446
Tel (215) 362-0700
SIC 3569 3494 3321 5085

VYGON CORP p 1567
2750 Morris Rd Ste 200 19446
Tel (215) 390-2002 SIC 5047

LANSDOWNE, PA

PENN WILLIAM SCHOOL DISTRICT p 1129
100 Green Ave 19050
Tel (610) 284-8080 SIC 8211

LATROBE, PA

EXCELA HEALTH LATROBE AREA HOSPITAL p 516
1 Mellon Way 15650
Tel (877) 771-1234 SIC 8062

■ **KENNAMETAL HOLDINGS EUROPE INC** p 810
1600 Technology Way 15650
Tel (724) 539-5000 SIC 6719

LATROBE AREA HOSPITAL INC p 846
1 Mellon Way 15650
Tel (724) 537-1000 SIC 8062

■ **LATROBE SPECIALTY METALS CO LLC** p 846
2626 Ligonier St 15650
Tel (724) 537-7711 SIC 3312 3369

ROBINDALE ENERGY SERVICES INC p 1242
1 Lloyd Ave Fl 2 15650
Tel (814) 446-6700 SIC 5052

WOLSELEY INVESTMENTS INC p 1621
1904 Ligonier St 15650
Tel (757) 874-7795
SIC 5074 5085 5075 5064 5211 5031

LAWRENCE, PA

▲ **BLACK BOX CORP** p 186
1000 Park Dr 15055
Tel (724) 746-5500
SIC 3577 3679 3661 5045 5065 5063

■ **BLACK BOX CORP OF PENNSYLVANIA** p 186
1000 Park Dr 15055
Tel (724) 746-5500
SIC 5045 5063 5065 3577 3679 3661

LEBANON, PA

GDT PROPERTIES INC p 595
312 N 8th St 17046
Tel (717) 273-4514 SIC 5063

GOOD SAMARITAN HEALTH SERVICES FOUNDATION p 623
259 S 4th St Fl 2 17042
Tel (717) 270-7864 SIC 8741 7389 8721

GOOD SAMARITAN HOSPITAL OF LEBANON PENNSYLVANIA p 623
252 S 4th St 17042
Tel (717) 270-7500 SIC 8062

GOOD SAMARITAN PHYSICIAN SERVICES p 623
259 S 4th St 17042
Tel (717) 270-7500 SIC 8062

LEBANON COUNTY p 850
400 S 8th St Ste 1 17042
Tel (717) 274-2801 SIC 9111

LEBANON SEABOARD CORP p 850
1600 E Cumberland St 17042
Tel (717) 273-1685 SIC 5191 2875 2048

■ **NEW PENN MOTOR EXPRESS LLC** p 1032
625 S 5th Ave 17042
Tel (800) 285-5000 SIC 4213 4231

PHILHAVEN HOSPITAL p 1143
283 Butler Rd 17042
Tel (717) 270-2414 SIC 8011 8063

WEABER INC p 1585
1231 Mount Wilson Rd 17042
Tel (717) 867-2212 SIC 2426

WT HARDWOODS GROUP INC p 1628
1231 Mount Wilson Rd 17042
Tel (717) 867-2212 SIC 2426

LEESPORT, PA

BERKS PRODUCTS CORP p 175
167 Berks Products Dr 19533
Tel (610) 374-5131
SIC 5031 3273 5983 5172 2439 1711

LEETSDALE, PA

ALMATIS INC p 59
501 W Park Rd 15056
Tel (412) 630-2800 SIC 2819

HCL LIQUIDATION LTD p 672
100 Washington St 15056
Tel (724) 251-4200 SIC 3351

LIBERTAS COPPER LLC p 861
100 Washington St 15056
Tel (724) 251-4200 SIC 3366 3351

LEMOYNE, PA

METRO BANK p 954
1249 Market St 17043
Tel (717) 972-2875 SIC 6022

LEOLA, PA

DART CONTAINER CORP OF PENNSYLVANIA p 413
60 E Main St 17540
Tel (717) 656-2236 SIC 3086

LEVITTOWN, PA

AIRGAS SAFETY INC p 40
2501 Green Ln 19057
Tel (215) 826-9000
SIC 5084 5085 3561 3841

BRISTOL TOWNSHIP SCHOOL DISTRICT AUTHORITY p 214
6401 Mill Creek Rd 19057
Tel (215) 943-3200 SIC 8211

COURIER TIMES INC p 383
8400 Bristol Pike 19057
Tel (215) 949-4011 SIC 2711

■ **HCSG SUPPLY INC** p 672
45 Runway Dr Ste H 19057
Tel (215) 269-0988 SIC 5099

PENNSBURY SCHOOL DISTRICT p 1130
19058-0338 Yardley Ave 19058
Tel (215) 428-4100 SIC 8211

LEWISBURG, PA

BUCKNELL UNIVERSITY p 223
1 Dent Dr 17837
Tel (570) 577-2000 SIC 8221

EVANGELICAL COMMUNITY HOSPITAL p 513
1 Hospital Dr 17837
Tel (570) 522-2000 SIC 8062

EVANGELICAL MEDICAL SERVICES ORGANIZATION p 513
1 Hospital Dr 17837
Tel (570) 522-2000 SIC 8011

HOME CARE PRODUCTS & PHARMACY p 703
1 Hospital Dr 17837
Tel (570) 522-2000 SIC 5912 7352 5999

LEWISTOWN, PA

FIRST QUALITY BABY PRODUCTS LLC p 549
97 Locust Rd 17044
Tel (717) 247-3516 SIC 2676

LEWISTOWN HOSPITAL p 859
400 Highland Ave 17044
Tel (717) 248-5411 SIC 8062 8221

LIMERICK, PA

■ **MARINE ACQUISITION (US) INC** p 906
640 N Lewis Rd 19468
Tel (610) 495-7011 SIC 3531 5551

LITITZ, PA

CARGILL COCOA & CHOCOLATE INC p 255
20 N Broad St 17543
Tel (717) 626-1131 SIC 2066

HALLER ENTERPRISES INC p 654
212 Bucky Dr 17543
Tel (888) 565-0546 SIC 1711 1731

R W SAUDER INC p 1203
570 Furnace Hills Pike 17543
Tel (717) 626-2074 SIC 5144

SKH MANAGEMENT CO p 1329
813 Lititz Pike 17543
Tel (717) 627-0090
SIC 5141 5092 5261 5411

SUSQUEHANNA BANCSHARES INC p 1409
26 N Cedar St 17543
Tel (717) 626-4721 SIC 6021

■ **SUSQUEHANNA BANK** p 1409
9 E Main St 17543
Tel (717) 627-1778 SIC 6022

WOODSTREAM CORP p 1623
69 N Locust St 17543
Tel (717) 626-2125 SIC 3496

LOCK HAVEN, PA

FIRST QUALITY TISSUE LLC p 549
904 Woods Ave 17745
Tel (570) 748-1200 SIC 2621

LORETTO, PA

SAINT FRANCIS UNIVERSITY p 1269
117 Evergreen Dr 15940
Tel (814) 472-3000 SIC 8221

LYON STATION, PA

EAST PENN MANUFACTURING CO p 470
102 Deka Rd 19536
Tel (610) 682-6361
SIC 3694 3691 5063 4225

MAINLAND, PA

ACCUPAC INC p 16
1501 Industrial Blvd 19451
Tel (215) 256-7000 SIC 7389

MALVERN, PA

ACME MARKETS INC p 18
75 Valley Stream Pkwy # 100 19355
Tel (610) 889-4000 SIC 5411

ALLAN MYERS MATERIALS INC p 52
638 Lancaster Ave 19355
Tel (610) 560-7900 SIC 1422

AMERICAN FUTURE SYSTEMS INC p 73
370 Technology Dr 19355
Tel (610) 695-8600 SIC 2741 8742

ARMSTRONG WORTHINGTON VENTURE p 112
101 Lindenwood Dr Ste 350 19355
Tel (610) 722-1200 SIC 3446 5051

AUXILIUM PHARMACEUTICALS INC p 135
1400 Atwater Dr 19355
Tel (484) 321-5900 SIC 2834

BALFOUR BEATTY COMMUNITIES LLC p 147
1 Country View Rd Ste 100 19355
Tel (610) 355-8100 SIC 6531

BALFOUR BEATTY INVESTMENTS INC p 148
1 Country View Rd Ste 100 19355
Tel (610) 355-8100
SIC 6531 8748 1731 8999 8741

BALFOUR BEATTY MILITARY HOUSING LLC p 148
1 Country View Rd 19355
Tel (610) 355-8100 SIC 1522 1542

BALFOUR BEATTY MILITARY HOUSING MANAGEMENT LLC p 148
1 Country View Rd Ste 100 19355
Tel (610) 355-8100 SIC 6531

▲ **BIOTELEMETRY INC** p 184
1000 Cedar Hollow Rd 19355
Tel (610) 729-7000 SIC 3845 8093

■ **CARDIONET LLC** p 253
1000 Cedar Hollow Rd 19355
Tel (610) 729-5060 SIC 3845

CEPHALON INC p 283
41 Moores Rd 19355
Tel (610) 344-0200 SIC 2834

CERTAINTEED CORP p 284
20 Moores Rd 19355
Tel (610) 893-5000
SIC 3221 3292 3259 3084 3089 3432

COMMUNICATION CABLE CO p 346
140 Quaker Ln 19355
Tel (610) 644-5155 SIC 5045 7379

■ **CRANE PAYMENT INNOVATIONS INC** p 389
3222 Phoenixville Pike # 200 19355
Tel (610) 430-2700 SIC 3578

CUBESMART p 399
5 Old Lancaster Rd 19355
Tel (610) 535-5000 SIC 6798

CUBESMART LP p 399
5 Old Lancaster Rd 19355
Tel (610) 535-5700 SIC 4225 6798

DFC GLOBAL CORP p 435
74 E Swedesford Rd # 150 19355
Tel (610) 296-3400 SIC 6099 6141

DFG WORLD INC p 435
74 E Swedesford Rd 19355
Tel (610) 296-3400 SIC 6099

DOLLAR FINANCIAL GROUP INC p 448
74 E Swedesford Rd 19355
Tel (610) 296-3400 SIC 6099 8721

ELLUCIAN CO LP p 489
4 Country View Rd 19355
Tel (610) 647-5930 SIC 7373 8741

ENDO HEALTH SOLUTIONS INC p 496
1400 Atwater Dr 19355
Tel (484) 216-0000 SIC 2834

ENDO PHARMACEUTICALS INC p 496
1400 Atwater Dr 19355
Tel (484) 216-0000 SIC 2834

ENVIRONMENTAL RESOURCES MANAGEMENT INC p 503
75 Valley Stream Pkwy # 200 19355
Tel (484) 913-0300 SIC 8748

ERM NORTH AMERICA INC p 508
75 Valley Stream Pkwy 19355
Tel (484) 913-0300 SIC 8748

ERM-NA HOLDINGS CORP p 508
75 Valley Stream Pkwy # 200 19355
Tel (484) 913-0300 SIC 8711 8748 8742

FUJIREBIO DIAGNOSTICS INC p 583
201 Great Valley Pkwy 19355
Tel (610) 240-3800 SIC 5047 8011

GAS BREAKER INC p 593
17 Lee Blvd Ste D 19355
Tel (610) 407-7200 SIC 3491

HARRON COMMUNICATIONS LP p 664
70 E Lancaster Ave 19355
Tel (610) 644-7500 SIC 8748

LIBERTY PROPERTY LIMITED PARTNERSHIP p 862
500 Chesterfield Pkwy 19355
Tel (610) 648-1700 SIC 6512

LIBERTY PROPERTY TRUST p 862
500 Chesterfield Pkwy 19355
Tel (610) 648-1700 SIC 6798

■ **NIAGARA HOLDINGS INC** p 1042
300 Lindenwood Dr 19355
Tel (610) 651-4200 SIC 2819 3231

NORWOOD CO p 1061
375 Technology Dr 19355
Tel (610) 240-4400 SIC 1541 1542 8741

POTTERS INDUSTRIES LLC p 1164
300 Lindenwood Dr 19355
Tel (610) 651-4700 SIC 3231

PQ CORP p 1166
300 Lindenwood Dr 19355
Tel (610) 651-4429 SIC 2819 3231

PQ HOLDING INC p 1166
300 Lindenwood Dr 19355
Tel (610) 651-4400 *SIC* 2819

RICOH AMERICAS CORP p 1233
70 Valley Stream Pkwy 19355
Tel (610) 296-8000
SIC 5044 5065 5045 5043 3861 3661

RICOH USA INC p 1233
70 Valley Stream Pkwy 19355
Tel (610) 296-8000
SIC 5044 5065 7359 5112 7334 6159

SAINT-GOBAIN CORP p 1271
20 Moores Rd 19355
Tel (610) 893-6000 *SIC* 2891 3269 3221

SIEMENS MEDICAL SOLUTIONS USA INC p 1320
40 Liberty Blvd 19355
Tel (610) 219-6300
SIC 5047 3845 3842 3843

SLATE PHARMACEUTICALS INC p 1331
1400 Atwater Dr 19355
Tel (484) 321-5900 *SIC* 2834

SMITHS GROUP NORTH AMERICA INC p 1334
101 Lindenwood Dr Ste 125 19355
Tel (772) 286-9300 *SIC* 3812 3841 3679

■ **SUSQUEHANNA COMMERCIAL FINANCE INC** p 1409
2 Country View Rd Ste 300 19355
Tel (610) 705-4999 *SIC* 8741

TURN 5 INC p 1492
7 Lee Blvd 19355
Tel (610) 251-2397 *SIC* 5531

VANGUARD CHARITABLE ENDOWMENT PROGRAM p 1543
100 Vanguard Blvd G19 19355
Tel (888) 383-4483 *SIC* 7389

VANGUARD FIDUCIARY TRUST CO INC p 1543
100 Vanguard Blvd 19355
Tel (610) 669-6000 *SIC* 6722

VANGUARD GROUP INC p 1543
100 Vanguard Blvd 19355
Tel (610) 669-1000 *SIC* 6722

VETERANS LIFE INSURANCE CO INC p 1553
20 Moores Rd 19355
Tel (610) 648-5000 *SIC* 6311 6321

▲ **VISHAY INTERTECHNOLOGY INC** p 1561
63 Lancaster Ave 19355
Tel (610) 644-1300
SIC 3676 3677 3675 3674 3613 3612

■ **VISHAY PRECISION FOIL INC** p 1561
3 Great Valley Pkwy # 150 19355
Tel (484) 321-5300 *SIC* 3676

▲ **VISHAY PRECISION GROUP INC** p 1561
3 Great Valley Pkwy # 150 19355
Tel (484) 321-5300 *SIC* 3676 3823

ZEOLYST INTERNATIONAL p 1642
300 Lindenwood Dr 19355
Tel (610) 651-4200 *SIC* 2819

MANHEIM, PA

KREIDER FARMS p 829
1461 Lancaster Rd 17545
Tel (717) 665-4415 *SIC* 0291

WORLEY & OBETZ INC p 1626
85 White Oak Rd 17545
Tel (717) 665-6891 *SIC* 5983 5541

MARIETTA, PA

■ **ATLANTIC STATES INSURANCE CO** p 127
1195 River Rd 17547
Tel (717) 426-1931 *SIC* 6331

CORIXA CORP p 370
325 N Bridge St 17547
Tel (717) 426-6557 *SIC* 5122

▲ **DONEGAL GROUP INC** p 450
1195 River Rd 17547
Tel (717) 426-1931 *SIC* 6331

■ **DONEGAL MUTUAL INSURANCE CO** p 450
1195 River Rd 17547
Tel (717) 426-1931 *SIC* 6331

MC CONNELLSBURG, PA

■ **JLG INDUSTRIES INC** p 786
1 J L G Dr 17233
Tel (717) 485-5161 *SIC* 3531

MC KEES ROCKS, PA

LANE STEEL CO INC p 844
4 River Rd Ste 2 15136
Tel (412) 331-1400 *SIC* 5051

MC MURRAY, PA

HENRY FTEICHMANN INC p 684
3009 Washington Rd 15317
Tel (724) 941-9550 *SIC* 1541 8711 8742

NATIONAL SLOVAK SOCIETY OF USA INC p 1016
351 Valley Brook Rd 15317
Tel (724) 731-0094 *SIC* 6311

MCKEESPORT, PA

ELG HANIEL METALS CORP p 486
369 River Rd 15132
Tel (412) 672-9200 *SIC* 5093 5051

ELG METALS INC p 486
369 River Rd 15132
Tel (412) 672-9200 *SIC* 5093 3341

MCKEESPORT AREA SCHOOL DISTRICT p 930
3590 Oneil Blvd 15132
Tel (412) 664-3610 *SIC* 8211

UPMC BRADDOCK p 1528
1500 5th Ave 15132
Tel (412) 636-5000 *SIC* 8062

UPMC MCKEESPORT p 1528
1500 5th Ave 15132
Tel (412) 664-2000 *SIC* 8062

MEADVILLE, PA

AINSWORTH PET NUTRITION LLC p 38
984 Water St 16335
Tel (814) 724-7710 *SIC* 2047

ALLEGHENY COLLEGE p 52
520 N Main St 16335
Tel (814) 332-3100 *SIC* 8221

MEADVILLE MEDICAL CENTER p 934
751 Liberty St 16335
Tel (814) 333-5000 *SIC* 8741 8062 8011

UNIQUE VENTURES GROUP LLC p 1505
231 Chestnut St Ste 302 16335
Tel (814) 337-6300 *SIC* 5812

■ **UNIVERSAL WELL SERVICES INC** p 1518
13549 S Mosiertown Rd 16335
Tel (814) 337-1983 *SIC* 1389 1382

MECHANICSBURG, PA

BALANCED CARE CORP p 147
5000 Ritter Rd Ste 202 17055
Tel (412) 487-6925 *SIC* 8741

COMMONWEALTH OF PENNSYLVANIA DEPARTMENT OF CORRECTIONS p 346
1920 Technology Pkwy 17050
Tel (717) 728-2573 *SIC* 9223

CUMBERLAND VALLEY SCHOOL DISTRICT p 400
6746 Carlisle Pike 17050
Tel (717) 697-1167 *SIC* 8211

■ **DLA DOCUMENT SERVICES** p 445
5450 Carlisle Pike Bldg 9 17050
Tel (717) 605-2362 *SIC* 9711

ESSINTIAL ENTERPRISE SOLUTIONS LLC p 510
100 Sterling Pkwy Ste 307 17050
Tel (717) 610-3200 *SIC* 8742

FRY COMMUNICATIONS INC p 582
800 W Church Rd 17055
Tel (717) 766-0211 *SIC* 2752

KARNS PRIME AND FANCY FOOD LTD p 804
675 Silver Spring Rd 17050
Tel (717) 766-6477 *SIC* 5411

MEMBERS 1ST FEDERAL CREDIT UNION p 941
5000 Louise Dr 17055
Tel (717) 697-1161 *SIC* 6061

MESSIAH COLLEGE p 951
1 College Ave Ste 3000 17055
Tel (717) 766-2511 *SIC* 8221

NOVITAS SOLUTIONS INC p 1063
2020 Tech Pkwy Ste 100 17050
Tel (717) 526-3459 *SIC* 6321

PENNSYLVANIA DENTAL SERVICE CORP p 1130
1 Delta Dr 17055
Tel (717) 766-8500 *SIC* 6324 8021

■ **REGENCY HOSPITAL CO LLC** p 1219
4714 Gettysburg Rd 17055
Tel (717) 972-1100 *SIC* 8742

■ **SELECT MEDICAL CORP** p 1301
4714 Gettysburg Rd 17055
Tel (717) 972-1100 *SIC* 8093 8051 8069

▲ **SELECT MEDICAL HOLDINGS CORP** p 1301
4714 Gettysburg Rd 17055
Tel (717) 972-1100 *SIC* 8093 8069

VIBRA HEALTHCARE LLC p 1555
4550 Lena Dr 17055
Tel (717) 591-5700 *SIC* 8051

MEDIA, PA

DELAWARE COUNTY PENNSYLVANIA p 423
201 W Front St 19063
Tel (610) 891-4000 *SIC* 9111

ELWYN p 490
111 Elwyn Rd 19063
Tel (610) 891-2000 *SIC* 8211

FAIR ACRES GERIATRIC CENTER p 524
340 N Middletown Rd 19063
Tel (610) 891-5600 *SIC* 8361

FAIR ACRES GERIATRIC CENTER p 524
340 N Middletown Rd 19063
Tel (610) 891-5700 *SIC* 8059

FOAMEX INTERNATIONAL INC p 562
1400 N Providence Rd 19063
Tel (610) 744-2300 *SIC* 3086

FOAMEX LP p 562
1400 N Providence Rd # 2000 19063
Tel (610) 565-2374 *SIC* 3086

FXI HOLDINGS INC p 586
1400 N Providence Rd # 2000 19063
Tel (610) 744-2300 *SIC* 3086

FXI INC p 586
1400 N Providence Rd # 2000 19063
Tel (610) 744-2300 *SIC* 3086

RIDDLE MEMORIAL HOSPITAL p 1234
1068 W Baltimore Pike 19063
Tel (610) 566-9400 *SIC* 8062

WAWA INC p 1584
260 W Baltimore Pike 19063
Tel (610) 358-8000 *SIC* 5411 2026

MERCERSBURG, PA

REGENTS OF MERCERSBURG COLLEGE p 1219
300 E Seminary St 17236
Tel (717) 328-6110 *SIC* 8299

MERION STATION, PA

SISTERS OF MERCY OF AMERICAS MID-ATLANTIC COMMUNITY INC p 1327
515 Montgomery Ave 19066
Tel (610) 664-6650 *SIC* 8661

MIDDLETOWN, PA

COUNTRY VIEW FAMILY FARMS INC p 375
1301 Fulling Mill Rd # 3000 17057
Tel (267) 663-0100 *SIC* 0213 0191

DIAKON LUTHERAN SOCIAL MINISTRIES p 436
1022 N Union St 17057
Tel (610) 682-1262 *SIC* 8051 8322

DIAKON LUTHERAN SOCIAL MINISTRIES p 436
1022 N Union St 17057
Tel (610) 682-1262 *SIC* 8322 8051

NOVINGER GROUP INC p 1063
1441 Stoneridge Dr 17057
Tel (717) 930-0300
SIC 1742 1799 5032 5033 5039

PHOENIX CONTACT SERVICES INC p 1144
586 Fulling Mill Rd 17057
Tel (717) 944-1300 *SIC* 5063 3678 3643

■ **PIEDMONT AIRLINES INC** p 1146
1000 Rosedale Ave 17057
Tel (410) 742-2996 *SIC* 4512

TURNPIKE COMMISSION PA p 1493
700 S Eisenhower Blvd 17057
Tel (717) 939-9551 *SIC* 9621

MIFFLINBURG, PA

RITZ-CRAFT CORP OF PENNSYLVANIA INC p 1237
15 Industrial Park Rd 17844
Tel (570) 966-1053 *SIC* 2452

MIFFLINTOWN, PA

■ **E K HOLDINGS INC** p 466
Rr 5 17059
Tel (717) 436-5921 *SIC* 2015

■ **EMPIRE KOSHER POULTRY INC** p 493
Chicken Plant Rd 17059
Tel (717) 436-5921 *SIC* 2015 5812

MILLERSBURG, PA

ADVANCED SCIENTIFICS INC p 26
163 Research Ln 17061
Tel (717) 692-2104 *SIC* 3069

MILLERSVILLE, PA

MILLERSVILLE UNIVERSITY OF PENNSYLVANIA p 971
1 S George St 17551
Tel (717) 872-3011 *SIC* 8221 9411

MILTON, PA

KRAMM HEALTHCARE CENTER INC p 829
743 Mahoning St 17847
Tel (570) 742-2681 *SIC* 8051

MONACA, PA

NOVA CHEMICALS INC p 1062
400 Frankfort Rd 15061
Tel (412) 490-4560 *SIC* 2821

PGT TRUCKING INC p 1141
1 Pgt Way 15061
Tel (724) 728-3500 *SIC* 4213 4731

MONONGAHELA, PA

MON-VALE HEALTH RESOURCES INC p 983
1163 Country Club Rd 15063
Tel (724) 258-1000 *SIC* 8062

MONONGAHELA VALLEY HOSPITAL INC p 984
1163 Country Club Rd 15063
Tel (724) 258-1000 *SIC* 8062 8063 8069

WESTMORELAND REALTY CORP p 1602
1428 Delberts Dr 15063
Tel (724) 258-9009 *SIC* 6531

MONROEVILLE, PA

BECHTEL PLANT MACHINERY INC p 167
3500 Technology Dr 15146
Tel (412) 829-8626 *SIC* 8711

COCHRAN OLDSMOBILE INC p 333
4520 William Penn Hwy 15146
Tel (412) 373-3333 *SIC* 5511

EMCON INC p 491
2790 Mosside Blvd 15146
Tel (412) 372-7701 *SIC* 8711 8999

THREE RIVERS HOLDINGS INC p 1450
300 Oxford Dr 15146
Tel (412) 858-4000 *SIC* 8011

UPMC EAST p 1528
2775 Mosside Blvd 15146
Tel (412) 357-3000 *SIC* 8062

MONTGOMERYVILLE, PA

MCCALLION TEMPS INC p 926
601 N Bthlhem Pike Bldg A 18936
Tel (215) 855-8000 *SIC* 7363 7361

MONTOURSVILLE, PA

K INVESTMENTS LIMITED PARTNERSHIP p 799
1500 Sycamore Rd Ste 10 17754
Tel (570) 327-0111 *SIC* 7011 5521 5712

MOON TOWNSHIP, PA

▲ **CALGON CARBON CORP** p 238
3000 Gsk Dr 15108
Tel (412) 787-6700
SIC 2819 7699 3589 3564

HARBISONWALKER INTERNATIONAL INC p 659
1305 Cherrington Pkwy # 100 15108
Tel (412) 375-6600 *SIC* 3297 3272 1459

IGATE INC p 730
1305 Cherrington Pkwy 15108
Tel (412) 787-2100 *SIC* 7373

■ **KINDER MORGAN MATERIALS SERVICES LLC** p 819
333 Rouser Rd Ste 4601 15108
Tel (412) 264-6068 *SIC* 4011

▲ **MASTECH DIGITAL INC** p 918
1305 Cherrington Pkwy # 400 15108
Tel (412) 787-2100 *SIC* 7361 7371

MICHAEL BAKER INTERNATIONAL HOLDCO CORP p 960
100 Airside Dr 15108
Tel (412) 269-6300 *SIC* 8711

SAPA EXTRUDER INC p 1281
Airport Offc Park 15108
Tel (412) 299-7600 *SIC* 3354

SAPA NORTH AMERICA INC p 1281
400 Rouser Rd Ste 300 15108
Tel (877) 922-7272 *SIC* 3354

■ **SERVICELINK NLS LLC** p 1307
1400 Cherrington Pkwy 15108
Tel (800) 777-8759 *SIC* 6361

VEOLIA WATER TECHNOLOGIES p 1549
250 Airside Dr 15108
Tel (412) 809-6000 *SIC* 8711

MOOSIC, PA

EDM AMERICAS INC p 478
10 Ed Preate Dr 18507
Tel (800) 852-9809
SIC 4226 7389 7334 8741

NORTHEAST BEHAVIORAL HEALTH CARE CONSORTIUM p 1054
72 Glenmaura Nat Blvd 18507
Tel (570) 344-9618 *SIC* 8082

MORGANTOWN, PA

MORGAN TRUCK BODY LLC p 989
111 Morgan Way 19543
Tel (610) 286-5025
SIC 3713 7532 5013 5084

RENKERT OIL LLC p 1224
3817 Main St 19543
Tel (610) 286-8010 *SIC* 5172

MORRISVILLE, PA

PUBLICIS HEALTHCARE SOLUTIONS INC p 1190
1000 Floral Vale Blvd # 400 19067
Tel (866) 616-4777 *SIC* 8742

MORTON, PA

DELAWARE COUNTY INTERMEDIATE UNIT EDUCATION FOUNDATION p 423
200 Yale Ave 19070
Tel (610) 938-9000 *SIC* 8211

MOSCOW, PA

MOZA LLC p 995
101 Church St Ofc 5 18444
Tel (570) 848-7926 *SIC* 5141 7389

MOUNT JOY, PA

HVAC DISTRIBUTORS INC p 722
2 Old Market St 17552
Tel (717) 653-6674 *SIC* 5075

■ PHYSICIAN SUPPORT SYSTEMS INC p 1145
15 Eby Chiques Rd 17552
Tel (717) 653-5340 *SIC* 8011

MOUNT MORRIS, PA

SHAFT DRILLERS INTERNATIONAL LLC p 1310
130 Madow Ridge Rd Ste 23 15349
Tel (800) 331-0175 *SIC* 1781

MOUNTAIN TOP, PA

CIW ENTERPRISES INC p 320
24 Elmwood Ave 18707
Tel (800) 233-8366 *SIC* 3442 3446 2431

CORNELLCOOKSON INC p 370
24 Elmwood Ave 18707
Tel (570) 474-6773 *SIC* 3442

MOUNTVILLE, PA

COMMUNITY SERVICES GROUP INC p 350
320 Highland Dr 17554
Tel (717) 285-7121 *SIC* 8093 8059

COOPER-BOOTH WHOLESALE CO LP p 367
200 Lincoln West Dr 17554
Tel (717) 285-8000
SIC 5194 5145 5122 5141

LIFT INC p 865
3745 Hempland Rd 17554
Tel (717) 295-1800 *SIC* 5084 7353

MUNCY, PA

INFINITY OILFIELD SERVICES LLC p 741
1 Eye Center Dr 17756
Tel (570) 567-7027 *SIC* 5172

MUNHALL, PA

FISHIN CO p 552
3714 Main St 15120
Tel (412) 464-9000 *SIC* 5146

MARCEGAGLIA USA INC p 905
1001 E Waterfront Dr 15120
Tel (412) 462-2185 *SIC* 3317 3312

MURRYSVILLE, PA

BECKWITH MACHINERY CO INC p 167
4565 William Penn Hwy 15668
Tel (724) 327-1300
SIC 5082 5084 7629 7353

CLEVELAND BROTHERS EQUIPMENT CO INC p 325
4565 William Penn Hwy 15668
Tel (724) 325-9421 *SIC* 5082

RESPIRONICS INC p 1227
1010 Murry Ridge Ln 15668
Tel (724) 387-5200
SIC 3641 3845 3841 3564 8351

MYERSTOWN, PA

DUTCH VALLEY FOOD DISTRIBUTORS INC p 463
7615 Lancaster Ave 17067
Tel (717) 933-4191 *SIC* 5141

NATRONA HEIGHTS, PA

ALLE-KISKI MEDICAL CENTER p 52
1301 Carlisle St 15065
Tel (724) 224-5100 *SIC* 8062

NAZARETH, PA

C F MARTIN & CO INC p 232
510 Sycamore St 18064
Tel (610) 759-2837 *SIC* 3931

ESSROC CEMENT CORP p 510
3251 Bath Pike 18064
Tel (610) 837-6725 *SIC* 3241

ESSROC CORP p 511
3251 Bath Pike 18064
Tel (610) 837-6725 *SIC* 3241 5032 3273

MORAVIAN SPRINGS HEALTH CENTER p 988
175 W North St 18064
Tel (610) 746-1000 *SIC* 8051

NESQUEHONING, PA

KOVATCH MOBILE EQUIPMENT CORP p 828
1 Industrial Complex 18240
Tel (570) 669-9461 *SIC* 3711

NEW BLOOMFIELD, PA

WOODEN HEART INC p 1623
64 Amanda Blvd 17068
Tel (717) 834-7144 *SIC* 5047

NEW BRITAIN, PA

MANGAR INDUSTRIES INC p 901
97 Britain Dr 18901
Tel (215) 230-0300 *SIC* 2671

NEW CASTLE, PA

ELLWOOD QUALITY STEELS CO p 489
700 Moravia St Ste 7 16101
Tel (724) 658-6502 *SIC* 3312

JAMESON HEALTH SYSTEM INC p 777
1211 Wilmington Ave 16105
Tel (724) 658-9001 *SIC* 8062

JAMESON MEMORIAL HOSPITAL p 777
1211 Wilmington Ave 16105
Tel (724) 658-9001 *SIC* 8062

■ NORDSON XALOY INC p 1048
1399 County Line Rd 16101
Tel (724) 656-5600 *SIC* 3544

NEW CUMBERLAND, PA

WEST SHORE SCHOOL BOARD p 1595
507 Fishing Creek Rd 17070
Tel (717) 938-9577 *SIC* 8211

WEST SHORE SCHOOL DISTRICT p 1595
507 Fishing Creek Rd 17070
Tel (717) 938-9577 *SIC* 8211

NEW ENTERPRISE, PA

NEW ENTERPRISE STONE & LIME CO INC p 1030
3912 Brumbaugh Rd 16664
Tel (814) 224-6883 *SIC* 1422 1611

NEW HOLLAND, PA

AFP ADVANCED FOOD PRODUCTS LLC p 33
402 S Custer Ave 17557
Tel (717) 355-8667
SIC 2026 2035 2032 2099 2022

ALOUETTE CHEESE USA LLC p 60
400 S Custer Ave 17557
Tel (717) 355-8500 *SIC* 5143 2022

BEANS-CLASS FORD MERCURY INC p 165
508 W Main St 17557
Tel (717) 354-4901 *SIC* 5511

BERK-TEK LLC p 174
132 White Oak Rd 17557
Tel (717) 354-6200 *SIC* 3357

CNH INC p 330
500 Diller Ave 17557
Tel (717) 355-1121 *SIC* 3523

NEW HOLLAND NORTH AMERICA INC p 1030
300 Diller Ave 17557
Tel (717) 355-1121 *SIC* 3523

VALCO COMPANIES INC p 1539
2710 Division Hwy 17557
Tel (717) 354-4586 *SIC* 5083

ZAUSNER FOODS CORP p 1641
400 S Custer Ave 17557
Tel (717) 355-8505 *SIC* 2022 2032 6794

NEW KENSINGTON, PA

LEEDSWORLD INC p 852
400 Hunt Valley Rd 15068
Tel (724) 334-9000
SIC 5199 5111 5112 3172 3161 2394

POLYCONCEPT NORTH AMERICA INC p 1160
400 Hunt Valley Rd 15068
Tel (724) 334-9000
SIC 5199 5111 5112 3172 3161 2394

NEW OXFORD, PA

AGRICULTURAL COMMODITIES INC p 36
2224 Oxford Rd 17350
Tel (717) 624-8249
SIC 5191 2048 2041 0723 2875

LINCOLN INTERMEDIATE UNIT 12 p 867
65 Billerbeck St 17350
Tel (717) 624-4616 *SIC* 8299

NEW PARIS, PA

CONEMAUGH HEALTH SYSTEM p 355
4186 Cortland Dr 15554
Tel (814) 839-4108 *SIC* 8099

NEWTOWN SQUARE, PA

APPLE LEISURE GROUP p 98
7 Campus Blvd Ste 100 19073
Tel (610) 359-6500 *SIC* 8699

CATHOLIC HEALTH EAST p 266
3805 West Chester Pike # 100 19073
Tel (610) 355-2000
SIC 8062 8051 8052 8059 8011

G M H COMMUNITIES LP p 587
10 Campus Blvd 19073
Tel (610) 355-8000 *SIC* 6531

■ GMH COMMUNITIES TRUST p 619
10 Campus Blvd 19073
Tel (610) 355-8000 *SIC* 6798 6513 8742

GRAHAM PARTNERS INC p 629
3811 West Chester Pike # 200 19073
Tel (610) 408-0500 *SIC* 8742 6799

MAIN LINE HEALTH INC p 897
3803 West Chester Pike # 250 19073
Tel (484) 565-1644 *SIC* 8741

MAXIS HEALTH SYSTEM p 922
3805 West Chester Pike # 100 19073
Tel (570) 281-1000 *SIC* 8062

NATIONAL ELEVATOR INDUSTRY HEALTH BENEFIT PLAN p 1011
19 Campus Blvd Ste 200 19073
Tel (610) 325-9100 *SIC* 6411

PROJECT MANAGEMENT INSTITUTE INC p 1182
14 Campus Blvd 19073
Tel (610) 356-4600 *SIC* 8699

SAP AMERICA INC p 1281
3999 West Chester Pike 19073
Tel (610) 661-1000 *SIC* 7371

■ SUNOCO INC p 1403
3801 West Chester Pike 19073
Tel (215) 977-3000
SIC 5541 2911 2869 2865 5171 5052

■ SUNOCO INC (R&M) p 1403
3801 West Chester Pike 19073
Tel (215) 977-3000
SIC 5541 2869 2911 5411

▲ SUNOCO LOGISTICS PARTNERS LP p 1403
3807 West Chester Pike 19073
Tel (866) 248-4344
SIC 4612 4613 5171 5172

■ SUNOCO PARTNERS LLC p 1403
3807 West Chester Pike 19073
Tel (866) 248-4344 *SIC* 4612

SUPPLYONE HOLDINGS CO INC p 1408
11 Campus Blvd 19073
Tel (484) 582-5005 *SIC* 2653 5113

SUPPLYONE INC p 1408
11 Campus Blvd Ste 150 19073
Tel (484) 582-1004 *SIC* 5113

WANHUA CHEMICAL (AMERICA) CO LTD p 1575
3803 West Chester Pike 19073
Tel (613) 796-1606 *SIC* 5169

XANITOS INC p 1630
3809 West Chester Pike # 210 19073
Tel (484) 654-2300 *SIC* 7349

NEWTOWN, PA

■ ALLIANCE GLOBAL SERVICES INC p 54
41 University Dr Ste 202 18940
Tel (610) 234-4301 *SIC* 7371

■ ALLIANCE GLOBAL SERVICES LLC p 54
41 University Dr Ste 202 18940
Tel (610) 234-4301 *SIC* 8742

COUNCIL ROCK SCHOOL DISTRICT p 374
30 N Chancellor St 18940
Tel (215) 944-1000 *SIC* 8211

▲ EPAM SYSTEMS INC p 504
41 University Dr Ste 202 18940
Tel (267) 759-9000 *SIC* 7371 8742

FITZ AND FLOYD ENTERPRISES LLC p 553
3 Friends Ln Ste 300 18940
Tel (800) 527-9550
SIC 5023 5199 5947 5719

PKF-MARK III INC p 1153
17 Blacksmith Rd Ste 101 18940
Tel (215) 968-5031
SIC 1611 1629 1711 1731 1771 8711

ROSE CASUAL DINING INC p 1250
826 Newtown Yardley Rd 18940
Tel (215) 579-9220 *SIC* 5812

ROSE MANAGEMENT SERVICES p 1250
29 Friends Ln 18940
Tel (215) 867-1802 *SIC* 5812

SECURITY AND DATA TECHNOLOGIES INC p 1299
101 Pheasant Run 18940
Tel (215) 579-7000 *SIC* 5063

WINPAK PORTION PACKAGING INC p 1617
828a Newtown Yardley Rd # 101 18940
Tel (267) 685-8200 *SIC* 3565 2671

NORRISTOWN, PA

A J CATAGNUS INC p 5
1299 W James St 19401
Tel (610) 275-5328 *SIC* 4953

ADT SECURITY SERVICES INC p 24
2450 Blvd Of The Generals 19403
Tel (800) 423-9637 *SIC* 7382

COUNTY OF MONTGOMERY p 380
530 Port Indian Rd 19403
Tel (610) 278-3072 *SIC* 9111

FARGO ASSEMBLY OF PA INC p 528
800 W Washington St 19401
Tel (610) 272-6850 *SIC* 3679

GAUDENZIA INC p 594
106 W Main St 19401
Tel (610) 239-9600 *SIC* 8361 8093

GENUARDIS FAMILY MARKETS LP p 605
301 E Germantown Pike 19401
Tel (610) 277-6000 *SIC* 5912 5411

HOUGHTON INTERNATIONAL INC p 711
945 Madison Ave 19403
Tel (610) 666-4000 *SIC* 2869 2992

METHACTON SCHOOL DISTRICT p 953
1001 Kriebel Mill Rd 19403
Tel (610) 489-5000 *SIC* 8211

PJM INTERCONNECTION LLC p 1153
2750 Monroe Blvd 19403
Tel (610) 666-8980 *SIC* 4911

NORTH EAST, PA

BETTER BAKED FOODS INC p 178
56 Smedley St 16428
Tel (814) 725-8778 *SIC* 2051

NE FOODS INC p 1022
1640 Freeport Rd 16428
Tel (814) 725-4835 *SIC* 2038

NORTH VERSAILLES, PA

BOLTTECH MANNINGS INC p 199
501 Mosside Blvd 15137
Tel (724) 872-4873
SIC 3546 5072 3599 7359 3545 3423

NORTH WALES, PA

BARR LABORATORIES INC p 156
1090 Horsham Rd 19454
Tel (215) 591-3000 *SIC* 2834

ICON CLINICAL RESEARCH LLC p 727
2100 Pennbrook Pkwy 19454
Tel (215) 616-3000 *SIC* 8731

MADLYN AND LEONARD ABRAMSON CENTER FOR JEWISH LIFE p 894
1425 Horsham Rd 19454
Tel (215) 371-3000 *SIC* 8051 8069 6513

TEVA PHARMACEUTICALS USA INC p 1441
1090 Horsham Rd 19454
Tel (215) 591-3000 *SIC* 2834 2833 5122

NORTHUMBERLAND, PA

FURMAN FOODS INC p 585
770 Cannery Rd 17857
Tel (570) 473-3516 *SIC* 2033

■ MOHAWK FLUSH DOORS p 982
980 Point Township Dr 17857
Tel (570) 473-3557 *SIC* 2431

NOTTINGHAM, PA

HERR FOODS INC p 687
20 Herr Dr 19362
Tel (610) 932-9330 *SIC* 2096

OAKMONT, PA

PRESBYTERIAN SENIORCARE p 1171
1215 Hulton Rd 15139
Tel (412) 828-5600
SIC 8051 8052 6513 8741

OAKS, PA

■ COMCAST OF SOUTHEAST PENNSYLVANIA LLC p 343
200 Cresson Blvd 19456
Tel (610) 650-1000 *SIC* 4841

▲ SEI INVESTMENTS CO p 1300
1 Freedom Valley Dr 19456
Tel (610) 676-1000 *SIC* 6722 8742

■ SEI PRIVATE TRUST CO p 1300
1 Freedom Valley Dr 19456
Tel (610) 676-1000 *SIC* 6733 6211

OLYPHANT, PA

CINRAM MANUFACTURING INC p 308
1400 E Lackawanna St 18448
Tel (570) 383-3291 *SIC* 3652

OREFIELD, PA

KIDSPEACE NATIONAL CENTERS OF NEW YORK INC p 817
5300 Kidspeace Dr 18069
Tel (800) 992-9543 *SIC* 8322

ORWIGSBURG, PA

BOYERS FOOD MARKETS INC p 205
301 S Warren St 17961
Tel (570) 366-1477 *SIC* 5411

OTTSVILLE, PA

ST LUKES PHYSICIANS GROUP p 1370
7790 Easton Rd 18942
Tel (610) 847-2071 *SIC* 8011

PALMERTON, PA

PENCOR SERVICES INC p 1128
613 3rd Street Palmerton 18071
Tel (610) 826-2115
SIC 2711 7371 4813 4841

TUTHILL CORP p 1493
1660 Blue Mountain Dr 18071
Tel (610) 826-7700 *SIC* 7011

PALMYRA, PA

DAS COMPANIES INC p 413
724 Lawn Rd 17078
Tel (717) 964-3642 *SIC* 5064

PAOLI, PA

MAIN LINE HEALTHCARE p 897
2 Industrial Blvd Ste 400 19301
Tel (610) 648-1644 *SIC* 8099 8011

PEACH BOTTOM, PA

PEACH BOTTOM TRANSPORT LLC p 1125
2663 Robert Fulton Hwy 17563
Tel (717) 278-8055 *SIC* 2873

PEACH GLEN, PA

KNOUSE FOODS COOPERATIVE INC p 825
800 Pach Glen Idaville Rd 17375
Tel (717) 677-8181 *SIC* 2033

PERKASIE, PA

PENNRIDGE SCHOOL DISTRICT p 1130
1200 N 5th St 18944
Tel (215) 257-5011 *SIC* 8211

PETROLIA, PA

■ INDSPEC CHEMICAL CORP p 739
133 Main St 16050
Tel (724) 756-2370 *SIC* 2865 2819

PHILADELPHIA, PA

ABERDEEN ASSET MANAGEMENT INC p 11
1735 Market St Fl 32 19103
Tel (215) 405-5700 *SIC* 6282

ACE AMERICAN INSURANCE CO p 16
436 Walnut St 19106
Tel (215) 640-1000 *SIC* 6321 6331 6351

ACE PROPERTY AND CASUALTY INSURANCE CO p 16
2 Liberty Pl 2 Liberty Place 19102
Tel (215) 761-1000 *SIC* 6321 6331 6351

ACE USA INC p 16
436 Walnut St 19106
Tel (215) 923-5352 *SIC* 6411 6321 6351

ALBERT EINSTEIN HEALTHCARE NETWORK p 46
5501 Old York Rd 19141
Tel (215) 456-7890 *SIC* 8062

ALBERT EINSTEIN MEDICAL ASSOCIATES INC p 46
5501 Old York Rd Ste 1 19141
Tel (215) 456-7890 *SIC* 8062 8051

ALBERT EINSTEIN MEDICAL CENTER p 46
5501 Old York Rd Ste 1 19141
Tel (215) 456-7890 *SIC* 8062

ALBERT M HOSPICE EINSTEIN p 46
5501 Old York Rd Ste 3 19141
Tel (215) 456-7890 *SIC* 8062

ALMO CORP p 59
2709 Commerce Way 19154
Tel (215) 698-4000 *SIC* 5064 5063

ALSTOM GRID INC p 61
2 International Plz # 325 19113
Tel (724) 483-7816 *SIC* 3613

AMERICAN ONCOLOGIC HOSPITAL INC p 77
333 Cottman Ave Frnt 19111
Tel (215) 214-3264 *SIC* 8069

AMERIHEALTH ADMINISTRATORS INC p 82
1900 Market St Ofc 624 19103
Tel (215) 657-8900 *SIC* 6321

AMERIHEALTH CARITAS HEALTH PLAN p 82
200 Stevens Dr 19113
Tel (215) 937-8000 *SIC* 6321

AMERIHEALTH INC p 82
1901 Market St Fl 32 19103
Tel (215) 241-3019 *SIC* 6411 6324 8748

■ ANTHROPOLOGIE INC p 94
5000 S Broad St 19112
Tel (215) 454-4421 *SIC* 5719 5621

ANTONIO ORIGLIO INC p 94
3000 Meetinghouse Rd 19154
Tel (215) 698-9500 *SIC* 5181

APPLABS TECHNOLOGIES PVT LTD p 98
1515 Market St Ste 1110 19102
Tel (215) 563-9396 *SIC* 7373

▲ ARAMARK CORP p 102
1101 Market St Ste 45 19107
Tel (215) 238-3000 *SIC* 5812 7218 5136

■ ARAMARK FACILITY SERVICES LLC p 102
1101 Market St 19107
Tel (215) 238-3000 *SIC* 7349

■ ARAMARK HEALTHCARE SUPPORT SERVICES OF TEXAS INC p 102
1101 Market St 19107
Tel (215) 238-3000 *SIC* 5812

■ ARAMARK INTERMEDIATE HOLDCO CORP p 102
1101 Market St Ste 45 19107
Tel (215) 238-3000 *SIC* 5812 7218 5136

■ ARAMARK REFRESHMENT SERVICES LLC p 102
1101 Market St 19107
Tel (215) 238-3000 *SIC* 5963

■ ARAMARK SERVICES INC p 102
1101 Market St Ste 45 19107
Tel (215) 238-3000 *SIC* 5812 7218 5136

■ ARAMARK SPORTS AND ENTERTAINMENT GROUP LLC p 102
1101 Market St 19107
Tel (215) 238-3000 *SIC* 5812

■ ARAMARK UNIFORM & CAREER APPAREL GROUP INC p 102
1101 Market St Ste 45 19107
Tel (215) 238-3000
SIC 2337 2311 5699 5961 5661 5812

ARIA HEALTH p 108
10800 Knights Rd 19114
Tel (215) 612-4000 *SIC* 8062

ATLANTIC PETROLEUM CORP p 127
1801 Market St Ste 1500 19103
Tel (215) 977-3000
SIC 5541 5172 2911 4612

■ ATLANTIC REFINING & MARKETING CORP p 127
1801 Market St 19103
Tel (215) 977-3000
SIC 2911 5171 5541 5411

■ AXALTA COATING SYSTEMS LLC p 139
2001 Market St Fl 36a 19103
Tel (215) 255-7932 *SIC* 2851 3479

▲ AXALTA COATING SYSTEMS LTD p 139
2001 Market St Ste 3600 19103
Tel (855) 547-1461 *SIC* 2851

BALLARD SPAHR LLP p 148
1735 Market St Fl 51 19103
Tel (215) 665-8500 *SIC* 8111

BDP INTERNATIONAL INC p 164
510 Walnut St Fl 14 19106
Tel (215) 629-8900 *SIC* 4731

■ BELL ATLANTIC GLOBAL WIRELESS INC p 170
1717 Arch St Fl 33 19103
Tel (215) 246-9494
SIC 4813 4812 5065 7379

■ BELL ATLANTIC INVESTMENT DEVELOPMENT CORP p 170
1717 Arch St Fl 22 19103
Tel (215) 963-6000 *SIC* 1731

▲ BENEFICIAL BANCORP INC p 172
1818 Market St 19103
Tel (215) 864-6000 *SIC* 6035

BENEFICIAL MUTUAL BANCORP INC p 172
1818 Market St 19103
Tel (215) 864-6000 *SIC* 6035

BENEFICIAL MUTUAL SAVINGS BANK p 172
1818 Market St Fl 8 19103
Tel (888) 742-5272 *SIC* 6036

BENEFICIAL SAVINGS BANK MHC p 173
1818 Market St Fl 8 19103
Tel (215) 864-6000 *SIC* 6411

BERWIND CONSOLIDATED HOLDINGS INC p 176
3000 Ctr Sq W 1500 Mkt St 1500 W 19102
Tel (215) 563-2800 *SIC* 6722

BERWIND CORP p 176
3000 Ctr Sq W 1500 Mkt St 1500 W 19102
Tel (215) 563-2800
SIC 6519 5052 4789 3625 3669 2899

BERWIND INDUSTRIES INC p 176
3000 Ctr Sq W 1500 Mkt St 19102
Tel (215) 563-2800 *SIC* 7389

BIOLIFE PLASMA SERVICES LP p 184
1435 Lake Cook Rd 19182
Tel (847) 940-5559 *SIC* 5122 8099

BLANK ROME LLP p 189
1 Logan Sq 19103
Tel (215) 569-5500 *SIC* 8111

BOARD OF PENSIONS OF PRESBYTERIAN CHURCH USA p 195
2000 Market St Fl 4 19103
Tel (800) 773-7752 *SIC* 6371

BODEK AND RHODES INC p 197
2951 Grant Ave 19114
Tel (215) 673-6767 *SIC* 5136 5137

■ BRANDYWINE GLOBAL INVESTMENT MANAGEMENT LLC p 208
2929 Arch St Ste 700 19104
Tel (215) 609-3500 *SIC* 6282

BRASKEM AMERICA INC p 208
1735 Market St Fl 28 19103
Tel (215) 841-3100 *SIC* 2821 2865 2869

■ CARDINAL HEALTH 407 INC p 253
3001 Red Lion Rd Ste Ag 19114
Tel (215) 501-1210 *SIC* 7389 3086 3089

CARDONE INDUSTRIES INC p 253
5501 Whitaker Ave 19124
Tel (215) 912-3000 *SIC* 3465 3714

CARING PEOPLE ALLIANCE p 256
8 Penn Ctr 19103
Tel (215) 545-5230 *SIC* 8351

CARPENTERS HEALTH AND WELFARE FUND p 260
1811 Spring Garden St # 1 19130
Tel (215) 568-0430 *SIC* 6371

▲ CDI CORP p 271
1735 Market St Ste 200 19103
Tel (215) 569-2200
SIC 8711 7371 7373 7376 7361 7363

■ CDI CORP p 271
1735 Market St Ste 200 19103
Tel (215) 569-2200
SIC 7363 8711 7361 6794

CEDAR FARMS CO INC p 272
2100 Hornig Rd 19116
Tel (215) 934-7100
SIC 5142 5144 5143 5149

CENTURY INDEMNITY CO p 282
1601 Chestnut St 19192
Tel (215) 761-1000 *SIC* 6321 6331 6351

▲ CHEMTURA CORP p 294
1818 Market St Ste 3700 19103
Tel (215) 446-3911
SIC 2869 2843 2821 2911 2899 2842

CHH LIQUIDATING CO p 296
8835 Germantown Ave 19118
Tel (215) 248-8200 *SIC* 8062

CHHC TRANSITION CO p 296
8835 Germantown Ave 19118
Tel (215) 248-8200 *SIC* 8062

■ CHHS HOSPITAL CO LLC p 296
8835 Germantown Ave 19118
Tel (215) 248-8200 *SIC* 8062

CHILDRENS HEALTH CARE ASSOCIATES INC p 299
100 N 20th St Ste 301 19103
Tel (215) 567-2422 *SIC* 8621

CHILDRENS HOSPITAL OF PHILADELPHIA p 300
3401 Civic Center Blvd 19104
Tel (215) 590-1000 *SIC* 8069

CHILDRENS HOSPITAL OF PHILADELPHIA FOUNDATION p 300
3401 Civic Center Blvd 19104
Tel (215) 590-1000 *SIC* 8741 8399

CHILDRENS SURGICAL ASSOCIATES LTD p 300
3400 Civic Center Blvd # 5 19104
Tel (215) 590-2700 *SIC* 8011

CHUBB US HOLDING INC p 304
1601 Chestnut St 19192
Tel (215) 640-1000 *SIC* 6411 6331

■ CIGNA LIFE INSURANCE CO OF NEW YORK p 306
Two Liberty Place 19192
Tel (215) 761-2355 *SIC* 6321 6311

■ CITIZENS BANK OF PENNSYLVANIA p 310
130 N 18th St 19103
Tel (267) 671-1000 *SIC* 6022 6021

CITY OF PHILADELPHIA p 317
215 City Hall 19107
Tel (215) 686-2181 *SIC* 9111

CLONDALKIN GROUP p 327
2000 Market St Ste 2810 19103
Tel (215) 440-0570 *SIC* 2657

CLONDALKIN HOLDINGS INC p 327
Crtis Centre Ste 19106
Tel (215) 440-0570
SIC 2673 2621 2752 8741

COLLECTION & CONSULTING FINANCIAL SERVICES INC p 336
2948 Reed St Ste 100 19146
Tel (215) 463-3477 *SIC* 7322

■ COLONIAL PENN LIFE INSURANCE CO p 338
399 Market St 19181
Tel (215) 928-8000 *SIC* 6321 6311

■ COMCAST CABLE COMMUNICATIONS LLC p 343
1701 John Fk Blvd 19103
Tel (215) 665-1700 *SIC* 4841

■ COMCAST CABLE HOLDINGS LLC p 343
1500 Market St Ste Lmw 3 19102
Tel (215) 665-1700 *SIC* 4841 7922 5961

■ COMCAST CABLEVISION OF MERCER COUNTY INC p 343
1500 Market St 19102
Tel (215) 665-1700 *SIC* 4841

▲ COMCAST CORP p 343
1701 Jfk Blvd 19103
Tel (215) 286-1700
SIC 4841 4813 7812 7996

■ COMCAST HOLDINGS CORP p 343
1701 John F Kennedy Blvd C100 19103
Tel (215) 665-1700 *SIC* 4841

■ COMCAST INTERACTIVE CAPITAL LP p 343
1701 John F Kennedy Blvd 19103
Tel (215) 981-8450 *SIC* 6799

■ COMCAST SPECTACOR INC p 343
3601 S Broad St Ste 2 19148
Tel (215) 875-5202 *SIC* 8742

■ COMCAST TELEPHONY COMMUNICATIONS LLC p 344
1701 Jfk Blvd 19103
Tel (215) 665-1700 *SIC* 4812

COMMUNITY BEHAVIORAL HEALTH p 347
801 Market St Ste 7000 19107
Tel (215) 413-3100 *SIC* 8322

COMMUNITY COLLEGE OF PHILADELPHIA FOUNDATION p 348
1700 Spring Garden St 19130
Tel (215) 751-8010 *SIC* 8221

COMPSERVICES INC p 352
1717 Arch St Fl 45 19103
Tel (215) 587-1829 *SIC* 6321

CONRAIL INC p 358
1717 Arch St Ste 1310 19103
Tel (215) 209-5027 *SIC* 4011

CONSOLIDATED RAIL CORP p 360
1717 Arch St Ste 1310 19103
Tel (800) 456-7509 *SIC* 4011

CONTRADO BBH HOLDINGS LLC p 364
2929 Arch St Fl 27 19104
Tel (215) 609-3400 *SIC* 3579

COZEN OCONNOR p 387
1650 Market St Ste 2800 19103
Tel (215) 665-2053 *SIC* 8111

■ CROWN CORK & SEAL CO INC p 395
1 Crown Way 19154
Tel (215) 698-5100 *SIC* 3411

■ CROWN CORK & SEAL USA INC p 395
1 Crown Way 19154
Tel (215) 698-5100 *SIC* 3411 3466

▲ CROWN HOLDINGS INC p 395
1 Crown Way 19154
Tel (215) 698-5100 *SIC* 3411 3466 3499

CRR HOLDINGS LLC p 396
1717 Arch St Fl 13 19103
Tel (215) 209-2000 *SIC* 4011

CSAA AFFINITY INSURANCE CO p 397
2040 Market St 19103
Tel (215) 864-5000 *SIC* 6331 6321

■ DANIEL J KEATING CONSTRUCTION CO p 411
130 N 18th St Ste 1500 19103
Tel (610) 668-4100 *SIC* 1542

DAY & ZIMMERMANN GROUP INC p 417
1500 Spring Garden St # 900 19130
Tel (215) 299-8000
SIC 8711 8712 8741 7381 7382 3489

DAY & ZIMMERMANN INTERNATIONAL INC p 417
1500 Spring Garden St # 900 19130
Tel (215) 299-8000 *SIC* 8711 1541 8741

DAY & ZIMMERMANN LLC CO p 417
1500 Spring Garden St # 900 19130
Tel (215) 299-8000 *SIC* 7381

DAY AND ZIMMERMANN INC p 417
1500 Spring Garden St # 900 19130
Tel (215) 299-8000
SIC 8744 8712 8711 3559 3483

DECHERT LLP p 421
2929 Arch St Ste 400 19104
Tel (202) 261-3300 *SIC* 8111

DELAVAU LLC p 423
10101 Roosevelt Blvd 19154
Tel (215) 671-1400 *SIC* 2087 2834

DIAMOND TOOL & FASTENERS INC p 437
2800 Grays Ferry Ave 19146
Tel (215) 952-1919 *SIC* 5082

DIETZ & WATSON INC p 438
5701 Tacony St 19135
Tel (800) 333-1974 *SIC* 2011 2013

DREXEL UNIVERSITY p 456
3141 Chestnut St 19104
Tel (215) 895-2000 *SIC* 8221

DRINKER BIDDLE & REATH LLP p 456
1 Logan Sq Ste 2000 19103
Tel (215) 988-2700 *SIC* 8111

DSI INC p 458
9401 Blue Grass Rd 19114
Tel (215) 676-6000 *SIC* 5621

DUANE MORRIS LLP p 459
30 S 17th St Fl 5 19103
Tel (215) 979-1000 *SIC* 8111

EASTERN REGIONAL MEDICAL CENTER INC p 472
1331 E Wyoming Ave 19124
Tel (215) 537-7400 *SIC* 8069

ECOG-ACRIN MEDICAL RESEARCH FOUNDATION INC p 476
1818 Market St 19103
Tel (215) 789-3600 *SIC* 8731

EINSTEIN COMMUNITY HEALTH ASSOCIATES p 482
5501 Old York Rd 19141
Tel (215) 456-7890 *SIC* 8011

EINSTEIN PRACTICE PLAN INC p 482
5501 Old York Rd Ste 2 19141
Tel (215) 456-6070 *SIC* 8741

ELLIOTT-LEWIS CORP p 488
2900 Black Lake Pl 19154
Tel (215) 698-4400 *SIC* 1711 7349 7353

EMD PERFORMANCE MATERIALS CORP p 491
1 International Plz # 300 19113
Tel (484) 652-5600 *SIC* 2819 2816

■ ENERGY PLUS HOLDINGS LLC p 498
3711 Market St Ste 1000 19104
Tel (877) 320-0356 *SIC* 4911

ERESEARCHTECHNOLOGY INC p 507
1818 Market St Ste 1000 19103
Tel (215) 972-0420 *SIC* 8734

ESIS INC p 509
436 Walnut St 19106
Tel (215) 640-1000 *SIC* 6411

■ EXCALIBUR REINSURANCE CORP p 516
1735 Market St Fl 30 19103
Tel (215) 665-5000 *SIC* 6331

FEDERAL RESERVE BANK OF PHILADELPHIA (INC) p 535
100 N Independence Mall W 19106
Tel (215) 574-6000 *SIC* 6011

▲ FIVE BELOW INC p 553
1818 Market St Ste 2000 19103
Tel (215) 546-7909 *SIC* 5331 5945

■ FLUIDICS INC p 561
9815 Roosevelt Blvd Ste A 19114
Tel (215) 671-7900 *SIC* 1711

▲ FMC CORP p 562
2929 Walnut St 19104
Tel (215) 299-6000 *SIC* 2812 2879 2869

FOX CHASE CANCER CENTER FOUNDATION p 572
333 Cottman Ave 19111
Tel (215) 728-6900 *SIC* 8069 8071 8062

FOX ROTHSCHILD LLP p 572
2000 Market St Fl 20 19103
Tel (215) 299-2000 *SIC* 8111

FRANKFORD CANDY LLC p 574
9300 Ashton Rd 19114
Tel (215) 735-5200 *SIC* 2066

FS ENERGY AND POWER FUND p 582
Cira Centre 2929 Arch St Cira Cent 19104
Tel (215) 495-1150 SIC 6722

FS INVESTMENT CORP p 582
201 Rouse Blvd 19112
Tel (215) 495-1150 SIC 6726 6722

FS INVESTMENT CORP II p 582
Cira Centre 2929 Arch St Cira Cent 19104
Tel (215) 495-1150 SIC 6282

GEODIS USA INC p 605
5101 S Broad St 19112
Tel (215) 238-8600 SIC 4731 8741

GLAXOSMITHKLINE LLC p 614
5 Crescent Dr 19112
Tel (215) 751-4000 SIC 2834 5122

GLENMEDE CORP p 615
1650 Market St Ste 1200 19103
Tel (215) 419-6000 SIC 6733 6732

GLOBAL HARNESS SYSTEMS INC p 616
3304 Danley Rd 19154
Tel (609) 815-2100 SIC 3679

GREEN ACQUISITION CORP p 636
2001 Market St 19103
Tel (215) 209-2000 SIC 4011

■ **GSA MID-ATLANTIC REGION OFC OF REGIONAL ADMINISTRATOR (3A)** p 643
20 N 8th St 19107
Tel (215) 446-4900 SIC 9199

HANUMAN BUSINESS INC p 659
5026 Wynnefield Ave 19131
Tel (609) 929-5146 SIC 5541 7538

■ **HARRY M STEVENS INC OF NEW JERSEY** p 664
1101 Market St 19107
Tel (215) 238-3000 SIC 5812

HAY GROUP HOLDINGS INC p 670
1650 Arch St Ste 2300 19103
Tel (215) 861-2000 SIC 8742 8249 8733

■ **HAY GROUP INC** p 670
1650 Arch St Ste 2300 19103
Tel (215) 861-2000 SIC 8742

HEALTH PARTNERS PLANS INC p 675
901 Market St Ste 500 19107
Tel (215) 849-9606 SIC 8011

HEALTH SERVICES OF FOX CHASE CANCER CENTER p 676
333 Cottman Ave 19111
Tel (215) 728-6900 SIC 8011 8062 8733

HERMAN GOLDNER CO INC p 687
7777 Brewster Ave 19153
Tel (215) 365-5400 SIC 1711 7699

▲ **HILL INTERNATIONAL INC** p 693
2005 Market St Fl 17 19103
Tel (215) 309-7700 SIC 8742 8741

HONOR HOLDINGS INC p 705
1801 N 5th St 19122
Tel (215) 236-1700 SIC 5141 5142

HORIZON HOUSE INC p 707
120 S 30th St 19104
Tel (215) 386-3838
SIC 8361 6512 8322 8093

HOSPITAL OF UNIVERSITY OF PENNSYLVANIA p 709
3400 Spruce St Ofc 19104
Tel (215) 301-3776 SIC 8062

INA CHUBB HOLDINGS INC p 735
436 Walnut St 19106
Tel (215) 640-1000 SIC 6411

INA CORP p 735
1601 Chestnut St Ste 1 19192
Tel (215) 761-1000 SIC 6331

INAMAR LTD p 735
1601 Chestnut St 19192
Tel (215) 640-1000 SIC 6321

INDEPENDENCE BLUE CROSS LLC p 736
1901 Market St Fl 32 19103
Tel (215) 241-2400 SIC 6324 6411 8748

INDEPENDENCE HEALTH GROUP INC p 736
1901 Market St 19103
Tel (215) 241-2400 SIC 6321

INDEPENDENCE HOSPITAL INDEMNITY PLAN INC p 736
1901 Market St 19103
Tel (215) 241-2400 SIC 6321

INDEPENDENCE REALTY TRUST INC p 736
2929 Arch St Ste 1650 19104
Tel (215) 243-9000 SIC 6798

INTECH CONSTRUCTION LLC p 748
3020 Market St Fl 2 19104
Tel (215) 243-2000 SIC 8741

J J WHITE INC p 771
5500 Bingham St 19120
Tel (215) 722-1000 SIC 1711 1542 7699

JANNEY MONTGOMERY SCOTT LLC p 777
1717 Arch St Fl 16 19103
Tel (215) 665-6000 SIC 6211

JEANES HOSPITAL p 781
7600 Central Ave 19111
Tel (215) 728-2000 SIC 8062

JEVS HUMAN SERVICES p 784
1845 Walnut St Ste 700 19103
Tel (215) 875-7387 SIC 8322 8331

JOSEPH STOKES INSTITUTE OF RESEARCH p 793
3615 Civic Center Blvd 19104
Tel (215) 590-3800 SIC 8062 8733

KEYSTONE FAMILY HEALTH PLAN p 815
200 Stevens Dr 19113
Tel (215) 937-8000 SIC 6324

KEYSTONE HEALTH PLAN EAST INC p 815
1901 Market St Ste 1000 19103
Tel (215) 241-2001 SIC 6324 8011

▲ **LANNETT CO INC** p 844
9000 State Rd 19136
Tel (215) 333-9000 SIC 2834

LASALLE UNIVERSITY p 846
1900 W Olney Ave 19141
Tel (215) 951-1000 SIC 8221

LAW ENFORCEMENT HEALTH BENEFITS INC p 847
2233 Spring Garden St 19130
Tel (215) 763-8290 SIC 8621

LEAF COMMERCIAL CAPITAL INC p 850
2005 Market St Fl 14 19103
Tel (800) 819-5556 SIC 6159 7359

■ **LIBERTY BELL EQUIPMENT CORP** p 861
3201 S 76th St 19153
Tel (215) 492-6700 SIC 5013

■ **LIFE INSURANCE CO OF NORTH AMERICA** p 863
1601 Chestnut St 19192
Tel (215) 761-1000 SIC 6321 6311

LOMBARD INTERNATIONAL AGENCY INC p 875
1 Liberty Pl Ste 1650 19103
Tel (484) 530-4800 SIC 6411

LUMINENT MORTGAGE CAPITAL INC p 885
1 Commerce Sq 19103
Tel (215) 564-5900 SIC 6798

MARSHALL DENNEHEY WARNER COLEMAN & GOGGIN PC p 911
2000 Market St Fl 23 19103
Tel (215) 575-2600 SIC 8111

■ **MASCOT PETROLEUM CO INC** p 915
1801 Market St Fl 10 19103
Tel (215) 977-3000 SIC 4932 5411

MCKEAN DEFENSE GROUP LLC p 930
1 Crescent Dr Ste 400 19112
Tel (215) 271-6108 SIC 8711

MCKEE SHEPARD & GRIASKA MEDICAL ASSOCIATES p 930
51 N 39th St Ste 1 19104
Tel (215) 662-8978 SIC 8011

MERCY HEALTH PLAN INC p 946
200 Stevens Dr Ste 350 19113
Tel (215) 937-8000 SIC 6324 6321

MORGAN LEWIS & BOCKIUS LLP p 988
1701 Market St Ste Con 19103
Tel (215) 963-5000 SIC 8111

MUTUAL INDUSTRIES NORTH INC p 1003
707 W Grange Ave Ste 1 19120
Tel (215) 927-6000 SIC 3842 2221

MUTUAL PHARMACEUTICAL CO INC p 1003
1100 Orthodox St 19124
Tel (215) 288-6500 SIC 2834

■ **NASDAQ OMX PHLX LLC** p 1008
1900 Market St Fl 2 19103
Tel (215) 496-5000 SIC 6231

NATIONAL BOARD OF MEDICAL EXAMINERS OF UNITED STATES OF AMERICA p 1010
3750 Market St 19104
Tel (215) 590-9500 SIC 8748

NATIONAL REFRIGERANTS INC p 1015
11401 Roosevelt Blvd 19154
Tel (215) 698-6620 SIC 5169

NAZARETH HOSPITAL p 1020
2601 Holme Ave 19152
Tel (215) 335-6000 SIC 8062

NELSON WORLDWIDE INC p 1025
222-230 Walnut St 19106
Tel (215) 925-6562 SIC 7389

OPEN SYSTEMS TECHNOLOGIES INC p 1089
1818 Market St Ste 2510 19103
Tel (215) 399-5800 SIC 7379

OPTICAL FOR EYES CO p 1090
1630 Walnut St 19103
Tel (800) 367-3937 SIC 5995

PACKAGING COORDINATORS LLC p 1106
3001 Red Lion Rd 19114
Tel (215) 613-3600 SIC 7389

■ **PECO ENERGY CO** p 1127
2301 Market St 19103
Tel (215) 841-4000 SIC 4911 4924 4923

PEI/GENESIS INC p 1128
2180 Hornig Rd Ste 2 19116
Tel (215) 464-1410 SIC 3678 3677

PENN DETROIT DIESEL ALLISON LLC p 1129
8330 State Rd 19136
Tel (215) 335-5010 SIC 7699 7538

PENN JERSEY PAPER CO p 1129
9355 Blue Grass Rd 19114
Tel (215) 671-9800 SIC 5113 5087

PENNONI ASSOCIATES INC p 1130
3001 Market St Ste 200 19104
Tel (215) 222-3000 SIC 8711

PENNSYLVANIA HOSPITAL OF UNIVERSITY OF PENNSYLVANIA HEALTH SYSTEM p 1130
800 Spruce St 19107
Tel (215) 829-3000 SIC 8062 8063

PENNSYLVANIA LUMBERMENS MUTUAL INSURANCE CO p 1130
2005 Market St Ste 1200 19103
Tel (800) 752-1895 SIC 6331

PENNSYLVANIA REAL ESTATE INVESTMENT TRUST p 1130
200 S Broad St 19102
Tel (215) 875-0700 SIC 6798 6531

■ **PEP BOYS - MANNY MOE & JACK** p 1133
3111 W Allegheny Ave 19132
Tel (215) 430-9000 SIC 5531 7539 7533

■ **PEP BOYS - MANNY MOE & JACK OF DELAWARE INC** p 1133
3111 W Allegheny Ave 19132
Tel (215) 229-7555 SIC 5531

■ **PEP BOYS MANNY MOE & JACK OF CALIFORNIA** p 1133
3111 W Allegheny Ave 19132
Tel (215) 430-9095 SIC 5531 7533 7539

■ **PEP BOYS-MANNY MOE & JACK OF PUERTO RICO INC** p 1133
3111 W Allegheny Ave 19132
Tel (215) 229-9000 SIC 5531

PEPPER HAMILTON LLP p 1133
3000 Two Logan Sq 19103
Tel (215) 981-4000 SIC 8111

■ **PEROXYCHEM LLC** p 1137
1 Commerce Sq 19103
Tel (267) 422-2400 SIC 5169 2819

PEW CHARITABLE TRUSTS p 1140
2005 Market St Fl 28 19103
Tel (215) 575-9050 SIC 8732 6732

PHILADELPHIA AGUSTAWESTLAND CORP p 1142
3050 Red Lion Rd 19114
Tel (215) 281-1400 SIC 3721 5088

PHILADELPHIA BUNZL p 1142
10814 Northeast Ave 19116
Tel (215) 969-0600
SIC 5087 5023 5113 7213

PHILADELPHIA CARPENTERS BENEFIT FUNDS p 1142
1811 Spring Garden St 19130
Tel (215) 568-0430 SIC 1751

■ **PHILADELPHIA COCA-COLA BOTTLING CO** p 1142
725 E Erie Ave 19134
Tel (215) 427-4500 SIC 2086

PHILADELPHIA COLLEGE OF OSTEOPATHIC MEDICINE p 1142
4190 City Ave 19131
Tel (215) 871-6100 SIC 8221

PHILADELPHIA CONTRIBUTIONSHIP FOR INSURANCE OF HOUSES FROM LOSS BY FIRE p 1142
212 S 4th St 19106
Tel (215) 627-1752
SIC 6331 6311 7382 6321

PHILADELPHIA CORP FOR AGING INC p 1142
642 N Broad St Fl 5 19130
Tel (215) 765-9040 SIC 8322

PHILADELPHIA ENERGY SOLUTIONS LLC p 1142
1735 Market St Fl 10 19103
Tel (267) 238-4300 SIC 2911

PHILADELPHIA ENERGY SOLUTIONS REFINING AND MARKETING LLC p 1142
1735 Market St Fl 11 19103
Tel (267) 238-4300 SIC 2911

PHILADELPHIA FACILITIES MANAGEMENT CORP p 1142
800 W Montgomery Ave 19122
Tel (215) 684-3000 SIC 8744

PHILADELPHIA HEALTH AND EDUCATION CORP p 1142
245 N 15th St 19102
Tel (215) 762-8288 SIC 8221

PHILADELPHIA HEALTH EDUCATION CORP p 1142
1601 Cherry St Ste 11511 19102
Tel (215) 255-7755 SIC 8011

PHILADELPHIA HOUSING AUTHORITY p 1142
12 S 23rd St 19103
Tel (215) 684-4000 SIC 9531

PHILADELPHIA MEDIA NETWORK PBC p 1143
801 Market St Ste 300 19107
Tel (215) 854-2000 SIC 2711

PHILADELPHIA MUSEUM OF ART INC p 1143
2600 Bnjmin Franklin Pkwy 19130
Tel (215) 763-8100 SIC 8412

PHILADELPHIA NORTH HEALTH SYSTEM p 1143
801 W Girard Ave 19122
Tel (215) 787-9001 SIC 8062 8069 8063

PHILADELPHIA PARKING AUTHORITY p 1143
701 Market St Ste 5400 19106
Tel (215) 222-0224 SIC 7521

PHILADELPHIA PHILLIES p 1143
1 Citizens Bank Way Ofc 19148
Tel (215) 463-5000 SIC 7941

PHILADELPHIA GAS WORKS p 1143
1800 N 9th St 19122
Tel (215) 684-6710 SIC 4923

PHILDELPHIA-NEWSPAPERS-LLC p 1143
801 Market St Ste 300 19107
Tel (215) 854-2000 SIC 2711

POLICE AND FIRE FEDERAL CREDIT UNION (INC) p 1159
901 Arch St 19107
Tel (215) 931-0300 SIC 6061 6163

PRESBYTERIAN MEDICAL CENTER OF UNIVERSITY OF PENNSYLVANIA HEALTH SYSTEM p 1171
51 N 39th St 19104
Tel (215) 662-8000 SIC 8062

PROCACCI BROS SALES CORP p 1179
3333 S Front St 19148
Tel (215) 463-8000 SIC 5148

PRWT SERVICES INC p 1187
1835 Market St Ste 800 19103
Tel (215) 563-7698 SIC 7374

PUBLIC HEALTH MANAGEMENT CORP p 1189
Centre Sq E 1500 Market 19102
Tel (215) 985-2500 SIC 8741

QUAKER VALLEY FOODS INC p 1196
2701 Red Lion Rd 19114
Tel (215) 992-0900 SIC 5142

RADIAN ASSET ASSURANCE INC p 1204
1601 Market St Fl 5 19103
Tel (212) 983-3100 SIC 6351

▲ **RADIAN GROUP INC** p 1204
1601 Market St Fl 12 19103
Tel (215) 231-1000 SIC 6351

■ **RADIAN GUARANTY INC** p 1204
1601 Market St Fl 5 19103
Tel (215) 564-6600 SIC 6351

RAIT FINANCIAL TRUST p 1206
2 Logan Sq Fl 23 19103
Tel (215) 243-9000 SIC 6798

RELIANCE STANDARD LIFE INSURANCE CO p 1222
2001 Market St Ste 1500 19103
Tel (267) 256-3500 SIC 6311 6321

RESOURCE AMERICA INC p 1227
1 Crescent Dr Ste 203 19112
Tel (215) 546-5005 SIC 6531 6722 7359

RESOURCE REAL ESTATE OPPORTUNITY REIT INC p 1227
1 Crescent Dr Ste 203 19112
Tel (215) 231-7050 SIC 6798

RESOURCES FOR HUMAN DEVELOPMENT INC p 1227
4700 Wphickon Ave Ste 126 19144
Tel (215) 951-0300
SIC 8322 8093 8052 8331 8361

■ **RIGHT MANAGEMENT INC** p 1234
1600 Jf Kennedy Blvd # 610 19103
Tel (952) 837-0955 SIC 7363

■ **ROHM AND HAAS CO** p 1246
100 N Independence Mall W 19106
Tel (215) 592-3000
SIC 2819 2851 2891 2899

SAINT JOSEPHS UNIVERSITY p 1270
5600 City Ave 19131
Tel (610) 660-1000 SIC 8221

SAMUELS AND SON SEAFOOD CO INC p 1275
3400 S Lawrence St 19148
Tel (215) 336-7810 SIC 5146

SAUL EWING LLP p 1283
1500 Market St Fl 38 19102
Tel (215) 972-7777 SIC 8111

SCA AMERICAS INC p 1285
2929 Arch St Ste 2600 19104
Tel (610) 499-3700 SIC 2621 3086 2676

SCHENKER INTERNATIONAL INC p 1286
3501 Island Ave 19153
Tel (724) 695-7886 SIC 4731

SCHOOL DISTRICT OF PHILADELPHIA p 1289
440 N Broad St 19130
Tel (215) 400-4000 SIC 8211

SNEAKER VILLA INC p 1335
1926 Arch St Fl 3 19103
Tel (215) 279-5600 SIC 5699 5661

SOCIETY OF CATHOLIC MEDICAL MISSIONARIES INC p 1336
8400 Pine Rd Ste A 19111
Tel (215) 742-6100 SIC 8661

SOLIS HEALTHCARE LP p 1338
5800 Ridge Ave 19128
Tel (215) 483-9900 SIC 8062

SONEPAR MANAGEMENT US INC p 1339
510 Walnut St Ste 400 19106
Tel (215) 399-5900 SIC 5063

SOUTHEASTERN PENNSYLVANIA TRANSPORTATION AUTHORITY p 1347
1234 Market St Fl 4 19107
Tel (215) 580-7800 SIC 4111

SOUTHWARK METAL MANUFACTURING CO p 1351
2800 Red Lion Rd 19114
Tel (215) 735-3401 SIC 3444

SPARKS MARKETING GROUP INC p 1354
2828 Charter Rd 19154
Tel (800) 925-7727 SIC 7389

■ **SPD ELECTRICAL SYSTEMS INC** p 1355
13500 Roosevelt Blvd 19116
Tel (215) 698-6426 SIC 3612 3699 3613

■ **SPECTRUM ARENA LIMITED PARTNERSHIP** p 1357
3601 S Broad St 19148
Tel (215) 389-9524 *SIC* 6512 7941

■ **SYSCO PHILADELPHIA LLC** p 1417
600 Packer Ave 19148
Tel (215) 218-1348 *SIC* 5149

■ **TARGA PIPELINE OPERATING PARTNERSHIP LP** p 1425
1845 Walnut St 19103
Tel (412) 489-0006 *SIC* 1311

■ **TASTY BAKING CO** p 1426
4300 S 26th St 19112
Tel (215) 221-8500 *SIC* 2051 2052

TAYLOR MCCORMICK INC p 1427
2001 Market St Fl 10 19103
Tel (215) 592-4200 *SIC* 8711

TEMPLE PHYSICIANS INC p 1436
3509 N Broad St 19140
Tel (215) 926-9050 *SIC* 8661

TEMPLE UNIVERSITY HEALTH SYSTEM FOUNDATION p 1436
3509 N Broad St Fl 9 19140
Tel (215) 707-2000 *SIC* 8211 8221

TEMPLE UNIVERSITY HEALTH SYSTEM INC p 1436
2450 W Hunting Park Ave 19129
Tel (215) 926-9050 *SIC* 8741

TEMPLE UNIVERSITY HOSPITAL INC p 1436
3401 N Broad St 19140
Tel (215) 707-2000 *SIC* 8062

TEMPLE UNIVERSITY-OF COMMONWEALTH SYSTEM OF HIGHER EDUCATION p 1436
1801 N Broad St 19122
Tel (215) 204-1380 *SIC* 8221

■ **TENET HEALTHSYSTEM HAHNEMANN LLC** p 1437
230 N Broad St 19102
Tel (215) 762-7000 *SIC* 8062

■ **TENET HEALTHSYSTEM ST CHRISTOPHERS HOSPITAL FOR CHILDREN LLC** p 1437
160 E Erie Ave 19134
Tel (215) 427-5000 *SIC* 8069

THOMAS JEFFERSON UNIVERSITY p 1449
1020 Walnut St Ste 1 19107
Tel (215) 955-6000 *SIC* 8062 8221

THOMAS JEFFERSON UNIVERSITY HOSPITALS INC p 1449
111 S 11th St 19107
Tel (215) 955-5806 *SIC* 8062

THOMSON REUTERS (SCIENTIFIC) INC p 1450
1500 Spring Garden St # 400 19130
Tel (215) 386-0100 *SIC* 8731

■ **THOMSON REUTERS (SCIENTIFIC) LLC** p 1450
1500 Spring Garden St # 400 19130
Tel (215) 386-0100 *SIC* 2741 7372

TIOGA PIPE INC p 1455
2450 Wheatsheaf Ln 19137
Tel (215) 831-0700 *SIC* 5051

TRONOX ALKALI CORP p 1484
1735 Market St 19103
Tel (215) 299-6904 *SIC* 2812

TRUSTEES OF UNIVERSITY OF PENNSYLVANIA p 1488
3451 Walnut St 19104
Tel (215) 898-6301 *SIC* 8221 9411

UNIQUE INDUSTRIES INC p 1505
4750 League Island Blvd 19112
Tel (215) 336-4300 *SIC* 2679

UNIVERSITY OF ARTS p 1520
320 S Broad St 19102
Tel (215) 717-6000 *SIC* 8221

UNIVERSITY OF PENNSYLVANIA p 1524
3451 Walnut St 19104
Tel (215) 898-6636 *SIC* 8221

UNIVERSITY OF SCIENCES IN PHILADELPHIA p 1525
600 S 43rd St 19104
Tel (215) 596-8800 *SIC* 8221

UNIVERSITY PLAZA ASSOCIATES p 1527
3901 Market St Ofc B 19104
Tel (215) 386-0351 *SIC* 6513

▲ **URBAN OUTFITTERS INC** p 1530
5000 S Broad St 19112
Tel (215) 454-5500
SIC 5621 5611 5632 5661 5719 5137

■ **VERIZON PENNSYLVANIA INC** p 1550
1717 Arch St Fl 15 19103
Tel (215) 466-9900
SIC 4813 8721 1731 7629

VERSA CAPITAL MANAGEMENT LLC p 1551
2929 Arch St Ste 1650 19104
Tel (215) 609-3400 *SIC* 6799

WESTCHESTER FIRE INSURANCE CO INC p 1596
436 Walnut St 19106
Tel (215) 640-1000 *SIC* 6411

WESTINGHOUSE LIGHTING CORP p 1601
12401 Mcnulty Rd Ofc 19154
Tel (215) 671-2000 *SIC* 5063 3641 3645

WILLIAM PENN FOUNDATION p 1611
2 Logan Sq Fl 11 19103
Tel (215) 988-1830 *SIC* 6732

WOLTERS KLUWER HEALTH INC p 1621
2001 Market St Lbby 1 19103
Tel (215) 521-8300
SIC 2721 2731 2741 7372 8748

YOH SERVICES LLC p 1636
1500 Spring Garden St 19130
Tel (215) 656-2650 *SIC* 7363

PHOENIXVILLE, PA

CUSTOMERS BANK p 403
99 Bridge St 19460
Tel (610) 933-2000 *SIC* 6022

■ **PHOENIXVILLE HOSPITAL CO LLC** p 1145
140 Nutt Rd 19460
Tel (610) 983-1000 *SIC* 8062

■ **PHOENIXVILLE HOSPITAL OF UNIVERSITY OF PENNSYLVANIA HEALTH SYSTEM** p 1145
140 Nutt Rd 19460
Tel (610) 983-1000 *SIC* 8062 8011

QMES LLC p 1195
122 Mill Rd Ste A130 19460
Tel (610) 630-6357 *SIC* 5047 6719

PIPERSVILLE, PA

WORTH & CO INC p 1626
6263 Kellers Church Rd 18947
Tel (267) 362-1100 *SIC* 1711

PITTSBURGH, PA

A A A EAST CENTRAL p 4
5900 Baum Blvd Ste 2 15206
Tel (412) 362-3300 *SIC* 6411

ABARTA INC p 9
200 Alpha Dr 15238
Tel (412) 963-6226
SIC 2086 2711 2721 5149 1382 5812

AEROTECH INC p 31
100 Zeta Dr 15238
Tel (412) 963-7470 *SIC* 3699 3825

■ **ALCOA MEXICO HOLDINGS LLC** p 47
201 Isabella St 15212
Tel (412) 553-4545 *SIC* 3334

■ **ALCOA WORLD ALUMINA LLC** p 47
201 Isabella St 15212
Tel (412) 553-4545 *SIC* 1099 1081 4911

ALLEGHENY COUNTY SANITARY AUTHORITY p 52
3300 Preble Ave 15233
Tel (412) 732-8020 *SIC* 4952

ALLEGHENY FOUNDATION p 52
301 Grant St Ste 1 15219
Tel (412) 392-2900 *SIC* 8641

ALLEGHENY GENERAL HOSPITAL INC p 52
320 E North Ave 15212
Tel (412) 359-3131 *SIC* 8062 8051

ALLEGHENY HEALTH NETWORK p 52
30 Isabella St Ste 320 15212
Tel (412) 330-2400 *SIC* 8099

■ **ALLEGHENY LUDLUM LLC** p 52
1000 Six Ppg Pl 15222
Tel (412) 394-2800 *SIC* 3312

▲ **ALLEGHENY TECHNOLOGIES INC** p 52
1000 Six Ppg Pl 15222
Tel (412) 394-2800 *SIC* 3312 3339 3545

■ **ALUMAX LLC** p 63
201 Isabella St 15212
Tel (412) 553-4545
SIC 3334 3353 3354 3449 3442 3446

▲ **AMERICAN EAGLE OUTFITTERS INC** p 71
77 Hot Metal St 15203
Tel (412) 432-3300
SIC 5621 5611 5661 5632

AMERICAN IRON OXIDE CO p 75
Fster Plz Ste 7 661 Adrsn 15220
Tel (412) 929-0177 *SIC* 4953 2816

ANSALDO STS USA INC p 93
1000 Technology Dr 15219
Tel (412) 688-2400 *SIC* 3669

ARCELORMITTAL TUBULAR PRODUCTS USA LLC p 104
4 Gateway Ctr 15222
Tel (419) 342-1200 *SIC* 3317

ARLANXEO USA HOLDINGS CORP p 110
111 Ridc Park West Dr 15275
Tel (412) 809-1000 *SIC* 2821 2824

ARLANXEO USA LLC p 110
111 Ridc Park West Dr 15275
Tel (412) 809-1000 *SIC* 2821 2824

ASSOCIATED CLEANING CONSULTANTS AND SERVICES INC p 120
431 Davidson Rd 15239
Tel (412) 795-9200 *SIC* 7349 8742

■ **ATC TECHNOLOGY CORP** p 124
100 Papercraft Park 15238
Tel (412) 820-3700 *SIC* 1541 3694 4225

■ **ATI OPERATING HOLDINGS LLC** p 124
1000 Six Ppg Pl 15222
Tel (412) 394-2800 *SIC* 3462

▲ **ATLAS ENERGY GROUP LLC** p 128
1000 Commerce Dr Ste 400 15275
Tel (412) 489-0006 *SIC* 1311 4922

ATLAS RESOURCE PARTNERS LP p 128
1000 Commerce Dr Ste 400 15275
Tel (800) 251-0171 *SIC* 1381

AXIALL LLC p 140
11 Stanwix St Ste 1900 15222
Tel (412) 515-8149 *SIC* 2899

AXIOM METALS INC p 140
401 Penn Ave 15221
Tel (412) 243-8000 *SIC* 5093

BAKER MICHAEL INTERNATIONAL INC p 146
500 Grant St Ste 5400 15219
Tel (412) 269-6300 *SIC* 8711 8741

BAYER BUSINESS AND TECHNOLOGY SERVICES LLC p 161
100 Bayer Rd 15205
Tel (412) 777-2000 *SIC* 8742

BAYER CORP p 161
100 Bayer Rd 15205
Tel (412) 777-2000
SIC 2821 2879 2819 2834 3841

■ **BNY MELLON NATIONAL ASSOCIATION** p 194
1 Mellon Center Ste 3831 15258
Tel (412) 234-5000 *SIC* 6021 6733

BOARD OF PUBLIC EDUCATION SCHOOL DISTRICT OF PITTSBURGH (INC) p 195
341 S Bellefield Ave 15213
Tel (412) 622-3500 *SIC* 8211

BOMBARDIER TRANSPORTATION (HOLDINGS) USA INC p 199
1501 Lebanon Church Rd 15236
Tel (412) 655-5700 *SIC* 3743 3315 3823

BROTHERS BROTHER FOUNDATION p 219
1200 Galveston Ave 15233
Tel (412) 321-3160 *SIC* 8399

BUCHANAN INGERSOLL & ROONEY PC p 222
301 Grant St Fl 20 15219
Tel (412) 562-8800 *SIC* 8111

CALANDRA FRANK INC p 238
258 Kappa Dr 15238
Tel (412) 963-9071 *SIC* 1241

CARMEUSE LIME & STONE INC p 258
11 Stanwix St Fl 21 15222
Tel (412) 995-5500 *SIC* 1422

CARMEUSE LIME INC p 258
11 Stanwix St Fl 21 15222
Tel (412) 995-5500 *SIC* 1422 3274

CARNEGIE INSTITUTE p 258
4400 Forbes Ave 15213
Tel (412) 622-3131 *SIC* 8412

CARNEGIE MELLON UNIVERSITY p 258
5000 Forbes Ave 15213
Tel (412) 268-2000 *SIC* 8221

CBCINNOVIS INC p 268
8 Parkway Ctr 15220
Tel (412) 503-9254 *SIC* 7323

CHEVRON AE RESOURCES LLC p 295
1000 Commerce Dr Fl 4 15275
Tel (800) 251-0171 *SIC* 4922 1311 4924

CHILDRENS HOSPITAL OF PITTSBURGH p 300
1 Childrens Hospital Dr 15224
Tel (412) 692-5437 *SIC* 8062

CHROMALOX INC p 304
103 Gamma Dr Ste 2 15238
Tel (412) 967-3800 *SIC* 3567

CITY OF PITTSBURGH p 317
414 Grant St 15219
Tel (412) 255-2640 *SIC* 9111

CIVIL & ENVIRONMENTAL CONSULTANTS INC p 320
333 Baldwin Rd Ste 1 15205
Tel (412) 429-2324 *SIC* 8711 0781

COMMUNITY CARE BEHAVIORAL HEALTH ORGANIZATION p 347
339 6th Ave Ste 1300 15222
Tel (412) 454-2120 *SIC* 6324

COMMUNITY COLLEGE OF ALLEGHENY COUNTY p 348
808 Ridge Ave 15212
Tel (412) 323-2323 *SIC* 8222

CORNELL ABRAXAS GROUP INC p 370
2840 Liberty Ave Ste 300 15222
Tel (412) 361-0695 *SIC* 8399

COUNTY OF ALLEGHENY p 376
436 Grant St Ste 104 15219
Tel (412) 350-5300 *SIC* 9111

COVESTRO LLC p 385
1 Covestro Cir 15205
Tel (412) 413-2000 *SIC* 2891 2821

CULWELL HEALTH INC p 400
4 Widgeon Dr 15238
Tel (412) 767-4103 *SIC* 8051

DCK WORLDWIDE LLC p 418
6 Ppg Pl Ste 710 15222
Tel (412) 384-1000 *SIC* 1542

DIOCESE OF PITTSBURGH p 440
111 Blvd Of The Allies 15222
Tel (412) 456-3000 *SIC* 8661

DIRECT ENERGY BUSINESS LLC p 441
1001 Liberty Ave Ste 1200 15222
Tel (800) 830-5923 *SIC* 4911

DOLLAR BANK FEDERAL SAVINGS BANK p 448
401 Liberty Ave 15222
Tel (412) 261-4900 *SIC* 6035 7359

DOLLAR BANK LEASING CORP p 448
401 Liberty Ave Lobby 15222
Tel (412) 261-4900 *SIC* 6035 7359

DQE HOLDINGS LLC p 454
411 7th Ave Ste 3 15219
Tel (412) 393-7100 *SIC* 6719

DUQUESNE LIGHT CO p 462
411 7th Ave 6-1 15219
Tel (412) 393-6000 *SIC* 4911

DUQUESNE LIGHT HOLDINGS INC p 462
411 7th Ave Ste 3 15219
Tel (412) 393-6000 *SIC* 4911

DUQUESNE UNIVERSITY OF HOLY SPIRIT p 462
600 Forbes Ave 15219
Tel (412) 396-6000 *SIC* 8221

ECKERT SEAMANS CHERIN & MELLOTT LLC p 475
600 Grant St Fl 44 15219
Tel (412) 566-6000 *SIC* 8111

▲ **EDUCATION MANAGEMENT CORP** p 479
210 6th Ave Fl 33 15222
Tel (412) 562-0900 *SIC* 8299

■ **EDUCATION MANAGEMENT CORP** p 479
210 6th Ave Ste 3300 15222
Tel (412) 562-0900 *SIC* 8221

■ **EMERSON PROCESS MANAGEMENT POWER & WATER SOLUTIONS INC** p 492
200 Beta Dr 15238
Tel (412) 963-4000 *SIC* 3823 5063

▲ **EQT CORP** p 506
625 Liberty Ave Ste 1700 15222
Tel (412) 553-5700
SIC 1311 4923 4924 4925

■ **EQT GATHERING HOLDINGS LLC** p 506
625 Liberty Ave Ste 1700 15222
Tel (412) 553-5700 *SIC* 4922

■ **EQT GP HOLDINGS LP** p 506
625 Liberty Ave Ste 1700 15222
Tel (412) 553-5700 *SIC* 4922

EQT MIDSTREAM PARTNERS LP p 506
625 Liberty Ave Ste 1700 15222
Tel (412) 553-5700 *SIC* 4922

■ **EQT PRODUCTION CO** p 506
625 Liberty Ave Ste 1700 15222
Tel (412) 553-5700 *SIC* 4911

■ **EQUITRANS LP** p 506
625 Liberty Ave Ste 1700 15222
Tel (412) 553-5700 *SIC* 4922

▲ **FAB UNIVERSAL CORP** p 523
5001 Baum Blvd Ste 770 15213
Tel (412) 621-0902
SIC 7371 7372 5735 5942 5994 5099

FEDERAL HOME LOAN BANK OF PITTSBURGH p 534
601 Grant St Ste 1000 15219
Tel (412) 288-3400 *SIC* 6019

▲ **FEDERATED INVESTORS INC** p 536
1001 Liberty Ave Ste 2100 15222
Tel (412) 288-1900 *SIC* 6282 6722

■ **FEDERATED INVESTORS SERVICES CORP** p 536
1001 Liberty Ave Ste 2100 15222
Tel (412) 288-1900 *SIC* 6722 6282

FENNER DUNLOP AMERICAS INC p 537
1000 Omega Dr Ste 1400 15205
Tel (412) 249-0700 *SIC* 3496

■ **FISHER SCIENTIFIC CO LLC** p 552
300 Industry Dr 15275
Tel (412) 490-8300
SIC 5049 5169 3821 3826 2869 2819

▲ **FNB CORP** p 562
1 N Shore Ctr 12 Fdral St 15212
Tel (800) 555-5455
SIC 6022 6021 6162 6411

FOREST SNAVELY PRODUCTS INC p 567
600 Delwar Rd 15236
Tel (412) 885-4005 *SIC* 5031

FORMS AND SURFACES INC p 568
30 Pine St 15223
Tel (412) 781-9003 *SIC* 3446

FRANK B FUHRER HOLDINGS INC p 574
3100 E Carson St 15203
Tel (412) 488-8844 *SIC* 5181

FRESH FOOD MANUFACTURING CO p 578
101 Kappa Dr 15238
Tel (412) 963-6200 *SIC* 2099

■ **GALYANS TRADING CO LLC** p 590
300 Industry Dr 15275
Tel (724) 273-3400 *SIC* 5941 5699 5661

GATEWAY HEALTH PLAN INC p 593
600 Grant St Fl 41 15219
Tel (412) 255-4640 *SIC* 6324

GATEWAY HEALTH PLAN LP p 594
4 Gateway Ctr 444 15222
Tel (412) 255-4640 *SIC* 6324

GBU FINANCIAL LIFE p 595
4254 Saw Mill Run Blvd 15227
Tel (412) 884-5100 *SIC* 6311

■ **GE ENERGY POWER CONVERSION USA INC** p 596
610 Epsilon Dr 15238
Tel (412) 967-0765 *SIC* 3629

■ **GENCO DISTRIBUTION SYSTEM INC** p 598
100 Papercraft Park 15238
Tel (412) 820-3700 *SIC* 4225 4731

GENCO OF LEBANON INC p 598
100 Papercraft Park 15238
Tel (412) 820-3747 *SIC* 6512

■ GENCO TRANSPORTATION MANAGEMENT LLC p 598
100 Papercraft Park 15238
Tel (412) 820-3700
SIC 4225 4111 5045 4789

■ GENERAL NUTRITION CENTERS INC p 601
300 6th Ave 15222
Tel (412) 288-4600 *SIC* 5499 2023

■ GENERAL NUTRITION COMPANIES INC p 601
300 6th Ave 15222
Tel (412) 288-4600 *SIC* 5499

■ GENERAL NUTRITION CORP p 601
300 6th Ave 15222
Tel (412) 288-4600
SIC 5499 5999 5941 5699 6794

GIANT EAGLE INC p 610
101 Kappa Dr 15238
Tel (800) 362-8899
SIC 5411 5141 5147 5148 5143 6794

▲ GNC HOLDINGS INC p 619
300 6th Ave Fl 2 15222
Tel (412) 288-4600 *SIC* 5499

■ GNC INC p 619
300 6th Ave Fl 2 15222
Tel (412) 288-4600 *SIC* 5499

GOODWILL OF SOUTHWESTERN PENNSYLVANIA p 625
118 52nd St 15201
Tel (412) 481-9005 *SIC* 8331

■ H J HEINZ CO LP p 650
357 6th Ave 15222
Tel (412) 237-5757 *SIC* 2038

HALCO (MINING) INC p 653
12 Federal St Ste 320 15212
Tel (412) 235-0265 *SIC* 1099

HANNA HOLDINGS INC p 658
1090 Freeport Rd Ste 1a 15238
Tel (412) 967-9000 *SIC* 6531 6162 6361

HEINZ ENDOWMENTS p 681
625 Liberty Ave Fl 30 15222
Tel (412) 281-5777 *SIC* 6732

■ HEINZ FROZEN FOOD CO p 681
357 6th Ave 15222
Tel (412) 237-5700 *SIC* 2038 2037 8741

■ HEINZ KRAFT FOODS CO p 681
1 Ppg Pl Ste 3200 15222
Tel (412) 456-5700
SIC 2033 2038 2032 2098

HFF HOLDINGS LLC p 689
1 Oxford Ctr 15219
Tel (412) 281-8714 *SIC* 6162

▲ HFF INC p 689
301 Grant St Ste 1100 15219
Tel (412) 281-8714 *SIC* 6162

HIGHMARK INC p 692
120 5th Ave 15222
Tel (412) 544-7000
SIC 6321 6324 6411 6512

HM HEALTH SOLUTIONS INC p 697
120 5th Ave 15222
Tel (412) 544-7226 *SIC* 8099 6321

HM INSURANCE GROUP INC p 697
120 5th Ave 15222
Tel (412) 544-1000 *SIC* 6311 6371

HORSEHEAD CORP p 708
4955 Steubenville Pike 15205
Tel (724) 774-1020 *SIC* 3339 3629

HORSEHEAD HOLDING CORP p 708
4955 Steubenville Pike 15205
Tel (724) 774-1020 *SIC* 3339

■ I GENCO INC p 725
100 Papercraft Park 15238
Tel (800) 677-3110 *SIC* 4225 4111 5045

■ IDL WORLDWIDE INC p 729
6515 Penn Ave 15206
Tel (412) 965-3954 *SIC* 3993 2752

INSTITUTE FOR TRANSFUSION MEDICINE p 747
5 Parkway Ctr 875 15220
Tel (412) 209-7316 *SIC* 8099

INTERTECH CI p 759
1501 Preble Ave 15233
Tel (412) 246-1200 *SIC* 5065

INTERTECH SECURITY GROUP LLC p 759
1501 Preble Ave Ste 6 15233
Tel (724) 742-4900 *SIC* 7382

IRON AGE HOLDINGS CORP p 764
3 Robinson Plz Ste 300 15205
Tel (412) 788-0888
SIC 5139 5661 3143 3144

JENNMAR CORP p 782
258 Kappa Dr 15238
Tel (412) 963-9071 *SIC* 3532

JOSH BIRT LLC p 794
2 Fordham Ave 15229
Tel (412) 719-7182 *SIC* 7812

K&L GATES LLP p 799
210 6th Ave Ste 1100 15222
Tel (412) 355-6500 *SIC* 8111

▲ KENNAMETAL INC p 810
600 Grant St Ste 5100 15219
Tel (412) 248-8200
SIC 3545 3532 3531 3313 3399

▲ KOPPERS HOLDINGS INC p 827
436 7th Ave 15219
Tel (412) 227-2001
SIC 2865 2491 2895 3312 2899

■ KOPPERS INC p 828
436 7th Ave 15219
Tel (412) 227-2001
SIC 2865 2491 3312 2899

▲ KRAFT HEINZ CO p 829
1 Ppg Pl 15222
Tel (412) 456-5700
SIC 2033 2038 2032 2098

▲ L B FOSTER CO p 833
415 Holiday Dr Ste 1 15220
Tel (412) 928-3417 *SIC* 3312 3272 3317

LABORERS COMBINED FUNDS OF WESTERN PENNSYLVANIA p 836
12 8th St 15222
Tel (412) 263-0900 *SIC* 6371

LANXESS CORP p 844
111 Parkwest Dr 15275
Tel (800) 526-9377
SIC 2869 2821 2822 2816 2819

LENMORE INC p 855
401 Penn Ave 15221
Tel (412) 243-8000 *SIC* 5093

LEWIS-GOETZ AND CO INC p 859
650 Washington Rd Ste 500 15228
Tel (800) 937-9070 *SIC* 5085

LIBERTY TIRE RECYCLING LLC p 862
1251 Waterfront Pl # 400 15222
Tel (412) 562-1700 *SIC* 5093 4953 8744

■ LIMBACH CO LLC p 866
31 35th St 15201
Tel (412) 359-2173 *SIC* 1711

■ LIMBACH FACILITY SERVICES LLC p 866
31 35th St 15201
Tel (412) 359-2100 *SIC* 1711 8741

▲ LIMBACH HOLDINGS LLC p 866
31 35th St 15201
Tel (412) 359-2173 *SIC* 1711

M & J MANAGEMENT CORP p 888
147 Delta Dr 15238
Tel (412) 963-6550 *SIC* 5812

MAGEE-WOMENS HOSPITAL OF UPMC p 895
300 Halket St 15213
Tel (412) 641-1000 *SIC* 8062

MANAGEMENT SCIENCE ASSOCIATES INC p 900
6565 Penn Ave 15206
Tel (412) 362-2000 *SIC* 8742 7371

MASCARO CONSTRUCTION CO LP p 915
1720 Metropolitan St 15233
Tel (412) 321-4901 *SIC* 1542

▲ MATTHEWS INTERNATIONAL CORP p 920
2 N Shore Ctr Ste 200 15212
Tel (412) 442-8200
SIC 3366 1542 3569 3995 3953 2796

MCKAMISH INC p 930
50 55th St 15201
Tel (412) 781-6262 *SIC* 1711

■ MED3000 GROUP INC p 935
680 Andersen Dr Foster Pl 15220
Tel (412) 937-8887 *SIC* 8742 8721

■ MED3000 INVESTMENTS INC p 935
680 Andersen Dr Ste 10 15220
Tel (412) 937-8887 *SIC* 8071

MERCY LIFE CENTER CORP p 947
1200 Reedsdale St Ste 1 15233
Tel (412) 578-6675 *SIC* 8322

MERCY LIFE CENTER CORP p 947
1200 Reedsdale St Ste 1 15233
Tel (412) 323-8026 *SIC* 8093

MERCY UPMC p 948
1400 Locust St 15219
Tel (412) 232-8111 *SIC* 8062

METAL TRADERS INC p 952
3480 Grand Ave 15225
Tel (412) 331-7772 *SIC* 5051

MICHAEL BAKER INTERNATIONAL LLC p 960
500 Grant St Ste 5400 15219
Tel (412) 918-4000 *SIC* 8711

MICROBAC LABORATORIES INC p 961
101 Bellevue Rd Ste 301 15229
Tel (412) 459-1060 *SIC* 8734

MONTEFIORE UNIVERSITY HOSPITAL p 986
3459 5th Ave 15213
Tel (412) 647-2345 *SIC* 8062

MOSITES CONSTRUCTION CO p 992
4839 Campbells Run Rd 15205
Tel (412) 923-2255 *SIC* 1542 1611

MT LEBANON SCHOOL DISTRICT p 997
7 Horsman Dr 15228
Tel (412) 344-2077 *SIC* 8211

NITYO INFOTECH CORP p 1045
2652 Hidden Valley Rd # 103 15241
Tel (412) 894-9054 *SIC* 7379

NORTH ALLEGHENY SCHOOL DISTRICT p 1049
200 Hillvue Ln Ste 1 15237
Tel (412) 369-5484 *SIC* 8211

O-N MINERALS CO (OHIO) p 1070
11 Stanwix St Fl 21 15222
Tel (412) 995-5500 *SIC* 1422

OXFORD DEVELOPMENT CO INC p 1101
301 Grant St Ste 4500 15219
Tel (412) 261-1500 *SIC* 7011

PACEC LLC p 1103
333 Baldwin Rd 15205
Tel (412) 429-2324 *SIC* 8748

PEOPLES NATURAL GAS CO p 1133
225 N Shore Dr Fl 2 15212
Tel (412) 208-6810 *SIC* 4924

■ PGW AUTO GLASS LLC p 1141
1 Ppg Pl Fl 6 15272
Tel (412) 434-4058 *SIC* 7536

PITT-OHIO EXPRESS LLC p 1152
15 27th St 15222
Tel (412) 232-3015 *SIC* 4213

PITTSBURGH p 1152
200 Lothrop St 15213
Tel (412) 648-8454 *SIC* 8011

PITTSBURGH CORNING CORP p 1152
800 Presque Isle Dr 15239
Tel (724) 327-6100 *SIC* 3296

PITTSBURGH FOUNDATION p 1152
5 Ppg Pl Ste 250 15222
Tel (412) 391-5122 *SIC* 6732

■ PITTSBURGH GLASS WORKS LLC p 1152
30 Isabella St Ste 500 15212
Tel (412) 995-6500 *SIC* 3211 5013

PITTSBURGH SCHOOL DISTRICT p 1152
341 S Bellefield Ave 15213
Tel (412) 622-3500 *SIC* 8211

PITTSBURGH WATER & SEWER AUTHORITY p 1152
1200 Penn Ave Ste 100 15222
Tel (412) 255-8935 *SIC* 4941 7389

PJ DICK INC p 1153
225 N Shore Dr 15212
Tel (412) 462-9300 *SIC* 1542 8741

■ PNC BANK NATIONAL ASSOCIATION p 1158
249 5th Ave Ste 1200 15222
Tel (412) 762-2000 *SIC* 6021

▲ PNC FINANCIAL SERVICES GROUP INC p 1158
300 5th Ave 15222
Tel (412) 762-2000
SIC 6021 6162 7389 6282 6211

■ PNC INVESTMENTS LLC p 1158
620 Liberty Ave Bsmt 15222
Tel (800) 762-6111 *SIC* 6799

POINT PARK UNIVERSITY p 1159
201 Wood St 15222
Tel (412) 391-4100 *SIC* 8221

PORT AUTHORITY OF ALLEGHENY COUNTY p 1162
345 6th Ave Fl 3 15222
Tel (412) 566-5500 *SIC* 4119

PORT AUTHORITY OF ALLEGHENY COUNTY p 1162
345 6th Ave Fl 3 15222
Tel (412) 566-5500 *SIC* 4131

■ PPG ARCHITECTURAL FINISHES INC p 1166
1 Ppg Pl 15272
Tel (412) 434-3131 *SIC* 2851 2891

▲ PPG INDUSTRIES INC p 1166
1 Ppg Pl 15272
Tel (412) 434-3131
SIC 2851 3211 3231 3229 2812 2821

PRESSLEY RIDGE FOUNDATION p 1173
5500 Corporate Dr Ste 400 15237
Tel (412) 872-9400 *SIC* 8399

R & R EXPRESS INC p 1201
3 Crafton Sq 15205
Tel (412) 920-1336 *SIC* 4731

R & R EXPRESS LOGISTICS INC p 1201
3 Crafton Sq 15205
Tel (800) 223-8973 *SIC* 4731

REED SMITH LLP p 1217
225 5th Ave Ste 1200 15222
Tel (412) 288-3131 *SIC* 8111

RESCO PRODUCTS INC p 1226
1 Robinson Plz Ste 300 15205
Tel (412) 494-4491
SIC 3297 3255 1455 1499 5032

RETIREES OF GOODYEAR TIRE AND RUBBER CO HEALTH CARE TRUST p 1229
60 Blvd Of The Allies 15222
Tel (866) 694-6477 *SIC* 5531

RUSSELL STANDARD CORP p 1259
285 Kappa Dr Ste 300 15238
Tel (412) 449-0700 *SIC* 1611 2951

RYCON CONSTRUCTION INC p 1260
2501 Smallman St Ste 100 15222
Tel (412) 392-2525 *SIC* 1542

SARGENT ELECTRIC CO p 1282
2767 Liberty Ave 15222
Tel (412) 338-8480 *SIC* 1731

SAUER HOLDINGS INC p 1283
30 51st St 15201
Tel (412) 687-4100 *SIC* 1711

SMS USA LLC p 1334
100 Sandusky St 15212
Tel (412) 231-1200 *SIC* 3547 3542

SOUTH UNIVERSITY ONLINE p 1345
1400 Penn Ave Ste 201 15222
Tel (412) 995-7424 *SIC* 8221

SPANG & CO p 1354
110 Delta Dr 15238
Tel (412) 963-9363
SIC 3672 3944 3612 3613 3312

ST CLAIR HEALTH CORP p 1365
1000 Bower Hill Rd 15243
Tel (412) 561-4900 *SIC* 8062

ST CLAIR MEMORIAL HOSPITAL p 1365
1000 Bower Hill Rd 15243
Tel (412) 561-4900 *SIC* 8062

ST CLAIR MEMORIAL HOSPITAL FOUNDATION p 1365
1000 Bower Hill Rd 15243
Tel (412) 942-4000 *SIC* 8062

ST MORITZ BUILDING SERVICES INC p 1372
4616 Clairton Blvd 15236
Tel (412) 885-2100 *SIC* 7349 5087

ST MORITZ SECURITY SERVICES INC p 1372
4600 Clairton Blvd 15236
Tel (412) 885-3144 *SIC* 7381

STELLA-JONES CORP p 1385
2 Gateway Ctr Ste 1000 15222
Tel (412) 894-2846 *SIC* 2491 2421 3531

STELLA-JONES CORP p 1385
603 Stanwix St Ste 1000 15222
Tel (412) 325-0202 *SIC* 2491

STELLA-JONES US HOLDING CORP p 1385
603 Stanwix St 15222
Tel (304) 372-2211 *SIC* 2491

SUBSIDIARIES OF INSTITUTE FOR TRANSFUSION MEDICINE p 1396
5 Parkway Ctr 15220
Tel (412) 209-7300 *SIC* 8733

SUPERIOR PETROLEUM CO p 1406
8199 Mcknight Rd 15237
Tel (412) 364-2200 *SIC* 7542

SYSTEM ONE HOLDINGS LLC p 1418
12 Federal St Ste 205 15212
Tel (412) 995-1900 *SIC* 7361

■ TARGA ENERGY LP p 1424
1000 Commerce Dr Ste 400 15275
Tel (412) 489-0006 *SIC* 1311 4922

■ TARGA PIPELINE PARTNERS LP p 1425
1000 Commerce Dr Ste 400 15275
Tel (877) 950-7473 *SIC* 4922

■ TDY INDUSTRIES LLC p 1429
1000 Six Ppg Pl 15222
Tel (412) 394-2896
SIC 3356 3312 3316 3339 3369

■ TRANSTAR INC p 1473
1200 Penn Ave Ste 300 15222
Tel (412) 433-4644 *SIC* 4449 4731

TRIB TOTAL MEDIA INC p 1479
503 Martin Street D L C 15212
Tel (412) 321-6460 *SIC* 5994

TRIBUNE REVIEW PUBLISHING CO p 1479
503 Marti St D L Clark B 15212
Tel (724) 834-1151 *SIC* 2711

■ TRISTATE CAPITAL BANK p 1483
301 Grant St Ste 2700 15219
Tel (412) 304-0304 *SIC* 6029

▲ TRISTATE CAPITAL HOLDINGS INC p 1483
301 Grant St Ste 2700 15219
Tel (412) 304-0304 *SIC* 6022

TRUFOOD MFG INC p 1486
610 Alpha Dr 15238
Tel (412) 963-2330 *SIC* 2066 2064

TRUMBULL CORP p 1486
225 N Shore Dr 15212
Tel (412) 807-2000 *SIC* 1611

U P M C SHADYSIDE p 1497
5230 Centre Ave 15232
Tel (412) 623-2121 *SIC* 8062

▲ UNITED STATES STEEL CORP p 1514
600 Grant St Ste 468 15219
Tel (412) 433-1121 *SIC* 3312 3317 3356

■ UNITED STATES STEEL INTERNATIONAL INC p 1514
600 Grant St Ste 468 15219
Tel (412) 433-1121 *SIC* 5051

UNITED STEEL PAPER AND FORESTRY RUBBER MANUFACTURING ENERGY ALLIED p 1514
5 Gateway Ctr 15222
Tel (412) 562-2400 *SIC* 8631

UNITED STEELWORKERS p 1514
60 Bolevard Of The Allies 15222
Tel (412) 562-2400 *SIC* 8631

UNIVERSITY OF PITTSBURGH p 1524
4200 5th Ave 15260
Tel (412) 624-4141 *SIC* 8221

UNIVERSITY OF PITTSBURGH MEDICAL CENTER p 1524
600 Grant St Fl 62 15219
Tel (412) 647-2345 *SIC* 8062

UNIVERSITY OF PITTSBURGH PHYSICIANS p 1524
200 Lothrop St 15213
Tel (412) 647-8762 *SIC* 8062

UPMC COMMUNITY PROVIDER SERVICES p 1528
200 Lthrpst Frbtwr 1005 Ste Forbes Tower 15213
Tel (412) 647-0548 *SIC* 8322

UPMC HEALTH PLAN INC p 1528
600 Grant St Fl 24 15219
Tel (412) 454-7642 *SIC* 6321

UPMC HEALTH SYSTEM p 1528
600 Grant St 15219
Tel (412) 281-6646 SIC 8099

UPMC PASSAVANT p 1528
9100 Babcock Blvd 15237
Tel (412) 367-6700 SIC 8062

UPMC PRESBYTERIAN SHADYSIDE p 1529
200 Lothrop St 15213
Tel (412) 647-8762 SIC 8062

UPMC ST MARGARET p 1529
815 Freeport Rd 15215
Tel (412) 784-4000 SIC 8062

UPMC ST MARGARET TRANSITIONAL CARE UNIT p 1529
815 Freeport Rd 15215
Tel (412) 784-4000 SIC 8062

URBAN LENDING SOLUTIONS p 1530
1001 Liberty Ave Ste 1050 15222
Tel (412) 325-7046 SIC 6163

V L H INC p 1538
600 Boyce Rd 15205
Tel (800) 245-4440 SIC 2833 5122 2834

■ VOCOLLECT INC p 1564
703 Rodi Rd 15235
Tel (412) 829-8145 SIC 3577 3571 7372

■ WESCO DISTRIBUTION INC p 1593
225 W Station Square Dr # 700 15219
Tel (412) 454-2200
SIC 5063 5085 5065 7389

▲ WESCO INTERNATIONAL INC p 1593
225 W Station Square Dr # 700 15219
Tel (412) 454-2200
SIC 5063 5084 5065 7389

WEST PENN ALLEGHENY HEALTH SYSTEM INC p 1595
4800 Friendship Ave 15224
Tel (412) 578-5000 SIC 8062

WESTERN PENNSYLVANIA HOSPITAL p 1599
4800 Friendship Ave 15224
Tel (412) 578-5000 SIC 8062

WEXFORD HEALTH SOURCES INC p 1603
501 Hlday Dr Foster Plz 4 15220
Tel (888) 633-6468 SIC 8741

WHEMCO INC p 1605
5 Hot Metal St Ste 300 15203
Tel (412) 390-2700
SIC 3312 3462 3731 3325 3441 3369

■ YORK GROUP INC p 1637
2 N Shore Ctr 15212
Tel (412) 995-1600 SIC 7261

ZOLL SERVICES LLC p 1644
121 Gamma Dr 15238
Tel (412) 968-3333 SIC 3845

PITTSTON, PA

BENCO DENTAL SUPPLY CO p 172
295 Centerpoint Blvd 18640
Tel (570) 602-7781 SIC 5047

■ ROCHESTER COCA COLA BOTTLING CORP p 1243
300 Oak St 18640
Tel (570) 655-2874 SIC 2086 5962

PLEASANT GAP, PA

TELE-MEDIA CORP p 1433
320 W College Ave 16823
Tel (814) 359-3481 SIC 4841

PLYMOUTH MEETING, PA

▲ CSS INDUSTRIES INC p 398
450 Plymouth Rd Ste 300 19462
Tel (610) 729-3959
SIC 2771 2679 2389 2396 2621 2865

DANELLA COMPANIES INC p 411
2290 Butler Pike 19462
Tel (610) 828-6200
SIC 7513 7353 8711 1623 8748

F&T APPAREL LLC p 522
4000 Chemical Rd Ste 500 19462
Tel (610) 828-8400 SIC 2311 2321 2325

FOX MANAGEMENT INC p 572
251 Stenton Ave 19462
Tel (610) 283-7561 SIC 8111

FOX NURSING HOME CORP p 572
251 Stenton Ave 19462
Tel (610) 828-2272 SIC 8051

GENERAL HEALTHCARE RESOURCES INC p 601
2250 Hickory Rd Ste 240 19462
Tel (610) 834-1122 SIC 8082

GENESIS ENGINEERS INC p 602
1850 Gravers Rd Ste 300 19462
Tel (610) 592-0280 SIC 8711 8741

NEW PENN FINANCIAL LLC p 1032
4000 Chemical Rd Ste 200 19462
Tel (484) 594-1000 SIC 6162

PORT MATILDA, PA

RAND-WHITNEY RECYCLING LLC p 1207
546 Smith Rd 16870
Tel (814) 692-8045 SIC 4953

POTTSTOWN, PA

BUCKMANS INC p 223
105 Airport Rd 19464
Tel (610) 495-7495 SIC 5169 5941

BUDGET MAINTENANCE CONCRETE SERVICES INC p 224
135 Walnut St 19464
Tel (610) 323-7702 SIC 5087 7349

■ EPLUS TECHNOLOGY OF PENNSYLVANIA INC p 505
130 Futura Dr 19464
Tel (610) 495-7800 SIC 5734 7378 8243

NEAPCO COMPONENTS LLC p 1023
740 Queen St 19464
Tel (610) 323-6000 SIC 3714 3568

POTTSTOWN AREA HEALTH & WELLNESS FOUNDATION p 1164
152 E High St Ste 500 19464
Tel (610) 323-2006 SIC 6324

POTTSTOWN HOSPITAL CO LLC p 1164
1600 E High St 19464
Tel (610) 327-7000 SIC 8062

■ POTTSTOWN MEMORIAL MEDICAL CENTER p 1164
1600 E High St 19464
Tel (610) 327-7000 SIC 8062

SCHUYLKILL VALLEY SPORTS INC p 1291
118 Industrial Dr Ste 1 19464
Tel (610) 495-8813 SIC 5091 5941

POTTSVILLE, PA

■ EEG INC p 480
396 Pttsvlle St Clair Hwy 17901
Tel (570) 429-4321 SIC 8299

EMPIRE BEAUTY SCHOOL INC p 493
396 Pttsvlle St Clair Hwy 17901
Tel (570) 429-4321 SIC 8249

QUAKERTOWN, PA

PENN STAINLESS PRODUCTS INC p 1129
190 Kelly Rd 18951
Tel (215) 536-3053 SIC 5051 3443 3471

RADNOR, PA

▲ ACTUA CORP p 20
555 E Lancaster Ave # 640 19087
Tel (610) 727-6900 SIC 7373

AIRGAS INC p 40
259 N Radnor Chester Rd # 100 19087
Tel (610) 687-5253
SIC 5169 5084 5085 2813 2819

AIRGAS USA LLC p 40
259 N Radnor Chester Rd # 100 19087
Tel (610) 687-5253
SIC 5169 5084 5085 2813 2819

BRANDYWINE OPERATING PARTNERSHIP LP p 208
555 E Lancaster Ave # 100 19087
Tel (610) 325-5600 SIC 6798

BRANDYWINE REALTY TRUST p 208
555 E Lancaster Ave # 100 19087
Tel (610) 325-5600 SIC 6798

▲ EMTEC INC p 495
150 N Radnor 19087
Tel (973) 376-4242 SIC 7371 7379

▲ J G WENTWORTH CO p 771
201 King Of Prussia Rd # 501 19087
Tel (484) 434-2300 SIC 7389 6798

▲ LINCOLN NATIONAL CORP p 867
150 N Rad Chester Rd A305 Ste A 19087
Tel (484) 583-1400
SIC 6311 6321 6371 6722 6411 6282

LINCOLN NATIONAL CORP VOLUNTARY EMPLOYEE BENEFICIARY ASSN p 867
150 N Radnor Chester Rd 19087
Tel (484) 583-1669 SIC 8699

MAIN LINE HEALTH SYSTEM p 897
240 N Radnor Chester Rd 19087
Tel (610) 225-6200
SIC 5999 8059 8361 8062

MILESTONE PARTNERS MANAGEMENT CO LP p 969
555 E Lancaster Ave 19087
Tel (610) 526-2700 SIC 6799

▲ PENN VIRGINIA CORP p 1129
100 Matsonford Rd Ste 200 19087
Tel (610) 687-8900 SIC 1311

■ PENN VIRGINIA OIL & GAS CORP p 1129
4 Radnor Corp Ctr Ste 200 19087
Tel (610) 687-8900 SIC 1382

PREFERRED SANDS LLC p 1169
1 Radnor Corp Ctr 1-101 19087
Tel (610) 834-1969 SIC 6719

PVR PARTNERS LP p 1193
3 Radnor Corp Ctr Ste 301 19087
Tel (610) 975-8200 SIC 1221 1311

QLIK PARENT INC p 1195
150 N Radnor Chester Rd 19087
Tel (888) 828-9768 SIC 6719 7371

QLIK TECHNOLOGIES INC p 1195
150 N Radnor Chester Rd 19087
Tel (866) 616-4960 SIC 7374 7371

ST JOHN HOLDINGS INC p 1367
320 King Of Prussia Rd 19087
Tel (610) 964-8702 SIC 6211

SYNOVOS INC p 1415
100 Matsonford Rd Ste 400 19087
Tel (610) 293-5940 SIC 5085 8741

VARIETAL DISTRIBUTION HOLDINGS LLC p 1544
100 Matsonford Rd 19087
Tel (610) 386-1700 SIC 5047

▲ VWR CORP p 1567
100 Matsonford Rd 1-200 19087
Tel (610) 386-1700
SIC 2869 2819 3821 5047

■ VWR FUNDING INC p 1567
100 Matsonford Rd 19087
Tel (610) 386-1700 SIC 5049 5169

■ VWR INTERNATIONAL LLC p 1567
100 Matsonford Rd Bldg 1 19087
Tel (610) 386-1700 SIC 5169 5049

READING, PA

ALLIANCE AIRCRAFT LTD p 53
4906 Penn Ave 19608
Tel (888) 233-1503 SIC 3721

BERKS COUNTY INTERMEDIATE UNIT p 175
1111 Commons Blvd 19605
Tel (610) 987-2248 SIC 9411

BOSCOVS DEPARTMENT STORE LLC p 202
4500 Perkiomen Ave 19606
Tel (610) 779-2000 SIC 8741 5311

BOSCOVS INC p 202
4500 Perkiomen Ave 19606
Tel (610) 779-2000 SIC 8741 5311

BRENNTAG NORTH AMERICA INC p 210
5083 Pottsville Pike 19605
Tel (610) 926-6100 SIC 5169

BRENNTAG NORTHEAST INC p 210
81 W Huller Ln 19605
Tel (610) 926-4151 SIC 5169

BRENTWOOD INDUSTRIES INC p 210
500 Spring Ridge Dr 19610
Tel (610) 374-5109 SIC 3089

C H BRIGGS CO p 232
2047 Kutztown Rd 19605
Tel (800) 355-1000 SIC 5072

CAMBRIDGE-LEE HOLDINGS INC p 244
86 Tube Dr 19605
Tel (610) 926-4141 SIC 5051 3351 5084

CENTRAL PENNSYLVANIA TEAMSTERS p 279
1055 Spring St 19610
Tel (610) 320-5500 SIC 8631

COUNTY OF BERKS p 376
633 Court St 19601
Tel (610) 478-6640 SIC 9111

DIGIORGIO MUSHROOM CORP p 439
1161 Park Rd 19605
Tel (610) 926-2139
SIC 2033 5148 2037 6512

▲ ENERSYS p 498
2366 Bernville Rd 19605
Tel (610) 208-1991 SIC 3691 3699

■ ENERSYS DELAWARE INC p 498
2366 Bernville Rd 19605
Tel (214) 324-8990 SIC 3691 5063

F M BROWNS SONS INC p 522
205 Woodrow Ave 19608
Tel (800) 334-8816
SIC 5191 2041 0723 2048

FROMM ELECTRIC SUPPLY CORP OF READING PENNA p 580
2101 Centre Ave Ste 4 19605
Tel (610) 374-4441 SIC 5063

GIORGIO FOODS INC p 613
1161 Park Rd 19605
Tel (610) 926-2139
SIC 2033 2037 5148 2038

GLEN-GERY CORP p 614
1166 Spring St 19610
Tel (610) 374-4011 SIC 3251

■ HOLLYWOOD CASINO CORP p 701
825 Berkshire Blvd # 200 19610
Tel (610) 373-2400 SIC 7011 8741

JC EHRLICH CHEMICAL CO p 780
1125 Berkshire Blvd # 150 19610
Tel (610) 372-9700 SIC 5191

LENTZ MILLING CO p 856
2045 N 11th St 19604
Tel (610) 921-0666 SIC 5149 5142

PENSKE DEDICATED LOGISTICS CORP p 1131
Green Hls Rr 10 19607
Tel (610) 775-6000 SIC 7513

PENSKE LOGISTICS LLC p 1131
Green Hls Rr 10 19603
Tel (800) 529-6531 SIC 7513 4213

PENSKE REALTY INC p 1131
Green Hls Rr 10 19607
Tel (610) 775-6000 SIC 6531

PENSKE TRUCK LEASING CO LP p 1131
2675 Morgantown Rd 19607
Tel (610) 775-6000 SIC 7513

PENSKE TRUCK LEASING CORP p 1131
2675 Morgantown Rd 19607
Tel (610) 775-6000 SIC 7513

PHOENIX FORGE GROUP LLC p 1145
1020 Macarthur Rd 19605
Tel (800) 234-8665 SIC 3089

QUADRANT EPP USA INC p 1196
2120 Fairmont Ave 19605
Tel (610) 320-6600 SIC 2821

R M PALMER CO p 1202
77 S 2nd Ave 19611
Tel (610) 372-8971 SIC 2066 2064

READING EAGLE CO p 1213
345 Penn St 19601
Tel (610) 371-5000 SIC 2711 2752

READING HEALTH SYSTEM p 1213
6th Ave And Spruce St 19611
Tel (610) 988-8000
SIC 8062 6512 8093 8721 8011 7219

READING HOSPITAL p 1213
6th And Spruce St 19611
Tel (484) 628-8000 SIC 8062 6512

READING SCHOOL DISTRICT p 1213
800 Washington St 19601
Tel (484) 258-7000 SIC 8211

READING TRUCK BODY LLC p 1213
201 Hancock Blvd 19611
Tel (610) 775-3301 SIC 3713 3792 3469

REDNERS MARKETS INC p 1217
3 Quarry Rd 19605
Tel (610) 926-3700 SIC 5411 5541 5912

ST JOSEPH REGIONAL HEALTH NETWORK p 1368
2500 Bernville Rd 19605
Tel (610) 378-2000 SIC 8062

SWEET STREET DESSERTS INC p 1411
722 Hiesters Ln 19605
Tel (610) 929-0616 SIC 2053

TRAY-PAK CORP p 1475
Tuckerton Rd And 19605
Tel (888) 926-1777 SIC 3089

TRG WIND DOWN LLC p 1476
201 Hancock Blvd 19611
Tel (610) 775-3301
SIC 3713 3792 3469 5531 7532

■ UGI ENERGY SERVICES LLC p 1499
1 Meridian Blvd Ste 2c01 19610
Tel (484) 663-5824 SIC 4924

■ UGI UTILITIES INC p 1499
2525 N 12th St Ste 360 19605
Tel (610) 796-3400 SIC 4939

■ VF INDUSTRIAL PARK INC p 1553
801 Hill Ave Ofc 19610
Tel (610) 378-0408 SIC 5611

■ VF OUTLET INC p 1553
801 Hill Ave Ste 1 19610
Tel (610) 378-0408 SIC 5651

WORLEYPARSONS OF VIRGINIA INC p 1626
2675 Morgantown Rd 19607
Tel (610) 855-2000 SIC 8712

REAMSTOWN, PA

DORMA USA INC p 451
1 Dorma Dr 17567
Tel (717) 336-3881 SIC 3429

RED HILL, PA

STAUFFER MANUFACTURING CO p 1383
361 E 6th St 18076
Tel (215) 679-4446 SIC 5085 5199

RHEEMS, PA

WENGER FEEDS LLC p 1592
101 W Harrisburg Ave 17570
Tel (717) 367-1195 SIC 2048 5144 0252

RIDGWAY, PA

■ METALDYNE SINTERED RIDGWAY LLC p 952
1149 Rocky Rd 15853
Tel (814) 776-1141 SIC 3399 3441 3462

RIDLEY PARK, PA

TAYLOR HOSPITAL p 1427
175 E Chester Pike 19078
Tel (610) 595-6000 SIC 8062

RIVERSIDE, PA

■ CHEROKEE PHARMACEUTICALS LLC p 294
100 Ave C 17868
Tel (570) 271-4195 SIC 5122

ROARING SPRING, PA

ROARING SPRING BLANK BOOK CO p 1240
740 Spang St 16673
Tel (814) 224-2306
SIC 2678 5149 2653 7389

SMITH TRANSPORT INC p 1333
153 Smith Transport Rd 16673
Tel (814) 224-5155 SIC 4213

ROBESONIA, PA

ASSOCIATED WHOLESALERS INC p 121
336 E Penn Ave 19551
Tel (610) 693-3161
SIC 5141 5147 5122 5142 5148 5411

■ READING ALLOYS INC p 1213
220 Old West Penn Ave 19551
Tel (610) 693-5822 SIC 3313 3341

ROYERSFORD, PA

SPRING-FORD AREA SCHOOL DISTRICT p 1360
857 S Lewis Rd 19468
Tel (610) 705-6000 SIC 8211

SPRING-FORD AREA SCHOOL DISTRICT OFFICE p 1360
857 S Lewis Rd 19468
Tel (610) 705-6000 SIC 8211

SACRAMENTO, PA

STERMAN MASSER INC p 1387
2 Fearnot Rd 17968
Tel (570) 682-3709 SIC 0134 2099

SAEGERTOWN, PA

GREENLEAF CORP p 638
18695 Greenleaf Dr 16433
Tel (814) 763-2915 SIC 3545 3541

SAINT MARYS, PA

■ AMPHENOL THERMOMETRICS INC p 86
967 Windfall Rd 15857
Tel (814) 834-9140 SIC 3823

ELK REGIONAL HEALTH SYSTEM p 487
763 Johnsonburg Rd 15857
Tel (814) 788-8000
SIC 8062 8051 8361 8399

KEYSTONE POWDERED METAL CO p 816
251 State St 15857
Tel (814) 781-1591 SIC 3499

SALTSBURG, PA

NORMA PENNSYLVANIA INC p 1048
3582 Tunnelton Rd 15681
Tel (724) 639-3571 SIC 3429

SAXONBURG, PA

▲ II-VI INC p 731
375 Saxonburg Blvd 16056
Tel (724) 352-4455
SIC 3827 3229 3674 3699

SAYRE, PA

GUTHRIE CLINIC p 648
1 Guthrie Sq Ste B 18840
Tel (570) 888-5858 SIC 8011 8062 8082

GUTHRIE HEALTHCARE SYSTEM p 648
1 Guthrie Sq Ste B 18840
Tel (570) 888-6666 SIC 8011 7352 8741

GUTHRIE MEDICAL GROUP PC p 648
1 Guthrie Sq Ste B 18840
Tel (570) 888-5858 SIC 8011

ROBERT PACKER HOSPITAL p 1241
1 Guthrie Sq Ste B 18840
Tel (570) 888-6666 SIC 8062

TWIN TIER MANAGEMENT CORP p 1495
Guthrie Sq 18840
Tel (570) 888-6666 SIC 8741 5912

SCHNECKSVILLE, PA

CARBON-LEHIGH INTERMEDIATE UNIT 21 p 252
4210 Independence Dr 18078
Tel (610) 799-4111 SIC 8211

KIDSPEACE NATIONAL CENTERS OF NORTH AMERICA INC p 817
4085 Independence Dr 18078
Tel (610) 799-8353 SIC 8322

SCHUYLKILL HAVEN, PA

EVANS DELIVERY CO INC p 513
100 W Columbia St Ste 110 17972
Tel (570) 385-9048 SIC 4213

M&Q HOLDINGS LLC p 890
3 Earl Ave 17972
Tel (570) 385-4991 SIC 3089 6719

SCOTTDALE, PA

PENN LINE SERVICE INC p 1129
300 Scottdale Ave 15683
Tel (724) 887-9110
SIC 1629 1623 1611 0782

SCRANTON, PA

ALLIED HEALTH CARE SERVICES p 56
475 Morgan Hwy 18508
Tel (570) 348-1300 SIC 8322

ARLINGTON INDUSTRIES INC p 110
1 Stauffer Industrial Par 18517
Tel (570) 562-0270 SIC 1731

CATHOLIC SOCIAL SERVICES OF DIOCESE OF SCRANTON INC p 267
516 Fig St 18505
Tel (570) 207-2283
SIC 8661 2711 8211 8322 6553

COMMUNITY PHARMACY SERVICES p 349
1822 Mulberry St 18510
Tel (570) 969-8000 SIC 8741

■ CPG INTERNATIONAL INC p 387
888 N Keyser Ave 18504
Tel (570) 558-8000 SIC 3089 3272

GEISINGER-COMMUNITY MEDICAL CENTER p 598
1822 Mulberry St 18510
Tel (570) 969-8000 SIC 8062

GERRITYS SUPER MARKET INC p 609
950 N South Rd Ste 5 18504
Tel (570) 342-4144 SIC 5411

LACKAWANNA COUNTY GOVERNMENT p 837
200 Adams Ave 18503
Tel (570) 963-6800 SIC 9611 9199

■ MERCY HEALTH PARTNERS p 946
746 Jefferson Ave 18510
Tel (570) 348-7100 SIC 8062

MERCY HOSPITAL SCRANTON PENNSYLVANIA p 947
746 Jefferson Ave 18510
Tel (570) 348-7100 SIC 8062 8051

NORTHEASTERN PENNSYLVANIA CENTER FOR INDEPENDENT LIVING INC p 1055
1142 Sanderson Ave 18509
Tel (570) 344-7211 SIC 8322

OAK HEALTH AND REHABILITATION CENTERS INC p 1070
5 Morgan Hwy 18508
Tel (215) 346-6454 SIC 8361

■ PRUDENTIAL TRUST CO p 1187
30 Ed Preate Dr 18507
Tel (570) 341-6000 SIC 6282 6722 6211

■ QUINCY SCRANTON HOSPITAL LLC p 1200
700 Quincy Ave 18510
Tel (570) 340-2100 SIC 8062 8051

■ SCRANTON HOSPITAL CO LLC p 1294
746 Jefferson Ave 18510
Tel (570) 348-7100 SIC 8062

SCRANTON SCHOOL DISTRICT p 1294
425 N Washington Ave 18503
Tel (570) 348-3474 SIC 8211

SCRANTON TIMES L P p 1294
149 Penn Ave Ste 1 18503
Tel (570) 348-9100 SIC 2711 4832

UNIVERSITY OF SCRANTON p 1525
800 Linden St 18510
Tel (888) 727-2686 SIC 8221

SELINSGROVE, PA

L/B WATER SERVICE INC p 835
540 S High St 17870
Tel (570) 374-2355 SIC 5074

SUNBURY GENERATION LP p 1401
2384 N Old Trl 17870
Tel (570) 884-1200 SIC 4911

SELLERSVILLE, PA

GRAND VIEW HOSPITAL p 630
700 Lawn Ave 18960
Tel (215) 453-4000 SIC 8062

SENECA, PA

UPMC NORTHWEST p 1528
100 Fairfield Dr 16346
Tel (814) 676-7600 SIC 8741

SEVEN FIELDS, PA

■ WATER SOLUTIONS HOLDINGS LLC p 1581
310 Seven Fields Blvd 16046
Tel (717) 508-0550 SIC 4952

SEWICKLEY, PA

ESMARK INC p 509
100 Hazel Ln Ste 300 15143
Tel (412) 259-8868 SIC 1382 3324

VALLEY MEDICAL FACILITIES INC p 1541
720 Blackburn Rd 15143
Tel (724) 728-7000 SIC 8011

SHADY GROVE, PA

■ GROVE US LLC p 642
1565 Buchanan Trl E 17256
Tel (717) 597-8121 SIC 3531 3537

SHARON, PA

LUBE HOLDINGS INC p 883
101 Chestnut Ave 16146
Tel (724) 981-3123 SIC 6719

■ SHARON REGIONAL HEALTH SYSTEM p 1312
740 E State St 16146
Tel (724) 983-3911 SIC 8062 8063 8069

WHEATLAND TUBE CO p 1604
700 S Dock St 16146
Tel (724) 342-6851 SIC 5051

SHARPSVILLE, PA

■ DEAN DAIRY PRODUCTS CO p 420
1690 Oneida Ln 16150
Tel (724) 962-7801 SIC 2026

SHAVERTOWN, PA

P D M CO INC p 1102
185 Ferguson Ave 18708
Tel (570) 675-3636 SIC 5812

SHIPPENSBURG, PA

BEISTLE CO p 169
1 Beistle Plz 17257
Tel (717) 532-2131
SIC 2679 3993 2675 2657 2631 2621

VOLVO CONSTRUCTION EQUIPMENT NORTH AMERICA LLC p 1565
312 Volvo Way 17257
Tel (717) 532-9181 SIC 5082

SIMPSON, PA

GENTEX CORP p 604
324 Main St 18407
Tel (570) 282-3550 SIC 3842 8731 2295

SKIPPACK, PA

HAINES & KIBBLEHOUSE INC p 653
2052 Lucon Rd 19474
Tel (610) 584-8500
SIC 1794 1611 1422 2951

■ MAR COR PURIFICATION INC p 904
4450 Township Line Rd 19474
Tel (800) 633-3080 SIC 3569 3677

SLIPPERY ROCK, PA

SLIPPERY ROCK UNIVERSITY p 1331
1 Morrow Way 16057
Tel (724) 738-9000 SIC 8221 9411

SMETHPORT, PA

INTERNATIONAL WAXES INC p 757
45 Route 446 16749
Tel (814) 887-5501 SIC 5169

SMITHTON, PA

SAM LEVIN INC p 1274
301 Fitz Henry Rd 15479
Tel (724) 872-2055 SIC 5712

SOMERSET, PA

DEVILBISS HEALTHCARE LLC p 434
100 Devilbiss Dr 15501
Tel (814) 443-4881 SIC 3845

SIEMON NURSING HOME INC p 1320
228 Siemon Dr 15501
Tel (814) 443-2811 SIC 8051

■ WHEELER BROS INC p 1605
384 Drum Ave 15501
Tel (814) 443-2444 SIC 5013

SOUDERTON, PA

ALMAC CLINICAL SERVICES LLC p 59
25 Fretz Rd 18964
Tel (215) 660-8500 SIC 7389

ALMAC GROUP INC p 59
25 Fretz Rd 18964
Tel (215) 660-8500 SIC 2834

BERGEYS INC p 174
462 Harleysville Pike 18964
Tel (215) 721-3430
SIC 5511 5531 7538 5013 5014

JBS SOUDERTON INC p 779
249 Allentown Rd 18964
Tel (215) 723-5555 SIC 2011 2077 2013

MOYER & SON INC p 995
113 E Reliance Rd 18964
Tel (215) 799-2000
SIC 5191 5983 2875 0782 1711

■ UNIVEST BANK AND TRUST CO p 1527
14 N Main St 18964
Tel (877) 723-5571 SIC 6021

▲ UNIVEST CORP OF PENNSYLVANIA p 1527
14 N Main St 18964
Tel (215) 721-2400 SIC 6022 6282 6411

SOUTHAMPTON, PA

▲ ENVIRONMENTAL TECTONICS CORP p 503
125 James Way 18966
Tel (215) 355-9100
SIC 3728 3842 3826 3823 3841

TANNER INDUSTRIES INC p 1424
735 Davisville Rd Ste 3 18966
Tel (215) 322-1238 SIC 5169

SPRING GROVE, PA

■ GLATFELTER PULP WOOD CO INC p 614
228 S Main St 17362
Tel (717) 225-4711 SIC 5099 2411 2621

SPRINGFIELD, PA

PROSPECT CROZER LLC p 1184
100 W Sproul Rd 19064
Tel (610) 338-8200 SIC 8741

STATE COLLEGE, PA

BEST LINE LEASING INC p 177
140 Hawbaker Indus Dr 16803
Tel (814) 237-9050 SIC 5082

■ ECLIPSE RESOURCES CORP p 475
2121 Old Gatesburg Rd # 110 16803
Tel (814) 308-9754 SIC 1311

▲ ECLIPSE RESOURCES HOLDINGS LP p 475
2121 Old Gatesburg Rd # 110 16803
Tel (814) 308-9754 SIC 1311

■ ECLIPSE RESOURCES I LP p 475
2121 Old Gteburg Rd Ste 1 16803
Tel (814) 308-9754 SIC 1311 1382

GLENN O HAWBAKER INC p 615
1952 Waddle Rd Ste 203 16803
Tel (814) 237-1444
SIC 2951 3281 1622 1794 1611 1422

HRI INC p 714
1750 W College Ave 16801
Tel (814) 238-5071 SIC 1611

MOUNT NITTANY HEALTH SYSTEM p 993
1800 E Park Ave 16803
Tel (814) 231-7040 SIC 8062

MOUNT NITTANY MEDICAL CENTER p 993
1800 E Park Ave 16803
Tel (814) 231-7000 SIC 8062

NITTANY OIL CO INC p 1045
1540 Martin St 16803
Tel (814) 237-4859 SIC 5171 1711

▲ REX ENERGY CORP p 1230
366 Walker Dr 16801
Tel (814) 278-7267 SIC 1311

SHANER HOTEL GROUP LIMITED PARTNERSHIP p 1311
1965 Waddle Rd 16803
Tel (814) 234-4460 SIC 7011

SHANER OPERATING CORP p 1311
1965 Waddle Rd 16803
Tel (814) 234-4460 SIC 8741

STATE COLLEGE AREA SCHOOL DISTRICT p 1380
131 W Nittany Ave 16801
Tel (814) 231-1016 SIC 8211

UNI-MARTS LLC p 1502
1155 Benner Pike 100 16801
Tel (814) 234-6000
SIC 5411 5541 5993 6794 5172

STEELTON, PA

ARCELORMITTAL STEELTON LLC p 104
215 S Front St 17113
Tel (717) 986-2000 SIC 3312

STEVENS, PA

JOHN F MARTIN & SONS INC p 788
55 Lower Hillside Rd 17578
Tel (717) 336-2804 SIC 2013 0212

STOYSTOWN, PA

RIGGS INDUSTRIES INC p 1234
2478 Lincoln Hwy 15563
Tel (814) 629-5621 SIC 3713 3441

STROUDSBURG, PA

POCONO PRODUCE CO INC p 1158
Chipperfield Dr Rr 191 18360
Tel (570) 421-1533 SIC 5149 5142 5148

SUNBURY, PA

BUTTER KRUST BAKING CO INC p 230
249 N 11th St 17801
Tel (570) 286-5845 SIC 2051

▲ WEIS MARKETS INC p 1588
1000 S 2nd St 17801
Tel (570) 286-4571 SIC 5411

SWARTHMORE, PA

SWARTHMORE COLLEGE p 1411
500 College Ave Ste 2 19081
Tel (610) 328-8000 SIC 8221

SWIFTWATER, PA

POCONO MOUNTAIN SCHOOL DISTRICT p 1158
134 Pocono Mtn Schl Rd 18370
Tel (570) 839-7121 SIC 8211

SANOFI PASTEUR INC p 1280
1 Discovery Dr 18370
Tel (570) 839-7187 SIC 2836

TAMAQUA, PA

SILBERLINE MANUFACTURING CO INC p 1322
130 Lincoln Dr 18252
Tel (570) 668-6050 SIC 2816 2819

TAYLOR, PA

KANE IS ABLE INC p 802
3 Stauffer Industrial Par 18517
Tel (570) 344-9801
SIC 4213 4222 4225 4214

TELFORD, PA

DATALOGIC AUTOMATION INC p 414
511 School House Rd 18969
Tel (215) 723-0981 SIC 3577

DRAEGER INC p 455
3135 Quarry Rd 18969
Tel (215) 721-5400 SIC 3841

FRES-CO SYSTEMS USA INC p 578
3005 State Rd 18969
Tel (215) 721-4600 SIC 5084 3565 2891

GODSHALLS QUALITY MEATS INC p 619
675 Mill Rd 18969
Tel (215) 256-8867 SIC 5147 5421

TIOGA, PA

HITACHI METALS AUTOMOTIVE COMPONENTS USA LLC p 697
18986 Route 287 16946
Tel (217) 347-0600 *SIC* 3465 3321 3559

PETROCHOICE LLC p 1139
18385 Route 287 16946
Tel (570) 835-5858 *SIC* 5172

TITUSVILLE, PA

INTERNATIONAL GROUP INC p 755
1007 E Spring St 16354
Tel (814) 827-4900 *SIC* 5169 2911

TOWANDA, PA

GLOBAL TUNGSTEN & POWDERS CORP p 617
1 Hawes St 18848
Tel (570) 268-5000 *SIC* 3313 3291

WILLIAMS OIL CO INC p 1611
44 Reuter Blvd 18848
Tel (570) 265-6673 *SIC* 5172 5983

TRAINER, PA

■ **MONROE ENERGY LLC** p 985
4101 Post Rd 19061
Tel (610) 364-8000 *SIC* 2911

TREVOSE, PA

ACTIVE DAY INC p 20
6 Neshaminy Interplex Dr # 401 19053
Tel (215) 642-6600 *SIC* 8322

ALLIANCEONE INC p 55
4850 E Street Rd Ste 300 19053
Tel (215) 354-5500 *SIC* 7322

BRODER BROS CO p 216
6 Neshaminy Interplex Dr 19053
Tel (215) 291-0300 *SIC* 5136 5137

CAPSULE INTERNATIONAL LLC p 251
1100 Northbrook Dr 19053
Tel (215) 552-3700 *SIC* 3089

CAPSULE PA INC p 252
1100 Northbrook Dr Fl 2 19053
Tel (215) 552-3700 *SIC* 3089 3085

CSI HOLDINGS INC p 397
4850 E Street Rd Ste 230 19053
Tel (215) 357-4400 *SIC* 6411 7532

■ **GE BETZ INC** p 595
4636 Somerton Rd 19053
Tel (215) 355-3300
SIC 2899 3826 5084 3823

▲ **STONEMOR PARTNERS LP** p 1391
3600 Horizon Blvd Ste 100 19053
Tel (215) 826-2800 *SIC* 6553 7261

TYRONE, PA

TEAMTEN LLC p 1430
1600 Pennsylvania Ave 16686
Tel (814) 684-1610 *SIC* 2621

UNIONTOWN, PA

HOSPITAL UNIONTOWN INC p 710
500 W Berkeley St 15401
Tel (724) 430-5000 *SIC* 8062

SENSUS METERING SYSTEMS-NORTH AMERICA INC p 1305
450 N Gallatin Ave 15401
Tel (724) 439-7700 *SIC* 3824

UNIVERSITY PARK, PA

PENNSYLVANIA STATE UNIVERSITY p 1130
201 Old Main 16802
Tel (814) 865-4700 *SIC* 8221

UPPER CHICHESTER, PA

PENTEC HEALTH INC p 1132
4 Creek Pkwy Ste A 19061
Tel (610) 494-8700 *SIC* 2834 8082

VALLEY FORGE, PA

GH HOLDINGS INC p 610
Madison & Van Buren Ave 19482
Tel (610) 666-4000 *SIC* 2869 2992

SAINT-GOBAIN CERAMICS & PLASTICS INC p 1271
750 E Swedesford Rd 19482
Tel (610) 341-7000
SIC 2819 3679 3544 3297

SAINT-GOBAIN DELAWARE CORP p 1271
750 E Swedesford Rd 19482
Tel (610) 341-7000
SIC 3291 3269 2891 3296 3084 3221

SAINT-GOBAIN VETROTEX AMERICA INC p 1271
20 Moores Rd 19482
Tel (610) 893-6000 *SIC* 3089

■ **UGI ENTERPRISES INC** p 1499
460 N Gulph Rd 19482
Tel (610) 337-1000 *SIC* 5172

VERONA, PA

AMERICAN BEVERAGE CORP p 68
1 Daily Way 15147
Tel (412) 828-9020 *SIC* 2033

VILLANOVA, PA

DEVEREUX FOUNDATION p 434
444 Devereux Dr 19085
Tel (610) 520-3000 *SIC* 8361

VILLANOVA UNIVERSITY IN STATE OF PENNSYLVANIA p 1557
800 E Lancaster Ave 19085
Tel (610) 519-4500 *SIC* 8221

WARMINSTER, PA

CENTENNIAL SCHOOL DISTRICT p 275
433 Centennial Rd 18974
Tel (215) 441-6000 *SIC* 8211

CRC INDUSTRIES INC p 390
885 Louis Dr 18974
Tel (215) 674-4300
SIC 2992 3471 2899 2842

GREEN ACRES HEALTH SYSTEMS INC p 636
4 Ivybrook Blvd 18974
Tel (215) 357-6055 *SIC* 8741 8051

K&D FUTURE INC p 799
908 W Street Rd 18974
Tel (215) 674-3555 *SIC* 5021

NAVMAR APPLIED SCIENCES CORP p 1020
65 W Street Rd Ste C 18974
Tel (215) 675-4900 *SIC* 8731 8711

S P INDUSTRIES INC p 1262
935 Mearns Rd 18974
Tel (215) 672-7800
SIC 3826 3585 7699 3821

VERTICAL SCREEN INC p 1552
251 Veterans Way 18974
Tel (215) 396-9870 *SIC* 7375

W ATLEE BURPEE CO p 1568
300 Park Ave 18974
Tel (215) 674-4900 *SIC* 0181 5961

WARREN, PA

BLAIR LLC p 188
220 Hickory St 16366
Tel (814) 723-3600 *SIC* 5961

WARRENDALE, PA

EVOQUA WATER TECHNOLOGIES LLC p 516
181 Thorn Hill Rd 15086
Tel (724) 772-0044
SIC 3589 3569 3823 3826 4941

GUARDIAN PROTECTION SERVICES INC p 645
174 Thorn Hill Rd 15086
Tel (412) 788-2580 *SIC* 1731 5999 7382

■ **JOY GLOBAL UNDERGROUND MINING LLC** p 794
40 Pennwood Pl Ste 100 15086
Tel (724) 779-4500 *SIC* 3535 3532

MITSUBISHI ELECTRIC POWER PRODUCTS INC p 977
530 Keystone Dr 15086
Tel (724) 772-2555 *SIC* 3613

NATCO INDUSTRIES INC DEL p 1009
150 Thorn Hill Rd 15086
Tel (724) 776-4857 *SIC* 6799

PARAGON WHOLESALE FOODS CORP p 1113
173 Thorn Hill Rd 15086
Tel (412) 621-2626 *SIC* 5148 5141

RHODES HOLDCO INC p 1232
800 Commonwealth Dr # 100 15086
Tel (724) 776-9780 *SIC* 6719

RUE21 INC p 1257
800 Commonwealth Dr 15086
Tel (724) 776-9780 *SIC* 5611 5621

VECTOR SECURITY INC p 1546
2000 Ericsson Dr Ste 250 15086
Tel (724) 741-2200 *SIC* 7382 1731

WARREN, PA

NORTHWEST BANCORP MHC p 1059
100 Liberty St 16365
Tel (814) 728-7260 *SIC* 6036

NORTHWEST BANCORP INC p 1059
100 Liberty St 16365
Tel (814) 726-2140 *SIC* 6036

▲ **NORTHWEST BANCSHARES INC** p 1059
100 Liberty St 16365
Tel (814) 726-2140 *SIC* 6021

NORTHWEST BANK p 1059
100 Liberty St 16365
Tel (814) 723-9696 *SIC* 6035

PENNSYLVANIA GENERAL ENERGY CORP p 1130
120 Market St 16365
Tel (814) 723-3230 *SIC* 1311

UNITED REFINING CO p 1511
15 Bradley St 16365
Tel (814) 723-1500 *SIC* 2911 5541 5411

UNITED REFINING CO OF PENNSYLVANIA p 1511
15 Bradley St 16365
Tel (814) 723-1500 *SIC* 5541 5411

UNITED REFINING INC p 1511
15 Bradley St 16365
Tel (814) 723-1500
SIC 2911 5541 5411 4612

WHIRLEY INDUSTRIES INC p 1605
618 4th Ave 16365
Tel (814) 723-7600 *SIC* 3089

WASHINGTON, PA

AUDIA GROUP LLC p 130
450 Racetrack Rd 15301
Tel (724) 228-1260 *SIC* 5169

AUDIA INTERNATIONAL INC p 130
450 Racetrack Rd 15301
Tel (724) 228-1260 *SIC* 2821

CHAPMAN CORP p 288
331 S Main St 15301
Tel (724) 228-1900 *SIC* 1541 1542

ENSINGER INDUSTRIES INC p 501
365 Meadowlands Blvd 15301
Tel (724) 746-6050 *SIC* 2821

FAIRMONT SUPPLY CO p 525
437 Jefferson Ave 15301
Tel (724) 223-2200 *SIC* 5085 5082

■ **FERRO COLOR & GLASS CORP** p 538
251 W Wylie Ave 15301
Tel (724) 223-5900 *SIC* 3231

SSSI INC p 1364
2755a Park Ave 15301
Tel (724) 743-5815 *SIC* 1611 3312 4925

WASHINGTON & JEFFERSON COLLEGE p 1577
60 S Lincoln St 15301
Tel (724) 222-4400 *SIC* 8221

WASHINGTON COUNTY p 1577
100 W Beau St Ste 403 15301
Tel (724) 228-6700 *SIC* 9111

WASHINGTON HEALTH CARE SERVICES INC p 1578
155 Wilson Ave 15301
Tel (724) 225-7000 *SIC* 6324

WASHINGTON HOSPITAL p 1578
155 Wilson Ave 15301
Tel (724) 225-7000 *SIC* 8062

WASHINGTON PENN PLASTIC CO INC p 1578
450 Racetrack Rd 15301
Tel (724) 228-1260 *SIC* 3083 3087

WATSONTOWN, PA

KRAMM NURSING HOME INC p 829
245 E 8th St 17777
Tel (570) 538-2561 *SIC* 8051

WAYNE, PA

■ **ARROW INTERNATIONAL INC** p 113
550 E Swedesford Rd # 400 19087
Tel (610) 225-6800 *SIC* 3841 3844

ATLANTIS PETROLEUM LLC p 127
998 Old Eagle School Rd # 1205 19087
Tel (610) 265-8081 *SIC* 5411 5541

BUSINESS & DECISION NORTH AMERICA INC p 229
900 W Valley Rd Ste 1000 19087
Tel (610) 230-2500 *SIC* 7372

CERTAINTEED GYPSUM INC p 284
750 E Swedesford Rd 19087
Tel (813) 286-3900 *SIC* 3275

■ **CITADEL PLASTICS HOLDINGS INC** p 309
150 N Radnor Chester Rd 19087
Tel (484) 844-0231 *SIC* 5162

DE LAGE LANDEN FINANCIAL SERVICES INC p 419
1111 Old Eagle School Rd 19087
Tel (610) 386-5000 *SIC* 6159

EASTERN UNIVERSITY p 472
1300 Eagle Rd 19087
Tel (610) 341-5800 *SIC* 8221

FIBRO SOURCE USA INC p 540
985 Old Eagle School Rd # 514 19087
Tel (610) 293-3200
SIC 5099 5113 5141 5112

■ **FIS EPROCESS INTELLIGENCE LLC** p 551
680 E Swedesford Rd 19087
Tel (888) 601-2361 *SIC* 7374 5045

■ **FIS SG LLC** p 551
680 E Swedesford Rd 19087
Tel (484) 582-5400 *SIC* 7372 7374

GENEX SERVICES LLC p 603
440 E Swedesford Rd # 1000 19087
Tel (610) 964-5100 *SIC* 6411

JUDGE GROUP INC p 796
151 S Warner Rd Ste 100 19087
Tel (610) 667-7700 *SIC* 7373 7361 7379

KENEXA CORP p 810
650 E Swedesford Rd # 200 19087
Tel (877) 971-9171 *SIC* 7361 7371

LIQUIDHUB INC p 870
500 E Swedesford Rd # 300 19087
Tel (610) 688-6531 *SIC* 8748

LUMBERMENS MERCHANDISING CORP p 885
137 W Wayne Ave 19087
Tel (610) 293-3678 *SIC* 5031 5072

MATTHEY JOHNSON HOLDINGS INC p 921
435 Devon Park Dr Ste 600 19087
Tel (610) 971-3000
SIC 3341 3339 3356 2834 3399 3714

MATTHEY JOHNSON INC p 921
435 Devon Park Dr Ste 600 19087
Tel (610) 971-3000
SIC 3341 3339 3356 2834 3399 3714

MEDECISION INC p 935
550 E Swedesford Rd # 220 19087
Tel (484) 588-0102 *SIC* 6324 7371

■ **MET-PRO TECHNOLOGIES LLC** p 952
460 E Swedesford Rd # 2030 19087
Tel (215) 717-7909 *SIC* 3564

METALLURG HOLDINGS INC p 952
435 Devon Park Dr Ste 200 19087
Tel (610) 293-0838 *SIC* 3313 1081

METALLURG INC p 952
435 Devon Park Dr Ste 200 19087
Tel (610) 293-2501 *SIC* 3313 1081

MTPCS LLC p 998
1170 Devon Park Dr # 104 19087
Tel (610) 688-1334 *SIC* 4812

NTHRIVE SOLUTIONS p 1065
1275 Drummers Ln Ste 200 19087
Tel (610) 688-2464 *SIC* 8742

NTHRIVE SOLUTIONS INC p 1065
1275 Drummers Ln Ste 200 19087
Tel (800) 555-2311 *SIC* 8099

PRECYSE ADVANCED TECHNOLOGIES LLC p 1169
1275 Drummers Ln Ste 200 19087
Tel (800) 555-2311 *SIC* 8748

PRECYSE HOLDINGS LLC p 1169
1275 Drummers Ln Ste 200 19087
Tel (800) 555-2311 *SIC* 8748

SAFEGUARD INTERNATIONAL FUND LP p 1266
435 Devon Park Dr Ste 200 19087
Tel (610) 254-4110 *SIC* 6282

WAYNESBURG, PA

CUMBERLAND COAL RESOURCES LP p 400
158 Portal Rd 15370
Tel (724) 852-5845 *SIC* 1222

WAYNE, PA

■ **SIGNAL** p 1321
676 E Swedesford Rd # 300 19087
Tel (610) 975-8901 *SIC* 6411

■ **SIGNAL HOLDINGS LLC** p 1322
676 E Swedesford Rd # 300 19087
Tel (610) 341-1300 *SIC* 6719

SUNGARD AVAILABILITY SERVICES LP p 1402
680 E Swedesford Rd 19087
Tel (484) 582-2000 *SIC* 7374

■ **SUNGARD BUSINESS SYSTEMS LLC** p 1402
680 E Swedesford Rd 19087
Tel (484) 582-2000 *SIC* 7374 5734

■ **SUNGARD CAPITAL CORP II** p 1402
680 E Swedesford Rd 19087
Tel (484) 582-2000 *SIC* 7372 7374

■ **SUNGARD HOLDCO LLC** p 1402
680 E Swedesford Rd 19087
Tel (484) 582-2000 *SIC* 7372 7374

■ **SUNGARD HOLDING CORP** p 1402
680 E Swedesford Rd 19087
Tel (888) 332-2564 *SIC* 7372 7374

TEKNI-PLEX INC p 1433
460 E Swedesford Rd # 3000 19087
Tel (484) 690-1520
SIC 2679 3462 3052 2672

▲ **TELEFLEX INC** p 1434
550 E Swedesford Rd # 400 19087
Tel (610) 225-6800 *SIC* 3841 3842

TRANSPORT INTERNATIONAL POOL INC p 1472
530 E Swedesford Rd 19087
Tel (484) 254-0100 *SIC* 5511 7519

TRANSPORT INTERNATIONAL POOL INC p 1472
530 E Swedesford Rd 19087
Tel (484) 254-0100
SIC 7519 7513 5511 5211

TREDYFFRIN-EASTTOWN SCHOOL DISTRICT (INC) p 1475
940 W Valley Rd Ste 1700 19087
Tel (610) 240-1900 *SIC* 8211

VELDOS LLC p 1547
435 Devon Park Dr Ste 500 19087
Tel (610) 254-4121 *SIC* 7389

WELLSBORO, PA

LAUREL HEALTH SYSTEM INC p 847
22 Walnut St 16901
Tel (570) 724-1010 *SIC* 8082 8741 8011

WELLSVILLE, PA

PENNEX ALUMINUM CO LLC p 1130
50 Community St 17365
Tel (717) 432-9647 *SIC* 5051

WEST CHESTER, PA

A DUIE PYLE INC p 5
650 Westtown Rd 19382
Tel (610) 696-5800 *SIC* 4214 4225 7519

ACADEMIC ACQUISITION CORP p 13
1615 W Chester Pike 19382
Tel (484) 947-2000 *SIC* 8211 8299

ACCESS GROUP INC p 14
10 N High St Fl 4 19380
Tel (484) 653-3300 *SIC* 6163

CHESTER COUNTY HOSPITAL p 295
701 E Marshall St 19380
Tel (610) 431-5000 *SIC* 8062

CHESTER COUNTY HOSPITAL AND HEALTH SYSTEM p 295
701 E Marshall St 19380
Tel (610) 431-5000 *SIC* 8062

COMMUNICATIONS TEST DESIGN INC p 347
1373 Enterprise Dr 19380
Tel (610) 436-5203
SIC 7629 7378 5065 5999

COUNTY OF CHESTER p 377
313 W Market St 19382
Tel (610) 344-6000 *SIC* 9111

■ **DEPUY SYNTHES INC** p 431
1302 Wrights Ln E 19380
Tel (610) 719-5000 *SIC* 3841

■ **EB INVESTMENT CORP** p 474
931 S Matlack St 19382
Tel (610) 430-8100 *SIC* 5734 5945

■ **HAAS GROUP** p 651
1475 Phoenixville Pike 19380
Tel (484) 564-4500 *SIC* 8741 3369

KEYSTONE FOODS LLC p 815
905 Airport Rd Ste 400 19380
Tel (610) 667-6700 *SIC* 2013 2015 5087

■ **KIDDE FIRE PROTECTION INC** p 817
350 E Union St 19382
Tel (610) 363-1400 *SIC* 3669 3999 3823

LASKO GROUP INC p 846
820 Lincoln Ave 19380
Tel (610) 692-7400 *SIC* 4789 3634

LASKO PRODUCTS INC p 846
820 Lincoln Ave 19380
Tel (610) 692-7400 *SIC* 4789 3585 3564

NOBEL LEARNING COMMUNITIES INC p 1046
1615 W Chester Pike # 200 19382
Tel (484) 947-2000 *SIC* 8211 8299

OMNI CABLE CORP p 1084
2 Hagerty Blvd 19382
Tel (610) 701-0100 *SIC* 5063

■ **QVC INC** p 1201
1200 Wilson Dr 19380
Tel (484) 701-1000 *SIC* 5961

SYNTHES (USA) LP p 1416
1302 Wrights Ln E 19380
Tel (610) 719-5000 *SIC* 3842 3841

■ **SYNTHES INC** p 1416
1302 Wrights Ln E 19380
Tel (610) 647-9700 *SIC* 3841 3842 6719

■ **VOYA INSURANCE AND ANNUITY CO** p 1566
1475 Dunwoody Dr 19380
Tel (610) 425-3400 *SIC* 6311

WEST CHESTER AREA SCHOOL DISTRICT p 1594
829 Paoli Pike 19380
Tel (484) 266-1000 *SIC* 8211

WEST CHESTER UNIVERSITY OF PENNSYLVANIA p 1594
700 S High St 19383
Tel (610) 436-1000 *SIC* 8221 9411

WESTON SOLUTIONS HOLDINGS INC p 1602
1400 Weston Way 19380
Tel (610) 692-7533 *SIC* 8748

WESTON SOLUTIONS INC p 1602
1400 Weston Way 19380
Tel (610) 701-3000 *SIC* 8742 8748

YMCA GREATER BRANDYWINE p 1636
1 E Chestnut St 19380
Tel (610) 643-9622
SIC 8641 7991 8351 7032 8322

WEST GROVE, PA

DANSKO HOLDINGS INC p 412
33 Federal Rd 19390
Tel (610) 869-8335 *SIC* 5139

WEST HAZLETON, PA

BRADLEY CALDWELL INC p 206
200 Kiwanis Blvd 18202
Tel (570) 455-7511 *SIC* 5191 5199 5072

WEST MIFFLIN, PA

LIBERTY USA INC p 863
920 Irwin Run Rd 15122
Tel (412) 461-2700
SIC 5194 5145 5122 5141

WEST POINT, PA

ACTS RETIREMENT-LIFE COMMUNITIES INC p 20
375 Morris Rd 19486
Tel (215) 699-3204 *SIC* 8361 8051

COLORCON INC p 339
420 Moyer Blvd 19486
Tel (215) 699-7733 *SIC* 2834

WEXFORD, PA

BAIERL CHEVROLET INC p 145
10432 Perry Hwy 15090
Tel (724) 935-3711 *SIC* 5511 5013

PTC GROUP HOLDINGS CORP p 1189
6051 Wallace Road Ext # 2 15090
Tel (412) 299-7900 *SIC* 3317

WHITEHALL, PA

EASTERN INDUSTRIES INC p 472
3724 Crescent Ct W 200 18052
Tel (610) 866-0932 *SIC* 5032 3273 1611

WILKES BARRE, PA

ALLONE HEALTH RESOURCES INC p 58
100 N Penna Ave 18701
Tel (877) 720-7770 *SIC* 6321

BRIDON-AMERICAN CORP p 212
C280 New Commerce Blvd 18706
Tel (570) 822-3349 *SIC* 3533 3532 5084

■ **CCE HOLDINGS LLC** p 270
1 Ugi Ctr Fl 2 18711
Tel (713) 989-2000 *SIC* 4922

COLOURS INC p 339
233 S Washington St 18701
Tel (570) 655-9510 *SIC* 5198 5085 5088

COMMUNITY SERVICE OFFICE p 350
84 W South St 18766
Tel (570) 408-5905 *SIC* 8999

GEISINGER WYOMING VALLEY MEDICAL CENTER p 597
1000 E Mountain Dr 18711
Tel (570) 808-7300 *SIC* 8062

■ **GUARD INSURANCE GROUP INC** p 645
16 S River St 18702
Tel (570) 825-9900 *SIC* 6331

HMO OF NORTHEASTERN PENNSYLVANIA INC p 698
19 N Main St 18711
Tel (570) 200-4300 *SIC* 6324

INTERMETRO INDUSTRIES CORP p 753
651 N Washington St 18705
Tel (570) 825-2741
SIC 3496 2542 3537 3411 3315 2441

LUZERNE COUNTY p 887
200 N River St 18711
Tel (570) 825-1500 *SIC* 9111

MCCARTHY TIRE SERVICE CO INC p 926
340 Kidder St 18702
Tel (570) 822-3151 *SIC* 5014 5531

PAGNOTTI ENTERPRISES INC p 1107
46 Public Sq Ste 600 18701
Tel (570) 825-8700 *SIC* 6411 1231 4841

RIVERSTREET MANOR p 1238
440 N River St 18702
Tel (570) 825-5611 *SIC* 8361 8059 8051

■ **SOUTHERN UNION PANHANDLE LLC** p 1350
1 Ugi Ctr Fl 2 18711
Tel (570) 820-2400 *SIC* 4922

STEP-BY-STEP INC p 1386
744 Kidder St Frnt 18702
Tel (570) 829-3477 *SIC* 8322 8361

WILKES UNIVERSITY p 1609
84 W South St 18766
Tel (570) 408-4200 *SIC* 8221

WILKES UNIVERSITY SECURITY DEPARTMENT p 1609
84 W South St 18766
Tel (570) 408-4999 *SIC* 7382

WILKES-BARRE AREA SCHOOL DISTRICT p 1609
730 S Main St 18702
Tel (570) 826-7127 *SIC* 8211

■ **WILKES-BARRE HOSPITAL CO LLC** p 1609
575 N River St 18764
Tel (570) 829-8111 *SIC* 8062 8069

■ **WYOMING VALLEY HEALTH & EDUCATION FOUNDATION** p 1630
575 N River St 18702
Tel (570) 829-8111 *SIC* 8062

WILLIAMSPORT, PA

BRODART CO p 216
500 Arch St 17701
Tel (570) 326-2461
SIC 5192 5942 2752 2782 2789 2531

DIVINE PROVIDENCE HOSPITAL OF SISTERS OF CHRISTIAN CHARITY p 444
1100 Grampian Blvd 17701
Tel (570) 321-1000 *SIC* 8062

PENNSYLVANIA COLLEGE OF TECHNOLOGY p 1130
1 College Ave 17701
Tel (570) 320-2400 *SIC* 8221

PRIMUS TECHNOLOGIES CORP p 1176
2333 Reach Rd 17701
Tel (570) 326-6591 *SIC* 3672

SHOP VAC CORP p 1318
2323 Reach Rd 17701
Tel (570) 326-0502 *SIC* 3589

SUSQUEHANNA HEALTH SYSTEM p 1409
700 High St 17701
Tel (570) 321-1000 *SIC* 8741

SUSQUEHANNA PHYSICIAN SERVICES p 1409
1100 Grampian Blvd 17701
Tel (570) 320-7444 *SIC* 8011

SUSQUEHANNA VENTURES INC p 1409
1100 Grampian Blvd 17701
Tel (570) 326-8718 *SIC* 8062

WILLIAMSPORT HOSPITAL p 1612
700 High St 17701
Tel (570) 321-1000 *SIC* 8062 7389

WILLIAMSPORT PATHOLOGY ASSOCS p 1612
700 High St 17701
Tel (570) 321-2321 *SIC* 8011

WIREROPE WORKS INC p 1618
100 Maynard St 17701
Tel (570) 327-4229 *SIC* 3496 2298 3315

WILLOW GROVE, PA

ASPLUNDH TREE EXPERT CO p 119
708 Blair Mill Rd 19090
Tel (215) 784-4200
SIC 0783 1629 1623 1611 6411

■ **HEALTHCARE RESOURCES CORP** p 676
1113 Easton Rd 19090
Tel (215) 659-3060 *SIC* 8059 8361

UTILICON SOLUTIONS LTD p 1537
708 Blair Mill Rd 19090
Tel (215) 784-4200 *SIC* 4939 4923

UTILITY VEGETATION SERVICES INC p 1537
708 Blair Mill Rd 19090
Tel (215) 784-4200 *SIC* 0783

WILLOW STREET, PA

WILLOW VALLEY COMMUNITIES p 1613
100 Willow Vly Lakes Dr 17584
Tel (717) 464-2741 *SIC* 8361 8059 8082

WILMERDING, PA

■ **WABTEC CORP** p 1570
1001 Airbrake Ave 15148
Tel (412) 825-1543 *SIC* 3743

▲ **WESTINGHOUSE AIR BRAKE TECHNOLOGIES CORP** p 1601
1001 Airbrake Ave 15148
Tel (412) 825-1000 *SIC* 3743

WORCESTER, PA

ALLAN MYERS INC p 51
1805 Berks Rd 19490
Tel (610) 222-8800
SIC 1629 1794 1611 1622 3281 5032

ALLAN MYERS LP p 51
1805 Berks Rd 19490
Tel (610) 584-3430
SIC 1629 1794 1611 1622

■ **TECHNI-TOOL INC** p 1431
1547 N Trooper Rd 19490
Tel (610) 941-2400 *SIC* 5085

WRIGHTSVILLE, PA

DONSCO INC p 451
124 N Front St 17368
Tel (717) 252-0690 *SIC* 3398 3321

WYNCOTE, PA

■ **CRESTVIEW CONVALESCENT HOME INC** p 392
1245 Church Rd 19095
Tel (215) 884-9990 *SIC* 8051

WYOMING, PA

■ **DIAMOND MANUFACTURING CO** p 437
243 W Eigth St 18644
Tel (570) 693-0300
SIC 3469 3471 3479 3089

WYOMISSING, PA

▲ **CARPENTER TECHNOLOGY CORP** p 260
2 Meridian Blvd 19610
Tel (610) 208-2000
SIC 3312 3443 3255 3316 3315

▲ **CUSTOMERS BANCORP INC** p 403
1015 Penn Ave Ste 103 19610
Tel (610) 933-2000 *SIC* 6022

▲ **GAMING AND LEISURE PROPERTIES INC** p 590
845 Berkshire Blvd 19610
Tel (610) 401-2900 *SIC* 6519

■ **GOLD MERGER SUB LLC** p 620
845 Berkshire Blvd # 200 19610
Tel (610) 401-2900 *SIC* 7999 7011

LOOMIS CO p 877
850 N Park Rd 19610
Tel (610) 374-4040 *SIC* 6411 8742

▲ **PENN NATIONAL GAMING INC** p 1129
825 Berkshire Blvd # 200 19610
Tel (610) 373-2400 *SIC* 7011 7948

RENTOKIL NORTH AMERICA INC p 1224
1125 Berkshire Blvd # 150 19610
Tel (610) 372-9700 *SIC* 7342 0781 5191

SAVOR STREET FOODS INC p 1284
1 Park Plz 19610
Tel (610) 320-7800 *SIC* 2052 2096 2099

SFS INTEC INC p 1310
1045 Spring St 19610
Tel (610) 376-5751 *SIC* 7699 5012 5085

YARDLEY, PA

CLINIGEN CTS INC p 326
790 Township Line Rd # 120 19067
Tel (215) 558-7001 *SIC* 5122

HERAEUS ELECTRO-NITE CO LLC p 685
770 Township Line Rd # 300 19067
Tel (215) 944-9000 *SIC* 3812 3823

HERAEUS INC HIC p 685
770 Township Line Rd 19067
Tel (212) 752-2180
SIC 3399 3823 3339 3469

MM USA HOLDINGS LLC p 979
780 Township Line Rd 19067
Tel (267) 685-2300 *SIC* 2741 8732

YORK, PA

■ **A&S SERVICES GROUP LLC** p 7
310 N Zarfoss Dr 17404
Tel (717) 235-2456 *SIC* 4214 4225

ARTHUR J GLATFELTER AGENCY INC p 114
183 Leaders Heights Rd 17402
Tel (717) 741-0911 *SIC* 6411 8742

▲ **BON-TON STORES INC** p 199
2801 E Market St Ofc C 17402
Tel (717) 757-7660 *SIC* 5311

C H R CORP p 232
2295 N Susquehanna Trl C 17404
Tel (717) 848-9827 *SIC* 5411

COUNTY OF YORK p 383
28 E Market St Rm 216 17401
Tel (717) 771-9964 *SIC* 9111

D F STAUFFER BISCUIT CO INC p 407
360 S Belmont St 17403
Tel (717) 815-4600 *SIC* 2052

▲ **DENTSPLY SIRONA INC** p 429
221 W Philadelphia St 17401
Tel (717) 845-7511 *SIC* 3843

ENGEL MACHINERY INC p 498
3740 Board Rd 17406
Tel (717) 764-6818 *SIC* 5084 7699

ETTLINE FOODS CORP p 512
525 N State St 17403
Tel (717) 848-1564 *SIC* 5141

GEA REFRIGERATION NORTH AMERICA INC p 597
3475 Board Rd 17406
Tel (717) 767-6411 *SIC* 3585

GPC CAPITAL CORP II p 627
2401 Pleasant Valley Rd # 2 17402
Tel (717) 849-8500 *SIC* 3089

GRAHAM ARCHITECTURAL PRODUCTS CORP p 628
1551 Mount Rose Ave 17403
Tel (717) 849-8100 *SIC* 3442

GRAHAM PACKAGING CO EUROPE LLC p 629
2401 Pleasant Valley Rd # 2 17402
Tel (717) 849-8500 *SIC* 3089

JMM SERVICES INC p 786
1431 N George St 17404
Tel (717) 848-1100 *SIC* 7361

KINSLEY CONSTRUCTION INC p 821
2700 Water St 17403
Tel (717) 741-3841 *SIC* 1541 1542 1611

LINCOLN GENERAL INSURANCE CO p 867
3501 Concord Rd Ste 120 17402
Tel (717) 757-0000 *SIC* 6331

MAGNESITA REFRACTORIES CO p 896
425 S Salem Church Rd 17408
Tel (717) 792-3611 *SIC* 3297 3274 1422

MAPLE DONUTS INC p 903
3455 E Market St 17402
Tel (717) 757-7826 *SIC* 2051 5461

MAPLE PRESS CO p 903
480 Willow Springs Ln 17406
Tel (717) 764-5911
SIC 2732 2791 2789 2752

MC WIL GROUP LTD p 925
209 N Beaver St 17401
Tel (717) 854-7857
SIC 8059 8051 8069 6513 8742 6552

NEW STANDARD CORP p 1033
74 Commerce Way 17406
Tel (717) 757-9450 *SIC* 3469 3465

NK LIQUIDATION INC p 1045
600 Arsenal Rd 17402
Tel (717) 854-1505 *SIC* 5411

▲ **P H GLATFELTER CO** p 1102
96 S Gorge St Ste 500 17401
Tel (717) 225-4711 *SIC* 2621

PACE RESOURCES INC p 1103
140 E Market St Fl 2 17401
Tel (717) 852-1300
SIC 2752 5049 7334 2789

■ **PFALTZGRAFF FACTORY STORES INC** p 1140
140 E Market St 17401
Tel (717) 848-5500 *SIC* 3269 5719

PRECISION CUSTOM COMPONENTS LLC p 1168
500 Lincoln St 17401
Tel (717) 848-1126 *SIC* 3443 3699

SUSQUEHANNA PFALTZGRAFF CO INC p 1409
140 E Market St 17401
Tel (717) 848-5500 *SIC* 4832 4841 6512

VOITH HYDRO INC p 1564
760 E Berlin Rd 17408
Tel (717) 792-7000 *SIC* 3511 7699

VOITH TURBO INC p 1564
25 Winship Rd 17406
Tel (717) 767-3200 *SIC* 5084 5013

WELLSPAN HEALTH p 1591
45 Monument Rd 17403
Tel (717) 851-2269 *SIC* 5912

WELLSPAN MEDICAL GROUP (INC) p 1591
140 N Duke St 17401
Tel (717) 851-6515 *SIC* 8011

WEXCO INC p 1603
3490 Board Rd 17406
Tel (717) 764-8585
SIC 3089 3949 3999 5091 3081

WILMAC CORP p 1613
209 N Beaver St 17401
Tel (717) 854-7857
SIC 8059 8051 8069 6513 8742 6552

YORK COLLEGE OF PENNSYLVANIA INC p 1637
441 Country Club Rd 17403
Tel (717) 815-1780 *SIC* 8221

YORK HOSPITAL p 1637
1001 S George St 17403
Tel (717) 851-2345 *SIC* 8062

YORK INTERNATIONAL CORP p 1637
631 S Richland Ave 17403
Tel (717) 771-7890 *SIC* 3585

YORK NAMI PA COUNTY p 1637
140 Roosevelt Ave Ste 200 17401
Tel (717) 848-3784 *SIC* 8299

YORK PENNSYLVANIA HOSPITAL CO LLC p 1637
325 S Belmont St 17403
Tel (717) 843-8623 *SIC* 8062 8082

YOUNGWOOD, PA

WESTMORELAND COUNTY COMMUNITY COLLEGE EDUCATIONAL FOUNDATION INC p 1602
145 Pavilion Ln 15697
Tel (724) 925-4000 *SIC* 8222

PUERTO RICO

AGUADILLA, PR

UNIVERSIDAD INTERAMERICANA DE PUERTO RICO INC p 1518
Recinto De Aguadil 00605
Tel (787) 891-0925 *SIC* 8221

ANASCO, PR

■ AMO PUERTO RICO MANUFACTURING INC p 86
Carr 402 Km 42 Zona Indus St Ca 00610
Tel (787) 826-2727 *SIC* 2834

ARECIBO, PR

■ CARIBE GE INTERNATIONAL OF PUERTO RICO INC p 256
980 Ave San Luis 00612
Tel (787) 878-1420 *SIC* 3613

CUTLER-HAMMER DE PUERTO RICO INC p 403
Carr 2 Km 67 6 Santana In St Ca 00612
Tel (787) 881-3640 *SIC* 3613

MUNICIPIO DE ARECIBO p 1000
Jose De Diego St 00612
Tel (787) 879-1561 *SIC* 9199

THERMO KING DE PUERTO RICO INC p 1447
517 Zona Industrial 00612
Tel (787) 878-1690 *SIC* 3585

ARROYO, PR

■ STRYKER PUERTO RICO LIMITED p 1394
Hwy 3 Km 131 2 Las Guasim 00714
Tel (787) 839-7688 *SIC* 3841

BARCELONETA, PR

■ ABBVIE BIOTECHNOLOGY LTD p 10
Road No 2 Km 59 2 00617
Tel (787) 846-3500
SIC 2834 2844 2835 3841 3826

■ PFIZER PHARMACEUTICALS INC p 1140
Km 58 Hm 2 Rr 2 00617
Tel (787) 846-4300 *SIC* 2834

BAYAMON, PR

B FERNANDEZ & HNOS INC p 142
Urb Luchetti Calle B 00960
Tel (787) 288-7272 *SIC* 5169

B FERNANDEZ & HNOS INC p 142
Carr 5 305 Urb Rr St Ca 00961
Tel (787) 288-7272 *SIC* 5181 5141 5182

C C 1 BEER DISTRIBUTORS INC p 232
107 Carr 174 00959
Tel (787) 288-6400 *SIC* 5181

C C 1 LIMITED PARTNERSHIP p 232
107 Carr 174 00959
Tel (787) 288-6400 *SIC* 2086

GOYA DE PUERTO RICO INC p 627
Esq Calle 5 Rr 28 00961
Tel (787) 740-4900 *SIC* 2032 2033

INSTITUCION EDUCATIVA NETS INC p 747
Urb Sierra Bayamn 00961
Tel (787) 785-5511 *SIC* 8299 8322

INTERNATIONAL SHIPPING AGENCY INC p 756
500 Paseo Monaco Apt 55 00956
Tel (787) 778-2355 *SIC* 4491 4731

JOSE SANTIAGO INC p 793
5 Calle Marginal # 5 00959
Tel (787) 288-8835 *SIC* 5142 5149

LUIS GARRATON INC p 884
Luchetti Ind Park Rd 28 C 00961
Tel (787) 788-6100 *SIC* 5122 5141

MUNICIPIO DE BAYAMON p 1000
Road 2 Km 11 Hm 3 St Ro 00959
Tel (787) 780-5552 *SIC* 9111

PAN PEPIN INC p 1110
Plaza Laurel 00956
Tel (787) 787-1717 *SIC* 2051

PUERTO RICO SUPPLIES GROUP INC p 1191
Parkeast 00961
Tel (787) 780-4043
SIC 5194 5149 5122 5143 5148

V SUAREZ & CO INC p 1538
Industrial Luchetti 300 C 00961
Tel (787) 792-1212 *SIC* 5182 5149

V SUAREZ & CO INC p 1538
Industrial Luchetti # 300 00961
Tel (787) 792-1212 *SIC* 5181 5141 5182

CABO ROJO, PR

PROPPER INTERNATIONAL INC p 1184
308 Km 0 6 375 Clljon Fas 00623
Tel (787) 254-8020 *SIC* 2311 2326

CAGUAS, PR

AIREKO CONSTRUCTION LLC p 40
Las Casas St Lot 20 00725
Tel (787) 653-6300
SIC 1542 1541 1731 1711

B M J FOODS PR INC p 142
Carr 175 Km 0 2 Bo Rio Ca St Ca 00725
Tel (787) 286-7040 *SIC* 5812

CAGUAS MUNICIPALITY p 237
Calle Padial Final Esq 00725
Tel (787) 743-2476 *SIC* 9111

CENTRO MEDICO DEL TURABO INC p 281
100 Ave Luis Munoz Marin 00725
Tel (787) 653-3434 *SIC* 8741

DROGUERIA BETANCES LLC p 456
Luis Munoz Marin Ave Esq 00725
Tel (787) 653-1200 *SIC* 5122

GRUPO HIMA-SAN PABLO INC p 643
100 Calle Munoz Rivera 00725
Tel (787) 653-3434 *SIC* 8062

HOSPITAL HIMA SAN PABLO CAGUAS p 709
100 Ave Luis Munoz Marin 00725
Tel (787) 653-3434 *SIC* 8062

KOMODIDAD DISTRIBUTORS INC p 827
156 Km 58 8 00727
Tel (787) 746-3188 *SIC* 5137 5136 5094

M T G LLC p 890
Carre 175km 27 2 Hc 34 Bo 00725
Tel (787) 783-1988 *SIC* 5147

NEOLPHARMA INC p 1026
99 Calle Jardines 00725
Tel (787) 286-4000 *SIC* 5122

P R PATHEON LLC p 1102
2 Calle Aquamarina Villa 00725
Tel (787) 746-8500 *SIC* 2834

STEEL AND PIPES INC p 1384
Road 1rio 00725
Tel (787) 747-9415
SIC 5051 3446 3317 5085

■ WAL-MART PUERTO RICO INC p 1572
Carr 1 Km 28 7 Bo St Ca 00725
Tel (787) 653-7777 *SIC* 5331 5411 5399

CANOVANAS, PR

I P R PHARMACEUTICAL INC p 725
San Isdro Indus Park Lot 00729
Tel (787) 957-1400 *SIC* 2834

CAROLINA, PR

CAROLINA MUNICIPALITY p 259
Ignacio Arzuaga St 00985
Tel (787) 757-2626 *SIC* 9111

■ ELI LILLY INDUSTRIES INC p 487
430 Calle Fabril 00987
Tel (787) 257-5555 *SIC* 2834

■ EXECUTIVE AIR LINES INC p 517
Lmm Int Airport Central 00983
Tel (787) 253-6401 *SIC* 4512 4212

GENESIS SECURITY SERVICE p 603
5900 Ave Isla Verde L 00979
Tel (787) 701-2830 *SIC* 7381

CATANO, PR

BACARDI CORP p 143
Km 2/6 Carretera 165 Rd S St 00962
Tel (787) 788-1500 *SIC* 2085

BALLESTER HERMANOS INC p 148
Carr 869 Parq 00962
Tel (787) 788-4110 *SIC* 5141 5182

CARIBBEAN PRODUCE EXCHANGE LLC p 256
2 Carr 869 00962
Tel (787) 793-0750 *SIC* 5148

CARIBBEAN RESTAURANTS LLC p 256
Rd 5 Km 27 4 Bldg 1 00962
Tel (787) 474-7777 *SIC* 5812

CAYEY, PR

CONGAR INTERNATIONAL CORP p 356
Km 72 Hm 2 Rr 14 00736
Tel (787) 738-2106 *SIC* 2121

MENNONITE GENERAL HOSPITAL INC p 943
Carr 14 Km 131 Sctor Lmas St Ca 00736
Tel (787) 535-1001 *SIC* 8062

■ NYPRO PUERTO RICO INC p 1069
15 Ave Luis Mnoz Rivera S 00736
Tel (787) 738-4211 *SIC* 3089

OLAY CO INC p 1080
Km 2 Hm 3 Rr 735 00736
Tel (787) 738-2191 *SIC* 2844

CIDRA, PR

■ CARIBBEAN REFRESCOS INC p 256
Carr 172 Km 13 4 Bo Monte St Ca 00739
Tel (787) 739-8452 *SIC* 2087

COAMO, PR

CE CARIBE LLC p 271
Carretera 14 Km 25 3 St Carrete 00769
Tel (787) 825-6000 *SIC* 3639 5064

COROZAL, PR

BLUEWATER DEFENSE INC p 193
Corozal Ind Pk Carr 159 00783
Tel (787) 746-5020
SIC 2393 2326 3842 2325

DORADO, PR

■ DORADO BEACH HOTEL CORP p 451
Km 12 7 Rr 693 00646
Tel (787) 796-1234 *SIC* 7011

■ GUIDANT PUERTO RICO BV p 645
12 Carr 698 Ste 171 00646
Tel (787) 796-2115 *SIC* 3845

FAJARDO, PR

EL CONQUISTADOR PARTNERSHIP LPSE (DE) p 482
1000 Ave El Conquistador 00738
Tel (787) 863-1000 *SIC* 7011

■ PALL LIFE SCIENCES PUERTO RICO LLC p 1108
Carr 194 Pall Blvd 98 00738
Tel (787) 863-1124 *SIC* 3842

■ PALL PUERTO RICO INC p 1108
Km 0 Hm 4 Rr 194 00738
Tel (787) 863-1124 *SIC* 3569

GUAYAMA, PR

■ AES PUERTO RICO LP p 31
Carretera Ste 3 Km 142 0 00784
Tel (787) 866-8117 *SIC* 4911

■ WYETH PHARMACEUTICALS CO INC p 1629
1 Carr 3 00784
Tel (787) 864-4010 *SIC* 5122

GUAYNABO, PR

■ BRISTOL-MYERS SQUIBB PUERTO RICO INC p 214
6 Calle Tabonuco 00968
Tel (787) 774-2800 *SIC* 2834

■ CARDINAL HEALTH PR 120 INC p 253
10 Carr 165 Km24 00968
Tel (787) 625-4100 *SIC* 5122 5047

CARIBBEAN ARCHITECTS & ENGINEERS p 256
D14 Calle 6 Apt 1101 00966
Tel (787) 783-5500 *SIC* 8711 8712

■ CELLULAR COMMUNICATIONS OF PUERTO RICO INC p 274
103 Ave Ortegon 00966
Tel (787) 397-1000 *SIC* 4812 5999

CEMEX DE PUERTO RICO INC p 274
Km 2/7 Carr 00968
Tel (787) 783-3000 *SIC* 3273 3241

CESAR CASTILLO INC p 284
Km 21 1 Pr 1 Rr 1 00971
Tel (787) 999-1616 *SIC* 5122 6552

■ COLGATE PALMOLIVE CO DISTRIBUTORS p 336
1 St Lot 8colgate 00968
Tel (787) 273-5000 *SIC* 5122

■ COMPAQ COMPUTER CARIBBEAN INC p 350
1 Calle Sonata 3 00969
Tel (787) 781-0505 *SIC* 5045 7378

■ FLUOR DANIEL CARIBBEAN INC p 561
Metro Office Park St2 1 # 2 00968
Tel (787) 783-5500 *SIC* 1542 1541

GFR MEDIA LLC p 610
50 Carr 165 Ste 1 00968
Tel (787) 641-8000 *SIC* 4789 2711 5963

GRUPO EDUK INC p 643
Marginal Rd 20 Km 2 3 00966
Tel (787) 982-3000
SIC 8249 8244 8243 8222 7231

INSTITUTO DE BANCA Y COMERCIO INC p 747
56 Carr 20 00966
Tel (787) 982-3000
SIC 8249 8244 8243 8222 7231

INTERNATIONAL RESTAURANT SERVICES INC p 756
Amelia Dist Ctr 23 Ema St 00968
Tel (787) 273-3131 *SIC* 5813 5812

JF MONTALVO CASH AND CARRY INC p 785
Amelia Ind Park 46 00968
Tel (787) 781-2962 *SIC* 5141

■ JOHNSON & JOHNSON INTERNATIONAL p 790
475 Calle C Ste 200 00969
Tel (787) 272-1905 *SIC* 5122

MENDEZ & CO INC p 943
Km 2/4 Mrtnez Nadal Rr 20 00969
Tel (787) 793-8888 *SIC* 5182 5141

MUNICPALITY OF GUAYNABO p 1000
Jose De Diego St Final 00969
Tel (787) 720-4040 *SIC* 9111

PAN AMERICAN GRAIN CO INC p 1110
Calle Claudia 9 Esqu 00968
Tel (787) 792-3355 *SIC* 2048

PAN AMERICAN GRAIN MANUFACTURING CO INC p 1110
Calle Caludia 9cnr 00968
Tel (787) 273-6100 *SIC* 2099

■ PEPSICO CARIBBEAN INC p 1134
668 Calle Cubitas 00969
Tel (787) 720-6825 *SIC* 2013

PLAZA PROVISION CO (PUERTO RICO) p 1156
Carretera 165 Esq 00965
Tel (787) 781-2070 *SIC* 5182 4222 2841

PUEBLO INC p 1190
Calle Diana Ste 14 00968
Tel (787) 757-3131 *SIC* 5411

RICO CLARO PUERTO p 1233
1515 Frnklin D Rsvelt Ave 00968
Tel (787) 766-2355 *SIC* 4812 8748

RICO PUERTO TELEPHONE CO INC p 1233
1515 Ave Fd Roosevelt 00968
Tel (787) 781-1314 *SIC* 8748

■ SANTANDER BANCORP p 1281
B7 Calle Tabonuco Fl 18 00968
Tel (787) 777-4100 *SIC* 6021 6411 6211

■ TRIPLE-S ADVANTAGE INC p 1482
1 Calle 1 Fl 3 00968
Tel (787) 620-1919 *SIC* 6321

UNIVERSAL GROUP INC p 1517
Calle 1 Lote 10 Metro Ofc St Cal 00968
Tel (787) 793-7202 *SIC* 6411

■ WALGREEN OF SAN PATRICIO INC p 1572
580 Marginal Buchanan 00966
Tel (787) 795-4200 *SIC* 5912

GURABO, PR

CONSOLIDATED WASTE SERVICES CORP p 360
Km 9 Rr 189 00778
Tel (787) 273-7649 *SIC* 4212

HATO REY, PR

AUTORIDAD PARA EL FINANCIAMIENTO DE LA VIVIENDA p 135
Ave Barbosa 606pisos St Ave Barbo 00917
Tel (787) 765-7577 *SIC* 7389

HUMACAO, PR

■ EC WASTE LLC p 475
Int 923 Km 1/7 Rr 3 00791
Tel (787) 852-4444 *SIC* 4953

■ SEAMLESS TEXTILES LLC p 1297
Km 86 3 Rr 3 00791
Tel (787) 850-3440 *SIC* 5137

JUANA DIAZ, PR

■ OCULAR SCIENCES PUERTO RICO INC p 1074
500 Carr 584 00795
Tel (787) 260-0555 *SIC* 3851

JUNCOS, PR

■ AMGEN MANUFACTURING LIMITED p 85
6 Carr 31 Km 00777
Tel (787) 656-2000 *SIC* 2836

MEDTECH PUERTO RICO INC p 939
Parque Industrial Carr Ca Que Industrial 00777
Tel (787) 561-2200 *SIC* 3841

LAS PIEDRAS, PR

RALPHS FOOD WAREHOUSE INC p 1206
Carr 183 Industrial Park 00771
Tel (787) 733-0959 *SIC* 5411 5149

MANATI, PR

DORADO HEALTH INC p 451
Carrion Hernandez St Urb 00674
Tel (787) 621-3700 *SIC* 8011

PATHEON PUERTO RICO INC p 1120
State Rd 670 Km 2/7 # 27 00674
Tel (787) 746-8500 *SIC* 2834

MAYAGUEZ, PR

MR SPECIAL SUPERMARKETS INC p 996
620 Ave Sta Tresa Journet 00682
Tel (787) 834-2695 *SIC* 5411

MUNICIPIO DE MAYAGUEZ p 1000
Betances St Crnr Mckinley Corner Mckinley 00680
Tel (787) 834-8585 *SIC* 9111

SAMUEL VAZQUEZ p 1275
108 Calle Mendez Vigo E 00680
Tel (787) 598-6107 *SIC* 5699

MERCEDITA, PR

DESTILERIA SERRALLES INC p 432
Calle Central 1 00715
Tel (787) 840-1000 *SIC* 2085 2084 5141

■ **ZIMMER CARIBE INC** p 1643
Road 1 Km 123 Hm 4 Bldg 1 00715
Tel (787) 259-5959 *SIC* 3842

PONCE, PR

ER EQUIPMENT INC p 507
Calle Sur Num 10 Mariani St Calle Sur N 00730
Tel (787) 841-2743 *SIC* 3531

HOSPITAL DAMAS INC p 709
2213 Ponce Byp 00717
Tel (787) 840-8686 *SIC* 8062

MEDTRONIC p 939
201 Sabanetas Ind Pk 00716
Tel (787) 844-4526 *SIC* 3841

METROPADIA HEALTH SYSTEM INC p 955
2445 Las America Ave 00731
Tel (787) 848-5600 *SIC* 8062

MUNICIPIO DE PONCE p 1000
Calle Comercio Frente 00731
Tel (787) 284-4141 *SIC* 9111

NATIONAL BUILDING MAINTENANCE CORP p 1010
855 Ave Hostos 00716
Tel (787) 290-7020 *SIC* 7349 5169

PONTIFICAL CATHOLIC UNIVERSITY OF PUERTO RICO p 1161
2250 Blvd Luis Ferre 00717
Tel (787) 841-2000 *SIC* 8221

■ **POPULAR FINANCE INC** p 1161
326 Salud St El El Senorial Cond 00716
Tel (787) 844-2760 *SIC* 6141

RIO GRANDE, PR

RIO MAR RESORT- WHG HOTEL PROPERTY LLC p 1236
6000 Rio Mar Blvd 00745
Tel (787) 888-6000 *SIC* 7011

RIO PIEDRAS, PR

■ **AT&T MOBILITY PUERTO RICO INC** p 123
996 Calle San Roberto 00926
Tel (787) 717-9600 *SIC* 4813 4812

CORPORACION DEL FONDO DEL SEGURO DEL ESTADO p 372
Urb La Riviera Se 1024 00921
Tel (787) 793-5959 *SIC* 9441

SAN JUAN, PR

ADMINISTRACION DE FAMILIAS Y NINOS p 23
Ave Ponce De Leon Stp2 00907
Tel (787) 625-4900 *SIC* 9431

ADMINISTRACION DE SERVICIOS MEDICOS DE PR p 23
Intersection Monacillos W 00921
Tel (787) 777-3535 *SIC* 8741

AUTORIDAD DE ACUEDUCTOS Y ALCANTARILLADOS DE PR p 135
604 Ave Barbosa 00917
Tel (787) 620-2482 *SIC* 9511

AUTORIDAD DE CARRETERAS p 135
Calle De Diego C 00923
Tel (787) 723-1390 *SIC* 9621

AUTORIDAD METROPOLITANA DE AUTOBUSES p 135
Bo Monacillos 37 Ave De D 37th 00919
Tel (787) 767-7979 *SIC* 4111

AUXILIO MUTUO HOSPITAL p 135
735 Ave Ponce De Leon 00917
Tel (787) 761-6600 *SIC* 8011 8062

■ **BANCO POPULAR DE PUERTO RICO (INC)** p 150
Popular Ctr 00918
Tel (787) 765-9800 *SIC* 6022 6159 6141

■ **BANCO SANTANDER-PUERTO RICO INC** p 150
207 Ave Ponce De Leon 00917
Tel (787) 274-7200 *SIC* 6022

BELLA INTERNATIONAL CORP p 170
Ave Kennedy Sector Bechar 00921
Tel (787) 620-7010 *SIC* 5511

BERMUDEZ LONGO DIAZ-MASSO LLC p 175
Km 0 5 Cupey Rr 845 00926
Tel (787) 761-3030 *SIC* 1731 1711

BETTEROADS ASPHALT CORP p 178
Edif Empresas Diaz 00926
Tel (787) 760-1050 *SIC* 1611 2951

CAPITOL SECURITY POLICE INC p 251
703 Calle Victor Lopez 00909
Tel (787) 727-1700 *SIC* 7381

CARIBBEAN TEMPORARY SERVICES INC p 256
1431 Ave Ponce De Leon 00907
Tel (787) 724-5643 *SIC* 7363

COMMONWEALTH OF PUERTO RICO p 346
63 Calle De La Fortaleza 00901
Tel (787) 721-7000 *SIC* 9111

COOPERATIVA DE SEGUROS MULTIPLES DE PUERTO RICO p 367
Expreso Ls America Y Mira 00927
Tel (787) 758-8585 *SIC* 6331 6351

DEPARTMENT OF EDUCATION OF PUERTO RICO p 430
150 Calle Federico Costa 00918
Tel (787) 759-2000 *SIC* 9411

DEPARTMENT OF FAMILY p 430
Sevilla Plz Bldg Se 00919
Tel (787) 643-1855 *SIC* 9441 8331

DORAL HOLDINGS DELAWARE LLC p 451
1451 Frnklin D Rsvelt Ave 00920
Tel (787) 474-6700
SIC 6162 6035 6211 6411

EUROBANCSHARES INC p 512
State Rd Pr 1 Km 24 5 00926
Tel (787) 751-7340 *SIC* 6022

▲ **EVERTEC INC** p 515
Km 1/3 Rr 176 00926
Tel (787) 759-9999
SIC 8741 8748 7379 8721

EXECUTIVE OFFICE OF COMMONWEALTH OF PUERTO RICO p 517
San Jose St Crn San 00901
Tel (787) 722-2121 *SIC* 9111

FAMOSA NORTH AMERICA INC p 527
1357 Ashford Ave Se 00907
Tel (206) 316-8315 *SIC* 5092

▲ **FIRST BANCORP** p 545
130 Mnoz Rvera Ave Fl 2 00908
Tel (787) 729-8200 *SIC* 6022 6411

HOSPITAL ESPANOL AUXILIO MUTUO DE PUERTO RICO INC p 709
Ave Ponce De Leon 00918
Tel (787) 758-2000 *SIC* 6324

K I INVESTMENTS INC p 799
Ave 65 De Infntria St1179 00924
Tel (787) 622-0600 *SIC* 6519 5012 5511

KRESS STORES OF PUERTO RICO INC p 829
598 Calle A 00920
Tel (787) 783-5374 *SIC* 7389 8741

LIBERTY CABLEVISION OF PUERTO RICO LLC p 861
Urb Indl Tres Monjitas 1 00918
Tel (787) 766-0909 *SIC* 4841

LIBERTY CABLEVISION OF PUERTO RICO LLC p 861
Urb Industrial Tres Monj 00919
Tel (787) 657-3050 *SIC* 4841

MANAGEMENT SSS INC p 900
Roosevlt Av 145a Fl 3 00918
Tel (787) 758-7700 *SIC* 8742

MANAGEMENT TEMPORARY & CONTRACT EMPLOYMENT SERVICES INC p 900
145 A Roosevelt Ave 00919
Tel (787) 758-7700 *SIC* 8742

MAPFRE PRAICO CORP p 903
297 Ave Chardon Urb Tres 00918
Tel (787) 250-6500 *SIC* 6411

MEDICAL CARD SYSTEM INC p 936
Mcs Plaza 255 Ponce St Mcs Pla 00917
Tel (787) 758-2500 *SIC* 6411

MEDICARE MUCHO MAS HOLDINGS INC p 937
Torrechardon 350 Av Chard 350th Avenue 00918
Tel (787) 622-3000 *SIC* 6324

MMM HEALTHCARE LLC p 979
350 Ave Carlos Chardon # 500 00918
Tel (787) 622-3000 *SIC* 6324

■ **MONDELEZ PUERTO RICO LLC** p 984
9615 Ave Los Romeros # 801 00926
Tel (787) 522-9810 *SIC* 5141

MUNICIPIO DE SAN JUAN p 1000
1306 Ave Fernandez Juncos 00909
Tel (787) 724-7171 *SIC* 9111

MUNICIPIO DE SAN JUAN p 1000
1205 Ave Ponce De Leon 00907
Tel (787) 289-0310 *SIC* 9611

NORTHWESTERN SELECTA INC p 1061
796 Calle C M Julia Indst 00920
Tel (787) 781-1950 *SIC* 5147 5146 5142

▲ **OFG BANCORP** p 1076
254 Ave Munoz Rivera Fl 8 00918
Tel (787) 771-6800 *SIC* 6022

■ **ORIENTAL BANK** p 1094
254 Ave Munoz Rivera 00918
Tel (787) 771-6800
SIC 6035 7359 7515 6733

▲ **POPULAR INC** p 1161
209 Munoz Rivera 00918
Tel (787) 765-9800 *SIC* 6022

PR RETAIL STORES INC p 1167
Edif Kodak Ave Campo 00924
Tel (787) 641-8200
SIC 5311 5712 5722 5331

PUBLIC BUILDING AUTHORITY p 1189
Cond Centro Plz 00909
Tel (787) 722-0101 *SIC* 8611

PUERTO RICO DEPARTMENT OF LABOR AND HUMAN RESOURCES p 1191
505 Ave Munoz Rivera 00918
Tel (787) 754-2119 *SIC* 9199

PUERTO RICO DEPARTMENT OF TREASURY p 1191
10 Paseo Covadonga 00901
Tel (787) 721-2020 *SIC* 9311

PUERTO RICO ELECTRIC POWER AUTHORITY p 1191
1110 Ave Ponce De Leon 00907
Tel (787) 289-3434 *SIC* 4911

PUERTO RICO FIREFIGHTERS CORPS p 1191
2432 Calle Loiza 00913
Tel (787) 725-3444 *SIC* 9224

PUERTO RICO PORTS AUTHORITY p 1191
Lindbergh St 64antigu 00907
Tel (787) 723-2260 *SIC* 9621

RANGER AMERICAN OF PUERTO RICO INC p 1208
605 Calle Lodi 00924
Tel (787) 999-6060 *SIC* 1731 7382 7381

■ **RICO FIRSTBANK PUERTO** p 1233
1519 Ave Ponce De Leon 00909
Tel (787) 729-8200 *SIC* 6022

RICO SOL PUERTO LIMITED p 1233
450 Ave De La Const 18c 00901
Tel (787) 721-0150 *SIC* 5171

SCOTIABANK DE PUERTO RICO p 1293
290 Ave Jesus T Pinero 00918
Tel (787) 766-4999 *SIC* 6022

■ **SEARS ROEBUCK DE PUERTO RICO INC** p 1297
383 Ave Fd Roosevelt # 105 00918
Tel (787) 773-7000 *SIC* 5311

SISTEMA UNIVERSITARIO ANA G MENDEZ INC p 1327
Carr 176 Km 0 3 Cpey Lowr St Ca 00928
Tel (787) 751-0178 *SIC* 8221 4833

SOCIEDAD ESPAOLA DE AUXILIO MUTUO Y BENEFICENCIA DE PUERTO RICO p 1336
Ponce De Leon Ave 00917
Tel (787) 758-2000 *SIC* 8062

SPECIAL CARE PHARMACY SERVICES INC p 1355
1221 Ave Americo Miranda 00921
Tel (787) 783-8579 *SIC* 5912 8082

ST JAMES SECURITY SERVICES INC p 1367
1604 Ave Ponce De Leon 00909
Tel (787) 754-8448 *SIC* 7381

SUIZA DAIRY CORP p 1397
131 De Diego Ave 00921
Tel (787) 792-7300 *SIC* 2026 2037

SUPREME COURT OF COMMONWEALTH OF PUERTO RICO p 1408
286 Munoz Rrivera Ave We Western 00919
Tel (787) 641-6600 *SIC* 9211

TELECOMUNICACIONES DE PUERTO RICO INC p 1434
1515 Ave Fd Roosevelt 14 Flr 14 00920
Tel (787) 782-8282 *SIC* 4813

TRAFON GROUP INC p 1469
Mercado Cntl 1229 Crr 28 St Mercado Centr 00920
Tel (787) 783-0011 *SIC* 5142

■ **TRIPLE - S SALUD INC** p 1482
1441 Ave Fd Roosevelt 00920
Tel (787) 749-4949 *SIC* 6321

▲ **TRIPLE-S MANAGEMENT CORP** p 1482
1441 Ave Fd Roosevelt 00920
Tel (787) 749-4949 *SIC* 6324 6311 6321

UNIVERSIDAD INTERAMERICANA DE PUERTO RICO INC p 1518
399 Calle Galileo 00927
Tel (787) 766-1912 *SIC* 8221

UNIVERSITY OF PUERTO RICO p 1524
Jardin Botanico Sur 1187 00926
Tel (787) 250-0000 *SIC* 8221

■ **VIDA TRIPLE-S INC** p 1556
1052 Ave Munoz Rivera 00927
Tel (800) 980-7651 *SIC* 6311

WENDCO OF PUERTO RICO INC p 1591
1155 Ave Ponce De Leon 00907
Tel (787) 792-2001 *SIC* 5812

TOA BAJA, PR

AMERICAN PETROLEUM CO INC p 77
Km 0 Hm 2 Cam Rr 865 00949
Tel (787) 794-1985 *SIC* 5172

BEST PETROLEUM CORP p 177
Km 20 Hm 5 Rr 2 00951
Tel (787) 251-6218 *SIC* 5172

HOLSUM DE PUERTO RICO INC p 702
Carr 2 Km 20 1 Bo Cndlria St Ca 00949
Tel (787) 798-8282 *SIC* 2051

PEPSI-COLA PUERTO RICO DISTRIBUTING LLC p 1134
Carr 865 Km 0 4 Barrio Ca St Ca 00949
Tel (787) 251-2000 *SIC* 2086

TRUJILLO ALTO, PR

IGLESIA EPISCOPAL PUERTORRIQUENA INC p 730
Carr 848 Km 1 1 Bo Sait J St Ca 00978
Tel (787) 761-9800 *SIC* 8661

VEGA BAJA, PR

■ **HARVEY HUBBELL CARIBE INC** p 667
Km 17 Hm 3 Rr 686 00693
Tel (787) 855-1075 *SIC* 3643

MATOSANTOS COMMERCIAL CORP p 920
Parque Industrial Ca 00693
Tel (787) 793-6900 *SIC* 5141 5113 5087

VILLALBA, PR

MEDTRONIC PUERTO RICO INC p 939
3 Carr 149 Km 00766
Tel (787) 847-3500 *SIC* 3841

YAUCO, PR

SARTORIUS STEDIM FILTERS INC p 1282
Intersection 376 Rr 128 00698
Tel (787) 856-5020 *SIC* 3569

RHODE ISLAND

ASHAWAY, RI

TE CONNECTIVITY SEACON PHOENIX INC p 1429
15 Gray Ln Ste 108 02804
Tel (401) 637-4952 *SIC* 3229

BARRINGTON, RI

ROCKWELL FUNDING LLC p 1245
310 Maple Ave Ste L04 02806
Tel (401) 466-4755 *SIC* 6153

BRISTOL, RI

ROGER WILLIAMS UNIVERSITY p 1246
1 Old Ferry Rd 02809
Tel (401) 253-1040 *SIC* 8221

COVENTRY, RI

RHODES PHARMACEUTICALS LP p 1232
498 Washington St 02816
Tel (401) 262-9200 *SIC* 2834

CRANSTON, RI

AIM SPECIALTY MATERIALS USA p 38
25 Kenney Dr 02920
Tel (401) 463-5605 *SIC* 3291

ALEX AND ANI LLC p 48
2000 Chapel View Blvd # 360 02920
Tel (401) 633-1486 *SIC* 3915 5944

ALLIANCE SECURITY INC p 55
85 Garfield Ave 02920
Tel (877) 746-2559 *SIC* 7382

CRANSTON PRINT WORKS CO INC p 389
1381 Cranston St 02920
Tel (401) 943-4800 *SIC* 2261 2262 2899

CRANSTON PUBLIC SCHOOLS p 389
845 Park Ave 02910
Tel (401) 270-8000 *SIC* 8211

DEPARTMENT OF BEHAVIORAL HEALTHCARE DEVELOPMENTAL DISABILITIES AND HOSPITALS p 429
14 Harrington Rd 02920
Tel (401) 462-3201 *SIC* 9431

EAST COAST DISTRIBUTORS INC p 470
1705 Broad St 02905
Tel (401) 780-8800 *SIC* 5147

GATEWAY WOODSIDE INC p 594
100 Midway Rd Ste 14 02920
Tel (401) 942-2800 *SIC* 6512

LUXURY BRAND HOLDINGS INC p 887
9 Ross Simons Dr 02920
Tel (401) 463-3100 *SIC* 5944

NORTH SAFETY PRODUCTS LLC p 1053
2000 Plainfield Pike 02921
Tel (401) 943-4400 *SIC* 3842

RHODE ISLAND AND PROVIDENCE PLANTATIONS DEPARTMENT OF CORRECTIONS p 1231
40 Howard Ave 02920
Tel (401) 462-2611 *SIC* 9223

RHODE ISLAND DEPT OF HUMAN SERVICES p 1231
57 Howard Ave Fl 2 02920
Tel (401) 462-1000 *SIC* 9441

SWAROVSKI NORTH AMERICA LIMITED p 1411
1 Kenney Dr 02920
Tel (401) 463-6400 *SIC* 3961 5023 3231

SWAROVSKI US HOLDING LIMITED p 1411
1 Kenney Dr 02920
Tel (401) 463-6400
SIC 3961 3231 5048 5099

TACO INC p 1421
1160 Cranston St 02920
Tel (401) 942-8000
SIC 3433 3561 3443 3822

TECHNIC INC p 1431
47 Molter St 02910
Tel (401) 781-6100 *SIC* 2899 3559

THIELSCH ENGINEERING INC p 1448
195 Frances Ave 02910
Tel (401) 785-0241
SIC 5084 5043 5172 5085

CUMBERLAND, RI

INMUSIC BRANDS INC p 744
200 Scenic View Dr 02864
Tel (401) 658-3131 SIC 5736

ION AUDIO LLC p 762
200 Scenic View Dr 02864
Tel (401) 658-3743 SIC 5999

JH LYNCH & SONS INC p 785
50 Lynch Pl 02864
Tel (401) 333-4300 SIC 1611 2951

NFA CORP p 1041
50 Martin St 02864
Tel (617) 232-6060 SIC 5012 2241

NUMARK INDUSTRIES LP p 1067
200 Scenic View Dr 02864
Tel (401) 658-3131 SIC 5736

EAST GREENWICH, RI

CORVIAS GROUP LLC p 373
1405 S County Trl 02818
Tel (401) 228-2800 SIC 7389

CORVIAS MILITARY LIVING LLC p 373
1405 S County Trl Ste 510 02818
Tel (401) 228-2800 SIC 1522

■ STANLEY FASTENING SYSTEMS LP p 1377
2 Briggs Dr 02818
Tel (401) 884-2500 SIC 3399 3579

EAST PROVIDENCE, RI

CITY OF EAST PROVIDENCE p 314
145 Taunton Ave 02914
Tel (401) 435-7521 SIC 9111

■ NORDSON EFD LLC p 1048
40 Catamore Blvd 02914
Tel (401) 434-1680 SIC 3548 3586 3699

EXETER, RI

CAROUSEL INDUSTRIES OF NORTH AMERICA INC p 260
659 South County Trl 02822
Tel (401) 667-5400 SIC 7389

JOHNSTON, RI

AFFILIATED FM INSURANCE CO p 32
270 Central Ave 02919
Tel (401) 275-3000 SIC 6512 6331

FACTORY MUTUAL INSURANCE CO p 524
270 Central Ave 02919
Tel (401) 275-3000 SIC 6331 8711 6512

KINGSTON, RI

UNIVERSITY OF RHODE ISLAND p 1524
75 Lower College Rd Ste 0 02881
Tel (401) 874-1000 SIC 8221

LINCOLN, RI

ACS INDUSTRIES INC p 19
1 New England Way Unit 1 02865
Tel (401) 769-4700
SIC 3291 3496 3312 3315 3569 3991

AMICA MUTUAL INSURANCE CO p 85
100 Amica Way 02865
Tel (800) 992-6422 SIC 6331

■ CAREMARK PHC LLC p 255
695 George Washington Hwy 02865
Tel (401) 334-0069 SIC 8011 5912

FORTUNE METAL INC OF RHODE ISLAND p 570
2 Crow Point Rd 02865
Tel (661) 387-1100 SIC 5093

■ MATERION TECHNICAL MATERIALS INC p 919
5 Wellington Rd 02865
Tel (401) 333-1700 SIC 3331 3339 3423

UTGR INC p 1536
100 Twin River Rd 02865
Tel (401) 723-3200 SIC 7011

MIDDLETOWN, RI

BANKNEWPORT p 152
184 John Clarke Rd 02842
Tel (401) 846-3400 SIC 6035

EMBRACE HOME LOANS INC p 490
25 Enterprise Ctr 02842
Tel (401) 846-3100 SIC 6162

▲ KVH INDUSTRIES INC p 832
50 Enterprise Ctr 02842
Tel (401) 847-3327 SIC 3663 3812

NEWPORT, RI

■ CDMI LLC p 271
130 Bellevue Ave Unit 201 02840
Tel (401) 619-5210 SIC 6324

NEWPORT HEALTH CARE CORP p 1038
11 Friendship St 02840
Tel (401) 846-6400 SIC 8062 6531 6732

NEWPORT HOSPITAL p 1038
11 Friendship St Ste 1 02840
Tel (401) 846-6400 SIC 8062

PANGAEA LOGISTICS SOLUTIONS LTD p 1111
109 Long Wharf 02840
Tel (401) 846-7790 SIC 4412

NORTH KINGSTOWN, RI

A & M SPECIAL PURCHASING INC p 4
375 Commerce Park Rd 02852
Tel (401) 295-2672 SIC 8721

ALL AMERICAN FOODS INC p 51
1 All American Way 02852
Tel (401) 294-5455 SIC 5147 5146 5142

AMWINS GROUP BENEFITS INC p 87
50 Whitecap Dr 02852
Tel (877) 739-3330 SIC 6311 6321

DDH INC p 419
211 Circuit Dr 02852
Tel (401) 667-0800 SIC 5047

FUJIFILM ELECTRONIC MATERIALS USA INC p 583
80 Circuit Dr 02852
Tel (401) 522-9499 SIC 5043 5065

HEXAGON METROLOGY INC p 688
250 Circuit Dr 02852
Tel (401) 886-2000 SIC 3823 3545

OCEAN STATE JOBBERS INC p 1073
375 Commerce Park Rd 02852
Tel (401) 295-2672 SIC 5331 5199

SENESCO MARINE LLC p 1303
10 Macnaught St 02852
Tel (401) 295-0373 SIC 3731

TORAY PLASTICS (AMERICA) INC p 1461
50 Belver Ave 02852
Tel (401) 667-2426 SIC 3081

NORTH PROVIDENCE, RI

FATIMA GIFT SHOP p 531
200 High Service Ave 02904
Tel (401) 456-3448 SIC 5947

PROSPECT CHARTERCARE SJHSRI LLC p 1184
200 High Service Ave 02904
Tel (401) 456-3000 SIC 8062

PAWTUCKET, RI

COOLEY GROUP HOLDINGS INC p 366
50 Esten Ave 02860
Tel (401) 724-0510 SIC 5211 3069

COOLEY INC p 366
50 Esten Ave 02860
Tel (401) 724-9000 SIC 2295 3069 2262

▲ HASBRO INC p 667
1027 Newport Ave 02861
Tel (401) 431-8697 SIC 3944 3942 3069

■ HASBRO INTERNATIONAL INC p 667
1027 Newport Ave 02861
Tel (401) 431-8697 SIC 3944

■ HASBRO MANAGERIAL SERVICES INC p 667
1027 Newport Ave 02861
Tel (401) 431-8697 SIC 8741

INTERNATIONAL PACKAGING CORP p 756
517 Mineral Spring Ave 02860
Tel (401) 724-1600 SIC 3499 3089

MATLET GROUP LLC p 920
60 Delta Dr 02860
Tel (401) 834-3007 SIC 2759

MEMORIAL HOSPITAL p 942
111 Brewster St 02860
Tel (401) 729-2000 SIC 8062 6513

■ NEPTCO INC p 1026
30 Hamlet St 02861
Tel (401) 722-5500 SIC 3496 3083 2672

PAWTUCKET SCHOOL DEPARTMENT p 1122
286 Main St 02860
Tel (401) 729-6300 SIC 8211 9411

PET FOOD EXPERTS INC p 1137
175 Main St 02860
Tel (401) 721-5593 SIC 5199 2047

SOUTHEASTERN HEALTHCARE SYSTEM INC p 1346
111 Brewster St 02860
Tel (401) 729-2000 SIC 8748

TEKNOR APEX CO p 1433
505 Central Ave 02861
Tel (401) 725-8000
SIC 3087 3069 3052 2869 3081 2821

PORTSMOUTH, RI

TALARIA CO LLC p 1422
1 Lil Hrbr Landing Prt 02871
Tel (401) 683-7100 SIC 3732

PROVIDENCE, RI

AAA NORTHEAST p 7
110 Royal Little Dr 02904
Tel (401) 868-2000 SIC 8699 6411 4724

BLUE CROSS & BLUE SHIELD OF RHODE ISLAND p 191
500 Exchange St 02903
Tel (401) 459-1000 SIC 6324

BROWN UNIVERSITY IN PROVIDENCE IN STATE OF RHODE ISLAND AND PROVIDENCE PLANTATIONS p 220
1 Prospect St 02912
Tel (401) 863-1000 SIC 8221

CARE NEW ENGLAND HEALTH SYSTEM INC p 254
45 Willard Ave 02905
Tel (401) 453-7900
SIC 8063 8062 8069 8093 8082

■ CITIZENS BANK NATIONAL ASSOCIATION p 310
1 Citizens Plz Ste 1 02903
Tel (401) 282-7000 SIC 6021

▲ CITIZENS FINANCIAL GROUP INC p 311
1 Citizens Plz Ste 1 02903
Tel (401) 456-7000 SIC 6022

CITY OF PROVIDENCE p 317
25 Dorrance St Unit 1 02903
Tel (401) 421-7740 SIC 9111

DELTA DENTAL OF RHODE ISLAND p 426
10 Charles St Ste 100 02904
Tel (401) 752-6246 SIC 6324 8021

DIMEO CONSTRUCTION CO p 440
75 Chapman St 02905
Tel (401) 781-9800 SIC 1542 1522 7353

■ DRYVIT HOLDINGS INC p 457
1 Energy Way 02903
Tel (401) 822-4100 SIC 2822 2899

EXECUTIVE OFFICE OF STATE OF RHODE ISLAND p 518
82 Smith St Ste 217 02903
Tel (401) 574-8423 SIC 9111

GILBANE BUILDING CO p 611
7 Jackson Walkway Ste 2 02903
Tel (401) 456-5800 SIC 1542

GILBANE INC p 611
7 Jackson Walkway 02903
Tel (401) 456-5800
SIC 1541 1542 8741 6513 6512

GREATER PROVIDENCE YOUNG MENS CHRISTIAN ASSOCIATION p 636
371 Pine St 02903
Tel (401) 521-9622
SIC 8641 7991 8351 7032 8322

GTECH HOLDINGS CORP p 644
10 Memorial Blvd Ste 101 02903
Tel (401) 392-1000 SIC 7999 7371

IGT GLOBAL SOLUTIONS CORP p 730
10 Memorial Blvd 02903
Tel (401) 392-1000
SIC 7999 3575 7372 7378 2752 7374

JOHNSON & WALES UNIVERSITY INC p 790
8 Abbott Park Pl 02903
Tel (401) 598-1000 SIC 7011

LIFESPAN CORP p 864
167 Point St Ste 2b 02903
Tel (401) 444-3500 SIC 8011

LIN TV CORP p 866
1 W Exchange St Ste 305 02903
Tel (401) 454-2880 SIC 4833 7311

MAHR FEDERAL INC p 897
1144 Eddy St 02905
Tel (401) 784-3100 SIC 5084

MARS 2000 INC p 910
40 Agnes St 02909
Tel (401) 421-5275 SIC 3089

MIRIAM HOSPITAL p 974
164 Summit Ave 02906
Tel (401) 793-2500 SIC 8062

NARRAGANSETT ELECTRIC CO p 1007
280 Melrose St 02907
Tel (401) 784-7000 SIC 4911

NAUTIC PARTNERS LLC p 1019
100 Westminster St # 1220 02903
Tel (401) 278-6770 SIC 6799 7629

NEIGHBORHOOD HEALTH PLAN OF RHODE ISLAND p 1024
299 Promenade St 02908
Tel (401) 459-6000 SIC 6411

NORTEK INC p 1049
500 Exchange St 02903
Tel (401) 751-1600
SIC 3585 3444 3634 3699 2434

PROSPECT CHARTERCARE LLC p 1184
825 Chalkstone Ave 02908
Tel (401) 456-2001 SIC 8082

PROVIDENCE COLLEGE p 1185
1 Cunningham Sq 02918
Tel (401) 865-1000 SIC 8221

PROVIDENCE EQUITY PARTNERS INC p 1185
100 Westminster St # 1800 02903
Tel (401) 751-1700 SIC 6211

PROVIDENCE PUBLIC SCHOOLS p 1186
797 Westminster St 02903
Tel (401) 456-9100 SIC 8211 8742

RHODE ISLAND HOSPITAL p 1231
593 Eddy St 02903
Tel (401) 444-4000 SIC 8062

RHODE ISLAND HOSPITAL EMR p 1232
1 Hoppin St Ste 106 02903
Tel (401) 444-6237 SIC 8062

RHODE ISLAND SCHOOL OF DESIGN INC p 1232
2 College St 02903
Tel (401) 454-6100 SIC 8221

ROGER WILLIAMS MEDICAL CENTER p 1246
825 Chalkstone Ave 02908
Tel (401) 456-2000 SIC 8062

ROGER WILLIAMS MEDICAL CENTER p 1246
825 Chalkstone Ave 02908
Tel (401) 456-2000 SIC 8062

ROMAN CATHOLIC BISHOP OF PROVIDENCE (INC) p 1248
1 Cathedral Sq 02903
Tel (401) 278-4616 SIC 8661

SRA COMPANIES INC p 1362
50 Kennedy Plz 18 02903
Tel (401) 277-1000 SIC 6211

STATE OF RHODE ISLAND p 1382
114 Enfield Ave 02908
Tel (401) 351-8448 SIC 7389

STATE OF RHODE ISLAND AND PROVIDENCE PLANTATIONS p 1382
82 Smith St Ste 102 02903
Tel (401) 222-2080 SIC 9111

STATE OF RHODE ISLAND DEPARTMENT OF ADMINISTRATION p 1382
1 Capitol Hl Ste 1 02908
Tel (401) 222-2280 SIC 9199

▲ TEXTRON INC p 1445
40 Westminster St 02903
Tel (401) 421-2800
SIC 3721 3724 3728 3799 3829 3546

■ TEXTRON LYCOMING CORP p 1445
40 Westminster St 02903
Tel (401) 421-2800 SIC 3728 3724

▲ UNITED NATURAL FOODS INC p 1510
313 Iron Horse Way 02908
Tel (401) 528-8634 SIC 5149 5122 5142

■ WARREN EQUITIES INC p 1577
27 Warren Way 02905
Tel (401) 781-9900 SIC 5172 5541 5411

WOMEN & INFANTS HOSPITAL OF RHODE ISLAND p 1621
101 Dudley St 02905
Tel (401) 274-1100 SIC 8062

RUMFORD, RI

■ REAL REEL CORP p 1214
50 Taylor Dr 02916
Tel (401) 438-4240 SIC 2631 2655 2621

SMITHFIELD, RI

BENNYS INC p 173
340 Waterman Ave 02917
Tel (401) 231-0965 SIC 5531

BRYANT UNIVERSITY p 221
1150 Douglas Pike 02917
Tel (401) 232-6000 SIC 8221

FGX INTERNATIONAL HOLDINGS LIMITED p 539
500 Washington Hwy 02917
Tel (401) 231-3800 SIC 5099 3851

FGX INTERNATIONAL INC p 539
500 George Washington Hwy 02917
Tel (401) 231-3800 SIC 5099 3851

NORCROSS SAFETY PRODUCTS LLC p 1047
900 Douglas Pike Ste 100 02917
Tel (800) 430-5490 SIC 3842 3021 3469

■ SPERIAN PROTECTION USA INC p 1358
900 Douglas Pike 02917
Tel (401) 232-1200
SIC 3851 3842 2311 7218 5999

WAKEFIELD, RI

SOUTH COUNTY HOSPITAL HEALTHCARE SYSTEM p 1344
100 Kenyon Ave 02879
Tel (401) 782-8000 SIC 8062

SOUTH COUNTY HOSPITAL HEALTHCARE SYSTEM ENDOWMENT AND AFFILIATES p 1344
100 Kenyon Ave 02879
Tel (401) 782-8000 SIC 8062

WARWICK, RI

■ A J OSTER LLC p 5
457 Warwick Industrial Dr 02886
Tel (401) 736-2600 SIC 5051

ATRION INC p 129
125 Metro Center Blvd 02886
Tel (401) 736-6400 SIC 7373 5065

ATW COMPANIES INC p 130
125 Metro Center Blvd # 3001 02886
Tel (401) 244-1002 SIC 3674 3498

BEACON MUTUAL INSURANCE CO p 165
1 Beacon Ctr Ste 100 02886
Tel (401) 825-2667 SIC 6331

KENNEY MANUFACTURING CO p 811
1000 Jefferson Blvd 02886
Tel (401) 739-2200
SIC 2591 3261 2511 3699 3499 2541

KENT COUNTY MEMORIAL HOSPITAL p 812
455 Toll Gate Rd 02886
Tel (401) 737-7000 SIC 8062

■ METROPOLITAN GROUP PROPERTIES & CASUALTY p 956
700 Quaker Ln 02886
Tel (401) 827-2400 SIC 6331 6351

■ METROPOLITAN PROPERTY AND CASUALTY INSURANCE CO p 956
700 Quaker Ln 02886
Tel (401) 827-2400 SIC 6411

PICERNE INVESTMENT CORP p 1146
75 Lambert Lind Hwy # 300 02886
Tel (401) 732-3700
SIC 6552 6531 1521 1522 1542

PLAN INTERNATIONAL INC p 1154
155 Plan Way Ste A 02886
Tel (401) 294-3693 SIC 8399

PLAN INTERNATIONAL USA INC p 1154
155 Plan Way Ste A 02886
Tel (401) 562-8400 SIC 8322

■ **SPRAGUE VISHAY INC** p 1360
111 Gilbane St 02886
Tel (401) 738-9150 SIC 3629

TRADESOURCE INC p 1469
205 Hallene Rd Unit 211 02886
Tel (401) 384-6148
SIC 7361 1751 1711 1731 1742 1721

■ **UNITEDHEALTHCARE OF NEW ENGLAND INC** p 1515
475 Kilvert St Ste 310 02886
Tel (401) 737-6900 SIC 6324

WARWICK PUBLIC SCHOOLS p 1577
34 Warwick Lake Ave 02889
Tel (401) 734-3000 SIC 8211

WEST GREENWICH, RI

J A M T LEYDEN ENTERPRISES INC p 770
179 Plain Meeting Hse Rd 02817
Tel (401) 258-9246 SIC 0811

WEST KINGSTON, RI

SCHNEIDER ELECTRIC IT CORP p 1287
132 Fairgrounds Rd 02892
Tel (401) 789-5735
SIC 3629 3612 3677 3585 7372 2542

SCHNEIDER ELECTRIC IT USA INC p 1288
132 Fairgrounds Rd 02892
Tel (401) 789-5735 SIC 3679

WEST WARWICK, RI

AMTROL HOLDINGS INC p 87
1400 Division Rd 02893
Tel (401) 884-6300 SIC 3822 3585 3443

AMTROL INC p 87
1400 Division Rd 02893
Tel (401) 884-6300 SIC 3443 3585

ARPIN GROUP INC p 112
99 James P Murphy Ind Hwy 02893
Tel (401) 828-8111 SIC 4213

▲ **ASTRONOVA INC** p 123
600 E Greenwich Ave 02893
Tel (401) 828-4000 SIC 3577 3829

BRADFORD SOAP INTERNATIONAL INC p 206
200 Providence St 02893
Tel (401) 821-2141 SIC 2841

■ **DRYVIT SYSTEMS INC** p 457
1 Energy Way 02893
Tel (401) 822-4100 SIC 2899

NATCO PRODUCTS CORP p 1009
155 Brookside Ave 02893
Tel (401) 828-0300 SIC 3996 2273 5023

ORIGINAL BRADFORD SOAP WORKS INC p 1094
200 Providence St 02893
Tel (401) 821-2141 SIC 2841

WESTERLY, RI

MOORE CO p 987
36 Beach St 02891
Tel (401) 596-2816
SIC 2258 2241 3069 3061 2821

▲ **WASHINGTON TRUST BANCORP INC** p 1579
23 Broad St Fl 1 02891
Tel (401) 348-1200 SIC 6022

■ **WASHINGTON TRUST CO OF WESTERLY** p 1579
23 Broad St Fl 1 02891
Tel (401) 348-1200 SIC 6022

WOONSOCKET, RI

■ **ARBOR DRUGS INC** p 103
1 Cvs Dr 02895
Tel (401) 765-1500 SIC 5912

ARC OF NORTHERN RHODE ISLAND INC p 103
80 Siaban St 1 Sox Ri 02895
Tel (401) 765-3700 SIC 8331 8361

CITY OF WOONSOCKET p 319
169 Main St 02895
Tel (401) 762-6400 SIC 9111

■ **CVS CAREMARK PART D SERVICES LLC** p 404
1 Cvs Dr 02895
Tel (401) 770-3317 SIC 6411

■ **CVS CENTER INC** p 404
1 Cvs Dr 02895
Tel (401) 765-1500 SIC 5912

▲ **CVS HEALTH CORP** p 404
1 Cvs Dr 02895
Tel (401) 765-1500 SIC 5912 5961 8099

■ **CVS OF DC AND VA INC** p 404
1 Cvs Dr 02895
Tel (401) 765-1500 SIC 5912

■ **CVS OF VIRGINIA INC** p 404
1 Cvs Dr 02895
Tel (401) 765-1500 SIC 5912

■ **CVS PHARMACY INC** p 404
1 Cvs Dr 02895
Tel (401) 765-1500 SIC 5912 5122

■ **CVS REVCO DS INC** p 404
1 Cvs Dr 02895
Tel (401) 765-1500 SIC 5912

■ **CVS VA DISTRIBUTION INC** p 404
1 Cvs Dr 02895
Tel (401) 765-1500 SIC 5122

LANDMARK MEDICAL CENTER p 843
115 Cass Ave 02895
Tel (401) 769-4100 SIC 8062

■ **LONGS DRUG STORES CALIFORNIA INC** p 877
1 Cvs Dr 02895
Tel (925) 937-1170 SIC 5912

■ **LONGS DRUG STORES CORP** p 877
1 Cvs Dr 02895
Tel (401) 770-1830 SIC 5912 5961

■ **MINUTECLINIC DIAGNOSTIC MEDICAL GROUP OF SAN DIEGO INC** p 974
1 Cvs Dr 02895
Tel (401) 765-1500 SIC 5912

■ **NASHUA HOLLIS CVS INC** p 1008
1 Cvs Dr 02895
Tel (401) 765-1500 SIC 5912

■ **PHARMACARE HOLDING CORP** p 1141
1 Cvs Dr 02895
Tel (401) 765-1500 SIC 5912

PRIME HEALTHCARE SERVICES-LANDMARK LLC p 1175
115 Cass Ave 02895
Tel (401) 769-4100 SIC 8062

■ **REVCO DISCOUNT DRUG CENTERS INC** p 1229
1 Cvs Dr 02895
Tel (401) 765-1500 SIC 5912

■ **RHODE CVS ISLAND INC** p 1231
1 Cvs Dr 02895
Tel (401) 765-1500 SIC 5912

■ **STEVEN MARK SERVICE MERCHANDISERS INC** p 1388
1 Cvs Dr 02895
Tel (401) 765-1500 SIC 7389

▲ **SUMMER INFANT INC** p 1398
1275 Park East Dr 02895
Tel (401) 671-6550
SIC 2514 2399 3842 3261

WOONSOCKET CITY SCHOOL DISTRICT p 1624
108 High St 02895
Tel (401) 767-4600 SIC 8211

SOUTH CAROLINA

ABBEVILLE, SC

FLEXIBLE TECHNOLOGIES INC p 556
528 Carwellyn Rd 29620
Tel (864) 366-5441 SIC 3052 3089

AIKEN, SC

AGY HOLDING CORP p 36
2556 Wagener Rd 29801
Tel (888) 434-0945 SIC 2221

AIKEN COUNTY SCHOOL DISTRICT p 38
1000 Brookhaven Dr 29803
Tel (803) 641-2428 SIC 8211

AIKEN ELECTRIC COOPERATIVE INC p 38
2790 Wagener Rd 29801
Tel (803) 649-6245 SIC 4911 4841

■ **AIKEN REGIONAL MEDICAL CENTERS LLC** p 38
302 University Pkwy 29801
Tel (803) 641-5000 SIC 8062

CB&I AREVA MOX SERVICES LLC p 268
Savannah River Site 29801
Tel (803) 819-2000 SIC 8741

FENIX MANUFACTURING SOLUTIONS LLC p 537
2063 University Pkwy 29801
Tel (803) 649-1381
SIC 3694 3825 3625 3354

SAVANNAH RIVER NUCLEAR SOLUTIONS LLC p 1284
203 Laurens St Sw Frnt 29801
Tel (803) 643-4570 SIC 8731

■ **SAVANNAH RIVER REMEDIATION LLC** p 1284
Savannah River Site 29808
Tel (803) 952-9630 SIC 4953

■ **WASHINGTON GOVERNMENT ENVIRONMENTAL SERVICES CO LLC** p 1578
106 Newberry St Sw 29801
Tel (803) 502-5710 SIC 1622

■ **WASHINGTON SAVANNAH RIVER CO LLC** p 1579
Savannah River Site Rd 1 29808
Tel (803) 725-6211 SIC 4959

ANDERSON, SC

ANDERSON COUNTY SCHOOL DISTRICT FIVE INC p 89
400 Pearman Dairy Rd 29625
Tel (864) 260-5000 SIC 8211

ANMED HEALTH p 92
800 Nh Fant St 29621
Tel (864) 261-1000 SIC 8062 8011

ANMED HEALTH RESOURCES INC p 92
800 N Fant St 29621
Tel (864) 512-1000 SIC 8062

ASSOCIATED FUEL PUMP SYSTEMS CORP p 120
1100 Scotts Bridge Rd 29621
Tel (864) 224-0012 SIC 3714 3561

BROOKSIDE LIVING CENTER LLC p 218
208 James St 29625
Tel (864) 226-3427 SIC 8051

▲ **HAMPSHIRE GROUP LIMITED** p 656
1924 Pearman Dairy Rd A 29625
Tel (212) 540-5666 SIC 2339 2329 2253

HOMELITE CONSUMER PRODUCTS INC p 703
1428 Pearman Dairy Rd 29625
Tel (864) 226-6511 SIC 5083

■ **JPS COMPOSITE MATERIALS CORP** p 795
2200 S Murray Ave 29624
Tel (864) 836-8011 SIC 3231

■ **JPS INDUSTRIES INC** p 795
2200 S Murray Ave 29624
Tel (864) 239-3900 SIC 2221 3081

ONE WORLD TECHNOLOGIES INC p 1086
1428 Pearman Dairy Rd 29625
Tel (864) 226-6511 SIC 5251

PLASTIC OMNIUM INDUSTRIES INC p 1155
5100 Old Pearman Dairy Rd 29625
Tel (864) 260-0000 SIC 3089

BALLENTINE, SC

LEXINGTON SCHOOL DISTRICT 5 p 859
1020 Dutchfork Rd 29002
Tel (803) 732-8011 SIC 8211

BAMBERG, SC

BRABHAM OIL CO INC p 206
525 Midway St 29003
Tel (803) 245-2471
SIC 5171 5541 5411 5921

BARNWELL, SC

BARNWELL COUNTY NURSING HOME p 156
31 Wren St 29812
Tel (803) 259-5547 SIC 8051 8052

BATESBURG, SC

AMICK FARMS LLC p 85
2079 Batesburg Hwy 29006
Tel (803) 532-1400 SIC 0751

BEAUFORT, SC

BEAUFORT COUNTY MEMORIAL HOSPITAL p 166
955 Ribaut Rd 29902
Tel (843) 522-5200 SIC 8062

BEAUFORT COUNTY SCHOOL DISTRICT p 166
2900 Mink Point Blvd 29902
Tel (843) 322-2300 SIC 8211

COUNTY OF BEAUFORT p 376
100 Ribaut Rd 29902
Tel (843) 255-7151 SIC 9111

BENNETTSVILLE, SC

■ **MARLEY ENGINEERED PRODUCTS LLC** p 909
470 Beauty Spot Rd E 29512
Tel (843) 479-4006 SIC 3634

BLACKVILLE, SC

AUGUSTA FIBERGLASS COATINGS INC p 131
86 Lake Cynthia Dr 29817
Tel (803) 284-2246 SIC 3089

BLUFFTON, SC

CARECORE NATIONAL LLC p 254
400 Buckwalter Place Blvd 29910
Tel (800) 918-8924 SIC 8011

BLYTHEWOOD, SC

PURE POWER TECHNOLOGIES INC p 1192
1410 Northpoint Blvd 29016
Tel (803) 744-7020 SIC 3363

SOUTH CAROLINA DEPARTMENT OF MOTOR VEHICLES p 1343
10311 Wilson Blvd 29016
Tel (803) 896-5000 SIC 9621

SOUTH CAROLINA DEPARTMENT OF PUBLIC SAFETY p 1343
10311 Wilson Blvd 29016
Tel (803) 896-9000 SIC 9229

CAMDEN, SC

HENGST OF NORTH AMERICA INC p 683
29 Hengst Blvd 29020
Tel (803) 432-5992 SIC 3714

HENGST USA INC p 683
29 Hengst Blvd 29020
Tel (803) 432-5992 SIC 3714

KERSHAW COUNTY SCHOOL DISTRICT p 813
2029 W Dekalb St 29020
Tel (803) 432-8416 SIC 8211

KERSHAW HEALTH MEDICAL CENTER p 813
1315 Roberts St 29020
Tel (803) 432-4311 SIC 8062 8051 8082

CASSATT, SC

PRESTAGE FARMS OF SOUTH CAROLINA LIMITED LIABILITY CO p 1173
1889 Highway 1 N 29032
Tel (803) 432-6396 SIC 5144 0253

CATAWBA, SC

RESOLUTE FP US INC p 1227
5300 Cureton Ferry Rd 29704
Tel (803) 981-8000
SIC 2621 2672 2611 2421

CAYCE, SC

▲ **SCANA CORP** p 1286
100 Scana Pkwy 29033
Tel (803) 217-9000
SIC 4931 4911 4924 4922

■ **SCANA SERVICES INC** p 1286
220 Operation Way 29033
Tel (803) 217-9000 SIC 8741

■ **SOUTH CAROLINA ELECTRIC & GAS CO** p 1343
100 Scana Pkwy 29033
Tel (803) 217-9000
SIC 4931 4911 4922 4924

SOUTH CAROLINA FARM BUREAU MUTUAL INSURANCE CO (INC) p 1343
724 Knox Abbott Dr 29033
Tel (803) 796-6700 SIC 6331

CHAPIN, SC

ELLETT BROTHERS LLC p 488
267 Columbia Ave 29036
Tel (803) 345-3751
SIC 5091 3949 2499 2541

UNITED SPORTING COMPANIES INC p 1512
267 Columbia Ave 29036
Tel (803) 345-3751 SIC 5091

CHARLESTON, SC

BEACH CO p 164
211 King St Ste 300 29401
Tel (843) 722-2615 SIC 6552 8741 1542

CARE ALLIANCE HEALTH INC p 254
2095 Henry Tecklenburg Dr 29414
Tel (843) 402-1000 SIC 8062

CAREALLIANCE HEALTH SERVICES p 254
316 Calhoun St 29401
Tel (843) 724-2000 SIC 8741

CAROLINA EASTERN INC p 259
1820 Savannah Hwy Ste G1 29407
Tel (843) 571-0411 SIC 5261 5191

CENTRAARCHY RESTAURANT MANAGEMENT CO p 277
236 Albemarle Rd 29407
Tel (843) 571-0096 SIC 5812

CHARLESTON COUNTY SCHOOL DISTRICT DEVELOPMENT CORP p 290
75 Calhoun St 29401
Tel (843) 937-6300 SIC 8211

CITY OF CHARLESTON p 313
116 Meeting St 29401
Tel (843) 795-7543 SIC 9111

COLLEGE OF CHARLESTON p 336
66 George St 29424
Tel (843) 953-5570 SIC 8221

COMMISSIONERS OF PUBLIC WORKS p 345
103 Saint Philip St 29403
Tel (843) 727-6800 SIC 4941

CORDILLERA COMMUNICATIONS LLC p 369
134 Columbus St 29403
Tel (843) 577-7111 SIC 2711 3663

COUNTY OF CHARLESTON p 377
4045 Bridge View Dr 29405
Tel (843) 958-4000 SIC 9111

EPI GROUP LLC p 505
134 Columbus St 29403
Tel (843) 577-7111 SIC 2711

GILDAN USA INC p 612
1980 Clements Ferry Rd 29492
Tel (843) 849-6191 SIC 2252 2254

GREYSTAR REAL ESTATE PARTNERS LLC p 639
18 Broad St Ste 300 29401
Tel (843) 579-9400 SIC 6531

HAGEMEYER PPS LTD p 652
1460 Tobias Gadson Blvd 29407
Tel (843) 745-2400 SIC 5063

MAHLE BEHR CHARLESTON INC p 897
4500 Leeds Ave Ste 101 29405
Tel (843) 745-1233 SIC 3714

MEDICAL UNIVERSITY HOSPITAL AUTHORITY p 937
169 Ashley Ave 29425
Tel (843) 792-1414 SIC 8062

MEDICAL UNIVERSITY OF SOUTH CAROLINA p 937
171 Ashley Ave 29425
Tel (843) 792-2123 SIC 8062 8221 8069

MVP GROUP INTERNATIONAL INC p 1003
1031 Legrand Blvd 29492
Tel (843) 216-8380 SIC 3999 5122

OSHAUGHNESSY REALTY CO INC p 1096
4024 Salt Pointe Pkwy 29405
Tel (843) 202-2016 SIC 6531

PIGGLY WIGGLY CAROLINA CO INC p 1147
176 Croghan Spur Ste 400 29407
Tel (843) 554-9880
SIC 7311 5411 5148 5141 2752 1542

QUEST SPECIALTY CHEMICALS INC p 1199
225 Sven Farms Dr Ste 204 29492
Tel (800) 966-7580 *SIC* 2851

RO HO HO INC p 1240
1479 Tobias Gadson Blvd 29407
Tel (877) 547-7272 *SIC* 5812

ROPER HOSPITAL INC p 1250
316 Calhoun St 29401
Tel (843) 724-2000 *SIC* 8062

ROPER ST FRANCIS PHYSICIANS NETWORK p 1250
125 Doughty St Ste 760 29403
Tel (843) 724-2903 *SIC* 8011

SHERMAN FINANCIAL GROUP LLC p 1316
200 Meeting St Ste 206 29401
Tel (212) 922-1616 *SIC* 6153 6726

SOUTH CAROLINA STATE PORTS AUTHORITY p 1343
176 Concord St 29401
Tel (843) 723-8651 *SIC* 4491 8111 2721

■ **TRIDENT MEDICAL CENTER LLC** p 1479
9330 Medical Plaza Dr 29406
Tel (843) 797-7000 *SIC* 8062 8011

VALLEN DISTRIBUTION INC p 1540
1460 Tobias Gadson Blvd 29407
Tel (843) 745-2400 *SIC* 5085

WHIT-MART INC p 1605
56 Wentworth St 29401
Tel (843) 720-5010 *SIC* 5812

CHERAW, SC

CAROLINA CANNERS INC p 259
300 Highway 1 S 29520
Tel (843) 537-5281 *SIC* 2086

CLEMSON, SC

CALHOUN MANAGEMENT CORP p 238
108f Elm St 29631
Tel (864) 624-9962 *SIC* 5812

CLEMSON UNIVERSITY p 325
201 Sikes Ave 29631
Tel (864) 656-6182 *SIC* 8221

CLINTON, SC

LANDAU APARTMENTS LIMITED PARTNERSHIP p 842
1321 S Broad St 29325
Tel (864) 833-3215 *SIC* 6513

RELATED CLINTON MANOR LLC p 1221
100 Clinton St 29325
Tel (864) 833-3836 *SIC* 6531 6513

CLOVER, SC

WDS INC p 1585
1632 Village Harbor Dr 29710
Tel (803) 619-0301 *SIC* 5085 1541 8742

COLUMBIA, SC

ADJUTANT GENERAL SOUTH CAROLINA p 23
1 National Guard Rd 29201
Tel (803) 299-4308 *SIC* 9711

ADVANTAGE HEALTH SYSTEMS INC p 26
106 Doctor Cir Ste A 29203
Tel (803) 376-4190 *SIC* 8099

AGFIRST FARM CREDIT BANK p 34
1901 Main St 29201
Tel (803) 799-5000 *SIC* 6111

BLUE CROSS BLUE SHIELD OF SOUTH CAROLINA p 192
I-20 Alpine Rd 29219
Tel (803) 788-3860 *SIC* 6321

BONITZ CONTRACTING CO INC p 200
645 Rosewood Dr 29201
Tel (803) 799-0181
SIC 1742 1752 1761 1542 1541

BONITZ INC p 200
645 Rosewood Dr 29201
Tel (803) 799-0181
SIC 3448 1542 1742 1541 1761 1752

BRUCE SEIBELS & CO p 220
1501 Lady St 29201
Tel (803) 748-2000 *SIC* 6411

BRUCE SEIBELS GROUP INC p 220
1501 Lady St 29201
Tel (803) 748-2000 *SIC* 6331 6321 6311

CAROLINA INTERNATIONAL TRUCKS INC p 259
1619 Bluff Rd 29201
Tel (803) 799-4923 *SIC* 5511

CENTRAL ELECTRIC POWER COOPERATIVE INC p 278
20 Cooperative Way 29210
Tel (803) 779-4975 *SIC* 4911

CITY OF COLUMBIA p 314
1737 Main St 29201
Tel (803) 545-3075 *SIC* 9111

CLIMATIC CORP p 326
1074 Pinnacle Point Dr 29223
Tel (803) 765-2595 *SIC* 5075

■ **COLONIAL LIFE & ACCIDENT INSURANCE CO INC** p 337
1200 Colonial Life Blvd W 29210
Tel (803) 798-7000 *SIC* 6321 6311

CONSOLIDATED SYSTEMS INC p 360
650 Rosewood Dr 29201
Tel (803) 771-7920 *SIC* 3444 3479 4213

■ **CONTINENTAL AMERICAN INSURANCE CO** p 362
1600 Williams St 29201
Tel (803) 256-6265 *SIC* 6411

COUNTY OF RICHLAND p 381
2020 Hampton St 29204
Tel (803) 576-2600 *SIC* 9111

DICK SMITH AUTOMOTIVE GROUP INC p 438
9940 Two Notch Rd 29223
Tel (800) 944-8570 *SIC* 5511 7515

DYER INC p 464
240 Killian Commons Pkwy 29203
Tel (803) 691-5602 *SIC* 5511 7532

EDENS & AVANT INC p 477
1221 Main St Ste 1000 29201
Tel (803) 779-4420 *SIC* 6798

EXECUTIVE OFFICE OF STATE OF SOUTH CAROLINA p 518
Wade Hampton Bldg Fl 6 29211
Tel (803) 734-2320 *SIC* 9111

FASTCO THREADED PRODUCTS INC p 531
539 Clemson Rd 29229
Tel (803) 788-1000 *SIC* 5085

FIRST CITIZENS BANK AND TRUST CO INC p 545
1230 Main St 29201
Tel (803) 733-2020 *SIC* 6022

GATEWAY SUPPLY CO INC p 594
1312 Hamrick St 29201
Tel (803) 771-7160 *SIC* 5075 5074

HEALTH SCIENCES SOUTH CAROLINA p 675
1320 Main St Ste 625 29201
Tel (803) 544-4772 *SIC* 8731

■ **HUBBELL POWER SYSTEMS INC** p 716
200 Center Point Cir # 200 29210
Tel (803) 216-2600 *SIC* 3643

INTERSTATE MANAGEMENT & INVESTMENT CORP p 758
1 Surrey Ct 29212
Tel (803) 772-2629 *SIC* 7011

JOHNSON FOOD SERVICES LLC p 791
Forney Smter St Bldg 3290 29207
Tel (803) 782-1461 *SIC* 5812

M B KAHN CONSTRUCTION CO INC p 889
101 Flintlake Rd 29223
Tel (803) 736-2950 *SIC* 1542 8742

MASHBURN CONSTRUCTION CO INC p 915
1820 Sumter St 29201
Tel (803) 400-1000 *SIC* 1542

MIDLANDS TECHNICAL COLLEGE FOUNDATION p 966
316 Beltline Blvd 29205
Tel (803) 738-8324 *SIC* 8222 8221

NELSON MULLINS RILEY & SCARBOROUGH LLP p 1025
1320 Main St Ste 1700 29201
Tel (803) 799-2000 *SIC* 8111

OWEN STEEL CO INC p 1100
727 Mauney Dr 29201
Tel (803) 251-7680 *SIC* 3441

PALMETTO GBA LLC p 1109
17 Technology Cir 29203
Tel (803) 735-1034 *SIC* 6324

PALMETTO HEALTH p 1109
1301 Taylor St Ste 8a 29201
Tel (803) 296-2100 *SIC* 8062

PALMETTO HEALTH ALLIANCE INC p 1109
293 Greystone Blvd 29210
Tel (803) 296-5220 *SIC* 8062

PALMETTO-RICHLAND MEMORIAL HOSPITAL p 1109
5 Richland Medical Pk Dr 29203
Tel (803) 434-3460 *SIC* 8062

PGBA LLC p 1140
I-20 Alpine Rd 29219
Tel (803) 788-3860 *SIC* 8322

PLANNED ADMINISTRATORS INC p 1154
17 Technology Cir E2ag 29203
Tel (803) 462-0151 *SIC* 6411

PROVIDENCE HOSPITAL FOUNDATION p 1186
2601 Laurel St 29204
Tel (803) 256-5300 *SIC* 7389

■ **PROVIDENCE HOSPITAL LLC** p 1186
2435 Forest Dr 29204
Tel (803) 256-5300 *SIC* 8062

■ **PURE FISHING INC** p 1192
7 Science Ct 29203
Tel (803) 754-7000 *SIC* 3949

QUILL.COM p 1200
300 Arbor Lake Dr # 1200 29223
Tel (803) 333-8300 *SIC* 7363

RICHLAND COUNTY SCHOOL DISTRICT 1 p 1233
1616 Richland St 29201
Tel (803) 231-7000 *SIC* 8211

RICHLAND SCHOOL DISTRICT TWO FOUNDATION p 1233
6831 Brookfield Rd 29206
Tel (803) 787-1910 *SIC* 8211

■ **SAFETY-KLEEN (TULSA) INC** p 1266
1301 Gervais St Ste 300 29201
Tel (800) 669-5740 *SIC* 4953

SC PUBLIC CHARTER SCHOOL DISTRICT p 1285
3700 Forest Dr Ste 406 29204
Tel (803) 734-8322 *SIC* 8211

SC STATE BOARD FOR TECHNICAL AND COMPREHENSIVE EDUCATION p 1285
111 Executive Center Dr # 1 29210
Tel (803) 896-5280 *SIC* 9411

■ **SHAKESPEARE CO LLC** p 1310
6111 Shakespeare Rd 29223
Tel (803) 754-7011
SIC 3089 3949 3679 3663

SOCIAL SERVICES SOUTH CAROLINA DEPARTMENT p 1336
1535 Confederate Ave 29201
Tel (803) 898-7601 *SIC* 9441

SOUTH CAROLINA DEPARTMENT OF COMMERCE p 1343
1201 Main St Ste 1600 29201
Tel (803) 737-0400 *SIC* 9611

SOUTH CAROLINA DEPARTMENT OF CORRECTIONS (INC) p 1343
4444 Broad River Rd 29210
Tel (803) 896-8500 *SIC* 9223

SOUTH CAROLINA DEPARTMENT OF DISABILITIES AND SPECIAL NEEDS p 1343
3440 Harden Street Ext 29203
Tel (803) 898-9600 *SIC* 9431

SOUTH CAROLINA DEPARTMENT OF EDUCATION p 1343
1429 Senate St 29201
Tel (803) 734-8500 *SIC* 9411

SOUTH CAROLINA DEPARTMENT OF EMPLOYMENT AND WORKFORCE p 1343
1550 Gadsden St 29201
Tel (803) 737-2400 *SIC* 9441

SOUTH CAROLINA DEPARTMENT OF HEALTH AND ENVIRONMENTAL CONTROL p 1343
2600 Bull St 29201
Tel (803) 898-3510 *SIC* 9431

SOUTH CAROLINA DEPARTMENT OF LAW ENFORCEMENT p 1343
4400 Broad River Rd 29210
Tel (803) 737-9000 *SIC* 9221

SOUTH CAROLINA DEPARTMENT OF MENTAL HEALTH p 1343
2414 Bull St 29201
Tel (803) 898-8581 *SIC* 9431

SOUTH CAROLINA DEPARTMENT OF TRANSPORTATION p 1343
955 Park St 29201
Tel (803) 737-1243 *SIC* 9621

SOUTH CAROLINA PUBLIC CHARTER SCHOOL DISTRICT p 1343
3710 Landmark Dr Ste 203 29204
Tel (803) 734-8322 *SIC* 8211

SOUTH CAROLINA RESEARCH AUTHORITY INC p 1343
1000 Catawba St Ste 100 29201
Tel (803) 799-4070 *SIC* 8733

SOUTH CAROLINA STUDENT LOAN CORP p 1343
8906 Two Notch Rd 29223
Tel (803) 798-0916 *SIC* 6111

SOUTH CAROLINA TELECOMMUNICATIONS GROUP HOLDING LLC p 1343
1500 Hampton St Ste 100 29201
Tel (803) 726-7000 *SIC* 4813

■ **SOUTH STATE BANK** p 1345
520 Gervais St Ste 310 29201
Tel (803) 771-2265 *SIC* 6022

▲ **SOUTH STATE CORP** p 1345
520 Gervais St Ste 310 29201
Tel (800) 277-2175 *SIC* 6712 6022

STATE OF SOUTH CAROLINA p 1382
1205 Pendleton St 29201
Tel (803) 734-2100 *SIC* 9111

SUSSEX INSURANCE CO p 1409
221 Dawson Rd 29223
Tel (803) 735-0672 *SIC* 6331

■ **SYSCO COLUMBIA LLC** p 1417
131 Sysco Ct 29209
Tel (803) 239-4000
SIC 5141 5046 5142 5147 5148

TERMINIX SERVICE INC p 1439
3618 Fernandina Rd 29210
Tel (803) 772-1783 *SIC* 7342

TIMBERLAKE & HITE CO INC p 1454
209 Flintlake Rd 29223
Tel (803) 276-0510 *SIC* 5141

TRAILBLAZER HEALTH ENTERPRISES LLC p 1469
I-20 At Alpine Road 29219
Tel (803) 788-4138 *SIC* 6324

U S C EDUCATIONAL FOUNDATION p 1497
1600 Hampton St Ste 814 29208
Tel (803) 777-1466 *SIC* 8221

UCI MEDICAL AFFILIATES INC p 1499
1818 Henderson St 29201
Tel (843) 782-4278 *SIC* 8093 8741

UNIVERSITY OF SOUTH CAROLINA p 1525
1400 Wheat St 29208
Tel (803) 777-2001 *SIC* 8221

UTI INTEGRATED LOGISTICS LLC p 1536
700 Gervais St Ste 100 29201
Tel (803) 771-6785 *SIC* 4226 4213

VENDORS SUPPLY INC p 1547
201 Saluda River Rd 29210
Tel (803) 772-6390 *SIC* 5141

WILBUR SMITH ASSOCIATES GROUP INC p 1608
1301 Gervais St Ste 1600 29201
Tel (803) 758-4500 *SIC* 8711

WILBUR SMITH ASSOCIATES INC p 1608
1301 Gervais St Ste 1600 29201
Tel (803) 758-4500 *SIC* 8711

CONWAY, SC

■ **BUILDERS FIRSTSOURCE- SOUTHEAST GROUP LLC** p 225
2451 E Highway 501 29526
Tel (843) 347-4224 *SIC* 5211 2431

COASTAL CAROLINA UNIVERSITY p 331
103 Tom Trout Dr 29526
Tel (843) 347-3161 *SIC* 8221

COASTAL CAROLINA UNIVERSITY p 331
642 Century Cir 29526
Tel (843) 347-3161 *SIC* 8221

CONWAY HOSPITAL AUXILIARY p 365
300 Singleton Ridge Rd 29526
Tel (843) 347-7111 *SIC* 8062

CONWAY HOSPITAL INC p 365
300 Singleton Ridge Rd 29526
Tel (843) 347-7111 *SIC* 8062

COUNTY OF HORRY p 378
1301 2nd Ave 29526
Tel (843) 915-5000 *SIC* 9111

GRAND STRAND WATER & SEWER AUTHORITY p 630
166 Jackson Bluff Rd 29526
Tel (843) 443-8200 *SIC* 4941 4952

HORRY COUNTY SCHOOL DISTRICT p 708
335 Four Mile Rd 29526
Tel (843) 488-6700 *SIC* 8211

HORRY TELEPHONE COOPERATIVE INC p 708
3480 Highway 701 N 29526
Tel (843) 365-2151 *SIC* 4813 4841 7382

PALMETTO CORP OF CONWAY p 1109
3873 Highway 701 N 29526
Tel (843) 365-2156 *SIC* 2951

PROFESSIONAL PLUMBING GROUP INC p 1180
2951 E Highway 501 29526
Tel (415) 124-5678 *SIC* 3432

WOLVERINE BRASS INC p 1621
2951 E Highway 501 29526
Tel (843) 347-3121 *SIC* 5074 3432 3431

DANIEL ISLAND, SC

▲ **BENEFITFOCUS INC** p 173
100 Benefitfocus Way 29492
Tel (843) 849-7476 *SIC* 7372

▲ **BLACKBAUD INC** p 187
2000 Daniel Island Dr 29492
Tel (843) 216-6200 *SIC* 7372 8748

■ **CIGNA HEALTHCARE OF SOUTH CAROLINA INC** p 306
146 Fairchild St Ste 100 29492
Tel (800) 949-0325 *SIC* 6324

DARLINGTON, SC

DARLINGTON COUNTY SCHOOL DISTRICT p 412
120 E Smith Ave 29532
Tel (843) 398-5100 *SIC* 8211

DARLINGTON VENEER CO INC p 412
225 4th St 29532
Tel (843) 393-3861 *SIC* 2426

DEE PEE ELECTRIC COOPERATIVE INC p 421
1355 E Mciver Rd 29532
Tel (843) 665-4070 *SIC* 4911 8611

DIAMOND HILL PLYWOOD CO INC p 436
600 E Broad St 29532
Tel (843) 393-4036 *SIC* 5031

DILLON, SC

SAINT EUGENE MEDICAL CENTER p 1269
301 E Jackson St 29536
Tel (843) 774-4111 *SIC* 8062

DUNCAN, SC

AFL NETWORK SERVICES INC p 33
170 Ridgeview Cnt Dr 29334
Tel (864) 433-0333 *SIC* 8711

AFL TELECOMMUNICATIONS LLC p 33
170 Ridgeview Center Dr 29334
Tel (864) 433-0333 *SIC* 3229 1731

AMERICA FUJIKURA LTD p 67
170 Ridgeview Cir 29334
Tel (864) 433-8281 *SIC* 3661

DAA DRAEXLMAIER AUTOMOTIVE OF AMERICA LLC p 407
1751 E Main St 29334
Tel (864) 433-8910 SIC 3714

ENGINEERED SYSTEMS INC p 499
1121 Duncan Reidville Rd 29334
Tel (864) 879-7438 SIC 5084

MORGAN CORP p 988
1800 E Main St 29334
Tel (864) 433-8800 SIC 1629

ROCHLING AUTOMOTIVE USA LLP p 1243
245 Parkway E 29334
Tel (864) 486-0888 SIC 3089

SPARTANBURG REGIONAL HEALTHCARE SYSTEM p 1355
411 Woodsberry Shoals Dr 29334
Tel (864) 560-1406 SIC 7389

TIRE CENTERS LLC p 1455
310 Inglesby Pkwy 29334
Tel (864) 329-2700 SIC 5014 5531 7534

WABCO PASSENGER TRANSPORTATION DIVISION p 1570
130 Ridgeview Center Dr 29334
Tel (864) 433-5900 SIC 3799

■ **WASTE CONNECTIONS US INC** p 1580
1010 Rogers Bridge Rd 29334
Tel (832) 801-1436 SIC 4953

EARLY BRANCH, SC

LE CREUSET OF AMERICA INC p 849
114 Bob Gifford Blvd 29916
Tel (803) 943-4308 SIC 5023

EASLEY, SC

ALICE MANUFACTURING CO INC p 50
208 E 1st Ave 29640
Tel (864) 859-6323 SIC 2211 2221

BAPTIST EASLEY HOSPITAL p 153
200 Fleetwood Dr 29640
Tel (864) 442-7200 SIC 8062

CONTRACT ENVIRONMENTAL SERVICES INC p 364
636 Powdersville Rd 29642
Tel (864) 306-7785 SIC 8748

HMR ADVANTAGE HEALTH SYSTEMS INC p 698
101 Grace Dr 29640
Tel (864) 269-3725 SIC 8741

SCHOOL DISTRICT OF PICKENS COUNTY p 1289
1348 Griffin Mill Rd 29640
Tel (864) 397-1000 SIC 8211

EFFINGHAM, SC

MCCALL FARMS INC p 926
6615 S Irby St 29541
Tel (843) 662-2223 SIC 2033

FLORENCE, SC

DILMAR OIL CO INC p 440
1951 W Darlington St 29501
Tel (843) 662-4179 SIC 5172 2819

FLORENCE SCHOOL DISTRICT ONE p 557
319 S Dargan St 29506
Tel (843) 669-4141 SIC 8211

MCLEOD HEALTH p 931
555 E Cheves St 29506
Tel (843) 777-2256 SIC 8099

MCLEOD HEALTH SERVICES INC p 931
555 E Cheves St 29506
Tel (843) 777-5146 SIC 8062

MCLEOD PHYSICIAN ASSOCIATES INC p 931
555 E Cheves St 29506
Tel (843) 777-7000 SIC 8011

MCLEOD REGIONAL MEDICAL CENTER OF PEE DEE INC p 931
555 E Cheves St 29506
Tel (843) 777-2000 SIC 8062

■ **QHG OF SOUTH CAROLINA INC** p 1195
805 Pamplico Hwy 29505
Tel (843) 674-5000 SIC 8062

YAHNIS CO p 1633
1440 N Schlitz Dr 29501
Tel (843) 662-6627 SIC 5181

FORT MILL, SC

AME INC p 66
2467 Coltharp Rd 29715
Tel (803) 548-7766 SIC 1541 7353 3443

ASHTEAD HOLDINGS LLC p 117
2341 Deerfield Dr 29715
Tel (803) 578-5811 SIC 7353 7359 5082

CARAUSTAR INDUSTRIAL AND CONSUMER PRODUCTS GROUP INC p 252
2031 Carolina Place Dr 29708
Tel (803) 548-5100 SIC 2655 2671 2679

CONTAINER CO OF CAROLINA p 362
3358 Highway 51 29715
Tel (704) 377-0161 SIC 4953

CONTINENTAL AUTOMOTIVE INC p 362
1830 Macmillan Park Dr 29707
Tel (704) 583-3900 SIC 3011 8711

CONTINENTAL TIRE AMERICAS LLC p 364
1830 Macmillan Park Dr 29707
Tel (800) 450-3187 SIC 3011

CONTINENTAL TIRE HOLDING US LLC p 364
1830 Macmillan Park Dr 29707
Tel (704) 588-5895 SIC 3011

DOMTAR INDUSTRIES LLC p 449
100 Kingsley Park Dr 29715
Tel (803) 802-7500 SIC 2621 5111

DOMTAR PAPER CO LLC p 449
100 Kingsley Park Dr 29715
Tel (803) 802-7500 SIC 2421 2621

FENNER ADVANCED SEALING TECHNOLOGIES INC p 537
975 Market St Ste 201a 29708
Tel (803) 547-8434 SIC 3061

FLAKEBOARD AMERICA LIMITED p 554
515 Rivercrossing Dr 29715
Tel (877) 273-7680 SIC 2493

FORT MILL SCHOOL DISTRICT 4 p 569
2233 Deerfield Dr 29715
Tel (803) 548-2527 SIC 8211

GREAT ATLANTIC NEWS LLC p 633
1962 Highway 160 W # 102 29708
Tel (803) 802-8630 SIC 5192

MACLEAN POWER LLC p 892
481 Munn Rd E Ste 300 29715
Tel (847) 455-0014 SIC 3493

MUZAK LLC p 1003
3318 Lakemont Blvd 29708
Tel (803) 396-3000 SIC 7389 6794

PTERIS GLOBAL (USA) INC p 1189
208 Shoreline Pkwy 29708
Tel (980) 253-3267 SIC 3535

RED VENTURES LLC p 1216
1101 Red Ventures Dr 29707
Tel (704) 971-2300 SIC 8742

SCHAEFFLER GROUP USA INC p 1286
308 Springhill Farm Rd 29715
Tel (803) 548-8500 SIC 3562

SOI HOLDINGS INC p 1337
3023 Hsbc Way Ste 100 29707
Tel (704) 523-2191 SIC 7361

SPRINGS GLOBAL US INC p 1361
205 N White St 29715
Tel (803) 547-1500 SIC 2299 5023

SUNBELT RENTALS INC p 1401
2341 Deerfield Dr 29715
Tel (803) 578-5811 SIC 7359 7353

SUNBELT RENTALS INDUSTRIAL SERVICES LLC p 1401
2341 Deerfield Dr 29715
Tel (803) 578-5811 SIC 7359

WIKOFF COLOR CORP p 1608
1886 Merritt Rd 29715
Tel (803) 548-2210 SIC 2893 2851

FOUNTAIN INN, SC

■ **AVX CORP** p 139
1 Avx Blvd 29644
Tel (864) 967-2150 SIC 3675 5065 3678

DELTA WOODSIDE INDUSTRIES INC p 427
700 N Woods Dr 29644
Tel (864) 255-4100 SIC 2221

FAURECIA INTERIOR SYSTEMS INC p 531
101 International Blvd 29644
Tel (864) 862-1900 SIC 5013

GAFFNEY, SC

CHEROKEE COUNTY SCHOOL DISTRICT 1 p 294
141 Twin Lake Rd 29341
Tel (864) 902-3500 SIC 8211

FREIGHTLINER CUSTOM CHASSIS CORP p 577
552 Hyatt St 29341
Tel (864) 487-1700 SIC 3711

HAMRICK MILLS INC p 656
515 W Buford St 29341
Tel (864) 489-4731 SIC 2211 2299

HAMRICKS INC p 656
742 Peachoid Rd 29341
Tel (864) 489-6095
SIC 5651 2337 2331 2335 2339 5087

GASTON, SC

G&P TRUCKING CO INC p 587
126 Access Rd 29053
Tel (803) 791-5500 SIC 4213

PALMETTO INDUSTRIAL CONSTRUCTION CO INC p 1109
831 Old Wire Rd 29053
Tel (803) 739-0381 SIC 1541

GEORGETOWN, SC

3V SIGMA USA INC p 3
888 Woodstock St 29440
Tel (843) 546-8556 SIC 2869 2899 8731

GEORGETOWN COUNTY SCHOOL DISTRICT p 606
2018 Church St 29440
Tel (843) 436-7000 SIC 8211

GEORGETOWN HEALTHCARE & REHAB INC p 606
2715 South Island Rd 29440
Tel (843) 546-4123 SIC 8011

GEORGETOWN MEMORIAL HOSPITAL p 606
606 Black River Rd 29440
Tel (843) 626-9040 SIC 8062

GOOSE CREEK, SC

■ **CENTURY ALUMINUM OF SOUTH CAROLINA INC** p 282
3575 U S Hwy 52 29445
Tel (843) 572-3700 SIC 3341

■ **JACOBS APPLIED TECHNOLOGY INC** p 775
2040 Bushy Park Rd 29445
Tel (843) 824-1100
SIC 3559 3443 8711 1629

■ **JW ALUMINUM HOLDING CORP** p 798
435 Old Mount Holly Rd 29445
Tel (843) 572-1100 SIC 3353 3497

GRAY COURT, SC

ZF TRANSMISSIONS GRAY COURT LLC p 1642
2846 N Old Laurens Rd 29645
Tel (864) 601-2500 SIC 3714

GREENVILLE, SC

ABITIBI CONSOLIDATED SALES CORP p 11
55 E Camperdown Way 29601
Tel (864) 656-3975 SIC 5111 5113

AGFA CORP p 34
10 S Academy St 29601
Tel (800) 526-5441 SIC 3861

■ **AMERICAN EQUIPMENT CO INC** p 71
2106 Anderson Rd 29611
Tel (864) 295-7800
SIC 7699 7359 5082 7353

AMERICAN SECURITY OF GREENVILLE LLC p 79
1300 Rutherford Rd 29609
Tel (864) 292-7450 SIC 7381

AMERICAN SERVICES INC p 79
1300 Rutherford Rd 29609
Tel (864) 292-7450 SIC 7381 7349 7363

ASCI HOLDINGS UK (DE) INC p 116
40 Emery St 29605
Tel (864) 240-2600 SIC 3714

ATHENE ANNUITY & LIFE ASSURANCE CO p 124
2000 Wade Hampton Blvd 29615
Tel (864) 609-1000 SIC 6719

BALDOR ELECTRIC CO p 147
6040 Ponders Ct 29615
Tel (864) 991-8492 SIC 3599

■ **BE&K BUILDING GROUP LLC** p 164
201 E Mcbee Ave Ste 400 29601
Tel (864) 250-5000 SIC 1542 1541 1522

■ **BENEFITFOCUS INC** p 173
1016 Woods Crossing Rd 29607
Tel (864) 234-2827 SIC 7371

BOB JONES UNIVERSITY INC OF GREENVILLE S C p 196
1700 Wade Hampton Blvd 29614
Tel (864) 242-5100
SIC 8221 8211 8231 8062 5942 0191

BWT LLC p 231
201 Brookfield Pkwy 29607
Tel (864) 990-0050 SIC 3398

C&S WHOLESALE SERVICES INC p 234
208 Bi Lo Blvd 29607
Tel (864) 234-1999 SIC 5141

CANAL INSURANCE CO p 246
400 E Stone Ave 29601
Tel (800) 452-6911 SIC 6331

■ **CERTUSBANK NATIONAL ASSOCIATION** p 284
935 S Main St 29601
Tel (864) 306-2540 SIC 6021

CHRISTIAN BLIND MISSION INTERNATIONAL INC p 302
228 Adley Way 29607
Tel (864) 239-0065 SIC 8661

COLINX LLC p 336
1 Independence Pt Ste 210 29615
Tel (864) 607-9431 SIC 4731

■ **COMPX SECURITY PRODUCTS INC** p 353
26 Old Mill Rd 29607
Tel (864) 286-1122 SIC 3429

COUNTY OF GREENVILLE p 378
301 University Rdg # 2400 29601
Tel (864) 467-7105 SIC 9111

COVERIS FLEXIBLES US LLC p 385
50 International Dr # 100 29615
Tel (773) 877-3300 SIC 2673

COVERIS RIGID NA INC p 385
50 International Dr # 100 29615
Tel (864) 225-9750 SIC 2671 3089

▲ **DELTA APPAREL INC** p 426
322 S Main St 29601
Tel (864) 232-5200
SIC 2321 2369 2339 2253

EASTERN INDUSTRIAL SUPPLIES INC p 472
11 Caledon Ct Ste A 29615
Tel (864) 451-5285 SIC 5085 5051

■ **ERWIN-PENLAND INC** p 508
125 E Broad St Ste 300 29601
Tel (864) 271-0500 SIC 7311

■ **FLUOR FEDERAL SERVICES INC** p 561
100 Fluor Daniel Dr 29607
Tel (864) 281-4400 SIC 8711

■ **FLUOR FEDERAL SOLUTIONS LLC** p 561
100 Fluor Daniel Dr 29607
Tel (864) 281-4400 SIC 4953

■ **FLUOR INTERCONTINENTAL INC** p 561
100 Fluor Daniel Dr 29607
Tel (864) 281-4400 SIC 1541 1542

■ **GABRIEL COMMUNICATIONS FINANCE CO** p 588
2 N Main St Ste 300 29601
Tel (864) 672-5000 SIC 4813

GOWER CORP p 627
355 Woodruff Rd Ste 101 29607
Tel (864) 458-3114 SIC 3535 5051 7373

GREENVILLE COUNTY SCHOOL DISTRICT p 638
301 E Camperdown Way 29601
Tel (864) 355-3100 SIC 8211

GREENVILLE TECHNICAL COLLEGE PUBLIC FACILITIES CORP p 638
506 S Pleasantburg Dr 29607
Tel (864) 250-8000 SIC 8222 8211 8221

GREENWOOD INC p 639
160 Milestone Way Ste A 29615
Tel (864) 288-5510 SIC 1541 7349

■ **HUBBELL LIGHTING INC** p 716
701 Millennium Blvd 29607
Tel (864) 678-1000 SIC 3648

IH SERVICES INC p 730
127 Tanner Rd 29607
Tel (864) 297-3748 SIC 7349 5014 7217

INTEGRATED POWER SERVICES LLC p 749
3 Independence Pt Ste 100 29615
Tel (864) 451-5600 SIC 7694

LIBERTY CORP p 861
135 S Main St Ste 1000 29601
Tel (864) 609-8111 SIC 4833

■ **LOCKHEED MARTIN AIRCRAFT CENTER** p 873
244 Terminal Rd 29605
Tel (864) 422-6262 SIC 3721 4581

■ **LOCKHEED MARTIN LOGISTIC SERVICES INC** p 873
244 Terminal Rd 29605
Tel (864) 236-3552 SIC 4581

■ **LOCKHEED MARTIN LOGISTICS MANAGEMENT INC** p 873
244 Terminal Rd 29605
Tel (864) 277-7230 SIC 8742

LOUIS BERGER SERVICES INC p 879
80 International Dr # 130 29615
Tel (864) 385-7500 SIC 6719

METROMONT CORP p 955
2802 White Horse Rd 29611
Tel (804) 222-6770 SIC 3272

MICHELIN CORP p 960
1 Parkway S 29615
Tel (864) 458-5000 SIC 5014

MICHELIN NORTH AMERICA INC p 960
1 Parkway S 29615
Tel (864) 458-5000 SIC 3011

MUSTANG PROCESS AND INDUSTRIAL INC p 1003
30 Patewood Dr Ste 200 29615
Tel (864) 288-3009 SIC 8741

NPI PROPERTY MANAGEMENT CORP p 1064
55 Beattie Pl 29601
Tel (864) 239-1000 SIC 6798

■ **NUVOX INC** p 1068
2 N Main St 29601
Tel (864) 672-5000 SIC 4813

OGLETREE DEAKINS NASH SMOAK & STEWART PC p 1077
300 N Main St Ste 500 29601
Tel (864) 271-1300 SIC 8111

ONEAL CONSTRUCTORS LLC p 1087
10 Falcon Crest Dr # 300 29607
Tel (864) 298-6510 SIC 8742

ONEAL INC p 1087
10 Falcon Crest Dr 29607
Tel (864) 298-2000 SIC 8711 8712

OPAL HOLDINGS LLC p 1089
208 Bi Lo Blvd 29607
Tel (864) 213-2500 SIC 5411 5541 5912

PATEWOOD MEMORIAL HOSPITAL p 1120
175 Patewood Dr 29615
Tel (864) 797-1000 SIC 8062

PINNACLE STAFFING INC p 1150
127 Tanner Rd 29607
Tel (864) 297-4212 SIC 7363

PRETTL INTERNATIONAL INC p 1173
1721 White Horse Rd 29605
Tel (864) 220-1010 SIC 3357

■ **PROGRESS LIGHTING INC** p 1181
701 Millennium Blvd 29607
Tel (864) 678-1000 SIC 3645 3646

RANGER AEROSPACE LLC p 1208
128 Millport Cir Ste 200 29607
Tel (864) 329-9000 SIC 6719

▲ **REGIONAL MANAGEMENT CORP** p 1219
509 W Butler Rd 29607
Tel (864) 422-8011 SIC 7389 6141

RELIANCE ELECTRIC CO p 1221
6040 Ponders Ct 29615
Tel (864) 297-4800 SIC 3714 3621

RENEWABLE WATER RESOURCES p 1224
561 Mauldin Rd 29607
Tel (864) 299-4000 SIC 4952

SAGE AUTOMOTIVE INTERIORS INC p 1267
3 Research Dr Ste 300 29607
Tel (864) 987-7778 SIC 2399

▲ **SCANSOURCE INC** p 1286
6 Logue Ct Ste G 29615
Tel (864) 288-2432 *SIC* 5045

SOUTHERN MANAGEMENT CORP p 1349
101 N Main St Ste 600 29601
Tel (864) 233-9033 *SIC* 6141

SPINX CO INC p 1358
1414 E Washington St N 29607
Tel (864) 233-5421 *SIC* 5541 5411 5812

ST FRANCIS HOSPITAL INC p 1366
1 Saint Francis Dr 29601
Tel (864) 255-1000 *SIC* 8062

STEVENS AVIATION INC p 1388
600 Delaware St 29605
Tel (864) 678-6000
SIC 4522 4581 5088 5599

SUNSHINE HOUSE INC p 1404
12 Interchange Blvd 29607
Tel (864) 990-1820 *SIC* 8351

UPSTATE AFFILIATE ORGANIZATION p 1529
701 Grove Rd 29605
Tel (864) 455-7000 *SIC* 8069 8051

■ **WINDSTREAM NUVOX INC** p 1615
2 N Main St 29601
Tel (864) 672-5000 *SIC* 4813

▲ **WORLD ACCEPTANCE CORP** p 1624
108 Frederick St 29607
Tel (864) 298-9800 *SIC* 6141

WYNIT DISTRIBUTION LLC p 1630
2 W Washington St Ste 500 29601
Tel (864) 605-9920
SIC 5045 5043 5046 5199 7372

GREENWOOD, SC

BAY ISLAND SPORTSWEAR INC p 161
1415 Emerald Rd 29646
Tel (864) 229-1298 *SIC* 2253 2339

CAPSUGEL MANUFACTURING INC p 251
535 Emerald Rd N 29646
Tel (864) 223-2270 *SIC* 2899

CAROLINA PRIDE FOODS INC p 259
1 Packer Ave 29646
Tel (864) 229-5611 *SIC* 2013

COLFIN JIH AHI OPCO LLC p 336
109 Enterprise Ct 29649
Tel (864) 942-0002 *SIC* 7011

FUJIFILM MANUFACTURING USA INC p 583
215 Puckett Ferry Rd 29649
Tel (864) 223-2888 *SIC* 2796 2752 3861

GREENWOOD MILLS INC p 639
300 Morgan Ave 29646
Tel (864) 227-2121
SIC 2211 2221 2241 2261 2262 6552

GREENWOOD SCHOOL DISTRICT 50 p 639
1855 Calhoun Rd 29649
Tel (864) 941-5400 *SIC* 8211

SELF REGIONAL HEALTHCARE p 1302
1325 Spring St 29646
Tel (864) 725-4150 *SIC* 8062

VELUX AMERICA LLC p 1547
450 Old Brickyard Rd 29649
Tel (864) 941-4700 *SIC* 5039

VELUX GREENWOOD INC p 1547
450 Old Brickyard Rd 29649
Tel (864) 941-4700 *SIC* 3442

GREER, SC

FOREST SPARTANBURG PRODUCTS INC p 567
1431 Highway 101 S 29651
Tel (864) 699-3100 *SIC* 7389

GBP MANAGEMENT INC p 594
979 Batesville Rd 29651
Tel (864) 297-6101 *SIC* 8741

GUARDIAN BUILDING PRODUCTS DISTRIBUTION INC p 645
979 Batesville Rd Ste A 29651
Tel (800) 569-4262
SIC 5031 5033 5051 5032 5039 5023

GUARDIAN BUILDING PRODUCTS INC p 645
979 Batesville Rd Ste A 29651
Tel (864) 297-6101 *SIC* 3296 2452 8741

KNAUF INSULATION LLC p 824
979 Batesville Rd Ste B 29651
Tel (517) 629-9464 *SIC* 3296

MITSUBISHI POLYESTER FILM INC p 978
2001 Hood Rd 29650
Tel (864) 879-5000 *SIC* 3081 2671

PIEDMONT LIVING CENTER LLC p 1147
401 Chandler Rd 29651
Tel (864) 879-1370 *SIC* 8051

PIEDMONT MUNICIPAL POWER AGENCY p 1147
121 Village Dr 29651
Tel (864) 877-9632 *SIC* 4911

HARTSVILLE, SC

HARTSVILLE LLC p 666
1304 W Bobo Newsom Hwy 29550
Tel (843) 339-2100 *SIC* 8011

HILEX POLY CO LLC p 692
101 E Carolina Ave 29550
Tel (843) 857-4800 *SIC* 2673 2674

NOVOLEX HOLDINGS INC p 1063
101 E Carolina Ave 29550
Tel (843) 857-4800 *SIC* 2673 2674

■ **SONOCO PLASTICS INC** p 1340
1 N 2nd St 29550
Tel (843) 383-7000 *SIC* 3082

▲ **SONOCO PRODUCTS CO** p 1340
1 N 2nd St 29550
Tel (843) 383-7000
SIC 2631 2671 2653 2655 3089 2499

■ **SONOCO PROTECTIVE SOLUTIONS INC** p 1340
1 N 2nd St 29550
Tel (843) 383-7000 *SIC* 3086 2679

■ **SONOCO RECYCLING LLC** p 1340
1 N 2nd St 29550
Tel (843) 383-0273 *SIC* 5093

WEST OIL INC p 1595
312 Lakeview Blvd 29550
Tel (843) 332-2201 *SIC* 5172 5541 5411

HILTON HEAD ISLAND, SC

HARGRAY COMMUNICATIONS GROUP INC p 661
856 William Hilton Pkwy 29928
Tel (843) 785-2166 *SIC* 4813

■ **HILTON HEAD HEALTH SYSTEM LP** p 695
25 Hospital Cntr Blvrd 29926
Tel (843) 681-6122 *SIC* 8062

HILTON HEAD HOSPITAL REHAB p 695
35 Bill Fries Dr Bldg D 29926
Tel (843) 681-4088 *SIC* 8049

HOPKINS, SC

DEFENDER SERVICES INC p 422
9031 Garners Ferry Rd 29061
Tel (803) 776-4220 *SIC* 7349 7361 7382

INMAN, SC

INMAN HOLDING CO INC p 744
300 Park Rd 29349
Tel (864) 472-2121 *SIC* 2211 2221

INMAN MILLS p 744
300 Park Rd 29349
Tel (864) 472-2121 *SIC* 2281

IRMO, SC

SCHOOL DISTRICT FIVE OF LEXINGTON AND RICHLAND COUNTIES p 1289
1020 Dutch Fork Rd 29063
Tel (803) 476-8000 *SIC* 8211

JOHNS ISLAND, SC

ISLAND OAKS LIVING CENTER LLC p 766
3647 Maybank Hwy 29455
Tel (843) 559-5888 *SIC* 8051

KIAWAH ISLAND INN CO p 816
1 Sanctuary Beach Dr 29455
Tel (843) 768-6000 *SIC* 7011

KIAWAH RESORT ASSOCIATES p 816
245 Gardners Cir 29455
Tel (843) 768-3400 *SIC* 6552

JOHNSONVILLE, SC

WELLMAN ADVANCED MATERIALS LLC p 1589
520 Kingsburg Hwy 29555
Tel (843) 386-8152 *SIC* 2824 2821

KINGSTREE, SC

FARMERS TELEPHONE COOPERATIVE INC p 530
1101 E Main St 29556
Tel (843) 382-2333 *SIC* 4813

SANTEE ELECTRIC COOPERATIVE INC p 1281
424 Sumter Hwy 29556
Tel (843) 355-6187 *SIC* 4911

LADSON, SC

■ **FORCE PROTECTION INC** p 565
9801 Highway 78 Bldg 1 29456
Tel (843) 569-8716 *SIC* 3711

LANCASTER, SC

FOUNDERS FEDERAL CREDIT UNION p 571
607 N Main St 29720
Tel (803) 283-5958 *SIC* 6061

JLJ HOME FURNISHINGS LLC p 786
4776 Charlotte Hwy 29720
Tel (704) 239-8630 *SIC* 5712

LANCASTER COUNTY SCHOOL DISTRICT p 841
300 S Catawba St 29720
Tel (803) 286-6972 *SIC* 8211

SPRINGS MEMORIAL HOSPITAL p 1361
800 W Meeting St 29720
Tel (803) 286-1477 *SIC* 8062 8069 8049

LAURENS, SC

LAURENS ELECTRIC COOPERATIVE INC p 847
2254 Highway 14 29360
Tel (864) 682-3141 *SIC* 4911

SC DJJ PIEDMONT REGIONAL OFFICE p 1285
300 E Courthouse Pub Sq 29360
Tel (864) 681-1035 *SIC* 8322

LEESVILLE, SC

COLUMBIA FARMS INC p 340
125 N Lee St 29070
Tel (803) 532-4488 *SIC* 2015

LEXINGTON, SC

BRANDI BOB STATIONS INC p 208
279 Cedarcrest Dr 29072
Tel (803) 957-3096 *SIC* 5411 5172

COOPER TOOLS INC p 367
670 Industrial Dr 29072
Tel (803) 359-1200 *SIC* 3546

COUNTY OF LEXINGTON p 379
212 S Lake Dr 29072
Tel (803) 785-8100 *SIC* 9111

LEXINGTON COUNTY SCHOOL DISTRICT NO 1 p 859
100 Tarrar Springs Rd 29072
Tel (803) 821-1000 *SIC* 8211

LEXINGTON SCHOOL DISTRICT 01 p 859
100 Tarrar Springs Rd 29072
Tel (803) 321-1002 *SIC* 8211

LEXMED INC p 860
815 Old Cherokee Rd 29072
Tel (803) 359-5181 *SIC* 8051

MEDICAL SERVICES OF AMERICA INC p 937
171 Monroe Ln 29072
Tel (803) 957-0500
SIC 8082 8741 8011 8071 7352 5999

MID-CAROLINA ELECTRIC COOPERATIVE INC p 963
254 Longs Pond Rd 29071
Tel (803) 749-6400 *SIC* 4911

PRYSMIAN CABLES AND SYSTEMS USA LLC p 1187
700 Industrial Dr 29072
Tel (803) 951-4800 *SIC* 3357

SEFA GROUP INC p 1300
217 Cedar Rd 29073
Tel (803) 520-9000 *SIC* 5093

SOUTHEASTERN FREIGHT LINES INC p 1346
420 Davega Dr 29073
Tel (803) 794-7300 *SIC* 4213

LIBERTY, SC

CORNELL-DUBILIER ELECTRONICS INC p 370
140 Technology Pl 29657
Tel (864) 843-2277 *SIC* 3675 3677

LONGS, SC

KRUGER LTD p 830
1513 Absco Dr 29568
Tel (843) 399-2165 *SIC* 5199

LYMAN, SC

SEW-EURODRIVE INC p 1309
1295 Old Spartanburg Hwy 29365
Tel (864) 439-7537 *SIC* 3566

MARIETTA, SC

FALLS CREEK LIVING CENTER LLC p 526
2906 Geer Hwy 29661
Tel (864) 836-6381 *SIC* 8051

MARION, SC

AVM INDUSTRIES LLC p 138
3108 W Highway 76 29571
Tel (843) 464-5406 *SIC* 3714

BENETEAU INC p 173
1313 W Highway 76 29571
Tel (843) 629-5300 *SIC* 3732

MAULDIN, SC

MOUNT VERNON MILLS INC p 994
503 S Main St 29662
Tel (864) 688-7100 *SIC* 2211 2221 2281

MONCKS CORNER, SC

BERKELEY COUNTY SCHOOL DISTRICT p 175
229 E Main St 29461
Tel (843) 899-8600 *SIC* 8211

BERKELEY COUNTY WATER AND SANITATION AUTHORITY p 175
212 Oakley Plantation Dr 29461
Tel (843) 761-8817 *SIC* 4941 4953

BERKELEY ELECTRIC COOPERATIVE INC p 175
551 Rmbert C. Dnnis Blvd 29461
Tel (843) 761-8200 *SIC* 4911

SOUTH CAROLINA PUBLIC SERVICE AUTHORITY (INC) p 1343
1 Riverwood Dr 29461
Tel (843) 761-4121 *SIC* 4911

MONETTA, SC

AMICK FARMS LLC p 85
3682 Highway 23 29105
Tel (803) 532-1400 *SIC* 5191

MOUNT PLEASANT, SC

■ **EAST COOPER COMMUNITY HOSPITAL INC** p 470
2000 Hospital Dr 29464
Tel (843) 881-0100 *SIC* 8062 8011

GREENBAX ENTERPRISES INC p 637
884 Johnnie Dodds Blvd B 29464
Tel (866) 891-1195 *SIC* 7389 6159 6512

MULLINS, SC

SO-PAK-CO INC p 1336
118 S Cypress St 29574
Tel (423) 639-1163 *SIC* 2099 4226

MURRELLS INLET, SC

WACCAMAW COMMUNITY HOSPITAL p 1570
4070 Highway 17 Business 29576
Tel (843) 527-7000 *SIC* 8062

MYRTLE BEACH, SC

BURROUGHS & CHAPIN CO INC p 228
8800 Marina Pkwy 29572
Tel (843) 448-5123
SIC 6552 6515 6519 6512

CANFOR SOUTHERN PINE LLC p 247
3700 Claypond Rd 29579
Tel (843) 236-8402 *SIC* 5031

GRAND STRAND REGIONAL MEDICAL CENTER LLC p 630
809 82nd Pkwy 29572
Tel (843) 449-4411 *SIC* 8062

HYATT AUTOMOTIVE LLC p 723
1887 Highway 501 29577
Tel (843) 626-3657 *SIC* 5511

INTELLIGENT INVESTMENTS LLC p 750
1010 Park Dr 29577
Tel (980) 989-4016 *SIC* 6726 7389

LEGACY BUSINESS SOLUTIONS LLC p 852
1144 Shine Ave 29577
Tel (843) 945-4358 *SIC* 7011

MYRTLE BEACH FARMS CO INC p 1005
8820 Marina Pkwy 29572
Tel (843) 448-5123 *SIC* 6552 7996 6512

NEW SOUTH COMPANIES INC p 1033
3700 Claypond Rd Ste 6 29579
Tel (843) 236-9399 *SIC* 2421 2491 2431

NEW SOUTH LUMBER CO INC p 1033
3700 Claypond Rd Ste 6 29579
Tel (843) 236-9399 *SIC* 2421

PRECISION SOUTHEAST INC p 1169
4900 Highway 501 29579
Tel (843) 347-4218 *SIC* 3089 8731 3083

SANDS PROPERTIES INC p 1278
201 74th Ave N 29572
Tel (843) 449-4431 *SIC* 6531

NEWBERRY, SC

NEWBERRY COUNTY SCHOOL DISTRICT p 1037
3419 Main St 29108
Tel (803) 321-2600 *SIC* 8211

RELATED NEWBERRY ARMS LLC p 1221
186 Newberry Arms 29108
Tel (803) 276-4053 *SIC* 6513

NORTH CHARLESTON, SC

ALLERGY CENTERS OF AMERICA LLC p 53
2430 Mall Dr Ste 210 29406
Tel (843) 747-4294 *SIC* 8011 8071

ASTENJOHNSON INC p 122
4399 Corporate Rd 29405
Tel (843) 747-7800 *SIC* 2221 2281 2299

BANKS CONSTRUCTION CO p 152
4902 Banco Rd 29418
Tel (843) 744-8261 *SIC* 1611

CHARLESTON SOUTHERN UNIVERSITY p 290
9200 University Blvd 29406
Tel (843) 863-7000 *SIC* 8221

CITY OF NORTH CHARLESTON p 317
2500 City Hall Ln 29406
Tel (843) 554-5700 *SIC* 9121

DETYENS SHIPYARDS INC p 433
1670 Dry Dock Ave # 236 29405
Tel (843) 746-1603 *SIC* 4499

FIRST FINANCIAL HOLDINGS INC p 547
2440 Mall Dr 29406
Tel (843) 529-5933 *SIC* 6035

▲ **INGEVITY CORP** p 742
5255 Virginia Ave 29406
Tel (843) 740-2300 *SIC* 2819

■ **INGEVITY SOUTH CAROLINA LLC** p 742
5255 Virginia Ave 29406
Tel (843) 740-2300 *SIC* 2611

INTERTECH GROUP INC p 759
4838 Jenkins Ave 29405
Tel (843) 744-5174 *SIC* 3949

■ **KAPSTONE CHARLESTON KRAFT LLC** p 803
5600 Virginia Ave 29406
Tel (843) 745-3000 *SIC* 2621

LANDMARK CONSTRUCTION CO INC p 842
3255 Industry Dr 29418
Tel (843) 552-6186
SIC 1542 1541 1623 1771 1794

LIFE CYCLE ENGINEERING INC p 863
4360 Corporate Rd Ste 100 29405
Tel (843) 744-7110
SIC 7371 7373 7376 7379 8711

PRODUCTION DESIGN ASSOCIATES INC p 1179
2799 Three Lakes Rd 29418
Tel (843) 554-3466 SIC 7812 1731

NORWAY, SC

■ NORWAY TELEPHONE CO INC p 1061
8432 Savannah Hwy 29113
Tel (608) 831-1000 SIC 4813

ORANGEBURG, SC

COX INDUSTRIES INC p 386
860 Cannon Bridge Rd 29115
Tel (803) 534-7467 SIC 2411 2491

COX WOOD PRESERVING CO p 386
860 Cannon Bridge Rd 29115
Tel (803) 534-7467 SIC 2491

ORANGEBURG CONSOLIDATED SCHOOL DISTRICT 5 p 1092
578 Ellis Ave 29115
Tel (803) 534-5454 SIC 8211

REGIONAL MEDICAL CENTER p 1219
3000 Saint Matthews Rd 29118
Tel (803) 395-2200 SIC 8062

REGIONAL MEDICAL CENTER OF ORANGEBURG & CALHOUN COUNTIES p 1219
3000 Saint Matthews Rd 29118
Tel (803) 395-2200 SIC 8062

SOUTH CAROLINA STATE UNIVERSITY p 1343
300 College Ave 29115
Tel (803) 536-7000 SIC 8221 9411

ZEUS INDUSTRIAL PRODUCTS INC p 1642
620 Magnolia St 29115
Tel (803) 268-9500 SIC 3082 3083

PAGELAND, SC

C M TUCKER LUMBER COMPANIES LLC p 233
601 N Pearl St 29728
Tel (843) 672-6135 SIC 2491

CM TUCKER LUMBER COMPANIES LLC p 328
601 N Pearl St 29728
Tel (843) 672-6135 SIC 2491

PAWLEYS ISLAND, SC

MERCOM CORP p 945
313 Commerce Dr 29585
Tel (843) 979-9957 SIC 5999

PELION, SC

WALTER P RAWL & SONS INC p 1574
824 Fairview Rd 29123
Tel (803) 894-1900 SIC 0161 0723 5148

PICKENS, SC

BLUE RIDGE ELECTRIC COOPERATIVE INC p 192
734 W Main St 29671
Tel (800) 240-3400 SIC 4911

LAUREL HILL INC p 847
716 E Cedar Rock St 29671
Tel (864) 878-4739 SIC 8052 8051

ROSEMOND NURSING CENTER INC p 1250
138 Rosemond St 29671
Tel (864) 878-9620 SIC 8051

PIEDMONT, SC

DRIVE AUTOMOTIVE INDUSTRIES OF AMERICA INC p 456
120 Moon Acres Rd 29673
Tel (864) 299-1349
SIC 3465 3714 3711 3469

FIRST SUN MANAGEMENT CORP p 549
127 Kiowa Ln 29673
Tel (864) 654-5099 SIC 5812

WAREHOUSE SERVICES INC p 1575
58 S Burty Rd 29673
Tel (812) 831-4053 SIC 1541 4225

RIDGELAND, SC

PALMETTO ELECTRIC COOPERATIVE INC p 1109
4063 Grays Hwy 29936
Tel (843) 726-5551 SIC 8611 4911

RIDGEVILLE, SC

ARBORGEN INC p 103
2011 Broadbank Ct 29472
Tel (843) 851-4129 SIC 0851

SHOWA DENKO CARBON INC p 1318
478 Ridge Rd 29472
Tel (843) 875-3200 SIC 3624

RIDGEWAY, SC

BEN ARNOLD-SUNBELT BEVERAGE CO OF SOUTH CAROLINA L P p 172
101 Beverage Blvd 29130
Tel (803) 337-3500 SIC 5182

BOMAG AMERICAS INC p 199
125 Blue Granite Pkwy 29130
Tel (803) 337-0700 SIC 3531 2951

ROCK HILL, SC

▲ 3D SYSTEMS CORP p 2
333 Three D Systems Cir 29730
Tel (803) 326-3900 SIC 3577 7372

■ 3D SYSTEMS INC p 2
333 Three D Systems Cir 29730
Tel (803) 326-3900 SIC 3571

■ AMISUB OF SOUTH CAROLINA INC p 85
222 S Herlong Ave 29732
Tel (803) 329-1234 SIC 8062

ATLAS COPCO COMPRESSORS LLC p 127
1800 Overview Dr 29730
Tel (803) 817-7000 SIC 3563 3999

C C DICKSON CO p 232
456 Lakeshore Pkwy 29730
Tel (803) 980-8000 SIC 5075 5078 5074

COMPORIUM INC p 351
330 E Black St 29730
Tel (803) 326-6011 SIC 4813

ROCK HILL SCHOOL DISTRICT 3 p 1243
660 Anderson Rd N 29730
Tel (803) 981-1000 SIC 8211

SPRINGS CREATIVE PRODUCTS GROUP LLC p 1361
300 Chatham Ave Ste 100 29730
Tel (803) 324-6300 SIC 5949 2759

TRANSAXLE MANUFACTURING OF AMERICA CORP p 1471
240 Waterford Park Dr 29730
Tel (803) 329-8900 SIC 3714

WINTHROP UNIVERSITY p 1617
701 Oakland Ave 29733
Tel (803) 323-2211 SIC 8221

ROEBUCK, SC

SPARTANBURG SCHOOL DISTRICT 6 p 1355
1390 Cavalier Way 29376
Tel (864) 576-4212 SIC 8211

SAINT GEORGE, SC

BID GROUP CONSTRUCTION US INC p 181
5154 Highway 78 29477
Tel (843) 563-7070 SIC 1542

SAINT STEPHEN, SC

SAINT STEPHEN NURSING FACILITY INC p 1270
1038 Mcgill Ln 29479
Tel (843) 567-2307 SIC 8051 8059

SCRANTON, SC

W LEE FLOWERS AND CO INC p 1568
127 E W Lee Flowers Rd 29591
Tel (843) 389-2731 SIC 5141 5147 5194

SENECA, SC

OCONEE MEDICAL CENTER p 1074
298 Memorial Dr 29672
Tel (864) 482-3100 SIC 8062 8051

SIMPSONVILLE, SC

▲ KEMET CORP p 809
2835 Kemet Way 29681
Tel (864) 963-6300 SIC 3675

SUMMIT PLACE LIVING CENTER LLC p 1399
807 Se Main St 29681
Tel (864) 963-6069 SIC 8051

SOCIETY HILL, SC

GALEY & LORD LLC p 589
670 N Main St 29593
Tel (843) 378-4511
SIC 2211 2221 2325 2339

■ MOR PPM INC p 988
1127 S Main St 29593
Tel (843) 378-4700 SIC 1731

SPARTANBURG, SC

ADVANCE AMERICA CASH ADVANCE CENTERS INC p 24
135 N Church St 29306
Tel (864) 342-5600 SIC 6141 6153

AURIGA POLYMERS INC p 131
1550 Dewberry Rd 29307
Tel (864) 579-5570 SIC 2821

CAROLINAS RECYCLING GROUP LLC p 259
2061 Nazareth Church Rd 29301
Tel (864) 439-7039 SIC 5093

CH2M HILL ENGINEERS INC p 286
1500 International Dr 29303
Tel (864) 578-2000 SIC 8711 8742 1629

■ COLUMBIA LIGHTING INC p 341
101 Corporate Dr Ste L 29303
Tel (864) 678-1000 SIC 3646

CONVERSE AND CO INC p 365
314 S Pine St Ste 200 29302
Tel (864) 542-2301 SIC 5052

COUNTY OF SPARTANBURG p 382
Main Level Ste 1000 366 N 29303
Tel (864) 596-2509 SIC 9121

COVERIS KEY HOLDINGS LLC p 385
345 Cedar Springs Ave 29302
Tel (864) 596-7300 SIC 2673 2631 6719

DEARYBURY OIL & GAS INC p 420
2560 Southport Rd 29302
Tel (864) 585-6226 SIC 5172 5983 4212

▲ DENNYS CORP p 428
203 E Main St 29319
Tel (864) 597-8000 SIC 5812 6794

■ DENNYS INC p 428
2306 Reidville Rd 29301
Tel (864) 597-8532 SIC 5812 6794

■ DENNYS INC p 428
203 E Main St P-73 29319
Tel (864) 597-8000 SIC 5812

■ DHI HOLDINGS INC p 435
105 Diversco Dr 29307
Tel (864) 579-3420 SIC 7361

DIVERSCO HOLDINGS INC p 443
105 Diversco Dr 29307
Tel (864) 579-3420 SIC 7381 7349

EAGLE US SUB INC p 468
135 N Church St 29306
Tel (864) 515-5600 SIC 6141 6153

J M SMITH CORP p 771
101 W Saint John St # 305 29306
Tel (864) 542-9419 SIC 5122 7374

■ KNIGHTS APPAREL INC p 824
5475 N Blackstock Rd 29303
Tel (864) 587-9690 SIC 5091 5699

MARTEX FIBER SOUTHERN CORP p 912
3200b Southport Rd 29302
Tel (864) 583-6412 SIC 5093

■ MARY BLACK HEALTH SYSTEMS INC p 914
1700 Skylyn Dr 29307
Tel (864) 573-3000 SIC 8062

MARY BLACK MEMORIAL HOSPITAL INC p 914
1700 Skylyn Dr 29307
Tel (864) 573-3004 SIC 8062

MERIT DISTRIBUTION GROUP LLC p 949
1310 Union St 29302
Tel (864) 583-3011 SIC 5198

MILLIKEN & CO p 971
920 Milliken Rd 29303
Tel (864) 503-2020
SIC 2221 2211 2231 2273 2821 4911

OAK WHITE MANOR INC p 1070
130 E Main St 29306
Tel (864) 582-7503 SIC 8051

■ OMNISOURCE SOUTHEAST LLC p 1085
2061 Nazareth Church Rd 29301
Tel (864) 439-7039 SIC 4953

R L JORDAN OIL CO OF NORTH CAROLINA INC p 1202
1451 Fernwood Glendale Rd 29307
Tel (864) 585-2784
SIC 5411 5172 5541 5812

SECURITY FINANCE CORP OF SPARTANBURG p 1299
181 Security Pl 29307
Tel (864) 582-8193 SIC 6141

SECURITY GROUP INC p 1299
181 Security Pl 29307
Tel (864) 582-8193 SIC 6141

SOUTHEASTERN PAPER GROUP INC p 1346
50 Old Blackstock Rd 29301
Tel (800) 858-7230 SIC 5113

SOUTHERN STATES PACKAGING CO p 1350
180 Brooks Blvd 29307
Tel (864) 579-3911 SIC 2679

SOUTHLAND CONTAINER CORP p 1351
60 Fairview Church Rd 29303
Tel (864) 578-0085 SIC 2653 3086

SPARTANBURG AUTOMOTIVE INC p 1355
1290 New Cut Rd 29303
Tel (864) 585-5211 SIC 3465 3412 3411

SPARTANBURG AUTOMOTIVE STEEL INC p 1355
1290 New Cut Rd 29303
Tel (864) 585-5211 SIC 3465

SPARTANBURG COUNTY SCHOOL DISTRICT NO 7 p 1355
610 Dupre Dr 29307
Tel (864) 594-4400 SIC 8211

SPARTANBURG REGIONAL HEALTH SERVICES DISTRICT INC p 1355
101 E Wood St 29303
Tel (864) 560-6000 SIC 8062

SPARTANBURG WATER SYSTEM p 1355
200 Commerce St 29306
Tel (864) 582-6375 SIC 4941 4952

TIETEX INTERNATIONAL LTD p 1453
3010 N Blackstock Rd 29301
Tel (864) 574-0500 SIC 2297 2258 2221

TINDALL CORP p 1455
3076 N Blackstock Rd 29301
Tel (864) 576-3230 SIC 3272

USLC LLC p 1535
100 Dunbar St Ste 100 29306
Tel (864) 577-0100 SIC 7389

WILLIAM BARNET & SON LLC p 1610
1300 Hayne St 29301
Tel (864) 327-4620
SIC 5199 2823 2221 2824

SUMMERVILLE, SC

ADVANCED TECHNOLOGY INTERNATIONAL p 26
315 Sigma Dr 29486
Tel (843) 760-3200 SIC 8741

DORCHESTER SCHOOL DISTRICT TWO p 451
102 Greenwave Blvd 29483
Tel (843) 873-2901 SIC 8211

SUMTER, SC

DELUXE MOTEL p 427
2700 N Main St 29153
Tel (803) 469-0236 SIC 7011

PALMETTO HEALTH TUOMEY p 1109
129 N Washington St 29150
Tel (803) 774-9000 SIC 8062

PIGGLY WIGGLY CENTRAL INC p 1147
415 N Salem Ave 29150
Tel (803) 775-3020 SIC 5411

SUMTER SCHOOL DISTRICT p 1399
1345 Wilson Hall Rd 29150
Tel (803) 469-6900 SIC 8211

■ SUMTER UTILITIES INC p 1399
1151 N Pike W 29153
Tel (803) 469-8585 SIC 1623

THOMPSON CONSTRUCTION GROUP INC p 1449
100 N Main St 29150
Tel (803) 773-8005
SIC 7349 1711 1721 1541

TUOMEY MEDICAL PROFESSIONALS p 1492
129 N Washington St 29150
Tel (803) 774-9000 SIC 8011

TAYLORS, SC

CAFE ENTERPRISES INC p 237
4324 Wade Hampton Blvd B 29687
Tel (864) 322-1331 SIC 5812

TOLT SOLUTIONS INC p 1459
3550 Rutherford Rd 29687
Tel (864) 322-4200
SIC 8748 7379 7374 7373

TIMMONSVILLE, SC

HONDA OF SOUTH CAROLINA MFG INC p 704
1111 Honda Way 29161
Tel (843) 346-8000 SIC 3799

UNION, SC

GESTAMP SOUTH CAROLINA LLC p 609
1 Lsp Dr 29379
Tel (864) 466-3960 SIC 3465

WALHALLA, SC

SCHOOL DISTRICT OF OCONEE COUNTY p 1289
414 S Pine St 29691
Tel (864) 886-4400 SIC 8211

WALTERBORO, SC

COLLETON COUNTY SCHOOL DISTRICT p 337
213 N Jefferies Blvd 29488
Tel (843) 549-5715 SIC 8211

WELLFORD, SC

■ WASTE MANAGEMENT OF SOUTH CAROLINA INC p 1581
390 Innovation Way 29385
Tel (864) 232-1537 SIC 4953 4212

WEST COLUMBIA, SC

■ ALLIED AIR ENTERPRISES LLC p 56
215 Metropolitan Dr 29170
Tel (803) 738-4000 SIC 3585 3433 5075

■ ARMSTRONG AIR CONDITIONING INC p 111
215 Metropolitan Dr 29170
Tel (803) 738-4000 SIC 3585

BLANCHARD MACHINERY CO p 188
3151 Charleston Hwy 29172
Tel (803) 791-7100 SIC 5082 7353

BOOKLAND CAYCE SCHOOL DISTRICT NO 2 p 200
715 9th St 29169
Tel (803) 739-4057 SIC 8211

COOPERATIVE ELECTRIC ENERGY UTILITY SUPPLY INC p 367
101 Enterprise Pkwy 29170
Tel (800) 922-3590 SIC 5063

CREGGER CO INC p 391
637 N 12th St 29169
Tel (803) 217-0710 SIC 5074 5064

FITTS AND GOODWIN INC p 553
120 Corporate Blvd 29169
Tel (803) 796-4660 SIC 1541 1542

LEXINGTON COUNTY HEALTH SERVICES DISTRICT INC p 859
2720 Sunset Blvd 29169
Tel (803) 791-2000
SIC 8062 8011 8299 8051

LEXINGTON MEDICAL CENTER p 859
2720 Sunset Blvd 29169
Tel (803) 791-2000 *SIC* 8062

LOXCREEN CO INC p 882
1630 Old Dunbar Rd 29172
Tel (803) 822-1600 *SIC* 3354 3442 3089

PRINCE GROUP LLC p 1176
3227 Sunset Blvd Ste E101 29169
Tel (803) 708-4789 *SIC* 2759 3479

SHEALY ELECTRICAL WHOLESALERS INC p 1313
120 Saxe Gotha Rd 29172
Tel (803) 252-5668 *SIC* 5063

WEST UNION, SC

■ **ITRON ELECTRICITY METERING INC** p 768
313 N Highway 11 29696
Tel (864) 638-8300
SIC 3825 3823 3824 3679 3829 3612

WESTMINSTER, SC

US ENGINE VALVE CORP p 1531
7039 S Highway 11 29693
Tel (864) 647-2061 *SIC* 3592

WILLISTON, SC

■ **CRANE MERCHANDISING SYSTEMS INC** p 389
3330 Crane Way 29853
Tel (803) 266-5000 *SIC* 3581 3531

■ **DIXIE-NARCO INC** p 445
3330 Dixie Narco Blvd 29853
Tel (803) 266-5000 *SIC* 3581

■ **WILLISTON TELEPHONE CO** p 1612
4670 West St 29853
Tel (803) 266-7411 *SIC* 4813

WINNSBORO, SC

FAIRFIELD COUNTY SCHOOL DISTRICT p 524
1226 Us Highway 321 Byp S 29180
Tel (803) 635-4607 *SIC* 8211

WINNSBORO PETROLEUM CO INC p 1617
401 S Congress St 29180
Tel (803) 635-4668 *SIC* 5171 5411

YORK, SC

COUNTY OF YORK p 383
6 S Congress St 29745
Tel (803) 684-8511 *SIC* 9111

SOUTH DAKOTA

ABERDEEN, SD

AVERA ST LUKES p 137
305 S State St 57401
Tel (605) 622-5000 *SIC* 8062 5912

DACOTAH BANK p 408
308 S Main St 57401
Tel (605) 225-5611 *SIC* 6022

DACOTAH BANKS INC p 408
401 S Main St Ste 212 57401
Tel (605) 225-1300 *SIC* 6712

SOUTH DAKOTA WHEAT GROWERS ASSOCIATION p 1344
908 Lamont St S 57401
Tel (605) 225-5500 *SIC* 5153

STUDENT LOAN FINANCE CORP p 1394
124 S 1st St 57401
Tel (605) 622-4400 *SIC* 6141

ALPENA, SD

S I L INC p 1262
39210 221st St 57312
Tel (605) 849-8800 *SIC* 2013

BIG STONE CITY, SD

NORTHERN GROWERS LLC p 1056
48416 144th St 57216
Tel (605) 862-7902 *SIC* 6719

BRANDON, SD

EASTERN FARMERS COOPERATIVE p 472
26033 482nd Ave 57005
Tel (605) 582-2415 *SIC* 5191 5171 5541

BRITTON, SD

FULL CIRCLE AG p 584
520 Vander Horck Ave 57430
Tel (605) 448-2231 *SIC* 5191 5153 5541

BROOKINGS, SD

AGFIRST FARMERS COOPERATIVE p 34
204 1st St S 57006
Tel (605) 692-6216 *SIC* 5191 5153

▲ **DAKTRONICS INC** p 409
201 Daktronics Dr 57006
Tel (605) 692-0200 *SIC* 3993 7372

HARMS OIL CO p 662
337 22nd Ave S 57006
Tel (605) 696-5000 *SIC* 5172

LARSON MANUFACTURING CO INC p 845
2333 Eastbrook Dr 57006
Tel (605) 692-6115 *SIC* 5031

LARSON MANUFACTURING CO OF SOUTH DAKOTA INC p 845
2333 Eastbrook Dr 57006
Tel (605) 692-6115 *SIC* 3442

SOUTH DAKOTA STATE UNIVERSITY p 1344
2201 Administration Lane 57007
Tel (605) 688-6101 *SIC* 8221

CANTON, SD

ADAMS THERMAL SYSTEMS INC p 21
47920 W 5th St 57013
Tel (605) 764-1260 *SIC* 3714

CHANCELLOR, SD

SASKER REPAIR p 1283
27535 460th Ave 57015
Tel (605) 647-5766 *SIC* 7699

DAKOTA DUNES, SD

BPI TECHNOLOGY INC p 206
891 Two Rivers Dr 57049
Tel (605) 217-8000 *SIC* 2011

FIMCO INC p 542
800 Stevens Port Dr 57049
Tel (605) 232-6800 *SIC* 3523 3524

STERLING COMPUTERS CORP p 1387
600 Stevens Port Dr 57049
Tel (605) 242-4000 *SIC* 7373

■ **TYSON FRESH MEATS INC** p 1496
800 Stevens Port Dr 57049
Tel (605) 235-2061 *SIC* 2011

FORT PIERRE, SD

FIRST NATIONAL BANK p 548
307 E Hustan Ave 57532
Tel (605) 223-2521 *SIC* 6021

HOT SPRINGS, SD

BLATCHFORDS INC p 189
207 S Chicago St 57747
Tel (605) 745-5173
SIC 5251 5712 5531 5947 5722

HURON, SD

DAKOTA TURKEY GROWERS LLC p 409
40253 Us Highway 14 57350
Tel (605) 352-1519 *SIC* 2015

■ **NORTHWESTERN SERVICES LLC** p 1061
600 Market St W 57350
Tel (605) 353-7478 *SIC* 4911 4924

IPSWICH, SD

NORTH CENTRAL FARMERS ELEVATOR p 1052
12 5th Ave 57451
Tel (605) 426-6021
SIC 5153 5191 5171 5541

LAKE PRESTON, SD

LAKE PRESTON COOPERATIVE ASSOCIATION p 839
106 2nd St Nw 57249
Tel (605) 847-4414 *SIC* 5153 5191 5172

LYONS, SD

ROSENBAUER AMERICA LLC p 1251
100 3rd St 57041
Tel (605) 543-5591 *SIC* 3711

ROSENBAUER SOUTH DAKOTA LLC p 1251
100 3rd St 57041
Tel (605) 543-5591 *SIC* 3711

MADISON, SD

ALLIED TRANSPORTATION SERVICES INC p 57
1533 Nw 2nd St 57042
Tel (877) 241-6237 *SIC* 7363 4731

EAST RIVER ELECTRIC POWER COOPERATIVE INC p 470
211 S Harth Ave 57042
Tel (605) 256-4536 *SIC* 4911 6163

MARION, SD

FREMAR LLC p 577
44608 273rd St 57043
Tel (605) 648-3941 *SIC* 5153 2873

■ **NUGEN ENERGY LLC** p 1067
27283 447th Ave 57043
Tel (605) 648-2100 *SIC* 0139 1731 5211

MILBANK, SD

ST BERNARDS PROVIDENCE HOSPITA p 1365
901 E Virgil Ave 57252
Tel (605) 432-4538 *SIC* 8062

VALLEY QUEEN CHEESE FACTORY INC p 1541
200 E Railway Ave 57252
Tel (605) 432-4563 *SIC* 2022

MITCHELL, SD

AVERA QUEEN OF PEACE p 137
525 N Foster St 57301
Tel (605) 995-2000 *SIC* 8062

AVERA QUEEN OF PEACE HOSPITAL p 137
525 N Foster St 57301
Tel (605) 995-2000 *SIC* 8062

TRAIL KING INDUSTRIES INC p 1469
300 E Norway Ave 57301
Tel (605) 996-2562 *SIC* 3715 3713

NORTH SIOUX CITY, SD

1ST FINANCIAL BANK USA p 1
331 Dakota Dunes Blvd 57049
Tel (605) 232-9310 *SIC* 6022

CONSUMERS SUPPLY DISTRIBUTING LLC p 362
718 N Derby Ln 57049
Tel (712) 255-6927 *SIC* 5122

■ **NUTRA-FLO CO** p 1067
200 S Derby Ln 57049
Tel (712) 277-2011 *SIC* 2873 2816 2048

PRINCE MANUFACTURING CORP p 1176
612 N Derby Ln 57049
Tel (605) 235-1220 *SIC* 3593 3492 3594

PIERRE, SD

DELTA DENTAL PLAN OF SOUTH DAKOTA p 426
720 N Euclid Ave 57501
Tel (605) 224-7345 *SIC* 6411

EXECUTIVE OFFICE OF STATE OF SOUTH DAKOTA p 518
500 E Capitol Ave 57501
Tel (605) 773-3411 *SIC* 9111

SOUTH DAKOTA BOARD OF REGENTS p 1344
306 E Capitol Ave Ste 200 57501
Tel (605) 773-3455 *SIC* 8221

SOUTH DAKOTA DEPARTMENT OF HUMAN SERVICES p 1344
500 E Capitol Ave 57501
Tel (605) 773-5990 *SIC* 9441

SOUTH DAKOTA DEPARTMENT OF SOCIAL SERVICES p 1344
700 Governors Dr 57501
Tel (605) 773-3165 *SIC* 9441

SOUTH DAKOTA DEPARTMENT OF TRANSPORTATION p 1344
700 E Broadway Ave 57501
Tel (605) 773-3265 *SIC* 9621

SOUTH DAKOTA HOUSING DEVELOPMENT AUTHORITY p 1344
3060 E Elizabeth St 57501
Tel (605) 773-3181 *SIC* 8748

STATE OF SOUTH DAKOTA p 1382
500 E Capitol Ave 57501
Tel (605) 773-3378 *SIC* 9111

RAPID CITY, SD

BIG D OIL CO p 181
3685 Sturgis Rd 57702
Tel (605) 342-6777 *SIC* 5541 5172 8741

▲ **BLACK HILLS CORP** p 187
625 9th St 57701
Tel (605) 721-1700 *SIC* 4911 4923 1241

■ **BLACK HILLS NON-REGULATED HOLDINGS LLC** p 187
625 9th St Ste 200 57701
Tel (605) 721-1700 *SIC* 4911 4923

■ **BLACK HILLS POWER INC** p 187
625 9th St 57701
Tel (605) 721-1700 *SIC* 4911

■ **BLACK HILLS UTILITY HOLDINGS INC** p 187
625 9th St Ste 200 57701
Tel (605) 721-1700 *SIC* 4911 4923

COCA-COLA BOTTLING CO HIGH COUNTRY p 333
2150 Coca Cola Ln 57702
Tel (605) 342-8222 *SIC* 2086

HEAVY CONSTRUCTORS INC p 679
4101 Deadwood Ave 57702
Tel (605) 342-3144
SIC 1542 1794 1623 1611

KNECHT LLC p 824
320 West Blvd 57701
Tel (605) 342-4840 *SIC* 5211 5251

MG OIL CO p 958
1180 Creek Dr 57703
Tel (605) 342-0527 *SIC* 5172 5541 5411

MOYLE PETROLEUM CO p 995
2504 W Main St 57702
Tel (605) 343-1966 *SIC* 5541 5411

▲ **NATIONAL AMERICAN UNIVERSITY HOLDINGS INC** p 1009
5301 S Highway 16 Ste 200 57701
Tel (605) 721-5220 *SIC* 8221 6531 1531

NEWKIRK HOLDING CO INC p 1037
320 West Blvd 57701
Tel (605) 342-4840 *SIC* 5251

PETE LIEN & SONS INC p 1138
3401 Universal Dr 57702
Tel (605) 342-7224
SIC 3273 3441 1422 3274

RAPID CITY AREA SCHOOL DISTRICT 51 4 p 1208
300 6th St Ste 2 57701
Tel (605) 394-4031 *SIC* 8211

RAPID CITY REGIONAL HOSPITAL INC p 1208
353 Fairmont Blvd 57701
Tel (605) 719-1000 *SIC* 8062

REGIONAL HEALTH INC p 1219
353 Fairmont Blvd 57701
Tel (605) 755-1000 *SIC* 8062

RIDDLES GROUP INC p 1234
2707 Mount Rushmore Rd 57701
Tel (605) 343-7099 *SIC* 3873 3911

SCULL CONSTRUCTION SERVICE INC p 1295
803 Industrial Ave 57702
Tel (605) 342-2379 *SIC* 1542

REDFIELD, SD

REDFIELD ENERGY LLC p 1216
38650 171st St 57469
Tel (605) 302-0090 *SIC* 0723 2869

SIOUX FALLS, SD

AKA WIRELESS INC p 42
7505 S Louise Ave 57108
Tel (605) 275-3733 *SIC* 4813

AVERA HEALTH p 137
3900 W Avera Dr 57108
Tel (605) 322-4700 *SIC* 8741 8721

AVERA MCKENNAN p 137
3900 W Avera Dr 57108
Tel (605) 322-7300 *SIC* 7389

AVERA MCKENNAN HOSPITAL MEDICAL STAFF p 137
1325 S Cliff Ave 57105
Tel (605) 322-8000 *SIC* 8062

BONNIE BERSCHEID p 200
800 N Lewis Ave 57103
Tel (605) 359-8208 *SIC* 4214

CHRIS CAM CORP p 302
808 W Cherokee St 57104
Tel (605) 336-1190 *SIC* 5113 5169 5111

■ **CITIBANK NATIONAL ASSOCIATION** p 310
701 E 60th St N 57104
Tel (605) 331-2626 *SIC* 6021

CITY OF SIOUX FALLS p 318
224 W 9th St 57104
Tel (605) 367-8000 *SIC* 9121

D M G INC p 407
809 W Russell St 57104
Tel (605) 336-3693
SIC 5063 7694 3599 1731

DAKOTA KING INC p 409
3800 W 53rd St 57106
Tel (605) 361-7714 *SIC* 5812

DAKOTA NEWS INC p 409
221 S Petro Ave 57107
Tel (605) 336-3000 *SIC* 5192

DHW LEASING LLC p 435
230 S Phillips Ave # 202 57104
Tel (605) 330-9414 *SIC* 6799

EARTHBEND LLC p 469
2300 E 54th St N Ste 3 57104
Tel (605) 789-5700 *SIC* 5065

EVANGELICAL LUTHERAN GOOD SAMARITAN SOCIETY p 513
4800 W 57th St 57108
Tel (866) 928-1635 *SIC* 8051 8052 8059

FURNITURE MART USA INC p 585
140 E Hinks Ln 57104
Tel (605) 336-5000 *SIC* 7641 5713

FURNITURE OUTLETS USA INC p 585
140 E Hinks Ln 57104
Tel (605) 336-5000 *SIC* 5712

▲ **GREAT WESTERN BANCORP INC** p 635
100 N Phillips Ave # 100 57104
Tel (605) 334-2548 *SIC* 6022

■ **GREAT WESTERN BANK** p 635
100 N Phillips Ave # 100 57104
Tel (605) 886-8401 *SIC* 6022

HEART HOSPITAL OF SOUTH DAKOTA LLC p 678
4500 W 69th St 57108
Tel (605) 977-7000 *SIC* 8062 3842

L G EVERIST INC p 834
300 S Phillips Ave # 200 57104
Tel (712) 552-1347 *SIC* 1442 1429

LEWIS DRUGS INC p 858
2701 S Minn Ave Ste 1 57105
Tel (605) 367-2800 *SIC* 5912

▲ **META FINANCIAL GROUP INC** p 952
5501 S Broadband Ln 57108
Tel (605) 782-1767 *SIC* 6035

MIDCO COMMUNICATIONS INC p 964
3901 N Louise Ave 57107
Tel (605) 334-1200
SIC 8748 5961 7389 4812

MIDLAND NATIONAL LIFE INSURANCE CO p 966
1 Sammons Plz 57193
Tel (605) 335-5700 *SIC* 6311

NORTH AMERICAN TRUCK & TRAILER INC p 1050
4500 N Cliff Ave 57104
Tel (605) 332-7112 *SIC* 5012 7538

▲ **NORTHWESTERN CORP** p 1060
3010 W 69th St 57108
Tel (605) 978-2900 *SIC* 4911 4924

■ **NORTHWESTERN ENERGY CORP** p 1060
3010 W 69th St 57108
Tel (605) 978-2900 *SIC* 4911 4924

■ NORWEST BANK SOUTH DAKOTA NATIONAL ASSOCIATION p 1061
101 N Phillips Ave Ste A 57104
Tel (605) 575-4900 *SIC* 6021

OCONNOR CO p 1074
4909 N Lewis Ave 57104
Tel (605) 336-0333 *SIC* 5075

ORION FOOD SYSTEMS LLC p 1094
2930 W Maple St 57107
Tel (605) 336-6961
SIC 5149 2033 2026 2041

POET LLC p 1159
4615 N Lewis Ave 57104
Tel (605) 965-2200 *SIC* 2869

PREMIER BANKCARD HOLDINGS LLC p 1170
3820 N Louise Ave 57107
Tel (605) 357-3440 *SIC* 6022

PREMIER BANKCARD LLC p 1170
3820 N Louise Ave 57107
Tel (605) 335-4000 *SIC* 7389

▲ RAVEN INDUSTRIES INC p 1209
205 E 6th St 57104
Tel (605) 336-2750
SIC 5065 3523 3081 3823 3083

REGENCY MIDWEST VENTURES LIMITED PARTNERSHIP p 1219
3211 W Sencore Dr 57107
Tel (605) 334-2371 *SIC* 7011

SANFORD HEALTH p 1279
1305 W 18th St 57105
Tel (605) 333-1720 *SIC* 8062 8011 8051

SANFORD HEALTH NETWORK p 1279
1305 W 18th St 57105
Tel (605) 328-2929 *SIC* 8741 8011

SIOUX FALLS SCHOOL DISTRICT NO 49-5 p 1326
201 E 38th St 57105
Tel (605) 367-7900 *SIC* 8211

SIOUX FALLS SPECIALTY HOSPITAL LLP p 1326
910 E 20th St 57105
Tel (605) 334-6730 *SIC* 8062

SIOUX STEEL CO p 1326
196 1/2 E 6th St 57104
Tel (605) 336-1750 *SIC* 3523 3448 2221

SONIFI SOLUTIONS INC p 1340
3900 W Innovation St 57107
Tel (605) 988-1000 *SIC* 7812 8082

SONSTEGARD FOODS CO p 1340
5005 S Bur Oak Pl 57108
Tel (605) 338-4642 *SIC* 5144

■ STARMARK CABINETRY p 1379
600 E 48th St N 57104
Tel (800) 755-7789 *SIC* 2434

SUMMIT GROUP INC p 1398
2701 S Minn Ave Ste 6 57105
Tel (512) 538-2300 *SIC* 7011

■ SUREWEST FINANCIAL CORP p 1408
101 S Phillips Ave 57104
Tel (605) 336-0850 *SIC* 6351

■ TEL-DRUG INC p 1433
4901 N 4th Ave 57104
Tel (605) 809-8166 *SIC* 5912 5961

UNITED NATIONAL CORP p 1510
601 S Minnesota Ave 57104
Tel (605) 357-3001 *SIC* 6021

■ WELLS FARGO FINANCIAL CARDS p 1590
3201 N 4th Ave 57104
Tel (605) 336-3933 *SIC* 6022

■ WESTERN SURETY CO p 1600
101 S Reid St Ste 300 57103
Tel (605) 336-0850 *SIC* 6351

SISSETON, SD

TEKAKWITHA LIVING CENTER INC p 1433
622 Veterans Ave 57262
Tel (605) 698-7693 *SIC* 8351

SPEARFISH, SD

DAVID M DORSETT HEALTH CARE p 415
1020 N 10th St 57783
Tel (605) 642-2716 *SIC* 8051

LANTIS ENTERPRISES INC p 844
4755 E Colorado Blvd 57783
Tel (605) 642-7736 *SIC* 8051 8052

VERMILLION, SD

UNIVERSITY OF SOUTH DAKOTA p 1525
414 E Clark St 57069
Tel (605) 677-5011 *SIC* 8221 9411

VOLGA, SD

SOUTH DAKOTA SOYBEAN PROCESSORS LLC p 1344
100 Caspian Ave 57071
Tel (605) 627-9240 *SIC* 2075

WALL, SD

GOLDEN WEST TELECOMMUNICATIONS COOPERATIVE INC p 622
415 Crown St 57790
Tel (605) 279-2161 *SIC* 4813

WATERTOWN, SD

HOLIEN INC p 700
312 9th Ave Se Ste B 57201
Tel (605) 886-3889 *SIC* 3612 3672 3993

PRAIRIE LAKES HEALTH CARE SYSTEM INC p 1167
401 9th Ave Nw 57201
Tel (605) 882-7000 *SIC* 8062

SCHULL CONSTRUCTION CO p 1290
405 1st Ave Ne 57201
Tel (605) 886-3495 *SIC* 5072

■ TEREX UTILITIES INC p 1439
500 Oakwood Rd 57201
Tel (605) 882-4000 *SIC* 3531 3537

WATERTOWN COOPERATIVE ELEVATOR ASSOCIATION p 1582
811 Burlington Northern D 57201
Tel (605) 886-8333 *SIC* 5153 5191 4221

■ WORTHINGTON INDUSTRIES ENGINEERED CABS INC p 1626
315 Airport Dr 57201
Tel (605) 886-5681 *SIC* 3537

WENTWORTH, SD

LAKE AREA CORN PROCESSORS CO-OPERATIVE p 838
46269 Sd Highway 34 57075
Tel (605) 483-2676 *SIC* 2869

WINNER, SD

COUNTRY PRIDE COOPERATIVE INC p 375
648 W 2nd St 57580
Tel (605) 842-2711
SIC 5153 5172 5191 5411 5211

YANKTON, SD

GEHL POWER PRODUCTS INC p 597
900 Ferdig St 57078
Tel (605) 665-6500 *SIC* 3537 3531 3535

■ KOLBERG-PIONEER INC p 826
700 W 21st St 57078
Tel (605) 665-9311 *SIC* 3532 3531 3535

SACRED HEART HEALTH SERVICES p 1265
501 Summit St 57078
Tel (605) 668-8000 *SIC* 8062 8011

STOCKMENS LIVESTOCK MARKET INC p 1390
1200 E Highway 50 57078
Tel (402) 640-8420 *SIC* 5154

TENNESSEE

ANTIOCH, TN

SYMMETRY SURGICAL INC p 1414
3034 Owen Dr 37013
Tel (615) 883-9090 *SIC* 5047

■ WASTE MANAGEMENT INC OF TENNESSEE p 1580
1428 Antioch Pike 37013
Tel (615) 831-9600 *SIC* 4953

WIRTGEN AMERICA INC p 1618
6030 Dana Way 37013
Tel (615) 501-0600 *SIC* 5082

ARLINGTON, TN

MICROPORT ORTHOPEDICS INC p 962
5677 Airline Rd 38002
Tel (866) 872-0211 *SIC* 5047

ASHLAND CITY, TN

CHEATHAM COUNTY SCHOOL DISTRICT (INC) p 292
102 Elizabeth St 37015
Tel (615) 792-5664 *SIC* 8211

■ STATE INDUSTRIES INC p 1381
500 Tennessee Waltz Pkwy 37015
Tel (615) 792-4371 *SIC* 3639 3443

ATHENS, TN

BARGAIN BARN INC p 155
2924 Lee Hwy 37303
Tel (423) 746-0746 *SIC* 5411 5141

DENSO MANUFACTURING ATHENS TENNESSEE INC p 428
2400 Denso Dr 37303
Tel (423) 746-0000 *SIC* 3694 3714

H-HOME DIVISION HACKNEY HOME FURNISHINGS FAX O p 651
3036 Highway 11 S 37303
Tel (423) 745-9127 *SIC* 5712

■ MAYFIELD DAIRY FARMS LLC p 923
806 E Madison Ave 37303
Tel (423) 745-2151 *SIC* 2026 2024

PI INC p 1146
213 Dennis St 37303
Tel (423) 745-6213
SIC 2519 3949 3089 2499 3086 3081

BARTLETT, TN

AMERICAN ESOTERIC LABORATORIES p 72
2763 Summer Oaks Dr 38134
Tel (901) 937-1910 *SIC* 8734

ORIANNA HEALTH SYSTEMS p 1094
2723 Summer Oaks Dr 38134
Tel (901) 937-7994 *SIC* 6282 8051

■ SAINT FRANCIS HOSPITAL - BARTLETT INC p 1269
2986 Kate Bond Rd 38133
Tel (901) 820-7000 *SIC* 8062

TOP RX LLC p 1460
2950 Brother Blvd Ste 102 38133
Tel (800) 542-8677 *SIC* 5122

BELLS, TN

PICTSWEET CO p 1146
10 Pictsweet Dr 38006
Tel (731) 663-7600 *SIC* 2037 4213

PICTSWEET LLC p 1146
10 Pictsweet Dr 38006
Tel (731) 422-7600 *SIC* 4213 2037

BLOUNTVILLE, TN

COUNTY OF SULLIVAN p 382
3411 Highway 126 Ste 201 37617
Tel (423) 323-6400 *SIC* 9111

SULLIVAN COUNTY SCHOOLS p 1397
154 Blountville Byp 37617
Tel (423) 354-1000 *SIC* 8211

UNITED COAL CO LLC p 1507
110 Sprint Dr 37617
Tel (276) 530-7411 *SIC* 1241

BRENTWOOD, TN

▲ AAC HOLDINGS INC p 8
200 Powell Pl 37027
Tel (615) 732-1231 *SIC* 8093

■ AGC LIFE INSURANCE CO p 34
American General Ctr 37027
Tel (615) 749-1000 *SIC* 6411

AHOM HOLDINGS INC (DE) p 37
5200 Maryland Way Ste 400 37027
Tel (615) 221-8884 *SIC* 8082

■ AMERICAN GENERAL LIFE & ACCIDENT INSURANCE CO p 73
2000 American General Way 37027
Tel (800) 265-5054 *SIC* 6311

AMERICAN HOMEPATIENT INC p 74
5200 Maryland Way Ste 400 37027
Tel (615) 221-8884 *SIC* 8049

■ AMERICAN RETIREMENT CORP p 78
111 Westwood Pl Ste 200 37027
Tel (615) 221-2250 *SIC* 8051

■ AMI METALS INC p 85
1738 Gen George Patton Dr 37027
Tel (615) 370-4917 *SIC* 5051

BELL & ASSOCIATES CONSTRUCTION LP p 169
255 Wilson Pike Cir 37027
Tel (615) 373-4343 *SIC* 1622 1541 1542

BOULEVARD TERRACE LLC p 204
6 Cadillac Dr Ste 310 37027
Tel (615) 896-4505 *SIC* 8051

BRIM HOLDINGS INC p 213
105 Westwood Pl Ste 300 37027
Tel (615) 309-6053 *SIC* 8741

▲ BROOKDALE SENIOR LIVING p 217
111 Westwood Pl Ste 400 37027
Tel (615) 221-2250 *SIC* 8059 8361 8051

CAPELLA HEALTHCARE INC p 248
103 Continental Pl # 200 37027
Tel (615) 764-3000 *SIC* 8062

CAPELLA HOLDINGS INC p 248
103 Continental Pl # 200 37027
Tel (615) 844-9800 *SIC* 8062 6719

CLARITY INDUSTRIES LLC p 322
9265 Hunterboro Dr 37027
Tel (330) 528-3400 *SIC* 3089

CLP HEALTHCARE SERVICES INC p 328
10 Cadillac Dr Ste 400 37027
Tel (615) 224-8028 *SIC* 8051

COGENT MEDICAL CARE PC p 334
5410 Maryland Way Ste 300 37027
Tel (615) 377-5600 *SIC* 8062

COMDATA HOLDINGS CORP p 344
5301 Maryland Way 37027
Tel (615) 370-7000 *SIC* 7374 7389 7375

COMDATA NETWORK INC p 344
5301 Maryland Way 37027
Tel (615) 370-7405 *SIC* 7374

CORIZON HEALTH INC p 370
103 Powell Ct 37027
Tel (800) 729-0069 *SIC* 8011

■ DELEK LOGISTICS PARTNERS LP p 424
7102 Commerce Way 37027
Tel (615) 771-6701 *SIC* 4612 4613

■ DELEK REFINING LIMITED PARTNERSHIP p 424
7102 Commerce Way 37027
Tel (615) 771-6701 *SIC* 4612 2911

▲ DELEK US HOLDINGS INC p 424
7102 Commerce Way 37027
Tel (615) 771-6701
SIC 2911 4612 5541 5411

▲ DIVERSICARE HEALTHCARE SERVICES INC p 443
1621 Galleria Blvd 37027
Tel (615) 771-7575 *SIC* 8051 8322

■ DLP HEALTHCARE LLC p 445
330 Seven Springs Way 37027
Tel (615) 372-8500 *SIC* 8062

■ DVA RENAL HEALTHCARE INC p 463
5200 Virginia Way 37027
Tel (615) 320-4200 *SIC* 8092 8071

GEODIS LOGISTICS LLC p 605
7101 Executive Center Dr # 333 37027
Tel (615) 401-6400
SIC 4225 8742 4226 4731

GUY BROWN MANAGEMENT LLC p 648
320 Seven Springs Way # 450 37027
Tel (615) 777-1500 *SIC* 5112

HEALTHTRUST PURCHASING GROUP LP p 678
155 Franklin Rd Ste 400 37027
Tel (615) 377-1294 *SIC* 7389

HIGHWAYS INC p 692
1623 Galleria Blvd 37027
Tel (615) 373-5445 *SIC* 1611

■ HISTORIC LIFEPOINT HOSPITALS INC p 696
330 Seven Springs Way 37027
Tel (615) 372-8500 *SIC* 8062

HYLANT GROUP p 724
8 Cadillac Dr Ste 230 37027
Tel (615) 732-6500 *SIC* 6361

INFRASTRUCTURE CORP OF AMERICA p 742
750 Old Hickory Blvd # 200 37027
Tel (615) 377-4730 *SIC* 8742 8711 8741

▲ KIRKLANDS INC p 822
5310 Maryland Way 37027
Tel (615) 872-4800 *SIC* 5999 5947

LHOIST NORTH AMERICA OF TENNESSEE INC p 861
750 Old Hickory Blvd 200-2 37027
Tel (615) 259-4222 *SIC* 1422

▲ LIFEPOINT HEALTH INC p 864
330 Seven Springs Way 37027
Tel (615) 920-7000 *SIC* 8062 8742

■ LION OIL CO p 869
7102 Commerce Way 37027
Tel (615) 771-6701 *SIC* 2911 4612 5172

LPS INTEGRATION INC p 882
5300 Virginia Way Ste 100 37027
Tel (866) 706-7904 *SIC* 5045 7379

MAPCO EXPRESS INC p 903
7102 Commerce Way 37027
Tel (615) 771-6701 *SIC* 5541 5411

NIXON POWER SERVICES LLC p 1045
5038 Thoroughbred Ln 37027
Tel (615) 309-5823 *SIC* 5063 4911

ONLIFE HEALTH INC p 1088
9020 Overlook Blvd # 300 37027
Tel (615) 844-2100 *SIC* 6324

OZBURN-HESSEY HOLDING CO LLC p 1101
7101 Executive Center Dr # 333 37027
Tel (615) 401-6400 *SIC* 4225 8742

PREMISE HEALTH HOLDING CORP p 1171
5500 Maryland Way Ste 200 37027
Tel (615) 468-6295 *SIC* 8099

■ PROVINCE HEALTHCARE CO p 1187
103 Powell Ct Ste 200 37027
Tel (205) 487-7900 *SIC* 8741

▲ QUORUM HEALTH CORP p 1201
1573 Mallory Ln 37027
Tel (615) 465-7189 *SIC* 8741

■ QUORUM HEALTH RESOURCES LLC p 1201
1573 Mallory Ln 200 37027
Tel (615) 371-7979
SIC 8742 8741 8082 8231 6324

REGIONAL CARE HOSPITAL PARTNERS INC p 1219
103 Continental Pl # 400 37027
Tel (615) 844-9800 *SIC* 8741

TAKE CARE EMPLOYER SOLUTIONS LLC p 1422
5500 Maryland Way Ste 200 37027
Tel (615) 665-9500 *SIC* 6324

▲ TRACTOR SUPPLY CO p 1468
5401 Virginia Way 37027
Tel (615) 440-4000
SIC 5999 5261 5251 5531 5699

■ TRACTOR SUPPLY CO OF TEXAS LP p 1468
5401 Virginia Way 37027
Tel (877) 718-6750 *SIC* 5084 5999

■ UNITED HEALTHCARE OF TENNESSEE INC p 1509
10 Cadillac Dr Ste 200 37027
Tel (615) 372-3622 *SIC* 6324

BRISTOL, TN

■ BRISTOL METALS LLC p 214
390 Bristol Metals Rd 37620
Tel (423) 968-2151 *SIC* 3312

■ KING PHARMACEUTICALS LLC p 820
501 5th St 37620
Tel (423) 989-8000 *SIC* 2834

SEND LIGHT DISTRIBUTION LLC p 1303
212 Industrial Dr 37620
Tel (423) 547-5100 *SIC* 5192

UNITED CENTRAL INDUSTRIAL SUPPLY CO LLC p 1507
1241 Vlntr Pkwy Ste 1000 37620
Tel (423) 573-7300 *SIC* 5082

UNITED DISTRIBUTORS GROUP INC p 1507
1241 Vlntr Pkwy Ste 1000 37620
Tel (423) 573-7300 *SIC* 5082

BROWNSVILLE, TN

LASCO FITTINGS INC p 846
414 Morgan St 38012
Tel (800) 776-2756 *SIC* 3494

SOUTHWEST TENNESSEE ELECTRIC MEMBERSHIP CORP p 1352
1009 E Main St 38012
Tel (731) 772-1322 *SIC* 4911

TEKNOR APEX TENNESSEE CO p 1433
751 N Dupree Ave 38012
Tel (731) 772-4842 *SIC* 3052

CARTHAGE, TN

UPPER CUMBERLAND ELECTRIC MEMBERSHIP CORP p 1529
907 Main St N 37030
Tel (615) 735-3208 *SIC* 4911

CELINA, TN

CLAY COUNTY MANOR INC p 323
120 Pitcock Ln 38551
Tel (931) 243-3139 *SIC* 8051

CENTERVILLE, TN

LEWIS MERIWETHER ELECTRIC COOPERATIVE p 858
1625 Highway 100 37033
Tel (931) 729-3558 *SIC* 4911

CHARLOTTE, TN

COUNTY OF DICKSON p 377
Court House Sq 37036
Tel (615) 789-5093 *SIC* 9111

CHATTANOOGA, TN

AMERICAN DISPLAY & FIXTURE LLC p 71
3600 N Hawthorne St 37406
Tel (423) 624-1191 *SIC* 2541

■ ASTEC INC p 122
4101 Jerome Ave 37407
Tel (423) 867-4210 *SIC* 3531 3433 3443

▲ ASTEC INDUSTRIES INC p 122
1725 Shepherd Rd 37421
Tel (423) 899-5898 *SIC* 3531 3433 3533

BLUECROSS BLUESHIELD OF TENNESSEE INC p 193
1 Cameron Hill Cir 37402
Tel (423) 535-5600 *SIC* 6324

▲ CBL & ASSOCIATES PROPERTIES INC p 268
2030 Hamilton Place Blvd 37421
Tel (423) 855-0001 *SIC* 6798

CHATTEM INC p 292
1715 W 38th St 37409
Tel (423) 821-4571
SIC 2834 2844 2023 5963

CITY OF CHATTANOOGA p 313
101 E 11th St Ste G13 37402
Tel (423) 425-3700 *SIC* 9111

CONTINUCARE HEALTHSERVICES INC p 364
1501 Riverside Dr Ste 350 37406
Tel (423) 386-1000 *SIC* 8099

COUNTY OF HAMILTON p 378
208 Courths 625 Ga Av 201 37402
Tel (423) 209-6100 *SIC* 9111

■ COVENANT TRANSPORT INC p 384
400 Birmingham Hwy 37419
Tel (423) 821-1212 *SIC* 4213

▲ COVENANT TRANSPORTATION GROUP INC p 384
400 Birmingham Hwy 37419
Tel (423) 821-1212 *SIC* 4213

CRAFTWORKS RESTAURANTS & BREWERIES LLC p 388
201 W Main St Ste 301 37408
Tel (423) 424-2000 *SIC* 5812

ELECTRIC POWER BOARD OF CHATTANOOGA p 484
10 W Martin Luther King B 37402
Tel (423) 756-2706 *SIC* 4911

EMJ CORP p 493
2034 Hamilton Place Blvd # 400 37421
Tel (423) 855-1550 *SIC* 1542

ERMC II LP p 508
1 Park Pl 6148 37421
Tel (423) 899-2753 *SIC* 7349 7382

ERMC III PROPERTY MANAGEMENT CO LLC p 508
6148 Lee Hwy Ste 300 37421
Tel (423) 899-2753 *SIC* 7349

FIRST AMERICAN HOLDING INC p 544
2504 Cross Winds Ln 37421
Tel (423) 894-8783 *SIC* 6163

FIVE STAR FOOD SERVICE INC p 553
6005 Century Oaks Dr # 100 37416
Tel (423) 490-4428 *SIC* 5962 5812 7389

FIVE STAR SERVICE GROUP INC p 553
6005 Century Oaks Dr # 100 37416
Tel (423) 643-2600 *SIC* 5963

GESTAMP CHATTANOOGA LLC p 609
3063 Hickory Valley Rd 37421
Tel (423) 305-6300 *SIC* 3465

GRAIN CRAFT INC p 629
201 W Main St Ste 203 37408
Tel (423) 265-2313 *SIC* 2041

HAMILTON CHATTANOOGA COUNTY HOSPITAL AUTHORITY p 655
975 E 3rd St 37403
Tel (423) 778-7000 *SIC* 5912

HAMILTON COUNTY ECONOMIC DEVELOPMENT FOUNDATION INC p 655
3074 Hickory Valley Rd 37421
Tel (423) 209-8400 *SIC* 9411

■ HEIL CO p 681
2030 Hamilton Place Blvd # 200 37421
Tel (866) 367-4345 *SIC* 3715

HUDSON CONSTRUCTION CO p 716
1615 Sholar Ave 37406
Tel (423) 624-2631 *SIC* 1542

JAT OIL INC p 779
600 W Main St 37402
Tel (423) 629-6611 *SIC* 5172

KENCO GROUP INC p 810
2001 Rverside Dr Ste 3100 37406
Tel (423) 622-1113 *SIC* 4225 6512

KENCO LOGISTIC SERVICES INC p 810
520 W 31st St 37410
Tel (423) 756-5552 *SIC* 4225 4783

KORDSA INC p 828
4501 N Access Rd 37415
Tel (423) 643-8300 *SIC* 5169

LAMBERTI SYNTHESIS USA INC p 841
4001 N Hawthorne St 37406
Tel (423) 697-0526 *SIC* 8741

LIPSEY LOGISTICS WORLDWIDE LLC p 870
5600 Brainerd Rd Ste E2 37411
Tel (678) 336-1180 *SIC* 4731 5499

MEMORIAL HEALTH CARE SYSTEM FOUNDATION INC p 941
2525 De Sales Ave 37404
Tel (423) 495-2525 *SIC* 8742

MEMORIAL HEALTH CARE SYSTEM INC p 941
2525 Desales Ave 37404
Tel (423) 495-2525 *SIC* 8082

METROPOLITAN SECURITY SERVICES INC p 956
100 E 10th St Ste 400 37402
Tel (423) 702-8200 *SIC* 7381

■ MUELLER CO LLC p 998
633 Chestnut St Ste 1200 37450
Tel (423) 209-4800 *SIC* 3823 3533 7699

NEW MOUNTAIN LAKE HOLDINGS LLC p 1032
4080 Jenkins Rd 37421
Tel (423) 510-3000 *SIC* 4213 4731

NU-FOAM PRODUCTS INC p 1066
1101 Wisdom St 37406
Tel (423) 698-6911 *SIC* 3086

OLAN MILLS INC p 1080
735 Broad St Ste 218 37402
Tel (423) 622-5141 *SIC* 7221 2752

■ PARKRIDGE MEDICAL CENTER INC p 1116
2333 Mccallie Ave 37404
Tel (423) 698-6061 *SIC* 8062

PLAYCORE HOLDINGS INC p 1155
401 Chestnut St Ste 410 37402
Tel (423) 756-0015 *SIC* 3949

PLAYCORE HOLDINGS LLC p 1155
401 Chestnut St Ste 410 37402
Tel (877) 762-7563 *SIC* 2452 3949 3448

PLAYCORE WISCONSIN INC p 1155
401 Chestnut St Ste 410 37402
Tel (423) 265-7529 *SIC* 3949

PROPEX HOLDING LLC p 1184
1110 Market St Ste 300 37402
Tel (800) 621-1273
SIC 6719 2221 2297 2262 2211

PROPEX OPERATING CO LLC p 1184
1110 Market St Ste 300 37402
Tel (423) 855-1466 *SIC* 2221

■ PROVIDENT LIFE & ACCIDENT INSURANCE CO p 1186
1 Fountain Sq Ste 1 37402
Tel (423) 755-1011 *SIC* 6311 6321

REPUBLIC PARKING SYSTEM LLC p 1225
633 Chestnut St Ste 2000 37450
Tel (423) 756-2771 *SIC* 8742 7521

■ ROADTEC INC p 1240
800 Manufacturers Rd 37405
Tel (423) 265-0600 *SIC* 3531

■ SERVICE ELECTRIC CO p 1307
1631 E 25th St 37404
Tel (423) 894-4336 *SIC* 1629 1731 1541

SERVICE GROUP INVESTMENTS LLC p 1307
6005 Century Oaks Dr # 100 37416
Tel (423) 643-2600 *SIC* 6282

SIGNAL ENERGY LLC p 1322
2034 Hamilton Place Blvd # 400 37421
Tel (423) 443-4190 *SIC* 1542 8731

■ SISKIN STEEL & SUPPLY CO INC p 1327
1901 Riverfront Pkwy 37408
Tel (423) 756-3671 *SIC* 3312 5051

SOUTHERN CHAMPION TRAY LP p 1347
220 Compress St 37405
Tel (423) 756-5121 *SIC* 2675

■ SOUTHERN MANAGEMENT CORP p 1349
5751 Uptain Rd Ste 408 37411
Tel (423) 510-0010 *SIC* 7349

STELLAR MANAGEMENT GROUP INC p 1385
412 Georgia Ave Ste 300 37403
Tel (423) 265-7090 *SIC* 5064

TUFTCO CORP p 1491
2318 S Holtzclaw Ave 37408
Tel (423) 648-3869 *SIC* 3552

U S XPRESS INC p 1497
4080 Jenkins Rd 37421
Tel (866) 266-7270 *SIC* 4213

▲ UNUM GROUP p 1528
1 Fountain Sq 37402
Tel (423) 294-1011
SIC 6321 6324 6311 6371

US XPRESS ENTERPRISES INC p 1533
4080 Jenkins Rd 37421
Tel (423) 510-3000 *SIC* 4213 4731

WESTROCK CONVERTING CO p 1602
2464 Amnicola Hwy 37406
Tel (423) 622-2254 *SIC* 2752 2759

XPRESS GLOBAL SYSTEMS LLC p 1633
6137 Shallowford Rd # 102 37421
Tel (706) 673-6551 *SIC* 4213

YMCA OF METROPOLITAN CHATTANOOGA p 1636
301 W 6th St 37402
Tel (423) 266-3766
SIC 8641 7991 8351 7032 8322

CLARKSVILLE, TN

BRIDGESTONE METALPHA USA INC p 211
570 International Blvd 37040
Tel (931) 552-2112 *SIC* 2296

CITY OF CLARKSVILLE p 314
1 Public Sq Ste 4 37040
Tel (931) 648-6106 *SIC* 9111

CLARKSVILLE VOLUNTEER HEALTH INC p 322
651 Dunlop Ln 37040
Tel (931) 220-2532 *SIC* 8062 8621

CLARKSVILLE-MONTGOMERY COUNTY SCHOOL SYS p 322
621 Gracey Ave 37040
Tel (931) 648-5600 *SIC* 8211

CUMBERLAND ELECTRIC MEMBERSHIP CORP p 400
1940 Madison St 37043
Tel (931) 645-2481 *SIC* 4911

DAELIM USA INC p 408
1200 International Blvd 37040
Tel (770) 530-3489 *SIC* 1541

DEL-JEN INC p 423
4465 Guthrie Hwy 37040
Tel (931) 552-0232 *SIC* 8744

FLORIM USA INC p 560
300 International Blvd 37040
Tel (931) 553-7548 *SIC* 3253

TENNESSEE ENERGY ACQUISITION CORP p 1438
1808 Ashland City Rd A 37043
Tel (931) 920-3499 *SIC* 4924

CLEVELAND, TN

CHECK INTO CASH INC p 292
201 Keith St Sw Ste 80 37311
Tel (423) 479-2400 *SIC* 6099

CHURCH OF GOD p 305
2490 Keith St Nw 37311
Tel (423) 472-3361 *SIC* 8661

CLEVELAND CHAIR CO INC p 325
370 9th St Se 37311
Tel (423) 476-8544 *SIC* 2512

■ CLEVELAND TENNESSEE HOSPITAL CO LLC p 326
2305 Chambliss Ave Nw 37311
Tel (423) 559-6000 *SIC* 8062

COUNTY OF BRADLEY p 376
155 Broad St Nw Ste H 37311
Tel (423) 728-7141 *SIC* 9111

JACKSON FURNITURE INDUSTRIES INC p 774
1910 King Edward Ave Se 37311
Tel (423) 476-8544 *SIC* 2512

LEE UNIVERSITY p 852
1120 N Ocoee St Ste 102 37311
Tel (423) 614-8000 *SIC* 8221 8661

LIFE CARE CENTERS OF AMERICA INC p 863
3570 Keith St Nw 37312
Tel (423) 472-9585 *SIC* 8051 8052

■ MANUFACTURERS CHEMICALS LLC p 903
4325 Old Tasso Rd Ne 37312
Tel (423) 476-6666 *SIC* 2899

■ OLIN CHLOR ALKALI LOGISTICS INC p 1082
490 Stuart Rd Ne 37312
Tel (423) 336-4850 *SIC* 2812

OPERATION COMPASSION p 1089
114 Stuart Rd Ne Ste 370 37312
Tel (423) 479-3770 *SIC* 8399

PIONEER CREDIT CO p 1150
1870 Executive Park Nw 37312
Tel (423) 476-6511 *SIC* 6141

SANTEK ENVIRONMENTAL INC p 1281
650 25th St Nw Ste 100 37311
Tel (423) 476-9160 *SIC* 4953

CLINTON, TN

ANDERSON COUNTY SCHOOLS p 90
101 S Main St Ste 500 37716
Tel (865) 463-8631 *SIC* 8211

CLINTON UTILITIES BOARD p 327
1001 Chrles G Sivers Blvd 37716
Tel (865) 457-9232 *SIC* 4911

COUNTY OF ANDERSON p 376
100 N Main St Rm 115 37716
Tel (865) 457-6200 *SIC* 9111

EAGLE BEND MFG INC p 467
1000 Jd Yrnell Indus Pkwy 37716
Tel (865) 457-3800 *SIC* 3465 3714

SL AMERICA CORP p 1330
312 Frank L Diggs Dr 37716
Tel (865) 457-8511 *SIC* 3714

SL TENNESSEE LLC p 1330
312 Frank Diggs Dr 37716
Tel (865) 457-8511 *SIC* 3714

TECHMER PM LLC p 1431
1 Quality Cir 37716
Tel (865) 457-6700 *SIC* 2821

COLLEGEDALE, TN

MCKEE FOODS CORP p 930
10260 Mckee Rd 37315
Tel (423) 238-7111
SIC 2051 2052 2099 2043

COLLIERVILLE, TN

ALPHA CORP OF TENNESSEE p 60
955 Highway 57 38017
Tel (901) 854-2800 *SIC* 3089 2865

AOC LLC p 94
955 Highway 57 38017
Tel (901) 854-2800 *SIC* 2295

HELENA CHEMICAL CO p 681
255 Schilling Blvd # 200 38017
Tel (901) 761-0050 *SIC* 5191 2819

HELENA INDUSTRIES INC p 681
225 Schilling Blvd # 400 38017
Tel (901) 820-5700 *SIC* 2879

JUICE PLUS CO LLC p 797
140 Crescent Dr 38017
Tel (901) 850-3000 *SIC* 5149

■ PEPSI BEVERAGES CO p 1134
110 S Byhalia Rd 38017
Tel (901) 853-5736 *SIC* 2086 5181

SHELBY GROUP INTERNATIONAL INC p 1314
1255 W Schilling Blvd 38017
Tel (901) 795-5810
SIC 3842 2381 3851 5137

COLUMBIA, TN

A-Z OFFICE RESOURCE INC p 7
809 S Garden St 38401
Tel (931) 388-1536
SIC 5112 5021 5044 5045 5087

COUNTY OF MAURY p 379
5 Public Sq 38401
Tel (931) 381-3690 *SIC* 9111

JRN INC p 795
209 W 7th St 38401
Tel (931) 381-3000 *SIC* 5812

LP COLUMBIA LLC p 882
1410 Trotwood Ave 38401
Tel (931) 388-6443 *SIC* 8051

MAURY COUNTY PUBLIC SCHOOLS p 921
501 W 8th St 38401
Tel (931) 388-8403 *SIC* 8211

MAURY REGIONAL HOSPITAL p 921
1224 Trotwood Ave 38401
Tel (931) 381-1111 *SIC* 8062

TENNESSEE FARMERS MUTUAL INSURANCE CO p 1438
147 Bear Creek Pike 38401
Tel (877) 876-2222 *SIC* 6331

WIREMASTERS INC p 1618
1788 N Pointe Rd 38401
Tel (615) 791-0281 *SIC* 5063

COOKEVILLE, TN

APHENA PHARMA SOLUTIONS HOLDINGS INC p 96
1920 Fisk Rd 38506
Tel (215) 953-5100 *SIC* 7389 2834

AVERITT EXPRESS INC p 137
1415 Neal St 38501
Tel (931) 526-3306 *SIC* 4214 4213

AVERITT INC p 137
1415 Neal St 38501
Tel (931) 526-3306 *SIC* 4213

■ CITIZENS TELECOMMUNICATIONS CO OF TENNESSEE LLC p 311
250 S Franklin Ave 38501
Tel (931) 528-0501 *SIC* 4813

COOKEVILLE REGIONAL MEDICAL CENTER p 366
1 Medical Center Blvd 38501
Tel (931) 528-2541 *SIC* 8062

DACCO INC p 407
741 Dacco Dr 38506
Tel (931) 303-0112 *SIC* 3714 5013

FLEXIAL CORP p 556
1483 Gould Dr 38506
Tel (931) 432-1853 SIC 5088

IDENTITY GROUP HOLDINGS CORP p 729
1480 Gould Dr 38506
Tel (931) 432-4000
SIC 3089 3086 3993 3953

IDENTITY GROUP HOLDINGS LLC p 729
1480 Gould Dr 38506
Tel (931) 432-4000 SIC 3953

IDENTITY HOLDING CO LLC p 729
1480 Gould Dr 38506
Tel (931) 432-4000 SIC 3953 2672

INSTITUTIONAL WHOLESALE CO INC p 747
535 Dry Valley Rd 38506
Tel (931) 537-4000 SIC 5141 5142

ORECK CORP p 1093
1400 Salem Rd 38506
Tel (800) 219-2044
SIC 3589 3564 5064 5087

TENNESSEE TECHNOLOGICAL UNIVERSITY p 1438
1 William L Jones Dr 38505
Tel (931) 372-3101 SIC 8221

TUTCO INC p 1493
500 Gould Dr 38506
Tel (931) 432-4141 SIC 3634

CORDOVA, TN

ABF NORTH AMERICA CORP p 11
7171 Goodlett Farms Pkwy 38016
Tel (901) 381-3000 SIC 2079 2099

ABF NORTH AMERICA HOLDINGS INC p 11
7171 Goodlett Farms Pkwy 38016
Tel (901) 381-3000 SIC 2079 2099

ACH FOOD COMPANIES INC p 17
7171 Goodlett Farms Pkwy 38016
Tel (901) 381-3000 SIC 2079 2099

AMERICAN INCOME LIFE p 74
8820 Trinity Rd 38018
Tel (901) 748-5584 SIC 6311

■ **CONCORD EFS INC** p 354
7000 Goodlett Farms Pkwy # 300 38016
Tel (901) 371-8000
SIC 6099 7389 6091 5044

LOUIS DREYFUS CO COTTON LLC p 879
7255 Goodlett Farms Pkwy 38016
Tel (901) 383-5000 SIC 5159 5131

STRATAS FOODS LLC p 1392
7130 Goodlett Frm Pkwy # 200 38016
Tel (888) 404-1004 SIC 2079

COVINGTON, TN

COUNTY OF TIPTON p 382
100 Court Sq E 38019
Tel (901) 476-0219 SIC 9111

TIPTON COUNTY SCHOOL DISTRICT INC p 1455
1580 Highway 51 S 38019
Tel (901) 476-7148 SIC 8211

CROSSVILLE, TN

COUNTY OF CUMBERLAND p 377
2 N Main St Ste 303 38555
Tel (931) 484-5730 SIC 9111

CROSSVILLE INC p 394
346 Sweeney Dr 38555
Tel (931) 484-2110 SIC 3253

CUMBERLAND MEDICAL CENTER INC p 400
421 S Main St 38555
Tel (931) 484-9511 SIC 8062

MASTERCORP INC p 918
3505 N Main St 38555
Tel (931) 484-1752 SIC 7349 7217

DANDRIDGE, TN

JEFFERSON COUNTY SCHOOL DISTRICT p 781
1221 Gay St 37725
Tel (865) 397-3138 SIC 8211

DAYTON, TN

ROBINSON MANUFACTURING CO p 1242
798 Market St 37321
Tel (423) 775-8331 SIC 2322 2339 2329

SUBURBAN MANUFACTURING CO p 1396
676 Broadway St 37321
Tel (423) 775-2131 SIC 3585

DECATUR, TN

VOLUNTEER ENERGY COOPERATIVE p 1565
18359 State Highway 58 N 37322
Tel (423) 334-1020 SIC 4911

DICKSON, TN

NEMAK USA INC p 1025
1635 Old Columbia Rd 37055
Tel (615) 446-8110 SIC 3363 3714

TENNSCO CORP p 1438
201 Tennsco Dr 37055
Tel (615) 446-8000 SIC 2542

DRESDEN, TN

COUNTY OF WEAKLEY p 383
8319 Highway 22 Ste B 38225
Tel (731) 364-5413 SIC 9111

DYERSBURG, TN

ELECTRIC RESEARCH AND MANUFACTURING COOPERATIVE INC p 484
2225 Industrial Rd 38024
Tel (731) 285-9121 SIC 3612

ROBERTS-GIBSON INC p 1242
115 Highway 51 Byp 38024
Tel (731) 285-4941 SIC 5171 5541

ELIZABETHTON, TN

SUMMERS-TAYLOR INC p 1398
300 W Elk Ave 37643
Tel (423) 543-3181 SIC 1611 1794 3273

FARRAGUT, TN

EDUCATIONAL SERVICES OF AMERICA INC p 479
12700 Kingston Pike 37934
Tel (865) 824-3051 SIC 7389

FRANKLIN, TN

▲ **ACADIA HEALTHCARE CO INC** p 13
6100 Tower Cir Ste 1000 37067
Tel (615) 861-6000 SIC 8093

■ **APCOM INC** p 96
125 Se Parkway 37064
Tel (615) 794-5574 SIC 3491 5064

CAMP RECOVERY CENTERS L P p 245
6100 Tower Cir Ste 1000 37067
Tel (408) 998-7260 SIC 8069

CARLSTAR GROUP LLC p 258
725 Cool Springs Blvd 37067
Tel (615) 503-0220
SIC 3714 5014 3499 5013 2296

■ **CENTERRE HEALTHCARE CORP** p 276
113 Seaboard Ln Ste 201b 37067
Tel (615) 846-9500 SIC 8011

■ **CHSPSC** p 304
4000 Meridian Blvd 37067
Tel (615) 465-7000 SIC 8062 6321

▲ **CLARCOR INC** p 321
840 Crescent Centre Dr # 600 37067
Tel (615) 771-3100
SIC 3714 3599 3564 3569 3411 3089

▲ **COMMUNITY HEALTH SYSTEMS INC** p 349
4000 Meridian Blvd 37067
Tel (615) 465-7000 SIC 8062 8742

CONSTRUCTION ENTERPRISES INC p 361
2179 Edward Curd Ln # 100 37067
Tel (615) 332-8880 SIC 1522 1542

■ **DIVERSICARE MANAGEMENT SERVICES CO** p 444
277 Mallory Station Rd # 130 37067
Tel (615) 771-7575 SIC 8741

EXPERIAN HEALTH INC p 519
720 Cool Springs Blvd 37067
Tel (615) 661-5657 SIC 7372 8399

GARDNER TRUCKING INC p 592
331 Premier Ct S 37067
Tel (909) 563-5606 SIC 4213 4212

GRANGES AMERICAS INC p 631
801 Crescent Centre Dr 37067
Tel (615) 778-2004 SIC 3353

HCTEC PARTNERS LLC p 672
7105 S Springs Dr Ste 208 37067
Tel (615) 577-4030 SIC 8741

▲ **HEALTHWAYS INC** p 678
701 Cool Springs Blvd 37067
Tel (615) 614-4929 SIC 8082 8099

IASIS HEALTHCARE CORP p 726
117 Seaboard Ln Bldg E 37067
Tel (615) 844-2747 SIC 8062

IASIS HEALTHCARE LLC p 726
117 Seaboard Ln Bldg E 37067
Tel (615) 844-2747 SIC 8062

IASIS INVESTMENT LLC p 726
113 Seaboard Ln Ste 200a 37067
Tel (615) 844-2747 SIC 8062

LAND SOUTHERN CO LLC p 842
1550 W Mcewen Dr Ste 200 37067
Tel (615) 778-3150 SIC 6552

LEE CO p 851
331 Mallory Station Rd 37067
Tel (615) 567-1000 SIC 1711

■ **LIFETRUST AMERICA INC** p 865
113 Seaboard Ln Ste 150a 37067
Tel (615) 342-0601
SIC 8361 8051 8052 8059

MAGOTTEAUX INC p 897
725 Cool Springs Blvd # 200 37067
Tel (615) 385-3055 SIC 3369

MANCHESTER TANK & EQUIPMENT CO INC p 901
1000 Corporate Centre Dr # 300 37067
Tel (615) 370-6104 SIC 3443

MARS PETCARE US INC p 910
315 Cool Springs Blvd 37067
Tel (615) 807-4626 SIC 2047

MEDHOST OF TENNESSEE INC p 935
6550 Carothers Pkwy # 100 37067
Tel (615) 761-1000 SIC 7371

MEDSOLUTIONS INC p 938
730 Cool Springs Blvd # 250 37067
Tel (615) 468-0600 SIC 6324 8322

MMODAL INC p 979
5000 Meridian Blvd # 200 37067
Tel (888) 840-4050 SIC 7374

MMODAL SERVICES INC p 979
5000 Meridian Blvd # 200 37067
Tel (615) 261-1500 SIC 7372 7371

MMODAL SERVICES LTD INC p 979
5000 Meridian Blvd # 200 37067
Tel (800) 233-3030 SIC 8999

■ **NATIONAL HEALTHCARE OF CLEVELAND INC** p 1013
4000 Meridian Blvd 37067
Tel (423) 339-4100 SIC 8062

NATIONAL SEATING & MOBILITY INC p 1016
320 Premier Ct S Ste 220 37067
Tel (615) 595-1115 SIC 3842 5999

NISSAN MOTOR ACCEPTANCE CORP p 1044
1 Nissan Way 37067
Tel (615) 725-1000 SIC 6141

NISSAN NORTH AMERICA INC p 1044
1 Nissan Way 37067
Tel (615) 725-1000
SIC 5012 8711 8734 6141 8741 3711

NORANDA ALUMINUM HOLDING CORP p 1047
801 Crescent Cntre Dr 6 Ste 600 37067
Tel (615) 771-5700 SIC 3334 2819 3353

NORANDA INTERMEDIATE HOLDING CORP p 1047
801 Crescent Centre Dr 37067
Tel (615) 771-5700
SIC 3353 3334 3714 3354

NORANDAL USA INC p 1047
801 Crescent Centre Dr # 600 37067
Tel (615) 778-2000 SIC 3353

NORTEL NETWORKS HPOCS INC p 1049
725 Cool Springs Blvd # 600 37067
Tel (800) 684-2228 SIC 3661

NUTRO CO p 1068
1550 W Mcewen Dr Ste 100 37067
Tel (888) 607-4081 SIC 2047 0742

■ **PARALLON BUSINESS SOLUTIONS LLC** p 1114
6640 Carothers Pkwy 37067
Tel (615) 344-3000 SIC 8082

■ **PRIMUS AUTOMOTIVE FINANCIAL SERVICES INC** p 1176
9009 Carothers Pkwy 37067
Tel (800) 374-7000 SIC 6141

■ **PSYCHIATRIC SOLUTIONS INC** p 1189
6640 Carothers Pkwy # 500 37067
Tel (615) 312-5700 SIC 8011 8063

PUREWORKS INC p 1192
5000 Meridian Blvd # 600 37067
Tel (615) 367-4404 SIC 4813

RESOURCE LABEL GROUP LLC p 1227
147 Seaboard Ln 37067
Tel (615) 661-5900 SIC 2759 2752

SP WIND DOWN INC p 1353
9009 Carothers Pkwy # 303 37067
Tel (615) 261-1500 SIC 7338

SPHERIS HOLDING III INC p 1358
720 Cool Springs Blvd 37067
Tel (615) 261-1500 SIC 7338

TOM JAMES CO p 1459
263 Seaboard Ln 37067
Tel (615) 771-6633
SIC 2311 2325 2323 2321 5611

TOTAL EMED INC p 1462
9009 Carothers Pkwy # 303 37067
Tel (615) 261-1500 SIC 7338

VIDEO GAMING TECHNOLOGIES INC p 1556
308 Mallory Station Rd 37067
Tel (615) 372-1000 SIC 3999 7993

WESTPORT PETROLEUM INC p 1602
810 Crescent Centre Dr # 530 37067
Tel (615) 771-6800 SIC 5172

WILLIAMSON COUNTY HOSPITAL INC p 1612
4321 Carothers Pkwy 37067
Tel (615) 791-0500 SIC 8062

WILLIAMSON COUNTY SCHOOL DISTRICT p 1612
1320 W Main St Ste 202 37064
Tel (615) 472-4000 SIC 8211

GALLATIN, TN

ASSOCIATED PACKAGING INC p 121
435 Calvert Dr 37066
Tel (615) 452-2131 SIC 5199 5084

CHARLES C PARKS CO INC p 289
500 N Belvedere Dr 37066
Tel (615) 452-2406 SIC 5149

COUNTY OF SUMNER p 382
355 N Belvedere Dr Rm 302 37066
Tel (615) 452-3604 SIC 9111

SERVPRO INDUSTRIES INC p 1308
801 Industrial Blvd 37066
Tel (615) 451-0200 SIC 5087

SERVPRO INTELLECTUAL PROPERTY INC p 1308
801 Industrial Blvd 37066
Tel (615) 451-0200 SIC 7349 8741 5087

■ **SRHS BANKRUPTCY INC** p 1363
555 Hartsville Pike 37066
Tel (615) 452-4210 SIC 8062

SUMNER COUNTY BOARD OF EDUCATION p 1399
695 E Main St 37066
Tel (615) 451-5200 SIC 8211

SUMNER COUNTY SCHOOL DISTRICT p 1399
695 E Main St 37066
Tel (615) 451-5200 SIC 8211

WESTERN REFLECTIONS LLC p 1599
261 Commerce Way 37066
Tel (615) 451-9700 SIC 5031

GERMANTOWN, TN

DYK AUTOMOTIVE LLC p 464
1900 Exeter Rd Ste 200 38138
Tel (763) 478-2360 SIC 6719

■ **MID-AMERICA APARTMENTS LP** p 963
6584 Poplar Ave 38138
Tel (866) 620-1130 SIC 6798

W2007 GRACE ACQUISITION I INC p 1569
7700 Wolf River Blvd 38138
Tel (901) 759-6000 SIC 6798

WEST FRASER INC p 1594
1900 Exeter Rd Ste 105 38138
Tel (901) 620-4200 SIC 2431 0831

WEST FRASER WOOD PRODUCTS INC p 1594
1900 Exeter Rd Ste 105 38138
Tel (901) 620-4200 SIC 2431

GOODLETTSVILLE, TN

31-W INSULATION CO INC p 2
7434 Cycle Ln 37072
Tel (615) 643-3900 SIC 1742

■ **DOLGENCORP LLC** p 448
100 Mission Rdg 37072
Tel (615) 855-4000 SIC 5331

■ **DOLGENCORP OF TEXAS INC** p 448
100 Mission Rdg 37072
Tel (615) 855-4000 SIC 5331

▲ **DOLLAR GENERAL CORP** p 448
100 Mission Rdg 37072
Tel (615) 855-4000 SIC 5331

GRAY, TN

FRONTIER HEALTH p 581
1167 Spratlin Park Dr 37615
Tel (423) 467-3600 SIC 8093 8322

GREENEVILLE, TN

COUNTY OF GREENE p 378
204 N Cutler St Ste 206 37745
Tel (423) 798-1703 SIC 9111

▲ **FORWARD AIR CORP** p 570
430 Airport Rd 37745
Tel (423) 636-7000 SIC 4731

■ **FORWARD AIR INC** p 570
430 Airport Rd 37745
Tel (423) 639-7196 SIC 4731

■ **GREEN BANKSHARES INC** p 636
100 N Main St 37743
Tel (704) 554-5901 SIC 6022

■ **GREENBANK** p 637
100 N Main St 37743
Tel (423) 639-5111 SIC 6022

GREENEVILLE LIGHT & POWER SYSTEM (INC) p 638
110 N College St 37743
Tel (423) 636-6200 SIC 4911

GREENEVILLE OIL & PETROLEUM INC p 638
860 W Andrew Johnson Hwy 37745
Tel (423) 638-3145 SIC 5172 5411 5541

■ **JARDEN ZINC PRODUCTS LLC** p 778
2500 Old Stage Rd 37745
Tel (423) 639-8111
SIC 2796 3364 3356 1031 2789

LANDAIR TRANSPORT INC p 842
1 Landair Way 37743
Tel (423) 783-1300 SIC 4213 4225

UNAKA CO INC p 1502
1500 Industrial Rd 37745
Tel (423) 639-1171
SIC 2099 3469 2514 2253 4226

HARROGATE, TN

LINCOLN MEMORIAL UNIVERSITY p 867
6965 Cumberland Gap Pkwy 37752
Tel (423) 869-3611 SIC 8221

HENDERSONVILLE, TN

ALADDIN TEMP-RITE LLC p 43
250 E Main St 37075
Tel (615) 537-3600 SIC 5047

APPALACHIAN PIPELINE CONTRACTORS LLP p 98
170 E Main St Ste D 37075
Tel (615) 264-8775 SIC 1623

DIRECT AUCTION SERVICES LLC p 441
101 Jessica Lauren Ct 37075
Tel (678) 570-3493
SIC 5012 7539 7549 7542 7361

DYNAMIC RESTAURANTS LLC p 464
313 E Mn St 37075
Tel (615) 277-1234 SIC 5812

HERMITAGE, TN

■ **HCA HEALTH SERVICES OF TENNESSEE INC** p 671
5655 Frist Blvd 37076
Tel (615) 316-3000 *SIC* 8062

HIXSON, TN

MEMORIAL NORTH PARK HOSPITAL p 942
2151 Hamill Rd 37343
Tel (423) 495-7100 *SIC* 8062

HOHENWALD, TN

HIGHLAND CORP p 691
108 Mill Ave 38462
Tel (800) 924-8514 *SIC* 5171 5411

JACKSON, TN

DEMENT CONSTRUCTION CO p 428
96 Smith Ln 38301
Tel (731) 424-6306 *SIC* 1622 1611

■ **DEVILBISS AIR POWER CO** p 434
4825 Highway 45 N 38305
Tel (800) 888-2468 *SIC* 3563 3621 3589

H AND M CONSTRUCTION CO INC p 649
50 Security Dr 38305
Tel (731) 660-3091 *SIC* 1541 1542

JACKSON CLINIC PHARMACY INC p 773
828 N Parkway 38305
Tel (731) 422-0330 *SIC* 5912

JACKSON CLINIC PROFESSIONAL ASSOCIATION p 773
828 N Parkway 38305
Tel (731) 422-0200 *SIC* 5912 8011 8062

JACKSON ENERGY AUTHORITY p 773
351 Dr Martin Luther 38301
Tel (731) 422-7500
SIC 4925 4911 4941 4952

■ **JACKSON HOSPITAL CORP** p 774
367 Hospital Blvd 38305
Tel (731) 661-2000 *SIC* 8062

JACKSON-MADISON COUNTY GENERAL HOSPITAL DISTRICT p 774
620 Skyline Dr 38301
Tel (731) 541-5000 *SIC* 8062

JACKSON-MADISON COUNTY SCHOOL SYSTEM p 774
310 N Parkway 38305
Tel (731) 664-2500 *SIC* 8211

MURRAY GUARD INC p 1001
58 Murray Guard Dr 38305
Tel (731) 668-3400 *SIC* 7381

PERSEUS DISTRIBUTION INC p 1137
210 American Dr 38301
Tel (731) 988-4440 *SIC* 5192

■ **PORTER-CABLE CORP** p 1162
4825 Highway 45 N Ste 880 38305
Tel (731) 660-5986 *SIC* 3546

RUSSEL JMS METALS CORP p 1259
25 College Park Cv 38301
Tel (731) 984-8121 *SIC* 5051

TENNESSEETBDN CO p 1438
1410 Us Highway 70 Byp 38301
Tel (731) 421-4800 *SIC* 3714

TENNESSEE WEST HEALTHCARE INC p 1438
620 Skyline Dr 38301
Tel (731) 541-5000 *SIC* 8062

UNION UNIVERSITY p 1505
1050 Union University Dr 38305
Tel (731) 668-1818 *SIC* 8221

■ **YOUNG TOUCHSTONE CO** p 1639
200 Smith Ln 38301
Tel (731) 424-5045 *SIC* 4911 3743

JOHNSON CITY, TN

ADMINISTRATIVE RESOURCES INC p 23
801 Sunset Dr F1 37604
Tel (423) 283-0296
SIC 8721 8741 8742 6794

■ **AMERICAN WATER HEATER CO** p 81
500 Princeton Rd 37601
Tel (423) 283-8000 *SIC* 3639

CITY OF JOHNSON CITY p 315
601 E Main St 37601
Tel (423) 434-6000 *SIC* 9111

EAST TENNESSEE STATE UNIVERSITY p 471
1276 Gilbreath Dr 37614
Tel (423) 439-1000 *SIC* 8221

GENERAL SHALE BRICK INC p 602
3015 Bristol Hwy 37601
Tel (423) 282-4661 *SIC* 5211 5031

■ **LAND-O-SUN DAIRIES LLC** p 842
2900 Bristol Hwy 37601
Tel (423) 283-5700 *SIC* 2026 2024 5143

MOUNTAIN EMPIRE OIL CO p 994
282 Christian Church Rd 37615
Tel (423) 928-7241 *SIC* 5541 5411

MOUNTAIN STATES HEALTH ALLIANCE p 994
400 N State Of Frnklin Rd 37604
Tel (423) 431-6111 *SIC* 8741

MOUNTAIN STATES HEALTH ALLIANCE p 994
400 N State Of Frnklin Rd 37604
Tel (423) 431-6111 *SIC* 8062

▲ **NN INC** p 1045
207 Mockingbird Ln Ste 10 37604
Tel (423) 743-9151 *SIC* 3562

POWELL CONSTRUCTION CO INC p 1165
3622 Bristol Hwy Ste 1 37601
Tel (423) 282-0111 *SIC* 1542 1221 1541

TPI CORP p 1467
114 Roscoe Fitz Rd 37615
Tel (800) 682-3398 *SIC* 3567 3564

JONESBOROUGH, TN

WASHINGTON COUNTY BOARD OF EDUCATION p 1578
405 W College St 37659
Tel (423) 753-1100 *SIC* 8211

KINGSPORT, TN

ALPHA NATURAL RESOURCES INC p 60
1989 E Stone Dr 37660
Tel (423) 723-8900 *SIC* 1221 1222

BAE SYSTEMS ORDNANCE SYSTEMS INC p 144
4509 W Stone Dr 37660
Tel (423) 578-6000 *SIC* 3483

▲ **EASTMAN CHEMICAL CO** p 473
200 S Wilcox Dr 37660
Tel (423) 229-2000
SIC 2821 2869 2865 2823

■ **EASTMAN CHEMICAL LTD CORP** p 473
200 S Wilcox Dr 37660
Tel (423) 229-2000 *SIC* 5169 8742

EASTMAN CREDIT UNION p 473
2021 Meadowview Ln # 200 37660
Tel (423) 229-8200 *SIC* 6062

HOLSTON MEDICAL GROUP PC p 702
2323 N John B Dennis Hwy 37660
Tel (423) 857-2000 *SIC* 8011

■ **TAMINCO CORP** p 1423
200 S Wilcox Dr 37660
Tel (423) 229-2000 *SIC* 2869

WELLMONT HEALTH SYSTEM p 1589
1905 American Way 37660
Tel (423) 230-8200 *SIC* 8062 8051 8063

KINGSTON, TN

ROANE COUNTY p 1240
200 E Race St Ste 1 37763
Tel (865) 376-3184 *SIC* 9111

ROANE COUNTY SCHOOLS p 1240
105 Bluff Rd 37763
Tel (865) 376-5592 *SIC* 8211

KNOXVILLE, TN

AMERICA PLASTICS LLC p 67
2636 Byington Solway Rd 37931
Tel (865) 457-7000 *SIC* 3089

AMERICAN BOOK CO p 69
10267 Kingston Pike 37922
Tel (865) 966-7454 *SIC* 5192 2731

AMERICAS COLLECTIBLES NETWORK INC p 81
9600 Parkside Dr 37922
Tel (865) 692-6000 *SIC* 5094

ANDERSON MEDIA CORP p 90
265 Brookview Town Ste 37919
Tel (865) 474-8500 *SIC* 5099 5192

ANDERSON NEWS LLC p 90
265 Brookview Town Ste 37919
Tel (865) 584-9765 *SIC* 5192

ANDERSON SERVICES LLC p 90
6016 Brookvale Ln 110b 37919
Tel (865) 584-6714 *SIC* 4212

APAC-ATLANTIC INC p 95
4817 Rutledge Pike 37914
Tel (865) 983-3100
SIC 5032 3531 3273 2951 1611

ARC AUTOMOTIVE INC p 103
1729 Midpark Rd Ste 100 37921
Tel (865) 583-7600 *SIC* 3714

ATWORK FRANCHISE INC p 130
3215 W Gov J Sevier Hwy 37920
Tel (865) 609-6911 *SIC* 6794 8742 8721

■ **BAPTIST HEALTH SYSTEM OF EAST TENNESSEE INC** p 154
137 E Blount Ave Ste 1b 37920
Tel (865) 632-5011 *SIC* 8062

BAPTIST HOSPITAL OF EAST TENNESSEE INC p 154
137 E Blount Ave 37920
Tel (865) 632-5200 *SIC* 8062

■ **BAPTIST HOSPITAL WEST INC** p 154
10820 Parkside Dr 37934
Tel (865) 218-7011 *SIC* 8062

BLAINE CONSTRUCTION CORP p 188
6510 Deane Hill Dr 37919
Tel (865) 693-8900 *SIC* 1541 1542

BROADWAY ELECTRIC SERVICE CORP p 216
1800 N Central St 37917
Tel (865) 524-1851 *SIC* 1731

BROS MANAGEMENT INC p 218
2501 E Magnolia Ave 37914
Tel (865) 523-2157 *SIC* 5812

BUSH BROTHERS & CO p 229
1016 E Weisgarber Rd 37909
Tel (865) 450-4130 *SIC* 2033 2032

■ **CARITEN INSURANCE CO** p 256
2160 Lakeside Centre Way # 200 37922
Tel (865) 470-7470 *SIC* 6324

CELLULAR SALES OF KNOXVILLE INC p 274
9040 Executive Park Dr 37923
Tel (865) 584-7555 *SIC* 5999

CFJ PROPERTIES LLC p 285
5508 Lonas Dr 37909
Tel (801) 624-1000 *SIC* 5541 5812 5411

CHEROKEE DISTRIBUTING CO INC p 294
200 Miller Main Cir 37919
Tel (865) 588-7641 *SIC* 5181

CITY OF KNOXVILLE p 316
400 W Main St Rm L108 37902
Tel (865) 215-2040 *SIC* 9111

COPPER CELLAR CORP p 368
3001 Industrial Pkwy E 37921
Tel (865) 673-3400 *SIC* 5812 5813

COUNTRYWIDE HR p 375
135 Fox Rd Ste F 37922
Tel (877) 257-6662 *SIC* 8721 7361

COUNTY OF KNOX p 379
400 W Main St Rm 615 37902
Tel (865) 215-2005 *SIC* 9111

COVENANT HEALTH p 384
100 Fort Sanders W Blvd 37922
Tel (865) 531-5555 *SIC* 8062

COVENANT HEALTHCARE INC p 384
1451 Bowell Springs Blvd 37909
Tel (865) 970-9800 *SIC* 8093

CUSTOM FOODS OF AMERICA INC p 403
3600 Pleasant Ridge Rd 37921
Tel (865) 525-0401 *SIC* 2038

DURA-LINE CORP p 462
11400 Parkside Dr Ste 300 37934
Tel (865) 218-3460 *SIC* 3644

EAST TENNESSEE CHILDRENS HOSPITAL ASSOCIATION INC p 471
2018 W Clinch Ave 37916
Tel (865) 541-8000 *SIC* 8069

EDFINANCIAL SERVICES LLC p 477
298 N Seven Oaks Dr 37922
Tel (865) 342-5500 *SIC* 6111

EDUCATIONAL FUNDING OF SOUTH INC p 479
12700 Kingston Pike 37934
Tel (865) 342-0684 *SIC* 6141

FORT SANDERS REGIONAL MEDICAL CENTER p 569
1901 W Clinch Ave 37916
Tel (865) 541-1111 *SIC* 8062

H T HACKNEY CO p 650
502 S Gay St Ste 300 37902
Tel (865) 546-1291
SIC 5141 5172 2434 5084

■ **HHC INC** p 689
6501 Deane Hill Dr 37919
Tel (865) 292-6000 *SIC* 8082

HOLSTON GASES INC p 702
545 W Baxter Ave 37921
Tel (865) 573-1917 *SIC* 5169 5084 2813

HOUSE-HASSON HARDWARE CO p 711
3125 Water Plant Rd 37914
Tel (800) 333-0520 *SIC* 5072 5031

■ **HOUSECALL MEDICAL RESOURCES INC** p 711
1400 Cntrpint Blvd St 100 37932
Tel (865) 689-7123 *SIC* 8082 8741 5999

JOHNSON & GALYON INC p 790
1130 Atlantic Ave 37917
Tel (865) 688-1111 *SIC* 1542 1541

KELSAN INC p 809
5109 N National Dr 37914
Tel (865) 525-7132 *SIC* 5087 5169 7699

■ **KNOXVILLE NEWS-SENTINEL CO** p 825
2332 News Sentinel Dr 37921
Tel (865) 523-3131 *SIC* 2711

KNOXVILLE UTILITIES BOARD p 825
445 S Gay St 37902
Tel (865) 594-7324
SIC 4911 4924 4941 4952

MAXUM PETROLEUM INC p 923
5508 Lonas Dr 37909
Tel (865) 588-7488 *SIC* 5172

■ **MERCY HEALTH PARTNERS INC** p 946
900 E Oak Hill Ave 37917
Tel (865) 545-8000 *SIC* 8062

METHODIST MEDICAL CENTER OF OAK RIDGE p 954
1420 Centerpoint Blvd C 37932
Tel (865) 374-6864 *SIC* 8011

MID AMERICA CORP p 962
2812 N Broadway St 37917
Tel (865) 524-3477 *SIC* 5812

NAVISTAR INC p 1020
Caller Service 59010 37950
Tel (865) 558-1904 *SIC* 5085

PARKWEST MEDICAL CENTER p 1117
9352 Park West Blvd 37923
Tel (865) 373-1000 *SIC* 8062

PARKWEST MEDICAL CENTER p 1117
1420 Centerpoint Blvd 37932
Tel (865) 374-6872 *SIC* 8011

PENNANT FOODS LLC p 1129
310 Corporate Dr Ste 103 37923
Tel (865) 691-1393 *SIC* 5812

PETERBILT OF KNOXVILLE INC p 1138
5218 Rutledge Pike 37924
Tel (800) 552-7779 *SIC* 5012 7538

PHILLIPS AND JORDAN INC p 1144
10201 Parkside Dr Ste 300 37922
Tel (865) 688-8342 *SIC* 1611 1629

PILOT CORP p 1148
5508 Lonas Dr 37909
Tel (865) 588-7488 *SIC* 5411 5541

PILOT TRAVEL CENTERS LLC p 1148
5508 Lonas Dr 37909
Tel (865) 588-7488 *SIC* 5411 5541

POWER EQUIPMENT CO p 1165
3300 Alcoa Hwy 37920
Tel (865) 577-5563 *SIC* 5082 3531 7353

PROLOGIC DISTRIBUTION SERVICES (EAST) LLC p 1182
6016 Brookvale Ln 110b 37919
Tel (865) 584-9765 *SIC* 4212 4213

RADIO SYSTEMS CORP p 1204
10427 Petsafe Way 37932
Tel (865) 777-5404 *SIC* 0752 1799 6794

■ **REGAL CINEMAS CORP** p 1218
7132 Regal Ln 37918
Tel (865) 922-1123 *SIC* 7832 5812

■ **REGAL CINEMAS INC** p 1218
7132 Regal Ln 37918
Tel (865) 922-1123 *SIC* 7832

▲ **REGAL ENTERTAINMENT GROUP** p 1218
7132 Regal Ln 37918
Tel (865) 922-1123 *SIC* 7832

■ **REGAL ENTERTAINMENT HOLDINGS INC** p 1218
7132 Regal Ln 37918
Tel (865) 922-1123 *SIC* 7832

RUSH FITNESS CORP p 1258
10708 Kingston Pike 37934
Tel (865) 671-6444 *SIC* 7991

■ **SAFETY & ECOLOGY HOLDINGS CORP** p 1266
2800 Solway Rd 37931
Tel (865) 690-0501 *SIC* 8744 8748

▲ **SCRIPPS NETWORKS INTERACTIVE INC** p 1294
9721 Sherrill Blvd 37932
Tel (865) 694-2700 *SIC* 4841

■ **SEA RAY BOATS INC** p 1295
800 S Gay St Ste 1200 37929
Tel (865) 522-4181 *SIC* 3732

SHONEYS OF KNOXVILLE INC p 1317
9720 Parkside Dr 37922
Tel (865) 690-6331 *SIC* 5812

SOUTHEAST SERVICE CORP p 1346
1845 Midpark Rd Ste 201 37921
Tel (865) 546-8880 *SIC* 7349

■ **STAR CONSTRUCTION LLC** p 1378
6621 Asheville Hwy 37924
Tel (865) 521-6795 *SIC* 1623

T & W OF KNOXVILLE INC p 1419
10315 Parkside Dr 37922
Tel (865) 218-3300 *SIC* 5511 7538 5531

▲ **TEAM HEALTH HOLDINGS INC** p 1430
265 Brookview Centre Way 37919
Tel (865) 693-1000 *SIC* 7363 8741

■ **TEAM HEALTH INC** p 1430
265 Brookview Centre Way 37919
Tel (865) 693-1000 *SIC* 8099

TED RUSSELL FORD INC p 1432
8551 Kingston Pike 37919
Tel (865) 693-7611 *SIC* 5511 5521 5531

■ **TENNESSEE VALLEY AUTHORITY** p 1438
400 W Summit Hill Dr 37902
Tel (865) 632-2101 *SIC* 4911 9631

TINDELLS INC p 1455
7751 Norris Fwy 37938
Tel (865) 922-7751 *SIC* 5031 5211 2439

■ **UNITED ARTISTS THEATRE CIRCUIT INC** p 1506
7132 Regal Ln 37918
Tel (865) 922-1123 *SIC* 7832

UNIVERSITY HEALTH SYSTEM INC p 1519
1924 Alcoa Hwy 37920
Tel (865) 305-9000 *SIC* 8062

UNIVERSITY HEALTH SYSTEM INC p 1519
9000 Executive Park Dr D240 37923
Tel (865) 251-3700 *SIC* 6324 8011

UNIVERSITY OF TENNESSEE p 1525
1331 Circle Park Dr 37916
Tel (865) 974-2303 *SIC* 8221

UT FOUNDATION INC p 1536
600 Henley St Ste 100 37996
Tel (865) 974-1558 *SIC* 8699

■ **WVLT-TV INC** p 1628
6450 Papermill Dr 37919
Tel (865) 450-8888 *SIC* 4833

LA VERGNE, TN

AJAX TURNER CO INC p 41
4010 Centre Pointe Dr 37086
Tel (615) 244-2424 *SIC* 5182

■ **CARDINAL HEALTH 108 LLC** p 253
305 Tech Park Dr Ste 113 37086
Tel (615) 287-5200 *SIC* 5122 5047

CINRAM GROUP INC p 308
437 New Sanford Rd 37086
Tel (615) 287-3800 *SIC* 3695

CONTENT INGRAM GROUP INC p 362
1 Ingram Blvd 37086
Tel (615) 793-5000 *SIC* 5192

DBI BEVERAGE INC p 418
2 Ingram Blvd 37089
Tel (615) 793-2337 *SIC* 5149

ESSEXTECHNOLOGY GROUP INC p 510
455 Industrial Blvd Ste C 37086
Tel (615) 620-5444 *SIC* 5045 8732 5261

■ **HENNESSY INDUSTRIES INC** p 683
1601 Jp Hennessy Dr 37086
Tel (615) 641-7533 *SIC* 3714 5013

INGRAM BOOK GROUP INC p 743
1 Ingram Blvd 37086
Tel (615) 213-5000 *SIC* 5192

INGRAM ENTERTAINMENT HOLDINGS INC p 743
2 Ingram Blvd 37089
Tel (615) 287-4000 *SIC* 5065 5045

INGRAM ENTERTAINMENT INC p 743
2 Ingram Blvd 37089
Tel (615) 287-4000 *SIC* 5065 5092 5099

QCH NASHVILLE LLC p 1194
1621 Heil Quaker Blvd 37086
Tel (615) 501-7500 *SIC* 5045 3577

QUANTA SERVICE NASHVILLE LLC p 1198
1621 Heil Quaker Blvd 37086
Tel (615) 501-7500 *SIC* 3577

SINGER SEWING CO p 1326
1224 Heil Quaker Blvd 37086
Tel (615) 213-0880 *SIC* 5064

STEELSUMMIT HOLDINGS INC p 1385
1718 Jp Hennessy Dr 37086
Tel (615) 641-8600 *SIC* 5051

TECHNICOLOR HOME ENTERTAINMENT p 1431
437 New Sanford Rd 37086
Tel (615) 372-9258 *SIC* 3652

TENNESSEE FARMERS COOPERATIVE INC p 1438
180 Old Nashville Hwy 37086
Tel (615) 793-8011
SIC 5191 5013 5014 5172 5122 2048

THOMPSON MACHINERY COMMERCE CORP p 1449
1245 Bridgestone Pkwy 37086
Tel (615) 256-2424 *SIC* 5082 7353

VENTURE EXPRESS INC p 1548
131 Industrial Blvd 37086
Tel (615) 793-9500 *SIC* 4213

LAFAYETTE, TN

TRI COUNTY ELECTRIC MEMBERSHIP CORP p 1476
405 College St 37083
Tel (615) 666-2111 *SIC* 4911

LAWRENCEBURG, TN

CENTRAL BAND OF CHEROKEE p 277
870 Lawrence Ave 38464
Tel (931) 242-6398 *SIC* 8641

EDWARDS OIL CO OF LAWRENCEBURG INC p 480
105 Helton Dr 38464
Tel (931) 762-5531 *SIC* 5172

SOUTHTENNESSEE OIL CO INC p 1345
105 Helton Dr 38464
Tel (931) 762-9600 *SIC* 5541 5411

LEBANON, TN

■ **CBOCSTEXAS LLC** p 268
305 S Hartmann Dr 37087
Tel (615) 235-4096 *SIC* 5812

▲ **CRACKER BARREL OLD COUNTRY STORE INC** p 388
305 S Hartmann Dr 37087
Tel (615) 444-5533 *SIC* 5812 5947

■ **KENNETH O LESTER CO INC** p 811
245 N Castle Heights Ave 37087
Tel (615) 444-9901 *SIC* 5141 5142 5148

■ **LEBANON HMA LLC** p 850
1411 W Baddour Pkwy 37087
Tel (615) 444-8262 *SIC* 8062

■ **LOCHINVAR LLC** p 873
300 Maddox Simpson Pkwy 37090
Tel (615) 889-8900 *SIC* 3639 3443 5074

LOJAC ENTERPRISES INC p 875
1401 Toshiba Dr 37087
Tel (615) 449-1401 *SIC* 1611 1794 5032

PERMOBIL INC p 1136
300 Duke Dr 37090
Tel (615) 547-1889 *SIC* 5047

■ **WILSON BANK ANDTRUST** p 1613
623 W Main St 37087
Tel (615) 444-2265 *SIC* 6022

▲ **WILSON BANK HOLDING CO** p 1613
623 W Main St 37087
Tel (615) 444-2265 *SIC* 6021

WILSON COUNTY BOARD OF EDUCATION p 1613
351 Stumpy Ln 37090
Tel (615) 444-3282 *SIC* 8211

WILSON COUNTY SCHOOLS p 1613
351 Stumpy Ln 37090
Tel (615) 444-3282 *SIC* 8211

LENOIR CITY, TN

JANUS GLOBAL HOLDINGS LLC p 778
2229 Old Highway 95 37771
Tel (865) 988-6063 *SIC* 8742

JANUS GLOBAL OPERATIONS LLC p 778
2229 Old Highway 95 37771
Tel (865) 988-6063
SIC 4959 7381 7373 7379 8742

LENOIR CITY UTILITIES BOARD p 855
200 Depot St 37771
Tel (865) 376-4421 *SIC* 4911

LEWISBURG, TN

WALKER DIE CASTING INC p 1573
1125 Higgs Rd 37091
Tel (931) 359-6206 *SIC* 3363

LEXINGTON, TN

■ **LEROY-SOMER INC** p 857
669 Natchez Trace Dr 38351
Tel (731) 967-3000 *SIC* 3621

MANUFACTURERS INDUSTRIAL GROUP LLC p 903
659 Natchez Trace Dr 38351
Tel (731) 968-3601 *SIC* 3499 2531

LOUDON, TN

▲ **MALIBU BOATS INC** p 899
5075 Kimberly Way 37774
Tel (865) 458-5478 *SIC* 3732

■ **MALIBU BOATS LLC** p 899
5075 Kimberly Way 37774
Tel (865) 458-5478 *SIC* 3732

NATION WIDE SERVICES INC p 1009
223 Sequoyah Rd 37774
Tel (248) 355-0500 *SIC* 7381

LYNCHBURG, TN

■ **JACK DANIEL DISTILLERY LEM MOTLOW PROP INC** p 773
Rr 1 37352
Tel (931) 759-4221 *SIC* 2085

MADISON, TN

NASHVILLE AUTOMOTIVE LLC p 1008
2340 Gallatin Pike N 37115
Tel (615) 851-8000 *SIC* 5511

MANCHESTER, TN

M-TEK INC p 890
1020 Volunteer Pkwy 37355
Tel (931) 728-4122 *SIC* 3089 3714 3429

MARYVILLE, TN

BLOUNT COUNTY SCHOOLS p 190
831 Grandview Dr 37803
Tel (865) 984-1212 *SIC* 8211

BLOUNT MEMORIAL HOSPITAL INC p 190
907 Lamar Alexander Pkwy 37804
Tel (865) 983-7211 *SIC* 8062

CITY OF MARYVILLE p 316
404 W Broadway Ave 37801
Tel (865) 273-3401 *SIC* 9121

■ **CLAYTON HOMES INC** p 323
5000 Clayton Rd 37804
Tel (865) 380-3000
SIC 2451 5271 6141 6351 6331

■ **CMH HOMES INC** p 329
5000 Clayton Rd 37804
Tel (865) 380-3000 *SIC* 5271

■ **CMH MANUFACTURING INC** p 329
5000 Clayton Rd 37804
Tel (865) 380-3000 *SIC* 2451

■ **CMH SERVICES INC** p 329
5000 Clayton Rd 37804
Tel (865) 380-3000 *SIC* 7389

COUNTY OF BLOUNT p 376
341 Court St 37804
Tel (865) 273-5700 *SIC* 9111

DENSO MANUFACTURINGTENNESSEE INC p 429
1720 Robert C Jackson Dr 37801
Tel (865) 982-7000 *SIC* 3694 3714

FOOTHILLS LAND CONSERVANCY INC p 564
373 Ellis Ave 37804
Tel (865) 681-8326 *SIC* 8641

MARYVILLE HEALTHCARE & REHABILITATION p 915
1012 Jamestown Way 37803
Tel (865) 984-7400 *SIC* 8322

▲ **RUBYTUESDAY INC** p 1257
150 W Church Ave 37801
Tel (865) 379-5700 *SIC* 5812 5813 6794

STANDARD AERO (ALLIANCE) INC p 1375
1029 Ross Dr 37801
Tel (865) 983-2992 *SIC* 3724

■ **VANDERBILT MORTGAGE AND FINANCE INC** p 1543
500 Alcoa Trl 37804
Tel (865) 380-3000 *SIC* 6141

MASCOT, TN

EXEDY AMERICA CORP p 518
2121 Holston Bend Dr 37806
Tel (865) 932-3700 *SIC* 3714

MC KENZIE, TN

BETHEL UNIVERSITY p 178
325 Cherry Ave 38201
Tel (731) 352-4000 *SIC* 8221 5942

MEMPHIS, TN

■ **ACCREDO HEALTH GROUP INC** p 15
1640 Century Center Pkwy # 110 38134
Tel (877) 222-7336 *SIC* 8051 8052 8093

■ **ACCREDO HEALTH INC** p 15
1640 Century Center Pkwy # 110 38134
Tel (901) 373-8958 *SIC* 2835 8092

AEROSPACE PRODUCTS INTERNATIONAL INC p 31
2871 Business Park Dr 38118
Tel (901) 365-3470 *SIC* 5088 4522

ALL-AMERICAN BOTTLING CORP p 51
5345 Hickory Hill Rd # 102 38141
Tel (901) 369-0483 *SIC* 2086

■ **AMERICAN HOME SHIELD CORP** p 74
889 Ridge Lake Blvd 38120
Tel (901) 597-8000 *SIC* 6351

■ **AMERICAN HOME SHIELD INSPECTION SERVICES INC** p 74
860 Ridge Lake Blvd # 101 38120
Tel (901) 537-8000 *SIC* 6351

AMERICAN LEBANESE SYRIAN ASSOCIATED CHARITIES INC p 75
501 Saint Jude Pl 38105
Tel (901) 578-2150 *SIC* 8399

AMERICAN RESIDENTIAL SERVICES LLC p 78
965 Ridge Lake Blvd # 201 38120
Tel (901) 271-9700 *SIC* 1711

APAC-TENNESSEE INC p 95
1210 Harbor Ave 38113
Tel (901) 947-5600 *SIC* 1611

ARMSTRONG TRANSFER AND STORAGE CO INC/ARMSTRONG RELOCATION CO MEMPHIS p 111
3927 Winchester Rd 38118
Tel (901) 363-1914 *SIC* 4213

ARS INVESTMENT HOLDINGS LLC p 113
965 Ridge Lake Blvd # 201 38120
Tel (901) 271-9700 *SIC* 6719

▲ **AUTOZONE INC** p 135
123 S Front St 38103
Tel (901) 495-6500 *SIC* 5531 5734

BAKER DONELSON BEARMAN CALDWELL & BERKOWITZ p 146
165 Madison Ave Ste 2000 38103
Tel (901) 526-2000 *SIC* 8111

BAPTIST AND PHYSICIANS LOCAL SERVICES BUREAU INC p 153
350 N Humphreys Blvd 38120
Tel (901) 227-5117 *SIC* 8741

BAPTIST MEMORIAL HEALTH CARE CORP p 154
350 N Humphreys Blvd 38120
Tel (901) 227-2727
SIC 8062 8011 8741 5047

BAPTIST MEMORIAL HOSPITAL p 154
6019 Walnut Grove Rd 38120
Tel (901) 226-5000 *SIC* 8062

BARNHART CRANE AND RIGGING CO p 156
2163 Airways Blvd 38114
Tel (901) 775-3000 *SIC* 7353 4213 1796

BELZ HOTEL GROUP LLC p 171
5118 Park Ave Ste 245 38117
Tel (901) 762-5466 *SIC* 8741 8721

BOARD OF EDUCATION-MEMPHIS CITY SCHOOLS p 195
160 S Hollywood St 38112
Tel (901) 416-5300 *SIC* 8211

BOSTON BASKIN CANCER FOUNDATION INC p 202
80 Humphreys Center Dr # 330 38120
Tel (901) 226-5000 *SIC* 8062

BROTHER INDUSTRIES (USA) INC p 219
7819 N Brother Blvd 38133
Tel (901) 377-7777 *SIC* 3579

■ **BROWNING-FERRIS INDUSTRIES OF TENNESSEE INC** p 220
3840 Homewood Rd 38118
Tel (901) 794-3800 *SIC* 4953

BRYCE CO LLC p 221
4505 Old Lamar Ave 38118
Tel (901) 369-4400 *SIC* 2671

BRYCE CORP p 221
4505 Old Lamar Ave 38118
Tel (901) 369-4400 *SIC* 6719

BUCKEYETECHNOLOGIES INC p 223
1001 Tillman St 38112
Tel (901) 320-8100 *SIC* 2611 3081

BUCKMAN LABORATORIES INC p 223
1256 N Mclean Blvd 38108
Tel (901) 278-0330 *SIC* 2869 2819

BUILDING PLASTICS INC p 225
3263 Sharpe Ave 38111
Tel (901) 744-6200 *SIC* 5023

BULAB HOLDINGS INC p 225
1256 N Mclean Blvd 38108
Tel (901) 278-0330 *SIC* 2819 2869

CARLISLE LLC p 257
263 Wagner Pl 38103
Tel (901) 526-5000 *SIC* 5812 8741 6531

CATHOLIC DIOCESE OF MEMPHIS p 266
5825 Shelby Oaks Dr 38134
Tel (901) 373-1200 *SIC* 8661

■ **CB RICHARD ELLIS MEMPHIS LLC** p 268
2620 Thousand Oaks Blvd # 4000 38118
Tel (901) 528-1000 *SIC* 6531 8742

■ **CDRSVM HOLDING LLC** p 271
860 Ridge Lake Blvd 38120
Tel (901) 597-1400 *SIC* 6719

CENTRAL DEFENSE SERVICES LLC p 278
6084 Apple Tree Dr Ste 1 38115
Tel (901) 322-9554 *SIC* 7381

CENTRAL NETWORK RETAIL GROUP LLC p 279
3753 Tyndale Dr Ste 102 38125
Tel (901) 205-9075 *SIC* 5211

CHUCK HUTTON CHEVROLET CO p 304
2471 Mount Moriah Rd 38115
Tel (901) 365-9700 *SIC* 5511

CITY OF MEMPHIS p 316
125 N Main St Ste 468 38103
Tel (901) 576-6657 *SIC* 9111

COMMUNITY FOUNDATION OF GREATER MEMPHIS INC p 348
1900 Union Ave 38104
Tel (901) 728-4600 *SIC* 8399

COMPREHENSIVE PHARMACY SERVICES LLC p 352
6409 N Quail Hollow Rd 38120
Tel (901) 748-0470 *SIC* 8742 8741

COUNTY OF SHELBY p 382
160 N Main St Fl 4 38103
Tel (901) 222-2050 *SIC* 5511

■ **CUMMINS MID-SOUTH LLC** p 401
3770 S Perkins Rd 38118
Tel (901) 577-0600 *SIC* 5999 5013

DDN/OBERGFEL LLC p 419
4580 S Mendenhall Rd 38141
Tel (901) 795-7117 *SIC* 5122

DIVERSIFIED CONVEYORS INC p 444
2163 Airways Blvd Ste 300 38114
Tel (901) 333-8346 *SIC* 8711

■ **DOUBLETREE INC** p 452
755 Crossover Ln 38117
Tel (901) 374-5000 *SIC* 7011 5812 5813

DREXEL CHEMICAL CO p 456
1700 Channel Ave 38106
Tel (901) 774-4370 *SIC* 2879

DUCKS UNLIMITED INC p 459
1 Waterfowl Way 38120
Tel (901) 758-3825 *SIC* 0971

DUNAVANT ENTERPRISES INC p 461
959 Ridg Loop Rd Ste 200 38120
Tel (901) 369-1500
SIC 5159 4221 4731 0131

EDUCATION REALTYTRUST INC p 479
999 Shady Grove Rd S # 600 38120
Tel (901) 259-2500 *SIC* 6798

■ **EFSTRANSPORTATION SERVICES INC** p 481
2525 Horizon Lake Dr # 120 38133
Tel (901) 371-8000 *SIC* 4731

EMPIRE EXPRESS INC p 493
999 Channel Ave 38106
Tel (901) 942-3300 *SIC* 4213

EMPIRE PACKING CO LP p 493
1837 Harbor Ave 38113
Tel (901) 948-4788 *SIC* 5147 2011

EVERGREEN PACKAGING INC p 514
5350 Poplar Ave Ste 600 38119
Tel (901) 821-5350 *SIC* 7389 2621

■ **FEDERAL EXPRESS CORP** p 534
3610 Hacks Cross Rd 38125
Tel (901) 369-3600
SIC 4513 4512 4215 4213

▲ **FEDEX CORP** p 536
942 Shady Grove Rd S 38120
Tel (901) 818-7500
SIC 4513 4512 4213 4215 7334

■ **FEDEX FREIGHT CORP** p 536
1715 Aaron Brenner Dr 38120
Tel (901) 434-3100 *SIC* 4213 7513

■ **FEDEXTRADE NETWORKS INC** p 537
6075 Poplar Ave Ste 300 38119
Tel (901) 684-4800 *SIC* 4731

▲ **FIRST HORIZON NATIONAL CORP** p 547
165 Madison Ave Fl 10 38103
Tel (901) 523-4444 *SIC* 6021

FIRSTTENN BROKERAGE p 549
4990 Poplar Ave Fl 3 38117
Tel (901) 818-6000 *SIC* 6211

■ **FIRSTTENNESSEE BANK NATIONAL ASSOCIATION** p 549
165 Madison Ave 38103
Tel (901) 523-4444 *SIC* 6021 6162

▲ **FREDS INC** p 576
4300 New Getwell Rd 38118
Tel (901) 365-8880
SIC 5331 5912 5199 6794

■ **FREDS STORES OFTENNESSEE INC** p 576
4300 New Getwell Rd 38118
Tel (901) 365-8880 *SIC* 5331 4731

GOSSETT MOTOR CARS INC p 626
1901 Covington Pike 38128
Tel (901) 363-6556 *SIC* 5511 5012

GREENPOINT AG p 638
3350 Players Club Pkwy 38125
Tel (901) 758-1341 *SIC* 5191

GUARDSMARK HOLDINGS INC p 645
22 S 2nd St 38103
Tel (901) 522-6000 *SIC* 7363

HEAVY MACHINES INC p 680
3926 E Raines Rd 38118
Tel (901) 260-2200
SIC 5082 7699 7353 3531 5063

HOPE CHRISTIAN COMMUNITY FOUNDATION p 706
4515 Poplar Ave Ste 324 38117
Tel (901) 682-6201 *SIC* 8661

HUNTER FAN CO p 719
7130 Goodlett Farms Pkwy Ste 400 38103
Tel (901) 743-1360 *SIC* 5064 3634 3645

IDEAL CHEMICAL AND SUPPLY CO p 729
4025 Air Park St 38118
Tel (901) 363-7720 *SIC* 5169 7389

IMPERIAL GUARD AND DETECTIVE SERVICES INC p 734
2555 Poplar Ave 38112
Tel (866) 840-2066 *SIC* 7381

▲ INTERNATIONAL PAPER CO p 756
6400 Poplar Ave 38197
Tel (901) 419-9000
SIC 2621 2653 2656 2631 2611

INTERNATIONAL PAPER CORP p 756
6400 Poplar Ave 38197
Tel (901) 818-5598 *SIC* 7389

INTERSTATE BLOOD BANK INC p 758
5700 Pleasant View Rd 38134
Tel (901) 384-6200 *SIC* 8099

KEITH DAVIS p 808
3574 Boxtown Rd 38109
Tel (901) 496-6477 *SIC* 4213

KELE INC p 808
3300 Brother Blvd 38133
Tel (901) 382-6084 *SIC* 5075 3822 3829

KTG (USA) LP p 831
400 Mahannah Ave 38107
Tel (901) 260-3900 *SIC* 2621

LEHMAN-ROBERTS CO p 854
1111 Wilson St 38106
Tel (901) 774-4000 *SIC* 1611 2951

LILLY CO p 866
3613 Knight Arnold Rd 38118
Tel (901) 363-6000
SIC 5084 7699 7359 5046

LRC EAGLES LANDING GP LLC p 882
555 Perkins Ext 38117
Tel (901) 435-7716 *SIC* 6798 6531

MALLORY ALEXANDER INTERNATIONAL LOGISTICS LLC p 900
4294 Swinnea Rd 38118
Tel (901) 367-9400 *SIC* 4731 4225 4789

MARIE CALLENDER PIE SHOPS INC p 906
6075 Poplar Ave Ste 800 38119
Tel (901) 766-6400 *SIC* 5812

MARTIN MONTGOMERY CONTRACTORS LLC p 913
8245 Tournament Dr # 300 38125
Tel (901) 374-9400 *SIC* 1542 1541 8741

MEDTRONIC SOFAMOR DANEK USA INC p 939
1800 Pyramid Pl 38132
Tel (901) 396-3133 *SIC* 3842 8099

MEMPHIS CITY BOARD OF EDUCATIO p 942
2597 Avery Ave 38112
Tel (901) 416-5444 *SIC* 8299

MEMPHIS-SHELBY COUNTY AIRPORT AUTHORITY p 942
2491 Winchester Rd # 113 38116
Tel (901) 922-8000 *SIC* 4581

■ MERRY MAIDS LIMITED PARTNERSHIP p 950
860 Ridge Lake Blvd Fl 3 38120
Tel (901) 597-8100 *SIC* 7349

METHODIST HEALTHCARE MEMPHIS HOSPITALS p 953
848 Adams Ave 38103
Tel (901) 287-5437 *SIC* 8069 8011

METHODIST HEALTHCARE MEMPHIS HOSPITALS p 953
1265 Union Ave 38104
Tel (901) 516-7000 *SIC* 8062

METHODIST LE BONHEUR HEALTHCARE p 954
1211 Union Ave Ste 700 38104
Tel (901) 516-7000 *SIC* 8062

▲ MID-AMERICA APARTMENT COMMUNITIES INC p 963
6584 Poplar Ave 38138
Tel (901) 682-6600 *SIC* 6798

MIRABILE INVESTMENT CORP p 974
1900 Whitten Rd 38133
Tel (901) 873-1187 *SIC* 5812

MONOGRAM FOOD SOLUTIONS LLC p 984
530 Oak Court Dr Ste 400 38117
Tel (901) 685-7167 *SIC* 5142 2013 5147

■ MS CARRIERS INC p 996
1940 E Brooks Rd Ste 20 38116
Tel (901) 332-2500 *SIC* 4213

■ MUELLER BRASS CO p 998
8285 Tournament Dr # 150 38125
Tel (901) 753-3200
SIC 3351 3463 3354 3494

■ MUELLER BRASS HOLDING CO INC p 998
8285 Tournament Dr # 150 38125
Tel (901) 753-3200 *SIC* 3351 3463 3494

■ MUELLER COPPERTUBE PRODUCTS INC p 998
8285 Tournament Dr # 150 38125
Tel (901) 753-3200 *SIC* 3351

▲ MUELLER INDUSTRIES INC p 998
8285 Tournament Dr # 150 38125
Tel (901) 753-3200 *SIC* 3463 3494 3089

■ NATIONAL BANK OF COMMERCE p 1010
1 Commerce Sq 38103
Tel (901) 523-3434
SIC 6021 6211 7374 6712

NBT INC p 1021
813 Ridge Lake Blvd 38120
Tel (901) 818-3309 *SIC* 6153

NEXAIR LLC p 1039
1385 Corporate Ave 38132
Tel (901) 396-5050
SIC 5169 5084 7699 7359

■ NUCOR STEEL MEMPHIS INC p 1066
3601 Paul R Lowry Rd 38109
Tel (901) 786-5837
SIC 3312 3441 3448 3452

ORGILL INC p 1094
3742 Tyndale Dr 38125
Tel (901) 754-8850 *SIC* 5072

OZARK MOTOR LINES INC p 1101
3934 Homewood Rd 38118
Tel (901) 251-9711 *SIC* 4213

■ PARK HOTELS & RESORTS INC p 1115
755 Crossover Ln 38117
Tel (901) 374-5000 *SIC* 7011

PERKINS & MARIE CALLENDERS HOLDING INC p 1136
6075 Poplar Ave Ste 800 38119
Tel (901) 766-6400 *SIC* 5812

PERKINS & MARIE CALLENDERS LLC p 1136
6075 Poplar Ave Ste 800 38119
Tel (901) 766-6400 *SIC* 5812 6794

PMC BIOGENIX INC p 1157
1231 Pope St 38108
Tel (901) 320-5800 *SIC* 2899

POWER & TELEPHONE SUPPLY CO p 1165
2673 Yale Ave 38112
Tel (901) 324-6116 *SIC* 5063 5999

PPS HOLDINGS INC p 1166
6409 N Quail Hollow Rd 38120
Tel (901) 748-0470 *SIC* 8741

PROMUS HOTEL CORP p 1183
755 Crossover Ln 38117
Tel (901) 374-5000 *SIC* 7011 8741 6794

■ PROMUS HOTELS LLC p 1183
755 Crossover Ln 38117
Tel (719) 265-6600 *SIC* 7011 8741 6794

■ PROMUS OPERATING CO INC p 1183
755 Crossover Ln 38117
Tel (901) 374-5000 *SIC* 7011 8741 6794

RADIANS INC p 1204
5305 Distriplex Farms Dr 38141
Tel (901) 388-7776 *SIC* 5085

RETRANSPORTATION INC p 1212
855 Ridge Lake Blvd # 500 38120
Tel (901) 271-8830 *SIC* 4731

SEDGWICK CLAIMS MANAGEMENT SERVICES INC p 1300
1100 Ridgeway Loop Rd # 200 38120
Tel (901) 415-7400 *SIC* 6411

SEDGWICK CMS HOLDINGS INC p 1300
1100 Ridgeway Loop Rd # 200 38120
Tel (901) 415-7400 *SIC* 6719

■ SEDGWICK JAMES INC p 1300
1000 Ridgeway Loop Rd # 4 38120
Tel (901) 415-7400 *SIC* 6411

■ SERVICEMASTER CO LLC p 1307
860 Ridge Lake Blvd Fl 3 38120
Tel (901) 597-1400
SIC 7349 7342 1711 1731 7641

■ SERVICEMASTER CONSUMER SERVICES LIMITED PARTNERSHIP p 1307
889 Ridge Lake Blvd Fl 2 38120
Tel (901) 597-7574 *SIC* 0782 6351 7349

▲ SERVICEMASTER GLOBAL HOLDINGS INC p 1308
860 Ridge Lake Blvd 38120
Tel (901) 597-1400 *SIC* 7342 7629 7641

SERVICEMASTER HOLDING CORP p 1308
860 Ridge Lake Blvd 38120
Tel (901) 597-1400
SIC 0782 7342 1711 1731 7349 7641

SHELBY COUNTY BOARD OF EDUCATION p 1314
160 S Hollywood St 38112
Tel (901) 321-2500 *SIC* 8211

SHELBY COUNTY HEALTH CARE CORP p 1314
877 Jefferson Ave 38103
Tel (901) 545-7928 *SIC* 8062

SHELBY COUNTY SCHOOLS p 1314
160 S Hollywood St 38112
Tel (901) 321-2500 *SIC* 8211

SMITH & NEPHEW INC p 1333
1450 E Brooks Rd 38116
Tel (901) 396-2121 *SIC* 3842 5047

SOUTH PLAZA CO p 1344
100 Peabody Pl Ste 1400 38103
Tel (901) 260-7400 *SIC* 6531

■ ST FRANCIS HOSPITAL INC p 1366
5959 Park Ave 38119
Tel (901) 765-1000 *SIC* 8062 8051

ST JUDE CHILDRENS RESEARCH HOSPITAL INC p 1369
262 Danny Thomas Pl 38105
Tel (901) 595-3300 *SIC* 8733 8062

STRATOS INC p 1392
66 N Main St 38103
Tel (901) 683-0064 *SIC* 7349

SUPPORT SOLUTIONS OF MID-SOUTH LLC p 1408
5909 Shelby Oaks Dr # 100 38134
Tel (901) 383-9193 *SIC* 8361

■ SUSA PARTNERSHIP LP p 1409
175 Toyota Plz 38103
Tel (901) 252-2000 *SIC* 4225

TAG TRUCK ENTERPRISES LLC p 1421
1650 E Brooks Rd 38116
Tel (901) 345-5633 *SIC* 5511

■ TERMINIX INTERNATIONAL CO LIMITED PARTNERSHIP p 1439
860 Ridge Lake Blvd 38120
Tel (901) 766-1400 *SIC* 7342 7389

■ TERMINIX INTERNATIONAL INC p 1439
860 Ridge Lake Blvd # 101 38120
Tel (901) 766-1100 *SIC* 7342

THOMAS & BETTS CORP p 1448
8155 T&B Blvd 38125
Tel (901) 252-5000 *SIC* 3643 3312 3567

THOMAS & BETTS INTERNATIONAL INC p 1448
8155 T And B Blvd 38125
Tel (901) 682-7766 *SIC* 3699 3678

THYSSENKRUPP ELEVATOR MANUFACTURING INC p 1451
9280 Crestwyn Hills Dr 38125
Tel (901) 261-1800 *SIC* 3534

TRI-STATE TRUCK CENTER INC p 1478
494 E Eh Crump Blvd 38126
Tel (901) 947-5000 *SIC* 5511 7513 5012

TRUCKPRO HOLDING CORP p 1485
1610 Century Center Pkwy 38134
Tel (901) 252-4200 *SIC* 5531 7539

TRUCKPRO LLC p 1485
1610 Century Center Pkwy 38134
Tel (901) 252-4200 *SIC* 5531 7539

TRUE TEMPER SPORTS INC p 1486
8275 Tournament Dr # 200 38125
Tel (901) 746-2000 *SIC* 5091 3949

TRUGREEN HOLDING CORP p 1486
1790 Kirby Pkwy Ste 300 38138
Tel (901) 251-4002 *SIC* 0782 6719

TRUGREEN LIMITED PARTNERSHIP p 1486
1790 Kirby Pkwy Forum Ii Ste 300 Forum Ii 38138
Tel (901) 681-1800 *SIC* 0782

TURNER HOLDINGS LLC p 1492
2040 Madison Ave 38104
Tel (901) 726-5684 *SIC* 2026

UNIVERSITY OF MEMPHIS p 1523
101 Wilder Tower 38152
Tel (901) 678-2111 *SIC* 8221

UT MEDICAL GROUP INC p 1536
1407 Union Ave Ste 700 38104
Tel (901) 866-8864 *SIC* 8011

VARCO PRUDEN HOLDING INC p 1544
3200 Players Club Cir 38125
Tel (901) 748-8000 *SIC* 3448

VARSITY BRANDS LLC p 1545
6745 Lenox Center Ct # 300 38115
Tel (901) 387-4306 *SIC* 5091

▲ VERSO CORP p 1552
6775 Lenox Center Ct # 400 38115
Tel (901) 369-4100 *SIC* 2621

■ VERSO PAPER HOLDINGS LLC p 1552
6775 Lenox Center Ct # 400 38115
Tel (901) 369-4100 *SIC* 2621

■ VERSO PAPER LLC p 1552
6775 Lenox Center Ct # 400 38115
Tel (901) 369-4100 *SIC* 2621

VINING-SPARKS IBG LIMITED PARTNERSHIP p 1558
775 Ridge Lake Blvd # 200 38120
Tel (901) 766-3000 *SIC* 6211

VVP HOLDINGS LLC p 1567
965 Ridge Lake Blvd # 300 38120
Tel (901) 767-7111
SIC 5039 5013 1793 3231 3444 5719

WENDELTA INC p 1592
263 Wagner Pl 38103
Tel (901) 526-5000 *SIC* 5812

WM BARR & CO INC p 1620
6750 Lenox Center Ct # 200 38115
Tel (901) 775-0100 *SIC* 2851

WRIGHT MEDICAL GROUP INC p 1627
1023 Cherry Rd 38117
Tel (800) 238-7117 *SIC* 3842

WRIGHT MEDICAL TECHNOLOGY INC p 1627
1023 Cherry Rd 38117
Tel (901) 867-9971 *SIC* 3842 3845

WUNDERLICH SECURITIES INC p 1628
6000 Poplar Ave Ste 150 38119
Tel (901) 251-1330 *SIC* 6211

YOUTH VILLAGES INC p 1639
3320 Brother Blvd 38133
Tel (901) 251-5000 *SIC* 8361 8322

MIDWAY, TN

TENNESSEE DTR INC p 1438
199 Pottertown Rd 37809
Tel (423) 422-4454 *SIC* 3069 3052

MORRISON, TN

YOROZU AUTOMOTIVE TENNESSEE INC p 1637
395 Mt View Industrial Dr 37357
Tel (931) 668-7700 *SIC* 3465

YOROZU NORTH AMERICA INC p 1637
395 Mt View Industrial Dr 37357
Tel (931) 668-7700 *SIC* 8711 8742

MORRISTOWN, TN

CHARTER FOODS INC p 291
5139 Old Highway 11e 37814
Tel (423) 587-0690 *SIC* 5812

COLORTECH INC p 339
5712 Commerce Blvd 37814
Tel (423) 587-0837 *SIC* 3087 2816

HAMBLEN COUNTY BOARD OF EDUCATION p 655
210 E Morris Blvd 37813
Tel (423) 586-7700 *SIC* 8211

HAMBLEN COUNTY SCHOOL DISTRICT p 655
210 E Morris Blvd 37813
Tel (423) 586-7700 *SIC* 8211

JTEKT AUTOMOTIVE TENNESSEE-MORRISTOWN INC p 796
5932 Commerce Blvd 37814
Tel (423) 585-2544 *SIC* 3714

MAHLE ENGINE COMPONENTS USA INC p 897
1 Mahle Dr 37815
Tel (423) 581-6603 *SIC* 3592 3443

MORRISTOWN UTILITY COMMISSION p 990
441 W Main St 37814
Tel (423) 317-8845 *SIC* 4931

ODDELLO INDUSTRIES LLC p 1074
425 Jones Franklin Rd 37813
Tel (423) 307-1240 *SIC* 2511

ROGERS PETROLEUM INC p 1246
1634 W 1st North St 37814
Tel (423) 581-7460 *SIC* 5171

TEAM TECHNOLOGIES INC p 1430
5949 Commerce Blvd 37814
Tel (423) 587-2199
SIC 2844 5122 5719 3991

TUFFTORQ CORP p 1491
5943 Commerce Blvd 37814
Tel (423) 585-2000 *SIC* 3679 3524

WALLACE HARDWARE CO INC p 1573
5050 S Davy Crockett Pkwy 37813
Tel (423) 586-5650
SIC 5072 5074 5085 5083 5211

MOUNT JULIET, TN

JONES BROS INC p 792
5760 Old Lebanon Dirt Rd 37122
Tel (615) 754-4710
SIC 1622 1771 1794 1629 1611

JONES INVESTMENT HOLDING INC p 792
5760 Old Lebanon Dirt Rd 37122
Tel (615) 754-4710
SIC 1622 1771 1794 1611

MOUNTAIN CITY, TN

MAYMEAD FARMS INC p 923
1995 Roan Creek Rd 37683
Tel (423) 727-2000 *SIC* 0212

MAYMEAD INC p 923
1995 Roan Creek Rd 37683
Tel (423) 727-2000
SIC 1611 2951 5032 5191

MURFREESBORO, TN

BACKER EHP INC p 143
4700 John Bragg Hwy 37127
Tel (615) 907-6900 *SIC* 3567 3585

CANNON COUNTY KNITTING MILLS INC p 247
237 Castlewood Dr Ste F 37129
Tel (615) 890-2938 *SIC* 2231

CITY OF MURFREESBORO p 316
111 W Vine St 37130
Tel (615) 849-2629 *SIC* 9111

COUNTY OF RUTHERFORD p 381
1 Public Sq Ste 101 37130
Tel (615) 898-7745 *SIC* 9199 9111

ENOVATE MEDICAL LLC p 500
1152 Park Ave 37129
Tel (615) 896-1652 *SIC* 3441

FIRSTENTERPRISES INC p 550
202 Heritage Park Dr 37129
Tel (615) 890-9229 *SIC* 4213

FIRSTFLEET INC p 550
202 Heritage Park Dr 37129
Tel (615) 890-9229 *SIC* 4213

HEALTH SERVICES MANAGEMENT INC p 676
206 Fortress Blvd 37128
Tel (615) 896-1191 *SIC* 8741

MAHLE FILTER SYSTEMS NORTH AMERICA INC p 897
906 Butler Dr 37127
Tel (615) 895-5572 *SIC* 3714

MIDDLE TENNESSEE MEDICAL CENTER p 964
1700 Medical Center Pkwy 37129
Tel (615) 396-4100 *SIC* 8062

MIDDLE TENNESSEE ELECTRIC MEMBERSHIP CORP p 964
555 New Salem Hwy 37129
Tel (615) 890-9762 *SIC* 4911

MIDDLE TENNESSEE STATE UNIVERSITY p 964
1301 E Main St 37132
Tel (615) 898-2300 *SIC* 8221

MURFREESBORO CITY SCHOOLS p 1001
2552 S Church St Ste 100 37127
Tel (615) 893-2313 *SIC* 8211

N H C O P LP p 1005
100 E Vine St 37130
Tel (615) 890-2020 *SIC* 8051

▲ NATIONAL HEALTH INVESTORS INC p 1013
222 Robert Rose Dr 37129
Tel (615) 890-9100 *SIC* 6798

▲ NATIONAL HEALTHCARE CORP p 1013
100 E Vine St 37130
Tel (615) 890-2020 *SIC* 8051 8082

OLD TIME POTTERY LLC p 1081
480 River Rock Blvd 37128
Tel (615) 890-6060 *SIC* 5999 5023

RAINBOW INTERNATIONAL OF MIDDLE TENNESEE p 1205
667 Patterson Ave Ste C 37129
Tel (615) 898-8258 *SIC* 1542 1521

SAINT THOMAS RUTHERFORD HOSPITAL p 1271
1700 Medical Center Pkwy 37129
Tel (615) 849-4100 *SIC* 8062

SCHWAN COSMETICS USA INC p 1291
3202 Elam Farms Pkwy 37127
Tel (931) 359-6253 *SIC* 2844

SETECH INC p 1308
410 New Salem Hwy Ste 106 37129
Tel (615) 890-1758 *SIC* 8742 8748 5085

NASHVILLE, TN

■ AEROSTRUCTURES CORP p 31
1431 Vultee Blvd 37217
Tel (615) 361-2000
SIC 3721 3728 3812 3769

AHS HILLCREST HEALTHCARE SYSTEM LLC p 37
1 Burton Hills Blvd # 250 37215
Tel (615) 296-3000 *SIC* 8062

AHS LEGACY OPERATIONS LLC p 37
1 Burton Hills Blvd 37215
Tel (615) 296-3000 *SIC* 8069

ALLEY-CASSETTY COMPANIES INC p 53
2 Oldham St 37213
Tel (615) 244-7077 *SIC* 5032 5052

AMERICAN BLUE RIBBON HOLDINGS LLC p 69
3038 Sidco Dr 37204
Tel (615) 256-8500 *SIC* 5812 6794

AMERICAN PAPER & TWINE CO p 77
7400 Cockrill Bend Blvd 37209
Tel (615) 350-9000 *SIC* 5113 5087 5112

▲ AMSURG CORP p 87
1a Burton Hills Bvld 37215
Tel (615) 665-1283 *SIC* 8011

ARDENT HEALTH PARTNERS LLC p 106
1 Burton Hills Blvd # 250 37215
Tel (615) 296-3000 *SIC* 8069 8062

ARDENT LEGACY ACQUISITIONS INC p 106
1 Burton Hills Blvd 37215
Tel (615) 296-3000 *SIC* 8069

ARDENT LEGACY HOLDINGS INC p 106
1 Burton Hills Blvd 37215
Tel (615) 296-3000 *SIC* 8069

ARIZONA II MERGER CORP p 109
15 Burton Hills Blvd 37215
Tel (615) 665-1283 *SIC* 6719

ASHLEY MEDICAL SUPPLY INC p 117
1911 Church St 37203
Tel (615) 329-3150 *SIC* 5047

ASURION INSURANCE SERVICES INC p 123
648 Grassmere Park # 300 37211
Tel (615) 837-3000 *SIC* 6411

ASURION LLC p 123
648 Grassmere Park # 300 37211
Tel (615) 837-3000 *SIC* 6399

ATHENS PAPER CO INC p 124
1898 Elm Tree Dr 37210
Tel (615) 889-7900 *SIC* 5111

B F NASHVILLE INC p 141
1101 Kermit Dr Ste 310 37217
Tel (615) 399-9700 *SIC* 5812

BAILEY CO INC p 145
501 Cowan St 37207
Tel (615) 242-0351 *SIC* 5084

BALDWIN PIANO INC p 147
309 Plus Park Blvd 37217
Tel (615) 277-2190 *SIC* 3931

BARGE WAGGONER SUMNER AND CANNON INC p 155
211 Commerce St Ste 600 37201
Tel (615) 254-1500 *SIC* 8711

■ BASIC AMERICAN MEDICAL INC p 158
1 Park Plz 37203
Tel (615) 344-9551 *SIC* 5912 2599 8093

BDT BEVERAGE LLC p 164
2712 Westwood Dr 37204
Tel (615) 742-3771 *SIC* 5149

BEAGLE PARENT CORP p 165
3055 Lebanon Pike # 1000 37214
Tel (615) 932-3000 *SIC* 7374

BEAMAN MOTOR CO p 165
1525 Broadway 37203
Tel (615) 251-8430 *SIC* 5511 7538

BELMONT UNIVERSITY p 171
1900 Belmont Blvd 37212
Tel (615) 460-6000 *SIC* 8221

BLEVINS INC p 189
421 Hart Ln 37216
Tel (615) 226-6453 *SIC* 5075

BRIDGESTONE AMERICAS INC p 211
535 Marriott Dr 37214
Tel (615) 937-1000
SIC 3011 3493 2952 2822 3229

BRIDGESTONE AMERICAS TIRE OPERATIONS LLC p 211
535 Marriott Dr 37214
Tel (615) 937-1000 *SIC* 3011 5531

BRIDGESTONE INDUSTRIAL PRODUCTS AMERICA INC p 211
402 Bna Dr Ste 212 37217
Tel (615) 365-0600 *SIC* 5085 8711

CAPTAIN DS LLC p 252
624 Grassmere Park Ste 30 37211
Tel (615) 391-5461 *SIC* 5812

■ CAREMARK RX INC p 255
445 Great Circle Rd 37228
Tel (615) 687-7400 *SIC* 5961

■ CAREMARKPCS HEALTH LLC p 255
211 Commerce St Ste 800 37201
Tel (615) 743-6600 *SIC* 8742

CARLEX GLASS AMERICA LLC p 257
7200 Centennial Blvd 37209
Tel (615) 350-7500 *SIC* 3231

■ CATERPILLAR FINANCIAL SERVICES CORP p 265
2120 West End Ave 37203
Tel (615) 341-1000 *SIC* 6159

CENTERSTONE OF TENNESSEE INC p 277
44 Vantage Way 37228
Tel (615) 463-6610 *SIC* 8093

■ CENTRAL PARKING CORP p 279
507 Mainstream Dr 37228
Tel (615) 297-4255 *SIC* 7521

■ CENTRAL PARKING SYSTEM INC p 279
507 Mainstream Dr 37228
Tel (615) 297-4255 *SIC* 7521

CENTRAL SHARED SERVICES LLC p 280
1 Park Plz 37203
Tel (615) 344-5228 *SIC* 7011

CGS ADMINISTRATORS LLC p 286
2 Vantage Way 37228
Tel (615) 244-5600 *SIC* 6411

CHANCELIGHT INC p 287
1321 Murfreesboro Pike 37217
Tel (615) 361-4000 *SIC* 8299

CHANGE HEALTHCARE HOLDINGS INC p 288
3055 Lebanon Pike # 1000 37214
Tel (615) 932-3000 *SIC* 7374

CHANGE HEALTHCARE OPERATIONS LLC p 288
3055 Lebanon Pike # 1000 37214
Tel (615) 932-3000 *SIC* 7374 8741 8099

■ CHILDRENS COMPREHENSIVE SERVICES INC p 299
3401 West End Ave Ste 400 37203
Tel (615) 250-0000 *SIC* 8322

■ CHRISTIAN HARPERCOLLINS PUBLISHING INC p 302
501 Nelson Pl 37214
Tel (615) 889-9000 *SIC* 2731

▲ CORECIVIC INC p 369
10 Burton Hills Blvd 37215
Tel (615) 263-3000
SIC 6798 8744 8361 8299

CORRECT CARE SOLUTIONS LLC p 372
1283 Murfreesboro Pike # 500 37217
Tel (800) 592-2974 *SIC* 8011

■ CUMMINS FILTRATION INC p 401
26 Century Blvd Ste 500 37214
Tel (615) 367-0040 *SIC* 3714

DELTA DENTAL OF TENNESSEE p 426
240 Venture Cir 37228
Tel (615) 255-3175 *SIC* 6324

DET DISTRIBUTING CO p 433
301 Great Circle Rd 37228
Tel (615) 244-4113 *SIC* 5181

DIALYSIS CLINIC INC p 436
1633 Church St Ste 500 37203
Tel (615) 327-3061 *SIC* 8092 5047 8071

DIALYSIS NEWCO INC p 436
424 Church St Ste 1900 37219
Tel (615) 777-8200 *SIC* 8092

■ DIRECT GENERAL CORP p 441
1281 Murfreesboro Pike # 150 37217
Tel (615) 399-4700
SIC 6311 6321 6331 6411

■ DIRECT GENERAL INSURANCE AGENCY INC p 441
1281 Murfreesboro Pike 37217
Tel (615) 226-2550 *SIC* 6411

■ DIRECT GENERAL INSURANCE CO p 441
1281 Murfreesboro Pike # 150 37217
Tel (615) 399-4700 *SIC* 6411

DISTRICT ATTORNEYS GENERAL CONFERENCE TENNESSEE p 443
226 Capitol Blvd Ste 800 37219
Tel (615) 741-1696 *SIC* 9222

DISTRICT PUBLIC DEFENDERS CONFERENCE TENNESSEE p 443
211 7th Ave N Ste 320 37219
Tel (615) 741-5562 *SIC* 9222

DSI HOLDING CO INC p 457
424 Church St Ste 1900 37219
Tel (615) 777-8201 *SIC* 8092 8069 8742

DSI RENAL HOLDINGS LLC p 458
424 Church St Ste 1900 37219
Tel (615) 777-8201 *SIC* 8092 8069 8742

■ ELARA HOLDINGS INC p 483
1281 Murfreesboro Pike 37217
Tel (615) 366-3723 *SIC* 6719

ELECTRIC POWER BOARD OF METROPOLITAN GOVERNMENT OF NASHVILLE & DAVIDSON COUNTY p 484
1214 Church St 37246
Tel (615) 747-3831 *SIC* 4911

ELECTRONIC EXPRESS INC p 485
418 Harding Industrial Dr 37211
Tel (615) 259-2031 *SIC* 5064

■ ELECTRONIC FUNDS SOURCE LLC p 485
3100 West End Ave # 1150 37203
Tel (888) 824-7378 *SIC* 7371 6099

EXECUTIVE OFFICE OF STATE OF TENNESSEE p 518
600 Charlotte Ave 37243
Tel (615) 741-2001 *SIC* 9111

▲ FB FINANCIAL CORP p 532
211 Commerce St Ste 300 37201
Tel (615) 313-0080 *SIC* 6022

■ FIFTH THIRD BANK NATIONAL ASSOCIATION p 542
424 Church St Ste 500 37219
Tel (615) 687-3100 *SIC* 6022

FIRESTONE NATURAL RUBBER CO LLC p 544
535 Marriott Dr Fl 3 37214
Tel (866) 900-3767 *SIC* 3069 2499

▲ FIRST ACCEPTANCE CORP p 544
3813 Green Hills Vlg Dr 37215
Tel (615) 844-2800 *SIC* 6331 6531

FIRST CALL AMBULANCE SERVICE LLC p 545
1930 Air Lane Dr 37210
Tel (615) 277-0900 *SIC* 4119

■ FIRSTBANK p 550
211 Commerce St Ste 300 37201
Tel (731) 968-4211 *SIC* 6022

■ GAYLORD OPRYLAND USA INC p 594
2800 Opryland Dr 37214
Tel (615) 889-1000 *SIC* 7011

▲ GENESCO INC p 602
1415 Murfreesboro Pike 37217
Tel (615) 367-7000 *SIC* 5661 5139 5961

GIBSON BRANDS INC p 611
309 Plus Park Blvd 37217
Tel (615) 871-4500 *SIC* 3931

GIDEONS INTERNATIONAL p 611
50 Century Blvd 37214
Tel (615) 564-5000 *SIC* 8661 5942

GOODWILL INDUSTRIES OF MIDDLE TENNESSEE INC p 624
1015 Herman St 37208
Tel (615) 742-4151 *SIC* 8641

GRAND OLE OPRY LLC p 629
1 Gaylord Dr 37214
Tel (615) 316-6180 *SIC* 8741

GRESHAM SMITH AND PARTNERS p 639
511 Union St 1400 Nashvle 37219
Tel (615) 770-8100 *SIC* 8712

HARDAWAY CONSTRUCTION CORP p 660
615 Main St 37206
Tel (615) 254-5461 *SIC* 1542 1541 1522

HARDAWAY GROUP INC p 660
615 Main St 37206
Tel (615) 254-5461
SIC 1542 1541 1522 6531

HARPETH FINANCIAL SERVICES LLC p 663
100 Oceanside Dr 37204
Tel (615) 341-5900 *SIC* 6162

HAVEN BEHAVIORAL HEALTHCARE INC p 668
3102 West End Ave # 1000 37203
Tel (615) 393-8800 *SIC* 8011

■ HCA HEALTH SERVICES OF FLORIDA INC p 671
1 Park Plz 37203
Tel (615) 344-9551 *SIC* 8062 8093

■ HCA HEALTH SERVICES OF TENNESSEE INC p 671
1 Park Plz 37203
Tel (615) 344-9551 *SIC* 8062

■ HCA HEALTH SERVICES OF TENNESSEE INC p 671
391 Wallace Rd 37211
Tel (615) 781-4000 *SIC* 8011 8062

■ HCA HEALTH SERVICES OF TEXAS INC p 671
1 Park Plz 37203
Tel (615) 344-9551 *SIC* 8062

▲ HCA HOLDINGS INC p 672
1 Park Plz 37203
Tel (615) 344-9551 *SIC* 8062

■ HCA INC p 672
1 Park Plz 37203
Tel (615) 344-9551
SIC 8063 8062 8069 8093

HCA INFORMATION SERVICES INC p 672
2555 Park Plz 37203
Tel (615) 344-9551 *SIC* 7374

■ HCA PSYCHIATRIC CO p 672
1 Park Plz 37203
Tel (615) 344-2390 *SIC* 8063 8011

■ HCA-HOSPITAL CORP OF AMERICA p 672
1 Park Plz 37203
Tel (615) 344-9551 *SIC* 8062 8063

HEALTHCARE REALTY TRUST INC p 676
3310 West End Ave Ste 700 37203
Tel (615) 269-8175 *SIC* 6798

■ HEALTHSPRING INC p 678
530 Great Circle Rd 37228
Tel (615) 291-7000 *SIC* 6324

■ HEALTHSPRING USA LLC p 678
44 Vantage Way Ste 300 37228
Tel (615) 291-7000 *SIC* 6324

▲ HEALTHSTREAM INC p 678
209 10th Ave S Ste 450 37203
Tel (615) 301-3100 *SIC* 7372 7371

HEALTHTECH HOLDINGS INC p 678
3102 West End Ave Ste 400 37203
Tel (615) 383-7300 *SIC* 7372

HERCULES HOLDING II LLC p 685
1 Park Plz 37203
Tel (615) 344-9551
SIC 8062 8063 8069 8093

■ HOSPITAL CORP OF AMERICA p 709
1 Park Plz 37203
Tel (615) 344-9551 *SIC* 8062 8063

■ HTI MEMORIAL HOSPITAL CORP p 715
3441 Dickerson Pike 37207
Tel (615) 769-2000 *SIC* 8062

INGRAM BARGE CO p 743
4400 Harding Pike 37205
Tel (615) 298-8200 *SIC* 4449

INGRAM INDUSTRIES INC p 743
4400 Harding Pike Ste 310 37205
Tel (615) 298-8200 *SIC* 5192 4449

INNOVATIVE HEARTH HOLDINGS LLC p 744
1508 Elm Hill Pike # 108 37210
Tel (714) 549-7782 *SIC* 3433

INNOVATIVE HEARTH PRODUCTS LLC p 744
1508 Elm Hill Pike # 108 37210
Tel (615) 925-3417 *SIC* 3634 3433

IPAYMENT INVESTORS INC p 763
40 Burton Hills Blvd 37215
Tel (615) 665-1858 *SIC* 7389

■ ISD RENAL INC p 766
424 Church St Ste 1900 37219
Tel (615) 777-8200 *SIC* 8069 8092 8742

J ALEXANDERS HOLDINGS INC p 770
3401 West End Ave Ste 260 37203
Tel (615) 250-1602 *SIC* 5812

■ J ALEXANDERS LLC p 770
3401 West End Ave Ste 260 37203
Tel (615) 269-1900 *SIC* 5812

■ KCPC HOLDINGS INC p 806
2401 21st Ave S Ste 200 37212
Tel (615) 297-4255 *SIC* 7521

KENNY PIPE & SUPPLY INC p 811
811 Cowan St 37207
Tel (615) 242-5909 *SIC* 5074

■ KEYSTONE AUTOMOTIVE INDUSTRIES INC p 815
655 Grassmere Park 37211
Tel (615) 781-5200 *SIC* 5013 5531 3714

■ KEYSTONE AUTOMOTIVE INDUSTRIES TN INC p 815
655 Grassmere Park 37211
Tel (615) 781-5200 *SIC* 5013

■ KEYSTONE EDUCATION AND YOUTH SERVICES LLC p 815
3401 West End Ave Ste 400 37203
Tel (615) 250-0000 *SIC* 8299 8322

LENDLEASE (US) PUBLIC PARTNERSHIPS LLC p 855
1201 Demonbreun St # 800 37203
Tel (615) 963-2600 *SIC* 1522

LIFEWAY CHRISTIAN RESOURCES OF SOUTHERN BAPTIST CONVENTION p 865
1 Lifeway Plz 37234
Tel (615) 251-2000
SIC 5942 5963 2731 5999 5735 5947

LIPMAN BROTHERS LLC p 870
411 Great Circle Rd 37228
Tel (615) 244-2230 *SIC* 5182

LIPSCOMB UNIVERSITY p 870
1 University Park Dr 37204
Tel (615) 966-1000 SIC 8221 8211

LOGANS ROADHOUSE INC p 874
3011 Armory Dr Ste 300 37204
Tel (615) 885-9056 SIC 5812

▲ LOUISIANA-PACIFIC CORP p 880
414 Union St Ste 2000 37219
Tel (615) 986-5600
SIC 2493 2436 2435 2421 2431

LRI HOLDINGS INC p 882
3011 Armory Dr Ste 300 37204
Tel (615) 885-9056 SIC 5812 6794

MAIN STREET OPERATING CO INC p 898
615 Main St 37206
Tel (615) 254-5461
SIC 1542 1541 1521 6531

MEDIFAX-EDI LLC p 938
26 Century Blvd 37214
Tel (615) 932-3226 SIC 7374 7389

MEHARRY MEDICAL COLLEGE p 940
1005 Dr Db Todd Jr Blvd 37208
Tel (615) 327-6111 SIC 8221

METROPOLITAN GOVERNMENT OF NASHVILLE & DAVIDSON COUNTY p 955
100 Metro Courthouse 37201
Tel (615) 862-5000 SIC 9111

METROPOLITAN NASHVILLE AIRPORT AUTHORITY p 956
1 Terminal Dr Ste 501 37214
Tel (615) 275-1600 SIC 4581

METROPOLITAN NASHVILLE PUBLIC SCHOOLS p 956
2601 Bransford Ave 37204
Tel (615) 259-4636 SIC 8211

■ MID STATE AUTOMOTIVE DISTRIBUTORS INC p 963
485 Craighead St 37204
Tel (615) 383-8566 SIC 5013 5531

MIDLAND ENTERPRISES INC p 965
4400 Harding Pike 37205
Tel (615) 298-8200
SIC 4449 4492 3731 4491

MYOFFICEPRODUCTS INC p 1004
22 Century Blvd Ste 420 37214
Tel (615) 507-3515 SIC 5112 5943

NASHVILLE WIRE PRODUCTS MFG CO p 1008
199 Polk Ave 37210
Tel (615) 743-2500 SIC 3496 3471 3643

NATIONAL FEDERATION OF INDEPENDENT BUSINESS p 1011
53 Century Blvd Ste 250 37214
Tel (615) 872-5800 SIC 8611

NEELY COBLE CO p 1024
319 Fesslers Ln 37210
Tel (615) 244-8900 SIC 6159

NEELY COBLE CO INC p 1024
319 Fesslers Ln 37210
Tel (615) 244-8900 SIC 5012 5013

NEW ASURION CORP p 1029
648 Grassmere Park 37211
Tel (615) 837-3000 SIC 6331

■ NEW PORT RICHEY HOSPITAL INC p 1033
1 Park Plz 37203
Tel (727) 848-1733 SIC 8062

■ NEWQUEST LLC p 1038
44 Vantage Way Ste 300 37228
Tel (615) 291-7000 SIC 6321

OCHARLEYS LLC p 1073
3038 Sidco Dr 37204
Tel (615) 256-8500 SIC 5812

OMNI VISION INC p 1085
301 S Perimeter Park Dr # 210 37211
Tel (615) 726-3603 SIC 8361

PARAGON REHABILITATION INC p 1113
3100 West End Ave Ste 400 37203
Tel (615) 345-2200 SIC 8049

PARMAN ENERGY CORP p 1117
7101 Cockrill Bend Blvd 37209
Tel (615) 350-7447 SIC 5172

PERMANENT GENERAL ASSURANCE CORP p 1136
2636 Elm Hill Pike # 510 37214
Tel (615) 744-1351 SIC 6331 6411 6141

PERMANENT GENERAL COMPANIES INC p 1136
2636 Elm Hill Pike # 510 37214
Tel (615) 242-1961 SIC 6411

■ PINNACLE BANK p 1149
150 3rd Ave S Ste 900 37201
Tel (615) 744-3700 SIC 6021

▲ PINNACLE FINANCIAL PARTNERS INC p 1149
150 3rd Ave S Ste 900 37201
Tel (615) 744-3700 SIC 6021

PURITY DAIRIES LLC p 1192
360 Murfreesboro Pike 37210
Tel (615) 760-2296 SIC 2026

QUALIFACTS SYSTEMS INC p 1196
200 2nd Ave S 37201
Tel (615) 386-6755 SIC 7373 7371

QUICKWAY DISTRIBUTION SERVICES INC p 1199
1116 Polk Ave 37210
Tel (615) 834-9470 SIC 4213 4212

RENAL CARE GROUP INC p 1223
2525 West End Ave Ste 600 37203
Tel (615) 345-5500 SIC 8092

RESTAURANT MANAGEMENT GROUP p 1228
902 Murfreesboro Pike 37217
Tel (423) 349-6204 SIC 5812

■ RESTON HOSPITAL CENTER LLC p 1228
1 Park Plz 37203
Tel (615) 344-9551 SIC 8011 8062

ROADHOUSE INTERMEDIATE INC p 1240
3011 Armory Dr Ste 300 37204
Tel (615) 885-9056 SIC 5812

ROADHOUSE MIDCO INC p 1240
3011 Armory Dr Ste 300 37204
Tel (615) 885-9056 SIC 5812 6794

ROADHOUSE PARENT INC p 1240
3011 Armory Dr Ste 300 37204
Tel (615) 885-9056 SIC 5812 6794

ROBERT J YOUNG CO INC p 1241
809 Division St 37203
Tel (615) 255-8551 SIC 5044

ROGERS GROUP INC p 1246
421 Great Circle Rd 37228
Tel (615) 242-0585 SIC 1611 1422

RYMAN HOSPITALITY PROPERTIES INC p 1261
1 Gaylord Dr 37214
Tel (615) 316-6000 SIC 6798 7011

SAINT THOMAS HEALTH SERVICES INC p 1271
4220 Harding Pike 37205
Tel (615) 222-2111 SIC 6512 6513 7011

SAINT THOMAS HOSPITAL p 1271
4220 Harding Pike 37205
Tel (615) 222-5976 SIC 8062

SHONEYS NORTH AMERICA LLC p 1317
1717 Elm Hill Pike Ste B1 37210
Tel (615) 231-2333 SIC 6794 8741 5812

SITEL LLC p 1327
3102 West End Ave Ste 900 37203
Tel (615) 301-7100 SIC 7389

SITEL OPERATING CORP p 1328
3102 West End Ave Ste 900 37203
Tel (615) 301-7100 SIC 7389 7375

SITEL WORLDWIDE CORP p 1328
3102 West End Ave Ste 900 37203
Tel (615) 301-7100 SIC 7389 7375

SMS HOLDINGS CORP p 1334
7135 Charlotte Pike # 100 37209
Tel (615) 399-1839 SIC 7349

SOUTHWESTERN/GREAT AMERICAN INC p 1353
2451 Atrium Way 37214
Tel (615) 391-2717 SIC 5192

SPECIALTY CARE SERVICES GROUP LLC p 1356
3100 West End Ave Ste 400 37203
Tel (615) 345-5400 SIC 8071

SPECIALTYCARE INC p 1356
3100 West End Ave Ste 800 37203
Tel (615) 345-5405 SIC 8099

SPEEDCO INC p 1358
535 Marriott Dr 37214
Tel (866) 773-3326 SIC 7549

ST THOMAS HOSPITAL p 1373
4220 Harding Pike 37205
Tel (615) 222-2111 SIC 8062

STATE OF TENNESSEE p 1382
312 Rosa L Prks Ave Fl 21 37243
Tel (615) 741-2001 SIC 9111

■ SUNTRUST COMMUNITY DEVELOPMENT CORP p 1405
201 4th Ave N Ste 1700 37219
Tel (615) 748-4000 SIC 6021

SUPREME COURT OF STATE OF TENNESSEE p 1408
511 Union St Ste 600 37219
Tel (615) 253-2868 SIC 9211

■ SURGERY PARTNERS INC p 1409
40 Burton Hills Blvd # 500 37215
Tel (615) 234-5900 SIC 8062 3851

SYMBION HOLDINGS CORP p 1414
40 Burton Hills Blvd # 500 37215
Tel (615) 234-5900 SIC 8011 8093 8062

SYMBION INC p 1414
40 Burton Hills Blvd # 500 37215
Tel (615) 234-5900 SIC 8011 8093 8062

■ SYSCO NASHVILLE LLC p 1417
1 Hermitage Plz 37209
Tel (615) 350-7100 SIC 5142 5149

TBHC DELIVERS LLC p 1427
2967 Sidco Dr 37204
Tel (800) 235-3798 SIC 5149

TCW INC p 1428
22 Stanley St 37210
Tel (615) 255-1122 SIC 4731 4225

TENNESSEE BOARD OF REGENTS p 1438
1 Bridgestone Park 37214
Tel (615) 366-4400 SIC 8211

TENNESSEE DEPARTMENT OF CHILDRENS SERVICES p 1438
Cordell Hull Bldg 7th Fl 37243
Tel (615) 741-9699 SIC 8322 9441

TENNESSEE DEPARTMENT OF CORRECTION p 1438
320 6th Ave N Fl 6 37243
Tel (615) 741-1000 SIC 9223

TENNESSEE DEPARTMENT OF EDUCATION p 1438
710 James Robertson Pkwy 37243
Tel (615) 741-5158 SIC 9411

TENNESSEE DEPARTMENT OF ENVIRONMENT AND CONSERVATION p 1438
312 Rosa L Parks Ave 37243
Tel (615) 532-0109 SIC 9511

TENNESSEE DEPARTMENT OF HUMAN SERVICES p 1438
400 Deaderick St Fl 15 37243
Tel (615) 313-4700 SIC 9441

TENNESSEE DEPARTMENT OF LABOR AND WORKFORCE DEVELOPMENT p 1438
220 French Landing Dr 37243
Tel (615) 741-3002 SIC 9651

TENNESSEE DEPARTMENT OF MENTAL HEALTH & SUBSTANCE ABUSE SERVICES p 1438
500 Deaderick St 37243
Tel (615) 770-0464 SIC 9431

TENNESSEE DEPARTMENT OF SAFETY p 1438
1150 Foster Ave Fl 2 37243
Tel (615) 251-5166 SIC 9229

TENNESSEE DEPARTMENT OF TRANSPORTATION p 1438
505 Deaderick St Ste 700 37243
Tel (615) 741-2848 SIC 9621

TENNESSEE DEPT OF HEALTH p 1438
710 James Robertson Pkwy 37243
Tel (615) 741-3111 SIC 9431

TENNESSEE MILITARY DEPARTMENT p 1438
3041 Sidco Dr Ste 401 37204
Tel (615) 313-3001 SIC 9711

TENNESSEE STATE UNIVERSITY p 1438
3500 John A Merritt Blvd 37209
Tel (615) 963-5000 SIC 8221

THERMAL SOLUTIONS MANUFACTURING INC p 1447
15 Century Blvd Ste 102 37214
Tel (615) 806-7907 SIC 3714

THOMAS SAINT MIDTOWN HOSPITAL p 1449
2000 Church St 37236
Tel (615) 284-5555 SIC 8062 8011

TRI STAR ENERGY LLC p 1477
1740 Ed Temple Blvd 37208
Tel (615) 313-3600 SIC 5331 5172

TWFRIERSON CONTRACTOR INC p 1494
2971 Kraft Dr 37204
Tel (615) 367-2434 SIC 1541 1542

UNITED METHODIST PUBLISHING HOUSE p 1510
2222 Rosa L Parks Blvd 37228
Tel (615) 749-6000
SIC 2731 5192 5942 2741 2721

UNIVERSAL LIGHTING TECHNOLOGIES INC p 1517
51 Century Blvd Ste 230 37214
Tel (615) 316-5100 SIC 3612

UNIVERSITY AND COMMUNITY COLLEGE SYSTEM TENNESSEE STATE p 1518
1415 Murfreesboro Pike 37217
Tel (615) 366-4400 SIC 8222

■ US SMOKELESS TOBACCO MANUFACTURING CO LLC p 1533
800 Harrison St 37203
Tel (615) 880-4400 SIC 2131

VANDERBILT CHILDRENS HOSPITAL p 1543
2200 Chld Way Ste 2410 37232
Tel (615) 322-7601 SIC 8062

VANDERBILT UNIVERSITY p 1543
211 Kirkland Hall 37240
Tel (615) 322-5000 SIC 8221 8062

VANDERBILT UNIVERSITY MEDICAL CENTER p 1543
1211 Medical Center Dr 37232
Tel (615) 875-9396 SIC 8062

■ VANGUARD HEALTH SYSTEMS INC p 1543
20 Burton Hills Blvd # 100 37215
Tel (615) 665-6000 SIC 8062 6324

■ VF IMAGEWEAR INC p 1553
545 Marriott Dr Ste 200 37214
Tel (615) 565-5000
SIC 2326 5099 2339 2311

■ VHS HOLDINGS LLC p 1554
20 Burton Hills Blvd 37215
Tel (615) 665-6000 SIC 8741

■ VHS SAN ANTONIO PARTNERS LLC p 1554
20 Burton Hills Blvd # 1 37215
Tel (615) 665-6036 SIC 8741

VISTA-PRO AUTOMOTIVE LLC p 1562
22 Century Blvd Ste 410 37214
Tel (615) 622-2200 SIC 3714

WASCO INC p 1577
1122 2nd Ave N B 37208
Tel (615) 244-9090 SIC 1741

WESTERN EXPRESS HOLDINGS INC p 1598
7135 Centennial Pl 37209
Tel (615) 259-9920 SIC 4213

WESTERN EXPRESS INC p 1598
7135 Centennial Pl 37209
Tel (615) 259-9920 SIC 4213

WILLIS ADMINISTRATIVE SERVICES CORP p 1612
26 Century Blvd Ste 101 37214
Tel (615) 872-3000 SIC 6411

WILLIS OF TENNESSEE INC p 1612
26 Century Blvd Ste 101 37214
Tel (615) 872-3000 SIC 6411

YOUNG MENS CHRISTIAN ASSOCIATION OF MIDDLE TENNESSEE p 1638
1000 Church St 37203
Tel (615) 259-9622
SIC 8641 7991 8351 7032 8322

NEW MARKET, TN

APPALACHIAN ELECTRIC COOPERATIVE p 98
1109 Hill Dr 37820
Tel (423) 586-4755 SIC 4911

OAK RIDGE, TN

ATKINS ENERGY GOVERNMENT GROUP INC p 125
545 Oak Ridge Tpke 37830
Tel (865) 481-6300 SIC 4959

■ BABCOCK & WILCOX TECHNICAL SERVICES Y-12 LLC p 143
301 Bear Creek Rd 37830
Tel (865) 574-1000 SIC 3483 3761

BECHTEL JACOBS CO LLC p 167
E Tennessee Techn 58 37831
Tel (865) 241-1151 SIC 8744

CONSOLIDATED NUCLEAR SECURITY LLC p 360
301 Bear Creek Rd 37830
Tel (865) 576-3456 SIC 9229

■ LOCKHEED MARTIN ENERGY RESEARCH CORP p 873
1 Bethel Valley Rd 37830
Tel (865) 574-1000 SIC 8733

METHODIST MEDICAL CENTER OF OAK RIDGE p 954
990 Oak Ridge Tpke 37830
Tel (865) 835-1000 SIC 8062

OAK RIDGE ASSOCIATED UNIVERSITIES INC p 1070
100 Orau Way 37830
Tel (865) 576-3000 SIC 8733

■ UNITED STATES DEPT OF ENERGY OAKRIDGE FIELD OFFICE p 1513
200 Administration Rd Fm-73 37830
Tel (865) 576-0770 SIC 9611

UT-BATTELLE LLC p 1536
1 Bethel Valley Rd 37830
Tel (865) 574-2227 SIC 8731

OAKLAND, TN

RING CONTAINER TECHNOLOGIES LLC p 1235
1 Industrial Park 38060
Tel (901) 465-6333 SIC 3085

RINGWOOD CONTAINERS LP p 1235
1 Industrial Park 38060
Tel (901) 465-3607 SIC 3085

OLD HICKORY, TN

■ FIBERWEB INC p 539
9335 Harris Corners Pkwy 37138
Tel (704) 697-5100 SIC 2281 5047 5137

OOLTEWAH, TN

■ CENTURY HOLDINGS INC p 282
8503 Hilltop Dr 37363
Tel (423) 238-4171 SIC 3713

GREAT AMERICAN DELI p 633
5828 Main St 37363
Tel (423) 238-5492 SIC 5812

■ HAWKER POWERSOURCE INC p 669
9404 Ooltewah Indus Blvd 37363
Tel (423) 238-5700 SIC 5063

▲ MILLER INDUSTRIES INC p 970
8503 Hilltop Dr 37363
Tel (423) 238-4171 SIC 3713

■ MILLER INDUSTRIES TOWING EQUIPMENT INC p 970
8503 Hilltop Dr 37363
Tel (423) 238-4171 SIC 3799

PARIS, TN

ADAMS & SULLIVAN LLC p 21
1188 N Market St 38242
Tel (731) 642-2752 SIC 5411

PARSONS, TN

AMERICAN HEALTH COMPANIES INC p 73
1971 Tennessee Ave N 38363
Tel (731) 847-6343 SIC 8051 8052 8059

■ KMT REFRIGERATION INC p 824
2915 Tennessee Ave N 38363
Tel (731) 847-6361 SIC 3585 3448 1711

PORTLAND, TN

■ **KIRBY BUILDING SYSTEMS LLC** p 821
124 Kirby Dr 37148
Tel (615) 325-4165 *SIC* 3448

KYOWA AMERICA CORP p 833
1039 Fred White Blvd 37148
Tel (615) 323-2194 *SIC* 5162

NASG TENNESSEE NORTH 2 LLC p 1008
160 Kirby Dr 37148
Tel (615) 323-0500 *SIC* 3465

NORTH AMERICAN STAMPING GROUP LLC p 1050
119 Kirby Dr 37148
Tel (615) 323-0500 *SIC* 3469 6719

UNIPRES USA INC p 1505
201 Kirby Dr 37148
Tel (615) 325-7311 *SIC* 3465

POWELL, TN

DEROYAL INDUSTRIES INC p 431
200 Debusk Ln 37849
Tel (865) 938-7828 *SIC* 3841

PULASKI, TN

COUNTY OF GILES p 378
222 W Madison St 38478
Tel (931) 424-4001 *SIC* 9111

SAARGUMMI TENNESSEE INC p 1263
200 Commerce Way 38478
Tel (931) 363-1363 *SIC* 3061

RIPLEY, TN

BEST-WADE PETROLEUM INC p 177
201 Dodge Dr 38063
Tel (731) 635-9661 *SIC* 5171 5541 5411

MARVIN WINDOWS OF TENNESSEE INC p 914
101 Marvin Dr 38063
Tel (731) 635-5190 *SIC* 2431 3231

ROCKWOOD, TN

■ **CHASE SCIENTIFIC GLASS INC** p 291
234 Cardiff Valley Rd 37854
Tel (865) 354-4206 *SIC* 3231

ROGERSVILLE, TN

PROFESSIONAL PERSONNEL SERVICE INC p 1180
3815 Highway 66 S Ste 4 37857
Tel (423) 764-1334 *SIC* 7363

SAVANNAH, TN

PRAXIS COMPANIES LLC p 1168
435 Industrial Rd 38372
Tel (731) 925-7656 *SIC* 3088

SEVIERVILLE, TN

CHARLES BLALOCK & SONS INC p 289
409 Robert Henderson Rd 37862
Tel (865) 429-5902
SIC 1611 7353 3271 3255 2951

SEVIER COUNTY BOARD OF EDUCATION p 1309
226 Cedar St 37862
Tel (865) 453-4671 *SIC* 8211

SEVIER COUNTY ELECTRIC SYSTEM INC p 1309
315 E Main St 37862
Tel (865) 453-2887 *SIC* 4911

SEVIER COUNTY SCHOOL SYSTEM p 1309
226 Cedar St 37862
Tel (865) 453-4671 *SIC* 8211

SEWANEE, TN

UNIVERSITY OF SOUTH p 1525
735 University Ave 37383
Tel (931) 598-1000 *SIC* 8221

SHELBYVILLE, TN

CALSONICKANSEI NORTH AMERICA INC p 243
1 Calsonic Way 37160
Tel (931) 684-4490 *SIC* 3585

CNA INC p 330
1 Calsonic Way 37160
Tel (931) 684-4490 *SIC* 3585

COOPERS STEEL FABRICATORS INC () p 367
503 N Hillcrest Dr 37160
Tel (931) 684-7962 *SIC* 3441 1791

DUCK RIVER ELECTRIC MEMBERSHIP CORP p 459
1411 Madison St 37160
Tel (931) 684-4621 *SIC* 4911

SMITHVILLE, TN

■ **FEDERAL-MOGUL FAP INC** p 536
1 Grizzly Ln 37166
Tel (615) 597-6700 *SIC* 3714

L&S SERVICES LLC p 834
501 W Broad St 37166
Tel (615) 597-6278 *SIC* 5812

SHIROKI NORTH AMERICA INC p 1317
1111 W Broad St 37166
Tel (615) 597-8870 *SIC* 3711

SMYRNA, TN

FRANKE FOODSERVICE SUPPLY INC p 574
800 Aviation Pkwy 37167
Tel (615) 459-3486 *SIC* 5084

FRANKE KITCHEN SYSTEMS LLC p 574
800 Aviation Pkwy 37167
Tel (800) 637-6485 *SIC* 3431 5074

FRANKE SSG INC p 574
800 Aviation Pkwy 37167
Tel (615) 462-4000 *SIC* 5046

IDEAL CLAMP PRODUCTS INC p 729
8100 Tridon Dr 37167
Tel (615) 459-5800 *SIC* 3429

KIMBERLAND SWAN HOLDINGS INC p 818
1 Swan Dr 37167
Tel (615) 459-8900 *SIC* 2844

NISSAN TRADING CORP AMERICAS p 1044
1974 Midway Ln 37167
Tel (615) 220-7100
SIC 5013 5012 5051 5084

■ **RUSH TRUCK LEASING INC** p 1259
900 Expo Dr 37167
Tel (615) 220-7600 *SIC* 5511

YATES SERVICES LLC p 1635
983 Nissan Dr 37167
Tel (615) 459-1701 *SIC* 7349

SOMERVILLE, TN

FAYETTE COUNTY SCHOOLS p 532
126 W Market St 38068
Tel (901) 465-5260 *SIC* 8211

SOUTH PITTSBURG, TN

SEQUACHEE VALLEY ELECTRIC CO-OPERATIVE INC p 1306
512 S Cedar Ave 37380
Tel (423) 837-8605 *SIC* 4911

SPRING HILL, TN

FHG CORP p 539
4637 Port Royal Rd 37174
Tel (931) 499-7070 *SIC* 7389 5122

SPRINGFIELD, TN

COUNTY OF ROBERTSON p 381
108 Crthuse 501 S Main St 37172
Tel (615) 384-2476 *SIC* 9111

■ **DELIGHT PRODUCTS CO** p 424
1200 Industrial Dr 37172
Tel (615) 384-7546 *SIC* 2047

FLETCHLINE INC p 555
5480 Lakeview Rd 37172
Tel (615) 382-0764 *SIC* 5084 1796

HOLLINGSWORTH OIL CO INC p 701
1503 Memorial Blvd Ste B 37172
Tel (615) 242-8466 *SIC* 5171

ROBERTSON COUNTY SCHOOL DISTRICT p 1242
800 Ms Couts Blvd Ste 2 37172
Tel (615) 384-5588 *SIC* 8211

UNARCO MATERIAL HANDLING INC p 1502
701 16th Ave E 37172
Tel (615) 384-3531 *SIC* 5084 2542

SWEETWATER, TN

SCHOTT GEMTRON CORP p 1290
615 Highway 68 37874
Tel (423) 337-3522 *SIC* 3211

TOONE, TN

KILGORE FLARES CO LLC p 818
155 Kilgore Rd 38381
Tel (731) 228-5200 *SIC* 2899 3728

TRENTON, TN

GIBSON ELECTRIC MEMBERSHIP CORP p 611
1207 S College St 38382
Tel (731) 855-4660 *SIC* 4911

MACLEAN POWER TN LLC p 892
1465 Industrial Park Dr 38382
Tel (847) 566-0010 *SIC* 3679

TULLAHOMA, TN

AEROSPACE CENTER SUPPORT p 30
100 Kindel Dr Ste A211 37389
Tel (931) 454-3000 *SIC* 8744

AEROSPACE TESTING ALLIANCE p 31
600 William Northern Blvd 37388
Tel (931) 454-3000 *SIC* 8711

■ **HARTON JOHN W REGIONAL MEDICAL CENTER INC** p 666
1801 N Jackson St 37388
Tel (931) 393-3000 *SIC* 8062

■ **JACOBS TECHNOLOGY INC** p 775
600 William Northern Blvd 37388
Tel (931) 455-6400 *SIC* 8711

TULLAHOMA INDUSTRIES LLC p 1491
401 Nw Atlantic St 37388
Tel (931) 455-1314 *SIC* 2311 2339 2326

UNION CITY, TN

CANDLE CORP OF AMERICA p 247
600 Sherwood Dr 38261
Tel (731) 885-7836 *SIC* 5023 5199

COX OIL CO INC p 386
623 Perkins St 38261
Tel (731) 885-6444 *SIC* 5541 5411

VONORE, TN

CARLEX GLASS CO LLC p 257
77 Excellence Way 37885
Tel (423) 884-1105 *SIC* 5013

■ **MASTERCRAFT BOAT CO LLC** p 918
100 Cherokee Cove Dr 37885
Tel (423) 884-2221 *SIC* 3799

■ **MCBC HOLDINGS INC** p 926
100 Cherokee Cove Dr 37885
Tel (423) 884-2221 *SIC* 3732 3799

SHORT BARK INDUSTRIES INC p 1318
139 Grand Vis 37885
Tel (423) 884-2010 *SIC* 2311

WHITES CREEK, TN

GRACE HEALTH CARE p 628
3425 Knight Dr 37189
Tel (615) 876-2754 *SIC* 8051

WINCHESTER, TN

■ **TENNESSEE SOUTHERN REGIONAL HEALTH** p 1438
185 Hospital Rd 37398
Tel (931) 967-8200 *SIC* 8062

TENNESSEE ZANINI INC p 1438
840 Industrial Dr 37398
Tel (931) 967-8544 *SIC* 5013

TEXAS

ABILENE, TX

■ **AB-TEX BEVERAGE LTD** p 9
650 Colonial Dr 79603
Tel (325) 673-7171 *SIC* 2086

ABILENE CHRISTIAN UNIVERSITY INC p 11
1600 Campus Ct 79601
Tel (325) 674-2000 *SIC* 8221

ABILENE INDEPENDENT SCHOOL DISTRICT p 11
241 Pine St 79601
Tel (325) 677-1444 *SIC* 8211

ABIMAR FOODS INC p 11
5425 N 1st St 79603
Tel (325) 691-5425 *SIC* 2052

ALLIED STAFFING INC p 57
4400 Buffalo Gap Rd # 4500 79606
Tel (325) 695-5822 *SIC* 7361 7363

■ **ARMC LP** p 111
6250 Highway 83 84 79606
Tel (325) 428-1000
SIC 8062 8093 8011 7991

CITY OF ABILENE p 312
555 Walnut St 79601
Tel (325) 676-6200 *SIC* 9111

■ **FIRST FINANCIAL BANK NATIONAL ASSOCIATION** p 546
400 Pine St 79601
Tel (325) 627-7000 *SIC* 6021

▲ **FIRST FINANCIAL BANKSHARES INC** p 546
400 Pine St 79601
Tel (325) 627-7155 *SIC* 6022

HENDRICK MEDICAL CENTER p 683
1900 Pine St 79601
Tel (325) 670-2000 *SIC* 8062

LAUREN CORP p 847
901 S 1st St 79602
Tel (325) 670-9660 *SIC* 1629

LAUREN ENGINEERS & CONSTRUCTORS INC p 847
901 S 1st St 79602
Tel (325) 670-9660 *SIC* 1541

PETROSMITH EQUIPMENT LP p 1139
7435 Us Highway 277 S 79606
Tel (325) 691-1085 *SIC* 5084 7353

RANGER PLANT CONSTRUCTIONAL CO INC p 1208
5851 E Interstate 20 79601
Tel (325) 677-2888 *SIC* 1623

RENTECH BOILER SYSTEMS INC p 1224
5025 E Business 20 79601
Tel (325) 672-3400 *SIC* 5074

SEARS METHODIST RETIREMENT SYSTEM INC p 1297
1 Village Dr Ste 400 79606
Tel (325) 691-5519 *SIC* 8361

WESTERN MARKETING INC p 1599
20 Exit 278 79601
Tel (800) 588-4662 *SIC* 5172

ADDISON, TX

ACCOR NORTH AMERICA INC p 15
5055 Kelle Sprin Rd Ste 2 75001
Tel (972) 360-9000 *SIC* 7011

ALLPLAYERS NETWORK INC p 58
4145 Belt Line Rd Ste 212 75001
Tel (214) 234-9770 *SIC* 5941

BL RESTAURANT OPERATIONS LLC p 186
4550 Beltway Dr 75001
Tel (972) 386-5567 *SIC* 5812 5813 6794

CADENCE MCSHANE CONSTRUCTION CO LLC p 236
5057 Keller Springs Rd 75001
Tel (972) 239-2336 *SIC* 1541 1542

CHARTWELL COMMUNITY SERVICES INC p 291
14295 Midway Rd Ste 400 75001
Tel (972) 713-3400 *SIC* 8082

■ **CONCENTRA HEALTH SERVICES INC** p 354
5080 Spectrum Dr Ste 400w 75001
Tel (972) 364-8000 *SIC* 8093 8011

■ **CONCENTRA INC** p 354
5080 Spectrum Dr Ste 400w 75001
Tel (972) 364-8000 *SIC* 8011

■ **CONCENTRA OPERATING CORP** p 354
5080 Spectrum Dr Ste 400w 75001
Tel (972) 364-8000 *SIC* 8093

DASEKE INC p 413
15455 Dallas Pkwy Ste 440 75001
Tel (972) 248-0412 *SIC* 4789

DASEKE LONE STAR INC p 413
15455 Dallas Pkwy 75001
Tel (972) 248-0412 *SIC* 4212

GRAND TEXAS HOMES INC p 630
15455 Dallas Pkwy # 1000 75001
Tel (972) 387-6000 *SIC* 1521

H Q GLOBAL HOLDINGS INC p 650
15305 Dallas Pkwy Ste 400 75001
Tel (972) 361-8100 *SIC* 6519 7389

■ **HOMEWARD RESIDENTIAL INC** p 704
16675 Addison Rd 75001
Tel (877) 304-3100 *SIC* 6162

HQ GLOBAL WORKPLACES INC p 714
15305 Dallas Pkwy Ste 400 75001
Tel (972) 361-8100 *SIC* 6519 7389

J-W ENERGY CO p 772
15505 Wright Brothers Dr 75001
Tel (972) 233-8191
SIC 1311 7353 3533 1381

J-W OPERATING CO p 772
15505 Wright Brothers Dr 75001
Tel (972) 233-8191 *SIC* 1382

JANI-KING INTERNATIONAL INC p 777
16885 Dallas Pkwy 75001
Tel (972) 991-0900 *SIC* 7349

LATTIMORE MATERIALS CO LP p 846
15900 Dooley Rd 75001
Tel (972) 221-4646 *SIC* 3273 1422 1442

LUMENATE TECHNOLOGIES LP p 885
16633 Dallas Pkwy Ste 450 75001
Tel (972) 248-8999 *SIC* 7379

MARY KAY HOLDING CORP p 914
16251 Dallas Pkwy 75001
Tel (972) 687-6300
SIC 5963 3961 3172 4724

MARY KAY INC p 914
16251 Dallas Pkwy 75001
Tel (972) 687-6300 *SIC* 5963

■ **MBNA TECHNOLOGY INC** p 925
16001 Dallas Pkwy 75001
Tel (972) 233-7101 *SIC* 7374 6282

METDALSPI LLC p 953
17101 Dallas Pkwy 75001
Tel (469) 248-3900 *SIC* 8069

NATIONS BROADBAND INC p 1017
15455 Dallas Pkwy Ste 600 75001
Tel (972) 851-7851 *SIC* 4813

NAUTILUS GROUP p 1019
15305 Dallas Pkwy Ste 950 75001
Tel (972) 720-6600 *SIC* 6411

NEW AFFIRMATIVE LLC p 1029
4450 Sojourn Dr Ste 500 75001
Tel (972) 728-6300 *SIC* 6331

NJ MALIN & ASSOCIATES LLC p 1045
15870 Midway Rd 75001
Tel (972) 458-2680 *SIC* 5046 5084

OLYMPUS REAL ESTATE CORP p 1083
5080 Spectrum Dr 75001
Tel (972) 980-2200 *SIC* 7011 6512

OSTEOMED LLC p 1097
3885 Arapaho Rd 75001
Tel (972) 677-4600 *SIC* 3841

RATCLIFF CONSTRUCTORS LP p 1209
4200 Beltway Dr 75001
Tel (972) 432-9969 *SIC* 1542

REGUS CORP p 1220
15305 Dallas Pkwy Ste 400 75001
Tel (972) 361-8100 *SIC* 7363 7389 6531

SMITH PROTECTIVE SERVICES INC p 1333
4440 Beltway Dr 75001
Tel (972) 960-8481 *SIC* 7381

SOUPER SALAD INC p 1342
4004 Belt Line Rd Ste 100 75001
Tel (972) 761-1790 *SIC* 5812

▲ **TRANSATLANTIC PETROLEUM LTD** p 1470
16803 Dallas Pkwy 75001
Tel (214) 220-4323 *SIC* 1311

UNITED SURGICAL PARTNERS INTERNATIONAL INC p 1514
15305 Dallas Pkwy # 1600 75001
Tel (972) 713-3500 *SIC* 8011

USP INTERNATIONAL HOLDINGS INC p 1535
15305 Dallas Pkwy 75001
Tel (972) 713-3500 *SIC* 8062

USPI GROUP HOLDINGS INC p 1535
15305 Dallas Pkwy # 1600 75001
Tel (972) 713-3500 *SIC* 8011

USPI HOLDINGS INC p 1535
15305 Dallas Pkwy # 1600 75001
Tel (972) 713-3500 *SIC* 8011

ALBANY, TX

ANDERSON PERFORATING LTD p 90
124 Welco Rd 76430
Tel (325) 762-2200 *SIC* 1389

ALICE, TX

ALICE INDEPENDENT SCHOOL DISTRICT p 50
2 Coyote Trl 78332
Tel (361) 664-0981 *SIC* 8211

FESCO LTD p 539
1000 Fesco Dr 78332
Tel (361) 664-3479 *SIC* 8711 5082

FORBES ENERGY SERVICES LTD p 565
3000 S Business Hwy 281 78332
Tel (361) 664-0549 *SIC* 1389

LIGHTNING FLUID SERVICES INC p 865
1310 Southwood St 78332
Tel (361) 396-0801 *SIC* 1389 7389

TEXAS ENERGY SERVICES LP p 1443
4932 N Us Hwy 281 78332
Tel (361) 664-5020 *SIC* 1389

ALLEN, TX

ALLEN INDEPENDENT SCHOOL DISTRICT p 53
612 E Bethany Dr 75002
Tel (972) 727-0511 *SIC* 8211

AMERICAS POWERSPORTS INC p 81
825 Market St Bldg M 75013
Tel (214) 383-4835 *SIC* 5571 7941

■ **ASSOCIATED AMERICAN INDUSTRIES INC** p 119
1307 N Watters Rd 75013
Tel (214) 421-7366
SIC 3914 3634 3469 3639

▲ **ATRION CORP** p 129
1 Allentown Pkwy 75002
Tel (972) 390-9800 *SIC* 3841

CVE TECHNOLOGY GROUP INC p 404
915 Enterprise Blvd 75013
Tel (972) 424-6606 *SIC* 3663

▲ **PFSWEB INC** p 1140
505 Millenium Dr 75013
Tel (972) 881-2900 *SIC* 8741 7389 8742

■ **PRIORITY FULFILLMENT SERVICES INC** p 1177
505 Millenium Dr 75013
Tel (972) 881-2900 *SIC* 7389

SUPPLIES DISTRIBUTORS INC p 1407
505 Millenium Dr 75013
Tel (972) 881-2900 *SIC* 5045 5112

ALVARADO, TX

NATIVE OILFIELD SERVICES LLC p 1018
7900 S Interstate 35 W 76009
Tel (817) 783-3636 *SIC* 1389

SABRE INDUSTRIES INC p 1264
8653 E Highway 67 76009
Tel (817) 852-1700 *SIC* 3441

ALVIN, TX

ALVIN INDEPENDENT SCHOOL DISTRICT p 63
301 E House St 77511
Tel (281) 388-1130 *SIC* 8211

K-3 RESOURCES LP p 799
850 County Road 149 77511
Tel (281) 585-2817 *SIC* 1389

■ **TEAM INDUSTRIAL SERVICES INC** p 1430
200 Hermann Dr 77511
Tel (281) 388-5525 *SIC* 8748 8711 7699

AMARILLO, TX

AFFILIATED FOODS INC p 32
1401 W Farmers Ave 79118
Tel (806) 345-7773
SIC 5141 2026 2051 5149 6153

AHS AMARILLO HEALTH SYSTEM LLC p 37
1600 Wallace Blvd 79106
Tel (806) 212-2000 *SIC* 8062

AMARILLO INDEPENDENT SCHOOL DISTRICT p 64
7200 W Interstate 40 79106
Tel (806) 326-1000 *SIC* 8211

AMARILLO JUNIOR COLLEGE DISTRICT p 64
2201 S Washington St 79109
Tel (806) 371-5000 *SIC* 8222 8221

AMARILLO NATIONAL BANCORP INC p 64
Plaza One 410 S Taylor St # 1 79101
Tel (806) 378-8000 *SIC* 6021

AMARILLO NATIONAL BANK p 64
410 S Taylor St 79101
Tel (806) 349-9760 *SIC* 6021

ANCONNECT LLC p 89
421 Se 34th Ave 79103
Tel (806) 376-6251 *SIC* 5099 5192

ATTEBURY GRAIN LLC p 129
3905 Bell St Ste A 79109
Tel (806) 335-1639 *SIC* 5153

BAPTIST ST ANTHONYS HOSPITAL CORP p 154
1600 Wallace Blvd 79106
Tel (806) 212-2000 *SIC* 8062

BAPTIST/ST ANTHONYS HEALTH SYSTEM p 154
1600 Wallace Blvd 79106
Tel (806) 212-2000 *SIC* 8062

BRUCKNER TRUCK SALES INC p 220
9471 E Interstate 40 79118
Tel (806) 376-6273 *SIC* 5511

BSA HEALTH SYSTEM OF AMARILLO LLC p 222
1600 Wallace Blvd 79106
Tel (806) 212-2000 *SIC* 8062

CACTUS FEEDERS INC p 236
2209 Sw 7th Ave Ste 200 79106
Tel (806) 373-2333 *SIC* 0211

CITY OF AMARILLO p 313
509 Se 7th Ave Rm 303 79101
Tel (806) 378-3000 *SIC* 9111

■ **CONSOLIDATED NUCLEAR SECURITY LLC** p 360
2373 Farm To Market Rd 79120
Tel (806) 477-3000 *SIC* 7382

DRAW ANOTHER CIRCLE LLC p 455
3601 Plains Blvd 79102
Tel (806) 351-2300 *SIC* 5735

FRIONA INDUSTRIES LP p 580
500 S Taylor St Unit 253 79101
Tel (806) 374-1811 *SIC* 0211

GOLDEN SPREAD ELECTRIC COOPERATIVE INC p 621
905 S Fillmore St Ste 300 79101
Tel (806) 379-7766 *SIC* 4911

HAPPY STATE BANK p 659
701 S Taylor St Lb120 79101
Tel (806) 373-2265 *SIC* 6022

HASTINGS ENTERTAINMENT INC p 667
3601 Plains Blvd 79102
Tel (806) 351-2300 *SIC* 5735 5942 7841

HIGH PLAINS BAPTIST HOSPITAL INC p 690
1600 Wallace Blvd 79106
Tel (806) 358-5800 *SIC* 8062 6513 8051

HIGH PLAINS CHRISTIAN MINISTRIES FDN p 690
701 Park Place Ave Fl 2 79101
Tel (806) 337-5292 *SIC* 8699

MAXOR NATIONAL PHARMACY SERVICES LLC p 922
320 S Polk St Ste 900 79101
Tel (806) 324-5400 *SIC* 5912

■ **MCCARTY-HULL CIGAR CO INC** p 926
4714 Ne 24th Ave 79107
Tel (806) 383-1313 *SIC* 5194 5145

MERRICK NATURAL PETWORKS INC p 950
101 Se 11th Ave Ste 200 79101
Tel (806) 322-2800 *SIC* 2047

■ **NORTHWEST TEXAS HEALTHCARE SYSTEM INC** p 1060
1501 S Coulter St 79106
Tel (806) 354-1000
SIC 8062 8063 8051 8049

PLAINS DAIRY LLC p 1153
300 N Taylor St 79107
Tel (806) 374-0385 *SIC* 2026 2086 2033

■ **SOUTHWESTERN PUBLIC SERVICE CO** p 1353
Tyler At Sixth 79101
Tel (303) 571-7511 *SIC* 4911

TOOT N TOTUM FOOD STORES LLC p 1460
1201 S Taylor St 79101
Tel (806) 373-4351 *SIC* 5411 5541

TOOT N TOTUM FOOD STORES LP p 1460
1201 S Taylor St 79101
Tel (806) 373-4351 *SIC* 5541 5411

VENABLES CONSTRUCTION INC p 1547
7410 Continental Pkwy 79119
Tel (806) 381-2121
SIC 1623 1794 1389 4922 4612 1799

WESTERN BUILDERS OF AMARILLO INC p 1597
700 S Grant St 79101
Tel (806) 376-4321 *SIC* 1542

ANDERSON, TX

TEXAS MUNICIPAL POWER AGENCY p 1444
12824 Fm 244 Rd 77830
Tel (936) 873-2013 *SIC* 4911

ANGLETON, TX

▲ **BENCHMARK ELECTRONICS INC** p 172
3000 Technology Rd 77515
Tel (979) 849-6550 *SIC* 3672 3679

COUNTY OF BRAZORIA p 376
111 E Locust St Ste 303 77515
Tel (979) 864-1275 *SIC* 9111

ARANSAS PASS, TX

J M DAVIDSON INC p 771
2564 County Road 1960 78336
Tel (361) 883-0983 *SIC* 1541 1731 3441

ARGYLE, TX

SMSA PALESTINE ACQUISITION CORP p 1334
174 E Fm 1830 76226
Tel (972) 233-0300 *SIC* 6799

US TRINITY ENERGY SERVICES LLC p 1533
200 Highland Cir 76226
Tel (940) 240-5800 *SIC* 1623

ARLINGTON, TX

■ **A E PETSCHE CO INC** p 5
1501 Nolan Ryan Expy 76011
Tel (817) 461-9473 *SIC* 5063

AGRILOGIC INSURANCE SERVICES LLC p 36
1000 Ballpark Way Ste 314 76011
Tel (888) 245-6442 *SIC* 6331

ARLINGTON INDEPENDENT SCHOOL DISTRICT p 110
1203 W Pioneer Pkwy 76013
Tel (682) 867-4611 *SIC* 8211

ARLINGTON MEMORIAL HOSPITAL ALLIANCE INC p 110
800 W Randol Mill Rd 76012
Tel (817) 548-6100 *SIC* 8062

■ **BUILDERS FIRSTSOURCE-TEXAS GROUP LP** p 225
3403 E Abram St 76010
Tel (214) 880-3500 *SIC* 5031 5033 2439

CATERAIR HOLDINGS CORP p 265
524 E Lamar Blvd 76011
Tel (817) 792-2100 *SIC* 5812

CHOICE HOMES INC p 302
1600 E Lamar Blvd Ste 400 76011
Tel (817) 652-5100 *SIC* 1521

CITY OF ARLINGTON p 313
101 W Abram St 76010
Tel (817) 275-3271 *SIC* 9111

■ **CUMMINS SOUTHERN PLAINS LLC** p 401
600 N Watson Rd 76011
Tel (817) 640-6801 *SIC* 5084 3519

DOLEX DOLLAR EXPRESS INC p 448
700 Highlander Blvd # 450 76015
Tel (817) 548-4700 *SIC* 6099

DON DAVIS AUTO GROUP INC p 449
1901 N Collins St 76011
Tel (817) 461-1000 *SIC* 5511

DOSKOCIL MANUFACTURING CO INC p 451
2300 E Randol Mill Rd 76011
Tel (877) 738-6283 *SIC* 3999 5999

▲ **FIRSTCASH INC** p 550
690 E Lamar Blvd Ste 400 76011
Tel (817) 460-3947 *SIC* 5932 6099

■ **ISCAR METALS INC** p 766
300 Westway Pl 76018
Tel (817) 258-3200 *SIC* 5084

MARTIN SPROCKET & GEAR INC p 913
3100 Sprocket Dr 76015
Tel (817) 258-3000
SIC 3566 3568 3535 3321 3462 3429

MORITZ PARTNERS LP p 989
2111 N Collins St Ste 323 76011
Tel (817) 461-9222 *SIC* 5511

NURSECORE MANAGEMENT SERVICES LLC p 1067
2201 Brookhollow Plaza Dr # 450 76006
Tel (817) 649-1166 *SIC* 8742 8082

■ **OIL STATES INDUSTRIES INC** p 1079
7701 S Cooper St 76001
Tel (817) 548-4200
SIC 1389 3061 3561 3533

OLAMETER CORP p 1080
2261 Brookhollow Plaza Dr # 111 76006
Tel (817) 385-0053 *SIC* 7389

■ **PAACO AUTOMOTIVE GROUP LP** p 1103
3200 E Randol Mill Rd 76011
Tel (817) 635-2000 *SIC* 5521

PETMATE HOLDINGS CO p 1138
2300 E Randol Mill Rd 76011
Tel (817) 467-5116 *SIC* 3999 5999

SCIS AIR SECURITY CORP p 1292
1521 N Cooper St Ste 300 76011
Tel (817) 792-4500 *SIC* 5063 7382

TEXAS HEALTH ARLINGTON MEMORIAL HOSPITAL p 1443
800 W Randol Mill Rd 76012
Tel (682) 236-6695 *SIC* 8062

TEXAS HEALTH RESOURCES p 1443
612 E Lamar Blvd Ste 400 76011
Tel (682) 236-7900 *SIC* 8062

TRNLWB LLC p 1483
1112 E Cpeland Rd Ste 500 76011
Tel (800) 581-3117 *SIC* 3271

UANT VENTURES LLP p 1498
612 E Lamar Blvd Ste 700 76011
Tel (817) 543-4905 *SIC* 6719

UNIVERSITY OF TEXAS AT ARLINGTON p 1525
701 S Nedderman Dr 76019
Tel (817) 272-2011 *SIC* 8221 8731

USMD HOSPITAL AT ARLINGTON LP p 1535
801 W Interstate 20 76017
Tel (817) 472-3400 *SIC* 8062

ATHENS, TX

SSC ATHENS OPERATING CO LLC p 1363
711 Lucas Dr 75751
Tel (903) 675-8538 *SIC* 8051

AUSTIN, TX

AAC GROUP HOLDING CORP p 8
7211 Circle S Rd 78745
Tel (512) 444-0571 *SIC* 3911

ABRAMS INTERNATIONAL INC p 12
111 Congress Ave Ste 2400 78701
Tel (512) 322-4000
SIC 1611 1622 1629 6799 7359 8742

ACCENT FOOD SERVICES LLC p 14
16209 Central Commerce Dr 73301
Tel (512) 251-9500 *SIC* 5046

ACCRUENT LLC p 16
11500 Alterra Pkwy # 110 78758
Tel (512) 861-0726 *SIC* 7372

■ **ACS COMMUNICATIONS INC** p 19
2535 Brockton Dr Ste 400 78758
Tel (512) 837-4400 *SIC* 1731

ACTIVANT SOLUTIONS HOLDINGS INC p 19
804 Las Cimas Pkwy 78746
Tel (512) 328-2300 *SIC* 7371

ALAMO CONCRETE PRODUCTS LTD p 44
6055 W Green Mountain Rd 78744
Tel (512) 444-2464 *SIC* 3272

ALL WEB LEADS INC p 51
7300 Rm Ste 100 78730
Tel (512) 349-7900 *SIC* 6411

AMERICAN ACHIEVEMENT CORP p 67
7211 Circle S Rd 78745
Tel (512) 444-0571 *SIC* 3911 2741

AMERICAN ACHIEVEMENT GROUP HOLDING CORP p 67
7211 Circle S Rd 78745
Tel (512) 444-0571 *SIC* 5094

▲ **AMERICAN CAMPUS COMMUNITIES INC** p 69
12700 Hill Country Blvd 78738
Tel (512) 732-1000 *SIC* 6798 6531

■ **AMERICAN CAMPUS COMMUNITIES OPERATING PARTNERSHIP LP** p 69
12700 Hill Country Blvd 78738
Tel (512) 732-1000 *SIC* 6531

AMERICAN EAGLE PROTECTIVE SERVICES CORP p 71
7700 Chevy Chase Dr 78752
Tel (512) 380-9700 *SIC* 8744

AMERICAN HABILITATION SERVICES INC p 73
9050 N Capital Of Texa 78759
Tel (325) 676-8992 *SIC* 8059

■ **AMERICAN PHYSICIANS SERVICE GROUP INC** p 77
1221 S Mo Pac Expy # 200 78746
Tel (512) 328-0888
SIC 6282 8741 6411 6211

▲ **AMPLIFY SNACK BRANDS INC** p 86
500 W 5th St Ste 1350 78701
Tel (512) 600-9893 *SIC* 2099 2064 2096

ARNOLD OIL CO OF AUSTIN GP LLC p 112
5909 Burleson Rd 78744
Tel (512) 476-2401 *SIC* 5013 5172

ARTHROCARE CORP p 114
7000 W William Cannon Dr # 1 78735
Tel (512) 391-3900 *SIC* 3841

■ **AT&T LABS INC** p 123
9505 Arboretum Blvd 78759
Tel (512) 372-5000 *SIC* 8748

ATTORNEY GENERAL TEXAS p 129
300 W 15th St 78701
Tel (512) 475-4375 *SIC* 9222

AUSTIN COMMUNITY COLLEGE p 132
5930 Middle Fiskville Rd 78752
Tel (512) 223-7000 *SIC* 8222

AUSTIN DIAGNOSTIC CLINIC ASSOCIATION p 132
12221 N Mo Pac Expy 78758
Tel (512) 901-1111 *SIC* 8011

AUSTIN INDEPENDENT SCHOOL DISTRICT (INC) p 133
1111 W 6th St 78703
Tel (512) 414-1700 *SIC* 8211

AUSTIN MATERIALS LLC p 133
9020 N Cpitl Of Texas Hwy 78759
Tel (512) 251-3713 *SIC* 1611 5032

AUSTIN TACALA CORP p 133
500 N Capitl Of Texas Hwy 78746
Tel (512) 327-4654 *SIC* 5812

AUSTIN VENTURES LP p 133
300 W 6th St Ste 2300 78701
Tel (512) 485-1900 *SIC* 6799 2038

BALCONES RESOURCES INC p 147
9301 Johnny Morris Rd 78724
Tel (512) 472-3355 *SIC* 4953

▲ **BAZAARVOICE INC** p 163
10901 Stonelake Blvd 78759
Tel (512) 551-6000 *SIC* 7372

BEXAR COUNTY CLINICAL SERVICES INC p 179
2801 Via Fortuna Ste 500 78746
Tel (512) 899-3995 *SIC* 8072 8071

BLACKHAWK HEALTHCARE LLC p 187
6836 Fm 2244 Rd Ste 202 78746
Tel (512) 617-6363 *SIC* 8741

BLUE SAGE CAPITAL LP p 192
114 W 7th St Ste 820 78701
Tel (512) 536-1900 *SIC* 6726

BOON GROUP INC p 200
6300 Bridge Point Pkwy 3-500 78730
Tel (512) 339-4441 *SIC* 6411

BOTTOM LINE FOOD PROCESSORS INC p 203
200 Michael Angelo Way 78728
Tel (512) 218-3500 *SIC* 2038

■ **BROSNA INC** p 218
5700 S Mo Pac Expy # 300 78749
Tel (512) 936-7600 *SIC* 5812

BROWN DISTRIBUTING CO LTD p 219
8711 Johnny Morris Rd 78724
Tel (512) 478-9353 *SIC* 5181

CALENDAR HOLDINGS LLC p 238
6411 Burleson Rd 78744
Tel (512) 386-7220 *SIC* 5943 5945

CAPITAL METROPOLITAN TRANSPORTATION AUTHORITY p 250
2910 E 5th St 78702
Tel (512) 389-7400 *SIC* 4111

■ **CENPATICO BEHAVIORAL HEALTH LLC** p 275
12515-8 Res Blvd Ste 400 78759
Tel (512) 406-7200 *SIC* 6324

▲ **CHUYS HOLDINGS INC** p 305
1623 Toomey Rd 78704
Tel (512) 473-2783 *SIC* 5812

■ **CHUYS ON HWY 183 INC** p 305
1623 Toomey Rd 78704
Tel (512) 473-2783 *SIC* 5812

CHUYS OPCO INC p 305
1623 Toomey Rd 78704
Tel (512) 473-2783 *SIC* 5812

■ **CICA LIFE INSURANCE CO OF AMERICA** p 306
400 E Anderson Ln 78752
Tel (512) 836-9730 *SIC* 6311

▲ **CIRRUS LOGIC INC** p 309
800 W 6th St 78701
Tel (512) 851-4000 *SIC* 3674

▲ **CITIZENS INC** p 311
400 E Anderson Ln Ste 600 78752
Tel (512) 837-7100 *SIC* 6311 6321

CITY OF AUSTIN p 313
301 W 2nd St 78701
Tel (512) 974-2000 *SIC* 9111

CLASSIC SOFTTRIM INC p 323
4516 Seton Center Pkwy # 135 78759
Tel (512) 873-7770 *SIC* 5199

CLEARESULT CONSULTING INC p 324
4301 Westbank Dr Ste A250 78746
Tel (512) 327-9200 *SIC* 8748

CLINICAL PATHOLOGY LABORATORIES INC p 326
9200 Wall St 78754
Tel (512) 339-1275 *SIC* 8071

COMMEMORATIVE BRANDS INC p 344
7211 Circle S Rd 78745
Tel (512) 444-0571 *SIC* 3911 5944 3961

COMPTROLLER OF PUBLIC ACCOUNTS TEXAS p 352
111 E 17th St Rm 138 78701
Tel (512) 763-8550 *SIC* 9311

COORS OF AUSTIN LP p 368
10300 Metropolitan Dr 78758
Tel (512) 837-6550 *SIC* 5181

COUNTY OF TRAVIS p 382
700 Lavaca St Fl 11 78701
Tel (512) 854-9125 *SIC* 9111

COVENANT MANAGEMENT SYSTEMS LP p 384
4515 Seton Center Pkwy # 220 78759
Tel (512) 338-8388 *SIC* 8011

COVERT BUICK INC p 385
11750 Research Blvd Ste D 78759
Tel (512) 583-3000 *SIC* 5511 7532

COX TEXAS NEWSPAPERS LP p 386
305 S Congress Ave 78704
Tel (512) 445-3500 *SIC* 2711

CRCI HOLDINGS INC p 390
4301 Westbank Dr A-250 78746
Tel (512) 327-9200 *SIC* 6719

D&S RESIDENTIAL SERVICES LP p 407
8911 N Capital Of Texas H 78759
Tel (512) 327-2325 *SIC* 8059

■ **DHI MORTGAGE CO LTD** p 435
10700 Pecan Park Blvd # 450 78750
Tel (512) 502-0545 *SIC* 6162

▲ **DIGITAL TURBINE INC** p 439
1300 Guadalupe St Ste 302 78701
Tel (512) 387-7717 *SIC* 7373

DIMENSIONAL FUND ADVISORS LP p 440
6300 Fm 2244 Rd Bldg 1 78746
Tel (512) 306-7400 *SIC* 6722

DRILLING INFO INC p 456
2901 Via Fortuna Bldg 6 78746
Tel (512) 477-9200 *SIC* 1381

DYNAMIC SYSTEMS INC p 464
3901 S Lamar Blvd Ste 300 78704
Tel (512) 443-4848 *SIC* 1711

EDUCATION AGENCY TEXAS p 479
1701 Congress Ave 78701
Tel (512) 463-9734 *SIC* 8211 9411

ELECTRIC RELIABILITY COUNCIL OF TEXAS INC p 484
7620 Metro Center Dr 78744
Tel (512) 225-7000 *SIC* 4911

EMBARCADERO TECHNOLOGIES INC p 490
10801 N Mopac Expy 1-100 78759
Tel (415) 834-3131 *SIC* 7371 7372

EMPLOYEES RETIREMENT SYSTEM OF TEXAS p 494
200 E 18th St 78701
Tel (512) 867-7199 *SIC* 6371 9441

■ **ENCORE MEDICAL LP** p 496
9800 Metric Blvd 78758
Tel (512) 832-9500 *SIC* 3842 5047

ENVIRONMENTAL QUALITY TEXAS COMMISSION ON p 503
12100 Pk Thirty Five Cir 78753
Tel (512) 239-5500 *SIC* 9511

EPICOR SOFTWARE CORP p 505
804 Las Cimas Pkwy 78746
Tel (512) 328-2300 *SIC* 7372

EXECUTIVE OFFICE OF STATE OF TEXAS p 518
1100 San Jacinto Blvd 78701
Tel (512) 463-2000 *SIC* 9111

▲ **EZCORP INC** p 522
2500 Bee Caves Rd B1-200 78746
Tel (512) 314-3400 *SIC* 5932 6141

FACILITY SOLUTIONS GROUP INC p 523
4401 West Gate Blvd # 310 78745
Tel (512) 440-7985 *SIC* 5063 1731

FARM CREDIT BANK OF TEXAS p 528
4801 Plaza On The Lk # 1200 78746
Tel (512) 330-9060 *SIC* 6111

FERROVIAL AGROMAN TEXAS LLC p 538
9600 Great Hills Trl 200e 78759
Tel (512) 637-8587 *SIC* 8711

FGI GROUP INC p 539
3901 S Lamar Blvd Ste 100 78704
Tel (512) 448-9898
SIC 1542 1541 1794 1611 7353 1711

FIRESTONE HOLDINGS LLC p 544
6501 W William Cannon Dr 78735
Tel (512) 895-2000 *SIC* 5531

FLARE INDUSTRIES LLC p 554
16310 Bratton Ln Ste 350 78728
Tel (512) 836-9473
SIC 3822 7359 3694 2899 1711 3569

■ **FOCUS POINT PARKING INC** p 562
14141 W Hwy 290 Ste 700 78737
Tel (512) 894-3556 *SIC* 7521

■ **FORCEPOINT LLC** p 565
10900 Stonelake Blvd 78759
Tel (858) 320-8000 *SIC* 7372

▲ **FORESTAR GROUP INC** p 567
6300 Fm 2244 Rd Bldg 500 78746
Tel (512) 433-5200 *SIC* 6531 1382

FOUR HANDS LLC p 571
2090 Woodward St 78744
Tel (512) 371-7575 *SIC* 5023 5712

FREESCALE SEMICONDUCTOR HOLDINGS V INC p 577
6501 W William Cannon Dr 78735
Tel (512) 895-2000 *SIC* 3674

FREESCALE SEMICONDUCTOR LTD p 577
6501 W William Cannon Dr 78735
Tel (512) 895-2000 *SIC* 3674

■ **FROST INSURANCE AGENCY INC** p 582
201 Lavaca St Apt 621 78701
Tel (512) 473-4520 *SIC* 6411

GEMALTO INC p 598
9442 Capital Of 78759
Tel (215) 340-2000 *SIC* 5045

GENTEX POWER CORP p 605
3701 Lake Austin Blvd 78703
Tel (512) 473-4084 *SIC* 1629

GIRLING HEALTH CARE INC p 613
1703 W 5th St Fl 7 78703
Tel (512) 452-5781 *SIC* 8082

■ **GOLFSMITH INTERNATIONAL HOLDINGS INC** p 622
11000 N Interstate 35 78753
Tel (512) 837-8810
SIC 5941 5699 5661 5961

GOODWILL INDUSTRIES OF CENTRAL TEXAS p 624
1015 Norwood Park Blvd 78753
Tel (512) 637-7100 *SIC* 8331

■ **GREEN MOUNTAIN ENERGY CO** p 637
901 S Mo Pac Expy Ste 300 78746
Tel (512) 691-6100 *SIC* 4911

■ **GSD&M IDEA CITY LLC** p 643
828 W 6th St 78703
Tel (512) 242-4736 *SIC* 7311

GTS TECHNOLOGY SOLUTIONS INC p 644
9211 Wterford Centre Blvd 78758
Tel (512) 452-0651 *SIC* 5045 5112

GUNZE ELECTRONICS USA CORP p 648
2113 Wells Branch Pkwy # 54 78728
Tel (512) 990-3400 *SIC* 3577

HANGER INC p 657
10910 Domain Dr Ste 300 78758
Tel (512) 777-3800 *SIC* 8093 5047 3842

HARDEN HEALTHCARE TEXAS LP p 660
8701 N Mopac Expy 78759
Tel (512) 615-4965 *SIC* 8059

HARDEN HOME HEALTH LLC p 660
8701 N Mopac Expy 78759
Tel (512) 634-4909 *SIC* 8082

HARRIS COUNTY CLINICAL SERVICES INC p 663
2801 Via Fortuna 78746
Tel (512) 899-3995 *SIC* 8071

HEALTH AND HUMAN SERVICES COMMISSION TEXAS p 674
4900 N Lamar Blvd 78751
Tel (512) 424-6500 *SIC* 9441 9431

HEALTHTRONICS INC p 678
9825 Spectrum Dr Bldg 3 78717
Tel (512) 328-2892 *SIC* 3845

HEALTHTRONICS SERVICE CENTER LLC p 678
9825 Spectrum Dr Bldg 3 78717
Tel (512) 328-2892 *SIC* 1389

HELLAS CONSTRUCTION INC p 681
12710 Res Blvd Ste 240 78759
Tel (512) 250-2910 *SIC* 1629

HID GLOBAL CORP p 690
611 Center Ridge Dr 78753
Tel (800) 237-7769 *SIC* 3825 1731 8741

■ **HILL COUNTRY ELECTRIC SUPPLY LP** p 693
4801 Freidrich Ln Ste 200 78744
Tel (512) 428-9300 *SIC* 5063

HOMEAWAY INC p 703
1011 W 5th St Ste 300 78703
Tel (512) 684-1100 *SIC* 6531 7389 7375

HOSPITAL HOUSEKEEPING SYSTEMS INC p 709
811 Barton Springs Rd # 300 78704
Tel (512) 478-1888 *SIC* 7349

HOSPITAL HOUSEKEEPING SYSTEMS LLC p 709
216 E 4th St 78701
Tel (512) 478-1888 *SIC* 7349

HOUSE OF REPRESENTATIVES TEXAS p 711
105 W 15th St 78701
Tel (512) 463-0865 *SIC* 9121

HT INTERMEDIATE CO LLC p 715
9825 Spectrum Dr Bldg 3 78717
Tel (512) 328-2892 *SIC* 3845

INDEPENDENCE TITLE CO p 736
5900 Sheph Mount Cove Bld 78730
Tel (512) 372-8455 *SIC* 6361

INLAND PAPERBOARD AND PACKAGING INC p 743
1300 S Mo Pac Expy Fl 3 78746
Tel (512) 234-5001
SIC 2653 2631 3086 2679 2657

J & J MAINTENANCE INC p 770
7710 Rialto Blvd Unit 200 78735
Tel (512) 444-7271 *SIC* 1799

JD ABRAMS LP p 780
5811 Trade Center Dr # 1 78744
Tel (512) 322-4000
SIC 1611 1622 1629 3272

JD RAMMING PAVING MANAGEMENT LLC p 780
9020 N Cptl Of Texas Hwy 78759
Tel (512) 251-3713 *SIC* 1611 1771

JEWELRY CHANNEL INC p 784
100 Mchl Agl Way Ste 400d 78728
Tel (512) 852-7000 *SIC* 3679

■ **JONES ENERGY HOLDINGS LLC** p 792
807 Las Cimas Pkwy # 350 78746
Tel (512) 328-2953 *SIC* 1311 1382

▲ **JONES ENERGY INC** p 792
807 Las Cimas Pkwy # 350 78746
Tel (512) 328-2953 *SIC* 1311

JOURNEYMAN CONSTRUCTION INC p 794
7701 N Lamar Blvd Ste 100 78752
Tel (512) 247-7000 *SIC* 1542

JUDICIARY COURTS OF STATE OF TEXAS p 797
205 W 14th St Ste 600 78701
Tel (512) 463-1312 *SIC* 9211

K & N MANAGEMENT INC p 798
11570 Research Blvd 78759
Tel (512) 418-0444 *SIC* 5411 5812

KASASA LTD p 804
4516 Seton Center Pkwy 78759
Tel (512) 418-9590 *SIC* 7371 7373 7379

KELLER WILLIAMS REALTY INC p 808
1221 S Mo Pac Expy # 400 78746
Tel (512) 327-3070 *SIC* 6531

KINGS BAY SERVICES GROUP LLC p 820
3755 S Cptl Of Tx Hwy # 35 78704
Tel (931) 241-1183 *SIC* 7349

■ **LDR HOLDING CORP** p 849
13785 Res Blvd Ste 200 78750
Tel (512) 344-3333 *SIC* 3841

LEGISLATIVE OFFICE TEXAS p 853
1200 N Congress Ave Ste 2 78701
Tel (512) 463-0001 *SIC* 9121

LEIF JOHNSON FORD INC p 854
501 E Koenig Ln 78751
Tel (512) 454-3711 *SIC* 5521 5511

■ **LIN TELEVISION CORP** p 866
701 Brazos St Ste 800 78701
Tel (512) 774-6110 *SIC* 4833

LINEBARGER GOGGAN BLAIR & SAMPSON LLP p 869
2700 Via Fortuna Ste 400 78746
Tel (512) 447-6675 *SIC* 8111

LONE STAR HOLDINGS LLC p 875
6500 River Place Blvd # 2 78730
Tel (512) 873-8067 *SIC* 4215 4513 4212

LOWER COLORADO RIVER AUTHORITY p 881
3700 Lake Austin Blvd 78703
Tel (512) 473-3200 *SIC* 4911 4941 1629

▲ **LUMINEX CORP** p 885
12212 Technology Blvd 78727
Tel (512) 219-8020 *SIC* 3841 8731

MC CARTY CORP p 925
13494 Pond Springs Rd 78729
Tel (512) 331-1344 *SIC* 1541 6411

MGI HOLDINGS LP p 958
5912 Balcones Dr 78731
Tel (512) 459-4796 *SIC* 5812 6794

MICHAEL & SUSAN DELL FOUNDATION p 959
4417 Westlake Dr 78746
Tel (512) 329-0799 *SIC* 7389

MOOD MEDIA CORP p 987
1703 W 5th St Ste 600 78703
Tel (800) 345-5000 *SIC* 7319 7389

MOOD MEDIA NORTH AMERICA LIMITED p 987
1703 W 5th St Ste 600 78703
Tel (512) 380-8500 *SIC* 6794 7389

MR GATTIS LP p 996
5912 Balcones Dr Ste 200 78731
Tel (512) 459-4796 *SIC* 6794 5812

MS PAWN LIMITED PARTNERSHIP p 996
1901 Capital Pkwy 78746
Tel (512) 314-3400 *SIC* 5932 6141

▲ **NATIONAL INSTRUMENTS CORP** p 1013
11500 N Mopac Expy 78759
Tel (512) 338-9119 *SIC* 7372

▲ **NATIONAL WESTERN LIFE INSURANCE CO** p 1017
850 E Anderson Ln 78752
Tel (512) 836-1010 *SIC* 6311

■ **NETSPEND CORP** p 1027
701 Brazos St 78701
Tel (512) 532-8200 *SIC* 6091

■ **NETSPEND HOLDINGS INC** p 1027
701 Brazos St Ste 1300 78701
Tel (512) 532-8200 *SIC* 6153

NEWGISTICS INC p 1037
2700 Via Fortuna Ste 300 78746
Tel (512) 225-6000 *SIC* 4731

■ **NEXTEL OF TEXAS INC** p 1040
8911 N Capital Of Texas 78759
Tel (512) 342-3800 *SIC* 4812

NIELSEN & BAINBRIDGE LLC p 1043
12303 Tech Blvd Ste 950 78727
Tel (512) 506-8844 *SIC* 2499 5023

NPPI INTERMEDIATE INC p 1064
106 E 6th St Ste 300 78701
Tel (512) 476-7100 *SIC* 3086

NXP USA INC p 1068
6501 W William Cannon Dr 78735
Tel (512) 933-8214 *SIC* 3674

OMGANICS INC p 1084
1821 Waterston Ave Unit B 78703
Tel (512) 560-3262 *SIC* 2676

ONE WATER SOURCE LLC p 1086
1114 Lost Creek Blvd # 100 78746
Tel (512) 347-9280 *SIC* 2086

OTTO BOCK HEALTHCARE LP p 1098
11501 Alterra Pkwy # 600 78758
Tel (800) 328-4058 *SIC* 5047

PAROLE DIVISION TEXAS p 1117
209 W 14th St Ste 500 78701
Tel (512) 926-7570 *SIC* 9223

▲ **PARSLEY ENERGY INC** p 1117
303 Colorado St Ste 3000 78701
Tel (737) 704-2300 *SIC* 1311

PINNERGY LTD p 1150
111 Congress Ave Ste 2020 78701
Tel (512) 343-8880 *SIC* 1389

PISCES FOODS LP p 1152
5407 Parkcrest Dr Ste 200 78731
Tel (512) 452-5454 *SIC* 5812

PLANVIEW INC p 1154
12301 Research Blvd 5-100 78759
Tel (512) 346-8600 *SIC* 7371 8748 8742

PLEASANT HILL PRESERVATION LP p 1156
2501 Anken Dr Ofc 78741
Tel (512) 447-7244 *SIC* 6513

PROFESSIONAL CONTRACT SERVICES INC p 1180
718 W Fm 1626 Bldg 100 78748
Tel (512) 358-8887 *SIC* 7349

▲ **Q2 HOLDINGS INC** p 1194
13785 Res Blvd Ste 150 78750
Tel (512) 275-0072 *SIC* 7372

■ **RAVEN POWER FINANCE LLC** p 1209
2901 Via Fortuna Ste 600 78746
Tel (512) 314-8600 *SIC* 4911

■ **RAVEN POWER GROUP LLC** p 1209
2901 Via Fortuna Ste 600 78746
Tel (512) 314-8600 *SIC* 4911

▲ **RETAILMENOT INC** p 1228
301 Congress Ave Ste 700 78701
Tel (512) 777-2970 *SIC* 7311

RIO HOLDINGS INC p 1235
600 Congress Ave Ste 200 78701
Tel (512) 917-1742 *SIC* 4813 4841

RK HALL LLC p 1239
1114 Lost Creek Blvd # 410 78746
Tel (903) 784-7280 *SIC* 1611

SACHEM INC p 1264
821 Woodward St 78704
Tel (512) 421-4900 *SIC* 2869

SAILPOINT TECHNOLOGIES INC p 1268
11305 Four Points Dr 2-100 78726
Tel (512) 346-2000 *SIC* 7372

SAINT EDWARDS UNIVERSITY INC p 1268
3001 S Congress Ave 78704
Tel (512) 448-8400 *SIC* 8221

SAMSUNG AUSTIN SEMICONDUCTOR LLC p 1275
12100 Samsung Blvd 78754
Tel (512) 672-1000 *SIC* 3674

SANDRIDGE PERMIAN TRUST p 1278
919 Congress Ave 78701
Tel (512) 236-6599 *SIC* 6733

■ SAPPHIRE POWER FINANCE LLC p 1282
2901 Via Fortuna Ste 600 78746
Tel (512) 314-8600 *SIC* 4911

■ SAPPHIRE POWER LLC p 1282
2901 Via Fortuna Ste 600 78746
Tel (512) 314-8600 *SIC* 4911

SCHOOL SERVICES AND LEASING INC p 1290
9011 Mtn Rdg Dr Ste 200 78759
Tel (512) 241-7050 *SIC* 4151 4141

■ SCHWAB RETIREMENT PLAN SERVICES CO p 1291
12401 Res Blvd Bldg 2 78759
Tel (512) 344-3000 *SIC* 6371

SELL-THRU SERVICES INC p 1302
4807 Spicewd Spgs Rd # 3120 78759
Tel (512) 346-5075 *SIC* 5141 8742

SERVICE LLOYDS INSURANCE CO p 1307
6907 N Capital Of Texas 78731
Tel (512) 343-0600 *SIC* 6331

SETON HEALTHCARE FAMILY p 1308
1201 W 38th St 78705
Tel (512) 324-1000 *SIC* 8062

SHA LLC p 1310
12940 N Hwy 183 78750
Tel (512) 257-6000 *SIC* 6324 6311 6321

SHI/GOVERNMENT SOLUTIONS INC p 1316
1301 St Mo Pac Expy Ste 78746
Tel (512) 634-8100 *SIC* 5045 7372

▲ SILICON LABORATORIES INC p 1323
400 W Cesar Chavez St 78701
Tel (512) 416-8500 *SIC* 3674

SIZMEK INC p 1328
500 W 5th St Ste 900 78701
Tel (512) 469-5900 *SIC* 7311

SOFTSERVE INC p 1337
111 Congress Ave 78701
Tel (512) 516-8880 *SIC* 7371

SOLARWINDS HOLDINGS INC p 1338
7171 Southwest Pkwy # 400 78735
Tel (512) 682-9300 *SIC* 7372

SOLARWINDS INC p 1338
7171 Southwest Pkwy # 400 78735
Tel (512) 682-9300 *SIC* 7372

SONIC HEALTHCARE USA INC p 1340
9737 Great Hills Trl # 100 78759
Tel (512) 439-1600 *SIC* 8099

SOUTHWEST KEY PROGRAMS INC p 1352
6002 Jain Ln 78721
Tel (512) 462-2181 *SIC* 8361

SPREDFAST INC p 1360
200 W Cesar Chavez St # 600 78701
Tel (512) 823-2320 *SIC* 7371

ST DAVIDS COMMUNITY HEALTH FOUNDATION INITIATIVE p 1365
1303 San Antonio St 78701
Tel (512) 879-6240 *SIC* 8062

ST DAVIDS FOUNDATION p 1365
1303 San Antonio St 78701
Tel (512) 879-6600 *SIC* 8062

ST DAVIDS HEALTH CARE FOUNDATION p 1365
811 Barton Springs Rd # 600 78704
Tel (512) 879-6600 *SIC* 8621

ST DAVIDS HEALTHCARE PARTNERSHIP LP LLP p 1365
98 San Jacinto Blvd 78701
Tel (512) 708-9700 *SIC* 8062

ST DAVIDS HOSPITAL (INC) p 1366
919 E 32nd St 78705
Tel (512) 476-7111 *SIC* 8062

ST DAVIDS NORTH AUSTIN MEDICAL CENTER p 1366
12221 N Mo Pac Expy 78758
Tel (512) 901-1000
SIC 8062 8011 8069 8049

■ ST DAVIDS SOUTH AUSTIN MEDICAL CENTER p 1366
901 W Ben White Blvd 78704
Tel (512) 447-2211 *SIC* 8062 8011

STATE OF TEXAS p 1382
1100 San Jacinto Blvd 78701
Tel (512) 463-2000 *SIC* 9111

STATOIL EXPLORATION CO p 1383
6300 Bridge Point Pkwy 78730
Tel (512) 427-3300 *SIC* 1311

SUCCESS FOODS MANAGEMENT GROUP LLC p 1396
4501 Springdale Rd 78723
Tel (512) 441-8900 *SIC* 8741 5812

■ SUMMIT HOTEL OP LP p 1399
12600 Hill Country Blvd 78738
Tel (512) 538-2300 *SIC* 7011

▲ SUMMIT HOTEL PROPERTIES INC p 1399
12600 Hill Country Blvd 78738
Tel (512) 538-2300 *SIC* 6798

SURVEYING AND MAPPING LLC p 1409
4801 Sw Pkwy Ste 100 78735
Tel (512) 447-0575 *SIC* 8713

TEXAS AMERICAN RESOURCES CO p 1442
401 Congress Ave Ste 1600 78701
Tel (512) 480-8700 *SIC* 1311 1382

TEXAS COUNTY AND DISTRICT RETIREMENT SYSTEM p 1442
901 S Mopac 78746
Tel (512) 328-8889 *SIC* 6733

TEXAS DEPARTMENT OF AGING AND DISABILITY SERVICES p 1442
701 W 51st St 78751
Tel (512) 438-3011 *SIC* 9441

TEXAS DEPARTMENT OF ASSISTIVE AND REHABILITATIVE SERVICES p 1442
4900 N Lamar Blvd 78751
Tel (512) 424-4601 *SIC* 9441

TEXAS DEPARTMENT OF INSURANCE p 1443
333 Guadalupe St Ste 2 78701
Tel (512) 463-6169 *SIC* 6411 9651

TEXAS DEPARTMENT OF MILITARY p 1443
2200 W 35th St Bldg 11 78703
Tel (512) 782-5001 *SIC* 9711

TEXAS DEPARTMENT OF PUBLIC SAFETY p 1443
5805 N Lamar Blvd 78752
Tel (512) 424-2000 *SIC* 9229 9221

TEXAS DEPARTMENT OF STATE HEALTH SERVICES p 1443
1100 W 49th St 78756
Tel (512) 776-6946 *SIC* 9431

TEXAS DEPARTMENT OF TRANSPORTATION p 1443
150 E Riverside Dr 78704
Tel (512) 463-8588 *SIC* 9621

TEXAS DEPT OF FAMILY AND PROTECTIVE SERVICES p 1443
701 W 51st St 78751
Tel (512) 438-3240 *SIC* 9441

TEXAS ELECTRIC COOPERATIVES INC p 1443
1122 Colorado St Ste 2400 78701
Tel (512) 454-0311 *SIC* 2491 3612 8621

TEXAS ENTERPRISES INC p 1443
5005 E 7th St 78702
Tel (512) 385-2167 *SIC* 5172

■TEXAS EZPAWN MANAGEMENT INC p 1443
1901 Capital Pkwy 78746
Tel (512) 314-3400 *SIC* 8741

TEXAS MEDICAL LIABILITY TRUST p 1444
901 S Mo Pac Expy V500 78746
Tel (512) 425-5800 *SIC* 6321

TEXAS MUTUAL INSURANCE CO p 1444
6210 E Hwy 290 78723
Tel (512) 322-3800 *SIC* 6331

TEXAS STATE UNIVERSITY SYSTEM p 1444
208 E 10th St Ste 600 78701
Tel (512) 463-1808 *SIC* 8221

TML MULTISTATE INTERGOVERNMENTAL EMPLOYEE BENEFITS POOL p 1457
1821 Rutherford Ln 300 78754
Tel (512) 719-6500 *SIC* 8611

TOKYO ELECTRON AMERICA INC p 1458
2400 Grove Blvd 78741
Tel (512) 424-1000 *SIC* 3559 8711

TOKYO ELECTRON US HOLDINGS INC p 1458
2400 Grove Blvd 78741
Tel (512) 424-1000 *SIC* 3674

TOUCH INTERNATIONAL INC p 1463
2222 W Rundberg Ln # 200 78758
Tel (512) 832-8292 *SIC* 3575 3577

TRISUN HEALTHCARE LLC p 1483
1703 W 5th St 78703
Tel (512) 634-4900 *SIC* 8051

ULTRA ELECTRONICS DEFENSE INC p 1501
4101 Smith School Rd 78744
Tel (512) 327-6795 *SIC* 3812 3825

■ UNITED TEACHER ASSOCIATES INC p 1514
11200 Lakeline Blvd 78717
Tel (512) 451-2224 *SIC* 6324

UNIVERSITY OF TEXAS AT AUSTIN p 1525
110 Inner Campus Dr G3400 78712
Tel (512) 471-3434 *SIC* 8221

UNIVERSITY OF TEXAS SYSTEM p 1526
210 W 6th St 78701
Tel (512) 499-4587 *SIC* 8221

USA COMPRESSION PARTNERS LLC p 1534
100 Congress Ave Ste 450 78701
Tel (512) 369-1380 *SIC* 1389

▲ USA COMPRESSION PARTNERS LP p 1534
100 Congress Ave Ste 450 78701
Tel (512) 473-2662 *SIC* 1389

VELOCITY ELECTRONICS LP p 1547
2208 Energy Dr 78758
Tel (512) 973-9500 *SIC* 5065

WAYNE FUELING SYSTEMS LLC p 1584
3814 Jarrett Way 78728
Tel (512) 388-8311 *SIC* 1389

■ WEBSENSE LLC p 1586
10900 Stonelake Blvd 78759
Tel (858) 320-8000 *SIC* 7372

▲ WHOLE FOODS MARKET INC p 1607
550 Bowie St 78703
Tel (512) 477-4455 *SIC* 5411

■ WILLIAMS INSULATION CO OF AUSTIN INC p 1611
4300 Nixon Ln 78725
Tel (512) 928-4002 *SIC* 1742

WILSHIRE HOMES LP p 1613
8200 N Mopac Expy Ste 350 78759
Tel (512) 502-2050 *SIC* 1521

■ WINCOR NIXDORF INC p 1615
12345 N Lamar Blvd # 200 78753
Tel (512) 676-5000 *SIC* 7379 5734 5251

WORKFORCE COMMISSION TEXAS p 1624
101 E 15th St 78778
Tel (512) 463-2222 *SIC* 9651

▲ XPLORE TECHNOLOGIES CORP p 1632
8601 Ranch Road 2222 Ii 78730
Tel (512) 336-7797 *SIC* 3577

AZLE, TX

QUALITY TRAILER PRODUCTS LP p 1197
604 W Main St 76020
Tel (817) 444-4518 *SIC* 3714 5013

TRI-COUNTY ELECTRIC COOPERATIVE INC p 1477
600 Northwest Pkwy 76020
Tel (817) 444-3201 *SIC* 4911

BALCH SPRINGS, TX

GLENN THURMAN INC p 615
3180 S Belt Line Rd 75181
Tel (972) 286-6333 *SIC* 1611 4212

BALLINGER, TX

MUELLER SUPPLY CO INC p 998
1913 Hutchins Ave 76821
Tel (325) 365-3555 *SIC* 3448 3496 5039

BASTROP, TX

BASTROP INDEPENDENT SCHOOL DISTRICT p 159
906 Farm St 78602
Tel (512) 321-2292 *SIC* 8211

BLUEBONNET ELECTRIC COOPERATIVE INC p 192
155 Electric Ave 78602
Tel (800) 842-7708 *SIC* 4911

BAYTOWN, TX

ANGEL BROTHERS ENTERPRISES LTD p 91
5210 West Rd 77521
Tel (281) 421-5721 *SIC* 1794 1611

ANGEL BROTHERS INC p 91
5210 West Rd 77521
Tel (281) 471-6730 *SIC* 1611

BBB TANK SERVICES INC p 163
162 Independence Pkwy N 77520
Tel (832) 695-2132 *SIC* 1389

CRYOGENIC VESSEL ALTERNATIVES INC p 396
1301 Transport Dr 77523
Tel (281) 738-2863 *SIC* 3559

GOOSE CREEK CONSOLIDATED INDEPENDENT SCHOOL DISTRICT p 625
4544 Interstate 10 E 77521
Tel (281) 420-4800 *SIC* 8211

JSW STEEL (USA) INC p 796
5200 E Mckinney Rd # 110 77523
Tel (281) 383-2525 *SIC* 3317 3312

KTB SERVICES LLC p 831
1108 Cedar Bayou Rd 77520
Tel (281) 428-7344 *SIC* 1711

SAN JACINTO METHODIST HOSPITAL p 1277
4401 Garth Rd 77521
Tel (281) 420-8600 *SIC* 8062 8063 8051

■TRIUMPH HOSPITAL BAYTOWN p 1483
1700 James Bowie Dr 77520
Tel (281) 420-7800 *SIC* 8062

BEASLEY, TX

HUDSON PRODUCTS CORP p 717
9660 Grunwald Rd 77417
Tel (281) 396-8195 *SIC* 3443

HUDSON PRODUCTS HOLDINGS INC p 717
9660 Grunwald Rd 77417
Tel (281) 396-8100 *SIC* 3443

BEAUMONT, TX

ALLCO LLC p 52
6720 College St 77707
Tel (409) 860-4459 *SIC* 1623 1542 1541

BAPTIST HOSPITALS OF SOUTHEAST TEXAS p 154
3080 College St 77701
Tel (409) 212-5000 *SIC* 8062

BEAUMONT INDEPENDENT SCHOOL DISTRICT p 166
3395 Harrison Ave 77706
Tel (409) 617-5000 *SIC* 8211

BO-MAC CONTRACTORS LTD p 194
1020 Lindbergh Dr 77707
Tel (409) 842-2125 *SIC* 1629 1771

CHRISTUS HEALTH SOUTHEAST TEXAS p 303
2830 Calder St 77702
Tel (409) 892-7171 *SIC* 8062

CITY OF BEAUMONT p 313
801 Main St 77701
Tel (409) 880-3716 *SIC* 9111

COBURN SUPPLY CO INC p 333
390 Park St Ste 100 77701
Tel (409) 838-6363
SIC 5063 5064 5072 5074 5075 5078

COMMUNITYBANK OF TEXAS NATIONAL ASSOCIATION p 350
5999 Delaware St 77706
Tel (409) 861-7200
SIC 6163 6029 6022 6021

COUNTY OF JEFFERSON p 378
1149 Pearl St Ste 301 77701
Tel (409) 835-8466 *SIC* 9111

DAWSON MARINE INC p 417
4230 College St 77707
Tel (409) 840-4111 *SIC* 4499

DELI MANAGEMENT INC p 424
2400 Broadway St 77702
Tel (409) 838-1976 *SIC* 5812

DRAGON PRODUCTS LTD p 455
1655 Louisiana St 77701
Tel (409) 833-2665 *SIC* 3443

E E R INC p 466
3000 W Cedar St 77702
Tel (409) 838-2002 *SIC* 5812

■ ENTERGY TEXAS INC p 502
350 Pine St 77701
Tel (409) 981-2000 *SIC* 4911

■ EXXONMOBIL OIL CORP p 521
2805 Sycamore St 77701
Tel (409) 757-3763
SIC 2911 5171 4613 1311

HELENA LABORATORIES CORP p 681
1530 Lindbergh Dr 77707
Tel (409) 842-3714 *SIC* 3841 3826

LAMAR UNIVERSITY p 841
4400 S M L King Jr Pkwy 77705
Tel (409) 880-8932 *SIC* 8221

MEMORIAL HERMANN BAPTIST HOSPITAL p 941
3080 College St 77701
Tel (409) 212-5000 *SIC* 8062

MODERN AG PRODUCTS LTD p 981
1655 Louisiana St 77701
Tel (409) 833-2665 *SIC* 7359 6792 0161

MODERN GROUP LTD p 981
1655 Louisiana St 77701
Tel (800) 231-8198 *SIC* 7359 3441

OFFSHORE RENTAL LTD p 1076
1655 Louisiana St 77701
Tel (409) 833-2665 *SIC* 2911

■ OHMSTEDE LTD p 1078
895 N Main St 77701
Tel (409) 833-6375 *SIC* 5075 3443

PRICE & CO p 1174
3530 W Cardinal Dr 77705
Tel (409) 842-0677
SIC 5194 5145 5122 5141

SOUTHEAST TEXAS CLASSIC AUTOMOTIVE INC p 1346
1000 Interstate 10 N 77702
Tel (409) 898-8001 *SIC* 5511 7515

TRANSIT MIX CONCRETE & MATERIALS CO p 1472
850 Pine St 77701
Tel (409) 835-4934 *SIC* 3273

TRI-CON INC p 1477
7076 W Port Arthur Rd 77705
Tel (409) 835-2237 *SIC* 5541 5172 5411

BEDFORD, TX

CARTER BLOODCARE p 261
2205 Highway 121 76021
Tel (817) 412-5000 *SIC* 2836

CARTER BLOODCARE FDN p 261
2205 Highway 121 76021
Tel (817) 412-5121 *SIC* 8011

HURST-EULESS-BEDFORD INDEPENDENT SCHOOL DISTRICT p 721
1849 Central Dr 76022
Tel (817) 267-3311 *SIC* 8211

NISSAN GRUBBS MID-CITIES LTD p 1044
310 Airport Fwy 76022
Tel (817) 268-1000 *SIC* 5511

STATE NATIONAL COMPANIES INC p 1381
1900 L Don Dodson Dr 76021
Tel (817) 265-2000 *SIC* 8742

STATE NATIONAL INSURANCE CO INC p 1381
1900 L Don Dodson Dr 76021
Tel (817) 265-2000 *SIC* 6331

TBA INSURANCE GROUP LIMITED PARTNERSHIP p 1427
1900 L Don Dodson Dr 76021
Tel (817) 265-2000 *SIC* 6331 6163

TEXAS HLTH HRS MTHDT HSPTL HEB p 1443
1615 Hospital Pkwy 76022
Tel (817) 848-4000 SIC 8062 8063 8069

■ WARRANTECH CORP p 1576
2200 Highway 121 76021
Tel (817) 785-6601 SIC 6399

WORD OF GOD FELLOWSHIP INC p 1624
3901 Highway 121 76021
Tel (817) 571-1229 SIC 4833

BELLAIRE, TX

■ CHEVRON PIPE LINE CO p 296
4800 Fournace Pl 77401
Tel (877) 596-2800 SIC 5541

CTECU p 399
4800 Fournace Pl 77401
Tel (713) 432-0038 SIC 6062

EMERALD FOODS INC p 491
6300 West Loop S 77401
Tel (713) 791-9167 SIC 5812

JONES & CARTER INC p 792
6330 West Loop S Ste 150 77401
Tel (713) 777-5337 SIC 8711

NEIGHBORHOOD CENTERS INC p 1024
4500 Bissonnet St Ste 200 77401
Tel (713) 667-9400 SIC 8351 8322

ROYWELL SERVICES INC p 1255
4545 Bissonnet St Ste 104 77401
Tel (713) 661-4747 SIC 1389

WORLEYPARSONS GROUP INC p 1626
6330 West Loop S 77401
Tel (713) 407-5000 SIC 8711 8742

WORLEYPARSONS INTERNATIONAL INC p 1626
6330 West Loop S Ste 200 77401
Tel (713) 407-5000 SIC 8742

BELLVILLE, TX

■ BELLVILLE TUBE CO LP p 171
141 Miller Rd E 77418
Tel (979) 865-9111 SIC 3312

WESTERN INTERNATIONAL GAS & CYLINDERS INC p 1598
7173 Highway 159 E 77418
Tel (979) 865-5991 SIC 5169 2813

BELTON, TX

BELL COUNTY TEXAS p 170
101 E Central Ave 76513
Tel (254) 933-5115 SIC 9111

BELTON INDEPENDENT SCHOOL DISTRICT p 171
400 N Wall St 76513
Tel (254) 215-2000 SIC 8211

■ MILLER SPRINGS MATERIALS LLC p 971
6218 State Highway 317 76513
Tel (254) 780-9959 SIC 5085 5999

UNIVERSITY OF MARY HARDIN-BAYLOR p 1522
900 College St 76513
Tel (254) 295-8642 SIC 8221

BOERNE, TX

JET SPECIALTY INC p 783
211 Market Ave 78006
Tel (830) 331-9457 SIC 5084 5085

TEXAS STAR NUT AND FOOD CO INC p 1444
206 Market Ave 78006
Tel (830) 249-8300 SIC 5145 2068

BOLING, TX

MAXIM FARM EGG CO INC p 922
580 Maxim Dr 77420
Tel (979) 657-2891 SIC 5144

WHARTON COUNTY FOODS LLC p 1604
4429 Fm 442 Rd 77420
Tel (979) 657-2891 SIC 5411

BONHAM, TX

KWIK CHEK FOOD STORES INC p 832
2207 N Center St 75418
Tel (903) 583-7484 SIC 5541 5411

KWIK CHEK REAL ESTATE TRUST INC p 832
2207 N Center St 75418
Tel (903) 583-7481 SIC 6798

TAYLOR-SMART LLC p 1427
2207 N Center St 75418
Tel (903) 583-7481 SIC 5171

BORGER, TX

SENIOR LIVING PROPERTIES LLC p 1304
1316 S Florida St 79007
Tel (806) 273-3785 SIC 8051

BRADY, TX

LOADCRAFT INDUSTRIES LTD p 872
3811 N Bridge St 76825
Tel (325) 597-2911 SIC 3533

BRENHAM, TX

BLINN COLLEGE p 189
902 College Ave 77833
Tel (979) 830-4000 SIC 8221 8222

BLUE BELL CREAMERIES INC p 190
1101 S Blue Bell Rd 77833
Tel (817) 560-1980 SIC 2024

BLUE BELL CREAMERIES LP p 190
1101 S Blue Bell Rd 77833
Tel (979) 836-7977 SIC 2024 5143

BLUE BELL CREAMERIES USA INC p 190
1101 S Blue Bell Rd 77833
Tel (979) 836-7977 SIC 2024

BRENHAM WHOLESALE GROCERY CO INC p 210
602 W First St 77833
Tel (979) 836-7925
SIC 5194 5147 5142 5141 5148

GERMANIA FARM MUTUAL INSURANCE ASSOCIATION p 609
507 Highway 290 E 77833
Tel (979) 836-5224 SIC 6311 6331

GERMANIA INSURANCE CO p 609
507 Highway 290 E 77833
Tel (979) 836-5224 SIC 6411

BRIDGE CITY, TX

STIS INC p 1390
3127 Texas Ave 77611
Tel (409) 697-3350 SIC 1541

BRIDGEPORT, TX

CRISP INDUSTRIES INC p 392
323 Energy Way 76426
Tel (940) 683-4070 SIC 5032

PEAK OILFIELD SERVICES LLC p 1126
1502 10th St Ste A 76426
Tel (940) 683-1627 SIC 1389

ROC HOLDINGS LLC p 1242
191 Energy Way 76426
Tel (940) 683-0159 SIC 1794 1731 6719

ROC SERVICE CO LLC p 1242
191 Energy Way 76426
Tel (940) 683-0109 SIC 1794 1731 1389

BRONTE, TX

EAST COKE COUNTY HOSPITAL DISTRICT p 470
900 S State St 76933
Tel (325) 473-3621 SIC 8059 8051

BROOKSHIRE, TX

ORIZON INDUSTRIES INC p 1095
7007 Fm 362 Rd 77423
Tel (281) 375-7700 SIC 3441

WEST HOU INC p 1594
907 Bains St 77423
Tel (281) 934-1500 SIC 1389

BROWNSVILLE, TX

ABUNDANT LIFE HOME HEALTH INC p 13
1900 Pecan 78520
Tel (956) 544-7714 SIC 8082

BROWNSVILLE INDEPENDENT SCHOOL DISTRICT p 220
1900 E Price Rd 78521
Tel (956) 548-8000 SIC 8211

CITY OF BROWNSVILLE p 313
1001 E Elizabeth St # 234 78520
Tel (956) 542-2064 SIC 9111

COUNTY OF CAMERON p 376
1100 E Monroe St 78520
Tel (956) 544-0823 SIC 9111

ESCO MARINE INC p 509
16200 Jose Garza Rd 78521
Tel (956) 554-5300 SIC 4499 5093 7389

INTERNATIONAL ASSEMBLY INC p 754
750 E Los Ebanos Blvd A 78520
Tel (956) 499-7933 SIC 5162

KEPPEL AMFELS LLC p 813
20000 State Highway 48 78521
Tel (956) 831-8220
SIC 1629 3731 1389 3449 3546 3443

PRONTO GENERAL AGENCY LTD p 1183
805 Media Luna St Ste 100 78520
Tel (956) 574-9787 SIC 6331 6361 7291

PUBLIC UTILITIES BOARD p 1190
1425 Robinhood St 78521
Tel (956) 350-8819 SIC 4931

TRICO TECHNOLOGIES CORP p 1479
1995 Billy Mitchell Blvd 78521
Tel (956) 544-2722 SIC 3714

UNIVERSITY OF TEXAS AT BROWNSVILLE p 1525
1 W University Blvd 78520
Tel (956) 882-8200 SIC 8221

VALLEY BAPTIST MEDICAL CENTER - BROWNSVILLE p 1540
1040 W Jefferson St 78520
Tel (956) 389-1100 SIC 8062

BROWNWOOD, TX

BROWNWOOD HOSPITAL LP p 220
1501 Burnet Rd 76801
Tel (325) 646-8541 SIC 8062

BRYAN, TX

■ ALENCO HOLDING CORP p 48
615 W Carson St 77801
Tel (979) 779-1051 SIC 3442

ANCO INSURANCE MANAGERS INC p 89
1111 Briarcrest Dr 77802
Tel (979) 776-2626 SIC 6411

BRYAN INDEPENDENT SCHOOL DISTRICT p 221
101 N Texas Ave 77803
Tel (979) 209-1000 SIC 8211

BRYAN TEXAS UTILITIES p 221
205 E 28th St 77803
Tel (979) 821-5700 SIC 4911

COUFAL-PRATER EQUIPMENT LLC p 374
3110 W Highway 21 77803
Tel (979) 822-7684 SIC 5999 7699 5082

KENT MOORE CABINETS LTD p 812
501 Industrial Blvd 77803
Tel (979) 775-2906 SIC 2434

ST JOSEPH REGIONAL HEALTH CENTER p 1368
2801 Franciscan Dr 77802
Tel (979) 776-3777 SIC 8062 8322

WOODBOLT DISTRIBUTION LLC p 1622
3891 S Traditions Dr 77807
Tel (800) 870-2070 SIC 5122

BUFFALO, TX

R CONSTRUCTION CO p 1201
1313 Hwy 79 S 75831
Tel (903) 322-4639 SIC 1389 1794

BUNA, TX

B & E RESOURCES LTD CO p 141
39772 Us Highway 96 S 77612
Tel (409) 994-2653 SIC 1799

SOUTHEAST TEXAS INDUSTRIES INC p 1346
35911 Us Highway 96 S 77612
Tel (409) 994-3570 SIC 3312 3443

BURKE, TX

FLEETWOOD TRANSPORTATION SERVICES INC p 555
7632 S Us Highway 59 75941
Tel (936) 829-4735 SIC 4213

BURLESON, TX

ADVENTIST HEALTH SYSTEMS/ SUN BELT p 27
11801 South Fwy 76028
Tel (817) 293-9110 SIC 8062

BURLESON INDEPENDENT SCHOOL DISTRICT p 227
1160 Sw Wilshire Blvd 76028
Tel (817) 245-1000 SIC 8211

BURNET, TX

■ ATMI MATERIALS LTD p 128
706 Houston Clinton Dr 78611
Tel (512) 715-5343 SIC 3674

CAMERON, TX

EBCO GENERAL CONTRACTOR LTD p 474
305 W Gillis Ave 76520
Tel (254) 697-8516 SIC 1542 8741

CANUTILLO, TX

BD VINTON LLC p 164
I-10 Vinton Rd 79835
Tel (915) 886-2000
SIC 5051 3312 3449 3316

CANYON, TX

CANYON INDEPENDENT SCHOOL DISTRICT p 248
3301 N 23rd St 79015
Tel (806) 677-2600 SIC 8211

LONE STAR DAIRY PRODUCTS LLC p 875
401 Highway 60 79015
Tel (806) 567-5623 SIC 2023

CARROLLTON, TX

4FRONT ENGINEERED SOLUTIONS INC p 3
1612 Hutton Dr Ste 140 75006
Tel (972) 466-0707 SIC 3537

4FRONT HOLDINGS INC p 3
1612 Hutton Dr Ste 140 75006
Tel (972) 466-0707 SIC 3537 3999 3448

AER MANUFACTURING LP p 30
1605 Surveyor Blvd 75006
Tel (972) 418-6499 SIC 3714

■ ALBERTA INVESTMENTS INC p 46
1445 Mac Arthur Dr Ste 13 75007
Tel (972) 242-4550 SIC 3273

■ AMERICAN TILE AND STONE INC p 80
2244 Luna Rd Ste 160 75006
Tel (972) 243-2377 SIC 5032

BAYLOR MEDICAL CENTER AT CARROLLTON p 162
4343 N Josey Ln 75010
Tel (972) 492-1010 SIC 8062

BRANDT COMPANIES LLC p 208
1728 Briercroft Ct 75006
Tel (972) 241-9411 SIC 1711 1731 7623

C H INDUSTRIES INC p 232
1700 Columbian Club Dr 75006
Tel (972) 416-1304 SIC 2599 3444 3469

CANTEX HEALTH CARE CENTERS LLC p 247
2537 Golden Bear Dr 75006
Tel (214) 954-4114 SIC 8051

CARROLLTON-FARMERS BRANCH INDEPENDENT SCHOOL DISTRICT p 261
1445 N Perry Rd 75006
Tel (972) 968-6100 SIC 8211

■ COOKTEK INDUCTION SYSTEM LLC p 366
2801 Trade Ctr 75007
Tel (312) 563-9600 SIC 5046

▲ CYRUSONE INC p 406
1649 W Frankford Rd 75007
Tel (972) 350-0060 SIC 6798

■ FIRST TEXAS HOSPITAL CARROLLTON LLC p 550
1401 E Trinity Mills Rd 75006
Tel (972) 810-0700 SIC 8062

G L SEAMAN & CO p 587
4201 International Pkwy 75007
Tel (214) 764-6400 SIC 5021

G6 HOSPITALITY LLC p 588
4001 International Pkwy 75007
Tel (972) 360-9000 SIC 8741

G6 HOSPITALITY LLC p 588
4001 International Pkwy 75007
Tel (972) 360-9000 SIC 7011

GUNDER & ASSOCIATES INC p 647
1215 W Crosby Rd Ste 206 75006
Tel (972) 620-2801 SIC 5075

HILITE INDUSTRIES INC p 692
1671 S Broadway St 75006
Tel (972) 242-2116 SIC 6719

HILITE INTERNATIONAL INC p 693
1671 S Broadway St 75006
Tel (972) 242-2116 SIC 5531

■ HILTON RESERVATIONS WORLDWIDE LLC p 695
2050 Chenault Dr 75006
Tel (972) 770-6100 SIC 7011

HUGH M CUNNINGHAM INC p 717
2029 Westgate Dr Ste 120 75006
Tel (972) 888-3833
SIC 5074 5085 5083 5199

HUMANETICS II LTD p 718
1700 Columbian Club Dr 75006
Tel (972) 416-1304 SIC 3444 3599

IBL LIMITED LLC p 726
4001 International Pkwy 75007
Tel (972) 360-9000 SIC 7011

INNOVATIVE IDM LLC p 745
1625 Wallace Dr Ste 110 75006
Tel (214) 574-9500 SIC 5063 7622 3699

LORIS GIFTS INC p 878
2125 Chenault Dr Ste 100 75006
Tel (972) 759-5000 SIC 5947 8099 5999

M&A TECHNOLOGY INC p 890
2045 Chenault Dr 75006
Tel (972) 490-5803 SIC 5045 7373

■ MCLANE FOODSERVICE INC p 931
2085 Midway Rd 75006
Tel (972) 364-2000
SIC 8742 5141 5311 5113

MOTEL 6 OPERATING LP p 992
4001 Intl Pkwy Ste 500 75007
Tel (972) 360-9000 SIC 7011

OPTEK TECHNOLOGY INC p 1090
1645 Wallace Dr 75006
Tel (972) 323-2200
SIC 3674 3825 3812 3661 3643

SAM PACKS FIVE STAR FORD LTD p 1274
1635 S Interstate 35e 75006
Tel (972) 447-0606 SIC 5511

SCHNEIDER ELECTRIC BUILDINGS AMERICAS INC p 1287
1650 W Crosby Rd 75006
Tel (972) 323-1111 SIC 3822 1731

SITE CONCRETE INC p 1327
1544 Valwood Pkwy Ste 100 75006
Tel (972) 313-0733 SIC 1611 1771 1794

STMICROELECTRONICS (NORTH AMERICA) HOLDING INC p 1390
1310 Electronics Dr 75006
Tel (972) 466-6000 SIC 3674

SWS RE-DISTRIBUTION CO INC p 1413
1440 Lemay Dr Ste 104 75007
Tel (214) 483-1076 SIC 5087

■ THOMSON REUTERS (TAX & ACCOUNTING) INC p 1450
2395 Midway Rd 75006
Tel (800) 431-9025 SIC 2721 7371

TRUCO ENTERPRISES LP p 1485
2727 Realty Dr Ste 134 75006
Tel (972) 869-4600 SIC 5145

VAREL INTERNATIONAL ENERGY SERVICES INC p 1544
1625 W Crosby Rd Ste 124 75006
Tel (800) 827-3526 SIC 1381 3545

VAREL INTERNATIONAL IND LP p 1544
1625 W Crosby Rd Ste 124 75006
Tel (972) 242-1160 SIC 3545 3532 1381

■ WOOT INC p 1624
4121 International Pkwy 75007
Tel (972) 417-3959 SIC 7389

■ WOOT SERVICES LLC p 1624
4121 Intl Pkwy Ste 900 75007
Tel (972) 417-3959 SIC 7389

CARTHAGE, TX

RITTER CONSTRUCTION CO p 1237
671 Ritter Dr 75633
Tel (903) 693-2397 *SIC* 1623

CEDAR PARK, TX

AMERICAN CONSTRUCTORS INC p 70
11900 W Parmer Ln Ste 200 78613
Tel (512) 328-2026 *SIC* 1541 1542

APAC-TEXAS INC p 95
1320 Arrow Point Dr # 600 78613
Tel (512) 861-7100 *SIC* 1611

■ CEDAR PARK HEALTH SYSTEM LP p 272
1401 Medical Pkwy 78613
Tel (512) 528-7000 *SIC* 8062

CENTER, TX

■ TYSON FARMS OF TEXAS INC p 1496
1019 Shelbyville St 75935
Tel (936) 598-2474 *SIC* 2015

CHANNELVIEW, TX

TAPCOENPRO LLC p 1424
16315 Market St 77530
Tel (281) 247-8100 *SIC* 3491

CHINA GROVE, TX

LONE STAR BAKERY INC p 875
6905 Us Highway 87 E 78263
Tel (210) 648-6400 *SIC* 2053 2051

CHRISTINE, TX

SAN MIGUEL ELECTRIC COOPERATIVE INC p 1277
6200 Fm 3387 78012
Tel (830) 784-3411 *SIC* 4911

CLEBURNE, TX

AGE INDUSTRIES LTD p 34
3601 County Road 316c 76031
Tel (817) 477-5266 *SIC* 2653 2655 2671

TECHNICAL CHEMICAL CO p 1431
3327 Pipeline Rd 76033
Tel (817) 645-6088 *SIC* 2992

TUTLE & TUTLE TRUCKING INC p 1493
3672 W Highway 67 76033
Tel (817) 556-2131 *SIC* 4212

UNITED ELECTRIC COOPERATIVE SERVICES INC p 1508
3309 N Main St 76033
Tel (817) 556-4000 *SIC* 4911

CLEVELAND, TX

MACK CLEVELAND SALES INC p 892
1263 Us Highway 59 N 77327
Tel (281) 593-8888 *SIC* 5012

TUBULAR MACHINED PRODUCTS p 1490
90 Campbell Acres Rd 77328
Tel (713) 504-8932 *SIC* 5051 3492 7389

CLUTE, TX

BRAZOSPORT INDEPENDENT SCHOOL DISTRICT (INC) p 209
301 W Brazoswood Dr 77531
Tel (979) 730-7000 *SIC* 8211

INFINITY CONSTRUCTION SERVICES LP p 741
926 Brazosport Blvd S 77531
Tel (979) 388-8579 *SIC* 1629 1542

COLLEGE STATION, TX

12TH MAN STUDENT FOUNDATION INC p 1
12th Man Fndtion The Zone 77844
Tel (979) 846-8892 *SIC* 7389

■ COLLEGE STATION HOSPITAL LP p 337
1604 Rock Prairie Rd 77845
Tel (979) 764-5100 *SIC* 8062

COLLEGE STATION INDEPENDENT SCHOOL DISTRICT p 337
1812 Welsh Ave 77840
Tel (979) 764-5400 *SIC* 8211

■ OI CORP p 1078
151 Graham Rd 77845
Tel (979) 690-1711 *SIC* 3826

TEXAS A & M RESEARCH FOUNDATION INC p 1441
400 Harvey Mtchl Pkwy 3 77845
Tel (979) 845-8600 *SIC* 8741

TEXAS A & M UNIVERSITY p 1441
301 Tarrow St Fl 6 77840
Tel (979) 862-3003 *SIC* 8221

TEXAS A&M AGRILIFE EXTENSION SERVICE p 1442
2147 Tamu 77843
Tel (979) 458-4383 *SIC* 8731 8221

TEXAS A&M AGRILIFE RESEARCH p 1442
2147 Tamu 77843
Tel (979) 458-4383 *SIC* 8731 8221

TEXAS A&M ENGINEERING EXPERIMENT STATION p 1442
7607 Eastmark Dr Ste 101 77840
Tel (979) 458-7643 *SIC* 8711

TEXAS A&M ENGINEERING EXTENSION SERVICE p 1442
301 Tarrow St 77840
Tel (979) 845-7641
SIC 8331 8711 8748 8111

TEXAS A&M FOUNDATION p 1442
401 George Bush Dr 77840
Tel (979) 845-8161 *SIC* 6732 8399

TEXAS A&M HEALTH SCIENCE CENTER p 1442
200 Technology Way 77845
Tel (979) 436-9200 *SIC* 8299 8221

TEXAS A&M UNIVERSITY SYSTEM p 1442
301 Tarrow St Fl 3 77840
Tel (979) 458-6100
SIC 8221 8731 8742 8011

COLLEYVILLE, TX

ALACRITY LENDING CO p 43
6209 Colleyville Blvd 76034
Tel (817) 481-1500 *SIC* 6162

■ ALAMO TITLE HOLDING CO p 44
6200 Colleyville Blvd 76034
Tel (817) 428-6996 *SIC* 6361

COLUMBUS, TX

ALLEYTON RESOURCE CO LLC p 53
755 Fm 762 78934
Tel (281) 238-1010 *SIC* 5251

COLORADO COUNTY OIL CO INC p 338
1348 Business 71 78934
Tel (979) 732-6870 *SIC* 5171

DRYMALLA CONSTRUCTION CO INC p 457
608 Harbert St 78934
Tel (281) 342-3853 *SIC* 1542

COMMERCE, TX

TAMU COMMERCE p 1423
P.O. Box 3011 75429
Tel (903) 886-5060 *SIC* 8611

TEXAS A&M UNIVERSITY-COMMERCE p 1442
2600 W Neal St 75428
Tel (903) 886-5041 *SIC* 8221

CONROE, TX

■ CHCA CONROE LP p 292
504 Medical Center Blvd 77304
Tel (936) 539-1111 *SIC* 8062

CONROE INDEPENDENT SCHOOL DISTRICT p 358
3205 W Davis St 77304
Tel (936) 709-7751 *SIC* 8211

■ CONSOLIDATED COMMUNICATIONS SERVICES CO p 359
350 S Loop 336 W 77304
Tel (936) 756-0611 *SIC* 4813

COUNTY OF MONTGOMERY p 380
501 N Thompson St 77301
Tel (936) 539-7885 *SIC* 9111

DMG EQUIPMENT CO LTD p 446
1575 Fm 1485 Rd 77301
Tel (936) 756-6960 *SIC* 1611 2951

HEMPEL (USA) INC p 682
600 Conroe Park North Dr 77303
Tel (936) 523-6000 *SIC* 2851

MULTI-SHOT LLC p 999
3335 Pollok Dr 77303
Tel (936) 441-6630 *SIC* 1389 1381

PROFESSIONAL DIRECTIONAL ENTERPRISES INC p 1180
850 Conroe Park West Dr 77303
Tel (936) 441-7266 *SIC* 1389 1381

TONY GULLO MOTORS I LP p 1460
500 Interstate 45 S 77304
Tel (936) 539-9191 *SIC* 7549 5511 5531

CONVERSE, TX

SOUTHWEST ELECTRICAL CONTRACTING SERVICES LTD p 1352
9435 E Loop 1604 N 78109
Tel (210) 568-1632 *SIC* 1731

COPPELL, TX

AAA TEXAS LLC p 7
1225 Freeport Pkwy 75019
Tel (469) 221-8285 *SIC* 6411

ALCO STORES INC p 47
751 Freeport Pkwy 75019
Tel (469) 322-2900 *SIC* 5311 5331

AVT GROCERY INC p 139
777 Freeport Pkwy 75019
Tel (972) 241-2184 *SIC* 5411 5912

BARCEL USA LLC p 154
301 S Nrthpint Dr Ste 100 75019
Tel (972) 607-4500 *SIC* 5145

BT AMERICAS INC p 222
8951 Cypress Waters Blvd # 200 75019
Tel (877) 272-0832 *SIC* 8748

▲ CONTAINER STORE GROUP INC p 362
500 Freeport Pkwy 75019
Tel (972) 538-6000 *SIC* 5719

■ CONTAINER STORE INC p 362
500 Freeport Pkwy Ste 100 75019
Tel (972) 538-6000 *SIC* 5719

COPPELL INDEPENDENT SCHOOL DISTRICT p 368
200 S Denton Tap Rd 75019
Tel (214) 496-6000 *SIC* 8211

CRAFTMADE INTERNATIONAL INC p 388
650 S Royal Ln Ste 100 75019
Tel (972) 393-3800 *SIC* 5064 5063

■ HOMEWARD RESIDENTIAL HOLDINGS INC p 704
1525 S Belt Line Rd 75019
Tel (877) 304-3100 *SIC* 7389

▲ IMPRESO INC p 735
652 Southwestern Blvd 75019
Tel (972) 462-0100 *SIC* 2761 2679 2086

▲ MANNATECH INC p 902
600 S Royal Ln Ste 200 75019
Tel (972) 471-7400 *SIC* 2833

▲ NATIONSTAR MORTGAGE HOLDINGS INC p 1017
8950 Cypress Waters Blvd 75019
Tel (469) 549-2000 *SIC* 6162

■ NATIONSTAR MORTGAGE LLC p 1017
8950 Cypress Waters Blvd 75019
Tel (469) 549-2000 *SIC* 6162

NEFAB COMPANIES INC p 1024
204 Airline Dr Ste 100 75019
Tel (866) 332-4425 *SIC* 2448 2449 2441

NEFAB PACKAGING NORTH EAST LLC p 1024
204 Airline Dr Ste 100 75019
Tel (469) 444-5264 *SIC* 2448 2449 2441

SHRED-IT DALLAS INC p 1319
825 W Sandy Lake Rd # 100 75019
Tel (972) 556-0197 *SIC* 7389 5093 5087

STMICROELECTRONICS INC p 1390
750 Canyon Dr Ste 300 75019
Tel (972) 466-6000 *SIC* 3674

STRATEGIC EQUIPMENT AND SUPPLY CORP p 1392
1461 S Belt Line Rd # 100 75019
Tel (469) 240-7200 *SIC* 5046

STRATEGIC EQUIPMENT LLC p 1392
1461 S Belt Line Rd # 100 75019
Tel (469) 240-7200 *SIC* 5046

TEKNI-PLEX MANAGEMENT LLC p 1433
260 N Denton Tap Rd 75019
Tel (972) 304-5077 *SIC* 3089 2631 2656

UNIVERSAL POWER GROUP INC p 1517
488 S Royal Ln 75019
Tel (469) 892-1122 *SIC* 5065 5063

COPPERAS COVE, TX

COPPERAS COVE INDEPENDENT SCHOOL DISTRICT p 368
703 W Avenue D 76522
Tel (254) 547-1227 *SIC* 8211

CORINTH, TX

COSERV UTILITY HOLDINGS LP p 373
7701 S Stemmons Fwy 76210
Tel (940) 321-4640 *SIC* 4911

DENTON COUNTY ELECTRIC COOPERATIVE INC p 429
7701 S Stemmons Fwy 76210
Tel (940) 321-7800 *SIC* 4911

CORPUS CHRISTI, TX

AIRGAS - SOUTHWEST INC p 40
4817 Agnes St 78405
Tel (361) 882-1141 *SIC* 5169 5084

AMERICAN STEEL INC p 80
2500 Agnes St 78405
Tel (361) 883-1706
SIC 5023 5051 5084 5191

ASSET PROTECTION & SECURITY SERVICES LP p 119
5502 Burnham Dr 78413
Tel (361) 906-1552 *SIC* 7381

■ BAY AREA HEALTHCARE GROUP LTD p 160
3315 S Alameda St 78411
Tel (361) 761-1400
SIC 8062 8063 8069 8093

BERRY CONTRACTING LP p 176
1414 Corn Product Rd 78409
Tel (361) 693-2100 *SIC* 2911 1611

BERRY GP INC p 176
1414 Corn Product Rd 78409
Tel (361) 693-2100 *SIC* 1541 1611 3498

BERRY HOLDINGS LP p 176
1414 Corn Product Rd 78409
Tel (361) 693-2100 *SIC* 1541 1611 3498

BRADFORD HOLDING CO INC p 206
4646 Corona Dr Ste 105 78411
Tel (361) 852-6392 *SIC* 7363

CHRISTUS SPOHN HEALTH SYSTEM CORP p 304
1702 Santa Fe St 78404
Tel (361) 881-3000 *SIC* 8062

CITY OF CORPUS CHRISTI p 314
1201 Leopard St 78401
Tel (361) 880-3000 *SIC* 9111

■ COLUMBIA HOSPITAL CORP OF BAY AREA p 341
7101 S Padre Island Dr 78412
Tel (361) 761-1200 *SIC* 8062

CORPUS CHRISTI INDEPENDENT SCHOOL DISTRICT p 372
801 Leopard St 78401
Tel (361) 886-9200 *SIC* 8211

COUNTY OF NUECES p 380
901 Leopard St Rm 304 78401
Tel (361) 888-0556 *SIC* 9111

DEL MAR COLLEGE DISTRICT p 423
101 Baldwin Blvd 78404
Tel (361) 698-1259 *SIC* 8222

DRISCOLL CHILDRENS HEALTH PLAN p 456
615 N Uppr Brdwy 1621 78401
Tel (361) 694-6432 *SIC* 8011 6399

DRISCOLL CHILDRENS HOSPITAL p 456
3533 S Alameda St 78411
Tel (361) 694-5000 *SIC* 8069

ED RACHAL FOUNDATION INC p 476
500 N Shoreline Blvd # 606 78401
Tel (361) 881-9040 *SIC* 8322

G BRADFORD CO INC p 586
4646 Corona Dr Ste 100 78411
Tel (361) 852-6392 *SIC* 7363

GARRY BRADFORD MANAGEMENT CO LTD p 592
4646 Corona Dr Ste 105 78411
Tel (361) 852-6392 *SIC* 8741

GULF COAST BROADCASTING CO p 646
409 S Staples St 78401
Tel (361) 886-6100 *SIC* 4833 5812

H & S CONSTRUCTORS INC p 649
1616 Corn Product Rd 78409
Tel (361) 668-8674 *SIC* 1711

HART RESTAURANT MANAGEMENT INC p 665
108 N Mesquite St 78401
Tel (361) 882-4100 *SIC* 5812

MILLER ENVIRONMENTAL SERVICES LLC p 970
401 Navigation Blvd 78408
Tel (361) 289-9800 *SIC* 4953 7375

NAVY ARMY COMMUNITY CREDIT UNION p 1020
2730 Rodd Field Rd 78414
Tel (361) 986-4500 *SIC* 6061

NORTHERN BEEF INDUSTRIES INC p 1055
719 S Shoreline Blvd # 204 78401
Tel (361) 654-6180 *SIC* 5147

■ QUALSPEC INC p 1198
5602 Ih 37 78407
Tel (281) 479-3300 *SIC* 8711

REPCON INC p 1224
7501 Up River Rd 78409
Tel (361) 289-6342 *SIC* 1629 1389

SAM KANE BEEF PROCESSORS LLC p 1274
9001 Leopard St 78409
Tel (361) 241-5000 *SIC* 2011

SANDIS DINER LLC p 1278
704 Ayers St 78404
Tel (361) 334-3850 *SIC* 7221

SCOTT ELECTRIC CO p 1293
2001 N Port Ave 78401
Tel (361) 884-6326 *SIC* 1731

■ STRIPES LLC p 1393
4433 Baldwin Blvd 9911 78408
Tel (361) 884-2463 *SIC* 5812

■ STRIPES LLC p 1394
4525 Ayers St 78415
Tel (361) 225-0129 *SIC* 5411

■ SUSSER CO LTD p 1409
4545 Ayers St 78415
Tel (361) 883-6321 *SIC* 6531

■ SUSSER HOLDINGS CORP p 1409
4525 Ayers St 78415
Tel (361) 884-2463 *SIC* 5411 5541 5172

■ SUSSER HOLDINGS LLC p 1409
4433 Baldwin Blvd 78408
Tel (361) 693-3698 *SIC* 5411

SWIFF-TRAIN CO LLC p 1412
2500 Agnes St 78405
Tel (361) 883-1706 *SIC* 5023

TEXAS A&M UNIVERSITY-CORPUS CHRISTI p 1442
6300 Ocean Dr Unit 5756 78412
Tel (361) 825-5700 *SIC* 8221

TRAFIGURA CORPUS CHRISTI HOLDINGS INC p 1469
7002 Marvin L Berry Rd 78409
Tel (361) 884-4000 *SIC* 6719

UNIQUE RISK AND ADMINISTRATIVE SERVICES (US) INC p 1505
4646 Corona Dr Ste 105 78411
Tel (361) 852-6392 *SIC* 7363

UNIQUE STAFF LEASING I LTD p 1505
4646 Corona Dr Ste 105 78411
Tel (361) 852-6392 *SIC* 7363

UNIQUE STAFF LEASING III LTD p 1505
4646 Corona Dr Ste 105 78411
Tel (361) 852-6392 *SIC* 7363

■ WILLIAMS CONSOLIDATED I LTD p 1611
1524 N Port Ave 78401
Tel (386) 304-2200 *SIC* 1742

CORSICANA, TX

CORSICANA BEDDING LLC p 373
3001 S Us Highway 287 75109
Tel (903) 872-2591 *SIC* 2515

WATKINS CONSTRUCTION CO LLC p 1582
3229 S 15th St 75110
Tel (903) 874-6587 *SIC* 1623

CREEDMOOR, TX

TEXAS DISPOSAL SYSTEMS INC p 1443
12200 Carl Rd 78610
Tel (512) 421-1300 *SIC* 4953

TEXAS LANDFILL MANAGEMENT LLC p 1444
12200 Carl Rd 78610
Tel (512) 421-1300 *SIC* 4953

CROWLEY, TX

CROWLEY INDEPENDENT SCHOOL DISTRICT 912 p 395
512 Peach St 76036
Tel (817) 297-5800 *SIC* 8211

■ HARBISON-FISCHER INC p 659
901 N Crowley Rd 76036
Tel (817) 297-2211 *SIC* 3533 3443

POWERHOUSE RETAIL SERVICES LLC p 1166
812 S Crowley Rd Ste A 76036
Tel (817) 297-8575 *SIC* 1542 1799

CRYSTAL CITY, TX

LOPEZ HEALTH SYSTEMS INC p 877
2209 N Highway 83 78839
Tel (830) 374-3525 *SIC* 8082

CYPRESS, TX

ATOS ORIGIN INC p 128
18062 Fm 529 Rd Ste 215 77433
Tel (914) 881-3000
SIC 7373 7374 7376 7379

CS&P TECHNOLOGIES LP p 397
18119 Telge Rd 77429
Tel (713) 467-0869 *SIC* 3561

NORTH CYPRESS MEDICAL CENTER OPERATING CO GP LLC p 1052
21214 Northwest Fwy 77429
Tel (832) 912-3500 *SIC* 8062

DAINGERFIELD, TX

DELTA FABRICATION AND MACHINE INC p 427
1379 County Road 2110 75638
Tel (903) 645-3994 *SIC* 1541 3599 3441

DALHART, TX

DALHART CONSUMERS FUEL ASSOCIATION INC p 409
919 Liberal St 79022
Tel (806) 249-4660
SIC 5153 5172 5191 5541

DALLAS, TX

▲ A H BELO CORP p 5
508 Young St 75202
Tel (214) 977-8222 *SIC* 2711 7313

■ A PLAINSCAPITAL PRIMELENDING CO p 6
18111 Preston Rd Ste 900 75252
Tel (800) 317-7463 *SIC* 6163 6021

ACCENTCARE INC p 14
17855 Dallas Pkwy 75287
Tel (800) 834-3059 *SIC* 8082

ACCUDYNE INDUSTRIES LLC p 16
2728 N Harwood St Ste 200 75201
Tel (469) 518-4777 *SIC* 3463

■ ACS ENTERPRISE SOLUTIONS INC p 19
2828 N Haskell Ave 75204
Tel (214) 841-6111 *SIC* 7374

■ ACS HEALTH CARE INC p 19
2828 N Haskell Ave 75204
Tel (214) 841-6111 *SIC* 7376 8742

■ ACS IMAGE SOLUTIONS INC p 19
3988 N Central Expy 75204
Tel (214) 818-3000
SIC 7389 5112 7374 7375

ACTIVE NETWORK LLC p 20
717 N Harwood St Ste 2500 75201
Tel (888) 543-7223 *SIC* 8742

■ ADVANCED HOMECARE MANAGEMENT INC p 25
6688 N Cntrl Expy # 1300 75206
Tel (214) 239-6500 *SIC* 8082

AEGIS COMMUNICATIONS GROUP LLC p 29
9999 Technology Blvd W 75220
Tel (972) 830-1800 *SIC* 7389

AIR LIQUIDE ELECTRONICS US LP p 39
9101 Lyndon B Johnson Fwy # 800 75243
Tel (972) 301-5200
SIC 2813 3564 8631 2819

■ AIRTRAN AIRWAYS INC p 41
2702 Love Field Dr 75235
Tel (407) 318-5600 *SIC* 4512

ALLFLEX USA INC p 53
2805 E 14th St 75261
Tel (972) 456-3686 *SIC* 6719

■ ALON USA DELAWARE LLC p 59
12700 Park Central Dr # 1600 75251
Tel (972) 367-3600 *SIC* 8741

▲ ALON USA ENERGY INC p 59
12700 Park Central Dr # 1600 75251
Tel (972) 367-3600 *SIC* 2911 5171 5411

■ ALON USA INC p 59
12700 Park Central Dr # 1600 75251
Tel (972) 367-3600 *SIC* 2911

■ ALON USA LP p 59
12700 Park Central Dr # 1600 75251
Tel (972) 367-3600
SIC 2911 4612 5172 5541 2895

■ ALON USA PARTNERS LP p 59
12700 Park Central Dr # 1600 75251
Tel (972) 367-3600 *SIC* 2911

AMBIT ENERGY HOLDINGS LLC p 65
1801 N Lamar St Ste 200 75202
Tel (214) 461-4736 *SIC* 4931

■ AMERICAN GYPSUM CO LLC p 73
3811 Turtle Creek Blvd # 1200 75219
Tel (214) 530-5500 *SIC* 3275 5031

AMERICAN HEART ASSOCIATION INC p 74
7272 Greenville Ave 75231
Tel (214) 373-6300 *SIC* 8399 2721

■ AMERICAN MARAZZI TILE INC p 75
7834 C F Hawn Fwy 75217
Tel (972) 232-3801 *SIC* 3253

▲ AMERICAN REALTY INVESTORS INC p 78
1603 Lbj Fwy Ste 800 75234
Tel (469) 522-4200
SIC 6798 6162 6513 6512

ANATOLE HOTEL INVESTORS L P p 88
2201 N Stemmons Fwy 75207
Tel (214) 748-1200 *SIC* 7011 5813 5812

ANDREWS DISTRIBUTING CO OF NORTH TEXAS LLC p 90
2730 Irving Blvd 75207
Tel (214) 525-9400 *SIC* 5181

ANTHELIO HEALTHCARE SOLUTIONS INC p 93
1 Lincoln Centre 5400 L 75240
Tel (214) 257-7000 *SIC* 8741 8071 7389

APEX CLEARING CORP p 96
350 N Paul St Ste 1300 75201
Tel (214) 765-1100
SIC 6099 7389 4813 6289

APPLIANCE PARTS DEPOT LP p 99
4754 Almond Ave 75247
Tel (214) 631-6331 *SIC* 5064 5722

■ ARMY & AIR FORCE EXCHANGE SERVICE p 112
3911 S Walton Walker Blvd 75236
Tel (214) 312-2011 *SIC* 5399 9711

■ ASHFORD HOSPITALITY LIMITED PARTNERSHIP p 117
14185 Dallas Pkwy # 1100 75254
Tel (972) 778-9452 *SIC* 6722

ASHFORD HOSPITALITY PRIME INC p 117
14185 Dallas Pkwy # 1100 75254
Tel (972) 490-9600 *SIC* 6798

ASHFORD HOSPITALITY TRUST INC p 117
14185 Dallas Pkwy # 1100 75254
Tel (972) 490-9600 *SIC* 6798 6733

ASSOCIATIONS INC p 121
5401 N Central Expy # 300 75205
Tel (214) 953-3009 *SIC* 6531

▲ AT&T INC p 123
208 S Akard St 75202
Tel (210) 821-4105
SIC 4813 4812 3663 3661 2741

■ AT&T SERVICES INC p 123
208 S Akard St Ste 110 75202
Tel (210) 821-4105 *SIC* 4813

▲ ATMOS ENERGY CORP p 128
5430 Lbj Fwy Ste 1800 75240
Tel (972) 934-9227 *SIC* 4924 4922 1629

■ ATMOS PIPELINE AND STORAGE LLC p 128
5420 Lyndon B Johnson Fwy 75240
Tel (972) 934-9227 *SIC* 4911 4922 4923

ATRIUM CORP p 129
13355 Noel Rd Ste 1250 75240
Tel (214) 583-1543 *SIC* 3442

ATRIUM WINDOWS AND DOORS INC p 129
3890 W Northwest Hwy # 500 75220
Tel (214) 956-8031
SIC 3442 2431 3089 3354 7629

AUSTIN COMMERCIAL INC p 132
3535 Travis St Ste 300 75204
Tel (214) 443-5700 *SIC* 1542

AUSTIN COMMERCIAL LP p 132
3535 Travis St Ste 300 75204
Tel (214) 443-5700 *SIC* 1542

AUSTIN INDUSTRIES INC p 133
3535 Travis St Ste 300 75204
Tel (214) 443-5500
SIC 1542 1629 1611 1622

AUTOMATED TELECOMMUNICATION SERVICES LP p 134
13355 Noel Rd Ste 2100 75240
Tel (972) 233-9614 *SIC* 3572

■ AVIALL INC p 137
2750 Rgent Blvd Dfw Arprt Dfw Airport 75261
Tel (972) 586-1000 *SIC* 5088

BALFOUR BEATTY CONSTRUCTION GROUP INC p 147
3100 Mckinnon St Fl 10 75201
Tel (214) 451-1000 *SIC* 1542 1541

BALFOUR BEATTY CONSTRUCTION LLC p 147
3100 Mckinnon St Fl 10 75201
Tel (214) 451-1000 *SIC* 1542 1541

BARNSCO INC p 156
2609 Willowbrook Rd 75220
Tel (214) 352-9091 *SIC* 5032

BAYLOR HEALTH CARE SYSTEM p 162
3500 Gaston Ave 75246
Tel (214) 820-0111 *SIC* 8062 8082 1542

BAYLOR HEALTH ENTERPRISES LP p 162
411 N Washington Ave # 7200 75246
Tel (214) 820-2492 *SIC* 5122 7011 7991

BAYLOR REGIONAL MEDICAL CENTER AT PLANO p 162
2001 Bryan St Ste 2200 75201
Tel (214) 820-4135 *SIC* 8011

BAYLOR SCOTT & WHITE HEALTH p 162
3500 Gaston Ave 75246
Tel (214) 820-1075 *SIC* 8082 8062

BAYLOR SCOTT & WHITE HOLDINGS p 162
350 N Saint Paul St # 2900 75201
Tel (214) 820-3151 *SIC* 8062

BAYLOR UNIVERSITY MEDICAL CENTER p 162
2001 Bryan St Ste 2200 75201
Tel (214) 820-3151 *SIC* 8062

BB&T p 163
8214 Westchester Dr # 100 75225
Tel (214) 234-7750 *SIC* 6021

BEARINGPOINT INC p 166
100 Crescent Ct Ste 700 75201
Tel (214) 459-2770 *SIC* 8748

BECK INTERNATIONAL LLC p 167
1807 Ross Ave Ste 500 75201
Tel (214) 303-6200 *SIC* 1542 8712

BENEFITMALL INC p 173
4851 Freeway Ste 100 75244
Tel (469) 791-3300 *SIC* 6411 8742 7375

■ BG STAFFING LLC p 180
14900 Landmark Blvd 75254
Tel (972) 692-2400 *SIC* 7361

BHG HOLDINGS LLC p 180
5001 Spring Valley Rd 600e 75244
Tel (214) 365-6100 *SIC* 8093

BJT PROPERTIES INC p 186
12770 Coit Rd Ste 1100 75251
Tel (210) 225-0290 *SIC* 2434

BODYCOTE THERMAL PROCESSING INC p 197
12700 Park Central Dr # 700 75251
Tel (214) 904-2420 *SIC* 3398

BODYCOTE USA INC p 197
12700 Park Central Dr # 700 75251
Tel (214) 904-2420 *SIC* 8721

BRANDT ENGINEERING CO INC p 208
1728 Briercrest Dr 75229
Tel (972) 395-6000 *SIC* 1711 8711

▲ BRIDGFORD INDUSTRIES INC p 212
1601 S Good Latimer Expy 75226
Tel (214) 428-1535
SIC 2045 2099 2015 2013 2022 2038

BRIGGS EQUIPMENT INC p 212
10540 N Stemmons Fwy 75220
Tel (214) 630-0808 *SIC* 5084

▲ BRINKER INTERNATIONAL INC p 213
6820 Lbj Fwy 75240
Tel (972) 980-9917 *SIC* 5812 6794

■ BRINKER RESTAURANT CORP p 213
6820 Lbj Fwy 75240
Tel (972) 980-9917 *SIC* 5812

BROADLANE GROUP INC p 215
13727 Noel Rd Ste 1400 75240
Tel (972) 813-7500 *SIC* 5047

BRUEGGERS ENTERPRISES INC p 220
12201 Merit Dr Ste 900 75251
Tel (802) 660-4020 *SIC* 5461

▲ BUILDERS FIRSTSOURCE INC p 225
2001 Bryan St Ste 1600 75201
Tel (214) 880-3500 *SIC* 2431 2421 5211

BURCH MANAGEMENT CO INC p 226
10723 Composite Dr 75220
Tel (214) 358-0055 *SIC* 8741 5813 5812

C C TEXAS INC p 232
3130 Lemmon Ave 75204
Tel (214) 526-4664 *SIC* 5812

C&M MARINE AVIATION SERVICES INC p 234
9200 King Arthur Dr 75247
Tel (214) 654-9270 *SIC* 2399

■ CAMBIUM LEARNING GROUP INC p 244
17855 Dallas Pkwy Ste 400 75287
Tel (214) 932-9500 *SIC* 8299 8211 7372

■ CAMBIUM LEARNING INC p 244
17855 Dallas Pkwy Ste 400 75287
Tel (214) 932-9500 *SIC* 2731

CAMPBELL RESOURCES LTD p 245
14800 Landmark Blvd # 155 75254
Tel (972) 716-2500 *SIC* 4724

▲ CAPITAL SENIOR LIVING CORP p 250
14160 Dallas Pkwy Ste 300 75254
Tel (972) 770-5600 *SIC* 8051 8052

■ CAPITAL SENIOR LIVING INC p 250
14160 Dallas Pkwy Ste 300 75254
Tel (972) 770-5600 *SIC* 6513

▲ CAPSTEAD MORTGAGE CORP p 251
8401 N Central Expy # 800 75225
Tel (214) 874-2323 *SIC* 6798

CARECYCLE SOLUTIONS LLC p 254
3406 Main St 75226
Tel (214) 698-0600 *SIC* 8082

CARLSON RESTAURANTS INC p 258
19111 Dallas Pkwy 75287
Tel (972) 662-5400 *SIC* 5812

CAS RESIDENTIAL LLC p 262
1201 Elm St Ste 1600 75270
Tel (214) 965-6000 *SIC* 6531

CBC RESTAURANT CORP p 268
12700 Park Central Dr # 1300 75251
Tel (972) 619-4100 *SIC* 5812 6794

■ CCA CLUB OPERATIONS HOLDINGS LLC p 269
3030 L B Johnson Fwy # 400 75234
Tel (972) 243-6191 *SIC* 7997

■ CELANESE ACETATE LLC p 273
1601 Lyndon B Johnson Fwy 75234
Tel (972) 443-4000 *SIC* 2281

■ CELANESE CHEMICALS INC p 273
1601 Lyndon B Johnson Fwy 75234
Tel (972) 443-4000
SIC 2821 2824 2865 2869

■ CELANESE HOLDINGS LLC p 273
1601 Lyndon B Johnson Fwy 75234
Tel (972) 443-4000 *SIC* 2821 2824

■ CELANESE US HOLDINGS LLC p 273
1601 Lyndon B Johnson Fwy 75234
Tel (972) 443-4000 *SIC* 2821 2879 2819

CENTENNIAL BEVERAGE GROUP LLC p 275
4011 Commerce St 75226
Tel (972) 668-7335 *SIC* 5921

CENTER OPERATING CO LP p 276
2500 Victory Ave 75219
Tel (214) 222-3687 *SIC* 7941

CENTERSTONE INSURANCE AND FINANCIAL SERVICES INC p 277
4851 Lyndon B Johnson Fwy 75244
Tel (469) 791-3300 *SIC* 7389

■ CENTEX CORP p 277
2728 N Harwood St Ste 200 75201
Tel (214) 981-5000
SIC 1531 2451 6162 1542 1541 1522

■ CENTEX FINANCIAL SERVICES LLC p 277
2728 N Harwood St 75201
Tel (214) 981-5000 *SIC* 6162

■ CENTEX HOME SERVICES CO LLC p 277
2728 N Harwood St Ste 200 75201
Tel (214) 981-5000 *SIC* 7342

■ CENTEX HOMES INC p 277
2728 N Harwood St 75201
Tel (800) 777-8583 *SIC* 1521

■ CENTEX INTERNATIONAL INC p 277
2728 N Harwood St Ste 200 75201
Tel (214) 981-5000 *SIC* 1521 1522

■ CENTEX REAL ESTATE CORP p 277
2728 N Harwood St Ste 800 75201
Tel (972) 304-2800 *SIC* 1521

CENTURY GOLF PARTNERS MANAGEMENT LP p 282
5430 L B Johnson Fwy 14 Ste 1400 75240
Tel (972) 419-1400 *SIC* 7999

■ CHARTER INDEMNITY CO p 291
8360 Lyndon B Johnson Fwy # 400 75243
Tel (972) 690-5500 *SIC* 6411

■ CHASE PAYMENTECH SOLUTIONS LLC p 291
14221 Dallas Pkwy Bldg 2 75254
Tel (214) 849-3000 *SIC* 6153 7389

CHILDRENS HEALTH SYSTEM OF TEXAS p 299
1935 Medical District Dr 75235
Tel (844) 424-4537 *SIC* 8069

CHILDRENS MEDICAL CENTER OF DALLAS p 300
1935 Medical District Dr 75235
Tel (214) 456-7000 *SIC* 8069

■ CHILIS INC p 300
6820 Lbj Fwy 75240
Tel (972) 980-9917 *SIC* 5812

CIM COMMERCIAL TRUST CORP p 307
17950 Preston Rd Ste 600 75252
Tel (972) 349-3200 *SIC* 6798

CITY ELECTRIC SUPPLY CO p 312
400 S Record St Ste 100 75202
Tel (214) 123-1234 *SIC* 5063

CITY OF DALLAS p 314
1500 Marilla St 75201
Tel (214) 670-3146 *SIC* 9111

CLAMPITT PAPER CO OF DALLAS GP LLC p 321
9207 Ambassador Row 75247
Tel (214) 638-3300 *SIC* 5111

CLEAVER-BROOKS SALES AND SERVICE INC p 325
1956 Singleton Blvd 75212
Tel (214) 637-0020 *SIC* 5074 7699 1711

■ CLUBCORP CLUB OPERATIONS INC p 328
3030 Lbj Fwy Ste 600 75234
Tel (972) 243-6191 *SIC* 7997

▲ CLUBCORP HOLDINGS INC p 328
3030 Lbj Fwy Ste 600 75234
Tel (972) 243-6191 *SIC* 7997

■ CLUBCORP USA INC p 328
3030 Lyndon B Johnson Fwy 75234
Tel (972) 243-6191 *SIC* 7011 7997

COACH AMERICA GROUP INC p 330
8150 N Central Expy # 1000 75206
Tel (972) 354-3500 *SIC* 4141

■ **COLUMBIA HOSPITAL AT MEDICAL CITY DALLAS SUBSIDIARY LP** p 340
7777 Forest Ln Ste C840 75230
Tel (972) 566-7000 *SIC* 8062

■ **COLUMBIA MEDICAL CENTER OF ARLINGTON SUBSIDIARY LP** p 341
13455 Noel Rd 75240
Tel (817) 465-3241 *SIC* 8062

■ **COMERICA BANK** p 344
1717 Main St Ste 2100 75201
Tel (214) 462-4000 *SIC* 6021

■ **COMERICA BANK-TEXAS** p 344
1601 Elm St 75201
Tel (214) 462-6831 *SIC* 6021

▲ **COMERICA INC** p 344
1717 Main St Mc6404 75201
Tel (214) 462-6831
SIC 6021 6022 6091 6082 6099 6141

COMMUNITIES FOUNDATION OF TEXAS p 347
5500 Caruth Haven Ln 75225
Tel (214) 378-4500 *SIC* 8399

COMPAREX USA INC p 350
600 N Pearl St Ste 1960 75201
Tel (972) 734-5223 *SIC* 5045 7371

COMPUCOM SYSTEMS HOLDING LLC p 352
7171 Forest Ln 75230
Tel (972) 856-3600
SIC 7373 5045 7378 8748

■ **COMPUSA INC** p 352
14951 Dallas Pkwy 75254
Tel (972) 982-4000 *SIC* 5734 5045 5961

■ **COMPX INTERNATIONAL INC** p 353
5430 Lbj Fwy Ste 1700 75240
Tel (972) 448-1400 *SIC* 3699 3714

▲ **CONCEPT DEVELOPMENT PARTNERS LLC** p 354
500 Crescent Ct Ste 250 75201
Tel (214) 871-6819 *SIC* 6726 5812 5813

CONSOLIDATED RESTAURANT COMPANIES INC p 360
12200 N Stemmons Fwy 75234
Tel (972) 241-5500 *SIC* 5812 6794

CONSOLIDATED RESTAURANT OPERATIONS INC p 360
12200 N Stemmons Fwy 75234
Tel (972) 241-5500 *SIC* 5812 6794

▲ **CONTRAN CORP** p 364
5430 Lyndon B Johnson Fwy 75240
Tel (972) 233-1700 *SIC* 2816

▲ **COPART INC** p 368
14185 Dallas Pkwy Ste 300 75254
Tel (972) 391-5000 *SIC* 5012

CORGAN ASSOCIATES INC p 370
401 N Houston St 75202
Tel (214) 748-2000 *SIC* 8712 7389

COUNTY OF DALLAS p 377
509 Main St Fl 6 75202
Tel (214) 653-6472 *SIC* 9111

COVEY PARK II LLC p 385
8401 N Central Expy # 700 75225
Tel (214) 548-6000 *SIC* 1311

■ **CPM-US LLC** p 387
1999 Bryan St Ste 3200 75201
Tel (800) 648-0722 *SIC* 7311

▲ **CSW INDUSTRIALS INC** p 398
5400 Lyndon B Johnson Fwy 75240
Tel (972) 233-8242 *SIC* 3569

CULINAIRE INTERNATIONAL INC p 400
8303 Elmbrook Dr 75247
Tel (214) 754-1645 *SIC* 8742 5812 8741

CUSTOM CRETE INC p 403
2624 Joe Field Rd 75229
Tel (972) 243-4466 *SIC* 5032 3273

CUSTOM FOOD GROUP LP p 403
12221 Merit Dr Ste 975 75251
Tel (214) 273-0500 *SIC* 5962

CYMI INDUSTRIAL INC p 405
12400 Coit Rd Ste 700 75251
Tel (214) 276-8950 *SIC* 1541

D&M HOLDING INC p 407
5001 Spring Valley Rd 800e 75244
Tel (214) 368-6391 *SIC* 8748

DAISY BRAND LLC p 409
12750 Merit Dr Ste 600 75251
Tel (972) 726-0800 *SIC* 2026

■ **DAL-TILE CORP** p 409
7834 C F Hawn Fwy 75217
Tel (214) 398-1411 *SIC* 3253

■ **DAL-TILE DISTRIBUTION INC** p 409
7834 C F Hawn Fwy 75217
Tel (214) 398-1411 *SIC* 5032

■ **DAL-TILE GROUP INC** p 409
7834 C F Hawn Fwy 75217
Tel (214) 398-1411 *SIC* 3253

DALLAS AREA RAPID TRANSIT p 410
1401 Pacific Ave 75202
Tel (214) 979-1111 *SIC* 4111

DALLAS BAPTIST UNIVERSITY p 410
3000 Mountain Creek Pkwy 75211
Tel (214) 333-5360 *SIC* 8221

DALLAS COUNTY HOSPITAL DISTRICT p 410
5200 Harry Hines Blvd 75235
Tel (214) 590-8000 *SIC* 8062

DALLAS COUNTY MENTAL HEALTH & MENTAL RETARDATION CENTER (INC) p 410
1345 River Bend Dr # 200 75247
Tel (214) 743-1200 *SIC* 8361

DALLAS COUNTY SCHOOLS p 410
5151 Samuell Blvd 75228
Tel (214) 944-4545 *SIC* 8211

DALLAS INDEPENDENT SCHOOL DISTRICT p 410
3700 Ross Ave 75204
Tel (972) 925-3700 *SIC* 8211

DALLAS MARKET CENTER DEVELOPMENT CO LTD p 410
2201 N Stemmons Fwy 75207
Tel (214) 748-1200 *SIC* 7011

DALLAS MEDICAL CENTER LLC p 410
7 Medical Pkwy 75234
Tel (972) 888-7000 *SIC* 8062

DALLAS PRODUCTION INC p 410
4600 Greenville Ave # 300 75206
Tel (214) 369-9266 *SIC* 1311

DATASPAN HOLDINGS INC p 414
1245 Viceroy Dr 75247
Tel (214) 905-1882 *SIC* 6719 7375

DATASPAN INC p 414
1245 Viceroy Dr 75247
Tel (800) 660-3586 *SIC* 5045 7375

DAVACO INC p 414
6688 N Cntrl Expy Ste 100 75206
Tel (214) 373-4700
SIC 1751 1799 1542 1796

▲ **DAVE & BUSTERS ENTERTAINMENT INC** p 415
2481 Manana Dr 75220
Tel (214) 357-9588 *SIC* 5812 7993

■ **DAVE & BUSTERS HOLDINGS INC** p 415
2481 Manana Dr 75220
Tel (214) 357-9588 *SIC* 5812

■ **DAVE & BUSTERS INC** p 415
2481 Manana Dr 75220
Tel (214) 357-9588
SIC 5812 5813 7999 7993

■ **DEAN DAIRY HOLDINGS LLC** p 420
2515 Mckinney Ave # 1100 75201
Tel (214) 303-3400 *SIC* 6719 2026

▲ **DEAN FOODS CO** p 420
2711 N Haskell Ave 75204
Tel (214) 303-3400 *SIC* 2026 2033 5143

■ **DEAN HOLDING CO** p 420
2711 N Haskell Ave 75204
Tel (214) 303-3400 *SIC* 2023 5143 5451

■ **DEAN WEST II LLC** p 420
2515 Mckinney Ave # 1100 75201
Tel (214) 303-3400 *SIC* 2026

DEGOLYER AND MACNAUGHTON CORP p 422
5001 Spring Valley Rd 800e 75244
Tel (214) 368-6391 *SIC* 1389

DG21 LLC p 435
14900 Landmark Blvd # 400 75254
Tel (972) 774-8850 *SIC* 8744

■ **DGSE CORP** p 435
15850 Dallas Pkwy 75248
Tel (972) 484-3662 *SIC* 5094

DICKEYS BARBECUE RESTAURANTS INC p 438
4514 Cole Ave Ste 1015 75205
Tel (972) 248-9899 *SIC* 5812

■ **DMN INC** p 446
508 Young St 75202
Tel (214) 977-8222 *SIC* 2711

DOUBLE DIAMOND - DELAWARE INC p 452
5495 Belt Line Rd Ste 200 75254
Tel (214) 706-9831 *SIC* 6552 7992

DOUBLE DIAMOND INC p 452
5495 Belt Line Rd Ste 200 75254
Tel (214) 706-9801 *SIC* 6552

DRIVING MOMENTUM USA INC p 456
2025 Irving Blvd Ste 102 75207
Tel (214) 651-1031 *SIC* 7361

▲ **EAGLE MATERIALS INC** p 468
3811 Turtle Creek Blvd # 1100 75219
Tel (214) 432-2000 *SIC* 3241 3275 3273

EB ACQUISITION CO LLC p 474
200 Crescent Ct 75201
Tel (214) 871-5151 *SIC* 6029

ECO-BAT AMERICA LLC p 476
2777 N Stemmons Fwy 75207
Tel (214) 688-4000 *SIC* 3356

ECOM ATLANTIC INC p 476
13760 Noel Rd Ste 500 75240
Tel (214) 520-1717 *SIC* 5159 5149

ECOM USA INC p 476
13760 Noel Rd Ste 500 75240
Tel (214) 520-1717 *SIC* 5159

ED BELL INVESTMENTS INC p 476
10605 Harry Hines Blvd 75220
Tel (214) 358-3414 *SIC* 1611 5082 4424

ED HIGHER HOLDINGS LLC p 476
600 N Pearl St Ste 900 75201
Tel (214) 210-7300 *SIC* 8211

■ **EHHI HOLDINGS INC** p 481
6688 N Cntrl Expy # 1300 75206
Tel (877) 330-7657 *SIC* 8082

EIGHT-O MANAGEMENT INC p 481
1722 S Harwood St 75215
Tel (214) 969-9321 *SIC* 8741

EL CHICO RESTAURANTS INC p 482
12200 N Stemmons Fwy 75234
Tel (972) 241-5500 *SIC* 5812 6794 5046

ELEMETAL LLC p 486
15850 Dallas Pkwy 75248
Tel (214) 956-7600 *SIC* 3341 3356 3339

ELK PREMIUM BUILDING PRODUCTS INC p 487
14911 Quorum Dr Ste 600 75254
Tel (972) 851-0400 *SIC* 2952 2273

ELKCORP p 488
14911 Quorum Dr Ste 600 75254
Tel (972) 851-0500
SIC 2952 5033 2426 2431 3471

■ **EMCARE HOLDINGS INC** p 491
13737 Noel Rd Ste 1600 75240
Tel (214) 712-2000 *SIC* 7363

■ **EMCARE INC** p 491
13737 Noel Rd Ste 1600 75240
Tel (214) 712-2000 *SIC* 7363

EMPIRE PETROLEUM PARTNERS LLC p 493
8350 N Central Expy M2175 75206
Tel (214) 750-9313 *SIC* 4924 5172

■ **EMPLOYERS GENERAL INSURANCE GROUP INC** p 494
1700 Pacific Ave Ste 1600 75201
Tel (214) 665-6100 *SIC* 6331 8742

EMR GOLD RECYCLING LLC p 495
4305 S Lamar St 75215
Tel (214) 421-0247 *SIC* 5093 6719

ENCORE ENTERPRISES INC p 496
5005 L B Johnson Fwy 12 Ste 1200 75244
Tel (214) 259-7009 *SIC* 6531 6512

ENERGY FUTURE COMPETITIVE HOLDINGS CO LLC p 497
1601 Bryan St Ste 510 75201
Tel (214) 812-4600 *SIC* 4911

ENERGY FUTURE HOLDINGS CORP p 497
1601 Bryan St Ste 510 75201
Tel (214) 812-4600 *SIC* 4911

ENERGY FUTURE INTERMEDIATE HOLDING CO LLC p 497
1601 Bryan St Ste 510 75201
Tel (214) 812-4600 *SIC* 4911

ENERGY SPECTRUM PARTNERS VI LP p 498
5956 Sherry Ln Ste 900 75225
Tel (214) 987-6100 *SIC* 6722

▲ **ENERGY TRANSFER EQUITY LP** p 498
8111 Westchester Dr # 600 75225
Tel (214) 981-0700 *SIC* 4922

ENERGY TRANSFER PARTNERS GP LP p 498
8111 Westchester Dr # 600 75225
Tel (214) 981-0700 *SIC* 4922

■ **ENERGY TRANSFER PARTNERS LLC** p 498
8111 Westchester Dr # 600 75225
Tel (214) 981-0700 *SIC* 8748

▲ **ENERGY TRANSFER PARTNERS LP** p 498
8111 Westchester Dr # 600 75225
Tel (214) 981-0700 *SIC* 4922 5984

■ **ENLINK MIDSTREAM GP LLC** p 500
2501 Cedar Springs Rd 75201
Tel (214) 953-9500 *SIC* 5172

■ **ENLINK MIDSTREAM INC** p 500
2501 Cedar Springs Rd 75201
Tel (214) 953-9500 *SIC* 1311 5712

■ **ENLINK MIDSTREAM LLC** p 500
2501 Cedar Springs Rd 75201
Tel (214) 953-9500 *SIC* 1311

▲ **ENLINK MIDSTREAM PARTNERS LP** p 500
2501 Cedar Springs Rd 75201
Tel (214) 953-9500 *SIC* 4922 1321

ENTECH SALES AND SERVICE INC p 501
3404 Garden Brook Dr 75234
Tel (972) 241-8188 *SIC* 1731 7623 1711

ENTRUST INC p 503
5430 Lyndon B Johnson Fwy 75240
Tel (972) 728-0447 *SIC* 7371

EPIC HEALTH SERVICES INC p 505
5220 Spring Valley Rd 75254
Tel (214) 466-1340 *SIC* 8082

ESSILOR LABORATORIES OF AMERICA INC p 510
13515 N Stemmons Fwy 75234
Tel (972) 241-4141 *SIC* 3851 5048

ESSILOR OF AMERICA INC p 510
13555 N Stemmons Fwy 75234
Tel (214) 496-4000 *SIC* 3851 5048

EVERCOM SYSTEMS INC p 513
14651 Dallas Pkwy Ste 600 75254
Tel (972) 277-0300 *SIC* 4813

EVERETT FINANCIAL INC p 514
14801 Quorum Dr Ste 300 75254
Tel (214) 340-5225 *SIC* 6163

EVERGREEN ALLIANCE GOLF LIMITED LP p 514
4851 Lydon B Johnson Ste 600 75244
Tel (214) 722-6000 *SIC* 7992 5091

■ **EXCO OPERATING CO LP** p 517
12377 Merit Dr Ste 1700 75251
Tel (214) 368-2084 *SIC* 1382

▲ **EXCO RESOURCES INC** p 517
12377 Merit Dr Ste 1700 75251
Tel (214) 368-2084 *SIC* 1311

■ **EXELON POWER CORP** p 519
2233 Mountain Creek Pkwy A 75211
Tel (214) 623-1051 *SIC* 4911

EYE-MART EXPRESS INC p 522
13800 Senlac Dr Ste 200 75234
Tel (972) 488-2002 *SIC* 5995

EYEMART EXPRESS LTD p 522
13800 Senlac Dr Ste 200 75234
Tel (972) 488-2002 *SIC* 5995

F & H ACQUISITION CORP p 522
200 Crescent Ct Ste 1400 75201
Tel (214) 661-7474 *SIC* 6799

FAMSA INC p 527
2727 Lyndon B Johnson Fwy 75234
Tel (972) 993-5800 *SIC* 5722 5712

FEDDERS CORP p 533
13455 Noel Rd Ste 2200 75240
Tel (604) 908-8686
SIC 3585 3674 3634 3564

FEDERAL RESERVE BANK DALLAS p 535
2200 N Pearl St 75201
Tel (214) 922-6000 *SIC* 6011

▲ **FIESTA RESTAURANT GROUP INC** p 541
14800 Landmark Blvd # 500 75254
Tel (972) 702-9300 *SIC* 5812 6794

FIREBIRD RESTAURANT GROUP LLC p 543
1845 Woodall Rodgers Fwy # 1100 75201
Tel (972) 241-2171 *SIC* 5812

FIRST SOUTHWEST CO p 549
325 N Saint Paul St # 800 75201
Tel (214) 953-4000 *SIC* 6211

FIRST TEXAS HOMES INC p 549
500 Crescent Ct Ste 350 75201
Tel (214) 613-3400 *SIC* 1521

FIRSTSERVICE RESIDENTIAL TEXAS INC p 551
3102 Oak Lawn Ave Ste 202 75219
Tel (214) 871-9700 *SIC* 8741

■ **FLOWTRONEX PSI LLC** p 560
10661 Newkirk St 75220
Tel (469) 221-1200
SIC 3561 3949 3523 3432

■ **FOGO DE CHAO CHURRASCARIA (LOS ANGELES) LLC** p 563
14881 Quorum Dr Ste 750 75254
Tel (972) 361-6200 *SIC* 5812

▲ **FOGO DE CHAO INC** p 563
14881 Quorum Dr Ste 750 75254
Tel (972) 960-9533 *SIC* 5812

FORD FINANCIAL FUND II LP p 565
200 Crescent Ct 75201
Tel (214) 871-5151 *SIC* 6282 6799 7389

FOREST PARK MEDICAL CENTER LLC p 567
11990 N Central Expy 75243
Tel (972) 234-1900 *SIC* 8011

FRANK KASMIR ASSOCIATES INC p 574
3191 Commonwealth Dr 75247
Tel (214) 631-8040 *SIC* 5131

■ **FREEDMAN MEATS INC** p 576
2901 S Polk St 75224
Tel (713) 229-8000 *SIC* 5147

FREEMAN DECORATING CO p 576
1600 Viceroy Dr Ste 100 75235
Tel (214) 445-1000 *SIC* 7389

FREEMAN EXPOSITIONS INC p 577
1600 Viceroy Dr Ste 100 75235
Tel (214) 445-1000 *SIC* 7389

■ **FRESHPOINT DALLAS INC** p 579
4721 Simonton Rd 75244
Tel (972) 385-5800 *SIC* 5148 5142

▲ **GAINSCO INC** p 589
3333 Lee Pkwy Ste 1200 75219
Tel (972) 629-4301 *SIC* 6331

GARDERE WYNNE SEWELL LLP p 591
1601 Elm St Ste 3000 75201
Tel (214) 999-3000 *SIC* 8111

GAS EQUIPMENT CO INC p 593
11616 Harry Hines Blvd 75229
Tel (972) 241-2333 *SIC* 5084 5085 3321

GENERAL DATATECH LP p 600
999 Metro Media Pl 75247
Tel (214) 857-6100 *SIC* 5065

GENERAL HEALTH SERVICES CORP p 601
7515 Grnvlle Ave Ste 1000 75231
Tel (214) 345-8345 *SIC* 6719

GEORGE W BUSH PRESIDENTIAL LIBRARY FOUNDATION p 606
6166 N Rental Expy 75206
Tel (214) 890-9943 *SIC* 8231

GEORGECO INC p 606
2609 Willowbrook Rd 75220
Tel (214) 352-9091 *SIC* 5032

GHM CORP p 610
12700 Hillcrest Rd # 291 75230
Tel (972) 840-1200
SIC 3448 1799 5999 5561

GOLD METAL RECYCLERS LTD p 620
4305 S Lamar St 75215
Tel (214) 421-0247 *SIC* 5093

GOLDS HOLDING CORP p 622
4001 Maple Ave Ste 200 75219
Tel (214) 574-4653 *SIC* 6719

GRAEBEL VANLINES HOLDINGS LLC p 628
12790 Merit Dr Bldg 9 75251
Tel (972) 694-0400 *SIC* 4213 4214 4212

GRAPHIC SOLUTIONS GROUP INC p 632
4601 Spring Valley Rd 75244
Tel (214) 748-3271 *SIC* 5084

GREATWIDE DEDICATED TRANSPORT LLC p 636
12404 Park Central Dr # 300 75251
Tel (972) 228-7344 *SIC* 4213 4731

GREATWIDE LOGISTICS SERVICES LLC p 636
12404 Park Central Dr # 300 75251
Tel (972) 228-7389 *SIC* 4213 4731

GREYHOUND LINES INC p 639
350 N Saint Paul St # 300 75201
Tel (214) 849-8000 *SIC* 4111 4215 4142

GREYSTAR RS GROUP LLC p 639
1201 Elm St Ste 1600 75270
Tel (214) 290-7300 *SIC* 8741

GROUP & PENSION ADMINISTRATORS INC p 641
12770 Merit Dr Ste 200 75251
Tel (972) 238-7900 *SIC* 6411

HALF PRICE BOOKS RECORDS MAGAZINES INC p 654
5803 E Northwest Hwy 75231
Tel (214) 379-8000 *SIC* 5942 5192

HALL FINANCIAL GROUP LTD p 654
2323 Ross Ave Ste 200 75201
Tel (972) 377-1100 *SIC* 6552 6531

HALLWOOD FINANCIAL LIMITED p 655
3710 Rawlins St Ste 1500 75219
Tel (214) 523-1288 *SIC* 5812

HALLWOOD GROUP INC p 655
3710 Rawlins St Ste 1500 75219
Tel (214) 528-5588 *SIC* 2221 7389

HARDIES FRUIT AND VEGETABLE CO LP p 660
1005 N Cockrell Hill Rd 75211
Tel (214) 426-5666 *SIC* 5148

HAWKWOOD ENERGY EAST TEXAS LLC p 670
1999 Bryan St Ste 900 75201
Tel (303) 823-4175 *SIC* 1382

HAYNES AND BOONE LLP p 670
2323 Victory Ave Ste 700 75219
Tel (214) 651-5000 *SIC* 8111

HEALTHTEXAS PROVIDER NETWORK p 678
8080 N Cntrl Expy Ste 600 75206
Tel (972) 860-8600 *SIC* 8011

HENSLEY INDUSTRIES INC p 685
2108 Joe Field Rd 75229
Tel (972) 241-2321 *SIC* 3325

HERITAGE CAPITAL CORP p 686
3500 Maple Ave Ste 1700 75219
Tel (214) 528-3500 *SIC* 5094

HFS HOLDING CORP p 689
8900 Ambassador Row 75247
Tel (214) 634-8600 *SIC* 2679 5112 2675

HICKS HOLDINGS LLC p 690
2200 Ross Ave Ste 5000 75201
Tel (214) 615-2300 *SIC* 3679

HIGHLAND CAPITAL MANAGEMENT LP p 691
300 Crescent Ct Ste 700 75201
Tel (972) 628-4100 *SIC* 6211

HIGHLAND PARK INDEPENDENT SCHOOL DISTRICT p 691
7015 Westchester Dr 75205
Tel (214) 780-3000 *SIC* 8211

HIGHLANDER PARTNERS LP p 691
300 Crescent Ct Ste 550 75201
Tel (214) 245-5000 *SIC* 6159

▲ HILLTOP HOLDINGS INC p 694
200 Crescent Ct Ste 1330 75201
Tel (214) 855-2177 *SIC* 6022 7389

■ HILLTOP SECURITIES HOLDINGS LLC p 694
200 Crescent Ct Ste 1330 75201
Tel (214) 855-2177 *SIC* 6211

■ HILLTOP SECURITIES INC p 694
1201 Elm St Ste 3500 75270
Tel (214) 859-1800 *SIC* 6211

HILLWOOD DEVELOPMENT CORP p 694
3090 Olive St Ste 300 75219
Tel (214) 303-5535 *SIC* 6552 6531

HITACHI CONSULTING CORP p 696
14643 Dallas Pkwy Ste 800 75254
Tel (214) 665-7000 *SIC* 7379 7374

HKS INC p 697
350 N Saint Paul St # 100 75201
Tel (214) 969-5599 *SIC* 8712

HOAK MEDIA LLC p 698
3963 Maple Ave Ste 450 75219
Tel (972) 960-4840 *SIC* 4833

■ HOLLY ENERGY PARTNERS LP p 701
2828 N Harwood St # 1300 75201
Tel (214) 871-3555 *SIC* 4612 4613 5171

▲ HOLLYFRONTIER CORP p 701
2828 N Harwood St # 1300 75201
Tel (214) 871-3555 *SIC* 2911 4613

■ HOLLYFRONTIER REFINING & MARKETING LLC p 701
2828 N Harwood St # 1300 75201
Tel (214) 871-3555 *SIC* 2911 4612

■ HOMETEAM PEST DEFENSE INC p 704
3100 Mckinnon St Ste 120 75201
Tel (214) 665-8700 *SIC* 7342

■ HOTELS.COM LP p 710
5400 Lyndon B Johnson Fwy # 500 75240
Tel (214) 361-7311 *SIC* 7389 7375

■ HOUSEWARES HOLDING CO INC p 711
14785 Preston Rd Ste 1100 75254
Tel (440) 449-9600 *SIC* 3634 5719

■ HOWARD HUGHES CORP p 713
13355 Noel Rd Fl 22 75240
Tel (702) 791-4000 *SIC* 6552 6512 7992

▲ HOWARD HUGHES CORP p 713
13355 Noel Rd Fl 22 75240
Tel (214) 741-7744 *SIC* 6798

HUNT CONSOLIDATED INC p 718
1900 N Akard St 75201
Tel (214) 978-8000
SIC 6799 1311 2911 1382 0212

HUNT DOMINION CORP p 719
1601 Elm St Ste 3900 75201
Tel (214) 880-8400 *SIC* 1311 1382 1241

HUNT OIL USA INC p 719
1900 N Akard St 75201
Tel (214) 978-8000 *SIC* 1311 1382 2911

HYDROCARBON EXCHANGE CORP p 723
5910 N Cntrl Expy # 1380 75206
Tel (214) 987-0257 *SIC* 4924

I2 TECHNOLOGIES INC p 725
11701 Luna Rd 75234
Tel (469) 357-1000 *SIC* 7372

INFRAREIT INC p 742
1807 Ross Ave Fl 4 75201
Tel (214) 855-6700 *SIC* 6798

INTERSTATE BATTERIES INC p 758
12770 Merit Dr Ste 400 75251
Tel (972) 991-1444 *SIC* 5531 3694

INTERSTATE BATTERY SYSTEM INTERNATIONAL INC p 758
12770 Merit Dr Ste 1000 75251
Tel (972) 991-1444 *SIC* 5531

■ INTERVOICE LLC p 759
17787 Waterview Pkwy 75252
Tel (972) 454-8000 *SIC* 3661

INTREPID USA INC p 760
4055 Valley View Ln # 500 75244
Tel (214) 445-3750 *SIC* 7363 8082

J BAXTER BRINKMANN INTERNATIONAL CORP p 770
4099 Mcewen Rd Ste 375 75244
Tel (972) 387-4939 *SIC* 3648 3631

JACKSON WALKER LLP p 774
2323 Ross Ave Ste 600 75201
Tel (214) 953-6000 *SIC* 8111

▲ JACOBS ENGINEERING GROUP INC p 775
1999 Bryan St Ste 1200 75201
Tel (214) 583-8500
SIC 8711 1629 1541 8748

JAMIESON MANUFACTURING CO p 777
4221 Platinum Way 75237
Tel (214) 339-8384 *SIC* 5039 2499

JBRE HOLDINGS LLC p 779
8150 N Central Expy 75206
Tel (214) 276-5504 *SIC* 7539 6719

JBRE LLC p 779
8150 N Central Expy M1008 75206
Tel (214) 276-5504 *SIC* 7539

JM BULLION INC p 786
12655 N Cntl Expy Ste 800 75243
Tel (800) 276-6508 *SIC* 5094

▲ JRJR33 INC p 795
2950 N Harwood St Fl 22 75201
Tel (469) 913-4115
SIC 5499 5023 5122 2721 5251

KAINOS GP LLC p 800
2100 Mckinney Ave # 1600 75201
Tel (214) 740-7300 *SIC* 5812

■ KEYSTONE CONSOLIDATED INDUSTRIES INC p 815
5430 Lyndon B Johnson Fwy # 1740 75240
Tel (800) 441-0308 *SIC* 3312 3315

KING SUPPLY CO LLC p 820
9611 E R L Thornton Fwy 75228
Tel (214) 388-9834 *SIC* 5039 5051

KRESTMARK INDUSTRIES LP p 830
3950 Bastille Rd Ste 100 75212
Tel (214) 237-5055 *SIC* 3442 3089

■ KRONOS INTERNATIONAL INC p 830
5430 L B Johnson Fwy 1700 75240
Tel (972) 233-1700 *SIC* 2816

▲ KRONOS WORLDWIDE INC p 830
5430 Lbj Fwy Ste 1700 75240
Tel (972) 233-1700 *SIC* 2816

KSF HOLDINGS LLP p 831
2100 Mckinney Ave # 1600 75201
Tel (214) 740-7300 *SIC* 5149

L S F 5 ACCREDITED INVESTMENTS LLC p 834
717 N Harwood St Ste 2200 75201
Tel (214) 754-8300 *SIC* 6798

■ LA GRANGE ACQUISITION LP p 835
8111 Westchester Dr 75225
Tel (214) 981-0700 *SIC* 4922

LALA BRANDED PRODUCTS LLC p 840
8750 N Central Expy # 400 75231
Tel (214) 459-1100 *SIC* 5143

LANYON SOLUTIONS INC p 844
717 N Harwood St Ste 2200 75201
Tel (817) 226-5656 *SIC* 5734

LE DUFF AMERICA INC p 849
12201 Merit Dr Ste 900 75251
Tel (214) 540-1867 *SIC* 5812

LEEWARD MEMBER LLC p 852
6688 N Central Expy # 500 75206
Tel (214) 515-1100 *SIC* 4911

LETCO GROUP LLC p 857
1901 Cal Crossing Rd 75220
Tel (972) 506-8575 *SIC* 2875

LINCOLN PROPERTY CO p 868
2000 Mckinney Ave # 1000 75201
Tel (214) 740-3300 *SIC* 6531

LOCAL & WESTERN OF TEXAS INC p 872
5445 La Sierra Dr Ste 100 75231
Tel (214) 750-6633 *SIC* 5142

LOCKE LORD LLP p 873
2200 Ross Ave Ste 2800 75201
Tel (214) 740-8000 *SIC* 8111

LONE STAR FUND IV (US) LP p 875
2711 N Haskell Ave 75204
Tel (214) 754-8300 *SIC* 6726

LONE STAR FUND V (US) LP p 875
2711 N Haskell Ave # 1700 75204
Tel (214) 754-8300 *SIC* 6799 5812

LONE STAR FUNDS p 875
2711 N Haskell Ave # 1700 75204
Tel (214) 754-8300 *SIC* 6211

LONE STAR REAL ESTATE FUND (US) LP p 876
2711 N Haskell Ave 75204
Tel (214) 754-8300 *SIC* 6733

■ LONE STAR TECHNOLOGIES INC p 876
15660 Dallas Pkwy Ste 500 75248
Tel (972) 770-6401 *SIC* 3317 3312

LPC COMMERCIAL SERVICES INC p 882
2000 Mckinney Ave # 1000 75201
Tel (202) 513-6710 *SIC* 6552

LSF5 WAGON HOLDINGS LLC p 883
2711 N Haskell Ave # 1700 75204
Tel (214) 515-6824 *SIC* 5812 5813

LSREF LODGING INVESTMENTS LLC p 883
2711 N Haskell Ave 75204
Tel (214) 754-8300 *SIC* 6798

LUMINANT GENERATION CO LLC p 885
1601 Bryan St 75201
Tel (214) 812-4600 *SIC* 4911 3621

LUMINANT MINING CO LLC p 885
1601 Bryan St 75201
Tel (214) 812-4600 *SIC* 1221

MAC ACQUISITION OF KANSAS LLC p 891
6750 Lyndon B Johnson Fwy 75240
Tel (972) 674-4300 *SIC* 5812

■ MAGGIANOS INC p 895
6820 Lyndon B Johnson Fwy 75240
Tel (972) 980-9917 *SIC* 5812

MAGNETIC TICKET & LABEL CORP p 896
8719 Diplomacy Row 75247
Tel (214) 634-8600 *SIC* 2679

▲ MALIBU ENTERTAINMENT WORLDWIDE INC p 899
717 N Harwood St Ste 1650 75201
Tel (214) 210-8701 *SIC* 1629 7999

MARIPOSA INTERMEDIATE HOLDINGS LLC p 907
1618 Main St 75201
Tel (214) 743-7600 *SIC* 5311

■ MARKETING ARM INC p 908
1999 Bryan St Fl 18 75201
Tel (214) 259-3200 *SIC* 8742

MARKETPLACE MINISTRIES INC p 908
2001 W Plano Pkwy 75201
Tel (972) 941-4400 *SIC* 8661

MASTER-HALCO INC p 918
3010 Lbj Fwy Ste 800 75234
Tel (972) 714-7300
SIC 3315 5039 3496 3446 5031 1799

▲ MATADOR RESOURCES CO p 918
5400 Lbj Fwy Ste 1500 75240
Tel (972) 371-5200 *SIC* 1311

■ MATCH GROUP INC p 919
8750 N Cntl Expy Ste 1400 75231
Tel (214) 576-9352 *SIC* 7299 7374

MAYA MANAGEMENT GROUP LLC p 923
11411 Hillguard Rd 75243
Tel (214) 751-2290 *SIC* 8742

■ MEDIA RECOVERY p 936
5501 L B Johnson Fwy 350 75240
Tel (800) 660-3586 *SIC* 7373

MEDICAL CITY DALLAS IMAGING CENTER LLP p 936
7777 Forest Ln Ste C840 75230
Tel (972) 566-7000 *SIC* 8062

MENZIES AVIATION (TEXAS) INC p 943
2520 W Airfield Dr 75261
Tel (972) 929-1020 *SIC* 4512

MERIT ENERGY CO LLC p 949
13737 Noel Rd Ste 1200 75240
Tel (972) 701-8377 *SIC* 1311

METHODIST HOSPITALS OF DALLAS INC p 954
1441 N Beckley Ave 75203
Tel (877) 637-4297 *SIC* 8062

■ MGA INSURANCE CO INC p 958
3333 Lee Pkwy 75219
Tel (972) 629-4301 *SIC* 6331

MILESTONE MANAGEMENTS LLC p 969
5429 Lyndon B Johnson Fwy # 800 75240
Tel (214) 561-1200 *SIC* 6513

MODEST BILLIONAIRES LLC p 981
3815 Martha Ln 75229
Tel (972) 672-0755 *SIC* 7374 7371 7389

MONARCH DENTAL CORP p 983
7989 Belt Line Rd Ste 90 75248
Tel (972) 720-9017 *SIC* 8021

▲ MONEYGRAM INTERNATIONAL INC p 984
2828 N Harwood St Fl 15 75201
Tel (214) 999-7552 *SIC* 6099

■ MONITRONICS INTERNATIONAL INC p 984
1990 Wittington Pl 75234
Tel (972) 243-7443 *SIC* 7382 1731

MOROCH HOLDINGS INC p 989
3625 N Hall St Ste 1100 75219
Tel (214) 520-9700 *SIC* 7311

MV TRANSPORTATION INC p 1003
5910 N Cntrl Expy # 1145 75206
Tel (972) 391-4600 *SIC* 4111

▲ N L INDUSTRIES INC p 1005
5430 Lbj Fwy Ste 1700 75240
Tel (972) 233-1700 *SIC* 2819 3572 3699

NATIONAL BANKRUPTCY SERVICES LLC p 1010
14841 Dallas Pkwy Ste 300 75254
Tel (972) 643-6600 *SIC* 7389

NATIONAL CONSUMER OUTDOORS CORP p 1011
4215 Mcewen Rd 75244
Tel (972) 716-4200
SIC 3999 2399 2394 3732

NATIONAL DAIRY LLC p 1011
8750 N Central Expy # 400 75231
Tel (469) 587-0190 *SIC* 5143

NATIONAL WHOLESALE SUPPLY INC p 1017
1972 Cal Crossing Rd 75220
Tel (972) 331-7770 *SIC* 5074

NATURAL GAS SUPPLY LLC p 1018
9233 Denton Dr Ste 300 75235
Tel (469) 305-1508 *SIC* 4212

NEIMAN MARCUS GROUP INC p 1025
1618 Main St 75201
Tel (214) 743-7600 *SIC* 5311 5961

NEIMAN MARCUS GROUP LLC p 1025
1618 Main St 75201
Tel (214) 741-6911 *SIC* 5311

NEIMAN MARCUS GROUP LTD LLC p 1025
1618 Main St 75201
Tel (214) 743-7600 *SIC* 5311 5961

NEWCASTLE CAPITAL MANAGEMENT LP p 1037
200 Crescent Ct Ste 1400 75201
Tel (317) 704-6000 *SIC* 6799

NGL CROSSTEX MARKETING L P p 1041
2501 Cedar Springs Rd 75201
Tel (214) 754-4752 *SIC* 5172

NOGALES PRODUCE INC p 1046
8220 Forney Rd 75227
Tel (214) 275-3500 *SIC* 5148

NORTH FOOD GROUP INC p 1052
1245 W Royal Ln 75261
Tel (972) 445-3322
SIC 5146 5147 5149 5113

NORTH TEXAS FOOD BANK p 1054
4500 S Cockrell Hill Rd 75236
Tel (214) 330-1396 *SIC* 8322

NOVATECH HOLDINGS CORP p 1063
8388 C F Hawn Fwy 75217
Tel (214) 398-1491 *SIC* 3491

■ OCCIDENTAL CHEMICAL CORP p 1072
5005 Lyndon B Johnson Fwy # 2200 75244
Tel (972) 404-3800 *SIC* 2812

OCULAR LCD INC p 1074
12700 Park Central Dr # 750 75251
Tel (972) 437-3888 *SIC* 3679

ODONNELL FOUNDATION p 1074
100 Crescent Ct Ste 1660 75201
Tel (214) 871-5800 *SIC* 8699

OLDCASTLE BUILDINGENVELOPE INC p 1082
5005 Lndn B Jnsn Fwy 10 Ste 1050 75244
Tel (214) 273-3400 *SIC* 3231 5231

OLMSTED-KIRK PAPER CO p 1083
1601 Valley View Ln # 101 75234
Tel (214) 637-2220 *SIC* 5111

OMNI HOTELS CORP p 1084
4001 Maple Ave Ste 500 75219
Tel (972) 730-6664 *SIC* 7011

OMNI HOTELS MANAGEMENT CORP p 1084
4001 Maple Ave Ste 500 75219
Tel (972) 871-5600 *SIC* 7011

OMNITRACS LLC p 1085
717 N Harwood St Ste 1300 75201
Tel (888) 627-2716 *SIC* 8741 4214

ONCOR ELECTRIC DELIVERY CO LLC p 1086
1616 Woodall Rodgers Fwy 75202
Tel (214) 486-2000 *SIC* 4911

ONCOR ELECTRIC DELIVERY HOLDINGS CO LLC p 1086
1616 Woodall Rodgers Fwy 75202
Tel (214) 486-2000 *SIC* 4911

ONCOR ELECTRIC DELIVERY TRANSITION BOND CO LLC p 1086
1616 Woodall Rodgers Fwy 75202
Tel (214) 486-2000 *SIC* 4911

ORIX USA CORP p 1095
1717 Main St Ste 1100 75201
Tel (214) 237-2000 *SIC* 6211 6282

OXEA CORP p 1100
1505 L B Johnson Fwy # 400 75234
Tel (972) 481-2700 *SIC* 2869

OXEA HOLDING CORP p 1100
1505 Lyndon B Johnson Fwy 75234
Tel (972) 481-2700 *SIC* 2899

OXY CHEMICAL CORP p 1101
5005 L B Johnson Fwy 2200 75244
Tel (972) 404-3800
SIC 2869 2873 2874 2899 3089

■ **OXY VINYLS LP** p 1101
5005 Lbj Fwy Ste 2200 75244
Tel (972) 720-7000
SIC 2821 2899 2819 1382

PAJ INC p 1108
18325 Waterview Pkwy Frnt 75252
Tel (214) 575-6080 *SIC* 5094

PANDA POWER GENERATION INFRASTRUCTURE FUND GP LP p 1111
5001 Spring Valley Rd 1150w 75244
Tel (972) 361-2000 *SIC* 1382

■ **PANHANDLE EASTERN PIPE LINE CO LP** p 1111
8111 Westchester Dr # 600 75225
Tel (214) 981-0700 *SIC* 4922

PARALLEL INVESTMENT PARTNERS LLC p 1113
3889 Maple Ave Ste 220 75219
Tel (214) 740-3600 *SIC* 6211

PARIVEDA SOLUTIONS INC p 1115
2811 Mckinney Ave Ste 220 75204
Tel (214) 777-4600 *SIC* 8748

PARK COVEY GAS LLC p 1115
8401 N Central Expy # 700 75225
Tel (214) 548-6000 *SIC* 4924

PARK PLACE MOTORCARS LTD p 1115
6113 Lemmon Ave 75209
Tel (214) 526-8701 *SIC* 5511

PARKLAND COMMUNITY HEALTH PLAN p 1116
2777 N Stemmons Fwy 75207
Tel (214) 266-2100 *SIC* 8099

PARKLAND HEALTH AND HOSPITAL SYSTEM AUXILIARY p 1116
5200 Harry Hines Blvd 75235
Tel (214) 590-4123 *SIC* 9431

PARRISH-HARE ELECTRICAL SUPPLY LP p 1117
1211 Regal Row 75247
Tel (214) 905-1001 *SIC* 5063

PENSON WORLDWIDE INC p 1131
1700 Pacific Ave Ste 1400 75201
Tel (214) 765-1100 *SIC* 6289

■ **PEPPER DINING HOLDING CORP** p 1133
6820 Lyndon B Johnson Fwy 75240
Tel (704) 943-5276 *SIC* 5812

■ **PEPPER DINING INC** p 1133
6820 Lyndon B Johnson Fwy 75240
Tel (704) 943-5276 *SIC* 5812

PEREZ CONCRETE INC p 1135
5502 Gregg St 75235
Tel (214) 522-9480 *SIC* 1771

PERSEUS HOLDING CORP p 1137
8350 N Central Expy 75206
Tel (214) 234-4000 *SIC* 7374

PETRO-HUNT LLC p 1139
2101 Cedar Springs Rd 75201
Tel (214) 880-8400 *SIC* 1311

■ **PIM HIGHLAND HOLDING LLC** p 1148
14185 Dallas Pkwy # 1100 75254
Tel (972) 778-9452 *SIC* 6719

PINNACLE LIGHT INDUSTRIAL LLC p 1150
5501 Lyndon B Johnson Fwy Fw600 75240
Tel (214) 740-2443 *SIC* 7361

■ **PIZZA HUT WEST INC** p 1153
14841 Dallas Pkwy Frnt 75254
Tel (972) 338-7700 *SIC* 5812

PLACID HOLDING CO p 1153
1601 Elm St Ste 3900 75201
Tel (214) 880-8479 *SIC* 2911

■ **PLAINSCAPITAL BANK** p 1153
2323 Victory Ave Ste 1400 75219
Tel (214) 252-4100 *SIC* 6022

■ **PLAINSCAPITAL CORP** p 1154
2323 Victory Ave Ste 1400 75219
Tel (214) 252-4100 *SIC* 7389

PMFG INC p 1157
14651 Dallas Pkwy Ste 500 75254
Tel (214) 357-6181 *SIC* 3569

POWERCARE AND SERVICE SOLUTIONS INC p 1166
12770 Merit Dr Ste 400 75251
Tel (972) 991-1444 *SIC* 5063

▲ **PRIMORIS SERVICES CORP** p 1176
2100 Mckinney Ave # 1500 75201
Tel (214) 740-5600 *SIC* 1623 8711

PURITY OILFIELD SERVICES LLC p 1192
2101 Cedar Springs Rd 75201
Tel (214) 880-8400 *SIC* 1389

PURVIS INDUSTRIES LTD p 1193
10500 N Stemmons Fwy 75220
Tel (214) 358-5500 *SIC* 5013 5085 3822

PXU ELECTRIC DELIVERY p 1193
500 N Akard St Ste 14 75201
Tel (214) 486-4760 *SIC* 4911

QUEMETCO INC p 1198
2777 N Stemmons Fwy 75207
Tel (317) 247-1303 *SIC* 3341 4953

QUEXCO INC p 1199
2777 N Stemmons Fwy 75207
Tel (214) 688-4000 *SIC* 3341

RAVE CINEMAS LLC p 1209
3333 Welborn St Ste 100 75219
Tel (214) 220-7600 *SIC* 7832

REDDY ICE CORP p 1216
5720 Lyndon B Johnson Fwy # 200 75240
Tel (214) 526-6740 *SIC* 2097

REDDY ICE GROUP INC p 1216
5720 Lbj Fwy Ste 200 75240
Tel (877) 295-0024 *SIC* 5199 2097

REDDY ICE HOLDINGS INC p 1216
5720 Lbj Fwy Ste 200 75240
Tel (214) 526-6740 *SIC* 2097

■ **REGENCY ENERGY PARTNERS LP** p 1218
8111 Westchester Dr # 600 75225
Tel (214) 750-1771
SIC 1321 4925 5172 4922

■ **REGENCY GAS SERVICES LP** p 1219
2001 Bryan St Ste 3700 75201
Tel (214) 750-1771 *SIC* 4932

REMINGTON HOSPITALITY SERVICES p 1222
14185 Dallas Pkwy # 1150 75254
Tel (972) 980-2700 *SIC* 7011

REMINGTON HOTEL CORP p 1222
14185 Dallas Pkwy # 1150 75254
Tel (972) 980-2700 *SIC* 8741

REMINGTON LODGING & HOSPITALITY LLC p 1222
14185 Dallas Pkwy # 1150 75254
Tel (972) 980-2700 *SIC* 7011

■ **REPUBLIC COMPANIES INC** p 1225
5525 Lyndon B Johnson Fwy 75240
Tel (972) 788-6001 *SIC* 6321 6311 6331

REPUBLIC INSURANCE CO INC p 1225
5525 Lyndon B Johnson Fwy 75240
Tel (972) 788-6001 *SIC* 6331

■ **REPUBLIC UNDERWRITERS INSURANCE CO** p 1226
5525 Lbj Fwy 75240
Tel (972) 788-6001 *SIC* 6331

REXEL HOLDINGS USA CORP p 1230
14951 Dallas Pkwy 75254
Tel (972) 387-3600 *SIC* 5063

REXEL INC p 1230
14951 Dallas Pkwy # 1000 75254
Tel (972) 387-3600 *SIC* 5063

REXEL INC p 1230
14951 Dallas Pkwy # 1000 75254
Tel (972) 387-3600 *SIC* 5063

RICHARDS GROUP INC p 1232
2801 N Cntl Expy Ste 100 75204
Tel (214) 891-5700 *SIC* 7311

ROMAN CATHOLIC DIOCESE OF DALLAS p 1248
3725 Blackburn St 75219
Tel (214) 528-2240 *SIC* 8661

ROOFING SUPPLY GROUP HOLDINGS INC p 1249
3890 W Northwest Hwy # 400 75220
Tel (214) 956-5100 *SIC* 5211

■ **ROOFING SUPPLY GROUP LLC** p 1249
3890 W Northwest Hwy # 400 75220
Tel (214) 956-5100 *SIC* 5033

■ **ROOFING SUPPLY GROUP-TUSCALOOSA LLC** p 1249
3890 W Northwest Hwy # 400 75220
Tel (214) 956-5100 *SIC* 5033

ROSEWOOD CORP p 1251
2101 Cedar Springs Rd # 1600 75201
Tel (214) 849-9000 *SIC* 6531 7382

ROSEWOOD PRIVATE INVESTMENTS INC p 1251
2101 Cedar Springs Rd # 1600 75201
Tel (214) 849-9000 *SIC* 6799 3423

RRH CORP p 1255
1900 N Akard St 75201
Tel (214) 978-8000
SIC 1382 1311 2911 0212 6799

▲ **RSP PERMIAN INC** p 1256
3141 Hood St Ste 500 75219
Tel (214) 252-2700 *SIC* 1311

■ **RSP PERMIAN LLC** p 1256
3141 Hood St Ste 700 75219
Tel (214) 252-2700 *SIC* 1382

RSR CORP p 1256
2777 N Stemmons Fwy 75207
Tel (317) 247-1303 *SIC* 3341

RYAN GOVERNMENT SERVICES LLC p 1260
13155 Noel Rd Ste 100 75240
Tel (972) 934-0022 *SIC* 8742

RYAN LLC p 1260
13155 Noel Rd Ste 100 75240
Tel (972) 934-0022 *SIC* 8721 7291 7389

■ **SAFEGUARD BUSINESS SYSTEMS INC** p 1266
8585 N Stemmons Fwy 75247
Tel (214) 640-3916
SIC 7374 2759 5112 5045

SAMMONS ENTERPRISES INC p 1274
5949 Sherry Ln Ste 1900 75225
Tel (214) 210-5000 *SIC* 5084 6311

SANDENVENDO AMERICA INC p 1278
10710 Sanden Dr 75238
Tel (800) 344-7216 *SIC* 3581

■ **SANTANDER CONSUMER USA HOLDINGS INC** p 1281
1601 Elm St Ste 800 75201
Tel (214) 634-1110 *SIC* 6141

■ **SANTANDER CONSUMER USA INC FOUNDATION** p 1281
8585 N Stemmons Fwy 75247
Tel (214) 634-1110 *SIC* 6141

SANWA USA INC p 1281
4020 Mcewen Rd Ste 118 75244
Tel (972) 503-3031
SIC 3442 2431 3699 3537

SAPUTO DAIRY FOODS USA LLC p 1282
2711 N Haske Ave Ste 3700 75204
Tel (214) 863-2300 *SIC* 2023 2015 2026

SAXTON GROUP INC p 1285
7859 Walnut Hill Ln # 325 75230
Tel (214) 373-3400 *SIC* 5812

SB RESTAURANT CO p 1285
18900 Dallas Pkwy Ste 125 75287
Tel (800) 227-5454 *SIC* 5812 5813

SCHWOB BUILDING CO LTD p 1291
2349 Glenda Ln 75229
Tel (972) 243-7674 *SIC* 1542

SECURUS HOLDINGS INC p 1299
14651 Dallas Pkwy Ste 600 75254
Tel (972) 241-1535 *SIC* 4813

SECURUS TECHNOLOGIES INC p 1299
14651 Dallas Pkwy Ste 600 75254
Tel (972) 241-1535 *SIC* 4813

SEKISUI SPECIALTY CHEMICALS AMERICA LLC p 1301
1501 Lyndo B Johns Fwy St Ste 530 75234
Tel (972) 277-2900 *SIC* 2899

SELECT PRODUCT GROUP LP p 1301
8214 Westchester Dr # 800 75225
Tel (214) 363-7427 *SIC* 5199

SENIOR CARE CENTERS LLC p 1304
600 N Pearl St Ste 1100 75201
Tel (214) 252-7600 *SIC* 8741

SEWELL CORP p 1309
6421 Lemmon Ave 75209
Tel (214) 352-8100 *SIC* 5511

SEWELL VILLAGE CADILLAC CO INC p 1309
7310 Lemmon Ave 75209
Tel (214) 350-2000 *SIC* 5511

SFG MANAGEMENT LIMITED LIABILITY CO p 1310
3114 S Haskell Ave 75223
Tel (214) 824-8163 *SIC* 2026

SHADE STRUCTURES INC p 1310
8505 Chancellor Row 75247
Tel (214) 905-9500 *SIC* 2394

SHARYLAND UTILITIES LP p 1312
1807 Ross Ave Ste 460 75201
Tel (214) 978-8958 *SIC* 4911

■ **SHOOTING STAR** p 1318
8144 Walnut Hill Ln Fl 16 75231
Tel (972) 770-1600 *SIC* 6411 8741

SILVERLEAF RESORTS INC p 1324
1201 Elm St Ste 4600 75270
Tel (214) 631-1166 *SIC* 6531

SIMMONS HAROLD C FAMILY TRUST p 1324
5430 Lyndon B Johnson Fwy # 1700 75240
Tel (972) 233-1700 *SIC* 2063

SMART CITY LOCATING INC p 1332
5555 Smu Blvd 75206
Tel (214) 586-0519 *SIC* 6531

SMITH GREENTECH TANNERY LLC p 1333
2233 Vantage St 75207
Tel (214) 566-8392 *SIC* 3111

SNELLING STAFFING LLC p 1335
4055 Valley View Ln # 700 75244
Tel (972) 239-7575 *SIC* 7363

SOFTLAYER TECHNOLOGIES INC p 1337
14001 Dallas Pkwy M100 75240
Tel (214) 442-0600 *SIC* 7374 4813

SOURCE INC p 1342
4550 Spring Valley Rd # 200 75244
Tel (972) 371-2600 *SIC* 5065 7629

▲ **SOUTHCROSS ENERGY PARTNERS LP** p 1345
1717 Main St Ste 5200 75201
Tel (214) 979-3720 *SIC* 4922

■ **SOUTHERN FOODS GROUP LLC** p 1348
3114 S Haskell Ave 75223
Tel (214) 824-8163 *SIC* 2026

SOUTHERN GLAZERS WINE AND SPIRITS OF CANADA LLC p 1348
14911 Quorum Dr Ste 150 75254
Tel (972) 392-8200 *SIC* 5182

SOUTHERN GLAZERS WINE AND SPIRITS OF TEXAS LLC p 1348
14911 Quorum Dr Ste 150 75254
Tel (972) 392-8200 *SIC* 2082 5182 5199

SOUTHERN METHODIST UNIVERSITY INC p 1349
6425 Boaz Ln 75205
Tel (214) 768-2000 *SIC* 8221

■ **SOUTHWEST A B Q RES CENTER** p 1351
2702 Love Field Dr 75235
Tel (214) 792-4000 *SIC* 4724

▲ **SOUTHWEST AIRLINES CO** p 1351
2702 Love Field Dr 75235
Tel (214) 792-4000 *SIC* 4512

SOUTHWEST INTERNATIONAL TRUCKS INC p 1352
3722 Irving Blvd 75247
Tel (214) 689-1400 *SIC* 5511 5531

SOUTHWESTERN FINANCIAL SERVICES CORP p 1353
12001 N Cntl Expy Ste 800 75243
Tel (800) 792-4368 *SIC* 6311

SPAGHETTI WAREHOUSE RESTAURANTS INC p 1354
1815 N Market St 75202
Tel (949) 336-5111 *SIC* 5812

SPIRIT REALTY CAPITAL INC p 1359
2727 N Harwood St Ste 300 75201
Tel (480) 606-0820 *SIC* 6798

STAFF ONE INC p 1374
8111 Lndn B Jnsn Fwy 13 Ste 1350 75251
Tel (214) 461-1140 *SIC* 7363

STANDARD SUPPLY AND DISTRIBUTING CO INC p 1376
1431 Regal Row 75247
Tel (214) 630-7800 *SIC* 5075

STATE FARM LLOYDS INC p 1381
17301 Preston Rd 75252
Tel (972) 732-5000 *SIC* 6411

STERLING GROUP PARTNERS II LP p 1387
3890 W Northwest Hwy # 400 75220
Tel (214) 956-5100 *SIC* 5211

STEVENS TRANSPORT INC p 1388
9757 Military Pkwy 75227
Tel (972) 216-9000 *SIC* 4213

■ **STEWART TITLE NORTH TEXAS INC** p 1389
15950 Dallas Pkwy Ste 100 75248
Tel (972) 386-9898 *SIC* 6361 6541

STREAM GAS & ELECTRIC LTD p 1393
1950 N Stemmons Fwy F 75207
Tel (214) 800-4400 *SIC* 4911

■ **SUIZA DAIRY GROUP LLC** p 1397
2515 Mckinney Ave # 1200 75201
Tel (214) 303-3400 *SIC* 0241

SUN HOLDINGS INC p 1400
3318 Forest Ln Ste 300 75234
Tel (972) 620-2287 *SIC* 5812

▲ **SUNOCO LP** p 1403
8020 Park Ln Ste 200 75231
Tel (214) 981-0700 *SIC* 5172 6519 5541

SUSAN G KOMEN BREAST CANCER FOUNDATION INC p 1409
5005 Lbj Fwy Ste 250 75244
Tel (972) 855-1600
SIC 8699 8069 8011 8099

SWH MIMIS CAFE LLC p 1412
12201 Merit Dr Ste 900 75251
Tel (866) 926-6636 *SIC* 5812

SWS GROUP INC p 1413
1201 Elm St Ste 3500 75270
Tel (214) 859-1800 *SIC* 6211 6029

TAYLOR FARMS TEXAS INC p 1427
1001 N Cockrell Hill Rd 75211
Tel (214) 421-1947 *SIC* 5149

TAYLOR PUBLISHING CO p 1427
1550 W Mockingbird Ln 75235
Tel (214) 819-8321 *SIC* 2731 2732

TD SERVICES INC p 1429
13850 Diplomat Dr 75234
Tel (972) 888-9500 *SIC* 8711

TDINDUSTRIES INC p 1429
13850 Diplomat Dr 75234
Tel (972) 888-9500 *SIC* 1711

TELVISTA INC p 1435
1605 Lyndon B Johnson Fwy 75234
Tel (972) 919-7800 *SIC* 4813

▲ **TENET HEALTHCARE CORP** p 1437
1445 Ross Ave Ste 1400 75202
Tel (469) 893-2200
SIC 8062 8069 8741 8063 8082 8011

■ **TENET HEALTHCARE FOUNDATION** p 1437
1445 Ross Ave Ste 1400 75202
Tel (469) 893-2000 *SIC* 8049

■ **TENET HEALTHSYSTEM HOSPITALS INC** p 1437
13737 Noel Rd Ste 100 75240
Tel (469) 893-2000 *SIC* 8062

■ **TENET HEALTHSYSTEM MEDICAL INC** p 1437
1445 Ross Ave Ste 1400 75202
Tel (469) 893-2000 *SIC* 8062 8063 6512

▲ **TEXAS CAPITAL BANCSHARES INC** p 1442
2000 Mckinney Ave Ste 700 75201
Tel (214) 932-6600 *SIC* 6022

■ **TEXAS CAPITAL BANK NATIONAL ASSOCIATION** p 1442
2000 Mckinney Ave Ste 700 75201
Tel (214) 932-6600 *SIC* 6021

TEXAS CLOTHING HOLDING CORP p 1442
11511 Luna Rd 75234
Tel (214) 956-4494
SIC 2325 2311 2321 5611

TEXAS COMPETITIVE ELECTRIC HOLDINGS CO LLC p 1442
1601 Bryan St Ste 510 75201
Tel (214) 812-4600 *SIC* 4911 4922

TEXAS DE BRAZIL (ADDISON) CORP p 1442
2952 N Stemmons Fwy 75247
Tel (214) 615-2184 *SIC* 5812

TEXAS HEALTH PRESBYTERIAN HOSPITAL DALLAS p 1443
8200 Walnut Hill Ln 75231
Tel (214) 345-6789 SIC 8062

■TEXAS INDUSTRIES INC p 1443
1503 Lyndon B Johnson Fwy # 400 75234
Tel (972) 647-6700
SIC 3241 3299 3281 3273

▲TEXAS INSTRUMENTS INC p 1443
12500 Ti Blvd 75243
Tel (214) 479-3773
SIC 3674 3613 3822 3578

TEXAS KENWORTH CO p 1444
4040 Irving Blvd 75247
Tel (214) 920-7300
SIC 5012 5013 7513 7538

TEXAS SCOTTISH RITE HOSPITAL FOR CHILDREN p 1444
2222 Welborn St 75219
Tel (214) 559-5000 SIC 8069

TEXAS SCOTTISH RITE HOSPITAL FOR CRIPPLED CHILDREN p 1444
2222 Welborn St 75219
Tel (214) 559-5000 SIC 8069

TEXAS WESTERN MANAGEMENT PARTNERS LP p 1445
13747 Montfort Dr Ste 115 75240
Tel (469) 385-6248 SIC 7011

TEXAS-HEALTH-PHYSICIANS-GROUP p 1445
9229 Lbj Fwy Ste 250 75243
Tel (214) 860-6300 SIC 8099

TF COURIER INC p 1445
5429 Lyndon B Johnson Fwy 75240
Tel (214) 560-9000 SIC 4513 4215 8741

TF FINAL MILE LLC p 1445
5429 Lbj Fwy Ste 900 75240
Tel (214) 560-9000 SIC 4215 4513

TFI HOLDINGS USA INC p 1445
5429 L B Johnson Fwy 10 Ste 1000 75240
Tel (877) 396-2639 SIC 4215 8741 4513

TGI FRIDAYS INC p 1446
19111 Dallas Pkwy 75287
Tel (972) 662-5400 SIC 5812 6794

THOMPSON & KNIGHT LLP p 1449
1 Arts Plz 1722 75201
Tel (214) 969-1700 SIC 8111

THOMPSON PETROLEUM CORP p 1449
325 N Saint Paul St # 4300 75201
Tel (214) 953-1177 SIC 1311

THR PROPERTY MANAGEMENT LP p 1450
1201 Elm St Ste 1600 75270
Tel (214) 965-6053 SIC 6531

TI EMPLOYEES HEALTH BENEFIT TRUST p 1452
7839 Churchill Way 75251
Tel (972) 995-3333 SIC 6351

TIER REIT INC p 1452
5950 Sherry Ln Ste 700 75225
Tel (972) 483-2400 SIC 6798

TITAN GLOBAL HOLDINGS INC p 1456
17760 Preston Rd 75252
Tel (214) 751-7777 SIC 5172 4813

■TITLE RESOURCES GUARANTY CO p 1456
8111 L B Johnson Fwy 12 Ste 1200 75251
Tel (972) 644-6500 SIC 6361

TOP GOLF USA INC p 1460
8750 N Cntl Expy Ste 1200 75231
Tel (214) 377-5053 SIC 7999 5812 5941

TOPGOLF INTERNATIONAL INC p 1461
8750 N Cntl Expy Ste 1200 75231
Tel (214) 377-0615 SIC 3949

TRAILBLAZER HEALTH ENTERPRISES LLC p 1469
8330 L B Johnson Fwy 10 Ste 100 75243
Tel (469) 372-2000 SIC 6324

■TRAMMELL CROW CENTRAL TEXAS LTD p 1469
2001 Ross Ave Ste 325 75201
Tel (214) 267-0400 SIC 6799 6552 6512

■TRAMMELL CROW CO p 1469
2100 Mckinney Ave Ste 900 75201
Tel (214) 863-3000 SIC 6512

TRAMMELL CROW RESIDENTIAL CO p 1469
3819 Maple Ave 75219
Tel (214) 922-8400 SIC 6513 6512 6531

▲TRANSCONTINENTAL REALTY INVESTORS INC p 1471
1603 Lbj Fwy Ste 800 75234
Tel (469) 522-4200 SIC 6798

TRANSITION CAPITAL PARTNERS LP p 1472
2100 Mckinney Ave # 1501 75201
Tel (214) 978-3800 SIC 6799

TRANSPLANT SERVICES DALLAS p 1472
3410 Worth St Ste 950 75246
Tel (214) 820-2050 SIC 8999

TRANSPORTATION 100 LLC p 1472
12404 Park Central Dr 300s 75251
Tel (972) 228-7300 SIC 4213 4731

■TRAVELOCITY.COM LP p 1474
5400 L B Johnson Fwy 50 Ste 500 75240
Tel (682) 605-1000 SIC 4724

■TRIAD FINANCIAL CORP p 1478
8585 N Stemmons Fwy 75247
Tel (817) 521-8127 SIC 7389

TRINITY CONSULTANTS INC p 1481
12700 Park Central Dr # 2100 75251
Tel (972) 661-8100 SIC 8748

▲TRINITY INDUSTRIES INC p 1481
2525 N Stemmons Fwy 75207
Tel (214) 631-4420
SIC 3743 3731 3531 3444 3441 3443

■TRINITY INDUSTRIES LEASING CO p 1481
2525 N Stemmons Fwy 75207
Tel (800) 227-8844 SIC 4741 4499

■TRINITY MEYER UTILITY STRUCTURES LLC p 1481
2525 N Stemmons Fwy 75207
Tel (901) 566-6500 SIC 1623

■TRINITY RAIL GROUP LLC p 1481
2525 N Stemmons Fwy 75207
Tel (214) 631-4420 SIC 3743

■TRINITY UNIVERSAL INSURANCE CO p 1482
12790 Merit Dr Ste 400 75251
Tel (312) 661-4930 SIC 6331

▲TRIUMPH BANCORP INC p 1483
12700 Park Central Dr # 1700 75251
Tel (214) 365-6930 SIC 6022

TRT DEVELOPMENT CO - CCB p 1485
4001 Maple Ave Ste 600 75219
Tel (800) 809-6664 SIC 7011

TRT HOLDINGS INC p 1485
4001 Maple Ave Ste 600 75219
Tel (214) 283-8500 SIC 7011 7991 1382

TRUCONNECT COMMUNICATIONS INC p 1485
10440 N Cntl Expy Ste 700 75231
Tel (877) 771-7736 SIC 4813

▲TUESDAY MORNING CORP p 1490
6250 Lbj Fwy 75240
Tel (972) 387-3562
SIC 5947 5719 5944 5948 5945 5712

■TUESDAY MORNING INC p 1490
6250 Lbj Fwy 75240
Tel (972) 387-3562 SIC 5311 2392 5719

■TXI OPERATIONS LP p 1495
1341 W Mockingbird Ln 700w 75247
Tel (972) 647-6700
SIC 3273 3271 3272 1442

TXU ENERGY INDUSTRIES CO p 1495
1601 Bryan St Ste 34-068 75201
Tel (214) 812-4600 SIC 4911

TXU ENERGY RETAIL CO LLC p 1495
1601 Bryan St 75201
Tel (214) 812-4449 SIC 4911

TXU ENERGY SERVICES CO LLC p 1495
1601 Bryan St 75201
Tel (214) 812-4600 SIC 3679

TXU TRANSITION BOND CO L L C p 1495
1601 Bryan St 75201
Tel (214) 814-4600 SIC 4911

TXU UNITED KINGDOM HOLDINGS CO p 1496
1601 Bryan St 75201
Tel (214) 812-4600 SIC 4911

UNION STREET MORTGAGE p 1505
4403 N Beltwood Pkwy 75244
Tel (866) 499-3411 SIC 6162

UNITED INVESTMENT LTD p 1509
11700 Preston Rd 660-388 75230
Tel (214) 632-9531 SIC 6726

■ UNITED STATES LIME & MINERALS INC p 1513
5429 Lbj Fwy Ste 230 75240
Tel (972) 991-8400 SIC 1422 3274 6289

UNIVERSITY OF TEXAS SOUTHWESTERN MEDICAL CENTER p 1526
5323 Harry Hines Blvd 75390
Tel (214) 648-3068 SIC 8733 8011

UNIVISION RADIO INC p 1527
2323 Bryan St Ste 1900 75201
Tel (214) 758-2300 SIC 4832

UPLIFT EDUCATION p 1528
1825 Market Center Blvd # 500 75207
Tel (469) 621-8500 SIC 8211

US STEEL TUBULAR PRODUCTS INC p 1533
15660 Dallas Pkwy Ste 500 75248
Tel (972) 386-3981 SIC 5051

USA CINEMA INVESTMENT HOLDINGS INC p 1534
14951 Dallas Pkwy 75254
Tel (972) 993-1553 SIC 7832

UT SOUTHWESTERN MEDICAL CENTER p 1536
5323 Harry Hines Blvd # 7200 75390
Tel (214) 648-2508 SIC 8059

UTILITY TRAILER OF DALLAS INC p 1537
34241 Lyndon B Jhnson Fwy 75241
Tel (972) 225-8845 SIC 5012 5015 5511

■ VALHI HOLDING CO p 1540
5430 Lyndon B Johnson Fwy # 1700 75240
Tel (972) 233-1700 SIC 2816

■ VALHI INC p 1540
5430 Lbj Fwy Ste 1700 75240
Tel (972) 233-1700
SIC 2816 2899 3429 4953

VG HOLDINGS LLC p 1553
200 Crescent Ct Ste 1600 75201
Tel (314) 727-2087 SIC 3672

■ VISTACARE INC p 1562
717 N Harwood St Ste 1500 75201
Tel (480) 648-4545 SIC 8082

VISTRA ENERGY CORP p 1562
1601 Bryan St 75201
Tel (214) 812-4600 SIC 5722

■ VOYAGER LEARNING CO p 1566
17855 Dallas Pkwy Ste 400 75287
Tel (214) 932-9500 SIC 2741 2759

■ WASTE CONTROL SPECIALISTS LLC p 1580
5430 Lyndon B Johnson Fwy # 1700 75240
Tel (888) 789-2783 SIC 4953

WESTDALE ASSET MANAGEMENT LTD p 1597
3100 Monticello Ave # 600 75205
Tel (214) 515-7000 SIC 6531

▲ WESTWOOD HOLDINGS GROUP INC p 1603
200 Crescent Ct Ste 1200 75201
Tel (214) 756-6900 SIC 6282

■ WHOLE FOODS MARKET ROCKY MOUNTAIN/SOUTHWEST LP p 1607
11770 Preston Rd Ste 119 75230
Tel (214) 361-8887 SIC 5411

▲ WILHELMINA INTERNATIONAL INC p 1609
200 Crescent Ct Ste 1400 75201
Tel (214) 661-7488 SIC 7363

WILLIAM DAVIS REALTY WOODLANDS LLC p 1610
17732 Creston Rd 75252
Tel (214) 621-9689 SIC 6531

WILLIAM HERBERT HUNT TRUST ESTATE p 1610
1601 Elm St Ste 3900 75201
Tel (214) 880-8400 SIC 8742 6799

WINGATE PARTNERS LP p 1616
750 N Saint Paul St # 1200 75201
Tel (214) 720-1313
SIC 2621 2672 3645 2519 5021 2521

WINGATE PARTNERS V LP p 1616
750 N Saint Paul St # 1200 75201
Tel (214) 720-1313 SIC 6726 3448

WINGSPAN PORTFOLIO HOLDINGS INC p 1616
18451 Dallas Pkwy Ste 100 75287
Tel (469) 737-2441 SIC 6211

X5 OPCO LLC p 1630
2828 N Harwood St # 1700 75201
Tel (214) 932-9293 SIC 4813

■ XEROX BUSINESS SERVICES LLC p 1631
2828 N Haskell Ave Fl 1 75204
Tel (214) 841-6111 SIC 7374 7375 7389

■ XEROX COMMERCIAL SOLUTIONS LLC p 1631
2828 N Haskell Ave Fl 9 75204
Tel (214) 841-6111 SIC 7374

YOUNG MENS CHRISTIAN ASSOCIATION OF METROPOLITAN p 1638
601 N Akard St 75201
Tel (214) 880-9622
SIC 8641 7991 8351 7032 8322

DAYTON, TX

GLOBAL TUBING LLC p 617
501 County Road 493 77535
Tel (713) 265-5000 SIC 1382

DECATUR, TX

JAMES WOOD MOTORS INC p 777
2111 S Highway 287 76234
Tel (940) 627-2177 SIC 5511

WISE HEALTH FOUNDATION p 1619
609 Medical Center Dr 76234
Tel (940) 627-5921 SIC 8062

DEER PARK, TX

24 HR SAFETY LLC p 2
4912 Railroad St 77536
Tel (337) 316-0541 SIC 5084

ATLANTIC SCAFFOLDING CO LLC p 127
1217 Georgia Ave 77536
Tel (281) 807-8200 SIC 1721 1799

BILFINGER TEPSCO INC p 182
2909 Aaron St 77536
Tel (281) 604-0309 SIC 1623

DEER PARK INDEPENDENT SCHOOL DISTRICT (INC) p 421
2800 Texas Ave 77536
Tel (832) 668-7080 SIC 8211

GARNER ENVIRONMENTAL SERVICES INC p 592
1717 W 13th St 77536
Tel (281) 930-1200 SIC 4959

HYDROCHEM LLC p 723
900 Georgia Ave 77536
Tel (713) 393-5600 SIC 7349

JONES INDUSTRIAL HOLDINGS INC p 792
806 Seaco Ct 77536
Tel (281) 479-6000 SIC 3564

■ ORION CONSTRUCTION LP p 1094
4440 Highway 225 Ste 180 77536
Tel (713) 852-6500 SIC 1629

■ PRIMORIS ENERGY SERVICES CORP p 1176
1109 W 13th St 77536
Tel (281) 478-5100 SIC 1623

■ ROHM AND HAAS TEXAS INC p 1247
6600 La Porte Fwy 77536
Tel (281) 476-8304 SIC 2869 2899 2819

USA ENVIRONMENT LP p 1534
316 Georgia Ave 77536
Tel (713) 425-6900 SIC 8748

DEL RIO, TX

■ GENTHERM (TEXAS) INC p 605
2121b Frontera Rd 78840
Tel (830) 774-3094 SIC 5013

SAN FELIPE DEL RIO CONSOLIDATED INDEPENDENT SCHOOL DISTRICT p 1276
315 Griner St 78840
Tel (830) 778-4000 SIC 8211

DENISON, TX

SIGNWAREHOUSE INC p 1322
2614 Texoma Dr 75020
Tel (903) 462-7700 SIC 7373

TEXOMA HEALTHCARE SYSTEM p 1445
1000 Memorial Dr 75020
Tel (903) 416-4000 SIC 8062 8059

UHS OF TEXOMA INC p 1500
5016 S Us Highway 75 75020
Tel (903) 416-4000 SIC 8062

DENTON, TX

■ BEAUTY SYSTEMS GROUP LLC p 166
3001 Colorado Blvd 76210
Tel (940) 297-2000 SIC 5999 5122 5087

CITY OF DENTON p 314
215 E Mckinney St 76201
Tel (940) 349-8200 SIC 9111

COUNTY OF DENTON p 377
110 W Hickory St 76201
Tel (940) 349-3100 SIC 9111

DAYBREAK VENTURE LLC p 417
401 N Elm St 76201
Tel (940) 387-4388 SIC 8051 8099

DENTON INDEPENDENT SCHOOL DISTRICT p 429
1307 N Locust St 76201
Tel (940) 369-0000 SIC 8211

■ DENTON REGIONAL MEDICAL CENTER INC p 429
3535 S Interstate 35 E 76210
Tel (940) 384-3535 SIC 8062 8011

DENTON TRANSITIONAL LTCH LP p 429
2813 S Mayhill Rd 76208
Tel (940) 320-2300 SIC 8062

■ ESAB GROUP INC p 509
2800 Airport Rd 76207
Tel (843) 669-4411 SIC 3548 2899

FIRST FINANCIAL RESOURCES INC p 547
611 Kimberly Dr 76208
Tel (940) 382-4599 SIC 4789 4953

HULCHER SERVICES INC p 718
611 Kimberly Dr 76208
Tel (940) 387-0099 SIC 4953 4789

IMPERIAL GROUP MANUFACTURING INC p 734
4545 Airport Rd 76207
Tel (940) 565-8505 SIC 3715

LABINAL LLC p 836
3790 Russell Newman Blvd # 100 76208
Tel (940) 272-5700 SIC 3728

R V MCCLAINS INC p 1203
5601 S I 35 E 76210
Tel (940) 498-4398 SIC 5561 7538

ROVIN INC p 1253
1332 Paisley St 76209
Tel (940) 383-0300 SIC 5812

▲ SALLY BEAUTY HOLDINGS INC p 1273
3001 Colorado Blvd 76210
Tel (940) 898-7500 SIC 5999 5087

■ SALLY BEAUTY SUPPLY LLC p 1273
3001 Colorado Blvd 76210
Tel (940) 898-7500 SIC 5999 5122 5087

■ SALLY HOLDINGS LLC p 1273
3001 Colorado Blvd 76210
Tel (940) 898-7500 SIC 5087

■ SALLY INVESTMENT HOLDINGS LLC p 1273
3001 Colorado Blvd 76210
Tel (940) 898-7500 SIC 7389

TETRA PAK INC p 1441
3300 Airport Rd 76207
Tel (940) 565-8800 SIC 2671 3565 5084

TEXAS WOMANS UNIVERSITY FOUNDATION p 1445
304 Administration Dr 76204
Tel (940) 898-3525 SIC 8221

UCI HOLDINGS LLC p 1499
2727 Geesling Rd 76208
Tel (940) 243-7676 SIC 3357

UNITED COPPER INDUSTRIES INC p 1507
2727 Geesling Rd 76208
Tel (940) 243-8200 SIC 3357

UNIVERSITY OF NORTH TEXAS SYSTEM p 1524
1302 Teasley Ln 76205
Tel (940) 565-2281 SIC 8221

■ VICTOR EQUIPMENT CO p 1555
2800 Airport Rd 76207
Tel (940) 566-2000 SIC 5088 3541 3548

■ VICTOR TECHNOLOGIES INTERNATIONAL INC p 1555
2800 Airport Rd 76207
Tel (940) 381-1353 SIC 3541 3548

DESOTO, TX

DESOTO INDEPENDENT SCHOOL DISTRICT p 432
200 E Belt Line Rd 75115
Tel (972) 223-6666 *SIC* 8211

DW DISTRIBUTION INC p 463
1200 E Centre Park Blvd 75115
Tel (214) 381-2200 *SIC* 5033 5031 5072

DFW AIRPORT, TX

■ **AVIALL SERVICES INC** p 137
2750 Regent Blvd 75261
Tel (972) 586-1000 *SIC* 5088 7699

DALLAS/FORT WORTH INTERNATIONAL AIRPORT p 410
3200 E Airfield Dr 75261
Tel (972) 973-8888 *SIC* 4581

DEX MEDIA HOLDINGS INC p 434
2200 W Airfield Dr 75261
Tel (972) 453-7000 *SIC* 8742

DEX MEDIA INC p 434
2200 W Airfield Dr 75261
Tel (972) 453-7000 *SIC* 2741 7311

SUPERMEDIA INC p 1407
2200 W Airfield Dr 75261
Tel (972) 453-7000 *SIC* 2741

SUPERMEDIA LLC p 1407
2200 W Airfield Dr 75261
Tel (972) 453-7000 *SIC* 2741 6719

DICKINSON, TX

DICKINSON INDEPENDENT SCHOOL DISTRICT p 438
2218 Fm 517 Rd E 77539
Tel (281) 229-6000 *SIC* 8211

DONNA, TX

DONNA INDEPENDENT SCHOOL DISTRICT p 450
116 N 10th St 78537
Tel (956) 464-1600 *SIC* 8211

DRIPPING SPRINGS, TX

SERENGETITRADING CO LP p 1306
19100 Hamilton Pool Rd 78620
Tel (512) 358-9593 *SIC* 5149

DUNCANVILLE, TX

DEFORD LUMBER CO LTD p 422
1018 N Duncanville Rd 75116
Tel (972) 298-7121 *SIC* 5031 5211

DUNCANVILLE INDEPENDENT SCHOOL DISTRICT p 461
710 S Cedar Ridge Dr 75137
Tel (972) 708-2000 *SIC* 8211

PIONEER FROZEN FOODS INC p 1150
627 Big Stone Gap Rd 75137
Tel (972) 298-4281 *SIC* 2051

EAGLE PASS, TX

EAGLE PASS INDEPENDENT SCHOOL DISTRICT p 468
1420 Eidson Rd 78852
Tel (830) 773-5181 *SIC* 8211

KICKAPOO TRADITIONAL TRIBE OF TEXAS p 817
2212 Rosita Valley Rd 78852
Tel (830) 773-2105 *SIC* 8322

EDGEWOOD, TX

EDGEWOOD INDEPENDENT SCHOOL DISTRICT 903 p 478
804 E Pine St 75117
Tel (903) 896-4332 *SIC* 8211 9411

EDINBURG, TX

AA TRADING LLC p 7
1702 S State Highway 336 B 78539
Tel (956) 618-3006 *SIC* 5147

COUNTY OF HIDALGO p 378
100 N Closner Blvd # 303 78539
Tel (956) 289-7850 *SIC* 9111

DOCTORS HOSPITAL AT RENAISSANCE LTD p 447
5501 S Mccoll Rd 78539
Tel (956) 362-8677 *SIC* 8062

EDINBURG CONSOLIDATED INDEPENDENT SCHOOL DISTRICT p 478
411 N 8th Ave 78541
Tel (956) 289-2300 *SIC* 8211

FIRST NATIONAL BANK p 548
100 W Cano St 78539
Tel (956) 380-8587 *SIC* 6021

J & D PRODUCE INC p 769
7310 N Expressway 281 78542
Tel (956) 380-0353 *SIC* 5148

MO-VAC SERVICE CO p 980
3721 S Mccoll Rd 78539
Tel (956) 682-6381 *SIC* 1389 4959

UNIVERSITY OF TEXAS RIO GRANDE VALLEY p 1526
1201 W University Dr 78539
Tel (956) 665-2110 *SIC* 8221

EL CAMPO, TX

■ **PROSPERITY BANK** p 1184
1301 N Mechanic St 77437
Tel (979) 543-1426 *SIC* 6022

UNITED AGRICULTURAL COOPERATIVE INC p 1506
911 S Wharton St 77437
Tel (979) 543-6284
SIC 5251 0724 5083 4221 5153

EL PASO, TX

AMBROSIA GUILLENTSVH p 65
9650 Kenworthy St 79924
Tel (915) 751-0967 *SIC* 8051

BASIC SPORTS APPAREL INC p 158
301 Williams St 79901
Tel (915) 532-0561 *SIC* 5136

BIG 8 FOODS LTD p 181
1480 George Dieter Dr 79936
Tel (915) 857-6080 *SIC* 5411

BORDER APPAREL LAUNDRY LTD p 201
6969 Industrial Ave 79915
Tel (915) 772-7170 *SIC* 2326 7211

CEMEX EL PASO INC p 274
1 Mckelligon Canyon Rd 79930
Tel (915) 565-4681
SIC 3273 2951 5032 1442

CITY OF EL PASO p 314
1 Civic Center Plz 79901
Tel (915) 541-4000 *SIC* 9111

CLINT INDEPENDENT SCHOOL DISTRICT p 326
14521 Horizon Blvd 79928
Tel (915) 926-4000 *SIC* 8211 9411

COUNTY OF EL PASO p 377
500 E San Antonio Ave # 314 79901
Tel (915) 546-2000 *SIC* 9111

DATAMARK INC p 414
123 W Mills Ave Ste 400 79901
Tel (915) 778-1944 *SIC* 7374

DAY EL PASO SURGERY LP p 417
1300 Murchison Dr Ste 200 79902
Tel (915) 225-7600 *SIC* 8011

DELPHI AUTOMOTIVE SYSTEMS CORP p 425
12170 Rojas Dr 79936
Tel (915) 612-2855 *SIC* 3694

EL PASO COUNTY COMMUNITY COLLEGE DISTRICT p 483
9050 Viscount Blvd 79925
Tel (915) 831-3722 *SIC* 8222

EL PASO COUNTY HOSPITAL DISTRICT p 483
4815 Alameda Ave 79905
Tel (915) 544-1200 *SIC* 8062

▲ **EL PASO ELECTRIC CO** p 483
Stanton Twr 100 N Stanton 79901
Tel (915) 543-5711 *SIC* 4911

EL PASO FIRST HEALTH PLANS INC p 483
1145 Westmoreland Dr 79925
Tel (915) 298-7198 *SIC* 8741

■ **EL PASO HEALTHCARE SYSTEM LTD** p 483
10301 Gateway Blvd W 79925
Tel (915) 595-9000 *SIC* 8062

EL PASO INDEPENDENT SCHOOL DISTRICT p 483
6531 Boeing Dr 79925
Tel (915) 230-2000 *SIC* 8211

EL PASO WATER UTILITIES PUBLIC SERVICE BOARD p 483
1154 Hawkins Blvd 79925
Tel (915) 594-5500 *SIC* 4941 1623

ELAMEX USA CORP p 483
1800 Northwestern Dr 79912
Tel (915) 298-3061 *SIC* 3694 2068 2064

ELCOM INC p 484
20 Butterfield Trail Blvd 79906
Tel (915) 298-2000 *SIC* 3679 3694

FIRST TEXAS HOLDING CORP p 549
1465 Henry Brennan Dr H 79936
Tel (915) 633-8354 *SIC* 3812

FIRST TEXAS PRODUCTS LLC p 550
1465 Henry Brennan Dr H 79936
Tel (915) 633-8354 *SIC* 3812

FORD CASA INC p 565
5815 Montana Ave 79925
Tel (915) 779-2272 *SIC* 5511

FRED LOYA INSURANCE AGENCY INC p 576
1800 N Lee Trevino Dr # 100 79936
Tel (915) 595-0595 *SIC* 6411

FRL INC p 580
1465 Henry Brennan Dr H 79936
Tel (915) 225-0333 *SIC* 3699

FURUKAWA WIRING SYSTEMS AMERICA INC p 585
950 Loma Verde Dr 79936
Tel (915) 791-5579 *SIC* 2531

GECU p 597
1225 Airway Blvd 79925
Tel (915) 778-9221 *SIC* 6062

GENPACT p 604
2004 Bassett Ave Pmb 2500 79901
Tel (915) 225-2500 *SIC* 7374

HELEN OF TROY LP p 681
1 Helen Of Troy Plz 79912
Tel (915) 225-8000 *SIC* 3999 3634

HELEN OF TROY TEXAS CORP p 681
1 Helen Of Troy Plz 79912
Tel (915) 225-8000 *SIC* 3999

HUNT BUILDING CO LTD p 718
4401 N Mesa St Ste 201 79902
Tel (915) 533-1122
SIC 1522 6531 1542 7389

HUNT COMPANIES INC p 718
4401 N Mesa St 79902
Tel (915) 533-1122 *SIC* 1522 6531 1542

JARRITOS INC p 778
500 W Overland Ave # 300 79901
Tel (915) 594-1618 *SIC* 5149

JOBE MATERIALS LP p 787
1150 Southview Dr Ste A 79928
Tel (915) 298-9900 *SIC* 3272

JORDAN CF CONSTRUCTION LLC p 793
7700 Cf Jordan Dr Ste 200 79912
Tel (915) 877-3333 *SIC* 1542 1541 1522

JORDAN CF INVESTMENTS LLP p 793
7700 Cf Jordan Dr 79912
Tel (915) 877-3333
SIC 1542 1541 1522 1611

JORDAN FOSTER CONSTRUCTION LLC p 793
7700 Cf Jordan Dr Ste 200 79912
Tel (915) 877-3333 *SIC* 1542

LARROC INC p 845
6420 Boeing Dr 79925
Tel (915) 772-3733 *SIC* 5141 5149

LOPEZ SCRAP METAL INC p 878
351 N Nevarez Rd 79927
Tel (915) 859-0770 *SIC* 5093 3341

MID-WEST TEXTILE CO p 964
1600 E San Antonio Ave 79901
Tel (915) 351-0231 *SIC* 5093 5137 5136

MOUNT FRANKLIN FOODS LLC p 993
1800 Northwestern Dr 79912
Tel (915) 877-4079 *SIC* 5145 2068 2064

MSDP GROUP LLC p 997
1350 Pullman Dr Dr14 79936
Tel (915) 857-5200 *SIC* 3694

NOVA USA INC p 1062
500 W Overland Ave # 300 79901
Tel (915) 594-1618 *SIC* 6719

PHILIPS CONSUMER ELECTRONIC CO p 1143
12430 Mercantile Ave 79928
Tel (915) 298-4111 *SIC* 3663

PIZZA PROPERTIES LTD p 1153
4445 N Mesa St Ste 100 79902
Tel (915) 544-8565 *SIC* 5812

PLASTICOS PROMEX USA INC p 1155
1220 Barranca Dr Ste 4c 79935
Tel (915) 592-5447 *SIC* 3089

■ **POLLOK INC** p 1160
6 Butterfield Trail Blvd 79906
Tel (915) 592-5700
SIC 5065 3823 3714 3545

READYONE INDUSTRIES INC p 1213
1414 Ability Dr 79936
Tel (915) 858-7277 *SIC* 2331 2311

RUDOLPH CHEVROLET LLC p 1257
5625 S Desert Blvd 79932
Tel (915) 544-4321 *SIC* 5511

SEISA MEDICAL INC p 1301
9005 Montana Ave 79925
Tel (915) 774-4321 *SIC* 3841

SOCORRO INDEPENDENT SCHOOL DISTRICT p 1336
12440 Rojas Dr 79928
Tel (915) 937-0100 *SIC* 8211

■ **STONERIDGE ELECTRONICS INC** p 1391
21 Butterfield Trail Blvd A 79906
Tel (915) 593-2011 *SIC* 3679 3714

T & T STAFF MANAGEMENT INC p 1419
511 Executive Center Blvd 79902
Tel (915) 771-0393 *SIC* 7361

TECMA GROUP L L C p 1432
2000 Wyoming Ave Ste A 79903
Tel (915) 534-4252 *SIC* 7389

■ **TENET HOSPITALS LIMITED** p 1437
2001 N Oregon St 79902
Tel (915) 577-6011 *SIC* 8062

TIME WARNER ENTERTAINMENT ADVANCE NEWHOUSE PARTNERSHIP p 1454
7010 Airport Rd 79906
Tel (512) 288-5440 *SIC* 4841

TIPP DISTRIBUTORS INC p 1455
500 W Overland Ave # 300 79901
Tel (915) 594-1618 *SIC* 5149

TRINITY BAY CITY HOLDINGS LLC p 1481
712 Waltham Ct 79922
Tel (915) 877-1700 *SIC* 5511

UNIVERSITY OF TEXAS AT EL PASO p 1525
500 W University Ave 79968
Tel (915) 747-5000 *SIC* 8221

■ **WESTERN REFINING CO LP** p 1599
123 W Mills Ave Ste 200 79901
Tel (915) 534-1400 *SIC* 2911

▲ **WESTERN REFINING INC** p 1599
123 W Mills Ave Ste 200 79901
Tel (915) 534-1400 *SIC* 2911 5983

■ **WESTERN REFINING LOGISTICS LP** p 1599
123 W Mills Ave Ste 200 79901
Tel (915) 534-1400 *SIC* 4613 4612

YSLETA INDEPENDENT SCHOOL DISTRICT p 1640
9600 Sims Dr 79925
Tel (915) 434-0240 *SIC* 8211

ENNIS, TX

ENNIS STEEL INDUSTRIES INC p 500
204 Metro Park Blvd 75119
Tel (972) 878-0400 *SIC* 3312 3441 1791

JTEKT AUTOMOTIVE TEXAS LP p 796
4400 Sterilite Dr 75119
Tel (972) 878-1800 *SIC* 3714

TRAC-WORK INC p 1468
3801 N I 45 75119
Tel (972) 875-6565 *SIC* 1629

EULESS, TX

■ **BEALL CONCRETE ENTERPRISES LTD** p 165
331 N Main St 76039
Tel (817) 835-4100 *SIC* 1611 1771

H M DUNN CO INC p 650
3301 House Anderson Rd 76040
Tel (817) 283-3722 *SIC* 3724 3599 3728

HM DUNN AEROSYSTEMS INC p 697
3301 House Anderson Rd 76040
Tel (817) 283-3722 *SIC* 3724

PIONEER FASTENERS & TOOL INC p 1150
202 S Ector Dr 76040
Tel (817) 545-0121 *SIC* 5085

SUPREME ENTERPRISES INC p 1408
204 N Ector Dr 76039
Tel (817) 267-6090 *SIC* 7363

▲ **US CONCRETE INC** p 1531
331 N Main St 76039
Tel (817) 835-4105 *SIC* 3273 3272

FARMERS BRANCH, TX

BSN SPORTS LLC p 222
1901 Diplomat Dr 75234
Tel (972) 484-9484 *SIC* 5091

CCS MEDICAL HOLDINGS INC p 270
1505 L B Johnson Fwy # 600 75234
Tel (972) 628-2100 *SIC* 5999 5912 5961

CCS MEDICAL INC p 270
1505 L B Johnson Fwy # 600 75234
Tel (972) 628-2100 *SIC* 5999 5912 5961

EYEMART EXPRESS LLC p 522
13800 Senlac Dr Ste 200 75234
Tel (972) 488-2002 *SIC* 5995

HAGGAR CLOTHING CO p 653
1507 Lbj Fwy Ste 100 75234
Tel (214) 352-8481
SIC 2325 2311 2321 5611 5651

HAGGAR CORP p 653
1507 Lyndon B Johnson Fwy 75234
Tel (214) 352-8481
SIC 2325 2311 2321 5611 6794

HYLA INC p 724
Prk W 1 & 2 1507 Lbj Fwy 75234
Tel (972) 573-0300 *SIC* 5084

INDEPENDENT BANKERS FINANCIAL CORP p 736
11701 Luna Rd 75234
Tel (972) 650-6000 *SIC* 6712

JMEG LP p 786
13995 Diplomat Dr Ste 400 75234
Tel (972) 590-5555 *SIC* 1731

LA BODEGA MEAT INC p 835
14330 Gillis Rd 75244
Tel (972) 926-6129 *SIC* 5147

TACO BUENO RESTAURANTS LP p 1421
1605 Lbj Fwy Ste 800 75234
Tel (800) 440-0778 *SIC* 5812 6794

TIB - INDEPENDENT BANKERSBANK p 1452
11701 Luna Rd 75234
Tel (972) 650-6000 *SIC* 6022

VARSITY BRANDS HOLDING CO INC p 1545
1901 Diplomat Dr 75234
Tel (972) 406-7162 *SIC* 5091 7299 6719

FERRIS, TX

TRINITY MATERIALS INC p 1481
401 N Interstate Hwy 45 75125
Tel (972) 544-5900 *SIC* 3273

FLOWER MOUND, TX

GENERAL ALUMINUM CO OF TEXAS LP p 599
1900 Lakeside Pkwy 75028
Tel (972) 242-5271 *SIC* 3442 5031

GREENLEAF ADVERTISING & MEDIA INC p 638
601 Silveron Ste 200 75028
Tel (972) 899-8750 *SIC* 7311

IVIE & ASSOCIATES INC p 769
601 Silveron Ste 200 75028
Tel (972) 899-5000 *SIC* 7311

LEWISVILLE INDEPENDENT SCHOOL DISTRICT p 859
1800 Timber Creek Rd 75028
Tel (469) 713-5200 *SIC* 8211

FORNEY, TX

STEVE SILVER CO p 1388
1000 Fm 548 75126
Tel (972) 564-2601 *SIC* 5021

FORT WORTH, TX

20/20 COMMUNICATIONS INC p 1
3575 Lone Star Cir # 200 76177
Tel (817) 490-0100 *SIC* 5963

ACCELERATE HOLDINGS CORP p 14
301 Commerce St Ste 3300 76102
Tel (817) 871-4000 *SIC* 6722

■ **ACME BRICK CO** p 17
3024 Acme Brick Plz 76109
Tel (817) 332-4101 *SIC* 3251 5032 5211

ACQUISITION VEHICLE TEXAS II LLC p 18
301 Commerce St Ste 3232 76102
Tel (972) 915-2895 *SIC* 5411 5912

ALCON LABORATORIES HOLDING CORP p 47
6201 South Fwy 76134
Tel (817) 293-0450 *SIC* 2834 3841

ALCON LABORATORIES INC p 47
6201 South Fwy 76134
Tel (817) 293-0450 *SIC* 3841 2834

ALCON MANUFACTURING LTD p 47
6201 South Fwy 76134
Tel (817) 293-0450 *SIC* 2834 3841

ALCON RESEARCH LTD p 47
6201 South Fwy 76134
Tel (817) 551-4555 *SIC* 8733 3841 2834

ALCON SURGICAL INC p 47
6201 South Fwy 76134
Tel (817) 293-0450 *SIC* 3841

ALLIED ELECTRONICS INC p 56
7151 Jack Newell Blvd S 76118
Tel (817) 595-3500 *SIC* 5065 7389 3999

AMERICAN AIRLINES FEDERAL CREDIT UNION INC p 67
4151 Amon Carter Blvd 76155
Tel (817) 963-6000 *SIC* 6061

▲ **AMERICAN AIRLINES GROUP INC** p 67
4333 Amon Carter Blvd 76155
Tel (817) 963-1234 *SIC* 4512 4581

■ **AMERICAN AIRLINES INC** p 67
4333 Amon Carter Blvd 76155
Tel (817) 963-1234 *SIC* 4512 4513

■ **AMERICAN EAGLE HOLDING LLC** p 71
14760 Trinity Blvd # 300 76155
Tel (817) 963-1234 *SIC* 7389

■ **AMERICREDIT FINANCIAL SERVICES INC** p 82
801 Cherry St Ste 3500 76102
Tel (817) 302-7000 *SIC* 6141

■ **AMR EAGLE INC** p 86
4333 Amon Carter Blvd 76155
Tel (214) 927-6016 *SIC* 4512

AMSCO STEEL CO LLC p 87
3430 Mccart Ave 76110
Tel (817) 926-3355 *SIC* 5051

APEX CAPITAL CORP p 96
6000 Western Pl Ste 1000 76107
Tel (800) 511-6022 *SIC* 6153

▲ **APPROACH RESOURCES INC** p 100
6500 West Fwy Ste 800 76116
Tel (817) 989-9000 *SIC* 1311

■ **ARBOR-CROWLEY INC** p 103
3100 W 7th St Ste 500 76107
Tel (817) 810-0095 *SIC* 3629

■ **ATC LOGISTICS & ELECTRONICS INC** p 124
13500 Independence Pkwy 76177
Tel (817) 491-7700 *SIC* 4225 3714 3694

ATCO RUBBER PRODUCTS INC p 124
7101 Atco Dr 76118
Tel (817) 589-7035
SIC 3443 3084 3585 3444 3083

ATHLON ENERGY INC p 124
420 Throckmorton St # 1200 76102
Tel (817) 984-8200 *SIC* 1311

AUI CONTRACTORS LLC p 131
4775 North Fwy 76106
Tel (817) 926-4377 *SIC* 1542 1623 1771

AUTOBAHN INC p 133
3000 White Settlement Rd 76107
Tel (817) 336-0885 *SIC* 5511

▲ **AZZ INC** p 141
3100 W 7th St Ste 500 76107
Tel (817) 810-0095
SIC 3699 3613 3494 3312

BAIRDS MRS BAKERIES BUSINESS TRUST p 145
7301 South Fwy 76134
Tel (817) 615-3100 *SIC* 2051

▲ **BASIC ENERGY SERVICES INC** p 158
801 Cherry St Unit 2 76102
Tel (817) 334-4100 *SIC* 1389 1794

■ **BASIC ENERGY SERVICES LP** p 158
801 Cherry St Unit 2 76102
Tel (817) 334-4100 *SIC* 1389

BASS ENTERPRISES PRODUCTION CO p 159
201 Main St Ste 2700 76102
Tel (817) 698-0200 *SIC* 1311 1382

BASSHAM WHOLESALE EGG CO INC p 159
5409 Hemphill St 76115
Tel (817) 921-1600
SIC 5144 5143 5141 5147

BAYLOR ALL SAINTS MEDICAL CENTER p 162
1400 8th Ave 76104
Tel (817) 926-2544 *SIC* 8062

■ **BELL HELICOPTER TEXTRON INC** p 170
3255 Bell Helicopter Blvd 76118
Tel (817) 280-2011 *SIC* 3728 5088 3721

BEN E KEITH CO p 172
601 E 7th St 76102
Tel (817) 877-5700 *SIC* 5181 5141

■ **BNSF RAILWAY CO** p 194
2650 Lou Menk Dr 76131
Tel (800) 795-2673 *SIC* 4731 4011

■ **BURLINGTON NORTHERN SANTA FE LLC** p 228
2650 Lou Menk Dr 76131
Tel (800) 795-2673 *SIC* 4731 4011

▲ **CALLOWAYS NURSERY INC** p 242
4200 Airport Fwy Ste 200 76117
Tel (817) 222-1122 *SIC* 5261

CANTEX INC p 247
301 Commerce St Ste 2700 76102
Tel (817) 215-7000 *SIC* 3084 3089

CARLILE BANCSHARES INC p 257
201 Main St Ste 1320 76102
Tel (817) 877-4440 *SIC* 6719

■ **CARTER & BURGESS INC** p 261
777 Main St Ste 2500 76102
Tel (817) 735-6000 *SIC* 8711 8712 8713

■ **CASH AMERICA FINANCIAL SERVICES INC** p 263
1600 W 7th St 76102
Tel (817) 335-1100 *SIC* 5932

CASH AMERICA INVESTMENTS INC p 263
1600 W 7th St 76102
Tel (817) 335-1100 *SIC* 5932 6099

CATHOLIC DIOCESE OF FORT WORTH p 266
800 W Loop 820 S 76108
Tel (817) 560-3300 *SIC* 8661

CDK PERFORATING LLC p 271
6500 West Fwy Ste 600 76116
Tel (817) 945-1051 *SIC* 1389

CEC ELECTRICAL INC p 272
14450 Trinity Blvd # 250 76155
Tel (817) 734-0040 *SIC* 1731

CIBA VISION CORP p 305
6201 South Fwy 76134
Tel (817) 551-6881 *SIC* 3851

■ **CITI ASSURANCE SERVICES INC** p 309
3001 Meacham Blvd Ste 100 76137
Tel (817) 348-7500 *SIC* 6321 6411

CITY OF FORT WORTH p 314
1000 Throckmorton St 76102
Tel (817) 392-6118 *SIC* 9111

COLONIAL SAVINGS FA p 338
2600 West Fwy 76102
Tel (817) 390-2000 *SIC* 6162 6035

■ **COLUMBIA PLAZA MEDICAL CENTER OF FORT WORTH SUBSIDIARY LP** p 341
900 8th Ave 76104
Tel (817) 336-2100 *SIC* 8062

COMPASS WELL SERVICES LLC p 351
4100 Intl Plz Ste 500 76109
Tel (817) 244-2555 *SIC* 1389 1382

CONNER INDUSTRIES INC p 358
3800 Sandshell Dr Ste 235 76137
Tel (817) 847-0361 *SIC* 5211 5031

COOK CHILDRENS HEALTH CARE SYSTEM p 365
801 7th Ave 76104
Tel (682) 885-4555 *SIC* 8069

COOK CHILDRENS HEALTH PLAN p 365
801 7th Ave 76104
Tel (817) 334-2247 *SIC* 8082

COOK CHILDRENS MEDICAL CENTER p 365
801 7th Ave 76104
Tel (682) 885-4000 *SIC* 8069

COOK CHILDRENS PHYSICIAN NETWORK p 365
801 7th Ave 76104
Tel (682) 885-6800 *SIC* 8011

COORS DISTRIBUTING CO OF FORT WORTH p 368
2550 Mcmillian Pkwy 76137
Tel (817) 838-1600 *SIC* 5181

CRESCENT REAL ESTATE EQUITIES CO p 391
777 Main St Ste 2260 76102
Tel (817) 321-2100 *SIC* 6798

CRESCENT REAL ESTATE HOLDINGS LLC p 391
777 Main St Ste 2260 76102
Tel (817) 321-2100 *SIC* 6798

CREST PUMPING TECHNOLOGIES LLC p 392
6500 West Fwy Ste 601 76116
Tel (817) 484-5100 *SIC* 1389

■ **CROSS TIMBERS OPERATING CO** p 394
810 Houston St Ste 2000 76102
Tel (817) 870-2800 *SIC* 1311

CUMMINGS ELECTRICAL LP p 401
14900 Grand River Rd # 124 76155
Tel (817) 355-5300 *SIC* 1731

D REYNOLDS CO LLC p 407
2680 Sylvania Cross Dr 76137
Tel (214) 630-9000 *SIC* 5063

DAVOIL INC p 416
6300 Ridglea Pl Ste 1208 76116
Tel (817) 737-6678 *SIC* 1382

DECATUR HOSPITAL AUTHORITY p 420
900 W Leuda St 76104
Tel (817) 332-7003 *SIC* 8062

DFB PHARMACEUTICALS LLC p 435
3909 Hulen St 76107
Tel (817) 900-4050 *SIC* 2834

DIMARE FRESH INC p 440
4629 Diplomacy Rd 76155
Tel (817) 385-3000 *SIC* 5148

■ **DR HORTON - TEXAS LTD** p 454
301 Commerce St Ste 500 76102
Tel (817) 856-8200 *SIC* 1521

▲ **DR HORTON INC** p 454
301 Commerce St Ste 500 76102
Tel (817) 390-8200 *SIC* 1531 6162

DUNLAP CO p 461
200 Bailey Ave Ste 100 76107
Tel (817) 336-4985 *SIC* 5311

■ **DYNA TEN CORP** p 464
4375 Diplomacy Rd 76155
Tel (817) 616-2200 *SIC* 1711

EAGLE MOUNTAIN-SAGINAW INDEPENDENT SCHOOL DISTRICT p 468
1200 Old Decatur Rd 76179
Tel (817) 232-0123 *SIC* 8211

ECOMMERCE INDUSTRIES INC p 476
4400 Alliance Gateway Fwy # 154 76177
Tel (682) 831-0827 *SIC* 7373

ED TUCKER DISTRIBUTOR INC p 477
4900 Alliance Gateway Fwy 76177
Tel (817) 258-9000 *SIC* 5013

EFW INC p 481
4700 Marine Creek Pkwy 76179
Tel (817) 916-1359 *SIC* 3812

EIGER HOLDCO LLC p 481
301 Commerce St Ste 1600 76102
Tel (817) 332-3235 *SIC* 6719

ELBIT SYSTEMS OF AMERICA LLC p 483
4700 Marine Creek Pkwy 76179
Tel (817) 234-6600 *SIC* 3827

ELEVATE CREDIT INC p 486
4150 Intl Plz Ste 300 76109
Tel (817) 928-1500 *SIC* 6141

FALCON PHARMACEUTICALS LTD p 526
6201 South Fwy 76134
Tel (800) 343-2133 *SIC* 2834 3841

▲ **FARMER BROS CO** p 529
13601 North Fwy Ste 200 76177
Tel (682) 549-6600 *SIC* 2095 5149

FIRST AMERICAN PAYMENT SYSTEMS LP p 544
100 Throckmorton St # 1800 76102
Tel (817) 317-9100 *SIC* 6153

FIRST COMMAND FINANCIAL PLANNING INC p 545
1 Firstcomm Plz 76109
Tel (817) 731-8621 *SIC* 6311 6211

FIRST COMMAND FINANCIAL SERVICES INC p 545
1 Firstcomm Plz 76109
Tel (817) 731-8621 *SIC* 7389

FLUID DELIVERY SOLUTIONS LLC p 561
6795 Corp Pkwy Ste 200 76126
Tel (817) 730-9761 *SIC* 4941

FORT WORTH INDEPENDENT SCHOOL DISTRICT p 569
100 N University Dr 76107
Tel (817) 871-2000 *SIC* 8211

FREESE AND NICHOLS INC p 577
4055 Intl Plz Ste 200 76109
Tel (817) 735-7491 *SIC* 8711

■ **FRONTIER MERGER SUB LLC** p 581
1600 W 7th St 76102
Tel (800) 223-8738 *SIC* 5932 6099

FRUIT OF EARTH INC p 582
3101 High Rver Rd Ste 175 76155
Tel (817) 510-1600 *SIC* 5122 2844

FTS INTERNATIONAL INC p 583
777 Main St Ste 3000 76102
Tel (682) 862-2000 *SIC* 1389

FTS INTERNATIONAL MANUFACTURING LLC p 583
777 Main St Ste 2900 76102
Tel (817) 850-8004 *SIC* 5082 7353 5211

FTS INTERNATIONAL SERVICES LLC p 583
777 Main St Ste 2900 76102
Tel (817) 850-1008
SIC 3561 8711 7353 4225

GALDERMA LABORATORIES LP p 589
14501 North Fwy 76177
Tel (817) 961-5000 *SIC* 2834

GAMTEX INDUSTRIES LP p 590
2600 Shamrock Ave 76107
Tel (800) 749-0423 *SIC* 5093

■ **GENERAL MOTORS FINANCIAL CO INC** p 601
801 Cherry St Ste 3500 76102
Tel (817) 302-7000 *SIC* 6141

■ **GSA GREATER SOUTHWEST REGION OFC OF REGIONAL ADMINISTRATOR** p 643
819 Taylor St Rm 11a00 76102
Tel (817) 978-2321 *SIC* 9199

▲ **HALLMARK FINANCIAL SERVICES INC** p 654
777 Main St Ste 1000 76102
Tel (817) 348-1600 *SIC* 6411 6311

HEALTHCARE TECHNOLOGY INTERMEDIATE HOLDINGS INC p 676
301 Commerce St Ste 3300 76102
Tel (817) 871-4000 *SIC* 8732

HIGGINBOTHAM INSURANCE AGENCY MCKINNEY INC p 690
500 W 13th St Ste 200 76102
Tel (817) 336-2377 *SIC* 6411

HIGGINBOTHAM INSURANCE GROUP INC p 690
500 W 13th St Ste 200 76102
Tel (800) 728-2374 *SIC* 6411

HOWARD SUPPLY CO LLC p 713
4100 Intl Plz Ste 850 76109
Tel (817) 529-9950 *SIC* 5084 5082

HYDRADYNE LLC p 723
15050 Faa Blvd 76155
Tel (817) 391-1547 *SIC* 5084

INTERMET CORP p 753
301 Commerce St Ste 2901 76102
Tel (817) 348-9190
SIC 3321 3714 3462 3365 3364

INTERSTATE RESTORATION LLC p 758
3401 Quorum Dr Ste 300 76137
Tel (817) 293-0035 *SIC* 1542 1522 7349

■ **JUSTIN BRANDS INC** p 798
610 W Daggett Ave 76104
Tel (817) 332-4385 *SIC* 3144 3143 3149

■ **JUSTIN INDUSTRIES INC** p 798
3024 Acme Brick Plz 76109
Tel (817) 332-4101
SIC 3251 3271 5211 5032

KDM HOLDING INC p 807
3700 Hulen St 76107
Tel (817) 732-8164 *SIC* 3274

KIEWIT TEXAS CONSTRUCTION LP p 817
13119 Old Denton Rd 76177
Tel (817) 337-7000 *SIC* 1611

▲ **KMG CHEMICALS INC** p 824
300 Throckmorton St 76102
Tel (817) 761-6100 *SIC* 2899

■ **KMG ELECTRONIC CHEMICALS INC** p 824
300 Throckmorton St 76102
Tel (817) 761-6100 *SIC* 1629

■ **KMG-BERNUTH INC** p 824
300 Throckmorton St 76102
Tel (817) 761-6100 *SIC* 5169 2869

KPS GLOBAL LLC p 829
4201 N Beach St 76137
Tel (817) 281-5121 *SIC* 3089 3585

LANDMARK STRUCTURES I LP p 843
1665 Harmon Rd 76177
Tel (817) 439-8888 *SIC* 1791 7699

LEGACY HOUSING LTD p 852
4801 Mark Iv Pkwy 76106
Tel (817) 624-7565 *SIC* 2451

LHOIST NORTH AMERICA INC p 861
3700 Hulen St 76107
Tel (817) 732-8164 *SIC* 3274

LIME HOLDING INC p 866
3700 Hulen St 76107
Tel (817) 732-8164 *SIC* 3274

LONE STAR TRANSPORTATION LLC p 876
1100 Northway Dr 76131
Tel (817) 306-1000 *SIC* 4213

LUTHER KING CAPITAL MANAGEMENT CORP p 886
301 Commerce St Ste 1600 76102
Tel (817) 429-6256 *SIC* 6282

■ **M&M MANUFACTURING INC** p 890
4001 Mark Iv Pkwy 76106
Tel (817) 336-2311 *SIC* 3444

MAALT LP p 891
4413 Carey St 76119
Tel (817) 205-0460 *SIC* 4225 4731

MARCO DISPLAY SPECIALISTS LP p 905
3209 Marquita Dr 76116
Tel (817) 244-8300
SIC 2521 2541 3993 3089 3081

MARCO DISPLAY SPECIALISTS LP p 905
3209 Marquita Dr 76116
Tel (817) 244-8300 *SIC* 2541 3993

MARKETING MANAGEMENT INC p 908
4717 Fletcher Ave 76107
Tel (817) 731-4176 *SIC* 5141

MAXUM ENTERPRISES LLC p 923
201 N Rupert St Ste 101 76107
Tel (877) 877-8300 *SIC* 5171 5172

MCDONALD TRANSIT ASSOCIATES INC p 927
3800 Sandshell Dr Ste 185 76137
Tel (817) 232-9551 *SIC* 8742

MENTAL HEALTH MENTAL RETARDATION OF TARRANT COUNTY p 943
3840 Hulen St 76107
Tel (817) 569-4300 *SIC* 8093 8322 8361

MORRISON SUPPLY CO p 990
311 E Vickery Blvd 76104
Tel (817) 336-0451 *SIC* 5074

MORSCO INC p 990
100 E 15th St Ste 200 76102
Tel (877) 709-2227 *SIC* 5074 1711

MORTEX PRODUCTS INC p 991
501 Terminal Rd 76106
Tel (817) 624-0820
SIC 3585 3433 1711 3999

MOTHER PARKERS TEA & COFFEE USA LTD p 992
7800 Will Rogers Blvd 76140
Tel (817) 551-5500 *SIC* 5149 2095 2099

MRS BAIRDS BAKERIES BUSINESS TRUST p 996
14401 Statler Blvd 76155
Tel (817) 864-2500 SIC 2051

■ **NORTH AMERICAN GALVANIZING & COATINGS INC** p 1050
3100 W 7th St Ste 500 76107
Tel (817) 810-0095 SIC 7539 3312

NORTHSTAR BANK OF TEXAS p 1058
1300 S University Dr # 100 76107
Tel (940) 591-1200 SIC 6022

NOVARIA GROUP LLC p 1062
6300 Ridglea Pl Ste 800 76116
Tel (817) 381-3810 SIC 6726

NOVO 1 INC p 1063
4301 Cambridge Rd 76155
Tel (817) 355-8909 SIC 7389

■ **NUCLEAR LOGISTICS INC** p 1066
7410 Pebble Dr 76118
Tel (817) 284-0077 SIC 5065 8711

PAE APPLIED TECHNOLOGIES LLC p 1107
6500 West Fwy Ste 600 76116
Tel (817) 737-1500
SIC 8741 8711 8744 4581 7381

PATTONAIR USA INC p 1121
1900 Robotics Pl 76118
Tel (817) 284-4449 SIC 5088

■ **PHYSASSIST SCRIBES INC** p 1145
6451 Brentwood Stair Rd # 100 76112
Tel (817) 496-1009 SIC 8011

■ **PIER 1 IMPORTS (US) INC** p 1147
100 Pier 1 Pl 76102
Tel (817) 252-8000 SIC 5713 5719

▲ **PIER 1 IMPORTS INC** p 1147
100 Pier 1 Pl 76102
Tel (817) 252-8000 SIC 5719 6794 5712

■ **PIER 1 LICENSING INC** p 1147
100 Pier 1 Pl 76102
Tel (817) 878-8000
SIC 5719 5712 5621 5632

PILOT THOMAS LOGISTICS LLC p 1148
201 N Rupert St Ste 101 76107
Tel (435) 789-1832 SIC 5172

PITTSBURGH HOLDINGS LLC p 1152
301 Commerce St Ste 3300 76102
Tel (817) 871-4000 SIC 2721

POINT 180 LLC p 1159
3575 Lone Star Cir 76177
Tel (817) 490-0100 SIC 8742

PREFERRED PUMP & EQUIPMENT LP p 1169
2201 Scott Ave Ste 100 76103
Tel (817) 536-9800
SIC 5084 5083 5074 3533 5082

PROGRESSIVE WASTE SOLUTIONS LTD p 1182
2301 Eagle Pkwy Ste 200 76177
Tel (817) 632-4000 SIC 4953

QES WIRELINE LLC p 1195
801 Cherry St Ste 800 76102
Tel (817) 546-4970 SIC 1389

▲ **QUICKSILVER RESOURCES INC** p 1199
801 Cherry St Unit 19 76102
Tel (817) 665-5000 SIC 1311 1321

▲ **RANGE RESOURCES CORP** p 1208
100 Throckmorton St # 1200 76102
Tel (817) 870-2601 SIC 1311

RAZZOOS INC p 1211
2950 Texas Sage Trl 76177
Tel (972) 233-6399 SIC 5812 5813

■ **RINGWOOD GATHERING CO** p 1235
810 Houston St Ste 2000 76102
Tel (817) 870-2800 SIC 4922

RS LEGACY CORP p 1255
300 Radioshack Cir 76102
Tel (817) 415-3011 SIC 5731 5999 5734

SID RICHARDSON CARBON & ENERGY CO p 1319
309 Main St 76102
Tel (817) 336-0494 SIC 2895

SIMONS PETROLEUM p 1325
201 N Rupert St Ste 101 76107
Tel (405) 551-2403
SIC 5172 5171 5541 5411

SIMONS PETROLEUM INC p 1325
201 N Rupert St Ste 101 76107
Tel (405) 848-3500 SIC 5171 5172

SITTON ENTERPRISES LLC p 1328
4100 Intl Plz Ste 820 76109
Tel (940) 328-6000 SIC 1389

SMITH TEMPORARIES INC p 1333
1200 Summit Ave Ste 518 76102
Tel (817) 332-5882 SIC 7363

SNYDER OIL CORP p 1336
777 Main St Ste 1400 76102
Tel (817) 338-4043 SIC 1311 4922

SOURCEHOV TAX INC p 1342
4150 International Plz 76109
Tel (817) 732-5494 SIC 8748

SOUTHWESTERN BAPTIST THEOLOGICAL SEMINARY p 1353
2001 W Seminary Dr 76115
Tel (817) 923-1921 SIC 8221

SPM FLOW CONTROL INC p 1359
601 Weir Way 76108
Tel (817) 246-2461 SIC 3533 3599

■ **STAR-TELEGRAM OPERATING LTD** p 1378
808 Throckmorton St 76102
Tel (817) 390-7400 SIC 2711

■ **SUPERIOR SILICA SANDS LLC** p 1407
6000 Western Pl Ste 465 76107
Tel (817) 841-8070 SIC 1429

SUPPLY SOURCE DYNAMICS INC p 1407
311 E Vickery Blvd 76104
Tel (817) 336-0451 SIC 5074

■ **T N P ENTERPRISES INC** p 1419
4100 Intl Plaza Ste 900 76109
Tel (817) 731-0099 SIC 4911

▲ **TANDY LEATHER FACTORY INC** p 1424
1900 Se Loop 820 76140
Tel (817) 872-3200 SIC 5948 5199 3111

TARRANT COUNTY COLLEGE DISTRICT p 1425
1500 Houston St 76102
Tel (817) 515-5220 SIC 5942 8221

TARRANT COUNTY HOSPITAL DISTRICT p 1425
1500 S Main St 76104
Tel (817) 921-3431 SIC 8062

TARRANT COUNTY TEXAS (INC) p 1425
100 E Weatherford St 76196
Tel (817) 884-1111 SIC 9111

TEX ROBBINS TRANSPORTATION LLC p 1441
1100 Northway Dr 76131
Tel (817) 306-1000 SIC 4213

TEXAS AERO ENGINE SERVICES LLC p 1442
2100 Eagle Pkwy 76177
Tel (817) 224-0711 SIC 7538

TEXAS CHRISTIAN UNIVERSITY INC p 1442
2800 S University Dr 76129
Tel (817) 257-7000 SIC 8221

TEXAS ENERGY FUTURE HOLDINGS LIMITED PARTNERSHIP p 1443
301 Commerce St Ste 3300 76102
Tel (817) 871-4000 SIC 4911 6211

TEXAS HEALTH HARRIS METHODIST HOSPITAL FORT WORTH p 1443
1301 Pennsylvania Ave 76104
Tel (817) 250-2000 SIC 8062

TEXAS WESLEYAN UNIVERSITY p 1444
1204 Nicole St Apt 1603 76120
Tel (817) 531-4444 SIC 8221

TEXLAND PETROLEUM LP p 1445
777 Main St Ste 3200 76102
Tel (817) 336-2751 SIC 1311 1382

TPG ASIA ADVISORS II INC p 1467
301 Commerce St Ste 3300 76102
Tel (817) 871-4000 SIC 3674

TPG CAPITAL MANAGEMENT LP p 1467
301 Commerce St Ste 3300 76102
Tel (817) 871-4000
SIC 6726 3674 6799 3993 6719

TPG PARTNERS LP p 1467
301 Commerce St Ste 3300 76102
Tel (817) 871-4000 SIC 6722

TPG SPECIALTY LENDING INC p 1467
301 Commerce St Ste 3300 76102
Tel (817) 871-4000 SIC 6726

■ **TRAULSEN & CO INC** p 1473
4401 Blue Mound Rd 76106
Tel (817) 625-9671 SIC 3585

■ **TTI INC** p 1489
2441 Northeast Pkwy 76106
Tel (817) 740-9000 SIC 5065

■ **TWA AIRLINES LLC** p 1494
4333 Amon Carter Blvd 76155
Tel (817) 963-1234 SIC 4512 4522 4581

■ **ULTERRA DRILLING TECHNOLOGIES LP** p 1500
420 Throckmorton St # 1110 76102
Tel (817) 293-7555 SIC 5084 3533

UNIDEN HOLDING INC p 1503
4700 Amon Carter Blvd 76155
Tel (817) 858-3300 SIC 5063 5065

UNIVERSITY OF NORTH TEXAS HEALTH SCIENCE CENTER AT FORT WORTH TEXAS p 1524
3500 Camp Bowie Blvd 76107
Tel (817) 735-2000 SIC 8221

UNT HEALTH SCIENCE CENTER p 1528
3500 Camp Bowie Blvd 76107
Tel (817) 735-2000 SIC 8031

US AIRWAYS GROUP INC p 1531
4333 Amon Carter Blvd 76155
Tel (480) 693-0800 SIC 4512

US HEALTH GROUP INC p 1532
300 Burnett St Ste 200 76102
Tel (817) 878-3300 SIC 6411

USHEALTH ADMINISTRATORS LLC p 1535
300 Burnett St Ste 200 76102
Tel (817) 878-3307 SIC 6321

UTECH INC p 1536
303 Arthur St 76107
Tel (817) 332-2770 SIC 1542

VASARI LLC p 1545
550 Bailey Ave Ste 650 76107
Tel (888) 685-1847 SIC 2024

VIRBAC CORP p 1558
3200 Meacham Blvd 76137
Tel (800) 338-3659 SIC 2834 5122

W M AUTOMOTIVE WAREHOUSE INC p 1568
208 Penland St 76111
Tel (817) 834-5559 SIC 5013

■ **WALCO INTERNATIONAL INC** p 1572
9500 Ray White Rd Ste 200 76244
Tel (817) 859-3000 SIC 5499

WASTE SERVICES INC p 1581
2301 Eagle Pkwy Ste 200 76177
Tel (817) 632-4000 SIC 4953

WEIR GROUP INC p 1588
7601 Wyatt Dr 76108
Tel (817) 246-2461 SIC 3561 8711

WELBILT WALK-INS LP p 1588
4201 N Beach St 76137
Tel (817) 281-5121 SIC 3089 3585

WILLBANKS METALS INC p 1610
1155 Ne 28th St 76106
Tel (817) 625-6161 SIC 5051 3449

■ **WILLBROS UTILITY T&D HOLDINGS LLC** p 1610
115 W 7th St Ste 1420 76102
Tel (682) 233-9010 SIC 8711

WILLIAMSON-DICKIE MANUFACTURING CO p 1612
509 W Vickery Blvd 76104
Tel (817) 336-7201 SIC 2326 2339

WL PLASTICS CORP p 1620
575 Lone Star Cir Ste 300 76177
Tel (682) 831-2701 SIC 3084

■ **XTO ENERGY INC** p 1633
810 Houston St Ste 2000 76102
Tel (817) 870-2800 SIC 1311

FREDERICKSBURG, TX

ML INDUSTRIES INC p 979
605 W Austin St 78624
Tel (956) 279-8678 SIC 7549

FREEPORT, TX

GULF STATES INC p 647
6711 E Highway 332 77541
Tel (979) 233-4461 SIC 1541 1629

FRIONA, TX

HI-PRO FEEDS INC p 689
1201 E 11th St 79035
Tel (806) 250-2791 SIC 2048

FRISCO, TX

ADI WORLDLINK LLC p 22
3880 Parkwood Blvd # 204 75034
Tel (972) 671-3434 SIC 7371

■ **AMERISOURCEBERGEN SPECIALTY GROUP INC** p 83
3101 Gaylord Pkwy 75034
Tel (866) 408-3761 SIC 5122

■ **ASD SPECIALTY HEALTHCARE INC** p 116
3101 Gaylord Pkwy Fl 3 75034
Tel (469) 365-8000 SIC 5122

CAREINGTON INTERNATIONAL CORP p 255
7400 Gaylord Pkwy 75034
Tel (972) 335-6970 SIC 6324 6411

■ **CENTENNIAL MEDICAL CENTER** p 275
12505 Lebanon Rd 75035
Tel (972) 963-3333 SIC 8069

CI (TRANSPLACE) HOLDINGS LLC p 305
3010 Gaylord Pkwy Ste 200 75034
Tel (972) 731-4500 SIC 4731

CLA USA INC p 321
9300 Wade Blvd Ste 100 75035
Tel (214) 472-5000 SIC 6411

▲ **COMSTOCK RESOURCES INC** p 353
5300 Town And Country Blv 75034
Tel (972) 668-8800 SIC 1311

■ **CONIFER HEALTH SOLUTIONS LLC** p 356
3560 Dallas Pkwy 75034
Tel (469) 803-3000 SIC 8082

FRISCO INDEPENDENT SCHOOL DISTRICT p 580
5515 Ohio Dr 75035
Tel (469) 633-6000 SIC 8211

FRISCO MEDICAL CENTER LLP p 580
5601 Warren Pkwy 75034
Tel (214) 618-2000 SIC 8062

GENBAND US LLC p 598
2801 Network Blvd Ste 300 75034
Tel (972) 521-5800 SIC 3661

GENESIS PURE INC p 603
7164 Tech Dr Ste 100 75033
Tel (469) 213-2900 SIC 5122

GOODMAN NETWORKS INC p 624
2801 Network Blvd Ste 300 75034
Tel (972) 406-9692 SIC 4899

IMAGINE COMMUNICATIONS CORP p 733
3001 Dallas Pkwy Ste 300 75034
Tel (469) 803-4900 SIC 4899 3663

■ **INDEPENDENT PROPANE CO LLC** p 737
2591 Dallas Pkwy Ste 105 75034
Tel (972) 731-5454 SIC 5984 5172

▲ **INTEGER HOLDINGS CORP** p 748
2595 Dallas Pkwy Ste 310 75034
Tel (716) 759-5600 SIC 3675 3692 3691

MARIO SINACOLA & SONS EXCAVATING INC p 907
10950 Research Rd 75033
Tel (214) 387-3900 SIC 1794

MULTIBAND CORP p 999
2801 Network Blvd Ste 300 75034
Tel (763) 504-3000 SIC 4841 4813

NEV HOLDINGS LLC p 1028
3211 Internet Blvd # 200 75034
Tel (972) 731-1100 SIC 2677

NEXIUS SOLUTIONS INC p 1040
2595 Dallas Pkwy Ste 300 75034
Tel (703) 650-7777 SIC 5045

PENN TREATY AMERICAN CORP p 1129
2500 Legacy Dr Ste 130 75034
Tel (469) 287-7044 SIC 6311

TANGO TRANSPORT LLC p 1424
2933 Belclaire Dr 75034
Tel (318) 683-6700 SIC 4213

TEXAS CITY OF FRISCO p 1442
6101 Frisco Square Blvd # 1000 75034
Tel (972) 335-5555 SIC 9111

TRANSPLACE TEXAS LP p 1472
3010 Gaylord Pkwy Ste 200 75034
Tel (972) 731-4500 SIC 4731

TRUE HEALTH DIAGNOSTICS LLC p 1486
6170 Research Rd Ste 211 75033
Tel (844) 341-1491 SIC 8011 8069

TTS LLC p 1490
11000 Frisco St Ste 100 75033
Tel (214) 778-0800 SIC 4214

GAINESVILLE, TX

BELL SUPPLY CO LLC p 170
114 E Foreline St 76240
Tel (940) 612-0612 SIC 5084

SELECT ENERGY SERVICES LLC p 1301
1820 N Interstate 35 76240
Tel (940) 668-1818 SIC 1389

SES HOLDINGS LLC p 1308
114 E Foreline St 76240
Tel (940) 668-0251 SIC 6719 5084

SYNERGY ENERGY HOLDINGS LLC p 1415
114 E Foreline St 76240
Tel (940) 612-0417 SIC 5084

TEXAS CES INC p 1442
3333 Ih 35 N Bldg F 76240
Tel (940) 668-5100 SIC 1389

ZODIAC SEATS US LLC p 1644
2000 Zodiac Dr 76240
Tel (940) 668-8541 SIC 5088 3728

GALENA PARK, TX

AMERICAN PLANT FOOD CORP p 77
903 Mayo Shell Rd 77547
Tel (713) 675-2231 SIC 2875

GALVESTON, TX

1859-HISTORIC HOTELS LTD p 1
2302 Post Office St # 500 77550
Tel (409) 763-8536 SIC 7011

▲ **AMERICAN NATIONAL INSURANCE CO INC** p 77
1 Moody Plz Fl 18 77550
Tel (409) 763-4661
SIC 6351 6311 6321 6324 6331

■ **AMERICAN NATIONAL LIFE INSURANCE CO OF TEXAS** p 77
1 Moody Plz Fl 8 77550
Tel (409) 763-4661 SIC 6411 6321

COUNTY OF GALVESTON p 378
722 21st St Fl 1 77550
Tel (409) 795-2100 SIC 9111

GAL-TEX HOTEL CORP p 589
2302 Pstoffice St Ste 500 77550
Tel (409) 763-8536 SIC 7011 8741

GALVESTON INDEPENDENT SCHOOL DISTRICT p 590
3904 Avenue T 77550
Tel (409) 765-2101 SIC 8211

MOODY GARDENS INC p 987
1 Hope Blvd 77554
Tel (409) 744-4673
SIC 8412 8422 7999 7011

REGENT MANAGEMENT SERVICES LIMITED PARTNERSHIP p 1219
2302 Post Office St # 402 77550
Tel (409) 763-6000 SIC 8741

■ **STANDARD LIFE & ACCIDENT INSURANCE CO INC** p 1376
1 Moody Plz 77550
Tel (409) 766-6036 SIC 6324 6311

UNIVERSITY OF TEXAS MEDICAL BRANCH AT GALVESTON p 1526
301 University Blvd 77555
Tel (409) 772-1011 SIC 8062

GARDENDALE, TX

CATALYST OILFIELD SERVICES 2016 LLC p 264
11999 E Us Highway 158 79758
Tel (432) 563-0727 SIC 1389

GARLAND, TX

ARENA BRANDS INC p 106
601 Marion Dr 75042
Tel (972) 494-7133 SIC 2353

ATLAS COPCO DRILLING SOLUTIONS LLC p 127
2100 N 1st St 75040
Tel (972) 496-7258 SIC 3541

BAYLOR MEDICAL CENTER AT GARLAND p 162
2300 Marie Curie Dr 75042
Tel (972) 487-5000
SIC 8062 8082 8011 8093

BEARCOM GROUP INC p 165
4009 Dist Dr Ste 200 75041
Tel (214) 340-8876 *SIC* 5999 5065

BEARCOM OPERATING LLC p 165
4009 Dist Dr Ste 200 75041
Tel (214) 765-7100 *SIC* 4812 5065

CITY OF GARLAND p 315
200 N 5th St 75040
Tel (972) 205-2000 *SIC* 9111

GARLAND INDEPENDENT SCHOOL DISTRICT p 592
501 S Jupiter Rd 75042
Tel (972) 494-8201 *SIC* 8211

HAT BRANDS HOLDING CORP p 667
601 Marion Dr 75042
Tel (972) 494-7133
SIC 2353 3914 3144 3143

■ IDQ ACQUISITION CORP p 729
2901 W Kingsley Rd 75041
Tel (214) 778-4600 *SIC* 3585

INTERCERAMIC INC p 751
2333 S Jupiter Rd 75041
Tel (214) 503-4967 *SIC* 3253 5032

MEXICO FOODS LLC p 957
2600 Mccree Rd Ste 101 75041
Tel (972) 526-7200 *SIC* 5411

OSBURN CONTRACTORS INC p 1096
2747 Oakland Ave Ste A 75041
Tel (972) 205-9086 *SIC* 1771

PC INTERNATIONAL SALES INC p 1123
730 S Jupiter Rd Ste B 75042
Tel (972) 487-0580 *SIC* 5199

PRISM ELECTRIC INC p 1178
2985 Market St 75041
Tel (972) 926-2000 *SIC* 1731

PRODUCT CENTRE - SW INC p 1179
730 S Jupiter Rd Ste B 75042
Tel (972) 487-0580 *SIC* 5099

RHE HATCO INC p 1231
601 Marion Dr 75042
Tel (972) 494-0511 *SIC* 2353

TIMBERLAKE & DICKSON INC p 1454
3520 W Miller Rd Ste 110 75041
Tel (214) 349-2320 *SIC* 5075

UNITED CENTRAL BANK p 1507
4555 W Walnut St 75042
Tel (972) 487-1505 *SIC* 6021

GATESVILLE, TX

CORYELL COUNTY MEMORIAL HOSPITAL AUTHORITY p 373
1507 W Main St 76528
Tel (254) 248-6247 *SIC* 8062

CORYELL STEEL INC p 373
2005 N Main St 136 76528
Tel (254) 223-3987 *SIC* 5051

GEORGETOWN, TX

AIRBORN INTERCONNECT INC p 39
3500 Airborn Cir 78626
Tel (512) 863-5585 *SIC* 3678 3679

COUNTY OF WILLIAMSON p 383
710 S Main St Ste 303 78626
Tel (512) 943-1550 *SIC* 9111

EMBREE CONSTRUCTION GROUP INC p 490
4747 Williams Dr 78633
Tel (512) 819-4700 *SIC* 1542

GEORGETOWN INDEPENDENT SCHOOL DISTRICT p 606
603 Lakeway Dr 78628
Tel (512) 943-5000 *SIC* 8211

SOUTHWESTERN UNIVERSITY p 1353
1001 E University Ave 78626
Tel (512) 863-6511 *SIC* 8221

TEXAS CRUSHED STONE CO INC p 1442
5300 S Interstate 35 78626
Tel (512) 255-4405 *SIC* 1422 2951 1442

GIDDINGS, TX

■ PUMPCO INC p 1192
1209 S Main St 78942
Tel (979) 542-9054 *SIC* 1623 1389

GILMER, TX

UPSHUR RURAL ELECTRIC COOPERATIVE CORP p 1529
1200 W Tyler St 75644
Tel (903) 843-2536 *SIC* 4911

GODLEY, TX

OWEN OIL TOOLS INC p 1099
12001 County Road 1000 76044
Tel (817) 396-4570 *SIC* 2892 3533

GONZALES, TX

BYK ADDITIVES INC p 231
1212 Church St 78629
Tel (830) 672-2891 *SIC* 1459 3295 3297

GUADALUPE VALLEY ELECTRIC COOPERATIVE INC p 644
825 E Sarah Dewitt Dr 78629
Tel (830) 857-1200 *SIC* 4911

J CINCO INC p 770
1113 E Sarah Dewitt Dr 78629
Tel (830) 672-9574 *SIC* 5172 5541

GRANBURY, TX

■ GRANBURY HOSPITAL CORP p 629
1310 Paluxy Rd 76048
Tel (817) 573-2273 *SIC* 8062

TOTAL EQUIPMENT AND SERVICE p 1462
4801 Glen Rose Hwy 76048
Tel (817) 573-3550 *SIC* 3533

GRAND PRAIRIE, TX

AIRBUS HELICOPTERS INC p 40
2701 N Forum Dr 75052
Tel (972) 641-0000 *SIC* 5088 7699 3721

ARNOLD TRANSPORTATION SERVICES INC p 112
3375 High Prairie Rd 75050
Tel (972) 986-3154 *SIC* 4213

CONDUMEX INC p 355
900 Avenue S 75050
Tel (800) 925-9473 *SIC* 7389 5063

■ GE ON WING SUPPORT INC p 596
3010 Red Hawk Dr Ste B 75052
Tel (214) 960-3322 *SIC* 7699 8711

GRAND PRAIRIE CITY OF (INC) p 630
317 College St 75050
Tel (972) 237-8000 *SIC* 9111

GRAND PRAIRIE INDEPENDENT SCHOOL DISTRICT p 630
2602 S Belt Line Rd 75052
Tel (972) 264-6141 *SIC* 8211

HANSON PRESSURE PIPE INC p 659
1003 Macarthur Blvd 75050
Tel (972) 262-3600 *SIC* 3317 3272 3999

LITEX INDUSTRIES LIMITED p 870
3401 Trinity Blvd 75050
Tel (972) 871-4350 *SIC* 5064 5063

■ PARTSCHANNEL INC p 1119
4003 Grand Lakes Way # 200 75050
Tel (214) 688-0018 *SIC* 5013

POLK MECHANICAL CO LLC p 1159
2425 Dillard St 75051
Tel (972) 339-1200
SIC 1711 3444 3498 3599 3999

POLLOCK INVESTMENTS INC p 1160
1 Pollock Pl 75050
Tel (972) 263-8448 *SIC* 5113 5087

POLY-AMERICA LP p 1160
2000 W Marshall Dr 75051
Tel (972) 337-7100 *SIC* 3081 2673

PROFESSIONAL PACKAGING SYSTEMS LLC p 1180
2010 S Great Sw Pkwy 75051
Tel (972) 988-0777 *SIC* 5199

RBLS INC p 1211
502 Fountain Pkwy 75050
Tel (817) 633-6838 *SIC* 5712

▲ SIX FLAGS ENTERTAINMENT CORP p 1328
924 E Avenue J 75050
Tel (972) 595-5000 *SIC* 7996

SIX FLAGS THEME PARKS INC p 1328
924 E Avenue J 75050
Tel (972) 595-5000 *SIC* 7996

TEXAS PLYWOOD AND LUMBER CO INC p 1444
1001 E Avenue K 75050
Tel (972) 262-1331 *SIC* 5031 2431

GRANDVIEW, TX

UFP GRANDVIEW LLC p 1499
1000 S 3rd St 76050
Tel (817) 866-3306 *SIC* 5031 2439

GRAPEVINE, TX

BAYLOR REGIONAL MEDICAL CENTER AT GRAPEVINE p 162
1650 W College St 76051
Tel (817) 481-1588 *SIC* 8062

CARROLL INDEPENDENT SCHOOL DISTRICT p 261
3051 Dove Rd 76051
Tel (817) 949-8230 *SIC* 8211

CLASSIC CHEVROLET LTD p 323
1101 W State Highway 114 76051
Tel (817) 421-1200 *SIC* 5511

COTTON PATCH CAF LLC p 374
600 E Dallas Rd Ste 300 76051
Tel (817) 865-6500 *SIC* 5812

DALLAS AIRMOTIVE INC p 409
900 Nolen Dr Ste 100 76051
Tel (214) 956-3001 *SIC* 7699

EARTHBOUND HOLDING LLC p 469
4051 Freeport Pkwy Ste 400 76051
Tel (972) 248-0228 *SIC* 5632

■ ELECTRONICS BOUTIQUE AMERICA INC p 486
625 Westport Pkwy 76051
Tel (817) 424-2000 *SIC* 5734

■ ELECTRONICS BOUTIQUE HOLDINGS CORP p 486
625 Westport Pkwy 76051
Tel (817) 424-2000 *SIC* 5734

■ ELECTRONICS BOUTIQUE OF AMERICA INC p 486
625 Westport Pkwy 76051
Tel (817) 424-2000 *SIC* 5734 5945

ENTACT LLC p 501
3129 Bass Pro Dr 76051
Tel (972) 580-1323 *SIC* 1629

▲ GAMESTOP CORP p 590
625 Westport Pkwy 76051
Tel (817) 424-2000
SIC 5945 5734 5932 2721

GRAPEVINE - COLLYVILLE INDEPENDENT SCHOOL DIST p 631
3051 Ira E Woods Ave 76051
Tel (817) 251-5466 *SIC* 8211

GRAPEVINE/COLLEYVILLE INDEPENDENT SCHOOL DISTRICT p 631
3051 Ira E Woods Ave 76051
Tel (817) 251-5200 *SIC* 8211

INTEGRACARE HOLDINGS INC p 748
2559 Sw Grapevine Pkwy 76051
Tel (817) 310-4999 *SIC* 6719

INTERNATIONAL AIRMOTIVE HOLDING CO INC p 754
900 Nolen Dr Ste 100 76051
Tel (214) 956-3000 *SIC* 7699 3724

JENISYS ENGINEERED PRODUCTS INC p 782
404 E Dallas Rd 76051
Tel (817) 481-3521 *SIC* 3444

LONESTAR FREIGHTLINER GROUP LLC p 876
2051 Hughes Rd 76051
Tel (817) 428-9736 *SIC* 5511 7538

LTG LONESTAR TRUCK GROUP EAST LLC p 883
2051 Hughes Rd 76051
Tel (817) 428-9736 *SIC* 5531

MASTER PUMPS & EQUIPMENT CORP p 918
805 Port America Pl # 100 76051
Tel (817) 251-6745 *SIC* 5084 7699

SMS INFOCOMM CORP p 1334
4051 N Highway 121 # 100 76051
Tel (972) 906-7800 *SIC* 7378

UNITED CELLULAR INC p 1507
1940 Enchanted Way 76051
Tel (940) 566-5735 *SIC* 4812

UNITED DEVELOPMENT FUNDING IV p 1507
1301 Municipal Way # 100 76051
Tel (214) 370-8960 *SIC* 6798

■ VERIZON SELECT SERVICES INC p 1550
4255 Patriot Dr Ste 400 76051
Tel (972) 724-6000 *SIC* 4813

GREENVILLE, TX

FARMERS ELECTRIC COOPERATIVE INC p 529
2000 I 30 E 75402
Tel (903) 455-1715 *SIC* 4911

HUNT MEMORIAL HOSPITAL DISTRICT p 719
4215 Joe Ramsey Blvd E 75401
Tel (903) 408-5000 *SIC* 8062 8071 8082

GREGORY, TX

NASHTEC LLC p 1008
4633 Hwy 361 78359
Tel (361) 777-2280 *SIC* 2819

HALLSVILLE, TX

■ SABINE MINING CO p 1264
6501 Fm 968 W 75650
Tel (903) 660-4200 *SIC* 1241 8711 1221

HALTOM CITY, TX

BIRDVILLE INDEPENDENT SCHOOL DISTRICT p 185
6125 E Belknap St 76117
Tel (817) 547-5700 *SIC* 8211

BMS ENTERPRISES INC p 194
5718 Airport Fwy 76117
Tel (877) 730-1948 *SIC* 7349

CLASSIC STAR GROUP LP p 323
6324 Eden Dr 76117
Tel (817) 834-2868 *SIC* 5172

HARKER HEIGHTS, TX

PM MANAGEMENT - KILLEEN II NC LLC p 1157
415 Indian Oaks Dr 76548
Tel (254) 699-5051 *SIC* 8051

HARLINGEN, TX

BALLENGER CONSTRUCTION CO p 148
24200 N Fm 509 78550
Tel (956) 421-9500 *SIC* 1542

HARLINGEN CONSOLIDATED INDEPENDENT SCHOOL DISTRICT p 662
407 N 77 Sunshinestrip 78550
Tel (956) 430-9500 *SIC* 8211

HARLINGEN MEDICAL CENTER LIMITED PARTNERSHIP p 662
5501 S Expressway 77 78550
Tel (956) 365-3947 *SIC* 8062

■ TEXAS GAS SERVICE CO p 1443
5602 E Grimes St 78550
Tel (956) 444-3900 *SIC* 1311

UNIVERSITY OF TEXAS RIO GRANDE VALLEY FOUNDATION UTRGV FOUNDATION p 1526
2102 Treasure Hills Blvd 78550
Tel (956) 365-8740 *SIC* 8221

VALLEY BAPTIST HEALTH SYSTEM p 1540
2101 Pease St 78550
Tel (956) 389-1100 *SIC* 6719

VALLEY BAPTIST MEDICAL CENTER HARLINGEN AUXILIARY INC p 1540
2101 Pease St 78550
Tel (956) 389-1100 *SIC* 8742

HEREFORD, TX

AZTX CATTLE CO LTD p 141
311 E Park Ave 79045
Tel (806) 364-8871 *SIC* 0211

CAVINESS BEEF PACKERS LTD p 267
3255 Us Highway 60 79045
Tel (806) 357-2443 *SIC* 2011

HIDALGO, TX

TST NA TRIM LLC p 1489
401 E Olmos Ave 78557
Tel (956) 843-3500 *SIC* 3465

HIGHLANDS, TX

ZXP TECHNOLOGIES LTD p 1645
409 Wallisville Rd 77562
Tel (281) 426-8800 *SIC* 2992 2879 7549

HILLSBORO, TX

BOBCAT CONTRACTING LLC p 196
1721 Hcr 3106 76645
Tel (254) 582-0205 *SIC* 1389

LIGHTHOUSE HOSPICE p 865
305 Coke Ave Ste 140 76645
Tel (254) 710-9800 *SIC* 8082 8069

HOCKLEY, TX

CHINA SUTONG TIRE RESOURCES INC p 301
33402 Highway 290 A 77447
Tel (713) 690-5500 *SIC* 5014

SCHULTE BUILDING SYSTEMS INC p 1290
17600 Badtke Rd 77447
Tel (281) 304-6111 *SIC* 3448

HOLLYWOOD PARK, TX

BUFFETS LLC p 224
120 Chula Vis 78232
Tel (651) 994-8608 *SIC* 5812 8741

CATALINA RESTAURANT GROUP INC p 264
120 Chula Vis 78232
Tel (760) 804-5750 *SIC* 5812

FOOD MANAGEMENT PARTNERS INC p 564
120 Chula Vis 78232
Tel (210) 248-9340 *SIC* 8742

HOUSTON, TX

1155 DISTRIBUTOR PARTNERS LLC p 1
4200 N Sam Houston Pkwy W 77086
Tel (832) 855-3400 *SIC* 5063

2ML REAL ESTATE INTERESTS INC p 2
952 Echo Ln Ste 314 77024
Tel (713) 747-5000 *SIC* 5141 5142 5122

A & B VALVE AND PIPING SYSTEMS LLC p 4
3845 Cypress Creek Pkwy # 451 77068
Tel (281) 444-6996 *SIC* 5082

A 3 H FOODS LP p 4
13636 Breton Ridge St C 77070
Tel (832) 678-3590 *SIC* 5812

ABIBOW RECYCLING LLC p 11
14950 Hathrow Forest Pkwy 77032
Tel (800) 874-1301 *SIC* 4212

■ ABM FACILITY SOLUTIONS GROUP LLC p 11
1201 Louisiana St 77002
Tel (832) 214-5500 *SIC* 8744

■ ABM JANITORIAL SERVICES INC p 12
1111 Fannin St Ste 1500 77002
Tel (713) 654-8924 *SIC* 7349

ABM SECURITY SERVICES INC p 12
3800 Buffalo Speedway # 325 77098
Tel (713) 928-5344 *SIC* 7382

ABS GROUP OF COMPANIES INC p 12
16855 Northchase Dr 77060
Tel (281) 673-2800 *SIC* 4785 8741

ABSG CONSULTING INC p 12
16855 Northchase Dr 77060
Tel (281) 673-2800 *SIC* 8748

ACT PIPE & SUPPLY INC p 19
6950 W Sam Houston Pkwy N 77041
Tel (713) 937-0600 *SIC* 5051 5085

ACTION GYPSUM SUPPLY LP p 19
9635 W Little York Rd 77040
Tel (713) 896-4002 *SIC* 5085

▲ ADAMS RESOURCES & ENERGY INC p 21
17 S Briar Hollow Ln 77027
Tel (713) 881-3600
SIC 5172 4212 1382 1311

ADDAX PETROLEUM US SERVICES CORP p 21
1301 Mckinney St Ste 2050 77010
Tel (713) 341-3150 *SIC* 5172

AEI SERVICES LLC p 29
2929 Allen Pkwy Ste 200 77019
Tel (713) 345-5200 *SIC* 4911

AES DRILLING FLUIDS LLC p 31
11767 Katy Fwy Ste 230 77079
Tel (888) 556-4533 *SIC* 1381

AGGREKO INTERNATIONAL PROJECTS p 35
2 Northpoint Dr Ste 810 77060
Tel (281) 848-1400 *SIC* 4911

AGILITY PROJECT LOGISTICS INC p 35
15600 Morales Rd 77032
Tel (504) 465-1000 *SIC* 4731 4225

■ AIG LIFE HOLDINGS INC p 38
2929 Allen Pkwy 77019
Tel (713) 522-1111
SIC 6311 6321 6331 6141 6162 6153

AIR LIQUIDE ADVANCED MATERIALS INC p 38
9811 Katy Fwy Ste 100 77024
Tel (713) 624-8000 *SIC* 2813

AIR LIQUIDE ADVANCED TECHNOLOGIES US LLC p 39
9807 Katy Fwy 77024
Tel (713) 624-8000 *SIC* 2813

AIR LIQUIDE AMERICA LP p 39
9811 Katy Fwy Ste 100 77024
Tel (713) 624-8000
SIC 5084 3533 2813 3569

AIR LIQUIDE AMERICA SPECIALTY GASES LLC p 39
2700 Post Oak Blvd 77056
Tel (800) 217-2688 *SIC* 2911 2813

AIR LIQUIDE INDUSTRIAL US LP p 39
2700 Post Oak Blvd # 1800 77056
Tel (713) 624-8000 *SIC* 2813

AIR LIQUIDE LARGE INDUSTRIES US LP p 39
9811 Katy Fwy Ste 100 77024
Tel (713) 624-8000 *SIC* 2813

AIR LIQUIDE USA LLC p 39
9811 Kepy Fwy Ste 100 77024
Tel (713) 402-2221 *SIC* 2813

AKER SUBSEA INC p 42
3010 Briarpark Dr 77042
Tel (713) 685-5700 *SIC* 3533 1389 8711

■ ALDERWOODS (DELAWARE) INC p 47
1929 Allen Pkwy 77019
Tel (713) 522-5141 *SIC* 7261 6553 6311

ALDINE INDEPENDENT SCHOOL DISTRICT p 48
2520 Ww Thorne Blvd 77073
Tel (281) 449-1011 *SIC* 8211

■ ALGONQUIN GASTRANSMISSION LLC p 50
5400 Westheimer Ct 77056
Tel (713) 627-5400 *SIC* 4923

ALIEF INDEPENDENT SCHOOL DISTRICT p 50
4250 Cook Rd 77072
Tel (281) 498-8110 *SIC* 8211

▲ ALLEGIANCE BANCSHARES INC p 52
8847 W Sam Houston Pkwy N 77040
Tel (281) 894-3200 *SIC* 6022

ALLIED ALLOYS LP p 56
6002 Donoho St 77033
Tel (713) 643-6966 *SIC* 5093

ALLIED FITTING LP p 56
7200 Mykawa Rd 77033
Tel (800) 969-5565 *SIC* 5085

ALLIED WIRELINE SERVICES LLC p 57
3200 Wilcrest Dr Ste 170 77042
Tel (713) 343-7280 *SIC* 1389

ALLIS-CHALMERS ENERGY INC p 58
12101 Cutten Rd 77066
Tel (281) 301-2600 *SIC* 1381 1389 7353

ALLTRAN FINANCIAL LP p 59
5800 N Course Dr 77072
Tel (800) 568-0399 *SIC* 7322

ALS GROUP USA CORP p 61
10450 Stncliff Rd Ste 210 77099
Tel (281) 530-5656 *SIC* 8734

ALTA MESA HOLDINGS LP p 61
15021 Katy Fwy Ste 400 77094
Tel (281) 530-0991 *SIC* 1311

ALTA MESA RESOURCES LP p 61
15021 Katy Fwy Ste 400 77094
Tel (281) 530-0991 *SIC* 5541

AMEC FOSTER WHEELER OIL & GAS INC p 66
585 N Dairy Ashford Rd 77079
Tel (713) 929-5000 *SIC* 8711 8742 8741

AMEC FOSTER WHEELER USA CORP p 66
585 N Dairy Ashford Rd 77079
Tel (713) 929-5000 *SIC* 8711 3443 1629

AMEGY BANK NATIONAL ASSOCIATION p 66
4400 Post Oak Pkwy 77027
Tel (713) 235-8800 *SIC* 6021

AMERICAN AIR LIQUIDE HOLDINGS INC p 67
2700 Post Oak Blvd 77056
Tel (713) 624-8000 *SIC* 2813 6719

AMERICAN ALLOY STEEL INC p 67
6230 N Houston Rosslyn Rd 77091
Tel (713) 462-8081 *SIC* 3443

AMERICAN BLOCK CO p 69
6311 Breen Dr 77086
Tel (800) 572-9087
SIC 3441 3599 3533 3496 3444 3429

AMERICAN BUREAU OF SHIPPING INC p 69
16855 Northchase Dr 77060
Tel (281) 877-5800 *SIC* 4785

■ AMERICAN GENERAL LIFE INSURANCE CO p 73
2727 Allen Pkwy Ste A 77019
Tel (713) 522-1111 *SIC* 6311

■ AMERICAN GENERAL LIFE INSURANCE CO p 73
10700 Northwest Fwy # 300 77092
Tel (713) 522-1111 *SIC* 6311

■ AMERICAN GENERAL LIFE INSURANCE CO OF DELAWARE p 73
2727 Allen Pkwy Ste A 77019
Tel (713) 522-1111 *SIC* 6411

AMERICAN INFOSOURCE LP p 74
5847 San Felipe St # 1200 77057
Tel (713) 532-8977 *SIC* 7374

▲ AMERICAN MIDSTREAM PARTNERS LP p 76
2103 Citywest Blvd # 800 77042
Tel (720) 457-6060 *SIC* 4922

■ AMERICAN NATURAL RESOURCES CO p 77
717 Texas St Ste 2400 77002
Tel (832) 320-5000 *SIC* 4922 1311 1222

AMERICUS MORTGAGE CORP p 82
6110 Pinemont Dr Ste 215 77092
Tel (713) 684-0725 *SIC* 6162

AMERIFORGE CORP p 82
13770 Industrial Rd 77015
Tel (713) 393-4200 *SIC* 3462

AMERIFORGE GROUP INC p 82
945 Bunker Hill Rd # 500 77024
Tel (713) 688-9705 *SIC* 3462

AMERIMEX MOTOR & CONTROLS LLC p 82
610 N Milby St 77003
Tel (713) 225-4300 *SIC* 5063 3625 7694

AMIGOS MEAT DISTRIBUTORS LP p 85
611 Crosstimbers St 77022
Tel (713) 928-3111 *SIC* 5147

AMSTAR MORTGAGE CORP p 87
10851 Scarsdale Blvd # 800 77089
Tel (281) 481-9040 *SIC* 6163

■ ANADARKO HOLDING CO p 88
17001 Northchase Dr 77060
Tel (832) 636-7200
SIC 1311 1321 5172 4922

ANCO INDUSTRIES LLC p 89
10343 Sam Houston Park Dr # 200 77064
Tel (281) 807-8200 *SIC* 1721 1799

ANDREWS KURTH LLP p 90
600 Travis St Ste 4200 77002
Tel (713) 220-4200 *SIC* 8111

ANGLO-SUISSE OFFSHORE PARTNERS LLC p 91
919 Milam St Ste 2300 77002
Tel (713) 358-9763 *SIC* 1311

■ ANR PIPELINE CO p 92
700 Louisiana St Ste 700 77002
Tel (832) 320-2000 *SIC* 4922

ANTELOPE OIL TOOL & MFG CO LLC p 93
8807 W Sam Houston Pkwy N # 200 77040
Tel (832) 756-2300 *SIC* 3533

AON RISK SERVICES SOUTHWEST INC p 95
5555 San Felipe St # 1500 77056
Tel (832) 476-6000 *SIC* 6411

▲ APACHE CORP p 95
2000 Post Oak Blvd # 100 77056
Tel (713) 296-6000 *SIC* 1311

■ APACHE GATHERING CO p 96
2000 Post Oak Blvd # 100 77056
Tel (713) 296-6000 *SIC* 4924

APACHE INDUSTRIAL SERVICES INC p 96
15423 Vantage Pkwy E 77032
Tel (281) 609-8800 *SIC* 1629 1541

AQUINAS CORP p 102
3900 Essex Ln Ste 1200 77027
Tel (713) 621-2350 *SIC* 1542

ARAMCO SERVICES CO p 102
9009 West Loop S 77096
Tel (713) 432-4000 *SIC* 8711 8742

ARCHER WELL CO INC p 105
10613 W Sh Pkwy N Ste 600 77064
Tel (713) 856-4222 *SIC* 1381

▲ ARCHROCK INC p 105
16666 Northchase Dr 77060
Tel (281) 836-8000 *SIC* 1389

■ ARCHROCK PARTNERS LP p 105
16666 Northchase Dr 77060
Tel (281) 836-8000 *SIC* 4922

ARGOS USA CORP p 107
757 N Eldridge Pkwy # 525 77079
Tel (281) 759-7392 *SIC* 3273

ASCEND PERFORMANCE MATERIALS HOLDINGS INC p 115
1010 Travis St Ste 900 77002
Tel (713) 315-5700 *SIC* 6722

ASCEND PERFORMANCE MATERIALS OPERATIONS LLC p 116
1010 Travis St Ste 900 77002
Tel (713) 315-5700 *SIC* 2821 2284

ASIA CHEMICAL CORP INC p 117
11950 Airline Dr Ste 300 77037
Tel (281) 445-1793 *SIC* 5162

ASP WESTWARD LP p 118
523 N Sam Houston Pkwy E # 600 77060
Tel (713) 256-0953 *SIC* 2711

ASPIRE HOLDINGS LLC p 118
811 Main St Ste 2100 77002
Tel (713) 307-8700 *SIC* 6719

ASSET PLUS CORP p 119
950 Corbindale Rd Ste 300 77024
Tel (713) 782-5800 *SIC* 7011

ASSOCIATED PIPE LINE CONTRACTORS INC p 121
3535 Briarpark Dr Ste 135 77042
Tel (713) 789-4311 *SIC* 1623

ASTRA OIL CO LLC p 122
5847 San Felipe St # 2850 77057
Tel (713) 357-0640 *SIC* 5172

ATLANTIC COFFEE INDUSTRIAL SOLUTIONS LLC p 126
3900 Harrisburg Blvd 77003
Tel (713) 228-9501 *SIC* 2095

ATLANTIC HOLDINGS I INC p 126
10343 Sam Houston Park Dr 77064
Tel (281) 807-8200 *SIC* 1721 1799

ATLANTIC HOLDINGS II INC p 126
10343 Sam Houston Park Dr 77064
Tel (281) 807-8200 *SIC* 1721 1799

ATLANTIC INDUSTRIAL LLC p 126
10343 Sam Houston Park Dr 77064
Tel (281) 807-8200 *SIC* 1721 1799

ATLANTIC METHANOL PRODUCTION CO LLC p 127
16945 Northchase Dr # 1950 77060
Tel (281) 872-8324 *SIC* 2869

ATLANTIC PACIFIC MARINE CORP p 127
2500 City W Blvd Ste 1850 77042
Tel (713) 346-4300 *SIC* 1389

■ ATLANTICTRADING & MARKETING INC p 127
5847 San Felipe St # 2100 77057
Tel (713) 243-2200 *SIC* 5172

▲ ATWOOD OCEANICS INC p 130
15011 Katy Fwy Ste 800 77094
Tel (281) 749-7800 *SIC* 1381

■ AXALTA POWDER COATING SYSTEMS USA INC p 139
9800 Genard Rd 77041
Tel (800) 247-3886 *SIC* 2851

AXIP ENERGY SERVICES LP p 140
1301 Mckinney St Ste 900 77010
Tel (832) 294-6500 *SIC* 5084 7699

AZKU INC p 140
1616 S Voss Rd Ste 550 77057
Tel (713) 782-1080 *SIC* 5082 8711

AZTEC FACILITY SERVICES INC p 140
11000 S Wilcrest Dr Ste 1 77099
Tel (281) 668-9000 *SIC* 7349

■ B JOHNSON NASA/LYNDON SPACE CENTER p 142
2101 Nasa Pkwy 77058
Tel (281) 483-0123 *SIC* 9661

BAE SYSTEMS RESOLUTION INC p 144
1000 La St Ste 4950 77002
Tel (713) 868-7700
SIC 3713 5084 3711 7699 3351 3829

BAKER BOTTS LLP p 145
910 Louisiana St Ste 3200 77002
Tel (713) 229-1234 *SIC* 8111

▲ BAKER HUGHES INC p 146
17021 Aldine Westfield Rd 77073
Tel (713) 439-8600 *SIC* 3533 3561

■ BAKER HUGHES OILFIELD OPERATIONS INC p 146
17021 Aldine Westfield Rd 77073
Tel (713) 439-8600
SIC 1381 1311 1389 2899

BANCOMERTRANSFER SERVICES INC p 150
16825 Northchase Dr Ste 1 77060
Tel (281) 765-1500 *SIC* 6099

BAYLOR COLLEGE OF MEDICINE p 162
1 Baylor Plz 77030
Tel (713) 798-4951 *SIC* 8221

BBVA COMPASS BANCSHARES INC p 163
2200 Post Oak Blvd Fl 18 77056
Tel (205) 297-3000 *SIC* 6022

BEACON PRINTING & GRAPHICS INC p 165
2748 Bingle Rd 77055
Tel (713) 464-8484 *SIC* 2752 2791 2789

BECHTEL OIL GAS AND CHEMICALS INC p 167
3000 Post Oak Blvd 77056
Tel (713) 235-2000 *SIC* 1629

BECHTEL-JACOBS JOINT VENTURE p 167
3000 Post Oak Blvd 77056
Tel (713) 235-2000 *SIC* 8711

BECK & MASTEN PONTIAC-GMC INC p 167
11300 Fm 1960 Rd W 77065
Tel (281) 469-5222 *SIC* 5511

BENCHMARK PERFORMANCE GROUP INC p 172
2801 Post Oak Blvd 77056
Tel (713) 986-2500 *SIC* 5169

BENTELER STEEL & TUBE p 173
3050 Post Oak Blvd # 1130 77056
Tel (713) 629-9111 *SIC* 5051

■ BERRY PETROLEUM CO LLC p 176
600 Travis St Ste 5100 77002
Tel (281) 840-4000 *SIC* 1311

BERTSCHI NORTH AMERICA INC p 176
16902 El Cmno Real 3b Ste 3 77058
Tel (281) 751-8800 *SIC* 4731

■ BEST EQUIPMENT SERVICE & SALES CO LLC p 177
8885 Monroe Rd 77061
Tel (713) 956-2002 *SIC* 5084

BG BRASILIA LLC p 179
910 Louisiana St 77002
Tel (713) 599-4000 *SIC* 1311

BG NORTH AMERICA LLC p 180
811 Main St Ste 3400 77002
Tel (713) 426-2786 *SIC* 1311

BHP BILLITON PETROLEUM (ARKANSAS) INC p 180
1360 Post Blvd Ste 150 77056
Tel (713) 961-8500 *SIC* 4922 1311

BHP BILLITON PETROLEUM (NORTH AMERICA) INC p 180
1360 Post Oak Blvd # 150 77056
Tel (713) 961-8500 *SIC* 1311 4922

BHP COPPER INC p 180
1360 Post Oak Blvd # 150 77056
Tel (713) 961-8500 *SIC* 1021 3341 1041

BHP HOLDINGS (RESOURCES) INC p 180
1360 Post Oak Blvd # 150 77056
Tel (713) 961-8500 *SIC* 1021 3341 1041

BHP MINERALS INTERNATIONAL INC p 180
1360 Post Oak Blvd # 150 77056
Tel (713) 961-8500 *SIC* 1222 1011 1021

BIOURJA TRADING LLC p 185
1080 Eldridge Pkwy # 1175 77077
Tel (832) 775-9000 *SIC* 5172

BISHOP LIFTING PRODUCTS INC p 185
125 Mccarty St 77029
Tel (713) 674-2266 *SIC* 1799 3531

■ BISON BUILDING MATERIALS OF TEXAS INC p 185
1445 W Sam Houston Pkwy N 77043
Tel (713) 467-6700 *SIC* 5031

BJ SERVICES CO USA LP p 186
5500 Nw Central Dr # 100 77092
Tel (713) 462-4239 *SIC* 1389

BLACK ELK ENERGY OFFSHORE OPERATIONS p 186
842 W Sam Houston Pkwy N # 500 77024
Tel (832) 973-4230 *SIC* 1389

BLACK STONE MINERALS LP p 187
1001 Fannin St Ste 2020 77002
Tel (713) 658-0647 *SIC* 1311

BLACKHAWK SPECIALTY TOOLS LLC p 187
11936 Brittmoore Park Dr 77041
Tel (713) 466-4200 *SIC* 1382

BLP SETTLEMENT CO p 190
125 Mccarty St 77029
Tel (713) 674-2266 *SIC* 5085 3496

■ BLUE DOLPHIN ENERGY CO p 192
801 Travis St Ste 2100 77002
Tel (713) 568-4725
SIC 1311 1382 4612 4922

BMC SOFTWARE INC p 193
2103 Citywest Blvd # 2100 77042
Tel (713) 918-8800 *SIC* 7372 7371

■ BOARDWALK PIPELINE PARTNERS LP p 196
9 Greenway Plz Ste 2800 77046
Tel (866) 913-2122 *SIC* 4922

■ BOARDWALK PIPELINES LP p 196
9 Greenway Plz Ste 2800 77046
Tel (713) 479-8000 *SIC* 4922 4923

BOCCARD PIPE FABRICATORS INC p 197
2500 Galveston Rd 77017
Tel (713) 643-0681 *SIC* 3498

BOMIN BUNKER OIL CORP p 199
333 Clay St Ste 2400 77002
Tel (713) 952-5151 *SIC* 5172

■ BOOTS & COOTS LLC p 200
3000 N Sam Houston Pkwy E 77032
Tel (281) 871-2699 *SIC* 1389

BORUSAN MANNESMANN PIPE US INC p 201
363 N Sam H Pkwy E Ste 63 77060
Tel (832) 399-6000 *SIC* 3317

BOWEN MICLETTE & BRITT INSURANCE AGENCY LLC p 204
1111 North Loop W Ste 400 77008
Tel (713) 802-6100 *SIC* 6411

BOXER PARENT CO INC p 205
2101 Citywest Blvd 77042
Tel (713) 918-8800 *SIC* 7372

BP AMERICA PRODUCTION CO p 205
501 Westlake Park Blvd 77079
Tel (281) 366-2000 *SIC* 1311 1321

BP CORP NORTH AMERICA INC p 205
501 Westlake Park Blvd 77079
Tel (281) 366-2000
SIC 2911 5541 5171 1311 4613 4612

BP ENERGY CO p 205
501 Westlake Park Blvd 77079
Tel (281) 679-9584 *SIC* 4924

BP PRODUCTS NORTH AMERICA INC p 206
501 Westlake Park Blvd 77079
Tel (281) 366-2000 *SIC* 5541 5171 4613

BPZ RESOURCES INC p 206
10497 Town And Country Wa 77024
Tel (281) 556-6200 *SIC* 1311

BRACE INC p 206
14950 Heathrow Forest Pkw 77032
Tel (281) 749-1020 *SIC* 6719

BRACE INDUSTRIAL GROUP INC p 206
14950 Heathrow Fore 77032
Tel (281) 749-1020 *SIC* 8748

BRACE INTEGRATED SERVICES INC p 206
14950 Heathrow Frst 77032
Tel (281) 749-1020 *SIC* 8748

BRACEWELL LLP p 206
711 Louisiana St Ste 2300 77002
Tel (713) 223-2300 *SIC* 8111

BRAY INTERNATIONAL INC p 209
13333 Westland East Blvd 77041
Tel (281) 894-7979 *SIC* 3491

BRENNTAG LATIN AMERICA INC p 210
5300 Memorial Dr Ste 1100 77007
Tel (713) 880-5400 *SIC* 5169

▲ BRISTOW GROUP INC p 214
2103 City West Blvd Fl 4 77042
Tel (713) 267-7600 *SIC* 4522

BROADSPECTRUM DOWNSTREAM SERVICES INC p 215
1330 Post Oak Blvd # 1250 77056
Tel (713) 964-2800 *SIC* 1382

BROCK GROUP INC p 216
10343 Sam Houston Park Dr 77064
Tel (281) 807-8200 *SIC* 1721 1799

BROCK HOLDINGS I LLC p 216
10343 Sam Houston Park Dr # 200 77064
Tel (281) 807-8200 *SIC* 1721 1799 7359

BROCK HOLDINGS II INC p 216
10343 Sam Houston Park Dr 77064
Tel (281) 807-8200 *SIC* 1721 1799

BROCK HOLDINGS III INC p 216
10343 Sam Houston Park Dr 77064
Tel (281) 807-8200 *SIC* 1721 7349

BROCK SERVICES HOLDINGS LLC p 216
10343 Sam Houston Park Dr # 200 77064
Tel (281) 807-8200 *SIC* 1721 1799

BROCK SERVICES LLC p 216
10343 Sam Houston Park Dr # 200 77064
Tel (281) 807-8200 *SIC* 1721 1799

BROTHERS PRODUCE INC p 219
3173 Produce Row 77023
Tel (713) 924-4196 *SIC* 5148

BROWN FOUNDATION INC p 219
2217 Welch St 77019
Tel (713) 523-6867 *SIC* 6732

■ BUCKEYE ENERGY SERVICES LLC p 223
1 Greenway Plz Ste 600 77046
Tel (832) 615-8600 *SIC* 8748

BUCKEYE GP HOLDINGS LP p 223
1 Greenway Plz Ste 600 77046
Tel (832) 615-8600
SIC 4789 4213 4226 4212

▲ BUCKEYE PARTNERS LP p 223
1 Greenway Plz Ste 600 77046
Tel (832) 615-8600
SIC 4612 4789 4226 4213

■ BUCKEYE TEXAS PARTNERS HOLDINGS LLC p 223
1 Greenway Plz Ste 600 77046
Tel (832) 615-8600 *SIC* 6719

■ BUCKEYE TEXAS PARTNERS LLC p 223
1 Greenway Plz Ste 600 77046
Tel (832) 615-8600 *SIC* 6719 4491

BUFFALO MARINE SERVICE INC p 224
8201 E Erath St 77012
Tel (713) 923-2106 *SIC* 5172

■ BURLINGTON RESOURCES INC p 228
600 N Dairy Ashford Rd 77079
Tel (281) 293-1000
SIC 1311 5172 4922 4612

BURNETT COMPANIES CONSOLIDATED INC p 228
9800 Richmond Ave Ste 800 77042
Tel (713) 977-4777 *SIC* 7361 8243

BURROW GLOBAL LLC p 228
6200 Savoy Dr Ste 800 77036
Tel (713) 963-0930 *SIC* 1542 6799

BURROW GLOBAL SERVICES LLC p 228
6200 Savoy Dr Ste 800 77036
Tel (713) 963-0930 *SIC* 1542 1541 8711

C&C INDUSTRIES INC p 233
10350 Clay Rd Ste 250 77041
Tel (713) 466-1644 *SIC* 3999 5085

C&J ENERGY SERVICES INC p 234
3990 Rogerdale Rd 77042
Tel (713) 325-6000 *SIC* 1382 1389

C&J SPEC-RENT SERVICES INC p 234
3990 Rogerdale Rd 77042
Tel (713) 260-9900 *SIC* 5065

C&J WELL SERVICES INC p 234
3990 Rogerdale Rd 77042
Tel (281) 874-0035 *SIC* 1389

▲ CABOT OIL & GAS CORP p 235
840 Gessner Rd Ste 1400 77024
Tel (281) 589-4600 *SIC* 1311

CACTUS WELLHEAD LLC p 236
1 Greenway Plz Ste 200 77046
Tel (713) 626-8800 *SIC* 3533

CADENCE BANCORP LLC p 236
2800 Post Oak Blvd # 3800 77056
Tel (713) 871-4000 *SIC* 6021

CAL DIVE INTERNATIONAL INC p 237
2500 Citywest Blvd # 2200 77042
Tel (713) 361-2600 *SIC* 7389 1623 1629

▲ CALPINE CORP p 242
717 Texas St Ste 1000 77002
Tel (713) 830-2000 *SIC* 4911

■ CALPINE ENERGY SERVICES LP p 242
717 Texas St Ste 1000 77002
Tel (713) 830-2000 *SIC* 4911

■ CALPINE MID-ATLANTIC ENERGY LLC p 242
717 Texas St Ste 1000 77002
Tel (713) 830-2000 *SIC* 4932

CAMAC INTERNATIONAL CORP p 243
1330 Post Oak Blvd Ste 22 77056
Tel (713) 965-5100
SIC 8711 6552 1382 8741 1389

CAMCORP INTERESTS LTD p 244
10410 Wndamere Lakes Blvd 77065
Tel (281) 671-9000 *SIC* 1521 6798 6552

CAMDEN DEVELOPMENT INC p 244
11 Greenway Plz Ste 2400 77046
Tel (713) 354-2500 *SIC* 6531 6552

CAMDEN PROPERTY TRUST p 245
11 Greenway Plz Ste 2400 77046
Tel (713) 354-2500 *SIC* 6798

CAMERON CO p 245
4646 W Sam Houston Pkwy N 77041
Tel (713) 513-3300 *SIC* 3823

CAMERON INTERNATIONAL CORP p 245
4646 W Sam Houston Pkwy N 77041
Tel (713) 513-3300 *SIC* 3533 3563 3491

CAMERON INTERNATIONAL HOLDING CORP p 245
4646 W Sam Houston Pkwy N 77041
Tel (713) 513-3300 *SIC* 1389

CAMERON SOLUTIONS INC p 245
11210 Equity Dr Ste 100 77041
Tel (713) 849-7500 *SIC* 3533 1389 3569

CAMERON TECHNOLOGIES INC p 245
4646 W Sam Houston Pkwy N 77041
Tel (713) 513-3300 *SIC* 5084 3533

CAMPBELL CONCRETE & MATERIALS LP p 245
16155 Park Row Ste 120 77084
Tel (281) 592-5201 *SIC* 3273

CANRIG DRILLING TECH LTD p 247
515 W Greens Rd Ste 1200 77067
Tel (281) 774-5600 *SIC* 3532

■ CAPROCK COMMUNICATIONS CORP p 251
4400 S Sam Houston Pkwy E 77048
Tel (281) 482-0289 *SIC* 4813

CARBER HOLDINGS INC p 252
12600 N Featherwood Dr # 450 77034
Tel (713) 797-2859 *SIC* 1389 7389

▲ CARBO CERAMICS INC p 252
575 N Dairy Ashford Rd # 30 77079
Tel (281) 921-6400
SIC 3291 5945 8742 7371

■ CARDINAL HEALTH 109 INC p 253
1330 Enclave Pkwy 77077
Tel (281) 749-4000 *SIC* 8741

▲ CARDTRONICS INC p 253
3250 Briarpark Dr Ste 400 77042
Tel (832) 308-4000 *SIC* 7389 5049

▲ CARRIAGE SERVICES INC p 260
3040 Post Oak Blvd # 300 77056
Tel (713) 332-8400 *SIC* 7261 6553

▲ CARRIZO OIL & GAS INC p 261
500 Dallas St Ste 2300 77002
Tel (713) 328-1000 *SIC* 1311

CARRUTH-DOGGETT INC p 261
7110 North Fwy 77076
Tel (713) 675-7000 *SIC* 5084 7359 7699

■ CC HOLDINGS GS V LLC p 269
1220 Augusta Dr Ste 500 77057
Tel (713) 570-3000 *SIC* 4812

■ CC SCN FIBER LLC p 269
1220 Augusta Dr Ste 600 77057
Tel (713) 570-3000 *SIC* 4899 7622 4812

CCJV p 270
5001 Rogerdale Rd 77072
Tel (713) 375-8051 *SIC* 4924

■ CDM RESOURCE MANAGEMENT LLC p 271
20405 State Hwy Ste 700 77070
Tel (281) 376-2980 *SIC* 1389

CEMEX CEMENT INC p 274
929 Gessner Rd Ste 1900 77024
Tel (713) 650-6200 *SIC* 3273 3241

CEMEX CONSTRUCTION MATERIALS LP p 274
929 Gessner Rd Ste 1900 77024
Tel (713) 650-6200 *SIC* 3273

CEMEX CONSTRUCTION MATERIALS SOUTH LLC p 274
920 Mmrial Cy Way Ste 100 77024
Tel (713) 650-6200
SIC 3271 3273 3272 1422

CEMEX INC p 274
929 Gessner Rd Ste 1900 77024
Tel (713) 650-6200
SIC 3273 3271 3272 5032

■ CENTERPOINT ENERGY HOUSTON ELECTRIC LLC p 276
1111 Louisiana St 77002
Tel (713) 207-1111 *SIC* 4911

▲ CENTERPOINT ENERGY INC p 276
1111 Louisiana St Ste 264 77002
Tel (713) 207-1111 *SIC* 4931

■ CENTERPOINT ENERGY RESOURCES CORP p 276
1111 Louisiana St 77002
Tel (713) 207-1111 *SIC* 4924 4922

■ CENTERPOINT ENERGY SERVICES INC p 276
1111 Louisiana St Ste 264 77002
Tel (713) 207-1111 *SIC* 4924

■ CENTERPOINT ENERGY SERVICES RETAIL LLC p 276
1111 La St Fl 20 77002
Tel (800) 752-8036 *SIC* 4924

■ CENTERPOINT ENERGY TRANSITION BOND CO LLC p 276
1111 La St Ste 4667 77002
Tel (713) 207-8272 *SIC* 4924

CENTRAL CRUDE INC p 278
10370 Richmond Ave # 975 77042
Tel (713) 783-2167 *SIC* 1382

CENTRAL UNITED LIFE INSURANCE CO INC p 280
10777 Northwest Fwy # 100 77092
Tel (713) 529-0045 *SIC* 6311

■ CENTURION PIPELINE LP p 281
5 Greenway Plz Ste 110 77046
Tel (713) 215-7000 *SIC* 1311

CENTURY ASPHALT LTD p 282
5303 Navigation Blvd 77011
Tel (713) 292-2868 *SIC* 5032

CENTURY CARE OF AMERICA INC p 282
14800 Saint Marys Ln # 175 77079
Tel (832) 448-3700 *SIC* 8051

■ CEVA FREIGHT LLC p 284
15350 Vickery Dr 77032
Tel (281) 618-3100
SIC 4214 4225 4412 4512 4522 4731

■ CEVA FREIGHT MANAGEMENT INTERNATIONAL GROUP INC p 284
15350 Vickery Dr 77032
Tel (281) 618-3100 *SIC* 4731

■ CEVA GROUND US LP p 284
15390 Vickery Dr 77032
Tel (281) 227-5000 *SIC* 4212 4213

■ CEVA LOGISTICS LLC p 284
15350 Vickery Dr 77032
Tel (281) 618-3100 *SIC* 4731

■ CEVA LOGISTICS US INC p 285
15350 Vickery Dr 77032
Tel (281) 618-3100 *SIC* 4731

CGG SERVICES (US) INC p 285
10300 Town Park Dr 77072
Tel (832) 351-8300 *SIC* 1382

CGGVERITAS LAND (US) INC p 285
10300 Town Park Dr 77072
Tel (832) 351-8300 *SIC* 7699

CHAMBERLIN WATERPROOFING & ROOFING SYSTEMS INC p 287
7510 Langtry St 77040
Tel (713) 880-1432 *SIC* 1799 1761

■ CHAMBERS DEVELOPMENT CO INC p 287
1001 Fannin St Ste 400 77002
Tel (713) 877-8793 *SIC* 4953

CHAMPION ENERGY HOLDINGS LLC p 287
1500 Rankin Rd Ste 200 77073
Tel (281) 653-5090 *SIC* 4911

■ CHAMPION ENERGY MARKETING LLC p 287
1500 Rankin Rd Ste 200 77073
Tel (281) 653-5090 *SIC* 4911

■ CHAMPION ENERGY SERVICES LLC p 287
1500 Rankin Rd Ste 200 77073
Tel (281) 653-5090 *SIC* 4911

CHAMPION WINDOW INC p 287
12427 Duncan Rd 77066
Tel (281) 440-7000 *SIC* 3442

CHAMPIONS CINCO PIPE & SUPPLY LLC p 287
4 Greenspoint Mall # 16945 77060
Tel (713) 468-6555 *SIC* 5051

CHARLIE CHARMING HOLDINGS INC p 290
5999 Savoy Dr 77036
Tel (713) 579-1936 *SIC* 5632

CHARMING CHARLIE LLC p 290
5999 Savoy Dr 77036
Tel (713) 579-1936 *SIC* 5632

CHASTANG ENTERPRISES INC p 291
6200 North Loop E 77026
Tel (713) 678-5000 *SIC* 5511

■ CHCA WOMANS HOSPITAL LP p 292
7600 Fannin St 77054
Tel (713) 791-7534 *SIC* 8062

■ CHEMICAL WASTE MANAGEMENT INC p 293
1001 Fannin St Ste 4000 77002
Tel (713) 512-6200 *SIC* 4953 4959

CHEMIUM INTERNATIONAL CORP p 293
1455 West Loop S Ste 550 77027
Tel (713) 622-7766 *SIC* 5172

▲ CHENIERE ENERGY INC p 294
700 Milam St Ste 1900 77002
Tel (713) 375-5000 *SIC* 1321 4925 4922

■ CHENIERE ENERGY INVESTMENTS LLC p 294
700 Louisiana St Ste 1900 77002
Tel (713) 375-5000 *SIC* 4922

■ CHENIERE ENERGY PARTNERS LP p 294
700 Milam St Ste 1900 77002
Tel (713) 375-5000 *SIC* 4924 4922

CHERRY CRUSHED CONCRETE INC p 294
6131 Selinsky Rd 77048
Tel (713) 987-0000 *SIC* 5032

CHESMAR HOMES LTD p 295
450 Gears Rd Ste 400 77067
Tel (832) 253-0100 *SIC* 1521

■ CHEVRON MARINE PRODUCTS LLC p 296
1500 Louisiana St 77002
Tel (832) 854-2767 *SIC* 5172 2992 2869

CHI ST LUKES HEALTH BAYLOR COLLEGE OF MEDICINE MEDICAL CENTER p 296
6624 Fannin St Ste 1100 77030
Tel (832) 355-1000 *SIC* 8062

CHICKASAW DISTRIBUTORS INC p 298
800 Bering Dr Ste 330 77057
Tel (713) 974-2905 *SIC* 5051

CHILL HOLDINGS INC p 300
5151 San Felipe St # 500 77056
Tel (713) 861-2500 *SIC* 3585

CHRISTUS HEALTH GULF COAST p 303
18300 Saint John Dr 77058
Tel (281) 333-5503 *SIC* 8062

CHUNGS PRODUCTS LP p 305
3907 Dennis St 77004
Tel (713) 741-2118 *SIC* 5142 2038

CIMA ENERGY LTD p 307
100 Waugh Dr Ste 500 77007
Tel (713) 209-1112 *SIC* 1311

■ CIRCLE INTERNATIONAL INC p 308
15350 Vickery Dr 77032
Tel (281) 618-3100 *SIC* 4731

CITATION CRUDE MARKETING INC p 309
14077 Cutten Rd 77069
Tel (281) 891-1000 *SIC* 5172

CITATION OIL & GAS CORP p 309
14077 Cutten Rd 77069
Tel (281) 891-1000 *SIC* 1311 1382

CITGO HOLDING INC p 309
1293 Eldridge Pkwy 77077
Tel (281) 531-0004
SIC 2911 2992 5171 4213

CITGO PETROLEUM CORP p 309
1293 Eldridge Pkwy 77077
Tel (832) 486-4000
SIC 2911 5171 4213 4612

CITRUS CORP p 311
1400 Smith St Ste 3902 77002
Tel (713) 853-6161 *SIC* 4923

CITY OF HOUSTON p 315
901 Bagby St 77002
Tel (713) 837-0311 *SIC* 9111

▲ CIVEO CORP p 320
333 Clay St Ste 4980 77002
Tel (713) 510-2400 *SIC* 7011

■ CIVEO US HOLDINGS LLC p 320
333 Clay St Ste 4980 77002
Tel (713) 510-2400 *SIC* 7011

CJ HOLDING CO p 320
3990 Rogerdale Rd 77042
Tel (713) 325-6086 *SIC* 6719

CLAIM JUMPER RESTAURANTS LLC p 321
1510 West Loop S 77027
Tel (949) 756-9001 *SIC* 5812

CLIFFS DRILLING CO p 326
14701 Saint Marys Ln 77079
Tel (281) 749-1000 *SIC* 1381

COD INTERMEDIATE LLC p 333
1330 Post Oak Blvd 77056
Tel (713) 292-2400 *SIC* 4953

COKINOS ENERGY CORP p 335
5718 Westheimer Rd # 900 77057
Tel (713) 974-0101 *SIC* 4924 1623

COKINOS NATURAL GAS CO INC p 335
5718 Westheimer Rd # 900 77057
Tel (713) 974-0101 *SIC* 4924 1623

■ COLORADO INTERSTATE GAS CO LLC p 339
1001 La St Ste 1000 77002
Tel (713) 369-9000 *SIC* 4922

■ COLUMBIA GULF TRANSMISSION LLC p 340
5151 San Felipe St # 2500 77056
Tel (713) 386-3701 *SIC* 4922

■ COLUMBIA PIPELINE GROUP INC p 341
5151 San Felipe St 77056
Tel (713) 386-3701 *SIC* 4922

■ COLUMBIA PIPELINE PARTNERS LP p 341
5151 San Felipe St # 2500 77056
Tel (713) 386-3701 SIC 4922

▲ COMFORT SYSTEMS USA INC p 344
675 Bering Dr Ste 400 77057
Tel (713) 830-9600 SIC 1711 1731

COMMUNITY HEALTH CHOICE INC p 348
2636 S Loop W Ste 700 77054
Tel (713) 295-2200 SIC 8062

■ COMPLETE ENERGY SERVICES INC p 351
1001 La St Ste 2900 77002
Tel (713) 654-2200 SIC 1382

■ COMPLETE PRODUCTION SERVICES INC p 351
1001 Louisiana St 77002
Tel (281) 372-2300 SIC 1389 1381

COMPLETERX LTD p 351
3100 S Gessner Rd Ste 640 77063
Tel (713) 355-1196 SIC 8742

COMPUGEN SYSTEMS INC p 352
5847 San Felipe St # 1700 77057
Tel (713) 821-1739 SIC 7379

▲ CONOCOPHILLIPS p 358
600 N Dairy Ashford Rd 77079
Tel (281) 293-1000 SIC 1311 1382

■ CONOCOPHILLIPS HOLDING CO p 358
600 N Dairy Ashford Rd 77079
Tel (281) 293-1000 SIC 2911 5171 5541

■ CONSOLIDATED GRAPHICS INC p 360
5858 Westheimer Rd # 200 77057
Tel (713) 787-0977 SIC 2752

▲ CONTANGO OIL & GAS CO p 362
717 Texas St Ste 2900 77002
Tel (713) 236-7400 SIC 1311

CONTINENTAL CARBON CO p 363
16850 Park Row 77084
Tel (281) 647-3700 SIC 2895 3624

COOPER INDUSTRIES LLC p 366
600 Travis St Ste 5400 77002
Tel (713) 209-8400
SIC 3646 3612 3613 3644 3546 3423

■ COPANO ENERGY LLC p 368
1001 La St Ste 1000 77002
Tel (713) 621-9547 SIC 4922 4925

CORE LABORATORIES LP p 369
6316 Windfern Rd 77040
Tel (713) 328-2673 SIC 1389

CORNERSTONE HOME LENDING INC p 371
1177 West Loop S Ste 200 77027
Tel (713) 599-2895 SIC 6162

CORPORATE SERVICES GROUP HOLDINGS INC p 372
10740 N Gessner Rd # 400 77064
Tel (713) 438-1411 SIC 7363

COUNTY OF HARRIS p 378
201 Caroline St Ste 800 77002
Tel (713) 755-6411 SIC 9111

COXS FOODARAMA INC p 387
10810 S Post Oak Rd 77035
Tel (713) 723-8683 SIC 5411

CPW AMERICA CO p 388
750 Town And Country Blvd # 920 77024
Tel (281) 752-7300 SIC 5051

CRANE WORLDWIDE LOGISTICS LLC p 389
1500 Rankin Rd 77073
Tel (281) 443-2777 SIC 4731

CRAWFORD ELECTRIC SUPPLY CO HOUSTON LTD p 389
7390 Northcourt Rd 77040
Tel (281) 501-4440 SIC 5063

CRAWFORD ELECTRIC SUPPLY CO INC p 389
7390 Northcourt Rd 77040
Tel (713) 476-0788 SIC 5063

CRESCENT DIRECTIONAL DRILLING LP p 391
2040 Aldine Western Rd 77038
Tel (281) 668-9500 SIC 1381

▲ CRESTWOOD EQUITY PARTNERS LP p 392
700 Louisiana St Ste 2550 77002
Tel (832) 519-2200 SIC 5984 5172

■ CRESTWOOD MIDSTREAM PARTNERS LP p 392
700 Louisiana St Ste 2550 77002
Tel (832) 519-2200 SIC 4922

CRESTWOOD MIDSTREAM PARTNERS LP p 392
700 Louisiana St Ste 2550 77002
Tel (832) 519-2200 SIC 4922

CRITERION CATALYSTS & TECHNOLOGIES LP p 393
910 Louisiana St Ste 2900 77002
Tel (713) 241-3000 SIC 2819 2869

▲ CROWN CASTLE INTERNATIONAL CORP p 395
1220 Augusta Dr Ste 600 77057
Tel (713) 570-3000
SIC 6798 4899 7622 4812

CROWN CASTLE INTERNATIONAL CORP p 395
1220 Augusta Dr Ste 600 77057
Tel (713) 570-3000
SIC 4899 7622 4812 6798

CSAT SOLUTIONS LP p 397
4949 Windfern Rd 77041
Tel (713) 934-5200 SIC 7378

CYBERONICS INC p 405
100 Cyberonics Blvd # 600 77058
Tel (281) 228-7200 SIC 3845

CYCLONE ENTERPRISES INC p 405
146 Knobcrest Dr 77060
Tel (281) 872-0087 SIC 5141

CYPRESS FAIRBANKS MEDICAL CENTER p 405
10655 Steepletop Dr 77065
Tel (281) 897-3172 SIC 5912

■ CYPRESS FAIRBANKS MEDICAL CENTER INC p 405
10655 Steepletop Dr 77065
Tel (281) 890-4285 SIC 8062

CYPRESS-FAIRBANKS INDEPENDENT SCHOOL DISTRICT p 405
10300 Jones Rd 77065
Tel (281) 897-4000 SIC 8211

■ D & I SILICA LLC p 406
3 Riverway Ste 1350 77056
Tel (713) 980-6200 SIC 5032

DAIKIN MANUFACTURING CO LP p 408
5151 San Felipe St # 500 77056
Tel (972) 245-1510 SIC 3585

DAN-BUNKERING (AMERICA) INC p 410
840 Gessner Rd Ste 210 77024
Tel (281) 833-5801 SIC 5172

■ DANIEL INDUSTRIES INC p 411
11100 Brittmoore Park Dr 77041
Tel (713) 467-6000
SIC 3823 3824 3494 3829 3826 3571

■ DANIEL MEASUREMENT AND CONTROL INC p 411
11100 Brittmoore Park Dr 77041
Tel (713) 467-6000
SIC 3824 3498 3499 3823 3571 3491

DAVID E HARVEY BUILDERS INC p 415
3630 Westchase Dr 77042
Tel (713) 783-8710 SIC 1542

DEARBORN RESOURCES INC p 420
2130 Inwood Dr 77019
Tel (713) 521-1950 SIC 1623

DELTA RIGGING & TOOLS INC p 427
125 Mccarty St 77029
Tel (713) 512-1700 SIC 7359 2298 3496

■ DELTA STEEL INC p 427
7355 Roundhouse Ln 77078
Tel (713) 635-1200 SIC 5051

DEMONTROND BUICK CO p 428
14101 North Fwy 77090
Tel (281) 872-7200 SIC 5511

DENALI INC p 428
550 Westcott St Ste 450 77007
Tel (713) 627-0933 SIC 3089

DEPARTMENT OF HEALTH AND HUMAN SERVICES p 430
8000 N Stadium Dr Fl 8 77054
Tel (713) 794-9370 SIC 9431

DERICHEBOURG RECYCLING USA INC p 431
7501 Wallisville Rd 77020
Tel (713) 675-2281 SIC 5093

■ DIAMOND OFFSHORE DRILLING INC p 437
15415 Katy Fwy Ste 400 77094
Tel (281) 492-5300 SIC 1381

DIOCESE OF GALVESTON-HOUSTON EDUCATION FOUNDATION p 440
1700 San Jacinto St 77002
Tel (713) 652-8248 SIC 8661

DIRECT ENERGY LP p 441
12 Greenway Plz Ste 250 77046
Tel (713) 877-3500 SIC 4911

DIRECT ENERGY SERVICES LLC p 441
12 Greenway Plz Ste 250 77046
Tel (713) 877-3500 SIC 4931

DISTRIBUTION INTERNATIONAL INC p 443
9000 Railwood Dr 77078
Tel (713) 428-3740 SIC 5033 5099

DISTRIBUTION INTERNATIONAL SOUTHWEST INC p 443
9000 Railwood Dr 77078
Tel (713) 428-3900 SIC 5087 5047

DMC BUILDERS CO INC p 446
3411 Richmond Ave Ste 200 77046
Tel (832) 209-1200 SIC 1522

■ DNOW LP p 446
7402 N Eldridge Pkwy 77041
Tel (281) 823-4700 SIC 5084 7353 3533

DOCKWISE USA LLC p 447
16340 Park Ten Pl Ste 200 77084
Tel (713) 934-7300 SIC 4493

DON MCGILL TOYOTA INC p 450
11800 Katy Fwy I10 77079
Tel (281) 496-2000 SIC 5511 5521

DRESSER-RAND GROUP INC p 455
10205 Westheimer Rd # 1000 77042
Tel (713) 354-6100 SIC 3563 3511

DRESSER-RAND LLC p 455
1200 W Sam Houston Pkwy N 77043
Tel (713) 354-6100 SIC 3563

▲ DRIL-QUIP INC p 456
6401 N Eldridge Pkwy 77041
Tel (713) 939-7711 SIC 3533

DRILLMEC INC p 456
18320 Imperial Valley Dr 77060
Tel (281) 885-0777 SIC 3533

DRIVING MOMENTUM INC p 456
17024 Butte Creek Rd # 107 77090
Tel (281) 893-3390 SIC 7363

DUBUIS HEALTH SYSTEM INC p 459
2707 North Loop W Ste 7 77008
Tel (713) 277-2300 SIC 8069

DUKE ENERGY NATURAL GAS CORP p 460
5400 Westheimer Ct 77056
Tel (713) 627-5400 SIC 4923

■ DUNCAN ENERGY PARTNERS LP p 461
1100 Louisiana St Fl 10 77002
Tel (713) 381-6500 SIC 4922

DX HOLDING CO INC p 464
300 Jackson Hill St 77007
Tel (713) 863-1947 SIC 2869 2819 5169

▲ DXP ENTERPRISES INC p 464
7272 Pinemont Dr 77040
Tel (713) 996-4700 SIC 5084 5063

■ DYNEGY CONESVILLE LLC p 465
601 Travis St Ste 1400 77002
Tel (713) 507-6400 SIC 4911

■ DYNEGY HOLDINGS LLC p 465
601 Travis St Ste 1400 77002
Tel (713) 507-6400 SIC 4911 4923 5172

▲ DYNEGY INC p 465
601 Travis St Ste 1400 77002
Tel (713) 507-6400 SIC 4911

■ DYNEGY MARKETING & TRADE LLC p 465
601 Travis St Ste 1400 77002
Tel (713) 507-6400 SIC 4911 4924

■ DYNEGY MIAMI FORT LLC p 465
601 Travis St Ste 1400 77002
Tel (713) 507-6400 SIC 4911

■ DYNEGY MIDWEST GENERATION LLC p 465
601 Travis St Ste 1400 77002
Tel (713) 507-6400 SIC 4911

■ DYNEGY POWER CORP p 465
601 Travis St Ste 1400 77002
Tel (713) 507-6400 SIC 4911

■ DYNEGY RESOURCE I LLC p 465
601 Travis St Ste 1400 77002
Tel (713) 507-6400 SIC 4911 4924 4931

■ DYNEGY RESOURCES GENERATING HOLDCO LLC p 465
601 Travis St Ste 1400 77002
Tel (713) 507-6400 SIC 4911

■ DYNEGY ZIMMER LLC p 465
601 Travis St Ste 1400 77002
Tel (713) 507-6400 SIC 4911

EAGLE PIPE LLC p 468
9525 Katy Fwy Ste 306 77024
Tel (713) 464-7473 SIC 3533 5082

■ EAGLE ROCK ENERGY PARTNERS LP p 468
5847 San Felipe St # 3000 77057
Tel (281) 408-1200 SIC 1311 1321

■ EAST TENNESSEE NATURAL GAS LLC p 471
5400 Westheimer Ct 77056
Tel (713) 627-5400 SIC 4923

EATON ELECTRIC HOLDINGS LLC p 473
600 Travis St Ste 5600 77002
Tel (713) 209-8400
SIC 3646 3612 3613 3644 3536 3423

■ EC SOURCE SERVICES LLC p 474
16055 Space Center Blvd # 700 77062
Tel (281) 480-4600 SIC 1623 8742

ECONOMY MUD PRODUCTS CO p 476
435 E Anderson Rd 77047
Tel (800) 231-2066 SIC 2869 2899

EDF TRADING NORTH AMERICA LLC p 477
4700 W Sam Houston Pkwy N 77041
Tel (281) 781-0333 SIC 6799

EDP RENEWABLES NORTH AMERICA LLC p 478
808 Travis St Ste 700 77002
Tel (713) 265-0350 SIC 4911

EDUCATIONAL PRODUCTS INC p 479
4100 N Sam Houston Pkwy W P 77086
Tel (800) 365-5345 SIC 5112 5049

■ EL PASO CGP CO LLC p 483
1001 Louisiana St 77002
Tel (713) 420-2600
SIC 2911 1311 4613 4612 5541 4922

■ EL PASO HOLDCO LLC p 483
1001 Louisiana St 77002
Tel (713) 420-2600 SIC 6719

■ EL PASO LLC p 483
1001 Louisiana St 77002
Tel (713) 420-2600 SIC 4922 1311

EL PASO PIPELINE PARTNERS LP p 483
1001 La St Ste 1000 77002
Tel (713) 369-9000 SIC 4922

■ EL PASO TENNESSEE PIPELINE CO LLC p 483
1001 Louisiana St 77002
Tel (713) 420-2131 SIC 4922

EMAS CHIYODA SUBSEA INC p 490
825 Town And Country Ln 77024
Tel (832) 487-7300 SIC 1381

EMPLOYEE OWNED HOLDINGS INC p 494
5500 N Sam Houston Pkwy W # 100 77086
Tel (281) 569-7000 SIC 5084

EMS ASSEMBLY LLC p 495
8807 Fallbrook Dr 77064
Tel (281) 668-1551 SIC 3575

EMS USA INC p 495
2000 Bering Dr Ste 600 77057
Tel (713) 595-7600 SIC 1389

■ ENABLE GAS TRANSMISSION LLC p 495
1111 Louisiana St 77002
Tel (713) 207-1111 SIC 4922

ENBRIDGE (US) INC p 495
1100 Louisiana St # 3300 77002
Tel (713) 821-2000 SIC 4612

▲ ENBRIDGE ENERGY PARTNERS LP p 495
1100 La St Ste 3300 77002
Tel (713) 821-2000 SIC 4612 4922 4924

■ ENBRIDGE MIDCOAST ENERGY INC p 495
1100 La St Ste 3300 77002
Tel (713) 650-8900 SIC 4923

ENBRIDGE OFFSHORE (GAS TRANSMISSION) LLC p 495
1100 La St Ste 3300 77002
Tel (713) 821-2000 SIC 4922

ENCORE BANCSHARES INC p 496
9 Greenway Plz Ste 1000 77046
Tel (713) 787-3100 SIC 6021

ENCORE BANK p 496
9 Greenway Plz Ste 1000 77046
Tel (713) 787-3100 SIC 6021 6035

ENDEAVOUR INTERNATIONAL CORP p 496
811 Main St Ste 2100 77002
Tel (713) 307-8700 SIC 1311

ENDURO COMPOSITES INC p 497
16602 Central Green Blvd 77032
Tel (713) 358-4000 SIC 5033

ENERFLEX ENERGY SYSTEMS INC p 497
10815 Telge Rd 77095
Tel (281) 345-9300
SIC 3585 7623 7699 3563

ENERGY MAINTENANCE SERVICES GROUP I INC p 497
2000 Bering Dr Ste 600 77057
Tel (713) 595-7600 SIC 1389

ENERGY RESOURCE TECHNOLOGY GOM LLC p 498
500 Dallas St Ste 2000 77002
Tel (281) 618-0590 SIC 1311 1389

ENERGY XXI GULF COAST INC p 498
1021 Main St Ste 2626 77002
Tel (713) 351-3000 SIC 4424 1311

ENERGY XXI USA INC p 498
1021 Main St Ste 2626 77002
Tel (713) 351-3000 SIC 1311

ENERVEST LTD p 498
1001 Fannin St Ste 800 77002
Tel (713) 659-3500 SIC 1311 1382

ENERVEST OPERATING LLC p 498
1001 Fannin St Ste 800 77002
Tel (713) 659-3500 SIC 1311

ENGIE NORTH AMERICA INC p 498
1990 Post Oak Blvd # 1900 77056
Tel (713) 636-0000 SIC 4911

ENGIE RESOURCES LLC p 498
1990 Post Oak Blvd # 1900 77056
Tel (713) 636-0000 SIC 4911

ENI PETROLEUM CO INC p 499
1201 La St Ste 3500 77002
Tel (713) 393-6100 SIC 1311

ENI TRADING & SHIPPING INC p 499
1200 Smith St Ste 1707 77002
Tel (713) 393-6340 SIC 5172

ENJET LLC p 499
5373 W Alabama St Ste 502 77056
Tel (713) 552-1559 SIC 5172

ENRON CREDITORS RECOVERY CORP p 500
1221 Lamar St Ste 1325 77010
Tel (713) 853-6161
SIC 5172 4922 4911 1311 1321 2911

ENRON ENERGY SERVICES INC p 500
1400 Smith St Ste 501 77002
Tel (713) 853-6161 SIC 4924 4911

ENRON NETWORKS LLC p 500
1400 Smith St 77002
Tel (713) 853-6161 SIC 7389

ENRON POWER CORP p 500
333 Clay St 400 77002
Tel (713) 853-6161 SIC 4911

ENRON TRANSPORTATION SERVICES CO p 500
1400 Smith St 77002
Tel (713) 853-6161 SIC 4922

ENSCO INTERNATIONAL INC p 500
5847 San Felipe St # 3300 77057
Tel (800) 423-8006 SIC 1381

ENTERGY-KOCH L P p 502
20 Greenway Plz Ste 950 77046
Tel (713) 544-6000 SIC 4923 4911

■ ENTERPRISE CRUDE OIL LLC p 502
1100 Louisiana St 77002
Tel (713) 381-6500 SIC 5172

ENTERPRISE PRODUCTS CO p 502
1100 Louisiana St 77002
Tel (713) 880-6500 SIC 1321 4925

ENTERPRISE PRODUCTS HOLDINGS LLC p 502
1100 Louisiana St Fl 10 77002
Tel (713) 381-6500 SIC 4922 4925 4923

■ ENTERPRISE PRODUCTS OPERATING LLC p 502
1100 La St Ste 1000 77002
Tel (713) 381-6500 SIC 4923

▲ ENTERPRISE PRODUCTS PARTNERS LP p 502
1100 Louisiana St Fl 10 77002
Tel (713) 381-6500 SIC 4922 4925 4923

ENTRIX HOLDING CO p 502
5252 Westchester St # 250 77005
Tel (713) 666-6223 SIC 8748

ENTRUST ENERGY INC p 503
1301 Mckinney St Ste 1200 77010
Tel (713) 338-2601 SIC 4911

ENVENTURE GLOBAL TECHNOLOGY INC p 503
15995 N Barkers Landing R 77079
Tel (281) 552-2200 SIC 7353

▲ EOG RESOURCES INC p 504
1111 Bagby St Lbby 2 77002
Tel (713) 651-7000 SIC 1311

▲ EP ENERGY CORP p 504
1001 Louisiana St 77002
Tel (713) 997-1200 SIC 1311

■ EP ENERGY E&P CO LP p 504
1001 Louisiana St 77002
Tel (713) 997-4858 SIC 1382

■ EP ENERGY GLOBAL LLC p 504
1001 Louisiana St 77002
Tel (713) 420-2600 SIC 8748

■ EP ENERGY LLC p 504
1001 Louisiana St 77002
Tel (713) 997-1200 SIC 1311 1382

EP ENERGY MANAGEMENT LLC p 504
1001 Louisiana St 77002
Tel (713) 997-1000 SIC 4922 1321

EP ENERGY RESALE CO LLC p 504
1001 Louisiana St 77002
Tel (713) 997-1000 SIC 2911

EPCO HOLDINGS INC p 504
1100 Louisiana St Fl 10 77002
Tel (713) 880-6500 SIC 7299

EPL OIL & GAS INC p 505
1021 Main St Ste 2626 77002
Tel (713) 351-3000 SIC 1311

EQUILON ENTERPRISES LLC p 506
910 Louisiana St Ste 2 77002
Tel (713) 241-6161
SIC 2911 4612 2992 5172

EQUIPMENT DEPOT LTD p 506
840 Gessner Rd Ste 950 77024
Tel (713) 365-2547
SIC 5083 5084 7359 7699 7353

EQUISTAR CHEMICALS LP p 506
1221 Mckinney St Ste 700 77010
Tel (713) 309-7200 SIC 2869 2822

EQUIVA SERVICES LLC p 507
1100 La St Ste 3030 77002
Tel (713) 241-6161 SIC 8741

▲ ERA GROUP INC p 507
818 Town And Country Blvd 77024
Tel (713) 369-4700 SIC 4512

■ ETC INTRASTATE PROCUREMENT CO LLC p 511
1300 Main St 77002
Tel (713) 989-2688 SIC 1311

ETHOSENERGY GTS HOLDINGS (US) LLC p 511
2800 North Loop W # 1100 77092
Tel (281) 227-5600 SIC 1731 7699 4581

▲ EV ENERGY PARTNERS LP p 513
1001 Fannin St Ste 800 77002
Tel (713) 651-1144 SIC 1311

EVEROSE HEALTHCARE INC p 515
11200 Westheimer Rd # 100 77042
Tel (919) 482-9036 SIC 8082

■ EXLP FINANCE CORP p 519
16666 Northchase Dr 77060
Tel (281) 836-7000 SIC 3533

EXPEDITED LOGISTICS AND FREIGHT SERVICES LLC p 519
4740 Consulate Plaza Dr 77032
Tel (281) 442-3323 SIC 4731

EXPRESS ENERGY SERVICES OPERATING LP p 520
9800 Richmond Ave Ste 500 77042
Tel (713) 625-7400 SIC 1389

■ EXPRESSJET HOLDINGS INC p 521
700 N Sam Hous Pkwy W # 200 77067
Tel (832) 353-1000 SIC 4512

▲ EXTERRAN CORP p 521
4444 Brittmoore Rd 77041
Tel (281) 836-7000 SIC 7359

■ EXTERRAN ENERGY SOLUTIONS LP p 521
263 N Sam Houston Pkwy E 77060
Tel (281) 836-7000 SIC 7353

■ EXTERRAN INC p 521
16666 Northchase Dr 77060
Tel (281) 836-7000 SIC 7353 5084

■ EXTERRAN TRINIDAD LLC p 521
12001 N Huston Rosslyn Rd 77086
Tel (281) 921-9337 SIC 7353 5084 1389

■ EXXON PIPELINE HOLDINGS INC p 521
800 Bell St Rm 2441 77002
Tel (713) 656-3636 SIC 4612 4613

■ EXXONMOBIL UPSTREAM RESEARCH CO p 522
3120 Buffalo Speedway 77098
Tel (713) 431-4222 SIC 2911

FABCO LLC p 523
13835 Beaumont Hwy 77049
Tel (713) 633-6500 SIC 3441 8741 8711

FAIRMONT SPECIALTY INSURANCE MANAGERS INC p 525
11490 Westheimer Rd # 300 77077
Tel (713) 954-8100 SIC 6411

FAROUK SYSTEMS INC p 530
880 E Richey Rd 77073
Tel (281) 876-2000 SIC 2844

FAUST DC LTD p 531
10040 East Fwy 77029
Tel (713) 673-5111 SIC 5181

FERTITTA GROUP INC p 538
1510 West Loop S 77027
Tel (713) 850-1010 SIC 6799

■ FET HOLDINGS LLC p 539
920 Memorial City Way 77024
Tel (281) 949-2500 SIC 5084

FIELDWOOD ENERGY LLC p 541
2000 W Sam Houston Pkwy S # 1200 77042
Tel (713) 969-1000 SIC 1382

FIESTA MART INC p 541
5235 Katy Fwy 77007
Tel (713) 869-5060 SIC 5411

■ FIRST AMERICAN TITLE INSURANCE CO OF TEXAS p 544
1500 S Dairy Ashford Rd # 300 77077
Tel (281) 588-2200 SIC 6361

FIRST SERVICE CREDIT UNION p 549
9621 W Sam Houston Pkwy N 77064
Tel (832) 688-1000 SIC 6061

■ FIRST SIERRA FINANCIAL INC p 549
600 Travis St Ste 7050 77002
Tel (713) 221-8822 SIC 6159

■ FISK ACQUISITION INC p 552
111 T C Jester Blvd 77007
Tel (713) 868-6111 SIC 1731 1623

■ FISK ELECTRIC CO p 552
10855 Westview Dr 77043
Tel (713) 868-6111 SIC 1731

■ FLEETWOOD RETAIL CORP p 555
2150 W 18th St Ste 300 77008
Tel (713) 965-0520 SIC 5271

FLEXITALLIC GROUP INC p 556
201 Kingwood Med Dr B20 Ste B 200 77067
Tel (281) 604-2525
SIC 3053 3533 3463 3965

FLEXSTEEL PIPELINE TECHNOLOGIES INC p 556
1201 La St Ste 2700 77002
Tel (832) 531-8555 SIC 3312

FLORIDA GAS TRANSMISSION CO LLC p 558
1300 Main St 77002
Tel (713) 989-7000 SIC 4923

▲ FLOTEK INDUSTRIES INC p 560
10603 W Sam Houston Pkwy 77064
Tel (713) 849-9911
SIC 2087 2869 2899 3533 3491

FLOWORKS INTERNATIONAL LLC p 560
515 Post Oak Blvd Ste 800 77027
Tel (713) 839-1753 SIC 5051 5023

▲ FMC TECHNOLOGIES INC p 562
5875 N Sam Houston Pkwy W 77086
Tel (281) 591-4000 SIC 3533

FORD MAC HAIK LTD p 565
10333 Katy Fwy 77024
Tel (713) 932-5000 SIC 5511

FORETHOUGHT FINANCIAL GROUP INC p 567
3200 Southwest Fwy # 1300 77027
Tel (713) 599-0405 SIC 6311

FORGINGS FLANGES & FITTINGS LLC p 567
8900 Railwood Dr Unit B 77078
Tel (713) 695-5400 SIC 5085

▲ FORUM ENERGY TECHNOLOGIES INC p 570
920 Memorial City Way # 1000 77024
Tel (281) 949-2500 SIC 3533

■ FORUM US INC p 570
10344 Sam Houston Park Dr 77064
Tel (713) 351-7900 SIC 1382

FRAMEWORK CAPITAL PARTNERS LLC p 573
1700 Post Oak Blvd 77056
Tel (713) 826-9351 SIC 6719

▲ FRANCESCAS HOLDINGS CORP p 573
8760 Clay Rd 77080
Tel (713) 864-1358 SIC 5621 5632

FRANKS INTERNATIONAL LLC p 575
10260 Westheimer Rd 77042
Tel (281) 966-7300 SIC 1382 7353

■ FREEPORT-MCMORAN OIL & GAS LLC p 577
700 Milam St Ste 3100 77002
Tel (713) 579-6000 SIC 1382

■ FRESHPOINT INC p 579
1390 Enclave Pkwy 77077
Tel (281) 899-4242 SIC 5148

FRIEDKIN COMPANIES INC p 579
1345 Enclave Pkwy 77077
Tel (713) 580-3300 SIC 5012 6211

FRONTIER PETROLEUM RESOURCES INC p 581
6200 Savoy Dr Ste 650 77036
Tel (832) 242-1510 SIC 2911 5172

FSI DEVCO INC p 582
1510 West Loop S 77027
Tel (713) 850-1010 SIC 5812

FSI RESTAURANT DEVELOPMENT LIMITED p 582
1510 West Loop S 77027
Tel (713) 386-7176 SIC 5812

FUGRO (USA) INC p 583
6100 Hillcroft St Ste 700 77081
Tel (713) 772-3700 SIC 1389 8711 8999

FUGRO CONSULTANTS INC p 583
6100 Hillcroft St Ste 100 77081
Tel (713) 369-5400 SIC 8711

■ FURMANITE AMERICA INC p 585
10370 Richmond Ave # 600 77042
Tel (713) 634-7777 SIC 7699

■ FURMANITE CORP p 585
10370 Richmond Ave # 600 77042
Tel (713) 634-7777 SIC 7699 7389

■ FURMANITE WORLDWIDE INC p 585
10370 Richmond Ave # 600 77042
Tel (972) 699-4000 SIC 7699 3599 7389

GAMMA CONSTRUCTION CO INC p 590
2808 Joanel St 77027
Tel (713) 963-0086 SIC 1542

▲ GASTAR EXPLORATION INC p 593
1331 Lamar St Ste 650 77010
Tel (713) 739-1800 SIC 1311

GC SERVICES LIMITED PARTNERSHIP p 595
6330 Gulfton St 77081
Tel (713) 777-4441 SIC 7322 7389

GDF SUEZ ENERGY DEVELOPMENT NA INC p 595
1990 Post Oak Blvd # 1900 77056
Tel (713) 636-0000 SIC 4911

GDF SUEZ ENERGY NORTH AMERICA INC p 595
1990 Post Oak Blvd # 1900 77056
Tel (713) 636-0000 SIC 1311 8741 1629

■ GE ENERGY MANUFACTURING INC p 596
1333 West Loop S Ste 700 77027
Tel (713) 803-0900 SIC 3621 3568 5084

GE OIL & GAS COMPRESSION SYSTEMS LLC p 596
16250 Port Nw 77041
Tel (713) 354-1900 SIC 1389

■ GE OIL & GAS PRESSURE CONTROL LP p 596
4424 W Sam Houston Pkwy N # 100 77041
Tel (281) 398-8901 SIC 3491

■ GE PACKAGED POWER INC p 596
1330 West Loop S Ste 1000 77027
Tel (713) 803-0900 SIC 3511

■ GE PACKAGED POWER LP p 596
16415 Jacintoport Blvd 77015
Tel (281) 452-3610 SIC 3511

GENERAL PLASTICS & COMPOSITES LP p 601
6910 E Orem Dr 77075
Tel (713) 644-1449 SIC 3083

■ GENESIS CRUDE OIL LP p 602
919 Milam St Ste 2100 77002
Tel (713) 860-2500 SIC 4612

▲ GENESIS ENERGY LP p 602
919 Milam St Ste 2100 77002
Tel (713) 860-2500 SIC 4612 5171 4212

■ GENON ENERGY HOLDINGS INC p 604
1000 Main St 77002
Tel (832) 357-3000 SIC 4911

■ GENON POWER MIDWEST LP p 604
1000 Main St 77002
Tel (713) 497-3000 SIC 4911

GEOKINETICS INC p 606
1500 Citywest Blvd # 800 77042
Tel (713) 850-7600 SIC 1382 7374

GEOKINETICS MANAGEMENT INC p 606
1500 City W Blvd Ste 800 77042
Tel (281) 870-8506 SIC 1382

■ GEORGIA WASTE SYSTEMS INC p 608
1001 Fannin St Ste 4000 77002
Tel (713) 512-6200 SIC 4953

GERLAND CORP p 608
3131 Pawnee St 77054
Tel (713) 746-3600 SIC 5411

■ GEXA ENERGY LP p 609
20455 State Highway 249 # 200 77070
Tel (713) 961-9399 SIC 4911

GHX INDUSTRIAL LLC p 610
3430 S Sam Houston Pkwy E 77047
Tel (713) 222-2231 SIC 3053 3052 3061

GIBSON APPLIED TECHNOLOGY & ENGINEERING (TEXAS) INC p 611
16360 Park Ten Pl Ste 206 77084
Tel (281) 398-5781 SIC 8711

GILLMAN INTERESTS INC p 612
10595 W Sam Huston Pkwy S 77099
Tel (713) 776-7000 SIC 5511

GLAZIER FOODS CO p 614
11303 Antoine Dr 77066
Tel (713) 869-6411 SIC 5142 5141

GLOBAL ENERGY SERVICES INC p 616
10307 Wallisville Rd 77013
Tel (281) 447-9000 SIC 3533

GLOBAL MARINE INC p 617
4 Greenway Plz Ste 100 77046
Tel (713) 232-7500 SIC 1381 1311

GLOBAL STAINLESS SUPPLY INC p 617
8900 Railwood Dr Unit A 77078
Tel (713) 980-0733 SIC 5051

GOODMAN GLOBAL HOLDINGS INC p 624
5151 San Felipe St # 500 77056
Tel (713) 861-2500 SIC 3585 3564

GOODMAN GLOBAL INC p 624
5151 San Felipe St # 500 77056
Tel (713) 861-2500 SIC 3585 3564

GOODMAN MANUFACTURING CO LP p 624
5151 San Felipe St # 500 77056
Tel (877) 254-4729 SIC 3585

■ GRANT PRIDECO INC p 631
10100 Houston Oaks Dr 77064
Tel (281) 878-8000 SIC 3533

GRDG HOLDINGS LLC p 633
19411 Atrium Pl Ste 170 77084
Tel (281) 578-2334 SIC 5945

GREATER HOUSTON COMMUNITY FOUNDATION p 635
5120 Woodway Dr Ste 6000 77056
Tel (713) 333-2200 SIC 8733

▲ GREEN BANCORP INC p 636
4000 Greenbriar St 77098
Tel (713) 275-8220 SIC 6021

GREEN BANK NATIONAL ASSOCIATION p 636
4000 Greenbriar St 77098
Tel (713) 275-8200 SIC 6029

■ GREENSTAR MID-AMERICA LLC p 638
1001 Fannin St Ste 4000 77002
Tel (713) 512-6200 SIC 4953

GREGORY PRICE INTERNATIONAL INC p 639
920 Mmrial Cy Way Ste 600 77024
Tel (713) 780-7500 SIC 1623

GREYSTAR CORP p 639
10375 Richmond Ave # 900 77042
Tel (713) 953-7007 SIC 1389

GREYSTAR MANAGEMENT SERVICES LP p 639
750 Bering Dr Ste 300 77057
Tel (713) 966-5000 SIC 6513 6531 1522

▲ GROUP 1 AUTOMOTIVE INC p 641
800 Gessner Rd Ste 500 77024
Tel (713) 647-5700
SIC 5511 6141 7538 7532 5531

GROUP MANAGEMENT 0002 LLC p 642
1321 Upland Dr 3966 77043
Tel (716) 998-3386 SIC 6411

GROVES INDUSTRIAL SUPPLY CORP p 642
7301 Pinemont Dr 77040
Tel (713) 675-4747 SIC 5085 5084 5198

GSE ENVIRONMENTAL INC p 643
19103 Gundle Rd 77073
Tel (281) 443-8564 SIC 3081 1799

GSE ENVIRONMENTAL LLC p 643
19103 Gundle Rd 77073
Tel (281) 443-8564 SIC 3081

GSE HOLDING INC p 643
19103 Gundle Rd 77073
Tel (281) 443-8564 SIC 3081 6719

GULF COAST REGIONAL BLOOD CENTER p 646
1400 La Concha Ln 77054
Tel (713) 790-1200 SIC 8099 7371 7363

GULF INTERNATIONAL CORP p 646
16010 Barkers Point Ln 77079
Tel (713) 850-3400 SIC 8711

GULF INTERSTATE ENGINEERING CO p 646
16010 Barkers Point Ln # 600 77079
Tel (713) 850-3400 SIC 8711

▲ GULF ISLAND FABRICATION INC p 646
16225 Park Ten Pl Ste 280 77084
Tel (713) 714-6100 SIC 3441 1389

GULF PACIFIC INC p 646
12010 Taylor Rd 77041
Tel (713) 464-0606 SIC 5153 0723

■ GULF SOUTH PIPELINE CO LP p 647
9 Greenway Plz Ste 2800 77046
Tel (888) 315-5005 SIC 4923

GULF STATES FINANCIAL SERVICES INC p 647
1375 Enclave Pkwy 77077
Tel (713) 580-3000 SIC 6411

GULF STATES TOYOTA INC p 647
1375 Enclave Pkwy 77077
Tel (713) 580-3300 SIC 5012 5013

GULF WINDS INTERNATIONAL INC p 647
411 Brisbane St 77061
Tel (713) 747-4909 SIC 4225 4731

■ GULFMARK ENERGY INC p 647
17 S Briar Hollow Ln # 100 77027
Tel (210) 524-9725 SIC 5172

▲ GULFMARK OFFSHORE INC p 647
842 W Sam Houston Pkwy N 77024
Tel (713) 963-9522 SIC 4412

GYRODATA INC p 649
23000 Nw Lake Dr 77095
Tel (713) 461-3146 SIC 1389 8713

▲ HALCON RESOURCES CORP p 653
1000 La St Ste 6700 77002
Tel (832) 538-0300 SIC 1311

▲ HALLIBURTON CO p 654
3000 N Sam Houston Pkwy E 77032
Tel (281) 871-2699
SIC 1389 1382 1381 8711

■ **HALLIBURTON DELAWARE INC** p 654
3000 Houston Ave 77009
Tel (713) 759-2600
SIC 1629 1611 1622 8711 1389

■ **HALLIBURTON ENERGY SERVICES INC** p 654
10200 Bellaire Blvd 77072
Tel (713) 839-3950 SIC 1389

HANDY HARDWARE WHOLESALE INC p 657
8300 Tewantin Dr 77061
Tel (713) 644-1495
SIC 5072 5074 5063 5031 5198

HARMONY PUBLIC SCHOOLS p 662
9321 W Sam Houston Pkwy S 77099
Tel (281) 888-9764 SIC 8211

■ **HARRIS CAPROCK COMMUNICATIONS INC** p 663
4400 S Sam Houston Pkwy E 77048
Tel (888) 482-0289 SIC 4813

HARRIS CENTER FOR MENTAL HEALTH AND IDD p 663
9401 Southwest Fwy 77074
Tel (713) 970-7000 SIC 8063

HARRIS COUNTY DEPARTMENT OF EDUCATION PUBLIC FACILITY CORP p 663
6300 Irvington Blvd 77022
Tel (713) 694-6300 SIC 8299

HARRIS HEALTH SYSTEM p 663
2525 Holly Hall St 77054
Tel (713) 566-6400 SIC 8062 8011

HAVERHILL CHEMICALS LLC p 668
16800 Imperial Valley Dr # 499 77060
Tel (281) 885-8900 SIC 2899

HCC INSURANCE HOLDINGS INC p 672
13403 Northwest Fwy 77040
Tel (713) 690-7300 SIC 6311 6321 6331

HDC DISTRIBUTING LTD p 673
7100 High Life Dr 77066
Tel (281) 880-2730 SIC 5199

HEALTH CARE TEMPORARIES INC p 674
8926 Sherbourne St Ste D 77016
Tel (713) 631-7106
SIC 8082 1542 1522 1081 5082

HEARST NEWSPAPERS LLC p 678
4747 Southwest Fwy 77027
Tel (713) 220-7171 SIC 2711

HEAT TRANSFER SOLUTIONS INC p 679
3350 Yale St 77018
Tel (832) 328-1010 SIC 5075

HEATH CONSULTANTS INC p 679
9030 W Monroe Rd 77061
Tel (713) 844-1300 SIC 8711 3826 3812

▲ **HELIX ENERGY SOLUTIONS GROUP INC** p 681
3505 W Sam Houston Pkwy N 77043
Tel (281) 618-0400 SIC 1629 1389 1311

■ **HERCULES DRILLING CO LLC** p 685
9 Greenway Plz Ste 2200 77046
Tel (713) 350-5100 SIC 8741

▲ **HERCULES OFFSHORE INC** p 685
9 Greenway Plz Ste 2200 77046
Tel (713) 350-5100 SIC 1381 1389

▲ **HI-CRUSH PARTNERS LP** p 689
3 Riverway Ste 1350 77056
Tel (713) 960-4777 SIC 1442 1481

HIGHLANDS INSURANCE GROUP INC p 691
10370 Richmond Ave 77042
Tel (713) 952-0665 SIC 6331 6351

HIGHMOUNT EXPLORATION & PRODUCTION LLC p 692
16945 Northchase Dr # 1750 77060
Tel (281) 873-1500 SIC 1382

HIGHWAY TECHNOLOGIES INC p 692
6811 Dixie Dr 77087
Tel (713) 845-1800 SIC 1622 7359

HILCORP ENERGY CO p 692
1111 Travis St 77002
Tel (713) 209-2400 SIC 1311 1382

HINES GLOBAL REIT INC p 695
2800 Post Oak Blvd # 5000 77056
Tel (888) 220-6121 SIC 6798

HINES INTERESTS LIMITED PARTNERSHIP p 695
2800 Post Oak Blvd # 4800 77056
Tel (713) 621-8000 SIC 6552

HINES REAL ESTATE INVESTMENT TRUST INC p 695
2800 Post Oak Blvd # 4800 77056
Tel (713) 621-8000 SIC 6798

HIS CO INC p 696
6650 Concord Park Dr 77040
Tel (713) 934-1600 SIC 5065 5063

■ **HOLLIDAY FENOGLIO FOWLER LP** p 701
9 Greenway Plz Ste 700 77046
Tel (713) 852-3500 SIC 6162

HOLLOMAN CORP p 701
333 N Sam Houston Pkwy E 77060
Tel (281) 878-2600 SIC 1541 1623 1389

HOLLOWAY-HOUSTON INC p 701
5833 Armour Dr 77020
Tel (713) 674-5631 SIC 5072

HOOVER GROUP INC p 706
2135 Highway 6 S 77077
Tel (800) 844-8683
SIC 3496 3412 3443 3089 7359 3411

HOOVER MATERIALS HANDLING GROUP INC p 706
2135 Highway 6 S 77077
Tel (800) 844-8683 SIC 5113 3089

HOUSTON BAPTIST UNIVERSITY p 712
7502 Fondren Rd 77074
Tel (281) 649-3000 SIC 8221 8661

HOUSTON CASUALTY CO p 712
13403 Northwest Fwy 77040
Tel (713) 462-1000 SIC 6331

HOUSTON COMMUNITY COLLEGE INC p 712
3100 Main St Ste Mc1148 77002
Tel (713) 718-5001 SIC 8222

HOUSTON FOAM PLASTICS INC p 712
2019 Brooks St 77026
Tel (713) 224-3484 SIC 3086

HOUSTON FOOD BANK p 712
535 Portwall St 77029
Tel (713) 223-3700 SIC 8399

HOUSTON INDEPENDENT SCHOOL DISTRICT p 712
4400 W 18th St 77092
Tel (713) 556-6005 SIC 8211

HOUSTON INTERNATIONAL INSURANCE GROUP LTD p 712
800 Gessner Rd Ste 600 77024
Tel (713) 935-4800 SIC 6331

HOUSTON LIVESTOCK SHOW AND RODEO EDUCATIONAL FUND p 712
8334 Nrg Park Fl 2 77054
Tel (832) 667-1000 SIC 7999

HOUSTON LIVESTOCK SHOW AND RODEO INC p 712
8334 Nrg Park 77054
Tel (832) 667-1000 SIC 7313

■ **HOUSTON NORTH POLE LINE** p 712
1608 Margaret St 77093
Tel (713) 691-3616 SIC 1623

■ **HOUSTON NORTHWEST MEDICAL CENTER INC** p 712
710 Cypress Creek Pkwy # 34 77090
Tel (281) 440-1000 SIC 8062

■ **HOUSTON NORTHWEST MEDICAL CENTER EDUCATION FOUNDATION INC** p 712
710 Cypress Station Dr # 340 77090
Tel (281) 440-1000 SIC 8062

HOUSTON SERIES OF LOCKTON COMPANIES LLC p 712
5847 San Felipe St # 320 77057
Tel (713) 458-5200 SIC 6411

■ **HOUSTON SYSCO INC** p 712
10710 Grens Crossing Blvd 77038
Tel (713) 672-8080
SIC 5149 5142 5046 5141 2099

HOUSTON TRIBOLOGY SALES & MARKETING OFFICE p 712
10450 Stncliff Rd Ste 210 77099
Tel (281) 599-1242 SIC 8742

▲ **HOUSTON WIRE & CABLE CO INC** p 712
10201 North Loop E 77029
Tel (713) 609-2100 SIC 5063

HOUSTON-GALVESTON AREA COUNCIL p 712
3555 Timmons Ln Ste 120 77027
Tel (713) 627-3200 SIC 6035

HOWCO METALS MANAGEMENT LLC p 713
9611 Telge Rd 77095
Tel (281) 649-8800 SIC 5051 3999 8741

HTI LTD p 715
10555 Westpark Dr 77042
Tel (713) 266-3900 SIC 5075

HUNTER BUILDINGS LLC p 719
14935 Jacintoport Blvd 77015
Tel (281) 452-9800 SIC 1542

HUNTING ENERGY SERVICES INC p 719
2 Northpoint Dr Ste 400 77060
Tel (281) 820-3838 SIC 1389 8741

HUNTING INNOVA INC p 719
8383 N Sam Houston Pkwy W 77064
Tel (281) 653-5500 SIC 3672 3613 8711

■ **HWC WIRE & CABLE CO** p 722
10201 North Loop E 77029
Tel (713) 609-2160 SIC 5063

HYDRAQUIP INC p 723
16330 Central Green Blvd # 200 77032
Tel (713) 680-1951 SIC 5084

HYDRIL CO p 723
302 Mccarty St 77029
Tel (713) 670-3500 SIC 3533

■ **HYDRIL USA DISTRIBUTION LLC** p 723
3300 N Sam Houston Pkwy E 77032
Tel (281) 449-2000 SIC 3533

HYDRIL USA MANUFACTURING LLC p 723
3300 N Sam Houston Pkwy E 77032
Tel (281) 449-2000 SIC 3069

IDERA INC p 729
2950 North Loop W Ste 700 77092
Tel (713) 523-4433 SIC 7371 7372

■ **IES COMMERCIAL INC** p 730
5433 Westheimer Rd # 500 77056
Tel (713) 860-1500 SIC 1731

IFCO SYSTEMS NORTH AMERICA LLC p 730
13100 Nw Fwy Ste 625 77040
Tel (888) 714-2430 SIC 2448

▲ **IGNITE RESTAURANT GROUP INC** p 730
10555 Richmond Ave # 100 77042
Tel (713) 366-7500 SIC 5812 6794

IHI E&C INTERNATIONAL CORP p 731
1080 Eldridge Pkwy 77077
Tel (713) 270-3100 SIC 8711

■ **ILLINOIS POWER GENERATING CO** p 732
601 Travis St Ste 1400 77002
Tel (713) 507-6400 SIC 4911

INDEPENDENCE CONTRACT DRILLING INC p 736
11601 N Galayda St 77086
Tel (281) 598-1230 SIC 1381

INDUS ENTERPRISES INC p 739
7051 Southwest Fwy 77074
Tel (713) 784-4335 SIC 5149 5194 5912

INNOVATIVE ENERGY SERVICES INC p 744
16600 Park Row 77084
Tel (281) 392-5199 SIC 5084

INSPECTORATE AMERICA CORP p 746
12000 Aerospace Ave # 200 77034
Tel (713) 944-2000 SIC 7389 8734 8731

INSPECTORATE AMERICA HOLDING INC p 746
12000 Aerospace Ave # 200 77034
Tel (713) 944-2000 SIC 7389 8734

INSTITUTE FOR REHABILITATION & RESEARCH p 747
1333 Moursund St 77030
Tel (713) 799-5000 SIC 8062

INTEGRA US MARKETING LLC p 748
5075 Westheimer Rd # 790 77056
Tel (713) 224-2044 SIC 8742

▲ **INTEGRATED ELECTRICAL SERVICES INC** p 749
5433 Westheimer Rd # 500 77056
Tel (713) 860-1500 SIC 1731

■ **INTEGRATED PRODUCTION SERVICES INC** p 749
16800 Greenspt Pk Dr 200s 77060
Tel (281) 774-6700 SIC 1389 3599

INTERNATIONAL PAINT LLC p 756
6001 Antoine Dr 77091
Tel (713) 682-1711 SIC 2851

INTERNATIONAL TRUCKS OF HOUSTON LLC p 757
8900 North Loop E 77029
Tel (713) 674-3444 SIC 5511 5531

INTERTEK USA INC p 759
2 Riverway Ste 500 77056
Tel (713) 543-3600 SIC 4785 8734

INTSEL STEEL DISTRIBUTORS LLC p 760
11310 W Little York Rd 77041
Tel (713) 937-9500 SIC 5051 3312 3444

INVENSYS PROCESSS SYSTEMS INC p 761
10900 Equity Dr 77041
Tel (713) 329-1600 SIC 3822

INVENSYS SYSTEMS INC p 761
10900 Equity Dr 77041
Tel (713) 329-1600 SIC 3823 8711 8741

■ **INVESCO AIM ADVISORS INC** p 761
11 Greenway Plz Ste 2500 77046
Tel (713) 626-1919 SIC 6722

▲ **ION GEOPHYSICAL CORP** p 762
2105 Citywest Blvd # 900 77042
Tel (281) 933-3339 SIC 7372 3829

■ **IOS/PCI LLC** p 762
652 N Sam Houston Pkwy E 77060
Tel (281) 310-5357 SIC 1389 7389

■ **IPH II LLC** p 763
601 Travis St Ste 1400 77002
Tel (713) 507-6400 SIC 4939

■ **IPH LLC** p 763
601 Travis St Ste 1400 77002
Tel (713) 507-6400 SIC 4911

IPSCO TUBULARS INC p 764
10120 Houston Oaks Dr 77064
Tel (281) 949-1023 SIC 3498

IRONGATE ENERGY SERVICES LLC p 765
19500 State Highway 249 # 600 77070
Tel (832) 678-8585 SIC 1389

ISC ACQUISITION CORP p 766
7645 Railhead Ln 77086
Tel (281) 590-6000 SIC 5032 5031

J AND L HOLDING CO INC p 770
12235 Robin Blvd 77045
Tel (713) 434-7600 SIC 5171

J B POINDEXTER & CO INC p 770
600 Travis St Ste 200 77002
Tel (713) 655-9800 SIC 3713

J D FIELDS & CO INC p 770
55 Waugh Dr Ste 1250 77007
Tel (281) 558-7199 SIC 5051 7359 3443

J D RUSH CORP p 770
2 Northpoint Dr Ste 150 77060
Tel (281) 558-8004 SIC 3498 5051

JT VAUGHN ENTERPRISES INC p 772
10355 Westpark Dr 77042
Tel (713) 243-8300 SIC 1542

■ **JA APPAREL CORP** p 772
6380 Rogerdale Rd 77072
Tel (877) 986-9669 SIC 5136

■ **JACINTOPORT INTERNATIONAL LLC** p 773
16398 Jacintoport Blvd 77015
Tel (281) 457-2415 SIC 4491

JACKSON SUPPLY CO p 774
6655 Roxburgh Dr Ste 100 77041
Tel (713) 849-5865 SIC 5075

■ **JACOBS FIELD SERVICES NORTH AMERICA INC** p 775
5995 Rogerdale Rd 77072
Tel (832) 351-6000 SIC 8711

■ **JACOBS P&C US INC** p 775
3600 Briarpark Dr 77042
Tel (713) 988-2002 SIC 1629

JAKES INC p 776
13400 Hollister Dr 77086
Tel (713) 868-1301 SIC 5144 5142 5141

JAM DISTRIBUTING CO p 776
7010 Mykawa Rd 77033
Tel (713) 844-7788 SIC 5172

JEFFERSON ENERGY I LP p 781
3104 Edloe St Ste 205 77027
Tel (713) 552-0002 SIC 1389 5051

JIFFY LUBE INTERNATIONAL INC p 785
700 Milam St 77002
Tel (713) 546-1400 SIC 7549

JOHN L WORTHAM & SON LP p 789
2727 Allen Pkwy 77019
Tel (713) 526-3366 SIC 6411

JOHN WOOD GROUP US HOLDINGS INC p 789
17325 Park Row Ste 500 77084
Tel (281) 828-3500 SIC 4581

JOHNSON SUPPLY AND EQUIPMENT CORP p 791
10151 Stella Link Rd 77025
Tel (713) 830-2300 SIC 5075

JUST ENERGY (US) CORP p 797
5251 Westheimr Rd # 1000 77056
Tel (713) 850-6784 SIC 3621 4924

■ **K&G MENS CO INC** p 799
6380 Rogerdale Rd 77072
Tel (281) 776-7000 SIC 5611 5621

■ **KAYO OIL CO** p 805
600 N Dairy Ashford Rd 77079
Tel (281) 293-1000 SIC 5541 5411

■ **KBR HOLDINGS LLC** p 806
601 Jefferson St Ste 7911 77002
Tel (713) 753-4176 SIC 1629 8711 8741

▲ **KBR INC** p 806
601 Jefferson St Ste 3400 77002
Tel (713) 753-3011 SIC 1629 8711 8741

KEANE GROUP HOLDINGS LLC p 807
11200 Westheimer Rd # 900 77042
Tel (713) 960-0381 SIC 1381 7353 4212

■ **KELLOGG BROWN & ROOT LLC** p 808
601 Jefferson St Ste 100 77002
Tel (713) 753-2000 SIC 8711 1629

KENMOR ELECTRIC CO LP p 810
8330 Hansen Rd 77075
Tel (713) 869-0171 SIC 1731

KEY ENERGY DRILLING INC p 814
1301 Mckinney St Ste 1800 77010
Tel (432) 620-0300 SIC 1381

KEY ENERGY SERVICES INC p 814
1301 Mckinney St Ste 1800 77010
Tel (713) 651-4300 SIC 1389 1381 1311

■ **KHOU-TV INC** p 816
1945 Allen Pkwy 77019
Tel (713) 284-1011 SIC 4833

KIK INTERNATIONAL HOUSTON INC p 817
2921 Corder St 77054
Tel (713) 747-8710 SIC 5999

■ **KINDER MORGAN BULK TERMINALS LLC** p 819
1001 Louisiana St # 1000 77002
Tel (713) 369-9000 SIC 4491

■ **KINDER MORGAN ENERGY PARTNERS LP** p 819
1001 La St Ste 1000 77002
Tel (713) 369-9000
SIC 4613 4925 4922 4226 4619 5171

▲ **KINDER MORGAN INC** p 819
1001 La St Ste 1000 77002
Tel (713) 369-9000 SIC 4922

■ **KINDER MORGAN KANSAS INC** p 819
1001 La St Ste 1000 77002
Tel (713) 369-9000 SIC 4922 4924

■ **KINDER MORGAN LIQUIDS TERMINALS LLC** p 819
500 Dallas St Ste 1000 77002
Tel (713) 369-8758 SIC 4226

■ **KINDER MORGAN PRODUCTION CO LP** p 819
1001 La St Ste 1000 77002
Tel (800) 525-3752 SIC 5172

KING RANCH INC p 820
3 Riverway Ste 1600 77056
Tel (832) 681-5700
SIC 0212 2711 5083 5948

KIPP INC p 821
10711 Kipp Way Dr 77099
Tel (832) 328-1051 SIC 8211

▲ **KIRBY CORP** p 821
55 Waugh Dr Ste 1000 77007
Tel (713) 435-1000 SIC 4449 7699

■ **KIRBY INLAND MARINE LP** p 821
55 Waugh Dr Ste 1000 77007
Tel (713) 435-1000 SIC 4449

■ **KIRBY OFFSHORE MARINE LLC** p 821
55 Waugh Dr Ste 1000 77007
Tel (713) 435-1000 SIC 5172 4212 4213

KNIGHT-CHEMSTAR INC p 824
9204 Emmott Rd 77040
Tel (713) 466-8751 *SIC* 5169 5172

▲ KRATON CORP p 829
15710 John F Kennedy Blvd # 300 77032
Tel (281) 504-4700 *SIC* 2821

■ KRATON POLYMERS LLC p 829
15710 John F Kennedy Blvd # 300 77032
Tel (281) 504-4700 *SIC* 2822

■ KRATON POLYMERS US LLC p 829
15710 John F Kennedy Blvd # 300 77032
Tel (281) 504-4700 *SIC* 2822

■ KRONOS (US) INC p 830
14950 Heathrow Ste 230 77032
Tel (281) 423-3300 *SIC* 5169

KS MANAGEMENT SERVICES LLC p 831
2727 W Holcombe Blvd 77025
Tel (713) 442-0000 *SIC* 8741

KURARAY AMERICA INC p 832
2625 Bay Area Blvd # 600 77058
Tel (281) 474-1592 *SIC* 2821 3081 3843

KURARAY HOLDINGS USA INC p 832
2625 Bay Area Blvd 77058
Tel (713) 495-7311 *SIC* 5047 5049 2821

KW INTERNATIONAL LLC p 832
10880 Alcott Dr 77043
Tel (713) 468-9581 *SIC* 3533

L E SIMMONS & ASSOCIATES INC p 834
600 Travis St Ste 6600 77002
Tel (713) 227-7888 *SIC* 6799

LA VOZ PUBLISHING CORP p 836
4747 Southwest Fwy 77027
Tel (713) 664-4404 *SIC* 2711

■ LAKESHORE ENERGY SERVICES LLC p 840
1415 La St Ste 4200 77002
Tel (888) 200-3788 *SIC* 4924

■ LAMONS GASKET CO p 841
7300 Airport Blvd 77061
Tel (713) 547-9527 *SIC* 3053 5085

■ LANDCARE USA INC p 842
2603 Augusta Dr Ste 1300 77057
Tel (713) 692-6371 *SIC* 0783 0782

LANDMARK FBO LLC p 843
1500 Citywest Blvd # 600 77042
Tel (713) 895-9243 *SIC* 4581

■ LANDMARK GRAPHICS CORP p 843
2107 Citywest Blvd Bldg 2 77042
Tel (713) 839-2000 *SIC* 7371 7373

LANDMARK INDUSTRIES HOLDINGS LTD p 843
11111 S Wilcrest Dr 77099
Tel (713) 789-0310 *SIC* 5411 5541

LANDRYS GAMING INC p 843
1510 West Loop S 77027
Tel (713) 850-1010 *SIC* 7011

LANDRYS INC p 843
1510 West Loop S 77027
Tel (713) 850-1010 *SIC* 5812

LASON INC p 846
11850 Hempstead Rd # 270 77092
Tel (713) 957-0800 *SIC* 7376

LAURA AND JOHN ARNOLD FOUNDATION p 847
2800 Post Oak Blvd # 225 77056
Tel (713) 554-1349 *SIC* 8699

LAW OFFICES OF ETHERIDGE & OUGRAH LLP p 847
340 N Sam Houston Pkwy E 77060
Tel (832) 563-3620 *SIC* 8111

▲ LAZARUS ENERGY HOLDINGS LLC p 849
801 Travis St Ste 2100 77002
Tel (713) 850-0500 *SIC* 2911

LEE SUMMER HOLDINGS LLC p 851
600 Travis St Ste 5800 77002
Tel (713) 993-4610 *SIC* 6799

LEGACY COMMUNITY HEALTH SERVICES INC p 852
1415 California St 77006
Tel (713) 830-3000 *SIC* 8093 8011

LETSOS CO p 857
8435 Westglen Dr 77063
Tel (713) 783-3200 *SIC* 1711 7623

LEWIS FOOD TOWN INC p 858
3131 Pawnee St 77054
Tel (713) 746-3600 *SIC* 5411

LINBECK GROUP LLC p 866
3900 Essex Ln Ste 1200 77027
Tel (713) 621-2350 *SIC* 1542

■ LINN ACQUISITION CO LLC p 869
600 Travis St Ste 4900 77002
Tel (281) 840-4000 *SIC* 1311

▲ LINN ENERGY LLC p 869
600 Travis St Ste 5100 77002
Tel (281) 840-4000 *SIC* 1311

■ LINN OPERATING INC p 869
600 Travis St Ste 5100 77002
Tel (713) 227-1868 *SIC* 1382

▲ LINNCO LLC p 869
600 Travis St Ste 5100 77002
Tel (281) 840-4000 *SIC* 1311

LITTON LOAN SERVICING LP p 871
4828 Loop Central Dr # 104 77081
Tel (713) 960-9676 *SIC* 6162

LIVE NATION MUSIC GROUP TEXAS INC p 871
2000 West Loop S Ste 1300 77027
Tel (713) 693-8152 *SIC* 7922 6512

LNG FREEPORT DEVELOPMENT L P p 872
333 Clay St Ste 5050 77002
Tel (713) 980-2888 *SIC* 4922

LOCKWOOD INTERNATIONAL INC p 873
10203 Wallisville Rd 77013
Tel (866) 898-2583 *SIC* 5085

LOGAN OIL TOOLS INC p 874
11006 Lucerne St 77016
Tel (281) 219-6613 *SIC* 5082

LOGIX COMMUNICATIONS LP p 875
2950 North Loop W Ste 140 77092
Tel (713) 862-2000 *SIC* 4813

■ LONE STAR NGL PIPELINE LP p 876
1300 Main St 10 77002
Tel (210) 403-7300 *SIC* 4924 1321

LOOMIS ARMORED US LLC p 877
2500 Citywest Blvd # 2300 77042
Tel (713) 435-6700 *SIC* 7381 4789

■ LRR ENERGY LP p 882
1111 Bagby St Ste 4600 77002
Tel (713) 292-9510 *SIC* 1311

LSRI HOLDINGS INC p 883
1510 West Loop S 77027
Tel (713) 850-1010 *SIC* 5812

▲ LUBYS INC p 884
13111 Nw Fwy Ste 600 77040
Tel (713) 329-6800 *SIC* 5812

■ LUBYS RESTAURANTS LIMITED PARTNERSHIP p 884
13111 Nw Fwy Ste 600 77040
Tel (713) 329-6800 *SIC* 5812

LVDE CORP p 887
5100 San Felipe St 244e 77056
Tel (713) 840-1489 *SIC* 4911

LYONDELL CHEMICAL CO p 888
1221 Mckinney St Ste 300 77010
Tel (713) 309-7200 *SIC* 2869 2911

LYONDELL CHEMICAL WORLDWIDE INC p 888
1221 Mckinney St Ste 1600 77010
Tel (713) 652-7200 *SIC* 2869

LYONDELLBASELL INDUSTRIES INC p 888
1221 Mckinney St Ste 700 77010
Tel (713) 309-7200 *SIC* 2821

M-I LLC p 890
5950 N Course Dr 77072
Tel (281) 561-1300
SIC 1389 2865 2869 8711 8741

M3 MIDSTREAM LLC p 891
600 Travis St Ste 5600 77002
Tel (713) 783-3000 *SIC* 1311

MAC HAIK ENTERPRISES p 891
11757 Katy Fwy Ste 1500 77079
Tel (281) 496-7788 *SIC* 5511

MAC PARENT LLC p 891
3100 S Gessner Rd Ste 125 77063
Tel (832) 649-2260 *SIC* 5812 6794

MACQUARIE ENERGY LLC p 893
500 Dallas St 31 77002
Tel (713) 275-6100 *SIC* 6221

MAGNUM STAFFING SERVICES INC p 897
2900 Smith St Ste 250 77006
Tel (713) 658-0068 *SIC* 7363

MAHINDRA USA INC p 897
9020 Jackrabbit Rd # 600 77095
Tel (281) 449-7771 *SIC* 5083

▲ MAIN STREET CAPITAL CORP p 898
1300 Post Oak Blvd 77056
Tel (713) 350-6000 *SIC* 6211

■ MARATHON INTERNATIONAL OIL CO p 904
5555 San Felipe St # 2796 77056
Tel (713) 629-6600 *SIC* 1311 1382 6519

■ MARATHON OIL CO p 904
5555 San Felipe St # 2796 77056
Tel (713) 629-6600
SIC 2911 5171 5541 1311 4612 4613

▲ MARATHON OIL CORP p 904
5555 San Felipe St # 2796 77056
Tel (713) 629-6600
SIC 1311 2911 5171 5541

MAREK BROTHERS SYSTEMS INC p 905
2115 Judiway St 77018
Tel (713) 681-9213 *SIC* 1742

MARTIN ENERGY SERVICES LLC p 912
3 Riverway Ste 400 77056
Tel (713) 350-6800
SIC 5171 4492 5172 5551

MATTRESS FIRM HOLDING CORP p 921
10201 Main St 77025
Tel (713) 923-1090 *SIC* 5712

MATTRESS FIRM INC p 921
10201 Main St 77025
Tel (713) 923-1090 *SIC* 5712

MATTRESS GIANT CORP p 921
5815 Gulf Fwy 77023
Tel (713) 923-1090 *SIC* 5712

MATTRESS HOLDING CORP p 921
5815 Gulf Fwy 77023
Tel (713) 923-1090 *SIC* 5712

MAVERICK TUBE CORP p 921
2200 West Loop S Ste 800 77027
Tel (713) 767-4400 *SIC* 3317

MAXXAM INC p 923
1330 Post Oak Blvd # 2000 77056
Tel (832) 251-5960 *SIC* 6531 7948

MB BARTER (USA) INC p 924
3388 Sage Rd Unit 402e 77056
Tel (713) 505-1303 *SIC* 2821

MCCOMBS ENERGY LTD p 927
5599 Saint Felipe St 12 # 1200 77056
Tel (713) 621-0033 *SIC* 1311

MCCORMICK & SCHMICK MANAGEMENT GROUP p 927
1510 West Loop S 77027
Tel (512) 836-0500 *SIC* 5812

MCCORMICK & SCHMICKS SEAFOOD RESTAURANTS INC p 927
1510 West Loop S 77027
Tel (800) 552-6379 *SIC* 5812

MCCORVEY SHEET METAL WORKS LP p 927
8610 Wallisville Rd 77029
Tel (713) 672-7545 *SIC* 3444

MCCOY-ROCKFORD INC p 927
6869 Old Katy Rd 77024
Tel (713) 862-4600 *SIC* 5021 1799

■ MCDERMOTT INC p 927
757 N Eldridge Pkwy # 101 77079
Tel (281) 870-5000 *SIC* 1629

▲ MCDERMOTT INTERNATIONAL INC p 927
757 N Eldridge Pkwy 77079
Tel (281) 870-5000 *SIC* 1389 1623

■ MCDERMOTT INVESTMENTS LLC p 927
757 N Eldridge Pkwy # 101 77079
Tel (281) 870-5000 *SIC* 1629

MCGRAW-EDISON CO p 929
600 Travis St Ste 5400 77002
Tel (713) 209-8400
SIC 3613 3641 3645 3646

MCGUYER HOMEBUILDERS INC p 929
7676 Woodway Dr Ste 104 77063
Tel (713) 952-6767 *SIC* 1531 1521

MEDPLAST GROUP INC p 938
7865 Northcourt Rd # 100 77040
Tel (480) 553-6400 *SIC* 3089

MEI TECHNOLOGIES INC p 940
18050 Saturn Ln Ste 300 77058
Tel (281) 283-6200 *SIC* 8711 8733

MEMORIAL HERMANN HEALTH SYSTEM p 941
909 Frostwood Dr Fl 2 77024
Tel (713) 242-3000 *SIC* 8062 8093

MEMORIAL HERMANN HEALTHCARE SYSTEM p 941
929 Gessner Rd 77024
Tel (713) 338-5555 *SIC* 8059 8062

MEMORIAL HERMANN MEDICAL GROUP p 942
909 Frostwood Dr Fl 2 77024
Tel (713) 448-5555 *SIC* 8099

MEMORIAL HERMANN TEXAS MEDICAL p 942
6411 Fannin St 77030
Tel (713) 704-4000 *SIC* 8062

▲ MEMORIAL PRODUCTION PARTNERS LP p 942
500 Dallas St Ste 1800 77002
Tel (713) 588-8300 *SIC* 1311

■ MENS WEARHOUSE INC p 943
6380 Rogerdale Rd 77072
Tel (281) 776-7000
SIC 5611 5621 5632 5661 5699

MERICHEM CO p 948
5455 Old Spanish Trl 77023
Tel (713) 428-5000 *SIC* 2911

■ MERRILL LYNCH COMMODITIES INC p 950
20 Greenway Plz Ste 950 77046
Tel (832) 681-5904 *SIC* 6211 6091

METHODIST HEALTH CARE SYSTEM p 953
6565 Fannin St D200 77030
Tel (713) 793-1602 *SIC* 8011

METHODIST HOSPITAL p 953
6565 Fannin St 77030
Tel (713) 790-3311 *SIC* 8062

METHODIST WEST HOUSTON HOSPITAL p 954
18500 Katy Fwy 77094
Tel (832) 522-1000 *SIC* 8661 8062

METRO NATIONAL CORP p 955
945 Bunker Hill Rd # 400 77024
Tel (713) 973-6400 *SIC* 6512 6531 6722

METROPOLITAN TRANSIT AUTHORITY OF HARRIS COUNTY p 956
1900 Main St 77002
Tel (713) 635-4000 *SIC* 4119

MEXICAN RESTAURANTS INC p 957
12000 Aerospace Ave # 400 77034
Tel (832) 300-5858 *SIC* 5812 6794 5046

MHI PARTNERSHIP LTD p 959
7676 Woodway Dr Ste 104 77063
Tel (713) 952-6767 *SIC* 1531

MID-AMERICA PIPELINE CO LLC p 963
1100 La St Ste 1000 77002
Tel (713) 880-6500 *SIC* 4922

■ MIDCOAST ENERGY PARTNERS LP p 964
1100 La St Ste 3300 77002
Tel (713) 821-2000 *SIC* 1311 4923

■ MIDCOAST OPERATING LP p 964
1100 La St Ste 3300 77002
Tel (713) 821-2000 *SIC* 5172 1389

MIDWAY IMPORTING INC p 967
1807 Brittmoore Rd 77043
Tel (713) 802-9363 *SIC* 5122

■ MIKE HALL CHEVROLET INC p 968
8100 Highway 6 S 77083
Tel (281) 561-9900 *SIC* 5511

MIKEN SPECIALTIES LTD p 968
10343 Sam Houston Park Dr 77064
Tel (979) 265-9599 *SIC* 1721 1799

MILAGRO OIL & GAS INC p 968
1301 Mckinney St Ste 500 77010
Tel (713) 750-1600 *SIC* 1382

MITSUBISHI CATERPILLAR FORKLIFT AMERICA INC p 977
2121 W Sam Houston Pkwy N 77043
Tel (713) 365-1000 *SIC* 3537 5084

MITSUBISHI HEAVY INDUSTRIES AMERICA INC p 977
20 Greenway Plz Ste 830 77046
Tel (346) 308-8800 *SIC* 5084

■ MOBIL PRODUCING TEXAS AND NEW MEXICO INC p 980
9 Greenway Plz 2700 77046
Tel (713) 871-5000 *SIC* 1311

MODEC INTERNATIONAL INC p 980
15011 Katy Fwy Ste 500 77094
Tel (281) 529-8100 *SIC* 8711 2499 3731

MORRISON ENERGY GROUP p 990
16285 Park Ten Pl 77084
Tel (281) 616-8405 *SIC* 1389

MORTONS RESTAURANT GROUP INC p 991
1510 West Loop S 77027
Tel (713) 850-1010 *SIC* 5812

MOSSY HOLDING CO INC p 992
12150 Old Katy Rd 77079
Tel (281) 558-9970 *SIC* 5511 6159 7532

MOTIVA ENTERPRISES LLC p 992
500 Dallas St 77002
Tel (713) 241-6161 *SIC* 2911 5541

MPG PIPELINE CONTRACTORS LLC p 995
16770 Imperial Valley Dr # 105 77060
Tel (713) 904-1168 *SIC* 1623

■ MRC GLOBAL (US) INC p 996
1301 Mckinney St Ste 2300 77010
Tel (877) 294-7574 *SIC* 5051 5085

▲ MRC GLOBAL INC p 996
1301 Mckinney St Ste 2300 77010
Tel (877) 294-7574 *SIC* 5051 5085

MUNDY CONTRACT MAINTENANCE INC p 1000
11150 S Wilcrest Dr # 300 77099
Tel (281) 530-8711 *SIC* 7349

MUNDY PLANT MAINTENANCE INC p 1000
11150 S Wilcrest Dr # 300 77099
Tel (281) 530-8711 *SIC* 7699

■ MURPHY EXPLORATION & PRODUCTION CO - USA p 1001
9805 Katy Fwy Ste G200 77024
Tel (281) 599-8145 *SIC* 1382 1311

MUSEUM OF FINE ARTS OF HOUSTON p 1002
1001 Bissonnet St 77005
Tel (713) 639-7300 *SIC* 8412 5999

MUSTANG ENGINEERS AND CONSTRUCTORS LP p 1002
16001 Park Ten Pl 77084
Tel (713) 215-8000 *SIC* 1542 1541

MUSTANG MACHINERY CO LTD p 1002
12800 Northwest Fwy 77040
Tel (713) 861-1440 *SIC* 5082 5084

N F SMITH & ASSOCIATES LP p 1005
5306 Hollister St 77040
Tel (713) 430-3000 *SIC* 5065

NABORS DRILLING USA LP p 1006
515 W Greens Rd Ste 1200 77067
Tel (281) 874-0035 *SIC* 1381

NABORS INDUSTRIES INC p 1006
515 W Greens Rd Ste 1200 77067
Tel (281) 874-0035 *SIC* 1381 1389

NABORS INTERNATIONAL INC p 1006
515 W Greens Rd Ste 600 77067
Tel (281) 874-0035 *SIC* 1381 7353

NABORS OFFSHORE CORP p 1006
515 W Greens Rd Ste 1200 77067
Tel (281) 874-0406 *SIC* 1381 1389

NABORS WELL SERVICES CO p 1006
515 W Greens Rd Ste 1000 77067
Tel (281) 874-0035 *SIC* 1389

NABORS WELL SERVICES LTD p 1006
515 W Greens Rd Ste 1200 77067
Tel (281) 874-0035 *SIC* 1389 7353

NATCO GROUP INC p 1009
11210 Equity Dr Ste 100 77041
Tel (713) 849-7500 *SIC* 3533 1389

▲ NATIONAL OILWELL VARCO INC p 1014
7909 Parkwood Circle Dr 77036
Tel (713) 346-7500 *SIC* 3533 3594 5084

■ NATIONAL OILWELL VARCO LP p 1014
1530 W Sam Houston Pkwy N 77043
Tel (713) 960-5100 *SIC* 3533 5082 5084

NATIONAL PROCESSING CO p 1015
20405 State Highway 249 # 700 77070
Tel (281) 376-3399 *SIC* 5065

NATIONWIDE ARGOSY SOLUTIONS LLC p 1017
2764 Bingle Rd 77055
Tel (713) 961-4700 *SIC* 2759

■ **NATURAL GAS PIPELINE CO OF AMERICA LLC** p 1018
1001 Louisiana St 77002
Tel (713) 369-9000 SIC 4922 1311 8741

▲ **NATURAL RESOURCE PARTNERS LP** p 1018
1201 La St Ste 3400 77002
Tel (713) 751-7507 SIC 1221 1474

■ **NBL TEXAS LLC** p 1021
1001 Noble Energy Way 77070
Tel (281) 872-3100 SIC 1311

▲ **NCI BUILDING SYSTEMS INC** p 1022
10943 N Sam Huston Pkwy W 77064
Tel (281) 897-7788
SIC 3448 3444 3442 1542 1541 7389

■ **NCI GROUP INC** p 1022
10943 N Sam Huston Pkwy W 77064
Tel (281) 897-7500 SIC 3448 3446

NCS MULTISTAGE LLC p 1022
19450 State Highway 249 # 200 77070
Tel (281) 453-2222 SIC 5084

NES GLOBAL LLC p 1026
800 Gessner Rd Ste 310 77024
Tel (713) 551-4444 SIC 1799

NETIQ CORP p 1027
515 Post Oak Blvd # 1000 77027
Tel (713) 548-1700 SIC 7372 7371

NETVERSANT SOLUTIONS LLC p 1028
9750 W Sam Houston Pkwy N # 100 77064
Tel (800) 540-2739 SIC 7373 8999 7381

NEW PROCESS STEEL HOLDING CO INC p 1033
5800 Westview Dr 77055
Tel (713) 686-9631 SIC 5051

NEW PROCESS STEEL LP p 1033
1322 N Post Oak Rd 77055
Tel (713) 686-9631 SIC 5051 3469

■ **NEWFIELD EXPLORATION GULF COAST INC** p 1037
363 N Sam Houston Pkwy E # 2020 77060
Tel (713) 243-3100 SIC 1311

NINE ENERGY SERVICE INC p 1044
16945 Northchase Dr 77060
Tel (281) 730-5100 SIC 5211 1382

▲ **NOBILIS HEALTH CORP** p 1046
11700 Katy Fwy Ste 300 77079
Tel (713) 355-8614 SIC 8011

▲ **NOBLE ENERGY INC** p 1046
1001 Noble Energy Way 77070
Tel (281) 872-3100 SIC 1311

NORTH FOREST INDEPENDENT SCHOOL DISTRICT p 1052
4400 W 18th St 77092
Tel (713) 633-1600 SIC 8211

NORTH FOREST ISD p 1052
4400 W 18th St 77092
Tel (713) 633-1600 SIC 8211

NORTH SHORE SUPPLY CO INC p 1053
1566 Miles St 77015
Tel (713) 453-3533 SIC 5051 5085 3441

NORTHERN BORDER PIPELINE CO p 1055
700 Louisiana St Ste 700 77002
Tel (832) 320-5000 SIC 4922

NORTHERN STAR GENERATION LLC p 1056
2929 Allen Pkwy Ste 2200 77019
Tel (713) 580-6300 SIC 4911

NORTHERN STAR GENERATION SERVICES LLC p 1056
2929 Allen Pkwy Ste 2200 77019
Tel (713) 580-6300 SIC 4911

NORTHSTAR MEMORIAL GROUP LLC p 1059
1900 Saint James Pl # 300 77056
Tel (713) 979-9690 SIC 8748

NORTON ROSE FULBRIGHT US LLP p 1061
1301 Mckinney St Ste 5100 77010
Tel (713) 651-5151 SIC 8111

▲ **NOW INC** p 1064
7402 N Eldridge Pkwy 77041
Tel (281) 823-4700 SIC 5084

■ **NRG REMA LLC** p 1064
1000 Main St 77002
Tel (713) 497-3000 SIC 4911

■ **NRG TEXAS POWER LLC** p 1064
1301 Mckinney St Ste 2300 77010
Tel (713) 537-3000 SIC 3621

NW PIPELINE INC p 1068
3535 Briarpark Dr Ste 135 77042
Tel (713) 789-4311 SIC 1623

▲ **OASIS PETROLEUM INC** p 1072
1001 Fannin St Ste 1500 77002
Tel (281) 404-9500 SIC 1311

■ **OCCIDENTAL ENERGY MARKETING INC** p 1072
5 Greenway Plz Ste 110 77046
Tel (713) 215-7000 SIC 5172 1382 4924

■ **OCCIDENTAL OIL AND GAS CORP** p 1072
5 Greenway Plz Ste 110 77046
Tel (713) 215-7000 SIC 1311

■ **OCCIDENTAL PERMIAN LTD** p 1072
5 Greenway Plz Ste 110 77046
Tel (713) 215-7000 SIC 1382 1311

▲ **OCCIDENTAL PETROLEUM CORP** p 1072
5 Greenway Plz Ste 110 77046
Tel (713) 215-7000 SIC 1382 1311

▲ **OCEANEERING INTERNATIONAL INC** p 1073
11911 Fm 529 Rd 77041
Tel (713) 329-4500 SIC 1389 3731 8711

ODONNELL/SNIDER CONSTRUCTION LLC p 1074
1900 West Loop S Ste 350 77027
Tel (713) 782-7660 SIC 1542

OIL & GAS ASSET CLEARINGHOUSE LP p 1079
1235 North Loop W Ste 500 77008
Tel (281) 873-4600 SIC 6531

OIL PATCH GROUP INC p 1079
11767 Katy Fwy Ste 510a 77079
Tel (832) 300-0000 SIC 1389 7353

■ **OIL STATES ENERGY SERVICES LLC** p 1079
333 Clay St Ste 2100 77002
Tel (713) 425-2400 SIC 3533 5082

▲ **OIL STATES INTERNATIONAL INC** p 1079
333 Clay St Ste 4620 77002
Tel (713) 652-0582
SIC 3353 3061 3053 3561 3491

OLD GES INC p 1080
11757 Katy Fwy Ste 700 77079
Tel (281) 598-6830
SIC 1389 7353 3599 7359 1382

▲ **OMEGA PROTEIN CORP** p 1084
2105 Citywest Blvd # 500 77042
Tel (713) 623-0060 SIC 2077 5199

ONESUBSEA LLC p 1088
4646 W Sam Houston Pkwy N 77041
Tel (713) 939-2211 SIC 3533 3563 3491

▲ **ORION GROUP HOLDINGS INC** p 1094
12000 Aerospace Ave # 300 77034
Tel (713) 852-6500 SIC 1629

OROURKE DISTRIBUTING CO INC p 1095
223 Mccarty St 77029
Tel (713) 672-4500 SIC 5171 5172

■ **ORTHOPEDIC HOSPITAL LTD** p 1096
7401 Main St 77030
Tel (713) 799-8600 SIC 8069

■ **OXY INC** p 1101
5 Greenway Plz Ste 2400 77046
Tel (713) 215-7000 SIC 1311 1382

PAPPAS PARTNERS LP p 1112
6894 Southwest Fwy 1 77074
Tel (713) 869-7151 SIC 5812

PAPPAS RESTAURANTS INC p 1112
13939 Nw Fwy 77040
Tel (713) 869-0151 SIC 5812 5813

■ **PAR HAWAII REFINING LLC** p 1113
800 Gessner Rd Ste 875 77024
Tel (281) 899-4800 SIC 5541 2911

▲ **PAR PACIFIC HOLDINGS INC** p 1113
800 Gessner Rd Ste 875 77024
Tel (713) 969-3293 SIC 1311 2911 4923

PARAGON OFFSHORE PLC p 1113
3151 Briarpark Dr Ste 700 77042
Tel (832) 783-4000 SIC 1382

PARK GALENA INDEPENDENT SCHOOL DISTRICT p 1115
14705 Woodforest Blvd A 77015
Tel (832) 386-1000 SIC 8211

PARK PLAZA HOSPITAL p 1115
5209 Chenevert St 77004
Tel (713) 527-5000 SIC 6719

■ **PARK PLAZA HOSPITAL INC** p 1115
1313 Hermann Dr 77004
Tel (713) 527-5128 SIC 8071

▲ **PARKER DRILLING CO** p 1116
5 Greenway Plz Ste 100 77046
Tel (281) 406-2000 SIC 1381 7353

PARKER SCHOOL UNIFORMS LLC p 1116
6300 W By Northwest Blvd # 100 77040
Tel (713) 957-1511 SIC 2389

PARMAN CAPITAL GROUP LLC p 1117
1000 La St Ste 5900 77002
Tel (713) 751-2700 SIC 1389 7353

▲ **PATTERSON-UTI ENERGY INC** p 1121
10713 W Sam Huston Pkwy N 77064
Tel (281) 765-7100 SIC 1381 1389 1311

PB ENERGY STORAGE SERVICES INC p 1123
16200 Park Row Ste 200 77084
Tel (281) 496-5590 SIC 8711

PCPC DIRECT LTD p 1124
10690 Shadow Wood Dr # 132 77043
Tel (713) 984-8808 SIC 5045 7378 7379

PCPC INC p 1124
10690 Shadow Wood Dr # 132 77043
Tel (713) 984-8808 SIC 5045 7378 7379

PEARCE INDUSTRIES INC p 1126
12320 Main St 77035
Tel (713) 723-1050 SIC 5084 3533 5082

PENNZOIL-QUAKER STATE CO p 1131
700 Milam St Ste 125 77002
Tel (713) 546-4000 SIC 2992

PENNZOIL-QUAKER STATE NOMINEE CO p 1131
700 Milam St Ste 400 77002
Tel (713) 546-4000 SIC 5172

PENTAIR VALVES & CONTROLS LLC p 1132
10707 Clay Rd Ste 200 77041
Tel (713) 986-4665 SIC 3491

PENTAIR VALVES & CONTROLS US LP p 1132
10707 Clay Rd Ste 200 77041
Tel (713) 986-4665 SIC 3491 3625 3494

PENTHOL LLC p 1132
333 Clay St Ste 3300 77002
Tel (832) 548-5832 SIC 5172

PERMIAN MUD SERVICE INC p 1136
3200 Southwest Fwy # 2700 77027
Tel (713) 627-1101 SIC 2819

PETROBRAS AMERICA INC p 1139
10350 Richmond Ave 77042
Tel (713) 808-2000 SIC 5172 1382 2911

PETROHAWK ENERGY CORP p 1139
1360 Post Oak Blvd # 150 77056
Tel (713) 961-8500 SIC 1311

PETROLEUM GEO-SERVICES INC p 1139
15375 Memorial Dr Ste 100 77079
Tel (281) 509-8000 SIC 3827 8713 1382

PETROSANTANDER (COLOMBIA) INC p 1139
6363 Woodway Dr Ste 350 77057
Tel (713) 784-8700 SIC 1311 1382

PETROSANTANDER INC p 1139
6363 Woodway Dr Ste 350 77057
Tel (713) 784-8700 SIC 1311

▲ **PHILLIPS 66** p 1144
2331 City West Blvd 77042
Tel (832) 765-3300 SIC 1311 2911 2869

■ **PHILLIPS 66 CO** p 1144
1075 W Sam Houston Pkwy N # 200 77043
Tel (281) 293-6600 SIC 2911

■ **PHILLIPS 66 PARTNERS LP** p 1144
3010 Briarpark Dr 77042
Tel (855) 283-9237 SIC 4612 1311 5541

■ **PHILLIPS PETROLEUM CO** p 1144
600 N Dairy Ashford Rd 77079
Tel (281) 293-1000
SIC 1382 2911 5171 5541

PHOENIX TECHNOLOGY SERVICES USA INC p 1145
12329 Cutten Rd 77066
Tel (713) 337-0600 SIC 1381

PIEDMONT HAWTHORNE AVIATION LLC p 1147
1500 City W Blvd Ste 600 77042
Tel (713) 895-9243
SIC 5599 4581 4522 5172

PINNACLE SUMMER INVESTMENTS INC p 1150
600 Travis St Ste 5800 77002
Tel (781) 749-7409 SIC 6282 8741

PIONEER EXPLORATION CO p 1150
15603 Kuykendahl Rd 77090
Tel (281) 893-9400 SIC 1311 1321

PIPELINE SUPPLY & SERVICE LLC p 1151
1010 Lamar St Ste 710 77002
Tel (713) 741-8127 SIC 4922 5085 1623

PIPING TECHNOLOGY & PRODUCTS INC p 1151
3701 Holmes Rd 77051
Tel (800) 787-5914 SIC 3494 8711 3441

■ **PLAINS ALL AMERICAN PIPELINE LP** p 1153
333 Clay St Ste 1600 77002
Tel (713) 646-4100 SIC 4612 5172

▲ **PLAINS GP HOLDINGS LP** p 1153
333 Clay St Ste 1600 77002
Tel (713) 646-4100 SIC 4612 1321

■ **PLAINS MARKETING LP** p 1153
333 Clay St Ste 1600 77002
Tel (713) 646-4100 SIC 5172 4213

PLAZA GROUP INC p 1156
10375 Richmond Ave # 1620 77042
Tel (713) 266-0707 SIC 8742

PLG HOLDINGS INC p 1156
1 Greenway Plz Ste 400 77046
Tel (713) 439-1010 SIC 4214

PM REALTY GROUP LP p 1157
1000 Main St Ste 2400 77002
Tel (713) 209-5800 SIC 6531

PON MATERIAL HANDLING NA INC p 1161
840 Gessner Rd Ste 950 77024
Tel (713) 365-2547 SIC 5084

PON NORTH AMERICA INC p 1161
840 Gessner Rd Ste 950 77024
Tel (713) 365-2547 SIC 5942 5082

PORT OF HOUSTON AUTHORITY p 1162
111 East Loop N 77029
Tel (713) 670-2662 SIC 4491

■ **POWELL ELECTRICAL SYSTEMS INC** p 1165
8550 Mosley Rd 77075
Tel (708) 409-1200 SIC 3625

▲ **POWELL INDUSTRIES INC** p 1165
8550 Mosley Rd 77075
Tel (713) 944-6900
SIC 3612 3613 3625 3643 3823

PRECISION DRILLING CO LP p 1168
10350 Richmond Ave # 700 77042
Tel (713) 435-6100 SIC 1381

PRECISION DRILLING CORP p 1168
10350 Richmond Ave # 700 77042
Tel (713) 435-6100 SIC 1381

PRECISION ENERGY SERVICES INC p 1168
2000 Saint James Pl 77056
Tel (713) 693-4000 SIC 3533 1389

■ **PRECISION INDUSTRIES INC** p 1168
7272 Pinemont Dr 77040
Tel (713) 996-4700 SIC 5211 5085

PREDICTIF SOLUTIONS p 1169
8588 Katy Fwy Ste 435 77024
Tel (713) 457-7471 SIC 7379

PREFERRED FOODS MARTIN L P p 1169
2011 Silver St 77007
Tel (713) 869-6191
SIC 5142 2015 2011 5141 5144

PREMIER GRAPHICS HOLDINGS INC p 1170
2500 West Loop S Ste 500 77027
Tel (713) 961-4700 SIC 2752

PRIDE INTERNATIONAL INC p 1174
5847 San Felipe St # 3400 77057
Tel (713) 789-1400 SIC 1381 1389 8711

PRIME NATURAL RESOURCES LLC p 1175
2500 Citywest Blvd # 1750 77042
Tel (713) 953-3200 SIC 1311

PRINCE ENERGY LLC p 1176
7707 Wallisville Rd 77020
Tel (713) 673-5176 SIC 7389

PRITCHARD INDUSTRIES SOUTHWEST INC p 1178
4040 Directors Row 77092
Tel (713) 957-1387 SIC 7349

PRO OILFIELD SERVICES LLC p 1178
3 Riverway Ste 1110 77056
Tel (281) 496-5810 SIC 1381

PRODUCTION SERVICES NETWORK US INC p 1180
9821 Katy Fwy Ste 400 77024
Tel (713) 984-1000 SIC 8742

PROFESSIONAL COMPOUNDING CENTERS OF AMERICA INC p 1180
9901 S Wilcrest Dr 77099
Tel (281) 933-6948 SIC 5047 5122

PROLER SOUTHWEST INC p 1182
90 Hirsch Rd 77020
Tel (713) 671-2900 SIC 5051

▲ **PROS HOLDINGS INC** p 1184
3100 Main St Ste 900 77002
Tel (713) 335-5151 SIC 7371 7372

■ **PROS INC** p 1184
3100 Main St Ste 900 77002
Tel (713) 335-5151 SIC 7372

PROSERV OPERATIONS INC p 1184
13105 Nw Fwy Ste 250 77040
Tel (281) 407-2405 SIC 1389

▲ **PROSPERITY BANCSHARES INC** p 1184
4295 San Felipe St 77027
Tel (281) 269-7199 SIC 6022

■ **PSC ENVIRONMENTAL SERVICES LLC** p 1188
5151 San Felipe St # 1100 77056
Tel (713) 623-8777 SIC 4953 4959 5093

PSC HOLDINGS I LP p 1188
5151 San Felipe St # 1600 77056
Tel (713) 623-8777 SIC 4212

PSC HOLDINGS II LP p 1188
5151 San Felipe St # 1600 77056
Tel (713) 623-8777 SIC 4953 8748

PSC HOLDINGS INC p 1188
5151 San Felipe St # 1100 77056
Tel (713) 623-8777 SIC 4953 4959

PSC LLC p 1188
5151 San Felipe St Ste 11 77056
Tel (713) 623-8777 SIC 4953 4959

PVI HOLDINGS INC p 1193
840 Gessner Rd Ste 950 77024
Tel (713) 365-6805 SIC 5085 5084 7699

▲ **QUANEX BUILDING PRODUCTS CORP** p 1198
1800 West Loop S Ste 1500 77027
Tel (713) 961-4600 SIC 3272 3353

■ **QUANTA FIBER NETWORKS INC** p 1198
1360 Post Oak Blvd # 2100 77056
Tel (713) 629-7600 SIC 1731 8742

▲ **QUANTA SERVICES INC** p 1198
2800 Post Oak Blvd # 2600 77056
Tel (713) 629-7600 SIC 1731

QUIETFLEX MANUFACTURING CO LP p 1199
4518 Brittmoore Rd 77041
Tel (713) 849-2163 SIC 3444 1799 3599

QUINTANA ENERGY SERVICES LP p 1200
601 Jefferson St Ste 3600 77002
Tel (713) 751-7500 SIC 1389

R & B FALCON DRILLING INTERNATIONAL DEEPWATER INC p 1201
2000 W Sam Houston Pkwy S 77042
Tel (713) 278-6000 SIC 1381 8711

RAINFOREST CAFE INC p 1206
1510 West Loop S 77027
Tel (713) 850-1010 SIC 5812

RAINTREE RESORTS INTERNATIONAL INC p 1206
10000 Memorial Dr Ste 480 77024
Tel (713) 613-2800 SIC 7011

RANDALLS FOOD MARKETS INC p 1207
3663 Briarpark Dr 77042
Tel (713) 268-3500 SIC 5411 5912

■ **RANGE RESOURCES - LOUISIANA INC** p 1208
500 Dallas St Ste 1800 77002
Tel (713) 588-8300 SIC 1311

RAWSON LP p 1209
2010 Mcallister Rd 77092
Tel (713) 684-1400 *SIC* 5085 5084

▲ RCI HOSPITALITY HOLDINGS INC p 1212
10959 Cutten Rd 77066
Tel (281) 397-6730 *SIC* 5813 5812

REC SILICON INC p 1214
3700 Buffalo Speedway # 620 77098
Tel (281) 325-3800 *SIC* 3339

REECE GREGORY MD p 1217
1515 Holcombe Blvd 77030
Tel (713) 794-1247 *SIC* 8011

REEF SERVICES LLC p 1217
515 Post Oak Blvd Ste 600 77027
Tel (432) 560-5600 *SIC* 3533

RELIANCE HOLDING USA INC p 1221
2000 W Sam Houston Pkwy S # 700 77042
Tel (713) 430-8700 *SIC* 6719

RELIANCE STANDARD LIFE INSURANCE CO OF TEXAS p 1222
7600 W Tidwell Rd Ste 111 77040
Tel (713) 468-2603 *SIC* 6311 6321

■ RELIANT ENERGY RETAIL HOLDINGS LLC p 1222
1000 Main St 77002
Tel (713) 497-3000 *SIC* 4911

REMEDIAL CONSTRUCTION SVCS LP p 1222
9977 W Sam Houston Pkwy N 77064
Tel (281) 955-2442 *SIC* 8744 1629

RENAISSANCE OFFSHORE LLC p 1223
920 Mmrial Cy Way Ste 800 77024
Tel (832) 333-7700 *SIC* 1389 1311

REPUBLIC NATIONAL DISTRIBUTING CO LLC p 1225
8045 Northcourt Rd 77040
Tel (813) 885-3200 *SIC* 5182

RETAIL CONCEPTS INC p 1228
10560 Bissonnet St # 100 77099
Tel (281) 340-5000 *SIC* 5941

REYNOLDS AND REYNOLDS CO p 1230
6700 Hollister St 77040
Tel (713) 718-1800 *SIC* 7371

RICE EPICUREAN MARKETS INC p 1232
5333 Gulfton St 77081
Tel (713) 662-7700 *SIC* 5411 5812

▲ RIGNET INC p 1235
1880 S Dairy Ashford Rd # 300 77077
Tel (281) 674-0100 *SIC* 4899 4813

RIL USA INC p 1235
2000 W Sam Houston Pkwy S # 1155 77042
Tel (713) 430-8700 *SIC* 1382

RIMKUS CONSULTING GROUP INC p 1235
8 Greenway Plz Ste 500 77046
Tel (713) 621-3550 *SIC* 8711

RIO ENERGY INTERNATIONAL INC p 1235
5718 Westheimer Rd # 1806 77057
Tel (713) 977-5718 *SIC* 5172

RIVIANA FOODS INC p 1239
2777 Allen Pkwy Fl 15 77019
Tel (713) 529-3251
SIC 2044 2052 2033 5141

RMC USA INC p 1239
920 Memorial City Way 77024
Tel (713) 650-6200
SIC 3273 3272 3271 5031

■ ROBERTSON-CECO II CORP p 1242
10943 N Sam Huston Pkwy W 77064
Tel (281) 897-7788 *SIC* 3448

ROCTX LAKESIDE LLC p 1242
1455 Lakeside Estates Dr 77042
Tel (801) 284-5960 *SIC* 8741

ROCKWATER ENERGY SOLUTIONS INC p 1245
515 Post Oak Blvd Ste 200 77027
Tel (713) 235-9500 *SIC* 8731 8748

ROSETTA RESOURCES INC p 1251
1111 Bagby St Ste 1600 77002
Tel (713) 335-4000 *SIC* 1311 1381

■ ROSETTA RESOURCES OFFSHORE LLC p 1251
1111 Bagby St Ste 1600 77002
Tel (713) 335-4000 *SIC* 1382

ROWAN COMPANIES INC p 1253
2800 Post Oak Blvd # 5450 77056
Tel (713) 621-7800 *SIC* 1381 3531 3533

ROWAN DRILLING CO INC p 1253
2800 Post Oak Blvd # 5450 77056
Tel (713) 621-7800 *SIC* 1381

ROYAL BATHS MANUFACTURING CO LTD p 1254
14635 Chrisman Rd 77039
Tel (281) 442-3400
SIC 3842 3949 3432 3281

■ RRI ENERGY BROADBAND INC p 1255
1000 Main St 77002
Tel (713) 537-3000 *SIC* 4911

RTU INC p 1256
1445 Langham Creek Dr 77084
Tel (800) 247-4793 *SIC* 7319 2752

RUSHLAKE HOTELS (USA) INC p 1259
333 Clay St Ste 4980 77002
Tel (713) 759-0790 *SIC* 7011

RUSSELL & SMITH FORD INC p 1259
3440 South Loop W 77025
Tel (713) 663-4111 *SIC* 5511

RYAN DIRECTIONAL SERVICES INC p 1260
19510 Oil Center Blvd 77073
Tel (281) 443-1414 *SIC* 1389

S & B HOLDINGS LTD p 1261
7809 Park Place Blvd 77087
Tel (713) 645-4141 *SIC* 1629 8711

S AND B ENGINEERS AND CONSTRUCTORS LTD p 1261
7825 Park Place Blvd 77087
Tel (713) 645-4141 *SIC* 1629 8711

SABIC AMERICAS INC p 1264
2500 Citywest Blvd 77042
Tel (713) 532-4999 *SIC* 5172 5169

▲ SABINE OIL & GAS CORP p 1264
1415 Louisiana St # 1600 77002
Tel (832) 242-9600 *SIC* 1311

■ SABINE PASS LIQUEFACTION LLC p 1264
700 Milam St Ste 1900 77002
Tel (713) 375-5000 *SIC* 4924

■ SABINE PASS LNG LP p 1264
700 Milam St Ste 1900 77002
Tel (713) 375-5000 *SIC* 4922

■ SABINE PASS LNG-LP LLC p 1264
700 Milam St Ste 800 77002
Tel (713) 375-5000 *SIC* 4922

SAETOWERS HOLDINGS LLC p 1265
16945 Northchase Dr # 1910 77060
Tel (281) 763-2282 *SIC* 6719

SAIPEM AMERICA INC p 1271
15950 Park Row 77084
Tel (281) 552-5600 *SIC* 8711 1389

SALTGRASS INC p 1273
1510 West Loop S 77027
Tel (713) 850-1010 *SIC* 5812

SAMEDAN OIL CORP p 1274
1001 Noble Energy Way 77070
Tel (580) 223-4110 *SIC* 1311

▲ SANCHEZ ENERGY CORP p 1277
1000 Main St Ste 3000 77002
Tel (713) 783-8000 *SIC* 1311

SANCHEZ OIL & GAS CORP p 1277
1000 Main St Ste 3000 77002
Tel (956) 722-8092 *SIC* 1311

SASOL (USA) CORP p 1283
12120 Wickchester Ln 77079
Tel (281) 588-3000 *SIC* 1382

SASOL CHEMICALS (USA) LLC p 1283
12120 Wickchester Ln 77079
Tel (281) 588-3000 *SIC* 2869 5169

SATTERFIELD AND PONTIKES CONSTRUCTION INC p 1283
11000 Equity Dr Ste 100 77041
Tel (713) 996-1393 *SIC* 1542 1541

SAYBOLT LP p 1285
6316 Windfern Rd 77040
Tel (713) 328-2673 *SIC* 1389

SBMC HEALTHCARE LLC p 1285
1301 Mckinney St Ste 2025 77010
Tel (713) 953-1055 *SIC* 8011

SBP HOLDING LP p 1285
125 Mccarty St 77029
Tel (281) 953-1113 *SIC* 5085 3496

SCAN DRILLING CO INC p 1286
11777 Katy Fwy Ste 470 77079
Tel (281) 496-5571 *SIC* 1381

■ SCCI HOSPITALS OF AMERICA INC p 1286
7333 North Fwy Ste 500 77076
Tel (713) 807-8686 *SIC* 8062

SCHLUMBERGER INTERNATIONAL INC p 1287
7030 Ardmore St 77054
Tel (713) 747-4000
SIC 1389 3561 3492 3533

SCHLUMBERGER LIMITED p 1287
5599 San Felipe St Fl 17 77056
Tel (713) 513-2000
SIC 1381 1389 1382 3825 3824 3823

SCHLUMBERGER OMNES INC p 1287
5599 San Felipe St Fl 17 77056
Tel (713) 375-3400 *SIC* 1382 1389

SCHOENMANN PRODUCE CO INC p 1288
6950 Neuhaus St 77061
Tel (713) 923-2728 *SIC* 5148

■ SCI FUNERAL SERVICES OF NEW YORK INC p 1292
1929 Allen Pkwy 77019
Tel (713) 522-5141 *SIC* 7261

■ SCI SHARED RESOURCES LLC p 1292
1929 Allen Pkwy 77019
Tel (713) 522-5141 *SIC* 7261 6553

■ SCI VIRGINIA FUNERAL SERVICES INC p 1292
1929 Allen Pkwy 77019
Tel (713) 522-5141 *SIC* 8741

SCIENTIFIC DRILLING INTERNATIONAL INC p 1292
16071 Greenspoint Park Ste 200 77060
Tel (281) 443-3300 *SIC* 1381 1389

SCOMI EQUIPMENT INC p 1293
6607 Theall Rd 77066
Tel (281) 260-6016 *SIC* 1389

SCULLY SERVICES LLC p 1295
19319 Oil Center Blvd 77073
Tel (281) 230-7500 *SIC* 1771

SEATRAX INC p 1297
13223 Fm 529 Rd 77041
Tel (713) 896-6500 *SIC* 3531 3536

SEATTLE AIRPORT HOSPITALITY LLC p 1297
5847 San Felipe St # 4650 77057
Tel (713) 787-6222 *SIC* 7011

■ SEC ENERGY PRODUCTS & SERVICES LP p 1298
9523 Frbanks N Houston Rd 77064
Tel (281) 890-9977 *SIC* 3563

SECOND BAPTIST CHURCH p 1298
6400 Woodway Dr 77057
Tel (713) 465-3408 *SIC* 8661

SEDKO GROUP INC p 1300
5847 San Felipe St # 4650 77057
Tel (713) 782-9100 *SIC* 7011

SEITEL HOLDINGS INC p 1301
10811 S Westview Circle D 77043
Tel (713) 881-8900 *SIC* 1382

SEITEL INC p 1301
10811 S Westvw Cir Dr 100 77043
Tel (713) 881-8900 *SIC* 1382

SELECTRANSPORTATION RESOURCES LLC p 1302
9550 North Loop E 77029
Tel (713) 672-4115
SIC 5012 5013 5511 7538

SELLERS BROS INC p 1302
4580 S Wayside Dr 77087
Tel (713) 640-1611 *SIC* 5411

■ SENECA RESOURCES CORP p 1303
1201 Louisiana St Ste 400 77002
Tel (713) 654-2600 *SIC* 1382

■ SEQUENT ENERGY MANAGEMENT LP p 1306
1200 Smith St 77002
Tel (832) 397-1700 *SIC* 4924

SERCEL INC p 1306
17200 Park Row 77084
Tel (281) 492-6688 *SIC* 3829

▲ SERVICE CORP INTERNATIONAL p 1307
1929 Allen Pkwy 77019
Tel (713) 522-5141 *SIC* 7261

SERVICE STEEL WAREHOUSE CO LP p 1307
8415 Clinton Dr 77029
Tel (713) 675-2631 *SIC* 5051

SERVISAIR LLC p 1308
151 Northpoint Dr 77060
Tel (281) 260-3900 *SIC* 4581

■ SESI LLC p 1308
1001 Louisiana St 77002
Tel (504) 587-7374 *SIC* 7353 1389

■ SFI-GRAY STEEL LLC p 1310
3511 W 12th St 77008
Tel (713) 864-6450 *SIC* 3325 5051

SHAWCOR INC p 1313
3838 N Sam Houston Pkwy E # 300 77032
Tel (281) 886-2350 *SIC* 8734

SHAWCOR PIPE PROTECTION LLC p 1313
3838 N Sam Houston Pkwy E # 300 77032
Tel (281) 886-2350 *SIC* 3479

SHELF DRILLING DISTRIBUTION LTD p 1314
1 Riverway 77056
Tel (713) 457-8220 *SIC* 6719

SHELL CATALYST VENTURES INC p 1314
910 Louisiana St 77002
Tel (713) 241-5766 *SIC* 2819

SHELL CHEMICAL LP p 1314
910 Louisiana St 77002
Tel (855) 697-4355 *SIC* 2869

SHELL ENERGY NORTH AMERICA (US) LP p 1314
1000 Main St 77002
Tel (713) 230-3822 *SIC* 1311

SHELL EXPLORATION & PRODUCTION CO p 1314
200 N Dairy Ashford Rd 77079
Tel (832) 337-0369 *SIC* 4922

SHELL GLOBAL SOLUTIONS (US) INC p 1314
3333 Highway 6 S 77082
Tel (281) 544-7709 *SIC* 1311

SHELL INFORMATION TECHNOLOGY INTERNATIONAL INC p 1314
910 Louisiana St 77002
Tel (855) 697-4355 *SIC* 8742 7371

SHELL MIDSTREAM PARTNERS LP p 1314
910 Louisiana St 77002
Tel (713) 241-6161 *SIC* 4612

SHELL OFFSHORE INC p 1314
200 N Dairy Ashford Rd 77079
Tel (281) 544-4800 *SIC* 5172

SHELL OIL CO p 1314
910 Louisiana St Ste 1500 77002
Tel (713) 241-6161
SIC 5541 4612 1311 2821 2869 2911

SHELL PETROLEUM INC p 1314
910 Louisiana St Ste 420 77002
Tel (713) 241-6161 *SIC* 2911 4613 5172

SHELL PIPE LINE CORP p 1314
2 Shell Plz Ste 1160 77002
Tel (713) 241-6161 *SIC* 4612

SHELL TRADING NORTH AMERICA CO p 1314
1000 Main St 77002
Tel (713) 241-6161 *SIC* 5172

SHELL US GAS & POWER LLC p 1314
1301 Mckinney St Ste 700 77010
Tel (713) 658-0509 *SIC* 4922

SHERIDAN PRODUCTION CO LLC p 1316
9 Greenway Plz Ste 1300 77046
Tel (713) 548-1000 *SIC* 1381

SHINTECH INC p 1317
3 Greenway Plz Ste 1150 77046
Tel (713) 965-0713 *SIC* 2821

SIDEWINDER DRILLING INC p 1319
952 Echo Ln Ste 460 77024
Tel (832) 320-7600 *SIC* 1381

SIGNATURE HOSPITAL CORP p 1322
363 N Sam Houston Pkwy E 77060
Tel (281) 598-9800 *SIC* 8062

SILVER EAGLE DISTRIBUTORS LIMITED PARTNERSHIP p 1323
7777 Washington Ave 77007
Tel (713) 869-4361 *SIC* 5181

SILVER EAGLE DISTRIBUTORS LLC p 1323
7777 Washington Ave 77007
Tel (713) 869-4361 *SIC* 5181

SINGER EQUITIES INC p 1326
125 Mccarty St 77029
Tel (713) 714-3610 *SIC* 8741

SJ MEDICAL CENTER LLC p 1328
1401 St Joseph Pkwy 77002
Tel (713) 757-1000 *SIC* 8062

SK LUBRICANTS AMERICAS INC p 1329
11700 Katy Fwy Ste 900 77079
Tel (713) 341-5828 *SIC* 5169

SMITH INTERNATIONAL INC p 1333
1310 Rankin Rd 77073
Tel (281) 443-3370 *SIC* 3532 3533

SOFEC INC p 1337
15011 Katy Fwy Ste 500 77094
Tel (713) 510-6600 *SIC* 3533 8742

SOLVAY AMERICA INC p 1339
3737 Buffalo Ste 800 77098
Tel (713) 525-4000 *SIC* 2819

SOLVAY CHEMICALS INC p 1339
3737 Buffalo Speedway 77098
Tel (713) 525-6800 *SIC* 1474 2819

SOLVAY INTEROX INC p 1339
3737 Buffalo Speedway 77098
Tel (713) 525-6500 *SIC* 2819 2899

■ SONIC AUTOMOTIVE OF TEXAS LP p 1340
8477 North Fwy 77037
Tel (281) 931-3300 *SIC* 5511 7538

SOS CUETARA USA INC p 1341
10700 North Fwy Ste 800 77037
Tel (281) 272-8800 *SIC* 2044

SOUTHEAST SUPPLY HEADER LLC p 1346
5400 Westheimer Ct 77056
Tel (713) 627-5400 *SIC* 4923

SOUTHERN NEWSPAPERS INC p 1349
5701 Woodway Dr Ste 131 77057
Tel (713) 266-5481 *SIC* 2711

SOUTHERN PETROLEUM LABORATORIES INC p 1350
8850 Interchange Dr 77054
Tel (713) 660-0901 *SIC* 5172 8999 8734

■ SOUTHERN UNION CO p 1350
1300 Main St 77002
Tel (713) 989-2000 *SIC* 4924

SOUTHWEST OILFIELD PRODUCTS INC p 1352
10340 Wallisville Rd 77013
Tel (713) 675-7541 *SIC* 3533 3561

SOUTHWEST STAINLESS LP p 1352
515 Post Oak Blvd Ste 800 77027
Tel (713) 943-3544 *SIC* 3498 5051 5085

■ SOUTHWESTERN ENERGY PRODUCTION CO INC p 1353
2350 N Sam Houston Pkwy E 77032
Tel (281) 618-4700 *SIC* 1382 1311

▲ SPARK ENERGY INC p 1354
12140 Wickchester Ln 77079
Tel (713) 600-2600 *SIC* 4931 4911

■ SPARK ENERGY LLC p 1354
12140 Wickchester Ln 77079
Tel (713) 977-5634 *SIC* 4911

SPAW GLASS CONSTRUCTION CORP p 1355
13800 West Rd 77041
Tel (281) 970-5300 *SIC* 1542 1522 1541

■ SPECIALTY RETAILERS INC p 1356
2425 West Loop S Ste 110 77027
Tel (713) 331-4970 *SIC* 5651

SPECS FAMILY PARTNERS LTD p 1356
2410 Smith St 77006
Tel (713) 526-8787 *SIC* 5921

▲ SPECTRA ENERGY CORP p 1356
5400 Westheimer Ct 77056
Tel (713) 627-5400 *SIC* 4922 4924

■ SPECTRA ENERGY PARTNERS LP p 1357
5400 Westheimer Ct 77056
Tel (713) 627-5400 *SIC* 4922 4924

■ SPECTRA ENERGY TRANSMISSION LLC p 1357
5400 Westheimer Ct 77056
Tel (713) 627-5400 *SIC* 4922 4924

SPITZER INDUSTRIES INC p 1359
12141 Wickc Ln Ste 750 77079
Tel (713) 466-1518 *SIC* 1389

SPRING BRANCH INDEPENDENT SCHOOL DISTRICT (INC) p 1360
955 Campbell Rd 77024
Tel (713) 464-1511 *SIC* 8211

SPRING BRANCH MEDICAL CENTER INC p 1360
6060 Richmond Ave Ste 315 77057
Tel (713) 722-3799 SIC 8062

SPRING INDEPENDENT SCHOOL DISTRICT p 1360
16717 Ella Blvd 77090
Tel (281) 891-6000 SIC 8211

ST JOSEPH MEDICAL CENTER CORP p 1368
1401 St Joseph Pkwy 77002
Tel (713) 757-1000 SIC 8051

ST LUKES EPISCOPAL HOSPITAL p 1370
6624 Fannin St 77030
Tel (713) 610-9326 SIC 8062

ST LUKES EPISCOPAL HOSPITAL INDEPENDENT PRACTICE ASSOCIATION INC p 1370
6720 Bertner Ave 77030
Tel (832) 355-1000 SIC 8062

ST LUKES HEALTH SYSTEM CORP p 1370
6624 Fannin St Ste 1100 77030
Tel (832) 355-1000 SIC 8062

▲ STAGE STORES INC p 1374
2425 West Loop S 77027
Tel (800) 579-2302 SIC 5651 5661

STALLION OILFIELD HOLDINGS LTD p 1375
950 Corbindale Rd Ste 300 77024
Tel (713) 528-5544 SIC 8999

STALLION OILFIELD SERVICES LTD p 1375
950 Corbindale Rd Ste 300 77024
Tel (713) 528-5544 SIC 1389

STATOIL USA PROPERTIES INC p 1383
2103 Citywest Blvd # 800 77042
Tel (713) 918-8200 SIC 1382

STEMCOR SPECIAL STEELS LLC p 1385
5847 San Felipe St # 2400 77057
Tel (281) 252-3625 SIC 5051

■ STERLING BANCSHARES INC p 1386
2950 North Loop W # 1200 77092
Tel (713) 466-8300 SIC 6022

■ STERLING BANK p 1386
2550 North Loop W Ste 600 77092
Tel (713) 466-8300 SIC 6022

STERLING GROUP L P p 1387
9 Greenway Plz Ste 2400 77046
Tel (713) 877-8257 SIC 6799

STEWART & STEVENSON CAPITAL CORP p 1388
601 W 38th St 77018
Tel (713) 868-7700
SIC 5084 5013 5078 5082 3711 3537

STEWART & STEVENSON LLC p 1389
1000 La St Ste 5900 77002
Tel (713) 751-2600
SIC 5084 5082 3533 7353

STEWART & STEVENSON POWER PRODUCTS LLC p 1389
1000 La St Ste 5900 77002
Tel (713) 751-2600
SIC 1389 5084 5082 3533 7353

▲ STEWART INFORMATION SERVICES CORP p 1389
1980 Post Oak Blvd 77056
Tel (713) 625-8100 SIC 6361 8742 7389

■ STEWART TITLE CO p 1389
1980 Post Oak Blvd Ste 80 77056
Tel (713) 625-8100
SIC 6361 7389 8713 8742 6541

■ STEWART TITLE GUARANTY CO p 1389
1980 Post Oak Blvd Ste 61 77056
Tel (713) 625-8100 SIC 6361 6541

STOLLER INTERNATIONAL INC p 1390
9090 Katy Fwy Ste 400 77024
Tel (713) 461-1493 SIC 5191 2879

STOLLER USA INC p 1390
9090 Katy Fwy Ste 400 77024
Tel (713) 461-1493 SIC 5191 8731

STOLT-NIELSEN USA INC p 1391
15635 Jacintoport Blvd 77015
Tel (203) 299-3600 SIC 4731

STRATEGIC MATERIALS INC p 1392
16365 Park Ten Pl Ste 200 77084
Tel (281) 647-2700 SIC 4953

STRESS ENGINEERING SERVICES INC p 1393
13800 Westfair East Dr 77041
Tel (281) 955-2900 SIC 8711

SUBSEA 7 (US) LLC p 1396
10787 Clay Rd 77041
Tel (281) 966-7600 SIC 1629 3731

SULZER PUMPS (US) INC p 1397
1255 Enclave Pkwy 300 77077
Tel (281) 934-6014 SIC 3594

SUMMIT CONSOLIDATION GROUP INC p 1398
10497 Town Cntry Way 3 77024
Tel (713) 554-2244 SIC 7373 7371 4813

SUN COAST RESOURCES INC p 1400
6405 Cavalcade St Bldg 1 77026
Tel (713) 844-9600
SIC 5172 2992 5084 1389

SUNCOAST POST-TENSION LTD p 1402
509 N Sam Houston Pkwy E # 300 77060
Tel (281) 445-8886
SIC 3315 3316 3496 3449

SUPERBAG USA CORP p 1406
9291 Baythorne Dr 77041
Tel (713) 462-1173 SIC 2673 5411

▲ SUPERIOR ENERGY SERVICES INC p 1406
1001 La St Ste 2900 77002
Tel (713) 654-2200 SIC 1389 3533 7353

■ SUSSER PETROLEUM CORP p 1409
555 E Airtex Dr 77073
Tel (832) 234-3746 SIC 5172 7389

■ SUSSER PETROLEUM OPERATING CO LLC p 1409
555 E Airtex Dr 77073
Tel (832) 234-3600 SIC 5172

■ SUSSER PETROLEUM PROPERTY CO LLC p 1409
555 E Airtex Dr 77073
Tel (832) 234-3600 SIC 5172 6519

SWEPI LP p 1412
200 N Dairy Ashford Rd 77079
Tel (713) 241-6161 SIC 1311 1382 5169

▲ SWIFT ENERGY CO p 1412
17001 Northchase Dr # 100 77060
Tel (281) 874-2700 SIC 1311

SWIFT ENERGY OPERATING LLC p 1412
17001 Northchase Dr # 100 77060
Tel (281) 874-2700 SIC 1311

SWISSPORT USA INC p 1413
151 Northpoint Dr 77060
Tel (281) 443-7687 SIC 4581

■ SWN DRILLING CO p 1413
2350 N Sam Hous 77032
Tel (281) 618-4700 SIC 1311

SYNDEX CORP p 1415
6950 Neuhaus St 77061
Tel (713) 923-1057 SIC 5148

▲ SYSCO CORP p 1417
1390 Enclave Pkwy 77077
Tel (281) 584-1390
SIC 5149 5142 5143 5144 5148 5137

■ SYSCO HOLDINGS LLC p 1417
1390 Enclave Pkwy 77077
Tel (281) 584-1728
SIC 5141 5142 5143 5144 5145 5146

■ SYSCO USA I INC p 1418
1390 Enclave Pkwy 77077
Tel (281) 584-1390
SIC 5141 5142 5143 5144 5145 5146

■ SYSCO USA II LLC p 1418
1390 Enclave Pkwy 77077
Tel (281) 584-1390
SIC 5141 5143 5144 5145 5146

T & L DISTRIBUTING p 1419
7350 Langfield Rd 77092
Tel (713) 461-7802 SIC 5023

■ T-3 ENERGY SERVICES INC p 1420
140 Cypress Station Dr # 225 77090
Tel (713) 944-5950 SIC 5211 3491 7699

▲ TAILORED BRANDS INC p 1421
6380 Rogerdale Rd 77072
Tel (281) 776-7000
SIC 5611 5621 5632 5661 5699

TALOS PRODUCTION LLC p 1423
1600 Smith St 77002
Tel (713) 328-3000 SIC 1382

TAM INTERNATIONAL INC p 1423
4620 Southerland Rd 77092
Tel (713) 462-7617 SIC 3533

▲ TARGA RESOURCES CORP p 1425
1000 La St Ste 4300 77002
Tel (713) 584-1000 SIC 4922 4924

■ TARGA RESOURCES LLC p 1425
1000 Louisiana St # 4300 77002
Tel (713) 873-1000 SIC 1389 6799

■ TARGA RESOURCES PARTNERS LP p 1425
1000 Louisiana St # 4300 77002
Tel (713) 584-1000 SIC 4922 4924 5172

■ TAS COMMERCIAL CONCRETE CONSTRUCTION LLC p 1425
19319 Oil Center Blvd 77073
Tel (281) 230-7500 SIC 1771

TAS COMMERCIAL CONCRETE LLC p 1425
19319 Oil Center Blvd 77073
Tel (281) 230-7500 SIC 8711

TAS CONSTRUCTION INC p 1425
19319 Oil Center Blvd 77073
Tel (281) 230-7500 SIC 1771

TASCO AUTO COLOR CORP p 1426
10323 Veterans Mem Dr 77038
Tel (281) 999-3761
SIC 5198 5013 5231 5531

TAUBER OIL CO p 1426
55 Waugh Dr Ste 700 77007
Tel (713) 869-8700 SIC 1311

▲ TC PIPELINES LP p 1428
700 Louisiana St Ste 700 77002
Tel (877) 290-2772 SIC 4922

TCH PEDIATRIC ASSOCIATES INC p 1428
8080 N Stadium Dr Ste 200 77054
Tel (832) 824-6626 SIC 8011

TE PRODUCTS PIPELINE CO LIMITED PARTNERSHIP p 1429
1100 La St Ste 1600 77002
Tel (713) 381-3636 SIC 4613 4922

TECHNIP STONE & WEBSTER PROCESS TECHNOLOGY INC p 1431
11740 Katy Fwy Ste 100 77079
Tel (281) 870-1111 SIC 8711

TECHNIP USA HOLDINGS INC p 1431
11740 Katy Fwy Ste 100 77079
Tel (281) 870-1111 SIC 8711

TECHNIP USA INC p 1431
11740 Katy Fwy Ste 100 77079
Tel (281) 870-1111 SIC 8711 8741

TEJAS TUBULAR PRODUCTS INC p 1433
8799 North Loop E Ste 300 77029
Tel (281) 822-3400 SIC 3317 3498

TEJAS TUBULAR PRODUCTS INC p 1433
8526 Green River Dr 77028
Tel (281) 822-3400 SIC 5051

TELCO INTERCONTINENTAL CORP p 1433
9812 Whithorn Dr 77095
Tel (281) 500-8270 SIC 5063 5065 3575

■ TELECHECK SERVICES INC p 1434
5251 Westheimr Rd B100 77056
Tel (713) 331-7600 SIC 7389 7374 6153

TELLEPSEN BUILDERS LP p 1435
777 Benmar Dr Ste 400 77060
Tel (281) 447-8100 SIC 1542

TELLEPSEN CORP p 1435
777 Benmar Dr Ste 400 77060
Tel (281) 447-8100 SIC 1521

TENARIS GLOBAL SERVICES (USA) CORP p 1437
2200 West Loop S Ste 800 77027
Tel (713) 767-4400 SIC 3317

■ TEPPCO PARTNERS LP p 1439
1100 Louisiana St # 1600 77002
Tel (713) 381-3636 SIC 4925 5171

TERRA ENERGY PARTNERS LLC p 1439
4828 Loop Central Dr # 900 77081
Tel (281) 936-0355 SIC 5172

TERRY ENERGY INC p 1440
3104 Edloe St Ste 205 77027
Tel (713) 552-0002 SIC 1389

TERRY FOUNDATION p 1440
600 Jefferson St Ste 1600 77002
Tel (713) 552-0002 SIC 8641

■ TERVITA LLC p 1440
10613 W Sam Huston Pkwy N 77064
Tel (832) 399-4500 SIC 1389

▲ TESCO CORP p 1440
11330 Clay Rd Ste 350 77041
Tel (713) 359-7000 SIC 3533

■ TESCO CORP (US) p 1440
11330 Clay Rd Ste 350 77041
Tel (713) 359-7000
SIC 7353 5082 1389 1381

TETON BUILDINGS LLC p 1441
2701 Magnet St 77054
Tel (713) 351-6300 SIC 1542

■ TEXACO EXPLORATION AND PRODUCTION INC p 1441
1500 Louisiana St 77002
Tel (800) 962-1223 SIC 5541 5511 1321

TEXAS AMERICAN TITLE CO p 1442
2000 Bering Dr Ste 900 77057
Tel (713) 988-9999 SIC 6361 8111

TEXAS AROMATICS LP p 1442
3555 Timmons Ln Ste 700 77027
Tel (713) 520-2900 SIC 5172

TEXAS CHILDRENS HEALTH PLAN INC p 1442
1919 S Braeswood Blvd 77030
Tel (832) 824-2939 SIC 6324

TEXAS CHILDRENS HOSPITAL p 1442
6621 Fannin St 77030
Tel (832) 824-1000 SIC 8011 8062

TEXAS CHILDRENS HOSPITAL FOUNDATION p 1442
6621 Fannin St Ste 210 77030
Tel (832) 824-6230 SIC 8011

TEXAS CHILDRENS PHYSICIAN GROUP INC p 1442
6621 Fannin St 77030
Tel (832) 824-2982 SIC 8011

■ TEXAS EASTERN TRANSMISSION LP p 1443
5400 Westheimer Ct 77056
Tel (713) 627-5400 SIC 4922

■ TEXAS GENCO HOLDINGS INC p 1443
12301 Kurland Dr 77034
Tel (281) 897-2610 SIC 4911

TEXAS HEART INSTITUTE p 1443
2450 Holcombe Blvd # 341 77021
Tel (832) 828-1000 SIC 8099

TEXAS PETROCHEMICALS LP p 1444
8600 Park Place Blvd 77017
Tel (713) 477-9211 SIC 2869

TEXAS PETROLEUM INVESTMENT CO INC p 1444
5850 San Felipe St # 250 77057
Tel (713) 789-9225 SIC 1382

TEXAS PIPE AND SUPPLY CO LTD p 1444
2330 Holmes Rd 77051
Tel (713) 799-9235 SIC 5051

TEXAS SOUTHERN UNIVERSITY p 1444
3100 Cleburne St 77004
Tel (713) 313-7011 SIC 8221

TEXAS STAFFING SERVICES INC p 1444
3000 Richmond Ave Ste 120 77098
Tel (713) 522-4800 SIC 7363

TEXAS STEEL CONVERSION INC p 1444
3101 Holmes Rd 77051
Tel (713) 733-6013 SIC 3498

■ TEXAS STEEL PROCESSING INC p 1444
5480 Windfern Rd 77041
Tel (281) 822-3200 SIC 5051

■ TEXAS STERLING CONSTRUCTION CO p 1444
20810 Fernbush Dr 77073
Tel (281) 821-9091 SIC 1611 1623

TEXAS UNITED CORP p 1444
4800 San Felipe St 77056
Tel (713) 877-1793
SIC 1479 2819 4619 2899 3299 7353

TEXICAN INDUSTRIAL ENERGY MARKETING LLC p 1445
1 Allen Ctr Ste 1150 77002
Tel (713) 650-6579 SIC 4924

TEXICAN NATURAL GAS CO p 1445
1 Allen Ctr 1 Allen Center 77002
Tel (713) 650-6579 SIC 4923

TEXON DISTRIBUTING LP p 1445
11757 Katy Fwy Ste 1400 77079
Tel (281) 531-8400 SIC 5172

TGS-NOPEC GEOPHYSICAL CO p 1446
10451 Clay Rd 77041
Tel (713) 860-2100 SIC 1382

THRUSTMASTER OF TEXAS INC p 1451
6900 Thrustmaster Dr 77041
Tel (713) 937-6295 SIC 3531

■ TIW CORP p 1457
12300 Main St 77035
Tel (713) 729-2110 SIC 3533

TMH PHYSICIAN ORGANIZATION p 1457
6565 Fannin St Ste D200 77030
Tel (713) 441-4182 SIC 8071

TMK IPSCO INC p 1457
10120 Houston Oaks Dr 77064
Tel (281) 949-1023 SIC 1389

TNT CRANE & RIGGING INC p 1458
925 S Loop W 77054
Tel (713) 644-6113 SIC 7353 1611

TODCO p 1458
2000 W Sam Houston Pkwy S # 800 77042
Tel (713) 278-6000 SIC 1381

TOM THUMB FOOD & DRUGS INC p 1459
3663 Briarpark Dr 77042
Tel (713) 268-3500
SIC 5411 5912 5499 6512 6552

TOMMIE VAUGHN MOTORS INC p 1459
1201 N Shepherd Dr 77008
Tel (713) 869-4661 SIC 5511

TORCH ENERGY ADVISORS INC p 1461
1331 Lamar St Ste 1450 77010
Tel (713) 650-1246
SIC 1311 1382 8741 8742

TOSHIBA INTERNATIONAL CORP p 1462
13131 W Little York Rd 77041
Tel (713) 466-0277
SIC 3621 5084 5063 3613 3594 3572

■ TOTAL DELAWARE INC p 1462
1201 La St Ste 1800 77002
Tel (713) 483-5000 SIC 1311 1382

■ TOTAL HOLDINGS USA INC p 1463
1201 La St Ste 1800 77002
Tel (713) 483-5000 SIC 1382 1311

■ TOTAL PETROCHEMICALS & REFINING USA INC p 1463
1201 La St Ste 1800 77002
Tel (713) 483-5000 SIC 2911 2899 2869

TOTAL SAFETY US INC p 1463
11111 Wilcrest Green Dr # 375 77042
Tel (713) 353-7100 SIC 8748 5084 7699

TPC GROUP INC p 1467
1 Allen Ctr Ste 1000 77002
Tel (713) 627-7474 SIC 2869

TPC GROUP LLC p 1467
1 Allen Center 500 77002
Tel (713) 477-9211 SIC 2869

TRACER CONSTRUCTION LLC p 1468
7433 Harwin Dr 77036
Tel (713) 868-5500 SIC 1731

TRACER INDUSTRIES INC p 1468
7433 Harwin Dr 77036
Tel (713) 868-5500 SIC 1711 1731

■ TRAFIGURA TERMINALS LLC p 1469
1401 Mckinney St Ste 1375 77010
Tel (832) 203-6400 SIC 4491

TRAFIGURA TRADING LLC p 1469
1401 Mckinney St Ste 1500 77010
Tel (832) 203-6400 SIC 6799

TRANS OCEAN LTD p 1470
4 Greenway Plz Ste 100 77046
Tel (713) 232-7500 SIC 1381

TRANS-GLOBAL SOLUTIONS INC p 1470
11811 East Fwy Ste 630 77029
Tel (713) 453-0341 SIC 4491 4013 4789

TRANSCONTINENTAL GAS PIPE LINE CO LLC p 1471
2800 Post Oak Blvd 77056
Tel (713) 215-2000 SIC 4922

TRANSOCEAN INC p 1472
4 Greenway Plz Ste 700 77046
Tel (713) 232-7500 SIC 1381

TRANSWESTERN COMMERCIAL SERVICES LLC p 1473
1900 West Loop S Ste 1300 77027
Tel (713) 270-7000 SIC 6512

■ TRANSWESTERN PIPELINE CO LLC p 1473
711 Louisiana St Ste 900 77002
Tel (281) 714-2000 SIC 4922

TRANSWORLD WORLDWIDE INC p 1473
4 Greenway Plz Ste 700 77046
Tel (713) 232-7500 SIC 1381 1311

TREES INC p 1475
650 N Sam Houston Pkwy E 77060
Tel (281) 447-1327 *SIC* 0783 0782

TRELLEBORG OFFSHORE US INC p 1476
1902 Rankin Rd 77073
Tel (281) 774-2600 *SIC* 3533

■ TRI RESOURCES INC p 1476
1000 Louisiana St # 4300 77002
Tel (713) 584-1000 *SIC* 1321 1381 1382

TRIBUTE ENERGY INC p 1479
2100 West Loop S Ste 1220 77027
Tel (281) 768-5300 *SIC* 5169 3295 2821

TRICAN WELL SERVICE LP p 1479
5825 N Sam Houston Pkwy W # 600 77086
Tel (281) 716-9152 *SIC* 2911 1481 1389

TRICO MARINE SERVICES INC p 1479
3200 Southwest Fwy # 2950 77027
Tel (888) 369-8929 *SIC* 4412

TRICON ENERGY INC p 1479
777 Post Oak Blvd Ste 550 77056
Tel (713) 963-0066 *SIC* 6719

TRICON INTERNATIONAL LTD p 1479
777 Post Oak Blvd Ste 550 77056
Tel (713) 963-0066 *SIC* 5169 7389 4789

TRIMAC ACTIVE INC p 1480
15333 John F Kennedy Blvd # 800 77032
Tel (281) 985-0000 *SIC* 4213

TRIMAC TRANSPORTATION INC p 1480
15333 John F Kenn Blvd 77032
Tel (281) 985-0000 *SIC* 4789

TRIPLE-S STEEL HOLDINGS INC p 1482
6000 Jensen Dr 77026
Tel (713) 697-7105 *SIC* 5051 6719

TRIPLE-S STEEL SUPPLY LLC p 1482
6000 Jensen Dr 77026
Tel (713) 354-4100 *SIC* 5051

■ TRIUMPH HEALTHCARE HOLDINGS INC p 1483
7333 North Fwy Ste 500 77076
Tel (713) 699-8879 *SIC* 6324

TROY CONSTRUCTION LLC p 1485
8521 Mchard Rd 77053
Tel (281) 437-8214 *SIC* 1623 8711

■ TRUNKLINE GAS CO LLC p 1487
5051 Westheimr Rd # 1428 77056
Tel (713) 989-2193 *SIC* 4922

TRUSSWAY HOLDINGS INC p 1487
9411 Alcorn St 77093
Tel (713) 691-6900 *SIC* 2439

TRUSSWAY INDUSTRIES INC p 1487
9411 Alcorn St 77093
Tel (713) 691-6900 *SIC* 2439

TRUSSWAY MANUFACTURING INC p 1487
9411 Alcorn St 77093
Tel (719) 322-9662 *SIC* 2439 5031

TSC OFFSHORE CORP p 1489
7611 Railhead Ln 77086
Tel (832) 456-3900 *SIC* 3533

TTS INC p 1490
333 N Sam Houston Pkwy E 77060
Tel (281) 716-2000 *SIC* 7213

▲ TTWF LP p 1490
2801 Post Oak Blvd 77056
Tel (713) 960-9111 *SIC* 2821 2869 2865

TUBOSCOPE INC p 1490
2919 Holmes Rd 77051
Tel (713) 799-5100 *SIC* 1381

TUBULAR RAIL INC p 1490
5000 Milwee St Apt 43 77092
Tel (713) 834-7905 *SIC* 4731

TUBULAR SERVICES LLC p 1490
1010 Mccarty St 77029
Tel (713) 675-6212 *SIC* 1389

TUCKER ENERGY SERVICES INC p 1490
411 N Sam Houston Pkwy E # 300 77060
Tel (281) 442-9095 *SIC* 1389 3533

TURBINE AIR SYSTEMS LTD p 1492
6110 Cullen Blvd 77021
Tel (713) 877-8700 *SIC* 3585

TWIN EAGLE RESOURCE MANAGEMENT LLC p 1495
8847 W Sam Houston Pkwy N 77040
Tel (713) 341-7332 *SIC* 4911 4924 5983

TYCO ENGINEERED PRODUCTS & SERVICES p 1496
9600 W Gulf Bank Rd 77040
Tel (609) 720-4200 *SIC* 3491 3625 3621

U S WEATHERFORD L P p 1497
2000 Saint James Pl 77056
Tel (713) 693-4000 *SIC* 3498 3533

ULTRA PETROLEUM CORP p 1501
400 N Sam Houston Pkwy E # 1200 77060
Tel (281) 876-0120 *SIC* 1311

ULTRAPAK LTD p 1501
9690 W Wingfoot Rd 77041
Tel (713) 329-9183 *SIC* 5162

UNI-CHARTERING USA LLC p 1502
840 Gessner Rd Ste 210 77024
Tel (281) 833-7271 *SIC* 4491

■ UNION CARBIDE CORP p 1504
1254 Enclave Pkwy 77077
Tel (281) 966-2727 *SIC* 2869 2821

UNION DRILLING INC p 1504
952 Echo Ln Ste 460 77024
Tel (817) 735-8793 *SIC* 1381

UNITED SPACE ALLIANCE LLC p 1512
3700 Bay Area Blvd # 100 77058
Tel (281) 212-6200 *SIC* 8711

UNITED STRUCTURES OF AMERICA INC p 1514
1912 Buschong St 77039
Tel (281) 442-8247 *SIC* 3448

UNITED WAY OF GREATER HOUSTON p 1515
50 Waugh Dr 77007
Tel (713) 685-2300 *SIC* 8399

UNIVERSAL COMPUTER SYSTEMS INC p 1516
6700 Hollister St 77040
Tel (713) 718-1800 *SIC* 5045

■ UNIVERSAL ENSCO INC p 1516
4848 Loop Central Dr # 137 77081
Tel (713) 425-6000 *SIC* 1389

UNIVERSAL WEATHER AND AVIATION INC p 1518
1150 Gemini St 77058
Tel (713) 944-1622 *SIC* 4725 4724

■ UNIVERSALPEGASUS INTERNATIONAL HOLDINGS INC p 1518
4848 Loop Central Dr # 600 77081
Tel (713) 425-6000 *SIC* 7389 8711 8713

■ UNIVERSALPEGASUS INTERNATIONAL INC p 1518
4848 Loop Central Dr # 600 77081
Tel (713) 425-6000 *SIC* 7389 8711 8713

UNIVERSITY GENERAL HEALTH SYSTEM INC p 1518
7501 Fannin St 77054
Tel (713) 375-7100 *SIC* 8062 8059

UNIVERSITY OF HOUSTON SYSTEM p 1521
4302 University Dr 77204
Tel (713) 743-0945 *SIC* 8221

UNIVERSITY OF TEXAS HEALTH SCIENCE CENTER AT HOUSTON p 1526
7000 Fannin St Ste 700a 77030
Tel (713) 500-4472 *SIC* 8221

UNIVERSITY OF TEXAS MD ANDERSON CANCER CENTER p 1526
1515 Holcombe Blvd # 207 77030
Tel (713) 745-4428 *SIC* 8069

UNIVERSITY TEXAS PHYSICIANS INF p 1527
6410 Fannin St Ste 600 77030
Tel (832) 325-7070 *SIC* 8011

■ US HOME CORP p 1532
10707 Clay Rd 77041
Tel (305) 559-4000 *SIC* 1531 6162 6552

US LEGAL SUPPORT INC p 1532
363 N Sam Houston Pkwy E # 1200 77060
Tel (713) 653-7100 *SIC* 8111

US METALS INC p 1532
19102 Gundle Rd 77073
Tel (281) 443-7473 *SIC* 5085

▲ US PHYSICAL THERAPY INC p 1533
1300 W Sam Houston Pkwy S # 300 77042
Tel (713) 297-7000 *SIC* 8049

US PIPELINE INC p 1533
950 Echo Ln Ste 100 77024
Tel (281) 531-6100 *SIC* 1623

US SHALE SOLUTIONS INC p 1533
7670 Woodway Dr Ste 250 77063
Tel (832) 742-7492 *SIC* 1382

US WELL SERVICES LLC p 1533
770 S Post Oak Ln Ste 405 77056
Tel (832) 562-3731 *SIC* 1389

US ZINC CORP p 1533
2727 Allen Pkwy Ste 800 77019
Tel (713) 514-0037 *SIC* 3356

USA (UNITED SPACE ALLIANCE PENSION) p 1533
600 Gemini St 77058
Tel (281) 212-6200 *SIC* 3812

UT PHYSICIANS p 1536
6410 Fannin St Ste 1500 77030
Tel (713) 500-5086 *SIC* 8011

UTC OVERSEAS INC p 1536
2 Northpoint Dr Ste 213 77060
Tel (713) 422-2850 *SIC* 4412 4581

UTEX INDUSTRIES INC p 1536
10810 Katy Fwy Ste 100 77043
Tel (713) 559-0203 *SIC* 3053 3061

■ UTILITY HOLDING LLC p 1537
1111 Louisiana St 77002
Tel (713) 207-1111 *SIC* 4924 4922

■ UTLX MANUFACTURING LLC p 1537
16923 Old Beaumont 90 77049
Tel (281) 847-8200 *SIC* 3795

V&M STAR A PARTNERSHIP WITH GENERAL AND LIMITED PARTNERS LP p 1538
8603 Sheldon Rd 77049
Tel (281) 456-6000 *SIC* 3317

VALERUS FIELD SOLUTIONS HOLDINGS LLC p 1540
919 Milam St Ste 1000 77002
Tel (713) 744-6100 *SIC* 1382 6719

VALLEN SAFETY SUPPLY CO p 1540
521 N Sam Houston Pkwy E # 300 77060
Tel (281) 500-5000
SIC 5099 5084 5047 5063

VALLOUREC & MANNESMANN HOLDINGS INC p 1541
4424 W Sam Houston Pkwy N # 150 77041
Tel (713) 479-3200 *SIC* 5082

VALLOUREC INDUSTRIES INC p 1541
19210 E Hardy Rd 77073
Tel (281) 821-5510 *SIC* 3498

VALLOUREC USA CORP p 1541
4424 W Sm Hstn Pkwy N 1 77041
Tel (713) 479-3277 *SIC* 5082

VAM USA LLC p 1542
4424 W S Houston N 150 77041
Tel (281) 821-5510 *SIC* 3498

▲ VANGUARD NATURAL RESOURCES LLC p 1543
5847 San Felipe St # 1910 77057
Tel (832) 327-2255 *SIC* 1311 1382

VANTAGE DRILLING CO p 1544
777 Post Oak Blvd Ste 800 77056
Tel (281) 404-4700 *SIC* 1381

■ VARCO LP p 1544
2835 Holmes Rd 77051
Tel (713) 799-5272 *SIC* 1389 3479

■ VARIABLE ANNUITY LIFE INSURANCE CO (INC) p 1544
2929 Allen Pkwy 77019
Tel (713) 522-1111 *SIC* 6311

VEOLIA ES INDUSTRIAL SERVICES INC p 1548
4760 World Houston Pkwy # 100 77032
Tel (713) 672-8004 *SIC* 1799

VEOLIA WATER NORTH AMERICA-NORTHEAST LLC p 1549
14950 Hathrow Forest Pkwy 77032
Tel (281) 449-1500 *SIC* 4952 4941

VERIFINC CORP p 1549
12000 Westheimer Rd # 380 77077
Tel (832) 858-5548 *SIC* 7371 5734 5122

VERSATECH AUTOMATION SERVICES LLC p 1551
11349 Fm 529 Rd 77041
Tel (713) 937-3100 *SIC* 5531 5013

▲ VERTEX ENERGY INC p 1552
1331 Gemini St Ste 250 77058
Tel (866) 660-8156 *SIC* 2911

■ VETCO GRAY INC p 1552
4424 W Sam Houston Pkwy N 77041
Tel (713) 683-2400 *SIC* 3533

■ VICTORY PACKAGING LP p 1556
3555 Timmons Ln Ste 1440 77027
Tel (888) 261-1268 *SIC* 5113 5199

VINMAR INTERNATIONAL HOLDINGS LTD p 1558
16800 Imperial Valley Dr 77060
Tel (281) 618-1300 *SIC* 5169

VINMAR INTERNATIONAL LTD p 1558
16800 Imperial Valley Dr 77060
Tel (281) 618-1300 *SIC* 5169

VINSON & ELKINS LLP p 1558
1001 Fannin St Ste 2500 77002
Tel (713) 758-2222 *SIC* 8111

VISTA HOST INC p 1562
10370 Richmond Ave # 150 77042
Tel (713) 267-5800 *SIC* 7011

VITOL INC p 1563
2925 Richmond Ave Ste 11 77098
Tel (713) 230-1000 *SIC* 6211

VOPAK NORTH AMERICA INC p 1565
2000 West Loop S Ste 1550 77027
Tel (713) 561-7200
SIC 4491 4226 4953 4789

VOTORANTIM METAIS NORTH AMERICA INC p 1566
6020 Navigation Blvd 77011
Tel (713) 926-1705 *SIC* 3356

VOTORANTIM US INC p 1566
3200 Southwest Fwy # 3030 77027
Tel (832) 726-0160 *SIC* 1031 1061

W S BELLOWS CONSTRUCTION CORP p 1569
1906 Afton St 77055
Tel (713) 680-2132 *SIC* 1542

W T BYLER CO INC p 1569
15203 Lillja Rd 77060
Tel (281) 445-2070 *SIC* 1794 1629

▲ W&T OFFSHORE INC p 1569
9 Greenway Plz Ste 300 77046
Tel (713) 626-8525 *SIC* 1311

W-H ENERGY SERVICES LLC p 1569
2000 W Sam Houston Pkwy S # 500 77042
Tel (713) 969-1000 *SIC* 1389 7353

WANG JING p 1575
1400 Hermann Pressler Dr 77030
Tel (713) 794-4190 *SIC* 8733

WARTSILA HOLDING INC p 1577
11710 N Gessner Rd Ste A 77064
Tel (281) 233-6200 *SIC* 5084 1629

WARTSILA NORTH AMERICA INC p 1577
11710 N Gessner Rd Ste A 77064
Tel (281) 233-6200
SIC 1629 5084 1382 4789 3731

■ WASTE AWAY GROUP INC p 1580
1001 Fannin St Ste 4000 77002
Tel (713) 512-6200 *SIC* 4953

WASTE CORP OF AMERICA INC p 1580
1330 Post Oak Blvd Fl 30 77056
Tel (713) 572-3802 *SIC* 4953

■ WASTE MANAGEMENT HOLDINGS INC p 1580
1001 Fannin St Ste 4000 77002
Tel (713) 512-6200 *SIC* 4953

▲ WASTE MANAGEMENT INC p 1580
1001 Fannin St Ste 4000 77002
Tel (713) 512-6200 *SIC* 4953

■ WASTE MANAGEMENT OF ILLINOIS INC p 1580
1001 Fannin St Ste 4000 77002
Tel (713) 512-6200 *SIC* 4953

■ WASTE MANAGEMENT OF OKLAHOMA INC p 1581
1001 Fannin St Ste 3900 77002
Tel (713) 512-6200 *SIC* 4953

■ WASTE MANAGEMENT OF TEXAS INC p 1581
1001 Fannin St Ste 4000 77002
Tel (713) 512-6200 *SIC* 4953

WAUKESHA-PEARCE INDUSTRIES INC p 1583
12320 Main St 77035
Tel (713) 723-1050 *SIC* 5084 5082 3621

WAVE ELECTRONICS INC p 1583
8648 Glenmont Dr Ste 130 77036
Tel (713) 849-2710 *SIC* 5064

WAYNE D ENTERPRISES INC p 1584
14300 Hollister St 77066
Tel (713) 856-0300 *SIC* 5136 5199

WCA WASTE CORP p 1585
1330 Post Oak Blvd # 3000 77056
Tel (713) 292-2400 *SIC* 4953

WEATHERFORD ARTIFICIAL LIFT SYSTEMS LLC p 1586
2000 Saint James Pl 77056
Tel (713) 836-4000 *SIC* 3561 5084

WEATHERFORD INTERNATIONAL LLC p 1586
2000 Saint James Pl 77056
Tel (713) 693-4000 *SIC* 1389

WEATHERFORD LABORATORIES INC p 1586
2000 Saint James Pl 77056
Tel (832) 237-4000 *SIC* 1389

WEDGE GROUP INC p 1587
1415 La St Ste 3000 77002
Tel (713) 739-6500 *SIC* 1389 1629 1311

WEDGE MEASUREMENT SYSTEMS LLC p 1587
1415 La St Ste 1500 77002
Tel (713) 490-9444 *SIC* 1389

WEEKLEY HOMES LLC p 1587
1111 N Post Oak Rd 77055
Tel (713) 963-0500 *SIC* 1531 1521

▲ WEINGARTEN REALTY INVESTORS p 1588
2600 Citadel Plaza Dr # 125 77008
Tel (713) 866-6000 *SIC* 6798

■ WELLS FARGO BANK SOUTH CENTRAL NATIONAL ASSOCIATION p 1590
2005 Taylor St 77007
Tel (713) 802-2717 *SIC* 6035

■ WESTERN NATIONAL LIFE INSURANCE CO p 1599
2929 Allen Pkwy Ste 3800 77019
Tel (713) 522-1111 *SIC* 6411

■ WESTERN WASTE OF TEXAS LLC p 1600
1001 Fannin St Ste 4000 77002
Tel (713) 512-6200 *SIC* 4953

WESTERNGECO LLC p 1600
10001 Richmond Ave 77042
Tel (713) 789-9600 *SIC* 1382

■ WESTLAKE CHEMICAL CORP p 1601
2801 Post Oak Blvd # 600 77056
Tel (713) 960-9111 *SIC* 2821

■ WESTLAKE CHEMICAL PARTNERS LP p 1601
2801 Post Oak Blvd # 600 77056
Tel (713) 585-2900 *SIC* 2869

■ WESTLAKE OLEFINS CORP p 1601
2801 Post Oak Blvd Fl 6 77056
Tel (713) 960-9111 *SIC* 2869 2822

■ WESTLAKE POLYMERS LLC p 1601
2801 Post Oak Blvd # 650 77056
Tel (713) 960-9111 *SIC* 2673 2869

■ WESTLAKE VINYLS CO LP p 1601
2801 Post Oak Blvd # 600 77056
Tel (713) 960-9111 *SIC* 2812 2869 2821

WESTWAY CONSTRUCTION SERVICES LLC p 1603
8611 Derrington Rd 77064
Tel (713) 375-2330 *SIC* 1522

WHIRLWIND HOLDING CO INC p 1605
8234 Hansen Rd 77075
Tel (713) 946-7140 *SIC* 3448

WHIRLWIND STEEL BUILDINGS INC p 1605
8234 Hansen Rd 77075
Tel (713) 946-7140 *SIC* 3448

WHITE DEER ENERGY LP II p 1606
700 Louisiana St Ste 4770 77002
Tel (713) 581-6900 *SIC* 6726

■ WHMC INC p 1607
12141 Richmond Ave 77082
Tel (281) 558-3444 *SIC* 8069

WHOLESALE ELECTRIC SUPPLY CO OF HOUSTON INC p 1607
4040 Gulf Fwy 77004
Tel (713) 748-6100 *SIC* 5065

■ **WILD WELL CONTROL INC** p 1609
2202 Oil Center Ct 77073
Tel (281) 784-4700 *SIC* 1389

■ **WILLBROS CONSTRUCTION (US) LLC** p 1610
4400 Post Oak Pkwy # 1000 77027
Tel (713) 403-8000 *SIC* 1623

▲ **WILLBROS GROUP INC** p 1610
4400 Post Oak Pkwy 77027
Tel (713) 403-8000 *SIC* 8711 1542

WILLBROS INTERNATIONAL INC p 1610
4400 Post Oak Pkwy # 1000 77027
Tel (713) 403-8000 *SIC* 8711

■ **WILLBROS UNITED STATES HOLDINGS INC** p 1610
4400 Post Oak Pkwy # 1000 77027
Tel (713) 403-8000 *SIC* 8711 1623

WILLIAM MARSH RICE UNIVERSITY INC p 1610
6100 Main St 77005
Tel (713) 348-4055 *SIC* 8221

WILLIAM STAMPS FARISH FUND p 1611
1100 La St Ste 1200 77002
Tel (713) 757-7313 *SIC* 7389

WILLIAMS BROTHERS CONSTRUCTION CO INC p 1611
3800 Milam St 77006
Tel (713) 522-9821 *SIC* 1622

■ **WILLIAMS GAS PIPELINE-TRANSCO** p 1611
2800 Post Oak Blvd # 300 77056
Tel (713) 215-2000 *SIC* 1321 1221 1222

WILLISTON HOLDINGS INC p 1612
12000 Aerospace Ave # 400 77034
Tel (832) 300-5858 *SIC* 5812 6794 5046

WINDSOR QUALITY FOOD CO LTD p 1615
3355 W Alabama St Ste 730 77098
Tel (713) 843-5200 *SIC* 2038

WINDWARD PRINT STAR INC p 1616
14950 Hethrw Frst Pkwy # 120 77032
Tel (281) 821-5522
SIC 2752 2791 2796 7335 7336 7331

WISENBAKER BUILDER SERVICES INC p 1619
1703 Westfield Loop Rd 77073
Tel (281) 233-4000 *SIC* 5023 5084 5031

■ **WM RECYCLE AMERICA LLC** p 1620
1001 Fannin St Ste 4000 77002
Tel (713) 512-6200 *SIC* 5093

WOMBLE CO INC p 1621
12821 Industrial Rd 77015
Tel (713) 636-8700 *SIC* 3479

WOOD GROUP MANAGEMENT SERVICES INC p 1622
17325 Park Row 77084
Tel (281) 828-3500 *SIC* 1389

WOOD GROUP MUSTANG INC p 1622
17325 Park Row 77084
Tel (832) 809-8000
SIC 8711 8742 7389 1389

WOOD GROUP PSN INC p 1622
17325 Park Row 77084
Tel (281) 647-1041 *SIC* 1629 1542 8711

WORLEYPARSONS CORP p 1626
575 N Gary Ashford 77079
Tel (713) 407-5000 *SIC* 8711 8742

WRRH INVESTMENTS LP p 1628
5747 San Felipe St # 4650 77057
Tel (713) 782-9100 *SIC* 7011

WYATT FIELD SERVICE CO p 1629
15415 Katy Fwy Ste 800 77094
Tel (281) 675-1300 *SIC* 1791

■ **WYMAN-GORDON FORGINGS INC** p 1629
10825 Telge Rd 77095
Tel (281) 897-2400 *SIC* 3462

■ **XJT HOLDINGS INC** p 1632
1600 Smith St 77002
Tel (713) 324-5236 *SIC* 4512

YES PREP PUBLIC SCHOOLS INC p 1636
6201 Bonhomme Rd Ste 168n 77036
Tel (713) 967-9001 *SIC* 8211

YOUNG MENS CHRISTIAN ASSOCIATION OF GREATER HOUSTON AREA p 1638
2600 North Loop W Ste 300 77092
Tel (713) 659-5566 *SIC* 8322

YOUNG MENS CHRISTIAN ASSOCIATION OF GREATER HOUSTON AREA INC p 1638
2600 North Loop W Ste 300 77092
Tel (713) 659-5566
SIC 8641 7991 8351 7032 8322

HUMBLE, TX

ABSOLUTE ENVIRONMENTAL SERVICES LTD LLP p 13
11315 Dogwood Dr 77338
Tel (281) 319-4789 *SIC* 1799

CDI ENERGY PRODUCTS INC p 271
8103 Rankin Rd 77396
Tel (281) 446-6662 *SIC* 3053

HUMBLE INDEPENDENT SCHOOL DISTRICT p 718
20200 Eastway Village Dr 77338
Tel (281) 641-1000 *SIC* 8211

NISSAN ROBBINS INC p 1044
18711 Highway 59 N 77338
Tel (281) 446-3181 *SIC* 5511

NORTHEAST HOSPITAL FOUNDATION p 1055
18951 N Memorial Dr 77338
Tel (281) 540-7817 *SIC* 8062

NORTHEAST MEDICAL CENTER HOSPITAL p 1055
9813 Memorial Blvd Ste H 77338
Tel (281) 540-7167 *SIC* 8062

HUNGERFORD, TX

STROUHAL TIRE RECAPPING PLANT LTD p 1394
8206 Hwy 59 77448
Tel (979) 532-1579 *SIC* 5014

HUNTSVILLE, TX

HOUSTON SAM STATE UNIVERSITY p 712
1806 Ave J 77340
Tel (936) 294-1111 *SIC* 8221

HUNTSVILLE INDEPENDENT SCHOOL DISTRICT p 720
441 Fm 2821 Rd E 77320
Tel (936) 435-6300 *SIC* 8211

HUNTSVILLE MEMORIAL HOSPITAL AUXILIARY p 721
110 Memorial Hospital Dr 77340
Tel (936) 291-3411 *SIC* 8062

TEXAS DEPARTMENT OF CRIMINAL JUSTICE p 1443
861 Interstate 45 N 227b 77320
Tel (936) 295-6371 *SIC* 9223 9229

HUTCHINS, TX

CONSOLIDATED CASTING CORP p 359
1501 S Interstate 45 75141
Tel (972) 225-7305 *SIC* 3324 3369

INGLESIDE, TX

KIEWIT OFFSHORE SERVICES LTD p 817
2440 Kiewit Rd 78362
Tel (361) 775-4300 *SIC* 1623

STATE SERVICE CO INC p 1382
1062 Harbor 2 Bishop Rd 78362
Tel (281) 347-2500 *SIC* 1629

IRVING, TX

7-ELEVEN INC p 3
3200 Hackberry Rd 75063
Tel (972) 828-0711 *SIC* 5411 6794

■ **AARON BROTHERS INC** p 8
8001 Ridgepoint Dr 75063
Tel (214) 492-6200 *SIC* 7699 5945

ACCURUS AEROSPACE CORP p 16
222 Las Colinas Blvd W 75039
Tel (469) 317-6140 *SIC* 3728

ACE CASH EXPRESS INC p 16
1231 Greenway Dr Ste 600 75038
Tel (972) 550-5000 *SIC* 7323 6099

ACM NEWSPAPERS HOLDINGS LLC p 17
7301 State Highway 161 75039
Tel (214) 691-4066 *SIC* 6719

■ **ALLSTATE TEXAS LLOYDS** p 58
8711 Freeport Pkwy 75063
Tel (847) 402-3029 *SIC* 6331

ANIMAL SUPPLY CO LLC p 91
600 Las Colinas Blvd E 75039
Tel (972) 616-9600 *SIC* 5199

ARBOR CONTRACT CARPET INC p 103
2313 E Pioneer Dr 75061
Tel (972) 445-2235 *SIC* 1752

■ **ASBURY AUTOMOTIVE SOUTHERN CALIFORNIA LLC** p 115
3700 W Airport Fwy 75062
Tel (972) 790-6000 *SIC* 5511

■ **ASSOCIATES CORP OF NORTH AMERICA** p 121
250 E John Carpenter Fwy 75062
Tel (972) 652-4000
SIC 6141 6153 6159 6311 6321 6331

■ **ASSOCIATES FIRST CAPITAL CORP** p 121
4000 Regent Blvd 75063
Tel (800) 922-6235
SIC 6162 6021 6141 6159 6153

AUSTIN BRIDGE & ROAD INC p 132
6330 Commerce Dr Ste 150 75063
Tel (214) 596-7300 *SIC* 1611 1622

AUSTIN BRIDGE & ROAD LP p 132
6330 Commerce Dr Ste 150 75063
Tel (214) 596-7300 *SIC* 1622 1611

AUTO AIR EXPORT INC p 133
1401 Valley View Ln # 100 75061
Tel (972) 812-7000 *SIC* 5075 3585 5531

AZTECA MILLING LP p 140
1159 Cottonwood Ln # 100 75038
Tel (972) 232-5339 *SIC* 0723

■ **BAKER HUGHES OILFIELD OPERATIONS INC** p 146
1333 Corporate Dr Ste 300 75038
Tel (972) 988-0111 *SIC* 1389

BANCTEC INC p 150
2701 E Grauwyler Rd 75061
Tel (972) 821-4000 *SIC* 7389

BAYLOR MEDICAL CENTER AT IRVING p 162
1901 N Macarthur Blvd 75061
Tel (972) 579-8100 *SIC* 8062

BELL SPORTS CORP p 170
6333 N State Highway 161 # 300 75038
Tel (469) 417-6600 *SIC* 3949 3751 5091

BELL SPORTS INC p 170
6333 N State Highway 161 # 300 75038
Tel (469) 417-6600 *SIC* 3949 3751

■ **BERKSHIRE HATHAWAY AUTOMOTIVE INC** p 175
8333 Royal Ridge Pkwy # 100 75063
Tel (972) 536-2900 *SIC* 7549 5511

BFN OPERATIONS LLC p 179
8700 Freeport Pkwy Ste 100 75063
Tel (972) 819-5030 *SIC* 0181

BIG 12 CONFERENCE INC p 181
400 E John Carpenter Fwy 75062
Tel (469) 524-1000 *SIC* 7941 7997

BIO WORLD MERCHANDISING INC p 183
2111 W Walnut Hill Ln 75038
Tel (888) 831-2138
SIC 2353 3161 2253 5199 3021

BOY SCOUTS OF AMERICA p 205
1325 W Walnut Hill Ln 75038
Tel (972) 580-2000
SIC 8641 5136 5091 2721

BROADVIEW SECURITY INC p 215
8880 Esters Blvd 75063
Tel (972) 871-3500 *SIC* 7382

C-III CAPITAL PARTNERS LLC p 234
5221 N O Connor Blvd 75039
Tel (972) 868-5300
SIC 6519 6726 6361 6411

CALIBER FUNDING LLC p 239
6031 Connection Dr # 200 75039
Tel (866) 373-2968 *SIC* 6153

CALIBER HOME LOANS INC p 239
3701 Regent Blvd 75063
Tel (800) 401-6587 *SIC* 6153

CEC ENTERTAINMENT INC p 272
1707 Market Pl Ste 200 75063
Tel (972) 258-8507 *SIC* 5812 7993 6794

■ **CELANESE AMERICAS LLC** p 273
222 Colinas Blvd W 900n 75039
Tel (972) 443-4000
SIC 2821 2819 2824 5169

▲ **CELANESE CORP** p 273
222 Las Colinas Blvd W # 900 75039
Tel (972) 443-4000 *SIC* 2819 2821 2869

■ **CELANESE INTERNATIONAL CORP** p 273
222 Las Colinas Blvd W 75039
Tel (972) 443-4000 *SIC* 2819 2869

CENTREX PRECISION PLASTICS p 281
7700 Bent Dr Ste 100 75063
Tel (972) 929-4804 *SIC* 3842

CH WILKINSON PHYSICIAN NETWORK p 286
919 Hidden Rdg 75038
Tel (469) 282-2000 *SIC* 8011

CHEDDARS CASUAL CAFE INC p 292
2900 Ranch Trl 75063
Tel (214) 596-6700 *SIC* 5812

CHRISTUS HEALTH p 303
919 Hidden Rdg 75038
Tel (469) 282-2000 *SIC* 8062 8051

CHRISTUS HEALTH p 303
919 Hidden Rdg 75038
Tel (281) 936-6000 *SIC* 8062

CHRISTUS HEALTH GULF COAST p 303
919 Hidden Rdg 75038
Tel (281) 599-5700 *SIC* 8062

■ **CITI FINANCIAL AUTO** p 309
250 E John Carpenter Fwy 75062
Tel (972) 652-4000 *SIC* 6141

CITY OF IRVING p 315
825 W Irving Blvd 75060
Tel (972) 721-2600 *SIC* 9111

■ **CNA HOLDINGS LLC** p 330
222 Las Colinas Blvd W 75039
Tel (972) 443-4000
SIC 2823 2821 2819 5169 8731

▲ **COMMERCIAL METALS CO** p 345
6565 N Mcarthr Blvd # 800 75039
Tel (214) 689-4300
SIC 3312 3441 5051 5093

CONSOLIDATED ELECTRICAL DISTRIBUTORS INC p 359
1920 Westridge Dr Ste 107 75038
Tel (972) 582-5300 *SIC* 5063 5211

■ **CONTEL FEDERAL SYSTEMS INC** p 362
600 Hidden Rdg 75038
Tel (972) 718-5600 *SIC* 3661 4813

CORPSOURCE HOLDINGS LLC p 372
2701 E Grauwyler Rd 75061
Tel (866) 321-5854 *SIC* 7375 7334 7374

COTTONWOOD FINANCIAL ADMINISTRATIVE SERVICES LLC p 374
1901 Gateway Dr Ste 200 75038
Tel (972) 753-0822 *SIC* 6141

▲ **DARLING INGREDIENTS INC** p 412
251 Oconnor Ridge Blvd 75038
Tel (972) 717-0300 *SIC* 2077

DEEP SOUTH HOLDING INC p 421
7701 Las Colinas Rdg # 600 75063
Tel (214) 493-4200 *SIC* 6411

DRIVER PIPELINE CO INC p 456
1200 N Union Bower Rd 75061
Tel (214) 638-7131 *SIC* 1623

ELECTRICAL DISTRIBUTORS LLC p 485
2301 Century Cir 75062
Tel (469) 533-6250 *SIC* 5063 5999

EMSI HOLDING CO p 495
3050 Regent Blvd Ste 400 75063
Tel (602) 288-4488 *SIC* 8099

■ **ENVOY AIR INC** p 504
4301 Regent Blvd 75063
Tel (972) 374-5200 *SIC* 4512

■ **EPSILON DATA MANAGEMENT LLC** p 505
6021 Connection Dr 75039
Tel (972) 582-9600 *SIC* 7375

ETHOS GROUP INC p 511
5215 N O Connor Blvd # 1450 75039
Tel (972) 331-1000 *SIC* 6411

EXAMINATION MANAGEMENT SERVICES INC p 516
3050 Regent Blvd Ste 100 75063
Tel (214) 689-3600 *SIC* 8099

■ **EXETER FINANCE CORP** p 519
222 Las Colinas Blvd W 75039
Tel (214) 572-8276 *SIC* 6153

▲ **EXXON MOBIL CORP** p 521
5959 Las Colinas Blvd 75039
Tel (972) 444-1000
SIC 2911 4612 5541 5171 4911

FEDERAL HOME LOAN BANK OF DALLAS p 534
8500 Freeport Pkwy # 600 75063
Tel (214) 441-8500 *SIC* 6111

FELCOR LODGING LIMITED PARTNERSHIP p 537
545 E John Carpenter Fwy # 1300 75062
Tel (972) 444-4900 *SIC* 7011

FELCOR LODGING TRUST INC p 537
545 E John Carpenter Fwy # 1300 75062
Tel (972) 444-4900 *SIC* 6798

FLEETPRIDE INC p 555
600 Las Colinas Blvd E # 400 75039
Tel (469) 249-7500 *SIC* 5531 5013

▲ **FLOWSERVE CORP** p 560
5215 N Oconnor Blvd Connor 75039
Tel (972) 443-6500
SIC 3561 3491 3621 3494 3463 3321

■ **FLOWSERVE US INC** p 560
5215 N Oconnor Blvd Ste 75039
Tel (972) 443-6500 *SIC* 3561 3491

▲ **FLUOR CORP** p 561
6700 Las Colinas Blvd 75039
Tel (469) 398-7000 *SIC* 8711 1629 1541

FLUOR EMPLOYEE BENEFIT TRUST p 561
6700 Las Colinas Blvd 75039
Tel (469) 398-7000 *SIC* 6411

■ **FLUOR ENTERPRISES INC** p 561
6700 Las Colinas Blvd 75039
Tel (469) 398-7000 *SIC* 1799 8711

■ **FORTERRA INC** p 569
511 E John Carpenter Fwy 75062
Tel (469) 284-8678 *SIC* 3272 3569

FORTERRA PIPE & PRECAST LLC p 569
511 E John Carpenter Fwy 75062
Tel (469) 458-7973 *SIC* 3272 1771

▲ **FORTERRA US HOLDINGS LLC** p 569
511 E John Carpenter Fwy 75062
Tel (469) 284-8678 *SIC* 6719

FOUR SEASONS RESORT & CLUB p 572
4150 N Macarthur Blvd 75038
Tel (972) 717-0700 *SIC* 7011

■ **FRONTIER SOUTHWEST INC** p 581
600 Hidden Rdg 75038
Tel (972) 718-5600 *SIC* 4813

G2 SECURE STAFF LLC p 588
400 Las Colinas Blvd E # 750 75039
Tel (972) 915-6979 *SIC* 6411 4789 4729

▲ **GLOBAL POWER EQUIPMENT GROUP INC** p 617
400 Las Colinas Blvd E 75039
Tel (214) 574-2000 *SIC* 3568 1796 7699

■ **GOLDMAN SACHS REALTY MANAGEMENT LP** p 622
6011 Connection Dr 75039
Tel (972) 368-2200 *SIC* 8741

GOLDS GYM INTERNATIONAL INC p 622
125 E J Carpentr Fwy 13 75062
Tel (972) 444-8527 *SIC* 7991 6794

GRUMA CORP p 642
5601 Executive Dr Ste 800 75038
Tel (972) 232-5000 *SIC* 0723 2096 2099

■ **GTE MIDWEST INC** p 644
600 Hidden Rdg 75038
Tel (972) 718-1856 *SIC* 4813

HANSON AGGREGATES LLC p 658
8505 Freeport Pkwy Ste 500 75063
Tel (469) 417-1200 *SIC* 3273 2951 5032

HANSON LEHIGH INC p 659
300 E John Carpenter Fwy 75062
Tel (972) 653-5500
SIC 1442 1422 1423 3297 3273 3272

■ **HEALTH MANAGEMENT SYSTEMS INC** p 675
5615 High Point Dr # 100 75038
Tel (214) 453-3000 *SIC* 7374 7372

HIGHGATE HOTELS INC p 691
545 E J Carpentr Fwy 14 75062
Tel (972) 444-9700 *SIC* 8741

▲ **HMS HOLDINGS CORP** p 698
5615 High Point Dr # 100 75038
Tel (214) 453-3000 *SIC* 7322

HOV SERVICES INC p 712
2701 E Grauwyler Rd 75061
Tel (248) 837-7100
SIC 7374 7334 7389 2752 7331 7379

HUNTLEIGH USA CORP p 720
545 E John Carpenter Fwy 75062
Tel (972) 719-9180 SIC 4581

HYUNDAI MERCHANT MARINE (AMERICA) INC p 724
222 Las Colinas Blvd W 75039
Tel (972) 501-1100 SIC 4731

IRVING BRAKEBUSH INC p 765
2230 E Union Bower Rd 75061
Tel (972) 554-0590 SIC 5144

IRVING INDEPENDENT SCHOOL DISTRICT INC p 765
2621 W Airport Fwy 75062
Tel (972) 600-5000 SIC 8211

IRVING MCDAVID HONDA LP p 765
3700 W Airport Fwy 75062
Tel (972) 790-2000 SIC 5511

▲ JP ENERGY PARTNERS LP p 794
600 Las Colinas Blvd E # 2000 75039
Tel (972) 444-0300 SIC 1321

JPI APARTMENT CONSTRUCTION LP p 795
600 Las Colinas Blvd E # 1800 75039
Tel (972) 556-1700 SIC 1522

JPI INVESTMENT CO LP p 795
600 Las Colinas Blvd E # 1800 75039
Tel (972) 556-1700 SIC 6552

JPI LIFESTYLE APARTMENT COMMUNITIES LP p 795
600 Las Colinas Blvd E 75039
Tel (972) 556-1700 SIC 6513 6552

JPI MANAGEMENT LLC p 795
600 Las Colinas Blvd E 75039
Tel (972) 556-1700 SIC 8741

▲ KIMBERLY-CLARK CORP p 818
351 Phelps Dr 75038
Tel (972) 281-1200 SIC 2621 2676

▲ LA QUINTA HOLDINGS INC p 836
909 Hidden Rdg Ste 600 75038
Tel (214) 492-6600 SIC 7011

■ LA QUINTA LLC p 836
909 Hidden Rdg Ste 600 75038
Tel (214) 492-6600 SIC 7011 6794 8741

LAIRD PLASTICS INC p 838
5800 Campus Circle Dr E 75063
Tel (469) 299-7000 SIC 5162 3089

LEHIGH CEMENT CO LLC p 853
300 E John Carpenter Fwy 75062
Tel (877) 534-4442 SIC 3241 3273 5032

■ LQ MANAGEMENT LLC p 882
909 Hidden Rdg Ste 600 75038
Tel (214) 492-6600 SIC 7011

LSG SKY CHEFS USA INC p 883
6191 N State Highway 161 # 100 75038
Tel (972) 793-9000 SIC 5812 5962

MAGNUM HUNTER RESOURCES CORP p 896
909 Lake Carolyn Pkwy # 600 75039
Tel (832) 369-6986 SIC 1311

MATRIX TELECOM LLC p 920
433 Las Colinas Blvd E # 500 75039
Tel (888) 411-0111 SIC 4813

■ MCDAVID IRVING-HON LP p 927
3700 W Airport Fwy 75062
Tel (972) 790-6100 SIC 5511

MEDIEVAL TIMES ENTERTAINMENT INC p 938
6363 N State Highway 161 # 400 75038
Tel (214) 596-7600 SIC 8741

MEDSYNERGIES INC p 939
909 Hidden Rdg Ste 300 75038
Tel (972) 791-1224 SIC 8741 8742 8721

MEDSYNERGIES NORTH TEXAS INC p 939
909 Hidden Rdg Ste 300 75038
Tel (972) 791-1224 SIC 8741

■ METLIFE HOME LOANS LLC p 954
7880 Bent Branch Dr # 100 75063
Tel (214) 441-4000 SIC 6162

▲ MICHAELS COMPANIES INC p 960
8000 Bent Branch Dr 75063
Tel (972) 409-1300 SIC 5945 3999 2273

■ MICHAELS FINCO HOLDINGS LLC p 960
8000 Bent Branch Dr 75063
Tel (972) 409-1300 SIC 5945

■ MICHAELS FUNDING INC p 960
8000 Bent Branch Dr 75063
Tel (972) 409-1300 SIC 5945

MICHAELS HOLDINGS LLC p 960
8000 Bent Branch Dr 75063
Tel (972) 409-1300
SIC 5945 5999 5949 5947 5199 5099

■ MICHAELS STORES INC p 960
8000 Bent Branch Dr 75063
Tel (972) 409-1300
SIC 5945 5999 5949 5947 5199 5099

MJB WOOD GROUP INC p 978
2201 W Royal Ln Ste 250 75063
Tel (972) 401-0005 SIC 5031

■ MOBIL CORP p 980
5959 Las Colinas Blvd 75039
Tel (972) 444-1000
SIC 2911 5171 4612 4613 1311

MOSAIC SALES SOLUTIONS US OPERATING CO LLC p 992
220 Las Colinas Blvd E 75039
Tel (972) 870-4800 SIC 8742 8743 7374

MULTI-VIEW INC p 999
7701 Las Colinas Rdg 75063
Tel (972) 402-7070 SIC 7313

NCH CORP p 1022
2727 Chemsearch Blvd 75062
Tel (972) 438-0211
SIC 2842 2899 3432 3548 3429

NEC CORP OF AMERICA p 1023
3929 W John Carpenter Fwy 75063
Tel (214) 262-6000 SIC 5045 5065

NEOVIA LOGISTICS SERVICES LLC p 1026
6363 N State Highway 161 # 700 75038
Tel (469) 513-7000 SIC 4789 5082

NEXCYCLE INC p 1039
5221 N O Connor Blvd # 850 75039
Tel (972) 506-7200 SIC 4953

▲ NEXSTAR BROADCASTING GROUP INC p 1040
545 E John Carpenter Fwy # 700 75062
Tel (972) 373-8800 SIC 4833

NOKIA INC p 1046
6363 N State Highway 161 # 800 75038
Tel (214) 496-0329 SIC 3663

NOKIA SOLUTIONS AND NETWORKS US LLC p 1046
6000 Connection Dr 75039
Tel (972) 374-3000 SIC 3663 5999 4813

■ ODYSSEY HEALTHCARE INC p 1075
7801 Mesquite Bend Dr # 105 75063
Tel (888) 600-2411 SIC 8051

ON BORDER CORP p 1085
2201 W Royal Ln Ste 240 75063
Tel (972) 499-3000 SIC 5812 5813

ONE SOURCE VIRTUAL HR INC p 1086
5601 N Macarthur Blvd 75038
Tel (972) 916-9847 SIC 8742

OTB ACQUISITION LLC p 1097
2201 W Royal Ln Ste 240 75063
Tel (972) 499-3000 SIC 5812

PACIFIC UNION FINANCIAL LLC p 1106
8900 Freeport Pkwy Ste 150 75063
Tel (800) 809-0421 SIC 6282

PARTSMASTER INC p 1119
1400 E Northgate Dr 75062
Tel (972) 438-0711 SIC 5085

PDS TECH INC p 1125
300 E John Carpenter Fwy # 700 75062
Tel (214) 647-9600 SIC 7361

PERIMETER INTERNATIONAL p 1136
2700 Story Rd W Ste 150 75038
Tel (877) 701-1919
SIC 7389 4412 4731 4581 4449

PINNACLE ONE PARTNERS LP p 1150
300 Decker Dr 75062
Tel (214) 812-4600 SIC 4813

PINNACLE PROPANE LLC p 1150
600 Las Colinas Blvd E # 2000 75039
Tel (972) 444-0300 SIC 1321

▲ PIONEER NATURAL RESOURCES CO p 1151
5205 N Oconnor Connor 75039
Tel (972) 444-9001 SIC 1311 1321

■ PIONEER NATURAL RESOURCES PUMPING SERVICES LLC p 1151
5205 N O Connor Blvd # 200 75039
Tel (972) 444-9001 SIC 1389

■ PIONEER NATURAL RESOURCES USA INC p 1151
5205 N Oconnor Blvd Ste 75039
Tel (972) 444-9001 SIC 1311 1321

PIONEER SOUTHWEST ENERGY PARTNERS LP p 1151
5205 N Oconner Blvd 200 Connor 75039
Tel (972) 444-9001 SIC 1311

PLH GROUP INC p 1156
400 Las Colinas Blvd E 75039
Tel (214) 272-0500 SIC 1623

PORT PLASTICS INC p 1162
5800 Campus Circle Dr E 150a 75063
Tel (469) 299-7000 SIC 5162

POTTER CONCRETE OF HOUSTON INC p 1164
2400 E Pioneer Dr 75061
Tel (214) 630-2191 SIC 1771

POWER LINE SERVICES INC p 1165
400 Las Colinas Blvd E 75039
Tel (214) 272-0500 SIC 1623

PREMIER DESIGNS INC p 1170
1551 Corporate Dr Ste 150 75038
Tel (972) 550-0955 SIC 5094

■ PREMIER SILICA LLC p 1171
5205 N O Connor Blvd # 200 75039
Tel (972) 444-9001 SIC 1446

PRIMESOURCE BUILDING PRODUCTS INC p 1175
1321 Greenway Dr 75038
Tel (972) 999-8500 SIC 5033 5031

PROGRESSIVE LABORATORIES INC p 1181
3131 Story Rd W 75038
Tel (972) 518-9660 SIC 2834

■ PULTE HOMES OF TEXAS LP p 1192
4800 Regent Blvd Ste 100 75063
Tel (972) 304-2800 SIC 6552 1521

S A ICTS-U INC p 1261
545 E John Carpenter Fwy 75062
Tel (972) 719-9180 SIC 6719

S C INTERNATIONAL SERVICES INC p 1262
6191 N State Highway 161 # 100 75038
Tel (972) 793-9000 SIC 5812 5962

■ SAXON MORTGAGE SERVICES INC p 1284
3701 Regent Blvd Ste 100 75063
Tel (972) 570-6000 SIC 6162

SHERMCO INDUSTRIES INC p 1316
2425 E Pioneer Dr 75061
Tel (972) 793-5523 SIC 8711 7694 5063

■ SIRIUS XM CONNECTED VEHICLE SERVICES INC p 1327
8550 Freeport Pkwy 75063
Tel (972) 753-6200 SIC 7375

SKY CHEFS INC p 1330
6191 N State Highway 161 # 100 75038
Tel (972) 793-9000 SIC 5812

SOURCECORP INC p 1342
2701 E Grauwyler Rd 75061
Tel (866) 321-5854 SIC 7375 7334 7374

SOURCEHOV HOLDINGS INC p 1342
2701 E Grauwyler Rd 75061
Tel (972) 821-4000 SIC 6719

SOURCEHOV LLC p 1342
2701 E Grauwyler Rd 75061
Tel (866) 321-5854 SIC 8748

SQS USA INC p 1362
545 E John Carpenter Fwy 75062
Tel (630) 596-6001 SIC 7373

SUPERIOR FIBERS INC p 1406
1333 Corporate Dr Ste 350 75038
Tel (972) 600-9953 SIC 3677 3569

TEXAS AIR SYSTEMS INC p 1442
6029 Campus Circle Dr W # 100 75063
Tel (972) 570-4700 SIC 5075 1711

TEXAS AIRSYSTEMS LLC p 1442
6029 Campus Circle Dr W 75063
Tel (210) 499-0004 SIC 3563

TEXAS WASATCH INSURANCE SERVICES LP p 1444
100 E Royal Ln Ste 320 75039
Tel (214) 838-5500 SIC 6411 6799

■ TICONA POLYMERS INC p 1452
222 Las Colinas Blvd W 900n 75039
Tel (972) 443-4000 SIC 3087

TRT HOTEL CO LLC p 1485
420 Decker Dr 75062
Tel (972) 730-6664 SIC 7011

TURBO RESTAURANT LLC p 1492
7750 N Macarthur Blvd 1 75063
Tel (972) 620-2287 SIC 5812

■ UNION STANDARD INSURANCE GROUP LLC p 1505
222 Las Colinas Blvd W # 1300 75039
Tel (972) 719-2400 SIC 6331

■ US HOME SYSTEMS INC p 1532
2951 Kinwest Pkwy 75063
Tel (214) 488-6300 SIC 3429 5031 1751

USMD HOLDINGS INC p 1535
6333 N State Highway 161 # 200 75038
Tel (214) 493-4000 SIC 8062

VCC LLC p 1545
600 Las Colinas Blvd E # 1525 75039
Tel (214) 574-4500 SIC 1542 8711 8742

■ VERIZON NORTHWEST INC p 1550
600 Hidden Rdg 75038
Tel (972) 718-5600
SIC 4813 6519 8721 5065 7629

■ VERIZON SOUTH INC p 1550
600 Hidden Rdg 75038
Tel (972) 718-5600 SIC 4813 5065 8721

VERMEER EQUIPMENT OF TEXAS INC p 1551
3025 State Highway 161 75062
Tel (972) 255-3500 SIC 5082 7699 7353

VIZIENT INC p 1563
290 E John Carpenter Fwy # 1500 75062
Tel (972) 830-0000 SIC 8742

W2005 WYN HOTELS LP p 1569
545 E J Carpntr Fwy 140 75062
Tel (972) 444-9700 SIC 7011

WALKER ENGINEERING INC p 1573
1505 W Walnut Hill Ln 75038
Tel (817) 540-7777 SIC 1731

WERE READY TO ASSEMBLE INC p 1592
2201 W Royal Ln Ste 230 75063
Tel (972) 373-9484 SIC 7389 5399

■ WINDSTREAM SOUTHWEST LONG DISTANCE LP p 1616
201 E John Carpenter Fwy 75062
Tel (972) 373-1000 SIC 4813

WORKWAY INC p 1624
105 Decker Ct Ste 560 75062
Tel (972) 514-1547 SIC 7361

WORLDWIDE FLIGHT SERVICES INC p 1626
1925 W John Carpenter Fwy # 450 75063
Tel (972) 629-5001 SIC 4581 4789

YOUNG PRESIDENTS ORGANIZATION p 1639
600 Las Colinas Blvd E # 10 75039
Tel (972) 587-1500 SIC 8621

ZALE CANADA CO p 1641
901 W Walnut Hill Ln 75038
Tel (972) 580-4000 SIC 5944

ZALE CORP p 1641
901 W Walnut Hill Ln 75038
Tel (972) 580-4000 SIC 5944

ZALE DELAWARE INC p 1641
901 W Walnut Hill Ln 75038
Tel (972) 580-4000 SIC 5944

JACKSONVILLE, TX

AUSTIN BANCORP INC p 132
200 E Commerce St 75766
Tel (903) 586-1526 SIC 6021 6211 6022

AUSTIN BANK TEXAS N A p 132
200 E Commerce St 75766
Tel (903) 586-1526 SIC 6021

SOUTHERN MULTIFOODS INC p 1349
101 E Cherokee St 75766
Tel (903) 586-1524 SIC 5812

JEFFERSON, TX

NORBORD TEXAS LP p 1047
500 Nexfor Blvd 75657
Tel (936) 568-8009 SIC 2493

JERSEY VILLAGE, TX

A2 HOLDINGS LTD p 7
15701 Nw Fwy 77040
Tel (713) 983-1100 SIC 5013

STEWART BUILDERS INC p 1389
16575 Village Dr 77040
Tel (713) 983-8002 SIC 1771

W CSE INDUSTRIES INC p 1568
11500 Charles Rd 77041
Tel (713) 466-9463
SIC 3625 3613 3594 3494

W-INDUSTRIES OF TEXAS LLC p 1569
11500 Charles Rd 77041
Tel (713) 466-9463 SIC 6719

JOHNSON CITY, TX

PEDERNALES ELECTRIC COOPERATIVE INC p 1127
201 S Avenue F 78636
Tel (830) 868-7155 SIC 4911

JUSTIN, TX

NORTHWEST INDEPENDENT SCHOOL DISTRICT p 1060
2001 Texan Dr 76247
Tel (817) 215-0000 SIC 8211

KATY, TX

ACADEMY LTD p 13
1800 N Mason Rd 77449
Tel (281) 646-5200 SIC 5941 5699 5661

DET NORSKE VERITAS HOLDING (USA) INC p 433
1400 Ravello Rd 77449
Tel (281) 396-1000
SIC 8711 7389 5734 8741

IGLOO PRODUCTS CORP p 730
777 Igloo Rd 77494
Tel (281) 394-6800 SIC 3086

KATY INDEPENDENT SCHOOL DISTRICT p 805
6301 S Stadium Ln 77494
Tel (281) 396-6000 SIC 8211

KATY INDEPENDENT SCHOOL DISTRICT DARE ADVISORY BOARD INC p 805
20380 Franz Rd 77449
Tel (281) 396-2500 SIC 8211

MEMORIAL HERMANN KATY HOSPITAL p 942
23900 Katy Fwy 77494
Tel (281) 644-7000 SIC 8062

■ NEWPARK DRILLING FLUIDS LLC p 1038
21920 Merchants Way 77449
Tel (281) 754-8600 SIC 5169 5172 4953

OPTIMIZED PROCESS DESIGNS LLC p 1090
25610 Clay Rd 77493
Tel (281) 371-7500 SIC 1629

PATHFINDER ENERGY SERVICES LLC p 1120
23500 Colonial Pkwy 77493
Tel (281) 769-4501 SIC 1389

PEPPER-LAWSON CONSTRUCTION LP p 1133
4555 Katy Hockley Rd 77493
Tel (281) 371-3100 SIC 1542

PERCHERON SERVICES p 1134
1904 W Grand Pkwy N 77449
Tel (832) 300-6400 SIC 6552

STAFF FORCE INC p 1374
419 Mason Park Blvd 77450
Tel (281) 492-6044 SIC 7363

TRENT SEVERN ENVIRONMENTAL SERVICES INC p 1476
2002 W Grand Pkwy N 77449
Tel (281) 578-4200 SIC 8741 3589

KAUFMAN, TX

TRINITY VALLEY ELECTRIC COOPERATIVE INC p 1482
1800 E State Highway 243 75142
Tel (972) 932-2214 SIC 4911

VILLAGE OF KAUFMAN p 1557
421 E 7th St 75142
Tel (972) 962-7328 SIC 6513

KELLER, TX

KELLER INDEPENDENT SCHOOL DISTRICT p 808
350 Keller Pkwy 76248
Tel (817) 744-1000 SIC 8211

KERRVILLE, TX

JAMES AVERY CRAFTSMAN INC p 776
145 Avery Rd 78028
Tel (830) 895-6800 SIC 3911

PETERSON SID MEMORIAL HOSPITAL p 1138
551 Hill Country Dr 78028
Tel (830) 896-4200 SIC 8051 8062

KILGORE, TX

▲ MARTIN MIDSTREAM PARTNERS LP p 913
4200 Stone Rd 75662
Tel (903) 983-6200
SIC 5171 4226 1321 4424 2819 2875

■ MARTIN OPERATING PARTNERSHIP LP p 913
4200 Stone Rd 75662
Tel (903) 983-6200 SIC 5172

MARTIN PRODUCT SALES LLC p 913
4200 Stone Rd 75662
Tel (903) 983-6200 SIC 5052 5032 5172

MARTIN RESOURCE MANAGEMENT CORP p 913
4200 Stone Rd 75662
Tel (903) 983-6200
SIC 2911 4924 5984 5172

MARTIN TRANSPORT INC p 913
4200 Stone Rd 75662
Tel (281) 860-4313 SIC 4213

VERTEX COMMUNICATIONS CORP p 1552
2600 N Longview St 75662
Tel (903) 984-0555 SIC 3663

KILLEEN, TX

CITY OF KILLEEN p 315
101 College St 76541
Tel (254) 501-7895 SIC 9111

■ FIRST NATIONAL BANK TEXAS p 548
507 N Gray St 76541
Tel (254) 554-6699 SIC 6021

KILLEEN INDEPENDENT SCHOOL DISTRICT p 818
200 N W S Young Dr 76543
Tel (254) 336-0000 SIC 8211

METROPLEX ADVENTIST HOSPITAL INC p 955
2201 S Clear Creek Rd 76549
Tel (254) 526-7523 SIC 8062

KINGSVILLE, TX

TEXAS A & M UNIVERSITY KINGSVILLE p 1441
700 University Blvd 78363
Tel (361) 593-3344 SIC 8221

KINGWOOD, TX

EPRODUCTION SOLUTIONS LLC p 505
22001 Northpark Dr 77339
Tel (281) 348-1000 SIC 3491 5084 1389

FGI ACQUISITION CORP p 539
201 Kingwood Medical Dr B200 77339
Tel (281) 604-2525 SIC 3053

■ INSPERITY HOLDINGS INC p 746
19001 Crescent Springs Dr 77339
Tel (281) 358-8986 SIC 7363

▲ INSPERITY INC p 746
19001 Crescent Springs Dr 77339
Tel (281) 358-8986
SIC 8742 7363 7361 6311

KINGWOOD MEDICAL CENTER p 821
22999 Highway 59 N # 134 77339
Tel (281) 348-8000 SIC 8011

ORION ENGINEERED CARBONS LLC p 1094
4501 Magnolia Cove Dr 77345
Tel (832) 445-3300 SIC 2895

KYLE, TX

HAYS CONSOLIDATED I S D p 670
21003 Interstate 35 78640
Tel (512) 268-8442 SIC 8211

LA JOYA, TX

LA JOYA INDEPENDENT SCHOOL DISTRICT p 835
200 W Expressway 83 78560
Tel (956) 580-2000 SIC 8211

LA PORTE, TX

AUSTIN INDUSTRIAL INC p 133
2801 E 13th St 77571
Tel (713) 641-3400 SIC 1629

AUSTIN MAINTENANCE & CONSTRUCTION INC p 133
2801 E 13th St 77571
Tel (713) 641-3400 SIC 1629

LA PORTE INDEPENDENT SCHOOL DISTRICT p 835
1002 San Jacinto St 77571
Tel (281) 604-7000 SIC 8211

MOBLEY INDUSTRIAL SERVICES INC p 980
1220 Miller Cut Off Rd 77571
Tel (281) 470-9120 SIC 1721 1799 5033

■ REPCONSTRICKLAND INC p 1224
1605 S Battleground Rd 77571
Tel (281) 478-6200 SIC 1541

SULZER TURBO SERVICES HOUSTON INC p 1397
11518 Old La Porte Rd 77571
Tel (713) 567-2700 SIC 3569

LA VILLA, TX

DE BRUYN PRODUCE CO p 419
26 Fm 491 78562
Tel (956) 262-6286 SIC 5148

LAKE JACKSON, TX

BRAZOSPORT MEMORIAL HOSPITAL p 209
194 Abner Jackson Pkwy 77566
Tel (979) 299-2882 SIC 8062

BUC-EES LTD p 222
327 Fm 2004 Rd 77566
Tel (979) 230-2930 SIC 8741

TEXAS DOW EMPLOYEES CREDIT UNION p 1443
1001 Fm 2004 Rd 77566
Tel (979) 297-1154 SIC 6062

LAKEWAY, TX

FORD RESTAURANT GROUP INC p 566
1514 Ranch Road 620 S 78734
Tel (512) 263-0929 SIC 5812

LANCASTER, TX

FFE LOGISTICS INC p 539
3400 Stonewall St 75134
Tel (214) 630-8090 SIC 4731

FFE TRANSPORTATION SERVICES INC p 539
3400 Stonewall St 75134
Tel (800) 569-9200 SIC 4213

FROZEN FOOD EXPRESS INDUSTRIES INC p 582
3400 Stonewall St 75134
Tel (800) 569-9200 SIC 4731 4213

LAREDO, TX

ABOUT TIME LTD p 12
7220 Bob Bullock Loop 78041
Tel (956) 723-1198 SIC 5092 5945

ARGUINDEGUI OIL CO II LTD p 108
6551 Star Ct 78041
Tel (956) 722-5251 SIC 5171

CITY OF LAREDO p 316
1110 Houston St 78040
Tel (956) 791-7308 SIC 9111

COUNTY OF WEBB p 383
1000 Houston St 78040
Tel (956) 523-4600 SIC 9111

▲ INTERNATIONAL BANCSHARES CORP p 754
1200 San Bernardo Ave 78040
Tel (956) 722-7611 SIC 6022

■ INTERNATIONAL BANK OF COMMERCE p 754
1200 San Bernardo Ave 78040
Tel (956) 722-7611 SIC 6022

LAREDO INDEPENDENT SCHOOL DISTRICT EDUCATIONAL FOUNDATION p 845
1702 Houston St 78040
Tel (956) 795-3200 SIC 8211

■ LAREDO MEDICAL CENTER p 845
1700 E Saunders St 78041
Tel (956) 796-5000 SIC 8062

■ LAREDO REGIONAL MEDICAL CENTER L P p 845
1700 E Saunders St 78041
Tel (956) 796-5000 SIC 8062 8071

MARIBEL RESENDIZ p 906
711 Mispola Dr 78046
Tel (956) 236-2907 SIC 5199

RAMSA ELECTROMECHANIC INC p 1207
207 W Ryan St 78041
Tel (956) 568-5354 SIC 7694

SIGMA ALIMENTOS INTERNATIONAL INC p 1321
1009 Black Diamond Cir 78045
Tel (956) 417-2693 SIC 5147

SSC LAREDO WEST OPERATING CO LLC p 1363
1200 E Lane St 78040
Tel (956) 722-0031 SIC 8051

UNITED INDEPENDENT SCHOOL DISTRICT p 1509
201 Lindenwood Dr 78045
Tel (956) 473-6201 SIC 8211

VITRO PACKAGING LLC p 1563
13481 Resource 78045
Tel (956) 717-4232 SIC 3221

LEAGUE CITY, TX

AMERICAN HOMESTAR CORP p 74
2450 S Shore Blvd Ste 300 77573
Tel (281) 334-9700
SIC 2451 4213 5271 6351 6515

BENSON - SABIN INC p 173
2112 Gulf Fwy S 77573
Tel (281) 338-9700 SIC 5511 7538

CEDA INTERNATIONAL INC p 272
2600 S Shore Blvd Ste 300 77573
Tel (281) 478-2600 SIC 1389

CLEAR CREEK INDEPENDENT SCHOOL DISTRICT p 324
2425 E Main St 77573
Tel (281) 284-0000 SIC 8211

INEOS AMERICAS LLC p 740
2600 S Shore Blvd Ste 500 77573
Tel (281) 535-6600 SIC 2873 2869

INEOS NITRILES USA LLC p 740
2600 S Shore Blvd Ste 250 77573
Tel (281) 535-6600 SIC 2821

INEOS USA LLC p 740
2600 S Shore Blvd Ste 500 77573
Tel (281) 535-6600 SIC 2821 3999

LEANDER, TX

LEANDER INDEPENDENT SCHOOL DISTRICT p 850
204 W South St 78641
Tel (512) 570-0000 SIC 8211

LEWISVILLE, TX

▲ ADEPTUS HEALTH INC p 22
2941 Lake Vista Dr # 200 75067
Tel (972) 899-6666 SIC 8741 8011

AMERICAN MESSAGING SERVICES LLC p 76
1720 Lakepointe Dr # 100 75057
Tel (888) 699-9014 SIC 4812

APPAREL GROUP LTD p 98
883 Trinity Dr 75056
Tel (214) 469-3300 SIC 2339 2321

CALIBER BODYWORKS OF TEXAS INC p 239
401 E Corp Dr Ste 150 75057
Tel (469) 948-9500 SIC 7532

CALIBER BODYWORKS PSA OF TEXAS INC p 239
401 E Corp Dr Ste 150 75057
Tel (469) 948-9500 SIC 7532

CALIBER HOLDINGS CORP p 239
401 E Corp Dr Ste 150 75057
Tel (469) 948-9500 SIC 6719

COMPUDATA PRODUCTS INC p 352
1301 Ridgeview Ste 100 75057
Tel (972) 280-0922 SIC 5112

CUNNINGHAM LINDSEY US INC p 401
405 State Highway 121 Byp A100 75067
Tel (214) 488-5139 SIC 6411

■ EMC MORTGAGE LLC p 490
2780 Lake Vista Dr 75067
Tel (214) 626-2735 SIC 6162

■ HORIZON HEALTH CORP p 707
1965 Lakepointe Dr # 100 75057
Tel (972) 420-8200 SIC 8093 8069

HOYA CORP p 714
651 E Corporate Dr 75057
Tel (972) 221-4141 SIC 3851

IRONSHORE SPECIALTY INSURANCE CO p 765
2850 Lake Vista Dr # 150 75067
Tel (646) 826-6600 SIC 6331

LEWISVILLE INDEPENDENT SCHOOL DISTRICT p 859
1565 W Main St Ste 101 75067
Tel (469) 713-5200 SIC 8211

■ NATIONSTAR CAPITAL CORP p 1017
350 Highland Dr 75067
Tel (469) 549-2000 SIC 6162

ORTHOFIX INC p 1096
3451 Plano Pkwy 75056
Tel (214) 937-2000 SIC 3841

OVERHEAD DOOR CORP p 1099
2501 S State Hwy 121 Ste 75067
Tel (469) 549-7100
SIC 3442 2431 3699 3537 3589

PARKWAY C&A LP p 1117
1000 Civic Cir 75067
Tel (972) 221-1979 SIC 1542

PARKWAY CONSTRUCTION & ARCHITECTURE LP p 1117
1000 Civic Cir 75067
Tel (972) 221-1979 SIC 1542

PARKWAY CONSTRUCTION & ASSOCIATES LP p 1117
1000 Civic Cir 75067
Tel (972) 221-1979 SIC 1542

PRESIDIO NETWORKED SOLUTIONS GROUP LLC p 1172
1955 Lakeway Dr Ste 220 75057
Tel (469) 549-3800 SIC 5045 7372 7373

PRIME CONTROLS LP p 1175
1725 Lakepointe Dr 75057
Tel (972) 221-4849 SIC 5065 1731

RESPONSIVE EDUCATION SOLUTIONS p 1228
1301 Waters Ridge Dr 75057
Tel (972) 420-7050 SIC 8211

ROBERTS TRUCK CENTER HOLDING CO LLC p 1242
1825 Lakeway Dr Ste 700 75057
Tel (469) 645-7111 SIC 5012 7513 7538

■ SOLUTIONSTAR HOLDINGS LLC p 1339
750 Hwy 121 Byp Ste 100 75067
Tel (888) 321-2192 SIC 6531

■ SYSCO NORTH TEXAS p 1417
800 Trinity Dr 75056
Tel (469) 384-6000 SIC 5141

■ TEXAS-NEW MEXICO POWER CO p 1445
577 N Garden Ridge Blvd 75067
Tel (972) 420-4189 SIC 4911

UNIVERSAL DISPLAY AND FIXTURE CO p 1516
726 E Hwy 121 75057
Tel (972) 434-8067 SIC 2542 3993

VINSON PROCESS CONTROLS CO LP p 1558
2747 Highpoint Oaks Dr 75067
Tel (972) 459-8200 SIC 5084 3533 3498

LITTLEFIELD, TX

AMERICAN TEXTILE HOLDINGS LLC p 80
1926 Fm 548 79339
Tel (806) 385-6401 SIC 2211

PAY AND SAVE INC p 1122
1804 Hall Ave 79339
Tel (806) 385-3366 SIC 5411

LIVE OAK, TX

BA & W ENTERPRISES INC p 143
13510 Toepperwein Rd 78233
Tel (361) 767-4100 SIC 5012

JORDAN FORD LTD p 793
13010 N Interstate 35 78233
Tel (210) 653-3673 SIC 5511

JUDSON INDEPENDENT SCHOOL DISTRICT p 797
8012 Shin Oak Dr 78233
Tel (210) 945-5100 SIC 8211

LIVINGSTON, TX

SAM HOUSTON ELECTRIC COOPERATIVE INC p 1274
1157 E Church St 77351
Tel (936) 327-5711 SIC 4911

LLANO, TX

BUTTERY CO LLP p 230
201 W Main St 78643
Tel (325) 247-4141
SIC 5072 5074 5063 5091 5211 5251

LOLITA, TX

AMTOPP CORP p 87
101 Interplast Blvd 77971
Tel (361) 874-3000 SIC 3081

INTEGRATED BAGGING SYSTEMS CORP p 749
101 Interplast Blvd 77971
Tel (361) 874-3000 SIC 3081

LONE STAR, TX

SCOT INDUSTRIES INC p 1293
3756 Fm 250 N 75668
Tel (903) 639-2551
SIC 7389 5051 3498 3471

LONGVIEW, TX

■ AAON COIL PRODUCTS INC p 8
203 Gum Springs Rd 75602
Tel (903) 236-4403 SIC 3585

ABC AUTO PARTS LTD p 10
920 W Marshall Ave 75604
Tel (903) 232-3010 SIC 5013 5531

APPLIED-CLEVELAND HOLDINGS INC p 100
2735 State Highway 322 75603
Tel (918) 358-5735 SIC 6719 7389

BRENNTAG SOUTHWEST INC p 210
610 Fisher Rd 75604
Tel (903) 241-7117 SIC 5169

CAPACITY OF TEXAS INC p 248
401 Capacity Dr 75604
Tel (903) 759-0610 SIC 3537

GIBSON SALES LP p 611
2321a W Loop 281 75604
Tel (903) 297-0966 SIC 5912

GOOD SHEPHERD HEALTH SYSTEM INC p 623
700 E Marshall Ave 75601
Tel (888) 784-4747 SIC 8062

■ JOY GLOBAL LONGVIEW OPERATIONS LLC p 794
2400 S Macarthur Dr 75602
Tel (903) 237-7000
SIC 3532 3533 3312 3531

LONGVIEW BRIDGE AND ROAD LTD p 877
792 Skinner Ln 75605
Tel (903) 663-0264 SIC 1611 1622 1794

LONGVIEW INDEPENDENT SCHOOL DISTRICT p 877
1301 E Young St 75602
Tel (903) 753-0206 SIC 8211

■ LONGVIEW MEDICAL CENTER LP p 877
2901 4th St 75605
Tel (903) 758-1818 SIC 8062 8099

NORTHEAST TEXAS ELECTRIC COOPERATIVE INC p 1055
2221 H G Mosley Pkwy # 100 75604
Tel (903) 757-3282 SIC 4911

SHEPHERD GOOD HOSPITAL INC p 1315
700 E Marshall Ave 75601
Tel (903) 315-2000 SIC 8062

■ STEMCO LP p 1385
300 Industrial Dr 75602
Tel (903) 232-3500 SIC 3714

T E C WELL SERVICE INC p 1419
851 W Harrison Rd 75604
Tel (903) 759-0082 SIC 1389

TEXAS BANK & TRUST CO p 1442
300 E Whaley St 75601
Tel (903) 237-5500 SIC 6022

LORENA, TX

BIG CREEK CONSTRUCTION LTD p 181
1617 Old Waco Temple Rd 76655
Tel (254) 857-3200 SIC 1611

LOS FRESNOS, TX

LOS FRESNOS CONSOLIDATED INDEPENDENT SCHOOL DISTRICT p 879
600 N Mesquite St 78566
Tel (956) 233-4407 SIC 8211

LOS INDIOS, TX

TOYODA GOSEI BROWNSVILLE TEXAS LLC p 1466
107 Joaquin Cavazos Rd 78567
Tel (956) 290-8802 SIC 3711

LUBBOCK, TX

■ ALAMOSA HOLDINGS INC p 44
5225 S Loop 289 Ste 120 79424
Tel (806) 722-1111 SIC 4813

ASSOCIATED SUPPLY CO INC p 121
2102 E Slaton Rd 79404
Tel (806) 745-2000 SIC 5084 5082 7353

CAPROCK HOME HEALTH SERVICES INC p 251
8806 University Ave 79423
Tel (806) 748-7722 SIC 8082

CITY BANK p 312
5219 City Bank Pkwy Fl 1 79407
Tel (806) 792-7101 SIC 6022

CITY OF LUBBOCK p 316
1625 13th St 79401
Tel (806) 775-2016 SIC 9111

COVENANT HEALTH SYSTEM p 384
3615 19th St 79410
Tel (806) 725-1011 SIC 8062

COVENANT MEDICAL GROUP p 384
3506 21st St Ste 506 79410
Tel (806) 725-4130 SIC 8011

COVENANT MEDICAL GROUP p 384
524 E 40th St Unit B 79404
Tel (806) 725-9800 SIC 8011

FOOD CONCEPTS INTERNATIONAL INC p 564
4401 82nd St 79424
Tel (806) 785-8686 SIC 5812

FRESH ACQUISITIONS LLC p 578
1001 E 33rd St 79404
Tel (806) 723-5600 SIC 5149 5146

GICON PUMPS & EQUIPMENT INC p 611
1001 Texas Ave 79401
Tel (806) 401-8287 SIC 5084 5074 5039

GVH DISTRIBUTION LTD p 648
2601 Se Loop 289 Lubbock 79404
Tel (806) 687-5264 SIC 5199

HEALTHSMART PREFERRED CARE II LP p 677
2002 W Loop 289 Ste 103 79407
Tel (806) 473-2500 SIC 6324

ITSQUEST INC p 768
4505 82nd St Ste 3 79424
Tel (806) 785-9100 SIC 7361

JIM BURNS AUTOMOTIVE GROUP INC p 785
8230 Urbana Ave 79424
Tel (806) 747-3211 SIC 5511

LEE LEWIS CONSTRUCTION INC p 851
7810 Orlando Ave 79423
Tel (806) 797-8400 SIC 1542 1541

LUBBOCK COUNTY HOSPITAL DISTRICT p 883
602 Indiana Ave 79415
Tel (806) 775-8200 SIC 8062

LUBBOCK INDEPENDENT SCHOOL DISTRICT p 883
1628 19th St 79401
Tel (806) 766-1000 SIC 8211

■ MCLANE HIGH PLAINS INC p 931
1717 E Loop 289 79403
Tel (806) 766-2900 SIC 5141 5142 5113

NTS COMMUNICATIONS INC p 1065
1220 Brdwy 79401
Tel (806) 791-0687 SIC 4813

NTS INC p 1065
1220 Broadway Ste 100 79401
Tel (806) 771-5212 SIC 4813

PLAINS COTTON COOPERATIVE ASSOCIATION p 1153
3301 E 50th St 79404
Tel (806) 763-8011 SIC 5159 4221

PRO PETROLEUM INC p 1178
4710 4th St 79416
Tel (806) 795-8785 SIC 5172

PYCO INDUSTRIES INC p 1193
2901 Avenue A 79404
Tel (806) 747-3434 SIC 2074

RIP GRIFFIN TRUCK SERVICE CENTER INC p 1236
4710 4th St 79416
Tel (806) 795-8785 SIC 6719

ROBERT MADDEN INDUSTRIES LTD p 1241
6021 43rd St 79407
Tel (806) 797-4251 SIC 5075

SOUTH PLAINS ELECTRIC COOPERATIVE INC p 1344
4727 S Loop 289 Ste 200 79424
Tel (806) 775-7732 SIC 4911

SOUTH PLAINS FINANCIAL INC p 1344
5219 City Bank Pkwy # 55 79407
Tel (806) 792-7101 SIC 6712

■ SYSCO WEST TEXAS INC p 1418
714 2nd Pl 79401
Tel (806) 747-2678 SIC 5146 5147

TEXAS TECH UNIVERSITY HEALTH SCIENCES CENTER p 1444
4004 82nd St C 79423
Tel (806) 743-1842 SIC 8221

TEXAS TECH UNIVERSITY SYSTEM p 1444
2500 Broadway 79409
Tel (806) 742-2011 SIC 8221

TTU HSC RESEARCH & GRADUATE SCHOOL p 1490
3601 4th St Rm 2b106 79430
Tel (806) 743-2556 SIC 8221

TYCO FIRE PRODUCTS LP p 1496
8902 N Interstate 27 79403
Tel (806) 472-2400 SIC 3569

UNITED SUPERMARKETS LLC p 1514
7830 Orlando Ave 79423
Tel (806) 791-0220 SIC 5411

LUFKIN, TX

BROOKSHIRE BROTHERS LTD p 218
1201 Ellen Trout Dr 75904
Tel (936) 634-8155 SIC 5411

■ LUFKIN INDUSTRIES LLC p 884
601 S Raguet St 75904
Tel (936) 634-2211 SIC 3561 3321 3462

MEMORIAL HEALTH SYSTEM OF EAST TEXAS p 941
1201 W Frank Ave 75904
Tel (936) 634-8111 SIC 8062

■ PINEY WOODS HEALTHCARE SYSTEM LP p 1149
505 S John Redditt Dr 75904
Tel (936) 634-8311
SIC 8062 8071 8099 8051

REDZONE COIL TUBING LLC p 1217
701 N 1st St Ste 109 75901
Tel (936) 632-2645 SIC 1389

LUMBERTON, TX

TRIPLE S INDUSTRIAL CORP p 1482
860 W Chance Rd 77657
Tel (409) 755-4077 SIC 1799 1791

MABANK, TX

MABANK INDEPENDENT SCHOOL DISTRICT p 891
310 E Market St 75147
Tel (903) 880-1300 SIC 8211

MAGNOLIA, TX

LINCOLN MANUFACTURING INC p 867
31209 Fm 2978 Rd 77354
Tel (281) 252-9494 SIC 3533 5082

MAGNOLIA INDEPENDENT SCHOOL DISTRICT p 896
31141 Nichols Sawmill Rd 77355
Tel (281) 356-3571 SIC 8211

MANOR, TX

MANOR INDEPENDENT SCHOOL DISTRICT p 902
10335 Us Highway 290 E 78653
Tel (512) 278-4000 SIC 8211

MANSFIELD, TX

MANSFIELD INDEPENDENT SCHOOL DISTRICT p 903
605 E Broad St 76063
Tel (817) 299-6300 SIC 8211

■ MOUSER ELECTRONICS INC p 995
1000 N Main St 76063
Tel (817) 804-3800 SIC 5065

REGAL METALS INTERNATIONAL INC p 1218
207 Sentry Dr 76063
Tel (817) 477-2568 SIC 5051

RJR CONSULTING GROUP INC p 1239
707 Dover Park Trl # 200 76063
Tel (817) 992-0124 SIC 7379

S J LOUIS CONSTRUCTION OF TEXAS LTD p 1262
520 S 6th Ave 76063
Tel (817) 477-0320 SIC 1623

SEVILLE FARMS INC p 1309
8805 Levy County Line Rd 76063
Tel (817) 473-2249 SIC 5193

TA SERVICES INC p 1420
241 Regency Pkwy 76063
Tel (800) 626-2185 SIC 4731 4213

MARSHALL, TX

HARRISON COUNTY HOSPITAL ASSOCIATION p 664
811 S Washington Ave 75670
Tel (903) 927-6000 SIC 8062

REPUBLIC NATIONAL CABINET CORP p 1225
1400 Warren Dr 75672
Tel (903) 935-3680 SIC 2434

REPUBLIC NATIONAL INDUSTRIES OF TEXAS LP p 1225
1400 Warren Dr 75672
Tel (903) 935-3680 SIC 2434 5211 2541

SHUNA & CAM p 1319
805 Van Zandt Ave Apt G 75670
Tel (903) 578-5478 SIC 8299

MC KINNEY, TX

MYCON GENERAL CONTRACTORS INC p 1004
208 E La St Ste 200 75069
Tel (972) 529-2444 SIC 1542

MC QUEENEY, TX

WUESTS INC p 1628
9318 Fm 725 78123
Tel (830) 379-3442 SIC 5141 5411 0173

MCALLEN, TX

AIM MEDIA TEXAS OPERATING LLC p 38
1400 E Nolana Ave 78504
Tel (956) 683-4000 SIC 2711 4899

AM-MEX PRODUCTS INC p 63
3801 W Military Hwy 78503
Tel (956) 631-7916 SIC 3714 7361 3672

CITY OF MC ALLEN p 316
1300 W Houston Ave 78501
Tel (956) 681-1000 SIC 9111

■ COLUMBIA RIO GRANDE HEALTHCARE LP p 341
101 E Ridge Rd 78503
Tel (956) 632-6000 SIC 8011 8062

■ GE ENGINE SERVICES - MCALLEN L P p 596
6200 S 42nd St 78503
Tel (956) 971-5200 SIC 3724

HEALTH CARE UNLIMITED INC p 674
1100 E Laurel Ave 78501
Tel (956) 994-9911 SIC 5047 8082

L & F DISTRIBUTORS LLC p 833
3900 N Mccoll Rd 78501
Tel (956) 687-7751 SIC 5181

LA VALENCIANA AVOCADOS CORP p 836
214 N 16th St Ste 127 78501
Tel (956) 994-0561 SIC 5148 0179

LONE STAR NATIONAL BANCSHARES—TEXAS INC p 876
4500 N 10th St Ste 305 78504
Tel (956) 781-4321 SIC 6712 6021

LONE STAR NATIONAL BANK p 876
520 E Nolana Ave Ste 110 78504
Tel (956) 781-4321 SIC 6021

MAGIC VALLEY FRESH FROZEN LLC p 895
3701 W Military Hwy 78503
Tel (956) 994-8947 SIC 5142

MCALLEN INDEPENDENT SCHOOL DISTRICT p 925
2000 N 23rd St 78501
Tel (956) 618-6000 SIC 8211

■ MCALLEN MEDICAL CENTER LP p 925
301 W Expressway 83 78503
Tel (956) 632-4000 SIC 8062

PANASONIC INDUSTRIAL DEVICES CORP OF AMERICA p 1111
4900 Gorge Mcvay Dr Ste C 78503
Tel (956) 984-3700 SIC 3651 3675 3471

RIO GRANDE REGIONAL HOSPITAL p 1235
101 E Ridge Rd 78503
Tel (956) 632-6000 SIC 8062

SOUTH TEXAS COLLEGE p 1345
3201 Pecan Blvd 78501
Tel (956) 872-8311 SIC 8222

SSC MCALLEN RETAMA OPERATING CO LLC p 1363
900 S 12th St 78501
Tel (956) 682-4171 SIC 8051

TEXAS REGIONAL DELAWARE INC p 1444
3900 N 10th St Fl 11 78501
Tel (956) 631-5400 SIC 6022 6541

MCKINNEY, TX

BAYLOR MEDICAL CENTER AT MCKINNEY p 162
5252 W University Dr 75071
Tel (469) 764-4600 SIC 8011

COLLIN COUNTY COMMUNITY COLLEGE DISTRICT p 337
3452 Spur 399 75069
Tel (972) 758-3100 SIC 8222

COUNTY OF COLLIN p 377
2300 Bloomdale Rd 75071
Tel (972) 424-1460 SIC 9111

■ EMERSON PROCESS MANAGEMENT REGULATOR TECHNOLOGIES INC p 492
3200 Emerson Way 75069
Tel (972) 548-3585 SIC 3491

▲ ENCORE WIRE CORP p 496
1329 Millwood Rd 75069
Tel (972) 562-9473 SIC 3357

▲ INDEPENDENT BANK GROUP INC p 736
1600 Redbud Blvd Ste 400 75069
Tel (972) 548-9004 SIC 6021

MCKINNEY DODGE INC p 930
321 N Central Expy # 240 75070
Tel (972) 569-9650 SIC 5511

MCKINNEY INDEPENDENT SCHOOL DISTRICT p 930
1 Duvall St 75069
Tel (469) 302-4000 SIC 8211

NORTH DALLAS HONEY CO LP p 1052
2910 Nature Nate Farms 75071
Tel (214) 642-9367 SIC 5149

POGUE CONSTRUCTION CO LP p 1159
1512 Bray Central Dr # 300 75069
Tel (972) 529-9401 SIC 1542

PROGRESSIVE WASTE SOLUTIONS LTD p 1182
2138 Country Ln 75069
Tel (469) 452-8000 SIC 4953

SRS DISTRIBUTION INC p 1363
5900 S Lake Forest Dr # 400 75070
Tel (214) 491-4149 SIC 5033

▲ TORCHMARK CORP p 1461
3700 S Stonebridge Dr 75070
Tel (972) 569-4000 SIC 6321 6311

■ UNITED AMERICAN INSURANCE CO p 1506
3700 S Stonebridge Dr 75070
Tel (800) 331-2512 SIC 6321 6311

MERCEDES, TX

MAGIC VALLEY ELECTRIC COOPERATIVE INC p 895
1 3/4 Mi W Hwy 83 78570
Tel (866) 225-5683 SIC 4911

MESQUITE, TX

ABATIX CORP p 9
2400 Skyline Dr Ste 400 75149
Tel (214) 381-1146 SIC 5084 5085

BAKER DRYWALL LTD p 146
401 Hwy 80 E 75150
Tel (972) 285-8878 SIC 8741

BAKER DRYWALL MANAGEMENT LLC p 146
401 Us Highway 80 E 75150
Tel (972) 285-8878 SIC 8741

BAKER DRYWALL PARTNERSHIP LLP p 146
401 Us Highway 80 E 75150
Tel (972) 288-9275 SIC 1742

CITY OF MESQUITE p 316
1515 N Galloway Ave 75149
Tel (972) 216-6218 SIC 9111

DALLAS COUNTY COMMUNITY COLLEGE DISTRICT p 410
4343 Interstate 30 75150
Tel (972) 860-7700 SIC 8222

DALLAS REGIONAL MEDICAL CENTER p 410
1011 N Galloway Ave 75149
Tel (214) 320-7000 SIC 8099

DEPENDABLE AUTO SHIPPERS INC p 430
3020 U S 80 Frontage Rd 75149
Tel (214) 381-0181 SIC 4213

FRITZ INDUSTRIES INC p 580
500 N Sam Houston Rd 75149
Tel (972) 285-5471 SIC 2899

GIBSON ENERGY MARKETING LLC p 611
3819 Towne Crossing Blvd 75150
Tel (214) 461-5600 SIC 5172 5984

INTEGRACOLOR LLC p 748
3210 Innovative Way 75149
Tel (972) 289-0705 SIC 2752 2754

K & S GROUP INC p 798
18601 Lyndn B Jhnsn 420 75150
Tel (214) 234-8871 SIC 6411

MESQUITE INDEPENDENT SCHOOL DISTRICT p 951
405 E Davis St 75149
Tel (972) 288-6411 SIC 8211

MESQUITE SPECIALTY HOSPITAL p 951
1024 N Galloway Ave 75149
Tel (972) 216-2300 SIC 8742

SUPERIOR TRAILER SALES CO p 1407
501 Us Highway 80 E 75182
Tel (972) 226-3893 SIC 5511

SUTTON HOLDING CORP p 1410
2330 Interstate 30 75150
Tel (972) 755-8200 SIC 7377

VAR RESOURCES LLC p 1544
2330 Interstate 30 75150
Tel (972) 755-8200 SIC 7377

MIDLAND, TX

ADVANCED STIMULATION TECHNOLOGIES INC p 26
2903 E Interstate 20 79706
Tel (432) 994-0900 SIC 1389

BENCHMARK ENERGY PRODUCTS LP p 172
4113 W Industrial Ave 79703
Tel (432) 697-8171 *SIC* 5169

BRAWLER INDUSTRIES LLC p 209
11701 County Rd W 125 125 W 79711
Tel (432) 563-4005 *SIC* 5162

▲ CLAYTON WILLIAMS ENERGY INC p 323
6 Desta Dr Ste 6500 79705
Tel (432) 682-6324 *SIC* 1311

■ COG OPERATING LLC p 334
600 W Illinois Ave 79701
Tel (432) 685-0727 *SIC* 1382

■ COMPRESSOR SYSTEMS INC p 352
3809 S Fm 1788 79706
Tel (432) 563-1170 *SIC* 7359 7699 3563

▲ CONCHO RESOURCES INC p 354
600 W Illinois Ave 79701
Tel (432) 683-7443 *SIC* 1311

CROWNROCK LP p 396
500 W Texas Ave Ste 500 79701
Tel (432) 818-0300 *SIC* 1382

▲ CSI COMPRESSCO LP p 397
3809 S Fm 1788 79706
Tel (432) 563-1170 *SIC* 1389 3533

▲ DAWSON GEOPHYSICAL CO p 417
508 W Wall St Ste 800 79701
Tel (432) 684-3000 *SIC* 1382 8713

▲ DIAMONDBACK ENERGY INC p 437
500 W Texas Ave Ste 1200 79701
Tel (432) 221-7400 *SIC* 1311

DIXIE ELECTRIC LLC p 444
701 Tradewinds Blvd 79706
Tel (432) 580-7095 *SIC* 1731

DON-NAN PUMP AND SUPPLY CO INC p 450
3427 E Garden Cy Hwy 158 79706
Tel (432) 682-7742 *SIC* 1389 3599 3561

ENDEAVOR ENERGY RESOURCES LP p 496
110 N Marienfeld St # 200 79701
Tel (432) 687-1575 *SIC* 1311 8748

IMPACT CHEMICAL TECHNOLOGIES INC p 734
10501 E Hwy 80 79706
Tel (432) 458-3500 *SIC* 5169

J L DAVIS CO p 771
211 N Colorado St 79701
Tel (432) 682-6311 *SIC* 5172 4923 1311

JIM F WEBB INC p 785
2401 E Interstate 20 79701
Tel (432) 684-4388 *SIC* 4911

KEL-TECH INC p 808
3408 E State Highway 158 79706
Tel (432) 684-4700 *SIC* 1389 8731

▲ LEGACY RESERVES LP p 852
303 W Wall St Ste 1800 79701
Tel (432) 689-5200 *SIC* 1311

LPC CRUDE OIL INC p 882
408 W Wall St Ste B 79701
Tel (432) 682-8555 *SIC* 5172

MIDLAND COUNTY HOSPITAL DISTRICT p 965
400 R Redfern Grover Pkwy 79701
Tel (432) 685-1111 *SIC* 8062

MIDLAND INDEPENDENT SCHOOL DISTRICT p 965
615 W Missouri Ave 79701
Tel (432) 689-1000 *SIC* 8211

MIDLAND MEMORIAL HOSPITAL p 966
400 Rosalind Rdfrn Grovr 79701
Tel (432) 221-1111 *SIC* 8049

MIDLAND MEMORIAL HOSPITAL & MEDICAL CENTER p 966
2200 W Illinois Ave 79701
Tel (432) 685-1111 *SIC* 8062

▲ NATURAL GAS SERVICES GROUP INC p 1018
508 W Wall St Ste 550 79701
Tel (432) 262-2700 *SIC* 7353 3563

■ PARSLEY ENERGY LLC p 1117
500 W Texas Ave Ste 200 79701
Tel (432) 818-2100 *SIC* 1311

POWER LINE INFRASTRUCTURE SERVICES INC p 1165
1031 Andrews Hwy 79701
Tel (432) 682-1991 *SIC* 1623

PRODUCTION SPECIALTY SERVICES LLC p 1180
511 W Missouri Ave 79701
Tel (432) 620-0059 *SIC* 5082 7699

PROPETRO SERVICES INC p 1184
1706 S Midkiff Rd Ste B 79701
Tel (432) 688-0012 *SIC* 1381

RELIANT HOLDINGS LTD p 1222
10817 W County Road 60 79707
Tel (432) 617-4200 *SIC* 5169

■ SOUTHWEST ROYALTIES INC p 1352
6 Desta Dr Ste 2100 79705
Tel (432) 688-3008 *SIC* 1311 6211 1389

TESSCO ENERGY SERVICES INC p 1440
1031 Andrews Hwy Ste 450 79701
Tel (432) 563-0071 *SIC* 4911

■ UNIVERSAL PRESSURE PUMPING INC p 1517
6 Desta Dr Ste 4400 79705
Tel (432) 221-7000 *SIC* 1381

WARREN EQUIPMENT CO p 1577
10325 Younger Rd 79706
Tel (432) 571-8462
SIC 5082 5084 7699 3563 7359

WARREN POWER & MACHINERY INC p 1577
10325 Younger Rd 79706
Tel (432) 571-4200 *SIC* 3531

WARREN POWER & MACHINERY INC p 1577
10325 Younger Rd 79706
Tel (432) 563-1170 *SIC* 5082

WEST TEXAS GAS INC p 1595
211 N Colorado St 79701
Tel (432) 682-4349 *SIC* 5411

MIDLOTHIAN, TX

ALPHA MATERIALS HANDLING INC p 60
313 N 9th St 76065
Tel (972) 775-2555 *SIC* 5084

▲ ENNIS INC p 500
2441 Presidential Pkwy 76065
Tel (972) 775-9801
SIC 2761 2759 2331 2329

GERDAU AMERISTEEL US INC p 608
300 Ward Rd 76065
Tel (972) 775-8241 *SIC* 3312

MIDLOTHIAN INDEPENDENT SCHOOL DISTRICT p 966
100 Walter Stephenson Rd 76065
Tel (972) 723-6290 *SIC* 8211

MIDWAY, TX

MIDWAY OILFIELD CONSTRUCTORS INC p 967
12627 State Highway 21 E 75852
Tel (936) 348-3721 *SIC* 1389 1623

MILLSAP, TX

GEODYNAMICS INC p 606
10500 W Interstate 20 76066
Tel (817) 341-5300 *SIC* 2892 3533

MINERAL WELLS, TX

■ PECOFACET (US) INC p 1127
118 Washington Ave 76067
Tel (940) 325-2575 *SIC* 3823 5082

MISSION, TX

J & K EXPRESS INC p 770
5046 N Conway Ave 78573
Tel (956) 584-3130 *SIC* 7389

LIMEX SICAR LTD CO p 866
701 Trinity St 78572
Tel (956) 581-6080 *SIC* 5148

MISSION CONSOLIDATED INDEPENDENT SCHOOL DISTRICT p 975
1201 Bryce Dr 78572
Tel (956) 323-5500 *SIC* 8211

MISSION HOSPITAL INC p 975
900 S Bryan Rd 78572
Tel (956) 323-9000 *SIC* 8062

MISSOURI CITY, TX

AMERICAN BULK PIPE & STEEL LLC p 69
607 Oyster Shell Ct 77459
Tel (281) 431-3473 *SIC* 3317

GLOBAL GEOPHYSICAL SERVICES INC p 616
13927 S Gessner Rd 77489
Tel (713) 972-9200 *SIC* 1382

MONT BELVIEU, TX

BARBERS HILL INDEPENDENT SCHOOL DISTRICT EDUCATION FOUNDATION p 154
9600 Eagle Dr 77580
Tel (281) 576-2221 *SIC* 8211

MOULTON, TX

GLADE OPERATING LLC p 614
110 S Main St 77975
Tel (361) 596-5050 *SIC* 1381

MOUNT PLEASANT, TX

BIG TEX TRAILER MANUFACTURING INC p 182
950 Interstate Hwy 30 E 75455
Tel (903) 575-0300 *SIC* 3523 5013 5599

MOUNT PLEASANT INDEPENDENT SCHOOL DISTRICT p 994
2230 N Edwards Ave 75455
Tel (903) 575-2000 *SIC* 8211

PRIEFERT MFG CO INC p 1174
2630 S Jefferson Ave 75455
Tel (903) 572-1741
SIC 3523 3446 3444 3317 3449

MOUNT VERNON, TX

JORDAN HEALTH CARE INC p 793
412 Texas Highway 37 S 75457
Tel (903) 537-3600 *SIC* 8082

JORDAN HEALTHCARE HOLDINGS INC p 793
412 Texas Highway 37 S 75457
Tel (903) 537-2445 *SIC* 6719 8082

NACOGDOCHES, TX

EAST TEXAS ELECTRIC COOPERATIVE INC p 471
2905 Westward Dr 75964
Tel (936) 560-9532 *SIC* 4939

ELLIOTT ELECTRIC SUPPLY INC p 488
2526 N Stallings Dr 75964
Tel (936) 569-1184 *SIC* 5063 5084

ETECH GLOBAL SERVICES LLC p 511
1903 Berry Dr 75964
Tel (936) 559-2200
SIC 7389 8742 7373 8741 8721 7374

SAM RAYBURN G & T ELECTRIC COOPERATIVE INC p 1274
2905 Westward Dr 75964
Tel (936) 560-9532 *SIC* 4911

STEPHEN F AUSTIN STATE UNIVERSITY p 1386
1936 North St 75965
Tel (936) 468-3401 *SIC* 8221

STEPHEN F AUSTIN STATE UNIVERSITY FOUNDATION INC p 1386
Vista At Alumni Dr 303 75962
Tel (936) 468-5406 *SIC* 8221

TEX-LA ELECTRIC COOPERATIVE OF TEXAS INC p 1441
2905 Westward Dr 75964
Tel (936) 560-9532 *SIC* 4911

NASH, TX

BWI COMPANIES INC p 231
1355 N Kings Hwy 75569
Tel (903) 838-8561 *SIC* 5191

NAVASOTA, TX

ELLWOOD TEXAS FORGE NAVASOTA LLC p 489
10908 County Road 419 77868
Tel (936) 825-7531 *SIC* 3462

NEDERLAND, TX

MARKET BASKET STORES INC p 908
2420 Nederland Ave 77627
Tel (409) 727-3104 *SIC* 5411

NEWTRON BEAUMONT LLC p 1039
1905 Industrial Park Rd 77627
Tel (409) 727-6344 *SIC* 1731

■ OCI PARTNERS LP p 1073
5470 N Twin City Hwy 77627
Tel (409) 723-1900 *SIC* 2861 2873

RETAIL INVESTORS OF TEXAS LTD p 1228
2420 Nederland Ave 77627
Tel (409) 727-3104 *SIC* 5411

NEW BRAUNFELS, TX

COMAL INDEPENDENT SCHOOL DISTRICT p 343
1404 N Interstate 35 78130
Tel (830) 221-2000 *SIC* 8611 8211

HARRISON WORLDWIDE ENTERPRISES INC p 664
1650 Independence Dr 78132
Tel (830) 608-9200 *SIC* 5571

HILL COUNTRY FURNITURE PARTNERS LTD p 693
1431 Fm 1101 78130
Tel (830) 515-1400 *SIC* 5712

HILL COUNTRY HOLDINGS LLC p 693
1431 Fm 1101 78130
Tel (830) 515-1400 *SIC* 6719

HUNTER INDUSTRIES LTD p 719
5080 Fm 2439 78132
Tel (512) 353-7757 *SIC* 1611 2951 1442

INGRAM READYMIX INC p 743
3580 Farm Market 482 78132
Tel (830) 625-9156 *SIC* 3273

KAHLIG ENTERPRISES INC p 800
351 S Interstate 35 78130
Tel (830) 606-8011 *SIC* 5511

MIDTEX OIL LP p 966
3455 Ih 35 S 78132
Tel (830) 625-4214 *SIC* 5541 5171

NEW BRAUNFELS UTILITIES p 1029
263 Main Plz 78130
Tel (830) 608-8867 *SIC* 4911 4941 4952

■ RUSH ADMINISTRATIVE SERVICES INC p 1258
555 S Interstate 35 # 500 78130
Tel (830) 626-5286
SIC 5012 7538 5531 5014 7513

▲ RUSH ENTERPRISES INC p 1258
555 S Ih 35 Ste 500 78130
Tel (830) 302-5200
SIC 5012 7538 5531 5014 7513

■ RUSH TRUCK CENTERS OF CALIFORNIA INC p 1259
555 S Interstate 35 # 500 78130
Tel (830) 626-5200 *SIC* 5511 5012

■ RUSH TRUCK CENTERS OF ILLINOIS INC p 1259
555 S Interstate 35 # 500 78130
Tel (830) 626-5200 *SIC* 5012

■ RUSH TRUCK CENTERS OF TEXAS INC p 1259
555 S Interstate 35 # 500 78130
Tel (830) 626-5200 *SIC* 5012 5511

SCOOTER STORE LTD p 1293
1650 Independence Dr 78132
Tel (877) 841-8159 *SIC* 5999

■ SYSCO CENTRAL TEXAS INC p 1416
1260 Schwab Rd 78132
Tel (830) 730-1000 *SIC* 5141

WORD CONSTRUCTORS LLC p 1624
1245 River Rd 78130
Tel (830) 625-2365 *SIC* 1622 1611

NEW CANEY, TX

NEW CANEY INDEPENDENT SCHOOL DISTRICT p 1029
21580 Loop 494 77357
Tel (281) 577-8600 *SIC* 8211

ONYX SERVICES LLC p 1088
22971 Keith Dr 77357
Tel (281) 577-5131 *SIC* 6531

NORTH RICHLAND HILLS, TX

D L ROGERS CORP p 407
5013 Davis Blvd 76180
Tel (817) 428-2077 *SIC* 5812 6552 6799

HEALTHMARKETS INC p 677
9151 Blvd 256 76180
Tel (817) 255-3100 *SIC* 6311 6321

HEALTHMARKETS LLC p 677
9151 Boulevard 26 76180
Tel (817) 255-3100 *SIC* 6311 6321

INSPHERE INSURANCE SOLUTIONS INC p 746
9151 Boulevard 26 76180
Tel (817) 255-3100 *SIC* 6411

SMURFIT KAPPA BATES LLC p 1335
6433 Davis Blvd 76182
Tel (817) 498-3200 *SIC* 2653 5113

NURSERY, TX

SOUTH TEXAS ELECTRIC COOPERATIVE INC p 1345
2849 Fm 447 77976
Tel (361) 575-6491 *SIC* 4911

OAKWOOD, TX

A GLEN BARRILLEAUX LLC p 5
1412 W Broad St 75855
Tel (903) 545-1231 *SIC* 1623 1629

ODESSA, TX

BLACK VIPER ENERGY SERVICES LTD p 187
11220 W County Road 127 79765
Tel (432) 561-8801 *SIC* 1381

CITY PIPE AND SUPPLY CORP p 319
2101 W 2nd St 79763
Tel (432) 332-1541 *SIC* 5051 5085

E L FARMER & CO p 466
3800 E 42nd St Ste 417 79762
Tel (432) 366-2010 *SIC* 1389

ECTOR COUNTY HOSPITAL DISTRICT p 476
500 W 4th St 79761
Tel (432) 640-4000 *SIC* 8062

ECTOR COUNTY INDEPENDENT SCHOOL DISTRICT p 476
802 N Sam Houston Ave 79761
Tel (432) 456-0002 *SIC* 8211

GRAHAM BROTHERS ENTERTAINMENT INC p 628
6999 E Business 20 79762
Tel (432) 362-0401 *SIC* 5813

NURSES UNLIMITED INC p 1067
511 N Lincoln Ave 79761
Tel (432) 580-2085 *SIC* 8049

■ ODESSA PUMPS AND EQUIPMENT INC p 1074
8161 Dorado Dr 79765
Tel (432) 333-2817 *SIC* 5084

ODESSA REGIONAL HOSPITAL LP p 1074
520 E 6th St 79761
Tel (432) 582-8000 *SIC* 8062

■ OXY USA INC p 1101
1001 S County Rd W 79763
Tel (432) 335-0995 *SIC* 1311

PERMIAN TANK & MANUFACTURING INC p 1136
2701 W Interstate 20 79766
Tel (432) 580-1050 *SIC* 3443

REF-CHEM LP p 1217
1128 S Grandview Ave 79761
Tel (432) 332-8531 *SIC* 1629

RUSH SALES CO p 1258
2700 E I 20 Service Rd 79766
Tel (432) 337-2397 *SIC* 3533 5511

SAULSBURY ELECTRIC CO LTD p 1283
2951 E Interstate 20 79766
Tel (432) 366-3686 *SIC* 1629

SAULSBURY INDUSTRIES INC p 1283
2951 E Interstate 20 79766
Tel (432) 366-3686 *SIC* 1629

SEWELL FAMILY OF COMPANIES INC p 1309
2425 E 8th St 79761
Tel (432) 498-0421 *SIC* 5511

■ SOUTHWEST CONVENIENCE STORES LLC p 1351
4001 Penbrook St Ste 400 79762
Tel (432) 580-8850 *SIC* 5411

STANDARD SALES CO LP p 1376
4800 E 42nd St Ste 400 79762
Tel (432) 367-7662 SIC 5181

TECHWELL SURVEYS CORP p 1432
610 W 83rd St 79764
Tel (432) 362-3711 SIC 4911 7389

TFORCE ENERGY SERVICES INC p 1445
3800 E 42nd St Ste 417 79762
Tel (303) 770-6511 SIC 4213

ORANGE, TX

BEACON MARITIME INC p 165
96 W Front St 77630
Tel (409) 670-1060 SIC 1629 3731

DUPHIL INC p 462
6608 Interstate 10 W 77632
Tel (409) 883-8550 SIC 1542

MEMORIAL HERMANN BAPTIST BELMONT p 941
608 Strickland Dr 77630
Tel (409) 883-9361 SIC 8062

PAMPA, TX

B S W INC p 142
111 Naida St 79065
Tel (806) 669-1103 SIC 5082 5084

BOURLAND & LEVERICH SUPPLY CO LLC p 204
11707 Highway 152 79065
Tel (806) 665-0061 SIC 3317

PAMPA REGIONAL MEDICAL CENTER AUXILIARY p 1110
1 Medical Plz 79065
Tel (806) 665-3721 SIC 8011

PARIS, TX

ESSENT PRMC LP p 510
865 Deshong Dr 75460
Tel (903) 785-9082 SIC 8062

R K HALL CONSTRUCTION LTD p 1202
2810 Nw Loop 286 75460
Tel (903) 785-8941 SIC 1611

PASADENA, TX

■ ALBEMARLE CATALYSTS CO LP p 46
13000 Baypark Rd 77507
Tel (281) 474-2864 SIC 2819

AMERICAN ACRYL LP p 67
4631 Old Highway 146 B 77507
Tel (281) 909-2600 SIC 2869

AMERICAN ACRYL NA LLC p 67
4631 Old Highway 146 B 77507
Tel (281) 909-2600 SIC 2869

■ ATLANTIC PLANT MAINTENANCE INC p 127
3225 Pasadena Blvd 77503
Tel (713) 475-4500 SIC 1629

INDUSTRIAL AIR TOOL p 739
1305 W Jackson Ave 77506
Tel (713) 477-3144 SIC 5084

JV INDUSTRIAL COMPANIES LTD p 798
4040 Red Bluff Rd 77503
Tel (713) 568-2600 SIC 7692 3441 8711

KANEKA AMERICAS HOLDING INC p 802
6250 Underwood Rd 77507
Tel (281) 474-7084 SIC 2023

KANEKA NORTH AMERICA LLC p 802
6161 Underwood Rd 77507
Tel (281) 474-7084 SIC 2821 3081 2023

LOOMIS INTERNATIONAL INC p 877
100 N Richey St 77506
Tel (713) 477-7148 SIC 1389

MEADOR STAFFING SERVICES INC p 934
722a Fairmont Pkwy 77504
Tel (713) 941-0616 SIC 7361 7363

OXITENO USA LLC p 1101
9801 Bay Area Blvd 77507
Tel (281) 909-7600 SIC 5172

■ PASADENA BAYSHORE HOSPITAL INC p 1119
4000 Spencer Hwy 77504
Tel (713) 359-2000 SIC 8062

PASADENA INDEPENDENT SCHOOL DISTRICT p 1119
1515 Cherrybrook Ln 77502
Tel (713) 740-0000 SIC 8211

PASADENA REFINING SYSTEM INC p 1119
111 Red Bluff Rd 77506
Tel (713) 920-1874 SIC 2911

SAN JACINTO COMMUNITY COLLEGE DISTRICT p 1277
4624 Fairmont Pkwy # 106 77504
Tel (281) 998-6306 SIC 8222

SDB TRADE INTERNATIONAL LP p 1295
817 Southmore Ave Ste 301 77502
Tel (713) 475-0048 SIC 3317

SUNBELT SUPPLY CO INC p 1401
3750 Hwy 225 77503
Tel (713) 672-2222 SIC 5085

UNITOR HOLDING INC p 1515
9400 New Century Dr 77507
Tel (281) 867-2000 SIC 5088

VENTECH ENGINEERS INTERNATIONAL CORP p 1548
1149 Ellsworth Dr Ofc 77506
Tel (713) 477-0201
SIC 1629 8711 3559 5084

VENTECH INC p 1548
1149 Ellsworth Dr Ofc 77506
Tel (713) 477-0201
SIC 8711 3491 5084 6512

■ VICEROY INC p 1555
3225 Pasadena Blvd 77503
Tel (713) 475-4518
SIC 1629 3443 1796 8742 8748 7363

WILHELMSEN SHIPS SERVICE INC p 1609
9400 New Century Dr 77507
Tel (281) 867-2000 SIC 5551 5088 7699

PEARLAND, TX

CYANCO CORP p 404
1920 Country Place Pkwy # 400 77584
Tel (775) 853-4300 SIC 1081

HOUSTON TUBULARS INC p 712
13600 Hatfield Rd 77581
Tel (281) 485-4014 SIC 1389

KELSEY-SEYBOLD MEDICAL GROUP PLLC p 809
11511 Shadow Creek Pkwy 77584
Tel (713) 442-0000 SIC 8011 5912

PACKAGING SERVICE CO INC p 1107
1904 Mykawa Rd 77581
Tel (281) 485-1458 SIC 3563

PEARLAND INDEPENDENT SCHOOL DISTRICT p 1126
1928 N Main St 77581
Tel (281) 485-3203 SIC 8211

SEI HOLDING I CORP p 1300
11233 Shadow Creek Pkwy # 235 77584
Tel (410) 553-9192 SIC 8741

THIRD COAST PACKAGING INC p 1448
1871 Mykawa Rd 77581
Tel (281) 412-0275 SIC 5172 4783 2899

PERRYTON, TX

PERRYTON EQUITY EXCHANGE p 1137
4219 S Main St 79070
Tel (806) 435-4016 SIC 5153 5191 5541

PFLUGERVILLE, TX

PFLUGERVILLE INDEPENDENT SCHOOL DISTRICT p 1140
1401 W Pecan St 78660
Tel (512) 594-0000 SIC 8211

PHARR, TX

FRENCH-ELLISON TRUCK CENTER LLC p 578
4300 N Cage Blvd 78577
Tel (956) 781-2401
SIC 5013 5531 5511 5012 7538

LACKS VALLEY STORES LTD p 837
1300 San Patricia Dr 78577
Tel (956) 702-3361 SIC 5712 5722

LONE STAR NATIONAL BANK SHARES NEVEDA p 876
100 W Ferguson St 78577
Tel (956) 781-4321 SIC 6021

PHARR SAN JUAN-ALAMO INDEPENDENT SCHOOL DISTRICT p 1141
601 E Kelly Ave 78577
Tel (956) 354-2000 SIC 8211

VILLITA AVOCADOS INC p 1557
9800 Keystone 78577
Tel (956) 843-1118 SIC 5148

PLAINVIEW, TX

GARRISON FRED OIL CO p 592
1107 Walter Griffin St 79072
Tel (806) 296-6353 SIC 5172 5541

RAY LEE EQUIPMENT CO LTD p 1209
910 N Date St 79072
Tel (806) 293-2538 SIC 5083 7699

PLANO, TX

ADVANCED INTEGRATION TECHNOLOGY LP p 26
2805 E Plano Pkwy Ste 300 75074
Tel (972) 423-8354 SIC 3728 3544

■ ADVANCED NEUROMODULATION SYSTEMS INC p 26
6901 Preston Rd 75024
Tel (972) 309-8000 SIC 3845

AEGON DIRECT MARKETING SERVICES INC p 29
2700 W Plano Pkwy 75075
Tel (972) 881-6000 SIC 7389

AIMBRIDGE HOSPITALITY LLC p 38
5851 Legacy Cir Ste 400 75024
Tel (972) 952-0200 SIC 8741

AIR DISTRIBUTION TECHNOLOGIES INC p 38
605 Shiloh Rd 75074
Tel (972) 943-6100 SIC 3585

AIR SYSTEM COMPONENTS INC p 39
605 Shiloh Rd 75074
Tel (972) 212-4888 SIC 3585

ALCATEL-LUCENT HOLDINGS INC p 47
601 Data Dr 75075
Tel (972) 477-2000 SIC 3661

▲ ALLIANCE DATA SYSTEMS CORP p 54
7500 Dallas Pkwy Ste 700 75024
Tel (214) 494-3000 SIC 7389

■ AMERICAN BOTTLING CO p 69
5301 Legacy Dr 75024
Tel (972) 673-7000 SIC 2086

ANDERSON MERCHANDISERS LLC p 90
5601 Gran Pkwy Ste 1400 75024
Tel (972) 987-5516 SIC 7389

ARGON MEDICAL DEVICES INC p 107
5151 Hdqtr Dr Ste 210 75024
Tel (903) 675-9321 SIC 3845 3842 3841

ARK-LA-TEX FINANCIAL SERVICES LLC p 109
5160 Tennyson Pkwy 2000w 75024
Tel (972) 398-7676 SIC 6163

■ ARROW SYSTEMS INTEGRATION INC p 113
1820 Preston Park Blvd # 2800 75093
Tel (972) 462-5800 SIC 4813 1731 5999

▲ AT HOME GROUP INC p 123
1600 E Plano Pkwy 75074
Tel (972) 265-6227 SIC 5719 5945

■ AT HOME STORES LLC p 123
1600 E Plano Pkwy 75074
Tel (972) 265-6227
SIC 5719 5992 5999 5947 5945

■ ATLANTIC AVIATION CORP p 125
6652 Pinecrest Dr Ste 300 75024
Tel (972) 905-2500
SIC 4581 5088 5172 6331 6159 4522

■ ATLANTIC AVIATION HOLDING CORP p 126
6652 Pinecrest Dr Ste 300 75024
Tel (972) 905-2500 SIC 5599

■ B27 LLC p 143
1417 Gables Ct Ste 201 75075
Tel (972) 244-4350 SIC 8741 5084

BAKERCORP INTERNATIONAL INC p 146
7800 Dallas Pkwy Ste 500 75024
Tel (888) 882-4895 SIC 7359

BAYLOR REGIONAL MEDICAL CENTER AT PLANO p 162
4700 Alliance Blvd 75093
Tel (469) 814-2000 SIC 8062

BEAL BANK p 165
6000 Legacy Dr 75024
Tel (469) 467-5000 SIC 6029

BEAL FINANCIAL CORP p 165
6000 Legacy Dr 75024
Tel (469) 467-5000 SIC 6036

▲ BG STAFFING INC p 180
5850 Granite Pkwy Ste 730 75024
Tel (972) 692-2400 SIC 7363

BLACK CREEK HOLDINGS LTD p 186
2400 Dallas Pkwy Ste 230 75093
Tel (972) 398-7100 SIC 3955 3861

■ CAPITAL ONE AUTO FINANCE INC p 250
7933 Preston Rd 75024
Tel (800) 946-0332 SIC 6141

CAPITAL TITLE OF TEXAS LLC p 250
2400 Dallas Pkwy Ste 560 75093
Tel (972) 682-2700 SIC 6361

■ CENTURY THEATRES INC p 282
3900 Dallas Pkwy Ste 500 75093
Tel (972) 665-1000 SIC 7833

CHANNEL POINT HOSPITALITY LLC p 288
5851 Legacy Cir Ste 400 75024
Tel (972) 952-0200 SIC 8741

CHILDRENS AND PRESBYTERIAN HEALTH CARE CENTER OF NORTH TEXAS p 299
6200 W Parker Rd Ofc 75093
Tel (972) 981-8000 SIC 8062

CHRONIC DISEASE FUND p 304
6900 Dallas Pkwy Ste 200 75024
Tel (972) 608-7175 SIC 7363

▲ CINEMARK HOLDINGS INC p 307
3900 Dallas Pkwy Ste 500 75093
Tel (972) 665-1000 SIC 6531

■ CINEMARK INC p 307
3900 Dallas Pkwy Ste 500 75093
Tel (800) 246-3627 SIC 7832

■ CINEMARK USA INC p 307
3900 Dallas Pkwy Ste 500 75093
Tel (972) 665-1000 SIC 7832

CITY OF PLANO p 317
1520 Ave K 75074
Tel (972) 941-7121 SIC 9111

COASTAL RESTAURANTS GP LLC p 332
6340 Intl Pkwy Ste 300 75093
Tel (214) 443-1920 SIC 5812

■ COLUMBIA MEDICAL CENTER OF PLANO SUBSIDIARY LP p 341
3901 W 15th St 75075
Tel (972) 596-6800 SIC 8062

COMPUCOM SYSTEMS INC p 352
8383 Dominion Pkwy 75024
Tel (972) 856-3600
SIC 7373 5045 7378 8748

CREATION TECHNOLOGIES KENTUCKY INC p 390
1001 Klein Rd Ste 100 75074
Tel (859) 253-3066 SIC 3679 3672

CREST CADILLAC INC p 392
2701 Northcrest Dr 75075
Tel (972) 423-7700 SIC 5511

CROSSMARK CONSUMER ENGAGEMENTS LLC p 394
5100 Legacy Dr 75024
Tel (469) 814-1000 SIC 8742

CROSSMARK INC p 394
5100 Legacy Dr 75024
Tel (469) 814-1000 SIC 5141 5912 7299

CUSTOM COMPUTER CABLES OF AMERICA INC p 403
2901 Summit Ave Ste 400 75074
Tel (972) 638-9309 SIC 5051 3357

DAY STAR RESTAURANT GROUP INC p 417
5055 W Park Blvd Ste 500 75093
Tel (972) 295-8600 SIC 6719

■ DENBURY ONSHORE LLC p 428
5320 Legacy Dr 75024
Tel (972) 673-2000 SIC 1311 1382

▲ DENBURY RESOURCES INC p 428
5320 Legacy Dr 75024
Tel (972) 673-2000 SIC 1311

DENTALONE PARTNERS INC p 429
7160 Dallas Pkwy Ste 400 75024
Tel (972) 755-0800 SIC 8621

▲ DIODES INC p 441
4949 Hedgcoxe Rd Ste 200 75024
Tel (972) 987-3900 SIC 3674

▲ DR PEPPER SNAPPLE GROUP INC p 454
5301 Legacy Dr 75024
Tel (972) 673-7000 SIC 2086

■ DR PEPPER/SEVEN UP INC p 454
5301 Legacy Dr Fl 1 75024
Tel (972) 673-7000 SIC 2087

■ DRESSER INC p 455
601 Shiloh Rd 75074
Tel (262) 549-2626
SIC 3491 3825 3594 3593 3561 3494

■ EDS ELECTRONIC FINANCIAL SERVICES INC p 478
5400 Legacy Dr 75024
Tel (972) 378-6985 SIC 7374

EGS CUSTOMER CARE INC p 481
5085 W Park Blvd Ste 300 75093
Tel (972) 943-7000 SIC 7389

ERICSSON HOLDING II INC p 507
6300 Legacy Dr 75024
Tel (972) 398-0183 SIC 3663

ERICSSON INC p 508
6300 Legacy Dr 75024
Tel (972) 583-0000 SIC 4899

EXPERT GLOBAL SOLUTIONS INC p 520
5085 W Park Blvd Ste 300 75093
Tel (800) 252-3996 SIC 7322

■ FEDEX OFFICE AND PRINT SERVICES INC p 536
7900 Legacy Dr 75024
Tel (214) 550-7000 SIC 7334

FOXWORTH GALBRAITH LUMBER CO p 573
4965 Preston Park Blvd # 400 75093
Tel (972) 665-2400
SIC 5211 5031 2439 2431

■ FRITO-LAY NORTH AMERICA INC p 580
7701 Legacy Dr 75024
Tel (972) 334-7000
SIC 2096 2052 2013 5812 6794 2086

FURNITURE MARKETING GROUP INC p 585
6100 W Plano Pkwy # 1400 75093
Tel (214) 556-4700 SIC 5021

FUTUREWEI TECHNOLOGIES INC p 586
5700 Tennyson Pkwy # 500 75024
Tel (972) 509-5599 SIC 4813

GARDEN RIDGE CORP p 591
1600 E Plano Pkwy 75074
Tel (972) 265-6227 SIC 5719 5999 5945

GARDEN RIDGE HOLDINGS INC p 591
1600 E Plano Pkwy 75074
Tel (832) 391-7201
SIC 5719 5945 5992 5947 5999

■ GE POWER ELECTRONICS INC p 596
601 Shiloh Rd 75074
Tel (972) 244-9288 SIC 3661

■ GE ZENITH CONTROLS INC p 597
601 Shiloh Rd 75074
Tel (903) 436-1503 SIC 3613

GGNSC HOLDINGS LLC p 610
5220 Tennyson Pkwy # 400 75024
Tel (972) 372-6300 SIC 8059

GOLDEN LIVING LLC p 621
5220 Tennyson Pkwy # 400 75024
Tel (972) 372-6300
SIC 8051 8082 8731 8093

▲ GREEN BRICK PARTNERS INC p 636
2805 Dallas Pkwy Ste 400 75093
Tel (469) 573-6755 SIC 1531 6531

HIGHLAND HOMES LTD p 691
5601 Democracy Dr Ste 300 75024
Tel (972) 789-3500 SIC 1521 1531

HILTI INC p 694
7250 Dallas Pkwy Ste 1000 75024
Tel (800) 879-8000 SIC 5072

HILTI OF AMERICA INC p 694
7250 Dallas Pkwy Ste 1000 75024
Tel (800) 879-8000 SIC 5084 3546 3825

HOMESTYLE DINING LLC p 704
3701 W Plano Pkwy Ste 200 75075
Tel (972) 244-8900 SIC 5812 6794

HOSPITAL ACQUISITION LLC p 709
5340 Legacy Dr Ste 150 75024
Tel (469) 241-2100 SIC 8069 8051

■ HP ENTERPRISE SERVICES LLC p 714
5400 Legacy Dr 75024
Tel (972) 604-6000 SIC 7374 7371 8742

HUAWEI DEVICE USA INC p 715
5700 Tennyson Pkwy # 600 75024
Tel (214) 919-6688 SIC 3663

HUAWEI TECHNOLOGIES USA INC p 715
5700 Tennyson Pkwy # 500 75024
Tel (214) 545-3700 SIC 8748

■ ICL HOLDING CO INC p 727
5340 Legacy Dr Bldg 4150 75024
Tel (469) 241-2100 SIC 8069 8051

▲ J C PENNEY CO INC p 770
6501 Legacy Dr 75024
Tel (972) 431-1000 SIC 5311 5961

■ J C PENNEY EUROPE INC p 770
6501 Legacy Dr 75024
Tel (972) 431-1000 SIC 5137 5136 5023

J C PENNEY LIFE INSURANCE CO p 770
2700 W Plano Pkwy 75075
Tel (972) 881-6000 SIC 6311 6321

■ J C PENNEY MEXICO INC p 770
6501 Legacy Dr 75024
Tel (972) 431-1000 SIC 5311

■ J C PENNEY PURCHASING CORP p 770
6501 Legacy Dr 75024
Tel (972) 431-1000 SIC 5137 5136 5023

■ JC PENNEY CORP INC p 780
6501 Legacy Dr 75024
Tel (972) 431-1000 SIC 5311 5961

■ JCP MEDIA INC p 780
6501 Legacy Dr 75024
Tel (972) 431-1000 SIC 8743

■ JCP PUBLICATIONS CORP p 780
6501 Legacy Dr 75024
Tel (972) 431-1000 SIC 5311

JOSH MCDOWELL MINISTRY p 794
2001 W Plano Pkwy # 2400 75075
Tel (972) 907-1000 SIC 8661

LCI HOLDCO LLC p 849
5340 Legacy Dr Ste 150 75024
Tel (469) 241-2100 SIC 8069 8051

■ LCI INTERMEDIATE HOLDCO INC p 849
5340 Legacy Dr Bldg 4150 75024
Tel (469) 241-2100 SIC 8069 8051

■ LEGACYTEXAS BANK p 853
5851 Legacy Cir Ste 1200 75024
Tel (972) 578-5000 SIC 6022

▲ LEGACYTEXAS FINANCIAL GROUP INC p 853
5851 Legacy Cir 75024
Tel (972) 578-5000 SIC 6022

LHP HOSPITAL GROUP INC p 861
2400 Dallas Pkwy Ste 450 75093
Tel (972) 943-1700 SIC 8062

LIFECARE HOLDINGS INC p 864
5340 Legacy Dr Ste 150 75024
Tel (469) 241-2100 SIC 8069 8051

■ LINEAGE POWER HOLDINGS INC p 869
601 Shiloh Rd 75074
Tel (974) 244-9288 SIC 6719

LONE STAR STEAKHOUSE & SALOON OF KANSAS INC p 876
5055 W Park Blvd Ste 500 75093
Tel (972) 295-8600 SIC 5812

LONE STAR STEAKS INC p 876
5055 W Park Blvd Ste 500 75093
Tel (972) 295-8600 SIC 5812

LSF5 CACTUS LLC p 883
5055 W Park Blvd Ste 500 75093
Tel (281) 830-0055 SIC 6799

LUMINATOR TECHNOLOGY GROUP LLC p 885
900 Klein Rd 75074
Tel (972) 424-6511
SIC 3613 3643 3646 3647

M+W AMERICAS INC p 890
1001 Klein Rd Ste 400 75074
Tel (972) 535-7300
SIC 3433 8712 8711 8741

MACH SPEED HOLDINGS LLC p 892
7200 Bishop Rd Ste 280 75024
Tel (214) 978-3800 SIC 5091 5065 3679

MAIN EVENT ENTERTAINMENT LP p 897
6652 Pinecrest Dr Ste 100 75024
Tel (972) 406-2600 SIC 7929 5813 5812

MASERGY COMMUNICATIONS INC p 915
2740 Dallas Pkwy Ste 260 75093
Tel (214) 442-5700 SIC 4813

MED ASSETS INC p 935
5543 Legacy Dr 75024
Tel (800) 390-7459 SIC 5099

METHANEX METHANOL CO LLC p 953
5850 Granite Pkwy Ste 400 75024
Tel (972) 702-0909 SIC 5169

MONOGRAM RESIDENTIAL TRUST INC p 984
5800 Gran Pkwy Ste 1000 75024
Tel (469) 250-5500 SIC 6798

MUREX LLC p 1001
7160 Dallas Pkwy Ste 300 75024
Tel (972) 702-0018 SIC 5172

■ NORTH AMERICAN COAL CORP p 1049
5340 Legacy Dr Ste 300 75024
Tel (972) 448-5400 SIC 1221

NTT DATA INC p 1065
5601 Gran Pkwy Ste 1000 75024
Tel (800) 745-3263 SIC 7373 7372 7379

NUKOTE INC p 1067
2400 Dallas Pkwy Ste 230 75093
Tel (972) 398-7100 SIC 3955 3861

OCEANS HEALTH CARE p 1073
5850 Granite Pkwy Ste 300 75024
Tel (972) 464-0022 SIC 8063

OLD FRITO-LAY INC p 1080
7701 Legacy Dr 75024
Tel (972) 334-7000
SIC 2096 2052 2013 5812 6794 2086

■ PEROT SYSTEMS CORP p 1137
2300 W Plano Pkwy 75075
Tel (972) 577-0000 SIC 7376 7379

■ PIZZA HUT INC p 1152
7100 Corporate Dr 75024
Tel (972) 338-7700 SIC 5812

■ PIZZA HUT OF TITUSVILLE INC p 1153
7100 Corporate Dr 75024
Tel (972) 338-7700 SIC 5812

PLANO INDEPENDENT SCHOOL DISTRICT p 1154
2700 W 15th St 75075
Tel (469) 752-8100 SIC 8211

PREFERRED CARE PARTNERS MANAGEMENT GROUP LP p 1169
5420 W Plano Pkwy 75093
Tel (972) 931-3800 SIC 8051 8052

PRESTIGE MAINTENANCE USA LTD p 1173
1808 10th St Ste 300 75074
Tel (800) 321-4773 SIC 7349

■ RENT-A-CENTER FRANCHISING INTERNATIONAL INC p 1224
5501 Headquarters Dr 75024
Tel (972) 403-4900 SIC 5722 5531

▲ RENT-A-CENTER INC p 1224
5501 Headquarters Dr 75024
Tel (972) 801-1100 SIC 7359 6794

■ REPUBLIC TITLE OF TEXAS INC p 1226
2701 W Plano Pkwy Ste 100 75075
Tel (972) 578-8611
SIC 6411 7372 6531 6541

RESEARCH NOW GROUP INC p 1226
5800 Tennyson Pkwy # 600 75024
Tel (214) 365-5000 SIC 8732

■ RETALIX USA INC p 1228
6100 Tennyson Pkwy # 150 75024
Tel (469) 241-8400 SIC 7371

RUG DOCTOR LLC p 1257
4701 Old Shepard Pl 75093
Tel (972) 673-1400 SIC 2842 3589 5087

SERVICE EXPERTS LLC p 1307
3820 American Dr Ste 200 75075
Tel (972) 231-5468
SIC 1711 5074 5075 8742

SIEMENS PRODUCT LIFECYCLE MANAGEMENT SOFTWARE INC p 1320
5800 Granite Pkwy Ste 600 75024
Tel (972) 987-3000 SIC 7372

■ SK HOLDING CO INC p 1328
5400 Legacy Dr Cluster Ii 75024
Tel (972) 265-2000 SIC 6719

SMCL LLC p 1332
5340 Legacy Dr 75024
Tel (469) 241-2100 SIC 8062 8069

■ SOFTWARE SPECTRUM INC p 1337
3480 Lotus Dr 75075
Tel (469) 443-3900 SIC 5045 7373

■ SOUTHWESTERN BELL MOBILE SYSTEMS LLC p 1353
5601 Legacy Dr 75024
Tel (972) 712-7305 SIC 4812

SYSTEM ELECTRIC CO p 1418
704 Central Pkwy E # 1200 75074
Tel (972) 422-2665 SIC 1731

TEXAS HEART HOSPITAL OF SOUTHWEST LLP p 1443
1100 Allied Dr 75093
Tel (469) 241-8900 SIC 8062

▲ TYLER TECHNOLOGIES INC p 1496
5101 Tennyson Pkwy 75024
Tel (972) 713-3700 SIC 7372

■ UGS CAPITAL CORP p 1500
5800 Gran Pkwy Ste 600 75024
Tel (972) 987-3000 SIC 7372

US RENAL CARE INC p 1533
5851 Legacy Cir Ste 900 75024
Tel (214) 736-2700 SIC 8092

VIEWPOINT BANK NA p 1556
1309 W 15th St Ste 210 75075
Tel (972) 578-5000 SIC 6062

W R STARKEY MORTGAGE LLP p 1569
6101 W Plano Pkwy 75093
Tel (972) 599-5510 SIC 6162

WHITE ENERGY INC p 1606
2745 Dallas Pkwy Ste 670 75093
Tel (972) 715-6490 SIC 2869

WINZER CORP p 1617
4060 E Plano Pkwy 75074
Tel (800) 527-4126
SIC 5072 3452 5251 5169

WSOL INC p 1628
1820 Preston Park Blvd # 1150 75093
Tel (972) 964-4800 SIC 7389

▲ ZOES KITCHEN INC p 1644
5760 State Highway 121 75024
Tel (214) 436-8765 SIC 5812 6794

ZOES KITCHEN USA LLC p 1644
5760 State Highway 121 # 250 75024
Tel (214) 872-4141 SIC 5812

POINT COMFORT, TX

FORMOSA PLASTICS CORP TEXAS p 568
201 Formosa Dr 77978
Tel (361) 987-7000 SIC 2821

FORMOSA UTILITY VENTURE LTD p 568
201 Formosa Dr 77978
Tel (361) 987-7000 SIC 2673

PORT ARTHUR, TX

CHRISTUS HEALTH SOUTHEAST TEXAS p 303
3600 Gates Blvd 77642
Tel (409) 985-7431 SIC 8062

ECHO MAINTENANCE LLC p 475
6711 N Twin City Hwy 77642
Tel (409) 724-0456 SIC 1541 3498 1623

GULF COPPER & MANUFACTURING CORP p 646
5700 Procter Ext 77642
Tel (409) 989-0300
SIC 3731 3599 3312 3732 3498 3441

MEDICAL CENTER OF SOUTHEAST TEXAS L P p 936
2555 Jimmy Johnson Blvd 77640
Tel (409) 724-7389 SIC 8062

PORT ARTHUR INDEPENDENT SCHOOL DISTRICT p 1162
4801 9th Ave 77642
Tel (409) 989-6100 SIC 8211

PORT LAVACA, TX

KING FISHER MARINE SERVICE LP p 820
159 Hwy 316 77979
Tel (361) 552-6751 SIC 1629

PORT NECHES, TX

LION ELASTOMERS LLC p 869
1615 Main St 77651
Tel (409) 722-8321 SIC 2822

PRAIRIE VIEW, TX

PRAIRIE VIEW A&M UNIVERSITY p 1167
100 University Dr 77445
Tel (936) 261-3311 SIC 8221

QUITMAN, TX

SSB HOLDINGS INC p 1363
4300 Fm 2225 75783
Tel (903) 878-7513 SIC 5122

RED OAK, TX

■ TRIUMPH AEROSTRUCTURES LLC p 1483
300 Austin Blvd 75154
Tel (972) 515-8276
SIC 3721 3728 3812 3769

RICHARDSON, TX

■ AMX LLC p 88
3000 Research Dr 75082
Tel (469) 624-8740 SIC 3625

BLUE CROSS AND BLUE SHIELD OF TEXAS INC p 191
1001 E Lookout Dr 75082
Tel (972) 766-6900 SIC 6324 6311

BOMBARDIER AEROSPACE CORP p 199
3400 Waterview Pkwy # 400 75080
Tel (972) 960-3810 SIC 5088 3721

CHILDRENS HOME HEALTHCARE INC p 299
901 Waterfall Way Ste 105 75080
Tel (972) 661-3737 SIC 8082

ELECTRONIC TRANSACTION CONSULTANTS CORP p 486
1705 N Plano Rd 75081
Tel (972) 470-5873 SIC 7371

ENGLISH COLOR & SUPPLY INC p 499
806 N Grove Rd 75081
Tel (972) 235-3108 SIC 5198 5231

EXFO AMERICA INC p 519
3400 Waterview Pkwy # 100 75080
Tel (972) 761-9271 SIC 3825 8734

▲ FOSSIL GROUP INC p 570
901 S Central Expy 75080
Tel (972) 234-2525
SIC 3873 5944 5094 5651 5632

■ FOSSIL PARTNERS LP p 570
901 S Central Expy 75080
Tel (972) 234-2525
SIC 5137 2389 2339 5094

FUJITSU NETWORK COMMUNICATIONS INC p 584
2801 Telecom Pkwy 75082
Tel (972) 479-6000 SIC 3661 3663

HALFF ASSOCIATES INC p 654
1201 N Bowser Rd 75081
Tel (214) 346-6200 SIC 8711 8713

HILL & WILKINSON CONSTRUCTION GROUP LTD p 693
2703 Telecom Pkwy Ste 120 75082
Tel (214) 299-4300 SIC 1541 1542

INFOVISION INC p 742
800 E Campbell Rd Ste 388 75081
Tel (972) 234-0058 SIC 8711 7371

■ LEGACYSTAR SERVICES LLC p 852
2435 N Central Expy # 700 75080
Tel (972) 699-4062 SIC 4613 5172

■ LENNOX INDUSTRIES INC p 855
2100 Lake Park Blvd 75080
Tel (972) 497-5000 SIC 5075

▲ LENNOX INTERNATIONAL INC p 855
2140 Lake Park Blvd 75080
Tel (972) 497-5350 SIC 3585 3621

MITEL MOBILITY INC p 977
1700 Intl Pkwy Ste 200 75081
Tel (469) 916-4393 SIC 4813

■ NUSTAR PIPELINE PARTNERS LP p 1067
2435 N Central Expy Ste 7 75080
Tel (972) 699-4062 SIC 4613

OUTREACH HEALTH CARE INC p 1099
269 W Renner Rd 75080
Tel (972) 840-7360 SIC 8093 8049 8082

PARSONS GOVERNMENT SUPPORT SERVICES INC p 1118
1301 W President George B 75080
Tel (972) 991-0800 SIC 8744

QORVO INC p 1195
500 W Renner Rd 75080
Tel (972) 994-8200 SIC 3663 3674 3679

■ QORVO TEXAS LLC p 1195
500 W Renner Rd 75080
Tel (972) 994-8200 SIC 3674

■ RADIATION SYSTEMS PRECISION CONTROLS INC p 1204
1219 Digital Dr Ste 101 75081
Tel (972) 907-9599 SIC 3663

■ RAYTHEON E-SYSTEMS INC p 1211
1727 Cityline Dr 75082
Tel (972) 205-9374
SIC 3663 3812 7373 3575 4581 3721

▲ REALPAGE INC p 1214
2201 Lakeside Blvd 75082
Tel (972) 820-3000 SIC 7371

RICHARDSON INDEPENDENT SCHOOL DISTRICT p 1232
400 S Greenville Ave # 205 75081
Tel (469) 593-0000 SIC 8211

■ RICHARDSON TRIDENT CO LLC p 1233
405 N Plano Rd 75081
Tel (972) 231-5176
SIC 5051 5085 5063 5065 3316

ROCKFISH SEAFOOD GRILL INC p 1244
801 E Campbell Rd Ste 300 75081
Tel (214) 887-9400 SIC 5812 5813

■ SAFETY-KLEEN ENVIROSYSTEMS CO p 1266
2600 N Central Expy # 400 75080
Tel (800) 323-5040 SIC 4953

■ SAFETY-KLEEN INC p 1266
2600 N Central Expy # 400 75080
Tel (800) 669-5740
SIC 4953 3559 4212 5172 5085 7389

■ SAFETY-KLEEN SYSTEMS INC p 1266
2600 N Central Expy # 400 75080
Tel (972) 265-2000
SIC 3559 7359 5172 4212 7389 5085

SAMSUNG TELECOMMUNICATIONS AMERICA LLC p 1275
1301 E Lookout Dr 75082
Tel (972) 761-7000 SIC 5065

SERVICE EXPERTS HEATING & AIR CONDITIONING LLC p 1307
2140 Lake Park Blvd 75080
Tel (972) 535-3800
SIC 1711 5074 5075 8742

SERVICE KING HOLDINGS LLC p 1307
2600 N Central Expy # 400 75080
Tel (972) 960-7595 SIC 7532

■ SERVICE KING PAINT & BODY LLC p 1307
2600 N Central Expy 75080
Tel (972) 960-7595 SIC 7532

■ SOUTHWESTERN BELL TELECOMMUNICATIONS INC p 1353
1651 N Collins Blvd 75080
Tel (972) 705-7658 SIC 5065 5999

SPEED COMMERCE INC p 1358
1303 E Arapaho Rd Ste 200 75081
Tel (866) 377-3331 SIC 5045 5099

■ STREAM INTERNATIONAL INC p 1393
3010 Waterview Pkwy 75080
Tel (469) 624-5000 SIC 8744

TPP ACQUISITION INC p 1467
1155 Kas Dr Ste 180 75081
Tel (972) 265-7600 SIC 7221

UNIVERSITY OF TEXAS AT DALLAS p 1525
800 W Campbell Rd 75080
Tel (972) 883-6325 SIC 8221

VCE CO LLC p 1545
1500 N Greenville Ave 75081
Tel (972) 656-5300 SIC 3572

VERTEX BUSINESS SERVICES LLC p 1552
501 W Pres G Bush Hwy 3 75080
Tel (214) 576-1000 SIC 7379

ZTE (USA) INC p 1644
2425 N Central Expy # 600 75080
Tel (972) 671-8885 SIC 5065 5999

RICHMOND, TX

COUNTY OF FORT BEND p 378
301 Jackson St Ste 719 77469
Tel (281) 342-3411 SIC 9111

MATRIX METALS HOLDINGS INC p 920
126 Collins Rd 77469
Tel (281) 633-4263 SIC 3325

MATRIX METALS LLC p 920
126 Collins Rd 77469
Tel (281) 342-5511 *SIC* 3325
OAKBEND MEDICAL CENTER p 1070
1705 Jackson St 77469
Tel (713) 453-0446 *SIC* 8062 8051
SAGERS SEAFOOD PLUS INC p 1268
4802 Bridal Wreath Dr 77406
Tel (281) 342-8833 *SIC* 5146

RIO GRANDE CITY, TX

RIO GRANDE CITY CONSOLIDATED INDEPENDENT SCHOOL DISTRICT p 1235
1 S Fort Ringgold St 78582
Tel (956) 716-6700 *SIC* 8211

ROANOKE, TX

FALCON HOLDINGS LLC p 526
1301 Solana Blvd Ste 2300 76262
Tel (817) 693-5151 *SIC* 5812
HERITAGE BAG CO p 686
501 Gateway Pkwy 76262
Tel (972) 241-5525 *SIC* 2673
J & D RESTAURANT GROUP LLC p 769
1301 Solana Blvd Ste 2300 76262
Tel (817) 693-5119 *SIC* 5812
JOHNSON BROS CORP p 790
608 Henrietta Creek Rd 76262
Tel (813) 685-5101 *SIC* 1623 1629 1622
OSCAR RENDA CONTRACTING INC p 1096
608 Henrietta Creek Rd 76262
Tel (817) 491-2703 *SIC* 1623 1799 1622
SOUTHLAND CONTRACTING INC p 1351
608 Henrietta Creek Rd 76262
Tel (817) 293-4263 *SIC* 1799 1622
SOUTHLAND HOLDINGS LLC p 1351
608 Henrietta Creek Rd 76262
Tel (817) 293-4263 *SIC* 1629

ROBSTOWN, TX

ATLAS TUBULAR LLC p 128
1710 S Highway 77 78380
Tel (361) 387-7505 *SIC* 5051 3498

ROCKDALE, TX

ROCKDALE HOSPITAL AUTHORITY (INC) p 1244
1700 Brazos Ave 76567
Tel (512) 446-4500 *SIC* 8062 8051

ROCKWALL, TX

FAMILY MEDICAL CENTER AT ROCKWALL p 527
1975 Alpha Dr 204 75087
Tel (972) 771-9155 *SIC* 8011
HATFIELD AND CO INC p 668
2475 Discovery Blvd 75032
Tel (972) 288-7625 *SIC* 5084 3677 5074
■ **L-3 COMMUNICATIONS INTEGRATED SYSTEMS LP** p 835
1309 Ridge Rd Ste 401 75087
Tel (903) 455-3450 *SIC* 4581
PRESBYTERIAN HOSPITAL OF ROCKWALL p 1171
3150 Horizon Rd 75032
Tel (469) 698-1000 *SIC* 8062
RAYBURN COUNTRY ELECTRIC COOPERATIVE INC p 1210
980 Sids Rd 75032
Tel (972) 771-1336 *SIC* 4911
RESOURCING EDGE INC p 1227
1309 Ridge Rd Ste 200 75087
Tel (214) 771-4411 *SIC* 8721 8742
ROCKWALL INDEPENDENT SCHOOL DISTRICT PUBLIC FACILITY CORP p 1245
1050 Williams St 75087
Tel (972) 771-0605 *SIC* 8211
TREND PERSONNEL SERVICES INC p 1476
2701 Sunset Ridge Dr 75032
Tel (214) 553-5505 *SIC* 7361

ROMA, TX

CITIZENS STATE BANK p 311
1709 N Grant St 78584
Tel (956) 849-2311 *SIC* 6022
ROMA INDEPENDENT SCHOOL DISTRICT p 1248
608 N Garcia St 78584
Tel (956) 849-1377 *SIC* 8211

ROSENBERG, TX

LAMAR CONSOLIDATED INDEPENDENT SCHOOL DISTRICT (INC) p 841
3911 Avenue I 77471
Tel (832) 223-0000 *SIC* 8211

ROSHARON, TX

■ **PRIMORIS PIPELINE SERVICES CORP** p 1176
1010 County Road 59 77583
Tel (281) 431-5900 *SIC* 1623

ROUND ROCK, TX

BAKER MICHAEL JR INC p 146
810 Hesters Crossing Rd # 163 78681
Tel (512) 248-8651 *SIC* 8711
CAPSTONE COMMODITIES LLC p 251
1311 Chisholm Trl 78681
Tel (512) 671-6626 *SIC* 5191 5999
CHASCO CONSTRUCTORS LTD LLP p 291
2801 E Old Settlers Blvd 78665
Tel (512) 244-0600
SIC 1542 1771 1794 1623
■ **DELL FINANCIAL SERVICES LLC** p 424
1 Dell Way 78682
Tel (800) 283-2210 *SIC* 7389
■ **DELL INC** p 425
1 Dell Way 78682
Tel (512) 338-4400
SIC 3571 3572 3575 3577 7372 7379
■ **DELL INTERNATIONAL INC** p 425
1 Dell Way 78682
Tel (512) 728-3500 *SIC* 3571
■ **DELL MARKETING LP** p 425
1 Dell Way 78682
Tel (512) 338-4400 *SIC* 5045
■ **DELL PRODUCTS LP** p 425
1 Dell Way 78682
Tel (512) 338-4400 *SIC* 3571
▲ **DELL TECHNOLOGIES INC** p 425
1 Dell Way 78682
Tel (800) 289-3355 *SIC* 8731 5734
■ **DELL USA CORP** p 425
1 Dell Way 78682
Tel (512) 338-4400 *SIC* 8741 5045
■ **DENALI INTERMEDIATE INC** p 428
1 Dell Way 78682
Tel (713) 627-0933
SIC 3571 3572 3577 7372
DNT CONSTRUCTION LLC p 446
2300 Picadilly Dr 78664
Tel (512) 837-6700 *SIC* 1623 1794 1611
■ **EMERSON PROCESS MANAGEMENT LLLP** p 492
1100 W Louis Henna Blvd 78681
Tel (512) 835-2190 *SIC* 8742
■ **FISHER-ROSEMOUNT SYSTEMS INC** p 552
1100 W Louis Henna Blvd 78681
Tel (512) 835-2190 *SIC* 3625 3621 7699
LIGHTHOUSE HOSPICE p 865
100 College St 78664
Tel (866) 678-0505 *SIC* 8052
ROUND ROCK INDEPENDENT SCHOOL DISTRICT (INC) p 1252
1311 Round Rock Ave 78681
Tel (512) 464-5000 *SIC* 8211 8748
SETON MEDICAL CENTER WILLIAMSON p 1309
201 Seton Pkwy 78665
Tel (512) 324-4000 *SIC* 8011
ST DAVIDS HEALTHCARE PARTNERSHIP LLP p 1365
2400 Round Rock Ave 78681
Tel (512) 341-1000 *SIC* 8062
TECO HOLDINGS USA INC p 1432
5100 N Interstate 35 78681
Tel (512) 255-4141 *SIC* 3621
TECO-WESTINGHOUSE MOTOR CO p 1432
5100 N Interstate 35 A 78681
Tel (512) 218-7448 *SIC* 3621
TEXAS GUARANTEED STUDENT LOAN CORP p 1443
301 Sundance Pkwy 78681
Tel (512) 219-5700 *SIC* 6111
TOPPAN PHOTOMASKS INC p 1461
131 E Old Settlers Blvd 78664
Tel (512) 310-6500 *SIC* 3559

ROWLETT, TX

■ **LAKE POINTE MEDICAL CENTER LTD** p 839
6800 Scenic Dr 75088
Tel (972) 412-2273 *SIC* 8011
LINK AMERICA LLC p 869
3002 Century Dr 75088
Tel (972) 463-0050 *SIC* 8748
NATIONS ROOF CENTRAL LLC p 1017
2914 Lawing Ln 75088
Tel (972) 278-9200 *SIC* 1761

SAGINAW, TX

BANA INC p 149
624 E Mcleroy Blvd 76179
Tel (817) 232-3750 *SIC* 5085 2441 2448

SAN ANGELO, TX

ALBERT REECE INC p 46
3001 Foster St 76903
Tel (325) 653-1241
SIC 1611 1794 1623 1622
HIRSCHFELD HOLDINGS LP p 696
112 W 29th St 76903
Tel (325) 486-4201 *SIC* 1622 3441
HIRSCHFELD STEEL GROUP LP p 696
112 W 29th St 76903
Tel (325) 486-4201 *SIC* 3441
■ **MULTI-CHEM GROUP LLC** p 999
424 S Chadbourne St 76903
Tel (325) 223-6200 *SIC* 1389
■ **PATTERSON DRILLING CO INC** p 1121
4105 S Chadbourne St 76904
Tel (325) 651-6603 *SIC* 1381
■ **SAN ANGELO HOSPITAL LP** p 1275
3501 Knickerbocker Rd 76904
Tel (325) 949-9511 *SIC* 8062
SAN ANGELO INDEPENDENT SCHOOL DISTRICT p 1275
1621 University Ave 76904
Tel (325) 947-3700 *SIC* 8211
SHANNON CLINIC p 1311
120 E Beauregard Ave 76903
Tel (325) 658-1511 *SIC* 8011
SHANNON HEALTH SYSTEM p 1311
120 E Harris Ave 76903
Tel (325) 653-6741 *SIC* 8011
SHANNON MEDICAL CENTER p 1311
120 E Harris Ave 76903
Tel (325) 653-6741 *SIC* 8062
■ **TCFS HOLDINGS INC** p 1428
3515 S Bryant Blvd 76903
Tel (325) 655-0676 *SIC* 5411
■ **TOWN & COUNTRY FOOD STORES INC** p 1464
3515 S Bryant Blvd 76903
Tel (325) 655-0676 *SIC* 5411
WESTERN-SHAMROCK CORP p 1600
801 S Abe St Ste 2a 76903
Tel (325) 653-6814 *SIC* 6141 6159 6153

SAN ANTONIO, TX

4E BRANDS NORTHAMERICA LLC p 3
17806 W Interstate 10 # 30 78257
Tel (210) 819-7385 *SIC* 2841
ACCORD MEDICAL MANAGEMENT LP p 15
414 Navarro St Ste 600 78205
Tel (210) 271-1800 *SIC* 8062
ACE MART RESTAURANT SUPPLY CO p 16
2653 Austin Hwy 78218
Tel (210) 323-4400 *SIC* 5169 5046
ACELITY LP INC p 17
12930 W Interstate 10 78249
Tel (210) 524-9000 *SIC* 3841 2834
ADVANCED TEMPORARIES INC p 26
5139 Fredericksburg Rd 78229
Tel (903) 561-0927 *SIC* 7363
ALAMO COMMUNITY COLLEGE DISTRICT p 44
201 W Sheridan 78204
Tel (210) 485-0000 *SIC* 8222
■ **ALAMO TITLE CO** p 44
18618 Tuscany Stone 78258
Tel (210) 490-1313 *SIC* 6361
■ **ALAMO TITLE INSURANCE CO** p 44
434 N Loop 1604 W # 2204 78232
Tel (210) 499-5872 *SIC* 6361
ALPHA BUILDING CORP p 60
24870 Blanco Rd 78260
Tel (210) 491-9925 *SIC* 1542
ALTERMAN GROUP INC p 62
14703 Jnes Maltsberger Rd 78247
Tel (210) 496-6888 *SIC* 1731
ALTERMAN INC p 62
14703 Jnes Maltsberger Rd 78247
Tel (210) 496-6888 *SIC* 1731
ANCIRA ENTERPRISES INC p 89
10855 W Interstate 10 78230
Tel (210) 681-4900 *SIC* 5511
ARCHDIOCESE OF SAN ANTONIO p 105
2718 W Woodlawn Ave 78228
Tel (210) 433-0411 *SIC* 8661
ARGO GROUP US INC p 107
10101 Reunion Pl Ste 500 78216
Tel (210) 321-8400 *SIC* 6331
ARGONAUT INSURANCE CO INC p 107
10101 Reunion Pl Ste 500 78216
Tel (210) 321-8400 *SIC* 6331
■ **AT&T MESSAGING LLC** p 123
4801 Nw Loop 410 Ste 850 78229
Tel (210) 523-4300 *SIC* 4813
■ **AUSTIN COCA-COLA BOTTLING CO** p 132
1 Coca Cola Pl 78219
Tel (210) 225-2601 *SIC* 2086
AVANZAR INTERIOR SYSTEMS LLC p 136
1 Lone Star Pass Bldg 41 78264
Tel (210) 271-2400 *SIC* 5013
AVANZAR INTERIOR TECHNOLOGIES LTD p 136
1 Lone Star Pass Bldg 41 78264
Tel (210) 271-2300 *SIC* 3559
AXEON MARKETING LLC p 140
2338 N Loop 1604 W 78248
Tel (210) 918-2000 *SIC* 1311
■ **BAPTIST HEALTH SYSTEM** p 153
215 E Quincy St Ste 200 78215
Tel (210) 297-1000 *SIC* 8062
BARTLETT COCKE GENERAL CONTRACTORS LLC p 157
8706 Lockway St 78217
Tel (210) 655-1031 *SIC* 1542
BAY CLUB LOS ANGELES INC p 160
15759 San Pedro Ave 78232
Tel (210) 490-1980 *SIC* 7991
BCFS HEALTH AND HUMAN SERVICES p 164
1506 Bexar Crossing St 78232
Tel (210) 832-5000 *SIC* 8322
BEXAR COUNTY BOARD OFTRUSTEES FOR MENTAL HEALTH MENTAL RETARDATION p 179
3031 W Interstate 10 78201
Tel (210) 261-1000 *SIC* 8361 8093
BEXAR COUNTY HOSPITAL DISTRICT p 179
4502 Medical Dr Ms651 78229
Tel (210) 358-4000 *SIC* 8062 8011
BEXAR COUNTY MARKETS INC p 179
340 Enrque M Barrera Pkwy 78237
Tel (210) 227-8755 *SIC* 5411
BEXAR METROPOLITAN WATER DISTRICT PUBLIC FACILITY CORP p 179
2047 W Malone Ave 78225
Tel (210) 233-2335 *SIC* 4941
▲ **BIGLARI HOLDINGS INC** p 182
17802 W Ih 10 Ste 400 78257
Tel (210) 344-3400 *SIC* 5812 6794
BLACKBRUSH OIL & GAS LP p 187
18615 Tuscany Stone 78258
Tel (210) 495-5577 *SIC* 1311
BORAL MATERIAL TECHNOLOGIES LLC p 201
45 Ne Loop 410 Ste 700 78216
Tel (210) 349-4069 *SIC* 5169
BROADWAY BANCSHARES INC p 216
1177 Ne Loop 410 78209
Tel (210) 283-6500 *SIC* 6021
BROADWAY NATIONAL BANK p 216
1177 Ne Loop 410 78209
Tel (210) 283-6500 *SIC* 6021
BUFFET PARTNERS LP p 224
120 Chula Vis 78232
Tel (210) 403-3725 *SIC* 5812
BUFFETS HOLDINGS LLC p 224
120 Chula Vista Hollywood 78232
Tel (210) 403-3725 *SIC* 5812
C H GUENTHER & SON INC p 232
2201 Broadway St 78215
Tel (210) 227-1401
SIC 2041 2051 2045 2052 2099
CAPITOL AGGREGATES INC p 250
11551 Nacogdoches Rd 78217
Tel (210) 655-3010
SIC 3241 1442 1422 2951 4011
CATHOLIC LIFE INSURANCE p 267
1635 Ne Loop 410 Ste 300 78209
Tel (210) 828-9921 *SIC* 6311 6411
CCC GROUP INC p 269
5797 Dietrich Rd 78219
Tel (210) 661-4251 *SIC* 1541 1629 1542
CHIRON GUERNSEY HOLDINGS LP INC p 301
12930 W Interstate 10 78249
Tel (210) 524-9000 *SIC* 3841
CHIRON HOLDINGS INC p 301
12930 W Interstate 10 78249
Tel (210) 524-9000 *SIC* 2599 7352
CHRISTUS SANTA ROSA HEALTH CARE CORP p 303
333 N Santa Rosa St 78207
Tel (210) 704-2011 *SIC* 8063 8069
CHRISTUS SANTA ROSA HOME CARE p 304
4241 Woodcock Dr Ste A100 78228
Tel (210) 704-2011 *SIC* 7389
■ **CHROMALLOY COMPONENT SERVICES INC** p 304
303 Industrial Park Rd 78226
Tel (210) 331-2300 *SIC* 7699 3724
CITY OF SAN ANTONIO p 318
City Hall 100 Military Plz 78205
Tel (210) 207-6000 *SIC* 9199
CITY PUBLIC SERVICES OF SAN ANTONIO p 319
145 Navarro St 78205
Tel (210) 353-2222 *SIC* 4931 4932
CLARKE AMERICAN CHECKS INC p 322
15955 La Cantera Pkwy 78256
Tel (210) 694-1492 *SIC* 2782 2759 2752
■ **CLEAR CHANNEL OUTDOOR HOLDINGS INC** p 324
200 E Basse Rd Ste 100 78209
Tel (210) 832-3700 *SIC* 7312 7999
COASTAL TRANSPORT CO INC p 332
1603 Ackerman Rd 78219
Tel (210) 661-4287 *SIC* 4212 4213
CONTINENTAL WHOLESALE FLORISTS INC p 364
1777 Ne Loop 410 78217
Tel (210) 654-6543 *SIC* 5193
COUNTY OF BEXAR p 376
101 W Nueva Ste 1019 78205
Tel (210) 335-2626 *SIC* 9111
▲ **CST BRANDS INC** p 398
19500 Bulverde Rd Ste 100 78259
Tel (210) 692-5000 *SIC* 5983 5411
▲ **CULLEN/FROST BANKERS INC** p 400
100 W Houston St 78205
Tel (210) 220-4011 *SIC* 6021 6411
CURTIS C GUNN INC p 402
227 Broadway St 78205
Tel (210) 472-2501 *SIC* 5511 6531
■ **DAHILL OFFICE TECHNOLOGY CORP** p 408
8200 W Interstate 10 # 400 78230
Tel (210) 805-8200 *SIC* 5999 3861 2759

DEE HOWARD CO p 421
9610 John Saunders Rd 78216
Tel (210) 828-1341 *SIC* 3721 3724 4581

■ DIAMOND SHAMROCK REFINING AND MARKETING CO p 437
6000 N Loop 1604 W 78249
Tel (210) 345-2000 *SIC* 5541 5171 2911

DISABILITY SERVICES OF SOUTHWEST INC p 442
6243 W Interstate 10 # 395 78201
Tel (210) 798-0123 *SIC* 8093

DPT LABORATORIES LTD p 454
318 Mccullough Ave 78215
Tel (866) 225-5378 *SIC* 2834

EAST CENTRAL INDEPENDENT SCHOOL DISTRICT p 470
6634 New Sulphur Sprng Rd 78263
Tel (210) 648-7861 *SIC* 8211

ECCA HOLDINGS CORP p 475
175 E Houston St Fl 6 78205
Tel (210) 340-3531 *SIC* 5995 3851

EDGEWOOD INDEPENDENT SCHOOL DISTRICT p 478
5358 W Comm St 78237
Tel (210) 444-4500 *SIC* 8211

EEMPLOYERS SOLUTIONS INC p 480
12211 Huebner Rd 78230
Tel (210) 495-1171 *SIC* 8742 6411

■ ENERGY TRANSFER CRUDE OIL CO LLC p 498
800 E Sonterra Blvd 78258
Tel (210) 403-7300 *SIC* 4612

■ ENTERPRISE HYDROCARBONS LP p 502
1100 La St Fl 10 78209
Tel (713) 381-6500 *SIC* 1389

FIESTA TEXAS INC p 541
17000 W Interstate 10 78257
Tel (210) 697-5000 *SIC* 7996

FIRE MOUNTAIN RESTAURANTS LLC p 543
120 Chula Vis 78232
Tel (651) 994-8608 *SIC* 5812

FITE DISTRIBUTION SERVICES CO LP p 552
1001 Donaldson Ave 78228
Tel (210) 736-3141 *SIC* 4214 4225

■ FLOWERS BAKING CO OF SAN ANTONIO LLC p 560
6000 Ne Loop 410 78218
Tel (210) 661-2361 *SIC* 2051

FRIEDRICH AIR CONDITIONING CO LTD p 579
10001 Reunion Pl Ste 500 78216
Tel (210) 546-0500 *SIC* 3585 5722

FROST & SULLIVAN p 581
7550 W Ih 10 Ste 400 78229
Tel (210) 348-1000 *SIC* 8732 8742

■ FROST BANK p 581
100 W Houston St Ste 100 78205
Tel (210) 220-4011 *SIC* 6021

GAMBRINUS CO p 590
14800 San Pedro Ave # 310 78232
Tel (210) 483-5100 *SIC* 5181 2082

GENESIS NETWORKS ENTERPRISES LLC p 603
600 N Loop 1604 E 78232
Tel (210) 489-6600 *SIC* 7373

GLI INC p 615
803 S Medina St 78207
Tel (210) 226-4376 *SIC* 5181

GOODWILL INDUSTRIES OF SAN ANTONIO p 625
406 W Commerce St 78207
Tel (210) 924-8581 *SIC* 8331

GROTHUES BROTHERS HOLDINGS LTD p 641
2651 Sw Military Dr 78224
Tel (830) 569-1131 *SIC* 5031 5211 6719

GUTHRIE & HUEBNER CO INC p 648
5797 Dietrich Rd 78219
Tel (210) 661-4251 *SIC* 1541 1629 1542

H E BUTT GROCERY CO p 650
646 S Flores St 78204
Tel (210) 938-8000 *SIC* 5411

HARCOURT ASSESSMENT INC p 660
19500 Bulverde Rd 78259
Tel (210) 339-5000 *SIC* 8748 2741

HARLAND CLARKE CORP p 661
15955 La Cantera Pkwy 78256
Tel (830) 609-5500 *SIC* 2782 2754 7389

HARLAND CLARKE HOLDINGS CORP p 661
15955 La Cantera Pkwy 78256
Tel (210) 697-8888 *SIC* 2782 2754 7389

HARLANDALE INDEPENDENT SCHOOL DISTRICT PUBLIC FACILITIES CORP p 661
102 Genevieve Dr 78214
Tel (210) 989-4340 *SIC* 8211

▲ HARTE HANKS INC p 665
9601 Mcallister Fwy # 610 78216
Tel (210) 829-9000 *SIC* 7331 7372

HASSLOCHER ENTERPRISES INC p 667
8520 Crownhill Blvd 78209
Tel (210) 828-1493 *SIC* 5812 5142 6552

HAWKINS ASSOCIATES INC p 669
909 Ne Loop 410 Ste 104 78209
Tel (210) 349-9911 *SIC* 7363 7361

HB ZACHRY CO p 671
527 Logwood Ave 78221
Tel (210) 475-8000
SIC 1611 1622 1623 1629

HEB GROCERY CO LP p 680
646 S Flores St 78204
Tel (210) 938-8000 *SIC* 5411

HEBCO PETROLEUM DISTRIBUTORS INC p 680
646 S Main Ave 78204
Tel (210) 938-8419 *SIC* 5172

HILL COUNTRY BAKERY LLC p 693
122 Stribling 78204
Tel (210) 475-9981 *SIC* 5149 5461

HOLT TEXAS LTD p 702
5665 Se Loop 410 78222
Tel (210) 648-1111
SIC 3531 5082 7353 7699

HOMETOWN BUFFET INC p 704
120 Chula Vis 78232
Tel (651) 994-8608 *SIC* 5812

■ HOUSTON PIPE LINE CO LP p 712
800 E Sonterra Blvd 78258
Tel (713) 222-0414 *SIC* 4922

HOWARD MIDSTREAM ENERGY PARTNERS LLC p 713
17806 W Ih 10 Ste 210 78257
Tel (210) 298-2222 *SIC* 5085

■ HPL HOUSTON PIPE LINE CO LLC p 714
800 E Sonterra Blvd 78258
Tel (713) 222-0414 *SIC* 4922

■ HUMANA HEALTH PLAN INC p 718
8431 Fredericksburg Rd # 340 78229
Tel (210) 615-5100 *SIC* 6324 6321 8011

HVHC INC p 722
175 E Houston St 78205
Tel (210) 340-3531 *SIC* 6324

■ IHEARTCOMMUNICATIONS INC p 731
200 E Basse Rd 78209
Tel (210) 822-2828 *SIC* 4832 4833 7312

■ IHEARTMEDIA CAPITAL I LLC p 731
200 E Basse Rd 78209
Tel (210) 822-2828 *SIC* 4813 4899

■ IHEARTMEDIA CAPITAL II LLC p 731
200 E Basse Rd 78209
Tel (210) 822-2828 *SIC* 4899 4813

▲ IHEARTMEDIA INC p 731
200 E Basse Rd Ste 100 78209
Tel (210) 822-2828 *SIC* 4832 7312

INSCO DISTRIBUTING INC p 745
12501 Network Blvd 78249
Tel (210) 690-8400 *SIC* 5078 5075

ISS FACILITY SERVICES HOLDING INC p 767
1019 Central Pkwy N # 100 78232
Tel (210) 495-6021 *SIC* 7349

ISS FACILITY SERVICES INC p 767
1019 Central Pkwy N # 100 78232
Tel (210) 495-6021 *SIC* 7699

ISS HOLDING INC p 767
1019 Central Pkwy N # 100 78232
Tel (210) 495-6021 *SIC* 7349

ISS MANAGEMENT & FINANCE CO INC p 767
1019 Central Pkwy N Ste 1 78232
Tel (210) 495-6021 *SIC* 7381

JOERIS GENERAL CONTRACTORS LTD p 787
823 Arion Pkwy 78216
Tel (210) 286-8696 *SIC* 1542

JOHNSON BROS BAKERY SUPPLY INC p 790
10731 N Ih 35 78233
Tel (210) 590-2575 *SIC* 5149 5046

JOJOS CALIFORNIA p 792
120 Chula Vis 78232
Tel (877) 225-4160 *SIC* 5812

KAHLIG MOTOR CO p 800
611 Lockhill Selma Rd 78216
Tel (210) 308-8900 *SIC* 5511 7515

KCI USA INC p 806
12930 W Interstate 10 78249
Tel (800) 275-4524 *SIC* 7352 3842 5047

KINETIC CONCEPTS INC p 819
12930 W Interstate 10 78249
Tel (800) 531-5346 *SIC* 3842

KOONTZ CONSTRUCTION INC p 827
755 E Mulberry Ave # 100 78212
Tel (210) 826-2600 *SIC* 1542 1522

LABATT FOOD SERVICE LLC p 836
4500 Industry Park Dr 78218
Tel (210) 661-4216 *SIC* 8742

LABATT INSTITUTIONAL SUPPLY CO INC p 836
4500 Industry Park Dr 78218
Tel (210) 661-4216 *SIC* 5141

LANCER CORP p 841
6655 Lancer Blvd 78219
Tel (210) 661-6964 *SIC* 3585

LEONARD FAMILY CORP p 856
647 Steves Ave 78210
Tel (210) 532-3241 *SIC* 5147

LEWIS ENERGY GROUP LP p 858
10101 Reunion Pl Ste 1000 78216
Tel (210) 384-3200 *SIC* 1311

LEWIS RESOURCE MANAGEMENT LLC p 859
10101 Reunion Pl Ste 1000 78216
Tel (210) 384-3200 *SIC* 4924

LGD MANAGEMENT LP p 860
608 Sandau Rd 78216
Tel (210) 564-0100 *SIC* 8741

LIBERTO SPECIALTY CO INC p 861
830 S Presa St 78210
Tel (210) 222-1415 *SIC* 5046 5145

■ LONE STAR NGL LLC p 876
800 E Sonterra Blvd # 400 78258
Tel (210) 403-7300 *SIC* 1321

LYND CO p 887
8000 W Interstate 10 # 1200 78230
Tel (210) 798-8114 *SIC* 6513 6512

■ MARTIN MARIETTA MATERIALS SOUTHWEST INC p 912
5710 W Hausman Rd Ste 121 78249
Tel (210) 208-4400
SIC 1422 3273 2951 3274 1442

MASS MARKETING INC p 916
401 Isom Rd Ste 210 78216
Tel (210) 314-7005 *SIC* 5411

MATERA PAPER CO INC p 919
835 N Ww White Rd 78219
Tel (210) 892-5101 *SIC* 5087

MCS & METROPLEX CONTROL SYSTEM p 932
12903 Delivery 78247
Tel (210) 495-5245 *SIC* 1731

METHODIST HEALTHCARE MINISTRIES OF SOUTH TEXAS INC p 953
4507 Medical Dr 78229
Tel (210) 692-0234 *SIC* 8011 7363

■ METHODIST HEALTHCARE SYSTEM OF SAN ANTONIO LTD LLP p 953
8109 Fredericksburg Rd 78229
Tel (210) 575-8110 *SIC* 8062 8011

METHODIST HOSPITAL p 953
7700 Floyd Curl Dr 78229
Tel (210) 575-4000 *SIC* 8062

MG BUILDING MATERIALS LTD p 958
2651 Sw Military Dr 78224
Tel (210) 924-8604 *SIC* 2421 4212 5211

MINER CORP p 973
11827 Tech Com Rd Ste 115 78233
Tel (210) 655-8600 *SIC* 5084

MINER HOLDING CO INC p 973
11827 Tech Com Rd Ste 115 78233
Tel (830) 627-8600 *SIC* 1799 6719

MISSION PHARMACAL CO p 975
10999 W Interstate 10 # 1000 78230
Tel (210) 696-8400 *SIC* 2834

MUY HAMBURGER PARTNERS LLC p 1003
17890 Blanco Rd Ste 401 78232
Tel (210) 408-2400 *SIC* 5812

■ NATIONAL CONVENIENCE STORES INC p 1011
6000 N Loop 1604 W 78249
Tel (830) 995-4303 *SIC* 5411 5812

NATURESWEET LTD p 1019
2338 N Loop 1604 W 78248
Tel (210) 408-8500 *SIC* 0161

NAVARRO MIDSTREAM SERVICES LLC p 1020
10101 Reunion Pl Ste 1000 78216
Tel (956) 728-6000 *SIC* 1382

■ NEW GALVESTON CO p 1030
100 W Houston St 78205
Tel (210) 220-4011 *SIC* 6712

NEWS GROUP INC p 1039
5130 Comm Pkwy 78218
Tel (210) 226-9333 *SIC* 5192 5994

NIX HOSPITALS SYSTEM LLC p 1045
414 Navarro St Ste 600 78205
Tel (210) 271-1800 *SIC* 8062

NORTH EAST INDEPENDENT SCHOOL DISTRICT p 1052
8961 Tesoro Dr 78217
Tel (210) 407-0359 *SIC* 8211

NORTHSIDE INDEPENDENT SCHOOL DISTRICT p 1058
5900 Evers Rd 78238
Tel (210) 397-8770 *SIC* 8211

NORTHWEST VISTA COLLEGE p 1060
3535 N Ellison Dr 78251
Tel (210) 706-9291 *SIC* 8222 8221

▲ NUSTAR ENERGY LP p 1067
19003 W Ih 10 78257
Tel (210) 918-2000 *SIC* 4612 4613 4226

▲ NUSTAR GP HOLDINGS LLC p 1067
19003 W Ih 10 78257
Tel (210) 918-2000 *SIC* 4612 4613

■ NUSTAR GP LLC p 1067
19003 W Interstate 10 78257
Tel (210) 370-2000 *SIC* 3533

■ NUSTAR LOGISTICS LP p 1067
19003 W Interstate 10 78257
Tel (210) 918-2000 *SIC* 1311

■ NUSTAR SUPPLY & TRADING LLC p 1067
19003 W Interstate 10 78257
Tel (210) 918-2000 *SIC* 5172

OCB RESTAURANT CO LLC p 1072
120 Chula Vis 78232
Tel (210) 403-3725 *SIC* 5812

OLMOS CONSTRUCTION INC p 1082
440 Pinn Rd 78227
Tel (210) 675-4990 *SIC* 1611 1794 1795

PARK NORTH LINCOLN-MERCURY INC p 1115
9207 San Pedro Ave 78216
Tel (210) 341-8841 *SIC* 5511

■ PIONEER DRILLING SERVICES LTD p 1150
1250 Ne Loop 410 Ste 1000 78209
Tel (210) 828-7689 *SIC* 1381

▲ PIONEER ENERGY SERVICES CORP p 1150
1250 Ne Loop 410 Ste 1000 78209
Tel (855) 884-0575 *SIC* 1381 7353

■ PIONEER WELL SERVICES LLC p 1151
1250 Ne Loop 410 Ste 1000 78209
Tel (210) 828-7689 *SIC* 1389

■ PIONEER WIRELINE SERVICES LLC p 1151
1250 Ne Loop 410 Ste 1000 78209
Tel (210) 828-7689 *SIC* 1389

PMG INTERNATIONAL LTD p 1157
1011 N Frio St 78207
Tel (210) 226-6820 *SIC* 5192

PRESIDIAN DESTINATIONS LTD p 1172
9000 Tesoro Dr Ste 300 78217
Tel (210) 646-8811 *SIC* 6512

■ QEP MIDSTREAM PARTNERS LP p 1195
19100 Ridgewood Pkwy 78259
Tel (210) 626-6000 *SIC* 4922

QUALTEX LABORATORIES p 1198
6211 W Interstate 10 78201
Tel (210) 736-8952 *SIC* 2836

R&L FOODS INC p 1203
7550 W Interstate 10 # 508 78229
Tel (210) 433-3371 *SIC* 5812

RABA KISTNER INC p 1203
12821 W Golden Ln 78249
Tel (210) 699-9090 *SIC* 8711

RACKSPACE HOSTING INC p 1203
1 Fanatical Pl 78218
Tel (210) 312-4000
SIC 7371 7374 7382 4813

RACKSPACE US INC p 1203
1 Fanatical Pl 78218
Tel (210) 312-4000 *SIC* 4813

RED MCCOMBS HYUNDAI LTD p 1215
4800 Nw Loop 410 78229
Tel (210) 684-7440 *SIC* 5511 5521

RITA RESTAURANT CORP p 1236
120 Chula Vis 78232
Tel (210) 403-3725 *SIC* 5812 6794

RYANS RESTAURANT GROUP LLC p 1260
120 Chula Vis 78232
Tel (651) 994-8608 *SIC* 5812

S C SAN ANTONIO INC p 1262
7400 Barlite Blvd 78224
Tel (210) 921-2000 *SIC* 8062

SAN ANTONIO FEDERAL CREDIT UNION p 1275
6061 W Ih 10 Fl 3 78201
Tel (210) 258-1414 *SIC* 6062

SAN ANTONIO FOOD BANK p 1275
5200 Enrique M Barrera Pa 78227
Tel (210) 337-3663 *SIC* 4225 8322

SAN ANTONIO INDEPENDENT SCHOOL DISTRICT FAC p 1275
141 Lavaca St 78210
Tel (210) 554-2200 *SIC* 8211

SAN ANTONIO SHOE INC p 1275
1717 Sas Dr 78224
Tel (877) 727-7463
SIC 3131 5661 5139 5632 3144

SAN ANTONIO STATE HOSPITAL p 1275
6711 S New Braunfels Ave 78223
Tel (210) 532-8811 *SIC* 8063

SAN ANTONIO WATER SYSTEM p 1275
2800 Us Highway 281 N 78212
Tel (210) 233-3814 *SIC* 4941

SECURITY SERVICE CUSO LLC p 1299
16211 La Cantera Pkwy 78256
Tel (210) 476-4151 *SIC* 6061 7381

SECURITY SERVICE FEDERAL CREDIT UNION p 1299
15000 W Interstate 10 78249
Tel (210) 476-4000 *SIC* 6061

SEGUNDO NAVARRO DRILLING LTD p 1300
10101 Reunion Pl Ste 1000 78216
Tel (210) 384-3200 *SIC* 1382 4925

SENIOR MANAGEMENT SERVICES OF NORMANDY AT SAN ANTONIO INC p 1304
841 Rice Rd 78220
Tel (210) 648-0101 *SIC* 8051

SIGMA SOLUTIONS GP INC p 1321
607 E Sonterra Blvd # 250 78258
Tel (210) 348-9876 *SIC* 7373 7379

SIGMA TECHNOLOGY SOLUTIONS INC p 1321
607 E Sonterra Blvd # 250 78258
Tel (888) 895-0495 *SIC* 7373

SIRIUS COMPUTER SOLUTIONS INC p 1327
10100 Reunion Pl Ste 500 78216
Tel (210) 369-8000 *SIC* 7373 5045

SOUTH SAN ANTONIO INDEPENDENT SCHOOL DISTRICT p 1345
5622 Ray Ellison Blvd 78242
Tel (210) 977-7000 *SIC* 8211

SOUTHWEST BUSINESS CORP p 1351
9311 San Pedro Ave # 600 78216
Tel (210) 525-1241 *SIC* 6411 6162 6282

SOUTHWEST INDEPENDENT SCHOOL DISTRICT p 1352
11914 Dragon Ln 78252
Tel (210) 622-4300 *SIC* 8211

SOUTHWEST RESEARCH INSTITUTE INC p 1352
6220 Culebra Rd 78238
Tel (210) 684-5111 *SIC* 8731 8711

SOUTHWEST TEXAS EQUIPMENT DISTRIBUTORS INC p 1352
1126 S Saint Marys St 78210
Tel (210) 354-0691 *SIC* 5078

SPFM LP p 1358
4310 West Ave 78213
Tel (210) 805-8931
SIC 5122 5149 2834 2833 2841 2844

SSC SAN ANTONIO NORTHGATE OPERATING CO LLC p 1363
5757 N Knoll 78240
Tel (210) 694-7951 *SIC* 8051

ST MARYS UNIVERSITY OF SAN ANTONIO TEXAS p 1372
1 Camino Santa Maria St 78228
Tel (210) 436-3506 *SIC* 8221

STANDARD AERO INC p 1375
3523 General Hudnell Dr 78226
Tel (210) 704-1100 *SIC* 7699

STEVES & SONS INC p 1388
203 Humble Ave 78225
Tel (210) 924-5111 *SIC* 2431

TEAM EXPRESS DISTRIBUTING LLC p 1429
5750 Northwest Pkwy # 100 78249
Tel (210) 525-9161 *SIC* 5941 5091

■TESORO COMPANIES INC p 1440
19100 Ridgewood Pkwy 78259
Tel (210) 626-7390 *SIC* 8741

▲TESORO CORP p 1440
19100 Ridgewood Pkwy 78259
Tel (210) 626-6000
SIC 2911 1311 5983 5984

▲TESORO LOGISTICS LP p 1440
19100 Ridgewood Pkwy 78259
Tel (210) 626-6000 *SIC* 1311 4612

■TESORO LOGISTICS OPERATIONS LLC p 1440
19100 Ridgewood Pkwy 78259
Tel (210) 626-4280 *SIC* 4922

■TESORO REFINING & MARKETING CO LLC p 1440
19100 Ridgewood Pkwy 78259
Tel (210) 828-8484 *SIC* 2911 5541

TETCO INC p 1441
1100 Ne Loop 410 Ste 900 78209
Tel (210) 821-5900
SIC 4213 5411 1611 5193

■TIME WARNER CABLE SAN ANTONIO LP p 1454
1900 Blue Crest Ln 78247
Tel (703) 713-9342 *SIC* 4841

TK HOLDINGS INC p 1457
4611 Wiseman Blvd 78251
Tel (210) 509-0762 *SIC* 2399

TOUCHSTONE COMMUNITIES INC p 1464
250 W Nottingham Dr # 200 78209
Tel (210) 828-5686 *SIC* 8741

TOYOTA MOTOR MANUFACTURING TEXAS INC p 1467
1 Lone Star Pass 78264
Tel (210) 263-4000 *SIC* 5511

■TPI PETROLEUM INC p 1467
6000 N Loop 1604 W 78249
Tel (210) 592-2000
SIC 2911 5541 4612 4212 4213

TRIDENT INSURANCE SERVICES LLC p 1479
175 E Houston St Ste 1300 78205
Tel (210) 342-8808 *SIC* 6411

TRINITY UNIVERSITY p 1482
1 Trinity Pl 78212
Tel (210) 999-7011 *SIC* 8221

■ ULTRAMAR DIAMOND SHAMROCK INC p 1501
6000 N Loop 1604 W 78249
Tel (210) 627-2003 *SIC* 6512

■ ULTRAMAR INC p 1501
1 Valero Way 78249
Tel (210) 345-2000 *SIC* 2911 5172 5541

UNITED FASHIONS HOLDINGS INC p 1508
4629 Marco Dr 78218
Tel (210) 662-7140 *SIC* 5621 5641

UNITED FASHIONS OF TEXAS LLC p 1508
4629 Macro 78218
Tel (210) 662-7140 *SIC* 5611 5621 5651

UNITED SERVICES AUTOMOBILE ASSOCIATION p 1511
9800 Fredericksburg Rd 78288
Tel (210) 498-2211 *SIC* 6331 6311 6351

UNIVERSITY HEALTH SYSTEM p 1518
355 Spencer Ln Ste 2 78201
Tel (210) 358-9185 *SIC* 8011 6512

UNIVERSITY HEALTH SYSTEM p 1519
4502 Medical Dr 78229
Tel (210) 358-4000 *SIC* 8099

UNIVERSITY OF INCARNATE WORD p 1521
4301 Broadway St 78209
Tel (210) 829-6000 *SIC* 8221

UNIVERSITY OF TEXAS AT SAN ANTONIO p 1525
1 Utsa Cir 78249
Tel (210) 458-4011 *SIC* 8221

UNIVERSITY OF TEXAS HEALTH SCIENCE CENTER AT SAN ANTONIO p 1526
7703 Floyd Curl Dr 78229
Tel (210) 567-7000 *SIC* 8221

URBAN CONCRETE CONTRACTORS INC p 1530
24114 Blanco Rd 78260
Tel (210) 490-0090 *SIC* 1771

US-LAS COLINAS LIMITED PARTNERSHIP p 1533
9830 Colonnade Blvd # 600 78230
Tel (210) 498-0626 *SIC* 7011 7997

USAA CAPITAL CORP p 1534
9800 Fredericksburg Rd 78288
Tel (210) 498-2211
SIC 6035 6798 6722 7299 4813 4724

USAA FEDERAL SAVINGS BANK p 1534
10750 Mcdermott Fwy 78288
Tel (210) 498-2211 *SIC* 6035

USAA GENERAL AGENCY INC p 1534
9800 Fredericksburg Rd 78288
Tel (210) 456-1800 *SIC* 6331 6321

USAA INSURANCE AGENCY INC p 1534
9800 Fredericksburg Rd B-2e 78288
Tel (210) 498-2211 *SIC* 6331 6321 8742

USAA LIFE INSURANCE CO p 1534
9800 Fredericksburg Rd 78288
Tel (210) 498-2211 *SIC* 6331 6311

USAA REAL ESTATE CO p 1534
9830 Colonnade Blvd # 600 78230
Tel (210) 641-8400 *SIC* 6552

UT MEDICINE SAN ANTONIO p 1536
6126 Wurzbach Rd 78238
Tel (210) 450-9000 *SIC* 8099

▲ VALERO ENERGY CORP p 1539
1 Valero Way 78249
Tel (210) 345-2000 *SIC* 2911 2869

VALERO ENERGY PARTNERS LP p 1539
1 Valero Way 78249
Tel (210) 345-2000 *SIC* 4612 4613 4789

■ VALERO MARKETING AND SUPPLY CO p 1539
1 Valero Way 78249
Tel (210) 345-2000 *SIC* 5171

■ VALERO REFINING CO (INC) p 1539
1 Valero Way 78249
Tel (210) 345-2000 *SIC* 2911

■ VALERO REFINING CO-CALIFORNIA p 1539
1 Valero Way 78249
Tel (210) 345-2000 *SIC* 2911

■ VALERO REFINING CO-NEW JERSEY p 1539
1 Valero Way 78249
Tel (210) 345-2000 *SIC* 2911 6163

■ VALERO REFINING-NEW ORLEANS LLC p 1539
1 Valero Way 78249
Tel (210) 345-2000 *SIC* 2911

■ VALERO REFINING-TEXAS LP p 1539
1 Valero Way 78249
Tel (210) 345-2000 *SIC* 2911

■ VALERO RENEWABLE FUELS CO LLC p 1539
1 Valero Way 78249
Tel (210) 345-2000 *SIC* 2911

VALERO SERVICES INC p 1539
1 Valero Way 78249
Tel (210) 345-2000 *SIC* 2911 5172 5411

VIA METROPOLITAN TRANSIT p 1554
800 W Myrtle St 78212
Tel (210) 362-2000 *SIC* 4111

VILORE FOODS CO INC p 1557
3838 Medical Dr Ste 207 78229
Tel (210) 509-9496 *SIC* 5149 5169

VISIONWARE INC p 1561
11103 West Ave 78213
Tel (210) 340-3531 *SIC* 5995

VISIONWORKS OF AMERICA INC p 1561
175 E Houston St 78205
Tel (210) 340-3531 *SIC* 5995

■ VITAL SIGNS MN INC p 1562
5859 Farinon Dr Ste 200 78249
Tel (952) 894-7523 *SIC* 3841

VNA AND HOSPICE OF SOUTH TEXAS p 1563
4241 Woodcock Dr Ste A100 78228
Tel (210) 785-5800 *SIC* 8082

VT SAN ANTONIO AEROSPACE INC p 1567
9800 John Saunders Rd 78216
Tel (210) 293-3200 *SIC* 7699

WALKER RESOURCES INC p 1573
1343 Hallmark Dr 78216
Tel (210) 341-6000 *SIC* 7514

■ WELLMED MEDICAL MANAGEMENT INC p 1589
8637 Fredericksburg Rd # 360 78240
Tel (210) 615-9355 *SIC* 8082

WHATABURGER RESTAURANTS LLC p 1604
300 Concord Plaza Dr 78216
Tel (210) 476-6000 *SIC* 5812 6794

WIND RIVER GROUP PT LLC p 1615
608 Sandau Rd 78216
Tel (210) 564-0100 *SIC* 8051

YANTIS CORP p 1635
3611 Paesanos Pkwy # 300 78231
Tel (210) 655-3780
SIC 1623 1611 1622 1629 6552 1521

YOUGHIOGHENY COMMUNICATIONS-TEXAS LLC p 1637
2118 Fredericksburg Rd 78201
Tel (210) 777-7777 *SIC* 4812

ZACHRY CONSOLIDATED LLC p 1640
527 Logwood Ave 78221
Tel (210) 871-2700
SIC 1611 1622 1623 1629 3241 1442

ZACHRY CONSTRUCTION & MATERIALS INC p 1640
2330 N Loop 1604 W 78248
Tel (210) 479-1027
SIC 1611 1622 1623 1629 1542 3241

ZACHRY CONSTRUCTION CORP p 1640
2330 N Loop 1604 W 78248
Tel (210) 871-2700
SIC 1623 1611 1622 1629 1542

ZACHRY HOLDINGS INC p 1640
527 Logwood Ave 78221
Tel (210) 588-5000
SIC 1541 8711 1629 1623

ZACHRY INDUSTRIAL INC p 1640
527 Logwood Ave 78221
Tel (210) 475-8000 *SIC* 1541 1629

ZACHRY INTERNATIONAL INC p 1640
2330 N Loop 1604 W 78248
Tel (210) 871-2700 *SIC* 1541 1542

SAN AUGUSTINE, TX

DEEP EAST TEXAS ELECTRIC p 421
880 State Highway 21 E 75972
Tel (936) 275-2314 *SIC* 4911

DEEP EAST TEXAS ELECTRIC COOPERATIVE INC p 421
U S Hwy 21 E 75972
Tel (936) 275-2314 *SIC* 4911

SAN BENITO, TX

SAN BENITO CONSOLIDATED INDEPENDENT SCHOOL DISTRICT PUBLIC FACILITIES p 1275
240 N Crockett St 78586
Tel (956) 361-6100 *SIC* 8211

SAN ISIDRO, TX

GRAVICK GROUP LLC p 632
4985 Fm 1017 78588
Tel (956) 330-5676 *SIC* 8742 7371 7389

SAN JUAN, TX

RIO FRESH INC p 1235
6504 S Stewart Rd 78589
Tel (956) 787-0023 *SIC* 5148

SPIRIT TRUCK LINES INC p 1359
200 W Nolana 78589
Tel (956) 781-7715 *SIC* 4731

SAN MARCOS, TX

ADVENTIST HEALTH SYSTEM/SUNBELT INC p 27
1301 Wonder World Dr 78666
Tel (512) 353-8979 *SIC* 8062

CFAN CO p 285
1000 Technology Way 78666
Tel (512) 754-3005 *SIC* 3724

GRANDE COMMUNICATIONS NETWORKS LLC p 630
401 Carlson Cir 78666
Tel (512) 878-4000 *SIC* 4841

MCCOY CORP p 927
1350 N Ih 35 78666
Tel (512) 353-5400 *SIC* 5211 5251 5231

SAN MARCOS CONSOLIDATED INDEPENDENT SCHOOL DISTRICT p 1277
501 S Lbj Dr 78666
Tel (512) 393-6700 *SIC* 8211

TELENETWORK PARTNERS LTD p 1434
350 Barnes Dr 78666
Tel (512) 707-3100 *SIC* 4813

TEXAS STATE UNIVERSITY-SAN MARCOS p 1444
601 University Dr 78666
Tel (512) 245-2111 *SIC* 8221

▲THERMON GROUP HOLDINGS INC p 1447
100 Thermon Dr 78666
Tel (512) 396-5801 *SIC* 8711

■THERMON HEAT TRACING SERVICES INC p 1447
100 Thermon Dr 78666
Tel (512) 396-5801 *SIC* 8711

■THERMON HOLDING CORP p 1447
100 Thermon Dr 78666
Tel (512) 396-5801 *SIC* 6719

■THERMON INDUSTRIES INC p 1447
100 Thermon Dr 78666
Tel (512) 396-5801 *SIC* 3643

■THERMON MANUFACTURING CO INC p 1447
100 Thermon Dr 78666
Tel (512) 396-5801 *SIC* 3643 3612

WARREN FUEL CO p 1577
1405 United Dr 78666
Tel (512) 395-8557 *SIC* 5541

SANTA ROSA, TX

RIO GRANDE VALLEY SUGAR GROWERS INC p 1235
2.5 Miles W Hwy 107 78593
Tel (956) 636-1411 *SIC* 2061

SCHERTZ, TX

PSP INDUSTRIES INC p 1188
9885 Doerr Ln 78154
Tel (210) 651-9595
SIC 3533 3531 3564 3532 3559

RNDC TEXAS LLC p 1240
6511 Tri County Pkwy 78154
Tel (210) 224-7531 *SIC* 5182

SCHERTZ-CIBOLO-UNIVERSAL CITY INDEPENDENT SCHOOL DISTRICT p 1286
1060 Elbel Rd 78154
Tel (210) 945-6200 *SIC* 8211

SEABROOK, TX

HOUSTON LBC L P p 712
11666 Port Rd 77586
Tel (281) 474-4433 *SIC* 5171

SEGUIN, TX

■ ALAMO GROUP (USA) INC p 44
1627 E Walnut St 78155
Tel (830) 379-1480 *SIC* 3523

▲ ALAMO GROUP INC p 44
1627 E Walnut St 78155
Tel (830) 379-1480 *SIC* 3523 3531

ALEXANDER OIL CO p 49
2993 N Hwy 123 Byp 78155
Tel (830) 379-1736 *SIC* 5171

■ C M C STEEL FABRICATORS INC p 233
1 Steel Mill Dr 78155
Tel (830) 372-8200 *SIC* 3312 3441

GUADALUPE REGIONAL MEDICAL CENTER p 644
1215 E Court St 78155
Tel (830) 379-2411 *SIC* 8062

GUADALUPE-BLANCO RIVER AUTHORITY INDUSTRIAL DEVELOPMENT CORP p 644
933 E Court St 78155
Tel (361) 575-6366 *SIC* 4911 4941 4952

RANDOLPH-BROOKS FEDERAL CREDIT UNION p 1208
1600 E Court St 78155
Tel (210) 945-3300 *SIC* 6061

SEGUIN INDEPENDENT SCHOOL DISTRICT p 1300
1221 E Kingsbury St 78155
Tel (830) 372-5771 *SIC* 8211

■ STRUCTURAL METALS INC p 1394
1 Steel Mill Dr 78155
Tel (830) 372-8200 *SIC* 3312 3441 3462

SELMA, TX

SPAW GLASS CONTRACTORS INC p 1355
9331 Corporate Dr 78154
Tel (210) 651-9000 *SIC* 1522

SPAW GLASS HOLDING LP p 1355
9331 Corporate Dr 78154
Tel (210) 651-9000 *SIC* 1542 1522 1541

SHENANDOAH, TX

■ KROGER TEXAS LP p 830
19245 David Memorial Dr 77385
Tel (713) 507-4800 *SIC* 5141 5411

SHERMAN, TX

AMERICAN BANK OF TEXAS p 68
2011 Texoma Pkwy Ste 101 75090
Tel (903) 893-7555 *SIC* 6022

DOUGLASS DISTRIBUTING RETAIL CO INC p 452
325 E Forest Ave 75090
Tel (903) 893-1181 *SIC* 5411 5541

■ MEMC SOUTHWEST INC p 941
6416 S Us Highway 75 75090
Tel (903) 891-5000 *SIC* 3674

SHERMAN INDEPENDENT SCHOOL DISTRICT p 1316
2701 N Loy Lake Rd 75090
Tel (903) 891-6400 *SIC* 8211

SHERMAN/GRAYSON HOSPITAL LLC p 1316
500 N Highland Ave 75092
Tel (903) 870-4611 *SIC* 8011

W DOUGLASS DISTRIBUTING LTD p 1568
325 E Forest Ave 75090
Tel (903) 893-1181 *SIC* 5812

SHINER, TX

KASPAR WIRE WORKS INC p 804
959 State Highway 95 N 77984
Tel (361) 594-3327 *SIC* 3496

SILVERTON, TX

CITY BANK p 312
500 Main St 79257
Tel (806) 823-2426 *SIC* 6022

SNYDER, TX

GLOBE ENERGY SERVICES LLC p 618
3204 W Highway 180 79549
Tel (325) 573-1310 SIC 1382

■ PATTERSON-UTI DRILLING SERVICES LP LLLP p 1121
4500 Lamesa Hwy 79549
Tel (325) 573-1104 SIC 1381

SOUTHLAKE, TX

AMERICAN TRAILER WORKS INC p 80
180 State St Ste 230 76092
Tel (817) 328-3686 SIC 3715

ANCOR HOLDINGS LP p 89
100 Throckmorton St St Ste 1600 76092
Tel (817) 877-4458 SIC 8741 8742

BLOOMFIELD HOMES LP p 190
1050 E State Hwy Ste 210 76092
Tel (817) 416-1572 SIC 1521

DARR EQUIPMENT LP p 412
350 Bank St 76092
Tel (254) 420-2650
SIC 5084 7353 5013 4959

■ DEL FRISCOS GRILLE OF TEXAS LLC p 423
1200 E Southlake Blvd 76092
Tel (817) 410-3777 SIC 5812 5813

■ DEL FRISCOS OF NORTH CAROLINA INC p 423
930 S Kimball Ave 76092
Tel (817) 601-3421 SIC 5812

▲ DEL FRISCOS RESTAURANT GROUP INC p 423
920 S Kimball Ave Ste 100 76092
Tel (817) 601-3421 SIC 5812 5813

▲ EMERGE ENERGY SERVICES LP p 491
180 State St Ste 225 76092
Tel (817) 865-5830 SIC 1311 1389 4613

FLOORS INC p 557
200 Bank St 76092
Tel (817) 421-8787 SIC 5023 5713

GATEWAY CHURCH p 593
500 S Nolen Dr Ste 300 76092
Tel (817) 328-1000 SIC 8661

INSIGHT EQUITY A P X L P p 746
1400 Civic Pl Ste 250 76092
Tel (817) 488-7775
SIC 6722 3441 3443 3556 3714 5171

INSIGHT EQUITY ACQUISITION CO LLC p 746
1400 Civic Pl Ste 250 76092
Tel (817) 354-2715
SIC 2911 6722 3851 3441

INSIGHT EQUITY HOLDINGS LLC p 746
1400 Civic Pl Ste 250 76092
Tel (817) 488-7775
SIC 6726 3851 2911 3441

INSIGHT EQUITY LP p 746
1400 Civic Pl Ste 250 76092
Tel (817) 488-7775
SIC 6722 3441 3443 3556 3714 5171

PROPHET EQUITY LP p 1184
1460 Main St Ste 200 76092
Tel (817) 898-1500 SIC 6282

▲ SABRE CORP p 1264
3150 Sabre Dr 76092
Tel (682) 605-1000 SIC 4724 7375

■ SABRE GLBL INC p 1264
3150 Sabre Dr 76092
Tel (682) 605-1000
SIC 7375 7371 7374 7389 8748

■ SABRE HOLDINGS CORP p 1264
3150 Sabre Dr 76092
Tel (682) 605-1000 SIC 4724

VICNRG LLC p 1555
930 S Kimball Ave Ste 100 76092
Tel (817) 562-4888 SIC 5172

SPRING, TX

APPLIED MACHINERY CORP p 99
20105 Krahn Rd 77388
Tel (281) 821-0700 SIC 3533

ATP OIL & GAS CORP p 128
26219 Oak Ridge Dr 77380
Tel (713) 622-3311 SIC 1311 1382

■ CONTINENTAL ALLOYS & SERVICES INC p 362
18334 Stuebner Airline Rd 77379
Tel (281) 376-9600 SIC 5051

ECO SERVICES OPERATIONS LLC p 475
2002 Timberloch Pl # 300 77380
Tel (800) 642-4200 SIC 2819

■ EGS HOLDINGS INC p 481
2001 Timberloch Pl 77380
Tel (409) 981-2000 SIC 4911 4924

ELECTRA LINK INC p 484
21755 Interstate 45 # 10 77388
Tel (281) 350-6096 SIC 1623

■ EXXONMOBIL CHEMICAL CO p 521
22777 Sprngwoods Vlg Pkwy 77389
Tel (281) 834-5200 SIC 2821

■ EXXONMOBIL PIPELINE CO p 521
22777 Sprngwoods Vlg Pkwy 77389
Tel (713) 656-3636 SIC 4612 4613 2911

■ EXXONMOBIL SALES AND SUPPLY LLC p 521
22777 Sprngwoods Vlg Pkwy 77389
Tel (800) 243-9966 SIC 2911

■ EXXONMOBIL SAUDI ARABIA INC p 522
22777 Sprngwoods Vlg Pkwy 77389
Tel (281) 288-4545 SIC 4213

ICI CONSTRUCTION INC p 727
24715 W Hardy Rd 77373
Tel (281) 355-5151 SIC 1542

■ ICO - SCHULMAN LLC p 727
24624 Interstate 45 77386
Tel (832) 663-3131 SIC 2821

▲ INTEGRATED DRILLING EQUIPMENT HOLDINGS CORP p 749
25311 I 45 N Bldg 6 77380
Tel (281) 465-9393 SIC 3533 7539 5084

■ KERR-MCGEE CORP p 813
1201 Lake Robbins Dr 77380
Tel (832) 636-1000
SIC 2816 2819 1311 1221 1222

KINGSLEY CONSTRUCTORS INC p 821
25250 Borough Park Dr # 106 77380
Tel (281) 363-1979 SIC 1623 1611

KLEIN INDEPENDENT SCHOOL DISTRICT p 823
7200 Spring Cypress Rd 77379
Tel (832) 249-4000 SIC 8211

■ MOBIL EXPLORATION & PRODUCING US INC p 980
22777 Sprngwoods Vlg Pkwy 77389
Tel (281) 288-4545 SIC 5541

■ MOBIL INTERNATIONAL PETROLEUM CORP p 980
22777 Sprngwoods Vlg Pkwy 77389
Tel (281) 288-4545 SIC 2911

■ MOBIL PETROLEUM CO INC p 980
22777 Sprngwoods Vlg Pkwy 77389
Tel (703) 846-3000 SIC 2911

NHM COMMUNITY COLLEGE DISTRICT p 1042
5000 Research Forest Dr 77381
Tel (832) 813-6500 SIC 8222

■ PHYSICIAN RELIANCE NETWORK INC p 1145
10101 Woodloch Forest Dr 77380
Tel (281) 863-1000 SIC 8741

■ RTI ENERGY SYSTEMS INC p 1256
7211 Spring Cypress Rd 77379
Tel (281) 379-4289 SIC 3533 3498

SEALTECH INC p 1296
28420 Hardy Toll Rd # 220 77373
Tel (281) 475-4770 SIC 5169

▲ SOUTHWESTERN ENERGY CO INC p 1353
10000 Energy Dr 77389
Tel (832) 796-1000 SIC 1311 1382

TALENTNET INC p 1422
2219 Sawdust Rd Ste 603 77380
Tel (844) 825-3686 SIC 7361

TALISMAN ENERGY USA INC p 1422
2445 Tech Forest Blvd # 1200 77381
Tel (281) 210-2100 SIC 1311

■ TETRA APPLIED TECHNOLOGIES INC p 1441
24955 Interstate 45 77380
Tel (281) 367-1983 SIC 1389

SPRINGTOWN, TX

SHOW SERVICES LLC p 1318
920 E Highway 199 76082
Tel (800) 737-8757 SIC 7389

SPRING, TX

WORLD CLASS AUTOMOTIVE GROUP LP p 1625
20403 Interstate 45 77388
Tel (281) 719-3700 SIC 5511

STAFFORD, TX

CASTLES OF WORLD INC p 264
11150 Cash Rd 77477
Tel (281) 269-2600 SIC 4724

EADS DISTRIBUTION LLC p 467
13843 N Promenade Blvd 77477
Tel (281) 243-2900 SIC 5085

GLEN GEO ENTERPRISES INC p 614
13395 Murphy Rd 77477
Tel (281) 242-6945 SIC 1799 5198 5084

GOLDEN MAX LLC p 621
12701 Directors Dr 77477
Tel (832) 886-5300 SIC 5047

■ IES RESIDENTIAL INC p 730
10203 Mula Cir 77477
Tel (281) 498-2212 SIC 1731

KITZ CORP OF AMERICA p 822
10750 Corporate Dr 77477
Tel (281) 491-7333 SIC 5085

LEEDO MANUFACTURING CO LP p 852
10707 Corp Dr Ste 250 77477
Tel (866) 465-3336 SIC 2434

MAINTENANCE SUPPLY HEADQUARTERS LP p 898
12315 Parc Crest Dr # 100 77477
Tel (281) 530-6300 SIC 5072

■ PLANT PERFORMANCE SERVICES LLC p 1154
4800 Sugar Grove Blvd # 450 77477
Tel (832) 532-5600 SIC 1731 1799 7699

PUFFER-SWEIVEN HOLDINGS INC p 1191
4230 Greenbriar Dr 77477
Tel (281) 240-2000 SIC 5084

REDI-CARPET INC p 1217
10225 Mula Rd Ste 120 77477
Tel (832) 310-2000 SIC 5023

STEPHENVILLE, TX

TARLETON STATE UNIVERSITY p 1425
1333 W Washington St 76401
Tel (254) 968-9107 SIC 8221

SUGAR LAND, TX

▲ APPLIED OPTOELECTRONICS INC p 100
13139 Jess Pirtle Blvd 77478
Tel (281) 295-1800 SIC 3674 3827 3699

APPLUS RTD USA INC p 100
3 Sugar Creek Center Blvd # 600 77478
Tel (832) 295-5000 SIC 7389

■ BAKER PETROLITE LLC p 146
12645 W Airport Blvd 77478
Tel (281) 276-5400 SIC 2899 2869

C & C NORTH AMERICA INC p 231
2245 Texas Dr Ste 600 77479
Tel (281) 207-4461 SIC 5032

■ COFFEYVILLE RESOURCES LLC p 334
2277 Plaza Dr Ste 500 77479
Tel (281) 207-3200 SIC 2911

■ COFFEYVILLE RESOURCES REFINING & MARKETING LLC p 334
2277 Plaza Dr Ste 500 77479
Tel (281) 207-3200 SIC 2911

▲ CVR ENERGY INC p 404
2277 Plaza Dr Ste 500 77479
Tel (281) 207-3200 SIC 2911 2873

■ CVR PARTNERS LP p 404
2277 Plaza Dr Ste 500 77479
Tel (281) 207-3200 SIC 2873

■ CVR REFINING HOLDINGS LLC p 404
2277 Plaza Dr Ste 500 77479
Tel (281) 207-3200 SIC 2911 4612

■ CVR REFINING LLC p 404
2277 Plaza Dr Ste 500 77479
Tel (281) 207-3200 SIC 2911

■ CVR REFINING LP p 404
2277 Plaza Dr Ste 500 77479
Tel (281) 207-3200 SIC 2911 4612

E E REED CONSTRUCTION LP p 466
333 Commerce Green Blvd 77478
Tel (281) 933-4000 SIC 1542

FAIRFIELD INDUSTRIES INC p 525
1111 Gillingham Ln 77478
Tel (281) 275-7627
SIC 7374 3829 1382 3429

FORT BEND INDEPENDENT SCHOOL DISTRICT p 568
16431 Lexington Blvd 77479
Tel (281) 634-1000 SIC 8211

FRONTIER DRILLING USA INC p 581
13135 Dairy Ashford Rd # 800 77478
Tel (713) 481-7500 SIC 1381

GAS UNLIMITED INC p 593
2277 Plaza Dr Ste 270 77479
Tel (281) 295-5600 SIC 7363

■ GE OIL & GAS LOGGING SERVICES INC p 596
13000 Executive Dr 77478
Tel (281) 579-9879 SIC 1389 4789

HERCULES FILMS LLC p 685
12600 Cardinal Mdw 77478
Tel (920) 284-0796 SIC 3081 5199

HOUSTON FOODS INC p 712
4415 Highway 6 77478
Tel (281) 201-2700 SIC 5812

IMPERIAL SUGAR CO p 734
3 Sugar Creek Center Blvd # 500 77478
Tel (281) 491-9181 SIC 2062 5149

LIBERTYTOWN USA 2 INC p 863
13131 Dairy Ashford Rd # 230 77478
Tel (832) 295-5024 SIC 6719

MEGLOBAL AMERICAS INC p 940
2150 Town Square Pl # 750 77479
Tel (844) 634-5622 SIC 5169

MONEY MANAGEMENT INTERNATIONAL INC p 984
14141 Southwest Fwy # 1000 77478
Tel (713) 923-2227 SIC 7389

■ NALCO CHAMPION LLC p 1006
7705 Highway 90a 77478
Tel (713) 627-3303 SIC 2819

■ NALCO ENERGY SERVICES LP p 1007
7705 Highway 90a 77478
Tel (281) 263-7000 SIC 2899

NOBLE DRILLING (US) INC p 1046
13135 Dry Ashfd 800 77478
Tel (281) 276-6100 SIC 1381

NOBLE DRILLING CORP p 1046
13135 Dairy Ashford Rd # 700 77478
Tel (281) 276-6100 SIC 1381 8711

NOBLE DRILLING HOLDING LLC p 1046
13135 Dairy Ashford Rd # 700 77478
Tel (281) 276-6100 SIC 1381

NOBLE DRILLING SERVICES INC p 1046
13135 Dairy Ashford Rd # 800 77478
Tel (281) 276-6100 SIC 3541

NOBLE HOLDING (US) CORP p 1046
3135 S Dairy Ashford Ste 800 77478
Tel (281) 276-6100 SIC 1381

PHYSICANS AT SUGAR CREEK p 1145
14023 Southwest Fwy 77478
Tel (281) 325-4100 SIC 8011

PRIME COMMUNICATIONS LP p 1174
12550 Reed Rd Ste 100 77478
Tel (281) 240-7800 SIC 4812

SCHLUMBERGER TECHNOLOGY CORP p 1287
100 Gillingham Ln 77478
Tel (281) 285-8500
SIC 1382 1389 3825 3824 3533 3586

SPRINT WASTE SERVICES LP p 1361
16011 W Bellfort St 77498
Tel (281) 491-7775 SIC 5093 4953

SULZER US HOLDING INC p 1397
2277 Plaza Dr Ste 600 77479
Tel (832) 886-2299 SIC 7699 3594

▲ TEAM INC p 1430
13131 Dar Ashford Ste 600 77478
Tel (281) 331-6154 SIC 7389 7699

TRAMONTINA USA INC p 1469
12955 W Airport Blvd 77478
Tel (281) 340-8400 SIC 5046 5072 5085

▲ TRECORA RESOURCES p 1475
1650 Highway 6 Ste 190 77478
Tel (409) 385-8300 SIC 2911

■ WESTERN CONTAINER CORP p 1597
2150 Town Square Pl # 400 77479
Tel (281) 302-4314 SIC 3085

WHOLESOME SWEETENERS INC p 1607
14141 Southwest Fwy # 160 77478
Tel (281) 275-3199 SIC 5141

SULPHUR SPRINGS, TX

GSC ENTERPRISES INC p 643
130 Hillcrest Dr 75482
Tel (903) 885-7621 SIC 5141 6099

PINNACLE COMPANIES INC p 1149
903 Interstate Hwy 30 E 75482
Tel (903) 885-6772 SIC 5082

SUMNER, TX

LOAD TRAIL LLC p 872
220 Farm Road 2216 75486
Tel (903) 783-3900 SIC 3799

PJ TRAILERS INC p 1153
1807 Farm Road 2352 75486
Tel (903) 785-6879 SIC 3715

PJ TRAILERS MANUFACTURING INC p 1153
1807 Farm Road 2352 75486
Tel (903) 785-6879 SIC 3799

SWEETWATER, TX

LUDLUM MEASUREMENTS INC p 884
501 Oak St 79556
Tel (325) 235-5494
SIC 3829 3826 3824 3823

MAL ENTERPRISES INC p 899
300 Hailey St 79556
Tel (325) 236-6351 SIC 5411

TEMPLE, TX

DELTA CENTRIFUGAL CORP p 426
3402 Center St 76504
Tel (254) 773-9055 SIC 5051 3325 3369

FIKES WHOLESALE INC p 542
6261 Central Pointe Pkwy 76504
Tel (254) 791-0009 SIC 5411 5171

GIRLING HEALTH CENTER p 613
1920 Birdcreek Dr 76502
Tel (254) 778-4210 SIC 8082

■ MCLANE CO INC p 930
4747 Mclane Pkwy 76504
Tel (254) 771-7500
SIC 5141 5149 5311 5113

■ MCLANE/SOUTHERN CALIFORNIA INC p 931
4472 Georgia Blvd 76504
Tel (909) 887-7500 SIC 5141

■ MCLANE/SUNEAST INC p 931
4747 Mclane Pkwy 76504
Tel (254) 771-7500 SIC 5141

MW BUILDERS INC p 1003
1701 N General Bruce Dr 76504
Tel (254) 778-4241 SIC 1542

SCOTT & WHITE CLINIC p 1293
2401 S 31st St 76508
Tel (254) 724-2111 SIC 8062

SCOTT & WHITE MEMORIAL HOSPITAL p 1293
2401 S 31st St 76508
Tel (254) 724-2111
SIC 8062 6512 7352 7363

TEMPLE INDEPENDENT SCHOOL DISTRICT p 1436
200 N 23rd St 76504
Tel (254) 215-7513 SIC 8211 8299

TEXAS HYDRAULICS INC p 1443
3410 Range Rd 76504
Tel (254) 778-4701 SIC 3593 3443

■ TRANSCO INC p 1471
4747 Mclane Pkwy 76504
Tel (254) 771-7500 SIC 4213

WILSONART INTERNATIONAL HOLDINGS LLC p 1614
2400 Wilson Pl 76504
Tel (254) 207-7000 SIC 2541

■ WILSONART INTERNATIONAL INC p 1614
2501 Wilsonart Dr 76503
Tel (254) 207-7000 SIC 2821 2541

WILSONART LLC p 1614
2501 Wilsonart Dr 76504
Tel (254) 207-7000 SIC 2541

TERRELL, TX

AMERICAN NATIONAL BANK OF TEXAS p 77
102 W Moore Ave Lbby 75160
Tel (972) 524-3411 SIC 6021

ANB CORP p 89
102 W Moore Ave Lbby Lbby 75160
Tel (972) 563-2611 SIC 6712

ANB HOLDING CO LTD p 89
102 W Moore Ave 75160
Tel (972) 524-3411 SIC 6712

MADIX INC p 894
500 Airport Rd 75160
Tel (214) 515-5400 SIC 2542 2541

RANDALL NOE CHRYSLER DODGE LLP p 1207
1608 W Moore Ave 75160
Tel (972) 524-3775 SIC 5511

RANDALL NOE FORD-MERCURY INC p 1207
1608 W Moore Ave 75160
Tel (972) 524-3775 SIC 5511 5521

TEXARKANA, TX

BRIM HEALTHCARE OF TEXAS LLC p 213
1000 Pine St 75501
Tel (903) 798-8000 SIC 8062

CHRISTUS HEALTH ARK-LA-TEX p 303
2600 Saint Michael Dr 75503
Tel (903) 614-1000 SIC 8062

E-Z MART STORES INC p 467
602 Falvey Ave 75501
Tel (903) 832-6502 SIC 5541 5411

JST ENTERPRISES p 796
5120 Summerhill Rd 75503
Tel (903) 794-3743 SIC 8741

LIBERTY-EYLAU INDEPENDENT SCHOOL DISTRICT p 863
2901 Leopard Dr 75501
Tel (903) 832-1535 SIC 8211

TRUMAN ARNOLD COMPANIES p 1486
701 S Robison Rd 75501
Tel (903) 794-3835 SIC 5172 4581

WADLEY REGIONAL MEDICAL CENTER p 1571
1000 Pine St 75501
Tel (903) 798-8000 SIC 8062

WHOLESALE ELECTRIC SUPPLY CO INC p 1607
1400 Waterall St 75501
Tel (903) 794-3404 SIC 5063

TEXAS CITY, TX

DEL PAPA DISTRIBUTING CO LP p 423
120 Gulf Fwy 77591
Tel (409) 842-5215 SIC 5181

THE COLONY, TX

ACPRODUCTS INC p 18
3551 Plano Pkwy 75056
Tel (214) 469-3000 SIC 2434

▲ QUEST RESOURCE HOLDING CORP p 1199
3481 Plano Pkwy 75056
Tel (972) 464-0004 SIC 4953

THE WOODLANDS, TX

ACCELERATED PRODUCTION SERVICES INC p 14
1585 Sawdust Rd Ste 210 77380
Tel (281) 403-5793 SIC 1389

AIM GROUP INC p 38
9450 Grogans Mill Rd # 120 77380
Tel (281) 847-2000 SIC 8711

AMERICAS STYRENICS LLC p 81
24 Waterway Ave Ste 1200 77380
Tel (832) 616-7800 SIC 2821 2865

■ ANADARKO E&P ONSHORE LLC p 88
1201 Lake Robbins Dr 77380
Tel (832) 636-1000 SIC 2911

▲ ANADARKO PETROLEUM CORP p 88
1201 Lake Robbins Dr 77380
Tel (832) 636-1000
SIC 1311 4924 5171 1382

ARENA ENERGY LP p 106
4200 Res Frest Dr Ste 500 77381
Tel (281) 681-9500 SIC 1311

BENCHMARK HOSPITALITY INC p 172
4 Waterway Square Pl # 300 77380
Tel (281) 367-5757 SIC 8741 5046

BLUELINE RENTAL LLC p 193
8401 New Trils Dr Ste 150 77381
Tel (832) 299-7515 SIC 7353 4789

CB&I LLC p 268
2103 Research Forest Dr 77380
Tel (832) 513-1000 SIC 1791 3443 3312

■ CHART ENERGY & CHEMICALS INC p 290
8665 New Trils Dr Ste 100 77381
Tel (281) 364-8700 SIC 3443

CHEVRON PHILLIPS CHEMICAL CO LLC p 296
10001 Six Pines Dr 77380
Tel (832) 813-4100 SIC 2821

CHEVRON PHILLIPS CHEMICAL CO LP p 296
10001 Six Pines Dr 77380
Tel (832) 813-4100
SIC 5169 3292 3089 3084 3432 2911

CHICAGO BRIDGE & IRON CO p 297
2103 Research Forest Dr 77380
Tel (832) 513-1000 SIC 1791

CHICAGO BRIDGE & IRON CO p 297
2103 Research Forest Dr 77380
Tel (832) 513-1000 SIC 8711

CHICAGO BRIDGE & IRON CO (DELAWARE) p 297
2103 Research Forest Dr 77380
Tel (832) 513-1000 SIC 8711 3325 3462

■ CONN APPLIANCES INC p 356
4055 Technology Frst 77381
Tel (409) 832-1696
SIC 5722 5731 7629 6141 7359

▲ CONNS INC p 358
4055 Technology Frst 77381
Tel (936) 230-5899
SIC 5722 5731 5261 5712

■ CUDD PRESSURE CONTROL INC p 400
2828 Tech Forest Blvd 77381
Tel (832) 295-5555 SIC 1389

ENERGY ALLOYS LLC p 497
3 Waterway Square Pl # 600 77380
Tel (832) 601-5800 SIC 5051

FK DELLIA LLC p 553
25025 North Fwy I45210 77380
Tel (817) 546-3358 SIC 1389

H M T TANK SERVICE INC p 650
24 Waterway Ave Ste 400 77380
Tel (281) 681-7000 SIC 1799

HMT INC p 698
24 Waterway Ave Ste 400 77380
Tel (281) 681-7000
SIC 7699 3443 7389 1791

■ HUNTSMAN ADVANCED MATERIALS AMERICAS LLC p 720
10003 Woodloch Forest Dr # 260 77380
Tel (281) 719-6000 SIC 2899

▲ HUNTSMAN CORP p 720
10003 Woodloch Forest Dr # 260 77380
Tel (281) 719-6000
SIC 2821 3081 2869 2816 2865

■ HUNTSMAN INTERNATIONAL LLC p 720
1003 Woodloch Forest Dr 77380
Tel (281) 719-6000
SIC 2821 3081 2869 2816 2865

■ HUNTSMAN INTERNATIONAL TRADING CORP p 720
10003 Woodloch Forest Dr # 260 77380
Tel (281) 719-6000 SIC 5169

■ INDEPENDENCE OILFIELD CHEMICALS LLC p 736
1450 Lake Robbins Dr # 400 77380
Tel (713) 936-4340 SIC 2899 5169

■ ISG INFORMATION SERVICES GROUP AMERICAS INC p 766
25025 N I 45 Ste 225 77380
Tel (281) 465-5700 SIC 7379

▲ LAYNE CHRISTENSEN CO p 848
1800 Hughes Landing Blvd 77380
Tel (281) 475-2600
SIC 1781 1623 5084 1481 8748

▲ LEXICON PHARMACEUTICALS INC p 859
8800 Technology Forest Pl 77381
Tel (281) 863-3000 SIC 2834

▲ LGI HOMES INC p 860
1450 Lake Robbins Dr # 430 77380
Tel (281) 362-8998 SIC 1531

LONE STAR COLLEGE SYSTEM p 875
5000 Research Forest Dr 77381
Tel (832) 813-6500 SIC 8222

■ MCC HOLDINGS INC p 926
4526 Res Frest Dr Ste 400 77381
Tel (936) 271-6500 SIC 3491 7699

▲ NEWFIELD EXPLORATION CO p 1037
4 Waterway Square Pl # 100 77380
Tel (281) 210-5100 SIC 1311

■ NEWPARK MATS & INTEGRATED SERVICES LLC p 1038
9320 Lkeside Blvd Ste 100 77381
Tel (281) 362-6800 SIC 1389

▲ NEWPARK RESOURCES INC p 1038
9320 Lkeside Blvd Ste 100 77381
Tel (281) 362-6800
SIC 1389 4959 4953 2273

■ NEXEO SOLUTIONS HOLDINGS LLC p 1039
3 Waterway Square Pl # 1000 77380
Tel (281) 297-0700 SIC 5169 5162

▲ NEXEO SOLUTIONS INC p 1040
3 Waterway Square Pl # 1000 77380
Tel (281) 297-0700 SIC 6799

■ NEXEO SOLUTIONS LLC p 1040
3 Waterway Square Pl # 1000 77380
Tel (281) 297-0700 SIC 5169 5162 2821

OXBOW SULPHUR INC p 1100
1450 Lake Robbins Dr # 500 77380
Tel (281) 907-9500 SIC 5191 5169

PETROLEUM WHOLESALE LP p 1139
8550 Technology Forest Pl 77381
Tel (281) 681-7500 SIC 5172 5541

REPSOL ENERGY NORTH AMERICA CORP p 1225
2455 Tech Forest Blvd 77381
Tel (832) 442-1000 SIC 1321

REPSOL SERVICES CO p 1225
2455 Tech Forest Blvd 77381
Tel (832) 442-1000 SIC 1382

SAVANNA ENERGY SERVICES (USA) CORP p 1284
2445 Technology Ste 200 77381
Tel (281) 907-4800 SIC 1381 1389

SHRIEVE CHEMICAL CO p 1319
1755 Woodstead Ct 77380
Tel (281) 367-4226 SIC 5169

ST LUKES COMMUNITY HEALTH SERVICES p 1370
17200 St Lukes Way 77384
Tel (936) 266-2000 SIC 8011 8062

▲ STERLING CONSTRUCTION CO INC p 1387
1800 Hughes Landing Blvd # 250 77380
Tel (281) 214-0800 SIC 1611 1622 1623

STRIKE LLC p 1393
1800 Hughes Landing Blvd # 500 77380
Tel (713) 389-2400 SIC 1623

▲ SUMMIT MIDSTREAM PARTNERS LP p 1399
1790 Hughes 77380
Tel (832) 413-4770 SIC 4922

▲ TETRA TECHNOLOGIES INC p 1441
24955 Interstate 45 77380
Tel (281) 367-1983 SIC 2819 1389

■ US ONCOLOGY HOLDINGS INC p 1532
10101 Woodloch Forest Dr 77380
Tel (281) 863-1000 SIC 8093 8099 8011

■ US ONCOLOGY INC p 1532
10101 Woodloch Forest Dr 77380
Tel (800) 381-2637 SIC 8093 8099 8011

USER FRIENDLY PHONE BOOK LLC p 1535
10200 Grogans Mill Rd # 440 77380
Tel (281) 465-5400 SIC 2741

VICTORY HOSPITAL PROPERTIES LLC p 1556
2201 Timberloch Pl # 200 77380
Tel (281) 863-2100 SIC 8062

VICTORY PARENT CO LLC p 1556
2201 Timberloch Pl # 200 77380
Tel (281) 863-2100 SIC 8062

VOLGA DNEPR - UNIQUE AIR CARGO INC p 1564
9400 Grogans Mill Rd 77380
Tel (832) 585-8611 SIC 4522

WEBBER LLC p 1586
9303 New Trils Dr Ste 200 77381
Tel (281) 372-0274 SIC 1611

■ WESTERN GAS EQUITY PARTNERS LP p 1598
1201 Lake Robbins Dr 77380
Tel (832) 636-6000 SIC 1311

■ WESTERN GAS PARTNERS LP p 1598
1201 Lake Robbins Dr 77380
Tel (832) 636-6000 SIC 4923 4924 4922

WOODFOREST FINANCIAL GROUP INC p 1623
1330 Lake Robbins Dr # 150 77380
Tel (832) 375-2000 SIC 6021

WOODFOREST NATIONAL BANK p 1623
25231 Grogans Mill Rd # 175 77380
Tel (713) 455-7000 SIC 6021

■ WOODLANDS OPERATING CO L P p 1623
24 Waterway Ave Ste 1100 77380
Tel (281) 719-6100
SIC 6552 7997 7389 6513 6512

■ XOMOX CORP p 1632
4526 Res Frest Dr Ste 400 77381
Tel (936) 271-6500 SIC 3491 3593 3494

TOMBALL, TX

ACCENT PACKAGING INC p 14
10131 Fm 2920 Rd 77375
Tel (281) 251-3700 SIC 5051 5084 5085

FOREST TOMBALL PRODUCTS INC p 567
16801 Fm 2920 Rd 77377
Tel (281) 357-8196 SIC 5083 5211 5031

NRG MANUFACTURING INC p 1064
11311 Holderrieth Rd # 100 77375
Tel (281) 320-2525 SIC 3449 3441

PARKWAY CHEVROLET INC p 1117
25500 State Highway 249 77375
Tel (281) 351-8211 SIC 5511 7549 5531

TOMBALL HOSPITAL AUTHORITY p 1459
605 Holderrieth Blvd 77375
Tel (281) 351-1623 SIC 8062

TOMBALL INDEPENDENT SCHOOL DISTRICT p 1459
310 S Cherry St 77375
Tel (281) 357-3100 SIC 8211

TOMBALL TEXAS HOSPITAL CO LLC p 1459
605 Holderrieth Blvd 77375
Tel (281) 401-7500 SIC 8062

TROY, TX

ANDERTON CASTINGS LLC p 90
222 Lely Dr 76579
Tel (254) 938-2541 SIC 3465

TYLER, TX

BROOKSHIRE GROCERY CO INC p 218
1600 W Southwest Loop 323 75701
Tel (903) 534-3000 SIC 5411 5983

CAVENDER STORES LTD p 267
7820 S Broadway Ave 75703
Tel (903) 509-9509 SIC 5699 5661

CHRISTUS TRINITY MOTHER FRANCES HEALTH SYSTEM p 304
800 E Dawson St 75701
Tel (903) 593-8441 SIC 8062

COX SOUTHWEST HOLDINGS LP p 386
3015 S Southeast Loop 323 75701
Tel (903) 595-3701 SIC 4841

EAST TEXAS MEDICAL CENTER p 471
1000 S Beckham Ave 75701
Tel (903) 597-0351 SIC 8062 8011

EAST TEXAS MEDICAL CENTER REGIONAL HEALTH SERVICES INC p 471
1000 S Beckham Ave 75701
Tel (903) 597-0351 SIC 8062

EAST TEXAS MEDICAL CENTER REGIONAL HEALTHCARE SYST p 471
1000 S Beckham Ave 75701
Tel (866) 333-3862 SIC 8062 8741

EAST TEXAS SPECIALTY HOSP p 471
1000 S Beckham Ave Fl 5 75701
Tel (903) 596-3600 SIC 8062

HEIGHTS OF TYLER p 681
2650 Elkton Trl 75703
Tel (903) 266-7200 SIC 8322

JOHN SOULES FOODS INC p 789
10150 Fm 14 75706
Tel (903) 592-9800 SIC 2013 2015 5147

MCWANE INC p 933
11910 County Road 492 75706
Tel (800) 527-8478 SIC 3321

MEWBOURNE HOLDINGS INC p 957
3901 S Broadway Ave 75701
Tel (903) 561-2900 SIC 1311

MEWBOURNE OIL CO p 957
3620 Old Bullard Rd 75701
Tel (903) 561-2900 SIC 1311

MOTHER FRANCES HOSPITAL REGIONAL HEALTH CARE CENTER p 992
800 E Dawson St 75701
Tel (903) 593-8441 SIC 8062

POSADOS CAFE INC p 1163
204 W Main St 75701
Tel (903) 534-1076 SIC 5812

REX-HIDE INC p 1230
705 S Lyons Ave 75702
Tel (903) 593-7387
SIC 3061 3069 2891 6799

▲ SOUTHSIDE BANCSHARES INC p 1351
1201 S Beckham Ave 75701
Tel (903) 531-7111 SIC 6022

■ SOUTHSIDE BANK p 1351
1201 S Beckham Ave 75701
Tel (903) 531-7111 SIC 6022

TORQUED-UP ENERGY SERVICES INC p 1462
110 N College Ave # 1000 75702
Tel (903) 363-0300 SIC 1381

TRINITY MOTHER FRANCES HEALTH SYSTEM FOUNDATION p 1481
800 E Dawson St 75701
Tel (903) 531-5057 SIC 8062

TRINITY MOTHER FRANCIS HEALTH SYSTEM p 1481
910 E Houston St Ste 550 75702
Tel (903) 526-2644 SIC 8011

TYLER INDEPENDENT SCHOOL DISTRICT p 1496
1319 Earl Campbell Pkwy 75701
Tel (903) 262-1000 SIC 8211

UNIVERSAL CABLE HOLDINGS INC p 1516
6151 Paluxy Dr 75703
Tel (330) 872-0462 SIC 4841

UNIVERSITY OF TEXAS AT TYLER p 1526
3900 University Blvd 75799
Tel (903) 566-7000 SIC 8221

UNIVERSITY OF TEXAS HEALTH SCIENCE CENTER AT TYLER p 1526
11937 Us Highway 271 75708
Tel (903) 877-7777 SIC 8062 8221

VALLEY VIEW, TX

ALAN RITCHEY INC p 44
740 S Frontage Rd 76272
Tel (940) 726-3276
SIC 7389 4213 2048 0291

VAN ALSTYNE, TX

GRAYSON-COLLIN ELECTRIC CO-OP INC p 633
902 N Waco St 75495
Tel (903) 482-7100 SIC 4911

VANDERBILT, TX

INDUSTRIAL INDEPENDENT SCHOOL DISTRICT p 740
511 5th St 77991
Tel (361) 284-3226 SIC 8211

VENUS, TX

CHALK MOUNTAIN SERVICES OF TEXAS LLC p 286
2828 Chambers St 76084
Tel (817) 473-1931 SIC 1389

VICTORIA, TX

CITIZENS MEDICAL CENTER p 311
2701 Hospital Dr 77901
Tel (361) 573-9181 SIC 8062

CL THOMAS INC p 320
9701 Us Highway 59 N 77905
Tel (361) 573-7662 SIC 5411 5541

ELITE COMPRESSION SERVICES LLC p 487
10375 Richmond Ave Ste 450 77901
Tel (361) 894-6320 SIC 1389

FIRST VICTORIA NATIONAL BANK p 550
101 S Main St 77901
Tel (361) 573-6321 SIC 6021

FORDYCE LTD p 566
120 S Main St 77901
Tel (361) 573-4309 SIC 1442

GULF COAST PAPER CO INC p 646
3705 Houston Hwy 77901
Tel (361) 852-5252 SIC 5113 5087

MID-COAST ELECTRIC SUPPLY INC p 963
1801 Stolz St 77901
Tel (361) 575-6311 SIC 5063

NEW DISTRIBUTING CO INC p 1029
4102 Us Highway 59 N 77905
Tel (361) 575-1981 SIC 5171

REGENCY INTEGRATED HEALTH SERVICES p 1219
101 W Goodwin Ave Ste 600 77901
Tel (361) 576-0694 SIC 8051

SPEEDY STOP FOOD STORES LLC p 1358
8701 N Navarro St 77904
Tel (361) 573-7662 SIC 5812 5541 5411

THOMAS PETROLEUM LLC p 1449
9701 Us Highway 59 N 77905
Tel (361) 582-5100 SIC 5171 4225

VICTORIA INDEPENDENT SCHOOL DISTRICT p 1555
102 Profit Dr 77901
Tel (361) 576-3131 SIC 8211

VIDOR, TX

ORANGE COUNTY EMERGENCY SERVICES DISTRICT p 1092
2351 Highway 12 77662
Tel (409) 769-6241 SIC 9224

VINTON, TX

W SILVER INC p 1569
9059 Doniphan Dr 79821
Tel (915) 886-3553 SIC 3312 3462

WACO, TX

■ **AMERICAN INCOME LIFE INSURANCE CO INC** p 74
1200 Wooded Acres Dr 76710
Tel (254) 741-5701 SIC 6311

BAYLOR UNIVERSITY p 162
700 S University Parks Dr 76706
Tel (254) 710-1561 SIC 8221

BIG 3 HOLDING CO INC p 181
1625 N Valley Mills Dr 76710
Tel (254) 772-8850 SIC 5511 5571

BRAZOS ELECTRIC POWER COOPERATIVE INC p 209
7616 Bagby Ave 76712
Tel (254) 750-6500 SIC 4911

CENTRAL FREIGHT LINES INC p 278
5601 W Waco Dr 76710
Tel (254) 772-2120 SIC 6719 4213

CENTRAL FREIGHT LINES INC p 278
5601 W Waco Dr 76710
Tel (254) 772-2120 SIC 4212

CITY OF WACO p 319
300 Austin Ave 76701
Tel (254) 750-5600 SIC 9111

DEALERS ELECTRICAL SUPPLY CO p 420
2320 Columbus Ave 76701
Tel (254) 756-7251 SIC 5063 5719

EXTRACO CORP p 521
1700 N Vly Mills Dr Ste 1 76710
Tel (254) 776-0330 SIC 6712

HILLCREST BAPTIST MEDICAL CENTER p 693
100 Hillcrest Med Blvd 76712
Tel (254) 202-8675 SIC 8062

HOBBS BONDED FIBERS LLC p 699
200 Commerce Dr 76710
Tel (254) 741-0040 SIC 2297 2299

HOBBS BONDED FIBERS NA LLC p 699
200 Commerce Dr 76710
Tel (254) 741-0040 SIC 2297 2299

PROVIDENCE HEALTH SERVICES OF WACO p 1186
6901 Medical Pkwy 76712
Tel (254) 751-4000 SIC 8062

TEXAS FARM BUREAU MUTUAL INSURANCE CO p 1443
7420 Fish Pond Rd 76710
Tel (254) 772-3030 SIC 6411

TEXAS LIFE INSURANCE CO p 1444
900 Washington Ave # 400 76701
Tel (254) 752-6521 SIC 6311

TEXAS STATE TECHNICAL COLLEGE p 1444
3801 Campus Dr Bldg 3210 76705
Tel (254) 799-3611 SIC 8221 8222

UNITED AMERICAN ACQUISITION CORP p 1506
3022 Franklin Ave 76710
Tel (859) 987-5389
SIC 2211 0782 3423 2875

WACO INDEPENDENT SCHOOL DISTRICT p 1570
501 Franklin Ave Ofc 76701
Tel (254) 755-9473 SIC 8211

WADSWORTH, TX

STP NUCLEAR OPERATING CO p 1392
8 Miles W Wdsworth Fm 521 77483
Tel (361) 972-3611 SIC 4911

WAELDER, TX

J & B SAUSAGE CO INC p 769
100 Main 78959
Tel (830) 788-7661 SIC 2011 5147 2013

WAXAHACHIE, TX

BAYLOR MEDICAL CENTER AT WAXAHACHIE p 162
1405 W Jefferson St 75165
Tel (972) 923-7000 SIC 8062

MAGNABLEND INC p 896
326 N Grand Ave 75165
Tel (972) 938-2028 SIC 2899

▲ **TANDY BRANDS ACCESSORIES INC** p 1424
501 N College St 75165
Tel (214) 519-5200 SIC 3172 5961

WEATHERFORD, TX

BOOTS SMITH PIPELINE SERVICES LLC p 200
500 Dennis Rd 76087
Tel (601) 682-0761 SIC 1623

BRAZOS ROCK INC p 209
1813 Banks Dr 76087
Tel (817) 594-0772 SIC 1623

■ **C D HARTNETT CO** p 232
302 N Main St 76086
Tel (817) 594-3813 SIC 5141 5122

■ **WEATHERFORD REGIONAL MEDICAL CENTER** p 1586
713 E Anderson St 76086
Tel (682) 582-1000 SIC 8062

WEBSTER, TX

ABC PROFESSIONAL TREE SERVICES INC p 10
201 Flint Ridge Rd 77598
Tel (281) 280-1100 SIC 0783

ALIMAK HEK INC p 50
12552 Galveston Rd Ste A 160 77598
Tel (713) 640-8500
SIC 5084 7699 3535 3534

■ **CHCA CLEAR LAKE LP** p 292
500 W Medical Center Blvd 77598
Tel (281) 332-2511 SIC 8062

■ **CLEAR LAKE REGIONAL MEDICAL CENTER INC** p 324
500 W Medical Center Blvd 77598
Tel (713) 371-5000 SIC 8062

■ **COLT INTERNATIONAL LLC** p 339
300 Flint Ridge Rd 77598
Tel (281) 280-2100 SIC 6411 5172

MCHS - WEBSTER p 929
750 W Texas Ave 77598
Tel (281) 332-3496 SIC 8051

TECHNOLOGY TRANSFER INC p 1432
16969 N Texas Ave Ste 400 77598
Tel (281) 488-7961 SIC 7361 7379

WESTLINK TRADING LLC p 1601
17926 Highway 3 77598
Tel (832) 295-9778
SIC 5032 5099 5074 5051 5031

WESLACO, TX

IDEA PUBLIC SCHOOLS p 729
505 Angelita Dr Ste 9 78599
Tel (956) 377-8000 SIC 8211

KNAPP MEDICAL CENTER p 824
1401 E 8th St 78596
Tel (956) 968-8567 SIC 8011

MID VALLEY HEALTH SYSTEM p 963
1401 E 8th St 78596
Tel (956) 969-5112 SIC 6719

WESLACO INDEPENDENT SCHOOL DISTRICT p 1593
319 W 4th St 78596
Tel (956) 969-6500 SIC 8211

■ **WOODCRAFTERS HOME PRODUCTS HOLDING LLC** p 1622
3700 Camino De Verdad Rd 78596
Tel (956) 647-8300 SIC 2434

■ **WOODCRAFTERS HOME PRODUCTS LLC** p 1622
3700 Camino De Verdad Rd 78596
Tel (956) 565-6329 SIC 2434

WEST LAKE HILLS, TX

■ **BROADWING CORP** p 216
1122 Capital Of Texas Hwy 78746
Tel (512) 742-3700 SIC 3661

EANES INDEPENDENT SCHOOL DISTRICT p 468
601 Camp Craft Rd 78746
Tel (512) 732-9000 SIC 8211

■ **EVERI GAMES HOLDING INC** p 515
206 Wild Basin Rd 78746
Tel (512) 334-7500 SIC 3944

KESTRA FINANCIAL INC p 814
1250 Capital Of Tex 78746
Tel (512) 697-6890 SIC 7389

KESTRA INVESTMENT SERVICES LLC p 814
1250 Capital Of Texas Hwy 78746
Tel (512) 697-6940 SIC 6211

MEYERTONS HOOD KIVLIN KOWERT & GOETZEL P C p 957
1120 S Capital Of Texas 78746
Tel (512) 853-8800 SIC 8011

ORTHOPAEDIC & NEUROLOGICAL REHABILITATION SPEECH PATHOLOGY INC p 1096
1101 S Cpitl Of Texas Hwy 78746
Tel (512) 327-4444 SIC 8049

WESTLAKE, TX

SOLERA HOLDINGS INC p 1338
1301 Solana Blvd Ste 2100 76262
Tel (817) 961-2100 SIC 7371

SOLERA LLC p 1338
1301 Solana Blvd Ste 2100 76262
Tel (817) 961-2100 SIC 7371

SUMMERTIME HOLDING CORP p 1398
1301 Solana Blvd Ste 2100 76262
Tel (817) 961-2100 SIC 6719 7371

WHITE SETTLEMENT, TX

PDX INC p 1125
101 S Jim Wright Fwy # 100 76108
Tel (817) 246-6760 SIC 7371

WICHITA FALLS, TX

CARDIOVASCULAR & THORACIC SURGICAL GROUP OF WICHITA FALLS P A p 253
912 Burnett St 76301
Tel (940) 764-8570 SIC 8011

CITY OF WICHITA FALLS p 319
1300 7th St 76301
Tel (940) 761-7462 SIC 9111

LONE STAR MILK PRODUCERS INC p 876
2716 Commerce St 76301
Tel (817) 781-1194 SIC 5143

MA ACQUISITION CO LLC p 891
501 Galveston St 76301
Tel (940) 397-2100 SIC 6733

PATTERSON AUTO CENTER INC p 1121
315 Central Fwy E 76301
Tel (940) 766-0293 SIC 5511

UNITED ELECTRIC CO LP p 1508
501 Galveston St 76301
Tel (940) 397-2100 SIC 3585

UNITED REGIONAL HEALTH CARE SYSTEM INC p 1511
1600 11th St 76301
Tel (940) 764-3211 SIC 8062

VERNON HOME HEALTH CARE AGENCY INC p 1551
2733 Midwestern Pkwy # 120 76308
Tel (972) 840-3401 SIC 8093 8049 8082

WICHITA FALLS INDEPENDENT SCHOOL DISTRICT p 1607
1104 Broad St 76301
Tel (940) 235-1000 SIC 8211

WILLIS, TX

DIRECTIONAL DRILLING CO LP p 441
11390 Fm 830 Rd 77318
Tel (936) 856-4332 SIC 1381

KONGSBERG POWER PRODUCTS SYSTEMS I INC p 827
300 S Cochran St 77378
Tel (936) 856-2971 SIC 3714

■ **ROBBIN & MEYERS ENERGY SYSTEMS LP** p 1240
10586 N Highway 75 77378
Tel (936) 890-1064 SIC 3491 3533

■ **ROBBINS & MYERS INC** p 1241
10586 N Highway 75 77378
Tel (936) 890-1064
SIC 3533 3443 3823 5084

WOODWAY, TX

MIDWAY INDEPENDENT SCHOOL DISTRICT p 967
13885 Woodway Dr 76712
Tel (254) 761-5610 SIC 8211

WYLIE, TX

BAYCO PRODUCTS INC p 161
640 Sanden Blvd 75098
Tel (214) 342-0288 SIC 5063

NORTH TEXAS MUNICIPAL WATER DISTRICT p 1054
505 E Brown St 75098
Tel (972) 442-5405 SIC 4953 4941

SANDEN INTERNATIONAL (USA) INC p 1278
601 Sanden Blvd 75098
Tel (972) 442-8941
SIC 3714 1711 3585 3563

SANDEN OF AMERICA INC p 1278
601 Sanden Blvd 75098
Tel (972) 442-8400 SIC 3585 3581

WYLIE INDEPENDENT SCHOOL DISTRICT p 1629
951 S Ballard Ave 75098
Tel (972) 442-5444 SIC 8211

YOAKUM, TX

EDDY PACKING CO INC p 477
404 Airport Rd 77995
Tel (361) 580-3800 SIC 2011 2013

UTAH

AMERICAN FORK, UT

ALPINE SCHOOL DISTRICT p 60
575 N 100 E 84003
Tel (801) 610-8400 SIC 8211

MORINDA BIOACTIVES INC p 989
737 E 1180 S 84003
Tel (801) 234-1000 SIC 6719

MORINDA HOLDINGS INC p 989
737 E 1180 S 84003
Tel (801) 234-1000 SIC 5149 8099 3999

■ **PIZZA HUT OF UTAH INC** p 1153
76 N 100 E Ste 3 84003
Tel (801) 756-9696 SIC 5812

SHELF RELIANCE LLC p 1314
691 S Auto Mall Dr 84003
Tel (801) 756-9902 SIC 5021

BOUNTIFUL, UT

CITY FIRST MORTGAGE SERVICES LLC p 312
750 S Main St Ste 104 84010
Tel (801) 299-1770 SIC 6162

DESERET HEALTH GROUP LLC p 432
190 S Main St 84010
Tel (801) 296-5105 SIC 8051

LAKEVIEW HOSPITAL p 840
630 Medical Dr 84010
Tel (801) 292-6231 SIC 8062

BRIGHAM CITY, UT

ASSOCIATED BRIGHAM CONTRACTORS INC p 120
75 N 900 W 84302
Tel (435) 723-8529 SIC 1541 1771

BOX ELDER COUNTY SCHOOL DISTRICT p 204
960 S Main St Ste 1 84302
Tel (435) 734-4800 SIC 8211

HONEYVILLE INC p 705
1080 N Main St Ste 101 84302
Tel (435) 494-4193 SIC 5153

CEDAR CITY, UT

AMERICAN PACIFIC CORP p 77
10622 W 6400 N 84721
Tel (435) 865-5000 SIC 2899

LEAVITT GROUP ENTERPRISES INC p 850
216 S 200 W 84720
Tel (435) 586-1555 SIC 6153 8741 6411

SOUTHERN UTAH UNIVERSITY FOUNDATION p 1351
351 W University Blvd 84720
Tel (435) 586-7700 SIC 8221

CENTERVILLE, UT

MANAGEMENT & TRAINING CORP p 900
500 N Market Place Dr # 100 84014
Tel (801) 693-2600
SIC 8744 8331 7349 8741 8249

CLEARFIELD, UT

■ **ATK SPACE SYSTEMS INC** p 125
Freeport Ctr Bldg A15 84016
Tel (801) 775-1141 SIC 3728 3769

LIFETIME LLC p 865
Freeport Ctr Bldg D-11 84016
Tel (801) 776-1532 SIC 3089

LIFETIME PRODUCTS INC p 865
Freeport Ctr Bldg D-11 84016
Tel (801) 776-1532
SIC 2519 3949 2531 2511

CORINNE, UT

■ **ATK LAUNCH SYSTEMS INC** p 125
9160 N Highway 83 84307
Tel (801) 251-2512 SIC 3764

COTTONWOOD HEIGHTS, UT

TETRA FINANCIAL GROUP LLC p 1441
6995 S Union Park Ctr # 400 84047
Tel (801) 748-2200 SIC 6153

DELTA, UT

INTERMOUNTAIN POWER SERVICE CORP p 753
850 W Brush Wellman Rd 84624
Tel (435) 864-4414 SIC 4911

■ **MATERION NATURAL RESOURCES INC** p 919
10 Miles North Hwy 6 84624
Tel (435) 864-2701 SIC 1099 3339

DRAPER, UT

1-800 CONTACTS INC p 1
261 W Data Dr 84020
Tel (801) 316-5000 SIC 5961 3851

ACADEMY MORTGAGE CORP p 13
339 W 13490 S 84020
Tel (801) 233-7237 SIC 6163

CASTLE & COOKE MORTGAGE LLC p 264
13751 S Wadsworth Park Dr # 101 84020
Tel (866) 461-7101 SIC 6162

▲ **CONTROL4 CORP** p 364
11734 S Election Rd 84020
Tel (801) 523-3100 SIC 3679 7372

CSS CORP p 398
11778 S Election Rd # 160 84020
Tel (801) 619-4014 SIC 7299

DEPARTMENT OF CORRECTIONS UTAH p 430
14717 S Minuteman Dr 84020
Tel (801) 545-5500 SIC 9223

▲ **HEALTHEQUITY INC** p 677
15 W Scenic Pointe Dr # 100 84020
Tel (801) 727-1000
SIC 8399 6371 6036 6321 6282

M & M AUTOMOTIVE INC p 888
11453 S Lone Peak Pkwy 84020
Tel (801) 553-5800 SIC 5511

NATIONAL GUARD UTAH p 1013
12953 S Minuteman Dr 84020
Tel (801) 432-4439 SIC 9711

PENTALON CONSTRUCTION INC p 1132
132 E 13065 S Ste 175 84020
Tel (801) 619-1900 SIC 1522 1542

PROG FINANCE LLC p 1180
11629 S 700 E Ste 200 84020
Tel (877) 898-1970 SIC 6141

■ **RALPH L WADSWORTH CONSTRUCTION CO LLC** p 1206
166 E 14000 S Ste 200 84020
Tel (801) 553-1661 SIC 1629 1611

SWIRE PACIFIC HOLDINGS INC p 1412
12634 S 265 W Bldg A 84020
Tel (801) 816-5300 SIC 2086

■ **SYNCHRONY BANK** p 1414
170 W Election Rd Ste 125 84020
Tel (801) 619-4760 SIC 6035

EAGLE MOUNTAIN, UT

MTA DEVELOPMENT INC p 997
3222 E Autumn Ln 84005
Tel (801) 647-3247 SIC 8741

FARMINGTON, UT

DAVIS SCHOOL DISTRICT p 416
45 E St St 84025
Tel (801) 402-5261 SIC 8211

PLURALSIGHT LLC p 1157
182 N Union Ave 84025
Tel (801) 784-9007 SIC 8742

▲ **VISTA OUTDOOR INC** p 1562
262 N University Ave 84025
Tel (801) 447-3000
SIC 3482 3483 3827 3949 3484 3812

GRANTSVILLE, UT

■ **ATI TITANIUM LLC** p 124
12633 N Rowley Rd 84029
Tel (801) 443-9958 SIC 3462

HEBER CITY, UT

PROBST ELECTRIC INC p 1178
875 S 600 W 84032
Tel (435) 657-1955 SIC 1623 1731

HIGHLAND, UT

GRABBER CONSTRUCTION PRODUCTS INC p 628
5255 W 11000 N Ste 100 84003
Tel (801) 492-3880 SIC 5072 5211

HILDALE, UT

PHAZE CONCRETE INC p 1141
1280 W Utah Ave 84784
Tel (435) 656-9500 SIC 1542

HOLLADAY, UT

SNOWBIRD CORP p 1336
3165 E Millrock Dr # 150 84121
Tel (801) 742-2222 SIC 6531 7011

TPUSA INC p 1468
6510 S Millrock Dr # 150 84121
Tel (801) 257-5800 SIC 7389

HUNTINGTON, UT

NIELSON CONSTRUCTION AND MATERIALS p 1043
825 N Loop Rd 84528
Tel (435) 687-2494 SIC 1611

HURRICANE, UT

ALDEN PADFIELD INC p 47
203 N 5500 W 84737
Tel (435) 674-9883 SIC 5014 5531

DATS TRUCKING INC p 414
321 N Old Highway 91 84737
Tel (435) 673-1886 SIC 4212 4213 5171

KAYSVILLE, UT

GREAT BASIN INDUSTRIAL LLC p 633
1284 Flint Meadow Dr A 84037
Tel (801) 543-2100 SIC 3443 7699 1731

LAYTON, UT

DAVIS HOSPITAL & MEDICAL CENTER INC p 416
1600 W Antelope Dr 84041
Tel (801) 807-1000 SIC 8062

YOUNG AUTOMOTIVE GROUP INC p 1638
645 N Main St 84041
Tel (801) 544-1234 SIC 5511

LEHI, UT

313 ACQUISITION LLC p 2
3301 N Thanksgiving Way 84043
Tel (877) 404-4129 SIC 5074

ANCESTRY.COM INC p 89
1300 W Traverse Pkwy 84043
Tel (801) 705-7000 SIC 7374

ANCESTRY.COM LLC p 89
1300 W Traverse Pkwy 84043
Tel (801) 705-7000 SIC 7374

■ **IM FLASH TECHNOLOGIES LLC** p 733
4000 N Flash Dr 84043
Tel (801) 767-4000 SIC 3674

MARITZCX HOLDINGS LLC p 907
3451 N Triumph Blvd 84043
Tel (385) 695-2800 SIC 8742 6719

▲ **NATURES SUNSHINE PRODUCTS INC** p 1019
2500 W Executive Pkwy # 100 84043
Tel (801) 341-7900 SIC 2834

SIRSI CORP p 1327
3300 N Ashton Blvd # 500 84043
Tel (801) 223-5200 SIC 7371

■ **VIVINT SOLAR DEVELOPER LLC** p 1563
1800 W Ashton Blvd 84043
Tel (801) 377-9111 SIC 1711

▲ **VIVINT SOLAR INC** p 1563
1850 W Ashton Blvd 84043
Tel (877) 404-4129 SIC 5074

WORKFRONT INC p 1624
3301 N Thank Way Ste 100 84043
Tel (801) 373-3266 SIC 7371

XANGO LLC p 1630
2889 W Ashton Blvd Ste 1 84043
Tel (801) 753-3000 SIC 5122

ZIJA INTERNATIONAL INC p 1643
3300 N Ashton Blvd # 100 84043
Tel (801) 494-2300 SIC 5149

LINDON, UT

ACCESSDATA GROUP INC p 15
588 W 400 S Ste 350 84042
Tel (801) 377-5410 SIC 7373

MOUNTAIN STATES STEEL INC p 994
325 S Geneva Rd Ste 1 84042
Tel (801) 785-5085 SIC 3441

SOFTWARE FORENSICS INC p 1337
384 S 400 W Ste 200 84042
Tel (801) 377-5410 SIC 7371 8243

SUNROC BUILDING MATERIALS INC p 1404
520 S 800 W 84042
Tel (801) 802-6952 SIC 5031

LOGAN, UT

CACHE VALLEY ELECTRIC CO p 235
875 N 1000 W 84321
Tel (435) 752-6405 SIC 1731

DIRECT FINANCIAL SOLUTIONS LLC p 441
84 E 2400 N 84341
Tel (435) 774-8207 SIC 7389

GOSSNER FOODS INC p 626
1051 N 1000 W 84321
Tel (435) 713-6100 SIC 2022 2026 2021

HF HOLDINGS INC p 688
1500 S 1000 W 84321
Tel (435) 750-5000 SIC 3949 3088

■ **HYCLONE LABORATORIES INC** p 723
925 W 1800 S 84321
Tel (435) 792-8000 SIC 2836 8071

ICON HEALTH & FITNESS INC p 727
1500 S 1000 W 84321
Tel (435) 750-5000 SIC 3949

PRIME INTERNATIONAL LLC p 1175
1047 S 100 W Ste 240 84321
Tel (435) 753-6533 SIC 5147

UTAH STATE UNIVERSITY p 1536
1000 Old Main Hl 84322
Tel (435) 797-1057 SIC 8221

MAGNA, UT

KENNECOTT CORP p 810
8315 W 3595 S 84044
Tel (801) 913-8335
SIC 1041 1021 1061 1221

MIDVALE, UT

■ **ALLY BANK** p 59
6985 S Union Park Ctr # 435 84047
Tel (801) 790-5005
SIC 6153 6021 6311 6331 6162

CARDWELL DISTRIBUTING INC p 253
8137 S State St Bldg 1 84047
Tel (801) 561-4251
SIC 5171 7549 5172 5983

DOE FL SMIDTH p 447
7158 Fl Smidth Dr 84047
Tel (801) 526-2500 SIC 5039

FLSMIDTH USA INC p 561
7158 S Flsmidth Dr 84047
Tel (801) 871-7000 SIC 5049

▲ **OVERSTOCK.COM INC** p 1099
799 W Coliseum Way 84047
Tel (801) 947-3100 SIC 5961

SAVAGE COMPANIES p 1283
901 W Legacy Center Way 84047
Tel (801) 944-6600 SIC 4212 4213

SAVAGE SERVICES CORP p 1284
901 W Legacy Center Way 84047
Tel (801) 944-6600 SIC 4212

▲ **SPORTSMANS WAREHOUSE HOLDINGS INC** p 1360
7035 S High Tech Dr # 100 84047
Tel (801) 566-6681 SIC 5941 5699 5661

■ **SPORTSMANS WAREHOUSE INC** p 1360
7035 S High Tech Dr 84047
Tel (801) 566-6681 SIC 5941 5699 5661

■ **WEX INC** p 1603
7090 S Union Park Ave # 350 84047
Tel (801) 270-8166 SIC 6021

▲ **ZAGG INC** p 1641
910 W Legacy Center Way 84047
Tel (801) 263-0699 SIC 5731 6794

MURRAY, UT

GENEVA ROCK PRODUCTS INC p 603
302 W 5400 S Ste 201 84107
Tel (801) 765-7800 SIC 5032

INTERMOUNTAIN HEALTH CARE HEALTH SERVICES p 753
5121 S Cottonwood St 84107
Tel (801) 507-5358 SIC 8011

SELECTHEALTH BENEFIT ASSURANCE p 1302
5381 S Green St 84123
Tel (801) 442-5000 SIC 6321

SELECTHEALTH INC p 1302
5381 S Green St 84123
Tel (801) 442-5000 SIC 6321

NORTH LOGAN, UT

CACHE COUNTY SCHOOL DISTRICT p 235
2063 N 1200 E 84341
Tel (435) 752-3925 SIC 8211

UTAH STATE UNIVERSITY RESEARCH FOUNDATION p 1536
1695 N Research Pkwy 84341
Tel (435) 713-3400
SIC 8711 8734 8733 7371

NORTH SALT LAKE, UT

BIG WEST OIL LLC p 182
333 W Center St 84054
Tel (801) 624-1000 SIC 2911 5172

■ **MOTOR CARGO** p 992
845 W Center St 84054
Tel (801) 936-1111 SIC 4213

ORBIT IRRIGATION PRODUCTS INC p 1092
845 Overland St 84054
Tel (801) 299-5555 SIC 3523

PRO-MARK INC p 1178
845 Overland St 84054
Tel (801) 299-5500 SIC 7311 7336

OGDEN, UT

AFJ LLC p 33
1104 Country Hills Dr 84403
Tel (801) 624-1000 SIC 5541 5963

AMERICA FIRST CREDIT UNION p 67
1344 W 4675 S Ste 130 84405
Tel (801) 627-0900 SIC 6062

■ **AUTOLIV ASP INC** p 134
3350 Airport Rd 84405
Tel (801) 625-4800 SIC 3714 3563

▲ **AUTOLIV INC** p 134
3350 Airport Rd 84405
Tel (801) 629-9800 SIC 3714

BOARD OF EDUC OF OGDEN CITY SD p 195
1950 Monroe Blvd 84401
Tel (801) 737-8000 SIC 8211

CARE-A-LOT FUND p 254
1344 W 4675 S 84405
Tel (801) 627-0900 SIC 7389

■ **COLUMBIA OGDEN MEDICAL CENTER INC** p 341
5475 S 500 E 84405
Tel (801) 479-2111 SIC 8062 8099

CORNERSTONE RESEARCH & DEVELOPMENT INC p 371
900 S Depot Dr 84404
Tel (801) 337-9400 SIC 2834

G S L CORP p 587
765 N 10500 W 84404
Tel (801) 731-3100 SIC 2819 2899 3339

GREAT WESTERN SUPPLY INC p 635
2626 Industrial Dr 84401
Tel (801) 621-5412
SIC 5074 5051 5999 1711

JM THOMAS FOREST PRODUCTS CO p 786
2525 N Hwy 89 91 84404
Tel (801) 782-8090 SIC 5031

KIER CONSTRUCTION CORP p 817
3710 Quincy Ave 84403
Tel (801) 627-1414 SIC 1522 1542 1541

■ **LOFTHOUSE BAKERY PRODUCTS INC** p 874
215 N 700 W Ste A10 84404
Tel (801) 776-3500 SIC 5149

■ **MARKETSTAR CORP** p 908
2475 Washington Blvd 84401
Tel (801) 393-1155 SIC 8742

OGDEN CITY SCHOOL DISTRICT p 1076
1950 Monroe Blvd 84401
Tel (801) 737-8000 SIC 8211

OVERLAND WEST INC p 1099
2805 Washington Blvd 84401
Tel (801) 621-5663 SIC 7514

PETERSEN INC p 1138
1527 N 2000 W 84404
Tel (801) 731-1366
SIC 5084 3441 7692 3444

R & O CONSTRUCTION CO INC p 1201
933 Wall Ave Ste 2 84404
Tel (801) 627-1403 SIC 1542 1521

STAKER & PARSON COMPANIES p 1374
2350 S 1900 W Ste 100 84401
Tel (801) 298-7500
SIC 1611 5032 3273 4212 2951 1771

WADMAN CORP p 1571
2920 S 925 W 84401
Tel (801) 621-4185 SIC 1542 1541

WEBER SCHOOL DISTRICT p 1586
5320 Adams Ave Pkwy 84405
Tel (801) 476-7800 SIC 8211

WEBER STATE UNIVERSITY p 1586
3848 Harrison Blvd 84408
Tel (801) 626-6606 SIC 8221

OREM, UT

CLYDE COMPANIES INC p 328
730 N 1500 W 84057
Tel (801) 802-6900 SIC 1611 5031 6411

M L E HOLDINGS INC p 889
1301 W 400 N 84057
Tel (801) 224-0589 SIC 2531 2522 2521

MITY-LITE INC p 978
1301 W 400 N 84057
Tel (801) 224-0589 SIC 2531 2522 7359

■ **OMNITURE LLC** p 1085
550 E Tmpngos Cle Bldng G 84097
Tel (801) 722-7000 SIC 7371

OPINIONOLOGY LLC p 1089
701 Timpanogos Pkwy Ste M 84097
Tel (801) 373-7735 SIC 7389 8732

■ **TIMPANOGOS REGIONAL HOSPITAL** p 1455
750 W 800 N 84057
Tel (801) 714-6000 SIC 8062

TIMPANOGOS REGIONAL HOSPITAL p 1455
750 W 800 N 84057
Tel (801) 714-6000 SIC 8062

UNICITY INTERNATIONAL INC p 1502
1201 N 800 E 84097
Tel (801) 226-2600 SIC 5149

■ **US SYNTHETIC CORP** p 1533
1260 S 1600 W 84058
Tel (801) 235-9001 SIC 3915

UTAH VALLEY UNIVERSITY p 1536
800 W University Pkwy 84058
Tel (801) 863-8000 SIC 8221

VERIO INC p 1549
1203 Research Way 84097
Tel (303) 645-1900 SIC 4813

VIA MOTORS INC p 1554
165 Mountain Way Dr 84058
Tel (801) 764-9111 SIC 5012

WESTLAND CONSTRUCTION INC p 1601
1411 W 1250 S Ste 200 84058
Tel (801) 374-6085 SIC 1542 1541

PARK CITY, UT

ASC UTAH INC p 115
4000 Canyons Resort Dr 84098
Tel (435) 649-5400 SIC 7011 5812

BACKCOUNTRY.COM LLC p 143
1678 Redstone Center Dr # 210 84098
Tel (801) 746-7580 SIC 5091 4813

DEER VALLEY RESORT p 422
2250 Deer Valley Dr 84060
Tel (435) 649-1000 SIC 7999

■ **MAKERS OF KAL INC** p 899
1500 Kearns Blvd 84060
Tel (435) 655-6000 SIC 5122

■ **NUTRACEUTICAL CORP** p 1067
1400 Kearns Blvd Ste 200 84060
Tel (435) 655-6000 SIC 2834

▲ **NUTRACEUTICAL INTERNATIONAL CORP** p 1067
1400 Kearns Blvd Fl 2 84060
Tel (435) 655-6106 SIC 2833

PACIFIC GROUP RESORTS INC p 1104
1389 Center Dr Ste 200 84098
Tel (435) 241-7000 SIC 7011

POWDR CORP p 1164
1790 Bonanza Dr Ste W201 84060
Tel (435) 647-5490 SIC 7011

SHC SERVICES INC p 1313
1640 Redstone Center Dr # 200 84098
Tel (435) 645-0788 SIC 7361

SKULLCANDY INC p 1330
1441 Ute Blvd Ste 250 84098
Tel (435) 940-1545 SIC 3679

■ **TRIUMPH GEAR SYSTEMS INC** p 1483
6125 Silver Creek Dr 84098
Tel (435) 649-1900 SIC 3593 3728 3812

PAYSON, UT

ABOUT TIME TECHNOLOGIES LLC p 12
58 N 1100 W Apt 2 84651
Tel (801) 465-8181 SIC 5045 7372 7375

■ **LIBERTY SAFE AND SECURITY PRODUCTS INC** p 862
1199 W Utah Ave 84651
Tel (801) 925-1000 SIC 3499

PLEASANT GROVE, UT

DOTERRA INTERNATIONAL LLC p 452
389 S 1300 W 84062
Tel (801) 615-7200 SIC 2899

■ **NIELS FUGAL SONS CO LLC** p 1043
1005 S Main St 84062
Tel (801) 785-3152 SIC 1623

PRICE, UT

INTERMOUNTAIN ELECTRONICS INC OF PRICE UTAH p 753
1511 S Highway 6 84501
Tel (435) 637-7160 SIC 3699 5063

PROVO, UT

ANCESTRY US HOLDINGS INC p 89
360 W 4800 N 84604
Tel (801) 705-7000 SIC 7375

ANCESTRY.COM HOLDINGS LLC p 89
360 W 4800 N 84604
Tel (801) 705-7000 SIC 7374 7375

APX GROUP HOLDINGS INC p 101
4931 N 300 W 84604
Tel (801) 377-9111
SIC 7382 5065 3822 1711

APX GROUP INC p 101
4931 N 300 W 84604
Tel (801) 377-9111
SIC 8711 3822 1711 5065

APX PARENT HOLDCO INC p 101
4931 N 300 W 84604
Tel (801) 377-9111
SIC 6719 3822 1711 8711 5065 5074

BRIGHAM YOUNG UNIVERSITY p 212
A 41 Asb Brgham Yung Univ 84602
Tel (801) 422-1211 SIC 8221

DYNIX CORP p 465
400 W 5050 N 84604
Tel (800) 288-8820 SIC 8231

NOVELL INC p 1063
1800 Novell Pl 84606
Tel (801) 861-4272 SIC 7372

▲ **NU SKIN ENTERPRISES INC** p 1066
75 W Center St 84601
Tel (801) 345-1000 SIC 2844 5122

■ **NU SKIN ENTERPRISES UNITED STATES INC** p 1066
75 W Center St 84601
Tel (801) 377-6056 SIC 5122

■ **NU SKIN INTERNATIONAL INC** p 1066
75 W Center St 84601
Tel (801) 345-1000 SIC 2844

PROVO CITY SCHOOL DISTRICT p 1187
280 W 940 N 84604
Tel (801) 374-4800 SIC 8211

QUALTRICS LABS INC p 1198
400 W Qualtrics Dr # 100 84604
Tel (800) 340-9194 SIC 8713

QUALTRICS LLC p 1198
333 River Park Dr 84604
Tel (801) 374-6682 SIC 7371

UTAH VALLEY REGIONAL MEDICAL CENTER p 1536
1034 N 500 W 84604
Tel (801) 357-7850 SIC 8062

VIVINT INC p 1563
4931 N 300 W 84604
Tel (801) 705-6253 SIC 3822

RIVERTON, UT

MORRELL INTERNATIONAL INC p 990
14901 S Heritagecrest Way 84065
Tel (801) 495-3111 SIC 4213 4226 5039

STAMPIN UP INC p 1375
12907 S 3600 W 84065
Tel (801) 257-5400 SIC 3953

ROOSEVELT, UT

RN INDUSTRIES TRUCKING p 1239
188 W 200 N 84066
Tel (435) 722-2800 SIC 1389

UINTAH BASIN MEDICAL CENTER p 1500
250 W 300 N 84066
Tel (435) 725-2008
SIC 8062 8082 7352 8092 8361

ROY, UT

FOCUS SERVICES LLC p 563
4102 S 1900 W 84067
Tel (801) 393-1635 SIC 7389

SALT LAKE CITY, UT

A & K RAILROAD MATERIALS INC p 4
1505 S Redwood Rd 84104
Tel (801) 974-5484 SIC 5088

ADESA UTAH LLC p 22
780 S 5600 W 84104
Tel (801) 322-1234 SIC 5012 5521 5084

AGRESERVES INC p 35
79 S Main St Ste 1100 84111
Tel (801) 715-9100 SIC 0762

ALSCO INC p 61
505 E South Temple 84102
Tel (801) 328-8831 SIC 7213

■ **AMERICAN EXPRESS BANK FSB** p 72
4315 S 2700 W 84184
Tel (801) 945-5000 SIC 6029

AMSCO WINDOWS p 87
1880 S 1045 W 84104
Tel (801) 972-6444 SIC 3442

ARNOLD MACHINERY CO p 112
2975 W 2100 S 84119
Tel (801) 972-4000
SIC 5082 5084 5012 5083

ARUP LABORATORIES INC p 114
500 S Chipeta Way 84108
Tel (801) 583-2787 SIC 8071

ASAHI REFINING USA INC p 115
4601 W 2100 S 84120
Tel (801) 972-6466 SIC 1041

ASSOCIATED FOOD STORES INC p 120
1850 W 2100 S 84119
Tel (801) 973-4400
SIC 5141 5147 5142 5148 5122 5023

AVALON HEALTH CARE INC p 136
206 N 2100 W Ste 300 84116
Tel (801) 596-8844 SIC 8741 8051

■ **BARD ACCESS SYSTEMS INC** p 155
605 N 5600 W 84116
Tel (801) 522-5000 SIC 3841

BARRICK GOLD OF NORTH AMERICA INC p 157
460 W 50 N Ste 500 84101
Tel (416) 861-9911 SIC 8741 1041

BEAR RIVER MUTUAL INSURANCE CO p 165
778 E Winchester St 84107
Tel (801) 267-5000 SIC 6331 6411

BENEFICIAL LIFE INSURANCE CO p 172
55 N 300 W Ste 375 84101
Tel (801) 933-1272 SIC 6311

BIG-D CAPITAL CORP p 182
420 E South Temple 84111
Tel (801) 415-6086 SIC 1521

BIG-D CONSTRUCTION CORP p 182
404 W 400 S 84101
Tel (801) 415-6000 SIC 1541 1542

BIOFIRE DEFENSE LLC p 183
79 W 4500 S Ste 14 84107
Tel (801) 262-3592 SIC 3829 3826 6794

BMW BANK OF NORTH AMERICA p 194
2735 E Parleys Way # 301 84109
Tel (801) 461-6415 SIC 6022

BOART LONGYEAR CO p 196
2570 W 1700 S 84104
Tel (801) 972-6430
SIC 1481 3532 3559 1771

BOART LONGYEAR MANUFACTURING AND DISTRIBUTION INC p 196
2640 W 1700 S 84104
Tel (801) 972-6430 SIC 1381 5084 3533

BODELL CONSTRUCTION CO INC p 197
586 W Fine Dr 84115
Tel (801) 261-4343 SIC 1542 1541

BONNEVILLE INTERNATIONAL CORP p 200
55 N 300 W 84101
Tel (801) 575-5555 SIC 4832

BRAHMA GROUP p 207
1132 S 500 W 84101
Tel (801) 521-5200 SIC 1791

BRIDGE INVESTMENT GROUP PARTNERS LLC p 211
5295 S Commerce Dr # 100 84107
Tel (801) 716-4500 SIC 6513 6531

BURTON LUMBER & HARDWARE CO p 229
1170 S 4400 W 84104
Tel (801) 952-3700 SIC 5211 5251

CBTRAVEL CORP p 268
5588 S Green St Ste 300 84123
Tel (801) 327-7700 SIC 4724

CHG HEALTHCARE SERVICES INC p 296
6440 S Millrock Dr # 175 84121
Tel (801) 930-3000 SIC 7363

CHILDRENS MIRACLE NETWORK p 300
205 W 700 S 84101
Tel (801) 214-7400 SIC 8399

CIT BANK p 309
2150 S 1300 E Ste 400 84106
Tel (801) 412-6800 SIC 6036

CITY OF SALT LAKE CITY p 318
451 S State St Rm 145 84111
Tel (801) 535-7704 SIC 9111

CLI HOLDINGS INC p 326
3950 S 700 E Ste 301 84107
Tel (801) 262-3942 SIC 1411

CODALE ELECTRIC SUPPLY INC p 333
5225 W 2400 S England Ct 84120
Tel (801) 975-7300 SIC 5063

■ **COMENITY CAPITAL BANK** p 344
2795 E Cottonwood Pkwy # 100 84121
Tel (801) 527-2272 SIC 6022

CORP OF PRESIDENT OF CHURCH OF JESUS CHRIST OF LATTER-DAY SAINTS p 371
50 W North Temple 84150
Tel (801) 240-1000 SIC 8661 8221

CORP OF PRESIDING BISHOP OF CHURCH OF JESUS CHRIST OF LATTER-DAY SAINTS p 371
50 E North Temple 84150
Tel (801) 240-1000 SIC 8661

COUNTY OF SALT LAKE p 381
2001 S State St S2-200 84190
Tel (801) 468-3225 SIC 9111

CR ENGLAND INC p 388
4701 W 2100 S 84120
Tel (800) 421-9004 SIC 4213

DEPARTMENT OF HEALTH UTAH p 430
288 N 1460 W 84116
Tel (801) 538-6111 SIC 9431

DESERET BOOK CO p 432
57 W South Temple 84101
Tel (801) 517-3294 SIC 5192 5942 2731

DESERET MANAGEMENT CORP p 432
55 N 300 W Ste 800 84101
Tel (801) 538-0651
SIC 4832 4833 5932 6512 6531 6411

▲ **DIAMOND BLACK INC** p 436
2084 E 3900 S 84124
Tel (801) 278-5552 SIC 3949 2329 2339

DOWNEAST OUTFITTERS INC p 453
375 W Hope Ave 84115
Tel (801) 467-7520
SIC 5611 5621 5963 2512

DYNO NOBEL HOLDINGS USA INC p 465
2795 E Cottonwood Pkwy # 500 84121
Tel (801) 364-4800 SIC 2892

DYNO NOBEL INC p 465
2795 E Cottonwood Pkwy # 500 84121
Tel (801) 364-4800 SIC 2892

EDURO HEALTHCARE LLC p 479
1376 E 3300 S 84106
Tel (801) 601-1450 SIC 8051

ENERGYSOLUTIONS INC p 498
299 S Main St Ste 1700 84111
Tel (801) 649-2000 SIC 4953 8711

ENERGYSOLUTIONS LLC p 498
299 Suth Main St Ste 1700 84111
Tel (801) 649-2000 SIC 4953 8711

ENERGYSOLUTIONS SERVICES INC p 498
299 S Main St Ste 1700 84111
Tel (801) 649-2000 SIC 4953

ENGLAND LOGISTICS INC p 499
1325 S 4700 W 84104
Tel (801) 656-4500 SIC 8742

ENVIROTECH PUMPSYSTEMS INC p 504
440 W 800 S 84101
Tel (801) 359-8731 SIC 3561 3491 3089

EQUITABLE LIFE & CASUALTY INSURANCE CO p 506
3 Triad Ctr 84180
Tel (801) 579-3400 SIC 6411 6311

EXECUTIVE OFFICE OF STATE OF UTAH p 518
2110 State Ofc Bldg 84114
Tel (801) 538-3020 SIC 9111

■ **EXTRA SPACE MANAGEMENT INC** p 521
2795 E Cottonwood Pkwy # 400 84121
Tel (801) 562-5556 SIC 4225

▲ **EXTRA SPACE STORAGE INC** p 521
2795 E Cottonwood Pkwy # 400 84121
Tel (801) 365-4600 SIC 6798

FARMLAND RESERVE INC p 530
50 E North Temple 84150
Tel (801) 240-6301 SIC 0762

FC ORGANIZATIONAL PRODUCTS LLC p 532
2250 W Parkway Blvd 84119
Tel (801) 817-1776 SIC 5942 5734

FIRETROL PROTECTION SYSTEMS INC p 544
3696 W 900 S Ste A 84104
Tel (801) 485-6900 SIC 1711 1731

FIRST MANHATTAN FUNDING LLC p 547
261 E Broadway Ste 255 84111
Tel (801) 643-3022 SIC 6162

FJ MANAGEMENT INC p 553
185 S State St Ste 201 84111
Tel (801) 624-1000
SIC 5541 2911 5411 1382 6022

▲ **FRANKLIN COVEY CO** p 575
2200 W Parkway Blvd 84119
Tel (801) 817-1776 SIC 8742 8331 2741

FRED A MORETON & CO p 575
101 S 200 E Ste 300 84111
Tel (801) 531-1234 SIC 6411

■ **FUSION-IO INC** p 585
2855 E Cottonwood Pkwy # 200 84121
Tel (801) 424-5569 SIC 3572

GARFF ENTERPRISES INC p 592
405 S Main St Ste 1200 84111
Tel (801) 257-3400 SIC 5511 6512

GENERAL DISTRIBUTING CO p 600
5350 W Amelia Earhart Dr 84116
Tel (801) 531-7895 SIC 5181

GRAND AMERICA HOTELS & RESORTS INC p 629
555 S Main St 84111
Tel (801) 596-5717 SIC 7011

GRANITE SCHOOL DISTRICT p 631
2500 S State St 84115
Tel (385) 646-5000 SIC 8211

GRAYMONT INC p 632
301 S 700 E 3950 84102
Tel (801) 262-3942 SIC 1429 2951 3273

GRAYMONT WESTERN US INC p 632
3950 S 700 E Ste 301 84107
Tel (801) 262-3942 SIC 1411

■ **GREENBACKS INC** p 637
2369 W Orton Cir 84119
Tel (801) 977-7777 SIC 5331

HARMON CITY INC p 662
3540 S 4000 W 84120
Tel (801) 969-8261 SIC 5411

■ **HUNTSMAN ADVANCED MATERIALS LLC** p 720
500 S Huntsman Way 84108
Tel (801) 584-5700 SIC 2821 2891 3087

■ **HUNTSMAN HOLDINGS LLC** p 720
500 S Huntsman Way 84108
Tel (801) 584-5700
SIC 2821 2911 3081 2869

■ **HUNTSMAN PETROCHEMICAL LLC** p 720
500 S Huntsman Way 84108
Tel (801) 584-5700 SIC 2911

■ **HUNTSMAN-COOPER LLC** p 720
500 S Huntsman Way 84108
Tel (801) 584-5700 SIC 2821

INDUSTRIAL SUPPLY CO INC p 740
1635 S 300 W 84115
Tel (801) 484-8644 SIC 5084 5085

INTERMOUNTAIN HEALTH CARE INC p 753
36 S State St Ste 1600 84111
Tel (801) 442-2000 SIC 8062

INTERMOUNTAIN PLASTIC DISTRIBUTION INC p 753
2300 S Decker Lake Blvd B 84119
Tel (801) 201-1212 SIC 5162

JACOBSEN CONSTRUCTION CO INC p 775
3131 W 2210 S 84119
Tel (801) 973-0500 SIC 1542 1541

JAS D EASTON INC p 778
5215 W Wiley Post Way # 130 84116
Tel (801) 526-6211 SIC 3949 5091 6552

JOB INDUSTRIAL SERVICES INC p 787
1805 S Redwood Rd # 150 84104
Tel (801) 433-0901 SIC 8711

■ **KERN RIVER GAS SUPPLY CORP** p 813
2755 E Cottonwood Pkwy # 300 84121
Tel (801) 937-6000 SIC 4922

KILGORE COMPANIES LLC p 818
7057 W 2100 S 84128
Tel (801) 250-0132 SIC 1721

KIMBALL ELECTRONICS INC p 818
2233 S 300 E 84115
Tel (801) 466-0569 SIC 5065 5063

L-3 COMMUNICATIONS CORP p 834
322 N 2200 W 84116
Tel (801) 594-2000 SIC 3812

LDS HOSPITAL p 849
8th Ave C St 84143
Tel (801) 408-1100 SIC 8062

LES OLSON CO p 857
3244 S 300 W 84115
Tel (435) 586-2345 SIC 5044

LONGYEAR HOLDINGS INC p 877
2340 W 1700 S 84104
Tel (801) 972-6430 SIC 1481 3532 3559

■ **MARLIN BUSINESS BANK** p 909
2795 E Cottonwood Pkwy # 120 84121
Tel (888) 479-9111 SIC 6111

MAVERIK INC p 921
185 S State St Ste 800 84111
Tel (801) 936-9155 SIC 5541 5411

■ MEDALLION BANK p 935
1100 E 6600 S Ste 510 84121
Tel (801) 284-7065 SIC 6029

MORRIS MURDOCK LLC p 990
101 S 200 E Ste 100 84111
Tel (801) 483-6441 SIC 4724

▲ MYRIAD GENETICS INC p 1005
320 S Wakara Way 84108
Tel (801) 584-3600 SIC 2835 8731

NAARTJIE CUSTOM KIDS INC p 1006
3676 W Ca Ave Ste D100 84104
Tel (801) 973-7988 SIC 5641

NATIONAL WOOD PRODUCTS INC p 1017
2705 S 600 W 84115
Tel (801) 977-1171 SIC 5031

NELSON LABORATORIES INC p 1025
6280 S Redwood Rd 84123
Tel (801) 290-7500 SIC 8734

NICHOLAS & CO INC p 1042
5520 W Harold Gatty Dr 84116
Tel (801) 531-1100 SIC 5046 5141 5142

■ NORTHERN UTAH HEALTHCARE CORP p 1057
1200 E 3900 S 84124
Tel (801) 268-7111 SIC 8062 8082 8011

NORTHWEST PIPELINE LLC p 1060
295 S Chipeta Way Fl 4 84108
Tel (801) 583-8800 SIC 4923

O C TANNER CO p 1070
1930 S State St 84115
Tel (801) 486-2430 SIC 3911 2759 2741

O C TANNER MANUFACTURING p 1070
1930 S State St 84115
Tel (801) 486-2430 SIC 3911

O C TANNER RECOGNITION CO p 1070
1930 S State St 84115
Tel (801) 486-2430 SIC 5094

■ OEC MEDICAL SYSTEMS INC p 1075
384 N Wright Brothers Dr 84116
Tel (801) 328-9300 SIC 3844 7699

OKLAND CONSTRUCTION CO INC p 1080
1978 S West Temple 84115
Tel (801) 486-0144 SIC 1542 1541

ONRAMP TRANSPORTATION SERVICES LLC p 1088
5416 W Amelia Earhart Dr # 201 84116
Tel (801) 736-9420 SIC 4789

PACKSIZE LLC p 1107
6440 S Wasatch Blvd # 305 84121
Tel (801) 944-4814 SIC 7389

PADFIELD INC p 1107
1335 W 2100 S 84119
Tel (801) 972-1944 SIC 5014 5531 3711

PINNACLE ENERGY MARKETING LLC p 1149
90 S 400 W Ste 320 84101
Tel (435) 940-9001 SIC 5172

■ PITNEY BOWES BANK INC p 1152
1245 E Brickyard Rd # 250 84106
Tel (801) 832-4440 SIC 6141

PRIDE TRANSPORT INC p 1174
5499 W 2455 S 84120
Tel (801) 972-8890 SIC 4213

PRIMARY RESIDENTIAL MORTGAGE INC p 1174
1480 N 2200 W 84116
Tel (801) 596-8707 SIC 6163

■ QUESTAR CORP p 1199
333 S State St 84111
Tel (801) 324-5900 SIC 4922 1311 5172

■ QUESTAR GAS CO p 1199
333 S State St 84111
Tel (801) 324-5900 SIC 4924 4923

■ QUESTAR PIPELINE LLC p 1199
333 S State St 84111
Tel (801) 324-5173 SIC 4922 4923

RC HUNT ELECTRIC INC p 1212
1863 W Alexander St 84119
Tel (801) 975-8844 SIC 1731

■ RC WILLEY HOME FURNISHINGS p 1212
2301 S 300 W 84115
Tel (801) 461-3900 SIC 5712 5731 5722

REDWOOD INDUSTRIES INC p 1217
2345 S Cci Way 84119
Tel (801) 973-9000 SIC 1711

REGENCE BLUECROSS BLUESHIELD OF UTAH p 1218
2890 E Cottonwood Pkwy 84121
Tel (801) 942-9205 SIC 6324

ROCKY MOUNTAIN FABRICATION INC p 1245
1125 W 2300 N 84116
Tel (801) 532-5400 SIC 3443

ROCKY MOUNTAIN RECYCLING LLC p 1245
2950 W 900 S 84104
Tel (801) 975-1820 SIC 5093

ROOFERS SUPPLY INC p 1249
3359 S 500 W 84115
Tel (801) 266-1311 SIC 5033

■ RUSH TRUCK CENTERS OF UTAH INC p 1259
964 S 3800 W 84104
Tel (801) 972-5320 SIC 5012 7538 5531

■ SALLIE MAE BANK p 1273
175 S West Temple Ste 600 84101
Tel (801) 320-3700 SIC 6021

SALT LAKE CITY CORP p 1273
4380 W 2100 S 84120
Tel (801) 535-7704 SIC 9111

SALT LAKE CITY SCHOOL DISTRICT p 1273
440 E 100 S 84111
Tel (801) 578-8307 SIC 8211

SALT LAKE COMMUNITY COLLEGE (INC) p 1273
4600 S Redwood Rd 84123
Tel (801) 957-4111 SIC 8222 8221

SALT LAKE REGIONAL MEDICAL CENTER LP p 1273
1050 E South Temple 84102
Tel (801) 350-4631 SIC 8062

▲ SECURITY NATIONAL FINANCIAL CORP p 1299
5300 S 360 W Ste 250 84123
Tel (801) 264-1060 SIC 6311 6531 6162

SINCLAIR COMPANIES p 1326
550 E South Temple 84102
Tel (801) 363-5100
SIC 2911 4612 1382 5541 7011 0212

SINCLAIR OIL CORP p 1326
550 E South Temple 84102
Tel (801) 524-2700 SIC 2911 5172

SINCLAIR SERVICES CO p 1326
550 E South Temple 84102
Tel (801) 363-5100 SIC 5172

SIZZLING PLATTER LLC p 1328
348 E Winchester St # 200 84107
Tel (801) 268-3400 SIC 5812

SLAYMAKER GROUP INC p 1331
404 E 4500 S Ste A12 84107
Tel (801) 261-3700 SIC 5812

SMITH POWER PRODUCTS INC p 1333
3065 W California Ave 84104
Tel (801) 262-2631
SIC 5084 7538 3714 5063

■ SMITHS FOOD & DRUG CENTERS INC p 1334
1550 S Redwood Rd 84104
Tel (801) 974-1400 SIC 5912 5499

SNOWBIRD HOLDINGS LLC p 1336
2721 E Kelly Ln 84117
Tel (801) 277-2840 SIC 6719

SPS HOLDINGS CORP p 1362
3815 S West Temple 84115
Tel (801) 293-1883 SIC 6162 6798

STATE OF UTAH p 1382
350 N State St Ste 200 84114
Tel (801) 538-1000 SIC 9111

TAX COMMISSION UTAH STATE p 1426
210 N 1950 W 84134
Tel (801) 297-2200 SIC 9311

THATCHER GROUP INC p 1446
1905 W Fortune Rd 84104
Tel (801) 972-4587 SIC 2819

TPUSA INC p 1468
1991 S 4650 W 84104
Tel (801) 257-5800 SIC 7389

TRAEGER PELLET GRILLS LLC p 1469
1215 E Wilmington Ave # 200 84106
Tel (855) 382-2560 SIC 3631

TURNER GAS CO INC p 1492
2825 W 500 S 84104
Tel (801) 973-6886 SIC 5172 4213

UBS BANK USA p 1498
299 S Main St Ste 2275 84111
Tel (801) 532-2741 SIC 6021

UNION PACIFIC RAILROAD EMPLOYES HEALTH SYSTEMS p 1505
1040 N 2200 W Ste 200 84116
Tel (801) 595-4300 SIC 6371

UNIVERSITY OF UTAH p 1526
201 Presidents Cir Rm 203 84112
Tel (801) 581-7200 SIC 8221

UNIVERSITY OF UTAH HOSPITALS AND CLINICS p 1526
50 N Medical Dr 84132
Tel (801) 581-2121 SIC 8062 8011

UNIVERSITY PATHOLOGY ASSOCIATES p 1527
50 N Medical Dr 5c124 84132
Tel (801) 581-5406 SIC 8071 8011

US GOLD INC p 1532
299 S Main St Ste 1800 84111
Tel (800) 607-4600 SIC 6799

US MAGNESIUM LLC p 1532
238 N 2200 W 84116
Tel (801) 532-2043 SIC 3356 2819

▲ USANA HEALTH SCIENCES INC p 1534
3838 W Parkway Blvd 84120
Tel (801) 954-7100 SIC 2833

UTAH ASSOCIATED MUNICIPAL POWER SYSTEMS p 1536
155 N 400 W 84103
Tel (801) 566-3938 SIC 4911

UTAH DEPARTMENT OF HUMAN SERVICES p 1536
195 N 1950 W 84116
Tel (801) 538-4001 SIC 8322 9441

UTAH DEPARTMENT OF NATURAL RESOURCES p 1536
1594 W North Temple 84116
Tel (801) 538-7200 SIC 9512

UTAH DEPT OF WORKFORCE SERVICES p 1536
140 E Broadway 84111
Tel (801) 526-9432 SIC 9441

UTAH RETIREMENT SYSTEMS p 1536
540 E 200 S 84102
Tel (801) 366-7700 SIC 6371

UTAH TRANSIT AUTHORITY (UTA) p 1536
669 W 200 S Bldg 1 84101
Tel (801) 262-5626 SIC 4111

UTILITY TRAILER SALES OF UTAH INC p 1537
4970 W 2100 S 84120
Tel (801) 973-4040 SIC 5511 5531 7539

VALLEY MENTAL HEALTH INC p 1541
5965 S 900 E 84121
Tel (801) 263-7100 SIC 8093

VMI NUTRITION INC p 1563
391 S Orange St Ste C 84104
Tel (801) 954-0471 SIC 2087

WEIR GROUP LP p 1588
440 W 800 S 84101
Tel (801) 530-7937 SIC 3561

WESTECH ENGINEERING INC p 1597
3665 S West Temple 84115
Tel (801) 265-1000 SIC 3589

WESTERN EXPLOSIVES SYSTEMS CO p 1598
3135 S Richmond St 84106
Tel (801) 484-6557
SIC 5169 1629 1241 1081 1481 2892

WESTERN GOVERNORS UNIVERSITY p 1598
4001 S 700 E Ste 700 84107
Tel (801) 274-3280 SIC 8299 8221

WESTMINSTER COLLEGE p 1601
1840 S 1300 E 84105
Tel (801) 484-7651 SIC 8221

WHEELER MACHINERY CO p 1605
4901 W 2100 S 84120
Tel (801) 974-0511
SIC 5082 5084 7359 7353

WOODSIDE GROUP INC p 1623
460 W 50 N Ste 200 84101
Tel (801) 299-6700 SIC 1531

YOUNG ELECTRIC SIGN CO INC p 1638
2401 S Foothill Dr 84109
Tel (801) 464-4600
SIC 3993 7359 1799 6794

■ ZB NATIONAL ASSOCIATION p 1641
1 S Main St 84133
Tel (801) 974-8800 SIC 6021

▲ ZIONS BANCORPORATION p 1643
1 S Main St Fl 15 84133
Tel (801) 844-7637 SIC 6022 6021

■ ZIONS CREDIT CORP p 1643
310 S Main St Ste 1300 84101
Tel (801) 524-2230 SIC 6159

ZIONS MOUNTAIN VIEW HOME AND ASSOCIATES LTD p 1643
2730 E 3300 S 84109
Tel (801) 487-0896 SIC 8741

SANDY, UT

■ ACS COMMERCIAL SOLUTIONS INC p 18
510 W Parkland Dr 84070
Tel (801) 567-5000 SIC 7374 7389

■ BECTON DICKINSON INFUSION THERAPY HOLDINGS INC p 167
9450 S State St 84070
Tel (801) 565-2300 SIC 3841 3842

■ BECTON DICKINSON INFUSION THERAPY SYSTEMS INC p 167
9450 S State St 84070
Tel (801) 565-2300 SIC 3841 3842

CANYONS SCHOOL DISTRICT p 248
9361 S 300 E 84070
Tel (801) 826-5340 SIC 8211

CEMENTATION USA INC p 274
10150 S Centennial Pkwy # 110 84070
Tel (801) 937-4120 SIC 1081

CHALLENGER SCHOOLS p 287
9424 S 300 W 84070
Tel (801) 569-2700 SIC 8351 8211

DIAMOND WIRELESS LLC p 437
10450 S State St 84070
Tel (801) 501-7683 SIC 4812

DIAMOND WIRELESS-OREGON LLC p 437
7927 High Point Pkwy # 300 84094
Tel (801) 733-6929 SIC 4812

IBAHN CORP p 726
126 W 10000 S Ste 100 84070
Tel (801) 952-2000 SIC 4813

INCONTACT INC p 735
75 W Towne Ridge Pkwy # 1 84070
Tel (801) 320-3200 SIC 7372 4813

LARRY H MILLER GROUP OF COMPANIES p 845
9350 S 150 E Ste 1000 84070
Tel (801) 563-4100 SIC 8741

LARRY H MILLER THEATRES INC p 845
35 E 9270 S 84070
Tel (801) 304-4500 SIC 7832

LAYTON COMPANIES INC p 848
9090 S Sandy Pkwy 84070
Tel (801) 568-9090 SIC 1542 1541

▲ LIFEVANTAGE CORP p 865
9785 S Monroe St Ste 300 84070
Tel (801) 432-9000 SIC 2834

STANDARD PLUMBING SUPPLY CO INC p 1376
9150 S 300 W Bldg 5 84070
Tel (801) 255-7145 SIC 5074

WORKERS COMPENSATION FUND p 1624
100 W Towne Ridge Pkwy 84070
Tel (385) 351-8000 SIC 6331

SNOWBIRD, UT

SNOWBIRD LTD p 1336
State Rd 210 84092
Tel (801) 742-2222 SIC 1531 6519

SNOWBIRD RESORT LLC p 1336
9385 S Snowbird Center Dr 84092
Tel (801) 933-4670 SIC 7011

SOUTH JORDAN, UT

AMERICAN SMARTPHONE INC p 79
10421 S Jordan Gtwy # 500 84095
Tel (801) 748-1780 SIC 3663

DESERET GENERATION AND TRANSMISSION CO-OPERATIVE p 432
10714 S Jordan Gtwy # 300 84095
Tel (435) 781-5737 SIC 4911

▲ HEADWATERS INC p 673
10701 S River Front Pkwy # 300 84095
Tel (801) 984-9400
SIC 3272 3271 3281 2952

■ HEADWATERS RESOURCES INC p 673
10701 S River Front Pkwy # 300 84095
Tel (801) 984-9400 SIC 5032 4953 8711

INNOVATIVE STAFFING INC p 745
859 W South Jordan Pkwy # 77 84095
Tel (801) 984-0252 SIC 7363

INTERMOUNTAIN POWER AGENCY p 753
10653 S River Front Pkwy # 120 84095
Tel (801) 938-1333 SIC 4911

ISI HR INC p 766
859 W South Jordan Pkwy # 77 84095
Tel (801) 984-0252 SIC 7361

KENNECOTT UTAH COPPER LLC p 811
4700 W Daybreak Pkwy 84009
Tel (801) 204-2000
SIC 1021 1041 1044 1061

LANDESK SOFTWARE INC p 842
698 W 10000 S Ste 500 84095
Tel (801) 208-1500 SIC 7371

LONGYEAR CO p 877
10808 S River Front Pkwy 84095
Tel (801) 972-6430 SIC 1481

▲ MERIT MEDICAL SYSTEMS INC p 949
1600 W Merit Pkwy 84095
Tel (801) 253-1600 SIC 3841

MERRICK BANK CORP p 950
10705 S Jordan Gtwy # 200 84095
Tel (801) 545-6600 SIC 6021

MONAVIE LLC p 983
10855 S River Front Pkwy # 100 84095
Tel (801) 748-3100 SIC 5963

■ MORGAN STANLEY BANK p 989
680 W 10000 S Fl 2 84095
Tel (212) 761-4000 SIC 6022

OOCL (USA) INC p 1088
10913 S River Front Pkwy # 200 84095
Tel (801) 302-6625 SIC 4731

PROVO CRAFT & NOVELTY INC p 1187
10855 S Rvr Frnt Pkwy # 400 84095
Tel (800) 937-7686
SIC 5092 5199 5945 5947

■ RIO TINTO SERVICES INC p 1236
4700 W Daybreak Pkwy 84009
Tel (801) 204-2000 SIC 8721 8741

ULTRADENT PRODUCTS INC p 1501
505 W 10200 S 84095
Tel (801) 572-4200 SIC 3843

SOUTH SALT LAKE, UT

INTERMOUNTAIN FARMERS ASSOCIATION p 753
1147 W 2100 S 84119
Tel (801) 972-2122 SIC 5999 5191

T&N ASPHALT SERVICES INC p 1420
3643 S 700 W Ste C 84119
Tel (801) 266-1626 SIC 1611

USI SENIOR HOLDINGS INC p 1535
895 W 2600 S 84119
Tel (801) 983-0390 SIC 1742

SPANISH FORK, UT

NEBO SCHOOL DISTRICT p 1023
350 S Main St 84660
Tel (801) 354-7400 SIC 8211

SPRINGVILLE, UT

■ FLOWSERVE FCD CORP p 560
1350 N Mtn Spring Pkwy 84663
Tel (801) 489-8611 SIC 3491

MAPLE MOUNTAIN ENTERPRISES INC p 903
588 S 2000 W 84663
Tel (801) 418-2000 SIC 2023

MAPLE MOUNTAIN GROUP INC p 903
588 S 2000 W 84663
Tel (801) 418-2000 SIC 5999

W W CLYDE & CO p 1569
1375 N Main St 84663
Tel (801) 802-6800 SIC 1611 1794 1629

ST GEORGE, UT

IHC HEALTH SERVICES INC p 730
1380 E Medical Center Dr 84790
Tel (801) 442-5000
SIC 8062 8011 8322 8049 8093 8069

M CASPERSON ENTERPRISE LLC p 889
220 S 100 E 84770
Tel (800) 275-8802 *SIC* 5063 1731

■ SKYWEST AIRLINES INC p 1330
444 S River Rd 84790
Tel (435) 634-3000 *SIC* 4512

▲ SKYWEST INC p 1330
444 S River Rd 84790
Tel (435) 634-3000 *SIC* 4512

ST GEORGE CITY GOVERNMENT (INC) p 1367
175 E 200 N 84770
Tel (435) 627-4000 *SIC* 9532

SUNROC CORP p 1404
3657 S River Rd 84790
Tel (435) 634-2200
SIC 5031 3273 5032 3271 1442

WASHINGTON COUNTY SCHOOL DISTRICT p 1578
121 W Tabernacle St 84770
Tel (435) 673-3553 *SIC* 8211

SYRACUSE, UT

CRAIG F SORENSEN CONSTRUCTION INC p 388
918 S 2000 W 84075
Tel (801) 773-4390 *SIC* 1623 1731

TAYLORSVILLE, UT

UTAH DEPARTMENT OF PUBLIC SAFETY p 1536
4501 S Constitution Blvd 84129
Tel (801) 965-4461 *SIC* 9229

UTAH DEPARTMENT OF TRANSPORTATION p 1536
4501 S Constitution Blvd 84129
Tel (801) 965-4000 *SIC* 9621

UTAH NATIONAL SECURITY INC p 1536
2600 W 4700 S 84129
Tel (801) 963-0397 *SIC* 5651

WOLF TRANSPORTATION LLC p 1621
5204 S Redwood Rd Ste B1 84123
Tel (801) 759-9465 *SIC* 4212

TOOELE, UT

DETROIT DIESEL REMANUFACTURING-WEST INC p 433
100 Lodestone Way 84074
Tel (435) 843-6000 *SIC* 3519 3714 5013

TOOELE COUNTY SCHOOL DISTRICT p 1460
92 Lodestone Way 84074
Tel (435) 833-1900 *SIC* 8211

TREMONTON, UT

BOX ELDER SCHOOL DISTRICT p 205
515 N 800 W 84337
Tel (435) 257-2560 *SIC* 8211 8742

WEST JORDAN, UT

JORDAN SCHOOL DISTRICT p 793
7387 S Campus View Dr 84084
Tel (801) 280-3689 *SIC* 8211

JORDAN VALLEY MEDICAL CENTER LP p 793
3580 W 9000 S 84088
Tel (801) 561-8888 *SIC* 8062

MOUNTAIN AMERICA FEDERAL CREDIT UNION p 994
7181 S Campus View Dr 84084
Tel (801) 325-6228 *SIC* 6062

SME INDUSTRIES INC p 1332
5801 W Wells Park Rd 84081
Tel (801) 280-3960 *SIC* 1791 3441

■ STOCK BUILDING SUPPLY WEST LLC p 1390
1133 W 9000 S 84088
Tel (801) 561-9000 *SIC* 5031 5211 2439

WEST VALLEY CITY, UT

CCI MECHANICAL INC p 270
2345 S Cci Way 84119
Tel (801) 973-9000 *SIC* 1711

CENTRAL REFRIGERATED SERVICE LLC p 280
5175 W 2100 S 84120
Tel (801) 924-7000 *SIC* 4213

FREIGHTLINER OF UTAH A LIMITED LIABILITY CO p 577
2240 S 5370 W 84120
Tel (801) 978-8000
SIC 5012 5013 7539 7538 5511

KENWORTH SALES CO p 813
2125 S Constitution Blvd 84119
Tel (801) 487-4161
SIC 5012 5013 7538 3519

SELECT PORTFOLIO SERVICING INC p 1301
3217 Decker Lake Dr 84119
Tel (800) 258-8602 *SIC* 6162

UTAH HOUSING CORP p 1536
2479 S Lake Park Blvd 84120
Tel (801) 902-8200 *SIC* 6211 6162

VERMONT

ARLINGTON, VT

MACK GROUP INC p 892
608 Warm Brook Rd 05250
Tel (802) 375-2511 *SIC* 3089 3577 6719

MACK MOLDING CO INC p 892
608 Warm Brook Rd 05250
Tel (802) 375-2511 *SIC* 3089 3577

BARRE, VT

BOND AUTO PARTS INC p 199
272 Morrison Rd 05641
Tel (802) 479-0571 *SIC* 5013 5531

CAPITAL CANDY CO INC p 249
32 Burnham St 05641
Tel (802) 476-6689
SIC 5145 5194 5122 5141 5149

BENNINGTON, VT

SOUTHWESTERN VERMONT HEALTH CARE CORP p 1353
100 Hospital Dr 05201
Tel (802) 442-6361 *SIC* 8741

SOUTHWESTERN VERMONT MEDICAL CENTER INC p 1353
100 Hospital Dr 05201
Tel (802) 442-6361 *SIC* 8062

BERLIN, VT

CENTRAL VERMONT MEDICAL CENTER INC p 281
130 Fisher Rd Unit 1 05602
Tel (802) 371-4100 *SIC* 8062

EASTER SEALS VERMONT INC p 471
641 Comstock Rd Ste 1 05602
Tel (802) 223-4744 *SIC* 8322

BETHEL, VT

G W PLASTICS INC p 587
239 Pleasant St 05032
Tel (802) 234-9941 *SIC* 3089 3544

BRATTLEBORO, VT

G S PRECISION INC p 587
101 John Seitz Dr 05301
Tel (802) 257-5200 *SIC* 3728

WORLD LEARNING INC p 1625
1 Kipling Rd 05301
Tel (802) 257-7751 *SIC* 8221 8299

BURLINGTON, VT

■ ARCONIC SECURITIES LLC p 106
101 Cherry St Ste 400 05401
Tel (802) 658-2661 *SIC* 3353

BURTON CORP p 229
80 Industrial Pkwy 05401
Tel (802) 862-4500 *SIC* 3949

CHAMPLAIN COLLEGE INC p 287
246 S Willard St 05401
Tel (802) 860-2700 *SIC* 8222

CORNELL TRADING INC p 370
131 Battery St 05401
Tel (802) 879-1271
SIC 5023 5137 5719 5621

DEALER DOT COM INC p 419
1 Howard St 05401
Tel (888) 894-8989 *SIC* 7374

FLETCHER ALLEN HEALTH VENTURES INC p 555
111 Colchester Ave 05401
Tel (802) 847-5669 *SIC* 8011

HOWARDCENTER INC p 713
208 Flynn Ave Ste 3j 05401
Tel (802) 488-6900 *SIC* 8322

INDEPENDENT BREWERS UNITED CORP p 736
431 Pine St Ste G12 05401
Tel (802) 862-6114 *SIC* 2082 2084

UNIVERSITY OF VERMONT & STATE AGRICULTURAL COLLEGE p 1526
85 S Prospect St 05405
Tel (802) 656-3131 *SIC* 8221

UNIVERSITY OF VERMONT MEDICAL CENTER INC p 1526
111 Colchester Ave 05401
Tel (802) 847-0000 *SIC* 8062

VERMONT ENERGY INVESTMENT CORP p 1551
128 Lakeside Ave Ste 401 05401
Tel (802) 860-4095 *SIC* 8748

COLCHESTER, VT

DEPARTMENT OF MILITARY VERMONT p 430
789 National Guard Rd 05446
Tel (802) 338-3310 *SIC* 9711

GREEN MOUNTAIN POWER CORP p 637
163 Acorn Ln 05446
Tel (888) 835-4672 *SIC* 4911 1623 1731

NOKIAN TYRES INC p 1046
1945 Main St 05446
Tel (800) 852-5222 *SIC* 5014

SAINT MICHAELS COLLEGE INC p 1270
1 Winooski Park 05439
Tel (802) 654-2000 *SIC* 8221

KILLINGTON, VT

KILLINGTON/PICO SKI RESORT PARTNERS LLC p 818
4763 Killington Rd 05751
Tel (802) 422-3333 *SIC* 7011

LYNDONVILLE, VT

LYNDON STATE COLLEGE p 888
1001 College Rd 05851
Tel (802) 626-6200 *SIC* 8221

MANCHESTER CENTER, VT

VERMONT COUNTRY STORE INC p 1551
5650 Main St 05255
Tel (802) 362-4667 *SIC* 5961 5399 5812

MIDDLEBURY, VT

PRESIDENT AND FELLOWS OF MIDDLEBURY COLLEGE p 1172
38 College St 05753
Tel (802) 443-5000 *SIC* 8221

MILTON, VT

BURLINGTON DRUG CO INC p 228
91 Catamount Dr 05468
Tel (802) 893-5105 *SIC* 5122

HUSKY INJECTION MOLDING SYSTEMS INC p 721
288 North Rd 05468
Tel (905) 951-5000 *SIC* 5084 7699

MONTPELIER, VT

BLUE CROSS AND BLUE SHIELD OF VERMONT p 192
445 Industrial Ln 05602
Tel (802) 223-6131 *SIC* 6321

EXECUTIVE OFFICE OF STATE OF VERMONT p 518
109 State St Ste 5 05609
Tel (802) 828-3333 *SIC* 9111

NATIONAL LIFE HOLDING CO p 1014
1 National Life Dr 05604
Tel (802) 229-3333 *SIC* 6311 6321

NATIONAL LIFE INSURANCE CO p 1014
1 National Life Dr 05604
Tel (802) 229-3333 *SIC* 6311

NLV FINANCIAL CORP p 1045
1 National Life Dr 05604
Tel (802) 229-3333 *SIC* 6311 6321

STATE OF VERMONT p 1382
109 State St Ste 4 05609
Tel (802) 828-1452 *SIC* 9111

VERMONT AGENCY OF TRANSPORTATION p 1551
1 National Life Dr # 20 05602
Tel (802) 828-2657 *SIC* 9621

VERMONT MUTUAL INSURANCE CO p 1551
89 State St 05602
Tel (802) 223-2341 *SIC* 6331

VERMONT STATE COLLEGES p 1551
660 Elm St 05602
Tel (802) 828-2800 *SIC* 8221

NORTHFIELD, VT

NORWICH UNIVERSITY p 1061
158 Harmon Dr 05663
Tel (802) 485-2000 *SIC* 8221

NORWICH, VT

KING ARTHUR FLOUR CO INC p 820
135 Us Route 5 S 05055
Tel (802) 649-3881
SIC 5149 5961 5461 8299

RUTLAND, VT

■ CASELLA WASTE MANAGEMENT INC p 263
25 Green Hill Ln 05701
Tel (802) 775-0325 *SIC* 4953 4212

▲ CASELLA WASTE SYSTEMS INC p 263
25 Green Hill Ln 05701
Tel (802) 775-0325 *SIC* 4953

RUTLAND HOSPITAL INC ACT 220 p 1260
160 Allen St 05701
Tel (802) 775-7111 *SIC* 8062

RUTLAND REGIONAL HEALTH SERVICES p 1260
160 Allen St 05701
Tel (802) 775-7111 *SIC* 8062 7352 8059

SHERMAN V ALLEN INC p 1316
126 Post St 05701
Tel (802) 775-7421
SIC 5172 5984 5411 4923

VERMONT ELECTRIC POWER CO INC p 1551
366 Pinnacle Ridge Rd 05701
Tel (802) 773-9161 *SIC* 4911

VERMONT TRANSCO LLC p 1551
366 Pinnacle Ridge Rd 05701
Tel (802) 773-9161 *SIC* 1731

VERMONT YANKEE NUCLEAR POWER CORP p 1551
45 Union St 05701
Tel (802) 258-4120 *SIC* 1731

SAINT ALBANS, VT

A N DERINGER INC p 6
64 N Main St 05478
Tel (802) 524-8110 *SIC* 4731

HANDY PONTIAC CADILLAC BUICK G M C INC p 657
405 Swanton Rd 05478
Tel (802) 524-6531 *SIC* 5511

NORTHWESTERN MEDICAL CENTER INC p 1060
133 Fairfield St 05478
Tel (802) 524-5911 *SIC* 8062

R L VALLEE INC p 1202
282 S Main St 05478
Tel (802) 524-8710 *SIC* 5172 5541

ST ALBANS COOPERATIVE CREAMERY INC p 1364
140 Federal St 05478
Tel (802) 524-9366 *SIC* 2026 2023

SAINT JOHNSBURY, VT

NSA INDUSTRIES LLC p 1064
210 Pierce Rd 05819
Tel (802) 748-5007 *SIC* 3444 1799 1796

SOUTH BURLINGTON, VT

BEN & JERRYS HOMEMADE INC p 172
30 Community Dr Ste 1 05403
Tel (802) 846-1500 *SIC* 2024 5812 6794

CHAMPLAIN OIL CO INC p 287
45 San Remo Dr 05403
Tel (802) 864-5380 *SIC* 5172 5984

■ IDX SYSTEMS CORP p 729
40 Idx Dr 05403
Tel (802) 658-2664 *SIC* 7371

NORTHERN NEW ENGLAND ENERGY CORP p 1056
85 Swift St 05403
Tel (802) 658-6555 *SIC* 4911

PC CONSTRUCTION CO p 1123
193 Tilley Dr 05403
Tel (802) 658-4100 *SIC* 1629 1542

SYMQUEST GROUP INC p 1414
30 Community Dr Ste 5 05403
Tel (802) 658-9890 *SIC* 5044 8243

SOUTH LONDONDERRY, VT

■ STRATTON CORP p 1393
5 Village Lodge Rd 05155
Tel (802) 297-2200
SIC 7011 7992 1531 6512 5941

STRATTON MOUNTAIN COUNTRY CLUB p 1393
Stratton Mtn Access Rd 05155
Tel (802) 297-1005 *SIC* 7997

STOWE, VT

■ MT MANSFIELD CO INC p 997
5781 Mountain Rd 05672
Tel (802) 253-7311 *SIC* 6331 5812 5813

SUNDERLAND, VT

ORVIS CO INC p 1096
178 Conservation Way 05250
Tel (802) 362-3622 *SIC* 5961 5941 3949

VERGENNES, VT

■ SIMMONDS PRECISION PRODUCTS INC p 1324
100 Panton Rd 05491
Tel (802) 877-4000
SIC 3829 3694 3724 3728

WAITSFIELD, VT

CABOT CREAMERY COOPERATIVE INC p 235
193 Home Farm Way 05673
Tel (978) 552-5500 *SIC* 2022 5143 5451

WATERBURY, VT

KEURIG GREEN MOUNTAIN INC p 814
33 Coffee Ln 05676
Tel (802) 244-5621 *SIC* 5046

VERMONT AGENCY OF HUMAN SERVICES p 1551
280 State Dr 05671
Tel (802) 871-3007 *SIC* 9441

WHITE RIVER JUNCTION, VT

KING ARTHUR FLOUR CO INC p 820
62 Fogg Farm Rd 05001
Tel (802) 649-3881 *SIC* 5149

WILLISTON, VT

LAND-AIR EXPRESS OF NEW ENGLAND LTD p 842
59 Avenue C 05495
Tel (800) 639-3095 *SIC* 4214

VELAN VALVE CORP p 1547
94 Avenue C 05495
Tel (802) 863-2561 *SIC* 3491

VIRGIN ISLANDS

CHARLOTTE AMALIE, VI

GOVERNMENT OF US VIRGIN ISLANDS p 627
21-22 Kongens Gade 00802
Tel (340) 774-0001 SIC 9111

CHRISTIANSTED, VI

ALTISOURCE RESIDENTIAL CORP p 62
36c Strand St 00820
Tel (340) 692-1055 SIC 6798

GOVERNOR JUAN F LUIS HOSPITAL & MEDICAL CENTER p 627
4007 Estate Diamond Ruby 00820
Tel (340) 778-6311 SIC 8062

HOVENSA LLC p 713
1 Estate Hope 00820
Tel (340) 692-3000 SIC 1382

LIMETREE BAY TERMINALS LLC p 866
1 Estate Hope 00820
Tel (340) 692-3000 SIC 4225

ST THOMAS, VI

DIRECT BEAUTY INC p 441
33 Estate Fryndendahl 00802
Tel (340) 775-4612 SIC 7231

INNOVATIVE COMMUNICATIONS CORP p 744
4611 Tutu Park Mall # 200 00802
Tel (340) 777-7700 SIC 4813 4841

VIRGIN ISLANDS WATER & POWER AUTHORITY p 1558
9702 Estate Thomas 00802
Tel (340) 774-3552 SIC 4911

VIRGINIA

ABINGDON, VA

JOHNSTON MEMORIAL HOSPITAL INC p 791
16000 Johnston Memorial D 24211
Tel (276) 258-1000 SIC 8062 8011

K-VA-T FOOD STORES INC p 799
1 Food City Cir E 24210
Tel (800) 826-8451 SIC 5411 5141 6512

MID-MOUNTAIN FOODS INC p 963
26331 Hillman Hwy 24210
Tel (276) 623-5000 SIC 5141

ALEXANDRIA, VA

A & G QUALITY BUILDERS INC p 4
1413 Powhatan St 22314
Tel (703) 549-8682 SIC 1522

ABC IMAGING OF WASHINGTON INC p 10
5290 Shawnee Rd Ste 300 22312
Tel (202) 429-8870 SIC 2759

AHL SERVICES INC p 36
102 S Union St 22314
Tel (703) 682-0729 SIC 8742

ALEXANDRIA CITY PUBLIC SCHOOLS p 49
1340 Braddock Pl Ste 100 22314
Tel (703) 619-8000 SIC 8211

ALEXANDRIA INOVA HOSPITAL p 49
4320 Seminary Rd 22304
Tel (703) 504-3000 SIC 8062

AMERICAN SERVICE CENTER ASSOCIATES OF ALEXANDRIA LLC p 79
200 S Pickett St 22304
Tel (703) 284-2490 SIC 5511 7538

AMERICAN SOCIETY OF CLINICAL ONCOLOGY INC p 79
2318 Mill Rd Ste 800 22314
Tel (571) 483-1300 SIC 8621

ARMED FORCES BENEFIT ASSOCIATION p 111
909 N Washington St # 767 22314
Tel (703) 549-4455 SIC 7389

■ BOAT AMERICA CORP p 196
880 S Pickett St 22304
Tel (703) 823-0984 SIC 6331

BOSTON COACH-WASHINGTON CORP p 202
5775c General Wash Dr 22312
Tel (703) 813-6280 SIC 4119

▲ BURKE & HERBERT BANK & TRUST CO INC p 227
100 S Fairfax St 22314
Tel (703) 299-8491 SIC 6022

CALIBRE SYSTEMS INC p 239
6354 Walker Ln Ste 300 22310
Tel (703) 797-8500 SIC 7379 8748

CATAPULT TECHNOLOGY LTD p 265
11 Canal Center Plz Fl 2 22314
Tel (240) 482-2100 SIC 7373 8742

CB&I FEDERAL SERVICES LLC p 268
1725 Duke St Ste 400 22314
Tel (202) 261-1900 SIC 1521

CHARITIES AID FOUNDATION AMERICA p 288
1800 Diagonal Rd Ste 150 22314
Tel (703) 549-8931 SIC 8399

CITY OF ALEXANDRIA p 312
301 King St 22314
Tel (703) 746-4000 SIC 9111

COMPUTER SECURITY SOLUTIONS LLC p 353
11 Canal Center Plz Fl 2 22314
Tel (703) 956-5700 SIC 5045

DCS CORP p 418
6909 Metro Park Dr # 500 22310
Tel (571) 227-6000 SIC 7373

■ DEFENSE HUMAN RESOURCES ACTIVITY p 422
4800 Mark Center Dr D 22350
Tel (571) 372-1949 SIC 9711

■ DEPARTMENT OF DEFENSE EDUCATION ACTIVITY p 430
4800 Mark Center Dr 22350
Tel (571) 372-1337 SIC 9711 9411

DONORS TRUST INC p 451
1800 Diagonal Rd Ste 280 22314
Tel (703) 535-3563 SIC 6732 8733

■ FLUOR-LANE LLC p 561
6315 Bren Mar Dr Ste 250 22312
Tel (571) 480-4641 SIC 8711

■ FOOD & NUTRITION SERVICE p 563
3101 Park Center Dr # 200 22302
Tel (703) 305-2060 SIC 9641

GIANT CEMENT HOLDING INC p 610
1600 Duke St Ste 400 22314
Tel (571) 302-7150 SIC 3241 4953

GOOD360 p 624
675 N Washington St # 330 22314
Tel (703) 836-2121 SIC 8399

GRANISER LLC p 631
5650 General Wash Dr 22312
Tel (703) 256-5650 SIC 5032

INSTITUTE FOR DEFENSE ANALYSES INC p 747
4850 Mark Center Dr 22311
Tel (703) 845-2000 SIC 8733

KS INTERNATIONAL LLC p 831
3601 Eisenhower Ave # 600 22304
Tel (703) 676-3253 SIC 1522

LINDSAY MOTOR CAR CO p 868
1525 Kenwood Ave 22302
Tel (703) 998-6600 SIC 5511

MICHAEL & SON SERVICES INC p 959
5740 General Wash Dr 22312
Tel (703) 658-3998 SIC 1521 1731 5074

■ MILITARY SURFACE DEPLOYMENT & DISTRIBUTION COMMAND p 969
200 Stovall St Fl 18 22332
Tel (703) 428-2753 SIC 9711

MODERN TECHNOLOGY SOLUTIONS INC p 981
5285 Shawnee Rd Ste 400 22312
Tel (703) 564-3800
SIC 8711 8742 8731 7379

NES ASSOCIATES LLC p 1026
6400 Beulah St Ste 100 22310
Tel (703) 224-2600 SIC 7373

■ OFFICE OF THE INSPECTOR GENERAL p 1076
4800 Mark Center Dr 22350
Tel (703) 604-8669 SIC 9711

ON-SITE E DISCOVERY INC p 1086
806 N Henry St 22314
Tel (703) 683-9710 SIC 2759

PENTAGON FEDERAL CREDIT UNION p 1131
2930 Eisenhower Ave 22314
Tel (800) 247-5626 SIC 6061

PIERCE ASSOCIATES INC p 1147
4216 Wheeler Ave 22304
Tel (703) 751-2400 SIC 1711

R&R ENTERPRISES INC p 1203
1101 King St Ste 550 22314
Tel (703) 739-0084 SIC 8711

RAND CONSTRUCTION CORP p 1207
1029 N Royal St Ste 100 22314
Tel (202) 449-9840 SIC 1542

SAFRAN USA INC p 1267
700 S Washington St # 320 22314
Tel (703) 351-9898
SIC 3643 3621 7699 3724 5013 5088

SALVATION ARMY NATIONAL CORP p 1273
615 Slaters Ln 22314
Tel (703) 684-5500 SIC 8661 8699

SENTEL CORP p 1305
2800 Eisenhower Ave # 300 22314
Tel (571) 481-2000 SIC 8711 8742 8741

SOCIETY FOR HUMAN RESOURCE MANAGEMENT p 1336
1800 Duke St 22314
Tel (703) 548-3440 SIC 8621

STG INTERNATIONAL INC p 1389
99 Canal Center Plz # 500 22314
Tel (571) 970-3729 SIC 7361

TRANSFORCE INC p 1471
5520 Cherokee Ave Ste 200 22312
Tel (703) 838-5580 SIC 7363

■ UNITED STATES PATENT AND TRADEMARK OFFICE p 1513
600 Dulany St Ste 1 22314
Tel (571) 272-4100 SIC 9651

VISION TECHNOLOGIES ELECTRONICS INC p 1561
99 Canal Center Plz # 210 22314
Tel (703) 739-2610 SIC 8711

VISION TECHNOLOGIES SYSTEMS INC p 1561
99 Canal Center Plz # 220 22314
Tel (703) 739-2610 SIC 3731 3531

VOLUNTEERS OF AMERICA INC p 1565
1660 Duke St Ste 100 22314
Tel (703) 341-5000 SIC 8322 6531

▲ VSE CORP p 1566
6348 Walker Ln 22310
Tel (703) 960-4600 SIC 8711 8742 8741

ALTAVISTA, VA

MOORES ELECTRICAL & MECHANICAL CONSTRUCTION INC p 987
101 Edgewood Ave 24517
Tel (434) 369-4374 SIC 1731 1711

SCHRADER-BRIDGEPORT INTERNATIONAL INC p 1290
205 Frazier Rd 24517
Tel (434) 369-4741
SIC 3492 3714 3491 3011

ANNANDALE, VA

INOVA WOODBURN SURGERY CENTER LLC p 745
3289 Woodburn Rd Ste 100 22003
Tel (703) 226-2640 SIC 8011

ARLINGTON, VA

ACCENTURE FEDERAL SERVICES LLC p 14
800 N Glebe Rd Ste 300 22203
Tel (703) 947-2000 SIC 8742 7379

▲ AES CORP p 31
4300 Wilson Blvd Ste 1100 22203
Tel (703) 522-1315 SIC 4911

■ AES DPL HOLDINGS LLC p 31
4300 Wilson Blvd 22203
Tel (703) 522-1315 SIC 4911

AIRLINES REPORTING CORP p 40
3000 Wilson Blvd Ste 300 22201
Tel (703) 816-8000 SIC 7389 6099 7374

ALENIA AERMACCHI NORTH AMERICA INC p 48
1235 S Clark St Ste 700 22202
Tel (703) 413-2125 SIC 8711

■ ALLBRITTON COMMUNICATIONS CO p 52
1000 Wilson Blvd Ste 2700 22209
Tel (703) 647-8700 SIC 4833 7812

■ ALLBRITTON GROUP LLC p 52
1000 Wilson Blvd Ste 2700 22209
Tel (703) 647-8700 SIC 4833

▲ ARLINGTON ASSET INVESTMENT CORP p 110
1001 19th St N Ste 1900 22209
Tel (703) 373-0200 SIC 6798 6162

ARLINGTON PUBLIC SCHOOLS p 110
1426 N Quincy St 22207
Tel (703) 228-6000 SIC 8211

■ ARMED FORCES SERVICES CORP p 111
2800 S Shirlington Rd # 350 22206
Tel (571) 312-7670 SIC 8742

▲ AVALONBAY COMMUNITIES INC p 136
671 N Glebe Rd Ste 800 22203
Tel (703) 329-6300 SIC 6798

BAE SYSTEMS HOLDINGS INC p 144
1101 Wilson Blvd Ste 2000 22209
Tel (703) 312-6100 SIC 3699 3728 3812

BAE SYSTEMS INC p 144
1101 Wilson Blvd Ste 2000 22209
Tel (703) 312-6100 SIC 3812 3728

BAE SYSTEMS LAND & ARMAMENTS INC p 144
2000 15th Nw 22201
Tel (703) 907-8200 SIC 3721 3795

BAE SYSTEMS LAND & ARMAMENTS LP p 144
2000 15th Nw Fl 11 22201
Tel (703) 312-6100 SIC 3795 3812

BNG AMERICA LLC p 194
1235 S Clark St Ste 700a 22202
Tel (703) 412-2500
SIC 8711 8741 4953 2819

BUREAU OF NATIONAL AFFAIRS INC p 226
1801 S Bell St Ste Cn110 22202
Tel (703) 341-3000 SIC 2711 2721

■ CACI ENTERPRISE SOLUTIONS INC p 235
1100 N Glebe Rd Ste 200 22201
Tel (703) 841-7800 SIC 7373

■ CACI INC - FEDERAL p 235
1100 N Glebe Rd Ste 200 22201
Tel (703) 841-7800
SIC 7373 7372 7371 8711

▲ CACI INTERNATIONAL INC p 235
1100 N Glebe Rd Ste 200 22201
Tel (703) 841-7800 SIC 7373 4899 7371

■ CACI TECHNOLOGIES INC p 236
1100 N Glebe Rd Ste 200 22201
Tel (703) 841-7800 SIC 7373 8711

■ CACI-ISS INC p 236
1100 N Glebe Rd Ste 200 22201
Tel (703) 841-7800 SIC 7371

CATHOLIC DIOCESE OF ARLINGTON p 266
200 N Glebe Rd Ste 901 22203
Tel (703) 841-2500 SIC 8661

▲ CEB INC p 272
1919 N Lynn St 22209
Tel (571) 303-3000 SIC 8742

CHANGEIS INC p 288
1530 Wilson Blvd Ste 340 22209
Tel (301) 237-1622 SIC 8742

CHARLES G KOCH CHARITABLE FOUNDATION p 289
1515 N Courthouse Rd # 200 22201
Tel (703) 875-1600 SIC 8699

CLARK REALTY CAPITAL LLC p 322
4401 Wilson Blvd Ste 600 22203
Tel (703) 294-4500 SIC 1522 1531 1542

CNA CORP p 329
3003 Washington Blvd 22201
Tel (703) 824-2000 SIC 8732

COBHAM AES HOLDINGS INC p 332
2121 Crystal Dr Ste 625 22202
Tel (703) 414-5300 SIC 3679 3812

CONSERVATION FUND A NONPROFIT CORP p 358
1655 Fort Myer Dr # 1300 22209
Tel (703) 525-6300 SIC 8422

CONSERVATION INTERNATIONAL FOUNDATION p 358
2011 Crystal Dr Ste 500 22202
Tel (703) 341-2400 SIC 8748

CONSUMER TECHNOLOGY ASSOCIATION p 361
1919 S Eads St Ste Ll 22202
Tel (703) 907-7600 SIC 8611

COUNTY OF ARLINGTON p 376
2100 Clarendon Blvd # 500 22201
Tel (703) 228-3130 SIC 9111

DOMINION ELECTRIC SUPPLY CO INC p 449
5053 Lee Hwy 22207
Tel (703) 532-0741 SIC 5063 5719

DRS TECHNOLOGIES INC p 457
2345 Crystal Dr Ste 1000 22202
Tel (973) 898-1500
SIC 3812 3699 3572 3669 3679 8741

■ EMCOR GOVERNMENT SERVICES INC p 491
2800 Crystal Dr Ste 600 22202
Tel (571) 403-8900 SIC 8741 8711 1731

▲ EVOLENT HEALTH INC p 515
800 N Glebe Rd Ste 500 22203
Tel (571) 389-6000 SIC 8099

EXPERIENCE WORKS INC p 520
4401 Wilson Blvd Ste 1100 22203
Tel (703) 522-7272 SIC 8322 8331

▲ FBR & CO p 532
1300 17th St N 22209
Tel (703) 312-9500 SIC 6211

■ FISH & WILDLIFE SERVICE UNITED STATES p 551
4401 Fairfax Dr Ste 325 22203
Tel (703) 358-1742 SIC 9512

▲ GRAHAM HOLDINGS CO p 629
1300 17th St N Ste 1700 22209
Tel (703) 345-6300
SIC 8299 4833 4841 2721

GREATER WASHINGTON EDUCATIONAL TELECOMMUNICATIONS ASSOCIATION INC p 636
3939 Campbell Ave 22206
Tel (703) 998-2600 SIC 4833 4832

■ GSA FEDERAL ACQUISITION SERVICE (Q) p 643
2200 Crystal Dr Rm 1100 22202
Tel (703) 605-5400 SIC 9199

HIGH SIERRA POOLS INC p 691
2704 Columbia Pike 22204
Tel (703) 920-1750 SIC 8741 7389

IFES INC p 730
2011 Crystal Dr Fl 10 22202
Tel (202) 350-6750 SIC 8733

IMAGINE SCHOOLS NON-PROFIT INC p 733
1005 N Glebe Rd Ste 610 22201
Tel (703) 527-2600 SIC 8299

IMAGINE SCHOOLS ON BROADWAY p 733
1005 N Glebe Rd Ste 610 22201
Tel (703) 527-2600 SIC 8211

INTEGREON MANAGED SOLUTIONS INC p 749
2011 Crystal Dr Ste 200 22202
Tel (201) 213-6107 SIC 8111

INTERNATIONAL RELIEF AND DEVELOPMENT INC p 756
1621 N Kent St Ste 400 22209
Tel (703) 247-3068 SIC 8322

INTERSTATE HOTELS & RESORTS INC p 758
4501 Fairfax Dr Ste 500 22203
Tel (703) 387-3100 SIC 7011

INTERSTATE MANAGEMENT CO LLC p 758
4501 Fairfax Dr Ste 500 22203
Tel (703) 387-3100 SIC 8741

INTERSTATE RESOURCES INC p 758
1300 Wilson Blvd Ste 1075 22209
Tel (703) 243-3355 SIC 2631 2653 7389

■ KELLOGG BROWN & ROOT SERVICES INC p 808
200 12th St S Ste 300 22202
Tel (703) 526-7500 SIC 8741

KEOLIS AMERICA INC p 813
3003 Washington Blvd 22201
Tel (301) 251-5612 SIC 4111

L C VIRGINIA p 834
4600 Fairfax Dr Ste 1004 22203
Tel (703) 524-5454 SIC 1541 1542 1522

LINCOLN HOLDINGS LLC p 867
627 N Glebe Rd Ste 850 22203
Tel (202) 266-2200 *SIC* 7941

MANAGEMENT SYSTEMS INTERNATIONAL INC p 900
200 12th St S 22202
Tel (703) 979-7100 *SIC* 8742

MARYMOUNT UNIVERSITY p 915
2807 N Glebe Rd 22207
Tel (703) 284-1500 *SIC* 8221

MILLENNIUM ENGINEERING AND INTEGRATION CO p 970
1400 Crystal Dr Ste 800 22202
Tel (703) 413-7750 *SIC* 8711 8731

■ **MINE SAFETY AND HEALTH ADMINISTRATION** p 973
201 12th St S Ste 401 22202
Tel (202) 693-9899 *SIC* 9651

NATIONAL ASSOCIATION OF STATE DEPARTMENTS OF AGRICULTURE INC p 1010
4350 Fairfax Dr Ste 910 22203
Tel (202) 296-9680 *SIC* 8611

NATIONAL RURAL ELECTRIC COOPERATIVE ASSOCIATION p 1016
4301 Wilson Blvd Ste 1 22203
Tel (703) 907-5500 *SIC* 8611

■ **NATIONAL SCIENCE FOUNDATION** p 1016
4201 Wilson Blvd Ste 1205 22230
Tel (703) 292-5050 *SIC* 9199 9111

NATIONAL TELECOMMUNICATIONS COOPERATIVE ASSOCIATION p 1016
4121 Wilson Blvd Ste 1000 22203
Tel (703) 351-2000 *SIC* 8611 8741

NATURE CONSERVANCY p 1018
4245 Fairfax Dr Ste 100 22203
Tel (703) 841-5300 *SIC* 8641

NAVY MUTUAL AID ASSOCIATION p 1020
Henderson Hall, 29 22212
Tel (703) 945-1440 *SIC* 8641 6411

NORTH AMERICA SEKISUI HOUSE LLC p 1049
2001 Jefferson Davis Hwy 22202
Tel (703) 740-0229 *SIC* 6719

NORTHERN VIRGINIA TRANSPORTATION COMMISSION p 1057
2300 Wilson Blvd Ste 620 22201
Tel (703) 524-3322 *SIC* 4111

■ **OPOWER INC** p 1090
1515 N Courthouse Rd Fl 8 22201
Tel (703) 778-4544 *SIC* 7372

PACIFIC ARCHITECTS AND ENGINEERS INC p 1104
1320 N Courthouse Rd # 800 22201
Tel (888) 526-5416 *SIC* 8711 8712

PAE AVIATION AND TECHNICAL SERVICES LLC p 1107
1320 N Courthouse Rd # 800 22201
Tel (856) 866-2200 *SIC* 4581 3728 8742

PAE GOVERNMENT SERVICES INC p 1107
1320 N Courthouse Rd # 800 22201
Tel (703) 717-6000 *SIC* 8748

PAE HOLDING CORP p 1107
1320 N Courthouse Rd # 800 22201
Tel (703) 717-6000 *SIC* 6719 8742 8711

PAPPAS GROUP LLC p 1112
4100 Fairfax Dr Ste 400 22203
Tel (703) 349-7221 *SIC* 7311

PARTNERSHIP FOR SUPPLY CHAIN MANAGEMENT INC p 1118
1616 Fort Myer Dr Fl 12 22209
Tel (571) 227-8600 *SIC* 8399

■ **PERPETUAL CAPITAL PARTNERS LLC** p 1137
1000 Wilson Blvd Ste 2700 22209
Tel (703) 647-8709 *SIC* 6726

PHACIL INC p 1141
800 N Glebe Rd Ste 700 22203
Tel (703) 526-1800 *SIC* 7379 7371

PRINCE GROUP OF VIRGINIA LLC p 1176
901 N Glebe Rd Ste 901 22203
Tel (703) 953-0577 *SIC* 3479

■ **PRO-TELLIGENT LLC** p 1178
1320 N Courthouse Rd # 600 22201
Tel (703) 387-2100 *SIC* 7371 7379

PROMONTORY INTERFINANCIAL NETWORK LLC p 1183
1300 17th St N Ste 1800 22209
Tel (703) 292-3400 *SIC* 7389

PUBLIC BROADCASTING SERVICE p 1189
2100 Crystal Dr Ste 100 22202
Tel (703) 739-5000 *SIC* 4833

RAMBOLL ENVIRON INC p 1206
4350 Fairfax Dr Ste 300 22203
Tel (703) 516-2300 *SIC* 8748 8999

RAMBOLL ENVIRON US CORP p 1207
4350 Fairfax Dr Ste 300 22203
Tel (703) 516-2300 *SIC* 8748 8999

RELATIVITY CAPITAL LLC p 1221
1655 Fort Myer Dr Fl 7 22209
Tel (703) 812-3020 *SIC* 6282 4581

RELIANT ASSET MANAGEMENT LLC p 1222
2900 S Quincy St Ste 300a 22206
Tel (703) 820-2900 *SIC* 6512

▲ **ROSETTA STONE INC** p 1251
1621 N Kent St Ste 1200 22209
Tel (703) 387-5800 *SIC* 7372 4813 7371

■ **ROSETTA STONE INTL LTD** p 1251
1919 N Lynn St Fl 7 22209
Tel (540) 236-7719 *SIC* 7372

■ **SAVVIS FEDERAL SYSTEMS INC** p 1284
4250 Fairfax Dr 22203
Tel (703) 667-6000 *SIC* 4813 7379

SERVICES MANAGEMENT CORP p 1308
4121 Wilson Blvd Fl 10 22203
Tel (703) 351-2074 *SIC* 8741

SIEMENS GOVERNMENT TECHNOLOGIES INC p 1320
2231 Crystal Dr Ste 700 22202
Tel (703) 860-1574
SIC 8711 7373 7376 7379 8712 7378

■ **SIX3 SYSTEMS HOLDINGS II INC** p 1328
1100 N Glebe Rd 22201
Tel (703) 841-7800 *SIC* 7373

THALES INC p 1446
2733 Crystal Dr Ste 1200 22202
Tel (703) 838-9685 *SIC* 8742

THALES USA INC p 1446
2733 Crystal Dr 22202
Tel (703) 413-6029
SIC 5065 3699 3679 3841 8711 7371

TOWERS WATSON DELAWARE INC p 1464
901 N Glebe Rd 22203
Tel (703) 258-8000 *SIC* 8742

■ **TRANSPORTATION SECURITY ADMINISTRATION** p 1472
601 S 12th St 20598
Tel (877) 872-7990 *SIC* 9621

UNITED BANK p 1506
5350 Lee Hwy Ste 2 22207
Tel (703) 534-1382 *SIC* 6021

UNITED SERVICE ORGANIZATIONS INC p 1511
2111 Wilson Blvd Ste 1200 22201
Tel (703) 908-6400 *SIC* 8399

VIRGINIA COMMERCE BANCORP INC p 1558
5350 Lee Hwy 22207
Tel (703) 534-0700 *SIC* 6022

VIRGINIA HOSPITAL CENTER ARLINGTON AUXILIARY INC p 1559
1701 N George Mason Dr 22205
Tel (703) 558-5668 *SIC* 8062

VIRGINIA HOSPITAL CENTER ARLINGTON HEALTH SYSTEM p 1559
1701 N George Mason Dr 22205
Tel (703) 558-5000 *SIC* 8093

WTW DELAWARE HOLDINGS LLC p 1628
901 N Glebe Rd 22203
Tel (703) 258-8000 *SIC* 8742

ARRINGTON, VA

CENTRAL VIRGINIA ELECTRIC COOPERATIVE INC p 281
800 Cooperative Way 22922
Tel (434) 263-8336 *SIC* 4911

ASHBURN, VA

FCI FEDERAL INC p 533
20135 Lakeview Center Plz # 300 20147
Tel (703) 443-1888 *SIC* 8742 8748

■ **FORFEITURE SUPPORT ASSOCIATES LLC** p 567
20110 Ashbrook Pl Ste 220 20147
Tel (571) 291-8900 *SIC* 8111 8742

INTELLIGENT DECISIONS INC p 750
21445 Beaumeade Cir 20147
Tel (703) 554-1600 *SIC* 3571 5045

M V M INC p 890
44620 Guilford Dr Ste 150 20147
Tel (571) 223-4500 *SIC* 7381 8741

■ **MCI COMMUNICATIONS CORP** p 929
22001 Loudoun County Pkwy 20147
Tel (703) 886-5600
SIC 4813 4812 4822 7372

■ **MCI COMMUNICATIONS SERVICES INC** p 929
22001 Loudoun County Pkwy 20147
Tel (703) 886-5600 *SIC* 4813

■ **MCI INTERNATIONAL INC** p 929
22001 Loudoun County Pkwy 20147
Tel (703) 886-5600
SIC 4813 4812 4822 7372

■ **MCI INTERNATIONAL SERVICES INC** p 929
22001 Loudoun County Pkwy 20147
Tel (703) 886-5600 *SIC* 4813

SAAB NORTH AMERICA INC p 1263
20700 Loudoun County Pkwy # 152 20147
Tel (703) 406-7277 *SIC* 5088 3699 7371

▲ **TELOS CORP** p 1435
19886 Ashburn Rd 20147
Tel (703) 724-3800 *SIC* 7373

■ **UUNET TECHNOLOGIES INC** p 1537
22001 Loudoun County Pkwy 20147
Tel (703) 726-9240 *SIC* 4813

■ **VERIZON BUSINESS GLOBAL LLC** p 1550
22001 Loudoun County Pkwy 20147
Tel (703) 886-5600 *SIC* 4813 8721 4822

■ **VERIZON BUSINESS NETWORK SERVICES INC** p 1550
22001 Loudoun County Pkwy 20147
Tel (703) 729-5615 *SIC* 4813

VERIZON SELECT SERVICES INC p 1550
22001 Loudoun County Pkwy 20147
Tel (703) 886-7446 *SIC* 4813

■ **VERIZON SERVICES CORP** p 1550
22001 Loudoun County Pkwy 20147
Tel (703) 729-5931 *SIC* 4813

■ **VERIZON VIRGINIA LLC** p 1551
22001 Loudoun County Pkwy 20147
Tel (800) 837-4966 *SIC* 4813

ASHLAND, VA

CONCRETE PIPE & PRECAST LLC p 355
11352 Virginia Precast Rd 23005
Tel (804) 798-6068 *SIC* 3272

COUNTRY VINTNER INC p 375
12305 N Lakeridge Pkwy 23005
Tel (804) 752-3670 *SIC* 5182

CREATIVE OFFICE ENVIRONMENTS p 390
11798 N Lakeridge Pkwy 23005
Tel (804) 329-0400 *SIC* 5021

HANOVER COUNTY PUBLIC SCHOOLS p 658
200 Berkley St 23005
Tel (804) 365-4500 *SIC* 8211

HIGHWAY SERVICE VENTURES INC p 692
100 Arbor Oak Dr Ste 305 23005
Tel (804) 752-4966 *SIC* 5541 5411 5812

J L CULPEPPER & CO INC p 771
201 Haley Rd 23005
Tel (804) 752-6576 *SIC* 5141

JAMES RIVER EQUIPMENT INC p 777
11047 Leadbetter Rd 23005
Tel (804) 748-9324 *SIC* 5084 5082

JAMES RIVER EQUIPMENT VIRGINIA LLC p 777
11047 Leadbetter Rd 23005
Tel (804) 798-6001 *SIC* 5082

NORTHERN STAR VENTURES LLC p 1057
10440 Leadbetter Rd 23005
Tel (804) 368-0747 *SIC* 5149 5461

RANDOLPH-MACON COLLEGE p 1208
204 Henry St 23005
Tel (804) 752-7200 *SIC* 8221

VSC FIRE & SECURITY INC p 1566
10343b Kings Acres Rd 23005
Tel (804) 459-2200 *SIC* 1711 3494

AXTON, VA

A C FURNITURE CO INC p 5
3872 Martin Dr 24054
Tel (276) 650-3356 *SIC* 2521

BASSETT, VA

▲ **BASSETT FURNITURE INDUSTRIES INC** p 159
3525 Fairystone Park Hwy 24055
Tel (276) 629-6000
SIC 2511 2512 5021 5712

■ **BASSETT FURNITURE INDUSTRIES OF NORTH CAROLINA LLC** p 159
3525 Fairystone Park Hwy 24055
Tel (276) 629-6000 *SIC* 2511 2512

BEDFORD, VA

BEDFORD COUNTY SCHOOL DISTRICT p 168
310 S Bridge St 24523
Tel (540) 586-1045 *SIC* 8211

BERRYVILLE, VA

BERRYVILLE GRAPHICS INC p 176
25 Jack Enders Blvd 22611
Tel (540) 955-2750 *SIC* 2732 2752 2789

BLACKSBURG, VA

EDWARD VIA VIRGINIA COLLEGE OF OSTEOPATHIC MEDICINE p 480
2265 Kraft Dr 24060
Tel (540) 231-4000 *SIC* 8733

HHHUNT CORP p 689
800 Hethwood Blvd 24060
Tel (540) 552-3515 *SIC* 6513

HHHUNT PROPERTY MANAGEMENT INC p 689
800 Hethwood Blvd 24060
Tel (540) 552-3515 *SIC* 6513

■ **MONTGOMERY REGIONAL HOSPITAL INC** p 987
3700 S Main St 24060
Tel (540) 951-1111 *SIC* 8062

NEWCOMB ENTERPRISES INC JOHN p 1037
910 Triangle St 24060
Tel (540) 552-7718 *SIC* 5812

VIRGINIA POLYTECHNIC INSTITUTE & STATE UNIVERSITY p 1559
300 Turner St Nw Ste 4200 24061
Tel (540) 231-6000 *SIC* 8221

VIRGINIA TECH CORPORATE RESEARCH CENTER INC p 1560
1715 Pratt Dr Ste 1000 24060
Tel (540) 961-3600 *SIC* 8733

VIRGINIA TECH FOUNDATION INC p 1560
902 Prices Fork Rd 24060
Tel (540) 231-2861 *SIC* 7299

BLUE RIDGE, VA

BOXLEY MATERIALS CO p 205
15418 W Lynchburg 24064
Tel (540) 777-7600 *SIC* 1422 1423

BLUEFIELD, VA

AMMARS INC p 85
710 S College Ave 24605
Tel (276) 322-4686 *SIC* 5947

▲ **FIRST COMMUNITY BANCSHARES INC** p 546
1 Community Pl 24605
Tel (276) 326-9000 *SIC* 6022

■ **FIRST COMMUNITY BANK** p 546
1 Community Pl 24605
Tel (276) 326-9000 *SIC* 6021

■ **FIRST COMMUNITY BANK NA** p 546
29 College Dr 24605
Tel (304) 323-6300 *SIC* 6021

BRIDGEWATER, VA

DYNAMIC AVIATION GROUP INC p 464
1402 Airport Rd 22812
Tel (540) 828-6070 *SIC* 5088

BRISTOL, VA

ALPHA APPALACHIA HOLDINGS INC p 60
1 Alpha Pl 24209
Tel (276) 619-4410 *SIC* 1221 1222

ALPHA NATURAL RESOURCES LLC p 60
1 Alpha Pl 24209
Tel (276) 619-4410 *SIC* 1241

APPALACHIA HOLDING CO p 97
1 Alpha Pl 24202
Tel (276) 619-4410 *SIC* 1221

BRISTOL COMPRESSORS INTERNATIONAL LLC p 214
15185 Industrial Park Rd 24202
Tel (276) 466-4121 *SIC* 3585

BVU AUTHORITY p 230
15022 Lee Hwy 24202
Tel (276) 821-6100 *SIC* 4931

CONTURA COAL SALES LLC p 364
1 Alpha Pl 24209
Tel (276) 619-4451 *SIC* 5052

ELECTRO-MECHANICAL CORP p 485
329 Williams St 24201
Tel (276) 669-9428
SIC 3612 5063 3829 3822 3613 3354

KINGSWAY CHARITIES INC p 821
1119 Commonwealth Ave 24201
Tel (276) 466-3014 *SIC* 8699

STRONGWELL CORP p 1394
400 Commonwealth Ave 24201
Tel (276) 645-8000 *SIC* 3089

UNITED CO p 1507
1005 Glenway Ave 24201
Tel (276) 466-3322 *SIC* 1382 7992

UNIVERSAL FIBERS INC p 1516
14401 Industrial Park Rd 24202
Tel (276) 669-1161 *SIC* 2824 2281

BROADLANDS, VA

LOUDOUN COUNTY PUBLIC SCHOOL DISTRICT p 879
21000 Education Ct 20148
Tel (571) 252-1000 *SIC* 8211

BURKE, VA

CREVENNA OAKS PRESERVATION LP p 392
11550 Oak Bluff Ct 22015
Tel (703) 323-7964 *SIC* 6513 7389

CENTREVILLE, VA

ANDREWS INTERNATIONAL INC p 90
5870 Trinity Pkwy Ste 300 20120
Tel (703) 592-1400 *SIC* 7381

QINETIQ US HOLDINGS INC p 1195
5885 Trinity Pkwy Ste 130 20120
Tel (202) 429-6630 *SIC* 3812

SECURE MISSION SOLUTIONS INC p 1298
5875 Trinity Pkwy Ste 300 20120
Tel (703) 230-2804 *SIC* 7382

SECURE MISSION SOLUTIONS LLC p 1298
5875 Trinity Pkwy Ste 300 20120
Tel (703) 245-1300 *SIC* 7382

CHANTILLY, VA

AMERICAN SYSTEMS CORP p 80
14151 Pk Madow Dr Ste 500 20151
Tel (703) 968-6300
SIC 8711 1731 8742 7373

■ **APPTIS HOLDINGS INC** p 100
4800 Westfields Blvd # 1 20151
Tel (703) 745-6016 *SIC* 7371

BOWMAN CONSULTING GROUP LTD p 204
3863 Centerview Dr # 300 20151
Tel (703) 464-1000 *SIC* 8711 8713

BRITT FORD SALES INC TED p 214
4175 Auto Park Cir 20151
Tel (703) 673-2300 *SIC* 5511

CHENEGA INTEGRATED SYSTEMS LLC p 294
14295 Pk Madow Dr Ste 400 20151
Tel (571) 291-8500 *SIC* 7381 7382 8331

■ CORT BUSINESS SERVICES CORP p 373
15000 Conference Ste 440 20151
Tel (703) 968-8500 *SIC* 7359 5712 5932

■ CSRA SYSTEMS AND SOLUTIONS LLC p 398
15000 Conference Ctr Dr 20151
Tel (703) 641-2213 *SIC* 7299

▲ ENGILITY HOLDINGS INC p 499
3750 Centerview Dr 20151
Tel (703) 708-1400 *SIC* 8711 8741

■ ENGILITY LLC p 499
4803 Stonecroft Blvd 20151
Tel (703) 708-1400 *SIC* 8711

ENGINEERING CONSULTING SERVICES LTD p 499
14026 Thunderbolt Pl 20151
Tel (703) 471-8400 *SIC* 8711

ENGINEERING SOLUTIONS & PRODUCTS LLC p 499
14566 Lee Rd 20151
Tel (571) 375-1400
SIC 8711 7379 4813 8742 8748

FOUR POINTS TECHNOLOGY LLC p 571
14900 Confrnce Ctr Dr # 100 20151
Tel (703) 657-6102 *SIC* 5045

HAZEL INC WILLIAM A p 671
4305 Hazel Park Ct 20151
Tel (703) 378-8300 *SIC* 1623 1794

HENSEL PHELPS SERVICES LLC p 685
4437 Brookfield Corp 20 Ste 207 20151
Tel (703) 828-3200
SIC 1522 8744 1521 1541 1623 1611

▲ INTERSECTIONS INC p 757
3901 Stonecroft Blvd 20151
Tel (703) 488-6100 *SIC* 7323

IRON BOW HOLDINGS INC p 764
4800 Westfields Blvd # 300 20151
Tel (703) 279-3000 *SIC* 7379 7373

IRON BOW TECHNOLOGIES LLC p 764
4800 Westfields Blvd # 300 20151
Tel (703) 279-3000 *SIC* 3571

LONG & FOSTER COMPANIES INC p 876
14501 George Carter Way # 1 20151
Tel (888) 462-9111 *SIC* 6531 6794

NJVC LLC p 1045
14295 Park Meadow Dr 20151
Tel (703) 429-9000 *SIC* 7379

OBERTHUR TECHNOLOGIES OF AMERICA CORP p 1072
4250 Pleasant Valley Rd 20151
Tel (703) 263-0100
SIC 3089 7382 3953 3578 3499

OMNIPLEX WORLD SERVICES CORP p 1085
14151 Park Meadow Dr # 300 20151
Tel (703) 652-3100 *SIC* 7381

SOC LLC p 1336
15002 Northridge Dr # 100 20151
Tel (703) 955-5700 *SIC* 7382 1731

SRA COMPANIES INC p 1362
15036 Conference Ctr Dr 20151
Tel (703) 803-1500 *SIC* 7372 8742

■ SRA INTERNATIONAL INC p 1362
15036 Conference Ctr Dr 20151
Tel (703) 803-1500 *SIC* 7373 8748

SYBASE 365 INC p 1413
4511 Singer Ct Ste 300 20151
Tel (925) 236-5000 *SIC* 3577

UNICOM GOVERNMENT INC p 1502
15010 Conference Center D 20151
Tel (703) 502-2000 *SIC* 5045

VENCORE HOLDING CORP p 1547
15052 Conference Ctr Dr 20151
Tel (571) 313-6000
SIC 6719 8711 8733 3812 7372

VENCORE INC p 1547
15052 Conference Ctr Dr 20151
Tel (571) 313-6000
SIC 8711 8733 3812 7372

CHARLOTTESVILLE, VA

ALBEMARLE COUNTY PUBLIC SCHOOLS p 46
401 Mcintire Rd 22902
Tel (434) 296-5820 *SIC* 8211

CFA INSTITUTE p 285
915 E High St 22902
Tel (434) 951-5499 *SIC* 8621 6282 8221

CFA INSTITUTE RESEARCH FOUNDATION p 285
915 E High St 22902
Tel (434) 951-5499 *SIC* 8641

COMMONWEALTH ASSISTED LIVING LLC p 345
534 E Main St Ste B 22902
Tel (434) 220-1055 *SIC* 8741

COUNTY OF ALBEMARLE p 376
401 Mcintire Rd Rm 149 22902
Tel (434) 296-5855 *SIC* 9111

CRUTCHFIELD CORP p 396
1 Crutchfield Park 22911
Tel (434) 817-1000 *SIC* 5961

EAGLE CORP p 468
1020 Harris St 22903
Tel (434) 971-2686 *SIC* 3272 3271 3273

FAULCONER CONSTRUCTION CO INC p 531
2496 Old Ivy Rd 22903
Tel (434) 295-0033
SIC 1629 1611 1542 1623

■ GE INTELLIGENT PLATFORMS INC p 596
2500 Austin Dr 22911
Tel (434) 978-5000 *SIC* 3625 3674 7371

GREENBRIER INC p 637
200 Carlton Rd 22902
Tel (434) 817-2611 *SIC* 6719

MARTHA JEFFERSON HEALTH SERVICES CORP p 912
500 Martha Jefferson Dr 22911
Tel (434) 654-7000 *SIC* 8741

MARTHA JEFFERSON HOSPITAL p 912
500 Martha Jefferson Dr 22911
Tel (434) 982-7000 *SIC* 8062

MARTHA JEFFERSON HOSTIPAL p 912
459 Locust Ave 22902
Tel (434) 982-7000 *SIC* 8082

NATIONAL RADIO ASTRONOMY OBSERVATORY p 1015
520 Edgemont Rd 22903
Tel (434) 296-0211 *SIC* 8731

■ NORTHROP GRUMMAN MARITIME SYSTEMS p 1058
1070 Seminole Trl 22901
Tel (434) 974-2000 *SIC* 5088

PBM HOLDINGS INC p 1123
652 Peter Jefferson Pkwy # 300 22911
Tel (540) 832-3282 *SIC* 5149

PEPSI-COLA BOTTLING CO OF CENTRAL VIRGINIA p 1134
1150 Pepsi Pl 22901
Tel (434) 978-2140 *SIC* 2086

PETERSBURG MOTOR CO INC p 1138
100 Myers Dr 22901
Tel (434) 951-1000 *SIC* 5511 7515

RECTOR & VISITORS OF UNIVERSITY OF VIRGINIA p 1215
1001 Emmet St N 22903
Tel (434) 924-0311 *SIC* 8221

■ SNL FINANCIAL LC p 1335
1 Snl Plz 22902
Tel (434) 977-1600 *SIC* 7374

STELLARONE CORP p 1385
590 Peter Jefferson Pkwy 22911
Tel (434) 964-2211 *SIC* 6022

UNIVERSITY OF VIRGINIA p 1526
1215 Lee St 22908
Tel (434) 924-0000 *SIC* 8221

UNIVERSITY OF VIRGINIA INVESTMENT MANAGEMENT CO p 1526
Fontain 560 Ray C Hunt Dr 22903
Tel (434) 924-4245 *SIC* 6722

UNIVERSITY OF VIRGINIA MEDICAL CENTER p 1526
1215 Lee St 22908
Tel (434) 924-0211 *SIC* 8221

UNIVERSITY OF VIRGINIA PHYSICIANS GROUP p 1526
4105 Lewis And Clark Dr 22911
Tel (434) 980-6110 *SIC* 8721

CHATHAM, VA

DAVENPORT ENERGY INC p 415
108 Main St 24531
Tel (434) 432-0251 *SIC* 5172 5983 5984

FIRST PIEDMONT CORP p 549
108 S Main St 24531
Tel (434) 432-0211 *SIC* 4953 5084

PITTSYLVANIA COUNTY SCHOOL BOARD p 1152
39 Bank St 24531
Tel (434) 432-2761 *SIC* 8211

CHESAPEAKE, VA

AMERICAN MARITIME HOLDINGS INC p 75
813 Industrial Ave 23324
Tel (757) 961-9311 *SIC* 3731 7929

AMFAB INC p 85
1424 Campostella Rd 23320
Tel (757) 543-1485 *SIC* 3499

BAX GLOBAL INC p 160
1305 Executive Blvd # 200 23320
Tel (866) 744-7282 *SIC* 4731

BAZON-COX AND ASSOCIATES INC p 163
1244 Executive Blvd B113 23320
Tel (757) 410-2128 *SIC* 7373

CHESAPEAKE HOSPITAL AUTHORITY p 295
736 Battlefield Blvd N 23320
Tel (757) 312-8121 *SIC* 8062

CHESAPEAKE SCHOOL DISTRICT p 295
312 Cedar Rd 23322
Tel (757) 547-0153 *SIC* 8211

CITY OF CHESAPEAKE p 314
306 Cedar Rd 23322
Tel (757) 382-6586 *SIC* 9111

■ COAST GUARD EXCHANGE SYSTEM p 331
510 Independence Pkwy # 500 23320
Tel (757) 420-2480 *SIC* 5399 5311

■ DOLLAR TREE DISTRIBUTION INC p 448
500 Volvo Pkwy 23320
Tel (757) 321-5000 *SIC* 4225

▲ DOLLAR TREE INC p 448
500 Volvo Pkwy 23320
Tel (757) 321-5000 *SIC* 5331

■ DOLLAR TREE STORES INC p 448
500 Volvo Pkwy 23320
Tel (757) 321-5000 *SIC* 5331

FINCANTIERI MARINE SYSTEMS NORTH AMERICA INC p 543
800 Principal Ct Ste C 23320
Tel (757) 548-6000 *SIC* 7699 5084

■ GREENBRIER INTERNATIONAL INC p 637
500 Volvo Pkwy 23320
Tel (757) 321-5900 *SIC* 5199 7389

JO-KELL INC p 787
1716 Lambert Ct 23320
Tel (757) 523-2900 *SIC* 5063 8711

LTD MANAGEMENT CO LLC p 883
1564 Crossways Blvd 23320
Tel (757) 420-0900 *SIC* 8741 8721

MEB GENERAL CONTRACTORS INC p 934
4016 Holland Blvd 23323
Tel (757) 487-5858 *SIC* 1542 1629 1541

MONARCH BANK p 983
1435 Crossways Blvd 23320
Tel (757) 222-2100 *SIC* 6029

MONARCH FINANCIAL HOLDINGS INC p 983
1435 Crossways Blvd 23320
Tel (757) 389-5111 *SIC* 6022

NORFOLK DREDGING CO p 1048
110 Centerville Tpke N 23320
Tel (757) 547-9391 *SIC* 1629

PLASSER AMERICAN CORP p 1155
2001 Myers Rd 23324
Tel (757) 543-3526 *SIC* 3531

SUMITOMO MACHINERY CORP OF AMERICA p 1398
4200 Holland Blvd 23323
Tel (757) 485-3355 *SIC* 5063 3568

TECNICO CORP p 1432
831 Industrial Ave 23324
Tel (757) 545-4013
SIC 3446 3443 3441 3444 3731

VOLVO PENTA OF AMERICAS LLC p 1565
1300 Volvo Penta Dr 23320
Tel (757) 436-2800
SIC 5088 3519 5091 5063

YOUNG MENS CHRISTIAN ASSOCIATION OF SOUTH HAMPTON ROADS p 1639
920 Corporate Ln 23320
Tel (757) 624-9622 *SIC* 8641

CHESTER, VA

C W WRIGHT CONSTRUCTION CO INC p 233
11500 Iron Bridge Rd 23831
Tel (804) 768-1054 *SIC* 1623

■ COLUMBIA GAS OF VIRGINIA INC p 340
1809 Coyote Dr 23836
Tel (800) 543-8911 *SIC* 4924

DU PONT TEIJIN FILMS US LIMITED PARTNERSHIP p 459
3600 Discovery Dr 23836
Tel (804) 530-4076 *SIC* 3081

CHESTERFIELD, VA

CHESTERFIELD COUNTY PUBLIC SCHOOLS p 295
9900 Krause Rd 23832
Tel (804) 748-1405 *SIC* 8211

COUNTY OF CHESTERFIELD p 377
9901 Lori Rd 23832
Tel (804) 748-1000 *SIC* 9111

CHESTER, VA

SHAMIN HOTELS INC p 1311
2000 Ware Btm Spring Rd 23836
Tel (804) 777-9000
SIC 7011 8051 6512 6513

CHRISTIANSBURG, VA

CARILION NEW RIVER VALLEY MEDICAL CENTER p 256
2900 Lamb Cir Ste 150 24073
Tel (540) 731-2000 *SIC* 8062

COUNTY OF MONTGOMERY p 380
755 Roanoke St Ste 2e 24073
Tel (540) 382-5700 *SIC* 9111

MONTGOMERY COUNTY PUBLIC SCHOOLS p 986
750 Imperial St 24073
Tel (540) 382-5100 *SIC* 8211

NEW ENERGY INC p 1029
2300 Prospect Dr 24073
Tel (540) 382-7377 *SIC* 5021

SHELOR CHEVROLET CORP p 1314
2265 Roanoke St 24073
Tel (540) 382-2981 *SIC* 5511

CLOVERDALE, VA

AEW FOUNDATION p 32
2176 Lee Hwy S 24077
Tel (540) 992-2865 *SIC* 1623 1731

NEW RIVER ELECTRICAL CORP p 1033
15 Cloverdale Pl 24077
Tel (540) 966-1650 *SIC* 1731 1623

COEBURN, VA

DAVIS MINING & MANUFACTURING INC p 416
613 Front St E 24230
Tel (276) 395-3354
SIC 2892 5082 2426 1221 1222

COLLINSVILLE, VA

HENRY COUNTY SCHOOL DISTRICT p 684
3300 Kings Mountain Rd 24078
Tel (276) 634-4700 *SIC* 8211

CREWE, VA

SOUTHSIDE ELECTRIC COOPERATIVE INC p 1351
2000 W Virginia Ave 23930
Tel (800) 552-2118 *SIC* 4911

CULPEPER, VA

COUNTY OF CULPEPER p 377
302 N Main St 22701
Tel (540) 727-3427 *SIC* 9111

CULPEPER COUNTY PUBLIC SCHOOLS p 400
450 Radio Ln 22701
Tel (540) 825-3677 *SIC* 8211

MERCHANTS GROCERY CO INC p 944
800 Maddox Dr 22701
Tel (540) 825-0786 *SIC* 5194 5141 5145

■ STELLAR ONE BANK p 1385
102 S Main St 22701
Tel (540) 382-4951 *SIC* 6021

DANVILLE, VA

CITY OF DANVILLE p 314
427 Patton St 24541
Tel (434) 799-5100 *SIC* 9111

DALY SEVEN INC p 410
4829 Riverside Dr 24541
Tel (434) 822-2161 *SIC* 8741 1522 6531

DANVILLE REGIONAL HEALTH FOUNDATION p 412
142 S Main St 24541
Tel (434) 799-2100
SIC 8741 8062 8051 8011

■ DANVILLE REGIONAL MEDICAL CENTER p 412
142 S Main St 24541
Tel (434) 799-2100
SIC 8062 8011 8093 8069 8051

WOMACK ELECTRIC & SUPPLY CO INC p 1621
518 Newton St 24541
Tel (434) 793-5134 *SIC* 5063

DILLWYN, VA

KYANITE MINING CORP p 833
30 Willis Mountain Ln 23936
Tel (434) 983-2085 *SIC* 1459

DUBLIN, VA

PHOENIX PACKAGING OPERATIONS LLC p 1145
4800 Lina Ln 24084
Tel (540) 307-4084 *SIC* 2631

DUFFIELD, VA

■ TEMPUR PRODUCTION USA LLC p 1436
203 Tempur Pedic Dr # 102 24244
Tel (276) 431-7150 *SIC* 2515

DULLES, VA

AIRLINE TARIFF PUBLISHING CO p 40
45005 Aviation Dr Ste 400 20166
Tel (703) 661-7400 *SIC* 2721 7374 2731

CHG GROUP INC p 296
23031 Ladbrook Dr 20166
Tel (703) 661-0283 *SIC* 8741

DIGITEK IMAGING PRODUCTS INC p 439
44258 Mercure Cir 20166
Tel (703) 421-0300 *SIC* 5045

■ DYNALECTRIC CO p 464
22930 Shaw Rd Ste 100 20166
Tel (703) 288-2866 *SIC* 1731

GIESECKE & DEVRIENT AMERICA INC p 611
45925 Horseshoe Dr # 100 20166
Tel (703) 480-2000 *SIC* 2672 5044

GIESECKE & DEVRIENT MOBILE SECURITY AMERICA INC p 611
45925 Horseshoe Dr 20166
Tel (703) 480-2100
SIC 7382 3089 5045 7374

HARRIS TECHNICAL SERVICES CORP p 664
21000 Atl Blvd Ste 300 20166
Tel (703) 610-4200
SIC 7371 7379 8711 3577

■ HISTORIC AOL LLC p 696
22000 Aol Way 20166
Tel (703) 265-1000 *SIC* 4813 7299

NATIONAL RURAL UTILITIES COOPERATIVE FINANCE CORP p 1016
20701 Cooperative Way 20166
Tel (703) 467-1800 *SIC* 6141 6159

▲ ORBITAL ATK INC p 1092
45101 Warp Dr 20166
Tel (703) 406-5000
SIC 3764 3812 3483 3482 3489

■ ORBITAL SCIENCES CORP p 1092
45101 Warp Dr 20166
Tel (703) 406-5000 *SIC* 3812 4899 7372

RAYTHEON TECHNICAL SERVICES CO LLC p 1211
22270 Pacific Blvd 20166
Tel (571) 250-2100 SIC 8331 8711

■ SIX3 ADVANCED SYSTEMS INC p 1328
45200 Business Ct Ste 100 20166
Tel (703) 742-7660
SIC 3825 4899 8099 4789

SWISSPORT CARGO SERVICES LP p 1413
23723 Air Frt Ln Bldg 5 20166
Tel (703) 742-4300 SIC 4581

SWISSPORT CORP p 1413
45025 Aviation Dr Ste 350 20166
Tel (703) 742-4300 SIC 7363

SWISSPORT FUELING INC p 1413
45025 Aviation Dr Ste 350 20166
Tel (703) 742-4338 SIC 5172

SWISSPORT USA INC p 1413
45025 Aviation Dr Ste 350 20166
Tel (703) 742-4300 SIC 4581

TWO GUYS SERVICE LLC p 1495
45662 Terminal Dr 20166
Tel (703) 481-0222 SIC 7349 1541

ZEVACOR PHARMA INC p 1642
21000 Atl Blvd Ste 730 20166
Tel (703) 547-8161 SIC 5122 5047

EDINBURG, VA

▲ SHENANDOAH TELECOMMUNICATIONS CO p 1315
500 Shentel Way 22824
Tel (540) 984-4141 SIC 4813 4812 4841

ELLISTON, VA

ROWE FINE FURNITURE INC p 1253
2121 Gardner St 24087
Tel (540) 444-7693 SIC 2512 2511

ROWE FURNITURE CORP p 1253
2121 Gardner St 24087
Tel (540) 444-7693 SIC 2512 5712

ROWE FURNITURE INC p 1253
2121 Gardner St 24087
Tel (540) 389-8671 SIC 2512 2511 2421

FAIRFAX, VA

■ ARGON ST INC p 107
12701 Fair Lakes Cir # 800 22033
Tel (703) 322-0881 SIC 3812

ASM RESEARCH LLC p 118
4050 Legato Rd Ste 1100 22033
Tel (703) 645-0420 SIC 7371 8731

BARCELO CRESTLINE CORP p 154
3950 University Dr # 301 22030
Tel (571) 529-6000 SIC 6513 6531

BRITT TRANSPORTATION ENTERPRISES INCTED p 214
11165 Fairfax Blvd 22030
Tel (703) 591-8484 SIC 5511

BROOKFIELD HOMES CORP p 217
3201 Jermantown Rd # 150 22030
Tel (703) 270-1400 SIC 1521 1522

BROWN AUTOMOTIVE GROUP LTD p 219
12500 Fair Lakes Cir # 375 22033
Tel (703) 352-5555 SIC 5511

CAMBER GOVERNMENT SOLUTIONS INC p 243
12730 Fair Lakes Cir 22033
Tel (703) 653-8000 SIC 7371 7379

CAVALIER MAINTENANCE SERVICES INC p 267
2722 Merrilee Dr Ste 300 22031
Tel (703) 849-1100 SIC 7349

CDM FEDERAL PROGRAMS CORP p 271
3201 Jermantown Rd # 400 22030
Tel (703) 691-6500
SIC 8711 8742 8744 8748 8999

CDM-AECOM MULTIMEDIA JOINT VENTURE p 271
3201 Jermantown Rd # 400 22030
Tel (703) 691-6500 SIC 8711

CGI FEDERAL INC p 285
12601 Fair Lakes Cir 22033
Tel (703) 227-6000 SIC 7379 7389 8999

CGI TECHNOLOGIES AND SOLUTIONS INC p 286
11325 Random Hills Rd 22030
Tel (703) 267-8000
SIC 7379 7373 7372 7389

CRESCENT HOTELS & RESORTS LLC p 391
10306 Eaton Pl Ste 430 22030
Tel (703) 279-7820 SIC 7011

CUSTOMINK LLC p 403
2910 District Ave Ste 100 22031
Tel (703) 891-2273 SIC 2759 5699 5941

DEWBERRY COMPANIES INC p 434
8401 Arlington Blvd 22031
Tel (703) 849-0100 SIC 6719

DEWBERRY COMPANIES LC p 434
8401 Arlington Blvd Ste 1 22031
Tel (703) 849-0100 SIC 8711

DEWBERRY CONSULTANTS LLC p 434
8401 Arlington Blvd Ste 1 22031
Tel (703) 849-0311 SIC 8711 8712 8731

■ EAGLE GROUP INTERNATIONAL LLC p 468
10530 Rosehaven St # 500 22030
Tel (703) 272-6161 SIC 8742

ECS FEDERAL LLC p 476
2750 Prosperity Ave # 600 22031
Tel (703) 270-1540 SIC 7371 7379 8742

ELLUCIAN INC p 489
4375 Fair Lakes Ct 22033
Tel (407) 660-1199 SIC 7371 7373

FAIRFAX COUNTY VIRGINIA p 524
12000 Government Ste 214 22035
Tel (703) 324-3126 SIC 9121

FAIRFAX COUNTY WATER AUTHORITY p 524
8570 Executive Park Ave 22031
Tel (703) 698-5600 SIC 4941

FAIRFAX COUNTY WATER AUTHORITY WELFARE BENEFIT TRUST p 524
8570 Executive Park Ave 22031
Tel (703) 698-5600 SIC 6371

■ GENERAL DYNAMICS GOVERNMENT SYSTEMS OVERSEAS CORP p 600
3211 Jermantown Rd 22030
Tel (703) 995-8666 SIC 3663

■ GENERAL DYNAMICS INFORMATION TECHNOLOGY INC p 600
3211 Jermantown Rd 22030
Tel (703) 995-8700 SIC 7379 8711 7373

■ GENERAL DYNAMICS MISSION SYSTEMS INC p 600
12450 Fair Lakes Cir # 800 22033
Tel (703) 263-2800 SIC 3571

GEORGE MASON UNIVERSITY p 606
4400 University Dr 22030
Tel (703) 993-1000 SIC 8221

GUEST SERVICES INC p 645
3055 Prosperity Ave 22031
Tel (703) 849-9300 SIC 5148 8741

■ ICF CONSULTING GROUP INC p 727
9300 Lee Hwy 22031
Tel (703) 934-3000 SIC 8742

■ ICF INC LLC p 727
9300 Lee Hwy Ste 200 22031
Tel (703) 934-3000 SIC 8742 8748

▲ ICF INTERNATIONAL INC p 727
9300 Lee Hwy Ste 200 22031
Tel (703) 934-3000 SIC 8742 8748

INFORELIANCE CORP p 741
4050 Legato Rd Ste 700 22033
Tel (703) 246-9360 SIC 7371

▲ KAISER GROUP HOLDINGS INC p 800
9300 Lee Hwy 22031
Tel (703) 934-3000 SIC 4953

■ KFORCE GOVERNMENT SOLUTIONS INC p 816
2677 Prosperity Ave # 100 22031
Tel (703) 245-7350 SIC 7379

▲ MANTECH INTERNATIONAL CORP p 903
12015 Lee Jackson Hwy 22033
Tel (703) 218-6000 SIC 7373 8711 7379

■ MANTECH SYSTEMS ENGINEERING CORP p 903
12015 Lee Jackson Hwy 22033
Tel (703) 218-6000 SIC 7373 8711

■ MANTECH TELECOMMUNICATIONS AND INFORMATION SYSTEMS CORP p 903
12015 Lee Jackson Mem Hwy 22033
Tel (703) 218-6000 SIC 7373

NATIONAL RIFLE ASSOCIATION OF AMERICA p 1016
11250 Waples Mill Rd # 1 22030
Tel (703) 267-1000 SIC 8699

NORTHERN VIRGINIA SURGERY CENTER II LLC p 1057
3620 Joseph Siewick Dr # 406 22033
Tel (703) 766-6960 SIC 8011

OMEGA WORLD TRAVEL INC p 1084
3102 Omega Office Park # 1 22031
Tel (703) 359-0200 SIC 4724

PETERSON COMPANIES L C p 1138
12500 Fair Lakes Cir # 400 22033
Tel (703) 631-7570 SIC 6552

■ QSS GROUP INC p 1195
8270 Willow Oaks Corp Dr 22031
Tel (703) 289-8000 SIC 8711

RADIOLOGICAL CONSULTANTS FAIRFAX PC p 1204
2722 Merrilee Dr Ste 230 22031
Tel (703) 698-4444 SIC 8011

SALIENT CRGT HOLDINGS INC p 1272
4000 Legato Rd Ste 600 22033
Tel (703) 891-8200 SIC 7371 8748

SALIENT CRGT INC p 1272
4000 Legato Rd Ste 600 22033
Tel (703) 891-8200 SIC 7373 8748

SALIENT FEDERAL SOLUTIONS INC p 1272
4000 Legato Rd Ste 600 22033
Tel (703) 891-8200 SIC 7371

■ SIGNAL SOLUTIONS LLC p 1322
3211 Jermantown Rd # 700 22030
Tel (703) 205-0500
SIC 8711 7379 7374 4813 7373 8731

STANLEY ASSOCIATES INC p 1377
12601 Fair Lakes Cir 22033
Tel (703) 227-6000 SIC 7373

STANLEY INC p 1377
12601 Fair Lakes Cir 22033
Tel (703) 684-1125 SIC 7373

TEOCO CORP p 1439
12150 Monu Dr Ste 400 22033
Tel (703) 322-9200 SIC 7379

■ VANGENT INC p 1543
3211 Jermantown Rd 22030
Tel (703) 995-2666
SIC 8748 7371 7372 7373 7374 7376

■ WASHINGTONFIRST MORTGAGE CORP p 1579
12700 Fair Lakes Cir 22033
Tel (703) 564-9100 SIC 6162

■ XEROX FEDERAL SOLUTIONS LLC p 1631
8260 Willow Oaks Corp Dr 22031
Tel (703) 891-8774 SIC 8733

■ XEROX STATE & LOCAL SOLUTIONS INC p 1631
8260 Willow Oaks Crprt 22031
Tel (202) 378-2804 SIC 7373

FALLS CHURCH, VA

■ ACENTIA LLC p 17
3130 Frview Pk Dr Ste 800 22042
Tel (703) 712-4000 SIC 7371

ALEXANDRIA INOVA HEALTH SERVICES CORP p 49
8110 Gatehouse Rd 200e 22042
Tel (703) 289-2000 SIC 8062

APTARA INC p 101
3110 Frview Pk Dr Ste 900 22042
Tel (703) 352-0001 SIC 7379

BEYER MOTORS INC DON p 179
118 Gordon Rd 22046
Tel (703) 237-5000 SIC 5511

CAPITAL HOSPICE p 249
2900 Telestar Ct 22042
Tel (703) 538-2065 SIC 8082 8052

■ CSC COVANSYS CORP p 397
3170 Fairview Park Dr 22042
Tel (703) 876-1000 SIC 7371

▲ CSRA INC p 398
3170 Fairview Park Dr 22042
Tel (703) 641-2000 SIC 7373

■ CSRA LLC p 398
3170 Fairview Park Dr 22042
Tel (703) 876-1000
SIC 7371 8733 7376 7374 7379

■ DATATRAC INFORMATION SERVICES INC p 414
3170 Fairview Park Dr 22042
Tel (703) 876-1000 SIC 8742 0781 8721

■ DEFENSE HEALTH AGENCY p 422
7700 Arlington Blvd # 5101 22042
Tel (703) 681-1730 SIC 9431 9711

■ DOD PATIENT SAFETY PROGRAM p 447
5111 Leesburg Pike # 810 22041
Tel (703) 681-0064 SIC 9711

ENSCO INC p 500
3110 Frview Pk Dr Ste 300 22042
Tel (703) 321-4713 SIC 8731

FAIRFAX COUNTY PUBLIC SCHOOLS p 524
8115 Gatehouse Rd 22042
Tel (571) 423-1010 SIC 8211

▲ GENERAL DYNAMICS CORP p 600
2941 Frview Pk Dr Ste 100 22042
Tel (703) 876-3000
SIC 3721 3731 3795 3711 3812

■ GENERAL DYNAMICS GOVERNMENT SYSTEMS CORP p 600
2941 Fairview Park Dr 22042
Tel (703) 876-3000 SIC 6719

HITT CONTRACTING INC p 697
2900 Fairview Park Dr # 300 22042
Tel (703) 846-9000 SIC 1542

■ INNOVATION HEALTH PLAN INC p 744
3130 Fairview Park Dr # 300 22042
Tel (703) 914-2925 SIC 6324

INOVA HEALTH CARE SERVICES p 745
8110 Gatehouse Rd 200e 22042
Tel (703) 289-2000 SIC 8062 8093

INOVA HEALTH SYSTEM p 745
8110 Gatehouse Rd 200e 22042
Tel (703) 289-2069
SIC 8741 8011 8062 8049 8059 8051

INOVA HEALTH SYSTEM SERVICES p 745
8110 Gatehouse Rd 200e 22042
Tel (703) 289-2000 SIC 8062

JENNINGS INC L F p 782
407 N Washington St # 200 22046
Tel (703) 241-1200 SIC 1542

■ MANTECH GRAY HAWK SYSTEMS INC p 903
7799 Leesburg Pike 700s 22043
Tel (703) 610-9232 SIC 7373 7378

MILITARY PERSONNEL SERVICES CORP p 969
6066 Leesburg Pike # 900 22041
Tel (571) 481-4000 SIC 9451

NOBLIS INC p 1046
3150 Fairview Park Dr 22042
Tel (703) 610-2000 SIC 8733 8748

▲ NORTHROP GRUMMAN CORP p 1058
2980 Fairview Park Dr 22042
Tel (703) 280-2900 SIC 3812

■ NORTHROP GRUMMAN SYSTEMS CORP p 1058
2980 Fairview Park Dr 22042
Tel (703) 280-2900
SIC 3721 3761 3728 3812 3825 4581

ONE UP ENTERPRISES INC p 1086
7777 Lsburg Pike Ste 302s 22043
Tel (703) 448-7333
SIC 2731 2711 2092 6531

P & R ENTERPRISES INC p 1102
5681 Columbia Pike # 101 22041
Tel (703) 379-2018 SIC 7349

PACEM SOLUTION INTERNATIONAL LLC p 1103
2941 Frview Pk Dr Ste 550 22042
Tel (703) 309-1891 SIC 8748

■ STAR SECOND MERGER SUB LLC p 1378
3170 Fairview Park Dr 22042
Tel (703) 876-1000 SIC 7373 8748

FIELDALE, VA

■ CPFILMS INC p 387
4210 The Great Rd 24089
Tel (276) 627-3000 SIC 3081

FISHERSVILLE, VA

AUGUSTA HEALTH CARE FOR WOMEN p 131
70 Medical Center Cir 22939
Tel (540) 245-7007 SIC 8011

AUGUSTA HEALTH CARE INC p 131
78 Medical Center Dr 22939
Tel (540) 332-4000 SIC 8062

WILSON TRUCKING CORP p 1614
137 Wilson Blvd 22939
Tel (540) 949-3200 SIC 4213

FOREST, VA

SMITH MOUNTAIN INDUSTRIES OF VIRGINIA INC p 1333
1000 Dillard Dr 24551
Tel (800) 827-2231 SIC 5199 5947

WORKMAN OIL CO p 1624
14670 Forest Rd 24551
Tel (434) 525-1615 SIC 5541

FORT BELVOIR, VA

■ DEFENSE LOGISTICS AGENCY p 422
Andrew T Mcnamara Bld 22060
Tel (703) 767-4012 SIC 9711

FORT BELVOIR COMMUNITY HOSPITAL p 568
9300 Dewitt Loop 22060
Tel (703) 805-0510 SIC 8062

FORT LEE, VA

■ DEFENSE COMMISSARY AGENCY p 422
1300 E Ave 23801
Tel (804) 734-8000 SIC 9711

FORT MYER, VA

AMERICAN ARMED FORCES MUTUAL AID ASSOCIATION p 68
102 Sheridan Ave 22211
Tel (800) 522-5221 SIC 6411

FREDERICKSBURG, VA

A-T SOLUTIONS INC p 7
10304 Spotsylvania Ave A 22408
Tel (540) 604-5492 SIC 1731

EOIR TECHNOLOGIES INC p 504
10300 Spotsylvania Ave 22408
Tel (540) 834-4888
SIC 8711 7371 8731 8742

GET SOLD REALTY INC p 609
1171 Cntl Pk Blvd Ste 200 22401
Tel (540) 371-7653 SIC 6531

KAESER COMPRESSORS INC p 800
511 Sigma Dr 22408
Tel (540) 898-5500 SIC 5084

■ MCLANE/MID-ATLANTIC INC p 931
56 Mclane Dr 22406
Tel (540) 374-2000 SIC 5141

■ PATHWAYS HEALTH AND COMMUNITY SUPPORT LLC p 1120
10304 Spotsylvania Ave 22408
Tel (540) 710-6085 SIC 8093

RAPPAHANNOCK ELECTRIC COOPERATIVE p 1209
247 Industrial Ct 22408
Tel (540) 898-8500 SIC 4911

SPOTSYLVANIA COUNTY PUBLIC SCHOOLS p 1360
8020 River Stone Dr 22407
Tel (540) 834-2500 SIC 8211

SPOTSYLVANIA COUNTY SCHOOL BOARD p 1360
8020 River Stone Dr 22407
Tel (540) 898-6032 SIC 8211

■ SPOTSYLVANIA MEDICAL CENTER INC p 1360
4600 Spotsylvania Pkwy 22408
Tel (540) 498-4000 SIC 8011

UNIVERSITY OF MARY WASHINGTON p 1522
1301 College Ave 22401
Tel (540) 654-2060 SIC 8221 7389

WASHINGTON HEALTHCARE MARY p 1578
2300 Fall Hill Ave # 314 22401
Tel (540) 741-2507 SIC 8741

WASHINGTON HEALTHCARE PHYSICIANS MARY p 1578
2300 Fall Hill Ave # 314 22401
Tel (540) 741-1100 SIC 8099

WASHINGTON HOSPITAL INC MARY p 1578
1001 Sam Perry Blvd 22401
Tel (540) 741-1100 SIC 8062 8069

GAINESVILLE, VA

ATLANTIC COAST COTTON INC p 126
14251 John Marshall Hwy 20155
Tel (703) 753-7000 SIC 5136 5137

■ ATLANTIC RESEARCH CORP p 127
5945 Wellington Rd 20155
Tel (703) 754-5000 SIC 3764 3694

S W RODGERS CO INC p 1263
5816 Wellington Rd 20155
Tel (703) 591-8400
SIC 1611 1799 6552 1771 1623

GALAX, VA

CONSOLIDATED GLASS & MIRROR CORP p 359
110 Jack Guynn Dr 24333
Tel (276) 236-5196 SIC 3231

V-B/WILLIAMS FURNITURE CO INC p 1538
300 E Grayson St 24333
Tel (276) 236-6161 SIC 2511

VAUGHAN-BASSETT FURNITURE CO INC p 1545
300 E Grayson St 24333
Tel (276) 236-6161 SIC 2511

GLEN ALLEN, VA

ALLAN MYERS VA INC p 52
301 Cncourse Blvd Ste 300 23059
Tel (804) 290-8500
SIC 1623 1611 1542 1794

■ APEX SYSTEMS LLC p 96
4400 Cox Rd Ste 100 23060
Tel (804) 254-2600 SIC 7363 7361

ATLANTIC COAST DINING INC p 126
4701 Cox Rd Ste 345 23060
Tel (804) 747-5050 SIC 8741

■ BERKLEY MID-ATLANTIC GROUP LLC p 175
4820 Lake Brook Dr # 300 23060
Tel (804) 285-2700 SIC 6411

■ CHEMTREAT INC p 293
5640 Cox Rd Ste 300 23060
Tel (804) 935-2000 SIC 2899 3589

■ COMMONWEALTH LAND TITLE INSURANCE CO p 346
201 Cncourse Blvd Ste 200 23059
Tel (904) 854-8100 SIC 6361

■ CONSTELLATION PUMPS CORP p 361
10571 Telg Rd Ste 201 23059
Tel (804) 327-5664 SIC 3561

▲ DYNEX CAPITAL INC p 465
4991 Lake Brook Dr # 100 23060
Tel (804) 217-5800 SIC 6798

■ ESSEX INSURANCE CO p 510
4521 Highwoods Pkwy 23060
Tel (804) 273-1400 SIC 6331

■ FF ACQUISITION LLC p 539
4860 Cox Rd 23060
Tel (757) 306-7006 SIC 5411

GENERAL CIGAR CO INC p 599
10900 Nuckols Rd Ste 100 23060
Tel (860) 602-3500 SIC 2121 5199 0132

■ HAMILTON BEACH BRANDS INC p 655
4421 Waterfront Dr 23060
Tel (804) 273-9777 SIC 3634

■ HB PS HOLDING CO INC p 671
4421 Waterfront Dr 23060
Tel (804) 273-9777 SIC 5722

HEALTH DIAGNOSTIC LABORATORY INC p 674
4401 Dominion Blvd 23060
Tel (804) 343-2718 SIC 8734

■ MAGELLAN MEDICAID ADMINISTRATION INC p 895
11013 W Broad St Ste 500 23060
Tel (804) 548-0100
SIC 7374 8093 6411 8741

▲ MARKEL CORP p 908
4521 Highwoods Pkwy 23060
Tel (804) 747-0136 SIC 6331 6211

■ MARKEL INSURANCE CO p 908
4600 Cox Rd Ste 100 23060
Tel (800) 431-1270 SIC 6411

■ MARKEL SERVICE INC p 908
4600 Cox Rd Ste 100 23060
Tel (804) 747-0136 SIC 6411

■ MARKEL VENTURES INC p 908
4521 Highwoods Pkwy 23060
Tel (804) 747-0136 SIC 8741

OLD DOMINION ELECTRIC CO-OPERATIVE p 1080
4201 Dominion Blvd # 300 23060
Tel (804) 747-0592 SIC 4911

PATIENT FIRST CORP p 1120
5000 Cox Rd Ste 100 23060
Tel (804) 968-5700 SIC 8741

RETAIL DATA LLC p 1228
11013 W Broad St Ste 300 23060
Tel (804) 678-7500 SIC 7299

■ SAXON CAPITAL INC p 1284
4860 Cox Rd Ste 300 23060
Tel (804) 270-1468 SIC 6798

■ SERVICE PARTNERS LLC p 1307
1029 Technology Park Dr 23059
Tel (804) 515-7400 SIC 5033

▲ SYNALLOY CORP p 1414
4510 Cox Rd Ste 201 23060
Tel (864) 585-3605
SIC 3317 3443 2865 2899 2869

THALHIMER INC MORTON G p 1446
11100 W Broad St 23060
Tel (804) 648-5881
SIC 1542 6531 6799 6513 6512

■ UNITED DOMINION REALTY TRUST INC p 1508
4510 Cox Rd Ste 105 23060
Tel (804) 290-4705 SIC 6798

VIRGINIA UNITED METHODIST HOMES INC p 1560
5101 Cox Rd Ste 225 23060
Tel (804) 474-8700 SIC 8361

WINEBOW GROUP LLC p 1616
4800 Cox Rd Ste 300 23060
Tel (804) 752-3670 SIC 5182

GLOUCESTER, VA

GLOUCESTER COUNTY SCHOOLS p 618
6099 T C Walker Rd 23061
Tel (804) 693-5300 SIC 8211

RIVERSIDE MIDDLE PENINSULA HOSPITAL INC p 1238
7519 Hospital Dr 23061
Tel (757) 875-7545 SIC 8062

GORDONSVILLE, VA

KLOCKNER PENTAPLAST OF AMERICA INC p 823
3585 Kloeckner Rd 22942
Tel (540) 832-1400 SIC 3081 4213

KLOCKNER PENTAPLAST PARTICIPATION LLC p 823
3585 Kloeckner Rd 22942
Tel (540) 832-3600 SIC 3081 4213

HALIFAX, VA

HALIFAX COUNTY PUBLIC SCHOOLS p 654
1030 Mary Bethune St 24558
Tel (434) 476-2171 SIC 8211

HAMPTON, VA

CITY OF HAMPTON p 315
22 Lincoln St 23669
Tel (757) 728-5177 SIC 9111

■ FANEUIL INC p 527
2 Eaton St Ste 1002 23669
Tel (757) 722-3235 SIC 7389

FUTRELL & HOLT INC p 585
2000 Enterprise Pkwy 23666
Tel (757) 744-9552 SIC 7389

HAMPTON CITY SCHOOL DISTRICT p 656
1 Franklin St Fl 2 23669
Tel (757) 727-2000 SIC 8211

HAMPTON RUBBER CO p 656
1669 W Pembroke Ave 23661
Tel (757) 722-9818 SIC 5085

HAMPTON UNIVERSITY p 656
100 E Queen St 23668
Tel (757) 727-5000 SIC 8221

MEASUREMENT SPECIALTIES INC p 934
1000 Lucas Way 23666
Tel (757) 766-1500 SIC 3829

■ NASA LANGLEY RESEARCH CENTER p 1007
11 Langley Blvd 23681
Tel (757) 864-1000 SIC 9661

SENTARA CAREPLEX HOSPITAL p 1305
3000 Coliseum Dr 23666
Tel (757) 736-1000 SIC 8062

TRANSPORTATION DIST COMMISION OF HAMPTON ROADS p 1472
3400 Victoria Blvd 23661
Tel (757) 222-6000 SIC 4111

HANOVER, VA

COUNTY OF HANOVER p 378
7497 County Complex Rd 23069
Tel (804) 365-6000 SIC 9111

HARRISONBURG, VA

CLINE ENERGY INC p 326
1890 S Main St 22801
Tel (540) 434-7344 SIC 5172 5541 1521

JAMES MADISON UNIVERSITY INC p 776
800 S Main St 22807
Tel (540) 568-6211 SIC 8221

ROCKINGHAM CO-OPERATIVE FARM BUREAU INC p 1244
1040 S High St 22801
Tel (540) 434-3856 SIC 5999 5251

ROCKINGHAM COOPERATIVE p 1244
1044 S High St 22801
Tel (540) 434-3856 SIC 0191

ROCKINGHAM COUNTY SCHOOL DISTRICT p 1244
100 Mount Clinton Pike 22802
Tel (540) 564-3200 SIC 8211

■ ROSETTA STONE LTD p 1251
135 W Market St 22801
Tel (540) 432-6166 SIC 7372

TRUCK ENTERPRISES INC p 1485
3440 S Main St 22801
Tel (540) 564-6900
SIC 5511 5531 7538 7539

HAYMARKET, VA

LAMINATE CO p 841
6612 James Madison Hwy 20169
Tel (703) 753-0699 SIC 5031 2431

HENRICO, VA

■ CADMUS JOURNAL SERVICES INC p 236
2901 Byrdhill Rd 23228
Tel (804) 287-5680 SIC 2752 2721 2741

COUNTY OF HENRICO p 378
4301 E Parham Rd 23228
Tel (804) 501-4000 SIC 9111 9511

INTERBAKE FOODS LLC p 751
3951 Westerre Pkwy # 200 23233
Tel (804) 755-7107 SIC 2052 2051

■ MCKESSON MEDICAL-SURGICAL HOLDINGS INC p 930
9954 Mayland Dr Ste 4000 23233
Tel (804) 264-7500 SIC 5047

■ VIRGINIA FOODSERVICE GROUP LLC p 1559
7420 Ranco Rd 23228
Tel (804) 237-1001 SIC 5141 5046

HERNDON, VA

AFFIGENT LLC p 32
13873 Park Center Rd # 127 20171
Tel (866) 977-8524 SIC 5045

AIRBUS AMERICAS INC p 39
2550 Wasser Ter Ste 9100 20171
Tel (703) 834-3400 SIC 3721

AIRBUS DEFENSE AND SPACE HOLDINGS INC p 39
2550 Wasser Ter Ste 9000 20171
Tel (703) 466-5600 SIC 3721

AIRBUS DEFENSE AND SPACE INC p 39
2550 Wasser Ter Ste 9000 20171
Tel (703) 466-5600 SIC 3721

AIRLINE PILOTS ASSOCIATION INTERNATIONAL p 40
1625 Massachusetts Ave Nw 20172
Tel (703) 689-2270 SIC 8631 6512

AKIMA LLC p 42
13873 Park Center Rd 400n 20171
Tel (571) 323-5200 SIC 8741

AKIMA MANAGEMENT SERVICES LLC p 42
13873 Park Center Rd 400n 20171
Tel (571) 323-5200 SIC 4581

ANALEX CORP p 88
3076 Centreville Rd # 200 20171
Tel (703) 880-2800 SIC 7371

APEX DATA SERVICES INC p 96
198 Van Buren St Ste 200 20170
Tel (703) 709-3000 SIC 7374

APEX EPUBLISHING DATA SERVICES LLC p 96
198 Van Buren St Ste 120 20170
Tel (703) 709-3000 SIC 7373

▲ BEACON ROOFING SUPPLY INC p 165
505 Huntmar Park Dr # 300 20170
Tel (571) 323-3939 SIC 5033 5031

CHINA TELECOM (AMERICAS) CORP p 301
607 Herndon Pkwy Ste 201 20170
Tel (703) 787-0088 SIC 4813

▲ COMMAND SECURITY CORP p 344
512 Herndon Pkwy Ste A 20170
Tel (703) 464-4735 SIC 7381

■ CONTENT EPLUS SERVICES INC p 362
13595 Dulles Tech Dr 20171
Tel (703) 984-8400 SIC 7371

▲ CONTINENTAL BUILDING PRODUCTS INC p 363
12950 Worldgate Dr # 700 20170
Tel (703) 480-3800 SIC 3275

■ CSRA INFORMATION SYSTEMS LLC p 398
13857 Mclearen Rd 20171
Tel (703) 818-4000 SIC 7376

■ CUBIC GLOBAL DEFENSE INC p 399
205 Van Buren St Ste 310 20170
Tel (703) 821-8930
SIC 7379 7371 7373 8711

DELTEK INC p 427
2291 Wood Oak Dr Ste 100 20171
Tel (703) 734-8606 SIC 7371 7379

DLT MERGERCO LLC p 445
2411 Dulles Corner Park 20171
Tel (800) 262-4358 SIC 7373

DLT SOLUTIONS HOLDINGS INC p 445
13861 Sunrise Valley Dr # 400 20171
Tel (800) 262-4358 SIC 7371

DLT SOLUTIONS LLC p 445
2411 Dulles Corner Park # 800 20171
Tel (703) 709-7172 SIC 7373

DRS GLOBAL ENTERPRISE SOLUTIONS INC p 457
12930 Worldgate Dr 20170
Tel (703) 896-7100 SIC 7371 8731

ELECTRONIC WARFARE ASSOCIATES INC p 486
13873 Park Center Rd # 500 20171
Tel (703) 904-5700
SIC 7373 7374 3672 3699 3643 3441

■ EPLUS GROUP INC p 505
13595 Dulles Tech Dr 20171
Tel (703) 984-8400 SIC 7377 5734 5045

▲ EPLUS INC p 505
13595 Dulles Tech Dr 20171
Tel (703) 984-8400
SIC 5045 7377 7379 7372

■ EPLUS TECHNOLOGY INC p 505
13595 Dulles Tech Dr 20171
Tel (703) 984-8400 SIC 5045 5734

EXELIS INC p 518
2235 Monroe St 20171
Tel (703) 790-6300 SIC 3669 3823 3812

■ GEOEYE LLC p 606
2325 Dulles Corner Blvd # 1000 20171
Tel (703) 480-7500 SIC 4899

■ HARRIS IT SERVICES CORP p 663
2235 Monroe St 20171
Tel (703) 673-1400 SIC 8711 3663 3674

■ HOLDCO LLC p 700
13820 Sunrise Valley Dr 20171
Tel (703) 345-2400 SIC 4813

▲ K12 INC p 799
2300 Corporate Park Dr 20171
Tel (703) 483-7000 SIC 8211 8299

LCC INTERNATIONAL INC p 849
2201 Coop Way Ste 600 20171
Tel (703) 873-2065 SIC 4813 4812

▲ LEARNING TREE INTERNATIONAL INC p 850
13650 Dulles Tech Dr # 400 20171
Tel (703) 709-9119 SIC 8243

LGS INNOVATIONS LLC p 860
13665 Dulles Technology D 20171
Tel (866) 547-4243 SIC 4813

MARINE SPILL RESPONSE CORP p 906
220 Spring St Ste 500 20170
Tel (703) 326-5600 SIC 4959

■ NETWORK SOLUTIONS LLC p 1028
13861 Sunrise Valley Dr # 300 20171
Tel (703) 668-4600
SIC 7375 7389 4813 7374

■ NEXTIRAONE FEDERAL LLC p 1040
510 Spring St Ste 200 20170
Tel (703) 885-7900 SIC 5065

■ NORTHROP GRUMMAN ENTERPRISE MANAGEMENT SERVICES CORP p 1058
2340 Dulles Corner Blvd 20171
Tel (703) 713-4000
SIC 8741 8744 4731 8331 7349

■ NORTHROP GRUMMAN TECHNICAL SERVICES INC p 1058
2340 Dulles Corner Blvd 20171
Tel (703) 713-4096 SIC 4581 7699

■ NTT DATA SERVICES FEDERAL GOVERNMENT INC p 1066
13880 Dulles Corner Ln 20171
Tel (703) 289-8000 SIC 8711 7373 7374

ORANGE BUSINESS SERVICES HOLDINGS US INC p 1091
13775 Mclearen Rd 20171
Tel (703) 471-2300 SIC 4813

ORANGE BUSINESS SERVICES US INC p 1091
13775 Mclearen Rd 20171
Tel (866) 849-4185 SIC 4813 8748

PARAGON SYSTEMS INC p 1113
13655 Dulles Tech Dr # 100 20171
Tel (703) 263-7176 SIC 7381 7382 7374

PARSONS BRINCKERHOFF CONSTRUCTION SERVICES INC p 1117
13530 Dulles Tech Dr # 100 20171
Tel (703) 742-5700 SIC 8741

PCCW GLOBAL INC p 1123
450 Springpark Pl Ste 100 20170
Tel (703) 621-1600 SIC 4813

■ RAYTHEON BLACKBIRD TECHNOLOGIES INC p 1211
13900 Lincoln Park Dr # 400 20171
Tel (703) 796-1420 SIC 7371 7382

RETIREE HEALTH PLAN AND TRUST FOR CERTAIN EMPOF AIR LINE PILOTS ASSNINTL p 1228
535 Herndon Pkwy 20170
Tel (703) 689-4238 SIC 6733

SECURITY CONSULTANTS GROUP INC p 1299
13655 Dulles Tech Dr 20171
Tel (703) 263-7176 SIC 7381

SIDERA NETWORKS INC p 1319
196 Van Buren St Ste 250 20170
Tel (703) 434-8500 SIC 4841 4813 7375

SOTERA DEFENSE SOLUTIONS INC p 1341
2121 Coop Way Ste 400 20171
Tel (703) 230-8200 SIC 7371 7379

▲ STRAYER EDUCATION INC p 1393
2303 Dulles Station Blvd 20171
Tel (703) 561-1600 SIC 8221

STRAYER UNIVERSITY INC p 1393
2303 Dulles Station Blvd # 100 20171
Tel (703) 561-1710 SIC 8221

TATA COMMUNICATIONS (AMERICA) INC p 1426
2355 Dulles Corner Blvd # 700 20171
Tel (703) 657-8400 SIC 4813

VION CORP p 1558
196 Van Buren St Ste 300 20170
Tel (571) 353-6000 SIC 5045

VOLKSWAGEN GROUP OF AMERICA CHATTANOOGA OPERATIONS LLC p 1564
2200 Ferdinand Porsche Dr 20171
Tel (703) 364-7000 SIC 5012 5013

VOLKSWAGEN GROUP OF AMERICA INC p 1564
2200 Ferdinand Porsche Dr 20171
Tel (703) 364-7000
SIC 5511 5012 5013 6153 6141 4899

VT IDIRECT INC p 1567
13861 Sunrise Valley Dr 20171
Tel (703) 648-8002 SIC 3663

VW CREDIT INC p 1567
2200 Ferdinand Porsche Dr 20171
Tel (248) 340-5000 SIC 6141

XO COMMUNICATIONS LLC p 1632
13865 Sunrise Valley Dr # 400 20171
Tel (703) 547-2000 SIC 4813

XO COMMUNICATIONS SERVICES LLC p 1632
13865 Sunrise Valley Dr 20171
Tel (703) 547-2000 SIC 4813

XO HOLDINGS INC p 1632
13865 Sunrise Vley Dr 4 Ste 400 20171
Tel (703) 547-2000 SIC 4813

HINTON, VA

VIRGINIA POULTRY GROWERS COOPERATIVE INC p 1559
6349 Rawley Pike 22831
Tel (540) 867-4000 SIC 2015

KING GEORGE, VA

BIRCHWOOD POWER PARTNERS LP p 185
10900 Birchwood Dr 22485
Tel (540) 775-6303 SIC 4911

LANGLEY AFB, VA

192D COMMUNICATIONS FLIGHT p 1
165 Sweeney Blvd Ste 214 23665
Tel (757) 764-1607 SIC 9711

LANSDOWNE, VA

SSP AMERICA INC p 1364
19465 Drfield Ave Ste 105 20176
Tel (703) 723-7235 SIC 5812

LEESBURG, VA

ARMFIELD HARRISON & THOMAS INC p 111
20 S King St Ste 300 20175
Tel (703) 777-2341 SIC 6411

K2M GROUP HOLDINGS INC p 799
600 Hope Pkwy Se 20175
Tel (703) 777-3155 SIC 3842

LOUDOUN COUNTY p 879
1 Harrison St Se Fl 1 20175
Tel (703) 777-0100 SIC 9199

LOUDOUN HEALTHCARE INC p 879
44045 Riverside Pkwy 20176
Tel (703) 777-3300 SIC 8062 8059

LOUDOUN HOSPITAL CENTER p 879
44045 Riverside Pkwy 20176
Tel (703) 858-6000 SIC 8062

LOUDOUN MEDICAL GROUP PC p 879
224d Cornwall St Nw 20176
Tel (703) 737-6010 SIC 8011

REHAU INC p 1220
1501 Edwards Ferry Rd Ne 20176
Tel (703) 777-5255 SIC 3089

LEXINGTON, VA

WASHINGTON AND LEE UNIVERSITY p 1577
204 W Washington St 24450
Tel (540) 458-8400 SIC 8221

LORTON, VA

MILLERS SUPPLIES AT WORK INC p 971
8600 Cinder Bed Rd 22079
Tel (703) 644-2200 SIC 5112 5044 5021

SHIRLEY CONTRACTING CO LLC p 1317
8435 Backlick Rd 22079
Tel (703) 550-8100 SIC 1611

LOUISA, VA

TRI-DIM FILTER CORP p 1477
93 Industrial Dr 23093
Tel (540) 967-2600 SIC 3564

LURAY, VA

PANAMERICA COMPUTERS INC p 1111
1386 Big Oak Rd 22835
Tel (540) 635-4402 SIC 5045

LYNCHBURG, VA

■ BELVAC PRODUCTION MACHINERY INC p 171
237 Graves Mill Rd 24502
Tel (434) 239-0358 SIC 3565

▲ BWX TECHNOLOGIES INC p 231
800 Main St Ste 4 24504
Tel (980) 365-4300 SIC 3621 3829

■ BWXT GOVERNMENT GROUP INC p 231
2016 Mount Athos Rd 24504
Tel (434) 522-6000 SIC 3443

■ BWXT NUCLEAR OPERATIONS GROUP INC p 231
2016 Mount Athos Rd 24504
Tel (434) 522-6000 SIC 3443

■ BWXT TECHNICAL SERVICES GROUP INC p 231
2016 Mount Athos Rd 24504
Tel (434) 522-6000 SIC 8711 8731

C B FLEET CO INC p 232
4615 Murray Pl 24502
Tel (434) 528-4000 SIC 2834

CENTRA HEALTH INC p 277
1920 Atherholt Rd 24501
Tel (434) 200-3204 SIC 8062

CITY OF LYNCHBURG p 316
900 Church St Ste 102 24504
Tel (434) 455-3990 SIC 9111

DELTA STAR INC p 427
3550 Mayflower Dr 24501
Tel (434) 845-0921 SIC 3612

ENGLISH CONSTRUCTION CO INC p 499
615 Church St Ste 2 24504
Tel (434) 845-0301
SIC 1611 1629 1623 1542

■ GENWORTH FINANCIAL CAPITAL INC p 605
700 Main St 24504
Tel (434) 845-0911 SIC 6411

GRIFFIN PIPE PRODUCTS CO INC p 640
10 Adams St 24504
Tel (434) 845-8021 SIC 3317

HANDY CO N B p 657
65 10th St 24504
Tel (434) 847-4495 SIC 5051 5074 5075

LIBERTY UNIVERSITY INC p 862
1971 University Blvd 24515
Tel (434) 582-2000 SIC 8221

LYNCHBURG COLLEGE p 887
1501 Lakeside Dr 24501
Tel (434) 544-8100 SIC 8221

PIEDMONT COMMUNITY HEALTH PLAN INC p 1146
2316 Atherholt Rd 24501
Tel (434) 947-4463 SIC 6321

PIEDMONT COMMUNITY HEALTHCARE INC p 1147
2316 Atherholt Rd 24501
Tel (434) 947-4463 SIC 8011

SCHEWEL FURNITURE CO INC p 1286
1031 Main St 24504
Tel (434) 522-0200 SIC 5712 5722 5713

SOUTHERN AIR INC p 1347
2655 Lakeside Dr 24501
Tel (434) 385-6200 SIC 1711 1731

■ WESTOVER DAIRY p 1602
2801 Fort Ave 24501
Tel (434) 528-2560 SIC 2099

MADISON HEIGHTS, VA

CENTRAL VIRGINIA TRAINING CENTER p 281
521 Colony Rd 24572
Tel (804) 947-6313 SIC 8299

MADISON, VA

PLOW & HEARTH LLC p 1156
7021 Wolftown Hood Rd 22727
Tel (540) 948-2272 SIC 5961 5251

MANAKIN SABOT, VA

LUCK STONE CORP p 884
515 Stone Mill Dr 23103
Tel (804) 784-3383
SIC 1423 2899 3281 5211 8741

MANASSAS PARK, VA

CAPITOL BUILDING SUPPLY INC p 251
8429 Euclid Ave 20111
Tel (703) 631-6772
SIC 5032 5039 5033 5051

MANASSAS, VA

AMERICAN DISPOSAL SERVICES INC p 71
10370 Central Park Dr 20110
Tel (703) 789-7935 SIC 4953

AURORA FLIGHT SCIENCES CORP p 132
9950 Wakeman Dr 20110
Tel (703) 369-3633 SIC 3721

DIDLAKE INC p 438
8641 Breeden Ave Ste 101 20110
Tel (703) 361-4195
SIC 8331 7331 7349 7334

ENVIROSOLUTIONS HOLDINGS INC p 503
9650 Hawkins Dr 20109
Tel (703) 633-3000 SIC 8748

ENVIROSOLUTIONS INC p 503
9650 Hawkins Dr 20109
Tel (703) 633-3000 SIC 4953

MERCHANTS INC p 945
9073 Euclid Ave 20110
Tel (703) 368-3171 SIC 5014 7539 5531

NORTHERN VIRGINIA ELECTRIC COOPERATIVE p 1057
10323 Lomond Dr 20109
Tel (703) 335-0500
SIC 4911 8611 8741 4939

OBERON ASSOCIATES INC p 1072
9700 Capital Ct Ste 301 20110
Tel (703) 365-8801 SIC 7379

PRINCE WILLIAM COUNTY SCHOOL BOARD p 1176
14800 Joplin Rd 20112
Tel (703) 791-8308 SIC 8211

PROGENY SYSTEMS CORP p 1180
9500 Innovation Dr 20110
Tel (703) 368-6107 SIC 7373

THREE SAINTS BAY LLC p 1450
10440 Balls Ford Rd 20109
Tel (703) 365-0450 SIC 8742

WILLIAM PRINCE HEALTH SYSTEM p 1611
8650 Sudley Rd Ste 411 20110
Tel (703) 369-8270 SIC 8741

WILLIAM PRINCE HOSPITAL p 1611
8700 Sudley Rd 20110
Tel (703) 369-8484 SIC 8062

MARTINSVILLE, VA

CARTER BANK & TRUST p 261
1300 Kings Mountain Rd 24112
Tel (276) 656-1776 SIC 6022

GILDAN DELAWARE INC p 612
3375 Joseph Martin Hwy 24112
Tel (276) 956-2305 SIC 2252 2254

▲ HOOKER FURNITURE CORP p 705
440 Commonwealth Blvd E 24112
Tel (276) 632-2133
SIC 2511 2512 2517 2521

MONOGRAM SNACKS MARTINSVILLE LLC p 984
200 Knauss Dr 24112
Tel (901) 685-7167 SIC 5147

MC LEAN, VA

ACTIVEOPS USA INC p 20
8300 Greensboro Dr # 800 22102
Tel (703) 918-4918 SIC 8741

ADSUMMA GROUP INC p 24
1431 Cedar Ave 22101
Tel (703) 883-0404 SIC 6719

ADVANCED COMPUTER CONCEPTS INC p 25
7927 Jones Branch Dr 600n 22102
Tel (703) 276-7800 SIC 5045

ALION SCIENCE AND TECHNOLOGY CORP p 50
1750 Tysons Blvd Ste 1300 22102
Tel (703) 918-4480 SIC 8711 8731

BAE SYSTEMS INFORMATION SOLUTIONS INC p 144
8201 Greensboro Dr # 1200 22102
Tel (703) 847-5820 SIC 8742

■ BELO CORP p 171
7950 Jones Branch Dr 22102
Tel (703) 854-6000 SIC 4833

BH HOTELS HOLDCO LLC p 180
7930 Jones Branch Dr 22102
Tel (703) 883-1000 SIC 7011

▲ BOOZ ALLEN HAMILTON HOLDING CORP p 201
8283 Greensboro Dr 22102
Tel (703) 902-5000 SIC 8742

■ BOOZ ALLEN HAMILTON INC p 201
8283 Greensboro Dr # 700 22102
Tel (703) 902-5000 SIC 8742

CAPITAL AUTOMOTIVE REAL ESTATE SERVICES INC p 249
8270 Greensboro Dr # 950 22102
Tel (703) 288-3075 SIC 6798

■ CAPITAL ONE BANK p 250
1680 Capital One Dr 22102
Tel (804) 967-1000 SIC 6021

▲ CAPITAL ONE FINANCIAL CORP p 250
1680 Capital One Dr 22102
Tel (703) 720-1000 SIC 6021 6141

CAPITAL ONE FSB p 250
1680 Capital One Dr 22102
Tel (610) 350-9074 SIC 6021

■ CAPITAL ONE NATIONAL ASSOCIATION p 250
1680 Capital One Dr 22102
Tel (800) 655-2265 SIC 6021

■ CAPITAL ONE SERVICES LLC p 250
1680 Capital One Dr 22102
Tel (703) 720-1000 SIC 6141

■ CARDINAL BANK p 252
8270 Greensboro Dr # 100 22102
Tel (703) 584-3400 SIC 6021 6162

▲ CARDINAL FINANCIAL CORP p 253
8270 Greensboro Dr # 500 22102
Tel (703) 584-3400 SIC 6021 6211 8741

CELERITY IT LLC p 273
8401 Greensboro Dr # 500 22102
Tel (703) 848-1900 SIC 7379

CII / OCI JOINT VENTURE p 307
6862 Elm St Ste 500 22101
Tel (703) 358-8800 SIC 1542

COGNOSANTE HOLDINGS LLC p 334
8200 Greensboro Dr # 1200 22102
Tel (703) 206-6000 SIC 7389

COGNOSANTE LLC p 334
8200 Greensboro Dr # 1200 22102
Tel (703) 206-6000 SIC 7379 8748

CONTRACK WATTS INC p 364
6862 Elm St Fl 5 22101
Tel (703) 358-8800 SIC 1541

CORCENTRIC COLLECTIVE BUSINESS SYSTEM CORP p 368
7927 Jones Branch Dr # 3200 22102
Tel (703) 790-7272 SIC 7372

DIGITAL INTELLIGENCE SYSTEMS LLC p 439
8270 Greensboro Dr # 1000 22102
Tel (703) 752-7900 SIC 7373 7371

■ DOUBLETREE LLC p 452
7930 Jones Branch Dr 22102
Tel (703) 883-1000 SIC 7011

■ DYN SPECIALTY CONTRACTING INC p 464
1420 Spring Hill Rd # 500 22102
Tel (703) 556-8000 SIC 1711 1731

■ DYNCORP p 465
1700 Old Meadow Rd 22102
Tel (571) 722-0210
SIC 7373 7371 7374 7375 8744 4581

■ DYNCORP INTERNATIONAL INC p 465
1700 Old Meadow Rd 22102
Tel (571) 722-0210
SIC 8741 7371 7381 7361 7363

■ EC AMERICA INC p 474
8444 Westpark Dr Ste 200 22102
Tel (703) 752-0610 SIC 5045

■ EMBASSY SUITES CLUB NO 1 INC p 490
7930 Jones Branch Dr 22102
Tel (703) 883-1000 SIC 7011

▲ FEDERAL HOME LOAN MORTGAGE CORP p 534
8200 Jones Branch Dr 22102
Tel (703) 903-2000 SIC 6111

FN AMERICA LLC p 562
7918 Jones Branch Dr # 400 22102
Tel (703) 288-3500 SIC 3484

■ GANNETT BROADCASTING INC p 590
7950 Jones Branch Dr 22102
Tel (703) 854-6000 SIC 4833

▲ GANNETT CO INC p 590
7950 Jones Branch Dr 22102
Tel (703) 854-6000 SIC 2711 7375

■ GANNETT RIVER STATES PUBLISHING CORP p 591
7950 Jones Branch Dr 22102
Tel (703) 284-6000 SIC 2711 2741

■ GANNETT SATELLITE INFORMATION NETWORK LLC p 591
7950 Jones Branch Dr 22102
Tel (703) 854-6000 SIC 2711

▲ GLADSTONE COMMERCIAL CORP p 614
1521 Westbranch Dr # 200 22102
Tel (703) 287-5800 SIC 6798

■ GLOBAL TELECOM & TECHNOLOGY AMERICAS INC p 617
7900 Tysons One Pl 22102
Tel (703) 442-5500 SIC 4813

▲ GTT COMMUNICATIONS INC p 644
7900 Tysons One Pl # 1450 22102
Tel (703) 442-5500 SIC 4813

GW CONSULTING INC p 648
1760 Old Madow Rd Ste 400 22102
Tel (703) 253-8080 SIC 7381

■ HILTON GARDEN INNS MANAGEMENT LLC p 694
7930 Jones Branch Dr 22102
Tel (703) 448-6100 SIC 7011

HILTON GLOBAL HOLDINGS LLC p 694
7930 Jones Branch Dr # 1100 22102
Tel (703) 883-1000 SIC 6794 7011

■ HILTON HAWAII CORP p 695
7930 Jones Branch Dr 22102
Tel (703) 883-1000 SIC 7011

■ HILTON HOTELS HOLDINGS LLC p 695
7930 Jones Branch Dr 22102
Tel (703) 883-1000 SIC 7011

■ HILTON ILLINOIS HOLDINGS LLC p 695
7930 Jones Branch Dr 22102
Tel (703) 883-1000 SIC 7011

■ HILTON SUPPLY MANAGEMENT LLC p 695
7930 Jones Branch Dr # 400 22102
Tel (703) 883-1000 SIC 5046 5021

▲ HILTON WORLDWIDE HOLDINGS INC p 695
7930 Jones Branch Dr # 100 22102
Tel (703) 883-1000 SIC 7011 6794

■ HLT ESP INTERNATIONAL FRANCHISE LLC p 697
7930 Jones Branch Dr 22102
Tel (703) 883-1000 SIC 7011

HSBC BANK USA NATIONAL ASSOCIATION p 714
1800 Tysons Blvd Ste 50 22102
Tel (800) 975-4722 SIC 6021

■ IMMIXGROUP INC p 734
8444 Westpark Dr Ste 200 22102
Tel (703) 752-0610 SIC 7371 7379

■ IMMIXTECHNOLOGY INC p 734
8444 Westpark Dr Ste 200 22102
Tel (703) 752-0610 SIC 5045

INTELSAT CORP p 750
7900 Tysons One Pl 22102
Tel (703) 559-6800 *SIC* 4841

INTELSAT GLOBAL SERVICE LLC p 750
7900 Tysons One Pl 22102
Tel (703) 559-7129 *SIC* 4899

INTELSAT HOLDING CORP p 750
7900 Tysons One Pl Fl 14 22102
Tel (202) 703-5599 *SIC* 4899

INTELSAT USA SALES CORP p 750
7900 Tysons One Pl 22102
Tel (703) 559-6800 *SIC* 4899

▲ **IRIDIUM COMMUNICATIONS INC** p 764
1750 Tysons Blvd Ste 1400 22102
Tel (703) 287-7400 *SIC* 4899

■ **ITT DEFENSE & ELECTRONICS INC** p 768
1650 Tysons Blvd Ste 1700 22102
Tel (703) 790-6300
SIC 3679 3678 3674 3769 3489

JER INVESTORS TRUST INC p 783
1650 Tysons Blvd Ste 1600 22102
Tel (703) 714-8000 *SIC* 6798

■ **LOCKHEED MARTIN GLOBAL TELECOMMUNICATIONS INC** p 873
1600 Tysons Blvd Ste 550 22102
Tel (703) 556-9500 *SIC* 4813 1731

LOGISTICS MANAGEMENT INSTITUTE p 874
7940 Jones Branch Dr 22102
Tel (703) 917-9800 *SIC* 8742

MARS INC p 910
6885 Elm St 22101
Tel (703) 821-4900
SIC 2044 2024 2066 2064 5812

MILLER AND SMITH INC p 970
8401 Greensboro Dr # 450 22102
Tel (703) 821-2500 *SIC* 1799 1531

■ **NORTHROP GRUMMAN INFORMATION TECHNOLOGY GLOBAL CORP** p 1058
7575 Colshire Dr 22102
Tel (703) 556-3187 *SIC* 8733

■ **NORTHROP GRUMMAN INFORMATION TECHNOLOGY INC** p 1058
7575 Colshire Dr 22102
Tel (703) 556-1000 *SIC* 7373 7372 8733

NOVETTA SOLUTIONS LLC p 1063
7921 Jones Branch Dr # 500 22102
Tel (571) 282-3000 *SIC* 7373

ORASCOM E&C USA INC p 1092
6862 Elm St Ste 400 22101
Tel (703) 358-8800 *SIC* 1521 1522 1542

■ **PARK HOTELS & RESORTS INC** p 1115
7930 Jones Branch Dr # 700 22102
Tel (703) 883-1000 *SIC* 7011 6794

PREFERRED SYSTEMS SOLUTIONS INC p 1169
7925 Jones Branch Dr # 6200 22102
Tel (703) 663-2777 *SIC* 7379

SALIENT FEDERAL-SGIS INC p 1272
8255 Greensboro Dr # 400 22102
Tel (703) 891-8200 *SIC* 7373 8711 7382

▲ **SCIENCE APPLICATIONS INTERNATIONAL CORP** p 1292
1710 Saic Dr Ste B 22102
Tel (703) 676-6942 *SIC* 7373 7374

SECURIGUARD INC p 1298
6858 Old Dominion Dr # 307 22101
Tel (703) 821-6777 *SIC* 7381 8744

SIMPLY WIRELESS INC p 1325
8484 Westpark Dr Ste 800 22102
Tel (703) 343-2700 *SIC* 4812

■ **SIX3 SYSTEMS INC** p 1328
1430 Spring Hill Rd # 525 22102
Tel (703) 442-6650 *SIC* 7373

SMS DATA PRODUCTS GROUP INC p 1334
1751 Pinnacle Dr Ste 1200 22102
Tel (703) 288-8100 *SIC* 5045 7373

SOURCE HOME ENTERTAINMENT LLC p 1342
8251 Greensboro Dr # 400 22102
Tel (239) 949-4450
SIC 5192 5099 8742 2541

SPORT & HEALTH CLUBS LC p 1359
1760 Old Madow Rd Ste 300 22102
Tel (703) 556-6556 *SIC* 7991

STRATEGIC RESOURCES INC p 1392
7927 Jones Branch Dr 600w 22102
Tel (703) 749-3040 *SIC* 8742 8748 7373

■ **SUNRISE SENIOR LIVING LLC** p 1404
7902 Westpark Dr 22102
Tel (703) 273-7500 *SIC* 6513

■ **SUNRISE SENIOR LIVING MANAGEMENT INC** p 1404
7902 Westpark Dr 22102
Tel (703) 273-7500 *SIC* 8361 8741 8052

▲ **TEGNA INC** p 1432
7950 Jones Branch Dr 22102
Tel (703) 854-7000
SIC 2711 4813 4841 4833

TVAR SOLUTIONS LLC p 1494
1320 Old Chain Bridge Rd # 445 22101
Tel (703) 635-3900 *SIC* 5045 7379 3571

TWD & ASSOCIATES INC p 1494
1751 Pinnacle Dr Ste 900 22102
Tel (703) 820-9777 *SIC* 7371

WATTS CONSTRUCTORS LLC p 1583
6862 Elm St Ste 500 22101
Tel (703) 358-8800 *SIC* 1542 1623

MCLEAN, VA

ACUMEN SOLUTIONS INC p 20
1660 Intl Dr Ste 500 22102
Tel (703) 600-4000 *SIC* 8748

MECHANICSVILLE, VA

AMF BOWLING CENTERS HOLDINGS INC p 84
7313 Bell Creek Rd 23111
Tel (804) 417-2008 *SIC* 7933

AMF BOWLING CENTERS INC p 84
7313 Bell Creek Rd 23111
Tel (855) 263-7278 *SIC* 7933

AMF BOWLING WORLDWIDE INC p 84
7313 Bell Creek Rd 23111
Tel (804) 730-4000 *SIC* 3949 7933

BON SECOURS-MEMORIAL REGIONAL MEDICAL CENTER INC p 199
8260 Atlee Rd Ste 1203 23116
Tel (804) 764-1253 *SIC* 8062 8071

■ **OWENS & MINOR DISTRIBUTION INC** p 1100
9120 Lockwood Blvd 23116
Tel (804) 723-7000 *SIC* 5047

▲ **OWENS & MINOR INC** p 1100
9120 Lockwood Blvd 23116
Tel (804) 723-7000 *SIC* 5047

■ **OWENS & MINOR MEDICAL INC** p 1100
9120 Lockwood Blvd 23116
Tel (804) 723-7000 *SIC* 5047

QUBICAAMF WORLDWIDE LLC p 1198
8100 Amf Dr 23111
Tel (804) 569-1000 *SIC* 3949 7933

■ **RICHFOOD INC** p 1233
8258 Richfood Rd 23116
Tel (804) 746-6000
SIC 5141 5147 5142 5148 5143 2026

RINK MANAGEMENT SERVICES CORP p 1235
9414 Charter Crossing Dr 23116
Tel (804) 550-7002 *SIC* 7999

MIDLOTHIAN, VA

PATIENT SERVICES INC p 1120
3104 E Boundary Ct 23112
Tel (804) 744-3813 *SIC* 8699

MILLWOOD, VA

PROJECT HOPE-PEOPLE-TO-PEOPLE HEALTH FOUNDATION INC p 1182
255 Carter Hall Ln 22646
Tel (540) 837-2100 *SIC* 8399

MOUNT CRAWFORD, VA

■ **RIDDLEBERGER BROTHERS INC** p 1234
6127 S Valley Pike 22841
Tel (540) 434-1731 *SIC* 3444 1711

SHENANDOAH VALLEY ELECTRIC COOPERATIVE INC p 1315
147 Dinkel Ave 22841
Tel (540) 434-2200 *SIC* 4911

MOUNT JACKSON, VA

BOWMAN ANDROS PRODUCTS LLC p 204
10119 Old Valley Pike 22842
Tel (540) 217-4100 *SIC* 2033 2099 2037

HOLTZMAN OIL CORP p 702
5534 Main St 22842
Tel (540) 477-3131 *SIC* 5172

NATURAL BRIDGE, VA

SENECA COAL RESOURCES LLC p 1303
15 Appledore Ln 24578
Tel (304) 369-8175 *SIC* 1222

SENECA NORTH AMERICAN COAL LLC p 1303
15 Appledore Ln 24578
Tel (304) 369-8175 *SIC* 1222

NELLYSFORD, VA

WINTERGREEN RESORTS INC p 1617
11 Grassy Ridge Dr 22958
Tel (434) 325-8237 *SIC* 8721 7011 5812

NEW CASTLE, VA

■ **NEW CASTLE TELEPHONE CO** p 1029
320 Salem Ave 24127
Tel (608) 831-1000 *SIC* 4813

NEWPORT NEWS, VA

CANON VIRGINIA INC p 247
12000 Canon Blvd 23606
Tel (757) 881-6000
SIC 3861 3577 3555 4953

CHRISTOPHER NEWPORT UNIVERSITY p 303
1 Avenue Of The Arts 23606
Tel (757) 594-7000 *SIC* 8221

CITY LINE APTS p 312
155a Mytilene Dr 23605
Tel (757) 838-5553 *SIC* 6513

CITY OF NEWPORT NEWS p 317
2400 Washington Ave Main 23607
Tel (757) 926-8411 *SIC* 9111

■ **DAILY PRESS INC** p 408
703 Mariners Row 23606
Tel (757) 245-3737 *SIC* 2711

FERGUSON ENTERPRISES INC p 538
12500 Jefferson Ave 23602
Tel (757) 874-7795
SIC 5074 5085 5075 5064

■ **HUNTINGTON INGALLS INC** p 720
4101 Washington Ave 23607
Tel (757) 380-2000 *SIC* 3731

▲ **HUNTINGTON INGALLS INDUSTRIES INC** p 720
4101 Washington Ave 23607
Tel (757) 380-2000 *SIC* 3731

LIEBHERR MINING & CONSTRUCTION EQUIPMENT INC p 863
4100 Chestnut Ave 23607
Tel (757) 245-5251 *SIC* 5082 5084 3532

MARY IMMACULATE HOSPITAL INC p 914
2 Bernardine Dr 23602
Tel (757) 886-6440 *SIC* 8062 8099

NEWPORT NEWS PUBLIC SCHOOL DISTRICT p 1038
12465 Warwick Blvd 23606
Tel (757) 591-4500 *SIC* 8211

■ **NORTHROP GRUMMAN NEWPORT NEWS INC** p 1058
4101 Washington Ave 23607
Tel (757) 380-2000 *SIC* 3731

PATRICK HENRY HOSPITAL INC p 1120
1000 Old Denbigh Blvd 23602
Tel (757) 875-2000 *SIC* 8052 8059 8051

RIVERSIDE HEALTHCARE ASSOCIATION INC p 1238
701 Town Center Dr # 1000 23606
Tel (757) 534-7000 *SIC* 8741

RIVERSIDE HEALTHCARE SERVICES INC p 1238
608 Denbigh Blvd Ste 800 23608
Tel (757) 856-7038 *SIC* 8741

RIVERSIDE HOSPITAL INC p 1238
500 J Clyde Morris Blvd 23601
Tel (757) 594-2000 *SIC* 8062

RIVERSIDE REGIONAL MEDIAL CENTER p 1238
500 J Clyde Morris Blvd 23601
Tel (757) 856-7030 *SIC* 5999

THOMAS JEFFERSON NATIONAL ACCELERATOR FACILITY p 1449
12000 Jefferson Ave # 12 23606
Tel (757) 269-7100 *SIC* 8731

■ **TITAN II INC** p 1456
4101 Washington Ave 23607
Tel (757) 380-2000
SIC 3728 3761 7373 3721 4581 3812

WMJORDAN CO INC p 1620
11010 Jefferson Ave 23601
Tel (757) 596-6341 *SIC* 1542 1541

WOLSELEY REAL ESTATE INC p 1621
618 Bland Blvd 23602
Tel (757) 874-7795 *SIC* 6531

NORFOLK, VA

■ **ALABAMA GREAT SOUTHERN RAILROAD CO** p 43
3 Commercial Pl 23510
Tel (540) 981-4049 *SIC* 4011

ALTERNATIVE BEHAVIORAL SERVICES INC p 62
240 Corporate Blvd 23502
Tel (757) 459-5200 *SIC* 8741

BAE SYSTEMS NORFOLK SHIP REPAIR INC p 144
750 W Berkley Ave 23523
Tel (757) 494-4000 *SIC* 3731 3732 7699

BAE SYSTEMS SHIP REPAIR INC p 144
750 W Berkley Ave 23523
Tel (757) 494-4000 *SIC* 3731 3732

BEACON HEALTH OPTIONS INC p 164
240 Corporate Blvd # 100 23502
Tel (757) 459-5100 *SIC* 6324 8322 6411

BON SECOURS - DEPAUL MEDICAL CENTER INC p 199
150 Kingsley Ln 23505
Tel (757) 889-5000 *SIC* 8062

■ **CAROLINA NORTH MIDLAND RAILROAD CO** p 259
3 Commercial Pl 23510
Tel (757) 629-2645 *SIC* 4011

■ **CDI MARINE CO LLC** p 271
4600 Village Ave 23502
Tel (757) 763-6666
SIC 8711 8712 3732 3731

CHILDRENS HEALTH SYSTEM INC p 299
601 Childrens Ln 23507
Tel (757) 622-2134 *SIC* 8741

CHILDRENS HOSPITAL OF KINGS DAUGHTERS INC p 300
601 Childrens Ln 23507
Tel (757) 668-7000 *SIC* 8069 8011

CMA CGM (AMERICA) LLC p 328
5701 Lake Wright Dr 23502
Tel (757) 961-2100 *SIC* 4731

COX AUTOTRADER PUBLICATIONS INC p 386
100 W Plume St 23510
Tel (757) 531-7000 *SIC* 2721

DOMINION ENTERPRISES p 449
150 Granby St Ste 150 23510
Tel (757) 351-7000 *SIC* 7374 2721 2741

EASTERN VIRGINIA MEDICAL SCHOOL p 472
714 Woodis Ave 23510
Tel (757) 446-6052 *SIC* 8221 8099

FHC HEALTH SYSTEMS INC p 539
240 Corporate Blvd # 100 23502
Tel (757) 459-5100 *SIC* 6719

■ **GE MOBILE WATER INC** p 596
4545 Patent Rd 23502
Tel (757) 855-9000 *SIC* 3589

HENDERSON & PHILLIPS INC p 682
101 W Main St Ste 900 23510
Tel (757) 625-1800 *SIC* 6411

I S O INDUSTRIES INC p 725
5353 E Princess Anne Rd F 23502
Tel (757) 855-0900 *SIC* 5172

IAT INTERNATIONAL INC p 726
555 E Main St Ste 1101 23510
Tel (757) 622-7239 *SIC* 5088

LANDMARK MEDIA ENTERPRISES LLC p 843
150 Granby St 23510
Tel (757) 351-7000
SIC 2711 5045 2721 6531

■ **LIVE OAK PERRY AND SOUTH GEORGIA RAILWAY CO** p 871
3 Commercial Pl 23510
Tel (757) 629-2600 *SIC* 4011

MAERSK LINE LIMITED p 895
1 Commercial Pl Fl 20 23510
Tel (757) 857-4800 *SIC* 4499

■ **METRO MACHINE CORP** p 955
200 Ligon St 23523
Tel (757) 543-6801 *SIC* 3731

MILLER OIL CO INC p 970
1000 E City Hall Ave 23504
Tel (757) 623-6600
SIC 5411 5172 5983 7549

■ **NORFOLK AND WESTERN RAILWAY CO (INC)** p 1048
3 Commercial Pl 23510
Tel (757) 629-2600 *SIC* 4011

NORFOLK PUBLIC SCHOOLS p 1048
800 E City Hall Ave # 1201 23510
Tel (757) 628-3830 *SIC* 8211

▲ **NORFOLK SOUTHERN CORP** p 1048
3 Commercial Pl Ste 1a 23510
Tel (757) 629-2680 *SIC* 4011

■ **NORFOLK SOUTHERN RAILWAY CO** p 1048
3 Commercial Pl Ste 1a 23510
Tel (757) 629-2680 *SIC* 4011

NORFOLK STATE UNIVERSITY p 1048
700 Park Ave 23504
Tel (757) 823-8600 *SIC* 8221 9411

OHL GLOBAL FREIGHT MANAGEMENT p 1078
223 E Cy Hall Ave Ste 208 23510
Tel (757) 314-4300 *SIC* 8741

OLD DOMINION UNIVERSITY p 1080
5115 Hampton Blvd 23529
Tel (757) 683-3000 *SIC* 8221 9411

■ **PRA GOVERNMENT SERVICES LLC** p 1167
120 Corporate Blvd # 100 23502
Tel (757) 519-9300 *SIC* 7322

▲ **PRA GROUP INC** p 1167
120 Corporate Blvd # 100 23502
Tel (888) 772-7326 *SIC* 7322

RCMA AMERICAS INC p 1212
150 Boush St Ste 1000 23510
Tel (757) 627-4000 *SIC* 5199 6221

SCHOOL BOARD OF CITY OF NORFOLK p 1289
800 E City Hall Ave # 1201 23510
Tel (757) 628-3830 *SIC* 8211

SENTARA ENTERPRISES p 1305
6015 Poplar Hall Dr 23502
Tel (757) 455-7000 *SIC* 8011

SENTARA HEALTHCARE p 1305
6015 Poplar Hall Dr 23502
Tel (757) 455-7976 *SIC* 8062 6324

SENTARA HOSPITALS - NORFOLK p 1305
600 Gresham Dr 23507
Tel (757) 388-3000 *SIC* 8062

SENTARA LIFE CARE CORP p 1305
249 S Newtown Rd 23502
Tel (757) 892-5500 *SIC* 8051

SENTARA MEDICAL GROUP p 1305
835 Glenrock Rd 23502
Tel (757) 252-3070 *SIC* 8093 8082

SHIP COLONNAS YARD INC p 1317
400 E Indian River Rd 23523
Tel (757) 545-2414 *SIC* 3731 3443 3499

TARMAC MID-ATLANTIC INC p 1425
1151 Azalea Garden Rd 23502
Tel (757) 858-6500
SIC 3273 1442 3272 3271

TITAN AMERICA LLC p 1456
1151 Azalea Garden Rd 23502
Tel (757) 858-6500
SIC 3241 3273 3271 4213

TITAN FLORIDA LLC p 1456
1151 Azalea Garden Rd 23502
Tel (757) 858-2095 *SIC* 3273

■ VIRGINIA & SOUTHWESTERN RAILWAY CO p 1558
3 Commercial Pl 23510
Tel (757) 629-2645 *SIC* 4011

VIRGINIA INTERNATIONAL TERMINALS LLC p 1559
601 World Trade Ctr 23510
Tel (757) 440-7120 *SIC* 4491 4213

VIRGINIA PALACE NEWSPAPERS INC p 1559
150 W Brambleton Ave 23510
Tel (757) 446-2000 *SIC* 8222

VIRGINIA PORT AUTHORITY p 1559
600 World Trade Ctr 23510
Tel (757) 683-8000 *SIC* 9621 9111

VIRGINIA WESLEYAN COLLEGE p 1560
1584 Wesleyan Dr 23502
Tel (757) 455-3200 *SIC* 8221

VIRGINIAN-PILOT MEDIA COMPANIES LLC p 1560
150 W Brambleton Ave 23510
Tel (757) 446-2056 *SIC* 2711

ZIM AMERICAN INTEGRATED SHIPPING SERVICES CO INC p 1643
5801 Lake Wright Dr 23502
Tel (757) 228-1300 *SIC* 4731

NORTH CHESTERFIELD, VA

ABILENE MOTOR EXPRESS p 11
1700 Willis Rd 23237
Tel (804) 275-0224 *SIC* 4213 6221 4212

ATLANTIC CONSTRUCTORS INC p 126
1401 Battery Brooke Pkwy 23237
Tel (804) 222-3400 *SIC* 1796 1711 3444

JOHNSTON-WILLIS HOSPITAL NURSES ALUMNAE ASSOCIATION p 791
1401 Johnston Willis Dr 23235
Tel (804) 560-5800 *SIC* 8062

SWEET FROG LLC p 1411
10800 Midlothian Tpke # 300 23235
Tel (804) 893-3151 *SIC* 5812 6794

TIMMONS GROUP INC p 1455
1001 Boulders Pkwy # 300 23225
Tel (804) 200-6500 *SIC* 8711 8713

▲ TREDEGAR CORP p 1475
1100 Boulders Pkwy # 200 23225
Tel (804) 330-1000
SIC 3081 2671 3083 3354

■ TREDEGAR FILM PRODUCTS CORP p 1475
1100 Boulders Pkwy # 200 23225
Tel (804) 330-1000 *SIC* 3081

UPPYS CONVENIENCE STORES INC p 1529
1011 Boulder Springs Dr 23225
Tel (804) 706-4702 *SIC* 5411 5541

VIRGINIA COMMUNITY COLLEGE SYSTEM OFFICE p 1558
300 Arboretum Pl Ste 200 23236
Tel (804) 819-4901 *SIC* 8222

VIRGINIA CREDIT UNION INC p 1558
7500 Boulder View Dr 23225
Tel (804) 323-6800 *SIC* 6062 6163

VIRGINIA DEPARTMENT OF STATE POLICE p 1559
7700 Midlothian Tpke 23235
Tel (804) 674-2000 *SIC* 9221

VIRGINIA MARUCHAN INC p 1559
8101 Whitepine Rd 23237
Tel (804) 275-0800 *SIC* 2098 2099

WILLIAM L BONNELL CO INC p 1610
1100 Boulders Pkwy 23225
Tel (804) 330-1147 *SIC* 3354

NORTH DINWIDDIE, VA

VIRGINIA CHAPARRAL INC p 1558
25801 Hofheimer Way 23803
Tel (804) 520-0286 *SIC* 3312

NORTON, VA

MAXXIM REBUILD CO LLC p 923
5703 Crutchfield Dr 24273
Tel (276) 679-7020 *SIC* 1241

OAKTON, VA

COYANOSA GAS SERVICES CORP p 387
10214 Walkerton Ln 22124
Tel (703) 938-7984 *SIC* 4924

SERVICESOURCE INC p 1308
10467 White Granite Dr # 100 22124
Tel (703) 461-6000 *SIC* 8331 7331

PETERSBURG, VA

CARRIAGE HOUSE PRESERVATION LP p 260
135 W Old St 23803
Tel (804) 733-6225 *SIC* 6513

■ PETERSBURG HOSPITAL CO LLC p 1138
200 Medical Park Blvd 23805
Tel (804) 765-5000 *SIC* 8062

QUALITY PLUS SERVICES INC p 1197
2929 Quality Dr 23805
Tel (804) 863-0191 *SIC* 1711 1731

VIRGINIA SOUTHSIDE TRAINING CENTER INC p 1559
W Washington St 23803
Tel (804) 524-7333 *SIC* 8361 8052

VIRGINIA STATE UNIVERSITY p 1559
1 Hayden Dr 23803
Tel (804) 524-5000 *SIC* 8221 9411

VIRGINIA TS INC p 1560
2001 Anchor Ave 23803
Tel (804) 862-2600 *SIC* 5136 5137

PORTSMOUTH, VA

CITY OF PORTSMOUTH p 317
801 Crawford St Fl 5 23704
Tel (757) 393-8000 *SIC* 9111

MARYVIEW HOSPITAL p 915
3636 High St 23707
Tel (757) 398-2200 *SIC* 8062

PORTSMOUTH CITY PUBLIC SCHOOLS p 1163
801 Crawford St 23704
Tel (757) 393-8751 *SIC* 8211

PORTSMOUTH CITY SCHOOL BOARD p 1163
801 Crawford St Fl 3 23704
Tel (757) 393-8751 *SIC* 8211

WESTERN BRANCH DIESEL INC p 1597
3504 Shipwright St 23703
Tel (757) 673-7000 *SIC* 5084 7699

WHEELABRATOR PORTSMOUTH INC p 1604
3809 Elm Ave 23704
Tel (757) 393-3100 *SIC* 4953 4911

PRINCE GEORGE, VA

PRINCE GEORGE COUNTY SCHOOL BOARD p 1176
6410 Courts Dr 23875
Tel (804) 733-2700 *SIC* 8211

QUANTICO, VA

■ BUSINESS AND SUPPORT SERVICES p 229
3044 Catlin Ave 22134
Tel (703) 432-0109 *SIC* 7997

■ DEFENSE SECURITY SERVICE p 422
27130 Telegraph Rd 22134
Tel (571) 305-6751 *SIC* 9711

RADFORD, VA

■ ALLIANT TECHSYSTEMS OPERATIONS LLC p 55
Hc 114 24143
Tel (540) 831-4788 *SIC* 2892

■ KOLLMORGEN CORP p 826
203a W Rock Rd 24141
Tel (540) 639-2495
SIC 3621 3825 3827 3861

RADFORD UNIVERSITY p 1204
801 E Main St 24142
Tel (540) 831-5000 *SIC* 8221

RESTON, VA

ACADEMI LLC p 13
12018 Sunrise Valley Dr # 140 20191
Tel (252) 435-2488 *SIC* 7382 8742

ACE INFO SOLUTIONS INC p 16
11490 Commerce Park Dr # 340 20191
Tel (703) 391-2800 *SIC* 7379

■ AMERICHOICE CORP p 81
12018 Sunrise Valley Dr # 400 20191
Tel (571) 262-8933 *SIC* 6324

APOGEN TECHNOLOGIES INC p 97
11091 Sunset Hills Rd # 200 20190
Tel (703) 644-6433 *SIC* 7373 7379

APPIAN CORP p 98
11955 Democracy Dr # 1700 20190
Tel (703) 442-8844 *SIC* 7379 7371

ASHGROVE HOLDINGS LLC p 117
12001 Sunrise Valley Dr 20191
Tel (703) 821-1175 *SIC* 5032

BECHTEL MARINE PROPULSION CORP p 167
12011 Sunset Hills Rd 20190
Tel (301) 228-6000 *SIC* 8731

BECHTEL NUCLEAR SECURITY & ENVIRONMENTAL INC p 167
12021 Sunset Hills Rd 20190
Tel (415) 768-1234 *SIC* 8711 1629 8742

■ CACI NSS INC p 236
11955 Freedom Dr Fl 2 20190
Tel (703) 434-4000 *SIC* 7373 8711

CARAHSOFT TECHNOLOGY CORP p 252
1860 Michael Faraday Dr # 100 20190
Tel (703) 871-8500 *SIC* 5045

CENTENNIAL CONTRACTORS ENTERPRISES INC p 275
11111 Sunset Hills Rd # 350 20190
Tel (703) 885-4600 *SIC* 1542 1541

CLEARPATH SOLUTIONS GROUP LLC p 324
12100 Sunset Hills Rd # 610 20190
Tel (703) 673-9370 *SIC* 5045

▲ COMSCORE INC p 353
11950 Democracy Dr # 600 20190
Tel (703) 438-2000 *SIC* 7372

■ CONTACT SOLUTIONS LLC p 362
11950 Democracy Dr # 250 20190
Tel (703) 480-1620 *SIC* 7379 7371 7389

EMERALD DAIRY INC p 491
11990 Market St Unit 205 20190
Tel (703) 867-9247 *SIC* 5451

FEDERAL HOME LOAN BANK - OFFICE OF FINANCE p 534
1818 Library St Ste 200 20190
Tel (703) 467-3600 *SIC* 6019

■ FEDERAL NETWORK SYSTEMS LLC p 535
11710 Plaza America Dr 20190
Tel (703) 694-7200 *SIC* 8748

FRIENDS & CO p 580
1760 Reston Pkwy Ste 200 20190
Tel (703) 796-0333 *SIC* 7361

GATE GOURMET US INC p 593
1880 Campus Commons Dr # 200 20191
Tel (703) 964-2300 *SIC* 5812 8742

GATEGROUP US HOLDING INC p 593
11710 Plaza America Dr # 800 20190
Tel (703) 964-2300 *SIC* 5812 8742

GENEVA ENTERPRISES INC p 603
1902 Association Dr 20191
Tel (703) 553-4300 *SIC* 5511

GOVERNMENT SCIENTIFIC SOURCE INC p 627
12351 Sunrise Valley Dr 20191
Tel (703) 734-1805 *SIC* 5049 5047

GRADUATE MANAGEMENT ADMISSION COUNCIL INC p 628
11921 Freedom Dr Ste 300 20190
Tel (703) 668-9600 *SIC* 8748

HEADSTRONG CORP p 673
11921 Freedom Dr Ste 550 20190
Tel (703) 272-6761 *SIC* 7379 8999

INDYNE INC p 740
11800 Sunrise Valley Dr # 250 20191
Tel (703) 903-6900 *SIC* 8744 8748 7382

■ LEIDOS ENGINEERING LLC p 854
11951 Freedom Dr 20190
Tel (571) 526-6000 *SIC* 8711 1541

▲ LEIDOS HOLDINGS INC p 854
11951 Freedom Dr Ste 500 20190
Tel (571) 526-6000
SIC 8731 7371 7373 8742 3674

■ LEIDOS INC p 854
11951 Freedom Dr Ste 500 20190
Tel (571) 526-6000 *SIC* 8731 7373

MA FEDERAL INC p 891
12030 Sunrise Valley Dr # 300 20191
Tel (703) 356-1160 *SIC* 5045

MARYLAND AND VIRGINIA MILK PRODUCERS COOPERATIVE ASSOCIATION INC p 914
1985 Isaac Newton Sq W # 200 20190
Tel (703) 742-6800 *SIC* 5143 2026 5084

■ MAXIMUS FEDERAL SERVICES INC p 922
1891 Metro Center Dr 20190
Tel (703) 251-8500 *SIC* 8742

▲ MAXIMUS INC p 922
1891 Metro Center Dr 20190
Tel (703) 251-8500 *SIC* 8742 8741

MEDICAL TEAM INC p 937
1902 Campus Commons Dr # 650 20191
Tel (703) 390-2300 *SIC* 8082

■ NAVIENT SOLUTIONS INC p 1020
2001 Edmund Halley Dr 20191
Tel (703) 810-3000 *SIC* 6111

▲ NCI INC p 1022
11730 Plaza America Dr # 700 20190
Tel (703) 707-6900 *SIC* 7373 8711

■ NCI INFORMATION SYSTEMS INC p 1022
11730 Plaza America Dr # 700 20190
Tel (703) 707-6900 *SIC* 7373

■ NEXTEL COMMUNICATIONS INC p 1040
12502 Sunrise Valley Dr 20191
Tel (703) 433-4000 *SIC* 4812

■ NEXTEL FINANCE CO p 1040
2001 Edmund Halley Dr 20191
Tel (703) 433-4000 *SIC* 4812 6719

▲ NII HOLDINGS INC p 1043
1875 Explorer St Ste 800 20190
Tel (703) 390-5100 *SIC* 4812

▲ NVR INC p 1068
11700 Plaza America Dr # 500 20190
Tel (703) 956-4000 *SIC* 1531 6162

PRAGMATICS INC p 1167
1761 Business Center Dr # 110 20190
Tel (703) 890-8500 *SIC* 7379

QUADRAMED CORP p 1196
12110 Sunset Hills Rd # 600 20190
Tel (703) 709-2300 *SIC* 7372

REINFORCED EARTH CO p 1221
12001 Sunrise Valley Dr # 400 20191
Tel (703) 821-1175 *SIC* 5032

RL2 INC p 1239
10802 Parkridge Blvd 20191
Tel (703) 390-1899 *SIC* 4899

ROLLS-ROYCE NORTH AMERICA (USA) HOLDINGS CO p 1247
1875 Explorer St Ste 200 20190
Tel (703) 834-1700
SIC 5088 8741 6159 3724

ROLLS-ROYCE NORTH AMERICA HOLDINGS INC p 1248
1875 Explorer St Ste 200 20190
Tel (703) 834-1700 *SIC* 5088 8741 7699

ROLLS-ROYCE NORTH AMERICA INC p 1248
1875 Explorer St Ste 200 20190
Tel (703) 834-1700 *SIC* 5088 8741 1731

■ SCITOR CORP p 1292
12010 Sunset Hills Rd 20190
Tel (703) 961-4000 *SIC* 8711

■ SCITOR HOLDINGS INC p 1292
12010 Sunset Hills Rd # 800 20190
Tel (703) 481-5892 *SIC* 7382 5065 7373

SERCO GROUP INC p 1306
1818 Library St Ste 1000 20190
Tel (703) 939-6000 *SIC* 8744

SERCO INC p 1306
1818 Library St Ste 1000 20190
Tel (703) 939-6000 *SIC* 8999

SERCO NORTH AMERICA (HOLDINGS) INC p 1306
1818 Library St Ste 1000 20190
Tel (703) 939-6000 *SIC* 8744

SERCO SERVICES INC p 1306
1818 Library St Ste 1000 20190
Tel (703) 939-6000 *SIC* 7371

SES GOVERNMENT SOLUTIONS INC p 1308
11790 Sunrise Valley Dr # 300 20191
Tel (703) 610-1000 *SIC* 7389 3663

SI INTERNATIONAL ZEN TECHNOLOGY INC p 1319
1818 Library St 20190
Tel (703) 939-6671 *SIC* 7379

SOFTWARE AG INC p 1337
11700 Plaza America Dr # 700 20190
Tel (703) 860-5050 *SIC* 7372

SOFTWARE AG USA INC p 1337
11700 Plaza America Dr # 700 20190
Tel (703) 860-5050 *SIC* 7371

STANLEY MARTIN COMPANIES INC p 1377
11710 Plaza America Dr # 1100 20190
Tel (703) 964-5000 *SIC* 1531

STG INC p 1389
11091 Sunset Hills Rd # 200 20190
Tel (703) 691-2480 *SIC* 4813

TALKAMERICA INC p 1422
12020 Sunrise Valley Dr # 250 20191
Tel (703) 391-7518 *SIC* 4813

THOMPSON HOSPITALITY CORP p 1449
1741 Bus Ctr Dr Ste 200 20190
Tel (703) 757-5500 *SIC* 5812

THOMPSON HOSPITALITY SERVICES LLC p 1449
1741 Bus Ctr Dr Ste 200 20190
Tel (703) 757-5560 *SIC* 5812

THUNDERCAT TECHNOLOGY LLC p 1451
1925 Isaac Newton Sq E # 180 20190
Tel (703) 674-0216 *SIC* 5045

TNS INC p 1458
10740 Parkridge Blvd # 100 20191
Tel (703) 453-8300 *SIC* 4813 7374

TRANSACTION NETWORK SERVICES INC p 1470
10740 Parkridge Blvd # 100 20191
Tel (703) 453-8300 *SIC* 4813 7389 7374

TRIPLE CANOPY INC p 1482
12018 Sunrise Valley Dr # 140 20191
Tel (703) 673-5000 *SIC* 7381 8748

TRULAND SYSTEMS CORP p 1486
1900 Oracle Way Ste 700 20190
Tel (703) 464-3000 *SIC* 1731

■ UNITED STATES DEPT OF GEOLOGICAL SURVEY p 1513
12201 Sunrise Valley Dr 20192
Tel (703) 648-4000 *SIC* 9511

VENCORE SERVICES AND SOLUTIONS INC p 1547
1835 Alexander Bell Dr 20191
Tel (703) 391-7017 *SIC* 7379 7373 3812

▲ VERISIGN INC p 1549
12061 Bluemont Way 20190
Tel (703) 948-3200 *SIC* 7375 7372

RICHLANDS, VA

■ CLINCH VALLEY MEDICAL CENTER INC p 326
6801 Gov Gc Peery Hwy 24641
Tel (276) 596-6000 *SIC* 8062

RICHMOND, VA

■ AFFLINK HOLDING CORP p 32
12500 West Creek Pkwy 23238
Tel (804) 484-6217 *SIC* 5141

■ AFTON CHEMICAL CORP p 33
500 Spring St 23219
Tel (804) 788-5086 *SIC* 2899 2999 3999

AGA (VIRGINIA) INC p 34
9950 Mayland Dr 23233
Tel (804) 285-3300 *SIC* 6411 4724

AGA SERVICE CO p 34
2805 N Parham Rd 23294
Tel (804) 285-3300 *SIC* 6719

ALFA LAVAL INC p 49
5400 Intl Trade Dr 23231
Tel (804) 222-5300
SIC 3491 3433 3585 3569 3821

ALFA LAVAL US HOLDING INC p 49
5400 Intl Trade Dr 23231
Tel (804) 222-5300 *SIC* 3569 5085

ALFA LAVAL USA INC p 49
5400 Intl Trade Dr 23231
Tel (804) 222-5300 *SIC* 3443 3585

ALLIANZ GLOBAL ASSISTANCE (AGA) SERVICE CO p 55
9950 Mayland Dr 23233
Tel (800) 628-4908 *SIC* 6411

■ ALTRIA GROUP DISTRIBUTION CO p 63
6601 W Broad St 23230
Tel (804) 274-2000 *SIC* 5159

▲ ALTRIA GROUP INC p 63
6601 W Broad St 23230
Tel (804) 274-2200 *SIC* 2111 2084

AMF AUTOMATION TECHNOLOGIES LLC p 84
2115 W Laburnum Ave 23227
Tel (804) 355-7961 *SIC* 3556

■ ANTHEM HEALTH PLANS OF VIRGINIA INC p 93
2015 Staples Mill Rd 23230
Tel (804) 354-7000 *SIC* 6324

APPLE EIGHT HOSPITALITY MANAGEMENT INC p 98
814 E Main St 23219
Tel (804) 727-6337 *SIC* 8741

APPLE HOSPITALITY REIT INC p 98
814 E Main St 23219
Tel (804) 344-8121 *SIC* 6798

APPLE REIT EIGHT INC p 99
14 E Main St 23219
Tel (804) 344-8121 *SIC* 6798

APPLE REIT EIGHT INC p 99
814 E Main St 23219
Tel (804) 344-8121 *SIC* 7011

APPLE REIT SEVEN INC p 99
814 E Main St 23219
Tel (804) 344-8121 *SIC* 7011

APPLE REIT TEN INC p 99
814 E Main St 23219
Tel (804) 344-8121 *SIC* 6798

ARCET EQUIPMENT CO p 104
1700 Chamberlayne Ave 23222
Tel (804) 644-4521 *SIC* 5085 5084 5169

AUDIO FIDELITY COMMUNICATIONS CORP p 130
12820 West Creek Pkwy 23238
Tel (804) 273-9100 *SIC* 5044 5065

BLEDSOE COAL CORP p 189
901 E Byrd St Ste 1140 23219
Tel (606) 878-7411 *SIC* 1221

BMG METALS INC p 194
950 Masonic Ln 23223
Tel (804) 226-1024 *SIC* 5051

BON SECOURS - ST MARYS HOSPITAL OF RICHMOND INC p 199
5801 Bremo Rd 23226
Tel (804) 288-5415 *SIC* 8062

▲ BRINKS CO p 213
1801 Bayberry Ct Ste 400 23226
Tel (804) 289-9600 *SIC* 7382 7381

■ BRINKS INC p 213
1801 Bayberry Ct Ste 400 23226
Tel (804) 289-9600 *SIC* 7381

C F SAUER CO p 232
2000 W Broad St 23220
Tel (804) 359-5786 *SIC* 2087

■ CADMUS JOURNAL SERVICES INC p 236
2901 Byrdhill Rd 23228
Tel (804) 264-2711 *SIC* 2752

▲ CARMAX INC p 258
12800 Tuckahoe Creek Pkwy 23238
Tel (804) 747-0422 *SIC* 5521 5511 6141

CARPENTER CO p 260
5016 Monument Ave 23230
Tel (804) 359-0800
SIC 3086 1311 2869 2297 2392 2821

CARPENTER HOLDINGS INC p 260
5016 Monument Ave 23230
Tel (804) 359-0800 *SIC* 3086

■ CAVALIER TELEPHONE CORP p 267
2134 W Laburnum Ave 23227
Tel (804) 422-4000 *SIC* 4813

CAVALIER TELEPHONE LLC p 267
2134 W Laburnum Ave 23227
Tel (804) 422-4100 *SIC* 4813 4812

CAVALIER TELEPHONE MID-ATLANTIC LLC p 267
2134 W Laburnum Ave 23227
Tel (804) 422-4100 *SIC* 4813 4812

■ CAVTEL HOLDINGS LLC p 268
2134 W Laburnum Ave 23227
Tel (804) 422-4107 *SIC* 4813

CHERRY BEKAERT LLP p 294
200 S 10th St Ste 900 23219
Tel (804) 673-5700 *SIC* 8721

CHILDFUND INTERNATIONAL USA p 298
2821 Emerywood Pkwy 23294
Tel (804) 756-2700 *SIC* 8399

■ CHIPPENHAM & JOHNSTON-WILLIS HOSPITALS INC p 301
7101 Jahnke Rd 23225
Tel (804) 327-4046 *SIC* 8062

■ CHIPPENHAM HOSPITAL INC p 301
7101 Jahnke Rd 23225
Tel (804) 320-3911 *SIC* 8062

CHURCH SCHOOLS IN DIOCESE OF VIRGINIA p 305
8727 River Rd 23229
Tel (804) 288-6045 *SIC* 8211

CITY OF RICHMOND p 318
900 E Broad St Ste 201 23219
Tel (804) 646-7970 *SIC* 9111

■ COLONIALWEBB CONTRACTORS CO p 338
2820 Ackley Ave 23228
Tel (804) 916-1400 *SIC* 1711 7623

COLONY INSURANCE CO p 338
8720 Stony Point Pkwy # 400 23235
Tel (804) 560-2000 *SIC* 6351

COMMONWEALTH OF VIRGINIA p 346
101 N 14st James Monroe St 23219
Tel (804) 225-3131 *SIC* 9111

■ CONSOLIDATED NATURAL GAS CO p 360
120 Tredegar St 23219
Tel (804) 819-2000 *SIC* 1311 4922 4924

CORNETT HOSPITALITY LLC p 371
2120 Staples Mill Rd 23230
Tel (804) 678-9000 *SIC* 8741

CORNETT MANAGEMENT CO INC p 371
2120 Staples Mill Rd # 300 23230
Tel (804) 678-9000 *SIC* 5812

■ DANVILLE LEAF TOBACCO CO INC p 412
9201 Forest Hill Ave Fl 1 23235
Tel (804) 359-9311 *SIC* 2141

DAVENPORT & CO LLC p 415
901 E Cary St Ste 1200 23219
Tel (804) 780-2000 *SIC* 6211 6282

DNC/MFS FOOD GROUP p 446
1 Richard E Byrd Trml Dr 23250
Tel (804) 222-1227 *SIC* 5812

■ DOMINION CAPITAL INC p 449
120 Tredegar St 23219
Tel (804) 819-2000 *SIC* 4911

■ DOMINION COVE POINT INC p 449
120 Tredegar St 23219
Tel (804) 819-2000 *SIC* 4911 4923 1311

■ DOMINION ENERGY INC p 449
120 Tredegar St 23219
Tel (804) 819-2000 *SIC* 4911

■ DOMINION MIDSTREAM PARTNERS LP p 449
120 Tredegar St 23219
Tel (804) 819-2000 *SIC* 4925 4922

■ DOMINION MLP HOLDING CO LLC p 449
120 Tredegar St 23219
Tel (804) 819-2000 *SIC* 4911 4923 1311

■ DOMINION NUCLEAR CONNECTICUT INC p 449
120 Tredegar St 23219
Tel (866) 366-4357 *SIC* 4931

▲ DOMINION RESOURCES INC p 449
120 Tredegar St 23219
Tel (804) 819-2000 *SIC* 4911 4923 1311

■ DOMINION RESOURCES SERVICES INC p 449
120 Tredegar St 23219
Tel (804) 775-2500 *SIC* 4911

■ DOMINION TRANSMISSION INC p 449
120 Tredegar St 23219
Tel (804) 771-4795 *SIC* 4922 4923

EASTERN SLEEP PRODUCTS CO p 472
4901 Fitzhugh Ave 23230
Tel (804) 254-1711
SIC 2515 2512 7641 4213

ECK ENTERPRISES INC p 475
1405 W Main St 23220
Tel (804) 359-5781 *SIC* 5063 6512

ECK SUPPLY CO p 475
1405 W Main St 23220
Tel (804) 359-5781 *SIC* 5063

EMPLOYMENT COMMISSION VIRGINIA p 494
703 E Main St 23219
Tel (804) 786-3021 *SIC* 9441

ESTES EXPRESS LINES INC p 511
3901 W Broad St 23230
Tel (804) 353-1900 *SIC* 4213

■ ETHYL CORP p 511
330 S 4th St 23219
Tel (804) 788-5000
SIC 2869 5169 2899 2841 2865

EVERGREEN ENTERPRISES INC p 514
5915 Midlothian Tpke 23225
Tel (804) 231-1800
SIC 3253 2399 5193 5999

EXECUTIVE OFFICE OF VIRGINIA p 518
1111 E Broad St Fl 3 23219
Tel (804) 225-4534 *SIC* 9111

FEDERAL RESERVE BANK OF RICHMOND p 535
701 E Byrd St Fl 2 23219
Tel (804) 697-8000 *SIC* 6029

FIRE & LIFE SAFETY AMERICA INC p 543
3017 Vernon Rd 23228
Tel (804) 222-1381 *SIC* 5063

FIRE AND LIFE SAFETY AMERICA HOLDINGS INC p 543
3017 Vernon Rd Ste 100 23228
Tel (804) 222-1381 *SIC* 1711 1731

FRISCHKORN INC p 580
1801 Roseneath Rd 23230
Tel (804) 353-0181 *SIC* 5085

FROEHLING & ROBERTSON INC p 580
3015 Dumbarton Rd 23228
Tel (804) 264-2701 *SIC* 8711 8734

■ GE FINANCIAL ASSURANCE HOLDINGS INC p 596
6604 W Broad St 23230
Tel (804) 281-6000 *SIC* 6311

▲ GENWORTH FINANCIAL INC p 605
6620 W Broad St Ste 270 23230
Tel (804) 281-6000 *SIC* 6311 6371 6351

■ GENWORTH LIFE AND ANNUITY INSURANCE CO p 605
6610 W Broad St 23230
Tel (804) 281-6000 *SIC* 6311 6211

■ GENWORTH LIFE INSURANCE CO p 605
6620 W Broad St 23230
Tel (804) 281-6000 *SIC* 6311

■ GENWORTH NORTH AMERICA CORP p 605
6620 W Broad St Bldg 3 23230
Tel (804) 281-6000 *SIC* 6141

GOODWILL OF CENTRAL AND COASTAL VIRGINIA INC p 625
6301 Midlothian Tpke 23225
Tel (804) 745-6300 *SIC* 8331

GPM INVESTMENTS LLC p 627
8565 Magellan Pkwy # 400 23227
Tel (804) 266-1363 *SIC* 5541 5411 5172

GREATER RICHMOND BUSINESS INC p 636
1833 Commerce Rd 23224
Tel (804) 232-3492
SIC 5511 5013 5531 7513

■ HCA HEALTH SERVICES OF VIRGINIA INC p 672
1602 Skipwith Rd 23229
Tel (804) 289-4500 *SIC* 8062 8093

HENRICO COUNTY PUBLIC SCHOOLS p 683
3820 Nine Mile Rd Ste A 23223
Tel (804) 652-3717 *SIC* 8211

HENRICO DOCTORS HOSPITAL p 683
1602 Skipwith Rd 23229
Tel (804) 289-4500 *SIC* 8069

HILB GROUP LLC p 692
8720 Stony Point Pkwy # 125 23235
Tel (804) 414-6501 *SIC* 6411

HUNTON & WILLIAMS LLP p 720
Riverfront Plz E Towe 951 23219
Tel (804) 788-8200 *SIC* 8111

INDIVIOR INC p 739
10710 Midlothian Turnpik Ste 430 23235
Tel (804) 379-1090 *SIC* 5122

INTERNATIONAL MISSION BOARD OF SOUTHERN BAPTIST CONVENTION p 756
3806 Monument Ave 23230
Tel (804) 353-0151 *SIC* 8661 2731 7812

JAMES RIVER COAL CO p 777
901 E Byrd St Ste 1600 23219
Tel (804) 780-3000 *SIC* 1221

JAMES RIVER COAL SERVICE CO p 777
901 E Byrd St Ste 1600 23219
Tel (606) 878-7411 *SIC* 1222 1221

JUDICIARY COURTS OF COMMONWEALTH OF VIRGINIA p 796
100 N 9th St 23219
Tel (804) 786-6455 *SIC* 9211

K LINE AMERICA INC p 799
8730 Stony Point Pkwy # 400 23235
Tel (804) 560-3600 *SIC* 4412 4491

KBS INC p 806
8050 Kimway Dr 23228
Tel (804) 262-0100 *SIC* 1542

KJELLSTROM AND LEE INC p 822
1607 Ownby Ln 23220
Tel (804) 288-0082 *SIC* 1541 1542

KSB AMERICA CORP p 831
4415 Sarellen Rd 23231
Tel (804) 222-1818
SIC 3561 3494 3625 5084

LANDMARK APARTMENT TRUST INC p 842
4901 Dickens Rd Ste 101 23230
Tel (804) 237-1335 *SIC* 6798 6513

LANDOR INTERNATIONAL INC p 843
2120 Staples Mill Rd # 300 23230
Tel (804) 346-8200 *SIC* 6552 8741 4724

LANSING BUILDING PRODUCTS INC p 844
8501 Sanford Dr 23228
Tel (804) 266-8893 *SIC* 5033 5031 5032

LECLAIRRYAN A PROFESSNL CORP p 851
951 E Byrd St Fl 8 23219
Tel (804) 783-2003 *SIC* 8111

■ MARTIN AGENCY INC p 912
1 Shockoe Plz 23219
Tel (804) 649-1496
SIC 7331 7311 8743 7313

MCGUIREWOODS LLP p 929
800 E Canal St 23219
Tel (804) 775-1000 *SIC* 8111

■ MCKESSON MEDICAL-SURGICAL INC p 930
9954 Mayland Dr Ste 4000 23233
Tel (804) 264-7500 *SIC* 5047

MCV ASSOCIATED PHYSICIANS p 933
830 E Main St Ste 1900 23219
Tel (804) 358-6100 *SIC* 8741 8721

■ MEDIA GENERAL COMMUNICATIONS INC p 935
333 E Franklin St 23219
Tel (804) 649-6000 *SIC* 2711

▲ MEDIA GENERAL INC p 936
333 E Franklin St 23219
Tel (804) 887-5000 *SIC* 4833

■ MEDIA GENERAL OPERATIONS INC p 936
333 E Franklin St 23219
Tel (804) 887-5000 *SIC* 2711 4833

■ MGOC INC p 958
333 E Franklin St 23219
Tel (804) 887-5000 *SIC* 4833 4841

NATURAL RESOURCES VIRGINIA p 1018
1111 E Broad St 23219
Tel (804) 786-0044 *SIC* 9511 9512

▲ NEWMARKET CORP p 1038
330 S 4th St 23219
Tel (804) 788-5000
SIC 2869 2899 2841 2865

PEARSON COMPANIES INC p 1126
9530 Midlothian Pike 23225
Tel (804) 745-0300 *SIC* 5511

▲ PERFORMANCE FOOD GROUP CO p 1135
12500 West Creek Pkwy 23238
Tel (804) 484-7700 *SIC* 5141

■ PERFORMANCE FOOD GROUP INC p 1135
12500 West Creek Pkwy 23238
Tel (804) 484-7700 *SIC* 5149

PFG HOLDINGS LLC p 1140
12500 West Creek Pkwy 23238
Tel (804) 484-7700
SIC 5141 5144 5147 5146 5142 5148

■ PFGC INC p 1140
12500 West Creek Pkwy 23238
Tel (804) 484-7700 *SIC* 5141 5142

■ PHILIP MORRIS USA INC p 1143
6601 W Brd St 23230
Tel (804) 274-2000 *SIC* 2111 2141 5194

■ REYNOLDS METALS CO LLC p 1230
6603 W Broad St 23230
Tel (804) 281-2000 *SIC* 3411

REYNOLDS PACKAGING GROUP LTD p 1231
6641 W Broad St Fl 5 23230
Tel (804) 281-2000 *SIC* 7389

REYNOLDS PACKAGING INC p 1231
6641 W Broad St Fl 4 23230
Tel (804) 281-2000 *SIC* 7389

RICHMOND CITY PUBLIC SCHOOLS p 1233
301 N 9th St Fl 17 23219
Tel (804) 780-7775 *SIC* 8211

ROMAN CATHOLIC DIOCESE OF RICHMOND p 1249
7800 Carousel Ln 23294
Tel (804) 359-5661 *SIC* 8661

S & K FAMOUS BRANDS INC p 1261
20 N 8th St 23219
Tel (804) 827-1000 *SIC* 5611 5661

■ SCOTT & STRINGFELLOW LLC p 1293
901 E Byrd St Ste 300 23219
Tel (804) 643-1811 *SIC* 6211

SHONEYS OF RICHMOND INC p 1317
7202 Glen Forest Dr # 104 23226
Tel (804) 346-3414 *SIC* 5812

SLURRY PAVERS INC p 1331
3617 Nine Mile Rd 23223
Tel (804) 264-0707 *SIC* 2951 1611

■ SOUTHEAST SERVICES INC p 1346
2015 Staples Mill Rd 23230
Tel (804) 354-7000 *SIC* 6324

SOUTHERN STATES COOPERATIVE INC p 1350
6606 W Broad St Ste B 23230
Tel (804) 281-1000
SIC 2048 0181 2873 2874 5191 5172

SOUTHERN STATES HOLDINGS INC p 1350
6606 W Broad St Ste B 23230
Tel (804) 281-1206 *SIC* 5191 5261 0724

STATE COUNCIL OF HIGHER EDUCATION FOR VIRGINIA p 1380
101 N 14th St Fl 9 23219
Tel (804) 225-2627 *SIC* 9411

■ SUNTRUST MORTGAGE INC p 1405
901 Semmes Ave 23224
Tel (804) 291-0740 *SIC* 6162

SWEDISH MATCH NORTH AMERICA LLC p 1411
1021 E Cary St Ste 1600 23219
Tel (804) 787-5100 *SIC* 2131 5199

TALK AMERICA HOLDINGS INC p 1422
2134 W Laburnum Ave 23227
Tel (804) 422-4100 *SIC* 4813

THOMAS & BETTS POWER SOLUTIONS LLC p 1448
5900 Eastport Blvd Bldg 5 23231
Tel (804) 236-3300 *SIC* 3629

UKROPS SUPER MARKETS INC p 1500
2001 Maywill St Ste 100 23230
Tel (804) 304-3000 *SIC* 5411

▲ UNION BANKSHARES CORP p 1504
1051 E Cary St Ste 1200 23219
Tel (804) 633-5031 *SIC* 6022

▲ UNIVERSAL CORP p 1516
9201 Forest Hill Ave 23235
Tel (804) 359-9311 *SIC* 5159 2141

■ UNIVERSAL CORP p 1516
9201 Forest Hl Ave Stony 23235
Tel (804) 359-9311 *SIC* 5194

UNIVERSITY OF RICHMOND p 1524
28 Westhampton Way 23173
Tel (804) 289-8133 *SIC* 8221

■ UPS FREIGHT SERVICES INC p 1529
1000 Semmes Ave 23224
Tel (804) 231-8000 *SIC* 4215

■ UPS GROUND FREIGHT INC p 1529
1000 Semmes Ave 23224
Tel (866) 372-5619 *SIC* 4213

■ **US SMOKELESS TOBACCO CO** p 1533
6603 W Broad St 23230
Tel (804) 274-2000 SIC 2131

VCU HEALTH SYSTEM AUTHORITY p 1546
1250 E Marshall St 23298
Tel (804) 828-9000 SIC 8062

VIRGINIA COMMONWEALTH UNIVERSITY p 1558
912 W Franklin St 23284
Tel (804) 828-0100 SIC 8221

VIRGINIA DEPARTMENT OF ALCOHOLIC BEVERAGE CONTROL p 1559
2901 Hermitage Rd 23220
Tel (804) 213-4400 SIC 9651

VIRGINIA DEPARTMENT OF CONSERVATION AND RECREATION p 1559
600 E Main St Fl 24 23219
Tel (804) 371-0099 SIC 9512

VIRGINIA DEPARTMENT OF CORRECTIONS p 1559
6900 Atmore Dr 23225
Tel (804) 674-3000 SIC 9223

VIRGINIA DEPARTMENT OF HEALTH p 1559
109 Governor St Ste 1221 23219
Tel (804) 864-7045 SIC 9431

VIRGINIA DEPARTMENT OF JUVENILE JUSTICE p 1559
7th & Franklin Sts 23219
Tel (804) 371-0700 SIC 9223

VIRGINIA DEPARTMENT OF MOTOR VEHICLES p 1559
2300 W Broad St 23220
Tel (804) 367-0538 SIC 9621

VIRGINIA DEPARTMENT OF SOCIAL SERVICES p 1559
801 E Main St Fl 3 23219
Tel (804) 726-7000 SIC 9441

VIRGINIA DEPARTMENT OF TRANSPORTATION p 1559
1401 E Broad St 23219
Tel (804) 786-2836 SIC 8711

VIRGINIA DEPARTMENT OF TRANSPORTATION p 1559
1401 E Broad St 23219
Tel (804) 786-2701 SIC 9621

■ **VIRGINIA ELECTRIC AND POWER CO** p 1559
120 Tredegar St 23219
Tel (804) 819-2000 SIC 4911

VIRGINIA HOUSING DEVELOPMENT AUTHORITY p 1559
601 S Belvidere St 23220
Tel (804) 780-0789 SIC 6162

■ **VIRGINIA POWER SERVICES ENERGY CORP INC** p 1559
120 Tredegar St 23219
Tel (804) 819-2000 SIC 4911

VIRGINIA PREMIER HEALTH PLAN INC p 1559
600 E Broad St Ste 400 23219
Tel (804) 819-5164 SIC 8011

VIRGINIA SECRETARY OF COMMERCE AND TRADE p 1559
Ninth St Off Bldg Ste 723 23219
Tel (804) 786-7831 SIC 9611

VIRGINIA SECRETARY OF EDUCATION p 1559
1111 E Broad St Fl 5 23219
Tel (804) 786-1151 SIC 9411

VIRGINIA SECRETARY OF FINANCE p 1559
1111 E Broad St Ste 5035 23219
Tel (804) 786-1148 SIC 9311

VIRGINIA SECRETARY OF HEALTH AND HUMAN RESOURCES p 1559
202 E 9th St 23224
Tel (804) 786-7765 SIC 9431 9441

VIRGINIA SECRETARY OF PUBLIC SAFETY AND HOMELAND SECURITY p 1559
1111 E Broad St 23219
Tel (804) 786-5351 SIC 9111

VIRGINIA SECRETARY OF TRANSPORTATION p 1559
1111 E Broad St Fl 3 23219
Tel (804) 786-8032 SIC 9621

■ **WACHOVIA SECURITIES FINANCIAL HOLDINGS LLC** p 1570
901 E Byrd St Ste 500 23219
Tel (804) 782-4174 SIC 6211

■ **WESTROCK MWV LLC** p 1603
501 S 5th St 23219
Tel (804) 444-1000
SIC 2631 2671 2678 2677 2861 2611

WOODFIN HEATING INC p 1623
1823 N Hamilton St 23230
Tel (804) 730-4500
SIC 5172 5983 1711 7382

■ **WORLD MEDIA ENTERPRISES INC** p 1625
300 E Franklin St 23219
Tel (804) 643-1276 SIC 2711

■ **WYETH CONSUMER HEALTHCARE LLC** p 1629
1405 Cummings Dr 23220
Tel (804) 257-2000 SIC 2834

▲ **XENITH BANKSHARES INC** p 1631
901 E Cary St Ste 1700 23219
Tel (804) 433-2200 SIC 6021

YOUNG MENS CHRISTIAN ASSOCIATION OF GREATER RICHMOND p 1638
2 W Franklin St 23220
Tel (804) 644-9622
SIC 8641 7991 8351 7032 8322

RIDGEWAY, VA

NILIT AMERICA INC p 1043
420 Industrial Park Rd 24148
Tel (276) 638-2434 SIC 5199 2299 5531

ROANOKE, VA

ADAMS CONSTRUCTION CO p 21
523 Rutherford Ave Ne 24016
Tel (540) 982-2366 SIC 1611 2951

▲ **ADVANCE AUTO PARTS INC** p 24
5008 Airport Rd Nw 24012
Tel (877) 238-2623 SIC 5531

■ **ADVANCE STORES CO INC** p 25
5008 Airport Rd Nw 24012
Tel (540) 362-4911 SIC 5531

AMERICAN HEALTHCARE LLC p 74
3131 Electric Rd 24018
Tel (540) 774-4263 SIC 8052 8051 8059

ASSOCIATED ASPHALT INC p 119
130 Church Ave Sw 24011
Tel (540) 345-8867 SIC 5032

■ **BELLSOUTH COMMUNICATION SYSTEMS LLC** p 171
1936 Blue Hills Dr Ne 24012
Tel (540) 983-6000 SIC 5065 4813 4812

BRANCH & ASSOCIATES INC p 207
5732 Airport Rd Nw 24012
Tel (540) 989-5215 SIC 1542

BRANCH GROUP INC p 207
442 Rutherford Ave Ne 24016
Tel (540) 982-1678
SIC 1542 1611 1711 1731 1541

BRANCH HIGHWAYS INC p 207
442 Rutherford Ave Ne 24016
Tel (540) 982-1678 SIC 1611

BRENNER HOLDINGS INC p 210
2580 Broadway Ave Sw 24014
Tel (540) 981-1211
SIC 4953 5093 3341 3231

CARILION CLINIC p 256
1906 Belleview Ave Se 24014
Tel (540) 981-7900 SIC 8741

CARILION MEDICAL CENTER p 256
1906 Belleview Ave Se 24014
Tel (540) 981-7000 SIC 8011 8062

CITY OF ROANOKE p 318
215 Church Ave Sw Ste 461 24011
Tel (540) 853-2333 SIC 9111

CONCORDIA HEALTHCARE USA INC p 355
4950 Brambleton Ave Ste F 24018
Tel (434) 980-8146 SIC 5122

COORDINATED SERVICES MANAGEMENT INC p 367
3333 Peters Creek Rd Nw 24019
Tel (540) 366-0622 SIC 8741

COUNTY OF ROANOKE p 381
5204 Bernard Dr 24018
Tel (540) 772-2004 SIC 9111

DELTA DENTAL OF VIRGINIA p 426
4818 Starkey Rd 24018
Tel (540) 989-8000 SIC 6411 6321

DYNAX AMERICA CORP p 464
568 Eastpark Dr 24019
Tel (540) 966-6010 SIC 3714

EXCEL TRUCK GROUP p 516
267 Lee Hwy 24019
Tel (540) 777-7700
SIC 5511 5013 7538 5012

GRAND PIANO & FURNITURE CO p 630
4235 Electric Rd Ste 100 24018
Tel (540) 776-7000 SIC 5712 5021

■ **HAYES SEAY MATTERN & MATTERN INC** p 670
10 S Jefferson St # 1600 24011
Tel (540) 857-3100 SIC 8711 8712

JAMES C JUSTICE COMPANIES INC p 776
302 S Jefferson St # 400 24011
Tel (540) 776-7890 SIC 6719

LAWRENCE TRANSPORTATION SYSTEMS INC p 848
872 Lee Hwy 24019
Tel (540) 966-4000 SIC 4225 4213 4212

MASTIN KIRKLAND BOLLING INC p 918
3801 Electric Rd 24018
Tel (540) 989-4555 SIC 6531

MEDICAL FACILITIES OF AMERICA VI AND XIII (LIMITED PARTNERSHIP) p 936
2917 Penn Forest Blvd 24018
Tel (540) 989-3618 SIC 8051

METALSA-ROANOKE INC p 953
184 Vista Dr 24019
Tel (540) 966-5300 SIC 3713

PARTS DEPOT INC p 1118
401 Albemarle Ave Se 24013
Tel (540) 345-1001 SIC 5013 5531

ROANOKE CITY PUBLIC SCHOOL DISTRICT p 1240
40 Douglas Ave Nw 24012
Tel (540) 853-2502 SIC 8211

ROANOKE CITY PUBLIC SCHOOLS p 1240
40 Douglas Ave Nw 24012
Tel (540) 853-2381 SIC 8211

■ **ROANOKE ELECTRIC STEEL CORP** p 1240
102 Westside Blvd Nw 24017
Tel (540) 342-1831 SIC 3312

SHENANDOAH LIFE INSURANCE CO p 1315
4415 Pheasant Ridge Rd # 300 24014
Tel (540) 985-4400 SIC 6311

■ **STOP IN FOOD STORES INC** p 1391
3000 Ogden Rd 24018
Tel (540) 772-4900 SIC 5411

WESTERN VIRGINIA WATER AUTHORITY p 1600
601 S Jefferson St # 100 24011
Tel (540) 853-5700 SIC 4941

ROCKINGHAM, VA

ROCKINGHAM HEALTH CARE INC p 1244
2010 Health Campus Dr 22801
Tel (540) 433-4100 SIC 8062

SENTARA RMH MEDICAL CENTER p 1305
2010 Health Campus Dr 22801
Tel (540) 433-4100 SIC 8062

■ **SYSCO VIRGINIA LLC** p 1418
5081 S Valley Pike 22801
Tel (540) 434-0761
SIC 5149 5142 5113 5148 5147 5143

ROCKY MOUNT, VA

COUNTY OF FRANKLIN p 378
1255 Franklin St Ste 106 24151
Tel (540) 483-3030 SIC 9111

FRANKLIN COUNTY PUBLIC SCHOOLS p 575
25 Bernard Rd 24151
Tel (540) 483-5138 SIC 8211

FRANKLIN COUNTY SCHOOL BOARD p 575
25 Bernard Rd 24151
Tel (540) 483-5138 SIC 8211

■ **MW MANUFACTURERS INC** p 1004
433 N Main St 24151
Tel (540) 483-0211 SIC 2431

RONILE INC p 1249
701 Orchard Ave 24151
Tel (540) 483-0261 SIC 2269 5949 2273

UTTERMOST CO p 1537
3325 Grassy Hill Rd 24151
Tel (540) 483-5103 SIC 2392 5023

RUSTBURG, VA

COUNTY OF CAMPBELL p 376
47 Court House Ln 24588
Tel (434) 332-9667 SIC 9111

SALEM, VA

BLUE RIDGE BEVERAGE CO INC p 192
4446 Barley Dr 24153
Tel (540) 380-2000 SIC 5181 5182

CARTER MACHINERY CO INC p 262
1330 Lynchburg Tpke 24153
Tel (540) 387-1111 SIC 5082 3531

CITY OF SALEM p 318
114 N Broad St 24153
Tel (540) 375-4112 SIC 9111

■ **GE DRIVES & CONTROLS INC** p 596
1501 Roanoke Blvd 24153
Tel (540) 387-7000 SIC 3612

■ **LEWIS-GALE HOSPITAL INC** p 859
1900 Electric Rd 24153
Tel (540) 776-4000 SIC 8062

SALEM TOOLS INC p 1272
1602 Midland Rd 24153
Tel (540) 389-0726 SIC 5085

TMEIC CORP p 1457
1325 Electric Rd 24153
Tel (540) 283-2000 SIC 8711

TRUSTEES OF ROANOKE COLLEGE p 1488
221 College Ln 24153
Tel (540) 375-2500 SIC 8221 7929

YOKOHAMA CORP OF NORTH AMERICA p 1637
1500 Indiana St 24153
Tel (540) 389-5426 SIC 3011 5014

YOKOHAMA TIRE MANUFACTURING VIRGINIA LLC p 1637
1500 Indiana St 24153
Tel (540) 389-5426 SIC 3011

SANDSTON, VA

ASSOCIATED DISTRIBUTORS LLC p 120
5800 Technology Blvd 23150
Tel (757) 424-6300 SIC 5182

WACO INC p 1570
5450 Lewis Rd 23150
Tel (804) 222-8440
SIC 1711 1799 3448 5033

SMITHFIELD, VA

SMITHFIELD FARMLAND CORP p 1333
111 Commerce St 23430
Tel (757) 357-3131 SIC 2011 2013

SMITHFIELD FARMLAND SALES CORP p 1333
111 Commerce St 23430
Tel (757) 357-3131 SIC 5147 8743 5963

SMITHFIELD FOODS INC p 1333
200 Commerce St 23430
Tel (757) 365-3000 SIC 2011 2013 2015

SMITHFIELD PACKING CO INC p 1334
601 N Church St 23430
Tel (757) 357-3131 SIC 2011 2013

SOUTH CHESTERFIELD, VA

ESSENTRA HOLDINGS CORP p 510
1625 Ashton Park Dr Ste A 23834
Tel (804) 518-0322
SIC 3081 3082 3999 3951 2823

ESSENTRA POROUS TECHNOLOGIES CORP p 510
1625 Ashton Park Dr Ste A 23834
Tel (804) 524-4983
SIC 3081 3951 3082 2823 3999

SOUTH HILL, VA

COMMUNITY MEMORIAL HEALTH CENTER PHYSICIAN-HOSPITAL ORGANIZATION LLC p 349
125 Buena Vista Cir 23970
Tel (434) 447-3151 SIC 8062 8051

GLOBAL SAFETY TEXTILES LLC p 617
1556 Montgomery St 23970
Tel (434) 447-7629 SIC 3714 2211 3496

PARKER HOLDING CO INC p 1116
1428 W Danville St 23970
Tel (434) 447-3146 SIC 5171 5541 5983

PARKER OIL CO INC p 1116
1428 W Danville St 23970
Tel (434) 447-3146 SIC 5171 5541 5983

SPRINGFIELD, VA

■ **ARCH WIRELESS INC** p 104
6850 Versar Ctr Ste 420 22151
Tel (703) 269-6850 SIC 5999 4812

CORNET TECHNOLOGY INC p 371
6800 Versar Ctr 22151
Tel (703) 658-3400 SIC 5065 3669 3577

■ **DRUG ENFORCEMENT ADMINISTRATION** p 457
8701 Morrissette Dr 22152
Tel (202) 307-1000 SIC 9229

GREENSPRING VILLAGE INC p 638
7440 Spring Village Dr 22150
Tel (703) 313-7800 SIC 8059

INFORMATION INNOVATORS INC p 742
7400 Fullerton Rd Ste 210 22153
Tel (703) 635-7088 SIC 7379

MIDDLE EAST BROADCASTING NETWORKS INC p 964
7600 Boston Blvd 22153
Tel (703) 852-9000 SIC 4841 4832

PROGRESSIVE NURSING STAFFERS OF VIRGINIA INC p 1181
5531 Hempstead Way Ste B 22151
Tel (703) 750-3991 SIC 7363

SECURITAS CRITICAL INFRASTRUCTURE SERVICES INC p 1298
6850 Versar Ctr Ste 400 22151
Tel (703) 750-1098 SIC 7381

▲ **SPOK HOLDINGS INC** p 1359
6850 Versar Ctr Ste 420 22151
Tel (800) 611-8488 SIC 4812 4822 7372

■ **SPOK INC** p 1359
6850 Versar Ctr Ste 420 22151
Tel (703) 269-6850 SIC 4812

TRIPLE-I HOLDINGS LLC p 1482
7400 Fullerton Rd Ste 210 22153
Tel (703) 635-7088 SIC 7379 6719

▲ **VERSAR INC** p 1551
6850 Versar Ctr Ste 201 22151
Tel (703) 750-3000
SIC 8711 8748 8712 8731

STAFFORD, VA

HILLDRUP COMPANIES INC p 693
4022 Jefferson Davis Hwy 22554
Tel (703) 221-7155 SIC 4212

STAFFORD COUNTY PUBLIC SCHOOL BOARD p 1374
31 Stafford Ave 22554
Tel (540) 658-6000 SIC 8211

STAFFORD COUNTY PUBLIC SCHOOLS p 1374
31 Stafford Ave 22554
Tel (540) 658-6000 SIC 8211

STAUNTON, VA

FARM CREDIT OF VIRGINIAS ACA p 528
106 Sangers Ln 24401
Tel (540) 899-0989 SIC 6159

FISHER AUTO PARTS INC p 552
512 Greenville Ave 24401
Tel (540) 885-8901 SIC 5013 5531 4225

STERLING, VA

CSC/TECHNOLOGY MGMT GRP p 397
P.O. Box 1728 20167
Tel (703) 876-3636 SIC 5112

EXEL GLOBAL LOGISTICS INC p 518
22879 Glenn Dr Ste 100 20164
Tel (703) 350-1298 SIC 4731 4225

HR SOLUTIONS LLC p 714
47632 Loweland Ter 20165
Tel (703) 493-0084 *SIC* 8742

J K MOVING & STORAGE INC p 771
44112 Mercure Cir Ste 1 20166
Tel (703) 260-4282 *SIC* 4226

MC DEAN INC p 925
22980 Indian Creek Dr 20166
Tel (571) 262-8234 *SIC* 1731

NATIONAL ELECTRONICS WARRANTY LLC p 1011
22894 Pacific Blvd 20166
Tel (703) 375-8100 *SIC* 6411

▲ **NEUSTAR INC** p 1028
21575 Ridgetop Cir 20166
Tel (571) 434-5400 *SIC* 7375 4899

NEW CUSTOMER SERVICE COMPANIES INC p 1029
22894 Pacific Blvd 20166
Tel (703) 318-7700 *SIC* 8748

■ **RAYTHEON TECHNICAL SERVICES INTERNATIONAL CO LLC** p 1211
22265 Pacific Blvd 20166
Tel (310) 647-9438 *SIC* 8711

SABMD LLC p 1264
22705 Commerce Center Ct 20166
Tel (703) 790-1000 *SIC* 5521

SCHNABEL FOUNDATION CO INC p 1287
45240 Business Ct Ste 250 20166
Tel (703) 742-0020 *SIC* 1741

■ **VIASYSTEMS NORTH AMERICA INC** p 1554
1200 Severn Way 20166
Tel (703) 450-2600 *SIC* 3672

STONY CREEK, VA

ILUKA RESOURCES INC p 733
12472 St John Church Rd 23882
Tel (434) 348-4300 *SIC* 1481

STRASBURG, VA

VALLEY MILK PRODUCTS LLC p 1541
412 E King St 22657
Tel (540) 465-5113 *SIC* 2023 2021

SUFFOLK, VA

COOKE SEAFOOD USA INC p 366
2000 Nrthgate Cmmrce Pkwy 23435
Tel (757) 673-4500 *SIC* 2092

LOUISE OBICI MEMORIAL HOSPITAL INC p 880
2800 Godwin Blvd 23434
Tel (757) 934-4000 *SIC* 8062

MASSIMO ZANETTI BEVERAGE USA INC p 917
1370 Progress Rd 23434
Tel (757) 215-7300 *SIC* 0179

SENTARA LOUISE OBICI MEMORIAL HOSPITAL p 1305
2800 Godwin Blvd 23434
Tel (757) 934-4827 *SIC* 8062

SUFFOLK CITY OF PUBLIC SCHOOLS p 1396
100 N Main St Ste 1 23434
Tel (757) 925-6754 *SIC* 8211

■ **SYSCO HAMPTON ROADS INC** p 1417
7000 Harbour View Blvd 23435
Tel (757) 399-2451 *SIC* 5141 5147 5148

▲ **TOWNEBANK** p 1466
6001 Harbour View Blvd 23435
Tel (757) 638-6700 *SIC* 6022

TAZEWELL, VA

TAZEWELL COUNTY BOARD OF EDUCATION p 1427
209 W Fincastle Tpke 24651
Tel (276) 988-5511 *SIC* 8211

TOANO, VA

■ **AVID MEDICAL INC** p 138
9000 Westmont Dr 23168
Tel (757) 566-3510 *SIC* 5047

▲ **LUMBER LIQUIDATORS HOLDINGS INC** p 885
3000 John Deere Rd 23168
Tel (757) 259-4280 *SIC* 5211

■ **LUMBER LIQUIDATORS INC** p 885
3000 John Deere Rd 23168
Tel (757) 259-4280 *SIC* 5031 5211

TYSONS CORNER, VA

▲ **ALARM.COM HOLDINGS INC** p 44
8281 Greensboro Dr # 100 22102
Tel (877) 389-4033 *SIC* 7382

ALVAREZ LLC p 63
8251 Greensboro Dr # 230 22102
Tel (301) 830-4020
SIC 8742 8741 7379 5044

CVENT INC p 404
1765 Grnsboro Stn Pl Fl 7 22102
Tel (703) 226-3500 *SIC* 7372

▲ **MICROSTRATEGY INC** p 962
1850 Towers Crescent Plz # 700 22182
Tel (703) 848-8600 *SIC* 7372 7371

TYSONS, VA

▲ **COMPUTER SCIENCES CORP** p 353
1775 Tysons Blvd 22102
Tel (703) 245-9675
SIC 7376 7374 7379 7373 7323

■ **CSC CREDIT SERVICES INC** p 397
1775 Tysons Blvd 22102
Tel (703) 876-1000 *SIC* 7323 7322

VERONA, VA

AUGUSTA COUNTY SCHOOL BOARD p 131
18 Government Center Ln 24482
Tel (540) 245-5100 *SIC* 8211

VIENNA, VA

ACTIONET INC p 19
2600 Park Twr Dr Ste 1000 22180
Tel (703) 204-0090
SIC 7379 7373 7372 7371

■ **AT&T GOVERNMENT SOLUTIONS INC** p 123
1900 Gallows Rd Ste 105 22182
Tel (703) 506-5000
SIC 5999 8742 7373 7371

CREATIVE HAIRDRESSERS INC p 390
1577 Spring Hill Rd # 600 22182
Tel (703) 269-5400 *SIC* 5999 7231

■ **GENESYS CONFERENCING INC** p 603
8020 Towers Crescent Dr 22182
Tel (703) 749-2500 *SIC* 4813

JIM KOONS MANAGEMENT CO p 785
2000 Chain Bridge Rd 22182
Tel (703) 448-7000 *SIC* 8741

LASERSHIP INC p 846
1912 Woodford Rd Ste Ll 22182
Tel (703) 761-9030 *SIC* 7389

MARYLAND FOODS INC p 915
1960 Gallows Rd Ste 200 22182
Tel (703) 827-0320 *SIC* 5812 5813

MHM SERVICES INC p 959
1593 Spring Hill Rd # 600 22182
Tel (703) 749-4600 *SIC* 8093 8361

MICROTECHNOLOGIES LLC p 962
8330 Boone Blvd Ste 600 22182
Tel (703) 891-1073 *SIC* 7379

NAVY FEDERAL CREDIT UNION p 1020
820 Follin Ln Se 22180
Tel (703) 255-8000 *SIC* 6061

RATNER COMPANIES LC p 1209
1577 Spring Hill Rd # 500 22182
Tel (703) 269-5400 *SIC* 7231

RED DOOR SALONS INC p 1215
8075 Leesburg Pike # 110 22182
Tel (602) 760-2519 *SIC* 7231

RNGLNG BRS BRNM & BLY COMB SHO p 1240
8607 Westwood Center Dr # 500 22182
Tel (703) 448-4000 *SIC* 7999

SOURCEAMERICA p 1342
8401 Old Courthouse Rd 22182
Tel (888) 411-8424 *SIC* 8399

SOUTHERN MANAGEMENT CORP p 1349
1950 Old Gallows Rd # 600 22182
Tel (703) 902-2000 *SIC* 6531

TEAM WASHINGTON INC p 1430
8381 Old Courthouse Rd # 100 22182
Tel (703) 734-7080 *SIC* 5812

■ **UNITED BANK** p 1506
2071 Chain Bridge Rd 22182
Tel (703) 442-7118 *SIC* 6022

VIE DE FRANCE YAMAZAKI INC p 1556
2070 Chain Bridge Rd # 500 22182
Tel (703) 442-9205 *SIC* 5142 5461

■ **WGL ENERGY SERVICES INC** p 1604
8614 Westwood Center Dr # 1200 22182
Tel (703) 333-3900 *SIC* 4931 1711

VIRGINIA BEACH, VA

ADS TACTICAL INC p 24
621 Lynnhven Pkwy Ste 400 23452
Tel (757) 781-7758 *SIC* 7389

■ **AMERIGROUP CORP** p 82
4425 Corp Ln Ste 160 23462
Tel (757) 473-2737 *SIC* 6324

■ **AMSEC CORP** p 87
5701 Cleveland St 23462
Tel (757) 463-6666 *SIC* 8711

■ **AMSEC LLC** p 87
5701 Cleveland St 23462
Tel (757) 463-6666 *SIC* 8711

ARCHITECTURAL GRAPHICS INC p 105
2655 International Pkwy 23452
Tel (757) 427-1900 *SIC* 3993

▲ **ARMADA HOFFLER PROPERTIES INC** p 110
222 Central Park Ave # 2100 23462
Tel (757) 366-4000 *SIC* 6798

ARMADA/HOFFLER PROPERTIES LLC p 110
222 Central Park Ave # 2100 23462
Tel (757) 366-4000 *SIC* 6552

ATLANTIC BAY MORTGAGE GROUP LLC p 126
596 Lynnhven Pkwy Ste 102 23452
Tel (757) 498-6789 *SIC* 6211

ATLANTIC DIVING SUPPLY INC p 126
621 Lynnhven Pkwy Ste 400 23452
Tel (757) 481-7758 *SIC* 5091

BURGERBUSTERS INC p 227
2242 W Great Neck Rd 23451
Tel (757) 412-0112 *SIC* 5812

BUSCH CONSOLIDATED INC p 229
516 Viking Dr 23452
Tel (757) 463-7800 *SIC* 5084 3563

CENTURY CONCRETE INC p 282
1364 Air Rail Ave 23455
Tel (757) 460-5366 *SIC* 1622 1611 1771

CHECKERED FLAG MOTOR CAR CO INC p 292
5225 Virginia Beach Blvd 23462
Tel (757) 490-1111 *SIC* 5511 7532

CHRISTIAN BROADCASTING NETWORK INC p 302
977 Centerville Tpke 23463
Tel (757) 226-3030
SIC 8661 4833 4832 5999 4724

CITY OF VIRGINIA BEACH p 319
2401 Courthouse Dr 23456
Tel (757) 385-4508 *SIC* 9111

CUBE CORP p 399
529 Viking Dr 23452
Tel (770) 952-1479 *SIC* 1542

DARKA HOLDINGS LLC p 412
1528 Taylor Farm Rd # 105 23453
Tel (757) 689-4400 *SIC* 6719

■ **EAGLE INDUSTRIES UNLIMITED INC** p 468
2645 Intl Pkwy Ste 102 23454
Tel (888) 343-7547 *SIC* 3842

EHW CONSTRUCTORS A JOINT VENTURE p 481
295 Bendix Rd Ste 400 23452
Tel (757) 420-4140 *SIC* 1629

■ **ELECTRONIC SYSTEMS INC** p 486
369 Edwin Dr 23462
Tel (757) 497-8000 *SIC* 5044

GENERAL FOAM PLASTICS CORP p 601
4429 Bonney Rd Ste 500 23462
Tel (757) 857-0153 *SIC* 3089

HALL AUTOMOTIVE LLC p 654
441 Viking Dr 23452
Tel (757) 431-9944 *SIC* 5511

HAMPTON ROADS SANITATION DISTRICT (INC) p 656
1434 Air Rail Ave 23455
Tel (757) 460-2261 *SIC* 4952

HAYNES FURNITURE CO INC p 670
5324 Virginia Beach Blvd 23462
Tel (804) 276-1060 *SIC* 5713 5712

▲ **LIBERTY TAX INC** p 862
1716 Corp Landing Pkwy 23454
Tel (757) 493-8855 *SIC* 7291

LIFENET HEALTH p 864
1864 Concert Dr 23453
Tel (757) 464-4761 *SIC* 8099

MANAGEMENT CONSULTING INC p 900
1961 Diamond Springs Rd 23455
Tel (757) 460-0879 *SIC* 8742

MYTHICS INC p 1005
1439 N Great Neck Rd 23454
Tel (757) 965-6756 *SIC* 5045

■ **NAVY EXCHANGE SERVICE COMMAND** p 1020
3280 Virginia Beach Blvd 23452
Tel (757) 631-3696 *SIC* 5399 9711

OLD DOMINION TOBACCO CO INC p 1080
5400 Virginia Beach Blvd 23462
Tel (757) 497-1001 *SIC* 5194 5145

OPERATION BLESSING INTERNATIONAL RELIEF AND DEVELOPMENT CORP p 1089
977 Centerville Tpke 23463
Tel (757) 226-3401 *SIC* 8699

OPTIMA HEALTH PLAN p 1090
4417 Corp Ln Ste 150 23462
Tel (757) 552-7401 *SIC* 6324

■ **PAPCO INC** p 1112
4920 Southern Blvd 23462
Tel (757) 499-5977 *SIC* 4923

PENROD CO p 1131
272 Bendix Rd Ste 550 23452
Tel (757) 498-0186 *SIC* 3429 5039 2821

PROFESSIONAL HOSPITALITY RESOURCES INC p 1180
932 Laskin Rd 23451
Tel (757) 491-3000 *SIC* 7011 7389 5812

QED SYSTEMS INC p 1194
4646 N Witchduck Rd 23455
Tel (757) 490-5000 *SIC* 8711 3731

S B BALLARD CONSTRUCTION CO p 1261
2828 Shipps Corner Rd 23453
Tel (757) 440-5555 *SIC* 1542 1771

SCHOOL BOARD OF CITY OF VIRGINIA BEACH p 1289
2512 George Mason Dr 23456
Tel (757) 263-1033 *SIC* 8211

SENTARA PRINCESS ANNE HOSPITAL p 1305
1925 Glenn Mitchell Dr 23456
Tel (757) 507-1660 *SIC* 8062

SKANSKA USA CIVIL SOUTHEAST INC p 1329
295 Bendix Rd Ste 400 23452
Tel (757) 420-4140
SIC 1622 1629 3272 1541

SLAIT PARTNERS INC p 1331
100 Landmark Sq 23452
Tel (757) 313-6500
SIC 5045 3571 8748 7373

STIHL INC p 1389
536 Viking Dr 23452
Tel (757) 486-9100 *SIC* 3546 3398

TIDEWATER FINANCE CO p 1452
6520 Indian River Rd 23464
Tel (757) 579-6444 *SIC* 6141

TTEC-TESORO JOINT VENTURE p 1489
5250 Challedon Dr 23462
Tel (770) 825-7100 *SIC* 1542

VIRGINIA INTEGRATED COMMUNICATION INC p 1559
5361 Cleveland St 23462
Tel (757) 490-7777 *SIC* 5065

■ **VIRGINIA NATURAL GAS INC** p 1559
544 S Independence Blvd 23452
Tel (757) 466-5400 *SIC* 4924

VT SERVICES INC p 1567
529 Viking Dr 23452
Tel (912) 573-3671 *SIC* 8744 8711

WARRENTON, VA

COUNTY OF FAUQUIER p 378
70 Culpeper St 20186
Tel (540) 422-8080 *SIC* 8322

FAUQUIER COUNTY PUBLIC SCHOOLS p 531
320 Hospital Dr Ste 40 20186
Tel (540) 422-7000 *SIC* 8211

FAUQUIER HEALTH SYSTEM INC p 531
500 Hospital Dr 20186
Tel (540) 316-5000 *SIC* 8062

FHI SERVICES p 539
500 Hospital Dr 20186
Tel (540) 347-2550 *SIC* 8062

MID-ATLANTIC HOME HEALTH NETWORK INC p 963
25 Winchester St 20186
Tel (540) 347-4901 *SIC* 8082

WAYNESBORO, VA

HARDWOOD LUMBER MANUFACTURING INC p 661
567 N Charlotte Ave 22980
Tel (540) 946-9150 *SIC* 2426

▲ **LUMOS NETWORKS CORP** p 885
1 Lumos Plz 22980
Tel (540) 946-2000 *SIC* 4813

■ **NTELOS HOLDINGS CORP** p 1065
1154 Shenandoah Vlg Dr 22980
Tel (540) 946-3500 *SIC* 4813 4812

■ **NTELOS INC** p 1065
1154 Shenandoah Vlg Dr 22980
Tel (540) 946-3500 *SIC* 4899

■ **NTELOS NET LLC** p 1065
1 Lumos Plz 22980
Tel (540) 946-3500 *SIC* 4813

WEST POINT, VA

▲ **C&F FINANCIAL CORP** p 234
802 Main St 23181
Tel (804) 843-2360 *SIC* 6022

■ **CITIZENS AND FARMERS BANK** p 310
802 Main St 23181
Tel (804) 843-2360 *SIC* 6022

WILLIAMSBURG, VA

COLLEGE OF WILLIAM & MARY p 337
261 Richmond Rd 23185
Tel (757) 221-3966 *SIC* 8221 9411

COLONIAL WILLIAMSBURG CO p 338
101 Visitor Center Dr 23185
Tel (888) 965-7254 *SIC* 8741

COLONIAL WILLIAMSBURG FOUNDATION p 338
427 Franklin St Rm 212 23185
Tel (757) 229-1000
SIC 5947 8412 5812 7011

RIVERSIDE PHYSICIAN SVCS INC p 1238
608 Denbigh Blvd 23185
Tel (757) 442-6600 *SIC* 8011

SENTARA WILLIAMSBURG REGIONAL MEDICAL CENTER p 1305
100 Sentara Cir 23188
Tel (757) 984-6000 *SIC* 8062

▲ **SOTHERLY HOTELS INC** p 1342
410 W Francis St 23185
Tel (757) 229-5648 *SIC* 6798

WILLIAMSBURG JAMES CITY COUNTY PUBLIC SCHOOLS p 1612
117 Ironbound Rd 23185
Tel (757) 603-6400 *SIC* 8299

WILLIAMSBURG-JAMES CITY COUNTY PUBLIC SCHOOLS p 1612
117 Ironbound Rd 23185
Tel (757) 603-6400 *SIC* 8211

WINCHESTER, VA

▲ AMERICAN WOODMARK CORP p 81
3102 Shawnee Dr 22601
Tel (540) 665-9100 SIC 2434

FREDERICK COUNTY SCHOOL DISTRICT p 576
1415 Amherst St 22601
Tel (540) 662-3888 SIC 8211

FUNKHOUSER AND CO H N p 585
2150 S Loudoun St 22601
Tel (540) 662-9000 SIC 5461 5013

NATIONAL FRUIT PRODUCT CO INC p 1012
550 Fairmont Ave 22601
Tel (540) 662-3401
SIC 0723 2033 2035 2099

OSULLIVAN FILMS INC p 1097
1944 Valley Ave 22601
Tel (540) 667-6666 SIC 3081

■ RUBBERMAID COMMERCIAL PRODUCTS LLC p 1256
3124 Valley Ave 22601
Tel (540) 677-8700 SIC 3089 2673

SCHENCK FOODS CO INC p 1286
3578 Valley Pike 22602
Tel (540) 869-1870
SIC 5141 5142 5087 5147 5148

SHENANDOAH UNIVERSITY p 1315
1460 University Dr 22601
Tel (540) 665-4500 SIC 8221

▲ TREX CO INC p 1476
160 Exeter Dr 22603
Tel (540) 542-6300 SIC 2421

VALLEY HEALTH SYSTEM p 1540
1840 Amherst St 22601
Tel (540) 536-8000
SIC 8062 8051 5047 8699

VALLEY HEALTH SYSTEM GROUP RETURN p 1540
220 Campus Blvd Ste 310 22601
Tel (540) 536-4302 SIC 8062

VALLEY PROTEINS (DE) INC p 1541
151 Valpro Dr 22603
Tel (540) 877-2533 SIC 2048

VALLEY PROTEINS INC p 1541
151 Valpro Dr 22603
Tel (540) 877-2590 SIC 2077

WINCHESTER MEDICAL CENTER p 1614
1840 Amherst St 22601
Tel (540) 536-8000 SIC 8059

WINCHESTER MEDICAL CENTER AUXILIARY INC p 1614
1840 Amherst St 22601
Tel (540) 536-8000 SIC 8062

WISE, VA

WISE COUNTY PUBLIC SCHOOLS p 1619
628 Lake St Ne 24293
Tel (276) 328-8017 SIC 8211

WOODBRIDGE, VA

COUNTY OF PRINCE WILLIAM p 381
1 County Complex Ct 22192
Tel (703) 792-4640 SIC 9111

E & C ENTERPRISES INC p 465
2359 Research Ct 22192
Tel (703) 494-5800 SIC 5541

FRU-CON CONSTRUCTION LLC p 582
4310 Prince William Pkwy # 200 22192
Tel (703) 586-6100 SIC 1629

MINNIELAND PRIVATE DAY SCHOOL INC p 974
4300 Prince William Pkwy 22192
Tel (703) 680-2548 SIC 8351 8211

ONSITE HEALTH INC p 1088
1308 Devils Reach Rd # 302 22192
Tel (949) 441-9530 SIC 8099

POTOMAC HOSPITAL CORP OF PRINCE WILLIAM p 1164
2300 Opitz Blvd 22191
Tel (703) 523-1000 SIC 8062

PRINCE WILLIAM COUNTY SERVICE AUTHORITY INC p 1176
4 County Complex Ct 22192
Tel (703) 335-7900 SIC 4941 4952 4953

ZEIDERS ENTERPRISES INC p 1641
2750 Killarney Dr Ste 100 22192
Tel (703) 496-9000 SIC 8742

YORKTOWN, VA

YORK COUNTY SCHOOL DIVISION p 1637
302 Dare Rd 23692
Tel (757) 898-0300 SIC 8211

WASHINGTON

ABERDEEN, WA

GRAYS HARBOR COMMUNITY HOSPITAL p 632
1006 N H St 98520
Tel (360) 532-8330 SIC 8062

GRAYS HARBOR COMMUNITY HOSPITAL FOUNDATION p 632
915 Anderson Dr 98520
Tel (360) 537-5000 SIC 8062

PUBLIC UTILITY DISTRICT NO 1 OF GRAYS HARBOR COUNTY p 1190
2720 Sumner Ave 98520
Tel (360) 532-4220 SIC 4911

ANACORTES, WA

DAKOTA CREEK INDUSTRIES INC p 409
820 4th St 98221
Tel (360) 293-9575 SIC 3732 3731

SKAGIT COUNTY PUBLIC HOSPITAL DISTRICT 2 p 1329
1211 24th St 98221
Tel (360) 299-1300 SIC 8062

ARLINGTON, WA

BRUNSWICK FAMILY BOAT CO INC p 221
17825 59th Ave Ne 98223
Tel (360) 435-5571 SIC 3732

SMOKEY POINT DISTRIBUTING INC p 1334
19201 63rd Ave Ne 98223
Tel (360) 435-5737 SIC 4213 4212 4214

AUBURN, WA

AIM AEROSPACE SUMNER INC p 38
1502 20th St Nw 98001
Tel (253) 804-3355 SIC 3728 3543

■ AUBURN REGIONAL MEDICAL CENTER INC p 130
Plz 1 202 N Div St 98001
Tel (253) 833-7711 SIC 8062

AUBURN SCHOOL DISTRICT p 130
915 4th St Ne 98002
Tel (253) 931-4900 SIC 8211

FLOYD PETERSON CO p 561
1102 D St Ne 98002
Tel (253) 735-0313 SIC 5141 5149 5143

GREEN RIVER COLLEGE p 637
12401 Se 320th St 98092
Tel (253) 833-9111 SIC 8222 8299 8221

KING COUNTY HOUSING AUTHORITY p 820
401 37th St Se 98002
Tel (206) 205-8837 SIC 6515

MUCKLESHOOT INDIAN TRIBE p 998
39015 172nd Ave Se 98092
Tel (253) 333-8741 SIC 9131

OAK HARBOR FREIGHT LINES INC p 1070
1339 W Valley Hwy N 98001
Tel (206) 246-2600 SIC 4213 4214

OLDCASTLE PRECAST INC p 1082
1002 15th St Sw Ste 110 98001
Tel (253) 833-2777 SIC 3272 3446

PLY GEM PACIFIC WINDOWS CORP p 1157
5001 D St Nw 98001
Tel (253) 850-9000 SIC 1751

■ PRIMUS INTERNATIONAL INC p 1176
610 Bllvue Way Ne Ste 200 98001
Tel (425) 688-0444 SIC 3728

ZONES INC p 1644
1102 15th St Sw Ste 102 98001
Tel (253) 205-3000 SIC 7373 5734

ZONES PUBLIC SECTOR LLC p 1644
1102 15th St Sw Ste 102 98001
Tel (253) 205-3000 SIC 5961

BELLEVUE, WA

AAA WASHINGTON p 8
3605 132nd Ave Se 98006
Tel (425) 646-2015 SIC 8699

AMARGOSA INC p 64
10401 Ne 8th St Ste 500 98004
Tel (425) 755-6100
SIC 5611 5699 5941 5719 5947 5961

■ AMAZON COM DEDC LLC p 64
1227 124th Ave Ne Ste 200 98005
Tel (206) 266-5363 SIC 5961

▲ APPTIO INC p 100
11100 Ne 8th St Ste 600 98004
Tel (425) 453-5861 SIC 7372

BELLEVUE COLLEGE FOUNDATION p 170
3000 Landerholm Cir Se 98007
Tel (425) 564-1000 SIC 8222 8221

BELLEVUE SCHOOL DISTRICT p 170
12111 Ne 1st St 98005
Tel (425) 456-4000 SIC 8211

▲ BLUCORA INC p 190
10900 Ne 8th St Ste 800 98004
Tel (425) 201-6100 SIC 7375 7374

■ BOSTON PRIVATE BANK & TRUST CO p 203
10885 Ne 4th St Ste 100 98004
Tel (425) 586-5038 SIC 6022

▲ BSQUARE CORP p 222
110 110th Ave Ne Ste 300 98004
Tel (425) 519-5900 SIC 7371 8711

■ CHEMPOINT.COM INC p 293
411 108th Ave Ne Ste 1050 98004
Tel (425) 378-8600 SIC 5169

CITY OF BELLEVUE p 313
450 110th Ave Ne 98004
Tel (425) 452-6800 SIC 9111

■ CLEAR WIRELESS LLC p 324
1475 120th Ave Ne 98005
Tel (425) 216-7974 SIC 4813

COASTAL HOTEL GROUP INC p 331
15375 Se 30th Pl Ste 290 98007
Tel (206) 388-0400 SIC 7011

COCA-COLA BOTTLING OF HAWAII LLC p 333
11400 Se 8th St Ste 300 98004
Tel (800) 767-6366 SIC 5149

■ COINSTAR LLC p 335
1800 114th Ave Se 98004
Tel (425) 943-8000 SIC 7299 7841

CONCUR TECHNOLOGIES INC p 355
601 108th Ave Ne Ste 1000 98004
Tel (425) 702-8808 SIC 7372 7371

DIRECT SOURCE SEAFOOD LLC p 441
840 140th Ave Ne 98005
Tel (908) 240-9374 SIC 5146

EDDIE BAUER LLC p 477
10401 Ne 8th St Ste 500 98004
Tel (425) 755-6100 SIC 5611 5961 5621

EFINANCIAL LLC p 480
13810 Se Eastgate Way # 300 98005
Tel (800) 482-6616 SIC 6411

▲ ESTERLINE TECHNOLOGIES CORP p 511
500 108th Ave Ne Ste 1500 98004
Tel (425) 453-9400 SIC 3728 3812 3429

EVEREST HOLDINGS LLC p 514
10401 Ne 8th St Ste 500 98004
Tel (425) 755-6544 SIC 5699 5611 5961

▲ EXPEDIA INC p 519
333 108th Ave Ne 98004
Tel (425) 679-7200 SIC 4724

GENE JUAREZ SALONS LLC p 598
3633 136th Pl Se Ste 200 98006
Tel (425) 748-1400 SIC 7231

GJS HOLDING LLC p 613
3633 136th Pl Se Ste 200 98006
Tel (425) 748-1400 SIC 7231

GLY CONSTRUCTION INC p 618
200 112th Ave Ne Ste 300 98004
Tel (425) 451-8877 SIC 1542

H D FOWLER CO INC p 649
13440 Se 30th St 98005
Tel (425) 746-8400
SIC 5084 5083 5085 3321

HEALTH CARE MANAGEMENT ADMINISTRATORS INC p 674
220 120th Ave Ne 98005
Tel (425) 462-1000 SIC 6411

INTELLECTUAL VENTURES LLC p 750
3150 139th Ave Se Ste 500 98005
Tel (425) 467-2300 SIC 7379

MAINVUE HOMES LLC p 898
1110 112th Ave Ne Ste 202 98004
Tel (425) 646-4022 SIC 7389 1521

NINTEX USA LLC p 1044
10900 Ne 8th St Ste 230 98004
Tel (425) 324-2455 SIC 5734

ODOM CORP p 1074
11400 Se 8th St Ste 300 98004
Tel (425) 456-3535 SIC 5149

OVERLAKE HOSPITAL ASSOCIATION p 1099
1035 116th Ave Ne 98004
Tel (425) 688-5000 SIC 8621

OVERLAKE HOSPITAL MEDICAL CENTER p 1099
1035 116th Ave Ne 98004
Tel (425) 688-5000 SIC 8062

■ PACCAR FINANCIAL CORP p 1103
777 106th Ave Ne 98004
Tel (425) 468-7100 SIC 6153

▲ PACCAR INC p 1103
777 106th Ave Ne 98004
Tel (425) 468-7400
SIC 3711 3714 3713 3537 5013 6153

PARALLELS INC p 1113
110 110th Ave Ne Ste 410 98004
Tel (425) 728-8239 SIC 7379

PARKER SMITH & FEEK INC p 1116
2233 112th Ave Ne 98004
Tel (425) 709-3600 SIC 6411 6351 8748

PEOPLETECH GROUP INC p 1132
601108 Ave Ne Ste 310 98004
Tel (425) 880-7981 SIC 7361

PUGET ENERGY INC p 1191
10885 Ne 4th St Ste 1200 98004
Tel (425) 454-6363 SIC 4931 4924

PUGET EQUICO LLC p 1191
10885 Ne 4th St Ste 1200 98004
Tel (425) 454-6363 SIC 4911

PUGET HOLDING CO LLC p 1191
10885 Ne 4th St Ste 1200 98004
Tel (425) 454-6363 SIC 4911 4922 4924

PUGET SOUND ENERGY INC p 1191
10885 Ne 4th St Ste 1200 98004
Tel (425) 454-6363 SIC 4939 4911

■ QUALITY FOOD CENTERS INC p 1197
10116 Ne 8th St 98004
Tel (425) 455-0870 SIC 5411

▲ RADIANT LOGISTICS INC p 1204
405 114th Ave Se Fl 3 98004
Tel (425) 943-4599 SIC 4731

SAVERS INC p 1284
11400 Se 6th St Ste 220 98004
Tel (425) 462-1515 SIC 5932 5311 5331

SOUTHERN WINE & SPIRITS-PACIFIC NORTHWEST HOLDINGS LLC p 1351
10500 Ne 8th St Ste 2000 98004
Tel (425) 456-3535 SIC 5182

SUMITOMO FORESTRY AMERICA INC p 1398
1110 112th Ave Ne Ste 202 98004
Tel (425) 454-2355 SIC 8741 5099

■ SUNCOM WIRELESS HOLDINGS INC p 1402
12920 Se 38th St 98006
Tel (425) 378-4000 SIC 4812

SYMETRA FINANCIAL CORP p 1414
777 108th Ave Ne Ste 1200 98004
Tel (425) 256-8000 SIC 6311 6411

SYMETRA LIFE INSURANCE CO p 1414
777 108th Ave Ne Ste 1200 98004
Tel (877) 796-3872 SIC 6311 6324 6411

■ T-MOBILE US INC p 1420
12920 Se 38th St 98006
Tel (425) 378-4000 SIC 4813

■ T-MOBILE USA INC p 1420
12920 Se 38th St 98006
Tel (425) 378-4000 SIC 4812 4899

TVI INC p 1494
11400 Se 6th St Ste 220 98004
Tel (425) 462-1515
SIC 5932 5251 5311 5331

UNIGARD INC p 1503
2125 158th Ct Ne 98008
Tel (425) 641-4321 SIC 6321 6331

UNIGARD INSURANCE CO p 1503
15800 Northup Way 98008
Tel (425) 641-4321 SIC 6331

UNIGARD PACIFIC INSURANCE CO p 1503
15800 Northup Way 98008
Tel (425) 644-5236 SIC 6331 6411

WAGGENER EDSTROM WORLDWIDE INC p 1571
225 108th Ave Ne Ste 700 98004
Tel (425) 638-7000 SIC 8743

BELLINGHAM, WA

ALPHA TECHNOLOGIES INC p 60
3767 Alpha Way 98226
Tel (360) 647-2360 SIC 8742 8711

BELLINGHAM PUBLIC SCHOOLS p 171
1306 Dupont St 98225
Tel (360) 676-6400 SIC 8211

BELLINGHAM SCHOOL BOARD p 171
1306 Dupont St 98225
Tel (360) 676-6400 SIC 8211

DENISE THRASHER p 428
959 E Axton Rd 98226
Tel (360) 223-4917 SIC 5945

GRIZZLY INDUSTRIAL INC p 641
1821 Valencia St 98229
Tel (360) 676-6090 SIC 5251

HAGGEN ACQUISITION LLC p 653
2211 Rimland Dr Ste 300 98226
Tel (360) 733-8720 SIC 8748

HAGGEN INC p 653
2211 Rimland Dr Ste 300 98226
Tel (360) 733-8720 SIC 5411 5912

HAGGEN OPERATIONS HOLDINGS LLC p 653
2211 Rimland Dr Ste 300 98226
Tel (360) 733-8720 SIC 8748

HASKELL CORP p 667
1001 Meador Ave 98229
Tel (360) 734-1200 SIC 1542

HEATH TECNA INC p 679
3225 Woburn St 98226
Tel (360) 738-2005 SIC 3728 5088

INTERFOR US INC p 752
2211 Rimland Dr Ste 220 98226
Tel (360) 788-2299 SIC 0811 2421 5031

MARKETS LLC p 908
4350 Cordata Pkwy 98226
Tel (360) 714-9797 SIC 5411

NORCO INC p 1047
101 E Stuart Rd 98226
Tel (360) 746-0826 SIC 7352

SMITH GARDENS INC p 1333
4164 Meridian St Ste 400 98226
Tel (800) 755-6256 SIC 0181

■ STERLING LIFE INSURANCE CO p 1387
2219 Rimland Dr Ste 100 98226
Tel (360) 647-9080 SIC 6411

TRANS-OCEAN PRODUCTS INC p 1470
350 W Orchard Dr 98225
Tel (360) 671-6886 SIC 2091

WESTERN WASHINGTON UNIVERSITY p 1600
516 High St 98225
Tel (360) 650-3720 SIC 8221

BINGEN, WA

■ INSITU INC p 746
118 Columbia River Way 98605
Tel (509) 493-8600 SIC 8711 3999

BLAINE, WA

BP WEST COAST PRODUCTS LLC p 206
4519 Grandview Rd 98230
Tel (310) 549-6204 SIC 5541

BRITISH PETROLEUM p 214
4519 Grandview Rd 98230
Tel (360) 371-1300 SIC 1629

BOTHELL, WA

FALCK USA INC p 526
21540 30th Dr Se Ste 250 98021
Tel (425) 892-1180 SIC 4119

FUJIFILM SONOSITE INC p 583
21919 30th Dr Se 98021
Tel (425) 951-1200 SIC 3845

JACO ENVIRONMENTAL INC p 775
18323 Bothell Everett Hwy # 110 98012
Tel (425) 398-6200 SIC 8748

■ MOLINA HEALTHCARE OF WASHINGTON INC p 982
21540 30th Dr Se Ste 400 98021
Tel (425) 424-1100 SIC 8011

NORTHSHORE SCHOOL DISTRICT p 1058
3330 Monte Villa Pkwy 98021
Tel (425) 408-6000 SIC 8211

PANASONIC AVIONICS CORP p 1111
3303 Monte Villa Pkwy 98021
Tel (425) 415-9000 SIC 8711

PHILIPS ORAL HEALTHCARE LLC p 1143
22100 Bothell Everett Hwy 98021
Tel (425) 487-7000 SIC 3843

PHILIPS ULTRASOUND INC p 1143
22100 Bothell Everett Hwy 98021
Tel (800) 982-2011 SIC 3845

RILEY GROUP INC p 1235
17522 Bthell Way Ne Ste A 98011
Tel (425) 415-0551 SIC 8748

▲ SEATTLE GENETICS INC p 1297
21823 30th Dr Se 98021
Tel (425) 527-4000 SIC 2836

SNC-LAVALIN CONSTRUCTORS INC p 1335
19015 North Creek Pkwy # 300 98011
Tel (425) 489-3300 SIC 1629

■ VERATHON INC p 1549
20001 North Creek Pkwy 98011
Tel (425) 867-1348 SIC 3845

VERTAFORE INC p 1552
11724 Ne 195th St 98011
Tel (425) 402-1000 SIC 7374

BREMERTON, WA

HARRISON MEDICAL CENTER p 664
2520 Cherry Ave 98310
Tel (360) 744-6510 SIC 8062

HARRISON MEMORIAL HOSPITAL INC p 664
2520 Cherry Ave 98310
Tel (360) 377-3911 SIC 8062

SKOOKUM EDUCATIONAL PROGRAMS INC p 1330
4525 Auto Center Way 98312
Tel (360) 475-0756 SIC 8744

WA STATE COMMUNITY COLLEGE DIST 3 p 1569
1600 Chester Ave 98337
Tel (360) 792-6050 SIC 8221

BREWSTER, WA

BREWSTER HEIGHTS PACKING & ORCHARDS LP p 210
25985 Hwy 97 98812
Tel (509) 689-3424 SIC 0723

BRUSH PRAIRIE, WA

BATTLE GROUND SCHOOL DISTRICT p 160
11104 Ne 149th St 98606
Tel (360) 885-5300 SIC 8211

BURIEN, WA

HIGHLINE MEDICAL CENTER p 692
16251 Sylvester Rd Sw 98166
Tel (206) 244-9970 SIC 8062 8051

HIGHLINE MEDICAL SERVICES INC p 692
16255 Sylvester Rd Sw # 202 98166
Tel (206) 431-5304 SIC 8011

HIGHLINE PUBLIC SCHOOLS p 692
15675 Ambaum Blvd Sw 98166
Tel (206) 631-3000 SIC 8211

BURLINGTON, WA

SKAGIT FARMERS SUPPLY p 1329
1833 Park Ln 98233
Tel (360) 757-6053
SIC 5191 5172 5983 5451 5331 5261

CAMAS, WA

C-TECH INDUSTRIES INC p 234
4275 Nw Pacific Rim Blvd 98607
Tel (360) 833-1600 SIC 3589 2841 3559

FISHER INVESTMENTS INC p 552
5525 Nw Fisher Creek Dr 98607
Tel (888) 823-9566 SIC 6282

TSMC DEVELOPMENT INC p 1489
5509 Nw Parker St 98607
Tel (360) 817-3000 SIC 3674

WAFERTECH LLC p 1571
5509 Nw Parker St 98607
Tel (360) 817-3000 SIC 3674 7361

CASHMERE, WA

CRUNCH PAK LLC p 396
300 Sunset Hwy 98815
Tel (509) 782-2807 SIC 0723

CENTRALIA, WA

TRANS ALTA p 1470
913 Big Hanaford Rd 98531
Tel (360) 736-9901 SIC 4911

TRANSALTA CENTRALIA GENERATION LLC p 1470
913 Big Hanaford Rd 98531
Tel (360) 330-8130 SIC 4911

CHEHALIS, WA

ALTA FOREST PRODUCTS LLC p 61
810 Nw Alta Way 98532
Tel (360) 219-0008 SIC 2421

CHELAN, WA

TROUT-BLUE CHELAN-MAGI INC p 1484
8 Howser Rd 98816
Tel (509) 682-2591 SIC 0723 0175 4222

CHENEY, WA

EASTERN WASHINGTON UNIVERSITY INC p 472
307 Showalter Hall 99004
Tel (509) 359-6200 SIC 8221

TRANS-SYSTEM INC p 1470
7405 S Hayford Rd 99004
Tel (509) 623-4001 SIC 4213 4731

COLFAX, WA

MCGREGOR CO p 929
401 Colfax Airport Rd 99111
Tel (509) 397-4355 SIC 5191 3523 2874

COUPEVILLE, WA

WHIDBEY ISLAND PUBLIC HOSPITAL DISTRICT p 1605
101 N Main St 98239
Tel (360) 678-5151 SIC 8062

COWICHE, WA

EVANS FRUIT CO INC p 513
200 Cowiche City Rd 98923
Tel (509) 678-4127 SIC 0175

DES MOINES, WA

AMERICAN BAPTIST HOMES OF WASHINGTON INC p 68
23600 Marine View Dr S 98198
Tel (206) 870-6641 SIC 8051 8059 8052

EAST WENATCHEE, WA

EAGLE GROUP SYSTEMS INC p 468
230 Grant Rd 98802
Tel (509) 665-0319
SIC 4214 4119 4522 7373 7374 8741

NORTHERN FRUIT CO p 1056
220 2nd St Ne 98802
Tel (509) 884-6651 SIC 0723

EDMONDS, WA

HOTEL GROUP INC p 710
201 5th Ave S Ste 200 98020
Tel (425) 771-1788 SIC 7011

SWEDISH EDMONDS p 1411
21601 76th Ave W 98026
Tel (425) 640-4000 SIC 8062

TOWN & COUNTRY MARKETS INC p 1464
130 5th Ave S Ste 126 98020
Tel (360) 598-7300 SIC 5411

ELLENSBURG, WA

ANDERSON HAY & GRAIN CO INC p 90
910 Anderson Rd 98926
Tel (509) 925-9818 SIC 5191

CENTRAL WASHINGTON UNIVERSITY INC p 281
400 E University Way 98926
Tel (509) 963-1111 SIC 8221

ENUMCLAW, WA

MUTUAL OF ENUMCLAW INSURANCE CO p 1003
1460 Wells St 98022
Tel (360) 825-2591 SIC 6331 6311

SCHREINER CORP p 1290
28210 Se 440th St 98022
Tel (253) 736-5774 SIC 7374

EPHRATA, WA

PUBLIC UTILITY DISTRICT 2 GRANT COUNTY p 1190
30 C St Sw 98823
Tel (509) 754-0500 SIC 4911

EVERETT, WA

APPLIED TECHNICAL SERVICES CORP p 100
6300 Merrill Creek Pkwy A100 98203
Tel (425) 249-5555 SIC 3672

AVIATION TECHNICAL SERVICES INC p 138
3121 109th St Sw 98204
Tel (425) 347-3030 SIC 4581 8711

■ AVTECHTYEE INC p 139
6500 Merrill Creek Pkwy 98203
Tel (206) 695-8000 SIC 3728 3648 3812

CITY OF EVERETT p 314
2930 Wetmore Ave Ste 100 98201
Tel (425) 257-8700 SIC 9111

COUNTY OF SNOHOMISH p 382
3000 Rockefeller Ave Ms508 98201
Tel (425) 388-3460 SIC 9111

■ EVERETT CLINIC PLLC p 514
3901 Hoyt Ave 98201
Tel (425) 339-5465 SIC 8011

EVERETT MSO INC p 514
3901 Hoyt Ave 98201
Tel (425) 339-5465 SIC 8011

EVERETT PUBLIC SCHOOLS p 514
3900 Broadway 98201
Tel (425) 385-4000 SIC 8211

■ FLUKE CORP p 561
6920 Seaway Blvd 98203
Tel (425) 446-5400 SIC 3823 5065 7629

■ FLUKE ELECTRONICS CORP p 561
6920 Seaway Blvd 98203
Tel (425) 446-5610 SIC 3825 3823

■ FLUKE INTERNATIONAL CORP p 561
6920 Seaway Blvd 98203
Tel (425) 347-6100 SIC 5063

▲ FORTIVE CORP p 570
6920 Seaway Blvd 98203
Tel (425) 446-5000 SIC 3823

■ FRONTIER COMMUNICATIONS WEST COAST INC p 581
1800 41st St 98203
Tel (425) 261-5321 SIC 4813

JAMCO AMERICA INC p 776
1018 80th St Sw 98203
Tel (425) 347-4735 SIC 3728

■ KORRY ELECTRONICS CO p 828
11910 Beverly Park Rd 98204
Tel (425) 297-9700 SIC 3613

MUKILTEO SCHOOL DISTRICT p 999
9401 Sharon Dr 98204
Tel (425) 356-1274 SIC 8211

NATIONAL FOOD CORP p 1012
808 134th St Sw Ste 116 98204
Tel (425) 349-4257 SIC 0252

NORCO INC p 1047
3030 Hoyt Ave 98201
Tel (425) 205-4200 SIC 7352

NORTH PUGET SOUND CENTER FOR SLEEP DISORDERS LLC p 1053
1728 W Marine View Dr 98201
Tel (425) 339-5460 SIC 8011

PROVIDENCE EVERETT MEDICAL CENTER p 1185
900 Pacific Ave Ste 501 98201
Tel (425) 258-7311 SIC 8099

PUBLIC UTILITY DISTRICT 1 OF SNOHOMISH COUNTY p 1190
2320 California St 98201
Tel (425) 257-9288 SIC 4911 4941

QUALITEL CORP p 1196
11831 Beverly Park Rd A 98204
Tel (425) 423-8388 SIC 3679

SOUND PUBLISHING INC p 1342
11323 Commando Rd W Main 98204
Tel (360) 394-5800 SIC 2711

STRATA INC p 1392
3501 Everett Ave 98201
Tel (425) 259-6016 SIC 1799

FEDERAL WAY, WA

FEDERAL WAY PUBLIC SCHOOLS p 536
33330 8th Ave S 98003
Tel (253) 830-6246 SIC 8211

GENERAL CONSTRUCTION CO p 600
33455 6th Ave S 98003
Tel (253) 943-4200 SIC 1622 1629

ST FRANCIS HOSPITAL p 1366
34515 9th Ave S 98003
Tel (253) 944-8100 SIC 8062

■ WEYERHAEUSER INTERNATIONAL INC p 1603
33663 Weyerhaeuser Way S 98001
Tel (253) 924-2345 SIC 5031

WORLD VISION INC p 1625
34834 Weyerhaeuser Way S 98001
Tel (253) 815-1000 SIC 6732

FERNDALE, WA

IMCO GENERAL CONSTRUCTION INC p 733
2116 Buchanan Loop 98248
Tel (360) 671-3936 SIC 1541 1629 1542

■ INTALCO ALUMINUM LLC p 748
4050 Mountain View Rd 98248
Tel (360) 384-7061 SIC 3334

FIFE, WA

AFF INC p 32
7400 45th Street Ct E 98424
Tel (253) 926-5000 SIC 4731 4213 7389

AMERICAN FAST FREIGHT INC p 72
7400 45th Street Ct E 98424
Tel (253) 926-5000
SIC 4731 4213 7389 4214

GENSCO INC p 604
4402 20th St E 98424
Tel (253) 620-8203 SIC 5074 3444

GREAT PACIFIC NEWS CO INC p 634
3995 70th Ave E Ste B 98424
Tel (425) 226-3250 SIC 5192

■ MILGARD MANUFACTURING INC p 969
1010 54th Ave E 98424
Tel (253) 922-6030 SIC 3089 3442

PROLOGIX DISTRIBUTION SERVICES (WEST) LLC p 1183
3995 70th Ave E Ste B 98424
Tel (253) 952-7150 SIC 5199

GIG HARBOR, WA

PENINSULA SCHOOL DISTRICT p 1129
14015 62nd Ave Nw 98332
Tel (253) 530-1000 SIC 8299

GRANDVIEW, WA

POWELL - CHRISTENSEN INC p 1164
501 E Wine Country Rd 98930
Tel (509) 882-2115 SIC 5171 4212

R H SMITH DISTRIBUTING CO INC p 1202
315 E Wine Country Rd 98930
Tel (509) 882-3377
SIC 5171 5541 5411 5172

WYCKOFF FARMS INC p 1629
160602 Evans Rd 98930
Tel (509) 882-3934 SIC 0191

ISSAQUAH, WA

COSTCO WHOLESALE CANADA LTD p 374
999 Lake Dr Ste 200 98027
Tel (425) 313-8100 SIC 5141

▲ COSTCO WHOLESALE CORP p 374
999 Lake Dr Ste 200 98027
Tel (425) 313-8100 SIC 5399

ISSAQUAH SCHOOL DISTRICT 411 p 767
565 Nw Holly St 98027
Tel (425) 837-7000 SIC 8211 9411

JOHN L SCOTT INC p 789
1700 Nw Gilman Blvd # 300 98027
Tel (425) 392-1211 SIC 6531 6794

KING COUNTY LIBRARY SYSTEM p 820
960 Newport Way Nw 98027
Tel (425) 369-3200 SIC 8231

LAKESIDE INDUSTRIES INC p 840
6505 226th Pl Se Ste 200 98027
Tel (425) 313-2600 SIC 1611 2951 5032

NAES CORP p 1006
1180 Nw Maple St Ste 200 98027
Tel (425) 961-4700 SIC 4911

■ PRICE CO p 1174
999 Lake Dr Ste 200 98027
Tel (425) 313-8100 SIC 5399

SANMAR CORP p 1279
22833 Se Black Nugget Rd 98029
Tel (206) 727-3200 SIC 5136 5137

VANGUARD INTERNATIONAL INC p 1543
22605 Se 56th St Ste 200 98029
Tel (425) 557-8250 SIC 5148

WAREHOUSE DEMO SERVICES INC p 1575
1301 4th Ave Nw Ste 202 98027
Tel (425) 889-0797 SIC 7389

KALAMA, WA

RSG FOREST PRODUCTS INC p 1256
985 Nw 2nd St 98625
Tel (360) 673-2825 SIC 2421 2499

STEELSCAPE LLC p 1385
222 W Kalama River Rd 98625
Tel (360) 673-8200 SIC 3479

KENMORE, WA

KANAWAY SEAFOODS INC p 802
6425 Ne 175th St 98028
Tel (425) 485-7755 SIC 2091

KENNEWICK, WA

APOLLO INC p 97
1133 W Columbia Dr 99336
Tel (509) 586-1104 SIC 1542

APOLLO SHEET METAL INC p 97
1201 W Columbia Dr 99336
Tel (509) 586-1104 SIC 1711 3444

■ CASCADE NATURAL GAS CORP p 262
8113 W Grandridge Blvd 99336
Tel (509) 734-4500 SIC 4924

KENNEWICK PUBLIC HOSPITAL DISTRICT p 811
900 S Auburn St 99336
Tel (509) 586-6111 SIC 8062

KENNEWICK SCHOOL DISTRICT 17 p 811
1000 W 4th Ave 99336
Tel (509) 222-5000 SIC 8211 9411

PUBLIC UTILITY DISTRICT 1 OF BENTON COUNTY p 1190
2721 W 10th Ave 99336
Tel (509) 582-2175 SIC 4911

SUN PACIFIC ENERGY INC p 1400
501 W Canal Dr 99336
Tel (509) 586-1135 SIC 5172 5541 5411

■ WESTON LAMB INC p 1602
8701 W Gage Blvd 99336
Tel (509) 735-4651 SIC 2037

■ WESTON LAMB SALES INC p 1602
8701 W Gage Blvd 99336
Tel (509) 735-4651 SIC 2037

KENT, WA

ALASKAN COPPER COMPANIES INC p 45
27402 72nd Ave S 98032
Tel (206) 623-5800 SIC 5051 3498 3443

ALCO INVESTMENT CO p 47
27402 72nd Ave S 98032
Tel (206) 623-5800 SIC 5051 3498 3443

BEST FRIENDS PET CARE INC p 177
19717 62nd Ave S Ste F103 98032
Tel (253) 981-3998 SIC 0752 0742 5999

BEVERLY RICARDO HILLS INC p 179
6329 S 226th St Unit 101 98032
Tel (425) 207-1900 SIC 5099

BOX MAKER INC p 205
6412 S 190th St 98032
Tel (425) 251-0655
SIC 5113 2653 2672 3086 5199 2631

CARLISLE INC p 257
7911 S 188th St Ste 100 98032
Tel (425) 251-0700 SIC 3643 5065 5063

CARLYLE HOLDINGS INC p 258
7911 S 188th St Ste 100 98032
Tel (425) 251-0700 SIC 3643 5065 5063

COLUMBIA DISTRIBUTING OF SEATTLE LLC p 340
20301 59th Pl S 98032
Tel (425) 251-9300 SIC 5182

EXOTIC METALS FORMING CO LLC p 519
5411 S 226th St 98032
Tel (253) 220-5900 SIC 3728 3724

FLOW INTERNATIONAL CORP p 560
23500 64th Ave S 98032
Tel (253) 850-3500 SIC 3561

HERMANSON CO LLP p 687
1221 2nd Ave N 98032
Tel (206) 575-9700 SIC 1711

KENT SCHOOL DISTRICT p 812
12033 Se 256th St 98030
Tel (253) 373-7000 SIC 8211

MIKRON INDUSTRIES INC p 968
1034 6th Ave N 98032
Tel (253) 854-8020 SIC 3089

NOVINIUM INC p 1063
22820 Russell Rd 98032
Tel (253) 288-7100 SIC 1521

OBERTO SAUSAGE CO p 1072
7060 S 238th St 98032
Tel (253) 437-6100 SIC 2013

OMAX CORP p 1084
21409 72nd Ave S 98032
Tel (253) 872-2300 SIC 3545 3561

PETROCARD INC p 1139
730 Central Ave S 98032
Tel (253) 852-7801 SIC 5172

PUGET SOUND PIPE AND SUPPLY CO p 1191
7816 S 202nd St 98032
Tel (206) 682-9350 SIC 5074 5085

RECREATIONAL EQUIPMENT INC p 1215
6750 S 228th St 98032
Tel (253) 395-3780
SIC 2329 3949 2399 5941 5961 5699

SHAPE TECHNOLOGIES GROUP INC p 1311
23500 64th Ave S 98032
Tel (253) 246-3200 SIC 6719

SHAPE TECHNOLOGIES GROUP PARENT HOLDINGS INC p 1311
23500 64th Ave S 98032
Tel (253) 850-3500 SIC 7379

■ **SYSCO SEATTLE INC** p 1418
22820 54th Ave S 98032
Tel (206) 622-2261 SIC 5142 5141

T & A SUPPLY CO INC p 1419
6821 S 216th St Bldg A 98032
Tel (206) 282-3770
SIC 1771 5023 1752 2431

TIGERS GLOBAL LOGISTICS INC p 1453
20024 85th Ave S 98031
Tel (253) 246-4184 SIC 4789

UTILX CORP p 1537
22820 Russell Rd 98032
Tel (253) 395-4535 SIC 1623

WEST COAST PAPER CO p 1594
6703 S 234th St Ste 120 98032
Tel (253) 850-1900
SIC 5085 5169 5084 2677

WESTERN INTEGRATED TECHNOLOGIES INC p 1598
13406 Se 32nd St 98032
Tel (800) 456-6248 SIC 5084

WORLDWIDE DISTRIBUTORS p 1626
8211 S 194th St 98032
Tel (253) 872-8746
SIC 5091 5136 5137 5139 5199 5023

KIRKLAND, WA

■ **ALLIED TRADE GROUP LLC** p 57
11410 Ne 122nd Way Ste 20 98034
Tel (425) 814-2515 SIC 5063

ASTRONICS ADVANCED ELECTRONIC SYSTEMS CORP p 122
12950 Willows Rd Ne 98034
Tel (425) 881-1700 SIC 3825

■ **BHC FAIRFAX HOSPITAL INC** p 180
10200 Ne 132nd St 98034
Tel (425) 821-2000 SIC 8063

BITTITAN INC p 185
3933 Lk Wa Blvd Ne # 200 98033
Tel (206) 428-6030 SIC 7372

CHANG INTERNATIONAL INC p 288
1611 Market St 98033
Tel (206) 283-9098 SIC 5146

COBALT MORTGAGE INC p 332
11241 Slater Ave Ne # 110 98033
Tel (425) 605-3100 SIC 6163

EAGLE HEALTHCARE INC p 468
12015 115th Ave Ne 98034
Tel (425) 285-3880 SIC 8051

GREENPOINT TECHNOLOGIES INC p 638
4600 Carillon Pt 98033
Tel (425) 828-2777 SIC 1799

■ **GTS DRYWALL SUPPLY CO** p 644
10819 120th Ave Ne 98033
Tel (425) 828-0608 SIC 5032

INRIX INC p 745
10210 Ne Pints Dr Ste 400 98033
Tel (425) 284-3800 SIC 3651

KING COUNTY PUBLIC HOSPITAL DISTRICT 2 p 820
12040 Ne 128th St 98034
Tel (425) 899-2769 SIC 8062

KING COUNTY PUBLIC HOSPITAL DISTRICT NO 2 p 820
12040 Ne 128th St 98034
Tel (425) 899-1000 SIC 8741

MAD ANTHONYS INC p 893
10502 Ne 37th Cir Bldg 8 98033
Tel (425) 455-0732 SIC 5812 5813

NABTESCO AEROSPACE INC p 1006
12413 Willows Rd Ne 98034
Tel (425) 602-8400 SIC 3728 3812 3593

■ **NEXTEL PARTNERS INC** p 1040
4500 Carillon Pt 98033
Tel (425) 576-3600 SIC 4812

NOBLE HOUSE HOTELS & RESORTS LTD p 1046
600 6th St S 98033
Tel (425) 827-8737 SIC 7011

PAINT SUNDRIES SOLUTIONS INC p 1108
930 7th Ave 98033
Tel (425) 827-9200 SIC 5198

R D WING CO INC p 1202
517 6th St S 98033
Tel (425) 821-7222 SIC 3299

▲ **RIGHTSIDE GROUP LTD** p 1234
5808 Lake Washington Blvd 98033
Tel (425) 298-2500 SIC 7374 7375

■ **WASTE MANAGEMENT OF WASHINGTON INC** p 1581
720 4th Ave Ste 400 98033
Tel (425) 823-6164 SIC 4953

WAVEDIVISION HOLDINGS LLC p 1584
401 Kirkland Prk Pl Ste 500 98033
Tel (425) 576-8200 SIC 4841

LACEY, WA

HARBOR WHOLESALE GROCERY INC p 660
3901 Hogum Bay Rd Ne 98516
Tel (360) 754-4484
SIC 5141 5194 5142 5122

THURSTON NORTH PUBLIC SCHOOLS p 1451
305 College St Ne 98516
Tel (360) 412-4400 SIC 8211

LAKE STEVENS, WA

LAKE STEVENS SCHOOL DISTRICT p 839
12309 22nd St Ne 98258
Tel (425) 335-1500 SIC 8211

LAKEWOOD, WA

PARK CLOVER SCHOOL DISTRICT p 1115
10903 Gravelly Lake Dr Sw 98499
Tel (253) 583-5494 SIC 8211

RAM INTERNATIONAL LTD p 1206
10013 59th Ave Sw 98499
Tel (253) 588-1788 SIC 5812

LIBERTY LAKE, WA

▲ **ITRON INC** p 768
2111 N Molter Rd 99019
Tel (509) 924-9900 SIC 3829 7371

TELECT INC p 1434
22245 E Appleway Blvd Ste 99019
Tel (509) 926-6000 SIC 3661

LONGVIEW, WA

EGT LLC p 481
150 E Mill Rd 98632
Tel (503) 827-4066 SIC 5153

J H KELLY INVESTMENTS INC p 771
821 3rd Ave 98632
Tel (360) 423-5510 SIC 1711

JH KELLY LLC p 785
821 3rd Ave 98632
Tel (360) 423-5510 SIC 1711

KELLY JH HOLDING LLC p 809
821 3rd Ave 98632
Tel (360) 423-5510 SIC 1711 1542 1731

■ **LONGVIEW FIBRE PAPER AND PACKAGING INC** p 877
300 Fibre Way 98632
Tel (360) 425-1550 SIC 2621

MALLORY CO p 900
1040 Industrial Way 98632
Tel (360) 636-5750 SIC 5099

MALLORY SAFETY AND SUPPLY LLC p 900
1040 Industrial Way 98632
Tel (360) 636-5750 SIC 5099 8331

NORTH PACIFIC PAPER CO LLC p 1053
3001 Indl Way 98632
Tel (360) 636-6400 SIC 2621 5084 3554

NP PAPER CO LLC p 1064
3001 Industrial Way 98632
Tel (360) 636-6400 SIC 2621

PUBLIC UTILITY DISTRICT NO 1 OF COWLITZ COUNTY p 1190
961 12th Ave 98632
Tel (360) 577-7507 SIC 4911

WHITTEN GROUP INTERNATIONAL CORP p 1607
2622 Lilac St 98632
Tel (360) 560-3319 SIC 5172 3559

WILSON OIL INC p 1614
95 Panel Way 98632
Tel (360) 575-9222 SIC 5541 5983 5172

LYNNWOOD, WA

EDMONDS COMMUNITY COLLEGE FOUNDATION p 478
20000 68th Ave W 98036
Tel (425) 640-1459 SIC 8222

EDMONDS SCHOOL DISTRICT 15 p 478
20420 68th Ave W 98036
Tel (425) 431-7000 SIC 8211

■ **ELDEC CORP** p 484
16700 13th Ave W 98037
Tel (425) 743-8362
SIC 3812 3728 3824 3769 3674 3613

■ **INTERMEC INC** p 753
16201 25th Ave W 98087
Tel (425) 348-2600 SIC 3577

■ **INTERMEC TECHNOLOGIES CORP** p 753
16201 25th Ave W 98087
Tel (425) 348-2600 SIC 3577 2759

KLB CONSTRUCTION INC p 823
3405 121st St Sw 98087
Tel (425) 355-7335 SIC 1623 1611

WASHINGTON ENERGY SERVICES CO p 1578
3909 196th St Sw 98036
Tel (800) 398-4663 SIC 5074 1711 8711

▲ **ZUMIEZ INC** p 1645
4001 204th St Sw 98036
Tel (425) 551-1500 SIC 5941

MEAD, WA

MEAD SCHOOL DISTRICT #354 p 933
2323 E Farwell Rd 99021
Tel (509) 465-7480 SIC 8211

MERCER ISLAND, WA

BAYLEY CONSTRUCTION A GENERAL PARTNERSHIP p 161
8005 Se 28th St Ste 100 98040
Tel (206) 621-8884 SIC 1542 1541

FARMERS NEW WORLD LIFE INSURANCE CO INC p 530
3003 77th Ave Se 98040
Tel (206) 232-1093 SIC 6311 6411

MOSES LAKE, WA

MOSES LAKE SCHOOL DIST 161 p 992
920 W Ivy Ave 98837
Tel (509) 766-2650 SIC 8211

MOUNT VERNON, WA

DRAPER VALLEY HOLDINGS LLC p 455
1000 Jason Ln 98273
Tel (360) 424-7947 SIC 0254 2015

PUBLIC HOSPITAL DISTRICT 1 SKAGIT COUNTY p 1189
1415 E Kincaid St 98274
Tel (360) 424-4111 SIC 8062

MOUNTLAKE TERRACE, WA

■ **HAIN REFRIGERATED FOODS INC** p 653
21707 66th Ave W 98043
Tel (425) 485-2476 SIC 2024 5143

PREMERA BLUE CROSS p 1170
7001 220th St Sw Bldg 1 98043
Tel (425) 670-4000 SIC 6321

MUKILTEO, WA

ELECTROIMPACT INC p 485
4413 Chennault Beach Rd 98275
Tel (425) 348-8090 SIC 3542

EMERALD CITY PIZZA LLC p 491
12121 Harbour Rch Dr 20 Ste 200 98275
Tel (425) 493-8077 SIC 5812

GLUTH CONTRACT FLOORING LLC p 618
12003 Mukilteo Speedway # 102 98275
Tel (425) 493-9100 SIC 1752

NESPELEM, WA

COLVILLE CONFEDERATED TRIBES INC p 343
44 School Loop Rd 99155
Tel (509) 634-2200 SIC 9199

CONFEDERATED TRIBES OF COLVILLE RESERVATION p 355
1 Colville St 99155
Tel (509) 634-2857 SIC 9131

OAK HARBOR, WA

WASHINGTON BANKING CO p 1577
450 Sw Bayshore Dr 98277
Tel (360) 679-3121 SIC 6022

OLYMPIA, WA

ASSOCIATION OF WASHINGTON CITIES p 121
1076 Franklin St Se 98501
Tel (360) 753-4137 SIC 8621

ATTORNEY GENERAL OFFICE OF p 129
1125 Washington St Se 98501
Tel (360) 753-6200 SIC 9222

CAPITAL MEDICAL CENTER p 250
3900 Capital Mall Dr Sw 98502
Tel (360) 754-5858 SIC 8062 8011

COUNTY OF THURSTON p 382
2000 Lakeridge Dr Sw 98502
Tel (360) 754-3800 SIC 9111

CUBIC GLOBAL DEFENSE INC p 399
400 Union Ave Se Ste 300 98501
Tel (360) 493-6275
SIC 7373 8744 8711 7376 8748 8741

DAIRY FRESH FARMS INC p 409
9636 Blomberg St Sw 98512
Tel (360) 357-9411 SIC 5143

EXECUTIVE OFFICE OF STATE OF WASHINGTON p 518
1115 Washington St Se 98501
Tel (360) 753-6780 SIC 9111

■ **HERITAGE BANK** p 686
201 5th Ave Sw Ste 101 98501
Tel (360) 943-1500 SIC 6022

▲ **HERITAGE FINANCIAL CORP** p 686
201 5th Ave Sw 98501
Tel (360) 943-1500 SIC 6036

JUDICIARY COURTS OF STATE OF WASHINGTON p 797
Temple Of Justice 98504
Tel (360) 357-2077 SIC 9211

OLYMPIA SCHOOL DISTRICT p 1083
1113 Legion Way Se 98501
Tel (360) 596-6100 SIC 8211

PROVIDENCE HEALTH AND SERVICES p 1186
413 Lilly Rd Ne 98506
Tel (360) 491-9480 SIC 8062

STATE OF WASHINGTON p 1382
106 Legislative Building 98504
Tel (360) 902-4111 SIC 9111

WASHINGTON STATE DEPARTMENT OF ECOLOGY p 1579
300 Desmond Dr Se 98503
Tel (360) 407-6000 SIC 9511

WASHINGTON STATE DEPARTMENT OF EMPLOYMENT SECURITY p 1579
212 Maple Park Ave Se 98501
Tel (360) 902-9500 SIC 9441

WASHINGTON STATE DEPARTMENT OF ENTERPRISE SERVICES p 1579
1500 Jefferson St Se 98501
Tel (360) 407-2200 SIC 9111

WASHINGTON STATE DEPARTMENT OF FISH & WILDLIFE p 1579
600 Capitol Way N 98501
Tel (360) 902-2200 SIC 9512

WASHINGTON STATE DEPARTMENT OF LICENSING p 1579
421 Black Lake Blvd Sw 98502
Tel (360) 902-3900 SIC 9631

WASHINGTON STATE DEPARTMENT OF LICENSING p 1579
1125 Washington St Se 98501
Tel (360) 920-3600 SIC 9111

WASHINGTON STATE DEPARTMENT OF LICENSING p 1579
1125 Washington St Se 98501
Tel (360) 902-3600 SIC 9651 9621

WASHINGTON STATE DEPARTMENT OF NATURAL RESOURCES p 1579
1111 Washington St Se 98501
Tel (360) 902-1000 SIC 9512

WASHINGTON STATE DEPARTMENT OF REVENUE p 1579
1025 Union Ave Se Ste 500 98501
Tel (360) 570-5900 SIC 9311

WASHINGTON STATE DEPARTMENT OF SOCIAL AND HEALTH SERVICES p 1579
14th And Jefferson 98504
Tel (360) 902-8400 SIC 9441

WASHINGTON STATE DEPARTMENT OF TRANSPORTATION p 1579
310 Maple Park Ave Se 98501
Tel (360) 705-7000 SIC 9621

WASHINGTON STATE EMPLOYEES CREDIT UNION p 1579
330 Union Ave Se 98501
Tel (360) 943-7911 SIC 6062

WASHINGTON STATE LIQUOR CONTROL BOARD p 1579
3000 Pacific Ave Se 98501
Tel (360) 664-1600 SIC 9651

WASHINGTON STATE PATROL p 1579
210 11th Ave Sw Rm 116 98501
Tel (360) 753-6540 SIC 9221

PACIFIC, WA

■ GORDON TRUCKING INC p 626
151 Stewart Rd Sw 98047
Tel (253) 863-7777 SIC 4213

PASCO, WA

BASIN GOLD COOPERATIVE p 159
5802 N Industrial Way C 99301
Tel (509) 545-4161 SIC 5148

CONNELL OIL INC p 358
1015 N Oregon Ave 99301
Tel (509) 547-3326 SIC 5171

FRANKLIN PUD p 575
1411 W Clark St 99301
Tel (509) 547-5591 SIC 4911

MCCURLEY INTEGRITY DEALERSHIPS LLC p 927
1325 N Autoplex Way 99301
Tel (509) 547-5555 SIC 5511

OREGON POTATO CO p 1094
6610 W Court St Ste B 99301
Tel (509) 349-8803 SIC 2034

OUR LADY OF LOURDES HOSPITAL AT PASCO p 1098
520 N 4th Ave 99301
Tel (509) 547-7704 SIC 8062 8063

PASCO SCHOOL DISTRICT 1 p 1119
1215 W Lewis St 99301
Tel (509) 546-2691 SIC 8211

TWO RIVERS TERMINAL LLC p 1495
3300c N Glade Rd 99301
Tel (509) 547-7776 SIC 5191 5999

PORT ANGELES, WA

CLALLAM COUNTY PUBLIC HOSPITAL DISTRICT 2 p 321
939 Caroline St 98362
Tel (360) 417-7000 SIC 8062

PORT ORCHARD, WA

COUNTY OF KITSAP p 379
619 Division St 98366
Tel (360) 337-7164 SIC 9111

FRANCISCAN HEALTH SYSTEMS p 573
451 Sw Sedgwick Rd 98367
Tel (360) 874-5900 SIC 8011

SOUTH KITSAP SCHOOL DISTRICT 402 p 1344
2689 Hoover Ave Se 98366
Tel (360) 874-7000 SIC 8211

PORT TOWNSEND, WA

CROWN PAPER GROUP INC p 396
100 Mill Rd 98368
Tel (770) 330-9137 SIC 2621

JEFFERSON COUNTY PUBLIC HOSPITAL DISTRICT 2 p 781
834 Sheridan St 98368
Tel (360) 379-8031 SIC 8062

PORT TOWNSEND HOLDINGS CO INC p 1162
100 Mill Rd 98368
Tel (360) 385-3170 SIC 2611 2653

PORT TOWNSEND PAPER CORP p 1162
100 Mill Rd 98368
Tel (360) 385-3170 SIC 2631

POULSBO, WA

POULSBO RV INC p 1164
19705 Viking Ave Nw 98370
Tel (360) 697-4445 SIC 5561

SOUND PUBLISHING HOLDING INC p 1342
19351 8th Ave Ne Ste 106 98370
Tel (360) 394-5800 SIC 2711

PRESCOTT, WA

BROETJE ORCHARDS LLC p 216
1111 Fishook Park Rd 99348
Tel (509) 749-2217 SIC 0175

PULLMAN, WA

SCHWEITZER ENGINEERING LABORATORIES INC p 1291
2440 Ne Hopkins Ct 99163
Tel (509) 332-1890 SIC 3731

WASHINGTON STATE UNIVERSITY INC p 1579
240 French Adm Bldg 99164
Tel (509) 335-2022 SIC 8221

PUYALLUP, WA

ABSHER CONSTRUCTION CO p 13
1001 Shaw Rd 98372
Tel (253) 845-9544 SIC 1542

GOOD SAMARITAN COMMUNITY HEALTHCARE INC p 623
407 14th Ave Se 98372
Tel (253) 848-6661 SIC 8062

GOOD SAMARITAN HOSPITAL p 623
401 15th Ave Se 98372
Tel (253) 697-4000 SIC 8062 8069

MILES SAND & GRAVEL CO p 969
400 Valley Ave Ne 98372
Tel (253) 833-3705 SIC 3273 5032

NORTHWEST CASCADE INC p 1059
10412 John Bananola Way E 98374
Tel (253) 848-2371
SIC 1623 7359 7699 3272 1711

PARAMETRIX INC p 1114
1019 39th Ave Se Ste 100 98374
Tel (206) 394-3700
SIC 8748 8711 8742 1389 4789

PUYALLUP SCHOOL DISTRICT p 1193
302 2nd St Se 98372
Tel (253) 840-8971 SIC 8211

QUIL CEDA VILLAGE, WA

TULALIP RESORT CASINO p 1491
10200 Quil Ceda Blvd 98271
Tel (360) 716-6000 SIC 7011

REDMOND, WA

3MD INC p 3
17735 Ne 65th St Ste 130 98052
Tel (425) 467-8000 SIC 5045 8742

■ ADVANCED DIGITAL INFORMATION CORP p 25
11431 Willows Rd Ne 98052
Tel (425) 881-8004 SIC 3572

ALTIG INTERNATIONAL INC p 62
15440 Bel Red Rd 98052
Tel (425) 885-2838 SIC 6411

■ AT&T WIRELESS SERVICES OF CALIFORNIA LLC p 123
7277 164th Ave Ne 98052
Tel (425) 827-4500 SIC 4812 4833

C M T PARTNERS p 233
7277 164th Ave Ne Rtc1 98052
Tel (425) 580-6000 SIC 4812

CADMAN INC p 236
7554 185th Ave Ne Ste 100 98052
Tel (425) 867-1234 SIC 3273

CLUB WORLDMARK p 328
9805 Willows Rd Ne 98052
Tel (425) 498-2500 SIC 6531

■ CRANE ELECTRONICS INC p 388
10301 Willows Rd Ne 98052
Tel (425) 882-3100 SIC 3679

■ GENIE HOLDINGS INC p 604
18340 Ne 76th St 98052
Tel (425) 881-1800 SIC 3536

■ GENIE INDUSTRIES INC p 604
18340 Ne 76th St 98052
Tel (425) 881-1800 SIC 3536

■ GENIE MANUFACTURING INC p 604
18340 Ne 76th St 98052
Tel (425) 881-1800 SIC 3531

LAKE WASHINGTON SCHOOL DISTRICT p 839
16250 Ne 74th St 98052
Tel (425) 936-1200 SIC 8211

■ LANOGA CORP p 844
17946 Ne 65th St 98052
Tel (425) 883-4125 SIC 5211 5031

▲ MICROSOFT CORP p 962
1 Microsoft Way 98052
Tel (425) 882-8080
SIC 7372 7371 3577 7375

■ MICROSOFT NETWORK L L C p 962
1 Microsoft Way 98052
Tel (425) 538-2948 SIC 4813

■ NEW CINGULAR WIRELESS SERVICES INC p 1029
7277 164th Ave Ne 98052
Tel (425) 827-4500 SIC 4812

■ NEXTEL WEST CORP p 1040
10545 Willows Rd Ne # 100 98052
Tel (253) 924-8545 SIC 4812

NINTENDO OF AMERICA INC p 1044
4600 150th Ave Ne 98052
Tel (425) 882-2040 SIC 5092

NIPPON SUISAN (USA) INC p 1044
15400 Ne 90th St 100 98052
Tel (425) 869-1703 SIC 5146

PAC WORLDWIDE CORP p 1103
15435 Ne 92nd St 98052
Tel (425) 202-4015 SIC 5199

PAC WORLDWIDE HOLDING CO p 1103
15435 Ne 92nd St 98052
Tel (800) 535-0039 SIC 5199

PACTERA TECHNOLOGIES NA INC p 1107
14980 Ne 31st Way Ste 120 98052
Tel (425) 233-8578 SIC 7371 8742

PHYSIO-CONTROL INC p 1146
11811 Willows Rd Ne 98052
Tel (425) 867-4000
SIC 3841 3845 7699 7372

■ PHYSIO-CONTROL INTERNATIONAL INC p 1146
11811 Willows Rd Ne 98052
Tel (425) 867-4000 SIC 3845

REDAPT INC p 1216
12226 134th Ct Ne Bldg D 98052
Tel (425) 882-0400 SIC 5045

REDAPT SYSTEMS INC p 1216
12226 134th Ct Ne Bldg D 98052
Tel (206) 210-5440 SIC 5045

SENIOR AEGIS COMMUNITIES LLC p 1303
17602 Ne Union Hill Rd 98052
Tel (866) 688-5829 SIC 8082

■ UNIVAR USA INC p 1516
17411 Ne Union Hill Rd 98052
Tel (331) 777-6000 SIC 5169 5191 8741

■ WYNDHAM RESORT DEVELOPMENT CORP p 1630
9805 Willows Rd Ne 98052
Tel (425) 498-2500 SIC 7389

RENTON, WA

AIM GROUP USA INC p 38
705 Sw 7th St 98057
Tel (425) 235-2750 SIC 3728

ALLIANCE PACKAGING LLC p 55
1000 Sw 43rd St 98057
Tel (425) 291-3500 SIC 2653 3086

GREENSOURCE BRAND APPAREL INC p 638
1020 Sw 34th St 98057
Tel (425) 656-9123 SIC 5136 5137

JAVA TRADING CO LLC p 779
801 Houser Way N 98057
Tel (425) 917-2920 SIC 5149 2095

K AND L DISTRIBUTORS INC p 798
3215 Lind Ave Sw 98057
Tel (206) 454-8800 SIC 5182

MCLENDON HARDWARE INC p 931
440 Rainier Ave S 98057
Tel (425) 264-1541 SIC 5031 5251

NORTH WEST HANDLING SYSTEMS INC p 1054
1100 Sw 7th St 98057
Tel (425) 255-0500 SIC 5084 7699

PROVIDENCE HEALTH & SERVICES p 1185
1801 Lind Ave Sw 98057
Tel (425) 525-3355 SIC 8062

PROVIDENCE HEALTH & SERVICES - OREGON p 1185
1801 Lind Ave Sw 98057
Tel (425) 525-3355 SIC 8062

PROVIDENCE HEALTH & SERVICES AND SWEDISH HEALTH SERVICES p 1185
1801 Lind Ave Sw 98057
Tel (425) 525-3355 SIC 8062

PROVIDENCE HEALTH & SERVICES-WASHINGTON p 1186
1801 Lind Ave Sw 9016 98057
Tel (425) 525-3355
SIC 8062 8051 8052 6513 8069

PROVIDENCE HEALTH SYSTEM-SOUTHERN CALIFORNIA p 1186
1801 Lind Ave Sw 98057
Tel (425) 525-3355 SIC 8062

PUBLIC HOSPITAL DISTRICT 1 OF KING COUNTY p 1189
400 S 43rd St 98055
Tel (425) 228-3440 SIC 8062

RENTON SCHOOL DISTRICT p 1224
300 Sw 7th St 98057
Tel (425) 204-2300 SIC 8211

RHEM LLC p 1231
700 Powell Ave Sw 98057
Tel (425) 228-4111 SIC 5033 3086 1742

WASHINGTON GAMING INC p 1578
711 Powell Ave Sw 98057
Tel (425) 264-1050 SIC 7999

■ WIZARDS OF COAST LLC p 1619
1600 Lind Ave Sw Ste 400 98057
Tel (425) 226-6500 SIC 3944

RICHLAND, WA

BATTELLE MEMORIAL INSTITUTE p 159
900 Battelle Blvd 99354
Tel (509) 371-7608 SIC 8733

ENERGY NORTHWEST p 498
76 N Power Plant Loop 99354
Tel (509) 372-5000 SIC 4911 7699

■ FLUOR HANFORD INC p 561
3160 George Wash Way 99354
Tel (509) 372-2000 SIC 4953

KADLEC REGIONAL MEDICAL CENTER p 800
888 Swift Blvd 99352
Tel (509) 946-4611 SIC 8062

MISSION SUPPORT ALLIANCE LLC p 975
2490 Garlick Blvd 99354
Tel (509) 376-6770 SIC 8741

RICHLAND SCHOOL DISTRICT p 1233
615 Snow Ave 99352
Tel (509) 967-6000 SIC 8211

■ UNITED STATES DEPT OF ENERGY RICHLAND OPERATIONS OFFICE p 1513
825 Jadwin Ave Ste 700 99352
Tel (509) 376-7395 SIC 9611

■ WASHINGTON RIVER PROTECTION SOLUTIONS LLC p 1579
2425 Stevens Center Pl 99354
Tel (509) 376-8103 SIC 8711

RITZVILLE, WA

RITZVILLE WAREHOUSE CO p 1237
201 E 1st Ave 99169
Tel (509) 659-0130 SIC 5153 4221

ROY, WA

WILCOX FARMS INC p 1608
40400 Harts Lake Vly Rd 98580
Tel (360) 458-7774 SIC 0252 2015 2875

SALKUM, WA

■ MCDANIEL TELEPHONE CO p 927
160 Stowell Rd 98582
Tel (608) 831-1000 SIC 4813

SAMMAMISH, WA

WORLD WIDE TECHNOLOGY p 1625
26017 Se 23rd Pl 98075
Tel (425) 269-2678 SIC 7371

SEATAC, WA

▲ ALASKA AIR GROUP INC p 44
19300 International Blvd 98188
Tel (206) 392-5040 SIC 4512 4731

ALASKA AIRLINES p 44
20833 International Blvd 98198
Tel (206) 392-5885 SIC 4512

■ ALASKA AIRLINES INC p 44
19300 International Blvd 98188
Tel (206) 433-3200 SIC 4512

■ HORIZON AIR INDUSTRIES INC p 706
19521 International Blvd 98188
Tel (206) 241-6757 SIC 4512 4522

LYNDEN AIR FREIGHT INC p 888
18000 Intl Blvd Ste 700 98188
Tel (206) 777-5300 SIC 4731

LYNDEN INC p 888
18000 Intl Blvd Ste 800 98188
Tel (206) 241-8778 SIC 4213 4731 4424

MARSHALLS HOLDING CO p 911
20220 International Blvd 98198
Tel (206) 433-5911 SIC 5012 5013

SEATTLE, WA

A POLYCLINIC PROFESSIONAL CORP p 6
904 7th Ave 98104
Tel (206) 292-2249 SIC 8011

ACCRETIVE TECHNOLOGY GROUP INC p 16
800 Stewart St 98101
Tel (206) 443-6401 SIC 4813

ACG SEATTLE INC p 17
24 Roy St 442 98109
Tel (206) 524-5300 SIC 8732

■ ACKERLEY VENTURES INC p 17
1301 5th Ave Ste 3525 98101
Tel (206) 624-2888
SIC 7941 4833 4832 7319 7312

ADAPTIS INC p 21
999 3rd Ave Ste 1700 98104
Tel (206) 521-8833 SIC 7389

ALLEN INSTITUTE FOR BRAIN SCIENCE p 53
1441 N 34th St 98103
Tel (206) 548-7000 SIC 8733

■ AMAZON FULFILLMENT SERVICES INC p 64
410 Terry Ave N 98109
Tel (206) 266-1000
SIC 5735 5961 5731 5945

▲ AMAZON.COM INC p 64
410 Terry Ave N 98109
Tel (206) 266-1000 SIC 5961

■ AMAZON.COMDEDC LLC p 65
410 Terry Ave N 98109
Tel (206) 266-1000
SIC 5961 5735 5731 5945

AMAZON.COMINDC LLC p 65
440 Terry Ave N 98109
Tel (206) 266-1000 SIC 4813 5999 7371

AMERICAN MANAGEMENT SERVICES LLC p 75
2801 Alaskan Way Ste 200 98121
Tel (206) 215-9700 SIC 8742

AMERICAN MANAGEMENT SERVICES WEST LLC p 75
2801 Alaskan Way Ste 200 98121
Tel (206) 215-9700 SIC 6531

AMERICAN MOTELS ACQUISITION CO LLC p 76
2101 4th Ave Ste 1020 98121
Tel (206) 443-3550 SIC 7011

AMERICAN SEAFOODS CO LLC p 79
2025 1st Ave Ste 900 98121
Tel (206) 448-0300 SIC 0912 0921 2092

AMERICAN SEAFOODS GROUP LLC p 79
2025 1st Ave Ste 900 98121
Tel (206) 374-1515 SIC 5421 5146

AMERICAN SEAFOODS LP p 79
2025 1st Ave Ste 900 98121
Tel (206) 374-1515 SIC 5421 5146

AQUA STAR (USA) CORP p 101
2025 1st Ave Ste 200 98121
Tel (206) 448-5400 SIC 5146

ASG CONSOLIDATED LLC p 116
2025 1st Ave Ste 900 98121
Tel (206) 374-1515 SIC 5421 5146

ASSOCIATED GROCERS INC p 120
3301 S Norfolk St 98118
Tel (206) 762-2100
SIC 5141 5147 5143 5122 5148 5142

ASSOCIATION OF UNIVERSITY PHYSICIANS p 121
701 5th Ave Ste 700 98104
Tel (206) 520-5388 *SIC* 8621

ATTACHMATE CORP p 129
705 5th Ave S Ste 1000 98104
Tel (206) 217-7100 *SIC* 7373 7371 7372

ATTACHMATE GROUP INC p 129
705 5th Ave S Ste 1100 98104
Tel (206) 217-7100 *SIC* 7371 7372 7373

AVANADE INC p 136
818 Stewart St Ste 400 98101
Tel (206) 239-5600 *SIC* 7379 8742

BARTELL DRUG CO p 157
4025 Delridge Way Sw # 400 98106
Tel (206) 763-2626 *SIC* 5912

BASEBALL CLUB OF SEATTLE LLLP p 158
1250 1st Ave S 98134
Tel (206) 346-4000 *SIC* 7941

■ BEN BRIDGE - JEWELER INC p 172
2901 3rd Ave Ste 200 98121
Tel (206) 448-8800 *SIC* 5944 7631

■ BIG FISH GAMES INC p 181
333 Elliott Ave W Ste 200 98119
Tel (206) 213-5753 *SIC* 5734

BILL & MELINDA GATES FOUNDATION p 182
440 5th Ave N 98109
Tel (206) 709-3100 *SIC* 8699

BLETHEN CORP p 189
1120 John St 98109
Tel (206) 464-2471 *SIC* 2711

BLOODWORKS p 189
921 Terry Ave 98104
Tel (206) 292-6500
SIC 8071 8099 8733 8732

▲ BLUE NILE INC p 192
411 1st Ave S Ste 700 98104
Tel (206) 336-6700 *SIC* 5944

BNBUILDERS INC p 194
2601 4th Ave Ste 350 98121
Tel (206) 382-3443 *SIC* 1542

BRANDED ENTERTAINMENT NETWORK INC p 208
710 2nd Ave Ste 200 98104
Tel (206) 373-6000 *SIC* 7335

■ BROOKS SPORTS INC p 218
3400 Stone Way N Ste 500 98103
Tel (425) 488-3131 *SIC* 5139

BUFFALO CHECK BEER LLC p 224
P.O. Box 9635 98109
Tel (312) 320-3717 *SIC* 2082

CALLISON ARCHITECTURE HOLDING LLC p 242
1420 5th Ave Ste 2400 98101
Tel (206) 623-4646 *SIC* 6719

CAR TOYS INC p 252
400 Fairview Ave N # 900 98109
Tel (206) 443-2726 *SIC* 5731 5999

CARRIX INC p 261
1131 Sw Klickitat Way 98134
Tel (206) 623-0304 *SIC* 4491

CASCADE DESIGNS INC p 262
4000 1st Ave S 98134
Tel (206) 583-0583
SIC 2515 3089 3949 8733

CATALYST PAPER (USA) INC p 264
2200 6th Ave Ste 800 98121
Tel (206) 838-2070 *SIC* 5111

CATALYST PAPER HOLDINGS INC p 264
2200 6th Ave Ste 800 98121
Tel (604) 247-4018 *SIC* 6719

CATALYST PAPER OPERATIONS INC p 264
2200 6th Ave Ste 800 98121
Tel (604) 247-4018 *SIC* 2611

CATHOLIC COMMUNITY SERVICES OF WESTERN WASHINGTON p 266
100 23rd Ave S 98144
Tel (206) 328-5696 *SIC* 8322

CEDAR GROVE COMPOSTING INC p 272
7343 E Marginal Way S 98108
Tel (206) 832-3000 *SIC* 4953

CHARTER CONSTRUCTION INC p 291
980 S Harney St 98108
Tel (206) 382-1900 *SIC* 1542

CHIEF SEATTLE COUNCIL BOY SCOUTS OF AMERICA p 298
3120 Rainier Ave S 98144
Tel (206) 725-5200 *SIC* 8641

CHP OF WASHINGTON p 302
720 Olive Way Ste 300 98101
Tel (206) 521-8833 *SIC* 6411

CITY OF SEATTLE p 318
700 5th Ave Ste 4350 98104
Tel (206) 684-0702 *SIC* 9111

CITY OF SEATTLE-CITY LIGHT DEPARTMENT p 318
700 5th Ave Ste 3200 98104
Tel (206) 684-3200 *SIC* 4911

■ COBALT GROUP INC p 332
605 5th Ave S Ste 800 98104
Tel (206) 269-6363 *SIC* 7372

COCHRAN INC p 333
12500 Aurora Ave N Main 98133
Tel (206) 367-1900 *SIC* 1731 7382

COLLIERS INTERNATIONAL PROPERTY CONSULTANTS INC p 337
601 Union St Ste 3320 98101
Tel (206) 695-4200 *SIC* 6531

COLLIERS INTERNATIONAL WA LLC p 337
601 Union St Ste 3320 98101
Tel (206) 223-0866 *SIC* 6531

COMMUNITY HEALTH NETWORK OF WASHINGTON p 348
720 Olive Way Ste 300 98101
Tel (206) 521-8833 *SIC* 6324

COMMUNITY HEALTH PLAN OF WASHINGTON p 348
720 Olive Way Ste 300 98101
Tel (206) 521-8833 *SIC* 6324

CORP OF CATHOLIC ARCHBISHOP OF SEATTLE p 371
910 Marion St 98104
Tel (206) 382-4884 *SIC* 8661

COUNTY OF KING p 379
401 5th Ave Ste 3 98104
Tel (206) 296-4040 *SIC* 9111

▲ CRAY INC p 389
901 5th Ave Ste 1000 98164
Tel (206) 701-2000 *SIC* 3571 7379

CROWLEY MARINE SERVICES INC p 395
1102 Sw Massachusetts St 98134
Tel (206) 332-8000 *SIC* 4499

DAIRY EXPORT CO INC p 408
635 Elliott Ave W 98119
Tel (206) 284-7220 *SIC* 5191 5083 2033

DAPTIV SOLUTIONS LLC p 412
1111 3rd Ave Ste 700 98101
Tel (206) 341-9117 *SIC* 5045

DARIGOLD INC p 412
1130 Rainier Ave S 98144
Tel (206) 284-7220
SIC 2023 2026 2022 5143

DAVID OPPENHEIMER & CO I LLC p 415
180 Nickerson St Ste 211 98109
Tel (206) 284-1705 *SIC* 5141

DAVIS WRIGHT TREMAINE LLP p 416
1201 3rd Ave Ste 2200 98101
Tel (206) 622-3150 *SIC* 8111

DELTA DENTAL OF WASHINGTON p 426
9706 4th Ave Ne Ste 100 98115
Tel (206) 522-2300 *SIC* 6324

DELTA MARINE INDUSTRIES INC p 427
1608 S 96th St 98108
Tel (206) 763-0760 *SIC* 3732

DELTA WESTERN INC p 427
1177 Fairview Ave N 98109
Tel (907) 276-2688 *SIC* 5171 5251 5411

DENDREON CORP p 428
601 Union St Ste 4900 98101
Tel (206) 256-4545 *SIC* 2834

DIAMOND PARKING SERVICES LLC p 437
605 1st Ave Ste 600 98104
Tel (206) 284-2732 *SIC* 7521 6512

DOUBLE E FOODS LLC p 452
801 S Fidalgo St Ste 100 98108
Tel (206) 768-8979 *SIC* 8741

E & E FOODS INC p 465
801 S Fidalgo St Ste 100 98108
Tel (206) 768-8979 *SIC* 5146 2092

EMERALD SERVICES INC p 491
7343 E Marginal Way S 98108
Tel (206) 430-7795
SIC 4953 7699 2911 8748 7359

EVERGREEN PACIFIC PARTNERS MANAGEMENT CO INC p 514
1700 7th Ave Ste 2300 98101
Tel (206) 262-4709 *SIC* 7389 6282

▲ EXPEDITORS INTERNATIONAL OF WASHINGTON INC p 519
1015 3rd Ave Fl 12 98104
Tel (206) 674-3400 *SIC* 4731

▲ F5 NETWORKS INC p 523
401 Elliott Ave W Ste 500 98119
Tel (206) 272-5555 *SIC* 7373 7372

FEDERAL HOME LOAN BANK OF SEATTLE p 534
1001 4th Ave Ste 2600 98154
Tel (206) 340-2421 *SIC* 6019

FIRST & GOAL INC p 544
800 Occidental Ave S 98134
Tel (206) 381-7940 *SIC* 1542 7941

FIRST CHOICE HEALTH NETWORK INC p 545
600 University St # 1400 98101
Tel (206) 292-8255 *SIC* 6324

FIRST NATIONAL INSURANCE CO OF AMERICA p 548
4333 Rootland Ave Ne 98185
Tel (206) 545-5000 *SIC* 6331

■ FISHER COMMUNICATIONS INC p 552
140 4th Ave N Ste 500 98109
Tel (206) 404-7000 *SIC* 4833 4832

FOSS MARITIME CO p 570
1151 Fairview Ave N 98109
Tel (206) 281-4001
SIC 4412 4424 4492 4491 3731 4959

FR UTILITY SERVICES p 573
1424 4th Ave 98101
Tel (425) 890-1425 *SIC* 1731

FRANK RUSSELL CO p 574
1301 2nd Ave Fl 18 98101
Tel (206) 505-7877 *SIC* 6282 6211 6722

FRAZIER HEALTHCARE II LP p 575
601 Union St Ste 3200 98101
Tel (206) 621-7200 *SIC* 8742

FRAZIER MANAGEMENT LLC p 575
601 Union St Ste 3200 98101
Tel (206) 621-7200 *SIC* 6799

FRED HUTCHINSON CANCER RESEARCH CENTER p 575
1100 Fairview Ave N 98109
Tel (206) 667-4877 *SIC* 8733

FRS CAPITAL CORP p 582
1131 Sw Klickitat Way 98134
Tel (206) 623-0304 *SIC* 4491

GARY MERLINO CONSTRUCTION CO INC p 593
9125 10th Ave S 98108
Tel (206) 763-9552 *SIC* 1611 1623 3273

■ GETTY IMAGES INC p 609
605 5th Ave S Ste 400 98104
Tel (206) 925-5000 *SIC* 5961

GLANT PACIFIC INC p 614
2230 4th Ave S 98134
Tel (206) 628-6222
SIC 5949 5093 5094 5945

GLOBAL DIVING & SALVAGE INC p 616
3840 W Marginal Way Sw 98106
Tel (206) 623-0621 *SIC* 4959 1629 7389

GM NAMEPLATE INC p 618
2040 15th Ave W 98119
Tel (206) 284-2200 *SIC* 3479 2679 3679

GRANGE INSURANCE ASSOCIATION INC p 630
200 Cedar St 98121
Tel (206) 448-4911 *SIC* 8611

GROUP HEALTH COOPERATIVE p 641
320 Westlake Ave N # 100 98109
Tel (206) 448-4141
SIC 6324 5999 8093 6321

GROUP HEALTH PERMANENTE p 641
320 Westlake Ave N # 100 98109
Tel (206) 448-4491 *SIC* 8011

GWP HOLDINGS LLC p 648
3801 Airport Way S 98108
Tel (206) 624-7383
SIC 5511 7513 7538 5012

HARBORVIEW MEDICAL CENTER p 660
325 9th Ave 98104
Tel (206) 731-3000 *SIC* 8062

HARLEY MARINE SERVICES INC p 661
910 Sw Spokane St 98134
Tel (206) 628-0051 *SIC* 4449 4492

■ HOLLAND AMERICA LINE INC p 700
300 Elliott Ave W Ste 100 98119
Tel (206) 281-3535 *SIC* 4725

HOLLAND AMERICA LINE NV DBA HOLLAND AMERICA LINE NV LLC p 700
300 Elliott Ave W Ste 100 98119
Tel (206) 281-3535 *SIC* 4489

■ HOMESTREET BANK p 704
601 Union St Ste 2000 98101
Tel (206) 623-3050 *SIC* 6036

▲ HOMESTREET INC p 704
601 Union St Ste 2000 98101
Tel (206) 623-3050 *SIC* 6036 6022

ICICLE SEAFOODS INC p 727
4019 21st Ave W Ste 300 98199
Tel (206) 282-0988 *SIC* 2092 2091

■ IMMUNEX CORP p 734
51 University St 98101
Tel (206) 551-5169 *SIC* 2834 8731 2836

IQUIQUE US LLC p 764
2320 W Commodore Way # 200 98199
Tel (206) 286-1661 *SIC* 0921

ISSC INC p 767
3660 E Marginal Way S 98134
Tel (206) 343-0700 *SIC* 5051

JGC FOOD CO LLC p 785
1425 4th Ave Ste 420 98101
Tel (206) 622-0420 *SIC* 2099 2092

JR ABBOTT CONSTRUCTION INC p 795
3408 1st Ave S Ste 101 98134
Tel (206) 467-8500 *SIC* 1542

KAMILCHE CO p 802
1301 5th Ave Ste 2700 98101
Tel (206) 224-5800
SIC 2621 2611 2421 2435 2431

KELLER SUPPLY CO p 808
3209 17th Ave W 98119
Tel (206) 285-3300 *SIC* 5074

KIDDER MATHEWS LLC p 817
601 Union St Ste 4720 98101
Tel (206) 296-9600 *SIC* 6531

KPFF INC p 828
1601 5th Ave Ste 1600 98101
Tel (206) 622-5822 *SIC* 8711

LAIRD NORTON CO LLC p 838
801 2nd Ave Ste 1700 98104
Tel (206) 464-5245 *SIC* 5211

LANE POWELL PC p 843
1420 5th Ave Ste 4200 98101
Tel (206) 223-7000 *SIC* 8111

LEISURE CARE LLC p 854
999 3rd Ave Ste 4500 98104
Tel (800) 327-3490 *SIC* 8361

LEWIS LEASE CRUTCHER WA LLC p 858
2200 Western Ave 98121
Tel (206) 264-1985 *SIC* 1542 1521

MACDONALD-MILLER FACILITY SOLUTIONS INC p 892
7717 Detroit Ave Sw 98106
Tel (206) 763-9400 *SIC* 1711 1731

MANSON CONSTRUCTION CO p 903
5209 E Marginal Way S 98134
Tel (206) 762-0850 *SIC* 1629

MANSON CONSTRUCTION HOLDING CO p 903
5209 E Marginal Way S 98134
Tel (206) 762-0850 *SIC* 1629

▲ MARCHEX INC p 905
520 Pike St Ste 2000 98101
Tel (206) 331-3300 *SIC* 7313

MARUHA CAPITAL INVESTMENT INC p 913
2101 4th Ave Ste 1700 98121
Tel (206) 382-0640 *SIC* 6799 2091

MCKINSTRY CO LLC p 930
5005 3rd Ave S 98134
Tel (206) 762-3311
SIC 1711 1623 3446 3444

MERRILL GARDENS LLC p 950
1938 Frview Ave E Ste 300 98102
Tel (206) 676-5300 *SIC* 6531

METROPOLITAN MARKET LLC p 956
4025 Delridge Way Sw # 100 98106
Tel (206) 284-2530 *SIC* 5411

MILLIMAN INC p 971
1301 5th Ave Ste 3800 98101
Tel (206) 624-7940 *SIC* 8742 8999 7389

MOSS ADAMS LLP p 992
999 3rd Ave Ste 2800 98104
Tel (206) 302-6500 *SIC* 8721

NATIONAL FROZEN FOODS CORP p 1012
1600 Frview Ave E Ste 200 98102
Tel (206) 322-8900 *SIC* 2037

NBBJ LP p 1021
223 Yale Ave N 98109
Tel (206) 223-5555 *SIC* 8712

▲ NORDSTROM INC p 1048
1617 6th Ave 98101
Tel (206) 628-2111
SIC 5651 5661 5632 5611 5641 5961

NORTH COAST ELECTRIC CO p 1052
2450 8th Ave S Ste 200 98134
Tel (206) 442-9898 *SIC* 5063

NORTH PACIFIC SEAFOODS INC p 1053
4 Nickerson St Ste 400 98109
Tel (206) 726-9900 *SIC* 2091

NORTHLAND TELECOMMUNICATIONS CORP p 1057
101 Stewart St Ste 700 98101
Tel (206) 621-1351 *SIC* 4841 7371

NORTHWEST ADMINISTRATORS INC p 1059
2323 Eastlake Ave E 98102
Tel (206) 329-4900 *SIC* 6371

NORTHWEST CAPITAL APPRECIATION INC p 1059
1200 Westlake Ave N # 310 98109
Tel (206) 689-5615 *SIC* 2611

NORTHWEST DAIRY ASSOCIATION p 1059
1130 Rainier Ave S 98144
Tel (206) 284-7220 *SIC* 8611

NORTHWEST HOSPITAL & MEDICAL CENTER p 1060
1550 N 115th St 98133
Tel (206) 364-0500 *SIC* 8741 8062

NORTHWEST KIDNEY CENTERS p 1060
700 Broadway 98122
Tel (206) 292-2771 *SIC* 8092

NW CENTER INDUSTRIES 5307 p 1068
7272 W Marginal Way S 98108
Tel (206) 285-9140 *SIC* 3999

OCEAN BEAUTY SEAFOODS LLC p 1073
1100 W Ewing St 98119
Tel (206) 285-6800 *SIC* 2092 2091

ODYSSEY ENTERPRISES INC p 1075
2729 6th Ave S 98134
Tel (206) 285-7445 *SIC* 5146

OPUS NORTHWEST LLC p 1091
2025 1st Ave Ph B 98121
Tel (425) 467-2701 *SIC* 6552 1542

PACIFIC COAST FEATHER CO p 1104
1964 4th Ave S 98134
Tel (206) 624-1057 *SIC* 2392

PACIFIC RAIL SERVICES LLC p 1105
1131 Sw Klickitat Way 98134
Tel (206) 382-4462 *SIC* 4789

PACMED CLINICS p 1107
1200 12th Ave S 98144
Tel (206) 326-2400 *SIC* 8011

PAINTED POST PARTNERS p 1108
3131 Elliott Ave Ste 500 98121
Tel (206) 298-2909 *SIC* 8059

PATH p 1120
2201 Westlake Ave Ste 200 98121
Tel (206) 285-3500 *SIC* 8399

PAUL G ALLEN FAMILY FOUNDATION p 1121
505 5th Ave S Ste 900 98104
Tel (206) 342-2000 *SIC* 8699

PEMCO MUTUAL INSURANCE CO p 1128
1300 Dexter Ave N 98109
Tel (425) 712-7700 *SIC* 6331

PERKINS COIE LLP p 1136
1201 3rd Ave Ste 4900 98101
Tel (206) 359-8000 *SIC* 8111

PETER PAN SEAFOODS INC p 1138
The Tenth Fl 2200 6th Ave 98121
Tel (206) 728-6000 SIC 2092 2091

PHYSICIANS INSURANCE A MUTUAL CO p 1145
1301 2nd Ave Ste 2700 98101
Tel (206) 343-7300 SIC 6411

PINNACLE REALTY MANAGEMENT CO p 1150
2801 Alaskan Way Ste 200 98121
Tel (206) 215-9700
SIC 6531 8741 6513 6512 1522

■ PLUM CREEK MANUFACTURING LP p 1156
999 3rd Ave Ste 4300 98104
Tel (206) 467-3600
SIC 2421 2436 2493 5031

PLUM CREEK TIMBER CO INC p 1156
601 Union St Ste 3100 98101
Tel (206) 467-3600 SIC 6798 1311

■ PLUM CREEK TIMBERLANDS LP p 1156
601 Union St Ste 3100 98101
Tel (206) 467-3600
SIC 2421 2436 2493 5031

PORT OF SEATTLE p 1162
2711 Alaskan Way Pier 69 98121
Tel (206) 728-3000 SIC 4491

PRECEPT BRANDS LLC p 1168
1910 Frview Ave E Ste 400 98102
Tel (206) 267-5252 SIC 5182

PUGET CONSUMERS CO-OP p 1191
4201 Roosevelt Way Ne 98105
Tel (206) 547-1222 SIC 5411

PUGET SOUND COMMERCE CENTER INC p 1191
1801 16th Ave Sw 98134
Tel (206) 623-1635 SIC 3731

R D MERRILL CO p 1202
1938 Frview Ave E Ste 300 98102
Tel (206) 676-5600 SIC 6513

R U CORP p 1203
411 1st Ave S Ste 200n 98104
Tel (206) 634-0550 SIC 5812 5813 5461

RAD POWER BIKES LLC p 1203
2622 Nw Market St Ste B 98107
Tel (800) 939-0310 SIC 5941

RAYTHEON PIKEWERKS CORP p 1211
321 3rd Ave S Ste 203 98104
Tel (310) 647-9438 SIC 8711

RAZORFISH LLC p 1211
424 2nd Ave W 98119
Tel (206) 816-8800 SIC 7375 7319

▲ REALNETWORKS INC p 1214
1501 1st Ave S Ste 600 98134
Tel (206) 674-2700 SIC 7371 7372

REGENCE BLUESHIELD p 1218
1800 9th Ave Ste 200 98101
Tel (206) 340-6600 SIC 6324

RESTAURANTS UNLIMITED INC p 1228
411 1st Ave S Ste 200 98104
Tel (206) 634-0550 SIC 5812

SAFECO ADMINISTRATIVE SERVICES INC p 1266
1001 4th Ave 98154
Tel (206) 545-5000 SIC 6411

SAFECO CORP p 1266
1001 4th Ave Ste 800 98185
Tel (206) 545-5000
SIC 6411 6311 6321 6324 6351

SAFECO INSURANCE CO OF AMERICA p 1266
1001 4th Ave Ste 800 98185
Tel (206) 545-5000 SIC 6411

SALTCHUK RESOURCES INC p 1273
1111 Fairview Ave N 98109
Tel (206) 652-1111 SIC 4492 4412 4499

SATTERBERG FOUNDATION p 1283
1904 3rd Ave Ste 825 98101
Tel (206) 441-3045 SIC 8641

SEA MAR COMMUNITY CARE CENTER p 1295
1040 S Henderson St 98108
Tel (206) 763-5210 SIC 8051 8351

SEA-MAR COMMUNITY HEALTH CENTER p 1295
1040 S Henderson St 98108
Tel (206) 763-5277
SIC 8322 8082 8093 8051

■ SEABOURN CRUISE LINE LIMITED p 1296
300 Elliott Ave W Ste 100 98119
Tel (206) 626-9179 SIC 4481

SEABRIGHT HOLDINGS INC p 1296
1111 3rd Ave Ste 1450 98101
Tel (206) 269-8500 SIC 6331

SEATTLE CANCER CARE ALLIANCE p 1297
825 Eastlake Ave E 98109
Tel (206) 288-7222 SIC 8069

SEATTLE CHILDRENS HEALTHCARE SYSTEM p 1297
4800 Sand Point Way Ne 98105
Tel (206) 987-2000 SIC 8069

SEATTLE CHILDRENS HEALTHCARE SYSTEM p 1297
P.O. Box 5371 98145
Tel (206) 987-4846 SIC 8062

SEATTLE CHILDRENS HOSPITAL p 1297
4800 Sand Point Way Ne 98105
Tel (206) 987-2000 SIC 8062 8069

SEATTLE COLLEGES p 1297
1500 Harvard Ave 98122
Tel (206) 934-4100 SIC 8222

SEATTLE FOUNDATION p 1297
1200 5th Ave Ste 1300 98101
Tel (206) 622-2294 SIC 8399

SEATTLE GOODWILL INDUSTRIES INC p 1297
700 Dearborn Pl S 98144
Tel (206) 329-1000 SIC 5932

SEATTLE PACIFIC INDUSTRIES INC p 1297
1633 Westlake Ave N # 300 98109
Tel (253) 872-8822 SIC 5136 5137

SEATTLE PACIFIC UNIVERSITY INC p 1298
3307 3rd Ave W 98119
Tel (206) 281-2000 SIC 8221 8661

SEATTLE PUBLIC SCHOOLS p 1298
2445 3rd Ave S 98134
Tel (206) 252-0000 SIC 8211

SEATTLE TIMES CO p 1298
1000 Denny Way Ste 501 98109
Tel (206) 464-2111 SIC 2711

SEATTLE UNIVERSITY p 1298
901 12th Ave 98122
Tel (206) 296-6150 SIC 8221

SEIU HEALTHCARE NW HEALTH BENEFITS TRUST p 1301
215 Columbia St Ste 300 98104
Tel (425) 771-7359 SIC 6733

SELLEN CONSTRUCTION CO INC p 1302
227 Westlake Ave N 98109
Tel (206) 682-7770 SIC 1542 8741

■ SEQUOIA SPRINGS COTTAGES p 1306
3131 Elliott Ave Ste 500 98121
Tel (206) 298-2909 SIC 8051

SILVARIS CORP p 1323
505 5th Ave S Ste 610 98104
Tel (888) 856-6677 SIC 5031

SIMPSON INVESTMENT CO INC p 1325
1301 5th Ave Ste 2700 98101
Tel (253) 272-0158
SIC 2621 2611 2421 2431 3084

SK FOOD GROUP INC p 1328
4600 37th Ave Sw Ste 300 98126
Tel (206) 935-8100 SIC 2099

SLALOM LLC p 1331
821 2nd Ave Ste 1900 98104
Tel (206) 374-4200 SIC 8742 7373

SMITH JOHNSON LAVEY AND BELL INC p 1333
2025 1st Ave Ste 11150 98121
Tel (206) 443-8846 SIC 8743

SSA MARINE INC p 1363
1131 Sw Klickitat Way 98134
Tel (206) 623-0304 SIC 4491 4731

■ STARBUCKS COFFEE INTERNATIONAL INC p 1378
2401 Utah Ave S Ste 800 98134
Tel (206) 447-1575 SIC 5812

▲ STARBUCKS CORP p 1378
2401 Utah Ave S 98134
Tel (206) 447-1575
SIC 5812 5499 5461 5149

STONEPATH GROUP INC p 1391
2200 Alaskan Way Ste 200 98121
Tel (206) 336-5400 SIC 4731

STUSSER ELECTRIC CO p 1395
660 S Andover St 98108
Tel (206) 623-1501 SIC 5063

SUGAR MOUNTAIN CAPITAL LLC p 1397
801 Blanchard St Ste 300 98121
Tel (206) 322-1644 SIC 5142

SUMITOMO METAL MINING AMERICA INC p 1398
701 5th Ave Ste 2150 98104
Tel (206) 405-2800 SIC 1081

SUR LA TABLE INC p 1408
6100 4th Ave S Ste 500 98108
Tel (206) 613-6000 SIC 5719

SWEDISH HEALTH SERVICES p 1411
747 Broadway 98122
Tel (206) 386-6000 SIC 8011

SWEDISH PHYSICIANS DIVISION p 1411
600 University St # 1200 98101
Tel (206) 320-2700 SIC 8011 8741

▲ TABLEAU SOFTWARE INC p 1420
837 N 34th St Ste 200 98103
Tel (206) 633-3400 SIC 7372

TC GLOBAL INC p 1428
2003 Western Ave Ste 660 98121
Tel (206) 233-2070 SIC 2095 5149

■ TOMMY BAHAMA GROUP INC p 1459
400 Fairview Ave N # 488 98109
Tel (206) 622-8688
SIC 7389 5651 5136 5137

TRIDENT SEAFOODS CORP p 1479
5303 Shilshole Ave Nw 98107
Tel (206) 783-3818
SIC 2092 5146 5091 0912

TRIPLE "B" CORP p 1482
4103 2nd Ave S 98134
Tel (206) 625-1412 SIC 5148

TRUPANION INC p 1487
6100 4th Ave S Ste 200 98108
Tel (855) 727-9079 SIC 6324 8011

UNITED WAY OF KING COUNTY p 1515
720 2nd Ave 98104
Tel (206) 461-3700 SIC 8399

■ UNITEDHEALTHCARE OF WASHINGTON INC p 1515
1111 3rd Ave Ste 1100 98101
Tel (206) 236-2500 SIC 6324 6321

UNIVERSITY OF WASHINGTON INC p 1526
4311 11th Ave Ne Ste 600 98105
Tel (206) 543-2100 SIC 8221

UW MEDICINE/NORTHWEST p 1538
1550 N 115th St 98133
Tel (206) 364-0500 SIC 8062

UW MEDICINE/NORTHWEST p 1538
1550 N 115th St 98133
Tel (206) 364-0500 SIC 8062

UWAJIMAYA INC p 1538
4601 6th Ave S 98108
Tel (206) 624-6248 SIC 5141 5411

VAUPELL INDUSTRIAL PLASTICS INC p 1545
1144 Nw 53rd St 98107
Tel (206) 784-9050 SIC 3089

■ VIEWPOINT INTERNATIONAL INC p 1556
428 Westlake Ave N # 388 98109
Tel (206) 622-8688 SIC 5136 5137

VIGOR SHIPYARDS INC p 1556
1801 16th Ave Sw 98134
Tel (206) 623-1635 SIC 3731

VIRGINIA MASON HEALTH SYSTEM p 1559
1100 9th Ave 98101
Tel (206) 233-6600 SIC 8741

VIRGINIA MASON MEDICAL CENTER p 1559
1100 9th Ave 98101
Tel (206) 223-6600
SIC 8011 8051 6513 8062

VIRGINIA MASON SEATTLE MAIN CLINIC p 1559
1100 9th Ave 98101
Tel (206) 223-6600 SIC 8011

VULCAN INC p 1567
505 5th Ave S Ste 900 98104
Tel (206) 342-2000 SIC 6531 6722 7941

W LEASE LEWIS CO p 1568
2200 Western Ave 98121
Tel (206) 622-0500 SIC 1542

▲ WASHINGTON FEDERAL INC p 1578
425 Pike St Ste 100 98101
Tel (206) 624-7930 SIC 6021

■ WASHINGTON FEDERAL NATIONAL ASSOCIATION p 1578
425 Pike St 98101
Tel (206) 624-7930 SIC 6035

WASHINGTON REAL ESTATE HOLDINGS LLC p 1578
600 University St # 2820 98101
Tel (206) 613-5300 SIC 6512

WASHINGTON TEAMSTERS WELFARE TRUST p 1579
2323 Eastlake Ave E 98102
Tel (206) 329-4900 SIC 8631

WATCHGUARD TECHNOLOGIES INC p 1581
505 5th Ave S Ste 500 98104
Tel (206) 613-6600 SIC 7372

WESTERN CONFERENCE OF TEAMSTERS PENSION TRUST FUND p 1597
2323 Eastlake Ave E 98102
Tel (206) 329-4900 SIC 6733

WESTERN TEAMSTERS WELFARE TRUST p 1600
2323 Eastlake Ave E 98102
Tel (206) 329-4900 SIC 8631

▲ WEYERHAEUSER CO p 1603
220 Occidental Ave S 98104
Tel (253) 924-2345
SIC 6798 0811 2411 2435 2611 2621

■ WEYERHAEUSER NR CO p 1603
220 Occidental Ave S 98104
Tel (253) 924-2345 SIC 0811

■ WHITE PASS & YOKON MOTOR COACHES INC p 1606
300 Elliott Ave W 98119
Tel (206) 281-3535 SIC 4141

WIRELESS ADVOCATES LLC p 1618
400 Fairview Ave N # 900 98109
Tel (206) 428-2400 SIC 5999

▲ WMI HOLDINGS CORP p 1620
800 5th Ave Ste 4100 98104
Tel (206) 432-8887 SIC 6035

WORKSPACE DEVELOPMENT LLC p 1624
5601 6th Ave S Ste 470 98108
Tel (206) 768-8000 SIC 5021

YOUNG MENS CHRISTIAN ASSOCIATION OF GREATER SEATTLE p 1638
909 4th Ave 98104
Tel (206) 382-5342 SIC 8641 8322

▲ ZILLOW GROUP INC p 1643
1301 2nd Ave Fl 31 98101
Tel (206) 470-7000 SIC 7372 6531 4813

■ ZILLOW INC p 1643
1301 2nd Ave Fl 31 98101
Tel (206) 470-7000 SIC 7371 8742

ZULILY INC p 1644
2601 Elliott Ave Ste 200 98121
Tel (877) 779-5614 SIC 5961

■ ZULILY LLC p 1645
2601 Elliott Ave Ste 200 98121
Tel (877) 779-5614 SIC 5961

SEDRO WOOLLEY, WA

JANICKI INDUSTRIES INC p 777
719 Metcalf St 98284
Tel (360) 856-5143 SIC 3728

SNELSON COMPANIES INC p 1335
601 W State St 98284
Tel (360) 856-6511 SIC 1623

SELAH, WA

TREE TOP INC p 1475
220 E 2nd Ave 98942
Tel (509) 697-7251 SIC 2033 2034 2037

ZIRKLE FRUIT CO p 1643
352 Harrison Rd 98942
Tel (509) 697-6101 SIC 0175 0723 4222

SHELTON, WA

MASON COUNTY PUBLIC UTILITY DISTRICT NO 3 p 916
2621 E Johns Prairie Rd 98584
Tel (360) 426-8255 SIC 4911

SQUAXIN ISLAND TRIBE OF SQUAXIN ISLAND RESERVATION p 1362
10 Se Squaxin Ln 98584
Tel (360) 426-9781
SIC 5411 5146 7011 0132

SHORELINE, WA

CRISTA MINISTRIES p 392
19303 Fremont Ave N 98133
Tel (206) 546-7200 SIC 8322 8051 8211

SHORELINE SCHOOL DISTRICT p 1318
18560 1st Ave Ne 98155
Tel (206) 367-6111 SIC 8211

SHORELINE SCHOOL DISTRICT p 1318
18560 1st Ave Ne 98155
Tel (206) 361-4208 SIC 8211

SILVERDALE, WA

CENTRAL KITSAP SCHOOL DISTRICT p 279
9210 Silverdale Way Nw 98383
Tel (360) 662-1610 SIC 8211

SNOHOMISH, WA

SNOHOMISH SCHOOL DISTRICT 201 p 1335
1601 Avenue D 98290
Tel (360) 563-7263 SIC 8211

SNOQUALMIE, WA

SNOQUALMIE ENTERTAINMENT p 1336
37500 Se North Bend Way 98065
Tel (425) 888-1234 SIC 7993 7011

■ SPACELABS HEALTHCARE (WASHINGTON) INC p 1354
35301 Se Center St 98065
Tel (425) 396-3300
SIC 3845 3841 3575 7699 7378

■ SPACELABS HEALTHCARE INC p 1354
35301 Se Center St 98065
Tel (425) 396-3302
SIC 3841 3845 3575 7699 7378

SPANAWAY, WA

BETHEL SCHOOL DISTRICT p 178
516 176th St E 98387
Tel (253) 683-6000 SIC 8211

SPOKANE VALLEY, WA

ALLIANCE MACHINE SYSTEMS INTERNATIONAL LLC p 54
5303 E Desmet Ave 99212
Tel (509) 842-5104 SIC 3554

ALSAKER CORP p 61
6409 E Sharp Ave 99212
Tel (509) 242-6327 SIC 5541 5411

CENTRAL VALLEY SCHOOL DISTRICT p 280
19307 E Cataldo Ave 99016
Tel (509) 228-5404 SIC 8211

CPM DEVELOPMENT CORP p 387
5111 E Broadway Ave 99212
Tel (509) 534-6221 SIC 3273 1771 3272

HEALTHCARE RESOURCE GROUP INC p 676
12610 E Mirabeau Pkwy # 900 99216
Tel (509) 209-2000
SIC 6411 7322 8742 8721

■ HONEYWELL ELECTRONIC MATERIALS INC p 705
15128 E Euclid Ave 99216
Tel (509) 252-2200 SIC 3679 3674 3643

HOSPITALITY INVESTMENTS LIMITED PARTNERSHIP p 710
3808 N Sullivan Rd # 34 99216
Tel (509) 928-3736 SIC 6799

▲ KEY TRONIC CORP p 815
4424 N Sullivan Rd 99216
Tel (509) 928-8000 SIC 3577

LYDIG CONSTRUCTION INC p 887
11001 E Montgomery Dr 99206
Tel (509) 534-0451 SIC 1542 1541

NUMERICA CREDIT UNION p 1067
14610 E Sprague Ave 99216
Tel (509) 535-7613 SIC 6062

SKYLINE EXHIBITS INLAND NW INC p 1330
10102 E Knox Ave Ste 450 99206
Tel (509) 892-5354 SIC 7389

■ SPOKANE VALLEY WASHINGTON HOSPITAL CO LLC p 1359
12606 E Mission Ave 99216
Tel (509) 924-6650 *SIC* 8062

TIDYMANS LLC p 1452
10020 E Knox Ave Ste 500 99206
Tel (509) 928-7480 *SIC* 5411

TIDYMANS MANAGEMENT SERVICES INC p 1452
10020 E Knox Ave Ste 500 99206
Tel (509) 928-7480 *SIC* 5411

WAGSTAFF INC p 1571
3910 N Flora Rd 99216
Tel (509) 922-1404 *SIC* 3542 3364

WINDOW PRODUCTS INC p 1615
10507 E Montgomery Dr 99206
Tel (800) 442-8544 *SIC* 3442 5211

YOKES FOODS INC p 1636
3426 S University Rd 99206
Tel (509) 921-2292 *SIC* 5912

SPOKANE, WA

AMERICANWEST BANCORPORATION p 81
41 W Rverside Ave Ste 300 99201
Tel (509) 467-6993 *SIC* 6022

AMERICANWEST BANK p 81
41 W Rverside Ave Ste 300 99201
Tel (509) 232-1515 *SIC* 6021

■ APPLEWAY CHEVROLET INC p 99
8600 E Sprague Ave 99212
Tel (509) 924-1150 *SIC* 5511

ASEA AFSCME LOCAL 52 HEALTH BENEFITS TRUST p 116
111 W Cataldo Ave 99201
Tel (509) 328-0300 *SIC* 8631

▲ AVISTA CORP p 138
1411 E Mission Ave 99202
Tel (509) 489-0500 *SIC* 4911 4924 3499

■ AVISTA UTILITIES INC p 138
1411 E Mission Ave 99202
Tel (509) 489-0500 *SIC* 4939

CITY OF SPOKANE p 318
808 W Spokane Falls Blvd 99201
Tel (509) 625-6200 *SIC* 9111

▲ CLEARWATER PAPER CORP p 324
601 W Riverside Ave # 1100 99201
Tel (509) 344-5900 *SIC* 2621 2631

CORP OF GONZAGA UNIVERSITY p 371
502 E Boone Ave 99258
Tel (509) 328-4220 *SIC* 8221

COUNTY OF SPOKANE p 382
1116 W Broadway Ave 99260
Tel (509) 477-2265 *SIC* 9121

COWLES PUBLISHING CO p 386
999 W Riverside Ave 99201
Tel (509) 459-5000
SIC 2711 2611 2621 4833

■ DEACONESS MEDICAL CENTER p 419
800 W 5th Ave 99204
Tel (509) 458-5800 *SIC* 8062

DOMINICAN HEALTH SERVICES p 449
5633 N Lidgerwood St 99208
Tel (509) 482-0111 *SIC* 8062

ECOVA INC p 476
1313 N Atl St Ste 5000 99201
Tel (509) 747-5069 *SIC* 8742

EMBASSY MANAGEMENT LLC p 490
5709 W Sunset Hwy Ste 100 99224
Tel (509) 328-2740 *SIC* 8741

EMPIRE HEALTH CENTERS GROUP p 493
800 W 5th Ave 99204
Tel (509) 473-5800 *SIC* 8062

ENGIE HOLDINGS INC p 498
1313 N Atl St Ste 5000 99201
Tel (509) 329-7600 *SIC* 8742

GARCO CONSTRUCTION INC p 591
4114 E Broadway Ave 99202
Tel (509) 536-1649 *SIC* 1541

■ HASKINS STEEL CO INC p 667
3613 E Main Ave 99202
Tel (509) 252-9724 *SIC* 5051

JENSEN-BYRD CO LLC p 783
314 W Riverside Ave 99201
Tel (509) 624-1321 *SIC* 5072

JUBILANT HOLLISTERSTIER LLC p 796
3525 N Regal St 99207
Tel (509) 482-4945 *SIC* 2834

NORTHWEST FARM CREDIT SERVICES p 1059
2001 S Flint Rd 99224
Tel (509) 838-2429 *SIC* 6111

PATHOLOGY ASSOCIATES MEDICAL LABORATORIES LLC p 1120
110 W Cliff Dr 99204
Tel (800) 541-7891 *SIC* 8071

▲ POTLATCH CORP p 1164
601 W 1st Ave Ste 1600 99201
Tel (509) 835-1500 *SIC* 0831 6798

PROVIDENCE HEALTH & SERVICES-WASHINGTON p 1186
5633 N Lidgerwood St 99208
Tel (509) 482-0111 *SIC* 8062

PYROTEK INC p 1194
705 W 1st Ave 99201
Tel (509) 926-6212 *SIC* 3365

▲ RED LION HOTELS CORP p 1215
201 W North River Dr # 100 99201
Tel (509) 459-6100 *SIC* 7011

■ RED LION HOTELS HOLDINGS INC p 1215
201 W North River Dr # 100 99201
Tel (509) 459-6100 *SIC* 7011

■ RL VENTURE LLC p 1239
201 W North River Dr # 100 99201
Tel (509) 459-6100 *SIC* 7011

ROCKWOOD CLINIC PS p 1245
400 E 5th Ave Frnt 99202
Tel (509) 838-2531 *SIC* 8011

ROSAUERS SUPERMARKETS INC p 1250
1815 W Garland Ave 99205
Tel (509) 326-8900 *SIC* 5411

SACRED HEART MEDICAL CENTER p 1265
101 W 8th Ave 99204
Tel (509) 455-3131 *SIC* 8062 8071

SCAFCO CORP p 1285
2800 E Main Ave 99202
Tel (509) 343-9000
SIC 3523 5065 6531 3444

SPOKANE PRODUCE INC p 1359
1905 S Geiger Blvd 99224
Tel (509) 455-8970 *SIC* 5148

SPOKANE PUBLIC SCHOOLS p 1359
200 N Bernard St 99201
Tel (509) 354-5900 *SIC* 8211

■ SPOKANE WASHINGTON HOSPITAL CO LLC p 1359
800 W 5th Ave 99204
Tel (509) 458-5800 *SIC* 8062

STERLING FINANCIAL CORP p 1387
111 N Wall St 99201
Tel (509) 358-8097 *SIC* 6036

STERLING SAVINGS BANK p 1387
111 N Wall St 99201
Tel (509) 624-4121
SIC 6036 6162 6035 6141 6153

STONEWAY ELECTRIC SUPPLY CO p 1391
402 N Perry St 99202
Tel (509) 535-2933 *SIC* 5063

STONEWAY ELECTRIC SUPPLY CO OF SPOKANE (INC) p 1391
1212 E Front Ave 99202
Tel (509) 535-2933 *SIC* 5063

TECK AMERICAN INC p 1432
501 N Riverpoint Blvd # 300 99202
Tel (509) 747-6111 *SIC* 1081

TRAVIS PATTERN & FOUNDRY INC p 1475
1413 E Hawthorne Rd 99218
Tel (509) 466-1798
SIC 3523 3369 3313 3321 3625

■ TRIUMPH COMPOSITE SYSTEMS INC p 1483
1514 S Flint Rd 99224
Tel (509) 623-8536 *SIC* 3724 3728

URM STORES INC p 1530
7511 N Freya St 99217
Tel (509) 467-2620 *SIC* 5141 5147

VEBA TRUST FOR PUBLIC EMPLOYEES IN NORTHWEST p 1546
906 W 2nd Ave 99201
Tel (509) 838-5571 *SIC* 6733

WASHINGTON TRUST BANK p 1579
717 W Sprague Ave Fl 7 99201
Tel (509) 353-4204 *SIC* 6022

WTB FINANCIAL CORP p 1628
717 W Sprague Ave Fl 7 99201
Tel (509) 353-4204 *SIC* 6712

STANWOOD, WA

TWIN CITY FOODS INC p 1495
10120 269th Pl Nw 98292
Tel (206) 515-2400 *SIC* 2037

SUMNER, WA

HELLY HANSEN (US) INC p 682
14218 Stewart Rd Ste 100a 98390
Tel (800) 435-5901
SIC 5137 5699 2339 2329

LULULEMON USA INC p 885
2201 140th Ave E 98390
Tel (604) 732-6124 *SIC* 5137 5331

METRIE INC p 954
2200 140th Ave E Ste 600 98390
Tel (253) 470-5050 *SIC* 5031

NORTHERN SALES CO INC p 1056
15022 Puyallup St E # 101 98390
Tel (253) 299-0500
SIC 5145 5149 5194 5141

■ POTELCO INC p 1164
14103 Stewart Rd 98390
Tel (253) 826-7300 *SIC* 1623

SEFNCO COMMUNICATIONS INC p 1300
4610 Tacoma Ave 98390
Tel (877) 385-2903 *SIC* 1623

WASHINGTON TRACTOR INC p 1579
2700 136th Avenue Ct E 98390
Tel (253) 863-4436
SIC 3523 5083 5261 7699 7353

TACOMA, WA

AUTO WAREHOUSING CO INC p 133
2810 Marshall Ave Ste B 98421
Tel (253) 719-1700 *SIC* 4226

BARGREEN-ELLINGSON INC p 155
6626 Tacoma Mall Blvd B 98409
Tel (253) 475-9201 *SIC* 5046 2541

BURKHART DENTAL SUPPLY CO p 227
2502 S 78th St 98409
Tel (253) 474-7761 *SIC* 5047

CATHOLIC HEALTH INITIATIVES WESTERN REGION p 266
1149 Market St 98402
Tel (253) 552-4100 *SIC* 8742

CITY OF TACOMA p 319
747 Market St 98402
Tel (253) 591-5088 *SIC* 9111

CITY OF TACOMA DEPARTMENT OF PUBLIC UTILITIES p 319
3628 S 35th St 98409
Tel (253) 502-8900
SIC 4911 4941 4899 4013 4841

■ CLP RESOURCES INC p 328
1015 A St 98402
Tel (775) 321-8000 *SIC* 8742

▲ COLUMBIA BANKING SYSTEM INC p 340
1301 A St 98402
Tel (253) 305-1900 *SIC* 6022

■ COLUMBIA STATE BANK p 342
1301 A St Ste 800 98402
Tel (253) 305-1900 *SIC* 6022

COUNTY OF PIERCE p 381
615 S 9th St Ste 100 98405
Tel (253) 798-7285 *SIC* 9111

FRANCISCAN HEALTH SYSTEM p 573
1717 S J St 98405
Tel (253) 426-4101 *SIC* 8062

FRANCISCAN MEDICAL GROUP p 573
1717 S J St 98405
Tel (253) 792-4365 *SIC* 8011

FRANKLIN-PIERCE SCHOOL DISTRICT p 575
315 129th St S 98444
Tel (253) 298-3000 *SIC* 8211

INTERSTATE DISTRIBUTOR CO p 758
11707 21st Avenue Ct S 98444
Tel (253) 537-9455 *SIC* 4213

■ LABOR READY MIDWEST INC p 836
1015 A St Unit A 98402
Tel (253) 383-9101 *SIC* 7363

■ LABOR READY NORTHWEST INC p 836
P.O. Box 2910 98401
Tel (253) 383-9101 *SIC* 7363

■ LABOR READY SOUTHEAST III LP p 836
1015 A St Unit A 98402
Tel (253) 383-9101 *SIC* 7363

■ LABOR READY SOUTHEAST INC p 836
1016 S 28th St 98409
Tel (253) 383-9101 *SIC* 7363

LABOR READY SOUTHWEST INC p 836
1015 A St Unit A 98402
Tel (800) 610-8920 *SIC* 7361

LD MCFARLAND CO LIMITED p 849
1640 E Marc St 98421
Tel (253) 572-5670 *SIC* 2499 2491 2411

MANKE LUMBER CO INC p 902
1717 Marine View Dr 98422
Tel (253) 572-6252 *SIC* 2421 2491 2499

MCFARLAND CASCADE HOLDINGS INC p 928
1640 E Marc St 98421
Tel (253) 572-3033 *SIC* 2491 6552 6531

MIDDLETON BRATRUD INSURANCE BROKERS INC p 965
1201 Pacific Ave Ste 1000 98402
Tel (253) 759-2200 *SIC* 6411

MOOR INNOVATIVE TECHNOLOGIES LLC p 987
4812 64th St E 98443
Tel (253) 343-2216 *SIC* 2326

MULTICARE HEALTH SYSTEM p 999
316 M L King Jr Way # 314 98405
Tel (253) 403-1000 *SIC* 8062 8093 8069

NORTHWEST HARDWOODS INC p 1059
820 A St Ste 500 98402
Tel (253) 568-6800 *SIC* 2426 5031

PACIFIC LUTHERAN UNIVERSITY INC p 1105
12180 Park Ave S 98447
Tel (253) 531-6900 *SIC* 8221

PORT OF TACOMA p 1162
1 Sitcum Way 98421
Tel (253) 383-5841 *SIC* 4491

SIMPSON TIMBER CO p 1325
917 E 11th St 98421
Tel (253) 779-6400 *SIC* 2421 2439

SOUND INPATIENT PHYSICIANS HOLDINGS LLC p 1342
1498 Pacific Ave Ste 400 98402
Tel (253) 682-1710 *SIC* 8011 6719

SOUND INPATIENT PHYSICIANS INC p 1342
1498 Pacific Ave Ste 400 98402
Tel (253) 682-1710 *SIC* 8011

ST ANDREWS ACQUISITION INC p 1364
9720 South Tacoma Way 98499
Tel (253) 584-2170 *SIC* 8322 8361

ST JOSEPH MEDICAL CENTER p 1368
1717 S J St 98405
Tel (253) 627-4101 *SIC* 8062

TACOMA COMMUNITY COLLEGE p 1421
6501 S 19th St Bldg 14 98466
Tel (253) 566-5058 *SIC* 8222 8351

TACOMA PUBLIC SCHOOLS p 1421
601 S 8th St 98405
Tel (253) 571-1000 *SIC* 8211

TORAY COMPOSITES (AMERICA) INC p 1461
19002 50th Ave E 98446
Tel (253) 846-1777 *SIC* 3624

▲ TRUEBLUE INC p 1486
1015 A St 98402
Tel (253) 383-9101 *SIC* 7363

UNIVERSITY OF PUGET SOUND p 1524
1500 N Warner St 98416
Tel (253) 879-3100 *SIC* 8221

US OIL TRADING LLC p 1532
3001 Marshall Ave 98421
Tel (253) 383-1651 *SIC* 5172

YOUNG MENS CHRISTIAN ASSOCIATION OF PIERCE AND KITSAP COUNTY p 1639
4717 S 19th St Ste 201 98405
Tel (253) 534-7800
SIC 8699 7991 7032 8322

TOLEDO, WA

TOLEDO SCHOOL DISTRICT 237 p 1459
130 N 5th St 98591
Tel (360) 864-6325 *SIC* 8211

TOPPENISH, WA

AB FOODS LLC p 9
201 Elmwood Rd 98948
Tel (509) 865-2121 *SIC* 5147

WASHINGTON BEEF LLC p 1577
201 Elmwood Rd 98948
Tel (509) 865-2121 *SIC* 2011

YAKIMA VALLEY FARM WORKERS CLINIC INC p 1634
518 W 1st Ave 98948
Tel (509) 865-5898
SIC 8011 8021 8093 1799

TUKWILA, WA

BOEING EMPLOYEES CREDIT UNION p 197
12770 Gateway Dr S 98168
Tel (206) 439-5700 *SIC* 6062 6061

CONTINENTAL MILLS INC p 363
18100 Andover Park W 98188
Tel (253) 872-8400 *SIC* 2045 2038

DOW HOTEL CO LLC p 453
16400 Southcenter Pkwy # 208 98188
Tel (206) 575-3600 *SIC* 7011

GENOA A QOL HEALTHCARE CO LLC p 604
18300 Cascade Ave S 98188
Tel (253) 218-0830 *SIC* 2834

GENOA HEALTHCARE LLC p 604
18300 Cascade Ave S # 251 98188
Tel (800) 519-1139 *SIC* 5912

HARNISH GROUP INC p 662
17035 W Valley Hwy 98188
Tel (425) 251-9800 *SIC* 5082 5013 5083

HARTUNG GLASS INDUSTRIES INC p 666
17830 W Valley Hwy 98188
Tel (425) 656-2626 *SIC* 5023

HOLADAY-PARKS-FABRICATORS INC p 700
4600 S 134th Pl 98168
Tel (206) 248-9700 *SIC* 1711

INNOVASIAN CUISINE ENTERPRISES INC p 744
18251 Cascade Ave S 98188
Tel (425) 251-3706 *SIC* 5149

L&L ENERGY INC p 834
130 Andover Park E # 200 98188
Tel (206) 264-8065 *SIC* 1241 1221 5052

MONEYTREE INC p 984
6720 Fort Dent Way # 230 98188
Tel (888) 516-6643 *SIC* 6099

MUSEUM OF FLIGHT FOUNDATION p 1002
9404 E Marginal Way S 98108
Tel (206) 764-5720 *SIC* 8412

N C MACHINERY CO p 1005
17025 W Valley Hwy 98188
Tel (425) 251-9800 *SIC* 5082 5013 5083

N C POWER SYSTEMS CO p 1005
17900 W Valley Hwy 98188
Tel (425) 251-5877 *SIC* 5013 5082 5083

PSF MECHANICAL INC p 1188
11621 E Marginal Way S 98168
Tel (206) 764-9663 *SIC* 1711 8711

RED DOT CORP p 1215
495 Andover Park E 98188
Tel (206) 151-3840 *SIC* 3714 3585

SAFEWORKS LLC p 1267
365 Upland Dr 98188
Tel (206) 575-6445
SIC 3536 3531 3446 5082

TRACTOR & EQUIPMENT CO p 1468
17035 W Valley Hwy 98188
Tel (425) 251-9800 *SIC* 5082

TULALIP, WA

TULALIP TRIBES OF WASHINGTON p 1491
2832 116th St Ne 98271
Tel (360) 716-4000 *SIC* 4841

TUMWATER, WA

DEPARTMENT OF CORRECTIONS WASHINGTON STATE p 430
7345 Linderson Way Sw 98501
Tel (360) 725-8213 *SIC* 9223

WASHINGTON STATE DEPARTMENT OF HEALTH p 1579
101 Israel Rd Se 98501
Tel (360) 236-4300 *SIC* 9431

WASHINGTON STATE DEPARTMENT OF LABOR AND INDUSTRIES p 1579
7273 Linderson Way Sw 98501
Tel (360) 902-5743 *SIC* 9311

UNION GAP, WA

G S LONG CO INC p 587
2517 Old Town Rd 98903
Tel (509) 575-8382 *SIC* 5191

VANCOUVER, WA

AHO CONSTRUCTION I INC p 37
5512 Ne 109th Ct Ste 101 98662
Tel (360) 254-0493 *SIC* 1531 1521

▲ BARRETT BUSINESS SERVICES INC p 157
8100 Ne Parkway Dr # 200 98662
Tel (360) 828-0700 *SIC* 7361 8742

CITY OF VANCOUVER p 319
415 W 6th St 98660
Tel (360) 619-1068 *SIC* 9121

COLUMBIA UNITED PROVIDERS INC p 342
19120 Se 34th St Ste 201 98683
Tel (360) 891-1520 *SIC* 6324

CONSOLIDATED METCO INC p 360
5701 Se Columbia Way 98661
Tel (360) 828-2599
SIC 3365 3363 3089 3714 3443 3312

CORE HEALTH & FITNESS LLC p 369
4400 Ne 77th Ave Ste 300 98662
Tel (360) 326-4090 *SIC* 5091

CORE INDUSTRIES LLC p 369
4400 Ne 77th Ave Ste 300 98662
Tel (360) 326-4090 *SIC* 5091

COUNTY OF CLARK p 377
1300 Franklin St 98660
Tel (360) 397-2232 *SIC* 9111

DOTSTER INC p 452
8100 Ne Parkway Dr # 300 98662
Tel (360) 883-5589 *SIC* 4813

ELECTRIC LIGHTWAVE COMMUNICATIONS INC p 484
18110 Se 34th St Bldg 1s 98683
Tel (360) 558-6900 *SIC* 7389 4813

ELECTRIC LIGHTWAVE HOLDINGS INC p 484
18110 Se 34th St 98683
Tel (360) 558-6900 *SIC* 4813

ELECTRIC LIGHTWAVE LLC p 484
18110 Se 34th St Bldg 1s 98683
Tel (360) 558-6900 *SIC* 4813

EMERALD PERFORMANCE MATERIALS LLC p 491
1499 Se Tech Center Pl 98683
Tel (330) 916-6700 *SIC* 2821

EMPRES FINANCIAL SERVICES LLC p 494
4601 Ne 77th Ave Ste 300 98662
Tel (360) 892-6628 *SIC* 8051

EVERGREEN HEALTHCARE INC p 514
4601 Ne 77th Ave Ste 300 98662
Tel (360) 892-6472
SIC 8051 6513 8059 8741

EVERGREEN PUBLIC SCHOOLS p 514
13501 Ne 28th St 98682
Tel (360) 604-4000 *SIC* 8211

GREENBERRY INDUSTRIAL LLC p 637
600 Se Maritime Ave # 190 98661
Tel (360) 567-0006
SIC 1711 1541 3443 3441

HANNAH MOTOR CO p 658
3400 Ne Auto Mall Dr 98662
Tel (360) 944-3424 *SIC* 5511

HOLLAND INC p 700
109 W 17th St 98660
Tel (360) 694-1521 *SIC* 8741

HOLLAND PARTNERS ROCK CREEK LANDING LLC p 700
1111 Main St Ste 700 98660
Tel (360) 694-7888 *SIC* 6531

HOLLAND RESIDENTIAL LLC p 700
1111 Main St Ste 700 98660
Tel (360) 694-7888 *SIC* 6513 8741

JERRY ERWIN ASSOCIATES INC p 783
12115 Ne 99th St Ste 1800 98682
Tel (800) 254-9442 *SIC* 6552 6531

▲ NAUTILUS INC p 1019
17750 Se 6th Way 98683
Tel (360) 859-2900 *SIC* 3949

NLIGHT INC p 1045
5408 Ne 88th St Ste E 98665
Tel (360) 566-4460 *SIC* 3674 3699

▲ NORTHWEST PIPE CO p 1060
5721 Se Columbia Way # 200 98661
Tel (360) 397-6250 *SIC* 3317 3443

PACIFIC BELLS LLC p 1104
111 W 39th St Ste A 98660
Tel (360) 694-7855 *SIC* 5812

PACIFIC NUTRITIONAL INC p 1105
6317 Ne 131st Ave Buildb 98682
Tel (360) 253-3197 *SIC* 5122 2099

PACIFIC POWER GROUP LLC p 1105
805 Broadway St Ste 700 98660
Tel (360) 887-7400
SIC 5088 3621 5063 3519 5084

▲ PAPA MURPHYS HOLDINGS INC p 1112
8000 Ne Parkway Dr # 350 98662
Tel (360) 260-7272 *SIC* 5812

PEACE HEALTH SOUTHWEST MEDICAL CENTER p 1125
602 Ne 92nd Ave Ste 120 98664
Tel (360) 514-2250 *SIC* 8062 7389

PEACEHEALTH p 1125
1115 Se 164th Ave 98683
Tel (360) 788-6841 *SIC* 8062 8011

PEACEHEALTH SOUTHWEST MEDICAL CENTER p 1125
400 Ne Mother Joseph Pl 98664
Tel (360) 514-2097 *SIC* 8099

PRESTIGE CARE INC p 1173
7700 Ne Parkway Dr # 300 98662
Tel (360) 735-7155 *SIC* 8051

PUBLIC UTILITY DISTRICT 1 OF CLARK COUNTY p 1190
1200 Fort Vancouver Way 98663
Tel (360) 992-3000 *SIC* 4911

SALMON LEGACY CREEK HOSPITAL p 1273
2211 Ne 139th St 98686
Tel (360) 487-1000 *SIC* 8062

SHIN-ETSU HANDOTAI AMERICA INC p 1316
4111 Ne 112th Ave 98682
Tel (360) 883-7000 *SIC* 3674 5065

SOUTHWEST WASHINGTON HEALTH SYSTEM p 1352
400 Ne Mother Joseph Pl 98664
Tel (360) 514-2000 *SIC* 8741

SOUTHWEST WASHINGTON MEDICAL CENTER p 1352
400 Ne Mother Joseph Pl 98664
Tel (360) 514-1900 *SIC* 8011

STEIN DISTRIBUTING INC p 1385
5408 Ne 88th St Ste B101 98665
Tel (360) 693-8251 *SIC* 5181 5182

SUNLIGHT SUPPLY INC p 1403
5408 Ne 88th St Ste A101 98665
Tel (360) 883-8846 *SIC* 3524 5191

SW WASHINGTON HOSPITAL INC p 1411
400 Ne Mother Joseph Pl 98664
Tel (360) 514-2000 *SIC* 8062

VANCOUVER CLINICAL SERVICES PC p 1543
700 Ne 87th Ave 98664
Tel (360) 397-1500 *SIC* 8011

VANCOUVER PUBLIC SCHOOLS p 1543
2901 Falk Rd 98661
Tel (360) 313-1000 *SIC* 8211

WELLONS INC p 1589
2525 W Firestone Ln 98660
Tel (360) 750-3500 *SIC* 3559 3443

WALLA WALLA, WA

■ BANNER BANK p 152
10 S 1st Ave 99362
Tel (800) 272-9933 *SIC* 6022

▲ BANNER CORP p 152
10 S 1st Ave 99362
Tel (509) 527-3636 *SIC* 6022 6036

COCA COLA BOTTLING CO (INC) p 333
155 Avery St 99362
Tel (509) 529-0753 *SIC* 2086

▲ KEYTECHNOLOGY INC p 814
150 Avery St 99362
Tel (509) 529-2161 *SIC* 3556 2834

PROVIDENCE ST MARY MEDICAL CENTER p 1186
401 W Poplar St 99362
Tel (509) 525-3320 *SIC* 8062

WATERBROOK WINERY INC p 1581
10518 W Highway 12 99362
Tel (509) 522-1262 *SIC* 5182

WHITMAN COLLEGE p 1607
345 Boyer Ave 99362
Tel (509) 527-5111 *SIC* 8221

WALLULA, WA

■ BOISE WHITE PAPER LLC p 198
31831 W Hwy 12 99363
Tel (509) 545-3318 *SIC* 2621

WENATCHEE, WA

CENTRAL WASHINGTON HEALTH SERVICES ASSOCIATION p 281
1201 S Miller St 98801
Tel (509) 662-1511 *SIC* 8062

CONFLUENCE HEALTH p 356
820 N Chelan Ave 98801
Tel (509) 663-8711 *SIC* 8011

GLENN DISTRIBUTOR INC p 615
1301 N Wenatchee Ave 98801
Tel (509) 663-7173 *SIC* 5172 5541 7359

GOODFELLOW BROS INC p 624
1407 Walla Walla Ave 98801
Tel (509) 667-9095 *SIC* 1611

ONEONTA TRADING CORP p 1088
1 Oneonta Dr 98801
Tel (509) 663-2631 *SIC* 5148

PUBLIC UTILITY DISTRICT NO 1 OF CHELAN COUNTY p 1190
327 N Wenatchee Ave 98801
Tel (509) 663-8121 *SIC* 4911

STEMILT GROWERS LLC p 1385
3135 Warehouse Rd 98801
Tel (509) 663-1451 *SIC* 0723

WENATCHEE PUBLIC SCHOOLS p 1591
235 Sunset Ave 98801
Tel (509) 663-8161 *SIC* 8211

WENATCHEE VALLEY HOSPITAL p 1591
820 N Chelan Ave 98801
Tel (509) 663-8711 *SIC* 8062

WENATCHEE VALLEY MEDICAL GROUP PS p 1591
820 N Chelan Ave 98801
Tel (509) 663-8711 *SIC* 8011

WOODINVILLE, WA

BENSUSSEN DEUTSCH & ASSOCIATES LLC p 173
15525 Woodinville Rdmnd 98072
Tel (425) 492-6111 *SIC* 5199 5136 5137

■ CABLECOM LLC p 235
8602 Maltby Rd 98072
Tel (360) 668-1300 *SIC* 1623 1731

HOMETOWN ENTERPRISES INC p 704
18815 139th Ave Ne Ste C 98072
Tel (425) 486-6336 *SIC* 5812

HOS BROTHERS CONSTRUCTION INC p 708
7733 W Bostian Rd 98072
Tel (425) 481-5569 *SIC* 1611 1629

LOUD TECHNOLOGIES INC p 879
16220 Wood Red Rd Ne 98072
Tel (425) 892-6500 *SIC* 3651

MATHEUS LUMBER CO INC p 920
15800 Woodinville Redmond 98072
Tel (206) 284-7500 *SIC* 5031

MOWAT CONSTRUCTION CO p 995
20210 142nd Ave Ne 98072
Tel (425) 398-0205 *SIC* 1611

NATIONAL INDUSTRIAL CONCEPTS INC p 1013
23518 63rd Ave Se 98072
Tel (425) 489-4300 *SIC* 3444

NORTHWEST RESTAURANTS INC p 1060
18815 139th Ave Ne Ste C 98072
Tel (425) 486-6336 *SIC* 5812

PRECOR INC p 1169
20031 142nd Ave Ne 98072
Tel (425) 486-9292 *SIC* 3949

WOODLAND, WA

COLUMBIA FRUIT LLC p 340
2530 Dike Rd 98674
Tel (360) 225-9575 *SIC* 5142 5411

USNR LLC p 1535
1981 Schurman Way 98674
Tel (360) 225-8267
SIC 3585 3553 3625 1221 5084

YAKIMA, WA

COUNTY OF YAKIMA p 383
128 N 2nd St Rm 408 98901
Tel (509) 574-1500 *SIC* 9111

DOLSEN COMPANIES p 448
301 N 3rd St 98901
Tel (509) 248-2831
SIC 0241 0211 2086 7359

HOLTZINGER FRUIT CO INC p 702
1312 N 6th Ave 98902
Tel (509) 457-5115 *SIC* 5148 4222

HOPUNION LLC p 706
203 Division St 98902
Tel (509) 453-4792 *SIC* 5181

MICHELSEN PACKAGING CO OF CALIFORNIA p 960
202 N 2nd Ave 98902
Tel (509) 248-6270 *SIC* 5113 2653

NOEL CORP p 1046
1001 S 1st St 98901
Tel (509) 248-4545
SIC 2086 7389 4212 6512 4225 5962

UNDERWOOD FRUIT AND WAREHOUSE CO LLC p 1502
401 N 1st Ave 98902
Tel (509) 457-6177 *SIC* 5149 2033

VALLEY ROZ ORCHARDS INC p 1541
10 E Mead Ave 98903
Tel (509) 457-4153 *SIC* 0175 5431

WASHINGTON FRUIT & PRODUCE CO p 1578
1111 River Rd 98902
Tel (509) 457-6177 *SIC* 5148 0723

WILKINSON CORP p 1609
212 N Naches Ave 98901
Tel (866) 914-2403 *SIC* 6552

■ YAKIMA HMA LLC p 1634
110 S 9th Ave 98902
Tel (509) 575-5000 *SIC* 8062

YAKIMA SCHOOL DISTRICT p 1634
104 N 4th Ave 98902
Tel (509) 573-7000 *SIC* 8211

YAKIMA VALLEY MEMORIAL HOSPITAL ASSOCIATION INC p 1634
2811 Tieton Dr 98902
Tel (509) 249-5129 *SIC* 8062 8082

WEST VIRGINIA

ALLOY, WV

WVA MANUFACTURING LLC p 1628
Rr 60 25002
Tel (304) 779-3200 *SIC* 3339 2819

BECKLEY, WV

JEAN NELL ENTERPRISES INC p 781
1 Nell Jean Sq 19 25801
Tel (304) 253-0200 *SIC* 5941 5082 5091

LITTLE GENERAL STORE INC p 871
4036 Robert C. Byrd Dr 25801
Tel (304) 253-9592 *SIC* 5411

RALEIGH COUNTY BOARD OF EDUCATION p 1206
105 Adair St 25801
Tel (304) 256-4500 *SIC* 8211 9111

RALEIGH COUNTY SCHOOL DISTRICT p 1206
105 Adair St 25801
Tel (304) 256-4500 *SIC* 8211

■ RALEIGH GENERAL HOSPITAL p 1206
1710 Harper Rd 25801
Tel (304) 256-4100 *SIC* 8062

VECELLIO & GROGAN INC p 1546
2251 Robert C Byrd Dr 25801
Tel (304) 252-6575 *SIC* 1611 1622 1629

BELLE, WV

PETROLEUM PRODUCTS LLC p 1139
500 River East Dr Ste 1 25015
Tel (304) 204-1720 *SIC* 5171

BLUEFIELD, WV

HEALTH SERVICES OF VIRGINIAS INC p 676
500 Cherry St 24701
Tel (304) 327-1100 *SIC* 8062

RISH EQUIPMENT CO p 1236
6384 Airport Rd 24701
Tel (304) 327-5124 *SIC* 5082 7699

BRIDGEPORT, WV

■ PRATT & WHITNEY ENGINE SERVICES INC p 1167
1525 Midway Park Rd 26330
Tel (860) 565-4321 *SIC* 7699 3724 4581

UNITED HOSPITAL CENTER INC p 1509
327 Medical Park Dr 26330
Tel (681) 342-1000 *SIC* 8062

BUCKHANNON, WV

JF ALLEN CO INC p 785
U.S 33 W Red Rock Rd 26201
Tel (304) 472-8890
SIC 3271 1611 3273 3281 2951

BUFFALO, WV

TOYOTA MOTOR MANUFACTURING WEST VIRGINIA INC p 1467
1 Sugar Maple Ln 25033
Tel (304) 937-7000 *SIC* 3714 3519

CHARLES TOWN, WV

▲ AMERICAN PUBLIC EDUCATION INC p 78
111 W Congress St 25414
Tel (304) 724-3700 *SIC* 8221

CHARLESTON, WV

AMFM INC p 85
240 Capitol St Ste 500 25301
Tel (304) 344-1623 *SIC* 8741 8742

APPALACHIAN TIRE PRODUCTS INC p 98
2907 4th Ave 25387
Tel (304) 744-9473
SIC 5014 5531 5013 7534

BRICKSTREET MUTUAL INSURANCE CO p 211
400 Quarrier St 25301
Tel (304) 941-1000 *SIC* 6321 6331

CAMC HEALTH SYSTEM INC p 244
501 Morris St 25301
Tel (304) 388-5432 *SIC* 8062

CAPITAL AREA SERVICE CO INC p 249
200 Kanawha Blvd E 25301
Tel (304) 346-3800 *SIC* 6324 6321

CHARLESTON AREA MEDICAL CENTER INC p 289
501 Morris St 25301
Tel (304) 348-5432 *SIC* 8062

CHARLESTON HOSPITAL INC p 290
333 Laidley St 25301
Tel (304) 347-6500 *SIC* 8062

▲ CITY HOLDING CO p 312
25 Gatewater Rd 25313
Tel (304) 769-1100 *SIC* 6021

■ CITY NATIONAL BANK OF WEST VIRGINIA p 312
3601 Maccorkle Ave Se 25304
Tel (304) 926-3301 *SIC* 6021

EASTERN AMERICAN ENERGY CORP *p* 471
500 Corporate Lndg 25311
Tel (304) 925-6100
SIC 1311 4922 5172 1321

EXECUTIVE OFFICE STATE OF WEST VIRGINIA *p* 518
1900 Kanawha Blvd E 25305
Tel (304) 558-2000 *SIC* 9111

■ FRONTIER WEST VIRGINIA INC *p* 581
1500 Maccorkle Ave Se 25396
Tel (304) 344-6409 *SIC* 4813 8721

HERBERT J THOMAS MEMORIAL HOSPITAL ASSOCIATION *p* 685
4605 Maccorkle Ave Sw 25309
Tel (304) 766-3600 *SIC* 8062

JUDICIARY COURTS OF STATE OF WEST VIRGINIA *p* 797
State Capital Bldg E100 25305
Tel (304) 558-0145 *SIC* 9211

KANAWHA COUNTY BOARD OF EDUCATION *p* 802
200 Elizabeth St 25311
Tel (304) 348-7770 *SIC* 8211

KANAWHA COUNTY SCHOOLS *p* 802
200 Elizabeth St 25311
Tel (304) 348-7770 *SIC* 8211

MOUNTAINEER GAS CO *p* 994
501 56th St Se 25304
Tel (888) 420-4427 *SIC* 4924

ST FRANCIS HOSPITAL *p* 1366
333 Laidley St 25301
Tel (304) 347-6860 *SIC* 8742

STATE OF WEST VIRGINIA *p* 1382
1900 Kanawha Blvd E # 714 25305
Tel (304) 558-2000 *SIC* 9111

▲ UNITED BANKSHARES INC *p* 1506
500 Virginia St E 25301
Tel (304) 424-8800 *SIC* 6022

■ VIRGINIA WEST AMERICAN WATER CO *p* 1560
1600 Pennsylvania Ave 25302
Tel (304) 353-6300 *SIC* 4941

■ WELLS FARGO INSURANCE SERVICES OF WEST VIRGINIA INC *p* 1591
1 Hillcrest Dr E 25311
Tel (304) 346-0611 *SIC* 6411

WEST VIRGINIA DEPARTMENT OF EDUCATION AND ARTS *p* 1596
1900 Kanawha Blvd E # 358 25305
Tel (304) 558-2440 *SIC* 9411

WEST VIRGINIA DEPARTMENT OF HEALTH AND HUMAN RESOURCES *p* 1596
1 Davis Sq Ste 100e 25301
Tel (304) 558-0684 *SIC* 9431 9441

WEST VIRGINIA DEPARTMENT OF MILITARY AFFAIRS AND PUBLIC SAFETY *p* 1596
1900 Kanawha Blvd E Rm 1 25305
Tel (304) 558-8045 *SIC* 9711 9221 9229

WEST VIRGINIA DEPARTMENT OF TRANSPORTATION *p* 1596
1900 Kanawha Blvd E # 109 25305
Tel (304) 558-0330 *SIC* 9621

CHESTER, WV

■ MTR GAMING GROUP INC *p* 998
Hc 2 Box S 26034
Tel (304) 387-8000 *SIC* 7011 7948

■ PARK MOUNTAINEER INC *p* 1115
Hc 2 26034
Tel (304) 387-8300
SIC 7999 7011 7389 6512

CLARKSBURG, WV

■ BIOMETRICS IDENTITY MANAGEMENT AGENCY *p* 184
340 Washington Ave 26301
Tel (304) 326-3000 *SIC* 9711

HARRISON COUNTY SCHOOL DISTRICT *p* 664
408 E B Saunders Way 26301
Tel (304) 326-7300 *SIC* 8211 9111

CROSS LANES, WV

CITY NATIONAL BANK OF WEST VIRGINIA *p* 312
25 Gatewater Rd 25313
Tel (304) 769-1189 *SIC* 6021

DRENNEN, WV

ALEX ENERGY INC *p* 48
2 Jerry Fork Rd 26667
Tel (304) 872-5065 *SIC* 1241

ELEANOR, WV

DIAMOND ELECTRIC MFG CORP *p* 436
Hc 62 25070
Tel (304) 586-0070 *SIC* 3694

FAIRMONT, WV

EXTREME PLASTICS PLUS INC *p* 521
360 Epic Circle Dr 26554
Tel (304) 534-3600 *SIC* 3083

MARION COUNTY BOARD OF EDUCATION *p* 907
200 Gaston Ave 26554
Tel (304) 367-2100 *SIC* 8211

MARION COUNTY SCHOOL TRANSPORTATION *p* 907
614 Virginia Ave 26554
Tel (304) 367-2161 *SIC* 4151

MARION COUNTY SCHOOLS *p* 907
200 Gaston Ave 26554
Tel (304) 367-2100 *SIC* 8211

■ MONONGAHELA POWER CO *p* 984
1310 Fairmont Ave 26554
Tel (800) 686-0022 *SIC* 4911

▲ MVB FINANCIAL CORP *p* 1003
301 Virginia Ave 26554
Tel (304) 363-4800 *SIC* 6022

FAYETTEVILLE, WV

FAYETTE COUNTY SCHOOLS *p* 532
111 Fayette Ave 25840
Tel (304) 574-1176 *SIC* 9111 8211

FOLLANSBEE, WV

WHEELING-NISSHIN INC *p* 1605
400 Penn St 26037
Tel (304) 527-2800 *SIC* 3312

FRIENDLY, WV

ALERIS RECYCLING BENS RUN LLC *p* 48
4203 S State Route 2 26146
Tel (304) 652-1415 *SIC* 3355

GASSAWAY, WV

GO-MART INC *p* 619
915 Riverside Dr 26624
Tel (304) 364-8000 *SIC* 5411 5541

GILBERT, WV

INTERNATIONAL INDUSTRIES INC *p* 755
210 Larry Joe Harless Dr 25621
Tel (304) 664-3227 *SIC* 6211

HAMLIN, WV

LINCOLN COUNTY SCHOOLS *p* 866
10 Marland Ave 25523
Tel (304) 824-3033 *SIC* 8211

HUNTINGTON, WV

CABELL COUNTY BOARD-EDUCATION *p* 235
2850 5th Ave 25702
Tel (304) 528-5000 *SIC* 8211

CABELL COUNTY SCHOOL DIST INC *p* 235
2850 5th Ave 25702
Tel (304) 528-5000 *SIC* 8211

DIRECTOR OF VOLUNTEERS SERVICE *p* 442
2900 1st Ave 25702
Tel (304) 526-1400 *SIC* 8999

▲ ENERGY SERVICES OF AMERICA CORP *p* 498
75 3rd Ave W 25701
Tel (304) 522-3868 *SIC* 1623 1731

FORTHS FOODS INC *p* 569
3090 Woodville Dr 25701
Tel (304) 525-3293 *SIC* 5141 5411

■ HUNTINGTON ALLOYS CORP *p* 719
3200 Riverside Dr 25705
Tel (304) 526-5100 *SIC* 3356

HUNTINGTON CABELL HOSPITAL INC *p* 720
1340 Hal Greer Blvd 25701
Tel (304) 526-2000 *SIC* 8062

J H FLETCHER & CO *p* 771
402 High St 25705
Tel (304) 525-7811
SIC 5082 3532 3743 3546 3541

MARSHALL UNIVERSITY *p* 911
1 John Marshall Dr 25755
Tel (304) 696-2385 *SIC* 8221

ST MARYS MEDICAL CENTER *p* 1371
2900 1st Ave 25702
Tel (304) 526-1234 *SIC* 8062

STATE ELECTRIC SUPPLY CO *p* 1380
2010 2nd Ave 25703
Tel (304) 523-7491 *SIC* 5063 3357

STATE ELECTRIC SUPPLY CO *p* 1380
2010 2nd Ave 25703
Tel (304) 523-7491 *SIC* 5063 3357

■ STEEL OF WEST VIRGINIA INC *p* 1384
17th St & 2nd Ave 25703
Tel (304) 696-8200 *SIC* 3441

■ SWVA INC *p* 1413
17th St & Second Ave 25703
Tel (304) 696-8200 *SIC* 3441 3312

UNIVERSITY PHYSICIANS & SURGEONS INC *p* 1527
1600 Med Ctr Dr Ste 1400 25701
Tel (304) 691-1630 *SIC* 8011

LEWISBURG, WV

■ 331 HOLT LANE OPERATIONS LLC *p* 2
331 Holt Ln 24901
Tel (304) 645-4453 *SIC* 8051

LOGAN, WV

LOGAN COUNTY SCHOOLS *p* 874
506 Holly Ave 25601
Tel (304) 792-2060 *SIC* 8211

■ LOGAN GENERAL HOSPITAL LLC *p* 874
20 Hospital Dr 25601
Tel (304) 831-1101 *SIC* 8011

MADISON, WV

SENECA COAL RESOURCES LLC *p* 1303
Shaffer Rd Exit 25130
Tel (304) 369-8316 *SIC* 1241

MARTINSBURG, WV

BERKELEY COUNTY SCHOOLS *p* 175
401 S Queen St 25401
Tel (304) 267-3500 *SIC* 8211

CITY HOSPITAL INC *p* 312
2500 Hospital Dr 25401
Tel (304) 264-1000 *SIC* 8062

CITY HOSPITAL INC *p* 312
2000 Foundation Way # 2310 25401
Tel (304) 264-1244 *SIC* 8062

R M ROACH & SONS INC *p* 1202
333 E John St 25401
Tel (304) 263-3329 *SIC* 5541 5172

MILLWOOD, WV

STAR PLASTICS INC *p* 1378
326 Jack Burlingame Dr 25262
Tel (304) 273-0352 *SIC* 5162 2821

MORGANTOWN, WV

AMCP RETAIL ACQUISITION CORP *p* 66
55 Scott Ave 26508
Tel (304) 292-6965 *SIC* 5611 5621

AMCP RETAIL HOLDINGS CORP *p* 66
55 Scott Ave 26508
Tel (304) 292-6965 *SIC* 5621 5611

BRUCETON FARM SERVICE INC *p* 220
1768 Mileground Rd 26505
Tel (304) 291-6980
SIC 5411 5172 5999 5983 5812 2048

GABRIEL BROTHERS INC *p* 588
55 Scott Ave 26508
Tel (304) 292-6965 *SIC* 5651

GREER INDUSTRIES INC *p* 639
570 Canyon Rd 26508
Tel (304) 296-2549
SIC 3316 3272 2951 1422 3274 1446

MONONGALIA COUNTY BOARD OF EDUCATION *p* 984
13 S High St 26501
Tel (304) 291-9210 *SIC* 8211

MONONGALIA COUNTY GENERAL HOSPITAL CO *p* 984
1200 J D Anderson Dr 26505
Tel (304) 598-1200 *SIC* 8062

MONONGALIA HEALTH SYSTEM INC *p* 984
1200 J D Anderson Dr 26505
Tel (304) 598-1200 *SIC* 8062 8011

MYLAN PHARMACEUTICALS INC *p* 1004
781 Chestnut Ridge Rd 26505
Tel (304) 599-2595 *SIC* 2834

MYLAN SPECIALTY LP *p* 1004
781 Chestnut Ridge Rd 26505
Tel (304) 554-4519 *SIC* 2834 8731

SWANSON INDUSTRIES INC *p* 1411
2608 Smithtown Rd 26508
Tel (304) 292-0021
SIC 3593 3471 7629 5084

URGENT CARE HOLDINGS INC *p* 1530
1751 Earl L Core Rd 26505
Tel (304) 225-2500 *SIC* 8011

VIRGINIA WEST UNIVERSITY FOUNDATION INC *p* 1560
1 Waterfront Pl Fl 7 26501
Tel (304) 293-3708 *SIC* 6732

VIRGINIA WEST UNIVERSITY HOSPITALS INC *p* 1560
1 Medical Center Dr 26506
Tel (304) 598-4000 *SIC* 8062

VIRGINIA WEST UNIVERSITY MEDICAL CORP *p* 1560
1 Stadium Dr 26506
Tel (304) 598-4200 *SIC* 8011

WEST VIRGINIA UNITED HEALTH SYSTEM INC *p* 1596
1 Medical Center Dr 26506
Tel (304) 598-4000 *SIC* 8741

WEST VIRGINIA UNIVERSITY *p* 1596
103 Stewart Hl 26506
Tel (304) 293-2545 *SIC* 8221

WEST VIRGINIA UNIVERSITY RESEARCH CORP *p* 1596
886 Chestnut Ridge Rd 26505
Tel (304) 293-7398 *SIC* 8733

MOUNT HOPE, WV

RALEIGH MINE AND INDUSTRIAL SUPPLY INC *p* 1206
1500 Mill Creek Rd 25880
Tel (304) 877-5503
SIC 5085 1629 3532 3441

NEWELL, WV

BELLOFRAM CORP *p* 171
8019 Ohio River Blvd 26050
Tel (304) 387-1200 *SIC* 3612 3829 3625

HOMER LAUGHLIN CHINA CO *p* 704
672 Fiesta Dr 26050
Tel (304) 387-1300 *SIC* 3262 5719

PARKERSBURG, WV

BUREAU OF THE PUBLIC DEBT *p* 226
200 3rd St 5f 26106
Tel (304) 480-6514 *SIC* 9311

CAMDEN CLARK MEDICAL CENTER - ST JOSEPH CAMPUS *p* 244
800 Garfield Ave 26101
Tel (304) 424-4111 *SIC* 8062

CAMDEN-CLARK MEMORIAL HOSPITAL CORP *p* 245
800 Garfield Ave 26101
Tel (304) 424-2111 *SIC* 8062

HIGHMARK BLUE CROSS BLUE SHIELD WEST VIRGINIA *p* 692
614 Market St 26101
Tel (304) 424-7700 *SIC* 6321

SIMONTON BUILDING PRODUCTS INC *p* 1325
5300 Briscoe Rd 26105
Tel (304) 659-2851 *SIC* 3089 3442 3231

TEKNETIX INC *p* 1433
2501 Garfield Ave 26101
Tel (304) 489-3600 *SIC* 3672 7371

■ UNITED BANK INC *p* 1506
514 Market St 26101
Tel (304) 424-8800 *SIC* 6022

■ UNITED BROKERAGE SERVICES INC *p* 1506
514 Market St 26101
Tel (304) 424-8781 *SIC* 6211

WOOD COUNTY SCHOOLS *p* 1622
1210 13th St 26101
Tel (304) 420-9663 *SIC* 8211

WOODCRAFT SUPPLY LLC *p* 1622
1177 Rosemar Rd 26105
Tel (304) 422-5412 *SIC* 5961 5251

PETERSBURG, WV

ALLEGHENY WOOD PRODUCTS INC *p* 52
240 Airport Rd 26847
Tel (304) 257-1082 *SIC* 2421

POINT PLEASANT, WV

FRUTH INC *p* 582
4016 Ohio River Rd 25550
Tel (304) 675-1612 *SIC* 5912

PRINCETON, WV

EXTERIOR SERVICES LLC *p* 521
209 Anderson Dr 24739
Tel (304) 487-1503 *SIC* 1611

MERCER COUNTY BOARD OF EDUCATION *p* 944
1403 Honaker Ave 24740
Tel (304) 487-1551 *SIC* 8211

MERCER COUNTY PUBLIC SCHOOLS *p* 944
1403 Honaker Ave 24740
Tel (304) 487-1551 *SIC* 8211

PRINCETON COMMUNITY HOSPITAL ASSOCIATION INC *p* 1177
122 12th St 24740
Tel (304) 487-7000 *SIC* 8062

RAVENSWOOD, WV

■ CONSTELLIUM ROLLED PRODUCTS RAVENSWOOD LLC *p* 361
859 Century Rd 26164
Tel (304) 273-7000 *SIC* 3353

SDR PLASTICS INC *p* 1295
1 Plastics Ave 26164
Tel (304) 273-5326 *SIC* 5093

RIPLEY, WV

JACKSON COUNTY SCHOOLS *p* 773
1 School St 25271
Tel (304) 372-7300 *SIC* 8211

SAINT ALBANS, WV

■ ICG LLC *p* 727
114 Smiley Dr 25177
Tel (304) 760-2400 *SIC* 1241

■ INTERNATIONAL COAL GROUP INC *p* 754
114 Smiley Dr 25177
Tel (304) 760-2400 *SIC* 1222 1221

MOORES SERVICE CENTER LLC *p* 987
82 Winfield Rd 25177
Tel (304) 722-1175 *SIC* 7538

ORDERS CONSTRUCTION CO INC *p* 1093
501 6th Ave 25177
Tel (304) 722-4237 *SIC* 1622 1611

SAINT MARYS, WV

SIMEX INC *p* 1324
181 Pleasant Indus Ctr 26170
Tel (304) 665-1104 *SIC* 5039 2431

SISSONVILLE, WV

NGK SPARK PLUGS (USA) INC *p* 1041
1 Ngk Dr 25320
Tel (304) 988-0060 *SIC* 5013 3694

SLATYFORK, WV

SNOWSHOE MOUNTAIN INC *p* 1336
10 Snowshoe Dr 26291
Tel (304) 572-5601
SIC 8741 7011 5813 5812

SOUTH CHARLESTON, WV

GESTAMP WEST VIRGINIA LLC p 609
3100 Maccorkle Ave Sw 25303
Tel (304) 744-4601 *SIC* 3469

LOVED ONES IN HOME CARE LLC p 881
144 7th Ave 25303
Tel (304) 744-4081 *SIC* 8082

THOMAS HEALTH SYSTEM INC p 1448
4605 Maccorkle Ave Sw 25309
Tel (304) 347-6500 *SIC* 8741

THOMAS HJ MEMORIAL HOSPITAL INC p 1448
4605 Maccorkle Ave Sw 25309
Tel (304) 766-3697 *SIC* 8062

WAYNE, WV

WAYNE COUNTY SCHOOLS p 1584
212 N Court St 25570
Tel (304) 272-5116 *SIC* 8211

WEIRTON, WV

ARCELORMITTAL WEIRTON INC p 104
100 Pennsylvania Ave 26062
Tel (304) 797-2000 *SIC* 3316

CORE METALS GROUP LLC p 369
324 1/2 Penco Rd 26062
Tel (304) 914-4360 *SIC* 5051

WEIRTON MEDICAL CENTER INC p 1588
601 Colliers Way 26062
Tel (304) 797-6000 *SIC* 8062 8051

WEIRTON MEDICAL CORP p 1588
601 Colliers Way 26062
Tel (304) 797-6000 *SIC* 8062

WEIRTON STEEL CORP p 1588
400 Three Springs Dr 26062
Tel (304) 797-2000 *SIC* 3312 3316

WHEELING, WV

FITZ VOGT & ASSOCIATES LTD p 553
21 Armory Dr Ste L-1 26003
Tel (603) 644-0117 *SIC* 5812 8742 7349

KALKREUTH ROOFING & SHEET METAL INC p 801
53 14th St Ste 100 26003
Tel (304) 232-8540
SIC 1761 3446 3444 3441

OGDEN NEWSPAPERS INC p 1076
1500 Main St 26003
Tel (304) 233-0100
SIC 2711 2754 2741 2791 2752

OGLEBAY RESORT CONFERENCE CENTER p 1076
Rr 88 Box N 26003
Tel (304) 243-4063 *SIC* 7011 7992 5812

OHIO VALLEY HEALTH SERVICES AND EDUCATION CORP p 1078
2000 Eoff St 26003
Tel (304) 234-8174 *SIC* 8741 8062 8011

OHIO VALLEY MEDICAL CENTER INC p 1078
2000 Eoff St 26003
Tel (304) 234-0123 *SIC* 8062 8011

RG STEEL WHEELING STEEL GROUP LLC p 1231
1134 Market St 26003
Tel (304) 234-2400 *SIC* 3312 3444

SLEDD CO CHAS M p 1331
100 E Cove Ave 26003
Tel (800) 333-0374 *SIC* 5194 5142 5149

TRI-STATE PETROLEUM CORP p 1478
2627 Vance Ave 26003
Tel (304) 277-3232 *SIC* 5171

■ WESBANCO BANK INC p 1593
1 Bank Plz 26003
Tel (304) 234-9000 *SIC* 6022

▲ WESBANCO INC p 1593
2100 National Rd 26003
Tel (304) 234-9000 *SIC* 6021

WHEELING HOSPITAL INC p 1605
1 Medical Park 26003
Tel (304) 243-3000 *SIC* 8062 8011

WHEELING ISLAND GAMING INC p 1605
1 S Stone St 26003
Tel (304) 232-5050 *SIC* 7948 7011 5813

WHT SPHR SPGS, WV

GREENBRIER HOTEL CORP p 637
300 W Main St 24986
Tel (304) 536-1110 *SIC* 7011

JUSTICE FAMILY GROUP LLC p 797
101 Main St W 24986
Tel (304) 252-1074 *SIC* 8741

WINFIELD, WV

INNOVATIVE MATTRESS SOLUTIONS LLC p 745
11060 Winfield Rd 25213
Tel (304) 586-2863 *SIC* 8741

WISCONSIN

ABBOTSFORD, WI

ABBYLAND FOODS INC p 10
502 E Linden St 54405
Tel (715) 223-6386 *SIC* 2013 2011

ADAMS, WI

ALLIED COOPERATIVE p 56
540 S Main St 53910
Tel (608) 339-3394 *SIC* 5191 5171 5251

AMHERST, WI

H O WOLDING INC p 650
9642 Western Way 54406
Tel (715) 824-5513 *SIC* 4213

ANTIGO, WI

LANGLADE HOSPITAL - HOTEL DIEU OF ST JOSEPH OF ANTIGO WISCONSIN p 844
112 E 5th Ave 54409
Tel (715) 623-2331 *SIC* 8062

VOLM COMPANIES INC p 1564
1804 Edison St 54409
Tel (715) 627-4826 *SIC* 5113 5199 3565

APPLETON, WI

AGROPUR INC p 36
3500 E Destination Dr # 200 54915
Tel (920) 944-0990 *SIC* 2022

AIR WISCONSIN AIRLINES CORP p 39
W6390 Challenger Dr # 203 54914
Tel (920) 739-5123 *SIC* 4512

APPLETON AREA SCHOOL DISTRICT p 99
122 E College Ave Ste 1a 54911
Tel (920) 832-6161 *SIC* 8211

APPLETON MEDICAL CENTER INC p 99
1818 N Meade St 54911
Tel (920) 731-4101 *SIC* 8062

APPVION INC p 100
825 E Wisconsin Ave 54911
Tel (920) 734-9841 *SIC* 2621 2754

BOLDT CO p 198
2525 N Roemer Rd 54911
Tel (920) 739-6321 *SIC* 1542

BOLDT GROUP INC p 198
2525 N Roemer Rd 54911
Tel (920) 739-7800 *SIC* 1542

CLARK THEDA MEDICAL CENTER p 322
5320 W Michaels Dr 54913
Tel (920) 735-7650 *SIC* 8011

COUNTY OF OUTAGAMIE p 380
410 S Walnut St 54911
Tel (920) 832-1684 *SIC* 9111

FLEET WHOLESALE SUPPLY CO LLC p 555
3035 W Wisconsin Ave 54914
Tel (920) 734-8231
SIC 5191 5331 5531 5211 5541

GREAT NORTHERN CORP p 634
395 Stroebe Rd 54914
Tel (920) 739-3671 *SIC* 2653 5199 2671

INDEPENDENT PROCUREMENT ALLIANCE PROGRAM LLC p 737
1650 Tri Park Way Ste B 54914
Tel (920) 832-1100 *SIC* 5143

■ JANSPORT INC p 777
N850 County Road Cb 54914
Tel (920) 734-5708
SIC 3949 3161 2339 2329 2321

MATERIAL LOGISTICS & SERVICES LLC p 919
1160 N Mayflower Dr 54913
Tel (920) 830-5000 *SIC* 4225

MCC INC p 926
2600 N Roemer Rd 54911
Tel (920) 749-3360 *SIC* 3273 1442 1611

■ MILLER ELECTRIC MFG CO p 970
1635 W Spencer St 54914
Tel (920) 734-9821 *SIC* 3548 3621

PACON CORP p 1107
2525 N Casaloma Dr 54913
Tel (920) 830-5050 *SIC* 2679

PAPERWEIGHT DEVELOPMENT CORP p 1112
825 E Wisconsin Ave 54911
Tel (920) 734-9841 *SIC* 2671

■ PIERCE MANUFACTURING INC p 1147
2600 American Dr 54914
Tel (920) 832-3000 *SIC* 3711

PROGRESSIVE CONVERTING INC p 1181
2430 E Glendale Ave 54911
Tel (800) 637-7310 *SIC* 2679

REYNOLDS PRESTO PRODUCTS INC p 1231
670 N Perkins St 54914
Tel (800) 558-3525 *SIC* 2671 2673 3842

RICE HEALTH CARE FACILITIES OF WISCONSIN INC p 1232
1726 N Ballard Rd Ste 2 54911
Tel (920) 991-9072 *SIC* 8051

SECURA INSURANCE A MUTUAL CO (INC) p 1298
2401 S Memorial Dr 54915
Tel (920) 739-3161 *SIC* 6331

ST ELIZABETH HOSPITAL INC p 1366
1506 S Oneida St 54915
Tel (920) 738-2000 *SIC* 8062

THEDACARE INC p 1446
122 E College Ave Ste 2a 54911
Tel (920) 735-5560 *SIC* 8062

US VENTURE INC p 1533
425 Better Way 54915
Tel (920) 739-6101 *SIC* 5171 5014 5013

VALLEY PACKAGING INDUSTRIES INC p 1541
110 N Kensington Dr 54915
Tel (920) 749-5840 *SIC* 7389 8331

VAN HOOF CORP p 1542
1160 N Mayflower Dr 54913
Tel (920) 830-5000 *SIC* 4225

VOITH HOLDING INC p 1564
2200 N Roemer Rd 54911
Tel (920) 731-7724
SIC 5131 3554 2221 6719

VOITH PAPER INC p 1564
2200 N Roemer Rd 54911
Tel (920) 731-0769 *SIC* 3554

WAREHOUSE SPECIALISTS LLC p 1575
1160 N Mayflower Dr 54913
Tel (920) 830-5000 *SIC* 4225

WERNER ELECTRIC SUPPLY CO p 1592
4800 W Prospect Ave 54914
Tel (920) 337-6700 *SIC* 5063

WOW LOGISTICS CO p 1627
3040 W Wisconsin Ave 54914
Tel (800) 236-3565 *SIC* 4225

ARCADIA, WI

ASHLEY DISTRIBUTION SERVICES LTD p 117
1 Ashley Way 54612
Tel (608) 323-3377 *SIC* 4213

ASHLEY FURNITURE INDUSTRIES INC p 117
1 Ashley Way 54612
Tel (608) 323-3377 *SIC* 2512 2511

ASHLAND, WI

CG BRETTING MANUFACTURING CO INC p 285
3401 Lake Park Rd 54806
Tel (715) 682-5231
SIC 3554 3599 3565 3555

BANCROFT, WI

RPE INC p 1255
8550 Central Sands Rd 54921
Tel (715) 335-8050 *SIC* 7389

BARABOO, WI

FLAMBEAU INC p 554
801 Lynn Ave 53913
Tel (608) 356-5551 *SIC* 3089 3949 3944

FOREMOST FARMS USA COOPERATIVE p 566
E10889 Penny Ln 53913
Tel (608) 355-8700
SIC 2022 2026 2023 2021

HAMMOND POWER SOLUTIONS INC p 656
1100 Lake St 53913
Tel (608) 356-3921 *SIC* 5084

NORDIC GROUP OF COMPANIES LTD p 1048
715 Lynn Ave Ste 100 53913
Tel (608) 356-7303 *SIC* 8742 8111 5561

■ SYSCO BARABOO LLC p 1416
910 South Blvd 53913
Tel (800) 733-8217
SIC 5141 5142 5046 5148

BEAVER DAM, WI

BEAVER DAM COMMUNITY HOSPITALS INC p 166
707 S University Ave 53916
Tel (920) 887-7181 *SIC* 8062 8051

UNITED COOPERATIVE p 1507
N7160 Raceway Rd 53916
Tel (920) 887-1756
SIC 5191 5171 5541 5153 5812

BELLEVILLE, WI

▲ DULUTH HOLDINGS INC p 460
170 Countryside Dr 53508
Tel (608) 424-1544 *SIC* 5961 5611 5621

BELOIT, WI

AMERICAN BUILDERS & CONTRACTORS SUPPLY CO INC p 69
1 Abc Pkwy 53511
Tel (608) 362-7777 *SIC* 5033 5031

BELOIT HEALTH SYSTEM INC p 171
1969 W Hart Rd 53511
Tel (608) 364-5011 *SIC* 8062

BELOIT MEMORIAL HOSPITAL FOUNDATION INC p 171
1969 W Hart Rd 53511
Tel (608) 363-5724 *SIC* 6733

BELOIT MEMORIAL HOSPITAL INC p 171
1969 W Hart Rd 53511
Tel (608) 364-5011 *SIC* 8062 8011

■ COLTEC INDUSTRIES INC p 340
701 White Ave 53511
Tel (608) 364-4411 *SIC* 3519

HENDRICKS HOLDING CO INC p 683
690 3rd St Ste 300 53511
Tel (608) 362-8981 *SIC* 6726

KERRY HOLDING CO p 813
3330 Millington Rd 53511
Tel (608) 363-1200
SIC 2099 2079 2023 2022 2087

KERRY INC p 813
3330 Millington Rd 53511
Tel (608) 363-1200 *SIC* 2099

■ REGAL BELOIT AMERICA INC p 1218
200 State St 53511
Tel (608) 364-8800 *SIC* 3644 3621

▲ REGAL BELOIT CORP p 1218
200 State St 53511
Tel (608) 364-8800 *SIC* 3621 3714 3566

UNITED STARS INC p 1512
1546 Henry Ave 53511
Tel (608) 368-4625
SIC 3317 3351 3463 3613 3621

BERLIN, WI

BADGER MINING CORP p 144
409 S Church St 54923
Tel (920) 361-2388 *SIC* 1446

THEDACARE MEDICAL CENTER - BERLIN INC p 1446
225 Memorial Dr 54923
Tel (920) 361-1313 *SIC* 8062 8051 8011

BLACK EARTH, WI

■ BLACK EARTH TELEPHONE CO LLC p 186
1125 Mills St 53515
Tel (608) 767-2229 *SIC* 4813

BLACK RIVER FALLS, WI

HO-CHUNK NATION p 698
W9814 Airport Rd 54615
Tel (800) 280-2843 *SIC* 9131

■ LUNDA CONSTRUCTION CO p 886
620 Gebhardt Rd 54615
Tel (715) 284-2322 *SIC* 1622 8711

MILLIS TRANSFER INC p 971
121 Gebhardt Rd 54615
Tel (715) 284-4384 *SIC* 4213 4231 4212

BLOOMER, WI

BLOOMER HOLDINGS INC p 190
1710 N Industrial Dr 54724
Tel (800) 638-0479 *SIC* 2371

BLUE MOUNDS, WI

DAIRYFOOD USA INC p 409
2819 County Road F 53517
Tel (608) 437-5598 *SIC* 5143 2022 2023

BOYCEVILLE, WI

BIG RIVER RESOURCES BOYCEVILLE LLC p 181
N10185 370th St 54725
Tel (715) 643-2602 *SIC* 5169

BRILLION, WI

ARIENS CO p 108
655 W Ryan St 54110
Tel (920) 756-2141 *SIC* 3524

■ BRILLION IRON WORKS INC p 213
200 Park Ave 54110
Tel (920) 756-2121 *SIC* 3321

ENDRIES INTERNATIONAL INC p 496
714 W Ryan St 54110
Tel (920) 756-2174 *SIC* 5085 5072

BRODHEAD, WI

KUHN NORTH AMERICA INC p 831
1501 W 7th Ave 53520
Tel (608) 897-4508 *SIC* 3523 3531

BROOKFIELD, WI

COMMUNITY CARE INC p 347
205 Bishops Way Ofc 53005
Tel (414) 385-6600 *SIC* 8322

▲ CONNECTURE INC p 357
18500 W Corp Dr Ste 250 53045
Tel (262) 432-8282 *SIC* 7371

■ FISERV CIR INC p 551
255 Fiserv Dr 53045
Tel (262) 879-5000 *SIC* 7374 7372 7373

▲ FISERV INC p 551
255 Fiserv Dr 53045
Tel (262) 879-5000 *SIC* 7374 7371

■ FISERV SOLUTIONS LLC p 551
255 Fiserv Dr 53045
Tel (262) 879-5000 *SIC* 7374 2754 5084

FRIENDS OF ELMBROOK MEMORIAL HOSPITAL INC p 580
19333 W North Ave 53045
Tel (262) 785-2000 *SIC* 8062

GUHRING INC p 645
1445 Commerce Ave 53045
Tel (262) 784-6730 *SIC* 3545

HYDRITE CHEMICAL CO p 723
300 N Patrick Blvd Fl 2 53045
Tel (262) 792-1450
SIC 5169 2819 2841 2869

JRS HOLDING INC p 795
20445 W Capitol Dr 53045
Tel (262) 781-2626 *SIC* 5511

MILWAUKEE ELECTRIC TOOL CORP p 972
13135 W Lisbon Rd 53005
Tel (800) 729-3878 *SIC* 3546 3425

PARAGON DEVELOPMENT SYSTEMS INC p 1113
13400 Bishops Ln Ste 190 53005
Tel (262) 569-5300 *SIC* 5734 7379

PROGRESSIVE ENTERPRISES HOLDINGS INC p 1181
250 N Sunny Slope Rd # 110 53005
Tel (262) 207-2101 *SIC* 7371

STONERIVER INC p 1391
250 N Sunny Slope Rd # 110 53005
Tel (262) 207-2101 *SIC* 7371

WISCONSIN LIFT TRUCK CORP p 1619
3125 Intertech Dr 53045
Tel (262) 790-6230 *SIC* 5084 5085 7699

BROWNSVILLE, WI

M10 INC p 890
817 W Main St 53006
Tel (920) 583-3132 *SIC* 6719

MICHELS CORP p 960
817 W Main St 53006
Tel (920) 583-3132
SIC 1623 1771 1381 1629 3498 1794

BURLINGTON, WI

WISCONSIN VISION ASSOCIATES INC p 1619
139 W Chestnut St 53105
Tel (262) 763-0100 *SIC* 5048 5122 5047

BUTLER, WI

ALLIED DIESEL INC p 56
13015 W Custer Ave 53007
Tel (262) 781-7100 *SIC* 5084 5531 7699

WESTERN STATES ENVELOPE CO p 1600
4480 N 132nd St 53007
Tel (262) 781-5540 *SIC* 2677

CALEDONIA, WI

MEETINGS & INCENTIVES WORLDWIDE INC p 939
10520 7 Mile Rd 53108
Tel (262) 835-6710 *SIC* 4724 8742 7389

CAMERON, WI

ADVANCED HEATING LLC p 25
2736 12 3/4 Ave 54822
Tel (715) 296-6107 *SIC* 1711

CHILTON, WI

■ **KAYTEE PRODUCTS INC** p 805
521 Clay St 53014
Tel (920) 849-2321 *SIC* 2048

CHIPPEWA FALLS, WI

MASON COMPANIES INC p 916
1251 1st Ave 54729
Tel (715) 720-4200 *SIC* 5961 5661

■ **TTM ADVANCED CIRCUITS INC** p 1490
234 Cashman Dr 54729
Tel (715) 720-5000 *SIC* 3672 3674

CLEVELAND, WI

■ **EASTCOAST TELECOM OF WISCONSIN LLC** p 471
1140 W Washington Ave 53015
Tel (920) 693-8121 *SIC* 4813

CLINTON, WI

DELONG CO INC p 425
513 Front St 53525
Tel (800) 356-0784 *SIC* 5153

CLINTONVILLE, WI

FWD SEAGRAVE HOLDINGS LP p 586
105 E 12th St 54929
Tel (715) 823-2141 *SIC* 3711

SEAGRAVE FIRE APPARATUS LLC p 1296
105 E 12th St 54929
Tel (715) 823-2141 *SIC* 5012 3713 8711

COMBINED LOCKS, WI

APPLETON COATED LLC p 99
540 Prospect St 54113
Tel (920) 788-3550 *SIC* 2621 2672

VIRTUS HOLDINGS LLC p 1560
540 Prospect St 54113
Tel (920) 788-3550 *SIC* 2672 2621

COTTAGE GROVE, WI

JOHNSON HEALTH TECH NORTH AMERICA INC p 791
1600 Landmark Dr 53527
Tel (608) 839-1240 *SIC* 5091 5941

LANDMARK SERVICES COOPERATIVE p 843
1401 Landmark Dr 53527
Tel (608) 819-3115
SIC 4221 5171 5191 1711

CROSS PLAINS, WI

PLASTIC INGENUITY INC p 1155
1017 Park St 53528
Tel (608) 798-3071 *SIC* 3089

CUDAHY, WI

■ **ATI LADISH LLC** p 124
5481 S Packard Ave 53110
Tel (414) 747-2611 *SIC* 3462 3463

■ **LUCAS-MILHAUPT INC** p 884
5656 S Pennsylvania Ave 53110
Tel (414) 769-6000 *SIC* 3356

PATRICK CUDAHY LLC p 1120
1 Sweet Applewood Ln 53110
Tel (414) 744-2000 *SIC* 2013

■ **ROADRUNNER TRANSPORTATION SERVICES INC** p 1240
4900 S Pennsylvania Ave 53110
Tel (414) 615-1500 *SIC* 4731

▲ **ROADRUNNER TRANSPORTATION SYSTEMS INC** p 1240
4900 S Pennsylvania Ave 53110
Tel (414) 615-1500 *SIC* 4731

■ **VILTER MANUFACTURING LLC** p 1557
5555 S Packard Ave 53110
Tel (414) 744-0111 *SIC* 5078

DE PERE, WI

■ **AMERIPRISE BANK FSB** p 83
3500 Packerland Dr 54115
Tel (920) 330-5835 *SIC* 6331

BELMARK INC p 171
600 Heritage Rd 54115
Tel (920) 336-2848 *SIC* 2759 2657 2671

BROWN COUNTY MSA CELLULAR LIMITED PARTNERSHIP p 219
1580 Mid Valley Dr 54115
Tel (920) 339-4004 *SIC* 4812 5999

■ **CONSTELLATION ENERGY SERVICES INC** p 361
1716 Lawrence Dr 54115
Tel (920) 617-6100 *SIC* 4911

FOTH & VAN DYKE LLC p 571
2121 Innovation Ct # 100 54115
Tel (920) 497-2500 *SIC* 6719

HAMILTON L FISHER L C p 655
1716 Lawrence Dr Ste 1 54115
Tel (920) 793-1121 *SIC* 3821

■ **MEGTEC SYSTEMS INC** p 940
830 Prosper St 54115
Tel (920) 336-5715
SIC 3822 3555 3567 3823

NEW-CELL LLC p 1036
1580 Mid Valley Dr 54115
Tel (920) 617-7800 *SIC* 4812

ROBINSON METAL INC p 1242
1740 Eisenhower Rd 54115
Tel (920) 494-7411 *SIC* 3444 3443 3599

WEL COMPANIES INC p 1588
1625 S Broadway 54115
Tel (800) 333-4415 *SIC* 4213

DEFOREST, WI

DON EVANS INC p 450
100 W North St 53532
Tel (608) 846-6000 *SIC* 3089

TRUCK COUNTRY OF WISCONSIN INC p 1485
4195 Anderson Rd 53532
Tel (608) 249-1090 *SIC* 5012 7538

DELAVAN, WI

STA-RITE INDUSTRIES LLC p 1374
293 S Wright St 53115
Tel (888) 782-7483 *SIC* 3561 5084 5251

DENMARK, WI

DETERVILLE LUMBER & SUPPLY LLC p 433
3749 S County Road T 54208
Tel (920) 863-2191 *SIC* 5211

DICKEYVILLE, WI

■ **DICKEYVILLE TELEPHONE LLC** p 438
200 W Main St 53808
Tel (608) 831-1000 *SIC* 4813

DODGEVILLE, WI

▲ **LANDS END INC** p 843
1 Lands End Ln 53595
Tel (608) 935-9341 *SIC* 5961 5611 5621

QUALITY LIQUID FEEDS INC p 1197
3586 State Road 23 53533
Tel (608) 935-2345 *SIC* 5191

DURAND, WI

BAUER BUILT INC p 160
1111 W Prospect St 54736
Tel (715) 672-8300
SIC 5531 5014 7534 5171

EAU CLAIRE, WI

CHIPPEWA VALLEY TECHNICAL COLLEGE FOUNDATION INC p 301
620 W Clairemont Ave 54701
Tel (715) 833-6200 *SIC* 8222

CHOICE PRODUCTS USA LLC p 302
3421 Truax Ct 54703
Tel (715) 833-8761 *SIC* 5199 7389 2041

CONSUMERS COOPERATIVE ASSOCIATION OF EAU CLAIRE p 362
1201 S Hastings Way 54701
Tel (715) 836-8700 *SIC* 5411 5541

CURT MANUFACTURING LLC p 402
6208 Industrial Dr 54701
Tel (715) 831-8713 *SIC* 3799

DITTO II LLC p 443
1201 S Hastings Way 54701
Tel (715) 836-8710 *SIC* 5541 5411

DORO INC p 451
3112 Golf Rd 54701
Tel (715) 836-6800 *SIC* 5812

EAU CLAIRE AREA SCHOOL DISTRICT p 474
500 Main St 54701
Tel (715) 852-3000 *SIC* 8211

INDIANHEAD FOODSERVICE DISTRIBUTOR INC p 739
313 N Hastings Pl 54703
Tel (715) 834-2777
SIC 5142 5141 5147 5143

INSURANCE CLAIMS MANAGEMENT INC p 748
404 S Barstow St 54701
Tel (715) 830-6000 *SIC* 6411

LUTHER HOSPITAL p 886
733 W Clairemont Ave 54701
Tel (715) 838-3060 *SIC* 8011

LUTHER MIDELFORT MAYO HEALTH SYSTEM p 886
733 W Clairemont Ave 54701
Tel (715) 838-5353 *SIC* 6324 8011

MARKET & JOHNSON INC p 908
2350 Galloway St 54703
Tel (715) 834-1213 *SIC* 1542 1541

MAYO CLINIC HEALTH SYSTEM p 923
733 W Clairemont Ave 54701
Tel (715) 838-6968 *SIC* 8011

MAYO CLINIC HEALTH SYSTEM-EAU CLAIRE CLINIC INC p 924
1400 Bellinger St 54703
Tel (715) 838-5222 *SIC* 8062

MAYO CLINIC HEALTH SYSTEM-NORTHWEST WISCONSIN REGION INC p 924
1221 Whipple St 54703
Tel (715) 838-3311 *SIC* 8062 8011

MENARD INC p 943
5101 Menard Dr 54703
Tel (715) 876-5911 *SIC* 2431 5211

MIDWEST MANUFACTURING INC p 967
5311 Kane Rd 54703
Tel (715) 876-5555 *SIC* 5033 5031 3965

▲ **NATIONAL PRESTO INDUSTRIES INC** p 1015
3925 N Hastings Way 54703
Tel (715) 839-2121 *SIC* 2211 3483 3634

■ **NORTHERN STATES POWER CO** p 1057
1414 W Hamilton Ave 54701
Tel (715) 839-2625 *SIC* 4931

■ **PRECISION PIPELINE LLC** p 1168
3314 56th St 54703
Tel (715) 874-4510 *SIC* 1623

SACRED HEART HOSPITAL INC p 1265
900 W Clairemont Ave 54701
Tel (715) 717-3926 *SIC* 8062

SACRED HEART HOSPITAL OF HOSPITAL SISTERS-3RD ORDER OF ST FRANCIS p 1265
1110 Oak Ridge Dr 54701
Tel (715) 717-4131 *SIC* 8099

EDEN, WI

EDEN STONE CO INC p 477
W4520 Lime Rd 53019
Tel (920) 477-2521 *SIC* 1411 5032

ELK MOUND, WI

CROSSROADS AG LLC p 394
N6055 State Road 40 54739
Tel (715) 879-5454 *SIC* 5191 5171

ELKHORN, WI

COUNTY OF WALWORTH p 382
100 W Walworth St Ste 116 53121
Tel (262) 741-4241 *SIC* 9111

ELM GROVE, WI

AURORA PHARMACY INC p 132
12500 W Bluemound Rd # 201 53122
Tel (262) 787-2136 *SIC* 5912

FITCHBURG, WI

■ **CDW TECHNOLOGIES LLC** p 271
5520 Research Park Dr 53711
Tel (608) 288-3000 *SIC* 7373 4813

CERTCO INC p 284
5321 Verona Rd 53711
Tel (608) 271-4500 *SIC* 5141

GENERAL BEVERAGE SALES CO-MILWAUKEE p 599
6169 Mckee Rd 53719
Tel (608) 271-1237 *SIC* 5182 5181

PROMEGA CORP p 1183
2800 Woods Hollow Rd 53711
Tel (608) 274-4330 *SIC* 2836

TRI-NORTH BUILDERS INC p 1477
2625 Research Park Dr 53711
Tel (608) 271-8717 *SIC* 1541 1542 1521

FOND DU LAC, WI

AGNESIAN HEALTHCARE INC p 35
430 E Division St 54935
Tel (920) 929-2300 *SIC* 8069

BADGER LIQUOR CO INC p 143
850 Morris St 54935
Tel (920) 923-8160 *SIC* 5182

■ **BRENNER TANK LLC** p 210
450 Arlington Ave 54935
Tel (920) 922-4530 *SIC* 3715 3714 3443

CD SMITH CONSTRUCTION INC p 270
889 E Johnson St 54935
Tel (920) 924-2900 *SIC* 1542 1541

FOND DU LAC SCHOOL DISTRICT p 563
72 W 9th St 54935
Tel (920) 929-2900 *SIC* 8211

GRANDE CHEESE CO p 630
250 Camelot Dr 54935
Tel (920) 952-7200 *SIC* 2022

J F AHERN CO p 771
855 Morris St 54935
Tel (920) 921-9020 *SIC* 1711

LAKELAND CARE DISTRICT p 839
N6654 Rolling Meadows Dr 54937
Tel (920) 906-5100 *SIC* 6321

■ **MERCURY MARINE INC** p 945
W6250 W Pioneer Rd 54935
Tel (920) 929-5000 *SIC* 3089 3535

MIKE SHANNON AUTOMOTIVE INC p 968
321 N Rolling Meadows Dr 54937
Tel (920) 921-8898 *SIC* 5511

NEB CORP p 1023
130 S Main St 54935
Tel (920) 921-7700 *SIC* 6029

SADOFF & RUDOY INDUSTRIES LLP p 1265
240 W Arndt St 272 54935
Tel (920) 921-2070 *SIC* 5093

SOCIETY INSURANCE A MUTUAL CO p 1336
150 Camelot Dr 54935
Tel (920) 922-1220 *SIC* 6411

ST AGNES HOSPITAL OF FOND DU LAC WISC INC p 1364
430 E Division St 54935
Tel (920) 929-2300 *SIC* 8062

WELLS VEHICLE ELECTRONICS LP p 1591
385 W Rolling Meadows Dr 54937
Tel (920) 922-5900
SIC 3714 3694 3644 3357

FORT ATKINSON, WI

CYGNUS BUSINESS MEDIA INC p 405
1233 Janesville Ave 53538
Tel (920) 563-6388 *SIC* 2721 7389 7319

FORT HEALTHCARE INC p 569
611 Sherman Ave E 53538
Tel (920) 568-5401 *SIC* 8062 8011

NASCO HEALTHCARE INC p 1008
901 Janesville Ave 53538
Tel (920) 568-5600 *SIC* 3999

SPACESAVER CORP p 1354
1450 Janesville Ave 53538
Tel (920) 563-6362 *SIC* 2542

FRANKLIN, WI

KRONES INC p 830
9600 S 58th St 53132
Tel (414) 409-4000 *SIC* 3565

SENIOR FLEXONICS GA PRECISION p 1304
5215 W Airways Ave 53132
Tel (414) 817-5300 *SIC* 3714

GERMANTOWN, WI

ALCAMI WISCONSIN CORP p 47
W130n10497 Washington Dr 53022
Tel (262) 251-5044 *SIC* 8731 8734

ELLSWORTH CORP p 489
W129n10825 Washington Dr 53022
Tel (262) 253-8600 *SIC* 5169 5085

GEHL FOODS LLC p 597
N116w15970 Main St 53022
Tel (262) 251-8570 *SIC* 2022 5451

MGS GROUP NORTH AMERICA INC p 958
W190n11701 Moldmakers Way 53022
Tel (262) 250-2950 *SIC* 3089

MGS MFG GROUP INC p 958
W188n11707 Maple Rd 53022
Tel (262) 255-5790 *SIC* 3089 5047 2821

SATISLOH NORTH AMERICA INC p 1283
N106w13131 Bradley Way # 200 53022
Tel (262) 255-6001 *SIC* 5049 5072

VULCAN INDUSTRIES CORP p 1567
N113w18830 Carnegie Dr 53022
Tel (262) 255-1090 *SIC* 3469 3498

WAGO CORP p 1571
N120 W 19129 Freistadt Rd N 120 W 53022
Tel (262) 255-6333 *SIC* 5063 3643 3678

■ **WASTE MANAGEMENT OF WISCONSIN INC** p 1581
N96 W 13600 Cnty Line Rd St N 96 53022
Tel (262) 251-4000 *SIC* 4953 4212

GLEASON, WI

AURORA HEALTH CARE SOUTHERN LAKES INC p 132
36500 Aurora Dr 54435
Tel (262) 434-1000 *SIC* 8099

GLENDALE, WI

COLUMBIA ST MARYS HOSPITAL OZAUKEE INC p 341
4425 N Port Washington Rd 53212
Tel (414) 326-2230 *SIC* 8062

▲ WEYCO GROUP INC p 1603
333 W Estabrook Blvd # 1 53212
Tel (414) 908-1600 *SIC* 5139 5661

WHEATON FRANCISCAN HEALTHCARE - ALL SAINTS FOUNDATION INC p 1604
400 W River Woods Pkwy 53212
Tel (414) 465-3000 *SIC* 8062

GRAFTON, WI

AURORA MEDICAL CENTER GRAFTON LLC p 132
975 Port Washington Rd 53024
Tel (262) 329-2723 *SIC* 8049

CPL INDUSTRIES INC p 387
1111 Cedar Creek Rd 53024
Tel (262) 377-2210 *SIC* 6712

■ LEESON ELECTRIC CORP p 852
1051 Cheyenne Ave 53024
Tel (262) 377-8810 *SIC* 3621

GREEN BAY, WI

AMERHART LIMITED p 66
2455 Century Rd 54303
Tel (920) 494-4744 *SIC* 5031

AMERICAN FOODS GROUP LLC p 72
500 S Washington St 54301
Tel (320) 759-5900 *SIC* 2011

■ AMERICAN MEDICAL SECURITY GROUP INC PAC p 76
3100 Ams Blvd 54313
Tel (920) 661-1111 *SIC* 6321 6311

■ AMERICAN MEDICAL SECURITY INC p 76
3100 Ams Blvd 54313
Tel (920) 661-1111 *SIC* 6324

▲ ASSOCIATED BANC-CORP p 119
433 Main St 54301
Tel (920) 491-7500 *SIC* 6022

■ ASSOCIATED BANK NATIONAL ASSOCIATION p 120
200 N Adams St 54301
Tel (920) 433-3200 *SIC* 6021 6211

AURORA BAYCARE MEDICAL CENTER p 131
2845 Greenbrier Rd 54311
Tel (920) 288-8000 *SIC* 8011

AWS/GB CORP p 139
2929 Walker Dr 54311
Tel (920) 406-4000
SIC 5031 2431 3442 5033 1542 1541

BAY INDUSTRIES INC p 161
2929 Walker Dr 54311
Tel (920) 406-4000 *SIC* 5031 5033

■ BAY VALLEY FOODS LLC p 161
3200 Riverside Dr Ste A 54301
Tel (800) 558-4700 *SIC* 2099

BAYCARE HEALTH SYSTEMS LLC p 161
164 N Broadway 54303
Tel (920) 490-9046 *SIC* 8011

BELGIOIOSO CHEESE p 169
4200 Main St 54311
Tel (920) 863-2123 *SIC* 2022

BELLIN HEALTH SYSTEMS INC p 170
744 S Webster Ave 54301
Tel (920) 433-3500 *SIC* 8062 8063 7352

BELLIN MEMORIAL HOSPITAL INC p 170
744 S Webster Ave 54301
Tel (920) 433-3500 *SIC* 8062

BROADWAY AUTOMOTIVE - GREEN BAY INC p 216
2700 S Ashland Ave 54304
Tel (920) 498-6666 *SIC* 5511

BROADWAY ENTERPRISES INC p 216
1106 S Military Ave 54304
Tel (920) 429-6249 *SIC* 5511 7514

BROADWAY FORD-HYUNDAI INC p 216
1010 S Military Ave 54304
Tel (920) 499-3131
SIC 7515 5511 7513 5521 5012

COUNTY OF BROWN p 376
2077 Airport Dr Ste 18 54313
Tel (920) 448-4035 *SIC* 9111

EILLIENS CANDIES INC p 481
1301 Waube Ln 54304
Tel (920) 336-7549 *SIC* 5145

ENGLEWOOD MARKETING GROUP INC p 499
1471 Partnership Rd 54304
Tel (920) 337-9800 *SIC* 5064

ENZYMATIC THERAPY LLC p 504
825 Challenger Dr 54311
Tel (920) 469-1313 *SIC* 2834

FABIO PERINI NORTH AMERICA INC p 523
3060 S Ridge Rd 54304
Tel (920) 336-5000 *SIC* 5084

GREEN BAY AREA PUBLIC SCHOOL DISTRICT p 636
200 S Broadway 54303
Tel (920) 448-2101 *SIC* 8211

GREEN BAY CONVERTING INC p 636
600 Packerland Dr 54303
Tel (920) 498-5100 *SIC* 5113

GREEN BAY DRESSED BEEF LLC p 636
544 Acme St 54302
Tel (920) 436-4220 *SIC* 2011 2013

GREEN BAY PACKAGING INC p 636
1700 N Webster Ave 54302
Tel (920) 433-5111
SIC 2631 2672 2653 2491

H J MARTIN & SON INC p 650
320 S Military Ave 54303
Tel (920) 494-3461
SIC 5713 1793 1522 1542 1742

■ HUMANA INSURANCE CO p 718
1100 Employers Blvd 54344
Tel (502) 580-1000 *SIC* 6311 6321

IOD INC p 762
1030 Ontario Rd 54311
Tel (920) 469-5000 *SIC* 7375

JBS PACKERLAND INC p 779
1330 Lime Kiln Rd 54311
Tel (920) 468-4000 *SIC* 2011 4213

KRUEGER INTERNATIONAL INC p 830
1330 Bellevue St 54302
Tel (920) 468-8100 *SIC* 2531

LA FORCE INC p 835
1060 W Mason St 54303
Tel (920) 497-7100 *SIC* 5072 5031 3442

LAMERS BUS LINES INC p 841
2407 S Point Rd 54313
Tel (920) 496-3600
SIC 4151 4142 4119 4725 4141

LITTLE RAPIDS CORP p 871
2273 Larsen Rd 54303
Tel (920) 490-5400 *SIC* 2621

NORTHEAST COMMUNICATIONS OF WISCONSIN INC p 1054
450 Security Blvd 54313
Tel (920) 617-7000 *SIC* 4812 4813

NORTHEAST WISCONSIN TECHNICAL COLLEGE DISTRICT p 1055
2740 W Mason St 54303
Tel (920) 498-5400 *SIC* 8221 8222

PAPER CONVERTING MACHINE CO p 1112
2300 S Ashland Ave 54304
Tel (920) 494-5601 *SIC* 3554

PAPER TRANSPORT INC p 1112
2701 Executive Dr 54304
Tel (920) 497-6222 *SIC* 4213

PIONEER METAL FINISHING LLC p 1151
480 Pilgrim Way Ste 1400 54304
Tel (920) 499-6996 *SIC* 3471

POMPS TIRE SERVICE INC p 1161
1122 Cedar St 54301
Tel (920) 435-8301 *SIC* 5531 5014 7534

PREVEA CLINIC INC p 1173
2710 Executive Dr 54304
Tel (920) 272-1100 *SIC* 8011

SANIMAX CORP p 1279
2099 Badgerland Dr 54303
Tel (920) 494-5233 *SIC* 5199 2077

SANIMAX USA LLC p 1279
2099 Badgerland Dr 54303
Tel (920) 494-5233 *SIC* 5199 2077

SANTA MARIA NURSING HOME INC p 1281
430 S Clay St 54301
Tel (920) 432-5231 *SIC* 8051

SCHNEIDER LOGISTICS INC p 1288
3101 Packerland Dr 54313
Tel (920) 592-0000
SIC 4731 4225 4789 4212

SCHNEIDER NATIONAL CARRIERS INC p 1288
3101 Packerland Dr 54313
Tel (920) 592-2000 *SIC* 4731

SCHNEIDER NATIONAL INC p 1288
3101 Packerland Dr 54313
Tel (920) 592-2000 *SIC* 8742 4213

SCHNEIDER RESOURCES INC p 1288
3101 Packerland Dr 54313
Tel (920) 592-2000 *SIC* 4213

SCHREIBER FOODS INC p 1290
400 N Washington St 54301
Tel (920) 437-7601 *SIC* 2022 3556 3565

SCHREIBER INTERNATIONAL INC p 1290
425 Pine St 54301
Tel (920) 437-7601 *SIC* 5143

SCHWABE NORTH AMERICA INC p 1291
825 Challenger Dr 54311
Tel (920) 469-1313 *SIC* 2834 2099

SHOPKO HOLDING CO INC p 1318
700 Pilgrim Way 54304
Tel (920) 429-2211 *SIC* 5311

SHOPKO STORES OPERATING CO LLC p 1318
700 Pilgrim Way 54304
Tel (920) 429-2211 *SIC* 5311 5912 8042

SPECIALTY RETAIL SHOPS HOLDING CORP p 1356
700 Pilgrim Way 54304
Tel (920) 429-2211 *SIC* 6719

ST MARYS HOSPITAL p 1371
1726 Shawano Ave 54303
Tel (920) 498-4200 *SIC* 8011 8062

ST VINCENT HOSPITAL OF HOSPITAL SISTERS OF THIRD ORDER OF S p 1373
835 S Van Buren St 54301
Tel (920) 433-0111 *SIC* 8062 8011

TUFCO HOLDINGS LLC p 1490
3161 S Ridge Rd 54304
Tel (920) 336-0054 *SIC* 2679

TUFCO LP p 1491
3161 S Ridge Rd 54304
Tel (920) 336-0054 *SIC* 5122 5112 2676

TUFCO TECHNOLOGIES INC p 1491
3161 S Ridge Rd 54304
Tel (920) 336-0054 *SIC* 2679

TWEET-GAROT MECHANICAL INC p 1494
2545 Larsen Rd 54303
Tel (920) 498-0400 *SIC* 1711 3444

■ UNITEDHEALTHCARE LIFE INSURANCE CO p 1515
3100 Ams Blvd 54313
Tel (800) 232-5432
SIC 6411 6324 6311 8322

VHC INC p 1553
3090 Holmgren Way 54304
Tel (920) 336-7278
SIC 1731 1542 1541 1521 1711 6512

VOS ELECTRIC INC p 1566
3131 Market St 54304
Tel (920) 336-0781 *SIC* 1731

W/S PACKAGING GROUP INC p 1569
2571 S Hemlock Rd 54229
Tel (920) 866-6300 *SIC* 2679 2752

■ WISCONSIN PUBLIC SERVICE CORP p 1619
700 N Adams St 54301
Tel (800) 450-7260 *SIC* 4931

GREENDALE, WI

GOODWILL INDUSTRIES OF SOUTHEASTERN WISCONSIN INC p 625
5400 S 60th St 53129
Tel (414) 847-4200 *SIC* 8331 7349

GOODWILL RETAIL SERVICES INC p 625
5400 S 60th St 53129
Tel (414) 847-4200 *SIC* 5651 4226

GREENFIELD, WI

EVERBRITE LLC p 513
4949 S 110th St 53228
Tel (414) 529-3500 *SIC* 3993

GREENVILLE, WI

SCHOOL SPECIALTY INC p 1290
W6316 Design Dr 54942
Tel (920) 734-5712 *SIC* 5049 5021

▲ SCHOOL SPECIALTY INC p 1290
W6316 Design Dr 54942
Tel (920) 734-5712 *SIC* 5049 5021 5961

VALLEY BAKERS COOPERATIVE ASSOCIATION p 1540
W6470 Quality Dr 54942
Tel (920) 560-3200 *SIC* 5149 5046

VEOLIA ES SPECIAL SERVICES INC p 1548
W6490b Specialty Dr 54942
Tel (800) 932-6216 *SIC* 4953

GREENWOOD, WI

GRASSLAND DAIRY PRODUCTS INC p 632
N8790 Fairground Ave 54437
Tel (715) 267-6182 *SIC* 2021 5143

HALES CORNERS, WI

HOLZ MOTORS INC p 702
5961 S 108th Pl 53130
Tel (414) 425-2400 *SIC* 5511

HARTFORD, WI

BROAN-NUTONE LLC p 216
926 W State St 53027
Tel (262) 673-4340
SIC 3634 3699 3635 3639 2514 3669

HELGESEN INDUSTRIES INC p 681
7261 State Road 60 53027
Tel (262) 709-4444 *SIC* 3443

SIGNICAST LLC p 1322
1800 Innovation Way 53027
Tel (262) 673-2700 *SIC* 3324

WENDORFF BROS CO INC p 1592
105 Steelcraft Dr 53027
Tel (262) 673-6770
SIC 3469 3089 5013 3479

HARTLAND, WI

JX ENTERPRISES INC p 798
1320 Walnut Ridge Dr 53029
Tel (800) 810-3410
SIC 5012 5511 7538 6159 7513

ONETOUCHPOINT CORP p 1088
1225 Walnut Ridge Dr 53029
Tel (630) 586-9002 *SIC* 2759

ONETOUCHPOINT MIDWEST CORP p 1088
1225 Walnut Ridge Dr 53029
Tel (262) 369-6000 *SIC* 2752

PRICE ENGINEERING CO INC p 1174
1175 Cottonwood Ave 53029
Tel (262) 369-2147 *SIC* 5084

HUDSON, WI

■ ERICKSON OIL PRODUCTS INC p 507
1231 Industrial St 54016
Tel (715) 386-8241 *SIC* 5541 5411

PHILLIPS-MEDISIZE CORP p 1144
1201 Hanley Rd 54016
Tel (715) 386-4320 *SIC* 3089 3444 3544

S/S/G CORP p 1263
512 2nd St Ste 12 54016
Tel (715) 386-8281 *SIC* 5541 5411

HURLEY, WI

AVANTI HEALTH SYSTEMS INC p 136
300 Villa Dr 54534
Tel (715) 561-3200 *SIC* 8399

JANESVILLE, WI

■ AMTEC CORP p 87
4230 Capital Cir 53546
Tel (608) 752-2699 *SIC* 3483

BLAIN SUPPLY INC p 188
3507 E Racine St 53546
Tel (608) 754-2821
SIC 5083 5072 5039 5013 5023 5198

BLISS COMMUNICATIONS INC p 189
1 S Parker Dr 53545
Tel (608) 741-6650 *SIC* 2711 4832

CHAMBERS & OWEN INC p 287
1733 Morse St 53545
Tel (608) 752-7865
SIC 5194 5145 5113 5141

COUNTY OF ROCK p 381
51 S Main St 53545
Tel (608) 757-5660 *SIC* 9111

CPT INC p 388
3706 Enterprise Dr 53546
Tel (608) 314-2020 *SIC* 3089 5162

FARM & FLEET OF JANESVILLE INC p 528
2421 Old Humes Rd Hwy 14 53545
Tel (608) 752-6377 *SIC* 5331

FARM & FLEET OF MADISON INC p 528
3507 E Racine St 53546
Tel (608) 754-2821
SIC 5199 5531 5251 5261 5039

FARM & FLEET OF RICE LAKE INC p 528
3507 E Racine St 53546
Tel (608) 754-2821 *SIC* 5191 5251 5531

■ GHC SPECIALTY BRANDS LLC p 610
401 S Wright Rd 53546
Tel (608) 754-2345 *SIC* 5961

HUFCOR INC p 717
2101 Kennedy Rd 53545
Tel (608) 756-1241 *SIC* 2542 3442

J P CULLEN & SONS INC p 772
330 E Delavan Dr 53546
Tel (608) 754-6601 *SIC* 1541 1542

JANESVILLE SCHOOL DISTRICT p 777
527 S Franklin St 53548
Tel (608) 743-5000 *SIC* 8211

JOHNSON BANK NA p 790
1 S Main St Ste 100 53545
Tel (262) 639-6010 *SIC* 6021

LEMANS CORP p 854
3501 Kennedy Rd 53545
Tel (608) 758-1111 *SIC* 5013

MERCY HEALTH SYSTEM CORP p 946
1000 Mineral Point Ave 53548
Tel (608) 741-6891 *SIC* 8062

PRENT CORP p 1171
2225 Kennedy Rd 53545
Tel (608) 754-0276 *SIC* 3081

■ RATHGIBSON HOLDING CO LLC p 1209
2505 Foster Ave 53545
Tel (608) 754-2222 *SIC* 3317 5051

■ RATHGIBSON LLC p 1209
2505 Foster Ave 53545
Tel (608) 754-2222 *SIC* 3317

RYAN INC CENTRAL p 1260
2700 E Racine St 53545
Tel (608) 754-2291 *SIC* 1794

SSI TECHNOLOGIES INC p 1364
3200 Palmer Dr 53546
Tel (608) 758-1500 *SIC* 3399 3825

WOODMANS FOOD MARKET INC p 1623
2631 Liberty Ln 53545
Tel (608) 754-8382 *SIC* 5411

JOHNSON CREEK, WI

DIDION MILLING INC p 438
520 Hartwig Blvd Ste C 53038
Tel (920) 348-5868 *SIC* 5153 2041

■ RIVERSIDE TELECOM LLC p 1238
121 Depot St 53038
Tel (608) 831-1000 *SIC* 4813

KAUKAUNA, WI

EXPERA SPECIALTY SOLUTIONS LLC p 519
600 Thilmany Rd 54130
Tel (920) 766-4611 *SIC* 2621

KELLER INC p 808
N216 State Highway 55 54130
Tel (920) 766-5795 *SIC* 1542 1541 7336

KENOSHA, WI

CARTHAGE COLLEGE p 262
2001 Alford Park Dr 53140
Tel (262) 551-8500 SIC 8221

COUNTY OF KENOSHA p 379
1010 56th St 53140
Tel (262) 653-2552 SIC 9111

■ **HEARTLAND-WASHINGTON MANOR OF KENOSHA WI LLC** p 679
3100 Washington Rd 53144
Tel (262) 658-4622 SIC 8051

■ **IDSC HOLDINGS LLC** p 729
2801 80th St 53143
Tel (262) 656-5200
SIC 3423 3559 7372 6794 5013 3546

JOCKEY INTERNATIONAL DOMESTIC INC p 787
2300 60th St 53140
Tel (262) 658-8111 SIC 5651 5611

JOCKEY INTERNATIONAL GLOBAL INC p 787
2300 60th St 53140
Tel (262) 658-8111 SIC 2211 5611

JOCKEY INTERNATIONAL INC p 787
2300 60th St 53140
Tel (262) 658-8111 SIC 2254 2341 2322

KENOSHA BEEF INTERNATIONAL LTD p 811
3111 152nd Ave 53144
Tel (800) 541-1684 SIC 2011

KENOSHA UNIFIED SCHOOL DISTRICT 1 p 811
3600 52nd St 53144
Tel (262) 359-6300 SIC 8211

NATIONAL COALITION OF CERTIFICATION CENTERS p 1010
4940 88th Ave 53144
Tel (262) 914-1515 SIC 8734

RILEY CONSTRUCTION CO INC p 1235
5301 99th Ave 53144
Tel (262) 658-4381 SIC 1542 1541

▲ **SNAP-ON INC** p 1335
2801 80th St 53143
Tel (262) 656-5200 SIC 3546 3559 3825

■ **SNAP-ON-TOOLS CORP** p 1335
2801 80th St 53143
Tel (262) 656-5200 SIC 5251

UHS INC p 1500
6308 8th Ave 53143
Tel (262) 656-2273 SIC 8062

UNITED HOSPITAL SYSTEM INC p 1509
6308 8th Ave 53143
Tel (262) 656-2011 SIC 8062

KEWASKUM, WI

REGAL WARE INC p 1218
1675 Reigle Dr 53040
Tel (262) 626-2121 SIC 3634 3469

KIELER, WI

KAISER CONTRACT CLEANING SPECIALISTS LLC p 800
3691 Prism Ln 53812
Tel (608) 568-3413 SIC 7349

KIMBERLY, WI

CRANE ENGINEERING SALES INC p 389
707 Ford St 54136
Tel (920) 733-4425 SIC 5084 5085 5074

PRN HEALTH SERVICES INC p 1178
740 Ford St Ste A 54136
Tel (920) 830-8811 SIC 7361 7363

KOHLER, WI

KOHLER CO p 826
444 Highland Dr 53044
Tel (920) 457-4441
SIC 3431 3432 3261 2511 2521 3519

KRONENWETTER, WI

WAUSAU PAPER CORP p 1583
100 Paper Pl 54455
Tel (715) 693-4470 SIC 2621

WAUSAU PAPER MILLS LLC p 1583
100 Paper Pl 54455
Tel (715) 693-4470 SIC 2621

LA CROSSE, WI

AGROPUR MSI LLC p 36
2340 Enterprise Ave 54603
Tel (608) 781-2345 SIC 2023

■ **AMERIPRISE FINANCIAL SERVICES INC** p 83
500 2nd St S Ste 101 54601
Tel (608) 783-2639
SIC 6282 6411 6211 8742

BADGER CORRUGATING CO p 143
1801 West Ave S 54601
Tel (608) 788-0100 SIC 5031

CITY BREWING CO LLC p 312
925 3rd St S 54601
Tel (608) 785-4200 SIC 2082

CITY OF LA CROSSE p 316
400 La Crosse St 54601
Tel (608) 784-8477 SIC 9111

CONSUMER LOAN SERVICES LLC p 361
811 Monitor St 54603
Tel (877) 791-1257 SIC 6162

COUNTY OF LA CROSSE p 379
400 4th St N 54601
Tel (608) 785-9581 SIC 9111

DAIRYLAND POWER COOPERATIVE p 409
3200 East Ave S 54601
Tel (608) 788-4000 SIC 4911

FORTNEY HOSPITALITY GROUP INC p 570
308 3rd St S 54601
Tel (608) 784-1225 SIC 7011

GUNDERSEN CLINIC LTD p 647
1836 South Ave 54601
Tel (608) 782-7300 SIC 8011

GUNDERSEN LUTHERAN ADMINISTRATIVE SERVICES INC p 647
1900 South Ave 54601
Tel (608) 782-7300 SIC 8621

GUNDERSEN LUTHERAN HEALTH SYSTEM INC p 647
1900 South Ave 54601
Tel (608) 782-7300 SIC 8062

GUNDERSEN LUTHERAN MEDICAL CENTER INC p 647
1900 South Ave 54601
Tel (608) 782-7300 SIC 8062 5912

GUNDERSON LUTHERAN INC p 647
1836 South Ave 54601
Tel (608) 782-7300 SIC 8011

INLAND LABEL AND MARKETING SERVICES LLC p 743
2009 West Ave S 54601
Tel (608) 788-5800 SIC 2754 2752

KWIK TRIP INC p 832
1626 Oak St 54603
Tel (608) 781-8988
SIC 5921 5993 5541 5983 5461

■ **LOGISTICS HEALTH INC** p 874
328 Front St S 54601
Tel (866) 284-8788 SIC 8011

MAYO CLINIC HEALTH SYSTEM-FRANCISCAN HEALTHCARE INC p 924
700 West Ave S 54601
Tel (608) 785-0940 SIC 8062 8051

MAYO CLINIC HEALTH SYSTEM-FRANCISCAN MEDICAL CENTER INC p 924
700 West Ave S 54601
Tel (608) 785-0940 SIC 8062

REINHART FOODSERVICE LLC p 1221
1500 Saint James St 54603
Tel (608) 782-2660 SIC 5963

ROTTINGHAUS CO INC p 1252
510 Gillette St 54603
Tel (608) 784-2774 SIC 5812

SCHOOL DISTRICT OF LACROSSE p 1289
807 East Ave S 54601
Tel (608) 789-7600 SIC 8211

TRANE CO p 1469
3600 Pammel Creek Rd 54601
Tel (608) 787-2000 SIC 3585

VITERBO UNIVERSITY INC p 1563
900 Viterbo Dr 54601
Tel (608) 796-3000 SIC 8221

WESTERN TECHNICAL COLLEGE p 1600
400 7th St N 54601
Tel (608) 785-9200 SIC 8222 8221

LA FARGE, WI

COOPERATIVE REGIONS OF ORGANIC PRODUCER POOLS p 367
1 Organic Way 54639
Tel (608) 625-2602 SIC 5148 5143

LAC DU FLAMBEAU, WI

LAC DU FLAMBEAU BAND OF LAKE SUPERIOR CHIPPEWA INDIANS (INC) p 836
418 Little Pines Rd 54538
Tel (715) 588-3303
SIC 8011 7999 5411 5541 8031

LADYSMITH, WI

INDIANHEAD COMMUNITY ACTION AGENCY INC p 739
1000 College Ave W 54848
Tel (715) 532-4222 SIC 8399

LAKE MILLS, WI

DAYBREAK FOODS INC p 417
533 E Tyranena Park Rd 53551
Tel (920) 648-8341 SIC 5144

LARSEN, WI

LARSEN COOPERATIVE CO p 845
8290 County Hwy T 54947
Tel (920) 982-1111 SIC 5191 5172 5541

LITTLE CHUTE, WI

HEARTLAND LABEL PRINTERS LLC p 679
1700 Stephen St 54140
Tel (920) 788-7720 SIC 5065 2672

TRILLIANT FOOD AND NUTRITION LLC p 1480
1101 Moasis Dr 54140
Tel (920) 788-1252 SIC 5149 2099 2095

MADISON, WI

AFFILIATED ENGINEERS INC p 32
5802 Research Park Blvd 53719
Tel (608) 238-2616 SIC 8711

▲ **ALLIANT ENERGY CORP** p 55
4902 N Biltmore Ln # 1000 53718
Tel (608) 458-3311 SIC 4911 4924

ALTER METAL RECYCLING p 62
4400 Sycamore Ave 53714
Tel (608) 241-7191 SIC 5093

AMERICAN FAMILY LIFE INSURANCE CO p 72
6000 American Pkwy 53783
Tel (608) 249-2111 SIC 6411

AMERICAN FAMILY MUTUAL INSURANCE CO INC p 72
6000 American Pkwy 53783
Tel (608) 249-2111 SIC 6331 6311

AMERICAN TV & APPLIANCE OF MADISON INC p 80
2404 W Beltline Hwy 53713
Tel (608) 515-5020 SIC 5731 5712 5722

AMFAM INC p 85
6000 American Pkwy 53783
Tel (608) 249-2111 SIC 6331 6311 6141

ANCHOR BANCORP WISCONSIN INC p 89
25 W Main St 53703
Tel (608) 252-8700 SIC 6035

ANCHORBANK FSB p 89
25 W Main St Lowr 53703
Tel (608) 252-8700 SIC 6036

APPLICA CONSUMER PRODUCTS INC p 99
601 Ray O Vac Dr 53711
Tel (608) 275-4562 SIC 3634 3631

BELL LABORATORIES INC p 170
3699 Kinsman Blvd 53704
Tel (608) 241-0202 SIC 2879

CAPITOL LAKES RETIREMENT COMMUNITY p 251
110 S Henry St 53703
Tel (608) 283-2000
SIC 6513 8051 8052 8361

CAPTEL INC p 252
450 Science Dr 53711
Tel (608) 238-5400 SIC 3842

CARE WISCONSIN FIRST INC p 254
1617 Sherman Ave 53704
Tel (608) 240-0020 SIC 8322

■ **CENTRAL STATE TELEPHONE CO LLC** p 280
525 Junction Rd 53717
Tel (608) 831-1000 SIC 4813

CITY OF MADISON p 316
210 Martin Luther 53703
Tel (608) 266-4671 SIC 9111

CMFG LIFE INSURANCE CO p 329
5910 Mineral Point Rd 53705
Tel (800) 356-2644 SIC 6321 6311

COMMUNITY LIVING ALLIANCE INC p 349
1414 Macarthur Rd 53714
Tel (608) 242-8335 SIC 8322

COUNTY OF DANE p 377
210 M Lthr Kng Jr Blv 425 53703
Tel (608) 266-4114 SIC 9121

■ **COVANCE LABORATORIES INC** p 384
3301 Kinsman Blvd 53704
Tel (608) 241-4471 SIC 8734

CSM COMPANIES INC p 398
5100 Estpark Blvd Ste 210 53718
Tel (608) 241-5616 SIC 5012 5013

CUNA MUTUAL GROUP p 401
5910 Mineral Point Rd 53705
Tel (608) 238-5851
SIC 6331 6311 6351 6411 7515

CUNA MUTUAL INSURANCE AGENCY INC p 401
5910 Mineral Point Rd 53705
Tel (608) 238-5851 SIC 6411

■ **DATEX-OHMEDA INC** p 414
3030 Ohmeda Dr 53718
Tel (608) 221-1551 SIC 3845

DEAN HEALTH SYSTEMS INC p 420
1808 W Beltline Hwy 53713
Tel (608) 250-1435 SIC 8099

DEMCO INC p 428
4810 Forest Run Rd 53704
Tel (800) 356-1200 SIC 5021 2521

DOUGLAS STEWART CO INC p 452
2402 Advance Rd 53718
Tel (608) 221-1155 SIC 5045 5044 5049

ERDMAN CO p 507
1 Erdman Pl 53717
Tel (608) 410-8000 SIC 1542

EXECUTIVE OFFICE OF STATE OF WISCONSIN p 518
115 E State Capitol 53702
Tel (608) 266-1212 SIC 9111

FAIRWAY INDEPENDENT MORTGAGE CORP p 525
4801 S Biltmore Ln 53718
Tel (608) 837-4800 SIC 6162

FARMFIRST DAIRY COOPERATIVE p 530
4001 Nakoosa Trl Ste 100 53714
Tel (608) 244-3373 SIC 5143 8611

▲ **FIRST BUSINESS FINANCIAL SERVICES INC** p 545
401 Charmany Dr 53719
Tel (608) 238-8008 SIC 6022

FORD KAYSER INC p 565
2303 W Beltline Hwy 53713
Tel (608) 271-6000
SIC 5511 7538 7532 7515 5521

■ **FPC FINANCIAL F S B** p 573
8402 Excelsior Dr 53717
Tel (608) 821-2000 SIC 6035

GREAT WOLF RESORTS HOLDINGS INC p 635
525 Junction Rd Ste 6000 53717
Tel (608) 662-4700 SIC 7011

GROUP HEALTH CO-OPERATIVE OF SOUTH CENTRAL WISCONSIN p 641
1265 John Q Hammons Dr # 200 53717
Tel (608) 251-4156 SIC 6324

GROUP HEALTH COOPERATIVE ADMINISTRATION p 641
1265 John Q Hammons Dr # 200 53717
Tel (608) 251-4156 SIC 8099

HARTUNG BROTHERS INC p 666
708 Heartland Trl # 2000 53717
Tel (608) 829-6000 SIC 0161 0115 8748

HOLLIS TELEPHONE CO INC p 701
515 Junction Rd 53717
Tel (608) 831-1000 SIC 4813

HOOPER CORP p 706
2030 Pennsylvania Ave 53704
Tel (608) 249-0451 SIC 1623 1711

HORIZON CONSTRUCTION GROUP INC p 707
5201 E Terrace Dr Ste 300 53718
Tel (608) 354-0900 SIC 1542 1522

HY CITE ENTERPRISES LLC p 722
333 Holtzman Rd 53713
Tel (608) 273-3373 SIC 5023

INTERVARSITY CHRISTIAN FELLOWSHIP/USA p 759
635 Science Dr 53711
Tel (608) 274-9001 SIC 8661 2731 7032

J H FINDORFF & SON INC p 771
300 S Bedford St 53703
Tel (608) 257-5321
SIC 1542 1541 8741 1522

M3 INSURANCE SOLUTIONS INC p 891
828 John Nolen Dr 53713
Tel (608) 273-0655 SIC 6411

MADISON AREA TECHNICAL COLLEGE DISTRICT p 894
1701 Wright St 53704
Tel (608) 246-6100 SIC 8222

■ **MADISON GAS AND ELECTRIC CO** p 894
133 S Blair St 53788
Tel (608) 252-7000 SIC 4931

MADISON METROPOLITAN SCHOOL DISTRICT p 894
545 W Dayton St 53703
Tel (608) 663-1879 SIC 8211

MADISON ONE HOLDINGS LLC p 894
2001 S Stoughton Rd 53716
Tel (608) 222-3484 SIC 3523

MADISON-KIPP CORP p 894
201 Waubesa St 53704
Tel (608) 244-3511 SIC 3363

MERITER HEALTH SERVICES INC p 949
202 S Park St 53715
Tel (608) 417-5800 SIC 8741

MERITER HOSPITAL INC p 949
202 S Park St 53715
Tel (608) 417-6000 SIC 8062

▲ **MGE ENERGY INC** p 958
133 S Blair St 53788
Tel (608) 252-7000 SIC 4939 4911 4924

MIDVALE INDEMNITY CO p 966
6000 American Pkwy 53783
Tel (847) 320-2000 SIC 6331 8099

NATIONAL GUARDIAN LIFE INSURANCE CO (INC) p 1013
2 E Gilman St Stop 1 53703
Tel (608) 257-5611 SIC 6311

PACIFIC CYCLE INC p 1104
4902 Hammersley Rd 53711
Tel (608) 268-2468 SIC 5091 5941

PAYMENT SERVICE NETWORK INC p 1122
2901 International Ln # 100 53704
Tel (608) 442-5100 SIC 7389 6531 8721

PIZZA HUT OF SOUTHERN WISCONSIN INC p 1152
434 S Yellowstone Dr D 53719
Tel (608) 833-2113 SIC 5812

PNA HOLDINGS LLC p 1158
3150 Pleasant View Rd 53713
Tel (608) 203-1500
SIC 5044 5045 5112 7699

■ **PROGRESSIVE NORTHERN INSURANCE CO** p 1181
44 E Mifflin St 53703
Tel (440) 461-5000 SIC 6331

REGIONAL DIVISION INC p 1219
600 Highland Ave 53792
Tel (608) 263-7923 SIC 8741

RESEARCH PRODUCTS CORP p 1226
1015 E Washington Ave 53703
Tel (608) 257-8801 SIC 5075 3564 3569

RIVERS END HOLDINGS LLC p 1237
301 N Broom St Fl 2 53703
Tel (952) 912-2500 *SIC* 5137 5136

ROMAN CATHOLIC DIOCESE OF MADISON INC p 1249
702 S High Point Rd 53719
Tel (608) 821-3000 *SIC* 8661

RURAL MUTUAL INSURANCE CO p 1258
1241 John Q Hammons Dr # 200 53717
Tel (608) 836-5525 *SIC* 6411

SSM HEALTH CARE OF WISCONSIN INC p 1364
1808 W Beltline Hwy 53713
Tel (608) 258-6551 *SIC* 8062

ST MARYS DEAN VENTURES INC p 1371
1808 W Beltline Hwy 53713
Tel (608) 250-1311 *SIC* 8011

ST MARYS HOSPITAL p 1371
700 S Park St 53715
Tel (608) 251-6100 *SIC* 8062

ST MARYS HOSPITAL MEDICAL CENTER AUXILIARY (INC) p 1371
700 S Park St 53715
Tel (608) 251-6100 *SIC* 6321

STATE OF WISCONSIN p 1382
115 E Capitol 53702
Tel (608) 266-1212 *SIC* 9111

STATE OF WISCONSIN p 1382
2135 Rimrock Rd 53713
Tel (608) 266-6466 *SIC* 9311

STEVENS CONSTRUCTION CORP p 1388
2 Buttonwood Ct 53718
Tel (608) 222-5100 *SIC* 1522 1542

SUB-ZERO GROUP INC p 1395
4717 Hammersley Rd 53711
Tel (608) 271-2233 *SIC* 3632

SUB-ZERO INC p 1395
4717 Hammersley Rd 53711
Tel (608) 271-2233 *SIC* 3632

SUMMIT CREDIT UNION p 1398
2424 Rimrock Rd 53713
Tel (608) 244-2400 *SIC* 6062

■ TDS LONG DISTANCE CORP p 1429
525 Junction Rd Ste 6000 53717
Tel (608) 831-1000 *SIC* 4813

■ TDS TELECOMMUNICATIONS CORP p 1429
525 Junction Rd Ste 1000 53717
Tel (608) 664-4000 *SIC* 4813

TELEVISION WISCONSIN INC p 1435
7025 Raymond Rd 53719
Tel (608) 271-4321 *SIC* 4833

■ TOMOTHERAPY INC p 1459
1240 Deming Way 53717
Tel (608) 824-2800 *SIC* 3829

TRI-COUNTY TELEPHONE CO INC p 1477
525 Junction Rd 53717
Tel (608) 661-3114 *SIC* 4813

UNIVERSITY OF WISCONSIN FOUNDATION p 1527
1848 University Ave 53726
Tel (608) 263-4545 *SIC* 8699

UNIVERSITY OF WISCONSIN HOSPITAL AND CLINICS AUTHORITY p 1527
600 Highland Ave 53792
Tel (608) 263-6400 *SIC* 8062 8069

UNIVERSITY OF WISCONSIN HOSPITALS AND CLINICS p 1527
600 Highland Ave 53792
Tel (608) 263-8991 *SIC* 8062

UNIVERSITY OF WISCONSIN SYSTEM p 1527
1700 Van Hise Ave 53726
Tel (608) 262-2321 *SIC* 8221 8741

UNIVERSITY OF WISCONSIN-MADISON p 1527
500 Lincoln Dr 53706
Tel (608) 262-9946 *SIC* 8221

VOGEL BROS BUILDING CO p 1564
2701 Packers Ave 53704
Tel (608) 241-5454 *SIC* 1542 1541 4941

VP HOLDINGS CORP p 1566
2514 Fish Hatchery Rd 53713
Tel (608) 256-1988 *SIC* 2048 5191 5153

WEA INSURANCE CORP p 1585
45 Nob Hill Rd 53713
Tel (608) 276-4000 *SIC* 6324 6311 6321

WEA INSURANCE CORP p 1585
45 Nob Hill Rd 53713
Tel (608) 276-4000 *SIC* 6324

WISCONSIN ALUMNI RESEARCH FOUNDATION p 1618
614 Walnut St Fl 13 53726
Tel (608) 263-2500 *SIC* 6799 6794

WISCONSIN DEPARTMENT OF ADMINISTRATION p 1618
101 E Wilson St Fl 10 53703
Tel (608) 266-1741 *SIC* 9611

WISCONSIN DEPARTMENT OF CORRECTIONS p 1618
3099 E Washington Ave 53704
Tel (608) 240-5000 *SIC* 9223

WISCONSIN DEPARTMENT OF HEALTH SERVICES p 1618
1 W Wilson St Rm 650 53703
Tel (608) 266-1865 *SIC* 9431 9441

WISCONSIN DEPARTMENT OF TRANSPORTATION p 1618
4802 Sheboygan Ave 53705
Tel (608) 266-2878 *SIC* 9621

WISCONSIN DEPARTMENT OF WORKFORCE DEVELOPMENT p 1618
201 E Wa Ave Rm 400x 53703
Tel (608) 266-3131 *SIC* 9651

WISCONSIN DEPT OF NATURAL RESOURCES p 1618
101 S Webster St 53703
Tel (608) 266-2621 *SIC* 9512

WISCONSIN EDUCATION ASSOCIATION INSURANCE TRUST p 1618
45 Nob Hill Rd 53713
Tel (608) 276-4000 *SIC* 6411

WISCONSIN EDUCATIONAL COMMUNICATIONS BOARD p 1618
3319 W Beltline Hwy 53713
Tel (608) 264-9600 *SIC* 4833 4832

■ WISCONSIN POWER AND LIGHT CO p 1619
4902 N Biltmore Ln # 1000 53718
Tel (608) 458-3311 *SIC* 4931

WISCONSIN TECHNICAL COLLEGE SYSTEM BOARD p 1619
4622 University Ave 53705
Tel (608) 266-1207 *SIC* 8222

ZIMBRICK INC p 1643
1601 W Beltline Hwy 53713
Tel (608) 277-2277 *SIC* 5511 7538 5521

MANAWA, WI

■ STURM FOODS INC p 1395
215 Center St 54949
Tel (920) 596-2511 *SIC* 5149

MANITOWOC, WI

■ BROADWIND TOWERS INC p 216
101 S 16th St 54220
Tel (920) 684-5531 *SIC* 3511

FRANCISCAN SISTERS OF CHRISTIAN CHARITY SPONSORED MINISTRIES INC p 573
1415 S Rapids Rd 54220
Tel (920) 684-7071 *SIC* 8741 8062

GREAT LAKES UTILITIES p 634
1323 S 7th St 54221
Tel (920) 686-4342 *SIC* 7539

HOLY FAMILY MEMORIAL INC p 702
2300 Western Ave 54220
Tel (920) 320-2011 *SIC* 8062

LAKESIDE FOODS INC p 840
808 Hamilton St 54220
Tel (920) 684-3356
SIC 2033 2037 2032 2038

▲ MANITOWOC CO INC p 902
2400 S 44th St 54220
Tel (920) 684-4410
SIC 3536 3537 3531 3585

■ MANITOWOC CRANES LLC p 902
2401 S 30th St 54220
Tel (920) 684-6621 *SIC* 3531

MANITOWOC TOOL AND MACHINING LLC p 902
4211 Clipper Dr 54220
Tel (920) 682-8825 *SIC* 3441

NORTHERN LABS INC p 1056
5800 West Dr 54220
Tel (920) 684-7137 *SIC* 2842 2841

MARATHON, WI

COUNTY MATERIALS CORP p 375
205 North St 54448
Tel (715) 443-2434
SIC 3271 5211 3273 3272 1442

MARATHON CHEESE CORP p 904
304 East St 54448
Tel (715) 443-2211 *SIC* 2022 5143

MARINETTE, WI

BAY AREA MEDICAL CENTER INC p 160
3100 Shore Dr 54143
Tel (715) 735-4200 *SIC* 8062

GREAT LAKES FINANCIAL MANAGEMENT GROUP INC p 633
2033 Marinette Ave 54143
Tel (715) 732-9955
SIC 6211 8742 6282 6411

KS KOLBENSCHMIDT US INC p 831
1731 Industrial Pkwy N 54143
Tel (715) 732-0181 *SIC* 3592

KSPG HOLDING USA INC p 831
1731 Industrial Pkwy N 54143
Tel (715) 732-0181 *SIC* 3592 3714 6719

KSPG NORTH AMERICA INC p 831
1731 Industrial Pkwy N 54143
Tel (715) 732-0181 *SIC* 3592

SAMUEL PRESSURE VESSEL GROUP INC p 1275
2121 Cleveland Ave 54143
Tel (715) 735-9311 *SIC* 3443

MARSHFIELD, WI

FAMILY HEALTH CENTER OF A MARSHFIELD INC p 527
1000 N Oak Ave 54449
Tel (715) 387-9137 *SIC* 8621

MARSHFIELD CLINIC HEALTH SYSTEM INC p 911
1000 N Oak Ave 54449
Tel (715) 387-5511 *SIC* 8011

MARSHFIELD CLINIC INC p 911
1000 N Oak Ave 54449
Tel (715) 387-5511 *SIC* 8011

■ MARSHFIELD DOORSYSTEMS INC p 911
1401 E 4th St 54449
Tel (715) 384-2141 *SIC* 2431 3442

NELSON-JAMESON INC p 1025
2400 E 5th St 54449
Tel (715) 387-1151 *SIC* 5084

PRINCE CORP p 1176
8351 County Road H 54449
Tel (800) 777-2486
SIC 5031 5191 2048 5083 5072

PROVISION PARTNERS COOPERATIVE p 1187
2327 W Veterans Pkwy 54449
Tel (715) 687-4443 *SIC* 5191 5984 5541

ROEHL TRANSPORT INC p 1246
1916 E 29th St 54449
Tel (715) 591-3795 *SIC* 4213

SAINT JOSEPHS HOSPITAL OF MARSHFIELD INC p 1269
611 N Saint Joseph Ave 54449
Tel (715) 387-1713 *SIC* 8062

SECURITY HEALTH PLAN OF WISCONSIN INC p 1299
1515 N Saint Joseph Ave 54449
Tel (715) 221-9555 *SIC* 8011

V & H INC p 1538
1505 S Central Ave 54449
Tel (715) 387-2545 *SIC* 5511 7513

MAYVILLE, WI

MAYVILLE ENGINEERING CO INC p 924
715 South St 53050
Tel (920) 387-4500 *SIC* 3469

METALCRAFT OF MAYVILLE INC p 952
1000 Metalcraft Dr 53050
Tel (920) 387-3150 *SIC* 3523 3444

MC FARLAND, WI

CITY WIDE INSULATION OF MADISON INC p 320
4501 Triangle St 53558
Tel (608) 838-4141 *SIC* 1742

MEDFORD, WI

HWD ACQUISITION INC p 722
575 S Whelen Ave 54451
Tel (800) 433-4873 *SIC* 2431

JAMES PETERSON SONS INC p 777
N2251 Gibson Dr 54451
Tel (715) 748-3010 *SIC* 1611

PEACHTREE COMPANIES INC p 1125
1 Weathershield Plz 54451
Tel (715) 748-6555 *SIC* 3442 2431

WEATHER SHIELD MFG INC p 1585
1 Weathershield Plz 54451
Tel (715) 748-2100 *SIC* 2431 3089 3442

MENASHA, WI

AFFINITY HEALTH SYSTEM p 32
1570 Midway Pl 54952
Tel (920) 720-1700 *SIC* 8741 8062

AZCO INC p 140
806 Valley Rd 54952
Tel (920) 734-5791 *SIC* 1629

■ BANTA CORP p 153
1457 Earl St 54952
Tel (312) 326-8000 *SIC* 2759 8742

FAITH TECHNOLOGIES INC p 526
225 Main St 54952
Tel (920) 738-1500 *SIC* 1731

GOODWILL INDUSTRIES OF NORTH CENTRAL WISCONSIN INC p 624
1800 Appleton Rd 54952
Tel (920) 731-6601 *SIC* 5932 7389 8331

NETWORK HEALTH SYSTEM INC p 1028
1165 Appleton Rd 54952
Tel (920) 831-8920 *SIC* 8011

NETWORK PLAN OF WISCONSIN INC p 1028
1570 Midway Pl 54952
Tel (920) 720-1200 *SIC* 6324

MENOMONEE FALLS, WI

▲ ACTUANT CORP p 20
N86w12500 Westbrook Xing 53051
Tel (262) 293-1500
SIC 3593 3492 3594 3625 7359

AID HOLDINGS LLC p 37
W140n8981 Lilly Rd 53051
Tel (262) 257-8888
SIC 8052 8051 8059 8082

ARANDELL CORP p 102
N82w13118 Leon Rd 53051
Tel (262) 255-4400 *SIC* 2752

BRADLEY CORP p 206
W142n9101 Fountain Blvd 53051
Tel (262) 251-6000 *SIC* 3431 3272

COMMUNITY MEMORIAL HOSPITAL OF MENOMONEE FALLS INC p 349
W180n8085 Town Hall Rd 53051
Tel (262) 251-1000 *SIC* 8062

COUSINS SUBMARINES INC p 383
N83w13400 Leon Rd 53051
Tel (262) 253-7700 *SIC* 5812

DARROW RUSS GROUP INC p 412
W133n8569 Executive Pkwy 53051
Tel (262) 250-9600 *SIC* 5511 7538

ENGMAN-TAYLOR CO INC p 499
W142n9351 Fountain Blvd 53051
Tel (262) 255-9300 *SIC* 5084 5085

FROEDTERT HEALTH INC p 580
400 Wood Prim Ste 53051
Tel (262) 251-1000 *SIC* 8062

▲ KOHLS CORP p 826
N56w17000 Ridgewood Dr 53051
Tel (262) 703-7000 *SIC* 5311 5961

■ KOHLS DEPARTMENT STORES INC p 826
N56w17000 Ridgewood Dr 53051
Tel (262) 703-7000 *SIC* 5311

LAMPLIGHT FARMS INC p 841
W140n4900 Lilly Rd 53051
Tel (262) 781-9590
SIC 3648 3999 3229 2911

■ MAGNETEK INC p 896
N49w13650 Campbell Dr 53051
Tel (262) 783-3500 *SIC* 3625

POWER PRODUCTS LLC p 1165
N85w12545 Westbrook Xing 53051
Tel (262) 293-0600 *SIC* 3679 3699 3691

PROHEALTH CARE MEDICAL ASSOCIATES INC p 1182
W180n8000 Town Hall Rd 53051
Tel (262) 255-2500 *SIC* 8011

WACKER NEUSON CORP p 1570
N92w15000 Anthony Ave 53051
Tel (262) 255-0500
SIC 3531 3621 3561 3546 3423

MENOMONIE, WI

MAYO CLINIC HEALTH SYSTEM-RED CEDAR INC p 924
2415 Stout Rd 54751
Tel (715) 235-5531 *SIC* 8062

UNIVERSITY OF WISCONSIN-SYSTEM p 1527
712s Brdwy 125m Admn Bld 54751
Tel (715) 232-2441 *SIC* 8221

MEQUON, WI

CHARTER MANUFACTURING CO INC p 291
1212 W Glen Oaks Ln 53092
Tel (262) 243-4700 *SIC* 3312 3496

COLUMBIA ST MARYS HOSPITAL OZAUKEE INC p 341
13111 N Port Wash Rd 53097
Tel (262) 243-7300 *SIC* 8062

CONCORDIA UNIVERSITY WISCONSIN INC p 355
12800 N Lake Shore Dr 53097
Tel (262) 243-5700 *SIC* 8221

DENTAQUEST LLC p 429
12121 Corporate Pkwy 53092
Tel (262) 241-7140 *SIC* 6324

HB PERFORMANCE SYSTEMS INC p 671
5800 W Donges Bay Rd 53092
Tel (262) 242-4300 *SIC* 3714 3751

■ TELSMITH INC p 1435
10910 N Industrial Dr 53092
Tel (262) 242-6600 *SIC* 3531 3532

MERRILL, WI

CHURCH MUTUAL INSURANCE CO p 305
3000 Schuster Ln 54452
Tel (715) 536-5577 *SIC* 6411

MIDDLETON, WI

■ AMERICAN GIRL BRANDS LLC p 73
8400 Fairway Pl 53562
Tel (608) 836-4848 *SIC* 5945 2731

■ CAPITOL INDEMNITY CORP p 251
1600 Aspen Cmns Ste 400 53562
Tel (608) 829-4200 *SIC* 6331 6351

■ CAPITOL TRANSAMERICA CORP p 251
1600 Aspen Cmns Ste 400 53562
Tel (608) 829-4200 *SIC* 6331 6351

ELECTRONIC THEATRE CONTROLS INC p 486
3031 Pleasant View Rd 53562
Tel (608) 831-4116 *SIC* 5063

ERDMAN HOLDINGS INC p 507
6720 Frank Llyd Wright Av 53562
Tel (608) 662-2205 *SIC* 1542 2599

EXTREME ENGINEERING SOLUTIONS INC p 521
3225 Deming Way Ste 120 53562
Tel (608) 833-1155 *SIC* 5045

FISKARS BRANDS INC p 552
7800 Discovery Dr 53562
Tel (608) 259-1649
SIC 3052 3679 3421 3069 3423

FRANK LIQUOR CO INC p 574
2115 Pleasant View Rd 53562
Tel (608) 836-6000 *SIC* 5182 5181

MEAD AND HUNT INC p 933
2440 Deming Way 53562
Tel (608) 273-6380 *SIC* 8712 8711

MIDDLETON-CROSS PLAINS-AREA SCHOOL DISTRICT p 965
7106 South Ave 53562
Tel (608) 829-9000 SIC 8211

RAYMOND MANAGEMENT CO INC p 1210
8333 Greenway Blvd # 200 53562
Tel (608) 833-4100 SIC 6552 8741 7011

RURAL ELECTRIC SUPPLY COOPERATIVE p 1258
2250 Pinehurst Dr 53562
Tel (608) 831-2600 SIC 5063

SHELTERED WINGS INC p 1315
2120 W Greenview Dr Ste 4 53562
Tel (608) 664-9856 SIC 5049

■ **SPECTRUM BRANDS HOLDINGS INC** p 1357
3001 Deming Way 53562
Tel (608) 275-3340
SIC 3692 2879 3999 3648

■ **SPECTRUM BRANDS INC** p 1357
3001 Deming Way 53562
Tel (608) 275-3340
SIC 3692 3634 2879 3999 3648

SPRINGS INDUSTRIES INC p 1361
7549 Graber Rd 53562
Tel (608) 836-1011 SIC 2591

SPRINGS WINDOW FASHIONS LLC p 1361
7549 Graber Rd 53562
Tel (608) 836-1011 SIC 2591

U W PROVISION CO INC p 1497
2315 Pleasant View Rd 53562
Tel (608) 836-7421 SIC 5147

UNIVERSITY OF WISCONSIN MEDICAL FOUNDATION INC p 1527
7974 Uw Health Ct 53562
Tel (608) 821-4223
SIC 8221 8011 2834 8299 8042 8043

UW HEALTH p 1537
7974 Uw Health Ct 53562
Tel (608) 829-5217 SIC 8099

MILTON, WI

CHARTER NEX HOLDING CO p 291
1264 E High St 53563
Tel (608) 531-1405 SIC 3081

FGS-WI LLC p 539
1101 S Janesville St 53563
Tel (608) 373-6500 SIC 2752 7331

MBK-WI INC p 925
1101 S Janesville St 53563
Tel (608) 373-6500 SIC 2752

UNITED ETHANOL LLC p 1508
1250 Chicago St 53563
Tel (608) 868-5900 SIC 2869

MILWAUKEE, WI

▲ **A O SMITH CORP** p 6
11270 W Park Pl Ste 1200 53224
Tel (414) 359-4000 SIC 3639 3433

AA MANAGEMENT GROUP INC p 7
411 E Wisconsin Ave # 1900 53202
Tel (414) 271-7240 SIC 6531 7389

ALBERT TROSTEL & SONS CO p 46
800 N Marshall St 53202
Tel (414) 223-1560 SIC 3111

■ **ALDEN JOHN LIFE INSURANCE CO** p 47
501 W Michigan St 53203
Tel (414) 271-3011 SIC 6311

ALDRICH CHEMICAL CO LLC p 48
6000 N Teutonia Ave 53209
Tel (414) 438-3850
SIC 2869 2819 3821 7371 2741

ALVERNO COLLEGE p 63
3400 S 43rd St 53219
Tel (414) 382-6000 SIC 8221

AMERICAN APPRAISAL ASSOCIATES INC p 68
411 E Wisconsin Ave # 1900 53202
Tel (630) 541-4650 SIC 8748 7389 6531

■ **AMERICAN GENERAL LIFE BROKERAGE GROUP** p 73
1200 N Mayfair Rd Ste 300 53226
Tel (414) 443-5800 SIC 6311 6411

ARBON EQUIPMENT CORP p 103
8900 N Arbon Dr 53223
Tel (414) 355-2600 SIC 5211

ARTISAN PARTNERS ASSET MANAGEMENT INC p 114
875 E Wscnsin Ave Ste 800 53202
Tel (414) 390-6100 SIC 6282

ASSOCIATED SALES & BAG CO p 121
400 W Boden St 53207
Tel (414) 769-1000 SIC 5113

ASTRONAUTICS CORP OF AMERICA p 122
4115 N Teutonia Ave 53209
Tel (414) 449-4000
SIC 3812 3571 3572 3769

ATLAS COPCO CONSTRUCTION MINING TECHNIQUE USA LLC p 127
11825 W Carmen Ave 53225
Tel (414) 760-1193 SIC 1521

AURORA HEALTH CARE CENTRAL INC p 132
3031 W Montana St 53215
Tel (414) 647-3211 SIC 8099

AURORA HEALTH CARE INC p 132
750 W Virginia St 53204
Tel (414) 647-3000 SIC 8741 8062

AURORA HEALTH CARE METRO INC p 132
2900 W Oklahoma Ave 53215
Tel (414) 649-6000 SIC 8062

AURORA MEDICAL GROUP INC p 132
750 W Virginia St 53204
Tel (414) 299-1781 SIC 8011

AURORA SINAI MEDICAL CENTER INC p 132
945 N 12th St 53233
Tel (414) 219-2000 SIC 8062

AURORA WEST ALLIS MEDICAL CENTER p 132
8901 W Lincoln Ave 53227
Tel (414) 328-6000 SIC 8062

▲ **BADGER METER INC** p 144
4545 W Brown Deer Rd 53223
Tel (414) 355-0400 SIC 3824 3491 3823

BAIRD FINANCIAL CORP p 145
777 E Wisconsin Ave 53202
Tel (414) 765-3500 SIC 6719

BAIRD HOLDING CO p 145
777 E Wisconsin Ave 53202
Tel (414) 765-3500 SIC 6719

■ **BANK MUTUAL** p 151
4949 W Brown Deer Rd 53223
Tel (414) 354-1500
SIC 6036 6163 6029 6022

▲ **BANK MUTUAL CORP** p 151
4949 W Brown Deer Rd 53223
Tel (414) 354-1500 SIC 6036

BENTLEY WORLD-PACKAGING LTD p 173
4080 N Port Washington Rd 53212
Tel (414) 967-8000 SIC 4783 5199

BINGO POTAWATOMI p 183
1721 W Canal St 53233
Tel (414) 645-6888 SIC 7999 5812 5947

BLOODCENTER OF WISCONSIN INC p 189
638 N 18th St 53233
Tel (414) 933-5000 SIC 8099

BOSTIK FINDLEY F S C INC p 202
11320 W Wtertown Plank Rd 53226
Tel (414) 774-2250 SIC 5085

▲ **BRADY CORP** p 207
6555 W Good Hope Rd 53223
Tel (414) 358-6600
SIC 3993 2672 3695 3577

■ **BRADY WORLDWIDE INC** p 207
6555 W Good Hope Rd 53223
Tel (414) 358-6600 SIC 3999

BRENNTAG GREAT LAKES LLC p 210
4420 N Hrley Davidson Ave 53225
Tel (262) 252-3550 SIC 5169

C G SCHMIDT INC p 232
11777 W Lake Park Dr 53224
Tel (414) 577-1177 SIC 1542 8741

■ **C&H DISTRIBUTORS LLC** p 234
11200 W Parkland Ave 53224
Tel (800) 607-8520 SIC 5084

CARDINAL STRITCH UNIVERSITY INC p 253
6801 N Yates Rd 53217
Tel (414) 410-4000 SIC 8221

CATHEDRAL SQUARE PHARMACY p 265
732 N Jackson St Ste 300 53202
Tel (414) 277-6510 SIC 5912

CATHOLIC FINANCIAL SERVICES CORP p 266
1100 W Wells St Ste 1 53233
Tel (414) 278-6550 SIC 6311 6211

CATHOLIC KNIGHTS INSURANCE SOCIETY INC p 267
1100 W Wells St Ste 1 53233
Tel (414) 273-6266
SIC 6311 6411 6211 6141

CHILDRENS HOSPITAL AND HEALTH SYSTEM INC p 299
8915 W Connell Ave 53226
Tel (414) 266-2000
SIC 8069 8082 7389 7322

CHILDRENS HOSPITAL OF WISCONSIN INC p 300
9000 W Wscnsin Ave Stop 1 53226
Tel (414) 266-2000 SIC 8069

CHILDRENS SPECIALTY GROUP INC p 300
999 N 92nd St Ste C740 53226
Tel (414) 292-7858 SIC 8011

CHR HANSEN p 302
9015 W Maple St 53214
Tel (414) 607-5700 SIC 2099

CHRYSALIS PACKAGING AND ASSEMBLY CORP p 304
130 W Edger Avenu Sut 53207
Tel (414) 744-8550 SIC 7389

CITY OF MILWAUKEE p 316
200 E Wells St 53202
Tel (414) 286-3321 SIC 9111

CLEAN POWER LLC p 324
124 N 121st St 53226
Tel (414) 302-3000 SIC 7349 7217

COLUMBIA HOSPITAL INC p 341
4425 N Pt Wshngton Rd 1 1 Stop 53212
Tel (414) 961-3300 SIC 8062

COLUMBIA ST MARYS HOSPITAL MILWAUKEE INC p 341
2301 N Lake Dr 53211
Tel (414) 291-1000 SIC 8062

COLUMBIA ST MARYS INC p 342
4425 N Port Washington Rd 53212
Tel (414) 326-2495 SIC 8062

COMMUNITY CARE ORGANIZATION p 347
3220 W Vliet St 53208
Tel (414) 231-4000 SIC 8011

CORPORATE GROUP INC p 372
7123 W Calumet Rd 53223
Tel (414) 355-7740 SIC 8711 1731

COVENANT HEALTH CARE SYSTEM INC p 384
1126 S 70th St Ste S306 53214
Tel (414) 456-3000 SIC 8062

■ **DERCO AEROSPACE INC** p 431
8000 W Tower Ave 53223
Tel (414) 355-3066 SIC 5065 5088

DERSE INC p 431
3800 W Canal St 53208
Tel (414) 257-2000 SIC 3993 7312

DESK BC MERGER LLC p 432
333 W State St 53203
Tel (414) 224-2000 SIC 4832

DIRECT SUPPLY INC p 441
6767 N Industrial Rd 53223
Tel (414) 358-2805 SIC 5047

▲ **DOUGLAS DYNAMICS INC** p 452
7777 N 73rd St 53223
Tel (414) 354-2310 SIC 3531

■ **DOUGLAS DYNAMICS LLC** p 452
7777 N 73rd St 53223
Tel (414) 354-2310 SIC 3531

DRS POWER & CONTROL TECHNOLOGIES INC p 457
4265 N 30th St 53216
Tel (414) 875-4314 SIC 3812

■ **EMERITUS CORP** p 492
3131 Elliott Ave Ste 500 53214
Tel (206) 298-2909 SIC 8052

EVERETT SMITH GROUP LTD p 514
330 E Kilbourn Ave # 1400 53202
Tel (414) 223-1560 SIC 3111 6282

■ **EXPERIS FINANCE US LLC** p 520
100 W Manpower Pl 53212
Tel (414) 319-3400 SIC 8721

■ **EXPERIS US INC** p 520
100 W Manpower Pl 53212
Tel (414) 961-1000 SIC 7361

EXTENDICARE FOUNDATION INC p 521
111 W Michigan St 53203
Tel (414) 908-8000 SIC 8051

EXTENDICARE HEALTH SERVICES INC p 521
111 W Michigan St 53203
Tel (414) 908-6720 SIC 8051 7389 5912

EXTENDICARE HOLDINGS LLC p 521
111 W Michigan St 53203
Tel (414) 908-8000 SIC 8051

EXTENDICARE HOMES INC p 521
111 W Michigan St 53203
Tel (414) 908-8000 SIC 8051

F DOHMEN CO p 522
190 N Milwaukee St 53202
Tel (414) 299-4913 SIC 5122 5045 7374

■ **FALK SERVICE CORP** p 526
3001 W Canal St 53208
Tel (414) 342-3131 SIC 5085

FOLEY & LARDNER LLP p 563
777 E Wisconsin Ave # 3800 53202
Tel (414) 271-2400 SIC 8111

■ **FORTIS INSURANCE CO** p 569
501 W Michigan St 53203
Tel (262) 646-4633 SIC 6311 6321

FOUR KEYS LLC p 571
5505 S 27th St 53221
Tel (414) 282-9300 SIC 5511

FROEDTERT AND COMMUNITY HEALTH INC p 580
9200 W Wisconsin Ave 53226
Tel (414) 777-0960 SIC 8062

FROEDTERT HEALTH HOSPITAL p 580
9200 W Wisconsin Ave 53226
Tel (414) 805-3000 SIC 8062

GARDNER DENVER INC p 592
222 E Erie St Ste 500 53202
Tel (414) 212-4700 SIC 3564 3561 3563

GENERAL PET SUPPLY INC p 601
7711 N 81st St 53223
Tel (414) 365-3400 SIC 5199

GILBANE BUILDING CO / CG SCHMIDT A JOINT VENTURE p 611
11777 W Lake Park Dr 53224
Tel (414) 577-1177 SIC 1542

GOSSEN CORP p 626
2030 W Bender Rd 53209
Tel (800) 558-8984 SIC 2431 3089 2452

GREATER MILWAUKEE FOUNDATION INC p 635
101 W Pleasant St Ste 210 53212
Tel (414) 272-5805 SIC 8699 8733

GUARANTY FINANCIAL MHC p 644
4000 W Brown Deer Rd 53209
Tel (414) 362-4000 SIC 6035

HAL LEONARD CORP p 653
7777 W Bluemound Rd 53213
Tel (414) 774-3630 SIC 2741

▲ **HARLEY-DAVIDSON INC** p 661
3700 W Juneau Ave 53208
Tel (414) 342-4680
SIC 3751 6153 6141 6411 6399

■ **HARLEY-DAVIDSON MOTOR CO INC** p 662
3700 W Juneau Ave 3800 53208
Tel (414) 343-4056 SIC 3751

HATCO CORP p 668
635 S 28th St 53215
Tel (414) 671-6350 SIC 3589

HELLERMANNTYTON CORP p 681
7930 N Faulkner Rd 53224
Tel (414) 355-1130 SIC 3089 2891

HUF NORTH AMERICA AUTOMOTIVE PARTS MANUFACTURING CORP p 717
9020 W Dean Rd 53224
Tel (414) 365-4950 SIC 3714

■ **INTEGRYS HOLDING INC** p 750
231 W Michigan St 53201
Tel (414) 221-2345 SIC 4931

INTERNATIONAL COMMERCE & MARKETING CORP p 755
500 W Oklahoma Ave 53207
Tel (414) 290-1500 SIC 5085 5961

JACOBUS ENERGY INC p 775
11815 W Bradley Rd 53224
Tel (414) 577-0217 SIC 5983 5172

JASON HOLDINGS INC p 778
411 E Wisconsin Ave # 2120 53202
Tel (414) 277-9300
SIC 2297 3465 3469 3844 3443

■ **JASON INC** p 778
411 E Wisconsin Ave 53202
Tel (414) 277-9300
SIC 3465 2297 3625 3469 3844 3443

▲ **JASON INDUSTRIES INC** p 778
833 E Michigan St Ste 900 53202
Tel (414) 277-9300
SIC 3465 2297 3625 3469 3844 3443

JOHNSON CONTROLS BATTERY GROUP INC p 791
5757 N Green Bay Ave 53209
Tel (414) 524-1200 SIC 3691

JOHNSON CONTROLS HOLDING CO INC p 791
5757 N Green Bay Ave 53209
Tel (414) 524-1200 SIC 6719

JOHNSON CONTROLS INC p 791
5757 N Green Bay Ave 53209
Tel (414) 524-1200
SIC 2531 3714 3691 3822 8744

JOURNAL BROADCAST GROUP INC p 794
720 E Capitol Dr 53212
Tel (414) 799-9494 SIC 4833

JOURNAL COMMUNICATIONS INC p 794
333 W State St 53203
Tel (414) 224-2000
SIC 4832 4833 2711 2759 4813

■ **JOURNAL MEDIA GROUP INC** p 794
333 W State St 53203
Tel (414) 224-2000 SIC 2711

JOURNAL SENTINEL INC p 794
333 W State St 53203
Tel (414) 224-2000 SIC 2711

▲ **JOY GLOBAL INC** p 794
100 E Wisconsin Ave # 2780 53202
Tel (414) 319-8500 SIC 3532

■ **JOY GLOBAL SURFACE MINING INC** p 794
4400 W National Ave 53214
Tel (414) 671-4400 SIC 3462

■ **JPHI HOLDINGS INC** p 795
411 E Wisconsin Ave 53202
Tel (414) 277-9445
SIC 3465 2297 3625 3469 3844 3443

KLEMENT SAUSAGE CO INC p 823
1036 W Juneau Ave 400 53233
Tel (414) 744-2330 SIC 2013

KRIETE TRUCK CENTER MILWAUKEE INC p 830
4444 W Blue Mound Rd 53208
Tel (414) 258-8484 SIC 5511

LAKESIDE INTERNATIONAL LLC p 840
11000 W Silver Spring Dr 53225
Tel (414) 353-4800
SIC 5511 5531 7538 7532 6159 7513

LESAFFRE INTERNATIONAL CORP p 857
7475 W Main St 53214
Tel (414) 615-3300 SIC 2099

LESAFFREYEAST CORP p 857
7475 W Main St 53214
Tel (414) 615-3300 SIC 5149

LUBAR & CO INC p 883
700 N Water St Ste 1200 53202
Tel (414) 291-9000 SIC 6722

LUTHERAN SOCIAL SERVICES OF WISCONSIN AND UPPER MICHIGAN INC p 886
647 W Virginia St Ste 200 53204
Tel (262) 896-3446 SIC 8322 8082

■ **M G I C MORTGAGE INSURANCE CORP** p 889
250 E Kilbourn Ave 53202
Tel (414) 347-6480 SIC 6351

■ **MANPOWER INC OF NEW YORK** p 902
100 W Manpower Pl 53212
Tel (414) 961-1000 SIC 7363

▲ **MANPOWERGROUP INC** p 903
100 W Manpower Pl 53212
Tel (414) 961-1000 SIC 7363 7361

▲ **MARCUS CORP** p 905
100 E Wisconsin Ave # 1 53202
Tel (414) 905-1000 *SIC* 7011 7833

■ **MARCUS HOTELS INC** p 905
100 E Wisconsin Ave 53202
Tel (414) 905-1200 *SIC* 7011

■ **MARCUS THEATRES CORP** p 905
100 E Wisconsin Ave 53202
Tel (414) 905-1500 *SIC* 7832

MARK TRAVEL CORP p 907
8907 N Port Washington Rd 53217
Tel (414) 228-7472 *SIC* 4725

MARQUETTE UNIVERSITY p 910
1250 W Wisconsin Ave 53233
Tel (414) 288-7223 *SIC* 8221

MARSHALL & ILSLEY TRUST CO NATIONAL ASSOCIATION p 911
111 E Kilbourn Ave # 200 53202
Tel (414) 287-8700 *SIC* 6733

■ **MARSHALL & SWIFT/BOECKH LLC** p 911
10001 W Innovation Dr # 102 53226
Tel (262) 780-2800 *SIC* 6411

MASON WELLS BUYOUT FUND II LIMITED PARTNERSHIP p 916
411 E Wisconsin Ave 53202
Tel (414) 727-6400
SIC 3594 3492 3593 6211

MASON WELLS INC p 916
411 E Wisconsin Ave # 1280 53202
Tel (414) 727-6400 *SIC* 6799

MEDICAL COLLEGE OF WISCONSIN INC p 936
8701 W Watertown Plank Rd 53226
Tel (414) 456-8296 *SIC* 8221

MERCO GROUP INC p 945
7711 N 81st St 53223
Tel (414) 365-2600 *SIC* 5199 5047

MERIDIAN INDUSTRIES INC p 949
735 N Water St Ste 630 53202
Tel (414) 224-0610
SIC 3069 2843 2269 7389

■ **METAVANTE CORP** p 953
4900 W Brown Deer Rd 53223
Tel (904) 438-6000 *SIC* 7374 8742 6153

▲ **MGIC INVESTMENT CORP** p 958
250 E Kilbourn Ave 53202
Tel (414) 347-6480 *SIC* 6351 6411

MICHAEL BEST & FRIEDRICH LLP p 960
100 E Wisconsin Ave # 3300 53202
Tel (414) 271-6560 *SIC* 8111

■ **MILLER BREWERIES EAST INC** p 970
3939 W Highland Blvd 53208
Tel (414) 931-2000 *SIC* 2082

■ **MILSCO MANUFACTURING CO** p 972
9009 N 51st St 53223
Tel (414) 354-0500 *SIC* 2531

MILWAUKEE AREA TECHNICAL COLLEGE FOUNDATION INC p 972
700 W State St 53233
Tel (414) 297-6792 *SIC* 8222 8221

MILWAUKEE COUNTY BEHAVORIAL HEALTH DIVISION p 972
9455 W Watertown Plank Rd 53226
Tel (414) 257-6995 *SIC* 8063

MILWAUKEE PUBLIC SCHOOLS (INC) p 972
5225 W Vliet St 53208
Tel (414) 475-8393 *SIC* 8211

MILWAUKEE SCHOOL OF ENGIINEERING p 972
1025 N Broadway 53202
Tel (414) 277-6763 *SIC* 8221

MILWAUKEE SCHOOL OF ENGINEERING p 972
1025 N Broadway 53202
Tel (414) 277-7300 *SIC* 8221

MILWAUKEE TRANSPORT SERVICES INC p 972
1942 N 17th St 53205
Tel (414) 344-6711 *SIC* 4131

MILWAUKEE WORLD FESTIVAL INC p 972
114 N Jackson St 53202
Tel (414) 273-2680 *SIC* 7999

MINISTRY HEALTH CARE INC p 973
400 W River Woods Pkwy 53212
Tel (414) 359-1060 *SIC* 8011 8051

MINISTRY MEDICAL GROUP INC p 973
11925 W Lake Park Dr 53224
Tel (414) 359-1060 *SIC* 8011

MORTARA INSTRUMENT INC p 991
7865 N 86th St 53224
Tel (414) 354-1600 *SIC* 8731 3845

■ **MORTGAGE GUARANTY INSURANCE CORP** p 991
270 E Kilbourn Ave 53202
Tel (414) 347-6480 *SIC* 6351

■ **MORTGAGE GUARANTY REINSURANCE CORP** p 991
250 E Kilbourn Ave 270 53202
Tel (414) 347-6480 *SIC* 6351

NATIONAL BUSINESS FURNITURE LLC p 1010
770 S 70th St 53214
Tel (414) 276-8511 *SIC* 5021

NORTHWESTERN MUTUAL LIFE INSURANCE CO p 1060
720 E Wisconsin Ave 53202
Tel (414) 271-1444 *SIC* 6311 6321 7389

NORTHWESTERN MUTUAL WEALTH MANAGEMENT CO p 1061
611 E Wisconsin Ave 53202
Tel (206) 623-8801 *SIC* 6411

OGLETREE DEAKINS NASH SMOAK & STEWART PC p 1077
1243 N 10th St Ste 210 53205
Tel (414) 239-6400 *SIC* 8111

OLDENBURG GROUP INC p 1082
1717 W Civic Dr 53209
Tel (414) 354-6600 *SIC* 3537 3532 3646

PALERMO VILLA INC p 1108
3301 W Canal St 53208
Tel (414) 342-8898 *SIC* 5149

PAX HOLDINGS LLC p 1122
758 N Broadway Ste 910 53202
Tel (414) 803-9983
SIC 5199 2759 2672 2671 2657 2752

PENTAIR FILTRATION INC p 1131
5730 N Glen Park Rd 53209
Tel (800) 645-0267 *SIC* 3561

PHOENIX CARE SYSTEMS INC p 1144
1744 N Farwell Ave 53202
Tel (414) 225-4460 *SIC* 8361

PHYSICIANS REALTY TRUST p 1146
309 N Water St Ste 500 53202
Tel (414) 367-5600 *SIC* 6798

PPC PARTNERS INC p 1166
5464 N Port Washington Rd E 53217
Tel (414) 831-1251 *SIC* 1731

QUARLES & BRADY LLP p 1198
411 E Wisconsin Ave # 2040 53202
Tel (414) 277-5000 *SIC* 8111

■ **RBS GLOBAL INC** p 1211
4701 W Greenfield Ave 53214
Tel (414) 643-3000
SIC 3562 3566 3568 3272 3261

RED STAR YEAST CO LLC p 1216
7475 W Main St Ste 150 53214
Tel (800) 445-4746 *SIC* 2099

REV GROUP INC p 1229
111 E Kilbourn Ave # 2600 53202
Tel (414) 290-0190 *SIC* 3711

▲ **REXNORD CORP** p 1230
4701 W Greenfield Ave 53214
Tel (414) 643-3739 *SIC* 3491

■ **REXNORD INDUSTRIES LLC** p 1230
247 W Freshwater Way # 200 53204
Tel (414) 643-3000
SIC 3568 3566 3625 3714

■ **REXNORD LLC** p 1230
3001 W Canal St 53208
Tel (414) 342-3131 *SIC* 3566 3325 3599

■ **REXNORD-ZURN HOLDINGS INC** p 1230
4701 W Greenfield Ave 53214
Tel (414) 643-3000
SIC 3568 3566 3625 3714

RITE-HITE CO LLC p 1236
8900 N Arbon Dr 53223
Tel (414) 355-2600 *SIC* 5084 3842 3448

RITE-HITE HOLDING CORP p 1237
8900 N Arbon Dr 53223
Tel (414) 355-2600 *SIC* 5084 3449 3537

ROBERT W BAIRD & CO INC p 1241
777 E Wisconsin Ave Fl 29 53202
Tel (414) 765-3500 *SIC* 6719

▲ **ROCKWELL AUTOMATION INC** p 1245
1201 S 2nd St 53204
Tel (414) 382-2000
SIC 3625 3621 3566 3661

■ **ROUNDYS INC** p 1253
875 E Wisconsin Ave 53202
Tel (414) 231-5000 *SIC* 5411

■ **ROUNDYS SUPERMARKETS INC** p 1253
875 E Wscnsin Ave Ste 100 53202
Tel (414) 231-5000 *SIC* 5411 5141

RUSSEL METALS WILLIAMS BAHCALL INC p 1259
999 W Armour Ave 53221
Tel (414) 481-7100 *SIC* 5051

RYAN ROBERTSON AND ASSOCIATES INC p 1260
330 E Kilbourn Ave # 650 53202
Tel (414) 271-3575 *SIC* 6411

SCHWERMAN TRUCKING CO p 1291
611 S 28th St 53215
Tel (414) 671-1600 *SIC* 4213

■ **SENIOR BROOKDALE LIVING COMMUNITIES INC** p 1303
6737 W Wa St Ste 2300 53214
Tel (414) 918-5000 *SIC* 8059 8051 8361

SENIOR BROOKDALE LIVING INC p 1303
6737 W Wa St Ste 2300 53214
Tel (941) 625-1220 *SIC* 8059

▲ **SENSIENT TECHNOLOGIES CORP** p 1304
777 E Wisconsin Ave # 1100 53202
Tel (414) 271-6755 *SIC* 2087 2099

■ **SOUTHERN ASSISTED LIVING INC** p 1347
6737 W Wa St Ste 2300 53214
Tel (414) 588-0431 *SIC* 6513

ST FRANCIS HOSPITAL INC p 1366
3237 S 16th St 53215
Tel (414) 647-5000 *SIC* 8062

ST MICHAEL HOSPITAL OF FRANCISCAN SISTERS MILWAUKEE INC p 1372
5000 W Chambers St 53210
Tel (414) 447-2000 *SIC* 8062 8011

STEIN GARDEN CENTERS INC p 1385
5400 S 27th St 53221
Tel (414) 761-5400 *SIC* 5261 5992

▲ **STRATTEC SECURITY CORP** p 1393
3333 W Good Hope Rd 53209
Tel (414) 247-3333 *SIC* 3714 3364 3429

SUPER STEEL LLC p 1406
7900 W Tower Ave 53223
Tel (414) 362-9114
SIC 3443 3444 3441 3446

TAKKT AMERICA HOLDING INC p 1422
770 S 70th St 53214
Tel (414) 443-1700 *SIC* 5084

TANKSTAR USA INC p 1424
611 S 28th St 53215
Tel (414) 671-3039 *SIC* 4213

TENDERCARE (MICHIGAN) INC p 1437
111 W Michigan St 53203
Tel (800) 395-5000 *SIC* 8051

■ **TIME INSURANCE CO** p 1454
501 W Michigan St 53203
Tel (414) 271-3011 *SIC* 6321

TRAFFIC AND PARKING CONTROL CO INC p 1469
5100 W Brown Deer Rd 53223
Tel (262) 814-7000 *SIC* 5063 3444 3646

UNITED P&H SUPPLY CO p 1510
9947 W Carmen Ave 53225
Tel (414) 393-6600
SIC 5085 5074 3312 3463

■ **UNITEDHEALTHCARE OF WISCONSIN INC** p 1515
10701 W Research Dr 53226
Tel (414) 443-4060 *SIC* 6324 6411 6321

V & J EMPLOYMENT SERVICES INC p 1538
53223 W Brown Deer Rd 53223
Tel (414) 365-9003 *SIC* 5812

V & J HOLDING COMPANIES INC p 1538
6933 W Brown Deer Rd Fl 2 53223
Tel (414) 365-9003 *SIC* 5812

■ **VEOLIA ENVIRONMENTAL SERVICES NORTH AMERICA LLC** p 1548
125 S 84th St Ste 200 53214
Tel (414) 479-7800 *SIC* 4953 4212

■ **WE ENERGIES** p 1585
231 W Michigan St 53203
Tel (414) 221-2345 *SIC* 4911 4924 4961

▲ **WEC ENERGY GROUP INC** p 1587
231 W Michigan St 53203
Tel (414) 221-2345 *SIC* 4911 4924

WEST ALLIS-WEST MILWAUKEE p 1593
1205 S 70th St 53214
Tel (414) 604-3033 *SIC* 8211

WHEATON FRANCISCAN p 1604
3070 N 51st St Ste 601 53210
Tel (414) 447-2000 *SIC* 8062

WHEATON FRANCISCAN HEALTHCARE-ST FRANCIS INC p 1604
3237 S 16th St Ste 1005 53215
Tel (414) 647-5000 *SIC* 8399

WHEATON FRANCISCAN HEALTHCARE-FRANKLIN p 1604
3070 N 51st St Ste 210 53210
Tel (414) 874-1171 *SIC* 8062

WILDE OF WEST ALLIS INC p 1609
3225 S 108th St 53227
Tel (414) 329-6043
SIC 5511 5521 7538 7515 7513 5012

WILLOWGLEN ACADEMY-WISCONSIN INC p 1613
1744 N Farwell Ave 53202
Tel (414) 225-4460 *SIC* 8361

WIPFLI LLP p 1618
10000 W Innovation Dr 250-260 53226
Tel (414) 431-9300 *SIC* 8748 8721

■ **WISCONSIN BELL INC** p 1618
722 N Broadway 53202
Tel (414) 271-9619 *SIC* 4813 8721

■ **WISCONSIN GAS LLC** p 1618
231 W Michigan St 53203
Tel (414) 221-3236 *SIC* 4924

WISCONSIN MILWAUKEE COUNTY p 1619
901 N 9th St Ste 306 53233
Tel (414) 278-4211 *SIC* 9111

WIXON INDUSTRIES INC p 1619
1390 E Bolivar Ave 53235
Tel (800) 841-5304 *SIC* 2099 2087 2899

WT WALKER GROUP INC p 1628
222 E Erie St Ste 300 53202
Tel (414) 223-2000 *SIC* 3462 3398

XENTEL INC p 1631
720 W Virginia St 53204
Tel (954) 522-5200 *SIC* 7389

YANFENG US AUTOMOTIVE INTERIOR SYSTEMS II LLC p 1634
5757 N Green Bay Ave 53209
Tel (205) 477-4225 *SIC* 2531

YOUNG MENS CHRISTIAN ASSOCIATION OF METROPOLITAN MILWAUKEE INC p 1638
161 W Wisconsin Ave 53203
Tel (414) 291-9622
SIC 8641 7991 8351 7032 8322

MINOCQUA, WI

T A SOLBERG CO INC p 1419
420 Oneida St 54548
Tel (715) 356-7711 *SIC* 5541

MINONG, WI

LINK SNACKS INC p 869
1 Snack Food Ln 54859
Tel (715) 466-2234 *SIC* 2013

MONDOVI, WI

▲ **MARTEN TRANSPORT LTD** p 912
129 Marten St 54755
Tel (715) 926-4216 *SIC* 4213

MONONA, WI

FIRST SUPPLY LLC p 549
6800 Gisholt Dr 53713
Tel (608) 222-7799
SIC 5074 5078 5075 5712 5713

WISCONSIN PHYSICIANS SERVICE INSURANCE CORP p 1619
1717 W Broadway 53713
Tel (608) 221-4711 *SIC* 6324

MONROE, WI

COLONY BRANDS INC p 338
1112 7th Ave 53566
Tel (608) 328-8400 *SIC* 5961 5143 2051

MONROE CLINIC INC p 985
515 22nd Ave 53566
Tel (608) 324-2775 *SIC* 8062 8011

MONROE TRUCK EQUIPMENT INC p 985
1051 W 7th St 53566
Tel (608) 328-8127 *SIC* 5013 3441 3599

SC DATA CENTER INC p 1285
1112 7th Ave 53566
Tel (608) 328-8600 *SIC* 7374

WISCONSIN CHEESE GROUP LLC p 1618
105 3rd St 53566
Tel (608) 325-8342 *SIC* 5143 2022

MOSINEE, WI

■ **MOSINEE TELEPHONE CO LLC** p 992
410 4th St 54455
Tel (715) 693-2622 *SIC* 4813

MOUNT HOREB, WI

PREMIER COOPERATIVE p 1170
501 W Main St 53572
Tel (608) 251-0199
SIC 5211 5171 5191 5541

MOUNT PLEASANT, WI

ALL SAINTS HEALTH CARE SYSTEM INC p 51
3801 Spring St 53405
Tel (262) 687-4011 *SIC* 8062

CNH INDUSTRIAL CAPITAL LLC p 330
5729 Washington Ave 53406
Tel (262) 636-6011 *SIC* 6159

MUKWONAGO, WI

GS GLOBAL RESOURCES INC p 643
926 Perkins Dr 53149
Tel (262) 786-0100 *SIC* 5084

LINDENGROVE MUKWONAGO p 868
837 County Road Nn E 53149
Tel (262) 363-6830 *SIC* 8051

MUSKEGO, WI

INPRO CORP p 745
S80w18766 Apollo Dr 53150
Tel (262) 679-9010 *SIC* 3081

NASHOTAH, WI

TECHNIPLAS LLC p 1431
N44w33341 Wtrtwn Plnk Rd 53058
Tel (262) 369-5555 *SIC* 3089 3544

NEENAH, WI

AIA CORP p 37
800 W Winneconne Ave 54956
Tel (920) 886-3700 *SIC* 5199

ALTA RESOURCES CORP p 61
120 N Commercial St 54956
Tel (877) 464-2582 *SIC* 7389 8742

▲ **BEMIS CO INC** p 171
1 Neenah Ctr Fl 4 54956
Tel (920) 527-5000 *SIC* 2671 2672

BERGSTROM CHEVROLET-BUICK-CADILLAC INC p 174
150 N Green Bay Rd 54956
Tel (866) 575-8036 *SIC* 5511

BERGSTROM CORP p 174
1 Neenah Ctr Ste 700 54956
Tel (920) 725-4444 *SIC* 5511

■ **CELLU TISSUE CORP-NEENAH** p 274
249 N Lake St 54956
Tel (920) 721-9800 *SIC* 2621

■ **DUNSIRN INDUSTRIES INC** p 461
2415 Industrial Dr 54956
Tel (920) 725-3814
SIC 2671 5113 3081 2672 2621

■ **ELECTRONIC ASSEMBLY CORP** p 485
55 Jewelers Park Dr 54956
Tel (920) 722-3451
SIC 3672 3679 3825 3841

J J KELLER & ASSOCIATES INC p 771
3003 Breezewood Ln 54956
Tel (920) 722-2848 *SIC* 2741 8742

JEWELERS MUTUAL INSURANCE CO p 784
24 Jewelers Park Dr 54956
Tel (800) 558-6411 *SIC* 6331

MENASHA CORP p 943
1645 Bergstrom Rd 54956
Tel (920) 751-1000
SIC 2631 2653 2679 3086 0811

MENASHA PACKAGING CO LLC p 943
1645 Bergstrom Rd 54956
Tel (920) 751-1000 *SIC* 2653

MIRON CONSTRUCTION CO INC p 974
1471 Mcmahon Rd 54956
Tel (920) 969-7000 *SIC* 1542 1541 1796

▲ NEENAH ENTERPRISES INC p 1024
2121 Brooks Ave 54956
Tel (920) 725-7000 *SIC* 3272 3312

■ NEENAH FOUNDRY CO p 1024
2121 Brooks Ave 54956
Tel (920) 725-7000 *SIC* 3321 3315

■ NEENAH PAPER FR LLC p 1024
1376 Kimberly Dr 54956
Tel (800) 558-8327 *SIC* 2679 2621

■ NFC CASTINGS INC p 1041
2121 Brooks Ave 54956
Tel (920) 725-7000 *SIC* 3325 3321

▲ PLEXUS CORP p 1156
1 Plexus Way 54956
Tel (920) 969-6000 *SIC* 3672 3825

SCA TISSUE NORTH AMERICA LLC p 1285
984 Winchester Rd 54956
Tel (920) 725-7031 *SIC* 2621

THEDA CLARK MEMORIAL HOSPITAL (INC) p 1446
130 2nd St 54956
Tel (920) 729-3100 *SIC* 8062

TIDI PRODUCTS LLC p 1452
570 Enterprise Dr 54956
Tel (920) 751-4300 *SIC* 3843 3841 5047

WEBEX INC p 1586
1035 Breezewood Ln 54956
Tel (920) 729-6666 *SIC* 5084

NEW BERLIN, WI

BEECHWOOD DISTRIBUTORS INC p 168
5350 S Emmer Dr 53151
Tel (262) 717-2831 *SIC* 5181

DYNATECT MANUFACTURING INC p 464
2300 S Calhoun Rd 53151
Tel (262) 786-1500
SIC 3069 3499 3714 3599

■ EMTEQ LLC p 495
5349 S Emmer Dr 53151
Tel (262) 679-6170 *SIC* 8711

■ GMR MARKETING LLC p 619
5000 S Towne Dr 53151
Tel (262) 786-5600 *SIC* 8743

IEWC CORP p 730
5001 S Towne Dr 53151
Tel (262) 782-2255 *SIC* 5063

■ INFRASOURCE LLC p 742
2936 S 166th St 53151
Tel (713) 629-7600 *SIC* 1623 1542

INFRATROL MANUFACTURING CORP p 742
2500 S 162nd St 53151
Tel (262) 797-8140 *SIC* 3567

KS ENERGY SERVICES LLC p 831
19705 W Lincoln Ave 53146
Tel (262) 574-5100 *SIC* 1623

LANDMARK CREDIT UNION p 842
5445 S Westridge Dr 53151
Tel (262) 796-4500 *SIC* 6062

LINDENGROVE INC p 868
13700 W National Ave # 9 53151
Tel (262) 797-4600 *SIC* 8051 5912

MILWAUKEE VALVE CO INC p 972
16550 W Stratton Dr 53151
Tel (262) 432-2800 *SIC* 3494 3492 3432

STERLING INC p 1387
2900 S 160th St 53151
Tel (414) 354-0970 *SIC* 3823 3542 3559

NEW LISBON, WI

■ WALKER GROUP HOLDINGS LLC p 1573
625 W State St 53950
Tel (608) 562-7500 *SIC* 3443

■ WALKER STAINLESS EQUIPMENT CO LLC p 1573
625 W State St 53950
Tel (608) 562-7500 *SIC* 3443 3556 3715

NEW RICHMOND, WI

BOSCH PACKAGING TECHNOLOGY INC p 202
869 S Knowles Ave 54017
Tel (715) 246-6511 *SIC* 3565

OAK CREEK, WI

BRIDGEMAN FOODS II INC p 211
2025 Ws Branch Blvd 53154
Tel (502) 254-7130 *SIC* 5812

CREATION TECHNOLOGIES WISCONSIN INC p 390
2250 W South Branch Blvd 53154
Tel (414) 761-0400 *SIC* 3672

GRUNAU CO INC p 642
1100 W Anderson Ct 53154
Tel (414) 216-6900 *SIC* 1711

■ MASTER LOCK CO LLC p 918
137 W Forest Hill Ave 53154
Tel (414) 444-2800 *SIC* 3429 3462

PHMH HOLDING CO p 1144
315 W Forest Hill Ave 53154
Tel (414) 764-6200 *SIC* 3625 6719

■ SENTRY SAFE INC p 1305
137 W Forest Hill Ave 53154
Tel (585) 381-4900 *SIC* 3089 3499 2522

STEEL WAREHOUSE OF WISCONSIN INC p 1384
535 W Forest Hill Ave 53154
Tel (414) 764-4800 *SIC* 5051

SUPERIOR DIE SET CORP p 1406
900 W Drexel Ave 53154
Tel (414) 764-4900 *SIC* 3544 3443 3599

OCONOMOWOC, WI

BRUNO INDEPENDENT LIVING AIDS INC p 221
1780 Executive Dr 53066
Tel (262) 953-5405 *SIC* 3842

KERLEY BIOKIMICA INC p 813
33707 Prairieview Ln 53066
Tel (262) 567-8840 *SIC* 7389

LANDLOVERS LLC p 842
1833 Executive Dr Ste 105 53066
Tel (262) 560-9786 *SIC* 6163

OCONOMOWOC RESIDENTIAL PROGRAMS INC p 1074
1746 Executive Dr 53066
Tel (262) 569-5515 *SIC* 8052 8361

ORBIS CORP p 1092
1055 Corporate Center Dr 53066
Tel (262) 560-5000 *SIC* 3089

PROHEALTHCARE FOUNDATION p 1182
791 Summit Ave 53066
Tel (262) 569-9400 *SIC* 8062 8011

ROGERS MEMORIAL HOSPITAL INC p 1246
34700 Valley Rd 53066
Tel (800) 767-4411 *SIC* 8063

OCONTO, WI

KCS INTERNATIONAL INC p 806
804 Pecor St 54153
Tel (920) 834-2211 *SIC* 3732

ONALASKA, WI

COURTESY CORP p 383
2700 National Dr Ste 100 54650
Tel (608) 781-8080 *SIC* 5812

MATHY CONSTRUCTION CO p 920
920 10th Ave N 54650
Tel (608) 783-6411
SIC 1611 1771 1442 5171

MDSFEST INC p 933
237 2nnd Ave S 54650
Tel (608) 779-2720 *SIC* 5411

PETROENERGY LLC p 1139
920 10th Ave N 54650
Tel (608) 783-6411 *SIC* 5171 4925 5172

SKOGENS FOODLINER INC p 1330
3800 Emerald Dr E 54650
Tel (608) 783-5500 *SIC* 5411 5461 5421

TEXPAR ENERGY LLC p 1445
920 10th Ave N 54650
Tel (800) 323-7350 *SIC* 5171 4925 5172

ONEIDA, WI

ONEIDA TRIBE OF INDIANS OF WISCONSIN p 1087
N7210 Seminary Rd 54155
Tel (920) 869-2214 *SIC* 9131

OOSTBURG, WI

DUTCHLAND PLASTICS LLC p 463
54 Enterprise Ct 53070
Tel (920) 564-3633 *SIC* 3089 3544

OREGON, WI

GORMAN & CO INC p 626
200 N Main St 53575
Tel (608) 835-3900 *SIC* 6552 6531

OSHKOSH, WI

4IMPRINT INC p 3
101 Commerce St 54901
Tel (920) 236-7272 *SIC* 5199

AURORA MEDICAL CENTER OSHKOSH p 132
855 N Westhaven Dr 54904
Tel (920) 303-8730 *SIC* 8011

■ BEMIS HEALTHCARE PACKAGING INC p 171
3500 N Main St 54901
Tel (920) 527-7464 *SIC* 2671 3565

■ BEMIS HEALTHCARE PACKAGING INC p 171
3500 N Main St 54901
Tel (920) 527-3000 *SIC* 2671

■ BEMIS PACKAGING INC p 172
3550 Moser St 54901
Tel (920) 527-2300 *SIC* 2671

C R MEYER AND SONS CO p 233
895 W 20th Ave 54902
Tel (920) 235-3350 *SIC* 1542 1796 1541

COUNTY OF WINNEBAGO p 383
112 Otter Ave 54901
Tel (920) 236-4800 *SIC* 9131

GENERAC POWER SYSTEMS INC p 599
3815 Oregon St 54902
Tel (262) 544-4811 *SIC* 3621

HOFFMASTER GROUP INC p 699
2920 N Main St 54901
Tel (920) 235-9330 *SIC* 2676

MERCY MEDICAL CENTER OF OSHKOSH INC p 948
2700 W 9th Ave Ste 100 54904
Tel (920) 223-2000 *SIC* 8062

OSHKOSH AREA SCHOOL DISTRICT p 1096
215 S Eagle St 54902
Tel (920) 424-0160 *SIC* 8211

▲ OSHKOSH CORP p 1096
2307 Oregon St 54902
Tel (920) 235-9151 *SIC* 3711 3531 3715

■ OSHKOSH DEFENSE LLC p 1096
2307 Oregon St 54902
Tel (920) 235-9151 *SIC* 3711 3531 3715

■ TOTAL MIXER TECHNOLOGIES LLC p 1463
2307 Oregon St 54902
Tel (920) 235-9150 *SIC* 3531

OSSEO, WI

GLOBAL FINISHING SOLUTIONS LLC p 616
12731 Norway Rd 54758
Tel (715) 597-8007 *SIC* 3444

PARK FALLS, WI

FLAMBEAU RIVER PAPER CORP p 554
200 1st Ave N 54552
Tel (715) 762-4612 *SIC* 2621

FLAMBEAU RIVER PAPERS LLC p 554
200 1st Ave N 54552
Tel (715) 762-5229 *SIC* 2621

PEWAUKEE, WI

CARNES CO INC p 258
600 College Ave 53072
Tel (262) 691-9900
SIC 3822 3444 3585 3669

GUSTAVE A LARSON CO p 648
W233n2869 Roundy Cir W 53072
Tel (262) 542-0200
SIC 5075 5078 5084 5046

NEW LIFECARE HOSPITALS OF MILWAUKEE LLC p 1032
2400 Golf Rd 53072
Tel (262) 524-2600 *SIC* 8062

TOTAL MECHANICAL INC p 1463
W234n2830 Paul Rd 53072
Tel (262) 523-2510 *SIC* 1711 1791 3823

VENTUREDYNE LTD p 1548
600 College Ave 53072
Tel (262) 691-9900
SIC 3568 3829 3826 3823 3625

■ WAUKESHA BEARINGS CORP p 1583
W231n2811 Roundy Cir E 53072
Tel (262) 506-3000 *SIC* 3568 3566

WAUKESHA COUNTY AREA TECHNICAL COLLEGE DISTRICT p 1583
800 Main St 53072
Tel (262) 691-5566 *SIC* 8222

PHILLIPS, WI

BARRY-WEHMILLER PAPERSYSTEMS INC p 157
1300 N Airport Rd 54555
Tel (314) 862-8000 *SIC* 3554

MARQUIP LLC p 910
1300 N Airport Rd 54555
Tel (715) 339-2191 *SIC* 3554

PLAIN, WI

EDWARD KRAEMER & SONS INC p 480
1 Plainview Rd 53577
Tel (608) 546-2311 *SIC* 1622 1442

PLEASANT PRAIRIE, WI

ACTIVE TRUCK TRANSPORT LLC p 20
10801 Corporate Dr 53158
Tel (800) 558-3271 *SIC* 4213

■ ALBANY-CHICAGO CO LLC p 45
8200 100th St 53158
Tel (262) 947-7600 *SIC* 3363

EMCO CHEMICAL DISTRIBUTORS INC p 491
8601 95th St 53158
Tel (262) 427-0400 *SIC* 5169 7389 2819

FAIR OAKS FARMS LLC p 524
7600 95th St 53158
Tel (262) 947-0320 *SIC* 2013

GOOD FOODS GROUP LLC p 623
10100 88th Ave 53158
Tel (262) 465-6900 *SIC* 2038 5149

IRIS USA INC p 764
11111 80th Ave 53158
Tel (262) 612-1000 *SIC* 3089

JHT HOLDINGS INC p 785
10801 Corporate Dr 53158
Tel (800) 558-3271 *SIC* 4213

REHRIG PENN LOGISTICS INC p 1220
7800 100th St 53158
Tel (262) 947-0032 *SIC* 3089

ULINE INC p 1500
12575 Uline Dr 53158
Tel (262) 612-4200 *SIC* 5113

UNIFIED SOLUTIONS INC p 1503
9801 80th Ave 53158
Tel (262) 942-5200 *SIC* 4783

PLOVER, WI

■ BANTA GLOBAL TURNKEY LTD p 153
1600 Disk Dr 54467
Tel (715) 341-0544 *SIC* 3577

GOLDEN COUNTY FOODS INC p 620
300 Moore Rd 54467
Tel (800) 489-7783 *SIC* 2099

PLYMOUTH, WI

LAKELAND COLLEGE p 840
W3718 South Dr 53073
Tel (920) 565-2111 *SIC* 8221

MASTERS GALLERY FOODS INC p 918
328 Count Hwy Pp Pp 53073
Tel (920) 893-8431 *SIC* 5143

SARGENTO FOODS INC p 1282
1 Persnickety Pl 53073
Tel (920) 893-8484 *SIC* 2022

SARTORI CO p 1282
107 N Pleasant View Rd 53073
Tel (920) 893-6061 *SIC* 2022

PORT WASHINGTON, WI

ALLEN EDMONDS CORP p 53
201 E Seven Hills Rd 53074
Tel (262) 235-6000 *SIC* 3143 5661

FRANKLIN ENERGY SERVICES LLC p 575
102 N Franklin St 53074
Tel (800) 598-4376 *SIC* 8711

KLEEN TEST PRODUCTS CORP p 823
1611 S Sunset Rd 53074
Tel (262) 284-6600 *SIC* 2842 2675

PORTAGE, WI

DIVINE SAVIOR HEALTHCARE INC p 444
2817 New Pinery Rd # 202 53901
Tel (608) 745-4598 *SIC* 8062 8011 8051

PENDA CORP p 1128
2344 W Wisconsin St 53901
Tel (608) 742-5301
SIC 5013 3714 3792 3713 2273

PRAIRIE DU CHIEN, WI

DESIGN HOMES INC p 432
600 N Marquette Rd 53821
Tel (608) 326-8406 *SIC* 2452 3663 5211

PULASKI, WI

RIESTERER & SCHNELL INC p 1234
N2909 State Highway 32 54162
Tel (920) 775-4146 *SIC* 5083 5261

RACINE, WI

CASE CONSTRUCTION EQUIPMENT INC p 263
700 State St 53404
Tel (262) 636-6011 *SIC* 6159 3531 3523

CASE NEW HOLLAND INDUSTRIAL INC p 263
700 State St 53404
Tel (262) 636-6011 *SIC* 3523 3531

CITY OF RACINE p 317
730 Washington Ave 53403
Tel (262) 636-9101 *SIC* 9111

CNH INDUSTRIAL AMERICA LLC p 330
700 St St 53404
Tel (262) 636-6011 *SIC* 3523 3531 6159

J V LABORATORIES INC p 772
1320 Wisconsin Ave # 101 53403
Tel (262) 687-2150 *SIC* 8071

JOHNSON FINANCIAL GROUP INC p 791
555 Main St Ste 400 53403
Tel (262) 619-2700
SIC 6022 6021 6712 6733 6311

▲ JOHNSON OUTDOORS INC p 791
555 Main St 53403
Tel (262) 631-6600 *SIC* 3949 3732 3812

▲ MODINE MANUFACTURING CO INC p 981
1500 Dekoven Ave 53403
Tel (262) 636-1200
SIC 3443 3714 3433 3585

RACINE UNIFIED SCHOOL DISTRICT p 1203
3109 Mount Pleasant St 53404
Tel (262) 635-5600 *SIC* 8211

ROGAN SHOES INC p 1246
1750 Ohio St 53405
Tel (262) 637-3613 *SIC* 5661

S C JOHNSON & SON INC p 1262
1525 Howe St 53403
Tel (262) 260-2000
SIC 2842 2844 2879 2865 7342 7349

▲ TWIN DISC INC p 1495
1328 Racine St 53403
Tel (262) 638-4000 *SIC* 3568 3566 3714

WARREN INDUSTRIES INC p 1577
3100 Mount Pleasant St 53404
Tel (262) 639-7800 *SIC* 7389

RANDOM LAKE, WI

TIMES PRINTING LLC p 1454
100 Industrial Dr 53075
Tel (920) 994-4396 *SIC* 2752

REEDSBURG, WI

■ **NUK USA LLC** p 1067
728 Booster Blvd 53959
Tel (608) 524-4343 *SIC* 2676

SEATS INC p 1297
1515 Industrial St 53959
Tel (608) 524-8261 *SIC* 2531

RHINELANDER, WI

FOSTER AND SMITH INC p 570
2253 Air Park Rd 54501
Tel (715) 369-3305 *SIC* 4813 5961

MINISTRY MEDICAL GROUP p 973
2251 N Shore Dr Ste 200 54501
Tel (715) 361-4700 *SIC* 8011

RICE LAKE, WI

LAKEVIEW MEDICAL CENTER INC OF RICE LAKE p 840
1700 W Stout St 54868
Tel (715) 234-1515 *SIC* 8062

■ **QUANEX HOMESHIELD LLC** p 1198
311 W Coleman St 54868
Tel (715) 234-9061 *SIC* 3448

RICE LAKE WEIGHING SYSTEMS INC p 1232
230 W Coleman St 54868
Tel (715) 234-9171 *SIC* 3596 3545

RICHFIELD, WI

RITEWAY BUS SERVICE INC p 1237
W201 N13900 Fond Du Lac 53076
Tel (262) 677-3282 *SIC* 4151 4142 4141

RIPON, WI

ALLIANCE LAUNDRY HOLDINGS LLC p 54
221 Shepard St 54971
Tel (920) 748-3121 *SIC* 3582 3633

ALLIANCE LAUNDRY SYSTEMS LLC p 54
221 Shepard St 54971
Tel (920) 748-3121 *SIC* 3582 3633

CONDON OIL CO p 355
126 E Jackson St 54971
Tel (920) 748-3186 *SIC* 5541

ROTHSCHILD, WI

WAUSAUTILE INC p 1583
9001 Business Highway 51 54474
Tel (715) 359-3121 *SIC* 3272

SAUK CITY, WI

UNITY HEALTH PLANS INSURANCE CORP p 1515
840 Carolina St 53583
Tel (608) 643-2491 *SIC* 6324

SCHOFIELD, WI

CRYSTAL FINISHING SYSTEMS INC p 396
4704 Bayberry St 54476
Tel (715) 355-5351 *SIC* 3479

GREENHECK FAN CORP p 638
1100 Greenheck Dr 54476
Tel (715) 359-6171 *SIC* 3564 3444

L & S ELECTRIC INC p 833
5101 Mesker St 54476
Tel (715) 359-3155
SIC 7694 5063 8711 3613

SAINT CLARES HOSPITAL OF WESTON INC p 1268
3400 Ministry Pkwy 54476
Tel (715) 393-3000 *SIC* 8062

WAUSAU SUPPLY CO p 1583
7102 Commerce Dr 54476
Tel (715) 359-2524 *SIC* 5033

SHAWANO, WI

COOPERATIVE RESOURCES INTERNATIONAL INC p 367
117 E Green Bay St 54166
Tel (715) 526-2141
SIC 0751 5159 0762 8731

GENEX COOPERATIVE INC p 603
100 Mbc Dr 54166
Tel (715) 526-2141 *SIC* 0751 5159

SHEBOYGAN FALLS, WI

BEMIS MANUFACTURING CO INC p 171
300 Mill St 53085
Tel (920) 467-4621 *SIC* 3089

CURT G JOA INC p 402
100 Crocker Ave 53085
Tel (920) 467-6136 *SIC* 3554

JOHNSONVILLE SAUSAGE LLC p 791
N6928 Johnsonville Way 53085
Tel (920) 453-6900 *SIC* 2013

RICHARDSON INDUSTRIES INC p 1232
635 Old County Road Pp 53085
Tel (920) 467-2950
SIC 2511 2439 5211 2491 2434 2426

SHEBOYGAN, WI

A ACUITY MUTUAL INSURANCE CO p 4
2800 S Taylor Dr 53081
Tel (920) 458-9131 *SIC* 6411 6331

AMERICAN ORTHODONTICS CORP p 77
3524 Washington Ave 53081
Tel (920) 457-5051 *SIC* 3843 8021

COUNTY OF SHEBOYGAN p 381
508 New York Ave 53081
Tel (920) 459-3000 *SIC* 9111

FRENCH HOLDINGS LLC p 578
3101 S Taylor Dr 53081
Tel (920) 458-7724 *SIC* 3363 3341 8711

GARDNER DENVER THOMAS INC p 592
1419 Illinois Ave 53081
Tel (920) 457-4891 *SIC* 3563

JL FRENCH AUTOMOTIVE LLC p 786
3101 S Taylor Dr 53081
Tel (920) 458-7724 *SIC* 3465

JL FRENCH LLC p 786
3101 S Taylor Dr 53081
Tel (920) 458-7724 *SIC* 3363

NEMAK AUTOMOTIVE CASTINGS INC p 1025
3101 S Taylor Dr 53081
Tel (920) 458-7724 *SIC* 3341 3363 8711

PIGGLY WIGGLY MIDWEST LLC p 1147
2215 Union Ave 53081
Tel (920) 457-4433 *SIC* 5141 5411

QUALITY STATE OIL CO INC p 1197
2201 Calumet Dr 53083
Tel (920) 459-5640 *SIC* 5171 5541 5411

ROCKLINE INDUSTRIES INC p 1245
4343 S Taylor Dr 53081
Tel (800) 558-7790 *SIC* 2679 2297

SHEBOYGAN AREA SCHOOL DISTRICT p 1313
830 Virginia Ave 53081
Tel (920) 459-3500 *SIC* 8211 8741

TVCI HOLDING INC p 1494
1236 N 18th St 53081
Tel (920) 457-4851 *SIC* 3914 3365 3089

VOLLRATH CO LLC p 1564
1236 N 18th St 53081
Tel (920) 459-6568
SIC 3089 3365 3421 3556 3914

WINDWAY CAPITAL CORP p 1616
630 Riverfront Dr Ste 200 53081
Tel (920) 457-8600
SIC 3469 2394 3624 3732

SHELL LAKE, WI

WISCONSIN INDIANHEAD TECHNICAL COLLEGE FOUNDATION INC p 1618
505 Pine Ridge Dr 54871
Tel (715) 468-2815 *SIC* 8222

SHERWOOD, WI

■ **STOCKBRIDGE & SHERWOOD TELEPHONE CO LLC** p 1390
N287 Military Rd 54169
Tel (920) 989-1501 *SIC* 4813

SLINGER, WI

H WOLF EDWARD AND SONS INC p 651
414 Kettle Moraine Dr S 53086
Tel (262) 644-5030 *SIC* 5983 5171

SOMERSET, WI

SCIENTIFIC MOLDING CORP LTD p 1292
330 Smc Dr 54025
Tel (715) 247-3500 *SIC* 3089 3544

SOUTH MILWAUKEE, WI

■ **CATERPILLAR GLOBAL MINING LLC** p 265
1100 Milwaukee Ave 53172
Tel (414) 762-0376 *SIC* 3531 3532 3599

SPARTA, WI

■ **CENTURY FOODS INTERNATIONAL LLC** p 282
400 Century Ct 54656
Tel (608) 269-1900 *SIC* 2023

LAKE STATES LUMBER INC p 839
312 S Chester St 54656
Tel (608) 269-6714 *SIC* 5031

LAWRENCE HOLDING INC p 848
803 S Black River St 54656
Tel (608) 269-6911 *SIC* 3469 3089 3544

NORTHERN ENGRAVING CORP p 1056
803 S Black River St 54656
Tel (608) 269-6911 *SIC* 3469 3544 3089

SPRING GREEN, WI

HANOR CO OF WISCONSIN LLC p 658
E4614 Us Hwy 14 And 60 53588
Tel (608) 588-9170 *SIC* 0291

STEVENS POINT, WI

■ **ASSOCIATED BANC-CORP** p 119
1305 Main St Ms7722 54481
Tel (715) 341-0400 *SIC* 6035

CARE p 254
2000 Polk St 54481
Tel (715) 345-5620 *SIC* 8299

DAIRYLAND INSURANCE CO p 409
1800 Northpoint Dr 54481
Tel (715) 346-6000 *SIC* 6331

DELTA DENTAL OF WISCONSIN INC p 426
2801 Hoover Rd 54481
Tel (715) 344-6087 *SIC* 6324

SCHIERL INC p 1287
2201 Madison St 54481
Tel (715) 345-5060
SIC 5171 5014 5531 5983

SENTRY INSURANCE A MUTUAL CO p 1305
1800 Northpoint Dr 54481
Tel (715) 346-6000
SIC 6331 6311 6411 6321

SENTRY LIFE INSURANCE CO p 1305
1800 Northpoint Dr 54481
Tel (715) 346-6000 *SIC* 6411 6321

ST MICHAELS HOSPITAL INC p 1372
900 Illinois Ave 54481
Tel (715) 346-5000 *SIC* 8062

STEEL KING INDUSTRIES INC p 1384
2700 Chamber St 54481
Tel (715) 341-3120
SIC 3441 3537 3412 2542

STEVENS POINT AREA PUBLIC SCHOOL DISTRICT p 1388
1900 Polk St 54481
Tel (715) 345-5444 *SIC* 8211

■ **STEVENS POINT DISTRIBUTION CENTER LLC** p 1388
2828 Wayne St 54481
Tel (952) 828-4000 *SIC* 5411

■ **TRAVEL GUARD GROUP INC** p 1473
3300 Business Park Dr 54482
Tel (715) 345-0505 *SIC* 6411

UNIVERSITY OF WISCONSIN STEVENS POINT p 1527
1015 Reserve St 54481
Tel (715) 346-0123 *SIC* 8221

VIKING INSURANCE CO OF WISCONSIN p 1557
1800 Northpoint Dr 54481
Tel (715) 346-6000 *SIC* 6331

WORZALLA PUBLISHING CO p 1626
3535 Jefferson St 54481
Tel (715) 344-9600 *SIC* 2732

STOUGHTON, WI

NELSON GLOBAL PRODUCTS INC p 1025
1560 Williams Dr 53589
Tel (608) 719-1800 *SIC* 3714 3317

■ **NELSON INDUSTRIES INC** p 1025
1801 Us Highway 51 & 138 53589
Tel (608) 873-4200 *SIC* 3714 3519 3569

STI HOLDINGS INC p 1389
416 S Academy St 53589
Tel (608) 873-2500 *SIC* 6719

STOUGHTON TRAILERS LLC p 1392
416 S Academy St 53589
Tel (608) 873-2500 *SIC* 3715

UNIVERSAL ACOUSTIC & EMISSION TECHNOLOGIES INC p 1516
1925 Us Highway 51 & 138 53589
Tel (608) 873-4272 *SIC* 3569 3441

STRATFORD, WI

■ **A & B PROCESS SYSTEMS CORP** p 4
201 S Wisconsin Ave 54484
Tel (715) 687-4332 *SIC* 3443 1799 8711

STURGEON BAY, WI

FINCANTIERI MARINE GROUP HOLDINGS INC p 543
605 N 3rd Ave 54235
Tel (920) 743-3406 *SIC* 3731

FINCANTIERI MARINE GROUP LLC p 543
605 N 3rd Ave 54235
Tel (920) 743-3406 *SIC* 3731

PALMER JOHNSON ENTERPRISES INC p 1109
128 Kentucky St 54235
Tel (920) 746-6342 *SIC* 5085 4493 3732

PALMER JOHNSON YACHTS LLC p 1109
128 Kentucky St 54235
Tel (920) 743-4412 *SIC* 3732

STURTEVANT, WI

BRP US INC p 220
10101 Science Dr 53177
Tel (715) 842-8886 *SIC* 3732

■ **DIVERSEY HOLDINGS INC** p 443
8310 16th St 53177
Tel (262) 631-4001 *SIC* 2842

HORIZON RETAIL CONSTRUCTION p 707
1500 Horizon Dr 53177
Tel (262) 638-6000 *SIC* 1542

POCLAIN HYDRAULICS INC p 1158
1300 Grandview Pkwy 53177
Tel (262) 321-0676 *SIC* 5084

PUTZMEISTER AMERICA INC p 1193
1733 90th St 53177
Tel (262) 886-3200 *SIC* 3561

SUN PRAIRIE, WI

INDEPENDENT PHARMACY COOPERATIVE p 736
1550 Columbus St 53590
Tel (608) 825-9556 *SIC* 5122 7299

QBE AMERICAS INC p 1194
1 General Dr 53596
Tel (608) 837-4440 *SIC* 6331

QBE INVESTMENTS (NORTH AMERICA) INC p 1194
1 General Dr 53596
Tel (608) 837-4440 *SIC* 6331

WINTERTHUR U S HOLDINGS INC p 1617
1 General Dr 53596
Tel (608) 837-4440 *SIC* 6411 6163

WPPI ENERGY p 1627
1425 Corporate Center Dr 53590
Tel (608) 834-4500 *SIC* 4911

SUPERIOR, WI

AMSOIL INC p 87
925 Tower Ave 54880
Tel (715) 392-7101
SIC 2992 3589 2873 3714

■ **CALUMET SUPERIOR LLC** p 243
2407 Stinson Ave 54880
Tel (715) 398-3533 *SIC* 2992

EVENING TELEGRAM CO p 513
1226 Ogden Ave 54880
Tel (715) 394-4411 *SIC* 4833

GRAYMONT (WI) LLC p 632
800 Hill Ave 54880
Tel (715) 392-5146 *SIC* 3274

HALVOR LINES INC p 655
217 Grand Ave 54880
Tel (715) 392-8161 *SIC* 4213

LAKEHEAD CONSTRUCTORS INC p 839
2916 Hill Ave 54880
Tel (715) 392-5181 *SIC* 1541 1542

LAKEHEAD HOLDING CORP p 839
2916 Hill Ave 54880
Tel (715) 392-5181 *SIC* 1541 1542

SUSSEX, WI

BEER CAPITOL DISTRIBUTING INC p 168
W222n5700 Miller Way 53089
Tel (262) 932-2337 *SIC* 5181

■ **QG LLC** p 1195
N61w23044 Harrys Way 53089
Tel (414) 566-6000 *SIC* 2754

■ **QG PRINTING CORP** p 1195
N61w23044 Harrys Way 53089
Tel (414) 566-6000 *SIC* 2752

■ **QG PRINTING II CORP** p 1195
N61w23044 Harrys Way 53089
Tel (414) 566-6000 *SIC* 2752

▲ **QUAD/GRAPHICS INC** p 1195
N61w23044 Harrys Way 53089
Tel (414) 566-6000 *SIC* 2752 2754 2721

REINDERS INC p 1221
W227n6225 Sussex Rd 53089
Tel (262) 786-3300
SIC 5191 5169 5074 5999 5083

SUSSEX IM INC p 1409
N65w24770 Main St 53089
Tel (262) 246-8022 *SIC* 3089

TOMAH, WI

R G REZIN INC p 1202
1602 Rezin Rd 54660
Tel (608) 372-5956
SIC 1623 3443 3613 3561 3523 3599

TWO RIVERS, WI

EGGERS INDUSTRIES INC p 481
1 Eggers Dr 54241
Tel (920) 793-1351 *SIC* 2431 2435

■ **NEXTERA ENERGY POINT BEACH LLC** p 1040
6610 Nuclear Rd 54241
Tel (920) 755-7705 *SIC* 4911

UNION GROVE, WI

AMERICAN ROLLER CO LLC p 78
1440 13th Ave 53182
Tel (262) 878-8665 *SIC* 3549 3548

VALDERS, WI

CP FEEDS LLC p 387
16322 W Washington St 54245
Tel (920) 775-9600 *SIC* 5153 5191

VERONA, WI

CLEARY BUILDING CORP p 324
190 Paoli St 53593
Tel (608) 845-9700 *SIC* 1541 3448

EPIC SYSTEMS CORP p 505
1979 Milky Way 53593
Tel (608) 271-9000 *SIC* 7371

FULL COMPASS SYSTEMS LTD p 584
9770 Silicon Prairie Pkwy 53593
Tel (608) 831-7330 *SIC* 5999

JT PACKARD LLC p 796
275 Investment Ct 53593
Tel (800) 972-9778 *SIC* 4911

VIROQUA, WI

CITIZENS FIRST BANK p 311
101 S Main St 54665
Tel (608) 637-3133 *SIC* 6022

WALWORTH, WI

MINIATURE PRECISION COMPONENTS INC p 973
820 Wisconsin St 53184
Tel (262) 275-5791 *SIC* 3089

WARRENS, WI

■ UFP WARRENS LLC p 1499
County Rd 0 610 Rr St 54666
Tel (608) 378-4904 *SIC* 5031

WATERFORD, WI

HYPRO INC p 724
600 S Jefferson St 53185
Tel (608) 348-4810 *SIC* 3599

SOUTHEAST TELEPHONE CO OF WISCONSIN LLC p 1346
311 Elizabeth St 53185
Tel (608) 831-1000 *SIC* 4813

WATERLOO, WI

TREK BICYCLE CORP p 1476
801 W Madison St 53594
Tel (920) 478-2191 *SIC* 5941 3429

WATERTOWN, WI

B-G WESTERN INC p 142
1141 S 10th St 53094
Tel (920) 261-0660 *SIC* 3443 3469 3444

BETHESDA LUTHERAN COMMUNITIES INC p 178
600 Hoffmann Dr 53094
Tel (920) 261-3050 *SIC* 8361

FISHER-BARTON INC p 552
576 Bluemound Road 53188 53094
Tel (920) 261-0131 *SIC* 6719

GREATER WATERTOWN COMMUNITY HEALTH FOUNDATION INC p 636
125 Hospital Dr 53098
Tel (920) 261-4210 *SIC* 8062 8011 8059

WESTERN INDUSTRIES INC p 1598
1141 S 10th St 53094
Tel (920) 261-0660
SIC 3443 3469 3089 3444 1761 3491

WIS - PAK INC p 1618
860 West St 53094
Tel (920) 262-6300 *SIC* 2086

WAUKESHA, WI

AMERICAN TRANSMISSION CO LLC p 80
W234n2000 Rdgview Pky Ct 53188
Tel (262) 506-6700 *SIC* 4911

BOELTER COMPANIES INC p 197
N22 W23685 Rdgview Pkwy W 53188
Tel (262) 523-6200
SIC 5113 5046 7389 5087

BUILDING SERVICE p 225
W222n630 Cheaney Rd 53186
Tel (414) 358-5080 *SIC* 5021 1542 5023

COOPER POWER SYSTEMS LLC p 367
2300 Badger Dr 53188
Tel (262) 524-4227
SIC 3612 3613 3644 3643 3629 3679

COUNTY OF WAUKESHA p 382
515 W Mrland Blvd Ste G72 53188
Tel (262) 548-7902 *SIC* 9111

CS ESTATE INC p 397
N7w22025 Johnson Dr 53186
Tel (262) 953-3500 *SIC* 3841 3663 7374

DEDICATED COMPUTING LLC p 421
N26w23880 Commerce Cir B 53188
Tel (262) 951-7200 *SIC* 3571 3577 5045

■ FIDELITY & GUARANTY INSURANCE UNDERWRITERS INC p 540
20800 Swenson Dr Ste 300 53186
Tel (414) 784-5530 *SIC* 6331

▲ GENERAC HOLDINGS INC p 599
S45w29290 Hwy 59 53189
Tel (262) 544-4811 *SIC* 3621

■ GENERAC POWER SYSTEMS INC p 599
S45w29290 Wisconsin 59 St S 45 53189
Tel (262) 544-4811 *SIC* 3621

HOPSON OIL CO INC p 706
1225 Whiterock Ave 53186
Tel (262) 542-5343 *SIC* 5171 5983 1711

HUSCO INTERNATIONAL INC p 721
2239 Pewaukee Rd 53188
Tel (262) 513-4200 *SIC* 3492

KHS USA INC p 816
880 Bahcall Ct 53186
Tel (262) 797-7200 *SIC* 3556

■ MARKEL AMERICAN INSURANCE CO p 908
N14w23800 Stone Ridge Dr # 300 53188
Tel (262) 548-9880 *SIC* 6411

METALTEK INTERNATIONAL INC p 953
905 E Saint Paul Ave 53188
Tel (262) 544-7777 *SIC* 3366 3443 3364

METSO MINERALS INDUSTRIES INC p 957
20965 Crossroads Cir 53186
Tel (262) 798-3994
SIC 3321 3069 3561 3535 3532

NATIONS ROOF NORTH LLC p 1017
901 Sentry Dr 53186
Tel (262) 542-0002 *SIC* 1761

PROHEALTH CARE INC p 1182
725 American Ave 53188
Tel (262) 544-2011 *SIC* 8011 8062

SAFWAY GROUP HOLDING LLC p 1267
N19w24200 Riverwood Dr 53188
Tel (262) 523-6500 *SIC* 1799

SAFWAY SERVICES LLC p 1267
N19w24200 Riverwood Dr # 200 53188
Tel (262) 523-6500 *SIC* 5082

SOFTWARE ONE INC p 1337
20875 Crssroads Cir Ste 1 53186
Tel (262) 317-5555 *SIC* 5045

SPANCRETE GROUP INC p 1354
N16 W 23415 Stone Rdge Dr St N 16 53188
Tel (414) 290-9000 *SIC* 3272 3531

■ SPX TRANSFORMER SOLUTIONS INC p 1362
400 S Prairie Ave 53186
Tel (262) 547-0121 *SIC* 7629 3612

VENTURE ELECTRICAL CONTRACTORS p 1548
2110 Pewaukee Rd Ste 110 53188
Tel (262) 542-2727 *SIC* 1731

WALTER USA LLC p 1574
N22 W 23855 Rdg St N 22 53188
Tel (800) 945-5554 *SIC* 3545

WAUKESHA MEMORIAL HOSPITAL INC p 1583
725 American Ave 53188
Tel (262) 928-2292 *SIC* 8062

WAUKESHA SCHOOL DISTRICT p 1583
222 Maple Ave 53186
Tel (262) 970-1038 *SIC* 8211

■ WAUKESHA WHOLESALE FOODS INC p 1583
900 Gale St 53186
Tel (262) 542-8841 *SIC* 5141

WESTERN POWER PRODUCTS INC p 1599
2300 Badger Dr 53188
Tel (262) 896-2400 *SIC* 3644

WILDE AUTOS INC p 1609
1710a State Road 164 S 53186
Tel (262) 970-5900 *SIC* 5511

WAUNAKEE, WI

INTERCON CONSTRUCTION INC p 752
5512 State Rd 19 & 113 53597
Tel (608) 850-4820 *SIC* 1623

SCIENTIFIC PROTEIN LABORATORIES LLC p 1292
700 E Main St 53597
Tel (608) 849-5944 *SIC* 2834 2833

WAUPACA, WI

HITACHI METALS FOUNDRY AMERICA INC p 697
1955 Brunner Dr 54981
Tel (715) 258-6600 *SIC* 3321

JOURNAL COMMUNITY PUBLISHING GROUP INC p 794
600 Industrial Dr 54981
Tel (715) 258-8450 *SIC* 2741 2711

WAUPACA FOUNDRY INC p 1583
1955 Brunner Dr 54981
Tel (715) 258-6611 *SIC* 3321

WAUSAU, WI

■ APOGEE WAUSAU GROUP INC p 97
7800 International Dr 54401
Tel (715) 845-2161
SIC 3479 3442 3471 3449

ASPIRUS EMPLOYEE ASSISTANCE p 118
3000 Westhill Dr Ste 102 54401
Tel (715) 847-2772 *SIC* 8011

ASPIRUS INC p 118
425 Pine Ridge Blvd # 300 54401
Tel (715) 847-2121 *SIC* 8062

ASPIRUS WAUSAU HOSPITAL INC p 119
425 Pine Ridge Blvd # 1 54401
Tel (715) 847-2121 *SIC* 8062

CORNERSTONE ADVISORS p 370
2711 Stewart Ave 54401
Tel (715) 849-3697 *SIC* 6211

E O JOHNSON CO INC p 466
8400 Stewart Ave 54401
Tel (715) 842-9999 *SIC* 5112 7699 5045

■ EASTBAY INC p 471
111 S 1st Ave 54401
Tel (800) 826-2205 *SIC* 5699 5661 5941

EMPLOYERS INSURANCE OF WAUSAU A MUTUAL CO p 494
2000 Westwood Dr 54401
Tel (715) 845-5211 *SIC* 6331 6311

■ FOOTLOCKER.COM INC p 564
111 S 1st Ave 54401
Tel (715) 842-3890 *SIC* 5961 5661

KOLBE & KOLBE MILLWORK CO INC p 826
1323 S 11th Ave 54401
Tel (715) 842-5666 *SIC* 5031 2431

■ LINETEC p 869
7500 Stewart Ave 54401
Tel (715) 843-4100 *SIC* 3442

■ UMR INC p 1502
11 Scott St 54403
Tel (800) 826-9781 *SIC* 6324 8748

WAUSAU COATED PRODUCTS INC p 1583
7801 Stewart Ave 54401
Tel (715) 848-2741 *SIC* 2672 3554

■ WAUSAU FINANCIAL SYSTEMS INC p 1583
400 Westwood Dr 54401
Tel (715) 359-0427 *SIC* 7373

WAUSAU SERVICE CORP p 1583
2000 Westwood Dr 54401
Tel (715) 845-5211 *SIC* 6331 6311

WAUWATOSA, WI

BOSTIK INC p 202
11320 W Wtertown Plank Rd 53226
Tel (414) 774-2250 *SIC* 2891

▲ BRIGGS & STRATTON CORP p 212
12301 W Wirth St 53222
Tel (414) 259-5333 *SIC* 3519 3524

■ BRIGGS & STRATTON POWER PRODUCTS GROUP LLC p 212
12301 W Wirth St 53222
Tel (414) 259-5333 *SIC* 3621

CORIX UTILITIES (US) INC p 370
11020 W Plank Ct Ste 100 53226
Tel (414) 203-8700 *SIC* 1731 7389

GREAT LAKES DENTAL LLC p 633
10101 W Innovation Dr # 700 53226
Tel (262) 966-2428 *SIC* 8021

WATERSTONE BANK p 1582
11200 W Plank Ct 53226
Tel (414) 459-4211 *SIC* 6029

▲ WATERSTONE FINANCIAL INC p 1582
11200 W Plank Ct 53226
Tel (414) 761-1000 *SIC* 6035

WAUWATOSA SCHOOL DISTRICT p 1583
12121 W North Ave 53226
Tel (414) 773-1000 *SIC* 8211

WEBSTER, WI

ST CROIX CHIPPEWA INDIANS OF WISCONSIN p 1365
24663 Angeline Ave 54893
Tel (715) 349-2195 *SIC* 9131

WEST ALLIS, WI

SCHOOL DISTRICT OF WEST ALLIS-WEST MILWAUKEE ET AL p 1290
1205 S 70th St Ste 440 53214
Tel (414) 604-3000 *SIC* 8211

WEST BEND, WI

MANITOU AMERICAS INC p 902
1 Gehl Way 53095
Tel (262) 334-9461 *SIC* 3531 3523

MATENAER CORP p 919
810 Schoenhaar Dr 53090
Tel (262) 338-0700 *SIC* 5051 3452

SAINT JOSEPHS COMMUNITY HOSPITAL p 1269
3200 Pleasant Valley Rd 53095
Tel (262) 334-5533 *SIC* 8062

SERIGRAPH INC p 1306
3801 Decorah Rd 53095
Tel (262) 335-7200 *SIC* 2759 2752 2396

WEST BEND JOINT SCHOOL DISTRICT NO 1 p 1593
735 S Main St Stop 2 53095
Tel (262) 335-5435 *SIC* 8211

WEST BEND MUTUAL INSURANCE CO p 1593
1900 S 18th Ave 53095
Tel (262) 334-5571 *SIC* 6331

WESTFIELD, WI

BRAKEBUSH BROTHERS INC p 207
N4993 6th Dr 53964
Tel (608) 296-2121 *SIC* 2013 2015

DW SAWMILL LLC p 463
N8972 County Road Jj 53964
Tel (608) 296-1863 *SIC* 5099 2491 5211

WHITEWATER, WI

S & R EGG FARM INC p 1261
N9416 Tamarack Rd 53190
Tel (262) 495-6220 *SIC* 0252

WINDSOR, WI

CLACK CORP p 321
4462 Duraform Ln 53598
Tel (608) 846-3010 *SIC* 3589 3089

WISCONSIN DELLS, WI

■ DELLONA ENTERPRISES INC p 425
S944 Christmas Mtn Rd 53965
Tel (608) 253-1000 *SIC* 7011 7992 5812

HOLIDAY WHOLESALE INC p 700
225 Pioneer Dr 53965
Tel (608) 253-0404
SIC 5194 5145 5113 5199

KALAHARI DEVELOPMENT LLC p 801
1305 Kalahari Dr 53965
Tel (608) 254-5466 *SIC* 7011 5812 5813

WISCONSIN RAPIDS, WI

NEWPAGE WISCONSIN SYSTEM INC p 1038
111 W Jackson St 54495
Tel (715) 422-3111
SIC 2621 2611 2653 7011

RENAISSANCE LEARNING INC p 1223
2911 Peach St 54494
Tel (715) 424-4242 *SIC* 7372 5072

RIVERVIEW HOSPITAL ASSOCIATION p 1238
410 Dewey St 54494
Tel (715) 423-6060 *SIC* 8062

WITTENBERG, WI

■ ASSOCIATED BANK NA p 120
303 S 1st Ave 54499
Tel (715) 845-4301 *SIC* 6022

WOODVILLE, WI

OEM FABRICATORS INC p 1075
300 Mcmillan Rd 54028
Tel (715) 698-2111 *SIC* 3599

WRIGHTSTOWN, WI

COATING EXCELLENCE INTERNATIONAL LLC p 332
975 Brdwy St 54180
Tel (920) 996-1900 *SIC* 2671

WYOMING

BUFFALO, WY

CKT SERVICES INC p 320
412 N Main St Ste 100 82834
Tel (713) 581-0819 *SIC* 5172 7699

CASPER, WY

■ JW WILLIAMS INC p 798
2180 W Renauna Ave 82601
Tel (307) 237-8345
SIC 3533 3443 3547 1761 3291

NATRONA COUNTY SCHOOL DISTRICT p 1018
970 N Glenn Rd 82601
Tel (307) 253-5200 *SIC* 8211

TIC - INDUSTRIAL CO WYOMING INC p 1452
1474 Willer Dr 82604
Tel (307) 235-9958 *SIC* 1629

TRUE OIL LLC p 1486
455 N Poplar St 82601
Tel (307) 237-9301 *SIC* 1311

WERCS p 1592
400 E 1st St Ste 100 82601
Tel (307) 235-6200
SIC 6211 6163 6411 6321 6531 6099

WYOMING MACHINERY CO p 1630
5300 W Old Yllowstone Hwy 82604
Tel (307) 686-1500 *SIC* 5082

WYOMING MEDICAL CENTER p 1630
1233 E 2nd St 82601
Tel (307) 577-7201 *SIC* 8062

CHEYENNE, WY

BLUE CROSS & BLUE SHIELD OF WYOMING p 191
4000 House Ave 82001
Tel (307) 634-1393 *SIC* 6321

DEPARTMENT OF CORRECTIONS WYOMING p 430
1934 Wyott Dr Ste 100 82007
Tel (307) 777-7208 *SIC* 9223

DEPARTMENT OF MILITARY WYOMING p 430
5500 Bishop Blvd 82009
Tel (307) 772-6201 *SIC* 9711

EXECUTIVE OFFICE OF STATE OF WYOMING p 518
200 W 24th St Rm 124 82001
Tel (307) 777-7434 *SIC* 9111

■ FRONTIER REFINING LLC p 581
300 Morrie Ave 82007
Tel (307) 634-3551 *SIC* 2951 2911

LARAMIE COUNTY SCHOOL DISTRICT 1 p 845
2810 House Ave 82001
Tel (307) 771-2100 *SIC* 8211

M C HOLDINGS INC p 889
5709 Education Dr Apt 205 82009
Tel (307) 514-1510 *SIC* 6719 7389

MEMORIAL HOSPITAL OF LARAMIE COUNTY p 942
214 E 23rd St 82001
Tel (307) 633-7667 *SIC* 8062

OMEGA PROBE INC p 1084
308 Southwest Dr 82007
Tel (877) 323-2201 *SIC* 7371 6552

■ SIERRA TRADING POST INC p 1321
5025 Campstool Rd 82007
Tel (307) 775-8050 *SIC* 5961

SIMON CONTRACTORS p 1324
1103 Old Town Ln Ste 1a 82009
Tel (307) 635-9005 *SIC* 1611

STATE OF WYOMING p 1382
122 W 25th St Fl 4 82001
Tel (307) 777-7758 *SIC* 9111

WYOMING DEPARTMENT OF HEALTH p 1630
2300 Capitol Ave Ste 1 82001
Tel (307) 777-6780 *SIC* 9431

WYOMING DEPARTMENT OF TRANSPORTATION p 1630
5300 Bishop Blvd 82009
Tel (307) 777-4375 *SIC* 9621

CODY, WY

WEST PARK HOSPITAL DISTRICT p 1595
707 Sheridan Ave 82414
Tel (307) 527-7501 *SIC* 8062

EVANSTON, WY

ELKHORN CONSTRUCTION INC p 488
71 Allegiance Cir 82930
Tel (307) 789-1595 *SIC* 1629 1731 1623

GILLETTE, WY

ALPHA COAL WEST INC p 60
2273 Bishop Rd 82718
Tel (307) 687-3400 *SIC* 1221

CAMPBELL COUNTY HOSPITAL DISTRICT p 245
501 S Burma Ave 82716
Tel (307) 688-1551 *SIC* 8062

CAMPBELL COUNTY SCHOOL DISTRICT 1 p 245
1000 W 8th St 82716
Tel (307) 682-5171 *SIC* 8211

▲ CLOUD PEAK ENERGY INC p 327
505 S Gillette Ave 82716
Tel (307) 687-6000 *SIC* 1221

■ CLOUD PEAK ENERGY RESOURCES LLC p 327
505 S Gillette Ave 82716
Tel (303) 956-7596 *SIC* 1221

■ CLOUD PEAK ENERGY SERVICES CO p 327
505 S Gillette Ave 82716
Tel (307) 687-6000 *SIC* 1221

GREEN RIVER, WY

■ CINER WYOMING LLC p 308
254 County Rd 4/6 82935
Tel (307) 875-2600 *SIC* 2812

TRONOX ALKALI WYOMING CORP p 1484
580 Westvaco Rd 82935
Tel (307) 875-2580 *SIC* 2812

HULETT, WY

NEIMAN ENTERPRISES INC p 1025
51 State Highway 112 82720
Tel (307) 467-5252 *SIC* 2421

JACKSON, WY

KUSSY INC p 832
1260 Huff Ln Ste B 83001
Tel (307) 739-9465 *SIC* 1752 5713

TETON COUNTY HOSPITAL DISTRICT p 1441
625 E Broadway Ave 83001
Tel (307) 733-3636 *SIC* 8062 8052 8051

LANDER, WY

NATIONAL OUTDOOR LEADERSHIP SCHOOL p 1014
284 Lincoln St 82520
Tel (800) 710-6657 *SIC* 8299 5941

LARAMIE, WY

ALBANY COUNTY SCHOOL DISTRICT ONE p 45
1948 E Grand Ave 82070
Tel (307) 721-4400 *SIC* 8211

UNIVERSITY OF WYOMING p 1527
1000 E University Ave # 3434 82071
Tel (307) 766-5766 *SIC* 8221

MORAN, WY

■ GRAND TETON LODGE CO p 630
Highway 89 5 Mls N Moran 83013
Tel (307) 543-2811 *SIC* 7011

MOUNTAIN VIEW, WY

UNION TELEPHONE CO p 1505
850 N Hwy 414 82939
Tel (307) 782-6131 *SIC* 4813 4812

RIVERTON, WY

HIGH PLAINS POWER INC p 690
1775 E Monroe 82501
Tel (800) 826-3446 *SIC* 4911

ROCK SPRINGS, WY

SWEETWATER COUNTY SCHOOL DISTRICT 1 p 1411
3550 Foothill Blvd 82901
Tel (307) 352-3400 *SIC* 8211

TEAM REAL ESTATE INC p 1430
601 Broadway St 82901
Tel (307) 362-1275 *SIC* 6531

SINCLAIR, WY

SINCLAIR WYOMING REFINING CO p 1326
100 E Lincoln Ave 82334
Tel (307) 328-3539 *SIC* 2911

SUNDANCE, WY

POWDER RIVER ENERGY CORP p 1164
221 Main St 82729
Tel (307) 283-3531 *SIC* 4911

TETON VILLAGE, WY

JACKSON HOLE MOUNTAIN RESORT CORP p 774
3395 Cody Ln 83025
Tel (307) 733-2292 *SIC* 7999 6552

WORLAND, WY

ADMIRAL BEVERAGE CORP p 23
821 Pulliam Ave 82401
Tel (801) 782-5072 *SIC* 5149 2086

WRIGHT, WY

■ THUNDER BASIN COAL CO LLC p 1451
5669 Hwy 450 82732
Tel (307) 939-1300 *SIC* 1221

Section III

Businesses by Industry Classification

SIC 0111 Wheat

F & W FARMS INC p 522
177 Woody Cir, New Hope AL 35760
Tel (256) 599-6422
SIC 0116 0115 0131 0111

■YASHENG GROUP p 1635
805 Veterans Blvd Ste 228, Redwood City CA 94063
Tel (650) 363-8345
SIC 2879 0111 0115 0116 0112

BLAINE LARSEN FARMS INC p 188
2650 N 2375 E, Hamer ID 83425
Tel (208) 662-5501
SIC 5148 2099 0111 0139

PIONEER FEEDYARD LLC p 1150
1021 County Road Cc, Oakley KS 67748
Tel (785) 672-3257
SIC 0111 0211 0115 0212

WHEAT MONTANA FARMS INC p 1604
10778 Us Highway 287, Three Forks MT 59752
Tel (406) 285-3614 SIC 5149 0111

W B JOHNSTON GRAIN CO p 1568
411 W Chestnut Ave, Enid OK 73701
Tel (580) 233-5800
SIC 5153 5191 4491 4213 0111 0211

SIC 0112 Rice

■YASHENG GROUP p 1635
805 Veterans Blvd Ste 228, Redwood City CA 94063
Tel (650) 363-8345
SIC 2879 0111 0115 0116 0112

SIC 0115 Corn

F & W FARMS INC p 522
177 Woody Cir, New Hope AL 35760
Tel (256) 599-6422
SIC 0116 0115 0131 0111

■YASHENG GROUP p 1635
805 Veterans Blvd Ste 228, Redwood City CA 94063
Tel (650) 363-8345
SIC 2879 0111 0115 0116 0112

HOWE-OTTO INC p 713
951 E 3300 North Rd, Farmer City IL 61842
Tel (309) 928-9730 SIC 0116 0115 7389

PIONEER FEEDYARD LLC p 1150
1021 County Road Cc, Oakley KS 67748
Tel (785) 672-3257
SIC 0111 0211 0115 0212

SCOTT FARMS INC p 1293
7965a Simpson Rd, Lucama NC 27851
Tel (919) 284-4030
SIC 0132 0115 0116 0161 0139

HARTUNG BROTHERS INC p 666
708 Heartland Trl # 2000, Madison WI 53717
Tel (608) 829-6000 SIC 0161 0115 8748

SIC 0116 Soybeans

F & W FARMS INC p 522
177 Woody Cir, New Hope AL 35760
Tel (256) 599-6422
SIC 0116 0115 0131 0111

E RITTER & CO p 466
10 Elm St, Marked Tree AR 72365
Tel (870) 358-7333
SIC 0131 0116 0724 4813 5211 5083

■YASHENG GROUP p 1635
805 Veterans Blvd Ste 228, Redwood City CA 94063
Tel (650) 363-8345
SIC 2879 0111 0115 0116 0112

HOWE-OTTO INC p 713
951 E 3300 North Rd, Farmer City IL 61842
Tel (309) 928-9730 SIC 0116 0115 7389

SCOTT FARMS INC p 1293
7965a Simpson Rd, Lucama NC 27851
Tel (919) 284-4030
SIC 0132 0115 0116 0161 0139

SIC 0119 Cash Grains, NEC

TALLGRASS COMMODITIES LLC p 1423
420 Lincoln St, Wamego KS 66547
Tel (855) 494-8484 SIC 0119

FORNAZOR INTERNATIONAL INC A NEW JERSEY CORP p 568
455 Hillsdale Ave, Hillsdale NJ 07642
Tel (201) 664-4000
SIC 0119 2034 2044 2045 2075 4449

UNGERER & CO INC p 1502
4 Bridgewater Ln, Lincoln Park NJ 07035
Tel (973) 628-0600 SIC 0119

SIC 0131 Cotton

F & W FARMS INC p 522
177 Woody Cir, New Hope AL 35760
Tel (256) 599-6422
SIC 0116 0115 0131 0111

AK-CHIN INDIAN COMMUNITY DEVELOPMENT CORP p 41
42507 W Peters & Nall Rd, Maricopa AZ 85138
Tel (520) 568-1000
SIC 0131 0139 5251 7993

E RITTER & CO p 466
10 Elm St, Marked Tree AR 72365
Tel (870) 358-7333
SIC 0131 0116 0724 4813 5211 5083

E RITTER AGRIBUSINESS HOLDINGS INC p 466
10 Elm St, Marked Tree AR 72365
Tel (870) 336-7310 SIC 0131 4813

J G BOSWELL CO p 771
101 W Walnut St, Pasadena CA 91103
Tel (626) 356-7492 SIC 0131 6552

BARNHARDT MANUFACTURING CO p 156
1100 Hawthorne Ln, Charlotte NC 28205
Tel (704) 376-0380 SIC 0131 3086

DUNAVANT ENTERPRISES INC p 461
959 Ridg Loop Rd Ste 200, Memphis TN 38120
Tel (901) 369-1500
SIC 5159 4221 4731 0131

SIC 0132 Tobacco

COLONIAL GROCERS INC p 337
4001 E Lake Ave, Tampa FL 33610
Tel (813) 621-8880 SIC 0132 5141

SCOTT FARMS INC p 1293
7965a Simpson Rd, Lucama NC 27851
Tel (919) 284-4030
SIC 0132 0115 0116 0161 0139

GENERAL CIGAR CO INC p 599
10900 Nuckols Rd Ste 100, Glen Allen VA 23060
Tel (860) 602-3500 SIC 2121 5199 0132

SQUAXIN ISLAND TRIBE OF SQUAXIN ISLAND RESERVATION p 1362
10 Se Squaxin Ln, Shelton WA 98584
Tel (360) 426-9781
SIC 5411 5146 7011 0132

SIC 0133 Sugarcane & Sugar Beets

UNITED STATES SUGAR CORP p 1514
111 Ponce De Leon Ave, Clewiston FL 33440
Tel (863) 983-8121
SIC 0133 2061 2062 2033

▲ALICO INC p 50
10070 Daniels Interstate, Fort Myers FL 33913
Tel (239) 226-2000
SIC 0174 0212 0133 6519

A DUDA & SONS INC p 5
1200 Duda Trl, Oviedo FL 32765
Tel (407) 365-2111
SIC 0161 5148 2033 0133 6552 0174

FANJUL CORP p 527
1 N Clematis St Ste 200, West Palm Beach FL 33401
Tel (561) 655-6303
SIC 0133 2061 2099 6552

■ALEXANDER & BALDWIN LLC p 49
822 Bishop St, Honolulu HI 96813
Tel (808) 525-6611
SIC 6531 0133 0179 6552

■AMFAC HAWAII LLC A HAWAII LIMITED LIABILITY CO p 85
700 Bishop St Ste 2002, Honolulu HI 96813
Tel (808) 543-8900
SIC 6531 6552 0133 0179

▲SEABOARD CORP p 1295
9000 W 67th St, Merriam KS 66202
Tel (913) 676-8800
SIC 2011 0133 4412 6221 0723 0213

SIC 0134 Irish Potatoes

RD OFFUTT CO p 1212
700 7th St S, Fargo ND 58103
Tel (701) 526-9670 SIC 0134 2038

BLACK GOLD FARMS p 186
4320 18th Ave S, Grand Forks ND 58201
Tel (701) 792-3414 SIC 0134 0191

STERMAN MASSER INC p 1387
2 Fearnot Rd, Sacramento PA 17968
Tel (570) 682-3709 SIC 0134 2099

SIC 0139 Field Crops, Except Cash Grains, NEC

AK-CHIN INDIAN COMMUNITY DEVELOPMENT CORP p 41
42507 W Peters & Nall Rd, Maricopa AZ 85138
Tel (520) 568-1000
SIC 0131 0139 5251 7993

▲S&W SEED CO p 1263
7108 N Fresno St Ste 380, Fresno CA 93720
Tel (559) 884-2535 SIC 0139 0723

CHRISTOPHER RANCH LLC p 303
305 Bloomfield Ave, Gilroy CA 95020
Tel (408) 847-1100 SIC 0139 0175

JOHN I HAAS INC p 789
5185 Mcarthur Blvd Nw # 300, Washington DC 20016
Tel (202) 777-4800 SIC 0139 5159

BLAINE LARSEN FARMS INC p 188
2650 N 2375 E, Hamer ID 83425
Tel (208) 662-5501
SIC 5148 2099 0111 0139

WAYNE BAILEY INC p 1584
490 Old Hwy 74, Chadbourn NC 28431
Tel (910) 654-5163 SIC 5148 0139

SCOTT FARMS INC p 1293
7965a Simpson Rd, Lucama NC 27851
Tel (919) 284-4030
SIC 0132 0115 0116 0161 0139

■NUGEN ENERGY LLC p 1067
27283 447th Ave, Marion SD 57043
Tel (605) 648-2100 SIC 0139 1731 5211

SIC 0161 Vegetables & Melons

EAGLE PRODUCE LLC p 468
7332 E Butherus Dr # 200, Scottsdale AZ 85260
Tel (480) 998-1444 SIC 0161

ROUSSEAU SONS LLC p 1253
102 S 95th Ave, Tolleson AZ 85353
Tel (623) 936-7100 SIC 0161 0191

AV THOMAS PRODUCE INC p 135
3900 Sultana Ave, Atwater CA 95301
Tel (209) 394-7514 SIC 0161

■BOLTHOUSE FARMS p 199
3200 E Brundage Ln, Bakersfield CA 93304
Tel (661) 366-7205 SIC 0161

■BOLTHOUSE HOLDING CORP p 199
7200 E Brundage Ln, Bakersfield CA 93307
Tel (310) 566-8350 SIC 0161 2099

SUN WORLD INTERNATIONAL INC p 1401
16351 Driver Rd, Bakersfield CA 93308
Tel (661) 392-5000
SIC 0723 0172 0174 0175 0179 0161

■WM BOLTHOUSE FARMS INC p 1620
7200 E Brundage Ln, Bakersfield CA 93307
Tel (661) 366-7205 SIC 0161 2099 0723

SUN AND SANDS ENTERPRISES LLC p 1399
86705 Avenue 54 Ste A, Coachella CA 92236
Tel (760) 399-4278 SIC 0161

BOSKOVICH FARMS INC p 202
711 Diaz Ave, Oxnard CA 93030
Tel (805) 487-2299 SIC 0723 5812 0161

DARRIGO BROSCOOF CALIFORNIA p 412
21777 Harris Rd, Salinas CA 93908
Tel (831) 455-4500 SIC 0161

TANIMURA & ANTLE FRESH FOODS INC p 1424
1 Harris Rd, Salinas CA 93908
Tel (831) 455-2950
SIC 0161 0182 0723 2099

BETTERAVIA FARMS LLC p 178
1850 W Stowell Rd, Santa Maria CA 93458
Tel (805) 925-2585 SIC 0161

DFC HOLDINGS LLC p 435
1 Dole Dr, Westlake Village CA 91362
Tel (818) 879-6600
SIC 0174 0175 0161 5148 2033

DHM HOLDING CO INC p 435
1 Dole Dr, Westlake Village CA 91362
Tel (818) 879-6600
SIC 0179 0174 0175 0161 5148 2033

DOLE FOOD CO INC p 448
1 Dole Dr, Westlake Village CA 91362
Tel (818) 874-4000
SIC 0179 0174 0175 0161 5148 2033

DOLE HOLDING CO LLC p 448
1 Dole Dr, Westlake Village CA 91362
Tel (818) 879-6600
SIC 0179 0174 0175 0161 5148 2033

CHIQUITA BRANDS INTERNATIONAL INC p 301
2051 Se 35th St, Fort Lauderdale FL 33316
Tel (954) 453-1201
SIC 0179 0174 0161 0175 2033

CHIQUITA BRANDS LLC p 301
2051 Se 35th St, Fort Lauderdale FL 33316
Tel (954) 453-1201
SIC 0175 0174 0179 0161 5148 7389

VILLAGE FARMS LP p 1557
195 International Pkwy # 100, Heathrow FL 32746
Tel (407) 936-1190 SIC 0161

CUSTOM-PAK INC p 403
315 New Market Rd E, Immokalee FL 34142
Tel (239) 657-4421 SIC 0161

J & J PRODUCE INC p 770
4003 Seminole Pratt, Loxahatchee FL 33470
Tel (561) 422-9777 SIC 5148 0161

A DUDA & SONS INC p 5
1200 Duda Trl, Oviedo FL 32765
Tel (407) 365-2111
SIC 0161 5148 2033 0133 6552 0174

DUDA FARM FRESH FOODS INC p 459
1200 Duda Trl, Oviedo FL 32765
Tel (407) 365-2111 SIC 5148 0161 0174

MCCLURE PROPERTIES LTD p 927
502 6th Ave W, Palmetto FL 34221
Tel (941) 722-4545 SIC 0161

PACIFIC TOMATO GROWERS LTD p 1106
503 10th St W, Palmetto FL 34221
Tel (941) 729-8410 SIC 0161 0174 0723

AYCO FARMS INC p 140
1501 Nw 12th Ave, Pompano Beach FL 33069
Tel (954) 788-6800 SIC 5148 0161

POTANDON PRODUCE LLC p 1164
1210 Pier View Dr, Idaho Falls ID 83402
Tel (208) 419-4200 SIC 5148 0161 0722

R J VAN DRUNEN & SONS INC p 1202
300 W 6th St, Momence IL 60954
Tel (815) 472-3100
SIC 2034 2037 0161 2099

SCOTT FARMS INC p 1293
7965a Simpson Rd, Lucama NC 27851
Tel (919) 284-4030
SIC 0132 0115 0116 0161 0139

STAHLBUSH ISLAND FARMS INC p 1374
3122 Se Stahlbush Is, Corvallis OR 97333
Tel (541) 753-8942 SIC 2037 0161

WALTER P RAWL & SONS INC p 1574
824 Fairview Rd, Pelion SC 29123
Tel (803) 894-1900 SIC 0161 0723 5148

MODERN AG PRODUCTS LTD p 981
1655 Louisiana St, Beaumont TX 77701
Tel (409) 833-2665 SIC 7359 6792 0161

NATURESWEET LTD p 1019
2338 N Loop 1604 W, San Antonio TX 78248
Tel (210) 408-8500 SIC 0161

HARTUNG BROTHERS INC p 666
708 Heartland Trl # 2000, Madison WI 53717
Tel (608) 829-6000 SIC 0161 0115 8748

SIC 0171 Berry Crops

RED BLOSSOM SALES INC p 1215
400 W Ventura Blvd # 140, Camarillo CA 93010
Tel (805) 686-4747 SIC 0171

GEM-PACK BERRIES LLC p 598
8 Corporate Park Ste 110, Irvine CA 92606
Tel (949) 861-4919 SIC 0171

BERRY ECLIPSE FARMS LLC p 176
11812 San Vicente Blvd # 250, Los Angeles CA 90049
Tel (310) 207-7879 SIC 0171 5148

RAMCO ENTERPRISES LP p 1207
320 Airport Blvd, Salinas CA 93905
Tel (831) 758-5272 SIC 0171 7361 0723

AG-MART PRODUCE INC p 34
4006 Airport Rd, Plant City FL 33563
Tel (877) 606-5003 SIC 0171

SIC 0172 Grapes

SUN WORLD INTERNATIONAL INC p 1401
16351 Driver Rd, Bakersfield CA 93308
Tel (661) 392-5000
SIC 0723 0172 0174 0175 0179 0161

GRAPEMAN FARMS LP p 631
9777 Wilshire Blvd # 918, Beverly Hills CA 90212
Tel (310) 273-9540 SIC 0172

GIUMARRA VINEYARDS CORP p 613
11220 Edison Hwy, Edison CA 93220
Tel (661) 395-7000 SIC 0172 2084 2086

F KORBEL & BROS p 522
13250 River Rd, Guerneville CA 95446
Tel (707) 824-7000 SIC 2084 0172

E & J GALLO WINERY p 465
600 Yosemite Blvd, Modesto CA 95354
Tel (209) 341-3111 SIC 2084 0172

SUTTER HOME WINERY INC p 1410
100 Saint Helena Hwy S, Saint Helena CA 94574
Tel (707) 963-3104 SIC 2084 0172

JACKSON FAMILY WINES INC p 774
421 And 425 Aviation Blvd, Santa Rosa CA 95403
Tel (707) 544-4000 SIC 2084 0172 5813

MOET HENNESSY USA INC p 982
85 10th Ave Fl 2, New York NY 10011
Tel (212) 888-7575
SIC 0172 2844 6153 5182 5122

SIC 0173 Tree Nuts

FOSTER POULTRY FARMS p 570
1000 Davis St, Livingston CA 95334
Tel (209) 394-6914
SIC 0254 2015 5812 0173 5191 4212

WONDERFUL ORCHARDS LLC p 1622
6801 E Lerdo Hwy, Shafter CA 93263
Tel (661) 399-4456 SIC 0173 0179

SELECT HARVEST USA LLC p 1301
14827 W Harding Rd, Turlock CA 95380
Tel (209) 668-2471 SIC 5159 0173

WUESTS INC p 1628
9318 Fm 725, Mc Queeney TX 78123
Tel (830) 379-3442 SIC 5141 5411 0173

SIC 0174 Citrus Fruits

SUN WORLD INTERNATIONAL INC p 1401
16351 Driver Rd, Bakersfield CA 93308
Tel (661) 392-5000
SIC 0723 0172 0174 0175 0179 0161

WILEMAN BROS & ELLIOTT INC p 1609
40232 Road 128, Cutler CA 93615
Tel (559) 651-8378
SIC 0723 2653 0174 0175

WONDERFUL CITRUS PACKING LLC p 1622
1901 S Lexington St, Delano CA 93215
Tel (661) 720-2400 SIC 0723 0174 2033

IRVINE CO LLC p 765
550 Newport Center Dr # 160, Newport Beach CA 92660
Tel (949) 720-2000
SIC 6552 6531 0174 0191 4841

▲LIMONEIRA CO p 866
1141 Cummings Rd Ofc, Santa Paula CA 93060
Tel (805) 525-5541
SIC 0723 0174 0179 6531 6799

DFC HOLDINGS LLC p 435
1 Dole Dr, Westlake Village CA 91362
Tel (818) 879-6600
SIC 0174 0175 0161 5148 2033

DHM HOLDING CO INC p 435
1 Dole Dr, Westlake Village CA 91362
Tel (818) 879-6600
SIC 0179 0174 0175 0161 5148 2033

DOLE FOOD CO INC p 448
1 Dole Dr, Westlake Village CA 91362
Tel (818) 874-4000
SIC 0179 0174 0175 0161 5148 2033

DOLE HOLDING CO LLC p 448
1 Dole Dr, Westlake Village CA 91362
Tel (818) 879-6600
SIC 0179 0174 0175 0161 5148 2033

CHIQUITA BRANDS INTERNATIONAL INC p 301
2051 Se 35th St, Fort Lauderdale FL 33316
Tel (954) 453-1201
SIC 0179 0174 0161 0175 2033

CHIQUITA BRANDS LLC p 301
2051 Se 35th St, Fort Lauderdale FL 33316
Tel (954) 453-1201
SIC 0175 0174 0179 0161 5148 7389

▲ALICO INC p 50
10070 Daniels Interstate, Fort Myers FL 33913
Tel (239) 226-2000
SIC 0174 0212 0133 6519

BERNARD EGAN & CO p 176
1900 N Old Dixie Hwy, Fort Pierce FL 34946
Tel (772) 465-7555 SIC 0723 8741 0174

BEN HILL GRIFFIN INC p 172
700 S Scenic Hwy, Frostproof FL 33843
Tel (863) 635-2281 SIC 2875 0174 2033

A DUDA & SONS INC p 5
1200 Duda Trl, Oviedo FL 32765
Tel (407) 365-2111
SIC 0161 5148 2033 0133 6552 0174

DUDA FARM FRESH FOODS INC p 459
1200 Duda Trl, Oviedo FL 32765
Tel (407) 365-2111 SIC 5148 0161 0174

PACIFIC TOMATO GROWERS LTD p 1106
503 10th St W, Palmetto FL 34221
Tel (941) 729-8410 SIC 0161 0174 0723

LYKES BROS INC p 887
400 N Tampa St Ste 1900, Tampa FL 33602
Tel (813) 223-3911 SIC 0174 6331

■H J M P CORP p 650
1930 George St Ste 2, Melrose Park IL 60160
Tel (708) 345-5370
SIC 2033 5149 0174 2037

SIC 0175 Deciduous Tree Fruits

SUN WORLD INTERNATIONAL INC p 1401
16351 Driver Rd, Bakersfield CA 93308
Tel (661) 392-5000
SIC 0723 0172 0174 0175 0179 0161

WILEMAN BROS & ELLIOTT INC p 1609
40232 Road 128, Cutler CA 93615
Tel (559) 651-8378
SIC 0723 2653 0174 0175

CHRISTOPHER RANCH LLC p 303
305 Bloomfield Ave, Gilroy CA 95020
Tel (408) 847-1100 SIC 0139 0175

DFC HOLDINGS LLC p 435
1 Dole Dr, Westlake Village CA 91362
Tel (818) 879-6600
SIC 0174 0175 0161 5148 2033

DHM HOLDING CO INC p 435
1 Dole Dr, Westlake Village CA 91362
Tel (818) 879-6600
SIC 0179 0174 0175 0161 5148 2033

DOLE FOOD CO INC p 448
1 Dole Dr, Westlake Village CA 91362
Tel (818) 874-4000
SIC 0179 0174 0175 0161 5148 2033

DOLE HOLDING CO LLC p 448
1 Dole Dr, Westlake Village CA 91362
Tel (818) 879-6600
SIC 0179 0174 0175 0161 5148 2033

CHIQUITA BRANDS INTERNATIONAL INC p 301
2051 Se 35th St, Fort Lauderdale FL 33316
Tel (954) 453-1201
SIC 0179 0174 0161 0175 2033

CHIQUITA BRANDS LLC p 301
2051 Se 35th St, Fort Lauderdale FL 33316
Tel (954) 453-1201
SIC 0175 0174 0179 0161 5148 7389

NAUMES INC p 1019
2 W Barnett St, Medford OR 97501
Tel (541) 772-6268 *SIC* 0175 0723 4222

UNITED SALAD CO p 1511
8448 Ne 33rd Dr Ste 100, Portland OR 97211
Tel (503) 288-8300 *SIC* 5148 0175 2033

TROUT-BLUE CHELAN-MAGI INC p 1484
8 Howser Rd, Chelan WA 98816
Tel (509) 682-2591 *SIC* 0723 0175 4222

EVANS FRUIT CO INC p 513
200 Cowiche City Rd, Cowiche WA 98923
Tel (509) 678-4127 *SIC* 0175

BROETJE ORCHARDS LLC p 216
1111 Fishook Park Rd, Prescott WA 99348
Tel (509) 749-2217 *SIC* 0175

ZIRKLE FRUIT CO p 1643
352 Harrison Rd, Selah WA 98942
Tel (509) 697-6101 *SIC* 0175 0723 4222

VALLEY ROZ ORCHARDS INC p 1541
10 E Mead Ave, Yakima WA 98903
Tel (509) 457-4153 *SIC* 0175 5431

SIC 0179 Fruits & Tree Nuts, NEC

SUN WORLD INTERNATIONAL INC p 1401
16351 Driver Rd, Bakersfield CA 93308
Tel (661) 392-5000
SIC 0723 0172 0174 0175 0179 0161

HENRY AVOCADO CORP p 684
2355 E Lincoln Ave, Escondido CA 92027
Tel (760) 745-6632 *SIC* 0179 4213

▲ LIMONEIRA CO p 866
1141 Cummings Rd Ofc, Santa Paula CA 93060
Tel (805) 525-5541
SIC 0723 0174 0179 6531 6799

WONDERFUL ORCHARDS LLC p 1622
6801 E Lerdo Hwy, Shafter CA 93263
Tel (661) 399-4456 *SIC* 0173 0179

DHM HOLDING CO INC p 435
1 Dole Dr, Westlake Village CA 91362
Tel (818) 879-6600
SIC 0179 0174 0175 0161 5148 2033

DOLE FOOD CO INC p 448
1 Dole Dr, Westlake Village CA 91362
Tel (818) 874-4000
SIC 0179 0174 0175 0161 5148 2033

DOLE HOLDING CO LLC p 448
1 Dole Dr, Westlake Village CA 91362
Tel (818) 879-6600
SIC 0179 0174 0175 0161 5148 2033

CHIQUITA BRANDS INTERNATIONAL INC p 301
2051 Se 35th St, Fort Lauderdale FL 33316
Tel (954) 453-1201
SIC 0179 0174 0161 0175 2033

CHIQUITA BRANDS LLC p 301
2051 Se 35th St, Fort Lauderdale FL 33316
Tel (954) 453-1201
SIC 0175 0174 0179 0161 5148 7389

■ ALEXANDER & BALDWIN LLC p 49
822 Bishop St, Honolulu HI 96813
Tel (808) 525-6611
SIC 6531 0133 0179 6552

■ AMFAC HAWAII LLC A HAWAII LIMITED LIABILITY CO p 85
700 Bishop St Ste 2002, Honolulu HI 96813
Tel (808) 543-8900
SIC 6531 6552 0133 0179

LA VALENCIANA AVOCADOS CORP p 836
214 N 16th St Ste 127, Mcallen TX 78501
Tel (956) 994-0561 *SIC* 5148 0179

MASSIMO ZANETTI BEVERAGE USA INC p 917
1370 Progress Rd, Suffolk VA 23434
Tel (757) 215-7300 *SIC* 0179

SIC 0181 Ornamental Floriculture & Nursery Prdts

FLOWERWOOD NURSERY INC p 560
6470 Dauphin Island Pkwy, Mobile AL 36605
Tel (251) 443-6540 *SIC* 0181

SUN VALLEY GROUP INC p 1401
3160 Upper Bay Rd, Arcata CA 95521
Tel (707) 822-2885 *SIC* 0181

MONROVIA NURSERY CO p 985
817 E Monrovia Pl, Azusa CA 91702
Tel (626) 334-9321 *SIC* 0181 5193 5261

KEITHLY-WILLIAMS SEEDS INC p 808
420 Palm Ave, Holtville CA 92250
Tel (760) 356-5533 *SIC* 5191 0721 0181

DUARTE NURSERY INC p 459
1555 Baldwin Rd, Hughson CA 95326
Tel (209) 531-0351 *SIC* 0181

HINES HORTICULTURE INC p 695
12621 Jeffrey Rd, Irvine CA 92620
Tel (949) 559-4444 *SIC* 0181 5261

HMCLAUSE INC p 697
260 Cousteau Pl Ste 210, Modesto CA 95357
Tel (530) 747-3700 *SIC* 0181

NORMANS NURSERY INC p 1049
8665 Duarte Rd, San Gabriel CA 91775
Tel (626) 285-9795 *SIC* 5193 0181

SIERRA-CASCADE NURSERY INC p 1321
472-715 Johnson Rd, Susanville CA 96130
Tel (530) 254-6867 *SIC* 0181

COLOR SPOT HOLDINGS INC p 338
27368 Via Industria Ste 2, Temecula CA 92590
Tel (760) 695-1430 *SIC* 0181

COLOR SPOT NURSERIES INC p 338
27368 Via Ste 201, Temecula CA 92590
Tel (760) 695-1430 *SIC* 0181

AMERICAN CIVIL CONSTRUCTORS LLC p 70
4901 S Windermere St, Littleton CO 80120
Tel (303) 795-2582 *SIC* 1629 0783 0181

COSTA FARMS LLC p 374
21800 Sw 162nd Ave, Miami FL 33170
Tel (305) 247-3248 *SIC* 0181

WOERNER HOLDINGS LP p 1620
525 Okeechobee Blvd # 720, West Palm Beach FL 33401
Tel (561) 835-3747 *SIC* 0181

BURPEE HOLDING CO INC p 228
800 Roosevelt Rd Ste 216, Glen Ellyn IL 60137
Tel (215) 674-4900 *SIC* 0181 5191

BALL HORTICULTURAL CO p 148
622 Town Rd, West Chicago IL 60185
Tel (630) 231-3600 *SIC* 0181

BACHMANS INC p 143
6010 Lyndale Ave S, Minneapolis MN 55419
Tel (612) 861-7600
SIC 5992 5261 0181 5193 7359

BUSCH AGRICULTURAL RESOURCES LLC p 229
3636 S Geyer Rd Fl 2, Saint Louis MO 63127
Tel (314) 577-2000
SIC 2044 2083 0181 5153

▲ MONSANTO CO p 985
800 N Lindbergh Blvd, Saint Louis MO 63167
Tel (314) 694-1000 *SIC* 2879 0181

F&S PRODUCE CO INC p 522
913 Bridgeton Ave, Rosenhayn NJ 08352
Tel (856) 453-0316
SIC 0723 2099 2032 0181

KURT WEISS GREENHOUSES INC p 832
95 Main St, Center Moriches NY 11934
Tel (631) 878-2500 *SIC* 0181 5193

S BAUCOM NURSERY CO p 1262
10020 John Russell Rd, Charlotte NC 28213
Tel (704) 596-3220 *SIC* 0181 5193

METROLINA GREENHOUSES INC p 955
16400 Hntrsvle Concrd Rd, Huntersville NC 28078
Tel (704) 659-9400 *SIC* 0181

ARIS HORTICULTURE INC p 108
115 3rd St Se, Barberton OH 44203
Tel (330) 745-2143 *SIC* 0181

DAVEY TREE EXPERT CO p 415
1500 N Mantua St, Kent OH 44240
Tel (330) 673-9511
SIC 0783 0782 0811 0181

GREEN CIRCLE GROWERS INC p 636
51051 Us Highway 20, Oberlin OH 44074
Tel (440) 775-1411 *SIC* 0181

GREENLEAF NURSERY CO p 638
28406 Highway 82, Park Hill OK 74451
Tel (918) 457-5172 *SIC* 0181

INTERNATIONAL GARDEN PRODUCTS INC p 755
30590 Se Kelso Rd, Boring OR 97009
Tel (503) 663-1698 *SIC* 0181

W ATLEE BURPEE CO p 1568
300 Park Ave, Warminster PA 18974
Tel (215) 674-4900 *SIC* 0181 5961

BFN OPERATIONS LLC p 179
8700 Freport Pkwy Ste 100, Irving TX 75063
Tel (972) 819-5030 *SIC* 0181

SOUTHERN STATES COOPERATIVE INC p 1350
6606 W Broad St Ste B, Richmond VA 23230
Tel (804) 281-1000
SIC 2048 0181 2873 2874 5191 5172

SMITH GARDENS INC p 1333
4164 Meridian St Ste 400, Bellingham WA 98226
Tel (800) 755-6256 *SIC* 0181

SIC 0182 Food Crops Grown Under Cover

SAKATA SEED AMERICA INC p 1271
18095 Serene Dr, Morgan Hill CA 95037
Tel (408) 778-7758 *SIC* 5191 0182

TANIMURA & ANTLE FRESH FOODS INC p 1424
1 Harris Rd, Salinas CA 93908
Tel (831) 455-2950
SIC 0161 0182 0723 2099

MONTEREY MUSHROOMS INC p 986
260 Westgate Dr, Watsonville CA 95076
Tel (831) 763-5300 *SIC* 0182

KAOLIN MUSHROOM FARMS INC p 803
649 W South St, Kennett Square PA 19348
Tel (610) 444-4800 *SIC* 0182

SIC 0191 Crop Farming, Misc

BONNIE PLANTS INC p 200
1727 Highway 223, Union Springs AL 36089
Tel (334) 738-3104 *SIC* 0191

ROUSSEAU SONS LLC p 1253
102 S 95th Ave, Tolleson AZ 85353
Tel (623) 936-7100 *SIC* 0161 0191

HARRIS FARMS INC p 663
29475 Fresno Coalinga Rd, Coalinga CA 93210
Tel (559) 884-2435
SIC 0191 0211 2011 7011 5812 5541

BRITZ INC p 214
3265 W Figarden Dr, Fresno CA 93711
Tel (559) 448-8000 *SIC* 0723 0724 0191

IRVINE CO LLC p 765
550 Newport Center Dr # 160, Newport Beach CA 92660
Tel (949) 720-2000
SIC 6552 6531 0174 0191 4841

CB NORTH LLC p 268
480 W Beach St, Watsonville CA 95076
Tel (831) 786-1642 *SIC* 0191

DAN ENNIS FARMS INC p 410
6910 Egbert Rd, Martinsville IN 46151
Tel (765) 342-2711 *SIC* 0191

REMINGTON HYBRID SEED CO INC p 1222
4746 W Us Highway 24, Remington IN 47977
Tel (219) 261-3444 *SIC* 0191

AGSPRING LLC p 36
5250 W 116th Pl Ste 200, Leawood KS 66211
Tel (913) 333-3035 *SIC* 0191 8748

CLAY FARMS p 323
85 Cypress Ln, Yazoo City MS 39194
Tel (662) 836-7629 *SIC* 0191

NAVAJO AGRICULTURAL PRODUCTS INDUSTRY p 1019
10086 Nm Hwy 371, Farmington NM 87499
Tel (505) 326-2730 *SIC* 0191

LAKE SPIRIT TRIBE p 839
816 3rd Ave N, Fort Totten ND 58335
Tel (701) 766-1270
SIC 9131 0191 2394 2298 7999

BLACK GOLD FARMS p 186
4320 18th Ave S, Grand Forks ND 58201
Tel (701) 792-3414 *SIC* 0134 0191

COUNTRY VIEW FAMILY FARMS INC p 375
1301 Fulling Mill Rd # 3000, Middletown PA 17057
Tel (267) 663-0100 *SIC* 0213 0191

BOB JONES UNIVERSITY INC OF GREENVILLE S C p 196
1700 Wade Hampton Blvd, Greenville SC 29614
Tel (864) 242-5100
SIC 8221 8211 8231 8062 5942 0191

ROCKINGHAM COOPERATIVE p 1244
1044 S High St, Harrisonburg VA 22801
Tel (540) 434-3856 *SIC* 0191

WYCKOFF FARMS INC p 1629
160602 Evans Rd, Grandview WA 98930
Tel (509) 882-3934 *SIC* 0191

SIC 0211 Beef Cattle Feedlots

HARRIS FARMS INC p 663
29475 Fresno Coalinga Rd, Coalinga CA 93210
Tel (559) 884-2435
SIC 0191 0211 2011 7011 5812 5541

JBS FIVE RIVERS CATTLE FEEDING LLC p 779
1770 Promontory Cir, Greeley CO 80634
Tel (970) 506-8000 *SIC* 0211

JR SIMPLOT CO p 795
999 W Main St Ste 1300, Boise ID 83702
Tel (208) 336-2110
SIC 0211 2879 2037 2874 2873

SIMPLOT LIVESTOCK CO p 1325
1301 Highway 67, Grand View ID 83624
Tel (208) 834-2231 *SIC* 0211

PIONEER FEEDYARD LLC p 1150
1021 County Road Cc, Oakley KS 67748
Tel (785) 672-3257
SIC 0111 0211 0115 0212

W B JOHNSTON GRAIN CO p 1568
411 W Chestnut Ave, Enid OK 73701
Tel (580) 233-5800
SIC 5153 5191 4491 4213 0111 0211

CACTUS FEEDERS INC p 236
2209 Sw 7th Ave Ste 200, Amarillo TX 79106
Tel (806) 373-2333 *SIC* 0211

FRIONA INDUSTRIES LP p 580
500 S Taylor St Unit 253, Amarillo TX 79101
Tel (806) 374-1811 *SIC* 0211

AZTX CATTLE CO LTD p 141
311 E Park Ave, Hereford TX 79045
Tel (806) 364-8871 *SIC* 0211

DOLSEN COMPANIES p 448
301 N 3rd St, Yakima WA 98901
Tel (509) 248-2831
SIC 0241 0211 2086 7359

SIC 0212 Beef Cattle, Except Feedlots

▲ ALICO INC p 50
10070 Daniels Interstate, Fort Myers FL 33913
Tel (239) 226-2000
SIC 0174 0212 0133 6519

GRAHAM COMPANIES p 628
6843 Main St, Miami Lakes FL 33014
Tel (305) 821-1130
SIC 1531 7011 0212 6552 6512 2711

AGRI BEEF CO p 36
1555 W Shoreline Dr # 320, Boise ID 83702
Tel (208) 338-2500 *SIC* 2011 0212

PIONEER FEEDYARD LLC p 1150
1021 County Road Cc, Oakley KS 67748
Tel (785) 672-3257
SIC 0111 0211 0115 0212

HEMPT BROS INC p 682
205 Creek Rd, Camp Hill PA 17011
Tel (717) 774-2911
SIC 1611 3273 2951 1442 0212

JOHN F MARTIN & SONS INC p 788
55 Lower Hillside Rd, Stevens PA 17578
Tel (717) 336-2804 *SIC* 2013 0212

MAYMEAD FARMS INC p 923
1995 Roan Creek Rd, Mountain City TN 37683
Tel (423) 727-2000 *SIC* 0212

HUNT CONSOLIDATED INC p 718
1900 N Akard St, Dallas TX 75201
Tel (214) 978-8000
SIC 6799 1311 2911 1382 0212

RRH CORP p 1255
1900 N Akard St, Dallas TX 75201
Tel (214) 978-8000
SIC 1382 1311 2911 0212 6799

KING RANCH INC p 820
3 Riverway Ste 1600, Houston TX 77056
Tel (832) 681-5700
SIC 0212 2711 5083 5948

SINCLAIR COMPANIES p 1326
550 E South Temple, Salt Lake City UT 84102
Tel (801) 363-5100
SIC 2911 4612 1382 5541 7011 0212

SIC 0213 Hogs

CENTRAL STATES ENTERPRISES LLC p 280
1275 Lake Heathrow Ln # 101, Heathrow FL 32746
Tel (407) 333-3503 *SIC* 5153 0213 0723

MASCHHOFFS LLC p 915
7475 State Route 127, Carlyle IL 62231
Tel (618) 594-2125 *SIC* 0213

JBS UNITED INC p 780
4310 W State Road 38, Sheridan IN 46069
Tel (317) 758-4495 *SIC* 2048 5153 0213

IOWA SELECT FARMS LLP p 763
811 S Oak St, Iowa Falls IA 50126
Tel (641) 648-4479 *SIC* 0213

TRIOAK FOODS INC p 1482
103 W Railroad St, Oakville IA 52646
Tel (319) 766-2230 *SIC* 0213 5153

▲ SEABOARD CORP p 1295
9000 W 67th St, Merriam KS 66202
Tel (913) 676-8800
SIC 2011 0133 4412 6221 0723 0213

■ SEABOARD FOODS LLC p 1295
9000 W 67th St Ste 200, Shawnee Mission KS 66202
Tel (913) 261-2600 *SIC* 0213 5147 2011

AUSTIN JACK DE COSTER p 133
Plains Rd, Turner ME 04282
Tel (207) 224-8222 *SIC* 0252 0213 0723

CHRISTENSEN FARMS & FEEDLOTS INC p 302
23971 County Road 10, Sleepy Eye MN 56085
Tel (507) 794-5310 *SIC* 0213

NPP LLC p 1064
4860 33rd Ave, Columbus NE 68601
Tel (402) 564-9464 *SIC* 0213

PRESTAGE FARMS INC p 1173
4651 Taylors Bridge Hwy, Clinton NC 28328
Tel (910) 596-5700 *SIC* 0213 0253

MAXWELL FOODS LLC p 923
938 Millers Chapel Rd, Goldsboro NC 27534
Tel (919) 778-3130 *SIC* 0213

HOG SLAT INC p 699
206 Fayetteville St, Newton Grove NC 28366
Tel (866) 464-7528
SIC 1542 3272 3523 0213

MURPHY FARMS LLC p 1001
600 Rte Hwy A, Rose Hill NC 28458
Tel (910) 289-6439 *SIC* 0213

MURPHY-BROWN LLC p 1001
2822 W Nc 24 Hwy, Warsaw NC 28398
Tel (910) 293-3434 *SIC* 0213

■ SEABOARD FARMS INC p 1295
424 N Main St Ste 200, Guymon OK 73942
Tel (580) 338-1470 *SIC* 0213 2011

CLEMENS FAMILY CORP p 325
2700 Clemens Rd, Hatfield PA 19440
Tel (800) 523-5291
SIC 0213 2011 4222 8661

COUNTRY VIEW FAMILY FARMS INC p 375
1301 Fulling Mill Rd # 3000, Middletown PA 17057
Tel (267) 663-0100 *SIC* 0213 0191

SIC 0219 General Livestock, NEC

TARTER GATE CO LLC p 1425
10739 S Us 127, Dunnville KY 42528
Tel (435) 744-0770 *SIC* 3446 0219

SIC 0241 Dairy Farms

■ BERKELEY FARMS LLC p 175
25500 Clawiter Rd, Hayward CA 94545
Tel (510) 265-8600 *SIC* 5143 2026 0241

FOSTER DAIRY FARMS p 570
529 Kansas Ave, Modesto CA 95351
Tel (209) 576-3400 *SIC* 0241

GH DAIRY p 610
14651 Grove Ave, Ontario CA 91762
Tel (909) 606-6455 *SIC* 0241

AURORA DAIRY CORP p 132
1919 14th St Ste 300, Boulder CO 80302
Tel (720) 564-6296 *SIC* 0241

WHITE CONSTRUCTION CO INC p 1606
2811 N Young Blvd, Chiefland FL 32626
Tel (352) 493-1444 *SIC* 1611 0241 3531

ANDERSON ERICKSON DAIRY CO p 90
2420 E University Ave, Des Moines IA 50317
Tel (515) 265-2521 *SIC* 0241

DELAVAL INC p 423
11100 N Congress Ave, Kansas City MO 64153
Tel (816) 891-7700
SIC 5083 3523 2842 0241

■ SUIZA DAIRY GROUP LLC p 1397
2515 Mckinney Ave # 1200, Dallas TX 75201
Tel (214) 303-3400 *SIC* 0241

DOLSEN COMPANIES p 448
301 N 3rd St, Yakima WA 98901
Tel (509) 248-2831
SIC 0241 0211 2086 7359

SIC 0251 Chicken & Poultry Farms

ROD GOLDEN HATCHERY INC p 1246
85 13th St Ne, Cullman AL 35055
Tel (256) 734-0941 *SIC* 0251

PECO FOODS INC p 1127
145 2nd Ave Nw, Gordo AL 35466
Tel (205) 364-7121 *SIC* 0251

MARSHALL DURBIN FOOD CORP p 911
2830 Commerce Blvd, Irondale AL 35210
Tel (205) 841-7315
SIC 0252 0254 2048 0251 2015 5144

SYLVEST FARMS INC p 1414
3500 West Blvd, Montgomery AL 36108
Tel (334) 281-0400 *SIC* 0251 2015

PECO FOODS INC p 1127
1020 Lurleen B Wallace, Tuscaloosa AL 35401
Tel (205) 345-4711
SIC 0254 0251 2015 2048

OK INDUSTRIES INC p 1079
4601 N 6th St, Fort Smith AR 72904
Tel (479) 783-4186 SIC 2048 2015 0251

GEORGES INC p 606
402 W Robinson Ave, Springdale AR 72764
Tel (479) 927-7000 SIC 2015 0254 0251

■TYSON CHICKEN INC p 1496
2200 W Don Tyson Pkwy, Springdale AR 72762
Tel (479) 290-4000
SIC 0252 0253 0254 0251 2015 2013

COLEMAN NATURAL FOODS LLC p 336
1767 Denver West Blvd # 200, Golden CO 80401
Tel (303) 468-2500 SIC 2011 5147 0251

ALLEN HARIM FOODS LLC p 53
126 N Shipley St, Seaford DE 19973
Tel (302) 629-9136 SIC 0251

FRIES FARMS LLC p 580
8816 Us Highway 301, Claxton GA 30417
Tel (912) 739-3181 SIC 0251 2015

HOUSE OF RAEFORD FARMS OF LOUISIANA LLC p 711
3867 2nd St, Arcadia LA 71001
Tel (318) 263-9004 SIC 0251 2015

GOLDEN PUMP POULTRY INC p 621
4150 2nd St S Ste 200, Saint Cloud MN 56301
Tel (320) 240-6234 SIC 2015 0251

JFC LLC p 785
4150 2nd St S Ste 200, Saint Cloud MN 56301
Tel (320) 251-3570 SIC 2015 0251

▲ SANDERSON FARMS INC p 1278
127 Flynt Rd, Laurel MS 39443
Tel (601) 649-4030 SIC 0251 2015

■ SANDERSON FARMS INC (PRODUCTION DIVISION) p 1278
127 Flynt Rd, Laurel MS 39443
Tel (601) 425-2552 SIC 0251

NASH JOHNSON & SONS FARMS INC p 1008
3385 S Us Highway 117, Rose Hill NC 28458
Tel (910) 289-3113
SIC 2015 0254 0253 0251 2048

SIC 0252 Chicken Egg Farms

MARSHALL DURBIN FOOD CORP p 911
2830 Commerce Blvd, Irondale AL 35210
Tel (205) 841-7315
SIC 0252 0254 2048 0251 2015 5144

■TYSON CHICKEN INC p 1496
2200 W Don Tyson Pkwy, Springdale AR 72762
Tel (479) 290-4000
SIC 0252 0253 0254 0251 2015 2013

FOSTER FARMS LLC p 570
1000 Davis St, Livingston CA 95334
Tel (970) 874-7503 SIC 0252

VALLEY FRESH FOODS INC p 1540
3600 E Linwood Ave, Turlock CA 95380
Tel (209) 669-5600 SIC 0252 2015

▲ PILGRIMS PRIDE CORP p 1148
1770 Promontory Cir, Greeley CO 80634
Tel (970) 506-8000
SIC 2015 0254 0252 2048 5999

MOARK LLC p 980
28 Under The Mountain Rd, North Franklin CT 06254
Tel (951) 332-3300
SIC 5144 2048 0252 2015

ROSE ACRE FARMS INC p 1250
6874 N Base Rd, Seymour IN 47274
Tel (812) 497-2557 SIC 0252

SUNRISE FARMS INC p 1404
2060 White Ave, Harris IA 51345
Tel (712) 735-6010 SIC 0252

AUSTIN JACK DE COSTER p 133
Plains Rd, Turner ME 04282
Tel (207) 224-8222 SIC 0252 0213 0723

HERBRUCK POULTRY RANCH INC p 685
6425 Grand River Ave, Saranac MI 48881
Tel (616) 642-9421 SIC 0252

■ MFI HOLDING CORP p 958
301 Carlson Pkwy Ste 400, Minnetonka MN 55305
Tel (952) 258-4000 SIC 6719 0252

■ MICHAEL FOODS GROUP INC p 960
301 Carlson Pkwy Ste 400, Minnetonka MN 55305
Tel (952) 258-4000
SIC 0252 2015 5144 5143 5148 6719

■ MICHAEL FOODS INC p 960
301 Carlson Pkwy Ste 400, Minnetonka MN 55305
Tel (507) 237-4600
SIC 0252 2015 5144 5143 5148 5499

■ MICHAEL FOODS OF DELAWARE INC p 960
301 Carlson Pkwy Ste 400, Minnetonka MN 55305
Tel (952) 258-4000
SIC 0252 2015 5144 5143 5148 2024

▲ CAL-MAINE FOODS INC p 238
3320 W Woodrow Wilson Ave, Jackson MS 39209
Tel (601) 948-6813 SIC 0252

OPAL FOODS LLC p 1089
1100 Blair Ave, Neosho MO 64850
Tel (417) 455-5000 SIC 0252

WENGER FEEDS LLC p 1592
101 W Harrisburg Ave, Rheems PA 17570
Tel (717) 367-1195 SIC 2048 5144 0252

NATIONAL FOOD CORP p 1012
808 134th St Sw Ste 116, Everett WA 98204
Tel (425) 349-4257 SIC 0252

WILCOX FARMS INC p 1608
40400 Harts Lake Vly Rd, Roy WA 98580
Tel (360) 458-7774 SIC 0252 2015 2875

S & R EGG FARM INC p 1261
N9416 Tamarack Rd, Whitewater WI 53190
Tel (262) 495-6220 SIC 0252

SIC 0253 Turkey & Turkey Egg Farms

■TYSON CHICKEN INC p 1496
2200 W Don Tyson Pkwy, Springdale AR 72762
Tel (479) 290-4000
SIC 0252 0253 0254 0251 2015 2013

HARVEST LAND COOPERATIVE p 666
711 Front St W, Morgan MN 56266
Tel (507) 249-3196 SIC 5153 5191 0253

PRINSBURG FARMERS CO-OP p 1177
404 Railroad Ave, Prinsburg MN 56281
Tel (320) 978-8100 SIC 5153 5191 0253

■ JENNIE-O TURKEY STORE INC p 782
2505 Willmar Ave Sw, Willmar MN 56201
Tel (320) 235-2622 SIC 2015 0253

WILLMAR POULTRY CO INC p 1612
1800 Technology Dr Ne, Willmar MN 56201
Tel (320) 235-8850 SIC 0254 0253

WILLMAR POULTRY FARMS INC p 1613
3939 1st Ave W, Willmar MN 56201
Tel (320) 235-8870 SIC 0253 2048

PRESTAGE FARMS INC p 1173
4651 Taylors Bridge Hwy, Clinton NC 28328
Tel (910) 596-5700 SIC 0213 0253

NASH JOHNSON & SONS FARMS INC p 1008
3385 S Us Highway 117, Rose Hill NC 28458
Tel (910) 289-3113
SIC 2015 0254 0253 0251 2048

V H COOPER & CO INC p 1538
2321 State Route 49, Fort Recovery OH 45846
Tel (419) 375-4116 SIC 0253 2015 2011

COOPER HATCHERY INC p 366
22348 Road 140, Oakwood OH 45873
Tel (419) 594-3325
SIC 0254 0253 2015 5153 2048

PRESTAGE FARMS OF SOUTH CAROLINA LIMITED LIABILITY CO p 1173
1889 Highway 1 N, Cassatt SC 29032
Tel (803) 432-6396 SIC 5144 0253

SIC 0254 Poultry Hatcheries

MARSHALL DURBIN FOOD CORP p 911
2830 Commerce Blvd, Irondale AL 35210
Tel (205) 841-7315
SIC 0252 0254 2048 0251 2015 5144

PECO FOODS INC p 1127
1020 Lurleen B Wallace, Tuscaloosa AL 35401
Tel (205) 345-4711
SIC 0254 0251 2015 2048

GEORGES INC p 606
402 W Robinson Ave, Springdale AR 72764
Tel (479) 927-7000 SIC 2015 0254 0251

■TYSON BREEDERS INC p 1496
2200 W Don Tyson Pkwy, Springdale AR 72762
Tel (479) 290-4000 SIC 0254

■TYSON CHICKEN INC p 1496
2200 W Don Tyson Pkwy, Springdale AR 72762
Tel (479) 290-4000
SIC 0252 0253 0254 0251 2015 2013

FOSTER POULTRY FARMS p 570
1000 Davis St, Livingston CA 95334
Tel (209) 394-6914
SIC 0254 2015 5812 0173 5191 4212

▲ PILGRIMS PRIDE CORP p 1148
1770 Promontory Cir, Greeley CO 80634
Tel (970) 506-8000
SIC 2015 0254 0252 2048 5999

■ PILGRIMS PRIDE CORP OF GEORGIA INC p 1148
244 Perimeter Ctr Pkwy Ne, Atlanta GA 30346
Tel (770) 393-5000 SIC 2015 0254

HARRISON POULTRY INC p 664
107 Star St W, Bethlehem GA 30620
Tel (770) 867-9105
SIC 0254 2015 5984 2013 2011

EQUITY GROUP - GEORGIA DIVISION LLC p 506
7220 Us Highway 19, Camilla GA 31730
Tel (229) 336-1001 SIC 2015 0254 2048

MAR-JAC POULTRY INC p 904
1020 Aviation Blvd, Gainesville GA 30501
Tel (770) 531-5000 SIC 0254

PINE MANOR INC p 1149
9622 W 350 N, Orland IN 46776
Tel (800) 532-4186 SIC 2048 2015 0254

HY-LINE NORTH AMERICA LLC p 722
1755 West Lakes Pkwy A, West Des Moines IA 50266
Tel (515) 225-6030 SIC 0254

WILLMAR POULTRY CO INC p 1612
1800 Technology Dr Ne, Willmar MN 56201
Tel (320) 235-8850 SIC 0254 0253

AG PROCESSING INC A COOPERATIVE p 33
12700 W Dodge Rd, Omaha NE 68154
Tel (402) 496-7809
SIC 5153 2075 2048 5999 0254

NASH JOHNSON & SONS FARMS INC p 1008
3385 S Us Highway 117, Rose Hill NC 28458
Tel (910) 289-3113
SIC 2015 0254 0253 0251 2048

COOPER HATCHERY INC p 366
22348 Road 140, Oakwood OH 45873
Tel (419) 594-3325
SIC 0254 0253 2015 5153 2048

DRAPER VALLEY HOLDINGS LLC p 455
1000 Jason Ln, Mount Vernon WA 98273
Tel (360) 424-7947 SIC 0254 2015

SIC 0259 Poultry & Eggs Farms, NEC

MAPLE LEAF INC p 903
101 E Church St, Leesburg IN 46538
Tel (574) 453-4455 SIC 0259 2015 5159

MAPLE LEAF FARMS INC p 903
9166 N 200 E, Milford IN 46542
Tel (574) 453-4500 SIC 0259 2015

SIC 0273 Animal Aquaculture Farms

CLEAR SPRINGS FOODS INC p 324
4424 N 1500 E, Buhl ID 83316
Tel (208) 543-4316 SIC 0273 2048

AMERICAS CATCH INC p 81
46623 County Road 523, Itta Bena MS 38941
Tel (662) 254-7207 SIC 2092 0273

PRECISION VALVE CORP p 1169
800 Westchester Ave, Rye Brook NY 10573
Tel (914) 969-6500 SIC 3499 0273 5085

SIC 0279 Animal Specialties, NEC

■ CHARLES RIVER LABORATORIES INC p 289
251 Ballardvale St, Wilmington MA 01887
Tel (978) 658-6000
SIC 8742 8734 8731 0279

TACONIC BIOSCIENCES INC p 1421
1 Hudson City Ctr, Hudson NY 12534
Tel (609) 860-0806 SIC 0279

■ COVANCE RESEARCH PRODUCTS INC p 384
310 Swamp Bridge Rd, Denver PA 17517
Tel (717) 336-4921 SIC 0279 2836 2834

SIC 0291 Animal Production, NEC

PHOENIX RANCH MARKET III p 1145
1602 E Roosevelt St, Phoenix AZ 85006
Tel (602) 254-6676 SIC 0291

ARMAND AGRA INC p 110
1330 Capital Blvd, Reno NV 89502
Tel (775) 322-4073 SIC 0291 5147

KREIDER FARMS p 829
1461 Lancaster Rd, Manheim PA 17545
Tel (717) 665-4415 SIC 0291

ALAN RITCHEY INC p 44
740 S Frontage Rd, Valley View TX 76272
Tel (940) 726-3276
SIC 7389 4213 2048 0291

HANOR CO OF WISCONSIN LLC p 658
E4614 Us Hwy 14 And 60, Spring Green WI 53588
Tel (608) 588-9170 SIC 0291

SIC 0711 Soil Preparation Svcs

WILBUR-ELLIS CO LLC p 1608
345 California St Fl 27, San Francisco CA 94104
Tel (415) 772-4000 SIC 5191 0711

SIC 0721 Soil Preparation, Planting & Cultivating Svc

KEITHLY-WILLIAMS SEEDS INC p 808
420 Palm Ave, Holtville CA 92250
Tel (760) 356-5533 SIC 5191 0721 0181

COAST PUMP & SUPPLY CO INC p 331
610 Groveland Ave, Venice FL 34285
Tel (352) 258-2291 SIC 0721

■ DOW AGROSCIENCES LLC p 453
9330 Zionsville Rd, Indianapolis IN 46268
Tel (317) 337-3000
SIC 2879 5191 0721 8731

■ MYCOGEN CORP p 1004
9330 Zionsville Rd, Indianapolis IN 46268
Tel (317) 337-3000
SIC 5191 2879 0721 8731

PANHANDLE COOPERATIVE ASSOCIATION p 1111
401 S Beltline Hwy W, Scottsbluff NE 69361
Tel (308) 632-5301 SIC 5541 0721

SYNGENTA CROP PROTECTION LLC p 1415
410 S Swing Rd, Greensboro NC 27409
Tel (336) 632-6000 SIC 0721

SIC 0722 Crop Harvesting By Machine

NOBLESSE OBLIGE INC p 1046
2015 Silsbee Rd, El Centro CA 92243
Tel (760) 353-3336 SIC 0722

MANN PACKING CO INC p 902
1333 Schilling Pl, Salinas CA 93901
Tel (831) 422-7405 SIC 0723 4783 0722

POTANDON PRODUCE LLC p 1164
1210 Pier View Dr, Idaho Falls ID 83402
Tel (208) 419-4200 SIC 5148 0161 0722

SIC 0723 Crop Preparation, Except Cotton Ginning

GRIMMWAY ENTERPRISES INC p 640
14141 Di Giorgio Rd, Arvin CA 93203
Tel (661) 854-6250 SIC 0723

SUN WORLD INTERNATIONAL INC p 1401
16351 Driver Rd, Bakersfield CA 93308
Tel (661) 392-5000
SIC 0723 0172 0174 0175 0179 0161

■WM BOLTHOUSE FARMS INC p 1620
7200 E Brundage Ln, Bakersfield CA 93307
Tel (661) 366-7205 SIC 0161 2099 0723

WAWONA PACKING CO LLC p 1584
12133 Avenue 408, Cutler CA 93615
Tel (559) 528-4000 SIC 0723

WILEMAN BROS & ELLIOTT INC p 1609
40232 Road 128, Cutler CA 93615
Tel (559) 651-8378
SIC 0723 2653 0174 0175

WONDERFUL CITRUS PACKING LLC p 1622
1901 S Lexington St, Delano CA 93215
Tel (661) 720-2400 SIC 0723 0174 2033

EXETER PACKERS INC p 519
1250 E Myer Ave, Exeter CA 93221
Tel (559) 592-5168 SIC 0723

SUNSHINE RAISIN CORP p 1404
626 S 5th St, Fowler CA 93625
Tel (559) 834-5981 SIC 2064 0723

BRITZ INC p 214
3265 W Figarden Dr, Fresno CA 93711
Tel (559) 448-8000 SIC 0723 0724 0191

OLAM AMERICAS INC p 1080
25 Union Pl Ste 3, Fresno CA 93720
Tel (559) 447-1390 SIC 0723

▲ S&W SEED CO p 1263
7108 N Fresno St Ste 380, Fresno CA 93720
Tel (559) 884-2535 SIC 0139 0723

■ APIO INC p 97
4575 W Main St, Guadalupe CA 93434
Tel (800) 454-1355 SIC 2099 0723

L A HEARNE CO p 833
512 Metz Rd, King City CA 93930
Tel (831) 385-5441
SIC 5191 0723 5699 4214 2048 5261

REYNOLDS PACKING CO p 1231
33 E Tokay St, Lodi CA 95240
Tel (209) 369-2725 SIC 0723 5148 2449

WONDERFUL CO LLC p 1622
11444 W Olympic Blvd # 210, Los Angeles CA 90064
Tel (310) 966-5700 SIC 0723 2084

S STAMOULES INC p 1262
904 S Lyon Ave, Mendota CA 93640
Tel (559) 655-9777 SIC 0723

JS WEST & COMPANIES p 795
501 9th St, Modesto CA 95354
Tel (209) 577-3221
SIC 5172 5211 5251 0723 5499

DOLE FRESH VEGETABLES INC p 448
2959 Salinas Hwy, Monterey CA 93940
Tel (831) 422-8871 SIC 2099 0723

WEST PAK AVOCADO INC p 1595
38655 Sky Canyon Dr, Murrieta CA 92563
Tel (951) 296-5757 SIC 0723

BOSKOVICH FARMS INC p 202
711 Diaz Ave, Oxnard CA 93030
Tel (805) 487-2299 SIC 0723 5812 0161

■ SEMINIS VEGETABLE SEEDS INC p 1302
2700 Camino Del Sol, Oxnard CA 93030
Tel (855) 733-3834 SIC 5191 0723

BUTTE COUNTY RICE GROWERS ASSOCIATION INC p 230
1193 Richvale Hwy, Richvale CA 95974
Tel (530) 345-7103 SIC 5191 0723 5261

MANN PACKING CO INC p 902
1333 Schilling Pl, Salinas CA 93901
Tel (831) 422-7405 SIC 0723 4783 0722

RAMCO ENTERPRISES LP p 1207
320 Airport Blvd, Salinas CA 93905
Tel (831) 758-5272 SIC 0171 7361 0723

TANIMURA & ANTLE FRESH FOODS INC p 1424
1 Harris Rd, Salinas CA 93908
Tel (831) 455-2950
SIC 0161 0182 0723 2099

TAYLOR FARMS CALIFORNIA INC p 1427
150 Main St Ste 500, Salinas CA 93901
Tel (831) 754-0471 SIC 0723

TAYLOR FRESH FOODS INC p 1427
150 Main St Ste 400, Salinas CA 93901
Tel (831) 676-9023 SIC 0723

■ EARTHBOUND FARM LLC p 469
1721 San Juan Hwy, San Juan Bautista CA 95045
Tel (831) 623-7880 SIC 0723 2037 2099

■ EARTHBOUND HOLDINGS I LLC p 469
1721 San Juan Hwy, San Juan Bautista CA 95045
Tel (831) 623-2767 SIC 0723 2099

■ EARTHBOUND HOLDINGS II LLC p 469
1721 San Juan Hwy, San Juan Bautista CA 95045
Tel (831) 623-2767 SIC 0723 2099

■ EARTHBOUND HOLDINGS III LLC p 469
1721 San Juan Hwy, San Juan Bautista CA 95045
Tel (831) 623-7880 SIC 0723 2099 6719

■ EB SAV INC p 474
1721 San Juan Hwy, San Juan Bautista CA 95045
Tel (303) 635-4500 SIC 0723 2099

▲ LIMONEIRA CO p 866
1141 Cummings Rd Ofc, Santa Paula CA 93060
Tel (805) 525-5541
SIC 0723 0174 0179 6531 6799

SATICOY LEMON ASSOCIATION p 1283
103 N Peck Rd, Santa Paula CA 93060
Tel (805) 654-6500 SIC 0723

MORADA PRODUCE CO LP p 988
500 N Jack Tone Rd, Stockton CA 95215
Tel (209) 546-0426 SIC 0723

MARIANI PACKING CO INC p 906
500 Crocker Dr, Vacaville CA 95688
Tel (707) 452-2800 SIC 0723 2034 5148

VPS COMPANIES INC p 1566
310 Walker St, Watsonville CA 95076
Tel (831) 724-7551 SIC 5142 0723 4731

BERNARD EGAN & CO p 176
1900 N Old Dixie Hwy, Fort Pierce FL 34946
Tel (772) 465-7555 SIC 0723 8741 0174

CENTRAL STATES ENTERPRISES LLC p 280
1275 Lake Heathrow Ln # 101, Heathrow FL 32746
Tel (407) 333-3503 SIC 5153 0213 0723

PACIFIC TOMATO GROWERS LTD p 1106
503 10th St W, Palmetto FL 34221
Tel (941) 729-8410 SIC 0161 0174 0723

FRESH EXPRESS INC p 578
4757 The Grove Dr Ste 260, Windermere FL 34786
Tel (980) 636-5530 SIC 0723 2099

■ GOLDEN PEANUT CO LLC p 621
100 N Point Ctr E Ste 400, Alpharetta GA 30022
Tel (770) 752-8160 SIC 0723

OLAM US HOLDINGS INC p 1080
2077 Convention Ctr 150, College Park GA 30337
Tel (404) 209-2676 SIC 0723

■ PENNINGTON SEED INC p 1130
1280 Atlanta Hwy, Madison GA 30650
Tel (706) 342-1234
SIC 5261 2873 5191 6799 0723

PRECISION SOYA LLC p 1169
6501 Constitution Dr, Fort Wayne IN 46804
Tel (260) 459-9353 SIC 0723

MAXYIELD COOPERATIVE p 923
313 3rd Ave Nw, West Bend IA 50597
Tel (515) 887-7211
SIC 5153 5191 2999 0723

▲ SEABOARD CORP p 1295
9000 W 67th St, Merriam KS 66202
Tel (913) 676-8800
SIC 2011 0133 4412 6221 0723 0213

ALLIANCE AG AND GRAIN LLC p 53
313 N Main, Spearville KS 67876
Tel (620) 385-2898 SIC 0723

AUSTIN JACK DE COSTER p 133
Plains Rd, Turner ME 04282
Tel (207) 224-8222 SIC 0252 0213 0723

TAYLOR FARMS MARYLAND INC p 1427
9055 Junction Dr, Annapolis Junction MD 20701
Tel (301) 617-2942 *SIC* 5431 0723

COASTAL SUNBELT INC p 332
9001 Whiskey Bottom Rd, Laurel MD 20723
Tel (410) 799-8000
SIC 5148 4214 0723 2099

INDIAN SUMMER COOPERATIVE INC p 738
3958 W Chauvez Rd Ste 1, Ludington MI 49431
Tel (231) 845-6248
SIC 2033 0723 4213 2035

PETERSON FARMS INC p 1138
3104 W Baseline Rd, Shelby MI 49455
Tel (231) 861-6333 *SIC* 2037 0723

FARMERS CO-OPERATIVE ELEVATOR CO p 529
1972 510th St, Hanley Falls MN 56245
Tel (507) 768-3448 *SIC* 0723

MEADOWLAND FARMERS COOP p 934
25861 Us Highway 14, Lamberton MN 56152
Tel (507) 752-7335 *SIC* 5153 5191 0723

REICHEL FOODS INC p 1220
3706 Enterprise Dr Sw, Rochester MN 55902
Tel (507) 289-7264
SIC 2011 5812 2013 0723

F&S PRODUCE CO INC p 522
913 Bridgeton Ave, Rosenhayn NJ 08352
Tel (856) 453-0316
SIC 0723 2099 2032 0181

EASTERN CAROLINA ORGANICS LLC p 472
2210 E Pettigrew St, Durham NC 27703
Tel (919) 542-3264 *SIC* 0723

▲ANDERSONS INC p 90
480 W Dussel Dr, Maumee OH 43537
Tel (419) 893-5050
SIC 5153 0723 5191 2874 4789 4741

AZURE FARMS INC p 141
79709 Dufur Valley Rd, Dufur OR 97021
Tel (971) 200-8350 *SIC* 5149 0723 2099

RIVER POINT FARMS LLC p 1237
115 W Hermiston Ave # 240, Hermiston OR 97838
Tel (541) 567-4781 *SIC* 0723

NAUMES INC p 1019
2 W Barnett St, Medford OR 97501
Tel (541) 772-6268 *SIC* 0175 0723 4222

AGRICULTURAL COMMODITIES INC p 36
2224 Oxford Rd, New Oxford PA 17350
Tel (717) 624-8249
SIC 5191 2048 2041 0723 2875

F M BROWNS SONS INC p 522
205 Woodrow Ave, Reading PA 19608
Tel (800) 334-8816
SIC 5191 2041 0723 2048

WALTER P RAWL & SONS INC p 1574
824 Fairview Rd, Pelion SC 29123
Tel (803) 894-1900 *SIC* 0161 0723 5148

REDFIELD ENERGY LLC p 1216
38650 171st St, Redfield SD 57469
Tel (605) 302-0090 *SIC* 0723 2869

GULF PACIFIC INC p 646
12010 Taylor Rd, Houston TX 77041
Tel (713) 464-0606 *SIC* 5153 0723

AZTECA MILLING LP p 140
1159 Cottonwood Ln # 100, Irving TX 75038
Tel (972) 232-5339 *SIC* 0723

GRUMA CORP p 642
5601 Executive Dr Ste 800, Irving TX 75038
Tel (972) 232-5000 *SIC* 0723 2096 2099

NATIONAL FRUIT PRODUCT CO INC p 1012
550 Fairmont Ave, Winchester VA 22601
Tel (540) 662-3401
SIC 0723 2033 2035 2099

BREWSTER HEIGHTS PACKING & ORCHARDS LP p 210
25985 Hwy 97, Brewster WA 98812
Tel (509) 689-3424 *SIC* 0723

CRUNCH PAK LLC p 396
300 Sunset Hwy, Cashmere WA 98815
Tel (509) 782-2807 *SIC* 0723

TROUT-BLUE CHELAN-MAGI INC p 1484
8 Howser Rd, Chelan WA 98816
Tel (509) 682-2591 *SIC* 0723 0175 4222

NORTHERN FRUIT CO p 1056
220 2nd St Ne, East Wenatchee WA 98802
Tel (509) 884-6651 *SIC* 0723

ZIRKLE FRUIT CO p 1643
352 Harrison Rd, Selah WA 98942
Tel (509) 697-6101 *SIC* 0175 0723 4222

STEMILT GROWERS LLC p 1385
3135 Warehouse Rd, Wenatchee WA 98801
Tel (509) 663-1451 *SIC* 0723

WASHINGTON FRUIT & PRODUCE CO p 1578
1111 River Rd, Yakima WA 98902
Tel (509) 457-6177 *SIC* 5148 0723

SIC 0724 Cotton Ginning

■LEESBURG KNITTING MILLS INC p 852
400 Industrial Blvd, Leesburg AL 35983
Tel (256) 526-6522 *SIC* 2281 0724

E RITTER & CO p 466
10 Elm St, Marked Tree AR 72365
Tel (870) 358-7333
SIC 0131 0116 0724 4813 5211 5083

BRITZ INC p 214
3265 W Figarden Dr, Fresno CA 93711
Tel (559) 448-8000 *SIC* 0723 0724 0191

UNITED AGRICULTURAL COOPERATIVE INC p 1506
911 S Wharton St, El Campo TX 77437
Tel (979) 543-6284
SIC 5251 0724 5083 4221 5153

SOUTHERN STATES HOLDINGS INC p 1350
6606 W Broad St Ste B, Richmond VA 23230
Tel (804) 281-1206 *SIC* 5191 5261 0724

SIC 0742 Veterinary Animal Specialties

PETSMART INC p 1139
19601 N 27th Ave, Phoenix AZ 85027
Tel (623) 580-6100 *SIC* 5999 0742 0752

NATIONAL VETERINARY ASSOCIATES INC p 1016
29229 Canwood St Ste 100, Agoura Hills CA 91301
Tel (805) 777-7722 *SIC* 0742

■ANTECH DIAGNOSTICS INC p 93
17672 Cowan Bldg B, Irvine CA 92614
Tel (800) 745-4725 *SIC* 0742

▲VCA INC p 1545
12401 W Olympic Blvd, Los Angeles CA 90064
Tel (310) 571-6500 *SIC* 0742 5999 5047

BLUEPEARL FLORIDA LLC p 193
3000 Busch Lake Blvd, Tampa FL 33614
Tel (813) 933-8944 *SIC* 0742

■FOUNDATION FOR MARINE ANIMAL HUSBANDRY INC p 571
222 Berkeley St, Boston MA 02116
Tel (617) 351-5072 *SIC* 0742

■ZOETIS P&U LLC p 1644
100 Campus Dr, Florham Park NJ 07932
Tel (973) 822-7000 *SIC* 5159 0742 8734

MEDVET ASSOCIATES INC p 939
300 E Wilson Bridge Rd # 100, Worthington OH 43085
Tel (614) 846-5800 *SIC* 0742

A CARING DOCTOR (TEXAS) PC p 5
8000 Ne Tillamook St, Portland OR 97213
Tel (503) 922-5000 *SIC* 0742 5047

A CARING DOCTOR MINNESOTA PA p 5
8000 Ne Tillamook St, Portland OR 97213
Tel (503) 922-5000 *SIC* 0742 5047

MEDICAL MANAGEMENT INTERNATIONAL INC p 937
8000 Ne Tillamook St, Portland OR 97213
Tel (503) 922-5000 *SIC* 0742 5047

NUTRO CO p 1068
1550 W Mcewen Dr Ste 100, Franklin TN 37067
Tel (888) 607-4081 *SIC* 2047 0742

BEST FRIENDS PET CARE INC p 177
19717 62nd Ave S Ste F103, Kent WA 98032
Tel (253) 981-3998 *SIC* 0752 0742 5999

SIC 0751 Livestock Svcs, Except Veterinary

MOUNTAIRE FARMS OF DELAWARE INC p 994
1901 Napa Valley Dr, Little Rock AR 72212
Tel (501) 372-6524 *SIC* 0751

■COBB-VANTRESS INC p 332
4703 Highway 412 E, Siloam Springs AR 72761
Tel (479) 524-3166 *SIC* 0751

AMERICAN BEEF PACKERS INC p 68
13677 Yorba Ave, Chino CA 91710
Tel (909) 628-4888 *SIC* 0751 2011 5147

FIELDALE FARMS CORP p 541
555 Broiler Blvd, Baldwin GA 30511
Tel (706) 778-5100 *SIC* 2015 2013 0751

WAYNE FARMS INC p 1584
4110 Continental Dr, Oakwood GA 30566
Tel (678) 450-3111 *SIC* 0751

MIDWEST POULTRY SERVICES LP p 967
9951 W State Road 25, Mentone IN 46539
Tel (574) 353-7232 *SIC* 0751 2015

KEENELAND ASSOCIATION INC p 807
4201 Versailles Rd, Lexington KY 40510
Tel (859) 288-4236 *SIC* 5154 7948 0751

SELECT SIRES INC p 1301
11740 U S 42 N, Plain City OH 43064
Tel (614) 873-4683 *SIC* 0751

AMICK FARMS LLC p 85
2079 Batesburg Hwy, Batesburg SC 29006
Tel (803) 532-1400 *SIC* 0751

COOPERATIVE RESOURCES INTERNATIONAL INC p 367
117 E Green Bay St, Shawano WI 54166
Tel (715) 526-2141
SIC 0751 5159 0762 8731

GENEX COOPERATIVE INC p 603
100 Mbc Dr, Shawano WI 54166
Tel (715) 526-2141 *SIC* 0751 5159

SIC 0752 Animal Specialty Svcs, Exc Veterinary

PETSMART INC p 1139
19601 N 27th Ave, Phoenix AZ 85027
Tel (623) 580-6100 *SIC* 5999 0742 0752

PETCO ANIMAL SUPPLIES INC p 1137
10850 Via Frontera, San Diego CA 92127
Tel (858) 453-7845 *SIC* 0752 5199 5999

PETCO ANIMAL SUPPLIES STORES INC p 1137
9125 Rehco Rd, San Diego CA 92121
Tel (858) 453-7845 *SIC* 5999 0752 5199

WESTKUSTE INC p 1601
29330 Calle De Caballos, Sun City CA 92585
Tel (951) 775-2534 *SIC* 0752

NOVUS INTERNATIONAL INC p 1063
20 Research Park Dr, Saint Charles MO 63304
Tel (314) 576-8886 *SIC* 0752

ROYAL CANIN USA INC p 1254
500 Fountain Lakes Blvd # 100, Saint Charles MO 63301
Tel (636) 724-1692 *SIC* 2047 0752

ARGOS HOLDINGS INC p 107
650 Madison Ave Fl 15, New York NY 10022
Tel (212) 891-2880 *SIC* 0752

RADIO SYSTEMS CORP p 1204
10427 Petsafe Way, Knoxville TN 37932
Tel (865) 777-5404 *SIC* 0752 1799 6794

BEST FRIENDS PET CARE INC p 177
19717 62nd Ave S Ste F103, Kent WA 98032
Tel (253) 981-3998 *SIC* 0752 0742 5999

SIC 0761 Farm Labor Contractors & Crew Leaders

HARO & HARO ENTERPRISES INC p 662
115 W Walnut St Ste 4, Lodi CA 95240
Tel (209) 334-2035 *SIC* 0761

MOUNTAIN VIEW AG SERVICES INC p 994
13281 Avenue 416, Orosi CA 93647
Tel (559) 528-6004 *SIC* 0761

SIC 0762 Farm Management Svcs

WEST COAST GRAPE FARMING INC p 1594
800 E Keyes Rd, Ceres CA 95307
Tel (209) 538-3131 *SIC* 0762

SUN PACIFIC FARMING COOPERATIVE INC p 1400
1250 E Myer Ave, Exeter CA 93221
Tel (559) 592-7121 *SIC* 0762

SYAR INDUSTRIES INC p 1413
2301 Napa Vallejo Hwy, Napa CA 94558
Tel (707) 252-8711
SIC 5032 2951 0762 7992 5932

FARMLAND MANAGEMENT SERVICES p 530
301 E Main St, Turlock CA 95380
Tel (209) 669-0742 *SIC* 0762

LAZER SPOT INC p 849
6525 Shiloh Rd Ste 900, Alpharetta GA 30005
Tel (770) 886-6851 *SIC* 0762 4212

HEARTLAND CO-OP p 679
2829 Westown Pkwy Ste 350, West Des Moines IA 50266
Tel (515) 225-1334 *SIC* 5153 0762 2048

AGRESERVES INC p 35
79 S Main St Ste 1100, Salt Lake City UT 84111
Tel (801) 715-9100 *SIC* 0762

FARMLAND RESERVE INC p 530
50 E North Temple, Salt Lake City UT 84150
Tel (801) 240-6301 *SIC* 0762

COOPERATIVE RESOURCES INTERNATIONAL INC p 367
117 E Green Bay St, Shawano WI 54166
Tel (715) 526-2141
SIC 0751 5159 0762 8731

SIC 0781 Landscape Counseling & Planning

BRIGHTVIEW COMPANIES LLC p 213
24151 Ventura Blvd, Calabasas CA 91302
Tel (818) 223-8500 *SIC* 1629 0782 0781

BRIGHTVIEW LANDSCAPE DEVELOPMENT INC p 213
24151 Ventura Blvd, Calabasas CA 91302
Tel (818) 223-8500 *SIC* 0781

BRIGHTVIEW LANDSCAPE SERVICES INC p 213
24151 Ventura Blvd, Calabasas CA 91302
Tel (818) 223-8500 *SIC* 0781

■EDAW INC p 477
300 California St Fl 5, San Francisco CA 94104
Tel (415) 955-2800 *SIC* 6552 0781

HELLMUTH OBATA & KASSABAUM INC p 682
1 Bush St Ste 200, San Francisco CA 94104
Tel (415) 243-0555
SIC 8712 8711 8742 7389 0781

DMS FACILITY SERVICES LLC p 446
1040 Arroyo Dr, South Pasadena CA 91030
Tel (626) 305-8500 *SIC* 8711 7349 0781

AMERICAN CIVIL CONSTRUCTORS HOLDINGS INC p 70
4901 S Windermere St, Littleton CO 80120
Tel (303) 795-2582 *SIC* 1622 0781

YELLOWSTONE LANDSCAPE GROUP INC p 1635
3235 N State St, Bunnell FL 32110
Tel (386) 437-6211 *SIC* 0782 0781

YELLOWSTONE LANDSCAPE-SOUTHEAST LLC p 1635
3235 N State St, Bunnell FL 32110
Tel (386) 437-6211 *SIC* 0781 0782

QGS DEVELOPMENT INC p 1195
17502 County Road 672, Lithia FL 33547
Tel (813) 634-3326 *SIC* 0782 0781 1711

SEA ISLAND ACQUISITION LP p 1295
100 Cloister Dr, Sea Island GA 31561
Tel (912) 638-3611 *SIC* 7011 0781 7992

SEA ISLAND CO p 1295
100 Cloister Dr, Sea Island GA 31561
Tel (888) 732-4752 *SIC* 7011 0781 7992

LANDSCAPE INNOVATIONS LLC p 843
11101 Fairview 189, Eagle ID 83616
Tel (208) 841-7666 *SIC* 0781

AQUASCAPE DESIGNS INC p 101
901 Aqualand Way, Saint Charles IL 60174
Tel (630) 659-2000
SIC 5191 1629 0782 0781

ACRES ENTERPRISES INC p 18
610 W Liberty St, Wauconda IL 60084
Tel (847) 526-4554 *SIC* 0782 0781 4959

MAINSCAPE INC p 898
13418 Britton Park Rd, Fishers IN 46038
Tel (317) 577-3155 *SIC* 0781

BG INTERMEDIATE CORP p 179
18227 Flower Hill Way, Gaithersburg MD 20879
Tel (301) 987-9200 *SIC* 0782 0781

RUPPERT LANDSCAPE INC p 1258
23601 Laytonsville Rd, Laytonsville MD 20882
Tel (301) 482-0300 *SIC* 0781 0783 0782

BG HOLDING LLC p 179
2275 Res Blvd Ste 600, Rockville MD 20850
Tel (301) 987-9200 *SIC* 0781 0782

BRICKMAN ACQUISITION HOLDINGS INC p 211
2275 Res Blvd Ste 600, Rockville MD 20850
Tel (240) 683-2000 *SIC* 0781

BRICKMAN PARENT LP p 211
2275 Res Blvd Ste 600, Rockville MD 20850
Tel (240) 683-2000 *SIC* 0781

BRIGHTVIEW COMPANIES LLC p 213
2275 Research Blvd, Rockville MD 20850
Tel (240) 683-2000 *SIC* 0781 0782

BRIGHTVIEW LANDSCAPES LLC p 213
2275 Res Blvd Ste 600, Rockville MD 20850
Tel (301) 987-9200 *SIC* 0781 0782

RESIDEX LLC p 1226
46495 Humboldt Dr, Novi MI 48377
Tel (855) 737-4339
SIC 5191 7342 0781 0782

HOK INC p 699
10 S Broadway Ste 200, Saint Louis MO 63102
Tel (314) 421-2000 *SIC* 0781 8712 8711

LANGAN ENGINEERING ENVIRONMENTAL SURVEYING AND LANDSCAPE ARCHITECTURE DPC p 844
300 Kimball Dr Ste 4, Parsippany NJ 07054
Tel (973) 560-4900
SIC 8711 8748 1389 0781

NATURES TREES INC p 1019
550 Bedford Rd, Bedford Hills NY 10507
Tel (914) 241-4999
SIC 0783 0782 0781 1629

FERRANDINO & SON INC p 538
71 Carolyn Blvd, Farmingdale NY 11735
Tel (866) 571-4609
SIC 1542 0781 3531 7299

LANDDESIGN INC p 842
223 N Graham St, Charlotte NC 28202
Tel (704) 333-0325 *SIC* 0781

BUDD GROUP INC p 223
2325 S Stratford Rd, Winston Salem NC 27103
Tel (336) 765-9324 *SIC* 0781 7349

OTAK INC p 1097
808 Sw 3rd Ave Ste 220, Portland OR 97204
Tel (503) 274-5445
SIC 0781 8712 8711 8713 8742 8999

CIVIL & ENVIRONMENTAL CONSULTANTS INC p 320
333 Baldwin Rd Ste 1, Pittsburgh PA 15205
Tel (412) 429-2324 *SIC* 8711 0781

RENTOKIL NORTH AMERICA INC p 1224
1125 Berkshire Blvd # 150, Wyomissing PA 19610
Tel (610) 372-9700 *SIC* 7342 0781 5191

■DATATRAC INFORMATION SERVICES INC p 414
3170 Fairview Park Dr, Falls Church VA 22042
Tel (703) 876-1000 *SIC* 8742 0781 8721

SIC 0782 Lawn & Garden Svcs

WEST COAST ARBORISTS INC p 1594
2200 E Via Burton, Anaheim CA 92806
Tel (714) 991-1900 *SIC* 0782

BRIGHTVIEW COMPANIES LLC p 213
24151 Ventura Blvd, Calabasas CA 91302
Tel (818) 223-8500 *SIC* 1629 0782 0781

ARMSTRONG GARDEN CENTERS INC p 111
2200 E Route 66 Ste 200, Glendora CA 91740
Tel (626) 914-1091 *SIC* 5261 0782

CAGWIN & DORWARD p 237
1565 S Novato Blvd, Novato CA 94947
Tel (415) 892-7710 *SIC* 0782

OCONNELL LANDSCAPE MAINTENANCE INC p 1074
23091 Arroyo Vis, Rcho Sta Marg CA 92688
Tel (949) 589-2007 *SIC* 0782

PARK WEST COMPANIES INC p 1116
22421 Gilberto Ste A, Rcho Sta Marg CA 92688
Tel (949) 546-8300 *SIC* 0782 1629 6719

JENSEN CORPORATE HOLDINGS INC p 782
1983 Concourse Dr, San Jose CA 95131
Tel (408) 446-1118 *SIC* 0782

RESOURCE COLLECTION INC p 1227
3771 W 242nd St Ste 205, Torrance CA 90505
Tel (310) 219-3272
SIC 7349 7381 0782 3564

GOTHIC LANDSCAPING INC p 626
27502 Avenue Scott, Valencia CA 91355
Tel (661) 257-1266 *SIC* 0782

LANDSCAPE DEVELOPMENT INC p 843
28447 Witherspoon Pkwy, Valencia CA 91355
Tel (661) 295-1970 *SIC* 0782 5039

YELLOWSTONE LANDSCAPE GROUP INC p 1635
3235 N State St, Bunnell FL 32110
Tel (386) 437-6211 *SIC* 0782 0781

YELLOWSTONE LANDSCAPE-SOUTHEAST LLC p 1635
3235 N State St, Bunnell FL 32110
Tel (386) 437-6211 *SIC* 0781 0782

QGS DEVELOPMENT INC p 1195
17502 County Road 672, Lithia FL 33547
Tel (813) 634-3326 *SIC* 0782 0781 1711

GLENWOOD TREE EXPERTS p 615
21457 Milwaukee Ave, Deerfield IL 60015
Tel (847) 459-0200 *SIC* 0783 0782

AQUASCAPE DESIGNS INC p 101
901 Aqualand Way, Saint Charles IL 60174
Tel (630) 659-2000
SIC 5191 1629 0782 0781

ACRES ENTERPRISES INC p 18
610 W Liberty St, Wauconda IL 60084
Tel (847) 526-4554 *SIC* 0782 0781 4959

LANDCARE USA LLC p 842
5295 Westview Dr Ste 100, Frederick MD 21703
Tel (301) 874-3300 *SIC* 0782

BG INTERMEDIATE CORP p 179
18227 Flower Hill Way, Gaithersburg MD 20879
Tel (301) 987-9200 *SIC* 0782 0781

RUPPERT LANDSCAPE INC p 1258
23601 Laytonsville Rd, Laytonsville MD 20882
Tel (301) 482-0300 *SIC* 0781 0783 0782

BG HOLDING LLC p 179
2275 Res Blvd Ste 600, Rockville MD 20850
Tel (301) 987-9200 *SIC* 0781 0782

BRICKMAN GROUP HOLDINGS INC p 211
2275 Res Blvd Ste 700, Rockville MD 20850
Tel (301) 987-9200 *SIC* 0782 4959

BRIGHTVIEW COMPANIES LLC p 213
2275 Research Blvd, Rockville MD 20850
Tel (240) 683-2000 *SIC* 0781 0782

BRIGHTVIEW LANDSCAPES LLC p 213
2275 Res Blvd Ste 600, Rockville MD 20850
Tel (301) 987-9200 *SIC* 0781 0782

SUNGROW HORTICULTURE CANADA INC p 1402
770 Silver St, Agawam MA 01001
Tel (800) 732-8667 *SIC* 0782

RESIDEX LLC p 1226
46495 Humboldt Dr, Novi MI 48377
Tel (855) 737-4339
SIC 5191 7342 0781 0782

TURFIX LLC p 1492
2228 Mount Curve Ave, Saint Joseph MI 49085
Tel (888) 495-3195 SIC 0782

CONTROL ENVIRONMENTAL SERVICES INC p 364
737 New Durham Rd Ste 1, Edison NJ 08817
Tel (732) 548-5272 SIC 0782

JERSEY CITY INCINERATOR AUTHORITY p 783
501 State Rt 440, Jersey City NJ 07305
Tel (201) 432-4645 SIC 4953 0782 4212

CONTROL BUILDING SERVICES INC p 364
333 Meadowlands Pkwy Fl 1, Secaucus NJ 07094
Tel (201) 864-1900 SIC 7349 0782

NATURES TREES INC p 1019
550 Bedford Rd, Bedford Hills NY 10507
Tel (914) 241-4999
SIC 0783 0782 0781 1629

A & A MAINTENANCE ENTERPRISE INC p 4
965 Midland Ave, Yonkers NY 10704
Tel (914) 969-0009
SIC 7349 1721 1542 4959 0782

KOENIG EQUIPMENT INC p 826
15213 State Route 274, Botkins OH 45306
Tel (937) 693-5000 SIC 5999 0782

DAVEY TREE EXPERT CO p 415
1500 N Mantua St, Kent OH 44240
Tel (330) 673-9511
SIC 0783 0782 0811 0181

■ SCOTTS CO LLC p 1294
14111 Scottslawn Rd, Marysville OH 43040
Tel (937) 644-0011
SIC 2873 2874 2879 0782 2499 3524

▲ SCOTTS MIRACLE-GRO CO p 1294
14111 Scottslawn Rd, Marysville OH 43040
Tel (937) 644-0011 SIC 3542 0782 7342

DEANGELO BROTHERS LLC p 420
100 N Conahan Dr, Hazleton PA 18201
Tel (570) 459-5800 SIC 0782

PENN LINE SERVICE INC p 1129
300 Scottdale Ave, Scottdale PA 15683
Tel (724) 887-9110
SIC 1629 1623 1611 0782

MOYER & SON INC p 995
113 E Reliance Rd, Souderton PA 18964
Tel (215) 799-2000
SIC 5191 5983 2875 0782 1711

■ SERVICEMASTER CONSUMER SERVICES LIMITED PARTNERSHIP p 1307
889 Ridge Lake Blvd Fl 2, Memphis TN 38120
Tel (901) 597-7574 SIC 0782 6351 7349

SERVICEMASTER HOLDING CORP p 1308
860 Ridge Lake Blvd, Memphis TN 38120
Tel (901) 597-1400
SIC 0782 7342 1711 1731 7349 7641

TRUGREEN HOLDING CORP p 1486
1790 Kirby Pkwy Ste 300, Memphis TN 38138
Tel (901) 251-4002 SIC 0782 6719

TRUGREEN LIMITED PARTNERSHIP p 1486
1790 Kirby Pkwy Forum Ii Ste 300 Forum Ii, Memphis TN 38138
Tel (901) 681-1800 SIC 0782

■ LANDCARE USA INC p 842
2603 Augusta Dr Ste 1300, Houston TX 77057
Tel (713) 692-6371 SIC 0783 0782

TREES INC p 1475
650 N Sam Houston Pkwy E, Houston TX 77060
Tel (281) 447-1327 SIC 0783 0782

UNITED AMERICAN ACQUISITION CORP p 1506
3022 Franklin Ave, Waco TX 76710
Tel (859) 987-5389
SIC 2211 0782 3423 2875

SIC 0783 Ornamental Shrub & Tree Svc

DAVEY TREE SURGERY CO p 415
2617 S Vasco Rd, Livermore CA 94550
Tel (925) 443-1723 SIC 0783

AMERICAN CIVIL CONSTRUCTORS LLC p 70
4901 S Windermere St, Littleton CO 80120
Tel (303) 795-2582 SIC 1629 0783 0181

F A BARTLETT TREE EXPERT CO p 522
1290 E Main St Ste 2, Stamford CT 06902
Tel (203) 323-1131 SIC 0783

GLENWOOD TREE EXPERTS p 615
21457 Milwaukee Ave, Deerfield IL 60015
Tel (847) 459-0200 SIC 0783 0782

TOWNSEND CORP p 1466
1015 W Jackson St, Muncie IN 47305
Tel (765) 468-3007 SIC 0783

WRIGHT SERVICE CORP p 1627
5930 Grand Ave Ste 100, West Des Moines IA 50266
Tel (515) 271-1197 SIC 0783

WRIGHT TREE SERVICE INC p 1627
5930 Grand Ave Ste 100, West Des Moines IA 50266
Tel (515) 277-6291 SIC 0783

ASPLUNDISH TREE EXPERT CO p 119
4070 North Point Rd, Baltimore MD 21222
Tel (443) 242-6666 SIC 0783

RUPPERT LANDSCAPE INC p 1258
23601 Laytonsville Rd, Laytonsville MD 20882
Tel (301) 482-0300 SIC 0781 0783 0782

NATURES TREES INC p 1019
550 Bedford Rd, Bedford Hills NY 10507
Tel (914) 241-4999
SIC 0783 0782 0781 1629

LEWIS TREE SERVICE INC p 859
300 Lucius Gordon Dr, West Henrietta NY 14586
Tel (585) 436-3208 SIC 0783

DAVEY TREE EXPERT CO p 415
1500 N Mantua St, Kent OH 44240
Tel (330) 673-9511
SIC 0783 0782 0811 0181

MCCOY TREE SURGERY CO p 927
3201 Broce Dr, Norman OK 73072
Tel (405) 579-6000 SIC 0783

J FRANK SCHMIDT & SON CO p 771
9500 Se 327th Ave, Boring OR 97009
Tel (503) 663-4128 SIC 0783 2875

ASPLUNDH TREE EXPERT CO p 119
708 Blair Mill Rd, Willow Grove PA 19090
Tel (215) 784-4200
SIC 0783 1629 1623 1611 6411

UTILITY VEGETATION SERVICES INC p 1537
708 Blair Mill Rd, Willow Grove PA 19090
Tel (215) 784-4200 SIC 0783

■ LANDCARE USA INC p 842
2603 Augusta Dr Ste 1300, Houston TX 77057
Tel (713) 692-6371 SIC 0783 0782

TREES INC p 1475
650 N Sam Houston Pkwy E, Houston TX 77060
Tel (281) 447-1327 SIC 0783 0782

ABC PROFESSIONAL TREE SERVICES INC p 10
201 Flint Ridge Rd, Webster TX 77598
Tel (281) 280-1100 SIC 0783

SIC 0811 Timber Tracts

TATITLEK CORP p 1426
561 E 36th Ave, Anchorage AK 99503
Tel (907) 278-4000 SIC 0811 6552 7361

BEARDEN LEASING CO LTD p 165
111 S Plum St, Bearden AR 71720
Tel (870) 687-2246 SIC 7359 0811

▲ DELTIC TIMBER CORP p 427
210 E Elm St, El Dorado AR 71730
Tel (870) 881-9400
SIC 0811 2411 6531 8741

FRUIT GROWERS SUPPLY CO INC p 582
27770 N Entrmt Dr Fl 3, Valencia CA 91355
Tel (818) 986-6480
SIC 2653 0811 5191 2448 5113

BOETHING TREELAND FARMS INC p 197
23475 Long Valley Rd, Woodland Hills CA 91367
Tel (818) 883-1222 SIC 0811 5261

COASTAL FOREST RESOURCES CO p 331
8007 Florida Georgia Hwy, Havana FL 32333
Tel (850) 539-6432
SIC 2436 2491 0811 0851

▲ ST JOE CO p 1367
133 S Watersound Pkwy A, Watersound FL 32461
Tel (850) 231-6400
SIC 6531 6552 6512 0811 0851

MARTIN COMPANIES LLC ROM p 912
2189 Memorial Dr, Alexandria LA 71301
Tel (318) 445-1973 SIC 0811

ANDERSON-TULLY CO p 90
1725 N Washington St, Vicksburg MS 39183
Tel (601) 629-3283 SIC 2421 0811

JM HUBER CORP p 786
499 Thornall St Ste 8, Edison NJ 08837
Tel (732) 603-3630
SIC 0811 1311 1455 2493 2819

DAVEY TREE EXPERT CO p 415
1500 N Mantua St, Kent OH 44240
Tel (330) 673-9511
SIC 0783 0782 0811 0181

HAMPTON RESOURCES INC p 656
9600 Sw Barnes Rd Ste 200, Portland OR 97225
Tel (503) 297-7691 SIC 5031 2421 0811

ROSEBURG FOREST PRODUCTS CO p 1250
3660 Gateway St Ste A, Springfield OR 97477
Tel (541) 679-3311
SIC 2436 2421 2493 5031 5211 0811

CONFEDERATED TRIBES OF WARM SPRINGS RESERVATION OF OREGON p 356
1233 Veterans St, Warm Springs OR 97761
Tel (541) 553-1161 SIC 7011 4832 0811

J A M T LEYDEN ENTERPRISES INC p 770
179 Plain Meeting Hse Rd, West Greenwich RI 02817
Tel (401) 258-9246 SIC 0811

INTERFOR US INC p 752
2211 Rimland Dr Ste 220, Bellingham WA 98226
Tel (360) 788-2299 SIC 0811 2421 5031

▲ WEYERHAEUSER CO p 1603
220 Occidental Ave S, Seattle WA 98104
Tel (253) 924-2345
SIC 6798 0811 2411 2435 2611 2621

■ WEYERHAEUSER NR CO p 1603
220 Occidental Ave S, Seattle WA 98104
Tel (253) 924-2345 SIC 0811

MENASHA CORP p 943
1645 Bergstrom Rd, Neenah WI 54956
Tel (920) 751-1000
SIC 2631 2653 2679 3086 0811

SIC 0831 Forest Prdts

CHEP RECYCLED PALLET SOLUTIONS LLC p 294
8517 Suthpark Cir Ste 140, Orlando FL 32819
Tel (713) 332-6145 SIC 2448 0831

■ IDAHO TIMBER LLC p 728
3540 E Longwing Ln # 270, Meridian ID 83646
Tel (208) 377-3000 SIC 0831

INTERNATIONAL FOREST PRODUCTS LLC p 755
1 Patriot Pl, Foxboro MA 02035
Tel (508) 698-4600 SIC 0831

WEST FRASER INC p 1594
1900 Exeter Rd Ste 105, Germantown TN 38138
Tel (901) 620-4200 SIC 2431 0831

▲ POTLATCH CORP p 1164
601 W 1st Ave Ste 1600, Spokane WA 99201
Tel (509) 835-1500 SIC 0831 6798

SIC 0851 Forestry Svcs

AFOGNAK NATIVE CORP p 33
3909 Arctic Blvd Ste 500, Anchorage AK 99503
Tel (907) 222-9500 SIC 0851

CHUGACH ALASKA CORP p 304
3800 Cntrpint Dr Ste 1200, Anchorage AK 99503
Tel (907) 563-8866
SIC 8744 4959 7361 0851 7373

COASTAL FOREST RESOURCES CO p 331
8007 Florida Georgia Hwy, Havana FL 32333
Tel (850) 539-6432
SIC 2436 2491 0811 0851

■ FOREST RAYONIER RESOURCES LP p 567
50 N Laura St Ste 1900, Jacksonville FL 32202
Tel (904) 357-9100 SIC 0851

▲ ST JOE CO p 1367
133 S Watersound Pkwy A, Watersound FL 32461
Tel (850) 231-6400
SIC 6531 6552 6512 0811 0851

TIMBER PRODUCTS INSPECTION INC p 1454
1641 Sigman Rd Nw, Conyers GA 30012
Tel (770) 922-8000 SIC 0851 8734

PERFOREX LLC p 1135
2663 E Coulee Crossing Rd, Woodworth LA 71485
Tel (318) 445-6799 SIC 0851

ARBORGEN INC p 103
2011 Broadbank Ct, Ridgeville SC 29472
Tel (843) 851-4129 SIC 0851

SIC 0912 Finfish

▲ UMAMI SUSTAINABLE SEAFOOD INC p 1501
1230 Columbia St Ste 440, San Diego CA 92101
Tel (619) 544-9177 SIC 5146 0912

AMERICAN SEAFOODS CO LLC p 79
2025 1st Ave Ste 900, Seattle WA 98121
Tel (206) 448-0300 SIC 0912 0921 2092

TRIDENT SEAFOODS CORP p 1479
5303 Shilshole Ave Nw, Seattle WA 98107
Tel (206) 783-3818
SIC 2092 5146 5091 0912

SIC 0921 Finfish Farming & Fish Hatcheries

AMERICAN SEAFOODS CO LLC p 79
2025 1st Ave Ste 900, Seattle WA 98121
Tel (206) 448-0300 SIC 0912 0921 2092

IQUIQUE US LLC p 764
2320 W Commodore Way # 200, Seattle WA 98199
Tel (206) 286-1661 SIC 0921

SIC 0971 Hunting & Trapping

DUCKS UNLIMITED INC p 459
1 Waterfowl Way, Memphis TN 38120
Tel (901) 758-3825 SIC 0971

SIC 1011 Iron Ores

FARREL CORP p 530
1 Farrell Blvd, Ansonia CT 06401
Tel (203) 736-5500 SIC 3559 1011 3089

ARCELORMITTAL HOLDINGS LLC p 104
3210 Watling St, East Chicago IN 46312
Tel (219) 399-1200 SIC 3312 1011

ARCELORMITTAL MINORCA MINE INC p 104
3210 Watling St, East Chicago IN 46312
Tel (219) 399-1200 SIC 1011

MAGNETATION LLC p 896
102 Ne 3rd St Ste 120, Grand Rapids MN 55744
Tel (218) 398-0079 SIC 1011

■ BLOOM LAKE IRON ORE MINE LTD p 189
200 Public Sq, Cleveland OH 44114
Tel (216) 694-5700 SIC 1011

▲ CLIFFS NATURAL RESOURCES INC p 326
200 Public Sq Ste 3300, Cleveland OH 44114
Tel (216) 694-5700 SIC 1011

EMPIRE IRON MINING PARTNERSHIP p 493
1100 Superior Ave E Fl 15, Cleveland OH 44114
Tel (216) 694-5700 SIC 1011

HIBBING TACONITE CO (A JOINT VENTURE) p 690
200 Public Sq Ste 3300, Cleveland OH 44114
Tel (216) 694-5700 SIC 1011

■ NORTHSHORE MINING CO p 1058
1100 Superior Ave E # 1500, Cleveland OH 44114
Tel (216) 694-5700 SIC 1011 4931

TILDEN MINING CO LC p 1453
1100 Superior Ave E, Cleveland OH 44114
Tel (216) 694-5278 SIC 1011

■ UNITED TACONITE LLC p 1514
1100 Superior Ave E # 1500, Cleveland OH 44114
Tel (218) 744-7800 SIC 1011

BHP MINERALS INTERNATIONAL INC p 180
1360 Post Oak Blvd # 150, Houston TX 77056
Tel (713) 961-8500 SIC 1222 1011 1021

SIC 1021 Copper Ores

■ FREEPORT-MCMORAN SIERRITA INC p 577
6200 W Duval Mine Rd, Green Valley AZ 85622
Tel (520) 648-8500 SIC 1021

■ SILVER BELL MINING LLC p 1323
25000 W Avra Valley Rd, Marana AZ 85653
Tel (520) 682-2420 SIC 1021

■ CYPRUS AMAX MINERALS CO p 405
333 N Central Ave, Phoenix AZ 85004
Tel (602) 366-8100
SIC 1221 1222 1021 1061 1479 1041

■ CYPRUS METALS CO p 406
333 N Central Ave, Phoenix AZ 85004
Tel (928) 473-7000 SIC 1021

■ CYPRUS MINES CORP p 406
1 N Central Ave, Phoenix AZ 85004
Tel (602) 366-8100
SIC 1221 1021 1031 1061

■ FREEPORT MINERALS CORP p 577
333 N Central Ave, Phoenix AZ 85004
Tel (602) 366-8100
SIC 1061 1021 3312 3351

▲ FREEPORT-MCMORAN INC p 577
333 N Central Ave, Phoenix AZ 85004
Tel (602) 366-8100
SIC 1021 1041 1061 1044

■ FREEPORT-MCMORAN MIAMI INC p 577
333 N Central Ave, Phoenix AZ 85004
Tel (602) 366-8100 SIC 1021

■ SOUTHERN COPPER CORP p 1348
1440 E Missouri Ave # 160, Phoenix AZ 85014
Tel (602) 264-1375
SIC 1021 3331 1031 1061 1044

▲ AMERICAS MINING CORP p 81
1150 N 7th Ave, Tucson AZ 85705
Tel (520) 798-7500
SIC 1021 1044 1031 1041 3331

■ AR SILVER BELL INC p 102
5285 E Williams Cir, Tucson AZ 85711
Tel (520) 798-7500
SIC 1021 1044 1031 1041 3331 3339

■ ASARCO LLC p 115
5285 E Williams Cir # 2000, Tucson AZ 85711
Tel (520) 798-7500
SIC 1021 1044 1031 1041 3331 3339

▲ NEWMONT MINING CORP p 1038
6363 S Fiddlers Green Cir # 800, Greenwood Village CO 80111
Tel (303) 863-7414 SIC 1041 1021

■ NEWMONT USA LIMITED p 1038
6363 Sout Fidd Gree Cir, Greenwood Village CO 80111
Tel (303) 863-7414 SIC 1041 1021

THOMPSON CREEK METALS CO INC p 1449
26 W Dry Creek Cir, Littleton CO 80120
Tel (303) 761-8801
SIC 1021 1041 1044 1061

TRELLEBORG CORP p 1476
200 Veterans Blvd Ste 3, South Haven MI 49090
Tel (269) 639-9891
SIC 3341 1021 1044 1031 4226 1041

AMES CONSTRUCTION INC p 84
14420 County Road 5, Burnsville MN 55306
Tel (952) 435-7106
SIC 1611 1041 1021 1794

DOE RUN RESOURCES CORP p 447
1801 Park 270 Dr Ste 300, Saint Louis MO 63146
Tel (314) 453-7100 SIC 1031 1021 3339

▲ TAHOE RESOURCES INC p 1421
5310 Kietzke Ln Ste 200, Reno NV 89511
Tel (775) 825-8574
SIC 1021 1041 1044 1031 1311

BHP COPPER INC p 180
1360 Post Oak Blvd # 150, Houston TX 77056
Tel (713) 961-8500 SIC 1021 3341 1041

BHP HOLDINGS (RESOURCES) INC p 180
1360 Post Oak Blvd # 150, Houston TX 77056
Tel (713) 961-8500 SIC 1021 3341 1041

BHP MINERALS INTERNATIONAL INC p 180
1360 Post Oak Blvd # 150, Houston TX 77056
Tel (713) 961-8500 SIC 1222 1011 1021

KENNECOTT CORP p 810
8315 W 3595 S, Magna UT 84044
Tel (801) 913-8335
SIC 1041 1021 1061 1221

KENNECOTT UTAH COPPER LLC p 811
4700 W Daybreak Pkwy, South Jordan UT 84009
Tel (801) 204-2000
SIC 1021 1041 1044 1061

SIC 1031 Lead & Zinc Ores

■ CYPRUS MINES CORP p 406
1 N Central Ave, Phoenix AZ 85004
Tel (602) 366-8100
SIC 1221 1021 1031 1061

■ SOUTHERN COPPER CORP p 1348
1440 E Missouri Ave # 160, Phoenix AZ 85014
Tel (602) 264-1375
SIC 1021 3331 1031 1061 1044

▲ AMERICAS MINING CORP p 81
1150 N 7th Ave, Tucson AZ 85705
Tel (520) 798-7500
SIC 1021 1044 1031 1041 3331

■ AR SILVER BELL INC p 102
5285 E Williams Cir, Tucson AZ 85711
Tel (520) 798-7500
SIC 1021 1044 1031 1041 3331 3339

■ ASARCO LLC p 115
5285 E Williams Cir # 2000, Tucson AZ 85711
Tel (520) 798-7500
SIC 1021 1044 1031 1041 3331 3339

▲ HECLA MINING CO p 680
6500 N Mineral Dr Ste 200, Coeur D Alene ID 83815
Tel (208) 769-4100
SIC 1041 1044 1031 1081

TRELLEBORG CORP p 1476
200 Veterans Blvd Ste 3, South Haven MI 49090
Tel (269) 639-9891
SIC 3341 1021 1044 1031 4226 1041

DOE RUN RESOURCES CORP p 447
1801 Park 270 Dr Ste 300, Saint Louis MO 63146
Tel (314) 453-7100 SIC 1031 1021 3339

▲ TAHOE RESOURCES INC p 1421
5310 Kietzke Ln Ste 200, Reno NV 89511
Tel (775) 825-8574
SIC 1021 1041 1044 1031 1311

■ JARDEN ZINC PRODUCTS LLC p 778
2500 Old Stage Rd, Greeneville TN 37745
Tel (423) 639-8111
SIC 2796 3364 3356 1031 2789

VOTORANTIM US INC p 1566
3200 Southwest Fwy # 3030, Houston TX 77027
Tel (832) 726-0160 SIC 1031 1061

SIC 1041 Gold Ores

SUMITOMO METAL MINING POGO LLC p 1398
50 Mile Pogo Mile Rd, Delta Junction AK 99737
Tel (907) 895-2740 SIC 1041

■ CYPRUS AMAX MINERALS CO p 405
333 N Central Ave, Phoenix AZ 85004
Tel (602) 366-8100
SIC 1221 1222 1021 1061 1479 1041

▲ FREEPORT-MCMORAN INC p 577
333 N Central Ave, Phoenix AZ 85004
Tel (602) 366-8100
SIC 1021 1041 1061 1044

▲ AMERICAS MINING CORP p 81
1150 N 7th Ave, Tucson AZ 85705
Tel (520) 798-7500
SIC 1021 1044 1031 1041 3331

■ AR SILVER BELL INC p 102
5285 E Williams Cir, Tucson AZ 85711
Tel (520) 798-7500
SIC 1021 1044 1031 1041 3331 3339

■ASARCO LLC p 115
5285 E Williams Cir # 2000, Tucson AZ 85711
Tel (520) 798-7500
SIC 1021 1044 1031 1041 3331 3339

▲GOLD RESOURCE CORP p 620
2886 Carriage Manor Pt, Colorado Springs CO 80906
Tel (303) 320-7708 SIC 1041 1044

KINROSS GOLD USA INC p 821
5075 S Syracuse St, Denver CO 80237
Tel (775) 829-1666 SIC 1041 1044

ALACER MANAGEMENT CORP p 43
9635 Maroon Cir Ste 300, Englewood CO 80112
Tel (303) 292-1299 SIC 1041

■NEWMONT GOLD CO p 1038
6363 S Fiddlers Green Cir, Greenwood Village CO 80111
Tel (303) 863-7414 SIC 1041

▲NEWMONT MINING CORP p 1038
6363 S Fiddlers Green Cir # 800, Greenwood Village CO 80111
Tel (303) 863-7414 SIC 1041 1021

■NEWMONT USA LIMITED p 1038
6363 Sout Fidd Gree Cir, Greenwood Village CO 80111
Tel (303) 863-7414 SIC 1041 1021

GOLDEN STAR RESOURCES LTD p 621
10901 W Toller Dr Ste 300, Littleton CO 80127
Tel (303) 830-9000 SIC 1041

THOMPSON CREEK METALS CO INC p 1449
26 W Dry Creek Cir, Littleton CO 80120
Tel (303) 761-8801
SIC 1021 1041 1044 1061

▲HECLA MINING CO p 680
6500 N Mineral Dr Ste 200, Coeur D Alene ID 83815
Tel (208) 769-4100
SIC 1041 1044 1031 1081

▲COEUR MINING INC p 333
104 S Michigan Ave # 900, Chicago IL 60603
Tel (312) 489-5800 SIC 1041 1044

TRELLEBORG CORP p 1476
200 Veterans Blvd Ste 3, South Haven MI 49090
Tel (269) 639-9891
SIC 3341 1021 1044 1031 4226 1041

AMES CONSTRUCTION INC p 84
14420 County Road 5, Burnsville MN 55306
Tel (952) 435-7106
SIC 1611 1041 1021 1794

BARRICK GOLDSTRIKE MINES INC p 157
905 W Main St, Elko NV 89801
Tel (775) 748-1001 SIC 1041

ARGONAUT GOLD INC p 107
9600 Prototype Ct, Reno NV 89521
Tel (775) 284-4422 SIC 1081 1041

HYCROFT MINING CORP p 723
9790 Gateway Dr Ste 200, Reno NV 89521
Tel (775) 358-4455 SIC 1041 1044

▲TAHOE RESOURCES INC p 1421
5310 Kietzke Ln Ste 200, Reno NV 89511
Tel (775) 825-8574
SIC 1021 1041 1044 1031 1311

BHP COPPER INC p 180
1360 Post Oak Blvd # 150, Houston TX 77056
Tel (713) 961-8500 SIC 1021 3341 1041

BHP HOLDINGS (RESOURCES) INC p 180
1360 Post Oak Blvd # 150, Houston TX 77056
Tel (713) 961-8500 SIC 1021 3341 1041

KENNECOTT CORP p 810
8315 W 3595 S, Magna UT 84044
Tel (801) 913-8335
SIC 1041 1021 1061 1221

ASAHI REFINING USA INC p 115
4601 W 2100 S, Salt Lake City UT 84120
Tel (801) 972-6466 SIC 1041

BARRICK GOLD OF NORTH AMERICA INC p 157
460 W 50 N Ste 500, Salt Lake City UT 84101
Tel (416) 861-9911 SIC 8741 1041

KENNECOTT UTAH COPPER LLC p 811
4700 W Daybreak Pkwy, South Jordan UT 84009
Tel (801) 204-2000
SIC 1021 1041 1044 1061

SIC 1044 Silver Ores

▲FREEPORT-MCMORAN INC p 577
333 N Central Ave, Phoenix AZ 85004
Tel (602) 366-8100
SIC 1021 1041 1061 1044

■SOUTHERN COPPER CORP p 1348
1440 E Missouri Ave # 160, Phoenix AZ 85014
Tel (602) 264-1375
SIC 1021 3331 1031 1061 1044

▲AMERICAS MINING CORP p 81
1150 N 7th Ave, Tucson AZ 85705
Tel (520) 798-7500
SIC 1021 1044 1031 1041 3331

■AR SILVER BELL INC p 102
5285 E Williams Cir, Tucson AZ 85711
Tel (520) 798-7500
SIC 1021 1044 1031 1041 3331 3339

■ASARCO LLC p 115
5285 E Williams Cir # 2000, Tucson AZ 85711
Tel (520) 798-7500
SIC 1021 1044 1031 1041 3331 3339

▲GOLD RESOURCE CORP p 620
2886 Carriage Manor Pt, Colorado Springs CO 80906
Tel (303) 320-7708 SIC 1041 1044

KINROSS GOLD USA INC p 821
5075 S Syracuse St, Denver CO 80237
Tel (775) 829-1666 SIC 1041 1044

RIO TINTO AMERICA INC p 1236
8051 E Maplewood Ave # 100, Greenwood Village CO 80111
Tel (303) 713-5000 SIC 3412 5082 1044

THOMPSON CREEK METALS CO INC p 1449
26 W Dry Creek Cir, Littleton CO 80120
Tel (303) 761-8801
SIC 1021 1041 1044 1061

■COEUR-ROCHESTER INC p 334
505 E Front Ave, Coeur D Alene ID 83814
Tel (312) 489-5800 SIC 1044

▲HECLA MINING CO p 680
6500 N Mineral Dr Ste 200, Coeur D Alene ID 83815
Tel (208) 769-4100
SIC 1041 1044 1031 1081

▲COEUR MINING INC p 333
104 S Michigan Ave # 900, Chicago IL 60603
Tel (312) 489-5800 SIC 1041 1044

TRELLEBORG CORP p 1476
200 Veterans Blvd Ste 3, South Haven MI 49090
Tel (269) 639-9891
SIC 3341 1021 1044 1031 4226 1041

HYCROFT MINING CORP p 723
9790 Gateway Dr Ste 200, Reno NV 89521
Tel (775) 358-4455 SIC 1041 1044

▲TAHOE RESOURCES INC p 1421
5310 Kietzke Ln Ste 200, Reno NV 89511
Tel (775) 825-8574
SIC 1021 1041 1044 1031 1311

KENNECOTT UTAH COPPER LLC p 811
4700 W Daybreak Pkwy, South Jordan UT 84009
Tel (801) 204-2000
SIC 1021 1041 1044 1061

SIC 1061 Ferroalloy Ores, Except Vanadium

■CLIMAX MOLYBDENUM MARKETING CORP p 326
333 N Central Ave Ste 100, Phoenix AZ 85004
Tel (602) 366-8100 SIC 1061 3313

■CYPRUS AMAX MINERALS CO p 405
333 N Central Ave, Phoenix AZ 85004
Tel (602) 366-8100
SIC 1221 1222 1021 1061 1479 1041

■CYPRUS MINES CORP p 406
1 N Central Ave, Phoenix AZ 85004
Tel (602) 366-8100
SIC 1221 1021 1031 1061

■FREEPORT MINERALS CORP p 577
333 N Central Ave, Phoenix AZ 85004
Tel (602) 366-8100
SIC 1061 1021 3312 3351

▲FREEPORT-MCMORAN INC p 577
333 N Central Ave, Phoenix AZ 85004
Tel (602) 366-8100
SIC 1021 1041 1061 1044

■SOUTHERN COPPER CORP p 1348
1440 E Missouri Ave # 160, Phoenix AZ 85014
Tel (602) 264-1375
SIC 1021 3331 1031 1061 1044

THOMPSON CREEK METALS CO INC p 1449
26 W Dry Creek Cir, Littleton CO 80120
Tel (303) 761-8801
SIC 1021 1041 1044 1061

THOMPSON CREEK METALS CO USA p 1449
26 W Dry Creek Cir, Littleton CO 80120
Tel (303) 761-8801 SIC 1061

THOMPSON CREEK MINING CO p 1449
26 W Dry Creek Cir # 810, Littleton CO 80120
Tel (303) 783-6413 SIC 2899 1061

THOMPSON CREEK MINING LTD p 1449
26 W Dry Creek Cir # 810, Littleton CO 80120
Tel (303) 761-8801 SIC 1061 2899 2819

GEORGIAN AMERICAN ALLOYS INC p 608
200 S Biscayne Blvd # 5500, Miami FL 33131
Tel (305) 375-7560 SIC 1061

VOTORANTIM US INC p 1566
3200 Southwest Fwy # 3030, Houston TX 77027
Tel (832) 726-0160 SIC 1031 1061

KENNECOTT CORP p 810
8315 W 3595 S, Magna UT 84044
Tel (801) 913-8335
SIC 1041 1021 1061 1221

KENNECOTT UTAH COPPER LLC p 811
4700 W Daybreak Pkwy, South Jordan UT 84009
Tel (801) 204-2000
SIC 1021 1041 1044 1061

SIC 1081 Metal Mining Svcs

BERING STRAITS NATIVE CORP p 174
110 Front St Ste 300, Nome AK 99762
Tel (907) 443-5252 SIC 1081

NATIONAL EWP INC p 1011
500 Main St, Woodland CA 95695
Tel (530) 419-2117 SIC 1081

■AECOM ENERGY & CONSTRUCTION INC p 28
6200 S Quebec St, Greenwood Village CO 80111
Tel (303) 228-3000
SIC 1622 1629 1081 4953

TERRANE METALS CORP p 1439
26 W Dry Creek Cir # 810, Littleton CO 80120
Tel (303) 761-8801 SIC 1081

■TRADEMARK METALS RECYCLING LLC p 1468
The Lincoln Center 5401 W, Tampa FL 33609
Tel (813) 226-0088 SIC 5093 1081

SMALL MINE DEVELOPMENT LLC p 1332
670 E Riverpark Ln # 100, Boise ID 83706
Tel (208) 338-8880 SIC 1081

WASHINGTON GROUP INTERNATIONAL INC p 1578
720 E Park Blvd, Boise ID 83712
Tel (208) 386-5000
SIC 1611 1629 1221 1081 4959 1475

▲HECLA MINING CO p 680
6500 N Mineral Dr Ste 200, Coeur D Alene ID 83815
Tel (208) 769-4100
SIC 1041 1044 1031 1081

CAMBRIAN COAL CORP p 244
15888 Ferrells Creek Rd, Belcher KY 41513
Tel (606) 754-9898 SIC 1081

CHARAH INC p 288
12601 Plantside Dr, Louisville KY 40299
Tel (502) 245-1353 SIC 1081 4953

PENSE BROTHERS DRILLING CO INC p 1131
800 Newberry St, Fredericktown MO 63645
Tel (573) 783-3011 SIC 1081 1381

ARGONAUT GOLD INC p 107
9600 Prototype Ct, Reno NV 89521
Tel (775) 284-4422 SIC 1081 1041

CORAL REEF CAPITAL GROUP LLC p 368
757 3rd Ave, New York NY 10017
Tel (646) 599-9680 SIC 6799 1081

■ALCOA WORLD ALUMINA LLC p 47
201 Isabella St, Pittsburgh PA 15212
Tel (412) 553-4545 SIC 1099 1081 4911

METALLURG HOLDINGS INC p 952
435 Devon Park Dr Ste 200, Wayne PA 19087
Tel (610) 293-0838 SIC 3313 1081

METALLURG INC p 952
435 Devon Park Dr Ste 200, Wayne PA 19087
Tel (610) 293-2501 SIC 3313 1081

HEALTH CARE TEMPORARIES INC p 674
8926 Sherbourne St Ste D, Houston TX 77016
Tel (713) 631-7106
SIC 8082 1542 1522 1081 5082

CYANCO CORP p 404
1920 Country Place Pkwy # 400, Pearland TX 77584
Tel (775) 853-4300 SIC 1081

WESTERN EXPLOSIVES SYSTEMS CO p 1598
3135 S Richmond St, Salt Lake City UT 84106
Tel (801) 484-6557
SIC 5169 1629 1241 1081 1481 2892

CEMENTATION USA INC p 274
10150 S Centennial Pkwy # 110, Sandy UT 84070
Tel (801) 937-4120 SIC 1081

SUMITOMO METAL MINING AMERICA INC p 1398
701 5th Ave Ste 2150, Seattle WA 98104
Tel (206) 405-2800 SIC 1081

TECK AMERICAN INC p 1432
501 N Riverpoint Blvd # 300, Spokane WA 99202
Tel (509) 747-6111 SIC 1081

SIC 1094 Uranium, Radium & Vanadium Ores

■PHOSPHATE RESOURCE PARTNERS LIMITED PARTNERSHIP p 1145
100 Saunders Rd Ste 300, Lake Forest IL 60045
Tel (847) 739-1200
SIC 2874 1311 1475 2819 1094

▲CENTRUS ENERGY CORP p 281
6901 Rockledge Dr Ste 800, Bethesda MD 20817
Tel (301) 564-3200 SIC 1094

■MOS HOLDINGS INC p 991
3033 Campus Dr Ste E490, Plymouth MN 55441
Tel (763) 577-2700
SIC 2874 1475 2819 1094 1481

LOUISIANA ENERGY SERVICES LLC p 880
275 Andrews Hwy, Eunice NM 88231
Tel (575) 394-4646 SIC 1094

SIC 1099 Metal Ores, NEC

▲MOLYCORP INC p 983
5619 Denver Tech Ste, Greenwood Village CO 80111
Tel (303) 843-8040 SIC 1099

▲STILLWATER MINING CO p 1390
26 W Dry Creek Cir, Littleton CO 80120
Tel (406) 373-8700 SIC 1099

C-E MINERALS INC p 234
100 Mansell Ct E Ste 615, Roswell GA 30076
Tel (770) 225-7900
SIC 1099 1446 3295 6512

■JOHNSON KADANT INC p 791
805 Wood St, Three Rivers MI 49093
Tel (269) 278-1715
SIC 3494 8711 1389 3052 1099

▲ARCONIC INC p 106
390 Park Ave, New York NY 10022
Tel (212) 836-2674 SIC 3334 3353 1099

■ALCOA WORLD ALUMINA LLC p 47
201 Isabella St, Pittsburgh PA 15212
Tel (412) 553-4545 SIC 1099 1081 4911

HALCO (MINING) INC p 653
12 Federal St Ste 320, Pittsburgh PA 15212
Tel (412) 235-0265 SIC 1099

■MATERION NATURAL RESOURCES INC p 919
10 Miles North Hwy 6, Delta UT 84624
Tel (435) 864-2701 SIC 1099 3339

SIC 1221 Bituminous Coal & Lignite: Surface Mining

MCWANE INC p 933
2900 Highway 280 S # 300, Birmingham AL 35223
Tel (205) 414-3100
SIC 3491 1221 3321 3312 3494

DRUMMOND CO INC p 457
1000 Urban Center Dr # 300, Vestavia AL 35242
Tel (205) 945-6500
SIC 1221 1222 3312 5052 5085 5172

USIBELLI COAL MINE INC p 1535
100 River Rd, Healy AK 99743
Tel (907) 683-2226 SIC 1221

■CYPRUS AMAX MINERALS CO p 405
333 N Central Ave, Phoenix AZ 85004
Tel (602) 366-8100
SIC 1221 1222 1021 1061 1479 1041

■CYPRUS MINES CORP p 406
1 N Central Ave, Phoenix AZ 85004
Tel (602) 366-8100
SIC 1221 1021 1031 1061

■CHEVRON MINING INC p 296
116 Invrneco Dr E Ste 207, Englewood CO 80112
Tel (303) 930-3600 SIC 1221

▲WESTMORELAND COAL CO p 1601
9540 Maroon Cir Unit 200, Englewood CO 80112
Tel (855) 922-6463 SIC 1221 4911

■WESTMORELAND RESOURCE PARTNERS LP p 1602
9540 Maroon Cir Unit 200, Englewood CO 80112
Tel (614) 643-0337 SIC 1221

WEXFORD CAPITAL LP p 1603
411 W Putnam Ave Ste 125, Greenwich CT 06830
Tel (203) 862-7000
SIC 8741 6282 1221 1222

■PROGRESS FUELS CORP p 1181
1 Progress Plz Fl 11, Saint Petersburg FL 33701
Tel (727) 824-6600 SIC 1221

TECO DIVERSIFIED INC p 1432
702 N Franklin St, Tampa FL 33602
Tel (813) 228-4111 SIC 1221

TECO ENERGY INC p 1432
702 N Franklin St, Tampa FL 33602
Tel (813) 228-1111
SIC 4911 4924 4424 1221 1222

WASHINGTON GROUP INTERNATIONAL INC p 1578
720 E Park Blvd, Boise ID 83712
Tel (208) 386-5000
SIC 1611 1629 1221 1081 4959 1475

■MATERIAL SERVICE RESOURCES CORP p 919
222 N La Salle St # 1200, Chicago IL 60601
Tel (630) 325-7736 SIC 1442 1221

PEABODY BEAR RUN MINING LLC p 1125
7100 Eagle Crest Blvd, Evansville IN 47715
Tel (812) 659-7126 SIC 1221

VIGO COAL OPERATING CO INC p 1556
250 N Cross Pointe Blvd, Evansville IN 47715
Tel (812) 759-8446 SIC 1221 8748

SOLAR SOURCES INC p 1338
6755 Gray Rd, Indianapolis IN 46237
Tel (317) 788-0084 SIC 1221

PEABODY MIDWEST MINING LLC p 1125
566 Dickeyville Rd, Lynnville IN 47619
Tel (812) 434-8500 SIC 1221 1222 1241

■WEBSTER COUNTY COAL LLC p 1587
1758 State Route 874, Clay KY 42404
Tel (270) 249-2205 SIC 1221

LESLIE RESOURCES INC p 857
1021 Tori Dr, Hazard KY 41701
Tel (606) 439-0946 SIC 1221

RHINO RESOURCE PARTNERS LP p 1231
424 Lewis Hargett Cir # 250, Lexington KY 40503
Tel (859) 389-6500 SIC 1221 1222

BOWIE RESOURCE PARTNERS LLC p 204
6100 Dutchmans Ln Ste 902, Louisville KY 40205
Tel (502) 584-6022 SIC 1221

BOWIE RESOURCES LLC p 204
6100 Dutchmans Ln Ste 902, Louisville KY 40205
Tel (502) 584-6022 SIC 1221

LOTUS INTERNATIONAL CO p 879
6880 Commerce Blvd, Canton MI 48187
Tel (734) 245-0140 SIC 8711 3651 1221

▲ARCH COAL INC p 104
1 Cityplace Dr Ste 300, Saint Louis MO 63141
Tel (314) 994-2700 SIC 1221 1222

■ARCH WESTERN RESOURCES LLC p 104
1 Cityplace Dr Ste 300, Saint Louis MO 63141
Tel (314) 994-2700 SIC 1221

▲FORESIGHT ENERGY LP p 566
211 N Broadway Ste 2600, Saint Louis MO 63102
Tel (314) 932-6160 SIC 1221

PEABODY COAL CO p 1125
701 Market St, Saint Louis MO 63101
Tel (314) 342-3400 SIC 1222 1221

PEABODY ENERGY CORP p 1125
701 Market St, Saint Louis MO 63101
Tel (314) 342-3400 SIC 1221 1222

PEABODY HOLDING CO LLC p 1125
701 Market St Ste 700, Saint Louis MO 63101
Tel (314) 342-3400
SIC 1221 1222 5052 2873 6719

PEABODY NATURAL RESOURCES CO p 1125
701 Market St Ste 700, Saint Louis MO 63101
Tel (314) 342-3400 SIC 1221

■WESTERN ENERGY CO p 1598
148 Rosebud Ln, Colstrip MT 59323
Tel (406) 748-5100 SIC 1221

PETER KIEWIT SONS INC p 1138
3555 Farnam St Ste 1000, Omaha NE 68131
Tel (402) 342-2052
SIC 1611 1622 1711 1542 1629 1221

■FLORIDA PROGRESS CORP p 559
410 S Wilmington St, Raleigh NC 27601
Tel (919) 546-6111
SIC 1221 4911 4011 4449

■COTEAU PROPERTIES CO p 374
204 County Road 15, Beulah ND 58523
Tel (701) 873-2281 SIC 1221

■CENTENNIAL ENERGY HOLDINGS INC p 275
Schuchart Bldg 918e, Bismarck ND 58501
Tel (701) 222-7900 SIC 1382 8748 1221

■KNIFE RIVER CORP p 824
1150 W Century Ave, Bismarck ND 58503
Tel (701) 530-1400 SIC 1442 3273 1221

▲MDU RESOURCES GROUP INC p 933
1200 W Century Ave, Bismarck ND 58503
Tel (701) 530-1000
SIC 4911 4924 4922 1221 1442 1311

■FALKIRK MINING CO p 526
2801 1st St Sw, Underwood ND 58576
Tel (701) 442-5751 SIC 1221

▲NACCO INDUSTRIES INC p 1006
5875 Landerbrook Dr # 300, Cleveland OH 44124
Tel (440) 229-5151
SIC 3634 1221 5719 3631

■OXFORD MINING CO INC p 1101
544 Chestnut St, Coshocton OH 43812
Tel (740) 622-6302 SIC 1221

■OXFORD MINING CO-KENTUCKY LLC p 1101
544 Chestnut St, Coshocton OH 43812
Tel (740) 622-6302 SIC 1221

KIMBLE CO p 818
3596 State Route 39 Nw, Dover OH 44622
Tel (330) 343-1226 SIC 1221

WATERLOO COAL CO INC p 1582
3675 Dixon Run Rd, Jackson OH 45640
Tel (740) 286-5633 SIC 1221 1411 1459

■ALLIANCE COAL LLC p 54
1717 S Boulder Ave # 400, Tulsa OK 74119
Tel (918) 295-7600 SIC 1221 1222

▲ALLIANCE HOLDINGS GP LP p 54
1717 S Boulder Ave # 400, Tulsa OK 74119
Tel (918) 295-1415 SIC 1221 1222

ALLIANCE RESOURCE HOLDINGS INC p 55
1717 S Boulder Ave Fl 6, Tulsa OK 74119
Tel (918) 295-7600 SIC 1221 1222

■ **ALLIANCE RESOURCE OPERATING PARTNERS LP** p 55
1717 S Boulder Ave # 600, Tulsa OK 74119
Tel (918) 295-7600 SIC 1221

▲ **ALLIANCE RESOURCE PARTNERS LP** p 55
1717 S Boulder Ave # 400, Tulsa OK 74119
Tel (918) 295-7600 SIC 1221 1222 1241

▲ **CONSOL ENERGY INC** p 359
1000 Consol Energy Dr, Canonsburg PA 15317
Tel (724) 485-4000 SIC 1221 1222 1311

CONSOLIDATION COAL CO INC p 360
1000 Consol Energy Dr, Canonsburg PA 15317
Tel (740) 338-3100 SIC 1221

PBS COALS INC p 1123
1576 Stoystown Rd, Friedens PA 15541
Tel (814) 443-4668 SIC 1221

ROSEBUD MINING CO p 1250
301 Market St, Kittanning PA 16201
Tel (724) 545-6222 SIC 1222 1221

PVR PARTNERS LP p 1193
3 Radnor Corp Ctr Ste 301, Radnor PA 19087
Tel (610) 975-8200 SIC 1221 1311

POWELL CONSTRUCTION CO INC p 1165
3622 Bristol Hwy Ste 1, Johnson City TN 37601
Tel (423) 282-0111 SIC 1542 1221 1541

ALPHA NATURAL RESOURCES INC p 60
1989 E Stone Dr, Kingsport TN 37660
Tel (423) 723-8900 SIC 1221 1222

LUMINANT MINING CO LLC p 885
1601 Bryan St, Dallas TX 75201
Tel (214) 812-4600 SIC 1221

■ **SABINE MINING CO** p 1264
6501 Fm 968 W, Hallsville TX 75650
Tel (903) 660-4200 SIC 1241 8711 1221

▲ **NATURAL RESOURCE PARTNERS LP** p 1018
1201 La St Ste 3400, Houston TX 77002
Tel (713) 751-7507 SIC 1221 1474

■ **WILLIAMS GAS PIPELINE-TRANSCO** p 1611
2800 Post Oak Blvd # 300, Houston TX 77056
Tel (713) 215-2000 SIC 1321 1221 1222

■ **NORTH AMERICAN COAL CORP** p 1049
5340 Legacy Dr Ste 300, Plano TX 75024
Tel (972) 448-5400 SIC 1221

■ **KERR-MCGEE CORP** p 813
1201 Lake Robbins Dr, Spring TX 77380
Tel (832) 636-1000
SIC 2816 2819 1311 1221 1222

KENNECOTT CORP p 810
8315 W 3595 S, Magna UT 84044
Tel (801) 913-8335
SIC 1041 1021 1061 1221

ALPHA APPALACHIA HOLDINGS INC p 60
1 Alpha Pl, Bristol VA 24209
Tel (276) 619-4410 SIC 1221 1222

APPALACHIA HOLDING CO p 97
1 Alpha Pl, Bristol VA 24202
Tel (276) 619-4410 SIC 1221

DAVIS MINING & MANUFACTURING INC p 416
613 Front St E, Coeburn VA 24230
Tel (276) 395-3354
SIC 2892 5082 2426 1221 1222

BLEDSOE COAL CORP p 189
901 E Byrd St Ste 1140, Richmond VA 23219
Tel (606) 878-7411 SIC 1221

JAMES RIVER COAL CO p 777
901 E Byrd St Ste 1600, Richmond VA 23219
Tel (804) 780-3000 SIC 1221

JAMES RIVER COAL SERVICE CO p 777
901 E Byrd St Ste 1600, Richmond VA 23219
Tel (606) 878-7411 SIC 1222 1221

L&L ENERGY INC p 834
130 Andover Park E # 200, Tukwila WA 98188
Tel (206) 264-8065 SIC 1241 1221 5052

USNR LLC p 1535
1981 Schurman Way, Woodland WA 98674
Tel (360) 225-8267
SIC 3585 3553 3625 1221 5084

■ **INTERNATIONAL COAL GROUP INC** p 754
114 Smiley Dr, Saint Albans WV 25177
Tel (304) 760-2400 SIC 1222 1221

ALPHA COAL WEST INC p 60
2273 Bishop Rd, Gillette WY 82718
Tel (307) 687-3400 SIC 1221

▲ **CLOUD PEAK ENERGY INC** p 327
505 S Gillette Ave, Gillette WY 82716
Tel (307) 687-6000 SIC 1221

■ **CLOUD PEAK ENERGY RESOURCES LLC** p 327
505 S Gillette Ave, Gillette WY 82716
Tel (303) 956-7596 SIC 1221

■ **CLOUD PEAK ENERGY SERVICES CO** p 327
505 S Gillette Ave, Gillette WY 82716
Tel (307) 687-6000 SIC 1221

■ **THUNDER BASIN COAL CO LLC** p 1451
5669 Hwy 450, Wright WY 82732
Tel (307) 939-1300 SIC 1221

SIC 1222 Bituminous Coal: Underground Mining

WALTER JIM RESOURCES INC p 1574
16243 Highway 216, Brookwood AL 35444
Tel (205) 554-6150 SIC 1222

DRUMMOND CO INC p 457
1000 Urban Center Dr # 300, Vestavia AL 35242
Tel (205) 945-6500
SIC 1221 1222 3312 5052 5085 5172

■ **CYPRUS AMAX MINERALS CO** p 405
333 N Central Ave, Phoenix AZ 85004
Tel (602) 366-8100
SIC 1221 1222 1021 1061 1479 1041

TWENTYMILE COAL LLC p 1494
29515 Routt County Rd 2 # 27, Oak Creek CO 80467
Tel (970) 879-3800 SIC 1222

WEXFORD CAPITAL LP p 1603
411 W Putnam Ave Ste 125, Greenwich CT 06830
Tel (203) 862-7000
SIC 8741 6282 1221 1222

TECO ENERGY INC p 1432
702 N Franklin St, Tampa FL 33602
Tel (813) 228-1111
SIC 4911 4924 4424 1221 1222

OXBOW CARBON & MINERALS HOLDINGS INC p 1100
1601 Forum Pl Ste 1400, West Palm Beach FL 33401
Tel (561) 907-5400 SIC 5052 1222

AMERICAN COAL CO p 70
9085 Highway 34 N, Galatia IL 62935
Tel (618) 268-6311 SIC 1222 5052

KNIGHT HAWK COAL LLC p 824
500 Cutler Trico Rd, Percy IL 62272
Tel (618) 426-3662 SIC 1241 1222

PEABODY MIDWEST MINING LLC p 1125
566 Dickeyville Rd, Lynnville IN 47619
Tel (812) 434-8500 SIC 1221 1222 1241

SUNRISE COAL LLC p 1403
1183 E Canvasback Dr, Terre Haute IN 47802
Tel (812) 299-2800 SIC 1222

PLM HOLDING CO LLC p 1156
200 Allison Blvd, Corbin KY 40701
Tel (606) 523-4444 SIC 1222

HNRC DISSOLUTION CO p 698
201 E Main St 100, Lexington KY 40507
Tel (606) 327-5450 SIC 1222

RHINO RESOURCE PARTNERS LP p 1231
424 Lewis Hargett Cir # 250, Lexington KY 40503
Tel (859) 389-6500 SIC 1221 1222

SHAMROCK COAL CO INC p 1311
1374 Highway 192 E, London KY 40741
Tel (606) 878-7411 SIC 1222

BEECH FORK PROCESSING INC p 168
Rr 292, Lovely KY 41231
Tel (606) 395-6841 SIC 1222

▲ **ARCH COAL INC** p 104
1 Cityplace Dr Ste 300, Saint Louis MO 63141
Tel (314) 994-2700 SIC 1221 1222

PEABODY COAL CO p 1125
701 Market St, Saint Louis MO 63101
Tel (314) 342-3400 SIC 1222 1221

PEABODY ENERGY CORP p 1125
701 Market St, Saint Louis MO 63101
Tel (314) 342-3400 SIC 1221 1222

PEABODY HOLDING CO LLC p 1125
701 Market St Ste 700, Saint Louis MO 63101
Tel (314) 342-3400
SIC 1221 1222 5052 2873 6719

MURRAY ENERGY CORP p 1001
46226 National Rd W, Saint Clairsville OH 43950
Tel (740) 338-3100 SIC 1222

■ **ALLIANCE COAL LLC** p 54
1717 S Boulder Ave # 400, Tulsa OK 74119
Tel (918) 295-7600 SIC 1221 1222

▲ **ALLIANCE HOLDINGS GP LP** p 54
1717 S Boulder Ave # 400, Tulsa OK 74119
Tel (918) 295-1415 SIC 1221 1222

ALLIANCE RESOURCE HOLDINGS INC p 55
1717 S Boulder Ave Fl 6, Tulsa OK 74119
Tel (918) 295-7600 SIC 1221 1222

▲ **ALLIANCE RESOURCE PARTNERS LP** p 55
1717 S Boulder Ave # 400, Tulsa OK 74119
Tel (918) 295-7600 SIC 1221 1222 1241

▲ **CONSOL ENERGY INC** p 359
1000 Consol Energy Dr, Canonsburg PA 15317
Tel (724) 485-4000 SIC 1221 1222 1311

■ **CONSOL PENNSYLVANIA COAL CO LLC** p 359
1000 Consol Energy Dr, Canonsburg PA 15317
Tel (724) 485-4000 SIC 1311 1222

ROSEBUD MINING CO p 1250
301 Market St, Kittanning PA 16201
Tel (724) 545-6222 SIC 1222 1221

SNYDER ASSOCIATED COMPANIES INC p 1336
1 Glade Park Dr, Kittanning PA 16201
Tel (724) 548-8101 SIC 1442 3281 1222

CUMBERLAND COAL RESOURCES LP p 400
158 Portal Rd, Waynesburg PA 15370
Tel (724) 852-5845 SIC 1222

ALPHA NATURAL RESOURCES INC p 60
1989 E Stone Dr, Kingsport TN 37660
Tel (423) 723-8900 SIC 1221 1222

■ **AMERICAN NATURAL RESOURCES CO** p 77
717 Texas St Ste 2400, Houston TX 77002
Tel (832) 320-5000 SIC 4922 1311 1222

BHP MINERALS INTERNATIONAL INC p 180
1360 Post Oak Blvd # 150, Houston TX 77056
Tel (713) 961-8500 SIC 1222 1011 1021

■ **WILLIAMS GAS PIPELINE-TRANSCO** p 1611
2800 Post Oak Blvd # 300, Houston TX 77056
Tel (713) 215-2000 SIC 1321 1221 1222

■ **KERR-MCGEE CORP** p 813
1201 Lake Robbins Dr, Spring TX 77380
Tel (832) 636-1000
SIC 2816 2819 1311 1221 1222

ALPHA APPALACHIA HOLDINGS INC p 60
1 Alpha Pl, Bristol VA 24209
Tel (276) 619-4410 SIC 1221 1222

DAVIS MINING & MANUFACTURING INC p 416
613 Front St E, Coeburn VA 24230
Tel (276) 395-3354
SIC 2892 5082 2426 1221 1222

SENECA COAL RESOURCES LLC p 1303
15 Appledore Ln, Natural Bridge VA 24578
Tel (304) 369-8175 SIC 1222

SENECA NORTH AMERICAN COAL LLC p 1303
15 Appledore Ln, Natural Bridge VA 24578
Tel (304) 369-8175 SIC 1222

JAMES RIVER COAL SERVICE CO p 777
901 E Byrd St Ste 1600, Richmond VA 23219
Tel (606) 878-7411 SIC 1222 1221

■ **INTERNATIONAL COAL GROUP INC** p 754
114 Smiley Dr, Saint Albans WV 25177
Tel (304) 760-2400 SIC 1222 1221

SIC 1231 Anthracite Mining

▲ **ALLETE INC** p 53
30 W Superior St, Duluth MN 55802
Tel (218) 279-5000
SIC 4931 4924 4941 1231 6552

PAGNOTTI ENTERPRISES INC p 1107
46 Public Sq Ste 600, Wilkes Barre PA 18701
Tel (570) 825-8700 SIC 6411 1231 4841

SIC 1241 Coal Mining Svcs

WALTER ENERGY INC p 1574
3000 Riverchase Galleria # 1700, Hoover AL 35244
Tel (205) 745-2000 SIC 1241 4925

▲ **HALLADOR ENERGY CO** p 654
1660 Lincoln St Ste 2700, Denver CO 80264
Tel (303) 839-5504 SIC 1241 1311 1382

ASBURY CARBONS INC p 115
103 Foulk Rd Ste 202, Wilmington DE 19803
Tel (302) 652-0266
SIC 1499 3295 1241 5051 3952 3069

OXBOW CARBON LLC p 1100
1601 Forum Pl Ste 1400, West Palm Beach FL 33401
Tel (561) 907-5400 SIC 1241 2999 5052

■ **WHITE OAK RESOURCES LLC** p 1606
18033 County Road 500 E, Dahlgren IL 62828
Tel (618) 643-5500 SIC 1241

▲ **SUNCOKE ENERGY INC** p 1402
1011 Warrenville Rd # 600, Lisle IL 60532
Tel (630) 824-1000 SIC 3312 1241

KNIGHT HAWK COAL LLC p 824
500 Cutler Trico Rd, Percy IL 62272
Tel (618) 426-3662 SIC 1241 1222

■ **FREEMAN ENERGY CORP** p 576
3008 Happy Landing Dr, Springfield IL 62711
Tel (217) 698-3949 SIC 1241

▲ **VECTREN CORP** p 1546
1 Vectren Sq, Evansville IN 47708
Tel (812) 491-4000
SIC 4924 4911 1241 1623 6531

PEABODY MIDWEST MINING LLC p 1125
566 Dickeyville Rd, Lynnville IN 47619
Tel (812) 434-8500 SIC 1221 1222 1241

BLACKHAWK MINING LLC p 187
3228 Summit Square Pl # 180, Lexington KY 40509
Tel (859) 543-0515 SIC 1241

LICKING RIVER RESOURCES INC p 863
6301 Old Richmond Rd, Lexington KY 40515
Tel (859) 223-8820 SIC 1241

US COAL CORP p 1531
6301 Old Richmond Rd, Lexington KY 40515
Tel (859) 223-8820 SIC 1241

CANYON FUEL CO LLC p 248
6100 Dutchmans Ln Fl 9, Louisville KY 40205
Tel (502) 584-6022 SIC 1241

CRISTAL p 392
20 Wight Ave Ste 100, Hunt Valley MD 21030
Tel (410) 229-4440
SIC 1241 3531 2816 2869 1321 3631

■ **WESTMORELAND MINING LLC** p 1602
490 N 31st St Ste 308, Billings MT 59101
Tel (719) 442-2600 SIC 1241

KIEWIT MINING GROUP INC p 817
Kiewit Plz, Omaha NE 68131
Tel (402) 342-2052 SIC 1241

OHIO VALLEY RESOURCES INC p 1078
29325 Chagrin Blvd # 300, Beachwood OH 44122
Tel (216) 765-1240 SIC 1241

OHIO VALLEY COAL CO p 1078
46226 National Rd W, Saint Clairsville OH 43950
Tel (740) 926-1351 SIC 1241

OHIO VALLEY TRANSLOADING CO INC p 1078
46226 National Rd W, Saint Clairsville OH 43950
Tel (740) 795-4967 SIC 1241

▲ **ALLIANCE RESOURCE PARTNERS LP** p 55
1717 S Boulder Ave # 400, Tulsa OK 74119
Tel (918) 295-7600 SIC 1221 1222 1241

CNX COAL RESOURCES LP p 330
1000 Consol Energy Dr, Canonsburg PA 15317
Tel (724) 485-4009 SIC 1241

EARTH SUPPORT SERVICES INC p 469
25 Allegheny Sq, Glassport PA 15045
Tel (412) 664-7788 SIC 1241

CALANDRA FRANK INC p 238
258 Kappa Dr, Pittsburgh PA 15238
Tel (412) 963-9071 SIC 1241

▲ **BLACK HILLS CORP** p 187
625 9th St, Rapid City SD 57701
Tel (605) 721-1700 SIC 4911 4923 1241

UNITED COAL CO LLC p 1507
110 Sprint Dr, Blountville TN 37617
Tel (276) 530-7411 SIC 1241

HUNT DOMINION CORP p 719
1601 Elm St Ste 3900, Dallas TX 75201
Tel (214) 880-8400 SIC 1311 1382 1241

■ **SABINE MINING CO** p 1264
6501 Fm 968 W, Hallsville TX 75650
Tel (903) 660-4200 SIC 1241 8711 1221

WESTERN EXPLOSIVES SYSTEMS CO p 1598
3135 S Richmond St, Salt Lake City UT 84106
Tel (801) 484-6557
SIC 5169 1629 1241 1081 1481 2892

ALPHA NATURAL RESOURCES LLC p 60
1 Alpha Pl, Bristol VA 24209
Tel (276) 619-4410 SIC 1241

MAXXIM REBUILD CO LLC p 923
5703 Crutchfield Dr, Norton VA 24273
Tel (276) 679-7020 SIC 1241

L&L ENERGY INC p 834
130 Andover Park E # 200, Tukwila WA 98188
Tel (206) 264-8065 SIC 1241 1221 5052

ALEX ENERGY INC p 48
2 Jerry Fork Rd, Drennen WV 26667
Tel (304) 872-5065 SIC 1241

SENECA COAL RESOURCES LLC p 1303
Shaffer Rd Exit, Madison WV 25130
Tel (304) 369-8316 SIC 1241

■ **ICG LLC** p 727
114 Smiley Dr, Saint Albans WV 25177
Tel (304) 760-2400 SIC 1241

SIC 1311 Crude Petroleum & Natural Gas

▲ **ENERGEN CORP** p 497
605 Richard Arrington Jr, Birmingham AL 35203
Tel (205) 326-2700
SIC 1311 4924 4922 1321

BP TRANSPORTATION (ALASKA) INC p 206
900 E Benson Blvd, Anchorage AK 99508
Tel (907) 561-5111 SIC 1311

▲ **MURPHY OIL CORP** p 1001
300 E Peach St, El Dorado AR 71730
Tel (870) 862-6411 SIC 1311 1382 2911

■ **MURPHY OIL USA INC** p 1001
200 E Peach St, El Dorado AR 71730
Tel (870) 862-6411
SIC 8742 2911 1311 4213

■ **CALIFORNIA RESOURCES PRODUCTION CORP** p 241
11109 River Run Blvd, Bakersfield CA 93311
Tel (661) 869-8000 SIC 1311 1382

E & B NATURAL RESOURCES MANAGEMENT CORP p 465
1600 Norris Rd, Bakersfield CA 93308
Tel (661) 679-1714 SIC 1311

▲ **CALIFORNIA RESOURCES CORP** p 241
9200 Oakdale Ave Fl 9, Chatsworth CA 91311
Tel (888) 848-4754 SIC 1311

RYZE SYNTHETICS PORT ARTHUR LLC p 1261
20 Pacifica Ste 1010, Irvine CA 92618
Tel (310) 200-2081 SIC 1311

BREITBURN ENERGY PARTNERS LP p 209
707 Wilshire Blvd # 4600, Los Angeles CA 90017
Tel (213) 225-5900 SIC 1311

STRAND ENERGY CO p 1392
515 S Flower St Ste 4800, Los Angeles CA 90071
Tel (213) 225-5900 SIC 1311

TPG PARTNERS III LP p 1467
345 California St # 3300, San Francisco CA 94104
Tel (415) 743-1500
SIC 1311 1389 4922 5082

▲ **CHEVRON CORP** p 295
6001 Bollinger Canyon Rd, San Ramon CA 94583
Tel (925) 842-1000
SIC 2911 1311 1382 1321 5541

■ **CHEVRON ORONITE CO LLC** p 296
6001 Bollinger Canyon Rd, San Ramon CA 94583
Tel (713) 432-2500
SIC 2821 2899 2869 1311

▲ **ANTERO RESOURCES CORP** p 93
1615 Wynkoop St, Denver CO 80202
Tel (303) 357-7310 SIC 1311

ANTERO RESOURCES LLC p 93
1625 17th St Ste 300, Denver CO 80202
Tel (303) 357-7310 SIC 1311

▲ **BILL BARRETT CORP** p 182
1099 18th St Ste 2300, Denver CO 80202
Tel (303) 293-9100 SIC 1311

▲ **BONANZA CREEK ENERGY INC** p 199
410 17th St Ste 1400, Denver CO 80202
Tel (720) 440-6100 SIC 1311

▲ **CIMAREX ENERGY CO** p 307
1700 N Lincoln St # 3700, Denver CO 80203
Tel (303) 295-3995 SIC 1311

EMERALD OIL INC p 491
200 Columbine St Ste 500, Denver CO 80206
Tel (303) 595-5600 SIC 1311

ENCANA OIL & GAS (USA) INC p 495
370 17th St Ste 1700, Denver CO 80202
Tel (303) 623-2300 SIC 2911 1311

■ **EVERGREEN RESOURCES INC** p 515
1401 17th St Ste 1200, Denver CO 80202
Tel (303) 298-8100 SIC 1311 1382 1381

▲ **HALLADOR ENERGY CO** p 654
1660 Lincoln St Ste 2700, Denver CO 80264
Tel (303) 839-5504 SIC 1241 1311 1382

■ **NEWFIELD PRODUCTION CO** p 1037
1001 17th St Ste 2000, Denver CO 80202
Tel (303) 893-0102 SIC 1311

▲ **PDC ENERGY INC** p 1124
1775 N Sherman St # 3000, Denver CO 80203
Tel (303) 860-5800 SIC 1311 1381

■ **QEP ENERGY CO** p 1195
1050 17th St Ste 800, Denver CO 80265
Tel (303) 672-6900
SIC 1311 1382 1389 5172

▲ **QEP RESOURCES INC** p 1195
1050 17th St Ste 800, Denver CO 80265
Tel (303) 672-6900 SIC 1311 1321 1382

▲ **RESOLUTE ENERGY CORP** p 1227
1700 N Lincoln St # 2800, Denver CO 80203
Tel (303) 534-4600 SIC 1311

■ **RESOLUTE NATURAL RESOURCES CO LLC** p 1227
1700 N Lincoln St # 2800, Denver CO 80203
Tel (303) 573-4886 SIC 1311

▲ **SM ENERGY CO** p 1331
1775 N Sherman St # 1200, Denver CO 80203
Tel (303) 861-8140 SIC 1311

■ **ST MARY OPERATING CO** p 1371
1775 N Sherman St # 1200, Denver CO 80203
Tel (303) 861-8140 SIC 1311

▲ **TRIANGLE PETROLEUM CORP** p 1478
1200 17th St Ste 2500, Denver CO 80202
Tel (303) 260-7125 SIC 1311 1382

▲ **WARREN RESOURCES INC** p 1577
1331 17th St Ste 720, Denver CO 80202
Tel (720) 403-8125 SIC 1311

■ **WESTERN GAS RESOURCES INC** p 1598
1099 18th St, Denver CO 80202
Tel (303) 452-5603
SIC 4923 4925 1311 5172

■ **WHITING OIL AND GAS CORP** p 1607
1700 Broadway Ste 2300, Denver CO 80290
Tel (303) 837-1661 SIC 1311

▲WHITING PETROLEUM CORP p 1607
1700 Broadway Ste 2300, Denver CO 80290
Tel (303) 837-1661 SIC 1311 1382

FRC FOUNDERS CORP p 575
1 Lafayette Pl Ste 3, Greenwich CT 06830
Tel (203) 661-6601
SIC 8741 1311 1389 8731 5084

■NORTHERN TIER ENERGY LLC p 1057
38c Grove St Ste 5, Ridgefield CT 06877
Tel (203) 244-6550 SIC 1311

DIRECT ENERGY INC p 441
263 Tresser Blvd Fl 8, Stamford CT 06901
Tel (800) 260-0300 SIC 4911 1311

NOBLE AMERICAS CORP p 1046
107 Elm St Fl 1, Stamford CT 06902
Tel (203) 324-8555 SIC 5052 1311

LOUIS DREYFUS HOLDING CO INC p 879
10 Westport Rd Ste 200, Wilton CT 06897
Tel (203) 761-2000
SIC 6221 5153 6512 6531 1311

NEW SOURCE ENERGY PARTNERS LP p 1033
300 Delaware Ave Ste 1100, Wilmington DE 19801
Tel (405) 272-3028 SIC 1311 1389

SHELL ENERGY RESOURCES INC p 1314
1105 N Market St Ste 1300, Wilmington DE 19801
Tel (302) 658-3676 SIC 1311 1382

■PHOSPHATE RESOURCE PARTNERS LIMITED PARTNERSHIP p 1145
100 Saunders Rd Ste 300, Lake Forest IL 60045
Tel (847) 739-1200
SIC 2874 1311 1475 2819 1094

COUNTRYMARK COOPERATIVE HOLDING CORP p 375
225 S East St Ste 144, Indianapolis IN 46202
Tel (800) 808-3170
SIC 5172 2911 1382 1311 6719

FERRELL COMPANIES INC p 538
7500 College Blvd # 1000, Overland Park KS 66210
Tel (913) 661-1500 SIC 1311 5984

BEREXCO LLC p 174
2020 N Bramblewood St, Wichita KS 67206
Tel (316) 265-3311 SIC 1382 1311

■KENTUCKY WEST VIRGINIA GAS CO p 812
748 N Lake Dr, Prestonsburg KY 41653
Tel (606) 886-2311 SIC 1311 1389 4922

LLOG EXPLORATION CO LLC p 872
1001 Ochsner Blvd Ste 200, Covington LA 70433
Tel (504) 833-7700 SIC 1311 1382

JP OIL CO LLC p 795
1604 W Pinhook Rd Ste 300, Lafayette LA 70508
Tel (337) 234-1170 SIC 1311

MARLIN ENERGY LLC p 909
3861 Ambassador Caffery P, Lafayette LA 70503
Tel (337) 769-0032 SIC 1311 1382

▲PETROQUEST ENERGY INC p 1139
400 E Kaliste Saloom Rd # 6000, Lafayette LA 70508
Tel (337) 232-7028 SIC 1311

▲STONE ENERGY CORP p 1391
625 E Kaliste Saloom Rd # 201, Lafayette LA 70508
Tel (337) 237-0410 SIC 1311 1382

RAAM GLOBAL ENERGY CO p 1203
3838 N Causeway Blvd # 2800, Metairie LA 70002
Tel (859) 253-1300 SIC 1311

NATIONAL GRID USA SERVICE CO INC p 1013
40 Sylvan Rd, Waltham MA 02451
Tel (800) 260-0054 SIC 4911 1311

BARTLETT HOLDINGS INC p 157
97 Libbey Industrial Pkwy # 400, Weymouth MA 02189
Tel (800) 225-0385 SIC 1311

▲DTE ENERGY CO p 458
1 Energy Plz, Detroit MI 48226
Tel (313) 235-4000 SIC 4911 4923 1311

OPTION ENERGY LLC p 1090
5481 N Whitetail Ln, Ludington MI 49431
Tel (269) 329-4317
SIC 4924 1311 4931 1711

DART ENERGY CORP p 413
600 Dart Rd, Mason MI 48854
Tel (517) 676-2900 SIC 1311 1382

SUMMIT-REED CITY INC p 1399
1315 S Mission Rd, Mount Pleasant MI 48858
Tel (989) 772-2028 SIC 1311

CENEX INC p 275
5500 Cenex Dr, Inver Grove Heights MN 55077
Tel (800) 232-3639
SIC 1311 2911 4613 4922 4789 4213

▲CHS INC p 304
5500 Cenex Dr, Inver Grove Heights MN 55077
Tel (651) 355-6000
SIC 5153 5191 2075 1311 2911 4613

NORTHERN OIL AND GAS INC p 1056
315 Manitoba Ave Ste 200, Wayzata MN 55391
Tel (952) 476-9800 SIC 1311

■CALLON OFFSHORE PRODUCTION INC p 242
200 N Canal St, Natchez MS 39120
Tel (601) 442-1601 SIC 1311 1382

▲CALLON PETROLEUM CO p 242
200 N Canal St, Natchez MS 39120
Tel (601) 442-1601 SIC 1311

■CALLON PETROLEUM OPERATING CO p 242
200 N Canal St, Natchez MS 39120
Tel (601) 442-1601 SIC 1311

TELLUS OPERATING GROUP LLC p 1435
602 Crescent Pl Ste 100, Ridgeland MS 39157
Tel (601) 898-7444 SIC 1311

BALLARD PETROLEUM HOLDINGS LLC p 148
845 12th St W, Billings MT 59102
Tel (406) 259-8790 SIC 1311

▲TAHOE RESOURCES INC p 1421
5310 Kietzke Ln Ste 200, Reno NV 89511
Tel (775) 825-8574
SIC 1021 1041 1044 1031 1311

LIBERTY ENERGY UTILITIES (NEW HAMPSHIRE) CORP p 861
15 Buttrick Rd, Londonderry NH 03053
Tel (905) 287-2061 SIC 1311

JM HUBER CORP p 786
499 Thornall St Ste 8, Edison NJ 08837
Tel (732) 603-3630
SIC 0811 1311 1455 2493 2819

MACK ENERGY CORP p 892
11344 Lovington Hwy, Artesia NM 88210
Tel (575) 748-1288 SIC 1311 2911

YATES PETROLEUM CORP p 1635
105 S 4th St, Artesia NM 88210
Tel (575) 748-1471 SIC 1311

ROCKET TECH FUEL CORP p 1244
20 Corbin Ave, Bay Shore NY 11706
Tel (516) 810-8947 SIC 1311

NATIONAL GRID CORPORATE SERVICES LLC p 1013
175 E Old Country Rd, Hicksville NY 11801
Tel (718) 403-2000
SIC 4924 4911 1311 4922

CHINA NORTH EAST PETROLEUM HOLDINGS LIMITED p 301
445 Park Ave Ste 900, New York NY 10022
Tel (212) 307-3568 SIC 1311

▲HESS CORP p 688
1185 Ave Of The Americas, New York NY 10036
Tel (212) 997-8500
SIC 1311 2911 5171 5541 4911

LUKOIL AMERICAS CORP p 885
505 5th Ave Fl 9, New York NY 10017
Tel (212) 421-4141 SIC 1311

■ORANGE AND ROCKLAND UTILITIES INC p 1091
1 Blue Hill Plz Ste 20, Pearl River NY 10965
Tel (845) 352-6000
SIC 4924 4911 1311 6552

▲NATIONAL FUEL GAS CO p 1012
6363 Main St, Williamsville NY 14221
Tel (716) 857-7000
SIC 4924 4922 1311 1382

BASIN ELECTRIC POWER COOPERATIVE p 158
1717 E Interstate Ave, Bismarck ND 58503
Tel (701) 223-0441 SIC 4911 1311

DAKOTA GASIFICATION CO INC p 409
1717 E Interstate Ave, Bismarck ND 58503
Tel (701) 223-0441 SIC 2873 5169 1311

▲MDU RESOURCES GROUP INC p 933
1200 W Century Ave, Bismarck ND 58503
Tel (701) 530-1000
SIC 4911 4924 4922 1221 1442 1311

UNITED ENERGY CORP p 1508
919 S 7th St Ste 405, Bismarck ND 58504
Tel (701) 255-7970 SIC 1311

■WBI ENERGY TRANSMISSION INC p 1585
1250 W Century Ave, Bismarck ND 58503
Tel (701) 530-1601 SIC 4922 1311

■WBI HOLDINGS INC p 1585
1250 W Century Ave, Bismarck ND 58503
Tel (701) 530-1600 SIC 4922 1311

■COLUMBIA ENERGY GROUP p 340
200 Civic Center Dr, Columbus OH 43215
Tel (614) 460-4683 SIC 4922 1311 1731

INTERSTATE GAS SUPPLY INC p 758
6100 Emerald Pkwy, Dublin OH 43016
Tel (614) 659-5000 SIC 1311

AMERICAN ENERGY PARTNERS LP p 71
301 Nw 63rd St Ste 600, Oklahoma City OK 73116
Tel (405) 418-8000 SIC 1311

CHAPARRAL ENERGY INC p 288
701 Cedar Lake Blvd, Oklahoma City OK 73114
Tel (405) 478-8770 SIC 1311 1382

CHAPARRAL ENERGY LLC p 288
701 Cedar Lake Blvd, Oklahoma City OK 73114
Tel (405) 478-8770 SIC 1311 1382

▲CHESAPEAKE ENERGY CORP p 295
6100 N Western Ave, Oklahoma City OK 73118
Tel (405) 848-8000 SIC 1311

■CHESAPEAKE OPERATING LLC p 295
6100 N Western Ave, Oklahoma City OK 73118
Tel (405) 848-8000 SIC 1311 1389 4212

▲CONTINENTAL RESOURCES INC p 363
20 N Broadway, Oklahoma City OK 73102
Tel (405) 234-9000 SIC 1311

▲DEVON ENERGY CORP p 434
333 W Sheridan Ave, Oklahoma City OK 73102
Tel (405) 235-3611 SIC 1311 1382

■DEVON ENERGY PRODUCTION CO LP p 434
333 W Sheridan Ave, Oklahoma City OK 73102
Tel (405) 235-3611 SIC 1311 5172

■DEVON OEI OPERATING INC p 434
20 N Broadway, Oklahoma City OK 73102
Tel (405) 235-3611
SIC 4922 4924 1311 4613

▲GULFPORT ENERGY CORP p 647
14313 N May Ave Ste 100, Oklahoma City OK 73134
Tel (405) 848-8807 SIC 1311

MUSTANG FUEL CORP p 1002
9800 N Oklahoma Ave, Oklahoma City OK 73114
Tel (405) 884-2092 SIC 1311 4923

OKLAHOMA PUBLISHING CO OF OKLAHOMA p 1080
9000 N Brdwy, Oklahoma City OK 73114
Tel (405) 475-3311
SIC 2711 1311 6512 7375 2752

POSTROCK ENERGY CORP p 1164
210 Park Ave Ste 2750, Oklahoma City OK 73102
Tel (405) 600-7704 SIC 1311

▲SANDRIDGE ENERGY INC p 1278
123 Robert S Kerr Ave, Oklahoma City OK 73102
Tel (405) 429-5500 SIC 1311

THUNDERBIRD RESOURCES EQUITY INC p 1451
9400 Broadway Ext Ste 600, Oklahoma City OK 73114
Tel (405) 600-0711 SIC 1311

EVANS & ASSOCIATES ENTERPRISES INC p 513
3320 N 14th St, Ponca City OK 74601
Tel (580) 765-6693
SIC 5032 2951 1442 1611 3273 1311

GBK CORP p 594
6733 S Yale Ave, Tulsa OK 74136
Tel (918) 494-0000 SIC 1311

KAISER-FRANCIS OIL CO p 800
6733 S Yale Ave, Tulsa OK 74136
Tel (918) 494-0000 SIC 1382 1311

▲LAREDO PETROLEUM INC p 845
15 W 6th St Ste 1800, Tulsa OK 74119
Tel (918) 513-4570 SIC 1311

▲MID-CON ENERGY PARTNERS LP p 963
2431 E 61st St Ste 850, Tulsa OK 74136
Tel (972) 479-5980 SIC 1311

▲MIDSTATES PETROLEUM CO INC p 966
321 S Boston Ave Ste 1000, Tulsa OK 74103
Tel (918) 947-8550 SIC 1311

NADEL AND GUSSMAN LLC p 1006
15 E 5th St Ste 3300, Tulsa OK 74103
Tel (918) 583-3333 SIC 1311

■NEWFIELD EXPLORATION MID-CONTINENT INC p 1037
101 E 2nd St, Tulsa OK 74103
Tel (918) 582-2690 SIC 1311

▲ONE GAS INC p 1086
15 E 5th St, Tulsa OK 74103
Tel (918) 947-7000 SIC 1311 4924

▲ONEOK INC p 1087
100 W 5th St Ste Ll, Tulsa OK 74103
Tel (918) 588-7000
SIC 4922 4924 1311 1321 5172

■ONEOK ROCKIES MIDSTREAM LLC p 1087
100 W 5th St Ste Ll, Tulsa OK 74103
Tel (918) 588-7000 SIC 1311

ROSE ROCK MIDSTREAM LP p 1250
6120 S Yale Ave Ste 1500, Tulsa OK 74136
Tel (918) 524-7700 SIC 1311 4612

SAMSON INVESTMENT CO p 1274
2 W 2nd St Ste 1500, Tulsa OK 74103
Tel (918) 583-1791 SIC 1311 7353 5082

SAMSON RESOURCES CO p 1274
2 W 2nd St Ste 1500, Tulsa OK 74103
Tel (918) 583-1791 SIC 1311 2911

SAMSON RESOURCES CORP p 1274
2 W 2nd St Ste 1600, Tulsa OK 74103
Tel (918) 591-1791 SIC 1311

SANGUINE GAS EXPLORATION LLC p 1279
110 W 7th St Ste 2700, Tulsa OK 74119
Tel (918) 494-6070 SIC 1311

▲UNIT CORP p 1506
8200 S Unit Dr, Tulsa OK 74132
Tel (918) 493-7700 SIC 1381 1382 1311

■UNIT PETROLEUM CO p 1506
8200 S Unit Dr, Tulsa OK 74132
Tel (918) 493-7700 SIC 1311

▲WILLIAMS COMPANIES INC p 1611
1 Williams Ctr, Tulsa OK 74172
Tel (918) 573-2000
SIC 4922 4924 1311 1321

■WILLIAMS FIELD SERVICES CO LLC p 1611
1 Williams Ctr, Tulsa OK 74172
Tel (918) 573-2000 SIC 1311

▲WILLIAMS PARTNERS LP p 1611
1 Williams Ctr, Tulsa OK 74172
Tel (918) 573-2000 SIC 1311 4922

▲WPX ENERGY INC p 1627
3500 One Williams Ctr, Tulsa OK 74172
Tel (855) 979-2012 SIC 1311

■CNX GAS CORP p 330
1000 Consol Energy Dr, Canonsburg PA 15317
Tel (724) 485-4000 SIC 1311

▲CONSOL ENERGY INC p 359
1000 Consol Energy Dr, Canonsburg PA 15317
Tel (724) 485-4000 SIC 1221 1222 1311

■CONSOL PENNSYLVANIA COAL CO LLC p 359
1000 Consol Energy Dr, Canonsburg PA 15317
Tel (724) 485-4000 SIC 1311 1222

▲RICE ENERGY INC p 1232
2200 Rice Dr, Canonsburg PA 15317
Tel (724) 271-7200 SIC 1311

■EXCO RESOURCES (PA) LLC p 517
260 Executive Dr Ste 100, Cranberry Township PA 16066
Tel (724) 720-2500
SIC 1382 1381 1311 8741 6211

■TARGA PIPELINE OPERATING PARTNERSHIP LP p 1425
1845 Walnut St, Philadelphia PA 19103
Tel (412) 489-0006 SIC 1311

▲ATLAS ENERGY GROUP LLC p 128
1000 Commerce Dr Ste 400, Pittsburgh PA 15275
Tel (412) 489-0006 SIC 1311 4922

CHEVRON AE RESOURCES LLC p 295
1000 Commerce Dr Fl 4, Pittsburgh PA 15275
Tel (800) 251-0171 SIC 4922 1311 4924

▲EQT CORP p 506
625 Liberty Ave Ste 1700, Pittsburgh PA 15222
Tel (412) 553-5700
SIC 1311 4923 4924 4925

■TARGA ENERGY LP p 1424
1000 Commerce Dr Ste 400, Pittsburgh PA 15275
Tel (412) 489-0006 SIC 1311 4922

▲PENN VIRGINIA CORP p 1129
100 Matsonford Rd Ste 200, Radnor PA 19087
Tel (610) 687-8900 SIC 1311

PVR PARTNERS LP p 1193
3 Radnor Corp Ctr Ste 301, Radnor PA 19087
Tel (610) 975-8200 SIC 1221 1311

■ECLIPSE RESOURCES CORP p 475
2121 Old Gatesburg Rd # 110, State College PA 16803
Tel (814) 308-9754 SIC 1311

▲ECLIPSE RESOURCES HOLDINGS LP p 475
2121 Old Gatesburg Rd # 110, State College PA 16803
Tel (814) 308-9754 SIC 1311

■ECLIPSE RESOURCES I LP p 475
2121 Old Gteburg Rd Ste 1, State College PA 16803
Tel (814) 308-9754 SIC 1311 1382

▲REX ENERGY CORP p 1230
366 Walker Dr, State College PA 16801
Tel (814) 278-7267 SIC 1311

PENNSYLVANIA GENERAL ENERGY CORP p 1130
120 Market St, Warren PA 16365
Tel (814) 723-3230 SIC 1311

J-W ENERGY CO p 772
15505 Wright Brothers Dr, Addison TX 75001
Tel (972) 233-8191
SIC 1311 7353 3533 1381

▲TRANSATLANTIC PETROLEUM LTD p 1470
16803 Dallas Pkwy, Addison TX 75001
Tel (214) 220-4323 SIC 1311

■JONES ENERGY HOLDINGS LLC p 792
807 Las Cimas Pkwy # 350, Austin TX 78746
Tel (512) 328-2953 SIC 1311 1382

▲JONES ENERGY INC p 792
807 Las Cimas Pkwy # 350, Austin TX 78746
Tel (512) 328-2953 SIC 1311

▲PARSLEY ENERGY INC p 1117
303 Colorado St Ste 3000, Austin TX 78701
Tel (737) 704-2300 SIC 1311

STATOIL EXPLORATION CO p 1383
6300 Bridge Point Pkwy, Austin TX 78730
Tel (512) 427-3300 SIC 1311

TEXAS AMERICAN RESOURCES CO p 1442
401 Congress Ave Ste 1600, Austin TX 78701
Tel (512) 480-8700 SIC 1311 1382

■EXXONMOBIL OIL CORP p 521
2805 Sycamore St, Beaumont TX 77701
Tel (409) 757-3763
SIC 2911 5171 4613 1311

COVEY PARK II LLC p 385
8401 N Central Expy # 700, Dallas TX 75225
Tel (214) 548-6000 SIC 1311

DALLAS PRODUCTION INC p 410
4600 Greenville Ave # 300, Dallas TX 75206
Tel (214) 369-9266 SIC 1311

■ENLINK MIDSTREAM INC p 500
2501 Cedar Springs Rd, Dallas TX 75201
Tel (214) 953-9500 SIC 1311 5712

■ENLINK MIDSTREAM LLC p 500
2501 Cedar Springs Rd, Dallas TX 75201
Tel (214) 953-9500 SIC 1311

▲EXCO RESOURCES INC p 517
12377 Merit Dr Ste 1700, Dallas TX 75251
Tel (214) 368-2084 SIC 1311

HUNT CONSOLIDATED INC p 718
1900 N Akard St, Dallas TX 75201
Tel (214) 978-8000
SIC 6799 1311 2911 1382 0212

HUNT DOMINION CORP p 719
1601 Elm St Ste 3900, Dallas TX 75201
Tel (214) 880-8400 SIC 1311 1382 1241

HUNT OIL USA INC p 719
1900 N Akard St, Dallas TX 75201
Tel (214) 978-8000 SIC 1311 1382 2911

▲MATADOR RESOURCES CO p 918
5400 Lbj Fwy Ste 1500, Dallas TX 75240
Tel (972) 371-5200 SIC 1311

MERIT ENERGY CO LLC p 949
13737 Noel Rd Ste 1200, Dallas TX 75240
Tel (972) 701-8377 SIC 1311

PETRO-HUNT LLC p 1139
2101 Cedar Springs Rd, Dallas TX 75201
Tel (214) 880-8400 SIC 1311

RRH CORP p 1255
1900 N Akard St, Dallas TX 75201
Tel (214) 978-8000
SIC 1382 1311 2911 0212 6799

▲RSP PERMIAN INC p 1256
3141 Hood St Ste 500, Dallas TX 75219
Tel (214) 252-2700 SIC 1311

THOMPSON PETROLEUM CORP p 1449
325 N Saint Paul St # 4300, Dallas TX 75201
Tel (214) 953-1177 SIC 1311

▲APPROACH RESOURCES INC p 100
6500 West Fwy Ste 800, Fort Worth TX 76116
Tel (817) 989-9000 SIC 1311

ATHLON ENERGY INC p 124
420 Throckmorton St # 1200, Fort Worth TX 76102
Tel (817) 984-8200 SIC 1311

BASS ENTERPRISES PRODUCTION CO p 159
201 Main St Ste 2700, Fort Worth TX 76102
Tel (817) 698-0200 SIC 1311 1382

■CROSS TIMBERS OPERATING CO p 394
810 Houston St Ste 2000, Fort Worth TX 76102
Tel (817) 870-2800 SIC 1311

▲QUICKSILVER RESOURCES INC p 1199
801 Cherry St Unit 19, Fort Worth TX 76102
Tel (817) 665-5000 SIC 1311 1321

▲RANGE RESOURCES CORP p 1208
100 Throckmorton St # 1200, Fort Worth TX 76102
Tel (817) 870-2601 SIC 1311

SNYDER OIL CORP p 1336
777 Main St Ste 1400, Fort Worth TX 76102
Tel (817) 338-4043 SIC 1311 4922

TEXLAND PETROLEUM LP p 1445
777 Main St Ste 3200, Fort Worth TX 76102
Tel (817) 336-2751 SIC 1311 1382

■XTO ENERGY INC p 1633
810 Houston St Ste 2000, Fort Worth TX 76102
Tel (817) 870-2800 SIC 1311

▲COMSTOCK RESOURCES INC p 353
5300 Town And Country Blv, Frisco TX 75034
Tel (972) 668-8800 SIC 1311

■TEXAS GAS SERVICE CO p 1443
5602 E Grimes St, Harlingen TX 78550
Tel (956) 444-3900 SIC 1311

▲ADAMS RESOURCES & ENERGY INC p 21
17 S Briar Hollow Ln, Houston TX 77027
Tel (713) 881-3600
SIC 5172 4212 1382 1311

ALTA MESA HOLDINGS LP p 61
15021 Katy Fwy Ste 400, Houston TX 77094
Tel (281) 530-0991 SIC 1311

■AMERICAN NATURAL RESOURCES CO p 77
717 Texas St Ste 2400, Houston TX 77002
Tel (832) 320-5000 SIC 4922 1311 1222

■ **ANADARKO HOLDING CO** p 88
17001 Northchase Dr, Houston TX 77060
Tel (832) 636-7200
SIC 1311 1321 5172 4922

ANGLO-SUISSE OFFSHORE PARTNERS LLC p 91
919 Milam St Ste 2300, Houston TX 77002
Tel (713) 358-9763 *SIC* 1311

▲ **APACHE CORP** p 95
2000 Post Oak Blvd # 100, Houston TX 77056
Tel (713) 296-6000 *SIC* 1311

■ **BAKER HUGHES OILFIELD OPERATIONS INC** p 146
17021 Aldine Westfield Rd, Houston TX 77073
Tel (713) 439-8600
SIC 1381 1311 1389 2899

■ **BERRY PETROLEUM CO LLC** p 176
600 Travis St Ste 5100, Houston TX 77002
Tel (281) 840-4000 *SIC* 1311

BG BRASILIA LLC p 179
910 Louisiana St, Houston TX 77002
Tel (713) 599-4000 *SIC* 1311

BG NORTH AMERICA LLC p 180
811 Main St Ste 3400, Houston TX 77002
Tel (713) 428-2786 *SIC* 1311

BHP BILLITON PETROLEUM (ARKANSAS) INC p 180
1360 Post Blvd Ste 150, Houston TX 77056
Tel (713) 961-8500 *SIC* 4922 1311

BHP BILLITON PETROLEUM (NORTH AMERICA) INC p 180
1360 Post Oak Blvd # 150, Houston TX 77056
Tel (713) 961-8500 *SIC* 1311 4922

BLACK STONE MINERALS LP p 187
1001 Fannin St Ste 2020, Houston TX 77002
Tel (713) 658-0647 *SIC* 1311

■ **BLUE DOLPHIN ENERGY CO** p 192
801 Travis St Ste 2100, Houston TX 77002
Tel (713) 568-4725
SIC 1311 1382 4612 4922

BP AMERICA PRODUCTION CO p 205
501 Westlake Park Blvd, Houston TX 77079
Tel (281) 366-2000 *SIC* 1311 1321

BP CORP NORTH AMERICA INC p 205
501 Westlake Park Blvd, Houston TX 77079
Tel (281) 366-2000
SIC 2911 5541 5171 1311 4613 4612

BPZ RESOURCES INC p 206
10497 Town And Country Wa, Houston TX 77024
Tel (281) 556-6200 *SIC* 1311

■ **BURLINGTON RESOURCES INC** p 228
600 N Dairy Ashford Rd, Houston TX 77079
Tel (281) 293-1000
SIC 1311 5172 4922 4612

▲ **CABOT OIL & GAS CORP** p 235
840 Gessner Rd Ste 1400, Houston TX 77024
Tel (281) 589-4600 *SIC* 1311

▲ **CARRIZO OIL & GAS INC** p 261
500 Dallas St Ste 2300, Houston TX 77002
Tel (713) 328-1000 *SIC* 1311

■ **CENTURION PIPELINE LP** p 281
5 Greenway Plz Ste 110, Houston TX 77046
Tel (713) 215-7000 *SIC* 1311

CIMA ENERGY LTD p 307
100 Waugh Dr Ste 500, Houston TX 77007
Tel (713) 209-1112 *SIC* 1311

CITATION OIL & GAS CORP p 309
14077 Cutten Rd, Houston TX 77069
Tel (281) 891-1000 *SIC* 1311 1382

▲ **CONOCOPHILLIPS** p 358
600 N Dairy Ashford Rd, Houston TX 77079
Tel (281) 293-1000 *SIC* 1311 1382

▲ **CONTANGO OIL & GAS CO** p 362
717 Texas St Ste 2900, Houston TX 77002
Tel (713) 236-7400 *SIC* 1311

■ **EAGLE ROCK ENERGY PARTNERS LP** p 468
5847 San Felipe St # 3000, Houston TX 77057
Tel (281) 408-1200 *SIC* 1311 1321

■ **EL PASO CGP CO LLC** p 483
1001 Louisiana St, Houston TX 77002
Tel (713) 420-2600
SIC 2911 1311 4613 4612 5541 4922

■ **EL PASO LLC** p 483
1001 Louisiana St, Houston TX 77002
Tel (713) 420-2600 *SIC* 4922 1311

ENDEAVOUR INTERNATIONAL CORP p 496
811 Main St Ste 2100, Houston TX 77002
Tel (713) 307-8700 *SIC* 1311

ENERGY RESOURCE TECHNOLOGY GOM LLC p 498
500 Dallas St Ste 2000, Houston TX 77002
Tel (281) 618-0590 *SIC* 1311 1389

ENERGY XXI GULF COAST INC p 498
1021 Main St Ste 2626, Houston TX 77002
Tel (713) 351-3000 *SIC* 4424 1311

ENERGY XXI USA INC p 498
1021 Main St Ste 2626, Houston TX 77002
Tel (713) 351-3000 *SIC* 1311

ENERVEST LTD p 498
1001 Fannin St Ste 800, Houston TX 77002
Tel (713) 659-3500 *SIC* 1311 1382

ENERVEST OPERATING LLC p 498
1001 Fannin St Ste 800, Houston TX 77002
Tel (713) 659-3500 *SIC* 1311

ENI PETROLEUM CO INC p 499
1201 La St Ste 3500, Houston TX 77002
Tel (713) 393-6100 *SIC* 1311

ENRON CREDITORS RECOVERY CORP p 500
1221 Lamar St Ste 1325, Houston TX 77010
Tel (713) 853-6161
SIC 5172 4922 4911 1311 1321 2911

▲ **EOG RESOURCES INC** p 504
1111 Bagby St Lbby 2, Houston TX 77002
Tel (713) 651-7000 *SIC* 1311

▲ **EP ENERGY CORP** p 504
1001 Louisiana St, Houston TX 77002
Tel (713) 997-1200 *SIC* 1311

■ **EP ENERGY LLC** p 504
1001 Louisiana St, Houston TX 77002
Tel (713) 997-1200 *SIC* 1311 1382

EPL OIL & GAS INC p 505
1021 Main St Ste 2626, Houston TX 77002
Tel (713) 351-3000 *SIC* 1311

■ **ETC INTRASTATE PROCUREMENT CO LLC** p 511
1300 Main St, Houston TX 77002
Tel (713) 989-2688 *SIC* 1311

▲ **EV ENERGY PARTNERS LP** p 513
1001 Fannin St Ste 800, Houston TX 77002
Tel (713) 651-1144 *SIC* 1311

▲ **GASTAR EXPLORATION INC** p 593
1331 Lamar St Ste 650, Houston TX 77010
Tel (713) 739-1800 *SIC* 1311

GDF SUEZ ENERGY NORTH AMERICA INC p 595
1990 Post Oak Blvd # 1900, Houston TX 77056
Tel (713) 636-0000 *SIC* 1311 8741 1629

GLOBAL MARINE INC p 617
4 Greenway Plz Ste 100, Houston TX 77046
Tel (713) 232-7500 *SIC* 1381 1311

▲ **HALCON RESOURCES CORP** p 653
1000 La St Ste 6700, Houston TX 77002
Tel (832) 538-0300 *SIC* 1311

▲ **HELIX ENERGY SOLUTIONS GROUP INC** p 681
3505 W Sam Houston Pkwy N, Houston TX 77043
Tel (281) 618-0400 *SIC* 1629 1389 1311

HILCORP ENERGY CO p 692
1111 Travis St, Houston TX 77002
Tel (713) 209-2400 *SIC* 1311 1382

KEY ENERGY SERVICES INC p 814
1301 Mckinney St Ste 1800, Houston TX 77010
Tel (713) 651-4300 *SIC* 1389 1381 1311

■ **LINN ACQUISITION CO LLC** p 869
600 Travis St Ste 4900, Houston TX 77002
Tel (281) 840-4000 *SIC* 1311

▲ **LINN ENERGY LLC** p 869
600 Travis St Ste 5100, Houston TX 77002
Tel (281) 840-4000 *SIC* 1311

▲ **LINNCO LLC** p 869
600 Travis St Ste 5100, Houston TX 77002
Tel (281) 840-4000 *SIC* 1311

■ **LRR ENERGY LP** p 882
1111 Bagby St Ste 4600, Houston TX 77002
Tel (713) 292-9510 *SIC* 1311

M3 MIDSTREAM LLC p 891
600 Travis St Ste 5600, Houston TX 77002
Tel (713) 783-3000 *SIC* 1311

■ **MARATHON INTERNATIONAL OIL CO** p 904
5555 San Felipe St # 2796, Houston TX 77056
Tel (713) 629-6600 *SIC* 1311 1382 6519

■ **MARATHON OIL CO** p 904
5555 San Felipe St # 2796, Houston TX 77056
Tel (713) 629-6600
SIC 2911 5171 5541 1311 4612 4613

▲ **MARATHON OIL CORP** p 904
5555 San Felipe St # 2796, Houston TX 77056
Tel (713) 629-6600
SIC 1311 2911 5171 5541

MCCOMBS ENERGY LTD p 927
5599 Saint Felipe St 12 # 1200, Houston TX 77056
Tel (713) 621-0033 *SIC* 1311

▲ **MEMORIAL PRODUCTION PARTNERS LP** p 942
500 Dallas St Ste 1800, Houston TX 77002
Tel (713) 588-8300 *SIC* 1311

■ **MIDCOAST ENERGY PARTNERS LP** p 964
1100 La St Ste 3300, Houston TX 77002
Tel (713) 821-2000 *SIC* 1311 4923

■ **MOBIL PRODUCING TEXAS AND NEW MEXICO INC** p 980
9 Greenway Plz Ste 2700, Houston TX 77046
Tel (713) 871-5000 *SIC* 1311

■ **MURPHY EXPLORATION & PRODUCTION CO - USA** p 1001
9805 Katy Fwy Ste G200, Houston TX 77024
Tel (281) 599-8145 *SIC* 1382 1311

■ **NATURAL GAS PIPELINE CO OF AMERICA LLC** p 1018
1001 Louisiana St, Houston TX 77002
Tel (713) 369-9000 *SIC* 4922 1311 8741

■ **NBL TEXAS LLC** p 1021
1001 Noble Energy Way, Houston TX 77070
Tel (281) 872-3100 *SIC* 1311

■ **NEWFIELD EXPLORATION GULF COAST INC** p 1037
363 N Sam Houston Pkwy E # 2020, Houston TX 77060
Tel (713) 243-3100 *SIC* 1311

▲ **NOBLE ENERGY INC** p 1046
1001 Noble Energy Way, Houston TX 77070
Tel (281) 872-3100 *SIC* 1311

▲ **OASIS PETROLEUM INC** p 1072
1001 Fannin St Ste 1500, Houston TX 77002
Tel (281) 404-9500 *SIC* 1311

■ **OCCIDENTAL OIL AND GAS CORP** p 1072
5 Greenway Plz Ste 110, Houston TX 77046
Tel (713) 215-7000 *SIC* 1311

■ **OCCIDENTAL PERMIAN LTD** p 1072
5 Greenway Plz Ste 110, Houston TX 77046
Tel (713) 215-7000 *SIC* 1382 1311

▲ **OCCIDENTAL PETROLEUM CORP** p 1072
5 Greenway Plz Ste 110, Houston TX 77046
Tel (713) 215-7000 *SIC* 1382 1311

■ **OXY INC** p 1101
5 Greenway Plz Ste 2400, Houston TX 77046
Tel (713) 215-7000 *SIC* 1311 1382

▲ **PAR PACIFIC HOLDINGS INC** p 1113
800 Gessner Rd Ste 875, Houston TX 77024
Tel (713) 969-3293 *SIC* 1311 2911 4923

▲ **PATTERSON-UTI ENERGY INC** p 1121
10713 W Sam Huston Pkwy N, Houston TX 77064
Tel (281) 765-7100 *SIC* 1381 1389 1311

PETROHAWK ENERGY CORP p 1139
1360 Post Oak Blvd # 150, Houston TX 77056
Tel (713) 961-8500 *SIC* 1311

PETROSANTANDER (COLOMBIA) INC p 1139
6363 Woodway Dr Ste 350, Houston TX 77057
Tel (713) 784-8700 *SIC* 1311 1382

PETROSANTANDER INC p 1139
6363 Woodway Dr Ste 350, Houston TX 77057
Tel (713) 784-8700 *SIC* 1311

▲ **PHILLIPS 66** p 1144
2331 City West Blvd, Houston TX 77042
Tel (832) 765-3300 *SIC* 1311 2911 2869

■ **PHILLIPS 66 PARTNERS LP** p 1144
3010 Briarpark Dr, Houston TX 77042
Tel (855) 283-9237 *SIC* 4612 1311 5541

PIONEER EXPLORATION CO p 1150
15603 Kuykendahl Rd, Houston TX 77090
Tel (281) 893-9400 *SIC* 1311 1321

PRIME NATURAL RESOURCES LLC p 1175
2500 Citywest Blvd # 1750, Houston TX 77042
Tel (713) 953-3200 *SIC* 1311

■ **RANGE RESOURCES - LOUISIANA INC** p 1208
500 Dallas St Ste 1800, Houston TX 77002
Tel (713) 588-8300 *SIC* 1311

RENAISSANCE OFFSHORE LLC p 1223
920 Mmrial Cy Way Ste 800, Houston TX 77024
Tel (832) 333-7700 *SIC* 1389 1311

ROSETTA RESOURCES INC p 1251
1111 Bagby St Ste 1600, Houston TX 77002
Tel (713) 335-4000 *SIC* 1311 1381

▲ **SABINE OIL & GAS CORP** p 1264
1415 Louisiana St # 1600, Houston TX 77002
Tel (832) 242-9600 *SIC* 1311

SAMEDAN OIL CORP p 1274
1001 Noble Energy Way, Houston TX 77070
Tel (580) 223-4110 *SIC* 1311

▲ **SANCHEZ ENERGY CORP** p 1277
1000 Main St Ste 3000, Houston TX 77002
Tel (713) 783-8000 *SIC* 1311

SANCHEZ OIL & GAS CORP p 1277
1000 Main St Ste 3000, Houston TX 77002
Tel (956) 722-8092 *SIC* 1311

SHELL ENERGY NORTH AMERICA (US) LP p 1314
1000 Main St, Houston TX 77002
Tel (713) 230-3822 *SIC* 1311

SHELL GLOBAL SOLUTIONS (US) INC p 1314
3333 Highway 6 S, Houston TX 77082
Tel (281) 544-7709 *SIC* 1311

SHELL OIL CO p 1314
910 Louisiana St Ste 1500, Houston TX 77002
Tel (713) 241-6161
SIC 5541 4612 1311 2821 2869 2911

■ **SOUTHWESTERN ENERGY PRODUCTION CO INC** p 1353
2350 N Sam Houston Pkwy E, Houston TX 77032
Tel (281) 618-4700 *SIC* 1382 1311

SWEPI LP p 1412
200 N Dairy Ashford Rd, Houston TX 77079
Tel (713) 241-6161 *SIC* 1311 1382 5169

▲ **SWIFT ENERGY CO** p 1412
17001 Northchase Dr # 100, Houston TX 77060
Tel (281) 874-2700 *SIC* 1311

SWIFT ENERGY OPERATING LLC p 1412
17001 Northchase Dr # 100, Houston TX 77060
Tel (281) 874-2700 *SIC* 1311

■ **SWN DRILLING CO** p 1413
2350 N Sam Hous, Houston TX 77032
Tel (281) 618-4700 *SIC* 1311

TAUBER OIL CO p 1426
55 Waugh Dr Ste 700, Houston TX 77007
Tel (713) 869-8700 *SIC* 1311

TORCH ENERGY ADVISORS INC p 1461
1331 Lamar St Ste 1450, Houston TX 77010
Tel (713) 650-1246
SIC 1311 1382 8741 8742

■ **TOTAL DELAWARE INC** p 1462
1201 La St Ste 1800, Houston TX 77002
Tel (713) 483-5000 *SIC* 1311 1382

■ **TOTAL HOLDINGS USA INC** p 1463
1201 La St Ste 1800, Houston TX 77002
Tel (713) 483-5000 *SIC* 1382 1311

TRANSWORLD WORLDWIDE INC p 1473
4 Greenway Plz Ste 700, Houston TX 77046
Tel (713) 232-7500 *SIC* 1381 1311

ULTRA PETROLEUM CORP p 1501
400 N Sam Houston Pkwy E # 1200, Houston TX 77060
Tel (281) 876-0120 *SIC* 1311

▲ **VANGUARD NATURAL RESOURCES LLC** p 1543
5847 San Felipe St # 1910, Houston TX 77057
Tel (832) 327-2255 *SIC* 1311 1382

▲ **W&T OFFSHORE INC** p 1569
9 Greenway Plz Ste 300, Houston TX 77046
Tel (713) 626-8525 *SIC* 1311

WEDGE GROUP INC p 1587
1415 La St Ste 3000, Houston TX 77002
Tel (713) 739-6500 *SIC* 1389 1629 1311

MAGNUM HUNTER RESOURCES CORP p 896
909 Lake Carolyn Pkwy # 600, Irving TX 75039
Tel (832) 369-6986 *SIC* 1311

■ **MOBIL CORP** p 980
5959 Las Colinas Blvd, Irving TX 75039
Tel (972) 444-1000
SIC 2911 5171 4612 4613 1311

▲ **PIONEER NATURAL RESOURCES CO** p 1151
5205 N Oconnor Connor, Irving TX 75039
Tel (972) 444-9001 *SIC* 1311 1321

■ **PIONEER NATURAL RESOURCES USA INC** p 1151
5205 N Oconnor Blvd Ste, Irving TX 75039
Tel (972) 444-9001 *SIC* 1311 1321

PIONEER SOUTHWEST ENERGY PARTNERS LP p 1151
5205 N Oconner Blvd 200 Connor, Irving TX 75039
Tel (972) 444-9001 *SIC* 1311

▲ **CLAYTON WILLIAMS ENERGY INC** p 323
6 Desta Dr Ste 6500, Midland TX 79705
Tel (432) 682-6324 *SIC* 1311

▲ **CONCHO RESOURCES INC** p 354
600 W Illinois Ave, Midland TX 79701
Tel (432) 683-7443 *SIC* 1311

▲ **DIAMONDBACK ENERGY INC** p 437
500 W Texas Ave Ste 1200, Midland TX 79701
Tel (432) 221-7400 *SIC* 1311

ENDEAVOR ENERGY RESOURCES LP p 496
110 N Marienfeld St # 200, Midland TX 79701
Tel (432) 687-1575 *SIC* 1311 8748

J L DAVIS CO p 771
211 N Colorado St, Midland TX 79701
Tel (432) 682-6311 *SIC* 5172 4923 1311

▲ **LEGACY RESERVES LP** p 852
303 W Wall St Ste 1800, Midland TX 79701
Tel (432) 689-5200 *SIC* 1311

■ **PARSLEY ENERGY LLC** p 1117
500 W Texas Ave Ste 200, Midland TX 79701
Tel (432) 818-2100 *SIC* 1311

■ **SOUTHWEST ROYALTIES INC** p 1352
6 Desta Dr Ste 2100, Midland TX 79705
Tel (432) 688-3008 *SIC* 1311 6211 1389

■ **OXY USA INC** p 1101
1001 S County Rd W, Odessa TX 79763
Tel (432) 335-0995 *SIC* 1311

■ **DENBURY ONSHORE LLC** p 428
5320 Legacy Dr, Plano TX 75024
Tel (972) 673-2000 *SIC* 1311 1382

▲ **DENBURY RESOURCES INC** p 428
5320 Legacy Dr, Plano TX 75024
Tel (972) 673-2000 *SIC* 1311

AXEON MARKETING LLC p 140
2338 N Loop 1604 W, San Antonio TX 78248
Tel (210) 918-2000 *SIC* 1311

BLACKBRUSH OIL & GAS LP p 187
18615 Tuscany Stone, San Antonio TX 78258
Tel (210) 495-5577 *SIC* 1311

LEWIS ENERGY GROUP LP p 858
10101 Reunion Pl Ste 1000, San Antonio TX 78216
Tel (210) 384-3200 *SIC* 1311

■ **NUSTAR LOGISTICS LP** p 1067
19003 W Interstate 10, San Antonio TX 78257
Tel (210) 918-2000 *SIC* 1311

▲ **TESORO CORP** p 1440
19100 Ridgewood Pkwy, San Antonio TX 78259
Tel (210) 626-6000
SIC 2911 1311 5983 5984

▲ **TESORO LOGISTICS LP** p 1440
19100 Ridgewood Pkwy, San Antonio TX 78259
Tel (210) 626-6000 *SIC* 1311 4612

▲ **EMERGE ENERGY SERVICES LP** p 491
180 State St Ste 225, Southlake TX 76092
Tel (817) 865-5830 *SIC* 1311 1389 4613

ATP OIL & GAS CORP p 128
26219 Oak Ridge Dr, Spring TX 77380
Tel (713) 622-3311 *SIC* 1311 1382

■ **KERR-MCGEE CORP** p 813
1201 Lake Robbins Dr, Spring TX 77380
Tel (832) 636-1000
SIC 2816 2819 1311 1221 1222

▲ **SOUTHWESTERN ENERGY CO INC** p 1353
10000 Energy Dr, Spring TX 77389
Tel (832) 796-1000 *SIC* 1311 1382

TALISMAN ENERGY USA INC p 1422
2445 Tech Forest Blvd # 1200, Spring TX 77381
Tel (281) 210-2100 *SIC* 1311

▲ **ANADARKO PETROLEUM CORP** p 88
1201 Lake Robbins Dr, The Woodlands TX 77380
Tel (832) 636-1000
SIC 1311 4924 5171 1382

ARENA ENERGY LP p 106
4200 Res Frest Dr Ste 500, The Woodlands TX 77381
Tel (281) 681-9500 *SIC* 1311

▲ **NEWFIELD EXPLORATION CO** p 1037
4 Waterway Square Pl # 100, The Woodlands TX 77380
Tel (281) 210-5100 *SIC* 1311

■ **WESTERN GAS EQUITY PARTNERS LP** p 1598
1201 Lake Robbins Dr, The Woodlands TX 77380
Tel (832) 636-6000 *SIC* 1311

MEWBOURNE HOLDINGS INC p 957
3901 S Broadway Ave, Tyler TX 75701
Tel (903) 561-2900 *SIC* 1311

MEWBOURNE OIL CO p 957
3620 Old Bullard Rd, Tyler TX 75701
Tel (903) 561-2900 *SIC* 1311

■ **QUESTAR CORP** p 1199
333 S State St, Salt Lake City UT 84111
Tel (801) 324-5900 *SIC* 4922 1311 5172

CARPENTER CO p 260
5016 Monument Ave, Richmond VA 23230
Tel (804) 359-0800
SIC 3086 1311 2869 2297 2392 2821

■ **CONSOLIDATED NATURAL GAS CO** p 360
120 Tredegar St, Richmond VA 23219
Tel (804) 819-2000 *SIC* 1311 4922 4924

■ **DOMINION COVE POINT INC** p 449
120 Tredegar St, Richmond VA 23219
Tel (804) 819-2000 *SIC* 4911 4923 1311

■ **DOMINION MLP HOLDING CO LLC** p 449
120 Tredegar St, Richmond VA 23219
Tel (804) 819-2000 *SIC* 4911 4923 1311

▲ **DOMINION RESOURCES INC** p 449
120 Tredegar St, Richmond VA 23219
Tel (804) 819-2000 *SIC* 4911 4923 1311

PLUM CREEK TIMBER CO INC p 1156
601 Union St Ste 3100, Seattle WA 98101
Tel (206) 467-3600 *SIC* 6798 1311

EASTERN AMERICAN ENERGY CORP p 471
500 Corporate Lndg, Charleston WV 25311
Tel (304) 925-6100
SIC 1311 4922 5172 1321

TRUE OIL LLC p 1486
455 N Poplar St, Casper WY 82601
Tel (307) 237-9301 *SIC* 1311

SIC 1321 Natural Gas Liquids

▲ ENERGEN CORP p 497
605 Richard Arrington Jr, Birmingham AL 35203
Tel (205) 326-2700
SIC 1311 4924 4922 1321

■ ENERGEN RESOURCES CORP p 497
605 Richard Arrington Jr, Birmingham AL 35203
Tel (205) 326-2710 *SIC* 1382 1321

ATLANTIC RICHFIELD CO INC p 127
4 Centerpointe Dr Ste 200, La Palma CA 90623
Tel (800) 333-3991 *SIC* 5541 1321 2911

▲ CHEVRON CORP p 295
6001 Bollinger Canyon Rd, San Ramon CA 94583
Tel (925) 842-1000
SIC 2911 1311 1382 1321 5541

■ TEXACO INC p 1441
6001 Bollinger Canyon Rd, San Ramon CA 94583
Tel (925) 842-1000
SIC 5541 5511 1321 4612 4613 4412

■ MARKWEST ENERGY PARTNERS LP p 909
1515 Arapahoe St, Denver CO 80202
Tel (303) 925-9200 *SIC* 1321 4922 1389

■ MARKWEST HYDROCARBON LLC p 909
1515 Arapahoe St, Denver CO 80202
Tel (303) 290-8700 *SIC* 1321 4924

▲ QEP RESOURCES INC p 1195
1050 17th St Ste 800, Denver CO 80265
Tel (303) 672-6900 *SIC* 1311 1321 1382

AUX SABLE LIQUID PRODUCTS LP p 135
6155 E Us Route 6, Morris IL 60450
Tel (815) 941-5800 *SIC* 1321

CRISTAL p 392
20 Wight Ave Ste 100, Hunt Valley MD 21030
Tel (410) 229-4440
SIC 1241 3531 2816 2869 1321 3631

PROJECT VIKING LLC p 1182
501 Highway 212 W, Granite Falls MN 56241
Tel (320) 564-3324 *SIC* 1321

HERON LAKE BIOENERGY LLC p 687
91246 390th Ave, Heron Lake MN 56137
Tel (507) 793-0077 *SIC* 1321 2869

PARACO GAS CORP p 1113
800 Westchester Ave S604, Rye Brook NY 10573
Tel (800) 647-4427 *SIC* 1321

■ PANENERGY CORP p 1111
526 S Church St, Charlotte NC 28202
Tel (704) 594-6200
SIC 4922 1321 2813 5172 4911 4613

■ ENABLE OKLAHOMA INTRASTATE TRANSMISSION LLC p 495
211 N Robinson Ave N950, Oklahoma City OK 73102
Tel (405) 525-7788
SIC 4922 1321 4923 2911

■ ONEOK FIELD SERVICES CO LLC p 1087
100 W 5th St Ste Ll, Tulsa OK 74103
Tel (918) 588-7000 *SIC* 1321

▲ ONEOK INC p 1087
100 W 5th St Ste Ll, Tulsa OK 74103
Tel (918) 588-7000
SIC 4922 4924 1311 1321 5172

▲ ONEOK PARTNERS LP p 1087
100 W 5th St Ste Ll, Tulsa OK 74103
Tel (918) 588-7000
SIC 4922 1321 1381 4925

▲ WILLIAMS COMPANIES INC p 1611
1 Williams Ctr, Tulsa OK 74172
Tel (918) 573-2000
SIC 4922 4924 1311 1321

WILLIAMS PARTNERS LP p 1611
1 Williams Ctr Bsmt 2, Tulsa OK 74172
Tel (918) 573-2000 *SIC* 4922 1321 4925

UGI EUROPE INC p 1499
460 N Gulph Rd, King Of Prussia PA 19406
Tel (610) 337-1000 *SIC* 1321

▲ ENLINK MIDSTREAM PARTNERS LP p 500
2501 Cedar Springs Rd, Dallas TX 75201
Tel (214) 953-9500 *SIC* 4922 1321

■ REGENCY ENERGY PARTNERS LP p 1218
8111 Westchester Dr # 600, Dallas TX 75225
Tel (214) 750-1771
SIC 1321 4925 5172 4922

▲ QUICKSILVER RESOURCES INC p 1199
801 Cherry St Unit 19, Fort Worth TX 76102
Tel (817) 665-5000 *SIC* 1311 1321

■ ANADARKO HOLDING CO p 88
17001 Northchase Dr, Houston TX 77060
Tel (832) 636-7200
SIC 1311 1321 5172 4922

BP AMERICA PRODUCTION CO p 205
501 Westlake Park Blvd, Houston TX 77079
Tel (281) 366-2000 *SIC* 1311 1321

▲ CHENIERE ENERGY INC p 294
700 Milam St Ste 1900, Houston TX 77002
Tel (713) 375-5000 *SIC* 1321 4925 4922

■ EAGLE ROCK ENERGY PARTNERS LP p 468
5847 San Felipe St # 3000, Houston TX 77057
Tel (281) 408-1200 *SIC* 1311 1321

ENRON CREDITORS RECOVERY CORP p 500
1221 Lamar St Ste 1325, Houston TX 77010
Tel (713) 853-6161
SIC 5172 4922 4911 1311 1321 2911

ENTERPRISE PRODUCTS CO p 502
1100 Louisiana St, Houston TX 77002
Tel (713) 880-6500 *SIC* 1321 4925

EP ENERGY MANAGEMENT LLC p 504
1001 Louisiana St, Houston TX 77002
Tel (713) 997-1000 *SIC* 4922 1321

■ LONE STAR NGL PIPELINE LP p 876
1300 Main St 10, Houston TX 77002
Tel (210) 403-7300 *SIC* 4924 1321

PIONEER EXPLORATION CO p 1150
15603 Kuykendahl Rd, Houston TX 77090
Tel (281) 893-9400 *SIC* 1311 1321

▲ PLAINS GP HOLDINGS LP p 1153
333 Clay St Ste 1600, Houston TX 77002
Tel (713) 646-4100 *SIC* 4612 1321

■ TEXACO EXPLORATION AND PRODUCTION INC p 1441
1500 Louisiana St, Houston TX 77002
Tel (800) 962-1223 *SIC* 5541 5511 1321

■ TRI RESOURCES INC p 1476
1000 Louisiana St # 4300, Houston TX 77002
Tel (713) 584-1000 *SIC* 1321 1381 1382

■ WILLIAMS GAS PIPELINE-TRANSCO p 1611
2800 Post Oak Blvd # 300, Houston TX 77056
Tel (713) 215-2000 *SIC* 1321 1221 1222

▲ JP ENERGY PARTNERS LP p 794
600 Las Colinas Blvd E # 2000, Irving TX 75039
Tel (972) 444-0300 *SIC* 1321

PINNACLE PROPANE LLC p 1150
600 Las Colinas Blvd E # 2000, Irving TX 75039
Tel (972) 444-0300 *SIC* 1321

▲ PIONEER NATURAL RESOURCES CO p 1151
5205 N Oconnor Connor, Irving TX 75039
Tel (972) 444-9001 *SIC* 1311 1321

■ PIONEER NATURAL RESOURCES USA INC p 1151
5205 N Oconnor Blvd Ste, Irving TX 75039
Tel (972) 444-9001 *SIC* 1311 1321

▲ MARTIN MIDSTREAM PARTNERS LP p 913
4200 Stone Rd, Kilgore TX 75662
Tel (903) 983-6200
SIC 5171 4226 1321 4424 2819 2875

■ LONE STAR NGL LLC p 876
800 E Sonterra Blvd # 400, San Antonio TX 78258
Tel (210) 403-7300 *SIC* 1321

REPSOL ENERGY NORTH AMERICA CORP p 1225
2455 Tech Forest Blvd, The Woodlands TX 77381
Tel (832) 442-1000 *SIC* 1321

EASTERN AMERICAN ENERGY CORP p 471
500 Corporate Lndg, Charleston WV 25311
Tel (304) 925-6100
SIC 1311 4922 5172 1321

SIC 1381 Drilling Oil & Gas Wells

DOYON DRILLING INC p 454
11500 C St Ste 200, Anchorage AK 99515
Tel (907) 563-5530 *SIC* 1381

NABORS ALASKA DRILLING INC p 1006
2525 C St Ste 200, Anchorage AK 99503
Tel (907) 263-6000 *SIC* 1381

VECO CORP p 1546
949 E 36th Ave Ste 500, Anchorage AK 99508
Tel (907) 762-1500
SIC 1711 1389 1731 1381 4959

DOYON LIMITED p 454
1 Doyon Pl Ste 300, Fairbanks AK 99701
Tel (907) 459-2000 *SIC* 1381 1382

AERA ENERGY LLC p 30
10000 Ming Ave, Bakersfield CA 93311
Tel (661) 665-5000 *SIC* 1381

AGILITY LOGISTICS CORP p 35
240 Commerce, Irvine CA 92602
Tel (714) 617-6300
SIC 4731 8742 7372 1381

KENAI DRILLING LIMITED p 810
6430 Cat Canyon Rd, Santa Maria CA 93454
Tel (805) 937-7871 *SIC* 1381

CRESTONE PEAK RESOURCES LLC p 392
370 17th St Ste 2170, Denver CO 80202
Tel (720) 410-8500 *SIC* 1381

ENSIGN UNITED STATES DRILLING INC p 500
410 17th St Ste 1200, Denver CO 80202
Tel (303) 292-1206 *SIC* 1381

■ EVERGREEN RESOURCES INC p 515
1401 17th St Ste 1200, Denver CO 80202
Tel (303) 298-8100 *SIC* 1311 1382 1381

▲ PDC ENERGY INC p 1124
1775 N Sherman St # 3000, Denver CO 80203
Tel (303) 860-5800 *SIC* 1311 1381

SYNERGY RESOURCES CORP p 1415
1625 Broadway Ste 300, Denver CO 80202
Tel (720) 616-4300 *SIC* 1381

■ WHITING CANADIAN HOLDING CO ULC p 1606
1700 Broadway Ste 2300, Denver CO 80290
Tel (303) 837-1661 *SIC* 1381

▲ KLX INC p 823
1300 Corporate Center Way # 200, Wellington FL 33414
Tel (561) 383-5100 *SIC* 3728 2911 1381

MURFIN DRILLING CO INC p 1001
250 N Water St Ste 300, Wichita KS 67202
Tel (316) 267-3241
SIC 1381 1382 5082 6512 6514

BLAKE INTERNATIONAL USA RIGS LLC p 188
410 S Van Ave, Houma LA 70363
Tel (985) 274-2200 *SIC* 1381

OFFSHORE DRILLING CO p 1076
24 Concord Rd, Houma LA 70360
Tel (985) 876-6987 *SIC* 1381

ODYSSEA MARINE HOLDINGS INC p 1075
11864 Highway 308, Larose LA 70373
Tel (985) 385-0189 *SIC* 1381

INTERMOOR INC p 753
101 Youngswood Rd, Morgan City LA 70380
Tel (985) 385-3083 *SIC* 1381

KELLEY BROTHERS CONTRACTORS INC p 808
401 County Farm Rd, Waynesboro MS 39367
Tel (601) 735-2541 *SIC* 1389 1382 1381

PENSE BROTHERS DRILLING CO INC p 1131
800 Newberry St, Fredericktown MO 63645
Tel (573) 783-3011 *SIC* 1081 1381

AZTEC WELL SERVICING CO p 140
300 Legion Rd, Aztec NM 87410
Tel (505) 334-6194 *SIC* 1381 4213

▲ LOEWS CORP p 874
667 Madison Ave Fl 7, New York NY 10065
Tel (212) 521-2000
SIC 6331 6311 1381 4922 7011

▲ STEEL PARTNERS HOLDINGS LP p 1384
590 Madison Ave Rm 3202, New York NY 10022
Tel (212) 520-2300
SIC 3479 3497 1381 6141

ARCHER PRESSURE PUMPING LLC p 105
4500 Se 59th St, Oklahoma City OK 73135
Tel (405) 285-5812 *SIC* 1381

FRONTIER DRILLING LLC p 581
1608 Nw Epwy Ste 102, Oklahoma City OK 73118
Tel (405) 745-7700 *SIC* 1381

▲ MAMMOTH ENERGY PARTNERS LP p 900
4727 Gaillardia Pkwy # 200, Oklahoma City OK 73142
Tel (405) 265-4600 *SIC* 1389 1381

MERIDIAN DRILLING CO LLC p 948
11500 S Meridian Ave, Oklahoma City OK 73173
Tel (405) 691-1202 *SIC* 1381 1799 5084

HORIZON ENERGY SERVICES LLC p 707
203 E 80th St, Stillwater OK 74074
Tel (405) 533-4800 *SIC* 1381

MUSTANG HEAVY HAUL LLC p 1002
4905 S Perkins Rd, Stillwater OK 74074
Tel (405) 743-0085 *SIC* 1381

▲ HELMERICH & PAYNE INC p 682
1437 S Boulder Ave # 1400, Tulsa OK 74119
Tel (918) 742-5531 *SIC* 1381 1389 6512

■ HELMERICH & PAYNE INTERNATIONAL DRILLING CO INC p 682
1437 S Boulder Ave # 1400, Tulsa OK 74119
Tel (918) 742-5531 *SIC* 1381

LATSHAW DRILLING & EXPLORATION CO p 846
4500 S 129th East Ave # 150, Tulsa OK 74134
Tel (918) 355-4380 *SIC* 1381

▲ ONEOK PARTNERS LP p 1087
100 W 5th St Ste Ll, Tulsa OK 74103
Tel (918) 588-7000
SIC 4922 1321 1381 4925

▲ UNIT CORP p 1506
8200 S Unit Dr, Tulsa OK 74132
Tel (918) 493-7700 *SIC* 1381 1382 1311

■ UNIT DRILLING CO p 1506
8200 S Unit Dr, Tulsa OK 74132
Tel (918) 493-7700 *SIC* 1381

■ EXCO RESOURCES (PA) LLC p 517
260 Executive Dr Ste 100, Cranberry Township PA 16066
Tel (724) 720-2500
SIC 1382 1381 1311 8741 6211

ATLAS RESOURCE PARTNERS LP p 128
1000 Commerce Dr Ste 400, Pittsburgh PA 15275
Tel (800) 251-0171 *SIC* 1381

J-W ENERGY CO p 772
15505 Wright Brothers Dr, Addison TX 75001
Tel (972) 233-8191
SIC 1311 7353 3533 1381

DRILLING INFO INC p 456
2901 Via Fortuna Bldg 6, Austin TX 78746
Tel (512) 477-9200 *SIC* 1381

VAREL INTERNATIONAL ENERGY SERVICES INC p 1544
1625 W Crosby Rd Ste 124, Carrollton TX 75006
Tel (800) 827-3526 *SIC* 1381 3545

VAREL INTERNATIONAL IND LP p 1544
1625 W Crosby Rd Ste 124, Carrollton TX 75006
Tel (972) 242-1160 *SIC* 3545 3532 1381

MULTI-SHOT LLC p 999
3335 Pollok Dr, Conroe TX 77303
Tel (936) 441-6630 *SIC* 1389 1381

PROFESSIONAL DIRECTIONAL ENTERPRISES INC p 1180
850 Conroe Park West Dr, Conroe TX 77303
Tel (936) 441-7266 *SIC* 1389 1381

AES DRILLING FLUIDS LLC p 31
11767 Katy Fwy Ste 230, Houston TX 77079
Tel (888) 556-4533 *SIC* 1381

ALLIS-CHALMERS ENERGY INC p 58
12101 Cutten Rd, Houston TX 77066
Tel (281) 301-2600 *SIC* 1381 1389 7353

ARCHER WELL CO INC p 105
10613 W Sh Pkwy N Ste 600, Houston TX 77064
Tel (713) 856-4222 *SIC* 1381

▲ ATWOOD OCEANICS INC p 130
15011 Katy Fwy Ste 800, Houston TX 77094
Tel (281) 749-7800 *SIC* 1381

■ BAKER HUGHES OILFIELD OPERATIONS INC p 146
17021 Aldine Westfield Rd, Houston TX 77073
Tel (713) 439-8600
SIC 1381 1311 1389 2899

CLIFFS DRILLING CO p 326
14701 Saint Marys Ln, Houston TX 77079
Tel (281) 749-1000 *SIC* 1381

■ COMPLETE PRODUCTION SERVICES INC p 351
1001 Louisiana St, Houston TX 77002
Tel (281) 372-2300 *SIC* 1389 1381

CRESCENT DIRECTIONAL DRILLING LP p 391
2040 Aldine Western Rd, Houston TX 77038
Tel (281) 668-9500 *SIC* 1381

■ DIAMOND OFFSHORE DRILLING INC p 437
15415 Katy Fwy Ste 400, Houston TX 77094
Tel (281) 492-5300 *SIC* 1381

EMAS CHIYODA SUBSEA INC p 490
825 Town And Country Ln, Houston TX 77024
Tel (832) 487-7300 *SIC* 1381

ENSCO INTERNATIONAL INC p 500
5847 San Felipe St # 3300, Houston TX 77057
Tel (800) 423-8006 *SIC* 1381

GLOBAL MARINE INC p 617
4 Greenway Plz Ste 100, Houston TX 77046
Tel (713) 232-7500 *SIC* 1381 1311

▲ HALLIBURTON CO p 654
3000 N Sam Houston Pkwy E, Houston TX 77032
Tel (281) 871-2699
SIC 1389 1382 1381 8711

▲ HERCULES OFFSHORE INC p 685
9 Greenway Plz Ste 2200, Houston TX 77046
Tel (713) 350-5100 *SIC* 1381 1389

INDEPENDENCE CONTRACT DRILLING INC p 736
11601 N Galayda St, Houston TX 77086
Tel (281) 598-1230 *SIC* 1381

KEANE GROUP HOLDINGS LLC p 807
11200 Westheimer Rd # 900, Houston TX 77042
Tel (713) 960-0381 *SIC* 1381 7353 4212

KEY ENERGY DRILLING INC p 814
1301 Mckinney St Ste 1800, Houston TX 77010
Tel (432) 620-0300 *SIC* 1381

KEY ENERGY SERVICES INC p 814
1301 Mckinney St Ste 1800, Houston TX 77010
Tel (713) 651-4300 *SIC* 1389 1381 1311

NABORS DRILLING USA LP p 1006
515 W Greens Rd Ste 1200, Houston TX 77067
Tel (281) 874-0035 *SIC* 1381

NABORS INDUSTRIES INC p 1006
515 W Greens Rd Ste 1200, Houston TX 77067
Tel (281) 874-0035 *SIC* 1381 1389

NABORS INTERNATIONAL INC p 1006
515 W Greens Rd Ste 600, Houston TX 77067
Tel (281) 874-0035 *SIC* 1381 7353

NABORS OFFSHORE CORP p 1006
515 W Greens Rd Ste 1200, Houston TX 77067
Tel (281) 874-0406 *SIC* 1381 1389

▲ PARKER DRILLING CO p 1116
5 Greenway Plz Ste 100, Houston TX 77046
Tel (281) 406-2000 *SIC* 1381 7353

▲ PATTERSON-UTI ENERGY INC p 1121
10713 W Sam Huston Pkwy N, Houston TX 77064
Tel (281) 765-7100 *SIC* 1381 1389 1311

PHOENIX TECHNOLOGY SERVICES USA INC p 1145
12329 Cutten Rd, Houston TX 77066
Tel (713) 337-0600 *SIC* 1381

PRECISION DRILLING CO LP p 1168
10350 Richmond Ave # 700, Houston TX 77042
Tel (713) 435-6100 *SIC* 1381

PRECISION DRILLING CORP p 1168
10350 Richmond Ave # 700, Houston TX 77042
Tel (713) 435-6100 *SIC* 1381

PRIDE INTERNATIONAL INC p 1174
5847 San Felipe St # 3400, Houston TX 77057
Tel (713) 789-1400 *SIC* 1381 1389 8711

PRO OILFIELD SERVICES LLC p 1178
3 Riverway Ste 1110, Houston TX 77056
Tel (281) 496-5810 *SIC* 1381

R & B FALCON DRILLING INTERNATIONAL DEEPWATER INC p 1201
2000 W Sam Houston Pkwy S, Houston TX 77042
Tel (713) 278-6000 *SIC* 1381 8711

ROSETTA RESOURCES INC p 1251
1111 Bagby St Ste 1600, Houston TX 77002
Tel (713) 335-4000 *SIC* 1311 1381

ROWAN COMPANIES INC p 1253
2800 Post Oak Blvd # 5450, Houston TX 77056
Tel (713) 621-7800 *SIC* 1381 3531 3533

ROWAN DRILLING CO INC p 1253
2800 Post Oak Blvd # 5450, Houston TX 77056
Tel (713) 621-7800 *SIC* 1381

SCAN DRILLING CO INC p 1286
11777 Katy Fwy Ste 470, Houston TX 77079
Tel (281) 496-5571 *SIC* 1381

SCHLUMBERGER LIMITED p 1287
5599 San Felipe St Fl 17, Houston TX 77056
Tel (713) 513-2000
SIC 1381 1389 1382 3825 3824 3823

SCIENTIFIC DRILLING INTERNATIONAL INC p 1292
16071 Greenspoint Park Ste 200, Houston TX 77060
Tel (281) 443-3300 *SIC* 1381 1389

SHERIDAN PRODUCTION CO LLC p 1316
9 Greenway Plz Ste 1300, Houston TX 77046
Tel (713) 548-1000 *SIC* 1381

SIDEWINDER DRILLING INC p 1319
952 Echo Ln Ste 460, Houston TX 77024
Tel (832) 320-7600 *SIC* 1381

■ TESCO CORP (US) p 1440
11330 Clay Rd Ste 350, Houston TX 77041
Tel (713) 359-7000
SIC 7353 5082 1389 1381

TODCO p 1458
2000 W Sam Houston Pkwy S # 800, Houston TX 77042
Tel (713) 278-6000 *SIC* 1381

TRANS OCEAN LTD p 1470
4 Greenway Plz Ste 100, Houston TX 77046
Tel (713) 232-7500 *SIC* 1381

TRANSOCEAN INC p 1472
4 Greenway Plz Ste 700, Houston TX 77046
Tel (713) 232-7500 *SIC* 1381

TRANSWORLD WORLDWIDE INC p 1473
4 Greenway Plz Ste 700, Houston TX 77046
Tel (713) 232-7500 *SIC* 1381 1311

■ TRI RESOURCES INC p 1476
1000 Louisiana St # 4300, Houston TX 77002
Tel (713) 584-1000 *SIC* 1321 1381 1382

TUBOSCOPE INC p 1490
2919 Holmes Rd, Houston TX 77051
Tel (713) 799-5100 *SIC* 1381

UNION DRILLING INC p 1504
952 Echo Ln Ste 460, Houston TX 77024
Tel (817) 735-8793 *SIC* 1381

VANTAGE DRILLING CO p 1544
777 Post Oak Blvd Ste 800, Houston TX 77056
Tel (281) 404-4700 *SIC* 1381

PROPETRO SERVICES INC p 1184
1706 S Midkiff Rd Ste B, Midland TX 79701
Tel (432) 688-0012 *SIC* 1381

■ UNIVERSAL PRESSURE PUMPING INC p 1517
6 Desta Dr Ste 4400, Midland TX 79705
Tel (432) 221-7000 *SIC* 1381

GLADE OPERATING LLC p 614
110 S Main St, Moulton TX 77975
Tel (361) 596-5050 *SIC* 1381

BLACK VIPER ENERGY SERVICES LTD p 187
11220 W County Road 127, Odessa TX 79765
Tel (432) 561-8801 *SIC* 1381

■ PATTERSON DRILLING CO INC p 1121
4105 S Chadbourne St, San Angelo TX 76904
Tel (325) 651-6603 *SIC* 1381

■ **PIONEER DRILLING SERVICES LTD** p 1150
1250 Ne Loop 410 Ste 1000, San Antonio TX 78209
Tel (210) 828-7689 *SIC* 1381

▲ **PIONEER ENERGY SERVICES CORP** p 1150
1250 Ne Loop 410 Ste 1000, San Antonio TX 78209
Tel (855) 884-0575 *SIC* 1381 7353

■ **PATTERSON-UTI DRILLING SERVICES LP LLLP** p 1121
4500 Lamesa Hwy, Snyder TX 79549
Tel (325) 573-1104 *SIC* 1381

FRONTIER DRILLING USA INC p 581
13135 Dairy Ashford Rd # 800, Sugar Land TX 77478
Tel (713) 481-7500 *SIC* 1381

NOBLE DRILLING (US) INC p 1046
13135 Dry Ashfd 800, Sugar Land TX 77478
Tel (281) 276-6100 *SIC* 1381

NOBLE DRILLING CORP p 1046
13135 Dairy Ashford Rd # 700, Sugar Land TX 77478
Tel (281) 276-6100 *SIC* 1381 8711

NOBLE DRILLING HOLDING LLC p 1046
13135 Dairy Ashford Rd # 700, Sugar Land TX 77478
Tel (281) 276-6100 *SIC* 1381

NOBLE HOLDING (US) CORP p 1046
3135 S Dairy Ashford Ste 800, Sugar Land TX 77478
Tel (281) 276-6100 *SIC* 1381

SAVANNA ENERGY SERVICES (USA) CORP p 1284
2445 Technology Ste 200, The Woodlands TX 77381
Tel (281) 907-4800 *SIC* 1381 1389

TORQUED-UP ENERGY SERVICES INC p 1462
110 N College Ave # 1000, Tyler TX 75702
Tel (903) 363-0300 *SIC* 1381

DIRECTIONAL DRILLING CO LP p 441
11390 Fm 830 Rd, Willis TX 77318
Tel (936) 856-4332 *SIC* 1381

BOART LONGYEAR MANUFACTURING AND DISTRIBUTION INC p 196
2640 W 1700 S, Salt Lake City UT 84104
Tel (801) 972-6430 *SIC* 1381 5084 3533

MICHELS CORP p 960
817 W Main St, Brownsville WI 53006
Tel (920) 583-3132
SIC 1623 1771 1381 1629 3498 1794

SIC 1382 Oil & Gas Field Exploration Svcs

■ **ENERGEN RESOURCES CORP** p 497
605 Richard Arrington Jr, Birmingham AL 35203
Tel (205) 326-2710 *SIC* 1382 1321

COOK INLET REGION INC p 366
725 E Fireweed Ln Ste 800, Anchorage AK 99503
Tel (907) 274-8638
SIC 6552 1382 1389 6519 4832 4833

HILCORP ALASKA LLC p 692
3800 Centerpoint Dr, Anchorage AK 99503
Tel (907) 777-8300 *SIC* 1382

DOYON LIMITED p 454
1 Doyon Pl Ste 300, Fairbanks AK 99701
Tel (907) 459-2000 *SIC* 1381 1382

▲ **MURPHY OIL CORP** p 1001
300 E Peach St, El Dorado AR 71730
Tel (870) 862-6411 *SIC* 1311 1382 2911

■ **CALIFORNIA RESOURCES PRODUCTION CORP** p 241
11109 River Run Blvd, Bakersfield CA 93311
Tel (661) 869-8000 *SIC* 1311 1382

OCCIDENTAL PETROLEUM INVESTMENT CO INC p 1072
10889 Wilshire Blvd Fl 10, Los Angeles CA 90024
Tel (310) 208-8800 *SIC* 1382 8744

▲ **CHEVRON CORP** p 295
6001 Bollinger Canyon Rd, San Ramon CA 94583
Tel (925) 842-1000
SIC 2911 1311 1382 1321 5541

GREKA INTEGRATED INC p 639
1700 Sinton Rd, Santa Maria CA 93458
Tel (805) 347-8700 *SIC* 1382

DCOR LLC p 418
290 Maple Ct Ste 290, Ventura CA 93003
Tel (805) 535-2000 *SIC* 1382

ANSCHUTZ CORP p 93
555 17th St Ste 2400, Denver CO 80202
Tel (303) 298-1000 *SIC* 2711 1382 7941

■ **BLACK HILLS EXPLORATION AND PRODUCTION INC** p 187
1515 Wynkoop St Ste 500, Denver CO 80202
Tel (720) 210-1300 *SIC* 1382

ENERGY CORP OF AMERICA p 497
4643 S Ulster St Ste 1100, Denver CO 80237
Tel (303) 694-2667
SIC 4924 4932 1382 4922 5172

■ **EVERGREEN RESOURCES INC** p 515
1401 17th St Ste 1200, Denver CO 80202
Tel (303) 298-8100 *SIC* 1311 1382 1381

▲ **EXTRACTION OIL & GAS INC** p 521
370 17th St Ste 5300, Denver CO 80202
Tel (720) 557-8300 *SIC* 1382

■ **FIDELITY EXPLORATION & PRODUCTION CO** p 540
1801 Calif St Ste 2500, Denver CO 80202
Tel (303) 893-3133 *SIC* 1382

GATES GLOBAL LLC p 593
1551 Wewatta St, Denver CO 80202
Tel (303) 744-1911 *SIC* 1382

▲ **HALLADOR ENERGY CO** p 654
1660 Lincoln St Ste 2700, Denver CO 80264
Tel (303) 839-5504 *SIC* 1241 1311 1382

HAWKWOOD ENERGY LLC p 670
4582 S Ulster St Ste 500, Denver CO 80237
Tel (303) 823-4175 *SIC* 1382

JONAH ENERGY LLC p 792
707 17th St Ste 2700, Denver CO 80202
Tel (720) 577-1000 *SIC* 1382

LIBERTY OILFIELD SERVICES LLC p 862
950 17th St Ste 2000, Denver CO 80202
Tel (303) 515-2800 *SIC* 1382

LOCKHART GEOPHYSICAL CO p 873
1600 Broadway Ste 1660, Denver CO 80202
Tel (303) 592-5220 *SIC* 1382

P2 ENERGY SOLUTIONS INC p 1103
1670 Broadway Ste 2800, Denver CO 80202
Tel (303) 292-0990 *SIC* 1382

■ **QEP ENERGY CO** p 1195
1050 17th St Ste 800, Denver CO 80265
Tel (303) 672-6900
SIC 1311 1382 1389 5172

▲ **QEP RESOURCES INC** p 1195
1050 17th St Ste 800, Denver CO 80265
Tel (303) 672-6900 *SIC* 1311 1321 1382

▲ **TRIANGLE PETROLEUM CORP** p 1478
1200 17th St Ste 2500, Denver CO 80202
Tel (303) 260-7125 *SIC* 1311 1382

▲ **WHITING PETROLEUM CORP** p 1607
1700 Broadway Ste 2300, Denver CO 80290
Tel (303) 837-1661 *SIC* 1311 1382

PEAK EXPLORATION & PRODUCTION LLC p 1125
1910 Main Ave, Durango CO 81301
Tel (970) 247-1500 *SIC* 1382

ANATOLIA MINERALS DEVELOPMENT LTD p 88
3721 Hwy 74 Ste 14, Evergreen CO 80439
Tel (303) 670-9945 *SIC* 1382 8748

STATOIL US HOLDINGS INC p 1383
120 Long Ridge Rd, Stamford CT 06902
Tel (203) 978-6900 *SIC* 5172 1382

SHELL ENERGY RESOURCES INC p 1314
1105 N Market St Ste 1300, Wilmington DE 19801
Tel (302) 658-3676 *SIC* 1311 1382

SOLENIS INTERNATIONAL LP p 1338
500 Hercules Rd, Wilmington DE 19808
Tel (302) 994-1698 *SIC* 2911 2611 1382

COUNTRYMARK COOPERATIVE HOLDING CORP p 375
225 S East St Ste 144, Indianapolis IN 46202
Tel (800) 808-3170
SIC 5172 2911 1382 1311 6719

BEREXCO LLC p 174
2020 N Bramblewood St, Wichita KS 67206
Tel (316) 265-3311 *SIC* 1382 1311

FLINT HILLS RESOURCES LP p 557
4111 E 37th St N, Wichita KS 67220
Tel (800) 292-3133
SIC 5172 4612 1382 2911

MURFIN DRILLING CO INC p 1001
250 N Water St Ste 300, Wichita KS 67202
Tel (316) 267-3241
SIC 1381 1382 5082 6512 6514

TIM ICENHOWER OIL AND GAS INC p 1454
5916 Industrial Drive Ext, Bossier City LA 71112
Tel (318) 752-2293 *SIC* 1382

OMNI ENERGY SERVICES CORP p 1084
4500 Ne Evangeline Trwy, Carencro LA 70520
Tel (337) 896-6664 *SIC* 1382 1389 7349

■ **HORNBECK OFFSHORE SERVICES LLC** p 708
103 Northpark Blvd # 300, Covington LA 70433
Tel (985) 727-2000 *SIC* 1382

LLOG EXPLORATION CO LLC p 872
1001 Ochsner Blvd Ste 200, Covington LA 70433
Tel (504) 833-7700 *SIC* 1311 1382

LLOG EXPLORATION OFFSHORE LLC p 872
1001 Ochsner Blvd Ste 200, Covington LA 70433
Tel (985) 801-4300 *SIC* 1382

GULFSTREAM SERVICES INC p 647
103 Dickson Rd, Houma LA 70363
Tel (985) 868-0303 *SIC* 1382 7359

MARLIN ENERGY LLC p 909
3861 Ambassador Caffery P, Lafayette LA 70503
Tel (337) 769-0032 *SIC* 1311 1382

▲ **STONE ENERGY CORP** p 1391
625 E Kaliste Saloom Rd # 201, Lafayette LA 70508
Tel (337) 237-0410 *SIC* 1311 1382

DOMINION EXPLORATION & PRODUCTION INC p 449
1250 Poydras St Ste 2000, New Orleans LA 70113
Tel (504) 593-7000 *SIC* 1382

■ **CMS ENTERPRISES CO** p 329
1 Energy Plaza Dr, Jackson MI 49201
Tel (517) 788-0550 *SIC* 1382 4911

BECKMAN PRODUCTION SERVICES INC p 167
3786 Beebe Rd Ne, Kalkaska MI 49646
Tel (231) 258-9524 *SIC* 1382

DART ENERGY CORP p 413
600 Dart Rd, Mason MI 48854
Tel (517) 676-2900 *SIC* 1311 1382

EBERSEN INC p 474
7401 Central Ave Ne Ste 2, Minneapolis MN 55432
Tel (763) 572-2661
SIC 4911 1521 6211 1382 4731 8711

■ **CALLON OFFSHORE PRODUCTION INC** p 242
200 N Canal St, Natchez MS 39120
Tel (601) 442-1601 *SIC* 1311 1382

KELLEY BROTHERS CONTRACTORS INC p 808
401 County Farm Rd, Waynesboro MS 39367
Tel (601) 735-2541 *SIC* 1389 1382 1381

BURNS & MCDONNELL ENGINEERING CO INC p 228
9400 Ward Pkwy, Kansas City MO 64114
Tel (816) 333-9400 *SIC* 1382 8711

ELLIOTT ASSOCIATES LP p 488
712 5th Ave Fl 36, New York NY 10019
Tel (212) 586-9431 *SIC* 6282 1382

▲ **LEUCADIA NATIONAL CORP** p 858
520 Madison Ave Bsmt A, New York NY 10022
Tel (212) 460-1900
SIC 6798 6211 1382 2011 2426

▲ **NATIONAL FUEL GAS CO** p 1012
6363 Main St, Williamsville NY 14221
Tel (716) 857-7000
SIC 4924 4922 1311 1382

■ **CENTENNIAL ENERGY HOLDINGS INC** p 275
Schuchart Bldg 918e, Bismarck ND 58501
Tel (701) 222-7900 *SIC* 1382 8748 1221

■ **ALSATE EXPLORATION INC** p 61
1601 Nw Expwy St Ste 400, Oklahoma City OK 73118
Tel (405) 753-5500 *SIC* 1382

ASCENT RESOURCES LLC p 116
3501 Nw 63rd St, Oklahoma City OK 73116
Tel (405) 608-5544 *SIC* 1382 6719

CHAPARRAL ENERGY INC p 288
701 Cedar Lake Blvd, Oklahoma City OK 73114
Tel (405) 478-8770 *SIC* 1311 1382

CHAPARRAL ENERGY LLC p 288
701 Cedar Lake Blvd, Oklahoma City OK 73114
Tel (405) 478-8770 *SIC* 1311 1382

▲ **DEVON ENERGY CORP** p 434
333 W Sheridan Ave, Oklahoma City OK 73102
Tel (405) 235-3611 *SIC* 1311 1382

■ **LARIAT SERVICES INC** p 845
123 Robert S Kerr Ave, Oklahoma City OK 73102
Tel (405) 753-5500 *SIC* 1382

■ **QUEST ENERGY PARTNERS LP** p 1199
210 Park Ave Ste 2750, Oklahoma City OK 73102
Tel (405) 600-7704 *SIC* 1382

RIVER ROCK ENERGY LLC p 1237
211 N Robinson Ave S1525, Oklahoma City OK 73102
Tel (405) 606-7481 *SIC* 1382

KAISER-FRANCIS OIL CO p 800
6733 S Yale Ave, Tulsa OK 74136
Tel (918) 494-0000 *SIC* 1382 1311

▲ **UNIT CORP** p 1506
8200 S Unit Dr, Tulsa OK 74132
Tel (918) 493-7700 *SIC* 1381 1382 1311

■ **RANGE RESOURCES - APPALACHIA LLC** p 1208
3000 Town Center Blvd, Canonsburg PA 15317
Tel (724) 743-6700 *SIC* 1382

■ **EXCO RESOURCES (PA) LLC** p 517
260 Executive Dr Ste 100, Cranberry Township PA 16066
Tel (724) 720-2500
SIC 1382 1381 1311 8741 6211

■ **UNIVERSAL WELL SERVICES INC** p 1518
13549 S Mosiertown Rd, Meadville PA 16335
Tel (814) 337-1983 *SIC* 1389 1382

ABARTA INC p 9
200 Alpha Dr, Pittsburgh PA 15238
Tel (412) 963-6226
SIC 2086 2711 2721 5149 1382 5812

■ **PENN VIRGINIA OIL & GAS CORP** p 1129
4 Radnor Corp Ctr Ste 200, Radnor PA 19087
Tel (610) 687-8900 *SIC* 1382

ESMARK INC p 509
100 Hazel Ln Ste 300, Sewickley PA 15143
Tel (412) 259-8868 *SIC* 1382 3324

■ **ECLIPSE RESOURCES I LP** p 475
2121 Old Gteburg Rd Ste 1, State College PA 16803
Tel (814) 308-9754 *SIC* 1311 1382

J-W OPERATING CO p 772
15505 Wright Brothers Dr, Addison TX 75001
Tel (972) 233-8191 *SIC* 1382

▲ **FORESTAR GROUP INC** p 567
6300 Fm 2244 Rd Bldg 500, Austin TX 78746
Tel (512) 433-5200 *SIC* 6531 1382

■ **JONES ENERGY HOLDINGS LLC** p 792
807 Las Cimas Pkwy # 350, Austin TX 78746
Tel (512) 328-2953 *SIC* 1311 1382

TEXAS AMERICAN RESOURCES CO p 1442
401 Congress Ave Ste 1600, Austin TX 78701
Tel (512) 480-8700 *SIC* 1311 1382

■ **EXCO OPERATING CO LP** p 517
12377 Merit Dr Ste 1700, Dallas TX 75251
Tel (214) 368-2084 *SIC* 1382

HAWKWOOD ENERGY EAST TEXAS LLC p 670
1999 Bryan St Ste 900, Dallas TX 75201
Tel (303) 823-4175 *SIC* 1382

HUNT CONSOLIDATED INC p 718
1900 N Akard St, Dallas TX 75201
Tel (214) 978-8000
SIC 6799 1311 2911 1382 0212

HUNT DOMINION CORP p 719
1601 Elm St Ste 3900, Dallas TX 75201
Tel (214) 880-8400 *SIC* 1311 1382 1241

HUNT OIL USA INC p 719
1900 N Akard St, Dallas TX 75201
Tel (214) 978-8000 *SIC* 1311 1382 2911

■ **OXY VINYLS LP** p 1101
5005 Lbj Fwy Ste 2200, Dallas TX 75244
Tel (972) 720-7000
SIC 2821 2899 2819 1382

PANDA POWER GENERATION INFRASTRUCTURE FUND GP LP p 1111
5001 Spring Valley Rd 1150w, Dallas TX 75244
Tel (972) 361-2000 *SIC* 1382

RRH CORP p 1255
1900 N Akard St, Dallas TX 75201
Tel (214) 978-8000
SIC 1382 1311 2911 0212 6799

■ **RSP PERMIAN LLC** p 1256
3141 Hood St Ste 700, Dallas TX 75219
Tel (214) 252-2700 *SIC* 1382

TRT HOLDINGS INC p 1485
4001 Maple Ave Ste 600, Dallas TX 75219
Tel (214) 283-8500 *SIC* 7011 7991 1382

GLOBAL TUBING LLC p 617
501 County Road 493, Dayton TX 77535
Tel (713) 265-5000 *SIC* 1382

BASS ENTERPRISES PRODUCTION CO p 159
201 Main St Ste 2700, Fort Worth TX 76102
Tel (817) 698-0200 *SIC* 1311 1382

COMPASS WELL SERVICES LLC p 351
4100 Intl Plz Ste 500, Fort Worth TX 76109
Tel (817) 244-2555 *SIC* 1389 1382

DAVOIL INC p 416
6300 Ridglea Pl Ste 1208, Fort Worth TX 76116
Tel (817) 737-6678 *SIC* 1382

TEXLAND PETROLEUM LP p 1445
777 Main St Ste 3200, Fort Worth TX 76102
Tel (817) 336-2751 *SIC* 1311 1382

▲ **ADAMS RESOURCES & ENERGY INC** p 21
17 S Briar Hollow Ln, Houston TX 77027
Tel (713) 881-3600
SIC 5172 4212 1382 1311

BLACKHAWK SPECIALTY TOOLS LLC p 187
11936 Brittmoore Park Dr, Houston TX 77041
Tel (713) 466-4200 *SIC* 1382

■ **BLUE DOLPHIN ENERGY CO** p 192
801 Travis St Ste 2100, Houston TX 77002
Tel (713) 568-4725
SIC 1311 1382 4612 4922

BROADSPECTRUM DOWNSTREAM SERVICES INC p 215
1330 Post Oak Blvd # 1250, Houston TX 77056
Tel (713) 964-2800 *SIC* 1382

C&J ENERGY SERVICES INC p 234
3990 Rogerdale Rd, Houston TX 77042
Tel (713) 325-6000 *SIC* 1382 1389

CAMAC INTERNATIONAL CORP p 243
1330 Post Oak Blvd Ste 22, Houston TX 77056
Tel (713) 965-5100
SIC 8711 6552 1382 8741 1389

CENTRAL CRUDE INC p 278
10370 Richmond Ave # 975, Houston TX 77042
Tel (713) 783-2167 *SIC* 1382

CGG SERVICES (US) INC p 285
10300 Town Park Dr, Houston TX 77072
Tel (832) 351-8300 *SIC* 1382

CITATION OIL & GAS CORP p 309
14077 Cutten Rd, Houston TX 77069
Tel (281) 891-1000 *SIC* 1311 1382

■ **COMPLETE ENERGY SERVICES INC** p 351
1001 La St Ste 2900, Houston TX 77002
Tel (713) 654-2200 *SIC* 1382

▲ **CONOCOPHILLIPS** p 358
600 N Dairy Ashford Rd, Houston TX 77079
Tel (281) 293-1000 *SIC* 1311 1382

ENERVEST LTD p 498
1001 Fannin St Ste 800, Houston TX 77002
Tel (713) 659-3500 *SIC* 1311 1382

■ **EP ENERGY E&P CO LP** p 504
1001 Louisiana St, Houston TX 77002
Tel (713) 997-4858 *SIC* 1382

■ **EP ENERGY LLC** p 504
1001 Louisiana St, Houston TX 77002
Tel (713) 997-1200 *SIC* 1311 1382

FIELDWOOD ENERGY LLC p 541
2000 W Sam Houston Pkwy S # 1200, Houston TX 77042
Tel (713) 969-1000 *SIC* 1382

■ **FORUM US INC** p 570
10344 Sam Houston Park Dr, Houston TX 77064
Tel (713) 351-7900 *SIC* 1382

FRANKS INTERNATIONAL LLC p 575
10260 Westheimer Rd, Houston TX 77042
Tel (281) 966-7300 *SIC* 1382 7353

■ **FREEPORT-MCMORAN OIL & GAS LLC** p 577
700 Milam St Ste 3100, Houston TX 77002
Tel (713) 579-6000 *SIC* 1382

GEOKINETICS INC p 606
1500 Citywest Blvd # 800, Houston TX 77042
Tel (713) 850-7600 *SIC* 1382 7374

GEOKINETICS MANAGEMENT INC p 606
1500 City W Blvd Ste 800, Houston TX 77042
Tel (281) 870-8506 *SIC* 1382

▲ **HALLIBURTON CO** p 654
3000 N Sam Houston Pkwy E, Houston TX 77032
Tel (281) 871-2699
SIC 1389 1382 1381 8711

HIGHMOUNT EXPLORATION & PRODUCTION LLC p 692
16945 Northchase Dr # 1750, Houston TX 77060
Tel (281) 873-1500 *SIC* 1382

HILCORP ENERGY CO p 692
1111 Travis St, Houston TX 77002
Tel (713) 209-2400 *SIC* 1311 1382

■ **LINN OPERATING INC** p 869
600 Travis St Ste 5100, Houston TX 77002
Tel (713) 227-1868 *SIC* 1382

■ **MARATHON INTERNATIONAL OIL CO** p 904
5555 San Felipe St # 2796, Houston TX 77056
Tel (713) 629-6600 *SIC* 1311 1382 6519

MILAGRO OIL & GAS INC p 968
1301 Mckinney St Ste 500, Houston TX 77010
Tel (713) 750-1600 *SIC* 1382

■ **MURPHY EXPLORATION & PRODUCTION CO - USA** p 1001
9805 Katy Fwy Ste G200, Houston TX 77024
Tel (281) 599-8145 *SIC* 1382 1311

NINE ENERGY SERVICE INC p 1044
16945 Northchase Dr, Houston TX 77060
Tel (281) 730-5100 *SIC* 5211 1382

■ **OCCIDENTAL ENERGY MARKETING INC** p 1072
5 Greenway Plz Ste 110, Houston TX 77046
Tel (713) 215-7000 *SIC* 5172 1382 4924

■ **OCCIDENTAL PERMIAN LTD** p 1072
5 Greenway Plz Ste 110, Houston TX 77046
Tel (713) 215-7000 *SIC* 1382 1311

▲ **OCCIDENTAL PETROLEUM CORP** p 1072
5 Greenway Plz Ste 110, Houston TX 77046
Tel (713) 215-7000 *SIC* 1382 1311

OLD GES INC p 1080
11757 Katy Fwy Ste 700, Houston TX 77079
Tel (281) 598-6830
SIC 1389 7353 3599 7359 1382

■ **OXY INC** p 1101
5 Greenway Plz Ste 2400, Houston TX 77046
Tel (713) 215-7000 *SIC* 1311 1382

PARAGON OFFSHORE PLC p 1113
3151 Briarpark Dr Ste 700, Houston TX 77042
Tel (832) 783-4000 *SIC* 1382

PETROBRAS AMERICA INC p 1139
10350 Richmond Ave, Houston TX 77042
Tel (713) 808-2000 *SIC* 5172 1382 2911

PETROLEUM GEO-SERVICES INC p 1139
15375 Memorial Dr Ste 100, Houston TX 77079
Tel (281) 509-8000 *SIC* 3827 8713 1382

PETROSANTANDER (COLOMBIA) INC p 1139
6363 Woodway Dr Ste 350, Houston TX 77057
Tel (713) 784-8700 SIC 1311 1382

■ **PHILLIPS PETROLEUM CO** p 1144
600 N Dairy Ashford Rd, Houston TX 77079
Tel (281) 293-1000
SIC 1382 2911 5171 5541

RIL USA INC p 1235
2000 W Sam Houston Pkwy S # 1155, Houston TX 77042
Tel (713) 430-8700 SIC 1382

■ **ROSETTA RESOURCES OFFSHORE LLC** p 1251
1111 Bagby St Ste 1600, Houston TX 77002
Tel (713) 335-4000 SIC 1382

SASOL (USA) CORP p 1283
12120 Wickchester Ln, Houston TX 77079
Tel (281) 588-3000 SIC 1382

SCHLUMBERGER LIMITED p 1287
5599 San Felipe St Fl 17, Houston TX 77056
Tel (713) 513-2000
SIC 1381 1389 1382 3825 3824 3823

SCHLUMBERGER OMNES INC p 1287
5599 San Felipe St Fl 17, Houston TX 77056
Tel (713) 375-3400 SIC 1382 1389

SEITEL HOLDINGS INC p 1301
10811 S Westview Circle D, Houston TX 77043
Tel (713) 881-8900 SIC 1382

SEITEL INC p 1301
10811 S Westvw Cir Dr 100, Houston TX 77043
Tel (713) 881-8900 SIC 1382

■ **SENECA RESOURCES CORP** p 1303
1201 Louisiana St Ste 400, Houston TX 77002
Tel (713) 654-2600 SIC 1382

■ **SOUTHWESTERN ENERGY PRODUCTION CO INC** p 1353
2350 N Sam Houston Pkwy E, Houston TX 77032
Tel (281) 618-4700 SIC 1382 1311

STATOIL USA PROPERTIES INC p 1383
2103 Citywest Blvd # 800, Houston TX 77042
Tel (713) 918-8200 SIC 1382

SWEPI LP p 1412
200 N Dairy Ashford Rd, Houston TX 77079
Tel (713) 241-6161 SIC 1311 1382 5169

TALOS PRODUCTION LLC p 1423
1600 Smith St, Houston TX 77002
Tel (713) 328-3000 SIC 1382

TEXAS PETROLEUM INVESTMENT CO INC p 1444
5850 San Felipe St # 250, Houston TX 77057
Tel (713) 789-9225 SIC 1382

TGS-NOPEC GEOPHYSICAL CO p 1446
10451 Clay Rd, Houston TX 77041
Tel (713) 860-2100 SIC 1382

TORCH ENERGY ADVISORS INC p 1461
1331 Lamar St Ste 1450, Houston TX 77010
Tel (713) 650-1246
SIC 1311 1382 8741 8742

■ **TOTAL DELAWARE INC** p 1462
1201 La St Ste 1800, Houston TX 77002
Tel (713) 483-5000 SIC 1311 1382

■ **TOTAL HOLDINGS USA INC** p 1463
1201 La St Ste 1800, Houston TX 77002
Tel (713) 483-5000 SIC 1382 1311

■ **TRI RESOURCES INC** p 1476
1000 Louisiana St # 4300, Houston TX 77002
Tel (713) 584-1000 SIC 1321 1381 1382

US SHALE SOLUTIONS INC p 1533
7670 Woodway Dr Ste 250, Houston TX 77063
Tel (832) 742-7492 SIC 1382

VALERUS FIELD SOLUTIONS HOLDINGS LLC p 1540
919 Milam St Ste 1000, Houston TX 77002
Tel (713) 744-6100 SIC 1382 6719

▲ **VANGUARD NATURAL RESOURCES LLC** p 1543
5847 San Felipe St # 1910, Houston TX 77057
Tel (832) 327-2255 SIC 1311 1382

WARTSILA NORTH AMERICA INC p 1577
11710 N Gessner Rd Ste A, Houston TX 77064
Tel (281) 233-6200
SIC 1629 5084 1382 4789 3731

WESTERNGECO LLC p 1600
10001 Richmond Ave, Houston TX 77042
Tel (713) 789-9600 SIC 1382

■ **COG OPERATING LLC** p 334
600 W Illinois Ave, Midland TX 79701
Tel (432) 685-0727 SIC 1382

CROWNROCK LP p 396
500 W Texas Ave Ste 500, Midland TX 79701
Tel (432) 818-0300 SIC 1382

▲ **DAWSON GEOPHYSICAL CO** p 417
508 W Wall St Ste 800, Midland TX 79701
Tel (432) 684-3000 SIC 1382 8713

GLOBAL GEOPHYSICAL SERVICES INC p 616
13927 S Gessner Rd, Missouri City TX 77489
Tel (713) 972-9200 SIC 1382

■ **DENBURY ONSHORE LLC** p 428
5320 Legacy Dr, Plano TX 75024
Tel (972) 673-2000 SIC 1311 1382

NAVARRO MIDSTREAM SERVICES LLC p 1020
10101 Reunion Pl Ste 1000, San Antonio TX 78216
Tel (956) 728-6000 SIC 1382

SEGUNDO NAVARRO DRILLING LTD p 1300
10101 Reunion Pl Ste 1000, San Antonio TX 78216
Tel (210) 384-3000 SIC 1382 4925

GLOBE ENERGY SERVICES LLC p 618
3204 W Highway 180, Snyder TX 79549
Tel (325) 573-1310 SIC 1382

ATP OIL & GAS CORP p 128
26219 Oak Ridge Dr, Spring TX 77380
Tel (713) 622-3311 SIC 1311 1382

▲ **SOUTHWESTERN ENERGY CO INC** p 1353
10000 Energy Dr, Spring TX 77389
Tel (832) 796-1000 SIC 1311 1382

FAIRFIELD INDUSTRIES INC p 525
1111 Gillingham Ln, Sugar Land TX 77478
Tel (281) 275-7627
SIC 7374 3829 1382 3429

SCHLUMBERGER TECHNOLOGY CORP p 1287
100 Gillingham Ln, Sugar Land TX 77478
Tel (281) 285-8500
SIC 1382 1389 3825 3824 3533 3586

▲ **ANADARKO PETROLEUM CORP** p 88
1201 Lake Robbins Dr, The Woodlands TX 77380
Tel (832) 636-1000
SIC 1311 4924 5171 1382

REPSOL SERVICES CO p 1225
2455 Tech Forest Blvd, The Woodlands TX 77381
Tel (832) 442-1000 SIC 1382

FJ MANAGEMENT INC p 553
185 S State St Ste 201, Salt Lake City UT 84111
Tel (801) 624-1000
SIC 5541 2911 5411 1382 6022

SINCLAIR COMPANIES p 1326
550 E South Temple, Salt Lake City UT 84102
Tel (801) 363-5100
SIC 2911 4612 1382 5541 7011 0212

HOVENSA LLC p 713
1 Estate Hope, Christiansted VI 00820
Tel (340) 692-3000 SIC 1382

UNITED CO p 1507
1005 Glenway Ave, Bristol VA 24201
Tel (276) 466-3322 SIC 1382 7992

SIC 1389 Oil & Gas Field Svcs, NEC

OIMO HOLDINGS INC p 1079
2735 Middle Rd, Mobile AL 36605
Tel (251) 443-5550 SIC 1389

ARCTIC SLOPE REGIONAL CORP p 106
3900 C St Ste 801, Anchorage AK 99503
Tel (907) 339-6000 SIC 1389 2911 1623

ASRC ENERGY SERVICES LLC p 119
3900 C St Ste 701, Anchorage AK 99503
Tel (907) 339-6200 SIC 1389

CH2M HILL ALASKA INC p 286
949 E 36th Ave Ste 500, Anchorage AK 99508
Tel (907) 762-1500 SIC 1389

COOK INLET REGION INC p 366
725 E Fireweed Ln Ste 800, Anchorage AK 99503
Tel (907) 274-8638
SIC 6552 1382 1389 6519 4832 4833

HARDING HOLDINGS INC p 661
184 E 53rd Ave, Anchorage AK 99518
Tel (907) 344-1577 SIC 1389 1542

NANA DEVELOPMENT CORP p 1007
909 W 9th Ave, Anchorage AK 99501
Tel (907) 265-4100 SIC 7381 1389

PEAK OILFIELD SERVICE CO LLC p 1126
5015 Business Park Blvd # 4000, Anchorage AK 99503
Tel (907) 263-7000 SIC 7699 1389

SAEXPLORATION INC p 1265
8240 Sandlewood Pl # 102, Anchorage AK 99507
Tel (907) 522-4499 SIC 1389

VECO CORP p 1546
949 E 36th Ave Ste 500, Anchorage AK 99508
Tel (907) 762-1500
SIC 1711 1389 1731 1381 4959

UKPEAGVIK INUPIAT CORP p 1500
1250 Agvik St, Barrow AK 99723
Tel (907) 852-4460
SIC 1542 6512 6331 1389 4449

▲ **NUVERRA ENVIRONMENTAL SOLUTIONS INC** p 1068
14624 N Scottsdale Rd, Scottsdale AZ 85254
Tel (602) 903-7802 SIC 1389 4953

RELIANCE WELL SERVICE INC p 1222
237 Highway 79 S, Magnolia AR 71753
Tel (870) 234-2700 SIC 1389

PACIFIC PROCESS SYSTEMS INC p 1105
7401 Rosedale Hwy, Bakersfield CA 93308
Tel (661) 321-9681 SIC 1389 7353 5082

VANDERRA RESOURCES LLC p 1543
1801 Century Park E # 2400, Los Angeles CA 90067
Tel (817) 439-2220 SIC 1389

TOTAL-WESTERN INC p 1463
8049 Somerset Blvd, Paramount CA 90723
Tel (562) 220-1450 SIC 1389

TPG PARTNERS III LP p 1467
345 California St # 3300, San Francisco CA 94104
Tel (415) 743-1500
SIC 1311 1389 4922 5082

OIL WELL SERVICE CO p 1079
10840 Norwalk Blvd, Santa Fe Springs CA 90670
Tel (562) 612-0600 SIC 1389

ALL AROUND ROUSTABOUT LLC p 51
41350 County Road 33, Ault CO 80610
Tel (970) 518-2479 SIC 1389

DESCO ACQUISITION LLC p 431
230 Commerce Rd, Berthoud CO 80513
Tel (970) 532-0600 SIC 1796 3533 1389

■ **FLINT ENERGY SERVICES INC** p 557
6901 S Havana St, Centennial CO 80112
Tel (918) 294-3030 SIC 1389 3594 1623

CALFRAC WELL SERVICES CORP p 238
717 17th St Ste 1445, Denver CO 80202
Tel (303) 293-2931 SIC 1389

CANARY LLC p 246
410 17th St Ste 1320, Denver CO 80202
Tel (303) 309-1185 SIC 1389

EASTERN COLORADO WELL SERVICE LLC p 472
1400 W 122nd Ave Ste 120, Denver CO 80234
Tel (719) 767-5100 SIC 1389

■ **MARKWEST ENERGY PARTNERS LP** p 909
1515 Arapahoe St, Denver CO 80202
Tel (303) 925-9200 SIC 1321 4922 1389

MERITAGE MIDSTREAM SERVICES II LLC p 949
1331 17th St Ste 1100, Denver CO 80202
Tel (303) 551-8150 SIC 1389

■ **QEP ENERGY CO** p 1195
1050 17th St Ste 800, Denver CO 80265
Tel (303) 672-6900
SIC 1311 1382 1389 5172

ROCKPILE ENERGY SERVICES LLC p 1245
1200 17th St Ste 2700, Denver CO 80202
Tel (303) 825-8170 SIC 1389

SANJEL (USA) INC p 1279
1630 Welton St Ste 400, Denver CO 80202
Tel (303) 893-6866 SIC 1389

AKA ENERGY GROUP LLC p 41
65 Mercado St Ste 250, Durango CO 81301
Tel (970) 764-6650 SIC 1389

CROSSFIRE LLC p 394
820 Airport Rd, Durango CO 81303
Tel (970) 884-4869 SIC 1389

SUMMIT SLICKLINE INC p 1399
20701 County Road 50, La Salle CO 80645
Tel (970) 397-1808 SIC 1389 7389

■ **A & W WATER SERVICE INC** p 4
1900 S Sunset St Unit 1f, Longmont CO 80501
Tel (303) 659-6523 SIC 1389

ACUREN INSPECTION INC p 20
30 Main St Ste 402, Danbury CT 06810
Tel (203) 702-8740 SIC 1389 8071

FRC FOUNDERS CORP p 575
1 Lafayette Pl Ste 3, Greenwich CT 06830
Tel (203) 661-6601
SIC 8741 1311 1389 8731 5084

LONGVIEW HOLDING CORP p 877
43 Arch St, Greenwich CT 06830
Tel (203) 869-6734 SIC 6719 1389

HEIDMAR INC p 680
20 Glover Ave Ste 14, Norwalk CT 06850
Tel (203) 662-2600 SIC 1389

NEW SOURCE ENERGY PARTNERS LP p 1033
300 Delaware Ave Ste 1100, Wilmington DE 19801
Tel (405) 272-3028 SIC 1311 1389

AMERICAN PETROLEUM INSTITUTE INC p 77
1220 L St Nw Ste 900, Washington DC 20005
Tel (202) 682-8000 SIC 1389

MC ASSEMBLY INTERNATIONAL LLC p 925
425 North Dr, Melbourne FL 32934
Tel (321) 253-0541 SIC 3825 1389

OFFSHORE INLAND MARINE & OILFIELD SERVICES INC p 1076
700 S Barracks St, Pensacola FL 32502
Tel (251) 443-5550 SIC 1389

COLONIAL PIPELINE CO p 338
1185 Sanctuary Pkwy # 100, Alpharetta GA 30009
Tel (678) 762-2200
SIC 4613 4612 4226 1389 5171

RFPS MANAGEMENT CO II LP p 1231
2170 Piedmont Rd Ne, Atlanta GA 30324
Tel (404) 888-2000 SIC 1389

▲ **RPC INC** p 1255
2801 Buford Hwy Ne # 520, Brookhaven GA 30329
Tel (404) 321-2140 SIC 1389

PETCO PETROLEUM CORP p 1138
108 E Ogden Ave Ste 100, Hinsdale IL 60521
Tel (630) 654-1740 SIC 1389

BADGER DAYLIGHTING CORP p 143
8930 Motorsports Way, Brownsburg IN 46112
Tel (317) 456-1432 SIC 1389

BADGER DAYLIGHTING USA INC p 143
8930 Motorsports Way, Brownsburg IN 46112
Tel (317) 456-1050 SIC 1389

TRADEBE GP p 1468
4343 Kennedy Ave, East Chicago IN 46312
Tel (800) 388-7242 SIC 4953 7699 1389

TRADEBE ENVIRONMENTAL SERVICES LLC p 1468
1433 E 83rd Ave Ste 200, Merrillville IN 46410
Tel (800) 388-7242 SIC 4953 7699 1389

CONSOLIDATED OIL WELL SERVICES LLC p 360
1322 S Grant Ave, Chanute KS 66720
Tel (620) 431-9210 SIC 1389

Q CONSOLIDATED OIL WELL SERVICES LLC p 1194
1322 S Grant Ave, Chanute KS 66720
Tel (620) 431-9210 SIC 1389

■ **KENTUCKY WEST VIRGINIA GAS CO** p 812
748 N Lake Dr, Prestonsburg KY 41653
Tel (606) 886-2311 SIC 1311 1389 4922

■ **INTERNATIONAL SNUBBING SERVICES LLC** p 756
190 Industries Ln, Arnaudville LA 70512
Tel (337) 754-7233 SIC 1389 7353

CAJUN DEEP FOUNDATIONS LLC p 237
15635 Airline Hwy, Baton Rouge LA 70817
Tel (225) 753-5857 SIC 1389

CAJUN INDUSTRIES LLC p 237
15635 Airline Hwy, Baton Rouge LA 70817
Tel (225) 753-5857 SIC 1389

DELMAR SYSTEMS INC p 425
8114 Highway 90 E, Broussard LA 70518
Tel (337) 365-0180 SIC 1389

OFFSHORE ENERGY SERVICES p 1076
5900 Highway 90 E, Broussard LA 70518
Tel (337) 837-1024 SIC 1389

■ **SUPERIOR ENERGY SERVICES LLC** p 1406
5801 Highway 90 E, Broussard LA 70518
Tel (337) 714-4545 SIC 1389 7353

■ **WARRIOR ENERGY SERVICES CORP** p 1577
5801 Highway 90 E, Broussard LA 70518
Tel (662) 329-1047 SIC 1389

ZEDI US INC p 1641
208 Rue Park Dr, Broussard LA 70518
Tel (337) 233-2066 SIC 1389

OMNI ENERGY SERVICES CORP p 1084
4500 Ne Evangeline Trwy, Carencro LA 70520
Tel (337) 896-6664 SIC 1382 1389 7349

■ **CETCO ENERGY SERVICES CO LLC** p 284
1001 Ochsner Blvd Ste 425, Covington LA 70433
Tel (985) 871-4700 SIC 1389 2869 3533

LOOP LLC p 877
137 Northpark Blvd, Covington LA 70433
Tel (985) 632-6970 SIC 1389

FRANCIS DRILLING FLUIDS LTD p 573
240 Jasmine Rd, Crowley LA 70526
Tel (337) 783-8685 SIC 5169 1389 7353

OFFSHORE MARINE CONTRACTORS INC p 1076
133 W 113th St, Cut Off LA 70345
Tel (985) 632-7927 SIC 1389

GRAND ISLE SHIPYARD INC p 629
18838 Highway 3235, Galliano LA 70354
Tel (985) 475-5238 SIC 1389

DANOS AND CUROLE MARINE CONTRACTORS LLC p 412
3878 W Main St, Gray LA 70359
Tel (985) 693-3313 SIC 1389

CAMERON INC p 245
1036 Destrehan Ave, Harvey LA 70058
Tel (504) 371-3000 SIC 1389

CHET MORRISON CONTRACTORS LLC p 295
9 Bayou Dularge Rd, Houma LA 70363
Tel (985) 868-1950
SIC 1623 3498 1629 1389

PERFORMANCE ENERGY SERVICES LLC p 1135
132 Valhi Lagoon Xing, Houma LA 70360
Tel (985) 868-4895 SIC 1623 1389 7363

QUALITY ENERGY SERVICES INC p 1197
230 Menard Rd, Houma LA 70363
Tel (985) 850-0025 SIC 1389

ANALYTIC STRESS RELIEVING INC p 88
3118 W Pinhook Rd Ste 202, Lafayette LA 70508
Tel (337) 237-8790 SIC 1389

FRANKS CASING CREW & RENTAL TOOLS INC p 575
700 E Verot School Rd, Lafayette LA 70508
Tel (337) 233-0303 SIC 7353 1389

TIMCO SERVICES INC p 1454
1724 E Milton Ave, Lafayette LA 70508
Tel (337) 233-5185 SIC 1389

UV LOGISTICS LLC p 1537
4021 Ambssdor Cffery Pkwy, Lafayette LA 70503
Tel (337) 837-4757 SIC 4213 1389

PROJECT CONSULTING SERVICES INC p 1182
3300 W Esplanade Ave S, Metairie LA 70002
Tel (504) 219-3426 SIC 1389

■ **PRODUCTION MANAGEMENT INDUSTRIES LLC** p 1179
1204 Youngs Rd, Morgan City LA 70380
Tel (985) 631-3837 SIC 1389 8731 4789

ASRC ENERGY SERVICES OMEGA LLC p 119
4418 Pesson Rd, New Iberia LA 70560
Tel (337) 365-6028 SIC 1389 3533

■ **BAYOU HOLDINGS OF NEW IBERIA LLC** p 162
5200 Curtis Ln, New Iberia LA 70560
Tel (337) 369-3761 SIC 1389

■ **J RAY MCDERMOTT & CO INC** p 772
1340 Poydras St Ste 1200, New Orleans LA 70112
Tel (504) 587-5000 SIC 1629 1389 1623

DIVERSIFIED WELL LOGGING INC p 444
711 W 10th St, Reserve LA 70084
Tel (985) 536-4143 SIC 1389

ISLAND OPERATING CO INC p 766
108 Zachary Dr, Scott LA 70583
Tel (337) 262-0620 SIC 1389

ARKLATEX ENERGY SERVICES LLC p 110
6913 Westport Ave, Shreveport LA 71129
Tel (318) 688-9850 SIC 1389

BRAMMER ENGINEERING INC p 207
400 Texas St Ste 600, Shreveport LA 71101
Tel (318) 429-2345 SIC 1389

TRACO PRODUCTION SERVICES INC p 1468
425 Griffin Rd, Youngsville LA 70592
Tel (337) 857-6000 SIC 5082 1389

■ **DTE ENERGY RESOURCES INC** p 458
414 S Main St Ste 600, Ann Arbor MI 48104
Tel (734) 302-4800 SIC 4911 1389

■ **ALLY SERVICING LLC** p 59
500 Woodward Ave Fl 1, Detroit MI 48226
Tel (248) 948-7702 SIC 1389

■ **JOHNSON KADANT INC** p 791
805 Wood St, Three Rivers MI 49093
Tel (269) 278-1715
SIC 3494 8711 1389 3052 1099

WCE OIL FIELD SERVICES LLC p 1585
601 Carlson Pkwy Ste 110, Hopkins MN 55305
Tel (701) 356-7303 SIC 1389

KELLEY BROTHERS CONTRACTORS INC p 808
401 County Farm Rd, Waynesboro MS 39367
Tel (601) 735-2541 SIC 1389 1382 1381

T K STANLEY INC p 1419
6739 Highway 184, Waynesboro MS 39367
Tel (601) 735-2855 SIC 1389

PAS TECHNOLOGIES INC p 1119
1234 Atlantic Ave, North Kansas City MO 64116
Tel (816) 556-5113 SIC 7699 1389

AIH FLINTCO LLC p 38
8800 Page Ave, Saint Louis MO 63114
Tel (314) 733-2000 SIC 1389 1522

MITCHELLS OILFIELD SERVICE INC p 977
409 N Central Ave, Sidney MT 59270
Tel (406) 482-4927 SIC 1389 3273

▲ **SOUTHWEST GAS CORP** p 1352
5241 Spring Mountain Rd, Las Vegas NV 89150
Tel (702) 876-0711 SIC 4923 1623 1389

HIGHLANDS FUEL DELIVERY LLC p 691
190 Commerce Way, Portsmouth NH 03801
Tel (603) 559-8700 SIC 5172 5541 1389

LANGAN ENGINEERING ENVIRONMENTAL SURVEYING AND LANDSCAPE ARCHITECTURE DPC p 844
300 Kimball Dr Ste 4, Parsippany NJ 07054
Tel (973) 560-4900
SIC 8711 8748 1389 0781

OTIS EASTERN SERVICE LLC p 1097
2971 Andover Rd, Wellsville NY 14895
Tel (585) 593-4760 SIC 1623 1389

■ **STEEL EXCEL INC** p 1384
1133 Westchester Ave N-222, White Plains NY 10604
Tel (914) 461-1300 SIC 1389 7353 7032

MISSOURI BASIN WELL SERVICE INC p 976
12980 35th St Sw, Belfield ND 58622
Tel (701) 575-8242 SIC 4213 1389

ALLIED RESOURCES LLC p 57
387 15th St W 366, Dickinson ND 58601
Tel (800) 677-1142 SIC 1389

WYOMING CASING SERVICE INC p 1630
198 40th St E, Dickinson ND 58601
Tel (701) 225-8521 SIC 1389

STINGRAY ENERGY SERVICES p 1390
42739 National Rd, Belmont OH 43718
Tel (405) 648-4177 SIC 1389

BDI INC p 164
8000 Hub Pkwy, Cleveland OH 44125
Tel (216) 642-9100 SIC 1389

KELCHNER INC p 808
50 Advanced Dr, Springboro OH 45066
Tel (937) 704-9890 SIC 1794 1389

PSC HOLDINGS INC p 1188
109 Graham St, Zanesville OH 43701
Tel (740) 454-6253 SIC 1389

O-TEX PUMPING LLC p 1070
7045 N Highway 81, Duncan OK 73533
Tel (580) 255-3111 SIC 1389

G & G STEAM SERVICE INC p 586
120 W 12th St, Elk City OK 73644
Tel (580) 225-4254 SIC 1389

MARSAU ENTERPRISES INC p 910
1209 N 30th St, Enid OK 73701
Tel (580) 233-3910 SIC 1389

HAMMER CONSTRUCTION INC p 656
4320 Adams Rd, Norman OK 73069
Tel (405) 310-3160 SIC 1389 1794

■ CHESAPEAKE OPERATING LLC p 295
6100 N Western Ave, Oklahoma City OK 73118
Tel (405) 848-8000 SIC 1311 1389 4212

CRESCENT SERVICES LLC p 391
5721 Nw 132nd St, Oklahoma City OK 73142
Tel (405) 603-1200 SIC 1389

LEGEND ENERGY SERVICES LLC p 853
5801 Broadway Ext Ste 210, Oklahoma City OK 73118
Tel (405) 600-1264 SIC 1389

▲ MAMMOTH ENERGY PARTNERS LP p 900
4727 Gaillardia Pkwy # 200, Oklahoma City OK 73142
Tel (405) 265-4600 SIC 1389 1381

PANHANDLE OILFIELD SERVICE COMPANIES INC p 1111
14000 Quail Springs Pkwy # 300, Oklahoma City OK 73134
Tel (405) 608-5330
SIC 1389 7389 3498 4212 5082 1794

SEVENTY SEVEN ENERGY INC p 1309
777 Nw 63rd St, Oklahoma City OK 73116
Tel (405) 608-7777 SIC 1389

SEVENTY SEVEN OPERATING LLC p 1309
777 Nw 63rd St, Oklahoma City OK 73116
Tel (405) 608-7777 SIC 3533 1389

■ STINGER WELLHEAD PROTECTION INC p 1390
4301 Will Rogers Pkwy # 600, Oklahoma City OK 73108
Tel (405) 702-6575 SIC 1389

■ THRU TUBING SOLUTIONS INC p 1451
11515 S Portland Ave, Oklahoma City OK 73170
Tel (405) 692-1900 SIC 1389

▲ CYPRESS ENERGY PARTNERS LP p 405
5727 S Lewis Ave Ste 300, Tulsa OK 74105
Tel (918) 748-3900 SIC 1389 7389

■ DOVER ARTIFICIAL LIFT SYSTEMS LLC p 453
15 E 5th St Ste 1421, Tulsa OK 74103
Tel (918) 396-0558 SIC 1389

▲ HELMERICH & PAYNE INC p 682
1437 S Boulder Ave # 1400, Tulsa OK 74119
Tel (918) 742-5531 SIC 1381 1389 6512

SAMSON ENERGY CO LLC p 1274
110 W 7th St Ste 2000, Tulsa OK 74119
Tel (918) 879-0279 SIC 1389 1741

▲ SEMGROUP CORP p 1302
6120 S Yale Ave Ste 700, Tulsa OK 74136
Tel (918) 524-8100
SIC 1389 4612 5171 2951

■ TARGA PIPELINE MID-CONTINENT LLC p 1425
110 W 7th St Ste 2300, Tulsa OK 74119
Tel (918) 574-3500 SIC 1389

CASEDHOLE SOLUTIONS INC p 263
1720 N Airport Rd, Weatherford OK 73096
Tel (580) 772-8900 SIC 1389

■ UNIVERSAL WELL SERVICES INC p 1518
13549 S Mosiertown Rd, Meadville PA 16335
Tel (814) 337-1983 SIC 1389 1382

ANDERSON PERFORATING LTD p 90
124 Welco Rd, Albany TX 76430
Tel (325) 762-2200 SIC 1389

FORBES ENERGY SERVICES LTD p 565
3000 S Business Hwy 281, Alice TX 78332
Tel (361) 664-0549 SIC 1389

LIGHTNING FLUID SERVICES INC p 865
1310 Southwood St, Alice TX 78332
Tel (361) 396-0801 SIC 1389 7389

TEXAS ENERGY SERVICES LP p 1443
4932 N Us Hwy 281, Alice TX 78332
Tel (361) 664-5020 SIC 1389

NATIVE OILFIELD SERVICES LLC p 1018
7900 S Interstate 35 W, Alvarado TX 76009
Tel (817) 783-3636 SIC 1389

K-3 RESOURCES LP p 799
850 County Road 149, Alvin TX 77511
Tel (281) 585-2817 SIC 1389

VENABLES CONSTRUCTION INC p 1547
7410 Continental Pkwy, Amarillo TX 79119
Tel (806) 381-2121
SIC 1623 1794 1389 4922 4612 1799

■ OIL STATES INDUSTRIES INC p 1079
7701 S Cooper St, Arlington TX 76001
Tel (817) 548-4200
SIC 1389 3061 3561 3533

HEALTHTRONICS SERVICE CENTER LLC p 676
9825 Spectrum Dr Bldg 3, Austin TX 78717
Tel (512) 328-2892 SIC 1389

PINNERGY LTD p 1150
111 Congress Ave Ste 2020, Austin TX 78701
Tel (512) 343-8880 SIC 1389

USA COMPRESSION PARTNERS LLC p 1534
100 Congress Ave Ste 450, Austin TX 78701
Tel (512) 369-1380 SIC 1389

▲ USA COMPRESSION PARTNERS LP p 1534
100 Congress Ave Ste 450, Austin TX 78701
Tel (512) 473-2662 SIC 1389

WAYNE FUELING SYSTEMS LLC p 1584
3814 Jarrett Way, Austin TX 78728
Tel (512) 388-8311 SIC 1389

BBB TANK SERVICES INC p 163
162 Independence Pkwy N, Baytown TX 77520
Tel (832) 695-2132 SIC 1389

ROYWELL SERVICES INC p 1255
4545 Bissonnet St Ste 104, Bellaire TX 77401
Tel (713) 661-4747 SIC 1389

PEAK OILFIELD SERVICES LLC p 1126
1502 10th St Ste A, Bridgeport TX 76426
Tel (940) 683-1627 SIC 1389

ROC SERVICE CO LLC p 1242
191 Energy Way, Bridgeport TX 76426
Tel (940) 683-0109 SIC 1794 1731 1389

WEST HOU INC p 1594
907 Bains St, Brookshire TX 77423
Tel (281) 934-1500 SIC 1389

KEPPEL AMFELS LLC p 813
20000 State Highway 48, Brownsville TX 78521
Tel (956) 831-8220
SIC 1629 3731 1389 3449 3546 3443

R CONSTRUCTION CO p 1201
1313 Hwy 79 S, Buffalo TX 75831
Tel (903) 322-4639 SIC 1389 1794

MULTI-SHOT LLC p 999
3335 Pollok Dr, Conroe TX 77303
Tel (936) 441-6630 SIC 1389 1381

PROFESSIONAL DIRECTIONAL ENTERPRISES INC p 1180
850 Conroe Park West Dr, Conroe TX 77303
Tel (936) 441-7266 SIC 1389 1381

REPCON INC p 1224
7501 Up River Rd, Corpus Christi TX 78409
Tel (361) 289-6342 SIC 1629 1389

DEGOLYER AND MACNAUGHTON CORP p 422
5001 Spring Valley Rd 800e, Dallas TX 75244
Tel (214) 368-6391 SIC 1389

PURITY OILFIELD SERVICES LLC p 1192
2101 Cedar Springs Rd, Dallas TX 75201
Tel (214) 880-8400 SIC 1389

MO-VAC SERVICE CO p 980
3721 S Mccoll Rd, Edinburg TX 78539
Tel (956) 682-6381 SIC 1389 4959

▲ BASIC ENERGY SERVICES INC p 158
801 Cherry St Unit 2, Fort Worth TX 76102
Tel (817) 334-4100 SIC 1389 1794

■ BASIC ENERGY SERVICES LP p 158
801 Cherry St Unit 2, Fort Worth TX 76102
Tel (817) 334-4100 SIC 1389

CDK PERFORATING LLC p 271
6500 West Fwy Ste 600, Fort Worth TX 76116
Tel (817) 945-1051 SIC 1389

COMPASS WELL SERVICES LLC p 351
4100 Intl Plz Ste 500, Fort Worth TX 76109
Tel (817) 244-2555 SIC 1389 1382

CREST PUMPING TECHNOLOGIES LLC p 392
6500 West Fwy Ste 601, Fort Worth TX 76116
Tel (817) 484-5100 SIC 1389

FTS INTERNATIONAL INC p 583
777 Main St Ste 3000, Fort Worth TX 76102
Tel (682) 862-2000 SIC 1389

QES WIRELINE LLC p 1195
801 Cherry St Ste 800, Fort Worth TX 76102
Tel (817) 546-4970 SIC 1389

SITTON ENTERPRISES LLC p 1328
4100 Intl Plz Ste 820, Fort Worth TX 76109
Tel (940) 328-6000 SIC 1389

SELECT ENERGY SERVICES LLC p 1301
1820 N Interstate 35, Gainesville TX 76240
Tel (940) 668-1818 SIC 1389

TEXAS CES INC p 1442
3333 Ih 35 N Bldg F, Gainesville TX 76240
Tel (940) 668-5100 SIC 1389

CATALYST OILFIELD SERVICES 2016 LLC p 264
11999 E Us Highway 158, Gardendale TX 79758
Tel (432) 563-0727 SIC 1389

■ PUMPCO INC p 1192
1209 S Main St, Giddings TX 78942
Tel (979) 542-9054 SIC 1623 1389

BOBCAT CONTRACTING LLC p 196
1721 Hcr 3106, Hillsboro TX 76645
Tel (254) 582-0205 SIC 1389

AKER SUBSEA INC p 42
3010 Briarpark Dr, Houston TX 77042
Tel (713) 685-5700 SIC 3533 1389 8711

ALLIED WIRELINE SERVICES LLC p 57
3200 Wilcrest Dr Ste 170, Houston TX 77042
Tel (713) 343-7280 SIC 1389

ALLIS-CHALMERS ENERGY INC p 58
12101 Cutten Rd, Houston TX 77066
Tel (281) 301-2600 SIC 1381 1389 7353

▲ ARCHROCK INC p 105
16666 Northchase Dr, Houston TX 77060
Tel (281) 836-8000 SIC 1389

ATLANTIC PACIFIC MARINE CORP p 127
2500 City W Blvd Ste 1850, Houston TX 77042
Tel (713) 346-4300 SIC 1389

■ BAKER HUGHES OILFIELD OPERATIONS INC p 146
17021 Aldine Westfield Rd, Houston TX 77073
Tel (713) 439-8600
SIC 1381 1311 1389 2899

BJ SERVICES CO USA LP p 186
5500 Nw Central Dr # 100, Houston TX 77092
Tel (713) 462-4239 SIC 1389

BLACK ELK ENERGY OFFSHORE OPERATIONS p 186
842 W Sam Houston Pkwy N # 500, Houston TX 77024
Tel (832) 973-4230 SIC 1389

■ BOOTS & COOTS LLC p 200
3000 N Sam Houston Pkwy E, Houston TX 77032
Tel (281) 871-2699 SIC 1389

C&J ENERGY SERVICES INC p 234
3990 Rogerdale Rd, Houston TX 77042
Tel (713) 325-6000 SIC 1382 1389

C&J WELL SERVICES INC p 234
3990 Rogerdale Rd, Houston TX 77042
Tel (281) 874-0035 SIC 1389

CAMAC INTERNATIONAL CORP p 243
1330 Post Oak Blvd Ste 22, Houston TX 77056
Tel (713) 965-5100
SIC 8711 6552 1382 8741 1389

CAMERON INTERNATIONAL HOLDING CORP p 245
4646 W Sam Houston Pkwy N, Houston TX 77041
Tel (713) 513-3300 SIC 1389

CAMERON SOLUTIONS INC p 245
11210 Equity Dr Ste 100, Houston TX 77041
Tel (713) 849-7500 SIC 3533 1389 3569

CARBER HOLDINGS INC p 252
12600 N Featherwood Dr # 450, Houston TX 77034
Tel (713) 797-2859 SIC 1389 7389

■ CDM RESOURCE MANAGEMENT LLC p 271
20405 State Hwy Ste 700, Houston TX 77070
Tel (281) 376-2980 SIC 1389

■ COMPLETE PRODUCTION SERVICES INC p 351
1001 Louisiana St, Houston TX 77002
Tel (281) 372-2300 SIC 1389 1381

CORE LABORATORIES LP p 369
6316 Windfern Rd, Houston TX 77040
Tel (713) 328-2673 SIC 1389

EMS USA INC p 495
2000 Bering Dr Ste 600, Houston TX 77057
Tel (713) 595-7600 SIC 1389

ENERGY MAINTENANCE SERVICES GROUP I INC p 497
2000 Bering Dr Ste 600, Houston TX 77057
Tel (713) 595-7600 SIC 1389

ENERGY RESOURCE TECHNOLOGY GOM LLC p 498
500 Dallas St Ste 2000, Houston TX 77002
Tel (281) 618-0590 SIC 1311 1389

EXPRESS ENERGY SERVICES OPERATING LP p 520
9800 Richmond Ave Ste 500, Houston TX 77042
Tel (713) 625-7400 SIC 1389

■ EXTERRAN TRINIDAD LLC p 521
12001 N Huston Rosslyn Rd, Houston TX 77086
Tel (281) 921-9337 SIC 7353 5084 1389

FUGRO (USA) INC p 583
6100 Hillcroft St Ste 700, Houston TX 77081
Tel (713) 772-3700 SIC 1389 8711 8999

GE OIL & GAS COMPRESSION SYSTEMS LLC p 596
16250 Port Nw, Houston TX 77041
Tel (713) 354-1900 SIC 1389

GREYSTAR CORP p 639
10375 Richmond Ave # 900, Houston TX 77042
Tel (713) 953-7007 SIC 1389

▲ GULF ISLAND FABRICATION INC p 646
16225 Park Ten Pl Ste 280, Houston TX 77084
Tel (713) 714-6100 SIC 3441 1389

GYRODATA INC p 649
23000 Nw Lake Dr, Houston TX 77095
Tel (713) 461-3146 SIC 1389 8713

▲ HALLIBURTON CO p 654
3000 N Sam Houston Pkwy E, Houston TX 77032
Tel (281) 871-2699
SIC 1389 1382 1381 8711

■ HALLIBURTON DELAWARE INC p 654
3000 Houston Ave, Houston TX 77009
Tel (713) 759-2600
SIC 1629 1611 1622 8711 1389

■ HALLIBURTON ENERGY SERVICES INC p 654
10200 Bellaire Blvd, Houston TX 77072
Tel (713) 839-3950 SIC 1389

▲ HELIX ENERGY SOLUTIONS GROUP INC p 681
3505 W Sam Houston Pkwy N, Houston TX 77043
Tel (281) 618-0400 SIC 1629 1389 1311

▲ HERCULES OFFSHORE INC p 685
9 Greenway Plz Ste 2200, Houston TX 77046
Tel (713) 350-5100 SIC 1381 1389

HOLLOMAN CORP p 701
333 N Sam Houston Pkwy E, Houston TX 77060
Tel (281) 878 2600 SIC 1541 1623 1389

HUNTING ENERGY SERVICES INC p 719
2 Northpoint Dr Ste 400, Houston TX 77060
Tel (281) 820-3838 SIC 1389 8741

■ INTEGRATED PRODUCTION SERVICES INC p 749
16800 Greenspt Pk Dr 200s, Houston TX 77060
Tel (281) 774-6700 SIC 1389 3599

■ IOS/PCI LLC p 762
652 N Sam Houston Pkwy E, Houston TX 77060
Tel (281) 310-5357 SIC 1389 7389

IRONGATE ENERGY SERVICES LLC p 765
19500 State Highway 249 # 600, Houston TX 77070
Tel (832) 678-8585 SIC 1389

JEFFERSON ENERGY I LP p 781
3104 Edloe St Ste 205, Houston TX 77027
Tel (713) 552-0002 SIC 1389 5051

KEY ENERGY SERVICES INC p 814
1301 Mckinney St Ste 1800, Houston TX 77010
Tel (713) 651-4300 SIC 1389 1381 1311

M-I LLC p 890
5950 N Course Dr, Houston TX 77072
Tel (281) 561-1300
SIC 1389 2865 2869 8711 8741

▲ MCDERMOTT INTERNATIONAL INC p 927
757 N Eldridge Pkwy, Houston TX 77079
Tel (281) 870-5000 SIC 1389 1623

■ MIDCOAST OPERATING LP p 964
1100 La St Ste 3300, Houston TX 77002
Tel (713) 821-2000 SIC 5172 1389

MORRISON ENERGY GROUP p 990
16285 Park Ten Pl, Houston TX 77084
Tel (281) 616-8405 SIC 1389

NABORS INDUSTRIES INC p 1006
515 W Greens Rd Ste 1200, Houston TX 77067
Tel (281) 874-0035 SIC 1381 1389

NABORS OFFSHORE CORP p 1006
515 W Greens Rd Ste 1200, Houston TX 77067
Tel (281) 874-0406 SIC 1381 1389

NABORS WELL SERVICES CO p 1006
515 W Greens Rd Ste 1000, Houston TX 77067
Tel (281) 874-0035 SIC 1389

NABORS WELL SERVICES LTD p 1006
515 W Greens Rd Ste 1200, Houston TX 77067
Tel (281) 874-0035 SIC 1389 7353

NATCO GROUP INC p 1009
11210 Equity Dr Ste 100, Houston TX 77041
Tel (713) 849-7500 SIC 3533 1389

▲ OCEANEERING INTERNATIONAL INC p 1073
11911 Fm 529 Rd, Houston TX 77041
Tel (713) 329-4500 SIC 1389 3731 8711

OIL PATCH GROUP INC p 1079
11767 Katy Fwy Ste 510a, Houston TX 77079
Tel (832) 300-0000 SIC 1389 7353

OLD GES INC p 1080
11757 Katy Fwy Ste 700, Houston TX 77079
Tel (281) 598-6830
SIC 1389 7353 3599 7359 1382

PARMAN CAPITAL GROUP LLC p 1117
1000 La St Ste 5900, Houston TX 77002
Tel (713) 751-2700 SIC 1389 7353

▲ PATTERSON-UTI ENERGY INC p 1121
10713 W Sam Huston Pkwy N, Houston TX 77064
Tel (281) 765-7100 SIC 1381 1389 1311

PRECISION ENERGY SERVICES INC p 1168
2000 Saint James Pl, Houston TX 77056
Tel (713) 693-4000 SIC 3533 1389

PRIDE INTERNATIONAL INC p 1174
5847 San Felipe St # 3400, Houston TX 77057
Tel (713) 789-1400 SIC 1381 1389 8711

PROSERV OPERATIONS INC p 1184
13105 Nw Fwy Ste 250, Houston TX 77040
Tel (281) 407-2405 SIC 1389

QUINTANA ENERGY SERVICES LP p 1200
601 Jefferson St Ste 3600, Houston TX 77002
Tel (713) 751-7500 SIC 1389

RENAISSANCE OFFSHORE LLC p 1223
920 Mmrial Cy Way Ste 800, Houston TX 77024
Tel (832) 333-7700 SIC 1389 1311

RYAN DIRECTIONAL SERVICES INC p 1260
19510 Oil Center Blvd, Houston TX 77073
Tel (281) 443-1414 SIC 1389

SAIPEM AMERICA INC p 1271
15950 Park Row, Houston TX 77084
Tel (281) 552-5600 SIC 8711 1389

SAYBOLT LP p 1285
6316 Windfern Rd, Houston TX 77040
Tel (713) 328-2673 SIC 1389

SCHLUMBERGER INTERNATIONAL INC p 1287
7030 Ardmore St, Houston TX 77054
Tel (713) 747-4000
SIC 1389 3561 3492 3533

SCHLUMBERGER LIMITED p 1287
5599 San Felipe St Fl 17, Houston TX 77056
Tel (713) 513-2000
SIC 1381 1389 1382 3825 3824 3823

SCHLUMBERGER OMNES INC p 1287
5599 San Felipe St Fl 17, Houston TX 77056
Tel (713) 375-3400 SIC 1382 1389

SCIENTIFIC DRILLING INTERNATIONAL INC p 1292
16071 Greenspoint Park Ste 200, Houston TX 77060
Tel (281) 443-3300 SIC 1381 1389

SCOMI EQUIPMENT INC p 1293
6607 Theall Rd, Houston TX 77066
Tel (281) 260-6016 SIC 1389

■ SESI LLC p 1308
1001 Louisiana St, Houston TX 77002
Tel (504) 587-7374 SIC 7353 1389

SPITZER INDUSTRIES INC p 1359
12141 Wickc Ln Ste 750, Houston TX 77079
Tel (713) 466-1518 SIC 1389

STALLION OILFIELD SERVICES LTD p 1375
950 Corbindale Rd Ste 300, Houston TX 77024
Tel (713) 528-5544 SIC 1389

STEWART & STEVENSON POWER PRODUCTS LLC p 1389
1000 La St Ste 5900, Houston TX 77002
Tel (713) 751-2600
SIC 1389 5084 5082 3533 7353

SUN COAST RESOURCES INC p 1400
6405 Cavalcade St Bldg 1, Houston TX 77026
Tel (713) 844-9600
SIC 5172 2992 5084 1389

▲ SUPERIOR ENERGY SERVICES INC p 1406
1001 La St Ste 2900, Houston TX 77002
Tel (713) 654-2200 SIC 1389 3533 7353

■ TARGA RESOURCES LLC p 1425
1000 Louisiana St # 4300, Houston TX 77002
Tel (713) 873-1000 SIC 1389 6799

TERRY ENERGY INC p 1440
3104 Edloe St Ste 205, Houston TX 77027
Tel (713) 552-0002 SIC 1389

■ TERVITA LLC p 1440
10613 W Sam Huston Pkwy N, Houston TX 77064
Tel (832) 399-4500 SIC 1389

■ TESCO CORP (US) p 1440
11330 Clay Rd Ste 350, Houston TX 77041
Tel (713) 359-7000
SIC 7353 5082 1389 1381

TMK IPSCO INC p 1457
10120 Houston Oaks Dr, Houston TX 77064
Tel (281) 949-1023 SIC 1389

TRICAN WELL SERVICE LP p 1479
5825 N Sam Houston Pkwy W # 600, Houston TX 77086
Tel (281) 716-9152 SIC 2911 1481 1389

TUBULAR SERVICES LLC p 1490
1010 Mccarty St, Houston TX 77029
Tel (713) 675-6212 SIC 1389

TUCKER ENERGY SERVICES INC p 1490
411 N Sam Houston Pkwy E # 300, Houston TX 77060
Tel (281) 442-9095 *SIC* 1389 3533

■ **UNIVERSAL ENSCO INC** p 1516
4848 Loop Central Dr # 137, Houston TX 77081
Tel (713) 425-6000 *SIC* 1389

US WELL SERVICES LLC p 1533
770 S Post Oak Ln Ste 405, Houston TX 77056
Tel (832) 562-3731 *SIC* 1389

■ **VARCO LP** p 1544
2835 Holmes Rd, Houston TX 77051
Tel (713) 799-5272 *SIC* 1389 3479

W-H ENERGY SERVICES LLC p 1569
2000 W Sam Houston Pkwy S # 500, Houston TX 77042
Tel (713) 969-1000 *SIC* 1389 7353

WEATHERFORD INTERNATIONAL LLC p 1586
2000 Saint James Pl, Houston TX 77056
Tel (713) 693-4000 *SIC* 1389

WEATHERFORD LABORATORIES INC p 1586
2000 Saint James Pl, Houston TX 77056
Tel (832) 237-4000 *SIC* 1389

WEDGE GROUP INC p 1587
1415 La St Ste 3000, Houston TX 77002
Tel (713) 739-6500 *SIC* 1389 1629 1311

WEDGE MEASUREMENT SYSTEMS LLC p 1587
1415 La St Ste 1500, Houston TX 77002
Tel (713) 490-9444 *SIC* 1389

■ **WILD WELL CONTROL INC** p 1609
2202 Oil Center Ct, Houston TX 77073
Tel (281) 784-4700 *SIC* 1389

WOOD GROUP MANAGEMENT SERVICES INC p 1622
17325 Park Row, Houston TX 77084
Tel (281) 828-3500 *SIC* 1389

WOOD GROUP MUSTANG INC p 1622
17325 Park Row, Houston TX 77084
Tel (832) 809-8000
SIC 8711 8742 7389 1389

■ **BAKER HUGHES OILFIELD OPERATIONS INC** p 146
1333 Corporate Dr Ste 300, Irving TX 75038
Tel (972) 988-0111 *SIC* 1389

■ **PIONEER NATURAL RESOURCES PUMPING SERVICES LLC** p 1151
5205 N O Connor Blvd # 200, Irving TX 75039
Tel (972) 444-9001 *SIC* 1389

PATHFINDER ENERGY SERVICES LLC p 1120
23500 Colonial Pkwy, Katy TX 77493
Tel (281) 769-4501 *SIC* 1389

EPRODUCTION SOLUTIONS LLC p 505
22001 Northpark Dr, Kingwood TX 77339
Tel (281) 348-1000 *SIC* 3491 5084 1389

CEDA INTERNATIONAL INC p 272
2600 S Shore Blvd Ste 300, League City TX 77573
Tel (281) 478-2600 *SIC* 1389

T E C WELL SERVICE INC p 1419
851 W Harrison Rd, Longview TX 75604
Tel (903) 759-0082 *SIC* 1389

REDZONE COIL TUBING LLC p 1217
701 N 1st St Ste 109, Lufkin TX 75901
Tel (936) 632-2645 *SIC* 1389

ADVANCED STIMULATION TECHNOLOGIES INC p 26
2903 E Interstate 20, Midland TX 79706
Tel (432) 994-0900 *SIC* 1389

▲ **CSI COMPRESSCO LP** p 397
3809 S Fm 1788, Midland TX 79706
Tel (432) 563-1170 *SIC* 1389 3533

DON-NAN PUMP AND SUPPLY CO INC p 450
3427 E Garden Cy Hwy 158, Midland TX 79706
Tel (432) 682-7742 *SIC* 1389 3599 3561

KEL-TECH INC p 808
3408 E State Highway 158, Midland TX 79706
Tel (432) 684-4700 *SIC* 1389 8731

■ **SOUTHWEST ROYALTIES INC** p 1352
6 Desta Dr Ste 2100, Midland TX 79705
Tel (432) 688-3008 *SIC* 1311 6211 1389

MIDWAY OILFIELD CONSTRUCTORS INC p 967
12627 State Highway 21 E, Midway TX 75852
Tel (936) 348-3721 *SIC* 1389 1623

E L FARMER & CO p 466
3800 E 42nd St Ste 417, Odessa TX 79762
Tel (432) 366-2010 *SIC* 1389

LOOMIS INTERNATIONAL INC p 877
100 N Richey St, Pasadena TX 77506
Tel (713) 477-7148 *SIC* 1389

HOUSTON TUBULARS INC p 712
13600 Hatfield Rd, Pearland TX 77581
Tel (281) 485-4014 *SIC* 1389

■ **MULTI-CHEM GROUP LLC** p 999
424 S Chadbourne St, San Angelo TX 76903
Tel (325) 223-6200 *SIC* 1389

■ **ENTERPRISE HYDROCARBONS LP** p 502
1100 La St Fl 10, San Antonio TX 78209
Tel (713) 381-6500 *SIC* 1389

■ **PIONEER WELL SERVICES LLC** p 1151
1250 Ne Loop 410 Ste 1000, San Antonio TX 78209
Tel (210) 828-7689 *SIC* 1389

■ **PIONEER WIRELINE SERVICES LLC** p 1151
1250 Ne Loop 410 Ste 1000, San Antonio TX 78209
Tel (210) 828-7689 *SIC* 1389

▲ **EMERGE ENERGY SERVICES LP** p 491
180 State St Ste 225, Southlake TX 76092
Tel (817) 865-5830 *SIC* 1311 1389 4613

■ **TETRA APPLIED TECHNOLOGIES INC** p 1441
24955 Interstate 45, Spring TX 77380
Tel (281) 367-1983 *SIC* 1389

■ **GE OIL & GAS LOGGING SERVICES INC** p 596
13000 Executive Dr, Sugar Land TX 77478
Tel (281) 579-9879 *SIC* 1389 4789

SCHLUMBERGER TECHNOLOGY CORP p 1287
100 Gillingham Ln, Sugar Land TX 77478
Tel (281) 285-8500
SIC 1382 1389 3825 3824 3533 3586

ACCELERATED PRODUCTION SERVICES INC p 14
1585 Sawdust Rd Ste 210, The Woodlands TX 77380
Tel (281) 403-5793 *SIC* 1389

■ **CUDD PRESSURE CONTROL INC** p 400
2828 Tech Forest Blvd, The Woodlands TX 77381
Tel (832) 295-5555 *SIC* 1389

FK DELLIA LLC p 553
25025 North Fwy I45210, The Woodlands TX 77380
Tel (817) 546-3358 *SIC* 1389

■ **NEWPARK MATS & INTEGRATED SERVICES LLC** p 1038
9320 Lkeside Blvd Ste 100, The Woodlands TX 77381
Tel (281) 362-6800 *SIC* 1389

▲ **NEWPARK RESOURCES INC** p 1038
9320 Lkeside Blvd Ste 100, The Woodlands TX 77381
Tel (281) 362-6800
SIC 1389 4959 4953 2273

SAVANNA ENERGY SERVICES (USA) CORP p 1284
2445 Technology Ste 200, The Woodlands TX 77381
Tel (281) 907-4800 *SIC* 1381 1389

▲ **TETRA TECHNOLOGIES INC** p 1441
24955 Interstate 45, The Woodlands TX 77380
Tel (281) 367-1983 *SIC* 2819 1389

CHALK MOUNTAIN SERVICES OF TEXAS LLC p 286
2828 Chambers St, Venus TX 76084
Tel (817) 473-1931 *SIC* 1389

ELITE COMPRESSION SERVICES LLC p 487
10375 Rchmond Ave Ste 450, Victoria TX 77901
Tel (361) 894-6320 *SIC* 1389

RN INDUSTRIES TRUCKING p 1239
188 W 200 N, Roosevelt UT 84066
Tel (435) 722-2800 *SIC* 1389

PARAMETRIX INC p 1114
1019 39th Ave Se Ste 100, Puyallup WA 98374
Tel (206) 394-3700
SIC 8748 8711 8742 1389 4789

SIC 1411 Dimension Stone

ASH GROVE MATERIALS CORP p 117
11011 Cody St Ste 300, Overland Park KS 66210
Tel (913) 345-2030
SIC 3273 3272 1411 7389 4212

HAMM INC p 656
609 Perry Pl, Perry KS 66073
Tel (785) 597-5111 *SIC* 1411 1771 1611

AGGREGATE INDUSTRIES p 34
6211 N Ann Arbor Rd, Dundee MI 48131
Tel (734) 529-5876
SIC 3273 2951 1442 1411 1771 5211

▲ **MINERALS TECHNOLOGIES INC** p 973
622 3rd Ave Fl 38, New York NY 10017
Tel (212) 878-1800
SIC 3295 2819 3274 1411 3281 5032

CAROLINA SUNROCK LLC p 259
1001 W B St, Butner NC 27509
Tel (919) 575-4502
SIC 1429 3273 2951 1411

SUNROCK GROUP HOLDINGS CORP p 1404
200 Horizon Dr Ste 100, Raleigh NC 27615
Tel (919) 747-6400
SIC 1429 3273 2951 1411

WATERLOO COAL CO INC p 1582
3675 Dixon Run Rd, Jackson OH 45640
Tel (740) 286-5633 *SIC* 1221 1411 1459

CLI HOLDINGS INC p 326
3950 S 700 E Ste 301, Salt Lake City UT 84107
Tel (801) 262-3942 *SIC* 1411

GRAYMONT WESTERN US INC p 632
3950 S 700 E Ste 301, Salt Lake City UT 84107
Tel (801) 262-3942 *SIC* 1411

EDEN STONE CO INC p 477
W4520 Lime Rd, Eden WI 53019
Tel (920) 477-2521 *SIC* 1411 5032

SIC 1422 Crushed & Broken Limestone

■ **LEGACY VULCAN LLC** p 852
1200 Urban Center Dr, Shoal Creek AL 35242
Tel (205) 298-3000
SIC 1422 1423 1442 2951 3273

■ **LEGACY VULCAN LLC** p 852
1200 Urban Center Dr, Vestavia AL 35242
Tel (205) 298-3000
SIC 1422 1423 1442 2951 3273

■ **VULCAN CONSTRUCTION MATERIALS LLC** p 1567
1200 Urban Center Dr, Vestavia AL 35242
Tel (205) 298-3000 *SIC* 1422

▲ **VULCAN MATERIALS CO** p 1567
1200 Urban Center Dr, Vestavia AL 35242
Tel (205) 298-3000
SIC 1422 1423 2951 1442 3273 3272

▲ **SUMMIT MATERIALS INC** p 1399
1550 Wynkoop St Fl 3, Denver CO 80202
Tel (303) 893-0012 *SIC* 1422 1622 1795

UNIMIN CORP p 1504
258 Elm St, New Canaan CT 06840
Tel (203) 966-8880
SIC 1446 1499 1422 1459 4011 1442

■ **FLORIDA ROCK INDUSTRIES** p 559
4707 Gordon St, Jacksonville FL 32216
Tel (904) 355-1781 *SIC* 1422

CEMEX MATERIALS LLC p 274
1501 Belvedere Rd, West Palm Beach FL 33406
Tel (561) 833-5555
SIC 3271 3273 3272 1422

IMERYS USA INC p 733
100 Mansell Ct E Ste 300, Roswell GA 30076
Tel (770) 645-3300
SIC 1455 1459 1429 1422 2819

RIVERSTONE GROUP INC p 1238
1701 5th Ave, Moline IL 61265
Tel (309) 757-8250 *SIC* 1422

MATERIAL SERVICE CORP p 919
2235 Entp Dr Ste 3504, Westchester IL 60154
Tel (708) 731-2600 *SIC* 1422 1442

MULZER CRUSHED STONE INC p 1000
534 Mozart St, Tell City IN 47586
Tel (812) 547-7921
SIC 1422 3273 5191 5085

OMG MID WEST INC p 1084
2401 SeTones Dr Ste 13, Ankeny IA 50021
Tel (515) 266-9928 *SIC* 1442 1422

WENDLING QUARRIES INC p 1592
2647 225th St, De Witt IA 52742
Tel (563) 659-9181 *SIC* 1422 1611 1442

IOWA LIMESTONE CO p 763
3301 106th Cir, Urbandale IA 50322
Tel (515) 243-3160 *SIC* 1422 5191

ASH GROVE CEMENT CO p 116
11011 Cody St Ste 300, Overland Park KS 66210
Tel (913) 451-8900
SIC 3241 3273 1422 3271

HANSON AGGREGATES MIDWEST LLC p 659
207 Old Harrods Creek Rd, Louisville KY 40223
Tel (502) 244-7550 *SIC* 1422 1611

WALKER CO OF KENTUCKY INC p 1573
105 Apperson Hts, Mount Sterling KY 40353
Tel (859) 498-0092
SIC 1611 2951 1542 3273 1422

YAGER MATERIALS LLC p 1633
5001 Highway 2830, Owensboro KY 42303
Tel (270) 926-0893
SIC 1442 1422 1611 3273 4491 3731

HINKLE CONTRACTING CORP p 695
395 N Middletown Rd, Paris KY 40361
Tel (859) 987-3670
SIC 1611 1422 3273 3272 3271 2951

LAFARGE MID-ATLANTIC LLC p 837
300 E Joppa Rd Ste 200, Baltimore MD 21286
Tel (410) 847-9445 *SIC* 3273 1422

LAUREL SAND & GRAVEL INC p 847
14504 Greenview Dr # 210, Laurel MD 20708
Tel (410) 792-7234 *SIC* 1422 1442

HUNT MIDWEST ENTERPRISES INC p 719
8300 Ne Underground Dr # 100, Kansas City MO 64161
Tel (816) 455-2500 *SIC* 6552 1422 6211

MISSISSIPPI LIME CO p 975
3870 S Lindbergh Blvd # 200, Saint Louis MO 63127
Tel (314) 543-6300
SIC 3274 2819 2879 1422

LEO JOURNAGAN CONSTRUCTION CO INC p 856
3003 E Chestnut Expy, Springfield MO 65802
Tel (417) 869-7222 *SIC* 1422 1611 1623

COBLESKILL STONE PRODUCTS INC p 333
112 Rock Rd, Cobleskill NY 12043
Tel (518) 234-0221 *SIC* 1422

■ **SPECIALTY MINERALS INC** p 1356
622 3rd Ave Fl 38, New York NY 10017
Tel (212) 878-1800
SIC 2819 5032 1422 5169 2899

▲ **MARTIN MARIETTA MATERIALS INC** p 912
2710 Wycliff Rd, Raleigh NC 27607
Tel (919) 781-4550
SIC 1423 1422 1442 3295 3297

OMYA INDUSTRIES INC p 1085
9987 Carver Rd Ste 300, Blue Ash OH 45242
Tel (513) 387-4600 *SIC* 1422

NATIONAL LIME AND STONE CO p 1014
551 Lake Cascade Pkwy, Findlay OH 45840
Tel (419) 422-4341
SIC 1422 1442 3273 1423 1499

SHELLY MATERIALS INC p 1314
80 Park Dr, Thornville OH 43076
Tel (740) 246-6315
SIC 1422 1442 2951 4492

DOLESE BROS CO p 448
20 Nw 13th St, Oklahoma City OK 73103
Tel (405) 235-2311 *SIC* 3273 1422 1442

MARTIN LIMESTONE INC p 912
3580 Division Hwy, East Earl PA 17519
Tel (717) 335-4500
SIC 3273 3271 1611 1422 8741 5211

MILL SERVICES CORP p 969
12 Monongahela Ave, Glassport PA 15045
Tel (412) 678-6141
SIC 3295 1422 8742 3341

PENNSY SUPPLY INC p 1130
1001 Paxton St, Harrisburg PA 17104
Tel (717) 233-4511
SIC 1422 2951 3273 4212 5032

INTERNATIONAL MILL SERVICE INC p 756
1155 Bus Ctr Dr Ste 200, Horsham PA 19044
Tel (215) 956-5500
SIC 3295 3341 1422 8742

ALLAN MYERS MATERIALS INC p 52
638 Lancaster Ave, Malvern PA 19355
Tel (610) 560-7900 *SIC* 1422

NEW ENTERPRISE STONE & LIME CO INC p 1030
3912 Brumbaugh Rd, New Enterprise PA 16664
Tel (814) 224-6883 *SIC* 1422 1611

CARMEUSE LIME & STONE INC p 258
11 Stanwix St Fl 21, Pittsburgh PA 15222
Tel (412) 995-5500 *SIC* 1422

CARMEUSE LIME INC p 258
11 Stanwix St Fl 21, Pittsburgh PA 15222
Tel (412) 995-5500 *SIC* 1422 3274

O-N MINERALS CO (OHIO) p 1070
11 Stanwix St Fl 21, Pittsburgh PA 15222
Tel (412) 995-5500 *SIC* 1422

HAINES & KIBBLEHOUSE INC p 653
2052 Lucon Rd, Skippack PA 19474
Tel (610) 584-8500
SIC 1794 1611 1422 2951

GLENN O HAWBAKER INC p 615
1952 Waddle Rd Ste 203, State College PA 16803
Tel (814) 237-1444
SIC 2951 3281 1622 1794 1611 1422

MAGNESITA REFRACTORIES CO p 896
425 S Salem Church Rd, York PA 17408
Tel (717) 792-3611 *SIC* 3297 3274 1422

PETE LIEN & SONS INC p 1138
3401 Universal Dr, Rapid City SD 57702
Tel (605) 342-7224
SIC 3273 3441 1422 3274

LHOIST NORTH AMERICA OF TENNESSEE INC p 861
750 Old Hickory Blvd 200-2, Brentwood TN 37027
Tel (615) 259-4222 *SIC* 1422

ROGERS GROUP INC p 1246
421 Great Circle Rd, Nashville TN 37228
Tel (615) 242-0585 *SIC* 1611 1422

LATTIMORE MATERIALS CO LP p 846
15900 Dooley Rd, Addison TX 75001
Tel (972) 221-4646 *SIC* 3273 1422 1442

■ **UNITED STATES LIME & MINERALS INC** p 1513
5429 Lbj Fwy Ste 230, Dallas TX 75240
Tel (972) 991-8400 *SIC* 1422 3274 6289

TEXAS CRUSHED STONE CO INC p 1442
5300 S Interstate 35, Georgetown TX 78626
Tel (512) 255-4405 *SIC* 1422 2951 1442

CEMEX CONSTRUCTION MATERIALS SOUTH LLC p 274
920 Mmrial Cy Way Ste 100, Houston TX 77024
Tel (713) 650-6200
SIC 3271 3273 3272 1422

HANSON LEHIGH INC p 659
300 E John Carpenter Fwy, Irving TX 75062
Tel (972) 653-5500
SIC 1442 1422 1423 3297 3273 3272

CAPITOL AGGREGATES INC p 250
11551 Nacogdoches Rd, San Antonio TX 78217
Tel (210) 655-3010
SIC 3241 1442 1422 2951 4011

■ **MARTIN MARIETTA MATERIALS SOUTHWEST INC** p 912
5710 W Hausman Rd Ste 121, San Antonio TX 78249
Tel (210) 208-4400
SIC 1422 3273 2951 3274 1442

BOXLEY MATERIALS CO p 205
15418 W Lynchburg, Blue Ridge VA 24064
Tel (540) 777-7600 *SIC* 1422 1423

GREER INDUSTRIES INC p 639
570 Canyon Rd, Morgantown WV 26508
Tel (304) 296-2549
SIC 3316 3272 2951 1422 3274 1446

SIC 1423 Crushed & Broken Granite

■ **LEGACY VULCAN LLC** p 852
1200 Urban Center Dr, Shoal Creek AL 35242
Tel (205) 298-3000
SIC 1422 1423 1442 2951 3273

■ **LEGACY VULCAN LLC** p 852
1200 Urban Center Dr, Vestavia AL 35242
Tel (205) 298-3000
SIC 1422 1423 1442 2951 3273

▲ **VULCAN MATERIALS CO** p 1567
1200 Urban Center Dr, Vestavia AL 35242
Tel (205) 298-3000
SIC 1422 1423 2951 1442 3273 3272

MCGEORGE CONTRACTING CO INC p 929
1501 Heartwood St, White Hall AR 71602
Tel (870) 534-7120 *SIC* 1611 1423

HANSON AGGREGATES SOUTHEAST INC p 659
2310 Parklake Dr Ne # 550, Atlanta GA 30345
Tel (770) 491-2777 *SIC* 1423 1442

WAKE STONE CORP p 1572
6821 Knightdale Blvd, Knightdale NC 27545
Tel (919) 266-1100 *SIC* 1423

▲ **MARTIN MARIETTA MATERIALS INC** p 912
2710 Wycliff Rd, Raleigh NC 27607
Tel (919) 781-4550
SIC 1423 1422 1442 3295 3297

NATIONAL LIME AND STONE CO p 1014
551 Lake Cascade Pkwy, Findlay OH 45840
Tel (419) 422-4341
SIC 1422 1442 3273 1423 1499

HANSON LEHIGH INC p 659
300 E John Carpenter Fwy, Irving TX 75062
Tel (972) 653-5500
SIC 1442 1422 1423 3297 3273 3272

BOXLEY MATERIALS CO p 205
15418 W Lynchburg, Blue Ridge VA 24064
Tel (540) 777-7600 *SIC* 1422 1423

LUCK STONE CORP p 884
515 Stone Mill Dr, Manakin Sabot VA 23103
Tel (804) 784-3383
SIC 1423 2899 3281 5211 8741

SIC 1429 Crushed & Broken Stone, NEC

OLIVER DE SILVA INC p 1082
11555 Dublin Blvd, Dublin CA 94568
Tel (925) 829-9220 *SIC* 1429

■ **CALMAT CO** p 242
500 N Brand Blvd Ste 500, Glendale CA 91203
Tel (818) 553-8821
SIC 2951 1442 1429 3273 6512 6552

DUTRA GROUP p 463
2350 Kerner Blvd Ste 200, San Rafael CA 94901
Tel (415) 258-6876 *SIC* 1629 8711 1429

IMERYS USA INC p 733
100 Mansell Ct E Ste 300, Roswell GA 30076
Tel (770) 645-3300
SIC 1455 1459 1429 1422 2819

GRACE PACIFIC LLC p 628
949 Kamokila Blvd Ste 200, Kapolei HI 96707
Tel (808) 674-8383 *SIC* 1611 1429 3272

MOUNTAIN WEST LLC p 994
4212 S Highway 191, Rexburg ID 83440
Tel (208) 359-5640 *SIC* 1429

TRAP ROCK INDUSTRIES INC p 1473
460 River Rd, Kingston NJ 08528
Tel (609) 924-0300
SIC 3273 3272 1429 1611

TILCON NEW YORK INC p 1453
162 Old Mill Rd, West Nyack NY 10994
Tel (845) 358-4500 SIC 1429

CAROLINA SUNROCK LLC p 259
1001 W B St, Butner NC 27509
Tel (919) 575-4502
SIC 1429 3273 2951 1411

SUNROCK GROUP HOLDINGS CORP p 1404
200 Horizon Dr Ste 100, Raleigh NC 27615
Tel (919) 747-6400
SIC 1429 3273 2951 1411

M & B ASPHALT CO INC p 888
1525 W Seneca Cnty Rd 42, Tiffin OH 44883
Tel (419) 992-4235
SIC 1429 2951 1611 2952 1771

L G EVERIST INC p 834
300 S Phillips Ave # 200, Sioux Falls SD 57104
Tel (712) 552-1347 SIC 1442 1429

■ **SUPERIOR SILICA SANDS LLC** p 1407
6000 Western Pl Ste 465, Fort Worth TX 76107
Tel (817) 841-8070 SIC 1429

GRAYMONT INC p 632
301 S 700 E 3950, Salt Lake City UT 84102
Tel (801) 262-3942 SIC 1429 2951 3273

SIC 1442 Construction Sand & Gravel

■ **LEGACY VULCAN LLC** p 852
1200 Urban Center Dr, Shoal Creek AL 35242
Tel (205) 298-3000
SIC 1422 1423 1442 2951 3273

■ **LEGACY VULCAN LLC** p 852
1200 Urban Center Dr, Vestavia AL 35242
Tel (205) 298-3000
SIC 1422 1423 1442 2951 3273

▲ **VULCAN MATERIALS CO** p 1567
1200 Urban Center Dr, Vestavia AL 35242
Tel (205) 298-3000
SIC 1422 1423 2951 1442 3273 3272

SALT RIVER SAND & ROCK p 1273
8800 E Chaparral Rd # 155, Scottsdale AZ 85250
Tel (480) 850-5757 SIC 5032 1442

PINE BLUFF SAND AND GRAVEL CO p 1148
1501 Heartwood St, White Hall AR 71602
Tel (870) 534-7120
SIC 2951 3273 1442 5032 1629

ROBERTSONS READY MIX LTD A CALIFORNIA LIMITED PARTNERSHIP p 1242
200 S Main St Ste 200, Corona CA 92882
Tel (951) 493-6500
SIC 3273 3531 5032 2951 1442

■ **CALMAT CO** p 242
500 N Brand Blvd Ste 500, Glendale CA 91203
Tel (818) 553-8821
SIC 2951 1442 1429 3273 6512 6552

■ **AMERON INTERNATIONAL CORP** p 84
245 S Los Robles Ave, Pasadena CA 91101
Tel (626) 683-4000
SIC 3272 3317 3273 1442 3084

A TEICHERT & SON INC p 6
3500 American River Dr, Sacramento CA 95864
Tel (916) 484-3011
SIC 5032 3273 1611 1442 1521

TEICHERT INC p 1433
3500 American River Dr, Sacramento CA 95864
Tel (916) 484-3011
SIC 3273 5032 1611 1442 1521 5039

▲ **GRANITE CONSTRUCTION INC** p 631
585 W Beach St, Watsonville CA 95076
Tel (831) 724-1011
SIC 1611 1622 1629 1442

GRANITE ROCK CO p 631
350 Technology Dr, Watsonville CA 95076
Tel (831) 768-2000
SIC 1442 3273 5032 2951 1611 3271

AGGREGATE INDUSTRIES-WCR INC p 35
1687 Cole Blvd Ste 300, Lakewood CO 80401
Tel (303) 716-5200
SIC 1611 1442 1499 2951

TRADEBE TREATMENT AND RECYCLING NORTHEAST LLC p 1468
47 Gracey Ave, Meriden CT 06451
Tel (203) 238-8102 SIC 4953 1442 4212

UNIMIN CORP p 1504
258 Elm St, New Canaan CT 06840
Tel (203) 966-8880
SIC 1446 1499 1422 1459 4011 1442

HANSON AGGREGATES SOUTHEAST INC p 659
2310 Parklake Dr Ne # 550, Atlanta GA 30345
Tel (770) 491-2777 SIC 1423 1442

CONCRETE CO p 355
1030 1st Ave, Columbus GA 31901
Tel (706) 256-5700 SIC 1442 3272

FELDSPAR CORP p 537
100 Mansell Ct E Ste 300, Roswell GA 30076
Tel (770) 594-0660 SIC 1459 1442

EUCON CORP p 512
4201 Snake River Ave, Lewiston ID 83501
Tel (509) 533-1615 SIC 1442 1611

LAFARGE NORTH AMERICA INC p 837
8700 W Bryn Mawr Ave Ll, Chicago IL 60631
Tel (703) 480-3600
SIC 3241 3273 3272 3271 1442 2951

■ **MATERIAL SERVICE RESOURCES CORP** p 919
222 N La Salle St # 1200, Chicago IL 60601
Tel (630) 325-7736 SIC 1442 1221

ELMHURST-CHICAGO STONE CO p 489
400 W 1st St, Elmhurst IL 60126
Tel (630) 832-4000 SIC 1442 3273 3272

SOUTHFIELD CORP p 1351
8995 W 95th St, Palos Hills IL 60465
Tel (708) 344-1000
SIC 3273 1442 3241 4212 4213 5032

MATERIAL SERVICE CORP p 919
2235 Entp Dr Ste 3504, Westchester IL 60154
Tel (708) 731-2600 SIC 1422 1442

ASPHALT MATERIALS INC p 118
5400 W 86th St, Indianapolis IN 46268
Tel (317) 872-6010 SIC 2951 1442

OMG MID WEST INC p 1084
2401 Se Tones Dr Ste 13, Ankeny IA 50021
Tel (515) 266-9928 SIC 1442 1422

MANATTS INC p 900
1775 Old 6 Rd, Brooklyn IA 52211
Tel (641) 522-9206
SIC 1611 1442 2951 3273

WENDLING QUARRIES INC p 1592
2647 225th St, De Witt IA 52742
Tel (563) 659-9181 SIC 1422 1611 1442

HSG RESOURCES INC p 715
9660 Legler Rd, Shawnee Mission KS 66219
Tel (913) 492-5920 SIC 1442

YAGER MATERIALS LLC p 1633
5001 Highway 2830, Owensboro KY 42303
Tel (270) 926-0893
SIC 1442 1422 1611 3273 4491 3731

CHANEY ENTERPRISES LIMITED PARTNERSHIP p 288
2410 Evergreen Rd Ste 201, Gambrills MD 21054
Tel (410) 451-0197
SIC 3273 1442 5032 3429

LAUREL SAND & GRAVEL INC p 847
14504 Greenview Dr # 210, Laurel MD 20708
Tel (410) 792-7234 SIC 1422 1442

BOSTON SAND & GRAVEL CO INC p 203
100 N Washington St Fl 2, Boston MA 02114
Tel (617) 227-9000 SIC 3273 1442

BROX INDUSTRIES INC p 220
1471 Methuen St, Dracut MA 01826
Tel (978) 454-9105
SIC 1442 1499 1611 1629 1794 2951

P A LANDERS INC p 1102
351 Winter St, Hanover MA 02339
Tel (781) 826-8818 SIC 1611 1442

PETRICCA INDUSTRIES INC p 1139
550 Cheshire Rd, Pittsfield MA 01201
Tel (413) 499-1441
SIC 1611 1623 3273 3272 1442

AGGREGATE INDUSTRIES p 34
6211 N Ann Arbor Rd, Dundee MI 48131
Tel (734) 529-5876
SIC 3273 2951 1442 1411 1771 5211

TILLER CORP p 1453
7200 Hemlock Ln N Ste 200, Maple Grove MN 55369
Tel (763) 424-5400 SIC 1442 2951

CEMSTONE PRODUCTS CO p 274
2025 Centr Poin Blvd Ste 300, Mendota Heights MN 55120
Tel (651) 688-9292 SIC 3273 5032 1442

TWIN CITY CONCRETE PRODUCTS CO INC p 1495
2025 Centre Pointe Blvd # 300, Mendota Heights MN 55120
Tel (651) 688-9116
SIC 5032 3273 3255 1442

■ **KNIFE RIVER CORP - NORTH CENTRAL** p 824
4787 Shadowwood Dr Ne, Sauk Rapids MN 56379
Tel (320) 251-9472
SIC 1611 1442 3273 2951

FRED WEBER INC p 576
2320 Creve Coeur Mill Rd, Maryland Heights MO 63043
Tel (314) 344-0070
SIC 1611 1442 3272 1622 1542

NEBCO INC p 1023
1815 Y St, Lincoln NE 68508
Tel (402) 434-1212
SIC 5999 3273 3272 3271 1442 4013

LYMAN-RICHEY CORP p 887
4315 Cuming St, Omaha NE 68131
Tel (402) 556-3600
SIC 3273 1442 3271 5211 5032

HANSON AGGREGATES WRP INC p 659
1333 Campus Pkwy, Wall Township NJ 07753
Tel (972) 653-5500
SIC 3281 3272 2951 1442

DALRYMPLE HOLDING CORP p 410
2105 S Broadway, Pine City NY 14871
Tel (607) 737-6200
SIC 3273 1611 1442 1622 3281

BONSAL AMERICAN INC p 200
625 Griffith Rd Ste 100, Charlotte NC 28217
Tel (704) 525-1621
SIC 3272 1442 3253 2899

▲ **MARTIN MARIETTA MATERIALS INC** p 912
2710 Wycliff Rd, Raleigh NC 27607
Tel (919) 781-4550
SIC 1423 1422 1442 3295 3297

B V HEDRICK GRAVEL & SAND CO p 142
120 1/2 N Church St, Salisbury NC 28144
Tel (704) 633-5982
SIC 1442 7359 6512 3273 1541 1542

■ **KNIFE RIVER CORP** p 824
1150 W Century Ave, Bismarck ND 58503
Tel (701) 530-1400 SIC 1442 3273 1221

▲ **MDU RESOURCES GROUP INC** p 933
1200 W Century Ave, Bismarck ND 58503
Tel (701) 530-1000
SIC 4911 4924 4922 1221 1442 1311

FISHER SAND & GRAVEL CO p 552
3020 Energy Dr, Dickinson ND 58601
Tel (701) 456-9184 SIC 1442 3532 5084

STRATA CORP p 1392
1600 N 48th St, Grand Forks ND 58203
Tel (701) 775-4205
SIC 1611 3273 1442 5032

BEST SAND CORP p 177
11830 Ravenna Rd, Chardon OH 44024
Tel (440) 285-3132 SIC 1446 1442

TECHNISAND INC p 1431
11833 Ravenna Rd, Chardon OH 44024
Tel (440) 285-3132 SIC 1442

HILLTOP BASIC RESOURCES INC p 694
1 W 4th St Ste 1100, Cincinnati OH 45202
Tel (513) 651-5000 SIC 1442 3273

OLEN CORP p 1082
4755 S High St, Columbus OH 43207
Tel (614) 491-1515 SIC 1442

NATIONAL LIME AND STONE CO p 1014
551 Lake Cascade Pkwy, Findlay OH 45840
Tel (419) 422-4341
SIC 1422 1442 3273 1423 1499

SHELLY MATERIALS INC p 1314
80 Park Dr, Thornville OH 43076
Tel (740) 246-6315
SIC 1422 1442 2951 4492

SHELLY AND SANDS INC p 1314
3570 S River Rd, Zanesville OH 43701
Tel (740) 453-0721 SIC 1611 1442 2951

DOLESE BROS CO p 448
20 Nw 13th St, Oklahoma City OK 73103
Tel (405) 235-2311 SIC 3273 1422 1442

EVANS & ASSOCIATES ENTERPRISES INC p 513
3320 N 14th St, Ponca City OK 74601
Tel (580) 765-6693
SIC 5032 2951 1442 1611 3273 1311

HEMPT BROS INC p 682
205 Creek Rd, Camp Hill PA 17011
Tel (717) 774-2911
SIC 1611 3273 2951 1442 0212

SNYDER ASSOCIATED COMPANIES INC p 1336
1 Glade Park Dr, Kittanning PA 16201
Tel (724) 548-8101 SIC 1442 3281 1222

L G EVERIST INC p 834
300 S Phillips Ave # 200, Sioux Falls SD 57104
Tel (712) 552-1347 SIC 1442 1429

LATTIMORE MATERIALS CO LP p 846
15900 Dooley Rd, Addison TX 75001
Tel (972) 221-4646 SIC 3273 1422 1442

■ **TXI OPERATIONS LP** p 1495
1341 W Mockingbird Ln 700w, Dallas TX 75247
Tel (972) 647-6700
SIC 3273 3271 3272 1442

CEMEX EL PASO INC p 274
1 Mckelligon Canyon Rd, El Paso TX 79930
Tel (915) 565-4681
SIC 3273 2951 5032 1442

TEXAS CRUSHED STONE CO INC p 1442
5300 S Interstate 35, Georgetown TX 78626
Tel (512) 255-4405 SIC 1422 2951 1442

▲ **HI-CRUSH PARTNERS LP** p 689
3 Riverway Ste 1350, Houston TX 77056
Tel (713) 960-4777 SIC 1442 1481

HANSON LEHIGH INC p 659
300 E John Carpenter Fwy, Irving TX 75062
Tel (972) 653-5500
SIC 1442 1422 1423 3297 3273 3272

HUNTER INDUSTRIES LTD p 719
5080 Fm 2439, New Braunfels TX 78132
Tel (512) 353-7757 SIC 1611 2951 1442

CAPITOL AGGREGATES INC p 250
11551 Nacogdoches Rd, San Antonio TX 78217
Tel (210) 655-3010
SIC 3241 1442 1422 2951 4011

■ **MARTIN MARIETTA MATERIALS SOUTHWEST INC** p 912
5710 W Hausman Rd Ste 121, San Antonio TX 78249
Tel (210) 208-4400
SIC 1422 3273 2951 3274 1442

ZACHRY CONSOLIDATED LLC p 1640
527 Logwood Ave, San Antonio TX 78221
Tel (210) 871-2700
SIC 1611 1622 1623 1629 3241 1442

FORDYCE LTD p 566
120 S Main St, Victoria TX 77901
Tel (361) 573-4309 SIC 1442

SUNROC CORP p 1404
3657 S River Rd, St George UT 84790
Tel (435) 634-2200
SIC 5031 3273 5032 3271 1442

TARMAC MID-ATLANTIC INC p 1425
1151 Azalea Garden Rd, Norfolk VA 23502
Tel (757) 858-6500
SIC 3273 1442 3272 3271

MCC INC p 926
2600 N Roemer Rd, Appleton WI 54911
Tel (920) 749-3360 SIC 3273 1442 1611

COUNTY MATERIALS CORP p 375
205 North St, Marathon WI 54448
Tel (715) 443-2434
SIC 3271 5211 3273 3272 1442

MATHY CONSTRUCTION CO p 920
920 10th Ave N, Onalaska WI 54650
Tel (608) 783-6411
SIC 1611 1771 1442 5171

EDWARD KRAEMER & SONS INC p 480
1 Plainview Rd, Plain WI 53577
Tel (608) 546-2311 SIC 1622 1442

SIC 1446 Industrial Sand

UNIMIN CORP p 1504
258 Elm St, New Canaan CT 06840
Tel (203) 966-8880
SIC 1446 1499 1422 1459 4011 1442

C-E MINERALS INC p 234
100 Mansell Ct E Ste 615, Roswell GA 30076
Tel (770) 225-7900
SIC 1099 1446 3295 6512

■ **HOURGLASS HOLDINGS LLC** p 711
8490 Progress Dr Ste 300, Frederick MD 21701
Tel (301) 682-0600 SIC 1446

■ **U S SILICA CO** p 1497
8490 Progress Dr Ste 300, Frederick MD 21701
Tel (301) 682-0600 SIC 1446 1455 1459

▲ **US SILICA HOLDINGS INC** p 1533
8490 Progress Dr Ste 300, Frederick MD 21701
Tel (301) 682-0600 SIC 1446

SAND PRODUCTS CORP p 1278
13495 92nd St Se, Alto MI 49302
Tel (231) 722-6691 SIC 1446

BEST SAND CORP p 177
11830 Ravenna Rd, Chardon OH 44024
Tel (440) 285-3132 SIC 1446 1442

FAIRMOUNT MINERALS LLC p 525
8834 Mayfield Rd Ste A, Chesterland OH 44026
Tel (269) 926-9450 SIC 1446

FAIRMOUNT SANTROL HOLDINGS INC p 525
8834 Mayfield Rd Ste A, Chesterland OH 44026
Tel (800) 255-7263 SIC 1446

■ **PREMIER SILICA LLC** p 1171
5205 N O Connor Blvd # 200, Irving TX 75039
Tel (972) 444-9001 SIC 1446

GREER INDUSTRIES INC p 639
570 Canyon Rd, Morgantown WV 26508
Tel (304) 296-2549
SIC 3316 3272 2951 1422 3274 1446

BADGER MINING CORP p 144
409 S Church St, Berlin WI 54923
Tel (920) 361-2388 SIC 1446

SIC 1455 Kaolin & Ball Clay

IMERYS USA INC p 733
100 Mansell Ct E Ste 300, Roswell GA 30076
Tel (770) 645-3300
SIC 1455 1459 1429 1422 2819

■ **U S SILICA CO** p 1497
8490 Progress Dr Ste 300, Frederick MD 21701
Tel (301) 682-0600 SIC 1446 1455 1459

JM HUBER CORP p 786
499 Thornall St Ste 8, Edison NJ 08837
Tel (732) 603-3630
SIC 0811 1311 1455 2493 2819

RESCO PRODUCTS INC p 1226
1 Robinson Plz Ste 300, Pittsburgh PA 15205
Tel (412) 494-4491
SIC 3297 3255 1455 1499 5032

SIC 1459 Clay, Ceramic & Refractory Minerals, NEC

UNIMIN CORP p 1504
258 Elm St, New Canaan CT 06840
Tel (203) 966-8880
SIC 1446 1499 1422 1459 4011 1442

RT VANDERBILT CO INC p 1203
30 Winfield St, Norwalk CT 06855
Tel (203) 853-1400
SIC 5169 2869 2819 5052 1499 1459

RT VANDERBILT HOLDING CO INC p 1256
30 Winfield St, Norwalk CT 06855
Tel (203) 295-2141
SIC 5169 2869 2819 1499 1459

RHI REFRACTORIES HOLDING CO p 1231
1105 N Market St Ste 1300, Wilmington DE 19801
Tel (302) 655-6497
SIC 3297 3255 1459 3546 3272 3589

ENTEC POLYMERS LLC p 501
1900 Summit Tower Blvd # 900, Orlando FL 32810
Tel (407) 875-9595 SIC 5162 1459

FELDSPAR CORP p 537
100 Mansell Ct E Ste 300, Roswell GA 30076
Tel (770) 594-0660 SIC 1459 1442

IMERYS USA INC p 733
100 Mansell Ct E Ste 300, Roswell GA 30076
Tel (770) 645-3300
SIC 1455 1459 1429 1422 2819

■ **AMCOL INTERNATIONAL CORP** p 65
2870 Forbs Ave, Hoffman Estates IL 60192
Tel (847) 851-1500
SIC 1459 5032 4213 4731

■ **AMERICAN COLLOID CO** p 70
2870 Forbs Ave, Hoffman Estates IL 60192
Tel (847) 851-1700 SIC 1459 2899

■ **U S SILICA CO** p 1497
8490 Progress Dr Ste 300, Frederick MD 21701
Tel (301) 682-0600 SIC 1446 1455 1459

WATERLOO COAL CO INC p 1582
3675 Dixon Run Rd, Jackson OH 45640
Tel (740) 286-5633 SIC 1221 1411 1459

GLOBAL INDUSTRIAL TECHNOLOGIES INC p 616
1305 Chrrington Pkwy Moon, Coraopolis PA 15108
Tel (412) 375-6600
SIC 3297 3255 1459 3546 3272 3589

HARBISONWALKER INTERNATIONAL INC p 659
1305 Cherrington Pkwy # 100, Moon Township PA 15108
Tel (412) 375-6600 SIC 3297 3272 1459

BYK ADDITIVES INC p 231
1212 Church St, Gonzales TX 78629
Tel (830) 672-2891 SIC 1459 3295 3297

KYANITE MINING CORP p 833
30 Willis Mountain Ln, Dillwyn VA 23936
Tel (434) 983-2085 SIC 1459

SIC 1474 Potash, Soda & Borate Minerals

▲ **INTREPID POTASH INC** p 760
707 17th St Ste 4200, Denver CO 80202
Tel (303) 296-3006 SIC 1474

US BORAX INC p 1531
8051 E Maplewood Ave # 100, Greenwood Village CO 80111
Tel (303) 713-5000 SIC 1474 2819

■ **CINER ENTERPRISES INC** p 308
5 Concourse Pkwy Ste 2500, Atlanta GA 30328
Tel (770) 375-2300 SIC 1474 2812

■ **CINER RESOURCES CORP** p 308
5 Concourse Pkwy, Atlanta GA 30328
Tel (770) 375-2300 SIC 1474 2812

■ **CINER RESOURCES LP** p 308
5 Concourse Pkwy Ste 2500, Atlanta GA 30328
Tel (770) 375-2300 SIC 1474

■ **CINER WYOMING HOLDING CO** p 308
5 Concourse Pkwy, Atlanta GA 30328
Tel (770) 375-2300 SIC 1474 2812

PCS PHOSPHATE CO INC p 1124
1101 Skokie Blvd Ste 400, Northbrook IL 60062
Tel (847) 849-4200
SIC 1475 1474 2874 2819

▲ **COMPASS MINERALS INTERNATIONAL INC** p 351
9900 W 109th St Ste 100, Overland Park KS 66210
Tel (913) 344-9200 SIC 1474 2899 2819

■ MOSAIC CROP NUTRITION LLC p 991
3033 Campus Dr, Minneapolis MN 55441
Tel (763) 577-2700 *SIC* 2874 1474

■ MOSAIC GLOBAL HOLDINGS INC p 991
3033 Campus Dr Ste E490, Minneapolis MN 55441
Tel (763) 577-2700
SIC 2874 1474 1475 2875 2819

■ INTREPID POTASH-NEW MEXICO LLC p 760
1996 Potash Mines Rd, Carlsbad NM 88220
Tel (575) 887-5591 *SIC* 1474

▲ NATURAL RESOURCE PARTNERS LP p 1018
1201 La St Ste 3400, Houston TX 77002
Tel (713) 751-7507 *SIC* 1221 1474

SOLVAY CHEMICALS INC p 1339
3737 Buffalo Speedway, Houston TX 77098
Tel (713) 525-6800 *SIC* 1474 2819

SIC 1475 Phosphate Rock

WASHINGTON GROUP INTERNATIONAL INC p 1578
720 E Park Blvd, Boise ID 83712
Tel (208) 386-5000
SIC 1611 1629 1221 1081 4959 1475

■ PHOSPHATE RESOURCE PARTNERS LIMITED PARTNERSHIP p 1145
100 Saunders Rd Ste 300, Lake Forest IL 60045
Tel (847) 739-1200
SIC 2874 1311 1475 2819 1094

PCS PHOSPHATE CO INC p 1124
1101 Skokie Blvd Ste 400, Northbrook IL 60062
Tel (847) 849-4200
SIC 1475 1474 2874 2819

■ MOSAIC GLOBAL HOLDINGS INC p 991
3033 Campus Dr Ste E490, Minneapolis MN 55441
Tel (763) 577-2700
SIC 2874 1474 1475 2875 2819

■ MOS HOLDINGS INC p 991
3033 Campus Dr Ste E490, Plymouth MN 55441
Tel (763) 577-2700
SIC 2874 1475 2819 1094 1481

▲ MOSAIC CO p 991
3033 Campus Dr Ste E490, Plymouth MN 55441
Tel (800) 918-8270 *SIC* 2874 1475

SIC 1479 Chemical & Fertilizer Mining

■ CYPRUS AMAX MINERALS CO p 405
333 N Central Ave, Phoenix AZ 85004
Tel (602) 366-8100
SIC 1221 1222 1021 1061 1479 1041

MORTON INTERNATIONAL LLC p 991
123 N Wacker Dr Ste 2400, Chicago IL 60606
Tel (312) 807-2696
SIC 2891 2851 2822 1479 2899

MORTON SALT INC p 991
123 N Wacker Dr Fl 24, Chicago IL 60606
Tel (800) 725-8847
SIC 2891 2851 2822 1479 2899

■ COMPASS MINERALS AMERICA INC p 351
9900 W 109th St Ste 600, Overland Park KS 66210
Tel (913) 344-9100 *SIC* 2899 1479

KARNAVATI HOLDINGS INC p 804
9401 Indian Creek Pkwy # 1000, Overland Park KS 66210
Tel (913) 344-9500 *SIC* 1479

SEARLES VALLEY MINERALS INC p 1297
9401 Indn Crk Pkwy # 1000, Overland Park KS 66210
Tel (913) 344-9500 *SIC* 1479

SVM MINERALS HOLDINGS INC p 1410
9401 Indian Creek Pkwy, Overland Park KS 66210
Tel (913) 344-9500 *SIC* 1479

AMERICAN ROCK SALT CO LLC p 78
3846 Retsof Rd, Retsof NY 14539
Tel (585) 991-6878 *SIC* 1479 5169

TEXAS UNITED CORP p 1444
4800 San Felipe St, Houston TX 77056
Tel (713) 877-1793
SIC 1479 2819 4619 2899 3299 7353

SIC 1481 Nonmetallic Minerals Svcs, Except Fuels

■ MOS HOLDINGS INC p 991
3033 Campus Dr Ste E490, Plymouth MN 55441
Tel (763) 577-2700
SIC 2874 1475 2819 1094 1481

EP MINERALS LLC p 504
9785 Gateway Dr Ste 1000, Reno NV 89521
Tel (775) 824-7600 *SIC* 1481

B H P MINERALS INTERNATIONAL INC p 142
300 W Arrington Ste 101, Waterflow NM 87421
Tel (505) 598-4200 *SIC* 1481

▲ HI-CRUSH PARTNERS LP p 689
3 Riverway Ste 1350, Houston TX 77056
Tel (713) 960-4777 *SIC* 1442 1481

TRICAN WELL SERVICE LP p 1479
5825 N Sam Houston Pkwy W # 600, Houston TX 77086
Tel (281) 716-9152 *SIC* 2911 1481 1389

▲ LAYNE CHRISTENSEN CO p 848
1800 Hughes Landing Blvd, The Woodlands TX 77380
Tel (281) 475-2600
SIC 1781 1623 5084 1481 8748

BOART LONGYEAR CO p 196
2570 W 1700 S, Salt Lake City UT 84104
Tel (801) 972-6430
SIC 1481 3532 3559 1771

LONGYEAR HOLDINGS INC p 877
2340 W 1700 S, Salt Lake City UT 84104
Tel (801) 972-6430 *SIC* 1481 3532 3559

WESTERN EXPLOSIVES SYSTEMS CO p 1598
3135 S Richmond St, Salt Lake City UT 84106
Tel (801) 484-6557
SIC 5169 1629 1241 1081 1481 2892

LONGYEAR CO p 877
10808 S River Front Pkwy, South Jordan UT 84095
Tel (801) 972-6430 *SIC* 1481

ILUKA RESOURCES INC p 733
12472 St John Church Rd, Stony Creek VA 23882
Tel (434) 348-4300 *SIC* 1481

SIC 1499 Miscellaneous Nonmetallic Mining

IMERYS MINERALS CALIFORNIA INC p 733
2500 San Miguelito Rd, Lompoc CA 93436
Tel (805) 736-1221 *SIC* 1499 3295

IMERYS FILTRATION MINERALS INC p 733
1732 N 1st St Ste 450, San Jose CA 95112
Tel (805) 562-0200 *SIC* 1499

IMERYS PERLITE USA INC p 733
1732 N 1st St Ste 450, San Jose CA 95112
Tel (408) 643-0215 *SIC* 1499

IMERYS TALC AMERICA INC p 733
1732 N 1st St Ste 450, San Jose CA 95112
Tel (805) 562-0260 *SIC* 3295 1499

AGGREGATE INDUSTRIES-WCR INC p 35
1687 Cole Blvd Ste 300, Lakewood CO 80401
Tel (303) 716-5200
SIC 1611 1442 1499 2951

UNIMIN CORP p 1504
258 Elm St, New Canaan CT 06840
Tel (203) 966-8880
SIC 1446 1499 1422 1459 4011 1442

R T VANDERBILT CO INC p 1203
30 Winfield St, Norwalk CT 06855
Tel (203) 853-1400
SIC 5169 2869 2819 5052 1499 1459

R T VANDERBILT HOLDING CO INC p 1256
30 Winfield St, Norwalk CT 06855
Tel (203) 295-2141
SIC 5169 2869 2819 1499 1459

ASBURY CARBONS INC p 115
103 Foulk Rd Ste 202, Wilmington DE 19803
Tel (302) 652-0266
SIC 1499 3295 1241 5051 3952 3069

SUN GRO HORTICULTURE DISTRIBUTION INC p 1400
770 Silver St, Agawam MA 01001
Tel (413) 786-4343 *SIC* 1499 2875

BROX INDUSTRIES INC p 220
1471 Methuen St, Dracut MA 01826
Tel (978) 454-9105
SIC 1442 1499 1611 1629 1794 2951

BARTON MINES CO LLC p 158
6 Warren St, Glens Falls NY 12801
Tel (518) 798-5462 *SIC* 1499 3291 5085

NYCO MINERALS INC p 1069
803 Mountain View Dr, Willsboro NY 12996
Tel (518) 963-4262
SIC 1499 5052 3295 3291

NATIONAL LIME AND STONE CO p 1014
551 Lake Cascade Pkwy, Findlay OH 45840
Tel (419) 422-4341
SIC 1422 1442 3273 1423 1499

GRAFTECH HOLDINGS INC p 628
6100 Oak Tree Blvd # 300, Independence OH 44131
Tel (216) 676-2000 *SIC* 1499 3624

HARRISON GYPSUM LLC p 664
1550 Double C Dr, Norman OK 73069
Tel (405) 366-9500 *SIC* 1499 4213

RESCO PRODUCTS INC p 1226
1 Robinson Plz Ste 300, Pittsburgh PA 15205
Tel (412) 494-4491
SIC 3297 3255 1455 1499 5032

SIC 1521 General Contractors, Single Family Houses

RENAISSANCE WOODWORKING CO INC p 1223
13 Walnut St Ne, Decatur AL 35601
Tel (256) 308-1231 *SIC* 1542 1521

■ KBR CONSTRUCTION CO LLC p 806
3000 Riverchase Galleria, Hoover AL 35244
Tel (205) 972-6538
SIC 1541 1796 1711 1629 1799 1521

AHTNA INC p 37
110 W 38th Ave Ste 100, Anchorage AK 99503
Tel (907) 868-8250
SIC 1629 7389 1542 1521

ACHEN-GARDNER INC p 17
550 S 79th St, Chandler AZ 85226
Tel (480) 940-1300
SIC 1611 1542 1521 1751 6552

NATIONWIDE HOMES INC p 1018
1100 London Bridge Rd G102, Lake Havasu City AZ 86404
Tel (928) 453-6600 *SIC* 1521 6531

KITCHELL CONTRACTORS INC OF ARIZONA p 822
1707 E Highland Ave # 200, Phoenix AZ 85016
Tel (602) 264-4411 *SIC* 1541 1542 1521

KITCHELL CORP p 822
1707 E Highland Ave # 100, Phoenix AZ 85016
Tel (602) 264-4411
SIC 1542 1541 1521 8711 5078 6552

HAPPY HOUSE LLC p 659
8116 E Vista Bonita Dr, Scottsdale AZ 85255
Tel (480) 854-0788 *SIC* 1521

▲ MERITAGE HOMES CORP p 949
8800 E Raintree Dr # 300, Scottsdale AZ 85260
Tel (480) 515-8100 *SIC* 1521

■ MERITAGE HOMES OF FLORIDA INC p 949
8800 E Raintree Dr # 300, Scottsdale AZ 85260
Tel (480) 515-8500 *SIC* 1521

MNI ENTERPRISES INC p 980
8080 E Gelding Dr Ste 108, Scottsdale AZ 85260
Tel (480) 505-4600 *SIC* 1521

▲ TAYLOR MORRISON HOME CORP p 1427
4900 N Scottsdale Rd # 2000, Scottsdale AZ 85251
Tel (480) 840-8100 *SIC* 1521

■ TAYLOR MORRISON INC p 1427
4900 N Scottsdale Rd # 2000, Scottsdale AZ 85251
Tel (480) 840-8100 *SIC* 1521

PREMIER BUILDERS LLC p 1170
3191 E 44th St, Tucson AZ 85713
Tel (520) 293-0300 *SIC* 1521

■ LENNAR HOMES OF CALIFORNIA INC p 855
25 Enterprise Ste 400, Aliso Viejo CA 92656
Tel (949) 349-8000 *SIC* 1521 6552

A CLARK/MCCARTHY JOINT VENTURE p 5
18201 Von Karman Ave # 800, Irvine CA 92612
Tel (714) 429-9779 *SIC* 1521

▲ CALATLANTIC GROUP INC p 238
15360 Barranca Pkwy, Irvine CA 92618
Tel (949) 789-1600
SIC 1531 1521 6162 6541

K HOVNANIAN COMPANIES OF CALIFORNIA INC p 798
400 Exchange Ste 200, Irvine CA 92602
Tel (949) 222-7700 *SIC* 1521

RIDGESIDE CONSTRUCTION INC p 1234
4345 E Lowell St Ste A, Ontario CA 91761
Tel (909) 218-7593 *SIC* 1521

AMERICAN TECHNOLOGIES INC p 80
210 W Baywood Ave, Orange CA 92865
Tel (714) 283-9990
SIC 1521 1541 1742 1731 1721 1711

A TEICHERT & SON INC p 6
3500 American River Dr, Sacramento CA 95864
Tel (916) 484-3011
SIC 5032 3273 1611 1442 1521

TEICHERT INC p 1433
3500 American River Dr, Sacramento CA 95864
Tel (916) 484-3011
SIC 3273 5032 1611 1442 1521 5039

HARPER CONSTRUCTION CO INC p 663
2241 Kettner Blvd Ste 300, San Diego CA 92101
Tel (619) 233-7900 *SIC* 1542 1521

HARBOR VIEW HOLDINGS INC p 660
433 California St Fl 7, San Francisco CA 94104
Tel (415) 982-7777
SIC 1522 1521 6512 8741

■ UCP INC p 1499
99 Almaden Blvd Ste 400, San Jose CA 95113
Tel (408) 207-9499 *SIC* 1521 1531 6552

HAR-BRO INC p 659
2750 Signal Pkwy, Signal Hill CA 90755
Tel (562) 528-8000 *SIC* 1542 1521 1522

JF SHEA CONSTRUCTION INC p 785
655 Brea Canyon Rd, Walnut CA 91789
Tel (909) 595-4397 *SIC* 1521 1622 6512

SHEA HOMES LIMITED PARTNERSHIP A CALIFORNIA LIMITED PARTNERSHIP p 1313
655 Brea Canyon Rd, Walnut CA 91789
Tel (909) 594-9500 *SIC* 1521

EPISCOPAL HOMES FOUNDATION p 505
2185 N Calif Blvd Ste 275, Walnut Creek CA 94596
Tel (925) 956-7400 *SIC* 1521

RYLAND GROUP INC p 1261
3011 Townsgate Rd Ste 200, Westlake Village CA 91361
Tel (805) 367-3800 *SIC* 1531 1521 6162

WM KLORMAN CONSTRUCTION CORP p 1620
23047 Ventura Blvd # 200, Woodland Hills CA 91364
Tel (818) 591-5969 *SIC* 1521 1542

▲ MDC HOLDINGS INC p 933
4350 S Monaco St Ste 500, Denver CO 80237
Tel (303) 773-1100 *SIC* 1521 6162 7389

OAKWOOD HOMES LLC p 1071
4908 Tower Rd, Denver CO 80249
Tel (303) 486-8500 *SIC* 1521

■ RICHMOND AMERICAN HOMES OF COLORADO INC p 1233
4350 S Monaco St, Denver CO 80237
Tel (303) 773-1100 *SIC* 1521

ERIE COUNTY INVESTMENT CO p 508
601 Corporate Cir, Golden CO 80401
Tel (303) 384-0200
SIC 5812 6794 6531 6552 1542 1521

HENSEL PHELPS CONSTRUCTION CO p 684
420 6th Ave, Greeley CO 80631
Tel (970) 352-6565
SIC 1542 1521 1771 1522 1541 1622

▲ CENTURY COMMUNITIES INC p 282
8390 E Crescent Pkwy # 650, Greenwood Village CO 80111
Tel (303) 770-8300 *SIC* 1521

VILLAGE HOMES OF COLORADO INC p 1557
8480 E Orchard Rd # 1000, Greenwood Village CO 80111
Tel (303) 795-1976 *SIC* 1521

CARABETTA ENTERPRISES INC p 252
200 Pratt St Ofc, Meriden CT 06450
Tel (203) 237-7400
SIC 1522 1542 1521 6512

HOMESERVE USA CORP p 704
601 Merritt 7 Fl 6, Norwalk CT 06851
Tel (203) 351-4924 *SIC* 8741 1521

CODINA PARTNERS LLC p 333
135 San Lorenzo Ave # 750, Coral Gables FL 33146
Tel (305) 529-1300
SIC 6552 6531 1521 8742

INTERVEST CONSTRUCTION OF ORLANDO INC p 759
2379 Beville Rd, Daytona Beach FL 32119
Tel (386) 788-0820 *SIC* 1522 1521

■ TRUTEAM LLC p 1489
260 Jimmy Ann Dr, Daytona Beach FL 32114
Tel (386) 304-2200
SIC 1742 1761 1751 1521

ADAMS HOMES OF NORTHWEST FLORIDA INC p 21
3000 Gulf Breeze Pkwy, Gulf Breeze FL 32563
Tel (850) 934-0470 *SIC* 1521

TOUSA INC p 1464
4000 Hollywood Blvd # 555, Hollywood FL 33021
Tel (954) 364-4000
SIC 1521 1522 6162 6541

JR DAVIS CONSTRUCTION CO INC p 795
210 S Hoagland Blvd, Kissimmee FL 34741
Tel (407) 870-0066 *SIC* 1629 1521

VILLAGES OF LAKE-SUMTER INC p 1557
1000 Lake Sumter Lndg, Lady Lake FL 32162
Tel (352) 753-2270
SIC 6552 1521 7997 5812 7389

■ SEARS HOME IMPROVEMENT PRODUCTS INC p 1297
1024 Florida Central Pkwy, Longwood FL 32750
Tel (407) 767-0990 *SIC* 1521

HOLIDAY BUILDERS INC p 700
2293 W Eau Gallie Blvd, Melbourne FL 32935
Tel (321) 610-5156 *SIC* 1521

MANHATTAN CONSTRUCTION (FLORIDA) INC p 901
3705 Westview Dr Ste 1, Naples FL 34104
Tel (239) 643-6000
SIC 1542 8712 1531 1521 8741

ODC CONSTRUCTION LLC p 1074
5701 Carder Rd, Orlando FL 32810
Tel (407) 447-5999 *SIC* 1521

G L HOMES OF FLORIDA CORP p 587
1600 Sawgrs Corp Pkwy # 400, Sunrise FL 33323
Tel (954) 753-1730 *SIC* 1521

PEGASUS BUILDERS INC p 1127
3340 Frlane Frms Rd Ste 8, Wellington FL 33414
Tel (561) 791-7037 *SIC* 1521 1542

HABITAT FOR HUMANITY INTERNATIONAL INC p 651
121 Habitat St, Americus GA 31709
Tel (800) 422-4828
SIC 8399 8661 8322 1521 1531

ARROW EXTERMINATORS INC p 113
8613 Roswell Rd Bldg 4, Atlanta GA 30350
Tel (770) 993-8705
SIC 1742 7342 1521 1542

▲ BEAZER HOMES USA INC p 166
1000 Abernathy Rd Ste 260, Atlanta GA 30328
Tel (770) 829-3700 *SIC* 1521 1522

■ PULTE DIVERSIFIED COMPANIES INC p 1192
3350 Peachtree Rd Ne, Atlanta GA 30326
Tel (248) 647-2750 *SIC* 1521

AMERICAS HOME PLACE INC p 81
2144 Hilton Dr, Gainesville GA 30501
Tel (770) 532-1128 *SIC* 1521

SIVICA HOMES INC p 1328
1640 Pwrs Fy Rd Se 18-300, Marietta GA 30067
Tel (770) 645-5559 *SIC* 1521

HAWAIIAN DREDGING CONSTRUCTION CO INC p 669
201 Merchant St Ste 900, Honolulu HI 96813
Tel (808) 735-3211
SIC 1542 1611 1522 1521

ALBERT C KOBAYASHI INC p 46
94-535 Ukee St Ste 101, Waipahu HI 96797
Tel (808) 671-6460 *SIC* 1542 1521 1522

■ SELECTBUILD CONSTRUCTION INC p 1301
720 E Park Blvd Ste 115, Boise ID 83712
Tel (208) 331-4300
SIC 1521 1771 1751 2431 5031 5211

ARCHER WESTERN CONSTRUCTION LLC p 105
929 W Adams St, Chicago IL 60607
Tel (312) 563-5400
SIC 1521 1622 1629 1542

■ PERNIX BUILDING GROUP LLC p 1136
151 E 22nd St Ste 101e, Lombard IL 60148
Tel (630) 620-4787 *SIC* 1521

KIMBALL HILL INC p 818
5999 New Wilke Rd Ste 306, Rolling Meadows IL 60008
Tel (847) 364-7300 *SIC* 1521 1531

ALL AMERICAN GROUP INC p 51
2831 Dexter Dr, Elkhart IN 46514
Tel (574) 262-0123
SIC 3716 3792 2452 3714 1521

HALLMARK BUILDERS INC p 654
520 S Main St, Middlebury IN 46540
Tel (574) 825-9850 *SIC* 1521

R J PETERSON COMPANIES INC p 1202
32364 585th Ave, Cambridge IA 50046
Tel (515) 360-3337 *SIC* 1521

DEAN SNYDER CONSTRUCTION CO p 420
913 N 14th St, Clear Lake IA 50428
Tel (641) 357-2283 *SIC* 1542 1521 1541

ALENCO INC p 48
16201 W 110th St, Lenexa KS 66219
Tel (913) 438-1902 *SIC* 1521 1751 1761

MERRY TECHNOLOGY INC p 950
315 N Rverview St Apt 615, Wichita KS 67203
Tel (316) 371-9533 *SIC* 1521 1542

STEWART RICHEY CONSTRUCTION INC p 1389
2137 Glen Lily Rd, Bowling Green KY 42101
Tel (270) 842-5184 *SIC* 1542 1521 1541

DREES CO p 455
211 Grandview Dr Ste 300, Fort Mitchell KY 41017
Tel (859) 578-4200 *SIC* 1531 1522 1521

CLARK ENTERPRISES INC p 322
7500 Old Georgetown Rd # 7, Bethesda MD 20814
Tel (301) 657-7100
SIC 6552 4832 7359 1521 1542 6726

BOZZUTO CONTRACTING CO p 205
6406 Ivy Ln, Greenbelt MD 20770
Tel (301) 220-0100 *SIC* 1521 1542

■ K HOVNANIAN HOMES AT FAIRWOOD LLC p 798
1802 Brightseat Rd # 500, Landover MD 20785
Tel (301) 772-8900 *SIC* 1531 1522 1521

R H WHITE COMPANIES INC p 1202
41 Central St, Auburn MA 01501
Tel (508) 832-3295
SIC 1629 7359 1522 1521

SHARED TECHNOLOGY SERVICES GROUP INC p 1312
695 Atlantic Ave, Boston MA 02111
Tel (617) 720-1620 *SIC* 1521

POLYGON US CORP p 1160
15 Sharpners Pond Rd F, North Andover MA 01845
Tel (800) 422-6379 *SIC* 1521

■ INFRA SOURCE INC p 742
2311 Green Rd Ste D, Ann Arbor MI 48105
Tel (734) 434-2000 *SIC* 1521

BISHOP CONSTRUCTION INC p 185
3374 S Center Rd Ste C, Burton MI 48519
Tel (810) 744-4550 *SIC* 1521 1542

CHAMPION ENTERPRISES HOLDINGS LLC p 287
755 W Big Beaver Rd, Troy MI 48084
Tel (248) 614-8200 SIC 1521

CHAMPION HOME BUILDERS INC p 287
755 W Big Beaver Rd # 1000, Troy MI 48084
Tel (248) 614-8200 SIC 1521 2451

NOR-SON INC p 1047
7900 Hastings Rd, Baxter MN 56425
Tel (218) 828-1722 SIC 1521 1542 1541

■ **PULTE HOMES OF MINNESOTA LLC** p 1192
7500 Office Ridge Cir, Eden Prairie MN 55344
Tel (952) 936-7833 SIC 1521

EBERSEN INC p 474
7401 Central Ave Ne Ste 2, Minneapolis MN 55432
Tel (763) 572-2661
SIC 4911 1521 6211 1382 4731 8711

SILVER BAY REALTY TRUST CORP p 1323
3300 Fernbrook Ln N, Plymouth MN 55447
Tel (952) 358-4400 SIC 6798 6531 1521

LAMPERT YARDS INC p 841
1850 Como Ave, Saint Paul MN 55108
Tel (651) 695-3600
SIC 5211 1521 2439 2426

MC BRIDE & SON HOMES INC p 925
16091 Swingley Ridge Rd, Chesterfield MO 63017
Tel (636) 537-2000 SIC 1521

■ **VARIFORM INC** p 1545
303 W Major St, Kearney MO 64060
Tel (919) 677-3900 SIC 3089 1521 3444

KIEWIT BUILDING GROUP INC p 817
302 S 36th St Ste 500, Omaha NE 68131
Tel (402) 977-4500 SIC 1521

KB FRAMERS LLC p 805
5795 Rogers St, Las Vegas NV 89118
Tel (702) 873-9451 SIC 1751 1521

▲ **HOVNANIAN ENTERPRISES INC** p 713
110 W Front St, Red Bank NJ 07701
Tel (732) 747-7800
SIC 1521 1531 1522 6162 6361

ALLAN INDUSTRIES INC p 51
270 Us Highway 46 Ste E, Rockaway NJ 07866
Tel (973) 586-9400 SIC 1521 7349 1799

BBL LLC p 163
302 Washington Ave, Albany NY 12203
Tel (518) 452-8200
SIC 1542 1541 1521 1622 8741

MARRANO CORP p 910
2730 Transit Rd, Buffalo NY 14224
Tel (716) 675-1200 SIC 1521

KASSON & KELLER INC p 804
60 School St, Fonda NY 12068
Tel (518) 853-3421
SIC 3442 3089 1521 3231

■ **GREENSTAR SERVICES CORP** p 638
30 N Macquesten Pkwy, Mount Vernon NY 10550
Tel (914) 776-8000 SIC 1521

KUSHNER COMPANIES INC p 832
666 5th Ave Fl 15, New York NY 10103
Tel (212) 527-7000
SIC 1521 6513 6531 6512 1522 1531

LAHR CONSTRUCTION CORP p 838
75 Thruway Park Dr Ste 1, West Henrietta NY 14586
Tel (585) 334-4490 SIC 1521 1541

EASTWOOD CONSTRUCTION LLC p 473
2857 Westport Rd, Charlotte NC 28208
Tel (704) 399-4663 SIC 1521

MCGEE BROTHERS CO INC p 929
4608 Carriker Rd, Monroe NC 28110
Tel (704) 753-4582 SIC 1741 1521

50 X 20 HOLDING CO INC p 3
2715 Wise Ave Nw, Canton OH 44708
Tel (330) 478-4500 SIC 1521

NRP CONTRACTORS LLC p 1064
5309 Transportation Blvd, Cleveland OH 44125
Tel (216) 475-8900 SIC 1521 1522

DOMINION HOLDING CORP p 449
4900 Tuttle Crossing Blvd, Dublin OH 43016
Tel (614) 356-5000 SIC 1521

DOMINION HOMES INC p 449
4900 Tuttle Crossing Blvd, Dublin OH 43016
Tel (614) 356-5000 SIC 1521

LUKE THEIS ENTERPRISES INC p 885
14120 State Route 568, Findlay OH 45840
Tel (419) 422-2040 SIC 1542 1541 1521

MAROUS BROTHERS CONSTRUCTION INC p 910
1702 Joseph Lloyd Pkwy, Willoughby OH 44094
Tel (440) 951-3904 SIC 1521 1751

ORLEANS HOMEBUILDERS INC p 1095
3333 Street Rd Ste 101, Bensalem PA 19020
Tel (215) 245-7500 SIC 1531 1521

▲ **TOLL BROTHERS INC** p 1459
250 Gibraltar Rd, Horsham PA 19044
Tel (215) 938-8000 SIC 1521 1522

MARONDA INC p 910
11 Timberglen Dr, Imperial PA 15126
Tel (724) 695-1200 SIC 6552 1521

PICERNE INVESTMENT CORP p 1146
75 Lambert Lind Hwy # 300, Warwick RI 02886
Tel (401) 732-3700
SIC 6552 6531 1521 1522 1542

RAINBOW INTERNATIONAL OF MIDDLE TENNESSEE p 1205
667 Patterson Ave Ste C, Murfreesboro TN 37129
Tel (615) 898-8258 SIC 1542 1521

MAIN STREET OPERATING CO INC p 898
615 Main St, Nashville TN 37206
Tel (615) 254-5461
SIC 1542 1541 1521 6531

GRAND TEXAS HOMES INC p 630
15455 Dallas Pkwy # 1000, Addison TX 75001
Tel (972) 387-6000 SIC 1521

CHOICE HOMES INC p 302
1600 E Lamar Blvd Ste 400, Arlington TX 76011
Tel (817) 652-5100 SIC 1521

WILSHIRE HOMES LP p 1613
8200 N Mopac Expy Ste 350, Austin TX 78759
Tel (512) 502-2050 SIC 1521

■ **CENTEX HOMES INC** p 277
2728 N Harwood St, Dallas TX 75201
Tel (800) 777-8583 SIC 1521

■ **CENTEX INTERNATIONAL INC** p 277
2728 N Harwood St Ste 200, Dallas TX 75201
Tel (214) 981-5000 SIC 1521 1522

■ **CENTEX REAL ESTATE CORP** p 277
2728 N Harwood St Ste 800, Dallas TX 75201
Tel (972) 304-2800 SIC 1521

FIRST TEXAS HOMES INC p 549
500 Crescent Ct Ste 350, Dallas TX 75201
Tel (214) 613-3400 SIC 1521

■ **DR HORTON - TEXAS LTD** p 454
301 Commerce St Ste 500, Fort Worth TX 76102
Tel (817) 856-8200 SIC 1521

CAMCORP INTERESTS LTD p 244
10410 Wndamere Lakes Blvd, Houston TX 77065
Tel (281) 671-9000 SIC 1521 6798 6552

CHESMAR HOMES LTD p 295
450 Gears Rd Ste 400, Houston TX 77067
Tel (832) 253-0100 SIC 1521

MCGUYER HOMEBUILDERS INC p 929
7676 Woodway Dr Ste 104, Houston TX 77063
Tel (713) 952-6767 SIC 1531 1521

TELLEPSEN CORP p 1435
777 Benmar Dr Ste 400, Houston TX 77060
Tel (281) 447-8100 SIC 1521

WEEKLEY HOMES LLC p 1587
1111 N Post Oak Rd, Houston TX 77055
Tel (713) 963-0500 SIC 1531 1521

■ **PULTE HOMES OF TEXAS LP** p 1192
4800 Regent Blvd Ste 100, Irving TX 75063
Tel (972) 304-2800 SIC 6552 1521

HIGHLAND HOMES LTD p 691
5601 Democracy Dr Ste 300, Plano TX 75024
Tel (972) 789-3500 SIC 1521 1531

YANTIS CORP p 1635
3611 Paesanos Pkwy # 300, San Antonio TX 78231
Tel (210) 655-3780
SIC 1623 1611 1622 1629 6552 1521

BLOOMFIELD HOMES LP p 190
1050 E State Hwy Ste 210, Southlake TX 76092
Tel (817) 416-1572 SIC 1521

R & O CONSTRUCTION CO INC p 1201
933 Wall Ave Ste 2, Ogden UT 84404
Tel (801) 627-1403 SIC 1542 1521

BIG-D CAPITAL CORP p 182
420 E South Temple, Salt Lake City UT 84111
Tel (801) 415-6086 SIC 1521

CB&I FEDERAL SERVICES LLC p 268
1725 Duke St Ste 400, Alexandria VA 22314
Tel (202) 261-1900 SIC 1521

MICHAEL & SON SERVICES INC p 959
5740 General Wash Dr, Alexandria VA 22312
Tel (703) 658-3998 SIC 1521 1731 5074

HENSEL PHELPS SERVICES LLC p 685
4437 Brookfield Corp 20 Ste 207, Chantilly VA 20151
Tel (703) 828-3200
SIC 1522 8744 1521 1541 1623 1611

BROOKFIELD HOMES CORP p 217
3201 Jermantown Rd # 150, Fairfax VA 22030
Tel (703) 270-1400 SIC 1521 1522

CLINE ENERGY INC p 326
1890 S Main St, Harrisonburg VA 22801
Tel (540) 434-7344 SIC 5172 5541 1521

ORASCOM E&C USA INC p 1092
6862 Elm St Ste 400, Mc Lean VA 22101
Tel (703) 358-8800 SIC 1521 1522 1542

MAINVUE HOMES LLC p 898
1110 112th Ave Ne Ste 202, Bellevue WA 98004
Tel (425) 646-4022 SIC 7389 1521

NOVINIUM INC p 1063
22820 Russell Rd, Kent WA 98032
Tel (253) 288-7100 SIC 1521

LEWIS LEASE CRUTCHER WA LLC p 858
2200 Western Ave, Seattle WA 98121
Tel (206) 264-1985 SIC 1542 1521

AHO CONSTRUCTION I INC p 37
5512 Ne 109th Ct Ste 101, Vancouver WA 98662
Tel (360) 254-0493 SIC 1531 1521

TRI-NORTH BUILDERS INC p 1477
2625 Research Park Dr, Fitchburg WI 53711
Tel (608) 271-8717 SIC 1541 1542 1521

VHC INC p 1553
3090 Holmgren Way, Green Bay WI 54304
Tel (920) 336-7278
SIC 1731 1542 1541 1521 1711 6512

ATLAS COPCO CONSTRUCTION MINING TECHNIQUE USA LLC p 127
11825 W Carmen Ave, Milwaukee WI 53225
Tel (414) 760-1193 SIC 1521

SIC 1522 General Contractors, Residential Other Than Single Family

RACON INC p 1203
700 Energy Center Blvd # 404, Northport AL 35473
Tel (205) 333-8500 SIC 1611 1522

ABEINSA HOLDING INC p 10
2929 N Cent Ave Ste 1100, Phoenix AZ 85012
Tel (602) 265-6870 SIC 1522 1542

ERC PROPERTIES INC p 507
4107 Massard Rd, Fort Smith AR 72903
Tel (479) 478-5103 SIC 1522 6552 6513

CBM 2012 A CALIFORNIA LIMITED PARTNERSHIP p 268
1010 Racquet Club Dr # 108, Auburn CA 95603
Tel (530) 823-2477
SIC 1531 1522 6513 6531 8741

■ **SHAPELL INDUSTRIES LLC** p 1311
8383 Wilshire Blvd # 700, Beverly Hills CA 90211
Tel (323) 655-7330 SIC 6552 6514 1522

PALISADE BUILDERS INC p 1108
1875 S Bascom Ave # 2400, Campbell CA 95008
Tel (408) 429-7700 SIC 1522

MIKE ROVNER CONSTRUCTION INC p 968
5400 Tech Cir, Moorpark CA 93021
Tel (805) 584-5961 SIC 1522

FAIRFIELD DEVELOPMENT INC p 524
5510 Morehouse Dr Ste 200, San Diego CA 92121
Tel (858) 457-2123 SIC 1522

LEDCOR CMI INC p 851
6405 Mira Mesa Blvd # 100, San Diego CA 92121
Tel (602) 595-3017
SIC 1541 1611 1629 1623 1522 8999

HARBOR VIEW HOLDINGS INC p 660
433 California St Fl 7, San Francisco CA 94104
Tel (415) 982-7777
SIC 1522 1521 6512 8741

PJD CONSTRUCTION INC p 1153
447 London St, San Francisco CA 94112
Tel (415) 218-3031 SIC 1542 1522

SWINERTON BUILDERS p 1412
260 Townsend St, San Francisco CA 94107
Tel (415) 421-2980 SIC 1541 1522 1542

SWINERTON INC p 1412
260 Townsend St, San Francisco CA 94107
Tel (415) 421-2980
SIC 1542 1541 6531 1522

GREEN VALLEY CORP p 637
777 N 1st St Fl 5, San Jose CA 95112
Tel (408) 287-0246 SIC 1542 1522 6512

MORLEY BUILDERS INC p 989
3330 Ocean Park Blvd # 101, Santa Monica CA 90405
Tel (310) 399-1600
SIC 1541 1522 1542 1771

HAR-BRO INC p 659
2750 Signal Pkwy, Signal Hill CA 90755
Tel (562) 528-8000 SIC 1542 1521 1522

BROWN CONSTRUCTION INC p 219
1465 Entp Blvd Ste 100, West Sacramento CA 95691
Tel (916) 374-8616 SIC 1522 1542

MILENDER WHITE CONSTRUCTION CO p 969
12655 W 54th Dr, Arvada CO 80002
Tel (303) 216-0420 SIC 1542 1522

MERCY HOUSING INC p 947
1999 Broadway Ste 1000, Denver CO 80202
Tel (303) 830-3300 SIC 1522 6531

HENSEL PHELPS CONSTRUCTION CO p 684
420 6th Ave, Greeley CO 80631
Tel (970) 352-6565
SIC 1542 1521 1771 1522 1541 1622

CARABETTA ENTERPRISES INC p 252
200 Pratt St Ofc, Meriden CT 06450
Tel (203) 237-7400
SIC 1522 1542 1521 6512

HOLLADAY CORP p 700
3400 Idaho Ave Nw Ste 400, Washington DC 20016
Tel (202) 362-2400 SIC 1522 6531

PICERNE DEVELOPMENT CORP OF FLORIDA p 1146
247 N Westmonte Dr, Altamonte Springs FL 32714
Tel (407) 772-0200 SIC 1522

REAL ESTATE IN REAL TIME INC p 1213
100 Lakeshore Dr Ste 96, Altamonte Springs FL 32714
Tel (321) 312-0748 SIC 6531 1542 1522

ODEBRECHT CONSTRUCTION INC p 1074
201 Alhambra Cir Ste 1000, Coral Gables FL 33134
Tel (305) 341-8800 SIC 1622 1522

GLOBAL CONSTRUCTION SERVICES LLC p 616
934 N University Dr 453, Coral Springs FL 33071
Tel (954) 688-6255 SIC 1522

INTERVEST CONSTRUCTION OF ORLANDO INC p 759
2379 Beville Rd, Daytona Beach FL 32119
Tel (386) 788-0820 SIC 1522 1521

OCEAN PROPERTIES LTD p 1073
1001 E Atl Ave Ste 202, Delray Beach FL 33483
Tel (603) 559-2100
SIC 7011 6552 1522 5719 5812 5813

■ **WOODBRIDGE HOLDINGS LLC** p 1622
2100 W Cypress Creek Rd, Fort Lauderdale FL 33309
Tel (954) 950-4950 SIC 1522

TOUSA INC p 1464
4000 Hollywood Blvd # 555, Hollywood FL 33021
Tel (954) 364-4000
SIC 1521 1522 6162 6541

HASKELL CO p 667
111 Riverside Ave, Jacksonville FL 32202
Tel (904) 791-4500
SIC 1541 1542 1522 1623 8712 3272

HASKELL CO INC p 667
111 Riverside Ave, Jacksonville FL 32202
Tel (904) 791-4500
SIC 1541 1542 1522 1623 8712 3272

SUMMIT CONTRACTING GROUP INC p 1398
1000 Rverside Ave Ste 800, Jacksonville FL 32204
Tel (904) 268-5515 SIC 1522

GLF CONSTRUCTION CORP p 615
528 Nw 7th Ave, Miami FL 33136
Tel (305) 371-5228
SIC 1611 1622 1542 1541 1522

ON TOP OF WORLD COMMUNITIES INC p 1086
8445 Sw 80th St, Ocala FL 34481
Tel (352) 854-3600 SIC 6552 1522

ISLAND ONE INC p 766
7345 Greenbriar Pkwy, Orlando FL 32819
Tel (407) 859-8900 SIC 1522

PEOPLES FIRST PROPERTIES INC p 1132
1002 W 23rd St Ste 400, Panama City FL 32405
Tel (850) 769-8981 SIC 1522 6552

CURRENT BUILDERS CONSTRUCTION SERVICES INC p 402
2251 Blount Rd, Pompano Beach FL 33069
Tel (954) 977-4211 SIC 1522 1542

■ **HORIZON BAY MANAGEMENT LLC** p 707
5426 Bay Center Dr # 600, Tampa FL 33609
Tel (813) 287-3900 SIC 8611 6531 1522

KIMMINS CORP p 819
1501 E 2nd Ave, Tampa FL 33605
Tel (813) 248-3878 SIC 1799 1795 1522

▲ **BEAZER HOMES USA INC** p 166
1000 Abernathy Rd Ste 260, Atlanta GA 30328
Tel (770) 829-3700 SIC 1521 1522

CHOATE CONSTRUCTION CO p 301
8200 Roberts Dr Ste 600, Atlanta GA 30350
Tel (678) 892-1200 SIC 1522 1531 1542

JAMESON INNS INC p 777
41 Perimeter Ctr E # 4100, Atlanta GA 30346
Tel (770) 512-0462 SIC 7011 1522

KAJIMA USA INC p 801
3475 Piedmont Rd Ne, Atlanta GA 30305
Tel (404) 564-3900
SIC 1542 1541 6531 1522 6552 1622

FLOURNOY DEVELOPMENT CO p 560
900 Brookstone Ctr Pkwy, Columbus GA 31904
Tel (706) 324-4000 SIC 6552 1522 8741

AMBLING MANAGEMENT CO LLC p 65
348 Enterprise Dr, Valdosta GA 31601
Tel (866) 777-7228
SIC 1522 6552 6531 6513

HAWAIIAN DREDGING CONSTRUCTION CO INC p 669
201 Merchant St Ste 900, Honolulu HI 96813
Tel (808) 735-3211
SIC 1542 1611 1522 1521

ALBERT C KOBAYASHI INC p 46
94-535 Ukee St Ste 101, Waipahu HI 96797
Tel (808) 671-6460 SIC 1542 1521 1522

FH PASCHEN SN NIELSEN INC p 539
5515 N East River Rd, Chicago IL 60656
Tel (773) 444-3474
SIC 1611 1622 1522 1542

FRED TEITELBAUM CONSTRUCTION CO p 576
5526 N Kedzie Ave, Chicago IL 60625
Tel (954) 971-1700 SIC 1522

JAMES MCHUGH CONSTRUCTION CO p 776
1737 S Michigan Ave, Chicago IL 60616
Tel (312) 986-8000 SIC 1542 1522 1622

MCHUGH ENTERPRISES INC p 929
1737 S Michigan Ave, Chicago IL 60616
Tel (312) 986-8000
SIC 1542 1522 1622 1771 1742 6552

WALSH GROUP LTD p 1574
929 W Adams St, Chicago IL 60607
Tel (312) 563-5400
SIC 1542 1522 1622 1629 1541

INLAND REAL ESTATE GROUP OF COMPANIES p 743
2901 Butterfield Rd, Oak Brook IL 60523
Tel (630) 218-8000
SIC 6513 6512 6162 6282 1522 1542

GENE B GLICK CO INC p 598
8801 River Crossing Blvd # 200, Indianapolis IN 46240
Tel (317) 469-0400 SIC 1522 6531 6513

■ **DANIEL INDUSTRIES INC** p 411
8460 Valley View Dr, Martinsville IN 46151
Tel (317) 442-5294 SIC 1522

CITY WIDE HOLDING CO INC p 320
15447 W 100th Ter, Lenexa KS 66219
Tel (913) 888-5700
SIC 1542 1522 5087 7349

LAW CO INC p 847
345 N Rverview St Ste 300, Wichita KS 67203
Tel (316) 268-0200 SIC 1542 1522

FISCHER HOMES INC p 551
3940 Olympic Blvd Ste 100, Erlanger KY 41018
Tel (859) 341-4709 SIC 1522

DREES CO p 455
211 Grandview Dr Ste 300, Fort Mitchell KY 41017
Tel (859) 578-4200 SIC 1531 1522 1521

STRUEVER BROS ECCLES & ROUSE INC p 1394
2400 Boston St Ste 404, Baltimore MD 21224
Tel (443) 573-4000 SIC 1542 1522

BF SAUL PROPERTY CO p 179
7501 Wisconsin Ave, Bethesda MD 20814
Tel (301) 986-6000
SIC 6531 6519 1542 1522

CLARK CONSTRUCTION GROUP LLC p 322
7500 Old Georgetown Rd # 15, Bethesda MD 20814
Tel (301) 272-8100 SIC 1542 1611 1522

GEMCRAFT HOMES GROUP INC p 598
2205 Commerce Rd Ste A, Forest Hill MD 21050
Tel (410) 893-8458 SIC 1522

BOZZUTO & ASSOCIATES INC p 205
6406 Ivy Ln Ste 700, Greenbelt MD 20770
Tel (301) 220-0100 SIC 6513 1522 6552

BOZZUTO CONSTRUCTION CO INC p 205
6406 Ivy Ln Ste 700, Greenbelt MD 20770
Tel (301) 220-0100 SIC 1522 1542

■ **K HOVNANIAN HOMES AT FAIRWOOD LLC** p 798
1802 Brightseat Rd # 500, Landover MD 20785
Tel (301) 772-8900 SIC 1531 1522 1521

HARKINS BUILDERS INC p 661
2201 Warwick Way, Marriottsville MD 21104
Tel (410) 750-2600 SIC 1522 1542

R H WHITE COMPANIES INC p 1202
41 Central St, Auburn MA 01501
Tel (508) 832-3295
SIC 1629 7359 1522 1521

BEACON COMPANIES INC p 164
2 Center Plz Ste 700, Boston MA 02108
Tel (617) 574-1100 SIC 1522 6531 1542

DANIEL OCONNELLS SONS INC p 411
480 Hampden St, Holyoke MA 01040
Tel (413) 534-5667
SIC 1541 1542 1522 1611 1622 1629

MICHIGAN PAVING AND MATERIALS CO p 961
2575 S Haggerty Rd # 100, Canton MI 48188
Tel (734) 397-2050 SIC 1522 1541 2911

SACHSE CONSTRUCTION AND DEVELOPMENT CO LLC p 1264
1528 Woodward Ave Ste 600, Detroit MI 48226
Tel (313) 481-8200 SIC 1542 1522

P M GROUP INC p 1102
1050 Corporate Office Dr, Milford MI 48381
Tel (248) 529-2000 SIC 6531 1522 6552

ALPHA OIL & GAS SERVICES INC p 60
453 Tower St Nw, Clearbrook MN 56634
Tel (218) 776-2278 SIC 5172 1623 1522

RYAN COMPANIES US INC p 1260
50 S 10th St Ste 300, Minneapolis MN 55403
Tel (612) 492-4000
SIC 1542 1541 6552 6512 1522

WEIS BUILDERS INC p 1588
7645 Lyndale Ave S # 300, Minneapolis MN 55423
Tel (612) 243-5000 SIC 1522 1541 1542

OPUS DESIGN BUILD LLC p 1091
10350 Bren Rd W, Minnetonka MN 55343
Tel (952) 656-4444 SIC 1522 1541

UNITED SUBCONTRACTORS INC p 1514
445 Minnesota St Ste 2500, Saint Paul MN 55101
Tel (651) 225-6300
SIC 1742 1796 1542 1522

■ **ANDERSON COMPANIES INC** p 89
11400 Reichold Rd, Gulfport MS 39503
Tel (228) 896-4000 SIC 1542 1541 1522

■ **ROY ANDERSON CORP** p 1254
11400 Reichold Rd, Gulfport MS 39503
Tel (228) 896-4000 SIC 1542 1541 1522

MCBRIDE & SON ENTERPRISES INC p 926
16091 Swingley Ridge Rd # 300, Chesterfield MO 63017
Tel (636) 537-2000 SIC 1522 1542

CECO CONCRETE CONSTRUCTION DELAWARE LLC p 272
10100 N Ambassador Dr, Kansas City MO 64153
Tel (816) 459-7000 SIC 1542 1522

AIH FLINTCO LLC p 38
8800 Page Ave, Saint Louis MO 63114
Tel (314) 733-2000 SIC 1389 1522

KIEWIT INFRASTRUCTURE CO p 817
Kiewit Plz, Omaha NE 68131
Tel (402) 342-2052
SIC 1541 1542 1629 1622 1522

SAGEBRUSH ENTERPRISES INC p 1267
4730 S Fort Apache Rd, Las Vegas NV 89147
Tel (702) 873-5338
SIC 1522 1542 7992 6799

BLACKSTONE GROUP LLC p 188
570 Broad St Ste 1606, Newark NJ 07102
Tel (973) 624-6300 SIC 1542 1522 1541

▲ **HOVNANIAN ENTERPRISES INC** p 713
110 W Front St, Red Bank NJ 07701
Tel (732) 747-7800
SIC 1521 1531 1522 6162 6361

ELLICOTT DEVELOPMENT OF BUFFALO LLC p 488
295 Main St Rm 210, Buffalo NY 14203
Tel (716) 854-0060 SIC 1522 1542 6531

HELMSLEY ENTERPRISES INC p 682
230 Park Ave Rm 659, New York NY 10169
Tel (212) 679-3600 SIC 6513 8742 1522

HOCHTIEF USA INC p 699
375 Hudson St Fl 6, New York NY 10014
Tel (212) 229-6000
SIC 1542 1541 1522 8741 8742 6799

KUSHNER COMPANIES INC p 832
666 5th Ave Fl 15, New York NY 10103
Tel (212) 527-7000
SIC 1521 6513 6531 6512 1522 1531

LENDLEASE (US) CONSTRUCTION INC p 855
200 Park Ave Fl 9, New York NY 10166
Tel (212) 592-6700
SIC 1541 1542 1522 8741 8742

LENDLEASE (US) CONSTRUCTION LMB INC p 855
200 Park Ave Fl 9, New York NY 10166
Tel (212) 592-6700
SIC 1522 1541 1542 8741 8742

M/L BOVIS HOLDINGS LTD p 890
200 Park Ave Fl 9, New York NY 10166
Tel (212) 592-6700
SIC 1522 1541 1542 8741 8742

SHACKLEFORDS CONSTRUCTION & CONTRACTING LTD p 1310
303 Lexington Ave, New York NY 10016
Tel (646) 771-4470
SIC 1522 1542 1541 7389

TURNER CONSTRUCTION CO INC p 1492
375 Hudson St Fl 6, New York NY 10014
Tel (212) 229-6000
SIC 1542 1541 1522 8741 8742

TURNER CORP p 1492
375 Hudson St Rm 700, New York NY 10014
Tel (212) 229-6000
SIC 1542 1541 1522 8742

LIRO ENGINEERS INC p 870
3 Aerial Way, Syosset NY 11791
Tel (516) 938-5476 SIC 1522

PURCELL CONSTRUCTION CORP p 1192
566 Coffeen St, Watertown NY 13601
Tel (315) 782-1050 SIC 1542 1541 1522

BILL CLARK HOMES LLC p 182
200 E Arlington Blvd A, Greenville NC 27858
Tel (252) 355-5805 SIC 1522

DUGAN & MEYERS CONSTRUCTION CO p 460
11110 Kenwood Rd, Blue Ash OH 45242
Tel (513) 891-4300 SIC 1541 1542 1522

DUGAN & MEYERS INTERESTS INC p 460
11110 Kenwood Rd, Blue Ash OH 45242
Tel (513) 891-4300 SIC 1541 1542 1522

MESSER CONSTRUCTION CO p 951
5158 Fishwick Dr, Cincinnati OH 45216
Tel (513) 242-1541 SIC 1542 1541 1522

MV RESIDENTIAL CONSTRUCTION INC p 1003
9349 Waterstone Blvd # 200, Cincinnati OH 45249
Tel (513) 588-1000 SIC 1522

I & M J GROSS CO p 724
14300 Ridge Rd Ste 100, Cleveland OH 44133
Tel (440) 237-1681 SIC 1522

NRP CONTRACTORS LLC p 1064
5309 Transportation Blvd, Cleveland OH 44125
Tel (216) 475-8900 SIC 1521 1522

SAFEGUARD PROPERTIES MANAGEMENT LLC p 1266
7887 Hub Pkwy, Cleveland OH 44125
Tel (216) 739-2900 SIC 1522

▲ **INSTALLED BUILDING PRODUCTS INC** p 746
495 S High St Ste 50, Columbus OH 43215
Tel (614) 221-3399 SIC 1522 5033 5211

R&H CONSTRUCTION CO p 1203
1530 Sw Taylor St, Portland OR 97205
Tel (503) 228-7177 SIC 1542 1522

WALSH CONSTRUCTION CO p 1574
2905 Sw 1st Ave, Portland OR 97201
Tel (503) 228-1190 SIC 1522 1542

COLSON & COLSON GENERAL CONTRACTOR INC p 339
2260 Mcgilchrist St Se # 100, Salem OR 97302
Tel (503) 586-7401 SIC 1522 1542

▲ **TOLL BROTHERS INC** p 1459
250 Gibraltar Rd, Horsham PA 19044
Tel (215) 938-8000 SIC 1521 1522

BALFOUR BEATTY MILITARY HOUSING LLC p 148
1 Country View Rd, Malvern PA 19355
Tel (610) 355-8100 SIC 1522 1542

CORVIAS MILITARY LIVING LLC p 373
1405 S County Trl Ste 510, East Greenwich RI 02818
Tel (401) 228-2800 SIC 1522

DIMEO CONSTRUCTION CO p 440
75 Chapman St, Providence RI 02905
Tel (401) 781-9800 SIC 1542 1522 7353

PICERNE INVESTMENT CORP p 1146
75 Lambert Lind Hwy # 300, Warwick RI 02886
Tel (401) 732-3700
SIC 6552 6531 1521 1522 1542

■ **BE&K BUILDING GROUP LLC** p 164
201 E Mcbee Ave Ste 400, Greenville SC 29601
Tel (864) 250-5000 SIC 1542 1541 1522

CONSTRUCTION ENTERPRISES INC p 361
2179 Edward Curd Ln # 100, Franklin TN 37067
Tel (615) 332-8880 SIC 1522 1542

HARDAWAY CONSTRUCTION CORP p 660
615 Main St, Nashville TN 37206
Tel (615) 254-5461 SIC 1542 1541 1522

HARDAWAY GROUP INC p 660
615 Main St, Nashville TN 37206
Tel (615) 254-5461
SIC 1542 1541 1522 6531

LENDLEASE (US) PUBLIC PARTNERSHIPS LLC p 855
1201 Demonbreun St # 800, Nashville TN 37203
Tel (615) 963-2600 SIC 1522

■ **CENTEX CORP** p 277
2728 N Harwood St Ste 200, Dallas TX 75201
Tel (214) 981-5000
SIC 1531 2451 6162 1542 1541 1522

■ **CENTEX INTERNATIONAL INC** p 277
2728 N Harwood St Ste 200, Dallas TX 75201
Tel (214) 981-5000 SIC 1521 1522

HUNT BUILDING CO LTD p 718
4401 N Mesa St Ste 201, El Paso TX 79902
Tel (915) 533-1122
SIC 1522 6531 1542 7389

HUNT COMPANIES INC p 718
4401 N Mesa St, El Paso TX 79902
Tel (915) 533-1122 SIC 1522 6531 1542

JORDAN CF CONSTRUCTION LLC p 793
7700 Cf Jordan Dr Ste 200, El Paso TX 79912
Tel (915) 877-3333 SIC 1542 1541 1522

JORDAN CF INVESTMENTS LLP p 793
7700 Cf Jordan Dr, El Paso TX 79912
Tel (915) 877-3333
SIC 1542 1541 1522 1611

INTERSTATE RESTORATION LLC p 758
3401 Quorum Dr Ste 300, Fort Worth TX 76137
Tel (817) 293-0035 SIC 1542 1522 7349

DMC BUILDERS CO INC p 446
3411 Richmond Ave Ste 200, Houston TX 77046
Tel (832) 209-1200 SIC 1522

GREYSTAR MANAGEMENT SERVICES LP p 639
750 Bering Dr Ste 300, Houston TX 77057
Tel (713) 966-5000 SIC 6513 6531 1522

HEALTH CARE TEMPORARIES INC p 674
8926 Sherbourne St Ste D, Houston TX 77016
Tel (713) 631-7106
SIC 8082 1542 1522 1081 5082

SPAW GLASS CONSTRUCTION CORP p 1355
13800 West Rd, Houston TX 77041
Tel (281) 970-5300 SIC 1542 1522 1541

WESTWAY CONSTRUCTION SERVICES LLC p 1603
8611 Derrington Rd, Houston TX 77064
Tel (713) 375-2330 SIC 1522

JPI APARTMENT CONSTRUCTION LP p 795
600 Las Colinas Blvd E # 1800, Irving TX 75039
Tel (972) 556-1700 SIC 1522

KOONTZ CONSTRUCTION INC p 827
755 E Mulberry Ave # 100, San Antonio TX 78212
Tel (210) 826-2600 SIC 1542 1522

SPAW GLASS CONTRACTORS INC p 1355
9331 Corporate Dr, Selma TX 78154
Tel (210) 651-9000 SIC 1522

SPAW GLASS HOLDING LP p 1355
9331 Corporate Dr, Selma TX 78154
Tel (210) 651-9000 SIC 1542 1522 1541

PENTALON CONSTRUCTION INC p 1132
132 E 13065 S Ste 175, Draper UT 84020
Tel (801) 619-1900 SIC 1522 1542

KIER CONSTRUCTION CORP p 817
3710 Quincy Ave, Ogden UT 84403
Tel (801) 627-1414 SIC 1522 1542 1541

A & G QUALITY BUILDERS INC p 4
1413 Powhatan St, Alexandria VA 22314
Tel (703) 549-8682 SIC 1522

KS INTERNATIONAL LLC p 831
3601 Eisenhower Ave # 600, Alexandria VA 22304
Tel (703) 676-3253 SIC 1522

CLARK REALTY CAPITAL LLC p 322
4401 Wilson Blvd Ste 600, Arlington VA 22203
Tel (703) 294-4500 SIC 1522 1531 1542

L C VIRGINIA p 834
4600 Fairfax Dr Ste 1004, Arlington VA 22203
Tel (703) 524-5454 SIC 1541 1542 1522

HENSEL PHELPS SERVICES LLC p 685
4437 Brookfield Corp 20 Ste 207, Chantilly VA 20151
Tel (703) 828-3200
SIC 1522 8744 1521 1541 1623 1611

DALY SEVEN INC p 410
4829 Riverside Dr, Danville VA 24541
Tel (434) 822-2161 SIC 8741 1522 6531

BROOKFIELD HOMES CORP p 217
3201 Jermantown Rd # 150, Fairfax VA 22030
Tel (703) 270-1400 SIC 1521 1522

ORASCOM E&C USA INC p 1092
6862 Elm St Ste 400, Mc Lean VA 22101
Tel (703) 358-8800 SIC 1521 1522 1542

PINNACLE REALTY MANAGEMENT CO p 1150
2801 Alaskan Way Ste 200, Seattle WA 98121
Tel (206) 215-9700
SIC 6531 8741 6513 6512 1522

H J MARTIN & SON INC p 650
320 S Military Ave, Green Bay WI 54303
Tel (920) 494-3461
SIC 5713 1793 1522 1542 1742

HORIZON CONSTRUCTION GROUP INC p 707
5201 E Terrace Dr Ste 300, Madison WI 53718
Tel (608) 354-0900 SIC 1542 1522

J H FINDORFF & SON INC p 771
300 S Bedford St, Madison WI 53703
Tel (608) 257-5321
SIC 1542 1541 8741 1522

STEVENS CONSTRUCTION CORP p 1388
2 Buttonwood Ct, Madison WI 53718
Tel (608) 222-5100 SIC 1522 1542

SIC 1531 Operative Builders

▲ **AV HOMES INC** p 135
8601 N Scottsdale Rd # 220, Scottsdale AZ 85253
Tel (480) 214-7400 SIC 1531

▲ **NEW HOME CO INC** p 1031
85 Enterprise Ste 450, Aliso Viejo CA 92656
Tel (949) 382-7800 SIC 1531

CBM 2012 A CALIFORNIA LIMITED PARTNERSHIP p 268
1010 Racquet Club Dr # 108, Auburn CA 95603
Tel (530) 823-2477
SIC 1531 1522 6513 6531 8741

WARMINGTON HOMES p 1575
3090 Pullman St, Costa Mesa CA 92626
Tel (714) 434-4435 SIC 1531

▲ **CALATLANTIC GROUP INC** p 238
15360 Barranca Pkwy, Irvine CA 92618
Tel (949) 789-1600
SIC 1531 1521 6162 6541

DAHN CORP p 408
18552 Macarthur Blvd # 495, Irvine CA 92612
Tel (949) 752-1282 SIC 1531 6531 4225

▲ **TRI POINTE GROUP INC** p 1476
19540 Jamboree Rd Ste 300, Irvine CA 92612
Tel (949) 438-1400 SIC 1531

■ **TRI POINTE HOMES INC** p 1476
19520 Jamboree Rd Ste 300, Irvine CA 92612
Tel (949) 438-1400 SIC 1531

▲ **KB HOME** p 806
10990 Wilshire Blvd Fl 5, Los Angeles CA 90024
Tel (310) 231-4000 SIC 1531 6351 6162

▲ **WILLIAM LYON HOMES** p 1610
4695 Macarthur Ct Ste 800, Newport Beach CA 92660
Tel (949) 833-3600 SIC 1531

■ **EDISON MISSION GROUP INC** p 478
2244 Walnut Grove Ave, Rosemead CA 91770
Tel (626) 302-2222
SIC 4931 6799 1629 1531

■ **UCP INC** p 1499
99 Almaden Blvd Ste 400, San Jose CA 95113
Tel (408) 207-9499 SIC 1521 1531 6552

RYLAND GROUP INC p 1261
3011 Townsgate Rd Ste 200, Westlake Village CA 91361
Tel (805) 367-3800 SIC 1531 1521 6162

HOME BUYERS WARRANTY CORP p 703
10375 E Harvard Ave # 100, Denver CO 80231
Tel (720) 747-6000 SIC 6351 1531

▲ **WCI COMMUNITIES INC** p 1585
24301 Walden Center Dr, Bonita Springs FL 34134
Tel (239) 947-2600 SIC 1531 6531

SPACE GATEWAY SUPPORT LLC p 1354
1235 Evans Rd, Melbourne FL 32904
Tel (321) 853-3393 SIC 1531

▲ **LENNAR CORP** p 855
700 Nw 107th Ave Ste 400, Miami FL 33172
Tel (305) 559-4000 SIC 1531 6552 6163

■ **LENNAR HOMES INC** p 855
730 Nw 107th Ave Ste 300, Miami FL 33172
Tel (305) 559-4000 SIC 1531

■ **LENNAR HOMES LLC** p 855
700 Nw 107th Ave Ste 400, Miami FL 33172
Tel (305) 559-4000 SIC 1531

GRAHAM COMPANIES p 628
6843 Main St, Miami Lakes FL 33014
Tel (305) 821-1130
SIC 1531 7011 0212 6552 6512 2711

MANHATTAN CONSTRUCTION (FLORIDA) INC p 901
3705 Westview Dr Ste 1, Naples FL 34104
Tel (239) 643-6000
SIC 1542 8712 1531 1521 8741

EDGEWATER BEACH RESORT LLC p 477
11212 Front Beach Rd, Panama City FL 32407
Tel (850) 235-4044
SIC 1531 7011 5813 5812

KAST CONSTRUCTION CO LLC p 804
701 Nrthpint Pkwy Ste 400, West Palm Beach FL 33407
Tel (561) 689-2910 SIC 1531

HABITAT FOR HUMANITY INTERNATIONAL INC p 651
121 Habitat St, Americus GA 31709
Tel (800) 422-4828
SIC 8399 8661 8322 1521 1531

■ **BEAZER HOMES CORP** p 166
1000 Abernathy Rd, Atlanta GA 30328
Tel (770) 829-3700 SIC 1531

CHOATE CONSTRUCTION CO p 301
8200 Roberts Dr Ste 600, Atlanta GA 30350
Tel (678) 892-1200 SIC 1522 1531 1542

■ **PULTE HOME CORP** p 1192
3350 Peachtree Rd Ne # 150, Atlanta GA 30326
Tel (248) 647-2750 SIC 1531 6552 6162

▲ **PULTEGROUP INC** p 1192
3350 Peachtree Rd Ne # 150, Atlanta GA 30326
Tel (404) 978-6400 SIC 1531 6552 6162

BUILDER SUPPORT SERVICES INC p 224
4125 Atlanta Rd Se, Smyrna GA 30080
Tel (770) 907-3400 SIC 1531 6531

ENGINEERED STRUCTURES INC p 499
3330 E Louise Dr Ste 300, Meridian ID 83642
Tel (208) 362-3040 SIC 1542 1531

KIMBALL HILL INC p 818
5999 New Wilke Rd Ste 306, Rolling Meadows IL 60008
Tel (847) 364-7300 SIC 1521 1531

DREES CO p 455
211 Grandview Dr Ste 300, Fort Mitchell KY 41017
Tel (859) 578-4200 SIC 1531 1522 1521

WILLIAMS SCOTSMAN INC p 1611
901 S Bond St Ste 600, Baltimore MD 21231
Tel (410) 931-6000
SIC 1531 1541 5039 7359

■ **K HOVNANIAN HOMES AT FAIRWOOD LLC** p 798
1802 Brightseat Rd # 500, Landover MD 20785
Tel (301) 772-8900 SIC 1531 1522 1521

▲ **HOVNANIAN ENTERPRISES INC** p 713
110 W Front St, Red Bank NJ 07701
Tel (732) 747-7800
SIC 1521 1531 1522 6162 6361

■ **K HOVNANIAN DEVELOPMENTS OF NEW JERSEY INC** p 798
10 State Route 35, Red Bank NJ 07701
Tel (732) 747-7800 SIC 1531

■ **K HOVNANIAN DEVELOPMENTS OF NEW YORK INC** p 798
10 State Route 35, Red Bank NJ 07701
Tel (732) 747-7800 SIC 1531

GARDEN HOMES INC p 591
820 Morris Tpke Ste 301, Short Hills NJ 07078
Tel (973) 467-5000 SIC 1531 6531

KUSHNER COMPANIES INC p 832
666 5th Ave Fl 15, New York NY 10103
Tel (212) 527-7000
SIC 1521 6513 6531 6512 1522 1531

LETTIRE CONSTRUCTION CORP p 857
334 E 110th St 336, New York NY 10029
Tel (212) 996-6640 SIC 1531

▲ **WILLIAMS INDUSTRIES INC** p 1611
1128 Tyler Farms Dr, Raleigh NC 27603
Tel (919) 604-1746
SIC 3441 1531 1541 3315 1791

NRP HOLDINGS LLC p 1064
5309 Transportation Blvd, Cleveland OH 44125
Tel (216) 475-8900 SIC 1531

▲ **M/I HOMES INC** p 890
3 Easton Oval Ste 500, Columbus OH 43219
Tel (614) 418-8000 SIC 1531 6162

ASSOCIATED ESTATES REALTY CORP p 120
1 Aec Pkwy, Richmond Heights OH 44143
Tel (216) 261-5000 SIC 6798 1531

ORLEANS HOMEBUILDERS INC p 1095
3333 Street Rd Ste 101, Bensalem PA 19020
Tel (215) 245-7500 SIC 1531 1521

▲ **NATIONAL AMERICAN UNIVERSITY HOLDINGS INC** p 1009
5301 S Highway 16 Ste 200, Rapid City SD 57701
Tel (605) 721-5220 SIC 8221 6531 1531

■ **CENTEX CORP** p 277
2728 N Harwood St Ste 200, Dallas TX 75201
Tel (214) 981-5000
SIC 1531 2451 6162 1542 1541 1522

▲ **DR HORTON INC** p 454
301 Commerce St Ste 500, Fort Worth TX 76102
Tel (817) 390-8200 SIC 1531 6162

MCGUYER HOMEBUILDERS INC p 929
7676 Woodway Dr Ste 104, Houston TX 77063
Tel (713) 952-6767 SIC 1531 1521

MHI PARTNERSHIP LTD p 959
7676 Woodway Dr Ste 104, Houston TX 77063
Tel (713) 952-6767 SIC 1531

■ **US HOME CORP** p 1532
10707 Clay Rd, Houston TX 77041
Tel (305) 559-4000 SIC 1531 6162 6552

WEEKLEY HOMES LLC p 1587
1111 N Post Oak Rd, Houston TX 77055
Tel (713) 963-0500 SIC 1531 1521

▲ **GREEN BRICK PARTNERS INC** p 636
2805 Dallas Pkwy Ste 400, Plano TX 75093
Tel (469) 573-6755 SIC 1531 6531

HIGHLAND HOMES LTD p 691
5601 Democracy Dr Ste 300, Plano TX 75024
Tel (972) 789-3500 SIC 1521 1531

▲ **LGI HOMES INC** p 860
1450 Lake Robbins Dr # 430, The Woodlands TX 77380
Tel (281) 362-8998 SIC 1531

WOODSIDE GROUP INC p 1623
460 W 50 N Ste 200, Salt Lake City UT 84101
Tel (801) 299-6700 SIC 1531

SNOWBIRD LTD p 1336
State Rd 210, Snowbird UT 84092
Tel (801) 742-2222 SIC 1531 6519

■ **STRATTON CORP** p 1393
5 Village Lodge Rd, South Londonderry VT 05155
Tel (802) 297-2200
SIC 7011 7992 1531 6512 5941

CLARK REALTY CAPITAL LLC p 322
4401 Wilson Blvd Ste 600, Arlington VA 22203
Tel (703) 294-4500 SIC 1522 1531 1542

MILLER AND SMITH INC p 970
8401 Greensboro Dr # 450, Mc Lean VA 22102
Tel (703) 821-2500 SIC 1799 1531

▲ **NVR INC** p 1068
11700 Plaza America Dr # 500, Reston VA 20190
Tel (703) 956-4000 SIC 1531 6162

STANLEY MARTIN COMPANIES INC p 1377
11710 Plaza America Dr # 1100, Reston VA 20190
Tel (703) 964-5000 SIC 1531

AHO CONSTRUCTION I INC p 37
5512 Ne 109th Ct Ste 101, Vancouver WA 98662
Tel (360) 254-0493 SIC 1531 1521

SIC 1541 General Contractors, Indl Bldgs & Warehouses

■ **B E & K INC** p 141
2000 International Pk Dr, Birmingham AL 35243
Tel (205) 972-6000
SIC 1541 8711 1796 1711

HOAR CONSTRUCTION LLC p 698
2 Metroplex Dr Ste 400, Birmingham AL 35209
Tel (205) 803-2121 SIC 1541

GA WEST & CO INC p 588
12526 Celeste Rd, Chunchula AL 36521
Tel (251) 679-1965 SIC 1541

■ **KBR CONSTRUCTION CO LLC** p 806
3000 Riverchase Galleria, Hoover AL 35244
Tel (205) 972-6538
SIC 1541 1796 1711 1629 1799 1521

YATES CONSTRUCTORS LLC p 1635
1855 Data Dr Ste 200, Hoover AL 35244
Tel (205) 380-8420 SIC 1542 1541

CADDELL CONSTRUCTION CO (DE) LLC p 236
2700 Lagoon Park Dr, Montgomery AL 36109
Tel (334) 272-7723 SIC 1542 1541

CADDELL CONSTRUCTION CO INC p 236
2700 Lagoon Park Dr, Montgomery AL 36109
Tel (334) 272-7723 SIC 1542 1541

SYS-CON LLC p 1416
4444 Park Blvd, Montgomery AL 36116
Tel (334) 281-1520 SIC 1541

UDELHOVEN OILFIELD SYSTEMS SERVICES INC p 1499
184 E 53rd Ave, Anchorage AK 99518
Tel (907) 344-1577 SIC 1541 1542 8711

CORE CONSTRUCTION INC p 369
3036 E Greenway Rd, Phoenix AZ 85032
Tel (602) 494-0800 SIC 1542 1541

HAYDON BUILDING CORP p 670
4640 E Cotton Gin Loop, Phoenix AZ 85040
Tel (602) 296-1496 SIC 1541 1542

KITCHELL CONTRACTORS INC OF ARIZONA p 822
1707 E Highland Ave # 200, Phoenix AZ 85016
Tel (602) 264-4411 SIC 1541 1542 1521

KITCHELL CORP p 822
1707 E Highland Ave # 100, Phoenix AZ 85016
Tel (602) 264-4411
SIC 1542 1541 1521 8711 5078 6552

■ **TUTOR PERINI BUILDING CORP** p 1493
5055 E Washington St # 210, Phoenix AZ 85034
Tel (602) 256-6777 SIC 1541 1542 8741

■ **HUNT CORP** p 719
6720 N Scottsdale Rd # 300, Scottsdale AZ 85253
Tel (480) 368-4755 SIC 1541 6531 6552

SUNDT CONSTRUCTION INC p 1402
2620 S 55th St, Tempe AZ 85282
Tel (480) 293-3000
SIC 1542 1611 1629 1541 8741

NABHOLZ CONSTRUCTION CORP p 1006
612 Garland St, Conway AR 72032
Tel (501) 505-5800 SIC 1541

BALDWIN & SHELL CONSTRUCTION CO INC p 147
1000 W Capitol Ave, Little Rock AR 72201
Tel (501) 374-8677 SIC 1541 1542

KINCO CONSTRUCTORS LLC p 819
12600 Lawson Rd, Little Rock AR 72210
Tel (501) 225-7606 SIC 1542 1541

BOMEL CONSTRUCTION CO INC p 199
8195 E Kaiser Blvd, Anaheim CA 92808
Tel (714) 921-1660 SIC 1541

ICE BUILDERS INC p 727
421 E Cerritos Ave, Anaheim CA 92805
Tel (714) 491-1317 SIC 1541

NTS INC p 1065
8200 Stockdale Hwy Ste M, Bakersfield CA 93311
Tel (661) 588-8514 SIC 1623 1541 1771

ROEBBELEN CONTRACTING INC p 1246
1241 Hawks Flight Ct, El Dorado Hills CA 95762
Tel (916) 939-4000 SIC 1542 1541 8741

LILJA CORP p 866
229 Rickenbacker Cir, Livermore CA 94551
Tel (925) 454-9544 SIC 1541

STEARNS CONRAD AND SCHMIDT CONSULTING ENGINEERS INC p 1384
3900 Kilroy Arprt Way # 100, Long Beach CA 90806
Tel (562) 426-9544 SIC 8711 1541 8748

MILLIE AND SEVERSON INC p 971
3601 Serpentine Dr, Los Alamitos CA 90720
Tel (562) 493-3611 SIC 1541

SEVERSON GROUP INC p 1309
3601 Serpentine Dr, Los Alamitos CA 90720
Tel (562) 493-3611 SIC 1542 1541

■ **AECOM E&C HOLDINGS INC** p 28
1999 Avenue Of Ste 2600, Los Angeles CA 90067
Tel (213) 593-8000
SIC 8711 1611 1629 1623 1541 1622

DEVCON CONSTRUCTION INC p 433
690 Gibraltar Dr, Milpitas CA 95035
Tel (408) 942-8200 SIC 1541

AMERICAN TECHNOLOGIES INC p 80
210 W Baywood Ave, Orange CA 92865
Tel (714) 283-9990
SIC 1521 1541 1742 1731 1721 1711

■ **PERFORMANCE MECHANICAL INC** p 1135
701 Willow Pass Rd Ste 2, Pittsburg CA 94565
Tel (925) 432-4080 SIC 1541 1711 8711

DPR CONSTRUCTION A GENERAL PARTNERSHIP p 454
1450 Veterans Blvd, Redwood City CA 94063
Tel (650) 474-1450 SIC 1541

DPR CONSTRUCTION INC p 454
1450 Veterans Blvd Ofc, Redwood City CA 94063
Tel (650) 474-1450 SIC 1541 1542

■ **RUDOLPH AND SLETTEN INC** p 1257
1600 Seaport Blvd Ste 350, Redwood City CA 94063
Tel (650) 216-3600 SIC 1542 1541

C OVERAA & CO p 233
200 Parr Blvd, Richmond CA 94801
Tel (510) 234-0926 SIC 1541

ALSTON CONSTRUCTION CO INC p 61
8775 Folsom Blvd Ste 201, Sacramento CA 95826
Tel (916) 340-2400 SIC 1541 1542

JOHN F OTTO INC p 788
1717 2nd St, Sacramento CA 95811
Tel (916) 441-6870 SIC 1542 1541

UNGER CONSTRUCTION CO p 1502
910 X St, Sacramento CA 95818
Tel (916) 325-5500 SIC 1542 1541

GERDAU REINFORCING STEEL p 608
3880 Murphy Canyon Rd # 100, San Diego CA 92123
Tel (858) 737-7700 SIC 1541

LEDCOR CMI INC p 851
6405 Mira Mesa Blvd # 100, San Diego CA 92121
Tel (602) 595-3017
SIC 1541 1611 1629 1623 1522 8999

ROEL CONSTRUCTION CO INC p 1246
1615 Murray Canyon Rd # 1000, San Diego CA 92108
Tel (619) 297-4156 SIC 1541 8741

T B PENICK & SONS INC p 1419
15435 Innovation Dr # 100, San Diego CA 92128
Tel (858) 558-1800 SIC 1541 1542

BERNARDS BROS INC p 176
555 1st St, San Fernando CA 91340
Tel (818) 898-1521 SIC 1542 1541

BECHTEL CONSTRUCTION OPERATIONS INC p 167
50 Beale St Bsmt 1, San Francisco CA 94105
Tel (415) 768-1234
SIC 1541 1629 1623 8741 7353

HERRERO BUILDERS INC p 687
2100 Oakdale Ave, San Francisco CA 94124
Tel (415) 824-7675 SIC 1541

SWINERTON BUILDERS p 1412
260 Townsend St, San Francisco CA 94107
Tel (415) 421-2980 SIC 1541 1522 1542

SWINERTON INC p 1412
260 Townsend St, San Francisco CA 94107
Tel (415) 421-2980
SIC 1542 1541 6531 1522

LUSARDI CONSTRUCTION CO p 886
1570 Linda Vista Dr, San Marcos CA 92078
Tel (760) 744-3133 SIC 1542 1541

MORLEY BUILDERS INC p 989
3330 Ocean Park Blvd # 101, Santa Monica CA 90405
Tel (310) 399-1600
SIC 1541 1522 1542 1771

DOME CONSTRUCTION CORP p 448
393 E Grand Ave, South San Francisco CA 94080
Tel (650) 416-5600 SIC 1542 1541

OLTMANS CONSTRUCTION CO p 1083
10005 Mission Mill Rd, Whittier CA 90601
Tel (562) 948-4242 SIC 1541 1542

GAYLE MANUFACTURING CO INC p 594
1455 E Kentucky Ave, Woodland CA 95776
Tel (707) 226-9136 SIC 3441 1541

HILBERS INC p 692
1210 Stabler Ln, Yuba City CA 95993
Tel (530) 673-2947 SIC 1542 1541

PCL CONSTRUCTION SERVICES INC p 1124
2000 S Colorado Blvd 2-500, Denver CO 80222
Tel (303) 365-6500 SIC 1542 1541

TIC HOLDINGS INC p 1452
9780 Pyramid Ct Ste 100, Englewood CO 80112
Tel (970) 879-2561
SIC 1541 1629 1623 1542

FCI CONSTRUCTORS INC p 533
3070 I 70 Bus Loop Ste A, Grand Junction CO 81504
Tel (970) 434-9093 SIC 1542 1541

GRANITE HENSEL PHELPS JV p 631
420 6th Ave, Greeley CO 80631
Tel (970) 352-6565 SIC 1541 1542

HENSEL PHELPS CONSTRUCTION CO p 684
420 6th Ave, Greeley CO 80631
Tel (970) 352-6565
SIC 1542 1521 1771 1522 1541 1622

HENSEL PHELPS SOLTEK JV p 685
420 6th Ave, Greeley CO 80631
Tel (970) 352-6565 SIC 1542 1541

HENSEL PHELPS-GRANITE JV p 685
420 6th Ave, Greeley CO 80631
Tel (970) 352-6565
SIC 1541 1542 1629 1611

CASEY INDUSTRIAL INC p 263
1400 W 122nd Ave Ste 200, Westminster CO 80234
Tel (541) 926-8641 SIC 1541 8741

FIP CONSTRUCTION INC p 543
1536 New Britain Ave, Farmington CT 06032
Tel (860) 470-1800 SIC 1542 1541

KBE BUILDING CORP p 806
76 Batterson Park Rd # 1, Farmington CT 06032
Tel (860) 284-7424 SIC 1542 1541

NEWFIELD CONSTRUCTION INC p 1037
225 Newfield Ave, Hartford CT 06106
Tel (860) 953-1477 SIC 1541 1542

A/Z CORP p 7
46 Norwich Westerly Rd, North Stonington CT 06359
Tel (800) 400-2420 SIC 1541 1542

O & G INDUSTRIES INC p 1070
112 Wall St, Torrington CT 06790
Tel (860) 489-9261
SIC 1542 1541 1611 1623 5032 2951

MCN BUILD LLC p 932
1214 28th St Nw, Washington DC 20007
Tel (202) 333-3424 SIC 1541 1542

IAP WORLD SERVICES INC p 725
7315 N Atlantic Ave, Cape Canaveral FL 32920
Tel (321) 784-7100
SIC 4731 4581 8744 4911 1541 4813

■ **JAMES A CUMMINGS INC** p 776
1 E Broward Blvd Ste 1300, Fort Lauderdale FL 33301
Tel (954) 484-1532 SIC 1542 1541

STILES CORP p 1389
301 E Las Olas Blvd, Fort Lauderdale FL 33301
Tel (954) 627-9150 SIC 1542 1541

PERRY CHARLES PARTNERS INC p 1137
8200 Nw 15th Pl, Gainesville FL 32606
Tel (352) 333-9292 SIC 1542 1541

HASKELL CO p 667
111 Riverside Ave, Jacksonville FL 32202
Tel (904) 791-4500
SIC 1541 1542 1522 1623 8712 3272

HASKELL CO INC p 667
111 Riverside Ave, Jacksonville FL 32202
Tel (904) 791-4500
SIC 1541 1542 1522 1623 8712 3272

STELLAR COMPANIES INC p 1385
2900 Hartley Rd, Jacksonville FL 32257
Tel (904) 899-9393 SIC 1542 8711 1541

GLF CONSTRUCTION CORP p 615
528 Nw 7th Ave, Miami FL 33136
Tel (305) 371-5228
SIC 1611 1622 1542 1541 1522

PCL INDUSTRIAL CONSTRUCTION CO p 1124
6445 Shiloh Rd Ste E, Alpharetta GA 30005
Tel (678) 965-3100 SIC 1629 1541

FACILITY HOLDINGS CORP p 523
2700 Cumberland Pkwy Se, Atlanta GA 30339
Tel (770) 437-2700 SIC 1541

KAJIMA INTERNATIONAL INC p 801
3475 Piedmont Rd Ne # 1600, Atlanta GA 30305
Tel (404) 564-3900 SIC 1541 3446 1542

KAJIMA USA INC p 801
3475 Piedmont Rd Ne, Atlanta GA 30305
Tel (404) 564-3900
SIC 1542 1541 6531 1522 6552 1622

NEW SOUTH CONSTRUCTION CO INC p 1033
1180 W Peachtree St Nw # 70, Atlanta GA 30309
Tel (404) 443-4000 SIC 1541 8741

WINTER CONSTRUCTION CO p 1617
191 Peachtree St Ne # 2100, Atlanta GA 30303
Tel (404) 588-3300 SIC 1541

ACC CONSTRUCTION CO INC p 14
635 Nw Frontage Rd Ste A, Augusta GA 30907
Tel (706) 868-1037 SIC 1542 1541

TFE LOGISTICS GROUP INC p 1445
3633 Wheeler Rd Ste 350, Augusta GA 30909
Tel (706) 855-1014 SIC 1541

AUBREY SILVEY ENTERPRISES INC p 130
371 Hamp Jones Rd, Carrollton GA 30117
Tel (770) 834-0738
SIC 1629 1541 3643 7389 3699 5063

MADISON INDUSTRIES INC OF GEORGIA p 894
1035 Iris Dr Sw, Conyers GA 30094
Tel (770) 483-4401 SIC 1541 3444

CONLAN CO p 356
1800 Parkway Pl Se # 1010, Marietta GA 30067
Tel (770) 423-8000 SIC 1542 1541

CAPE ENVIRONMENTAL MANAGEMENT INC p 248
500 Pinnacle Ct Ste 100, Norcross GA 30071
Tel (770) 908-7200 SIC 1542 1541

WINTER GROUP OF COMPANIES INC p 1617
191 Peachtree St Ne, Peachtree Corners GA 30071
Tel (404) 588-3300
SIC 1541 1542 1799 6512

SPIRIT CONSTRUCTION SERVICES INC p 1359
118 Coleman Blvd, Savannah GA 31408
Tel (912) 748-8055 SIC 1541 1542

FACILITY DESIGN/BUILDERS INC p 523
2233 Lake Park Dr Se # 450, Smyrna GA 30080
Tel (770) 437-2700 SIC 1541

BATSON-COOK CO p 159
817 4th Ave, West Point GA 31833
Tel (706) 643-2500 SIC 1542 5211 1541

ISEMOTO CONTRACTING CO LTD p 766
648 Piilani St, Hilo HI 96720
Tel (808) 935-7194 SIC 1629 1542 1541

■ **NATIONAL PROJECTS INC** p 1015
720 E Park Blvd, Boise ID 83712
Tel (208) 386-5000 SIC 1629 1542 1541

HANSEN-RICE INC p 658
1717 E Chisholm Dr, Nampa ID 83687
Tel (208) 465-0200 SIC 1541

AUTO TRUCK GROUP LLC p 133
1420 Brewster Creek Blvd, Bartlett IL 60103
Tel (630) 860-5600 SIC 3713 1541

A EPSTEIN AND SONS INTERNATIONAL INC p 5
600 W Fulton St Ste 800, Chicago IL 60661
Tel (312) 454-9100
SIC 8711 8712 7389 1542 1541 8742

BULLEY & ANDREWS p 225
1755 W Armitage Ave, Chicago IL 60622
Tel (773) 235-2433 SIC 1542 1541

BULLEY & ANDREWS LLC p 225
1755 W Armitage Ave, Chicago IL 60622
Tel (312) 207-2100 SIC 1541 1542

CLAYCO INC p 323
35 E Wacker Dr Ste 1300, Chicago IL 60601
Tel (312) 658-0747 SIC 1541

ONEIL INDUSTRIES INC p 1087
1245 W Washington Blvd, Chicago IL 60607
Tel (773) 244-6003 SIC 1542 1541

PEPPER COMPANIES INC p 1133
643 N Orleans St, Chicago IL 60654
Tel (312) 266-4703 SIC 1542 1541

PEPPER CONSTRUCTION CO p 1133
643 N Orleans St, Chicago IL 60654
Tel (312) 266-4700 SIC 1542 1541

POWER CONSTRUCTION CO LLC p 1165
8750 W Bryn Mawr Ave, Chicago IL 60631
Tel (312) 596-6960 SIC 1541 1542

W E ONEIL CONSTRUCTION CO p 1568
1245 W Washington Blvd, Chicago IL 60607
Tel (773) 244-6003 SIC 1541

WALSH CONSTRUCTION CO p 1574
929 W Adams St, Chicago IL 60607
Tel (312) 563-5400
SIC 1541 1622 1542 1611

WALSH GROUP LTD p 1574
929 W Adams St, Chicago IL 60607
Tel (312) 563-5400
SIC 1542 1522 1622 1629 1541

■ **KENNY CONSTRUCTION A GRANITE CO** p 811
2215 Sanders Rd Ste 400, Northbrook IL 60062
Tel (847) 919-8200
SIC 1622 1611 1629 1623 1541

■ **KENNY INDUSTRIES INC** p 811
2215 Sanders Rd Ste 400, Northbrook IL 60062
Tel (847) 919-8200
SIC 1611 1622 1629 1623 1541 6552

GRAYCOR INC p 632
2 Mid America Plz Ste 400, Oakbrook Terrace IL 60181
Tel (630) 684-7110 SIC 1541 1542

GRAYCOR INDUSTRIAL CONSTRUCTORS INC p 632
2 Mid America Plz Ste 400, Oakbrook Terrace IL 60181
Tel (630) 684-7110 SIC 1542 1541

WEDDLE BROS CONSTRUCTION CO INC p 1587
1201 W 3rd St, Bloomington IN 47404
Tel (812) 339-9500 SIC 1542 1622 1541

INDUSTRIAL CONTRACTORS SKANSKA INC p 739
401 Nw 1st St, Evansville IN 47708
Tel (812) 423-7832 SIC 1541 1542

TIPPMANN CONSTRUCTION LLC p 1455
9009 Coldwater Rd Ste 300, Fort Wayne IN 46825
Tel (260) 490-3000 SIC 1541 1796

MORRISON CONSTRUCTION CO INC p 990
1834 Summer St, Hammond IN 46320
Tel (219) 932-5036 SIC 1541

BOWEN ENGINEERING CORP p 204
8802 N Meridian St Ste X, Indianapolis IN 46260
Tel (219) 661-9770 SIC 1629 1623 1541

PEPPER CONSTRUCTION CO OF INDIANA LLC p 1133
1850 W 15th St, Indianapolis IN 46202
Tel (317) 681-1000 SIC 1542 1541

SHIEL SEXTON CO INC p 1316
902 N Capitol Ave, Indianapolis IN 46204
Tel (317) 423-6000 SIC 1542 1541

WILHELM CONSTRUCTION INC p 1609
3914 Prospect St, Indianapolis IN 46203
Tel (317) 359-5411 SIC 1542 1541 1761

CIMC USA INC p 307
289 Water Tower Dr, Monon IN 47959
Tel (219) 253-2054 SIC 1541

DIY/GROUP INC p 445
2401 W 26th St, Muncie IN 47302
Tel (765) 284-9000 SIC 1541

SUPERIOR CONSTRUCTION CO INC p 1406
1455 Louis Sullivan Dr, Portage IN 46368
Tel (219) 886-3728 SIC 1541 1629 1622

FBI BUILDINGS INC p 532
3823 W 1800 S, Remington IN 47977
Tel (219) 261-2157 SIC 1542 5031 1541

MICHAELS G L CONSTRUCTION INC p 960
554 W Cedarwood Ave, West Terre Haute IN 47885
Tel (812) 478-3154 SIC 1542 1541

SARGENT GROUP INC p 1282
2905 Se 5th St, Ames IA 50010
Tel (515) 232-0442 SIC 1541 1796

TODD & SARGENT INC p 1458
2905 Se 5th St, Ames IA 50010
Tel (515) 232-0442 SIC 1541 1542

DEAN SNYDER CONSTRUCTION CO p 420
913 N 14th St, Clear Lake IA 50428
Tel (641) 357-2283 SIC 1542 1521 1541

WEITZ CO LLC p 1588
5901 Thornton Ave, Des Moines IA 50321
Tel (515) 698-4260 SIC 1542 1541 1629

CONLON CONSTRUCTION CO OF IOWA p 356
1100 Rockdale Rd, Dubuque IA 52003
Tel (563) 583-1724 SIC 1542 8741 1541

KLINGER COMPANIES INC p 823
2015 7th St, Sioux City IA 51101
Tel (712) 277-3900 SIC 1542 1541

DONDLINGER & SONS CONSTRUCTION CO INC p 450
2656 S Sheridan Ave, Wichita KS 67217
Tel (316) 945-0555 SIC 1622 1541 1542

EBY CORP p 474
2525 E 36th Cir N, Wichita KS 67219
Tel (316) 268-3500
SIC 1629 1623 1622 1541 1542 7353

KEY CONSTRUCTION INC p 814
741 W 2nd St N, Wichita KS 67203
Tel (316) 263-9515 SIC 1542 1541

STEWART RICHEY CONSTRUCTION INC p 1389
2137 Glen Lily Rd, Bowling Green KY 42101
Tel (270) 842-5184 SIC 1542 1521 1541

DENHAM-BLYTHE CO INC p 428
100 Trade St Ste 250, Lexington KY 40511
Tel (859) 255-7405 SIC 1541 1542

GRAY CONSTRUCTION INC p 632
10 Quality St, Lexington KY 40507
Tel (859) 281-5000 SIC 1541 1542 8712

GRAY INC *p* 632
10 Quality St, Lexington KY 40507
Tel (859) 281-5000 *SIC* 1541 1542

ABEL CONSTRUCTION CO INC *p* 11
3401 Bashford Avenue Ct, Louisville KY 40218
Tel (502) 451-2235 *SIC* 1541 1542

HALL CONTRACTING OF KENTUCKY INC *p* 654
3800 Crittenden Dr, Louisville KY 40209
Tel (502) 367-6151
SIC 1541 1623 1761 1731

A & K CONSTRUCTION INC *p* 4
100 Calloway Ct, Paducah KY 42001
Tel (270) 441-7752 *SIC* 1542 1541

BRANSCUM CONSTRUCTION CO/ROBINS & MORTON A JOINT VENTURE *p* 208
90 Key Village Rd, Russell Springs KY 42642
Tel (270) 866-5107 *SIC* 1541 8741 1542

CAJUN CONSTRUCTORS LLC *p* 237
15635 Airline Hwy, Baton Rouge LA 70817
Tel (225) 753-5857
SIC 1623 4952 1541 1542

CB&I CONTRACTORS INC *p* 268
4171 Essen Ln, Baton Rouge LA 70809
Tel (225) 932-2500 *SIC* 1541

CB&I GOVERNMENT SOLUTIONS INC *p* 268
4171 Essen Ln, Baton Rouge LA 70809
Tel (225) 932-2500
SIC 8711 8734 8748 1541 1542 1611

FORD BACON & DAVIS LLC *p* 565
12021 Lakeland Park Blvd # 212, Baton Rouge LA 70809
Tel (225) 297-3431 *SIC* 8711 1541 1623

PALA GROUP INC *p* 1108
16347 Old Hammond Hwy, Baton Rouge LA 70816
Tel (225) 272-5194 *SIC* 1629 1541

PALA INTERSTATE LLC *p* 1108
16347 Old Hammond Hwy, Baton Rouge LA 70816
Tel (225) 272-5194 *SIC* 1541 8711

PERFORMANCE CONTRACTORS INC *p* 1135
9901 Pecue Ln, Baton Rouge LA 70810
Tel (225) 490-2000 *SIC* 1541 3498

TURNER INDUSTRIES OF CALIFORNIA *p* 1493
8687 United Plaza Blvd, Baton Rouge LA 70809
Tel (225) 922-5050 *SIC* 1541

TURNER SPECIALTY SERVICES LLC *p* 1493
8687 United Plaza Blvd, Baton Rouge LA 70809
Tel (225) 922-5050 *SIC* 1541 7699

W H C INC *p* 1568
300 Industrial Trce, Broussard LA 70518
Tel (337) 837-4500 *SIC* 1623 1541

SMITH TANK & STEEL INC *p* 1333
42422 Highway 30, Gonzales LA 70737
Tel (225) 644-8747 *SIC* 1541

GIBBS CONSTRUCTION LLC *p* 611
5736 Citrus Blvd Ste 200, Harahan LA 70123
Tel (504) 733-4336 *SIC* 1542 1541

VISCARDI INDUSTRIAL SERVICES LLC *p* 1561
815 Lucerne Dr, New Iberia LA 70563
Tel (337) 367-0824 *SIC* 1541

WALTON CONSTRUCTION - A CORE CO LLC *p* 1575
2 Commerce Ct, New Orleans LA 70123
Tel (504) 733-2212 *SIC* 1541 1542

WOODWARD DESIGN + BUILD LLC *p* 1623
1000 S Jffrson Dvis Pkwy, New Orleans LA 70125
Tel (504) 822-6443 *SIC* 1541 1542

CROWN ENTERPRISES LLC *p* 395
52410 Clarke Rd, White Castle LA 70788
Tel (225) 545-3040 *SIC* 1541 1791 4212

CIANBRO COMPANIES *p* 305
1 Hunnewell Ave, Pittsfield ME 04967
Tel (207) 487-3311
SIC 1629 1622 1542 1541 8742

CIANBRO CORP *p* 305
101 Cianbro Sq, Pittsfield ME 04967
Tel (207) 487-3311
SIC 1622 1629 1542 1541 8742

REED & REED INC *p* 1217
275 River Rd, Woolwich ME 04579
Tel (207) 443-9747 *SIC* 1622 1629 1541

WHITING-TURNER CONTRACTING CO *p* 1607
300 E Joppa Rd Ste 800, Baltimore MD 21286
Tel (410) 821-1100
SIC 1542 1541 1629 8741

WILLIAMS SCOTSMAN INC *p* 1611
901 S Bond St Ste 600, Baltimore MD 21231
Tel (410) 931-6000
SIC 1531 1541 5039 7359

MORGAN-KELLER INC *p* 989
70 Thomas Johnson Dr # 200, Frederick MD 21702
Tel (301) 663-0626 *SIC* 1542 1541

EMD MILLIPORE CORP *p* 491
290 Concord Rd, Billerica MA 01821
Tel (781) 533-6000 *SIC* 3559 1541 3999

CDM CONSTRUCTORS INC *p* 271
75 State St Ste 701, Boston MA 02109
Tel (617) 452-6000 *SIC* 1541 1623

■ **PERINI MANAGEMENT SERVICES INC** *p* 1136
73 Mount Wayte Ave, Framingham MA 01702
Tel (508) 628-2000
SIC 1541 1542 1611 1629

DANIEL OCONNELLS SONS INC *p* 411
480 Hampden St, Holyoke MA 01040
Tel (413) 534-5667
SIC 1541 1542 1522 1611 1622 1629

OCONNELL COMPANIES INC *p* 1074
480 Hampden St, Holyoke MA 01040
Tel (413) 534-0246 *SIC* 1541

RAND WHITNEY PACKAGING *p* 1207
580 Fort Pond Rd, Lancaster MA 01523
Tel (978) 870-1188 *SIC* 1541

CONSIGLI CONSTRUCTION CO INC *p* 359
72 Sumner St, Milford MA 01757
Tel (508) 473-2580 *SIC* 1541 1542

WT RICH CO INC *p* 1569
29 Crafts St Ste 300, Newton MA 02458
Tel (617) 467-6010 *SIC* 1541 1542

DF PRAY INC *p* 435
25 Anthony St, Seekonk MA 02771
Tel (508) 336-3366 *SIC* 1542 1541

DEVERE CONSTRUCTION CO INC *p* 433
1030 Devere Dr, Alpena MI 49707
Tel (989) 356-4411
SIC 1542 1541 1629 8741

COMMERCIAL CONTRACTING CORP *p* 345
4260 N Atlantic Blvd, Auburn Hills MI 48326
Tel (248) 209-0500 *SIC* 1541 1796

MICHIGAN PAVING AND MATERIALS CO *p* 961
2575 S Haggerty Rd # 100, Canton MI 48188
Tel (734) 397-2050 *SIC* 1522 1541 2911

DEVON INDUSTRIAL GROUP *p* 434
535 Griswold St Ste 2050, Detroit MI 48226
Tel (313) 965-3455 *SIC* 1541

WALBRIDGE ALDINGER LLC *p* 1572
777 Woodward Ave Ste 300, Detroit MI 48226
Tel (313) 963-8000 *SIC* 1541 1542 8741

TRIANGLE ASSOCIATES INC *p* 1478
3769 3 Mile Rd Nw, Grand Rapids MI 49534
Tel (616) 453-3950 *SIC* 1542 1541

WOLVERINE BUILDING GROUP INC *p* 1621
4045 Barden St Se, Grand Rapids MI 49512
Tel (616) 281-6236 *SIC* 1541 1542

LAMAR CONSTRUCTION CO *p* 841
4404 Central Pkwy, Hudsonville MI 49426
Tel (616) 662-2933 *SIC* 1542 1541

CHRISTMAN CO *p* 303
208 N Capitol Ave Fl 4, Lansing MI 48933
Tel (517) 482-1488
SIC 8741 1542 1541 1629

GRANGER CONSTRUCTION CO INC *p* 631
6267 Aurelius Rd, Lansing MI 48911
Tel (517) 393-1670 *SIC* 1542 1541

ARISTEO CONSTRUCTION CO *p* 108
12811 Farmington Rd, Livonia MI 48150
Tel (734) 427-9111 *SIC* 1541

ARISTEO INSTALLATION LLC *p* 108
12811 Farmington Rd, Livonia MI 48150
Tel (734) 427-9111 *SIC* 1541

RAM CONSTRUCTION SERVICES OF MICHIGAN INC *p* 1206
13800 Eckles Rd, Livonia MI 48150
Tel (734) 464-3800 *SIC* 1799 1541 1542

STENCO CONSTRUCTION CO LLC *p* 1385
12741 Farmington Rd, Livonia MI 48150
Tel (734) 427-8843 *SIC* 1541

THREE RIVERS CORP *p* 1450
3069 E Vantage Point Dr, Midland MI 48642
Tel (989) 631-9726 *SIC* 1542 1541

LEE CONTRACTING INC *p* 851
631 Cesar E Chavez Ave, Pontiac MI 48342
Tel (888) 833-8776 *SIC* 1731 1542 1541

WOLGAST CORP *p* 1621
4835 Towne Centre Rd # 203, Saginaw MI 48604
Tel (989) 233-5228 *SIC* 1542 1541

BARTON MALOW ENTERPRISES INC *p* 158
26500 American Dr, Southfield MI 48034
Tel (248) 436-5000 *SIC* 8741 1542 1541

RONCELLI INC *p* 1249
6471 Metropolitan Pkwy, Sterling Heights MI 48312
Tel (586) 264-2060 *SIC* 1541 8711

NOR-SON INC *p* 1047
7900 Hastings Rd, Baxter MN 56425
Tel (218) 828-1722 *SIC* 1521 1542 1541

VIGEN CONSTRUCTION INC *p* 1556
42247 180th St Sw, East Grand Forks MN 56721
Tel (218) 773-1159 *SIC* 1541

MET-CON CONSTRUCTION INC *p* 952
15760 Acorn Trl, Faribault MN 55021
Tel (507) 332-2266 *SIC* 1541 1542 5251

FAGEN INC *p* 524
501 Highway 212 W, Granite Falls MN 56241
Tel (320) 564-3324 *SIC* 1541 1731 1711

KNUTSON CONSTRUCTION SERVICES INC *p* 825
7515 Wayzata Blvd, Minneapolis MN 55426
Tel (763) 546-1400 *SIC* 1542 1541

KNUTSON HOLDINGS INC *p* 825
7515 Wayzata Blvd, Minneapolis MN 55426
Tel (763) 546-1400 *SIC* 1542 1541

RYAN COMPANIES US INC *p* 1260
50 S 10th St Ste 300, Minneapolis MN 55403
Tel (612) 492-4000
SIC 1542 1541 6552 6512 1522

WEIS BUILDERS INC *p* 1588
7645 Lyndale Ave S # 300, Minneapolis MN 55423
Tel (612) 243-5000 *SIC* 1522 1541 1542

OPUS DESIGN BUILD LLC *p* 1091
10350 Bren Rd W, Minnetonka MN 55343
Tel (952) 656-4444 *SIC* 1522 1541

MCGOUGH CONSTRUCTION CO INC *p* 929
2737 Fairview Ave N, Saint Paul MN 55113
Tel (651) 633-5050 *SIC* 1541 1542

SHAW-LUNDQUIST ASSOCIATES INC *p* 1313
2757 W Service Rd, Saint Paul MN 55121
Tel (651) 454-0670 *SIC* 1542 1541

HILL BROTHERS CONSTRUCTION CO INC *p* 693
20831 Highway 15, Falkner MS 38629
Tel (662) 837-3041
SIC 1611 1622 1541 1542

■ **ANDERSON COMPANIES INC** *p* 89
11400 Reichold Rd, Gulfport MS 39503
Tel (228) 896-4000 *SIC* 1542 1541 1522

■ **ROY ANDERSON CORP** *p* 1254
11400 Reichold Rd, Gulfport MS 39503
Tel (228) 896-4000 *SIC* 1542 1541 1522

W G YATES & SONS CONSTRUCTION CO *p* 1568
1 Gully Ave, Philadelphia MS 39350
Tel (904) 714-1376
SIC 1542 1541 2339 1611 5211 1731

YATES COMPANIES INC *p* 1635
1 Gully Ave, Philadelphia MS 39350
Tel (601) 656-5411
SIC 1542 1541 1611 5211 1731

JESCO INC *p* 783
2020 Mccullough Blvd, Tupelo MS 38801
Tel (662) 842-3240 *SIC* 1541

BILFINGER INDUSTRIAL SERVICES INC *p* 182
15933 Clayton Rd Ste 305, Ballwin MO 63011
Tel (636) 391-4500
SIC 1541 1731 1796 8711 8744

BEN HUR CONSTRUCTION CO *p* 172
3783 Rider Trl S, Earth City MO 63045
Tel (314) 298-8007
SIC 1542 1791 1541 3441

FOLEY CO *p* 563
7501 E Front St, Kansas City MO 64120
Tel (816) 241-3335 *SIC* 1623 1711 1541

KISSICK CONSTRUCTION CO INC *p* 822
8131 Indiana Ave, Kansas City MO 64132
Tel (816) 363-5530
SIC 1541 1623 1771 1794

ARIZON COMPANIES INC *p* 108
11880 Dorsett Rd, Maryland Heights MO 63043
Tel (314) 739-0037
SIC 3585 1711 2394 1541 1542 8611

ALBERICI CONSTRUCTORS INC *p* 46
8800 Page Ave, Saint Louis MO 63114
Tel (314) 733-2000 *SIC* 1541 1542 1622

ALBERICI CORP *p* 46
8800 Page Ave, Saint Louis MO 63114
Tel (314) 733-2000
SIC 1541 1542 1622 1629

ALBERICI GROUP INC *p* 46
8800 Page Ave, Saint Louis MO 63114
Tel (314) 733-2000 *SIC* 1541 1542 1622

ARCO NATIONAL CONSTRUCTION CO *p* 105
900 N Rock Hill Rd, Saint Louis MO 63119
Tel (314) 963-0715 *SIC* 1541

■ **JACOBS FACILITIES INC** *p* 775
501 N Broadway, Saint Louis MO 63102
Tel (314) 335-4000
SIC 8712 8711 8713 8741 1542 1541

KORTE CONSTRUCTION CO *p* 828
5700 Oakland Ave Ste 275, Saint Louis MO 63110
Tel (314) 231-3700 *SIC* 1541 1542

L KEELEY CONSTRUCTION CO *p* 834
500 S Ewing Ave Ste G, Saint Louis MO 63103
Tel (314) 421-5933 *SIC* 1541 1611 1623

LIEBEL-FLARSHEIM CO LLC *p* 863
1034 S Brentwood Blvd, Saint Louis MO 63117
Tel (314) 654-8625 *SIC* 1541

MC INDUSTRIAL INC *p* 925
3117 S Big Bend Blvd, Saint Louis MO 63143
Tel (314) 646-4100 *SIC* 1541

MCCARTHY BUILDING COMPANIES INC *p* 926
1341 N Rock Hill Rd, Saint Louis MO 63124
Tel (314) 968-3300 *SIC* 1542 1541

MCCARTHY HOLDINGS INC *p* 926
1341 N Rock Hill Rd, Saint Louis MO 63124
Tel (314) 968-3300 *SIC* 1542 1541

NOOTER CONSTRUCTION CO *p* 1047
1500 S 2nd St, Saint Louis MO 63104
Tel (314) 621-6000 *SIC* 1541

PARIC CORP *p* 1114
77 West Port Plz Ste 250, Saint Louis MO 63146
Tel (636) 561-9500 *SIC* 1542 1541

S M WILSON & CO *p* 1262
2185 Hampton Ave, Saint Louis MO 63139
Tel (314) 645-9595 *SIC* 1541 1542

SLETTEN CONSTRUCTION CO *p* 1331
1000 25th St N Ste 4, Great Falls MT 59401
Tel (406) 761-7920 *SIC* 1541 1542 1611

SLETTEN INC *p* 1331
1000 25th St N Ste 4, Great Falls MT 59401
Tel (406) 761-7920 *SIC* 1542 1541 1611

SAMPSON CONSTRUCTION CO INC *p* 1274
3730 S 14th St, Lincoln NE 68502
Tel (308) 865-1375 *SIC* 1542 1541

HAWKINS CONSTRUCTION CO *p* 669
2516 Deer Park Blvd, Omaha NE 68105
Tel (402) 342-4455 *SIC* 1542 1611 1541

KIEWIT CORP *p* 817
3555 Farnam St Ste 1000, Omaha NE 68131
Tel (402) 342-2052
SIC 1542 1541 1611 1622 1629

KIEWIT INFRASTRUCTURE CO *p* 817
Kiewit Plz, Omaha NE 68131
Tel (402) 342-2052
SIC 1541 1542 1629 1622 1522

KIEWIT INFRASTRUCTURE WEST CO *p* 817
4004 S 60th St, Omaha NE 68117
Tel (402) 342-2052
SIC 1611 1629 1541 1622 1623

MARTIN-HARRIS CONSTRUCTION LLC *p* 913
3030 S Highland Dr, Las Vegas NV 89109
Tel (702) 385-5257 *SIC* 1541 1542

UNITED CONSTRUCTION CO *p* 1507
5300 Mill St, Reno NV 89502
Tel (775) 858-8090 *SIC* 1541 1542

PRO CON INC *p* 1178
1359 Hooksett Rd Ste 16, Hooksett NH 03106
Tel (603) 623-8811 *SIC* 1542 1541

STEBBINS ENTERPRISES INC *p* 1384
1359 Hooksett Rd, Hooksett NH 03106
Tel (603) 623-8811 *SIC* 1542 1541

HUTTER CONSTRUCTION CORP *p* 722
810 Turnpike Rd, New Ipswich NH 03071
Tel (603) 878-2300 *SIC* 1541 1542

FURINO & SON INC *p* 585
66 Columbia Rd, Branchburg NJ 08876
Tel (908) 756-7736 *SIC* 1541 1542

JOSEPH JINGOLI & SON INC *p* 793
100 Lenox Dr Ste 100, Lawrenceville NJ 08648
Tel (609) 896-3111 *SIC* 1541

■ **COVANTA ENERGY GROUP INC** *p* 384
445 South St, Morristown NJ 07960
Tel (862) 345-5000
SIC 1541 1629 4953 4931

BLACKSTONE GROUP LLC *p* 188
570 Broad St Ste 1606, Newark NJ 07102
Tel (973) 624-6300 *SIC* 1542 1522 1541

SKANSKA USA BUILDING INC *p* 1329
389 Interpace Pkwy Ste 5, Parsippany NJ 07054
Tel (973) 753-3500 *SIC* 1541 1542 8741

CORNELL & CO INC *p* 370
224 Cornell Ln, Westville NJ 08093
Tel (856) 742-1900 *SIC* 1542 1541

JAYNES CORP *p* 779
2906 Broadway Blvd Ne, Albuquerque NM 87107
Tel (505) 345-8591 *SIC* 1542 1541

BBL LLC *p* 163
302 Washington Ave, Albany NY 12203
Tel (518) 452-8200
SIC 1542 1541 1521 1622 8741

BAST HATFIELD INC *p* 159
1399 Vischers Ferry Rd, Clifton Park NY 12065
Tel (518) 373-2000 *SIC* 1542 1541 8741

BETTE & CRING LLC *p* 178
22 Century Hill Dr # 201, Latham NY 12110
Tel (518) 213-1010
SIC 1541 1542 1622 1611

WELLIVER MCGUIRE INC *p* 1589
250 N Genesee St, Montour Falls NY 14865
Tel (704) 454-5500 *SIC* 1542 1541

BARR & BARR INC *p* 156
460 W 34th St Fl 10, New York NY 10001
Tel (212) 563-2330 *SIC* 1542 1541

CLARENDON NATIONAL INSURANCE CO (MD CORP) *p* 321
411 5th Ave Fl 5, New York NY 10016
Tel (212) 790-9700
SIC 6321 1542 1541 7011

HOCHTIEF USA INC *p* 699
375 Hudson St Fl 6, New York NY 10014
Tel (212) 229-6000
SIC 1542 1541 1522 8741 8742 6799

LEND LEASE AMERICAS INC *p* 855
200 Park Ave Fl 9, New York NY 10166
Tel (212) 592-6700 *SIC* 1542 1541

LENDLEASE (US) CONSTRUCTION HOLDINGS INC *p* 855
200 Park Ave Fl 9, New York NY 10166
Tel (212) 592-6700 *SIC* 1542 1541 8742

LENDLEASE (US) CONSTRUCTION INC *p* 855
200 Park Ave Fl 9, New York NY 10166
Tel (212) 592-6700
SIC 1541 1542 1522 8741 8742

LENDLEASE (US) CONSTRUCTION LMB INC *p* 855
200 Park Ave Fl 9, New York NY 10166
Tel (212) 592-6700
SIC 1522 1541 1542 8741 8742

M/L BOVIS HOLDINGS LTD *p* 890
200 Park Ave Fl 9, New York NY 10166
Tel (212) 592-6700
SIC 1522 1541 1542 8741 8742

SHACKLEFORDS CONSTRUCTION & CONTRACTING LTD *p* 1310
303 Lexington Ave, New York NY 10016
Tel (646) 771-4470
SIC 1522 1542 1541 7389

STANTEC CONSULTING SERVICES INC *p* 1377
50 W 23rd St Fl 8, New York NY 10010
Tel (212) 366-5600 *SIC* 8731 8711 1541

TURNER CONSTRUCTION CO INC *p* 1492
375 Hudson St Fl 6, New York NY 10014
Tel (212) 229-6000
SIC 1542 1541 1522 8741 8742

TURNER CORP *p* 1492
375 Hudson St Rm 700, New York NY 10014
Tel (212) 229-6000
SIC 1542 1541 1522 8742

NOVA CORP INC *p* 1062
1 Main St, Nyack NY 10960
Tel (201) 567-4404 *SIC* 1541 8748

HOLT CONSTRUCTION CORP *p* 702
50 E Washington Ave, Pearl River NY 10965
Tel (845) 735-4054 *SIC* 1541 8742

BELL CO LLC *p* 170
1340 Lexington Ave, Rochester NY 14606
Tel (585) 277-1000 *SIC* 1541 1542

LECHASE CONSTRUCTION SERVICES LLC *p* 850
205 Indigo Creek Dr, Rochester NY 14626
Tel (585) 254-3510 *SIC* 1541 1542

PURCELL CONSTRUCTION CORP *p* 1192
566 Coffeen St, Watertown NY 13601
Tel (315) 782-1050 *SIC* 1542 1541 1522

LAHR CONSTRUCTION CORP *p* 838
75 Thruway Park Dr Ste 1, West Henrietta NY 14586
Tel (585) 334-4490 *SIC* 1521 1541

■ **BWXT INVESTMENT CO** *p* 231
11525 N Community House, Charlotte NC 28277
Tel (704) 625-4900
SIC 3511 3443 3564 1629 1541 7699

RODGERS BUILDERS INC *p* 1246
5701 N Sharon Amity Rd, Charlotte NC 28215
Tel (704) 537-6044 *SIC* 1542 1541

SHELCO LLC *p* 1314
2320 Cascade Pointe Blvd # 100, Charlotte NC 28208
Tel (704) 367-5600 *SIC* 1541 1542

CARDINAL LOGISTICS MANAGEMENT INC *p* 253
5333 Davidson Hwy, Concord NC 28027
Tel (704) 786-6125 *SIC* 4212 4213 1541

TA LOVING CO *p* 1420
400 Patetown Rd, Goldsboro NC 27530
Tel (919) 734-8400 *SIC* 1541 1542 1623

SAMET CORP *p* 1274
309 Gallimore Dairy Rd # 102, Greensboro NC 27409
Tel (336) 544-2600 *SIC* 1541 1542

JAMES R VANNOY & SONS CONSTRUCTION CO INC *p* 777
1608 Us Highway 221 N, Jefferson NC 28640
Tel (336) 846-7191 *SIC* 1542 1541 1799

CENTURY CONTRACTORS INC *p* 282
5100 Smith Farm Rd, Matthews NC 28104
Tel (704) 821-8050 *SIC* 1541

CLANCY & THEYS CONSTRUCTION CO INC *p* 321
516 W Cabarrus St, Raleigh NC 27603
Tel (919) 834-3601 *SIC* 1542 1541

▲WILLIAMS INDUSTRIES INC p 1611
1128 Tyler Farms Dr, Raleigh NC 27603
Tel (919) 604-1746
SIC 3441 1531 1541 3315 1791

BARNHILL CONTRACTING CO INC p 156
800 Tiffany Blvd Ste 200, Rocky Mount NC 27804
Tel (252) 823-1021 *SIC* 1771 1541

B V HEDRICK GRAVEL & SAND CO p 142
120 1/2 N Church St, Salisbury NC 28144
Tel (704) 633-5982
SIC 1442 7359 6512 3273 1541 1542

■ROBERTS CO FIELD SERVICES INC p 1242
133 Forlines Rd, Winterville NC 28590
Tel (252) 355-9353 *SIC* 1541

WESTCON INC p 1597
7401 Yukon Dr, Bismarck ND 58503
Tel (701) 222-0076 *SIC* 1541 3498 8741

■WANZEK CONSTRUCTION INC p 1575
2028 2nd Ave Nw, West Fargo ND 58078
Tel (701) 282-6171
SIC 1542 1623 1622 1799 1541 1629

DUGAN & MEYERS CONSTRUCTION CO p 460
11110 Kenwood Rd, Blue Ash OH 45242
Tel (513) 891-4300 *SIC* 1541 1542 1522

DUGAN & MEYERS INTERESTS INC p 460
11110 Kenwood Rd, Blue Ash OH 45242
Tel (513) 891-4300 *SIC* 1541 1542 1522

ENERFAB INC p 497
4955 Spring Grove Ave, Cincinnati OH 45232
Tel (513) 641-0500
SIC 3443 1629 1541 1711 3479

MESSER CONSTRUCTION CO p 951
5158 Fishwick Dr, Cincinnati OH 45216
Tel (513) 242-1541 *SIC* 1542 1541 1522

ALBERT M HIGLEY CO p 46
2926 Chester Ave, Cleveland OH 44114
Tel (216) 404-5783 *SIC* 1542 1541

AUSTIN BUILDING AND DESIGN INC p 132
6095 Parkland Blvd # 100, Cleveland OH 44124
Tel (440) 544-2600
SIC 1541 1542 8742 8711 8712

STEVENS ENGINEERS & CONSTRUCTORS INC p 1388
7850 Freeway Cir Ste 100, Cleveland OH 44130
Tel (440) 234-7888 *SIC* 1541 1711 8711

CONTINENTAL REAL ESTATE COMPANIES p 363
150 E Broad St Ste 200, Columbus OH 43215
Tel (614) 221-1800 *SIC* 1542 1541

ELFORD INC p 486
1220 Dublin Rd, Columbus OH 43215
Tel (614) 488-4000 *SIC* 1542 1541 8741

KOKOSING CONSTRUCTION CO INC p 826
886 Mckinley Ave, Columbus OH 43222
Tel (614) 228-1029
SIC 1611 1622 1629 1542 1541 1623

ADAMS-ROBINSON ENTERPRISES INC p 21
2735 Needmore Rd, Dayton OH 45414
Tel (937) 274-5318 *SIC* 1541

MV COMMERCIAL CONSTRUCTION LLC p 1003
137 N Main St Ste 900, Dayton OH 45402
Tel (937) 293-0900 *SIC* 1541

SHOOK NATIONAL CORP p 1318
4977 Northcutt Pl, Dayton OH 45414
Tel (937) 276-6666
SIC 8741 1542 1629 1541

LUKE THEIS ENTERPRISES INC p 885
14120 State Route 568, Findlay OH 45840
Tel (419) 422-2040 *SIC* 1542 1541 1521

MOSSER CONSTRUCTION INC p 992
122 S Wilson Ave, Fremont OH 43420
Tel (419) 334-3801 *SIC* 1541 1542

WMOG INC p 1620
122 S Wilson Ave, Fremont OH 43420
Tel (419) 334-3801 *SIC* 1541 7359 1611

DANIS BUILDING CONSTRUCTION CO p 411
3233 Newmark Dr, Miamisburg OH 45342
Tel (937) 228-1225 *SIC* 1542 1541

FORTNEY & WEYGANDT INC p 570
31269 Bradley Rd, North Olmsted OH 44070
Tel (440) 716-4000 *SIC* 1541 1542

RUHLIN CO p 1257
6931 Ridge Rd, Sharon Center OH 44274
Tel (330) 239-2800
SIC 1542 1541 1622 1611

FERGUSON CONSTRUCTION CO INC p 538
400 Canal St, Sidney OH 45365
Tel (937) 498-2381 *SIC* 1541 1542

SSOE INC p 1364
1001 Madison Ave Ste A, Toledo OH 43604
Tel (419) 255-3830
SIC 8711 8712 8742 1541 7389

RUDOLPH LIBBE INC p 1257
6494 Latcha Rd, Walbridge OH 43465
Tel (419) 241-5000 *SIC* 1541 1542

RUDOLPH/LIBBE COMPANIES INC p 1257
6494 Latcha Rd, Walbridge OH 43465
Tel (419) 241-5000 *SIC* 1541 1542

CORNA KOKOSING CONSTRUCTION CO p 370
6235 Westerville Rd, Westerville OH 43081
Tel (614) 901-8844 *SIC* 1541 1542 8741

MCGRAW/KOKOSING INC p 929
101 Clark Blvd, Westerville OH 43081
Tel (614) 212-5700 *SIC* 1541 1542

OKLAHOMA ROOF MASTERS INC p 1080
601 Evergreen Dr, Guthrie OK 73044
Tel (405) 814-6440
SIC 1761 1541 4731 4212 4213

TIMBERLAKE CONSTRUCTION CO INC p 1454
7613 N Classen Blvd, Oklahoma City OK 73116
Tel (405) 840-2521 *SIC* 1542 1541

FLINTCO LLC p 557
1624 W 21st St, Tulsa OK 74107
Tel (918) 587-8451 *SIC* 1541 1542

■HARRY & DAVID HOLDINGS INC p 664
2500 S Pacific Hwy, Medford OR 97501
Tel (541) 864-2362 *SIC* 5961 1541

ANDERSEN CONSTRUCTION CO p 89
6712 N Cutter Cir, Portland OR 97217
Tel (503) 283-6712 *SIC* 1542 1541

HOFFMAN CORP p 699
805 Sw Broadway Ste 2100, Portland OR 97205
Tel (503) 221-8811
SIC 8741 1541 1542 1623 1629

LOBAR INC p 872
1 Old Mill Rd, Dillsburg PA 17019
Tel (717) 432-9728
SIC 1541 1542 8741 1629 1731 7371

QUANDEL CONSTRUCTION GROUP INC p 1198
3003 N Front St Ste 203, Harrisburg PA 17110
Tel (717) 657-0909
SIC 1542 1541 1629 8741

HIGH STEEL STRUCTURES LLC p 691
1915 Old Philadelphia Pike, Lancaster PA 17602
Tel (717) 299-5211 *SIC* 1541

HORST GROUP INC p 708
320 Granite Run Dr, Lancaster PA 17601
Tel (717) 560-1919 *SIC* 1542 1541 6531

WOHLSEN CONSTRUCTION CO INC p 1620
548 Steel Way, Lancaster PA 17601
Tel (717) 299-2500 *SIC* 1542 1541 8741

NORWOOD CO p 1061
375 Technology Dr, Malvern PA 19355
Tel (610) 240-4400 *SIC* 1541 1542 8741

HENRY F TEICHMANN INC p 684
3009 Washington Rd, Mc Murray PA 15317
Tel (724) 941-9550 *SIC* 1541 8711 8742

DAY & ZIMMERMANN INTERNATIONAL INC p 417
1500 Spring Garden St # 900, Philadelphia PA 19130
Tel (215) 299-8000 *SIC* 8711 1541 8741

■ATC TECHNOLOGY CORP p 124
100 Papercraft Park, Pittsburgh PA 15238
Tel (412) 820-3700 *SIC* 1541 3694 4225

CHAPMAN CORP p 288
331 S Main St, Washington PA 15301
Tel (724) 228-1900 *SIC* 1541 1542

KINSLEY CONSTRUCTION INC p 821
2700 Water St, York PA 17403
Tel (717) 741-3841 *SIC* 1541 1542 1611

AIREKO CONSTRUCTION LLC p 40
Las Casas St Lot 20, Caguas PR 00725
Tel (787) 653-6300
SIC 1542 1541 1731 1711

■FLUOR DANIEL CARIBBEAN INC p 561
Metro Office Park St2 1 # 2, Guaynabo PR 00968
Tel (787) 783-5500 *SIC* 1542 1541

GILBANE INC p 611
7 Jackson Walkway, Providence RI 02903
Tel (401) 456-5800
SIC 1541 1542 8741 6513 6512

WDS INC p 1585
1632 Village Harbor Dr, Clover SC 29710
Tel (803) 619-0301 *SIC* 5085 1541 8742

BONITZ CONTRACTING CO INC p 200
645 Rosewood Dr, Columbia SC 29201
Tel (803) 799-0181
SIC 1742 1752 1761 1542 1541

BONITZ INC p 200
645 Rosewood Dr, Columbia SC 29201
Tel (803) 799-0181
SIC 3448 1542 1742 1541 1761 1752

AME INC p 66
2467 Coltharp Rd, Fort Mill SC 29715
Tel (803) 548-7766 *SIC* 1541 7353 3443

PALMETTO INDUSTRIAL CONSTRUCTION CO INC p 1109
831 Old Wire Rd, Gaston SC 29053
Tel (803) 739-0381 *SIC* 1541

■BE&K BUILDING GROUP LLC p 164
201 E Mcbee Ave Ste 400, Greenville SC 29601
Tel (864) 250-5000 *SIC* 1542 1541 1522

■FLUOR INTERCONTINENTAL INC p 561
100 Fluor Daniel Dr, Greenville SC 29607
Tel (864) 281-4400 *SIC* 1541 1542

GREENWOOD INC p 639
160 Milestone Way Ste A, Greenville SC 29615
Tel (864) 288-5510 *SIC* 1541 7349

LANDMARK CONSTRUCTION CO INC p 842
3255 Industry Dr, North Charleston SC 29418
Tel (843) 552-6186
SIC 1542 1541 1623 1771 1794

WAREHOUSE SERVICES INC p 1575
58 S Burty Rd, Piedmont SC 29673
Tel (812) 831-4053 *SIC* 1541 4225

THOMPSON CONSTRUCTION GROUP INC p 1449
100 N Main St, Sumter SC 29150
Tel (803) 773-8005
SIC 7349 1711 1721 1541

FITTS AND GOODWIN INC p 553
120 Corporate Blvd, West Columbia SC 29169
Tel (803) 796-4660 *SIC* 1541 1542

BELL & ASSOCIATES CONSTRUCTION LP p 169
255 Wilson Pike Cir, Brentwood TN 37027
Tel (615) 373-4343 *SIC* 1622 1541 1542

■SERVICE ELECTRIC CO p 1307
1631 E 25th St, Chattanooga TN 37404
Tel (423) 894-4336 *SIC* 1629 1731 1541

DAELIM USA INC p 408
1200 International Blvd, Clarksville TN 37040
Tel (770) 530-3489 *SIC* 1541

H AND M CONSTRUCTION CO INC p 649
50 Security Dr, Jackson TN 38305
Tel (731) 660-3091 *SIC* 1541 1542

POWELL CONSTRUCTION CO INC p 1165
3622 Bristol Hwy Ste 1, Johnson City TN 37601
Tel (423) 282-0111 *SIC* 1542 1221 1541

BLAINE CONSTRUCTION CORP p 188
6510 Deane Hill Dr, Knoxville TN 37919
Tel (865) 693-8900 *SIC* 1541 1542

JOHNSON & GALYON INC p 790
1130 Atlantic Ave, Knoxville TN 37917
Tel (865) 688-1111 *SIC* 1542 1541

MARTIN MONTGOMERY CONTRACTORS LLC p 913
8245 Tournament Dr # 300, Memphis TN 38125
Tel (901) 374-9400 *SIC* 1542 1541 8741

HARDAWAY CONSTRUCTION CORP p 660
615 Main St, Nashville TN 37206
Tel (615) 254-5461 *SIC* 1542 1541 1522

HARDAWAY GROUP INC p 660
615 Main St, Nashville TN 37206
Tel (615) 254-5461
SIC 1542 1541 1522 6531

MAIN STREET OPERATING CO INC p 898
615 Main St, Nashville TN 37206
Tel (615) 254-5461
SIC 1542 1541 1521 6531

TWFRIERSON CONTRACTOR INC p 1494
2971 Kraft Dr, Nashville TN 37204
Tel (615) 367-2434 *SIC* 1541 1542

LAUREN ENGINEERS & CONSTRUCTORS INC p 847
901 S 1st St, Abilene TX 79602
Tel (325) 670-9660 *SIC* 1541

CADENCE MCSHANE CONSTRUCTION CO LLC p 236
5057 Keller Springs Rd, Addison TX 75001
Tel (972) 239-2336 *SIC* 1541 1542

J M DAVIDSON INC p 771
2564 County Road 1960, Aransas Pass TX 78336
Tel (361) 883-0983 *SIC* 1541 1731 3441

FGI GROUP INC p 539
3901 S Lamar Blvd Ste 100, Austin TX 78704
Tel (512) 448-9898
SIC 1542 1541 1794 1611 7353 1711

MC CARTY CORP p 925
13494 Pond Springs Rd, Austin TX 78729
Tel (512) 331-1344 *SIC* 1541 6411

ALLCO LLC p 52
6720 College St, Beaumont TX 77707
Tel (409) 860-4459 *SIC* 1623 1542 1541

STIS INC p 1390
3127 Texas Ave, Bridge City TX 77611
Tel (409) 697-3350 *SIC* 1541

AMERICAN CONSTRUCTORS INC p 70
11900 W Parmer Ln Ste 200, Cedar Park TX 78613
Tel (512) 328-2026 *SIC* 1541 1542

BERRY GP INC p 176
1414 Corn Product Rd, Corpus Christi TX 78409
Tel (361) 693-2100 *SIC* 1541 1611 3498

BERRY HOLDINGS LP p 176
1414 Corn Product Rd, Corpus Christi TX 78409
Tel (361) 693-2100 *SIC* 1541 1611 3498

DELTA FABRICATION AND MACHINE INC p 427
1379 County Road 2110, Daingerfield TX 75638
Tel (903) 645-3994 *SIC* 1541 3599 3441

BALFOUR BEATTY CONSTRUCTION GROUP INC p 147
3100 Mckinnon St Fl 10, Dallas TX 75201
Tel (214) 451-1000 *SIC* 1542 1541

BALFOUR BEATTY CONSTRUCTION LLC p 147
3100 Mckinnon St Fl 10, Dallas TX 75201
Tel (214) 451-1000 *SIC* 1542 1541

■CENTEX CORP p 277
2728 N Harwood St Ste 200, Dallas TX 75201
Tel (214) 981-5000
SIC 1531 2451 6162 1542 1541 1522

CYMI INDUSTRIAL INC p 405
12400 Coit Rd Ste 700, Dallas TX 75251
Tel (214) 276-8950 *SIC* 1541

▲JACOBS ENGINEERING GROUP INC p 775
1999 Bryan St Ste 1200, Dallas TX 75201
Tel (214) 583-8500
SIC 8711 1629 1541 8748

JORDAN CF CONSTRUCTION LLC p 793
7700 Cf Jordan Dr Ste 200, El Paso TX 79912
Tel (915) 877-3333 *SIC* 1542 1541 1522

JORDAN CF INVESTMENTS LLP p 793
7700 Cf Jordan Dr, El Paso TX 79912
Tel (915) 877-3333
SIC 1542 1541 1522 1611

GULF STATES INC p 647
6711 E Highway 332, Freeport TX 77541
Tel (979) 233-4461 *SIC* 1541 1629

APACHE INDUSTRIAL SERVICES INC p 96
15423 Vantage Pkwy E, Houston TX 77032
Tel (281) 609-8800 *SIC* 1629 1541

BURROW GLOBAL SERVICES LLC p 228
6200 Savoy Dr Ste 800, Houston TX 77036
Tel (713) 963-0930 *SIC* 1542 1541 8711

HOLLOMAN CORP p 701
333 N Sam Houston Pkwy E, Houston TX 77060
Tel (281) 878-2600 *SIC* 1541 1623 1389

MUSTANG ENGINEERS AND CONSTRUCTORS LP p 1002
16001 Park Ten Pl, Houston TX 77084
Tel (713) 215-8000 *SIC* 1542 1541

▲NCI BUILDING SYSTEMS INC p 1022
10943 N Sam Huston Pkwy W, Houston TX 77064
Tel (281) 897-7788
SIC 3448 3444 3442 1542 1541 7389

SATTERFIELD AND PONTIKES CONSTRUCTION INC p 1283
11000 Equity Dr Ste 100, Houston TX 77041
Tel (713) 996-1393 *SIC* 1542 1541

SPAW GLASS CONSTRUCTION CORP p 1355
13800 West Rd, Houston TX 77041
Tel (281) 970-5300 *SIC* 1542 1522 1541

▲FLUOR CORP p 561
6700 Las Colinas Blvd, Irving TX 75039
Tel (469) 398-7000 *SIC* 8711 1629 1541

■REPCONSTRICKLAND INC p 1224
1605 S Battleground Rd, La Porte TX 77571
Tel (281) 478-6200 *SIC* 1541

LEE LEWIS CONSTRUCTION INC p 851
7810 Orlando Ave, Lubbock TX 79423
Tel (806) 797-8400 *SIC* 1542 1541

ECHO MAINTENANCE LLC p 475
6711 N Twin City Hwy, Port Arthur TX 77642
Tel (409) 724-0456 *SIC* 1541 3498 1623

HILL & WILKINSON CONSTRUCTION GROUP LTD p 693
2703 Telecom Pkwy Ste 120, Richardson TX 75082
Tel (214) 299-4300 *SIC* 1541 1542

CCC GROUP INC p 269
5797 Dietrich Rd, San Antonio TX 78219
Tel (210) 661-4251 *SIC* 1541 1629 1542

GUTHRIE & HUEBNER CO INC p 648
5797 Dietrich Rd, San Antonio TX 78219
Tel (210) 661-4251 *SIC* 1541 1629 1542

ZACHRY HOLDINGS INC p 1640
527 Logwood Ave, San Antonio TX 78221
Tel (210) 588-5000
SIC 1541 8711 1629 1623

ZACHRY INDUSTRIAL INC p 1640
527 Logwood Ave, San Antonio TX 78221
Tel (210) 475-8000 *SIC* 1541 1629

ZACHRY INTERNATIONAL INC p 1640
2330 N Loop 1604 W, San Antonio TX 78248
Tel (210) 871-2700 *SIC* 1541 1542

SPAW GLASS HOLDING LP p 1355
9331 Corporate Dr, Selma TX 78154
Tel (210) 651-9000 *SIC* 1542 1522 1541

ASSOCIATED BRIGHAM CONTRACTORS INC p 120
75 N 900 W, Brigham City UT 84302
Tel (435) 723-8529 *SIC* 1541 1771

KIER CONSTRUCTION CORP p 817
3710 Quincy Ave, Ogden UT 84403
Tel (801) 627-1414 *SIC* 1522 1542 1541

WADMAN CORP p 1571
2920 S 925 W, Ogden UT 84401
Tel (801) 621-4185 *SIC* 1542 1541

WESTLAND CONSTRUCTION INC p 1601
1411 W 1250 S Ste 200, Orem UT 84058
Tel (801) 374-6085 *SIC* 1542 1541

BIG-D CONSTRUCTION CORP p 182
404 W 400 S, Salt Lake City UT 84101
Tel (801) 415-6000 *SIC* 1541 1542

BODELL CONSTRUCTION CO INC p 197
586 W Fine Dr, Salt Lake City UT 84115
Tel (801) 261-4343 *SIC* 1542 1541

JACOBSEN CONSTRUCTION CO INC p 775
3131 W 2210 S, Salt Lake City UT 84119
Tel (801) 973-0500 *SIC* 1542 1541

OKLAND CONSTRUCTION CO INC p 1080
1978 S West Temple, Salt Lake City UT 84115
Tel (801) 486-0144 *SIC* 1542 1541

LAYTON COMPANIES INC p 848
9090 S Sandy Pkwy, Sandy UT 84070
Tel (801) 568-9090 *SIC* 1542 1541

L C VIRGINIA p 834
4600 Fairfax Dr Ste 1004, Arlington VA 22203
Tel (703) 524-5454 *SIC* 1541 1542 1522

HENSEL PHELPS SERVICES LLC p 685
4437 Brookfield Corp 20 Ste 207, Chantilly VA 20151
Tel (703) 828-3200
SIC 1522 8744 1521 1541 1623 1611

MEB GENERAL CONTRACTORS INC p 934
4016 Holland Blvd, Chesapeake VA 23323
Tel (757) 487-5858 *SIC* 1542 1629 1541

TWO GUYS SERVICE LLC p 1495
45662 Terminal Dr, Dulles VA 20166
Tel (703) 481-0222 *SIC* 7349 1541

CONTRACK WATTS INC p 364
6862 Elm St Fl 5, Mc Lean VA 22101
Tel (703) 358-8800 *SIC* 1541

WMJORDAN CO INC p 1620
11010 Jefferson Ave, Newport News VA 23601
Tel (757) 596-6341 *SIC* 1542 1541

CENTENNIAL CONTRACTORS ENTERPRISES INC p 275
11111 Sunset Hills Rd # 350, Reston VA 20190
Tel (703) 885-4600 *SIC* 1542 1541

■LEIDOS ENGINEERING LLC p 854
11951 Freedom Dr, Reston VA 20190
Tel (571) 526-6000 *SIC* 8711 1541

KJELLSTROM AND LEE INC p 822
1607 Ownby Ln, Richmond VA 23220
Tel (804) 288-0082 *SIC* 1541 1542

BRANCH GROUP INC p 207
442 Rutherford Ave Ne, Roanoke VA 24016
Tel (540) 982-1678
SIC 1542 1611 1711 1731 1541

SKANSKA USA CIVIL SOUTHEAST INC p 1329
295 Bendix Rd Ste 400, Virginia Beach VA 23452
Tel (757) 420-4140
SIC 1622 1629 3272 1541

IMCO GENERAL CONSTRUCTION INC p 733
2116 Buchanan Loop, Ferndale WA 98248
Tel (360) 671-3936 *SIC* 1541 1629 1542

BAYLEY CONSTRUCTION A GENERAL PARTNERSHIP p 161
8005 Se 28th St Ste 100, Mercer Island WA 98040
Tel (206) 621-8884 *SIC* 1542 1541

GARCO CONSTRUCTION INC p 591
4114 E Broadway Ave, Spokane WA 99202
Tel (509) 536-1649 *SIC* 1541

LYDIG CONSTRUCTION INC p 887
11001 E Montgomery Dr, Spokane Valley WA 99206
Tel (509) 534-0451 *SIC* 1542 1541

GREENBERRY INDUSTRIAL LLC p 637
600 Se Maritime Ave # 190, Vancouver WA 98661
Tel (360) 567-0006
SIC 1711 1541 3443 3441

MARKET & JOHNSON INC p 908
2350 Galloway St, Eau Claire WI 54703
Tel (715) 834-1213 *SIC* 1542 1541

TRI-NORTH BUILDERS INC p 1477
2625 Research Park Dr, Fitchburg WI 53711
Tel (608) 271-8717 *SIC* 1541 1542 1521

CD SMITH CONSTRUCTION INC p 270
889 E Johnson St, Fond Du Lac WI 54935
Tel (920) 924-2900 *SIC* 1542 1541

AWS/GB CORP p 139
2929 Walker Dr, Green Bay WI 54311
Tel (920) 406-4000
SIC 5031 2431 3442 5033 1542 1541

VHC INC p 1553
3090 Holmgren Way, Green Bay WI 54304
Tel (920) 336-7278
SIC 1731 1542 1541 1521 1711 6512

J P CULLEN & SONS INC p 772
330 E Delavan Dr, Janesville WI 53546
Tel (608) 754-6601 SIC 1541 1542

KELLER INC p 808
N216 State Highway 55, Kaukauna WI 54130
Tel (920) 766-5795 SIC 1542 1541 7336

RILEY CONSTRUCTION CO INC p 1235
5301 99th Ave, Kenosha WI 53144
Tel (262) 658-4381 SIC 1542 1541

J H FINDORFF & SON INC p 771
300 S Bedford St, Madison WI 53703
Tel (608) 257-5321
SIC 1542 1541 8741 1522

VOGEL BROS BUILDING CO p 1564
2701 Packers Ave, Madison WI 53704
Tel (608) 241-5454 SIC 1542 1541 4941

MIRON CONSTRUCTION CO INC p 974
1471 Mcmahon Rd, Neenah WI 54956
Tel (920) 969-7000 SIC 1542 1541 1796

C R MEYER AND SONS CO p 233
895 W 20th Ave, Oshkosh WI 54902
Tel (920) 235-3350 SIC 1542 1796 1541

LAKEHEAD CONSTRUCTORS INC p 839
2916 Hill Ave, Superior WI 54880
Tel (715) 392-5181 SIC 1541 1542

LAKEHEAD HOLDING CORP p 839
2916 Hill Ave, Superior WI 54880
Tel (715) 392-5181 SIC 1541 1542

CLEARY BUILDING CORP p 324
190 Paoli St, Verona WI 53593
Tel (608) 845-9700 SIC 1541 3448

SIC 1542 General Contractors, Nonresidential & Non-indl Bldgs

BL HARBERT HOLDINGS LLC p 186
820 Shades Creek Pkwy # 3000, Birmingham AL 35209
Tel (205) 802-2800 SIC 1542

BL HARBERT INTERNATIONAL LLC p 186
820 Shades Creek Pkwy # 3000, Birmingham AL 35209
Tel (205) 802-2800 SIC 1542

BRASFIELD & GORRIE LLC p 208
3021 7th Ave S, Birmingham AL 35233
Tel (205) 328-4000 SIC 1542

DOSTER CONSTRUCTION CO INC p 451
2100 International Pk Dr, Birmingham AL 35243
Tel (205) 443-3800 SIC 1542

DUNN INVESTMENT CO p 461
3900 Messer Airport Hwy, Birmingham AL 35222
Tel (205) 592-3866 SIC 1542 1611 3273

ROBINS & MORTON GROUP p 1242
400 Shades Creek Pkwy, Birmingham AL 35209
Tel (205) 870-1000 SIC 1542

RENAISSANCE WOODWORKING CO INC p 1223
13 Walnut St Ne, Decatur AL 35601
Tel (256) 308-1231 SIC 1542 1521

CAM BUILDERS LLC p 243
537 Highway 26, Hatchechubbee AL 36858
Tel (334) 667-6695 SIC 1542

MJ HARRIS CONSTRUCTION SERVICES LLC p 978
1 Riverchase Rdg Ste 300, Hoover AL 35244
Tel (205) 380-6800 SIC 1542

YATES CONSTRUCTORS LLC p 1635
1855 Data Dr Ste 200, Hoover AL 35244
Tel (205) 380-8420 SIC 1542 1541

CORNERSTONE DETENTION PRODUCTS INC p 371
14000 Al Highway 20, Madison AL 35756
Tel (256) 355-2396 SIC 1542

INFIRMARY HEALTH SYSTEM INC p 741
5 Mobile Infirmary Cir, Mobile AL 36607
Tel (251) 435-3030
SIC 8062 6512 1542 7322 5047 7389

CADDELL CONSTRUCTION CO (DE) LLC p 236
2700 Lagoon Park Dr, Montgomery AL 36109
Tel (334) 272-7723 SIC 1542 1541

CADDELL CONSTRUCTION CO INC p 236
2700 Lagoon Park Dr, Montgomery AL 36109
Tel (334) 272-7723 SIC 1542 1541

AHTNA INC p 37
110 W 38th Ave Ste 100, Anchorage AK 99503
Tel (907) 868-8250
SIC 1629 7389 1542 1521

ALEUT CORP p 48
4000 Old Seward Hwy # 300, Anchorage AK 99503
Tel (907) 561-4300 SIC 6799 1542 8742

CHUGACH FEDERAL SOLUTIONS INC p 305
3800 Cntrpint Dr Ste 1200, Anchorage AK 99503
Tel (907) 563-8866 SIC 1542

CHUGACH GOVERNMENT SERVICES INC p 305
3800 Cntrpint Dr Ste 1200, Anchorage AK 99503
Tel (907) 563-8866 SIC 1542

DAVIS CONSTRUCTORS & ENGINEERS INC p 416
6591 A St Ste 300, Anchorage AK 99518
Tel (907) 562-2336 SIC 1542

HARDING HOLDINGS INC p 661
184 E 53rd Ave, Anchorage AK 99518
Tel (907) 344-1577 SIC 1389 1542

NEESER CONSTRUCTION INC p 1024
2501 Blueberry Rd Ste 100, Anchorage AK 99503
Tel (907) 276-1058 SIC 1542

UDELHOVEN OILFIELD SYSTEMS SERVICES INC p 1499
184 E 53rd Ave, Anchorage AK 99518
Tel (907) 344-1577 SIC 1541 1542 8711

UKPEAGVIK INUPIAT CORP p 1500
1250 Agvik St, Barrow AK 99723
Tel (907) 852-4460
SIC 1542 6512 6331 1389 4449

SEALASKA CORP p 1296
1 Sealaska Plz Ste 400, Juneau AK 99801
Tel (907) 586-1512
SIC 5099 8744 7371 8748 1542

ACHEN-GARDNER INC p 17
550 S 79th St, Chandler AZ 85226
Tel (480) 940-1300
SIC 1611 1542 1521 1751 6552

ABEINSA HOLDING INC p 10
2929 N Cent Ave Ste 1100, Phoenix AZ 85012
Tel (602) 265-6870 SIC 1522 1542

CORE CONSTRUCTION INC p 369
3036 E Greenway Rd, Phoenix AZ 85032
Tel (602) 494-0800 SIC 1542 1541

HAYDON BUILDING CORP p 670
4640 E Cotton Gin Loop, Phoenix AZ 85040
Tel (602) 296-1496 SIC 1541 1542

KITCHELL CONTRACTORS INC OF ARIZONA p 822
1707 E Highland Ave # 200, Phoenix AZ 85016
Tel (602) 264-4411 SIC 1541 1542 1521

KITCHELL CORP p 822
1707 E Highland Ave # 100, Phoenix AZ 85016
Tel (602) 264-4411
SIC 1542 1541 1521 8711 5078 6552

■TUTOR PERINI BUILDING CORP p 1493
5055 E Washington St # 210, Phoenix AZ 85034
Tel (602) 256-6777 SIC 1541 1542 8741

W M GRACE COS INC p 1569
7575 N 16th St Ste 1, Phoenix AZ 85020
Tel (602) 956-8254 SIC 1542 6512 7011

DMB ASSOCIATES INC p 445
7600 E Doubletree Ste 300, Scottsdale AZ 85258
Tel (480) 367-6874
SIC 5999 6512 5961 1542 3446

SDB INC p 1295
810 W 1st St, Tempe AZ 85281
Tel (480) 967-5810 SIC 1542

SUNDT CONSTRUCTION INC p 1402
2620 S 55th St, Tempe AZ 85282
Tel (480) 293-3000
SIC 1542 1611 1629 1541 8741

SUNDT COMPANIES INC p 1402
2015 W River Rd Ste 101, Tucson AZ 85704
Tel (520) 750-4600 SIC 1542 1771 1611

CRAWFORD CR CONSTRUCTION LLC p 389
1102 S Happy Hollow Rd, Fayetteville AR 72701
Tel (479) 251-1161 SIC 1542

HOBBS & CURRY FAMILY LIMITED PARTNERSHIP LLLP p 699
4119 Massard Rd, Fort Smith AR 72903
Tel (479) 785-0844 SIC 1542

BALDWIN & SHELL CONSTRUCTION CO INC p 147
1000 W Capitol Ave, Little Rock AR 72201
Tel (501) 374-8677 SIC 1541 1542

■ CDI CONTRACTORS LLC p 271
3000 Cantrell Rd, Little Rock AR 72202
Tel (501) 666-4300 SIC 1542

CLARK CONTRACTORS LLC p 322
15825 Cantrell Rd, Little Rock AR 72223
Tel (501) 868-3133 SIC 1542

KINCO CONSTRUCTORS LLC p 819
12600 Lawson Rd, Little Rock AR 72210
Tel (501) 225-7606 SIC 1542 1541

CIRKS CONSTRUCTION INC p 308
2570 E Cerritos Ave, Anaheim CA 92806
Tel (714) 632-6717 SIC 1542

PINNER CONSTRUCTION CO INC p 1150
1255 S Lewis St, Anaheim CA 92805
Tel (714) 490-4000 SIC 1542

TECHNO COATINGS INC p 1431
1391 S Allec St, Anaheim CA 92805
Tel (714) 635-1130
SIC 1542 1629 1721 1799

■ METALS USA BUILDING PRODUCTS LP p 952
955 Columbia St, Brea CA 92821
Tel (713) 946-9000 SIC 3355 5031 1542

NEVELL GROUP INC p 1029
3001 Enterprise St # 200, Brea CA 92821
Tel (714) 579-7501 SIC 1542

ENVIRONMENTAL CHEMICAL CORP p 503
1240 Bayshore Hwy, Burlingame CA 94010
Tel (650) 347-1555 SIC 8711 1542 8744

B C C S INC p 141
1711 Dell Ave, Campbell CA 95008
Tel (408) 379-5500 SIC 1542

CAMERON DICKINSON CONSTRUCTION CO INC p 245
6184 Innovation Way, Carlsbad CA 92009
Tel (760) 438-9114 SIC 1542 8741

SD DEACON CORP p 1295
7745 Greenback Ln Ste 250, Citrus Heights CA 95610
Tel (916) 969-0900 SIC 1542

MERUELO ENTERPRISES INC p 951
9550 Firestone Blvd # 105, Downey CA 90241
Tel (562) 745-2300 SIC 1542

DESILVA GATES CONSTRUCTION LP p 432
11555 Dublin Blvd, Dublin CA 94568
Tel (925) 361-1380 SIC 1611 1794 1542

ROEBBELEN CONTRACTING INC p 1246
1241 Hawks Flight Ct, El Dorado Hills CA 95762
Tel (916) 939-4000 SIC 1542 1541 8741

■WALT DISNEY IMAGINEERING RESEARCH & DEVELOPMENT INC p 1574
1401 Flower St, Glendale CA 91201
Tel (818) 544-6500
SIC 7819 8712 1542 8741 8711

HENSEL PHELPS GRANITE HANGAR JOINT VENTURE p 684
18850 Von Kamon 100, Irvine CA 92612
Tel (949) 852-0111 SIC 1542 1629

HPM CONSTRUCTION LLC p 714
17911 Mitchell S, Irvine CA 92614
Tel (949) 474-9170 SIC 1542

PACIFIC NATIONAL GROUP p 1105
2392 Bateman Ave, Irwindale CA 91010
Tel (626) 357-4400 SIC 1542

IRWIN INDUSTRIES INC p 765
1580 W Carson St, Long Beach CA 90810
Tel (310) 233-3000
SIC 1629 1731 1796 7353 1542

TURELK INC p 1492
3700 Santa Fe Ave Ste 200, Long Beach CA 90810
Tel (310) 835-3736 SIC 1542

SEVERSON GROUP INC p 1309
3601 Serpentine Dr, Los Alamitos CA 90720
Tel (562) 493-3611 SIC 1542 1541

NOVO CONSTRUCTION INC p 1063
1460 Obrien Dr, Menlo Park CA 94025
Tel (650) 701-1500 SIC 1542

XL CONSTRUCTION CORP p 1632
851 Buckeye Ct, Milpitas CA 95035
Tel (408) 240-6000 SIC 1542

MAKAR PROPERTIES LLC p 899
4100 Macarthur Blvd # 150, Newport Beach CA 92660
Tel (949) 255-1100 SIC 6552 1542

■ HOLMES & NARVER INC p 701
999 W Town And Country Rd, Orange CA 92868
Tel (714) 567-2400
SIC 8711 8742 8741 1542

C W DRIVER INC p 233
468 N Rosemead Blvd, Pasadena CA 91107
Tel (626) 351-8800 SIC 1542

CHARLES PANKOW BUILDERS LTD A CALIFORNIA LIMITED PARTNERSHIP p 289
199 S Los Robles Ave # 300, Pasadena CA 91101
Tel (626) 304-1190 SIC 1542

PARSONS GOVERNMENT SERVICES INTERNATIONAL INC p 1118
100 W Walnut St, Pasadena CA 91124
Tel (626) 440-6000 SIC 1542

SILVER CREEK INDUSTRIES INC p 1323
2830 Barrett Ave, Perris CA 92571
Tel (951) 943-5393 SIC 1542 2452

DPR CONSTRUCTION INC p 454
1450 Veterans Blvd Ofc, Redwood City CA 94063
Tel (650) 474-1450 SIC 1541 1542

■ RUDOLPH AND SLETTEN INC p 1257
1600 Seaport Blvd Ste 350, Redwood City CA 94063
Tel (650) 216-3600 SIC 1542 1541

S J AMOROSO CONSTRUCTION CO INC p 1262
390 Bridge Pkwy, Redwood City CA 94065
Tel (650) 654-1900 SIC 1542

W L BUTLER CONSTRUCTION INC p 1568
204 Franklin St, Redwood City CA 94063
Tel (650) 361-1270 SIC 1542

ALSTON CONSTRUCTION CO INC p 61
8775 Folsom Blvd Ste 201, Sacramento CA 95826
Tel (916) 340-2400 SIC 1541 1542

JOHN F OTTO INC p 788
1717 2nd St, Sacramento CA 95811
Tel (916) 441-6870 SIC 1542 1541

UNGER CONSTRUCTION CO p 1502
910 X St, Sacramento CA 95818
Tel (916) 325-5500 SIC 1542 1541

BARNHART INC p 156
10620 Treena St Ste 300, San Diego CA 92131
Tel (858) 635-7400 SIC 1542 8741

HARPER CONSTRUCTION CO INC p 663
2241 Kettner Blvd Ste 300, San Diego CA 92101
Tel (619) 233-7900 SIC 1542 1521

LEDCOR CONSTRUCTION INC p 851
6405 Mira Mesa Blvd # 100, San Diego CA 92121
Tel (858) 527-6400 SIC 1542

SOLPAC CONSTRUCTION INC p 1338
2424 Congress St, San Diego CA 92110
Tel (619) 296-6247 SIC 8741 1542 1611

T B PENICK & SONS INC p 1419
15435 Innovation Dr # 100, San Diego CA 92128
Tel (858) 558-1800 SIC 1541 1542

BERNARDS BROS INC p 176
555 1st St, San Fernando CA 91340
Tel (818) 898-1521 SIC 1542 1541

BCCI CONSTRUCTION CO p 163
1160 Battery St Ste 250, San Francisco CA 94111
Tel (415) 817-5100 SIC 1542

BUILD GROUP INC p 224
457 Minna St Ste 100, San Francisco CA 94103
Tel (415) 367-9399 SIC 1542

CAHILL CONTRACTORS INC p 237
425 California St # 2200, San Francisco CA 94104
Tel (415) 986-0600 SIC 1542

GCI INC p 595
875 Battery St Fl 1, San Francisco CA 94111
Tel (415) 978-2790 SIC 1542

HATHAWAY DINWIDDIE CONSTRUCTION CO p 668
275 Battery St Ste 300, San Francisco CA 94111
Tel (415) 986-2718 SIC 1542

HATHAWAY DINWIDDIE CONSTRUCTION GROUP p 668
275 Battery St Ste 300, San Francisco CA 94111
Tel (415) 986-2718 SIC 1542

PJD CONSTRUCTION INC p 1153
447 London St, San Francisco CA 94112
Tel (415) 218-3031 SIC 1542 1522

PLANT CONSTRUCTION CO LP p 1154
300 Newhall St, San Francisco CA 94124
Tel (415) 285-0500 SIC 1542

SKYLINE COMMERCIAL INTERIORS INC p 1330
731 Sansome St Fl 4, San Francisco CA 94111
Tel (415) 908-1020 SIC 1542

SWINERTON BUILDERS p 1412
260 Townsend St, San Francisco CA 94107
Tel (415) 421-2980 SIC 1541 1522 1542

SWINERTON INC p 1412
260 Townsend St, San Francisco CA 94107
Tel (415) 421-2980
SIC 1542 1541 6531 1522

GREEN VALLEY CORP p 637
777 N 1st St Fl 5, San Jose CA 95112
Tel (408) 287-0246 SIC 1542 1522 6512

MCLARNEY CONSTRUCTION INC p 931
355 S Daniel Way, San Jose CA 95128
Tel (408) 246-8600 SIC 1542

LUSARDI CONSTRUCTION CO p 886
1570 Linda Vista Dr, San Marcos CA 92078
Tel (760) 744-3133 SIC 1542 1541

MOOREFIELD CONSTRUCTION INC p 987
600 N Tustin Ave Ste 210, Santa Ana CA 92705
Tel (714) 972-0700 SIC 1542

MORLEY BUILDERS INC p 989
3330 Ocean Park Blvd # 101, Santa Monica CA 90405
Tel (310) 399-1600
SIC 1541 1522 1542 1771

HAR-BRO INC p 659
2750 Signal Pkwy, Signal Hill CA 90755
Tel (562) 528-8000 SIC 1542 1521 1522

DOME CONSTRUCTION CORP p 448
393 E Grand Ave, South San Francisco CA 94080
Tel (650) 416-5600 SIC 1542 1541

USS CAL BUILDERS INC p 1535
8051 Main St, Stanton CA 90680
Tel (714) 828-4882 SIC 1542

GRUPE CO p 642
3255 W March Ln Ste 400, Stockton CA 95219
Tel (209) 473-6000 SIC 6531 1542

LEVEL 10 CONSTRUCTION LP p 858
1050 Entp Way Ste 250, Sunnyvale CA 94089
Tel (408) 747-5000 SIC 1542

▲TUTOR PERINI CORP p 1493
15901 Olden St, Sylmar CA 91342
Tel (818) 362-8391
SIC 1542 8741 1611 1791 8711

TUTOR PERINI CORP p 1493
15901 Olden St, Sylmar CA 91342
Tel (818) 362-8391 SIC 1542 1611 1622

■TUTOR-SALIBA CORP p 1493
15901 Olden St, Sylmar CA 91342
Tel (818) 362-8391
SIC 1542 1629 7353 1799 6552

TURLOCK DAIRY & REFRIGERATION INC p 1492
1819 S Walnut Rd, Turlock CA 95380
Tel (209) 667-6455 SIC 5083 7699 1542

BROWN CONSTRUCTION INC p 219
1465 Entp Blvd Ste 100, West Sacramento CA 95691
Tel (916) 374-8616 SIC 1522 1542

OLTMANS CONSTRUCTION CO p 1083
10005 Mission Mill Rd, Whittier CA 90601
Tel (562) 948-4242 SIC 1541 1542

WM KLORMAN CONSTRUCTION CORP p 1620
23047 Ventura Blvd # 200, Woodland Hills CA 91364
Tel (818) 591-5969 SIC 1521 1542

HILBERS INC p 692
1210 Stabler Ln, Yuba City CA 95993
Tel (530) 673-2947 SIC 1542 1541

MILENDER WHITE CONSTRUCTION CO p 969
12655 W 54th Dr, Arvada CO 80002
Tel (303) 216-0420 SIC 1542 1522

AP MOUNTAIN STATES LLC p 95
797 Ventura St, Aurora CO 80011
Tel (303) 363-7101 SIC 1542

HASELDEN CONSTRUCTION LLC p 667
6950 S Potomac St Ste 100, Centennial CO 80112
Tel (303) 751-1478 SIC 1542

SAUNDERS CONSTRUCTION INC p 1283
6950 S Jordan Rd, Centennial CO 80112
Tel (303) 699-9000 SIC 1542

G E JOHNSON CONSTRUCTION CO INC p 586
25 N Cascade Ave Ste 400, Colorado Springs CO 80903
Tel (719) 473-5321 SIC 1542

■ INTERMOUNTAIN ELECTRIC INC p 753
5050 Osage St Ste 500, Denver CO 80221
Tel (303) 733-7248 SIC 1542 8742 3671

PCL CONSTRUCTION ENTERPRISES INC p 1124
2000 S Colorado Blvd 2-500, Denver CO 80222
Tel (303) 365-6500 SIC 1542

PCL CONSTRUCTION SERVICES INC p 1124
2000 S Colorado Blvd 2-500, Denver CO 80222
Tel (303) 365-6500 SIC 1542 1541

PCL US HOLDINGS INC p 1124
2000 S Colorado Blvd 2-500, Denver CO 80222
Tel (303) 365-6591 SIC 1542 1611

SHAW CONSTRUCTION LLC p 1312
300 Kalamath St, Denver CO 80223
Tel (303) 825-4740 SIC 1542

SUMMIT MATERIALS CORPS I INC p 1399
1550 Wynkoop St Fl 3, Denver CO 80202
Tel (303) 893-0012 SIC 1542 1611

SUMMIT MATERIALS HOLDINGS II LLC p 1399
1550 Wynkoop St Fl 3, Denver CO 80202
Tel (303) 893-0012 SIC 1542 1611

SUMMIT MATERIALS HOLDINGS LLC p 1399
1550 Wynkoop St Fl 3, Denver CO 80202
Tel (303) 893-0012 SIC 1542 1611

SUMMIT MATERIALS HOLDINGS LP p 1399
1550 Wynkoop St Fl 3, Denver CO 80202
Tel (303) 893-0012 SIC 1542 1611

SUMMIT MATERIALS INTERMEDIATE HOLDINGS LLC p 1399
1550 Wynkoop St Fl 3, Denver CO 80202
Tel (303) 893-0012 SIC 1542 1611

SUMMIT MATERIALS LLC p 1399
1550 Wynkoop St Fl 3, Denver CO 80202
Tel (303) 893-0012 SIC 1542 1611

TIC HOLDINGS INC p 1452
9780 Pyramid Ct Ste 100, Englewood CO 80112
Tel (970) 879-2561
SIC 1541 1629 1623 1542

NEENAN CO LLLP p 1024
3325 S Timberline Rd # 100, Fort Collins CO 80525
Tel (970) 493-8747 SIC 1542

ERIE COUNTY INVESTMENT CO p 508
601 Corporate Cir, Golden CO 80401
Tel (303) 384-0200
SIC 5812 6794 6531 6552 1542 1521

FCI CONSTRUCTORS INC p 533
3070 I 70 Bus Loop Ste A, Grand Junction CO 81504
Tel (970) 434-9093 SIC 1542 1541

GRANITE HENSEL PHELPS JV p 631
420 6th Ave, Greeley CO 80631
Tel (970) 352-6565 SIC 1541 1542

HENSEL PHELPS CONSTRUCTION CO p 684
420 6th Ave, Greeley CO 80631
Tel (970) 352-6565
SIC 1542 1521 1771 1522 1541 1622

HENSEL PHELPS SOLTEK JV p 685
420 6th Ave, Greeley CO 80631
Tel (970) 352-6565 *SIC* 1542 1541

HENSEL PHELPS-GRANITE JV p 685
420 6th Ave, Greeley CO 80631
Tel (970) 352-6565
SIC 1541 1542 1629 1611

GERALD H PHIPPS INC p 608
5995 Greenwood Ste 100, Greenwood Village CO 80111
Tel (303) 571-5377 *SIC* 1542 3399

CATAMOUNT CONSTRUCTORS INC p 264
1527 Cole Blvd Ste 100, Lakewood CO 80401
Tel (303) 679-0087 *SIC* 1542

FIP CONSTRUCTION INC p 543
1536 New Britain Ave, Farmington CT 06032
Tel (860) 470-1800 *SIC* 1542 1541

KBE BUILDING CORP p 806
76 Batterson Park Rd # 1, Farmington CT 06032
Tel (860) 284-7424 *SIC* 1542 1541

NEWFIELD CONSTRUCTION INC p 1037
225 Newfield Ave, Hartford CT 06106
Tel (860) 953-1477 *SIC* 1541 1542

CARABETTA ENTERPRISES INC p 252
200 Pratt St Ofc, Meriden CT 06450
Tel (203) 237-7400
SIC 1522 1542 1521 6512

A/Z CORP p 7
46 Norwich Westerly Rd, North Stonington CT 06359
Tel (800) 400-2420 *SIC* 1541 1542

SCHIMENTI CONSTRUCTION CO LLC p 1287
650 Danbury Rd Ste 4, Ridgefield CT 06877
Tel (914) 244-9100 *SIC* 1542

PAVARINI NORTH EAST CONSTRUCTION CO INC p 1122
30 Oak St Fl 3, Stamford CT 06905
Tel (203) 327-0100 *SIC* 1542 8741

O & G INDUSTRIES INC p 1070
112 Wall St, Torrington CT 06790
Tel (860) 489-9261
SIC 1542 1541 1611 1623 5032 2951

BALFOUR BEATTY LLC p 148
1011 Centre Rd Ste 322, Wilmington DE 19805
Tel (302) 573-3873 *SIC* 1542 8712 8741

DONOHOE COMPANIES INC p 451
2101 Wisconsin Ave Nw, Washington DC 20007
Tel (202) 333-0880 *SIC* 6552 1542

MCN BUILD LLC p 932
1214 28th St Nw, Washington DC 20007
Tel (202) 333-3424 *SIC* 1541 1542

REAL ESTATE IN REAL TIME INC p 1213
100 Lakeshore Dr Ste 96, Altamonte Springs FL 32714
Tel (321) 312-0748 *SIC* 6531 1542 1522

■ **JAMES A CUMMINGS INC** p 776
1 E Broward Blvd Ste 1300, Fort Lauderdale FL 33301
Tel (954) 484-1532 *SIC* 1542 1541

STILES CORP p 1389
301 E Las Olas Blvd, Fort Lauderdale FL 33301
Tel (954) 627-9150 *SIC* 1542 1541

PERRY CHARLES PARTNERS INC p 1137
8200 Nw 15th Pl, Gainesville FL 32606
Tel (352) 333-9292 *SIC* 1542 1541

ELKINS CONSTRUCTORS INC p 488
701 W Adams St Ste 1, Jacksonville FL 32204
Tel (904) 353-6500 *SIC* 1542

HASKELL CO p 667
111 Riverside Ave, Jacksonville FL 32202
Tel (904) 791-4500
SIC 1541 1542 1522 1623 8712 3272

HASKELL CO INC p 667
111 Riverside Ave, Jacksonville FL 32202
Tel (904) 791-4500
SIC 1541 1542 1522 1623 8712 3272

MILTON J WOOD CO p 972
3805 Faye Rd, Jacksonville FL 32226
Tel (904) 353-5527 *SIC* 1711 1542

STELLAR COMPANIES INC p 1385
2900 Hartley Rd, Jacksonville FL 32257
Tel (904) 899-9393 *SIC* 1542 8711 1541

J RAYMOND & ASSOCIATES INC p 772
465 W Warren Ave, Longwood FL 32750
Tel (407) 339-2988 *SIC* 1542

CONDOTTE AMERICA INC p 355
10790 Nw 127th St, Medley FL 33178
Tel (305) 670-7585 *SIC* 1611 1622 1542

GLF CONSTRUCTION CORP p 615
528 Nw 7th Ave, Miami FL 33136
Tel (305) 371-5228
SIC 1611 1622 1542 1541 1522

AJAX BUILDING CORP p 41
1080 Commerce Blvd, Midway FL 32343
Tel (850) 224-9571 *SIC* 1542

MANHATTAN CONSTRUCTION (FLORIDA) INC p 901
3705 Westview Dr Ste 1, Naples FL 34104
Tel (239) 643-6000
SIC 1542 8712 1531 1521 8741

ROONEY HOLDINGS INC p 1249
3705 Westview Dr Ste 1, Naples FL 34104
Tel (239) 403-0375 *SIC* 1542

CURRENT BUILDERS CONSTRUCTION SERVICES INC p 402
2251 Blount Rd, Pompano Beach FL 33069
Tel (954) 977-4211 *SIC* 1522 1542

WHARTON-SMITH INC p 1604
750 Monroe Rd, Sanford FL 32771
Tel (407) 321-8410 *SIC* 1542

MUNILLA CONSTRUCTION MANAGEMENT LLC p 1000
6201 Sw 70th St Fl 2, South Miami FL 33143
Tel (305) 541-0000 *SIC* 1622 1542

BMP INTERNATIONAL INC p 194
5139 W Idlewild Ave, Tampa FL 33634
Tel (727) 458-0544 *SIC* 1542

KEENAN HOPKINS SCHMIDT AND STOWELL CONTRACTORS INC p 807
5422 Bay Center Dr # 200, Tampa FL 33609
Tel (813) 627-2219 *SIC* 1542 1742

HAWKINS CONSTRUCTION INC p 670
1430 L&R Industrial Blvd, Tarpon Springs FL 34689
Tel (727) 937-2690 *SIC* 1542

PEGASUS BUILDERS INC p 1127
3340 Frlane Frms Rd Ste 8, Wellington FL 33414
Tel (561) 791-7037 *SIC* 1521 1542

HEDRICK BROTHERS CONSTRUCTION CO INC p 680
2200 Centre Park West Dr # 100, West Palm Beach FL 33409
Tel (561) 689-8880 *SIC* 1542

MOSS & ASSOCIATES LLC p 992
2101 N Andrews Ave, Wilton Manors FL 33311
Tel (954) 524-5678 *SIC* 1542

ARCHER WESTERN CONTRACTORS LLC p 105
2410 Paces Ferry Rd Se # 600, Atlanta GA 30339
Tel (404) 495-8700
SIC 1542 1622 1611 1629

ARROW EXTERMINATORS INC p 113
8613 Roswell Rd Bldg 4, Atlanta GA 30350
Tel (770) 993-8705
SIC 1742 7342 1521 1542

CHOATE CONSTRUCTION CO p 301
8200 Roberts Dr Ste 600, Atlanta GA 30350
Tel (678) 892-1200 *SIC* 1522 1531 1542

H J RUSSELL & CO p 650
171 17th St Nw Ste 1600, Atlanta GA 30363
Tel (404) 330-1000
SIC 1542 8741 7389 8742

HOLDER CONSTRUCTION CO p 700
3333 Riverwood Pkwy Se # 400, Atlanta GA 30339
Tel (770) 988-3000 *SIC* 1542

HOLDER CONSTRUCTION GROUP LLC p 700
3333 Riverwood Pkwy Se # 400, Atlanta GA 30339
Tel (770) 988-3000 *SIC* 1542

HOLDER CORP p 700
3300 Cumberland Blvd Se # 400, Atlanta GA 30339
Tel (770) 988-3000 *SIC* 6552 1542

KAJIMA INTERNATIONAL INC p 801
3475 Piedmont Rd Ne # 1600, Atlanta GA 30305
Tel (404) 564-3900 *SIC* 1541 3446 1542

KAJIMA USA INC p 801
3475 Piedmont Rd Ne, Atlanta GA 30305
Tel (404) 564-3900
SIC 1542 1541 6531 1522 6552 1622

MERCHANDISING SOLUTIONS GROUP INC p 944
260 Peachtree St Nw, Atlanta GA 30303
Tel (800) 417-1320 *SIC* 5199 1542

ACC CONSTRUCTION CO INC p 14
635 Nw Frontage Rd Ste A, Augusta GA 30907
Tel (706) 868-1037 *SIC* 1542 1541

ORDNER CONSTRUCTION CO INC p 1093
1600 Executive Dr Ste 100, Duluth GA 30096
Tel (678) 380-7400 *SIC* 1542

SOUTHERN PAN SERVICES CO p 1350
2385 Lithonia Indus Blvd, Lithonia GA 30058
Tel (678) 301-2400 *SIC* 1542

CONLAN CO p 356
1800 Parkway Pl Se # 1010, Marietta GA 30067
Tel (770) 423-8000 *SIC* 1542 1541

CAPE ENVIRONMENTAL MANAGEMENT INC p 248
500 Pinnacle Ct Ste 100, Norcross GA 30071
Tel (770) 908-7200 *SIC* 1542 1541

VENTURE CONSTRUCTION CO INC p 1548
5660 Peachtree Indus Blvd, Norcross GA 30071
Tel (770) 441-2404 *SIC* 1542

WINTER GROUP OF COMPANIES INC p 1617
191 Peachtree St Ne, Peachtree Corners GA 30071
Tel (404) 588-3300
SIC 1541 1542 1799 6512

PARRISH CONSTRUCTION GROUP INC p 1117
221 Industrial Park Dr, Perry GA 31069
Tel (478) 987-5544 *SIC* 1542

SPIRIT CONSTRUCTION SERVICES INC p 1359
118 Coleman Blvd, Savannah GA 31408
Tel (912) 748-8055 *SIC* 1541 1542

HUMPHRIES AND CO LLC p 718
4581 S Cobb Dr Se Ste 200, Smyrna GA 30080
Tel (770) 434-1890 *SIC* 1542

BATSON-COOK CO p 159
817 4th Ave, West Point GA 31833
Tel (706) 643-2500 *SIC* 1542 5211 1541

PRIMUS BUILDERS INC p 1176
8294 Highway 92 Ste 210, Woodstock GA 30189
Tel (770) 928-7120 *SIC* 1542

ISEMOTO CONTRACTING CO LTD p 766
648 Piilani St, Hilo HI 96720
Tel (808) 935-7194 *SIC* 1629 1542 1541

DAWSON TECHNICAL LLC p 417
900 Fort Street Mall # 1850, Honolulu HI 96813
Tel (808) 536-5500 *SIC* 8711 1542

DCK PACIFIC CONSTRUCTION LLC p 418
707 Richards St Ste 410, Honolulu HI 96813
Tel (808) 533-5000 *SIC* 1542

HAWAIIAN DREDGING CONSTRUCTION CO INC p 669
201 Merchant St Ste 900, Honolulu HI 96813
Tel (808) 735-3211
SIC 1542 1611 1522 1521

MARYL GROUP INC p 914
55 Merchant St Ste 2000, Honolulu HI 96813
Tel (808) 545-2920 *SIC* 6552 1542

NAN INC p 1007
636 Laumaka St, Honolulu HI 96819
Tel (808) 842-4929 *SIC* 1542

ALBERT C KOBAYASHI INC p 46
94-535 Ukee St Ste 101, Waipahu HI 96797
Tel (808) 671-6460 *SIC* 1542 1521 1522

■ **NATIONAL PROJECTS INC** p 1015
720 E Park Blvd, Boise ID 83712
Tel (208) 386-5000 *SIC* 1629 1542 1541

RECORD STEEL AND CONSTRUCTION INC p 1214
333 W Rossi St Ste 200, Boise ID 83706
Tel (208) 887-1401 *SIC* 1542 1791

ENGINEERED STRUCTURES INC p 499
3330 E Louise Dr Ste 300, Meridian ID 83642
Tel (208) 362-3040 *SIC* 1542 1531

PERFORMANCE SYSTEMS INC p 1135
2204 E Lanark St, Meridian ID 83642
Tel (208) 287-0800 *SIC* 1542

POETTKER CONSTRUCTION CO p 1159
380 S Germantown Rd, Breese IL 62230
Tel (314) 994-0004 *SIC* 1542

A EPSTEIN AND SONS INTERNATIONAL INC p 5
600 W Fulton St Ste 800, Chicago IL 60661
Tel (312) 454-9100
SIC 8711 8712 7389 1542 1541 8742

ARCHER WESTERN CONSTRUCTION LLC p 105
929 W Adams St, Chicago IL 60607
Tel (312) 563-5400
SIC 1521 1622 1629 1542

BERGLUND CONSTRUCTION CO p 174
8410 S South Chicago Ave, Chicago IL 60617
Tel (773) 374-1000 *SIC* 1542

BULLEY & ANDREWS p 225
1755 W Armitage Ave, Chicago IL 60622
Tel (773) 235-2433 *SIC* 1542 1541

BULLEY & ANDREWS LLC p 225
1755 W Armitage Ave, Chicago IL 60622
Tel (312) 207-2100 *SIC* 1541 1542

CLUNE CONSTRUCTION CO LP p 328
10 S Riverside Plz # 2200, Chicago IL 60606
Tel (312) 609-3635 *SIC* 1542

FH PASCHEN SN NIELSEN INC p 539
5515 N East River Rd, Chicago IL 60656
Tel (773) 444-3474
SIC 1611 1622 1522 1542

JAMES MCHUGH CONSTRUCTION CO p 776
1737 S Michigan Ave, Chicago IL 60616
Tel (312) 986-8000 *SIC* 1542 1522 1622

■ **JONES LANG LASALLE AMERICAS INC** p 792
200 E Randolph St # 4300, Chicago IL 60601
Tel (312) 782-5800 *SIC* 6282 1542

MCHUGH ENTERPRISES INC p 929
1737 S Michigan Ave, Chicago IL 60616
Tel (312) 986-8000
SIC 1542 1522 1622 1771 1742 6552

ONEIL INDUSTRIES INC p 1087
1245 W Washington Blvd, Chicago IL 60607
Tel (773) 244-6003 *SIC* 1542 1541

PEPPER COMPANIES INC p 1133
643 N Orleans St, Chicago IL 60654
Tel (312) 266-4703 *SIC* 1542 1541

PEPPER CONSTRUCTION CO p 1133
643 N Orleans St, Chicago IL 60654
Tel (312) 266-4700 *SIC* 1542 1541

PEPPER CONSTRUCTION GROUP LLC p 1133
643 N Orleans St, Chicago IL 60654
Tel (312) 266-4700 *SIC* 1542

POWER CONSTRUCTION CO LLC p 1165
8750 W Bryn Mawr Ave, Chicago IL 60631
Tel (312) 596-6960 *SIC* 1541 1542

SKENDER CONSTRUCTION CO p 1329
200 W Madison St Ste 1300, Chicago IL 60606
Tel (312) 781-0265 *SIC* 1542

WALSH CONSTRUCTION CO p 1574
929 W Adams St, Chicago IL 60607
Tel (312) 563-5400
SIC 1541 1622 1542 1611

WALSH CONSTRUCTION CO II LLC p 1574
929 W Adams St, Chicago IL 60607
Tel (312) 563-5400 *SIC* 1542 1611

WALSH CONSTRUCTION GROUP LLC p 1574
929 W Adams St, Chicago IL 60607
Tel (312) 563-5400 *SIC* 1542

WALSH GROUP LTD p 1574
929 W Adams St, Chicago IL 60607
Tel (312) 563-5400
SIC 1542 1522 1622 1629 1541

■ **GLOBAL BRASS AND COPPER INC** p 615
305 Lewis And Clark Blvd, East Alton IL 62024
Tel (618) 258-5000
SIC 3351 3341 3469 1542

RIVER CITY CONSTRUCTION LLC p 1237
101 Hoffer Ln, East Peoria IL 61611
Tel (309) 694-3120 *SIC* 1542 1629

WILLIAM A RANDOLPH INC p 1610
820 Lakeside Dr Ste 3, Gurnee IL 60031
Tel (847) 856-0123 *SIC* 1542

PLOCHER CONSTRUCTION CO INC p 1156
2808 Thole Plocher Rd, Highland IL 62249
Tel (618) 654-9408 *SIC* 1542

LEOPARDO COMPANIES INC p 856
5200 Prairie Stone Pkwy, Hoffman Estates IL 60192
Tel (847) 783-3000 *SIC* 1542 8741

CARLSON BROS INC p 257
17250 New Lenox Rd B, Joliet IL 60433
Tel (815) 727-2200 *SIC* 1542

▲ **PERNIX GROUP INC** p 1136
151 E 22nd St Ste 101e, Lombard IL 60148
Tel (630) 620-4787 *SIC* 1542 4911

INLAND REAL ESTATE GROUP OF COMPANIES p 743
2901 Butterfield Rd, Oak Brook IL 60523
Tel (630) 218-8000
SIC 6513 6512 6162 6282 1522 1542

GRAYCOR INC p 632
2 Mid America Plz Ste 400, Oakbrook Terrace IL 60181
Tel (630) 684-7110 *SIC* 1541 1542

GRAYCOR INDUSTRIAL CONSTRUCTORS INC p 632
2 Mid America Plz Ste 400, Oakbrook Terrace IL 60181
Tel (630) 684-7110 *SIC* 1542 1541

P J HOERR INC p 1102
107 N Commerce Pl, Peoria IL 61604
Tel (309) 688-9567 *SIC* 1542

WILLIAMS BROTHERS CONSTRUCTION INC p 1611
1200 E Kelly Ave, Peoria IL 61616
Tel (309) 688-0416 *SIC* 1542

RUBLOFF CONSTRUCTION INC p 1257
6723 Weaver Rd Ste 108, Rockford IL 61114
Tel (815) 316-5410 *SIC* 1542

BEAR CONSTRUCTION CO p 165
1501 Rohlwing Rd, Rolling Meadows IL 60008
Tel (847) 222-1900 *SIC* 1542

WEDDLE BROS CONSTRUCTION CO INC p 1587
1201 W 3rd St, Bloomington IN 47404
Tel (812) 339-9500 *SIC* 1542 1622 1541

INDUSTRIAL CONTRACTORS SKANSKA INC p 739
401 Nw 1st St, Evansville IN 47708
Tel (812) 423-7832 *SIC* 1541 1542

MEYER & NAJEM CONSTRUCTION LLC p 957
11787 Lantern Rd Ste 100, Fishers IN 46038
Tel (317) 577-0007 *SIC* 1542

MEYER & NAJEM INC p 957
11787 Lantern Rd Ste 100, Fishers IN 46038
Tel (317) 577-0007 *SIC* 1542

WEIGAND CONSTRUCTION CO INC p 1587
7808 Honeywell Dr, Fort Wayne IN 46825
Tel (260) 413-6349 *SIC* 1542

CROWN CORR INC p 395
7100 W 21st Ave, Gary IN 46406
Tel (219) 944-7537 *SIC* 1542 1761

DUKE REALTY CORP p 460
600 E 96th St Ste 100, Indianapolis IN 46240
Tel (317) 808-6000 *SIC* 6798 1542

FLAHERTY & COLLINS CONSTRUCTION INC p 554
8900 Keystone Xing # 1200, Indianapolis IN 46240
Tel (317) 816-9300 *SIC* 1542

PEPPER CONSTRUCTION CO OF INDIANA LLC p 1133
1850 W 15th St, Indianapolis IN 46202
Tel (317) 681-1000 *SIC* 1542 1541

SHIEL SEXTON CO INC p 1316
902 N Capitol Ave, Indianapolis IN 46204
Tel (317) 423-6000 *SIC* 1542 1541

WILHELM CONSTRUCTION INC p 1609
3914 Prospect St, Indianapolis IN 46203
Tel (317) 359-5411 *SIC* 1542 1541 1761

TONN AND BLANK CONSTRUCTION LLC p 1460
1623 Greenwood Ave, Michigan City IN 46360
Tel (219) 879-7321 *SIC* 1542

FBI BUILDINGS INC p 532
3823 W 1800 S, Remington IN 47977
Tel (219) 261-2157 *SIC* 1542 5031 1541

WHITLEY EVERGREEN INC p 1607
201 W 1st St, South Whitley IN 46787
Tel (260) 723-5131 *SIC* 1542

THOMPSON THRIFT CONSTRUCTION INC p 1449
901 Wabash Ave Ste 300, Terre Haute IN 47807
Tel (812) 235-5959 *SIC* 1542 6531

MICHAELS G L CONSTRUCTION INC p 960
554 W Cedarwood Ave, West Terre Haute IN 47885
Tel (812) 478-3154 *SIC* 1542 1541

STORY CONSTRUCTION CO p 1392
300 S Bell Ave, Ames IA 50010
Tel (515) 232-4358 *SIC* 1542 1629

TODD & SARGENT INC p 1458
2905 Se 5th St, Ames IA 50010
Tel (515) 232-0442 *SIC* 1541 1542

DEAN SNYDER CONSTRUCTION CO p 420
913 N 14th St, Clear Lake IA 50428
Tel (641) 357-2283 *SIC* 1542 1521 1541

ARCHITECTURAL WALL SYSTEMS CO p 105
12345 University Ave # 100, Clive IA 50325
Tel (515) 255-1556 *SIC* 1542

RUSSELL CONSTRUCTION CO INC p 1259
4600 E 53rd St, Davenport IA 52807
Tel (563) 355-1845 *SIC* 1542

ALLIED CONSTRUCTION SERVICES INC p 56
2122 Fleur Dr, Des Moines IA 50321
Tel (515) 288-4855
SIC 1742 1752 1721 1751 1542

KBC GROUP INC p 806
3400 109th St, Des Moines IA 50322
Tel (515) 270-2417 *SIC* 1542 5083

WEITZ CO LLC p 1588
5901 Thornton Ave, Des Moines IA 50321
Tel (515) 698-4260 *SIC* 1542 1541 1629

CONLON CONSTRUCTION CO OF IOWA p 356
1100 Rockdale Rd, Dubuque IA 52003
Tel (563) 583-1724 *SIC* 1542 8741 1541

KLINGER COMPANIES INC p 823
2015 7th St, Sioux City IA 51101
Tel (712) 277-3900 *SIC* 1542 1541

CROSSLAND CONSTRUCTION CO INC p 394
833 S East Ave, Columbus KS 66725
Tel (620) 429-1414 *SIC* 1542

CITY WIDE HOLDING CO INC p 320
15447 W 100th Ter, Lenexa KS 66219
Tel (913) 888-5700
SIC 1542 1522 5087 7349

MMC CORP p 979
10955 Lowell Ave Ste 350, Overland Park KS 66210
Tel (913) 469-0101 *SIC* 1542 1711

MW BUILDERS GROUP INC p 1003
10955 Lowell Ave Ste 350, Shawnee Mission KS 66210
Tel (913) 345-0007 *SIC* 1542

CORNEJO & SONS LLC p 370
2060 E Tulsa St, Wichita KS 67216
Tel (316) 522-5100
SIC 1542 1794 1795 1611

DONDLINGER & SONS CONSTRUCTION CO INC p 450
2656 S Sheridan Ave, Wichita KS 67217
Tel (316) 945-0555 *SIC* 1622 1541 1542

EBY CORP p 474
2525 E 36th Cir N, Wichita KS 67219
Tel (316) 268-3500
SIC 1629 1623 1622 1541 1542 7353

HUTTON CONSTRUCTION CORP p 722
2229 S West St, Wichita KS 67213
Tel (316) 942-8855 *SIC* 1542

KEY CONSTRUCTION INC p 814
741 W 2nd St N, Wichita KS 67203
Tel (316) 263-9515 *SIC* 1542 1541

LAW CO INC p 847
345 N Rverview St Ste 300, Wichita KS 67203
Tel (316) 268-0200 *SIC* 1542 1522

MARTIN K EBY CONSTRUCTION CO INC p 912
2525 E 36th Cir N, Wichita KS 67219
Tel (316) 268-3500 *SIC* 1542

MERRY TECHNOLOGY INC p 950
315 N Rverview St Apt 615, Wichita KS 67203
Tel (316) 371-9533 *SIC* 1521 1542

STEWART RICHEY CONSTRUCTION INC p 1389
2137 Glen Lily Rd, Bowling Green KY 42101
Tel (270) 842-5184 *SIC* 1542 1521 1541

CORPOREX REALTY & INVESTMENT LLC p 372
100 E Riverctr Ste 1100, Covington KY 41011
Tel (859) 292-5500
SIC 1542 6531 6552 8741 6512

DENHAM-BLYTHE CO INC p 428
100 Trade St Ste 250, Lexington KY 40511
Tel (859) 255-7405 *SIC* 1541 1542

GRAY CONSTRUCTION INC p 632
10 Quality St, Lexington KY 40507
Tel (859) 281-5000 *SIC* 1541 1542 8712

GRAY INC p 632
10 Quality St, Lexington KY 40507
Tel (859) 281-5000 *SIC* 1541 1542

ABEL CONSTRUCTION CO INC p 11
3401 Bashford Avenue Ct, Louisville KY 40218
Tel (502) 451-2235 *SIC* 1541 1542

BUFFALO CONSTRUCTION INC p 224
2700 Stanley Gault Pkwy # 130, Louisville KY 40223
Tel (502) 327-4686 *SIC* 1542

KELLEY CONSTRUCTION INC p 808
12550 Lake Station Pl, Louisville KY 40299
Tel (502) 239-2848 *SIC* 1542

TRILOGY REHAB SERVICES LLC p 1480
2701 Chestnut Station Ct, Louisville KY 40299
Tel (800) 335-1060
SIC 8059 1542 8741 8051

WALKER CO OF KENTUCKY INC p 1573
105 Apperson Hts, Mount Sterling KY 40353
Tel (859) 498-0092
SIC 1611 2951 1542 3273 1422

A & K CONSTRUCTION INC p 4
100 Calloway Ct, Paducah KY 42001
Tel (270) 441-7752 *SIC* 1542 1541

HARPER INDUSTRIES INC p 663
960 N Hc Mathis Dr, Paducah KY 42001
Tel (270) 442-2753
SIC 3273 1711 1611 1542

BRANSCUM CONSTRUCTION CO/ROBINS & MORTON A JOINT VENTURE p 208
90 Key Village Rd, Russell Springs KY 42642
Tel (270) 866-5107 *SIC* 1541 8741 1542

ARKEL INTERNATIONAL LLC p 110
1048 Florida Blvd, Baton Rouge LA 70802
Tel (225) 343-0500 *SIC* 1542

CAJUN CONSTRUCTORS LLC p 237
15635 Airline Hwy, Baton Rouge LA 70817
Tel (225) 753-5857
SIC 1623 4952 1541 1542

CB&I GOVERNMENT SOLUTIONS INC p 268
4171 Essen Ln, Baton Rouge LA 70809
Tel (225) 932-2500
SIC 8711 8734 8748 1541 1542 1611

MAPP CONSTRUCTION LLC p 904
344 3rd St, Baton Rouge LA 70801
Tel (225) 757-0111 *SIC* 1542

GIBBS CONSTRUCTION LLC p 611
5736 Citrus Blvd Ste 200, Harahan LA 70123
Tel (504) 733-4336 *SIC* 1542 1541

LEMOINE CO L L C p 855
214 Jefferson St Ste 200, Lafayette LA 70501
Tel (337) 896-7720 *SIC* 1542

CORE CONSTRUCTION SERVICES LLC p 369
3131 N I 10 Service Rd E # 401, Metairie LA 70002
Tel (504) 733-2212 *SIC* 1542

MCC GROUP L L C p 926
3001 17th St, Metairie LA 70002
Tel (504) 833-8291 *SIC* 1711 1542 1731

WALTON CONSTRUCTION - A CORE CO LLC p 1575
2 Commerce Ct, New Orleans LA 70123
Tel (504) 733-2212 *SIC* 1541 1542

WOODWARD DESIGN + BUILD LLC p 1623
1000 S Jffrson Dvis Pkwy, New Orleans LA 70125
Tel (504) 822-6443 *SIC* 1541 1542

LINCOLN BUILDERS INC p 866
1809 Nrthpinte Ln Ste 201, Ruston LA 71270
Tel (318) 255-3822 *SIC* 1542

QUALITY CONSTRUCTION & PRODUCTION LLC p 1197
425 Griffin Rd, Youngsville LA 70592
Tel (337) 857-6000 *SIC* 1542

CIANBRO COMPANIES p 305
1 Hunnewell Ave, Pittsfield ME 04967
Tel (207) 487-3311
SIC 1629 1622 1542 1541 8742

CIANBRO CORP p 305
101 Cianbro Sq, Pittsfield ME 04967
Tel (207) 487-3311
SIC 1622 1629 1542 1541 8742

CCE/DFS INC p 270
201 Defense Hwy Ste 202, Annapolis MD 21401
Tel (410) 263-6422 *SIC* 1542 8711 8744

STRUEVER BROS ECCLES & ROUSE INC p 1394
2400 Boston St Ste 404, Baltimore MD 21224
Tel (443) 573-4000 *SIC* 1542 1522

WHITING-TURNER CONTRACTING CO p 1607
300 E Joppa Rd Ste 800, Baltimore MD 21286
Tel (410) 821-1100
SIC 1542 1541 1629 8741

BF SAUL PROPERTY CO p 179
7501 Wisconsin Ave, Bethesda MD 20814
Tel (301) 986-6000
SIC 6531 6519 1542 1522

CLARK CONSTRUCTION GROUP LLC p 322
7500 Old Georgetown Rd # 15, Bethesda MD 20814
Tel (301) 272-8100 *SIC* 1542 1611 1522

CLARK CONSTRUCTION LLC p 322
7500 Old Georgetown Rd # 1500, Bethesda MD 20814
Tel (301) 272-8337 *SIC* 1542

CLARK ENTERPRISES INC p 322
7500 Old Georgetown Rd # 7, Bethesda MD 20814
Tel (301) 657-7100
SIC 6552 4832 7359 1521 1542 6726

COAKLEY & WILLIAMS CONSTRUCTION INC p 331
7475 Wisconsin Ave # 900, Bethesda MD 20814
Tel (301) 963-5000 *SIC* 1542

CARL BELT INC p 256
11521 Milnor Ave, Cumberland MD 21502
Tel (240) 362-0270 *SIC* 1542

MORGAN-KELLER INC p 989
70 Thomas Johnson Dr # 200, Frederick MD 21702
Tel (301) 663-0626 *SIC* 1542 1541

BOZZUTO CONSTRUCTION CO INC p 205
6406 Ivy Ln Ste 700, Greenbelt MD 20770
Tel (301) 220-0100 *SIC* 1522 1542

BOZZUTO CONTRACTING CO p 205
6406 Ivy Ln, Greenbelt MD 20770
Tel (301) 220-0100 *SIC* 1521 1542

CA LINDMAN INC p 234
10401 Guilford Rd, Jessup MD 20794
Tel (410) 724-0040 *SIC* 1542

FACCHINA CONSTRUCTION CO INC p 523
102 Centennial St Ste 201, La Plata MD 20646
Tel (240) 776-7000
SIC 1542 1799 1623 1611 1622 1629

BUCH CONSTRUCTION INC p 222
11292 Buch Way, Laurel MD 20723
Tel (301) 369-3500 *SIC* 1542

HARKINS BUILDERS INC p 661
2201 Warwick Way, Marriottsville MD 21104
Tel (410) 750-2600 *SIC* 1522 1542

DAVIS CONSTRUCTION CORP JAMES G p 416
12530 Parklawn Dr Ste 100, Rockville MD 20852
Tel (301) 881-2990 *SIC* 1542

FORRESTER CONSTRUCTION CO p 568
12231 Parklawn Dr, Rockville MD 20852
Tel (301) 816-1700 *SIC* 1542

GRUNLEY CONSTRUCTION CO INC p 642
15020 Shady Ste 500, Rockville MD 20850
Tel (240) 399-2000 *SIC* 1542

HBW PROPERTIES INC p 671
1055 1st St Ste 200, Rockville MD 20850
Tel (301) 424-2900 *SIC* 1542 6512 6531

JOHN C GRIMBERG CO INC p 787
3200 Tower Oaks Blvd Fl 3, Rockville MD 20852
Tel (301) 881-5120 *SIC* 1542

BEACON COMPANIES INC p 164
2 Center Plz Ste 700, Boston MA 02108
Tel (617) 574-1100 *SIC* 1522 6531 1542

SHAWMUT WOODWORKING & SUPPLY INC p 1313
560 Harrison Ave Ste 200, Boston MA 02118
Tel (617) 338-6200 *SIC* 1542

SUFFOLK CONSTRUCTION CO INC p 1396
65 Allerton St, Boston MA 02119
Tel (617) 445-3500 *SIC* 1542

SUFFOLK/KRAFT CONSTRUCTION CO LLC p 1397
65 Allerton St, Boston MA 02119
Tel (617) 445-3500 *SIC* 1542

CALLAHAN INC p 242
80 1st St, Bridgewater MA 02324
Tel (508) 279-0012 *SIC* 1542

BOND BROTHERS INC p 199
145 Spring St, Everett MA 02149
Tel (617) 387-3400 *SIC* 1542

■ **PERINI MANAGEMENT SERVICES INC** p 1136
73 Mount Wayte Ave, Framingham MA 01702
Tel (508) 628-2000
SIC 1541 1542 1611 1629

DANIEL OCONNELLS SONS INC p 411
480 Hampden St, Holyoke MA 01040
Tel (413) 534-5667
SIC 1541 1542 1522 1611 1622 1629

CONSIGLI BUILDING GROUP INC p 358
72 Sumner St, Milford MA 01757
Tel (508) 473-2580 *SIC* 1542

CONSIGLI CONSTRUCTION CO INC p 359
72 Sumner St, Milford MA 01757
Tel (508) 473-2580 *SIC* 1541 1542

WT RICH CO INC p 1569
29 Crafts St Ste 300, Newton MA 02458
Tel (617) 467-6010 *SIC* 1541 1542

J CALNAN & ASSOCIATES INC p 770
3 Batterymarch Park # 500, Quincy MA 02169
Tel (617) 801-0200 *SIC* 8741 1542

LEE KENNEDY CO INC p 851
122 Quincy Shore Dr Ste 1, Quincy MA 02171
Tel (617) 825-6930 *SIC* 1542

DF PRAY INC p 435
25 Anthony St, Seekonk MA 02771
Tel (508) 336-3366 *SIC* 1542 1541

DEVERE CONSTRUCTION CO INC p 433
1030 Devere Dr, Alpena MI 49707
Tel (989) 356-4411
SIC 1542 1541 1629 8741

BISHOP CONSTRUCTION INC p 185
3374 S Center Rd Ste C, Burton MI 48519
Tel (810) 744-4550 *SIC* 1521 1542

FUTURENET GROUP INC p 586
12801 Auburn St, Detroit MI 48223
Tel (313) 544-7117 *SIC* 1542 8748

IDEAL CONTRACTING LLC p 729
2525 Clark St, Detroit MI 48209
Tel (313) 843-8000
SIC 1542 1742 1771 1791

SACHSE CONSTRUCTION AND DEVELOPMENT CO LLC p 1264
1528 Woodward Ave Ste 600, Detroit MI 48226
Tel (313) 481-8200 *SIC* 1542 1522

WALBRIDGE ALDINGER LLC p 1572
777 Woodward Ave Ste 300, Detroit MI 48226
Tel (313) 963-8000 *SIC* 1541 1542 8741

WALBRIDGE GROUP INC p 1572
777 Woodward Ave Ste 300, Detroit MI 48226
Tel (313) 963-8000 *SIC* 1542

BOUMA CORP p 204
4101 Roger B Chaffee Mem, Grand Rapids MI 49548
Tel (616) 538-3600 *SIC* 1542 1752 1742

BOUMA GROUP INC p 204
4101 Roger B Chaffee Mem, Grand Rapids MI 49548
Tel (616) 538-3600 *SIC* 1542 1752 1742

ROCKFORD CONSTRUCTION CO p 1244
601 1st St Nw, Grand Rapids MI 49504
Tel (616) 285-6933 *SIC* 1542

TRIANGLE ASSOCIATES INC p 1478
3769 3 Mile Rd Nw, Grand Rapids MI 49534
Tel (616) 453-3950 *SIC* 1542 1541

WOLVERINE BUILDING GROUP INC p 1621
4045 Barden St Se, Grand Rapids MI 49512
Tel (616) 281-6236 *SIC* 1541 1542

LAMAR CONSTRUCTION CO p 841
4404 Central Pkwy, Hudsonville MI 49426
Tel (616) 662-2933 *SIC* 1542 1541

CHAMPION INC p 287
180 Traders Mine Rd, Iron Mountain MI 49801
Tel (906) 779-2300
SIC 8741 1542 5063 5082 3273 3272

CHRISTMAN CO p 303
208 N Capitol Ave Fl 4, Lansing MI 48933
Tel (517) 482-1488
SIC 8741 1542 1541 1629

GRANGER CONSTRUCTION CO INC p 631
6267 Aurelius Rd, Lansing MI 48911
Tel (517) 393-1670 *SIC* 1542 1541

RAM CONSTRUCTION SERVICES OF MICHIGAN INC p 1206
13800 Eckles Rd, Livonia MI 48150
Tel (734) 464-3800 *SIC* 1799 1541 1542

THREE RIVERS CORP p 1450
3069 E Vantage Point Dr, Midland MI 48642
Tel (989) 631-9726 *SIC* 1542 1541

LEE CONTRACTING INC p 851
631 Cesar E Chavez Ave, Pontiac MI 48342
Tel (888) 833-8776 *SIC* 1731 1542 1541

WOLGAST CORP p 1621
4835 Towne Centre Rd # 203, Saginaw MI 48604
Tel (989) 233-5228 *SIC* 1542 1541

BARTON MALOW ENTERPRISES INC p 158
26500 American Dr, Southfield MI 48034
Tel (248) 436-5000 *SIC* 8741 1542 1541

NOR-SON INC p 1047
7900 Hastings Rd, Baxter MN 56425
Tel (218) 828-1722 *SIC* 1521 1542 1541

MILLER MANUFACTURING CO p 970
2910 Waters Rd Ste 150, Eagan MN 55121
Tel (651) 982-5100 *SIC* 1542 5199

MET-CON CONSTRUCTION INC p 952
15760 Acorn Trl, Faribault MN 55021
Tel (507) 332-2266 *SIC* 1541 1542 5251

ESSAR PROJECTS (USA) LLC p 510
555 W 27th St, Hibbing MN 55746
Tel (218) 263-3331 *SIC* 1542

ADOLFSON & PETERSON INC p 24
6701 W 23rd St, Minneapolis MN 55426
Tel (952) 544-1561 *SIC* 1542

AP MIDWEST LLC p 95
6701 W 23rd St, Minneapolis MN 55426
Tel (952) 544-1561 *SIC* 1542

KNUTSON CONSTRUCTION SERVICES INC p 825
7515 Wayzata Blvd, Minneapolis MN 55426
Tel (763) 546-1400 *SIC* 1542 1541

KNUTSON HOLDINGS INC p 825
7515 Wayzata Blvd, Minneapolis MN 55426
Tel (763) 546-1400 *SIC* 1542 1541

M A MORTENSON CO p 889
700 Meadow Ln N, Minneapolis MN 55422
Tel (763) 522-2100 *SIC* 1542 1629

M A MORTENSON COMPANIES INC p 889
700 Meadow Ln N, Minneapolis MN 55422
Tel (763) 522-2100 *SIC* 1542 1629

RYAN COMPANIES US INC p 1260
50 S 10th St Ste 300, Minneapolis MN 55403
Tel (612) 492-4000
SIC 1542 1541 6552 6512 1522

SATELLITE SHELTERS INC p 1283
2530 Xenium Ln N Ste 150, Minneapolis MN 55441
Tel (763) 553-1900 *SIC* 1542 7353

WEIS BUILDERS INC p 1588
7645 Lyndale Ave S # 300, Minneapolis MN 55423
Tel (612) 243-5000 *SIC* 1522 1541 1542

MCGOUGH CONSTRUCTION CO INC p 929
2737 Fairview Ave N, Saint Paul MN 55113
Tel (651) 633-5050 *SIC* 1541 1542

SHAW-LUNDQUIST ASSOCIATES INC p 1313
2757 W Service Rd, Saint Paul MN 55121
Tel (651) 454-0670 *SIC* 1542 1541

UNITED SUBCONTRACTORS INC p 1514
445 Minnesota St Ste 2500, Saint Paul MN 55101
Tel (651) 225-6300
SIC 1742 1796 1542 1522

HILL BROTHERS CONSTRUCTION CO INC p 693
20831 Highway 15, Falkner MS 38629
Tel (662) 837-3041
SIC 1611 1622 1541 1542

HEMPHILL CONSTRUCTION CO INC p 682
1858 Highway 49 S, Florence MS 39073
Tel (601) 932-2060 *SIC* 1623 1542

F L CRANE AND SONS INC p 522
508 S Spring St, Fulton MS 38843
Tel (662) 862-2172 *SIC* 1542

■ **ANDERSON COMPANIES INC** p 89
11400 Reichold Rd, Gulfport MS 39503
Tel (228) 896-4000 *SIC* 1542 1541 1522

■ **ROY ANDERSON CORP** p 1254
11400 Reichold Rd, Gulfport MS 39503
Tel (228) 896-4000 *SIC* 1542 1541 1522

W G YATES & SONS CONSTRUCTION CO p 1568
1 Gully Ave, Philadelphia MS 39350
Tel (904) 714-1376
SIC 1542 1541 2339 1611 5211 1731

YATES COMPANIES INC p 1635
1 Gully Ave, Philadelphia MS 39350
Tel (601) 656-5411
SIC 1542 1541 1611 5211 1731

MCBRIDE & SON ENTERPRISES INC p 926
16091 Swingley Ridge Rd # 300, Chesterfield MO 63017
Tel (636) 537-2000 *SIC* 1522 1542

R G BRINKMANN CO p 1202
16650 Chstrfield Grove Rd, Chesterfield MO 63005
Tel (636) 537-9700 *SIC* 1542

BEN HUR CONSTRUCTION CO p 172
3783 Rider Trl S, Earth City MO 63045
Tel (314) 298-8007
SIC 1542 1791 1541 3441

BLUESCOPE BUILDINGS NORTH AMERICA INC p 193
1540 Genessee St, Kansas City MO 64102
Tel (816) 245-6000 *SIC* 1542

BLUESCOPE CONSTRUCTION INC p 193
1540 Genessee St, Kansas City MO 64102
Tel (816) 245-6000 *SIC* 1542

BLUESCOPE STEEL NORTH AMERICA CORP p 193
1540 Genessee St, Kansas City MO 64102
Tel (816) 968-1700 *SIC* 1542 3448

CECO CONCRETE CONSTRUCTION DELAWARE LLC p 272
10100 N Ambassador Dr, Kansas City MO 64153
Tel (816) 459-7000 *SIC* 1542 1522

GORDON MCCOWN CONSTRUCTION LLC p 626
422 Admiral Blvd, Kansas City MO 64106
Tel (816) 960-1111 *SIC* 1542

JE DUNN CONSTRUCTION CO p 781
1001 Locust St, Kansas City MO 64106
Tel (816) 474-8600 *SIC* 1542

JE DUNN CONSTRUCTION GROUP INC p 781
1001 Locust St, Kansas City MO 64106
Tel (816) 474-8600 *SIC* 1542

POPULOUS HOLDINGS INC p 1161
4800 Main St Ste 300, Kansas City MO 64112
Tel (816) 221-1500 *SIC* 1542

VSMA INC p 1566
1540 Genessee St, Kansas City MO 64102
Tel (816) 968-3000 *SIC* 1542

ARIZON COMPANIES INC p 108
11880 Dorsett Rd, Maryland Heights MO 63043
Tel (314) 739-0037
SIC 3585 1711 2394 1541 1542 8611

FRED WEBER INC p 576
2320 Creve Coeur Mill Rd, Maryland Heights MO 63043
Tel (314) 344-0070
SIC 1611 1442 3272 1622 1542

ALBERICI CONSTRUCTORS INC p 46
8800 Page Ave, Saint Louis MO 63114
Tel (314) 733-2000 *SIC* 1541 1542 1622

ALBERICI CORP p 46
8800 Page Ave, Saint Louis MO 63114
Tel (314) 733-2000
SIC 1541 1542 1622 1629

ALBERICI GROUP INC p 46
8800 Page Ave, Saint Louis MO 63114
Tel (314) 733-2000 *SIC* 1541 1542 1622

DRURY DEVELOPMENT CORP p 457
721 Emerson Rd Ste 200, Saint Louis MO 63141
Tel (314) 423-6698 *SIC* 6512 1542 5812

HBE CORP p 671
11330 Olive Blvd, Saint Louis MO 63141
Tel (314) 567-9000 *SIC* 1542 8742

■ **JACOBS FACILITIES INC** p 775
501 N Broadway, Saint Louis MO 63102
Tel (314) 335-4000
SIC 8712 8711 8713 8741 1542 1541

KCI CONSTRUCTION CO p 806
10315 Lake Bluff Dr, Saint Louis MO 63123
Tel (314) 894-8888 *SIC* 1542 1611 1629

KORTE CONSTRUCTION CO p 828
5700 Oakland Ave Ste 275, Saint Louis MO 63110
Tel (314) 231-3700 *SIC* 1541 1542

MCCARTHY BUILDING COMPANIES INC p 926
1341 N Rock Hill Rd, Saint Louis MO 63124
Tel (314) 968-3300 *SIC* 1542 1541

MCCARTHY HOLDINGS INC p 926
1341 N Rock Hill Rd, Saint Louis MO 63124
Tel (314) 968-3300 *SIC* 1542 1541

MCCARTHY STRAUB JV I p 926
1341 N Rock Hill Rd, Saint Louis MO 63124
Tel (314) 646-4189 *SIC* 1542

NOOTER CORP p 1047
1500 S 2nd St, Saint Louis MO 63104
Tel (314) 421-7200
SIC 3443 3479 1796 8711 7699 1542

PARIC CORP p 1114
77 West Port Plz Ste 250, Saint Louis MO 63146
Tel (636) 561-9500 *SIC* 1542 1541

S M WILSON & CO p 1262
2185 Hampton Ave, Saint Louis MO 63139
Tel (314) 645-9595 *SIC* 1541 1542

SLETTEN CONSTRUCTION CO p 1331
1000 25th St N Ste 4, Great Falls MT 59401
Tel (406) 761-7920 *SIC* 1541 1542 1611

SLETTEN INC p 1331
1000 25th St N Ste 4, Great Falls MT 59401
Tel (406) 761-7920 *SIC* 1542 1541 1611

DICK ANDERSON CONSTRUCTION INC p 437
3424 E Us Highway 12, Helena MT 59601
Tel (406) 443-3225 SIC 1542 1622 1611

SWANK ENTERPRISES p 1411
615 Pondera Ave, Valier MT 59486
Tel (406) 279-3241 SIC 1542 5211

PAULSEN INC p 1122
1116 E Highway 30, Cozad NE 69130
Tel (308) 784-3333 SIC 1611 1542 3273

SAMPSON CONSTRUCTION CO INC p 1274
3730 S 14th St, Lincoln NE 68502
Tel (308) 865-1375 SIC 1542 1541

HAWKINS CONSTRUCTION CO p 669
2516 Deer Park Blvd, Omaha NE 68105
Tel (402) 342-4455 SIC 1542 1611 1541

KIEWIT CORP p 817
3555 Farnam St Ste 1000, Omaha NE 68131
Tel (402) 342-2052
SIC 1542 1541 1611 1622 1629

KIEWIT INFRASTRUCTURE CO p 817
Kiewit Plz, Omaha NE 68131
Tel (402) 342-2052
SIC 1541 1542 1629 1622 1522

PETER KIEWIT SONS INC p 1138
3555 Farnam St Ste 1000, Omaha NE 68131
Tel (402) 342-2052
SIC 1611 1622 1711 1542 1629 1221

A & K EARTH MOVERS INC p 4
515 Windmill Dr, Fallon NV 89406
Tel (775) 825-1636 SIC 1611 1542

MARTIN-HARRIS CONSTRUCTION LLC p 913
3030 S Highland Dr, Las Vegas NV 89109
Tel (702) 385-5257 SIC 1541 1542

PENTA BUILDING GROUP INC p 1131
181 E Warm Springs Rd, Las Vegas NV 89119
Tel (702) 614-1678 SIC 1542

SAGEBRUSH ENTERPRISES INC p 1267
4730 S Fort Apache Rd, Las Vegas NV 89147
Tel (702) 873-5338
SIC 1522 1542 7992 6799

UNITED CONSTRUCTION CO p 1507
5300 Mill St, Reno NV 89502
Tel (775) 858-8090 SIC 1541 1542

PRO CON INC p 1178
1359 Hooksett Rd Ste 16, Hooksett NH 03106
Tel (603) 623-8811 SIC 1542 1541

STEBBINS ENTERPRISES INC p 1384
1359 Hooksett Rd, Hooksett NH 03106
Tel (603) 623-8811 SIC 1542 1541

HUTTER CONSTRUCTION CORP p 722
810 Turnpike Rd, New Ipswich NH 03071
Tel (603) 878-2300 SIC 1541 1542

FURINO & SON INC p 585
66 Columbia Rd, Branchburg NJ 08876
Tel (908) 756-7736 SIC 1541 1542

C&H INDUSTRIAL SERVICES INC p 234
542 Penny St, Franklinville NJ 08322
Tel (856) 875-8152 SIC 7349 1542

BLACKSTONE GROUP LLC p 188
570 Broad St Ste 1606, Newark NJ 07102
Tel (973) 624-6300 SIC 1542 1522 1541

SKANSKA USA BUILDING INC p 1329
389 Interpace Pkwy Ste 5, Parsippany NJ 07054
Tel (973) 753-3500 SIC 1541 1542 8741

TORCON INC p 1461
328 Newman Springs Rd # 5, Red Bank NJ 07701
Tel (732) 704-9800 SIC 1542

NEW JERSEY SCHOOLS DEVELOPMENT AUTHORITY p 1031
32 E Front St, Trenton NJ 08608
Tel (609) 943-5955 SIC 1542

CORNELL & CO INC p 370
224 Cornell Ln, Westville NJ 08093
Tel (856) 742-1900 SIC 1542 1541

JAYNES CORP p 779
2906 Broadway Blvd Ne, Albuquerque NM 87107
Tel (505) 345-8591 SIC 1542 1541

BBL LLC p 163
302 Washington Ave, Albany NY 12203
Tel (518) 452-8200
SIC 1542 1541 1521 1622 8741

M+W US INC p 890
201 Fuller Rd Ste 400, Albany NY 12203
Tel (518) 266-3400 SIC 1542 8711

ELLICOTT DEVELOPMENT OF BUFFALO LLC p 488
295 Main St Rm 210, Buffalo NY 14203
Tel (716) 854-0060 SIC 1522 1542 6531

BAST HATFIELD INC p 159
1399 Vischers Ferry Rd, Clifton Park NY 12065
Tel (518) 373-2000 SIC 1542 1541 8741

FERRANDINO & SON INC p 538
71 Carolyn Blvd, Farmingdale NY 11735
Tel (866) 571-4609
SIC 1542 0781 3531 7299

POSILLICO CIVIL INC p 1163
1750 New Hwy, Farmingdale NY 11735
Tel (631) 249-1872 SIC 1611 1542

BETTE & CRING LLC p 178
22 Century Hill Dr # 201, Latham NY 12110
Tel (518) 213-1010
SIC 1541 1542 1622 1611

NEW YORK CITY SCHOOL CONSTRUCTION AUTHORITY p 1034
3030 Thomson Ave Fl 3, Long Island City NY 11101
Tel (718) 472-8000 SIC 1542

WELLIVER MCGUIRE INC p 1589
250 N Genesee St, Montour Falls NY 14865
Tel (704) 454-5500 SIC 1542 1541

COMMODORE CONSTRUCTION CORP p 345
602 S 3rd Ave, Mount Vernon NY 10550
Tel (914) 663-4394 SIC 1542

BARR & BARR INC p 156
460 W 34th St Fl 10, New York NY 10001
Tel (212) 563-2330 SIC 1542 1541

CLARENDON NATIONAL INSURANCE CO (MD CORP) p 321
411 5th Ave Fl 5, New York NY 10016
Tel (212) 790-9700
SIC 6321 1542 1541 7011

HOCHTIEF USA INC p 699
375 Hudson St Fl 6, New York NY 10014
Tel (212) 229-6000
SIC 1542 1541 1522 8741 8742 6799

HUNTER ROBERTS CONSTRUCTION GROUP LLC p 719
55 Water St Fl 51, New York NY 10041
Tel (212) 321-6800 SIC 8742 1542

JRM CONSTRUCTION MANAGEMENT LLC p 795
242 W 36th St Rm 901, New York NY 10018
Tel (212) 545-0500 SIC 1542

JT MAGEN & CO INC p 796
44 W 28th St Fl 11, New York NY 10001
Tel (212) 790-4200 SIC 1542

LEND LEASE AMERICAS INC p 855
200 Park Ave Fl 9, New York NY 10166
Tel (212) 592-6700 SIC 1542 1541

LENDLEASE (US) CONSTRUCTION HOLDINGS INC p 855
200 Park Ave Fl 9, New York NY 10166
Tel (212) 592-6700 SIC 1542 1541 8742

LENDLEASE (US) CONSTRUCTION INC p 855
200 Park Ave Fl 9, New York NY 10166
Tel (212) 592-6700
SIC 1541 1542 1522 8741 8742

LENDLEASE (US) CONSTRUCTION LMB INC p 855
200 Park Ave Fl 9, New York NY 10166
Tel (212) 592-6700
SIC 1522 1541 1542 8741 8742

M/L BOVIS HOLDINGS LTD p 890
200 Park Ave Fl 9, New York NY 10166
Tel (212) 592-6700
SIC 1522 1541 1542 8741 8742

PLAZA CONSTRUCTION LLC p 1155
1065 Avenue Of The Americ, New York NY 10018
Tel (212) 849-4800 SIC 1542 8741

SH GROUP INC p 1310
1515 Broadway, New York NY 10036
Tel (212) 921-2300 SIC 8748 8711 1542

SHACKLEFORDS CONSTRUCTION & CONTRACTING LTD p 1310
303 Lexington Ave, New York NY 10016
Tel (646) 771-4470
SIC 1522 1542 1541 7389

SKANSKA INC p 1329
350 5th Ave Fl 32, New York NY 10118
Tel (917) 438-4500 SIC 8741 1542

SKANSKA USA INC p 1329
350 5th Ave Fl 32, New York NY 10118
Tel (917) 438-4500 SIC 8741 1542

TURNER CONSTRUCTION CO INC p 1492
375 Hudson St Fl 6, New York NY 10014
Tel (212) 229-6000
SIC 1542 1541 1522 8741 8742

TURNER CORP p 1492
375 Hudson St Rm 700, New York NY 10014
Tel (212) 229-6000
SIC 1542 1541 1522 8742

TURNER INTERNATIONAL INDUSTRIES INC p 1493
375 Hudson St Fl 6, New York NY 10014
Tel (212) 229-6000 SIC 8741 8712 1542

CONSIGLI CONSTRUCTION NY LLC p 359
199 West Rd Ste 100, Pleasant Valley NY 12569
Tel (845) 635-1121 SIC 1542

BELL CO LLC p 170
1340 Lexington Ave, Rochester NY 14606
Tel (585) 277-1000 SIC 1541 1542

LECHASE CONSTRUCTION SERVICES LLC p 850
205 Indigo Creek Dr, Rochester NY 14626
Tel (585) 254-3510 SIC 1541 1542

PIKE CO INC p 1147
1 Circle St, Rochester NY 14607
Tel (585) 271-5256 SIC 1542

PURCELL CONSTRUCTION CORP p 1192
566 Coffeen St, Watertown NY 13601
Tel (315) 782-1050 SIC 1542 1541 1522

A & A MAINTENANCE ENTERPRISE INC p 4
965 Midland Ave, Yonkers NY 10704
Tel (914) 969-0009
SIC 7349 1721 1542 4959 0782

MB HAYNES CORP p 925
187 Deaverview Rd, Asheville NC 28806
Tel (828) 254-6141
SIC 1542 1623 1711 7382

EDIFICE INC p 478
1401 W Morehead St Ste A, Charlotte NC 28208
Tel (704) 332-0900 SIC 1542

ENVIRONAMICS INC p 503
13935 S Point Blvd, Charlotte NC 28273
Tel (704) 376-3613 SIC 1542

OBRIEN & GERE/ CROWDER JOINT VENTURE p 1072
6425 Brookshire Blvd, Charlotte NC 28216
Tel (704) 372-3541 SIC 1542

RODGERS BUILDERS INC p 1246
5701 N Sharon Amity Rd, Charlotte NC 28215
Tel (704) 537-6044 SIC 1542 1541

SHELCO LLC p 1314
2320 Cascade Pointe Blvd # 100, Charlotte NC 28208
Tel (704) 367-5600 SIC 1541 1542

TA LOVING CO p 1420
400 Patetown Rd, Goldsboro NC 27530
Tel (919) 734-8400 SIC 1541 1542 1623

SAMET CORP p 1274
309 Gallimore Dairy Rd # 102, Greensboro NC 27409
Tel (336) 544-2600 SIC 1541 1542

JAMES R VANNOY & SONS CONSTRUCTION CO INC p 777
1608 Us Highway 221 N, Jefferson NC 28640
Tel (336) 846-7191 SIC 1542 1541 1799

HOG SLAT INC p 699
206 Fayetteville St, Newton Grove NC 28366
Tel (866) 464-7528
SIC 1542 3272 3523 0213

CLANCY & THEYS CONSTRUCTION CO INC p 321
516 W Cabarrus St, Raleigh NC 27603
Tel (919) 834-3601 SIC 1542 1541

B V HEDRICK GRAVEL & SAND CO p 142
120 1/2 N Church St, Salisbury NC 28144
Tel (704) 633-5982
SIC 1442 7359 6512 3273 1541 1542

BILFINGER WESTCON INC p 182
7401 Yukon Dr, Bismarck ND 58503
Tel (701) 222-0076 SIC 1542

MILLER INSULATION CO INC p 970
3520 E Century Ave, Bismarck ND 58503
Tel (701) 258-4323 SIC 1742 1542

GATEWAY BUILDING SYSTEMS INC p 593
2138 Main Ave W, West Fargo ND 58078
Tel (701) 293-7202 SIC 1542 5083

INDUSTRIAL BUILDERS INC p 739
1307 County Road 17 N, West Fargo ND 58078
Tel (701) 282-4977
SIC 1629 1622 1542 1611 1623

■ **WANZEK CONSTRUCTION INC** p 1575
2028 2nd Ave Nw, West Fargo ND 58078
Tel (701) 282-6171
SIC 1542 1623 1622 1799 1541 1629

DUGAN & MEYERS CONSTRUCTION CO p 460
11110 Kenwood Rd, Blue Ash OH 45242
Tel (513) 891-4300 SIC 1541 1542 1522

DUGAN & MEYERS INTERESTS INC p 460
11110 Kenwood Rd, Blue Ash OH 45242
Tel (513) 891-4300 SIC 1541 1542 1522

J & R ASSOCIATES p 770
14803 Holland Rd, Brookpark OH 44142
Tel (440) 250-4080 SIC 1542 8361 6514

MESSER CONSTRUCTION CO p 951
5158 Fishwick Dr, Cincinnati OH 45216
Tel (513) 242-1541 SIC 1542 1541 1522

ALBERT M HIGLEY CO p 46
2926 Chester Ave, Cleveland OH 44114
Tel (216) 404-5783 SIC 1542 1541

AUSTIN BUILDING AND DESIGN INC p 132
6095 Parkland Blvd # 100, Cleveland OH 44124
Tel (440) 544-2600
SIC 1541 1542 8742 8711 8712

COLUMBIA NATIONAL GROUP INC p 341
6600 Grant Ave, Cleveland OH 44105
Tel (216) 883-4972 SIC 5051 5093 1542

DONLEYS INC p 450
5430 Warner Rd, Cleveland OH 44125
Tel (216) 524-6800 SIC 1542

CONTINENTAL REAL ESTATE COMPANIES p 363
150 E Broad St Ste 200, Columbus OH 43215
Tel (614) 221-1800 SIC 1542 1541

ELFORD INC p 486
1220 Dublin Rd, Columbus OH 43215
Tel (614) 488-4000 SIC 1542 1541 8741

KOKOSING CONSTRUCTION CO INC p 826
886 Mckinley Ave, Columbus OH 43222
Tel (614) 228-1029
SIC 1611 1622 1629 1542 1541 1623

■ **L BRANDS STORE DESIGN & CONSTRUCTION INC** p 834
3 Ltd Pkwy, Columbus OH 43230
Tel (614) 415-7000 SIC 1542

DUNCAN OIL CO p 461
849 Factory Rd, Dayton OH 45434
Tel (937) 426-5945
SIC 5172 5411 5983 1542

SHOOK CONSTRUCTION CO p 1318
4977 Northcutt Pl, Dayton OH 45414
Tel (937) 276-6666 SIC 1629 1542 8741

SHOOK NATIONAL CORP p 1318
4977 Northcutt Pl, Dayton OH 45414
Tel (937) 276-6666
SIC 8741 1542 1629 1541

LUKE THEIS ENTERPRISES INC p 885
14120 State Route 568, Findlay OH 45840
Tel (419) 422-2040 SIC 1542 1541 1521

BECK SUPPLIERS INC p 167
1000 N Front St, Fremont OH 43420
Tel (419) 332-5527
SIC 5171 5541 5411 5984 1542

MOSSER CONSTRUCTION INC p 992
122 S Wilson Ave, Fremont OH 43420
Tel (419) 334-3801 SIC 1541 1542

CLEVELAND CONSTRUCTION INC p 325
8620 Tyler Blvd, Mentor OH 44060
Tel (513) 398-8900 SIC 1542 1742 1752

DANIS BUILDING CONSTRUCTION CO p 411
3233 Newmark Dr, Miamisburg OH 45342
Tel (937) 228-1225 SIC 1542 1541

WINSUPPLY INC p 1617
3110 Kettering Blvd, Moraine OH 45439
Tel (937) 294-5331 SIC 1542 5074 5085

FRED OLIVIERI CONSTRUCTION CO p 576
6315 Promway Ave Nw, North Canton OH 44720
Tel (330) 494-1007 SIC 1542

FORTNEY & WEYGANDT INC p 570
31269 Bradley Rd, North Olmsted OH 44070
Tel (440) 716-4000 SIC 1541 1542

R L FORTNEY MANAGEMENT INC p 1202
31269 Bradley Rd, North Olmsted OH 44070
Tel (440) 716-4000 SIC 1542

RUHLIN CO p 1257
6931 Ridge Rd, Sharon Center OH 44274
Tel (330) 239-2800
SIC 1542 1541 1622 1611

FERGUSON CONSTRUCTION CO INC p 538
400 Canal St, Sidney OH 45365
Tel (937) 498-2381 SIC 1541 1542

RUDOLPH LIBBE INC p 1257
6494 Latcha Rd, Walbridge OH 43465
Tel (419) 241-5000 SIC 1541 1542

RUDOLPH/LIBBE COMPANIES INC p 1257
6494 Latcha Rd, Walbridge OH 43465
Tel (419) 241-5000 SIC 1541 1542

PETERSON CONSTRUCTION CO p 1138
18817 State Route 501, Wapakoneta OH 45895
Tel (419) 941-2233 SIC 1542 1629

CORNA KOKOSING CONSTRUCTION CO p 370
6235 Westerville Rd, Westerville OH 43081
Tel (614) 901-8844 SIC 1541 1542 8741

MCGRAW/KOKOSING INC p 929
101 Clark Blvd, Westerville OH 43081
Tel (614) 212-5700 SIC 1541 1542

TIMBERLAKE CONSTRUCTION CO INC p 1454
7613 N Classen Blvd, Oklahoma City OK 73116
Tel (405) 840-2521 SIC 1542 1541

FLINTCO LLC p 557
1624 W 21st St, Tulsa OK 74107
Tel (918) 587-8451 SIC 1541 1542

MANHATTAN CONSTRUCTION CO p 901
5601 S 122nd East Ave, Tulsa OK 74146
Tel (918) 583-6900 SIC 1542

MANHATTAN CONSTRUCTION GROUP INC p 901
5601 S 122nd East Ave, Tulsa OK 74146
Tel (918) 878-3341 SIC 1542

■ **MATRIX PDM ENGINEERING INC** p 920
5100 E Skelly Dr Ste 800, Tulsa OK 74135
Tel (918) 624-6300 SIC 1542 1623 8711

▲ **MATRIX SERVICE CO** p 920
5100 E Skelly Dr Ste 700, Tulsa OK 74135
Tel (918) 838-8822
SIC 1542 1623 7349 8711

ROSS GROUP CONSTRUCTION CORP p 1251
510 E 2nd St, Tulsa OK 74120
Tel (918) 878-2838 SIC 1542

WILDISH LAND CO p 1609
3600 Wildish Ln, Eugene OR 97408
Tel (541) 485-1700 SIC 1611 1542

ANDERSEN CONSTRUCTION CO p 89
6712 N Cutter Cir, Portland OR 97217
Tel (503) 283-6712 SIC 1542 1541

FORTIS CONSTRUCTION INC p 569
1705 Sw Taylor St Ste 200, Portland OR 97205
Tel (503) 459-4477 SIC 1542 1611

HOFFMAN CORP p 699
805 Sw Broadway Ste 2100, Portland OR 97205
Tel (503) 221-8811
SIC 8741 1541 1542 1623 1629

R&H CONSTRUCTION CO p 1203
1530 Sw Taylor St, Portland OR 97205
Tel (503) 228-7177 SIC 1542 1522

WALSH CONSTRUCTION CO p 1574
2905 Sw 1st Ave, Portland OR 97201
Tel (503) 228-1190 SIC 1522 1542

COLSON & COLSON GENERAL CONTRACTOR INC p 339
2260 Mcgilchrist St Se # 100, Salem OR 97302
Tel (503) 586-7401 SIC 1522 1542

SLAYDEN CONSTRUCTION GROUP INC p 1331
500 Willamette Ave, Stayton OR 97383
Tel (503) 769-1969 SIC 1542

LEONARD S FIORE INC p 856
5506 6th Ave Rear, Altoona PA 16602
Tel (814) 946-3686 SIC 1542

MODULAR SPACE CORP p 981
1200 W Swedesford Rd Fl 2, Berwyn PA 19312
Tel (610) 232-1200 SIC 7359 1542

KVAERNER NORTH AMERICAN CONSTRUCTION INC p 832
701 Technology Dr, Canonsburg PA 15317
Tel (724) 416-6900 SIC 1542 8741

AMERICAN BRIDGE HOLDING CO p 69
1000 American Bridge Way, Coraopolis PA 15108
Tel (412) 631-1000 SIC 1791 1542

ECICONSTRUCTION LLC p 475
124 W Church St, Dillsburg PA 17019
Tel (717) 638-3000 SIC 1542

EICHELBERGER CONSTRUCTION INC p 481
124 W Church St, Dillsburg PA 17019
Tel (717) 638-2000 SIC 1542

LOBAR INC p 872
1 Old Mill Rd, Dillsburg PA 17019
Tel (717) 432-9728
SIC 1541 1542 8741 1629 1731 7371

QUANDEL CONSTRUCTION GROUP INC p 1198
3003 N Front St Ste 203, Harrisburg PA 17110
Tel (717) 657-0909
SIC 1542 1541 1629 8741

QUANDEL ENTERPRISES INC p 1198
3003 N Front St Ste 203, Harrisburg PA 17110
Tel (717) 657-0909 SIC 1542 1629 8741

BORO DEVELOPERS INC p 201
400 Feheley Dr Ste B, King Of Prussia PA 19406
Tel (610) 272-7400 SIC 1542

HORST GROUP INC p 708
320 Granite Run Dr, Lancaster PA 17601
Tel (717) 560-1919 SIC 1542 1541 6531

WOHLSEN CONSTRUCTION CO INC p 1620
548 Steel Way, Lancaster PA 17601
Tel (717) 299-2500 SIC 1542 1541 8741

BALFOUR BEATTY MILITARY HOUSING LLC p 148
1 Country View Rd, Malvern PA 19355
Tel (610) 355-8100 SIC 1522 1542

NORWOOD CO p 1061
375 Technology Dr, Malvern PA 19355
Tel (610) 240-4400 SIC 1541 1542 8741

■ **DANIEL J KEATING CONSTRUCTION CO** p 411
130 N 18th St Ste 1500, Philadelphia PA 19103
Tel (610) 668-4100 SIC 1542

J J WHITE INC p 771
5500 Bingham St, Philadelphia PA 19120
Tel (215) 722-1000 SIC 1711 1542 7699

DCK WORLDWIDE LLC p 418
6 Ppg Pl Ste 710, Pittsburgh PA 15222
Tel (412) 384-1000 SIC 1542

MASCARO CONSTRUCTION CO LP p 915
1720 Metropolitan St, Pittsburgh PA 15233
Tel (412) 321-4901 *SIC* 1542

▲ MATTHEWS INTERNATIONAL CORP p 920
2 N Shore Ctr Ste 200, Pittsburgh PA 15212
Tel (412) 442-8200
SIC 3366 1542 3569 3995 3953 2796

MOSITES CONSTRUCTION CO p 992
4839 Campbells Run Rd, Pittsburgh PA 15205
Tel (412) 923-2255 *SIC* 1542 1611

PJ DICK INC p 1153
225 N Shore Dr, Pittsburgh PA 15212
Tel (412) 462-9300 *SIC* 1542 8741

RYCON CONSTRUCTION INC p 1260
2501 Smallman St Ste 100, Pittsburgh PA 15222
Tel (412) 392-2525 *SIC* 1542

CHAPMAN CORP p 288
331 S Main St, Washington PA 15301
Tel (724) 228-1900 *SIC* 1541 1542

KINSLEY CONSTRUCTION INC p 821
2700 Water St, York PA 17403
Tel (717) 741-3841 *SIC* 1541 1542 1611

AIREKO CONSTRUCTION LLC p 40
Las Casas St Lot 20, Caguas PR 00725
Tel (787) 653-6300
SIC 1542 1541 1731 1711

■ FLUOR DANIEL CARIBBEAN INC p 561
Metro Office Park St2 1 # 2, Guaynabo PR 00968
Tel (787) 783-5500 *SIC* 1542 1541

DIMEO CONSTRUCTION CO p 440
75 Chapman St, Providence RI 02905
Tel (401) 781-9800 *SIC* 1542 1522 7353

GILBANE BUILDING CO p 611
7 Jackson Walkway Ste 2, Providence RI 02903
Tel (401) 456-5800 *SIC* 1542

GILBANE INC p 611
7 Jackson Walkway, Providence RI 02903
Tel (401) 456-5800
SIC 1541 1542 8741 6513 6512

PICERNE INVESTMENT CORP p 1146
75 Lambert Lind Hwy # 300, Warwick RI 02886
Tel (401) 732-3700
SIC 6552 6531 1521 1522 1542

BEACH CO p 164
211 King St Ste 300, Charleston SC 29401
Tel (843) 722-2615 *SIC* 6552 8741 1542

PIGGLY WIGGLY CAROLINA CO INC p 1147
176 Croghan Spur Ste 400, Charleston SC 29407
Tel (843) 554-9880
SIC 7311 5411 5148 5141 2752 1542

BONITZ CONTRACTING CO INC p 200
645 Rosewood Dr, Columbia SC 29201
Tel (803) 799-0181
SIC 1742 1752 1761 1542 1541

BONITZ INC p 200
645 Rosewood Dr, Columbia SC 29201
Tel (803) 799-0181
SIC 3448 1542 1742 1541 1761 1752

M B KAHN CONSTRUCTION CO INC p 889
101 Flintlake Rd, Columbia SC 29223
Tel (803) 736-2950 *SIC* 1542 8742

MASHBURN CONSTRUCTION CO INC p 915
1820 Sumter St, Columbia SC 29201
Tel (803) 400-1000 *SIC* 1542

■ BE&K BUILDING GROUP LLC p 164
201 E Mcbee Ave Ste 400, Greenville SC 29601
Tel (864) 250-5000 *SIC* 1542 1541 1522

■ FLUOR INTERCONTINENTAL INC p 561
100 Fluor Daniel Dr, Greenville SC 29607
Tel (864) 281-4400 *SIC* 1541 1542

LANDMARK CONSTRUCTION CO INC p 842
3255 Industry Dr, North Charleston SC 29418
Tel (843) 552-6186
SIC 1542 1541 1623 1771 1794

BID GROUP CONSTRUCTION US INC p 181
5154 Highway 78, Saint George SC 29477
Tel (843) 563-7070 *SIC* 1542

FITTS AND GOODWIN INC p 553
120 Corporate Blvd, West Columbia SC 29169
Tel (803) 796-4660 *SIC* 1541 1542

HEAVY CONSTRUCTORS INC p 679
4101 Deadwood Ave, Rapid City SD 57702
Tel (605) 342-3144
SIC 1542 1794 1623 1611

SCULL CONSTRUCTION SERVICE INC p 1295
803 Industrial Ave, Rapid City SD 57702
Tel (605) 342-2379 *SIC* 1542

BELL & ASSOCIATES CONSTRUCTION LP p 169
255 Wilson Pike Cir, Brentwood TN 37027
Tel (615) 373-4343 *SIC* 1622 1541 1542

EMJ CORP p 493
2034 Hamilton Place Blvd # 400, Chattanooga TN 37421
Tel (423) 855-1550 *SIC* 1542

HUDSON CONSTRUCTION CO p 716
1615 Sholar Ave, Chattanooga TN 37406
Tel (423) 624-2631 *SIC* 1542

SIGNAL ENERGY LLC p 1322
2034 Hamilton Place Blvd # 400, Chattanooga TN 37421
Tel (423) 443-4190 *SIC* 1542 8731

CONSTRUCTION ENTERPRISES INC p 361
2179 Edward Curd Ln # 100, Franklin TN 37067
Tel (615) 332-8880 *SIC* 1522 1542

H AND M CONSTRUCTION CO INC p 649
50 Security Dr, Jackson TN 38305
Tel (731) 660-3091 *SIC* 1541 1542

POWELL CONSTRUCTION CO INC p 1165
3622 Bristol Hwy Ste 1, Johnson City TN 37601
Tel (423) 282-0111 *SIC* 1542 1221 1541

BLAINE CONSTRUCTION CORP p 188
6510 Deane Hill Dr, Knoxville TN 37919
Tel (865) 693-8900 *SIC* 1541 1542

JOHNSON & GALYON INC p 790
1130 Atlantic Ave, Knoxville TN 37917
Tel (865) 688-1111 *SIC* 1542 1541

MARTIN MONTGOMERY CONTRACTORS LLC p 913
8245 Tournament Dr # 300, Memphis TN 38125
Tel (901) 374-9400 *SIC* 1542 1541 8741

RAINBOW INTERNATIONAL OF MIDDLE TENNESEE p 1205
667 Patterson Ave Ste C, Murfreesboro TN 37129
Tel (615) 898-8258 *SIC* 1542 1521

HARDAWAY CONSTRUCTION CORP p 660
615 Main St, Nashville TN 37206
Tel (615) 254-5461 *SIC* 1542 1541 1522

HARDAWAY GROUP INC p 660
615 Main St, Nashville TN 37206
Tel (615) 254-5461
SIC 1542 1541 1522 6531

MAIN STREET OPERATING CO INC p 898
615 Main St, Nashville TN 37206
Tel (615) 254-5461
SIC 1542 1541 1521 6531

TWFRIERSON CONTRACTOR INC p 1494
2971 Kraft Dr, Nashville TN 37204
Tel (615) 367-2434 *SIC* 1541 1542

CADENCE MCSHANE CONSTRUCTION CO LLC p 236
5057 Keller Springs Rd, Addison TX 75001
Tel (972) 239-2336 *SIC* 1541 1542

RATCLIFF CONSTRUCTORS LP p 1209
4200 Beltway Dr, Addison TX 75001
Tel (972) 432-9969 *SIC* 1542

WESTERN BUILDERS OF AMARILLO INC p 1597
700 S Grant St, Amarillo TX 79101
Tel (806) 376-4321 *SIC* 1542

FGI GROUP INC p 539
3901 S Lamar Blvd Ste 100, Austin TX 78704
Tel (512) 448-9898
SIC 1542 1541 1794 1611 7353 1711

JOURNEYMAN CONSTRUCTION INC p 794
7701 N Lamar Blvd Ste 100, Austin TX 78752
Tel (512) 247-7000 *SIC* 1542

ALLCO LLC p 52
6720 College St, Beaumont TX 77707
Tel (409) 860-4459 *SIC* 1623 1542 1541

EBCO GENERAL CONTRACTOR LTD p 474
305 W Gillis Ave, Cameron TX 76520
Tel (254) 697-8516 *SIC* 1542 8741

AMERICAN CONSTRUCTORS INC p 70
11900 W Parmer Ln Ste 200, Cedar Park TX 78613
Tel (512) 328-2026 *SIC* 1541 1542

INFINITY CONSTRUCTION SERVICES LP p 741
926 Brazosport Blvd S, Clute TX 77531
Tel (979) 388-8579 *SIC* 1629 1542

DRYMALLA CONSTRUCTION CO INC p 457
608 Harbert St, Columbus TX 78934
Tel (281) 342-3853 *SIC* 1542

POWERHOUSE RETAIL SERVICES LLC p 1166
812 S Crowley Rd Ste A, Crowley TX 76036
Tel (817) 297-8575 *SIC* 1542 1799

AUSTIN COMMERCIAL INC p 132
3535 Travis St Ste 300, Dallas TX 75204
Tel (214) 443-5700 *SIC* 1542

AUSTIN COMMERCIAL LP p 132
3535 Travis St Ste 300, Dallas TX 75204
Tel (214) 443-5700 *SIC* 1542

AUSTIN INDUSTRIES INC p 133
3535 Travis St Ste 300, Dallas TX 75204
Tel (214) 443-5500
SIC 1542 1629 1611 1622

BALFOUR BEATTY CONSTRUCTION GROUP INC p 147
3100 Mckinnon St Fl 10, Dallas TX 75201
Tel (214) 451-1000 *SIC* 1542 1541

BALFOUR BEATTY CONSTRUCTION LLC p 147
3100 Mckinnon St Fl 10, Dallas TX 75201
Tel (214) 451-1000 *SIC* 1542 1541

BAYLOR HEALTH CARE SYSTEM p 162
3500 Gaston Ave, Dallas TX 75246
Tel (214) 820-0111 *SIC* 8062 8082 1542

BECK INTERNATIONAL LLC p 167
1807 Ross Ave Ste 500, Dallas TX 75201
Tel (214) 303-6200 *SIC* 1542 8712

■ CENTEX CORP p 277
2728 N Harwood St Ste 200, Dallas TX 75201
Tel (214) 981-5000
SIC 1531 2451 6162 1542 1541 1522

DAVACO INC p 414
6688 N Cntrl Expy Ste 100, Dallas TX 75206
Tel (214) 373-4700
SIC 1751 1799 1542 1796

SCHWOB BUILDING CO LTD p 1291
2349 Glenda Ln, Dallas TX 75229
Tel (972) 243-7674 *SIC* 1542

HUNT BUILDING CO LTD p 718
4401 N Mesa St Ste 201, El Paso TX 79902
Tel (915) 533-1122
SIC 1522 6531 1542 7389

HUNT COMPANIES INC p 718
4401 N Mesa St, El Paso TX 79902
Tel (915) 533-1122 *SIC* 1522 6531 1542

JORDAN CF CONSTRUCTION LLC p 793
7700 Cf Jordan Dr Ste 200, El Paso TX 79912
Tel (915) 877-3333 *SIC* 1542 1541 1522

JORDAN CF INVESTMENTS LLP p 793
7700 Cf Jordan Dr, El Paso TX 79912
Tel (915) 877-3333
SIC 1542 1541 1522 1611

JORDAN FOSTER CONSTRUCTION LLC p 793
7700 Cf Jordan Dr Ste 200, El Paso TX 79912
Tel (915) 877-3333 *SIC* 1542

AUI CONTRACTORS LLC p 131
4775 North Fwy, Fort Worth TX 76106
Tel (817) 926-4377 *SIC* 1542 1623 1771

INTERSTATE RESTORATION LLC p 758
3401 Quorum Dr Ste 300, Fort Worth TX 76137
Tel (817) 293-0035 *SIC* 1542 1522 7349

UTECH INC p 1536
303 Arthur St, Fort Worth TX 76107
Tel (817) 332-2770 *SIC* 1542

EMBREE CONSTRUCTION GROUP INC p 490
4747 Williams Dr, Georgetown TX 78633
Tel (512) 819-4700 *SIC* 1542

BALLENGER CONSTRUCTION CO p 148
24200 N Fm 509, Harlingen TX 78550
Tel (956) 421-9500 *SIC* 1542

AQUINAS CORP p 102
3900 Essex Ln Ste 1200, Houston TX 77027
Tel (713) 621-2350 *SIC* 1542

BURROW GLOBAL LLC p 228
6200 Savoy Dr Ste 800, Houston TX 77036
Tel (713) 963-0930 *SIC* 1542 6799

BURROW GLOBAL SERVICES LLC p 228
6200 Savoy Dr Ste 800, Houston TX 77036
Tel (713) 963-0930 *SIC* 1542 1541 8711

DAVID E HARVEY BUILDERS INC p 415
3630 Westchase Dr, Houston TX 77042
Tel (713) 783-8710 *SIC* 1542

GAMMA CONSTRUCTION CO INC p 590
2808 Joanel St, Houston TX 77027
Tel (713) 963-0086 *SIC* 1542

HEALTH CARE TEMPORARIES INC p 674
8926 Sherbourne St Ste D, Houston TX 77016
Tel (713) 631-7106
SIC 8082 1542 1522 1081 5082

HUNTER BUILDINGS LLC p 719
14935 Jacintoport Blvd, Houston TX 77015
Tel (281) 452-9800 *SIC* 1542

J T VAUGHN ENTERPRISES INC p 772
10355 Westpark Dr, Houston TX 77042
Tel (713) 243-8300 *SIC* 1542

LINBECK GROUP LLC p 866
3900 Essex Ln Ste 1200, Houston TX 77027
Tel (713) 621-2350 *SIC* 1542

MUSTANG ENGINEERS AND CONSTRUCTORS LP p 1002
16001 Park Ten Pl, Houston TX 77084
Tel (713) 215-8000 *SIC* 1542 1541

▲ NCI BUILDING SYSTEMS INC p 1022
10943 N Sam Huston Pkwy W, Houston TX 77064
Tel (281) 897-7788
SIC 3448 3444 3442 1542 1541 7389

ODONNELL/SNIDER CONSTRUCTION LLC p 1074
1900 West Loop S Ste 350, Houston TX 77027
Tel (713) 782-7660 *SIC* 1542

SATTERFIELD AND PONTIKES CONSTRUCTION INC p 1283
11000 Equity Dr Ste 100, Houston TX 77041
Tel (713) 996-1393 *SIC* 1542 1541

SPAW GLASS CONSTRUCTION CORP p 1355
13800 West Rd, Houston TX 77041
Tel (281) 970-5300 *SIC* 1542 1522 1541

TELLEPSEN BUILDERS LP p 1435
777 Benmar Dr Ste 400, Houston TX 77060
Tel (281) 447-8100 *SIC* 1542

TETON BUILDINGS LLC p 1441
2701 Magnet St, Houston TX 77054
Tel (713) 351-6300 *SIC* 1542

W S BELLOWS CONSTRUCTION CORP p 1569
1906 Afton St, Houston TX 77055
Tel (713) 680-2132 *SIC* 1542

▲ WILLBROS GROUP INC p 1610
4400 Post Oak Pkwy, Houston TX 77027
Tel (713) 403-8000 *SIC* 8711 1542

WOOD GROUP PSN INC p 1622
17325 Park Row, Houston TX 77084
Tel (281) 647-1041 *SIC* 1629 1542 8711

VCC LLC p 1545
600 Las Colinas Blvd E # 1525, Irving TX 75039
Tel (214) 574-4500 *SIC* 1542 8711 8742

PEPPER-LAWSON CONSTRUCTION LP p 1133
4555 Katy Hockley Rd, Katy TX 77493
Tel (281) 371-3100 *SIC* 1542

PARKWAY C&A LP p 1117
1000 Civic Cir, Lewisville TX 75067
Tel (972) 221-1979 *SIC* 1542

PARKWAY CONSTRUCTION & ARCHITECTURE LP p 1117
1000 Civic Cir, Lewisville TX 75067
Tel (972) 221-1979 *SIC* 1542

PARKWAY CONSTRUCTION & ASSOCIATES LP p 1117
1000 Civic Cir, Lewisville TX 75067
Tel (972) 221-1979 *SIC* 1542

LEE LEWIS CONSTRUCTION INC p 851
7810 Orlando Ave, Lubbock TX 79423
Tel (806) 797-8400 *SIC* 1542 1541

MYCON GENERAL CONTRACTORS INC p 1004
208 E La St Ste 200, Mc Kinney TX 75069
Tel (972) 529-2444 *SIC* 1542

POGUE CONSTRUCTION CO LP p 1159
1512 Bray Central Dr # 300, Mckinney TX 75069
Tel (972) 529-9401 *SIC* 1542

DUPHIL INC p 462
6608 Interstate 10 W, Orange TX 77632
Tel (409) 883-8550 *SIC* 1542

HILL & WILKINSON CONSTRUCTION GROUP LTD p 693
2703 Telecom Pkwy Ste 120, Richardson TX 75082
Tel (214) 299-4300 *SIC* 1541 1542

CHASCO CONSTRUCTORS LTD LLP p 291
2801 E Old Settlers Blvd, Round Rock TX 78665
Tel (512) 244-0600
SIC 1542 1771 1794 1623

ALPHA BUILDING CORP p 60
24870 Blanco Rd, San Antonio TX 78260
Tel (210) 491-9925 *SIC* 1542

BARTLETT COCKE GENERAL CONTRACTORS LLC p 157
8706 Lockway St, San Antonio TX 78217
Tel (210) 655-1031 *SIC* 1542

CCC GROUP INC p 269
5797 Dietrich Rd, San Antonio TX 78219
Tel (210) 661-4251 *SIC* 1541 1629 1542

GUTHRIE & HUEBNER CO INC p 648
5797 Dietrich Rd, San Antonio TX 78219
Tel (210) 661-4251 *SIC* 1541 1629 1542

JOERIS GENERAL CONTRACTORS LTD p 787
823 Arion Pkwy, San Antonio TX 78216
Tel (210) 286-8696 *SIC* 1542

KOONTZ CONSTRUCTION INC p 827
755 E Mulberry Ave # 100, San Antonio TX 78212
Tel (210) 826-2600 *SIC* 1542 1522

ZACHRY CONSTRUCTION & MATERIALS INC p 1640
2330 N Loop 1604 W, San Antonio TX 78248
Tel (210) 479-1027
SIC 1611 1622 1623 1629 1542 3241

ZACHRY CONSTRUCTION CORP p 1640
2330 N Loop 1604 W, San Antonio TX 78248
Tel (210) 871-2700
SIC 1623 1611 1622 1629 1542

ZACHRY INTERNATIONAL INC p 1640
2330 N Loop 1604 W, San Antonio TX 78248
Tel (210) 871-2700 *SIC* 1541 1542

SPAW GLASS HOLDING LP p 1355
9331 Corporate Dr, Selma TX 78154
Tel (210) 651-9000 *SIC* 1542 1522 1541

ICI CONSTRUCTION INC p 727
24715 W Hardy Rd, Spring TX 77373
Tel (281) 355-5151 *SIC* 1542

E E REED CONSTRUCTION LP p 466
333 Commerce Green Blvd, Sugar Land TX 77478
Tel (281) 933-4000 *SIC* 1542

MW BUILDERS INC p 1003
1701 N General Bruce Dr, Temple TX 76504
Tel (254) 778-4241 *SIC* 1542

PENTALON CONSTRUCTION INC p 1132
132 E 13065 S Ste 175, Draper UT 84020
Tel (801) 619-1900 *SIC* 1522 1542

PHAZE CONCRETE INC p 1141
1280 W Utah Ave, Hildale UT 84784
Tel (435) 656-9500 *SIC* 1542

KIER CONSTRUCTION CORP p 817
3710 Quincy Ave, Ogden UT 84403
Tel (801) 627-1414 *SIC* 1522 1542 1541

R & O CONSTRUCTION CO INC p 1201
933 Wall Ave Ste 2, Ogden UT 84404
Tel (801) 627-1403 *SIC* 1542 1521

WADMAN CORP p 1571
2920 S 925 W, Ogden UT 84401
Tel (801) 621-4185 *SIC* 1542 1541

WESTLAND CONSTRUCTION INC p 1601
1411 W 1250 S Ste 200, Orem UT 84058
Tel (801) 374-6085 *SIC* 1542 1541

BIG-D CONSTRUCTION CORP p 182
404 W 400 S, Salt Lake City UT 84101
Tel (801) 415-6000 *SIC* 1541 1542

BODELL CONSTRUCTION CO INC p 197
586 W Fine Dr, Salt Lake City UT 84115
Tel (801) 261-4343 *SIC* 1542 1541

JACOBSEN CONSTRUCTION CO INC p 775
3131 W 2210 S, Salt Lake City UT 84119
Tel (801) 973-0500 *SIC* 1542 1541

OKLAND CONSTRUCTION CO INC p 1080
1978 S West Temple, Salt Lake City UT 84115
Tel (801) 486-0144 *SIC* 1542 1541

LAYTON COMPANIES INC p 848
9090 S Sandy Pkwy, Sandy UT 84070
Tel (801) 568-9090 *SIC* 1542 1541

PC CONSTRUCTION CO p 1123
193 Tilley Dr, South Burlington VT 05403
Tel (802) 658-4100 *SIC* 1629 1542

RAND CONSTRUCTION CORP p 1207
1029 N Royal St Ste 100, Alexandria VA 22314
Tel (202) 449-9840 *SIC* 1542

CLARK REALTY CAPITAL LLC p 322
4401 Wilson Blvd Ste 600, Arlington VA 22203
Tel (703) 294-4500 *SIC* 1522 1531 1542

L C VIRGINIA p 834
4600 Fairfax Dr Ste 1004, Arlington VA 22203
Tel (703) 524-5454 *SIC* 1541 1542 1522

FAULCONER CONSTRUCTION CO INC p 531
2496 Old Ivy Rd, Charlottesville VA 22903
Tel (434) 295-0033
SIC 1629 1611 1542 1623

MEB GENERAL CONTRACTORS INC p 934
4016 Holland Blvd, Chesapeake VA 23323
Tel (757) 487-5858 *SIC* 1542 1629 1541

HITT CONTRACTING INC p 697
2900 Fairview Park Dr # 300, Falls Church VA 22042
Tel (703) 846-9000 *SIC* 1542

JENNINGS INC L F p 782
407 N Washington St # 200, Falls Church VA 22046
Tel (703) 241-1200 *SIC* 1542

ALLAN MYERS VA INC p 52
301 Cncourse Blvd Ste 300, Glen Allen VA 23059
Tel (804) 290-8500
SIC 1623 1611 1542 1794

THALHIMER INC MORTON G p 1446
11100 W Broad St, Glen Allen VA 23060
Tel (804) 648-5881
SIC 1542 6531 6799 6513 6512

ENGLISH CONSTRUCTION CO INC p 499
615 Church St Ste 2, Lynchburg VA 24504
Tel (434) 845-0301
SIC 1611 1629 1623 1542

CII / OCI JOINT VENTURE p 307
6862 Elm St Ste 500, Mc Lean VA 22101
Tel (703) 358-8800 *SIC* 1542

ORASCOM E&C USA INC p 1092
6862 Elm St Ste 400, Mc Lean VA 22101
Tel (703) 358-8800 *SIC* 1521 1522 1542

WATTS CONSTRUCTORS LLC p 1583
6862 Elm St Ste 500, Mc Lean VA 22101
Tel (703) 358-8800 *SIC* 1542 1623

WMJORDAN CO INC p 1620
11010 Jefferson Ave, Newport News VA 23601
Tel (757) 596-6341 *SIC* 1542 1541

CENTENNIAL CONTRACTORS ENTERPRISES INC p 275
11111 Sunset Hills Rd # 350, Reston VA 20190
Tel (703) 885-4600 *SIC* 1542 1541

KBS INC p 806
8050 Kimway Dr, Richmond VA 23228
Tel (804) 262-0100 *SIC* 1542

KJELLSTROM AND LEE INC p 822
1607 Ownby Ln, Richmond VA 23220
Tel (804) 288-0082 *SIC* 1541 1542

BRANCH & ASSOCIATES INC p 207
5732 Airport Rd Nw, Roanoke VA 24012
Tel (540) 989-5215 *SIC* 1542

BRANCH GROUP INC p 207
442 Rutherford Ave Ne, Roanoke VA 24016
Tel (540) 982-1678
SIC 1542 1611 1711 1731 1541

CUBE CORP p 399
529 Viking Dr, Virginia Beach VA 23452
Tel (770) 952-1479 *SIC* 1542

S B BALLARD CONSTRUCTION CO p 1261
2828 Shipps Corner Rd, Virginia Beach VA 23453
Tel (757) 440-5555 *SIC* 1542 1771

TTEC-TESORO JOINT VENTURE p 1489
5250 Challedon Dr, Virginia Beach VA 23462
Tel (770) 825-7100 *SIC* 1542

GLY CONSTRUCTION INC p 618
200 112th Ave Ne Ste 300, Bellevue WA 98004
Tel (425) 451-8877 *SIC* 1542

HASKELL CORP p 667
1001 Meador Ave, Bellingham WA 98229
Tel (360) 734-1200 *SIC* 1542

IMCO GENERAL CONSTRUCTION INC p 733
2116 Buchanan Loop, Ferndale WA 98248
Tel (360) 671-3936 *SIC* 1541 1629 1542

APOLLO INC p 97
1133 W Columbia Dr, Kennewick WA 99336
Tel (509) 586-1104 *SIC* 1542

KELLY JH HOLDING LLC p 809
821 3rd Ave, Longview WA 98632
Tel (360) 423-5510 *SIC* 1711 1542 1731

BAYLEY CONSTRUCTION A GENERAL PARTNERSHIP p 161
8005 Se 28th St Ste 100, Mercer Island WA 98040
Tel (206) 621-8884 *SIC* 1542 1541

ABSHER CONSTRUCTION CO p 13
1001 Shaw Rd, Puyallup WA 98372
Tel (253) 845-9544 *SIC* 1542

BNBUILDERS INC p 194
2601 4th Ave Ste 350, Seattle WA 98121
Tel (206) 382-3443 *SIC* 1542

CHARTER CONSTRUCTION INC p 291
980 S Harney St, Seattle WA 98108
Tel (206) 382-1900 *SIC* 1542

FIRST & GOAL INC p 544
800 Occidental Ave S, Seattle WA 98134
Tel (206) 381-7940 *SIC* 1542 7941

JR ABBOTT CONSTRUCTION INC p 795
3408 1st Ave S Ste 101, Seattle WA 98134
Tel (206) 467-8500 *SIC* 1542

LEWIS LEASE CRUTCHER WA LLC p 858
2200 Western Ave, Seattle WA 98121
Tel (206) 264-1985 *SIC* 1542 1521

OPUS NORTHWEST LLC p 1091
2025 1st Ave Ph B, Seattle WA 98121
Tel (425) 467-2701 *SIC* 6552 1542

SELLEN CONSTRUCTION CO INC p 1302
227 Westlake Ave N, Seattle WA 98109
Tel (206) 682-7770 *SIC* 1542 8741

W LEASE LEWIS CO p 1568
2200 Western Ave, Seattle WA 98121
Tel (206) 622-0500 *SIC* 1542

LYDIG CONSTRUCTION INC p 887
11001 E Montgomery Dr, Spokane Valley WA 99206
Tel (509) 534-0451 *SIC* 1542 1541

BOLDT CO p 198
2525 N Roemer Rd, Appleton WI 54911
Tel (920) 739-6321 *SIC* 1542

BOLDT GROUP INC p 198
2525 N Roemer Rd, Appleton WI 54911
Tel (920) 739-7800 *SIC* 1542

MARKET & JOHNSON INC p 908
2350 Galloway St, Eau Claire WI 54703
Tel (715) 834-1213 *SIC* 1542 1541

TRI-NORTH BUILDERS INC p 1477
2625 Research Park Dr, Fitchburg WI 53711
Tel (608) 271-8717 *SIC* 1541 1542 1521

CD SMITH CONSTRUCTION INC p 270
889 E Johnson St, Fond Du Lac WI 54935
Tel (920) 924-2900 *SIC* 1542 1541

AWS/GB CORP p 139
2929 Walker Dr, Green Bay WI 54311
Tel (920) 406-4000
SIC 5031 2431 3442 5033 1542 1541

H J MARTIN & SON INC p 650
320 S Military Ave, Green Bay WI 54303
Tel (920) 494-3461
SIC 5713 1793 1522 1542 1742

VHC INC p 1553
3090 Holmgren Way, Green Bay WI 54304
Tel (920) 336-7278
SIC 1731 1542 1541 1521 1711 6512

J P CULLEN & SONS INC p 772
330 E Delavan Dr, Janesville WI 53546
Tel (608) 754-6601 *SIC* 1541 1542

KELLER INC p 808
N216 State Highway 55, Kaukauna WI 54130
Tel (920) 766-5795 *SIC* 1542 1541 7336

RILEY CONSTRUCTION CO INC p 1235
5301 99th Ave, Kenosha WI 53144
Tel (262) 658-4381 *SIC* 1542 1541

ERDMAN CO p 507
1 Erdman Pl, Madison WI 53717
Tel (608) 410-8000 *SIC* 1542

HORIZON CONSTRUCTION GROUP INC p 707
5201 E Terrace Dr Ste 300, Madison WI 53718
Tel (608) 354-0900 *SIC* 1542 1522

J H FINDORFF & SON INC p 771
300 S Bedford St, Madison WI 53703
Tel (608) 257-5321
SIC 1542 1541 8741 1522

STEVENS CONSTRUCTION CORP p 1388
2 Buttonwood Ct, Madison WI 53718
Tel (608) 222-5100 *SIC* 1522 1542

VOGEL BROS BUILDING CO p 1564
2701 Packers Ave, Madison WI 53704
Tel (608) 241-5454 *SIC* 1542 1541 4941

ERDMAN HOLDINGS INC p 507
6720 Frank Llyd Wright Av, Middleton WI 53562
Tel (608) 662-2205 *SIC* 1542 2599

C G SCHMIDT INC p 232
11777 W Lake Park Dr, Milwaukee WI 53224
Tel (414) 577-1177 *SIC* 1542 8741

GILBANE BUILDING CO / CG SCHMIDT A JOINT VENTURE p 611
11777 W Lake Park Dr, Milwaukee WI 53224
Tel (414) 577-1177 *SIC* 1542

MIRON CONSTRUCTION CO INC p 974
1471 Mcmahon Rd, Neenah WI 54956
Tel (920) 969-7000 *SIC* 1542 1541 1796

■ INFRASOURCE LLC p 742
2936 S 166th St, New Berlin WI 53151
Tel (713) 629-7600 *SIC* 1623 1542

C R MEYER AND SONS CO p 233
895 W 20th Ave, Oshkosh WI 54902
Tel (920) 235-3350 *SIC* 1542 1796 1541

HORIZON RETAIL CONSTRUCTION p 707
1500 Horizon Dr, Sturtevant WI 53177
Tel (262) 638-6000 *SIC* 1542

LAKEHEAD CONSTRUCTORS INC p 839
2916 Hill Ave, Superior WI 54880
Tel (715) 392-5181 *SIC* 1541 1542

LAKEHEAD HOLDING CORP p 839
2916 Hill Ave, Superior WI 54880
Tel (715) 392-5181 *SIC* 1541 1542

BUILDING SERVICE p 225
W222n630 Cheaney Rd, Waukesha WI 53186
Tel (414) 358-5080 *SIC* 5021 1542 5023

SIC 1611 Highway & Street Construction

DUNN CONSTRUCTION CO INC p 461
3905 Airport Hwy, Birmingham AL 35222
Tel (205) 592-3866 *SIC* 1611 2951

DUNN INVESTMENT CO p 461
3900 Messer Airport Hwy, Birmingham AL 35222
Tel (205) 592-3866 *SIC* 1542 1611 3273

PREFERRED MATERIALS INC p 1169
500 Rvrhills Bus Park, Birmingham AL 35242
Tel (205) 995-5900
SIC 1611 1771 3531 5032

WIREGRASS CONSTRUCTION CO INC p 1618
170 E Main St, Dothan AL 36301
Tel (334) 699-6800 *SIC* 1611 2951

REED CONTRACTING SERVICES INC p 1217
2512 Triana Blvd Sw, Huntsville AL 35805
Tel (256) 533-0505
SIC 1771 1794 1623 1629 1611

RACON INC p 1203
700 Energy Center Blvd # 404, Northport AL 35473
Tel (205) 333-8500 *SIC* 1611 1522

ACHEN-GARDNER INC p 17
550 S 79th St, Chandler AZ 85226
Tel (480) 940-1300
SIC 1611 1542 1521 1751 6552

HUNTER CONTRACTING CO p 719
701 N Cooper Rd, Gilbert AZ 85233
Tel (480) 892-0521 *SIC* 1611 1629 1622

ACE ASPHALT OF ARIZONA INC p 16
3030 S 7th St, Phoenix AZ 85040
Tel (602) 243-4100 *SIC* 1611

ARIZONA PARKING LOT SERVICE p 109
1415 E Bethany Home Rd, Phoenix AZ 85014
Tel (602) 277-8007 *SIC* 1799 1611

KIEWIT WESTERN CO p 817
3888 E Broadway Rd, Phoenix AZ 85040
Tel (602) 437-7878
SIC 1622 1629 1794 1611 1623

MEADOW VALLEY CORP p 934
3333 E Camelback Rd # 240, Phoenix AZ 85018
Tel (602) 437-5400 *SIC* 1611 5032

MEADOW VALLEY HOLDINGS LLC p 934
4602 E Thomas Rd, Phoenix AZ 85018
Tel (602) 437-5400 *SIC* 1611 5032

PULICE CONSTRUCTION INC p 1191
2033 W Mountain View Rd, Phoenix AZ 85021
Tel (602) 944-2241 *SIC* 1611 8711

FNF CONSTRUCTION INC p 562
115 S 48th St, Tempe AZ 85281
Tel (480) 784-2910 *SIC* 1611 1794 2951

INFRASTRUCTURE HOLDINGS CO LLC p 742
115 S 48th St, Tempe AZ 85281
Tel (480) 784-2910 *SIC* 1611 1794 2591

SUNDT CONSTRUCTION INC p 1402
2620 S 55th St, Tempe AZ 85282
Tel (480) 293-3000
SIC 1542 1611 1629 1541 8741

SUNDT COMPANIES INC p 1402
2015 W River Rd Ste 101, Tucson AZ 85704
Tel (520) 750-4600 *SIC* 1542 1771 1611

APAC-CENTRAL INC p 95
755 E Millsap Rd, Fayetteville AR 72703
Tel (417) 226-4833 *SIC* 3272 1611

MCGEORGE CONTRACTING CO INC p 929
1501 Heartwood St, White Hall AR 71602
Tel (870) 534-7120 *SIC* 1611 1423

O C JONES & SONS INC p 1070
1520 4th St, Berkeley CA 94710
Tel (510) 526-3424 *SIC* 1611

GRIFFITH CO p 640
3050 E Birch St, Brea CA 92821
Tel (714) 984-5500 *SIC* 1611

SULLY-MILLER CONTRACTING CO INC p 1397
135 Sstate College Ste 400, Brea CA 92821
Tel (714) 578-9600 *SIC* 1611

R & L BROSAMER INC p 1201
1390 Willow Pass Rd # 950, Concord CA 94520
Tel (925) 627-1700 *SIC* 1611

ALL AMERICAN ASPHALT p 51
400 E 6th St, Corona CA 92879
Tel (951) 736-7600 *SIC* 1611 5032

DESILVA GATES CONSTRUCTION LP p 432
11555 Dublin Blvd, Dublin CA 94568
Tel (925) 361-1380 *SIC* 1611 1794 1542

CASS CONSTRUCTION INC p 263
1100 Wagner Dr, El Cajon CA 92020
Tel (619) 590-0929 *SIC* 1623 1611

SUPERIOR READY MIX CONCRETE LP p 1407
1508 Mission Rd, Escondido CA 92029
Tel (760) 745-0556 *SIC* 3273 1611 5032

CHRISP CO p 302
43650 Osgood Rd, Fremont CA 94539
Tel (510) 656-2840 *SIC* 1611

DRYCO CONSTRUCTION INC p 457
42745 Boscell Rd, Fremont CA 94538
Tel (510) 438-6500 *SIC* 1611 1721 5211

FOOTHILL / EASTERN TRANSPORTATION CORRIDOR AGENCY p 564
125 Pacifica Ste 100, Irvine CA 92618
Tel (949) 754-3400 *SIC* 1611

SAN JOAQUIN HILLS TRANSPORTATION CORRIDOR AGENCY p 1277
125 Pacifica Ste 100, Irvine CA 92618
Tel (949) 754-3400 *SIC* 1611

PAVEMENT RECYCLING SYSTEMS INC p 1122
10240 San Sevaine Way, Jurupa Valley CA 91752
Tel (951) 682-1091 *SIC* 5093 1611

RGW CONSTRUCTION INC p 1231
550 Greenville Rd, Livermore CA 94550
Tel (925) 606-2400 *SIC* 1611

■ AECOM E&C HOLDINGS INC p 28
1999 Avenue Of Ste 2600, Los Angeles CA 90067
Tel (213) 593-8000
SIC 8711 1611 1629 1623 1541 1622

BASIC RESOURCES INC p 158
928 12th St Ste 700, Modesto CA 95354
Tel (209) 521-9771
SIC 1611 3273 2951 3532 3531

PARSONS CORP p 1118
100 W Walnut St, Pasadena CA 91124
Tel (626) 440-2000
SIC 1629 1611 8711 8741

SKANSKA USA CIVIL WEST CALIFORNIA DISTRICT INC p 1329
1995 Agua Mansa Rd, Riverside CA 92509
Tel (951) 684-5360
SIC 1611 1622 1629 8711 2951

STRONGHOLD ENGINEERING INC p 1394
2000 Market St, Riverside CA 92501
Tel (951) 684-9303 *SIC* 1611

A TEICHERT & SON INC p 6
3500 American River Dr, Sacramento CA 95864
Tel (916) 484-3011
SIC 5032 3273 1611 1442 1521

MYERS & SONS CONSTRUCTION LP p 1004
4600 Northgate Blvd # 100, Sacramento CA 95834
Tel (916) 283-9950 *SIC* 1611

TEICHERT INC p 1433
3500 American River Dr, Sacramento CA 95864
Tel (916) 484-3011
SIC 3273 5032 1611 1442 1521 5039

DON CHAPIN CO INC p 449
560 Crazy Horse Canyon Rd, Salinas CA 93907
Tel (831) 449-4273 *SIC* 1623 1611 1771

LEDCOR CMI INC p 851
6405 Mira Mesa Blvd # 100, San Diego CA 92121
Tel (602) 595-3017
SIC 1541 1611 1629 1623 1522 8999

SOLPAC CONSTRUCTION INC p 1338
2424 Congress St, San Diego CA 92110
Tel (619) 296-6247 *SIC* 8741 1542 1611

FLATIRON WEST INC p 555
1770 La Costa Meadows Dr, San Marcos CA 92078
Tel (760) 916-9100 *SIC* 1622 1611

GHILOTTI BROS INC p 610
525 Jacoby St, San Rafael CA 94901
Tel (415) 454-7011 *SIC* 1611 1794 1623

TUTOR PERINI CORP p 1493
15901 Olden St, Sylmar CA 91342
Tel (818) 362-8391 *SIC* 1542 1611 1622

▲ TUTOR PERINI CORP p 1493
15901 Olden St, Sylmar CA 91342
Tel (818) 362-8391
SIC 1542 8741 1611 1791 8711

C A RASMUSSEN INC p 232
28548 Livingston Ave, Valencia CA 91355
Tel (661) 367-9040 *SIC* 1629 1611

■ GRANITE CONSTRUCTION CO p 631
585 W Beach St, Watsonville CA 95076
Tel (831) 724-1011 *SIC* 1611 1622

▲ GRANITE CONSTRUCTION INC p 631
585 W Beach St, Watsonville CA 95076
Tel (831) 724-1011
SIC 1611 1622 1629 1442

GRANITE ROCK CO p 631
350 Technology Dr, Watsonville CA 95076
Tel (831) 768-2000
SIC 1442 3273 5032 2951 1611 3271

FLATIRON CONSTRUCTION CORP p 554
385 Interlocken Blvd, Broomfield CO 80021
Tel (303) 485-4050 *SIC* 1622 1629 1611

FLATIRON CONSTRUCTORS INC p 555
385 Interlocken, Broomfield CO 80021
Tel (303) 485-4050 *SIC* 1611 1622 1629

INTERSTATE HIGHWAY CONSTRUCTION INC p 758
7135 S Tucson Way, Centennial CO 80112
Tel (303) 790-7132 *SIC* 1611

ROCKY MOUNTAIN MATERIALS AND ASPHALT INC p 1245
1910 Rand Ave, Colorado Springs CO 80905
Tel (719) 473-3100
SIC 1611 1771 1794 5032

BRANNAN SAND AND GRAVEL CO LLC p 208
2500 Brannan Way, Denver CO 80229
Tel (303) 534-1231 *SIC* 1611 5032

PCL CIVIL CONSTRUCTORS INC p 1124
2000 S Colo Blvd Ste 2-50, Denver CO 80222
Tel (303) 365-6500
SIC 1611 1622 1623 1629

PCL US HOLDINGS INC p 1124
2000 S Colorado Blvd 2-500, Denver CO 80222
Tel (303) 365-6591 *SIC* 1542 1611

SUMMIT MATERIALS CORPS I INC p 1399
1550 Wynkoop St Fl 3, Denver CO 80202
Tel (303) 893-0012 *SIC* 1542 1611

SUMMIT MATERIALS HOLDINGS II LLC p 1399
1550 Wynkoop St Fl 3, Denver CO 80202
Tel (303) 893-0012 *SIC* 1542 1611

SUMMIT MATERIALS HOLDINGS LLC p 1399
1550 Wynkoop St Fl 3, Denver CO 80202
Tel (303) 893-0012 *SIC* 1542 1611

SUMMIT MATERIALS HOLDINGS LP p 1399
1550 Wynkoop St Fl 3, Denver CO 80202
Tel (303) 893-0012 *SIC* 1542 1611

SUMMIT MATERIALS INTERMEDIATE HOLDINGS LLC p 1399
1550 Wynkoop St Fl 3, Denver CO 80202
Tel (303) 893-0012 *SIC* 1542 1611

SUMMIT MATERIALS LLC p 1399
1550 Wynkoop St Fl 3, Denver CO 80202
Tel (303) 893-0012 *SIC* 1542 1611

GUY F ATKINSON CONSTRUCTION LLC p 648
350 Indiana St Ste 600, Golden CO 80401
Tel (303) 985-1660 *SIC* 1611

OLDCASTLE SW GROUP INC p 1082
2273 River Rd, Grand Junction CO 81505
Tel (970) 243-4900 *SIC* 1611 3273 5032

HENSEL PHELPS-GRANITE JV p 685
420 6th Ave, Greeley CO 80631
Tel (970) 352-6565
SIC 1541 1542 1629 1611

ASPHALT SPECIALTIES CO INC p 118
10100 Dallas St, Henderson CO 80640
Tel (303) 289-8555 *SIC* 1611

AGGREGATE INDUSTRIES-WCR INC p 35
1687 Cole Blvd Ste 300, Lakewood CO 80401
Tel (303) 716-5200
SIC 1611 1442 1499 2951

LAFARGE WEST INC p 837
10170 Church Ranch Way # 200, Westminster CO 80021
Tel (303) 657-4355 *SIC* 5032 1611 3273

LANE CONSTRUCTION CORP p 843
90 Fieldstone Ct, Cheshire CT 06410
Tel (203) 235-3351
SIC 1622 1611 1629 3272 5032

LANE INDUSTRIES INC p 843
90 Fieldstone Ct, Cheshire CT 06410
Tel (203) 235-3351
SIC 1629 1611 5032 3272 1622

TILCON CONNECTICUT INC p 1453
642 Black Rock Ave, New Britain CT 06052
Tel (860) 224-6010
SIC 5032 1611 3273 2951

TILCON INC p 1453
301 Hartford Ave, Newington CT 06111
Tel (860) 223-3651
SIC 1611 5032 3273 2951

O & G INDUSTRIES INC p 1070
112 Wall St, Torrington CT 06790
Tel (860) 489-9261
SIC 1542 1541 1611 1623 5032 2951

GEORGE & LYNCH INC p 606
150 Lafferty Ln, Dover DE 19901
Tel (302) 736-3031
SIC 1623 1611 1629 1731

WHITE CONSTRUCTION CO INC p 1606
2811 N Young Blvd, Chiefland FL 32626
Tel (352) 493-1444 *SIC* 1611 0241 3531

SUPERIOR CONSTRUCTION CO SOUTHEAST LLC p 1406
7072 Business Park Blvd N, Jacksonville FL 32256
Tel (904) 292-4240 *SIC* 1611

ANDERSON COLUMBIA CO INC p 89
871 Nw Guerdon St, Lake City FL 32055
Tel (386) 752-7585 *SIC* 1611 2951

COMMUNITY ASPHALT CORP p 347
9675 Nw 117th Ave Ste 108, Medley FL 33178
Tel (305) 884-9444 *SIC* 1611 2951

CONDOTTE AMERICA INC p 355
10790 Nw 127th St, Medley FL 33178
Tel (305) 670-7585 *SIC* 1611 1622 1542

DE MOYA GROUP INC p 419
14600 Sw 136th St, Miami FL 33186
Tel (305) 255-5713 *SIC* 1611 1622

DOWNRITE HOLDINGS INC p 453
14241 Sw 143rd Ct, Miami FL 33186
Tel (305) 232-2340
SIC 1611 1623 8711 1794

GLF CONSTRUCTION CORP p 615
528 Nw 7th Ave, Miami FL 33136
Tel (305) 371-5228
SIC 1611 1622 1542 1541 1522

■ POOLE & KENT CO OF FLORIDA p 1161
1781 Nw North River Dr, Miami FL 33125
Tel (305) 325-1930 *SIC* 1611

AJAX PAVING INDUSTRIES OF FLORIDA LLC p 41
1 Ajax Dr, North Venice FL 34275
Tel (941) 486-3600 *SIC* 1611 2951

GAC CONTRACTORS INC p 588
4116 N Highway 231, Panama City FL 32404
Tel (850) 785-4675 *SIC* 1611 1629

C W ROBERTS CONTRACTING INC p 233
3372 Capital Cir Ne, Tallahassee FL 32308
Tel (850) 385-5060 *SIC* 1611

PRINCE CONTRACTING LLC p 1176
10210 Highland Manor Dr # 110, Tampa FL 33610
Tel (813) 699-5900 *SIC* 1611

RANGER CONSTRUCTION INDUSTRIES INC p 1208
101 Sansburys Way, West Palm Beach FL 33411
Tel (561) 793-9400 *SIC* 1611

VECELLIO GROUP INC p 1546
101 Sansburys Way, West Palm Beach FL 33411
Tel (561) 793-2102 *SIC* 1611

GECOS INC p 597
1938 Lee Rd, Winter Park FL 32789
Tel (407) 645-5500 *SIC* 1611 2951 1623

HUBBARD CONSTRUCTION CO p 716
1936 Lee Rd Ste 101, Winter Park FL 32789
Tel (407) 645-5500 *SIC* 1611 2951 1623

HUBBARD GROUP INC p 716
1936 Lee Rd Ste 101, Winter Park FL 32789
Tel (407) 645-5500 *SIC* 1611 2951 1623

OXFORD CONSTRUCTION CO p 1101
3200 Palmyra Rd, Albany GA 31707
Tel (229) 883-3232 *SIC* 1611 1629

APAC HOLDINGS INC p 95
900 Ashwood Pkwy Ste 700, Atlanta GA 30338
Tel (770) 392-5300 *SIC* 1611 3531 5032

APAC-SOUTHEAST INC p 95
900 Ashwood Pkwy Ste 700, Atlanta GA 30338
Tel (770) 392-5300 *SIC* 1611 1622 2951

ARCHER WESTERN CONTRACTORS LLC p 105
2410 Paces Ferry Rd Se # 600, Atlanta GA 30339
Tel (404) 495-8700
SIC 1542 1622 1611 1629

BALFOUR BEATTY INFRASTRUCTURE INC p 148
999 Peachtree St Ne # 900, Atlanta GA 30309
Tel (404) 875-0356 *SIC* 1611

OLDCASTLE MATERIALS INC p 1082
900 Ashwood Pkwy Ste 700, Atlanta GA 30338
Tel (770) 522-5600
SIC 3272 1622 1611 2951 5032

REEVES CONSTRUCTION CO p 1217
101 Sheraton Ct, Macon GA 31210
Tel (478) 474-9092 *SIC* 1611

BALDWIN PAVING CO INC p 147
1014 Kenmill Dr Nw, Marietta GA 30060
Tel (770) 425-9191 *SIC* 1611 2951

E R SNELL CONTRACTOR INC p 466
1785 Oak Rd, Snellville GA 30078
Tel (770) 985-0600 *SIC* 1611

HAWAIIAN DREDGING CONSTRUCTION CO INC p 669
201 Merchant St Ste 900, Honolulu HI 96813
Tel (808) 735-3211
SIC 1542 1611 1522 1521

GRACE PACIFIC LLC p 628
949 Kamokila Blvd Ste 200, Kapolei HI 96707
Tel (808) 674-8383 *SIC* 1611 1429 3272

WASHINGTON GROUP INTERNATIONAL INC p 1578
720 E Park Blvd, Boise ID 83712
Tel (208) 386-5000
SIC 1611 1629 1221 1081 4959 1475

EUCON CORP p 512
4201 Snake River Ave, Lewiston ID 83501
Tel (509) 533-1615 *SIC* 1442 1611

STARK EXCAVATING INC p 1379
1805 W Washington St, Bloomington IL 61701
Tel (309) 828-5034 *SIC* 1611 1794

FH PASCHEN SN NIELSEN INC p 539
5515 N East River Rd, Chicago IL 60656
Tel (773) 444-3474
SIC 1611 1622 1522 1542

ROADSAFE TRAFFIC SYSTEMS INC p 1240
8750 W Bryn Mawr Ave # 400, Chicago IL 60631
Tel (773) 724-3300 *SIC* 1721 1611 7389

WALSH CONSTRUCTION CO p 1574
929 W Adams St, Chicago IL 60607
Tel (312) 563-5400
SIC 1541 1622 1542 1611

WALSH CONSTRUCTION CO II LLC p 1574
929 W Adams St, Chicago IL 60607
Tel (312) 563-5400 *SIC* 1542 1611

D CONSTRUCTION INC p 406
1488 S Broadway St, Coal City IL 60416
Tel (815) 634-2555 *SIC* 1611

CURRAN GROUP INC p 402
286 Memorial Ct, Crystal Lake IL 60014
Tel (815) 455-5100 *SIC* 1799 3253 1611

ILLINOIS CONSTRUCTORS CORP p 732
39w866 Fabyan Pkwy, Elburn IL 60119
Tel (630) 232-7280 *SIC* 1611

HELM GROUP INC p 682
2283 Business Us 20 E, Freeport IL 61032
Tel (815) 235-2244 *SIC* 1611 1622 1629

K-FIVE CONSTRUCTION CORP p 799
13769 Main St, Lemont IL 60439
Tel (630) 257-5600 *SIC* 1611

■ **KENNY CONSTRUCTION A GRANITE CO** p 811
2215 Sanders Rd Ste 400, Northbrook IL 60062
Tel (847) 919-8200
SIC 1622 1611 1629 1623 1541

■ **KENNY INDUSTRIES INC** p 811
2215 Sanders Rd Ste 400, Northbrook IL 60062
Tel (847) 919-8200
SIC 1611 1622 1629 1623 1541 6552

L & H CO INC p 833
2215 York Rd Ste 304, Oak Brook IL 60523
Tel (630) 571-7200
SIC 1731 1611 1623 3621

WILLIAM CHARLES LTD p 1610
1401 N 2nd St, Rockford IL 61107
Tel (815) 963-7400
SIC 1611 5211 1731 4953

E & B PAVING INC p 465
286 W 300 N, Anderson IN 46012
Tel (765) 643-5358 *SIC* 1611 2951 1794

SKANSKA US CIVIL MIDWEST INC p 1329
401 Nw 1st St, Evansville IN 47708
Tel (812) 423-7832 *SIC* 1611

BROOKS CONSTRUCTION CO INC p 218
6525 Ardmore Ave, Fort Wayne IN 46809
Tel (260) 478-1990 *SIC* 1611

RIETH-RILEY CONSTRUCTION CO INC p 1234
3626 Elkhart Rd, Goshen IN 46526
Tel (574) 875-5183 *SIC* 1611 1771 1622

ITR CONCESSION CO LLC p 768
52551 Ash Rd, Granger IN 46530
Tel (574) 674-8836 *SIC* 1611

MILESTONE CONTRACTORS LP p 969
5950 S Belmont Ave, Indianapolis IN 46217
Tel (317) 788-6885 *SIC* 1611

MANATTS INC p 900
1775 Old 6 Rd, Brooklyn IA 52211
Tel (641) 522-9206
SIC 1611 1442 2951 3273

WENDLING QUARRIES INC p 1592
2647 225th St, De Witt IA 52742
Tel (563) 659-9181 *SIC* 1422 1611 1442

RASMUSSEN GROUP INC p 1209
5550 Ne 22nd St, Des Moines IA 50313
Tel (515) 266-5173 *SIC* 1622 1611 3272

REILLY CONSTRUCTION CO INC p 1221
110 E Main St, Ossian IA 52161
Tel (563) 532-9211 *SIC* 1611

PETERSON CONTRACTORS INC p 1138
104 Blackhawk St, Reinbeck IA 50669
Tel (319) 345-2713 *SIC* 1611

APAC-KANSAS INC p 95
7415 W 130th St Ste 300, Overland Park KS 66213
Tel (913) 371-1003
SIC 1611 1771 2951 7353 1622

HAMM INC p 656
609 Perry Pl, Perry KS 66073
Tel (785) 597-5111 *SIC* 1411 1771 1611

KOSS CONSTRUCTION CO p 828
5830 Sw Drury Ln, Topeka KS 66604
Tel (785) 228-2928 *SIC* 1611

CORNEJO & SONS LLC p 370
2060 E Tulsa St, Wichita KS 67216
Tel (316) 522-5100
SIC 1542 1794 1795 1611

WILDCAT CONSTRUCTION CO INC p 1609
3219 W May St, Wichita KS 67213
Tel (316) 945-9408
SIC 1623 1622 1771 1611 1629

SCOTTYS CONTRACTING AND STONE LLC p 1294
2300 Barren River Rd, Bowling Green KY 42101
Tel (270) 781-3998 *SIC* 1629 1611 2951

ELMO GREER & SONS LLC p 489
3138 N Us Highway 25, East Bernstadt KY 40729
Tel (606) 862-4233 *SIC* 1611 2951

HANSON AGGREGATES MIDWEST LLC p 659
207 Old Harrods Creek Rd, Louisville KY 40223
Tel (502) 244-7550 *SIC* 1422 1611

WALKER CO OF KENTUCKY INC p 1573
105 Apperson Hts, Mount Sterling KY 40353
Tel (859) 498-0092
SIC 1611 2951 1542 3273 1422

YAGER MATERIALS LLC p 1633
5001 Highway 2830, Owensboro KY 42303
Tel (270) 926-0893
SIC 1442 1422 1611 3273 4491 3731

HARPER INDUSTRIES INC p 663
960 N Hc Mathis Dr, Paducah KY 42001
Tel (270) 442-2753
SIC 3273 1711 1611 1542

HINKLE CONTRACTING CORP p 695
395 N Middletown Rd, Paris KY 40361
Tel (859) 987-3670
SIC 1611 1422 3273 3272 3271 2951

DIAMOND B CONSTRUCTION CO INC p 436
2090 Industrial Park Rd, Alexandria LA 71303
Tel (318) 427-1300 *SIC* 1611

CB&I GOVERNMENT SOLUTIONS INC p 268
4171 Essen Ln, Baton Rouge LA 70809
Tel (225) 932-2500
SIC 8711 8734 8748 1541 1542 1611

■ **JAMES CONSTRUCTION GROUP LLC** p 776
18484 E Petroleum Dr, Baton Rouge LA 70809
Tel (225) 293-0274 *SIC* 1611 1622

JB JAMES CONSTRUCTION LLC p 779
1881 Wooddale Blvd, Baton Rouge LA 70806
Tel (225) 927-3131 *SIC* 1611

BARRIERE CONSTRUCTION CO LLC p 157
1 Galleria Blvd Ste 1650, Metairie LA 70001
Tel (504) 581-7283 *SIC* 1611 1629

MADDEN CONTRACTING CO LLC p 893
11288 Hwy 371, Minden LA 71055
Tel (318) 377-0927 *SIC* 1611 2951

BOH BROS CONSTRUCTION CO LLC p 197
730 S Tonti St, New Orleans LA 70119
Tel (504) 821-2400
SIC 1611 1622 1629 1623

CG ENTERPRISES INC p 285
12001 Guilford Rd Ste 1, Annapolis Junction MD 20701
Tel (301) 953-3366 *SIC* 1611 1623

CORMAN CONSTRUCTION INC p 370
12001 Guilford Rd, Annapolis Junction MD 20701
Tel (301) 953-0900 *SIC* 1611 1622 1623

P FLANIGAN AND SONS INC p 1102
2444 Loch Raven Rd, Baltimore MD 21218
Tel (410) 467-5900 *SIC* 1611

RUMMEL KLEPPER & KAHL LLP p 1257
81 Mosher St, Baltimore MD 21217
Tel (410) 728-2900
SIC 8711 8741 1623 8999 8713 1611

CLARK CONSTRUCTION GROUP LLC p 322
7500 Old Georgetown Rd # 15, Bethesda MD 20814
Tel (301) 272-8100 *SIC* 1542 1611 1522

DIXIE CONSTRUCTION CO INC p 444
260 Hopewell Rd, Churchville MD 21028
Tel (410) 879-8055 *SIC* 1611 1623

PLEASANTS CONSTRUCTION INC p 1156
24024 Frederick Rd, Clarksburg MD 20871
Tel (301) 428-0800 *SIC* 1794 1623 1611

ALLAN MYERS MD INC p 52
2011 Bel Air Rd, Fallston MD 21047
Tel (410) 879-3055 *SIC* 1611 1623

■ **CHERRY HILL CONSTRUCTION INC** p 294
8211 Washington Blvd, Jessup MD 20794
Tel (410) 799-3577 *SIC* 1611 1622

FACCHINA CONSTRUCTION CO INC p 523
102 Centennial St Ste 201, La Plata MD 20646
Tel (240) 776-7000
SIC 1542 1799 1623 1611 1622 1629

GRAY & SON INC p 632
430 W Padonia Rd, Lutherville Timonium MD 21093
Tel (410) 771-4311 *SIC* 1611 1623 1794

MCCOURT CONSTRUCTION CO INC p 927
60 K St, Boston MA 02127
Tel (617) 269-2330 *SIC* 1611 1622

BROX INDUSTRIES INC p 220
1471 Methuen St, Dracut MA 01826
Tel (978) 454-9105
SIC 1442 1499 1611 1629 1794 2951

■ **PERINI MANAGEMENT SERVICES INC** p 1136
73 Mount Wayte Ave, Framingham MA 01702
Tel (508) 628-2000
SIC 1541 1542 1611 1629

P A LANDERS INC p 1102
351 Winter St, Hanover MA 02339
Tel (781) 826-8818 *SIC* 1611 1442

DANIEL OCONNELLS SONS INC p 411
480 Hampden St, Holyoke MA 01040
Tel (413) 534-5667
SIC 1541 1542 1522 1611 1622 1629

MIDDLESEX CORP p 965
1 Spectacle Pond Rd, Littleton MA 01460
Tel (978) 742-4400 *SIC* 1611 1794 1622

PETRICCA INDUSTRIES INC p 1139
550 Cheshire Rd, Pittsfield MA 01201
Tel (413) 499-1441
SIC 1611 1623 3273 3272 1442

PRINCE MANUFACTURING CORP p 1176
36 W 8th St Ste 250, Holland MI 49423
Tel (616) 494-5374 *SIC* 1611 3613 5013

AJAX PAVING INDUSTRIES INC p 41
1957 Crooks Rd A, Troy MI 48084
Tel (248) 244-3300
SIC 1611 2951 3273 3272

HHJ HOLDINGS LIMITED p 689
1957 Crooks Rd A, Troy MI 48084
Tel (248) 652-9716 *SIC* 1611 2951

ANGELO IAFRATE CONSTRUCTION CO p 91
26300 Sherwood Ave, Warren MI 48091
Tel (586) 756-1070 *SIC* 1623 1794 1611

AMES CONSTRUCTION INC p 84
14420 County Road 5, Burnsville MN 55306
Tel (952) 435-7106
SIC 1611 1041 1021 1794

CS MCCROSSAN INC p 397
7865 Jefferson Hwy, Maple Grove MN 55369
Tel (763) 425-4167 *SIC* 1611 1622 1799

PARK CONSTRUCTION CO p 1115
1481 81st Ave Ne, Minneapolis MN 55432
Tel (763) 786-9800 *SIC* 1611 1622 1629

DUININCK INC p 460
408 6th St, Prinsburg MN 56281
Tel (320) 978-6011 *SIC* 1629 1611

HARDRIVES INC p 661
14475 Quiram Dr Ste 1, Rogers MN 55374
Tel (763) 428-8886 *SIC* 1611 2951

VEIT & CO INC p 1547
14000 Veit Pl, Rogers MN 55374
Tel (763) 428-2242 *SIC* 1611 1795 4953

ASPHALT SURFACE TECHNOLOGIES CORP p 118
8348 Ridgewood Rd, Saint Joseph MN 56374
Tel (320) 363-8500 *SIC* 1611 4959

■ **KNIFE RIVER CORP - NORTH CENTRAL** p 824
4787 Shadowwood Dr Ne, Sauk Rapids MN 56379
Tel (320) 251-9472
SIC 1611 1442 3273 2951

EUTAW CONSTRUCTION CO INC p 513
109 W Commerce St, Aberdeen MS 39730
Tel (662) 369-7121 *SIC* 1611 1623 1794

TL WALLACE CONSTRUCTION INC p 1457
4025 Highway 35 N, Columbia MS 39429
Tel (601) 736-4525 *SIC* 1611 4212 8322

HILL BROTHERS CONSTRUCTION CO INC p 693
20831 Highway 15, Falkner MS 38629
Tel (662) 837-3041
SIC 1611 1622 1541 1542

W G YATES & SONS CONSTRUCTION CO p 1568
1 Gully Ave, Philadelphia MS 39350
Tel (904) 714-1376
SIC 1542 1541 2339 1611 5211 1731

YATES COMPANIES INC p 1635
1 Gully Ave, Philadelphia MS 39350
Tel (601) 656-5411
SIC 1542 1541 1611 5211 1731

APAC-MISSISSIPPI INC p 95
101 Riverview Dr, Richland MS 39218
Tel (601) 376-4000
SIC 1611 1771 3531 5032 2951

DELTA COMPANIES INC p 426
114 S Silver Springs Rd, Cape Girardeau MO 63703
Tel (573) 334-5261 *SIC* 2951 1611

APAC-MISSOURI INC p 95
1591 E Prathersville Rd, Columbia MO 65202
Tel (573) 449-0886 *SIC* 1611

EMERY SAPP & SONS INC p 492
2301 Interstate 70 Dr Nw, Columbia MO 65202
Tel (573) 445-8331 *SIC* 1622 1629 1611

CLARKSON CONSTRUCTION CO INC p 322
4133 Gardner Ave, Kansas City MO 64120
Tel (816) 483-5444 *SIC* 1611

GARNEY HOLDING CO p 592
1333 Nw Vivion Rd, Kansas City MO 64118
Tel (816) 741-4600 *SIC* 1623 1611 1629

FRED WEBER INC p 576
2320 Creve Coeur Mill Rd, Maryland Heights MO 63043
Tel (314) 344-0070
SIC 1611 1442 3272 1622 1542

CHESTER BROSS CONSTRUCTION CO p 295
6739 County Road 423, Palmyra MO 63461
Tel (573) 221-5958 *SIC* 1611 1629

HERZOG CONTRACTING CORP p 688
600 S Riverside Rd, Saint Joseph MO 64507
Tel (816) 233-9001 *SIC* 1629 1611 4953

KCI CONSTRUCTION CO p 806
10315 Lake Bluff Dr, Saint Louis MO 63123
Tel (314) 894-8888 *SIC* 1542 1611 1629

L KEELEY CONSTRUCTION CO p 834
500 S Ewing Ave Ste G, Saint Louis MO 63103
Tel (314) 421-5933 *SIC* 1541 1611 1623

LIONMARK CONSTRUCTION COMPANIES LLC p 870
1620 Woodson Rd, Saint Louis MO 63114
Tel (314) 991-2180 *SIC* 1611 2951 1622

MISSOURI PETROLEUM PRODUCTS CO LLC p 976
1620 Woodson Rd, Saint Louis MO 63114
Tel (314) 219-7305 *SIC* 5033 1611 2951

LEO JOURNAGAN CONSTRUCTION CO INC p 856
3003 E Chestnut Expy, Springfield MO 65802
Tel (417) 869-7222 *SIC* 1422 1611 1623

■ **JTL GROUP INC** p 796
4014 Hesper Rd, Billings MT 59106
Tel (406) 655-2010 *SIC* 1611

BARNARD CONSTRUCTION CO INC p 155
701 Gold Ave, Bozeman MT 59715
Tel (406) 586-1995
SIC 1623 1629 1611 1622

SLETTEN CONSTRUCTION CO p 1331
1000 25th St N Ste 4, Great Falls MT 59401
Tel (406) 761-7920 *SIC* 1541 1542 1611

SLETTEN INC p 1331
1000 25th St N Ste 4, Great Falls MT 59401
Tel (406) 761-7920 *SIC* 1542 1541 1611

DICK ANDERSON CONSTRUCTION INC p 437
3424 E Us Highway 12, Helena MT 59601
Tel (406) 443-3225 *SIC* 1542 1622 1611

OFTEDAL CONSTRUCTION INC p 1076
434 Highway 59 N 59n, Miles City MT 59301
Tel (406) 232-5911 *SIC* 1629 3273 1611

PAULSEN INC p 1122
1116 E Highway 30, Cozad NE 69130
Tel (308) 784-3333 *SIC* 1611 1542 3273

HAWKINS CONSTRUCTION CO p 669
2516 Deer Park Blvd, Omaha NE 68105
Tel (402) 342-4455 *SIC* 1542 1611 1541

KIEWIT CORP p 817
3555 Farnam St Ste 1000, Omaha NE 68131
Tel (402) 342-2052
SIC 1542 1541 1611 1622 1629

KIEWIT INFRASTRUCTURE GROUP INC p 817
3555 Farnam St, Omaha NE 68131
Tel (402) 342-2052 *SIC* 1611 1622

KIEWIT INFRASTRUCTURE SOUTH CO p 817
Kiewit Plz No 1044, Omaha NE 68131
Tel (402) 342-2052 *SIC* 1622 1611

KIEWIT INFRASTRUCTURE WEST CO p 817
4004 S 60th St, Omaha NE 68117
Tel (402) 342-2052
SIC 1611 1629 1541 1622 1623

PETER KIEWIT SONS INC p 1138
3555 Farnam St Ste 1000, Omaha NE 68131
Tel (402) 342-2052
SIC 1611 1622 1711 1542 1629 1221

A & K EARTH MOVERS INC p 4
515 Windmill Dr, Fallon NV 89406
Tel (775) 825-1636 *SIC* 1611 1542

LAS VEGAS PAVING CORP p 845
4420 S Decatur Blvd, Las Vegas NV 89103
Tel (702) 251-5800 *SIC* 1611 1629 8711

AGGREGATE INDUSTRIES-SWR INC p 35
3101 E Craig Rd, North Las Vegas NV 89030
Tel (702) 281-9696 *SIC* 1611 5032

PIKE INDUSTRIES INC p 1148
3 Eastgate Park Dr, Belmont NH 03220
Tel (603) 527-5100 *SIC* 1611 2951 3295

FERREIRA CONSTRUCTION CO INC p 538
31 Tannery Rd, Branchburg NJ 08876
Tel (908) 534-8655 *SIC* 1611

CONTI ENTERPRISES INC p 362
2045 Lincoln Hwy, Edison NJ 08817
Tel (732) 520-5000 *SIC* 1611 1622 1623

J FLETCHER CREAMER & SON INC p 771
101 E Broadway, Hackensack NJ 07601
Tel (201) 488-9800
SIC 1623 1611 1771 1622 1629

TRAP ROCK INDUSTRIES INC p 1473
460 River Rd, Kingston NJ 08528
Tel (609) 924-0300
SIC 3273 3272 1429 1611

CCA CIVIL INC p 269
445 South St Ste 310, Morristown NJ 07960
Tel (862) 701-7200 *SIC* 1611

COLAS INC p 335
163 Madison Ave Ste 500, Morristown NJ 07960
Tel (973) 290-9082 *SIC* 1611 1622 2951

BARRETT INDUSTRIES CORP p 157
3 Becker Farm Rd Ste 307, Roseland NJ 07068
Tel (973) 533-1001
SIC 1611 2951 4213 1799 1794

BARRETT PAVING MATERIALS INC p 157
3 Becker Farm Rd Ste 307, Roseland NJ 07068
Tel (973) 533-1001
SIC 1611 2951 4213 1799 1794

JAG COMPANIES INC p 776
1433 State Route 34 Ste 5, Wall Township NJ 07727
Tel (732) 557-6100
SIC 1623 1622 1629 1611

NORTHEAST REMSCO CONSTRUCTION INC p 1055
1433 State Route 34 Ste 6, Wall Township NJ 07727
Tel (732) 557-6100
SIC 1623 1622 1629 1611

JAYNES COMPANIES p 779
2906 Broadway Blvd Ne, Albuquerque NM 87107
Tel (505) 345-8591 *SIC* 1611

NAVAJO ENGINEERING & CONSTRUCTION AUTHORITY p 1019
1 Uranium Blvd, Shiprock NM 87420
Tel (505) 368-5151 *SIC* 1611 1623

JETT INDUSTRIES INC p 784
121 Willow Ln, Colliersville NY 13747
Tel (607) 433-2100 *SIC* 1611 1623

SUIT-KOTE CORP p 1397
1911 Lorings Crossing Rd, Cortland NY 13045
Tel (607) 753-1100 *SIC* 2951 1611

SKANSKA USA CIVIL INC p 1329
7520 Astoria Blvd Ste 200, East Elmhurst NY 11370
Tel (718) 340-0777 *SIC* 1611

POSILLICO CIVIL INC p 1163
1750 New Hwy, Farmingdale NY 11735
Tel (631) 249-1872 *SIC* 1611 1542

JUDLAU CONTRACTING INC p 797
2615 Ulmer St, Flushing NY 11354
Tel (718) 554-2320 *SIC* 1611 1623

TULLY CONSTRUCTION CO INC p 1491
12750 Northern Blvd, Flushing NY 11368
Tel (718) 446-7000 *SIC* 1611

BETTE & CRING LLC p 178
22 Century Hill Dr # 201, Latham NY 12110
Tel (518) 213-1010
SIC 1541 1542 1622 1611

JOHN P PICONE INC p 789
31 Garden Ln, Lawrence NY 11559
Tel (516) 239-1600
SIC 1611 1622 1623 1629

NEW YORK PAVING INC p 1035
3718 Railroad Ave, Long Island City NY 11101
Tel (718) 482-0780 *SIC* 1611

DRAGADOS USA INC p 455
810 7th Ave Fl 9, New York NY 10019
Tel (212) 779-0900 *SIC* 1611

SOLVATION INC p 1339
885 3rd Ave Fl 34, New York NY 10022
Tel (212) 888-5500 *SIC* 6153 1611 3272

■TISHMAN CONSTRUCTION CORP p 1455
100 Park Ave Fl 5, New York NY 10017
Tel (212) 708-6800 *SIC* 8741 1611

DALRYMPLE HOLDING CORP p 410
2105 S Broadway, Pine City NY 14871
Tel (607) 737-6200
SIC 3273 1611 1442 1622 3281

SEALAND CONTRACTORS CORP p 1296
85 High Tech Dr, Rush NY 14543
Tel (704) 522-1102 *SIC* 1622 1611 1623

YONKERS CONTRACTING CO INC p 1637
969 Midland Ave, Yonkers NY 10704
Tel (914) 965-1500 *SIC* 1611

TRIANGLE GRADING & PAVING INC p 1478
1521 Huffman Mill Rd, Burlington NC 27215
Tel (336) 584-1745 *SIC* 1611 1794

BLYTHE CONSTRUCTION INC p 193
2911 N Graham St, Charlotte NC 28206
Tel (704) 375-8474 *SIC* 1611 1622 2951

BLYTHE DEVELOPMENT CO p 193
1415 E Westinghouse Blvd, Charlotte NC 28273
Tel (704) 588-0023 *SIC* 1611

APAC-ATLANTIC INC p 95
300 S Benbow Rd, Greensboro NC 27401
Tel (336) 412-6800
SIC 1611 1771 3531 5032

THALLE CONSTRUCTION CO INC p 1446
900 Nc Highway 86 N, Hillsborough NC 27278
Tel (919) 245-1490
SIC 1611 1622 1623 1629

SANFORD CONTRACTORS INC p 1279
628 Rocky Fork Church Rd, Sanford NC 27332
Tel (919) 775-7882
SIC 1611 1622 1629 6552 1794 1623

S T WOOTEN CORP p 1263
3801 Black Creek Rd Se, Wilson NC 27893
Tel (252) 637-4294 *SIC* 1611 3273 1623

MCCORMICK INC p 927
4000 12th Ave N, Fargo ND 58102
Tel (701) 277-1225 *SIC* 1611 1629 1623

NORTHERN IMPROVEMENT CO p 1056
4000 12th Ave N, Fargo ND 58102
Tel (701) 277-1225 *SIC* 1611 1629

STRATA CORP p 1392
1600 N 48th St, Grand Forks ND 58203
Tel (701) 775-4205
SIC 1611 3273 1442 5032

INDUSTRIAL BUILDERS INC p 739
1307 County Road 17 N, West Fargo ND 58078
Tel (701) 282-4977
SIC 1629 1622 1542 1611 1623

KENMORE CONSTRUCTION CO INC p 810
700 Home Ave, Akron OH 44310
Tel (330) 762-8936 *SIC* 1611 5032

MBC HOLDINGS INC p 925
1613 S Defiance St, Archbold OH 43502
Tel (419) 445-1015 *SIC* 1622 1611

BEAVER EXCAVATING CO p 166
2000 Beaver Place Ave Sw, Canton OH 44706
Tel (330) 478-2151
SIC 1794 1611 1771 1623

VALLEY ASPHALT CORP p 1540
11641 Mosteller Rd, Cincinnati OH 45241
Tel (513) 771-0820 *SIC* 1611 2951

KOKOSING CONSTRUCTION CO INC p 826
886 Mckinley Ave, Columbus OH 43222
Tel (614) 228-1029
SIC 1611 1622 1629 1542 1541 1623

WMOG INC p 1620
122 S Wilson Ave, Fremont OH 43420
Tel (419) 334-3801 *SIC* 1541 7359 1611

INDEPENDENCE EXCAVATING INC p 736
5720 E Schaaf Rd, Independence OH 44131
Tel (216) 524-1700
SIC 1629 1794 1611 1771 1795

BAKER CONCRETE CONSTRUCTION INC p 146
900 N Garver Rd, Monroe OH 45050
Tel (513) 539-4000 *SIC* 1771 1611

RUHLIN CO p 1257
6931 Ridge Rd, Sharon Center OH 44274
Tel (330) 239-2800
SIC 1542 1541 1622 1611

SHELLY CO p 1314
80 Park Dr, Thornville OH 43076
Tel (740) 246-6315 *SIC* 1611

M & B ASPHALT CO INC p 888
1525 W Seneca Cnty Rd 42, Tiffin OH 44883
Tel (419) 992-4235
SIC 1429 2951 1611 2952 1771

KOKOSING INC p 826
6235 Wstrville Rd Ste 200, Westerville OH 43081
Tel (614) 212-5700 *SIC* 1611

KOKOSING CONSTRUCTION INC p 826
1516 Timken Rd, Wooster OH 44691
Tel (330) 263-4168 *SIC* 1611

SHELLY AND SANDS INC p 1314
3570 S River Rd, Zanesville OH 43701
Tel (740) 453-0721 *SIC* 1611 1442 2951

HASKELL LEMON CONSTRUCTION CO p 667
3800 Sw 10th St, Oklahoma City OK 73108
Tel (405) 947-6069
SIC 5032 1611 3272 2951

EVANS & ASSOCIATES ENTERPRISES INC p 513
3320 N 14th St, Ponca City OK 74601
Tel (580) 765-6693
SIC 5032 2951 1442 1611 3273 1311

APAC-OKLAHOMA INC p 95
4150 S 100th East Ave # 300, Tulsa OK 74146
Tel (918) 438-2020 *SIC* 1611

WILDISH LAND CO p 1609
3600 Wildish Ln, Eugene OR 97408
Tel (541) 485-1700 *SIC* 1611 1542

FORTIS CONSTRUCTION INC p 569
1705 Sw Taylor St Ste 200, Portland OR 97205
Tel (503) 459-4477 *SIC* 1542 1611

■ KNIFE RIVER CORP - NORTHWEST p 824
32260 Old Highway 34, Tangent OR 97389
Tel (541) 928-6491 *SIC* 1611 3273

J D ECKMAN INC p 770
4781 Lower Valley Rd, Atglen PA 19310
Tel (610) 593-5300 *SIC* 1611

GLEN BLOOMING CONTRACTORS INC p 614
901 Minsi Trl, Blooming Glen PA 18911
Tel (215) 257-9400 *SIC* 1611 1794

HEMPT BROS INC p 682
205 Creek Rd, Camp Hill PA 17011
Tel (717) 774-2911
SIC 1611 3273 2951 1442 0212

MARTIN LIMESTONE INC p 912
3580 Division Hwy, East Earl PA 17519
Tel (717) 335-4500
SIC 3273 3271 1611 1422 8741 5211

IA CONSTRUCTION CORP p 725
24 Gibb Rd, Franklin PA 16323
Tel (814) 432-3184
SIC 1611 2951 1622 1623

GLASGOW INC p 614
104 Willow Grove Ave, Glenside PA 19038
Tel (215) 884-8800 *SIC* 2951 1611 1623

STABLER COMPANIES INC p 1374
635 Lucknow Rd, Harrisburg PA 17110
Tel (717) 236-9307
SIC 5032 3089 7359 3531 1611 3648

GOLDEN TRIANGLE CONSTRUCTION CO INC p 621
8555 Old Strubenville Pik, Imperial PA 15126
Tel (724) 828-2800 *SIC* 1623 1611

NEW ENTERPRISE STONE & LIME CO INC p 1030
3912 Brumbaugh Rd, New Enterprise PA 16664
Tel (814) 224-6883 *SIC* 1422 1611

PKF-MARK III INC p 1153
17 Blacksmith Rd Ste 101, Newtown PA 18940
Tel (215) 968-5031
SIC 1611 1629 1711 1731 1771 8711

MOSITES CONSTRUCTION CO p 992
4839 Campbells Run Rd, Pittsburgh PA 15205
Tel (412) 923-2255 *SIC* 1542 1611

RUSSELL STANDARD CORP p 1259
285 Kappa Dr Ste 300, Pittsburgh PA 15238
Tel (412) 449-0700 *SIC* 1611 2951

TRUMBULL CORP p 1486
225 N Shore Dr, Pittsburgh PA 15212
Tel (412) 807-2000 *SIC* 1611

PENN LINE SERVICE INC p 1129
300 Scottdale Ave, Scottdale PA 15683
Tel (724) 887-9110
SIC 1629 1623 1611 0782

HAINES & KIBBLEHOUSE INC p 653
2052 Lucon Rd, Skippack PA 19474
Tel (610) 584-8500
SIC 1794 1611 1422 2951

GLENN O HAWBAKER INC p 615
1952 Waddle Rd Ste 203, State College PA 16803
Tel (814) 237-1444
SIC 2951 3281 1622 1794 1611 1422

HRI INC p 714
1750 W College Ave, State College PA 16801
Tel (814) 238-5071 *SIC* 1611

SSSI INC p 1364
2755a Park Ave, Washington PA 15301
Tel (724) 743-5815 *SIC* 1611 3312 4925

EASTERN INDUSTRIES INC p 472
3724 Crescent Ct W 200, Whitehall PA 18052
Tel (610) 866-0932 *SIC* 5032 3273 1611

ASPLUNDH TREE EXPERT CO p 119
708 Blair Mill Rd, Willow Grove PA 19090
Tel (215) 784-4200
SIC 0783 1629 1623 1611 6411

ALLAN MYERS INC p 51
1805 Berks Rd, Worcester PA 19490
Tel (610) 222-8800
SIC 1629 1794 1611 1622 3281 5032

ALLAN MYERS LP p 51
1805 Berks Rd, Worcester PA 19490
Tel (610) 584-3430
SIC 1629 1794 1611 1622

KINSLEY CONSTRUCTION INC p 821
2700 Water St, York PA 17403
Tel (717) 741-3841 *SIC* 1541 1542 1611

BETTEROADS ASPHALT CORP p 178
Edif Empresas Diaz, San Juan PR 00926
Tel (787) 760-1050 *SIC* 1611 2951

JH LYNCH & SONS INC p 785
50 Lynch Pl, Cumberland RI 02864
Tel (401) 333-4300 *SIC* 1611 2951

BANKS CONSTRUCTION CO p 152
4902 Banco Rd, North Charleston SC 29418
Tel (843) 744-8261 *SIC* 1611

HEAVY CONSTRUCTORS INC p 679
4101 Deadwood Ave, Rapid City SD 57702
Tel (605) 342-3144
SIC 1542 1794 1623 1611

HIGHWAYS INC p 692
1623 Galleria Blvd, Brentwood TN 37027
Tel (615) 373-5445 *SIC* 1611

SUMMERS-TAYLOR INC p 1398
300 W Elk Ave, Elizabethton TN 37643
Tel (423) 543-3181 *SIC* 1611 1794 3273

DEMENT CONSTRUCTION CO p 428
96 Smith Ln, Jackson TN 38301
Tel (731) 424-6306 *SIC* 1622 1611

APAC-ATLANTIC INC p 95
4817 Rutledge Pike, Knoxville TN 37914
Tel (865) 983-3100
SIC 5032 3531 3273 2951 1611

PHILLIPS AND JORDAN INC p 1144
10201 Parkside Dr Ste 300, Knoxville TN 37922
Tel (865) 688-8342 *SIC* 1611 1629

LOJAC ENTERPRISES INC p 875
1401 Toshiba Dr, Lebanon TN 37087
Tel (615) 449-1401 *SIC* 1611 1794 5032

APAC-TENNESSEE INC p 95
1210 Harbor Ave, Memphis TN 38113
Tel (901) 947-5600 *SIC* 1611

LEHMAN-ROBERTS CO p 854
1111 Wilson St, Memphis TN 38106
Tel (901) 774-4000 *SIC* 1611 2951

JONES BROS INC p 792
5760 Old Lebanon Dirt Rd, Mount Juliet TN 37122
Tel (615) 754-4710
SIC 1622 1771 1794 1629 1611

JONES INVESTMENT HOLDING INC p 792
5760 Old Lebanon Dirt Rd, Mount Juliet TN 37122
Tel (615) 754-4710
SIC 1622 1771 1794 1611

MAYMEAD INC p 923
1995 Roan Creek Rd, Mountain City TN 37683
Tel (423) 727-2000
SIC 1611 2951 5032 5191

ROGERS GROUP INC p 1246
421 Great Circle Rd, Nashville TN 37228
Tel (615) 242-0585 *SIC* 1611 1422

CHARLES BLALOCK & SONS INC p 289
409 Robert Henderson Rd, Sevierville TN 37862
Tel (865) 429-5902
SIC 1611 7353 3271 3255 2951

ABRAMS INTERNATIONAL INC p 12
111 Congress Ave Ste 2400, Austin TX 78701
Tel (512) 322-4000
SIC 1611 1622 1629 6799 7359 8742

AUSTIN MATERIALS LLC p 133
9020 N Cpitl Of Texas Hwy, Austin TX 78759
Tel (512) 251-3713 *SIC* 1611 5032

FGI GROUP INC p 539
3901 S Lamar Blvd Ste 100, Austin TX 78704
Tel (512) 448-9898
SIC 1542 1541 1794 1611 7353 1711

JD ABRAMS LP p 780
5811 Trade Center Dr # 1, Austin TX 78744
Tel (512) 322-4000
SIC 1611 1622 1629 3272

JD RAMMING PAVING MANAGEMENT LLC p 780
9020 N Cpitl Of Texas Hwy, Austin TX 78759
Tel (512) 251-3713 *SIC* 1611 1771

RK HALL LLC p 1239
1114 Lost Creek Blvd # 410, Austin TX 78746
Tel (903) 784-7280 *SIC* 1611

GLENN THURMAN INC p 615
3180 S Belt Line Rd, Balch Springs TX 75181
Tel (972) 286-6333 *SIC* 1611 4212

ANGEL BROTHERS ENTERPRISES LTD p 91
5210 West Rd, Baytown TX 77521
Tel (281) 421-5721 *SIC* 1794 1611

ANGEL BROTHERS INC p 91
5210 West Rd, Baytown TX 77521
Tel (281) 471-6730 *SIC* 1611

SITE CONCRETE INC p 1327
1544 Valwood Pkwy Ste 100, Carrollton TX 75006
Tel (972) 313-0733 *SIC* 1611 1771 1794

APAC-TEXAS INC p 95
1320 Arrow Point Dr # 600, Cedar Park TX 78613
Tel (512) 861-7100 *SIC* 1611

DMG EQUIPMENT CO LTD p 446
1575 Fm 1485 Rd, Conroe TX 77301
Tel (936) 756-6960 *SIC* 1611 2951

BERRY CONTRACTING LP p 176
1414 Corn Product Rd, Corpus Christi TX 78409
Tel (361) 693-2100 *SIC* 2911 1611

BERRY GP INC p 176
1414 Corn Product Rd, Corpus Christi TX 78409
Tel (361) 693-2100 *SIC* 1541 1611 3498

BERRY HOLDINGS LP p 176
1414 Corn Product Rd, Corpus Christi TX 78409
Tel (361) 693-2100 *SIC* 1541 1611 3498

AUSTIN INDUSTRIES INC p 133
3535 Travis St Ste 300, Dallas TX 75204
Tel (214) 443-5500
SIC 1542 1629 1611 1622

ED BELL INVESTMENTS INC p 476
10605 Harry Hines Blvd, Dallas TX 75220
Tel (214) 358-3414 *SIC* 1611 5082 4424

JORDAN CF INVESTMENTS LLP p 793
7700 Cf Jordan Dr, El Paso TX 79912
Tel (915) 877-3333
SIC 1542 1541 1522 1611

■ BEALL CONCRETE ENTERPRISES LTD p 165
331 N Main St, Euless TX 76039
Tel (817) 835-4100 *SIC* 1611 1771

KIEWIT TEXAS CONSTRUCTION LP p 817
13119 Old Denton Rd, Fort Worth TX 76177
Tel (817) 337-7000 *SIC* 1611

■ HALLIBURTON DELAWARE INC p 654
3000 Houston Ave, Houston TX 77009
Tel (713) 759-2600
SIC 1629 1611 1622 8711 1389

■TEXAS STERLING CONSTRUCTION CO p 1444
20810 Fernbush Dr, Houston TX 77073
Tel (281) 821-9091 *SIC* 1611 1623

TNT CRANE & RIGGING INC p 1458
925 S Loop W, Houston TX 77054
Tel (713) 644-6113 *SIC* 7353 1611

AUSTIN BRIDGE & ROAD INC p 132
6330 Commerce Dr Ste 150, Irving TX 75063
Tel (214) 596-7300 *SIC* 1611 1622

AUSTIN BRIDGE & ROAD LP p 132
6330 Commerce Dr Ste 150, Irving TX 75063
Tel (214) 596-7300 *SIC* 1622 1611

LONGVIEW BRIDGE AND ROAD LTD p 877
792 Skinner Ln, Longview TX 75605
Tel (903) 663-0264 *SIC* 1611 1622 1794

BIG CREEK CONSTRUCTION LTD p 181
1617 Old Waco Temple Rd, Lorena TX 76655
Tel (254) 857-3200 *SIC* 1611

HUNTER INDUSTRIES LTD p 719
5080 Fm 2439, New Braunfels TX 78132
Tel (512) 353-7757 *SIC* 1611 2951 1442

WORD CONSTRUCTORS LLC p 1624
1245 River Rd, New Braunfels TX 78130
Tel (830) 625-2365 *SIC* 1622 1611

R K HALL CONSTRUCTION LTD p 1202
2810 Nw Loop 286, Paris TX 75460
Tel (903) 785-8941 *SIC* 1611

DNT CONSTRUCTION LLC p 446
2300 Picadilly Dr, Round Rock TX 78664
Tel (512) 837-6700 *SIC* 1623 1794 1611

ALBERT REECE INC p 46
3001 Foster St, San Angelo TX 76903
Tel (325) 653-1241
SIC 1611 1794 1623 1622

HB ZACHRY CO p 671
527 Logwood Ave, San Antonio TX 78221
Tel (210) 475-8000
SIC 1611 1622 1623 1629

OLMOS CONSTRUCTION INC p 1082
440 Pinn Rd, San Antonio TX 78227
Tel (210) 675-4990 *SIC* 1611 1794 1795

TETCO INC p 1441
1100 Ne Loop 410 Ste 900, San Antonio TX 78209
Tel (210) 821-5900
SIC 4213 5411 1611 5193

YANTIS CORP p 1635
3611 Paesanos Pkwy # 300, San Antonio TX 78231
Tel (210) 655-3780
SIC 1623 1611 1622 1629 6552 1521

ZACHRY CONSOLIDATED LLC p 1640
527 Logwood Ave, San Antonio TX 78221
Tel (210) 871-2700
SIC 1611 1622 1623 1629 3241 1442

ZACHRY CONSTRUCTION & MATERIALS INC p 1640
2330 N Loop 1604 W, San Antonio TX 78248
Tel (210) 479-1027
SIC 1611 1622 1623 1629 1542 3241

ZACHRY CONSTRUCTION CORP p 1640
2330 N Loop 1604 W, San Antonio TX 78248
Tel (210) 871-2700
SIC 1623 1611 1622 1629 1542

KINGSLEY CONSTRUCTORS INC p 821
25250 Borough Park Dr # 106, Spring TX 77380
Tel (281) 363-1979 *SIC* 1623 1611

▲ STERLING CONSTRUCTION CO INC p 1387
1800 Hughes Landing Blvd # 250, The Woodlands TX 77380
Tel (281) 214-0800 *SIC* 1611 1622 1623

WEBBER LLC p 1586
9303 New Trils Dr Ste 200, The Woodlands TX 77381
Tel (281) 372-0274 *SIC* 1611

■ RALPH L WADSWORTH CONSTRUCTION CO LLC p 1206
166 E 14000 S Ste 200, Draper UT 84020
Tel (801) 553-1661 *SIC* 1629 1611

NIELSON CONSTRUCTION AND MATERIALS p 1043
825 N Loop Rd, Huntington UT 84528
Tel (435) 687-2494 *SIC* 1611

STAKER & PARSON COMPANIES p 1374
2350 S 1900 W Ste 100, Ogden UT 84401
Tel (801) 298-7500
SIC 1611 5032 3273 4212 2951 1771

CLYDE COMPANIES INC p 328
730 N 1500 W, Orem UT 84057
Tel (801) 802-6900 *SIC* 1611 5031 6411

T&N ASPHALT SERVICES INC p 1420
3643 S 700 W Ste C, South Salt Lake UT 84119
Tel (801) 266-1626 *SIC* 1611

W W CLYDE & CO p 1569
1375 N Main St, Springville UT 84663
Tel (801) 802-6800 *SIC* 1611 1794 1629

HENSEL PHELPS SERVICES LLC p 685
4437 Brookfield Corp 20 Ste 207, Chantilly VA 20151
Tel (703) 828-3200
SIC 1522 8744 1521 1541 1623 1611

FAULCONER CONSTRUCTION CO INC p 531
2496 Old Ivy Rd, Charlottesville VA 22903
Tel (434) 295-0033
SIC 1629 1611 1542 1623

S W RODGERS CO INC p 1263
5816 Wellington Rd, Gainesville VA 20155
Tel (703) 591-8400
SIC 1611 1799 6552 1771 1623

ALLAN MYERS VA INC p 52
301 Cncourse Blvd Ste 300, Glen Allen VA 23059
Tel (804) 290-8500
SIC 1623 1611 1542 1794

SHIRLEY CONTRACTING CO LLC p 1317
8435 Backlick Rd, Lorton VA 22079
Tel (703) 550-8100 *SIC* 1611

ENGLISH CONSTRUCTION CO INC p 499
615 Church St Ste 2, Lynchburg VA 24504
Tel (434) 845-0301
SIC 1611 1629 1623 1542

SLURRY PAVERS INC p 1331
3617 Nine Mile Rd, Richmond VA 23223
Tel (804) 264-0707 *SIC* 2951 1611

ADAMS CONSTRUCTION CO p 21
523 Rutherford Ave Ne, Roanoke VA 24016
Tel (540) 982-2366 *SIC* 1611 2951

BRANCH GROUP INC p 207
442 Rutherford Ave Ne, Roanoke VA 24016
Tel (540) 982-1678
SIC 1542 1611 1711 1731 1541

BRANCH HIGHWAYS INC p 207
442 Rutherford Ave Ne, Roanoke VA 24016
Tel (540) 982-1678 *SIC* 1611

CENTURY CONCRETE INC p 282
1364 Air Rail Ave, Virginia Beach VA 23455
Tel (757) 460-5366 *SIC* 1622 1611 1771

LAKESIDE INDUSTRIES INC p 840
6505 226th Pl Se Ste 200, Issaquah WA 98027
Tel (425) 313-2600 *SIC* 1611 2951 5032

KLB CONSTRUCTION INC p 823
3405 121st St Sw, Lynnwood WA 98087
Tel (425) 355-7335 *SIC* 1623 1611

GARY MERLINO CONSTRUCTION CO INC p 593
9125 10th Ave S, Seattle WA 98108
Tel (206) 763-9552 *SIC* 1611 1623 3273

GOODFELLOW BROS INC p 624
1407 Walla Walla Ave, Wenatchee WA 98801
Tel (509) 667-9095 *SIC* 1611

HOS BROTHERS CONSTRUCTION INC p 708
7733 W Bostian Rd, Woodinville WA 98072
Tel (425) 481-5569 *SIC* 1611 1629

MOWAT CONSTRUCTION CO p 995
20210 142nd Ave Ne, Woodinville WA 98072
Tel (425) 398-0205 *SIC* 1611

VECELLIO & GROGAN INC p 1546
2251 Robert C Byrd Dr, Beckley WV 25801
Tel (304) 252-6575 *SIC* 1611 1622 1629

JF ALLEN CO INC p 785
U.S 33 W Red Rock Rd, Buckhannon WV 26201
Tel (304) 472-8890
SIC 3271 1611 3273 3281 2951

EXTERIOR SERVICES LLC p 521
209 Anderson Dr, Princeton WV 24739
Tel (304) 487-1503 *SIC* 1611

ORDERS CONSTRUCTION CO INC p 1093
501 6th Ave, Saint Albans WV 25177
Tel (304) 722-4237 *SIC* 1622 1611

MCC INC p 926
2600 N Roemer Rd, Appleton WI 54911
Tel (920) 749-3360 *SIC* 3273 1442 1611

JAMES PETERSON SONS INC p 777
N2251 Gibson Dr, Medford WI 54451
Tel (715) 748-3010 *SIC* 1611

MATHY CONSTRUCTION CO p 920
920 10th Ave N, Onalaska WI 54650
Tel (608) 783-6411
SIC 1611 1771 1442 5171

SIMON CONTRACTORS p 1324
1103 Old Town Ln Ste 1a, Cheyenne WY 82009
Tel (307) 635-9005 *SIC* 1611

SIC 1622 Bridge, Tunnel & Elevated Hwy Construction

SCOTT BRIDGE CO INC p 1293
2641 Interstate Dr, Opelika AL 36801
Tel (334) 749-5045 *SIC* 1622

HUNTER CONTRACTING CO p 719
701 N Cooper Rd, Gilbert AZ 85233
Tel (480) 892-0521 *SIC* 1611 1629 1622

KIEWIT WESTERN CO p 817
3888 E Broadway Rd, Phoenix AZ 85040
Tel (602) 437-7878
SIC 1622 1629 1794 1611 1623

■ **FLUOR DANIEL CONSTRUCTION CO** p 561
3 Polaris Way, Aliso Viejo CA 92656
Tel (949) 349-2000 *SIC* 1622

■ **VADNAIS TRENCHLESS SERVICES INC** p 1538
26000 Commercentre Dr, Lake Forest CA 92630
Tel (858) 550-1460 *SIC* 1623 1622

■ **AECOM E&C HOLDINGS INC** p 28
1999 Avenue Of Ste 2600, Los Angeles CA 90067
Tel (213) 593-8000
SIC 8711 1611 1629 1623 1541 1622

NOVA GROUP INC p 1062
185 Devlin Rd, Napa CA 94558
Tel (707) 265-1100
SIC 1629 1623 1622 5172

MCM CONSTRUCTION INC p 932
6413 32nd St, North Highlands CA 95660
Tel (916) 334-1221 *SIC* 1622

C C MYERS INC p 232
3286 Fitzgerald Rd, Rancho Cordova CA 95742
Tel (916) 635-9370 *SIC* 1622

SKANSKA USA CIVIL WEST CALIFORNIA DISTRICT INC p 1329
1995 Agua Mansa Rd, Riverside CA 92509
Tel (951) 684-5360
SIC 1611 1622 1629 8711 2951

FLATIRON WEST INC p 555
1770 La Costa Meadows Dr, San Marcos CA 92078
Tel (760) 916-9100 *SIC* 1622 1611

TUTOR PERINI CORP p 1493
15901 Olden St, Sylmar CA 91342
Tel (818) 362-8391 *SIC* 1542 1611 1622

JF SHEA CONSTRUCTION INC p 785
655 Brea Canyon Rd, Walnut CA 91789
Tel (909) 595-4397 *SIC* 1521 1622 6512

■ **GRANITE CONSTRUCTION CO** p 631
585 W Beach St, Watsonville CA 95076
Tel (831) 724-1011 *SIC* 1611 1622

▲ **GRANITE CONSTRUCTION INC** p 631
585 W Beach St, Watsonville CA 95076
Tel (831) 724-1011
SIC 1611 1622 1629 1442

FLATIRON CONSTRUCTION CORP p 554
385 Interlocken Blvd, Broomfield CO 80021
Tel (303) 485-4050 *SIC* 1622 1629 1611

FLATIRON CONSTRUCTORS INC p 555
385 Interlocken, Broomfield CO 80021
Tel (303) 485-4050 *SIC* 1611 1622 1629

FLATIRON HOLDING INC p 555
385 Interlocken Cres, Broomfield CO 80021
Tel (303) 485-4050 *SIC* 1622 1629

SEMA CONSTRUCTION INC p 1302
7353 S Eagle St, Centennial CO 80112
Tel (303) 627-2600 *SIC* 1622 1771

PCL CIVIL CONSTRUCTORS INC p 1124
2000 S Colo Blvd Ste 2-50, Denver CO 80222
Tel (303) 365-6500
SIC 1611 1622 1623 1629

▲ **SUMMIT MATERIALS INC** p 1399
1550 Wynkoop St Fl 3, Denver CO 80202
Tel (303) 893-0012 *SIC* 1422 1622 1795

HENSEL PHELPS CONSTRUCTION CO p 684
420 6th Ave, Greeley CO 80631
Tel (970) 352-6565
SIC 1542 1521 1771 1522 1541 1622

■ **AECOM ENERGY & CONSTRUCTION INC** p 28
6200 S Quebec St, Greenwood Village CO 80111
Tel (303) 228-3000
SIC 1622 1629 1081 4953

AMERICAN CIVIL CONSTRUCTORS HOLDINGS INC p 70
4901 S Windermere St, Littleton CO 80120
Tel (303) 795-2582 *SIC* 1622 0781

LANE CONSTRUCTION CORP p 843
90 Fieldstone Ct, Cheshire CT 06410
Tel (203) 235-3351
SIC 1622 1611 1629 3272 5032

LANE INDUSTRIES INC p 843
90 Fieldstone Ct, Cheshire CT 06410
Tel (203) 235-3351
SIC 1629 1611 5032 3272 1622

MANAFORT BROTHERS INC p 900
414 New Britain Ave, Plainville CT 06062
Tel (860) 229-4853
SIC 1794 1771 1622 1795 4953

ODEBRECHT CONSTRUCTION INC p 1074
201 Alhambra Cir Ste 1000, Coral Gables FL 33134
Tel (305) 341-8800 *SIC* 1622 1522

CONDOTTE AMERICA INC p 355
10790 Nw 127th St, Medley FL 33178
Tel (305) 670-7585 *SIC* 1611 1622 1542

DE MOYA GROUP INC p 419
14600 Sw 136th St, Miami FL 33186
Tel (305) 255-5713 *SIC* 1611 1622

GLF CONSTRUCTION CORP p 615
528 Nw 7th Ave, Miami FL 33136
Tel (305) 371-5228
SIC 1611 1622 1542 1541 1522

MUNILLA CONSTRUCTION MANAGEMENT LLC p 1000
6201 Sw 70th St Fl 2, South Miami FL 33143
Tel (305) 541-0000 *SIC* 1622 1542

APAC-SOUTHEAST INC p 95
900 Ashwood Pkwy Ste 700, Atlanta GA 30338
Tel (770) 392-5300 *SIC* 1611 1622 2951

ARCHER WESTERN CONTRACTORS LLC p 105
2410 Paces Ferry Rd Se # 600, Atlanta GA 30339
Tel (404) 495-8700
SIC 1542 1622 1611 1629

KAJIMA USA INC p 801
3475 Piedmont Rd Ne, Atlanta GA 30305
Tel (404) 564-3900
SIC 1542 1541 6531 1522 6552 1622

OLDCASTLE MATERIALS INC p 1082
900 Ashwood Pkwy Ste 700, Atlanta GA 30338
Tel (770) 522-5600
SIC 3272 1622 1611 2951 5032

ARCHER WESTERN CONSTRUCTION LLC p 105
929 W Adams St, Chicago IL 60607
Tel (312) 563-5400
SIC 1521 1622 1629 1542

FH PASCHEN SN NIELSEN INC p 539
5515 N East River Rd, Chicago IL 60656
Tel (773) 444-3474
SIC 1611 1622 1522 1542

JAMES MCHUGH CONSTRUCTION CO p 776
1737 S Michigan Ave, Chicago IL 60616
Tel (312) 986-8000 *SIC* 1542 1522 1622

MCHUGH ENTERPRISES INC p 929
1737 S Michigan Ave, Chicago IL 60616
Tel (312) 986-8000
SIC 1542 1522 1622 1771 1742 6552

WALSH CONSTRUCTION CO p 1574
929 W Adams St, Chicago IL 60607
Tel (312) 563-5400
SIC 1541 1622 1542 1611

WALSH GROUP LTD p 1574
929 W Adams St, Chicago IL 60607
Tel (312) 563-5400
SIC 1542 1522 1622 1629 1541

LORIG CONSTRUCTION CO p 878
250 E Touhy Ave, Des Plaines IL 60018
Tel (847) 298-0360 *SIC* 1622

HELM GROUP INC p 682
2283 Business Us 20 E, Freeport IL 61032
Tel (815) 235-2244 *SIC* 1611 1622 1629

■ **KENNY CONSTRUCTION A GRANITE CO** p 811
2215 Sanders Rd Ste 400, Northbrook IL 60062
Tel (847) 919-8200
SIC 1622 1611 1629 1623 1541

■ **KENNY INDUSTRIES INC** p 811
2215 Sanders Rd Ste 400, Northbrook IL 60062
Tel (847) 919-8200
SIC 1611 1622 1629 1623 1541 6552

FREESEN INC p 577
3151 Robbins Rd Ste A, Springfield IL 62704
Tel (217) 546-6192 *SIC* 1622 1771 1629

UNITED CONTRACTORS MIDWEST INC p 1507
3151 Robbins Rd Ste A, Springfield IL 62704
Tel (217) 546-6192 *SIC* 8742 1622 5082

WEDDLE BROS CONSTRUCTION CO INC p 1587
1201 W 3rd St, Bloomington IN 47404
Tel (812) 339-9500 *SIC* 1542 1622 1541

TRAYLOR BROS INC p 1475
835 N Congress Ave, Evansville IN 47715
Tel (812) 477-1542 *SIC* 1622

RIETH-RILEY CONSTRUCTION CO INC p 1234
3626 Elkhart Rd, Goshen IN 46526
Tel (574) 875-5183 *SIC* 1611 1771 1622

MAC CONSTRUCTION & EXCAVATING INC p 891
1908 Unruh Ct, New Albany IN 47150
Tel (812) 284-4250 *SIC* 1623 1622 1794

SUPERIOR CONSTRUCTION CO INC p 1406
1455 Louis Sullivan Dr, Portage IN 46368
Tel (219) 886-3728 *SIC* 1541 1629 1622

JENSEN CONSTRUCTION CO p 782
5550 Ne 22nd St, Des Moines IA 50313
Tel (515) 266-5173 *SIC* 1622 1629

RASMUSSEN GROUP INC p 1209
5550 Ne 22nd St, Des Moines IA 50313
Tel (515) 266-5173 *SIC* 1622 1611 3272

GODBERSEN-SMITH CONSTRUCTION CO INC p 619
121 E State Highway 175, Ida Grove IA 51445
Tel (712) 364-3388 *SIC* 3531 1622

L G BARCUS AND SONS INC p 834
1430 State Ave, Kansas City KS 66102
Tel (913) 621-1100 *SIC* 1629 1622

MASSMAN CONSTRUCTION CO p 917
4400 W 109th St Ste 300, Leawood KS 66211
Tel (913) 291-2600 *SIC* 1629 1622

APAC-KANSAS INC p 95
7415 W 130th St Ste 300, Overland Park KS 66213
Tel (913) 371-1003
SIC 1611 1771 2951 7353 1622

DONDLINGER & SONS CONSTRUCTION CO INC p 450
2656 S Sheridan Ave, Wichita KS 67217
Tel (316) 945-0555 *SIC* 1622 1541 1542

EBY CORP p 474
2525 E 36th Cir N, Wichita KS 67219
Tel (316) 268-3500
SIC 1629 1623 1622 1541 1542 7353

WILDCAT CONSTRUCTION CO INC p 1609
3219 W May St, Wichita KS 67213
Tel (316) 945-9408
SIC 1623 1622 1771 1611 1629

COASTAL BRIDGE CO LLC p 331
4825 Jamestown Ave, Baton Rouge LA 70808
Tel (225) 766-0244 *SIC* 1622

■ **JAMES CONSTRUCTION GROUP LLC** p 776
18484 E Petroleum Dr, Baton Rouge LA 70809
Tel (225) 293-0274 *SIC* 1611 1622

BOH BROS CONSTRUCTION CO LLC p 197
730 S Tonti St, New Orleans LA 70119
Tel (504) 821-2400
SIC 1611 1622 1629 1623

CIANBRO COMPANIES p 305
1 Hunnewell Ave, Pittsfield ME 04967
Tel (207) 487-3311
SIC 1629 1622 1542 1541 8742

CIANBRO CORP p 305
101 Cianbro Sq, Pittsfield ME 04967
Tel (207) 487-3311
SIC 1622 1629 1542 1541 8742

REED & REED INC p 1217
275 River Rd, Woolwich ME 04579
Tel (207) 443-9747 *SIC* 1622 1629 1541

CORMAN CONSTRUCTION INC p 370
12001 Guilford Rd, Annapolis Junction MD 20701
Tel (301) 953-0900 *SIC* 1611 1622 1623

STRUCTURAL TECHNOLOGIES LLC p 1394
10150 Old Columbia Rd, Columbia MD 21046
Tel (410) 850-7000 *SIC* 1622 8711

FLIPPO CONSTRUCTION CO INC p 557
3820 Penn Belt Pl, District Heights MD 20747
Tel (301) 967-6800 *SIC* 1623 1622

MCLEAN CONTRACTING CO p 931
6700 Mclean Way, Glen Burnie MD 21060
Tel (410) 553-6700
SIC 1622 1623 1629 3449

■ **CHERRY HILL CONSTRUCTION INC** p 294
8211 Washington Blvd, Jessup MD 20794
Tel (410) 799-3577 *SIC* 1611 1622

FACCHINA CONSTRUCTION CO INC p 523
102 Centennial St Ste 201, La Plata MD 20646
Tel (240) 776-7000
SIC 1542 1799 1623 1611 1622 1629

MCCOURT CONSTRUCTION CO INC p 927
60 K St, Boston MA 02127
Tel (617) 269-2330 *SIC* 1611 1622

TREVI ICOS CORP p 1476
38 3rd Ave, Charlestown MA 02129
Tel (617) 241-4800 *SIC* 1629 1622

J F WHITE CONTRACTING CO p 771
10 Burr St, Framingham MA 01701
Tel (508) 879-4700 *SIC* 1622

DANIEL OCONNELLS SONS INC p 411
480 Hampden St, Holyoke MA 01040
Tel (413) 534-5667
SIC 1541 1542 1522 1611 1622 1629

MIDDLESEX CORP p 965
1 Spectacle Pond Rd, Littleton MA 01460
Tel (978) 742-4400 *SIC* 1611 1794 1622

CS MCCROSSAN INC p 397
7865 Jefferson Hwy, Maple Grove MN 55369
Tel (763) 425-4167 *SIC* 1611 1622 1799

PARK CONSTRUCTION CO p 1115
1481 81st Ave Ne, Minneapolis MN 55432
Tel (763) 786-9800 *SIC* 1611 1622 1629

HILL BROTHERS CONSTRUCTION CO INC p 693
20831 Highway 15, Falkner MS 38629
Tel (662) 837-3041
SIC 1611 1622 1541 1542

EMERY SAPP & SONS INC p 492
2301 Interstate 70 Dr Nw, Columbia MO 65202
Tel (573) 445-8331 *SIC* 1622 1629 1611

FRED WEBER INC p 576
2320 Creve Coeur Mill Rd, Maryland Heights MO 63043
Tel (314) 344-0070
SIC 1611 1442 3272 1622 1542

SAK CONSTRUCTION LLC p 1271
864 Hoff Rd, O Fallon MO 63366
Tel (636) 674-9104 *SIC* 1623 1622

ALBERICI CONSTRUCTORS INC p 46
8800 Page Ave, Saint Louis MO 63114
Tel (314) 733-2000 *SIC* 1541 1542 1622

ALBERICI CORP p 46
8800 Page Ave, Saint Louis MO 63114
Tel (314) 733-2000
SIC 1541 1542 1622 1629

ALBERICI GROUP INC p 46
8800 Page Ave, Saint Louis MO 63114
Tel (314) 733-2000 *SIC* 1541 1542 1622

LIONMARK CONSTRUCTION COMPANIES LLC p 870
1620 Woodson Rd, Saint Louis MO 63114
Tel (314) 991-2180 *SIC* 1611 2951 1622

COP CONSTRUCTION LLC p 368
242 S 64th St W, Billings MT 59106
Tel (406) 656-4632 *SIC* 1622 1629

BARNARD CONSTRUCTION CO INC p 155
701 Gold Ave, Bozeman MT 59715
Tel (406) 586-1995
SIC 1623 1629 1611 1622

DICK ANDERSON CONSTRUCTION INC p 437
3424 E Us Highway 12, Helena MT 59601
Tel (406) 443-3225 *SIC* 1542 1622 1611

KIEWIT CORP p 817
3555 Farnam St Ste 1000, Omaha NE 68131
Tel (402) 342-2052
SIC 1542 1541 1611 1622 1629

KIEWIT INFRASTRUCTURE CO p 817
Kiewit Plz, Omaha NE 68131
Tel (402) 342-2052
SIC 1541 1542 1629 1622 1522

KIEWIT INFRASTRUCTURE GROUP INC p 817
3555 Farnam St, Omaha NE 68131
Tel (402) 342-2052 *SIC* 1611 1622

KIEWIT INFRASTRUCTURE SOUTH CO p 817
Kiewit Plz No 1044, Omaha NE 68131
Tel (402) 342-2052 *SIC* 1622 1611

KIEWIT INFRASTRUCTURE WEST CO p 817
4004 S 60th St, Omaha NE 68117
Tel (402) 342-2052
SIC 1611 1629 1541 1622 1623

PETER KIEWIT SONS INC p 1138
3555 Farnam St Ste 1000, Omaha NE 68131
Tel (402) 342-2052
SIC 1611 1622 1711 1542 1629 1221

SKANSKA KOCH INC p 1329
400 Roosevelt Ave, Carteret NJ 07008
Tel (732) 969-1700 *SIC* 1622

CONTI ENTERPRISES INC p 362
2045 Lincoln Hwy, Edison NJ 08817
Tel (732) 520-5000 *SIC* 1611 1622 1623

J FLETCHER CREAMER & SON INC p 771
101 E Broadway, Hackensack NJ 07601
Tel (201) 488-9800
SIC 1623 1611 1771 1622 1629

COLAS INC p 335
163 Madison Ave Ste 500, Morristown NJ 07960
Tel (973) 290-9082 *SIC* 1611 1622 2951

S S K CONSTRUCTORS JV p 1262
150 Meadowlands Pkwy Fl 3, Secaucus NJ 07094
Tel (201) 867-5070 *SIC* 1622

SCHIAVONE CONSTRUCTION CO LLC p 1287
150 Meadowlands Pkwy # 2, Secaucus NJ 07094
Tel (201) 867-5070 *SIC* 1622 1629

JAG COMPANIES INC p 776
1433 State Route 34 Ste 5, Wall Township NJ 07727
Tel (732) 557-6100
SIC 1623 1622 1629 1611

NORTHEAST REMSCO CONSTRUCTION INC p 1055
1433 State Route 34 Ste 6, Wall Township NJ 07727
Tel (732) 557-6100
SIC 1623 1622 1629 1611

BBL LLC p 163
302 Washington Ave, Albany NY 12203
Tel (518) 452-8200
SIC 1542 1541 1521 1622 8741

SKANSKA USA CIVIL NORTHEAST INC p 1329
7520 Astoria Blvd Ste 200, East Elmhurst NY 11370
Tel (718) 340-0811 *SIC* 1622

BETTE & CRING LLC p 178
22 Century Hill Dr # 201, Latham NY 12110
Tel (518) 213-1010
SIC 1541 1542 1622 1611

JOHN P PICONE INC p 789
31 Garden Ln, Lawrence NY 11559
Tel (516) 239-1600
SIC 1611 1622 1623 1629

DALRYMPLE HOLDING CORP p 410
2105 S Broadway, Pine City NY 14871
Tel (607) 737-6200
SIC 3273 1611 1442 1622 3281

SEALAND CONTRACTORS CORP p 1296
85 High Tech Dr, Rush NY 14543
Tel (704) 522-1102 *SIC* 1622 1611 1623

BLYTHE CONSTRUCTION INC p 193
2911 N Graham St, Charlotte NC 28206
Tel (704) 375-8474 *SIC* 1611 1622 2951

CROWDER CONSTRUCTION CO INC p 394
6425 Brookshire Blvd, Charlotte NC 28216
Tel (800) 849-2966 *SIC* 1622 1629 1623

THALLE CONSTRUCTION CO INC p 1446
900 Nc Highway 86 N, Hillsborough NC 27278
Tel (919) 245-1490
SIC 1611 1622 1623 1629

SMITH-ROWE LLC p 1333
639 Old Us 52 S, Mount Airy NC 27030
Tel (336) 789-8221 *SIC* 1622

SANFORD CONTRACTORS INC p 1279
628 Rocky Fork Church Rd, Sanford NC 27332
Tel (919) 775-7882
SIC 1611 1622 1629 6552 1794 1623

INDUSTRIAL BUILDERS INC p 739
1307 County Road 17 N, West Fargo ND 58078
Tel (701) 282-4977
SIC 1629 1622 1542 1611 1623

■ WANZEK CONSTRUCTION INC p 1575
2028 2nd Ave Nw, West Fargo ND 58078
Tel (701) 282-6171
SIC 1542 1623 1622 1799 1541 1629

MBC HOLDINGS INC p 925
1613 S Defiance St, Archbold OH 43502
Tel (419) 445-1015 SIC 1622 1611

KOKOSING CONSTRUCTION CO INC p 826
886 Mckinley Ave, Columbus OH 43222
Tel (614) 228-1029
SIC 1611 1622 1629 1542 1541 1623

RUHLIN CO p 1257
6931 Ridge Rd, Sharon Center OH 44274
Tel (330) 239-2800
SIC 1542 1541 1622 1611

MANHATTAN ROAD & BRIDGE CO p 901
5601 S 122nd East Ave, Tulsa OK 74146
Tel (918) 583-6900 SIC 1622

HAMILTON CONSTRUCTION CO p 655
2213 S F St, Springfield OR 97477
Tel (541) 746-2426 SIC 1622 3441

AMERICAN BRIDGE CO p 69
1000 American Bridge Way, Coraopolis PA 15108
Tel (412) 631-1000 SIC 1791 8711 1622

IA CONSTRUCTION CORP p 725
24 Gibb Rd, Franklin PA 16323
Tel (814) 432-3184
SIC 1611 2951 1622 1623

GLENN O HAWBAKER INC p 615
1952 Waddle Rd Ste 203, State College PA 16803
Tel (814) 237-1444
SIC 2951 3281 1622 1794 1611 1422

ALLAN MYERS INC p 51
1805 Berks Rd, Worcester PA 19490
Tel (610) 222-8800
SIC 1629 1794 1611 1622 3281 5032

ALLAN MYERS LP p 51
1805 Berks Rd, Worcester PA 19490
Tel (610) 584-3430
SIC 1629 1794 1611 1622

■ WASHINGTON GOVERNMENT ENVIRONMENTAL SERVICES CO LLC p 1578
106 Newberry St Sw, Aiken SC 29801
Tel (803) 502-5710 SIC 1622

BELL & ASSOCIATES CONSTRUCTION LP p 169
255 Wilson Pike Cir, Brentwood TN 37027
Tel (615) 373-4343 SIC 1622 1541 1542

DEMENT CONSTRUCTION CO p 428
96 Smith Ln, Jackson TN 38301
Tel (731) 424-6306 SIC 1622 1611

JONES BROS INC p 792
5760 Old Lebanon Dirt Rd, Mount Juliet TN 37122
Tel (615) 754-4710
SIC 1622 1771 1794 1629 1611

JONES INVESTMENT HOLDING INC p 792
5760 Old Lebanon Dirt Rd, Mount Juliet TN 37122
Tel (615) 754-4710
SIC 1622 1771 1794 1611

ABRAMS INTERNATIONAL INC p 12
111 Congress Ave Ste 2400, Austin TX 78701
Tel (512) 322-4000
SIC 1611 1622 1629 6799 7359 8742

JD ABRAMS LP p 780
5811 Trade Center Dr # 1, Austin TX 78744
Tel (512) 322-4000
SIC 1611 1622 1629 3272

AUSTIN INDUSTRIES INC p 133
3535 Travis St Ste 300, Dallas TX 75204
Tel (214) 443-5500
SIC 1542 1629 1611 1622

■ HALLIBURTON DELAWARE INC p 654
3000 Houston Ave, Houston TX 77009
Tel (713) 759-2600
SIC 1629 1611 1622 8711 1389

HIGHWAY TECHNOLOGIES INC p 692
6811 Dixie Dr, Houston TX 77087
Tel (713) 845-1800 SIC 1622 7359

WILLIAMS BROTHERS CONSTRUCTION CO INC p 1611
3800 Milam St, Houston TX 77006
Tel (713) 522-9821 SIC 1622

AUSTIN BRIDGE & ROAD INC p 132
6330 Commerce Dr Ste 150, Irving TX 75063
Tel (214) 596-7300 SIC 1611 1622

AUSTIN BRIDGE & ROAD LP p 132
6330 Commerce Dr Ste 150, Irving TX 75063
Tel (214) 596-7300 SIC 1622 1611

LONGVIEW BRIDGE AND ROAD LTD p 877
792 Skinner Ln, Longview TX 75605
Tel (903) 663-0264 SIC 1611 1622 1794

WORD CONSTRUCTORS LLC p 1624
1245 River Rd, New Braunfels TX 78130
Tel (830) 625-2365 SIC 1622 1611

JOHNSON BROS CORP p 790
608 Henrietta Creek Rd, Roanoke TX 76262
Tel (813) 685-5101 SIC 1623 1629 1622

OSCAR RENDA CONTRACTING INC p 1096
608 Henrietta Creek Rd, Roanoke TX 76262
Tel (817) 491-2703 SIC 1623 1799 1622

SOUTHLAND CONTRACTING INC p 1351
608 Henrietta Creek Rd, Roanoke TX 76262
Tel (817) 293-4263 SIC 1799 1622

ALBERT REECE INC p 46
3001 Foster St, San Angelo TX 76903
Tel (325) 653-1241
SIC 1611 1794 1623 1622

HIRSCHFELD HOLDINGS LP p 696
112 W 29th St, San Angelo TX 76903
Tel (325) 486-4201 SIC 1622 3441

HB ZACHRY CO p 671
527 Logwood Ave, San Antonio TX 78221
Tel (210) 475-8000
SIC 1611 1622 1623 1629

YANTIS CORP p 1635
3611 Paesanos Pkwy # 300, San Antonio TX 78231
Tel (210) 655-3780
SIC 1623 1611 1622 1629 6552 1521

ZACHRY CONSOLIDATED LLC p 1640
527 Logwood Ave, San Antonio TX 78221
Tel (210) 871-2700
SIC 1611 1622 1623 1629 3241 1442

ZACHRY CONSTRUCTION & MATERIALS INC p 1640
2330 N Loop 1604 W, San Antonio TX 78248
Tel (210) 479-1027
SIC 1611 1622 1623 1629 1542 3241

ZACHRY CONSTRUCTION CORP p 1640
2330 N Loop 1604 W, San Antonio TX 78248
Tel (210) 871-2700
SIC 1623 1611 1622 1629 1542

▲ STERLING CONSTRUCTION CO INC p 1387
1800 Hughes Landing Blvd # 250, The Woodlands TX 77380
Tel (281) 214-0800 SIC 1611 1622 1623

CENTURY CONCRETE INC p 282
1364 Air Rail Ave, Virginia Beach VA 23455
Tel (757) 460-5366 SIC 1622 1611 1771

SKANSKA USA CIVIL SOUTHEAST INC p 1329
295 Bendix Rd Ste 400, Virginia Beach VA 23452
Tel (757) 420-4140
SIC 1622 1629 3272 1541

GENERAL CONSTRUCTION CO p 600
33455 6th Ave S, Federal Way WA 98003
Tel (253) 943-4200 SIC 1622 1629

VECELLIO & GROGAN INC p 1546
2251 Robert C Byrd Dr, Beckley WV 25801
Tel (304) 252-6575 SIC 1611 1622 1629

ORDERS CONSTRUCTION CO INC p 1093
501 6th Ave, Saint Albans WV 25177
Tel (304) 722-4237 SIC 1622 1611

■ LUNDA CONSTRUCTION CO p 886
620 Gebhardt Rd, Black River Falls WI 54615
Tel (715) 284-2322 SIC 1622 8711

EDWARD KRAEMER & SONS INC p 480
1 Plainview Rd, Plain WI 53577
Tel (608) 546-2311 SIC 1622 1442

SIC 1623 Water, Sewer & Utility Line Construction

UTILITIES BOARD OF CITY OF FOLEY p 1537
413 E Laurel Ave, Foley AL 36535
Tel (251) 943-5001 SIC 4911 1623 4841

L E BELL CONSTRUCTION CO INC p 834
1226 County Road 11, Heflin AL 36264
Tel (256) 253-2434 SIC 1623

REED CONTRACTING SERVICES INC p 1217
2512 Triana Blvd Sw, Huntsville AL 35805
Tel (256) 533-0505
SIC 1771 1794 1623 1629 1611

ARCTIC SLOPE REGIONAL CORP p 106
3900 C St Ste 801, Anchorage AK 99503
Tel (907) 339-6000 SIC 1389 2911 1623

KIEWIT WESTERN CO p 817
3888 E Broadway Rd, Phoenix AZ 85040
Tel (602) 437-7878
SIC 1622 1629 1794 1611 1623

■ NPL CONSTRUCTION CO p 1064
2355 W Utopia Rd, Phoenix AZ 85027
Tel (623) 582-1235 SIC 1623

■ PAULEY CONSTRUCTION LLC p 1121
2021 W Melinda Ln, Phoenix AZ 85027
Tel (623) 581-1200 SIC 1623

DEPCOM POWER INC p 430
9200 E Pima Center Pkwy # 180, Scottsdale AZ 85258
Tel (480) 270-6910 SIC 1623 5211

SULPHUR SPRINGS VALLEY ELECTRIC COOPERATIVE INC CHARITABLE p 1397
311 E Wilcox Dr, Sierra Vista AZ 85635
Tel (520) 384-2221 SIC 4911 1731 1623

PIMA COUNTY p 1148
97 E Congress St Fl 3, Tucson AZ 85701
Tel (520) 243-1800 SIC 9111 1623

ARKANSAS ELECTRIC COOPERATIVES INC p 109
1 Cooperative Way, Little Rock AR 72209
Tel (501) 570-2361
SIC 5063 1623 1629 7629

LINKUS ENTERPRISES LLC p 869
18631 Lloyd Ln, Anderson CA 96007
Tel (530) 229-9197 SIC 1623 5731 4813

KEN SMALL CONSTRUCTION INC p 810
6205 District Blvd, Bakersfield CA 93313
Tel (661) 617-1700 SIC 1623

KS INDUSTRIES LP p 831
6205 District Blvd, Bakersfield CA 93313
Tel (661) 617-1700 SIC 1623

NTS INC p 1065
8200 Stockdale Hwy Ste M, Bakersfield CA 93311
Tel (661) 588-8514 SIC 1623 1541 1771

ROBERT HEELY INC p 1241
5401 Woodmere Dr, Bakersfield CA 93313
Tel (661) 617-1400 SIC 1623

WEST VALLEY CONSTRUCTION CO INC p 1596
580 E Mcglincy Ln, Campbell CA 95008
Tel (408) 371-5510 SIC 1623

HP COMMUNICATIONS INC p 714
13341 Temescal Canyon Rd, Corona CA 92883
Tel (951) 572-1200 SIC 1623

KOBELCO COMPRESSORS AMERICA INC p 825
1450 W Rincon St, Corona CA 92880
Tel (951) 739-3030 SIC 1623 3563

CASS CONSTRUCTION INC p 263
1100 Wagner Dr, El Cajon CA 92020
Tel (619) 590-0929 SIC 1623 1611

■ UNIVERSITY MECHANICAL & ENGINEERING CONTRACTORS INC p 1519
1168 Fesler St, El Cajon CA 92020
Tel (619) 956-2500 SIC 1711 1623 8741

JR FILANC CONSTRUCTION CO INC p 795
740 N Andreasen Dr, Escondido CA 92029
Tel (760) 941-7130 SIC 1623 1629

W M LYLES CO p 1569
1210 W Olive Ave, Fresno CA 93728
Tel (951) 973-7393 SIC 1623

ARIZONA PIPE LINE CO p 109
17372 Lilac St, Hesperia CA 92345
Tel (760) 244-8212 SIC 1623

■ ARB INC p 102
26000 Commercentre Dr, Lake Forest CA 92630
Tel (949) 598-9242 SIC 1629 1623

■ VADNAIS TRENCHLESS SERVICES INC p 1538
26000 Commercentre Dr, Lake Forest CA 92630
Tel (858) 550-1460 SIC 1623 1622

W A RASIC CONSTRUCTION CO INC p 1568
4150 Long Beach Blvd, Long Beach CA 90807
Tel (562) 928-6111 SIC 1623

■ AECOM E&C HOLDINGS INC p 28
1999 Avenue Of Ste 2600, Los Angeles CA 90067
Tel (213) 593-8000
SIC 8711 1611 1629 1623 1541 1622

PRESTON PIPELINES INC p 1173
133 Bothelo Ave, Milpitas CA 95035
Tel (408) 262-1418 SIC 1623

NOVA GROUP INC p 1062
185 Devlin Rd, Napa CA 94558
Tel (707) 265-1100
SIC 1629 1623 1622 5172

HCI INC p 672
3166 Hrseless Carriage Rd, Norco CA 92860
Tel (951) 520-4202 SIC 1623

LOMBARDY HOLDINGS INC p 875
3166 Hrseless Carriage Rd, Norco CA 92860
Tel (951) 808-4550 SIC 1623 5211

DOTY BROS EQUIPMENT CO p 452
11232 Firestone Blvd, Norwalk CA 90650
Tel (562) 864-6566 SIC 1623

MCGUIRE AND HESTER p 929
9009 Railroad Ave, Oakland CA 94603
Tel (510) 632-7676 SIC 1623 7353

SHIMMICK CONSTRUCTION CO INC p 1316
8201 Edgewater Dr Ste 202, Oakland CA 94621
Tel (510) 777-5000 SIC 1629 1623

HERMAN WEISSKER INC p 687
1645 Brown Ave, Riverside CA 92509
Tel (951) 826-8800 SIC 1623 8711 1731

DON CHAPIN CO INC p 449
560 Crazy Horse Canyon Rd, Salinas CA 93907
Tel (831) 449-4273 SIC 1623 1611 1771

LEDCOR CMI INC p 851
6405 Mira Mesa Blvd # 100, San Diego CA 92121
Tel (602) 595-3017
SIC 1541 1611 1629 1623 1522 8999

BECHTEL CONSTRUCTION OPERATIONS INC p 167
50 Beale St Bsmt 1, San Francisco CA 94105
Tel (415) 768-1234
SIC 1541 1629 1623 8741 7353

■ REC SOLAR COMMERCIAL CORP p 1214
3450 Broad St Ste 105, San Luis Obispo CA 93401
Tel (844) 732-7652 SIC 1623

GHILOTTI BROS INC p 610
525 Jacoby St, San Rafael CA 94901
Tel (415) 454-7011 SIC 1611 1794 1623

OTAY WATER DISTRICT (INC) p 1097
2554 Swetwater Sprng Blvd, Spring Valley CA 91978
Tel (619) 670-2222 SIC 4941 1623

■ GREAT SOUTHWESTERN CONSTRUCTION INC p 634
1100 Topeka Way, Castle Rock CO 80109
Tel (303) 688-5816 SIC 1623

■ FLINT ENERGY SERVICES INC p 557
6901 S Havana St, Centennial CO 80112
Tel (918) 294-3030 SIC 1389 3594 1623

PCL CIVIL CONSTRUCTORS INC p 1124
2000 S Colo Blvd Ste 2-50, Denver CO 80222
Tel (303) 365-6500
SIC 1611 1622 1623 1629

■ UNITED PIPELINE SYSTEMS USA INC p 1510
135 Turner Dr, Durango CO 81303
Tel (970) 259-0354 SIC 1623

TIC HOLDINGS INC p 1452
9780 Pyramid Ct Ste 100, Englewood CO 80112
Tel (970) 879-2561
SIC 1541 1629 1623 1542

■ STURGEON ELECTRIC CO INC p 1395
12150 E 112th Ave, Henderson CO 80640
Tel (303) 227-6990 SIC 1731 1623

STERLING CONSTRUCTION MANAGEMENT LLC p 1387
3158 Baron Ln Unit E, Rifle CO 81650
Tel (307) 362-7906 SIC 1623

■ EVERSOURCE ENERGY SERVICE CO p 515
107 Selden St, Berlin CT 06037
Tel (860) 665-5000 SIC 1623

▲ CONNECTICUT WATER SERVICE INC p 357
93 W Main St, Clinton CT 06413
Tel (860) 669-8636 SIC 4941 6531 1623

O & G INDUSTRIES INC p 1070
112 Wall St, Torrington CT 06790
Tel (860) 489-9261
SIC 1542 1541 1611 1623 5032 2951

GEORGE & LYNCH INC p 606
150 Lafferty Ln, Dover DE 19901
Tel (302) 736-3031
SIC 1623 1611 1629 1731

■ PEPCO ENERGY SERVICES INC p 1133
701 9th St Nw Ste 2100, Washington DC 20001
Tel (703) 253-1800
SIC 1711 1731 1623 4961

▲ MASTEC INC p 917
800 S Douglas Rd Ste 1200, Coral Gables FL 33134
Tel (305) 599-1800 SIC 1623 8741

■ MASTEC NORTH AMERICA INC p 918
800 S Douglas Rd Ste 1200, Coral Gables FL 33134
Tel (305) 599-1800 SIC 1623

HYPOWER INC p 724
5913 Nw 31st Ave, Fort Lauderdale FL 33309
Tel (954) 978-9300 SIC 1623 1731

HASKELL CO p 667
111 Riverside Ave, Jacksonville FL 32202
Tel (904) 791-4500
SIC 1541 1542 1522 1623 8712 3272

HASKELL CO INC p 667
111 Riverside Ave, Jacksonville FL 32202
Tel (904) 791-4500
SIC 1541 1542 1522 1623 8712 3272

JEA p 781
21 W Church St Fl 1, Jacksonville FL 32202
Tel (904) 665-6000 SIC 4911 1623

UTILITY BOARD OF CITY OF KEY WEST p 1537
1001 James St, Key West FL 33040
Tel (305) 295-1000 SIC 1623

▲ GOLDFIELD CORP DEL p 622
1684 W Hibiscus Blvd, Melbourne FL 32901
Tel (321) 724-1700 SIC 1623 1731

DOWNRITE HOLDINGS INC p 453
14241 Sw 143rd Ct, Miami FL 33186
Tel (305) 232-2340
SIC 1611 1623 8711 1794

▲ DYCOM INDUSTRIES INC p 464
11780 Us Highway 1 # 600, Palm Beach Gardens FL 33408
Tel (561) 627-7171 SIC 1623 1731

■ DYCOM INVESTMENTS INC p 464
11770 Us Highway 1 # 101, Palm Beach Gardens FL 33408
Tel (561) 627-7171 SIC 1623

■ POWER CORP OF AMERICA p 1165
4647 Clyde Morris Blvd, Port Orange FL 32129
Tel (386) 333-6441 SIC 1731 1623

KIMMINS CONTRACTING CORP p 819
1501 E 2nd Ave, Tampa FL 33605
Tel (813) 248-3878 SIC 1623

FLORIDA KEYS ELECTRIC COOPERATIVE ASSOCIATION INC p 559
91630 Overseas Hwy, Tavernier FL 33070
Tel (305) 852-2431 SIC 4911 1731 1623

GECOS INC p 597
1936 Lee Rd, Winter Park FL 32789
Tel (407) 645-5500 SIC 1611 2951 1623

HUBBARD CONSTRUCTION CO p 716
1936 Lee Rd Ste 101, Winter Park FL 32789
Tel (407) 645-5500 SIC 1611 2951 1623

HUBBARD GROUP INC p 716
1936 Lee Rd Ste 101, Winter Park FL 32789
Tel (407) 645-5500 SIC 1611 2951 1623

■ UTILIQUEST LLC p 1537
2575 Westside Pkwy # 100, Alpharetta GA 30004
Tel (678) 461-3900 SIC 1623 3812

MUNICIPAL ELECTRIC AUTHORITY OF GEORGIA p 1000
1470 Riveredge Pkwy, Atlanta GA 30328
Tel (770) 563-0300 SIC 1623

■ ANSCO & ASSOCIATES LLC p 93
736 Park North Blvd, Clarkston GA 30021
Tel (404) 508-5700 SIC 1623

LATEX CONSTRUCTION CO INC p 846
1353 Farmer Rd Nw, Conyers GA 30012
Tel (770) 760-0820 SIC 1623

SOUTHEAST CONNECTIONS LLC p 1345
2720 Dogwood Dr Se, Conyers GA 30013
Tel (678) 509-0165 SIC 1623

BRENT SCARBROUGH & CO INC p 210
155 Robinson Dr, Fayetteville GA 30214
Tel (770) 461-8603 SIC 1623

INFRATECH CORP p 742
2036 Baker Ct Nw, Kennesaw GA 30144
Tel (770) 792-8700 SIC 1623

SIGNAL POINT SYSTEMS INC p 1322
1270 Shiloh Rd Nw Ste 100, Kennesaw GA 30144
Tel (770) 499-0439 SIC 1623

OSMOSE UTILITIES SERVICES INC p 1097
635 Highway 74 S, Peachtree City GA 30269
Tel (770) 632-6700 SIC 8741 8711 1623

MIDWEST UNDERGROUND TECHNOLOGY INC p 968
2626 Midwest Ct, Champaign IL 61822
Tel (217) 819-3040 SIC 1731 1623

LSC COMMUNICATIONS US LLC p 883
35 W Wacker Dr, Chicago IL 60601
Tel (844) 572-5720 SIC 1623

CONTRACTING & MATERIAL CO p 364
9550 W 55th St Ste A, Countryside IL 60525
Tel (708) 588-6000
SIC 4922 1623 4612 1731

■ KENNY CONSTRUCTION A GRANITE CO p 811
2215 Sanders Rd Ste 400, Northbrook IL 60062
Tel (847) 919-8200
SIC 1622 1611 1629 1623 1541

■ KENNY INDUSTRIES INC p 811
2215 Sanders Rd Ste 400, Northbrook IL 60062
Tel (847) 919-8200
SIC 1611 1622 1629 1623 1541 6552

L & H CO INC p 833
2215 York Rd Ste 304, Oak Brook IL 60523
Tel (630) 571-7200
SIC 1731 1611 1623 3621

■ L E MYERS CO p 834
1701 Golf Rd Ste 3-1012, Rolling Meadows IL 60008
Tel (847) 290-1891 SIC 1623

▲ MYR GROUP INC p 1004
1701 Golf Rd Ste 3-1012, Rolling Meadows IL 60008
Tel (847) 290-1891 SIC 1623 1731

INTREN INC p 760
18202 W Union Rd, Union IL 60180
Tel (815) 923-2300 SIC 1623

▲ VECTREN CORP p 1546
1 Vectren Sq, Evansville IN 47708
Tel (812) 491-4000
SIC 4924 4911 1241 1623 6531

CONSOLIDATED FABRICATION AND CONSTRUCTORS INC p 359
3851 Ellsworth St, Gary IN 46408
Tel (219) 884-6150 *SIC* 1623

BOWEN ENGINEERING CORP p 204
8802 N Meridian St Ste X, Indianapolis IN 46260
Tel (219) 661-9770 *SIC* 1629 1623 1541

■ MILLER PIPELINE LLC p 971
8850 Crawfordsville Rd, Indianapolis IN 46234
Tel (317) 293-0278 *SIC* 1623

RELIANT SERVICE LLC p 1222
8850 Crawfordsville Rd, Indianapolis IN 46234
Tel (317) 295-6407 *SIC* 1623

USIC LLC p 1535
9045 River Rd Ste 300, Indianapolis IN 46240
Tel (317) 575-7800 *SIC* 1623 8713

USIC LOCATING SERVICES LLC p 1535
9045 River Rd Ste 300, Indianapolis IN 46240
Tel (317) 816-2207 *SIC* 1623

MITCHELL & STARK CONSTRUCTION CO INC p 976
170 W 1st St, Medora IN 47260
Tel (812) 966-2151 *SIC* 1623 1629

MAC CONSTRUCTION & EXCAVATING INC p 891
1908 Unruh Ct, New Albany IN 47150
Tel (812) 284-4250 *SIC* 1623 1622 1794

■ LAYNE HEAVY CIVIL INC p 848
4520 N State Road 37, Orleans IN 47452
Tel (812) 865-3232 *SIC* 1623 1781 1629

■ LAYNE INLINER LLC p 848
4520 N State Rd State 37, Orleans IN 47452
Tel (812) 865-3232 *SIC* 1623

GREEN COMPANIES INC p 636
8710 Earhart Ln Sw, Cedar Rapids IA 52404
Tel (319) 841-4000
SIC 8711 8748 8713 4911 1623

MCANINCH CORP p 926
4001 Delaware Ave, Des Moines IA 50313
Tel (515) 267-2500 *SIC* 1623 1794

■ COFFEYVILLE RESOURCES LLC p 334
10 E Cambridge Circle Dr, Kansas City KS 66103
Tel (913) 982-0500 *SIC* 1623

CIMARRON UNDERGROUND INC p 307
8375 Melrose Dr, Lenexa KS 66214
Tel (913) 438-2981 *SIC* 1623 1731

EBY CORP p 474
2525 E 36th Cir N, Wichita KS 67219
Tel (316) 268-3500
SIC 1629 1623 1622 1541 1542 7353

WILDCAT CONSTRUCTION CO INC p 1609
3219 W May St, Wichita KS 67213
Tel (316) 945-9408
SIC 1623 1622 1771 1611 1629

DAVIS H ELLIOT CONSTRUCTION CO INC p 416
673 Blue Sky Pkwy, Lexington KY 40509
Tel (859) 263-5148 *SIC* 1623 1731

HALL CONTRACTING OF KENTUCKY INC p 654
3800 Crittenden Dr, Louisville KY 40209
Tel (502) 367-6151
SIC 1541 1623 1761 1731

■ ERVIN CABLE CONSTRUCTION LLC p 508
450 Pryor Blvd, Sturgis KY 42459
Tel (270) 333-3366 *SIC* 1623

T & D SOLUTIONS LLC p 1419
6411 Masonic Dr, Alexandria LA 71301
Tel (318) 442-8138 *SIC* 1623

CAJUN CONSTRUCTORS LLC p 237
15635 Airline Hwy, Baton Rouge LA 70817
Tel (225) 753-5857
SIC 1623 4952 1541 1542

FORD BACON & DAVIS LLC p 565
12021 Lakeland Park Blvd # 212, Baton Rouge LA 70809
Tel (225) 297-3431 *SIC* 8711 1541 1623

CELLXION LLC p 274
5031 Hazel Jones Rd, Bossier City LA 71111
Tel (318) 213-2900
SIC 4812 1623 3448 3441

W H C INC p 1568
300 Industrial Trce, Broussard LA 70518
Tel (337) 837-4500 *SIC* 1623 1541

LOUISIANA CRANE & CONSTRUCTION LLC p 880
1045 Highway 190, Eunice LA 70535
Tel (337) 550-6217 *SIC* 7389 7353 1623

SUNLAND CONSTRUCTION INC p 1403
2532 Aymond St, Eunice LA 70535
Tel (337) 546-0241 *SIC* 1623

CHET MORRISON CONTRACTORS LLC p 295
9 Bayou Dularge Rd, Houma LA 70363
Tel (985) 868-1950
SIC 1623 3498 1629 1389

PERFORMANCE ENERGY SERVICES LLC p 1135
132 Valhi Lagoon Xing, Houma LA 70360
Tel (985) 868-4895 *SIC* 1623 1389 7363

BOH BROS CONSTRUCTION CO LLC p 197
730 S Tonti St, New Orleans LA 70119
Tel (504) 821-2400
SIC 1611 1622 1629 1623

■ J RAY MCDERMOTT & CO INC p 772
1340 Poydras St Ste 1200, New Orleans LA 70112
Tel (504) 587-5000 *SIC* 1629 1389 1623

CG ENTERPRISES INC p 285
12001 Guilford Rd Ste 1, Annapolis Junction MD 20701
Tel (301) 953-3366 *SIC* 1611 1623

CORMAN CONSTRUCTION INC p 370
12001 Guilford Rd, Annapolis Junction MD 20701
Tel (301) 953-0900 *SIC* 1611 1622 1623

RUMMEL KLEPPER & KAHL LLP p 1257
81 Mosher St, Baltimore MD 21217
Tel (410) 728-2900
SIC 8711 8741 1623 8999 8713 1611

DIXIE CONSTRUCTION CO INC p 444
260 Hopewell Rd, Churchville MD 21028
Tel (410) 879-8055 *SIC* 1611 1623

PLEASANTS CONSTRUCTION INC p 1156
24024 Frederick Rd, Clarksburg MD 20871
Tel (301) 428-0800 *SIC* 1794 1623 1611

FLIPPO CONSTRUCTION CO INC p 557
3820 Penn Belt Pl, District Heights MD 20747
Tel (301) 967-6800 *SIC* 1623 1622

ALLAN MYERS MD INC p 52
2011 Bel Air Rd, Fallston MD 21047
Tel (410) 879-3055 *SIC* 1611 1623

MCLEAN CONTRACTING CO p 931
6700 Mclean Way, Glen Burnie MD 21060
Tel (410) 553-6700
SIC 1622 1623 1629 3449

B FRANK JOY LLC p 142
5355 Kilmer Pl, Hyattsville MD 20781
Tel (301) 779-9400 *SIC* 1623

FACCHINA CONSTRUCTION CO INC p 523
102 Centennial St Ste 201, La Plata MD 20646
Tel (240) 776-7000
SIC 1542 1799 1623 1611 1622 1629

GRAY & SON INC p 632
430 W Padonia Rd, Lutherville Timonium MD 21093
Tel (410) 771-4311 *SIC* 1611 1623 1794

▲ ARGAN INC p 107
1 Church St Ste 201, Rockville MD 20850
Tel (301) 315-0027 *SIC* 4813 1623 8748

CDM CONSTRUCTORS INC p 271
75 State St Ste 701, Boston MA 02109
Tel (617) 452-6000 *SIC* 1541 1623

MASSACHUSETTS WATER RESOURCES AUTHORITY p 917
Charl Navy Yard 100 First, Boston MA 02129
Tel (617) 788-4917 *SIC* 1623

PETRICCA INDUSTRIES INC p 1139
550 Cheshire Rd, Pittsfield MA 01201
Tel (413) 499-1441
SIC 1611 1623 3273 3272 1442

TRI-WIRE ENGINEERING SOLUTIONS INC p 1478
890 East St, Tewksbury MA 01876
Tel (978) 640-6899 *SIC* 1623 8748

MASS ELECTRIC CONSTRUCTION CO p 916
400 Totten Pond Rd # 400, Waltham MA 02451
Tel (781) 290-1000 *SIC* 1731 1623

UNIBAR SERVICES INC p 1502
4325 Concourse Dr, Ann Arbor MI 48108
Tel (734) 769-2600 *SIC* 1623

AERO COMMUNICATIONS HOLDING INC p 30
5711 Research Dr, Canton MI 48188
Tel (734) 467-8121 *SIC* 1623

AERO COMMUNICATIONS INC p 30
5711 Research Dr, Canton MI 48188
Tel (734) 467-8121 *SIC* 1623

R ROESE CONTRACTING CO INC p 1202
2674 S Huron Rd, Kawkawlin MI 48631
Tel (989) 684-5121 *SIC* 1623

POWERTEAM SERVICES LLC p 1166
477 S Main St, Plymouth MI 48170
Tel (919) 372-8614 *SIC* 1623 1629

■ MEARS GROUP INC p 934
4500 N Mission Rd, Rosebush MI 48878
Tel (989) 433-2929 *SIC* 1623 8711

ANGELO IAFRATE CONSTRUCTION CO p 91
26300 Sherwood Ave, Warren MI 48091
Tel (586) 756-1070 *SIC* 1623 1794 1611

MINNESOTA LIMITED LLC p 973
18640 200th St Nw, Big Lake MN 55309
Tel (763) 262-7000 *SIC* 1623

ALPHA OIL & GAS SERVICES INC p 60
453 Tower St Nw, Clearbrook MN 56634
Tel (218) 776-2278 *SIC* 5172 1623 1522

■ TELCOM CONSTRUCTION INC p 1433
2218 200th St E, Clearwater MN 55320
Tel (320) 558-9485 *SIC* 1623

UNITED PIPING INC p 1510
4510 Airport Rd, Duluth MN 55811
Tel (218) 727-7676 *SIC* 1623

MP NEXLEVEL LLC p 995
500 County Road 37, Maple Lake MN 55358
Tel (320) 963-2400 *SIC* 1623

■ PRIMORIS AV ENERGY & ELECTRICAL CONSTRUCTION CORP p 1176
3030 24th Ave S, Moorhead MN 56560
Tel (218) 284-9500 *SIC* 1731 1623

SJ LOUIS CONSTRUCTION INC p 1328
1351 Broadway St W, Rockville MN 56369
Tel (320) 685-4164 *SIC* 1623

■ Q3 CONTRACTING INC p 1194
3066 Spruce St, Saint Paul MN 55117
Tel (651) 224-2424 *SIC* 1623 7699 3669

EUTAW CONSTRUCTION CO INC p 513
109 W Commerce St, Aberdeen MS 39730
Tel (662) 369-7121 *SIC* 1611 1623 1794

HEMPHILL CONSTRUCTION CO INC p 682
1858 Highway 49 S, Florence MS 39073
Tel (601) 932-2060 *SIC* 1623 1542

BOOTS SMITH OILFIELD SERVICES LLC p 200
2501 Airport Dr, Laurel MS 39440
Tel (601) 649-1220 *SIC* 1623

PROGRESSIVE PIPELINE CONSTRUCTION LLC p 1182
12340 Qitman Meridian Hwy, Meridian MS 39301
Tel (601) 693-8777 *SIC* 1623

PROGRESSIVE PIPELINE HOLDINGS LLC p 1182
12340 Qitman Meridian Hwy, Meridian MS 39301
Tel (601) 693-8777 *SIC* 6719 1623

SOUTHERN PIPE & SUPPLY CO INC p 1350
4330 Highway 39 N, Meridian MS 39301
Tel (601) 693-2911 *SIC* 5074 1711 1623

■ IRBY CONSTRUCTION CO p 764
318 Old Highway 49 S, Richland MS 39218
Tel (601) 709-4729 *SIC* 1623 1731

▲ AEGION CORP p 29
17988 Edison Ave, Chesterfield MO 63005
Tel (636) 530-8000 *SIC* 1623

■ INSITUFORM TECHNOLOGIES LLC p 746
17988 Edison Ave, Chesterfield MO 63005
Tel (636) 530-8000 *SIC* 1623

FOLEY CO p 563
7501 E Front St, Kansas City MO 64120
Tel (816) 241-3335 *SIC* 1623 1711 1541

GARNEY COMPANIES INC p 592
1333 Nw Vivion Rd, Kansas City MO 64118
Tel (816) 741-4600 *SIC* 1623 1629

GARNEY HOLDING CO p 592
1333 Nw Vivion Rd, Kansas City MO 64118
Tel (816) 741-4600 *SIC* 1623 1611 1629

KISSICK CONSTRUCTION CO INC p 822
8131 Indiana Ave, Kansas City MO 64132
Tel (816) 363-5530
SIC 1541 1623 1771 1794

■ PAR ELECTRICAL CONTRACTORS INC p 1112
4770 N Belleview Ave # 300, Kansas City MO 64116
Tel (816) 474-9340 *SIC* 1623

SAK CONSTRUCTION LLC p 1271
864 Hoff Rd, O Fallon MO 63366
Tel (636) 674-9104 *SIC* 1623 1622

CORRIGAN BROTHERS INC p 373
3545 Gratiot St, Saint Louis MO 63103
Tel (314) 771-6200 *SIC* 1711 1761 1623

L KEELEY CONSTRUCTION CO p 834
500 S Ewing Ave Ste G, Saint Louis MO 63103
Tel (314) 421-5933 *SIC* 1541 1611 1623

SIKESTON BOARD OF MUNICIPAL UTILITIES p 1322
107 E Malone Ave, Sikeston MO 63801
Tel (573) 471-5000 *SIC* 4911 1623

LEO JOURNAGAN CONSTRUCTION CO INC p 856
3003 E Chestnut Expy, Springfield MO 65802
Tel (417) 869-7222 *SIC* 1422 1611 1623

BARNARD CONSTRUCTION CO INC p 155
701 Gold Ave, Bozeman MT 59715
Tel (406) 586-1995
SIC 1623 1629 1611 1622

G4S SECURE INTEGRATION LLC p 588
1299 Farnam St Ste 1300, Omaha NE 68102
Tel (402) 233-7700 *SIC* 1623 7382

KIEWIT INFRASTRUCTURE WEST CO p 817
4004 S 60th St, Omaha NE 68117
Tel (402) 342-2052
SIC 1611 1629 1541 1622 1623

▲ SOUTHWEST GAS CORP p 1352
5241 Spring Mountain Rd, Las Vegas NV 89150
Tel (702) 876-0711 *SIC* 4923 1623 1389

Q AND D CONSTRUCTION INC p 1194
1050 S 21st St, Sparks NV 89431
Tel (775) 353-1104 *SIC* 1623

CONTI ENTERPRISES INC p 362
2045 Lincoln Hwy, Edison NJ 08817
Tel (732) 520-5000 *SIC* 1611 1622 1623

CORBAN ENERGY GROUP CORP p 368
418 Falmouth Ave, Elmwood Park NJ 07407
Tel (201) 509-8555 *SIC* 1623 3443 5085

J FLETCHER CREAMER & SON INC p 771
101 E Broadway, Hackensack NJ 07601
Tel (201) 488-9800
SIC 1623 1611 1771 1622 1629

▲ MIDDLESEX WATER CO p 965
1500 Ronson Rd, Iselin NJ 08830
Tel (732) 634-1500 *SIC* 4941 1623

TREVCON CONSTRUCTION CO INC p 1476
30 Church St, Liberty Corner NJ 07938
Tel (908) 580-0200 *SIC* 1629 1623

SPINIELLO COMPANIES p 1358
354 Eisenhower Pkwy # 1200, Livingston NJ 07039
Tel (973) 808-8383 *SIC* 1623

J F KIELY CONSTRUCTION CO INC p 771
700 Mcclellan St, Long Branch NJ 07740
Tel (732) 222-4400 *SIC* 1623 7353

TYCOM LIMITED p 1496
10 Park Ave, Morristown NJ 07960
Tel (973) 753-3040 *SIC* 3643 1623

WIRELESS NETWORK GROUP INC p 1618
220 W Parkway Ste 10a, Pompton Plains NJ 07444
Tel (973) 831-4015 *SIC* 1623

▲ AMERICAN WATER WORKS CO INC p 81
1025 Laurel Oak Rd, Voorhees NJ 08043
Tel (856) 346-8200 *SIC* 4941 1629 1623

JAG COMPANIES INC p 776
1433 State Route 34 Ste 5, Wall Township NJ 07727
Tel (732) 557-6100
SIC 1623 1622 1629 1611

NORTHEAST REMSCO CONSTRUCTION INC p 1055
1433 State Route 34 Ste 6, Wall Township NJ 07727
Tel (732) 557-6100
SIC 1623 1622 1629 1611

BROKEN ARROW COMMUNICATIONS INC p 216
8316 Corona Loop Ne, Albuquerque NM 87113
Tel (505) 877-2100 *SIC* 4899 1623

■ B & H MAINTENANCE AND CONSTRUCTION INC p 141
S Loop 207, Eunice NM 88231
Tel (575) 394-2588 *SIC* 1623

NAVAJO ENGINEERING & CONSTRUCTION AUTHORITY p 1019
1 Uranium Blvd, Shiprock NM 87420
Tel (505) 368-5151 *SIC* 1611 1623

■ BRESNAN BROADBAND HOLDINGS LLC p 210
1111 Stewart Ave, Bethpage NY 11714
Tel (516) 803-2300 *SIC* 1623

JETT INDUSTRIES INC p 784
121 Willow Ln, Colliersville NY 13747
Tel (607) 433-2100 *SIC* 1611 1623

JUDLAU CONTRACTING INC p 797
2615 Ulmer St, Flushing NY 11354
Tel (718) 554-2320 *SIC* 1611 1623

PREMIER UTILITY SERVICES LLC p 1171
100 Marcus Blvd Ste 1, Hauppauge NY 11788
Tel (631) 758-7038 *SIC* 1623

HALLEN CONSTRUCTION CO INC p 654
4270 Austin Blvd, Island Park NY 11558
Tel (516) 432-8300 *SIC* 1623

JOHN P PICONE INC p 789
31 Garden Ln, Lawrence NY 11559
Tel (516) 239-1600
SIC 1611 1622 1623 1629

IFM GLOBAL INFRASTRUCTURE FUND p 730
114 W 47th St Fl 26, New York NY 10036
Tel (212) 784-2260 *SIC* 6799 1623

SEALAND CONTRACTORS CORP p 1296
85 High Tech Dr, Rush NY 14543
Tel (704) 522-1102 *SIC* 1622 1611 1623

JWD GROUP INC p 798
300 Colvin Woods Pkwy, Tonawanda NY 14150
Tel (716) 832-1940 *SIC* 1711 1629 1623

OTIS EASTERN SERVICE LLC p 1097
2971 Andover Rd, Wellsville NY 14895
Tel (585) 593-4760 *SIC* 1623 1389

MB HAYNES CORP p 925
187 Deaverview Rd, Asheville NC 28806
Tel (828) 254-6141
SIC 1542 1623 1711 7382

■ SPECTRASITE COMMUNICATIONS LLC p 1357
400 Regency Forest Dr # 300, Cary NC 27518
Tel (919) 468-0112
SIC 4812 8748 1623 3661 4813 4899

CROWDER CONSTRUCTION CO INC p 394
6425 Brookshire Blvd, Charlotte NC 28216
Tel (800) 849-2966 *SIC* 1622 1629 1623

CROWDER CONSTRUCTORS INC p 394
6425 Brookshire Blvd, Charlotte NC 28216
Tel (704) 372-3541 *SIC* 1623

TA LOVING CO p 1420
400 Patetown Rd, Goldsboro NC 27530
Tel (919) 734-8400 *SIC* 1541 1542 1623

THALLE CONSTRUCTION CO INC p 1446
900 Nc Highway 86 N, Hillsborough NC 27278
Tel (919) 245-1490
SIC 1611 1622 1623 1629

S & N COMMUNICATIONS INC p 1261
636 Gralin St, Kernersville NC 27284
Tel (336) 992-5420 *SIC* 1623 1731

SANFORD CONTRACTORS INC p 1279
628 Rocky Fork Church Rd, Sanford NC 27332
Tel (919) 775-7882
SIC 1611 1622 1629 6552 1794 1623

S T WOOTEN CORP p 1263
3801 Black Creek Rd Se, Wilson NC 27893
Tel (252) 637-4294 *SIC* 1611 3273 1623

MCCORMICK INC p 927
4000 12th Ave N, Fargo ND 58102
Tel (701) 277-1225 *SIC* 1611 1629 1623

■ VARISTAR CORP p 1545
4334 18th Ave S Ste 200, Fargo ND 58103
Tel (701) 232-6414
SIC 6719 4899 1623 5047 1731 4213

INDUSTRIAL BUILDERS INC p 739
1307 County Road 17 N, West Fargo ND 58078
Tel (701) 282-4977
SIC 1629 1622 1542 1611 1623

■ WANZEK CONSTRUCTION INC p 1575
2028 2nd Ave Nw, West Fargo ND 58078
Tel (701) 282-6171
SIC 1542 1623 1622 1799 1541 1629

BEAVER EXCAVATING CO p 166
2000 Beaver Place Ave Sw, Canton OH 44706
Tel (330) 478-2151
SIC 1794 1611 1771 1623

DLZ CORP p 445
6121 Huntley Rd, Columbus OH 43229
Tel (614) 888-0040 *SIC* 1623 8713 8712

FISHEL CO p 551
1366 Dublin Rd, Columbus OH 43215
Tel (614) 274-8100 *SIC* 1623 1731 8711

GEORGE J IGEL & CO INC p 606
2040 Alum Creek Dr, Columbus OH 43207
Tel (614) 445-8421 *SIC* 1794 1623 6552

KOKOSING CONSTRUCTION CO INC p 826
886 Mckinley Ave, Columbus OH 43222
Tel (614) 228-1029
SIC 1611 1622 1629 1542 1541 1623

BI-CON SERVICES INC p 180
10901 Clay Pike Rd, Derwent OH 43733
Tel (740) 685-2542 *SIC* 1623 3498 3443

■ MATRIX NORTH AMERICAN CONSTRUCTION INC p 920
5100 E Skelly Dr Ste 700, Tulsa OK 74135
Tel (918) 838-8822 *SIC* 1731 1623 1629

■ MATRIX PDM ENGINEERING INC p 920
5100 E Skelly Dr Ste 800, Tulsa OK 74135
Tel (918) 624-6300 *SIC* 1542 1623 8711

▲ MATRIX SERVICE CO p 920
5100 E Skelly Dr Ste 700, Tulsa OK 74135
Tel (918) 838-8822
SIC 1542 1623 7349 8711

■ MATRIX SERVICE INC p 920
5100 E Skelly Dr Ste 700, Tulsa OK 74135
Tel (918) 838-8822
SIC 1623 1629 1799 7699

WILSON CONSTRUCTION CO p 1613
1190 Nw 3rd Ave, Canby OR 97013
Tel (503) 263-6882 *SIC* 1623

HOFFMAN CORP p 699
805 Sw Broadway Ste 2100, Portland OR 97205
Tel (503) 221-8811
SIC 8741 1541 1542 1623 1629

■ INTERNATIONAL LINE BUILDERS INC p 755
19020 Sw Cipole Rd Ste A, Tualatin OR 97062
Tel (503) 692-0193 *SIC* 1623

ALEX E PARIS CONTRACTING CO INC p 48
1595 Smith Township State, Atlasburg PA 15004
Tel (724) 947-2235 *SIC* 1623 1629

HENKELS & MCCOY GROUP INC p 683
985 Jolly Rd, Blue Bell PA 19422
Tel (215) 283-7600 *SIC* 1623

HENKELS & MCCOY INC p 683
985 Jolly Rd, Blue Bell PA 19422
Tel (215) 283-7600 *SIC* 1623

■ AQUA PENNSYLVANIA INC p 101
762 W Lancaster Ave, Bryn Mawr PA 19010
Tel (610) 525-1400
SIC 4941 8741 4971 1623

CROWN ATLANTIC CO LLC p 395
200 Corporate Dr, Canonsburg PA 15317
Tel (724) 416-2000 SIC 1623

DAVID H MARTIN EXCAVATING INC p 415
4961 Cumberland Hwy, Chambersburg PA 17202
Tel (717) 264-1312 SIC 1623 1794 1711

UTILITY LINE SERVICES INC p 1537
1302 Conshohocken Rd # 100, Conshohocken PA 19428
Tel (484) 685-3489 SIC 1623

IA CONSTRUCTION CORP p 725
24 Gibb Rd, Franklin PA 16323
Tel (814) 432-3184
SIC 1611 2951 1622 1623

GLASGOW INC p 614
104 Willow Grove Ave, Glenside PA 19038
Tel (215) 884-8800 SIC 2951 1611 1623

GOLDEN TRIANGLE CONSTRUCTION CO INC p 621
8555 Old Strubenville Pik, Imperial PA 15126
Tel (724) 828-2800 SIC 1623 1611

DANELLA COMPANIES INC p 411
2290 Butler Pike, Plymouth Meeting PA 19462
Tel (610) 828-6200
SIC 7513 7353 8711 1623 8748

PENN LINE SERVICE INC p 1129
300 Scottdale Ave, Scottdale PA 15683
Tel (724) 887-9110
SIC 1629 1623 1611 0782

ASPLUNDH TREE EXPERT CO p 119
708 Blair Mill Rd, Willow Grove PA 19090
Tel (215) 784-4200
SIC 0783 1629 1623 1611 6411

LANDMARK CONSTRUCTION CO INC p 842
3255 Industry Dr, North Charleston SC 29418
Tel (843) 552-6186
SIC 1542 1541 1623 1771 1794

■ SUMTER UTILITIES INC p 1399
1151 N Pike W, Sumter SC 29153
Tel (803) 469-8585 SIC 1623

HEAVY CONSTRUCTORS INC p 679
4101 Deadwood Ave, Rapid City SD 57702
Tel (605) 342-3144
SIC 1542 1794 1623 1611

APPALACHIAN PIPELINE CONTRACTORS LLP p 98
170 E Main St Ste D, Hendersonville TN 37075
Tel (615) 264-8775 SIC 1623

■ STAR CONSTRUCTION LLC p 1378
6621 Asheville Hwy, Knoxville TN 37924
Tel (865) 521-6795 SIC 1623

RANGER PLANT CONSTRUCTIONAL CO INC p 1208
5851 E Interstate 20, Abilene TX 79601
Tel (325) 677-2888 SIC 1623

VENABLES CONSTRUCTION INC p 1547
7410 Continental Pkwy, Amarillo TX 79119
Tel (806) 381-2121
SIC 1623 1794 1389 4922 4612 1799

US TRINITY ENERGY SERVICES LLC p 1533
200 Highland Cir, Argyle TX 76226
Tel (940) 240-5800 SIC 1623

ALLCO LLC p 52
6720 College St, Beaumont TX 77707
Tel (409) 860-4459 SIC 1623 1542 1541

RITTER CONSTRUCTION CO p 1237
671 Ritter Dr, Carthage TX 75633
Tel (903) 693-2397 SIC 1623

WATKINS CONSTRUCTION CO LLC p 1582
3229 S 15th St, Corsicana TX 75110
Tel (903) 874-6587 SIC 1623

▲ PRIMORIS SERVICES CORP p 1176
2100 Mckinney Ave # 1500, Dallas TX 75201
Tel (214) 740-5600 SIC 1623 8711

■ TRINITY MEYER UTILITY STRUCTURES LLC p 1481
2525 N Stemmons Fwy, Dallas TX 75207
Tel (901) 566-6500 SIC 1623

BILFINGER TEPSCO INC p 182
2909 Aaron St, Deer Park TX 77536
Tel (281) 604-0309 SIC 1623

■ PRIMORIS ENERGY SERVICES CORP p 1176
1109 W 13th St, Deer Park TX 77536
Tel (281) 478-5100 SIC 1623

EL PASO WATER UTILITIES PUBLIC SERVICE BOARD p 483
1154 Hawkins Blvd, El Paso TX 79925
Tel (915) 594-5500 SIC 4941 1623

AUI CONTRACTORS LLC p 131
4775 North Fwy, Fort Worth TX 76106
Tel (817) 926-4377 SIC 1542 1623 1771

■ PUMPCO INC p 1192
1209 S Main St, Giddings TX 78942
Tel (979) 542-9054 SIC 1623 1389

ASSOCIATED PIPE LINE CONTRACTORS INC p 121
3535 Briarpark Dr Ste 135, Houston TX 77042
Tel (713) 789-4311 SIC 1623

CAL DIVE INTERNATIONAL INC p 237
2500 Citywest Blvd # 2200, Houston TX 77042
Tel (713) 361-2600 SIC 7389 1623 1629

COKINOS ENERGY CORP p 335
5718 Westheimer Rd # 900, Houston TX 77057
Tel (713) 974-0101 SIC 4924 1623

COKINOS NATURAL GAS CO INC p 335
5718 Westheimer Rd # 900, Houston TX 77057
Tel (713) 974-0101 SIC 4924 1623

DEARBORN RESOURCES INC p 420
2130 Inwood Dr, Houston TX 77019
Tel (713) 521-1950 SIC 1623

■ EC SOURCE SERVICES LLC p 474
16055 Space Center Blvd # 700, Houston TX 77062
Tel (281) 480-4600 SIC 1623 8742

■ FISK ACQUISITION INC p 552
111 T C Jester Blvd, Houston TX 77007
Tel (713) 868-6111 SIC 1731 1623

GREGORY PRICE INTERNATIONAL INC p 639
920 Mmrial Cy Way Ste 600, Houston TX 77024
Tel (713) 780-7500 SIC 1623

HOLLOMAN CORP p 701
333 N Sam Houston Pkwy E, Houston TX 77060
Tel (281) 878-2600 SIC 1541 1623 1389

■ HOUSTON NORTH POLE LINE p 712
1608 Margaret St, Houston TX 77093
Tel (713) 691-3616 SIC 1623

▲ MCDERMOTT INTERNATIONAL INC p 927
757 N Eldridge Pkwy, Houston TX 77079
Tel (281) 870-5000 SIC 1389 1623

MPG PIPELINE CONTRACTORS LLC p 995
16770 Imperial Valley Dr # 105, Houston TX 77060
Tel (713) 904-1168 SIC 1623

NW PIPELINE INC p 1068
3535 Briarpark Dr Ste 135, Houston TX 77042
Tel (713) 789-4311 SIC 1623

PIPELINE SUPPLY & SERVICE LLC p 1151
1010 Lamar St Ste 710, Houston TX 77002
Tel (713) 741-8127 SIC 4922 5085 1623

■ TEXAS STERLING CONSTRUCTION CO p 1444
20810 Fernbush Dr, Houston TX 77073
Tel (281) 821-9091 SIC 1611 1623

TROY CONSTRUCTION LLC p 1485
8521 Mchard Rd, Houston TX 77053
Tel (281) 437-8214 SIC 1623 8711

US PIPELINE INC p 1533
950 Echo Ln Ste 100, Houston TX 77024
Tel (281) 531-6100 SIC 1623

■ WILLBROS CONSTRUCTION (US) LLC p 1610
4400 Post Oak Pkwy # 1000, Houston TX 77027
Tel (713) 403-8000 SIC 1623

■ WILLBROS UNITED STATES HOLDINGS INC p 1610
4400 Post Oak Pkwy # 1000, Houston TX 77027
Tel (713) 403-8000 SIC 8711 1623

KIEWIT OFFSHORE SERVICES LTD p 817
2440 Kiewit Rd, Ingleside TX 78362
Tel (361) 775-4300 SIC 1623

DRIVER PIPELINE CO INC p 456
1200 N Union Bower Rd, Irving TX 75061
Tel (214) 638-7131 SIC 1623

PLH GROUP INC p 1156
400 Las Colinas Blvd E, Irving TX 75039
Tel (214) 272-0500 SIC 1623

POWER LINE SERVICES INC p 1165
400 Las Colinas Blvd E, Irving TX 75039
Tel (214) 272-0500 SIC 1623

S J LOUIS CONSTRUCTION OF TEXAS LTD p 1262
520 S 6th Ave, Mansfield TX 76063
Tel (817) 477-0320 SIC 1623

POWER LINE INFRASTRUCTURE SERVICES INC p 1165
1031 Andrews Hwy, Midland TX 79701
Tel (432) 682-1991 SIC 1623

MIDWAY OILFIELD CONSTRUCTORS INC p 967
12627 State Highway 21 E, Midway TX 75852
Tel (936) 348-3721 SIC 1389 1623

A GLEN BARRILLEAUX LLC p 5
1412 W Broad St, Oakwood TX 75855
Tel (903) 545-1231 SIC 1623 1629

ECHO MAINTENANCE LLC p 475
6711 N Twin City Hwy, Port Arthur TX 77642
Tel (409) 724-0456 SIC 1541 3498 1623

JOHNSON BROS CORP p 790
608 Henrietta Creek Rd, Roanoke TX 76262
Tel (813) 685-5101 SIC 1623 1629 1622

OSCAR RENDA CONTRACTING INC p 1096
608 Henrietta Creek Rd, Roanoke TX 76262
Tel (817) 491-2703 SIC 1623 1799 1622

■ PRIMORIS PIPELINE SERVICES CORP p 1176
1010 County Road 59, Rosharon TX 77583
Tel (281) 431-5900 SIC 1623

CHASCO CONSTRUCTORS LTD LLP p 291
2801 E Old Settlers Blvd, Round Rock TX 78665
Tel (512) 244-0600
SIC 1542 1771 1794 1623

DNT CONSTRUCTION LLC p 446
2300 Picadilly Dr, Round Rock TX 78664
Tel (512) 837-6700 SIC 1623 1794 1611

ALBERT REECE INC p 46
3001 Foster St, San Angelo TX 76903
Tel (325) 653-1241
SIC 1611 1794 1623 1622

HB ZACHRY CO p 671
527 Logwood Ave, San Antonio TX 78221
Tel (210) 475-8000
SIC 1611 1622 1623 1629

YANTIS CORP p 1635
3611 Paesanos Pkwy # 300, San Antonio TX 78231
Tel (210) 655-3780
SIC 1623 1611 1622 1629 6552 1521

ZACHRY CONSOLIDATED LLC p 1640
527 Logwood Ave, San Antonio TX 78221
Tel (210) 871-2700
SIC 1611 1622 1623 1629 3241 1442

ZACHRY CONSTRUCTION & MATERIALS INC p 1640
2330 N Loop 1604 W, San Antonio TX 78248
Tel (210) 479-1027
SIC 1611 1622 1623 1629 1542 3241

ZACHRY CONSTRUCTION CORP p 1640
2330 N Loop 1604 W, San Antonio TX 78248
Tel (210) 871-2700
SIC 1623 1611 1622 1629 1542

ZACHRY HOLDINGS INC p 1640
527 Logwood Ave, San Antonio TX 78221
Tel (210) 588-5000
SIC 1541 8711 1629 1623

ELECTRA LINK INC p 484
21755 Interstate 45 # 10, Spring TX 77388
Tel (281) 350-6096 SIC 1623

KINGSLEY CONSTRUCTORS INC p 821
25250 Borough Park Dr # 106, Spring TX 77380
Tel (281) 363-1979 SIC 1623 1611

▲ LAYNE CHRISTENSEN CO p 848
1800 Hughes Landing Blvd, The Woodlands TX 77380
Tel (281) 475-2600
SIC 1781 1623 5084 1481 8748

▲ STERLING CONSTRUCTION CO INC p 1387
1800 Hughes Landing Blvd # 250, The Woodlands TX 77380
Tel (281) 214-0800 SIC 1611 1622 1623

STRIKE LLC p 1393
1800 Hughes Landing Blvd # 500, The Woodlands TX 77380
Tel (713) 389-2400 SIC 1623

BOOTS SMITH PIPELINE SERVICES LLC p 200
500 Dennis Rd, Weatherford TX 76087
Tel (601) 682-0761 SIC 1623

BRAZOS ROCK INC p 209
1813 Banks Dr, Weatherford TX 76087
Tel (817) 594-0772 SIC 1623

PROBST ELECTRIC INC p 1178
875 S 600 W, Heber City UT 84032
Tel (435) 657-1955 SIC 1623 1731

■ NIELS FUGAL SONS CO LLC p 1043
1005 S Main St, Pleasant Grove UT 84062
Tel (801) 785-3152 SIC 1623

CRAIG F SORENSEN CONSTRUCTION INC p 388
918 S 2000 W, Syracuse UT 84075
Tel (801) 773-4390 SIC 1623 1731

GREEN MOUNTAIN POWER CORP p 637
163 Acorn Ln, Colchester VT 05446
Tel (888) 835-4672 SIC 4911 1623 1731

HAZEL INC WILLIAM A p 671
4305 Hazel Park Ct, Chantilly VA 20151
Tel (703) 378-8300 SIC 1623 1794

HENSEL PHELPS SERVICES LLC p 685
4437 Brookfield Corp 20 Ste 207, Chantilly VA 20151
Tel (703) 828-3200
SIC 1522 8744 1521 1541 1623 1611

FAULCONER CONSTRUCTION CO INC p 531
2496 Old Ivy Rd, Charlottesville VA 22903
Tel (434) 295-0033
SIC 1629 1611 1542 1623

C W WRIGHT CONSTRUCTION CO INC p 233
11500 Iron Bridge Rd, Chester VA 23831
Tel (804) 768-1054 SIC 1623

AEW FOUNDATION p 32
2176 Lee Hwy S, Cloverdale VA 24077
Tel (540) 992-2865 SIC 1623 1731

NEW RIVER ELECTRICAL CORP p 1033
15 Cloverdale Pl, Cloverdale VA 24077
Tel (540) 966-1650 SIC 1731 1623

S W RODGERS CO INC p 1263
5816 Wellington Rd, Gainesville VA 20155
Tel (703) 591-8400
SIC 1611 1799 6552 1771 1623

ALLAN MYERS VA INC p 52
301 Cncourse Blvd Ste 300, Glen Allen VA 23059
Tel (804) 290-8500
SIC 1623 1611 1542 1794

ENGLISH CONSTRUCTION CO INC p 499
615 Church St Ste 2, Lynchburg VA 24504
Tel (434) 845-0301
SIC 1611 1629 1623 1542

WATTS CONSTRUCTORS LLC p 1583
6862 Elm St Ste 500, Mc Lean VA 22101
Tel (703) 358-8800 SIC 1542 1623

UTILX CORP p 1537
22820 Russell Rd, Kent WA 98032
Tel (253) 395-4535 SIC 1623

KLB CONSTRUCTION INC p 823
3405 121st St Sw, Lynnwood WA 98087
Tel (425) 355-7335 SIC 1623 1611

NORTHWEST CASCADE INC p 1059
10412 John Bananola Way E, Puyallup WA 98374
Tel (253) 848-2371
SIC 1623 7359 7699 3272 1711

GARY MERLINO CONSTRUCTION CO INC p 593
9125 10th Ave S, Seattle WA 98108
Tel (206) 763-9552 SIC 1611 1623 3273

MCKINSTRY CO LLC p 930
5005 3rd Ave S, Seattle WA 98134
Tel (206) 762-3311
SIC 1711 1623 3446 3444

SNELSON COMPANIES INC p 1335
601 W State St, Sedro Woolley WA 98284
Tel (360) 856-6511 SIC 1623

■ POTELCO INC p 1164
14103 Stewart Rd, Sumner WA 98390
Tel (253) 826-7300 SIC 1623

SEFNCO COMMUNICATIONS INC p 1300
4610 Tacoma Ave, Sumner WA 98390
Tel (877) 385-2903 SIC 1623

■ CABLECOM LLC p 235
8602 Maltby Rd, Woodinville WA 98072
Tel (360) 668-1300 SIC 1623 1731

▲ ENERGY SERVICES OF AMERICA CORP p 498
75 3rd Ave W, Huntington WV 25701
Tel (304) 522-3868 SIC 1623 1731

MICHELS CORP p 960
817 W Main St, Brownsville WI 53006
Tel (920) 583-3132
SIC 1623 1771 1381 1629 3498 1794

■ PRECISION PIPELINE LLC p 1168
3314 56th St, Eau Claire WI 54703
Tel (715) 874-4510 SIC 1623

HOOPER CORP p 706
2030 Pennsylvania Ave, Madison WI 53704
Tel (608) 249-0451 SIC 1623 1711

■ INFRASOURCE LLC p 742
2936 S 166th St, New Berlin WI 53151
Tel (713) 629-7600 SIC 1623 1542

KS ENERGY SERVICES LLC p 831
19705 W Lincoln Ave, New Berlin WI 53146
Tel (262) 574-5100 SIC 1623

R G REZIN INC p 1202
1602 Rezin Rd, Tomah WI 54660
Tel (608) 372-5956
SIC 1623 3443 3613 3561 3523 3599

INTERCON CONSTRUCTION INC p 752
5512 State Rd 19 & 113, Waunakee WI 53597
Tel (608) 850-4820 SIC 1623

ELKHORN CONSTRUCTION INC p 488
71 Allegiance Cir, Evanston WY 82930
Tel (307) 789-1595 SIC 1629 1731 1623

SIC 1629 Heavy Construction, NEC

C & C HOLDING INC p 231
2238 Pinson Valley Pkwy, Birmingham AL 35217
Tel (205) 841-6666 SIC 5082 1629 5084

■ KBR CONSTRUCTION CO LLC p 806
3000 Riverchase Galleria, Hoover AL 35244
Tel (205) 972-6538
SIC 1541 1796 1711 1629 1799 1521

REED CONTRACTING SERVICES INC p 1217
2512 Triana Blvd Sw, Huntsville AL 35805
Tel (256) 533-0505
SIC 1771 1794 1623 1629 1611

MCABEE CONSTRUCTION INC p 925
5724 21st St, Tuscaloosa AL 35401
Tel (205) 349-2212
SIC 1629 1791 1796 3443 3498

AHTNA INC p 37
110 W 38th Ave Ste 100, Anchorage AK 99503
Tel (907) 868-8250
SIC 1629 7389 1542 1521

HUNTER CONTRACTING CO p 719
701 N Cooper Rd, Gilbert AZ 85233
Tel (480) 892-0521 SIC 1611 1629 1622

KIEWIT WESTERN CO p 817
3888 E Broadway Rd, Phoenix AZ 85040
Tel (602) 437-7878
SIC 1622 1629 1794 1611 1623

SUNDT CONSTRUCTION INC p 1402
2620 S 55th St, Tempe AZ 85282
Tel (480) 293-3000
SIC 1542 1611 1629 1541 8741

SYSTEMS PLANT SERVICES INC p 1419
214 N Wa Ave Ste 700, El Dorado AR 71730
Tel (870) 862-1315 SIC 1629

ARKANSAS ELECTRIC COOPERATIVES INC p 109
1 Cooperative Way, Little Rock AR 72209
Tel (501) 570-2361
SIC 5063 1623 1629 7629

LEXICON INC p 859
8900 Fourche Dam Pike, Little Rock AR 72206
Tel (501) 490-4200 SIC 1629 3441

PINE BLUFF SAND AND GRAVEL CO p 1148
1501 Heartwood St, White Hall AR 71602
Tel (870) 534-7120
SIC 2951 3273 1442 5032 1629

STACY AND WITBECK INC p 1374
2800 Harbor Bay Pkwy, Alameda CA 94502
Tel (510) 748-1870 SIC 1629

TECHNO COATINGS INC p 1431
1391 S Allec St, Anaheim CA 92805
Tel (714) 635-1130
SIC 1542 1629 1721 1799

BRIGHTVIEW COMPANIES LLC p 213
24151 Ventura Blvd, Calabasas CA 91302
Tel (818) 223-8500 SIC 1629 0782 0781

BRIGHTVIEW GOLF MAINTENANCE INC p 213
24151 Ventura Blvd, Calabasas CA 91302
Tel (818) 223-8500 SIC 1629

JR FILANC CONSTRUCTION CO INC p 795
740 N Andreasen Dr, Escondido CA 92029
Tel (760) 941-7130 SIC 1623 1629

■ BRINDERSON LP p 213
19000 Macarthur Blvd # 800, Irvine CA 92612
Tel (714) 466-7100 SIC 8711 1629

HENSEL PHELPS GRANITE HANGAR JOINT VENTURE p 684
18850 Von Kamon 100, Irvine CA 92612
Tel (949) 852-0111 SIC 1542 1629

■ ARB INC p 102
26000 Commercentre Dr, Lake Forest CA 92630
Tel (949) 598-9242 SIC 1629 1623

IRWIN INDUSTRIES INC p 765
1580 W Carson St, Long Beach CA 90810
Tel (310) 233-3000
SIC 1629 1731 1796 7353 1542

■ AECOM E&C HOLDINGS INC p 28
1999 Avenue Of Ste 2600, Los Angeles CA 90067
Tel (213) 593-8000
SIC 8711 1611 1629 1623 1541 1622

NOVA GROUP INC p 1062
185 Devlin Rd, Napa CA 94558
Tel (707) 265-1100
SIC 1629 1623 1622 5172

BRIGHTSOURCE ENERGY INC p 213
1999 Harrison St Ste 2150, Oakland CA 94612
Tel (510) 550-8161 SIC 1629

SHIMMICK CONSTRUCTION CO INC p 1316
8201 Edgewater Dr Ste 202, Oakland CA 94621
Tel (510) 777-5000 SIC 1629 1623

■ JACOBS ENGINEERING CO p 775
1111 S Arroyo Pkwy, Pasadena CA 91105
Tel (626) 449-2171 SIC 8711 1629

PARSONS CORP p 1118
100 W Walnut St, Pasadena CA 91124
Tel (626) 440-2000
SIC 1629 1611 8711 8741

PARK WEST COMPANIES INC p 1116
22421 Gilberto Ste A, Rcho Sta Marg CA 92688
Tel (949) 546-8300 SIC 0782 1629 6719

SKANSKA USA CIVIL WEST CALIFORNIA DISTRICT INC p 1329
1995 Agua Mansa Rd, Riverside CA 92509
Tel (951) 684-5360
SIC 1611 1622 1629 8711 2951

■ **EDISON MISSION GROUP INC** p 478
2244 Walnut Grove Ave, Rosemead CA 91770
Tel (626) 302-2222
SIC 4931 6799 1629 1531

LEDCOR CMI INC p 851
6405 Mira Mesa Blvd # 100, San Diego CA 92121
Tel (602) 595-3017
SIC 1541 1611 1629 1623 1522 8999

BECHTEL CONSTRUCTION OPERATIONS INC p 167
50 Beale St Bsmt 1, San Francisco CA 94105
Tel (415) 768-1234
SIC 1541 1629 1623 8741 7353

BECHTEL CORP p 167
50 Beale St, San Francisco CA 94105
Tel (415) 768-1234 *SIC* 8711 1629 8742

BECHTEL GROUP INC p 167
50 Beale St Bsmt 1, San Francisco CA 94105
Tel (415) 768-1234 *SIC* 8711 1629 8742

BECHTEL POWER CORP p 167
50 Beale St Bsmt 2, San Francisco CA 94105
Tel (415) 768-1234 *SIC* 8711 8742 1629

HUNTER INDUSTRIES L P p 719
1940 Diamond St, San Marcos CA 92078
Tel (760) 744-5240 *SIC* 1629

DUTRA GROUP p 463
2350 Kerner Blvd Ste 200, San Rafael CA 94901
Tel (415) 258-6876 *SIC* 1629 8711 1429

GHILOTTI CONSTRUCTION CO INC p 610
246 Ghillotti Ave, Santa Rosa CA 95407
Tel (707) 585-1221 *SIC* 1629

■ **FRONTIER-KEMPER CONSTRUCTORS INC** p 581
15900 Olden St, Sylmar CA 91342
Tel (818) 362-2062 *SIC* 1629

■ **TUTOR-SALIBA CORP** p 1493
15901 Olden St, Sylmar CA 91342
Tel (818) 362-8391
SIC 1542 1629 7353 1799 6552

C A RASMUSSEN INC p 232
28548 Livingston Ave, Valencia CA 91355
Tel (661) 367-9040 *SIC* 1629 1611

TIMEC ACQUISITIONS INC p 1454
155 Corporate Pl, Vallejo CA 94590
Tel (707) 642-2222 *SIC* 1629

TIMEC COMPANIES INC p 1454
155 Corporate Pl, Vallejo CA 94590
Tel (707) 642-2222 *SIC* 1629 1799

▲ **GRANITE CONSTRUCTION INC** p 631
585 W Beach St, Watsonville CA 95076
Tel (831) 724-1011
SIC 1611 1622 1629 1442

FLATIRON CONSTRUCTION CORP p 554
385 Interlocken Blvd, Broomfield CO 80021
Tel (303) 485-4050 *SIC* 1622 1629 1611

FLATIRON CONSTRUCTORS INC p 555
385 Interlocken, Broomfield CO 80021
Tel (303) 485-4050 *SIC* 1611 1622 1629

FLATIRON HOLDING INC p 555
385 Interlocken Cres, Broomfield CO 80021
Tel (303) 485-4050 *SIC* 1622 1629

MWH CONSTRUCTORS INC p 1004
370 Interlocken Blvd # 300, Broomfield CO 80021
Tel (303) 439-2800 *SIC* 8711 1629

RES AMERICA CONSTRUCTION INC p 1226
11101 W 120th Ave Ste 400, Broomfield CO 80021
Tel (512) 617-1960 *SIC* 1629

PCL CIVIL CONSTRUCTORS INC p 1124
2000 S Colo Blvd Ste 2-50, Denver CO 80222
Tel (303) 365-6500
SIC 1611 1622 1623 1629

TIC HOLDINGS INC p 1452
9780 Pyramid Ct Ste 100, Englewood CO 80112
Tel (970) 879-2561
SIC 1541 1629 1623 1542

HENSEL PHELPS-GRANITE JV p 685
420 6th Ave, Greeley CO 80631
Tel (970) 352-6565
SIC 1541 1542 1629 1611

■ **AECOM ENERGY & CONSTRUCTION INC** p 28
6200 S Quebec St, Greenwood Village CO 80111
Tel (303) 228-3000
SIC 1622 1629 1081 4953

AMERICAN CIVIL CONSTRUCTORS LLC p 70
4901 S Windermere St, Littleton CO 80120
Tel (303) 795-2582 *SIC* 1629 0783 0181

ASI CONSTRUCTORS INC p 117
1850 E Platteville Blvd, Pueblo West CO 81007
Tel (719) 647-2821 *SIC* 1629

LANE CONSTRUCTION CORP p 843
90 Fieldstone Ct, Cheshire CT 06410
Tel (203) 235-3351
SIC 1622 1611 1629 3272 5032

LANE INDUSTRIES INC p 843
90 Fieldstone Ct, Cheshire CT 06410
Tel (203) 235-3351
SIC 1629 1611 5032 3272 1622

▲ **FUELCELL ENERGY INC** p 583
3 Great Pasture Rd, Danbury CT 06810
Tel (203) 825-6000 *SIC* 1629

■ **TALEN ENERGY SERVICES NORTHEAST INC** p 1422
50 Inwood Rd Ste 3, Rocky Hill CT 06067
Tel (860) 513-1036 *SIC* 1711 1629

GEORGE & LYNCH INC p 606
150 Lafferty Ln, Dover DE 19901
Tel (302) 736-3031
SIC 1623 1611 1629 1731

CROM CORP p 393
250 Sw 36th Ter, Gainesville FL 32607
Tel (352) 372-3436 *SIC* 1629

JR DAVIS CONSTRUCTION CO INC p 795
210 S Hoagland Blvd, Kissimmee FL 34741
Tel (407) 870-0066 *SIC* 1629 1521

GAC CONTRACTORS INC p 588
4116 N Highway 231, Panama City FL 32404
Tel (850) 785-4675 *SIC* 1611 1629

■ **MWSTAR WASTE HOLDINGS CORP** p 1004
90 Fort Wade Rd Ste 200, Ponte Vedra FL 32081
Tel (904) 737-7900 *SIC* 1629 4953

■ **ORION MARINE CONSTRUCTION INC** p 1095
5440 W Tyson Ave, Tampa FL 33611
Tel (813) 839-8441 *SIC* 1629

OXFORD CONSTRUCTION CO p 1101
3200 Palmyra Rd, Albany GA 31707
Tel (229) 883-3232 *SIC* 1611 1629

PCL INDUSTRIAL CONSTRUCTION CO p 1124
6445 Shiloh Rd Ste E, Alpharetta GA 30005
Tel (678) 965-3100 *SIC* 1629 1541

ARCHER WESTERN CONTRACTORS LLC p 105
2410 Paces Ferry Rd Se # 600, Atlanta GA 30339
Tel (404) 495-8700
SIC 1542 1622 1611 1629

AUBREY SILVEY ENTERPRISES INC p 130
371 Hamp Jones Rd, Carrollton GA 30117
Tel (770) 834-0738
SIC 1629 1541 3643 7389 3699 5063

W A KENDALL AND CO INC p 1568
400 Farmer Ct, Lawrenceville GA 30046
Tel (770) 963-6017 *SIC* 1629

■ **WILLIAMS PLANT SERVICES LLC** p 1611
100 Crescent Center Pkwy # 1240, Tucker GA 30084
Tel (770) 879-4500 *SIC* 1629 8744

C TERRY HUNT INDUSTRIES INC p 233
5420 Perimeter Rd, Valdosta GA 31601
Tel (229) 244-6707 *SIC* 1629

ISEMOTO CONTRACTING CO LTD p 766
648 Piilani St, Hilo HI 96720
Tel (808) 935-7194 *SIC* 1629 1542 1541

■ **NATIONAL PROJECTS INC** p 1015
720 E Park Blvd, Boise ID 83712
Tel (208) 386-5000 *SIC* 1629 1542 1541

WASHINGTON GROUP INTERNATIONAL INC p 1578
720 E Park Blvd, Boise ID 83712
Tel (208) 386-5000
SIC 1611 1629 1221 1081 4959 1475

ARCHER WESTERN CONSTRUCTION LLC p 105
929 W Adams St, Chicago IL 60607
Tel (312) 563-5400
SIC 1521 1622 1629 1542

CARYLON CORP p 262
2500 W Arthington St, Chicago IL 60612
Tel (312) 666-7700
SIC 7699 1629 7349 8748 4959

CROWN GOLF PROPERTIES LP p 395
222 N La Salle St # 2000, Chicago IL 60601
Tel (312) 395-7701 *SIC* 8742 1629

WALSH GROUP LTD p 1574
929 W Adams St, Chicago IL 60607
Tel (312) 563-5400
SIC 1542 1522 1622 1629 1541

LUHR BROS INC p 884
250 W Sand Bank Rd, Columbia IL 62236
Tel (618) 281-4106 *SIC* 1629

RIVER CITY CONSTRUCTION LLC p 1237
101 Hoffer Ln, East Peoria IL 61611
Tel (309) 694-3120 *SIC* 1542 1629

HELM GROUP INC p 682
2283 Business Us 20 E, Freeport IL 61032
Tel (815) 235-2244 *SIC* 1611 1622 1629

ONYX ENVIRONMENTAL SERVICES LLC p 1088
700 E Bttrfeld Rd Ste 201, Lombard IL 60148
Tel (630) 218-1500
SIC 8711 4953 2869 1799 1629

■ **KENNY CONSTRUCTION A GRANITE CO** p 811
2215 Sanders Rd Ste 400, Northbrook IL 60062
Tel (847) 919-8200
SIC 1622 1611 1629 1623 1541

■ **KENNY INDUSTRIES INC** p 811
2215 Sanders Rd Ste 400, Northbrook IL 60062
Tel (847) 919-8200
SIC 1611 1622 1629 1623 1541 6552

■ **GREAT LAKES DREDGE & DOCK CO LLC** p 633
2122 York Rd Ste 200, Oak Brook IL 60523
Tel (630) 574-3000 *SIC* 1629

▲ **GREAT LAKES DREDGE & DOCK CORP** p 633
2122 York Rd Ste 200, Oak Brook IL 60523
Tel (630) 574-3000 *SIC* 1629 1741

CBI SERVICES INC p 268
14107 S Route 59, Plainfield IL 60544
Tel (815) 439-6668 *SIC* 1629 8741

CASE FOUNDATION CO p 263
1325 Lake St, Roselle IL 60172
Tel (630) 529-2911 *SIC* 1629

AQUASCAPE DESIGNS INC p 101
901 Aqualand Way, Saint Charles IL 60174
Tel (630) 659-2000
SIC 5191 1629 0782 0781

FREESEN INC p 577
3151 Robbins Rd Ste A, Springfield IL 62704
Tel (217) 546-6192 *SIC* 1622 1771 1629

NATIONAL SALVAGE & SERVICE CORP p 1016
6755 S Old State Road 37, Bloomington IN 47401
Tel (812) 339-8437
SIC 5088 1629 1795 5099 5093

■ **SHAMBAUGH & SON LP** p 1311
7614 Opportunity Dr, Fort Wayne IN 46825
Tel (260) 487-7777
SIC 1711 1799 1731 1796 1629

BMWC GROUP INC p 194
1740 W Michigan St, Indianapolis IN 46222
Tel (317) 267-0400 *SIC* 1629

BOWEN ENGINEERING CORP p 204
8802 N Meridian St Ste X, Indianapolis IN 46260
Tel (219) 661-9770 *SIC* 1629 1623 1541

MITCHELL & STARK CONSTRUCTION CO INC p 976
170 W 1st St, Medora IN 47260
Tel (812) 966-2151 *SIC* 1623 1629

■ **ENERGY SYSTEMS GROUP LLC** p 498
4655 Rosebud Ln, Newburgh IN 47630
Tel (812) 492-3734 *SIC* 8711 1711 1629

■ **LAYNE HEAVY CIVIL INC** p 848
4520 N State Road 37, Orleans IN 47452
Tel (812) 865-3232 *SIC* 1623 1781 1629

SUPERIOR CONSTRUCTION CO INC p 1406
1455 Louis Sullivan Dr, Portage IN 46368
Tel (219) 886-3728 *SIC* 1541 1629 1622

STORY CONSTRUCTION CO p 1392
300 S Bell Ave, Ames IA 50010
Tel (515) 232-4358 *SIC* 1542 1629

JENSEN CONSTRUCTION CO p 782
5550 Ne 22nd St, Des Moines IA 50313
Tel (515) 266-5173 *SIC* 1622 1629

WEITZ CO LLC p 1588
5901 Thornton Ave, Des Moines IA 50321
Tel (515) 698-4260 *SIC* 1542 1541 1629

L G BARCUS AND SONS INC p 834
1430 State Ave, Kansas City KS 66102
Tel (913) 621-1100 *SIC* 1629 1622

MASSMAN CONSTRUCTION CO p 917
4400 W 109th St Ste 300, Leawood KS 66211
Tel (913) 291-2600 *SIC* 1629 1622

EBY CORP p 474
2525 E 36th Cir N, Wichita KS 67219
Tel (316) 268-3500
SIC 1629 1623 1622 1541 1542 7353

WILDCAT CONSTRUCTION CO INC p 1609
3219 W May St, Wichita KS 67213
Tel (316) 945-9408
SIC 1623 1622 1771 1611 1629

SCOTTYS CONTRACTING AND STONE LLC p 1294
2300 Barren River Rd, Bowling Green KY 42101
Tel (270) 781-3998 *SIC* 1629 1611 2951

■ **JACOBS CONSTRUCTORS INC** p 775
4949 Essen Ln, Baton Rouge LA 70809
Tel (225) 769-7700 *SIC* 1629

PALA GROUP INC p 1108
16347 Old Hammond Hwy, Baton Rouge LA 70816
Tel (225) 272-5194 *SIC* 1629 1541

SHAW GROUP INC p 1312
4171 Essen Ln, Baton Rouge LA 70809
Tel (225) 932-2500
SIC 8711 8734 1629 3498

BERRY BROS GENERAL CONTRACTORS INC p 176
1414 River Rd, Berwick LA 70342
Tel (985) 384-8770 *SIC* 1629 4959

CHET MORRISON CONTRACTORS LLC p 295
9 Bayou Dularge Rd, Houma LA 70363
Tel (985) 868-1950
SIC 1623 3498 1629 1389

MAX FOOTE CONSTRUCTION CO LLC p 922
225 Antibes St W Ste 3, Mandeville LA 70448
Tel (985) 624-8569 *SIC* 1629

BARRIERE CONSTRUCTION CO LLC p 157
1 Galleria Blvd Ste 1650, Metairie LA 70001
Tel (504) 581-7283 *SIC* 1611 1629

BOH BROS CONSTRUCTION CO LLC p 197
730 S Tonti St, New Orleans LA 70119
Tel (504) 821-2400
SIC 1611 1622 1629 1623

■ **J RAY MCDERMOTT & CO INC** p 772
1340 Poydras St Ste 1200, New Orleans LA 70112
Tel (504) 587-5000 *SIC* 1629 1389 1623

PCE CONSTRUCTORS INC p 1124
13544 Eads Rd, Prairieville LA 70769
Tel (225) 677-9100 *SIC* 1629

MAINE DRILLING AND BLASTING INC p 898
544 Brunswick Ave, Gardiner ME 04345
Tel (207) 582-4300 *SIC* 1629

CIANBRO COMPANIES p 305
1 Hunnewell Ave, Pittsfield ME 04967
Tel (207) 487-3311
SIC 1629 1622 1542 1541 8742

CIANBRO CORP p 305
101 Cianbro Sq, Pittsfield ME 04967
Tel (207) 487-3311
SIC 1622 1629 1542 1541 8742

SARGENT CORP p 1282
378 Bennoch Rd, Stillwater ME 04489
Tel (207) 827-4435 *SIC* 1629

SC HOLDINGS INC p 1285
378 Bennoch Rd, Stillwater ME 04489
Tel (207) 827-4435 *SIC* 1629

REED & REED INC p 1217
275 River Rd, Woolwich ME 04579
Tel (207) 443-9747 *SIC* 1622 1629 1541

WHITING-TURNER CONTRACTING CO p 1607
300 E Joppa Rd Ste 800, Baltimore MD 21286
Tel (410) 821-1100
SIC 1542 1541 1629 8741

BECHTEL NATIONAL INC p 167
5275 Westview Dr, Frederick MD 21703
Tel (415) 768-1234 *SIC* 8711 1629 8742

MCLEAN CONTRACTING CO p 931
6700 Mclean Way, Glen Burnie MD 21060
Tel (410) 553-6700
SIC 1622 1623 1629 3449

FACCHINA CONSTRUCTION CO INC p 523
102 Centennial St Ste 201, La Plata MD 20646
Tel (240) 776-7000
SIC 1542 1799 1623 1611 1622 1629

R H WHITE COMPANIES INC p 1202
41 Central St, Auburn MA 01501
Tel (508) 832-3295
SIC 1629 7359 1522 1521

TREVI ICOS CORP p 1476
38 3rd Ave, Charlestown MA 02129
Tel (617) 241-4800 *SIC* 1629 1622

BROX INDUSTRIES INC p 220
1471 Methuen St, Dracut MA 01826
Tel (978) 454-9105
SIC 1442 1499 1611 1629 1794 2951

■ **PERINI MANAGEMENT SERVICES INC** p 1136
73 Mount Wayte Ave, Framingham MA 01702
Tel (508) 628-2000
SIC 1541 1542 1611 1629

■ **COVANTA HAVERHILL INC** p 384
100 Recovery Way, Haverhill MA 01835
Tel (978) 372-6288 *SIC* 4953 1629 4931

DANIEL OCONNELLS SONS INC p 411
480 Hampden St, Holyoke MA 01040
Tel (413) 534-5667
SIC 1541 1542 1522 1611 1622 1629

CASHMAN DREDGING AND MARINE CONTRACTING CO LLC p 263
549 South St, Quincy MA 02169
Tel (617) 890-0600 *SIC* 1629

JAY CASHMAN INC p 779
549 South St Bldg 19, Quincy MA 02169
Tel (617) 890-0600 *SIC* 1629

JCI HOLDINGS LLC p 780
549 South St Bldg 19, Quincy MA 02169
Tel (617) 890-0600 *SIC* 1629

DEVERE CONSTRUCTION CO INC p 433
1030 Devere Dr, Alpena MI 49707
Tel (989) 356-4411
SIC 1542 1541 1629 8741

CHRISTMAN CO p 303
208 N Capitol Ave Fl 4, Lansing MI 48933
Tel (517) 482-1488
SIC 8741 1542 1541 1629

NEWKIRK ELECTRIC ASSOCIATES INC p 1037
1875 Roberts St, Muskegon MI 49442
Tel (231) 722-1691 *SIC* 1731 1629 8711

POWERTEAM SERVICES LLC p 1166
477 S Main St, Plymouth MI 48170
Tel (919) 372-8614 *SIC* 1623 1629

CHERNE CONTRACTING CORP p 294
9855 W 78th St Ste 400, Eden Prairie MN 55344
Tel (952) 944-4300 *SIC* 1629

RAILWORKS TRACK SYSTEMS INC p 1205
8485 210th St W, Lakeville MN 55044
Tel (212) 502-7900 *SIC* 1629

M A MORTENSON CO p 889
700 Meadow Ln N, Minneapolis MN 55422
Tel (763) 522-2100 *SIC* 1542 1629

M A MORTENSON COMPANIES INC p 889
700 Meadow Ln N, Minneapolis MN 55422
Tel (763) 522-2100 *SIC* 1542 1629

PARK CONSTRUCTION CO p 1115
1481 81st Ave Ne, Minneapolis MN 55432
Tel (763) 786-9800 *SIC* 1611 1622 1629

DUININCK INC p 460
408 6th St, Prinsburg MN 56281
Tel (320) 978-6011 *SIC* 1629 1611

EMERY SAPP & SONS INC p 492
2301 Interstate 70 Dr Nw, Columbia MO 65202
Tel (573) 445-8331 *SIC* 1622 1629 1611

GARNEY COMPANIES INC p 592
1333 Nw Vivion Rd, Kansas City MO 64118
Tel (816) 741-4600 *SIC* 1623 1629

GARNEY HOLDING CO p 592
1333 Nw Vivion Rd, Kansas City MO 64118
Tel (816) 741-4600 *SIC* 1623 1611 1629

CHESTER BROSS CONSTRUCTION CO p 295
6739 County Road 423, Palmyra MO 63461
Tel (573) 221-5958 *SIC* 1611 1629

ROBINSON MECHANICAL CONTRACTORS INC p 1242
2411 Walters Ln, Perryville MO 63775
Tel (573) 547-8397 *SIC* 1629 1711

HERZOG CONTRACTING CORP p 688
600 S Riverside Rd, Saint Joseph MO 64507
Tel (816) 233-9001 *SIC* 1629 1611 4953

ALBERICI CORP p 46
8800 Page Ave, Saint Louis MO 63114
Tel (314) 733-2000
SIC 1541 1542 1622 1629

KCI CONSTRUCTION CO p 806
10315 Lake Bluff Dr, Saint Louis MO 63123
Tel (314) 894-8888 *SIC* 1542 1611 1629

PROENERGY SERVICES LLC p 1180
2001 Proenergy Blvd, Sedalia MO 65301
Tel (660) 829-5100 *SIC* 1629

COP CONSTRUCTION LLC p 368
242 S 64th St W, Billings MT 59106
Tel (406) 656-4632 *SIC* 1622 1629

BARNARD CONSTRUCTION CO INC p 155
701 Gold Ave, Bozeman MT 59715
Tel (406) 586-1995
SIC 1623 1629 1611 1622

OFTEDAL CONSTRUCTION INC p 1076
434 Highway 59 N 59n, Miles City MT 59301
Tel (406) 232-5911 *SIC* 1629 3273 1611

LANDSCAPES UNLIMITED LLC p 843
1201 Aries Dr, Lincoln NE 68512
Tel (402) 423-6653 *SIC* 1629

KIEWIT CORP p 817
3555 Farnam St Ste 1000, Omaha NE 68131
Tel (402) 342-2052
SIC 1542 1541 1611 1622 1629

KIEWIT INDUSTRIAL GROUP INC p 817
3555 Farnam St, Omaha NE 68131
Tel (402) 342-2052 *SIC* 1629

KIEWIT INFRASTRUCTURE CO p 817
Kiewit Plz, Omaha NE 68131
Tel (402) 342-2052
SIC 1541 1542 1629 1622 1522

KIEWIT INFRASTRUCTURE WEST CO p 817
4004 S 60th St, Omaha NE 68117
Tel (402) 342-2052
SIC 1611 1629 1541 1622 1623

PETER KIEWIT SONS INC p 1138
3555 Farnam St Ste 1000, Omaha NE 68131
Tel (402) 342-2052
SIC 1611 1622 1711 1542 1629 1221

LAS VEGAS PAVING CORP p 845
4420 S Decatur Blvd, Las Vegas NV 89103
Tel (702) 251-5800 *SIC* 1611 1629 8711

BECHTEL NEVADA CORP p 167
2621 Losee Rd, North Las Vegas NV 89030
Tel (702) 295-1000 *SIC* 8711 1629

NATIONAL SECURITY TECHNOLOGIES LLC p 1016
2621 Losee Rd, North Las Vegas NV 89030
Tel (702) 295-1000 SIC 8711 1629

LUMMUS OVERSEAS CORP p 885
1515 Broad St, Bloomfield NJ 07003
Tel (973) 893-1515 SIC 8711 1629 8741

SIMPSON & BROWN INC p 1325
119 North Ave W, Cranford NJ 07016
Tel (908) 276-2776 SIC 1629 1771

WEEKS MARINE INC p 1587
4 Commerce Dr Fl 2, Cranford NJ 07016
Tel (908) 272-4010 SIC 1629

J FLETCHER CREAMER & SON INC p 771
101 E Broadway, Hackensack NJ 07601
Tel (201) 488-9800
SIC 1623 1611 1771 1622 1629

FOSTER WHEELER ZACK INC p 571
53 Frontage Rd, Hampton NJ 08827
Tel (908) 730-4000
SIC 8711 1629 3569 4931

TREVCON CONSTRUCTION CO INC p 1476
30 Church St, Liberty Corner NJ 07938
Tel (908) 580-0200 SIC 1629 1623

■ COVANTA ENERGY GROUP INC p 384
445 South St, Morristown NJ 07960
Tel (862) 345-5000
SIC 1541 1629 4953 4931

■ DELAWARE CITY REFINING CO LLC p 423
1 Sylvan Way Ste 2, Parsippany NJ 07054
Tel (320) 834-6000 SIC 1629

MORETRENCH AMERICAN CORP p 988
100 Stickle Ave, Rockaway NJ 07866
Tel (262) 652-4444 SIC 1629

SCHIAVONE CONSTRUCTION CO LLC p 1287
150 Meadowlands Pkwy # 2, Secaucus NJ 07094
Tel (201) 867-5070 SIC 1622 1629

HAMON CORP p 656
58 E Main St, Somerville NJ 08876
Tel (908) 333-2000
SIC 1629 3564 3499 5084

■ AMERICAN INDUSTRIAL WATER LLC p 74
1025 Laurel Oak Rd, Voorhees NJ 08043
Tel (856) 346-8200 SIC 1629

▲ AMERICAN WATER WORKS CO INC p 81
1025 Laurel Oak Rd, Voorhees NJ 08043
Tel (856) 346-8200 SIC 4941 1629 1623

JAG COMPANIES INC p 776
1433 State Route 34 Ste 5, Wall Township NJ 07727
Tel (732) 557-6100
SIC 1623 1622 1629 1611

NORTHEAST REMSCO CONSTRUCTION INC p 1055
1433 State Route 34 Ste 6, Wall Township NJ 07727
Tel (732) 557-6100
SIC 1623 1622 1629 1611

NATURES TREES INC p 1019
550 Bedford Rd, Bedford Hills NY 10507
Tel (914) 241-4999
SIC 0783 0782 0781 1629

JOHN P PICONE INC p 789
31 Garden Ln, Lawrence NY 11559
Tel (516) 239-1600
SIC 1611 1622 1623 1629

MARUBENI POWER SERVICES INC p 913
375 Lexington Ave, New York NY 10017
Tel (212) 450-0640 SIC 1629 4911 8711

RAILWORKS CORP p 1205
5 Penn Plz, New York NY 10001
Tel (212) 502-7900 SIC 1629

RWL HOLDINGS LLC p 1260
767 5th Ave Ste 4200, New York NY 10153
Tel (212) 572-5700 SIC 1629

JWD GROUP INC p 798
300 Colvin Woods Pkwy, Tonawanda NY 14150
Tel (716) 832-1940 SIC 1711 1629 1623

■ BWXT INVESTMENT CO p 231
11525 N Community House, Charlotte NC 28277
Tel (704) 625-4900
SIC 3511 3443 3564 1629 1541 7699

CROWDER CONSTRUCTION CO INC p 394
6425 Brookshire Blvd, Charlotte NC 28216
Tel (800) 849-2966 SIC 1622 1629 1623

THALLE CONSTRUCTION CO INC p 1446
900 Nc Highway 86 N, Hillsborough NC 27278
Tel (919) 245-1490
SIC 1611 1622 1623 1629

■ SOUTHERN INDUSTRIAL CONSTRUCTORS INC p 1349
6101 Triangle Dr, Raleigh NC 27617
Tel (919) 782-4600
SIC 1629 1799 1731 1796 1791 7353

SANFORD CONTRACTORS INC p 1279
628 Rocky Fork Church Rd, Sanford NC 27332
Tel (919) 775-7882
SIC 1611 1622 1629 6552 1794 1623

MCCORMICK INC p 927
4000 12th Ave N, Fargo ND 58102
Tel (701) 277-1225 SIC 1611 1629 1623

NORTHERN IMPROVEMENT CO p 1056
4000 12th Ave N, Fargo ND 58102
Tel (701) 277-1225 SIC 1611 1629

INDUSTRIAL BUILDERS INC p 739
1307 County Road 17 N, West Fargo ND 58078
Tel (701) 282-4977
SIC 1629 1622 1542 1611 1623

■ WANZEK CONSTRUCTION INC p 1575
2028 2nd Ave Nw, West Fargo ND 58078
Tel (701) 282-6171
SIC 1542 1623 1622 1799 1541 1629

■ BABCOCK & WILCOX CO p 143
20 S Van Buren Ave, Barberton OH 44203
Tel (330) 753-4511
SIC 1629 1711 3443 7699 8741 3822

■ BABCOCK & WILCOX CONSTRUCTION CO INC p 143
74 Robinson Ave, Barberton OH 44203
Tel (330) 860-6301 SIC 1629

WHEELING CORP p 1605
100 1st St Se, Brewster OH 44613
Tel (330) 767-3401 SIC 1629 4011

ENERFAB INC p 497
4955 Spring Grove Ave, Cincinnati OH 45232
Tel (513) 641-0500
SIC 3443 1629 1541 1711 3479

GOETTLE HOLDING CO INC p 619
12071 Hamilton Ave, Cincinnati OH 45231
Tel (513) 825-8100
SIC 1799 1629 1771 1794

KOKOSING CONSTRUCTION CO INC p 826
886 Mckinley Ave, Columbus OH 43222
Tel (614) 228-1029
SIC 1611 1622 1629 1542 1541 1623

SHOOK CONSTRUCTION CO p 1318
4977 Northcutt Pl, Dayton OH 45414
Tel (937) 276-6666 SIC 1629 1542 8741

SHOOK NATIONAL CORP p 1318
4977 Northcutt Pl, Dayton OH 45414
Tel (937) 276-6666
SIC 8741 1542 1629 1541

INDEPENDENCE EXCAVATING INC p 736
5720 E Schaaf Rd, Independence OH 44131
Tel (216) 524-1700
SIC 1629 1794 1611 1771 1795

ULLIMAN SCHUTTE CONSTRUCTION LLC p 1500
9111 Springboro Pike, Miamisburg OH 45342
Tel (937) 247-0375 SIC 1629

■ TOLEDO REFINING CO LLC p 1459
1819 Woodville Rd, Oregon OH 43616
Tel (419) 698-6600 SIC 1629

PETERSON CONSTRUCTION CO p 1138
18817 State Route 501, Wapakoneta OH 45895
Tel (419) 941-2233 SIC 1542 1629

R & D MAINTENANCE SERVICES INC p 1201
409 N Main St, Hennessey OK 73742
Tel (405) 853-7108 SIC 1629

LINDE PROCESS PLANTS INC p 868
6100 S Yale Ave Ste 1200, Tulsa OK 74136
Tel (918) 477-1200 SIC 3444 8711 1629

■ MATRIX NORTH AMERICAN CONSTRUCTION INC p 920
5100 E Skelly Dr Ste 700, Tulsa OK 74135
Tel (918) 838-8822 SIC 1731 1623 1629

■ MATRIX SERVICE INC p 920
5100 E Skelly Dr Ste 700, Tulsa OK 74135
Tel (918) 838-8822
SIC 1623 1629 1799 7699

GRAND RIVER DAM AUTHORITY p 630
226 W Dwain Willis Ave, Vinita OK 74301
Tel (918) 256-5545 SIC 4911 1629

HOFFMAN CORP p 699
805 Sw Broadway Ste 2100, Portland OR 97205
Tel (503) 221-8811
SIC 8741 1541 1542 1623 1629

ALEX E PARIS CONTRACTING CO INC p 48
1595 Smith Township State, Atlasburg PA 15004
Tel (724) 947-2235 SIC 1623 1629

NICHOLSON CONSTRUCTION CO p 1042
2400 Ansys Dr Ste 303, Canonsburg PA 15317
Tel (412) 221-4500 SIC 1629 1771 1799

LOBAR INC p 872
1 Old Mill Rd, Dillsburg PA 17019
Tel (717) 432-9728
SIC 1541 1542 8741 1629 1731 7371

QUANDEL CONSTRUCTION GROUP INC p 1198
3003 N Front St Ste 203, Harrisburg PA 17110
Tel (717) 657-0909
SIC 1542 1541 1629 8741

QUANDEL ENTERPRISES INC p 1198
3003 N Front St Ste 203, Harrisburg PA 17110
Tel (717) 657-0909 SIC 1542 1629 8741

■ CEI HOLDING CO p 273
334 S Warminster Rd, Hatboro PA 19040
Tel (215) 734-1400 SIC 1629

PKF-MARK III INC p 1153
17 Blacksmith Rd Ste 101, Newtown PA 18940
Tel (215) 968-5031
SIC 1611 1629 1711 1731 1771 8711

PENN LINE SERVICE INC p 1129
300 Scottdale Ave, Scottdale PA 15683
Tel (724) 887-9110
SIC 1629 1623 1611 0782

ASPLUNDH TREE EXPERT CO p 119
708 Blair Mill Rd, Willow Grove PA 19090
Tel (215) 784-4200
SIC 0783 1629 1623 1611 6411

ALLAN MYERS INC p 51
1805 Berks Rd, Worcester PA 19490
Tel (610) 222-8800
SIC 1629 1794 1611 1622 3281 5032

ALLAN MYERS LP p 51
1805 Berks Rd, Worcester PA 19490
Tel (610) 584-3430
SIC 1629 1794 1611 1622

MORGAN CORP p 988
1800 E Main St, Duncan SC 29334
Tel (864) 433-8800 SIC 1629

■ JACOBS APPLIED TECHNOLOGY INC p 775
2040 Bushy Park Rd, Goose Creek SC 29445
Tel (843) 824-1100
SIC 3559 3443 8711 1629

CH2M HILL ENGINEERS INC p 286
1500 International Dr, Spartanburg SC 29303
Tel (864) 578-2000 SIC 8711 8742 1629

■ SERVICE ELECTRIC CO p 1307
1631 E 25th St, Chattanooga TN 37404
Tel (423) 894-4336 SIC 1629 1731 1541

PHILLIPS AND JORDAN INC p 1144
10201 Parkside Dr Ste 300, Knoxville TN 37922
Tel (865) 688-8342 SIC 1611 1629

JONES BROS INC p 792
5760 Old Lebanon Dirt Rd, Mount Juliet TN 37122
Tel (615) 754-4710
SIC 1622 1771 1794 1629 1611

LAUREN CORP p 847
901 S 1st St, Abilene TX 79602
Tel (325) 670-9660 SIC 1629

ABRAMS INTERNATIONAL INC p 12
111 Congress Ave Ste 2400, Austin TX 78701
Tel (512) 322-4000
SIC 1611 1622 1629 6799 7359 8742

GENTEX POWER CORP p 605
3701 Lake Austin Blvd, Austin TX 78703
Tel (512) 473-4084 SIC 1629

HELLAS CONSTRUCTION INC p 681
12710 Res Blvd Ste 240, Austin TX 78759
Tel (512) 250-2910 SIC 1629

JD ABRAMS LP p 780
5811 Trade Center Dr # 1, Austin TX 78744
Tel (512) 322-4000
SIC 1611 1622 1629 3272

LOWER COLORADO RIVER AUTHORITY p 881
3700 Lake Austin Blvd, Austin TX 78703
Tel (512) 473-3200 SIC 4911 4941 1629

BO-MAC CONTRACTORS LTD p 194
1020 Lindbergh Dr, Beaumont TX 77707
Tel (409) 842-2125 SIC 1629 1771

KEPPEL AMFELS LLC p 813
20000 State Highway 48, Brownsville TX 78521
Tel (956) 831-8220
SIC 1629 3731 1389 3449 3546 3443

INFINITY CONSTRUCTION SERVICES LP p 741
926 Brazosport Blvd S, Clute TX 77531
Tel (979) 388-8579 SIC 1629 1542

REPCON INC p 1224
7501 Up River Rd, Corpus Christi TX 78409
Tel (361) 289-6342 SIC 1629 1389

▲ ATMOS ENERGY CORP p 128
5430 Lbj Fwy Ste 1800, Dallas TX 75240
Tel (972) 934-9227 SIC 4924 4922 1629

AUSTIN INDUSTRIES INC p 133
3535 Travis St Ste 300, Dallas TX 75204
Tel (214) 443-5500
SIC 1542 1629 1611 1622

▲ JACOBS ENGINEERING GROUP INC p 775
1999 Bryan St Ste 1200, Dallas TX 75201
Tel (214) 583-8500
SIC 8711 1629 1541 8748

▲ MALIBU ENTERTAINMENT WORLDWIDE INC p 899
717 N Harwood St Ste 1650, Dallas TX 75201
Tel (214) 210-8701 SIC 1629 7999

■ ORION CONSTRUCTION LP p 1094
4440 Highway 225 Ste 180, Deer Park TX 77536
Tel (713) 852-6500 SIC 1629

TRAC-WORK INC p 1468
3801 N I 45, Ennis TX 75119
Tel (972) 875-6565 SIC 1629

■ KMG ELECTRONIC CHEMICALS INC p 824
300 Throckmorton St, Fort Worth TX 76102
Tel (817) 761-6100 SIC 1629

GULF STATES INC p 647
6711 E Highway 332, Freeport TX 77541
Tel (979) 233-4461 SIC 1541 1629

ENTACT LLC p 501
3129 Bass Pro Dr, Grapevine TX 76051
Tel (972) 580-1323 SIC 1629

AMEC FOSTER WHEELER USA CORP p 66
585 N Dairy Ashford Rd, Houston TX 77079
Tel (713) 929-5000 SIC 8711 3443 1629

APACHE INDUSTRIAL SERVICES INC p 96
15423 Vantage Pkwy E, Houston TX 77032
Tel (281) 609-8800 SIC 1629 1541

BECHTEL OIL GAS AND CHEMICALS INC p 167
3000 Post Oak Blvd, Houston TX 77056
Tel (713) 235-2000 SIC 1629

CAL DIVE INTERNATIONAL INC p 237
2500 Citywest Blvd # 2200, Houston TX 77042
Tel (713) 361-2600 SIC 7389 1623 1629

GDF SUEZ ENERGY NORTH AMERICA INC p 595
1990 Post Oak Blvd # 1900, Houston TX 77056
Tel (713) 636-0000 SIC 1311 8741 1629

■ HALLIBURTON DELAWARE INC p 654
3000 Houston Ave, Houston TX 77009
Tel (713) 759-2600
SIC 1629 1611 1622 8711 1389

▲ HELIX ENERGY SOLUTIONS GROUP INC p 681
3505 W Sam Houston Pkwy N, Houston TX 77043
Tel (281) 618-0400 SIC 1629 1389 1311

■ JACOBS P&C US INC p 775
3600 Briarpark Dr, Houston TX 77042
Tel (713) 988-2002 SIC 1629

■ KBR HOLDINGS LLC p 806
601 Jefferson St Ste 7911, Houston TX 77002
Tel (713) 753-4176 SIC 1629 8711 8741

▲ KBR INC p 806
601 Jefferson St Ste 3400, Houston TX 77002
Tel (713) 753-3011 SIC 1629 8711 8741

■ KELLOGG BROWN & ROOT LLC p 808
601 Jefferson St Ste 100, Houston TX 77002
Tel (713) 753-2000 SIC 8711 1629

■ MCDERMOTT INC p 927
757 N Eldridge Pkwy # 101, Houston TX 77079
Tel (281) 870-5000 SIC 1629

■ MCDERMOTT INVESTMENTS LLC p 927
757 N Eldridge Pkwy # 101, Houston TX 77079
Tel (281) 870-5000 SIC 1629

▲ ORION GROUP HOLDINGS INC p 1094
12000 Aerospace Ave # 300, Houston TX 77034
Tel (713) 852-6500 SIC 1629

REMEDIAL CONSTRUCTION SVCS LP p 1222
9977 W Sam Houston Pkwy N, Houston TX 77064
Tel (281) 955-2442 SIC 8744 1629

S & B HOLDINGS LTD p 1261
7809 Park Place Blvd, Houston TX 77087
Tel (713) 645-4141 SIC 1629 8711

S AND B ENGINEERS AND CONSTRUCTORS LTD p 1261
7825 Park Place Blvd, Houston TX 77087
Tel (713) 645-4141 SIC 1629 8711

SUBSEA 7 (US) LLC p 1396
10787 Clay Rd, Houston TX 77041
Tel (281) 966-7600 SIC 1629 3731

WT BYLER CO INC p 1569
15203 Lillja Rd, Houston TX 77060
Tel (281) 445-2070 SIC 1794 1629

WARTSILA HOLDING INC p 1577
11710 N Gessner Rd Ste A, Houston TX 77064
Tel (281) 233-6200 SIC 5084 1629

WARTSILA NORTH AMERICA INC p 1577
11710 N Gessner Rd Ste A, Houston TX 77064
Tel (281) 233-6200
SIC 1629 5084 1382 4789 3731

WEDGE GROUP INC p 1587
1415 La St Ste 3000, Houston TX 77002
Tel (713) 739-6500 SIC 1389 1629 1311

WOOD GROUP PSN INC p 1622
17325 Park Row, Houston TX 77084
Tel (281) 647-1041 SIC 1629 1542 8711

STATE SERVICE CO INC p 1382
1062 Harbor 2 Bishop Rd, Ingleside TX 78362
Tel (281) 347-2500 SIC 1629

▲ FLUOR CORP p 561
6700 Las Colinas Blvd, Irving TX 75039
Tel (469) 398-7000 SIC 8711 1629 1541

OPTIMIZED PROCESS DESIGNS LLC p 1090
25610 Clay Rd, Katy TX 77493
Tel (281) 371-7500 SIC 1629

AUSTIN INDUSTRIAL INC p 133
2801 E 13th St, La Porte TX 77571
Tel (713) 641-3400 SIC 1629

AUSTIN MAINTENANCE & CONSTRUCTION INC p 133
2801 E 13th St, La Porte TX 77571
Tel (713) 641-3400 SIC 1629

A GLEN BARRILLEAUX LLC p 5
1412 W Broad St, Oakwood TX 75855
Tel (903) 545-1231 SIC 1623 1629

REF-CHEM LP p 1217
1128 S Grandview Ave, Odessa TX 79761
Tel (432) 332-8531 SIC 1629

SAULSBURY ELECTRIC CO LTD p 1283
2951 E Interstate 20, Odessa TX 79766
Tel (432) 366-3686 SIC 1629

SAULSBURY INDUSTRIES INC p 1283
2951 E Interstate 20, Odessa TX 79766
Tel (432) 366-3686 SIC 1629

BEACON MARITIME INC p 165
96 W Front St, Orange TX 77630
Tel (409) 670-1060 SIC 1629 3731

■ ATLANTIC PLANT MAINTENANCE INC p 127
3225 Pasadena Blvd, Pasadena TX 77503
Tel (713) 475-4500 SIC 1629

VENTECH ENGINEERS INTERNATIONAL CORP p 1548
1149 Ellsworth Dr Ofc, Pasadena TX 77506
Tel (713) 477-0201
SIC 1629 8711 3559 5084

■ VICEROY INC p 1555
3225 Pasadena Blvd, Pasadena TX 77503
Tel (713) 475-4518
SIC 1629 3443 1796 8742 8748 7363

KING FISHER MARINE SERVICE LP p 820
159 Hwy 316, Port Lavaca TX 77979
Tel (361) 552-6751 SIC 1629

JOHNSON BROS CORP p 790
608 Henrietta Creek Rd, Roanoke TX 76262
Tel (813) 685-5101 SIC 1623 1629 1622

SOUTHLAND HOLDINGS LLC p 1351
608 Henrietta Creek Rd, Roanoke TX 76262
Tel (817) 293-4263 SIC 1629

CCC GROUP INC p 269
5797 Dietrich Rd, San Antonio TX 78219
Tel (210) 661-4251 SIC 1541 1629 1542

GUTHRIE & HUEBNER CO INC p 648
5797 Dietrich Rd, San Antonio TX 78219
Tel (210) 661-4251 SIC 1541 1629 1542

HB ZACHRY CO p 671
527 Logwood Ave, San Antonio TX 78221
Tel (210) 475-8000
SIC 1611 1622 1623 1629

YANTIS CORP p 1635
3611 Paesanos Pkwy # 300, San Antonio TX 78231
Tel (210) 655-3780
SIC 1623 1611 1622 1629 6552 1521

ZACHRY CONSOLIDATED LLC p 1640
527 Logwood Ave, San Antonio TX 78221
Tel (210) 871-2700
SIC 1611 1622 1623 1629 3241 1442

ZACHRY CONSTRUCTION & MATERIALS INC p 1640
2330 N Loop 1604 W, San Antonio TX 78248
Tel (210) 479-1027
SIC 1611 1622 1623 1629 1542 3241

ZACHRY CONSTRUCTION CORP p 1640
2330 N Loop 1604 W, San Antonio TX 78248
Tel (210) 871-2700
SIC 1623 1611 1622 1629 1542

ZACHRY HOLDINGS INC p 1640
527 Logwood Ave, San Antonio TX 78221
Tel (210) 588-5000
SIC 1541 8711 1629 1623

ZACHRY INDUSTRIAL INC p 1640
527 Logwood Ave, San Antonio TX 78221
Tel (210) 475-8000 SIC 1541 1629

■ RALPH L WADSWORTH CONSTRUCTION CO LLC p 1206
166 E 14000 S Ste 200, Draper UT 84020
Tel (801) 553-1661 SIC 1629 1611

WESTERN EXPLOSIVES SYSTEMS CO p 1598
3135 S Richmond St, Salt Lake City UT 84106
Tel (801) 484-6557
SIC 5169 1629 1241 1081 1481 2892

W W CLYDE & CO p 1569
1375 N Main St, Springville UT 84663
Tel (801) 802-6800 SIC 1611 1794 1629

PC CONSTRUCTION CO p 1123
193 Tilley Dr, South Burlington VT 05403
Tel (802) 658-4100 SIC 1629 1542

FAULCONER CONSTRUCTION CO INC p 531
2496 Old Ivy Rd, Charlottesville VA 22903
Tel (434) 295-0033
SIC 1629 1611 1542 1623

MEB GENERAL CONTRACTORS INC p 934
4016 Holland Blvd, Chesapeake VA 23323
Tel (757) 487-5858 SIC 1542 1629 1541

NORFOLK DREDGING CO p 1048
110 Centerville Tpke N, Chesapeake VA 23320
Tel (757) 547-9391 SIC 1629

ENGLISH CONSTRUCTION CO INC p 499
615 Church St Ste 2, Lynchburg VA 24504
Tel (434) 845-0301
SIC 1611 1629 1623 1542

BECHTEL NUCLEAR SECURITY & ENVIRONMENTAL INC p 167
12021 Sunset Hills Rd, Reston VA 20190
Tel (415) 768-1234 SIC 8711 1629 8742

EHW CONSTRUCTORS A JOINT VENTURE p 481
295 Bendix Rd Ste 400, Virginia Beach VA 23452
Tel (757) 420-4140 SIC 1629

SKANSKA USA CIVIL SOUTHEAST INC p 1329
295 Bendix Rd Ste 400, Virginia Beach VA 23452
Tel (757) 420-4140
SIC 1622 1629 3272 1541

FRU-CON CONSTRUCTION LLC p 582
4310 Prince William Pkwy # 200, Woodbridge VA 22192
Tel (703) 586-6100 SIC 1629

BRITISH PETROLEUM p 214
4519 Grandview Rd, Blaine WA 98230
Tel (360) 371-1300 SIC 1629

SNC-LAVALIN CONSTRUCTORS INC p 1335
19015 North Creek Pkwy # 300, Bothell WA 98011
Tel (425) 489-3300 SIC 1629

GENERAL CONSTRUCTION CO p 600
33455 6th Ave S, Federal Way WA 98003
Tel (253) 943-4200 SIC 1622 1629

IMCO GENERAL CONSTRUCTION INC p 733
2116 Buchanan Loop, Ferndale WA 98248
Tel (360) 671-3936 SIC 1541 1629 1542

GLOBAL DIVING & SALVAGE INC p 616
3840 W Marginal Way Sw, Seattle WA 98106
Tel (206) 623-0621 SIC 4959 1629 7389

MANSON CONSTRUCTION CO p 903
5209 E Marginal Way S, Seattle WA 98134
Tel (206) 762-0850 SIC 1629

MANSON CONSTRUCTION HOLDING CO p 903
5209 E Marginal Way S, Seattle WA 98134
Tel (206) 762-0850 SIC 1629

HOS BROTHERS CONSTRUCTION INC p 708
7733 W Bostian Rd, Woodinville WA 98072
Tel (425) 481-5569 SIC 1611 1629

VECELLIO & GROGAN INC p 1546
2251 Robert C Byrd Dr, Beckley WV 25801
Tel (304) 252-6575 SIC 1611 1622 1629

RALEIGH MINE AND INDUSTRIAL SUPPLY INC p 1206
1500 Mill Creek Rd, Mount Hope WV 25880
Tel (304) 877-5503
SIC 5085 1629 3532 3441

MICHELS CORP p 960
817 W Main St, Brownsville WI 53006
Tel (920) 583-3132
SIC 1623 1771 1381 1629 3498 1794

AZCO INC p 140
806 Valley Rd, Menasha WI 54952
Tel (920) 734-5791 SIC 1629

TIC - INDUSTRIAL CO WYOMING INC p 1452
1474 Willer Dr, Casper WY 82604
Tel (307) 235-9958 SIC 1629

ELKHORN CONSTRUCTION INC p 488
71 Allegiance Cir, Evanston WY 82930
Tel (307) 789-1595 SIC 1629 1731 1623

SIC 1711 Plumbing, Heating & Air Conditioning Contractors

■ B E & K INC p 141
2000 International Pk Dr, Birmingham AL 35243
Tel (205) 972-6000
SIC 1541 8711 1796 1711

BURKES MECHANICAL INC p 227
2 Industrial Rd, Brent AL 35034
Tel (205) 926-5847 SIC 1711

■ KBR CONSTRUCTION CO LLC p 806
3000 Riverchase Galleria, Hoover AL 35244
Tel (205) 972-6538
SIC 1541 1796 1711 1629 1799 1521

VECO CORP p 1546
949 E 36th Ave Ste 500, Anchorage AK 99508
Tel (907) 762-1500
SIC 1711 1389 1731 1381 4959

■ COMFORT SYSTEMS USA (SOUTHWEST) INC p 344
6875 W Galveston St, Chandler AZ 85226
Tel (480) 940-8400 SIC 1711

INTERSTATE MECHANICAL CORP p 758
1841 E Washington St, Phoenix AZ 85034
Tel (800) 628-0211 SIC 1711

TELGIAN CORP p 1435
10230 S 50th Pl, Phoenix AZ 85044
Tel (480) 753-5444
SIC 1711 8711 1731 8748

■ COMFORT SYSTEMS USA (ARKANSAS) INC p 344
4806 Rixie Rd, North Little Rock AR 72117
Tel (501) 834-3320 SIC 1711

MULTI-CRAFT CONTRACTORS INC p 999
2300 N Lowell Rd, Springdale AR 72764
Tel (479) 751-4330 SIC 1711 3441 1731

CONTROL AIR CONDITIONING CORP p 364
5200 E La Palma Ave, Anaheim CA 92807
Tel (714) 777-8600 SIC 1711

SOURCE REFRIGERATION & HVAC INC p 1342
800 E Orangethorpe Ave, Anaheim CA 92801
Tel (714) 578-2300 SIC 1711 1731

AMPAM PARKS MECHANICAL INC p 86
17036 Avalon Blvd, Carson CA 90746
Tel (310) 835-1532 SIC 1711

US AIRCONDITIONING DISTRIBUTORS INC p 1530
16900 Chestnut St, City Of Industry CA 91748
Tel (626) 854-4500 SIC 5075 1711

LDI MECHANICAL INC p 849
1587 E Bentley Dr, Corona CA 92879
Tel (951) 340-9685 SIC 1711

MURRAY PLUMBING AND HEATING CORP p 1002
18414 S Santa Fe Ave, E Rncho Dmngz CA 90221
Tel (310) 637-1500 SIC 1711

■ UNIVERSITY MECHANICAL & ENGINEERING CONTRACTORS INC p 1519
1168 Fesler St, El Cajon CA 92020
Tel (619) 956-2500 SIC 1711 1623 8741

CONFORTI PLUMBING INC p 356
6080 Pleasant Valley Rd C, El Dorado CA 95623
Tel (530) 622-0202 SIC 1711

MATERIAL SUPPLY INC p 919
11700 Industry Ave, Fontana CA 92337
Tel (951) 727-2200
SIC 3444 5075 7623 1711

PAN-PACIFIC MECHANICAL LLC p 1111
18250 Euclid St, Fountain Valley CA 92708
Tel (949) 474-9170 SIC 1711

KINETIC SYSTEMS INC p 820
48400 Fremont Blvd, Fremont CA 94538
Tel (510) 683-6000 SIC 1711

SOUTHLAND INDUSTRIES p 1351
7390 Lincoln Way, Garden Grove CA 92841
Tel (800) 613-6240 SIC 1711

ACCO ENGINEERED SYSTEMS INC p 15
6265 San Fernando Rd, Glendale CA 91201
Tel (818) 244-6571 SIC 1711 7623

■ MESA ENERGY SYSTEMS INC p 951
2 Cromwell, Irvine CA 92618
Tel (949) 460-0460 SIC 1711 7623

MX HOLDINGS US p 1004
153 Technology Dr Ste 200, Irvine CA 92618
Tel (949) 727-3277 SIC 1711 1731 5999

VILLARA CORP p 1557
4700 Lang Ave, Mcclellan CA 95652
Tel (916) 646-2700 SIC 1711

SUNGEVITY INC p 1402
66 Franklin St Ste 310, Oakland CA 94607
Tel (510) 496-5500 SIC 1711 8713

AMERICAN TECHNOLOGIES INC p 80
210 W Baywood Ave, Orange CA 92865
Tel (714) 283-9990
SIC 1521 1541 1742 1731 1721 1711

■ PERFORMANCE MECHANICAL INC p 1135
701 Willow Pass Rd Ste 2, Pittsburg CA 94565
Tel (925) 432-4080 SIC 1541 1711 8711

ET SOLAR INC p 511
4900 Hopyard Rd Ste 310, Pleasanton CA 94588
Tel (925) 460-9898 SIC 1711

SUPERIOR ELECTRICAL MECHANICAL & PLUMBING INC p 1406
8613 Helms Ave, Rancho Cucamonga CA 91730
Tel (909) 357-9400 SIC 1731 1711

PENTAIR THERMAL MANAGEMENT LLC p 1132
899 Broadway St, Redwood City CA 94063
Tel (650) 474-7414 SIC 1711 3822

SOLIGENT HOLDINGS INC p 1338
1500 Valley House Dr, Rohnert Park CA 94928
Tel (707) 992-3100 SIC 5074 7359 1711

AIRCO MECHANICAL INC p 40
8210 Demetre Ave, Sacramento CA 95828
Tel (916) 381-4523 SIC 1711 8711

A O REED & CO p 6
4777 Ruffner St, San Diego CA 92111
Tel (858) 565-4131 SIC 1711

■ CALIFORNIA COMFORT SYSTEMS USA p 239
7740 Kenamar Ct, San Diego CA 92121
Tel (858) 564-1100 SIC 1711

PACIFIC RIM MECHANICAL CONTRACTORS INC p 1105
7655 Convoy Ct, San Diego CA 92111
Tel (858) 974-6500 SIC 1711

AIR SYSTEMS INC p 39
940 Remillard Ct Frnt, San Jose CA 95122
Tel (408) 280-1666 SIC 1711 7623

CALIFORNIA UNITED MECHANICAL INC p 241
2185 Oakland Rd, San Jose CA 95131
Tel (408) 232-9000 SIC 1711

CRITCHFIELD MECHANICAL INC p 393
1901 Junction Ave, San Jose CA 95131
Tel (408) 437-7000 SIC 1711

COSCO FIRE PROTECTION INC p 373
29222 Rancho Viejo Rd # 205, San Juan Capistrano CA 92675
Tel (714) 974-8770 SIC 1711 1731 5999

■ SOLARCITY CORP p 1338
3055 Clearview Way, San Mateo CA 94402
Tel (650) 638-1028 SIC 1711

■ DESERT MECHANICAL INC p 432
15870 Olden St, Sylmar CA 91342
Tel (702) 873-7333 SIC 1711

WESTERN STATES FIRE PROTECTION CO INC p 1600
7026 S Tucson Way, Centennial CO 80112
Tel (303) 792-0022 SIC 1711

HEATING AND PLUMBING ENGINEERS INC p 679
407 Fillmore Pl, Colorado Springs CO 80907
Tel (719) 633-5571 SIC 1711

RK MECHANICAL INC p 1239
3800 Xanthia St, Denver CO 80238
Tel (303) 576-9696 SIC 1711 3498 3441

LONG BUILDING TECHNOLOGIES INC p 876
5001 S Zuni St, Littleton CO 80120
Tel (303) 975-2100 SIC 5075 1711

AMI MECHANICAL INC p 85
12141 Pennsylvania St, Thornton CO 80241
Tel (303) 280-1401 SIC 1711

■ EMCOR CONSTRUCTION SERVICES INC p 491
301 Merritt 7 Fl 6, Norwalk CT 06851
Tel (203) 849-7800 SIC 1711 1731

▲ EMCOR GROUP INC p 491
301 Merritt 7 Fl 6, Norwalk CT 06851
Tel (203) 849-7800 SIC 1731 1711 7349

■ EMCOR MECHANICAL/ELECTRICAL SERVICES (WEST) INC p 491
301 Merritt 7, Norwalk CT 06851
Tel (203) 849-7800 SIC 1711 1731

■ M E S HOLDING CORP p 889
301 Merritt 7, Norwalk CT 06851
Tel (203) 849-7800 SIC 1711 1731

■ TALEN ENERGY SERVICES NORTHEAST INC p 1422
50 Inwood Rd Ste 3, Rocky Hill CT 06067
Tel (860) 513-1036 SIC 1711 1629

▲ STAR GAS PARTNERS LP p 1378
9 W Broad St Ste 3, Stamford CT 06902
Tel (203) 328-7310 SIC 1711 5172

MERCURY FUEL SERVICE INC p 945
43 Lafayette St, Waterbury CT 06708
Tel (203) 756-7284
SIC 5172 5541 5411 5983 1711 2911

HORIZON SERVICES INC p 707
320 Century Blvd, Wilmington DE 19808
Tel (302) 762-1200 SIC 1711

■ PEPCO ENERGY SERVICES INC p 1133
701 9th St Nw Ste 2100, Washington DC 20001
Tel (703) 253-1800
SIC 1711 1731 1623 4961

SIMPLEXGRINNELL LP p 1325
4700 Exchange Ct, Boca Raton FL 33431
Tel (561) 988-7200
SIC 5087 1711 3669 7382

SERVICE AMERICA ENTEPRISE INC p 1307
2755 Nw 63rd Ct, Fort Lauderdale FL 33309
Tel (954) 979-1100 SIC 1711 1731

B & I CONTRACTORS INC p 141
2701 Prince St, Fort Myers FL 33916
Tel (239) 344-3213 SIC 1711 1731

HUGHES SUPPLY INC p 717
2920 Ford St, Fort Myers FL 33916
Tel (239) 334-2205
SIC 5063 5074 5075 5085 1711

MASTER PROTECTION HOLDINGS INC p 918
13050 Metro Pkwy Ste 1, Fort Myers FL 33966
Tel (239) 896-1680 SIC 7389 1711 5999

MILTON J WOOD CO p 972
3805 Faye Rd, Jacksonville FL 32226
Tel (904) 353-5527 SIC 1711 1542

WW GAY MECHANICAL CONTRACTOR INC p 1628
524 Stockton St, Jacksonville FL 32204
Tel (904) 388-2696 SIC 1711

BCH MECHANICAL INC p 164
6354 118th Ave, Largo FL 33773
Tel (727) 546-3561 SIC 1711 3444

QGS DEVELOPMENT INC p 1195
17502 County Road 672, Lithia FL 33547
Tel (813) 634-3326 SIC 0782 0781 1711

WAYNE AUTOMATIC FIRE SPRINKLERS INC p 1584
222 Capitol Ct, Ocoee FL 34761
Tel (407) 656-3030 SIC 1711

DEL-AIR HEATING AIR CONDITIONING & REFRIGERATION CORP p 423
531 Codisco Way, Sanford FL 32771
Tel (866) 796-4874 SIC 1711

WIGINTON CORP p 1608
699 Aero Ln, Sanford FL 32771
Tel (407) 585-3200 SIC 1711 7699 7389

CLEVELAND ELECTRIC CO INC p 325
1281 Fulton Indus Blvd Nw, Atlanta GA 30336
Tel (404) 696-4550 SIC 1731 1711 1796

CLEVELAND GROUP INC p 325
1281 Fulton Indus Blvd Nw, Atlanta GA 30336
Tel (404) 696-4550 SIC 1731 8741 1711

MCKENNEYS INC p 930
1056 Moreland Indus Blvd, Atlanta GA 30316
Tel (404) 622-5000 SIC 1711 8711

CENTRAL GEORGIA ELECTRIC MEMBERSHIP CORP p 278
923 S Mulberry St, Jackson GA 30233
Tel (770) 775-7857 SIC 4911 1711

FIRST CALL JEWEL INC p 545
1410 Hollipark Dr, Idaho Falls ID 83401
Tel (208) 522-7777
SIC 1731 1711 5078 5063

ANTARCTIC MECHANICAL SERVICES INC p 93
140 Tower Dr, Burr Ridge IL 60527
Tel (630) 887-7700 SIC 1711 1731

HAYES MECHANICAL LLC p 670
5959 S Harlem Ave, Chicago IL 60638
Tel (773) 784-0000 SIC 1711

HILL MECHANICAL CORP p 693
11045 Gage Ave, Franklin Park IL 60131
Tel (847) 451-5000 SIC 1711

CHICAGO BLOWER CORP p 297
1675 Glen Ellyn Rd, Glendale Heights IL 60139
Tel (630) 858-2600 SIC 3564 1711

US BUILDER SERVICES LLC p 1531
272 E Deerpath Ste 308, Lake Forest IL 60045
Tel (847) 735-2066 SIC 1742 1731 1711

LEXINGTON CORPORATE ENTERPRISES INC p 859
17725 Volbrecht Rd, Lansing IL 60438
Tel (708) 418-0700 SIC 5075 1711

■ TRADEWINDS HEATING & AIR CONDITIONING p 1469
2019 Corporate Ln Ste 159, Naperville IL 60563
Tel (630) 718-2700 SIC 1711

ARMON INC p 111
2265 Carlson Dr, Northbrook IL 60062
Tel (847) 498-4800 SIC 1711 7515 6552

F E MORAN INC p 522
2265 Carlson Dr, Northbrook IL 60062
Tel (847) 498-4800 SIC 1711

SCHNEIDER ELECTRIC BUILDINGS LLC p 1287
839 N Perryville Rd, Rockford IL 61107
Tel (815) 381-5000
SIC 3822 1711 3625 3823 3621

SCHNEIDER ELECTRIC HOLDINGS INC p 1287
200 N Martingale Rd # 100, Schaumburg IL 60173
Tel (717) 944-5460
SIC 3822 1711 3625 3823 3621

STERLING BOILER AND MECHANICAL INC p 1387
1420 Kimber Ln, Evansville IN 47715
Tel (812) 479-5447 SIC 1711 3443

■ SHAMBAUGH & SON LP p 1311
7614 Opportunity Dr, Fort Wayne IN 46825
Tel (260) 487-7777
SIC 1711 1799 1731 1796 1629

WAGNER-MEINERT LLC p 1571
7617 Freedom Way, Fort Wayne IN 46818
Tel (260) 489-7555 SIC 5078 1711 1799

DEEM LLC p 421
6831 E 32nd St Ste 200, Indianapolis IN 46226
Tel (317) 860-2990 SIC 1731 1711

■ ENERGY SYSTEMS GROUP LLC p 498
4655 Rosebud Ln, Newburgh IN 47630
Tel (812) 492-3734 SIC 8711 1711 1629

BAKER MECHANICAL INC p 146
4224 Hubbell Ave, Des Moines IA 50317
Tel (515) 262-4000 SIC 1711 3444

WALDINGER CORP p 1572
2601 Bell Ave, Des Moines IA 50321
Tel (515) 284-1911 SIC 1711

IOWA FIRE PROTECTION INC p 762
735 Robins Rd, Hiawatha IA 52233
Tel (319) 378-0820 SIC 1711

P1 GROUP INC p 1103
13605 W 96th Ter, Lenexa KS 66215
Tel (913) 529-5000 SIC 1711 1731

MMC CORP p 979
10955 Lowell Ave Ste 350, Overland Park KS 66210
Tel (913) 469-0101 SIC 1542 1711

SHELL TOPCO LP p 1314
2533 S West St, Wichita KS 67217
Tel (316) 942-7266 SIC 3625 1711

HARSHAW SERVICE INC p 664
12700 Plantside Dr, Louisville KY 40299
Tel (502) 499-7000 SIC 5075 1711 5074

TITAN CONTRACTING & LEASING CO INC p 1456
2205 Ragu Dr, Owensboro KY 42303
Tel (270) 683-6564 SIC 1711

HARPER INDUSTRIES INC p 663
960 N Hc Mathis Dr, Paducah KY 42001
Tel (270) 442-2753
SIC 3273 1711 1611 1542

MCC GROUP L L C p 926
3001 17th St, Metairie LA 70002
Tel (504) 833-8291 SIC 1711 1542 1731

CONSTELLATION ENERGY GROUP INC p 361
100 Constellation Way, Baltimore MD 21202
Tel (410) 470-2800 SIC 4911 4924 1711

W E BOWERS & ASSOCIATES INC p 1568
12401a Kiln Ct Ste A, Beltsville MD 20705
Tel (800) 989-0011 SIC 1711

WE BOWERS INC p 1585
12401 Kiln Ct Ste A, Beltsville MD 20705
Tel (301) 419-2488 SIC 1711

JOHN J KIRLIN INC p 789
515 Dover Rd Ste 2100, Rockville MD 20850
Tel (301) 424-3410 SIC 1711

JOHN J KIRLIN INC p 789
515 Dover Rd Ste 2200, Rockville MD 20850
Tel (301) 424-3410 SIC 1711

SHAPIRO & DUNCAN INC p 1311
14620 Rothgeb Dr, Rockville MD 20850
Tel (240) 453-0280 SIC 1711

FIDELITY ENGINEERING CORP p 540
25 Loveton Cir, Sparks MD 21152
Tel (410) 771-9400
SIC 1711 5063 1799 8711

▲ ATN INTERNATIONAL INC p 128
500 Cummings Ctr Ste 2450, Beverly MA 01915
Tel (978) 619-1300 SIC 4813 4812 1711

THOMAS G GALLAGHER INC p 1448
109 Smith Pl, Cambridge MA 02138
Tel (617) 661-7000 SIC 1711

E M DUGGAN INC p 466
140 Will Dr, Canton MA 02021
Tel (781) 828-2292 SIC 1711

HARRY GRODSKY & CO INC p 664
33 Shaws Ln, Springfield MA 01104
Tel (413) 785-1947 SIC 1711

■ JC HIGGINS CORP p 780
70 Hawes Way, Stoughton MA 02072
Tel (781) 341-1500 SIC 1711

JC CANNISTRARO LLC p 780
80 Rosedale Rd, Watertown MA 02472
Tel (617) 926-0092 SIC 1711

SIMPLEX TIME RECORDER LLC p 1325
50 Technology Dr, Westminster MA 01441
Tel (978) 731-2500 SIC 7382 3669 1711

RILEY POWER INC p 1235
5 Neponset St, Worcester MA 01606
Tel (508) 852-7100
SIC 3569 3443 3433 1711 3564 3511

JOHN E GREEN CO p 788
220 Victor St, Detroit MI 48203
Tel (313) 868-2400 SIC 1711

OPTION ENERGY LLC p 1090
5481 N Whitetail Ln, Ludington MI 49431
Tel (269) 329-4317
SIC 4924 1311 4931 1711

W SOULE & CO p 1569
7125 S Sprinkle Rd, Portage MI 49002
Tel (269) 324-7001 SIC 1711 3444

CONTI CORP p 362
6417 Center Dr Ste 120, Sterling Heights MI 48312
Tel (586) 274-4800 SIC 1731 1711

EGAN CO p 481
7625 Boone Ave N, Brooklyn Park MN 55428
Tel (763) 595-4358
SIC 1711 1731 3444 7623 1793

JAMAR CO p 776
4701 Mike Colalillo Dr, Duluth MN 55807
Tel (218) 628-1027
SIC 1711 1761 1742 5033 7699 3444

METROPOLITAN MECHANICAL CONTRACTORS INC p 956
7450 Flying Cloud Dr, Eden Prairie MN 55344
Tel (952) 941-7010 SIC 1711 8711

FAGEN INC p 524
501 Highway 212 W, Granite Falls MN 56241
Tel (320) 564-3324 SIC 1541 1731 1711

CANNON VALLEY COOPERATIVE p 247
1500 Highway 3 S, Northfield MN 55057
Tel (507) 645-9556
SIC 5541 5171 1711 5191 5153 5211

WRIGHT-HENNEPIN SECURITY CORP p 1627
6800 Electric Dr, Rockford MN 55373
Tel (763) 477-3664
SIC 1731 1711 7382 5063 4911

API GROUP INC p 96
1100 Old Highway 8 Nw, Saint Paul MN 55112
Tel (651) 636-4320
SIC 1711 1742 7699 1799

HARRIS CONTRACTING CO p 663
909 Montreal Cir, Saint Paul MN 55102
Tel (651) 602-6500 SIC 1711

NORTHERN AIR CORP p 1055
1001 Labore Industrial Ct B, Saint Paul MN 55110
Tel (651) 490-9868 SIC 1711

SUMMIT FIRE PROTECTION CO p 1398
575 Minnehaha Ave W, Saint Paul MN 55103
Tel (651) 288-0777 SIC 1711

PIONEER POWER INC p 1151
2500 Ventura Dr, Woodbury MN 55125
Tel (651) 438-5561 SIC 1711

IVEY MECHANICAL CO LLC p 769
514 N Wells St, Kosciusko MS 39090
Tel (662) 289-8601 SIC 1711

SOUTHERN PIPE & SUPPLY CO INC p 1350
4330 Highway 39 N, Meridian MS 39301
Tel (601) 693-2911 SIC 5074 1711 1623

FOLEY CO p 563
7501 E Front St, Kansas City MO 64120
Tel (816) 241-3335 SIC 1623 1711 1541

MMC CONTRACTORS NATIONAL INC p 979
13800 Wyandotte St, Kansas City MO 64145
Tel (816) 215-3422 SIC 1711

U S ENGINEERING CO p 1497
3433 Roanoke Rd, Kansas City MO 64111
Tel (816) 753-6969 SIC 1711

ARIZON COMPANIES INC p 108
11880 Dorsett Rd, Maryland Heights MO 63043
Tel (314) 739-0037
SIC 3585 1711 2394 1541 1542 8611

ROBINSON MECHANICAL CONTRACTORS INC p 1242
2411 Walters Ln, Perryville MO 63775
Tel (573) 547-8397 SIC 1629 1711

AMERICAN RESIDENTIAL SERVICES OF INDIANA INC p 78
10403 Baur Blvd Ste E, Saint Louis MO 63132
Tel (314) 812-6000
SIC 1711 1731 1799 5722

CORRIGAN BROTHERS INC p 373
3545 Gratiot St, Saint Louis MO 63103
Tel (314) 771-6200 SIC 1711 1761 1623

MURPHY CO MECHANICAL CONTRACTORS AND ENGINEERS p 1001
1233 N Price Rd, Saint Louis MO 63132
Tel (314) 997-6600 SIC 1711

PETER KIEWIT SONS INC p 1138
3555 Farnam St Ste 1000, Omaha NE 68131
Tel (402) 342-2052
SIC 1611 1622 1711 1542 1629 1221

WORLD AND MAIN LLC p 1624
324a Half Acre Rd, Cranbury NJ 08512
Tel (609) 860-9990 SIC 1711 3429

PRO-TECH ENERGY SOLUTIONS LLC p 1178
215 Executive Dr, Moorestown NJ 08057
Tel (856) 437-6220 SIC 1711

LIME ENERGY CO p 866
4 Gateway Ctr Fl 4, Newark NJ 07102
Tel (201) 416-2575 SIC 1711 8711

F M SYLVAN INC p 522
1001 State St, Perth Amboy NJ 08861
Tel (732) 826-7474 SIC 1711

SYLVAN FM HOLDING LLC p 1413
1001 State St, Perth Amboy NJ 08861
Tel (732) 826-7474 SIC 1711

BINSKY & SNYDER LLC p 183
281 Centennial Ave Ste 1, Piscataway NJ 08854
Tel (732) 885-0700 SIC 1711 8711

TYCO INTERNATIONAL MANAGEMENT CO LLC p 1496
9 Roszel Rd Ste 2, Princeton NJ 08540
Tel (609) 720-4200
SIC 3999 1711 1731 3669 3491

RAY ANGELINI INC p 1209
105 Blckwood Barnsboro Rd, Sewell NJ 08080
Tel (856) 228-5566 SIC 1731 1711 8741

FALASCA MECHANICAL INC p 526
3329 N Mill Rd, Vineland NJ 08360
Tel (856) 794-2010 SIC 1711

▲ SUBURBAN PROPANE PARTNERS LP p 1396
240 Route 10 W, Whippany NJ 07981
Tel (973) 887-5300
SIC 5984 5172 4939 1711

T L C CO INC p 1419
5000 Edith Blvd Ne, Albuquerque NM 87107
Tel (505) 761-9696 SIC 1711

YEAROUT MECHANICAL INC p 1635
8501 Washington St Ne, Albuquerque NM 87113
Tel (505) 884-0994 SIC 1711

PRECISION-AIRE INC p 1169
2100 Artic Ave Unit 9, Bohemia NY 11716
Tel (631) 563-8280 SIC 1711

S J FUEL CO INC p 1262
601 Union St, Brooklyn NY 11215
Tel (718) 855-6060 SIC 5983 1711

JOHN W DANFORTH CO p 789
4770 Bickert Dr, Clarence NY 14031
Tel (716) 832-1940 SIC 1711

SLOMINS INC p 1331
125 Lauman Ln, Hicksville NY 11801
Tel (516) 932-7000 SIC 5983 1731 1711

PAR PLUMBING CO INC p 1113
60 N Prospect Ave, Lynbrook NY 11563
Tel (516) 887-4000 SIC 1711

WDF INC p 1585
30 N Macquesten Pkwy, Mount Vernon NY 10550
Tel (914) 776-8000 SIC 1711

JWD GROUP INC p 798
300 Colvin Woods Pkwy, Tonawanda NY 14150
Tel (716) 832-1940 SIC 1711 1629 1623

MB HAYNES CORP p 925
187 Deaverview Rd, Asheville NC 28806
Tel (828) 254-6141
SIC 1542 1623 1711 7382

■ BAHNSON HOLDINGS INC p 145
4731 Commercial Park Ct, Clemmons NC 27012
Tel (336) 760-3111
SIC 8711 1711 3585 3564

■ BAHNSON INC p 145
4731 Commercial Park Ct, Clemmons NC 27012
Tel (336) 760-3111 SIC 8711 1711

AC CORP p 13
301 Creek Ridge Rd, Greensboro NC 27406
Tel (336) 273-4472
SIC 1711 1731 3556 3823 3625 3535

BRADY TRANE SERVICE INC p 207
1915 N Church St, Greensboro NC 27405
Tel (919) 781-0458 SIC 5075 1711 7623

■ ENVIRONMENTAL AIR SYSTEMS LLC p 503
521 Banner Ave, Greensboro NC 27401
Tel (336) 273-1975 SIC 1711

DELCOR INC p 424
834 Rivit St, Greenville NC 27834
Tel (252) 321-8868 SIC 1711

SUNENERGY1 LLC p 1402
192 Raceway Dr, Mooresville NC 28117
Tel (704) 662-0375 SIC 1711

SPC MECHANICAL CORP p 1355
1908 Baldree Rd S, Wilson NC 27893
Tel (252) 237-9035 SIC 3494 1711 3444

■ BABCOCK & WILCOX CO p 143
20 S Van Buren Ave, Barberton OH 44203
Tel (330) 753-4511
SIC 1629 1711 3443 7699 8741 3822

■ S A COMUNALE CO INC p 1261
2900 Newpark Dr, Barberton OH 44203
Tel (330) 706-3040 SIC 1711

VAUGHN INDUSTRIES LLC p 1545
1201 E Findlay St, Carey OH 43316
Tel (419) 396-3900 SIC 1731 1711

▲ CHEMED CORP p 293
255 E 5th St Ste 2600, Cincinnati OH 45202
Tel (513) 762-6690 SIC 8082 1711 7699

ENERFAB INC p 497
4955 Spring Grove Ave, Cincinnati OH 45232
Tel (513) 641-0500
SIC 3443 1629 1541 1711 3479

■ ROTO-ROOTER DEVELOPMENT CO p 1252
255 E 5th St Ste 2600, Cincinnati OH 45202
Tel (513) 762-6690 SIC 7699 1711

■ ROTO-ROOTER SERVICES CO p 1252
2500 Chemed Ctr 255e5th, Cincinnati OH 45202
Tel (513) 762-6690 SIC 7699 1711

THOMAS J DYER CO p 1448
5240 Lester Rd, Cincinnati OH 45213
Tel (513) 321-8100 SIC 1711

PARK CORP p 1115
6200 Riverside Dr, Cleveland OH 44135
Tel (216) 267-4870
SIC 3547 1711 3443 5084 6512 7999

STEVENS ENGINEERS & CONSTRUCTORS INC p 1388
7850 Freeway Cir Ste 100, Cleveland OH 44130
Tel (440) 234-7888 SIC 1541 1711 8711

PIONEER PIPE INC p 1151
2021 Hanna Rd, Marietta OH 45750
Tel (740) 376-2400
SIC 3498 1711 3443 3441 3312

AIRTRON INC p 41
9260 Marketpl Dr, Miamisburg OH 45342
Tel (937) 898-0826 SIC 1711

DIRECT ENERGY US HOME SERVICES INC p 441
9260 Marketplace Dr, Miamisburg OH 45342
Tel (937) 898-0826 SIC 1711

GARDINER SERVICE CO p 592
31200 Bainbridge Rd Ste 1, Solon OH 44139
Tel (440) 349-5588 SIC 5075 1711 7623

DUNBAR MECHANICAL INC p 461
2806 N Reynolds Rd, Toledo OH 43615
Tel (734) 856-6601 SIC 1711

ROTH BROS INC p 1252
3847 Crum Rd, Youngstown OH 44515
Tel (330) 793-5571 SIC 1711 1761

LOCKE SUPPLY CO p 873
1300 Se 82nd St, Oklahoma City OK 73149
Tel (405) 635-3230
SIC 5063 5074 5075 1711

HARDER MECHANICAL CONTRACTORS INC p 660
2148 Ne Mlk Blvd, Portland OR 97212
Tel (503) 281-1112 SIC 1711 7389

TEMP-CONTROL MECHANICAL CORP p 1436
4800 N Channel Ave, Portland OR 97217
Tel (503) 285-9851 SIC 1711 3444 1731

JET INDUSTRIES INC p 783
1935 Silverton Rd Ne, Salem OR 97301
Tel (503) 363-2334 SIC 1711 1731

■ H T LYONS INC p 650
7165 Ambassador Dr, Allentown PA 18106
Tel (610) 530-2600 SIC 1711

TALEN ENERGY SERVICES HOLDINGS LLC p 1422
835 Hamilton St, Allentown PA 18101
Tel (610) 774-5151 SIC 4911 1711 3625

BRADFORD-WHITE CORP p 206
725 Talamore Dr, Ambler PA 19002
Tel (215) 641-9400 SIC 3433 1711

■ MCCARLS INC p 926
1413 9th Ave, Beaver Falls PA 15010
Tel (724) 843-5660 SIC 1711

DAVID H MARTIN EXCAVATING INC p 415
4961 Cumberland Hwy, Chambersburg PA 17202
Tel (717) 264-1312 SIC 1623 1794 1711

W G TOMKO INC p 1568
2559 State Route 88, Finleyville PA 15332
Tel (724) 348-2000 SIC 1711

■ MC CLURE CO INC p 925
4101 N 6th St, Harrisburg PA 17110
Tel (717) 232-9743 SIC 1711

BERKS PRODUCTS CORP p 175
167 Berks Products Dr, Leesport PA 19533
Tel (610) 374-5131
SIC 5031 3273 5983 5172 2439 1711

HALLER ENTERPRISES INC p 654
212 Bucky Dr, Lititz PA 17543
Tel (888) 565-0546 SIC 1711 1731

PKF-MARK III INC p 1153
17 Blacksmith Rd Ste 101, Newtown PA 18940
Tel (215) 968-5031
SIC 1611 1629 1711 1731 1771 8711

ELLIOTT-LEWIS CORP p 488
2900 Black Lake Pl, Philadelphia PA 19154
Tel (215) 698-4400 SIC 1711 7349 7353

■ FLUIDICS INC p 561
9815 Roosevelt Blvd Ste A, Philadelphia PA 19114
Tel (215) 671-7900 SIC 1711

HERMAN GOLDNER CO INC p 687
7777 Brewster Ave, Philadelphia PA 19153
Tel (215) 365-5400 SIC 1711 7699

J J WHITE INC p 771
5500 Bingham St, Philadelphia PA 19120
Tel (215) 722-1000 SIC 1711 1542 7699

WORTH & CO INC p 1626
6263 Kellers Church Rd, Pipersville PA 18947
Tel (267) 362-1100 SIC 1711

■ LIMBACH CO LLC p 866
31 35th St, Pittsburgh PA 15201
Tel (412) 359-2173 SIC 1711

■ LIMBACH FACILITY SERVICES LLC p 866
31 35th St, Pittsburgh PA 15201
Tel (412) 359-2100 SIC 1711 8741

▲ LIMBACH HOLDINGS LLC p 866
31 35th St, Pittsburgh PA 15201
Tel (412) 359-2173 SIC 1711

MCKAMISH INC p 930
50 55th St, Pittsburgh PA 15201
Tel (412) 781-6262 SIC 1711

SAUER HOLDINGS INC p 1283
30 51st St, Pittsburgh PA 15201
Tel (412) 687-4100 SIC 1711

MOYER & SON INC p 995
113 E Reliance Rd, Souderton PA 18964
Tel (215) 799-2000
SIC 5191 5983 2875 0782 1711

NITTANY OIL CO INC p 1045
1540 Martin St, State College PA 16803
Tel (814) 237-4859 SIC 5171 1711

AIREKO CONSTRUCTION LLC p 40
Las Casas St Lot 20, Caguas PR 00725
Tel (787) 653-6300
SIC 1542 1541 1731 1711

BERMUDEZ LONGO DIAZ-MASSO LLC p 175
Km 0 5 Cupey Rr 845, San Juan PR 00926
Tel (787) 761-3030 SIC 1731 1711

TRADESOURCE INC p 1469
205 Hallene Rd Unit 211, Warwick RI 02886
Tel (401) 384-6148
SIC 7361 1751 1711 1731 1742 1721

THOMPSON CONSTRUCTION GROUP INC p 1449
100 N Main St, Sumter SC 29150
Tel (803) 773-8005
SIC 7349 1711 1721 1541

LEE CO p 851
331 Mallory Station Rd, Franklin TN 37067
Tel (615) 567-1000 SIC 1711

AMERICAN RESIDENTIAL SERVICES LLC p 78
965 Ridge Lake Blvd # 201, Memphis TN 38120
Tel (901) 271-9700 SIC 1711

■ SERVICEMASTER CO LLC p 1307
860 Ridge Lake Blvd Fl 3, Memphis TN 38120
Tel (901) 597-1400
SIC 7349 7342 1711 1731 7641

SERVICEMASTER HOLDING CORP p 1308
860 Ridge Lake Blvd, Memphis TN 38120
Tel (901) 597-1400
SIC 0782 7342 1711 1731 7349 7641

■ KMT REFRIGERATION INC p 824
2915 Tennessee Ave N, Parsons TN 38363
Tel (731) 847-6361 SIC 3585 3448 1711

DYNAMIC SYSTEMS INC p 464
3901 S Lamar Blvd Ste 300, Austin TX 78704
Tel (512) 443-4848 SIC 1711

FGI GROUP INC p 539
3901 S Lamar Blvd Ste 100, Austin TX 78704
Tel (512) 448-9898
SIC 1542 1541 1794 1611 7353 1711

FLARE INDUSTRIES LLC p 554
16310 Bratton Ln Ste 350, Austin TX 78728
Tel (512) 836-9473
SIC 3822 7359 3694 2899 1711 3569

KTB SERVICES LLC p 831
1108 Cedar Bayou Rd, Baytown TX 77520
Tel (281) 428-7344 SIC 1711

BRANDT COMPANIES LLC p 208
1728 Briercroft Ct, Carrollton TX 75006
Tel (972) 241-9411 SIC 1711 1731 7623

H & S CONSTRUCTORS INC p 649
1616 Corn Product Rd, Corpus Christi TX 78409
Tel (361) 668-8674 SIC 1711

BRANDT ENGINEERING CO INC p 208
1728 Briercrest Dr, Dallas TX 75229
Tel (972) 395-6000 SIC 1711 8711

CLEAVER-BROOKS SALES AND SERVICE INC p 325
1956 Singleton Blvd, Dallas TX 75212
Tel (214) 637-0020 SIC 5074 7699 1711

ENTECH SALES AND SERVICE INC p 501
3404 Garden Brook Dr, Dallas TX 75234
Tel (972) 241-8188 SIC 1731 7623 1711

TDINDUSTRIES INC p 1429
13850 Diplomat Dr, Dallas TX 75234
Tel (972) 888-9500 SIC 1711

■ DYNA TEN CORP p 464
4375 Diplomacy Rd, Fort Worth TX 76155
Tel (817) 616-2200 SIC 1711

MORSCO INC p 990
100 E 15th St Ste 200, Fort Worth TX 76102
Tel (877) 709-2227 SIC 5074 1711

MORTEX PRODUCTS INC p 991
501 Terminal Rd, Fort Worth TX 76106
Tel (817) 624-0820
SIC 3585 3433 1711 3999

POLK MECHANICAL CO LLC p 1159
2425 Dillard St, Grand Prairie TX 75051
Tel (972) 339-1200
SIC 1711 3444 3498 3599 3999

▲ COMFORT SYSTEMS USA INC p 344
675 Bering Dr Ste 400, Houston TX 77057
Tel (713) 830-9600 SIC 1711 1731

LETSOS CO p 857
8435 Westglen Dr, Houston TX 77063
Tel (713) 783-3200 SIC 1711 7623

TRACER INDUSTRIES INC p 1468
7433 Harwin Dr, Houston TX 77036
Tel (713) 868-5500 SIC 1711 1731

TEXAS AIR SYSTEMS INC p 1442
6029 Campus Circle Dr W # 100, Irving TX 75063
Tel (972) 570-4700 SIC 5075 1711

SERVICE EXPERTS LLC p 1307
3820 American Dr Ste 200, Plano TX 75075
Tel (972) 231-5468
SIC 1711 5074 5075 8742

SERVICE EXPERTS HEATING & AIR CONDITIONING LLC p 1307
2140 Lake Park Blvd, Richardson TX 75080
Tel (972) 535-3800
SIC 1711 5074 5075 8742

SANDEN INTERNATIONAL (USA) INC p 1278
601 Sanden Blvd, Wylie TX 75098
Tel (972) 442-8941
SIC 3714 1711 3585 3563

■ VIVINT SOLAR DEVELOPER LLC p 1563
1800 W Ashton Blvd, Lehi UT 84043
Tel (801) 377-9111 SIC 1711

GREAT WESTERN SUPPLY INC p 635
2626 Industrial Dr, Ogden UT 84401
Tel (801) 621-5412
SIC 5074 5051 5999 1711

APX GROUP HOLDINGS INC p 101
4931 N 300 W, Provo UT 84604
Tel (801) 377-9111
SIC 7382 5065 3822 1711

APX GROUP INC p 101
4931 N 300 W, Provo UT 84604
Tel (801) 377-9111
SIC 8711 3822 1711 5065

APX PARENT HOLDCO INC p 101
4931 N 300 W, Provo UT 84604
Tel (801) 377-9111
SIC 6719 3822 1711 8711 5065 5074

FIRETROL PROTECTION SYSTEMS INC p 544
3696 W 900 S Ste A, Salt Lake City UT 84104
Tel (801) 485-6900 SIC 1711 1731

REDWOOD INDUSTRIES INC p 1217
2345 S Cci Way, Salt Lake City UT 84119
Tel (801) 973-9000 SIC 1711

CCI MECHANICAL INC p 270
2345 S Cci Way, West Valley City UT 84119
Tel (801) 973-9000 SIC 1711

PIERCE ASSOCIATES INC p 1147
4216 Wheeler Ave, Alexandria VA 22304
Tel (703) 751-2400 SIC 1711

MOORES ELECTRICAL & MECHANICAL CONSTRUCTION INC p 987
101 Edgewood Ave, Altavista VA 24517
Tel (434) 369-4374 SIC 1731 1711

VSC FIRE & SECURITY INC p 1566
10343b Kings Acres Rd, Ashland VA 23005
Tel (804) 459-2200 SIC 1711 3494

SOUTHERN AIR INC p 1347
2655 Lakeside Dr, Lynchburg VA 24501
Tel (434) 385-6200 SIC 1711 1731

■ DYN SPECIALTY CONTRACTING INC p 464
1420 Spring Hill Rd # 500, Mc Lean VA 22102
Tel (703) 556-8000 SIC 1711 1731

■ RIDDLEBERGER BROTHERS INC p 1234
6127 S Valley Pike, Mount Crawford VA 22841
Tel (540) 434-1731 SIC 3444 1711

ATLANTIC CONSTRUCTORS INC p 126
1401 Battery Brooke Pkwy, North Chesterfield VA 23237
Tel (804) 222-3400 SIC 1796 1711 3444

QUALITY PLUS SERVICES INC p 1197
2929 Quality Dr, Petersburg VA 23805
Tel (804) 863-0191 SIC 1711 1731

■ COLONIALWEBB CONTRACTORS CO p 338
2820 Ackley Ave, Richmond VA 23228
Tel (804) 916-1400 SIC 1711 7623

FIRE AND LIFE SAFETY AMERICA HOLDINGS INC p 543
3017 Vernon Rd Ste 100, Richmond VA 23228
Tel (804) 222-1381 *SIC* 1711 1731

WOODFIN HEATING INC p 1623
1823 N Hamilton St, Richmond VA 23230
Tel (804) 730-4500
SIC 5172 5983 1711 7382

BRANCH GROUP INC p 207
442 Rutherford Ave Ne, Roanoke VA 24016
Tel (540) 982-1678
SIC 1542 1611 1711 1731 1541

WACO INC p 1570
5450 Lewis Rd, Sandston VA 23150
Tel (804) 222-8440
SIC 1711 1799 3448 5033

■ WGL ENERGY SERVICES INC p 1604
8614 Westwood Center Dr # 1200, Vienna VA 22182
Tel (703) 333-3900 *SIC* 4931 1711

APOLLO SHEET METAL INC p 97
1201 W Columbia Dr, Kennewick WA 99336
Tel (509) 586-1104 *SIC* 1711 3444

HERMANSON CO LLP p 687
1221 2nd Ave N, Kent WA 98032
Tel (206) 575-9700 *SIC* 1711

J H KELLY INVESTMENTS INC p 771
821 3rd Ave, Longview WA 98632
Tel (360) 423-5510 *SIC* 1711

JH KELLY LLC p 785
821 3rd Ave, Longview WA 98632
Tel (360) 423-5510 *SIC* 1711

KELLY JH HOLDING LLC p 809
821 3rd Ave, Longview WA 98632
Tel (360) 423-5510 *SIC* 1711 1542 1731

WASHINGTON ENERGY SERVICES CO p 1578
3909 196th St Sw, Lynnwood WA 98036
Tel (800) 398-4663 *SIC* 5074 1711 8711

NORTHWEST CASCADE INC p 1059
10412 John Bananola Way E, Puyallup WA 98374
Tel (253) 848-2371
SIC 1623 7359 7699 3272 1711

MACDONALD-MILLER FACILITY SOLUTIONS INC p 892
7717 Detroit Ave Sw, Seattle WA 98106
Tel (206) 763-9400 *SIC* 1711 1731

MCKINSTRY CO LLC p 930
5005 3rd Ave S, Seattle WA 98134
Tel (206) 762-3311
SIC 1711 1623 3446 3444

HOLADAY-PARKS-FABRICATORS INC p 700
4600 S 134th Pl, Tukwila WA 98168
Tel (206) 248-9700 *SIC* 1711

PSF MECHANICAL INC p 1188
11621 E Marginal Way S, Tukwila WA 98168
Tel (206) 764-9663 *SIC* 1711 8711

GREENBERRY INDUSTRIAL LLC p 637
600 Se Maritime Ave # 190, Vancouver WA 98661
Tel (360) 567-0006
SIC 1711 1541 3443 3441

ADVANCED HEATING LLC p 25
2736 12 3/4 Ave, Cameron WI 54822
Tel (715) 296-6107 *SIC* 1711

LANDMARK SERVICES COOPERATIVE p 843
1401 Landmark Dr, Cottage Grove WI 53527
Tel (608) 819-3115
SIC 4221 5171 5191 1711

J F AHERN CO p 771
855 Morris St, Fond Du Lac WI 54935
Tel (920) 921-9020 *SIC* 1711

TWEET-GAROT MECHANICAL INC p 1494
2545 Larsen Rd, Green Bay WI 54303
Tel (920) 498-0400 *SIC* 1711 3444

VHC INC p 1553
3090 Holmgren Way, Green Bay WI 54304
Tel (920) 336-7278
SIC 1731 1542 1541 1521 1711 6512

HOOPER CORP p 706
2030 Pennsylvania Ave, Madison WI 53704
Tel (608) 249-0451 *SIC* 1623 1711

GRUNAU CO INC p 642
1100 W Anderson Ct, Oak Creek WI 53154
Tel (414) 216-6900 *SIC* 1711

TOTAL MECHANICAL INC p 1463
W234n2830 Paul Rd, Pewaukee WI 53072
Tel (262) 523-2510 *SIC* 1711 1791 3823

HOPSON OIL CO INC p 706
1225 Whiterock Ave, Waukesha WI 53186
Tel (262) 542-5343 *SIC* 5171 5983 1711

SIC 1721 Painting & Paper Hanging Contractors

■ CENTRAL VALLEY SPECIALTIES INC p 281
3846 E Winslow Ave, Phoenix AZ 85040
Tel (602) 437-2046 *SIC* 1742 1721

KEENAN HOPKINS SUDER & STOWELL CONTRACTORS INC p 807
5109 E La Palma Ave Ste A, Anaheim CA 92807
Tel (714) 695-3670
SIC 1742 1751 1743 1741 1721

TECHNO COATINGS INC p 1431
1391 S Allec St, Anaheim CA 92805
Tel (714) 635-1130
SIC 1542 1629 1721 1799

DRYCO CONSTRUCTION INC p 457
42745 Boscell Rd, Fremont CA 94538
Tel (510) 438-6500 *SIC* 1611 1721 5211

NATIONAL SERVICES GROUP INC p 1016
1682 Langley Ave, Irvine CA 92614
Tel (714) 564-7900 *SIC* 1721

AMERICAN TECHNOLOGIES INC p 80
210 W Baywood Ave, Orange CA 92865
Tel (714) 283-9990
SIC 1521 1541 1742 1731 1721 1711

GENERAL COATINGS CORP p 599
6711 Nancy Ridge Dr, San Diego CA 92121
Tel (858) 587-1277 *SIC* 1721 1799

BRAND ENERGY SOLUTIONS LLC p 207
1325 Cobb International D, Kennesaw GA 30152
Tel (678) 285-1400
SIC 1751 1742 1799 1721

ROADSAFE TRAFFIC SYSTEMS INC p 1240
8750 W Bryn Mawr Ave # 400, Chicago IL 60631
Tel (773) 724-3300 *SIC* 1721 1611 7389

BROCK INDUSTRIAL SERVICES LLC p 216
2210 Oak Leaf St, Joliet IL 60436
Tel (815) 730-3350 *SIC* 1721 1799

SUPERIOR CONSOLIDATED INDUSTRIES INC p 1406
801 Sw Jefferson Ave, Peoria IL 61605
Tel (309) 677-5980 *SIC* 7389 1721

ALLIED CONSTRUCTION SERVICES INC p 56
2122 Fleur Dr, Des Moines IA 50321
Tel (515) 288-4855
SIC 1742 1752 1721 1751 1542

A & A MAINTENANCE ENTERPRISE INC p 4
965 Midland Ave, Yonkers NY 10704
Tel (914) 969-0009
SIC 7349 1721 1542 4959 0782

TRADESOURCE INC p 1469
205 Hallene Rd Unit 211, Warwick RI 02886
Tel (401) 384-6148
SIC 7361 1751 1711 1731 1742 1721

THOMPSON CONSTRUCTION GROUP INC p 1449
100 N Main St, Sumter SC 29150
Tel (803) 773-8005
SIC 7349 1711 1721 1541

ATLANTIC SCAFFOLDING CO LLC p 127
1217 Georgia Ave, Deer Park TX 77536
Tel (281) 807-8200 *SIC* 1721 1799

ANCO INDUSTRIES LLC p 89
10343 Sam Houston Park Dr # 200, Houston TX 77064
Tel (281) 807-8200 *SIC* 1721 1799

ATLANTIC HOLDINGS I INC p 126
10343 Sam Houston Park Dr, Houston TX 77064
Tel (281) 807-8200 *SIC* 1721 1799

ATLANTIC HOLDINGS II INC p 126
10343 Sam Houston Park Dr, Houston TX 77064
Tel (281) 807-8200 *SIC* 1721 1799

ATLANTIC INDUSTRIAL LLC p 126
10343 Sam Houston Park Dr, Houston TX 77064
Tel (281) 807-8200 *SIC* 1721 1799

BROCK GROUP INC p 216
10343 Sam Houston Park Dr, Houston TX 77064
Tel (281) 807-8200 *SIC* 1721 1799

BROCK HOLDINGS I LLC p 216
10343 Sam Houston Park Dr # 200, Houston TX 77064
Tel (281) 807-8200 *SIC* 1721 1799 7359

BROCK HOLDINGS II INC p 216
10343 Sam Houston Park Dr, Houston TX 77064
Tel (281) 807-8200 *SIC* 1721 1799

BROCK HOLDINGS III INC p 216
10343 Sam Houston Park Dr, Houston TX 77064
Tel (281) 807-8200 *SIC* 1721 7349

BROCK SERVICES HOLDINGS LLC p 216
10343 Sam Houston Park Dr # 200, Houston TX 77064
Tel (281) 807-8200 *SIC* 1721 1799

BROCK SERVICES LLC p 216
10343 Sam Houston Park Dr # 200, Houston TX 77064
Tel (281) 807-8200 *SIC* 1721 1799

MIKEN SPECIALTIES LTD p 968
10343 Sam Houston Park Dr, Houston TX 77064
Tel (979) 265-9599 *SIC* 1721 1799

MOBLEY INDUSTRIAL SERVICES INC p 980
1220 Miller Cut Off Rd, La Porte TX 77571
Tel (281) 470-9120 *SIC* 1721 1799 5033

KILGORE COMPANIES LLC p 818
7057 W 2100 S, Salt Lake City UT 84128
Tel (801) 250-0132 *SIC* 1721

SIC 1731 Electrical Work

■ VALMONT NEWMARK INC p 1542
2 Perimeter Park S 475w, Birmingham AL 35243
Tel (205) 968-7200 *SIC* 3272 1731 3317

HILLER COMPANIES INC p 693
3751 Joy Springs Dr, Mobile AL 36693
Tel (251) 661-1275 *SIC* 1731 5084 5088

D & G ELECTRIC CO LLC p 406
8297 Old Tenn Pike Rd, Pinson AL 35126
Tel (205) 365-4074 *SIC* 1731

BAGBY AND RUSSELL ELECTRIC CO INC p 144
5500 Plantation Rd, Theodore AL 36582
Tel (251) 344-5987 *SIC* 1731

CHUGACH ELECTRIC p 304
5601 Electron Dr, Anchorage AK 99518
Tel (907) 563-7494 *SIC* 1731

VECO CORP p 1546
949 E 36th Ave Ste 500, Anchorage AK 99508
Tel (907) 762-1500
SIC 1711 1389 1731 1381 4959

MOHAVE ELECTRIC CO-OPERATIVE INC p 982
928 Hancock Rd, Bullhead City AZ 86442
Tel (928) 763-4115 *SIC* 4911 1731

■ AMERICAN TRAFFIC SOLUTIONS INC p 80
1150 N Alma School Rd, Mesa AZ 85201
Tel (480) 443-7000 *SIC* 7374 1731 5084

INTER-TEL TECHNOLOGIES INC p 751
1146 N Alma School Rd, Mesa AZ 85201
Tel (480) 858-9600
SIC 5999 1731 5065 3661 3577

MITEL (DELAWARE) INC p 977
1146 N Alma School Rd, Mesa AZ 85201
Tel (480) 449-8900
SIC 3661 5045 4813 5065 1731 7359

MITEL NETWORKS INC p 977
1146 N Alma School Rd, Mesa AZ 85201
Tel (480) 961-9000
SIC 3661 7359 1731 7373

CLIMATEC LLC p 326
2851 W Kathleen Rd, Phoenix AZ 85053
Tel (602) 944-3330 *SIC* 1731 7373

JAVINE VENTURES INC p 779
2851 W Kathleen Rd, Phoenix AZ 85053
Tel (602) 944-3330 *SIC* 5075 1731

TELGIAN CORP p 1435
10230 S 50th Pl, Phoenix AZ 85044
Tel (480) 753-5444
SIC 1711 8711 1731 8748

SULPHUR SPRINGS VALLEY ELECTRIC COOPERATIVE INC CHARITABLE p 1397
311 E Wilcox Dr, Sierra Vista AZ 85635
Tel (520) 384-2221 *SIC* 4911 1731 1623

DELTA DIVERSIFIED ENTERPRISES INC p 427
425 W Gemini Dr, Tempe AZ 85283
Tel (480) 831-0532 *SIC* 1731

STALEY INC p 1375
8101 Fourche Rd, Little Rock AR 72209
Tel (501) 565-3006 *SIC* 1731

MULTI-CRAFT CONTRACTORS INC p 999
2300 N Lowell Rd, Springdale AR 72764
Tel (479) 751-4330 *SIC* 1711 3441 1731

SOURCE REFRIGERATION & HVAC INC p 1342
800 E Orangethorpe Ave, Anaheim CA 92801
Tel (714) 578-2300 *SIC* 1711 1731

SR BRAY LLC p 1362
1210 N Red Gum St, Anaheim CA 92806
Tel (714) 765-7551 *SIC* 1731 7359

HOT LINE CONSTRUCTION INC p 710
9020 Brentwood Blvd Ste H, Brentwood CA 94513
Tel (925) 634-9333 *SIC* 1731 1799

MORROW-MEADOWS CORP p 990
231 Benton Ct, City Of Industry CA 91789
Tel (858) 974-3650 *SIC* 1731

BAKER ELECTRIC INC p 146
1298 Pacific Oaks Pl, Escondido CA 92029
Tel (760) 745-2001 *SIC* 1731 8711

ELECTRIC MOTOR SHOP p 484
253 Fulton St, Fresno CA 93721
Tel (559) 233-1153
SIC 5063 1731 7694 7922

SASCO p 1283
2750 Moore Ave, Fullerton CA 92833
Tel (714) 870-0217 *SIC* 1731

SASCO ELECTRIC INC p 1283
2750 Moore Ave, Fullerton CA 92833
Tel (714) 870-0217 *SIC* 7373 1731

MX HOLDINGS US p 1004
153 Technology Dr Ste 200, Irvine CA 92618
Tel (949) 727-3277 *SIC* 1711 1731 5999

IRWIN INDUSTRIES INC p 765
1580 W Carson St, Long Beach CA 90810
Tel (310) 233-3000
SIC 1629 1731 1796 7353 1542

BERGELECTRIC CORP p 174
5650 W Centinela Ave, Los Angeles CA 90045
Tel (310) 337-1377 *SIC* 1731

STEINY AND CO INC p 1385
221 N Ardmore Ave, Los Angeles CA 90004
Tel (626) 962-1055 *SIC* 1731

INFOGAIN CORP p 741
485 Alberto Way Ste 100, Los Gatos CA 95032
Tel (408) 355-6000
SIC 7379 7373 8742 8748 7374 1731

■ CONTRA COSTA ELECTRIC INC p 364
825 Howe Rd, Martinez CA 94553
Tel (925) 229-4250 *SIC* 1731

AMERICAN TECHNOLOGIES INC p 80
210 W Baywood Ave, Orange CA 92865
Tel (714) 283-9990
SIC 1521 1541 1742 1731 1721 1711

BAY ALARM CO p 160
60 Berry Dr, Pacheco CA 94553
Tel (925) 935-1100 *SIC* 1731 7382 5063

SUPERIOR ELECTRICAL MECHANICAL & PLUMBING INC p 1406
8613 Helms Ave, Rancho Cucamonga CA 91730
Tel (909) 357-9400 *SIC* 1731 1711

HERMAN WEISSKER INC p 687
1645 Brown Ave, Riverside CA 92509
Tel (951) 826-8800 *SIC* 1623 8711 1731

■ INTERNATIONAL LINE BUILDERS INC p 755
2520 Rubidoux Blvd, Riverside CA 92509
Tel (951) 682-2982 *SIC* 1731

REX MOORE ELECTRICAL CONTRACTORS & ENGINEERS INC p 1230
6001 Outfall Cir, Sacramento CA 95828
Tel (916) 372-1300 *SIC* 1731

REX MOORE GROUP INC p 1230
6001 Outfall Cir, Sacramento CA 95828
Tel (916) 372-1300 *SIC* 1731 8711

■ CUBIC TRANSPORTATION SYSTEMS INC p 399
5650 Kearny Mesa Rd, San Diego CA 92111
Tel (858) 268-3100 *SIC* 3829 1731

HELIX ELECTRIC INC p 681
6795 Flanders Dr, San Diego CA 92121
Tel (858) 535-0505 *SIC* 1731

DECKER ELECTRIC CO INC ELECTRICAL CONTRACTORS p 421
1282 Folsom St, San Francisco CA 94103
Tel (415) 552-1622 *SIC* 1731

CUPERTINO ELECTRIC INC p 401
1132 N 7th St, San Jose CA 95112
Tel (408) 808-8000 *SIC* 1731

ROSENDIN ELECTRIC INC p 1251
880 Mabury Rd, San Jose CA 95133
Tel (408) 286-2800 *SIC* 1731

COSCO FIRE PROTECTION INC p 373
29222 Rancho Viejo Rd # 205, San Juan Capistrano CA 92675
Tel (714) 974-8770 *SIC* 1711 1731 5999

■ SUNRUN INSTALLATION SERVICES INC p 1404
775 Fiero Ln Ste 200, San Luis Obispo CA 93401
Tel (805) 528-9705 *SIC* 1731

REDWOOD ELECTRIC GROUP INC p 1217
2775 Northwestern Pkwy, Santa Clara CA 95051
Tel (707) 451-7348 *SIC* 1731

CSI ELECTRICAL CONTRACTORS INC p 397
10623 Fulton Wells Ave, Santa Fe Springs CA 90670
Tel (562) 946-0700 *SIC* 1731

WALTERS WHOLESALE ELECTRIC CO p 1574
2825 Temple Ave, Signal Hill CA 90755
Tel (562) 988-3100 *SIC* 5063 3699 1731

VECTOR RESOURCES INC p 1546
3530 Voyager St, Torrance CA 90503
Tel (310) 436-1000 *SIC* 1731 3651 7373

■ QWEST BUSINESS & GOVERNMENT SERVICES INC p 1201
1801 Calif St Ste 3800, Denver CO 80202
Tel (303) 391-8300
SIC 5999 1731 7629 7373 7371 7622

■ TIMKEN MOTOR & CRANE SERVICES LLC p 1455
4850 Moline St, Denver CO 80239
Tel (303) 623-8658
SIC 5063 1731 7694 3613 3536

■ STURGEON ELECTRIC CO INC p 1395
12150 E 112th Ave, Henderson CO 80640
Tel (303) 227-6990 *SIC* 1731 1623

ENCORE ELECTRIC INC p 496
7125 W Jefferson Ave # 400, Lakewood CO 80235
Tel (303) 934-1234 *SIC* 1731

ASPEN ELECTRIC AND SUPPLY INC p 118
1890 Loggers Ln Unit C, Steamboat Springs CO 80487
Tel (970) 879-3905 *SIC* 5719 1731

NORTHERN ELECTRIC INC p 1056
12789 Emerson St, Thornton CO 80241
Tel (303) 428-6969 *SIC* 1731

MCPHEE ELECTRIC LTD p 932
505 Main St, Farmington CT 06032
Tel (860) 677-9797 *SIC* 1731

PHALCON LTD p 1141
505 Main St, Farmington CT 06032
Tel (860) 677-9797 *SIC* 1731

CRIUS ENERGY LLC p 393
535 Connecticut Ave # 400, Norwalk CT 06854
Tel (203) 663-5089 *SIC* 6719 1731

■ EMCOR CONSTRUCTION SERVICES INC p 491
301 Merritt 7 Fl 6, Norwalk CT 06851
Tel (203) 849-7800 *SIC* 1711 1731

▲ EMCOR GROUP INC p 491
301 Merritt 7 Fl 6, Norwalk CT 06851
Tel (203) 849-7800 *SIC* 1731 1711 7349

■ EMCOR MECHANICAL/ELECTRICAL SERVICES (WEST) INC p 491
301 Merritt 7, Norwalk CT 06851
Tel (203) 849-7800 *SIC* 1711 1731

■ M E S HOLDING CORP p 889
301 Merritt 7, Norwalk CT 06851
Tel (203) 849-7800 *SIC* 1711 1731

DMG INFORMATION INC p 446
46 Southfield Ave Ste 400, Stamford CT 06902
Tel (203) 973-2940 *SIC* 6719 1731 8748

GEORGE & LYNCH INC p 606
150 Lafferty Ln, Dover DE 19901
Tel (302) 736-3031
SIC 1623 1611 1629 1731

■ PRINCE TELECOM LLC p 1176
551 Mews Dr Ste A, New Castle DE 19720
Tel (302) 324-1800 *SIC* 1731

■ CONECTIV LLC p 355
800 N King St Ste 400, Wilmington DE 19801
Tel (202) 872-2680
SIC 4911 4924 1731 5172

CONSTRUCTION MANAGEMENT SERVICES INC p 361
3600 Silverside Rd, Wilmington DE 19810
Tel (302) 478-4200 *SIC* 1731 8741

HATZEL & BUEHLER INC p 668
3600 Silverside Rd Ste A, Wilmington DE 19810
Tel (302) 478-4200 *SIC* 1731

■ PEPCO ENERGY SERVICES INC p 1133
701 9th St Nw Ste 2100, Washington DC 20001
Tel (703) 253-1800
SIC 1711 1731 1623 4961

TRI-CITY ELECTRICAL CONTRACTORS INC p 1477
430 West Dr, Altamonte Springs FL 32714
Tel (407) 788-3500 *SIC* 1731

ADT HOLDINGS INC p 24
1501 Nw 51st St, Boca Raton FL 33431
Tel (888) 298-9274 *SIC* 7381 1731

TYCO INTEGRATED SECURITY LLC p 1496
4700 Exchange Ct Ste 300, Boca Raton FL 33431
Tel (561) 226-8201 *SIC* 7382 7381 1731

MEISNER ELECTRIC INC OF FLORIDA p 940
220 Ne 1st St, Delray Beach FL 33444
Tel (561) 278-8362 *SIC* 1731

HYPOWER INC p 724
5913 Nw 31st Ave, Fort Lauderdale FL 33309
Tel (954) 978-9300 *SIC* 1623 1731

SERVICE AMERICA ENTEPRISE INC p 1307
2755 Nw 63rd Ct, Fort Lauderdale FL 33309
Tel (954) 979-1100 *SIC* 1711 1731

B & I CONTRACTORS INC p 141
2701 Prince St, Fort Myers FL 33916
Tel (239) 344-3213 *SIC* 1711 1731

■ C AND C POWER LINE INC p 232
12035 Palm Lake Dr, Jacksonville FL 32218
Tel (904) 751-6020 *SIC* 4911 1731

MILLER ELECTRIC CO p 970
2251 Rosselle St, Jacksonville FL 32204
Tel (904) 388-8000 *SIC* 1731

▲ GOLDFIELD CORP DEL p 622
1684 W Hibiscus Blvd, Melbourne FL 32901
Tel (321) 724-1700 *SIC* 1623 1731

▲ DYCOM INDUSTRIES INC p 464
11780 Us Highway 1 # 600, Palm Beach Gardens FL 33408
Tel (561) 627-7171 *SIC* 1623 1731

SANDERS BROTHERS ELECTRIC INC p 1278
8195 Kipling St, Pensacola FL 32514
Tel (850) 857-0701 *SIC* 1731

LS ENERGIA INC p 882
1200 S Pine Island Rd # 420, Plantation FL 33324
Tel (954) 628-3059 *SIC* 1731

■ POWER CORP OF AMERICA p 1165
4647 Clyde Morris Blvd, Port Orange FL 32129
Tel (386) 333-6441 *SIC* 1731 1623

POWER DESIGN INC p 1165
11600 9th St N, Saint Petersburg FL 33716
Tel (727) 210-0492 *SIC* 1731

AVI-SPL HOLDINGS INC p 137
6301 Benjamin Rd Ste 101, Tampa FL 33634
Tel (866) 708-5034
SIC 3669 3861 3663 3651 1731 5064

MCS OFTAMPA INC p 932
8510 Sunstate St, Tampa FL 33634
Tel (813) 872-0217
SIC 1731 7373 4813 7378

FLORIDA KEYS ELECTRIC COOPERATIVE ASSOCIATION INC p 559
91630 Overseas Hwy, Tavernier FL 33070
Tel (305) 852-2431 *SIC* 4911 1731 1623

■ SOUTHEAST POWER CORP p 1346
1805 Hammock Rd, Titusville FL 32796
Tel (321) 268-0540 *SIC* 1731

COMVEST INVESTMENT PARTNERS III LP p 353
525 Okeechobee Blvd # 1050, West Palm Beach FL 33401
Tel (561) 727-2000
SIC 4731 5912 5999 3652 8742 1731

QUINCO ELECTRICAL INC p 1200
4224 Metric Dr, Winter Park FL 32792
Tel (407) 478-6005 *SIC* 1731

METROPOWER INC p 957
798 21st Ave, Albany GA 31701
Tel (229) 432-7345 *SIC* 1731

LIN R ROGERS ELECTRICAL CONTRACTORS INC p 866
2050 Marconi Dr Ste 100, Alpharetta GA 30005
Tel (770) 772-3400 *SIC* 1731

CBEYOND INC p 268
320 Interstate N Pkwy 500, Atlanta GA 30339
Tel (678) 424-2400
SIC 4813 7389 4899 1731

CLEVELAND ELECTRIC CO INC p 325
1281 Fulton Indus Blvd Nw, Atlanta GA 30336
Tel (404) 696-4550 *SIC* 1731 1711 1796

CLEVELAND GROUP INC p 325
1281 Fulton Indus Blvd Nw, Atlanta GA 30336
Tel (404) 696-4550 *SIC* 1731 8741 1711

SNAPPING SHOALS ELECTRIC MEMBERSHIP CORP p 1335
14750 Brown Bridge Rd, Covington GA 30016
Tel (770) 786-3484 *SIC* 1731

SOUTHERN STATES LLC p 1350
30 Georgia Ave, Hampton GA 30228
Tel (770) 946-4562 *SIC* 3613 4013 1731

BROOKS-BERRY-HAYNIE & ASSOCIATES INC p 218
600 Discovery Pl, Mableton GA 30126
Tel (770) 874-1162 *SIC* 1731

I & S ACQUISITION CORP p 724
5200 Riverview Rd Se, Mableton GA 30126
Tel (404) 881-1199 *SIC* 1731

INGLETT & STUBBS LLC p 743
5200 Riverview Rd Se, Mableton GA 30126
Tel (404) 881-1199 *SIC* 1731

MCSI INC p 933
2975 Northwoods Pkwy, Peachtree Corners GA 30071
Tel (770) 441-5263 *SIC* 1731 5065 7359

ALLISON-SMITH CO LLC p 58
1869 S Cobb Indus Blvd Se, Smyrna GA 30082
Tel (404) 351-6430 *SIC* 1731 7389

FIRST CALL JEWEL INC p 545
1410 Hollipark Dr, Idaho Falls ID 83401
Tel (208) 522-7777
SIC 1731 1711 5078 5063

GURTZ ELECTRIC CO p 648
77 W Seegers Rd, Arlington Heights IL 60005
Tel (847) 734-2400 *SIC* 1731

HUEN ELECTRIC INC p 717
1801 W 16th St, Broadview IL 60155
Tel (708) 343-5511 *SIC* 1731

SIEMENS INDUSTRY INC p 1320
1000 Deerfield Pkwy, Buffalo Grove IL 60089
Tel (847) 215-1000
SIC 3822 5063 3669 1731 7382 3625

ANTARCTIC MECHANICAL SERVICES INC p 93
140 Tower Dr, Burr Ridge IL 60527
Tel (630) 887-7700 *SIC* 1711 1731

MIDWEST UNDERGROUND TECHNOLOGY INC p 968
2626 Midwest Ct, Champaign IL 61822
Tel (217) 819-3040 *SIC* 1731 1623

HEICO COMPANIES L L C p 680
5600 Three First Nat Plz, Chicago IL 60602
Tel (312) 419-8220
SIC 3315 3589 3448 3531 1731 3663

REX ELECTRIC & TECHNOLOGIES LLC p 1230
200 W Monroe St Ste 1700, Chicago IL 60606
Tel (312) 251-3620 *SIC* 1731

■ MAVERICK TECHNOLOGIES HOLDINGS LLC p 921
265 Admiral Trost Rd, Columbia IL 62236
Tel (618) 281-9100 *SIC* 8711 8748 1731

■ MAVERICK TECHNOLOGIES LLC p 921
265 Admiral Trost Rd, Columbia IL 62236
Tel (618) 281-9100 *SIC* 8711 8748 1731

CONTRACTING & MATERIAL CO p 364
9550 W 55th St Ste A, Countryside IL 60525
Tel (708) 588-6000
SIC 4922 1623 4612 1731

MEADE ELECTRIC CO INC p 933
9550 W 55th St Ste A, Countryside IL 60525
Tel (708) 588-2500 *SIC* 1731

RATHJE ENTERPRISES INC p 1209
1845 N 22nd St, Decatur IL 62526
Tel (217) 423-2593 *SIC* 1731 7694 5063

■ GIBSON ELECTRIC CO INC p 611
3100 Woodcreek Dr, Downers Grove IL 60515
Tel (630) 288-3800 *SIC* 1731

SENTINEL TECHNOLOGIES INC p 1305
2550 Warrenville Rd, Downers Grove IL 60515
Tel (630) 769-4300 *SIC* 7378 1731

JF ELECTRIC INC p 785
100 Lake Front Pkwy, Edwardsville IL 62025
Tel (618) 797-5353 *SIC* 1731

S & S AUTOMOTIVE INC p 1261
740 N Larch Ave, Elmhurst IL 60126
Tel (630) 279-1613
SIC 5013 5999 5065 1731

MORSE ELECTRIC INC p 990
500 W South St, Freeport IL 61032
Tel (815) 266-4200 *SIC* 1731

MORSE GROUP INC p 990
500 W South St, Freeport IL 61032
Tel (815) 266-4200 *SIC* 1731

US BUILDER SERVICES LLC p 1531
272 E Deerpath Ste 308, Lake Forest IL 60045
Tel (847) 735-2066 *SIC* 1742 1731 1711

TELLABS INC p 1435
1415 W Diehl Rd, Naperville IL 60563
Tel (630) 798-8800 *SIC* 3661 1731

L & H CO INC p 833
2215 York Rd Ste 304, Oak Brook IL 60523
Tel (630) 571-7200
SIC 1731 1611 1623 3621

WILLIAM CHARLES LTD p 1610
1401 N 2nd St, Rockford IL 61107
Tel (815) 963-7400
SIC 1611 5211 1731 4953

▲ MYR GROUP INC p 1004
1701 Golf Rd Ste 3-1012, Rolling Meadows IL 60008
Tel (847) 290-1891 *SIC* 1623 1731

CELLULAR CONNECTION LLC p 274
525 Congressional Blvd, Carmel IN 46032
Tel (765) 651-2001
SIC 5065 1731 5999 5731

INFRASTRUCTURE AND ENERGY ALTERNATIVES LLC p 742
3900 White Ave, Clinton IN 47842
Tel (708) 397-4200 *SIC* 8731 1731

■ SHAMBAUGH & SON LP p 1311
7614 Opportunity Dr, Fort Wayne IN 46825
Tel (260) 487-7777
SIC 1711 1799 1731 1796 1629

DEEM LLC p 421
6831 E 32nd St Ste 200, Indianapolis IN 46226
Tel (317) 860-2990 *SIC* 1731 1711

ERMCO INC p 508
1625 W Thompson Rd, Indianapolis IN 46217
Tel (317) 780-2923 *SIC* 1731

KOORSEN FIRE & SECURITY INC p 827
2719 N Arlington Ave, Indianapolis IN 46218
Tel (317) 542-1800
SIC 5099 7389 5199 5063 1731

NORTH ELECTRIC INC p 1052
2438 W Robin Rd, Scottsburg IN 47170
Tel (812) 752-4804 *SIC* 1731

DANFOSS POWER SOLUTIONS INC p 411
2800 E 13th St, Ames IA 50010
Tel (515) 239-6000 *SIC* 1731

TRI-CITY ELECTRIC CO OF IOWA p 1477
6225 N Brady St, Davenport IA 52806
Tel (563) 322-7181 *SIC* 1731

BAKER ELECTRIC INC p 146
111 Jackson Ave, Des Moines IA 50315
Tel (515) 288-6774 *SIC* 1731

ELECTRO MANAGEMENT CORP p 485
111 Jackson Ave, Des Moines IA 50315
Tel (515) 288-6774 *SIC* 1731

HARBOR GROUP INC p 659
1520 N Main Ave, Sioux Center IA 51250
Tel (712) 722-1661 *SIC* 1731

INTERSTATES CONSTRUCTION SERVICES INC p 758
1520 N Main Ave, Sioux Center IA 51250
Tel (712) 722-1662 *SIC* 1731 3629

SABRE COMMUNICATIONS CORP p 1264
7101 Southbridge Dr, Sioux City IA 51111
Tel (712) 258-6690 *SIC* 3663 3441 1731

CIMARRON UNDERGROUND INC p 307
8375 Melrose Dr, Lenexa KS 66214
Tel (913) 438-2981 *SIC* 1623 1731

P1 GROUP INC p 1103
13605 W 96th Ter, Lenexa KS 66215
Tel (913) 529-5000 *SIC* 1711 1731

WACHTER INC p 1570
16001 W 99th St, Lenexa KS 66219
Tel (913) 541-2500 *SIC* 1731

ALEXANDER OPEN SYSTEMS INC p 49
12980 Foster St Ste 300, Overland Park KS 66213
Tel (913) 307-2300
SIC 5045 7373 8748 7376 3577 1731

EAST KENTUCKY NETWORK LLC p 470
101 Technology Trl, Ivel KY 41642
Tel (606) 477-2355 *SIC* 4812 1731

AMTECK OF KENTUCKY INC p 87
2421 Fortune Dr Ste 150, Lexington KY 40509
Tel (859) 255-9546 *SIC* 1731

DAVIS H ELLIOT CONSTRUCTION CO INC p 416
673 Blue Sky Pkwy, Lexington KY 40509
Tel (859) 263-5148 *SIC* 1623 1731

HALL CONTRACTING OF KENTUCKY INC p 654
3800 Crittenden Dr, Louisville KY 40209
Tel (502) 367-6151
SIC 1541 1623 1761 1731

AWC INC p 139
6655 Exchequer Dr, Baton Rouge LA 70809
Tel (225) 752-3939 *SIC* 1731

EXCEL CONTRACTORS INC p 516
8641 United Plaza Blvd, Baton Rouge LA 70809
Tel (225) 408-1300 *SIC* 1731

ISC CONSTRUCTORS LLC p 766
20480 Highland Rd, Baton Rouge LA 70817
Tel (225) 756-8001 *SIC* 1731

ISC GROUP L L C p 766
20480 Highland Rd, Baton Rouge LA 70817
Tel (225) 756-8001 *SIC* 1731

MMR CONSTRUCTORS INC p 979
15961 Airline Hwy, Baton Rouge LA 70817
Tel (225) 756-5090 *SIC* 1731

MMR GROUP INC p 979
15961 Airline Hwy, Baton Rouge LA 70817
Tel (225) 756-5090 *SIC* 1731

NEWTRON GROUP L L C p 1039
8183 W El Cajon Dr, Baton Rouge LA 70815
Tel (225) 927-8921 *SIC* 1731

NEWTRON HOLDINGS LLC p 1039
8183 W El Cajon Dr, Baton Rouge LA 70815
Tel (225) 927-8921 *SIC* 1731

TRIAD E&C HOLDINGS LLC p 1478
8183 W El Cajon Dr, Baton Rouge LA 70815
Tel (225) 927-8921 *SIC* 1731

TRIAD ELECTRIC & CONTROLS INC p 1478
2288 N Airway Dr, Baton Rouge LA 70815
Tel (225) 923-0604 *SIC* 1731

■ ARDENT SERVICES LLC p 106
170 New Camellia Blvd, Covington LA 70433
Tel (985) 792-3000 *SIC* 1731

ALL STAR ELECTRIC INC p 51
1032 Bert St, La Place LA 70068
Tel (985) 618-1200 *SIC* 1731

MCC GROUP L L C p 926
3001 17th St, Metairie LA 70002
Tel (504) 833-8291 *SIC* 1711 1542 1731

JE RICHARDS INC p 781
10401 Tucker St, Beltsville MD 20705
Tel (301) 345-1300 *SIC* 1731

POWER SOLUTIONS LLC p 1165
17201 Melford Blvd Ste C, Bowie MD 20715
Tel (301) 794-0330 *SIC* 1731

MONA ELECTRIC GROUP INC p 983
7915 Malcolm Rd Ste 400w, Clinton MD 20735
Tel (301) 868-8400 *SIC* 1731

CHOPTANK ELECTRIC COOPERATIVE INC p 302
24820 Meeting House Rd, Denton MD 21629
Tel (410) 479-0420 *SIC* 4911 1731

BFPE INTERNATIONAL INC p 179
7512 Connelley Dr, Hanover MD 21076
Tel (410) 768-2200 *SIC* 1731 7382 7389

■ WA CHESTER LLC p 1569
4390 Parliament Pl Ste Q, Lanham MD 20706
Tel (202) 466-1940 *SIC* 1731

AES ELECTRICAL INC p 31
13335 Mid Atlantic Blvd, Laurel MD 20708
Tel (301) 770-2060 *SIC* 1731

SULLIVAN & MCLAUGHLIN COMPANIES INC p 1397
74 Lawley St, Boston MA 02122
Tel (617) 474-0500 *SIC* 1731

EGENERA INC p 481
80 Central St Ste 300, Boxborough MA 01719
Tel (978) 206-6300 *SIC* 7373 1731 8741

▲ AMERESCO INC p 66
111 Speen St Ste 410, Framingham MA 01701
Tel (508) 661-2200 *SIC* 8711 1731

CENTURY FIBER OPTICS p 282
79 Lowland St, Holliston MA 01746
Tel (508) 429-2342 *SIC* 1731

WAYNE J GRIFFIN ELECTRIC INC p 1584
116 Hopping Brook Rd, Holliston MA 01746
Tel (508) 429-8830 *SIC* 1731

COMMUNICATION TECHNOLOGY SERVICES LLC p 346
33 Locke Dr Ste 201, Marlborough MA 01752
Tel (508) 382-2700 *SIC* 1731

INTERSTATE ELECTRICAL SERVICES CORP p 758
70 Treble Cove Rd, North Billerica MA 01862
Tel (978) 667-5200 *SIC* 1731

MASS ELECTRIC CONSTRUCTION CO p 916
400 Totten Pond Rd # 400, Waltham MA 02451
Tel (781) 290-1000 *SIC* 1731 1623

COGHLIN CONSTRUCTION SERVICES INC p 334
100 Prescott St Ste 3, Worcester MA 01605
Tel (508) 793-0300 *SIC* 1731

COGHLIN ELECTRICAL CONTRACTORS INC p 334
100 Prescott St, Worcester MA 01605
Tel (508) 793-0300 *SIC* 1731

CANTON WIND-DOWN CO p 247
5711 Research Dr, Canton MI 48188
Tel (734) 467-8121 *SIC* 1731

MOTOR CITY ELECTRIC CO p 992
9440 Grinnell St, Detroit MI 48213
Tel (313) 567-5300 *SIC* 1731

NEWKIRK ELECTRIC ASSOCIATES INC p 1037
1875 Roberts St, Muskegon MI 49442
Tel (231) 722-1691 *SIC* 1731 1629 8711

LEE CONTRACTING INC p 851
631 Cesar E Chavez Ave, Pontiac MI 48342
Tel (888) 833-8776 *SIC* 1731 1542 1541

CONTI CORP p 362
6417 Center Dr Ste 120, Sterling Heights MI 48312
Tel (586) 274-4800 *SIC* 1731 1711

BLATTNER ENERGY INC p 189
392 County Road 50, Avon MN 56310
Tel (320) 356-7351 *SIC* 1731

EGAN CO p 481
7625 Boone Ave N, Brooklyn Park MN 55428
Tel (763) 595-4358
SIC 1711 1731 3444 7623 1793

BOSCH SECURITY SYSTEMS INC p 202
12000 Portland Ave, Burnsville MN 55337
Tel (952) 884-4051 *SIC* 1731 3669 3679

CONVERGEONE HOLDINGS CORP p 365
3344 Highway 149, Eagan MN 55121
Tel (651) 994-6800 *SIC* 4813 5999 1731

CONVERGEONE INC p 365
3344 Highway 149, Eagan MN 55121
Tel (651) 994-6800 *SIC* 4813 5999 1731

BLUESTREAM PROFESSIONAL SERVICES LLC p 193
3305 Highway 60 W, Faribault MN 55021
Tel (678) 355-6200 *SIC* 1731

▲ OTTER TAIL CORP p 1098
215 S Cascade St, Fergus Falls MN 56537
Tel (218) 739-8200
SIC 4911 3084 5047 2099 1731

FAGEN INC p 524
501 Highway 212 W, Granite Falls MN 56241
Tel (320) 564-3324 *SIC* 1541 1731 1711

HUNT ELECTRIC CORP p 719
7900 Chicago Ave S, Minneapolis MN 55420
Tel (651) 646-2911 *SIC* 1731

■ NEXTIRAONE LLC p 1040
5050 Lincoln Dr Ste 300, Minneapolis MN 55436
Tel (952) 352-4410
SIC 5065 7629 1731 5999 4813 4841

■ NORSTAN COMMUNICATIONS INC p 1049
5050 Lincoln Dr Ste 300, Minneapolis MN 55436
Tel (952) 935-9002 *SIC* 5065 1731 7629

PARSONS ELECTRIC LLC p 1118
5960 Main St Ne, Minneapolis MN 55432
Tel (763) 571-8000 *SIC* 1731 7382 8711

■ AEV INC p 31
3030 24th Ave S, Moorhead MN 56560
Tel (218) 284-9518 *SIC* 1731

■ PRIMORIS AV ENERGY & ELECTRICAL CONSTRUCTION CORP p 1176
3030 24th Ave S, Moorhead MN 56560
Tel (218) 284-9500 *SIC* 1731 1623

WRIGHT-HENNEPIN SECURITY CORP p 1627
6800 Electric Dr, Rockford MN 55373
Tel (763) 477-3664
SIC 1731 1711 7382 5063 4911

MARSDEN HOLDING LLC p 910
2124 University Ave W, Saint Paul MN 55114
Tel (651) 641-1717 *SIC* 1731

CHAIN ELECTRIC CO p 286
1308 1/2 W Pine St, Hattiesburg MS 39401
Tel (601) 545-3800 *SIC* 1731

YTG LLC p 1640
6222 Saint Louis St, Meridian MS 39307
Tel (601) 483-2384 *SIC* 1731

W G YATES & SONS CONSTRUCTION CO p 1568
1 Gully Ave, Philadelphia MS 39350
Tel (904) 714-1376
SIC 1542 1541 2339 1611 5211 1731

YATES COMPANIES INC p 1635
1 Gully Ave, Philadelphia MS 39350
Tel (601) 656-5411
SIC 1542 1541 1611 5211 1731

■ IRBY CONSTRUCTION CO p 764
318 Old Highway 49 S, Richland MS 39218
Tel (601) 709-4729 *SIC* 1623 1731

BILFINGER INDUSTRIAL SERVICES INC p 182
15933 Clayton Rd Ste 305, Ballwin MO 63011
Tel (636) 391-4500
SIC 1541 1731 1796 8711 8744

SACHS ELECTRIC CO p 1264
1572 Larkin Williams Rd, Fenton MO 63026
Tel (636) 532-2000 *SIC* 1731

■ CAPITAL ELECTRIC CONSTRUCTION CO INC p 249
600 Broadway Blvd Ste 600, Kansas City MO 64105
Tel (816) 472-9500 *SIC* 1731

MARK ONE ELECTRIC CO INC p 907
909 Troost Ave, Kansas City MO 64106
Tel (816) 842-7023 *SIC* 1731

ELECTRICAL CORP OF AMERICA INC p 485
7320 Arlington Ave, Raytown MO 64133
Tel (816) 737-3206 *SIC* 1731

AMERICAN RESIDENTIAL SERVICES OF INDIANA INC p 78
10403 Baur Blvd Ste E, Saint Louis MO 63132
Tel (314) 812-6000
SIC 1711 1731 1799 5722

GUARANTEE ELECTRICAL CO p 644
3405 Bent Ave, Saint Louis MO 63116
Tel (314) 772-5400 *SIC* 1731

PAYNECREST ELECTRIC INC p 1122
10411 Baur Blvd, Saint Louis MO 63132
Tel (314) 996-0400 *SIC* 1731

EPC SERVICES CO p 504
3521 Gabel Rd Ste B, Billings MT 59102
Tel (406) 294-8544 *SIC* 1731 8711

COMMONWEALTH ELECTRIC CO OF MIDWEST p 346
1901 Y St Ste 100, Lincoln NE 68503
Tel (402) 473-2214 *SIC* 1731

MILLER ELECTRIC CO p 970
2501 Saint Marys Ave, Omaha NE 68105
Tel (402) 341-6479 *SIC* 1731

■ BOMBARD ELECTRIC LLC p 199
3570 W Post Rd, Las Vegas NV 89118
Tel (702) 263-3570 *SIC* 1731

CALVI ELECTRIC CO p 243
14 S California Ave Ste 1, Atlantic City NJ 08401
Tel (609) 345-0151 *SIC* 1731

RIGGS DISTLER & CO INC p 1234
4 Esterbrook Ln, Cherry Hill NJ 08003
Tel (856) 433-6000 *SIC* 1731

EII INC p 481
530 South Ave E, Cranford NJ 07016
Tel (908) 276-1000 *SIC* 1731

NEAD ELECTRIC INC p 1023
187 E Union Ave, East Rutherford NJ 07073
Tel (201) 460-5200 *SIC* 1731

NEAD ORGANIZATION INC p 1023
187 E Union Ave, East Rutherford NJ 07073
Tel (201) 460-5200 *SIC* 1731

EMPIRE TECHNOLOGIES LLC p 494
246 Industrial Way W # 1, Eatontown NJ 07724
Tel (732) 625-3200 *SIC* 5065 1731 5999

TYCO ELECTRONICS SUBSEA COMMUNICATIONS LLC p 1496
250 Industrial Way W, Eatontown NJ 07724
Tel (732) 578-7000
SIC 3661 5063 7373 1731 8999

ACUATIVE CORP p 20
30 Two Bridges Rd Ste 240, Fairfield NJ 07004
Tel (862) 926-5600 SIC 7373 5065 1731

NICE SYSTEMS INC p 1042
461 From Rd Ste 103, Paramus NJ 07652
Tel (201) 964-2600
SIC 7372 7382 1731 8741

SCHOLES ELECTRIC & COMMUNICATIONS p 1288
1021 Centennial Ave, Piscataway NJ 08854
Tel (732) 562-1900 SIC 1731

TYCO INTERNATIONAL MANAGEMENT CO LLC p 1496
9 Roszel Rd Ste 2, Princeton NJ 08540
Tel (609) 720-4200
SIC 3999 1711 1731 3669 3491

CRESTRON ELECTRONICS INC p 392
15 Volvo Dr, Rockleigh NJ 07647
Tel (201) 767-3400
SIC 3571 3651 1731 3663 3499 3669

RAY ANGELINI INC p 1209
105 Blckwood Barnsboro Rd, Sewell NJ 08080
Tel (856) 228-5566 SIC 1731 1711 8741

■ COMCAST CABLEVISION OF NEW JERSEY INC p 343
800 Rahway Ave, Union NJ 07083
Tel (908) 206-8640 SIC 4841 1731 7375

JNET COMMUNICATIONS LLC p 786
25 Independence Blvd # 103, Warren NJ 07059
Tel (203) 951-6400 SIC 4899 1731

STAR-LO ELECTRIC INC p 1378
32 S Jefferson Rd, Whippany NJ 07981
Tel (973) 515-0500 SIC 1731

B & G ELECTRICAL CONTRACTORS OF NY INC p 141
7100 New Horizons Blvd, Amityville NY 11701
Tel (631) 669-6000 SIC 1731

▲ NAPCO SECURITY TECHNOLOGIES INC p 1007
333 Bayview Ave, Amityville NY 11701
Tel (631) 842-9400
SIC 3669 3699 3429 1731 7373

LANCE INVESTIGATION SERVICE INC p 841
1438 Boston Rd, Bronx NY 10460
Tel (718) 893-1400 SIC 7381 1731

EDWARDS TELEPHONE CO INC p 480
159 Main St, Edwards NY 13635
Tel (315) 562-9913 SIC 1731 4813

UNITY ELECTRIC CO INC p 1515
6545 Fresh Meadow Ln, Flushing NY 11365
Tel (718) 539-4300 SIC 1731

UNITY INTERNATIONAL GROUP INC p 1515
6545 Fresh Meadow Ln, Flushing NY 11365
Tel (718) 539-4300 SIC 1731

SLOMINS INC p 1331
125 Lauman Ln, Hicksville NY 11801
Tel (516) 932-7000 SIC 5983 1731 1711

E-J ELECTRIC INSTALLATION CO INC p 467
4641 Vernon Blvd, Long Island City NY 11101
Tel (718) 786-9400 SIC 1731

■ ATLANTIC AVIATION FBO HOLDINGS LLC p 126
600 5th Ave Fl 21, New York NY 10020
Tel (212) 548-6538 SIC 4581 4785 1731

ETRALI NORTH AMERICA LLC p 512
1500 Broadway Ste 708, New York NY 10036
Tel (212) 418-9328 SIC 5045 7378 1731

■ FOREST ELECTRIC CORP p 566
1375 Broadway Fl 7, New York NY 10018
Tel (212) 318-1500 SIC 1731 7349

■ FRONTIER CALIFORNIA INC p 581
140 West St, New York NY 10007
Tel (212) 395-1000
SIC 4813 6519 8721 5065 1731 7629

MCROBERTS PROTECTIVE AGENCY INC p 932
42 Broadway Ste 1836, New York NY 10004
Tel (732) 886-0990 SIC 7381 1731

■ FIVE STAR ELECTRIC CORP p 553
10132 101st St, Ozone Park NY 11416
Tel (718) 641-5000 SIC 1731

UNITED STATES INFORMATION SYSTEMS INC p 1513
35 W Jefferson Ave, Pearl River NY 10965
Tel (845) 358-7755 SIC 1731

ODYSSEY GROUP OF COMPANIES p 1075
11 Overlook Way, Setauket NY 11733
Tel (631) 751-8400
SIC 7373 3577 7371 1731

ADCO ELECTRICAL CORP p 21
201 Edward Curry Ave, Staten Island NY 10314
Tel (718) 494-4400 SIC 1731

OCONNELL ELECTRIC CO INC p 1074
7001 Performance Dr, Syracuse NY 13212
Tel (585) 924-2176 SIC 1731

LEE ELECTRICAL CONSTRUCTION INC p 851
12828 Us Highway 15 501, Aberdeen NC 28315
Tel (910) 944-9728 SIC 1731

WECTEC GLOBAL PROJECT SERVICES INC p 1587
128 S Tryon St Ste 1000, Charlotte NC 28202
Tel (980) 859-6837 SIC 1731 8712

AC CORP p 13
301 Creek Ridge Rd, Greensboro NC 27406
Tel (336) 273-4472
SIC 1711 1731 3556 3823 3625 3535

STARR ELECTRIC CO INC p 1379
6 Battleground Ct, Greensboro NC 27408
Tel (336) 275-0241 SIC 1731

S & N COMMUNICATIONS INC p 1261
636 Gralin St, Kernersville NC 27284
Tel (336) 992-5420 SIC 1623 1731

PIKE CORP p 1147
100 Pike Way, Mount Airy NC 27030
Tel (336) 789-2171 SIC 1731 8711

PIKE ELECTRIC LLC p 1148
100 Pike Way, Mount Airy NC 27030
Tel (336) 789-2171 SIC 1731 8711

PIONEER PARENT INC p 1151
100 Pike Way, Mount Airy NC 27030
Tel (336) 789-2171 SIC 1731 8711

■ SOUTHERN INDUSTRIAL CONSTRUCTORS INC p 1349
6101 Triangle Dr, Raleigh NC 27617
Tel (919) 782-4600
SIC 1629 1799 1731 1796 1791 7353

WATSON ELECTRICAL CONSTRUCTION CO LLC p 1583
1500 Charleston St Se, Wilson NC 27893
Tel (252) 237-7511 SIC 1731

■ VARISTAR CORP p 1545
4334 18th Ave S Ste 200, Fargo ND 58103
Tel (701) 232-6414
SIC 6719 4899 1623 5047 1731 4213

VAUGHN INDUSTRIES LLC p 1545
1201 E Findlay St, Carey OH 43316
Tel (419) 396-3900 SIC 1731 1711

MORGENTHALER MANAGEMENT PARTNERS VI LLC p 989
50 Public Sq Ste 2700, Cleveland OH 44113
Tel (216) 416-7500
SIC 1731 5065 7622 7373 5999

ZENITH SYSTEMS LLC p 1642
5055 Corbin Dr, Cleveland OH 44128
Tel (216) 587-9510 SIC 1731

ATLAS INDUSTRIAL CONTRACTORS LLC p 128
5275 Sinclair Rd, Columbus OH 43229
Tel (614) 841-4500 SIC 1731 3498 1796

■ COLUMBIA ENERGY GROUP p 340
200 Civic Center Dr, Columbus OH 43215
Tel (614) 460-4683 SIC 4922 1311 1731

FISHEL CO p 551
1366 Dublin Rd, Columbus OH 43215
Tel (614) 274-8100 SIC 1623 1731 8711

DYNEGY ZIMMER LLC p 465
1781 Us Rte 52, Moscow OH 45153
Tel (713) 767-0483 SIC 1731

ERIE LAKE ELECTRIC INC p 508
25730 1st St, Westlake OH 44145
Tel (440) 835-5565 SIC 1731

FORD AUDIO-VIDEO SYSTEMS LLC p 565
4800 W Interstate 40, Oklahoma City OK 73128
Tel (405) 946-9966 SIC 1731 8711

■ MATRIX NORTH AMERICAN CONSTRUCTION INC p 920
5100 E Skelly Dr Ste 700, Tulsa OK 74135
Tel (918) 838-8822 SIC 1731 1623 1629

EC CO p 474
2121 Nw Thurman St, Portland OR 97210
Tel (503) 224-3511
SIC 1731 7694 5063 5084

■ ON ELECTRIC GROUP INC p 1086
1709 Se 3rd Ave, Portland OR 97214
Tel (503) 234-9900 SIC 1731 3613

TEMP-CONTROL MECHANICAL CORP p 1436
4800 N Channel Ave, Portland OR 97217
Tel (503) 285-9851 SIC 1711 3444 1731

JET INDUSTRIES INC p 783
1935 Silverton Rd Ne, Salem OR 97301
Tel (503) 363-2334 SIC 1711 1731

ARMSTRONG HOLDINGS INC p 111
1 Armstrong Pl, Butler PA 16001
Tel (724) 283-0925 SIC 1731 5999 7382

LIGHTHOUSE ELECTRIC CO INC p 865
1957 Route 519, Canonsburg PA 15317
Tel (724) 873-3500 SIC 1731

LOBAR INC p 872
1 Old Mill Rd, Dillsburg PA 17019
Tel (717) 432-9728
SIC 1541 1542 8741 1629 1731 7371

■ TRANSCORE LP p 1471
3721 Tecport Dr Ste 102, Harrisburg PA 17111
Tel (615) 988-8960 SIC 1731

DIRECTSAT USA LLC p 442
2010 Renaissance Blvd, King Of Prussia PA 19406
Tel (267) 464-1700 SIC 1731

UNITEK GLOBAL SERVICES INC p 1515
2010 Renaissance Blvd, King Of Prussia PA 19406
Tel (267) 464-1700
SIC 1731 8741 8742 8711

HALLER ENTERPRISES INC p 654
212 Bucky Dr, Lititz PA 17543
Tel (888) 565-0546 SIC 1711 1731

BALFOUR BEATTY INVESTMENTS INC p 148
1 Country View Rd Ste 100, Malvern PA 19355
Tel (610) 355-8100
SIC 6531 8748 1731 8999 8741

PKF-MARK III INC p 1153
17 Blacksmith Rd Ste 101, Newtown PA 18940
Tel (215) 968-5031
SIC 1611 1629 1711 1731 1771 8711

■ BELL ATLANTIC INVESTMENT DEVELOPMENT CORP p 170
1717 Arch St Fl 22, Philadelphia PA 19103
Tel (215) 963-6000 SIC 1731

■ VERIZON PENNSYLVANIA INC p 1550
1717 Arch St Fl 15, Philadelphia PA 19103
Tel (215) 466-9900
SIC 4813 8721 1731 7629

SARGENT ELECTRIC CO p 1282
2767 Liberty Ave, Pittsburgh PA 15222
Tel (412) 338-8480 SIC 1731

ARLINGTON INDUSTRIES INC p 110
1 Stauffer Industrial Par, Scranton PA 18517
Tel (570) 562-0270 SIC 1731

GUARDIAN PROTECTION SERVICES INC p 645
174 Thorn Hill Rd, Warrendale PA 15086
Tel (412) 788-2580 SIC 1731 5999 7382

VECTOR SECURITY INC p 1546
2000 Ericsson Dr Ste 250, Warrendale PA 15086
Tel (724) 741-2200 SIC 7382 1731

AIREKO CONSTRUCTION LLC p 40
Las Casas St Lot 20, Caguas PR 00725
Tel (787) 653-6300
SIC 1542 1541 1731 1711

BERMUDEZ LONGO DIAZ-MASSO LLC p 175
Km 0 5 Cupey Rr 845, San Juan PR 00926
Tel (787) 761-3030 SIC 1731 1711

RANGER AMERICAN OF PUERTO RICO INC p 1208
605 Calle Lodi, San Juan PR 00924
Tel (787) 999-6060 SIC 1731 7382 7381

TRADESOURCE INC p 1469
205 Hallene Rd Unit 211, Warwick RI 02886
Tel (401) 384-6148
SIC 7361 1751 1711 1731 1742 1721

AFL TELECOMMUNICATIONS LLC p 33
170 Ridgeview Center Dr, Duncan SC 29334
Tel (864) 433-0333 SIC 3229 1731

PRODUCTION DESIGN ASSOCIATES INC p 1179
2799 Three Lakes Rd, North Charleston SC 29418
Tel (843) 554-3466 SIC 7812 1731

■ MOR PPM INC p 988
1127 S Main St, Society Hill SC 29593
Tel (843) 378-4700 SIC 1731

■ NUGEN ENERGY LLC p 1067
27283 447th Ave, Marion SD 57043
Tel (605) 648-2100 SIC 0139 1731 5211

D M G INC p 407
809 W Russell St, Sioux Falls SD 57104
Tel (605) 336-3693
SIC 5063 7694 3599 1731

■ SERVICE ELECTRIC CO p 1307
1631 E 25th St, Chattanooga TN 37404
Tel (423) 894-4336 SIC 1629 1731 1541

BROADWAY ELECTRIC SERVICE CORP p 216
1800 N Central St, Knoxville TN 37917
Tel (865) 524-1851 SIC 1731

■ SERVICEMASTER CO LLC p 1307
860 Ridge Lake Blvd Fl 3, Memphis TN 38120
Tel (901) 597-1400
SIC 7349 7342 1711 1731 7641

SERVICEMASTER HOLDING CORP p 1308
860 Ridge Lake Blvd, Memphis TN 38120
Tel (901) 597-1400
SIC 0782 7342 1711 1731 7349 7641

J M DAVIDSON INC p 771
2564 County Road 1960, Aransas Pass TX 78336
Tel (361) 883-0983 SIC 1541 1731 3441

■ ACS COMMUNICATIONS INC p 19
2535 Brockton Dr Ste 400, Austin TX 78758
Tel (512) 837-4400 SIC 1731

FACILITY SOLUTIONS GROUP INC p 523
4401 West Gate Blvd # 310, Austin TX 78745
Tel (512) 440-7985 SIC 5063 1731

HID GLOBAL CORP p 690
611 Center Ridge Dr, Austin TX 78753
Tel (800) 237-7769 SIC 3825 1731 8741

ROC HOLDINGS LLC p 1242
191 Energy Way, Bridgeport TX 76426
Tel (940) 683-0159 SIC 1794 1731 6719

ROC SERVICE CO LLC p 1242
191 Energy Way, Bridgeport TX 76426
Tel (940) 683-0109 SIC 1794 1731 1389

BRANDT COMPANIES LLC p 208
1728 Briercroft Ct, Carrollton TX 75006
Tel (972) 241-9411 SIC 1711 1731 7623

SCHNEIDER ELECTRIC BUILDINGS AMERICAS INC p 1287
1650 W Crosby Rd, Carrollton TX 75006
Tel (972) 323-1111 SIC 3822 1731

SOUTHWEST ELECTRICAL CONTRACTING SERVICES LTD p 1352
9435 E Loop 1604 N, Converse TX 78109
Tel (210) 568-1632 SIC 1731

SCOTT ELECTRIC CO p 1293
2001 N Port Ave, Corpus Christi TX 78401
Tel (361) 884-6326 SIC 1731

ENTECH SALES AND SERVICE INC p 501
3404 Garden Brook Dr, Dallas TX 75234
Tel (972) 241-8188 SIC 1731 7623 1711

■ MONITRONICS INTERNATIONAL INC p 984
1990 Wittington Pl, Dallas TX 75234
Tel (972) 243-7443 SIC 7382 1731

JMEG LP p 786
13995 Diplomat Dr Ste 400, Farmers Branch TX 75234
Tel (972) 590-5555 SIC 1731

CEC ELECTRICAL INC p 272
14450 Trinity Blvd # 250, Fort Worth TX 76155
Tel (817) 734-0040 SIC 1731

CUMMINGS ELECTRICAL LP p 401
14900 Grand River Rd # 124, Fort Worth TX 76155
Tel (817) 355-5300 SIC 1731

PRISM ELECTRIC INC p 1178
2985 Market St, Garland TX 75041
Tel (972) 926-2000 SIC 1731

▲ COMFORT SYSTEMS USA INC p 344
675 Bering Dr Ste 400, Houston TX 77057
Tel (713) 830-9600 SIC 1711 1731

ETHOSENERGY GTS HOLDINGS (US) LLC p 511
2800 North Loop W # 1100, Houston TX 77092
Tel (281) 227-5600 SIC 1731 7699 4581

■ FISK ACQUISITION INC p 552
111 T C Jester Blvd, Houston TX 77007
Tel (713) 868-6111 SIC 1731 1623

■ FISK ELECTRIC CO p 552
10855 Westview Dr, Houston TX 77043
Tel (713) 868-6111 SIC 1731

■ IES COMMERCIAL INC p 730
5433 Westheimer Rd # 500, Houston TX 77056
Tel (713) 860-1500 SIC 1731

▲ INTEGRATED ELECTRICAL SERVICES INC p 749
5433 Westheimer Rd # 500, Houston TX 77056
Tel (713) 860-1500 SIC 1731

KENMOR ELECTRIC CO LP p 810
8330 Hansen Rd, Houston TX 77075
Tel (713) 869-0171 SIC 1731

■ QUANTA FIBER NETWORKS INC p 1198
1360 Post Oak Blvd # 2100, Houston TX 77056
Tel (713) 629-7600 SIC 1731 8742

▲ QUANTA SERVICES INC p 1198
2800 Post Oak Blvd # 2600, Houston TX 77056
Tel (713) 629-7600 SIC 1731

TRACER CONSTRUCTION LLC p 1468
7433 Harwin Dr, Houston TX 77036
Tel (713) 868-5500 SIC 1731

TRACER INDUSTRIES INC p 1468
7433 Harwin Dr, Houston TX 77036
Tel (713) 868-5500 SIC 1711 1731

WALKER ENGINEERING INC p 1573
1505 W Walnut Hill Ln, Irving TX 75038
Tel (817) 540-7777 SIC 1731

PRIME CONTROLS LP p 1175
1725 Lakepointe Dr, Lewisville TX 75057
Tel (972) 221-4849 SIC 5065 1731

DIXIE ELECTRIC LLC p 444
701 Tradewinds Blvd, Midland TX 79706
Tel (432) 580-7095 SIC 1731

NEWTRON BEAUMONT LLC p 1039
1905 Industrial Park Rd, Nederland TX 77627
Tel (409) 727-6344 SIC 1731

■ ARROW SYSTEMS INTEGRATION INC p 113
1820 Preston Park Blvd # 2800, Plano TX 75093
Tel (972) 462-5800 SIC 4813 1731 5999

SYSTEM ELECTRIC CO p 1418
704 Central Pkwy E # 1200, Plano TX 75074
Tel (972) 422-2665 SIC 1731

ALTERMAN GROUP INC p 62
14703 Jnes Maltsberger Rd, San Antonio TX 78247
Tel (210) 496-6888 SIC 1731

ALTERMAN INC p 62
14703 Jnes Maltsberger Rd, San Antonio TX 78247
Tel (210) 496-6888 SIC 1731

MCS & METROPLEX CONTROL SYSTEM p 932
12903 Delivery, San Antonio TX 78247
Tel (210) 495-5245 SIC 1731

■ IES RESIDENTIAL INC p 730
10203 Mula Cir, Stafford TX 77477
Tel (281) 498-2212 SIC 1731

■ PLANT PERFORMANCE SERVICES LLC p 1154
4800 Sugar Grove Blvd # 450, Stafford TX 77477
Tel (832) 532-5600 SIC 1731 1799 7699

PROBST ELECTRIC INC p 1178
875 S 600 W, Heber City UT 84032
Tel (435) 657-1955 SIC 1623 1731

GREAT BASIN INDUSTRIAL LLC p 633
1284 Flint Meadow Dr A, Kaysville UT 84037
Tel (801) 543-2100 SIC 3443 7699 1731

CACHE VALLEY ELECTRIC CO p 235
875 N 1000 W, Logan UT 84321
Tel (435) 752-6405 SIC 1731

FIRETROL PROTECTION SYSTEMS INC p 544
3696 W 900 S Ste A, Salt Lake City UT 84104
Tel (801) 485-6900 SIC 1711 1731

RC HUNT ELECTRIC INC p 1212
1863 W Alexander St, Salt Lake City UT 84119
Tel (801) 975-8844 SIC 1731

M CASPERSON ENTERPRISE LLC p 889
220 S 100 E, St George UT 84770
Tel (800) 275-8802 SIC 5063 1731

CRAIG F SORENSEN CONSTRUCTION INC p 388
918 S 2000 W, Syracuse UT 84075
Tel (801) 773-4390 SIC 1623 1731

GREEN MOUNTAIN POWER CORP p 637
163 Acorn Ln, Colchester VT 05446
Tel (888) 835-4672 SIC 4911 1623 1731

VERMONT TRANSCO LLC p 1551
366 Pinnacle Ridge Rd, Rutland VT 05701
Tel (802) 773-9161 SIC 1731

VERMONT YANKEE NUCLEAR POWER CORP p 1551
45 Union St, Rutland VT 05701
Tel (802) 258-4120 SIC 1731

MICHAEL & SON SERVICES INC p 959
5740 General Wash Dr, Alexandria VA 22312
Tel (703) 658-3998 SIC 1521 1731 5074

MOORES ELECTRICAL & MECHANICAL CONSTRUCTION INC p 987
101 Edgewood Ave, Altavista VA 24517
Tel (434) 369-4374 SIC 1731 1711

■ EMCOR GOVERNMENT SERVICES INC p 491
2800 Crystal Dr Ste 600, Arlington VA 22202
Tel (571) 403-8900 SIC 8741 8711 1731

AMERICAN SYSTEMS CORP p 80
14151 Pk Meadow Dr Ste 500, Chantilly VA 20151
Tel (703) 968-6300
SIC 8711 1731 8742 7373

SOC LLC p 1336
15002 Northridge Dr # 100, Chantilly VA 20151
Tel (703) 955-5700 SIC 7382 1731

AEW FOUNDATION p 32
2176 Lee Hwy S, Cloverdale VA 24077
Tel (540) 992-2865 SIC 1623 1731

NEW RIVER ELECTRICAL CORP p 1033
15 Cloverdale Pl, Cloverdale VA 24077
Tel (540) 966-1650 SIC 1731 1623

■ DYNALECTRIC CO p 464
22930 Shaw Rd Ste 100, Dulles VA 20166
Tel (703) 288-2866 SIC 1731

A-T SOLUTIONS INC p 7
10304 Spotsylvania Ave A, Fredericksburg VA 22408
Tel (540) 604-5492 SIC 1731

SOUTHERN AIR INC p 1347
2655 Lakeside Dr, Lynchburg VA 24501
Tel (434) 385-6200 SIC 1711 1731

■ DYN SPECIALTY CONTRACTING INC p 464
1420 Spring Hill Rd # 500, Mc Lean VA 22102
Tel (703) 556-8000 SIC 1711 1731

■ LOCKHEED MARTIN GLOBAL TELECOMMUNICATIONS INC p 873
1600 Tysons Blvd Ste 550, Mc Lean VA 22102
Tel (703) 556-9500 SIC 4813 1731

QUALITY PLUS SERVICES INC p 1197
2929 Quality Dr, Petersburg VA 23805
Tel (804) 863-0191 SIC 1711 1731

ROLLS-ROYCE NORTH AMERICA INC p 1248
1875 Explorer St Ste 200, Reston VA 20190
Tel (703) 834-1700 SIC 5088 8741 1731

TRULAND SYSTEMS CORP p 1486
1900 Oracle Way Ste 700, Reston VA 20190
Tel (703) 464-3000 *SIC* 1731

FIRE AND LIFE SAFETY AMERICA HOLDINGS INC p 543
3017 Vernon Rd Ste 100, Richmond VA 23228
Tel (804) 222-1381 *SIC* 1711 1731

BRANCH GROUP INC p 207
442 Rutherford Ave Ne, Roanoke VA 24016
Tel (540) 982-1678
SIC 1542 1611 1711 1731 1541

MC DEAN INC p 925
22980 Indian Creek Dr, Sterling VA 20166
Tel (571) 262-8234 *SIC* 1731

KELLY JH HOLDING LLC p 809
821 3rd Ave, Longview WA 98632
Tel (360) 423-5510 *SIC* 1711 1542 1731

SCHWEITZER ENGINEERING LABORATORIES INC p 1291
2440 Ne Hopkins Ct, Pullman WA 99163
Tel (509) 332-1890 *SIC* 1731

COCHRAN INC p 333
12500 Aurora Ave N Main, Seattle WA 98133
Tel (206) 367-1900 *SIC* 1731 7382

FR UTILITY SERVICES p 573
1424 4th Ave, Seattle WA 98101
Tel (425) 890-1425 *SIC* 1731

MACDONALD-MILLER FACILITY SOLUTIONS INC p 892
7717 Detroit Ave Sw, Seattle WA 98106
Tel (206) 763-9400 *SIC* 1711 1731

■ **CABLECOM LLC** p 235
8602 Maltby Rd, Woodinville WA 98072
Tel (360) 668-1300 *SIC* 1623 1731

▲ **ENERGY SERVICES OF AMERICA CORP** p 498
75 3rd Ave W, Huntington WV 25701
Tel (304) 522-3868 *SIC* 1623 1731

VHC INC p 1553
3090 Holmgren Way, Green Bay WI 54304
Tel (920) 336-7278
SIC 1731 1542 1541 1521 1711 6512

VOS ELECTRIC INC p 1566
3131 Market St, Green Bay WI 54304
Tel (920) 336-0781 *SIC* 1731

FAITH TECHNOLOGIES INC p 526
225 Main St, Menasha WI 54952
Tel (920) 738-1500 *SIC* 1731

CORPORATE GROUP INC p 372
7123 W Calumet Rd, Milwaukee WI 53223
Tel (414) 355-7740 *SIC* 8711 1731

PPC PARTNERS INC p 1166
5464 N Port Washington Rd E, Milwaukee WI 53217
Tel (414) 831-1251 *SIC* 1731

VENTURE ELECTRICAL CONTRACTORS p 1548
2110 Pewaukee Rd Ste 110, Waukesha WI 53188
Tel (262) 542-2727 *SIC* 1731

CORIX UTILITIES (US) INC p 370
11020 W Plank Ct Ste 100, Wauwatosa WI 53226
Tel (414) 203-8700 *SIC* 1731 7389

ELKHORN CONSTRUCTION INC p 488
71 Allegiance Cir, Evanston WY 82930
Tel (307) 789-1595 *SIC* 1629 1731 1623

SIC 1741 Masonry & Other Stonework

KEENAN HOPKINS SUDER & STOWELL CONTRACTORS INC p 807
5109 E La Palma Ave Ste A, Anaheim CA 92807
Tel (714) 695-3670
SIC 1742 1751 1743 1741 1721

PENHALL CO p 1128
2121 W Crescent Ave Ste A, Anaheim CA 92801
Tel (714) 772-6450 *SIC* 1741 1795

J T THORPE & SON INC p 772
1060 Hensley St, Richmond CA 94801
Tel (510) 233-2500 *SIC* 1741 8711

TERRA MILLENNIUM CORP p 1439
1060 Hensley St, Richmond CA 94801
Tel (510) 233-2500 *SIC* 1741 8711

▲ **GREAT LAKES DREDGE & DOCK CORP** p 633
2122 York Rd Ste 200, Oak Brook IL 60523
Tel (630) 574-3000 *SIC* 1629 1741

TRI-STATE REFRACTORIES CORP p 1478
1127 E Virginia St, Evansville IN 47711
Tel (812) 425-3466 *SIC* 1741 5085

SEEDORFF MASONRY INC p 1300
408 W Mission St, Strawberry Point IA 52076
Tel (563) 933-2296 *SIC* 1741 2448

BERKEL & CO CONTRACTORS INC p 175
2649 S 142nd St, Bonner Springs KS 66012
Tel (913) 422-5125 *SIC* 1771 1741

INSULATIONS INC p 747
1101 Edwards Ave, Harahan LA 70123
Tel (504) 733-5033 *SIC* 1799 1761 1741

MANGANARO MIDATLANTIC LLC p 901
6405d Ammendale Rd, Beltsville MD 20705
Tel (301) 937-0580 *SIC* 1741 1742 1799

MANGANARO INDUSTRIES INC p 901
52 Cummings Park, Woburn MA 01801
Tel (781) 937-8880
SIC 1742 1741 1799 1743

COLD SPRING GRANITE CO INC p 335
17482 Granite West Rd, Cold Spring MN 56320
Tel (320) 685-3621 *SIC* 3281 1741 3366

COUGHLAN COMPANIES INC p 374
1710 Roe Crest Dr, North Mankato MN 56003
Tel (507) 345-8100 *SIC* 7361 1741

ENCLOS CORP p 495
2770 Blue Waters Rd # 100, Saint Paul MN 55121
Tel (651) 796-6100 *SIC* 1741

WESTERN CONSTRUCTION GROUP INC p 1597
1637 N Warson Rd, Saint Louis MO 63132
Tel (314) 427-1637
SIC 1799 1761 1741 1771

WESTERN WATERPROOFING CO INC p 1600
1637 N Warson Rd, Saint Louis MO 63132
Tel (314) 427-5461
SIC 1799 1761 1741 1771

NAVILLUS TILE INC p 1020
633 3rd Ave Fl 17, New York NY 10017
Tel (212) 750-1808 *SIC* 1741 1771 1743

MCGEE BROTHERS CO INC p 929
4608 Carriker Rd, Monroe NC 28110
Tel (704) 753-4582 *SIC* 1741 1521

■ **RMI TITANIUM CO LLC** p 1239
1000 Warren Ave, Niles OH 44446
Tel (330) 652-9952
SIC 3399 3356 1741 3533

SAMSON ENERGY CO LLC p 1274
110 W 7th St Ste 2000, Tulsa OK 74119
Tel (918) 879-0279 *SIC* 1389 1741

WASCO INC p 1577
1122 2nd Ave N B, Nashville TN 37208
Tel (615) 244-9090 *SIC* 1741

SCHNABEL FOUNDATION CO INC p 1287
45240 Business Ct Ste 250, Sterling VA 20166
Tel (703) 742-0020 *SIC* 1741

SIC 1742 Plastering, Drywall, Acoustical & Insulation Work

■ **CENTRAL VALLEY SPECIALTIES INC** p 281
3846 E Winslow Ave, Phoenix AZ 85040
Tel (602) 437-2046 *SIC* 1742 1721

KENYON COMPANIES p 813
2602 N 35th Ave, Phoenix AZ 85009
Tel (602) 233-1191 *SIC* 1742 2819

KENYON CONSTRUCTION INC p 813
4001 W Indian School Rd, Phoenix AZ 85019
Tel (602) 484-0080 *SIC* 1742

KENYON PLASTERING INC p 813
4001 W Indian School Rd, Phoenix AZ 85019
Tel (602) 233-1191 *SIC* 1742

KEENAN HOPKINS SUDER & STOWELL CONTRACTORS INC p 807
5109 E La Palma Ave Ste A, Anaheim CA 92807
Tel (714) 695-3670
SIC 1742 1751 1743 1741 1721

■ **B S I HOLDINGS INC** p 142
100 Clock Tower Pl # 200, Carmel CA 93923
Tel (831) 622-1840 *SIC* 1742

E M P INTERIORS INC p 466
9902 Channel Rd, Lakeside CA 92040
Tel (619) 443-7034 *SIC* 1742

STANDARD DRYWALL INC p 1376
9902 Channel Rd, Lakeside CA 92040
Tel (619) 443-7034 *SIC* 1742

ANSCHUTZ FILM GROUP p 93
1888 Century Park E # 1400, Los Angeles CA 90067
Tel (310) 887-1000 *SIC* 1742

AMERICAN TECHNOLOGIES INC p 80
210 W Baywood Ave, Orange CA 92865
Tel (714) 283-9990
SIC 1521 1541 1742 1731 1721 1711

FOUNDATION BUILDING MATERIALS LLC p 571
2552 Walnut Ave Ste 160, Tustin CA 92780
Tel (714) 380-3127 *SIC* 1742

PETROCHEM INSULATION INC p 1139
110 Corporate Pl, Vallejo CA 94590
Tel (707) 644-7455 *SIC* 1742 1799

■ **JOHNS MANVILLE CORP** p 790
717 17th St Ste 800, Denver CO 80202
Tel (303) 978-2000 *SIC* 2952 1761 1742

■ **BUILDER SERVICES GROUP INC** p 224
260 Jimmy Ann Dr, Daytona Beach FL 32114
Tel (386) 304-2222 *SIC* 1742

▲ **TOPBUILD CORP** p 1460
260 Jimmy Ann Dr, Daytona Beach FL 32114
Tel (386) 304-2200
SIC 1742 1761 1751 5033

■ **TOPBUILD SERVICES GROUP CORP** p 1461
260 Jimmy Ann Dr, Daytona Beach FL 32114
Tel (386) 304-2200 *SIC* 1742

■ **TRUTEAM LLC** p 1489
260 Jimmy Ann Dr, Daytona Beach FL 32114
Tel (386) 304-2200
SIC 1742 1761 1751 1521

ACOUSTI ENGINEERING CO OF FLORIDA p 18
4656 Sw 34th St, Orlando FL 32811
Tel (407) 425-3467 *SIC* 1742 5713

KEENAN HOPKINS SCHMIDT AND STOWELL CONTRACTORS INC p 807
5422 Bay Center Dr # 200, Tampa FL 33609
Tel (813) 627-2219 *SIC* 1542 1742

ARROW EXTERMINATORS INC p 113
8613 Roswell Rd Bldg 4, Atlanta GA 30350
Tel (770) 993-8705
SIC 1742 7342 1521 1542

BRAND ENERGY SOLUTIONS LLC p 207
1325 Cobb International D, Kennesaw GA 30152
Tel (678) 285-1400
SIC 1751 1742 1799 1721

TRILOK INDUSTRIES INC p 1480
670 Village Trce Ne, Marietta GA 30067
Tel (678) 325-2960 *SIC* 1799 1742

MED-ACOUSTICS INC p 935
1685 E Park Place Blvd, Stone Mountain GA 30087
Tel (770) 498-8075 *SIC* 5047 1742

MCHUGH ENTERPRISES INC p 929
1737 S Michigan Ave, Chicago IL 60616
Tel (312) 986-8000
SIC 1542 1522 1622 1771 1742 6552

TRANSCO INC p 1471
200 N La Salle St # 1550, Chicago IL 60601
Tel (312) 896-8527
SIC 4789 3743 3296 1742

US BUILDER SERVICES LLC p 1531
272 E Deerpath Ste 308, Lake Forest IL 60045
Tel (847) 735-2066 *SIC* 1742 1731 1711

ANNING-JOHNSON CO p 92
1959 Anson Dr, Melrose Park IL 60160
Tel (708) 681-1300
SIC 1742 1752 1799 1761

ANSON INDUSTRIES INC p 93
1959 Anson Dr, Melrose Park IL 60160
Tel (708) 681-1300
SIC 1742 1752 1761 1799

ALLIED CONSTRUCTION SERVICES INC p 56
2122 Fleur Dr, Des Moines IA 50321
Tel (515) 288-4855
SIC 1742 1752 1721 1751 1542

PERFORMANCE CONTRACTING GROUP INC p 1135
11145 Thompson Ave, Lenexa KS 66219
Tel (913) 888-8600 *SIC* 1799 1742

PERFORMANCE CONTRACTING INC p 1135
11145 Thompson Ave, Lenexa KS 66219
Tel (913) 888-8600 *SIC* 1742 8711

MIDWEST DRYWALL CO INC p 967
1351 S Reca Ct Ste 101, Wichita KS 67209
Tel (316) 722-9559 *SIC* 1742

MANGANARO MIDATLANTIC LLC p 901
6405d Ammendale Rd, Beltsville MD 20705
Tel (301) 937-0580 *SIC* 1741 1742 1799

MANGANARO INDUSTRIES INC p 901
52 Cummings Park, Woburn MA 01801
Tel (781) 937-8880
SIC 1742 1741 1799 1743

IDEAL CONTRACTING LLC p 729
2525 Clark St, Detroit MI 48209
Tel (313) 843-8000
SIC 1542 1742 1771 1791

BOUMA CORP p 204
4101 Roger B Chaffee Mem, Grand Rapids MI 49548
Tel (616) 538-3600 *SIC* 1542 1752 1742

BOUMA GROUP INC p 204
4101 Roger B Chaffee Mem, Grand Rapids MI 49548
Tel (616) 538-3600 *SIC* 1542 1752 1742

▲ **MASCO CORP** p 915
21001 Van Born Rd, Taylor MI 48180
Tel (313) 274-7400
SIC 2434 3432 3088 3429 1742

JAMAR CO p 776
4701 Mike Colalillo Dr, Duluth MN 55807
Tel (218) 628-1027
SIC 1711 1761 1742 5033 7699 3444

A P I INC p 6
1100 Old Highway 8 Nw, Saint Paul MN 55112
Tel (651) 636-4320 *SIC* 1742 5033

API GROUP INC p 96
1100 Old Highway 8 Nw, Saint Paul MN 55112
Tel (651) 636-4320
SIC 1711 1742 7699 1799

UNITED SUBCONTRACTORS INC p 1514
445 Minnesota St Ste 2500, Saint Paul MN 55101
Tel (651) 225-6300
SIC 1742 1796 1542 1522

INDUSTRIAL ACOUSTICS CO INC p 739
233 S 13th St Ste 1100, Lincoln NE 68508
Tel (718) 931-8000 *SIC* 3448 1742

ELIASON & KNUTH COMPANIES INC p 487
13324 Chandler Rd, Omaha NE 68138
Tel (402) 896-1614 *SIC* 1742 5032

WALLBOARD SYSTEMS HAWAII p 1573
696 Turtlewood Pl, Henderson NV 89052
Tel (702) 233-3654 *SIC* 1742

■ **MASCO CONTRACTOR SERVICES EAST INC** p 915
612 River Rd, Fair Haven NJ 07704
Tel (732) 933-4433 *SIC* 1742

GF INVESTORS LLC p 609
60 E 42nd St Rm 4510, New York NY 10165
Tel (212) 457-1138 *SIC* 1742

COMPONENT ASSEMBLY SYSTEMS INC p 351
620 Fifth Ave Ste 1, Pelham NY 10803
Tel (212) 567-5737 *SIC* 1751 1742

PRECISION WALLS INC p 1169
1230 Ne Maynard Rd, Cary NC 27513
Tel (919) 832-0380 *SIC* 1743 1742 1799

MILLER INSULATION CO INC p 970
3520 E Century Ave, Bismarck ND 58503
Tel (701) 258-4323 *SIC* 1742 1542

VALLEY INTERIOR SYSTEMS INC p 1541
2203 Fowler St, Cincinnati OH 45206
Tel (513) 961-0400 *SIC* 1742

IBP CORP HOLDINGS INC p 726
495 S High St Ste 50, Columbus OH 43215
Tel (614) 692-6360 *SIC* 1742 6719

■ **INSTALLED BUILDING PRODUCTS LLC** p 746
495 S High St Ste 50, Columbus OH 43215
Tel (614) 221-3399 *SIC* 1742 5211 1761

CLEVELAND CONSTRUCTION INC p 325
8620 Tyler Blvd, Mentor OH 44060
Tel (513) 398-8900 *SIC* 1542 1742 1752

WESTERN PARTITIONS INC p 1599
8300 Sw Hunziker St, Tigard OR 97223
Tel (503) 620-1600 *SIC* 1742

MARCON & BOYER INC p 905
645 Hamilton St Ste 300, Allentown PA 18101
Tel (610) 866-5959
SIC 3448 1742 1743 1799

NOVINGER GROUP INC p 1063
1441 Stoneridge Dr, Middletown PA 17057
Tel (717) 930-0300
SIC 1742 1799 5032 5033 5039

TRADESOURCE INC p 1469
205 Hallene Rd Unit 211, Warwick RI 02886
Tel (401) 384-6148
SIC 7361 1751 1711 1731 1742 1721

BONITZ CONTRACTING CO INC p 200
645 Rosewood Dr, Columbia SC 29201
Tel (803) 799-0181
SIC 1742 1752 1761 1542 1541

BONITZ INC p 200
645 Rosewood Dr, Columbia SC 29201
Tel (803) 799-0181
SIC 3448 1542 1742 1541 1761 1752

31-W INSULATION CO INC p 2
7434 Cycle Ln, Goodlettsville TN 37072
Tel (615) 643-3900 *SIC* 1742

■ **WILLIAMS INSULATION CO OF AUSTIN INC** p 1611
4300 Nixon Ln, Austin TX 78725
Tel (512) 928-4002 *SIC* 1742

■ **WILLIAMS CONSOLIDATED I LTD** p 1611
1524 N Port Ave, Corpus Christi TX 78401
Tel (386) 304-2200 *SIC* 1742

MAREK BROTHERS SYSTEMS INC p 905
2115 Judiway St, Houston TX 77018
Tel (713) 681-9213 *SIC* 1742

BAKER DRYWALL PARTNERSHIP LLP p 146
401 Us Highway 80 E, Mesquite TX 75150
Tel (972) 288-9275 *SIC* 1742

USI SENIOR HOLDINGS INC p 1535
895 W 2600 S, South Salt Lake UT 84119
Tel (801) 983-0390 *SIC* 1742

RHEM LLC p 1231
700 Powell Ave Sw, Renton WA 98057
Tel (425) 228-4111 *SIC* 5033 3086 1742

H J MARTIN & SON INC p 650
320 S Military Ave, Green Bay WI 54303
Tel (920) 494-3461
SIC 5713 1793 1522 1542 1742

CITY WIDE INSULATION OF MADISON INC p 320
4501 Triangle St, Mc Farland WI 53558
Tel (608) 838-4141 *SIC* 1742

SIC 1743 Terrazzo, Tile, Marble & Mosaic Work

KEENAN HOPKINS SUDER & STOWELL CONTRACTORS INC p 807
5109 E La Palma Ave Ste A, Anaheim CA 92807
Tel (714) 695-3670
SIC 1742 1751 1743 1741 1721

LOUISVILLE TILE DISTRIBUTORS INC p 881
4520 Bishop Ln, Louisville KY 40218
Tel (502) 452-2037 *SIC* 5032 5211 1743

MANGANARO INDUSTRIES INC p 901
52 Cummings Park, Woburn MA 01801
Tel (781) 937-8880
SIC 1742 1741 1799 1743

NAVILLUS TILE INC p 1020
633 3rd Ave Fl 17, New York NY 10017
Tel (212) 750-1808 *SIC* 1741 1771 1743

PRECISION WALLS INC p 1169
1230 Ne Maynard Rd, Cary NC 27513
Tel (919) 832-0380 *SIC* 1743 1742 1799

MARCON & BOYER INC p 905
645 Hamilton St Ste 300, Allentown PA 18101
Tel (610) 866-5959
SIC 3448 1742 1743 1799

SIC 1751 Carpentry Work

ACHEN-GARDNER INC p 17
550 S 79th St, Chandler AZ 85226
Tel (480) 940-1300
SIC 1611 1542 1521 1751 6552

YOUNGER BROTHERS GROUP INC p 1639
8525 N 75th Ave, Peoria AZ 85345
Tel (623) 979-1111 *SIC* 1751

ROYSTON HOLDING LLC p 1255
111 Center St Ste 2500, Little Rock AR 72201
Tel (770) 735-3456 *SIC* 7389 1751 2542

KEENAN HOPKINS SUDER & STOWELL CONTRACTORS INC p 807
5109 E La Palma Ave Ste A, Anaheim CA 92807
Tel (714) 695-3670
SIC 1742 1751 1743 1741 1721

CLOSET WORLD INC p 327
3860 Capitol Ave, City Of Industry CA 90601
Tel (562) 699-9945 *SIC* 1751 5211

MCCLONE CONSTRUCTION CO p 926
5170 Hillsdale Cir Ste B, El Dorado Hills CA 95762
Tel (916) 358-5495 *SIC* 1771 1751

CARPENTERS HEALTH AND WELFARE TRUST FOR p 260
533 S Fremont Ave Ste 410, Los Angeles CA 90071
Tel (213) 386-8590 *SIC* 1751

PACIFIC STATES INDUSTRIES INC p 1106
10 Madrone Ave, Morgan Hill CA 95037
Tel (408) 779-7354 *SIC* 5031 2421 1751

HERITAGE INTERESTS LLC p 686
4300 Jetway Ct, North Highlands CA 95660
Tel (916) 481-5030 *SIC* 1751 5031 2431

ISEC INC p 766
6000 Greenwood Plaza Blvd # 200, Greenwood Village CO 80111
Tel (410) 381-6049 *SIC* 1751

■ **STANLEY ACCESS TECHNOLOGIES LLC** p 1377
65 Scott Swamp Rd, Farmington CT 06032
Tel (860) 409-6502 *SIC* 1751

BRYNWOOD PARTNERS V LIMITED PARTNERSHIP p 222
8 Sound Shore Dr Ste 265, Greenwich CT 06830
Tel (203) 622-1790
SIC 6282 1751 3442 5031 3354

▲ **TOPBUILD CORP** p 1460
260 Jimmy Ann Dr, Daytona Beach FL 32114
Tel (386) 304-2200
SIC 1742 1761 1751 5033

■ **TRUTEAM LLC** p 1489
260 Jimmy Ann Dr, Daytona Beach FL 32114
Tel (386) 304-2200
SIC 1742 1761 1751 1521

RC ALUMINUM INDUSTRIES INC p 1211
2805 Nw 75th Ave, Miami FL 33122
Tel (305) 592-1515 *SIC* 3442 1751

ISI DESIGN AND INSTALLATION SOLUTIONS INC p 766
6321 Emperor Dr Ste 201, Orlando FL 32809
Tel (407) 872-1865
SIC 7389 1752 1799 1751

CARPENTER CONTRACTORS OF AMERICA INC p 260
3900 Ave D Nw, Winter Haven FL 33880
Tel (863) 294-6449 *SIC* 1751 2439 2431

▲ **HOME DEPOT INC** p 703
2455 Paces Ferry Rd Se, Atlanta GA 30339
Tel (770) 433-8211
SIC 5261 5211 5231 5251 1751 1752

ROYSTON LLC p 1255
1 Pickroy Rd, Jasper GA 30143
Tel (770) 735-3456 *SIC* 7389 2542 1751

BRAND ENERGY SOLUTIONS LLC p 207
1325 Cobb International D, Kennesaw GA 30152
Tel (678) 285-1400
SIC 1751 1742 1799 1721

■ SELECTBUILD CONSTRUCTION INC p 1301
720 E Park Blvd Ste 115, Boise ID 83712
Tel (208) 331-4300
SIC 1521 1771 1751 2431 5031 5211

ALLIED CONSTRUCTION SERVICES INC p 56
2122 Fleur Dr, Des Moines IA 50321
Tel (515) 288-4855
SIC 1742 1752 1721 1751 1542

ALENCO INC p 48
16201 W 110th St, Lenexa KS 66219
Tel (913) 438-1902 *SIC* 1521 1751 1761

HANSONS WINDOWS AND SIDING OF LANSING LLC p 659
977 E 14 Mile Rd, Troy MI 48083
Tel (248) 681-9202 *SIC* 1751

NORTHERN CONTOURS INC p 1056
1355 Mendota Heights Rd # 100, Saint Paul MN 55120
Tel (651) 695-1698 *SIC* 3083 1751 2435

KB FRAMERS LLC p 805
5795 Rogers St, Las Vegas NV 89118
Tel (702) 873-9451 *SIC* 1751 1521

CRYSTAL WINDOW & DOOR SYSTEMS LTD p 397
3110 Whitestone Expy, Flushing NY 11354
Tel (718) 961-7300
SIC 5031 3442 3231 3211 2431 1751

▲ GRIFFON CORP p 640
712 5th Ave Fl 18, New York NY 10019
Tel (212) 957-5000
SIC 3442 2431 1751 1799 3083 3663

COMPONENT ASSEMBLY SYSTEMS INC p 351
620 Fifth Ave Ste 1, Pelham NY 10803
Tel (212) 567-5737 *SIC* 1751 1742

■ FORTUNE BRANDS WINDOWS INC p 570
3948 Townsfair Way # 200, Columbus OH 43219
Tel (614) 532-3500 *SIC* 1751 5211

MAROUS BROTHERS CONSTRUCTION INC p 910
1702 Joseph Lloyd Pkwy, Willoughby OH 44094
Tel (440) 951-3904 *SIC* 1521 1751

POWER HOME REMODELING GROUP LLC p 1165
2501 Seaport Dr Lbby 1, Chester PA 19013
Tel (610) 874-5000 *SIC* 1751 1761

PHILADELPHIA CARPENTERS BENEFIT FUNDS p 1142
1811 Spring Garden St, Philadelphia PA 19130
Tel (215) 568-0430 *SIC* 1751

TRADESOURCE INC p 1469
205 Hallene Rd Unit 211, Warwick RI 02886
Tel (401) 384-6148
SIC 7361 1751 1711 1731 1742 1721

DAVACO INC p 414
6688 N Cntrl Expy Ste 100, Dallas TX 75206
Tel (214) 373-4700
SIC 1751 1799 1542 1796

■ US HOME SYSTEMS INC p 1532
2951 Kinwest Pkwy, Irving TX 75063
Tel (214) 488-6300 *SIC* 3429 5031 1751

PLY GEM PACIFIC WINDOWS CORP p 1157
5001 D St Nw, Auburn WA 98001
Tel (253) 850-9000 *SIC* 1751

SIC 1752 Floor Laying & Other Floor Work, NEC

JR MC DADE CO INC p 795
1102 N 21st Ave, Phoenix AZ 85009
Tel (602) 258-7134 *SIC* 5023 1752

INTERIOR SPECIALISTS INC p 753
1630 Faraday Ave, Carlsbad CA 92008
Tel (760) 929-6700 *SIC* 1752 1799

VALIANT PRODUCTS CORP p 1540
2727 W 5th Ave, Denver CO 80204
Tel (303) 892-1234
SIC 5131 5023 7389 2511 2599 1752

■ DGPM INVESTMENTS INC p 435
300 E River Dr, East Hartford CT 06108
Tel (860) 528-9981
SIC 5044 5021 5713 1752

US INSTALLATION GROUP INC p 1532
951 Brkn Snd Pkwy Nw # 100, Boca Raton FL 33487
Tel (561) 962-0452 *SIC* 1752

ISI DESIGN AND INSTALLATION SOLUTIONS INC p 766
6321 Emperor Dr Ste 201, Orlando FL 32809
Tel (407) 872-1865
SIC 7389 1752 1799 1751

MASTER-TEC FLOORS INC p 918
3109 N T St, Pensacola FL 32505
Tel (850) 454-0008 *SIC* 1752 5713

CHADWELL SUPPLY INC p 286
4907 Joanne Kearney Blvd, Tampa FL 33619
Tel (888) 341-2423 *SIC* 5031 1752

BURKS COMPANIES p 227
191 Peachtree St Ne # 800, Atlanta GA 30303
Tel (404) 589-4600
SIC 1752 5085 7349 4953 8999

■ HD BUILDER SOLUTIONS GROUP LLC p 672
2455 Paces Ferry Rd Se C9, Atlanta GA 30339
Tel (770) 443-8211 *SIC* 5023 1752 1799

▲ HOME DEPOT INC p 703
2455 Paces Ferry Rd Se, Atlanta GA 30339
Tel (770) 433-8211
SIC 5261 5211 5231 5251 1751 1752

■ SHAW CONTRACT FLOORING SERVICES INC p 1312
616 E Walnut Ave, Dalton GA 30721
Tel (706) 278-3812 *SIC* 1752

GREAT FLOORS LLC p 633
524 E Sherman Ave, Coeur D Alene ID 83814
Tel (208) 664-5405 *SIC* 1752 5713

■ COLEMAN FLOOR LLC p 336
1331 Davis Rd, Elgin IL 60123
Tel (847) 907-3109 *SIC* 1752

MR DAVIDS FLOORING INTERNATIONAL LLC p 996
865 W Irving Park Rd, Itasca IL 60143
Tel (847) 250-4600 *SIC* 1752

ANNING-JOHNSON CO p 92
1959 Anson Dr, Melrose Park IL 60160
Tel (708) 681-1300
SIC 1742 1752 1799 1761

ANSON INDUSTRIES INC p 93
1959 Anson Dr, Melrose Park IL 60160
Tel (708) 681-1300
SIC 1742 1752 1761 1799

ALLIED CONSTRUCTION SERVICES INC p 56
2122 Fleur Dr, Des Moines IA 50321
Tel (515) 288-4855
SIC 1742 1752 1721 1751 1542

BOUMA CORP p 204
4101 Roger B Chaffee Mem, Grand Rapids MI 49548
Tel (616) 538-3600 *SIC* 1542 1752 1742

BOUMA GROUP INC p 204
4101 Roger B Chaffee Mem, Grand Rapids MI 49548
Tel (616) 538-3600 *SIC* 1542 1752 1742

■ TREMCO INC p 1476
3735 Green Rd, Beachwood OH 44122
Tel (216) 292-5000
SIC 2891 2952 1761 1752 2851 2842

CONTINENTAL OFFICE FURNITURE CORP p 363
2601 Silver Dr, Columbus OH 43211
Tel (614) 262-5010 *SIC* 6021 1752

CLEVELAND CONSTRUCTION INC p 325
8620 Tyler Blvd, Mentor OH 44060
Tel (513) 398-8900 *SIC* 1542 1742 1752

BONITZ CONTRACTING CO INC p 200
645 Rosewood Dr, Columbia SC 29201
Tel (803) 799-0181
SIC 1742 1752 1761 1542 1541

BONITZ INC p 200
645 Rosewood Dr, Columbia SC 29201
Tel (803) 799-0181
SIC 3448 1542 1742 1541 1761 1752

ARBOR CONTRACT CARPET INC p 103
2313 E Pioneer Dr, Irving TX 75061
Tel (972) 445-2235 *SIC* 1752

T & A SUPPLY CO INC p 1419
6821 S 216th St Bldg A, Kent WA 98032
Tel (206) 282-3770
SIC 1771 5023 1752 2431

GLUTH CONTRACT FLOORING LLC p 618
12003 Mukilteo Speedway # 102, Mukilteo WA 98275
Tel (425) 493-9100 *SIC* 1752

KUSSY INC p 832
1260 Huff Ln Ste B, Jackson WY 83001
Tel (307) 739-9465 *SIC* 1752 5713

SIC 1761 Roofing, Siding & Sheet Metal Work

KOVACH INC p 828
3195 W Armstrong Pl, Chandler AZ 85286
Tel (480) 926-9292 *SIC* 1761

DIVERSIFIED ROOFING CORP p 444
2015 W Mountain View Rd, Phoenix AZ 85021
Tel (602) 850-8218 *SIC* 1761

PROGRESSIVE SERVICES INC p 1182
23 N 35th Ave, Phoenix AZ 85009
Tel (602) 278-4900 *SIC* 1761

PETERSEN-DEAN INC p 1138
39300 Civic Center Dr # 300, Fremont CA 94538
Tel (707) 469-7470 *SIC* 1761

BEST CONTRACTING SERVICES INC p 177
19027 S Hamilton Ave, Gardena CA 90248
Tel (310) 328-6969 *SIC* 1761

BORAL ROOFING LLC p 201
7575 Irvine Center Dr # 100, Irvine CA 92618
Tel (949) 756-1605 *SIC* 1761 3272 3259

PACIFIC COAST BUILDING PRODUCTS INC p 1104
10600 White Rock Rd # 100, Rancho Cordova CA 95670
Tel (916) 631-6500
SIC 3275 3271 5031 1761 2952 2426

GENERAL ROOFING SERVICES INC p 602
3300 S Parker Rd Ste 500, Aurora CO 80014
Tel (303) 923-2200 *SIC* 1761

DOUGLASS COLONY GROUP INC p 452
5901 E 58th Ave, Commerce City CO 80022
Tel (303) 288-2635 *SIC* 1761

■ JOHNS MANVILLE CORP p 790
717 17th St Ste 800, Denver CO 80202
Tel (303) 978-2000 *SIC* 2952 1761 1742

NATIONS ROOF OF CONNECTICUT LLC p 1017
1400 Honeyspot Road Ext, Stratford CT 06615
Tel (203) 335-8109 *SIC* 1761

▲ TOPBUILD CORP p 1460
260 Jimmy Ann Dr, Daytona Beach FL 32114
Tel (386) 304-2200
SIC 1742 1761 1751 5033

■ TRUTEAM LLC p 1489
260 Jimmy Ann Dr, Daytona Beach FL 32114
Tel (386) 304-2200
SIC 1742 1761 1751 1521

NATIONS ROOF OF FLORIDA LLC p 1017
1313 E Landstreet Rd, Orlando FL 32824
Tel (407) 649-1333 *SIC* 1761

PEACH STATE ROOFING INC p 1125
1655 Spectrum Dr Ste A, Lawrenceville GA 30043
Tel (770) 962-7885 *SIC* 1761

NATIONS ROOF LLC p 1017
1633 Blairs Bridge Rd, Lithia Springs GA 30122
Tel (678) 567-1533 *SIC* 1761

ANNING-JOHNSON CO p 92
1959 Anson Dr, Melrose Park IL 60160
Tel (708) 681-1300
SIC 1742 1752 1799 1761

ANSON INDUSTRIES INC p 93
1959 Anson Dr, Melrose Park IL 60160
Tel (708) 681-1300
SIC 1742 1752 1761 1799

TECTA AMERICA CORP p 1432
9450 Bryn Mawr Ave, Rosemont IL 60018
Tel (847) 581-3888 *SIC* 1761

TECTA HOLDING INC p 1432
6450 Brayn Mawr Ste 500, Rosemont IL 60018
Tel (847) 581-3888 *SIC* 1761

CROWN CORR INC p 395
7100 W 21st Ave, Gary IN 46406
Tel (219) 944-7537 *SIC* 1542 1761

WILHELM CONSTRUCTION INC p 1609
3914 Prospect St, Indianapolis IN 46203
Tel (317) 359-5411 *SIC* 1542 1541 1761

D C TAYLOR CO p 406
312 29th St Ne, Cedar Rapids IA 52402
Tel (319) 363-2073 *SIC* 1761

ALENCO INC p 48
16201 W 110th St, Lenexa KS 66219
Tel (913) 438-1902 *SIC* 1521 1751 1761

HALL CONTRACTING OF KENTUCKY INC p 654
3800 Crittenden Dr, Louisville KY 40209
Tel (502) 367-6151
SIC 1541 1623 1761 1731

INSULATIONS INC p 747
1101 Edwards Ave, Harahan LA 70123
Tel (504) 733-5033 *SIC* 1799 1761 1741

CIRAULO BROTHERS BUILDING CO p 308
7670 19 Mile Rd, Sterling Heights MI 48314
Tel (586) 731-3670 *SIC* 5031 5211 1761

JAMAR CO p 776
4701 Mike Colalillo Dr, Duluth MN 55807
Tel (218) 628-1027
SIC 1711 1761 1742 5033 7699 3444

A ZAHNER CO p 7
1400 E 9th St, Kansas City MO 64106
Tel (816) 474-8882 *SIC* 1799 1761

CORRIGAN BROTHERS INC p 373
3545 Gratiot St, Saint Louis MO 63103
Tel (314) 771-6200 *SIC* 1711 1761 1623

WESTERN CONSTRUCTION GROUP INC p 1597
1637 N Warson Rd, Saint Louis MO 63132
Tel (314) 427-1637
SIC 1799 1761 1741 1771

WESTERN WATERPROOFING CO INC p 1600
1637 N Warson Rd, Saint Louis MO 63132
Tel (314) 427-5461
SIC 1799 1761 1741 1771

■ INSTALLED BUILDING PRODUCTS LLC p 747
62 King St, Auburn NH 03032
Tel (603) 645-1604
SIC 1761 5021 5719 2515

NATIONS ROOF EAST LLC p 1017
255 Lake Ave, Yonkers NY 10701
Tel (914) 423-6171 *SIC* 1761

NATIONS ROOF OF NEW YORK LLC p 1017
70 Saint Casimir Ave, Yonkers NY 10701
Tel (914) 509-7020 *SIC* 1761

NORTH AMERICAN ROOFING SERVICES INC p 1050
41 Dogwood Rd, Asheville NC 28806
Tel (828) 687-7767 *SIC* 1761

BAKER ROOFING CO p 146
517 Mercury St, Raleigh NC 27603
Tel (919) 828-2975 *SIC* 1761 1799

■ TREMCO INC p 1476
3735 Green Rd, Beachwood OH 44122
Tel (216) 292-5000
SIC 2891 2952 1761 1752 2851 2842

■ CECO GROUP INC p 272
4625 Red Bank Rd Ste 200, Cincinnati OH 45227
Tel (513) 458-2600
SIC 8711 3564 8734 3443 3444 1761

CHAMPION OPCO LLC p 287
12121 Champion Way, Cincinnati OH 45241
Tel (513) 924-4858 *SIC* 3089 1761 3442

■ INSTALLED BUILDING PRODUCTS LLC p 746
495 S High St Ste 50, Columbus OH 43215
Tel (614) 221-3399 *SIC* 1742 5211 1761

NATIONS ROOF OF OHIO LLC p 1017
275 S Pioneer Blvd, Springboro OH 45066
Tel (937) 439-4160 *SIC* 1761

■ OWENS CORNING SALES LLC p 1100
1 Owens Corning Pkwy, Toledo OH 43659
Tel (419) 248-8000
SIC 3296 2952 3229 3089 1761

ROTH BROS INC p 1252
3847 Crum Rd, Youngstown OH 44515
Tel (330) 793-5571 *SIC* 1711 1761

OKLAHOMA ROOF MASTERS INC p 1080
601 Evergreen Dr, Guthrie OK 73044
Tel (405) 814-6440
SIC 1761 1541 4731 4212 4213

CENTIMARK CORP p 277
12 Grandview Cir, Canonsburg PA 15317
Tel (724) 743-7777 *SIC* 1761

POWER HOME REMODELING GROUP LLC p 1165
2501 Seaport Dr Lbby 1, Chester PA 19013
Tel (610) 874-5000 *SIC* 1751 1761

■ CENTRIA INC p 281
1005 Beaver Grade Rd # 2, Coraopolis PA 15108
Tel (412) 299-8000
SIC 3444 1761 3564 3449

TW METALS INC p 1494
760 Constitution Dr # 204, Exton PA 19341
Tel (610) 458-1300 *SIC* 1761

BONITZ CONTRACTING CO INC p 200
645 Rosewood Dr, Columbia SC 29201
Tel (803) 799-0181
SIC 1742 1752 1761 1542 1541

BONITZ INC p 200
645 Rosewood Dr, Columbia SC 29201
Tel (803) 799-0181
SIC 3448 1542 1742 1541 1761 1752

CHAMBERLIN WATERPROOFING & ROOFING SYSTEMS INC p 287
7510 Langtry St, Houston TX 77040
Tel (713) 880-1432 *SIC* 1799 1761

NATIONS ROOF CENTRAL LLC p 1017
2914 Lawing Ln, Rowlett TX 75088
Tel (972) 278-9200 *SIC* 1761

KALKREUTH ROOFING & SHEET METAL INC p 801
53 14th St Ste 100, Wheeling WV 26003
Tel (304) 232-8540
SIC 1761 3446 3444 3441

WESTERN INDUSTRIES INC p 1598
1141 S 10th St, Watertown WI 53094
Tel (920) 261-0660
SIC 3443 3469 3089 3444 1761 3491

NATIONS ROOF NORTH LLC p 1017
901 Sentry Dr, Waukesha WI 53186
Tel (262) 542-0002 *SIC* 1761

■ JW WILLIAMS INC p 798
2180 W Renauna Ave, Casper WY 82601
Tel (307) 237-8345
SIC 3533 3443 3547 1761 3291

SIC 1771 Concrete Work

PREFERRED MATERIALS INC p 1169
500 Rvrhills Bus Park, Birmingham AL 35242
Tel (205) 995-5900
SIC 1611 1771 3531 5032

REED CONTRACTING SERVICES INC p 1217
2512 Triana Blvd Sw, Huntsville AL 35805
Tel (256) 533-0505
SIC 1771 1794 1623 1629 1611

STEWARTS CONCRETE & BOBCAT p 1389
8771 S Desoto Dr, Mohave Valley AZ 86440
Tel (928) 788-4453 *SIC* 1771

SHASTA INDUSTRIES INC p 1312
6031 N 16th St, Phoenix AZ 85016
Tel (602) 532-3750
SIC 1799 1771 5169 7389 3088 5091

SUNDT COMPANIES INC p 1402
2015 W River Rd Ste 101, Tucson AZ 85704
Tel (520) 750-4600 *SIC* 1542 1771 1611

PENHALL INTERNATIONAL CORP p 1129
320 N Crescent Way, Anaheim CA 92801
Tel (714) 772-6450 *SIC* 1795 1771

NTS INC p 1065
8200 Stockdale Hwy Ste M, Bakersfield CA 93311
Tel (661) 588-8514 *SIC* 1623 1541 1771

GONSALVES & SANTUCCI INC p 623
5141 Commercial Cir, Concord CA 94520
Tel (925) 685-6799 *SIC* 1771

SERVICON SYSTEMS INC p 1308
3965 Landmark St, Culver City CA 90232
Tel (310) 204-5040 *SIC* 8744 7349 1771

MCCLONE CONSTRUCTION CO p 926
5170 Hillsdale Cir Ste B, El Dorado Hills CA 95762
Tel (916) 358-5495 *SIC* 1771 1751

DON CHAPIN CO INC p 449
560 Crazy Horse Canyon Rd, Salinas CA 93907
Tel (831) 449-4273 *SIC* 1623 1611 1771

PACIFIC STRUCTURES INC p 1106
953 Mission St Ste 200, San Francisco CA 94103
Tel (415) 367-9399 *SIC* 1771

JOSEPH J ALBANESE INC p 793
851 Martin Ave, Santa Clara CA 95050
Tel (408) 727-5700 *SIC* 1771

MORLEY BUILDERS INC p 989
3330 Ocean Park Blvd # 101, Santa Monica CA 90405
Tel (310) 399-1600
SIC 1541 1522 1542 1771

LARGO CONCRETE INC p 845
2741 Walnut Ave Ste 110, Tustin CA 92780
Tel (714) 731-3600 *SIC* 1771

SEMA CONSTRUCTION INC p 1302
7353 S Eagle St, Centennial CO 80112
Tel (303) 627-2600 *SIC* 1622 1771

ROCKY MOUNTAIN MATERIALS AND ASPHALT INC p 1245
1910 Rand Ave, Colorado Springs CO 80905
Tel (719) 473-3100
SIC 1611 1771 1794 5032

BRUNDAGE-BONE CONCRETE PUMPING INC p 221
6461 Downing St, Denver CO 80229
Tel (303) 289-4444 *SIC* 1771

HENSEL PHELPS CONSTRUCTION CO p 684
420 6th Ave, Greeley CO 80631
Tel (970) 352-6565
SIC 1542 1521 1771 1522 1541 1622

MANAFORT BROTHERS INC p 900
414 New Britain Ave, Plainville CT 06062
Tel (860) 229-4853
SIC 1794 1771 1622 1795 4953

PRECISION CONCRETE CONSTRUCTION INC p 1168
2075 Brandon Trl, Alpharetta GA 30004
Tel (770) 751-9158 *SIC* 1771

INTERFACE FLOORING SYSTEMS INC p 752
2859 Paces Ferry Rd Se, Atlanta GA 30339
Tel (800) 336-0225 *SIC* 3272 1771 3999

UNITED FORMING INC p 1508
470 Riverside Pkwy, Austell GA 30168
Tel (678) 945-4224 *SIC* 1771

CORESLAB STRUCTURES (ATLANTA) INC p 370
1655 Noahs Ark Rd, Jonesboro GA 30236
Tel (770) 471-1150 *SIC* 3272 1771

FLOOR AND DECOR OUTLETS OF AMERICA INC p 557
2233 Lake Park Dr Se # 400, Smyrna GA 30080
Tel (404) 471-1634 *SIC* 5713 1771

■ SELECTBUILD CONSTRUCTION INC p 1301
720 E Park Blvd Ste 115, Boise ID 83712
Tel (208) 331-4300
SIC 1521 1771 1751 2431 5031 5211

MCHUGH ENTERPRISES INC p 929
1737 S Michigan Ave, Chicago IL 60616
Tel (312) 986-8000
SIC 1542 1522 1622 1771 1742 6552

FREESEN INC p 577
3151 Robbins Rd Ste A, Springfield IL 62704
Tel (217) 546-6192 SIC 1622 1771 1629

RIETH-RILEY CONSTRUCTION CO INC p 1234
3626 Elkhart Rd, Goshen IN 46526
Tel (574) 875-5183 SIC 1611 1771 1622

3-D CONCRETE CORRECTION INC p 2
20115 Jackson Rd, South Bend IN 46614
Tel (574) 291-0771 SIC 1771

BERKEL & CO CONTRACTORS INC p 175
2649 S 142nd St, Bonner Springs KS 66012
Tel (913) 422-5125 SIC 1771 1741

APAC-KANSAS INC p 95
7415 W 130th St Ste 300, Overland Park KS 66213
Tel (913) 371-1003
SIC 1611 1771 2951 7353 1622

HAMM INC p 656
609 Perry Pl, Perry KS 66073
Tel (785) 597-5111 SIC 1411 1771 1611

WILDCAT CONSTRUCTION CO INC p 1609
3219 W May St, Wichita KS 67213
Tel (316) 945-9408
SIC 1623 1622 1771 1611 1629

GILCHRIST CONSTRUCTION CO LLC p 612
5709 New York Ave, Alexandria LA 71302
Tel (318) 448-3565 SIC 1771

MILLER & LONG CO INC p 970
4824 Rugby Ave, Bethesda MD 20814
Tel (301) 657-8000 SIC 1771

STRUCTURAL GROUP INC p 1394
10150 Old Columbia Rd, Columbia MD 21046
Tel (410) 850-7000 SIC 1771

STRUCTURAL PRESERVATION SYSTEMS LLC p 1394
10150 Old Columbia Rd, Columbia MD 21046
Tel (410) 850-7000 SIC 1771

DANIEL G SCHUSTER LLC p 411
3717 Crondall Ln Ste B, Owings Mills MD 21117
Tel (410) 363-9620 SIC 5032 1771

IDEAL CONTRACTING LLC p 729
2525 Clark St, Detroit MI 48209
Tel (313) 843-8000
SIC 1542 1742 1771 1791

AGGREGATE INDUSTRIES p 34
6211 N Ann Arbor Rd, Dundee MI 48131
Tel (734) 529-5876
SIC 3273 2951 1442 1411 1771 5211

FABCON COMPANIES LLC p 523
6111 Highway 13 W, Savage MN 55378
Tel (952) 890-4444 SIC 3272 1771

FABCON INC p 523
6111 Highway 13 W, Savage MN 55378
Tel (952) 890-4444 SIC 3272 1771

APAC-MISSISSIPPI INC p 95
101 Riverview Dr, Richland MS 39218
Tel (601) 376-4000
SIC 1611 1771 3531 5032 2951

KISSICK CONSTRUCTION CO INC p 822
8131 Indiana Ave, Kansas City MO 64132
Tel (816) 363-5530
SIC 1541 1623 1771 1794

WESTERN CONSTRUCTION GROUP INC p 1597
1637 N Warson Rd, Saint Louis MO 63132
Tel (314) 427-1637
SIC 1799 1761 1741 1771

WESTERN WATERPROOFING CO INC p 1600
1637 N Warson Rd, Saint Louis MO 63132
Tel (314) 427-5461
SIC 1799 1761 1741 1771

SIMPSON & BROWN INC p 1325
119 North Ave W, Cranford NJ 07016
Tel (908) 276-2776 SIC 1629 1771

J FLETCHER CREAMER & SON INC p 771
101 E Broadway, Hackensack NJ 07601
Tel (201) 488-9800
SIC 1623 1611 1771 1622 1629

NAVILLUS TILE INC p 1020
633 3rd Ave Fl 17, New York NY 10017
Tel (212) 750-1808 SIC 1741 1771 1743

APAC-ATLANTIC INC p 95
300 S Benbow Rd, Greensboro NC 27401
Tel (336) 412-6800
SIC 1611 1771 3531 5032

BARNHILL CONTRACTING CO INC p 156
800 Tiffany Blvd Ste 200, Rocky Mount NC 27804
Tel (252) 823-1021 SIC 1771 1541

MACK INDUSTRIES INC p 892
1321 Industrial Pkwy N # 500, Brunswick OH 44212
Tel (330) 460-7005 SIC 3272 1771

BEAVER EXCAVATING CO p 166
2000 Beaver Place Ave Sw, Canton OH 44706
Tel (330) 478-2151
SIC 1794 1611 1771 1623

GOETTLE HOLDING CO INC p 619
12071 Hamilton Ave, Cincinnati OH 45231
Tel (513) 825-8100
SIC 1799 1629 1771 1794

INDEPENDENCE EXCAVATING INC p 736
5720 E Schaaf Rd, Independence OH 44131
Tel (216) 524-1700
SIC 1629 1794 1611 1771 1795

LITHKO CONTRACTING LLC p 870
5353 Hmlton Middletown Rd, Liberty Twp OH 45011
Tel (513) 863-5100 SIC 1771

BAKER CONCRETE CONSTRUCTION INC p 146
900 N Garver Rd, Monroe OH 45050
Tel (513) 539-4000 SIC 1771 1611

R W SIDLEY INC p 1203
436 Casement Ave, Painesville OH 44077
Tel (440) 352-9343 SIC 1771 3299

M & B ASPHALT CO INC p 888
1525 W Seneca Cnty Rd 42, Tiffin OH 44883
Tel (419) 992-4235
SIC 1429 2951 1611 2952 1771

MILL CREEK LUMBER & SUPPLY CO INC p 969
6974 E 38th St, Tulsa OK 74145
Tel (405) 671-3540
SIC 3442 1771 5031 5211

NICHOLSON CONSTRUCTION CO p 1042
2400 Ansys Dr Ste 303, Canonsburg PA 15317
Tel (412) 221-4500 SIC 1629 1771 1799

SOLETANCHE INC p 1338
2400 Ansys Dr Ste 303, Canonsburg PA 15317
Tel (412) 221-4500 SIC 1771

PKF-MARK III INC p 1153
17 Blacksmith Rd Ste 101, Newtown PA 18940
Tel (215) 968-5031
SIC 1611 1629 1711 1731 1771 8711

LANDMARK CONSTRUCTION CO INC p 842
3255 Industry Dr, North Charleston SC 29418
Tel (843) 552-6186
SIC 1542 1541 1623 1771 1794

JONES BROS INC p 792
5760 Old Lebanon Dirt Rd, Mount Juliet TN 37122
Tel (615) 754-4710
SIC 1622 1771 1794 1629 1611

JONES INVESTMENT HOLDING INC p 792
5760 Old Lebanon Dirt Rd, Mount Juliet TN 37122
Tel (615) 754-4710
SIC 1622 1771 1794 1611

JD RAMMING PAVING MANAGEMENT LLC p 780
9020 N Cpitl Of Texas Hwy, Austin TX 78759
Tel (512) 251-3713 SIC 1611 1771

BO-MAC CONTRACTORS LTD p 194
1020 Lindbergh Dr, Beaumont TX 77707
Tel (409) 842-2125 SIC 1629 1771

SITE CONCRETE INC p 1327
1544 Valwood Pkwy Ste 100, Carrollton TX 75006
Tel (972) 313-0733 SIC 1611 1771 1794

PEREZ CONCRETE INC p 1135
5502 Gregg St, Dallas TX 75235
Tel (214) 522-9480 SIC 1771

■ **BEALL CONCRETE ENTERPRISES LTD** p 165
331 N Main St, Euless TX 76039
Tel (817) 835-4100 SIC 1611 1771

AUI CONTRACTORS LLC p 131
4775 North Fwy, Fort Worth TX 76106
Tel (817) 926-4377 SIC 1542 1623 1771

OSBURN CONTRACTORS INC p 1096
2747 Oakland Ave Ste A, Garland TX 75041
Tel (972) 205-9086 SIC 1771

SCULLY SERVICES LLC p 1295
19319 Oil Center Blvd, Houston TX 77073
Tel (281) 230-7500 SIC 1771

■ **TAS COMMERCIAL CONCRETE CONSTRUCTION LLC** p 1425
19319 Oil Center Blvd, Houston TX 77073
Tel (281) 230-7500 SIC 1771

TAS CONSTRUCTION INC p 1425
19319 Oil Center Blvd, Houston TX 77073
Tel (281) 230-7500 SIC 1771

FORTERRA PIPE & PRECAST LLC p 569
511 E John Carpenter Fwy, Irving TX 75062
Tel (469) 458-7973 SIC 3272 1771

POTTER CONCRETE OF HOUSTON INC p 1164
2400 E Pioneer Dr, Irving TX 75061
Tel (214) 630-2191 SIC 1771

STEWART BUILDERS INC p 1389
16575 Village Dr, Jersey Village TX 77040
Tel (713) 983-8002 SIC 1771

CHASCO CONSTRUCTORS LTD LLP p 291
2801 E Old Settlers Blvd, Round Rock TX 78665
Tel (512) 244-0600
SIC 1542 1771 1794 1623

URBAN CONCRETE CONTRACTORS INC p 1530
24114 Blanco Rd, San Antonio TX 78260
Tel (210) 490-0090 SIC 1771

ASSOCIATED BRIGHAM CONTRACTORS INC p 120
75 N 900 W, Brigham City UT 84302
Tel (435) 723-8529 SIC 1541 1771

STAKER & PARSON COMPANIES p 1374
2350 S 1900 W Ste 100, Ogden UT 84401
Tel (801) 298-7500
SIC 1611 5032 3273 4212 2951 1771

BOART LONGYEAR CO p 196
2570 W 1700 S, Salt Lake City UT 84104
Tel (801) 972-6430
SIC 1481 3532 3559 1771

S W RODGERS CO INC p 1263
5816 Wellington Rd, Gainesville VA 20155
Tel (703) 591-8400
SIC 1611 1799 6552 1771 1623

CENTURY CONCRETE INC p 282
1364 Air Rail Ave, Virginia Beach VA 23455
Tel (757) 460-5366 SIC 1622 1611 1771

S B BALLARD CONSTRUCTION CO p 1261
2828 Shipps Corner Rd, Virginia Beach VA 23453
Tel (757) 440-5555 SIC 1542 1771

T & A SUPPLY CO INC p 1419
6821 S 216th St Bldg A, Kent WA 98032
Tel (206) 282-3770
SIC 1771 5023 1752 2431

CPM DEVELOPMENT CORP p 387
5111 E Broadway Ave, Spokane Valley WA 99212
Tel (509) 534-6221 SIC 3273 1771 3272

MICHELS CORP p 960
817 W Main St, Brownsville WI 53006
Tel (920) 583-3132
SIC 1623 1771 1381 1629 3498 1794

MATHY CONSTRUCTION CO p 920
920 10th Ave N, Onalaska WI 54650
Tel (608) 783-6411
SIC 1611 1771 1442 5171

SIC 1781 Water Well Drilling

■ **LAYNE HEAVY CIVIL INC** p 848
4520 N State Road 37, Orleans IN 47452
Tel (812) 865-3232 SIC 1623 1781 1629

SHAFT DRILLERS INTERNATIONAL LLC p 1310
130 Madow Ridge Rd Ste 23, Mount Morris PA 15349
Tel (800) 331-0175 SIC 1781

▲ **LAYNE CHRISTENSEN CO** p 848
1800 Hughes Landing Blvd, The Woodlands TX 77380
Tel (281) 475-2600
SIC 1781 1623 5084 1481 8748

SIC 1791 Structural Steel Erection

MCABEE CONSTRUCTION INC p 925
5724 21st St, Tuscaloosa AL 35401
Tel (205) 349-2212
SIC 1629 1791 1796 3443 3498

■ **DBM GLOBAL INC** p 418
3020 E Camelback Rd # 100, Phoenix AZ 85016
Tel (602) 252-7787 SIC 3441 1791

ARCHITECTURAL GLASS & ALUMINUM CO INC p 105
6400 Brisa St, Livermore CA 94550
Tel (925) 583-2460
SIC 5051 1793 1791 3442

BRAGG INVESTMENT CO INC p 207
6251 N Paramount Blvd, Long Beach CA 90805
Tel (562) 984-2400 SIC 7389 7353 1791

▲ **TUTOR PERINI CORP** p 1493
15901 Olden St, Sylmar CA 91342
Tel (818) 362-8391
SIC 1542 8741 1611 1791 8711

CENTRAL MAINTENANCE AND WELDING INC p 279
2620 E Keysville Rd, Lithia FL 33547
Tel (813) 229-0012 SIC 3443 1791 7692

RECORD STEEL AND CONSTRUCTION INC p 1214
333 W Rossi St Ste 200, Boise ID 83706
Tel (208) 887-1401 SIC 1542 1791

▲ **ATKORE INTERNATIONAL GROUP INC** p 125
16100 Lathrop Ave, Harvey IL 60426
Tel (708) 339-1610
SIC 3441 1791 3446 3448 3496

■ **ATKORE INTERNATIONAL HOLDINGS INC** p 125
16100 Lathrop Ave, Harvey IL 60426
Tel (708) 225-2051
SIC 6719 3441 1791 3446 3448 3496

■ **UNISTRUT INTERNATIONAL CORP** p 1505
16100 Lathrop Ave, Harvey IL 60426
Tel (800) 882-5543
SIC 3441 1791 3446 3448 3496 3429

CROWN ENTERPRISES LLC p 395
52410 Clarke Rd, White Castle LA 70788
Tel (225) 545-3040 SIC 1541 1791 4212

IDEAL CONTRACTING LLC p 729
2525 Clark St, Detroit MI 48209
Tel (313) 843-8000
SIC 1542 1742 1771 1791

MIDWEST STEEL INC p 968
2525 E Grand Blvd, Detroit MI 48211
Tel (313) 873-2220 SIC 3441 1791

CH HOLDINGS USA INC p 286
2770 Blue Waters Rd # 100, Eagan MN 55121
Tel (651) 796-6100 SIC 1791

STEEL SERVICE CORP p 1384
2260 Flowood Dr, Jackson MS 39232
Tel (601) 939-9222
SIC 3441 1791 3496 3443

BEN HUR CONSTRUCTION CO p 172
3783 Rider Trl S, Earth City MO 63045
Tel (314) 298-8007
SIC 1542 1791 1541 3441

CONCRETE STRATEGIES LLC p 355
2199 Innerbelt Bus Ctr Dr, Saint Louis MO 63114
Tel (314) 595-6300 SIC 1791 1799

IRON WORK 40 361 & 417 HLTH FND p 765
451 Park Ave S, New York NY 10016
Tel (212) 684-1586 SIC 1791

CMD SALES LLC p 329
355 Industrial Park Dr, Boone NC 28607
Tel (828) 355-7121 SIC 1791

C P BUCKNER STEEL ERECTION INC p 233
4732 S Nc Highway 54, Graham NC 27253
Tel (336) 376-8888 SIC 1791 7353

■ **SOUTHERN INDUSTRIAL CONSTRUCTORS INC** p 1349
6101 Triangle Dr, Raleigh NC 27617
Tel (919) 782-4600
SIC 1629 1799 1731 1796 1791 7353

▲ **WILLIAMS INDUSTRIES INC** p 1611
1128 Tyler Farms Dr, Raleigh NC 27603
Tel (919) 604-1746
SIC 3441 1531 1541 3315 1791

AMERICAN BRIDGE CO p 69
1000 American Bridge Way, Coraopolis PA 15108
Tel (412) 631-1000 SIC 1791 8711 1622

AMERICAN BRIDGE HOLDING CO p 69
1000 American Bridge Way, Coraopolis PA 15108
Tel (412) 631-1000 SIC 1791 1542

HIGH CONCRETE GROUP LLC p 690
125 Denver Rd, Denver PA 17517
Tel (717) 336-9300 SIC 1791 3272

HIGH INDUSTRIES INC p 690
1853 William Penn Way, Lancaster PA 17601
Tel (717) 293-4444
SIC 1791 3272 5051 3441

COOPERS STEEL FABRICATORS INC () p 367
503 N Hillcrest Dr, Shelbyville TN 37160
Tel (931) 684-7962 SIC 3441 1791

ENNIS STEEL INDUSTRIES INC p 500
204 Metro Park Blvd, Ennis TX 75119
Tel (972) 878-0400 SIC 3312 3441 1791

LANDMARK STRUCTURES I LP p 843
1665 Harmon Rd, Fort Worth TX 76177
Tel (817) 439-8888 SIC 1791 7699

WYATT FIELD SERVICE CO p 1629
15415 Katy Fwy Ste 800, Houston TX 77094
Tel (281) 675-1300 SIC 1791

TRIPLE S INDUSTRIAL CORP p 1482
860 W Chance Rd, Lumberton TX 77657
Tel (409) 755-4077 SIC 1799 1791

CB&I LLC p 268
2103 Research Forest Dr, The Woodlands TX 77380
Tel (832) 513-1000 SIC 1791 3443 3312

CHICAGO BRIDGE & IRON CO p 297
2103 Research Forest Dr, The Woodlands TX 77380
Tel (832) 513-1000 SIC 1791

HMT INC p 698
24 Waterway Ave Ste 400, The Woodlands TX 77380
Tel (281) 681-7000
SIC 7699 3443 7389 1791

BRAHMA GROUP p 207
1132 S 500 W, Salt Lake City UT 84101
Tel (801) 521-5200 SIC 1791

SME INDUSTRIES INC p 1332
5801 W Wells Park Rd, West Jordan UT 84081
Tel (801) 280-3960 SIC 1791 3441

TOTAL MECHANICAL INC p 1463
W234n2830 Paul Rd, Pewaukee WI 53072
Tel (262) 523-2510 SIC 1711 1791 3823

SIC 1793 Glass & Glazing Work

ARCH ALUMINUM & GLASS CO OF ARIZONA INC p 104
1825 S 43rd Ave Ste A, Phoenix AZ 85009
Tel (602) 484-9777 SIC 3442 1793

WALTERS & WOLF GLASS CO p 1574
41450 Boscell Rd, Fremont CA 94538
Tel (510) 490-1115 SIC 1793

ARCHITECTURAL GLASS & ALUMINUM CO INC p 105
6400 Brisa St, Livermore CA 94550
Tel (925) 583-2460
SIC 5051 1793 1791 3442

WOODBRIDGE GLASS INC p 1622
14321 Myford Rd, Tustin CA 92780
Tel (714) 838-4444 SIC 1793 5231

PERMASTEELISA NORTH AMERICA CORP p 1136
123 Day Hill Rd, Windsor CT 06095
Tel (860) 298-2000 SIC 1793 1799

EGAN CO p 481
7625 Boone Ave N, Brooklyn Park MN 55428
Tel (763) 595-4358
SIC 1711 1731 3444 7623 1793

■ **BENSON INDUSTRIES INC** p 173
1650 Nw Naito Pkwy # 250, Portland OR 97209
Tel (503) 226-7611
SIC 5031 1793 3231 3211

CONSOLIDATED GLASS HOLDINGS INC p 359
500 Grant Ave Ste 201, East Butler PA 16029
Tel (866) 412-6977
SIC 5039 3211 6719 1793

VVP HOLDINGS LLC p 1567
965 Ridge Lake Blvd # 300, Memphis TN 38120
Tel (901) 767-7111
SIC 5039 5013 1793 3231 3444 5719

H J MARTIN & SON INC p 650
320 S Military Ave, Green Bay WI 54303
Tel (920) 494-3461
SIC 5713 1793 1522 1542 1742

SIC 1794 Excavating & Grading Work

SAIIA CONSTRUCTION CO LLC p 1268
4400 Lewisburg Rd, Birmingham AL 35207
Tel (205) 290-0400 SIC 1794

ACTION RESOURCES INC p 19
40 County Road 517, Hanceville AL 35077
Tel (256) 352-2689 SIC 4212 4213 1794

REED CONTRACTING SERVICES INC p 1217
2512 Triana Blvd Sw, Huntsville AL 35805
Tel (256) 533-0505
SIC 1771 1794 1623 1629 1611

KIEWIT WESTERN CO p 817
3888 E Broadway Rd, Phoenix AZ 85040
Tel (602) 437-7878
SIC 1622 1629 1794 1611 1623

FNF CONSTRUCTION INC p 562
115 S 48th St, Tempe AZ 85281
Tel (480) 784-2910 SIC 1611 1794 2951

INFRASTRUCTURE HOLDINGS CO LLC p 742
115 S 48th St, Tempe AZ 85281
Tel (480) 784-2910 SIC 1611 1794 2591

AMPCO CONTRACTING INC p 86
1540 S Lewis St, Anaheim CA 92805
Tel (949) 955-2255 SIC 4959 1795 1794

DESILVA GATES CONSTRUCTION LP p 432
11555 Dublin Blvd, Dublin CA 94568
Tel (925) 361-1380 SIC 1611 1794 1542

TOPCON POSITIONING SYSTEMS INC p 1461
7400 National Dr, Livermore CA 94550
Tel (925) 245-8300
SIC 3829 3625 3823 3699 8713 1794

GHILOTTI BROS INC p 610
525 Jacoby St, San Rafael CA 94901
Tel (415) 454-7011 SIC 1611 1794 1623

PIONEER SAND CO INC p 1151
5000 Northpark Dr, Colorado Springs CO 80918
Tel (719) 599-8100 SIC 5211 5031 1794

ROCKY MOUNTAIN MATERIALS AND ASPHALT INC p 1245
1910 Rand Ave, Colorado Springs CO 80905
Tel (719) 473-3100
SIC 1611 1771 1794 5032

MANAFORT BROTHERS INC p 900
414 New Britain Ave, Plainville CT 06062
Tel (860) 229-4853
SIC 1794 1771 1622 1795 4953

RAM EXCAVATING INC p 1206
3349 Hannah Way E, Dunedin FL 34698
Tel (727) 463-6428 SIC 1794

RONCO CONSULTING CORP p 1249
1395 University Blvd, Jupiter FL 33458
Tel (571) 551-2934 SIC 1794 7389 7382

DOWNRITE HOLDINGS INC p 453
14241 Sw 143rd Ct, Miami FL 33186
Tel (305) 232-2340
SIC 1611 1623 8711 1794

SWS ENVIRONMENTAL SERVICES p 1413
1619 Moylan Rd, Panama City Beach FL 32407
Tel (850) 234-8428 *SIC* 1794

PLATEAU EXCAVATION INC p 1155
375 Lee Industrial Blvd, Austell GA 30168
Tel (770) 944-0205 *SIC* 1794

STARK EXCAVATING INC p 1379
1805 W Washington St, Bloomington IL 61701
Tel (309) 828-5034 *SIC* 1611 1794

E & B PAVING INC p 465
286 W 300 N, Anderson IN 46012
Tel (765) 643-5358 *SIC* 1611 2951 1794

MAC CONSTRUCTION & EXCAVATING INC p 891
1908 Unruh Ct, New Albany IN 47150
Tel (812) 284-4250 *SIC* 1623 1622 1794

MCANINCH CORP p 926
4001 Delaware Ave, Des Moines IA 50313
Tel (515) 267-2500 *SIC* 1623 1794

CORNEJO & SONS LLC p 370
2060 E Tulsa St, Wichita KS 67216
Tel (316) 522-5100
SIC 1542 1794 1795 1611

SHERWOOD CONSTRUCTION CO INC p 1316
3219 W May St, Wichita KS 67213
Tel (316) 943-0211 *SIC* 1794 4522

CB&I ENVIRONMENTAL & INFRASTRUCTURE INC p 268
3867 Plaza Tower Dr, Baton Rouge LA 70816
Tel (225) 932-2500
SIC 8748 1794 1795 8744 8741

PLEASANTS CONSTRUCTION INC p 1156
24024 Frederick Rd, Clarksburg MD 20871
Tel (301) 428-0800 *SIC* 1794 1623 1611

MCKINNEY DRILLING CO LLC p 930
7550 Teague Rd Ste 300, Hanover MD 21076
Tel (410) 874-1235 *SIC* 1794 5082

GRAY & SON INC p 632
430 W Padonia Rd, Lutherville Timonium MD 21093
Tel (410) 771-4311 *SIC* 1611 1623 1794

BROX INDUSTRIES INC p 220
1471 Methuen St, Dracut MA 01826
Tel (978) 454-9105
SIC 1442 1499 1611 1629 1794 2951

MIDDLESEX CORP p 965
1 Spectacle Pond Rd, Littleton MA 01460
Tel (978) 742-4400 *SIC* 1611 1794 1622

GRANGER ASSOCIATES INC p 630
16980 Wood Rd, Lansing MI 48906
Tel (517) 372-2800 *SIC* 4953 1794 6552

ANGELO IAFRATE CONSTRUCTION CO p 91
26300 Sherwood Ave, Warren MI 48091
Tel (586) 756-1070 *SIC* 1623 1794 1611

AMES CONSTRUCTION INC p 84
14420 County Road 5, Burnsville MN 55306
Tel (952) 435-7106
SIC 1611 1041 1021 1794

EUTAW CONSTRUCTION CO INC p 513
109 W Commerce St, Aberdeen MS 39730
Tel (662) 369-7121 *SIC* 1611 1623 1794

KISSICK CONSTRUCTION CO INC p 822
8131 Indiana Ave, Kansas City MO 64132
Tel (816) 363-5530
SIC 1541 1623 1771 1794

BARRETT INDUSTRIES CORP p 157
3 Becker Farm Rd Ste 307, Roseland NJ 07068
Tel (973) 533-1001
SIC 1611 2951 4213 1799 1794

BARRETT PAVING MATERIALS INC p 157
3 Becker Farm Rd Ste 307, Roseland NJ 07068
Tel (973) 533-1001
SIC 1611 2951 4213 1799 1794

TRIANGLE GRADING & PAVING INC p 1478
1521 Huffman Mill Rd, Burlington NC 27215
Tel (336) 584-1745 *SIC* 1611 1794

SANFORD CONTRACTORS INC p 1279
628 Rocky Fork Church Rd, Sanford NC 27332
Tel (919) 775-7882
SIC 1611 1622 1629 6552 1794 1623

BEAVER EXCAVATING CO p 166
2000 Beaver Place Ave Sw, Canton OH 44706
Tel (330) 478-2151
SIC 1794 1611 1771 1623

GOETTLE HOLDING CO INC p 619
12071 Hamilton Ave, Cincinnati OH 45231
Tel (513) 825-8100
SIC 1799 1629 1771 1794

GEORGE J IGEL & CO INC p 606
2040 Alum Creek Dr, Columbus OH 43207
Tel (614) 445-8421 *SIC* 1794 1623 6552

INDEPENDENCE EXCAVATING INC p 736
5720 E Schaaf Rd, Independence OH 44131
Tel (216) 524-1700
SIC 1629 1794 1611 1771 1795

KELCHNER INC p 808
50 Advanced Dr, Springboro OH 45066
Tel (937) 704-9890 *SIC* 1794 1389

HAMMER CONSTRUCTION INC p 656
4320 Adams Rd, Norman OK 73069
Tel (405) 310-3160 *SIC* 1389 1794

PANHANDLE OILFIELD SERVICE COMPANIES INC p 1111
14000 Quail Springs Pkwy # 300, Oklahoma City OK 73134
Tel (405) 608-5330
SIC 1389 7389 3498 4212 5082 1794

GLEN BLOOMING CONTRACTORS INC p 614
901 Minsi Trl, Blooming Glen PA 18911
Tel (215) 257-9400 *SIC* 1611 1794

DAVID H MARTIN EXCAVATING INC p 415
4961 Cumberland Hwy, Chambersburg PA 17202
Tel (717) 264-1312 *SIC* 1623 1794 1711

HAINES & KIBBLEHOUSE INC p 653
2052 Lucon Rd, Skippack PA 19474
Tel (610) 584-8500
SIC 1794 1611 1422 2951

GLENN O HAWBAKER INC p 615
1952 Waddle Rd Ste 203, State College PA 16803
Tel (814) 237-1444
SIC 2951 3281 1622 1794 1611 1422

ALLAN MYERS INC p 51
1805 Berks Rd, Worcester PA 19490
Tel (610) 222-8800
SIC 1629 1794 1611 1622 3281 5032

ALLAN MYERS LP p 51
1805 Berks Rd, Worcester PA 19490
Tel (610) 584-3430
SIC 1629 1794 1611 1622

LANDMARK CONSTRUCTION CO INC p 842
3255 Industry Dr, North Charleston SC 29418
Tel (843) 552-6186
SIC 1542 1541 1623 1771 1794

HEAVY CONSTRUCTORS INC p 679
4101 Deadwood Ave, Rapid City SD 57702
Tel (605) 342-3144
SIC 1542 1794 1623 1611

SUMMERS-TAYLOR INC p 1398
300 W Elk Ave, Elizabethton TN 37643
Tel (423) 543-3181 *SIC* 1611 1794 3273

LOJAC ENTERPRISES INC p 875
1401 Toshiba Dr, Lebanon TN 37087
Tel (615) 449-1401 *SIC* 1611 1794 5032

JONES BROS INC p 792
5760 Old Lebanon Dirt Rd, Mount Juliet TN 37122
Tel (615) 754-4710
SIC 1622 1771 1794 1629 1611

JONES INVESTMENT HOLDING INC p 792
5760 Old Lebanon Dirt Rd, Mount Juliet TN 37122
Tel (615) 754-4710
SIC 1622 1771 1794 1611

VENABLES CONSTRUCTION INC p 1547
7410 Continental Pkwy, Amarillo TX 79119
Tel (806) 381-2121
SIC 1623 1794 1389 4922 4612 1799

FGI GROUP INC p 539
3901 S Lamar Blvd Ste 100, Austin TX 78704
Tel (512) 448-9898
SIC 1542 1541 1794 1611 7353 1711

ANGEL BROTHERS ENTERPRISES LTD p 91
5210 West Rd, Baytown TX 77521
Tel (281) 421-5721 *SIC* 1794 1611

ROC HOLDINGS LLC p 1242
191 Energy Way, Bridgeport TX 76426
Tel (940) 683-0159 *SIC* 1794 1731 6719

ROC SERVICE CO LLC p 1242
191 Energy Way, Bridgeport TX 76426
Tel (940) 683-0109 *SIC* 1794 1731 1389

R CONSTRUCTION CO p 1201
1313 Hwy 79 S, Buffalo TX 75831
Tel (903) 322-4639 *SIC* 1389 1794

SITE CONCRETE INC p 1327
1544 Valwood Pkwy Ste 100, Carrollton TX 75006
Tel (972) 313-0733 *SIC* 1611 1771 1794

▲ BASIC ENERGY SERVICES INC p 158
801 Cherry St Unit 2, Fort Worth TX 76102
Tel (817) 334-4100 *SIC* 1389 1794

MARIO SINACOLA & SONS EXCAVATING INC p 907
10950 Research Rd, Frisco TX 75033
Tel (214) 387-3900 *SIC* 1794

W T BYLER CO INC p 1569
15203 Lillja Rd, Houston TX 77060
Tel (281) 445-2070 *SIC* 1794 1629

LONGVIEW BRIDGE AND ROAD LTD p 877
792 Skinner Ln, Longview TX 75605
Tel (903) 663-0264 *SIC* 1611 1622 1794

CHASCO CONSTRUCTORS LTD LLP p 291
2801 E Old Settlers Blvd, Round Rock TX 78665
Tel (512) 244-0600
SIC 1542 1771 1794 1623

DNT CONSTRUCTION LLC p 446
2300 Picadilly Dr, Round Rock TX 78664
Tel (512) 837-6700 *SIC* 1623 1794 1611

ALBERT REECE INC p 46
3001 Foster St, San Angelo TX 76903
Tel (325) 653-1241
SIC 1611 1794 1623 1622

OLMOS CONSTRUCTION INC p 1082
440 Pinn Rd, San Antonio TX 78227
Tel (210) 675-4990 *SIC* 1611 1794 1795

W W CLYDE & CO p 1569
1375 N Main St, Springville UT 84663
Tel (801) 802-6800 *SIC* 1611 1794 1629

HAZEL INC WILLIAM A p 671
4305 Hazel Park Ct, Chantilly VA 20151
Tel (703) 378-8300 *SIC* 1623 1794

ALLAN MYERS VA INC p 52
301 Cncourse Blvd Ste 300, Glen Allen VA 23059
Tel (804) 290-8500
SIC 1623 1611 1542 1794

MICHELS CORP p 960
817 W Main St, Brownsville WI 53006
Tel (920) 583-3132
SIC 1623 1771 1381 1629 3498 1794

RYAN INC CENTRAL p 1260
2700 E Racine St, Janesville WI 53545
Tel (608) 754-2291 *SIC* 1794

SIC 1795 Wrecking & Demolition Work

AMPCO CONTRACTING INC p 86
1540 S Lewis St, Anaheim CA 92805
Tel (949) 955-2255 *SIC* 4959 1795 1794

PENHALL CO p 1128
2121 W Crescent Ave Ste A, Anaheim CA 92801
Tel (714) 772-6450 *SIC* 1741 1795

PENHALL INTERNATIONAL CORP p 1129
320 N Crescent Way, Anaheim CA 92801
Tel (714) 772-6450 *SIC* 1795 1771

NORTHSTAR DEMOLITION AND REMEDIATION LP p 1058
404 N Berry St, Brea CA 92821
Tel (714) 672-3500 *SIC* 1795 1799 8744

▲ SUMMIT MATERIALS INC p 1399
1550 Wynkoop St Fl 3, Denver CO 80202
Tel (303) 893-0012 *SIC* 1422 1622 1795

MANAFORT BROTHERS INC p 900
414 New Britain Ave, Plainville CT 06062
Tel (860) 229-4853
SIC 1794 1771 1622 1795 4953

KIMMINS CORP p 819
1501 E 2nd Ave, Tampa FL 33605
Tel (813) 248-3878 *SIC* 1799 1795 1522

■ WASHINGTON CLOSURE CO LLC p 1577
720 E Park Blvd Bsmt, Boise ID 83712
Tel (208) 386-5000
SIC 4959 1799 1795 4226

BRANDENBURG INDUSTRIAL SERVICE CO p 208
2625 S Loomis St, Chicago IL 60608
Tel (312) 326-5800 *SIC* 4959 1795 5093

METAL MANAGEMENT INC p 952
2500 S Paulina St, Chicago IL 60608
Tel (312) 645-0700 *SIC* 5093 1795

NATIONAL SALVAGE & SERVICE CORP p 1016
6755 S Old State Road 37, Bloomington IN 47401
Tel (812) 339-8437
SIC 5088 1629 1795 5099 5093

CORNEJO & SONS LLC p 370
2060 E Tulsa St, Wichita KS 67216
Tel (316) 522-5100
SIC 1542 1794 1795 1611

CB&I ENVIRONMENTAL & INFRASTRUCTURE INC p 268
3867 Plaza Tower Dr, Baton Rouge LA 70816
Tel (225) 932-2500
SIC 8748 1794 1795 8744 8741

VEIT & CO INC p 1547
14000 Veit Pl, Rogers MN 55374
Tel (763) 428-2242 *SIC* 1611 1795 4953

ENVIROCON INC p 503
101 International Dr, Missoula MT 59808
Tel (406) 523-1150 *SIC* 1795

LVI PARENT CORP p 887
370 7th Ave Ste 1803, New York NY 10001
Tel (212) 951-3660 *SIC* 1795

NORTHSTAR GROUP HOLDINGS LLC p 1059
370 7th Ave Ste 1803, New York NY 10001
Tel (212) 951-3660 *SIC* 1795

NORTHSTAR GROUP SERVICES INC p 1059
370 7th Ave Ste 1803, New York NY 10001
Tel (212) 951-3660 *SIC* 1795 1799

SEVENSON ENVIRONMENTAL SERVICES INC p 1309
2749 Lockport Rd, Niagara Falls NY 14305
Tel (716) 284-0431 *SIC* 4959 1795

D H GRIFFIN WRECKING CO INC p 407
4716 Hilltop Rd, Greensboro NC 27407
Tel (336) 855-7030 *SIC* 1795 5093

INDEPENDENCE EXCAVATING INC p 736
5720 E Schaaf Rd, Independence OH 44131
Tel (216) 524-1700
SIC 1629 1794 1611 1771 1795

FLUOR-BWXT PORTSMOUTH LLC p 561
1862 Shyville Rd Ste 216, Piketon OH 45661
Tel (866) 706-6992 *SIC* 1795

OLMOS CONSTRUCTION INC p 1082
440 Pinn Rd, San Antonio TX 78227
Tel (210) 675-4990 *SIC* 1611 1794 1795

SIC 1796 Installation Or Erection Of Bldg Eqpt & Machinery, NEC

■ B E & K INC p 141
2000 International Pk Dr, Birmingham AL 35243
Tel (205) 972-6000
SIC 1541 8711 1796 1711

■ KBR CONSTRUCTION CO LLC p 806
3000 Riverchase Galleria, Hoover AL 35244
Tel (205) 972-6538
SIC 1541 1796 1711 1629 1799 1521

MCABEE CONSTRUCTION INC p 925
5724 21st St, Tuscaloosa AL 35401
Tel (205) 349-2212
SIC 1629 1791 1796 3443 3498

TANADGUSIX CORP p 1424
615 E 82nd Ave Ste 200, Anchorage AK 99518
Tel (907) 278-2312 *SIC* 1796 7011 7359

MITSUBISHI ELECTRIC US INC p 977
5900 Katella Ave Ste A, Cypress CA 90630
Tel (714) 220-2500
SIC 5065 5045 1796 3534

IRWIN INDUSTRIES INC p 765
1580 W Carson St, Long Beach CA 90810
Tel (310) 233-3000
SIC 1629 1731 1796 7353 1542

BIGGE CRANE AND RIGGING CO p 182
10700 Bigge St, San Leandro CA 94577
Tel (510) 638-8100 *SIC* 1796

DESCO ACQUISITION LLC p 431
230 Commerce Rd, Berthoud CO 80513
Tel (970) 532-0600 *SIC* 1796 3533 1389

■ OTIS ELEVATOR CO p 1097
10 Farm Springs Rd, Farmington CT 06032
Tel (860) 676-6000 *SIC* 3534 1796 7699

MITSUBISHI HITACHI POWER SYSTEMS AMERICAS INC p 977
400 Colonial Center Pkwy # 400, Lake Mary FL 32746
Tel (407) 688-6100 *SIC* 5084 1796

THYSSENKRUPP ELEVATOR AMERICAS CORP p 1451
11605 Haynes Bridge Rd, Alpharetta GA 30009
Tel (678) 319-3240 *SIC* 7699 3534 1796

THYSSENKRUPP ELEVATOR CORP p 1451
11605 Haynes Bridge Rd # 650, Alpharetta GA 30009
Tel (678) 319-3240 *SIC* 3534 1796 7699

CLEVELAND ELECTRIC CO INC p 325
1281 Fulton Indus Blvd Nw, Atlanta GA 30336
Tel (404) 696-4550 *SIC* 1731 1711 1796

MANSFIELD ENERGY CORP p 903
1025 Airport Pkwy, Gainesville GA 30501
Tel (678) 450-2000 *SIC* 5172 4212 1796

KONE INC p 827
1 Kone Ct, Moline IL 61265
Tel (309) 764-6771 *SIC* 7699 3534 1796

■ SHAMBAUGH & SON LP p 1311
7614 Opportunity Dr, Fort Wayne IN 46825
Tel (260) 487-7777
SIC 1711 1799 1731 1796 1629

TIPPMANN CONSTRUCTION LLC p 1455
9009 Coldwater Rd Ste 300, Fort Wayne IN 46825
Tel (260) 490-3000 *SIC* 1541 1796

CENTURION INDUSTRIES INC p 281
1107 N Taylor Rd, Garrett IN 46738
Tel (260) 357-6665 *SIC* 3444 1796

SARGENT GROUP INC p 1282
2905 Se 5th St, Ames IA 50010
Tel (515) 232-0442 *SIC* 1541 1796

RYKO SOLUTIONS INC p 1261
1500 Se 37th St, Grimes IA 50111
Tel (515) 986-3700 *SIC* 3589 1796 7699

COMMERCIAL CONTRACTING CORP p 345
4260 N Atlantic Blvd, Auburn Hills MI 48326
Tel (248) 209-0500 *SIC* 1541 1796

COMMERCIAL CONTRACTING GROUP INC p 345
4260 N Atlantic Blvd, Auburn Hills MI 48326
Tel (248) 209-0500 *SIC* 1796

WALBRIDGE INDUSTRIAL PROCESS LLC p 1572
777 Woodward Ave Ste 300, Detroit MI 48226
Tel (313) 963-8000 *SIC* 1796

DEMATIC CORP p 428
507 Plymouth Ave Ne, Grand Rapids MI 49505
Tel (678) 695-4500 *SIC* 3535 1796 8711

▲ UNIVERSAL FOREST PRODUCTS INC p 1516
2801 E Beltline Ave Ne, Grand Rapids MI 49525
Tel (616) 364-6161 *SIC* 2421 1796

UNITED SUBCONTRACTORS INC p 1514
445 Minnesota St Ste 2500, Saint Paul MN 55101
Tel (651) 225-6300
SIC 1742 1796 1542 1522

BILFINGER INDUSTRIAL SERVICES INC p 182
15933 Clayton Rd Ste 305, Ballwin MO 63011
Tel (636) 391-4500
SIC 1541 1731 1796 8711 8744

NOOTER CORP p 1047
1500 S 2nd St, Saint Louis MO 63104
Tel (314) 421-7200
SIC 3443 3479 1796 8711 7699 1542

SCHINDLER ELEVATOR CORP p 1287
20 Whippany Rd, Morristown NJ 07960
Tel (973) 397-6500 *SIC* 3534 7699 1796

SCHINDLER ENTERPRISES INC p 1287
20 Whippany Rd, Morristown NJ 07960
Tel (973) 397-6500 *SIC* 3534 7699 1796

FARREN INTERNATIONAL LLC p 530
1578 Sussex Tpke, Randolph NJ 07869
Tel (800) 253-3203 *SIC* 4213 1796 6719

NOUVEAU ELEVATOR INDUSTRIES INC p 1062
4755 37th St, Long Island City NY 11101
Tel (718) 349-4700 *SIC* 7699 1796

STEAM GENERATING TEAM LLC p 1384
7207 Ibm Dr 3a, Charlotte NC 28262
Tel (704) 805-2810 *SIC* 1796

ASSA ABLOY ENTRANCE SYSTEMS US INC p 119
1900 Airport Rd, Monroe NC 28110
Tel (704) 290-5520 *SIC* 3699 1796 3442

■ SOUTHERN INDUSTRIAL CONSTRUCTORS INC p 1349
6101 Triangle Dr, Raleigh NC 27617
Tel (919) 782-4600
SIC 1629 1799 1731 1796 1791 7353

ATLAS INDUSTRIAL CONTRACTORS LLC p 128
5275 Sinclair Rd, Columbus OH 43229
Tel (614) 841-4500 *SIC* 1731 3498 1796

HY-TEK MATERIAL HANDLING INC p 722
2222 Rickenbacker Pkwy W, Columbus OH 43217
Tel (614) 497-2500
SIC 5084 5013 7538 7513 1796

■ CLOPAY CORP p 327
8585 Duke Blvd, Mason OH 45040
Tel (800) 282-2260
SIC 3081 3442 2431 1796

NK PARTS INDUSTRIES INC p 1045
777 S Kuther Rd, Sidney OH 45365
Tel (937) 498-4651 *SIC* 5013 1796 4731

MORGAN INDUSTRIAL INC p 988
23810 Nw Huffman St, Hillsboro OR 97124
Tel (503) 647-7474 *SIC* 1796 4213

BARNHART CRANE AND RIGGING CO p 156
2163 Airways Blvd, Memphis TN 38114
Tel (901) 775-3000 *SIC* 7353 4213 1796

FLETCHLINE INC p 555
5480 Lakeview Rd, Springfield TN 37172
Tel (615) 382-0764 *SIC* 5084 1796

DAVACO INC p 414
6688 N Cntrl Expy Ste 100, Dallas TX 75206
Tel (214) 373-4700
SIC 1751 1799 1542 1796

▲ GLOBAL POWER EQUIPMENT GROUP INC p 617
400 Las Colinas Blvd E, Irving TX 75039
Tel (214) 574-2000 *SIC* 3568 1796 7699

■ VICEROY INC p 1555
3225 Pasadena Blvd, Pasadena TX 77503
Tel (713) 475-4518
SIC 1629 3443 1796 8742 8748 7363

NSA INDUSTRIES LLC p 1064
210 Pierce Rd, Saint Johnsbury VT 05819
Tel (802) 748-5007 *SIC* 3444 1799 1796

ATLANTIC CONSTRUCTORS INC p 126
1401 Battery Brooke Pkwy, North Chesterfield VA 23237
Tel (804) 222-3400 *SIC* 1796 1711 3444

MIRON CONSTRUCTION CO INC p 974
1471 Mcmahon Rd, Neenah WI 54956
Tel (920) 969-7000 SIC 1542 1541 1796

C R MEYER AND SONS CO p 233
895 W 20th Ave, Oshkosh WI 54902
Tel (920) 235-3350 SIC 1542 1796 1541

SIC 1799 Special Trade Contractors, NEC

SHOOK & FLETCHER INSULATION CO INC p 1317
4625 Valleydale Rd, Birmingham AL 35242
Tel (205) 991-7606 SIC 5033 1799 5085

■ KBR CONSTRUCTION CO LLC p 806
3000 Riverchase Galleria, Hoover AL 35244
Tel (205) 972-6538
SIC 1541 1796 1711 1629 1799 1521

ARIZONA PARKING LOT SERVICE p 109
1415 E Bethany Home Rd, Phoenix AZ 85014
Tel (602) 277-8007 SIC 1799 1611

SHASTA INDUSTRIES INC p 1312
6031 N 16th St, Phoenix AZ 85016
Tel (602) 532-3750
SIC 1799 1771 5169 7389 3088 5091

WELSPUN PIPES INC p 1591
9301 Frazier Pike, Little Rock AR 72206
Tel (501) 301-8800 SIC 1799 3494

TECHNO COATINGS INC p 1431
1391 S Allec St, Anaheim CA 92805
Tel (714) 635-1130
SIC 1542 1629 1721 1799

NORTHSTAR DEMOLITION AND REMEDIATION LP p 1058
404 N Berry St, Brea CA 92821
Tel (714) 672-3500 SIC 1795 1799 8744

HOT LINE CONSTRUCTION INC p 710
9020 Brentwood Blvd Ste H, Brentwood CA 94513
Tel (925) 634-9333 SIC 1731 1799

INTERIOR SPECIALISTS INC p 753
1630 Faraday Ave, Carlsbad CA 92008
Tel (760) 929-6700 SIC 1752 1799

HALABI INC p 653
2100 Huntington Dr, Fairfield CA 94533
Tel (707) 402-1600 SIC 3281 1799

FENCEWORKS INC p 537
870 Main St, Riverside CA 92501
Tel (951) 788-5620 SIC 1799

GENERAL COATINGS CORP p 599
6711 Nancy Ridge Dr, San Diego CA 92121
Tel (858) 587-1277 SIC 1721 1799

MALCOLM DRILLING CO INC p 899
92 Natoma St Ste 400, San Francisco CA 94105
Tel (415) 901-4400 SIC 1799

PAVESCAPES p 1122
1340 E Pomona St, Santa Ana CA 92705
Tel (714) 581-5931 SIC 1799

■ TUTOR-SALIBA CORP p 1493
15901 Olden St, Sylmar CA 91342
Tel (818) 362-8391
SIC 1542 1629 7353 1799 6552

PETROCHEM INSULATION INC p 1139
110 Corporate Pl, Vallejo CA 94590
Tel (707) 644-7455 SIC 1742 1799

TIMEC COMPANIES INC p 1454
155 Corporate Pl, Vallejo CA 94590
Tel (707) 642-2222 SIC 1629 1799

■ DISH NETWORK LLC p 442
9601 S Meridian Blvd, Englewood CO 80112
Tel (303) 723-1000 SIC 1799

■ DISH NETWORK SERVICE LLC p 442
9601 S Meridian Blvd, Englewood CO 80112
Tel (303) 723-1000 SIC 1799 4841

LAZ KARP ASSOCIATES INC p 848
15 Lewis St Fl 5, Hartford CT 06103
Tel (860) 522-7641 SIC 7521 1799

LAZ KARP ASSOCIATES LLC p 848
15 Lewis St Fl 5, Hartford CT 06103
Tel (860) 522-7641 SIC 1799

PERMASTEELISA NORTH AMERICA CORP p 1136
123 Day Hill Rd, Windsor CT 06095
Tel (860) 298-2000 SIC 1793 1799

ISI DESIGN AND INSTALLATION SOLUTIONS INC p 766
6321 Emperor Dr Ste 201, Orlando FL 32809
Tel (407) 872-1865
SIC 7389 1752 1799 1751

KIMMINS CORP p 819
1501 E 2nd Ave, Tampa FL 33605
Tel (813) 248-3878 SIC 1799 1795 1522

CREATIVE SURFACES INC p 390
1400 W Marietta St Nw, Atlanta GA 30318
Tel (205) 988-3246 SIC 2541 1799

■ HD BUILDER SOLUTIONS GROUP LLC p 672
2455 Paces Ferry Rd Se C9, Atlanta GA 30339
Tel (770) 443-8211 SIC 5023 1752 1799

BRAND ENERGY & INFRASTRUCTURE HOLDINGS INC p 207
1325 Cobb Intl Dr Nw A1, Kennesaw GA 30152
Tel (678) 285-1400 SIC 1799

BRAND ENERGY & INFRASTRUCTURE SERVICES INC p 207
1325 Cobb Intl Dr Nw A1, Kennesaw GA 30152
Tel (678) 285-1400 SIC 1799

BRAND ENERGY SOLUTIONS LLC p 207
1325 Cobb International D, Kennesaw GA 30152
Tel (678) 285-1400
SIC 1751 1742 1799 1721

BRAND SERVICES LLC p 208
1325 Cobb Intl Dr Nw A1, Kennesaw GA 30152
Tel (678) 285-1400 SIC 1799

TRILOK INDUSTRIES INC p 1480
670 Village Trce Ne, Marietta GA 30067
Tel (678) 325-2960 SIC 1799 1742

■ AZZ WSI LLC p 141
2225 Skyland Ct, Norcross GA 30071
Tel (678) 728-9200 SIC 1799

WINTER GROUP OF COMPANIES INC p 1617
191 Peachtree St Ne, Peachtree Corners GA 30071
Tel (404) 588-3300
SIC 1541 1542 1799 6512

■ WILLIAMS INDUSTRIAL SERVICES GROUP LLC p 1611
100 Crescent Center Pkwy # 1240, Tucker GA 30084
Tel (866) 851-4077 SIC 1799

■ WASHINGTON CLOSURE CO LLC p 1577
720 E Park Blvd Bsmt, Boise ID 83712
Tel (208) 386-5000
SIC 4959 1799 1795 4226

CURRAN GROUP INC p 402
286 Memorial Ct, Crystal Lake IL 60014
Tel (815) 455-5100 SIC 1799 3253 1611

BROCK INDUSTRIAL SERVICES LLC p 216
2210 Oak Leaf St, Joliet IL 60436
Tel (815) 730-3350 SIC 1721 1799

I3 GROUP INC p 725
550 Bond St, Lincolnshire IL 60069
Tel (847) 325-1000 SIC 5021 1799

ONYX ENVIRONMENTAL SERVICES LLC p 1088
700 E Bttrfeld Rd Ste 201, Lombard IL 60148
Tel (630) 218-1500
SIC 8711 4953 2869 1799 1629

ANNING-JOHNSON CO p 92
1959 Anson Dr, Melrose Park IL 60160
Tel (708) 681-1300
SIC 1742 1752 1799 1761

ANSON INDUSTRIES INC p 93
1959 Anson Dr, Melrose Park IL 60160
Tel (708) 681-1300
SIC 1742 1752 1761 1799

CONGLOBAL INDUSTRIES LLC p 356
8200 185th St Ste A, Tinley Park IL 60487
Tel (925) 543-0977
SIC 3743 4213 4231 1799 7699

■ SHAMBAUGH & SON LP p 1311
7614 Opportunity Dr, Fort Wayne IN 46825
Tel (260) 487-7777
SIC 1711 1799 1731 1796 1629

WAGNER-MEINERT LLC p 1571
7617 Freedom Way, Fort Wayne IN 46818
Tel (260) 489-7555 SIC 5078 1711 1799

K2 INDUSTRIAL SERVICES INC p 799
4527 Columbia Ave 2, Hammond IN 46327
Tel (708) 928-4765 SIC 2842 1799

COMLUX AMERICA LLC p 344
2910 S High School Rd, Indianapolis IN 46241
Tel (317) 472-7370 SIC 1799

HERITAGE ENVIRONMENTAL SERVICES INC p 686
7901 W Morris St, Indianapolis IN 46231
Tel (317) 243-0811
SIC 5093 4213 8731 7389 1799 8711

HERITAGE ENVIRONMENTAL SERVICES LLC p 686
7901 W Morris St, Indianapolis IN 46231
Tel (317) 243-0811
SIC 5093 4213 8731 7389 1799 8711

KW SERVICES LLC p 832
3801 Voorde Dr Ste B, South Bend IN 46628
Tel (574) 232-2051 SIC 6719 1799 5063

EATON HYDRAULICS INC p 473
803 32nd Ave W, Spencer IA 51301
Tel (712) 264-3269 SIC 1799

PERFORMANCE CONTRACTING GROUP INC p 1135
11145 Thompson Ave, Lenexa KS 66219
Tel (913) 888-8600 SIC 1799 1742

MANKO WINDOW SYSTEMS INC p 902
800 Hayes Dr, Manhattan KS 66502
Tel (785) 776-9643 SIC 3442 1799 5039

EMPIRE SCAFFOLD LLC p 493
9680 S Choctaw Dr, Baton Rouge LA 70815
Tel (225) 924-3170 SIC 1799

IBERVILLE INSULATIONS LLC p 726
11621 Sun Belt Ct, Baton Rouge LA 70809
Tel (225) 752-2194 SIC 1799

UNITED SCAFFOLDING INC p 1511
12021 Lakeland Park Blvd # 120, Baton Rouge LA 70809
Tel (225) 774-1480 SIC 1799

INSULATIONS INC p 747
1101 Edwards Ave, Harahan LA 70123
Tel (504) 733-5033 SIC 1799 1761 1741

■ INTERNATIONAL-MATEX TANK TERMINALS p 757
321 Saint Charles Ave, New Orleans LA 70130
Tel (504) 586-8300 SIC 4226 1799

PETRIN CORP p 1139
1405 Commercial Dr, Port Allen LA 70767
Tel (225) 343-0471 SIC 1799 2952

MANGANARO MIDATLANTIC LLC p 901
6405d Ammendale Rd, Beltsville MD 20705
Tel (301) 937-0580 SIC 1741 1742 1799

LONG FENCE CO INC p 876
8545 Edgeworth Dr, Capitol Heights MD 20743
Tel (301) 350-2400 SIC 1799

HAYWARD BAKER INC p 670
7550 Teague Rd Ste 300, Hanover MD 21076
Tel (410) 551-8200 SIC 1799

KELLER FOUNDATIONS LLC p 808
7550 Teague Rd Ste 300, Hanover MD 21076
Tel (410) 551-8200 SIC 1799 8711

NEXT DAY BLINDS CORP p 1040
8251 Preston Ct Ste B, Jessup MD 20794
Tel (240) 568-8800
SIC 5023 2591 5719 1799

FACCHINA CONSTRUCTION CO INC p 523
102 Centennial St Ste 201, La Plata MD 20646
Tel (240) 776-7000
SIC 1542 1799 1623 1611 1622 1629

CENTRAL WHOLESALERS INC p 281
13401 Konterra Dr, Laurel MD 20707
Tel (800) 935-2947
SIC 5074 5063 5087 5072 5211 1799

FIDELITY ENGINEERING CORP p 540
25 Loveton Cir, Sparks MD 21152
Tel (410) 771-9400
SIC 1711 5063 1799 8711

KCI HOLDINGS INC p 806
936 Ridgebrook Rd, Sparks Glencoe MD 21152
Tel (410) 316-7800 SIC 8711 1799

ROBERT N KARPP CO INC p 1241
480 E 1st St, Boston MA 02127
Tel (617) 269-5880 SIC 5031 1799

EXCEL MODULAR SCAFFOLD AND LEASING CORP p 516
720 Washington St Unit 5, Hanover MA 02339
Tel (508) 830-1111 SIC 1799

GZA GEOENVIRONMENTAL TECHNOLOGIES INC p 649
249 Vanderbilt Ave Unit 2, Norwood MA 02062
Tel (781) 278-3700
SIC 8711 8999 1799 8744

VOLTA OIL CO INC p 1565
1 Roberts Rd Ste 2, Plymouth MA 02360
Tel (508) 747-3778 SIC 5172 1799

MANGANARO INDUSTRIES INC p 901
52 Cummings Park, Woburn MA 01801
Tel (781) 937-8880
SIC 1742 1741 1799 1743

BELFOR USA GROUP INC p 169
185 Oakland Ave Ste 150, Birmingham MI 48009
Tel (248) 594-1144 SIC 1799

RAM CONSTRUCTION SERVICES OF MICHIGAN INC p 1206
13800 Eckles Rd, Livonia MI 48150
Tel (734) 464-3800 SIC 1799 1541 1542

AVI SYSTEMS INC p 137
9675 W 76th St Ste 200, Eden Prairie MN 55344
Tel (952) 949-3700
SIC 5065 7622 8748 1799

CS MCCROSSAN INC p 397
7865 Jefferson Hwy, Maple Grove MN 55369
Tel (763) 425-4167 SIC 1611 1622 1799

API GROUP INC p 96
1100 Old Highway 8 Nw, Saint Paul MN 55112
Tel (651) 636-4320
SIC 1711 1742 7699 1799

SOUTHEASTERN VENTURES INC p 1347
4803 29th Ave Ste B, Meridian MS 39305
Tel (601) 693-0900 SIC 1799

A ZAHNER CO p 7
1400 E 9th St, Kansas City MO 64106
Tel (816) 474-8882 SIC 1799 1761

AMERICAN RESIDENTIAL SERVICES OF INDIANA INC p 78
10403 Baur Blvd Ste E, Saint Louis MO 63132
Tel (314) 812-6000
SIC 1711 1731 1799 5722

CONCRETE STRATEGIES LLC p 355
2199 Innerbelt Bus Ctr Dr, Saint Louis MO 63114
Tel (314) 595-6300 SIC 1791 1799

WESTERN CONSTRUCTION GROUP INC p 1597
1637 N Warson Rd, Saint Louis MO 63132
Tel (314) 427-1637
SIC 1799 1761 1741 1771

WESTERN WATERPROOFING CO INC p 1600
1637 N Warson Rd, Saint Louis MO 63132
Tel (314) 427-5461
SIC 1799 1761 1741 1771

THOLL FENCE INC p 1448
800 Glendale Ave, Sparks NV 89431
Tel (775) 358-8680 SIC 1799

NATIONAL FIELD REPRESENTATIVES INC p 1012
136 Maple Ave, Claremont NH 03743
Tel (603) 543-5210 SIC 7389 1799

ALLAN INDUSTRIES INC p 51
270 Us Highway 46 Ste E, Rockaway NJ 07866
Tel (973) 586-9400 SIC 1521 7349 1799

BARRETT INDUSTRIES CORP p 157
3 Becker Farm Rd Ste 307, Roseland NJ 07068
Tel (973) 533-1001
SIC 1611 2951 4213 1799 1794

BARRETT PAVING MATERIALS INC p 157
3 Becker Farm Rd Ste 307, Roseland NJ 07068
Tel (973) 533-1001
SIC 1611 2951 4213 1799 1794

HANES SUPPLY INC p 657
55 James E Casey Dr, Buffalo NY 14206
Tel (716) 826-2636
SIC 5085 5082 3496 1799

FORT MILLER SERVICE CORP p 569
688 Wilbur Ave, Greenwich NY 12834
Tel (518) 695-5000
SIC 3272 3271 5211 1799

▲ GRIFFON CORP p 640
712 5th Ave Fl 18, New York NY 10019
Tel (212) 957-5000
SIC 3442 2431 1751 1799 3083 3663

LVI HOLDING CORP p 887
80 Broad St Fl 3, New York NY 10004
Tel (212) 951-3660 SIC 1799

NORTHSTAR GROUP SERVICES INC p 1059
370 7th Ave Ste 1803, New York NY 10001
Tel (212) 951-3660 SIC 1795 1799

SAFWAY HOLDINGS LLC p 1267
280 Park Ave Fl 38, New York NY 10017
Tel (212) 351-7900 SIC 7359 5082 1799

TRIANGLE SERVICES INC p 1478
10 5th St Ste 200, Valley Stream NY 11581
Tel (516) 561-1700
SIC 7349 4581 1799 7382

STEBBINS ENGINEERING AND MANUFACTURING CO p 1384
363 Eastern Blvd, Watertown NY 13601
Tel (315) 782-3000 SIC 1799 3443

PRECISION WALLS INC p 1169
1230 Ne Maynard Rd, Cary NC 27513
Tel (919) 832-0380 SIC 1743 1742 1799

SOUTHERN PUMP & TANK CO LLC p 1350
4800 N Graham St, Charlotte NC 28269
Tel (704) 596-4373 SIC 5084 1799

JAMES R VANNOY & SONS CONSTRUCTION CO INC p 777
1608 Us Highway 221 N, Jefferson NC 28640
Tel (336) 846-7191 SIC 1542 1541 1799

BAKER ROOFING CO p 146
517 Mercury St, Raleigh NC 27603
Tel (919) 828-2975 SIC 1761 1799

JF ACQUISITION LLC p 785
1330 Saint Marys St # 210, Raleigh NC 27605
Tel (757) 857-5700 SIC 5084 1799 7299

■ SOUTHERN INDUSTRIAL CONSTRUCTORS INC p 1349
6101 Triangle Dr, Raleigh NC 27617
Tel (919) 782-4600
SIC 1629 1799 1731 1796 1791 7353

■ WANZEK CONSTRUCTION INC p 1575
2028 2nd Ave Nw, West Fargo ND 58078
Tel (701) 282-6171
SIC 1542 1623 1622 1799 1541 1629

GOETTLE HOLDING CO INC p 619
12071 Hamilton Ave, Cincinnati OH 45231
Tel (513) 825-8100
SIC 1799 1629 1771 1794

BASF CONSTRUCTION CHEMICALS LLC p 158
23700 Chagrin Blvd, Cleveland OH 44122
Tel (216) 831-5500 SIC 2899 2851 1799

MERIDIAN DRILLING CO LLC p 948
11500 S Meridian Ave, Oklahoma City OK 73173
Tel (405) 691-1202 SIC 1381 1799 5084

AMERISTAR PERIMETER SECURITY USA INC p 83
1555 N Mingo Rd, Tulsa OK 74116
Tel (918) 835-0898 SIC 3089 3446 1799

■ MATRIX SERVICE INC p 920
5100 E Skelly Dr Ste 700, Tulsa OK 74135
Tel (918) 838-8822
SIC 1623 1629 1799 7699

MARCON & BOYER INC p 905
645 Hamilton St Ste 300, Allentown PA 18101
Tel (610) 866-5959
SIC 3448 1742 1743 1799

NICHOLSON CONSTRUCTION CO p 1042
2400 Ansys Dr Ste 303, Canonsburg PA 15317
Tel (412) 221-4500 SIC 1629 1771 1799

ANTHONY & SYLVAN POOLS CORP p 94
3739 N Eastern Rd, Doylestown PA 18901
Tel (215) 489-5600 SIC 1799 5999

IREX CORP p 764
120 N Lime St, Lancaster PA 17602
Tel (717) 397-3633 SIC 1799

NORTH LIME HOLDINGS CORP p 1053
120 N Lime St, Lancaster PA 17602
Tel (717) 397-3633 SIC 1799

NOVINGER GROUP INC p 1063
1441 Stoneridge Dr, Middletown PA 17057
Tel (717) 930-0300
SIC 1742 1799 5032 5033 5039

RADIO SYSTEMS CORP p 1204
10427 Petsafe Way, Knoxville TN 37932
Tel (865) 777-5404 SIC 0752 1799 6794

VENABLES CONSTRUCTION INC p 1547
7410 Continental Pkwy, Amarillo TX 79119
Tel (806) 381-2121
SIC 1623 1794 1389 4922 4612 1799

J & J MAINTENANCE INC p 770
7710 Rialto Blvd Unit 200, Austin TX 78735
Tel (512) 444-7271 SIC 1799

B & E RESOURCES LTD CO p 141
39772 Us Highway 96 S, Buna TX 77612
Tel (409) 994-2653 SIC 1799

POWERHOUSE RETAIL SERVICES LLC p 1166
812 S Crowley Rd Ste A, Crowley TX 76036
Tel (817) 297-8575 SIC 1542 1799

DAVACO INC p 414
6688 N Cntrl Expy Ste 100, Dallas TX 75206
Tel (214) 373-4700
SIC 1751 1799 1542 1796

GHM CORP p 610
12700 Hillcrest Rd # 291, Dallas TX 75230
Tel (972) 840-1200
SIC 3448 1799 5999 5561

MASTER-HALCO INC p 918
3010 Lbj Fwy Ste 800, Dallas TX 75234
Tel (972) 714-7300
SIC 3315 5039 3496 3446 5031 1799

ATLANTIC SCAFFOLDING CO LLC p 127
1217 Georgia Ave, Deer Park TX 77536
Tel (281) 807-8200 SIC 1721 1799

ANCO INDUSTRIES LLC p 89
10343 Sam Houston Park Dr # 200, Houston TX 77064
Tel (281) 807-8200 SIC 1721 1799

ATLANTIC HOLDINGS I INC p 126
10343 Sam Houston Park Dr, Houston TX 77064
Tel (281) 807-8200 SIC 1721 1799

ATLANTIC HOLDINGS II INC p 126
10343 Sam Houston Park Dr, Houston TX 77064
Tel (281) 807-8200 SIC 1721 1799

ATLANTIC INDUSTRIAL LLC p 126
10343 Sam Houston Park Dr, Houston TX 77064
Tel (281) 807-8200 SIC 1721 1799

BISHOP LIFTING PRODUCTS INC p 185
125 Mccarty St, Houston TX 77029
Tel (713) 674-2266 SIC 1799 3531

BROCK GROUP INC p 216
10343 Sam Houston Park Dr, Houston TX 77064
Tel (281) 807-8200 SIC 1721 1799

BROCK HOLDINGS I LLC p 216
10343 Sam Houston Park Dr # 200, Houston TX 77064
Tel (281) 807-8200 SIC 1721 1799 7359

BROCK HOLDINGS II INC p 216
10343 Sam Houston Park Dr, Houston TX 77064
Tel (281) 807-8200 SIC 1721 1799

BROCK SERVICES HOLDINGS LLC p 216
10343 Sam Houston Park Dr # 200, Houston TX 77064
Tel (281) 807-8200 SIC 1721 1799

BROCK SERVICES LLC p 216
10343 Sam Houston Park Dr # 200, Houston TX 77064
Tel (281) 807-8200 *SIC* 1721 1799

CHAMBERLIN WATERPROOFING & ROOFING SYSTEMS INC p 287
7510 Langtry St, Houston TX 77040
Tel (713) 880-1432 *SIC* 1799 1761

GSE ENVIRONMENTAL INC p 643
19103 Gundle Rd, Houston TX 77073
Tel (281) 443-8564 *SIC* 3081 1799

MCCOY-ROCKFORD INC p 927
6869 Old Katy Rd, Houston TX 77024
Tel (713) 862-4600 *SIC* 5021 1799

MIKEN SPECIALTIES LTD p 968
10343 Sam Houston Park Dr, Houston TX 77064
Tel (979) 265-9599 *SIC* 1721 1799

NES GLOBAL LLC p 1026
800 Gessner Rd Ste 310, Houston TX 77024
Tel (713) 551-4444 *SIC* 1799

QUIETFLEX MANUFACTURING CO LP p 1199
4518 Brittmoore Rd, Houston TX 77041
Tel (713) 849-2163 *SIC* 3444 1799 3599

VEOLIA ES INDUSTRIAL SERVICES INC p 1548
4760 World Houston Pkwy # 100, Houston TX 77032
Tel (713) 672-8004 *SIC* 1799

ABSOLUTE ENVIRONMENTAL SERVICES LTD LLP p 13
11315 Dogwood Dr, Humble TX 77338
Tel (281) 319-4789 *SIC* 1799

■ FLUOR ENTERPRISES INC p 561
6700 Las Colinas Blvd, Irving TX 75039
Tel (469) 398-7000 *SIC* 1799 8711

MOBLEY INDUSTRIAL SERVICES INC p 980
1220 Miller Cut Off Rd, La Porte TX 77571
Tel (281) 470-9120 *SIC* 1721 1799 5033

TRIPLE S INDUSTRIAL CORP p 1482
860 W Chance Rd, Lumberton TX 77657
Tel (409) 755-4077 *SIC* 1799 1791

OSCAR RENDA CONTRACTING INC p 1096
608 Henrietta Creek Rd, Roanoke TX 76262
Tel (817) 491-2703 *SIC* 1623 1799 1622

SOUTHLAND CONTRACTING INC p 1351
608 Henrietta Creek Rd, Roanoke TX 76262
Tel (817) 293-4263 *SIC* 1799 1622

MINER HOLDING CO INC p 973
11827 Tech Com Rd Ste 115, San Antonio TX 78233
Tel (830) 627-8600 *SIC* 1799 6719

GLEN GEO ENTERPRISES INC p 614
13395 Murphy Rd, Stafford TX 77477
Tel (281) 242-6945 *SIC* 1799 5198 5084

■ PLANT PERFORMANCE SERVICES LLC p 1154
4800 Sugar Grove Blvd # 450, Stafford TX 77477
Tel (832) 532-5600 *SIC* 1731 1799 7699

H M T TANK SERVICE INC p 650
24 Waterway Ave Ste 400, The Woodlands TX 77380
Tel (281) 681-7000 *SIC* 1799

YOUNG ELECTRIC SIGN CO INC p 1638
2401 S Foothill Dr, Salt Lake City UT 84109
Tel (801) 464-4600
SIC 3993 7359 1799 6794

NSA INDUSTRIES LLC p 1064
210 Pierce Rd, Saint Johnsbury VT 05819
Tel (802) 748-5007 *SIC* 3444 1799 1796

S W RODGERS CO INC p 1263
5816 Wellington Rd, Gainesville VA 20155
Tel (703) 591-8400
SIC 1611 1799 6552 1771 1623

MILLER AND SMITH INC p 970
8401 Greensboro Dr # 450, Mc Lean VA 22102
Tel (703) 821-2500 *SIC* 1799 1531

WACO INC p 1570
5450 Lewis Rd, Sandston VA 23150
Tel (804) 222-8440
SIC 1711 1799 3448 5033

STRATA INC p 1392
3501 Everett Ave, Everett WA 98201
Tel (425) 259-6016 *SIC* 1799

GREENPOINT TECHNOLOGIES INC p 638
4600 Carillon Pt, Kirkland WA 98033
Tel (425) 828-2777 *SIC* 1799

YAKIMA VALLEY FARM WORKERS CLINIC INC p 1634
518 W 1st Ave, Toppenish WA 98948
Tel (509) 865-5898
SIC 8011 8021 8093 1799

■ A & B PROCESS SYSTEMS CORP p 4
201 S Wisconsin Ave, Stratford WI 54484
Tel (715) 687-4332 *SIC* 3443 1799 8711

SAFWAY GROUP HOLDING LLC p 1267
N19w24200 Riverwood Dr, Waukesha WI 53188
Tel (262) 523-6500 *SIC* 1799

SIC 2011 Meat Packing Plants

EQUITY GROUP EUFAULA DIVISION LLC p 507
57 Melvin Clark Rd, Eufaula AL 36027
Tel (334) 687-7790
SIC 2015 2048 2041 2011

▲ TYSON FOODS INC p 1496
2200 W Don Tyson Pkwy, Springdale AR 72762
Tel (479) 290-4000
SIC 2011 2015 2032 2096 2048

AMERICAN BEEF PACKERS INC p 68
13677 Yorba Ave, Chino CA 91710
Tel (909) 628-4888 *SIC* 0751 2011 5147

HARRIS FARMS INC p 663
29475 Fresno Coalinga Rd, Coalinga CA 93210
Tel (559) 884-2435
SIC 0191 0211 2011 7011 5812 5541

HARRIS RANCH BEEF CO p 663
29475 Fresno Coalinga Rd, Five Points CA 93624
Tel (559) 884-2435 *SIC* 2011 2013

COLUMBUS FOODS LLC p 342
30977 San Antonio St, Hayward CA 94544
Tel (510) 921-3400 *SIC* 2011 5143 5147

■ CLOUGHERTY PACKING LLC p 327
3049 E Vernon Ave, Vernon CA 90058
Tel (323) 583-4621 *SIC* 2011 2013

COLEMAN NATURAL FOODS LLC p 336
1767 Denver West Blvd # 200, Golden CO 80401
Tel (303) 468-2500 *SIC* 2011 5147 0251

JBS USA FOOD CO HOLDINGS p 780
1770 Promontory Cir, Greeley CO 80634
Tel (970) 506-8000 *SIC* 2011

JBS USA HOLDINGS LLC p 780
1770 Promontory Cir, Greeley CO 80634
Tel (970) 506-8000 *SIC* 2011 5147

PACKERLAND HOLDINGS INC p 1107
1770 Promontory Cir, Greeley CO 80634
Tel (970) 506-8000 *SIC* 2011 4213

■ BUCKHEAD BEEF CO p 223
355 Progress Rd, Auburndale FL 33823
Tel (863) 508-1050 *SIC* 2011

SEMINOLE TRIBE OF FLORIDA INC p 1302
6300 Stirling Rd, Hollywood FL 33024
Tel (954) 966-6300
SIC 7999 5194 2011 5182 2911

FPL FOOD LLC p 573
1301 New Savannah Rd, Augusta GA 30901
Tel (706) 722-2694 *SIC* 2011

HARRISON POULTRY INC p 664
107 Star St W, Bethlehem GA 30620
Tel (770) 867-9105
SIC 0254 2015 5984 2013 2011

AGRI BEEF CO p 36
1555 W Shoreline Dr # 320, Boise ID 83702
Tel (208) 338-2500 *SIC* 2011 0212

■ BRUSS CO p 221
3548 N Kostner Ave, Chicago IL 60641
Tel (773) 282-2900
SIC 5147 5142 2013 2011

CHICAGO MEAT AUTHORITY INC p 297
1120 W 47th Pl, Chicago IL 60609
Tel (773) 254-3811 *SIC* 2011

TEYS (USA) INC p 1445
770 N Halsted St Ste 202, Chicago IL 60642
Tel (312) 492-7163 *SIC* 2011

PLUMROSE USA INC p 1157
1901 Butterfield Rd # 305, Downers Grove IL 60515
Tel (732) 257-6600
SIC 2011 5147 2013 5149

TOGO PACKING CO INC p 1458
2125 Rochester Rd, Montgomery IL 60538
Tel (800) 575-3365 *SIC* 2011

■ ROCHELLE FOODS LLC p 1243
1001 S Main St, Rochelle IL 61068
Tel (815) 562-4141 *SIC* 2013 2011

INDIANA PACKERS CORP p 738
Hwy 421 S & Cr 100 N, Delphi IN 46923
Tel (765) 564-3680 *SIC* 2011 2013

■ PINNACLE FOODS LLC p 1149
2467 Henry Ladyn Dr, Fort Madison IA 52627
Tel (319) 463-7111 *SIC* 2011

CREEKSTONE FARMS PREMIUM BEEF LLC p 391
604 Goff Industrial Pk Rd, Arkansas City KS 67005
Tel (620) 741-3100 *SIC* 2011

S&S QUALITY MEATS LLC p 1263
1542 S Highway 99, Emporia KS 66801
Tel (620) 342-6354 *SIC* 2011 2013

▲ SEABOARD CORP p 1295
9000 W 67th St, Merriam KS 66202
Tel (913) 676-8800
SIC 2011 0133 4412 6221 0723 0213

■ SEABOARD FOODS LLC p 1295
9000 W 67th St Ste 200, Shawnee Mission KS 66202
Tel (913) 261-2600 *SIC* 0213 5147 2011

CARGILL MEAT SOLUTIONS CORP p 255
151 N Main St Ste 900, Wichita KS 67202
Tel (316) 291-2500 *SIC* 2011 5147 4213

FIELD PACKING CO LLC p 541
6 Dublin Ln, Owensboro KY 42301
Tel (270) 926-2324 *SIC* 2011

KAYEM FOODS INC p 805
75 Arlington St, Chelsea MA 02150
Tel (781) 933-3115 *SIC* 2011 2013

WOLVERINE PACKING CO p 1621
2535 Rivard St, Detroit MI 48207
Tel (313) 259-7500 *SIC* 5147 2011 5142

▲ HORMEL FOODS CORP p 708
1 Hormel Pl, Austin MN 55912
Tel (507) 437-5611 *SIC* 2011 2013 2032

QUALITY PORK PROCESSORS INC p 1197
711 Hormel Century Pkwy, Austin MN 55912
Tel (507) 434-6300 *SIC* 2011

ROSENS DIVERSIFIED INC p 1251
1120 Lake Ave, Fairmont MN 56031
Tel (507) 238-4201
SIC 2011 8748 5149 2879

CURLYS FOODS INC p 402
5201 Eden Ave Ste 370, Minneapolis MN 55436
Tel (612) 920-3400 *SIC* 2011

REICHEL FOODS INC p 1220
3706 Enterprise Dr Sw, Rochester MN 55902
Tel (507) 289-7264
SIC 2011 5812 2013 0723

LONG PRAIRIE PACKING CO INC p 876
100 Bridgepoint Curv # 249, South Saint Paul MN 55075
Tel (651) 552-8230 *SIC* 2011

CARGILL INC p 255
15407 Mcginty Rd W, Wayzata MN 55391
Tel (952) 742-7575
SIC 5153 2075 2046 2048 2011 2015

MENU MAKER FOODS INC p 943
913 Big Horn Dr, Jefferson City MO 65109
Tel (573) 893-3000
SIC 5141 5087 2011 5149

FARMLAND FOODS INC p 530
11500 Nw Ambassa Ste 500, Kansas City MO 64153
Tel (816) 243-2700 *SIC* 2011

■ NATIONAL BEEF PACKING CO LLC p 1010
12200 N Ambassador Dr # 101, Kansas City MO 64163
Tel (800) 449-2333 *SIC* 2011

TRIUMPH FOODS LLC p 1483
5302 Stockyards Expy, Saint Joseph MO 64504
Tel (816) 396-2700 *SIC* 2011

■ MIDDENDORF MEAT CO LLC p 964
3737 N Broadway, Saint Louis MO 63147
Tel (314) 241-4800
SIC 5147 5141 5148 5146 5113 2011

GREATER OMAHA PACKING CO INC p 635
3001 L St, Omaha NE 68107
Tel (402) 731-1700 *SIC* 2011 5147

NEBRASKA BEEF LTD p 1023
4501 S 36th St, Omaha NE 68107
Tel (402) 734-6823 *SIC* 2011

QUALITY PORK INTERNATIONAL INC p 1197
10404 F Plz, Omaha NE 68127
Tel (402) 339-1911 *SIC* 2011

XL FOUR STAR BEEF INC p 1632
3435 Gomez Ave, Omaha NE 68107
Tel (402) 731-3370 *SIC* 2011

VERONI USA INC p 1551
1110 Commerce Blvd # 200, Logan Township NJ 08085
Tel (609) 970-0320 *SIC* 2011

RASTELLI BROTHERS INC p 1209
300 Heron Dr, Swedesboro NJ 08085
Tel (856) 803-1100 *SIC* 5147 5421 2011

DARTAGNAN INC p 413
600 Green Ln, Union NJ 07083
Tel (973) 344-0565
SIC 5147 5148 5149 2011

▲ LEUCADIA NATIONAL CORP p 858
520 Madison Ave Bsmt A, New York NY 10022
Tel (212) 460-1900
SIC 6798 6211 1382 2011 2426

PM BEEF HOLDINGS LLC p 1157
810 7th Ave Fl 29, New York NY 10019
Tel (507) 831-2761 *SIC* 5144 5147 2011

MORRELL JOHN & CO p 990
805 E Kemper Rd, Cincinnati OH 45246
Tel (513) 782-3800 *SIC* 2011

V H COOPER & CO INC p 1538
2321 State Route 49, Fort Recovery OH 45846
Tel (419) 375-4116 *SIC* 0253 2015 2011

FRESH MARK INC p 578
1888 Southway St Se, Massillon OH 44646
Tel (330) 834-3669 *SIC* 2013 5147 2011

▲ BOB EVANS FARMS INC p 196
8111 Smiths Mill Rd, New Albany OH 43054
Tel (614) 491-2225
SIC 5812 2011 2099 2035

J H ROUTH PACKING CO p 771
4413 W Bogart Rd, Sandusky OH 44870
Tel (419) 626-2251 *SIC* 2011

SUGAR CREEK PACKING CO p 1397
2101 Kenskill Ave, Wshngtn Ct Hs OH 43160
Tel (740) 335-7440 *SIC* 2013 2011

■ SEABOARD FARMS INC p 1295
424 N Main St Ste 200, Guymon OK 73942
Tel (580) 338-1470 *SIC* 0213 2011

LOPEZ FOODS INC p 877
6016 Nw 120th Ct, Oklahoma City OK 73162
Tel (405) 603-7500 *SIC* 2013 2011

BARTELS PACKING INC p 157
706 Oscar St, Eugene OR 97402
Tel (541) 344-4177 *SIC* 2011

CLEMENS FAMILY CORP p 325
2700 Clemens Rd, Hatfield PA 19440
Tel (800) 523-5291
SIC 0213 2011 4222 8661

CLEMENS FOOD GROUP LLC p 325
2700 Clemens Rd, Hatfield PA 19440
Tel (215) 368-2500 *SIC* 2011 2013

KUNZLER & CO INC p 832
652 Manor St, Lancaster PA 17603
Tel (717) 299-6301 *SIC* 2011 2013

DIETZ & WATSON INC p 438
5701 Tacony St, Philadelphia PA 19135
Tel (800) 333-1974 *SIC* 2011 2013

JBS SOUDERTON INC p 779
249 Allentown Rd, Souderton PA 18964
Tel (215) 723-5555 *SIC* 2011 2077 2013

BPI TECHNOLOGY INC p 206
891 Two Rivers Dr, Dakota Dunes SD 57049
Tel (605) 217-8000 *SIC* 2011

■ TYSON FRESH MEATS INC p 1496
800 Stevens Port Dr, Dakota Dunes SD 57049
Tel (605) 235-2061 *SIC* 2011

EMPIRE PACKING CO LP p 493
1837 Harbor Ave, Memphis TN 38113
Tel (901) 948-4788 *SIC* 5147 2011

SAM KANE BEEF PROCESSORS LLC p 1274
9001 Leopard St, Corpus Christi TX 78409
Tel (361) 241-5000 *SIC* 2011

CAVINESS BEEF PACKERS LTD p 267
3255 Us Highway 60, Hereford TX 79045
Tel (806) 357-2443 *SIC* 2011

PREFERRED FOODS MARTIN L P p 1169
2011 Silver St, Houston TX 77007
Tel (713) 869-6191
SIC 5142 2015 2011 5141 5144

J & B SAUSAGE CO INC p 769
100 Main, Waelder TX 78959
Tel (830) 788-7661 *SIC* 2011 5147 2013

EDDY PACKING CO INC p 477
404 Airport Rd, Yoakum TX 77995
Tel (361) 580-3800 *SIC* 2011 2013

SMITHFIELD FARMLAND CORP p 1333
111 Commerce St, Smithfield VA 23430
Tel (757) 357-3131 *SIC* 2011 2013

SMITHFIELD FOODS INC p 1333
200 Commerce St, Smithfield VA 23430
Tel (757) 365-3000 *SIC* 2011 2013 2015

SMITHFIELD PACKING CO INC p 1334
601 N Church St, Smithfield VA 23430
Tel (757) 357-3131 *SIC* 2011 2013

WASHINGTON BEEF LLC p 1577
201 Elmwood Rd, Toppenish WA 98948
Tel (509) 865-2121 *SIC* 2011

ABBYLAND FOODS INC p 10
502 E Linden St, Abbotsford WI 54405
Tel (715) 223-6386 *SIC* 2013 2011

AMERICAN FOODS GROUP LLC p 72
500 S Washington St, Green Bay WI 54301
Tel (320) 759-5900 *SIC* 2011

GREEN BAY DRESSED BEEF LLC p 636
544 Acme St, Green Bay WI 54302
Tel (920) 436-4220 *SIC* 2011 2013

JBS PACKERLAND INC p 779
1330 Lime Kiln Rd, Green Bay WI 54311
Tel (920) 468-4000 *SIC* 2011 4213

KENOSHA BEEF INTERNATIONAL LTD p 811
3111 152nd Ave, Kenosha WI 53144
Tel (800) 541-1684 *SIC* 2011

SIC 2013 Sausages & Meat Prdts

BAR-S FOODS CO p 154
5090 N 40th St Ste 300, Phoenix AZ 85018
Tel (602) 264-7272 *SIC* 2013

DIAL CORP p 436
7201 E Henkel Way, Scottsdale AZ 85255
Tel (480) 754-3425
SIC 2841 2844 2842 2032 2013

■ TYSON CHICKEN INC p 1496
2200 W Don Tyson Pkwy, Springdale AR 72762
Tel (479) 290-4000
SIC 0252 0253 0254 0251 2015 2013

■ BRIDGFORD FOODS CORP p 212
1308 N Patt St, Anaheim CA 92801
Tel (714) 526-5533
SIC 2045 2099 2015 2013 2022 2038

HARRIS RANCH BEEF CO p 663
29475 Fresno Coalinga Rd, Five Points CA 93624
Tel (559) 884-2435 *SIC* 2011 2013

TALL TREE FOODS HOLDINGS INC p 1423
400 Hamilton Ave Ste 230, Palo Alto CA 94301
Tel (650) 264-7750 *SIC* 2013

BEE BUMBLE HOLDINGS INC p 168
280 10th Ave, San Diego CA 92101
Tel (858) 715-4000 *SIC* 2013 2032 2033

BUMBLE BEE PARENT INC p 225
280 10th Ave, San Diego CA 92101
Tel (858) 715-4000 *SIC* 2013 2032 2033

■ AIDELLS SAUSAGE CO INC p 37
2411 Baumann Ave, San Lorenzo CA 94580
Tel (510) 614-5450 *SIC* 2013 5147

■ CLOUGHERTY PACKING LLC p 327
3049 E Vernon Ave, Vernon CA 90058
Tel (323) 583-4621 *SIC* 2011 2013

RANCHO FOODS INC p 1207
2528 E 37th St, Vernon CA 90058
Tel (323) 585-0503 *SIC* 5147 2013

FIELDALE FARMS CORP p 541
555 Broiler Blvd, Baldwin GA 30511
Tel (706) 778-5100 *SIC* 2015 2013 0751

HARRISON POULTRY INC p 664
107 Star St W, Bethlehem GA 30620
Tel (770) 867-9105
SIC 0254 2015 5984 2013 2011

ROGER WOOD FOODS INC p 1246
7 Alfred St, Savannah GA 31408
Tel (912) 652-9600 *SIC* 2013 5147

INTERMOUNTAIN NATURAL LLC p 753
1740 S Yellowstone Hwy, Idaho Falls ID 83402
Tel (208) 227-9000 *SIC* 5147 2013

CTI FOODS HOLDING CO LLC p 399
22303 Highway 95, Wilder ID 83676
Tel (208) 482-7844 *SIC* 2013 2032 2035

CTI-SSI FOOD SERVICES LLC p 399
22303 Highway 95, Wilder ID 83676
Tel (208) 602-0937 *SIC* 2013

STAMPEDE MEAT INC p 1375
7351 S 78th Ave, Bridgeview IL 60455
Tel (773) 376-4300 *SIC* 2013

■ BRIDGFORD FOODS CORP p 212
170 N Green St, Chicago IL 60607
Tel (312) 733-0300 *SIC* 2013

■ BRUSS CO p 221
3548 N Kostner Ave, Chicago IL 60641
Tel (773) 282-2900
SIC 5147 5142 2013 2011

▲ CONAGRA BRANDS INC p 354
222 Merchandise Mart Plz, Chicago IL 60654
Tel (312) 549-5000 *SIC* 2099 2038 2013

■ HILLSHIRE BRANDS CO p 694
400 S Jefferson St Fl 1, Chicago IL 60607
Tel (312) 614-6000 *SIC* 2013 2051 2053

NATIONWIDE FOODS INC p 1017
700 E 107th St, Chicago IL 60628
Tel (773) 787-4900 *SIC* 2013 5142 5147

VIENNA BEEF LTD p 1556
2501 N Damen Ave, Chicago IL 60647
Tel (773) 278-7800
SIC 2013 2035 2053 5411 5149 5147

▲ MONDELEZ INTERNATIONAL INC p 983
3 Parkway N Ste 300, Deerfield IL 60015
Tel (847) 943-4000
SIC 2022 2013 2095 2043 2035 2087

PLUMROSE USA INC p 1157
1901 Butterfield Rd # 305, Downers Grove IL 60515
Tel (732) 257-6600
SIC 2011 5147 2013 5149

FARMINGTON FOODS INC p 530
7419 Franklin St, Forest Park IL 60130
Tel (708) 771-3600 *SIC* 2013

KRONOS FOODS CORP p 830
1 Kronos, Glendale Heights IL 60139
Tel (773) 847-2250
SIC 2013 2051 5141 5963

CARL BUDDIG AND CO p 256
950 175th St, Homewood IL 60430
Tel (708) 798-0900 *SIC* 2013 2022

CAPITOL WHOLESALE MEATS INC p 251
8751 W 50th St, Mc Cook IL 60525
Tel (708) 485-4800 *SIC* 2013

■ ROCHELLE FOODS LLC p 1243
1001 S Main St, Rochelle IL 61068
Tel (815) 562-4141 *SIC* 2013 2011

BRANDING IRON HOLDINGS INC p 208
1682 Sauget Business Blvd, Sauget IL 62206
Tel (618) 337-8400 SIC 2013 5147

INDIANA PACKERS CORP p 738
Hwy 421 S & Cr 100 N, Delphi IN 46923
Tel (765) 564-3680 SIC 2011 2013

PARK 100 FOODS INC p 1115
326 E Adams St, Tipton IN 46072
Tel (765) 675-3480 SIC 2013 2032 2035

OAKLAND FOODS LLC p 1071
21876 Highway 59, Oakland IA 51560
Tel (712) 482-6640 SIC 2013

S&S QUALITY MEATS LLC p 1263
1542 S Highway 99, Emporia KS 66801
Tel (620) 342-6354 SIC 2011 2013

SPECIALTY FOODS HOLDINGS INC p 1356
6 Dublin Ln, Owensboro KY 42301
Tel (757) 952-1200 SIC 2013

CTI FOODS LLC p 399
59 Custom Foods Dr, Owingsville KY 40360
Tel (310) 637-0900 SIC 2013

SAVAL FOODS CORP p 1284
6740 Dorsey Rd, Elkridge MD 21075
Tel (410) 379-5100 SIC 5141 2013

KAYEM FOODS INC p 805
75 Arlington St, Chelsea MA 02150
Tel (781) 933-3115 SIC 2011 2013

HOME MARKET FOODS INC p 703
140 Morgan Dr Ste 100, Norwood MA 02062
Tel (781) 948-1500 SIC 2013

▲ HORMEL FOODS CORP p 708
1 Hormel Pl, Austin MN 55912
Tel (507) 437-5611 SIC 2011 2013 2032

REICHEL FOODS INC p 1220
3706 Enterprise Dr Sw, Rochester MN 55902
Tel (507) 289-7264
SIC 2011 5812 2013 0723

■ APPERTS INC p 98
900 Highway 10 S, Saint Cloud MN 56304
Tel (320) 251-3200
SIC 5142 5141 5411 5421 2013

BURGERS OZARK COUNTRY CURED HAMS INC p 227
32819 Highway 87, California MO 65018
Tel (573) 796-3134
SIC 5147 5812 2015 2013

FARMLAND FOODS INC p 530
200 S 2nd St, Lincoln NE 68508
Tel (402) 475-6700 SIC 2013

THUMANN INC p 1451
670 Dell Rd Ste 1, Carlstadt NJ 07072
Tel (201) 935-3636 SIC 2013

▲ B&G FOODS INC p 142
4 Gatehall Dr Ste 110, Parsippany NJ 07054
Tel (973) 401-6500
SIC 2013 2032 2033 2035 2099

BIRDS EYE HOLDINGS INC p 185
90 Linden Park, Rochester NY 14625
Tel (585) 383-1850
SIC 2033 2013 2035 2096

PALMER FISH CO INC p 1109
900 Jefferson Rd Ste 1000, Rochester NY 14623
Tel (585) 424-3210
SIC 5146 5147 5142 2013

CLOVERDALE FOODS CO p 328
3015 34th St Nw, Mandan ND 58554
Tel (701) 663-9511 SIC 2013 5147

▲ ADVANCEPIERRE FOODS HOLDINGS INC p 26
9987 Carver Rd, Blue Ash OH 45242
Tel (800) 969-2747 SIC 2099 2013

■ ADVANCEPIERRE FOODS INC p 26
9987 Carver Rd Ste 500, Blue Ash OH 45242
Tel (513) 874-8741 SIC 2013 2015

WHITE CASTLE SYSTEM INC p 1606
555 W Goodale St, Columbus OH 43215
Tel (614) 228-5781
SIC 5812 5142 2051 2013

JTM PROVISIONS CO INC p 796
200 Sales Ave, Harrison OH 45030
Tel (513) 367-4900 SIC 2013 2051

FRESH MARK INC p 578
1888 Southway St Se, Massillon OH 44646
Tel (330) 834-3669 SIC 2013 5147 2011

PIERRE HOLDING CORP p 1147
9990 Prnceton Glendale Rd, West Chester OH 45246
Tel (513) 874-8741 SIC 2013 2015 2051

■ ZARTIC LLC p 1641
9990 Prnceton Glendale Rd, West Chester OH 45246
Tel (513) 874-8741 SIC 2013 2015

SUGAR CREEK PACKING CO p 1397
2101 Kenskill Ave, Wshngtn Ct Hs OH 43160
Tel (740) 335-7440 SIC 2013 2011

■ ADVANCE FOOD CO INC p 24
221 W Oxford Ave, Enid OK 73701
Tel (800) 969-2747 SIC 2013 2015 2099

LOPEZ FOODS INC p 877
6016 Nw 120th Ct, Oklahoma City OK 73162
Tel (405) 603-7500 SIC 2013 2011

NATIONAL STEAK PROCESSORS INC p 1016
301 E 5th Ave, Owasso OK 74055
Tel (918) 274-8787 SIC 2013 2015

OFD FOODS INC p 1075
525 25th Ave Sw, Albany OR 97322
Tel (541) 926-6001
SIC 2013 2015 2091 2032 2023

BRUCE PACKING CO INC p 220
380 S Pacific Hwy 99e, Woodburn OR 97071
Tel (503) 874-3000 SIC 2013

JDB INC p 781
380 S Pacific Hwy, Woodburn OR 97071
Tel (503) 874-3000 SIC 2015 2013

CLEMENS FOOD GROUP LLC p 325
2700 Clemens Rd, Hatfield PA 19440
Tel (215) 368-2500 SIC 2011 2013

KUNZLER & CO INC p 832
652 Manor St, Lancaster PA 17603
Tel (717) 299-6301 SIC 2011 2013

DIETZ & WATSON INC p 438
5701 Tacony St, Philadelphia PA 19135
Tel (800) 333-1974 SIC 2011 2013

JBS SOUDERTON INC p 779
249 Allentown Rd, Souderton PA 18964
Tel (215) 723-5555 SIC 2011 2077 2013

JOHN F MARTIN & SONS INC p 788
55 Lower Hillside Rd, Stevens PA 17578
Tel (717) 336-2804 SIC 2013 0212

KEYSTONE FOODS LLC p 815
905 Airport Rd Ste 400, West Chester PA 19380
Tel (610) 667-6700 SIC 2013 2015 5087

■ PEPSICO CARIBBEAN INC p 1134
668 Calle Cubitas, Guaynabo PR 00969
Tel (787) 720-6825 SIC 2013

CAROLINA PRIDE FOODS INC p 259
1 Packer Ave, Greenwood SC 29646
Tel (864) 229-5611 SIC 2013

S I L INC p 1262
39210 221st St, Alpena SD 57312
Tel (605) 849-8800 SIC 2013

MONOGRAM FOOD SOLUTIONS LLC p 984
530 Oak Court Dr Ste 400, Memphis TN 38117
Tel (901) 685-7167 SIC 5142 2013 5147

▲ BRIDGFORD INDUSTRIES INC p 212
1601 S Good Latimer Expy, Dallas TX 75226
Tel (214) 428-1535
SIC 2045 2099 2015 2013 2022 2038

■ FRITO-LAY NORTH AMERICA INC p 580
7701 Legacy Dr, Plano TX 75024
Tel (972) 334-7000
SIC 2096 2052 2013 5812 6794 2086

OLD FRITO-LAY INC p 1080
7701 Legacy Dr, Plano TX 75024
Tel (972) 334-7000
SIC 2096 2052 2013 5812 6794 2086

JOHN SOULES FOODS INC p 789
10150 Fm 14, Tyler TX 75706
Tel (903) 592-9800 SIC 2013 2015 5147

J & B SAUSAGE CO INC p 769
100 Main, Waelder TX 78959
Tel (830) 788-7661 SIC 2011 5147 2013

EDDY PACKING CO INC p 477
404 Airport Rd, Yoakum TX 77995
Tel (361) 580-3800 SIC 2011 2013

SMITHFIELD FARMLAND CORP p 1333
111 Commerce St, Smithfield VA 23430
Tel (757) 357-3131 SIC 2011 2013

SMITHFIELD FOODS INC p 1333
200 Commerce St, Smithfield VA 23430
Tel (757) 365-3000 SIC 2011 2013 2015

SMITHFIELD PACKING CO INC p 1334
601 N Church St, Smithfield VA 23430
Tel (757) 357-3131 SIC 2011 2013

OBERTO SAUSAGE CO p 1072
7060 S 238th St, Kent WA 98032
Tel (253) 437-6100 SIC 2013

ABBYLAND FOODS INC p 10
502 E Linden St, Abbotsford WI 54405
Tel (715) 223-6386 SIC 2013 2011

PATRICK CUDAHY LLC p 1120
1 Sweet Applewood Ln, Cudahy WI 53110
Tel (414) 744-2000 SIC 2013

GREEN BAY DRESSED BEEF LLC p 636
544 Acme St, Green Bay WI 54302
Tel (920) 436-4220 SIC 2011 2013

KLEMENT SAUSAGE CO INC p 823
1036 W Juneau Ave 400, Milwaukee WI 53233
Tel (414) 744-2330 SIC 2013

LINK SNACKS INC p 869
1 Snack Food Ln, Minong WI 54859
Tel (715) 466-2234 SIC 2013

FAIR OAKS FARMS LLC p 524
7600 95th St, Pleasant Prairie WI 53158
Tel (262) 947-0320 SIC 2013

JOHNSONVILLE SAUSAGE LLC p 791
N6928 Johnsonville Way, Sheboygan Falls WI 53085
Tel (920) 453-6900 SIC 2013

BRAKEBUSH BROTHERS INC p 207
N4993 6th Dr, Westfield WI 53964
Tel (608) 296-2121 SIC 2013 2015

SIC 2015 Poultry Slaughtering, Dressing & Processing

ALBERTVILLE QUALITY FOODS INC p 47
130 Quality Dr, Albertville AL 35950
Tel (256) 840-9923 SIC 2015

EQUITY GROUP EUFAULA DIVISION LLC p 507
57 Melvin Clark Rd, Eufaula AL 36027
Tel (334) 687-7790
SIC 2015 2048 2041 2011

ALATRADE FOODS LLC p 45
725 Blount Ave, Guntersville AL 35976
Tel (256) 571-9696 SIC 2015

AVIAGEN INC p 137
920 Explorer Blvd Nw, Huntsville AL 35806
Tel (256) 890-3800 SIC 2015

MARSHALL DURBIN FOOD CORP p 911
2830 Commerce Blvd, Irondale AL 35210
Tel (205) 841-7315
SIC 0252 0254 2048 0251 2015 5144

SYLVEST FARMS INC p 1414
3500 West Blvd, Montgomery AL 36108
Tel (334) 281-0400 SIC 0251 2015

PECO FOODS INC p 1127
1020 Lurleen B Wallace, Tuscaloosa AL 35401
Tel (205) 345-4711
SIC 0254 0251 2015 2048

TWIN RIVERS FOODS INC p 1495
1 E Colt Square Dr, Fayetteville AR 72703
Tel (479) 444-8898 SIC 2015

O K FOODS INC p 1070
4601 N 6th St, Fort Smith AR 72904
Tel (479) 783-4186 SIC 2015

OK INDUSTRIES INC p 1079
4601 N 6th St, Fort Smith AR 72904
Tel (479) 783-4186 SIC 2048 2015 0251

MOUNTAIRE CORP p 994
1901 Napa Valley Dr, Little Rock AR 72212
Tel (501) 372-6524 SIC 2015

MOUNTAIRE FARMS INC p 994
1901 Napa Valley Dr, Little Rock AR 72212
Tel (501) 372-6524 SIC 2015

OZARK MOUNTAIN POULTRY INC p 1101
750 W E St, Rogers AR 72756
Tel (479) 633-8700 SIC 2015 5144

SIMMONS FOODS INC p 1324
601 N Hico St, Siloam Springs AR 72761
Tel (479) 524-8151 SIC 2015

SIMMONS PREPARED FOODS INC p 1324
601 N Hico St, Siloam Springs AR 72761
Tel (479) 524-8151 SIC 2015

GEORGES INC p 606
402 W Robinson Ave, Springdale AR 72764
Tel (479) 927-7000 SIC 2015 0254 0251

GEORGES PROCESSING INC p 606
402 W Robinson Ave, Springdale AR 72764
Tel (479) 927-7000 SIC 2015

■ TYSON CHICKEN INC p 1496
2200 W Don Tyson Pkwy, Springdale AR 72762
Tel (479) 290-4000
SIC 0252 0253 0254 0251 2015 2013

▲ TYSON FOODS INC p 1496
2200 W Don Tyson Pkwy, Springdale AR 72762
Tel (479) 290-4000
SIC 2011 2015 2032 2096 2048

■ BRIDGFORD FOODS CORP p 212
1308 N Patt St, Anaheim CA 92801
Tel (714) 526-5533
SIC 2045 2099 2015 2013 2022 2038

ZACKY & SONS POULTRY LLC p 1641
2020 S East Ave, Fresno CA 93721
Tel (559) 443-2700 SIC 2015

FOSTER POULTRY FARMS p 570
1000 Davis St, Livingston CA 95334
Tel (209) 394-6914
SIC 0254 2015 5812 0173 5191 4212

VALLEY FRESH FOODS INC p 1540
3600 E Linwood Ave, Turlock CA 95380
Tel (209) 669-5600 SIC 0252 2015

▲ PILGRIMS PRIDE CORP p 1148
1770 Promontory Cir, Greeley CO 80634
Tel (970) 506-8000
SIC 2015 0254 0252 2048 5999

MOARK LLC p 980
28 Under The Mountain Rd, North Franklin CT 06254
Tel (951) 332-3300
SIC 5144 2048 0252 2015

OMTRON USA LLC p 1085
22855 Dupont Blvd, Georgetown DE 19947
Tel (302) 855-7131 SIC 2015

MOUNTAIRE FARMS OF DELAWARE INC p 994
29005 John J Williams Hwy, Millsboro DE 19966
Tel (302) 934-1100 SIC 2015

ALLEN BIOTECH LLC p 53
126 N Shipley St, Seaford DE 19973
Tel (302) 629-9136 SIC 2015

HARIM USA LTD p 661
126 N Shipley St, Seaford DE 19973
Tel (302) 629-9136 SIC 2015

■ PILGRIMS PRIDE CORP OF GEORGIA INC p 1148
244 Perimeter Ctr Pkwy Ne, Atlanta GA 30346
Tel (770) 393-5000 SIC 2015 0254

FIELDALE FARMS CORP p 541
555 Broiler Blvd, Baldwin GA 30511
Tel (706) 778-5100 SIC 2015 2013 0751

HARRISON POULTRY INC p 664
107 Star St W, Bethlehem GA 30620
Tel (770) 867-9105
SIC 0254 2015 5984 2013 2011

EQUITY GROUP - GEORGIA DIVISION LLC p 506
7220 Us Highway 19, Camilla GA 31730
Tel (229) 336-1001 SIC 2015 0254 2048

FRIES FARMS LLC p 580
8816 Us Highway 301, Claxton GA 30417
Tel (912) 739-3181 SIC 0251 2015

NORMAN W FRIES INC p 1049
8816 Us Highway 301, Claxton GA 30417
Tel (912) 739-1158 SIC 2015

PILGRIMS PRIDE CORP p 1148
1965 Evergreen Blvd # 100, Duluth GA 30096
Tel (770) 232-4200 SIC 2015 5144 5141

JOHN SOULES ACQUISITIONS LLC p 789
311 Green St Nw Ste 500, Gainesville GA 30501
Tel (770) 532-3058 SIC 2015

MARJAC HOLDINGS LLC p 907
1020 Aviation Blvd, Gainesville GA 30501
Tel (770) 531-5000 SIC 2015

TIP TOP POULTRY INC p 1455
327 Wallace Rd, Marietta GA 30062
Tel (770) 973-8070 SIC 2015

WAYNE FARMS LLC p 1584
4110 Continental Dr, Oakwood GA 30566
Tel (770) 538-2120 SIC 2015

FARBEST FOODS INC p 528
4689 S 400w, Huntingburg IN 47542
Tel (812) 683-4200 SIC 2015

MAPLE LEAF INC p 903
101 E Church St, Leesburg IN 46538
Tel (574) 453-4455 SIC 0259 2015 5159

MIDWEST POULTRY SERVICES LP p 967
9951 W State Road 25, Mentone IN 46539
Tel (574) 353-7232 SIC 0751 2015

MAPLE LEAF FARMS INC p 903
9166 N 200 E, Milford IN 46542
Tel (574) 453-4500 SIC 0259 2015

PINE MANOR INC p 1149
9622 W 350 N, Orland IN 46776
Tel (800) 532-4186 SIC 2048 2015 0254

REMBRANDT ENTERPRISES INC p 1222
1521 18th St, Spirit Lake IA 51360
Tel (712) 759-1800 SIC 2015 3556

WEST LIBERTY FOODS LLC p 1594
228 W 2nd St, West Liberty IA 52776
Tel (319) 627-6000 SIC 2015

HOUSE OF RAEFORD FARMS OF LOUISIANA LLC p 711
3867 2nd St, Arcadia LA 71001
Tel (318) 263-9004 SIC 0251 2015

■ BARBER FOODS p 154
56 Milliken St, Portland ME 04103
Tel (207) 482-5500 SIC 2015

PERDUE FARMS INC p 1134
31149 Old Ocean City Rd, Salisbury MD 21804
Tel (410) 543-3000 SIC 2015 2075 4213

MICHIGAN TURKEY PRODUCERS COOPERATIVE INC p 961
2140 Chicago Dr Sw, Wyoming MI 49519
Tel (616) 245-2221 SIC 2015

SPARBOE FARMS INC p 1354
23577 Mn Hwy 22, Litchfield MN 55355
Tel (320) 693-7241 SIC 2015

SPARBOE FOODS LLC p 1354
23577 Minnesota Hwy 22, Litchfield MN 55355
Tel (320) 593-9600 SIC 2015

TONY DOWNS FOODS CO p 1460
54934 210th Ln, Mankato MN 56001
Tel (507) 375-3111 SIC 2015 2099

TURKEY VALLEY FARMS LLC p 1492
112 S 6th St, Marshall MN 56258
Tel (507) 337-3100 SIC 2015

■ MG WALDBAUM CO p 958
301 Carlson Pkwy Ste 400, Minnetonka MN 55305
Tel (952) 258-4000 SIC 2015 5153 5191

■ MICHAEL FOODS GROUP INC p 960
301 Carlson Pkwy Ste 400, Minnetonka MN 55305
Tel (952) 258-4000
SIC 0252 2015 5144 5143 5148 6719

■ MICHAEL FOODS INC p 960
301 Carlson Pkwy Ste 400, Minnetonka MN 55305
Tel (507) 237-4600
SIC 0252 2015 5144 5143 5148 5499

■ MICHAEL FOODS OF DELAWARE INC p 960
301 Carlson Pkwy Ste 400, Minnetonka MN 55305
Tel (952) 258-4000
SIC 0252 2015 5144 5143 5148 2024

CARGILL KITCHEN SOLUTIONS INC p 255
206 W 4th St, Monticello MN 55362
Tel (763) 271-5600 SIC 2015

GNP CO p 619
4150 2nd St S Ste 200, Saint Cloud MN 56301
Tel (320) 251-3570 SIC 2015

GOLDEN PUMP POULTRY INC p 621
4150 2nd St S Ste 200, Saint Cloud MN 56301
Tel (320) 240-6234 SIC 2015 0251

JFC LLC p 785
4150 2nd St S Ste 200, Saint Cloud MN 56301
Tel (320) 251-3570 SIC 2015 0251

CARGILL INC p 255
15407 Mcginty Rd W, Wayzata MN 55391
Tel (952) 742-7575
SIC 5153 2075 2046 2048 2011 2015

■ JENNIE-O TURKEY STORE INC p 782
2505 Willmar Ave Sw, Willmar MN 56201
Tel (320) 235-2622 SIC 2015 0253

■ JENNIE-O TURKEY STORE INTERNATIONAL INC p 782
2505 Willmar Ave Sw, Willmar MN 56201
Tel (320) 235-2622 SIC 2015

▲ SANDERSON FARMS INC p 1278
127 Flynt Rd, Laurel MS 39443
Tel (601) 649-4030 SIC 0251 2015

■ SANDERSON FARMS INC (PROCESSING DIVISION) p 1278
127 Flynt Rd, Laurel MS 39443
Tel (601) 649-4030 SIC 2015

KOCH FOODS OF MISSISSIPPI LLC p 825
4688 Highway 80, Morton MS 39117
Tel (601) 732-8911 SIC 2015

BURGERS OZARK COUNTRY CURED HAMS INC p 227
32819 Highway 87, California MO 65018
Tel (573) 796-3134
SIC 5147 5812 2015 2013

▲ POST HOLDINGS INC p 1163
2503 S Hanley Rd, Saint Louis MO 63144
Tel (314) 644-7600
SIC 2015 2034 2038 2041 2099

■ PAPETTIS HYGRADE EGG PRODUCTS INC p 1112
1 Papetti Plz, Elizabethport NJ 07206
Tel (908) 282-7900 SIC 2015

CONTINENTAL GRAIN CO p 363
767 5th Ave Fl 15, New York NY 10153
Tel (212) 207-5930 SIC 2015 2041

BUTTERBALL LLC p 230
1 Butterball Ln, Garner NC 27529
Tel (919) 255-7900 SIC 2015

HOUSE OF RAEFORD FARMS INC p 711
1000 E Central Ave, Raeford NC 28376
Tel (910) 289-6900 SIC 2015

NASH JOHNSON & SONS FARMS INC p 1008
3385 S Us Highway 117, Rose Hill NC 28458
Tel (910) 289-3113
SIC 2015 0254 0253 0251 2048

PRESTAGE FOODS INC p 1173
4470 Hwy 20 E, Saint Pauls NC 28384
Tel (910) 865-6611 SIC 2015

CASE FARMS LLC p 263
385 Pilch Rd, Troutman NC 28166
Tel (704) 528-4501 SIC 2015 8731

CASE FARMS PROCESSING INC p 263
385 Pilch Rd, Troutman NC 28166
Tel (704) 528-4501 SIC 2015

CASE FOODS INC p 263
385 Pilch Rd, Troutman NC 28166
Tel (704) 528-4501 SIC 2015

■ ADVANCEPIERRE FOODS INC p 26
9987 Carver Rd Ste 500, Blue Ash OH 45242
Tel (513) 874-8741 SIC 2013 2015

OHIO FRESH EGGS LLC p 1077
11212 Croton Rd, Croton OH 43013
Tel (740) 893-7200 SIC 5144 2015

V H COOPER & CO INC p 1538
2321 State Route 49, Fort Recovery OH 45846
Tel (419) 375-4116 SIC 0253 2015 2011

COOPER HATCHERY INC p 366
22348 Road 140, Oakwood OH 45873
Tel (419) 594-3325
SIC 0254 0253 2015 5153 2048

PIERRE HOLDING CORP p 1147
9990 Prnceton Glendale Rd, West Chester OH 45246
Tel (513) 874-8741 SIC 2013 2015 2051

■ ZARTIC LLC p 1641
9990 Prnceton Glendale Rd, West Chester OH 45246
Tel (513) 874-8741 SIC 2013 2015

■ ADVANCE FOOD CO INC p 24
221 W Oxford Ave, Enid OK 73701
Tel (800) 969-2747 SIC 2013 2015 2099

NATIONAL STEAK PROCESSORS INC p 1016
301 E 5th Ave, Owasso OK 74055
Tel (918) 274-8787 SIC 2013 2015

OFD FOODS INC p 1075
525 25th Ave Sw, Albany OR 97322
Tel (541) 926-6001
SIC 2013 2015 2091 2032 2023

JDB INC p 781
380 S Pacific Hwy, Woodburn OR 97071
Tel (503) 874-3000 SIC 2015 2013

FARMERS PRIDE INC p 530
154 W Main St, Fredericksburg PA 17026
Tel (717) 865-6626 SIC 2015

SECHLER FAMILY FOODS INC p 1298
154 W Main St, Fredericksburg PA 17026
Tel (717) 865-6626 SIC 2015

■ E K HOLDINGS INC p 466
Rr 5, Mifflintown PA 17059
Tel (717) 436-5921 SIC 2015

■ EMPIRE KOSHER POULTRY INC p 493
Chicken Plant Rd, Mifflintown PA 17059
Tel (717) 436-5921 SIC 2015 5812

KEYSTONE FOODS LLC p 815
905 Airport Rd Ste 400, West Chester PA 19380
Tel (610) 667-6700 SIC 2013 2015 5087

COLUMBIA FARMS INC p 340
125 N Lee St, Leesville SC 29070
Tel (803) 532-4488 SIC 2015

DAKOTA TURKEY GROWERS LLC p 409
40253 Us Highway 14, Huron SD 57350
Tel (605) 352-1519 SIC 2015

■ TYSON FARMS OF TEXAS INC p 1496
1019 Shelbyville St, Center TX 75935
Tel (936) 598-2474 SIC 2015

▲ BRIDGFORD INDUSTRIES INC p 212
1601 S Good Latimer Expy, Dallas TX 75226
Tel (214) 428-1535
SIC 2045 2099 2015 2013 2022 2038

SAPUTO DAIRY FOODS USA LLC p 1282
2711 N Haske Ave Ste 3700, Dallas TX 75204
Tel (214) 863-2300 SIC 2023 2015 2026

PREFERRED FOODS MARTIN L P p 1169
2011 Silver St, Houston TX 77007
Tel (713) 869-6191
SIC 5142 2015 2011 5141 5144

JOHN SOULES FOODS INC p 789
10150 Fm 14, Tyler TX 75706
Tel (903) 592-9800 SIC 2013 2015 5147

VIRGINIA POULTRY GROWERS COOPERATIVE INC p 1559
6349 Rawley Pike, Hinton VA 22831
Tel (540) 867-4000 SIC 2015

SMITHFIELD FOODS INC p 1333
200 Commerce St, Smithfield VA 23430
Tel (757) 365-3000 SIC 2011 2013 2015

DRAPER VALLEY HOLDINGS LLC p 455
1000 Jason Ln, Mount Vernon WA 98273
Tel (360) 424-7947 SIC 0254 2015

WILCOX FARMS INC p 1608
40400 Harts Lake Vly Rd, Roy WA 98580
Tel (360) 458-7774 SIC 0252 2015 2875

BRAKEBUSH BROTHERS INC p 207
N4993 6th Dr, Westfield WI 53964
Tel (608) 296-2121 SIC 2013 2015

SIC 2021 Butter

CALIFORNIA DAIRIES INC p 239
2000 N Plaza Dr, Visalia CA 93291
Tel (559) 625-2200 SIC 2026 2021 2023

▲ WHITEWAVE FOODS CO p 1606
1225 17th St Ste 1000, Denver CO 80202
Tel (303) 635-4500 SIC 2026 2023 2021

BORDEN DAIRY CO OF FLORIDA LLC p 201
308 Avenue G Sw, Winter Haven FL 33880
Tel (863) 297-7300
SIC 5143 2026 2024 2022 2021

MICHIGAN MILK PRODUCERS ASSOCIATION p 961
41310 Bridge St, Novi MI 48375
Tel (248) 474-6672
SIC 5143 2023 2021 8611 2026

ASSOCIATED MILK PRODUCERS INC p 121
315 N Brdwy St, New Ulm MN 56073
Tel (507) 354-8295
SIC 2023 2022 2021 2024 2026 5143

BONGARDS CREAMERIES p 200
13200 County Road 51, Norwood MN 55368
Tel (952) 466-5521
SIC 2023 2022 5451 2021

PLAINVIEW MILK PRODUCTS COOPERATIVE p 1154
130 2nd St Sw, Plainview MN 55964
Tel (507) 534-3872 SIC 2023 2021

DAIRY FARMERS OF AMERICA INC p 408
10220 N Ambassador Dr, Kansas City MO 64153
Tel (816) 801-6455
SIC 2026 2023 2021 2022 5083 2024

O-AT-KA MILK PRODUCTS COOPERATIVE INC p 1070
700 Ellicott St, Batavia NY 14020
Tel (585) 343-0536 SIC 2023 2021 2026

TILLAMOOK COUNTY CREAMERY ASSOCIATION p 1453
4185 Highway 101 N, Tillamook OR 97141
Tel (503) 842-4481 SIC 2022 2024 2021

GOSSNER FOODS INC p 626
1051 N 1000 W, Logan UT 84321
Tel (435) 713-6100 SIC 2022 2026 2021

VALLEY MILK PRODUCTS LLC p 1541
412 E King St, Strasburg VA 22657
Tel (540) 465-5113 SIC 2023 2021

FOREMOST FARMS USA COOPERATIVE p 566
E10889 Penny Ln, Baraboo WI 53913
Tel (608) 355-8700
SIC 2022 2026 2023 2021

GRASSLAND DAIRY PRODUCTS INC p 632
N8790 Fairground Ave, Greenwood WI 54437
Tel (715) 267-6182 SIC 2021 5143

SIC 2022 Cheese

■ BRIDGFORD FOODS CORP p 212
1308 N Patt St, Anaheim CA 92801
Tel (714) 526-5533
SIC 2045 2099 2015 2013 2022 2038

CACIQUE INC p 236
14940 Proctor Ave, City Of Industry CA 91746
Tel (626) 961-3399 SIC 2022

HILMAR CHEESE CO INC p 694
8901 Lander Ave, Hilmar CA 95324
Tel (209) 667-6076 SIC 2022

IDB HOLDINGS INC p 728
601 S Rockefeller Ave, Ontario CA 91761
Tel (909) 390-5624 SIC 5143 2022

MARQUEZ BROTHERS INTERNATIONAL INC p 910
5801 Rue Ferrari, San Jose CA 95138
Tel (408) 960-2700 SIC 2022

SAPUTO CHEESE USA INC p 1282
800 E Paige Ave, Tulare CA 93274
Tel (559) 687-8411 SIC 2022

SSI-TURLOCK DAIRY DIVISION p 1364
2600 Spengler Way, Turlock CA 95380
Tel (209) 668-2100
SIC 5143 2024 5144 2022

LEPRINO FOODS CO p 857
1830 W 38th Ave, Denver CO 80211
Tel (303) 480-2600 SIC 2022

BORDEN DAIRY CO OF FLORIDA LLC p 201
308 Avenue G Sw, Winter Haven FL 33880
Tel (863) 297-7300
SIC 5143 2026 2024 2022 2021

GLANBIA INC p 614
121 4th Ave S, Twin Falls ID 83301
Tel (208) 733-7555 SIC 2022

CHEESE MERCHANTS OF AMERICA LLC p 292
1301 Schiferl Rd, Bartlett IL 60103
Tel (630) 221-0580 SIC 5143 2022

BEL BRANDS USA INC p 169
30 S Wacker Dr Ste 3000, Chicago IL 60606
Tel (312) 462-1500 SIC 2022

■ CONAGRA DAIRY FOODS CO INC p 354
222 Merchandise Mart Plz, Chicago IL 60654
Tel (630) 848-0975 SIC 2022

BERNER FOOD & BEVERAGE LLC p 176
2034 E Factory Rd, Dakota IL 61018
Tel (815) 563-4222
SIC 2022 2026 2095 2086 2033

■ MONDELEZ GLOBAL LLC p 983
3 Parkway N Ste 300, Deerfield IL 60015
Tel (847) 943-4000
SIC 2052 2066 3999 2067 2022 2087

▲ MONDELEZ INTERNATIONAL INC p 983
3 Parkway N Ste 300, Deerfield IL 60015
Tel (847) 943-4000
SIC 2022 2013 2095 2043 2035 2087

CARL BUDDIG AND CO p 256
950 175th St, Homewood IL 60430
Tel (708) 798-0900 SIC 2013 2022

SAPUTO CHEESE USA INC p 1282
1 Overlook Pt Ste 300, Lincolnshire IL 60069
Tel (847) 267-1100 SIC 2022

WISCON CORP p 1618
2050 N 15th Ave, Melrose Park IL 60160
Tel (708) 450-0074 SIC 5143 2022

KRAFT FOODS GROUP INC p 829
3 Lakes Dr, Northfield IL 60093
Tel (847) 646-2000
SIC 2022 3411 2095 2043 2035 2087

SWISS VALLEY FARMS COOPERATIVE p 1413
247 Research Pkwy, Davenport IA 52806
Tel (563) 468-6600
SIC 5143 2022 5191 2023

HP HOOD LLC p 714
6 Kimball Ln Ste 400, Lynnfield MA 01940
Tel (617) 887-8441 SIC 2026 2024 2022

AGRI-MARK INC p 36
100 Milk St Ste 5, Methuen MA 01844
Tel (978) 689-4442 SIC 2026 2022

DAVISCO FOODS INTERNATIONAL INC p 416
704 Mainstreet, Eden Prairie MN 55343
Tel (952) 914-0400 SIC 2023 2022

FIRST DISTRICT ASSOCIATION p 546
101 S Swift Ave, Litchfield MN 55355
Tel (320) 693-3236 SIC 2023 2022 2026

ASSOCIATED MILK PRODUCERS INC p 121
315 N Brdwy St, New Ulm MN 56073
Tel (507) 354-8295
SIC 2023 2022 2021 2024 2026 5143

BONGARDS CREAMERIES p 200
13200 County Road 51, Norwood MN 55368
Tel (952) 466-5521
SIC 2023 2022 5451 2021

DAIRY FARMERS OF AMERICA INC p 408
10220 N Ambassador Dr, Kansas City MO 64153
Tel (816) 801-6455
SIC 2026 2023 2021 2022 5083 2024

DAIRICONCEPTS LP p 408
3253 E Chestnut Expy, Springfield MO 65802
Tel (417) 829-3400 SIC 2022

ARTHUR SCHUMAN INC p 114
40 New Dutch Ln, Fairfield NJ 07004
Tel (973) 227-0030 SIC 2022

LOSURDO FOODS INC p 879
20 Owens Rd, Hackensack NJ 07601
Tel (201) 343-6680
SIC 5141 2022 2033 2045

TROPICAL CHEESE INDUSTRIES INC p 1484
452 Fayette St, Perth Amboy NJ 08861
Tel (732) 442-4898 SIC 2022 5143

SOUTHWEST CHEESE CO LLC p 1351
1141 Cr N Ste 4, Clovis NM 88101
Tel (575) 742-9200 SIC 5143 2022

LACTALIS AMERICAN GROUP INC p 837
2376 S Park Ave, Buffalo NY 14220
Tel (716) 823-6262 SIC 2022

EMPIRE CHEESE INC p 493
4520 County Road 6, Cuba NY 14727
Tel (585) 968-1552 SIC 2022

LACTALIS DELI INC p 837
77 Water St Fl Mezz, New York NY 10005
Tel (212) 758-6666 SIC 5143 2022

BREWSTER CHEESE CO p 210
800 Wabash Ave S, Brewster OH 44613
Tel (330) 767-3492 SIC 2022

■ INTER AMERICAN PRODUCTS INC p 750
1240 State Ave, Cincinnati OH 45204
Tel (800) 645-2233
SIC 2095 2099 2033 2079 2087 2022

LAKEVIEW FARMS LLC p 840
1600 Gressel Dr, Delphos OH 45833
Tel (419) 695-9925 SIC 2026 2099 2022

GREAT LAKES CHEESE CO INC p 633
17825 Great Lakes Pkwy, Hiram OH 44234
Tel (440) 834-2500 SIC 5143 2022

BIERY CHEESE CO p 181
6544 Paris Ave, Louisville OH 44641
Tel (330) 875-3381 SIC 2022

COLUMBIA RIVER PROCESSING INC p 341
79588 Rippee Rd, Boardman OR 97818
Tel (541) 481-3770 SIC 2022

TILLAMOOK COUNTY CREAMERY ASSOCIATION p 1453
4185 Highway 101 N, Tillamook OR 97141
Tel (503) 842-4481 SIC 2022 2024 2021

AFP ADVANCED FOOD PRODUCTS LLC p 33
402 S Custer Ave, New Holland PA 17557
Tel (717) 355-8667
SIC 2026 2035 2032 2099 2022

ALOUETTE CHEESE USA LLC p 60
400 S Custer Ave, New Holland PA 17557
Tel (717) 355-8500 SIC 5143 2022

ZAUSNER FOODS CORP p 1641
400 S Custer Ave, New Holland PA 17557
Tel (717) 355-8505 SIC 2022 2032 6794

VALLEY QUEEN CHEESE FACTORY INC p 1541
200 E Railway Ave, Milbank SD 57252
Tel (605) 432-4563 SIC 2022

▲ BRIDGFORD INDUSTRIES INC p 212
1601 S Good Latimer Expy, Dallas TX 75226
Tel (214) 428-1535
SIC 2045 2099 2015 2013 2022 2038

GOSSNER FOODS INC p 626
1051 N 1000 W, Logan UT 84321
Tel (435) 713-6100 SIC 2022 2026 2021

CABOT CREAMERY COOPERATIVE INC p 235
193 Home Farm Way, Waitsfield VT 05673
Tel (978) 552-5500 SIC 2022 5143 5451

DARIGOLD INC p 412
1130 Rainier Ave S, Seattle WA 98144
Tel (206) 284-7220
SIC 2023 2026 2022 5143

AGROPUR INC p 36
3500 E Destination Dr # 200, Appleton WI 54915
Tel (920) 944-0990 SIC 2022

FOREMOST FARMS USA COOPERATIVE p 566
E10889 Penny Ln, Baraboo WI 53913
Tel (608) 355-8700
SIC 2022 2026 2023 2021

KERRY HOLDING CO p 813
3330 Millington Rd, Beloit WI 53511
Tel (608) 363-1200
SIC 2099 2079 2023 2022 2087

DAIRYFOOD USA INC p 409
2819 County Road F, Blue Mounds WI 53517
Tel (608) 437-5598 SIC 5143 2022 2023

GRANDE CHEESE CO p 630
250 Camelot Dr, Fond Du Lac WI 54935
Tel (920) 952-7200 SIC 2022

GEHL FOODS LLC p 597
N116w15970 Main St, Germantown WI 53022
Tel (262) 251-8570 SIC 2022 5451

BELGIOIOSO CHEESE p 169
4200 Main St, Green Bay WI 54311
Tel (920) 863-2123 SIC 2022

SCHREIBER FOODS INC p 1290
400 N Washington St, Green Bay WI 54301
Tel (920) 437-7601 SIC 2022 3556 3565

MARATHON CHEESE CORP p 904
304 East St, Marathon WI 54448
Tel (715) 443-2211 SIC 2022 5143

WISCONSIN CHEESE GROUP LLC p 1618
105 3rd St, Monroe WI 53566
Tel (608) 325-8342 SIC 5143 2022

SARGENTO FOODS INC p 1282
1 Persnickety Pl, Plymouth WI 53073
Tel (920) 893-8484 SIC 2022

SARTORI CO p 1282
107 N Pleasant View Rd, Plymouth WI 53073
Tel (920) 893-6061 SIC 2022

SIC 2023 Milk, Condensed & Evaporated

NESTLE HOLDINGS INC p 1026
800 N Brand Blvd, Glendale CA 91203
Tel (818) 549-6000
SIC 2023 2032 2038 2033 2064 2026

NESTLE USA INC p 1027
800 N Brand Blvd, Glendale CA 91203
Tel (818) 549-6000
SIC 2023 2033 2064 2047 2099 2032

CALIFORNIA DAIRIES INC p 239
2000 N Plaza Dr, Visalia CA 93291
Tel (559) 625-2200 SIC 2026 2021 2023

■ CYTOSPORT INC p 406
1340 Treat Blvd Ste 350, Walnut Creek CA 94597
Tel (707) 751-3942 SIC 2023 2086

■ WWF OPERATING CO p 1629
12002 Airport Way, Broomfield CO 80021
Tel (214) 303-3400 SIC 2026 2023

▲ MUSCLEPHARM CORP p 1002
4721 Ironton St Unit A, Denver CO 80239
Tel (303) 396-6100 SIC 2023

▲ WHITEWAVE FOODS CO p 1606
1225 17th St Ste 1000, Denver CO 80202
Tel (303) 635-4500 SIC 2026 2023 2021

VALENTINE ENTERPRISES INC p 1539
1291 Progress Center Ave, Lawrenceville GA 30043
Tel (770) 995-0661 SIC 2023 2099

CREST FOODS CO INC p 392
905 Main St, Ashton IL 61006
Tel (800) 435-6972 SIC 2023 7336

▲ MEAD JOHNSON NUTRITION CO p 933
2701 Patriot Blvd, Glenview IL 60026
Tel (847) 832-2420 SIC 2023 2834

▲ LIFEWAY FOODS INC p 865
6431 Oakton St, Morton Grove IL 60053
Tel (847) 967-1010 SIC 2023 2026

▲ TREEHOUSE FOODS INC p 1475
2021 Spring Rd Ste 600, Oak Brook IL 60523
Tel (708) 483-1300
SIC 2035 2023 2032 2033 2087

SWISS VALLEY FARMS COOPERATIVE p 1413
247 Research Pkwy, Davenport IA 52806
Tel (563) 468-6600
SIC 5143 2022 5191 2023

CORBION AMERICA HOLDINGS INC p 368
7905 Quivira Rd, Lenexa KS 66215
Tel (913) 890-5500
SIC 2819 2869 2041 2023

▲ MEDIFAST INC p 938
3600 Crondall Ln, Owings Mills MD 21117
Tel (410) 581-8042 SIC 2099 2023 8093

▲ SYNUTRA INTERNATIONAL INC p 1416
2275 Res Blvd Ste 500, Rockville MD 20850
Tel (301) 840-3888 SIC 2023

■ PARTYLITE INC p 1119
59 Armstrong Rd, Plymouth MA 02360
Tel (203) 661-1926
SIC 2023 3999 3641 5199 5023

MICHIGAN MILK PRODUCERS ASSOCIATION p 961
41310 Bridge St, Novi MI 48375
Tel (248) 474-6672
SIC 5143 2023 2021 8611 2026

DAVISCO FOODS INTERNATIONAL INC p 416
704 Mainstreet, Eden Prairie MN 55343
Tel (952) 914-0400 SIC 2023 2022

RYT-WAY ACQUISITION CO LLC p 1261
21850 Grenada Ave, Lakeville MN 55044
Tel (952) 469-1417 SIC 7389 2023 3565

RYT-WAY INDUSTRIES LLC p 1261
21850 Grenada Ave, Lakeville MN 55044
Tel (952) 469-1417 SIC 7389 2023

RYT-WAY MIDCO LLC p 1261
21850 Grenada Ave, Lakeville MN 55044
Tel (952) 469-1417 SIC 7389 2023 3565

FIRST DISTRICT ASSOCIATION p 546
101 S Swift Ave, Litchfield MN 55355
Tel (320) 693-3236 SIC 2023 2022 2026

ASSOCIATED MILK PRODUCERS INC p 121
315 N Brdwy St, New Ulm MN 56073
Tel (507) 354-8295
SIC 2023 2022 2021 2024 2026 5143

BONGARDS CREAMERIES p 200
13200 County Road 51, Norwood MN 55368
Tel (952) 466-5521
SIC 2023 2022 5451 2021

PLAINVIEW MILK PRODUCTS COOPERATIVE p 1154
130 2nd St Sw, Plainview MN 55964
Tel (507) 534-3872 SIC 2023 2021

DAIRY FARMERS OF AMERICA INC p 408
10220 N Ambassador Dr, Kansas City MO 64153
Tel (816) 801-6455
SIC 2026 2023 2021 2022 5083 2024

GERBER PRODUCTS CO p 608
12 Vreeland Rd Fl 2, Florham Park NJ 07932
Tel (973) 593-7500
SIC 2023 2043 2037 2052 2086 2091

FARMLAND DAIRIES LLC p 530
520 Main Ave, Wallington NJ 07057
Tel (973) 777-2500 SIC 5143 2026 2023

O-AT-KA MILK PRODUCTS COOPERATIVE INC p 1070
700 Ellicott St, Batavia NY 14020
Tel (585) 343-0536 SIC 2023 2021 2026

RICH PRODUCTS CORP p 1232
1 Robert Rich Way, Buffalo NY 14213
Tel (716) 878-8422
SIC 2053 2092 2023 2099

■ BUY BUY BABY INC p 230
895 E Gate Blvd Ste 2, Garden City NY 11530
Tel (516) 507-3400 SIC 5641 5999 2023

▲ HAIN CELESTIAL GROUP INC p 653
1111 Marcus Ave Ste 100, New Hyde Park NY 11042
Tel (516) 587-5000
SIC 2023 2034 2096 2086 2844

SUGAR FOODS CORP p 1397
950 3rd Ave Fl 21, New York NY 10022
Tel (212) 753-6900
SIC 2869 2023 2099 2068 7389

BESTCO INC p 177
288 Mazeppa Rd, Mooresville NC 28115
Tel (704) 664-4300 SIC 2023

▲ J M SMUCKER CO p 771
1 Strawberry Ln, Orrville OH 44667
Tel (330) 682-3000
SIC 2099 2033 2023 2087 2035

EAGLE FAMILY FOODS GROUP LLC p 468
4020 Kinross Lakes Pkwy, Richfield OH 44286
Tel (330) 382-3725 SIC 2023

OFD FOODS INC p 1075
525 25th Ave Sw, Albany OR 97322
Tel (541) 926-6001
SIC 2013 2015 2091 2032 2023

■ GENERAL NUTRITION CENTERS INC p 601
300 6th Ave, Pittsburgh PA 15222
Tel (412) 288-4600 SIC 5499 2023

CHATTEM INC p 292
1715 W 38th St, Chattanooga TN 37409
Tel (423) 821-4571
SIC 2834 2844 2023 5963

LONE STAR DAIRY PRODUCTS LLC p 875
401 Highway 60, Canyon TX 79015
Tel (806) 567-5623 SIC 2023

■ DEAN HOLDING CO p 420
2711 N Haskell Ave, Dallas TX 75204
Tel (214) 303-3400 SIC 2023 5143 5451

SAPUTO DAIRY FOODS USA LLC p 1282
2711 N Haske Ave Ste 3700, Dallas TX 75204
Tel (214) 863-2300 SIC 2023 2015 2026

KANEKA AMERICAS HOLDING INC p 802
6250 Underwood Rd, Pasadena TX 77507
Tel (281) 474-7084 SIC 2023

KANEKA NORTH AMERICA LLC p 802
6161 Underwood Rd, Pasadena TX 77507
Tel (281) 474-7084 SIC 2821 3081 2023

MAPLE MOUNTAIN ENTERPRISES INC p 903
588 S 2000 W, Springville UT 84663
Tel (801) 418-2000 SIC 2023

ST ALBANS COOPERATIVE CREAMERY INC p 1364
140 Federal St, Saint Albans VT 05478
Tel (802) 524-9366 SIC 2026 2023

VALLEY MILK PRODUCTS LLC p 1541
412 E King St, Strasburg VA 22657
Tel (540) 465-5113 SIC 2023 2021

DARIGOLD INC p 412
1130 Rainier Ave S, Seattle WA 98144
Tel (206) 284-7220
SIC 2023 2026 2022 5143

FOREMOST FARMS USA COOPERATIVE p 566
E10889 Penny Ln, Baraboo WI 53913
Tel (608) 355-8700
SIC 2022 2026 2023 2021

KERRY HOLDING CO p 813
3330 Millington Rd, Beloit WI 53511
Tel (608) 363-1200
SIC 2099 2079 2023 2022 2087

DAIRYFOOD USA INC p 409
2819 County Road F, Blue Mounds WI 53517
Tel (608) 437-5598 SIC 5143 2022 2023

AGROPUR MSI LLC p 36
2340 Enterprise Ave, La Crosse WI 54603
Tel (608) 781-2345 SIC 2023

■ CENTURY FOODS INTERNATIONAL LLC p 282
400 Century Ct, Sparta WI 54656
Tel (608) 269-1900 SIC 2023

SIC 2024 Ice Cream

DREYERS GRAND ICE CREAM HOLDINGS INC p 456
5929 College Ave, Oakland CA 94618
Tel (510) 652-8187 SIC 5143 5451 2024

EDYS GRAND ICE CREAM p 480
5929 College Ave, Oakland CA 94618
Tel (510) 652-8187 SIC 2024 5143

NESTLE DREYERS ICE CREAM CO p 1026
5929 College Ave, Oakland CA 94618
Tel (510) 594-9466 SIC 5812 2024

VONS COMPANIES INC p 1565
5918 Stoneridge Mall Rd, Pleasanton CA 94588
Tel (626) 821-7000 SIC 5411 2026 2024

SUPER STORE INDUSTRIES p 1406
2800 W March Ln Ste 210, Stockton CA 95219
Tel (209) 473-8100
SIC 2026 2024 5149 5142

SSI-TURLOCK DAIRY DIVISION p 1364
2600 Spengler Way, Turlock CA 95380
Tel (209) 668-2100
SIC 5143 2024 5144 2022

STEVEN-ROBERT ORIGINALS LLC p 1388
2780 Tower Rd, Aurora CO 80011
Tel (303) 375-9925 SIC 2053 2024 2099

THOMAS J LIPTON INC p 1448
75 Merritt Blvd, Trumbull CT 06611
Tel (206) 381-3500
SIC 2099 2034 2035 2033 2098 2024

BORDEN DAIRY CO OF FLORIDA LLC p 201
308 Avenue G Sw, Winter Haven FL 33880
Tel (863) 297-7300
SIC 5143 2026 2024 2022 2021

BALDWIN RICHARDSON FOODS CO p 147
1 Tower Ln, Oakbrook Terrace IL 60181
Tel (815) 464-9994 SIC 2024

JEL SERT CO p 782
Conde St Rr 59, West Chicago IL 60185
Tel (630) 231-7590
SIC 2087 2024 2099 5499 5143

WELLS ENTERPRISES INC p 1590
1 Blue Bunny Dr Sw, Le Mars IA 51031
Tel (712) 546-4000 SIC 2024

SURE WINNER FOODS INC p 1408
2 Lehner Rd, Saco ME 04072
Tel (207) 282-1258 SIC 5143 4226 2024

HP HOOD LLC p 714
6 Kimball Ln Ste 400, Lynnfield MA 01940
Tel (617) 887-8441 SIC 2026 2024 2022

DIANNES FINE DESSERT INC p 437
4 Graf Rd, Newburyport MA 01950
Tel (978) 463-3832 SIC 2024

FREEZE OPERATIONS HOLDING CORP p 577
1855 Boston Rd, Wilbraham MA 01095
Tel (413) 543-2445 SIC 5812 2024 5143

FRIENDLYS ICE CREAM LLC p 580
1855 Boston Rd, Wilbraham MA 01095
Tel (413) 731-4000 SIC 2024 5812

■ COUNTRY FRESH LLC p 375
2555 Buchanan Ave Sw, Grand Rapids MI 49548
Tel (616) 243-0173 SIC 2026 2024 2097

SCHWAN FOOD CO p 1291
115 W College Dr, Marshall MN 56258
Tel (507) 532-3274 SIC 2038 2024 2037

▲ GENERAL MILLS INC p 601
1 General Mills Blvd, Minneapolis MN 55426
Tel (763) 764-7600
SIC 2099 2041 2045 2064 2024

■ MICHAEL FOODS OF DELAWARE INC p 960
301 Carlson Pkwy Ste 400, Minnetonka MN 55305
Tel (952) 258-4000
SIC 0252 2015 5144 5143 5148 2024

ASSOCIATED MILK PRODUCERS INC p 121
315 N Brdwy St, New Ulm MN 56073
Tel (507) 354-8295
SIC 2023 2022 2021 2024 2026 5143

KEMPS LLC p 810
1270 Energy Ln, Saint Paul MN 55108
Tel (651) 379-6500 SIC 2026 2024

DAIRY FARMERS OF AMERICA INC p 408
10220 N Ambassador Dr, Kansas City MO 64153
Tel (816) 801-6455
SIC 2026 2023 2021 2022 5083 2024

ICE CREAM SPECIALTIES INC p 727
8419 Hanley Industrial Ct, Saint Louis MO 63144
Tel (314) 962-2550 SIC 2024

HILAND DAIRY FOODS CO LLC p 692
1133 E Kearney St, Springfield MO 65803
Tel (417) 862-9311
SIC 2026 2024 2037 5143

CONOPCO INC p 358
700 Sylvan Ave, Englewood Cliffs NJ 07632
Tel (201) 894-2727
SIC 2035 2038 2086 2024 2844 2841

UNILEVER UNITED STATES INC p 1503
700 Sylvan Ave, Englewood Cliffs NJ 07632
Tel (201) 894-4000
SIC 2035 2086 2024 2038 2844 2841

▲ J & J SNACK FOODS CORP p 770
6000 Central Hwy, Pennsauken NJ 08109
Tel (856) 665-9533
SIC 2053 2087 2086 2024 2052 2051

CROWLEY FOODS INC p 394
93 Pennsylvania Ave, Binghamton NY 13903
Tel (800) 637-0019 SIC 2026 2024

FFC HOLDING CORP AND SUBSIDIARIES p 539
1 Ice Cream Dr, Dunkirk NY 14048
Tel (716) 366-5400 SIC 2024

FIELDBROOK FOODS CORP p 541
1 Ice Cream Dr, Dunkirk NY 14048
Tel (716) 366-5400 SIC 2024

HOUSE OF SPICES (INDIA) INC p 711
12740 Willets Point Blvd, Flushing NY 11368
Tel (718) 507-4900
SIC 5149 2099 5153 2033 2024

BYRNE DAIRY INC p 231
2394 Us Route 11, La Fayette NY 13084
Tel (315) 475-2121 SIC 2026 2024

ALAMANCE FOODS INC p 43
840 Plantation Dr, Burlington NC 27215
Tel (336) 226-6392
SIC 2026 2899 2024 2086

MAOLA MILK AND ICE CREAM CO LLC p 903
305 Avenue C, New Bern NC 28560
Tel (252) 638-1131 SIC 2026 2024

GRAETERS MANUFACTURING CO p 628
1175 Regina Graeter Way, Cincinnati OH 45216
Tel (513) 721-3323
SIC 2024 2051 2064 2066

UNITED DAIRY FARMERS INC p 1507
3955 Montgomery Rd, Cincinnati OH 45212
Tel (513) 396-8700
SIC 5411 5143 2026 2024 5541 5451

UNITED DAIRY INC p 1507
300 N 5th St, Martins Ferry OH 43935
Tel (740) 633-1451 SIC 2026 2024

SMITHFOODS ORRVILLE INC p 1334
1381 Dairy Ln, Orrville OH 44667
Tel (330) 683-8710 SIC 2026 2024

TILLAMOOK COUNTY CREAMERY ASSOCIATION p 1453
4185 Highway 101 N, Tillamook OR 97141
Tel (503) 842-4481 SIC 2022 2024 2021

■ TURKEY HILL LP p 1492
2601 River Rd, Conestoga PA 17516
Tel (717) 872-5461 SIC 2026 2024

HERSHEY CREAMERY CO p 687
301 S Cameron St, Harrisburg PA 17101
Tel (717) 238-8134 SIC 2024

GALLIKER DAIRY CO p 590
143 Donald Ln, Johnstown PA 15904
Tel (814) 266-8702 SIC 2026 2086 2024

■ MAYFIELD DAIRY FARMS LLC p 923
806 E Madison Ave, Athens TN 37303
Tel (423) 745-2151 SIC 2026 2024

■ LAND-O-SUN DAIRIES LLC p 842
2900 Bristol Hwy, Johnson City TN 37601
Tel (423) 283-5700 SIC 2026 2024 5143

BLUE BELL CREAMERIES INC p 190
1101 S Blue Bell Rd, Brenham TX 77833
Tel (817) 560-1980 SIC 2024

BLUE BELL CREAMERIES LP p 190
1101 S Blue Bell Rd, Brenham TX 77833
Tel (979) 836-7977 SIC 2024 5143

BLUE BELL CREAMERIES USA INC p 190
1101 S Blue Bell Rd, Brenham TX 77833
Tel (979) 836-7977 SIC 2024

VASARI LLC p 1545
550 Bailey Ave Ste 650, Fort Worth TX 76107
Tel (888) 685-1847 SIC 2024

BEN & JERRYS HOMEMADE INC p 172
30 Community Dr Ste 1, South Burlington VT 05403
Tel (802) 846-1500 SIC 2024 5812 6794

MARS INC p 910
6885 Elm St, Mc Lean VA 22101
Tel (703) 821-4900
SIC 2044 2024 2066 2064 5812

■ HAIN REFRIGERATED FOODS INC p 653
21707 66th Ave W, Mountlake Terrace WA 98043
Tel (425) 485-2476 SIC 2024 5143

SIC 2026 Milk

SHAMROCK FOODS CO p 1311
3900 E Camelback Rd # 300, Phoenix AZ 85018
Tel (602) 477-2500
SIC 5146 5149 5147 5148 5142 2026

■ ALTA-DENA CERTIFIED DAIRY LLC p 61
17637 E Valley Blvd, City Of Industry CA 91744
Tel (626) 964-6401 SIC 2026

ROCKVIEW DAIRIES INC p 1245
7011 Stewart And Gray Rd, Downey CA 90241
Tel (562) 927-5511 SIC 5149 5143 2026

DRIFTWOOD DAIRY INC p 456
10724 Lower Azusa Rd, El Monte CA 91731
Tel (626) 444-9591 SIC 2026

LYONS MAGNUS INC p 888
3158 E Hamilton Ave, Fresno CA 93702
Tel (559) 268-5966 SIC 2033 2026 2087

NESTLE HOLDINGS INC p 1026
800 N Brand Blvd, Glendale CA 91203
Tel (818) 549-6000
SIC 2023 2032 2038 2033 2064 2026

■ BERKELEY FARMS LLC p 175
25500 Clawiter Rd, Hayward CA 94545
Tel (510) 265-8600 SIC 5143 2026 0241

FOSTER DAIRY PRODUCTS DISTRIBUTING p 570
529 Kansas Ave, Modesto CA 95351
Tel (209) 576-3400 SIC 5143 2026

VONS COMPANIES INC p 1565
5918 Stoneridge Mall Rd, Pleasanton CA 94588
Tel (626) 821-7000 SIC 5411 2026 2024

STREMICKS HERITAGE FOODS LLC p 1393
4002 Westminster Ave, Santa Ana CA 92703
Tel (714) 775-5000 SIC 2026

SUPER STORE INDUSTRIES p 1406
2800 W March Ln Ste 210, Stockton CA 95219
Tel (209) 473-8100
SIC 2026 2024 5149 5142

CALIFORNIA DAIRIES INC p 239
2000 N Plaza Dr, Visalia CA 93291
Tel (559) 625-2200 SIC 2026 2021 2023

■ WWF OPERATING CO p 1629
12002 Airport Way, Broomfield CO 80021
Tel (214) 303-3400 SIC 2026 2023

SINTON DAIRY FOODS CO LLC p 1326
3801 Sinton Rd, Colorado Springs CO 80907
Tel (719) 633-3821 SIC 2026

▲ WHITEWAVE FOODS CO p 1606
1225 17th St Ste 1000, Denver CO 80202
Tel (303) 635-4500 SIC 2026 2023 2021

YOFARM CO p 1636
141a Sheridan Dr Ste A, Naugatuck CT 06770
Tel (203) 720-0000 SIC 2026

BORDEN DAIRY CO OF FLORIDA LLC p 201
308 Avenue G Sw, Winter Haven FL 33880
Tel (863) 297-7300
SIC 5143 2026 2024 2022 2021

PRAIRIE FARMS DAIRY INC p 1167
1100 Broadway, Carlinville IL 62626
Tel (217) 854-2547 SIC 2026

BERNER FOOD & BEVERAGE LLC p 176
2034 E Factory Rd, Dakota IL 61018
Tel (815) 563-4222
SIC 2022 2026 2095 2086 2033

▲ LIFEWAY FOODS INC p 865
6431 Oakton St, Morton Grove IL 60053
Tel (847) 967-1010 SIC 2023 2026

CLOVERLAND DAIRY LIMITED PARTNERSHIP p 328
2701 Loch Raven Rd, Baltimore MD 21218
Tel (410) 235-4477 SIC 2026

CUMBERLAND FARMS INC p 400
100 Crossing Blvd, Framingham MA 01702
Tel (508) 270-1400
SIC 5411 5541 5172 2086 2051 2026

■ GARELICK FARMS LLC p 592
1199 W Central St Ste 1, Franklin MA 02038
Tel (508) 528-9000 SIC 2026

HP HOOD LLC p 714
6 Kimball Ln Ste 400, Lynnfield MA 01940
Tel (617) 887-8441 SIC 2026 2024 2022

AGRI-MARK INC p 36
100 Milk St Ste 5, Methuen MA 01844
Tel (978) 689-4442 SIC 2026 2022

MELODY FOODS INC p 941
30777 Northwestern Hwy # 300, Farmington Hills MI 48334
Tel (248) 851-6990
SIC 5143 2026 5149 5145

■ COUNTRY FRESH LLC p 375
2555 Buchanan Ave Sw, Grand Rapids MI 49548
Tel (616) 243-0173 SIC 2026 2024 2097

MICHIGAN MILK PRODUCERS ASSOCIATION p 961
41310 Bridge St, Novi MI 48375
Tel (248) 474-6672
SIC 5143 2023 2021 8611 2026

MILK SPECIALTIES CO p 969
7500 Flying Cloud Dr # 500, Eden Prairie MN 55344
Tel (952) 942-7310 SIC 2026 2834 5149

FIRST DISTRICT ASSOCIATION p 546
101 S Swift Ave, Litchfield MN 55355
Tel (320) 693-3236 SIC 2023 2022 2026

ASSOCIATED MILK PRODUCERS INC p 121
315 N Brdwy St, New Ulm MN 56073
Tel (507) 354-8295
SIC 2023 2022 2021 2024 2026 5143

KEMPS LLC p 810
1270 Energy Ln, Saint Paul MN 55108
Tel (651) 379-6500 SIC 2026 2024

DAIRY FARMERS OF AMERICA INC p 408
10220 N Ambassador Dr, Kansas City MO 64153
Tel (816) 801-6455
SIC 2026 2023 2021 2022 5083 2024

HILAND DAIRY FOODS CO LLC p 692
1133 E Kearney St, Springfield MO 65803
Tel (417) 862-9311
SIC 2026 2024 2037 5143

ROBERTS DAIRY CO LLC p 1242
2901 Cuming St, Omaha NE 68131
Tel (402) 344-4321 SIC 2026 5812

■ MODEL DAIRY LLC p 981
500 Gould St, Reno NV 89502
Tel (775) 788-7900 SIC 2026 5143

JOHANNA FOODS INC p 787
20 Johanna Farms Rd, Flemington NJ 08822
Tel (908) 788-2200 SIC 2033 2026

WAKEFERN FOOD CORP p 1572
5000 Riverside Dr, Keasbey NJ 08832
Tel (908) 527-3300
SIC 5141 5149 5411 4213 2026

FARMLAND DAIRIES LLC p 530
520 Main Ave, Wallington NJ 07057
Tel (973) 777-2500 SIC 5143 2026 2023

READINGTON FARMS INC p 1213
12 Mill Rd, Whitehouse NJ 08888
Tel (908) 534-2121 SIC 2026

O-AT-KA MILK PRODUCTS COOPERATIVE INC p 1070
700 Ellicott St, Batavia NY 14020
Tel (585) 343-0536 SIC 2023 2021 2026

CROWLEY FOODS INC p 394
93 Pennsylvania Ave, Binghamton NY 13903
Tel (800) 637-0019 SIC 2026 2024

UPSTATE NIAGARA COOPERATIVE INC p 1530
25 Anderson Rd, Buffalo NY 14225
Tel (716) 892-3156 SIC 2026

STEUBEN FOODS INC p 1388
15504 Liberty Ave, Jamaica NY 11433
Tel (718) 291-3333 SIC 2032 2026

FAGE USA DAIRY INDUSTRY INC p 524
1 Opportunity Dr, Johnstown NY 12095
Tel (518) 762-5912 SIC 2026

FAGE USA HOLDINGS p 524
1 Opportunity Dr, Johnstown NY 12095
Tel (518) 762-5912 SIC 2026 5143

BYRNE DAIRY INC p 231
2394 Us Route 11, La Fayette NY 13084
Tel (315) 475-2121 SIC 2026 2024

CHOBANI LLC p 301
147 State Highway 320, Norwich NY 13815
Tel (607) 337-1246 SIC 2026

DANNON CO INC p 412
100 Hillside Ave Fl 3, White Plains NY 10603
Tel (914) 872-8400 SIC 2026

▲ INGLES MARKETS INC p 743
2913 Us Highway 70, Black Mountain NC 28711
Tel (828) 669-2941
SIC 5411 5912 5541 2026 6512

ALAMANCE FOODS INC p 43
840 Plantation Dr, Burlington NC 27215
Tel (336) 226-6392
SIC 2026 2899 2024 2086

MAOLA MILK AND ICE CREAM CO LLC p 903
305 Avenue C, New Bern NC 28560
Tel (252) 638-1131 SIC 2026 2024

UNITED DAIRY FARMERS INC p 1507
3955 Montgomery Rd, Cincinnati OH 45212
Tel (513) 396-8700
SIC 5411 5143 2026 2024 5541 5451

LAKEVIEW FARMS LLC p 840
1600 Gressel Dr, Delphos OH 45833
Tel (419) 695-9925 SIC 2026 2099 2022

UNITED DAIRY INC p 1507
300 N 5th St, Martins Ferry OH 43935
Tel (740) 633-1451 SIC 2026 2024

SMITHFOODS ORRVILLE INC p 1334
1381 Dairy Ln, Orrville OH 44667
Tel (330) 683-8710 SIC 2026 2024

■ TURKEY HILL LP p 1492
2601 River Rd, Conestoga PA 17516
Tel (717) 872-5461 SIC 2026 2024

GALLIKER DAIRY CO p 590
143 Donald Ln, Johnstown PA 15904
Tel (814) 266-8702 SIC 2026 2086 2024

WAWA INC p 1584
260 W Baltimore Pike, Media PA 19063
Tel (610) 358-8000 SIC 5411 2026

AFP ADVANCED FOOD PRODUCTS LLC p 33
402 S Custer Ave, New Holland PA 17557
Tel (717) 355-8667
SIC 2026 2035 2032 2099 2022

■ DEAN DAIRY PRODUCTS CO p 420
1690 Oneida Ln, Sharpsville PA 16150
Tel (724) 962-7801 SIC 2026

SUIZA DAIRY CORP p 1397
131 De Diego Ave, San Juan PR 00921
Tel (787) 792-7300 SIC 2026 2037

ORION FOOD SYSTEMS LLC p 1094
2930 W Maple St, Sioux Falls SD 57107
Tel (605) 336-6961
SIC 5149 2033 2026 2041

■ MAYFIELD DAIRY FARMS LLC p 923
806 E Madison Ave, Athens TN 37303
Tel (423) 745-2151 SIC 2026 2024

■ LAND-O-SUN DAIRIES LLC p 842
2900 Bristol Hwy, Johnson City TN 37601
Tel (423) 283-5700 SIC 2026 2024 5143

TURNER HOLDINGS LLC p 1492
2040 Madison Ave, Memphis TN 38104
Tel (901) 726-5684 SIC 2026

PURITY DAIRIES LLC p 1192
360 Murfreesboro Pike, Nashville TN 37210
Tel (615) 760-2296 SIC 2026

AFFILIATED FOODS INC p 32
1401 W Farmers Ave, Amarillo TX 79118
Tel (806) 345-7773
SIC 5141 2026 2051 5149 6153
PLAINS DAIRY LLC p 1153
300 N Taylor St, Amarillo TX 79107
Tel (806) 374-0385 *SIC* 2026 2086 2033
DAISY BRAND LLC p 409
12750 Merit Dr Ste 600, Dallas TX 75251
Tel (972) 726-0800 *SIC* 2026
■ **DEAN DAIRY HOLDINGS LLC** p 420
2515 Mckinney Ave # 1100, Dallas TX 75201
Tel (214) 303-3400 *SIC* 6719 2026
▲ **DEAN FOODS CO** p 420
2711 N Haskell Ave, Dallas TX 75204
Tel (214) 303-3400 *SIC* 2026 2033 5143
■ **DEAN WEST II LLC** p 420
2515 Mckinney Ave # 1100, Dallas TX 75201
Tel (214) 303-3400 *SIC* 2026
SAPUTO DAIRY FOODS USA LLC p 1282
2711 N Haske Ave Ste 3700, Dallas TX 75204
Tel (214) 863-2300 *SIC* 2023 2015 2026
SFG MANAGEMENT LIMITED LIABILITY CO p 1310
3114 S Haskell Ave, Dallas TX 75223
Tel (214) 824-8163 *SIC* 2026
■ **SOUTHERN FOODS GROUP LLC** p 1348
3114 S Haskell Ave, Dallas TX 75223
Tel (214) 824-8163 *SIC* 2026
GOSSNER FOODS INC p 626
1051 N 1000 W, Logan UT 84321
Tel (435) 713-6100 *SIC* 2022 2026 2021
ST ALBANS COOPERATIVE CREAMERY INC p 1364
140 Federal St, Saint Albans VT 05478
Tel (802) 524-9366 *SIC* 2026 2023
■ **RICHFOOD INC** p 1233
8258 Richfood Rd, Mechanicsville VA 23116
Tel (804) 746-6000
SIC 5141 5147 5142 5148 5143 2026
MARYLAND AND VIRGINIA MILK PRODUCERS COOPERATIVE ASSOCIATION INC p 914
1985 Isaac Newton Sq W # 200, Reston VA 20190
Tel (703) 742-6800 *SIC* 5143 2026 5084
DARIGOLD INC p 412
1130 Rainier Ave S, Seattle WA 98144
Tel (206) 284-7220
SIC 2023 2026 2022 5143
FOREMOST FARMS USA COOPERATIVE p 566
E10889 Penny Ln, Baraboo WI 53913
Tel (608) 355-8700
SIC 2022 2026 2023 2021

SIC 2032 Canned Specialties

DIAL CORP p 436
7201 E Henkel Way, Scottsdale AZ 85255
Tel (480) 754-3425
SIC 2841 2844 2842 2032 2013
LA COSTENA USA INC p 835
8755 S Rita Rd, Tucson AZ 85747
Tel (520) 663-4720 *SIC* 2032
▲ **TYSON FOODS INC** p 1496
2200 W Don Tyson Pkwy, Springdale AR 72762
Tel (479) 290-4000
SIC 2011 2015 2032 2096 2048
TEASDALE FOODS INC p 1430
901 Packers St, Atwater CA 95301
Tel (209) 358-5616 *SIC* 2034 2032
NESTLE HOLDINGS INC p 1026
800 N Brand Blvd, Glendale CA 91203
Tel (818) 549-6000
SIC 2023 2032 2038 2033 2064 2026
NESTLE USA INC p 1027
800 N Brand Blvd, Glendale CA 91203
Tel (818) 549-6000
SIC 2023 2033 2064 2047 2099 2032
BEE BUMBLE HOLDINGS INC p 168
280 10th Ave, San Diego CA 92101
Tel (858) 715-4000 *SIC* 2013 2032 2033
BUMBLE BEE PARENT INC p 225
280 10th Ave, San Diego CA 92101
Tel (858) 715-4000 *SIC* 2013 2032 2033
OLE MEXICAN FOODS INC p 1082
6585 Crescent Dr, Norcross GA 30071
Tel (770) 582-9200 *SIC* 2099 2032
CTI FOODS HOLDING CO LLC p 399
22303 Highway 95, Wilder ID 83676
Tel (208) 482-7844 *SIC* 2013 2032 2035
▲ **TREEHOUSE FOODS INC** p 1475
2021 Spring Rd Ste 600, Oak Brook IL 60523
Tel (708) 483-1300
SIC 2035 2023 2032 2033 2087
MORGAN FOODS INC p 988
90 W Morgan St, Austin IN 47102
Tel (812) 794-1170 *SIC* 2032
■ **MEAD JOHNSON & CO LLC** p 933
2400 W Lloyd Expy, Evansville IN 47712
Tel (812) 429-5000 *SIC* 2099 2834 2032
PARK 100 FOODS INC p 1115
326 E Adams St, Tipton IN 46072
Tel (765) 675-3480 *SIC* 2013 2032 2035
STONEWALL KITCHEN LLC p 1391
2 Stonewall Ln, York ME 03909
Tel (207) 351-2713
SIC 2033 2035 2032 5149 5064
KETTLE CUISINE LLC p 814
330 Lynnway Ste 405, Lynn MA 01901
Tel (617) 409-1100 *SIC* 2032 2035
AMWAY INTERNATIONAL INC p 87
7575 Fulton St E, Ada MI 49355
Tel (616) 787-1000
SIC 5169 5122 5099 5199 2099 2032
▲ **HORMEL FOODS CORP** p 708
1 Hormel Pl, Austin MN 55912
Tel (507) 437-5611 *SIC* 2011 2013 2032
FARIBAULT FOODS INC p 528
222 S 9th St Ste 3380, Minneapolis MN 55402
Tel (612) 333-6461 *SIC* 2099 2032 2033

■ **CONAGRA GROCERY PRODUCTS CO LLC** p 354
11 Conagra Dr, Omaha NE 68102
Tel (630) 857-1000
SIC 2033 2079 2099 2032 2066 5149
▲ **CAMPBELL SOUP CO** p 245
1 Campbell Pl, Camden NJ 08103
Tel (856) 342-4800
SIC 2032 2038 2033 2052 2051 2096
NESTLE HEALTHCARE NUTRITION INC p 1026
12 Vreeland Rd Fl 2, Florham Park NJ 07932
Tel (952) 848-6000 *SIC* 2099 2032
▲ **B&G FOODS INC** p 142
4 Gatehall Dr Ste 110, Parsippany NJ 07054
Tel (973) 401-6500
SIC 2013 2032 2033 2035 2099
F&S PRODUCE CO INC p 522
913 Bridgeton Ave, Rosenhayn NJ 08352
Tel (856) 453-0316
SIC 0723 2099 2032 0181
BEECH-NUT NUTRITION CO p 168
1 Nutritious Pl, Amsterdam NY 12010
Tel (518) 839-0300 *SIC* 2032
STEUBEN FOODS INC p 1388
15504 Liberty Ave, Jamaica NY 11433
Tel (718) 291-3333 *SIC* 2032 2026
NOVARTIS CORP p 1062
520 White Plains Rd, Tarrytown NY 10591
Tel (212) 307-1122
SIC 2834 2879 2032 2865
WORNICK CO p 1626
4700 Creek Rd, Blue Ash OH 45242
Tel (800) 860-4555 *SIC* 2032
WORNICK HOLDING CO INC p 1626
4700 Creek Rd, Blue Ash OH 45242
Tel (513) 794-9800 *SIC* 2032
SKYLINE CHILI INC p 1330
4180 Thunderbird Ln, Fairfield OH 45014
Tel (513) 874-1188
SIC 5812 2038 6794 5149 2032
OFD FOODS INC p 1075
525 25th Ave Sw, Albany OR 97322
Tel (541) 926-6001
SIC 2013 2015 2091 2032 2023
HANOVER FOODS CORP p 658
1486 York St, Hanover PA 17331
Tel (717) 632-6000
SIC 2033 2032 2037 2038 2099
AFP ADVANCED FOOD PRODUCTS LLC p 33
402 S Custer Ave, New Holland PA 17557
Tel (717) 355-8667
SIC 2026 2035 2032 2099 2022
ZAUSNER FOODS CORP p 1641
400 S Custer Ave, New Holland PA 17557
Tel (717) 355-8505 *SIC* 2022 2032 6794
■ **HEINZ KRAFT FOODS CO** p 681
1 Ppg Pl Ste 3200, Pittsburgh PA 15222
Tel (412) 456-5700
SIC 2033 2038 2032 2098
▲ **KRAFT HEINZ CO** p 829
1 Ppg Pl, Pittsburgh PA 15222
Tel (412) 456-5700
SIC 2033 2038 2032 2098
GOYA DE PUERTO RICO INC p 627
Esq Calle 5 Rr 28, Bayamon PR 00961
Tel (787) 740-4900 *SIC* 2032 2033
BUSH BROTHERS & CO p 229
1016 E Weisgarber Rd, Knoxville TN 37909
Tel (865) 450-4130 *SIC* 2033 2032
LAKESIDE FOODS INC p 840
808 Hamilton St, Manitowoc WI 54220
Tel (920) 684-3356
SIC 2033 2037 2032 2038

SIC 2033 Canned Fruits, Vegetables & Preserves

SAGER CREEK FOODS INC p 1268
305 E Main St, Siloam Springs AR 72761
Tel (479) 524-6431 *SIC* 2033
VEG LIQUIDATION INC p 1546
305 E Main St, Siloam Springs AR 72761
Tel (479) 524-6431 *SIC* 2033 5142
■ **SMUCKER NATURAL FOODS INC** p 1335
37 Speedway Ave, Chico CA 95928
Tel (530) 899-5000 *SIC* 2086 2033 2087
WONDERFUL CITRUS PACKING LLC p 1622
1901 S Lexington St, Delano CA 93215
Tel (661) 720-2400 *SIC* 0723 0174 2033
LYONS MAGNUS INC p 888
3158 E Hamilton Ave, Fresno CA 93702
Tel (559) 268-5966 *SIC* 2033 2026 2087
NESTLE HOLDINGS INC p 1026
800 N Brand Blvd, Glendale CA 91203
Tel (818) 549-6000
SIC 2023 2032 2038 2033 2064 2026
NESTLE USA INC p 1027
800 N Brand Blvd, Glendale CA 91203
Tel (818) 549-6000
SIC 2023 2033 2064 2047 2099 2032
BELL-CARTER FOODS INC p 170
3742 Mt Diablo Blvd, Lafayette CA 94549
Tel (925) 284-5933 *SIC* 2033
PACIFIC COAST PRODUCERS p 1104
631 N Cliff Ave, Lodi CA 95240
Tel (209) 367-8800 *SIC* 2033
INGOMAR PACKING CO LLC p 743
9950 S Ingomar Grade, Los Banos CA 93635
Tel (209) 826-9494 *SIC* 2033
▲ **LANDEC CORP** p 842
3603 Haven Ave, Menlo Park CA 94025
Tel (650) 306-1650 *SIC* 2033 5148 5999
■ **KINGSFORD PRODUCTS CO LLC** p 821
1221 Broadway Ste 1300, Oakland CA 94612
Tel (510) 271-7000
SIC 2861 2099 2035 2033 2879
T F LOUDERBACK INC p 1419
700 National Ct, Richmond CA 94804
Tel (510) 965-6120
SIC 5181 5149 2037 2033

BEE BUMBLE HOLDINGS INC p 168
280 10th Ave, San Diego CA 92101
Tel (858) 715-4000 *SIC* 2013 2032 2033
BUMBLE BEE PARENT INC p 225
280 10th Ave, San Diego CA 92101
Tel (858) 715-4000 *SIC* 2013 2032 2033
SUNKIST GROWERS INC p 1402
27770 N Entertainment Dr # 120, Valencia CA 91355
Tel (818) 986-4800
SIC 5148 2033 2037 2899 6794 5046
DEL MONTE FOODS INC p 423
3003 Oak Rd Ste 600, Walnut Creek CA 94597
Tel (925) 949-2772 *SIC* 2033 5149
SUNNYGEM LLC p 1403
500 N F St, Wasco CA 93280
Tel (661) 758-0491 *SIC* 2033 3556
DEL MAR FOOD PRODUCTS CORP p 423
1720 Beach Rd, Watsonville CA 95076
Tel (831) 722-3516 *SIC* 2033 2099
DFC HOLDINGS LLC p 435
1 Dole Dr, Westlake Village CA 91362
Tel (818) 879-6600
SIC 0174 0175 0161 5148 2033
DHM HOLDING CO INC p 435
1 Dole Dr, Westlake Village CA 91362
Tel (818) 879-6600
SIC 0179 0174 0175 0161 5148 2033
DOLE FOOD CO INC p 448
1 Dole Dr, Westlake Village CA 91362
Tel (818) 874-4000
SIC 0179 0174 0175 0161 5148 2033
DOLE HOLDING CO LLC p 448
1 Dole Dr, Westlake Village CA 91362
Tel (818) 879-6600
SIC 0179 0174 0175 0161 5148 2033
THOMAS J LIPTON INC p 1448
75 Merritt Blvd, Trumbull CT 06611
Tel (206) 381-3500
SIC 2099 2034 2035 2033 2098 2024
■ **TROPICANA PRODUCTS INC** p 1484
1275 26th Ave E, Bradenton FL 34208
Tel (941) 747-4461
SIC 2033 2037 2086 2048
UNITED STATES SUGAR CORP p 1514
111 Ponce De Leon Ave, Clewiston FL 33440
Tel (863) 983-8121
SIC 0133 2061 2062 2033
CHIQUITA BRANDS INTERNATIONAL INC p 301
2051 Se 35th St, Fort Lauderdale FL 33316
Tel (954) 453-1201
SIC 0179 0174 0161 0175 2033
BEN HILL GRIFFIN INC p 172
700 S Scenic Hwy, Frostproof FL 33843
Tel (863) 635-2281 *SIC* 2875 0174 2033
A DUDA & SONS INC p 5
1200 Duda Trl, Oviedo FL 32765
Tel (407) 365-2111
SIC 0161 5148 2033 0133 6552 0174
LOUIS DREYFUS CITRUS INC p 879
355 9th St, Winter Garden FL 34787
Tel (407) 656-1000 *SIC* 2037 2033
G ROE WM & SONS INC p 587
500 Avenue R Sw, Winter Haven FL 33880
Tel (863) 294-3577 *SIC* 2033
▲ **COCA-COLA CO** p 333
1 Coca Cola Plz Nw, Atlanta GA 30313
Tel (404) 676-2121
SIC 2087 2086 2033 2037
■ **ODWALLA INC** p 1074
1 Coca Cola Plz Nw, Atlanta GA 30313
Tel (479) 721-6260 *SIC* 2033
■ **MAUI PINEAPPLE CO LTD** p 921
200 Village Rd, Lahaina HI 96761
Tel (808) 877-1624 *SIC* 2033
LITEHOUSE INC p 870
100 Litehouse Dr, Sandpoint ID 83864
Tel (208) 920-2000 *SIC* 2035 2033
MULLINS FOOD PRODUCTS INC p 999
2200 S 25th Ave, Broadview IL 60155
Tel (708) 344-3224 *SIC* 2033 2035
BERNER FOOD & BEVERAGE LLC p 176
2034 E Factory Rd, Dakota IL 61018
Tel (815) 563-4222
SIC 2022 2026 2095 2086 2033
LAWRENCE FOODS INC p 847
2200 Lunt Ave, Elk Grove Village IL 60007
Tel (847) 437-2400 *SIC* 2033 2099
■ **H J M P CORP** p 650
1930 George St Ste 2, Melrose Park IL 60160
Tel (708) 345-5370
SIC 2033 5149 0174 2037
▲ **TREEHOUSE FOODS INC** p 1475
2021 Spring Rd Ste 600, Oak Brook IL 60523
Tel (708) 483-1300
SIC 2035 2023 2032 2033 2087
NATION PIZZA PRODUCTS LP p 1009
601 E Algonquin Rd, Schaumburg IL 60173
Tel (847) 397-3320 *SIC* 2038 2045 2033
RED GOLD INC p 1215
1500 Tomato Country Way, Elwood IN 46036
Tel (765) 557-5500 *SIC* 2033 2035
STONEWALL KITCHEN LLC p 1391
2 Stonewall Ln, York ME 03909
Tel (207) 351-2713
SIC 2033 2035 2032 5149 5064
WELCH FOODS INC A COOPERATIVE p 1588
300 Baker Ave Ste 101, Concord MA 01742
Tel (978) 371-1000 *SIC* 2033 2037
KENS FOODS INC p 812
1 Dangelo Dr, Marlborough MA 01752
Tel (508) 229-1100 *SIC* 2033
OCEAN SPRAY CRANBERRIES INC p 1073
1 Ocean Spray Dr, Middleboro MA 02349
Tel (508) 946-1000 *SIC* 2033 2034 2037
OCEAN SPRAY INTERNATIONAL INC p 1073
1 Ocean Spray Dr, Middleboro MA 02349
Tel (508) 946-1000 *SIC* 2037 2034 2033

ROHTSTEIN CORP p 1247
70 Olympia Ave, Woburn MA 01801
Tel (781) 935-8300
SIC 5149 2099 2087 2062 2041 2033
BURNETTE FOODS INC p 228
701 S Us Highway 31, Elk Rapids MI 49629
Tel (231) 264-8116 *SIC* 2033
■ **GRAY & CO** p 632
3325 W Polk Rd, Hart MI 49420
Tel (231) 873-5628 *SIC* 2033
INDIAN SUMMER COOPERATIVE INC p 738
3958 W Chauvez Rd Ste 1, Ludington MI 49431
Tel (231) 845-6248
SIC 2033 0723 4213 2035
CHERRY CENTRAL COOPERATIVE INC p 294
1771 N Us Highway 31 S, Traverse City MI 49685
Tel (231) 946-1860 *SIC* 2033
FARIBAULT FOODS INC p 528
222 S 9th St Ste 3380, Minneapolis MN 55402
Tel (612) 333-6461 *SIC* 2099 2032 2033
■ **CONAGRA GROCERY PRODUCTS CO LLC** p 354
11 Conagra Dr, Omaha NE 68102
Tel (630) 857-1000
SIC 2033 2079 2099 2032 2066 5149
▲ **CAMPBELL SOUP CO** p 245
1 Campbell Pl, Camden NJ 08103
Tel (856) 342-4800
SIC 2032 2038 2033 2052 2051 2096
LASSONDE PAPPAS AND CO INC p 846
1 Collins Dr Ste 200, Carneys Point NJ 08069
Tel (856) 455-1000 *SIC* 2033
PAPPAS LASSONDE HOLDINGS INC p 1112
1 Collins Dr Ste 200, Carneys Point NJ 08069
Tel (856) 455-1000 *SIC* 2033 6719
JOHANNA FOODS INC p 787
20 Johanna Farms Rd, Flemington NJ 08822
Tel (908) 788-2200 *SIC* 2033 2026
LOSURDO FOODS INC p 879
20 Owens Rd, Hackensack NJ 07601
Tel (201) 343-6680
SIC 5141 2022 2033 2045
▲ **B&G FOODS INC** p 142
4 Gatehall Dr Ste 110, Parsippany NJ 07054
Tel (973) 401-6500
SIC 2013 2032 2033 2035 2099
CLIFFSTAR LLC p 326
1 Cliffstar Dr, Dunkirk NY 14048
Tel (716) 366-6100 *SIC* 2033 2086
■ **MOTTS LLP** p 993
55 Hunter Ln, Elmsford NY 10523
Tel (972) 673-8088 *SIC* 2033 5149 2087
LIDESTRI FOODS INC p 863
815 Whitney Rd W, Fairport NY 14450
Tel (585) 377-7700 *SIC* 3221 2033
HOUSE OF SPICES (INDIA) INC p 711
12740 Willets Point Blvd, Flushing NY 11368
Tel (718) 507-4900
SIC 5149 2099 5153 2033 2024
■ **CARRIAGE HOUSE COMPANIES INC** p 260
196 Newton St, Fredonia NY 14063
Tel (716) 672-4321
SIC 2099 2033 2035 2087
▲ **SENECA FOODS CORP** p 1303
3736 S Main St, Marion NY 14505
Tel (315) 926-8100 *SIC* 2033 2037
■ **SPF HOLDINGS II LLC** p 1358
9 W 57th St Ste 4200, New York NY 10019
Tel (212) 750-8300
SIC 2033 5149 6719 2099
BIRDS EYE HOLDINGS INC p 185
90 Linden Park, Rochester NY 14625
Tel (585) 383-1850
SIC 2033 2013 2035 2096
NATIONAL GRAPE CO-OPERATIVE ASSOCIATION INC p 1012
80 State St, Westfield NY 14787
Tel (716) 326-5200 *SIC* 2033 2037
COUNTRY PURE FOODS INC p 375
681 W Waterloo Rd, Akron OH 44314
Tel (330) 753-2293 *SIC* 2033 2037 2086
NATURAL COUNTRY FARMS INC p 1018
681 W Waterloo Rd, Akron OH 44314
Tel (330) 753-2293 *SIC* 2033 2037 2086
■ **INTER AMERICAN PRODUCTS INC** p 750
1240 State Ave, Cincinnati OH 45204
Tel (800) 645-2233
SIC 2095 2099 2033 2079 2087 2022
■ **PORTION PAC INC** p 1163
7325 Snider Rd, Mason OH 45040
Tel (513) 398-0400 *SIC* 2033 2035
▲ **J M SMUCKER CO** p 771
1 Strawberry Ln, Orrville OH 44667
Tel (330) 682-3000
SIC 2099 2033 2023 2087 2035
WHITLOCK PACKAGING CORP p 1607
6655 S Lewis Ave Ste 105, Tulsa OK 74136
Tel (918) 524-4029 *SIC* 2033
UNITED SALAD CO p 1511
8448 Ne 33rd Dr Ste 100, Portland OR 97211
Tel (503) 288-8300 *SIC* 5148 0175 2033
NORPAC FOODS INC p 1049
3225 25th St Se, Salem OR 97302
Tel (503) 480-2100 *SIC* 2037 2033 2038
PACIFIC FOODS OF OREGON INC p 1104
19480 Sw 97th Ave, Tualatin OR 97062
Tel (503) 692-9666 *SIC* 2033 2099 2086
HANOVER FOODS CORP p 658
1486 York St, Hanover PA 17331
Tel (717) 632-6000
SIC 2033 2032 2037 2038 2099
FURMAN FOODS INC p 585
770 Cannery Rd, Northumberland PA 17857
Tel (570) 473-3516 *SIC* 2033
KNOUSE FOODS COOPERATIVE INC p 825
800 Pach Glen Idaville Rd, Peach Glen PA 17375
Tel (717) 677-8181 *SIC* 2033

■ HEINZ KRAFT FOODS CO p 681
1 Ppg Pl Ste 3200, Pittsburgh PA 15222
Tel (412) 456-5700
SIC 2033 2038 2032 2098

▲ KRAFT HEINZ CO p 829
1 Ppg Pl, Pittsburgh PA 15222
Tel (412) 456-5700
SIC 2033 2038 2032 2098

DIGIORGIO MUSHROOM CORP p 439
1161 Park Rd, Reading PA 19605
Tel (610) 926-2139
SIC 2033 5148 2037 6512

GIORGIO FOODS INC p 613
1161 Park Rd, Reading PA 19605
Tel (610) 926-2139
SIC 2033 2037 5148 2038

AMERICAN BEVERAGE CORP p 68
1 Daily Way, Verona PA 15147
Tel (412) 828-9020 *SIC* 2033

GOYA DE PUERTO RICO INC p 627
Esq Calle 5 Rr 28, Bayamon PR 00961
Tel (787) 740-4900 *SIC* 2032 2033

MCCALL FARMS INC p 926
6615 S Irby St, Effingham SC 29541
Tel (843) 662-2223 *SIC* 2033

ORION FOOD SYSTEMS LLC p 1094
2930 W Maple St, Sioux Falls SD 57107
Tel (605) 336-6961
SIC 5149 2033 2026 2041

BUSH BROTHERS & CO p 229
1016 E Weisgarber Rd, Knoxville TN 37909
Tel (865) 450-4130 *SIC* 2033 2032

PLAINS DAIRY LLC p 1153
300 N Taylor St, Amarillo TX 79107
Tel (806) 374-0385 *SIC* 2026 2086 2033

▲ DEAN FOODS CO p 420
2711 N Haskell Ave, Dallas TX 75204
Tel (214) 303-3400 *SIC* 2026 2033 5143

RIVIANA FOODS INC p 1239
2777 Allen Pkwy Fl 15, Houston TX 77019
Tel (713) 529-3251
SIC 2044 2052 2033 5141

BOWMAN ANDROS PRODUCTS LLC p 204
10119 Old Valley Pike, Mount Jackson VA 22842
Tel (540) 217-4100 *SIC* 2033 2099 2037

NATIONAL FRUIT PRODUCT CO INC p 1012
550 Fairmont Ave, Winchester VA 22601
Tel (540) 662-3401
SIC 0723 2033 2035 2099

DAIRY EXPORT CO INC p 408
635 Elliott Ave W, Seattle WA 98119
Tel (206) 284-7220 *SIC* 5191 5083 2033

TREE TOP INC p 1475
220 E 2nd Ave, Selah WA 98942
Tel (509) 697-7251 *SIC* 2033 2034 2037

UNDERWOOD FRUIT AND WAREHOUSE CO LLC p 1502
401 N 1st Ave, Yakima WA 98902
Tel (509) 457-6177 *SIC* 5149 2033

LAKESIDE FOODS INC p 840
808 Hamilton St, Manitowoc WI 54220
Tel (920) 684-3356
SIC 2033 2037 2032 2038

SIC 2034 Dried Fruits, Vegetables & Soup

TEASDALE FOODS INC p 1430
901 Packers St, Atwater CA 95301
Tel (209) 358-5616 *SIC* 2034 2032

OLAM WEST COAST INC p 1080
205 E Rver Pk Cir Ste 310, Fresno CA 93720
Tel (559) 447-1390 *SIC* 2034

TRUE LEAF FARMS LLC p 1486
1275 San Justo Rd, San Juan Bautista CA 95045
Tel (831) 623-4667 *SIC* 2034

SENSIENT DEHYDRATED FLAVORS CO p 1304
151 S Walnut Rd, Turlock CA 95380
Tel (209) 667-2777 *SIC* 2034

MARIANI PACKING CO INC p 906
500 Crocker Dr, Vacaville CA 95688
Tel (707) 452-2800 *SIC* 0723 2034 5148

BASIC AMERICAN INC p 158
2185 N Calif Blvd Ste 215, Walnut Creek CA 94596
Tel (925) 472-4000 *SIC* 2034 2099

SUNSWEET GROWERS INC p 1404
901 N Walton Ave, Yuba City CA 95993
Tel (530) 674-5010 *SIC* 2034 2037 2086

TRINIDAD/BENHAM CORP p 1481
3650 S Yosemite St # 300, Denver CO 80237
Tel (303) 220-1400
SIC 5149 5153 2034 2099

THOMAS J LIPTON INC p 1448
75 Merritt Blvd, Trumbull CT 06611
Tel (206) 381-3500
SIC 2099 2034 2035 2033 2098 2024

IDAHOAN FOODS LLC p 728
357 Constitution Way, Idaho Falls ID 83402
Tel (208) 542-3700 *SIC* 2034

■ IDAHO-PACIFIC CORP p 728
4723 E 100 N, Rigby ID 83442
Tel (208) 538-6971 *SIC* 2034

R J VAN DRUNEN & SONS INC p 1202
300 W 6th St, Momence IL 60954
Tel (815) 472-3100
SIC 2034 2037 0161 2099

KARLIN FOODS CORP p 804
1845 Oak St Ste 19, Northfield IL 60093
Tel (847) 441-8330 *SIC* 2034

DIVERSIFIED FOODS AND SEASONINGS LLC p 444
1115 N Causeway Blvd # 200, Mandeville LA 70471
Tel (985) 809-3600 *SIC* 2099 2034

OCEAN SPRAY CRANBERRIES INC p 1073
1 Ocean Spray Dr, Middleboro MA 02349
Tel (508) 946-1000 *SIC* 2033 2034 2037

OCEAN SPRAY INTERNATIONAL INC p 1073
1 Ocean Spray Dr, Middleboro MA 02349
Tel (508) 946-1000 *SIC* 2037 2034 2033

▲ POST HOLDINGS INC p 1163
2503 S Hanley Rd, Saint Louis MO 63144
Tel (314) 644-7600
SIC 2015 2034 2038 2041 2099

KELLEY BEAN CO INC p 808
2407 Circle Dr, Scottsbluff NE 69361
Tel (308) 635-6438 *SIC* 5153 2034

UNILEVER BESTFOODS NORTH AMERICA p 1503
800 Sylvan Ave, Englewood Cliffs NJ 07632
Tel (201) 894-4000
SIC 2046 2034 2035 2098 2099 2051

FORNAZOR INTERNATIONAL INC A NEW JERSEY CORP p 568
455 Hillsdale Ave, Hillsdale NJ 07642
Tel (201) 664-4000
SIC 0119 2034 2044 2045 2075 4449

▲ HAIN CELESTIAL GROUP INC p 653
1111 Marcus Ave Ste 100, New Hyde Park NY 11042
Tel (516) 587-5000
SIC 2023 2034 2096 2086 2844

KANAN ENTERPRISES INC p 802
31900 Solon Rd, Solon OH 44139
Tel (440) 248-8484 *SIC* 2068 2034

OREGON POTATO CO p 1094
6610 W Court St Ste B, Pasco WA 99301
Tel (509) 349-8803 *SIC* 2034

TREE TOP INC p 1475
220 E 2nd Ave, Selah WA 98942
Tel (509) 697-7251 *SIC* 2033 2034 2037

SIC 2035 Pickled Fruits, Vegetables, Sauces & Dressings

VENTURA FOODS LLC p 1548
40 Pointe Dr, Brea CA 92821
Tel (714) 257-3700 *SIC* 2079 2035

▲ CLOROX CO p 327
1221 Broadway Ste 1300, Oakland CA 94612
Tel (510) 271-7000
SIC 2842 2673 2035 2844 2879

■ KINGSFORD PRODUCTS CO LLC p 821
1221 Broadway Ste 1300, Oakland CA 94612
Tel (510) 271-7000
SIC 2861 2099 2035 2033 2879

HAMPTON CREEK INC p 656
2000 Folsom St, San Francisco CA 94110
Tel (844) 423-6637 *SIC* 2035 2052

KIKKOMAN SALES USA INC p 817
50 California St Ste 3600, San Francisco CA 94111
Tel (415) 956-7750 *SIC* 5149 2035

THOMAS J LIPTON INC p 1448
75 Merritt Blvd, Trumbull CT 06611
Tel (206) 381-3500
SIC 2099 2034 2035 2033 2098 2024

■ NATURALLY FRESH INC p 1018
1000 Naturally Fresh Blvd, Atlanta GA 30349
Tel (404) 765-9000 *SIC* 2035 2099

LITEHOUSE INC p 870
100 Litehouse Dr, Sandpoint ID 83864
Tel (208) 920-2000 *SIC* 2035 2033

CTI FOODS HOLDING CO LLC p 399
22303 Highway 95, Wilder ID 83676
Tel (208) 482-7844 *SIC* 2013 2032 2035

MULLINS FOOD PRODUCTS INC p 999
2200 S 25th Ave, Broadview IL 60155
Tel (708) 344-3224 *SIC* 2033 2035

VIENNA BEEF LTD p 1556
2501 N Damen Ave, Chicago IL 60647
Tel (773) 278-7800
SIC 2013 2035 2053 5411 5149 5147

▲ MONDELEZ INTERNATIONAL INC p 983
3 Parkway N Ste 300, Deerfield IL 60015
Tel (847) 943-4000
SIC 2022 2013 2095 2043 2035 2087

■ RALCORP FROZEN BAKERY PRODUCTS INC p 1206
3250 Lacey Rd Ste 600, Downers Grove IL 60515
Tel (630) 455-5200
SIC 2051 2053 2041 2035 2656

MIZKAN AMERICA INC p 978
1661 Feehanville Dr # 200, Mount Prospect IL 60056
Tel (847) 590-0059 *SIC* 2099 2035

KRAFT FOODS GROUP INC p 829
3 Lakes Dr, Northfield IL 60093
Tel (847) 646-2000
SIC 2022 3411 2095 2043 2035 2087

▲ TREEHOUSE FOODS INC p 1475
2021 Spring Rd Ste 600, Oak Brook IL 60523
Tel (708) 483-1300
SIC 2035 2023 2032 2033 2087

RED GOLD INC p 1215
1500 Tomato Country Way, Elwood IN 46036
Tel (765) 557-5500 *SIC* 2033 2035

PARK 100 FOODS INC p 1115
326 E Adams St, Tipton IN 46072
Tel (765) 675-3480 *SIC* 2013 2032 2035

WM B REILY & CO INC p 1620
640 Magazine St, New Orleans LA 70130
Tel (504) 539-5200
SIC 2095 2035 2079 5962 5963 2099

STONEWALL KITCHEN LLC p 1391
2 Stonewall Ln, York ME 03909
Tel (207) 351-2713
SIC 2033 2035 2032 5149 5064

KETTLE CUISINE LLC p 814
330 Lynnway Ste 405, Lynn MA 01901
Tel (617) 409-1100 *SIC* 2032 2035

INDIAN SUMMER COOPERATIVE INC p 738
3958 W Chauvez Rd Ste 1, Ludington MI 49431
Tel (231) 845-6248
SIC 2033 0723 4213 2035

■ TREEHOUSE PRIVATE BRANDS INC p 1475
800 Market St, Saint Louis MO 63101
Tel (314) 877-7300
SIC 2043 2052 2068 2035

■ BIRDS EYE FOODS INC p 185
121 Woodcrest Rd, Cherry Hill NJ 08003
Tel (585) 383-1850
SIC 2037 2096 2052 2038 2035

FRENCHS FOOD CO LLC p 578
4 Mill Ridge Ln, Chester NJ 07930
Tel (973) 404-2600 *SIC* 2035

CONOPCO INC p 358
700 Sylvan Ave, Englewood Cliffs NJ 07632
Tel (201) 894-2727
SIC 2035 2038 2086 2024 2844 2841

UNILEVER BESTFOODS NORTH AMERICA p 1503
800 Sylvan Ave, Englewood Cliffs NJ 07632
Tel (201) 894-4000
SIC 2046 2034 2035 2098 2099 2051

UNILEVER UNITED STATES INC p 1503
700 Sylvan Ave, Englewood Cliffs NJ 07632
Tel (201) 894-4000
SIC 2035 2086 2024 2038 2844 2841

▲ B&G FOODS INC p 142
4 Gatehall Dr Ste 110, Parsippany NJ 07054
Tel (973) 401-6500
SIC 2013 2032 2033 2035 2099

▲ PINNACLE FOODS INC p 1149
399 Jefferson Rd, Parsippany NJ 07054
Tel (973) 541-6620 *SIC* 2038 2035

RB MANUFACTURING LLC p 1211
399 Interpace Pkwy, Parsippany NJ 07054
Tel (973) 404-2600 *SIC* 2035 2842

RECKITT BENCKISER (NORTH AMERICA) INC p 1214
399 Interpace Pkwy # 101, Parsippany NJ 07054
Tel (973) 404-2600 *SIC* 2035 2842

RECKITT BENCKISER LLC p 1214
399 Interpace Pkwy # 101, Parsippany NJ 07054
Tel (973) 404-2600 *SIC* 2035 2842

■ CARRIAGE HOUSE COMPANIES INC p 260
196 Newton St, Fredonia NY 14063
Tel (716) 672-4321
SIC 2099 2033 2035 2087

BIRDS EYE HOLDINGS INC p 185
90 Linden Park, Rochester NY 14625
Tel (585) 383-1850
SIC 2033 2013 2035 2096

PERK-UP INC p 1136
399 Knollwood Rd Ste 309, White Plains NY 10603
Tel (914) 580-3200
SIC 5113 5149 2673 3411 2674 2035

SABRA DIPPING CO LLC p 1264
777 Westchester Ave Fl 3, White Plains NY 10604
Tel (914) 372-3900 *SIC* 2035

MOUNT OLIVE PICKLE CO INC p 994
1 Cucumber Blvd, Mount Olive NC 28365
Tel (919) 658-2535 *SIC* 2035

▲ LANCASTER COLONY CORP p 841
37 W Broad St Ste 500, Columbus OH 43215
Tel (614) 224-7141 *SIC* 2035 2038

■ TMARZETTI CO p 1457
1105 Schrock Rd Fl 3, Columbus OH 43229
Tel (614) 846-2232 *SIC* 2035 2098

■ PORTION PAC INC p 1163
7325 Snider Rd, Mason OH 45040
Tel (513) 398-0400 *SIC* 2033 2035

▲ BOB EVANS FARMS INC p 196
8111 Smiths Mill Rd, New Albany OH 43054
Tel (614) 491-2225
SIC 5812 2011 2099 2035

▲ J M SMUCKER CO p 771
1 Strawberry Ln, Orrville OH 44667
Tel (330) 682-3000
SIC 2099 2033 2023 2087 2035

MEDURI FARMS INC p 939
12375 Smithfield Rd, Dallas OR 97338
Tel (503) 623-0308 *SIC* 2035

AFP ADVANCED FOOD PRODUCTS LLC p 33
402 S Custer Ave, New Holland PA 17557
Tel (717) 355-8667
SIC 2026 2035 2032 2099 2022

NATIONAL FRUIT PRODUCT CO INC p 1012
550 Fairmont Ave, Winchester VA 22601
Tel (540) 662-3401
SIC 0723 2033 2035 2099

SIC 2037 Frozen Fruits, Juices & Vegetables

▲ INVENTURE FOODS INC p 761
5415 E High St Ste 350, Phoenix AZ 85054
Tel (623) 932-6200 *SIC* 2096 2037

LANGER JUICE CO INC p 844
16195 Stephens St, City Of Industry CA 91745
Tel (626) 336-3100 *SIC* 2037

WAWONA FROZEN FOODS p 1584
100 W Alluvial Ave, Clovis CA 93611
Tel (559) 299-2901 *SIC* 2037

WINDSOR AJINOMOTO INC p 1615
4200 Concours Ste 100, Ontario CA 91764
Tel (909) 477-4700 *SIC* 2038 2037

SUNRISE GROWERS INC p 1404
701 W Kimberly Ave # 210, Placentia CA 92870
Tel (714) 630-2170 *SIC* 5148 2037

T F LOUDERBACK INC p 1419
700 National Ct, Richmond CA 94804
Tel (510) 965-6120
SIC 5181 5149 2037 2033

■ EARTHBOUND FARM LLC p 469
1721 San Juan Hwy, San Juan Bautista CA 95045
Tel (831) 623-7880 *SIC* 0723 2037 2099

SUNKIST GROWERS INC p 1402
27770 N Entertainment Dr # 120, Valencia CA 91355
Tel (818) 986-4800
SIC 5148 2033 2037 2899 6794 5046

DOLE PACKAGED FOODS LLC p 448
3059 Townsgate Rd, Westlake Village CA 91361
Tel (805) 601-5500 *SIC* 2037

SUNSWEET GROWERS INC p 1404
901 N Walton Ave, Yuba City CA 95993
Tel (530) 674-5010 *SIC* 2034 2037 2086

CUTRALE CITRUS JUICES USA INC p 403
602 Mckean St, Auburndale FL 33823
Tel (863) 528-0396 *SIC* 2037

■ TROPICANA PRODUCTS INC p 1484
1275 26th Ave E, Bradenton FL 34208
Tel (941) 747-4461
SIC 2033 2037 2086 2048

CITRUS WORLD INC p 311
20205 Hwy 27, Lake Wales FL 33853
Tel (863) 676-1411 *SIC* 2037

LOUIS DREYFUS CITRUS INC p 879
355 9th St, Winter Garden FL 34787
Tel (407) 656-1000 *SIC* 2037 2033

▲ COCA-COLA CO p 333
1 Coca Cola Plz Nw, Atlanta GA 30313
Tel (404) 676-2121
SIC 2087 2086 2033 2037

JR SIMPLOT CO p 795
999 W Main St Ste 1300, Boise ID 83702
Tel (208) 336-2110
SIC 0211 2879 2037 2874 2873

MCCAIN FOODS USA INC p 926
2275 Cabot Dr, Lisle IL 60532
Tel (630) 955-0400 *SIC* 2037

MCCAIN USA INC p 926
2275 Cabot Dr, Lisle IL 60532
Tel (800) 938-7799 *SIC* 2037 2038 5411

■ H J M P CORP p 650
1930 George St Ste 2, Melrose Park IL 60160
Tel (708) 345-5370
SIC 2033 5149 0174 2037

R J VAN DRUNEN & SONS INC p 1202
300 W 6th St, Momence IL 60954
Tel (815) 472-3100
SIC 2034 2037 0161 2099

▲ MCCORMICK & CO INC p 927
18 Loveton Cir, Sparks MD 21152
Tel (410) 771-7301
SIC 2099 2087 2038 2037

WELCH FOODS INC A COOPERATIVE p 1588
300 Baker Ave Ste 101, Concord MA 01742
Tel (978) 371-1000 *SIC* 2033 2037

OCEAN SPRAY CRANBERRIES INC p 1073
1 Ocean Spray Dr, Middleboro MA 02349
Tel (508) 946-1000 *SIC* 2033 2034 2037

OCEAN SPRAY INTERNATIONAL INC p 1073
1 Ocean Spray Dr, Middleboro MA 02349
Tel (508) 946-1000 *SIC* 2037 2034 2033

PETERSON FARMS INC p 1138
3104 W Baseline Rd, Shelby MI 49455
Tel (231) 861-6333 *SIC* 2037 0723

SCHWAN FOOD CO p 1291
115 W College Dr, Marshall MN 56258
Tel (507) 532-3274 *SIC* 2038 2024 2037

HILAND DAIRY FOODS CO LLC p 692
1133 E Kearney St, Springfield MO 65803
Tel (417) 862-9311
SIC 2026 2024 2037 5143

SEABROOK BROTHERS & SONS INC p 1296
85 Finley Rd, Bridgeton NJ 08302
Tel (856) 455-8080 *SIC* 2037

■ BIRDS EYE FOODS INC p 185
121 Woodcrest Rd, Cherry Hill NJ 08003
Tel (585) 383-1850
SIC 2037 2096 2052 2038 2035

GERBER PRODUCTS CO p 608
12 Vreeland Rd Fl 2, Florham Park NJ 07932
Tel (973) 593-7500
SIC 2023 2043 2037 2052 2086 2091

▲ SENECA FOODS CORP p 1303
3736 S Main St, Marion NY 14505
Tel (315) 926-8100 *SIC* 2033 2037

▲ PEPSICO INC p 1134
700 Anderson Hill Rd, Purchase NY 10577
Tel (914) 253-2000
SIC 2096 2087 2086 2037 2052 2043

NATIONAL GRAPE CO-OPERATIVE ASSOCIATION INC p 1012
80 State St, Westfield NY 14787
Tel (716) 326-5200 *SIC* 2033 2037

COUNTRY PURE FOODS INC p 375
681 W Waterloo Rd, Akron OH 44314
Tel (330) 753-2293 *SIC* 2033 2037 2086

NATURAL COUNTRY FARMS INC p 1018
681 W Waterloo Rd, Akron OH 44314
Tel (330) 753-2293 *SIC* 2033 2037 2086

BEVERAGES HOLDINGS LLC p 178
10300 Alliance Rd Ste 500, Blue Ash OH 45242
Tel (513) 483-3300 *SIC* 2086 2037

NESTLE PREPARED FOODS CO p 1027
5750 Harper Rd, Solon OH 44139
Tel (440) 248-3600 *SIC* 2038 5411 2037

STAHLBUSH ISLAND FARMS INC p 1374
3122 Se Stahlbush Is, Corvallis OR 97333
Tel (541) 753-8942 *SIC* 2037 0161

HERMISTON FOODS INC p 687
2250 S Highway 395, Hermiston OR 97838
Tel (541) 567-8448 *SIC* 2037

AJINOMOTO NORTH AMERICA HOLDINGS INC p 41
7124 N Marine Dr, Portland OR 97203
Tel (503) 505-5783
SIC 5142 6719 2038 2037

NORPAC FOODS INC p 1049
3225 25th St Se, Salem OR 97302
Tel (503) 480-2100 *SIC* 2037 2033 2038

SMITH FROZEN FOODS INC p 1333
101 Depot St, Weston OR 97886
Tel (541) 566-3515 *SIC* 2037

HANOVER FOODS CORP p 658
1486 York St, Hanover PA 17331
Tel (717) 632-6000
SIC 2033 2032 2037 2038 2099

■ HEINZ FROZEN FOOD CO p 681
357 6th Ave, Pittsburgh PA 15222
Tel (412) 237-5700 *SIC* 2038 2037 8741

DIGIORGIO MUSHROOM CORP p 439
1161 Park Rd, Reading PA 19605
Tel (610) 926-2139
SIC 2033 5148 2037 6512

GIORGIO FOODS INC p 613
1161 Park Rd, Reading PA 19605
Tel (610) 926-2139
SIC 2033 2037 5148 2038

SUIZA DAIRY CORP p 1397
131 De Diego Ave, San Juan PR 00921
Tel (787) 792-7300 SIC 2026 2037

PICTSWEET CO p 1146
10 Pictsweet Dr, Bells TN 38006
Tel (731) 663-7600 SIC 2037 4213

PICTSWEET LLC p 1146
10 Pictsweet Dr, Bells TN 38006
Tel (731) 422-7600 SIC 4213 2037

BOWMAN ANDROS PRODUCTS LLC p 204
10119 Old Valley Pike, Mount Jackson VA 22842
Tel (540) 217-4100 SIC 2033 2099 2037

■WESTON LAMB INC p 1602
8701 W Gage Blvd, Kennewick WA 99336
Tel (509) 735-4651 SIC 2037

■WESTON LAMB SALES INC p 1602
8701 W Gage Blvd, Kennewick WA 99336
Tel (509) 735-4651 SIC 2037

NATIONAL FROZEN FOODS CORP p 1012
1600 Frview Ave E Ste 200, Seattle WA 98102
Tel (206) 322-8900 SIC 2037

TREE TOP INC p 1475
220 E 2nd Ave, Selah WA 98942
Tel (509) 697-7251 SIC 2033 2034 2037

TWIN CITY FOODS INC p 1495
10120 269th Pl Nw, Stanwood WA 98292
Tel (206) 515-2400 SIC 2037

LAKESIDE FOODS INC p 840
808 Hamilton St, Manitowoc WI 54220
Tel (920) 684-3356
SIC 2033 2037 2032 2038

SIC 2038 Frozen Specialties

JCG FOODS OF ALABAMA LLC p 780
764 George Cagle Dr, Collinsville AL 35961
Tel (256) 524-2147 SIC 2038

■BRIDGFORD FOODS CORP p 212
1308 N Patt St, Anaheim CA 92801
Tel (714) 526-5533
SIC 2045 2099 2015 2013 2022 2038

WEI-CHUAN USA INC p 1587
6655 Garfield Ave, Bell Gardens CA 90201
Tel (323) 587-2101 SIC 5142 2038

CEDARLANE NATURAL FOODS INC p 272
1135 E Artesia Blvd, Carson CA 90746
Tel (310) 886-7720 SIC 2038

RUIZ FOOD PRODUCTS INC p 1257
501 S Alta Ave, Dinuba CA 93618
Tel (559) 591-5510 SIC 2038 2099

NISSIN FOODS (USA) CO INC p 1044
2001 W Rosecrans Ave, Gardena CA 90249
Tel (310) 327-8478 SIC 2098 2038

NESTLE HOLDINGS INC p 1026
800 N Brand Blvd, Glendale CA 91203
Tel (818) 549-6000
SIC 2023 2032 2038 2033 2064 2026

TSC HOLDINGS INC p 1489
800 N Brand Blvd, Glendale CA 91203
Tel (818) 549-6000 SIC 2038

GOODMAN FOOD PRODUCTS INC p 624
200 E Beach Ave Fl 1, Inglewood CA 90302
Tel (310) 674-3180 SIC 2038

■ICEE CO p 727
1205 S Dupont Ave, Ontario CA 91761
Tel (800) 426-4233
SIC 2038 5145 3559 2087

SPECIALTY BRANDS INC p 1356
4200 Concours Ste 100, Ontario CA 91764
Tel (909) 477-4851 SIC 2038 5142

WINDSOR AJINOMOTO INC p 1615
4200 Concours Ste 100, Ontario CA 91764
Tel (909) 477-4700 SIC 2038 2037

DON MIGUEL MEXICAN FOODS INC p 450
333 S Anita Dr Ste 1000, Orange CA 92868
Tel (714) 385-4500 SIC 2038

AMYS KITCHEN INC p 88
2330 Northpoint Pkwy, Santa Rosa CA 95407
Tel (707) 578-7188 SIC 2038 2053

CAMINO REAL FOODS INC p 245
2638 E Vernon Ave, Vernon CA 90058
Tel (323) 585-6599 SIC 2038

OVERHILL FARMS INC p 1099
2727 E Vernon Ave, Vernon CA 90058
Tel (323) 582-9977 SIC 2038

FLAGSHIP FOOD GROUP LLC p 554
6455 S Yosemite St # 140, Greenwood Village CO 80111
Tel (303) 954-4979 SIC 2038

SOUTHEAST FROZEN FOODS INC p 1346
3261 Executive Way, Miramar FL 33025
Tel (866) 289-1198 SIC 2038

GA FOOD SERVICES OF PINELLAS COUNTY INC p 588
12200 32nd Ct N, Saint Petersburg FL 33716
Tel (727) 573-2211 SIC 2038 5812

▲WESTON LAMB HOLDINGS INC p 1602
599 S Rivershore Ln, Eagle ID 83616
Tel (208) 938-1047 SIC 2038

GAA HOLDINGS INC p 588
216 8th St N, Nampa ID 83687
Tel (208) 465-5111 SIC 2038

GREAT AMERICAN SNACKS INC p 633
216 8th St N, Nampa ID 83687
Tel (208) 465-5111 SIC 2038

▲CONAGRA BRANDS INC p 354
222 Merchandise Mart Plz, Chicago IL 60654
Tel (312) 549-5000 SIC 2099 2038 2013

HEARTHSIDE FOOD SOLUTIONS LLC p 678
3250 Lacey Rd Ste 200, Downers Grove IL 60515
Tel (630) 967-3600 SIC 2043 2038

LADY LITTLE FOODS INC p 837
2323 Pratt Blvd, Elk Grove Village IL 60007
Tel (847) 806-1440 SIC 2038 2099

KRAFT PIZZA CO INC p 829
1 Kraft Ct, Glenview IL 60025
Tel (847) 646-2000 SIC 2038

MCCAIN USA INC p 926
2275 Cabot Dr, Lisle IL 60532
Tel (800) 938-7799 SIC 2037 2038 5411

GONNELLA BAKING CO p 623
1117 Wiley Rd, Schaumburg IL 60173
Tel (312) 733-2020
SIC 2051 5812 2099 2038

NATION PIZZA PRODUCTS LP p 1009
601 E Algonquin Rd, Schaumburg IL 60173
Tel (847) 397-3320 SIC 2038 2045 2033

▲MCCORMICK & CO INC p 927
18 Loveton Cir, Sparks MD 21152
Tel (410) 771-7301
SIC 2099 2087 2038 2037

RICHELIEU FOODS INC p 1233
222 Forbes Rd Ste 401, Braintree MA 02184
Tel (781) 786-6800 SIC 2038

BLOUNT FINE FOODS CORP p 190
630 Currant Rd, Fall River MA 02720
Tel (774) 888-1300 SIC 2092 2038

▲KELLOGG CO p 808
1 Kellogg Sq, Battle Creek MI 49017
Tel (269) 961-2000
SIC 2043 2041 2052 2051 2038

BELLISIO FOODS INC p 171
525 S Lake Ave Ste 201, Duluth MN 55802
Tel (218) 723-5555 SIC 2038

BERNATELLOS PIZZA INC p 176
200 Congress St W, Maple Lake MN 55358
Tel (320) 963-6191 SIC 2038

SCHWAN FOOD CO p 1291
115 W College Dr, Marshall MN 56258
Tel (507) 532-3274 SIC 2038 2024 2037

SFC GLOBAL SUPPLY CHAIN INC p 1310
115 W College Dr, Marshall MN 56258
Tel (507) 532-3274 SIC 2045 2038

■SANDERSON FARMS INC (FOODS DIVISION) p 1278
127 Flynt Rd, Laurel MS 39443
Tel (601) 649-4030 SIC 2038 2092

▲POST HOLDINGS INC p 1163
2503 S Hanley Rd, Saint Louis MO 63144
Tel (314) 644-7600
SIC 2015 2034 2038 2041 2099

▲CAMPBELL SOUP CO p 245
1 Campbell Pl, Camden NJ 08103
Tel (856) 342-4800
SIC 2032 2038 2033 2052 2051 2096

■BIRDS EYE FOODS INC p 185
121 Woodcrest Rd, Cherry Hill NJ 08003
Tel (585) 383-1850
SIC 2037 2096 2052 2038 2035

■PEAK FINANCE HOLDINGS LLC p 1126
121 Woodcrest Rd, Cherry Hill NJ 08003
Tel (856) 969-7100
SIC 2038 2092 2099 2045

CONOPCO INC p 358
700 Sylvan Ave, Englewood Cliffs NJ 07632
Tel (201) 894-2727
SIC 2035 2038 2086 2024 2844 2841

UNILEVER UNITED STATES INC p 1503
700 Sylvan Ave, Englewood Cliffs NJ 07632
Tel (201) 894-4000
SIC 2035 2086 2024 2038 2844 2841

■PINNACLE FOODS FINANCE LLC p 1149
399 Jefferson Rd, Parsippany NJ 07054
Tel (973) 541-6620
SIC 2038 2092 2099 2045

■PINNACLE FOODS GROUP LLC p 1149
399 Jefferson Rd, Parsippany NJ 07054
Tel (856) 969-7100
SIC 2038 2092 2099 2045

▲PINNACLE FOODS INC p 1149
399 Jefferson Rd, Parsippany NJ 07054
Tel (973) 541-6620 SIC 2038 2035

DIAZ FOODS p 437
4 Rosol Ln, Saddle Brook NJ 07663
Tel (404) 629-3616 SIC 2038

EL ENCANTO INC p 482
2001 4th St Sw, Albuquerque NM 87102
Tel (505) 243-2722 SIC 2038 2099

PEAK HOLDINGS LLC p 1126
345 Park Ave Fl 30, New York NY 10154
Tel (212) 583-5000
SIC 2038 2092 2099 2045

RD OFFUTT CO p 1212
700 7th St S, Fargo ND 58103
Tel (701) 526-9670 SIC 0134 2038

▲LANCASTER COLONY CORP p 841
37 W Broad St Ste 500, Columbus OH 43215
Tel (614) 224-7141 SIC 2035 2038

SKYLINE CHILI INC p 1330
4180 Thunderbird Ln, Fairfield OH 45014
Tel (513) 874-1188
SIC 5812 2038 6794 5149 2032

NESTLE PREPARED FOODS CO p 1027
5750 Harper Rd, Solon OH 44139
Tel (440) 248-3600 SIC 2038 5411 2037

STOUFFER CORP p 1392
30003 Bainbridge Rd, Solon OH 44139
Tel (440) 349-5757 SIC 2038

AJINOMOTO NORTH AMERICA HOLDINGS INC p 41
7124 N Marine Dr, Portland OR 97203
Tel (503) 505-5783
SIC 5142 6719 2038 2037

NORPAC FOODS INC p 1049
3225 25th St Se, Salem OR 97302
Tel (503) 480-2100 SIC 2037 2033 2038

HANOVER FOODS CORP p 658
1486 York St, Hanover PA 17331
Tel (717) 632-6000
SIC 2033 2032 2037 2038 2099

NE FOODS INC p 1022
1640 Freeport Rd, North East PA 16428
Tel (814) 725-4835 SIC 2038

■H J HEINZ CO LP p 650
357 6th Ave, Pittsburgh PA 15222
Tel (412) 237-5757 SIC 2038

■HEINZ FROZEN FOOD CO p 681
357 6th Ave, Pittsburgh PA 15222
Tel (412) 237-5700 SIC 2038 2037 8741

■HEINZ KRAFT FOODS CO p 681
1 Ppg Pl Ste 3200, Pittsburgh PA 15222
Tel (412) 456-5700
SIC 2033 2038 2032 2098

▲KRAFT HEINZ CO p 829
1 Ppg Pl, Pittsburgh PA 15222
Tel (412) 456-5700
SIC 2033 2038 2032 2098

GIORGIO FOODS INC p 613
1161 Park Rd, Reading PA 19605
Tel (610) 926-2139
SIC 2033 2037 5148 2038

CUSTOM FOODS OF AMERICA INC p 403
3600 Pleasant Ridge Rd, Knoxville TN 37921
Tel (865) 525-0401 SIC 2038

AUSTIN VENTURES LP p 133
300 W 6th St Ste 2300, Austin TX 78701
Tel (512) 485-1900 SIC 6799 2038

BOTTOM LINE FOOD PROCESSORS INC p 203
200 Michael Angelo Way, Austin TX 78728
Tel (512) 218-3500 SIC 2038

▲BRIDGFORD INDUSTRIES INC p 212
1601 S Good Latimer Expy, Dallas TX 75226
Tel (214) 428-1535
SIC 2045 2099 2015 2013 2022 2038

CHUNGS PRODUCTS LP p 305
3907 Dennis St, Houston TX 77004
Tel (713) 741-2118 SIC 5142 2038

WINDSOR QUALITY FOOD CO LTD p 1615
3355 W Alabama St Ste 730, Houston TX 77098
Tel (713) 843-5200 SIC 2038

CONTINENTAL MILLS INC p 363
18100 Andover Park W, Tukwila WA 98188
Tel (253) 872-8400 SIC 2045 2038

LAKESIDE FOODS INC p 840
808 Hamilton St, Manitowoc WI 54220
Tel (920) 684-3356
SIC 2033 2037 2032 2038

GOOD FOODS GROUP LLC p 623
10100 88th Ave, Pleasant Prairie WI 53158
Tel (262) 465-6900 SIC 2038 5149

SIC 2041 Flour, Grain Milling

EQUITY GROUP EUFAULA DIVISION LLC p 507
57 Melvin Clark Rd, Eufaula AL 36027
Tel (334) 687-7790
SIC 2015 2048 2041 2011

ARDENT MILLS LLC p 106
1875 Lawrence St Ste 1400, Denver CO 80202
Tel (800) 851-9618 SIC 2041 4789 8741

SOUTHEASTERN MILLS INC p 1346
333 Old Lindale Rd Se, Rome GA 30161
Tel (706) 291-6528
SIC 2099 2041 5149 2045

▲ARCHER-DANIELS-MIDLAND CO p 105
77 W Wacker Dr Ste 4600, Chicago IL 60601
Tel (312) 634-8100
SIC 2046 2041 2075 2074 5153 2083

■RALCORP FROZEN BAKERY PRODUCTS INC p 1206
3250 Lacey Rd Ste 600, Downers Grove IL 60515
Tel (630) 455-5200
SIC 2051 2053 2041 2035 2656

SIEMER MILLING CO p 1320
111 W Main St, Teutopolis IL 62467
Tel (217) 857-3131 SIC 2041

AG PLUS INC p 33
401 N Main St, South Whitley IN 46787
Tel (260) 723-5141 SIC 5191 2041 5153

▲MGP INGREDIENTS INC p 958
100 Commercial St, Atchison KS 66002
Tel (913) 367-1480 SIC 2085 2041

■MGPI PROCESSING INC p 958
100 Commercial St, Atchison KS 66002
Tel (913) 367-1480 SIC 2085 2041

CORBION AMERICA HOLDINGS INC p 368
7905 Quivira Rd, Lenexa KS 66215
Tel (913) 890-5500
SIC 2819 2869 2041 2023

■ADM MILLING CO p 23
8000 W 110th St Ste 300, Overland Park KS 66210
Tel (913) 491-9400 SIC 2041

BAY STATE MILLING CO p 161
100 Congress St Ste 2, Quincy MA 02169
Tel (617) 328-4423 SIC 2041

ROHTSTEIN CORP p 1247
70 Olympia Ave, Woburn MA 01801
Tel (781) 935-8300
SIC 5149 2099 2087 2062 2041 2033

▲KELLOGG CO p 808
1 Kellogg Sq, Battle Creek MI 49017
Tel (269) 961-2000
SIC 2043 2041 2052 2051 2038

STAR OF WEST MILLING CO p 1378
121 E Tuscola St, Frankenmuth MI 48734
Tel (330) 673-2941 SIC 2041 5153 5191

CITIZENS LLC p 311
870 S Main St, Vermontville MI 49096
Tel (517) 726-0514
SIC 5191 5153 5999 2041

GRAIN MILLERS INC p 629
10400 Viking Dr Ste 301, Eden Prairie MN 55344
Tel (952) 829-8821 SIC 2041 5084

■POST FOODS LLC p 1163
20802 Kensington Blvd, Lakeville MN 55044
Tel (973) 658-2457 SIC 2041

▲GENERAL MILLS INC p 601
1 General Mills Blvd, Minneapolis MN 55426
Tel (763) 764-7600
SIC 2099 2041 2045 2064 2024

BARTLETT AGRI ENTERPRISES INC p 157
4900 Main St Ste 1200, Kansas City MO 64112
Tel (816) 753-6300 SIC 5153 5154 2041

BUNGE MILLING INC p 225
11720 Borman Dr, Saint Louis MO 63146
Tel (314) 292-2000 SIC 2041 2075

ITALGRANI USA INC p 767
7900 Van Buren St, Saint Louis MO 63111
Tel (314) 638-1447 SIC 2041 5153

▲POST HOLDINGS INC p 1163
2503 S Hanley Rd, Saint Louis MO 63144
Tel (314) 644-7600
SIC 2015 2034 2038 2041 2099

CONTINENTAL GRAIN CO p 363
767 5th Ave Fl 15, New York NY 10153
Tel (212) 207-5930 SIC 2015 2041

NORTH DAKOTA MILL & ELEVATOR ASSOCIATION INC p 1052
1823 Mill Rd, Grand Forks ND 58203
Tel (701) 795-7000 SIC 2052 2041

LEGACY FARMERS COOPERATIVE p 852
6566 County Road 236, Findlay OH 45840
Tel (419) 423-2611
SIC 5153 5191 5984 2875 2048 2041

■INTERNATIONAL MULTIFOODS CORP p 756
1 Strawberry Ln, Orrville OH 44667
Tel (330) 682-3000
SIC 5145 5149 5143 2048 2041

BAMA COMPANIES INC p 149
2745 E 11th St, Tulsa OK 74104
Tel (918) 592-0778 SIC 2053 2041 2051

KERR PACIFIC CORP p 813
1211 Sw 6th Ave, Portland OR 97204
Tel (503) 221-1301 SIC 5141 2041

AGRICULTURAL COMMODITIES INC p 36
2224 Oxford Rd, New Oxford PA 17350
Tel (717) 624-8249
SIC 5191 2048 2041 0723 2875

F M BROWNS SONS INC p 522
205 Woodrow Ave, Reading PA 19608
Tel (800) 334-8816
SIC 5191 2041 0723 2048

ORION FOOD SYSTEMS LLC p 1094
2930 W Maple St, Sioux Falls SD 57107
Tel (605) 336-6961
SIC 5149 2033 2026 2041

GRAIN CRAFT INC p 629
201 W Main St Ste 203, Chattanooga TN 37408
Tel (423) 265-2313 SIC 2041

C H GUENTHER & SON INC p 232
2201 Broadway St, San Antonio TX 78215
Tel (210) 227-1401
SIC 2041 2051 2045 2052 2099

CHOICE PRODUCTS USA LLC p 302
3421 Truax Ct, Eau Claire WI 54703
Tel (715) 833-8761 SIC 5199 7389 2041

DIDION MILLING INC p 438
520 Hartwig Blvd Ste C, Johnson Creek WI 53038
Tel (920) 348-5868 SIC 5153 2041

SIC 2043 Cereal Breakfast Foods

GILSTER-MARY LEE CORP p 612
1037 State St, Chester IL 62233
Tel (618) 826-2361
SIC 2043 2098 2099 2045 3089

■QUAKER OATS CO p 1196
555 W Monroe St Fl 1, Chicago IL 60661
Tel (312) 821-1000
SIC 2086 2043 2045 2052 2084 2099

▲MONDELEZ INTERNATIONAL INC p 983
3 Parkway N Ste 300, Deerfield IL 60015
Tel (847) 943-4000
SIC 2022 2013 2095 2043 2035 2087

HEARTHSIDE FOOD SOLUTIONS LLC p 678
3250 Lacey Rd Ste 200, Downers Grove IL 60515
Tel (630) 967-3600 SIC 2043 2038

KRAFT FOODS GROUP INC p 829
3 Lakes Dr, Northfield IL 60093
Tel (847) 646-2000
SIC 2022 3411 2095 2043 2035 2087

GREENCORE US HOLDINGS p 637
222 Rosewood Dr Ste 240, Danvers MA 01923
Tel (508) 586-8418 SIC 2043

■WEETABIX CO INC p 1587
500 Nickerson Rd Ste 150, Marlborough MA 01752
Tel (978) 365-1000 SIC 2043

▲KELLOGG CO p 808
1 Kellogg Sq, Battle Creek MI 49017
Tel (269) 961-2000
SIC 2043 2041 2052 2051 2038

■KELLOGG USA INC p 809
1 Kellogg Sq, Battle Creek MI 49017
Tel (269) 961-2000 SIC 2043

■POST FOODS LLC p 1163
275 Cliff St, Battle Creek MI 49014
Tel (269) 966-1000 SIC 2043

ROSKAM BAKING CO p 1251
4880 Corp Exch Blvd Se, Grand Rapids MI 49512
Tel (616) 574-5757 SIC 2051 2043 7389

ROTHBURY FARMS INC p 1252
3061 Shaffer Ave Se, Grand Rapids MI 49512
Tel (616) 574-5757 SIC 5149 2051 2043

■MOM BRANDS CO LLC p 983
20802 Kensington Blvd, Lakeville MN 55044
Tel (952) 322-8000 SIC 2043

MARY LEE PACKAGING CORP p 914
615 Saint Marys Rd, Perryville MO 63775
Tel (573) 547-1705
SIC 2043 2099 3089 2098

■TREEHOUSE PRIVATE BRANDS INC p 1475
800 Market St, Saint Louis MO 63101
Tel (314) 877-7300
SIC 2043 2052 2068 2035

GERBER PRODUCTS CO p 608
12 Vreeland Rd Fl 2, Florham Park NJ 07932
Tel (973) 593-7500
SIC 2023 2043 2037 2052 2086 2091

▲ PEPSICO INC p 1134
700 Anderson Hill Rd, Purchase NY 10577
Tel (914) 253-2000
SIC 2096 2087 2086 2037 2052 2043

MCKEE FOODS CORP p 930
10260 Mckee Rd, Collegedale TN 37315
Tel (423) 238-7111
SIC 2051 2052 2099 2043

SIC 2044 Rice Milling

PRODUCERS RICE MILL INC p 1179
518 E Harrison St, Stuttgart AR 72160
Tel (870) 673-4444 *SIC* 2044 5153 2099

RICELAND FOODS INC p 1232
2120 S Park Ave, Stuttgart AR 72160
Tel (870) 673-5500
SIC 2044 2079 5153 2075

MARS FOOD US LLC p 910
2001 E Cashdan St Ste 201, Rancho Dominguez CA 90220
Tel (310) 933-0670 *SIC* 2044

FARMERS RICE COOPERATIVE p 530
2566 River Plaza Dr, Sacramento CA 95833
Tel (916) 923-5100 *SIC* 2044

SAGE V FOODS LLC p 1267
1470 Walnut St Ste 202, Boulder CO 80302
Tel (303) 449-5626 *SIC* 2044

FLORIDA CRYSTALS CORP p 557
1 N Clematis St Ste 200, West Palm Beach FL 33401
Tel (561) 655-6303
SIC 2061 2062 2044 4911

LOUISIANA RICE MILL LLC p 880
4 S Avenue D, Crowley LA 70526
Tel (337) 783-9777 *SIC* 2044

BUSCH AGRICULTURAL RESOURCES LLC p 229
3636 S Geyer Rd Fl 2, Saint Louis MO 63127
Tel (314) 577-2000
SIC 2044 2083 0181 5153

FORNAZOR INTERNATIONAL INC A NEW JERSEY CORP p 568
455 Hillsdale Ave, Hillsdale NJ 07642
Tel (201) 664-4000
SIC 0119 2034 2044 2045 2075 4449

RIVIANA FOODS INC p 1239
2777 Allen Pkwy Fl 15, Houston TX 77019
Tel (713) 529-3251
SIC 2044 2052 2033 5141

SOS CUETARA USA INC p 1341
10700 North Fwy Ste 800, Houston TX 77037
Tel (281) 272-8800 *SIC* 2044

MARS INC p 910
6885 Elm St, Mc Lean VA 22101
Tel (703) 821-4900
SIC 2044 2024 2066 2064 5812

SIC 2045 Flour, Blended & Prepared

■ BRIDGFORD FOODS CORP p 212
1308 N Patt St, Anaheim CA 92801
Tel (714) 526-5533
SIC 2045 2099 2015 2013 2022 2038

ARYZTA HOLDINGS IV LLC p 115
6080 Center Dr Ste 900, Los Angeles CA 90045
Tel (310) 417-4700
SIC 2052 2053 2045 2051

BAKEMARK USA LLC p 145
7351 Crider Ave, Pico Rivera CA 90660
Tel (562) 949-1054
SIC 2045 5149 3556 2099

LAVOI CORP p 847
1749 Tullie Cir Ne, Atlanta GA 30329
Tel (404) 325-1016
SIC 2045 2053 2051 5149

SOUTHEASTERN MILLS INC p 1346
333 Old Lindale Rd Se, Rome GA 30161
Tel (706) 291-6528
SIC 2099 2041 5149 2045

GILSTER-MARY LEE CORP p 612
1037 State St, Chester IL 62233
Tel (618) 826-2361
SIC 2043 2098 2099 2045 3089

■ QUAKER OATS CO p 1196
555 W Monroe St Fl 1, Chicago IL 60661
Tel (312) 821-1000
SIC 2086 2043 2045 2052 2064 2099

RALCORP FROZEN BAKERY PRODUCTS INC p 1206
3250 Lacey Rd Ste 600, Downers Grove IL 60515
Tel (630) 455-5200 *SIC* 2053 2045

NATION PIZZA PRODUCTS LP p 1009
601 E Algonquin Rd, Schaumburg IL 60173
Tel (847) 397-3320 *SIC* 2038 2045 2033

HARLAN BAKERIES LLC p 661
7597 E Us Highway 36, Avon IN 46123
Tel (317) 272-3600 *SIC* 5149 2051 2045

HARLAN BAKERIES-AVON LLC p 661
7597 E Us Highway 36, Avon IN 46123
Tel (317) 272-3600 *SIC* 5149 2051 2045

MESA FOODS LLC p 951
3701 W Magnolia Ave, Louisville KY 40211
Tel (502) 772-2500 *SIC* 2096 2045 2099

■ PJ FOOD SERVICE INC p 1153
2002 Papa Johns Blvd, Louisville KY 40299
Tel (502) 261-7272 *SIC* 5149 5087 2045

CONCORD FOODS INC p 354
10 Minuteman Way, Brockton MA 02301
Tel (508) 580-1700 *SIC* 2099 2045

■ DOMINOS PIZZA LLC p 449
30 Frank Lloyd Wright Dr, Ann Arbor MI 48105
Tel (734) 930-3030
SIC 5812 6794 5046 5149 8741 2045

DAWN FOOD PRODUCTS INC p 416
3333 Sargent Rd, Jackson MI 49201
Tel (517) 789-4400 *SIC* 2045 5046 3556

DAWN FOODS INC p 416
3333 Sargent Rd, Jackson MI 49201
Tel (517) 789-4400
SIC 2053 2045 3556 5046 6719

SFC GLOBAL SUPPLY CHAIN INC p 1310
115 W College Dr, Marshall MN 56258
Tel (507) 532-3274 *SIC* 2045 2038

▲ GENERAL MILLS INC p 601
1 General Mills Blvd, Minneapolis MN 55426
Tel (763) 764-7600
SIC 2099 2041 2045 2064 2024

BEST BRANDS CORP p 177
111 Cheshire Ln Ste 100, Saint Paul MN 55121
Tel (952) 404-7500
SIC 5149 2045 2053 2052 2051

■ PEAK FINANCE HOLDINGS LLC p 1126
121 Woodcrest Rd, Cherry Hill NJ 08003
Tel (856) 969-7100
SIC 2038 2092 2099 2045

LOSURDO FOODS INC p 879
20 Owens Rd, Hackensack NJ 07601
Tel (201) 343-6680
SIC 5141 2022 2033 2045

FORNAZOR INTERNATIONAL INC A NEW JERSEY CORP p 568
455 Hillsdale Ave, Hillsdale NJ 07642
Tel (201) 664-4000
SIC 0119 2034 2044 2045 2075 4449

■ PINNACLE FOODS FINANCE LLC p 1149
399 Jefferson Rd, Parsippany NJ 07054
Tel (973) 541-6620
SIC 2038 2092 2099 2045

■ PINNACLE FOODS GROUP LLC p 1149
399 Jefferson Rd, Parsippany NJ 07054
Tel (856) 969-7100
SIC 2038 2092 2099 2045

PEAK HOLDINGS LLC p 1126
345 Park Ave Fl 30, New York NY 10154
Tel (212) 583-5000
SIC 2038 2092 2099 2045

■ PROCTER & GAMBLE MANUFACTURING CO p 1179
1 Procter And Gamble Plz, Cincinnati OH 45202
Tel (513) 983-1100
SIC 2841 2079 2099 2844 2045

▲ BRIDGFORD INDUSTRIES INC p 212
1601 S Good Latimer Expy, Dallas TX 75226
Tel (214) 428-1535
SIC 2045 2099 2015 2013 2022 2038

C H GUENTHER & SON INC p 232
2201 Broadway St, San Antonio TX 78215
Tel (210) 227-1401
SIC 2041 2051 2045 2052 2099

CONTINENTAL MILLS INC p 363
18100 Andover Park W, Tukwila WA 98188
Tel (253) 872-8400 *SIC* 2045 2038

SIC 2046 Wet Corn Milling

■ PENFORD CORP p 1128
345 Inverness Dr S # 200, Englewood CO 80112
Tel (303) 649-1900 *SIC* 2046 2869

STALEY HOLDINGS INC p 1375
501 Silverside Rd Ste 55, Wilmington DE 19809
Tel (302) 793-0289 *SIC* 2046

▲ ARCHER-DANIELS-MIDLAND CO p 105
77 W Wacker Dr Ste 4600, Chicago IL 60601
Tel (312) 634-8100
SIC 2046 2041 2075 2074 5153 2083

TATE & LYLE INGREDIENTS AMERICAS LLC p 1426
2200 E Eldorado St, Decatur IL 62521
Tel (217) 423-4411 *SIC* 2046

▲ INGREDION INC p 743
5 Westbrook Corporate Ctr # 500, Westchester IL 60154
Tel (708) 551-2600 *SIC* 2046

■ PENFORD PRODUCTS CO p 1128
1001 1st St Sw, Cedar Rapids IA 52404
Tel (319) 398-3700 *SIC* 2046

SOUTHWEST IOWA RENEWABLE ENERGY LLC p 1352
10868 189th St, Council Bluffs IA 51503
Tel (712) 366-0392 *SIC* 2869 2085 2046

ROQUETTE AMERICA INC p 1250
1003 S 5th St, Keokuk IA 52632
Tel (319) 524-5757 *SIC* 2046 2869

HOMELAND ENERGY SOLUTIONS LLC p 703
2779 Highway 24, Lawler IA 52154
Tel (563) 238-5555 *SIC* 2869 2085 2046

KENT CORP p 812
2905 N Highway 61, Muscatine IA 52761
Tel (563) 264-4211
SIC 2869 2085 2046 2048

GRANITE FALLS ENERGY LLC p 631
15045 Highway 23 Se, Granite Falls MN 56241
Tel (320) 564-3100 *SIC* 2869 2085 2046

CARGILL INC p 255
15407 Mcginty Rd W, Wayzata MN 55391
Tel (952) 742-7575
SIC 5153 2075 2046 2048 2011 2015

▲ GREEN PLAINS INC p 637
450 Regency Pkwy Ste 400, Omaha NE 68114
Tel (402) 884-8700 *SIC* 2869 2046

INDOPCO INC p 739
10 Finderne Ave Ste A, Bridgewater NJ 08807
Tel (908) 685-5000
SIC 2891 2046 2821 2869 2899 2099

■ NATIONAL STARCH AND CHEMICAL HOLDING CORP p 1016
10 Finderne Ave, Bridgewater NJ 08807
Tel (908) 685-5000 *SIC* 2891 2046 2869

UNILEVER BESTFOODS NORTH AMERICA p 1503
800 Sylvan Ave, Englewood Cliffs NJ 07632
Tel (201) 894-4000
SIC 2046 2034 2035 2098 2099 2051

SIC 2047 Dog & Cat Food

DEL MONTE p 423
1200 Market St Ne, Decatur AL 35601
Tel (256) 552-7453 *SIC* 2047

SUNSHINE MILLS INC p 1404
500 6th St Sw, Red Bay AL 35582
Tel (256) 356-9541 *SIC* 2047 2048 5149

SIMMONS PET FOOD INC p 1324
601 N Hico St, Siloam Springs AR 72761
Tel (479) 524-8151 *SIC* 2047

NESTLE USA INC p 1027
800 N Brand Blvd, Glendale CA 91203
Tel (818) 549-6000
SIC 2023 2033 2064 2047 2099 2032

REDBARN PET PRODUCTS INC p 1216
3229 E Spring St Ste 310, Long Beach CA 90806
Tel (562) 495-7315 *SIC* 5199 2047

BUMBLE BEE SEAFOODS INC p 225
280 10th Ave, San Diego CA 92101
Tel (858) 715-4068 *SIC* 2091 2047

■ BIG HEART PET BRANDS p 181
1 Maritime Plz Fl 2, San Francisco CA 94111
Tel (415) 247-3000 *SIC* 2047

ENSIGN-BICKFORD INDUSTRIES INC p 501
125 Pwder Frest Dr Fl 3, Simsbury CT 06070
Tel (860) 843-2000
SIC 3764 2047 2835 3829 2499 6552

■ BLUE BUFFALO CO LTD p 190
11 River Rd Ste 103, Wilton CT 06897
Tel (203) 762-9751 *SIC* 2047 5149

SIMMONS PET FOOD KS INC p 1324
1400 E Logan Ave, Emporia KS 66801
Tel (620) 342-1323 *SIC* 2047

TRIPLE - T FOODS INC p 1482
1601 W Mckay St, Frontenac KS 66763
Tel (620) 231-7779 *SIC* 2047

■ HILLS PET NUTRITION INC p 694
400 Sw 8th Ave Ste 101, Topeka KS 66603
Tel (785) 354-8523 *SIC* 5149 2048 2047

WELLPET LLC p 1589
200 Ames Pond Dr Ste 200, Tewksbury MA 01876
Tel (877) 869-2971 *SIC* 2047

KLN ENTERPRISES INC p 823
400 Lakeside Dr, Perham MN 56573
Tel (218) 346-7000 *SIC* 2047 2064

TUFFYS PET FOODS INC p 1491
245 1st Ave N, Perham MN 56573
Tel (218) 346-7500 *SIC* 2047

FARMERS UNION INDUSTRIES LLC p 530
590 W Park Rd, Redwood Falls MN 56283
Tel (507) 637-5210 *SIC* 2048 2047

ROYAL CANIN USA INC p 1254
500 Fountain Lakes Blvd # 100, Saint Charles MO 63301
Tel (636) 724-1692 *SIC* 2047 0752

NESTLE PURINA PETCARE CO p 1027
901 Chouteau Ave, Saint Louis MO 63102
Tel (314) 982-1000 *SIC* 2047

PURINA MILLS LLC p 1192
555 Maryvle Univ Dr 200, Saint Louis MO 63141
Tel (877) 454-7094 *SIC* 2048 2047

▲ FRESHPET INC p 579
400 Plaza Dr Fl 1, Secaucus NJ 07094
Tel (201) 520-4000 *SIC* 2047

▲ COLGATE-PALMOLIVE CO p 336
300 Park Ave Fl 5, New York NY 10022
Tel (212) 310-2000
SIC 2844 3991 2841 2842 2047

IAMS CO p 725
8700 S Masn Montgomery Rd, Mason OH 45040
Tel (800) 675-3849 *SIC* 2047 2048

AINSWORTH PET NUTRITION LLC p 38
984 Water St, Meadville PA 16335
Tel (814) 724-7710 *SIC* 2047

PET FOOD EXPERTS INC p 1137
175 Main St, Pawtucket RI 02860
Tel (401) 721-5593 *SIC* 5199 2047

MARS PETCARE US INC p 910
315 Cool Springs Blvd, Franklin TN 37067
Tel (615) 807-4626 *SIC* 2047

NUTRO CO p 1068
1550 W Mcewen Dr Ste 100, Franklin TN 37067
Tel (888) 607-4081 *SIC* 2047 0742

■ DELIGHT PRODUCTS CO p 424
1200 Industrial Dr, Springfield TN 37172
Tel (615) 384-7546 *SIC* 2047

MERRICK NATURAL PETWORKS INC p 950
101 Se 11th Ave Ste 200, Amarillo TX 79101
Tel (806) 322-2800 *SIC* 2047

SIC 2048 Prepared Feeds For Animals & Fowls

EQUITY GROUP EUFAULA DIVISION LLC p 507
57 Melvin Clark Rd, Eufaula AL 36027
Tel (334) 687-7790
SIC 2015 2048 2041 2011

MARSHALL DURBIN FOOD CORP p 911
2830 Commerce Blvd, Irondale AL 35210
Tel (205) 841-7315
SIC 0252 0254 2048 0251 2015 5144

SUNSHINE MILLS INC p 1404
500 6th St Sw, Red Bay AL 35582
Tel (256) 356-9541 *SIC* 2047 2048 5149

PECO FOODS INC p 1127
1020 Lurleen B Wallace, Tuscaloosa AL 35401
Tel (205) 345-4711
SIC 0254 0251 2015 2048

OK INDUSTRIES INC p 1079
4601 N 6th St, Fort Smith AR 72904
Tel (479) 783-4186 *SIC* 2048 2015 0251

▲ TYSON FOODS INC p 1496
2200 W Don Tyson Pkwy, Springdale AR 72762
Tel (479) 290-4000
SIC 2011 2015 2032 2096 2048

L A HEARNE CO p 833
512 Metz Rd, King City CA 93930
Tel (831) 385-5441
SIC 5191 0723 5699 4214 2048 5261

RECONSERVE INC p 1214
2811 Wilshire Blvd # 410, Santa Monica CA 90403
Tel (310) 458-1574 *SIC* 2048

BAKER COMMODITIES INC p 146
4020 Bandini Blvd, Vernon CA 90058
Tel (323) 268-2801 *SIC* 2077 2048

AGFINITY INC p 34
260 Factory Rd, Eaton CO 80615
Tel (970) 454-4000
SIC 5172 2048 7549 5191

▲ PILGRIMS PRIDE CORP p 1148
1770 Promontory Cir, Greeley CO 80634
Tel (970) 506-8000
SIC 2015 0254 0252 2048 5999

MOARK LLC p 980
28 Under The Mountain Rd, North Franklin CT 06254
Tel (951) 332-3300
SIC 5144 2048 0252 2015

H J BAKER & BRO INC p 650
2 Corporate Dr Ste 545, Shelton CT 06484
Tel (203) 682-9200 *SIC* 2048 5191 5052

▲ BLUE BUFFALO PET PRODUCTS INC p 191
11 River Rd Ste 103, Wilton CT 06897
Tel (203) 762-9751 *SIC* 2048

SOUTHEAST MILK INC p 1346
1950 Se County Hwy 484, Belleview FL 34420
Tel (352) 245-2437 *SIC* 5143 2048

■ TROPICANA PRODUCTS INC p 1484
1275 26th Ave E, Bradenton FL 34208
Tel (941) 747-4461
SIC 2033 2037 2086 2048

SUNSHINE STATE DAIRY FARMS LLC p 1404
3304 Sydney Rd, Plant City FL 33566
Tel (813) 754-1847 *SIC* 5143 2048

EQUITY GROUP - GEORGIA DIVISION LLC p 506
7220 Us Highway 19, Camilla GA 31730
Tel (229) 336-1001 *SIC* 2015 0254 2048

CLEAR SPRINGS FOODS INC p 324
4424 N 1500 E, Buhl ID 83316
Tel (208) 543-4316 *SIC* 0273 2048

FURST-MCNESS CO p 585
120 E Clark St, Freeport IL 61032
Tel (800) 435-5100 *SIC* 2048 5191

ADM ALLIANCE NUTRITION INC p 23
1000 N 30th St, Quincy IL 62301
Tel (217) 231-2674 *SIC* 2048 5154

PINE MANOR INC p 1149
9622 W 350 N, Orland IN 46776
Tel (800) 532-4186 *SIC* 2048 2015 0254

JBS UNITED INC p 780
4310 W State Road 38, Sheridan IN 46069
Tel (317) 758-4495 *SIC* 2048 5153 0213

FRICK SERVICES INC p 579
3154 Depot St, Wawaka IN 46794
Tel (260) 761-3311
SIC 5191 5153 5261 4221 2048 4213

AG PARTNERS LLC p 33
30 Main St, Albert City IA 50510
Tel (712) 843-2291 *SIC* 5153 5191 2048

■ CAMBREX CHARLES CITY INC p 244
1205 11th St, Charles City IA 50616
Tel (641) 257-1000
SIC 2834 2899 2865 2048

MID IOWA COOPERATIVE p 963
201 S Main St, Conrad IA 50621
Tel (641) 366-2740 *SIC* 5153 5191 2048

KENT CORP p 812
2905 N Highway 61, Muscatine IA 52761
Tel (563) 264-4211
SIC 2869 2085 2046 2048

KENT NUTRITION GROUP INC p 812
1600 Oregon St, Muscatine IA 52761
Tel (866) 647-1212 *SIC* 2048

WEST CENTRAL COOPERATIVE p 1594
406 1st St, Ralston IA 51459
Tel (712) 667-3200
SIC 5153 2075 2048 5191

UNITED FARMERS MERCANTILE COOPERATIVE p 1508
203 W Oak St, Red Oak IA 51566
Tel (712) 623-5453
SIC 5153 5191 5541 5211 2048

KEY COOPERATIVE p 814
13585 620th Ave, Roland IA 50236
Tel (515) 388-4341
SIC 5153 5541 2048 5191

■ FLO KAY INDUSTRIES INC p 557
1919 Grand Ave, Sioux City IA 51106
Tel (712) 277-2011 *SIC* 2873 2048 2816

HEARTLAND CO-OP p 679
2829 Westown Pkwy Ste 350, West Des Moines IA 50266
Tel (515) 225-1334 *SIC* 5153 0762 2048

■ HILLS PET NUTRITION INC p 694
400 Sw 8th Ave Ste 101, Topeka KS 66603
Tel (785) 354-8523 *SIC* 5149 2048 2047

EQUITY GROUP - KENTUCKY DIVISION LLC p 507
2294 Ky Highway 90 W, Albany KY 42602
Tel (606) 387-2300 *SIC* 2048 5144

ALLTECH INC p 58
3031 Catnip Hill Rd, Nicholasville KY 40356
Tel (859) 885-9613
SIC 2869 2048 3821 2819

CONTANDA LLC p 362
365 Canal St Ste 2900, New Orleans LA 70130
Tel (504) 525-9741 *SIC* 4226 2048

RIDLEY USA INC p 1234
111 W Cherry St Ste 500, Mankato MN 56001
Tel (507) 388-9400 *SIC* 2048

FARMERS UNION INDUSTRIES LLC p 530
590 W Park Rd, Redwood Falls MN 56283
Tel (507) 637-5210 *SIC* 2048 2047

CARGILL INC p 255
15407 Mcginty Rd W, Wayzata MN 55391
Tel (952) 742-7575
SIC 5153 2075 2046 2048 2011 2015

WILLMAR POULTRY FARMS INC p 1613
3939 1st Ave W, Willmar MN 56201
Tel (320) 235-8870 *SIC* 0253 2048

MAR-JAC POULTRY MS LLC p 904
261 Marshall Durbin Dr, Waynesboro MS 39367
Tel (601) 735-3132 *SIC* 2048

MFA INC p 957
201 Ray Young Dr, Columbia MO 65201
Tel (573) 874-5111
SIC 2875 2048 5191 5153

■ HEARTLAND PET FOODS MANUFACTURING INC p 679
8101 E 32nd St, Joplin MO 64804
Tel (417) 952-1400 *SIC* 2048

CENTRAL MISSOURI AGRISERVICE LLC p 279
211 N Lyon Ave, Marshall MO 65340
Tel (660) 886-7880 *SIC* 2875 2048 5251

3D CORPORATE SOLUTIONS LLC p 2
601 13th St, Monett MO 65708
Tel (417) 236-9602 *SIC* 5199 5149 2048

NUTRA BLEND LLC p 1067
3200 2nd St, Neosho MO 64850
Tel (417) 451-6111 *SIC* 2048

BUNGE NORTH AMERICA FOUNDATION p 226
11720 Borman Dr, Saint Louis MO 63146
Tel (314) 872-3030
SIC 2075 2079 2048 2834

PURINA MILLS LLC p 1192
555 Maryvle Univ Dr 200, Saint Louis MO 63141
Tel (877) 454-7094 *SIC* 2048 2047

SOUTHEAST NEBRASKA COOPERATIVE CO p 1346
403 S 3rd St, Beatrice NE 68310
Tel (402) 228-3458 *SIC* 5191 5153 2048

COOPERATIVE PRODUCERS INC p 367
265 N Showboat Blvd, Hastings NE 68901
Tel (402) 463-5148 *SIC* 2048 5153

AG PROCESSING INC A COOPERATIVE p 33
12700 W Dodge Rd, Omaha NE 68154
Tel (402) 496-7809
SIC 5153 2075 2048 5999 0254

SERGEANTS PET CARE PRODUCTS INC p 1306
10077 S 134th St, Omaha NE 68138
Tel (402) 938-7000 *SIC* 2834 5199 2048

GOLDSBORO MILLING CO p 622
938 Millers Chapel Rd, Goldsboro NC 27534
Tel (919) 778-3130 *SIC* 2048

NASH JOHNSON & SONS FARMS INC p 1008
3385 S Us Highway 117, Rose Hill NC 28458
Tel (910) 289-3113
SIC 2015 0254 0253 0251 2048

PROVIMI NORTH AMERICA INC p 1186
10 Collective Way, Brookville OH 45309
Tel (937) 770-2400 *SIC* 2048 5191

LEGACY FARMERS COOPERATIVE p 852
6566 County Road 236, Findlay OH 45840
Tel (419) 423-2611
SIC 5153 5191 5984 2875 2048 2041

IAMS CO p 725
8700 S Masn Montgomery Rd, Mason OH 45040
Tel (800) 675-3849 *SIC* 2047 2048

COOPER HATCHERY INC p 366
22348 Road 140, Oakwood OH 45873
Tel (419) 594-3325
SIC 0254 0253 2015 5153 2048

■ INTERNATIONAL MULTIFOODS CORP p 756
1 Strawberry Ln, Orrville OH 44667
Tel (330) 682-3000
SIC 5145 5149 5143 2048 2041

STILLWATER MILLING CO LLC p 1390
512 E 6th Ave, Stillwater OK 74074
Tel (405) 372-2766 *SIC* 2048 5999

M SIMON ZOOK CO p 890
4960 Horseshoe Pike, Honey Brook PA 19344
Tel (800) 327-4406 *SIC* 5149 2048 4013

LEBANON SEABOARD CORP p 850
1600 E Cumberland St, Lebanon PA 17042
Tel (717) 273-1685 *SIC* 5191 2875 2048

AGRICULTURAL COMMODITIES INC p 36
2224 Oxford Rd, New Oxford PA 17350
Tel (717) 624-8249
SIC 5191 2048 2041 0723 2875

F M BROWNS SONS INC p 522
205 Woodrow Ave, Reading PA 19608
Tel (800) 334-8816
SIC 5191 2041 0723 2048

WENGER FEEDS LLC p 1592
101 W Harrisburg Ave, Rheems PA 17570
Tel (717) 367-1195 *SIC* 2048 5144 0252

PAN AMERICAN GRAIN CO INC p 1110
Calle Claudia 9 Esqu, Guaynabo PR 00968
Tel (787) 792-3355 *SIC* 2048

■ NUTRA-FLO CO p 1067
200 S Derby Ln, North Sioux City SD 57049
Tel (712) 277-2011 *SIC* 2873 2816 2048

TENNESSEE FARMERS COOPERATIVE INC p 1438
180 Old Nashville Hwy, La Vergne TN 37086
Tel (615) 793-8011
SIC 5191 5013 5014 5172 5122 2048

HI-PRO FEEDS INC p 689
1201 E 11th St, Friona TX 79035
Tel (806) 250-2791 *SIC* 2048

ALAN RITCHEY INC p 44
740 S Frontage Rd, Valley View TX 76272
Tel (940) 726-3276
SIC 7389 4213 2048 0291

SOUTHERN STATES COOPERATIVE INC p 1350
6606 W Broad St Ste B, Richmond VA 23230
Tel (804) 281-1000
SIC 2048 0181 2873 2874 5191 5172

VALLEY PROTEINS (DE) INC p 1541
151 Valpro Dr, Winchester VA 22603
Tel (540) 877-2533 *SIC* 2048

BRUCETON FARM SERVICE INC p 220
1768 Mileground Rd, Morgantown WV 26505
Tel (304) 291-6980
SIC 5411 5172 5999 5983 5812 2048

■ KAYTEE PRODUCTS INC p 805
521 Clay St, Chilton WI 53014
Tel (920) 849-2321 *SIC* 2048

VP HOLDINGS CORP p 1566
2514 Fish Hatchery Rd, Madison WI 53713
Tel (608) 256-1988 *SIC* 2048 5191 5153

PRINCE CORP p 1176
8351 County Road H, Marshfield WI 54449
Tel (800) 777-2486
SIC 5031 5191 2048 5083 5072

SIC 2051 Bread, Bakery Prdts Exc Cookies & Crackers

■ ALPINE VALLEY BREAD CO p 61
300 W Southern Ave, Mesa AZ 85210
Tel (480) 483-2774 *SIC* 2051

■ HOLSUM BAKERY INC p 702
2322 W Lincoln St, Phoenix AZ 85009
Tel (602) 252-2351 *SIC* 2051

UNITED GENERAL BAKERY INC p 1508
3655 W Washington St, Phoenix AZ 85009
Tel (602) 255-0464 *SIC* 2051

CHAI BAGEL CORP p 286
14431 N 73rd St, Scottsdale AZ 85260
Tel (480) 860-0475
SIC 5149 5461 5812 2052 2051

FRESH START BAKERIES INC p 579
145 S State Ckkg Blvd 2 Ste 200, Brea CA 92821
Tel (714) 256-8900 *SIC* 2051

▲ CHEESECAKE FACTORY INC p 292
26901 Malibu Hills Rd, Calabasas Hills CA 91301
Tel (818) 871-3000 *SIC* 5812 2051

BAKKAVOR FOODS USA INC p 147
18201 Central Ave, Carson CA 90746
Tel (310) 533-0190 *SIC* 2051 5149

OAKHURST INDUSTRIES INC p 1071
2050 S Tubeway Ave, Commerce CA 90040
Tel (323) 724-3000 *SIC* 2051 5149

IL FORNAIO (AMERICA) CORP p 731
770 Tamalpais Dr Ste 400, Corte Madera CA 94925
Tel (415) 945-0500
SIC 5812 5813 5149 5461 2051

SVENHARDS SWEDISH BAKERY p 1410
701 Industrial Dr, Exeter CA 93221
Tel (831) 623-4375 *SIC* 2051

■ COTTAGE BAKERY INC p 374
1831 S Stockton St, Lodi CA 95240
Tel (209) 334-3616 *SIC* 5149 2051 2053

ARYZTA HOLDINGS IV LLC p 115
6080 Center Dr Ste 900, Los Angeles CA 90045
Tel (310) 417-4700
SIC 2052 2053 2045 2051

ARYZTA LLC p 115
6080 Center Dr Ste 900, Los Angeles CA 90045
Tel (310) 417-4700 *SIC* 2052 2053 2051

GALASSOS BAKERY p 589
10820 San Sevaine Way, Mira Loma CA 91752
Tel (951) 360-1211 *SIC* 2051

ANDRE-BOUDIN BAKERIES INC p 90
50 Francisco St Ste 200, San Francisco CA 94133
Tel (415) 882-1849
SIC 2051 5812 5961 5461

ARYZTA US HOLDINGS I CORP p 115
14490 Catalina St, San Leandro CA 94577
Tel (800) 938-1900 *SIC* 2052 2053 2051

LA BREA BAKERY CAFE INC p 835
14490 Catalina St, San Leandro CA 94577
Tel (818) 742-4242 *SIC* 2051 2052 2053

LA BREA BAKERY HOLDINGS INC p 835
14490 Catalina St, San Leandro CA 94577
Tel (818) 742-4242 *SIC* 2051

LA TORTILLA FACTORY INC p 836
3300 Westwind Blvd, Santa Rosa CA 95403
Tel (707) 586-4000 *SIC* 5149 2051

KINGS HAWAIIAN HOLDING CO INC p 820
19161 Harborgate Way, Torrance CA 90501
Tel (310) 755-7100 *SIC* 2051 5812

FIDELITY NEWPORT HOLDINGS LLC p 541
400 W 48th Ave, Denver CO 80216
Tel (303) 296-2121 *SIC* 5812 2051 6719

■ SOUTHERN BAKERIES INC p 1347
3355 W Memorial Blvd, Lakeland FL 33815
Tel (863) 682-1155 *SIC* 2051 5149

■ FLOWERS BAKING CO OF MIAMI LLC p 560
17800 Nw Miami Ct, Miami FL 33169
Tel (305) 652-3416 *SIC* 2051 5461

■ FLOWERS BAKING CO OF BRADENTON LLC p 560
6490 Parkland Dr, Sarasota FL 34243
Tel (941) 758-5656 *SIC* 2051

LAVOI CORP p 847
1749 Tullie Cir Ne, Atlanta GA 30329
Tel (404) 325-1016
SIC 2045 2053 2051 5149

■ MURRAY BISCUIT CO LLC p 1001
1550 Marvin Griffin Rd, Augusta GA 30906
Tel (706) 798-8600 *SIC* 2052 2051

■ DERST BAKING CO LLC p 431
1311 W 52nd St, Savannah GA 31405
Tel (912) 233-2235 *SIC* 2051 5461

■ FLOWERS BAKERIES LLC p 560
1919 Flowers Cir, Thomasville GA 31757
Tel (229) 226-9110 *SIC* 2051 2053

■ FLOWERS BAKING CO OF THOMASVILLE INC p 560
1919 Flowers Cir, Thomasville GA 31757
Tel (229) 226-9110 *SIC* 2051

▲ FLOWERS FOODS INC p 560
1919 Flowers Cir, Thomasville GA 31757
Tel (229) 226-9110 *SIC* 2051 2052

■ FLOWERS BAKING CO OF VILLA RICA LLC p 560
134 Doyle Mcclain Dr, Villa Rica GA 30180
Tel (770) 459-2883 *SIC* 2051

ALPHA BAKING CO INC p 60
5001 W Polk St, Chicago IL 60644
Tel (773) 489-5400 *SIC* 2051

■ HILLSHIRE BRANDS CO p 694
400 S Jefferson St Fl 1, Chicago IL 60607
Tel (312) 614-6000 *SIC* 2013 2051 2053

LE PETIT PAIN HOLDINGS LLC p 849
676 N Michigan Ave, Chicago IL 60611
Tel (312) 981-3770 *SIC* 2051

SCHULZE AND BURCH BISCUIT CO p 1291
1133 W 35th St, Chicago IL 60609
Tel (773) 927-6622 *SIC* 2051 2052 2099

WHOLESOME HARVEST BAKING LLC p 1607
1011 E Touhy Ave Ste 500, Des Plaines IL 60018
Tel (800) 550-6810 *SIC* 2051

■ RALCORP FROZEN BAKERY PRODUCTS INC p 1206
3250 Lacey Rd Ste 600, Downers Grove IL 60515
Tel (630) 455-5200
SIC 2051 2053 2041 2035 2656

KRONOS FOODS CORP p 830
1 Kronos, Glendale Heights IL 60139
Tel (773) 847-2250
SIC 2013 2051 5141 5963

HIGHLAND BAKING CO INC p 691
2301 Shermer Rd, Northbrook IL 60062
Tel (847) 677-2789 *SIC* 5149 2051

GONNELLA BAKING CO p 623
1117 Wiley Rd, Schaumburg IL 60173
Tel (312) 733-2020
SIC 2051 5812 2099 2038

OAK STATE PRODUCTS INC p 1070
775 State Route 251, Wenona IL 61377
Tel (815) 853-4348 *SIC* 2051

HARLAN BAKERIES LLC p 661
7597 E Us Highway 36, Avon IN 46123
Tel (317) 272-3600 *SIC* 5149 2051 2045

HARLAN BAKERIES-AVON LLC p 661
7597 E Us Highway 36, Avon IN 46123
Tel (317) 272-3600 *SIC* 5149 2051 2045

MAPLEHURST BAKERIES LLC p 904
50 Maplehurst Dr, Brownsburg IN 46112
Tel (317) 858-9000 *SIC* 2051

WESTON FOODS US INC p 1602
50 Maplehurst Dr, Brownsburg IN 46112
Tel (317) 858-9000 *SIC* 2051 2052

LEWIS BROTHERS BAKERIES INC p 858
500 N Fulton Ave, Evansville IN 47710
Tel (812) 425-4642 *SIC* 2051 5149

HOLSUM OF FORT WAYNE INC p 702
136 Murray St, Fort Wayne IN 46803
Tel (260) 456-2130 *SIC* 2051

PERFECTION BAKERIES INC p 1135
350 Pearl St, Fort Wayne IN 46802
Tel (260) 424-8245 *SIC* 2051

■ LEPAGE BAKERIES INC p 856
11 Adamian Dr, Auburn ME 04210
Tel (207) 783-9161 *SIC* 2051 5461

H & S BAKERY INC p 649
601 S Caroline St, Baltimore MD 21231
Tel (410) 558-3050 *SIC* 2051

NORTHEAST FOODS INC p 1054
601 S Caroline St, Baltimore MD 21231
Tel (410) 276-7254 *SIC* 2051 5149

SCHMIDT BAKING CO INC p 1287
7801 Fitch Ln, Baltimore MD 21236
Tel (410) 668-8200 *SIC* 2051

ABP CORP p 12
19 Fid Kennedy Ave, Boston MA 02210
Tel (617) 423-0629 *SIC* 5461 5812 2051

GOLD MEDAL BAKERY INC p 620
21 Penn St, Fall River MA 02724
Tel (508) 679-8958 *SIC* 2051

CUMBERLAND FARMS INC p 400
100 Crossing Blvd, Framingham MA 01702
Tel (508) 270-1400
SIC 5411 5541 5172 2086 2051 2026

■ KEEBLER CO p 807
1 Kellogg Sq, Battle Creek MI 49017
Tel (269) 961-2000 *SIC* 2052 2051

▲ KELLOGG CO p 808
1 Kellogg Sq, Battle Creek MI 49017
Tel (269) 961-2000
SIC 2043 2041 2052 2051 2038

ROSKAM BAKING CO p 1251
4880 Corp Exch Blvd Se, Grand Rapids MI 49512
Tel (616) 574-5757 *SIC* 2051 2043 7389

ROTHBURY FARMS INC p 1252
3061 Shaffer Ave Se, Grand Rapids MI 49512
Tel (616) 574-5757 *SIC* 5149 2051 2043

WAY BAKERY p 1584
2100 Enterprise St, Jackson MI 49203
Tel (517) 787-6720 *SIC* 2051

PAN-O-GOLD BAKING CO p 1110
444 E Saint Germain St, Saint Cloud MN 56304
Tel (320) 251-9361 *SIC* 5149 2051

BEST BRANDS CORP p 177
111 Cheshire Ln Ste 100, Saint Paul MN 55121
Tel (952) 404-7500
SIC 5149 2045 2053 2052 2051

TWIN CITY BAGEL INC p 1494
130 Hardman Ave S, South Saint Paul MN 55075
Tel (651) 554-0200 *SIC* 2051

EARTHGRAINS BAKERY GROUP INC p 469
3470 Rider Trl S, Earth City MO 63045
Tel (314) 291-5480 *SIC* 2051

▲ HOSTESS BRANDS INC p 710
1 E Armour Blvd, Kansas City MO 64111
Tel (816) 701-4600 *SIC* 2051 5461

■ HOSTESS BRANDS LLC p 710
1 E Armour Blvd, Kansas City MO 64111
Tel (816) 701-4600 *SIC* 2051

OLD HB INC p 1081
3101 Mercier St Ste 422, Kansas City MO 64111
Tel (816) 502-4000 *SIC* 2051 5461

ROTELLAS ITALIAN BAKERY INC p 1252
6949 S 108th St, La Vista NE 68128
Tel (402) 592-6600 *SIC* 2051

▲ CAMPBELL SOUP CO p 245
1 Campbell Pl, Camden NJ 08103
Tel (856) 342-4800
SIC 2032 2038 2033 2052 2051 2096

UNILEVER BESTFOODS NORTH AMERICA p 1503
800 Sylvan Ave, Englewood Cliffs NJ 07632
Tel (201) 894-4000
SIC 2046 2034 2035 2098 2099 2051

▲ J & J SNACK FOODS CORP p 770
6000 Central Hwy, Pennsauken NJ 08109
Tel (856) 665-9533
SIC 2053 2087 2086 2024 2052 2051

OMNI BAKING CO LLC p 1084
2621 Freddy Ln Bldg 7, Vineland NJ 08360
Tel (856) 205-1485 *SIC* 2051

BIMBO FOODS BAKERIES INC p 183
40 Harold Ct, Bay Shore NY 11706
Tel (631) 273-6000 *SIC* 2051

ENTENMANNS INC p 501
1724 5th Ave, Bay Shore NY 11706
Tel (631) 273-6000 *SIC* 2051

WENNER BREAD PRODUCTS INC p 1592
33 Rajon Rd, Bayport NY 11705
Tel (800) 869-6262 *SIC* 2051 2053 5461

FLOUR CITY BAGELS INC p 560
585 Moseley Rd Ste 3, Fairport NY 14450
Tel (585) 223-0450 *SIC* 5461 2051

ROCKLAND BAKERY INC p 1244
94 Demarest Mill Rd W, Nanuet NY 10954
Tel (845) 623-5800 *SIC* 2051

NERIS BAKERY PRODUCTS INC p 1026
31 Pearl St 37, Port Chester NY 10573
Tel (914) 937-3235 *SIC* 5149 5461 2051

CAROLINA FOODS INC p 259
1807 S Tryon St, Charlotte NC 28203
Tel (704) 333-9812 *SIC* 2051

■ FRANKLIN BAKING CO LLC p 574
500 W Grantham St, Goldsboro NC 27530
Tel (919) 735-0344 *SIC* 2051

KRISPY KREME DOUGHNUT CORP p 830
259 S Stratford Rd, Winston Salem NC 27103
Tel (336) 724-2484 *SIC* 5461 2051

KRISPY KREME DOUGHNUTS INC p 830
370 Knollwood St Ste 500, Winston Salem NC 27103
Tel (336) 726-8876 *SIC* 5461 5149 2051

GRAETERS MANUFACTURING CO p 628
1175 Regina Graeter Way, Cincinnati OH 45216
Tel (513) 721-3323
SIC 2024 2051 2064 2066

KLOSTERMAN BAKING CO p 823
4760 Paddock Rd, Cincinnati OH 45229
Tel (513) 242-5667 *SIC* 2051

ORLANDO BAKING CO p 1095
7777 Grand Ave, Cleveland OH 44104
Tel (216) 361-1872 *SIC* 2051

WHITE CASTLE SYSTEM INC p 1606
555 W Goodale St, Columbus OH 43215
Tel (614) 228-5781
SIC 5812 5142 2051 2013

JTM PROVISIONS CO INC p 796
200 Sales Ave, Harrison OH 45030
Tel (513) 367-4900 *SIC* 2013 2051

ALFRED NICKLES BAKERY INC p 50
26 Main St N, Navarre OH 44662
Tel (330) 879-5635 *SIC* 2051

NEW HORIZONS BAKING CO INC p 1031
211 Woodlawn Ave, Norwalk OH 44857
Tel (419) 668-8226 *SIC* 2051

PIERRE HOLDING CORP p 1147
9990 Prnceton Glendale Rd, West Chester OH 45246
Tel (513) 874-8741 *SIC* 2013 2015 2051

SCHWEBEL BAKING CO p 1291
965 E Midlothian Blvd, Youngstown OH 44502
Tel (330) 783-2860 *SIC* 2051

BAMA COMPANIES INC p 149
2745 E 11th St, Tulsa OK 74104
Tel (918) 592-0778 *SIC* 2053 2041 2051

■ AVB INC p 136
5209 Se International Way, Portland OR 97222
Tel (503) 335-8077 *SIC* 2051 2052

UNITED STATES BAKERY p 1512
315 Ne 10th Ave, Portland OR 97232
Tel (503) 232-2191 *SIC* 2051 5461

MARTINS FAMOUS PASTRY SHOPPE INC p 913
1000 Potato Roll Ln, Chambersburg PA 17202
Tel (717) 263-9580 *SIC* 2051

ARNOLD FOODS CO INC p 112
255 Business Center Dr # 200, Horsham PA 19044
Tel (215) 672-8010 *SIC* 2051 5149

BBU INC p 163
255 Business Center Dr # 200, Horsham PA 19044
Tel (215) 347-5500 *SIC* 2051

BIMBO BAKERIES USA INC p 183
255 Business Center Dr # 200, Horsham PA 19044
Tel (215) 347-5500 *SIC* 2051

OROGRAIN BAKERIES MANUFACTURING INC p 1095
255 Business Center Dr, Horsham PA 19044
Tel (518) 463-2221 *SIC* 2051

STROEHMANN BAKERIES LC p 1394
255 Business Center Dr # 200, Horsham PA 19044
Tel (215) 672-8010 *SIC* 2051 5461

AUNTIE ANNES INC p 131
48-50 W Chestnut St # 200, Lancaster PA 17603
Tel (717) 435-1435 *SIC* 6794 2051 5461

BETTER BAKED FOODS INC p 178
56 Smedley St, North East PA 16428
Tel (814) 725-8778 *SIC* 2051

■ TASTY BAKING CO p 1426
4300 S 26th St, Philadelphia PA 19112
Tel (215) 221-8500 *SIC* 2051 2052

BUTTER KRUST BAKING CO INC p 230
249 N 11th St, Sunbury PA 17801
Tel (570) 286-5845 *SIC* 2051

MAPLE DONUTS INC p 903
3455 E Market St, York PA 17402
Tel (717) 757-7826 *SIC* 2051 5461

PAN PEPIN INC p 1110
Plaza Laurel, Bayamon PR 00956
Tel (787) 787-1717 *SIC* 2051

HOLSUM DE PUERTO RICO INC p 702
Carr 2 Km 20 1 Bo Cndlria St Ca, Toa Baja PR 00949
Tel (787) 798-8282 SIC 2051

MCKEE FOODS CORP p 930
10260 Mckee Rd, Collegedale TN 37315
Tel (423) 238-7111
SIC 2051 2052 2099 2043

AFFILIATED FOODS INC p 32
1401 W Farmers Ave, Amarillo TX 79118
Tel (806) 345-7773
SIC 5141 2026 2051 5149 6153

LONE STAR BAKERY INC p 875
6905 Us Highway 87 E, China Grove TX 78263
Tel (210) 648-6400 SIC 2053 2051

PIONEER FROZEN FOODS INC p 1150
627 Big Stone Gap Rd, Duncanville TX 75137
Tel (972) 298-4281 SIC 2051

BAIRDS MRS BAKERIES BUSINESS TRUST p 145
7301 South Fwy, Fort Worth TX 76134
Tel (817) 615-3100 SIC 2051

MRS BAIRDS BAKERIES BUSINESS TRUST p 996
14401 Statler Blvd, Fort Worth TX 76155
Tel (817) 864-2500 SIC 2051

C H GUENTHER & SON INC p 232
2201 Broadway St, San Antonio TX 78215
Tel (210) 227-1401
SIC 2041 2051 2045 2052 2099

■ FLOWERS BAKING CO OF SAN ANTONIO LLC p 560
6000 Ne Loop 410, San Antonio TX 78218
Tel (210) 661-2361 SIC 2051

INTERBAKE FOODS LLC p 751
3951 Westerre Pkwy # 200, Henrico VA 23233
Tel (804) 755-7107 SIC 2052 2051

COLONY BRANDS INC p 338
1112 7th Ave, Monroe WI 53566
Tel (608) 328-8400 SIC 5961 5143 2051

SIC 2052 Cookies & Crackers

CHAI BAGEL CORP p 286
14431 N 73rd St, Scottsdale AZ 85260
Tel (480) 860-0475
SIC 5149 5461 5812 2052 2051

SONORA MILLS FOODS INC p 1340
3064 E Maria St, E Rncho Dmngz CA 90221
Tel (310) 639-5333 SIC 2052

CLIF BAR & CO p 326
1451 66th St, Emeryville CA 94608
Tel (510) 596-6300 SIC 2052 5149

SOUTH COAST BAKING LLC p 1343
1722 Kettering, Irvine CA 92614
Tel (949) 851-9654 SIC 2052 5149

■ BLOOMFIELD BAKERS p 190
10711 Bloomfield St, Los Alamitos CA 90720
Tel (626) 610-2253 SIC 2052 2064

ARYZTA HOLDINGS IV LLC p 115
6080 Center Dr Ste 900, Los Angeles CA 90045
Tel (310) 417-4700
SIC 2052 2053 2045 2051

ARYZTA LLC p 115
6080 Center Dr Ste 900, Los Angeles CA 90045
Tel (310) 417-4700 SIC 2052 2053 2051

HAMPTON CREEK INC p 656
2000 Folsom St, San Francisco CA 94110
Tel (844) 423-6637 SIC 2035 2052

ARYZTA US HOLDINGS I CORP p 115
14490 Catalina St, San Leandro CA 94577
Tel (800) 938-1900 SIC 2052 2053 2051

LA BREA BAKERY CAFE INC p 835
14490 Catalina St, San Leandro CA 94577
Tel (818) 742-4242 SIC 2051 2052 2053

■ J & J SNACK FOODS CORP OF CALIFORNIA p 770
5353 S Downey Rd, Vernon CA 90058
Tel (323) 581-0171 SIC 2052 5149

■ PEPPERIDGE FARM INC p 1134
595 Westport Ave, Norwalk CT 06851
Tel (203) 846-7000
SIC 5963 2052 2099 2053 5961

■ MURRAY BISCUIT CO LLC p 1001
1550 Marvin Griffin Rd, Augusta GA 30906
Tel (706) 798-8600 SIC 2052 2051

CSM BAKERY SOLUTIONS LLC p 398
5775 Glenridge Dr Bldg A, Sandy Springs GA 30328
Tel (404) 478-5400 SIC 2052

▲ FLOWERS FOODS INC p 560
1919 Flowers Cir, Thomasville GA 31757
Tel (229) 226-9110 SIC 2051 2052

FRESH BEGINNINGS INC p 578
4001 Coleman Rd N, Valdosta GA 31602
Tel (229) 242-0237 SIC 5199 2052 2064

■ QUAKER OATS CO p 1196
555 W Monroe St Fl 1, Chicago IL 60661
Tel (312) 821-1000
SIC 2086 2043 2045 2052 2064 2099

SCHULZE AND BURCH BISCUIT CO p 1291
1133 W 35th St, Chicago IL 60609
Tel (773) 927-6622 SIC 2051 2052 2099

■ MONDELEZ GLOBAL LLC p 983
3 Parkway N Ste 300, Deerfield IL 60015
Tel (847) 943-4000
SIC 2052 2066 3999 2067 2022 2087

TH FOODS INC p 1446
2134 Harlem Rd, Loves Park IL 61111
Tel (800) 896-2396 SIC 2052

PRETZELS INC p 1173
123 W Harvest Rd, Bluffton IN 46714
Tel (260) 824-4838 SIC 2052 2099

WESTON FOODS US INC p 1602
50 Maplehurst Dr, Brownsburg IN 46112
Tel (317) 858-9000 SIC 2051 2052

SHEARERS FOODS BURLINGTON LLC p 1313
3000 Mount Pleasant St, Burlington IA 52601
Tel (319) 754-6551 SIC 2052

■ KEEBLER CO p 807
1 Kellogg Sq, Battle Creek MI 49017
Tel (269) 961-2000 SIC 2052 2051

▲ KELLOGG CO p 808
1 Kellogg Sq, Battle Creek MI 49017
Tel (269) 961-2000
SIC 2043 2041 2052 2051 2038

■ KELLOGG NORTH AMERICA CO p 809
1 Kellogg Sq, Battle Creek MI 49017
Tel (269) 961-2000 SIC 2052

BEST BRANDS CORP p 177
111 Cheshire Ln Ste 100, Saint Paul MN 55121
Tel (952) 404-7500
SIC 5149 2045 2053 2052 2051

AB MAURI FOOD INC p 9
4240 Duncan Ave Ste 150, Saint Louis MO 63110
Tel (314) 392-0800 SIC 2052

■ BREMNER FOOD GROUP INC p 210
800 Market St Ste 2900, Saint Louis MO 63101
Tel (314) 877-7000 SIC 2052

■ TREEHOUSE PRIVATE BRANDS INC p 1475
800 Market St, Saint Louis MO 63101
Tel (314) 877-7300
SIC 2043 2052 2068 2035

▲ CAMPBELL SOUP CO p 245
1 Campbell Pl, Camden NJ 08103
Tel (856) 342-4800
SIC 2032 2038 2033 2052 2051 2096

■ BIRDS EYE FOODS INC p 185
121 Woodcrest Rd, Cherry Hill NJ 08003
Tel (585) 383-1850
SIC 2037 2096 2052 2038 2035

GERBER PRODUCTS CO p 608
12 Vreeland Rd Fl 2, Florham Park NJ 07932
Tel (973) 593-7500
SIC 2023 2043 2037 2052 2086 2091

▲ J & J SNACK FOODS CORP p 770
6000 Central Hwy, Pennsauken NJ 08109
Tel (856) 665-9533
SIC 2053 2087 2086 2024 2052 2051

▲ PEPSICO INC p 1134
700 Anderson Hill Rd, Purchase NY 10577
Tel (914) 253-2000
SIC 2096 2087 2086 2037 2052 2043

■ S-L SNACKS NATIONAL LLC p 1263
13024 Ballantyne Pl 350, Charlotte NC 28273
Tel (704) 554-1421 SIC 2052

■ S-L SNACKS NC LLC p 1263
13024 Balntyn Corp Pl, Charlotte NC 28277
Tel (717) 632-4477 SIC 2052

▲ SNYDERS-LANCE INC p 1336
13515 Balntyn Corp Pl, Charlotte NC 28277
Tel (704) 554-1421
SIC 2052 2064 2068 2096 5145

NORTH DAKOTA MILL & ELEVATOR ASSOCIATION INC p 1052
1823 Mill Rd, Grand Forks ND 58203
Tel (701) 795-7000 SIC 2052 2041

■ CHERYL & CO p 295
646 Mccorkle Blvd, Westerville OH 43082
Tel (614) 776-1500 SIC 2052

NONNIS FOODS LLC p 1047
3920 E Pine St, Tulsa OK 74115
Tel (918) 621-1200 SIC 2052 2053

■ AVB INC p 136
5209 Se International Way, Portland OR 97222
Tel (503) 335-8077 SIC 2051 2052

■ S-L SNACKS REAL ESTATE INC p 1263
1250 York St, Hanover PA 17331
Tel (717) 632-4477 SIC 2052 2096

UTZ QUALITY FOODS LLC p 1537
900 High St, Hanover PA 17331
Tel (800) 367-7629 SIC 2096 2052 2099

■ TASTY BAKING CO p 1426
4300 S 26th St, Philadelphia PA 19112
Tel (215) 221-8500 SIC 2051 2052

SAVOR STREET FOODS INC p 1284
1 Park Plz, Wyomissing PA 19610
Tel (610) 320-7800 SIC 2052 2096 2099

D F STAUFFER BISCUIT CO INC p 407
360 S Belmont St, York PA 17403
Tel (717) 815-4600 SIC 2052

MCKEE FOODS CORP p 930
10260 Mckee Rd, Collegedale TN 37315
Tel (423) 238-7111
SIC 2051 2052 2099 2043

ABIMAR FOODS INC p 11
5425 N 1st St, Abilene TX 79603
Tel (325) 691-5425 SIC 2052

RIVIANA FOODS INC p 1239
2777 Allen Pkwy Fl 15, Houston TX 77019
Tel (713) 529-3251
SIC 2044 2052 2033 5141

■ FRITO-LAY NORTH AMERICA INC p 580
7701 Legacy Dr, Plano TX 75024
Tel (972) 334-7000
SIC 2096 2052 2013 5812 6794 2086

OLD FRITO-LAY INC p 1080
7701 Legacy Dr, Plano TX 75024
Tel (972) 334-7000
SIC 2096 2052 2013 5812 6794 2086

C H GUENTHER & SON INC p 232
2201 Broadway St, San Antonio TX 78215
Tel (210) 227-1401
SIC 2041 2051 2045 2052 2099

INTERBAKE FOODS LLC p 751
3951 Westerre Pkwy # 200, Henrico VA 23233
Tel (804) 755-7107 SIC 2052 2051

SIC 2053 Frozen Bakery Prdts

■ COTTAGE BAKERY INC p 374
1831 S Stockton St, Lodi CA 95240
Tel (209) 334-3616 SIC 5149 2051 2053

ARYZTA HOLDINGS IV LLC p 115
6080 Center Dr Ste 900, Los Angeles CA 90045
Tel (310) 417-4700
SIC 2052 2053 2045 2051

ARYZTA LLC p 115
6080 Center Dr Ste 900, Los Angeles CA 90045
Tel (310) 417-4700 SIC 2052 2053 2051

HORIZON HOLDINGS LLC p 707
1 Bush St Ste 650, San Francisco CA 94104
Tel (415) 788-2000 SIC 6799 2053

ARYZTA US HOLDINGS I CORP p 115
14490 Catalina St, San Leandro CA 94577
Tel (800) 938-1900 SIC 2052 2053 2051

LA BREA BAKERY CAFE INC p 835
14490 Catalina St, San Leandro CA 94577
Tel (818) 742-4242 SIC 2051 2052 2053

AMYS KITCHEN INC p 88
2330 Northpoint Pkwy, Santa Rosa CA 95407
Tel (707) 578-7188 SIC 2038 2053

STEVEN-ROBERT ORIGINALS LLC p 1388
2780 Tower Rd, Aurora CO 80011
Tel (303) 375-9925 SIC 2053 2024 2099

■ PEPPERIDGE FARM INC p 1134
595 Westport Ave, Norwalk CT 06851
Tel (203) 846-7000
SIC 5963 2052 2099 2053 5961

LAVOI CORP p 847
1749 Tullie Cir Ne, Atlanta GA 30329
Tel (404) 325-1016
SIC 2045 2053 2051 5149

■ FLOWERS BAKERIES LLC p 560
1919 Flowers Cir, Thomasville GA 31757
Tel (229) 226-9110 SIC 2051 2053

■ HILLSHIRE BRANDS CO p 694
400 S Jefferson St Fl 1, Chicago IL 60607
Tel (312) 614-6000 SIC 2013 2051 2053

VIENNA BEEF LTD p 1556
2501 N Damen Ave, Chicago IL 60647
Tel (773) 278-7800
SIC 2013 2035 2053 5411 5149 5147

RALCORP FROZEN BAKERY PRODUCTS INC p 1206
3250 Lacey Rd Ste 600, Downers Grove IL 60515
Tel (630) 455-5200 SIC 2053 2045

■ RALCORP FROZEN BAKERY PRODUCTS INC p 1206
3250 Lacey Rd Ste 600, Downers Grove IL 60515
Tel (630) 455-5200
SIC 2051 2053 2041 2035 2656

QUALITY BAKERIES LLC p 1196
1750 E Main St Ste 260, Saint Charles IL 60174
Tel (630) 553-7377 SIC 2053

DAWN FOODS INC p 416
3333 Sargent Rd, Jackson MI 49201
Tel (517) 789-4400
SIC 2053 2045 3556 5046 6719

BEST BRANDS CORP p 177
111 Cheshire Ln Ste 100, Saint Paul MN 55121
Tel (952) 404-7500
SIC 5149 2045 2053 2052 2051

▲ J & J SNACK FOODS CORP p 770
6000 Central Hwy, Pennsauken NJ 08109
Tel (856) 665-9533
SIC 2053 2087 2086 2024 2052 2051

WENNER BREAD PRODUCTS INC p 1592
33 Rajon Rd, Bayport NY 11705
Tel (800) 869-6262 SIC 2051 2053 5461

RICH PRODUCTS CORP p 1232
1 Robert Rich Way, Buffalo NY 14213
Tel (716) 878-8422
SIC 2053 2092 2023 2099

CIRCLE PEAK CAPITAL MANAGEMENT LLC p 308
1325 Ave Of The Americas, New York NY 10019
Tel (646) 230-8812 SIC 2053 6799

BAMA COMPANIES INC p 149
2745 E 11th St, Tulsa OK 74104
Tel (918) 592-0778 SIC 2053 2041 2051

NONNIS FOODS LLC p 1047
3920 E Pine St, Tulsa OK 74115
Tel (918) 621-1200 SIC 2052 2053

SWEET STREET DESSERTS INC p 1411
722 Hiesters Ln, Reading PA 19605
Tel (610) 929-0616 SIC 2053

LONE STAR BAKERY INC p 875
6905 Us Highway 87 E, China Grove TX 78263
Tel (210) 648-6400 SIC 2053 2051

SIC 2061 Sugar, Cane

SUGAR CANE GROWERS COOPERATIVE OF FLORIDA p 1397
1500 W Sugar House Rd, Belle Glade FL 33430
Tel (561) 996-5556 SIC 2061

UNITED STATES SUGAR CORP p 1514
111 Ponce De Leon Ave, Clewiston FL 33440
Tel (863) 983-8121
SIC 0133 2061 2062 2033

FANJUL CORP p 527
1 N Clematis St Ste 200, West Palm Beach FL 33401
Tel (561) 655-6303
SIC 0133 2061 2099 6552

FLORIDA CRYSTALS CORP p 557
1 N Clematis St Ste 200, West Palm Beach FL 33401
Tel (561) 655-6303
SIC 2061 2062 2044 4911

■ HAWAIIAN COMMERCIAL & SUGAR CO p 669
1 Hansen St, Puunene HI 96784
Tel (808) 877-0081 SIC 2061

MA PATOUT & SON LIMITED LLC p 891
3512 J Patout Burns Rd, Jeanerette LA 70544
Tel (337) 276-4592 SIC 2061

RIO GRANDE VALLEY SUGAR GROWERS INC p 1235
2.5 Miles W Hwy 107, Santa Rosa TX 78593
Tel (956) 636-1411 SIC 2061

SIC 2062 Sugar, Cane Refining

SUGAR C&H CO INC p 1397
830 Loring Ave, Crockett CA 94525
Tel (510) 787-2121 SIC 2062

UNITED STATES SUGAR CORP p 1514
111 Ponce De Leon Ave, Clewiston FL 33440
Tel (863) 983-8121
SIC 0133 2061 2062 2033

FLORIDA CRYSTALS CORP p 557
1 N Clematis St Ste 200, West Palm Beach FL 33401
Tel (561) 655-6303
SIC 2061 2062 2044 4911

▲ ALEXANDER & BALDWIN INC p 49
822 Bishop St, Honolulu HI 96813
Tel (808) 525-6611 SIC 6512 2062

ROHTSTEIN CORP p 1247
70 Olympia Ave, Woburn MA 01801
Tel (781) 935-8300
SIC 5149 2099 2087 2062 2041 2033

SUGAR AMERICANE REFINING LLC p 1397
21010 Trolley Indus Dr, Taylor MI 48180
Tel (313) 299-1300 SIC 2062

AMERICAN SUGAR REFINING INC p 80
1 Federal St, Yonkers NY 10705
Tel (800) 729-4840 SIC 2062

ASR GROUP INTERNATIONAL INC p 119
1 Federal St, Yonkers NY 10705
Tel (914) 963-2400 SIC 2062

IMPERIAL SUGAR CO p 734
3 Sugar Creek Center Blvd # 500, Sugar Land TX 77478
Tel (281) 491-9181 SIC 2062 5149

SIC 2063 Sugar, Beet

WESTERN SUGAR COOPERATIVE p 1600
7555 E Hampden Ave # 600, Denver CO 80231
Tel (303) 830-3939 SIC 2063

AMALGAMATED SUGAR CO LLC p 64
1951 S Saturn Way Ste 100, Boise ID 83709
Tel (208) 383-6500 SIC 2063

SNAKE RIVER SUGAR CO p 1335
1951 S Saturn Way Ste 100, Boise ID 83709
Tel (208) 383-6500 SIC 8611 2063

MICHIGAN SUGAR CO p 961
122 Uptown Dr Unit 300, Bay City MI 48708
Tel (989) 686-0161 SIC 2063

AMERICAN CRYSTAL SUGAR CO p 70
101 3rd St N, Moorhead MN 56560
Tel (218) 236-4326 SIC 2063 7359

SOUTHERN MINNESOTA BEET SUGAR COOPERATIVE p 1349
83550 County Road 21, Renville MN 56284
Tel (320) 329-8305 SIC 2063

SIMMONS HAROLD C FAMILY TRUST p 1324
5430 Lyndon B Johnson Fwy # 1700, Dallas TX 75240
Tel (972) 233-1700 SIC 2063

SIC 2064 Candy & Confectionery Prdts

JOE TORNANTE-MDP HOLDING LLC p 787
233 S Beverly Dr, Beverly Hills CA 90212
Tel (310) 228-6800
SIC 5145 5092 5112 2064

GUITTARD CHOCOLATE CO p 646
10 Guittard Rd, Burlingame CA 94010
Tel (650) 697-4427 SIC 2066 2064

JELLY BELLY CANDY CO p 782
1 Jelly Belly Ln, Fairfield CA 94533
Tel (707) 428-2800 SIC 2064

SUNSHINE RAISIN CORP p 1404
626 S 5th St, Fowler CA 93625
Tel (559) 834-5981 SIC 2064 0723

NESTLE HOLDINGS INC p 1026
800 N Brand Blvd, Glendale CA 91203
Tel (818) 549-6000
SIC 2023 2032 2038 2033 2064 2026

NESTLE USA INC p 1027
800 N Brand Blvd, Glendale CA 91203
Tel (818) 549-6000
SIC 2023 2033 2064 2047 2099 2032

NELLSON NUTRACEUTICAL INC p 1025
5801 Ayala Ave, Irwindale CA 91706
Tel (626) 812-6522 SIC 2064

■ BLOOMFIELD BAKERS p 190
10711 Bloomfield St, Los Alamitos CA 90720
Tel (626) 610-2253 SIC 2052 2064

HARMONY FOODS CORP p 662
2200 Delaware Ave, Santa Cruz CA 95060
Tel (831) 457-3200 SIC 2834 2064

■ SEES CANDIES INC p 1300
210 El Camino Real, South San Francisco CA 94080
Tel (650) 761-2490 SIC 2064 5441

■ SEES CANDY SHOPS INC p 1300
210 El Camino Real, South San Francisco CA 94080
Tel (650) 761-2490 SIC 2064 5441

SIGNATURE BRANDS LLC p 1322
808 Sw 12th St, Ocala FL 34471
Tel (352) 622-3134 SIC 2064

FRESH BEGINNINGS INC p 578
4001 Coleman Rd N, Valdosta GA 31602
Tel (229) 242-0237 SIC 5199 2052 2064

■ QUAKER OATS CO p 1196
555 W Monroe St Fl 1, Chicago IL 60661
Tel (312) 821-1000
SIC 2086 2043 2045 2052 2064 2099

■ TOOTSIE ROLL CO INC p 1460
7401 S Cicero Ave, Chicago IL 60629
Tel (773) 838-3400 SIC 2064

▲ TOOTSIE ROLL INDUSTRIES INC p 1460
7401 S Cicero Ave, Chicago IL 60629
Tel (773) 838-3400 SIC 2064

■ TOOTSIE ROLL INDUSTRIES LLC p 1460
7401 S Cicero Ave, Chicago IL 60629
Tel (773) 245-4202 SIC 2064

WM WRIGLEY JR CO p 1620
930 W Evergreen Ave, Chicago IL 60642
Tel (312) 280-4710
SIC 2067 2064 2087 2899

▲ JOHN B SANFILIPPO & SON INC p 787
1703 N Randall Rd, Elgin IL 60123
Tel (847) 289-1800
SIC 2068 2064 2099 2096 2066

■ FANNIE MAY CONFECTIONS BRANDS INC p 527
2457 W North Ave, Melrose Park IL 60160
Tel (773) 693-9100 *SIC* 2064 5441

FERRARA CANDY CO p 538
1 Tower Ln Ste 2700, Oakbrook Terrace IL 60181
Tel (708) 366-0500 *SIC* 2064

AMERICAN LICORICE CO p 75
1900 Whirlpool Dr S, La Porte IN 46350
Tel (510) 487-5500 *SIC* 2064

PERFETTI VAN MELLE USA INC p 1135
3645 Turfway Rd, Erlanger KY 41018
Tel (859) 283-1234 *SIC* 5145 2064

ELMER CANDY CORP p 489
401 N 5th St, Ponchatoula LA 70454
Tel (985) 386-6166 *SIC* 2066 2064

BAKERY CRAFTS LLC p 147
3500 Thurston Ave 100, Anoka MN 55303
Tel (513) 942-0862 *SIC* 5046 5149 2064

▲ GENERAL MILLS INC p 601
1 General Mills Blvd, Minneapolis MN 55426
Tel (763) 764-7600
SIC 2099 2041 2045 2064 2024

KLN ENTERPRISES INC p 823
400 Lakeside Dr, Perham MN 56573
Tel (218) 346-7000 *SIC* 2047 2064

■ ANNS HOUSE OF NUTS INC p 92
380 Sint Pter St Ste 1000, Saint Paul MN 55102
Tel (651) 348-4100 *SIC* 2068 2064

RUSSELL STOVER CHOCOLATES LLC p 1259
4900 Oak St, Kansas City MO 64112
Tel (816) 842-9240 *SIC* 2064 5441

BELLA FOUR BAKERY INC p 170
1150 Trademark Dr Ste 101, Reno NV 89521
Tel (775) 883-2253 *SIC* 2064 5461

PROMOTION IN MOTION INC p 1183
25 Commerce Dr, Allendale NJ 07401
Tel (201) 962-8530
SIC 2064 5441 5145 2066

MARS CHOCOLATE NORTH AMERICA LLC p 910
800 High St, Hackettstown NJ 07840
Tel (908) 852-1000 *SIC* 2064 2066

FERRERO U S A INC p 538
600 Cottontail Ln, Somerset NJ 08873
Tel (732) 764-9300 *SIC* 5145 2064

SWEETWORKS INC p 1412
3500 Genesee St, Buffalo NY 14225
Tel (716) 634-4545 *SIC* 2066 2067 2064

GODIVA CHOCOLATIER INC p 619
333 W 34th St Fl 6, New York NY 10001
Tel (212) 984-5900
SIC 2066 5149 5441 2064

TOPPS CO INC p 1461
1 Whitehall St Fl 4, New York NY 10004
Tel (212) 376-0300
SIC 5145 5092 5112 2064

FIRST SOURCE LLC p 549
100 Pirson Pkwy, Tonawanda NY 14150
Tel (716) 877-0800 *SIC* 5499 2064

▲ SNYDERS-LANCE INC p 1336
13515 Balntyn Corp Pl, Charlotte NC 28277
Tel (704) 554-1421
SIC 2052 2064 2068 2096 5145

BESTCO HOLDINGS INC p 177
288 Mazeppa Rd, Mooresville NC 28115
Tel (704) 664-4300 *SIC* 2064

GRAETERS MANUFACTURING CO p 628
1175 Regina Graeter Way, Cincinnati OH 45216
Tel (513) 721-3323
SIC 2024 2051 2064 2066

JUST BORN INC p 797
1300 Stefko Blvd, Bethlehem PA 18017
Tel (610) 867-7568 *SIC* 2064

GERTRUDE HAWK CHOCOLATES INC p 609
9 Keystone Industrial Par, Dunmore PA 18512
Tel (570) 342-7556 *SIC* 2064 2066

▲ HERSHEY CO p 687
100 Crystal A Dr, Hershey PA 17033
Tel (717) 534-4200 *SIC* 2066 2064 2099

TRUFOOD MFG INC p 1486
610 Alpha Dr, Pittsburgh PA 15238
Tel (412) 963-2330 *SIC* 2066 2064

R M PALMER CO p 1202
77 S 2nd Ave, Reading PA 19611
Tel (610) 372-8971 *SIC* 2066 2064

▲ AMPLIFY SNACK BRANDS INC p 86
500 W 5th St Ste 1350, Austin TX 78701
Tel (512) 600-9893 *SIC* 2099 2064 2096

ELAMEX USA CORP p 483
1800 Northwestern Dr, El Paso TX 79912
Tel (915) 298-3061 *SIC* 3694 2068 2064

MOUNT FRANKLIN FOODS LLC p 993
1800 Northwestern Dr, El Paso TX 79912
Tel (915) 877-4079 *SIC* 5145 2068 2064

MARS INC p 910
6885 Elm St, Mc Lean VA 22101
Tel (703) 821-4900
SIC 2044 2024 2066 2064 5812

SIC 2066 Chocolate & Cocoa Prdts

GUITTARD CHOCOLATE CO p 646
10 Guittard Rd, Burlingame CA 94010
Tel (650) 697-4427 *SIC* 2066 2064

GHIRARDELLI CHOCOLATE CO p 610
1111 139th Ave, San Leandro CA 94578
Tel (510) 483-6970
SIC 5441 2066 5812 5149

T R TOPPERS INC p 1420
320 Fairchild Ave, Pueblo CO 81001
Tel (719) 948-4902 *SIC* 2066

STAR BRANDS NORTH AMERICA INC p 1378
30 Buxton Farm Rd Ste 100, Stamford CT 06905
Tel (203) 329-4545 *SIC* 2066

BARRY CALLEBAUT USA LLC p 157
600 W Chicago Ave Ste 860, Chicago IL 60654
Tel (312) 496-7491 *SIC* 2066 8741

WORLDS FINEST CHOCOLATE INC p 1626
4801 S Lawndale Ave, Chicago IL 60632
Tel (773) 847-4600 *SIC* 2066 5947

■ MONDELEZ GLOBAL LLC p 983
3 Parkway N Ste 300, Deerfield IL 60015
Tel (847) 943-4000
SIC 2052 2066 3999 2067 2022 2087

▲ JOHN B SANFILIPPO & SON INC p 787
1703 N Randall Rd, Elgin IL 60123
Tel (847) 289-1800
SIC 2068 2064 2099 2096 2066

SOUTH BEND CHOCOLATE CO INC p 1343
3300 W Sample St Ste 110, South Bend IN 46619
Tel (574) 233-2577
SIC 5149 2066 5441 5812

ELMER CANDY CORP p 489
401 N 5th St, Ponchatoula LA 70454
Tel (985) 386-6166 *SIC* 2066 2064

■ CONAGRA GROCERY PRODUCTS CO LLC p 354
11 Conagra Dr, Omaha NE 68102
Tel (630) 857-1000
SIC 2033 2079 2099 2032 2066 5149

LINDT & SPRUNGLI (USA) INC p 868
1 Fine Chocolate Pl, Stratham NH 03885
Tel (603) 778-8100 *SIC* 2066 5149 5441

PROMOTION IN MOTION INC p 1183
25 Commerce Dr, Allendale NJ 07401
Tel (201) 962-8530
SIC 2064 5441 5145 2066

MARS CHOCOLATE NORTH AMERICA LLC p 910
800 High St, Hackettstown NJ 07840
Tel (908) 852-1000 *SIC* 2064 2066

SWEETWORKS INC p 1412
3500 Genesee St, Buffalo NY 14225
Tel (716) 634-4545 *SIC* 2066 2067 2064

GODIVA CHOCOLATIER INC p 619
333 W 34th St Fl 6, New York NY 10001
Tel (212) 984-5900
SIC 2066 5149 5441 2064

GRAETERS MANUFACTURING CO p 628
1175 Regina Graeter Way, Cincinnati OH 45216
Tel (513) 721-3323
SIC 2024 2051 2064 2066

■ FANNIE MAY CONFECTIONS BRANDS INC p 527
5353 Lauby Rd, North Canton OH 44720
Tel (330) 494-0833 *SIC* 5441 2066

GERTRUDE HAWK CHOCOLATES INC p 609
9 Keystone Industrial Par, Dunmore PA 18512
Tel (570) 342-7556 *SIC* 2064 2066

▲ HERSHEY CO p 687
100 Crystal A Dr, Hershey PA 17033
Tel (717) 534-4200 *SIC* 2066 2064 2099

CARGILL COCOA & CHOCOLATE INC p 255
20 N Broad St, Lititz PA 17543
Tel (717) 626-1131 *SIC* 2066

FRANKFORD CANDY LLC p 574
9300 Ashton Rd, Philadelphia PA 19114
Tel (215) 735-5200 *SIC* 2066

TRUFOOD MFG INC p 1486
610 Alpha Dr, Pittsburgh PA 15238
Tel (412) 963-2330 *SIC* 2066 2064

R M PALMER CO p 1202
77 S 2nd Ave, Reading PA 19611
Tel (610) 372-8971 *SIC* 2066 2064

MARS INC p 910
6885 Elm St, Mc Lean VA 22101
Tel (703) 821-4900
SIC 2044 2024 2066 2064 5812

SIC 2067 Chewing Gum

WM WRIGLEY JR CO p 1620
930 W Evergreen Ave, Chicago IL 60642
Tel (312) 280-4710
SIC 2067 2064 2087 2899

WRIGLEY MANUFACTURING CO LLC p 1627
410 N Michigan Ave, Chicago IL 60611
Tel (312) 644-2121 *SIC* 2067

■ MONDELEZ GLOBAL LLC p 983
3 Parkway N Ste 300, Deerfield IL 60015
Tel (847) 943-4000
SIC 2052 2066 3999 2067 2022 2087

SWEETWORKS INC p 1412
3500 Genesee St, Buffalo NY 14225
Tel (716) 634-4545 *SIC* 2066 2067 2064

SIC 2068 Salted & Roasted Nuts & Seeds

SUNTREE LLC p 1405
4502 W Monterosa St, Phoenix AZ 85031
Tel (480) 719-6900 *SIC* 2068

SUNTREE SNACK FOODS LLC p 1405
4502 W Monterosa St, Phoenix AZ 85031
Tel (480) 719-6900 *SIC* 2068

WONDERFUL PISTACHIOS & ALMONDS LLC p 1622
11444 W Olympic Blvd, Los Angeles CA 90064
Tel (310) 966-4650 *SIC* 2068

■ DIAMOND FOODS LLC p 436
1050 Diamond St, Stockton CA 95205
Tel (415) 445-7444 *SIC* 2068 2096

PRIMEX FARMS LLC p 1176
16070 Wildwood Rd, Wasco CA 93280
Tel (661) 758-7790 *SIC* 2068

GOLDEN PEANUT & TREE NUTS p 621
275 Industrial Blvd, Camilla GA 31730
Tel (229) 336-7282 *SIC* 5159 2068

▲ JOHN B SANFILIPPO & SON INC p 787
1703 N Randall Rd, Elgin IL 60123
Tel (847) 289-1800
SIC 2068 2064 2099 2096 2066

KAR NUT PRODUCTS CO p 804
1200 E 14 Mile Rd Ste A, Madison Heights MI 48071
Tel (248) 588-1903 *SIC* 5145 2068

■ ANNS HOUSE OF NUTS INC p 92
380 Sint Pter St Ste 1000, Saint Paul MN 55102
Tel (651) 348-4100 *SIC* 2068 2064

■ FLAGSTONE FOODS INC p 554
380 Sint Pter St Ste 1000, Saint Paul MN 55102
Tel (651) 348-4100 *SIC* 5411 2068

■ TREEHOUSE PRIVATE BRANDS INC p 1475
800 Market St, Saint Louis MO 63101
Tel (314) 877-7300
SIC 2043 2052 2068 2035

STAR SNACKS CO LLC p 1378
105 Harbor Dr, Jersey City NJ 07305
Tel (201) 200-9820 *SIC* 2068

SUGAR FOODS CORP p 1397
950 3rd Ave Fl 21, New York NY 10022
Tel (212) 753-6900
SIC 2869 2023 2099 2068 7389

▲ SNYDERS-LANCE INC p 1336
13515 Balntyn Corp Pl, Charlotte NC 28277
Tel (704) 554-1421
SIC 2052 2064 2068 2096 5145

TROPICAL NUT & FRUIT CO p 1484
1100 Continental Blvd, Charlotte NC 28273
Tel (704) 588-0400
SIC 5149 5145 2099 2068

KANAN ENTERPRISES INC p 802
31900 Solon Rd, Solon OH 44139
Tel (440) 248-8484 *SIC* 2068 2034

TEXAS STAR NUT AND FOOD CO INC p 1444
206 Market Ave, Boerne TX 78006
Tel (830) 249-8300 *SIC* 5145 2068

ELAMEX USA CORP p 483
1800 Northwestern Dr, El Paso TX 79912
Tel (915) 298-3061 *SIC* 3694 2068 2064

MOUNT FRANKLIN FOODS LLC p 993
1800 Northwestern Dr, El Paso TX 79912
Tel (915) 877-4079 *SIC* 5145 2068 2064

SIC 2074 Cottonseed Oil Mills

▲ ARCHER-DANIELS-MIDLAND CO p 105
77 W Wacker Dr Ste 4600, Chicago IL 60601
Tel (312) 634-8100
SIC 2046 2041 2075 2074 5153 2083

SYNGENTA SEEDS INC p 1415
11055 Wayzata Blvd, Hopkins MN 55305
Tel (612) 656-8600
SIC 2074 2075 2076 5191

PYCO INDUSTRIES INC p 1193
2901 Avenue A, Lubbock TX 79404
Tel (806) 747-3434 *SIC* 2074

SIC 2075 Soybean Oil Mills

RICELAND FOODS INC p 1232
2120 S Park Ave, Stuttgart AR 72160
Tel (870) 673-5500
SIC 2044 2079 5153 2075

PULMUONE FOODS USA INC p 1191
2315 Moore Ave, Fullerton CA 92833
Tel (714) 578-2800 *SIC* 5149 5141 2075

PULMUONE USA INC p 1191
2315 Moore Ave, Fullerton CA 92833
Tel (714) 578-2800 *SIC* 5149 5141 2075

▲ ARCHER-DANIELS-MIDLAND CO p 105
77 W Wacker Dr Ste 4600, Chicago IL 60601
Tel (312) 634-8100
SIC 2046 2041 2075 2074 5153 2083

WEST CENTRAL COOPERATIVE p 1594
406 1st St, Ralston IA 51459
Tel (712) 667-3200
SIC 5153 2075 2048 5191

PERDUE FARMS INC p 1134
31149 Old Ocean City Rd, Salisbury MD 21804
Tel (410) 543-3000 *SIC* 2015 2075 4213

MINNESOTA SOYBEAN PROCESSORS p 974
121 Zeh Ave, Brewster MN 56119
Tel (507) 842-6677 *SIC* 5153 2075

SYNGENTA SEEDS INC p 1415
11055 Wayzata Blvd, Hopkins MN 55305
Tel (612) 656-8600
SIC 2074 2075 2076 5191

▲ CHS INC p 304
5500 Cenex Dr, Inver Grove Heights MN 55077
Tel (651) 355-6000
SIC 5153 5191 2075 1311 2911 4613

CARGILL INC p 255
15407 Mcginty Rd W, Wayzata MN 55391
Tel (952) 742-7575
SIC 5153 2075 2046 2048 2011 2015

BUNGE MILLING INC p 225
11720 Borman Dr, Saint Louis MO 63146
Tel (314) 292-2000 *SIC* 2041 2075

BUNGE NORTH AMERICA FOUNDATION p 226
11720 Borman Dr, Saint Louis MO 63146
Tel (314) 872-3030
SIC 2075 2079 2048 2834

■ SOLAE LLC p 1337
4300 Duncan Ave, Saint Louis MO 63110
Tel (314) 659-3000 *SIC* 2075 2076

AG PROCESSING INC A COOPERATIVE p 33
12700 W Dodge Rd, Omaha NE 68154
Tel (402) 496-7809
SIC 5153 2075 2048 5999 0254

FORNAZOR INTERNATIONAL INC A NEW JERSEY CORP p 568
455 Hillsdale Ave, Hillsdale NJ 07642
Tel (201) 664-4000
SIC 0119 2034 2044 2045 2075 4449

SOUTH DAKOTA SOYBEAN PROCESSORS LLC p 1344
100 Caspian Ave, Volga SD 57071
Tel (605) 627-9240 *SIC* 2075

SIC 2076 Vegetable Oil Mills

FUJI VEGETABLE OIL INC p 583
120 Brampton Rd, Savannah GA 31408
Tel (912) 966-5900 *SIC* 2076

SYNGENTA SEEDS INC p 1415
11055 Wayzata Blvd, Hopkins MN 55305
Tel (612) 656-8600
SIC 2074 2075 2076 5191

■ SOLAE LLC p 1337
4300 Duncan Ave, Saint Louis MO 63110
Tel (314) 659-3000 *SIC* 2075 2076

SIC 2077 Animal, Marine Fats & Oils

SIMMONS FEED INGREDIENTS INC p 1324
601 N Hico St, Siloam Springs AR 72761
Tel (479) 254-8151 *SIC* 2077

BAKER COMMODITIES INC p 146
4020 Bandini Blvd, Vernon CA 90058
Tel (323) 268-2801 *SIC* 2077 2048

■ GRIFFIN INDUSTRIES LLC p 640
4221 Alexandria Pike, Cold Spring KY 41076
Tel (859) 781-2010 *SIC* 2077

WENDY WEIHE STORLIE INC p 1592
4032 Shoreline Dr Ste 2, Spring Park MN 55384
Tel (952) 548-9306 *SIC* 2079 2077

VIGON INTERNATIONAL INC p 1556
127 Airport Rd, East Stroudsburg PA 18301
Tel (570) 476-4172 *SIC* 2869 5149 2077

JBS SOUDERTON INC p 779
249 Allentown Rd, Souderton PA 18964
Tel (215) 723-5555 *SIC* 2011 2077 2013

▲ OMEGA PROTEIN CORP p 1084
2105 Citywest Blvd # 500, Houston TX 77042
Tel (713) 623-0060 *SIC* 2077 5199

▲ DARLING INGREDIENTS INC p 412
251 Oconnor Ridge Blvd, Irving TX 75038
Tel (972) 717-0300 *SIC* 2077

VALLEY PROTEINS INC p 1541
151 Valpro Dr, Winchester VA 22603
Tel (540) 877-2590 *SIC* 2077

SANIMAX CORP p 1279
2099 Badgerland Dr, Green Bay WI 54303
Tel (920) 494-5233 *SIC* 5199 2077

SANIMAX USA LLC p 1279
2099 Badgerland Dr, Green Bay WI 54303
Tel (920) 494-5233 *SIC* 5199 2077

SIC 2079 Shortening, Oils & Margarine

RICELAND FOODS INC p 1232
2120 S Park Ave, Stuttgart AR 72160
Tel (870) 673-5500
SIC 2044 2079 5153 2075

VENTURA FOODS LLC p 1548
40 Pointe Dr, Brea CA 92821
Tel (714) 257-3700 *SIC* 2079 2035

WILSEY FOODS INC p 1613
40 Pointe Dr, Brea CA 92821
Tel (714) 257-3700 *SIC* 2079 5149

AMREP INC p 86
425 Franklin Gtwy Se # 530, Marietta GA 30067
Tel (770) 590-5960
SIC 2842 2079 2911 2869 2841 2819

LODERS CROKLAAN USA LLC p 873
24708 W Durkee Rd, Channahon IL 60410
Tel (815) 730-5200 *SIC* 2079

SOUTH CHICAGO PACKING LLC p 1343
16250 Vincennes Ave, South Holland IL 60473
Tel (708) 589-2400 *SIC* 2079

OWENSBORO GRAIN EDIBLE OILS LLC p 1100
822 E 2nd St, Owensboro KY 42303
Tel (270) 926-2032 *SIC* 2079

WM B REILY & CO INC p 1620
640 Magazine St, New Orleans LA 70130
Tel (504) 539-5200
SIC 2095 2035 2079 5962 5963 2099

WENDY WEIHE STORLIE INC p 1592
4032 Shoreline Dr Ste 2, Spring Park MN 55384
Tel (952) 548-9306 *SIC* 2079 2077

BUNGE NORTH AMERICA FOUNDATION p 226
11720 Borman Dr, Saint Louis MO 63146
Tel (314) 872-3030
SIC 2075 2079 2048 2834

■ CONAGRA GROCERY PRODUCTS CO LLC p 354
11 Conagra Dr, Omaha NE 68102
Tel (630) 857-1000
SIC 2033 2079 2099 2032 2066 5149

AARHUSKARLSHAMN USA INC p 8
499 Thornall St Ste 5, Edison NJ 08837
Tel (973) 344-1300 *SIC* 2079

SUPREME OIL CO INC p 1408
66 Grand Ave Ste 201, Englewood NJ 07631
Tel (201) 408-0800 *SIC* 5149 2079

■ INTER AMERICAN PRODUCTS INC p 750
1240 State Ave, Cincinnati OH 45204
Tel (800) 645-2233
SIC 2095 2099 2033 2079 2087 2022

■ PROCTER & GAMBLE MANUFACTURING CO p 1179
1 Procter And Gamble Plz, Cincinnati OH 45202
Tel (513) 983-1100
SIC 2841 2079 2099 2844 2045

ABF NORTH AMERICA CORP p 11
7171 Goodlett Farms Pkwy, Cordova TN 38016
Tel (901) 381-3000 *SIC* 2079 2099

ABF NORTH AMERICA HOLDINGS INC p 11
7171 Goodlett Farms Pkwy, Cordova TN 38016
Tel (901) 381-3000 *SIC* 2079 2099

ACH FOOD COMPANIES INC p 17
7171 Goodlett Farms Pkwy, Cordova TN 38016
Tel (901) 381-3000 *SIC* 2079 2099

STRATAS FOODS LLC p 1392
7130 Goodlett Frm Pkwy # 200, Cordova TN 38016
Tel (888) 404-1004 *SIC* 2079

KERRY HOLDING CO p 813
3330 Millington Rd, Beloit WI 53511
Tel (608) 363-1200
SIC 2099 2079 2023 2022 2087

SIC 2082 Malt Beverages

SIERRA NEVADA BREWING CO p 1320
1075 E 20th St, Chico CA 95928
Tel (530) 893-3520 *SIC* 2082 5812

PABST BREWING CO LLC p 1103
10635 Santa Monica Blvd, Los Angeles CA 90025
Tel (310) 470-0962 *SIC* 2082

HOME BREW MART INC p 703
9045 Carroll Way, San Diego CA 92121
Tel (858) 790-6900 *SIC* 2082 5999

▲ **MOLSON COORS BREWING CO** p 983
1801 Calif St Ste 4600, Denver CO 80202
Tel (303) 927-2337 SIC 2082

NEW BELGIUM BREWING CO INC p 1029
500 Linden St, Fort Collins CO 80524
Tel (970) 221-0524 SIC 2082

■ **COORS BREWING CO** p 367
17735 W 32nd Ave, Golden CO 80401
Tel (303) 279-6565 SIC 2082

■ **MILLERCOORS LLC** p 971
250 S Wacker Dr Ste 800, Chicago IL 60606
Tel (312) 496-2700 SIC 2082

GRAIN PROCESSING CORP p 629
1600 Oregon St, Muscatine IA 52761
Tel (563) 264-4265 SIC 2869 2085 2082

▲ **BOSTON BEER CO INC** p 202
1 Design Center Pl # 850, Boston MA 02210
Tel (617) 368-5000 SIC 2082

■ **BOSTON BEER CORP** p 202
1 Design Center Pl # 850, Boston MA 02210
Tel (617) 368-5000 SIC 2082

ANHEUSER BUSCH INVESTMENT p 91
1 Busch Pl, Saint Louis MO 63118
Tel (314) 577-2000 SIC 2082

ANHEUSER-BUSCH COMPANIES LLC p 91
1 Busch Pl, Saint Louis MO 63118
Tel (314) 632-6777 SIC 2082 3411 7996

ANHEUSER-BUSCH LLC p 91
1 Busch Pl, Saint Louis MO 63118
Tel (314) 632-6777 SIC 5181 2082

HIGH FALLS OPERATING CO LLC p 690
445 Saint Paul St, Rochester NY 14605
Tel (585) 546-1030 SIC 2082

NORTH AMERICAN BREWERIES INC p 1049
445 Saint Paul St, Rochester NY 14605
Tel (585) 546-1030 SIC 2082

▲ **CONSTELLATION BRANDS INC** p 360
207 High Point Dr # 100, Victor NY 14564
Tel (585) 678-7100
SIC 2084 5182 5181 2082 2085 2087

▲ **CRAFT BREW ALLIANCE INC** p 388
929 N Russell St, Portland OR 97227
Tel (503) 331-7270 SIC 2082

SAMUEL ADAMS PENNSYLVANIA BREWERY CO p 1275
7880 Penn Dr, Breinigsville PA 18031
Tel (610) 391-4700 SIC 2082

SOUTHERN GLAZERS WINE AND SPIRITS OF TEXAS LLC p 1348
14911 Quorum Dr Ste 150, Dallas TX 75254
Tel (972) 392-8200 SIC 2082 5182 5199

GAMBRINUS CO p 590
14800 San Pedro Ave # 310, San Antonio TX 78232
Tel (210) 483-5100 SIC 5181 2082

INDEPENDENT BREWERS UNITED CORP p 736
431 Pine St Ste G12, Burlington VT 05401
Tel (802) 862-6114 SIC 2082 2084

BUFFALO CHECK BEER LLC p 224
P.O. Box 9635, Seattle WA 98109
Tel (312) 320-3717 SIC 2082

CITY BREWING CO LLC p 312
925 3rd St S, La Crosse WI 54601
Tel (608) 785-4200 SIC 2082

■ **MILLER BREWERIES EAST INC** p 970
3939 W Highland Blvd, Milwaukee WI 53208
Tel (414) 931-2000 SIC 2082

SIC 2083 Malt

▲ **ARCHER-DANIELS-MIDLAND CO** p 105
77 W Wacker Dr Ste 4600, Chicago IL 60601
Tel (312) 634-8100
SIC 2046 2041 2075 2074 5153 2083

BUSCH AGRICULTURAL RESOURCES LLC p 229
3636 S Geyer Rd Fl 2, Saint Louis MO 63127
Tel (314) 577-2000
SIC 2044 2083 0181 5153

SIOUXLAND ETHANOL LLC p 1326
1501 Knox Blvd, Jackson NE 68743
Tel (402) 632-2676 SIC 2869 2083

MALT PRODUCTS CORP p 900
88 Market St, Saddle Brook NJ 07663
Tel (201) 845-4420 SIC 2083 2087

SIC 2084 Wine & Brandy

BRONCO WINE CO p 217
6342 Bystrum Rd, Ceres CA 95307
Tel (209) 538-3131 SIC 5182 2084

GIUMARRA VINEYARDS CORP p 613
11220 Edison Hwy, Edison CA 93220
Tel (661) 395-7000 SIC 0172 2084 2086

F KORBEL & BROS p 522
13250 River Rd, Guerneville CA 95446
Tel (707) 824-7000 SIC 2084 0172

WENTE BROS p 1592
5565 Tesla Rd, Livermore CA 94550
Tel (925) 456-2300 SIC 2084 8742

WONDERFUL CO LLC p 1622
11444 W Olympic Blvd # 210, Los Angeles CA 90064
Tel (310) 966-5700 SIC 0723 2084

E & J GALLO WINERY p 465
600 Yosemite Blvd, Modesto CA 95354
Tel (209) 341-3111 SIC 2084 0172

TREASURY WINE ESTATES AMERICAS CO p 1475
555 Gateway Dr, Napa CA 94558
Tel (707) 259-4500 SIC 2084

WINE GROUP INC p 1616
17000 E State Highway 120, Ripon CA 95366
Tel (209) 599-4111 SIC 2084

SUTTER HOME WINERY INC p 1410
100 Saint Helena Hwy S, Saint Helena CA 94574
Tel (707) 963-3104 SIC 2084 0172

OTSUKA AMERICA INC p 1097
1 Embarcadero Ctr # 2020, San Francisco CA 94111
Tel (415) 986-5300
SIC 3829 3499 5122 2833 2084 2086

JACKSON FAMILY WINES INC p 774
421 And 425 Aviation Blvd, Santa Rosa CA 95403
Tel (707) 544-4000 SIC 2084 0172 5813

DIAGEO NORTH AMERICA INC p 436
801 Main Ave, Norwalk CT 06851
Tel (203) 229-2100 SIC 2084 2085

UST LLC p 1536
6 High Ridge Park Bldg A, Stamford CT 06905
Tel (203) 817-3000
SIC 2131 2084 2621 3999

BUFKOR INC p 224
1801 Stonebrook Ln, Safety Harbor FL 34695
Tel (727) 572-9991 SIC 5199 2084

ELAN CHATEAU RESORTS LLC p 483
100 Rue Charlemagne Dr, Braselton GA 30517
Tel (678) 425-0900
SIC 2084 5812 7992 7011

COOPERS HAWK INTERMEDIATE HOLDING LLC p 367
5325 9th Ave, Countryside IL 60525
Tel (708) 839-2920
SIC 8741 2084 5182 5812

TERLATO WINE GROUP LTD p 1439
900 Armour Dr, Lake Bluff IL 60044
Tel (847) 604-8900 SIC 5182 2084 8743

▲ **BROWN-FORMAN CORP** p 220
850 Dixie Hwy, Louisville KY 40210
Tel (502) 585-1100 SIC 2085 2084 2449

GREAT LAKES WINE & SPIRITS LLC p 634
373 Victor St, Highland Park MI 48203
Tel (313) 278-5400 SIC 5182 2084

■ **CONSTELLATION BRANDS US OPERATIONS INC** p 361
235 N Bloomfield Rd, Canandaigua NY 14424
Tel (585) 396-7600 SIC 2084

SUNTORY INTERNATIONAL CORP p 1405
600 3rd Ave Fl 21, New York NY 10016
Tel (212) 891-6600
SIC 5149 2084 2086 5499 5812

▲ **CONSTELLATION BRANDS INC** p 360
207 High Point Dr # 100, Victor NY 14564
Tel (585) 678-7100
SIC 2084 5182 5181 2082 2085 2087

DESTILERIA SERRALLES INC p 432
Calle Central 1, Mercedita PR 00715
Tel (787) 840-1000 SIC 2085 2084 5141

INDEPENDENT BREWERS UNITED CORP p 736
431 Pine St Ste G12, Burlington VT 05401
Tel (802) 862-6114 SIC 2082 2084

▲ **ALTRIA GROUP INC** p 63
6601 W Broad St, Richmond VA 23230
Tel (804) 274-2200 SIC 2111 2084

SIC 2085 Liquors, Distilled, Rectified & Blended

FRANK-LIN DISTILLERS PRODUCTS LTD p 574
2455 Huntington Dr, Fairfield CA 94533
Tel (408) 259-8900 SIC 5182 2085

DIAGEO NORTH AMERICA INC p 436
801 Main Ave, Norwalk CT 06851
Tel (203) 229-2100 SIC 2084 2085

BEAM GLOBAL SPIRITS & WINE LLC p 165
510 Lake Cook Rd, Deerfield IL 60015
Tel (847) 948-8888 SIC 2085

BEAM SUNTORY INC p 165
510 Lake Cook Rd, Deerfield IL 60015
Tel (847) 948-8888 SIC 2085

JIM BEAM BRANDS CO p 785
510 Lake Cook Rd Ste 200, Deerfield IL 60015
Tel (847) 948-8903 SIC 2085

■ **ILLINOIS CORN PROCESSING LLC** p 732
1301 S Front St, Pekin IL 61554
Tel (309) 353-3990 SIC 2085

CARDINAL ETHANOL LLC p 252
1554 N County Rd 600 E, Union City IN 47390
Tel (765) 964-3137 SIC 2869 2085

SOUTHWEST IOWA RENEWABLE ENERGY LLC p 1352
10868 189th St, Council Bluffs IA 51503
Tel (712) 366-0392 SIC 2869 2085 2046

HOMELAND ENERGY SOLUTIONS LLC p 703
2779 Highway 24, Lawler IA 52154
Tel (563) 238-5555 SIC 2869 2085 2046

GRAIN PROCESSING CORP p 629
1600 Oregon St, Muscatine IA 52761
Tel (563) 264-4265 SIC 2869 2085 2082

KENT CORP p 812
2905 N Highway 61, Muscatine IA 52761
Tel (563) 264-4211
SIC 2869 2085 2046 2048

▲ **MGP INGREDIENTS INC** p 958
100 Commercial St, Atchison KS 66002
Tel (913) 367-1480 SIC 2085 2041

■ **MGPI PROCESSING INC** p 958
100 Commercial St, Atchison KS 66002
Tel (913) 367-1480 SIC 2085 2041

HEAVEN HILL DISTILLERIES INC p 679
1064 Loretto Rd, Bardstown KY 40004
Tel (502) 348-3921 SIC 2085

▲ **BROWN-FORMAN CORP** p 220
850 Dixie Hwy, Louisville KY 40210
Tel (502) 585-1100 SIC 2085 2084 2449

SAZERAC CO INC p 1285
3850 N Causeway Blvd # 1695, Metairie LA 70002
Tel (504) 831-9450 SIC 5182 2085

GRANITE FALLS ENERGY LLC p 631
15045 Highway 23 Se, Granite Falls MN 56241
Tel (320) 564-3100 SIC 2869 2085 2046

ROUST CORP p 1253
3000 Atrium Way Ste 265, Mount Laurel NJ 08054
Tel (856) 273-6980 SIC 5181 2085 5182

PERNOD RICARD USA LLC p 1136
250 Park Ave Ste 17a, New York NY 10177
Tel (914) 848-4800 SIC 2085

▲ **CONSTELLATION BRANDS INC** p 360
207 High Point Dr # 100, Victor NY 14564
Tel (585) 678-7100
SIC 2084 5182 5181 2082 2085 2087

RED TRAIL ENERGY LLC p 1216
3682 Highway 8, Richardton ND 58652
Tel (701) 974-3308 SIC 2869 2085

BACARDI CORP p 143
Km 2/6 Carretera 165 Rd S St, Catano PR 00962
Tel (787) 788-1500 SIC 2085

DESTILERIA SERRALLES INC p 432
Calle Central 1, Mercedita PR 00715
Tel (787) 840-1000 SIC 2085 2084 5141

■ **JACK DANIEL DISTILLERY LEM MOTLOW PROP INC** p 773
Rr 1, Lynchburg TN 37352
Tel (931) 759-4221 SIC 2085

SIC 2086 Soft Drinks

BUFFALO ROCK CO p 224
111 Oxmoor Rd, Birmingham AL 35209
Tel (205) 942-3435 SIC 2086 5962 5149

COCA-COLA BOTTLING CO UNITED INC p 333
4600 E Lake Blvd, Birmingham AL 35217
Tel (205) 238-3300 SIC 2086 5962

KALIL BOTTLING CO p 801
931 S Highland Ave, Tucson AZ 85719
Tel (520) 624-1788 SIC 2086 7359

SOUTHWEST CANNING & PACKAGING INC p 1351
931 S Highland Ave, Tucson AZ 85719
Tel (520) 622-5811 SIC 2086

■ **SMUCKER NATURAL FOODS INC** p 1335
37 Speedway Ave, Chico CA 95928
Tel (530) 899-5000 SIC 2086 2033 2087

■ **MONSTER BEVERAGE 1990 CORP** p 985
1 Monster Way, Corona CA 92879
Tel (951) 739-6200 SIC 2086

▲ **MONSTER BEVERAGE CORP** p 985
1 Monster Way, Corona CA 92879
Tel (951) 739-6200 SIC 2086

GIUMARRA VINEYARDS CORP p 613
11220 Edison Hwy, Edison CA 93220
Tel (661) 395-7000 SIC 0172 2084 2086

■ **SHASTA BEVERAGES INC** p 1312
26901 Indl Blvd, Hayward CA 94545
Tel (954) 581-0922 SIC 2086

■ **BCI COCA-COLA BOTTLING CO OF LOS ANGELES** p 164
1334 S Central Ave, Los Angeles CA 90021
Tel (213) 746-5555 SIC 2086

CG ROXANE LLC p 285
1210 State Hwy 395, Olancha CA 93549
Tel (760) 764-2885 SIC 2086

NIAGARA BOTTLING LLC p 1042
2560 E Philadelphia St, Ontario CA 91761
Tel (909) 230-5000 SIC 2086

OTSUKA AMERICA INC p 1097
1 Embarcadero Ctr # 2020, San Francisco CA 94111
Tel (415) 986-5300
SIC 3829 3499 5122 2833 2084 2086

■ **CYTOSPORT INC** p 406
1340 Treat Blvd Ste 350, Walnut Creek CA 94597
Tel (707) 751-3942 SIC 2023 2086

NOR-CAL BEVERAGE CO INC p 1047
2150 Stone Blvd, West Sacramento CA 95691
Tel (916) 372-0600 SIC 5181 2086

SUNSWEET GROWERS INC p 1404
901 N Walton Ave, Yuba City CA 95993
Tel (530) 674-5010 SIC 2034 2037 2086

■ **PEPSI-COLA METROPOLITAN BOTTLING CO INC** p 1134
3801 Brighton Blvd, Denver CO 80216
Tel (303) 292-9220 SIC 2086

DANONE HOLDINGS INC p 412
208 Harbor Dr Fl 3, Stamford CT 06902
Tel (203) 229-7000 SIC 2086

■ **TROPICANA PRODUCTS INC** p 1484
1275 26th Ave E, Bradenton FL 34208
Tel (941) 747-4461
SIC 2033 2037 2086 2048

■ **FLORIDA COCA-COLA BOTTLING CO** p 557
521 Lake Kathy Dr, Brandon FL 33510
Tel (813) 569-2600 SIC 2086

NUBO BOTTLE CO LLC p 1066
3700 Nw 124th Ave Ste 109, Coral Springs FL 33065
Tel (954) 283-9057 SIC 2086

C C 1 LIMITED PARTNERSHIP p 232
3201 Nw 72nd Ave, Miami FL 33122
Tel (305) 599-2337 SIC 2086

IBS PARTNERS LTD p 726
1 N University Dr Ut400a, Plantation FL 33324
Tel (954) 581-0922 SIC 2086

▲ **NATIONAL BEVERAGE CORP** p 1010
8100 Sw 10th St Ste 4000, Plantation FL 33324
Tel (954) 581-0922 SIC 2086

■ **NEWBEVCO INC** p 1037
1 N University Dr, Plantation FL 33324
Tel (954) 581-0922 SIC 2086

■ **PEPSI COLA BOTTLING FORT LAUNDERDALE** p 1134
7305 Garden Rd, Riviera Beach FL 33404
Tel (561) 848-1000 SIC 2086

■ **COCA-COLA BEVERAGES FLORIDA LLC** p 333
10117 Princess Plm Ave # 400, Tampa FL 33610
Tel (813) 327-7294 SIC 2086

COTT BEVERAGES INC p 374
5519 W Idlewild Ave, Tampa FL 33634
Tel (813) 313-1800 SIC 2086

COTT CORP p 374
5519 W Idlewild Ave, Tampa FL 33634
Tel (813) 313-1800 SIC 2086

■ **PEPSI-COLA BOTTLING CO OF TAMPA** p 1134
11315 N 30th St, Tampa FL 33612
Tel (813) 971-2550 SIC 2086

▲ **COCA-COLA CO** p 333
1 Coca Cola Plz Nw, Atlanta GA 30313
Tel (404) 676-2121
SIC 2087 2086 2033 2037

COCA-COLA ENTERPRISES INC p 333
2500 Windy Ridge Pkwy Se # 700, Atlanta GA 30339
Tel (678) 260-3000 SIC 2086

■ **COCA-COLA INTERAMERICAN CORP** p 333
1 Coca Cola Plz Nw, Atlanta GA 30313
Tel (404) 676-2121 SIC 2086

■ **COCA-COLA REFRESHMENTS USA INC** p 333
2500 Windy Ridge Pkwy Se, Atlanta GA 30339
Tel (770) 989-3000 SIC 2086 2087

DS WATERS HOLDINGS LLC p 457
5660 New Northside Dr # 500, Atlanta GA 30328
Tel (770) 933-1400 SIC 2086

■ **GREAT LAKES COCA-COLA DISTRIBUTION LLC** p 633
1 Coca Cola Plz Nw, Atlanta GA 30313
Tel (404) 374-8969 SIC 2086

■ **REFRESHMENT PRODUCT SERVICES INC** p 1217
1 Coca Cola Plz Nw, Atlanta GA 30313
Tel (404) 676-2121 SIC 2086

■ **GATORADE CO** p 594
555 W Monroe St Fl 1, Chicago IL 60661
Tel (312) 821-1000 SIC 2086 5149

HINCKLEY & SCHMITT INC p 695
6055 S Harlem Ave, Chicago IL 60638
Tel (773) 586-8600 SIC 2086 5149 7359

■ **QUAKER OATS CO** p 1196
555 W Monroe St Fl 1, Chicago IL 60661
Tel (312) 821-1000
SIC 2086 2043 2045 2052 2064 2099

BERNER FOOD & BEVERAGE LLC p 176
2034 E Factory Rd, Dakota IL 61018
Tel (815) 563-4222
SIC 2022 2026 2095 2086 2033

PEPSI MIDAMERICA CO p 1134
2605 W Main St, Marion IL 62959
Tel (618) 997-1377 SIC 2086

REFRESHMENT SERVICES INC p 1218
1121 Locust St, Quincy IL 62301
Tel (217) 223-8600 SIC 2086

■ **PEPSI-COLA GENERAL BOTTLERS INC** p 1134
1475 E Wdfeld Rd Ste 1300, Schaumburg IL 60173
Tel (847) 598-3000 SIC 2086 5149

■ **ROYAL CROWN BOTTLING CORP** p 1254
1100 Independence Ave, Evansville IN 47714
Tel (812) 424-7978 SIC 2086

ATLANTIC BOTTLING CO p 126
4 E 2nd St, Atlantic IA 50022
Tel (515) 987-1931 SIC 2086

CHESTERMAN CO p 295
4700 S Lewis Blvd, Sioux City IA 51106
Tel (712) 252-2653 SIC 2086

■ **WICHITA COCA-COLA BOTTLING CO** p 1607
10001 Industrial Blvd, Lenexa KS 66215
Tel (316) 612-6400 SIC 2086

■ **LOUISIANA COCA-COLA BOTTLING CO LIMITED** p 880
5601 Citrus Blvd, New Orleans LA 70123
Tel (504) 818-7000 SIC 2086 5962

■ **GE IONICS INC** p 596
3 Burlington Woods Dr # 200, Burlington MA 01803
Tel (781) 359-7000
SIC 3589 2086 4941 3559 2899 3823

CUMBERLAND FARMS INC p 400
100 Crossing Blvd, Framingham MA 01702
Tel (508) 270-1400
SIC 5411 5541 5172 2086 2051 2026

POLAR CORP p 1159
1001 Southbridge St, Worcester MA 01610
Tel (508) 753-6383 SIC 2086 5149

■ **FAYGO BEVERAGES INC** p 532
3579 Gratiot Ave, Detroit MI 48207
Tel (313) 925-1600 SIC 2086

■ **PEPSI AMERICAS INC** p 1134
60 S 6th St, Minneapolis MN 55402
Tel (612) 661-4000 SIC 2086

PREMIUM WATERS INC p 1171
2100 Summer St Ne Ste 200, Minneapolis MN 55413
Tel (612) 379-4141 SIC 2086

C C CLARK INC p 232
501 Academy Rd, Starkville MS 39759
Tel (662) 323-4317 SIC 5149 2086

OZARKS COCA-COLA/DR PEPPER BOTTLING CO p 1101
1777 N Packer Rd, Springfield MO 65803
Tel (417) 865-9900 SIC 2086 5149

COCA-COLA BOTTLING CO OF NORTHERN NEW ENGLAND INC p 333
1 Executive Park Dr # 330, Bedford NH 03110
Tel (603) 627-7871 SIC 2086

CONOPCO INC p 358
700 Sylvan Ave, Englewood Cliffs NJ 07632
Tel (201) 894-2727
SIC 2035 2038 2086 2024 2844 2841

UNILEVER UNITED STATES INC p 1503
700 Sylvan Ave, Englewood Cliffs NJ 07632
Tel (201) 894-4000
SIC 2035 2086 2024 2038 2844 2841

GERBER PRODUCTS CO p 608
12 Vreeland Rd Fl 2, Florham Park NJ 07932
Tel (973) 593-7500
SIC 2023 2043 2037 2052 2086 2091

▲ **J & J SNACK FOODS CORP** p 770
6000 Central Hwy, Pennsauken NJ 08109
Tel (856) 665-9533
SIC 2053 2087 2086 2024 2052 2051

PEPSI-COLA & NATIONAL BRAND BEVERAGES LTD (INC) p 1134
8275 N Crescent Blvd, Pennsauken NJ 08110
Tel (856) 665-6200 SIC 2086

BAI BRANDS LLC p 145
1800 E State St Ste 153, Trenton NJ 08609
Tel (609) 586-0500 SIC 2086

PEPSI-COLA BOTTLING CO OF NEW YORK INC p 1134
11402 15th Ave Ste 5, College Point NY 11356
Tel (718) 392-1000 SIC 2086

CLIFFSTAR LLC p 326
1 Cliffstar Dr, Dunkirk NY 14048
Tel (716) 366-6100 SIC 2033 2086

■ **CENTRAL COCA-COLA BOTTLING CO INC** p 277
555 Taxter Rd Ste 550, Elmsford NY 10523
Tel (914) 789-1100 SIC 5149 2086 8741

▲ HAIN CELESTIAL GROUP INC p 653
1111 Marcus Ave Ste 100, New Hyde Park NY 11042
Tel (516) 587-5000
SIC 2023 2034 2096 2086 2844

SUNTORY INTERNATIONAL CORP p 1405
600 3rd Ave Fl 21, New York NY 10016
Tel (212) 891-6600
SIC 5149 2084 2086 5499 5812

▲ PEPSICO INC p 1134
700 Anderson Hill Rd, Purchase NY 10577
Tel (914) 253-2000
SIC 2096 2087 2086 2037 2052 2043

ADIRONDACK BEVERAGE CO INC p 22
701 Corporation Park, Schenectady NY 12302
Tel (518) 370-3621 *SIC* 2086

■ GENERAL CINEMA BEVERAGES OF OHIO INC p 599
1 Pepsi Way Ste 1, Somers NY 10589
Tel (914) 767-6000 *SIC* 2086

■ BOTTLING GROUP LLC p 203
1111 Westchester Ave, White Plains NY 10604
Tel (800) 789-2626 *SIC* 2086

■ BOTTLING GROUP LLC p 203
1111 Westchester Ave, White Plains NY 10604
Tel (914) 767-6000 *SIC* 2086

■ PEPSI-COLA BOTTLING GROUP p 1134
1111 Westchester Ave, White Plains NY 10604
Tel (914) 767-6000 *SIC* 2086

■ PEPSI-COLA METROPOLITAN BOTTLING CO INC p 1134
1111 Westchester Ave, White Plains NY 10604
Tel (914) 767-6000 *SIC* 2086 2087

ALAMANCE FOODS INC p 43
840 Plantation Dr, Burlington NC 27215
Tel (336) 226-6392
SIC 2026 2899 2024 2086

■ CCBCC OPERATIONS LLC p 269
4100 Coca Cola Plz, Charlotte NC 28211
Tel (704) 364-8728 *SIC* 2086

▲ COCA-COLA BOTTLING CO CONSOLIDATED p 333
4100 Coca Cola Plz # 100, Charlotte NC 28211
Tel (704) 557-4400 *SIC* 2086

■ PIEDMONT COCA-COLA BOTTLING PARTNERSHIP p 1146
4115 Coca Cola Plz, Charlotte NC 28211
Tel (704) 551-4400 *SIC* 2086

S & D COFFEE INC p 1261
300 Concord Pkwy S, Concord NC 28027
Tel (704) 782-3121 *SIC* 2095 5149 2086

S&D COFFEE HOLDING CO p 1263
300 Concord Pkwy S, Concord NC 28027
Tel (704) 782-3121
SIC 6719 2095 5149 2086

PEPSI-COLA BOTTLING CO OF HICKORY NC INC p 1134
2401 14th Avenue Cir Nw, Hickory NC 28601
Tel (828) 322-8090 *SIC* 5149 2086

PEPSI BOTTLING VENTURES LLC p 1134
4141 Parklake Ave Ste 600, Raleigh NC 27612
Tel (919) 865-2300 *SIC* 5149 2086

COUNTRY PURE FOODS INC p 375
681 W Waterloo Rd, Akron OH 44314
Tel (330) 753-2293 *SIC* 2033 2037 2086

NATURAL COUNTRY FARMS INC p 1018
681 W Waterloo Rd, Akron OH 44314
Tel (330) 753-2293 *SIC* 2033 2037 2086

BEVERAGES HOLDINGS LLC p 178
10300 Alliance Rd Ste 500, Blue Ash OH 45242
Tel (513) 483-3300 *SIC* 2086 2037

SUNNY DELIGHT BEVERAGE CO p 1403
10300 Alliance Rd Ste 500, Blue Ash OH 45242
Tel (513) 483-3300 *SIC* 2086

G & J PEPSI-COLA BOTTLERS INC p 586
9435 Waterstone Blvd # 390, Cincinnati OH 45249
Tel (513) 785-6060 *SIC* 2086

BROWNE BOTTLING CO INC p 220
2712 Tealwood Dr, Oklahoma City OK 73120
Tel (405) 232-1158 *SIC* 2086

■ GREAT PLAINS COCA COLA BOTTLING CO p 634
600 N May Ave, Oklahoma City OK 73107
Tel (405) 280-2000 *SIC* 2086

PACIFIC FOODS OF OREGON INC p 1104
19480 Sw 97th Ave, Tualatin OR 97062
Tel (503) 692-9666 *SIC* 2033 2099 2086

■ GE INFRASTRUCTURE SENSING p 596
4636 Somerton Rd, Feasterville Trevose PA 19053
Tel (617) 926-1749
SIC 3589 2086 4941 3559 2899 3823

GALLIKER DAIRY CO p 590
143 Donald Ln, Johnstown PA 15904
Tel (814) 266-8702 *SIC* 2026 2086 2024

■ PHILADELPHIA COCA-COLA BOTTLING CO p 1142
725 E Erie Ave, Philadelphia PA 19134
Tel (215) 427-4500 *SIC* 2086

ABARTA INC p 9
200 Alpha Dr, Pittsburgh PA 15238
Tel (412) 963-6226
SIC 2086 2711 2721 5149 1382 5812

■ ROCHESTER COCA COLA BOTTLING CORP p 1243
300 Oak St, Pittston PA 18640
Tel (570) 655-2874 *SIC* 2086 5962

C C 1 LIMITED PARTNERSHIP p 232
107 Carr 174, Bayamon PR 00959
Tel (787) 288-6400 *SIC* 2086

PEPSI-COLA PUERTO RICO DISTRIBUTING LLC p 1134
Carr 865 Km 0 4 Barrio Ca St Ca, Toa Baja PR 00949
Tel (787) 251-2000 *SIC* 2086

CAROLINA CANNERS INC p 259
300 Highway 1 S, Cheraw SC 29520
Tel (843) 537-5281 *SIC* 2086

COCA-COLA BOTTLING CO HIGH COUNTRY p 333
2150 Coca Cola Ln, Rapid City SD 57702
Tel (605) 342-8222 *SIC* 2086

■ PEPSI BEVERAGES CO p 1134
110 S Byhalia Rd, Collierville TN 38017
Tel (901) 853-5736 *SIC* 2086 5181

ALL-AMERICAN BOTTLING CORP p 51
5345 Hickory Hill Rd # 102, Memphis TN 38141
Tel (901) 369-0483 *SIC* 2086

■ AB-TEX BEVERAGE LTD p 9
650 Colonial Dr, Abilene TX 79603
Tel (325) 673-7171 *SIC* 2086

PLAINS DAIRY LLC p 1153
300 N Taylor St, Amarillo TX 79107
Tel (806) 374-0385 *SIC* 2026 2086 2033

ONE WATER SOURCE LLC p 1086
1114 Lost Creek Blvd # 100, Austin TX 78746
Tel (512) 347-9280 *SIC* 2086

▲ IMPRESO INC p 735
652 Southwestern Blvd, Coppell TX 75019
Tel (972) 462-0100 *SIC* 2761 2679 2086

■ AMERICAN BOTTLING CO p 69
5301 Legacy Dr, Plano TX 75024
Tel (972) 673-7000 *SIC* 2086

▲ DR PEPPER SNAPPLE GROUP INC p 454
5301 Legacy Dr, Plano TX 75024
Tel (972) 673-7000 *SIC* 2086

■ FRITO-LAY NORTH AMERICA INC p 580
7701 Legacy Dr, Plano TX 75024
Tel (972) 334-7000
SIC 2096 2052 2013 5812 6794 2086

OLD FRITO-LAY INC p 1080
7701 Legacy Dr, Plano TX 75024
Tel (972) 334-7000
SIC 2096 2052 2013 5812 6794 2086

■ AUSTIN COCA-COLA BOTTLING CO p 132
1 Coca Cola Pl, San Antonio TX 78219
Tel (210) 225-2601 *SIC* 2086

SWIRE PACIFIC HOLDINGS INC p 1412
12634 S 265 W Bldg A, Draper UT 84020
Tel (801) 816-5300 *SIC* 2086

PEPSI-COLA BOTTLING CO OF CENTRAL VIRGINIA p 1134
1150 Pepsi Pl, Charlottesville VA 22901
Tel (434) 978-2140 *SIC* 2086

COCA COLA BOTTLING CO (INC) p 333
155 Avery St, Walla Walla WA 99362
Tel (509) 529-0753 *SIC* 2086

DOLSEN COMPANIES p 448
301 N 3rd St, Yakima WA 98901
Tel (509) 248-2831
SIC 0241 0211 2086 7359

NOEL CORP p 1046
1001 S 1st St, Yakima WA 98901
Tel (509) 248-4545
SIC 2086 7389 4212 6512 4225 5962

WIS - PAK INC p 1618
860 West St, Watertown WI 53094
Tel (920) 262-6300 *SIC* 2086

ADMIRAL BEVERAGE CORP p 23
821 Pulliam Ave, Worland WY 82401
Tel (801) 782-5072 *SIC* 5149 2086

SIC 2087 Flavoring Extracts & Syrups

■ SMUCKER NATURAL FOODS INC p 1335
37 Speedway Ave, Chico CA 95928
Tel (530) 899-5000 *SIC* 2086 2033 2087

LYONS MAGNUS INC p 888
3158 E Hamilton Ave, Fresno CA 93702
Tel (559) 268-5966 *SIC* 2033 2026 2087

GOLDEN STATE FOODS CORP p 621
18301 Von Karman Ave # 1100, Irvine CA 92612
Tel (949) 252-2000
SIC 5147 2087 5142 5148 5149

■ ICEE CO p 727
1205 S Dupont Ave, Ontario CA 91761
Tel (800) 426-4233
SIC 2038 5145 3559 2087

■ AMERICAN FRUITS AND FLAVORS LLC p 73
10725 Sutter Ave, Pacoima CA 91331
Tel (818) 899-9574 *SIC* 2087

▲ COCA-COLA CO p 333
1 Coca Cola Plz Nw, Atlanta GA 30313
Tel (404) 676-2121
SIC 2087 2086 2033 2037

■ COCA-COLA REFRESHMENTS USA INC p 333
2500 Windy Ridge Pkwy Se, Atlanta GA 30339
Tel (770) 989-3000 *SIC* 2086 2087

WM WRIGLEY JR CO p 1620
930 W Evergreen Ave, Chicago IL 60642
Tel (312) 280-4710
SIC 2067 2064 2087 2899

■ MONDELEZ GLOBAL LLC p 983
3 Parkway N Ste 300, Deerfield IL 60015
Tel (847) 943-4000
SIC 2052 2066 3999 2067 2022 2087

▲ MONDELEZ INTERNATIONAL INC p 983
3 Parkway N Ste 300, Deerfield IL 60015
Tel (847) 943-4000
SIC 2022 2013 2095 2043 2035 2087

FONA INTERNATIONAL INC p 563
1900 Averill Rd, Geneva IL 60134
Tel (630) 578-8600 *SIC* 2087

KRAFT FOODS GROUP INC p 829
3 Lakes Dr, Northfield IL 60093
Tel (847) 646-2000
SIC 2022 3411 2095 2043 2035 2087

▲ STEPAN CO p 1386
22 W Frontage Rd, Northfield IL 60093
Tel (847) 446-7500
SIC 2843 2821 2087 2865

▲ TREEHOUSE FOODS INC p 1475
2021 Spring Rd Ste 600, Oak Brook IL 60523
Tel (708) 483-1300
SIC 2035 2023 2032 2033 2087

JEL SERT CO p 782
Conde St Rr 59, West Chicago IL 60185
Tel (630) 231-7590
SIC 2087 2024 2099 5499 5143

■ SENSIENT FLAVORS LLC p 1304
5600 W Raymond St, Indianapolis IN 46241
Tel (317) 243-3521 *SIC* 2087

TONE BROTHERS INC p 1460
2301 Se Tones Dr, Ankeny IA 50021
Tel (515) 965-2711 *SIC* 2087 2099

CARAVAN INGREDIENTS INC p 252
7905 Quivira Rd, Lenexa KS 66215
Tel (913) 890-5500
SIC 2099 2821 5084 2087

▲ MCCORMICK & CO INC p 927
18 Loveton Cir, Sparks MD 21152
Tel (410) 771-7301
SIC 2099 2087 2038 2037

ROHTSTEIN CORP p 1247
70 Olympia Ave, Woburn MA 01801
Tel (781) 935-8300
SIC 5149 2099 2087 2062 2041 2033

JACOBS INDUSTRIES INC p 775
8096 Excelsior Blvd, Hopkins MN 55343
Tel (612) 339-9500
SIC 2841 2087 2099 2844 5084 6794

WATKINS INC p 1582
150 Liberty St, Winona MN 55987
Tel (507) 457-3300 *SIC* 2087 2841

■ SENSORYEFFECTS INC p 1305
13723 Rverport Dr Ste 201, Maryland Heights MO 63043
Tel (314) 291-5444 *SIC* 2087

UNGERER INDUSTRIES INC p 1502
4 Bridgewater Ln, Lincoln Park NJ 07035
Tel (973) 628-0600 *SIC* 2899 2844 2087

SODASTREAM USA INC p 1336
200 E Park Dr Ste 600, Mount Laurel NJ 08054
Tel (800) 763-2258 *SIC* 2087 3585

▲ J & J SNACK FOODS CORP p 770
6000 Central Hwy, Pennsauken NJ 08109
Tel (856) 665-9533
SIC 2053 2087 2086 2024 2052 2051

SOLVAY USA INC p 1339
504 Carnegie Ctr, Princeton NJ 08540
Tel (609) 860-4000
SIC 2899 2869 2821 2087 2865

MALT PRODUCTS CORP p 900
88 Market St, Saddle Brook NJ 07663
Tel (201) 845-4420 *SIC* 2083 2087

■ MOTTS LLP p 993
55 Hunter Ln, Elmsford NY 10523
Tel (972) 673-8088 *SIC* 2033 5149 2087

■ CARRIAGE HOUSE COMPANIES INC p 260
196 Newton St, Fredonia NY 14063
Tel (716) 672-4321
SIC 2099 2033 2035 2087

▲ INTERNATIONAL FLAVORS & FRAGRANCES INC p 755
521 W 57th St, New York NY 10019
Tel (212) 765-5500 *SIC* 2869 2844 2087

MACANDREWS & FORBES INC p 891
38 E 63rd St, New York NY 10065
Tel (212) 688-9000
SIC 2844 2087 2121 7819 2721 2731

▲ PEPSICO INC p 1134
700 Anderson Hill Rd, Purchase NY 10577
Tel (914) 253-2000
SIC 2096 2087 2086 2037 2052 2043

▲ CONSTELLATION BRANDS INC p 360
207 High Point Dr # 100, Victor NY 14564
Tel (585) 678-7100
SIC 2084 5182 5181 2082 2085 2087

■ PEPSI-COLA METROPOLITAN BOTTLING CO INC p 1134
1111 Westchester Ave, White Plains NY 10604
Tel (914) 767-6000 *SIC* 2086 2087

GIVAUDAN FLAVORS AND FRAGRANCES INC p 613
1199 Edison Dr, Cincinnati OH 45216
Tel (513) 948-8000 *SIC* 2869 2087

GIVAUDAN FLAVORS CORP p 613
1199 Edison Dr, Cincinnati OH 45216
Tel (513) 948-8000 *SIC* 2869 2087

GIVAUDAN ROURE (UNITED STATES) INC p 613
1199 Edison Dr, Cincinnati OH 45216
Tel (513) 948-8000 *SIC* 2869 2087

■ INTER AMERICAN PRODUCTS INC p 750
1240 State Ave, Cincinnati OH 45204
Tel (800) 645-2233
SIC 2095 2099 2033 2079 2087 2022

MANE INC p 901
2501 Henkle Dr, Lebanon OH 45036
Tel (513) 248-9876 *SIC* 2087 2099

▲ J M SMUCKER CO p 771
1 Strawberry Ln, Orrville OH 44667
Tel (330) 682-3000
SIC 2099 2033 2023 2087 2035

■ CESI CHEMICAL INC p 284
1004 S Plainsman Rd, Marlow OK 73055
Tel (580) 658-6608 *SIC* 2087

DELAVAU LLC p 423
10101 Roosevelt Blvd, Philadelphia PA 19154
Tel (215) 671-1400 *SIC* 2087 2834

■ CARIBBEAN REFRESCOS INC p 256
Carr 172 Km 13 4 Bo Monte St Ca, Cidra PR 00739
Tel (787) 739-8452 *SIC* 2087

▲ FLOTEK INDUSTRIES INC p 560
10603 W Sam Houston Pkwy, Houston TX 77064
Tel (713) 849-9911
SIC 2087 2869 2899 3533 3491

■ DR PEPPER/SEVEN UP INC p 454
5301 Legacy Dr Fl 1, Plano TX 75024
Tel (972) 673-7000 *SIC* 2087

VMI NUTRITION INC p 1563
391 S Orange St Ste C, Salt Lake City UT 84104
Tel (801) 954-0471 *SIC* 2087

C F SAUER CO p 232
2000 W Broad St, Richmond VA 23220
Tel (804) 359-5786 *SIC* 2087

KERRY HOLDING CO p 813
3330 Millington Rd, Beloit WI 53511
Tel (608) 363-1200
SIC 2099 2079 2023 2022 2087

▲ SENSIENT TECHNOLOGIES CORP p 1304
777 E Wisconsin Ave # 1100, Milwaukee WI 53202
Tel (414) 271-6755 *SIC* 2087 2099

WIXON INDUSTRIES INC p 1619
1390 E Bolivar Ave, Milwaukee WI 53235
Tel (800) 841-5304 *SIC* 2099 2087 2899

SIC 2091 Fish & Seafoods, Canned & Cured

COPPER RIVER SEAFOODS INC p 368
1118 E 5th Ave, Anchorage AK 99501
Tel (907) 424-3721 *SIC* 2091 5146

BEE BUMBLE FOODS LLC p 168
280 10th Ave, San Diego CA 92101
Tel (858) 715-4000 *SIC* 2091

BUMBLE BEE SEAFOODS LLC p 225
280 10th Ave, San Diego CA 92101
Tel (858) 715-4068 *SIC* 2091 2047

THAI UNION INTERNATIONAL INC p 1446
9330 Scranton Rd Ste 500, San Diego CA 92121
Tel (858) 558-9662 *SIC* 2091

TRI-UNION SEAFOODS LLC p 1478
9330 Scranton Rd Ste 500, San Diego CA 92121
Tel (858) 558-9662 *SIC* 5146 2091

PACIFIC AMERICAN FISH CO INC p 1104
5525 S Santa Fe Ave, Vernon CA 90058
Tel (323) 319-1551 *SIC* 5146 2091

SEA WATCH INTERNATIONAL LTD p 1295
8978 Glebe Park Dr, Easton MD 21601
Tel (410) 822-7501 *SIC* 2092 2091

GORTONS INC p 626
128 Rogers St, Gloucester MA 01930
Tel (978) 283-3000 *SIC* 2092 2091

MOREYS SEAFOOD INTERNATIONAL LLC p 988
742 Decatur Ave N, Minneapolis MN 55427
Tel (763) 541-0129 *SIC* 5146 2091

GERBER PRODUCTS CO p 608
12 Vreeland Rd Fl 2, Florham Park NJ 07932
Tel (973) 593-7500
SIC 2023 2043 2037 2052 2086 2091

OFD FOODS INC p 1075
525 25th Ave Sw, Albany OR 97322
Tel (541) 926-6001
SIC 2013 2015 2091 2032 2023

TRANS-OCEAN PRODUCTS INC p 1470
350 W Orchard Dr, Bellingham WA 98225
Tel (360) 671-6886 *SIC* 2091

KANAWAY SEAFOODS INC p 802
6425 Ne 175th St, Kenmore WA 98028
Tel (425) 485-7755 *SIC* 2091

ICICLE SEAFOODS INC p 727
4019 21st Ave W Ste 300, Seattle WA 98199
Tel (206) 282-0988 *SIC* 2092 2091

MARUHA CAPITAL INVESTMENT INC p 913
2101 4th Ave Ste 1700, Seattle WA 98121
Tel (206) 382-0640 *SIC* 6799 2091

NORTH PACIFIC SEAFOODS INC p 1053
4 Nickerson St Ste 400, Seattle WA 98109
Tel (206) 726-9900 *SIC* 2091

OCEAN BEAUTY SEAFOODS LLC p 1073
1100 W Ewing St, Seattle WA 98119
Tel (206) 285-6800 *SIC* 2092 2091

PETER PAN SEAFOODS INC p 1138
The Tenth Fl 2200 6th Ave, Seattle WA 98121
Tel (206) 728-6000 *SIC* 2092 2091

SIC 2092 Fish & Seafoods, Fresh & Frozen

ATLANTIS SEAFOOD LLC p 127
10501 Valley Blvd # 1820, El Monte CA 91731
Tel (626) 626-4900 *SIC* 2092

PROSPECT ENTERPRISES INC p 1184
625 Kohler St, Los Angeles CA 90021
Tel (213) 599-5700 *SIC* 5146 2092

CALIFORNIA SHELLFISH CO INC p 241
818 E Broadway C, San Gabriel CA 91776
Tel (415) 923-7400 *SIC* 2092

EAGLE CANYON CAPITAL LLC p 467
3130 Crow Canyon Pl # 240, San Ramon CA 94583
Tel (925) 884-0800 *SIC* 5411 5499 2092

FISHERMANS PRIDE PROCESSORS INC p 552
4510 S Alameda St, Vernon CA 90058
Tel (323) 232-1980 *SIC* 2092

TAMPA BAY FISHERIES INC p 1423
3060 Gallagher Rd, Dover FL 33527
Tel (813) 752-8883 *SIC* 2092

TAMPA MAID FOODS LLC p 1423
1600 Kathleen Rd, Lakeland FL 33805
Tel (863) 687-4411 *SIC* 2092

KING & PRINCE SEAFOOD CORP p 820
1 King And Prince Blvd, Brunswick GA 31520
Tel (912) 261-7025 *SIC* 2092

FOC ACQUISITION LLC p 562
146 Forest Pkwy Ste B, Forest Park GA 30297
Tel (404) 361-2201
SIC 5142 5421 5144 2092

SEA WATCH INTERNATIONAL LTD p 1295
8978 Glebe Park Dr, Easton MD 21601
Tel (410) 822-7501 *SIC* 2092 2091

BLOUNT FINE FOODS CORP p 190
630 Currant Rd, Fall River MA 02720
Tel (774) 888-1300 *SIC* 2092 2038

GORTONS INC p 626
128 Rogers St, Gloucester MA 01930
Tel (978) 283-3000 *SIC* 2092 2091

NATIONAL FISH AND SEAFOOD INC p 1012
11 15 Parker St, Gloucester MA 01930
Tel (978) 282-7880 *SIC* 5146 2092

CONSOLIDATED CATFISH COMPANIES LLC p 359
299 South St, Isola MS 38754
Tel (662) 962-3101 *SIC* 2092

AMERICAS CATCH INC p 81
46623 County Road 523, Itta Bena MS 38941
Tel (662) 254-7207 SIC 2092 0273

HEARTLAND CATFISH CO INC p 679
55001 Highway 82 W, Itta Bena MS 38941
Tel (662) 254-7100 SIC 2092

■ SANDERSON FARMS INC (FOODS DIVISION) p 1278
127 Flynt Rd, Laurel MS 39443
Tel (601) 649-4030 SIC 2038 2092

HIGH LINER FOODS (USA) INC p 690
1 Highliner Ave, Portsmouth NH 03801
Tel (603) 431-6865 SIC 2092

■ PEAK FINANCE HOLDINGS LLC p 1126
121 Woodcrest Rd, Cherry Hill NJ 08003
Tel (856) 969-7100
SIC 2038 2092 2099 2045

■ PINNACLE FOODS FINANCE LLC p 1149
399 Jefferson Rd, Parsippany NJ 07054
Tel (973) 541-6620
SIC 2038 2092 2099 2045

■ PINNACLE FOODS GROUP LLC p 1149
399 Jefferson Rd, Parsippany NJ 07054
Tel (856) 969-7100
SIC 2038 2092 2099 2045

RICH PRODUCTS CORP p 1232
1 Robert Rich Way, Buffalo NY 14213
Tel (716) 878-8422
SIC 2053 2092 2023 2099

PEAK HOLDINGS LLC p 1126
345 Park Ave Fl 30, New York NY 10154
Tel (212) 583-5000
SIC 2038 2092 2099 2045

DULCICH INC p 460
16797 Se 130th Ave, Clackamas OR 97015
Tel (503) 226-2200 SIC 5146 2092

HARRIS SOUP CO p 664
17711 Ne Riverside Pkwy, Portland OR 97230
Tel (503) 257-7687 SIC 2092 2099

ONE UP ENTERPRISES INC p 1086
7777 Lsburg Pike Ste 302s, Falls Church VA 22043
Tel (703) 448-7333
SIC 2731 2711 2092 6531

COOKE SEAFOOD USA INC p 366
2000 Nrthgate Cmmrce Pkwy, Suffolk VA 23435
Tel (757) 673-4500 SIC 2092

AMERICAN SEAFOODS CO LLC p 79
2025 1st Ave Ste 900, Seattle WA 98121
Tel (206) 448-0300 SIC 0912 0921 2092

E & E FOODS INC p 465
801 S Fidalgo St Ste 100, Seattle WA 98108
Tel (206) 768-8979 SIC 5146 2092

ICICLE SEAFOODS INC p 727
4019 21st Ave W Ste 300, Seattle WA 98199
Tel (206) 282-0988 SIC 2092 2091

JGC FOOD CO LLC p 785
1425 4th Ave Ste 420, Seattle WA 98101
Tel (206) 622-0420 SIC 2099 2092

OCEAN BEAUTY SEAFOODS LLC p 1073
1100 W Ewing St, Seattle WA 98119
Tel (206) 285-6800 SIC 2092 2091

PETER PAN SEAFOODS INC p 1138
The Tenth Fl 2200 6th Ave, Seattle WA 98121
Tel (206) 728-6000 SIC 2092 2091

TRIDENT SEAFOODS CORP p 1479
5303 Shilshole Ave Nw, Seattle WA 98107
Tel (206) 783-3818
SIC 2092 5146 5091 0912

SIC 2095 Coffee

ROYAL CUP INC p 1254
160 Cleage Dr, Birmingham AL 35217
Tel (205) 849-5836 SIC 2095 5149

RED DIAMOND INC p 1215
400 Park Ave, Moody AL 35004
Tel (205) 577-4000 SIC 5141 2095 2099

PEETS COFFEE & TEA LLC p 1127
1400 Park Ave, Emeryville CA 94608
Tel (510) 594-2100 SIC 2095 5149

JBR INC p 779
1731 Aviation Blvd, Lincoln CA 95648
Tel (916) 258-8000 SIC 2095 2099

HIE HOLDINGS INC p 690
2839 Mokumoa St, Honolulu HI 96819
Tel (808) 833-2244 SIC 2095 7993

BERNER FOOD & BEVERAGE LLC p 176
2034 E Factory Rd, Dakota IL 61018
Tel (815) 563-4222
SIC 2022 2026 2095 2086 2033

▲ MONDELEZ INTERNATIONAL INC p 983
3 Parkway N Ste 300, Deerfield IL 60015
Tel (847) 943-4000
SIC 2022 2013 2095 2043 2035 2087

KRAFT FOODS GROUP INC p 829
3 Lakes Dr, Northfield IL 60093
Tel (847) 646-2000
SIC 2022 3411 2095 2043 2035 2087

CCC HOLDING LLC p 269
3332 Partridge Ln Bldg A, Baton Rouge LA 70809
Tel (225) 368-3900 SIC 2095 5149 5812

COMMUNITY COFFEE CO LLC p 348
3332 Partridge Ln Bldg A, Baton Rouge LA 70809
Tel (800) 688-0990 SIC 2095

REILY FOODS CO p 1221
400 Poydras St Fl 10, New Orleans LA 70130
Tel (504) 524-6131 SIC 2099 2095

WM B REILY & CO INC p 1620
640 Magazine St, New Orleans LA 70130
Tel (504) 539-5200
SIC 2095 2035 2079 5962 5963 2099

EIGHT OCLOCK COFFEE CO p 481
155 Chestnut Ridge Rd # 2, Montvale NJ 07645
Tel (201) 571-9214 SIC 5149 2095

▲ COFFEE HOLDING CO INC p 334
3475 Victory Blvd Ste 4, Staten Island NY 10314
Tel (718) 832-0800 SIC 2095 5149 5499

S & D COFFEE INC p 1261
300 Concord Pkwy S, Concord NC 28027
Tel (704) 782-3121 SIC 2095 5149 2086

S&D COFFEE HOLDING CO p 1263
300 Concord Pkwy S, Concord NC 28027
Tel (704) 782-3121
SIC 6719 2095 5149 2086

■ INTER AMERICAN PRODUCTS INC p 750
1240 State Ave, Cincinnati OH 45204
Tel (800) 645-2233
SIC 2095 2099 2033 2079 2087 2022

■ MILLSTONE COFFEE INC p 971
1 Procter And Gamble Plz, Cincinnati OH 45202
Tel (513) 983-1100 SIC 2095

■ FOLGER COFFEE CO p 563
1 Strawberry Ln, Orrville OH 44667
Tel (800) 937-9745 SIC 2095

BOYD COFFEE CO p 205
19730 Ne Sandy Blvd, Portland OR 97230
Tel (503) 666-4545
SIC 2095 5499 5141 3634 2099

▲ FARMER BROS CO p 529
13601 North Fwy Ste 200, Fort Worth TX 76177
Tel (682) 549-6600 SIC 2095 5149

MOTHER PARKERS TEA & COFFEE USA LTD p 992
7800 Will Rogers Blvd, Fort Worth TX 76140
Tel (817) 551-5500 SIC 5149 2095 2099

ATLANTIC COFFEE INDUSTRIAL SOLUTIONS LLC p 126
3900 Harrisburg Blvd, Houston TX 77003
Tel (713) 228-9501 SIC 2095

JAVA TRADING CO LLC p 779
801 Houser Way N, Renton WA 98057
Tel (425) 917-2920 SIC 5149 2095

TC GLOBAL INC p 1428
2003 Western Ave Ste 660, Seattle WA 98121
Tel (206) 233-2070 SIC 2095 5149

TRILLIANT FOOD AND NUTRITION LLC p 1480
1101 Moasis Dr, Little Chute WI 54140
Tel (920) 788-1252 SIC 5149 2099 2095

SIC 2096 Potato Chips & Similar Prdts

GOLDEN ENTERPRISES INC p 620
1 Golden Flake Dr, Birmingham AL 35205
Tel (205) 458-7316 SIC 2096

GOLDEN FLAKE SNACK FOODS INC p 620
1 Golden Flake Dr, Birmingham AL 35205
Tel (205) 323-6161 SIC 2096

▲ INVENTURE FOODS INC p 761
5415 E High St Ste 350, Phoenix AZ 85054
Tel (623) 932-6200 SIC 2096 2037

▲ TYSON FOODS INC p 1496
2200 W Don Tyson Pkwy, Springdale AR 72762
Tel (479) 290-4000
SIC 2011 2015 2032 2096 2048

SNAK-KING CORP p 1335
16150 Stephens St, City Of Industry CA 91745
Tel (626) 336-7711 SIC 2096

■ DIAMOND FOODS LLC p 436
1050 Diamond St, Stockton CA 95205
Tel (415) 445-7444 SIC 2068 2096

■ BOULDER BRANDS INC p 204
1600 Pearl St Ste 300, Boulder CO 80302
Tel (303) 652-0521 SIC 2096 6719

▲ JOHN B SANFILIPPO & SON INC p 787
1703 N Randall Rd, Elgin IL 60123
Tel (847) 289-1800
SIC 2068 2064 2099 2096 2066

MESA FOODS LLC p 951
3701 W Magnolia Ave, Louisville KY 40211
Tel (502) 772-2500 SIC 2096 2045 2099

BARREL OFUN SNACK FOODS CO LLC p 157
400 Lakeside Dr, Perham MN 56573
Tel (218) 346-7000 SIC 2096

OLD DUTCH FOODS INC p 1080
2375 Terminal Rd, Saint Paul MN 55113
Tel (651) 633-8810 SIC 2096

▲ CAMPBELL SOUP CO p 245
1 Campbell Pl, Camden NJ 08103
Tel (856) 342-4800
SIC 2032 2038 2033 2052 2051 2096

■ BIRDS EYE FOODS INC p 185
121 Woodcrest Rd, Cherry Hill NJ 08003
Tel (585) 383-1850
SIC 2037 2096 2052 2038 2035

▲ HAIN CELESTIAL GROUP INC p 653
1111 Marcus Ave Ste 100, New Hyde Park NY 11042
Tel (516) 587-5000
SIC 2023 2034 2096 2086 2844

▲ PEPSICO INC p 1134
700 Anderson Hill Rd, Purchase NY 10577
Tel (914) 253-2000
SIC 2096 2087 2086 2037 2052 2043

BIRDS EYE HOLDINGS INC p 185
90 Linden Park, Rochester NY 14625
Tel (585) 383-1850
SIC 2033 2013 2035 2096

▲ SNYDERS-LANCE INC p 1336
13515 Balntyn Corp Pl, Charlotte NC 28277
Tel (704) 554-1421
SIC 2052 2064 2068 2096 5145

RUDOLPH FOODS CO INC p 1257
6575 Bellefontaine Rd, Lima OH 45804
Tel (909) 383-7463 SIC 2096 2099

WYANDOT INC p 1629
135 Wyandot Ave, Marion OH 43302
Tel (740) 383-4031 SIC 2096

SHEARERS FOODS LLC p 1313
100 Lincoln Way E, Massillon OH 44646
Tel (330) 834-4030 SIC 2096 5145

SNACK ALLIANCE INC p 1335
100 Lincoln Way E, Massillon OH 44646
Tel (330) 767-3426 SIC 2096

■ KETTLE FOODS INC p 814
3125 Kettle Ct Se, Salem OR 97301
Tel (503) 364-0399 SIC 2096

WISE FOODS INC p 1619
228 Rasely St, Berwick PA 18603
Tel (888) 759-4401 SIC 2096

■ S-L SNACKS REAL ESTATE INC p 1263
1250 York St, Hanover PA 17331
Tel (717) 632-4477 SIC 2052 2096

UTZ QUALITY FOODS LLC p 1537
900 High St, Hanover PA 17331
Tel (800) 367-7629 SIC 2096 2052 2099

HERR FOODS INC p 687
20 Herr Dr, Nottingham PA 19362
Tel (610) 932-9330 SIC 2096

SAVOR STREET FOODS INC p 1284
1 Park Plz, Wyomissing PA 19610
Tel (610) 320-7800 SIC 2052 2096 2099

▲ AMPLIFY SNACK BRANDS INC p 86
500 W 5th St Ste 1350, Austin TX 78701
Tel (512) 600-9893 SIC 2099 2064 2096

GRUMA CORP p 642
5601 Executive Dr Ste 800, Irving TX 75038
Tel (972) 232-5000 SIC 0723 2096 2099

■ FRITO-LAY NORTH AMERICA INC p 580
7701 Legacy Dr, Plano TX 75024
Tel (972) 334-7000
SIC 2096 2052 2013 5812 6794 2086

OLD FRITO-LAY INC p 1080
7701 Legacy Dr, Plano TX 75024
Tel (972) 334-7000
SIC 2096 2052 2013 5812 6794 2086

SIC 2097 Ice

■ COUNTRY FRESH LLC p 375
2555 Buchanan Ave Sw, Grand Rapids MI 49548
Tel (616) 243-0173 SIC 2026 2024 2097

ARCTIC GLACIER USA HOLDINGS LLC p 106
1654 Marthaler Ln, Saint Paul MN 55118
Tel (651) 455-0410 SIC 2097

ARCTIC GLACIER USA INC p 106
1654 Marthaler Ln, Saint Paul MN 55118
Tel (204) 784-5873 SIC 2097

UNITED STATES COLD STORAGE INC p 1512
201 Laurel Rd Ste 400, Voorhees NJ 08043
Tel (856) 354-8181 SIC 2097 4222

HOME CITY ICE CO p 703
6045 Bridgetown Rd Ste 1, Cincinnati OH 45248
Tel (513) 574-1800 SIC 2097

REDDY ICE CORP p 1216
5720 Lyndon B Johnson Fwy # 200, Dallas TX 75240
Tel (214) 526-6740 SIC 2097

REDDY ICE GROUP INC p 1216
5720 Lbj Fwy Ste 200, Dallas TX 75240
Tel (877) 295-0024 SIC 5199 2097

REDDY ICE HOLDINGS INC p 1216
5720 Lbj Fwy Ste 200, Dallas TX 75240
Tel (214) 526-6740 SIC 2097

SIC 2098 Macaroni, Spaghetti & Noodles

NISSIN FOODS (USA) CO INC p 1044
2001 W Rosecrans Ave, Gardena CA 90249
Tel (310) 327-8478 SIC 2098 2038

MARUCHAN INC p 913
15800 Laguna Canyon Rd, Irvine CA 92618
Tel (949) 789-2300 SIC 2098

NONGSHIM AMERICA INC p 1047
12155 6th St, Rancho Cucamonga CA 91730
Tel (909) 481-3698 SIC 5141 2098

THOMAS J LIPTON INC p 1448
75 Merritt Blvd, Trumbull CT 06611
Tel (206) 381-3500
SIC 2099 2034 2035 2033 2098 2024

GILSTER-MARY LEE CORP p 612
1037 State St, Chester IL 62233
Tel (618) 826-2361
SIC 2043 2098 2099 2045 3089

MARY LEE PACKAGING CORP p 914
615 Saint Marys Rd, Perryville MO 63775
Tel (573) 547-1705
SIC 2043 2099 3089 2098

UNILEVER BESTFOODS NORTH AMERICA p 1503
800 Sylvan Ave, Englewood Cliffs NJ 07632
Tel (201) 894-4000
SIC 2046 2034 2035 2098 2099 2051

■ DAKOTA GROWERS PASTA CO INC p 409
1 Pasta Ave, Carrington ND 58421
Tel (701) 652-2855 SIC 2098

■ TMARZETTI CO p 1457
1105 Schrock Rd Fl 3, Columbus OH 43229
Tel (614) 846-2232 SIC 2035 2098

NEW WORLD PASTA CO p 1033
85 Shannon Rd, Harrisburg PA 17112
Tel (717) 526-2200 SIC 2098

■ HEINZ KRAFT FOODS CO p 681
1 Ppg Pl Ste 3200, Pittsburgh PA 15222
Tel (412) 456-5700
SIC 2033 2038 2032 2098

▲ KRAFT HEINZ CO p 829
1 Ppg Pl, Pittsburgh PA 15222
Tel (412) 456-5700
SIC 2033 2038 2032 2098

VIRGINIA MARUCHAN INC p 1559
8101 Whitepine Rd, North Chesterfield VA 23237
Tel (804) 275-0800 SIC 2098 2099

SIC 2099 Food Preparations, NEC

RED DIAMOND INC p 1215
400 Park Ave, Moody AL 35004
Tel (205) 577-4000 SIC 5141 2095 2099

CAFE VALLEY INC p 237
7000 W Buckeye Rd, Phoenix AZ 85043
Tel (602) 278-2909 SIC 2099

PRODUCERS RICE MILL INC p 1179
518 E Harrison St, Stuttgart AR 72160
Tel (870) 673-4444 SIC 2044 5153 2099

■ BRIDGFORD FOODS CORP p 212
1308 N Patt St, Anaheim CA 92801
Tel (714) 526-5533
SIC 2045 2099 2015 2013 2022 2038

HARRIS FREEMAN & CO INC p 663
3110 E Miraloma Ave, Anaheim CA 92806
Tel (714) 765-1190 SIC 5149 2099

■ BOLTHOUSE HOLDING CORP p 199
7200 E Brundage Ln, Bakersfield CA 93307
Tel (310) 566-8350 SIC 0161 2099

■ WM BOLTHOUSE FARMS INC p 1620
7200 E Brundage Ln, Bakersfield CA 93307
Tel (661) 366-7205 SIC 0161 2099 0723

■ BERRY KNOTTS FARM LLC p 176
8039 Beach Blvd, Buena Park CA 90620
Tel (714) 827-1776 SIC 2099

NATROL LLC p 1018
21411 Prairie St, Chatsworth CA 91311
Tel (818) 739-6000 SIC 5122 2099

GOURMET FOODS INC p 627
2910 E Harcourt St, Compton CA 90221
Tel (310) 632-3300 SIC 5141 5812 2099

RUIZ FOOD PRODUCTS INC p 1257
501 S Alta Ave, Dinuba CA 93618
Tel (559) 591-5510 SIC 2038 2099

SALADINOS INC p 1271
3325 W Figarden Dr, Fresno CA 93711
Tel (559) 271-3700 SIC 5141 2099

NESTLE USA INC p 1027
800 N Brand Blvd, Glendale CA 91203
Tel (818) 549-6000
SIC 2023 2033 2064 2047 2099 2032

■ APIO INC p 97
4575 W Main St, Guadalupe CA 93434
Tel (800) 454-1355 SIC 2099 0723

READY PAC FOODS INC p 1213
4401 Foxdale St, Irwindale CA 91706
Tel (626) 856-8686 SIC 2099 5148

READY PAC PRODUCE INC p 1213
4401 Foxdale St, Irwindale CA 91706
Tel (800) 800-4088 SIC 2099 5148

CALIFORNIA NATURAL PRODUCTS p 240
15789 Mckinley Ave, Lathrop CA 95330
Tel (209) 249-1616 SIC 2099 8731 3612

JBR INC p 779
1731 Aviation Blvd, Lincoln CA 95648
Tel (916) 258-8000 SIC 2095 2099

PROPORTION FOODS LLC p 1184
4020 Compton Ave, Los Angeles CA 90011
Tel (323) 231-7777 SIC 2099

DOLE FRESH VEGETABLES INC p 448
2959 Salinas Hwy, Monterey CA 93940
Tel (831) 422-8871 SIC 2099 0723

DIANAS MEXICAN FOOD PRODUCTS INC p 437
16330 Pioneer Blvd, Norwalk CA 90650
Tel (562) 926-5802 SIC 2099 5812

■ KINGSFORD PRODUCTS CO LLC p 821
1221 Broadway Ste 1300, Oakland CA 94612
Tel (510) 271-7000
SIC 2861 2099 2035 2033 2879

■ SEMINIS INC p 1302
2700 Camino Del Sol, Oxnard CA 93030
Tel (805) 485-7317 SIC 8731 8742 2099

BAKEMARK USA LLC p 145
7351 Crider Ave, Pico Rivera CA 90660
Tel (562) 949-1054
SIC 2045 5149 3556 2099

■ RENAISSANCE FOOD GROUP LLC p 1223
11020 White Rock Rd # 100, Rancho Cordova CA 95670
Tel (916) 638-8825 SIC 2099

DIAMOND BLUE GROWERS p 436
1802 C St, Sacramento CA 95811
Tel (916) 442-0771 SIC 2099

TANIMURA & ANTLE FRESH FOODS INC p 1424
1 Harris Rd, Salinas CA 93908
Tel (831) 455-2950
SIC 0161 0182 0723 2099

SUN BASKET INC p 1400
1170 Olinder Ct, San Jose CA 95122
Tel (408) 669-4418 SIC 2099

■ EARTHBOUND FARM LLC p 469
1721 San Juan Hwy, San Juan Bautista CA 95045
Tel (831) 623-7880 SIC 0723 2037 2099

■ EARTHBOUND HOLDINGS I LLC p 469
1721 San Juan Hwy, San Juan Bautista CA 95045
Tel (831) 623-2767 SIC 0723 2099

■ EARTHBOUND HOLDINGS II LLC p 469
1721 San Juan Hwy, San Juan Bautista CA 95045
Tel (831) 623-2767 SIC 0723 2099

■ EARTHBOUND HOLDINGS III LLC p 469
1721 San Juan Hwy, San Juan Bautista CA 95045
Tel (831) 623-7880 SIC 0723 2099 6719

■ EB SAV INC p 474
1721 San Juan Hwy, San Juan Bautista CA 95045
Tel (303) 635-4500 SIC 0723 2099

FUJI FOOD PRODUCTS INC p 583
14420 Bloomfield Ave, Santa Fe Springs CA 90670
Tel (562) 404-2590 SIC 2099

BASIC AMERICAN INC p 158
2185 N Calif Blvd Ste 215, Walnut Creek CA 94596
Tel (925) 472-4000 SIC 2034 2099

DEL MAR FOOD PRODUCTS CORP p 423
1720 Beach Rd, Watsonville CA 95076
Tel (831) 722-3516 SIC 2033 2099

STEVEN-ROBERT ORIGINALS LLC p 1388
2780 Tower Rd, Aurora CO 80011
Tel (303) 375-9925 SIC 2053 2024 2099

TRINIDAD/BENHAM CORP p 1481
3650 S Yosemite St # 300, Denver CO 80237
Tel (303) 220-1400
SIC 5149 5153 2034 2099

RC BIGELOW INC p 1211
201 Black Rock Tpke, Fairfield CT 06825
Tel (888) 244-3569 SIC 2099

■ PEPPERIDGE FARM INC p 1134
595 Westport Ave, Norwalk CT 06851
Tel (203) 846-7000
SIC 5963 2052 2099 2053 5961

COFCO AMERICAS RESOURCES CORP p 334
4 Stamford Plz, Stamford CT 06902
Tel (203) 658-2820
SIC 6221 5153 5149 2099

THOMAS J LIPTON INC p 1448
75 Merritt Blvd, Trumbull CT 06611
Tel (206) 381-3500
SIC 2099 2034 2035 2033 2098 2024

TWINLAB CORP p 1495
2255 Glades Rd Ste 342w, Boca Raton FL 33431
Tel (212) 651-8500
SIC 2099 2834 2731 2721 2833

OSCEOLA FARMS CO p 1096
340 Royal Poinciana Way # 315, Palm Beach FL 33480
Tel (561) 655-6303 *SIC* 2099

FATHERS TABLE L L C p 531
2100 Country Club Rd, Sanford FL 32771
Tel (407) 324-1200 *SIC* 2099

FANJUL CORP p 527
1 N Clematis St Ste 200, West Palm Beach FL 33401
Tel (561) 655-6303
SIC 0133 2061 2099 6552

FRESH EXPRESS INC p 578
4757 The Grove Dr Ste 260, Windermere FL 34786
Tel (980) 636-5530 *SIC* 0723 2099

■ NATURALLY FRESH INC p 1018
1000 Naturally Fresh Blvd, Atlanta GA 30349
Tel (404) 765-9000 *SIC* 2035 2099

KEYSTONE FOODS EQUITY GROUP p 815
7220 Us Highway 19, Camilla GA 31730
Tel (229) 336-9747 *SIC* 2099

VALENTINE ENTERPRISES INC p 1539
1291 Progress Center Ave, Lawrenceville GA 30043
Tel (770) 995-0661 *SIC* 2023 2099

OLE MEXICAN FOODS INC p 1082
6585 Crescent Dr, Norcross GA 30071
Tel (770) 582-9200 *SIC* 2099 2032

FIVE STAR HOLDING CO INC p 553
248 Rollins Industrial Ct, Ringgold GA 30736
Tel (706) 937-5077
SIC 5962 5812 5963 2099

SOUTHEASTERN MILLS INC p 1346
333 Old Lindale Rd Se, Rome GA 30161
Tel (706) 291-6528
SIC 2099 2041 5149 2045

CRYSTAL DIAMOND BRANDS INC p 396
3000 Tremont Rd, Savannah GA 31405
Tel (912) 651-5112 *SIC* 7389 2099

CRIDER INC p 392
1 Plant Ave, Stillmore GA 30464
Tel (912) 562-4435 *SIC* 2099

NONPAREIL CORP p 1047
411 W Collins Rd, Blackfoot ID 83221
Tel (208) 785-5880 *SIC* 2099

PACIFIC NORTHWEST FARMERS COOPERATIVE INC p 1105
117 W Chestnut, Genesee ID 83832
Tel (208) 285-1141 *SIC* 5153 2099

BLAINE LARSEN FARMS INC p 188
2650 N 2375 E, Hamer ID 83425
Tel (208) 662-5501
SIC 5148 2099 0111 0139

RIDLEYS FOOD CORP p 1234
621 Washington St S, Twin Falls ID 83301
Tel (208) 324-4633 *SIC* 5411 2099

GRIFFITH FOODS GROUP INC p 640
1 Griffith Ctr, Alsip IL 60803
Tel (708) 371-0900 *SIC* 2099

GRIFFITH FOODS INC p 640
12200 S Central Ave, Alsip IL 60803
Tel (708) 371-0900 *SIC* 2099

GRIFFITH FOODS INTERNATIONAL INC p 640
1 Griffith Ctr, Alsip IL 60803
Tel (708) 371-0900 *SIC* 2099 7389

GRIFFITH FOODS WORLDWIDE INC p 640
12200 S Central Ave, Alsip IL 60803
Tel (708) 371-0900 *SIC* 2099

OSI GROUP LLC p 1096
1225 Corp Blvd Ste 300, Aurora IL 60505
Tel (630) 851-6600 *SIC* 2099

OSI INDUSTRIES LLC p 1096
1225 Corp Blvd Ste 105, Aurora IL 60505
Tel (630) 851-6600 *SIC* 2099

GILSTER-MARY LEE CORP p 612
1037 State St, Chester IL 62233
Tel (618) 826-2361
SIC 2043 2098 2099 2045 3089

▲ CONAGRA BRANDS INC p 354
222 Merchandise Mart Plz, Chicago IL 60654
Tel (312) 549-5000 *SIC* 2099 2038 2013

EL-MILAGRO INC p 483
3050 W 26th St, Chicago IL 60623
Tel (773) 579-6120 *SIC* 2099 5812

NEWLY WEDS FOODS INC p 1038
4140 W Fullerton Ave, Chicago IL 60639
Tel (773) 489-7000 *SIC* 2099

■ QUAKER OATS CO p 1196
555 W Monroe St Fl 1, Chicago IL 60661
Tel (312) 821-1000
SIC 2086 2043 2045 2052 2064 2099

SCHULZE AND BURCH BISCUIT CO p 1291
1133 W 35th St, Chicago IL 60609
Tel (773) 927-6622 *SIC* 2051 2052 2099

▲ JOHN B SANFILIPPO & SON INC p 787
1703 N Randall Rd, Elgin IL 60123
Tel (847) 289-1800
SIC 2068 2064 2099 2096 2066

LADY LITTLE FOODS INC p 837
2323 Pratt Blvd, Elk Grove Village IL 60007
Tel (847) 806-1440 *SIC* 2038 2099

LAWRENCE FOODS INC p 847
2200 Lunt Ave, Elk Grove Village IL 60007
Tel (847) 437-2400 *SIC* 2033 2099

R J VAN DRUNEN & SONS INC p 1202
300 W 6th St, Momence IL 60954
Tel (815) 472-3100
SIC 2034 2037 0161 2099

MIZKAN AMERICA HOLDINGS INC p 978
1661 Feehanville Dr # 300, Mount Prospect IL 60056
Tel (847) 590-0059 *SIC* 2099

MIZKAN AMERICA INC p 978
1661 Feehanville Dr # 200, Mount Prospect IL 60056
Tel (847) 590-0059 *SIC* 2099 2035

AMERICAN TRISTAR INC p 80
525 Dunham Rd, Saint Charles IL 60174
Tel (920) 872-2181 *SIC* 2099

CHEF SOLUTIONS HOLDINGS LLC p 292
20 N Martingale Rd # 600, Schaumburg IL 60173
Tel (847) 762-8500 *SIC* 2099

GONNELLA BAKING CO p 623
1117 Wiley Rd, Schaumburg IL 60173
Tel (312) 733-2020
SIC 2051 5812 2099 2038

JEL SERT CO p 782
Conde St Rr 59, West Chicago IL 60185
Tel (630) 231-7590
SIC 2087 2024 2099 5499 5143

H C SCHAU & SON INC p 649
10350 Argonne Dr Ste 400, Woodridge IL 60517
Tel (630) 783-1000 *SIC* 5147 2099

PRETZELS INC p 1173
123 W Harvest Rd, Bluffton IN 46714
Tel (260) 824-4838 *SIC* 2052 2099

TC HEARTLAND LLC p 1428
14300 Clay Terrace Blvd, Carmel IN 46032
Tel (317) 566-9750 *SIC* 2099

AMERIQUAL GROUP LLC p 83
18200 Highway 41 N, Evansville IN 47725
Tel (812) 867-1300 *SIC* 2099

■ MEAD JOHNSON & CO LLC p 933
2400 W Lloyd Expy, Evansville IN 47712
Tel (812) 429-5000 *SIC* 2099 2834 2032

SKJODT-BARRETT CONTRACT PACKAGING LLC p 1330
401 S Enterprise Blvd, Lebanon IN 46052
Tel (765) 482-6856 *SIC* 2099

LAURIDSEN GROUP INC p 847
2425 Se Oak Tree Ct, Ankeny IA 50021
Tel (515) 289-7600 *SIC* 2099

PURFOODS LLC p 1192
3210 Se Corp Woods Dr, Ankeny IA 50021
Tel (515) 963-0641 *SIC* 2099

TONE BROTHERS INC p 1460
2301 Se Tones Dr, Ankeny IA 50021
Tel (515) 965-2711 *SIC* 2087 2099

FRONTIER COOPERATIVE p 581
3021 78th St, Norway IA 52318
Tel (319) 227-7996 *SIC* 5122 2099 5149

GELITA NORTH AMERICA INC p 598
2445 Port Neal Rd, Sergeant Bluff IA 51054
Tel (712) 943-5516 *SIC* 5169 2099

CARAVAN INGREDIENTS INC p 252
7905 Quivira Rd, Lenexa KS 66215
Tel (913) 890-5500
SIC 2099 2821 5084 2087

■ DANISCO USA INC p 412
4 New Century Pkwy, New Century KS 66031
Tel (913) 764-8100 *SIC* 2099

MESA FOODS LLC p 951
3701 W Magnolia Ave, Louisville KY 40211
Tel (502) 772-2500 *SIC* 2096 2045 2099

▲ PAPA JOHNS INTERNATIONAL INC p 1112
2002 Papa Johns Blvd # 100, Louisville KY 40299
Tel (502) 261-7272 *SIC* 5812 6794 2099

DIVERSIFIED FOODS AND SEASONINGS LLC p 444
1115 N Causeway Blvd # 200, Mandeville LA 70471
Tel (985) 809-3600 *SIC* 2099 2034

REILY FOODS CO p 1221
400 Poydras St Fl 10, New Orleans LA 70130
Tel (504) 524-6131 *SIC* 2099 2095

WM B REILY & CO INC p 1620
640 Magazine St, New Orleans LA 70130
Tel (504) 539-5200
SIC 2095 2035 2079 5962 5963 2099

ELITE SPICE INC p 487
7151 Montevideo Rd, Jessup MD 20794
Tel (410) 796-1900 *SIC* 2099

COASTAL SUNBELT INC p 332
9001 Whiskey Bottom Rd, Laurel MD 20723
Tel (410) 799-8000
SIC 5148 4214 0723 2099

▲ MEDIFAST INC p 938
3600 Crondall Ln, Owings Mills MD 21117
Tel (410) 581-8042 *SIC* 2099 2023 8093

▲ MCCORMICK & CO INC p 927
18 Loveton Cir, Sparks MD 21152
Tel (410) 771-7301
SIC 2099 2087 2038 2037

CONCORD FOODS INC p 354
10 Minuteman Way, Brockton MA 02301
Tel (508) 580-1700 *SIC* 2099 2045

GREENCORE USA INC p 637
222 Rosewood Dr Fl 4, Danvers MA 01923
Tel (978) 716-2530 *SIC* 2099

ROHTSTEIN CORP p 1247
70 Olympia Ave, Woburn MA 01801
Tel (781) 935-8300
SIC 5149 2099 2087 2062 2041 2033

VITASOY USA INC p 1563
57 Russell St, Woburn MA 01801
Tel (781) 430-8988 *SIC* 5149 2099

AMWAY INTERNATIONAL INC p 87
7575 Fulton St E, Ada MI 49355
Tel (616) 787-1000
SIC 5169 5122 5099 5199 2099 2032

QUESTOR PARTNERS FUND II LP p 1199
101 Southfield Rd 2, Birmingham MI 48009
Tel (248) 593-1930 *SIC* 8742 2099

BIG BOY RESTAURANTS INTERNATIONAL LLC p 181
4199 Marcy St, Warren MI 48091
Tel (586) 759-6000 *SIC* 5812 2099

COUNTRYSIDE FOODS LLC p 375
26661 Bunert Rd, Warren MI 48089
Tel (586) 447-3500 *SIC* 5141 2099

E A SWEEN CO p 466
16101 W 78th St, Eden Prairie MN 55344
Tel (952) 937-9440 *SIC* 2099 5142

▲ OTTER TAIL CORP p 1098
215 S Cascade St, Fergus Falls MN 56537
Tel (218) 739-8200
SIC 4911 3084 5047 2099 1731

JACOBS INDUSTRIES INC p 775
8096 Excelsior Blvd, Hopkins MN 55343
Tel (612) 339-9500
SIC 2841 2087 2099 2844 5084 6794

■ ELAN NUTRITION INC p 483
21325 Hamburg Ave, Lakeville MN 55044
Tel (616) 940-6000 *SIC* 2099

TONY DOWNS FOODS CO p 1460
54934 210th Ln, Mankato MN 56001
Tel (507) 375-3111 *SIC* 2015 2099

FARIBAULT FOODS INC p 528
222 S 9th St Ste 3380, Minneapolis MN 55402
Tel (612) 333-6461 *SIC* 2099 2032 2033

▲ GENERAL MILLS INC p 601
1 General Mills Blvd, Minneapolis MN 55426
Tel (763) 764-7600
SIC 2099 2041 2045 2064 2024

■ AMERICAN ITALIAN PASTA CO p 75
1000 Italian Way, Excelsior Springs MO 64024
Tel (816) 502-6000 *SIC* 2099

MARY LEE PACKAGING CORP p 914
615 Saint Marys Rd, Perryville MO 63775
Tel (573) 547-1705
SIC 2043 2099 3089 2098

▲ POST HOLDINGS INC p 1163
2503 S Hanley Rd, Saint Louis MO 63144
Tel (314) 644-7600
SIC 2015 2034 2038 2041 2099

TROVERCO INC p 1485
727 N 1st St, Saint Louis MO 63102
Tel (800) 468-3354 *SIC* 2099 5149

■ CONAGRA GROCERY PRODUCTS CO LLC p 354
11 Conagra Dr, Omaha NE 68102
Tel (630) 857-1000
SIC 2033 2079 2099 2032 2066 5149

GEL SPICE CO INC p 598
48 Hook Rd, Bayonne NJ 07002
Tel (201) 339-0700 *SIC* 2099 5149

GEL SPICE CO LLC p 598
48 Hook Rd, Bayonne NJ 07002
Tel (201) 339-0700 *SIC* 2099

INDOPCO INC p 739
10 Finderne Ave Ste A, Bridgewater NJ 08807
Tel (908) 685-5000
SIC 2891 2046 2821 2869 2899 2099

■ PEAK FINANCE HOLDINGS LLC p 1126
121 Woodcrest Rd, Cherry Hill NJ 08003
Tel (856) 969-7100
SIC 2038 2092 2099 2045

METROPOLITAN FOODS INC p 955
174 Delawanna Ave, Clifton NJ 07014
Tel (973) 672-9400
SIC 5142 5149 2099 5141

TWININGS NORTH AMERICA INC p 1495
777 Passaic Ave Ste 230, Clifton NJ 07012
Tel (973) 591-0600 *SIC* 2099

ALBERTO-CULVER CO p 46
800 Sylvan Ave, Englewood Cliffs NJ 07632
Tel (708) 681-2668 *SIC* 2844 2842 2099

UNILEVER BESTFOODS NORTH AMERICA p 1503
800 Sylvan Ave, Englewood Cliffs NJ 07632
Tel (201) 894-4000
SIC 2046 2034 2035 2098 2099 2051

UNILEVER MANUFACTURING (US) INC p 1503
800 Sylvan Ave, Englewood Cliffs NJ 07632
Tel (800) 298-5018 *SIC* 2844 2099

NESTLE HEALTHCARE NUTRITION INC p 1026
12 Vreeland Rd Fl 2, Florham Park NJ 07932
Tel (952) 848-6000 *SIC* 2099 2032

PHARMACHEM LABORATORIES INC p 1141
265 Harrison Tpke, Kearny NJ 07032
Tel (201) 246-1000 *SIC* 2099 2834

▲ B&G FOODS INC p 142
4 Gatehall Dr Ste 110, Parsippany NJ 07054
Tel (973) 401-6500
SIC 2013 2032 2033 2035 2099

■ PINNACLE FOODS FINANCE LLC p 1149
399 Jefferson Rd, Parsippany NJ 07054
Tel (973) 541-6620
SIC 2038 2092 2099 2045

■ PINNACLE FOODS GROUP LLC p 1149
399 Jefferson Rd, Parsippany NJ 07054
Tel (856) 969-7100
SIC 2038 2092 2099 2045

F&S PRODUCE CO INC p 522
913 Bridgeton Ave, Rosenhayn NJ 08352
Tel (856) 453-0316
SIC 0723 2099 2032 0181

EL ENCANTO INC p 482
2001 4th St Sw, Albuquerque NM 87102
Tel (505) 243-2722 *SIC* 2038 2099

MARAMONT CORP p 904
5600 1st Ave, Brooklyn NY 11220
Tel (718) 439-8900 *SIC* 2099 8322

RICH PRODUCTS CORP p 1232
1 Robert Rich Way, Buffalo NY 14213
Tel (716) 878-8422
SIC 2053 2092 2023 2099

HOUSE OF SPICES (INDIA) INC p 711
12740 Willets Point Blvd, Flushing NY 11368
Tel (718) 507-4900
SIC 5149 2099 5153 2033 2024

■ CARRIAGE HOUSE COMPANIES INC p 260
196 Newton St, Fredonia NY 14063
Tel (716) 672-4321
SIC 2099 2033 2035 2087

DEAN & DE LUCA BRANDS INC p 420
560 Broadway Frnt 2, New York NY 10012
Tel (212) 226-6800 *SIC* 5499 5812 2099

DEAN & DELUCA INC p 420
560 Broadway Frnt 2, New York NY 10012
Tel (212) 226-6800
SIC 5499 5812 5961 2099

PEAK HOLDINGS LLC p 1126
345 Park Ave Fl 30, New York NY 10154
Tel (212) 583-5000
SIC 2038 2092 2099 2045

■ SPF HOLDINGS II LLC p 1358
9 W 57th St Ste 4200, New York NY 10019
Tel (212) 750-8300
SIC 2033 5149 6719 2099

SUGAR FOODS CORP p 1397
950 3rd Ave Fl 21, New York NY 10022
Tel (212) 753-6900
SIC 2869 2023 2099 2068 7389

WIN-HOLT EQUIPMENT CORP p 1614
20 Crossways Park Dr N # 205, Woodbury NY 11797
Tel (516) 222-0335 *SIC* 2099

STAR FOOD PRODUCTS INC p 1378
2050 Willow Spring Ln A, Burlington NC 27215
Tel (336) 227-4079 *SIC* 5147 2099

■ SHARK ACQUISITION SUB II LLC p 1312
13515 Balntyn Corp Pl, Charlotte NC 28277
Tel (704) 554-1421 *SIC* 2099

TROPICAL NUT & FRUIT CO p 1484
1100 Continental Blvd, Charlotte NC 28273
Tel (704) 588-0400
SIC 5149 5145 2099 2068

CAVENDISH FARMS INC p 267
5855 3rd St Se, Jamestown ND 58401
Tel (701) 252-5222 *SIC* 5142 2099

MINN-DAK FARMERS COOPERATIVE INC p 973
7525 Red River Rd, Wahpeton ND 58075
Tel (701) 642-8411 *SIC* 2099

▲ ADVANCEPIERRE FOODS HOLDINGS INC p 26
9987 Carver Rd, Blue Ash OH 45242
Tel (800) 969-2747 *SIC* 2099 2013

■ INTER AMERICAN PRODUCTS INC p 750
1240 State Ave, Cincinnati OH 45204
Tel (800) 645-2233
SIC 2095 2099 2033 2079 2087 2022

■ PROCTER & GAMBLE MANUFACTURING CO p 1179
1 Procter And Gamble Plz, Cincinnati OH 45202
Tel (513) 983-1100
SIC 2841 2079 2099 2844 2045

LAKEVIEW FARMS LLC p 840
1600 Gressel Dr, Delphos OH 45833
Tel (419) 695-9925 *SIC* 2026 2099 2022

MANE INC p 901
2501 Henkle Dr, Lebanon OH 45036
Tel (513) 248-9876 *SIC* 2087 2099

RUDOLPH FOODS CO INC p 1257
6575 Bellefontaine Rd, Lima OH 45804
Tel (909) 383-7463 *SIC* 2096 2099

SANDRIDGE FOOD CORP p 1278
133 Commerce Dr, Medina OH 44256
Tel (330) 725-2348 *SIC* 2099

▲ BOB EVANS FARMS INC p 196
8111 Smiths Mill Rd, New Albany OH 43054
Tel (614) 491-2225
SIC 5812 2011 2099 2035

▲ J M SMUCKER CO p 771
1 Strawberry Ln, Orrville OH 44667
Tel (330) 682-3000
SIC 2099 2033 2023 2087 2035

FRESHWAY FOODS INC p 579
601 Stolle Ave, Sidney OH 45365
Tel (937) 498-4664 *SIC* 5148 2099

■ ADVANCE FOOD CO INC p 24
221 W Oxford Ave, Enid OK 73701
Tel (800) 969-2747 *SIC* 2013 2015 2099

QUIKTRIP CORP p 1200
4705 S 129th East Ave, Tulsa OK 74134
Tel (918) 615-7700
SIC 5411 5541 5172 2099 5141 6512

RESERS FINE FOODS INC p 1226
15570 Sw Jenkins Rd, Beaverton OR 97006
Tel (503) 643-6431 *SIC* 2099 5141

AZURE FARMS INC p 141
79709 Dufur Valley Rd, Dufur OR 97021
Tel (971) 200-8350 *SIC* 5149 0723 2099

BOYD COFFEE CO p 205
19730 Ne Sandy Blvd, Portland OR 97230
Tel (503) 666-4545
SIC 2095 5499 5141 3634 2099

HARRIS SOUP CO p 664
17711 Ne Riverside Pkwy, Portland OR 97230
Tel (503) 257-7687 *SIC* 2092 2099

PACIFIC FOODS OF OREGON INC p 1104
19480 Sw 97th Ave, Tualatin OR 97062
Tel (503) 692-9666 *SIC* 2033 2099 2086

HANOVER FOODS CORP p 658
1486 York St, Hanover PA 17331
Tel (717) 632-6000
SIC 2033 2032 2037 2038 2099

UTZ QUALITY FOODS LLC p 1537
900 High St, Hanover PA 17331
Tel (800) 367-7629 *SIC* 2096 2052 2099

▲ HERSHEY CO p 687
100 Crystal A Dr, Hershey PA 17033
Tel (717) 534-4200 *SIC* 2066 2064 2099

NUTRITION INC p 1068
580 Wendel Rd Ste 100, Irwin PA 15642
Tel (724) 978-2100 *SIC* 5812 2099

DUTCH GOLD HONEY INC p 463
2220 Dutch Gold Dr, Lancaster PA 17601
Tel (717) 393-1716 *SIC* 2099 5149

AFP ADVANCED FOOD PRODUCTS LLC p 33
402 S Custer Ave, New Holland PA 17557
Tel (717) 355-8667
SIC 2026 2035 2032 2099 2022

FRESH FOOD MANUFACTURING CO p 578
101 Kappa Dr, Pittsburgh PA 15238
Tel (412) 963-6200 *SIC* 2099

STERMAN MASSER INC p 1387
2 Fearnot Rd, Sacramento PA 17968
Tel (570) 682-3709 *SIC* 0134 2099

SAVOR STREET FOODS INC p 1284
1 Park Plz, Wyomissing PA 19610
Tel (610) 320-7800 SIC 2052 2096 2099

PAN AMERICAN GRAIN MANUFACTURING CO INC p 1110
Calle Caludia 9cnr, Guaynabo PR 00968
Tel (787) 273-6100 SIC 2099

SO-PAK-CO INC p 1336
118 S Cypress St, Mullins SC 29574
Tel (423) 639-1163 SIC 2099 4226

MCKEE FOODS CORP p 930
10260 Mckee Rd, Collegedale TN 37315
Tel (423) 238-7111
SIC 2051 2052 2099 2043

ABF NORTH AMERICA CORP p 11
7171 Goodlett Farms Pkwy, Cordova TN 38016
Tel (901) 381-3000 SIC 2079 2099

ABF NORTH AMERICA HOLDINGS INC p 11
7171 Goodlett Farms Pkwy, Cordova TN 38016
Tel (901) 381-3000 SIC 2079 2099

ACH FOOD COMPANIES INC p 17
7171 Goodlett Farms Pkwy, Cordova TN 38016
Tel (901) 381-3000 SIC 2079 2099

UNAKA CO INC p 1502
1500 Industrial Rd, Greeneville TN 37745
Tel (423) 639-1171
SIC 2099 3469 2514 2253 4226

▲AMPLIFY SNACK BRANDS INC p 86
500 W 5th St Ste 1350, Austin TX 78701
Tel (512) 600-9893 SIC 2099 2064 2096

▲BRIDGFORD INDUSTRIES INC p 212
1601 S Good Latimer Expy, Dallas TX 75226
Tel (214) 428-1535
SIC 2045 2099 2015 2013 2022 2038

MOTHER PARKERS TEA & COFFEE USA LTD p 992
7800 Will Rogers Blvd, Fort Worth TX 76140
Tel (817) 551-5500 SIC 5149 2095 2099

■HOUSTON SYSCO INC p 712
10710 Grens Crossing Blvd, Houston TX 77038
Tel (713) 672-8080
SIC 5149 5142 5046 5141 2099

GRUMA CORP p 642
5601 Executive Dr Ste 800, Irving TX 75038
Tel (972) 232-5000 SIC 0723 2096 2099

C H GUENTHER & SON INC p 232
2201 Broadway St, San Antonio TX 78215
Tel (210) 227-1401
SIC 2041 2051 2045 2052 2099

■WESTOVER DAIRY p 1602
2801 Fort Ave, Lynchburg VA 24501
Tel (434) 528-2560 SIC 2099

BOWMAN ANDROS PRODUCTS LLC p 204
10119 Old Valley Pike, Mount Jackson VA 22842
Tel (540) 217-4100 SIC 2033 2099 2037

VIRGINIA MARUCHAN INC p 1559
8101 Whitepine Rd, North Chesterfield VA 23237
Tel (804) 275-0800 SIC 2098 2099

NATIONAL FRUIT PRODUCT CO INC p 1012
550 Fairmont Ave, Winchester VA 22601
Tel (540) 662-3401
SIC 0723 2033 2035 2099

JGC FOOD CO LLC p 785
1425 4th Ave Ste 420, Seattle WA 98101
Tel (206) 622-0420 SIC 2099 2092

SK FOOD GROUP INC p 1328
4600 37th Ave Sw Ste 300, Seattle WA 98126
Tel (206) 935-8100 SIC 2099

PACIFIC NUTRITIONAL INC p 1105
6317 Ne 131st Ave Buildb, Vancouver WA 98682
Tel (360) 253-3197 SIC 5122 2099

KERRY HOLDING CO p 813
3330 Millington Rd, Beloit WI 53511
Tel (608) 363-1200
SIC 2099 2079 2023 2022 2087

KERRY INC p 813
3330 Millington Rd, Beloit WI 53511
Tel (608) 363-1200 SIC 2099

■BAY VALLEY FOODS LLC p 161
3200 Riverside Dr Ste A, Green Bay WI 54301
Tel (800) 558-4700 SIC 2099

SCHWABE NORTH AMERICA INC p 1291
825 Challenger Dr, Green Bay WI 54311
Tel (920) 469-1313 SIC 2834 2099

TRILLIANT FOOD AND NUTRITION LLC p 1480
1101 Moasis Dr, Little Chute WI 54140
Tel (920) 788-1252 SIC 5149 2099 2095

CHR HANSEN p 302
9015 W Maple St, Milwaukee WI 53214
Tel (414) 607-5700 SIC 2099

LESAFFRE INTERNATIONAL CORP p 857
7475 W Main St, Milwaukee WI 53214
Tel (414) 615-3300 SIC 2099

RED STAR YEAST CO LLC p 1216
7475 W Main St Ste 150, Milwaukee WI 53214
Tel (800) 445-4746 SIC 2099

▲SENSIENT TECHNOLOGIES CORP p 1304
777 E Wisconsin Ave # 1100, Milwaukee WI 53202
Tel (414) 271-6755 SIC 2087 2099

WIXON INDUSTRIES INC p 1619
1390 E Bolivar Ave, Milwaukee WI 53235
Tel (800) 841-5304 SIC 2099 2087 2899

GOLDEN COUNTY FOODS INC p 620
300 Moore Rd, Plover WI 54467
Tel (800) 489-7783 SIC 2099

SIC 2111 Cigarettes

COMMONWEALTH-ALTADIS INC p 346
5900 N Andrews Ave # 1100, Fort Lauderdale FL 33309
Tel (800) 481-5814 SIC 2111 2621 2131

▲VECTOR GROUP LTD p 1546
4400 Biscayne Blvd Fl 10, Miami FL 33137
Tel (305) 579-8000 SIC 2111 6552

■VGR HOLDING LLC p 1553
4400 S Biscayne Blvd # 10, Miami FL 33131
Tel (305) 579-8000 SIC 2111 6552

▲SCHWEITZER-MAUDUIT INTERNATIONAL INC p 1291
100 N Point Ctr E Ste 600, Alpharetta GA 30022
Tel (800) 514-0186 SIC 2141 2111 2621

IRA HIGDON GROCERY CO p 764
150 Iga Way, Cairo GA 39828
Tel (229) 377-1272
SIC 5141 5147 5142 5143 2111 5194

▲PHILIP MORRIS INTERNATIONAL INC p 1143
120 Park Ave Fl 6, New York NY 10017
Tel (917) 663-2000 SIC 2111

FONTEM US INC p 563
1100 S Tryon St Ste 300, Charlotte NC 28203
Tel (888) 207-4588 SIC 2111 5993

ITG BRANDS LLC p 768
714 Green Valley Rd, Greensboro NC 27408
Tel (336) 335-7000 SIC 2111

LORILLARD TOBACCO CO LLC p 878
714 Green Valley Rd, Greensboro NC 27408
Tel (336) 335-6600 SIC 2111

■LIGGETT GROUP LLC p 865
100 Maple Ln, Mebane NC 27302
Tel (919) 304-7700 SIC 2111

■R J REYNOLDS TOBACCO HOLDINGS INC p 1202
401 N Main St, Winston Salem NC 27101
Tel (336) 741-5000 SIC 2111

▲REYNOLDS AMERICAN INC p 1230
401 N Main St, Winston Salem NC 27101
Tel (336) 741-2000 SIC 2111 2121 2131

▲ALTRIA GROUP INC p 63
6601 W Broad St, Richmond VA 23230
Tel (804) 274-2200 SIC 2111 2084

■PHILIP MORRIS USA INC p 1143
6601 W Brd St, Richmond VA 23230
Tel (804) 274-2000 SIC 2111 2141 5194

SIC 2121 Cigars

ALTADIS USA INC p 61
5900 N Andrews Ave # 1100, Fort Lauderdale FL 33309
Tel (954) 772-9000 SIC 2121

CONSOLIDATED CIGAR HOLDINGS INC p 359
5900 N Andrews Ave # 1100, Fort Lauderdale FL 33309
Tel (954) 772-9000 SIC 2121

MACANDREWS & FORBES INC p 891
38 E 63rd St, New York NY 10065
Tel (212) 688-9000
SIC 2844 2087 2121 7819 2721 2731

MAFCO CONSOLIDATED GROUP INC p 895
35 E 62nd St, New York NY 10065
Tel (212) 572-8600 SIC 2121 2131 2869

▲REYNOLDS AMERICAN INC p 1230
401 N Main St, Winston Salem NC 27101
Tel (336) 741-2000 SIC 2111 2121 2131

CONGAR INTERNATIONAL CORP p 356
Km 72 Hm 2 Rr 14, Cayey PR 00736
Tel (787) 738-2106 SIC 2121

GENERAL CIGAR CO INC p 599
10900 Nuckols Rd Ste 100, Glen Allen VA 23060
Tel (860) 602-3500 SIC 2121 5199 0132

SIC 2131 Tobacco, Chewing & Snuff

HAY ISLAND HOLDING CORP p 670
20 Thorndal Cir, Darien CT 06820
Tel (203) 656-8000 SIC 5194 2131

UST LLC p 1536
6 High Ridge Park Bldg A, Stamford CT 06905
Tel (203) 817-3000
SIC 2131 2084 2621 3999

COMMONWEALTH-ALTADIS INC p 346
5900 N Andrews Ave # 1100, Fort Lauderdale FL 33309
Tel (800) 481-5814 SIC 2111 2621 2131

■NORTH ATLANTIC TRADING CO INC p 1051
5201 Interchange Way, Louisville KY 40229
Tel (502) 778-4421 SIC 2131

▲TURNING POINT BRANDS INC p 1493
5201 Interchange Way, Louisville KY 40229
Tel (502) 778-4421 SIC 2131

MAFCO CONSOLIDATED GROUP INC p 895
35 E 62nd St, New York NY 10065
Tel (212) 572-8600 SIC 2121 2131 2869

■R J REYNOLDS TOBACCO CO p 1202
401 N Main St, Winston Salem NC 27101
Tel (336) 741-5000 SIC 2131

▲REYNOLDS AMERICAN INC p 1230
401 N Main St, Winston Salem NC 27101
Tel (336) 741-2000 SIC 2111 2121 2131

■US SMOKELESS TOBACCO MANUFACTURING CO LLC p 1533
800 Harrison St, Nashville TN 37203
Tel (615) 880-4400 SIC 2131

SWEDISH MATCH NORTH AMERICA LLC p 1411
1021 E Cary St Ste 1600, Richmond VA 23219
Tel (804) 787-5100 SIC 2131 5199

■US SMOKELESS TOBACCO CO p 1533
6603 W Broad St, Richmond VA 23230
Tel (804) 274-2000 SIC 2131

SIC 2141 Tobacco Stemming & Redrying

▲SCHWEITZER-MAUDUIT INTERNATIONAL INC p 1291
100 N Point Ctr E Ste 600, Alpharetta GA 30022
Tel (800) 514-0186 SIC 2141 2111 2621

■DANVILLE LEAF TOBACCO CO INC p 412
9201 Forest Hill Ave Fl 1, Richmond VA 23235
Tel (804) 359-9311 SIC 2141

■PHILIP MORRIS USA INC p 1143
6601 W Brd St, Richmond VA 23230
Tel (804) 274-2000 SIC 2111 2141 5194

▲UNIVERSAL CORP p 1516
9201 Forest Hill Ave, Richmond VA 23235
Tel (804) 359-9311 SIC 5159 2141

SIC 2211 Cotton, Woven Fabric

DAS NORTH AMERICA INC p 413
840 Industrial Park Blvd, Montgomery AL 36117
Tel (334) 694-5335 SIC 2211

■ALSTYLE APPAREL LLC p 61
1501 E Cerritos Ave, Anaheim CA 92805
Tel (714) 765-0400 SIC 2211

SCAPA NORTH AMERICA INC p 1286
111 Great Pond Dr, Windsor CT 06095
Tel (860) 688-8000
SIC 2231 3069 2211 2824 2672

■ENERGY SERVICES PROVIDERS INC p 498
3700 Lakeside Dr 6, Miramar FL 33027
Tel (305) 947-7880 SIC 2211

SWIFT DENIM SERVICES INC p 1412
5 Concourse Pkwy Ste 2, Atlanta GA 30328
Tel (770) 901-6300 SIC 2211

MOUNTVILLE MILLS INC p 995
1729 S Davis Rd, Lagrange GA 30241
Tel (706) 882-2961 SIC 2273 2211 2221

KING AMERICA FINISHING INC p 820
1351 Scarboro Hwy, Sylvania GA 30467
Tel (912) 863-4511 SIC 2211 2261

VELTEX CORP p 1547
123 W Madison St Ste 1500, Chicago IL 60602
Tel (312) 235-4014 SIC 2211 5199

■RUSSELL BRANDS LLC p 1259
1 Fruit Of The Loom Dr, Bowling Green KY 42103
Tel (270) 781-6400
SIC 2253 2211 2329 2339 3949 5091

▲CROWN CRAFTS INC p 395
916 S Burnside Ave, Gonzales LA 70737
Tel (225) 647-9100 SIC 2211 2389

FRANCO MANUFACTURING CO INC p 574
555 Prospect St, Metuchen NJ 08840
Tel (732) 494-0503
SIC 2269 2392 2211 5023 5131

▲DERMA SCIENCES INC p 431
214 Carnegie Ctr Ste 300, Princeton NJ 08540
Tel (609) 514-4744 SIC 3842 2211 2834

HANOVER DIRECT INC p 658
1200 Harbor Blvd Fl 9, Weehawken NJ 07086
Tel (201) 863-7300
SIC 5712 5961 7389 2211 2221

AEON USA INC p 29
1 Penn Plz Fl 36, New York NY 10119
Tel (212) 946-8780
SIC 5621 5961 2211 2391

HMX LLC p 698
125 Park Ave Fl 7, New York NY 10017
Tel (212) 682-9073 SIC 2211

JAY FRANCO & SONS INC p 779
295 5th Ave Ste 312, New York NY 10016
Tel (212) 679-3022 SIC 5023 2211

■WESTPOINT HOME LLC p 1602
28 E 28th St Rm 8, New York NY 10016
Tel (212) 930-2074 SIC 2211 2221

■WESTPOINT INTERNATIONAL INC p 1602
28 E 28th St Bsmt 2, New York NY 10016
Tel (212) 930-2044 SIC 2211

NORTHWEST CO LLC p 1059
49 Bryant Ave, Roslyn NY 11576
Tel (516) 484-6996 SIC 2211

AMERICAN FIBER & FINISHING INC p 72
225 N Depot St, Albemarle NC 28001
Tel (704) 983-6102
SIC 2211 3842 2844 2392

GLEN RAVEN INC p 614
1831 N Park Ave, Burlington NC 27217
Tel (336) 227-6211
SIC 2221 2281 2261 2211

BURLINGTON INDUSTRIES LLC p 228
804 Green Valley Rd # 300, Greensboro NC 27408
Tel (336) 379-6220
SIC 2231 2211 2221 2273 2262 2261

CONE DENIM LLC p 355
804 Green Valley Rd # 300, Greensboro NC 27408
Tel (336) 379-6220 SIC 2211

INTERNATIONAL TEXTILE GROUP INC p 757
804 Green Valley Rd # 300, Greensboro NC 27408
Tel (336) 379-6299
SIC 3714 3496 2211 2231 2221 2273

ITG HOLDINGS INC p 768
804 Green Valley Rd # 300, Greensboro NC 27408
Tel (336) 379-6220
SIC 2211 2231 2221 2273 2262 2261

■VF SERVICES LLC p 1553
105 Corporate Center Blvd, Greensboro NC 27408
Tel (336) 424-6000 SIC 2211

CV INDUSTRIES INC p 404
401 11th St Nw, Hickory NC 28601
Tel (828) 328-1851 SIC 2511 2512 2211

CAROLINA MILLS INC p 259
618 N Carolina Ave, Maiden NC 28650
Tel (828) 428-9911
SIC 2281 2211 2221 2257 2511 2512

TRELLEBORG COATED SYSTEMS US INC p 1476
715 Railroad Ave, Rutherfordton NC 28139
Tel (864) 576-1210
SIC 2295 2221 2394 2396 2211

VALDESE WEAVERS LLC p 1539
1000 Perkins Rd Se, Valdese NC 28690
Tel (828) 874-2181 SIC 2211 2221

BEKAERT TEXTILES USA INC p 169
240 Business Park Dr, Winston Salem NC 27107
Tel (336) 747-4900 SIC 5021 2211

▲OMNOVA SOLUTIONS INC p 1085
25435 Harvard Rd, Beachwood OH 44122
Tel (216) 682-7000
SIC 2819 2211 3069 3081

STANDARD TEXTILE CO INC p 1376
1 Knollcrest Dr, Cincinnati OH 45237
Tel (513) 761-9255
SIC 2389 2326 2337 2211 2391 5136

TRANZONIC COMPANIES p 1473
26301 Curtiss Wright Pkwy # 200, Richmond Heights OH 44143
Tel (216) 535-4300
SIC 2676 2211 2326 2842 2273 2262

TZ ACQUISITION CORP p 1496
26301 Curtiss Wright Pkwy, Richmond Heights OH 44143
Tel (216) 535-4300
SIC 2676 2211 2326 2842 2262

TOTES ISOTONER HOLDINGS CORP p 1463
9655 International Blvd, West Chester OH 45246
Tel (513) 682-8200
SIC 2381 3151 2211 3021 5699

R B PAMPLIN CORP p 1201
805 Sw Brdwy Ste 2400, Portland OR 97205
Tel (503) 248-1133
SIC 2211 2392 2361 2369

ALICE MANUFACTURING CO INC p 50
208 E 1st Ave, Easley SC 29640
Tel (864) 859-6323 SIC 2211 2221

HAMRICK MILLS INC p 656
515 W Buford St, Gaffney SC 29341
Tel (864) 489-4731 SIC 2211 2299

GREENWOOD MILLS INC p 639
300 Morgan Ave, Greenwood SC 29646
Tel (864) 227-2121
SIC 2211 2221 2241 2261 2262 6552

INMAN HOLDING CO INC p 744
300 Park Rd, Inman SC 29349
Tel (864) 472-2121 SIC 2211 2221

MOUNT VERNON MILLS INC p 994
503 S Main St, Mauldin SC 29662
Tel (864) 688-7100 SIC 2211 2221 2281

GALEY & LORD LLC p 589
670 N Main St, Society Hill SC 29593
Tel (843) 378-4511
SIC 2211 2221 2325 2339

MILLIKEN & CO p 971
920 Milliken Rd, Spartanburg SC 29303
Tel (864) 503-2020
SIC 2221 2211 2231 2273 2821 4911

PROPEX HOLDING LLC p 1184
1110 Market St Ste 300, Chattanooga TN 37402
Tel (800) 621-1273
SIC 6719 2221 2297 2262 2211

AMERICAN TEXTILE HOLDINGS LLC p 80
1926 Fm 548, Littlefield TX 79339
Tel (806) 385-6401 SIC 2211

UNITED AMERICAN ACQUISITION CORP p 1506
3022 Franklin Ave, Waco TX 76710
Tel (859) 987-5389
SIC 2211 0782 3423 2875

GLOBAL SAFETY TEXTILES LLC p 617
1556 Montgomery St, South Hill VA 23970
Tel (434) 447-7629 SIC 3714 2211 3496

▲NATIONAL PRESTO INDUSTRIES INC p 1015
3925 N Hastings Way, Eau Claire WI 54703
Tel (715) 839-2121 SIC 2211 3483 3634

JOCKEY INTERNATIONAL GLOBAL INC p 787
2300 60th St, Kenosha WI 53140
Tel (262) 658-8111 SIC 2211 5611

SIC 2221 Silk & Man-Made Fiber

PHIFER INC p 1142
4400 Kauloosa Ave, Tuscaloosa AL 35401
Tel (205) 345-2120
SIC 3496 2221 3357 2295 3442 3354

MOMENTUM TEXTILES LLC p 983
17811 Fitch, Irvine CA 92614
Tel (949) 833-8886 SIC 5131 2221

HOLLANDER SLEEP PRODUCTS LLC p 700
6501 Congress Ave Ste 300, Boca Raton FL 33487
Tel (561) 997-6900 SIC 2392 2221 5719

PBR INC p 1123
335 Athena Dr, Athens GA 30601
Tel (706) 354-3700 SIC 2297 2221 3089

CAROLE FABRICS CORP p 259
633 Nw Frontage Rd, Augusta GA 30907
Tel (706) 863-4742
SIC 2221 2591 5131 5949 2392 2391

MOUNTVILLE MILLS INC p 995
1729 S Davis Rd, Lagrange GA 30241
Tel (706) 882-2961 SIC 2273 2211 2221

NICOLON CORP p 1043
365 S Holland Dr, Pendergrass GA 30567
Tel (706) 693-2226 SIC 2221 5949

SOUTHERN MILLS INC p 1349
6501 Mall Blvd, Union City GA 30291
Tel (770) 969-1000 SIC 2221 2297

BP AMOCO CHEMICAL CO p 205
150 W Warrenville Rd, Naperville IL 60563
Tel (630) 420-5111
SIC 2221 2821 2869 2819 2865

GOLDSHIELD FIBER GLASS INC p 622
2004 Patterson St, Decatur IN 46733
Tel (260) 728-2476 SIC 2221

AMESBURY GROUP INC p 84
57 S Hunt Rd, Amesbury MA 01913
Tel (978) 834-3233
SIC 3053 3442 3086 2221 3089

MICROFIBRES INC p 962
124 Washington St Ste 101, Foxboro MA 02035
Tel (401) 725-4883
SIC 2221 2295 5131 2262

TK HOLDINGS INC p 1457
2500 Takata Dr, Auburn Hills MI 48326
Tel (248) 373-8040
SIC 2221 2399 2396 3714

TRUE TEXTILES INC p 1486
5300 Corprte Grv Dr Se, Grand Rapids MI 49512
Tel (616) 301-7540 SIC 2221

▲ALBANY INTERNATIONAL CORP p 45
216 Airport Dr, Rochester NH 03867
Tel (518) 445-2200
SIC 2221 3496 2399 2899 3089

HANOVER DIRECT INC p 658
1200 Harbor Blvd Fl 9, Weehawken NJ 07086
Tel (201) 863-7300
SIC 5712 5961 7389 2211 2221

SEFAR INC p 1300
111 Calumet St, Depew NY 14043
Tel (716) 683-4050
SIC 5131 5051 5084 3496 2297 2221

SPRINGFIELD LLC p 1361
100 Jericho Quadrangle # 340, Jericho NY 11753
Tel (516) 861-6250 *SIC* 2221

CHF INDUSTRIES INC p 296
1 Park Ave Fl 9, New York NY 10016
Tel (212) 951-7800 *SIC* 5023 2221

SCHNEIDER MILLS INC p 1288
1430 Broadway Rm 1202, New York NY 10018
Tel (212) 768-7500 *SIC* 2221

SIMPLICITY CREATIVE GROUP INC p 1325
261 Madison Ave Fl 4, New York NY 10016
Tel (212) 686-7676
SIC 2241 2221 2396 2298

■WESTPOINT HOME LLC p 1602
28 E 28th St Rm 8, New York NY 10016
Tel (212) 930-2074 *SIC* 2211 2221

ASHEBORO ELASTICS CORP p 117
150 N Park St, Asheboro NC 27203
Tel (336) 629-2626 *SIC* 2221 2241

GLEN RAVEN INC p 614
1831 N Park Ave, Burlington NC 27217
Tel (336) 227-6211
SIC 2221 2281 2261 2211

HYOSUNG USA INC p 724
15801 Brixham Hill Ave # 575, Charlotte NC 28277
Tel (704) 790-6136 *SIC* 2221 2296 5199

LOW & BONAR INC p 881
1301 Sand Hill Rd, Enka NC 28728
Tel (828) 665-5000
SIC 5199 3296 2899 2297 2221

BGF INDUSTRIES INC p 180
3802 Robert Porcher Way, Greensboro NC 27410
Tel (843) 537-3172
SIC 2221 3624 2241 2295

BURLINGTON INDUSTRIES LLC p 228
804 Green Valley Rd # 300, Greensboro NC 27408
Tel (336) 379-6220
SIC 2231 2211 2221 2273 2262 2261

INTERNATIONAL TEXTILE GROUP INC p 757
804 Green Valley Rd # 300, Greensboro NC 27408
Tel (336) 379-6299
SIC 3714 3496 2211 2231 2221 2273

ITG HOLDINGS INC p 768
804 Green Valley Rd # 300, Greensboro NC 27408
Tel (336) 379-6220
SIC 2211 2231 2221 2273 2262 2261

NOUVEAU VERRE HOLDINGS INC p 1062
3802 Robert Porcher Way, Greensboro NC 27410
Tel (336) 545-0011
SIC 2221 3624 2241 2295

NVH INC p 1068
3802 Robert Porcher Way, Greensboro NC 27410
Tel (336) 545-0011
SIC 2221 3624 2241 2295

PRECISION FABRICS GROUP INC p 1168
301 N Elm St Ste 600, Greensboro NC 27401
Tel (336) 510-8000 *SIC* 2262 2221

▲UNIFI INC p 1503
7201 W Friendly Ave, Greensboro NC 27410
Tel (336) 294-4410 *SIC* 2281 2282 2221

▲CULP INC p 400
1823 Eastchester Dr, High Point NC 27265
Tel (336) 889-5161 *SIC* 2221

HIGHLAND INDUSTRIES INC p 691
1350 Bridgeport Dr Ste 1, Kernersville NC 27284
Tel (336) 992-7500 *SIC* 2221

CAROLINA MILLS INC p 259
618 N Carolina Ave, Maiden NC 28650
Tel (828) 428-9911
SIC 2281 2211 2221 2257 2511 2512

TRELLEBORG COATED SYSTEMS US INC p 1476
715 Railroad Ave, Rutherfordton NC 28139
Tel (864) 576-1210
SIC 2295 2221 2394 2396 2211

VALDESE WEAVERS LLC p 1539
1000 Perkins Rd Se, Valdese NC 28690
Tel (828) 874-2181 *SIC* 2211 2221

■WEAVEXX LLC p 1586
14101 Capital Blvd, Youngsville NC 27596
Tel (919) 556-7235 *SIC* 2221

▲XERIUM TECHNOLOGIES INC p 1631
14101 Capital Blvd, Youngsville NC 27596
Tel (919) 526-1400 *SIC* 2221 3069

SEAMAN CORP p 1297
1000 Venture Blvd, Wooster OH 44691
Tel (330) 262-1111 *SIC* 2221

FABTEX INC p 523
111 Woodbine Ln, Danville PA 17821
Tel (570) 275-7500
SIC 5072 2221 5023 2512 2392 2391

MUTUAL INDUSTRIES NORTH INC p 1003
707 W Grange Ave Ste 1, Philadelphia PA 19120
Tel (215) 927-6000 *SIC* 3842 2221

AGY HOLDING CORP p 36
2556 Wagener Rd, Aiken SC 29801
Tel (888) 434-0945 *SIC* 2221

■JPS INDUSTRIES INC p 795
2200 S Murray Ave, Anderson SC 29624
Tel (864) 239-3900 *SIC* 2221 3081

ALICE MANUFACTURING CO INC p 50
208 E 1st Ave, Easley SC 29640
Tel (864) 859-6323 *SIC* 2211 2221

DELTA WOODSIDE INDUSTRIES INC p 427
700 N Woods Dr, Fountain Inn SC 29644
Tel (864) 255-4100 *SIC* 2221

GREENWOOD MILLS INC p 639
300 Morgan Ave, Greenwood SC 29646
Tel (864) 227-2121
SIC 2211 2221 2241 2261 2262 6552

INMAN HOLDING CO INC p 744
300 Park Rd, Inman SC 29349
Tel (864) 472-2121 *SIC* 2211 2221

MOUNT VERNON MILLS INC p 994
503 S Main St, Mauldin SC 29662
Tel (864) 688-7100 *SIC* 2211 2221 2281

ASTENJOHNSON INC p 122
4399 Corporate Rd, North Charleston SC 29405
Tel (843) 747-7800 *SIC* 2221 2281 2299

GALEY & LORD LLC p 589
670 N Main St, Society Hill SC 29593
Tel (843) 378-4511
SIC 2211 2221 2325 2339

MILLIKEN & CO p 971
920 Milliken Rd, Spartanburg SC 29303
Tel (864) 503-2020
SIC 2221 2211 2231 2273 2821 4911

TIETEX INTERNATIONAL LTD p 1453
3010 N Blackstock Rd, Spartanburg SC 29301
Tel (864) 574-0500 *SIC* 2297 2258 2221

WILLIAM BARNET & SON LLC p 1610
1300 Hayne St, Spartanburg SC 29301
Tel (864) 327-4620
SIC 5199 2823 2221 2824

SIOUX STEEL CO p 1326
196 1/2 E 6th St, Sioux Falls SD 57104
Tel (605) 336-1750 *SIC* 3523 3448 2221

PROPEX HOLDING LLC p 1184
1110 Market St Ste 300, Chattanooga TN 37402
Tel (800) 621-1273
SIC 6719 2221 2297 2262 2211

PROPEX OPERATING CO LLC p 1184
1110 Market St Ste 300, Chattanooga TN 37402
Tel (423) 855-1466 *SIC* 2221

HALLWOOD GROUP INC p 655
3710 Rawlins St Ste 1500, Dallas TX 75219
Tel (214) 528-5588 *SIC* 2221 7389

VOITH HOLDING INC p 1564
2200 N Roemer Rd, Appleton WI 54911
Tel (920) 731-7724
SIC 5131 3554 2221 6719

SIC 2231 Wool, Woven Fabric

511 INC p 3
1360 Reynolds Ave Ste 101, Irvine CA 92614
Tel (949) 800-1511
SIC 5699 2231 5139 2393

SCAPA NORTH AMERICA INC p 1286
111 Great Pond Dr, Windsor CT 06095
Tel (860) 688-8000
SIC 2231 3069 2211 2824 2672

BURLINGTON INDUSTRIES LLC p 228
804 Green Valley Rd # 300, Greensboro NC 27408
Tel (336) 379-6220
SIC 2231 2211 2221 2273 2262 2261

INTERNATIONAL TEXTILE GROUP INC p 757
804 Green Valley Rd # 300, Greensboro NC 27408
Tel (336) 379-6299
SIC 3714 3496 2211 2231 2221 2273

ITG HOLDINGS INC p 768
804 Green Valley Rd # 300, Greensboro NC 27408
Tel (336) 379-6220
SIC 2211 2231 2221 2273 2262 2261

MILLIKEN & CO p 971
920 Milliken Rd, Spartanburg SC 29303
Tel (864) 503-2020
SIC 2221 2211 2231 2273 2821 4911

CANNON COUNTY KNITTING MILLS INC p 247
237 Castlewood Dr Ste F, Murfreesboro TN 37129
Tel (615) 890-2938 *SIC* 2231

SIC 2241 Fabric Mills, Cotton, Wool, Silk & Man-Made

▲AMERICAN BILTRITE INC p 69
57 River St Ste 302, Wellesley MA 02481
Tel (781) 237-6655
SIC 3069 2672 2241 3961 5094

VELCRO INC p 1547
95 Sundial Ave, Manchester NH 03103
Tel (603) 669-4880 *SIC* 2241

VELCRO USA INC p 1547
95 Sundial Ave, Manchester NH 03103
Tel (603) 669-4880 *SIC* 2241 3965

SIMPLICITY CREATIVE GROUP INC p 1325
261 Madison Ave Fl 4, New York NY 10016
Tel (212) 686-7676
SIC 2241 2221 2396 2298

ASHEBORO ELASTICS CORP p 117
150 N Park St, Asheboro NC 27203
Tel (336) 629-2626 *SIC* 2221 2241

COATS & CLARK INC p 332
3430 Toringdon Way # 301, Charlotte NC 28277
Tel (704) 329-5800
SIC 2284 2281 3364 3089 2241 3965

COATS NORTH AMERICA DE REPUBLICA DOMINICANA INC p 332
3430 Toringdon Way # 301, Charlotte NC 28277
Tel (800) 242-8095
SIC 2284 2281 3364 3089 2241 3965

PARKDALE MILLS INC p 1116
531 Cotton Blossom Cir, Gastonia NC 28054
Tel (704) 864-8761 *SIC* 2281 2844 2241

US COTTON LLC p 1531
531 Cotton Blossom Cir, Gastonia NC 28054
Tel (216) 676-6400 *SIC* 2844 2241

BGF INDUSTRIES INC p 180
3802 Robert Porcher Way, Greensboro NC 27410
Tel (843) 537-3172
SIC 2221 3624 2241 2295

NOUVEAU VERRE HOLDINGS INC p 1062
3802 Robert Porcher Way, Greensboro NC 27410
Tel (336) 545-0011
SIC 2221 3624 2241 2295

NVH INC p 1068
3802 Robert Porcher Way, Greensboro NC 27410
Tel (336) 545-0011
SIC 2221 3624 2241 2295

▲WORLDTEX INC p 1626
990 3rd Ave Se, Hickory NC 28602
Tel (828) 322-2242 *SIC* 2241

SHORE TO SHORE INC p 1318
8170 Washington Vlg Dr, Dayton OH 45458
Tel (937) 866-1908 *SIC* 2679 2241

NFA CORP p 1041
50 Martin St, Cumberland RI 02864
Tel (617) 232-6060 *SIC* 5012 2241

MOORE CO p 987
36 Beach St, Westerly RI 02891
Tel (401) 596-2816
SIC 2258 2241 3069 3061 2821

GREENWOOD MILLS INC p 639
300 Morgan Ave, Greenwood SC 29646
Tel (864) 227-2121
SIC 2211 2221 2241 2261 2262 6552

SIC 2251 Hosiery, Women's Full & Knee Length

ACME - MCCRARY CORP p 17
159 North St, Asheboro NC 27203
Tel (336) 625-2161 *SIC* 2251

KAYSER-ROTH CORP p 805
102 Corporate Center Blvd, Greensboro NC 27408
Tel (336) 852-2030
SIC 2252 2251 5961 8741 3842

▲HANESBRANDS INC p 657
1000 E Hanes Mill Rd, Winston Salem NC 27105
Tel (336) 519-8080
SIC 2253 2342 2341 2322 2252 2251

SIC 2252 Hosiery, Except Women's

COOPER HOSIERY MILLS INC p 366
4005 Gault Ave N, Fort Payne AL 35967
Tel (256) 845-1491 *SIC* 2252

WIESNER PRODUCTS INC p 1608
1333 Brdwy Fl 6, New York NY 10018
Tel (212) 279-2466 *SIC* 5139 2252

KAYSER-ROTH CORP p 805
102 Corporate Center Blvd, Greensboro NC 27408
Tel (336) 852-2030
SIC 2252 2251 5961 8741 3842

RENFRO CORP p 1224
661 Linville Rd, Mount Airy NC 27030
Tel (336) 719-8000 *SIC* 2252

▲HANESBRANDS INC p 657
1000 E Hanes Mill Rd, Winston Salem NC 27105
Tel (336) 519-8080
SIC 2253 2342 2341 2322 2252 2251

GILDAN USA INC p 612
1980 Clements Ferry Rd, Charleston SC 29492
Tel (843) 849-6191 *SIC* 2252 2254

GILDAN DELAWARE INC p 612
3375 Joseph Martin Hwy, Martinsville VA 24112
Tel (276) 956-2305 *SIC* 2252 2254

SIC 2253 Knit Outerwear Mills

A AND G INC p 4
1501 E Cerritos Ave, Anaheim CA 92805
Tel (714) 765-0400 *SIC* 2329 2253

■ALSTYLE APPAREL & ACTIVEWEAR MANAGEMENT CO p 61
1501 E Cerritos Ave, Anaheim CA 92805
Tel (714) 765-0400 *SIC* 2253

VOLCOM LLC p 1564
1740 Monrovia Ave, Costa Mesa CA 92627
Tel (949) 646-2175
SIC 7389 2253 7822 5136 5137

GRAY VESTAR INVESTORS LLC p 632
17622 Armstrong Ave, Irvine CA 92614
Tel (949) 863-1171
SIC 2253 2339 2335 2337 3961 2387

ST JOHN KNITS INC p 1367
17522 Armstrong Ave, Irvine CA 92614
Tel (949) 863-1171 *SIC* 2339 2253 2389

■FRUIT OF LOOM INC p 582
1 Fruit Of The Loom Dr, Bowling Green KY 42103
Tel (270) 781-6400 *SIC* 2254 2253

■RUSSELL BRANDS LLC p 1259
1 Fruit Of The Loom Dr, Bowling Green KY 42103
Tel (270) 781-6400
SIC 2253 2211 2329 2339 3949 5091

ELDER MANUFACTURING CO INC p 484
999 Executive Parkway Dr # 300, Saint Louis MO 63141
Tel (314) 469-1120 *SIC* 2321 2361 2253

HANDWEAR SALES INC p 657
74 Bleecker St, Gloversville NY 12078
Tel (518) 725-8641
SIC 3151 3949 2253 3021

GCE INTERNATIONAL INC p 595
1385 Broadway Fl 21, New York NY 10018
Tel (212) 704-4800
SIC 2253 2389 2331 5137 5136

GILDAN APPAREL USA INC p 612
48 W 38th St Fl 8, New York NY 10018
Tel (212) 476-0341 *SIC* 2253 2331

▲PVH CORP p 1193
200 Madison Ave Bsmt 1, New York NY 10016
Tel (212) 381-3500
SIC 2321 2331 2253 3143 5621 5611

▲RALPH LAUREN CORP p 1206
650 Madison Ave Fl C1, New York NY 10022
Tel (212) 318-7000
SIC 2325 2321 2253 2323 2311 2329

▲HANESBRANDS INC p 657
1000 E Hanes Mill Rd, Winston Salem NC 27105
Tel (336) 519-8080
SIC 2253 2342 2341 2322 2252 2251

WINSTON-SALEM INDUSTRIES FOR BLIND INC p 1617
7730 N Point Blvd, Winston Salem NC 27106
Tel (336) 759-0551
SIC 2515 3021 2392 2253 2394 3851

▲HAMPSHIRE GROUP LIMITED p 656
1924 Pearman Dairy Rd A, Anderson SC 29625
Tel (212) 540-5666 *SIC* 2339 2329 2253

▲DELTA APPAREL INC p 426
322 S Main St, Greenville SC 29601
Tel (864) 232-5200
SIC 2321 2369 2339 2253

BAY ISLAND SPORTSWEAR INC p 161
1415 Emerald Rd, Greenwood SC 29646
Tel (864) 229-1298 *SIC* 2253 2339

UNAKA CO INC p 1502
1500 Industrial Rd, Greeneville TN 37745
Tel (423) 639-1171
SIC 2099 3469 2514 2253 4226

BIO WORLD MERCHANDISING INC p 183
2111 W Walnut Hill Ln, Irving TX 75038
Tel (888) 831-2138
SIC 2353 3161 2253 5199 3021

SIC 2254 Knit Underwear Mills

■FRUIT OF LOOM INC p 582
1 Fruit Of The Loom Dr, Bowling Green KY 42103
Tel (270) 781-6400 *SIC* 2254 2253

GILDAN USA INC p 612
1980 Clements Ferry Rd, Charleston SC 29492
Tel (843) 849-6191 *SIC* 2252 2254

GILDAN DELAWARE INC p 612
3375 Joseph Martin Hwy, Martinsville VA 24112
Tel (276) 956-2305 *SIC* 2252 2254

JOCKEY INTERNATIONAL INC p 787
2300 60th St, Kenosha WI 53140
Tel (262) 658-8111 *SIC* 2254 2341 2322

SIC 2257 Circular Knit Fabric Mills

MCMURRAY FABRICS INC p 932
105 Vann Pl, Aberdeen NC 28315
Tel (910) 944-2128 *SIC* 2257

CAROLINA MILLS INC p 259
618 N Carolina Ave, Maiden NC 28650
Tel (828) 428-9911
SIC 2281 2211 2221 2257 2511 2512

SIC 2258 Lace & Warp Knit Fabric Mills

■GUILFORD MILLS INC p 646
1001 Military Cutoff Rd # 300, Wilmington NC 28405
Tel (910) 794-5810 *SIC* 2258 2399

MOORE CO p 987
36 Beach St, Westerly RI 02891
Tel (401) 596-2816
SIC 2258 2241 3069 3061 2821

TIETEX INTERNATIONAL LTD p 1453
3010 N Blackstock Rd, Spartanburg SC 29301
Tel (864) 574-0500 *SIC* 2297 2258 2221

SIC 2259 Knitting Mills, NEC

BIG TIME PRODUCTS LLC p 182
2 Wilbanks Rd Se, Rome GA 30161
Tel (706) 295-3770 *SIC* 2259

SIC 2261 Cotton Fabric Finishers

MAD ENGINE INC p 893
6740 Cobra Way Ste 100, San Diego CA 92121
Tel (858) 558-5270 *SIC* 2261

KING AMERICA FINISHING INC p 820
1351 Scarboro Hwy, Sylvania GA 30467
Tel (912) 863-4511 *SIC* 2211 2261

DURO TEXTILES LLC p 463
110 Chace St, Fall River MA 02724
Tel (508) 675-0102 *SIC* 2261 2262

TOMEN AMERICA INC p 1459
805 3rd Ave Fl 16, New York NY 10022
Tel (212) 355-3600
SIC 5153 5169 5031 5131 2261

GLEN RAVEN INC p 614
1831 N Park Ave, Burlington NC 27217
Tel (336) 227-6211
SIC 2221 2281 2261 2211

BURLINGTON INDUSTRIES LLC p 228
804 Green Valley Rd # 300, Greensboro NC 27408
Tel (336) 379-6220
SIC 2231 2211 2221 2273 2262 2261

ITG HOLDINGS INC p 768
804 Green Valley Rd # 300, Greensboro NC 27408
Tel (336) 379-6220
SIC 2211 2231 2221 2273 2262 2261

■HANES COMPANIES INC p 657
815 Buxton St, Winston Salem NC 27101
Tel (336) 747-1600 *SIC* 2262 2261 2297

CRANSTON PRINT WORKS CO INC p 389
1381 Cranston St, Cranston RI 02920
Tel (401) 943-4800 *SIC* 2261 2262 2899

GREENWOOD MILLS INC p 639
300 Morgan Ave, Greenwood SC 29646
Tel (864) 227-2121
SIC 2211 2221 2241 2261 2262 6552

SIC 2262 Silk & Man-Made Fabric Finishers

DURO TEXTILES LLC p 463
110 Chace St, Fall River MA 02724
Tel (508) 675-0102 *SIC* 2261 2262

MICROFIBRES INC p 962
124 Washington St Ste 101, Foxboro MA 02035
Tel (401) 725-4883
SIC 2221 2295 5131 2262

P KAUFMANN INC p 1102
3 Park Ave, New York NY 10016
Tel (212) 292-2200
SIC 5131 5714 5712 2262

BURLINGTON INDUSTRIES LLC p 228
804 Green Valley Rd # 300, Greensboro NC 27408
Tel (336) 379-6220
SIC 2231 2211 2221 2273 2262 2261

ITG HOLDINGS INC p 768
804 Green Valley Rd # 300, Greensboro NC 27408
Tel (336) 379-6220
SIC 2211 2231 2221 2273 2262 2261

PRECISION FABRICS GROUP INC p 1168
301 N Elm St Ste 600, Greensboro NC 27401
Tel (336) 510-8000 *SIC* 2262 2221

■ **HANES COMPANIES INC** p 657
815 Buxton St, Winston Salem NC 27101
Tel (336) 747-1600 *SIC* 2262 2261 2297

TRANZONIC COMPANIES p 1473
26301 Curtiss Wright Pkwy # 200, Richmond Heights OH 44143
Tel (216) 535-4300
SIC 2676 2211 2326 2842 2273 2262

TZ ACQUISITION CORP p 1496
26301 Curtiss Wright Pkwy, Richmond Heights OH 44143
Tel (216) 535-4300
SIC 2676 2211 2326 2842 2262

CRANSTON PRINT WORKS CO INC p 389
1381 Cranston St, Cranston RI 02920
Tel (401) 943-4800 *SIC* 2261 2262 2899

COOLEY INC p 366
50 Esten Ave, Pawtucket RI 02860
Tel (401) 724-9000 *SIC* 2295 3069 2262

GREENWOOD MILLS INC p 639
300 Morgan Ave, Greenwood SC 29646
Tel (864) 227-2121
SIC 2211 2221 2241 2261 2262 6552

PROPEX HOLDING LLC p 1184
1110 Market St Ste 300, Chattanooga TN 37402
Tel (800) 621-1273
SIC 6719 2221 2297 2262 2211

SIC 2269 Textile Finishers, NEC

WEB INDUSTRIES INC p 1586
377 Simarano Dr Ste 220, Marlborough MA 01752
Tel (508) 898-2988
SIC 2671 5162 3089 2269 3441

FRANCO MANUFACTURING CO INC p 574
555 Prospect St, Metuchen NJ 08840
Tel (732) 494-0503
SIC 2269 2392 2211 5023 5131

RONILE INC p 1249
701 Orchard Ave, Rocky Mount VA 24151
Tel (540) 483-0261 *SIC* 2269 5949 2273

MERIDIAN INDUSTRIES INC p 949
735 N Water St Ste 630, Milwaukee WI 53202
Tel (414) 224-0610
SIC 3069 2843 2269 7389

SIC 2273 Carpets & Rugs

DAEHAN SOLUTION ALABAMA LLC p 408
9101 County Road 26, Hope Hull AL 36043
Tel (334) 404-5000 *SIC* 3625 2273

■ **TDG OPERATIONS LLC** p 1429
716 Bill Myles Dr, Saraland AL 36571
Tel (251) 675-9080 *SIC* 2273

MAPLES INDUSTRIES INC p 904
2210 Moody Ridge Rd, Scottsboro AL 35768
Tel (256) 259-1327 *SIC* 2273

BENTLEY MILLS INC p 173
14641 Don Julian Rd, City Of Industry CA 91746
Tel (626) 333-4585 *SIC* 2273 2299

ROYALTY CARPET MILLS INC p 1254
17111 Red Hill Ave, Irvine CA 92614
Tel (949) 474-4000 *SIC* 2273

■ **ETHAN ALLEN RETAIL INC** p 511
Ethan Allen Dr, Danbury CT 06811
Tel (203) 743-8000
SIC 5712 5719 5713 5231 2273

■ **INTERFACE AMERICAS INC** p 752
2859 Pcs Frry St 2000, Atlanta GA 30339
Tel (770) 437-6800 *SIC* 2273

▲ **INTERFACE INC** p 752
2859 Paces Ferry Rd Se # 2000, Atlanta GA 30339
Tel (770) 437-6800 *SIC* 2273

■ **ALADDIN MANUFACTURING CORP** p 43
160 S Industrial Blvd, Calhoun GA 30701
Tel (706) 629-7721 *SIC* 2273

APACHE MILLS INC p 96
197 Royal Dr Se, Calhoun GA 30701
Tel (706) 629-7791 *SIC* 2273

■ **MOHAWK CARPET DISTRIBUTION INC** p 982
160 S Industrial Blvd, Calhoun GA 30701
Tel (706) 695-9743 *SIC* 2273

■ **MOHAWK CARPET LLC** p 982
160 S Industrial Blvd, Calhoun GA 30701
Tel (706) 629-7721 *SIC* 2273

▲ **MOHAWK INDUSTRIES INC** p 982
160 S Industrial Blvd, Calhoun GA 30701
Tel (706) 629-7721 *SIC* 2273 3253

BEAULIEU GROUP LLC p 166
1502 Coronet Dr, Dalton GA 30720
Tel (706) 259-4511 *SIC* 2273 2281

BEAULIEU OF AMERICA INC p 166
1502 Coronet Dr, Dalton GA 30720
Tel (706) 278-6666 *SIC* 2273

BROWN INDUSTRIES INC p 219
205 W Industrial Blvd, Dalton GA 30720
Tel (706) 277-1977
SIC 2759 5131 2273 3552 3315 2671

▲ **DIXIE GROUP INC** p 444
475 Reed Rd, Dalton GA 30720
Tel (706) 876-5800 *SIC* 2273

ENGINEERED FLOORS LLC p 499
3510 Corporate Dr, Dalton GA 30721
Tel (706) 625-4334 *SIC* 2273

J & J INDUSTRIES INC p 770
818 J And J Dr, Dalton GA 30721
Tel (706) 529-2100 *SIC* 2273

LEXMARK CARPET MILLS INC p 860
285 Kraft Dr, Dalton GA 30721
Tel (706) 277-3000 *SIC* 2273

■ **SHAW INDUSTRIES INC** p 1313
616 E Walnut Ave, Dalton GA 30721
Tel (706) 278-3812 *SIC* 2273

TANDUS CENTIVA INC p 1424
311 Smith Industrial Blvd, Dalton GA 30721
Tel (706) 259-9711 *SIC* 2273

TANDUS GROUP INC p 1424
311 Smith Industrial Blvd, Dalton GA 30721
Tel (706) 259-9711 *SIC* 2273

■ **INTERFACEFLOR LLC** p 752
1503 Orchard Hill Rd, Lagrange GA 30240
Tel (706) 882-1891 *SIC* 2273

KLEEN-TEX INDUSTRIES INC p 823
101 N Greenwood St Ste C, Lagrange GA 30240
Tel (706) 882-0111 *SIC* 3069 2273 2392

MOUNTVILLE MILLS INC p 995
1729 S Davis Rd, Lagrange GA 30241
Tel (706) 882-2961 *SIC* 2273 2211 2221

SYNTEC INDUSTRIES LLC p 1416
438 Lavender Dr Nw, Rome GA 30165
Tel (706) 235-1158 *SIC* 2273 5023

SURYA CARPET INC p 1409
1 Surya Dr, White GA 30184
Tel (706) 625-4823 *SIC* 5023 2273

HP PELZER AUTOMOTIVE SYSTEMS INC p 714
1175 Crooks Rd, Troy MI 48084
Tel (248) 280-1010 *SIC* 3061 2273

BARI HOME CORP p 155
1215 Livingston Ave Ste 4, North Brunswick NJ 08902
Tel (973) 713-0591 *SIC* 2273

MANNINGTON MILLS INC p 902
75 Mannington Mills Rd, Salem NJ 08079
Tel (856) 935-3000
SIC 3996 3253 2273 2435

SAFAVIEH INC p 1265
40 Harbor Park Dr, Port Washington NY 11050
Tel (516) 945-1900 *SIC* 2273 5712

BURLINGTON INDUSTRIES LLC p 228
804 Green Valley Rd # 300, Greensboro NC 27408
Tel (336) 379-6220
SIC 2231 2211 2221 2273 2262 2261

INTERNATIONAL TEXTILE GROUP INC p 757
804 Green Valley Rd # 300, Greensboro NC 27408
Tel (336) 379-6299
SIC 3714 3496 2211 2231 2221 2273

ITG HOLDINGS INC p 768
804 Green Valley Rd # 300, Greensboro NC 27408
Tel (336) 379-6220
SIC 2211 2231 2221 2273 2262 2261

TRANZONIC COMPANIES p 1473
26301 Curtiss Wright Pkwy # 200, Richmond Heights OH 44143
Tel (216) 535-4300
SIC 2676 2211 2326 2842 2273 2262

NATCO PRODUCTS CORP p 1009
155 Brookside Ave, West Warwick RI 02893
Tel (401) 828-0300 *SIC* 3996 2273 5023

MILLIKEN & CO p 971
920 Milliken Rd, Spartanburg SC 29303
Tel (864) 503-2020
SIC 2221 2211 2231 2273 2821 4911

ELK PREMIUM BUILDING PRODUCTS INC p 487
14911 Quorum Dr Ste 600, Dallas TX 75254
Tel (972) 851-0400 *SIC* 2952 2273

▲ **MICHAELS COMPANIES INC** p 960
8000 Bent Branch Dr, Irving TX 75063
Tel (972) 409-1300 *SIC* 5945 3999 2273

▲ **NEWPARK RESOURCES INC** p 1038
9320 Lkeside Blvd Ste 100, The Woodlands TX 77381
Tel (281) 362-6800
SIC 1389 4959 4953 2273

RONILE INC p 1249
701 Orchard Ave, Rocky Mount VA 24151
Tel (540) 483-0261 *SIC* 2269 5949 2273

PENDA CORP p 1128
2344 W Wisconsin St, Portage WI 53901
Tel (608) 742-5301
SIC 5013 3714 3792 3713 2273

SIC 2281 Yarn Spinning Mills

■ **LEESBURG KNITTING MILLS INC** p 852
400 Industrial Blvd, Leesburg AL 35983
Tel (256) 526-8022 *SIC* 2281 0724

PHARR-PALOMAR INC p 1141
6781 8th St, Buena Park CA 90620
Tel (714) 522-4811 *SIC* 2282 2281

BEAULIEU GROUP LLC p 166
1502 Coronet Dr, Dalton GA 30720
Tel (706) 259-4511 *SIC* 2273 2281

GLEN RAVEN INC p 614
1831 N Park Ave, Burlington NC 27217
Tel (336) 227-6211
SIC 2221 2281 2261 2211

COATS & CLARK INC p 332
3430 Toringdon Way # 301, Charlotte NC 28277
Tel (704) 329-5800
SIC 2284 2281 3364 3089 2241 3965

COATS NORTH AMERICA DE REPUBLICA DOMINICANA INC p 332
3430 Toringdon Way # 301, Charlotte NC 28277
Tel (800) 242-8095
SIC 2284 2281 3364 3089 2241 3965

PARKDALE AMERICA LLC p 1116
531 Cotton Blossom Cir, Gastonia NC 28054
Tel (704) 864-8761 *SIC* 2281

PARKDALE MILLS INC p 1116
531 Cotton Blossom Cir, Gastonia NC 28054
Tel (704) 864-8761 *SIC* 2281 2844 2241

▲ **UNIFI INC** p 1503
7201 W Friendly Ave, Greensboro NC 27410
Tel (336) 294-4410 *SIC* 2281 2282 2221

■ **UNIFI MANUFACTURING INC** p 1503
7201 W Friendly Ave, Greensboro NC 27410
Tel (336) 294-4410 *SIC* 2281

CAROLINA MILLS INC p 259
618 N Carolina Ave, Maiden NC 28650
Tel (828) 428-9911
SIC 2281 2211 2221 2257 2511 2512

PHARR YARNS LLC p 1141
100 Main St, Mc Adenville NC 28101
Tel (704) 824-3551 *SIC* 2281 2282 2824

TUSCARORA YARNS INC p 1493
8760 Franklin St E, Mount Pleasant NC 28124
Tel (704) 436-6527 *SIC* 2281

FRONTIER SPINNING MILLS HOLDING CORP p 581
1823 Boone Trail Rd, Sanford NC 27330
Tel (919) 776-9940 *SIC* 2281

FRONTIER SPINNING MILLS INC p 581
1823 Boone Trail Rd, Sanford NC 27330
Tel (919) 777-2689 *SIC* 2281

GRP INC p 642
1823 Boone Trail Rd, Sanford NC 27330
Tel (919) 776-9940 *SIC* 2281

NATIONAL SPINNING CO INC p 1016
1481 W 2nd St, Washington NC 27889
Tel (252) 975-7111 *SIC* 2281

INMAN MILLS p 744
300 Park Rd, Inman SC 29349
Tel (864) 472-2121 *SIC* 2281

MOUNT VERNON MILLS INC p 994
503 S Main St, Mauldin SC 29662
Tel (864) 688-7100 *SIC* 2211 2221 2281

ASTENJOHNSON INC p 122
4399 Corporate Rd, North Charleston SC 29405
Tel (843) 747-7800 *SIC* 2221 2281 2299

■ **FIBERWEB INC** p 539
9335 Harris Corners Pkwy, Old Hickory TN 37138
Tel (704) 697-5100 *SIC* 2281 5047 5137

■ **CELANESE ACETATE LLC** p 273
1601 Lyndon B Johnson Fwy, Dallas TX 75234
Tel (972) 443-4000 *SIC* 2281

UNIVERSAL FIBERS INC p 1516
14401 Industrial Park Rd, Bristol VA 24202
Tel (276) 669-1161 *SIC* 2824 2281

SIC 2282 Yarn Texturizing, Throwing, Twisting & Winding Mills

PHARR-PALOMAR INC p 1141
6781 8th St, Buena Park CA 90620
Tel (714) 522-4811 *SIC* 2282 2281

▲ **UNIFI INC** p 1503
7201 W Friendly Ave, Greensboro NC 27410
Tel (336) 294-4410 *SIC* 2281 2282 2221

PHARR YARNS LLC p 1141
100 Main St, Mc Adenville NC 28101
Tel (704) 824-3551 *SIC* 2281 2282 2824

SIC 2284 Thread Mills

COATS & CLARK INC p 332
3430 Toringdon Way # 301, Charlotte NC 28277
Tel (704) 329-5800
SIC 2284 2281 3364 3089 2241 3965

COATS AMERICAN INC p 332
3430 Toringdon Way # 301, Charlotte NC 28277
Tel (704) 329-5800 *SIC* 2284

COATS NORTH AMERICA DE REPUBLICA DOMINICANA INC p 332
3430 Toringdon Way # 301, Charlotte NC 28277
Tel (800) 242-8095
SIC 2284 2281 3364 3089 2241 3965

■ **RUDDICK OPERATING CO LLC** p 1257
301 S Tryon St Ste 1800, Charlotte NC 28282
Tel (704) 372-5404 *SIC* 5411 2284

AMERICAN & EFIRD LLC p 67
22 American St, Mount Holly NC 28120
Tel (704) 827-4311 *SIC* 2284

ASCEND PERFORMANCE MATERIALS OPERATIONS LLC p 116
1010 Travis St Ste 900, Houston TX 77002
Tel (713) 315-5700 *SIC* 2821 2284

SIC 2295 Fabrics Coated Not Rubberized

KRONOSPAN INC p 830
1 Kronospan Way, Eastaboga AL 36260
Tel (256) 741-8755 *SIC* 2431 2295

PHIFER INC p 1142
4400 Kauloosa Ave, Tuscaloosa AL 35401
Tel (205) 345-2120
SIC 3496 2221 3357 2295 3442 3354

HENNIGES AUTOMOTIVE IOWA INC p 683
3200 Main St, Keokuk IA 52632
Tel (319) 524-4560
SIC 3069 3442 3429 2295

HAARTZ CORP p 651
87 Hayward Rd, Acton MA 01720
Tel (978) 264-2600 *SIC* 3069 2295

MICROFIBRES INC p 962
124 Washington St Ste 101, Foxboro MA 02035
Tel (401) 725-4883
SIC 2221 2295 5131 2262

SHAWMUT CORP p 1313
208 Manley St, West Bridgewater MA 02379
Tel (508) 588-3300 *SIC* 2295

DURO-LAST INC p 463
525 E Morley Dr, Saginaw MI 48601
Tel (800) 248-0280 *SIC* 2295

PRECISION CUSTOM COATINGS LLC p 1168
200 Maltese Dr, Totowa NJ 07512
Tel (973) 785-4390 *SIC* 2295

TONOGA INC p 1460
136 Coon Brook Rd, Petersburg NY 12138
Tel (518) 658-3202 *SIC* 2295 3629

■ **CARLISLE CORP** p 257
11605 N Community Hse Rd, Charlotte NC 28277
Tel (704) 501-1100
SIC 2952 2899 3011 2295 3089 3577

BGF INDUSTRIES INC p 180
3802 Robert Porcher Way, Greensboro NC 27410
Tel (843) 537-3172
SIC 2221 3624 2241 2295

NOUVEAU VERRE HOLDINGS INC p 1062
3802 Robert Porcher Way, Greensboro NC 27410
Tel (336) 545-0011
SIC 2221 3624 2241 2295

NVH INC p 1068
3802 Robert Porcher Way, Greensboro NC 27410
Tel (336) 545-0011
SIC 2221 3624 2241 2295

TRELLEBORG COATED SYSTEMS US INC p 1476
715 Railroad Ave, Rutherfordton NC 28139
Tel (864) 576-1210
SIC 2295 2221 2394 2396 2211

■ **SCHNELLER LLC** p 1288
6019 Powdermill Rd, Kent OH 44240
Tel (330) 676-7183 *SIC* 2295

GENTEX CORP p 604
324 Main St, Simpson PA 18407
Tel (570) 282-3550 *SIC* 3842 8731 2295

COOLEY INC p 366
50 Esten Ave, Pawtucket RI 02860
Tel (401) 724-9000 *SIC* 2295 3069 2262

AOC LLC p 94
955 Highway 57, Collierville TN 38017
Tel (901) 854-2800 *SIC* 2295

SIC 2296 Tire Cord & Fabric

KISWIRE PINE BLUFF INC p 822
5100 Industrial Dr S, Pine Bluff AR 71602
Tel (870) 247-2444 *SIC* 3312 2296

HYOSUNG HOLDINGS USA INC p 724
15801 Prixham Hll Ave 5 Ste 575, Charlotte NC 28277
Tel (704) 790-6100 *SIC* 2299 2296

HYOSUNG USA INC p 724
15801 Brixham Hill Ave # 575, Charlotte NC 28277
Tel (704) 790-6136 *SIC* 2221 2296 5199

BRIDGESTONE METALPHA USA INC p 211
570 International Blvd, Clarksville TN 37040
Tel (931) 552-2112 *SIC* 2296

CARLSTAR GROUP LLC p 258
725 Cool Springs Blvd, Franklin TN 37067
Tel (615) 503-0220
SIC 3714 5014 3499 5013 2296

SIC 2297 Fabrics, Nonwoven

▲ **LYDALL INC** p 887
1 Colonial Rd, Manchester CT 06042
Tel (860) 646-1233
SIC 2297 3053 2899 2631 3714 3564

AHLSTROM NONWOVENS LLC p 37
2 Elm St, Windsor Locks CT 06096
Tel (860) 654-8300 *SIC* 2297

SUOMINEN US HOLDING INC p 1405
3 Chirnside Rd, Windsor Locks CT 06096
Tel (860) 654-8331 *SIC* 2297

WINDSOR LOCKS NONWOVENS INC p 1615
3 Chirnside Rd Bldg D, Windsor Locks CT 06096
Tel (860) 292-5600 *SIC* 2297

PBR INC p 1123
335 Athena Dr, Athens GA 30601
Tel (706) 354-3700 *SIC* 2297 2221 3089

SOUTHERN MILLS INC p 1349
6501 Mall Blvd, Union City GA 30291
Tel (770) 969-1000 *SIC* 2221 2297

HOLLINGSWORTH & VOSE CO p 701
112 Washington St, East Walpole MA 02032
Tel (508) 850-2000
SIC 2621 3053 2297 2499

FOSS HOLDINGS LLC p 570
11 Merrill Industrial Dr A1, Hampton NH 03842
Tel (603) 929-6000 *SIC* 2297

FOSS MANUFACTURING CO LLC p 570
11 Merrill Industrial Dr A1, Hampton NH 03842
Tel (603) 929-6000 *SIC* 2297

SEFAR INC p 1300
111 Calumet St, Depew NY 14043
Tel (716) 683-4050
SIC 5131 5051 5084 3496 2297 2221

SAINT-GOBAIN ADFORS AMERICA INC p 1271
1795 Baseline Rd, Grand Island NY 14072
Tel (716) 775-3900 *SIC* 2297

■ **AVINTIV INC** p 138
9335 Harris Corners Pkwy, Charlotte NC 28269
Tel (704) 697-5100 *SIC* 2297

■ **AVINTIV SPECIALTY MATERIALS INC** p 138
9335 Harris Corners Pkwy, Charlotte NC 28269
Tel (704) 697-5100 *SIC* 2297 2392

■ **CHICOPEE INC** p 298
9335 Harr Corn Pkwy Ste 3, Charlotte NC 28269
Tel (704) 697-5100 *SIC* 2297

■ **PGI NONWOVEN/CHICOPEE INC** p 1140
9335 Harris Corners Pkwy, Charlotte NC 28269
Tel (704) 697-5100 *SIC* 2297 2392

■ **SCORPIO ACQUISITION CORP** p 1293
9335 Harris Corners Pkwy, Charlotte NC 28269
Tel (704) 697-5100 *SIC* 2297

LOW & BONAR INC p 881
1301 Sand Hill Rd, Enka NC 28728
Tel (828) 665-5000
SIC 5199 3296 2899 2297 2221

TENOWO INC p 1438
1968 Kawai Rd, Lincolnton NC 28092
Tel (704) 732-3525 *SIC* 2297

AVGOL AMERICA INC p 137
178 Avgol Dr, Mocksville NC 27028
Tel (336) 751-5007 *SIC* 2297

■ **HANES COMPANIES INC** p 657
815 Buxton St, Winston Salem NC 27101
Tel (336) 747-1600 *SIC* 2262 2261 2297

TIETEX INTERNATIONAL LTD p 1453
3010 N Blackstock Rd, Spartanburg SC 29301
Tel (864) 574-0500 *SIC* 2297 2258 2221

PROPEX HOLDING LLC p 1184
1110 Market St Ste 300, Chattanooga TN 37402
Tel (800) 621-1273
SIC 6719 2221 2297 2262 2211

HOBBS BONDED FIBERS LLC p 699
200 Commerce Dr, Waco TX 76710
Tel (254) 741-0040 *SIC* 2297 2299

HOBBS BONDED FIBERS NA LLC p 699
200 Commerce Dr, Waco TX 76710
Tel (254) 741-0040 *SIC* 2297 2299

CARPENTER CO p 260
5016 Monument Ave, Richmond VA 23230
Tel (804) 359-0800
SIC 3086 1311 2869 2297 2392 2821

JASON HOLDINGS INC p 778
411 E Wisconsin Ave # 2120, Milwaukee WI 53202
Tel (414) 277-9300
SIC 2297 3465 3469 3844 3443

■ **JASON INC** p 778
411 E Wisconsin Ave, Milwaukee WI 53202
Tel (414) 277-9300
SIC 3465 2297 3625 3469 3844 3443

▲ **JASON INDUSTRIES INC** p 778
833 E Michigan St Ste 900, Milwaukee WI 53202
Tel (414) 277-9300
SIC 3465 2297 3625 3469 3844 3443

■ **JPHI HOLDINGS INC** p 795
411 E Wisconsin Ave, Milwaukee WI 53202
Tel (414) 277-9445
SIC 3465 2297 3625 3469 3844 3443

ROCKLINE INDUSTRIES INC p 1245
4343 S Taylor Dr, Sheboygan WI 53081
Tel (800) 558-7790 *SIC* 2679 2297

SIC 2298 Cordage & Twine

NORTH AMERICAN INTERCONNECT LLC p 1050
7975 N Hayden Rd Ste D105, Scottsdale AZ 85258
Tel (480) 556-6066 *SIC* 2298

THUNDER BASIN CORP p 1451
103 Foulk Rd Ste 151, Wilmington DE 19803
Tel (610) 962-3770 *SIC* 3566 2298

■ **LEHIGH CONSUMER PRODUCTS LLC** p 853
3901 Liberty St, Aurora IL 60504
Tel (630) 851-7330
SIC 3965 2298 3462 3452 8742

UNIVERSAL COOPERATIVES INC p 1516
1300 Corporate Ctr Curv, Saint Paul MN 55121
Tel (651) 239-1000 *SIC* 2879 5169 2298

SIMPLICITY CREATIVE GROUP INC p 1325
261 Madison Ave Fl 4, New York NY 10016
Tel (212) 686-7676
SIC 2241 2221 2396 2298

LAKE SPIRIT TRIBE p 839
816 3rd Ave N, Fort Totten ND 58335
Tel (701) 766-1270
SIC 9131 0191 2394 2298 7999

■ **TVC COMMUNICATIONS LLC** p 1494
800 Airport Rd, Annville PA 17003
Tel (717) 838-3790 *SIC* 3663 2298

WIREROPE WORKS INC p 1618
100 Maynard St, Williamsport PA 17701
Tel (570) 327-4229 *SIC* 3496 2298 3315

DELTA RIGGING & TOOLS INC p 427
125 Mccarty St, Houston TX 77029
Tel (713) 512-1700 *SIC* 7359 2298 3496

SIC 2299 Textile Goods, NEC

BENTLEY MILLS INC p 173
14641 Don Julian Rd, City Of Industry CA 91746
Tel (626) 333-4585 *SIC* 2273 2299

COLUMBIA RECYCLING CORP p 341
1001 Chattanooga Ave, Dalton GA 30720
Tel (706) 278-4701 *SIC* 2299

ROYAL TEN CATE (USA) INC p 1254
365 S Holland Dr, Pendergrass GA 30567
Tel (706) 693-2226 *SIC* 2299

NOVIPAX LLC p 1063
2215 York Rd Ste 504, Oak Brook IL 60523
Tel (630) 686-2735 *SIC* 2821 2299

WM T BURNETT HOLDING LLC p 1620
1500 Bush St, Baltimore MD 21230
Tel (410) 837-3000 *SIC* 2299 3086

POLARTEC LLC p 1159
46 Stafford St, Lawrence MA 01841
Tel (978) 685-6341 *SIC* 2299

RTP INTERNATIONAL HOLDINGS INC p 1256
580 E Front St, Winona MN 55987
Tel (507) 454-6900 *SIC* 2299

F SCHUMACHER & CO p 522
875 Ave Of The Amrcs 14, New York NY 10001
Tel (212) 213-7900 *SIC* 5131 2299

SOLVAIRA SPECIALTIES INC p 1339
50 Bridge St, North Tonawanda NY 14120
Tel (716) 693-4040 *SIC* 2823 2299

HYOSUNG HOLDINGS USA INC p 724
15801 Prixham Hll Ave 5 Ste 575, Charlotte NC 28277
Tel (704) 790-6100 *SIC* 2299 2296

■ **HICKORY BUSINESS FURNITURE LLC** p 690
900 12th Street Dr Nw, Hickory NC 28601
Tel (828) 322-1169 *SIC* 2521 2299

WORLD TRADING CO INC p 1625
6754 Melrose Ln, Oklahoma City OK 73127
Tel (405) 787-1982 *SIC* 2299

▲ **KNOLL INC** p 824
1235 Water St, East Greenville PA 18041
Tel (215) 679-7991 *SIC* 2521 2522 2299

SPRINGS GLOBAL US INC p 1361
205 N White St, Fort Mill SC 29715
Tel (803) 547-1500 *SIC* 2299 5023

HAMRICK MILLS INC p 656
515 W Buford St, Gaffney SC 29341
Tel (864) 489-4731 *SIC* 2211 2299

ASTENJOHNSON INC p 122
4399 Corporate Rd, North Charleston SC 29405
Tel (843) 747-7800 *SIC* 2221 2281 2299

HOBBS BONDED FIBERS LLC p 699
200 Commerce Dr, Waco TX 76710
Tel (254) 741-0040 *SIC* 2297 2299

HOBBS BONDED FIBERS NA LLC p 699
200 Commerce Dr, Waco TX 76710
Tel (254) 741-0040 *SIC* 2297 2299

NILIT AMERICA INC p 1043
420 Industrial Park Rd, Ridgeway VA 24148
Tel (276) 638-2434 *SIC* 5199 2299 5531

SIC 2311 Men's & Boys' Suits, Coats & Overcoats

AMERICAN APPAREL INC p 68
107 Cecil Jackson Byp, Selma AL 36703
Tel (334) 872-6337 *SIC* 2311 2385

▲ **DIFFERENTIAL BRANDS GROUP INC** p 438
1231 S Gerhart Ave, Commerce CA 90022
Tel (323) 890-1800
SIC 2337 2339 2311 2325 3111 2387

AMERICAN APPAREL LLC p 68
747 Warehouse St, Los Angeles CA 90021
Tel (213) 488-0226 *SIC* 2389 2311 2331

TENNIER INDUSTRIES INC p 1438
755 Nw 17th Ave Ste 106, Delray Beach FL 33445
Tel (561) 999-9710 *SIC* 2311

▲ **OXFORD INDUSTRIES INC** p 1101
999 Peachtree St Ne # 688, Atlanta GA 30309
Tel (404) 659-2424 *SIC* 2321 2325 2311

PECKHAM VOCATIONAL INDUSTRIES INC p 1126
3510 Capitol City Blvd, Lansing MI 48906
Tel (517) 316-4000
SIC 8331 2396 2311 2331 2339 2326

GOLDEN MANUFACTURING CO INC p 621
125 Highway 366, Golden MS 38847
Tel (662) 454-3428
SIC 2311 2325 2321 2326

PII INC p 1147
17 Research Park Dr # 100, Weldon Spring MO 63304
Tel (636) 685-1047 *SIC* 2311 2326

DONNA KARAN CO LLC p 450
240 W 40th St, New York NY 10018
Tel (212) 789-1500
SIC 2335 2337 2331 2339 2311 2325

EXCELLED SHEEPSKIN & LEATHER COAT CORP p 516
1400 Brdwy Fl 31, New York NY 10018
Tel (212) 594-5843
SIC 2386 3172 2337 2311

▲ **G-III APPAREL GROUP LTD** p 588
512 7th Ave Fl 35, New York NY 10018
Tel (212) 403-0500
SIC 2337 2339 2311 2329 2386 5136

HUGO BOSS USA INC p 717
55 Water St Fl 48, New York NY 10041
Tel (212) 940-0600
SIC 2311 2325 2337 5136 5611 6794

▲ **RALPH LAUREN CORP** p 1206
650 Madison Ave Fl C1, New York NY 10022
Tel (212) 318-7000
SIC 2325 2321 2253 2323 2311 2329

XMH-HFI INC p 1632
1155 N Clinton Ave, Rochester NY 14621
Tel (585) 467-7240 *SIC* 2311 2325

■ **FECHHEIMER BROTHERS CO** p 533
4545 Malsbary Rd, Blue Ash OH 45242
Tel (513) 793-7819
SIC 2311 2337 2339 5699

LION APPAREL INC p 869
7200 Poe Ave Ste 400, Dayton OH 45414
Tel (937) 898-1949 *SIC* 2311

■ **ARAMARK UNIFORM & CAREER APPAREL GROUP INC** p 102
1101 Market St Ste 45, Philadelphia PA 19107
Tel (215) 238-3000
SIC 2337 2311 5699 5961 5661 5812

F&T APPAREL LLC p 522
4000 Chemical Rd Ste 500, Plymouth Meeting PA 19462
Tel (610) 828-8400 *SIC* 2311 2321 2325

PROPPER INTERNATIONAL INC p 1184
308 Km 0 6 375 Cljon Fas, Cabo Rojo PR 00623
Tel (787) 254-8020 *SIC* 2311 2326

■ **SPERIAN PROTECTION USA INC** p 1358
900 Douglas Pike, Smithfield RI 02917
Tel (401) 232-1200
SIC 3851 3842 2311 7218 5999

TOM JAMES CO p 1459
263 Seaboard Ln, Franklin TN 37067
Tel (615) 771-6633
SIC 2311 2325 2323 2321 5611

■ **VF IMAGEWEAR INC** p 1553
545 Marriott Dr Ste 200, Nashville TN 37214
Tel (615) 565-5000
SIC 2326 5099 2339 2311

TULLAHOMA INDUSTRIES LLC p 1491
401 Nw Atlantic St, Tullahoma TN 37388
Tel (931) 455-1314 *SIC* 2311 2339 2326

SHORT BARK INDUSTRIES INC p 1318
139 Grand Vis, Vonore TN 37885
Tel (423) 884-2010 *SIC* 2311

TEXAS CLOTHING HOLDING CORP p 1442
11511 Luna Rd, Dallas TX 75234
Tel (214) 956-4494
SIC 2325 2311 2321 5611

READYONE INDUSTRIES INC p 1213
1414 Ability Dr, El Paso TX 79936
Tel (915) 858-7277 *SIC* 2331 2311

HAGGAR CLOTHING CO p 653
1507 Lbj Fwy Ste 100, Farmers Branch TX 75234
Tel (214) 352-8481
SIC 2325 2311 2321 5611 5651

HAGGAR CORP p 653
1507 Lyndon B Johnson Fwy, Farmers Branch TX 75234
Tel (214) 352-8481
SIC 2325 2311 2321 5611 6794

SIC 2321 Men's & Boys' Shirts

■ **VANS INC** p 1544
6550 Katella Ave, Cypress CA 90630
Tel (714) 889-6100
SIC 3021 2321 2329 2325 2353 2393

ASICS AMERICA CORP p 117
80 Technology Dr, Irvine CA 92618
Tel (949) 453-8888
SIC 5139 5136 5137 2369 2339 2321

LEVI STRAUSS & CO p 858
1155 Battery St, San Francisco CA 94111
Tel (415) 501-6000
SIC 2325 2339 2321 2331 2337 2329

▲ **PERRY ELLIS INTERNATIONAL INC** p 1137
3000 Nw 107th Ave, Doral FL 33172
Tel (305) 592-2830
SIC 2321 2325 2339 2337 5611 5621

▲ **OXFORD INDUSTRIES INC** p 1101
999 Peachtree St Ne # 688, Atlanta GA 30309
Tel (404) 659-2424 *SIC* 2321 2325 2311

TAG HOLDINGS INC p 1421
6901 Riverport Dr Ste B, Louisville KY 40258
Tel (214) 469-3300 *SIC* 2321 2339 2369

GOLDEN MANUFACTURING CO INC p 621
125 Highway 366, Golden MS 38847
Tel (662) 454-3428
SIC 2311 2325 2321 2326

ELDER MANUFACTURING CO INC p 484
999 Executive Parkway Dr # 300, Saint Louis MO 63141
Tel (314) 469-1120 *SIC* 2321 2361 2253

TIMBERLAND LLC p 1454
200 Domain Dr, Stratham NH 03885
Tel (603) 772-9500
SIC 3143 3144 2386 2329 2321 2325

CENTRAL MILLS INC p 279
473 Ridge Rd, Dayton NJ 08810
Tel (732) 329-0032
SIC 2329 2339 2369 2322 2341 2321

CAPITAL-MERCURY APPAREL LTD p 250
1385 Broadway Rm 1800, New York NY 10018
Tel (212) 704-4800 *SIC* 2321 2331

DONNA KARAN INTERNATIONAL INC p 450
240 W 40th St, New York NY 10018
Tel (212) 789-1500
SIC 2335 2337 2331 2339 2321 2325

■ **GARAN INC** p 591
200 Madison Ave Fl 4, New York NY 10016
Tel (212) 563-1292
SIC 2361 2369 2331 2339 2321

JORDACHE ENTERPRISES INC p 793
1400 Broadway Rm 1404b, New York NY 10018
Tel (212) 643-8400
SIC 2339 2325 2369 2331 2321 2361

▲ **PVH CORP** p 1193
200 Madison Ave Bsmt 1, New York NY 10016
Tel (212) 381-3500
SIC 2321 2331 2253 3143 5621 5611

▲ **RALPH LAUREN CORP** p 1206
650 Madison Ave Fl C1, New York NY 10022
Tel (212) 318-7000
SIC 2325 2321 2253 2323 2311 2329

■ **WARNACO INC** p 1576
501 Fashion Ave Fl 14, New York NY 10018
Tel (212) 287-8000
SIC 2342 2341 2321 2329 2322 2323

■ **FUN-TEES INC** p 585
4735 Corp Dr Nw Ste 100, Concord NC 28027
Tel (704) 788-3003 *SIC* 2321 2361 2331

■ **MJ SOFFE LLC** p 978
1 Soffe Dr, Fayetteville NC 28312
Tel (910) 435-3138
SIC 2339 2329 2369 2321

▲ **VF CORP** p 1553
105 Corp Ctr Blvd, Greensboro NC 27408
Tel (336) 424-6000
SIC 2325 2321 2329 2339 2331 2369

F&T APPAREL LLC p 522
4000 Chemical Rd Ste 500, Plymouth Meeting PA 19462
Tel (610) 828-8400 *SIC* 2311 2321 2325

▲ **DELTA APPAREL INC** p 426
322 S Main St, Greenville SC 29601
Tel (864) 232-5200
SIC 2321 2369 2339 2253

TOM JAMES CO p 1459
263 Seaboard Ln, Franklin TN 37067
Tel (615) 771-6633
SIC 2311 2325 2323 2321 5611

TEXAS CLOTHING HOLDING CORP p 1442
11511 Luna Rd, Dallas TX 75234
Tel (214) 956-4494
SIC 2325 2311 2321 5611

HAGGAR CLOTHING CO p 653
1507 Lbj Fwy Ste 100, Farmers Branch TX 75234
Tel (214) 352-8481
SIC 2325 2311 2321 5611 5651

HAGGAR CORP p 653
1507 Lyndon B Johnson Fwy, Farmers Branch TX 75234
Tel (214) 352-8481
SIC 2325 2311 2321 5611 6794

APPAREL GROUP LTD p 98
883 Trinity Dr, Lewisville TX 75056
Tel (214) 469-3300 *SIC* 2339 2321

■ **JANSPORT INC** p 777
N850 County Road Cb, Appleton WI 54914
Tel (920) 734-5708
SIC 3949 3161 2339 2329 2321

SIC 2322 Men's & Boys' Underwear & Nightwear

VAL DOR APPAREL LLC p 1538
6820 Lyons Technology Pkw, Coconut Creek FL 33073
Tel (954) 363-7340
SIC 2322 2329 2331 2339 2341

CENTRAL MILLS INC p 279
473 Ridge Rd, Dayton NJ 08810
Tel (732) 329-0032
SIC 2329 2339 2369 2322 2341 2321

■ **WARNACO GROUP INC** p 1576
501 Fashion Ave, New York NY 10018
Tel (212) 287-8000
SIC 2322 2329 2339 2369 2342 2341

■ **WARNACO INC** p 1576
501 Fashion Ave Fl 14, New York NY 10018
Tel (212) 287-8000
SIC 2342 2341 2321 2329 2322 2323

▲ **HANESBRANDS INC** p 657
1000 E Hanes Mill Rd, Winston Salem NC 27105
Tel (336) 519-8080
SIC 2253 2342 2341 2322 2252 2251

ROBINSON MANUFACTURING CO p 1242
798 Market St, Dayton TN 37321
Tel (423) 775-8331 *SIC* 2322 2339 2329

JOCKEY INTERNATIONAL INC p 787
2300 60th St, Kenosha WI 53140
Tel (262) 658-8111 *SIC* 2254 2341 2322

SIC 2323 Men's & Boys' Neckwear

■ **PVH NECKWEAR INC** p 1193
1735 S Santa Fe Ave, Los Angeles CA 90021
Tel (213) 688-7970 *SIC* 2323

▲ **RALPH LAUREN CORP** p 1206
650 Madison Ave Fl C1, New York NY 10022
Tel (212) 318-7000
SIC 2325 2321 2253 2323 2311 2329

RANDA CORP p 1207
417 5th Ave Fl 11, New York NY 10016
Tel (212) 768-8800 *SIC* 2323 2389

■ **WARNACO INC** p 1576
501 Fashion Ave Fl 14, New York NY 10018
Tel (212) 287-8000
SIC 2342 2341 2321 2329 2322 2323

TOM JAMES CO p 1459
263 Seaboard Ln, Franklin TN 37067
Tel (615) 771-6633
SIC 2311 2325 2323 2321 5611

SIC 2325 Men's & Boys' Separate Trousers & Casual Slacks

▲ **DIFFERENTIAL BRANDS GROUP INC** p 438
1231 S Gerhart Ave, Commerce CA 90022
Tel (323) 890-1800
SIC 2337 2339 2311 2325 3111 2387

■ **VANS INC** p 1544
6550 Katella Ave, Cypress CA 90630
Tel (714) 889-6100
SIC 3021 2321 2329 2325 2353 2393

▲ **GUESS INC** p 645
1444 S Alameda St, Los Angeles CA 90021
Tel (213) 765-3100
SIC 2325 2339 5611 5621 5641

LUCKY BRAND DUNGAREES LLC p 884
540 S Santa Fe Ave, Los Angeles CA 90013
Tel (213) 443-5700 *SIC* 2325 2339

TRUE RELIGION APPAREL INC p 1486
1888 Rosecrans Ave # 1000, Manhattan Beach CA 90266
Tel (323) 266-3072 *SIC* 2369 2325 2339

LEVI STRAUSS & CO p 858
1155 Battery St, San Francisco CA 94111
Tel (415) 501-6000
SIC 2325 2339 2321 2331 2337 2329

SEVEN FOR ALL MANKIND LLC p 1309
4440 E 26th St, Vernon CA 90058
Tel (323) 406-5300 *SIC* 2325

▲ **PERRY ELLIS INTERNATIONAL INC** p 1137
3000 Nw 107th Ave, Doral FL 33172
Tel (305) 592-2830
SIC 2321 2325 2339 2337 5611 5621

■ **SUPREME INTERNATIONAL LLC** p 1408
3000 Nw 107th Ave, Doral FL 33172
Tel (305) 592-2830 *SIC* 2325

ISLAND APPAREL p 766
135 Renfrew Dr, Athens GA 30606
Tel (706) 548-3420 *SIC* 2325

▲ **OXFORD INDUSTRIES INC** p 1101
999 Peachtree St Ne # 688, Atlanta GA 30309
Tel (404) 659-2424 *SIC* 2321 2325 2311

■ **LEE JEANS CO INC** p 851
9001 W 67th St, Merriam KS 66202
Tel (913) 384-4000 *SIC* 2325 2339 2369

■ **LEE APPAREL CO INC** p 851
1 Lee Dr, Shawnee Mission KS 66202
Tel (913) 789-0330 *SIC* 2325 2339

FLYNN ENTERPRISES LLC p 562
2203 S Walnut St, Hopkinsville KY 42240
Tel (270) 886-0223 *SIC* 2325 2339 2337

CARHARTT INC p 255
5750 Mercury Dr, Dearborn MI 48126
Tel (313) 271-8460 *SIC* 2326 2329 2325

GOLDEN MANUFACTURING CO INC p 621
125 Highway 366, Golden MS 38847
Tel (662) 454-3428
SIC 2311 2325 2321 2326

TIMBERLAND LLC p 1454
200 Domain Dr, Stratham NH 03885
Tel (603) 772-9500
SIC 3143 3144 2386 2329 2321 2325

DONNA KARAN CO LLC p 450
240 W 40th St, New York NY 10018
Tel (212) 789-1500
SIC 2335 2337 2331 2339 2311 2325

DONNA KARAN INTERNATIONAL INC p 450
240 W 40th St, New York NY 10018
Tel (212) 789-1500
SIC 2335 2337 2331 2339 2321 2325

HUGO BOSS USA INC p 717
55 Water St Fl 48, New York NY 10041
Tel (212) 940-0600
SIC 2311 2325 2337 5136 5611 6794

JORDACHE ENTERPRISES INC p 793
1400 Broadway Rm 1404b, New York NY 10018
Tel (212) 643-8400
SIC 2339 2325 2369 2331 2321 2361

KALTEX AMERICA INC p 801
350 5th Ave Ste 7100, New York NY 10118
Tel (212) 971-0575 *SIC* 2339 2325

▲ **RALPH LAUREN CORP** p 1206
650 Madison Ave Fl C1, New York NY 10022
Tel (212) 318-7000
SIC 2325 2321 2253 2323 2311 2329

XMH-HFI INC p 1632
1155 N Clinton Ave, Rochester NY 14621
Tel (585) 467-7240 *SIC* 2311 2325

▲ **VF CORP** p 1553
105 Corp Ctr Blvd, Greensboro NC 27408
Tel (336) 424-6000
SIC 2325 2321 2329 2339 2331 2369

■VF JEANSWEAR LIMITED PARTNERSHIP p 1553
400 N Elm St, Greensboro NC 27401
Tel (336) 332-3400
SIC 2325 2339 2331 2329

APPAREL BRANDS INC p 98
434 Carolina Way, Highlands NC 28741
Tel (828) 526-0167 *SIC* 2325 2337 8721

F&T APPAREL LLC p 522
4000 Chemical Rd Ste 500, Plymouth Meeting PA 19462
Tel (610) 828-8400 *SIC* 2311 2321 2325

BLUEWATER DEFENSE INC p 193
Corozal Ind Pk Carr 159, Corozal PR 00783
Tel (787) 746-5020
SIC 2393 2326 3842 2325

GALEY & LORD LLC p 589
670 N Main St, Society Hill SC 29593
Tel (843) 378-4511
SIC 2211 2221 2325 2339

TOM JAMES CO p 1459
263 Seaboard Ln, Franklin TN 37067
Tel (615) 771-6633
SIC 2311 2325 2323 2321 5611

TEXAS CLOTHING HOLDING CORP p 1442
11511 Luna Rd, Dallas TX 75234
Tel (214) 956-4494
SIC 2325 2311 2321 5611

HAGGAR CLOTHING CO p 653
1507 Lbj Fwy Ste 100, Farmers Branch TX 75234
Tel (214) 352-8481
SIC 2325 2311 2321 5611 5651

HAGGAR CORP p 653
1507 Lyndon B Johnson Fwy, Farmers Branch TX 75234
Tel (214) 352-8481
SIC 2325 2311 2321 5611 6794

SIC 2326 Men's & Boys' Work Clothing

HOT TOPIC INC p 710
18305 San Jose Ave, City Of Industry CA 91748
Tel (626) 839-4681 *SIC* 2326 5632 5699

DOWLING TEXTILE CO p 453
615 Macon Rd, Mcdonough GA 30253
Tel (770) 957-3981 *SIC* 2326 2337 2389

ENCOMPASS GROUP LLC p 495
615 Macon St, Mcdonough GA 30253
Tel (770) 957-3981 *SIC* 2326 2337 2389

W DIAMOND GROUP CORP p 1568
1680 E Touhy Ave, Des Plaines IL 60018
Tel (646) 647-2791 *SIC* 2326 5611

MAGID GLOVE & SAFETY MANUFACTURING CO LLC p 895
1300 Naperville Dr, Romeoville IL 60446
Tel (773) 384-2070
SIC 3151 2381 5699 3842 2326

▲ UNIFIRST CORP p 1503
68 Jonspin Rd, Wilmington MA 01887
Tel (978) 658-8888 *SIC* 7218 2326

CARHARTT INC p 255
5750 Mercury Dr, Dearborn MI 48126
Tel (313) 271-8460 *SIC* 2326 2329 2325

PECKHAM VOCATIONAL INDUSTRIES INC p 1126
3510 Capitol City Blvd, Lansing MI 48906
Tel (517) 316-4000
SIC 8331 2396 2311 2331 2339 2326

GOLDEN MANUFACTURING CO INC p 621
125 Highway 366, Golden MS 38847
Tel (662) 454-3428
SIC 2311 2325 2321 2326

LANDAU UNIFORMS INC p 842
8410 W Sandidge Rd, Olive Branch MS 38654
Tel (662) 895-7200 *SIC* 2326 2337 2339

AEGIS CORP p 29
614 Dartmouth Terrace Ct, Ballwin MO 63011
Tel (636) 273-1011
SIC 3699 4812 3812 3444 2326

PII INC p 1147
17 Research Park Dr # 100, Weldon Spring MO 63304
Tel (636) 685-1047 *SIC* 2311 2326

ANSELL HEALTHCARE PRODUCTS LLC p 93
111 Wood Ave S Ste 210, Iselin NJ 08830
Tel (732) 345-5400
SIC 3069 3842 2822 2326

BILLION TOWER INTL LLC p 182
989 6th Ave Fl 8, New York NY 10018
Tel (212) 220-0608 *SIC* 2326 5136

▲ CINTAS CORP p 308
6800 Cintas Blvd, Cincinnati OH 45262
Tel (513) 459-1200
SIC 7218 2337 2326 5084

STANDARD TEXTILE CO INC p 1376
1 Knollcrest Dr, Cincinnati OH 45237
Tel (513) 761-9255
SIC 2389 2326 2337 2211 2391 5136

■ MORNING PRIDE MFG LLC p 989
1 Innovation Ct, Dayton OH 45414
Tel (937) 264-2662 *SIC* 3842 2326

TRANZONIC COMPANIES p 1473
26301 Curtiss Wright Pkwy # 200, Richmond Heights OH 44143
Tel (216) 535-4300
SIC 2676 2211 2326 2842 2273 2262

TZ ACQUISITION CORP p 1496
26301 Curtiss Wright Pkwy, Richmond Heights OH 44143
Tel (216) 535-4300
SIC 2676 2211 2326 2842 2262

PROPPER INTERNATIONAL INC p 1184
308 Km 0 6 375 Clljon Fas, Cabo Rojo PR 00623
Tel (787) 254-8020 *SIC* 2311 2326

BLUEWATER DEFENSE INC p 193
Corozal Ind Pk Carr 159, Corozal PR 00783
Tel (787) 746-5020
SIC 2393 2326 3842 2325

■VF IMAGEWEAR INC p 1553
545 Marriott Dr Ste 200, Nashville TN 37214
Tel (615) 565-5000
SIC 2326 5099 2339 2311

TULLAHOMA INDUSTRIES LLC p 1491
401 Nw Atlantic St, Tullahoma TN 37388
Tel (931) 455-1314 *SIC* 2311 2339 2326

BORDER APPAREL LAUNDRY LTD p 201
6969 Industrial Ave, El Paso TX 79915
Tel (915) 772-7170 *SIC* 2326 7211

WILLIAMSON-DICKIE MANUFACTURING CO p 1612
509 W Vickery Blvd, Fort Worth TX 76104
Tel (817) 336-7201 *SIC* 2326 2339

MOOR INNOVATIVE TECHNOLOGIES LLC p 987
4812 64th St E, Tacoma WA 98443
Tel (253) 343-2216 *SIC* 2326

SIC 2329 Men's & Boys' Clothing, NEC

ANTIGUA ENTERPRISES INC p 94
16651 N 84th Ave, Peoria AZ 85382
Tel (623) 523-6000 *SIC* 2329

■VF OUTDOOR LLC p 1553
2701 Harbor Bay Pkwy, Alameda CA 94502
Tel (510) 618-3500
SIC 2329 2339 3949 2394 2399 5941

A AND G INC p 4
1501 E Cerritos Ave, Anaheim CA 92805
Tel (714) 765-0400 *SIC* 2329 2253

▲ CALLAWAY GOLF CO p 242
2180 Rutherford Rd, Carlsbad CA 92008
Tel (760) 931-1771
SIC 3949 2329 2339 6794

STRATEGIC PARTNERS INC p 1392
9800 De Soto Ave, Chatsworth CA 91311
Tel (818) 671-2100
SIC 3143 3144 5139 2339 2389 2329

■ HURLEY INTERNATIONAL LLC p 721
1945 Placentia Ave, Costa Mesa CA 92627
Tel (949) 548-9375 *SIC* 2329 5137

■VANS INC p 1544
6550 Katella Ave, Cypress CA 90630
Tel (714) 889-6100
SIC 3021 2321 2329 2325 2353 2393

■ QUIKSILVER INC p 1200
5600 Argosy Ave Ste 100, Huntington Beach CA 92649
Tel (714) 889-2200
SIC 2329 2339 3949 5136 5137

BURLEIGH POINT LTD p 227
117 Waterworks Way, Irvine CA 92618
Tel (949) 428-3200 *SIC* 2339 2331 2329

■ MARMOT MOUNTAIN LLC p 909
5789 State Farm Dr # 100, Rohnert Park CA 94928
Tel (707) 544-4590 *SIC* 2329

LEVI STRAUSS & CO p 858
1155 Battery St, San Francisco CA 94111
Tel (415) 501-6000
SIC 2325 2339 2321 2331 2337 2329

PATAGONIA INC p 1120
259 W Santa Clara St, Ventura CA 93001
Tel (805) 643-8616 *SIC* 2329 2339

PATAGONIA WORKS p 1120
259 W Santa Clara St, Ventura CA 93001
Tel (805) 643-8616
SIC 5699 2339 2329 5961

■ OUTDOOR SPORTS GEAR INC p 1098
2320 Cousteau Ct Ste 100, Vista CA 92081
Tel (914) 967-9400
SIC 3949 3069 2339 2329

VAL DOR APPAREL LLC p 1538
6820 Lyons Technology Pkw, Coconut Creek FL 33073
Tel (954) 363-7340
SIC 2322 2329 2331 2339 2341

AUGUSTA SPORTSWEAR INC p 131
425 Park 20 W, Grovetown GA 30813
Tel (706) 860-4633
SIC 2329 2339 2393 2399

■ RUSSELL BRANDS LLC p 1259
1 Fruit Of The Loom Dr, Bowling Green KY 42103
Tel (270) 781-6400
SIC 2253 2211 2329 2339 3949 5091

▲ UNDER ARMOUR INC p 1502
1020 Hull St Ste 300, Baltimore MD 21230
Tel (410) 454-6428
SIC 2329 2353 2339 3021

REEBOK INTERNATIONAL LTD p 1217
1895 J W Foster Blvd, Canton MA 02021
Tel (781) 401-5000
SIC 3149 3143 3144 2329 2339 5661

SPORTS LICENSED DIVISION OF ADIDAS GROUP LLC p 1360
1895 J W Foster Blvd, Canton MA 02021
Tel (781) 401-5000 *SIC* 2329

GOLDEN FLEECE MANUFACTURING GROUP LLC p 620
25 Computer Dr, Haverhill MA 01832
Tel (978) 738-0855 *SIC* 2329

CARHARTT INC p 255
5750 Mercury Dr, Dearborn MI 48126
Tel (313) 271-8460 *SIC* 2326 2329 2325

▲ ARCTIC CAT INC p 106
500 N 3rd St, Minneapolis MN 55401
Tel (763) 354-1800
SIC 3799 2329 2339 3732

TIMBERLAND LLC p 1454
200 Domain Dr, Stratham NH 03885
Tel (603) 772-9500
SIC 3143 3144 2386 2329 2321 2325

CENTRAL MILLS INC p 279
473 Ridge Rd, Dayton NJ 08810
Tel (732) 329-0032
SIC 2329 2339 2369 2322 2341 2321

■VF SPORTSWEAR INC p 1553
545 Wshngton Blvd Fl 8, Jersey City NJ 07310
Tel (212) 541-5757
SIC 2329 2384 5136 5137 5611 6794

DAVID PEYSER SPORTSWEAR INC p 415
88 Spence St, Bay Shore NY 11706
Tel (631) 231-7788 *SIC* 2329

▲ G-III APPAREL GROUP LTD p 588
512 7th Ave Fl 35, New York NY 10018
Tel (212) 403-0500
SIC 2337 2339 2311 2329 2386 5136

MEE APPAREL LLC p 939
501 10th Ave Fl 7, New York NY 10018
Tel (917) 262-1000 *SIC* 2329

▲ RALPH LAUREN CORP p 1206
650 Madison Ave Fl C1, New York NY 10022
Tel (212) 318-7000
SIC 2325 2321 2253 2323 2311 2329

■WARNACO GROUP INC p 1576
501 Fashion Ave, New York NY 10018
Tel (212) 287-8000
SIC 2322 2329 2339 2369 2342 2341

■WARNACO INC p 1576
501 Fashion Ave Fl 14, New York NY 10018
Tel (212) 287-8000
SIC 2342 2341 2321 2329 2322 2323

■ MJ SOFFE LLC p 978
1 Soffe Dr, Fayetteville NC 28312
Tel (910) 435-3138
SIC 2339 2329 2369 2321

▲VF CORP p 1553
105 Corp Ctr Blvd, Greensboro NC 27408
Tel (336) 424-6000
SIC 2325 2321 2329 2339 2331 2369

■VF JEANSWEAR LIMITED PARTNERSHIP p 1553
400 N Elm St, Greensboro NC 27401
Tel (336) 332-3400
SIC 2325 2339 2331 2329

▲ ROCKY BRANDS INC p 1245
39 E Canal St, Nelsonville OH 45764
Tel (740) 753-1951
SIC 3143 3144 2329 2331 2339 2389

HOLLOWAY SPORTSWEAR INC p 701
2633 Campbell Rd, Sidney OH 45365
Tel (937) 497-7575 *SIC* 2329 2339 2392

▲ NIKE INC p 1043
1 Sw Bowerman Dr, Beaverton OR 97005
Tel (503) 671-6453
SIC 3021 2329 2339 5139 5661 5136

ADIDAS NORTH AMERICA INC p 22
5055 N Greeley Ave, Portland OR 97217
Tel (971) 234-2300 *SIC* 2329

▲ COLUMBIA SPORTSWEAR CO p 341
14375 Nw Science Park Dr, Portland OR 97229
Tel (503) 985-4000
SIC 2329 2339 3021 2353 3949

■ COLUMBIA SPORTSWEAR USA CORP p 341
14375 Nw Science Park Dr, Portland OR 97229
Tel (503) 985-4000
SIC 5137 5136 2329 2339 3021 2353

CYCLING SPORTS GROUP INC p 405
16 Trowbridge Dr, Bedford PA 15522
Tel (203) 749-7000 *SIC* 3751 2329

▲ HAMPSHIRE GROUP LIMITED p 656
1924 Pearman Dairy Rd A, Anderson SC 29625
Tel (212) 540-5666 *SIC* 2339 2329 2253

ROBINSON MANUFACTURING CO p 1242
798 Market St, Dayton TN 37321
Tel (423) 775-8331 *SIC* 2322 2339 2329

▲ ENNIS INC p 500
2441 Presidential Pkwy, Midlothian TX 76065
Tel (972) 775-9801
SIC 2761 2759 2331 2329

▲ DIAMOND BLACK INC p 436
2084 E 3900 S, Salt Lake City UT 84124
Tel (801) 278-5552 *SIC* 3949 2329 2339

RECREATIONAL EQUIPMENT INC p 1215
6750 S 228th St, Kent WA 98032
Tel (253) 395-3780
SIC 2329 3949 2399 5941 5961 5699

HELLY HANSEN (US) INC p 682
14218 Stewart Rd Ste 100a, Sumner WA 98390
Tel (800) 435-5901
SIC 5137 5699 2339 2329

■ JANSPORT INC p 777
N850 County Road Cb, Appleton WI 54914
Tel (920) 734-5708
SIC 3949 3161 2339 2329 2321

SIC 2331 Women's & Misses' Blouses

▲ BEBE STORES INC p 167
400 Valley Dr, Brisbane CA 94005
Tel (415) 715-3900 *SIC* 2331

OAKLEY INC p 1071
1 Icon, Foothill Ranch CA 92610
Tel (949) 951-0991
SIC 3851 2331 2339 3021 3873 3143

BURLEIGH POINT LTD p 227
117 Waterworks Way, Irvine CA 92618
Tel (949) 428-3200 *SIC* 2339 2331 2329

AMERICAN APPAREL LLC p 68
747 Warehouse St, Los Angeles CA 90021
Tel (213) 488-0226 *SIC* 2389 2311 2331

SUNRISE BRANDS LLC p 1403
801 S Figueroa St # 2500, Los Angeles CA 90017
Tel (323) 780-8250
SIC 2339 2331 2335 2337

ALL ACCESS APPAREL INC p 50
1515 Gage Rd, Montebello CA 90640
Tel (323) 889-4300 *SIC* 2331 2361 2335

BYER CALIFORNIA p 231
66 Potrero Ave, San Francisco CA 94103
Tel (415) 626-7844 *SIC* 2331

LEVI STRAUSS & CO p 858
1155 Battery St, San Francisco CA 94111
Tel (415) 501-6000
SIC 2325 2339 2321 2331 2337 2329

FYC APPAREL GROUP LLC p 586
30 Thompson Rd, Branford CT 06405
Tel (203) 481-2420
SIC 2331 2335 2337 5651

VAL DOR APPAREL LLC p 1538
6820 Lyons Technology Pkw, Coconut Creek FL 33073
Tel (954) 363-7340
SIC 2322 2329 2331 2339 2341

PECKHAM VOCATIONAL INDUSTRIES INC p 1126
3510 Capitol City Blvd, Lansing MI 48906
Tel (517) 316-4000
SIC 8331 2396 2311 2331 2339 2326

ELIE TAHARI LTD p 487
16 Bleeker St, Millburn NJ 07041
Tel (973) 671-6300
SIC 2331 2339 2335 2337 5621 5611

ALFRED DUNNER INC p 49
1411 Broadway Fl 24, New York NY 10018
Tel (212) 478-4300 *SIC* 2337 2331 2339

CAPITAL-MERCURY APPAREL LTD p 250
1385 Broadway Rm 1800, New York NY 10018
Tel (212) 704-4800 *SIC* 2321 2331

DONNA KARAN CO LLC p 450
240 W 40th St, New York NY 10018
Tel (212) 789-1500
SIC 2335 2337 2331 2339 2311 2325

DONNA KARAN INTERNATIONAL INC p 450
240 W 40th St, New York NY 10018
Tel (212) 789-1500
SIC 2335 2337 2331 2339 2321 2325

■ GARAN INC p 591
200 Madison Ave Fl 4, New York NY 10016
Tel (212) 563-1292
SIC 2361 2369 2331 2339 2321

GCE INTERNATIONAL INC p 595
1385 Broadway Fl 21, New York NY 10018
Tel (212) 704-4800
SIC 2253 2389 2331 5137 5136

GILDAN APPAREL USA INC p 612
48 W 38th St Fl 8, New York NY 10018
Tel (212) 476-0341 *SIC* 2253 2331

JEANJER LLC p 781
1400 Broadway Fl 15, New York NY 10018
Tel (212) 944-1330
SIC 2331 2337 2339 2369

JORDACHE ENTERPRISES INC p 793
1400 Broadway Rm 1404b, New York NY 10018
Tel (212) 643-8400
SIC 2339 2325 2369 2331 2321 2361

▲ KATE SPADE & CO p 804
2 Park Ave Fl 8, New York NY 10016
Tel (212) 354-4900
SIC 2331 5651 5136 5137 5961

▲ PVH CORP p 1193
200 Madison Ave Bsmt 1, New York NY 10016
Tel (212) 381-3500
SIC 2321 2331 2253 3143 5621 5611

TRIUMPH APPAREL CORP p 1483
530 Fashion Ave Ste M1, New York NY 10018
Tel (212) 302-2606 *SIC* 2331

TURN ON PRODUCTS INC p 1492
270 W 38th St Rm 1200, New York NY 10018
Tel (212) 764-2121 *SIC* 2339 2331

■ FUN-TEES INC p 585
4735 Corp Dr Nw Ste 100, Concord NC 28027
Tel (704) 788-3003 *SIC* 2321 2361 2331

▲VF CORP p 1553
105 Corp Ctr Blvd, Greensboro NC 27408
Tel (336) 424-6000
SIC 2325 2321 2329 2339 2331 2369

■VF JEANSWEAR LIMITED PARTNERSHIP p 1553
400 N Elm St, Greensboro NC 27401
Tel (336) 332-3400
SIC 2325 2339 2331 2329

WORTH BON INC p 1626
40 Francis Rd, Hendersonville NC 28792
Tel (828) 697-2216
SIC 2331 5621 2339 2335 2337 8741

▲ ROCKY BRANDS INC p 1245
39 E Canal St, Nelsonville OH 45764
Tel (740) 753-1951
SIC 3143 3144 2329 2331 2339 2389

HAMRICKS INC p 656
742 Peachoid Rd, Gaffney SC 29341
Tel (864) 489-6095
SIC 5651 2337 2331 2335 2339 5087

READYONE INDUSTRIES INC p 1213
1414 Ability Dr, El Paso TX 79936
Tel (915) 858-7277 *SIC* 2331 2311

▲ ENNIS INC p 500
2441 Presidential Pkwy, Midlothian TX 76065
Tel (972) 775-9801
SIC 2761 2759 2331 2329

SIC 2335 Women's & Misses' Dresses

GRAY VESTAR INVESTORS LLC p 632
17622 Armstrong Ave, Irvine CA 92614
Tel (949) 863-1171
SIC 2253 2339 2335 2337 3961 2387

SUNRISE BRANDS LLC p 1403
801 S Figueroa St # 2500, Los Angeles CA 90017
Tel (323) 780-8250
SIC 2339 2331 2335 2337

ALL ACCESS APPAREL INC p 50
1515 Gage Rd, Montebello CA 90640
Tel (323) 889-4300 *SIC* 2331 2361 2335

JESSICA MCCLINTOCK INC p 783
2307 Broadway St, San Francisco CA 94115
Tel (415) 553-8200 *SIC* 2361 2335 2844

BCBG MAX AZRIA GROUP LLC p 163
2761 Fruitland Ave, Vernon CA 90058
Tel (323) 589-2224 *SIC* 5137 5621 2335

FYC APPAREL GROUP LLC p 586
30 Thompson Rd, Branford CT 06405
Tel (203) 481-2420
SIC 2331 2335 2337 5651

ELIE TAHARI LTD p 487
16 Bleeker St, Millburn NJ 07041
Tel (973) 671-6300
SIC 2331 2339 2335 2337 5621 5611

DONNA KARAN CO LLC p 450
240 W 40th St, New York NY 10018
Tel (212) 789-1500
SIC 2335 2337 2331 2339 2311 2325

DONNA KARAN INTERNATIONAL INC p 450
240 W 40th St, New York NY 10018
Tel (212) 789-1500
SIC 2335 2337 2331 2339 2321 2325

KASPER GROUP LLC p 804
1412 Broadway Fl 5, New York NY 10018
Tel (212) 354-4311 SIC 2335

WORTH BON INC p 1626
40 Francis Rd, Hendersonville NC 28792
Tel (828) 697-2216
SIC 2331 5621 2339 2335 2337 8741

HAMRICKS INC p 656
742 Peachoid Rd, Gaffney SC 29341
Tel (864) 489-6095
SIC 5651 2337 2331 2335 2339 5087

SIC 2337 Women's & Misses' Suits, Coats & Skirts

▲ DIFFERENTIAL BRANDS GROUP INC p 438
1231 S Gerhart Ave, Commerce CA 90022
Tel (323) 890-1800
SIC 2337 2339 2311 2325 3111 2387

GRAY VESTAR INVESTORS LLC p 632
17622 Armstrong Ave, Irvine CA 92614
Tel (949) 863-1171
SIC 2253 2339 2335 2337 3961 2387

SUNRISE BRANDS LLC p 1403
801 S Figueroa St # 2500, Los Angeles CA 90017
Tel (323) 780-8250
SIC 2339 2331 2335 2337

LEVI STRAUSS & CO p 858
1155 Battery St, San Francisco CA 94111
Tel (415) 501-6000
SIC 2325 2339 2321 2331 2337 2329

JAYA APPAREL GROUP LLC p 779
5175 S Soto St, Vernon CA 90058
Tel (323) 584-3500 SIC 2339 2337

FYC APPAREL GROUP LLC p 586
30 Thompson Rd, Branford CT 06405
Tel (203) 481-2420
SIC 2331 2335 2337 5651

▲ PERRY ELLIS INTERNATIONAL INC p 1137
3000 Nw 107th Ave, Doral FL 33172
Tel (305) 592-2830
SIC 2321 2325 2339 2337 5611 5621

DOWLING TEXTILE CO p 453
615 Macon Rd, Mcdonough GA 30253
Tel (770) 957-3981 SIC 2326 2337 2389

ENCOMPASS GROUP LLC p 495
615 Macon St, Mcdonough GA 30253
Tel (770) 957-3981 SIC 2326 2337 2389

FLYNN ENTERPRISES LLC p 562
2203 S Walnut St, Hopkinsville KY 42240
Tel (270) 886-0223 SIC 2325 2339 2337

BLAUER MANUFACTURING CO INC p 189
20 Aberdeen St, Boston MA 02215
Tel (617) 536-6606 SIC 5099 3842 2337

LANDAU UNIFORMS INC p 842
8410 W Sandidge Rd, Olive Branch MS 38654
Tel (662) 895-7200 SIC 2326 2337 2339

ELIE TAHARI LTD p 487
16 Bleeker St, Millburn NJ 07041
Tel (973) 671-6300
SIC 2331 2339 2335 2337 5621 5611

ALFRED DUNNER INC p 49
1411 Broadway Fl 24, New York NY 10018
Tel (212) 478-4300 SIC 2337 2331 2339

DONNA KARAN CO LLC p 450
240 W 40th St, New York NY 10018
Tel (212) 789-1500
SIC 2335 2337 2331 2339 2311 2325

DONNA KARAN INTERNATIONAL INC p 450
240 W 40th St, New York NY 10018
Tel (212) 789-1500
SIC 2335 2337 2331 2339 2321 2325

EXCELLED SHEEPSKIN & LEATHER COAT CORP p 516
1400 Brdwy Fl 31, New York NY 10018
Tel (212) 594-5843
SIC 2386 3172 2337 2311

▲ G-III APPAREL GROUP LTD p 588
512 7th Ave Fl 35, New York NY 10018
Tel (212) 403-0500
SIC 2337 2339 2311 2329 2386 5136

HUGO BOSS USA INC p 717
55 Water St Fl 48, New York NY 10041
Tel (212) 940-0600
SIC 2311 2325 2337 5136 5611 6794

JEANJER LLC p 781
1400 Broadway Fl 15, New York NY 10018
Tel (212) 944-1330
SIC 2331 2337 2339 2369

LEVY GROUP INC p 858
1333 Broadway Fl 9, New York NY 10018
Tel (212) 398-0707 SIC 2337 2385

WORTH BON INC p 1626
40 Francis Rd, Hendersonville NC 28792
Tel (828) 697-2216
SIC 2331 5621 2339 2335 2337 8741

APPAREL BRANDS INC p 98
434 Carolina Way, Highlands NC 28741
Tel (828) 526-0167 SIC 2325 2337 8721

■ FECHHEIMER BROTHERS CO p 533
4545 Malsbary Rd, Blue Ash OH 45242
Tel (513) 793-7819
SIC 2311 2337 2339 5699

▲ CINTAS CORP p 308
6800 Cintas Blvd, Cincinnati OH 45262
Tel (513) 459-1200
SIC 7218 2337 2326 5084

STANDARD TEXTILE CO INC p 1376
1 Knollcrest Dr, Cincinnati OH 45237
Tel (513) 761-9255
SIC 2389 2326 2337 2211 2391 5136

PENDLETON WOOLEN MILLS INC p 1128
220 Nw Broadway, Portland OR 97209
Tel (503) 226-4801 SIC 2337

KASPER ASL LTD p 804
180 Rittenhouse Cir, Bristol PA 19007
Tel (215) 785-4000 SIC 2337

NINE WEST HOLDINGS INC p 1044
180 Rittenhouse Cir, Bristol PA 19007
Tel (215) 785-4000 SIC 2337

■ ARAMARK UNIFORM & CAREER APPAREL GROUP INC p 102
1101 Market St Ste 45, Philadelphia PA 19107
Tel (215) 238-3000
SIC 2337 2311 5699 5961 5661 5812

HAMRICKS INC p 656
742 Peachoid Rd, Gaffney SC 29341
Tel (864) 489-6095
SIC 5651 2337 2331 2335 2339 5087

SIC 2339 Women's & Misses' Outerwear, NEC

ANTIGUA GROUP INC p 94
16651 N 84th Ave, Peoria AZ 85382
Tel (623) 523-6000
SIC 5137 5136 2395 2339 3993

■ VF OUTDOOR LLC p 1553
2701 Harbor Bay Pkwy, Alameda CA 94502
Tel (510) 618-3500
SIC 2329 2339 3949 2394 2399 5941

MARIKA LLC p 906
5553-B Bandini Blvd, Bell CA 90201
Tel (323) 888-7755 SIC 2339

▲ CALLAWAY GOLF CO p 242
2180 Rutherford Rd, Carlsbad CA 92008
Tel (760) 931-1771
SIC 3949 2329 2339 6794

STRATEGIC PARTNERS INC p 1392
9800 De Soto Ave, Chatsworth CA 91311
Tel (818) 671-2100
SIC 3143 3144 5139 2339 2389 2329

▲ DIFFERENTIAL BRANDS GROUP INC p 438
1231 S Gerhart Ave, Commerce CA 90022
Tel (323) 890-1800
SIC 2337 2339 2311 2325 3111 2387

MANHATTAN BEACHWEAR INC p 901
10700 Valley View St, Cypress CA 90630
Tel (714) 892-7354 SIC 2339

OAKLEY INC p 1071
1 Icon, Foothill Ranch CA 92610
Tel (949) 951-0991
SIC 3851 2331 2339 3021 3873 3143

▲ DECKERS OUTDOOR CORP p 421
250 Coromar Dr, Goleta CA 93117
Tel (805) 967-7611 SIC 3021 2389 2339

■ QUIKSILVER INC p 1200
5600 Argosy Ave Ste 100, Huntington Beach CA 92649
Tel (714) 889-2200
SIC 2329 2339 3949 5136 5137

CITIZENS OF HUMANITY LLC p 311
5715 Bickett St, Huntington Park CA 90255
Tel (323) 923-1240 SIC 2339

ASICS AMERICA CORP p 117
80 Technology Dr, Irvine CA 92618
Tel (949) 453-8888
SIC 5139 5136 5137 2369 2339 2321

BURLEIGH POINT LTD p 227
117 Waterworks Way, Irvine CA 92618
Tel (949) 428-3200 SIC 2339 2331 2329

GRAY VESTAR INVESTORS LLC p 632
17622 Armstrong Ave, Irvine CA 92614
Tel (949) 863-1171
SIC 2253 2339 2335 2337 3961 2387

ST JOHN KNITS INC p 1367
17522 Armstrong Ave, Irvine CA 92614
Tel (949) 863-1171 SIC 2339 2253 2389

ST JOHN KNITS INTERNATIONAL INC p 1367
17622 Armstrong Ave, Irvine CA 92614
Tel (949) 863-1171 SIC 2339

FOH GROUP INC p 563
6255 W Sunset Blvd # 2212, Los Angeles CA 90028
Tel (323) 466-5151
SIC 2341 2342 2339 5621 5632

▲ GUESS INC p 645
1444 S Alameda St, Los Angeles CA 90021
Tel (213) 765-3100
SIC 2325 2339 5611 5621 5641

LUCKY BRAND DUNGAREES LLC p 884
540 S Santa Fe Ave, Los Angeles CA 90013
Tel (213) 443-5700 SIC 2325 2339

SUNRISE BRANDS LLC p 1403
801 S Figueroa St # 2500, Los Angeles CA 90017
Tel (323) 780-8250
SIC 2339 2331 2335 2337

UNGER FABRIK LLC p 1502
1515 E 15th St, Los Angeles CA 90021
Tel (213) 222-1010 SIC 2339

TRUE RELIGION APPAREL INC p 1486
1888 Rosecrans Ave # 1000, Manhattan Beach CA 90266
Tel (323) 266-3072 SIC 2369 2325 2339

MAX LEON INC p 922
3100 New York Dr, Pasadena CA 91107
Tel (626) 797-6886 SIC 2339 5632

LEVI STRAUSS & CO p 858
1155 Battery St, San Francisco CA 94111
Tel (415) 501-6000
SIC 2325 2339 2321 2331 2337 2329

C P SHADES INC p 233
403 Coloma St, Sausalito CA 94965
Tel (415) 331-4581 SIC 2339 5621

PATAGONIA INC p 1120
259 W Santa Clara St, Ventura CA 93001
Tel (805) 643-8616 SIC 2329 2339

PATAGONIA WORKS p 1120
259 W Santa Clara St, Ventura CA 93001
Tel (805) 643-8616
SIC 5699 2339 2329 5961

JAYA APPAREL GROUP LLC p 779
5175 S Soto St, Vernon CA 90058
Tel (323) 584-3500 SIC 2339 2337

■ OUTDOOR SPORTS GEAR INC p 1098
2320 Cousteau Ct Ste 100, Vista CA 92081
Tel (914) 967-9400
SIC 3949 3069 2339 2329

VAL DOR APPAREL LLC p 1538
6820 Lyons Technology Pkw, Coconut Creek FL 33073
Tel (954) 363-7340
SIC 2322 2329 2331 2339 2341

▲ PERRY ELLIS INTERNATIONAL INC p 1137
3000 Nw 107th Ave, Doral FL 33172
Tel (305) 592-2830
SIC 2321 2325 2339 2337 5611 5621

AUGUSTA SPORTSWEAR INC p 131
425 Park 20 W, Grovetown GA 30813
Tel (706) 860-4633
SIC 2329 2339 2393 2399

■ LEE JEANS CO INC p 851
9001 W 67th St, Merriam KS 66202
Tel (913) 384-4000 SIC 2325 2339 2369

■ LEE APPAREL CO INC p 851
1 Lee Dr, Shawnee Mission KS 66202
Tel (913) 789-0330 SIC 2325 2339

■ RUSSELL BRANDS LLC p 1259
1 Fruit Of The Loom Dr, Bowling Green KY 42103
Tel (270) 781-6400
SIC 2253 2211 2329 2339 3949 5091

FLYNN ENTERPRISES LLC p 562
2203 S Walnut St, Hopkinsville KY 42240
Tel (270) 886-0223 SIC 2325 2339 2337

TAG HOLDINGS INC p 1421
6901 Riverport Dr Ste B, Louisville KY 40258
Tel (214) 469-3300 SIC 2321 2339 2369

▲ UNDER ARMOUR INC p 1502
1020 Hull St Ste 300, Baltimore MD 21230
Tel (410) 454-6428
SIC 2329 2353 2339 3021

REEBOK INTERNATIONAL LTD p 1217
1895 J W Foster Blvd, Canton MA 02021
Tel (781) 401-5000
SIC 3149 3143 3144 2329 2339 5661

PECKHAM VOCATIONAL INDUSTRIES INC p 1126
3510 Capitol City Blvd, Lansing MI 48906
Tel (517) 316-4000
SIC 8331 2396 2311 2331 2339 2326

▲ ARCTIC CAT INC p 106
500 N 3rd St, Minneapolis MN 55401
Tel (763) 354-1800
SIC 3799 2329 2339 3732

LANDAU UNIFORMS INC p 842
8410 W Sandidge Rd, Olive Branch MS 38654
Tel (662) 895-7200 SIC 2326 2337 2339

W G YATES & SONS CONSTRUCTION CO p 1568
1 Gully Ave, Philadelphia MS 39350
Tel (904) 714-1376
SIC 1542 1541 2339 1611 5211 1731

CENTRAL MILLS INC p 279
473 Ridge Rd, Dayton NJ 08810
Tel (732) 329-0032
SIC 2329 2339 2369 2322 2341 2321

ELIE TAHARI LTD p 487
16 Bleeker St, Millburn NJ 07041
Tel (973) 671-6300
SIC 2331 2339 2335 2337 5621 5611

EILEEN FISHER INC p 481
2 Bridge St Ste 230, Irvington NY 10533
Tel (914) 591-5700 SIC 2339

ALFRED DUNNER INC p 49
1411 Broadway Fl 24, New York NY 10018
Tel (212) 478-4300 SIC 2337 2331 2339

COLLECTION XIIX LTD p 336
1370 Broadway Fl 17, New York NY 10018
Tel (212) 686-8990 SIC 2339

DONNA KARAN CO LLC p 450
240 W 40th St, New York NY 10018
Tel (212) 789-1500
SIC 2335 2337 2331 2339 2311 2325

DONNA KARAN INTERNATIONAL INC p 450
240 W 40th St, New York NY 10018
Tel (212) 789-1500
SIC 2335 2337 2331 2339 2321 2325

▲ G-III APPAREL GROUP LTD p 588
512 7th Ave Fl 35, New York NY 10018
Tel (212) 403-0500
SIC 2337 2339 2311 2329 2386 5136

■ GARAN INC p 591
200 Madison Ave Fl 4, New York NY 10016
Tel (212) 563-1292
SIC 2361 2369 2331 2339 2321

GBG WEST LLC p 594
350 5th Ave Fl 5, New York NY 10118
Tel (646) 839-7000 SIC 2339

JACQUES MORET INC p 775
1411 Broadway Fl 8, New York NY 10018
Tel (212) 354-2400 SIC 2339 5137

JEANJER LLC p 781
1400 Broadway Fl 15, New York NY 10018
Tel (212) 944-1330
SIC 2331 2337 2339 2369

JORDACHE ENTERPRISES INC p 793
1400 Broadway Rm 1404b, New York NY 10018
Tel (212) 643-8400
SIC 2339 2325 2369 2331 2321 2361

KALTEX AMERICA INC p 801
350 5th Ave Ste 7100, New York NY 10118
Tel (212) 971-0575 SIC 2339 2325

MERYL DIAMOND LTD p 951
1375 Broadway Fl 9, New York NY 10018
Tel (212) 730-0333 SIC 2339 2389

TURN ON PRODUCTS INC p 1492
270 W 38th St Rm 1200, New York NY 10018
Tel (212) 764-2121 SIC 2339 2331

■ WARNACO GROUP INC p 1576
501 Fashion Ave, New York NY 10018
Tel (212) 287-8000
SIC 2322 2329 2339 2369 2342 2341

ZAR GROUP LLC p 1641
1375 Broadway Fl 12, New York NY 10018
Tel (212) 944-2510 SIC 2339

■ MJ SOFFE LLC p 978
1 Soffe Dr, Fayetteville NC 28312
Tel (910) 435-3138
SIC 2339 2329 2369 2321

▲ VF CORP p 1553
105 Corp Ctr Blvd, Greensboro NC 27408
Tel (336) 424-6000
SIC 2325 2321 2329 2339 2331 2369

■ VF JEANSWEAR LIMITED PARTNERSHIP p 1553
400 N Elm St, Greensboro NC 27401
Tel (336) 332-3400
SIC 2325 2339 2331 2329

WORTH BON INC p 1626
40 Francis Rd, Hendersonville NC 28792
Tel (828) 697-2216
SIC 2331 5621 2339 2335 2337 8741

■ FECHHEIMER BROTHERS CO p 533
4545 Malsbary Rd, Blue Ash OH 45242
Tel (513) 793-7819
SIC 2311 2337 2339 5699

▲ ROCKY BRANDS INC p 1245
39 E Canal St, Nelsonville OH 45764
Tel (740) 753-1951
SIC 3143 3144 2329 2331 2339 2389

HOLLOWAY SPORTSWEAR INC p 701
2633 Campbell Rd, Sidney OH 45365
Tel (937) 497-7575 SIC 2329 2339 2392

▲ NIKE INC p 1043
1 Sw Bowerman Dr, Beaverton OR 97005
Tel (503) 671-6453
SIC 3021 2329 2339 5139 5661 5136

ADIDAS AMERICA INC p 22
5055 N Greeley Ave, Portland OR 97217
Tel (971) 234-2300
SIC 5139 5136 5137 3021 2339

▲ COLUMBIA SPORTSWEAR CO p 341
14375 Nw Science Park Dr, Portland OR 97229
Tel (503) 985-4000
SIC 2329 2339 3021 2353 3949

■ COLUMBIA SPORTSWEAR USA CORP p 341
14375 Nw Science Park Dr, Portland OR 97229
Tel (503) 985-4000
SIC 5137 5136 2329 2339 3021 2353

■ SUGARTOWN WORLDWIDE LLC p 1397
800 3rd Ave, King Of Prussia PA 19406
Tel (610) 878-5550
SIC 2339 2361 5136 5611

▲ HAMPSHIRE GROUP LIMITED p 656
1924 Pearman Dairy Rd A, Anderson SC 29625
Tel (212) 540-5666 SIC 2339 2329 2253

HAMRICKS INC p 656
742 Peachoid Rd, Gaffney SC 29341
Tel (864) 489-6095
SIC 5651 2337 2331 2335 2339 5087

▲ DELTA APPAREL INC p 426
322 S Main St, Greenville SC 29601
Tel (864) 232-5200
SIC 2321 2369 2339 2253

BAY ISLAND SPORTSWEAR INC p 161
1415 Emerald Rd, Greenwood SC 29646
Tel (864) 229-1298 SIC 2253 2339

GALEY & LORD LLC p 589
670 N Main St, Society Hill SC 29593
Tel (843) 378-4511
SIC 2211 2221 2325 2339

ROBINSON MANUFACTURING CO p 1242
798 Market St, Dayton TN 37321
Tel (423) 775-8331 SIC 2322 2339 2329

■ VF IMAGEWEAR INC p 1553
545 Marriott Dr Ste 200, Nashville TN 37214
Tel (615) 565-5000
SIC 2326 5099 2339 2311

TULLAHOMA INDUSTRIES LLC p 1491
401 Nw Atlantic St, Tullahoma TN 37388
Tel (931) 455-1314 SIC 2311 2339 2326

WILLIAMSON-DICKIE MANUFACTURING CO p 1612
509 W Vickery Blvd, Fort Worth TX 76104
Tel (817) 336-7201 SIC 2326 2339

APPAREL GROUP LTD p 98
883 Trinity Dr, Lewisville TX 75056
Tel (214) 469-3300 SIC 2339 2321

■ FOSSIL PARTNERS LP p 570
901 S Central Expy, Richardson TX 75080
Tel (972) 234-2525
SIC 5137 2389 2339 5094

▲ DIAMOND BLACK INC p 436
2084 E 3900 S, Salt Lake City UT 84124
Tel (801) 278-5552 SIC 3949 2329 2339

HELLY HANSEN (US) INC p 682
14218 Stewart Rd Ste 100a, Sumner WA 98390
Tel (800) 435-5901
SIC 5137 5699 2339 2329

■ JANSPORT INC p 777
N850 County Road Cb, Appleton WI 54914
Tel (920) 734-5708
SIC 3949 3161 2339 2329 2321

SIC 2341 Women's, Misses' & Children's Underwear & Nightwear

FOH GROUP INC p 563
6255 W Sunset Blvd # 2212, Los Angeles CA 90028
Tel (323) 466-5151
SIC 2341 2342 2339 5621 5632

HONEST CO INC p 705
12130 Millennium Ste 500, Playa Vista CA 90094
Tel (310) 917-9199 SIC 2341 2833

VAL DOR APPAREL LLC p 1538
6820 Lyons Technology Pkw, Coconut Creek FL 33073
Tel (954) 363-7340
SIC 2322 2329 2331 2339 2341

■ VANITY FAIR BRANDS LP p 1543
1 Fruit Of The Loom Dr, Bowling Green KY 42103
Tel (270) 781-6400 *SIC* 2341 2384 2342

CENTRAL MILLS INC p 279
473 Ridge Rd, Dayton NJ 08810
Tel (732) 329-0032
SIC 2329 2339 2369 2322 2341 2321

MAIDENFORM p 897
485 Us Highway 1 S, Iselin NJ 08830
Tel (732) 621-2216 *SIC* 2341

■ MAIDENFORM BRANDS INC p 897
485 Us Highway 1 S, Iselin NJ 08830
Tel (888) 573-0299 *SIC* 2341 2342 5621

MAIDENFORM INC p 897
485f Us Highway 1 S # 120, Iselin NJ 08830
Tel (732) 621-2500 *SIC* 2341 2342

CHARLES KOMAR & SONS INC p 289
16 E 34th St Fl 10, Jersey City NJ 07308
Tel (212) 725-1500 *SIC* 2341 2384 5137

WACOAL AMERICA INC p 1570
1 Wacoal Plz, Lyndhurst NJ 07071
Tel (201) 933-8400 *SIC* 2342 2341

WACOAL INTERNATIONAL CORP p 1571
1 Wacoal Plz, Lyndhurst NJ 07071
Tel (201) 933-8400 *SIC* 2341

DELTA GALIL USA INC p 427
1 Harmon Plz Fl 5, Secaucus NJ 07094
Tel (201) 392-9098 *SIC* 2341

■ WARNACO GROUP INC p 1576
501 Fashion Ave, New York NY 10018
Tel (212) 287-8000
SIC 2322 2329 2339 2369 2342 2341

■ WARNACO INC p 1576
501 Fashion Ave Fl 14, New York NY 10018
Tel (212) 287-8000
SIC 2342 2341 2321 2329 2322 2323

▲ HANESBRANDS INC p 657
1000 E Hanes Mill Rd, Winston Salem NC 27105
Tel (336) 519-8080
SIC 2253 2342 2341 2322 2252 2251

JOCKEY INTERNATIONAL INC p 787
2300 60th St, Kenosha WI 53140
Tel (262) 658-8111 *SIC* 2254 2341 2322

SIC 2342 Brassieres, Girdles & Garments

FOH GROUP INC p 563
6255 W Sunset Blvd # 2212, Los Angeles CA 90028
Tel (323) 466-5151
SIC 2341 2342 2339 5621 5632

DONGHIA INC p 450
500 Bic Dr Ste 20, Milford CT 06461
Tel (800) 366-4442
SIC 5198 5131 5021 2342

■ VANITY FAIR BRANDS LP p 1543
1 Fruit Of The Loom Dr, Bowling Green KY 42103
Tel (270) 781-6400 *SIC* 2341 2384 2342

■ MAIDENFORM BRANDS INC p 897
485 Us Highway 1 S, Iselin NJ 08830
Tel (888) 573-0299 *SIC* 2341 2342 5621

MAIDENFORM INC p 897
485f Us Highway 1 S # 120, Iselin NJ 08830
Tel (732) 621-2500 *SIC* 2341 2342

WACOAL AMERICA INC p 1570
1 Wacoal Plz, Lyndhurst NJ 07071
Tel (201) 933-8400 *SIC* 2342 2341

■ WARNACO GROUP INC p 1576
501 Fashion Ave, New York NY 10018
Tel (212) 287-8000
SIC 2322 2329 2339 2369 2342 2341

■ WARNACO INC p 1576
501 Fashion Ave Fl 14, New York NY 10018
Tel (212) 287-8000
SIC 2342 2341 2321 2329 2322 2323

▲ HANESBRANDS INC p 657
1000 E Hanes Mill Rd, Winston Salem NC 27105
Tel (336) 519-8080
SIC 2253 2342 2341 2322 2252 2251

SIC 2353 Hats, Caps & Millinery

BAE SYSTEMS PROTECTION SYSTEMS INC p 144
7822 S 46th St, Phoenix AZ 85044
Tel (602) 643-7233
SIC 3721 2353 3795 3842

■ VANS INC p 1544
6550 Katella Ave, Cypress CA 90630
Tel (714) 889-6100
SIC 3021 2321 2329 2325 2353 2393

▲ UNDER ARMOUR INC p 1502
1020 Hull St Ste 300, Baltimore MD 21230
Tel (410) 454-6428
SIC 2329 2353 2339 3021

PARAMOUNT APPAREL INTERNATIONAL INC p 1114
1 Paramount Dr, Bourbon MO 65441
Tel (573) 732-4411 *SIC* 2353

PARAMOUNT HOLDING INC p 1114
1 Paramount Dr, Bourbon MO 65441
Tel (573) 732-4411 *SIC* 2353

NEW ERA CAP CO INC p 1030
160 Delaware Ave, Buffalo NY 14202
Tel (716) 604-9000 *SIC* 2353

FLEXFIT LLC p 556
350 Karin Ln Unit A, Hicksville NY 11801
Tel (516) 932-8800 *SIC* 2353

▲ COLUMBIA SPORTSWEAR CO p 341
14375 Nw Science Park Dr, Portland OR 97229
Tel (503) 985-4000
SIC 2329 2339 3021 2353 3949

■ COLUMBIA SPORTSWEAR USA CORP p 341
14375 Nw Science Park Dr, Portland OR 97229
Tel (503) 985-4000
SIC 5137 5136 2329 2339 3021 2353

BOLLMAN HAT CO p 198
110 E Main St, Adamstown PA 19501
Tel (717) 484-4361 *SIC* 2353 5136

ARENA BRANDS INC p 106
601 Marion Dr, Garland TX 75042
Tel (972) 494-7133 *SIC* 2353

HAT BRANDS HOLDING CORP p 667
601 Marion Dr, Garland TX 75042
Tel (972) 494-7133
SIC 2353 3914 3144 3143

RHE HATCO INC p 1231
601 Marion Dr, Garland TX 75042
Tel (972) 494-0511 *SIC* 2353

BIO WORLD MERCHANDISING INC p 183
2111 W Walnut Hill Ln, Irving TX 75038
Tel (888) 831-2138
SIC 2353 3161 2253 5199 3021

SIC 2361 Children's & Infants' Dresses & Blouses

AVALON APPAREL LLC p 135
2520 W 6th St Ste 101, Los Angeles CA 90057
Tel (323) 581-3511 *SIC* 2361

ALL ACCESS APPAREL INC p 50
1515 Gage Rd, Montebello CA 90640
Tel (323) 889-4300 *SIC* 2331 2361 2335

JESSICA MCCLINTOCK INC p 783
2307 Broadway St, San Francisco CA 94115
Tel (415) 553-8200 *SIC* 2361 2335 2844

▲ CARTERS INC p 262
3438 Peachtree Rd Ne # 1800, Atlanta GA 30326
Tel (678) 791-1000 *SIC* 2361 2369

ELDER MANUFACTURING CO INC p 484
999 Executive Parkway Dr # 300, Saint Louis MO 63141
Tel (314) 469-1120 *SIC* 2321 2361 2253

■ GARAN INC p 591
200 Madison Ave Fl 4, New York NY 10016
Tel (212) 563-1292
SIC 2361 2369 2331 2339 2321

JORDACHE ENTERPRISES INC p 793
1400 Broadway Rm 1404b, New York NY 10018
Tel (212) 643-8400
SIC 2339 2325 2369 2331 2321 2361

■ FUN-TEES INC p 585
4735 Corp Dr Nw Ste 100, Concord NC 28027
Tel (704) 788-3003 *SIC* 2321 2361 2331

R B PAMPLIN CORP p 1201
805 Sw Brdwy Ste 2400, Portland OR 97205
Tel (503) 248-1133
SIC 2211 2392 2361 2369

■ SUGARTOWN WORLDWIDE LLC p 1397
800 3rd Ave, King Of Prussia PA 19406
Tel (610) 878-5550
SIC 2339 2361 5136 5611

SIC 2369 Girls' & Infants' Outerwear, NEC

ASICS AMERICA CORP p 117
80 Technology Dr, Irvine CA 92618
Tel (949) 453-8888
SIC 5139 5136 5137 2369 2339 2321

TRUE RELIGION APPAREL INC p 1486
1888 Rosecrans Ave # 1000, Manhattan Beach CA 90266
Tel (323) 266-3072 *SIC* 2369 2325 2339

▲ CARTERS INC p 262
3438 Peachtree Rd Ne # 1800, Atlanta GA 30326
Tel (678) 791-1000 *SIC* 2361 2369

■ RUBBERMAID INC p 1256
3 Glenlake Pkwy, Atlanta GA 30328
Tel (770) 418-7000
SIC 3089 2519 3944 2369 2392

■ LEE JEANS CO INC p 851
9001 W 67th St, Merriam KS 66202
Tel (913) 384-4000 *SIC* 2325 2339 2369

TAG HOLDINGS INC p 1421
6901 Riverport Dr Ste B, Louisville KY 40258
Tel (214) 469-3300 *SIC* 2321 2339 2369

CENTRAL MILLS INC p 279
473 Ridge Rd, Dayton NJ 08810
Tel (732) 329-0032
SIC 2329 2339 2369 2322 2341 2321

■ GARAN INC p 591
200 Madison Ave Fl 4, New York NY 10016
Tel (212) 563-1292
SIC 2361 2369 2331 2339 2321

JEANJER LLC p 781
1400 Broadway Fl 15, New York NY 10018
Tel (212) 944-1330
SIC 2331 2337 2339 2369

JORDACHE ENTERPRISES INC p 793
1400 Broadway Rm 1404b, New York NY 10018
Tel (212) 643-8400
SIC 2339 2325 2369 2331 2321 2361

■ WARNACO GROUP INC p 1576
501 Fashion Ave, New York NY 10018
Tel (212) 287-8000
SIC 2322 2329 2339 2369 2342 2341

■ MJ SOFFE LLC p 978
1 Soffe Dr, Fayetteville NC 28312
Tel (910) 435-3138
SIC 2339 2329 2369 2321

▲ VF CORP p 1553
105 Corp Ctr Blvd, Greensboro NC 27408
Tel (336) 424-6000
SIC 2325 2321 2329 2339 2331 2369

R B PAMPLIN CORP p 1201
805 Sw Brdwy Ste 2400, Portland OR 97205
Tel (503) 248-1133
SIC 2211 2392 2361 2369

▲ DELTA APPAREL INC p 426
322 S Main St, Greenville SC 29601
Tel (864) 232-5200
SIC 2321 2369 2339 2253

SIC 2371 Fur Goods

BLOOMER HOLDINGS INC p 190
1710 N Industrial Dr, Bloomer WI 54724
Tel (800) 638-0479 *SIC* 2371

SIC 2381 Dress & Work Gloves

KITTRICH CORP p 822
1585 W Mission Blvd, Pomona CA 91766
Tel (714) 736-1000 *SIC* 2591 2392 2381

■ WELLS LAMONT INDUSTRY GROUP LLC p 1591
6640 W Touhy Ave, Niles IL 60714
Tel (800) 247-3295 *SIC* 2381

MAGID GLOVE & SAFETY MANUFACTURING CO LLC p 895
1300 Naperville Dr, Romeoville IL 60446
Tel (773) 384-2070
SIC 3151 2381 5699 3842 2326

■ ACUSHNET CO p 20
333 Bridge St, Fairhaven MA 02719
Tel (508) 979-2000 *SIC* 3949 3149 2381

FOWNES BROTHERS & CO INC p 572
16 E 34th St Fl 5, New York NY 10016
Tel (212) 683-0150
SIC 3151 2381 5136 5137 3949

WCM HOLDINGS INC p 1585
1150 Canal Rd, Cincinnati OH 45241
Tel (513) 705-2100 *SIC* 5099 2381 3842

CHESTER WEST HOLDINGS INC p 295
11500 Canal Rd, Sharonville OH 45241
Tel (800) 647-1900
SIC 3842 5136 5099 5137 2381

TOTES ISOTONER HOLDINGS CORP p 1463
9655 International Blvd, West Chester OH 45246
Tel (513) 682-8200
SIC 2381 3151 2211 3021 5699

SHELBY GROUP INTERNATIONAL INC p 1314
1255 W Schilling Blvd, Collierville TN 38017
Tel (901) 795-5810
SIC 3842 2381 3851 5137

SIC 2384 Robes & Dressing Gowns

■ VANITY FAIR BRANDS LP p 1543
1 Fruit Of The Loom Dr, Bowling Green KY 42103
Tel (270) 781-6400 *SIC* 2341 2384 2342

CHARLES KOMAR & SONS INC p 289
16 E 34th St Fl 10, Jersey City NJ 07308
Tel (212) 725-1500 *SIC* 2341 2384 5137

■ VF SPORTSWEAR INC p 1553
545 Wshngton Blvd Fl 8, Jersey City NJ 07310
Tel (212) 541-5757
SIC 2329 2384 5136 5137 5611 6794

SIC 2385 Waterproof Outerwear

AMERICAN APPAREL INC p 68
107 Cecil Jackson Byp, Selma AL 36703
Tel (334) 872-6337 *SIC* 2311 2385

LEVY GROUP INC p 858
1333 Broadway Fl 9, New York NY 10018
Tel (212) 398-0707 *SIC* 2337 2385

SIC 2386 Leather & Sheep Lined Clothing

TIMBERLAND LLC p 1454
200 Domain Dr, Stratham NH 03885
Tel (603) 772-9500
SIC 3143 3144 2386 2329 2321 2325

EXCELLED SHEEPSKIN & LEATHER COAT CORP p 516
1400 Brdwy Fl 31, New York NY 10018
Tel (212) 594-5843
SIC 2386 3172 2337 2311

▲ G-III APPAREL GROUP LTD p 588
512 7th Ave Fl 35, New York NY 10018
Tel (212) 403-0500
SIC 2337 2339 2311 2329 2386 5136

SIC 2387 Apparel Belts

▲ DIFFERENTIAL BRANDS GROUP INC p 438
1231 S Gerhart Ave, Commerce CA 90022
Tel (323) 890-1800
SIC 2337 2339 2311 2325 3111 2387

GRAY VESTAR INVESTORS LLC p 632
17622 Armstrong Ave, Irvine CA 92614
Tel (949) 863-1171
SIC 2253 2339 2335 2337 3961 2387

▲ COACH INC p 330
10 Hudson Yards, New York NY 10001
Tel (212) 594-1850
SIC 3171 3172 2387 3143 3144

COACH STORES INC p 331
516 W 34th St Bsmt 5, New York NY 10001
Tel (212) 643-9727
SIC 3171 3161 3172 2387 5137 5099

SIC 2389 Apparel & Accessories, NEC

STRATEGIC PARTNERS INC p 1392
9800 De Soto Ave, Chatsworth CA 91311
Tel (818) 671-2100
SIC 3143 3144 5139 2339 2389 2329

▲ DECKERS OUTDOOR CORP p 421
250 Coromar Dr, Goleta CA 93117
Tel (805) 967-7611 *SIC* 3021 2389 2339

ST JOHN KNITS INC p 1367
17522 Armstrong Ave, Irvine CA 92614
Tel (949) 863-1171 *SIC* 2339 2253 2389

AMERICAN APPAREL LLC p 68
747 Warehouse St, Los Angeles CA 90021
Tel (213) 488-0226 *SIC* 2389 2311 2331

▲ CROCS INC p 393
7477 Dry Creek Pkwy, Niwot CO 80503
Tel (303) 848-7000
SIC 3021 5139 3069 5661 2389

MAUI ACQUISITION CORP p 921
13386 International Pkwy, Jacksonville FL 32218
Tel (904) 741-5400 *SIC* 3069 2389

INTRADECO APPAREL INC p 759
9500 Nw 108th Ave, Medley FL 33178
Tel (305) 264-8888 *SIC* 2389

▲ SUPERIOR UNIFORM GROUP INC p 1407
10055 Seminole Blvd, Seminole FL 33772
Tel (727) 397-9611 *SIC* 2389 3999 7389

DOWLING TEXTILE CO p 453
615 Macon Rd, Mcdonough GA 30253
Tel (770) 957-3981 *SIC* 2326 2337 2389

ENCOMPASS GROUP LLC p 495
615 Macon St, Mcdonough GA 30253
Tel (770) 957-3981 *SIC* 2326 2337 2389

■ BAXTER HEALTHCARE CORP p 160
1 Baxter Pkwy, Deerfield IL 60015
Tel (224) 948-2000
SIC 3841 2835 2389 3842 5047

IPC INTERNATIONAL CORP p 763
10255 W Hggi, Rosemont IL 60018
Tel (847) 444-2000
SIC 7381 8742 2389 3199

▲ CROWN CRAFTS INC p 395
916 S Burnside Ave, Gonzales LA 70737
Tel (225) 647-9100 *SIC* 2211 2389

■ CMRG APPAREL LLC p 329
555 Turnpike St, Canton MA 02021
Tel (781) 828-9300 *SIC* 5699 2389

■ VISANT CORP p 1560
3601 Minnesota Dr Ste 400, Minneapolis MN 55435
Tel (914) 595-8200
SIC 3911 2741 2389 7221

■ BLOOMINGDALES INC p 190
1000 3rd Ave, New York NY 10022
Tel (212) 705-2000 *SIC* 5311 2389

GCE INTERNATIONAL INC p 595
1385 Broadway Fl 21, New York NY 10018
Tel (212) 704-4800
SIC 2253 2389 2331 5137 5136

MERYL DIAMOND LTD p 951
1375 Broadway Fl 9, New York NY 10018
Tel (212) 730-0333 *SIC* 2339 2389

RANDA CORP p 1207
417 5th Ave Fl 11, New York NY 10016
Tel (212) 768-8800 *SIC* 2323 2389

RUBIES COSTUME CO INC p 1257
12008 Jamaica Ave, Richmond Hill NY 11418
Tel (718) 846-1008 *SIC* 2389 7299

▲ LAKELAND INDUSTRIES INC p 840
3555 Vtrans Mem Hwy Ste C, Ronkonkoma NY 11779
Tel (631) 981-9700 *SIC* 3842 2389

STANDARD TEXTILE CO INC p 1376
1 Knollcrest Dr, Cincinnati OH 45237
Tel (513) 761-9255
SIC 2389 2326 2337 2211 2391 5136

▲ ROCKY BRANDS INC p 1245
39 E Canal St, Nelsonville OH 45764
Tel (740) 753-1951
SIC 3143 3144 2329 2331 2339 2389

MTM RECOGNITION CORP p 998
3201 Se 29th St, Oklahoma City OK 73115
Tel (405) 609-6900
SIC 3911 3873 2499 2389 3499 2791

▲ CSS INDUSTRIES INC p 398
450 Plymouth Rd Ste 300, Plymouth Meeting PA 19462
Tel (610) 729-3959
SIC 2771 2679 2389 2396 2621 2865

PARKER SCHOOL UNIFORMS LLC p 1116
6300 W By Northwest Blvd # 100, Houston TX 77040
Tel (713) 957-1511 *SIC* 2389

■ FOSSIL PARTNERS LP p 570
901 S Central Expy, Richardson TX 75080
Tel (972) 234-2525
SIC 5137 2389 2339 5094

SIC 2391 Curtains & Draperies

CAROLE FABRICS CORP p 259
633 Nw Frontage Rd, Augusta GA 30907
Tel (706) 863-4742
SIC 2221 2591 5131 5949 2392 2391

MARIETTA DRAPERY & WINDOW COVERINGS CO INC p 906
22 Trammell St Sw, Marietta GA 30064
Tel (770) 428-3335
SIC 5023 2391 2591 2392

ASCOT ENTERPRISES INC p 116
503 S Main St, Nappanee IN 46550
Tel (877) 773-7751 *SIC* 2391 2591 2392

LAFAYETTE VENETIAN BLIND INC p 838
3000 Klondike Rd, West Lafayette IN 47906
Tel (765) 464-2500 *SIC* 2591 2391

COUNTRY CURTAINS INC p 375
705 Pleasant St, Stockbridge MA 01262
Tel (413) 243-1474 *SIC* 2391

AEON USA INC p 29
1 Penn Plz Fl 36, New York NY 10119
Tel (212) 946-8780
SIC 5621 5961 2211 2391

STANDARD TEXTILE CO INC p 1376
1 Knollcrest Dr, Cincinnati OH 45237
Tel (513) 761-9255
SIC 2389 2326 2337 2211 2391 5136

FABTEX INC p 523
111 Woodbine Ln, Danville PA 17821
Tel (570) 275-7500
SIC 5072 2221 5023 2512 2392 2391

SIC 2392 House furnishings: Textile

EMARICO INC p 490
146 Resource Center Pkwy, Birmingham AL 35242
Tel (205) 545-9362 *SIC* 2392

PLANTATION PATTERNS LLC p 1154
146 Resource Center Pkwy, Birmingham AL 35242
Tel (205) 545-9229 *SIC* 2392

BRENTWOOD ORIGINALS INC p 210
20639 S Fordyce Ave, Carson CA 90810
Tel (310) 637-6804 *SIC* 2392

KITTRICH CORP p 822
1585 W Mission Blvd, Pomona CA 91766
Tel (714) 736-1000 *SIC* 2591 2392 2381

HOLLANDER HOME FASHIONS HOLDINGS LLC p 700
6501 Congress Ave Ste 300, Boca Raton FL 33487
Tel (561) 997-6900 *SIC* 2392

HOLLANDER SLEEP PRODUCTS LLC p 700
6501 Congress Ave Ste 300, Boca Raton FL 33487
Tel (561) 997-6900 *SIC* 2392 2221 5719

■ RUBBERMAID INC p 1256
3 Glenlake Pkwy, Atlanta GA 30328
Tel (770) 418-7000
SIC 3089 2519 3944 2369 2392

CAROLE FABRICS CORP p 259
633 Nw Frontage Rd, Augusta GA 30907
Tel (706) 863-4742
SIC 2221 2591 5131 5949 2392 2391

KLEEN-TEX INDUSTRIES INC p 823
101 N Greenwood St Ste C, Lagrange GA 30240
Tel (706) 882-0111 *SIC* 3069 2273 2392

MARIETTA DRAPERY & WINDOW COVERINGS CO INC p 906
22 Trammell St Sw, Marietta GA 30064
Tel (770) 428-3335
SIC 5023 2391 2591 2392

QST INDUSTRIES INC p 1195
550 W Adams St Ste 200, Chicago IL 60661
Tel (312) 930-9400 *SIC* 2396 2392 2752

JORDAN MANUFACTURING CO INC p 793
1200 S 6th St, Monticello IN 47960
Tel (574) 583-6008 *SIC* 2392 5021

ASCOT ENTERPRISES INC p 116
503 S Main St, Nappanee IN 46550
Tel (877) 773-7751 *SIC* 2391 2591 2392

▲ VERA BRADLEY INC p 1549
12420 Stonebridge Rd, Roanoke IN 46783
Tel (877) 708-8372
SIC 3171 3111 2392 2844

▲ TEMPUR SEALY INTERNATIONAL INC p 1436
1000 Tempur Way, Lexington KY 40511
Tel (800) 878-8889 *SIC* 2515 2392

LOUISVILLE BEDDING CO INC p 880
10400 Bunsen Way, Louisville KY 40299
Tel (502) 491-3370 *SIC* 2392 3949

GOODWILL INDUSTRIES OF NORTHERN NEW ENGLAND p 625
75 Washington Ave Ste 300, Portland ME 04101
Tel (207) 774-6323 *SIC* 8331 2392

ARDEN COMPANIES INC p 106
30400 Telg Rd Ste 200, Bingham Farms MI 48025
Tel (248) 415-8500 *SIC* 2392

KRAMS ENTERPRISES INC p 829
30400 Telg Rd Ste 200, Bingham Farms MI 48025
Tel (248) 415-8500 *SIC* 2392

▲ LEGGETT & PLATT INC p 853
1 Leggett Rd, Carthage MO 64836
Tel (417) 358-8131
SIC 2515 2514 3495 2392 2542 3363

■ QUICKIE MANUFACTURING CORP p 1199
1150 Taylors Ln Ste 2, Cinnaminson NJ 08077
Tel (856) 829-7900 *SIC* 2392 3991

FRANCO MANUFACTURING CO INC p 574
555 Prospect St, Metuchen NJ 08840
Tel (732) 494-0503
SIC 2269 2392 2211 5023 5131

INNOCOR INC p 744
200 Schulz Dr Ste 2, Red Bank NJ 07701
Tel (844) 824-9348 *SIC* 2515 2392 3069

KRAVET FABRICS INC p 829
225 Central Ave S, Bethpage NY 11714
Tel (516) 293-2000 *SIC* 2392

KRAVET INC p 829
225 Cent Ave S, Bethpage NY 11714
Tel (516) 293-2000 *SIC* 5131 5198 2392

ARLEE HOME FASHIONS INC p 110
261 5th Ave Fl Mezz, New York NY 10016
Tel (212) 213-0425 *SIC* 2392

D E SHAW LAMINAR PORTFOLIOS LLC p 407
120 W 45th St Fl 22, New York NY 10036
Tel (212) 478-0000 *SIC* 6282 2392 5945

KALTEX NORTH AMERICA INC p 801
350 5th Ave Ste 7100, New York NY 10118
Tel (212) 894-3200 *SIC* 2392

MADISON INDUSTRIES INC p 894
295 5th Ave Ste 512, New York NY 10016
Tel (212) 679-5110 *SIC* 2392 5023

SUNHAM HOME FASHIONS LLC p 1402
136 Madison Ave Fl 16, New York NY 10016
Tel (212) 695-1218 *SIC* 2392

AMERICAN FIBER & FINISHING INC p 72
225 N Depot St, Albemarle NC 28001
Tel (704) 983-6102
SIC 2211 3842 2844 2392

■ AVINTIV SPECIALTY MATERIALS INC p 138
9335 Harris Corners Pkwy, Charlotte NC 28269
Tel (704) 697-5100 *SIC* 2297 2392

■ PGI NONWOVEN/CHICOPEE INC p 1140
9335 Harris Corners Pkwy, Charlotte NC 28269
Tel (704) 697-5100 *SIC* 2297 2392

BOB BARKER CO INC p 196
134 N Main St, Fuquay Varina NC 27526
Tel (800) 235-8586
SIC 5131 5122 2392 5136 3441

MANUAL WOODWORKERS & WEAVERS INC p 903
3737 Howard Gap Rd, Hendersonville NC 28792
Tel (828) 692-7333 *SIC* 2392

WINSTON-SALEM INDUSTRIES FOR BLIND INC p 1617
7730 N Point Blvd, Winston Salem NC 27106
Tel (336) 759-0551
SIC 2515 3021 2392 2253 2394 3851

EASY WAY LEISURE CORP p 473
8950 Rossash Rd, Cincinnati OH 45236
Tel (513) 731-5640 *SIC* 2392

DOWN-LITE INTERNATIONAL INC p 453
8153 Duke Blvd, Mason OH 45040
Tel (513) 229-3696 *SIC* 2392 5719

■ NATIONAL SEATING CO p 1016
7800 Walton Pkwy, New Albany OH 43054
Tel (219) 872-7295 *SIC* 2392

HOLLOWAY SPORTSWEAR INC p 701
2633 Campbell Rd, Sidney OH 45365
Tel (937) 497-7575 *SIC* 2329 2339 2392

■ IMPACT PRODUCTS LLC p 734
2840 Centennial Rd, Toledo OH 43617
Tel (419) 841-2891
SIC 5084 5087 2392 3089

R B PAMPLIN CORP p 1201
805 Sw Brdwy Ste 2400, Portland OR 97205
Tel (503) 248-1133
SIC 2211 2392 2361 2369

FABTEX INC p 523
111 Woodbine Ln, Danville PA 17821
Tel (570) 275-7500
SIC 5072 2221 5023 2512 2392 2391

AMERICAN TEXTILE CO INC p 80
10 N Linden St, Duquesne PA 15110
Tel (412) 948-1020 *SIC* 5719 2392

■ TUESDAY MORNING INC p 1490
6250 Lbj Fwy, Dallas TX 75240
Tel (972) 387-3562 *SIC* 5311 2392 5719

CARPENTER CO p 260
5016 Monument Ave, Richmond VA 23230
Tel (804) 359-0800
SIC 3086 1311 2869 2297 2392 2821

UTTERMOST CO p 1537
3325 Grassy Hill Rd, Rocky Mount VA 24151
Tel (540) 483-5103 *SIC* 2392 5023

PACIFIC COAST FEATHER CO p 1104
1964 4th Ave S, Seattle WA 98134
Tel (206) 624-1057 *SIC* 2392

SIC 2393 Textile Bags

■ VANS INC p 1544
6550 Katella Ave, Cypress CA 90630
Tel (714) 889-6100
SIC 3021 2321 2329 2325 2353 2393

511 INC p 3
1360 Reynolds Ave Ste 101, Irvine CA 92614
Tel (949) 800-1511
SIC 5699 2231 5139 2393

ADCO PRODUCTS INC p 21
27615 Avenue Hopkins, Valencia CA 91355
Tel (800) 541-2326 *SIC* 2393

MONDI BAGS USA LLC p 984
281 Hemphill Blvd, Eastman GA 31023
Tel (478) 374-7032 *SIC* 2393 2621

AUGUSTA SPORTSWEAR INC p 131
425 Park 20 W, Grovetown GA 30813
Tel (706) 860-4633
SIC 2329 2339 2393 2399

BLUEWATER DEFENSE INC p 193
Corozal Ind Pk Carr 159, Corozal PR 00783
Tel (787) 746-5020
SIC 2393 2326 3842 2325

SIC 2394 Canvas Prdts

■ VF OUTDOOR LLC p 1553
2701 Harbor Bay Pkwy, Alameda CA 94502
Tel (510) 618-3500
SIC 2329 2339 3949 2394 2399 5941

■ MOUNTAIN HARDWEAR INC p 994
1414 Harbour Way S, Richmond CA 94804
Tel (510) 558-3000 *SIC* 2399 2394 5651

BESTOP INC p 177
333 Centennial Pkwy B, Louisville CO 80027
Tel (303) 465-1755 *SIC* 2394 3714

OUTDOOR VENTURE CORP p 1099
30 Venture Dr, Stearns KY 42647
Tel (606) 376-5021 *SIC* 2394

MAGNA CAR TOP SYSTEMS OF AMERICA INC p 895
2725 Commerce Pkwy, Auburn Hills MI 48326
Tel (248) 836-4500 *SIC* 2394

ARIZON COMPANIES INC p 108
11880 Dorsett Rd, Maryland Heights MO 63043
Tel (314) 739-0037
SIC 3585 1711 2394 1541 1542 8611

TINGUE BROWN & CO p 1455
535 N Midland Ave, Saddle Brook NJ 07663
Tel (201) 796-4490 *SIC* 5087 3089 2394

TRI VANTAGE LLC p 1477
1831 N Park Ave, Burlington NC 27217
Tel (800) 786-1876
SIC 5199 5088 5099 5091 2394

TRIMACO LLC p 1480
2300 Gateway Centre Blvd # 200, Morrisville NC 27560
Tel (919) 674-3476
SIC 2851 2621 2672 2679 2394

TRELLEBORG COATED SYSTEMS US INC p 1476
715 Railroad Ave, Rutherfordton NC 28139
Tel (864) 576-1210
SIC 2295 2221 2394 2396 2211

WINSTON-SALEM INDUSTRIES FOR BLIND INC p 1617
7730 N Point Blvd, Winston Salem NC 27106
Tel (336) 759-0551
SIC 2515 3021 2392 2253 2394 3851

LAKE SPIRIT TRIBE p 839
816 3rd Ave N, Fort Totten ND 58335
Tel (701) 766-1270
SIC 9131 0191 2394 2298 7999

LEEDSWORLD INC p 852
400 Hunt Valley Rd, New Kensington PA 15068
Tel (724) 334-9000
SIC 5199 5111 5112 3172 3161 2394

POLYCONCEPT NORTH AMERICA INC p 1160
400 Hunt Valley Rd, New Kensington PA 15068
Tel (724) 334-9000
SIC 5199 5111 5112 3172 3161 2394

NATIONAL CONSUMER OUTDOORS CORP p 1011
4215 Mcewen Rd, Dallas TX 75244
Tel (972) 716-4200
SIC 3999 2399 2394 3732

SHADE STRUCTURES INC p 1310
8505 Chancellor Row, Dallas TX 75247
Tel (214) 905-9500 *SIC* 2394

WINDWAY CAPITAL CORP p 1616
630 Riverfront Dr Ste 200, Sheboygan WI 53081
Tel (920) 457-8600
SIC 3469 2394 3624 3732

SIC 2395 Pleating & Stitching For The Trade

ANTIGUA GROUP INC p 94
16651 N 84th Ave, Peoria AZ 85382
Tel (623) 523-6000
SIC 5137 5136 2395 2339 3993

GALLS LLC p 590
1340 Russell Cave Rd, Lexington KY 40505
Tel (859) 266-7227 *SIC* 5961 5399 2395

SHAMROCK COMPANIES INC p 1311
24090 Detroit Rd, Westlake OH 44145
Tel (440) 899-9510
SIC 5112 5199 7336 7389 2754 2395

SIC 2396 Automotive Trimmings, Apparel Findings, Related Prdts

TOPRE AMERICA CORP p 1461
1580 County Rd Ste 222, Cullman AL 35057
Tel (256) 735-2600 *SIC* 2396

ALLIED PRINTING SERVICES INC p 56
1 Allied Way, Manchester CT 06042
Tel (860) 643-1101
SIC 2396 2752 2759 2789 2791

▲ UNIROYAL GLOBAL ENGINEERED PRODUCTS INC p 1505
1800 2nd St Ste 970, Sarasota FL 34236
Tel (941) 906-8580 *SIC* 2824 2396

QST INDUSTRIES INC p 1195
550 W Adams St Ste 200, Chicago IL 60661
Tel (312) 930-9400 *SIC* 2396 2392 2752

RICO INDUSTRIES INC p 1233
7000 N Austin Ave, Niles IL 60714
Tel (312) 427-0313
SIC 5199 3172 2396 3993

FUTABA INDIANA OF AMERICA CORP p 585
3320 S Keller Rd, Vincennes IN 47591
Tel (812) 895-4700 *SIC* 3089 3465 2396

TK HOLDINGS INC p 1457
2500 Takata Dr, Auburn Hills MI 48326
Tel (248) 373-8040
SIC 2221 2399 2396 3714

YANFENG USA AUTOMOTIVE TRIM SYSTEMS INC p 1634
42150 Executive Dr, Harrison Township MI 48045
Tel (586) 354-2101 *SIC* 2396

PECKHAM VOCATIONAL INDUSTRIES INC p 1126
3510 Capitol City Blvd, Lansing MI 48906
Tel (517) 316-4000
SIC 8331 2396 2311 2331 2339 2326

CNI ENTERPRISES INC p 330
1451 E Lincoln Ave, Madison Heights MI 48071
Tel (248) 586-3300 *SIC* 2396

NICA INC p 1042
1451 E Lincoln Ave, Madison Heights MI 48071
Tel (248) 586-3300 *SIC* 2396

IRVIN AUTOMOTIVE PRODUCTS INC p 765
2600 Centerpoint Pkwy, Pontiac MI 48341
Tel (248) 451-4100 *SIC* 3429 2396

■ EAGLE OTTAWA LLC p 468
21557 Telegraph Rd, Southfield MI 48033
Tel (248) 364-7400 *SIC* 3111 2399 2396

▲ LEAR CORP p 850
21557 Telegraph Rd, Southfield MI 48033
Tel (248) 447-1500
SIC 3714 2531 2396 3643

SRG GLOBAL INC p 1363
800 Stephenson Hwy, Troy MI 48083
Tel (248) 509-1100 *SIC* 2396

TRAVEL TAGS INC p 1473
5842 Carmen Ave, Inver Grove Heights MN 55076
Tel (651) 450-1201 *SIC* 2396 3999 2752

VOMELA SPECIALTY CO p 1565
274 Fillmore Ave E, Saint Paul MN 55107
Tel (651) 228-2200 *SIC* 7336 2396 2752

SIMPLICITY CREATIVE GROUP INC p 1325
261 Madison Ave Fl 4, New York NY 10016
Tel (212) 686-7676
SIC 2241 2221 2396 2298

PETRALEX USA INC p 1139
4740 Coml Pk Ct Ste 2, Clemmons NC 27012
Tel (336) 778-1049 *SIC* 2396

TRELLEBORG COATED SYSTEMS US INC p 1476
715 Railroad Ave, Rutherfordton NC 28139
Tel (864) 576-1210
SIC 2295 2221 2394 2396 2211

HFI LLC p 689
59 Gender Rd, Canal Winchester OH 43110
Tel (614) 491-0700
SIC 2396 2821 3714 3429 3086

ANOMATIC CORP p 92
1650 Tamarack Rd, Newark OH 43055
Tel (740) 522-2203 *SIC* 3471 3469 2396

▲ CSS INDUSTRIES INC p 398
450 Plymouth Rd Ste 300, Plymouth Meeting PA 19462
Tel (610) 729-3959
SIC 2771 2679 2389 2396 2621 2865

SERIGRAPH INC p 1306
3801 Decorah Rd, West Bend WI 53095
Tel (262) 335-7200 *SIC* 2759 2752 2396

SIC 2399 Fabricated Textile Prdts, NEC

EXXEL OUTDOORS INC p 521
300 American Blvd, Haleyville AL 35565
Tel (205) 486-5258 *SIC* 2399

AMSAFE PARTNERS INC p 87
1043 N 47th Ave, Phoenix AZ 85043
Tel (602) 850-2850 *SIC* 2399

■ VF OUTDOOR LLC p 1553
2701 Harbor Bay Pkwy, Alameda CA 94502
Tel (510) 618-3500
SIC 2329 2339 3949 2394 2399 5941

■ MOUNTAIN HARDWEAR INC p 994
1414 Harbour Way S, Richmond CA 94804
Tel (510) 558-3000 *SIC* 2399 2394 5651

BBA US HOLDINGS INC p 163
201 S Orange Ave Ste 1425, Orlando FL 32801
Tel (407) 648-7230 *SIC* 3728 2399 3052

AUGUSTA SPORTSWEAR INC p 131
425 Park 20 W, Grovetown GA 30813
Tel (706) 860-4633
SIC 2329 2339 2393 2399

GRUPO ANTOLIN KENTUCKY INC p 643
208 Commerce Ct, Hopkinsville KY 42240
Tel (270) 885-2703 *SIC* 3559 2399

TK HOLDINGS INC p 1457
2500 Takata Dr, Auburn Hills MI 48326
Tel (248) 373-8040
SIC 2221 2399 2396 3714

TECHNOTRIM INC p 1432
49200 Halyard Dr, Plymouth MI 48170
Tel (734) 254-6600 *SIC* 2399

■ EAGLE OTTAWA LLC p 468
21557 Telegraph Rd, Southfield MI 48033
Tel (248) 364-7400 *SIC* 3111 2399 2396

KEY SAFETY SYSTEMS INC p 814
7000 19 Mile Rd, Sterling Heights MI 48314
Tel (586) 726-3800 *SIC* 2399 3714

WINCRAFT INC p 1615
960 E Mark St, Winona MN 55987
Tel (507) 454-5510
SIC 3499 2399 3089 3961 3999 3069

▲ ALBANY INTERNATIONAL CORP p 45
216 Airport Dr, Rochester NH 03867
Tel (518) 445-2200
SIC 2221 3496 2399 2899 3089

KID BRANDS INC p 817
1 Meadowlands Plz Ste 803, East Rutherford NJ 07073
Tel (201) 405-2400 *SIC* 2399 3944

ANNIN & CO p 92
105 Eisenhower Pkwy # 203, Roseland NJ 07068
Tel (973) 228-9400 *SIC* 2399

ROSE BRAND WIPERS INC p 1250
4 Emerson Ln, Secaucus NJ 07094
Tel (201) 809-1730 *SIC* 5049 2399

AIR CRUISERS CO LLC p 38
1747 State Route 34, Wall Township NJ 07727
Tel (732) 681-3527
SIC 2531 3069 3728 2399

HICKORY SPRINGS MANUFACTURING CO p 690
235 2nd Ave Nw, Hickory NC 28601
Tel (828) 328-2201
SIC 3069 3495 2514 5072 2399

■ GUILFORD MILLS INC p 646
1001 Military Cutoff Rd # 300, Wilmington NC 28405
Tel (910) 794-5810 *SIC* 2258 2399

▲ SUMMER INFANT INC p 1398
1275 Park East Dr, Woonsocket RI 02895
Tel (401) 671-6550
SIC 2514 2399 3842 3261

SAGE AUTOMOTIVE INTERIORS INC p 1267
3 Research Dr Ste 300, Greenville SC 29607
Tel (864) 987-7778 *SIC* 2399

C&M MARINE AVIATION SERVICES INC p 234
9200 King Arthur Dr, Dallas TX 75247
Tel (214) 654-9270 *SIC* 2399

NATIONAL CONSUMER OUTDOORS CORP p 1011
4215 Mcewen Rd, Dallas TX 75244
Tel (972) 716-4200
SIC 3999 2399 2394 3732

TK HOLDINGS INC p 1457
4611 Wiseman Blvd, San Antonio TX 78251
Tel (210) 509-0762 *SIC* 2399

EVERGREEN ENTERPRISES INC p 514
5915 Midlothian Tpke, Richmond VA 23225
Tel (804) 231-1800
SIC 3253 2399 5193 5999

RECREATIONAL EQUIPMENT INC p 1215
6750 S 228th St, Kent WA 98032
Tel (253) 395-3780
SIC 2329 3949 2399 5941 5961 5699

SIC 2411 Logging

▲ DELTIC TIMBER CORP p 427
210 E Elm St, El Dorado AR 71730
Tel (870) 881-9400
SIC 0811 2411 6531 8741

PRIDE MANUFACTURING CO LLC p 1174
10 N Main St, Burnham ME 04922
Tel (207) 487-3322 *SIC* 2411 3949

UTILITY SUPPLY AND CONSTRUCTION CO p 1537
420 S Roth St Ste A, Reed City MI 49677
Tel (231) 832-2297
SIC 2411 2491 2631 5063

BELL LUMBER & POLE CO p 170
778 1st St Nw, New Brighton MN 55112
Tel (651) 633-4334 *SIC* 5099 2411

MID SOUTH LUMBER INC p 963
1115 C St, Meridian MS 39301
Tel (601) 483-4389 *SIC* 2411

COLUMBIA HELICOPTERS INC p 340
14452 Arndt Rd Ne, Aurora OR 97002
Tel (503) 678-7510 *SIC* 7699 2411 4522

STIMSON LUMBER CO p 1390
520 Sw Yamhill St Ste 700, Portland OR 97204
Tel (503) 222-1676 *SIC* 2421 2493 2411

■ GLATFELTER PULP WOOD CO INC p 614
228 S Main St, Spring Grove PA 17362
Tel (717) 225-4711 *SIC* 5099 2411 2621

COX INDUSTRIES INC p 386
860 Cannon Bridge Rd, Orangeburg SC 29115
Tel (803) 534-7467 *SIC* 2411 2491

▲ WEYERHAEUSER CO p 1603
220 Occidental Ave S, Seattle WA 98104
Tel (253) 924-2345
SIC 6798 0811 2411 2435 2611 2621

LD MCFARLAND CO LIMITED p 849
1640 E Marc St, Tacoma WA 98421
Tel (253) 572-5670 SIC 2499 2491 2411

SIC 2421 Saw & Planing Mills

COOPER MARINE & TIMBERLANDS CORP p 367
118 N Royal St, Mobile AL 36602
Tel (251) 434-5000 SIC 5199 2421

SMITH COOPER/T CORP p 1333
118 N Royal St Ste 1000, Mobile AL 36602
Tel (251) 431-6100
SIC 4499 4492 2421 7692 4491

SOUTHEAST WOOD TREATING INC p 1346
3077 Carter Hill Rd, Montgomery AL 36111
Tel (321) 631-1003 SIC 2421 2491

HB&G BUILDING PRODUCTS INC p 671
1015 S Brundidge Blvd, Troy AL 36081
Tel (334) 566-5000 SIC 2431 2421 2821

WESTERVELT CO p 1600
1400 Jack Warner Pkwy Ne, Tuscaloosa AL 35404
Tel (205) 562-5295 SIC 3553 2421

MCDONOUGH HOLDINGS INC (FN) p 928
21050 N Pima Rd Ste 100, Scottsdale AZ 85255
Tel (602) 544-5900
SIC 2431 4449 2426 2421

ANTHONY TIMBERLANDS INC p 94
3 Executive Cir, Arkadelphia AR 71923
Tel (870) 245-3000 SIC 2421

ANTHONY TIMBERLAND INC p 94
111 S Plum St, Bearden AR 71720
Tel (870) 687-3611 SIC 2421

FOREST ANTHONY PRODUCTS CO p 566
309 N Washington Ave, El Dorado AR 71730
Tel (870) 862-3414 SIC 2421 2452

PRICE COMPANIES INC p 1174
218 Midway Rte, Monticello AR 71655
Tel (870) 367-9751 SIC 2421 2426

HIXSON LUMBER SALES INC p 697
310 S Tennessee St, Pine Bluff AR 71601
Tel (870) 535-1436 SIC 2421 5031

SIERRA PACIFIC INDUSTRIES p 1321
19794 Riverside Ave, Anderson CA 96007
Tel (530) 378-8000 SIC 2421 2431

RELIABLE WHOLESALE LUMBER INC p 1221
7600 Redondo Cir, Huntington Beach CA 92648
Tel (714) 848-8222 SIC 5031 2421

PACIFIC STATES INDUSTRIES INC p 1106
10 Madrone Ave, Morgan Hill CA 95037
Tel (408) 779-7354 SIC 5031 2421 1751

CALIFORNIA CASCADE INDUSTRIES p 239
7512 14th Ave, Sacramento CA 95820
Tel (916) 736-3353 SIC 2491 2421

MENDOCINO FOREST PRODUCTS CO LLC p 943
3700 Old Redwood Hwy # 200, Santa Rosa CA 95403
Tel (707) 620-2961 SIC 5031 2421

TRONOX INC p 1484
1 Stamford Plz, Stamford CT 06901
Tel (203) 705-3800 SIC 2819 2421

BRUNSWICK CELLULOSE LLC p 221
1400 9th St, Brunswick GA 31520
Tel (912) 265-5780
SIC 2611 2421 2899 2631

GILMAN BUILDING PRODUCTS LLC p 612
2500 Saint Marys Rd, Saint Marys GA 31558
Tel (912) 576-0300 SIC 2421

LANGDALE CO p 844
1202 Madison Hwy, Valdosta GA 31601
Tel (229) 242-7450
SIC 2421 2491 7011 7699 5031 5171

IDAHO FOREST GROUP LLC p 728
4447 E Chilco Rd, Athol ID 83801
Tel (208) 255-3200 SIC 2421

▲ BOISE CASCADE CO p 198
1111 W Jefferson St # 300, Boise ID 83702
Tel (208) 384-6161 SIC 2421

■ STONE SOUTHWEST INC p 1391
150 N Michigan Ave, Chicago IL 60601
Tel (312) 346-6600
SIC 2631 2611 2621 2435 2436 2421

TARTER GATE WOOD PRODUCTS INC p 1425
10739 S Us 127, Dunnville KY 42528
Tel (606) 787-2081
SIC 3446 2448 2499 2426 2421

FOREST HUNT PRODUCTS INC p 566
401 E Reynolds Dr, Ruston LA 71270
Tel (318) 255-2245 SIC 2436 2421

HAMMOND LUMBER CO p 656
2 Hammond Dr, Belgrade ME 04917
Tel (207) 495-3303 SIC 5211 2421 5031

ENVIVA PARTNERS LP p 504
7200 Wscnsin Ave Ste 1000, Bethesda MD 20814
Tel (301) 657-5660 SIC 2421

■ NORTH AMERICAN FOREST PRODUCTS LIQUIDATION INC p 1050
27263 May St, Edwardsburg MI 49112
Tel (269) 663-8500 SIC 2421 5031

▲ UNIVERSAL FOREST PRODUCTS INC p 1516
2801 E Beltline Ave Ne, Grand Rapids MI 49525
Tel (616) 364-6161 SIC 2421 1796

MIDWEST HARDWOOD CORP p 967
9540 83rd Ave N, Maple Grove MN 55369
Tel (763) 425-8700 SIC 5031 2421

HOOD INDUSTRIES INC p 705
15 Professional Pkwy # 8, Hattiesburg MS 39402
Tel (601) 264-2962 SIC 2436 2421 5031

JT SHANNON LUMBER CO INC p 796
2200 Cole Rd, Horn Lake MS 38637
Tel (662) 393-3765 SIC 5031 3559 2421

ANDERSON-TULLY CO p 90
1725 N Washington St, Vicksburg MS 39183
Tel (601) 629-3283 SIC 2421 0811

JELD-WEN INC p 782
440 S Church St Ste 400, Charlotte NC 28202
Tel (800) 535-3936 SIC 3442 5031 2421

MARSH FURNITURE CO p 911
1001 S Centennial St, High Point NC 27260
Tel (336) 884-7363 SIC 2434 5712 2421

■ UNILIN FLOORING NC LLC p 1503
550 Cloniger Dr, Thomasville NC 27360
Tel (336) 313-4000 SIC 2421 2426

ITL CORP p 768
23925 Commerce Park, Cleveland OH 44122
Tel (216) 831-3140 SIC 2421 2426

VANPORT MANUFACTURING INC p 1544
28590 Se Wally Rd, Boring OR 97009
Tel (503) 663-4447 SIC 2421 5099

RLC INDUSTRIES CO p 1239
10599 Old Hwy 99 S, Dillard OR 97432
Tel (541) 679-3311 SIC 2493 2436 2421

SENECA SAWMILL CO p 1303
90201 Highway 99 N, Eugene OR 97402
Tel (541) 689-1011 SIC 2421

SWANSON GROUP INC p 1411
2695 Glendale Valley Rd, Glendale OR 97442
Tel (541) 832-1121 SIC 2421 2436 4522

HAMPTON LUMBER MILLS INC p 656
9600 Sw Barnes Rd Ste 200, Portland OR 97225
Tel (503) 297-7691 SIC 2421

HAMPTON LUMBER SALES CO p 656
9600 Sw Barnes Rd Ste 200, Portland OR 97225
Tel (503) 297-7691 SIC 5031 2421 7389

HAMPTON RESOURCES INC p 656
9600 Sw Barnes Rd Ste 200, Portland OR 97225
Tel (503) 297-7691 SIC 5031 2421 0811

STIMSON LUMBER CO p 1390
520 Sw Yamhill St Ste 700, Portland OR 97204
Tel (503) 222-1676 SIC 2421 2493 2411

ROSBORO LLC p 1250
2509 Main St, Springfield OR 97477
Tel (541) 746-8411
SIC 2436 2421 2439 3441 2435

ROSEBURG FOREST PRODUCTS CO p 1250
3660 Gateway St Ste A, Springfield OR 97477
Tel (541) 679-3311
SIC 2436 2421 2493 5031 5211 0811

COLLINS PINE CO p 337
29190 Sw Town Center Loop, Wilsonville OR 97070
Tel (503) 227-1219
SIC 2421 2426 5211 4911 4013

STELLA-JONES CORP p 1385
2 Gateway Ctr Ste 1000, Pittsburgh PA 15222
Tel (412) 894-2846 SIC 2491 2421 3531

RESOLUTE FP US INC p 1227
5300 Cureton Ferry Rd, Catawba SC 29704
Tel (803) 981-8000
SIC 2621 2672 2611 2421

DOMTAR PAPER CO LLC p 449
100 Kingsley Park Dr, Fort Mill SC 29715
Tel (803) 802-7500 SIC 2421 2621

NEW SOUTH COMPANIES INC p 1033
3700 Claypond Rd Ste 6, Myrtle Beach SC 29579
Tel (843) 236-9399 SIC 2421 2491 2431

NEW SOUTH LUMBER CO INC p 1033
3700 Claypond Rd Ste 6, Myrtle Beach SC 29579
Tel (843) 236-9399 SIC 2421

▲ LOUISIANA-PACIFIC CORP p 880
414 Union St Ste 2000, Nashville TN 37219
Tel (615) 986-5600
SIC 2493 2436 2435 2421 2431

▲ BUILDERS FIRSTSOURCE INC p 225
2001 Bryan St Ste 1600, Dallas TX 75201
Tel (214) 880-3500 SIC 2431 2421 5211

MG BUILDING MATERIALS LTD p 958
2651 Sw Military Dr, San Antonio TX 78224
Tel (210) 924-8604 SIC 2421 4212 5211

ROWE FURNITURE INC p 1253
2121 Gardner St, Elliston VA 24087
Tel (540) 389-8671 SIC 2512 2511 2421

▲ TREX CO INC p 1476
160 Exeter Dr, Winchester VA 22603
Tel (540) 542-6300 SIC 2421

INTERFOR US INC p 752
2211 Rimland Dr Ste 220, Bellingham WA 98226
Tel (360) 788-2299 SIC 0811 2421 5031

ALTA FOREST PRODUCTS LLC p 61
810 Nw Alta Way, Chehalis WA 98532
Tel (360) 219-0008 SIC 2421

RSG FOREST PRODUCTS INC p 1256
985 Nw 2nd St, Kalama WA 98625
Tel (360) 673-2825 SIC 2421 2499

KAMILCHE CO p 802
1301 5th Ave Ste 2700, Seattle WA 98101
Tel (206) 224-5800
SIC 2621 2611 2421 2435 2431

■ PLUM CREEK MANUFACTURING LP p 1156
999 3rd Ave Ste 4300, Seattle WA 98104
Tel (206) 467-3600
SIC 2421 2436 2493 5031

■ PLUM CREEK TIMBERLANDS LP p 1156
601 Union St Ste 3100, Seattle WA 98101
Tel (206) 467-3600
SIC 2421 2436 2493 5031

SIMPSON INVESTMENT CO INC p 1325
1301 5th Ave Ste 2700, Seattle WA 98101
Tel (253) 272-0158
SIC 2621 2611 2421 2431 3084

MANKE LUMBER CO INC p 902
1717 Marine View Dr, Tacoma WA 98422
Tel (253) 572-6252 SIC 2421 2491 2499

SIMPSON TIMBER CO p 1325
917 E 11th St, Tacoma WA 98421
Tel (253) 779-6400 SIC 2421 2439

ALLEGHENY WOOD PRODUCTS INC p 52
240 Airport Rd, Petersburg WV 26847
Tel (304) 257-1082 SIC 2421

NEIMAN ENTERPRISES INC p 1025
51 State Highway 112, Hulett WY 82720
Tel (307) 467-5252 SIC 2421

SIC 2426 Hardwood Dimension & Flooring Mills

MCDONOUGH HOLDINGS INC (FN) p 928
21050 N Pima Rd Ste 100, Scottsdale AZ 85255
Tel (602) 544-5900
SIC 2431 4449 2426 2421

PRICE COMPANIES INC p 1174
218 Midway Rte, Monticello AR 71655
Tel (870) 367-9751 SIC 2421 2426

PACIFIC COAST BUILDING PRODUCTS INC p 1104
10600 White Rock Rd # 100, Rancho Cordova CA 95670
Tel (916) 631-6500
SIC 3275 3271 5031 1761 2952 2426

TARTER GATE WOOD PRODUCTS INC p 1425
10739 S Us 127, Dunnville KY 42528
Tel (606) 787-2081
SIC 3446 2448 2499 2426 2421

SOMERSET HARDWOOD FLOORING INC p 1339
70 W Racetrack Rd, Somerset KY 42503
Tel (606) 678-2842 SIC 2426

■ WOODCRAFT INDUSTRIES INC p 1622
525 Lincoln Ave Se, Saint Cloud MN 56304
Tel (320) 656-2345 SIC 2434 2431 2426

LAMPERT YARDS INC p 841
1850 Como Ave, Saint Paul MN 55108
Tel (651) 695-3600
SIC 5211 1521 2439 2426

DIXIE MAT AND HARDWOOD CO p 444
236 Herring Rd, Sandy Hook MS 39478
Tel (601) 876-2427 SIC 2448 2426

HAVCO WOOD PRODUCTS LLC p 668
3200 E Outer Rd, Scott City MO 63780
Tel (573) 334-0611 SIC 2426

■ AIRBORNE SYSTEMS NORTH AMERICA INC p 39
5800 Magnolia Ave, Pennsauken NJ 08109
Tel (856) 663-1275 SIC 2426 3429

ARTISTIC FRAME CORP p 114
979 3rd Ave Ste 1705, New York NY 10022
Tel (212) 289-2100 SIC 2426 5021

▲ LEUCADIA NATIONAL CORP p 858
520 Madison Ave Bsmt A, New York NY 10022
Tel (212) 460-1900
SIC 6798 6211 1382 2011 2426

HUGHES FURNITURE INDUSTRIES INC p 717
952 S Stout Rd, Randleman NC 27317
Tel (336) 498-8700 SIC 2512 7641 2426

■ UNILIN FLOORING NC LLC p 1503
550 Cloniger Dr, Thomasville NC 27360
Tel (336) 313-4000 SIC 2421 2426

ITL CORP p 768
23925 Commerce Park, Cleveland OH 44122
Tel (216) 831-3140 SIC 2421 2426

HAMPTON INVESTMENT CO p 656
9600 Sw Barnes Rd Ste 200, Portland OR 97225
Tel (503) 297-7691 SIC 5031 2435 2426

COLLINS PINE CO p 337
29190 Sw Town Center Loop, Wilsonville OR 97070
Tel (503) 227-1219
SIC 2421 2426 5211 4911 4013

STRICK CORP p 1393
225 Lincoln Hwy, Fairless Hills PA 19030
Tel (215) 949-3600
SIC 3715 2426 3713 3537

▲ ARMSTRONG FLOORING INC p 111
2500 Columbia Ave, Lancaster PA 17603
Tel (717) 672-9611 SIC 3996 2426

■ ARMSTRONG HARDWOOD FLOORING CO p 111
2500 Columbia Ave, Lancaster PA 17603
Tel (717) 672-9611 SIC 2426

■ ARMSTRONG WOOD PRODUCTS INC p 111
2500 Columbia Ave, Lancaster PA 17603
Tel (800) 233-3823 SIC 2426

WEABER INC p 1585
1231 Mount Wilson Rd, Lebanon PA 17042
Tel (717) 867-2212 SIC 2426

WT HARDWOODS GROUP INC p 1628
1231 Mount Wilson Rd, Lebanon PA 17042
Tel (717) 867-2212 SIC 2426

DARLINGTON VENEER CO INC p 412
225 4th St, Darlington SC 29532
Tel (843) 393-3861 SIC 2426

ELKCORP p 488
14911 Quorum Dr Ste 600, Dallas TX 75254
Tel (972) 851-0500
SIC 2952 5033 2426 2431 3471

DAVIS MINING & MANUFACTURING INC p 416
613 Front St E, Coeburn VA 24230
Tel (276) 395-3354
SIC 2892 5082 2426 1221 1222

HARDWOOD LUMBER MANUFACTURING INC p 661
567 N Charlotte Ave, Waynesboro VA 22980
Tel (540) 946-9150 SIC 2426

NORTHWEST HARDWOODS INC p 1059
820 A St Ste 500, Tacoma WA 98402
Tel (253) 568-6800 SIC 2426 5031

RICHARDSON INDUSTRIES INC p 1232
635 Old County Road Pp, Sheboygan Falls WI 53085
Tel (920) 467-2950
SIC 2511 2439 5211 2491 2434 2426

SIC 2429 Special Prdt Sawmills, NEC

PREMIER AG CO-OP INC p 1170
785 S Marr Rd, Columbus IN 47201
Tel (812) 379-9501
SIC 5153 5191 5172 5411 2429

SIC 2431 Millwork

KRONOSPAN INC p 830
1 Kronospan Way, Eastaboga AL 36260
Tel (256) 741-8755 SIC 2431 2295

HB&G BUILDING PRODUCTS INC p 671
1015 S Brundidge Blvd, Troy AL 36081
Tel (334) 566-5000 SIC 2431 2421 2821

MCDONOUGH HOLDINGS INC (FN) p 928
21050 N Pima Rd Ste 100, Scottsdale AZ 85255
Tel (602) 544-5900
SIC 2431 4449 2426 2421

SIERRA PACIFIC INDUSTRIES p 1321
19794 Riverside Ave, Anderson CA 96007
Tel (530) 378-8000 SIC 2421 2431

DECORE-ATIVE SPECIALTIES p 421
2772 Peck Rd, Monrovia CA 91016
Tel (626) 254-9191 SIC 2431

HERITAGE INTERESTS LLC p 686
4300 Jetway Ct, North Highlands CA 95660
Tel (916) 481-5030 SIC 1751 5031 2431

JUDSON ENTERPRISES INC p 797
2440 Gold River Rd # 100, Rancho Cordova CA 95670
Tel (916) 631-9300 SIC 2431 5031

T M COBB CO p 1419
500 Palmyrita Ave, Riverside CA 92507
Tel (951) 248-2400 SIC 2431 3442

SIERRAPINE A CALIFORNIA LIMITED PARTNERSHIP p 1321
1050 Melody Ln Ste 160, Roseville CA 95678
Tel (800) 676-3339 SIC 2431

RAYMOND BUILDING SUPPLY p 1210
7751 Bayshore Rd, Fort Myers FL 33917
Tel (941) 429-1212
SIC 5211 2439 2431 3442 2434 3634

▲ PGT INC p 1140
1070 Technology Dr, North Venice FL 34275
Tel (941) 480-1600 SIC 3442 2431 3211

■ PGT INDUSTRIES INC p 1140
1070 Technology Dr, North Venice FL 34275
Tel (352) 335-5556 SIC 3442 2431 3231

CWS HOLDING CO LLC p 404
1900 Sw 44th Ave, Ocala FL 34474
Tel (352) 368-6922 SIC 2431 3211

■ MASONITE CORP p 916
1 Tampa City Center 20, Tampa FL 33602
Tel (813) 877-2726 SIC 2431 3469

MASONITE HOLDINGS INC p 916
201 N Franklin St Ste 300, Tampa FL 33602
Tel (813) 877-2726 SIC 2431 3442

▲ MASONITE INTERNATIONAL CORP p 916
201 N Franklin St, Tampa FL 33602
Tel (813) 877-2726 SIC 2431 3442

SHAVER PROPERTIES INC p 1312
6010 Old Dixie Hwy Ste K, Vero Beach FL 32967
Tel (772) 569-3466 SIC 2431

CARPENTER CONTRACTORS OF AMERICA INC p 260
3900 Ave D Nw, Winter Haven FL 33880
Tel (863) 294-6449 SIC 1751 2439 2431

▲ BMC STOCK HOLDINGS INC p 193
980 Hammond Dr Ste 500, Atlanta GA 30328
Tel (678) 222-1219
SIC 5211 2431 5031 5713 5251

■ LARSON-JUHL US LLC p 845
3900 Steve Reynolds Blvd, Norcross GA 30093
Tel (770) 279-5200 SIC 2499 3499 2431

MAGBEE BROS LUMBER AND SUPPLY CO INC p 895
1065 Bankhead Hwy, Winder GA 30680
Tel (678) 425-2600
SIC 2431 5211 3531 2439

■ SELECTBUILD CONSTRUCTION INC p 1301
720 E Park Blvd Ste 115, Boise ID 83712
Tel (208) 331-4300
SIC 1521 1771 1751 2431 5031 5211

WINDSOR WINDOW CO p 1615
300 Nw 16th St, Fruitland ID 83619
Tel (800) 452-3801 SIC 2431

WOODGRAIN MILLWORK INC p 1623
300 Nw 16th St, Fruitland ID 83619
Tel (208) 452-3801 SIC 2431

NEISEWANDER ENTERPRISES INC p 1025
1101 E River Rd, Dixon IL 61021
Tel (815) 288-1431 SIC 3442 2431 3429

RAYNOR MFG CO p 1210
1101 E River Rd, Dixon IL 61021
Tel (815) 288-1431
SIC 3442 7011 3699 2431

ROBERT WEED PLYWOOD CORP p 1241
705 Maple St, Bristol IN 46507
Tel (574) 848-7631 SIC 5031 2435 2431

WOOD-MIZER HOLDINGS INC p 1622
8180 W 10th St, Indianapolis IN 46214
Tel (317) 271-1542
SIC 3553 3524 3425 2431

EAGLE WINDOW & DOOR INC p 468
2045 Kerper Blvd, Dubuque IA 52001
Tel (563) 556-2270 SIC 2431

V-T INDUSTRIES INC p 1538
1000 Industrial Park, Holstein IA 51025
Tel (712) 368-4381
SIC 3089 3083 4213 2435 2434 2431

WOODHARBOR MOLDING & MILLWORKS INC p 1623
3277 9th St Sw, Mason City IA 50401
Tel (641) 423-0444
SIC 2431 2521 2517 2434

PELLA CORP p 1128
102 Main St, Pella IA 50219
Tel (641) 621-1000 SIC 2431

CEDAR CREEK LLC p 272
5034 Grand Ridge Dr, West Des Moines IA 50265
Tel (405) 917-8300 SIC 2431 5031

COX INTERIOR INC p 386
1751 Old Columbia Rd, Campbellsville KY 42718
Tel (270) 789-3129 SIC 2431

KENTUCKY-INDIANA LUMBER CO INC p 812
4010 Collins Ln, Louisville KY 40245
Tel (502) 637-1401 SIC 5031 2439 2431

LEE THOMAS H EQUITY FUND V LIMITED PARTNERSHIP p 852
100 Federal St Ste 3500, Boston MA 02110
Tel (617) 737-3261
SIC 3585 3444 3634 2431 3699

THL-NORTEK INVESTORS LLC p 1448
100 Federal St Ste 3100, Boston MA 02110
Tel (617) 227-1050
SIC 3585 3444 3634 2431

NATIONAL LUMBER CO *p* 1014
245 Oakland St, Mansfield MA 02048
Tel (508) 337-8020 *SIC* 5211 2431

HARVEY INDUSTRIES INC *p* 667
1400 Main St Fl 3, Waltham MA 02451
Tel (781) 899-3500
SIC 5031 5033 3442 2431

EMPIRE CO LLC *p* 493
8181 Logistics Dr, Zeeland MI 49464
Tel (616) 772-7272 *SIC* 5031 2431

ODL INC *p* 1074
215 E Roosevelt Ave, Zeeland MI 49464
Tel (616) 772-9111 *SIC* 2431

ANDERSEN CORP *p* 89
100 4th Ave N, Bayport MN 55003
Tel (651) 264-5150 *SIC* 2431 3231

TRUTH HARDWARE CORP *p* 1489
700 W Bridge St, Owatonna MN 55060
Tel (507) 451-5620 *SIC* 2431 3442 3429

■ **WOODCRAFT INDUSTRIES INC** *p* 1622
525 Lincoln Ave Se, Saint Cloud MN 56304
Tel (320) 656-2345 *SIC* 2434 2431 2426

MARVIN LUMBER AND CEDAR CO *p* 914
Hwy 11 & W Lake St, Warroad MN 56763
Tel (218) 386-1430 *SIC* 2431

PAXTON WOOD SOURCE INC *p* 1122
6311 Saint John Ave, Kansas City MO 64123
Tel (816) 483-7000
SIC 5031 2431 5211 5072

PLY GEM PRIME HOLDINGS INC *p* 1157
2600 Grand Blvd Ste 900, Kansas City MO 64108
Tel (888) 975-9436 *SIC* 2431

BRIDGEWATER WHOLESALERS INC *p* 212
210 Industrial Pkwy, Branchburg NJ 08876
Tel (908) 526-7555 *SIC* 2431 5031

CRYSTAL WINDOW & DOOR SYSTEMS LTD *p* 397
3110 Whitestone Expy, Flushing NY 11354
Tel (718) 961-7300
SIC 5031 3442 3231 3211 2431 1751

▲ **GRIFFON CORP** *p* 640
712 5th Ave Fl 18, New York NY 10019
Tel (212) 957-5000
SIC 3442 2431 1751 1799 3083 3663

▲ **PLY GEM HOLDINGS INC** *p* 1157
5020 Weston Pkwy Ste 400, Cary NC 27513
Tel (919) 677-3900 *SIC* 2431 2952

■ **PLY GEM INDUSTRIES INC** *p* 1157
5020 Weston Pkwy Ste 400, Cary NC 27513
Tel (919) 677-3900 *SIC* 2431

ECMD INC *p* 475
2 Grandview St, North Wilkesboro NC 28659
Tel (336) 667-5976 *SIC* 2431 5031

BUILDING CENTER INC *p* 225
10201 Industrial Dr, Pineville NC 28134
Tel (704) 889-8182 *SIC* 5031 2431

■ **BMC EAST LLC** *p* 193
8020 Arco Corp Dr Ste 400, Raleigh NC 27617
Tel (919) 431-1000
SIC 5211 2431 5031 5713 5251

STOCK BUILDING SUPPLY HOLDINGS LLC *p* 1390
8020 Arco Corp Dr Ste 400, Raleigh NC 27617
Tel (919) 431-1000
SIC 5211 2431 5031 5713 5251

AMARR CO *p* 64
165 Carriage Ct, Winston Salem NC 27105
Tel (336) 744-5100
SIC 2431 3442 5031 5211

COOK & BOARDMAN GROUP LLC *p* 365
3916 Westpoint Blvd, Winston Salem NC 27103
Tel (336) 768-8872 *SIC* 2431

■ **PRIMEWOOD INC** *p* 1175
2217 9th St N, Wahpeton ND 58075
Tel (701) 642-2727 *SIC* 2434 2431

CASCADE OHIO INC *p* 262
1209 Maple Ave, Conneaut OH 44030
Tel (440) 593-5800 *SIC* 2431 3442

■ **CLOPAY BUILDING PRODUCTS CO INC** *p* 327
8585 Duke Blvd, Mason OH 45040
Tel (513) 770-4800 *SIC* 2431 3442 2436

■ **CLOPAY CORP** *p* 327
8585 Duke Blvd, Mason OH 45040
Tel (800) 282-2260
SIC 3081 3442 2431 1796

HRH DOOR CORP *p* 714
1 Door Dr, Mount Hope OH 44660
Tel (850) 208-3400 *SIC* 3442 2431

BRIGHT WOOD CORP *p* 213
335 Nw Hess St, Madras OR 97741
Tel (541) 475-2234 *SIC* 2431

CONESTOGA WOOD SPECIALTIES CORP *p* 355
245 Reading Rd, East Earl PA 17519
Tel (717) 445-6701 *SIC* 2431 2521 2434

84 LUMBER CO *p* 4
1019 Route 519, Eighty Four PA 15330
Tel (724) 228-8820
SIC 2431 2439 5031 5211

RITESCREEN CO LLC *p* 1237
4314 State Route 209, Elizabethville PA 17023
Tel (717) 362-7483 *SIC* 3442 2431

CIW ENTERPRISES INC *p* 320
24 Elmwood Ave, Mountain Top PA 18707
Tel (800) 233-8366 *SIC* 3442 3446 2431

■ **MOHAWK FLUSH DOORS** *p* 982
980 Point Township Dr, Northumberland PA 17857
Tel (570) 473-3557 *SIC* 2431

■ **BUILDERS FIRSTSOURCE- SOUTHEAST GROUP LLC** *p* 225
2451 E Highway 501, Conway SC 29526
Tel (843) 347-4224 *SIC* 5211 2431

NEW SOUTH COMPANIES INC *p* 1033
3700 Claypond Rd Ste 6, Myrtle Beach SC 29579
Tel (843) 236-9399 *SIC* 2421 2491 2431

WEST FRASER INC *p* 1594
1900 Exeter Rd Ste 105, Germantown TN 38138
Tel (901) 620-4200 *SIC* 2431 0831

WEST FRASER WOOD PRODUCTS INC *p* 1594
1900 Exeter Rd Ste 105, Germantown TN 38138
Tel (901) 620-4200 *SIC* 2431

▲ **LOUISIANA-PACIFIC CORP** *p* 880
414 Union St Ste 2000, Nashville TN 37219
Tel (615) 986-5600
SIC 2493 2436 2435 2421 2431

MARVIN WINDOWS OF TENNESSEE INC *p* 914
101 Marvin Dr, Ripley TN 38063
Tel (731) 635-5190 *SIC* 2431 3231

ATRIUM WINDOWS AND DOORS INC *p* 129
3890 W Northwest Hwy # 500, Dallas TX 75220
Tel (214) 956-8031
SIC 3442 2431 3089 3354 7629

▲ **BUILDERS FIRSTSOURCE INC** *p* 225
2001 Bryan St Ste 1600, Dallas TX 75201
Tel (214) 880-3500 *SIC* 2431 2421 5211

ELKCORP *p* 488
14911 Quorum Dr Ste 600, Dallas TX 75254
Tel (972) 851-0500
SIC 2952 5033 2426 2431 3471

SANWA USA INC *p* 1281
4020 Mcewen Rd Ste 118, Dallas TX 75244
Tel (972) 503-3031
SIC 3442 2431 3699 3537

TEXAS PLYWOOD AND LUMBER CO INC *p* 1444
1001 E Avenue K, Grand Prairie TX 75050
Tel (972) 262-1331 *SIC* 5031 2431

OVERHEAD DOOR CORP *p* 1099
2501 S State Hwy 121 Ste, Lewisville TX 75067
Tel (469) 549-7100
SIC 3442 2431 3699 3537 3589

FOXWORTH GALBRAITH LUMBER CO *p* 573
4965 Preston Park Blvd # 400, Plano TX 75093
Tel (972) 665-2400
SIC 5211 5031 2439 2431

STEVES & SONS INC *p* 1388
203 Humble Ave, San Antonio TX 78225
Tel (210) 924-5111 *SIC* 2431

LAMINATE CO *p* 841
6612 James Madison Hwy, Haymarket VA 20169
Tel (703) 753-0699 *SIC* 5031 2431

■ **MW MANUFACTURERS INC** *p* 1004
433 N Main St, Rocky Mount VA 24151
Tel (540) 483-0211 *SIC* 2431

T & A SUPPLY CO INC *p* 1419
6821 S 216th St Bldg A, Kent WA 98032
Tel (206) 282-3770
SIC 1771 5023 1752 2431

KAMILCHE CO *p* 802
1301 5th Ave Ste 2700, Seattle WA 98101
Tel (206) 224-5800
SIC 2621 2611 2421 2435 2431

SIMPSON INVESTMENT CO INC *p* 1325
1301 5th Ave Ste 2700, Seattle WA 98101
Tel (253) 272-0158
SIC 2621 2611 2421 2431 3084

SIMEX INC *p* 1324
181 Pleasant Indus Ctr, Saint Marys WV 26170
Tel (304) 665-1104 *SIC* 5039 2431

MENARD INC *p* 943
5101 Menard Dr, Eau Claire WI 54703
Tel (715) 876-5911 *SIC* 2431 5211

AWS/GB CORP *p* 139
2929 Walker Dr, Green Bay WI 54311
Tel (920) 406-4000
SIC 5031 2431 3442 5033 1542 1541

■ **MARSHFIELD DOORSYSTEMS INC** *p* 911
1401 E 4th St, Marshfield WI 54449
Tel (715) 384-2141 *SIC* 2431 3442

HWD ACQUISITION INC *p* 722
575 S Whelen Ave, Medford WI 54451
Tel (800) 433-4873 *SIC* 2431

PEACHTREE COMPANIES INC *p* 1125
1 Weathershield Plz, Medford WI 54451
Tel (715) 748-6555 *SIC* 3442 2431

WEATHER SHIELD MFG INC *p* 1585
1 Weathershield Plz, Medford WI 54451
Tel (715) 748-2100 *SIC* 2431 3089 3442

GOSSEN CORP *p* 626
2030 W Bender Rd, Milwaukee WI 53209
Tel (800) 558-8984 *SIC* 2431 3089 2452

EGGERS INDUSTRIES INC *p* 481
1 Eggers Dr, Two Rivers WI 54241
Tel (920) 793-1351 *SIC* 2431 2435

KOLBE & KOLBE MILLWORK CO INC *p* 826
1323 S 11th Ave, Wausau WI 54401
Tel (715) 842-5666 *SIC* 5031 2431

SIC 2434 Wood Kitchen Cabinets

WELLBORN CABINET INC *p* 1589
38669 Highway 77, Ashland AL 36251
Tel (256) 354-7151 *SIC* 2434 2511 5032

RSI HOME PRODUCTS INC *p* 1256
400 E Orangethorpe Ave, Anaheim CA 92801
Tel (714) 449-2200
SIC 2514 2541 3281 2434

ROYAL CABINETS INC *p* 1254
1299 E Phillips Blvd, Pomona CA 91766
Tel (909) 629-8565 *SIC* 2434 2511

ZWD PRODUCTS CORP *p* 1645
400 Lukens Dr, New Castle DE 19720
Tel (302) 326-8200 *SIC* 2434 2514

RAYMOND BUILDING SUPPLY *p* 1210
7751 Bayshore Rd, Fort Myers FL 33917
Tel (941) 429-1212
SIC 5211 2439 2431 3442 2434 3634

ELKAY MANUFACTURING CO INC *p* 487
2222 Camden Ct, Oak Brook IL 60523
Tel (630) 574-8484
SIC 3431 3585 3432 2434

■ **H-C LIQUIDATING CORP** *p* 651
1002 Eisenhower Dr N, Goshen IN 46526
Tel (574) 535-9300 *SIC* 2434

■ **MASTERBRAND CABINETS INC** *p* 918
1 Masterbrand Cabinets Dr, Jasper IN 47546
Tel (812) 482-2527 *SIC* 2434

SACO INDUSTRIES INC *p* 1264
17151 Morse St, Lowell IN 46356
Tel (219) 690-9900 *SIC* 2434

KOUNTRY WOOD PRODUCTS LLC *p* 828
352 Shawnee St, Nappanee IN 46550
Tel (574) 773-5673 *SIC* 2434 5211 5031

V-T INDUSTRIES INC *p* 1538
1000 Industrial Park, Holstein IA 51025
Tel (712) 368-4381
SIC 3089 3083 4213 2435 2434 2431

WOODHARBOR MOLDING & MILLWORKS INC *p* 1623
3277 9th St Sw, Mason City IA 50401
Tel (641) 423-0444
SIC 2431 2521 2517 2434

■ **OMEGA CABINETS LTD** *p* 1084
1205 Peters Dr, Waterloo IA 50703
Tel (319) 235-5700 *SIC* 2434 5211

■ **MASCO BUILDER CABINET GROUP** *p* 915
5353 W Us Highway 223, Adrian MI 49221
Tel (517) 264-9153 *SIC* 2434

■ **MERILLAT LP** *p* 949
5353 W Us Highway 223, Adrian MI 49221
Tel (517) 263-0771 *SIC* 2434

■ **MASCO CABINETRY LLC** *p* 915
4600 Arrowhead Dr, Ann Arbor MI 48105
Tel (734) 205-4600 *SIC* 2434

▲ **MASCO CORP** *p* 915
21001 Van Born Rd, Taylor MI 48180
Tel (313) 274-7400
SIC 2434 3432 3088 3429 1742

NORCRAFT HOLDINGS LP *p* 1047
950 Blue Gentian Rd, Eagan MN 55121
Tel (800) 297-0661 *SIC* 2434

■ **WOODCRAFT INDUSTRIES INC** *p* 1622
525 Lincoln Ave Se, Saint Cloud MN 56304
Tel (320) 656-2345 *SIC* 2434 2431 2426

■ **NORCRAFT COMPANIES INC** *p* 1047
950 Blue Gentian Rd # 200, Saint Paul MN 55121
Tel (800) 297-0661 *SIC* 2434

■ **NORCRAFT COMPANIES LP** *p* 1047
950 Blue Gentian Rd # 200, Saint Paul MN 55121
Tel (651) 234-3300 *SIC* 2434

ELKAY WOOD PRODUCTS CO *p* 488
1 Medallion Way, Waconia MN 55387
Tel (952) 442-5171 *SIC* 2434

MEDALLION CABINETRY INC *p* 935
1 Medallion Way Ste 10501, Waconia MN 55387
Tel (952) 442-5171 *SIC* 2434

FABUWOOD CABINETRY CORP *p* 523
99 Caven Point Rd, Jersey City NJ 07305
Tel (201) 432-6555 *SIC* 2434

MARSH FURNITURE CO *p* 911
1001 S Centennial St, High Point NC 27260
Tel (336) 884-7363 *SIC* 2434 5712 2421

■ **PRIMEWOOD INC** *p* 1175
2217 9th St N, Wahpeton ND 58075
Tel (701) 642-2727 *SIC* 2434 2431

■ **MASCO CABINETRY MIDDLEFIELD LLC** *p* 915
15535 S State Ave, Middlefield OH 44062
Tel (440) 632-5333 *SIC* 2434

CONESTOGA WOOD SPECIALTIES CORP *p* 355
245 Reading Rd, East Earl PA 17519
Tel (717) 445-6701 *SIC* 2431 2521 2434

WOOD-MODE INC *p* 1622
1 Second St, Kreamer PA 17833
Tel (570) 374-2711 *SIC* 2434

NORTEK INC *p* 1049
500 Exchange St, Providence RI 02903
Tel (401) 751-1600
SIC 3585 3444 3634 3699 2434

■ **STARMARK CABINETRY** *p* 1379
600 E 48th St N, Sioux Falls SD 57104
Tel (800) 755-7789 *SIC* 2434

H T HACKNEY CO *p* 650
502 S Gay St Ste 300, Knoxville TN 37902
Tel (865) 546-1291
SIC 5141 5172 2434 5084

KENT MOORE CABINETS LTD *p* 812
501 Industrial Blvd, Bryan TX 77803
Tel (979) 775-2906 *SIC* 2434

BJT PROPERTIES INC *p* 186
12770 Coit Rd Ste 1100, Dallas TX 75251
Tel (210) 225-0290 *SIC* 2434

REPUBLIC NATIONAL CABINET CORP *p* 1225
1400 Warren Dr, Marshall TX 75672
Tel (903) 935-3680 *SIC* 2434

REPUBLIC NATIONAL INDUSTRIES OF TEXAS LP *p* 1225
1400 Warren Dr, Marshall TX 75672
Tel (903) 935-3680 *SIC* 2434 5211 2541

LEEDO MANUFACTURING CO LP *p* 852
10707 Corp Dr Ste 250, Stafford TX 77477
Tel (866) 465-3336 *SIC* 2434

ACPRODUCTS INC *p* 18
3551 Plano Pkwy, The Colony TX 75056
Tel (214) 469-3000 *SIC* 2434

■ **WOODCRAFTERS HOME PRODUCTS HOLDING LLC** *p* 1622
3700 Camino De Verdad Rd, Weslaco TX 78596
Tel (956) 647-8300 *SIC* 2434

■ **WOODCRAFTERS HOME PRODUCTS LLC** *p* 1622
3700 Camino De Verdad Rd, Weslaco TX 78596
Tel (956) 565-6329 *SIC* 2434

▲ **AMERICAN WOODMARK CORP** *p* 81
3102 Shawnee Dr, Winchester VA 22601
Tel (540) 665-9100 *SIC* 2434

RICHARDSON INDUSTRIES INC *p* 1232
635 Old County Road Pp, Sheboygan Falls WI 53085
Tel (920) 467-2950
SIC 2511 2439 5211 2491 2434 2426

SIC 2435 Hardwood Veneer & Plywood

SWANER HARDWOOD CO INC *p* 1411
5 W Magnolia Blvd, Burbank CA 91502
Tel (818) 953-5350 *SIC* 2435 5031

GEORGIA PACIFIC HOLDINGS INC *p* 607
13208 Hadley St Apt 1, Whittier CA 90601
Tel (626) 926-1474
SIC 2676 2656 2435 2821

GEORGIA-PACIFIC LLC *p* 608
133 Peachtree St Ne # 4810, Atlanta GA 30303
Tel (404) 652-4000
SIC 2676 2656 2653 2435 2821 3275

■ **STONE SOUTHWEST INC** *p* 1391
150 N Michigan Ave, Chicago IL 60601
Tel (312) 346-6600
SIC 2631 2611 2621 2435 2436 2421

ROBERT WEED PLYWOOD CORP *p* 1241
705 Maple St, Bristol IN 46507
Tel (574) 848-7631 *SIC* 5031 2435 2431

▲ **PATRICK INDUSTRIES INC** *p* 1120
107 W Franklin St, Elkhart IN 46516
Tel (574) 294-7511
SIC 3275 2493 2435 5031 5033 2891

V-T INDUSTRIES INC *p* 1538
1000 Industrial Park, Holstein IA 51025
Tel (712) 368-4381
SIC 3089 3083 4213 2435 2434 2431

MARTCO LLC *p* 911
2189 Memorial Dr, Alexandria LA 71301
Tel (318) 448-0405 *SIC* 2493 2435

MARTIN SUSTAINABLE RESOURCES LLC *p* 913
2189 Memorial Dr, Alexandria LA 71301
Tel (318) 448-0405 *SIC* 2493 2435

NORTHERN CONTOURS INC *p* 1056
1355 Mendota Heights Rd # 100, Saint Paul MN 55120
Tel (651) 695-1698 *SIC* 3083 1751 2435

MANNINGTON MILLS INC *p* 902
75 Mannington Mills Rd, Salem NJ 08079
Tel (856) 935-3000
SIC 3996 3253 2273 2435

COLUMBIA FOREST PRODUCTS INC *p* 340
7900 Triad Center Dr # 200, Greensboro NC 27409
Tel (336) 605-0429 *SIC* 2435

SIMS-LOHMAN INC *p* 1326
6325 Este Ave, Cincinnati OH 45232
Tel (513) 651-3510 *SIC* 5031 2435

DECORATIVE PANELS INTERNATIONAL INC *p* 421
2900 Hill Ave, Toledo OH 43607
Tel (419) 535-5921 *SIC* 2435

MURPHY CO *p* 1001
2350 Prairie Rd, Eugene OR 97402
Tel (541) 461-4545 *SIC* 2435 2436

SWANSON GROUP MFG LLC *p* 1411
2695 Glendale Valley Rd, Glendale OR 97442
Tel (541) 832-1121 *SIC* 2435

COLUMBIA FOREST PRODUCTS CORP *p* 340
222 Sw Columbia St # 610, Portland OR 97201
Tel (503) 224-5300 *SIC* 2435

COLUMBIA PLYWOOD CORP *p* 341
222 Sw Columbia St # 1575, Portland OR 97201
Tel (503) 224-5300 *SIC* 2435

HAMPTON INVESTMENT CO *p* 656
9600 Sw Barnes Rd Ste 200, Portland OR 97225
Tel (503) 297-7691 *SIC* 5031 2435 2426

ROSBORO LLC *p* 1250
2509 Main St, Springfield OR 97477
Tel (541) 746-8411
SIC 2436 2421 2439 3441 2435

TIMBER PRODUCTS CO LIMITED PARTNERSHIP *p* 1454
305 S 4th St, Springfield OR 97477
Tel (541) 747-4577
SIC 2436 2435 5031 2493

INTERNATIONAL TIMBER AND VENEER LLC *p* 757
75 Mcquiston Dr, Jackson Center PA 16133
Tel (724) 662-0880 *SIC* 2435 5031

▲ **LOUISIANA-PACIFIC CORP** *p* 880
414 Union St Ste 2000, Nashville TN 37219
Tel (615) 986-5600
SIC 2493 2436 2435 2421 2431

KAMILCHE CO *p* 802
1301 5th Ave Ste 2700, Seattle WA 98101
Tel (206) 224-5800
SIC 2621 2611 2421 2435 2431

▲ **WEYERHAEUSER CO** *p* 1603
220 Occidental Ave S, Seattle WA 98104
Tel (253) 924-2345
SIC 6798 0811 2411 2435 2611 2621

EGGERS INDUSTRIES INC *p* 481
1 Eggers Dr, Two Rivers WI 54241
Tel (920) 793-1351 *SIC* 2431 2435

SIC 2436 Softwood Veneer & Plywood

MAXCO SUPPLY INC *p* 922
605 S Zediker Ave, Parlier CA 93648
Tel (559) 646-8449 *SIC* 5113 2436 3554

COASTAL FOREST RESOURCES CO *p* 331
8007 Florida Georgia Hwy, Havana FL 32333
Tel (850) 539-6432
SIC 2436 2491 0811 0851

■ **STONE SOUTHWEST INC** *p* 1391
150 N Michigan Ave, Chicago IL 60601
Tel (312) 346-6600
SIC 2631 2611 2621 2435 2436 2421

FOREST HUNT PRODUCTS INC *p* 566
401 E Reynolds Dr, Ruston LA 71270
Tel (318) 255-2245 *SIC* 2436 2421

HOOD INDUSTRIES INC *p* 705
15 Professional Pkwy # 8, Hattiesburg MS 39402
Tel (601) 264-2962 *SIC* 2436 2421 5031

BALTEK INC *p* 149
5240 National Center Dr, Colfax NC 27235
Tel (336) 398-1900 *SIC* 2436

■ **CLOPAY BUILDING PRODUCTS CO INC** *p* 327
8585 Duke Blvd, Mason OH 45040
Tel (513) 770-4800 *SIC* 2431 3442 2436

RLC INDUSTRIES CO *p* 1239
10599 Old Hwy 99 S, Dillard OR 97432
Tel (541) 679-3311 *SIC* 2493 2436 2421

MURPHY CO p 1001
2350 Prairie Rd, Eugene OR 97402
Tel (541) 461-4545 SIC 2435 2436

SWANSON GROUP INC p 1411
2695 Glendale Valley Rd, Glendale OR 97442
Tel (541) 832-1121 SIC 2421 2436 4522

ROSBORO LLC p 1250
2509 Main St, Springfield OR 97477
Tel (541) 746-8411
SIC 2436 2421 2439 3441 2435

ROSEBURG FOREST PRODUCTS CO p 1250
3660 Gateway St Ste A, Springfield OR 97477
Tel (541) 679-3311
SIC 2436 2421 2493 5031 5211 0811

TIMBER PRODUCTS CO LIMITED PARTNERSHIP p 1454
305 S 4th St, Springfield OR 97477
Tel (541) 747-4577
SIC 2436 2435 5031 2493

▲ LOUISIANA-PACIFIC CORP p 880
414 Union St Ste 2000, Nashville TN 37219
Tel (615) 986-5600
SIC 2493 2436 2435 2421 2431

■ PLUM CREEK MANUFACTURING LP p 1156
999 3rd Ave Ste 4300, Seattle WA 98104
Tel (206) 467-3600
SIC 2421 2436 2493 5031

■ PLUM CREEK TIMBERLANDS LP p 1156
601 Union St Ste 3100, Seattle WA 98101
Tel (206) 467-3600
SIC 2421 2436 2493 5031

SIC 2439 Structural Wood Members, NEC

■ ERICKSON BUILDING COMPONENTS LLC p 507
250 N Beck Ave, Chandler AZ 85226
Tel (480) 627-1100 SIC 2439 2452

CALIFORNIA TRUSFRAME LLC p 241
23665 Cajalco Rd, Perris CA 92570
Tel (951) 657-7491 SIC 2439

▲ EASTERN CO p 472
112 Bridge St, Naugatuck CT 06770
Tel (203) 729-2255
SIC 3429 3452 3316 2439

RAYMOND BUILDING SUPPLY p 1210
7751 Bayshore Rd, Fort Myers FL 33917
Tel (941) 429-1212
SIC 5211 2439 2431 3442 2434 3634

CARPENTER CONTRACTORS OF AMERICA INC p 260
3900 Ave D Nw, Winter Haven FL 33880
Tel (863) 294-6449 SIC 1751 2439 2431

MAGBEE BROS LUMBER AND SUPPLY CO INC p 895
1065 Bankhead Hwy, Winder GA 30680
Tel (678) 425-2600
SIC 2431 5211 3531 2439

MINOVA HOLDING INC p 974
150 Carley Ct, Georgetown KY 40324
Tel (502) 863-6800 SIC 2821 3564 2439

ORICA GROUND SUPPORT INC p 1094
150 Summer Ct, Georgetown KY 40324
Tel (502) 863-6800
SIC 5082 3564 2439 7699

KENTUCKY-INDIANA LUMBER CO INC p 812
4010 Collins Ln, Louisville KY 40245
Tel (502) 637-1401 SIC 5031 2439 2431

CREST INDUSTRIES p 392
4725 Highway 28 E, Pineville LA 71360
Tel (318) 767-5530
SIC 3699 3612 3441 5063 2439

CREST OPERATIONS LLC p 392
4725 Highway 28 E, Pineville LA 71360
Tel (318) 448-0274
SIC 3441 2439 3699 5063 3612

LAMPERT YARDS INC p 841
1850 Como Ave, Saint Paul MN 55108
Tel (651) 695-3600
SIC 5211 1521 2439 2426

WOODBRIDGE CORP p 1622
11 Cermak Blvd, Saint Peters MO 63376
Tel (636) 970-1002 SIC 2439

■ UFP MID-ATLANTIC LLC p 1499
5631 S Nc Highway 62, Burlington NC 27215
Tel (336) 226-9356 SIC 2439

STARK TRUSS CO INC p 1379
109 Miles Ave Sw, Canton OH 44710
Tel (330) 478-2100 SIC 5031 2439

ROSBORO LLC p 1250
2509 Main St, Springfield OR 97477
Tel (541) 746-8411
SIC 2436 2421 2439 3441 2435

84 LUMBER CO p 4
1019 Route 519, Eighty Four PA 15330
Tel (724) 228-8820
SIC 2431 2439 5031 5211

BERKS PRODUCTS CORP p 175
167 Berks Products Dr, Leesport PA 19533
Tel (610) 374-5131
SIC 5031 3273 5983 5172 2439 1711

TINDELLS INC p 1455
7751 Norris Fwy, Knoxville TN 37938
Tel (865) 922-7751 SIC 5031 5211 2439

■ BUILDERS FIRSTSOURCE-TEXAS GROUP LP p 225
3403 E Abram St, Arlington TX 76010
Tel (214) 880-3500 SIC 5031 5033 2439

UFP GRANDVIEW LLC p 1499
1000 S 3rd St, Grandview TX 76050
Tel (817) 866-3306 SIC 5031 2439

TRUSSWAY HOLDINGS INC p 1487
9411 Alcorn St, Houston TX 77093
Tel (713) 691-6900 SIC 2439

TRUSSWAY INDUSTRIES INC p 1487
9411 Alcorn St, Houston TX 77093
Tel (713) 691-6900 SIC 2439

TRUSSWAY MANUFACTURING INC p 1487
9411 Alcorn St, Houston TX 77093
Tel (719) 322-9662 SIC 2439 5031

FOXWORTH GALBRAITH LUMBER CO p 573
4965 Preston Park Blvd # 400, Plano TX 75093
Tel (972) 665-2400
SIC 5211 5031 2439 2431

■ STOCK BUILDING SUPPLY WEST LLC p 1390
1133 W 9000 S, West Jordan UT 84088
Tel (801) 561-9000 SIC 5031 5211 2439

SIMPSON TIMBER CO p 1325
917 E 11th St, Tacoma WA 98421
Tel (253) 779-6400 SIC 2421 2439

RICHARDSON INDUSTRIES INC p 1232
635 Old County Road Pp, Sheboygan Falls WI 53085
Tel (920) 467-2950
SIC 2511 2439 5211 2491 2434 2426

SIC 2441 Wood Boxes

CALPINE CONTAINERS INC p 242
6425 N Palm Ave Ste 104, Fresno CA 93704
Tel (559) 519-7199
SIC 5113 5085 2441 2448

EXPORT PACKAGING CO INC p 520
525 10th Ave E, Milan IL 61264
Tel (309) 756-4288 SIC 4783 2448 2441

ATLAS BOX AND CRATING CO INC p 127
223 Wrcster Prvdence Tpke, Sutton MA 01590
Tel (508) 865-1155 SIC 2441 2448 2653

INTERMETRO INDUSTRIES CORP p 753
651 N Washington St, Wilkes Barre PA 18705
Tel (570) 825-2741
SIC 3496 2542 3537 3411 3315 2441

NEFAB COMPANIES INC p 1024
204 Airline Dr Ste 100, Coppell TX 75019
Tel (866) 332-4425 SIC 2448 2449 2441

NEFAB PACKAGING NORTH EAST LLC p 1024
204 Airline Dr Ste 100, Coppell TX 75019
Tel (469) 444-5264 SIC 2448 2449 2441

BANA INC p 149
624 E Mcleroy Blvd, Saginaw TX 76179
Tel (817) 232-3750 SIC 5085 2441 2448

SIC 2448 Wood Pallets & Skids

COMMERCIAL LUMBER & PALLET CO INC p 345
135 Long Ln, City Of Industry CA 91746
Tel (626) 968-0631 SIC 2448 5031

CALPINE CONTAINERS INC p 242
6425 N Palm Ave Ste 104, Fresno CA 93704
Tel (559) 519-7199
SIC 5113 5085 2441 2448

FRUIT GROWERS SUPPLY CO INC p 582
27770 N Entrmt Dr Fl 3, Valencia CA 91355
Tel (818) 986-6480
SIC 2653 0811 5191 2448 5113

PALLETONE INC p 1108
1470 Us Highway 17 S, Bartow FL 33830
Tel (863) 533-1147 SIC 2448

CHEP RECYCLED PALLET SOLUTIONS LLC p 294
8517 Suthpark Cir Ste 140, Orlando FL 32819
Tel (713) 332-6145 SIC 2448 0831

ELBERTA CRATE & BOX CO p 483
606 Dothan Rd, Bainbridge GA 39817
Tel (229) 243-1268 SIC 2449 5023 2448

EXPORT PACKAGING CO INC p 520
525 10th Ave E, Milan IL 61264
Tel (309) 756-4288 SIC 4783 2448 2441

FCA LLC p 532
7601 John Deere Pkwy, Moline IL 61265
Tel (309) 792-3444
SIC 4783 5031 5085 2448

STERLING LUMBER CO p 1387
501 E 151st St, Phoenix IL 60426
Tel (708) 388-2223 SIC 5031 7389 2448

ANTHONY WAYNE REHABILITATION CENTER FOR HANDICAPPED AND BLIND INC p 94
8515 Bluffton Rd, Fort Wayne IN 46809
Tel (260) 744-6145
SIC 8331 7331 3441 3412 2449 2448

SEEDORFF MASONRY INC p 1300
408 W Mission St, Strawberry Point IA 52076
Tel (563) 933-2296 SIC 1741 2448

PRATT (LOVE BOX) LLC p 1167
700 E 37th St N, Wichita KS 67219
Tel (316) 838-0851 SIC 2653 2448 4213

TARTER GATE WOOD PRODUCTS INC p 1425
10739 S Us 127, Dunnville KY 42528
Tel (606) 787-2081
SIC 3446 2448 2499 2426 2421

ATLAS BOX AND CRATING CO INC p 127
223 Wrcster Prvdence Tpke, Sutton MA 01590
Tel (508) 865-1155 SIC 2441 2448 2653

KAMPS INC p 802
2900 Peach Ridge Ave Nw, Grand Rapids MI 49534
Tel (616) 453-9676 SIC 2448 2499

DIXIE MAT AND HARDWOOD CO p 444
236 Herring Rd, Sandy Hook MS 39478
Tel (601) 876-2427 SIC 2448 2426

NEFAB COMPANIES INC p 1024
204 Airline Dr Ste 100, Coppell TX 75019
Tel (866) 332-4425 SIC 2448 2449 2441

NEFAB PACKAGING NORTH EAST LLC p 1024
204 Airline Dr Ste 100, Coppell TX 75019
Tel (469) 444-5264 SIC 2448 2449 2441

IFCO SYSTEMS NORTH AMERICA LLC p 730
13100 Nw Fwy Ste 625, Houston TX 77040
Tel (888) 714-2430 SIC 2448

BANA INC p 149
624 E Mcleroy Blvd, Saginaw TX 76179
Tel (817) 232-3750 SIC 5085 2441 2448

SIC 2449 Wood Containers, NEC

REYNOLDS PACKING CO p 1231
33 E Tokay St, Lodi CA 95240
Tel (209) 369-2725 SIC 0723 5148 2449

VEGETABLE GROWERS SUPPLY CO p 1546
1360 Merrill St, Salinas CA 93901
Tel (831) 759-4600 SIC 5199 2449

L & L NURSERY SUPPLY INC p 833
2552 Shenandoah Way, San Bernardino CA 92407
Tel (909) 591-0461
SIC 5191 2875 2449 5193

■ GPI HOLDINGS INC p 627
1500 Riveredge Pkwy # 100, Atlanta GA 30328
Tel (770) 240-7200
SIC 2631 2653 2449 4922

ELBERTA CRATE & BOX CO p 483
606 Dothan Rd, Bainbridge GA 39817
Tel (229) 243-1268 SIC 2449 5023 2448

ANTHONY WAYNE REHABILITATION CENTER FOR HANDICAPPED AND BLIND INC p 94
8515 Bluffton Rd, Fort Wayne IN 46809
Tel (260) 744-6145
SIC 8331 7331 3441 3412 2449 2448

▲ BROWN-FORMAN CORP p 220
850 Dixie Hwy, Louisville KY 40210
Tel (502) 585-1100 SIC 2085 2084 2449

LANDSCAPE FORMS INC p 843
7800 E Michigan Ave, Kalamazoo MI 49048
Tel (269) 381-0396
SIC 2531 2522 2511 2449 3648

INDEPENDENT STAVE CO LLC p 737
1078 S Jefferson Ave, Lebanon MO 65536
Tel (417) 588-4151 SIC 2449 5947 2499

ISCO HOLDING CO INC p 766
1078 S Jefferson Ave, Lebanon MO 65536
Tel (417) 588-4151 SIC 2449

▲ GREIF INC p 639
425 Winter Rd, Delaware OH 43015
Tel (740) 549-6000
SIC 2653 2449 2655 3412 3089 2674

NEFAB COMPANIES INC p 1024
204 Airline Dr Ste 100, Coppell TX 75019
Tel (866) 332-4425 SIC 2448 2449 2441

NEFAB PACKAGING NORTH EAST LLC p 1024
204 Airline Dr Ste 100, Coppell TX 75019
Tel (469) 444-5264 SIC 2448 2449 2441

SIC 2451 Mobile Homes

■ CAVALIER HOME BUILDERS LLC p 267
32 Wilson Blvd 100, Addison AL 35540
Tel (256) 747-1575 SIC 2451

■ CAVALIER HOMES INC p 267
32 Wilson Blvd Ste 100, Addison AL 35540
Tel (256) 747-1575 SIC 2451

■ SOUTHERN ENERGY HOMES INC p 1348
144 Corporate Way, Addison AL 35540
Tel (256) 747-8589 SIC 2451 5271

▲ CAVCO INDUSTRIES INC p 267
1001 N Central Ave # 800, Phoenix AZ 85004
Tel (602) 256-6263 SIC 2451 5271

■ FH GROUP LLC p 539
1001 N Central Ave # 800, Phoenix AZ 85004
Tel (574) 773-7941 SIC 2451

■ FLEETWOOD HOMES INC p 555
1001 N Central Ave # 800, Phoenix AZ 85004
Tel (602) 256-6263 SIC 2451 5271

FLEETWOOD ENTERPRISES INC p 555
1351 Pomona Rd Ste 230, Corona CA 92882
Tel (951) 354-3000 SIC 3799 2451 5561

■ CMH CAPITAL INC p 329
1105 N Market St Ste 1300, Wilmington DE 19801
Tel (302) 651-7947
SIC 6719 2451 6515 6311

HORTON INDUSTRIES INC p 708
101 Industrial Blvd, Eatonton GA 31024
Tel (706) 485-8506 SIC 2451 5271

GENERAL HOUSING INC p 601
2255 Industrial Blvd, Waycross GA 31503
Tel (912) 285-5068 SIC 2451

▲ SKYLINE CORP p 1330
2520 Bypass Rd, Elkhart IN 46514
Tel (574) 294-6521 SIC 2451 2452 3792

■ SKYLINE HOMES INC p 1330
2520 Bypass Rd, Elkhart IN 46514
Tel (574) 294-6521 SIC 2451 3792

■ ZIEMAN MANUFACTURING CO INC p 1643
2703 College Ave, Goshen IN 46528
Tel (574) 535-1125
SIC 3715 3441 2451 3799

■ FAIRMONT HOMES LLC p 525
502 S Oakland Ave, Nappanee IN 46550
Tel (574) 773-7941 SIC 2451

GULF STREAM COACH INC p 647
503 S Oakland Ave, Nappanee IN 46550
Tel (574) 773-7761
SIC 3716 3792 3714 2451

WHITLEY MANUFACTURING CO INC p 1607
201 W 1st St, South Whitley IN 46787
Tel (260) 723-5131 SIC 2451

▲ SUN COMMUNITIES INC p 1400
27777 Franklin Rd Ste 200, Southfield MI 48034
Tel (248) 208-2500 SIC 6798 2451

CEI LIQUIDATION ESTATES p 273
755 W Big Beaver Rd, Troy MI 48084
Tel (248) 614-8200 SIC 2451 5271

CHAMPION HOME BUILDERS INC p 287
755 W Big Beaver Rd # 1000, Troy MI 48084
Tel (248) 614-8200 SIC 1521 2451

CHIEF INDUSTRIES INC p 298
3942 W Old Highway 30, Grand Island NE 68803
Tel (308) 389-7200
SIC 3448 2451 3523 2869 3442

■ CLAYTON HOMES INC p 323
5000 Clayton Rd, Maryville TN 37804
Tel (865) 380-3000
SIC 2451 5271 6141 6351 6331

■ CMH MANUFACTURING INC p 329
5000 Clayton Rd, Maryville TN 37804
Tel (865) 380-3000 SIC 2451

■ CENTEX CORP p 277
2728 N Harwood St Ste 200, Dallas TX 75201
Tel (214) 981-5000
SIC 1531 2451 6162 1542 1541 1522

LEGACY HOUSING LTD p 852
4801 Mark Iv Pkwy, Fort Worth TX 76106
Tel (817) 624-7565 SIC 2451

AMERICAN HOMESTAR CORP p 74
2450 S Shore Blvd Ste 300, League City TX 77573
Tel (281) 334-9700
SIC 2451 4213 5271 6351 6515

SIC 2452 Prefabricated Wood Buildings & Cmpnts

■ ERICKSON BUILDING COMPONENTS LLC p 507
250 N Beck Ave, Chandler AZ 85226
Tel (480) 627-1100 SIC 2439 2452

■ PALM HARBOR HOMES INC p 1109
1001 N Central Ave # 800, Phoenix AZ 85004
Tel (602) 256-6263 SIC 2452 5211 6141

FOREST ANTHONY PRODUCTS CO p 566
309 N Washington Ave, El Dorado AR 71730
Tel (870) 862-3414 SIC 2421 2452

SILVER CREEK INDUSTRIES INC p 1323
2830 Barrett Ave, Perris CA 92571
Tel (951) 943-5393 SIC 1542 2452

E B BRADLEY CO p 466
5602 Bickett St, Vernon CA 90058
Tel (323) 585-9917 SIC 5072 2452

TUFF SHED INC p 1491
1777 S Harrison St # 600, Denver CO 80210
Tel (303) 753-8833 SIC 2452

MORTON BUILDINGS INC p 991
252 W Adams St, Morton IL 61550
Tel (309) 263-7474 SIC 2452

ALL AMERICAN GROUP INC p 51
2831 Dexter Dr, Elkhart IN 46514
Tel (574) 262-0123
SIC 3716 3792 2452 3714 1521

■ HOMETTE CORP p 704
2520 Bypass Rd, Elkhart IN 46514
Tel (574) 294-6521 SIC 2452 3792

▲ SKYLINE CORP p 1330
2520 Bypass Rd, Elkhart IN 46514
Tel (574) 294-6521 SIC 2451 2452 3792

COMMODORE CORP p 345
1423 Lincolnway E, Goshen IN 46526
Tel (574) 533-7100 SIC 2452

LEISURE TIME PRODUCTS LLC p 854
3001 N Rouse St, Pittsburg KS 66762
Tel (620) 232-2400 SIC 3089 3949 2452

BACKYARD PRODUCTS LLC p 143
1000 Ternes Dr, Monroe MI 48162
Tel (734) 242-6900 SIC 2452 2511

BACKYARD STORAGE SOLUTIONS LLC p 143
1000 Ternes Dr, Monroe MI 48162
Tel (734) 242-6900 SIC 2452

SOURCE CAPITAL BACKYARD LLC p 1342
1000 Ternes Dr, Monroe MI 48162
Tel (734) 242-6900 SIC 2511 2452

LESTER BUILDING SYSTEMS LLC p 857
1111 2nd Ave S, Lester Prairie MN 55354
Tel (320) 395-5212 SIC 2452

RITZ-CRAFT CORP OF PENNSYLVANIA INC p 1237
15 Industrial Park Rd, Mifflinburg PA 17844
Tel (570) 966-1053 SIC 2452

GUARDIAN BUILDING PRODUCTS INC p 645
979 Batesville Rd Ste A, Greer SC 29651
Tel (864) 297-6101 SIC 3296 2452 8741

PLAYCORE HOLDINGS LLC p 1155
401 Chestnut St Ste 410, Chattanooga TN 37402
Tel (877) 762-7563 SIC 2452 3949 3448

GOSSEN CORP p 626
2030 W Bender Rd, Milwaukee WI 53209
Tel (800) 558-8984 SIC 2431 3089 2452

DESIGN HOMES INC p 432
600 N Marquette Rd, Prairie Du Chien WI 53821
Tel (608) 326-8406 SIC 2452 3663 5211

SIC 2491 Wood Preserving

GREAT SOUTHERN WOOD PRESERVING INC p 634
1100 Us Highway 431 S, Abbeville AL 36310
Tel (334) 585-2291 SIC 2491

SOUTHEAST WOOD TREATING INC p 1346
3077 Carter Hill Rd, Montgomery AL 36111
Tel (321) 631-1003 SIC 2421 2491

CALIFORNIA CASCADE INDUSTRIES p 239
7512 14th Ave, Sacramento CA 95820
Tel (916) 736-3353 SIC 2491 2421

ATLAS HOLDINGS LLC p 128
100 Northfield St, Greenwich CT 06830
Tel (203) 622-9138
SIC 5031 2491 5039 5153

BRIDGEWELL RESOURCES HOLDINGS LLC p 212
1 Sound Shore Dr Ste 302, Greenwich CT 06830
Tel (203) 622-9138
SIC 5031 2491 5039 5153

COASTAL FOREST RESOURCES CO p 331
8007 Florida Georgia Hwy, Havana FL 32333
Tel (850) 539-6432
SIC 2436 2491 0811 0851

ROBBINS MANUFACTURING CO INC p 1241
13001 N Nebraska Ave, Tampa FL 33612
Tel (813) 971-3030 SIC 2491

■ KOPPERS PERFORMANCE CHEMICALS INC p 828
1016 Everee Inn Rd, Griffin GA 30224
Tel (770) 228-8434 SIC 2491

ATLANTIC WOOD INDUSTRIES INC p 127
405 E Perry St, Savannah GA 31401
Tel (912) 966-7008 SIC 2491 3272

SAVANNAH WOOD PRESERVING CO INC p 1284
501 Stiles Ave, Savannah GA 31415
Tel (912) 236-4875 SIC 2491

LANGDALE CO p 844
1202 Madison Hwy, Valdosta GA 31601
Tel (229) 242-7450
SIC 2421 2491 7011 7699 5031 5171

UTILITY SUPPLY AND CONSTRUCTION CO p 1537
420 S Roth St Ste A, Reed City MI 49677
Tel (231) 832-2297
SIC 2411 2491 2631 5063

BIEWER LUMBER LLC p 181
812 S Riverside Ave, Saint Clair MI 48079
Tel (810) 326-3930 *SIC* 2491

JOHN A BIEWER LUMBER CO p 787
812 S Riverside Ave, Saint Clair MI 48079
Tel (810) 329-4789 *SIC* 2491

■ OSMOSE HOLDINGS INC p 1097
2475 George Urban Blvd # 160, Depew NY 14043
Tel (716) 882-5905 *SIC* 2491

▲ KOPPERS HOLDINGS INC p 827
436 7th Ave, Pittsburgh PA 15219
Tel (412) 227-2001
SIC 2865 2491 2895 3312 2899

■ KOPPERS INC p 828
436 7th Ave, Pittsburgh PA 15219
Tel (412) 227-2001
SIC 2865 2491 3312 2899

STELLA-JONES CORP p 1385
2 Gateway Ctr Ste 1000, Pittsburgh PA 15222
Tel (412) 894-2846 *SIC* 2491 2421 3531

STELLA-JONES CORP p 1385
603 Stanwix St Ste 1000, Pittsburgh PA 15222
Tel (412) 325-0202 *SIC* 2491

STELLA-JONES US HOLDING CORP p 1385
603 Stanwix St, Pittsburgh PA 15222
Tel (304) 372-2211 *SIC* 2491

NEW SOUTH COMPANIES INC p 1033
3700 Claypond Rd Ste 6, Myrtle Beach SC 29579
Tel (843) 236-9399 *SIC* 2421 2491 2431

COX INDUSTRIES INC p 386
860 Cannon Bridge Rd, Orangeburg SC 29115
Tel (803) 534-7467 *SIC* 2411 2491

COX WOOD PRESERVING CO p 386
860 Cannon Bridge Rd, Orangeburg SC 29115
Tel (803) 534-7467 *SIC* 2491

C M TUCKER LUMBER COMPANIES LLC p 233
601 N Pearl St, Pageland SC 29728
Tel (843) 672-6135 *SIC* 2491

CM TUCKER LUMBER COMPANIES LLC p 328
601 N Pearl St, Pageland SC 29728
Tel (843) 672-6135 *SIC* 2491

TEXAS ELECTRIC COOPERATIVES INC p 1443
1122 Colorado St Ste 2400, Austin TX 78701
Tel (512) 454-0311 *SIC* 2491 3612 8621

LD MCFARLAND CO LIMITED p 849
1640 E Marc St, Tacoma WA 98421
Tel (253) 572-5670 *SIC* 2499 2491 2411

MANKE LUMBER CO INC p 902
1717 Marine View Dr, Tacoma WA 98422
Tel (253) 572-6252 *SIC* 2421 2491 2499

MCFARLAND CASCADE HOLDINGS INC p 928
1640 E Marc St, Tacoma WA 98421
Tel (253) 572-3033 *SIC* 2491 6552 6531

GREEN BAY PACKAGING INC p 636
1700 N Webster Ave, Green Bay WI 54302
Tel (920) 433-5111
SIC 2631 2672 2653 2491

RICHARDSON INDUSTRIES INC p 1232
635 Old County Road Pp, Sheboygan Falls WI 53085
Tel (920) 467-2950
SIC 2511 2439 5211 2491 2434 2426

DW SAWMILL LLC p 463
N8972 County Road Jj, Westfield WI 53964
Tel (608) 296-1863 *SIC* 5099 2491 5211

SIC 2493 Reconstituted Wood Prdts

PANOLAM INDUSTRIES INTERNATIONAL INC p 1111
20 Progress Dr, Shelton CT 06484
Tel (203) 925-1556 *SIC* 2493 3089

CELOTEX CORP p 274
10301 Dr Martn L Kng Jr S, Saint Petersburg FL 33716
Tel (727) 563-5100
SIC 3086 3275 3296 2493 2952

■ RTS PACKAGING LLC p 1256
504 Thrasher St, Norcross GA 30071
Tel (800) 558-6984 *SIC* 2493

▲ PATRICK INDUSTRIES INC p 1120
107 W Franklin St, Elkhart IN 46516
Tel (574) 294-7511
SIC 3275 2493 2435 5031 5033 2891

MARTCO LLC p 911
2189 Memorial Dr, Alexandria LA 71301
Tel (318) 448-0405 *SIC* 2493 2435

MARTIN SUSTAINABLE RESOURCES LLC p 913
2189 Memorial Dr, Alexandria LA 71301
Tel (318) 448-0405 *SIC* 2493 2435

MOREHOUSE BIOENERGY LLC p 988
7070 Carl Rd, Bastrop LA 71220
Tel (770) 743-4300 *SIC* 2493

NEXFOR (USA) INC p 1040
82 Bridge Ave, Madawaska ME 04756
Tel (207) 728-3321 *SIC* 2621 2493

JM HUBER CORP p 786
499 Thornall St Ste 8, Edison NJ 08837
Tel (732) 603-3630
SIC 0811 1311 1455 2493 2819

STANDARD INDUSTRIES INC p 1376
1 Campus Dr, Parsippany NJ 07054
Tel (973) 628-3000 *SIC* 2493

BMCA HOLDINGS CORP p 194
1361 Alps Rd, Wayne NJ 07470
Tel (973) 628-3000 *SIC* 2493

HUBER ENGINEERED WOODS LLC p 716
10925 David Taylor Dr, Charlotte NC 28262
Tel (704) 547-0671 *SIC* 2493

RLC INDUSTRIES CO p 1239
10599 Old Hwy 99 S, Dillard OR 97432
Tel (541) 679-3311 *SIC* 2493 2436 2421

STIMSON LUMBER CO p 1390
520 Sw Yamhill St Ste 700, Portland OR 97204
Tel (503) 222-1676 *SIC* 2421 2493 2411

ROSEBURG FOREST PRODUCTS CO p 1250
3660 Gateway St Ste A, Springfield OR 97477
Tel (541) 679-3311
SIC 2436 2421 2493 5031 5211 0811

TIMBER PRODUCTS CO LIMITED PARTNERSHIP p 1454
305 S 4th St, Springfield OR 97477
Tel (541) 747-4577
SIC 2436 2435 5031 2493

COLLINS TIMBER CO LLC p 337
29100 Sw Town Ctr Loop W, Wilsonville OR 97070
Tel (503) 227-1219 *SIC* 2493

FLAKEBOARD AMERICA LIMITED p 554
515 Rivercrossing Dr, Fort Mill SC 29715
Tel (877) 273-7680 *SIC* 2493

▲ LOUISIANA-PACIFIC CORP p 880
414 Union St Ste 2000, Nashville TN 37219
Tel (615) 986-5600
SIC 2493 2436 2435 2421 2431

NORBORD TEXAS LP p 1047
500 Nexfor Blvd, Jefferson TX 75657
Tel (936) 568-8009 *SIC* 2493

■ PLUM CREEK MANUFACTURING LP p 1156
999 3rd Ave Ste 4300, Seattle WA 98104
Tel (206) 467-3600
SIC 2421 2436 2493 5031

■ PLUM CREEK TIMBERLANDS LP p 1156
601 Union St Ste 3100, Seattle WA 98101
Tel (206) 467-3600
SIC 2421 2436 2493 5031

SIC 2499 Wood Prdts, NEC

GEMSTONE FOODS p 598
412 8th Ave Ne, Decatur AL 35601
Tel (256) 686-3601 *SIC* 5411 2499

CALIFORNIA CEDAR PRODUCTS CO p 239
2385 Arch Airport Rd # 500, Stockton CA 95206
Tel (209) 932-5002 *SIC* 2499

▲ ACME UNITED CORP p 18
55 Walls Dr Ste 201, Fairfield CT 06824
Tel (203) 254-6060
SIC 3421 2499 3842 3579 3069 3999

ENSIGN-BICKFORD INDUSTRIES INC p 501
125 Pwder Frest Dr Fl 3, Simsbury CT 06070
Tel (860) 843-2000
SIC 3764 2047 2835 3829 2499 6552

■ ALBECCA INC p 46
3900 Steve Reynolds Blvd, Norcross GA 30093
Tel (770) 279-5210 *SIC* 2499 3499

■ LARSON-JUHL US LLC p 845
3900 Steve Reynolds Blvd, Norcross GA 30093
Tel (770) 279-5200 *SIC* 2499 3499 2431

COUNTRY STONE INC p 375
6300 75th Ave Ste A, Milan IL 61264
Tel (309) 787-1744
SIC 2499 2875 3273 3281

GROHE AMERICA INC p 641
200 N Gary Ave Ste G, Roselle IL 60172
Tel (630) 582-7711 *SIC* 2499

PRECISION INC p 1168
300 Se 14th St, Pella IA 50219
Tel (641) 628-3115 *SIC* 2499 3429

TARTER GATE WOOD PRODUCTS INC p 1425
10739 S Us 127, Dunnville KY 42528
Tel (606) 787-2081
SIC 3446 2448 2499 2426 2421

LOUISVILLE LADDER INC p 881
7765 National Tpke # 190, Louisville KY 40214
Tel (502) 636-2811 *SIC* 2499

HARDWARE RESOURCES INC p 661
4319 Marlena St, Bossier City LA 71111
Tel (318) 742-0660 *SIC* 5072 2499

AMERICAN WOOD FIBERS INC p 81
9841 Broken Land Pkwy # 302, Columbia MD 21046
Tel (410) 290-8700 *SIC* 2499

HOLLINGSWORTH & VOSE CO p 701
112 Washington St, East Walpole MA 02032
Tel (508) 850-2000
SIC 2621 3053 2297 2499

WALPOLE WOODWORKERS INC p 1574
767 East St, Walpole MA 02081
Tel (508) 668-2800 *SIC* 2499

US FENCE INC p 1531
3200 Rbert T Longway Blvd, Flint MI 48506
Tel (810) 235-0400 *SIC* 2499

KAMPS INC p 802
2900 Peach Ridge Ave Nw, Grand Rapids MI 49534
Tel (616) 453-9676 *SIC* 2448 2499

DIAMOND BRANDS INC p 436
1800 Cloquet Ave, Cloquet MN 55720
Tel (218) 879-6700 *SIC* 2499

INDEPENDENT STAVE CO LLC p 737
1078 S Jefferson Ave, Lebanon MO 65536
Tel (417) 588-4151 *SIC* 2449 5947 2499

DARAMIC LLC p 412
11430 N Cmnity Hse Rd # 350, Charlotte NC 28277
Tel (704) 587-8599 *SIC* 3069 2499 3269

■ L G SOURCING INC p 834
1605 Curtis Bridge Rd, North Wilkesboro NC 28659
Tel (866) 578-0563 *SIC* 5023 5031 2499

■ SCOTTS CO LLC p 1294
14111 Scottslawn Rd, Marysville OH 43040
Tel (937) 644-0011
SIC 2873 2874 2879 0782 2499 3524

MTM RECOGNITION CORP p 998
3201 Se 29th St, Oklahoma City OK 73115
Tel (405) 609-6900
SIC 3911 3873 2499 2389 3499 2791

MCS INDUSTRIES INC p 932
2280 Newlins Mill Rd, Easton PA 18045
Tel (610) 253-6268
SIC 2499 3089 3499 3993 3231

NEW WERNER HOLDING CO INC p 1033
93 Werner Rd, Greenville PA 16125
Tel (724) 588-2000
SIC 3499 3355 3089 3446 2499 6512

WERNER CO p 1592
93 Werner Rd, Greenville PA 16125
Tel (724) 588-2000
SIC 3499 3355 3089 3446 2499

WERNER HOLDING CO (PA) INC p 1593
93 Werner Rd, Greenville PA 16125
Tel (888) 523-3371
SIC 3499 3355 3089 3446 2499

ELLETT BROTHERS LLC p 488
267 Columbia Ave, Chapin SC 29036
Tel (803) 345-3751
SIC 5091 3949 2499 2541

▲ SONOCO PRODUCTS CO p 1340
1 N 2nd St, Hartsville SC 29550
Tel (843) 383-7000
SIC 2631 2671 2653 2655 3089 2499

PI INC p 1146
213 Dennis St, Athens TN 37303
Tel (423) 745-6213
SIC 2519 3949 3089 2499 3086 3081

FIRESTONE NATURAL RUBBER CO LLC p 544
535 Marriott Dr Fl 3, Nashville TN 37214
Tel (866) 900-3767 *SIC* 3069 2499

NIELSEN & BAINBRIDGE LLC p 1043
12303 Tech Blvd Ste 950, Austin TX 78727
Tel (512) 506-8844 *SIC* 2499 5023

JAMIESON MANUFACTURING CO p 777
4221 Platinum Way, Dallas TX 75237
Tel (214) 339-8384 *SIC* 5039 2499

MODEC INTERNATIONAL INC p 980
15011 Katy Fwy Ste 500, Houston TX 77094
Tel (281) 529-8100 *SIC* 8711 2499 3731

RSG FOREST PRODUCTS INC p 1256
985 Nw 2nd St, Kalama WA 98625
Tel (360) 673-2825 *SIC* 2421 2499

LD MCFARLAND CO LIMITED p 849
1640 E Marc St, Tacoma WA 98421
Tel (253) 572-5670 *SIC* 2499 2491 2411

MANKE LUMBER CO INC p 902
1717 Marine View Dr, Tacoma WA 98422
Tel (253) 572-6252 *SIC* 2421 2491 2499

SIC 2511 Wood Household Furniture

WELLBORN CABINET INC p 1589
38669 Highway 77, Ashland AL 36251
Tel (256) 354-7151 *SIC* 2434 2511 5032

STANDARD FURNITURE MANUFACTURING CO INC p 1376
801 S Us Highway 31, Bay Minette AL 36507
Tel (251) 937-6741 *SIC* 2511

RIVERSIDE FURNITURE CORP p 1238
1400 S 6th St, Fort Smith AR 72901
Tel (479) 785-8100 *SIC* 2511

▲ NOVA LIFESTYLE INC p 1062
6565 E Washington Blvd, Commerce CA 90040
Tel (323) 888-9999 *SIC* 2511 2512

BROWN JORDAN CO LIMITED PARTNERSHIP p 219
9860 Gidley St, El Monte CA 91731
Tel (626) 443-8971 *SIC* 2511 2514

ROYAL CABINETS INC p 1254
1299 E Phillips Blvd, Pomona CA 91766
Tel (909) 629-8565 *SIC* 2434 2511

▲ VIRCO MFG CORP p 1558
2027 Harpers Way, Torrance CA 90501
Tel (310) 533-0474 *SIC* 2531 2522 2511

SANDBERG FURNITURE MANUFACTURING CO INC p 1278
5685 Alcoa Ave, Vernon CA 90058
Tel (323) 582-0711 *SIC* 2511

BIG SUR WATERBEDS INC p 182
5603 Brdwy, Denver CO 80216
Tel (303) 566-8700 *SIC* 5712 2515 2511

VALIANT PRODUCTS CORP p 1540
2727 W 5th Ave, Denver CO 80204
Tel (303) 892-1234
SIC 5131 5023 7389 2511 2599 1752

▲ ETHAN ALLEN INTERIORS INC p 511
Ethan Allen Dr, Danbury CT 06811
Tel (203) 743-8000 *SIC* 2511 2512 5712

■ ETHAN ALLEN OPERATIONS INC p 511
Ethan Allen Dr, Danbury CT 06813
Tel (203) 743-8496 *SIC* 2511

■ CLOSETMAID CORP p 327
650 Sw 27th Ave, Ocala FL 34471
Tel (352) 401-6000 *SIC* 2511

GEM INDUSTRIES INC p 598
Hwy 123 N, Toccoa GA 30577
Tel (706) 886-8431
SIC 3429 2531 2511 3446 2821 2515

D D G INC p 407
1955 Shermer Rd Ste 300, Northbrook IL 60062
Tel (847) 412-0277 *SIC* 3317 2511 6512

STEVENS INDUSTRIES INC p 1388
704 W Main St, Teutopolis IL 62467
Tel (217) 540-3100 *SIC* 2531 2679 2511

COSCO INC p 373
2525 State St, Columbus IN 47201
Tel (812) 372-0141 *SIC* 3944 2511 2514

DOREL USA INC p 451
2525 State St, Columbus IN 47201
Tel (812) 372-0141 *SIC* 3944 2511 2514

OFS BRANDS HOLDINGS INC p 1076
1204 E 6th St, Huntingburg IN 47542
Tel (800) 521-5381
SIC 2521 2522 2511 2599

▲ KIMBALL INTERNATIONAL INC p 818
1600 Royal St, Jasper IN 47549
Tel (812) 482-1600
SIC 2511 2512 2521 2522 2517

▲ FLEXSTEEL INDUSTRIES INC p 556
385 Bell St, Dubuque IA 52001
Tel (563) 556-7730 *SIC* 2512 2515 2511

BROWN JORDAN CO p 219
20 Kingbrook Pkwy, Simpsonville KY 40067
Tel (323) 686-0951 *SIC* 2514 2511

LANDSCAPE FORMS INC p 843
7800 E Michigan Ave, Kalamazoo MI 49048
Tel (269) 381-0396
SIC 2531 2522 2511 2449 3648

BACKYARD PRODUCTS LLC p 143
1000 Ternes Dr, Monroe MI 48162
Tel (734) 242-6900 *SIC* 2452 2511

▲ LA-Z-BOY INC p 836
1 La Z Boy Dr, Monroe MI 48162
Tel (734) 242-1444 *SIC* 2512 2511 5712

SOURCE CAPITAL BACKYARD LLC p 1342
1000 Ternes Dr, Monroe MI 48162
Tel (734) 242-6900 *SIC* 2511 2452

FURNITURE BRANDS INTERNATIONAL INC p 585
1 N Brentwood Blvd # 700, Saint Louis MO 63105
Tel (314) 863-1100 *SIC* 2511 2512 2515

DOREL HOME FURNISHINGS INC p 451
410 E 1st St S, Wright City MO 63390
Tel (636) 745-3351 *SIC* 2511

BUSH INDUSTRIES INC p 229
1 Mason Dr, Jamestown NY 14701
Tel (716) 665-2000 *SIC* 2511 2521

L& JG STICKLEY INC p 834
1 Stickley Dr, Manlius NY 13104
Tel (315) 682-5500 *SIC* 2511 2519

RENCO GROUP INC p 1223
1 Rockefeller Plz Fl 29, New York NY 10020
Tel (212) 541-6000
SIC 3312 3316 2514 2511 3171 3496

COMMUNITY PRODUCTS LLC p 350
2032 Route 213 St, Rifton NY 12471
Tel (845) 658-8799 *SIC* 3842 2511 3844

CENTURY FURNITURE LLC p 282
401 11th St Nw, Hickory NC 28601
Tel (828) 267-8739 *SIC* 2511 2512

CV INDUSTRIES INC p 404
401 11th St Nw, Hickory NC 28601
Tel (828) 328-1851 *SIC* 2511 2512 2211

KOHLER INTERIORS FURNITURE CO p 826
1105 22nd St Se, Hickory NC 28602
Tel (828) 624-7000 *SIC* 2511 5021

SHERRILL FURNITURE CO INC p 1316
2405 Highland Ave Ne, Hickory NC 28601
Tel (828) 322-2640 *SIC* 2512 2511

HERITAGE HOME GROUP LLC p 686
1925 Eastchester Dr, High Point NC 27265
Tel (314) 863-1100 *SIC* 2511 2512 2515

HFI WIND DOWN INC p 689
1925 Eastchester Dr, High Point NC 27265
Tel (336) 888-4800 *SIC* 2511 2512

TFI WIND DOWN INC p 1445
1925 Eastchester Dr, High Point NC 27265
Tel (336) 472-4000 *SIC* 2511 2512

UNIVERSAL FURNITURE LIMITED p 1517
2575 Penny Rd, High Point NC 27265
Tel (336) 822-8888 *SIC* 2511 2512

■ KINCAID FURNITURE CO INC p 819
240 Pleasant Hill Rd, Hudson NC 28638
Tel (828) 728-3261 *SIC* 2511 2512

BERNHARDT FURNITURE CO INC p 176
1839 Morganton Blvd Sw, Lenoir NC 28645
Tel (828) 758-9811
SIC 2511 2512 2521 2522

BERNHARDT INDUSTRIES INC p 176
1839 Morganton Blvd Sw, Lenoir NC 28645
Tel (828) 758-9811
SIC 2511 2521 2512 2522

FAIRFIELD CHAIR CO p 524
1331 Harper Ave Sw, Lenoir NC 28645
Tel (828) 758-5571 *SIC* 2512 2511

CAROLINA MILLS INC p 259
618 N Carolina Ave, Maiden NC 28650
Tel (828) 428-9911
SIC 2281 2211 2221 2257 2511 2512

KENNEY MANUFACTURING CO p 811
1000 Jefferson Blvd, Warwick RI 02886
Tel (401) 739-2200
SIC 2591 3261 2511 3699 3499 2541

ODDELLO INDUSTRIES LLC p 1074
425 Jones Franklin Rd, Morristown TN 37813
Tel (423) 307-1240 *SIC* 2511

LIFETIME PRODUCTS INC p 865
Freeport Ctr Bldg D-11, Clearfield UT 84016
Tel (801) 776-1532
SIC 2519 3949 2531 2511

▲ BASSETT FURNITURE INDUSTRIES INC p 159
3525 Fairystone Park Hwy, Bassett VA 24055
Tel (276) 629-6000
SIC 2511 2512 5021 5712

■ BASSETT FURNITURE INDUSTRIES OF NORTH CAROLINA LLC p 159
3525 Fairystone Park Hwy, Bassett VA 24055
Tel (276) 629-6000 *SIC* 2511 2512

ROWE FINE FURNITURE INC p 1253
2121 Gardner St, Elliston VA 24087
Tel (540) 444-7693 *SIC* 2512 2511

ROWE FURNITURE INC p 1253
2121 Gardner St, Elliston VA 24087
Tel (540) 389-8671 *SIC* 2512 2511 2421

V-B/WILLIAMS FURNITURE CO INC p 1538
300 E Grayson St, Galax VA 24333
Tel (276) 236-6161 *SIC* 2511

VAUGHAN-BASSETT FURNITURE CO INC p 1545
300 E Grayson St, Galax VA 24333
Tel (276) 236-6161 *SIC* 2511

▲ HOOKER FURNITURE CORP p 705
440 Commonwealth Blvd E, Martinsville VA 24112
Tel (276) 632-2133
SIC 2511 2512 2517 2521

ASHLEY FURNITURE INDUSTRIES INC p 117
1 Ashley Way, Arcadia WI 54612
Tel (608) 323-3377 *SIC* 2512 2511

KOHLER CO p 826
444 Highland Dr, Kohler WI 53044
Tel (920) 457-4441
SIC 3431 3432 3261 2511 2521 3519

RICHARDSON INDUSTRIES INC p 1232
635 Old County Road Pp, Sheboygan Falls WI 53085
Tel (920) 467-2950
SIC 2511 2439 5211 2491 2434 2426

SIC 2512 Wood Household Furniture, Upholstered

▲ NOVA LIFESTYLE INC p 1062
6565 E Washington Blvd, Commerce CA 90040
Tel (323) 888-9999 *SIC* 2511 2512

JONATHAN LOUIS INTERNATIONAL LTD p 792
544 W 130th St, Gardena CA 90248
Tel (323) 770-3330 *SIC* 2512

DOUGLAS FURNITURE OF CALIFORNIA LLC p 452
809 Tyburn Rd, Palos Verdes Estates CA 90274
Tel (310) 749-0003 *SIC* 2514 2512

▲ ETHAN ALLEN INTERIORS INC p 511
Ethan Allen Dr, Danbury CT 06811
Tel (203) 743-8000 *SIC* 2511 2512 5712

BROWN JORDAN INTERNATIONAL INC p 220
475 W Town Pl Ste 200, Saint Augustine FL 32092
Tel (336) 622-2201 *SIC* 2512 2514

TRP ACQUISITION CORP p 1485
1000 N Rohlwing Rd Ste 46, Lombard IL 60148
Tel (630) 261-2380 *SIC* 2512

BEST CHAIRS INC p 177
1 Best Dr, Ferdinand IN 47532
Tel (812) 367-1761 *SIC* 2512

▲ KIMBALL INTERNATIONAL INC p 818
1600 Royal St, Jasper IN 47549
Tel (812) 482-1600
SIC 2511 2512 2521 2522 2517

▲ FLEXSTEEL INDUSTRIES INC p 556
385 Bell St, Dubuque IA 52001
Tel (563) 556-7730 *SIC* 2512 2515 2511

■ ENGLAND INC p 499
1 La Z Boy Dr, Monroe MI 48162
Tel (734) 242-1444 *SIC* 2512

▲ LA-Z-BOY INC p 836
1 La Z Boy Dr, Monroe MI 48162
Tel (734) 242-1444 *SIC* 2512 2511 5712

■ LZB MANUFACTURING INC p 888
1 Lazboy Dr, Monroe MI 48162
Tel (734) 242-1444 *SIC* 2512

CORINTHIAN INC p 370
41 Henson Rd, Corinth MS 38834
Tel (662) 287-7835 *SIC* 2512

HM RICHARDS INC p 697
120 H M Richards Way, Guntown MS 38849
Tel (662) 365-9485 *SIC* 2512

FRANKLIN CORP p 575
600 Franklin Dr, Houston MS 38851
Tel (662) 456-5771 *SIC* 2512

ALBANY INDUSTRIES INC p 45
504 N Glenfield Rd, New Albany MS 38652
Tel (662) 534-9800 *SIC* 2512

SOUTHERN MOTION INC p 1349
298 Henry Southern Dr, Pontotoc MS 38863
Tel (662) 488-4007 *SIC* 2512

BAUHAUS FURNITURE GROUP LLC p 160
1 Bauhaus Dr, Saltillo MS 38866
Tel (662) 869-2664 *SIC* 2512

LFI WIND DOWN INC p 860
5380 Highway 145 S, Tupelo MS 38801
Tel (662) 566-7211 *SIC* 2512

UNITED FURNITURE INDUSTRIES INC p 1508
5380 Highway 145 S, Tupelo MS 38801
Tel (662) 447-4000 *SIC* 2512

FURNITURE BRANDS INTERNATIONAL INC p 585
1 N Brentwood Blvd # 700, Saint Louis MO 63105
Tel (314) 863-1100 *SIC* 2511 2512 2515

KLAUSSNER CORP p 823
405 Lewallen Rd, Asheboro NC 27205
Tel (888) 732-5948 *SIC* 2512

KLAUSSNER FURNITURE INDUSTRIES INC p 823
405 Lewallen Rd, Asheboro NC 27205
Tel (336) 625-6174 *SIC* 2512

LEE INDUSTRIES INC p 851
210 4th St Sw, Conover NC 28613
Tel (828) 464-8318 *SIC* 2512

CENTURY FURNITURE LLC p 282
401 11th St Nw, Hickory NC 28601
Tel (828) 267-8739 *SIC* 2511 2512

CV INDUSTRIES INC p 404
401 11th St Nw, Hickory NC 28601
Tel (828) 328-1851 *SIC* 2511 2512 2211

SHERRILL FURNITURE CO INC p 1316
2405 Highland Ave Ne, Hickory NC 28601
Tel (828) 322-2640 *SIC* 2512 2511

CRAFTMASTER FURNITURE INC p 388
221 Craftmaster Rd, Hiddenite NC 28636
Tel (828) 632-9786 *SIC* 2512

HERITAGE HOME GROUP LLC p 686
1925 Eastchester Dr, High Point NC 27265
Tel (314) 863-1100 *SIC* 2511 2512 2515

HFI WIND DOWN INC p 689
1925 Eastchester Dr, High Point NC 27265
Tel (336) 888-4800 *SIC* 2511 2512

SAMSON INVESTMENT HOLDING INC p 1274
2575 Penny Rd, High Point NC 27265
Tel (336) 449-4600 *SIC* 2512

TFI WIND DOWN INC p 1445
1925 Eastchester Dr, High Point NC 27265
Tel (336) 472-4000 *SIC* 2511 2512

UNIVERSAL FURNITURE LIMITED p 1517
2575 Penny Rd, High Point NC 27265
Tel (336) 822-8888 *SIC* 2511 2512

■ KINCAID FURNITURE CO INC p 819
240 Pleasant Hill Rd, Hudson NC 28638
Tel (828) 728-3261 *SIC* 2511 2512

BERNHARDT FURNITURE CO INC p 176
1839 Morganton Blvd Sw, Lenoir NC 28645
Tel (828) 758-9811
SIC 2511 2512 2521 2522

BERNHARDT INDUSTRIES INC p 176
1839 Morganton Blvd Sw, Lenoir NC 28645
Tel (828) 758-9811
SIC 2511 2521 2512 2522

BFI WIND DOWN INC p 179
815 Visionary St, Lenoir NC 28645
Tel (828) 759-8000 *SIC* 5712 2512

FAIRFIELD CHAIR CO p 524
1331 Harper Ave Sw, Lenoir NC 28645
Tel (828) 758-5571 *SIC* 2512 2511

CAROLINA MILLS INC p 259
618 N Carolina Ave, Maiden NC 28650
Tel (828) 428-9911
SIC 2281 2211 2221 2257 2511 2512

MCCREARY MODERN INC p 927
2564 S Us 321 Hwy, Newton NC 28658
Tel (828) 464-6465 *SIC* 2512

HUGHES FURNITURE INDUSTRIES INC p 717
952 S Stout Rd, Randleman NC 27317
Tel (336) 498-8700 *SIC* 2512 7641 2426

MITCHELL GOLD CO p 977
135 One Comfortable Pl, Taylorsville NC 28681
Tel (828) 632-9200 *SIC* 2512

LEXINGTON FURNITURE INDUSTRIES INC p 859
1300 National Hwy, Thomasville NC 27360
Tel (336) 474-5300 *SIC* 2512

FABTEX INC p 523
111 Woodbine Ln, Danville PA 17821
Tel (570) 275-7500
SIC 5072 2221 5023 2512 2392 2391

CLEVELAND CHAIR CO INC p 325
370 9th St Se, Cleveland TN 37311
Tel (423) 476-8544 *SIC* 2512

JACKSON FURNITURE INDUSTRIES INC p 774
1910 King Edward Ave Se, Cleveland TN 37311
Tel (423) 476-8544 *SIC* 2512

DOWNEAST OUTFITTERS INC p 453
375 W Hope Ave, Salt Lake City UT 84115
Tel (801) 467-7520
SIC 5611 5621 5963 2512

▲ BASSETT FURNITURE INDUSTRIES INC p 159
3525 Fairystone Park Hwy, Bassett VA 24055
Tel (276) 629-6000
SIC 2511 2512 5021 5712

■ BASSETT FURNITURE INDUSTRIES OF NORTH CAROLINA LLC p 159
3525 Fairystone Park Hwy, Bassett VA 24055
Tel (276) 629-6000 *SIC* 2511 2512

ROWE FINE FURNITURE INC p 1253
2121 Gardner St, Elliston VA 24087
Tel (540) 444-7693 *SIC* 2512 2511

ROWE FURNITURE CORP p 1253
2121 Gardner St, Elliston VA 24087
Tel (540) 444-7693 *SIC* 2512 5712

ROWE FURNITURE INC p 1253
2121 Gardner St, Elliston VA 24087
Tel (540) 389-8671 *SIC* 2512 2511 2421

▲ HOOKER FURNITURE CORP p 705
440 Commonwealth Blvd E, Martinsville VA 24112
Tel (276) 632-2133
SIC 2511 2512 2517 2521

EASTERN SLEEP PRODUCTS CO p 472
4901 Fitzhugh Ave, Richmond VA 23230
Tel (804) 254-1711
SIC 2515 2512 7641 4213

ASHLEY FURNITURE INDUSTRIES INC p 117
1 Ashley Way, Arcadia WI 54612
Tel (608) 323-3377 *SIC* 2512 2511

SIC 2514 Metal Household Furniture

RSI HOME PRODUCTS INC p 1256
400 E Orangethorpe Ave, Anaheim CA 92801
Tel (714) 449-2200
SIC 2514 2541 3281 2434

BROWN JORDAN CO LIMITED PARTNERSHIP p 219
9860 Gidley St, El Monte CA 91731
Tel (626) 443-8971 *SIC* 2511 2514

TROPITONE FURNITURE CO INC p 1484
5 Marconi, Irvine CA 92618
Tel (949) 595-2000 *SIC* 2514 2522

DOUGLAS FURNITURE OF CALIFORNIA LLC p 452
809 Tyburn Rd, Palos Verdes Estates CA 90274
Tel (310) 749-0003 *SIC* 2514 2512

ZWD PRODUCTS CORP p 1645
400 Lukens Dr, New Castle DE 19720
Tel (302) 326-8200 *SIC* 2434 2514

■ AMERICAN HOUSEHOLD INC p 74
2381 Nw Executive Ctr Dr, Boca Raton FL 33431
Tel (561) 912-4100
SIC 3631 2514 3421 3634 3829 3841

■ SUNBEAM AMERICAS HOLDINGS LLC p 1401
2381 Nw Executive Ctr Dr, Boca Raton FL 33431
Tel (561) 912-4100
SIC 3631 2514 3421 3634 3829 3841

BROWN JORDAN INTERNATIONAL INC p 220
475 W Town Pl Ste 200, Saint Augustine FL 32092
Tel (336) 622-2201 *SIC* 2512 2514

■ GRACO CHILDRENS PRODUCTS INC p 628
3 Glenlake Pkwy, Atlanta GA 30328
Tel (770) 418-7200 *SIC* 2514

HENRY CROWN AND CO p 684
222 N La Salle St # 2000, Chicago IL 60601
Tel (312) 236-6300 *SIC* 2514

COSCO INC p 373
2525 State St, Columbus IN 47201
Tel (812) 372-0141 *SIC* 3944 2511 2514

DOREL USA INC p 451
2525 State St, Columbus IN 47201
Tel (812) 372-0141 *SIC* 3944 2511 2514

BROWN JORDAN CO p 219
20 Kingbrook Pkwy, Simpsonville KY 40067
Tel (323) 686-0951 *SIC* 2514 2511

▲ LEGGETT & PLATT INC p 853
1 Leggett Rd, Carthage MO 64836
Tel (417) 358-8131
SIC 2515 2514 3495 2392 2542 3363

RENCO GROUP INC p 1223
1 Rockefeller Plz Fl 29, New York NY 10020
Tel (212) 541-6000
SIC 3312 3316 2514 2511 3171 3496

HICKORY SPRINGS MANUFACTURING CO p 690
235 2nd Ave Nw, Hickory NC 28601
Tel (828) 328-2201
SIC 3069 3495 2514 5072 2399

▲ INVACARE CORP p 760
1 Invacare Way, Elyria OH 44035
Tel (440) 329-6000 *SIC* 3842 2514 2813

▲ SUMMER INFANT INC p 1398
1275 Park East Dr, Woonsocket RI 02895
Tel (401) 671-6550
SIC 2514 2399 3842 3261

UNAKA CO INC p 1502
1500 Industrial Rd, Greeneville TN 37745
Tel (423) 639-1171
SIC 2099 3469 2514 2253 4226

BROAN-NUTONE LLC p 216
926 W State St, Hartford WI 53027
Tel (262) 673-4340
SIC 3634 3699 3635 3639 2514 3669

SIC 2515 Mattresses & Bedsprings

FURNITURE FACTORY OUTLET LLC p 585
6500 Jenny Lind Rd Spc A, Fort Smith AR 72908
Tel (918) 427-0241 *SIC* 5712 2515

DAVID AND LUCILE PACKARD FOUNDATION p 415
343 2nd St, Los Altos CA 94022
Tel (650) 948-7658 *SIC* 2515

ZINUS INC p 1643
1951 Fairway Dr Ste A, San Leandro CA 94577
Tel (925) 417-2100 *SIC* 2515

VCP MOBILITY INC p 1545
6899 Winchester Cir # 200, Boulder CO 80301
Tel (303) 218-4500
SIC 3842 2599 2515 5047 3841

BIG SUR WATERBEDS INC p 182
5603 Brdwy, Denver CO 80216
Tel (303) 566-8700 *SIC* 5712 2515 2511

AOT BEDDING INTERMEDIATE HOLDINGS LLC p 95
1 Concrs Pkwy Ne Ste 800, Atlanta GA 30328
Tel (770) 512-7700 *SIC* 2515

SERTA SIMMONS BEDDING LLC p 1307
1 Concourse Pkwy Ste 800, Atlanta GA 30328
Tel (770) 512-7700 *SIC* 2515

SIMMONS HOLDINGS LLC p 1324
1 Concrs Pkwy Ne Ste 800, Atlanta GA 30328
Tel (770) 512-7700 *SIC* 2515

SIMMONS MANUFACTURING CO LLC p 1324
1 Concrse Pkwy Ne Ste 800, Atlanta GA 30328
Tel (770) 512-7700 *SIC* 2515

SSB MANUFACTURING CO p 1363
1 Concourse Pkwy Ste 800, Atlanta GA 30328
Tel (770) 512-7700 *SIC* 2515

GEM INDUSTRIES INC p 598
Hwy 123 N, Toccoa GA 30577
Tel (706) 886-8431
SIC 3429 2531 2511 3446 2821 2515

NATIONAL BEDDING CO LLC p 1010
2600 Forbs Ave, Hoffman Estates IL 60192
Tel (847) 645-0200 *SIC* 2515

SERTA INC p 1306
2600 Forbs Ave, Hoffman Estates IL 60192
Tel (847) 645-0200 *SIC* 2515

▲ FLEXSTEEL INDUSTRIES INC p 556
385 Bell St, Dubuque IA 52001
Tel (563) 556-7730 *SIC* 2512 2515 2511

▲ TEMPUR SEALY INTERNATIONAL INC p 1436
1000 Tempur Way, Lexington KY 40511
Tel (800) 878-8889 *SIC* 2515 2392

■ TEMPUR WORLD LLC p 1436
1713 Jaggie Fox Way, Lexington KY 40511
Tel (859) 259-4838 *SIC* 2515

AW INDUSTRIES INC p 139
8415 Ardwick Ardmore Rd, Landover MD 20785
Tel (301) 322-1000 *SIC* 2515

▲ SELECT COMFORT CORP p 1301
9800 59th Ave N, Minneapolis MN 55442
Tel (763) 551-7000 *SIC* 2515

▲ LEGGETT & PLATT INC p 853
1 Leggett Rd, Carthage MO 64836
Tel (417) 358-8131
SIC 2515 2514 3495 2392 2542 3363

FURNITURE BRANDS INTERNATIONAL INC p 585
1 N Brentwood Blvd # 700, Saint Louis MO 63105
Tel (314) 863-1100 *SIC* 2511 2512 2515

■ INSTALLED BUILDING PRODUCTS LLC p 747
62 King St, Auburn NH 03032
Tel (603) 645-1604
SIC 1761 5021 5719 2515

INNOCOR INC p 744
200 Schulz Dr Ste 2, Red Bank NJ 07701
Tel (844) 824-9348 *SIC* 2515 2392 3089

KKR MILLENNIUM GP LLC p 822
9 W 57th St Ste 4150, New York NY 10019
Tel (212) 750-8300 *SIC* 2515

VSM INVESTORS LLC p 1566
245 Park Ave Fl 41, New York NY 10167
Tel (212) 351-1600 *SIC* 3842 2599 2515

HERITAGE HOME GROUP LLC p 686
1925 Eastchester Dr, High Point NC 27265
Tel (314) 863-1100 *SIC* 2511 2512 2515

KINGSDOWN INC p 821
126 W Holt St, Mebane NC 27302
Tel (919) 563-3531 *SIC* 2515

■ OHIO MATTRESS CO LICENSING AND COMPONENTS GROUP p 1077
1 Office Parkway Rd, Trinity NC 27370
Tel (336) 861-3500 *SIC* 2515 6794

■ SEALY CORP p 1296
1 Office Parkway Rd, Trinity NC 27370
Tel (336) 861-3500 *SIC* 2515

■ SEALY MATTRESS CO p 1297
1 Office Parkway Rd, Trinity NC 27370
Tel (336) 861-3500 *SIC* 2515

■ SEALY MATTRESS MANUFACTURING CO INC p 1297
1 Office Parkway Rd, Trinity NC 27370
Tel (336) 861-3500 *SIC* 2515

WINSTON-SALEM INDUSTRIES FOR BLIND INC p 1617
7730 N Point Blvd, Winston Salem NC 27106
Tel (336) 759-0551
SIC 2515 3021 2392 2253 2394 3851

CORSICANA BEDDING LLC p 373
3001 S Us Highway 287, Corsicana TX 75109
Tel (903) 872-2591 *SIC* 2515

■ TEMPUR PRODUCTION USA LLC p 1436
203 Tempur Pedic Dr # 102, Duffield VA 24244
Tel (276) 431-7150 *SIC* 2515

EASTERN SLEEP PRODUCTS CO p 472
4901 Fitzhugh Ave, Richmond VA 23230
Tel (804) 254-1711
SIC 2515 2512 7641 4213

CASCADE DESIGNS INC p 262
4000 1st Ave S, Seattle WA 98134
Tel (206) 583-0583
SIC 2515 3089 3949 8733

SIC 2517 Wood T V, Radio, Phono & Sewing Cabinets

ANA GLOBAL LLC p 88
2360 Marconi Ct, San Diego CA 92154
Tel (619) 482-9990 *SIC* 2517 5999

ZENITH ELECTRONICS CORP p 1642
2000 Millbrook Dr, Lincolnshire IL 60069
Tel (847) 941-8000
SIC 3651 3671 3663 3674 2517 2519

▲ KIMBALL INTERNATIONAL INC p 818
1600 Royal St, Jasper IN 47549
Tel (812) 482-1600
SIC 2511 2512 2521 2522 2517

WOODHARBOR MOLDING & MILLWORKS INC p 1623
3277 9th St Sw, Mason City IA 50401
Tel (641) 423-0444
SIC 2431 2521 2517 2434

▲ HOOKER FURNITURE CORP p 705
440 Commonwealth Blvd E, Martinsville VA 24112
Tel (276) 632-2133
SIC 2511 2512 2517 2521

SIC 2519 Household Furniture, NEC

JL AUDIO INC p 786
10369 N Commerce Pkwy, Miramar FL 33025
Tel (954) 443-1100 *SIC* 5065 2519

■ RUBBERMAID INC p 1256
3 Glenlake Pkwy, Atlanta GA 30328
Tel (770) 418-7000
SIC 3089 2519 3944 2369 2392

SUNCAST CORP p 1401
701 N Kirk Rd, Batavia IL 60510
Tel (630) 879-2050 *SIC* 2519 3052 3432

ZENITH ELECTRONICS CORP p 1642
2000 Millbrook Dr, Lincolnshire IL 60069
Tel (847) 941-8000
SIC 3651 3671 3663 3674 2517 2519

WESTON PRESIDIO INC p 1602
200 Clarendon St Ste 5000, Boston MA 02116
Tel (617) 988-2500
SIC 6799 3944 2519 3085

AMERICAN FURNITURE MANUFACTURING INC p 73
604 Pontotoc County Indu, Ecru MS 38841
Tel (662) 489-2633 *SIC* 2519

L&JG STICKLEY INC p 834
1 Stickley Dr, Manlius NY 13104
Tel (315) 682-5500 *SIC* 2511 2519

SUNTERRACE CASUAL FURNITURE INC p 1405
2369 Chrles Rper Jnas Hwy, Stanley NC 28164
Tel (704) 263-1967 *SIC* 2519

SAUDER WOODWORKING CO p 1283
502 Middle St, Archbold OH 43502
Tel (419) 446-3828 *SIC* 2519 5021

LITTLE TIKES CO p 871
2180 Barlow Rd, Hudson OH 44236
Tel (330) 650-3000 *SIC* 3944 2519

EVENFLO CO INC p 513
225 Byers Rd, Miamisburg OH 45342
Tel (937) 415-3300 *SIC* 3944 2519

PI INC p 1146
213 Dennis St, Athens TN 37303
Tel (423) 745-6213
SIC 2519 3949 3089 2499 3086 3081

WINGATE PARTNERS LP p 1616
750 N Saint Paul St # 1200, Dallas TX 75201
Tel (214) 720-1313
SIC 2621 2672 3645 2519 5021 2521

LIFETIME PRODUCTS INC p 865
Freeport Ctr Bldg D-11, Clearfield UT 84016
Tel (801) 776-1532
SIC 2519 3949 2531 2511

SIC 2521 Wood Office Furniture

NORSTAR OFFICE PRODUCTS INC p 1049
5353 Jillson St, Commerce CA 90040
Tel (323) 262-1919 *SIC* 2521 2522

CORPORATE INTERIORS INC p 372
223 Lisa Dr, New Castle DE 19720
Tel (302) 322-1008 *SIC* 5021 2521

■ GEIGER INTERNATIONAL INC p 597
6095 Fulton Indus Blvd Sw, Atlanta GA 30336
Tel (404) 344-1100 *SIC* 2521

MAYLINE INVESTMENTS INC p 923
555 Skokie Blvd, Northbrook IL 60062
Tel (847) 948-9340 *SIC* 2522 2521

OFS BRANDS HOLDINGS INC p 1076
1204 E 6th St, Huntingburg IN 47542
Tel (800) 521-5381
SIC 2521 2522 2511 2599

JASPER SEATING CO INC p 778
225 Clay St, Jasper IN 47546
Tel (812) 482-3204 SIC 2521 2531 2522

■ **KIMBALL FURNITURE GROUP LLC** p 818
1600 Royal St, Jasper IN 47549
Tel (812) 482-1600 SIC 2521 2522

▲ **KIMBALL INTERNATIONAL INC** p 818
1600 Royal St, Jasper IN 47549
Tel (812) 482-1600
SIC 2511 2512 2521 2522 2517

■ **PAOLI LLC** p 1112
201 E Martin St, Orleans IN 47452
Tel (800) 457-7415 SIC 2521

WOODHARBOR MOLDING & MILLWORKS INC p 1623
3277 9th St Sw, Mason City IA 50401
Tel (641) 423-0444
SIC 2431 2521 2517 2434

▲ **HNI CORP** p 698
408 E 2nd St, Muscatine IA 52761
Tel (563) 272-7400
SIC 2522 2542 2521 2541 3433 3429

■ **HON CO LLC** p 704
200 Oak St, Muscatine IA 52761
Tel (563) 272-7100 SIC 2521

▲ **STEELCASE INC** p 1384
901 44th St Se, Grand Rapids MI 49508
Tel (616) 247-2710
SIC 2522 2521 3648 8748

HAWORTH INC p 670
1 Haworth Ctr, Holland MI 49423
Tel (616) 393-3000 SIC 2522 2521

HAWORTH INTERNATIONAL LTD p 670
1 Haworth Ctr, Holland MI 49423
Tel (616) 393-3000 SIC 2522 2521

JSJ FURNITURE CORP p 796
17237 Van Wagoner Rd, Spring Lake MI 49456
Tel (616) 847-6534 SIC 2521

▲ **HERMAN MILLER INC** p 687
855 E Main Ave, Zeeland MI 49464
Tel (616) 654-3000
SIC 2521 2522 2541 2542 2531

COLOR ART INTEGRATED INTERIORS LLC p 338
1325 N Warson Rd, Saint Louis MO 63132
Tel (314) 432-3000
SIC 5021 7641 5999 5712 5099 2521

BUSH INDUSTRIES INC p 229
1 Mason Dr, Jamestown NY 14701
Tel (716) 665-2000 SIC 2511 2521

HUMANSCALE CORP p 718
11 E 26th St Fl 8, New York NY 10010
Tel (212) 725-4749 SIC 3577 2521

■ **GUNLOCKE CO L L C** p 647
1 Gunlocke Dr, Wayland NY 14572
Tel (585) 728-5111 SIC 2521

■ **HICKORY BUSINESS FURNITURE LLC** p 690
900 12th Street Dr Nw, Hickory NC 28601
Tel (828) 322-1169 SIC 2521 2299

BERNHARDT FURNITURE CO INC p 176
1839 Morganton Blvd Sw, Lenoir NC 28645
Tel (828) 758-9811
SIC 2511 2512 2521 2522

BERNHARDT INDUSTRIES INC p 176
1839 Morganton Blvd Sw, Lenoir NC 28645
Tel (828) 758-9811
SIC 2511 2521 2512 2522

CONESTOGA WOOD SPECIALTIES CORP p 355
245 Reading Rd, East Earl PA 17519
Tel (717) 445-6701 SIC 2431 2521 2434

▲ **KNOLL INC** p 824
1235 Water St, East Greenville PA 18041
Tel (215) 679-7991 SIC 2521 2522 2299

WINGATE PARTNERS LP p 1616
750 N Saint Paul St # 1200, Dallas TX 75201
Tel (214) 720-1313
SIC 2621 2672 3645 2519 5021 2521

MARCO DISPLAY SPECIALISTS LP p 905
3209 Marquita Dr, Fort Worth TX 76116
Tel (817) 244-8300
SIC 2521 2541 3993 3089 3081

M L E HOLDINGS INC p 889
1301 W 400 N, Orem UT 84057
Tel (801) 224-0589 SIC 2531 2522 2521

A C FURNITURE CO INC p 5
3872 Martin Dr, Axton VA 24054
Tel (276) 650-3356 SIC 2521

▲ **HOOKER FURNITURE CORP** p 705
440 Commonwealth Blvd E, Martinsville VA 24112
Tel (276) 632-2133
SIC 2511 2512 2517 2521

KOHLER CO p 826
444 Highland Dr, Kohler WI 53044
Tel (920) 457-4441
SIC 3431 3432 3261 2511 2521 3519

DEMCO INC p 428
4810 Forest Run Rd, Madison WI 53704
Tel (800) 356-1200 SIC 5021 2521

SIC 2522 Office Furniture, Except Wood

NORSTAR OFFICE PRODUCTS INC p 1049
5353 Jillson St, Commerce CA 90040
Tel (323) 262-1919 SIC 2521 2522

EXEMPLIS LLC p 519
6415 Katella Ave, Cypress CA 90630
Tel (714) 995-4800 SIC 2522

TROPITONE FURNITURE CO INC p 1484
5 Marconi, Irvine CA 92618
Tel (949) 595-2000 SIC 2514 2522

▲ **VIRCO MFG CORP** p 1558
2027 Harpers Way, Torrance CA 90501
Tel (310) 533-0474 SIC 2531 2522 2511

EDSAL MANUFACTURING CO INC p 479
4400 S Packers Ave, Chicago IL 60609
Tel (773) 475-3020 SIC 2599 2542 2522

MARVEL GROUP INC p 913
3843 W 43rd St, Chicago IL 60632
Tel (773) 523-4804 SIC 2522

FELLOWES INC p 537
1789 Norwood Ave, Itasca IL 60143
Tel (630) 893-1600
SIC 2522 3589 2653 3577 3572 3579

MAYLINE INVESTMENTS INC p 923
555 Skokie Blvd, Northbrook IL 60062
Tel (847) 948-9340 SIC 2522 2521

OFS BRANDS HOLDINGS INC p 1076
1204 E 6th St, Huntingburg IN 47542
Tel (800) 521-5381
SIC 2521 2522 2511 2599

JASPER SEATING CO INC p 778
225 Clay St, Jasper IN 47546
Tel (812) 482-3204 SIC 2521 2531 2522

■ **KIMBALL FURNITURE GROUP LLC** p 818
1600 Royal St, Jasper IN 47549
Tel (812) 482-1600 SIC 2521 2522

▲ **KIMBALL INTERNATIONAL INC** p 818
1600 Royal St, Jasper IN 47549
Tel (812) 482-1600
SIC 2511 2512 2521 2522 2517

■ **KIMBALL OFFICE INC** p 818
1600 Royal St, Jasper IN 47549
Tel (812) 482-1600 SIC 2522

FKI SECURITY GROUP LLC p 554
101 Security Pkwy, New Albany IN 47150
Tel (812) 948-8400
SIC 2522 5044 3499 3429

■ **ALLSTEEL INC** p 58
2210 2nd Ave, Muscatine IA 52761
Tel (563) 272-4800 SIC 2522

▲ **HNI CORP** p 698
408 E 2nd St, Muscatine IA 52761
Tel (563) 272-7400
SIC 2522 2542 2521 2541 3433 3429

■ **MAXON FURNITURE INC** p 922
2210 2nd Ave, Muscatine IA 52761
Tel (800) 876-4274 SIC 2522

HIRSH INDUSTRIES INC p 696
3636 Westown Pkwy Ste 100, West Des Moines IA 50266
Tel (515) 299-3200 SIC 2522 2541

JSJ CORP p 796
700 Robbins Rd, Grand Haven MI 49417
Tel (616) 842-6350
SIC 3465 3469 3366 3089 3086 2522

AMERICAN SEATING CO p 79
401 Amrcan Seating Ctr Nw, Grand Rapids MI 49504
Tel (616) 732-6600 SIC 2522 2531

▲ **STEELCASE INC** p 1384
901 44th St Se, Grand Rapids MI 49508
Tel (616) 247-2710
SIC 2522 2521 3648 8748

HAWORTH INC p 670
1 Haworth Ctr, Holland MI 49423
Tel (616) 393-3000 SIC 2522 2521

HAWORTH INTERNATIONAL LTD p 670
1 Haworth Ctr, Holland MI 49423
Tel (616) 393-3000 SIC 2522 2521

LANDSCAPE FORMS INC p 843
7800 E Michigan Ave, Kalamazoo MI 49048
Tel (269) 381-0396
SIC 2531 2522 2511 2449 3648

SRG GLOBAL INC p 1363
800 Stephenson Hwy, Troy MI 48083
Tel (586) 757-7800
SIC 3089 3571 3494 2522 3826 3825

▲ **HERMAN MILLER INC** p 687
855 E Main Ave, Zeeland MI 49464
Tel (616) 654-3000
SIC 2521 2522 2541 2542 2531

CRENLO CAB PRODUCTS INC p 391
1600 4th Ave Nw, Rochester MN 55901
Tel (507) 289-3371
SIC 2522 3531 2542 3713 3469 3444

GLOBAL INDUSTRIES INC p 616
17 W Stow Rd, Marlton NJ 08053
Tel (856) 596-3390 SIC 2522 5021

BERNHARDT FURNITURE CO INC p 176
1839 Morganton Blvd Sw, Lenoir NC 28645
Tel (828) 758-9811
SIC 2511 2512 2521 2522

BERNHARDT INDUSTRIES INC p 176
1839 Morganton Blvd Sw, Lenoir NC 28645
Tel (828) 758-9811
SIC 2511 2521 2512 2522

▲ **KNOLL INC** p 824
1235 Water St, East Greenville PA 18041
Tel (215) 679-7991 SIC 2521 2522 2299

M L E HOLDINGS INC p 889
1301 W 400 N, Orem UT 84057
Tel (801) 224-0589 SIC 2531 2522 2521

MITY-LITE INC p 978
1301 W 400 N, Orem UT 84057
Tel (801) 224-0589 SIC 2531 2522 7359

■ **SENTRY SAFE INC** p 1305
137 W Forest Hill Ave, Oak Creek WI 53154
Tel (585) 381-4900 SIC 3089 3499 2522

SIC 2531 Public Building & Related Furniture

ADIENT CLANTON INC p 22
2541 7th St S, Clanton AL 35046
Tel (205) 755-9994 SIC 2531

BAE SYSTEMS p 144
7822 S 46th St, Phoenix AZ 85044
Tel (602) 643-7233 SIC 2531

CLARIDGE PRODUCTS AND EQUIPMENT INC p 321
601 Highway 62 65 S, Harrison AR 72601
Tel (870) 743-2200
SIC 2531 3354 2541 2542

KATZKIN LEATHER INC p 805
6868 W Acco St, Montebello CA 90640
Tel (323) 725-1243 SIC 5199 2531

IJOT DEVELOPMENT INC p 731
1300 Clay St Ste 600, Oakland CA 94612
Tel (925) 258-9909 SIC 2531 2599

▲ **VIRCO MFG CORP** p 1558
2027 Harpers Way, Torrance CA 90501
Tel (310) 533-0474 SIC 2531 2522 2511

▲ **B/E AEROSPACE INC** p 142
1400 Corporate Center Way, Wellington FL 33414
Tel (561) 791-5000 SIC 2531 3728 3647

GEM INDUSTRIES INC p 598
Hwy 123 N, Toccoa GA 30577
Tel (706) 886-8431
SIC 3429 2531 2511 3446 2821 2515

FREEDMAN SEATING CO p 576
4545 W Augusta Blvd, Chicago IL 60651
Tel (773) 524-2440 SIC 2531

▲ **FORTUNE BRANDS HOME & SECURITY INC** p 570
520 Lake Cook Rd, Deerfield IL 60015
Tel (847) 484-4400
SIC 2531 2599 3429 3469

STEVENS INDUSTRIES INC p 1388
704 W Main St, Teutopolis IL 62467
Tel (217) 540-3100 SIC 2531 2679 2511

TRANSPORTATION TECHNOLOGIES INDUSTRIES INC p 1473
7140 Office Cir, Evansville IN 47715
Tel (812) 962-5000
SIC 2531 3714 3321 4741 3471

JASPER SEATING CO INC p 778
225 Clay St, Jasper IN 47546
Tel (812) 482-3204 SIC 2521 2531 2522

SEARS MANUFACTURING CO p 1297
1718 S Concord St, Davenport IA 52802
Tel (563) 383-2800 SIC 2531

TRIM MASTERS INC p 1480
1360 Dolwick Rd Ste 125, Erlanger KY 41018
Tel (859) 887-6000 SIC 2531

BRIDGEWATER INTERIORS LLC p 212
4617 W Fort St, Detroit MI 48209
Tel (313) 842-3300 SIC 5013 2531

INTEGRATED MANUFACTURING & ASSEMBLY LLC p 749
6501 E Nevada St, Detroit MI 48234
Tel (734) 530-5600 SIC 2531

TACHI-S ENGINEERING USA INC p 1421
23227 Commerce Dr, Farmington Hills MI 48335
Tel (248) 478-5050 SIC 2531 8711

AMERICAN SEATING CO p 79
401 Amrcan Seating Ctr Nw, Grand Rapids MI 49504
Tel (616) 732-6600 SIC 2522 2531

IRWIN SEATING CO p 766
3251 Fruit Ridge Ave Nw, Grand Rapids MI 49544
Tel (616) 784-2621 SIC 2531

IRWIN SEATING HOLDING CO p 766
3251 Fruit Ridge Ave Nw, Grand Rapids MI 49544
Tel (616) 574-7400 SIC 2531 7641

LANDSCAPE FORMS INC p 843
7800 E Michigan Ave, Kalamazoo MI 49048
Tel (269) 381-0396
SIC 2531 2522 2511 2449 3648

HOOVER UNIVERSAL INC p 706
49200 Halyard Dr, Plymouth MI 48170
Tel (734) 454-0994 SIC 2531

YANFENG US AUTOMOTIVE INTERIOR SYSTEMS I LLC p 1634
45000 Helm St, Plymouth MI 48170
Tel (414) 524-1200 SIC 2531

RCO ENGINEERING INC p 1212
29200 Calahan Rd, Roseville MI 48066
Tel (586) 774-0100
SIC 3714 3089 3365 7361 3325 2531

FISHER & CO INC p 551
33300 Fisher Dr, Saint Clair Shores MI 48082
Tel (586) 746-2000 SIC 2531

▲ **LEAR CORP** p 850
21557 Telegraph Rd, Southfield MI 48033
Tel (248) 447-1500
SIC 3714 2531 2396 3643

WOODBRIDGE HOLDINGS INC p 1622
1515 Equity Dr, Troy MI 48084
Tel (248) 288-0100 SIC 2531 3086

▲ **HERMAN MILLER INC** p 687
855 E Main Ave, Zeeland MI 49464
Tel (616) 654-3000
SIC 2521 2522 2541 2542 2531

LANDSCAPE STRUCTURES INC p 843
601 7th St S, Delano MN 55328
Tel (763) 972-3391 SIC 3949 2531

AIR CRUISERS CO LLC p 38
1747 State Route 34, Wall Township NJ 07727
Tel (732) 681-3527
SIC 2531 3069 3728 2399

SAUDER MANUFACTURING CO p 1283
930 W Barre Rd, Archbold OH 43502
Tel (419) 445-7670 SIC 2531

JAY INDUSTRIES INC p 779
150 Longview Ave E, Mansfield OH 44903
Tel (419) 524-3778 SIC 2531 3089

SETEX INC p 1308
1111 Mckinley Rd, Saint Marys OH 45885
Tel (419) 394-7800 SIC 2531

BRODART CO p 216
500 Arch St, Williamsport PA 17701
Tel (570) 326-2461
SIC 5192 5942 2752 2782 2789 2531

MANUFACTURERS INDUSTRIAL GROUP LLC p 903
659 Natchez Trace Dr, Lexington TN 38351
Tel (731) 968-3601 SIC 3499 2531

FURUKAWA WIRING SYSTEMS AMERICA INC p 585
950 Loma Verde Dr, El Paso TX 79936
Tel (915) 791-5579 SIC 2531

LIFETIME PRODUCTS INC p 865
Freeport Ctr Bldg D-11, Clearfield UT 84016
Tel (801) 776-1532
SIC 2519 3949 2531 2511

M L E HOLDINGS INC p 889
1301 W 400 N, Orem UT 84057
Tel (801) 224-0589 SIC 2531 2522 2521

MITY-LITE INC p 978
1301 W 400 N, Orem UT 84057
Tel (801) 224-0589 SIC 2531 2522 7359

KRUEGER INTERNATIONAL INC p 830
1330 Bellevue St, Green Bay WI 54302
Tel (920) 468-8100 SIC 2531

JOHNSON CONTROLS INC p 791
5757 N Green Bay Ave, Milwaukee WI 53209
Tel (414) 524-1200
SIC 2531 3714 3691 3822 8744

■ **MILSCO MANUFACTURING CO** p 972
9009 N 51st St, Milwaukee WI 53223
Tel (414) 354-0500 SIC 2531

YANFENG US AUTOMOTIVE INTERIOR SYSTEMS II LLC p 1634
5757 N Green Bay Ave, Milwaukee WI 53209
Tel (205) 477-4225 SIC 2531

SEATS INC p 1297
1515 Industrial St, Reedsburg WI 53959
Tel (608) 524-8261 SIC 2531

SIC 2541 Wood, Office & Store Fixtures

CLARIDGE PRODUCTS AND EQUIPMENT INC p 321
601 Highway 62 65 S, Harrison AR 72601
Tel (870) 743-2200
SIC 2531 3354 2541 2542

■ **LA DARLING CO LLC** p 835
1401 Highway 49b, Paragould AR 72450
Tel (870) 239-9564 SIC 2541 2542

RSI HOME PRODUCTS INC p 1256
400 E Orangethorpe Ave, Anaheim CA 92801
Tel (714) 449-2200
SIC 2514 2541 3281 2434

RACKS INC p 1203
7565 Siempre Viva Rd, San Diego CA 92154
Tel (619) 661-0987 SIC 2542 3993 2541

LIST INDUSTRIES INC p 870
401 Jim Moran Blvd, Deerfield Beach FL 33442
Tel (954) 429-9155 SIC 2541 5021 2542

CREATIVE SURFACES INC p 390
1400 W Marietta St Nw, Atlanta GA 30318
Tel (205) 988-3246 SIC 2541 1799

LG HAUSYS AMERICA INC p 860
900 Circle 75 Pkwy Se # 15, Atlanta GA 30339
Tel (678) 486-8210 SIC 2541

■ **MARMON RETAIL SERVICES INC** p 909
181 W Madison St, Chicago IL 60602
Tel (312) 332-0317 SIC 2541 2542

WIND POINT PARTNERS VI LP p 1615
676 N Michigan Ave # 3700, Chicago IL 60611
Tel (312) 255-4800
SIC 6799 2542 2541 3429

TOP SHOP LLC p 1460
5515 Council St Ne, Cedar Rapids IA 52402
Tel (319) 393-1041 SIC 2541

▲ **HNI CORP** p 698
408 E 2nd St, Muscatine IA 52761
Tel (563) 272-7400
SIC 2522 2542 2521 2541 3433 3429

HIRSH INDUSTRIES INC p 696
3636 Westown Pkwy Ste 100, West Des Moines IA 50266
Tel (515) 299-3200 SIC 2522 2541

HARBOR INDUSTRIES INC p 659
14130 172nd Ave, Grand Haven MI 49417
Tel (616) 842-5330 SIC 2541 3993

KNAPE & VOGT MANUFACTURING CO p 824
2700 Oak Industrial Dr Ne, Grand Rapids MI 49505
Tel (616) 459-3311 SIC 2542 2541 3429

▲ **HERMAN MILLER INC** p 687
855 E Main Ave, Zeeland MI 49464
Tel (616) 654-3000
SIC 2521 2522 2541 2542 2531

■ **STREATER LLC** p 1393
411 S 1st Ave, Albert Lea MN 56007
Tel (800) 527-4197 SIC 2542 2541

PROCESS DISPLAYS LLC p 1179
7108 31st Ave N, Minneapolis MN 55427
Tel (763) 541-1245
SIC 2541 2542 2599 2675 2752 2759

WENGER CORP p 1592
555 Park Dr, Owatonna MN 55060
Tel (507) 455-4100 SIC 2541 3446

SWAN SURFACES LLC p 1411
515 Olive St Ste 900, Saint Louis MO 63101
Tel (314) 231-8148 SIC 2541 5722 3431

LOZIER CORP p 882
6336 John J Pershing Dr, Omaha NE 68110
Tel (402) 457-8000 SIC 2541 2542

MARIETTA CORP p 906
37 Huntington St, Cortland NY 13045
Tel (607) 753-6746 SIC 2844 2834 2541

FORMICA CORP p 567
10155 Reading Rd, Cincinnati OH 45241
Tel (513) 786-3400 SIC 2541 2679

KENNEY MANUFACTURING CO p 811
1000 Jefferson Blvd, Warwick RI 02886
Tel (401) 739-2200
SIC 2591 3261 2511 3699 3499 2541

ELLETT BROTHERS LLC p 488
267 Columbia Ave, Chapin SC 29036
Tel (803) 345-3751
SIC 5091 3949 2499 2541

AMERICAN DISPLAY & FIXTURE LLC p 71
3600 N Hawthorne St, Chattanooga TN 37406
Tel (423) 624-1191 SIC 2541

MARCO DISPLAY SPECIALISTS LP p 905
3209 Marquita Dr, Fort Worth TX 76116
Tel (817) 244-8300 SIC 2541 3993

MARCO DISPLAY SPECIALISTS LP p 905
3209 Marquita Dr, Fort Worth TX 76116
Tel (817) 244-8300
SIC 2521 2541 3993 3089 3081

REPUBLIC NATIONAL INDUSTRIES OF TEXAS LP p 1225
1400 Warren Dr, Marshall TX 75672
Tel (903) 935-3680 SIC 2434 5211 2541

WILSONART INTERNATIONAL HOLDINGS LLC p 1614
2400 Wilson Pl, Temple TX 76504
Tel (254) 207-7000 SIC 2541

■ WILSONART INTERNATIONAL INC p 1614
2501 Wilsonart Dr, Temple TX 76503
Tel (254) 207-7000 SIC 2821 2541

WILSONART LLC p 1614
2501 Wilsonart Dr, Temple TX 76504
Tel (254) 207-7000 SIC 2541

MADIX INC p 894
500 Airport Rd, Terrell TX 75160
Tel (214) 515-5400 SIC 2542 2541

SOURCE HOME ENTERTAINMENT LLC p 1342
8251 Greensboro Dr # 400, Mc Lean VA 22102
Tel (239) 949-4450
SIC 5192 5099 8742 2541

BARGREEN-ELLINGSON INC p 155
6626 Tacoma Mall Blvd B, Tacoma WA 98409
Tel (253) 475-9201 SIC 5046 2541

SIC 2542 Partitions & Fixtures, Except Wood

CLARIDGE PRODUCTS AND EQUIPMENT INC p 321
601 Highway 62 65 S, Harrison AR 72601
Tel (870) 743-2200
SIC 2531 3354 2541 2542

ROYSTON HOLDING LLC p 1255
111 Center St Ste 2500, Little Rock AR 72201
Tel (770) 735-3456 SIC 7389 1751 2542

■ LA DARLING CO LLC p 835
1401 Highway 49b, Paragould AR 72450
Tel (870) 239-9564 SIC 2541 2542

CHATSWORTH PRODUCTS INC p 292
29899 Agoura Rd Ste 120, Agoura Hills CA 91301
Tel (818) 735-6100 SIC 3499 2542

INNOVATIVE STORE SYSTEMS INC p 745
1351 S Beach Blvd Ste L, La Habra CA 90631
Tel (562) 947-4101 SIC 2542

RACKS INC p 1203
7565 Siempre Viva Rd, San Diego CA 92154
Tel (619) 661-0987 SIC 2542 3993 2541

IMI AMERICAS INC p 733
5400 S Delaware St, Littleton CO 80120
Tel (763) 488-5400 SIC 2542

WORLD INDUSTRIAL RESOURCES CORP p 1625
13100 56th Ct Ste 710, Clearwater FL 33760
Tel (727) 572-9991
SIC 3999 2542 5113 2671

LIST INDUSTRIES INC p 870
401 Jim Moran Blvd, Deerfield Beach FL 33442
Tel (954) 429-9155 SIC 2541 5021 2542

ISD HOLDINGS INC p 766
4715 Frederick Dr Sw, Atlanta GA 30336
Tel (404) 691-7400
SIC 7389 2542 2759 2752

MILLER ZELL INC p 971
6100 Fulton Indus Blvd Sw, Atlanta GA 30336
Tel (404) 691-7400
SIC 7389 2542 2759 2752

ROYSTON LLC p 1255
1 Pickroy Rd, Jasper GA 30143
Tel (770) 735-3456 SIC 7389 2542 1751

EDSAL MANUFACTURING CO INC p 479
4400 S Packers Ave, Chicago IL 60609
Tel (773) 475-3020 SIC 2599 2542 2522

■ MARMON RETAIL SERVICES INC p 909
181 W Madison St, Chicago IL 60602
Tel (312) 332-0317 SIC 2541 2542

WIND POINT PARTNERS VI LP p 1615
676 N Michigan Ave # 3700, Chicago IL 60611
Tel (312) 255-4800
SIC 6799 2542 2541 3429

■ ACCO BRANDS INC p 15
4 Corporate Dr, Lake Zurich IL 60047
Tel (847) 541-9500 SIC 2542

INTERLAKE MECALUX INC p 753
1600 N 25th Ave, Melrose Park IL 60160
Tel (708) 344-9999 SIC 5084 2542

LYON LLC p 888
420 N Main St, Montgomery IL 60538
Tel (630) 892-8941 SIC 2542

LYON WORKSPACE PRODUCTS LLC p 888
420 N Main St, Montgomery IL 60538
Tel (630) 892-8941 SIC 2542

SOUTHERN IMPERIAL INC p 1349
1400 Eddy Ave, Rockford IL 61103
Tel (815) 877-7041 SIC 5046 2542

▲ HNI CORP p 698
408 E 2nd St, Muscatine IA 52761
Tel (563) 272-7400
SIC 2522 2542 2521 2541 3433 3429

CHAMPION INDUSTRIES INC p 287
10848 Airline Hwy, Baton Rouge LA 70816
Tel (225) 291-9090
SIC 2542 2759 2791 2789 2752

KNAPE & VOGT MANUFACTURING CO p 824
2700 Oak Industrial Dr Ne, Grand Rapids MI 49505
Tel (616) 459-3311 SIC 2542 2541 3429

▲ HERMAN MILLER INC p 687
855 E Main Ave, Zeeland MI 49464
Tel (616) 654-3000
SIC 2521 2522 2541 2542 2531

■ STREATER LLC p 1393
411 S 1st Ave, Albert Lea MN 56007
Tel (800) 527-4197 SIC 2542 2541

SMEAD MANUFACTURING CO INC p 1332
600 Smead Blvd, Hastings MN 55033
Tel (651) 437-4111
SIC 2675 7372 2789 2759 2752 2542

ACTIVAR INC p 19
7808 Creekridge Cir # 200, Minneapolis MN 55439
Tel (952) 944-3533
SIC 2542 3479 3442 3429 3089

PROCESS DISPLAYS LLC p 1179
7108 31st Ave N, Minneapolis MN 55427
Tel (763) 541-1245
SIC 2541 2542 2599 2675 2752 2759

LIBERTY DIVERSIFIED INTERNATIONAL INC p 861
5600 Highway 169 N, New Hope MN 55428
Tel (763) 536-6600
SIC 2653 2631 5112 2542 3089 5961

CRENLO CAB PRODUCTS INC p 391
1600 4th Ave Nw, Rochester MN 55901
Tel (507) 289-3371
SIC 2522 3531 2542 3713 3469 3444

▲ LEGGETT & PLATT INC p 853
1 Leggett Rd, Carthage MO 64836
Tel (417) 358-8131
SIC 2515 2514 3495 2392 2542 3363

IDX CORP p 729
1 Rider Trail Plaza Dr, Earth City MO 63045
Tel (314) 739-4120 SIC 2542

HALLMARK MARKETING CO LLC p 654
2501 Mcgee St, Kansas City MO 64108
Tel (816) 274-5111 SIC 5947 2542 7389

LOZIER CORP p 882
6336 John J Pershing Dr, Omaha NE 68110
Tel (402) 457-8000 SIC 2541 2542

FRAZIER INDUSTRIAL CO p 575
91 Fairview Ave, Long Valley NJ 07853
Tel (908) 876-3001 SIC 3441 2542

PENCO PRODUCTS INC p 1128
1820 Stonehenge Dr, Greenville NC 27858
Tel (252) 917-5287 SIC 2599 2542

INDUSTRIAL MANUFACTURING CO LLC p 740
8223 Brecksville Rd Ste 1, Brecksville OH 44141
Tel (440) 838-4700 SIC 2542 3728 3566

REPUBLIC STORAGE SYSTEMS LLC p 1226
1038 Belden Ave Ne, Canton OH 44705
Tel (330) 438-5800 SIC 2542 3441

SUMMA HOLDINGS INC p 1398
8223 Brecksville Rd # 100, Cleveland OH 44141
Tel (440) 838-4700
SIC 2542 3462 3569 7359 3728

MIDMARK CORP p 966
60 Vista Dr, Versailles OH 45380
Tel (937) 526-3662
SIC 3648 3842 3843 2542 3841

INTERMETRO INDUSTRIES CORP p 753
651 N Washington St, Wilkes Barre PA 18705
Tel (570) 825-2741
SIC 3496 2542 3537 3411 3315 2441

SCHNEIDER ELECTRIC IT CORP p 1287
132 Fairgrounds Rd, West Kingston RI 02892
Tel (401) 789-5735
SIC 3629 3612 3677 3585 7372 2542

TENNSCO CORP p 1438
201 Tennsco Dr, Dickson TN 37055
Tel (615) 446-8000 SIC 2542

UNARCO MATERIAL HANDLING INC p 1502
701 16th Ave E, Springfield TN 37172
Tel (615) 384-3531 SIC 5084 2542

UNIVERSAL DISPLAY AND FIXTURE CO p 1516
726 E Hwy 121, Lewisville TX 75057
Tel (972) 434-8067 SIC 2542 3993

MADIX INC p 894
500 Airport Rd, Terrell TX 75160
Tel (214) 515-5400 SIC 2542 2541

SPACESAVER CORP p 1354
1450 Janesville Ave, Fort Atkinson WI 53538
Tel (920) 563-6362 SIC 2542

HUFCOR INC p 717
2101 Kennedy Rd, Janesville WI 53545
Tel (608) 756-1241 SIC 2542 3442

STEEL KING INDUSTRIES INC p 1384
2700 Chamber St, Stevens Point WI 54481
Tel (715) 341-3120
SIC 3441 3537 3412 2542

SIC 2591 Drapery Hardware, Window Blinds & Shades

INFRASTRUCTURE HOLDINGS CO LLC p 742
115 S 48th St, Tempe AZ 85281
Tel (480) 784-2910 SIC 1611 1794 2591

KITTRICH CORP p 822
1585 W Mission Blvd, Pomona CA 91766
Tel (714) 736-1000 SIC 2591 2392 2381

MARIAK INDUSTRIES INC p 906
575 W Manville St, Rancho Dominguez CA 90220
Tel (310) 661-4400 SIC 5023 2591

GGC ADMINISTRATION LLC p 610
1 Embarcadero Ctr Fl 39, San Francisco CA 94111
Tel (415) 983-2700 SIC 2591

HUNTER DOUGLAS WINDOW FASHIONS INC p 719
1 Duette Way, Broomfield CO 80020
Tel (303) 466-1848 SIC 2591

CAROLE FABRICS CORP p 259
633 Nw Frontage Rd, Augusta GA 30907
Tel (706) 863-4742
SIC 2221 2591 5131 5949 2392 2391

MARIETTA DRAPERY & WINDOW COVERINGS CO INC p 906
22 Trammell St Sw, Marietta GA 30064
Tel (770) 428-3335
SIC 5023 2391 2591 2392

■ NEWELL OPERATING CO p 1037
29 E Stephenson St, Freeport IL 61032
Tel (815) 235-4171
SIC 3365 3991 3089 2591 3965 3596

ASCOT ENTERPRISES INC p 116
503 S Main St, Nappanee IN 46550
Tel (877) 773-7751 SIC 2391 2591 2392

DRAPER INC p 455
411 S Pearl St, Spiceland IN 47385
Tel (765) 987-7999 SIC 3861 2591 3651

LAFAYETTE VENETIAN BLIND INC p 838
3000 Klondike Rd, West Lafayette IN 47906
Tel (765) 464-2500 SIC 2591 2391

NEXT DAY BLINDS CORP p 1040
8251 Preston Ct Ste B, Jessup MD 20794
Tel (240) 568-8800
SIC 5023 2591 5719 1799

▲ NEWELL BRANDS INC p 1037
221 River St, Hoboken NJ 07030
Tel (201) 610-6600
SIC 3089 3469 2591 3951 3999 3546

BLINDS TO GO (US) INC p 189
101 E State Rt 4, Paramus NJ 07652
Tel (201) 441-9260 SIC 2591

MECHOSHADE SYSTEMS INC p 934
4203 35th St, Long Island City NY 11101
Tel (718) 729-2020 SIC 2591

HUNTER DOUGLAS INC p 719
1 Blue Hill Plz Ste 1569, Pearl River NY 10965
Tel (845) 664-7000 SIC 2591 3444 5084

KENNEY MANUFACTURING CO p 811
1000 Jefferson Blvd, Warwick RI 02886
Tel (401) 739-2200
SIC 2591 3261 2511 3699 3499 2541

SPRINGS INDUSTRIES INC p 1361
7549 Graber Rd, Middleton WI 53562
Tel (608) 836-1011 SIC 2591

SPRINGS WINDOW FASHIONS LLC p 1361
7549 Graber Rd, Middleton WI 53562
Tel (608) 836-1011 SIC 2591

SIC 2599 Furniture & Fixtures, NEC

IJOT DEVELOPMENT INC p 731
1300 Clay St Ste 600, Oakland CA 94612
Tel (925) 258-9909 SIC 2531 2599

VCP MOBILITY INC p 1545
6899 Winchester Cir # 200, Boulder CO 80301
Tel (303) 218-4500
SIC 3842 2599 2515 5047 3841

VALIANT PRODUCTS CORP p 1540
2727 W 5th Ave, Denver CO 80204
Tel (303) 892-1234
SIC 5131 5023 7389 2511 2599 1752

EDSAL MANUFACTURING CO INC p 479
4400 S Packers Ave, Chicago IL 60609
Tel (773) 475-3020 SIC 2599 2542 2522

■ MARMON RETAIL & END USER TECHNOLOGIES INC p 909
181 W Madison St Fl 26, Chicago IL 60602
Tel (312) 372-9500 SIC 2599

▲ FORTUNE BRANDS HOME & SECURITY INC p 570
520 Lake Cook Rd, Deerfield IL 60015
Tel (847) 484-4400
SIC 2531 2599 3429 3469

EUROMARKET DESIGNS INC p 512
1250 Techny Rd, Northbrook IL 60062
Tel (847) 272-2888
SIC 5719 5947 5712 5961 2599

RTC INDUSTRIES INC p 1256
2800 Golf Rd, Rolling Meadows IL 60008
Tel (847) 640-2400 SIC 2599 5211

■ HILL-ROM INC p 693
1069 State Route 46 E, Batesville IN 47006
Tel (812) 934-7777 SIC 7352 2599

OFS BRANDS HOLDINGS INC p 1076
1204 E 6th St, Huntingburg IN 47542
Tel (800) 521-5381
SIC 2521 2522 2511 2599

▲ STRYKER CORP p 1394
2825 Airview Blvd, Portage MI 49002
Tel (269) 385-2600 SIC 3841 3842 2599

PROCESS DISPLAYS LLC p 1179
7108 31st Ave N, Minneapolis MN 55427
Tel (763) 541-1245
SIC 2541 2542 2599 2675 2752 2759

ADIRONDACK SCENIC INC p 23
439 County Route 45 Ste 1, Argyle NY 12809
Tel (518) 638-8000 SIC 2599

VSM INVESTORS LLC p 1566
245 Park Ave Fl 41, New York NY 10167
Tel (212) 351-1600 SIC 3842 2599 2515

PENCO PRODUCTS INC p 1128
1820 Stonehenge Dr, Greenville NC 27858
Tel (252) 917-5287 SIC 2599 2542

▲ KEWAUNEE SCIENTIFIC CORP p 814
2700 W Front St, Statesville NC 28677
Tel (704) 873-7202 SIC 3821 2599

■ BASIC AMERICAN MEDICAL INC p 158
1 Park Plz, Nashville TN 37203
Tel (615) 344-9551 SIC 5912 2599 8093

C H INDUSTRIES INC p 232
1700 Columbian Club Dr, Carrollton TX 75006
Tel (972) 416-1304 SIC 2599 3444 3469

CHIRON HOLDINGS INC p 301
12930 W Interstate 10, San Antonio TX 78249
Tel (210) 524-9000 SIC 2599 7352

ERDMAN HOLDINGS INC p 507
6720 Frank Llyd Wright Av, Middleton WI 53562
Tel (608) 662-2205 SIC 1542 2599

SIC 2611 Pulp Mills

GEORGIA-PACIFIC BREWTON LLC p 608
32224 Highway 31, Brewton AL 36426
Tel (251) 867-3622 SIC 2611 2679

ALABAMA RIVER CELLULOSE LLC p 43
2373 Lena Landegger Hwy Cnty, Perdue Hill AL 36470
Tel (251) 575-2000 SIC 2611

DOMTAR AW LLC p 449
285 Highway 71 S, Ashdown AR 71822
Tel (870) 898-2711 SIC 2611

SOLENIS INTERNATIONAL LP p 1338
500 Hercules Rd, Wilmington DE 19808
Tel (302) 994-1698 SIC 2911 2611 1382

BUCKEYE FLORIDA LIMITED PARTNERSHIP p 223
1 Buckeye Dr, Perry FL 32348
Tel (850) 584-1121 SIC 2611

FOLEY CELLULOSE LLC p 563
3510 Contractors Rd, Perry FL 32348
Tel (850) 584-1121 SIC 2611

GNN INVESTOR LLC p 619
133 Peachtree St Ne, Atlanta GA 30303
Tel (404) 652-4000
SIC 2621 2611 2631 2653 5111 2677

GP CELLULOSE LLC p 627
133 Peachtree St Ne # 1, Atlanta GA 30303
Tel (404) 652-6630 SIC 2611

BRUNSWICK CELLULOSE LLC p 221
1400 9th St, Brunswick GA 31520
Tel (912) 265-5780
SIC 2611 2421 2899 2631

PRATT PAPER (NY) INC p 1167
1800 Sarasota Business, Conyers GA 30013
Tel (770) 918-5678 SIC 2611

■ STONE SOUTHWEST INC p 1391
150 N Michigan Ave, Chicago IL 60601
Tel (312) 346-6600
SIC 2631 2611 2621 2435 2436 2421

WOODLAND PULP LLC p 1623
144 Main St, Baileyville ME 04694
Tel (207) 427-3311 SIC 2611

ESCANABA PAPER CO p 509
7100 County Rd 426, Escanaba MI 49829
Tel (906) 786-1660 SIC 2611 2621 2672

BURROWS PAPER CORP p 229
501 W Main St Ste 1, Little Falls NY 13365
Tel (315) 823-2300
SIC 2621 2671 2611 2679

CENIBRA INC p 275
335 Madison Ave Fl 23, New York NY 10017
Tel (212) 818-8242 SIC 2611 5159

PARSONS & WHITTEMORE ENTERPRISES CORP p 1117
4 International Dr # 300, Port Chester NY 10573
Tel (914) 937-9009 SIC 2611

CENTRAL NATIONAL PULP & PAPER SALES INC p 279
3 Manhattanville Rd, Purchase NY 10577
Tel (914) 696-9000 SIC 2611

■ NEWPAGE CORP p 1038
8540 Gander Creek Dr, Miamisburg OH 45342
Tel (877) 855-7243 SIC 2621 2611

NEWPAGE ENERGY SERVICES LLC p 1038
8540 Gander Creek Dr, Miamisburg OH 45342
Tel (877) 855-7243 SIC 2672 2621 2611

■ NEWPAGE HOLDING CORP p 1038
8540 Gander Creek Dr, Miamisburg OH 45342
Tel (877) 855-7243 SIC 2621 2672 2611

RESOLUTE FP US INC p 1227
5300 Cureton Ferry Rd, Catawba SC 29704
Tel (803) 981-8000
SIC 2621 2672 2611 2421

■ INGEVITY SOUTH CAROLINA LLC p 742
5255 Virginia Ave, North Charleston SC 29406
Tel (843) 740-2300 SIC 2611

BUCKEYE TECHNOLOGIES INC p 223
1001 Tillman St, Memphis TN 38112
Tel (901) 320-8100 SIC 2611 3081

▲ INTERNATIONAL PAPER CO p 756
6400 Poplar Ave, Memphis TN 38197
Tel (901) 419-9000
SIC 2621 2653 2656 2631 2611

■ WESTROCK MWV LLC p 1603
501 S 5th St, Richmond VA 23219
Tel (804) 444-1000
SIC 2631 2671 2678 2677 2861 2611

PORT TOWNSEND HOLDINGS CO INC p 1162
100 Mill Rd, Port Townsend WA 98368
Tel (360) 385-3170 SIC 2611 2653

CATALYST PAPER OPERATIONS INC p 264
2200 6th Ave Ste 800, Seattle WA 98121
Tel (604) 247-4018 SIC 2611

KAMILCHE CO p 802
1301 5th Ave Ste 2700, Seattle WA 98101
Tel (206) 224-5800
SIC 2621 2611 2421 2435 2431

NORTHWEST CAPITAL APPRECIATION INC p 1059
1200 Westlake Ave N # 310, Seattle WA 98109
Tel (206) 689-5615 SIC 2611

SIMPSON INVESTMENT CO INC p 1325
1301 5th Ave Ste 2700, Seattle WA 98101
Tel (253) 272-0158
SIC 2621 2611 2421 2431 3084

▲ WEYERHAEUSER CO p 1603
220 Occidental Ave S, Seattle WA 98104
Tel (253) 924-2345
SIC 6798 0811 2411 2435 2611 2621

COWLES PUBLISHING CO p 386
999 W Riverside Ave, Spokane WA 99201
Tel (509) 459-5000
SIC 2711 2611 2621 4833

NEWPAGE WISCONSIN SYSTEM INC p 1038
111 W Jackson St, Wisconsin Rapids WI 54495
Tel (715) 422-3111
SIC 2621 2611 2653 7011

SIC 2621 Paper Mills

LD PRODUCTS INC p 849
3700 Cover St, Long Beach CA 90808
Tel (562) 986-6940 SIC 5045 2621

NEW-INDY ONTARIO LLC p 1036
5100 Jurupa St, Ontario CA 91761
Tel (909) 390-1055 SIC 2621

NEW-INDY OXNARD LLC p 1036
5936 Perkins Rd, Oxnard CA 93033
Tel (805) 986-3881 SIC 2621

■ CELLU TISSUE CORP p 274
2 Forbes St, East Hartford CT 06108
Tel (860) 289-7496 SIC 2621 3842 2676

BRANT INDUSTRIES INC p 208
80 Field Point Rd, Greenwich CT 06830
Tel (203) 863-1200 SIC 2621

FINCH PAPER HOLDINGS LLC p 543
1 Sound Shore Dr Ste 302, Greenwich CT 06830
Tel (203) 622-9138 SIC 2621

UST LLC p 1536
6 High Ridge Park Bldg A, Stamford CT 06905
Tel (203) 817-3000
SIC 2131 2084 2621 3999

AHLSTROM USA INC p 37
2 Elm St, Windsor Locks CT 06096
Tel (860) 654-8300 SIC 2621

COMMONWEALTH-ALTADIS INC p 346
5900 N Andrews Ave # 1100, Fort Lauderdale FL 33309
Tel (800) 481-5814 SIC 2111 2621 2131

ATLAS PAPER MILLS LLC p 128
3301 Nw 107th St, Miami FL 33167
Tel (800) 562-2860 SIC 2621

RESOLUTE FP FLORIDA INC p 1227
3301 Nw 107th St, Miami FL 33167
Tel (800) 562-2860 SIC 2621

PALM BEACH CAPITAL FUND II LP p 1109
180 Royal Palm Way, Palm Beach FL 33480
Tel (561) 659-9022 SIC 6799 2621

AHLSTROM ATLANTA LLC p 36
3820 Mansell Rd Ste 200, Alpharetta GA 30022
Tel (770) 650-2100 SIC 2621

■ CELLU TISSUE HOLDINGS INC p 274
12725 Morris Road Ext # 210, Alpharetta GA 30004
Tel (678) 393-2651 SIC 2621

▲ NEENAH PAPER INC p 1024
3460 Preston Ridge Rd # 150, Alpharetta GA 30005
Tel (678) 566-6500 SIC 2621 2741

▲ SCHWEITZER-MAUDUIT INTERNATIONAL INC p 1291
100 N Point Ctr E Ste 600, Alpharetta GA 30022
Tel (800) 514-0186 SIC 2141 2111 2621

FORT JAMES CORP p 569
133 Peachtree St Ne, Atlanta GA 30303
Tel (404) 652-4000 SIC 2621

GNN INVESTOR LLC p 619
133 Peachtree St Ne, Atlanta GA 30303
Tel (404) 652-4000
SIC 2621 2611 2631 2653 5111 2677

MONDI BAGS USA LLC p 984
1200 Abernathy Rd Ste 450, Atlanta GA 30328
Tel (770) 243-5410 SIC 2621

SPG HOLDINGS LLC p 1358
133 Peachtree St Se, Atlanta GA 30303
Tel (404) 652-4000 SIC 2621 5199

AUGUSTA NEWSPRINT CO EMPLOYEES RECREATION ASSOCIATION INC p 131
2434 Doug Barnard Pkwy, Augusta GA 30906
Tel (706) 798-3440 SIC 2621

PRATT INDUSTRIES (USA) INC p 1167
1800-A Sarasota Pkwy, Conyers GA 30013
Tel (770) 918-5678 SIC 2621

■ SP FIBERTECHNOLOGIES SOUTHEAST LLC p 1353
709 Papermill Rd, Dublin GA 31027
Tel (478) 272-1600 SIC 2621

■ WESTROCK SP CO p 1603
709 Papermill Rd, Dublin GA 31027
Tel (504) 733-1954 SIC 2621

ICONEX LLC p 728
3097 Satellite Blvd, Duluth GA 30096
Tel (917) 282-0861 SIC 5111 2621

MONDI BAGS USA LLC p 984
281 Hemphill Blvd, Eastman GA 31023
Tel (478) 374-7032 SIC 2393 2621

FMK HOLDINGS LLC p 562
3081 Holcom Ste H 1, Norcross GA 30071
Tel (413) 736-4554 SIC 2631 2621 2672

■ BOISE INC p 198
1111 W Jefferson St # 50, Boise ID 83702
Tel (208) 384-7000 SIC 2671 2621 2631

■ BOISE PAPER HOLDINGS LLC p 198
1111 W Jefferson St # 200, Boise ID 83702
Tel (208) 384-7501 SIC 2621

■ BOISE WHITE PAPER LLC p 198
1111 W Jefferson St # 200, Boise ID 83702
Tel (208) 384-7000 SIC 2621

■ STONE SOUTHWEST INC p 1391
150 N Michigan Ave, Chicago IL 60601
Tel (312) 346-6600
SIC 2631 2611 2621 2435 2436 2421

MICHAEL LEWIS CO p 960
8900 W 50th St, Mc Cook IL 60525
Tel (708) 688-2200
SIC 5113 5141 5142 2782 2759 2621

SCHWARZ PAPER CO LLC p 1291
8338 Austin Ave, Morton Grove IL 60053
Tel (847) 966-2550 SIC 2621 5199 4225

AMCOR FLEXIBLES LLC p 65
1919 S Butterfield Rd, Mundelein IL 60060
Tel (847) 362-9000
SIC 2671 2621 2821 3081 3466

■ KAPSTONE KRAFT PAPER CORP p 803
1101 Skokie Blvd Ste 300, Northbrook IL 60062
Tel (252) 533-6000 SIC 2621

▲ KAPSTONE PAPER AND PACKAGING CORP p 803
1101 Skokie Blvd Ste 300, Northbrook IL 60062
Tel (847) 239-8800 SIC 2621

SIMU LTD p 1326
201 Mittel Dr, Wood Dale IL 60191
Tel (630) 350-1060
SIC 5113 5141 5142 2782 2759 2621

WOLF PACKAGING INC p 1621
2068 303rd Ave, Fort Madison IA 52627
Tel (319) 372-6643 SIC 2621 2676 2671

WAUSAU PAPER TOWEL & TISSUE LLC p 1583
1150 Industry Rd, Harrodsburg KY 40330
Tel (859) 734-0538 SIC 2621

AHLSTROM FILTRATION LLC p 36
215 Nebo Rd, Madisonville KY 42431
Tel (270) 821-0140 SIC 2621

HOOD CONTAINER OF LOUISIANA LLC p 705
2105 Highway 964, Saint Francisville LA 70775
Tel (225) 336-2530 SIC 2621

LINCOLN PAPER AND TISSUE LLC p 867
50 Katadin Ave, Lincoln ME 04457
Tel (207) 794-0600 SIC 2621

NEXFOR (USA) INC p 1040
82 Bridge Ave, Madawaska ME 04756
Tel (207) 728-3321 SIC 2621 2493

TWIN RIVERS PAPER CO CORP p 1495
82 Bridge Ave, Madawaska ME 04756
Tel (207) 523-2350 SIC 2621

TWIN RIVERS PAPER CO LLC p 1495
82 Bridge Ave, Madawaska ME 04756
Tel (207) 728-3321 SIC 2621

MADISON UPM p 894
1 Main St, Madison ME 04950
Tel (207) 696-3307 SIC 2621

■ LUKE PAPER CO p 885
300 Pratt St, Luke MD 21540
Tel (301) 359-3311 SIC 2621

S D WARREN CO p 1262
255 State St Fl 4, Boston MA 02109
Tel (617) 423-7300
SIC 2679 2674 2672 2621

SDW HOLDINGS CORP p 1295
255 State St Fl 7, Boston MA 02109
Tel (617) 423-5400 SIC 2621

CRANE & CO INC p 388
30 South St, Dalton MA 01226
Tel (617) 648-3714 SIC 2621 5943

HOLLINGSWORTH & VOSE CO p 701
112 Washington St, East Walpole MA 02032
Tel (508) 850-2000
SIC 2621 3053 2297 2499

CRANE STATIONARY p 389
1466 Curran Hwy, North Adams MA 01247
Tel (413) 664-2527 SIC 2621

▲ KADANT INC p 800
1 Technology Park Dr # 210, Westford MA 01886
Tel (978) 776-2000 SIC 3554 3321 2621

THETFORD CORP p 1447
7101 Jackson Rd, Ann Arbor MI 48103
Tel (734) 769-6000
SIC 3632 3089 2842 2621 3431 2899

ESCANABA PAPER CO p 509
7100 County Rd 426, Escanaba MI 49829
Tel (906) 786-1660 SIC 2611 2621 2672

DUNN PAPER HOLDINGS INC p 461
218 Riverview St, Port Huron MI 48060
Tel (810) 984-5521 SIC 2621 2672

E B EDDY PAPER INC p 466
1700 Washington Ave, Port Huron MI 48060
Tel (810) 982-0191 SIC 2621

BLANDIN PAPER CO p 189
115 Sw 1st St, Grand Rapids MN 55744
Tel (218) 327-6200 SIC 2621 2672

■ NASHUA CORP p 1008
59 Daniel Webster Hwy A, Merrimack NH 03054
Tel (603) 880-1100
SIC 2672 2754 2679 2621 2782

AMERICAN BANKNOTE CORP p 68
2200 Fletcher Ave Ste 501, Fort Lee NJ 07024
Tel (201) 592-3400 SIC 2759 2752 2621

ROSES SOUTHWEST PAPERS INC p 1251
1701 2nd St Sw, Albuquerque NM 87102
Tel (505) 842-0134 SIC 2676 2674 2621

MOHAWK FINE PAPERS INC p 982
465 Saratoga St, Cohoes NY 12047
Tel (518) 237-1740 SIC 2672 2621

IRVING CONSUMER PRODUCTS INC p 765
1 Eddy St, Fort Edward NY 12828
Tel (518) 747-4151 SIC 2621

BURROWS PAPER CORP p 229
501 W Main St Ste 1, Little Falls NY 13365
Tel (315) 823-2300
SIC 2621 2671 2611 2679

VERSO PAPER MANAGEMENT LP p 1552
60 W 42nd Ste 1942, New York NY 10165
Tel (212) 599-2700 SIC 2621

NICE-PAK PRODUCTS INC p 1042
2 Nice Pak Park, Orangeburg NY 10962
Tel (845) 365-2772 SIC 2621 7389 2676

PROFESSIONAL DISPOSABLES INC p 1180
2 Nice Pak Park, Orangeburg NY 10962
Tel (845) 365-1700 SIC 2676 7389 2621

AMPAC PAPER LLC p 86
30 Coldenham Rd, Walden NY 12586
Tel (845) 778-5511 SIC 2674 2621 5162

BLUE RIDGE PAPER PRODUCTS INC p 192
41 Main St, Canton NC 28716
Tel (828) 454-0676 SIC 2621

VON DREHLE CORP p 1565
612 3rd Ave Ne Ste 200, Hickory NC 28601
Tel (828) 322-1805 SIC 2621 2676

TRIMACO LLC p 1480
2300 Gateway Centre Blvd # 200, Morrisville NC 27560
Tel (919) 674-3476
SIC 2851 2621 2672 2679 2394

ATLANTIC CORP OF WILMINGTON INC p 126
806 N 23rd St, Wilmington NC 28405
Tel (910) 343-0624 SIC 5113 2621 2679

RANPAK CORP p 1208
7990 Auburn Rd, Concord Township OH 44077
Tel (440) 354-4445 SIC 2621

■ NEWPAGE CORP p 1038
8540 Gander Creek Dr, Miamisburg OH 45342
Tel (877) 855-7243 SIC 2621 2611

NEWPAGE ENERGY SERVICES LLC p 1038
8540 Gander Creek Dr, Miamisburg OH 45342
Tel (877) 855-7243 SIC 2672 2621 2611

■ NEWPAGE HOLDING CORP p 1038
8540 Gander Creek Dr, Miamisburg OH 45342
Tel (877) 855-7243 SIC 2621 2672 2611

FIRST QUALITY TISSUE LLC p 549
904 Woods Ave, Lock Haven PA 17745
Tel (570) 748-1200 SIC 2621

CLONDALKIN HOLDINGS INC p 327
Crtis Centre Ste, Philadelphia PA 19106
Tel (215) 440-0570
SIC 2673 2621 2752 8741

SCA AMERICAS INC p 1285
2929 Arch St Ste 2600, Philadelphia PA 19104
Tel (610) 499-3700 SIC 2621 3086 2676

▲ CSS INDUSTRIES INC p 398
450 Plymouth Rd Ste 300, Plymouth Meeting PA 19462
Tel (610) 729-3959
SIC 2771 2679 2389 2396 2621 2865

BEISTLE CO p 169
1 Beistle Plz, Shippensburg PA 17257
Tel (717) 532-2131
SIC 2679 3993 2675 2657 2631 2621

■ GLATFELTER PULP WOOD CO INC p 614
228 S Main St, Spring Grove PA 17362
Tel (717) 225-4711 SIC 5099 2411 2621

TEAM TEN LLC p 1430
1600 Pennsylvania Ave, Tyrone PA 16686
Tel (814) 684-1610 SIC 2621

▲ P H GLATFELTER CO p 1102
96 S Gorge St Ste 500, York PA 17401
Tel (717) 225-4711 SIC 2621

■ REAL REEL CORP p 1214
50 Taylor Dr, Rumford RI 02916
Tel (401) 438-4240 SIC 2631 2655 2621

RESOLUTE FP US INC p 1227
5300 Cureton Ferry Rd, Catawba SC 29704
Tel (803) 981-8000
SIC 2621 2672 2611 2421

DOMTAR INDUSTRIES LLC p 449
100 Kingsley Park Dr, Fort Mill SC 29715
Tel (803) 802-7500 SIC 2621 5111

DOMTAR PAPER CO LLC p 449
100 Kingsley Park Dr, Fort Mill SC 29715
Tel (803) 802-7500 SIC 2421 2621

■ KAPSTONE CHARLESTON KRAFT LLC p 803
5600 Virginia Ave, North Charleston SC 29406
Tel (843) 745-3000 SIC 2621

EVERGREEN PACKAGING INC p 514
5350 Poplar Ave Ste 600, Memphis TN 38119
Tel (901) 821-5350 SIC 7389 2621

▲ INTERNATIONAL PAPER CO p 756
6400 Poplar Ave, Memphis TN 38197
Tel (901) 419-9000
SIC 2621 2653 2656 2631 2611

KTG (USA) LP p 831
400 Mahannah Ave, Memphis TN 38107
Tel (901) 260-3900 SIC 2621

▲ VERSO CORP p 1552
6775 Lenox Center Ct # 400, Memphis TN 38115
Tel (901) 369-4100 SIC 2621

■ VERSO PAPER HOLDINGS LLC p 1552
6775 Lenox Center Ct # 400, Memphis TN 38115
Tel (901) 369-4100 SIC 2621

■ VERSO PAPER LLC p 1552
6775 Lenox Center Ct # 400, Memphis TN 38115
Tel (901) 369-4100 SIC 2621

WINGATE PARTNERS LP p 1616
750 N Saint Paul St # 1200, Dallas TX 75201
Tel (214) 720-1313
SIC 2621 2672 3645 2519 5021 2521

▲ KIMBERLY-CLARK CORP p 818
351 Phelps Dr, Irving TX 75038
Tel (972) 281-1200 SIC 2621 2676

■ LONGVIEW FIBRE PAPER AND PACKAGING INC p 877
300 Fibre Way, Longview WA 98632
Tel (360) 425-1550 SIC 2621

NORTH PACIFIC PAPER CO LLC p 1053
3001 Indl Way, Longview WA 98632
Tel (360) 636-6400 SIC 2621 5084 3554

NP PAPER CO LLC p 1064
3001 Industrial Way, Longview WA 98632
Tel (360) 636-6400 SIC 2621

CROWN PAPER GROUP INC p 396
100 Mill Rd, Port Townsend WA 98368
Tel (770) 330-9137 SIC 2621

KAMILCHE CO p 802
1301 5th Ave Ste 2700, Seattle WA 98101
Tel (206) 224-5800
SIC 2621 2611 2421 2435 2431

SIMPSON INVESTMENT CO INC p 1325
1301 5th Ave Ste 2700, Seattle WA 98101
Tel (253) 272-0158
SIC 2621 2611 2421 2431 3084

▲ WEYERHAEUSER CO p 1603
220 Occidental Ave S, Seattle WA 98104
Tel (253) 924-2345
SIC 6798 0811 2411 2435 2611 2621

▲ CLEARWATER PAPER CORP p 324
601 W Riverside Ave # 1100, Spokane WA 99201
Tel (509) 344-5900 SIC 2621 2631

COWLES PUBLISHING CO p 386
999 W Riverside Ave, Spokane WA 99201
Tel (509) 459-5000
SIC 2711 2611 2621 4833

■ BOISE WHITE PAPER LLC p 198
31831 W Hwy 12, Wallula WA 99363
Tel (509) 545-3318 SIC 2621

APPVION INC p 100
825 E Wisconsin Ave, Appleton WI 54911
Tel (920) 734-9841 SIC 2621 2754

APPLETON COATED LLC p 99
540 Prospect St, Combined Locks WI 54113
Tel (920) 788-3550 SIC 2621 2672

VIRTUS HOLDINGS LLC p 1560
540 Prospect St, Combined Locks WI 54113
Tel (920) 788-3550 SIC 2672 2621

LITTLE RAPIDS CORP p 871
2273 Larsen Rd, Green Bay WI 54303
Tel (920) 490-5400 SIC 2621

EXPERA SPECIALTY SOLUTIONS LLC p 519
600 Thilmany Rd, Kaukauna WI 54130
Tel (920) 766-4611 SIC 2621

WAUSAU PAPER CORP p 1583
100 Paper Pl, Kronenwetter WI 54455
Tel (715) 693-4470 SIC 2621

WAUSAU PAPER MILLS LLC p 1583
100 Paper Pl, Kronenwetter WI 54455
Tel (715) 693-4470 SIC 2621

■ CELLU TISSUE CORP-NEENAH p 274
249 N Lake St, Neenah WI 54956
Tel (920) 721-9800 SIC 2621

■ DUNSIRN INDUSTRIES INC p 461
2415 Industrial Dr, Neenah WI 54956
Tel (920) 725-3814
SIC 2671 5113 3081 2672 2621

■ NEENAH PAPER FR LLC p 1024
1376 Kimberly Dr, Neenah WI 54956
Tel (800) 558-8327 SIC 2679 2621

SCA TISSUE NORTH AMERICA LLC p 1285
984 Winchester Rd, Neenah WI 54956
Tel (920) 725-7031 SIC 2621

FLAMBEAU RIVER PAPER CORP p 554
200 1st Ave N, Park Falls WI 54552
Tel (715) 762-4612 SIC 2621

FLAMBEAU RIVER PAPERS LLC p 554
200 1st Ave N, Park Falls WI 54552
Tel (715) 762-5229 SIC 2621

NEWPAGE WISCONSIN SYSTEM INC p 1038
111 W Jackson St, Wisconsin Rapids WI 54495
Tel (715) 422-3111
SIC 2621 2611 2653 7011

SIC 2631 Paperboard Mills

THOMPSON OLDE INC p 1449
3250 Camino Del Sol, Oxnard CA 93030
Tel (800) 827-1565 SIC 5023 2631 5149

▲ LYDALL INC p 887
1 Colonial Rd, Manchester CT 06042
Tel (860) 646-1233
SIC 2297 3053 2899 2631 3714 3564

CONNECTICUT CONTAINER CORP p 356
455 Sackett Point Rd, North Haven CT 06473
Tel (203) 248-2161
SIC 2653 3993 3412 2631

MAFCOTE INC p 895
108 Main St Ste 3, Norwalk CT 06851
Tel (203) 847-8500
SIC 2631 2657 2679 2671

GNN INVESTOR LLC p 619
133 Peachtree St Ne, Atlanta GA 30303
Tel (404) 652-4000
SIC 2621 2611 2631 2653 5111 2677

■ GPI HOLDINGS INC p 627
1500 Riveredge Pkwy # 100, Atlanta GA 30328
Tel (770) 240-7200
SIC 2631 2653 2449 4922

▲ GRAPHIC PACKAGING HOLDING CO p 632
1500 Riveredge Pkwy # 100, Atlanta GA 30328
Tel (770) 240-7200 SIC 2631 2653 2671

■ GRAPHIC PACKAGING INTERNATIONAL INC p 632
1500 Riveredge Pkwy # 100, Atlanta GA 30328
Tel (770) 240-7200 SIC 2657 2631 7389

CARAUSTAR INDUSTRIES INC p 252
5000 Astell Pwdr Sprng Rd, Austell GA 30106
Tel (770) 948-3101
SIC 2655 2631 2679 2656 2652

BRUNSWICK CELLULOSE LLC p 221
1400 9th St, Brunswick GA 31520
Tel (912) 265-5780
SIC 2611 2421 2899 2631

FMK HOLDINGS LLC p 562
3081 Holcom Ste H 1, Norcross GA 30071
Tel (413) 736-4554 SIC 2631 2621 2672

▲ WESTROCK CO p 1602
504 Thrasher St, Norcross GA 30071
Tel (678) 291-7456
SIC 2631 2899 3699 6531

■ WESTROCK CONVERTING CO p 1602
504 Thrasher St, Norcross GA 30071
Tel (770) 246-9982 SIC 2631 2653 3081

■ WESTROCK MILL CO LLC p 1602
504 Thrasher St, Norcross GA 30071
Tel (770) 448-2193 SIC 2631

■ WESTROCK RKT CO p 1603
504 Thrasher St, Norcross GA 30071
Tel (770) 448-2193 SIC 2653 2652 2631

INTERSTATE PAPER LLC p 758
2366 Interstate Rd Ste 1, Riceboro GA 31323
Tel (912) 884-3371 SIC 2631

■ BOISE INC p 198
1111 W Jefferson St # 50, Boise ID 83702
Tel (208) 384-7000 SIC 2671 2621 2631

COVERIS HOLDING CORP p 385
8600 W Bryn Mawr Ave, Chicago IL 60631
Tel (773) 877-3300 SIC 6719 2673 2631

■ STONE SOUTHWEST INC p 1391
150 N Michigan Ave, Chicago IL 60601
Tel (312) 346-6600
SIC 2631 2611 2621 2435 2436 2421

▲ PACKAGING CORP OF AMERICA p 1106
1955 W Field Ct, Lake Forest IL 60045
Tel (847) 482-3000 SIC 2631 2653

■ NEENAH NORTHEAST LLC p 1024
70 Front St, West Springfield MA 01089
Tel (413) 533-0699 SIC 2631

RAND-WHITNEY CONTAINER LLC p 1207
1 Agrand St, Worcester MA 01607
Tel (508) 890-7000 SIC 2653 2631

RAND-WHITNEY GROUP LLC p 1207
1 Agrand St, Worcester MA 01607
Tel (508) 791-2301 SIC 2653 2657 2631

UTILITY SUPPLY AND CONSTRUCTION CO p 1537
420 S Roth St Ste A, Reed City MI 49677
Tel (231) 832-2297
SIC 2411 2491 2631 5063

LIBERTY DIVERSIFIED INTERNATIONAL INC p 861
5600 Highway 169 N, New Hope MN 55428
Tel (763) 536-6600
SIC 2653 2631 5112 2542 3089 5961

■ WESTROCK MINNESOTA CORP p 1603
2250 Wabash Ave, Saint Paul MN 55114
Tel (612) 641-4938 SIC 2631

NEWARK GROUP INC p 1037
20 Jackson Dr, Cranford NJ 07016
Tel (908) 276-4000 SIC 2679 2631

ROMARK LOGISTICS LLC p 1249
822 South Ave W, Westfield NJ 07090
Tel (908) 789-2800 SIC 4225 4789 2631

STEPHEN GOULD CORP p 1386
35 S Jefferson Rd, Whippany NJ 07981
Tel (973) 428-1500 SIC 2631 2759

CASCADES CONTAINERBOARD PACKAGING INC p 263
4001 Packard Rd, Niagara Falls NY 14303
Tel (716) 285-3681 *SIC* 2631 2653

BEISTLE CO p 169
1 Beistle Plz, Shippensburg PA 17257
Tel (717) 532-2131
SIC 2679 3993 2675 2657 2631 2621

■ REAL REEL CORP p 1214
50 Taylor Dr, Rumford RI 02916
Tel (401) 438-4240 *SIC* 2631 2655 2621

▲ SONOCO PRODUCTS CO p 1340
1 N 2nd St, Hartsville SC 29550
Tel (843) 383-7000
SIC 2631 2671 2653 2655 3089 2499

COVERIS KEY HOLDINGS LLC p 385
345 Cedar Springs Ave, Spartanburg SC 29302
Tel (864) 596-7300 *SIC* 2673 2631 6719

▲ INTERNATIONAL PAPER CO p 756
6400 Poplar Ave, Memphis TN 38197
Tel (901) 419-9000
SIC 2621 2653 2656 2631 2611

INLAND PAPERBOARD AND PACKAGING INC p 743
1300 S Mo Pac Expy Fl 3, Austin TX 78746
Tel (512) 234-5001
SIC 2653 2631 3086 2679 2657

TEKNI-PLEX MANAGEMENT LLC p 1433
260 N Denton Tap Rd, Coppell TX 75019
Tel (972) 304-5077 *SIC* 3089 2631 2656

INTERSTATE RESOURCES INC p 758
1300 Wilson Blvd Ste 1075, Arlington VA 22209
Tel (703) 243-3355 *SIC* 2631 2653 7389

PHOENIX PACKAGING OPERATIONS LLC p 1145
4800 Lina Ln, Dublin VA 24084
Tel (540) 307-4084 *SIC* 2631

■ WESTROCK MWV LLC p 1603
501 S 5th St, Richmond VA 23219
Tel (804) 444-1000
SIC 2631 2671 2678 2677 2861 2611

BOX MAKER INC p 205
6412 S 190th St, Kent WA 98032
Tel (425) 251-0655
SIC 5113 2653 2672 3086 5199 2631

PORT TOWNSEND PAPER CORP p 1162
100 Mill Rd, Port Townsend WA 98368
Tel (360) 385-3170 *SIC* 2631

▲ CLEARWATER PAPER CORP p 324
601 W Riverside Ave # 1100, Spokane WA 99201
Tel (509) 344-5900 *SIC* 2621 2631

GREEN BAY PACKAGING INC p 636
1700 N Webster Ave, Green Bay WI 54302
Tel (920) 433-5111
SIC 2631 2672 2653 2491

MENASHA CORP p 943
1645 Bergstrom Rd, Neenah WI 54956
Tel (920) 751-1000
SIC 2631 2653 2679 3086 0811

SIC 2652 Set-Up Paperboard Boxes

RUSKEN PACKAGING INC p 1259
64 Walnut St Nw, Cullman AL 35055
Tel (256) 734-0092 *SIC* 2652

AGI-SHOREWOOD GROUP US LLC p 35
300 Atlantic St Ste 206, Stamford CT 06901
Tel (203) 324-4839 *SIC* 2671 2652 2657

CARAUSTAR INDUSTRIES INC p 252
5000 Astell Pwdr Sprng Rd, Austell GA 30106
Tel (770) 948-3101
SIC 2655 2631 2679 2656 2652

■ WESTROCK RKT CO p 1603
504 Thrasher St, Norcross GA 30071
Tel (770) 448-2193 *SIC* 2653 2652 2631

SIC 2653 Corrugated & Solid Fiber Boxes

SOUND PACKAGING LLC p 1342
260 N Roosevelt Ave, Chandler AZ 85226
Tel (480) 940-2010 *SIC* 2653

AMCOR PACKAGING (USA) INC p 65
6600 Valley View St, Buena Park CA 90620
Tel (714) 562-6000 *SIC* 2653 5113

ORORA PACKAGING SOLUTIONS p 1095
6600 Valley View St, Buena Park CA 90620
Tel (714) 562-6000 *SIC* 5113 2653

SAYCO CONTAINER INC p 1285
13400 Nelson Ave, City Of Industry CA 91746
Tel (619) 440-4411 *SIC* 2653 3089 3086

SMURFIT KAPPA NORTH AMERICA LLC p 1335
13400 Nelson Ave, City Of Industry CA 91746
Tel (626) 333-6363 *SIC* 2653 2671 2657

WILEMAN BROS & ELLIOTT INC p 1609
40232 Road 128, Cutler CA 93615
Tel (559) 651-8378
SIC 0723 2653 0174 0175

PACKAGING INNOVATORS CORP p 1106
6650 National Dr, Livermore CA 94550
Tel (925) 371-2000 *SIC* 5113 2653 3993

ADVANCE PAPER BOX CO p 24
6100 S Gramercy Pl, Los Angeles CA 90047
Tel (323) 750-2550 *SIC* 2653 3082

OAK PAPER PRODUCTS CO INC p 1070
3686 E Olympic Blvd, Los Angeles CA 90023
Tel (323) 268-0507
SIC 5113 5199 5087 2653

PACIFIC SOUTHWEST CONTAINER LLC p 1106
4530 Leckron Rd, Modesto CA 95357
Tel (209) 526-0444
SIC 2671 2657 3086 2653 2752

CORRUGADOS DE BAJA CALIFORNIA p 373
2475 Paseo De Las A, San Diego CA 92154
Tel (619) 662-8672 *SIC* 2653

■ THARCO CONTAINER INC p 1446
2222 Grant Ave, San Lorenzo CA 94580
Tel (510) 276-8600 *SIC* 2653

■ THARCO HOLDINGS INC p 1446
2222 Grant Ave, San Lorenzo CA 94580
Tel (303) 373-1860 *SIC* 2653 3086 2675

PIONEER PACKING INC p 1151
2430 S Grand Ave, Santa Ana CA 92705
Tel (714) 540-9751 *SIC* 5113 2653

FRUIT GROWERS SUPPLY CO INC p 582
27770 N Entrmt Dr Fl 3, Valencia CA 91355
Tel (818) 986-6480
SIC 2653 0811 5191 2448 5113

CONNECTICUT CONTAINER CORP p 356
455 Sackett Point Rd, North Haven CT 06473
Tel (203) 248-2161
SIC 2653 3993 3412 2631

SCHWARZ PARTNERS PACKAGING LLC p 1291
2808 New Tampa Hwy, Lakeland FL 33815
Tel (863) 682-0123 *SIC* 2653

GEORGIA-PACIFIC LLC p 608
133 Peachtree St Ne # 4810, Atlanta GA 30303
Tel (404) 652-4000
SIC 2676 2656 2653 2435 2821 3275

GNN INVESTOR LLC p 619
133 Peachtree St Ne, Atlanta GA 30303
Tel (404) 652-4000
SIC 2621 2611 2631 2653 5111 2677

■ GPI HOLDINGS INC p 627
1500 Riveredge Pkwy # 100, Atlanta GA 30328
Tel (770) 240-7200
SIC 2631 2653 2449 4922

▲ GRAPHIC PACKAGING HOLDING CO p 632
1500 Riveredge Pkwy # 100, Atlanta GA 30328
Tel (770) 240-7200 *SIC* 2631 2653 2671

STRONGHAVEN INC p 1394
2727 Paces Ferry Rd Se 1-1850, Atlanta GA 30339
Tel (678) 235-2713 *SIC* 2653

JET CORR INC p 783
1800 Sarasot Bus Pkwy Ne B, Conyers GA 30013
Tel (770) 929-1300 *SIC* 2653

PRATT (JET CORR) INC p 1167
1800 Sarasot Bus Pkwy Ne B, Conyers GA 30013
Tel (770) 929-1300 *SIC* 2653

■ WESTROCK CONVERTING CO p 1602
504 Thrasher St, Norcross GA 30071
Tel (770) 246-9982 *SIC* 2631 2653 3081

■ WESTROCK RKT CO p 1603
504 Thrasher St, Norcross GA 30071
Tel (770) 448-2193 *SIC* 2653 2652 2631

ROYAL BOX GROUP LLC p 1254
1301 S 47th Ave, Cicero IL 60804
Tel (708) 656-2020 *SIC* 2653

FELLOWES INC p 537
1789 Norwood Ave, Itasca IL 60143
Tel (630) 893-1600
SIC 2522 3589 2653 3577 3572 3579

▲ PACKAGING CORP OF AMERICA p 1106
1955 W Field Ct, Lake Forest IL 60045
Tel (847) 482-3000 *SIC* 2631 2653

COLOR-BOX LLC p 338
623 S G St, Richmond IN 47374
Tel (765) 966-7588 *SIC* 2653

■ KAPSTONE CONTAINER CORP p 803
1601 Blairs Ferry Rd Ne, Cedar Rapids IA 52402
Tel (319) 393-3610 *SIC* 2653

PRATT (LOVE BOX) LLC p 1167
700 E 37th St N, Wichita KS 67219
Tel (316) 838-0851 *SIC* 2653 2448 4213

INTERLOCK INDUSTRIES INC p 753
545 S 3rd St Ste 310, Louisville KY 40202
Tel (502) 569-2007
SIC 3341 4121 3444 3354 2653

PACKAGING UNLIMITED LLC p 1107
1729 Mccloskey Ave, Louisville KY 40210
Tel (502) 515-3900 *SIC* 2653

KRAFT GROUP LLC p 829
1 Patriot Pl, Foxboro MA 02035
Tel (508) 384-4230 *SIC* 2653

■ NEW ENGLAND BUSINESS SERVICE INC p 1030
500 Main St, Groton MA 01471
Tel (978) 448-6111
SIC 2759 2771 5045 2653 3089 3069

ATLAS BOX AND CRATING CO INC p 127
223 Wrcster Prvdence Tpke, Sutton MA 01590
Tel (508) 865-1155 *SIC* 2441 2448 2653

PACIFIC PACKAGING PRODUCTS INC p 1105
24 Industrial Way, Wilmington MA 01887
Tel (978) 657-9100
SIC 5113 5199 5084 5162 2671 2653

RAND-WHITNEY CONTAINER LLC p 1207
1 Agrand St, Worcester MA 01607
Tel (508) 890-7000 *SIC* 2653 2631

RAND-WHITNEY GROUP LLC p 1207
1 Agrand St, Worcester MA 01607
Tel (508) 791-2301 *SIC* 2653 2657 2631

ADVANCE PACKAGING CORP p 24
4459 40th St Se, Grand Rapids MI 49512
Tel (616) 949-6610 *SIC* 2653 3412

LIBERTY CARTON CO p 861
870 Louisiana Ave S, Golden Valley MN 55426
Tel (763) 540-9600 *SIC* 2653

LIBERTY DIVERSIFIED INTERNATIONAL INC p 861
5600 Highway 169 N, New Hope MN 55428
Tel (763) 536-6600
SIC 2653 2631 5112 2542 3089 5961

BOXES OF ST LOUIS INC p 205
1833 Knox Ave, Saint Louis MO 63139
Tel (314) 781-2600 *SIC* 2653

SOUTHERN MISSOURI CONTAINERS INC p 1349
3131 E Division St, Springfield MO 65802
Tel (417) 831-2685 *SIC* 2671 2653

PRESIDENT CONTAINER INC p 1172
200 W Commercial Ave, Moonachie NJ 07074
Tel (201) 933-7500 *SIC* 2653

JAMESTOWN CONTAINER CORP p 777
14 Deming Dr, Falconer NY 14733
Tel (716) 665-4623 *SIC* 2653 3086

CASCADES CONTAINERBOARD PACKAGING INC p 263
4001 Packard Rd, Niagara Falls NY 14303
Tel (716) 285-3681 *SIC* 2631 2653

HIGHLAND CONTAINERS INC p 691
3520 Dillon Rd, Jamestown NC 27282
Tel (336) 887-5400 *SIC* 2653

■ ALLIANCE DISPLAY AND PACKAGING CO p 54
5921 Grassy Creek Blvd, Winston Salem NC 27105
Tel (336) 661-1700 *SIC* 2653

▲ GREIF INC p 639
425 Winter Rd, Delaware OH 43015
Tel (740) 549-6000
SIC 2653 2449 2655 3412 3089 2674

BUCKEYE CORRUGATED INC p 223
822 Kumho Dr Ste 400, Fairlawn OH 44333
Tel (330) 576-0590 *SIC* 2653

PAPERWORKS INDUSTRIES INC p 1112
40 Monument Rd Ste 200, Bala Cynwyd PA 19004
Tel (215) 984-7000 *SIC* 2653

■ PCA CORRUGATED AND DISPLAY LLC p 1123
148 Penn St, Hanover PA 17331
Tel (717) 632-4727 *SIC* 2653 5113

SUPPLYONE HOLDINGS CO INC p 1408
11 Campus Blvd, Newtown Square PA 19073
Tel (484) 582-5005 *SIC* 2653 5113

ROARING SPRING BLANK BOOK CO p 1240
740 Spang St, Roaring Spring PA 16673
Tel (814) 224-2306
SIC 2678 5149 2653 7389

▲ SONOCO PRODUCTS CO p 1340
1 N 2nd St, Hartsville SC 29550
Tel (843) 383-7000
SIC 2631 2671 2653 2655 3089 2499

SOUTHLAND CONTAINER CORP p 1351
60 Fairview Church Rd, Spartanburg SC 29303
Tel (864) 578-0085 *SIC* 2653 3086

▲ INTERNATIONAL PAPER CO p 756
6400 Poplar Ave, Memphis TN 38197
Tel (901) 419-9000
SIC 2621 2653 2656 2631 2611

INLAND PAPERBOARD AND PACKAGING INC p 743
1300 S Mo Pac Expy Fl 3, Austin TX 78746
Tel (512) 234-5001
SIC 2653 2631 3086 2679 2657

AGE INDUSTRIES LTD p 34
3601 County Road 316c, Cleburne TX 76031
Tel (817) 477-5266 *SIC* 2653 2655 2671

SMURFIT KAPPA BATES LLC p 1335
6433 Davis Blvd, North Richland Hills TX 76182
Tel (817) 498-3200 *SIC* 2653 5113

INTERSTATE RESOURCES INC p 758
1300 Wilson Blvd Ste 1075, Arlington VA 22209
Tel (703) 243-3355 *SIC* 2631 2653 7389

BOX MAKER INC p 205
6412 S 190th St, Kent WA 98032
Tel (425) 251-0655
SIC 5113 2653 2672 3086 5199 2631

PORT TOWNSEND HOLDINGS CO INC p 1162
100 Mill Rd, Port Townsend WA 98368
Tel (360) 385-3170 *SIC* 2611 2653

ALLIANCE PACKAGING LLC p 55
1000 Sw 43rd St, Renton WA 98057
Tel (425) 291-3500 *SIC* 2653 3086

MICHELSEN PACKAGING CO OF CALIFORNIA p 960
202 N 2nd Ave, Yakima WA 98902
Tel (509) 248-6270 *SIC* 5113 2653

GREAT NORTHERN CORP p 634
395 Stroebe Rd, Appleton WI 54914
Tel (920) 739-3671 *SIC* 2653 5199 2671

GREEN BAY PACKAGING INC p 636
1700 N Webster Ave, Green Bay WI 54302
Tel (920) 433-5111
SIC 2631 2672 2653 2491

MENASHA CORP p 943
1645 Bergstrom Rd, Neenah WI 54956
Tel (920) 751-1000
SIC 2631 2653 2679 3086 0811

MENASHA PACKAGING CO LLC p 943
1645 Bergstrom Rd, Neenah WI 54956
Tel (920) 751-1000 *SIC* 2653

NEWPAGE WISCONSIN SYSTEM INC p 1038
111 W Jackson St, Wisconsin Rapids WI 54495
Tel (715) 422-3111
SIC 2621 2611 2653 7011

SIC 2655 Fiber Cans, Tubes & Drums

GRAPHIC PACKAGING INTERNATIONAL CORP p 632
1795 Dogwood St Unit 100, Louisville CO 80027
Tel (303) 215-4600 *SIC* 2657 2671 2655

CARAUSTAR INDUSTRIES INC p 252
5000 Astell Pwdr Sprng Rd, Austell GA 30106
Tel (770) 948-3101
SIC 2655 2631 2679 2656 2652

MEXICO PLASTIC CO p 957
2000 W Boulevard St, Mexico MO 65265
Tel (573) 581-4128 *SIC* 2673 3089 2655

SCHUTZ CONTAINER SYSTEMS INC p 1291
200 Aspen Hill Rd, Branchburg NJ 08876
Tel (908) 429-1637 *SIC* 2655

SCHUTZ CORP p 1291
200 Aspen Hill Rd, Branchburg NJ 08876
Tel (908) 526-6161 *SIC* 2655

MAUSER USA LLC p 921
35 Cotters Ln, East Brunswick NJ 08816
Tel (732) 353-7100 *SIC* 3412 2655

BERENFIELD CONTAINERS INC p 174
4555 Lake Forest Dr # 205, Blue Ash OH 45242
Tel (513) 618-3780 *SIC* 3412 2655

▲ GREIF INC p 639
425 Winter Rd, Delaware OH 43015
Tel (740) 549-6000
SIC 2653 2449 2655 3412 3089 2674

■ HPC HOLDINGS LLC p 714
3637 Ridgewood Rd, Fairlawn OH 44333
Tel (330) 666-3751 *SIC* 2821 2655

■ REAL REEL CORP p 1214
50 Taylor Dr, Rumford RI 02916
Tel (401) 438-4240 *SIC* 2631 2655 2621

CARAUSTAR INDUSTRIAL AND CONSUMER PRODUCTS GROUP INC p 252
2031 Carolina Place Dr, Fort Mill SC 29708
Tel (803) 548-5100 *SIC* 2655 2671 2679

▲ SONOCO PRODUCTS CO p 1340
1 N 2nd St, Hartsville SC 29550
Tel (843) 383-7000
SIC 2631 2671 2653 2655 3089 2499

AGE INDUSTRIES LTD p 34
3601 County Road 316c, Cleburne TX 76031
Tel (817) 477-5266 *SIC* 2653 2655 2671

SIC 2656 Sanitary Food Containers

GEORGIA PACIFIC HOLDINGS INC p 607
13208 Hadley St Apt 1, Whittier CA 90601
Tel (626) 926-1474
SIC 2676 2656 2435 2821

GEORGIA-PACIFIC LLC p 608
133 Peachtree St Ne # 4810, Atlanta GA 30303
Tel (404) 652-4000
SIC 2676 2656 2653 2435 2821 3275

GEORGIA-PACIFIC PACKAGING LLC p 608
133 Peachtree St Ne # 4810, Atlanta GA 30303
Tel (404) 652-4000 *SIC* 2656

GEORGIA-PACIFIC WOOD PRODUCTS SOUTH LLC p 608
133 Peachtree St Ne, Atlanta GA 30303
Tel (404) 652-4000 *SIC* 2656

GP BUILDING PRODUCTS OPERATIONS LLC p 627
133 Peachtree St Ne, Atlanta GA 30303
Tel (404) 652-4000 *SIC* 2656

MOSCOW CAMDEN AND SAN AUGUSTINE RAILROAD LLC p 992
133 Peachtree St Ne, Atlanta GA 30303
Tel (404) 652-4000 *SIC* 2656

CARAUSTAR INDUSTRIES INC p 252
5000 Astell Pwdr Sprng Rd, Austell GA 30106
Tel (770) 948-3101
SIC 2655 2631 2679 2656 2652

CTI FOODS ACQUISITION LLC p 399
22303 Highway 95, Wilder ID 83676
Tel (208) 482-7844 *SIC* 2656

■ RALCORP FROZEN BAKERY PRODUCTS INC p 1206
3250 Lacey Rd Ste 600, Downers Grove IL 60515
Tel (630) 455-5200
SIC 2051 2053 2041 2035 2656

SOLO CUP INVESTMENT CORP p 1338
1700 Old Deerfield Rd, Highland Park IL 60035
Tel (847) 831-4800 *SIC* 3089 2656 3421

SCC HOLDING CO LLC p 1286
150 Saunders Rd Ste 150, Lake Forest IL 60045
Tel (847) 444-5000 *SIC* 3089 2656 3421

SF HOLDINGS GROUP INC p 1310
300 Tr State Intl Ste 200, Lincolnshire IL 60069
Tel (847) 831-4800 *SIC* 2656

SOLO CUP CO p 1338
300 Tri State Intl # 200, Lincolnshire IL 60069
Tel (847) 831-4800 *SIC* 3089 3421 2656

SOLO CUP CO LLC p 1338
300 Tri State Intl # 200, Lincolnshire IL 60069
Tel (847) 444-5000 *SIC* 3089 2656 3421

SOLO CUP OPERATING CORP p 1338
300 Tr State Intl Ste 200, Lincolnshire IL 60069
Tel (847) 444-5000 *SIC* 3089 2656 3556

TETRA PAK US HOLDINGS INC p 1441
101 Corporate Woods Pkwy, Vernon Hills IL 60061
Tel (940) 565-8800 *SIC* 2656

HUHTAMAKI INC p 718
9201 Packaging Dr, De Soto KS 66018
Tel (913) 583-3025 *SIC* 2656 3565

AJM PACKAGING CORP p 41
E-4111 Andover Rd, Bloomfield Hills MI 48302
Tel (249) 901-0040 *SIC* 2656 2674

LETICA CORP p 857
52585 Dequindre Rd, Rochester Hills MI 48307
Tel (248) 652-0557 *SIC* 2656 3089

SOUNDVIEW PAPER HOLDINGS LLC p 1342
1 Market St, Elmwood Park NJ 07407
Tel (201) 796-4000 *SIC* 2676 2656

■ AMSCAN INC p 87
80 Grasslands Rd Ste 3, Elmsford NY 10523
Tel (914) 345-2020
SIC 2656 3089 5113 2676

AMERICAN GREETINGS CORP p 73
1 American Rd, Cleveland OH 44144
Tel (216) 252-7300
SIC 2771 2679 2656 2678

CENTURY INTERMEDIATE HOLDING CO p 282
1 American Rd, Cleveland OH 44144
Tel (216) 252-7300
SIC 2771 2679 2656 2678

DOPACO INC p 451
461 Boot Rd, Downingtown PA 19335
Tel (610) 269-6048
SIC 2657 2656 3089 3792

▲ INTERNATIONAL PAPER CO p 756
6400 Poplar Ave, Memphis TN 38197
Tel (901) 419-9000
SIC 2621 2653 2656 2631 2611

TEKNI-PLEX MANAGEMENT LLC p 1433
260 N Denton Tap Rd, Coppell TX 75019
Tel (972) 304-5077 *SIC* 3089 2631 2656

SIC 2657 Folding Paperboard Boxes

SMURFIT KAPPA NORTH AMERICA LLC p 1335
13400 Nelson Ave, City Of Industry CA 91746
Tel (626) 333-6363 *SIC* 2653 2671 2657

PACIFIC SOUTHWEST CONTAINER LLC p 1106
4530 Leckron Rd, Modesto CA 95357
Tel (209) 526-0444
SIC 2671 2657 3086 2653 2752

GRAPHIC PACKAGING INTERNATIONAL CORP p 632
1795 Dogwood St Unit 100, Louisville CO 80027
Tel (303) 215-4600 *SIC* 2657 2671 2655

MAFCOTE INC p 895
108 Main St Ste 3, Norwalk CT 06851
Tel (203) 847-8500
SIC 2631 2657 2679 2671

AGI-SHOREWOOD GROUP US LLC p 35
300 Atlantic St Ste 206, Stamford CT 06901
Tel (203) 324-4839 *SIC* 2671 2652 2657

MALNOVE INC OF FLORIDA p 900
10500 Canada Dr, Jacksonville FL 32218
Tel (904) 696-1600 *SIC* 2657

■ GRAPHIC PACKAGING INTERNATIONAL INC p 632
1500 Riveredge Pkwy # 100, Atlanta GA 30328
Tel (770) 240-7200 *SIC* 2657 2631 7389

CARAUSTAR CUSTOM PACKAGING GROUP INC p 252
5000 Austell Powder Sprin, Austell GA 30106
Tel (770) 948-3101 *SIC* 2657

■ IMPAC GROUP INC p 734
1950 N Ruby St, Melrose Park IL 60160
Tel (708) 344-9100 *SIC* 2657

NOSCO INC p 1062
651 S MI King Jr Ave, Waukegan IL 60085
Tel (847) 336-4200 *SIC* 2752 2657

WELCH PACKAGING GROUP INC p 1588
1020 Herman St, Elkhart IN 46516
Tel (574) 295-2460 *SIC* 2657

AMERICRAFT CARTON INC p 82
7400 State Line Rd # 206, Prairie Village KS 66208
Tel (913) 387-3700 *SIC* 2657

NEFF PACKAGING SOLUTIONS INC p 1024
10 Kingbrook Pkwy, Simpsonville KY 40067
Tel (502) 722-5020 *SIC* 2657

HUB FOLDING BOX CO INC p 715
774 Norfolk St, Mansfield MA 02048
Tel (508) 339-0005 *SIC* 2657

RAND-WHITNEY GROUP LLC p 1207
1 Agrand St, Worcester MA 01607
Tel (508) 791-2301 *SIC* 2653 2657 2631

BURD & FLETCHER CO p 226
5151 E Geospace Dr, Independence MO 64056
Tel (816) 257-0291 *SIC* 2657 2752 6512

MALNOVE HOLDING CO INC p 900
13434 F St, Omaha NE 68137
Tel (402) 330-1100 *SIC* 2657

▲ MULTI PACKAGING SOLUTIONS INTERNATIONAL LIMITED p 999
150 E 52nd St Fl 28, New York NY 10022
Tel (646) 885-0005 *SIC* 2657

FLOWER CITY PRINTING INC p 560
1725 Mount Read Blvd, Rochester NY 14606
Tel (585) 663-9000 *SIC* 2657 2752

DOPACO INC p 451
461 Boot Rd, Downingtown PA 19335
Tel (610) 269-6048
SIC 2657 2656 3089 3792

CLONDALKIN GROUP p 327
2000 Market St Ste 2810, Philadelphia PA 19103
Tel (215) 440-0570 *SIC* 2657

BEISTLE CO p 169
1 Beistle Plz, Shippensburg PA 17257
Tel (717) 532-2131
SIC 2679 3993 2675 2657 2631 2621

INLAND PAPERBOARD AND PACKAGING INC p 743
1300 S Mo Pac Expy Fl 3, Austin TX 78746
Tel (512) 234-5001
SIC 2653 2631 3086 2679 2657

BELMARK INC p 171
600 Heritage Rd, De Pere WI 54115
Tel (920) 336-2848 *SIC* 2759 2657 2671

PAX HOLDINGS LLC p 1122
758 N Broadway Ste 910, Milwaukee WI 53202
Tel (414) 803-9983
SIC 5199 2759 2672 2671 2657 2752

SIC 2671 Paper Coating & Laminating for Packaging

SMURFIT KAPPA NORTH AMERICA LLC p 1335
13400 Nelson Ave, City Of Industry CA 91746
Tel (626) 333-6363 *SIC* 2653 2671 2657

AUDIO VIDEO COLOR CORP p 130
17707 S Santa Fe Ave, Compton CA 90221
Tel (424) 213-7500 *SIC* 2671

PACIFIC SOUTHWEST CONTAINER LLC p 1106
4530 Leckron Rd, Modesto CA 95357
Tel (209) 526-0444
SIC 2671 2657 3086 2653 2752

PGAC CORP p 1140
9630 Ridgehaven Ct Ste B, San Diego CA 92123
Tel (858) 560-8213 *SIC* 2671

GRAPHIC PACKAGING INTERNATIONAL CORP p 632
1795 Dogwood St Unit 100, Louisville CO 80027
Tel (303) 215-4600 *SIC* 2657 2671 2655

AGI NORTH AMERICA LLC p 35
100 Northfield St, Greenwich CT 06830
Tel (203) 622-9138 *SIC* 2671

ATLAS AGI HOLDINGS LLC p 127
100 Northfield St, Greenwich CT 06830
Tel (203) 622-9138 *SIC* 2671

SHOREWOOD PACKAGING HOLDINGS LLC p 1318
100 Northfield St, Greenwich CT 06830
Tel (203) 541-8100 *SIC* 2671

MAFCOTE INC p 895
108 Main St Ste 3, Norwalk CT 06851
Tel (203) 847-8500
SIC 2631 2657 2679 2671

AGI SHOREWOOD GRAVURE LLC p 35
400 Atlantic St, Stamford CT 06901
Tel (203) 541-8100 *SIC* 2671

AGI-SHOREWOOD GROUP US LLC p 35
300 Atlantic St Ste 206, Stamford CT 06901
Tel (203) 324-4839 *SIC* 2671 2652 2657

SUN CAPITAL PARTNERS INC p 1400
5200 Town Center Cir # 600, Boca Raton FL 33486
Tel (561) 962-3400
SIC 6799 2672 2671 5812 5411 5311

WORLD INDUSTRIAL RESOURCES CORP p 1625
13100 56th Ct Ste 710, Clearwater FL 33760
Tel (727) 572-9991
SIC 3999 2542 5113 2671

CONSOLIDATED CONTAINER HOLDINGS LLC p 359
3101 Towercreek Pkwy Se P, Atlanta GA 30339
Tel (678) 742-4600 *SIC* 2671 7389 5113

CONSOLIDATED CONTAINER INTERMEDIARY LLC p 359
3101 Towercreek Pkwy Se, Atlanta GA 30339
Tel (678) 742-4600 *SIC* 5113 2671

▲ GRAPHIC PACKAGING HOLDING CO p 632
1500 Riveredge Pkwy # 100, Atlanta GA 30328
Tel (770) 240-7200 *SIC* 2631 2653 2671

BROWN INDUSTRIES INC p 219
205 W Industrial Blvd, Dalton GA 30720
Tel (706) 277-1977
SIC 2759 5131 2273 3552 3315 2671

AMCOR TOBACCO PACKAGING AMERICAS LLC p 66
445 Dividend Dr, Peachtree City GA 30269
Tel (770) 486-9095 *SIC* 2671

WALLE CORP p 1573
200 Hembree Park Dr Ste H, Roswell GA 30076
Tel (800) 942-6761 *SIC* 2759 2752 2671

■ BOISE INC p 198
1111 W Jefferson St # 50, Boise ID 83702
Tel (208) 384-7000 *SIC* 2671 2621 2631

BAGCRAFTPAPERCON I LLC p 144
3900 W 43rd St, Chicago IL 60632
Tel (620) 856-2800
SIC 2671 2674 2673 3497 2759

PACKAGING DYNAMICS CORP p 1106
3900 W 43rd St, Chicago IL 60632
Tel (773) 254-8000 *SIC* 2671

PREGIS HOLDING I CORP p 1170
1650 Lake Cook Rd Ste 400, Deerfield IL 60015
Tel (847) 597-2200 *SIC* 2671 5199 7336

PREGIS LLC p 1170
1650 Lake Cook Rd Ste 400, Deerfield IL 60015
Tel (847) 597-2200 *SIC* 2671 2673 3086

■ TEGRANT CORP p 1433
1401 Pleasant St, Dekalb IL 60115
Tel (815) 756-8451 *SIC* 2671

CLEAR LAM PACKAGING INC p 324
1950 Pratt Blvd, Elk Grove Village IL 60007
Tel (847) 439-8570 *SIC* 2671

SIGNODE INDUSTRIAL GROUP LLC p 1322
3650 W Lake Ave, Glenview IL 60026
Tel (847) 724-7500 *SIC* 2671

WESTROCK CONSUMER PACKAGING GROUP LLC p 1602
1950 N Ruby St, Melrose Park IL 60160
Tel (708) 344-9100 *SIC* 2671

AMCOR FLEXIBLES LLC p 65
1919 S Butterfield Rd, Mundelein IL 60060
Tel (847) 362-9000
SIC 2671 2621 2821 3081 3466

TETRA PAK MATERIALS LP p 1441
101 Corporate Woods Pkwy, Vernon Hills IL 60061
Tel (847) 955-6000 *SIC* 2671

WOLF PACKAGING INC p 1621
2068 303rd Ave, Fort Madison IA 52627
Tel (319) 372-6643 *SIC* 2621 2676 2671

AMERICAN FUJI SEAL INC p 73
1051 Bloomfield Rd, Bardstown KY 40004
Tel (502) 348-9211 *SIC* 8748 2671

CCL LABEL INC p 270
161 Worcester Rd Ste 504, Framingham MA 01701
Tel (508) 872-4511 *SIC* 2759 3411 2671

WEB INDUSTRIES INC p 1586
377 Simarano Dr Ste 220, Marlborough MA 01752
Tel (508) 898-2988
SIC 2671 5162 3089 2269 3441

PROLAMINA CORP p 1182
132 N Elm St, Westfield MA 01085
Tel (413) 562-2315 *SIC* 2671 5199

PACIFIC PACKAGING PRODUCTS INC p 1105
24 Industrial Way, Wilmington MA 01887
Tel (978) 657-9100
SIC 5113 5199 5084 5162 2671 2653

▲ UNIQUE FABRICATING INC p 1505
800 Standard Pkwy, Auburn Hills MI 48326
Tel (248) 853-2333
SIC 3053 3086 3296 2671

■ LANSING MPS INC p 844
5800 W Grand River Ave, Lansing MI 48906
Tel (517) 323-9000
SIC 2759 2731 2761 3089 2671

NYX LLC p 1069
36111 Schoolcraft Rd, Livonia MI 48150
Tel (734) 462-2385
SIC 3089 3714 3565 2671

DUNN PAPER INC p 461
218 Riverview St, Port Huron MI 48060
Tel (810) 984-5521 *SIC* 2671 2672

CENTURION MEDICAL PRODUCTS CORP p 281
100 Centurion Way, Williamston MI 48895
Tel (517) 546-5400 *SIC* 3842 2759 2671

COMPUTYPE INC p 353
2285 County Road C W, Saint Paul MN 55113
Tel (651) 633-0633
SIC 2759 2672 2679 3565 3577 2671

BEDFORD INDUSTRIES INC p 168
1659 Rowe Ave, Worthington MN 56187
Tel (507) 376-4136 *SIC* 2671 2759

MONDI JACKSON LLC p 984
14591 State Highway 177, Jackson MO 63755
Tel (573) 335-4900 *SIC* 2671

PACKAGING CONCEPTS INC p 1106
9832 Evergreen Indus Dr, Saint Louis MO 63123
Tel (314) 329-9700 *SIC* 5113 2674 2671

ROBERT FAMILY HOLDINGS INC p 1241
12430 Tesson Ferry Rd, Saint Louis MO 63128
Tel (314) 821-5665
SIC 2671 3572 3491 3498 7699 3494

SOUTHERN MISSOURI CONTAINERS INC p 1349
3131 E Division St, Springfield MO 65802
Tel (417) 831-2685 *SIC* 2671 2653

FORTIFIBER CORP p 569
300 Industrial Dr, Fernley NV 89408
Tel (800) 773-4777 *SIC* 2671

■ SEALED AIR CORP (US) p 1296
200 Riverfront Blvd # 301, Elmwood Park NJ 07407
Tel (201) 791-7600
SIC 2673 2671 3087 3086 3089

UNIVERSAL PACKAGING SYSTEMS INC p 1517
6080 Jericho Tpke, Commack NY 11725
Tel (631) 543-2277
SIC 2844 7389 3565 2671

BURROWS PAPER CORP p 229
501 W Main St Ste 1, Little Falls NY 13365
Tel (315) 823-2300
SIC 2621 2671 2611 2679

■ MULTI PACKAGING SOLUTIONS INC p 999
150 E 52nd St Ste 2800, New York NY 10022
Tel (646) 885-0005
SIC 2759 2731 2761 3089 5092 2671

AMERICAN PACKAGING CORP p 77
777 Driving Park Ave, Rochester NY 14613
Tel (585) 254-9500
SIC 2673 3497 2671 2754 2674

▲ SEALED AIR CORP p 1296
8215 Forest Point Blvd # 100, Charlotte NC 28273
Tel (980) 221-3235
SIC 2673 2671 3087 3086 3089

NS FLEXIBLES LLC p 1064
2619 Phoenix Dr, Greensboro NC 27406
Tel (336) 292-9911 *SIC* 2671 7336 2759

ATLANTIC CORP p 126
806 N 23rd St, Wilmington NC 28405
Tel (910) 343-0624 *SIC* 2671

SHURTECH BRANDS LLC p 1319
32150 Just Imagine Dr, Avon OH 44011
Tel (440) 937-7000 *SIC* 2671

PROAMPAC LLC p 1178
12025 Tricon Rd, Cincinnati OH 45246
Tel (513) 671-1777 *SIC* 2671

POLYCHEM CORP p 1160
6277 Heisley Rd, Mentor OH 44060
Tel (440) 357-1500 *SIC* 2671

■ NEWPAGE GROUP INC p 1038
8540 Gander Creek Dr, Miamisburg OH 45342
Tel (937) 242-9500 *SIC* 2671

STOROPACK INC p 1392
4758 Devitt Dr, West Chester OH 45246
Tel (513) 874-0314 *SIC* 5199 3086 2671

OLIVER-TOLAS HEALTHCARE PACKAGING INC p 1082
905 Pennsylvania Blvd, Feasterville Trevose PA 19053
Tel (215) 322-7900 *SIC* 2671

NATIONAL LABEL CO p 1014
2025 Joshua Rd, Lafayette Hill PA 19444
Tel (610) 825-3250
SIC 2672 2679 2759 2671

MANGAR INDUSTRIES INC p 901
97 Britain Dr, New Britain PA 18901
Tel (215) 230-0300 *SIC* 2671

WINPAK PORTION PACKAGING INC p 1617
828a Newtown Yardley Rd # 101, Newtown PA 18940
Tel (267) 685-8200 *SIC* 3565 2671

CARAUSTAR INDUSTRIAL AND CONSUMER PRODUCTS GROUP INC p 252
2031 Carolina Place Dr, Fort Mill SC 29708
Tel (803) 548-5100 *SIC* 2655 2671 2679

COVERIS RIGID NA INC p 385
50 International Dr # 100, Greenville SC 29615
Tel (864) 225-9750 *SIC* 2671 3089

MITSUBISHI POLYESTER FILM INC p 978
2001 Hood Rd, Greer SC 29650
Tel (864) 879-5000 *SIC* 3081 2671

▲ SONOCO PRODUCTS CO p 1340
1 N 2nd St, Hartsville SC 29550
Tel (843) 383-7000
SIC 2631 2671 2653 2655 3089 2499

BRYCE CO LLC p 221
4505 Old Lamar Ave, Memphis TN 38118
Tel (901) 369-4400 *SIC* 2671

AGE INDUSTRIES LTD p 34
3601 County Road 316c, Cleburne TX 76031
Tel (817) 477-5266 *SIC* 2653 2655 2671

TETRA PAK INC p 1441
3300 Airport Rd, Denton TX 76207
Tel (940) 565-8800 *SIC* 2671 3565 5084

▲ TREDEGAR CORP p 1475
1100 Boulders Pkwy # 200, North Chesterfield VA 23225
Tel (804) 330-1000
SIC 3081 2671 3083 3354

■ WESTROCK MWV LLC p 1603
501 S 5th St, Richmond VA 23219
Tel (804) 444-1000
SIC 2631 2671 2678 2677 2861 2611

GREAT NORTHERN CORP p 634
395 Stroebe Rd, Appleton WI 54914
Tel (920) 739-3671 *SIC* 2653 5199 2671

PAPERWEIGHT DEVELOPMENT CORP p 1112
825 E Wisconsin Ave, Appleton WI 54911
Tel (920) 734-9841 *SIC* 2671

REYNOLDS PRESTO PRODUCTS INC p 1231
670 N Perkins St, Appleton WI 54914
Tel (800) 558-3525 *SIC* 2671 2673 3842

BELMARK INC p 171
600 Heritage Rd, De Pere WI 54115
Tel (920) 336-2848 *SIC* 2759 2657 2671

PAX HOLDINGS LLC p 1122
758 N Broadway Ste 910, Milwaukee WI 53202
Tel (414) 803-9983
SIC 5199 2759 2672 2671 2657 2752

▲ BEMIS CO INC p 171
1 Neenah Ctr Fl 4, Neenah WI 54956
Tel (920) 527-5000 *SIC* 2671 2672

■ DUNSIRN INDUSTRIES INC p 461
2415 Industrial Dr, Neenah WI 54956
Tel (920) 725-3814
SIC 2671 5113 3081 2672 2621

■ BEMIS HEALTHCARE PACKAGING INC p 171
3500 N Main St, Oshkosh WI 54901
Tel (920) 527-7464 *SIC* 2671 3565

■ BEMIS HEALTHCARE PACKAGING INC p 171
3500 N Main St, Oshkosh WI 54901
Tel (920) 527-3000 *SIC* 2671

■ BEMIS PACKAGING INC p 172
3550 Moser St, Oshkosh WI 54901
Tel (920) 527-2300 *SIC* 2671

COATING EXCELLENCE INTERNATIONAL LLC p 332
975 Brdwy St, Wrightstown WI 54180
Tel (920) 996-1900 *SIC* 2671

SIC 2672 Paper Coating & Laminating, Exc for Packaging

AVERY PRODUCTS CORP p 137
50 Pointe Dr, Brea CA 92821
Tel (714) 675-8500
SIC 2678 3951 2672 2891

NITTO AMERICAS INC p 1045
48500 Fremont Blvd, Fremont CA 94538
Tel (510) 445-5400
SIC 2672 3589 5162 5065

▲ AVERY DENNISON CORP p 137
207 N Goode Ave Fl 6, Glendale CA 91203
Tel (626) 304-2000
SIC 2672 3081 3497 2678

■ PRECISION DYNAMICS CORP p 1168
27770 N Entrmt Dr Ste 200, Valencia CA 91355
Tel (818) 897-1111
SIC 2672 2754 5047 3069

BEIERSDORF NORTH AMERICA INC p 169
45 Danbury Rd, Wilton CT 06897
Tel (203) 563-5800
SIC 2844 5122 3842 2841 2672

SCAPA NORTH AMERICA INC p 1286
111 Great Pond Dr, Windsor CT 06095
Tel (860) 688-8000
SIC 2231 3069 2211 2824 2672

SUN CAPITAL PARTNERS INC p 1400
5200 Town Center Cir # 600, Boca Raton FL 33486
Tel (561) 962-3400
SIC 6799 2672 2671 5812 5411 5311

INTERTAPE POLYMER CORP p 759
100 Paramount Dr Ste 300, Sarasota FL 34232
Tel (941) 727-5788 *SIC* 2672

IPG (US) HOLDINGS INC p 763
100 Paramount Dr Ste 300, Sarasota FL 34232
Tel (941) 727-5788 *SIC* 2672 3953

IPG (US) INC p 763
100 Paramount Dr Ste 300, Sarasota FL 34232
Tel (941) 727-5788 *SIC* 2672 3953

LEXJET LLC p 860
1605 Main St Ste 400, Sarasota FL 34236
Tel (941) 330-1210
SIC 5045 5112 5111 2672 5043

FMK HOLDINGS LLC p 562
3081 Holcom Ste H 1, Norcross GA 30071
Tel (413) 736-4554 *SIC* 2631 2621 2672

WEBER MARKING SYSTEMS INC p 1586
711 W Algonquin Rd, Arlington Heights IL 60005
Tel (847) 364-8500 *SIC* 3555 2672 2675

HOLDEN INDUSTRIES INC p 700
500 Lake Cook Rd Ste 400, Deerfield IL 60015
Tel (847) 940-1500
SIC 2752 2672 3545 3589 3541 3441

▲ ACCO BRANDS CORP p 15
4 Corporate Dr, Lake Zurich IL 60047
Tel (847) 541-9500
SIC 2782 3083 2761 2672

▲ ZEBRA TECHNOLOGIES CORP p 1641
3 Overlook Pt, Lincolnshire IL 60069
Tel (847) 634-6700
SIC 3577 2672 2679 5045

■ COVALENCE SPECIALTY COATINGS LLC p 383
101 Oakley St, Evansville IN 47710
Tel (812) 424-2904 *SIC* 2672

WARD-KRAFT INC p 1575
2401 Cooper St, Fort Scott KS 66701
Tel (800) 821-4021 *SIC* 2761 2672

LLFLEX LLC p 872
1225 W Burnett Ave, Louisville KY 40210
Tel (502) 635-6331 *SIC* 2672

S D WARREN CO p 1262
255 State St Fl 4, Boston MA 02109
Tel (617) 423-7300
SIC 2679 2674 2672 2621

KANZAKI SPECIALTY PAPERS INC p 803
20 Cummings St, Ware MA 01082
Tel (413) 967-6204 *SIC* 2672

▲ AMERICAN BILTRITE INC p 69
57 River St Ste 302, Wellesley MA 02481
Tel (781) 237-6655
SIC 3069 2672 2241 3961 5094

▲ TRIMAS CORP p 1480
39400 Woodward Ave # 130, Bloomfield Hills MI 48304
Tel (248) 631-5450
SIC 3799 3714 3443 2672 3452 3545

LOWRY HOLDING CO INC p 882
9420 Maltby Rd, Brighton MI 48116
Tel (810) 229-7200
SIC 5045 2672 8742 7373 5044 5734

ESCANABA PAPER CO p 509
7100 County Rd 426, Escanaba MI 49829
Tel (906) 786-1660 *SIC* 2611 2621 2672

OLIVER-TOLAS HEALTHCARE PACKAGING LLC p 1082
445 6th St Nw, Grand Rapids MI 49504
Tel (616) 456-7711 SIC 2672

DUNN PAPER HOLDINGS INC p 461
218 Riverview St, Port Huron MI 48060
Tel (810) 984-5521 SIC 2621 2672

DUNN PAPER INC p 461
218 Riverview St, Port Huron MI 48060
Tel (810) 984-5521 SIC 2671 2672

BLANDIN PAPER CO p 189
115 Sw 1st St, Grand Rapids MN 55744
Tel (218) 327-6200 SIC 2621 2672

▲ 3M CO p 2
3m Center Bldg 22011w02, Saint Paul MN 55144
Tel (651) 733-1110
SIC 3841 3842 3291 2842 2672 2891

COMPUTYPE INC p 353
2285 County Road C W, Saint Paul MN 55113
Tel (651) 633-0633
SIC 2759 2672 2679 3565 3577 2671

■ NASHUA CORP p 1008
59 Daniel Webster Hwy A, Merrimack NH 03054
Tel (603) 880-1100
SIC 2672 2754 2679 2621 2782

CYTEC INDUSTRIES INC p 406
5 Garret Mountain Plz, Woodland Park NJ 07424
Tel (973) 357-3100
SIC 2899 2821 2672 2851 2823 2819

MOHAWK FINE PAPERS INC p 982
465 Saratoga St, Cohoes NY 12047
Tel (518) 237-1740 SIC 2672 2621

ESSELTE HOLDINGS INC p 510
48 S Service Rd Ste 400, Melville NY 11747
Tel (631) 675-5700
SIC 2675 2782 3579 2672 3953 3596

LOPAREX LLC p 877
1255 Crescent Green # 400, Cary NC 27518
Tel (919) 678-7700 SIC 2672

SHURTAPE TECHNOLOGIES INC p 1319
1506 Highland Ave Ne, Hickory NC 28601
Tel (828) 322-2700 SIC 2672

SHURTAPE TECHNOLOGIES LLC p 1319
1712 8th Street Dr Se, Hickory NC 28602
Tel (828) 322-2700 SIC 2672

STM INDUSTRIES INC p 1390
1985 Tate Blvd Se Ste 2, Hickory NC 28602
Tel (828) 322-2700 SIC 2672

UPM RAFLATAC INC p 1528
400 Broadpointe Dr, Mills River NC 28759
Tel (828) 651-4800 SIC 2672 3083

TRIMACO LLC p 1480
2300 Gateway Centre Blvd # 200, Morrisville NC 27560
Tel (919) 674-3476
SIC 2851 2621 2672 2679 2394

ORACLE FLEXIBLE PACKAGING INC p 1091
220 Polo Rd, Winston Salem NC 27105
Tel (336) 777-4695 SIC 2672

▲ MULTI-COLOR CORP p 999
4053 Clough Woods Dr, Batavia OH 45103
Tel (513) 381-1480 SIC 2759 2679 2672

SRC LIQUIDATION LLC p 1363
600 Albany St, Dayton OH 45417
Tel (937) 221-1000
SIC 2761 2672 2677 2759

NEWPAGE ENERGY SERVICES LLC p 1038
8540 Gander Creek Dr, Miamisburg OH 45342
Tel (877) 855-7243 SIC 2672 2621 2611

■ NEWPAGE HOLDING CORP p 1038
8540 Gander Creek Dr, Miamisburg OH 45342
Tel (877) 855-7243 SIC 2621 2672 2611

TECHNICOTE INC p 1431
222 Mound Ave, Miamisburg OH 45342
Tel (800) 358-4448 SIC 2672

GBS CORP p 595
7233 Freedom Ave Nw, North Canton OH 44720
Tel (330) 494-5330
SIC 5045 5112 2675 2672 2761 2759

MORGAN ADHESIVES CO LLC p 988
4560 Darrow Rd, Stow OH 44224
Tel (330) 688-1111
SIC 2891 3565 2672 2823

NATIONAL LABEL CO p 1014
2025 Joshua Rd, Lafayette Hill PA 19444
Tel (610) 825-3250
SIC 2672 2679 2759 2671

TEKNI-PLEX INC p 1433
460 E Swedesford Rd # 3000, Wayne PA 19087
Tel (484) 690-1520
SIC 2679 3462 3052 2672

■ NEPTCO INC p 1026
30 Hamlet St, Pawtucket RI 02861
Tel (401) 722-5500 SIC 3496 3083 2672

RESOLUTE FP US INC p 1227
5300 Cureton Ferry Rd, Catawba SC 29704
Tel (803) 981-8000
SIC 2621 2672 2611 2421

IDENTITY HOLDING CO LLC p 729
1480 Gould Dr, Cookeville TN 38506
Tel (931) 432-4000 SIC 3953 2672

WINGATE PARTNERS LP p 1616
750 N Saint Paul St # 1200, Dallas TX 75201
Tel (214) 720-1313
SIC 2621 2672 3645 2519 5021 2521

GIESECKE & DEVRIENT AMERICA INC p 611
45925 Horseshoe Dr # 100, Dulles VA 20166
Tel (703) 480-2000 SIC 2672 5044

BOX MAKER INC p 205
6412 S 190th St, Kent WA 98032
Tel (425) 251-0655
SIC 5113 2653 2672 3086 5199 2631

APPLETON COATED LLC p 99
540 Prospect St, Combined Locks WI 54113
Tel (920) 788-3550 SIC 2621 2672

VIRTUS HOLDINGS LLC p 1560
540 Prospect St, Combined Locks WI 54113
Tel (920) 788-3550 SIC 2672 2621

GREEN BAY PACKAGING INC p 636
1700 N Webster Ave, Green Bay WI 54302
Tel (920) 433-5111
SIC 2631 2672 2653 2491

HEARTLAND LABEL PRINTERS LLC p 679
1700 Stephen St, Little Chute WI 54140
Tel (920) 788-7720 SIC 5065 2672

▲ BRADY CORP p 207
6555 W Good Hope Rd, Milwaukee WI 53223
Tel (414) 358-6600
SIC 3993 2672 3695 3577

PAX HOLDINGS LLC p 1122
758 N Broadway Ste 910, Milwaukee WI 53202
Tel (414) 803-9983
SIC 5199 2759 2672 2671 2657 2752

▲ BEMIS CO INC p 171
1 Neenah Ctr Fl 4, Neenah WI 54956
Tel (920) 527-5000 SIC 2671 2672

■ DUNSIRN INDUSTRIES INC p 461
2415 Industrial Dr, Neenah WI 54956
Tel (920) 725-3814
SIC 2671 5113 3081 2672 2621

WAUSAU COATED PRODUCTS INC p 1583
7801 Stewart Ave, Wausau WI 54401
Tel (715) 848-2741 SIC 2672 3554

SIC 2673 Bags: Plastics, Laminated & Coated

JONAH BROOKLYN INC p 792
9673 Topanga Canyon Pl, Chatsworth CA 91311
Tel (877) 964-2725 SIC 2673

MERCURY PLASTICS INC p 945
14825 Salt Lake Ave, City Of Industry CA 91746
Tel (626) 369-8457 SIC 2673 2759 3089

CROWN POLY INC p 396
5700 Bickett St, Huntington Park CA 90255
Tel (323) 268-1298 SIC 2673

TRANS WESTERN POLYMERS INC p 1470
7539 Las Positas Rd, Livermore CA 94551
Tel (925) 449-7800 SIC 2673 5023 3089

▲ CLOROX CO p 327
1221 Broadway Ste 1300, Oakland CA 94612
Tel (510) 271-7000
SIC 2842 2673 2035 2844 2879

■ GLAD PRODUCTS CO p 614
1221 Broadway Ste A, Oakland CA 94612
Tel (510) 271-7000
SIC 3081 2673 2842 3295

B & B PLASTICS RECYCLERS INC p 141
3040 N Locust Ave, Rialto CA 92377
Tel (909) 829-3606 SIC 5093 2673

EMERALD PACKAGING INC p 491
33050 Western Ave, Union City CA 94587
Tel (510) 429-5700 SIC 2673

GRAND PACKAGING INC p 630
3840 E 26th St, Vernon CA 90058
Tel (323) 980-0918 SIC 2673

RCRV INC p 1212
4715 S Alameda St, Vernon CA 90058
Tel (323) 235-8070 SIC 2673 5137 5136

PRINTPACK ENTERPRISES INC p 1177
River Rd & Grantham Ln, New Castle DE 19720
Tel (302) 323-0900 SIC 2673

FLEXSOL HOLDING CORP p 556
1531 Nw 12th Ave, Pompano Beach FL 33069
Tel (954) 941-6333 SIC 2673 3082 3081

PRINTPACK HOLDINGS INC p 1177
2800 Overlook Pkwy Ne, Atlanta GA 30339
Tel (404) 460-7000 SIC 2673

PRINTPACK INC p 1177
2800 Overlook Pkwy Ne, Atlanta GA 30339
Tel (404) 460-7000 SIC 2673 3081

BAGCRAFTPAPERCON I LLC p 144
3900 W 43rd St, Chicago IL 60632
Tel (620) 856-2800
SIC 2671 2674 2673 3497 2759

COVERIS HOLDING CORP p 385
8600 W Bryn Mawr Ave, Chicago IL 60631
Tel (773) 877-3300 SIC 6719 2673 2631

PREGIS LLC p 1170
1650 Lake Cook Rd Ste 400, Deerfield IL 60015
Tel (847) 597-2200 SIC 2671 2673 3086

PACTIV LLC p 1107
1900 W Field Ct, Lake Forest IL 60045
Tel (847) 482-2000 SIC 5113 3089 2673

■ PLIANT LLC p 1156
1701 Golf Rd Ste 2-900, Rolling Meadows IL 60008
Tel (812) 424-2904 SIC 3081 2673 3089

BAGMAKERS INC p 145
6606 S Union Rd, Union IL 60180
Tel (815) 923-2247 SIC 2673 2674

▲ BERRY PLASTICS GROUP INC p 176
101 Oakley St, Evansville IN 47710
Tel (812) 424-2904
SIC 3089 3085 2673 3081 3083

ENVISION INC p 504
2301 S Water St, Wichita KS 67213
Tel (316) 267-2244 SIC 2673 2676

OMEGA PLASTIC CORP p 1084
901 Commerce Cir, Shelbyville KY 40065
Tel (502) 633-0168 SIC 2673

CADILLAC PRODUCTS INC p 236
5800 Crooks Rd Ste 100, Troy MI 48098
Tel (248) 813-8200
SIC 3714 3081 2673 3089

HOOD CONTAINER CORP p 705
623 N Main St Ste 100, Hattiesburg MS 39401
Tel (601) 582-1545 SIC 2673

MEXICO PLASTIC CO p 957
2000 W Boulevard St, Mexico MO 65265
Tel (573) 581-4128 SIC 2673 3089 2655

▲ KATY INDUSTRIES INC p 805
11840 Westline Industrial, Saint Louis MO 63146
Tel (314) 656-4321 SIC 3589 2673

■ SEALED AIR CORP (US) p 1296
200 Riverfront Blvd # 301, Elmwood Park NJ 07407
Tel (201) 791-7600
SIC 2673 2671 3087 3086 3089

INTEPLAST GROUP CORP p 750
9 Peach Tree Hill Rd, Livingston NJ 07039
Tel (973) 994-8000 SIC 2673

TRINITY PLASTICS INC p 1481
9 Peach Tree Hill Rd, Livingston NJ 07039
Tel (973) 994-8018 SIC 2673 3081

ALPHA INDUSTRIES MANAGEMENT INC p 60
Page And Schuyler Ave, Lyndhurst NJ 07071
Tel (201) 933-6000 SIC 2673

OMEGA PLASTICS CORP p 1084
Page & Schuyler Ave Ste 5, Lyndhurst NJ 07071
Tel (201) 933-1270 SIC 2673

TRINITY PACKAGING CORP p 1481
357 Main St, Armonk NY 10504
Tel (914) 273-4111 SIC 2673 2679

POLY-PAK INDUSTRIES INC p 1160
125 Spagnoli Rd, Melville NY 11747
Tel (631) 293-6767 SIC 2673 2677

API INDUSTRIES INC p 96
2 Glenshaw St, Orangeburg NY 10962
Tel (845) 365-2200 SIC 2673 3081

AMERICAN PACKAGING CORP p 77
777 Driving Park Ave, Rochester NY 14613
Tel (585) 254-9500
SIC 2673 3497 2671 2754 2674

FUJIFILM NORTH AMERICA CORP p 583
200 Summit Lake Dr Fl 2, Valhalla NY 10595
Tel (914) 789-8100
SIC 7384 5043 5065 3695 2673 3861

PERK-UP INC p 1136
399 Knollwood Rd Ste 309, White Plains NY 10603
Tel (914) 580-3200
SIC 5113 5149 2673 3411 2674 2035

▲ SEALED AIR CORP p 1296
8215 Forest Point Blvd # 100, Charlotte NC 28273
Tel (980) 221-3235
SIC 2673 2671 3087 3086 3089

AMPAC HOLDINGS LLC p 86
12025 Tricon Rd, Cincinnati OH 45246
Tel (513) 671-1777
SIC 2673 2677 3081 2674 6719

AMPAC PACKAGING LLC p 86
12025 Tricon Rd, Cincinnati OH 45246
Tel (513) 671-1777 SIC 2673

LIQUI-BOX CORP p 870
480 Schrock Rd Ste G, Columbus OH 43229
Tel (804) 325-1400
SIC 2673 3585 3089 3081 5149

API ENTERPRISES INC p 96
4901 S I 35 Service Rd, Oklahoma City OK 73129
Tel (713) 580-4800 SIC 2673

▲ WEST PHARMACEUTICAL SERVICES INC p 1595
530 Herman O West Dr, Exton PA 19341
Tel (610) 594-2900
SIC 3069 3466 2673 3085 3089

CLONDALKIN HOLDINGS INC p 327
Crtis Centre Ste, Philadelphia PA 19106
Tel (215) 440-0570
SIC 2673 2621 2752 8741

COVERIS FLEXIBLES US LLC p 385
50 International Dr # 100, Greenville SC 29615
Tel (773) 877-3300 SIC 2673

HILEX POLY CO LLC p 692
101 E Carolina Ave, Hartsville SC 29550
Tel (843) 857-4800 SIC 2673 2674

NOVOLEX HOLDINGS INC p 1063
101 E Carolina Ave, Hartsville SC 29550
Tel (843) 857-4800 SIC 2673 2674

COVERIS KEY HOLDINGS LLC p 385
345 Cedar Springs Ave, Spartanburg SC 29302
Tel (864) 596-7300 SIC 2673 2631 6719

POLY-AMERICA LP p 1160
2000 W Marshall Dr, Grand Prairie TX 75051
Tel (972) 337-7100 SIC 3081 2673

SUPERBAG USA CORP p 1406
9291 Baythorne Dr, Houston TX 77041
Tel (713) 462-1173 SIC 2673 5411

■ WESTLAKE POLYMERS LLC p 1601
2801 Post Oak Blvd # 650, Houston TX 77056
Tel (713) 960-9111 SIC 2673 2869

FORMOSA UTILITY VENTURE LTD p 568
201 Formosa Dr, Point Comfort TX 77978
Tel (361) 987-7000 SIC 2673

HERITAGE BAG CO p 686
501 Gateway Pkwy, Roanoke TX 76262
Tel (972) 241-5525 SIC 2673

■ RUBBERMAID COMMERCIAL PRODUCTS LLC p 1256
3124 Valley Ave, Winchester VA 22601
Tel (540) 677-8700 SIC 3089 2673

REYNOLDS PRESTO PRODUCTS INC p 1231
670 N Perkins St, Appleton WI 54914
Tel (800) 558-3525 SIC 2671 2673 3842

SIC 2674 Bags: Uncoated Paper & Multiwall

BAGCRAFTPAPERCON I LLC p 144
3900 W 43rd St, Chicago IL 60632
Tel (620) 856-2800
SIC 2671 2674 2673 3497 2759

GATEWAY PACKAGING CO p 594
20 Central Industrial Dr, Granite City IL 62040
Tel (618) 451-0010 SIC 2674 2679

BAGMAKERS INC p 145
6606 S Union Rd, Union IL 60180
Tel (815) 923-2247 SIC 2673 2674

DURO BAG MANUFACTURING CO p 463
7600 Empire Dr, Florence KY 41042
Tel (859) 371-2150 SIC 2674

BANCROFT BAG INC p 150
425 Bancroft Blvd, West Monroe LA 71292
Tel (318) 387-2550 SIC 2674

S D WARREN CO p 1262
255 State St Fl 4, Boston MA 02109
Tel (617) 423-7300
SIC 2679 2674 2672 2621

AJM PACKAGING CORP p 41
E-4111 Andover Rd, Bloomfield Hills MI 48302
Tel (248) 901-0040 SIC 2656 2674

HOOD PACKAGING CORP p 705
25 Woodgreen Pl, Madison MS 39110
Tel (601) 853-7260 SIC 2674

ASPEN PRODUCTS INC p 118
4231 Clary Blvd, Kansas City MO 64130
Tel (816) 921-0234 SIC 2674

PACKAGING CONCEPTS INC p 1106
9832 Evergreen Indus Dr, Saint Louis MO 63123
Tel (314) 329-9700 SIC 5113 2674 2671

ROSES SOUTHWEST PAPERS INC p 1251
1701 2nd St Sw, Albuquerque NM 87102
Tel (505) 842-0134 SIC 2676 2674 2621

AMERICAN PACKAGING CORP p 77
777 Driving Park Ave, Rochester NY 14613
Tel (585) 254-9500
SIC 2673 3497 2671 2754 2674

AMPAC PAPER LLC p 86
30 Coldenham Rd, Walden NY 12586
Tel (845) 778-5511 SIC 2674 2621 5162

PERK-UP INC p 1136
399 Knollwood Rd Ste 309, White Plains NY 10603
Tel (914) 580-3200
SIC 5113 5149 2673 3411 2674 2035

AMPAC HOLDINGS LLC p 86
12025 Tricon Rd, Cincinnati OH 45246
Tel (513) 671-1777
SIC 2673 2677 3081 2674 6719

▲ GREIF INC p 639
425 Winter Rd, Delaware OH 43015
Tel (740) 549-6000
SIC 2653 2449 2655 3412 3089 2674

HILEX POLY CO LLC p 692
101 E Carolina Ave, Hartsville SC 29550
Tel (843) 857-4800 SIC 2673 2674

NOVOLEX HOLDINGS INC p 1063
101 E Carolina Ave, Hartsville SC 29550
Tel (843) 857-4800 SIC 2673 2674

SIC 2675 Die-Cut Paper & Board

■ THARCO HOLDINGS INC p 1446
2222 Grant Ave, San Lorenzo CA 94580
Tel (303) 373-1860 SIC 2653 3086 2675

WEBER MARKING SYSTEMS INC p 1586
711 W Algonquin Rd, Arlington Heights IL 60005
Tel (847) 364-8500 SIC 3555 2672 2675

RAPID DISPLAYS INC p 1208
4300 W 47th St, Chicago IL 60632
Tel (773) 927-5000 SIC 2675 3944

GRAPHIC CONVERTING INC p 631
877 N Larch Ave, Elmhurst IL 60126
Tel (630) 758-4100 SIC 2675

■ ACCO BRANDS USA LLC p 15
4 Corporate Dr, Lake Zurich IL 60047
Tel (800) 222-6462
SIC 3089 2761 3496 2675

SMEAD MANUFACTURING CO INC p 1332
600 Smead Blvd, Hastings MN 55033
Tel (651) 437-4111
SIC 2675 7372 2789 2759 2752 2542

PROCESS DISPLAYS LLC p 1179
7108 31st Ave N, Minneapolis MN 55427
Tel (763) 541-1245
SIC 2541 2542 2599 2675 2752 2759

RENAISSANCE LAKEWOOD LLC p 1223
1200 Paco Way, Lakewood NJ 08701
Tel (732) 367-9000 SIC 2834 2844 2675

PRO TAPES & SPECIALTIES INC p 1178
621 Us Highway 1 Unit A, North Brunswick NJ 08902
Tel (732) 346-0900 SIC 5113 2675

ESSELTE HOLDINGS INC p 510
48 S Service Rd Ste 400, Melville NY 11747
Tel (631) 675-5700
SIC 2675 2782 3579 2672 3953 3596

■ TOPS SLT INC p 1461
225 Broadhollow Rd # 300, Melville NY 11747
Tel (631) 675-5700 SIC 2675

GBS CORP p 595
7233 Freedom Ave Nw, North Canton OH 44720
Tel (330) 494-5330
SIC 5045 5112 2675 2672 2761 2759

ROHRER CORP p 1247
717 Seville Rd, Wadsworth OH 44281
Tel (330) 335-1541 SIC 3089 2675

BEISTLE CO p 169
1 Beistle Plz, Shippensburg PA 17257
Tel (717) 532-2131
SIC 2679 3993 2675 2657 2631 2621

SOUTHERN CHAMPION TRAY LP p 1347
220 Compress St, Chattanooga TN 37405
Tel (423) 756-5121 SIC 2675

HFS HOLDING CORP p 689
8900 Ambassador Row, Dallas TX 75247
Tel (214) 634-8600 SIC 2679 5112 2675

KLEEN TEST PRODUCTS CORP p 823
1611 S Sunset Rd, Port Washington WI 53074
Tel (262) 284-6600 SIC 2842 2675

SIC 2676 Sanitary Paper Prdts

GEORGIA PACIFIC HOLDINGS INC p 607
13208 Hadley St Apt 1, Whittier CA 90601
Tel (626) 926-1474
SIC 2676 2656 2435 2821

■ CELLU TISSUE CORP p 274
2 Forbes St, East Hartford CT 06108
Tel (860) 289-7496 SIC 2621 3842 2676

CAPRICORN INVESTORS II LP p 251
30 E Elm St, Greenwich CT 06830
Tel (203) 861-6600 SIC 2676 5461 6794

SOUNDVIEW PAPER MILLS LLC p 1342
1 Sound Shore Dr Ste 203, Greenwich CT 06830
Tel (201) 796-4000 SIC 2676

■ EDGEWELL PERSONAL CARE BRANDS LLC p 477
6 Research Dr, Shelton CT 06484
Tel (203) 944-5500 SIC 3421 2844 2676

■ **PLAYTEX PRODUCTS LLC** p 1155
6 Research Dr Ste 400, Shelton CT 06484
Tel (203) 944-5500
SIC 2676 3069 2844 3842

■ **PLAYTEX MANUFACTURING INC** p 1155
50 N Dupont Hwy, Dover DE 19901
Tel (302) 678-6000 *SIC* 2676 2844 2842

GEORGIA-PACIFIC LLC p 608
133 Peachtree St Ne # 4810, Atlanta GA 30303
Tel (404) 652-4000
SIC 2676 2656 2653 2435 2821 3275

EPS SOLUTIONS INC p 505
1525 W Lake Shore Dr, Woodstock IL 60098
Tel (815) 206-0868 *SIC* 2676

WOLF PACKAGING INC p 1621
2068 303rd Ave, Fort Madison IA 52627
Tel (319) 372-6643 *SIC* 2621 2676 2671

ENVISION INC p 504
2301 S Water St, Wichita KS 67213
Tel (316) 267-2244 *SIC* 2673 2676

LEAF RIVER CELLULOSE LLC p 850
157 Buck Creek Rd, New Augusta MS 39462
Tel (601) 964-8411 *SIC* 2676

▲ **EDGEWELL PERSONAL CARE CO** p 477
1350 Timberlake Manor Pkwy, Chesterfield MO 63017
Tel (314) 594-1900
SIC 3421 2844 2676 3069

MARCAL MANUFACTURING LLC p 904
1 Market St, Elmwood Park NJ 07407
Tel (201) 703-6225 *SIC* 2676

MARCAL PAPER MILLS LLC p 905
1 Market St, Elmwood Park NJ 07407
Tel (201) 791-0852 *SIC* 2676

SOUNDVIEW PAPER HOLDINGS LLC p 1342
1 Market St, Elmwood Park NJ 07407
Tel (201) 796-4000 *SIC* 2676 2656

▲ **JOHNSON & JOHNSON** p 790
1 Johnson And Johnson Plz, New Brunswick NJ 08933
Tel (732) 524-0400
SIC 2676 2844 3841 3842 2834

ROSES SOUTHWEST PAPERS INC p 1251
1701 2nd St Sw, Albuquerque NM 87102
Tel (505) 842-0134 *SIC* 2676 2674 2621

■ **AMSCAN INC** p 87
80 Grasslands Rd Ste 3, Elmsford NY 10523
Tel (914) 345-2020
SIC 2656 3089 5113 2676

FIRST QUALITY PRODUCTS INC p 549
80 Cuttermill Rd Ste 500, Great Neck NY 11021
Tel (516) 829-4949 *SIC* 2676

■ **HFC PRESTIGE INTERNATIONAL US LLC** p 689
350 5th Ave, New York NY 10118
Tel (212) 389-7800
SIC 2844 2676 3421 2842 2841

NICE-PAK PRODUCTS INC p 1042
2 Nice Pak Park, Orangeburg NY 10962
Tel (845) 365-2772 *SIC* 2621 7389 2676

PROFESSIONAL DISPOSABLES INC p 1180
2 Nice Pak Park, Orangeburg NY 10962
Tel (845) 365-1700 *SIC* 2676 7389 2621

ROCHESTER MIDLAND CORP p 1243
155 Paragon Dr, Rochester NY 14624
Tel (585) 336-2200 *SIC* 2842 2676 2899

ASSOCIATED HYGIENIC PRODUCTS LLC p 120
1029 Old Creek Rd, Greenville NC 27834
Tel (770) 476-3594 *SIC* 2676

VON DREHLE CORP p 1565
612 3rd Ave Ne Ste 200, Hickory NC 28601
Tel (828) 322-1805 *SIC* 2621 2676

PRINCIPLE BUSINESS ENTERPRISES INC p 1177
20189 Pine Lake Rd, Bowling Green OH 43402
Tel (419) 352-1551 *SIC* 2676 3142

▲ **PROCTER & GAMBLE CO** p 1179
1 Procter And Gamble Plz, Cincinnati OH 45202
Tel (513) 983-1100
SIC 2844 2676 3421 2842 2841

■ **PROCTER & GAMBLE FAR EAST INC** p 1179
1 Procter And Gamble Plz, Cincinnati OH 45202
Tel (513) 983-1100 *SIC* 2842 2844 2676

■ **PROCTER & GAMBLE PAPER PRODUCTS CO** p 1179
1 Procter And Gamble Plz, Cincinnati OH 45202
Tel (513) 983-1100 *SIC* 2676

■ **TAMBRANDS SALES CORP** p 1423
1 Procter And Gamble Plz, Cincinnati OH 45202
Tel (513) 983-1100 *SIC* 2676

TRANZONIC COMPANIES p 1473
26301 Curtiss Wright Pkwy # 200, Richmond Heights OH 44143
Tel (216) 535-4300
SIC 2676 2211 2326 2842 2273 2262

TZ ACQUISITION CORP p 1496
26301 Curtiss Wright Pkwy, Richmond Heights OH 44143
Tel (216) 535-4300
SIC 2676 2211 2326 2842 2262

ORCHIDS PAPER PRODUCTS CO p 1093
4826 Hunt St, Pryor OK 74361
Tel (918) 825-0616 *SIC* 2676

FIRST QUALITY BABY PRODUCTS LLC p 549
97 Locust Rd, Lewistown PA 17044
Tel (717) 247-3516 *SIC* 2676

SCA AMERICAS INC p 1285
2929 Arch St Ste 2600, Philadelphia PA 19104
Tel (610) 499-3700 *SIC* 2621 3086 2676

OMGANICS INC p 1084
1821 Waterston Ave Unit B, Austin TX 78703
Tel (512) 560-3262 *SIC* 2676

▲ **KIMBERLY-CLARK CORP** p 818
351 Phelps Dr, Irving TX 75038
Tel (972) 281-1200 *SIC* 2621 2676

TUFCO LP p 1491
3161 S Ridge Rd, Green Bay WI 54304
Tel (920) 336-0054 *SIC* 5122 5112 2676

HOFFMASTER GROUP INC p 699
2920 N Main St, Oshkosh WI 54901
Tel (920) 235-9330 *SIC* 2676

■ **NUK USA LLC** p 1067
728 Booster Blvd, Reedsburg WI 53959
Tel (608) 524-4343 *SIC* 2676

SIC 2677 Envelopes

■ **CENVEO CORP** p 283
200 First Stamford Pl # 200, Stamford CT 06902
Tel (303) 790-8023 *SIC* 2677 2752 2759

▲ **CENVEO INC** p 283
200 First Stamford Pl # 200, Stamford CT 06902
Tel (203) 595-3000 *SIC* 2677 2679

GNN INVESTOR LLC p 619
133 Peachtree St Ne, Atlanta GA 30303
Tel (404) 652-4000
SIC 2621 2611 2631 2653 5111 2677

■ **PRINTEGRA CORP** p 1177
5040 Highlands Pkwy Se, Smyrna GA 30082
Tel (770) 487-5151
SIC 2761 2782 2677 2678 2679

PAPERCONE CORP p 1112
3200 Fern Valley Rd, Louisville KY 40213
Tel (502) 961-9493 *SIC* 2677

MACKAY MITCHELL ENVELOPE CO LLC p 892
2100 Elm St Se, Minneapolis MN 55414
Tel (612) 331-9311 *SIC* 2677

TAYLOR CORP p 1427
1725 Roe Crest Dr, North Mankato MN 56003
Tel (507) 625-2828
SIC 8742 2752 2677 2759

TENSION ENVELOPE CORP p 1438
819 E 19th St, Kansas City MO 64108
Tel (816) 471-3800 *SIC* 2677

UNITED ENVELOPE LLC p 1508
65 Railroad Ave Ste 1a, Ridgefield NJ 07657
Tel (201) 699-5800 *SIC* 2759 2677

■ **COMMERCIAL ENVELOPE MANUFACTURING CO INC** p 345
900 Grand Blvd, Deer Park NY 11729
Tel (631) 242-2500 *SIC* 2677 5112

POLY-PAK INDUSTRIES INC p 1160
125 Spagnoli Rd, Melville NY 11747
Tel (631) 293-6767 *SIC* 2673 2677

AMPAC HOLDINGS LLC p 86
12025 Tricon Rd, Cincinnati OH 45246
Tel (513) 671-1777
SIC 2673 2677 3081 2674 6719

ENVELOPE 1 INC p 503
41969 State Route 344, Columbiana OH 44408
Tel (330) 482-3900 *SIC* 2677

SRC LIQUIDATION LLC p 1363
600 Albany St, Dayton OH 45417
Tel (937) 221-1000
SIC 2761 2672 2677 2759

TRI-STATE ENVELOPE CORP p 1477
20th Market St, Ashland PA 17921
Tel (570) 875-0433 *SIC* 2677

NEV HOLDINGS LLC p 1028
3211 Internet Blvd # 200, Frisco TX 75034
Tel (972) 731-1100 *SIC* 2677

■ **WESTROCK MWV LLC** p 1603
501 S 5th St, Richmond VA 23219
Tel (804) 444-1000
SIC 2631 2671 2678 2677 2861 2611

WEST COAST PAPER CO p 1594
6703 S 234th St Ste 120, Kent WA 98032
Tel (253) 850-1900
SIC 5085 5169 5084 2677

WESTERN STATES ENVELOPE CO p 1600
4480 N 132nd St, Butler WI 53007
Tel (262) 781-5540 *SIC* 2677

SIC 2678 Stationery Prdts

AVERY PRODUCTS CORP p 137
50 Pointe Dr, Brea CA 92821
Tel (714) 675-8500
SIC 2678 3951 2672 2891

▲ **AVERY DENNISON CORP** p 137
207 N Goode Ave Fl 6, Glendale CA 91203
Tel (626) 304-2000
SIC 2672 3081 3497 2678

■ **PRINTEGRA CORP** p 1177
5040 Highlands Pkwy Se, Smyrna GA 30082
Tel (770) 487-5151
SIC 2761 2782 2677 2678 2679

PRECISION PRESS INC p 1168
2020 Lookout Dr, North Mankato MN 56003
Tel (507) 625-7155 *SIC* 2678 2752

AMERICAN GREETINGS CORP p 73
1 American Rd, Cleveland OH 44144
Tel (216) 252-7300
SIC 2771 2679 2656 2678

CENTURY INTERMEDIATE HOLDING CO p 282
1 American Rd, Cleveland OH 44144
Tel (216) 252-7300
SIC 2771 2679 2656 2678

ROARING SPRING BLANK BOOK CO p 1240
740 Spang St, Roaring Spring PA 16673
Tel (814) 224-2306
SIC 2678 5149 2653 7389

■ **WESTROCK MWV LLC** p 1603
501 S 5th St, Richmond VA 23219
Tel (804) 444-1000
SIC 2631 2671 2678 2677 2861 2611

SIC 2679 Converted Paper Prdts, NEC

GEORGIA-PACIFIC BREWTON LLC p 608
32224 Highway 31, Brewton AL 36426
Tel (251) 867-3622 *SIC* 2611 2679

SCHURMAN FINE PAPERS p 1291
500 Chadbourne Rd, Fairfield CA 94534
Tel (707) 425-8006
SIC 5113 2679 2771 5947

MAFCOTE INC p 895
108 Main St Ste 3, Norwalk CT 06851
Tel (203) 847-8500
SIC 2631 2657 2679 2671

▲ **CENVEO INC** p 283
200 First Stamford Pl # 200, Stamford CT 06902
Tel (203) 595-3000 *SIC* 2677 2679

CARAUSTAR INDUSTRIES INC p 252
5000 Astell Pwdr Sprng Rd, Austell GA 30106
Tel (770) 948-3101
SIC 2655 2631 2679 2656 2652

INTERNATIONAL GREETINGS USA INC p 755
338 Industrial Blvd, Midway GA 31320
Tel (912) 884-9727 *SIC* 2679

■ **PRINTEGRA CORP** p 1177
5040 Highlands Pkwy Se, Smyrna GA 30082
Tel (770) 487-5151
SIC 2761 2782 2677 2678 2679

GATEWAY PACKAGING CO p 594
20 Central Industrial Dr, Granite City IL 62040
Tel (618) 451-0010 *SIC* 2674 2679

▲ **ZEBRA TECHNOLOGIES CORP** p 1641
3 Overlook Pt, Lincolnshire IL 60069
Tel (847) 634-6700
SIC 3577 2672 2679 5045

NORKOL INC p 1048
11650 W Grand Ave, Northlake IL 60164
Tel (708) 531-1000 *SIC* 2679

STEVENS INDUSTRIES INC p 1388
704 W Main St, Teutopolis IL 62467
Tel (217) 540-3100 *SIC* 2531 2679 2511

E K SUCCESS LTD p 466
2240 75th St, Woodridge IL 60517
Tel (630) 963-7100 *SIC* 5199 2679

SCHWARZ PARTNERS LP p 1291
3600 Woodview Trce # 300, Indianapolis IN 46268
Tel (317) 290-1140 *SIC* 2679

STUMP PRINTING CO INC p 1395
101 Carroll Rd, South Whitley IN 46787
Tel (260) 723-5171
SIC 5199 2679 5961 2759

S D WARREN CO p 1262
255 State St Fl 4, Boston MA 02109
Tel (617) 423-7300
SIC 2679 2674 2672 2621

COMPUTYPE INC p 353
2285 County Road C W, Saint Paul MN 55113
Tel (651) 633-0633
SIC 2759 2672 2679 3565 3577 2671

GG MCGUIGGAN CORP p 610
1085 Snelling Ave N, Saint Paul MN 55108
Tel (651) 646-4544 *SIC* 2679 3993 2752

SMYTH COMPANIES LLC p 1335
1085 Snelling Ave N, Saint Paul MN 55108
Tel (651) 646-4544
SIC 2679 2752 3993 7389 5084 7699

■ **NASHUA CORP** p 1008
59 Daniel Webster Hwy A, Merrimack NH 03054
Tel (603) 880-1100
SIC 2672 2754 2679 2621 2782

NEWARK GROUP INC p 1037
20 Jackson Dr, Cranford NJ 07016
Tel (908) 276-4000 *SIC* 2679 2631

ROOSEVELT PAPER CO p 1249
1 Roosevelt Dr, Mount Laurel NJ 08054
Tel (856) 303-4100 *SIC* 2679

TRINITY PACKAGING CORP p 1481
357 Main St, Armonk NY 10504
Tel (914) 273-4111 *SIC* 2673 2679

GRAPHIC CONTROLS ACQUISITION CORP p 631
400 Exchange St, Buffalo NY 14204
Tel (716) 853-7500 *SIC* 2752 2679

GRAPHIC CONTROLS HOLDINGS INC p 631
400 Exchange St, Buffalo NY 14204
Tel (716) 853-7500 *SIC* 2752 2679 6719

■ **AMSCAN HOLDINGS INC** p 87
80 Grasslands Rd Ste 3, Elmsford NY 10523
Tel (914) 345-2020
SIC 5947 2679 3089 3069 6794

▲ **PLUG POWER INC** p 1156
968 Albany Shaker Rd, Latham NY 12110
Tel (518) 782-7700 *SIC* 2679

BURROWS PAPER CORP p 229
501 W Main St Ste 1, Little Falls NY 13365
Tel (315) 823-2300
SIC 2621 2671 2611 2679

FELIX SCHOELLER NORTH AMERICA INC p 537
179 County Route 2a, Pulaski NY 13142
Tel (315) 298-5133 *SIC* 2679

CASCADES TISSUE GROUP - NEW YORK INC p 263
148 Hudson River Rd, Wynantskill NY 12198
Tel (518) 238-1900 *SIC* 2679

NEW NGC INC p 1032
2001 Rexford Rd, Charlotte NC 28211
Tel (704) 365-7300 *SIC* 2679

NGC INDUSTRIES LLC p 1041
2001 Rexford Rd, Charlotte NC 28211
Tel (704) 365-7300 *SIC* 2679

US GREENFIBER LLC p 1532
5500 77 Center Dr Ste 100, Charlotte NC 28217
Tel (704) 379-0640 *SIC* 2679

TRIMACO LLC p 1480
2300 Gateway Centre Blvd # 200, Morrisville NC 27560
Tel (919) 674-3476
SIC 2851 2621 2672 2679 2394

3A COMPOSITES USA INC p 2
3480 Taylorsville Hwy, Statesville NC 28625
Tel (704) 872-8974
SIC 3334 2679 3081 3449

ATLANTIC CORP OF WILMINGTON INC p 126
806 N 23rd St, Wilmington NC 28405
Tel (910) 343-0624 *SIC* 5113 2621 2679

▲ **MULTI-COLOR CORP** p 999
4053 Clough Woods Dr, Batavia OH 45103
Tel (513) 381-1480 *SIC* 2759 2679 2672

FORMICA CORP p 567
10155 Reading Rd, Cincinnati OH 45241
Tel (513) 786-3400 *SIC* 2541 2679

AMERICAN GREETINGS CORP p 73
1 American Rd, Cleveland OH 44144
Tel (216) 252-7300
SIC 2771 2679 2656 2678

CENTURY INTERMEDIATE HOLDING CO p 282
1 American Rd, Cleveland OH 44144
Tel (216) 252-7300
SIC 2771 2679 2656 2678

MILLCRAFT GROUP LLC p 970
6800 Grant Ave, Cleveland OH 44105
Tel (216) 441-5500 *SIC* 5111 5113 2679

SHORE TO SHORE INC p 1318
8170 Washington Vlg Dr, Dayton OH 45458
Tel (937) 866-1908 *SIC* 2679 2241

PMCO LLC p 1157
9220 Glades Dr, West Chester OH 45011
Tel (513) 825-7626 *SIC* 2679

NATIONAL LABEL CO p 1014
2025 Joshua Rd, Lafayette Hill PA 19444
Tel (610) 825-3250
SIC 2672 2679 2759 2671

UNIQUE INDUSTRIES INC p 1505
4750 League Island Blvd, Philadelphia PA 19112
Tel (215) 336-4300 *SIC* 2679

▲ **CSS INDUSTRIES INC** p 398
450 Plymouth Rd Ste 300, Plymouth Meeting PA 19462
Tel (610) 729-3959
SIC 2771 2679 2389 2396 2621 2865

BEISTLE CO p 169
1 Beistle Plz, Shippensburg PA 17257
Tel (717) 532-2131
SIC 2679 3993 2675 2657 2631 2621

TEKNI-PLEX INC p 1433
460 E Swedesford Rd # 3000, Wayne PA 19087
Tel (484) 690-1520
SIC 2679 3462 3052 2672

CARAUSTAR INDUSTRIAL AND CONSUMER PRODUCTS GROUP INC p 252
2031 Carolina Place Dr, Fort Mill SC 29708
Tel (803) 548-5100 *SIC* 2655 2671 2679

■ **SONOCO PROTECTIVE SOLUTIONS INC** p 1340
1 N 2nd St, Hartsville SC 29550
Tel (843) 383-7000 *SIC* 3086 2679

SOUTHERN STATES PACKAGING CO p 1350
180 Brooks Blvd, Spartanburg SC 29307
Tel (864) 579-3911 *SIC* 2679

INLAND PAPERBOARD AND PACKAGING INC p 743
1300 S Mo Pac Expy Fl 3, Austin TX 78746
Tel (512) 234-5001
SIC 2653 2631 3086 2679 2657

▲ **IMPRESO INC** p 735
652 Southwestern Blvd, Coppell TX 75019
Tel (972) 462-0100 *SIC* 2761 2679 2086

HFS HOLDING CORP p 689
8900 Ambassador Row, Dallas TX 75247
Tel (214) 634-8600 *SIC* 2679 5112 2675

MAGNETIC TICKET & LABEL CORP p 896
8719 Diplomacy Row, Dallas TX 75247
Tel (214) 634-8600 *SIC* 2679

GM NAMEPLATE INC p 618
2040 15th Ave W, Seattle WA 98119
Tel (206) 284-2200 *SIC* 3479 2679 3679

PACON CORP p 1107
2525 N Casaloma Dr, Appleton WI 54913
Tel (920) 830-5050 *SIC* 2679

PROGRESSIVE CONVERTING INC p 1181
2430 E Glendale Ave, Appleton WI 54911
Tel (800) 637-7310 *SIC* 2679

TUFCO HOLDINGS LLC p 1490
3161 S Ridge Rd, Green Bay WI 54304
Tel (920) 336-0054 *SIC* 2679

TUFCO TECHNOLOGIES INC p 1491
3161 S Ridge Rd, Green Bay WI 54304
Tel (920) 336-0054 *SIC* 2679

W/S PACKAGING GROUP INC p 1569
2571 S Hemlock Rd, Green Bay WI 54229
Tel (920) 866-6300 *SIC* 2679 2752

MENASHA CORP p 943
1645 Bergstrom Rd, Neenah WI 54956
Tel (920) 751-1000
SIC 2631 2653 2679 3086 0811

■ **NEENAH PAPER FR LLC** p 1024
1376 Kimberly Dr, Neenah WI 54956
Tel (800) 558-8327 *SIC* 2679 2621

ROCKLINE INDUSTRIES INC p 1245
4343 S Taylor Dr, Sheboygan WI 53081
Tel (800) 558-7790 *SIC* 2679 2297

SIC 2711 Newspapers: Publishing & Printing

COMMUNITY NEWSPAPER HOLDINGS INC p 349
445 Dexter Ave Ste 7000, Montgomery AL 36104
Tel (334) 293-5800 *SIC* 2711 4833

BOONE NEWSPAPERS INC p 200
1060 Fairfax Park Ste B, Tuscaloosa AL 35406
Tel (205) 330-4100 *SIC* 2711

CALISTA CORP p 242
5015 Bus Pk Blvd Ste 3000, Anchorage AK 99503
Tel (907) 279-5516 *SIC* 6512 7363 2711

■ **PHOENIX NEWSPAPERS INC** p 1145
200 E Van Buren St, Phoenix AZ 85004
Tel (602) 444-8000 *SIC* 2711

VILLAGE VOICE MEDIA HOLDINGS LLC p 1557
1201 E Jefferson St, Phoenix AZ 85034
Tel (602) 271-0040 *SIC* 2711

ARKANSAS DEMOCRAT-GAZETTE INC p 109
121 E Capitol Ave, Little Rock AR 72201
Tel (501) 378-3400 *SIC* 2711

WEHCO MEDIA INC p 1587
115 E Capitol Ave, Little Rock AR 72201
Tel (501) 378-3529 *SIC* 2711 4841

WEHCO NEWSPAPERS INC p 1587
115 E Capital & Scott Sts, Little Rock AR 72201
Tel (501) 378-3400 *SIC* 2711

NATIONAL HOT ROD ASSOCIATION p 1013
2035 E Financial Way, Glendora CA 91741
Tel (626) 914-4761 *SIC* 7948 2711 2741

ALAMEDA NEWSPAPERS INC p 44
22533 Foothill Blvd, Hayward CA 94541
Tel (510) 783-6111 *SIC* 2711

COPLEY PRESS INC p 368
7776 Ivanhoe Ave, La Jolla CA 92037
Tel (858) 454-0411 *SIC* 7383 2711 7011

DATA ANALYSIS INC p 413
12655 Beatrice St, Los Angeles CA 90066
Tel (310) 448-6800 *SIC* 6211 2711 7374

■ LOS ANGELES TIMES COMMUNICATIONS LLC p 879
202 W 1st St Ste 500, Los Angeles CA 90012
Tel (213) 237-3700 *SIC* 2711

CALIFORNIA NEWSPAPERS LIMITED PARTNERSHIP p 241
605 E Huntington Dr # 100, Monrovia CA 91016
Tel (626) 962-8811 *SIC* 2711

PRESS-ENTERPRISE CO p 1172
3450 14th St, Riverside CA 92501
Tel (951) 684-1200 *SIC* 2711

▲ MCCLATCHY CO p 926
2100 Q St, Sacramento CA 95816
Tel (916) 321-1846 *SIC* 2711

■ MCCLATCHY NEWSPAPERS INC p 926
2100 Q St, Sacramento CA 95816
Tel (916) 321-1000 *SIC* 2711 2759 7375

BREHM COMMUNICATIONS INC p 209
16644 W Bernardo Dr # 300, San Diego CA 92127
Tel (858) 451-6200 *SIC* 2752 2711

■ MLIM LLC p 979
350 Camino De La Reina, San Diego CA 92108
Tel (619) 299-3131 *SIC* 2711

■ SAN DIEGO UNION-TRIBUNE LLC p 1276
600 B St, San Diego CA 92101
Tel (619) 299-3131 *SIC* 2711 7313 7383

HEARST COMMUNICATIONS INC p 678
901 Mission St, San Francisco CA 94103
Tel (415) 777-1111 *SIC* 2711

SAN JOSE MERCURY-NEWS LLC p 1277
4 N 2nd St Fl 8, San Jose CA 95113
Tel (408) 920-5000 *SIC* 2711

2100 FREEDOM INC p 1
625 N Grand Ave, Santa Ana CA 92701
Tel (714) 796-7000
SIC 2711 2721 7313 2741 5963 4813

FREEDOM COMMUNICATIONS HOLDINGS INC p 576
625 N Grand Ave, Santa Ana CA 92701
Tel (714) 796-7000
SIC 6719 2711 4813 2721

FREEDOM COMMUNICATIONS INC p 576
625 N Grand Ave, Santa Ana CA 92701
Tel (714) 796-7000
SIC 2711 2721 7313 2741 5963

CALIFORNIA NEWSPAPER LIMITED PARTNERSHIP p 241
194 Ford Rd, Ukiah CA 95482
Tel (707) 467-9111 *SIC* 2711

CONTRA COSTA NEWSPAPERS INC p 364
175 Lennon Ln Ste 100, Walnut Creek CA 94598
Tel (925) 935-2525 *SIC* 2711

PRAIRIE MOUNTAIN PUBLISHING CO LLC p 1167
2500 55th St Ste 210, Boulder CO 80301
Tel (303) 442-1202 *SIC* 2711

ANSCHUTZ CORP p 93
555 17th St Ste 2400, Denver CO 80202
Tel (303) 298-1000 *SIC* 2711 1382 7941

DENVER POST CORP p 429
1560 Broadway Fl 4, Denver CO 80202
Tel (303) 321-7012 *SIC* 2711

DENVER POST LLC p 429
101 W Colfax Ave, Denver CO 80202
Tel (303) 892-5000 *SIC* 2711

MEDIANEWS GROUP INC p 936
101 W Colfax Ave Ste 1100, Denver CO 80202
Tel (303) 954-6360 *SIC* 2711

■ HARTFORD COURANT CO LLC p 665
285 Broad St, Hartford CT 06115
Tel (860) 241-6200 *SIC* 2711

■ THOMSON REUTERS US LLC p 1450
1 Station Pl Ste 6, Stamford CT 06902
Tel (203) 539-8000 *SIC* 2711

WILMINGTON TRUST SP SERVICES p 1613
1105 N Market St Ste 1300, Wilmington DE 19801
Tel (302) 427-7650 *SIC* 2711

NASH HOLDINGS LLC p 1008
1403 Hamlin St Ne, Washington DC 20017
Tel (202) 334-6727 *SIC* 2711 2721

NEWS WORLD COMMUNICATIONS INC p 1039
3600 New York Ave Ne, Washington DC 20002
Tel (202) 636-3000 *SIC* 2711

POST COMMUNITY MEDIA LLC p 1163
1301 K St Nw, Washington DC 20071
Tel (301) 670-2565 *SIC* 2711 2732 2721

WP CO LLC p 1627
1301 K St Nw, Washington DC 20071
Tel (202) 334-6242 *SIC* 2721 2711

AMERICAN MEDIA INC p 75
301 Yamato Rd Ste 4200, Boca Raton FL 33431
Tel (561) 997-7733 *SIC* 2711 2741

AMERICAN MEDIA OPERATIONS INC p 75
1000 American Media Way, Boca Raton FL 33464
Tel (561) 997-7733 *SIC* 2711 2741

COLORGRAPHX INC p 339
4721 110th Ave N, Clearwater FL 33762
Tel (727) 572-6364 *SIC* 2711

■ HALIFAX MEDIA GROUP LLC p 654
2339 Beville Rd, Daytona Beach FL 32119
Tel (386) 265-6700 *SIC* 2711

HALIFAX MEDIA HOLDINGS LLC p 654
901 6th St, Daytona Beach FL 32117
Tel (386) 681-2404 *SIC* 2711 2791

■ NEW YORK TIMES REGIONAL NEWSPAPER GROUP p 1036
2339 Beville Rd, Daytona Beach FL 32119
Tel (212) 556-4673 *SIC* 2711

NEWS-JOURNAL CORP p 1039
901 6th St, Daytona Beach FL 32117
Tel (386) 252-1511 *SIC* 2711

■ SUN-SENTINEL CO INC p 1401
500 E Broward Blvd # 800, Fort Lauderdale FL 33394
Tel (954) 356-4000 *SIC* 2711

GRAHAM COMPANIES p 628
6843 Main St, Miami Lakes FL 33014
Tel (305) 821-1130
SIC 1531 7011 0212 6552 6512 2711

■ GREATER MEDIA INC p 635
3033 Riviera Dr Ste 200, Naples FL 34103
Tel (239) 263-5000 *SIC* 2711 8999 4832

■ SENTINEL COMMUNICATIONS NEWS VENTURES INC p 1305
633 N Orange Ave, Orlando FL 32801
Tel (407) 420-5000 *SIC* 2711

TAMPA BAY SPORTS ENTERTAINMENT LLC p 1423
490 1st Ave S, Saint Petersburg FL 33701
Tel (727) 893-8111 *SIC* 2711

TIMES PUBLISHING CO p 1454
490 1st Ave S, Saint Petersburg FL 33701
Tel (727) 893-8111 *SIC* 2711 2721

BUSINESS JOURNAL PUBLICATIONS INC p 229
4350 W Cypress St Ste 800, Tampa FL 33607
Tel (813) 342-2472 *SIC* 2711

TAMPA MEDIA GROUP INC p 1423
202 S Parker St, Tampa FL 33606
Tel (813) 259-7711 *SIC* 2711

TRIBUNE CO p 1479
202 S Parker St, Tampa FL 33606
Tel (813) 259-7711 *SIC* 2711

PALM BEACH NEWSPAPERS INC p 1109
2751 S Dixie Hwy, West Palm Beach FL 33405
Tel (561) 820-4100 *SIC* 2711 2721

COX ENTERPRISES INC p 386
6205 Pachtree Dunwoody Rd, Atlanta GA 30328
Tel (678) 645-0000
SIC 4841 4813 2711 4833 7389 4832

COX NEWSPAPERS INC p 386
6205 Peachtree Dunwoody, Atlanta GA 30328
Tel (678) 645-0000 *SIC* 2711

COX TEXAS PUBLICATIONS INC p 386
6205 Peachtree Dunwoody Rd, Atlanta GA 30328
Tel (404) 843-5000 *SIC* 2711

GEORGIA MUNICIPAL ASSOCIATION INC p 607
201 Pryor St Sw, Atlanta GA 30303
Tel (404) 688-0472 *SIC* 2711 2741 8611

MORRIS COMMUNICATIONS CO LLC p 990
725 Broad St, Augusta GA 30901
Tel (706) 724-0851
SIC 2711 5199 2721 2731

MORRIS PUBLISHING GROUP LLC p 990
725 Broad St, Augusta GA 30901
Tel (706) 724-0851 *SIC* 2711

MPG NEWSPAPER HOLDING LLC p 995
725 Broad St, Augusta GA 30901
Tel (706) 724-0851 *SIC* 2711

QUESTO INC p 1199
725 Broad St, Augusta GA 30901
Tel (706) 724-0851 *SIC* 2711

SHIVERS TRADING & OPERATING CO p 1317
725 Broad St, Augusta GA 30901
Tel (706) 724-0851
SIC 2711 2721 2731 4832 7312 6512

SOUTHEASTERN NEWSPAPERS CO LLC p 1346
725 Broad St, Augusta GA 30901
Tel (706) 722-0011 *SIC* 2711

OAHU PUBLICATIONS INC p 1070
500 Ala Moana Blvd, Honolulu HI 96813
Tel (808) 529-4700 *SIC* 2711

HAGADONE INVESTMENT CO INC p 652
111 S 1st St, Coeur D Alene ID 83814
Tel (208) 667-3431 *SIC* 2711 7011

PADDOCK PUBLICATIONS INC p 1107
155 E Algonquin Rd, Arlington Heights IL 60005
Tel (847) 427-4300 *SIC* 2711

BELAIR HD STUDIOS LLC p 169
2233 S Throop St, Chicago IL 60608
Tel (312) 254-5188 *SIC* 7335 2711

CHICAGO SUN-TIMES FEATURES INC p 297
350 N Orleans St Fl 10, Chicago IL 60654
Tel (312) 321-3000 *SIC* 2711 2752

■ CHICAGO TRIBUNE CO p 298
435 N Michigan Ave # 200, Chicago IL 60611
Tel (312) 222-3232
SIC 2711 7383 7389 7331

CNLC-STC INC p 330
350 N Orleans St, Chicago IL 60654
Tel (312) 321-3000 *SIC* 2711

SUN-TIMES MEDIA GROUP INC p 1401
350 N Orleans St Fl 10, Chicago IL 60654
Tel (312) 321-2299 *SIC* 2711

SUN-TIMES MEDIA HOLDINGS LLC p 1401
350 N Orleans St Fl 10, Chicago IL 60654
Tel (312) 321-2299 *SIC* 2711

■ TRIBUNE PUBLISHING CO LLC p 1479
435 N Michigan Ave Fl 2, Chicago IL 60611
Tel (312) 222-9100 *SIC* 2711

▲ TRONC INC p 1484
435 N Michigan Ave, Chicago IL 60611
Tel (312) 222-9100 *SIC* 2711

WRAPPORTS LLC p 1627
350 N Orleans St 10thf, Chicago IL 60654
Tel (312) 321-3000 *SIC* 7379 2711

SMALL NEWSPAPER GROUP p 1332
8 Dearborn Sq, Kankakee IL 60901
Tel (815) 937-3300 *SIC* 2711 2791 2752

MOLINE DISPATCH PUBLISHING CO p 983
1720 5th Ave, Moline IL 61265
Tel (309) 764-4344 *SIC* 2711 2752

QUINCY MEDIA INC p 1200
130 S 5th St, Quincy IL 62301
Tel (217) 223-5100
SIC 2711 4833 2752 2741

NEWS MEDIA CORP p 1039
211 E Il Route 38, Rochelle IL 61068
Tel (815) 562-2061 *SIC* 2711

■ NEWS PUBLISHING CO INC p 1039
600 W Main St, Fort Wayne IN 46802
Tel (260) 461-8444 *SIC* 2711

■ INDIANA NEWSPAPERS LLC p 738
130 S Meridian St, Indianapolis IN 46225
Tel (317) 444-4000 *SIC* 2711 2752

■ SCHURZ COMMUNICATIONS INC p 1291
1301 E Douglas Rd, Mishawaka IN 46545
Tel (574) 247-7237 *SIC* 4833 2711

GAZETTE CO p 594
500 3rd Ave Se, Cedar Rapids IA 52401
Tel (319) 398-8211 *SIC* 2711 2752 4833

▲ LEE ENTERPRISES INC p 851
201 N Harrison St Ste 600, Davenport IA 52801
Tel (563) 383-2100 *SIC* 2711

■ LEE PUBLICATIONS INC p 851
201 N Harrison St Ste 600, Davenport IA 52801
Tel (563) 383-2100 *SIC* 2711

WOODWARD COMMUNICATIONS INC p 1623
801 Bluff St, Dubuque IA 52001
Tel (563) 588-5611
SIC 2711 2741 4832 2752 7311

FARM BUREAU PROPERTY & CASUALTY INSURANCE CO p 528
5400 University Ave, West Des Moines IA 50266
Tel (515) 225-5400 *SIC* 6411 2711 6211

ARCHDIOCESE OF KANSAS CITY IN KANSAS p 105
12615 Parallel Pkwy, Kansas City KS 66109
Tel (913) 721-1570
SIC 8661 8211 8222 2711

■ COURIER-JOURNAL INC p 383
525 W Broadway, Louisville KY 40202
Tel (502) 582-4011 *SIC* 2711

PAXTON MEDIA GROUP LLC p 1122
100 Television Ln, Paducah KY 42003
Tel (270) 575-8630 *SIC* 2711 4833

LANDMARK COMMUNITY NEWSPAPERS LLC p 842
601 Taylorsville Rd, Shelbyville KY 40065
Tel (502) 633-4334 *SIC* 2711 2759

LANDMARK COMMUNITY NEWSPAPERS OF KENTUCKY LLC p 842
601 Taylorsville Rd, Shelbyville KY 40065
Tel (502) 633-4334 *SIC* 2711 2752

CAPITAL CITY PRESS LLC p 249
10705 Reiger Rd, Baton Rouge LA 70809
Tel (225) 383-1111 *SIC* 2711 2752

MTM OLDCO INC p 998
1 City Ctr Fl 5, Portland ME 04101
Tel (207) 791-6650 *SIC* 2711

■ BALTIMORE SUN CO p 149
501 N Calvert St, Baltimore MD 21278
Tel (410) 539-7700 *SIC* 2711

BOSTON GLOBE LLC p 203
135 William T Mrrssey Blvd, Boston MA 02125
Tel (617) 929-2684 *SIC* 2711

HERALD MEDIA HOLDINGS INC p 685
70 Fargo St Ste 600, Boston MA 02210
Tel (617) 423-4545 *SIC* 2711

NE MEDIA GROUP INC p 1022
135 William T Mrrssey Blvd, Boston MA 02125
Tel (617) 929-2000 *SIC* 2711

■ GATEHOUSE MEDIA MASSACHUSETTS I INC p 593
75 Sylvan St Ste C105, Danvers MA 01923
Tel (585) 598-0030 *SIC* 2711

■ ENTERPRISE PUBLISHING CO LLC p 502
10 Purchase St, Fall River MA 02720
Tel (585) 598-0030 *SIC* 2711

EAGLE-TRIBUNE PUBLISHING CO p 468
100 Turnpike St, North Andover MA 01845
Tel (978) 946-2000 *SIC* 2711

■ ENTERPRISE NEWSMEDIA LLC p 502
400 Crown Colony Dr, Quincy MA 02169
Tel (585) 598-0030 *SIC* 2711

REPUBLICAN CO p 1226
1860 Main St, Springfield MA 01103
Tel (413) 788-1000 *SIC* 2711

21ST CENTURY NEWSPAPERS INC p 2
19176 Hall Rd Ste 200, Clinton Township MI 48038
Tel (586) 469-4510 *SIC* 2711

CRAIN COMMUNICATIONS INC p 388
1155 Gratiot Ave, Detroit MI 48207
Tel (313) 446-6000 *SIC* 2721 2711

■ DETROIT NEWSPAPER PARTNERSHIP LP p 433
160 W Fort St, Detroit MI 48226
Tel (313) 222-2300 *SIC* 2711

DOLAN LLC p 447
222 S 9th St Ste 2300, Minneapolis MN 55402
Tel (612) 317-9420
SIC 7375 2741 2711 2752

ECM PUBLISHERS INC p 475
4095 Coon Rapids Blvd Nw, Minneapolis MN 55433
Tel (763) 712-2400
SIC 2711 2741 7319 2789 2752

STAR TRIBUNE MEDIA CO LLC p 1378
650 3rd Ave S Ste 1300, Minneapolis MN 55488
Tel (612) 673-4000 *SIC* 2711

■ CYPRESS MEDIA LLC p 405
1729 Grand Blvd, Kansas City MO 64108
Tel (816) 234-4141 *SIC* 2711

NEWS-PRESS & GAZETTE CO INC p 1039
825 Edmond St, Saint Joseph MO 64501
Tel (816) 271-8500 *SIC* 2711

PULITZER INC p 1191
900 N Tucker Blvd, Saint Louis MO 63101
Tel (314) 340-8000 *SIC* 2711 4833 4832

■ PULITZER INC p 1191
900 N Tucker Blvd, Saint Louis MO 63101
Tel (314) 340-8000 *SIC* 2711

■ ST LOUIS POST-DISPATCH LLC p 1369
900 N Tucker Blvd, Saint Louis MO 63101
Tel (314) 340-8000 *SIC* 2711

■ BH MEDIA GROUP HOLDINGS INC p 180
Omaha World Herald Bldg 1, Omaha NE 68102
Tel (402) 444-1000 *SIC* 2711 7379

■ BH MEDIA GROUP INC p 180
Omaha Wrld Hrld Bldg 1314, Omaha NE 68102
Tel (402) 444-1000 *SIC* 2711 7379

■ OMAHA WORLD-HERALD CO p 1084
1314 Douglas St Ste 700, Omaha NE 68102
Tel (402) 444-1000 *SIC* 2711 7331

SWIFT COMMUNICATIONS INC p 1412
580 Mallory Way, Carson City NV 89701
Tel (775) 850-7676 *SIC* 2711

STEPHENS MEDIA LLC p 1386
1111 W Bonanza Rd, Las Vegas NV 89106
Tel (702) 383-0211 *SIC* 2711

DIOCESE OF CAMDEN NEW JERSEY p 440
631 Market St, Camden NJ 08102
Tel (856) 756-7900 *SIC* 2711 8661

BERGEN RECORD CORP p 174
150 River St, Hackensack NJ 07601
Tel (201) 646-4000 *SIC* 2711

MACROMEDIA INC p 893
150 River St, Hackensack NJ 07601
Tel (201) 646-4000 *SIC* 2711 2721

■ ASBURY PARK PRESS INC p 115
3600 Route 66, Neptune NJ 07753
Tel (732) 922-6000 *SIC* 2711 2752

NEWARK MORNING LEDGER CO p 1037
1 Gateway Ctr Ste 1100, Newark NJ 07102
Tel (973) 392-4141 *SIC* 2711

NEW JERSEY HERALD p 1031
2 Spring St, Newton NJ 07860
Tel (973) 383-1500 *SIC* 2711

NORTH JERSEY MEDIA GROUP INC p 1052
1 Garret Mountain Plz # 201, Woodland Park NJ 07424
Tel (201) 646-4000 *SIC* 2711 4813

IMPREMEDIA LLC p 735
1 Metrotech Ctr Fl 18, Brooklyn NY 11201
Tel (212) 807-4785 *SIC* 2711

US HISPANIC MEDIA INC p 1532
1 Metrotech Ctr Fl 18, Brooklyn NY 11201
Tel (212) 885-8000 *SIC* 2711

NEWSDAY LLC p 1039
235 Pinelawn Rd, Melville NY 11747
Tel (631) 843-4050 *SIC* 2711

■ LOCAL MEDIA GROUP INC p 873
40 Mulberry St, Middletown NY 10940
Tel (845) 341-1100 *SIC* 2711 7313

■ ABC INC p 10
77 W 66th St Rm 100, New York NY 10023
Tel (212) 456-7777
SIC 4833 4832 7812 6794 2711 2721

ALM MEDIA HOLDINGS INC p 59
120 Broadway Fl 5, New York NY 10271
Tel (212) 457-9400
SIC 2721 2711 2741 2731 7389

ALM MEDIA LLC p 59
120 Broadway Fl 5, New York NY 10271
Tel (212) 457-9400
SIC 2721 2711 2741 2731 7389

DAILY NEWS LP p 408
4 New York Plz Fl 6, New York NY 10004
Tel (212) 210-2100 *SIC* 2711

DIGITAL FIRST MEDIA LLC p 439
20 W 33rd St Fl 7, New York NY 10001
Tel (212) 257-7212 *SIC* 2711

■ DOW JONES & CO INC p 453
1211 Avenue Of The Americ, New York NY 10036
Tel (609) 627-2999 *SIC* 2711 2721

EVERCORE PARTNERS SERVICES EAST LLC p 514
55 E 52nd St, New York NY 10055
Tel (212) 857-3100 *SIC* 2711

FAIRCHILD PUBLICATIONS INC p 524
475 5th Ave, New York NY 10017
Tel (212) 630-4000 *SIC* 2721 2711 2731

HEARST CORP p 678
300 W 57th St Fl 42, New York NY 10019
Tel (212) 649-2000
SIC 2721 2731 2711 4832 4833 7383

JOURNAL REGISTER CO p 794
5 Hanover Sq Fl 25, New York NY 10004
Tel (212) 257-7212 *SIC* 2711

LEBHAR-FRIEDMAN INC p 850
150 W 30th St Fl 19, New York NY 10001
Tel (212) 756-5000 *SIC* 2721 2711

▲ NEW MEDIA INVESTMENT GROUP INC p 1032
1345 Avenue Of The Americ, New York NY 10105
Tel (212) 479-3160 *SIC* 2711 7373

▲ NEW YORK TIMES CO p 1036
620 8th Ave, New York NY 10018
Tel (212) 556-1234
SIC 2711 4832 4833 7383 7375

▲ NEWS CORP p 1039
1211 Ave Of The Americas, New York NY 10036
Tel (212) 416-3400 *SIC* 2711 2731 7375

■ NYP HOLDINGS INC p 1069
1211 Avenue Of The Amer, New York NY 10036
Tel (212) 997-9272 *SIC* 2711

PEARSON INC p 1126
1330 Hudson St, New York NY 10013
Tel (212) 641-2400 *SIC* 2711 2731

UBM INC p 1498
2 Penn Plz, New York NY 10121
Tel (212) 600-3000
SIC 2721 2711 8732 2741

UBM LLC p 1498
2 Penn Plz Fl 15, New York NY 10121
Tel (516) 562-5085
SIC 2721 2711 7319 7389

■ GATEHOUSE MEDIA LLC p 593
175 Sullys Trl Ste 300, Pittsford NY 14534
Tel (585) 598-0030 *SIC* 2711 7311 2759

HERALD NEWSPAPERS CO INC p 685
220 S Warren St, Syracuse NY 13202
Tel (315) 470-0011 *SIC* 2711

PEARSON LONGMAN LLC p 1126
10 Bank St Ste 1030, White Plains NY 10606
Tel (212) 641-2400 *SIC* 2731 2711

AMERICAN CITY BUSINESS JOURNALS INC p 70
120 W Morehead St Ste 400, Charlotte NC 28202
Tel (704) 973-1000 *SIC* 2711 2721

■ CHARLOTTE OBSERVER PUBLISHING CO p 290
550 S Caldwell St, Charlotte NC 28202
Tel (704) 358-5000 *SIC* 2711 4813

CIVITAS MEDIA LLC p 320
130 Harbour Place Dr # 300, Davidson NC 28036
Tel (704) 897-6020 *SIC* 2711

FAYETTEVILLE PUBLISHING CO INC p 532
458 Whitfield St, Fayetteville NC 28306
Tel (910) 486-2741
SIC 2711 2791 2759 2752

■ NEWS AND OBSERVER PUBLISHING CO p 1039
215 S Mcdowell St, Raleigh NC 27601
Tel (919) 829-4500
SIC 2711 2741 2721 2752

FORUM COMMUNICATIONS CO p 570
101 5th St N, Fargo ND 58102
Tel (701) 235-7311 *SIC* 2711 4833 4832

▲ E W SCRIPPS CO p 467
312 Walnut St Ste 2800, Cincinnati OH 45202
Tel (513) 977-3000
SIC 4841 2711 4833 7375

PLAIN DEALER PUBLISHING CO p 1153
4800 Tiedeman Rd, Cleveland OH 44144
Tel (216) 999-5000 *SIC* 2711

COX MEDIA GROUP OHIO INC p 386
1611 S Main St, Dayton OH 45409
Tel (937) 225-2000 *SIC* 2711

OCM LLC p 1074
4500 Lyons Rd, Miamisburg OH 45342
Tel (937) 247-2700 *SIC* 2711

SANDUSKY NEWSPAPERS INC p 1278
314 W Market St, Sandusky OH 44870
Tel (419) 625-5500 *SIC* 4832 2711 2752

BLOCK COMMUNICATIONS INC p 189
405 Madison Ave Ste 2100, Toledo OH 43604
Tel (419) 724-6212 *SIC* 4841 4833 2711

OKLAHOMA PUBLISHING CO OF OKLAHOMA p 1080
9000 N Brdwy, Oklahoma City OK 73114
Tel (405) 475-3311
SIC 2711 1311 6512 7375 2752

■ BH MEDIA GROUP HOLDINGS INC p 180
315 S Boulder Ave, Tulsa OK 74103
Tel (918) 583-2161 *SIC* 2711

OREGONIAN PUBLISHING CO LLC p 1094
1500 Sw 1st Ave Ste 500, Portland OR 97201
Tel (503) 221-8327 *SIC* 2711

■ MORNING CALL LLC p 989
101 N 6th St, Allentown PA 18101
Tel (610) 820-6500 *SIC* 2752 2711

CALKINS MEDIA INC p 242
333 N Broad St, Doylestown PA 18901
Tel (215) 949-4000 *SIC* 2711

NEWSPAPER HOLDING INC p 1039
425 Locust St, Johnstown PA 15901
Tel (814) 532-5102 *SIC* 2711

LNP MEDIA GROUP INC p 872
8 W King St, Lancaster PA 17603
Tel (717) 291-8811 *SIC* 2711 2752

COURIER TIMES INC p 383
8400 Bristol Pike, Levittown PA 19057
Tel (215) 949-4011 *SIC* 2711

PENCOR SERVICES INC p 1128
613 3rd Street Palmerton, Palmerton PA 18071
Tel (610) 826-2115
SIC 2711 7371 4813 4841

PHILADELPHIA MEDIA NETWORK PBC p 1143
801 Market St Ste 300, Philadelphia PA 19107
Tel (215) 854-2000 *SIC* 2711

PHILDELPHIA-NEWSPAPERS-LLC p 1143
801 Market St Ste 300, Philadelphia PA 19107
Tel (215) 854-2000 *SIC* 2711

ABARTA INC p 9
200 Alpha Dr, Pittsburgh PA 15238
Tel (412) 963-6226
SIC 2086 2711 2721 5149 1382 5812

TRIBUNE REVIEW PUBLISHING CO p 1479
503 Marti St D L Clark B, Pittsburgh PA 15212
Tel (724) 834-1151 *SIC* 2711

READING EAGLE CO p 1213
345 Penn St, Reading PA 19601
Tel (610) 371-5000 *SIC* 2711 2752

CATHOLIC SOCIAL SERVICES OF DIOCESE OF SCRANTON INC p 267
516 Fig St, Scranton PA 18505
Tel (570) 207-2283
SIC 8661 2711 8211 8322 6553

SCRANTON TIMES L P p 1294
149 Penn Ave Ste 1, Scranton PA 18503
Tel (570) 348-9100 *SIC* 2711 4832

GFR MEDIA LLC p 610
50 Carr 165 Ste 1, Guaynabo PR 00968
Tel (787) 641-8000 *SIC* 4789 2711 5963

CORDILLERA COMMUNICATIONS LLC p 369
134 Columbus St, Charleston SC 29403
Tel (843) 577-7111 *SIC* 2711 3663

EPI GROUP LLC p 505
134 Columbus St, Charleston SC 29403
Tel (843) 577-7111 *SIC* 2711

■ KNOXVILLE NEWS-SENTINEL CO p 825
2332 News Sentinel Dr, Knoxville TN 37921
Tel (865) 523-3131 *SIC* 2711

COX TEXAS NEWSPAPERS LP p 386
305 S Congress Ave, Austin TX 78704
Tel (512) 445-3500 *SIC* 2711

▲ A H BELO CORP p 5
508 Young St, Dallas TX 75202
Tel (214) 977-8222 *SIC* 2711 7313

■ DMN INC p 446
508 Young St, Dallas TX 75202
Tel (214) 977-8222 *SIC* 2711

■ STAR-TELEGRAM OPERATING LTD p 1378
808 Throckmorton St, Fort Worth TX 76102
Tel (817) 390-7400 *SIC* 2711

ASP WESTWARD LP p 118
523 N Sam Houston Pkwy E # 600, Houston TX 77060
Tel (713) 256-0953 *SIC* 2711

HEARST NEWSPAPERS LLC p 678
4747 Southwest Fwy, Houston TX 77027
Tel (713) 220-7171 *SIC* 2711

KING RANCH INC p 820
3 Riverway Ste 1600, Houston TX 77056
Tel (832) 681-5700
SIC 0212 2711 5083 5948

LA VOZ PUBLISHING CORP p 836
4747 Southwest Fwy, Houston TX 77027
Tel (713) 664-4404 *SIC* 2711

SOUTHERN NEWSPAPERS INC p 1349
5701 Woodway Dr Ste 131, Houston TX 77057
Tel (713) 266-5481 *SIC* 2711

AIM MEDIA TEXAS OPERATING LLC p 38
1400 E Nolana Ave, Mcallen TX 78504
Tel (956) 683-4000 *SIC* 2711 4899

BUREAU OF NATIONAL AFFAIRS INC p 226
1801 S Bell St Ste Cn110, Arlington VA 22202
Tel (703) 341-3000 *SIC* 2711 2721

ONE UP ENTERPRISES INC p 1086
7777 Lsburg Pike Ste 302s, Falls Church VA 22043
Tel (703) 448-7333
SIC 2731 2711 2092 6531

▲ GANNETT CO INC p 590
7950 Jones Branch Dr, Mc Lean VA 22102
Tel (703) 854-6000 *SIC* 2711 7375

■ GANNETT RIVER STATES PUBLISHING CORP p 591
7950 Jones Branch Dr, Mc Lean VA 22102
Tel (703) 284-6000 *SIC* 2711 2741

■ GANNETT SATELLITE INFORMATION NETWORK LLC p 591
7950 Jones Branch Dr, Mc Lean VA 22102
Tel (703) 854-6000 *SIC* 2711

▲ TEGNA INC p 1432
7950 Jones Branch Dr, Mc Lean VA 22102
Tel (703) 854-7000
SIC 2711 4813 4841 4833

■ DAILY PRESS INC p 408
703 Mariners Row, Newport News VA 23606
Tel (757) 245-3737 *SIC* 2711

LANDMARK MEDIA ENTERPRISES LLC p 843
150 Granby St, Norfolk VA 23510
Tel (757) 351-7000
SIC 2711 5045 2721 6531

VIRGINIAN-PILOT MEDIA COMPANIES LLC p 1560
150 W Brambleton Ave, Norfolk VA 23510
Tel (757) 446-2056 *SIC* 2711

■ MEDIA GENERAL COMMUNICATIONS INC p 935
333 E Franklin St, Richmond VA 23219
Tel (804) 649-6000 *SIC* 2711

■ MEDIA GENERAL OPERATIONS INC p 936
333 E Franklin St, Richmond VA 23219
Tel (804) 887-5000 *SIC* 2711 4833

■ WORLD MEDIA ENTERPRISES INC p 1625
300 E Franklin St, Richmond VA 23219
Tel (804) 643-1276 *SIC* 2711

SOUND PUBLISHING INC p 1342
11323 Commando Rd W Main, Everett WA 98204
Tel (360) 394-5800 *SIC* 2711

SOUND PUBLISHING HOLDING INC p 1342
19351 8th Ave Ne Ste 106, Poulsbo WA 98370
Tel (360) 394-5800 *SIC* 2711

BLETHEN CORP p 189
1120 John St, Seattle WA 98109
Tel (206) 464-2471 *SIC* 2711

SEATTLE TIMES CO p 1298
1000 Denny Way Ste 501, Seattle WA 98109
Tel (206) 464-2111 *SIC* 2711

COWLES PUBLISHING CO p 386
999 W Riverside Ave, Spokane WA 99201
Tel (509) 459-5000
SIC 2711 2611 2621 4833

OGDEN NEWSPAPERS INC p 1076
1500 Main St, Wheeling WV 26003
Tel (304) 233-0100
SIC 2711 2754 2741 2791 2752

BLISS COMMUNICATIONS INC p 189
1 S Parker Dr, Janesville WI 53545
Tel (608) 741-6650 *SIC* 2711 4832

JOURNAL COMMUNICATIONS INC p 794
333 W State St, Milwaukee WI 53203
Tel (414) 224-2000
SIC 4832 4833 2711 2759 4813

■ JOURNAL MEDIA GROUP INC p 794
333 W State St, Milwaukee WI 53203
Tel (414) 224-2000 *SIC* 2711

JOURNAL SENTINEL INC p 794
333 W State St, Milwaukee WI 53203
Tel (414) 224-2000 *SIC* 2711

JOURNAL COMMUNITY PUBLISHING GROUP INC p 794
600 Industrial Dr, Waupaca WI 54981
Tel (715) 258-8450 *SIC* 2741 2711

SIC 2721 Periodicals: Publishing & Printing

EBSCO INDUSTRIES INC p 474
5724 Highway 280 E, Birmingham AL 35242
Tel (205) 991-6600
SIC 7389 2782 3949 7375 2721 6552

HERITAGE CO INC p 686
2402 Wildwood Ave Ste 500, North Little Rock AR 72120
Tel (501) 835-9111 *SIC* 7389 2721

1105 MEDIA INC p 1
9201 Oakdale Ave Ste 101, Chatsworth CA 91311
Tel (818) 814-5200
SIC 7313 7389 2721 2741 8748

ACTIVE INTEREST MEDIA INC p 20
300 Continental Blvd # 650, El Segundo CA 90245
Tel (310) 356-4100 *SIC* 2721

CRUZ BAY PUBLISHING INC p 396
300 Continental Blvd # 650, El Segundo CA 90245
Tel (310) 356-4100 *SIC* 2721

KELLEY BLUE BOOK CO INC p 808
195 Technology Dr, Irvine CA 92618
Tel (949) 770-7704 *SIC* 2721

OPENGATE CAPITAL LLC p 1089
10250 Constellation Blvd, Los Angeles CA 90067
Tel (310) 432-7000 *SIC* 2721 6799 8621

WEIDER PUBLICATIONS LLC p 1587
6420 Wilshire Blvd # 720, Los Angeles CA 90048
Tel (818) 884-6800 *SIC* 2721

AFFINITY GROUP HOLDING LLC p 32
2750 Park View Ct Ste 240, Oxnard CA 93036
Tel (805) 667-4100 *SIC* 7997 2721

COMPETITOR GROUP INC p 351
9477 Waples St Ste 150, San Diego CA 92121
Tel (858) 450-6510 *SIC* 2721 7941

CALIFORNIA ACADEMY OF SCIENCES p 239
55 Music Concourse Dr, San Francisco CA 94118
Tel (415) 379-8000 *SIC* 8422 2721 8412

2100 FREEDOM INC p 1
625 N Grand Ave, Santa Ana CA 92701
Tel (714) 796-7000
SIC 2711 2721 7313 2741 5963 4813

FREEDOM COMMUNICATIONS HOLDINGS INC p 576
625 N Grand Ave, Santa Ana CA 92701
Tel (714) 796-7000
SIC 6719 2711 4813 2721

FREEDOM COMMUNICATIONS INC p 576
625 N Grand Ave, Santa Ana CA 92701
Tel (714) 796-7000
SIC 2711 2721 7313 2741 5963

GUARDSMARK LLC p 645
1551 N Tustin Ave Ste 650, Santa Ana CA 92705
Tel (714) 619-9700 *SIC* 7381 8742 2721

ADVANSTAR COMMUNICATIONS INC p 26
2501 Colorado Ave Ste 280, Santa Monica CA 90404
Tel (310) 857-7500 *SIC* 7389 2721 7331

■ SCHOLASTIC LIBRARY PUBLISHING INC p 1288
90 Sherman Tpke, Danbury CT 06816
Tel (203) 797-3500
SIC 2731 5963 5192 2721 5961 7371

YALE UNIVERSITY p 1634
105 Wall St, New Haven CT 06511
Tel (203) 432-2550
SIC 8221 2731 2721 2741

TAUNTON INC p 1426
63 S Main St, Newtown CT 06470
Tel (203) 426-8171
SIC 2721 2731 7812 5963

▲ WORLD WRESTLING ENTERTAINMENT INC p 1625
1241 E Main St, Stamford CT 06902
Tel (203) 352-8600 *SIC* 7812 7929 2721

COMMERCE CONNECT MEDIA INC p 345
830 Post Rd E Fl 2, Westport CT 06880
Tel (800) 547-7377 *SIC* 2721

REED ELSEVIER US HOLDINGS INC p 1217
1105 N Market St Ste 501, Wilmington DE 19801
Tel (302) 427-2672
SIC 2721 7999 8748 6719

AMERICAN ASSOCIATION FOR ADVANCEMENT OF SCIENCE p 68
1200 New York Ave Nw, Washington DC 20005
Tel (202) 898-0873 *SIC* 8621 2721

HARMAN MEDIA LLC p 662
1150 15th St Nw, Washington DC 20071
Tel (202) 334-6000 *SIC* 2721

HW HOLDCO LLC p 722
1 Thomas Cir Nw Ste 600, Washington DC 20005
Tel (202) 452-0800 *SIC* 2721 7389

NASH HOLDINGS LLC p 1008
1403 Hamlin St Ne, Washington DC 20017
Tel (202) 334-6727 *SIC* 2711 2721

NATIONAL GEOGRAPHIC SOCIETY p 1012
1145 17th St Nw, Washington DC 20036
Tel (202) 857-7000 *SIC* 2721

POST COMMUNITY MEDIA LLC p 1163
1301 K St Nw, Washington DC 20071
Tel (301) 670-2565 *SIC* 2711 2732 2721

WP CO LLC p 1627
1301 K St Nw, Washington DC 20071
Tel (202) 334-6242 *SIC* 2721 2711

NEWSMAX MEDIA INC p 1039
750 Park Of Commerce Dr # 100, Boca Raton FL 33487
Tel (561) 686-1165 *SIC* 2721 2741

SANDOW MEDIA LLC p 1278
3651 Nw 8th Ave Ste 200, Boca Raton FL 33431
Tel (561) 961-7700 *SIC* 2721

TAYLOR & FRANCIS GROUP LLC p 1426
6000 Broken Sound Pkwy Nw # 300, Boca Raton FL 33487
Tel (800) 634-7064 *SIC* 2721 2731

TWINLAB CORP p 1495
2255 Glades Rd Ste 342w, Boca Raton FL 33431
Tel (212) 651-8500
SIC 2099 2834 2731 2721 2833

TIMES PUBLISHING CO p 1454
490 1st Ave S, Saint Petersburg FL 33701
Tel (727) 893-8111 *SIC* 2711 2721

PALM BEACH NEWSPAPERS INC p 1109
2751 S Dixie Hwy, West Palm Beach FL 33405
Tel (561) 820-4100 *SIC* 2711 2721

BONNIER CORP p 200
460 N Orlando Ave Ste 200, Winter Park FL 32789
Tel (407) 622-1014 *SIC* 2721

MORRIS COMMUNICATIONS CO LLC p 990
725 Broad St, Augusta GA 30901
Tel (706) 724-0851
SIC 2711 5199 2721 2731

SHIVERS TRADING & OPERATING CO p 1317
725 Broad St, Augusta GA 30901
Tel (706) 724-0851
SIC 2711 2721 2731 4832 7312 6512

HEARST BUSINESS MEDIA CORP p 678
2620 Barrett Rd, Gainesville GA 30507
Tel (770) 532-4111 *SIC* 2721

NETWORK COMMUNICATIONS INC p 1028
2 Sun Ct Ste 300, Norcross GA 30092
Tel (678) 346-9300 *SIC* 2731 2721

AMERICAN BAR ASSOCIATION p 68
321 N Clark St Ste Ll2, Chicago IL 60654
Tel (312) 988-5000 *SIC* 8621 2721 2731

AMERICAN HOSPITAL ASSOCIATION p 74
155 N Wacker Dr Ste 400, Chicago IL 60606
Tel (312) 422-3000 *SIC* 2721 2731 8099

AMERICAN MEDICAL ASSOCIATION INC p 76
330 N Wabash Ave # 39300, Chicago IL 60611
Tel (312) 464-5000
SIC 8621 2721 6321 6282

NATIONAL ASSOCIATION OF REALTORS p 1010
430 N Michigan Ave Lowr 2, Chicago IL 60611
Tel (800) 874-6500 *SIC* 8611 2721 8299

GOOD SAM ENTERPRISES LLC p 623
250 Parkway Dr Ste 270, Lincolnshire IL 60069
Tel (847) 229-6720 *SIC* 5561 7997 2721

PUBLICATIONS INTERNATIONAL LTD p 1190
8140 Lehigh Ave, Morton Grove IL 60053
Tel (847) 676-3470 *SIC* 2731 2721

WILLIS STEIN & PARTNERS MANAGEMENT III LLC p 1612
1033 Skokie Blvd Ste 360, Northbrook IL 60062
Tel (312) 422-2400
SIC 6799 3479 2721 8721

CCH INC p 270
2700 Lake Cook Rd, Riverwoods IL 60015
Tel (847) 267-7000
SIC 2721 2731 7389 7338 8732 7371

WOLTERS KLUWER UNITED STATES INC p 1621
2700 Lake Cook Rd, Riverwoods IL 60015
Tel (847) 580-5000
SIC 2731 2721 2741 2759

WILTON BRANDS LLC p 1614
2240 75th St, Woodridge IL 60517
Tel (630) 963-7100
SIC 5023 2731 2721 7812 5199

WILTON HOLDINGS INC p 1614
2240 75th St, Woodridge IL 60517
Tel (630) 963-7100
SIC 5023 2731 2721 7812 5199

WILTON INDUSTRIES INC p 1614
2240 75th St, Woodridge IL 60517
Tel (630) 963-7100
SIC 5023 2731 2721 7812 5199

▲ EMMIS COMMUNICATIONS CORP p 493
40 Monument Cir Ste 700, Indianapolis IN 46204
Tel (317) 266-0100 *SIC* 4832 2721

HERFF JONES LLC p 685
4501 W 62nd St, Indianapolis IN 46268
Tel (800) 837-4235 *SIC* 3911 2721 2741

▲ MEREDITH CORP p 948
1716 Locust St, Des Moines IA 50309
Tel (515) 284-3000 *SIC* 2721 2731 4833

PENTON BUSINESS MEDIA INC p 1132
9800 Metcalf Ave, Shawnee Mission KS 66212
Tel (913) 341-1300 *SIC* 2721

KENTUCKY ASSOCIATION OF ELECTRIC COOPERATIVES INC p 812
4515 Bishop Ln, Louisville KY 40218
Tel (502) 451-2430
SIC 3612 2721 7629 5063

DIVERSIFIED BUSINESS COMMUNICATIONS p 444
121 Free St, Portland ME 04101
Tel (207) 842-5400
SIC 4833 4841 2721 7389

UNITED COMMUNICATIONS GROUP LIMITED PARTNERSHIP p 1507
9737 Washingtonian Blvd # 500, Gaithersburg MD 20878
Tel (301) 287-2700 *SIC* 2721 7375

ACCESS INTELLIGENCE LLC p 15
9211 Corp Blvd Fl 4, Rockville MD 20850
Tel (301) 354-2000 *SIC* 2741 2721

INTERNATIONAL DATA GROUP INC p 755
1 Exeter Plz Fl 15, Boston MA 02116
Tel (617) 534-1200 *SIC* 2721 8732 7389

HARVARD BUSINESS SCHOOL PUBLISHING CORP p 666
20 Guest St Ste 700, Brighton MA 02135
Tel (617) 783-7400 *SIC* 2721 2731 2741

DECISION RESOURCES INC p 421
800 District Ave Ste 600, Burlington MA 01803
Tel (781) 993-2500 *SIC* 8732 2721

PRESIDENT AND FELLOWS OF HARVARD COLLEGE p 1172
1350 Massachusetts Ave, Cambridge MA 02138
Tel (617) 496-4873 *SIC* 8221 8732 2721

IDG COMMUNICATIONS INC p 729
5 Speen St, Framingham MA 01701
Tel (508) 875-5000 *SIC* 2721 2731

EBSCO PUBLISHING INC p 474
10 Estes St, Ipswich MA 01938
Tel (978) 356-6500
SIC 2741 7375 2731 2721

MASSACHUSETTS MEDICAL SOCIETY INC p 917
860 Winter St, Waltham MA 02451
Tel (781) 893-4610 *SIC* 2721 8621

CRAIN COMMUNICATIONS INC p 388
1155 Gratiot Ave, Detroit MI 48207
Tel (313) 446-6000 *SIC* 2721 2711

TWINLAB HOLDINGS INC p 1495
3133 Orchard Vista Dr Se, Grand Rapids MI 49546
Tel (616) 464-5000
SIC 2833 2834 5149 2721

BNP MEDIA INC p 194
2401 W Big Beaver Rd # 700, Troy MI 48084
Tel (248) 362-3700 *SIC* 2721

ADVANSTAR HOLDINGS CORP p 26
131 W 1st St, Duluth MN 55802
Tel (218) 740-7200 *SIC* 7389 2721 7331

ROCKLER COMPANIES INC p 1245
4365 Willow Dr, Medina MN 55340
Tel (763) 478-8201 *SIC* 5251 5961 2721

UNIVERSITY OF ST THOMAS p 1525
2115 Summit Ave, Saint Paul MN 55105
Tel (651) 962-5000 *SIC* 8221 2741 2721

■ WEST SERVICES INC p 1595
610 Opperman Dr, Saint Paul MN 55123
Tel (651) 687-5882 *SIC* 2721

OMICS GROUP INC p 1084
2360 Corp Cir Ste 400, Henderson NV 89074
Tel (888) 843-8169 *SIC* 2721

MACROMEDIA INC p 893
150 River St, Hackensack NJ 07601
Tel (201) 646-4000 *SIC* 2711 2721

▲ JOHN WILEY & SONS INC p 789
111 River St Ste 2000, Hoboken NJ 07030
Tel (201) 748-6000 *SIC* 2731 2721

AM BEST CO INC p 63
1 Ambest Rd, Oldwick NJ 08858
Tel (908) 439-2200 *SIC* 2731 2721 2732

NORTHSTAR TRAVEL MEDIA LLC p 1059
100 Lighting Way Ste 200, Secaucus NJ 07094
Tel (201) 902-2000 *SIC* 2721 4789 4724

■ 21ST CENTURY FOX AMERICA INC p 1
1211 Ave Of The Americas, New York NY 10036
Tel (212) 852-7000
SIC 2752 2721 4833 7812

■ ABC INC p 10
77 W 66th St Rm 100, New York NY 10023
Tel (212) 456-7777
SIC 4833 4832 7812 6794 2711 2721

ADVANCE MAGAZINE PUBLISHERS INC p 24
1 World Trade Ctr Fl 28, New York NY 10007
Tel (212) 286-2860 *SIC* 2721

ADVANSTAR INC p 26
641 Lexington Ave Fl 8, New York NY 10022
Tel (212) 951-6600 *SIC* 2721 7389 8742

ALM MEDIA HOLDINGS INC p 59
120 Broadway Fl 5, New York NY 10271
Tel (212) 457-9400
SIC 2721 2711 2741 2731 7389

ALM MEDIA LLC p 59
120 Broadway Fl 5, New York NY 10271
Tel (212) 457-9400
SIC 2721 2711 2741 2731 7389

AMERICAN MANAGEMENT ASSOCIATION INTERNATIONAL p 75
1601 Broadway Fl 7, New York NY 10019
Tel (212) 586-8100
SIC 8299 2731 8621 7812 2721

BERTELSMANN INC p 176
1745 Broadway Fl 20, New York NY 10019
Tel (212) 782-1000
SIC 2731 2721 7819 3652 6512

BERTELSMANN PUBLISHING GROUP INC p 176
1540 Broadway Fl 24, New York NY 10036
Tel (212) 782-1000 *SIC* 2731 2721

CLP PB LLC p 328
250 W 57th St Fl 15, New York NY 10107
Tel (212) 340-8100 *SIC* 2721

CONDE NAST INTERNATIONAL INC p 355
1 World Trade Ctr, New York NY 10007
Tel (212) 286-2860 *SIC* 2721

COURT SQUARE CAPITAL PARTNERS LP p 383
55 E 52nd St Rm 3400, New York NY 10055
Tel (212) 752-6110 *SIC* 6799 2731 2721

■ DAVIS ZIFF PUBLISHING INC p 416
28 E 28th St Fl 10, New York NY 10016
Tel (212) 503-3500 *SIC* 2721 2731 7371

■ DOW JONES & CO INC p 453
1211 Avenue Of The Americ, New York NY 10036
Tel (609) 627-2999 *SIC* 2711 2721

■ DOW JONES AER CO INC p 453
1211 Av Of The Am Lwr C3r, New York NY 10036
Tel (212) 416-2000 *SIC* 2721

ECONOMIST NEWSPAPER GROUP INC p 476
750 3rd Ave Fl 5, New York NY 10017
Tel (212) 541-0500 *SIC* 2721 7313 5963

FAIRCHILD PUBLICATIONS INC p 524
475 5th Ave, New York NY 10017
Tel (212) 630-4000 *SIC* 2721 2711 2731

GIRL SCOUTS OF UNITED STATES OF AMERICA p 613
420 5th Ave Fl 13, New York NY 10018
Tel (212) 852-8000
SIC 8641 5137 6794 2721

GRUNER + JAHR USA GROUP INC p 642
1745 Broadway Fl 16, New York NY 10019
Tel (866) 323-9336 *SIC* 2721 2754

HEARST CORP p 678
300 W 57th St Fl 42, New York NY 10019
Tel (212) 649-2000
SIC 2721 2731 2711 4832 4833 7383

HEARST HOLDINGS INC p 678
300 W 57th St, New York NY 10019
Tel (212) 649-2000 *SIC* 2721 4841

■ HISTORIC TW INC p 696
75 Rockefeller Plz, New York NY 10019
Tel (212) 484-8000
SIC 3652 6794 2741 7812 4841 2721

JOBSON MEDICAL INFORMATION LLC p 787
440 9th Ave Fl 14, New York NY 10001
Tel (212) 274-7000 *SIC* 2721 2741

LAGARDERE NORTH AMERICA INC p 838
60 E 42nd St Ste 1940, New York NY 10165
Tel (212) 477-7373 *SIC* 2721

LEBHAR-FRIEDMAN INC p 850
150 W 30th St Fl 19, New York NY 10001
Tel (212) 756-5000 *SIC* 2721 2711

MACANDREWS & FORBES INC p 891
38 E 63rd St, New York NY 10065
Tel (212) 688-9000
SIC 2844 2087 2121 7819 2721 2731

MACMILLAN HOLDINGS LLC p 892
175 5th Ave, New York NY 10010
Tel (646) 307-5151 *SIC* 2721 2731

■ MARTHA STEWART LIVING OMNIMEDIA INC p 912
601 W 26th St Rm 900, New York NY 10001
Tel (212) 827-8000
SIC 2721 2731 4813 7812

■ MARVEL ENTERTAINMENT LLC p 913
135 W 50th St Fl 7, New York NY 10020
Tel (212) 576-4000
SIC 2721 6794 3944 7929

NATIONAL AUDUBON SOCIETY INC p 1010
225 Varick St Fl 7, New York NY 10014
Tel (212) 979-3000 *SIC* 8641 2721

NATURE AMERICA INC p 1018
1 New York Plz Ste 4500, New York NY 10004
Tel (212) 726-9200 *SIC* 2721

NEW YORK MEDIA LLC p 1035
75 Varick St, New York NY 10013
Tel (212) 508-0700 *SIC* 2721

PENTON MEDIA INC p 1132
1166 Avenue Of The Americ, New York NY 10036
Tel (212) 204-4200
SIC 2721 7389 7313 7375

RDA HOLDING CO p 1212
750 3rd Ave, New York NY 10017
Tel (914) 238-1000
SIC 2721 2731 5961 2741

RELX INC p 1222
230 Park Ave, New York NY 10169
Tel (212) 309-8100
SIC 2721 2731 7389 7374 8748

▲ SCHOLASTIC CORP p 1288
557 Broadway Lbby 1, New York NY 10012
Tel (212) 343-6100
SIC 2731 2721 7372 7812 6794 7311

■ SCHOLASTIC INC p 1288
557 Broadway Lbby 1, New York NY 10012
Tel (800) 724-6527
SIC 2731 2721 7372 7812

SOURCE MEDIA INC p 1342
1 State St Fl 26, New York NY 10004
Tel (212) 803-8200 *SIC* 2721

THOMAS PUBLISHING CO LLC p 1449
5 Penn Plz Fl 9, New York NY 10001
Tel (212) 695-0500
SIC 2741 2721 7374 7331

▲ TIME INC p 1454
225 Liberty St Ste C2, New York NY 10281
Tel (212) 522-1212 *SIC* 2721

▲ TIME WARNER INC p 1454
1 Time Warner Ctr Bsmt B, New York NY 10019
Tel (212) 484-8000
SIC 4841 7812 2731 2721

TNC (US) HOLDINGS INC p 1458
770 Broadway Fl 8, New York NY 10003
Tel (646) 654-5500
SIC 8732 2721 2732 2741

TRUSTED MEDIA BRANDS INC p 1487
750 3rd Ave Fl 3, New York NY 10017
Tel (914) 238-1000
SIC 2721 2731 5961 2741

TV GUIDE MAGAZINE LLC p 1493
50 Rockefeller Plz Fl 14, New York NY 10020
Tel (212) 852-7500 *SIC* 2721

UBM INC p 1498
2 Penn Plz, New York NY 10121
Tel (212) 600-3000
SIC 2721 2711 8732 2741

UBM LLC p 1498
2 Penn Plz Fl 15, New York NY 10121
Tel (516) 562-5085
SIC 2721 2711 7319 7389

US NEWS & WORLD REPORT INC p 1532
4 New York Plz Fl 6, New York NY 10004
Tel (212) 716-6800 *SIC* 2721

VSS-AHC CONSOLIDATED HOLDINGS CORP p 1567
350 Park Ave Fl 7, New York NY 10022
Tel (212) 935-4990 *SIC* 7389 2721 7331

WASSERSTEIN & CO LP p 1580
1185 Avenue Of The Americ, New York NY 10036
Tel (212) 702-5600 *SIC* 6799 2721 2741

WASSERSTEIN HOLDINGS LLC p 1580
1301 Avenue Of The Americ, New York NY 10019
Tel (212) 702-5600 *SIC* 6799 2721 2741

WENNER MEDIA LLC p 1592
1290 Ave Of The Amer Fl 2, New York NY 10104
Tel (212) 484-1616 *SIC* 2721

CONSUMERS UNION OF UNITED STATES INC p 362
101 Truman Ave, Yonkers NY 10703
Tel (914) 378-2000 *SIC* 2741 2721 7389

AMERICAN CITY BUSINESS JOURNALS INC p 70
120 W Morehead St Ste 400, Charlotte NC 28202
Tel (704) 973-1000 *SIC* 2711 2721

AMERICAN INSTITUTE OF CERTIFIED PUBLIC ACCOUNTANTS p 75
220 Leigh Farm Rd, Durham NC 27707
Tel (919) 402-0682 *SIC* 8299 8621 2721

■ NEWS AND OBSERVER PUBLISHING CO p 1039
215 S Mcdowell St, Raleigh NC 27601
Tel (919) 829-4500
SIC 2711 2741 2721 2752

F+W MEDIA INC p 523
10151 Carver Rd Ste 200, Blue Ash OH 45242
Tel (513) 531-2690 *SIC* 2731 2721

ANGSTROM GRAPHICS INC p 91
4437 E 49th St, Cleveland OH 44125
Tel (216) 271-5300 *SIC* 2721 2754 2752

HIGHLIGHTS FOR CHILDREN INC p 692
1800 Watermark Dr, Columbus OH 43215
Tel (614) 486-0631 *SIC* 2721

OKLAHOMA ELECTRIC CO-OPERATIVE INC p 1079
242 24th Ave Nw, Norman OK 73069
Tel (405) 321-2024 *SIC* 4911 2721

PENNWELL CORP p 1131
1421 S Sheridan Rd, Tulsa OK 74112
Tel (918) 835-3161
SIC 2721 2731 2741 7389

RODALE INC p 1246
400 S 10th St, Emmaus PA 18049
Tel (800) 848-4735 *SIC* 2721 2731

ADVERTISING SPECIALTY INSTITUTE INC p 27
4800 E Street Rd Ste 100a, Feasterville Trevose PA 19053
Tel (215) 953-4000 *SIC* 2721 7372

KAPPA MEDIA GROUP INC p 803
40 Skippack Pike, Fort Washington PA 19034
Tel (215) 643-5800 *SIC* 2721 2741 5111

WOLTERS KLUWER HEALTH INC p 1621
2001 Market St Lbby 1, Philadelphia PA 19103
Tel (215) 521-8300
SIC 2721 2731 2741 7372 8748

ABARTA INC p 9
200 Alpha Dr, Pittsburgh PA 15238
Tel (412) 963-6226
SIC 2086 2711 2721 5149 1382 5812

SOUTH CAROLINA STATE PORTS AUTHORITY p 1343
176 Concord St, Charleston SC 29401
Tel (843) 723-8651 *SIC* 4491 8111 2721

UNITED METHODIST PUBLISHING HOUSE p 1510
2222 Rosa L Parks Blvd, Nashville TN 37228
Tel (615) 749-6000
SIC 2731 5192 5942 2741 2721

■ THOMSON REUTERS (TAX & ACCOUNTING) INC p 1450
2395 Midway Rd, Carrollton TX 75006
Tel (800) 431-9025 *SIC* 2721 7371

AMERICAN HEART ASSOCIATION INC p 74
7272 Greenville Ave, Dallas TX 75231
Tel (214) 373-6300 *SIC* 8399 2721

▲ JRJR33 INC p 795
2950 N Harwood St Fl 22, Dallas TX 75201
Tel (469) 913-4115
SIC 5499 5023 5122 2721 5251

PITTSBURGH HOLDINGS LLC p 1152
301 Commerce St Ste 3300, Fort Worth TX 76102
Tel (817) 871-4000 *SIC* 2721

▲ GAMESTOP CORP p 590
625 Westport Pkwy, Grapevine TX 76051
Tel (817) 424-2000
SIC 5945 5734 5932 2721

BOY SCOUTS OF AMERICA p 205
1325 W Walnut Hill Ln, Irving TX 75038
Tel (972) 580-2000
SIC 8641 5136 5091 2721

BUREAU OF NATIONAL AFFAIRS INC p 226
1801 S Bell St Ste Cn110, Arlington VA 22202
Tel (703) 341-3000 *SIC* 2711 2721

▲ GRAHAM HOLDINGS CO p 629
1300 17th St N Ste 1700, Arlington VA 22209
Tel (703) 345-6300
SIC 8299 4833 4841 2721

AIRLINE TARIFF PUBLISHING CO p 40
45005 Aviation Dr Ste 400, Dulles VA 20166
Tel (703) 661-7400 *SIC* 2721 7374 2731

■ CADMUS JOURNAL SERVICES INC p 236
2901 Byrdhill Rd, Henrico VA 23228
Tel (804) 287-5680 *SIC* 2752 2721 2741

COX AUTO TRADER PUBLICATIONS INC p 386
100 W Plume St, Norfolk VA 23510
Tel (757) 531-7000 *SIC* 2721

DOMINION ENTERPRISES p 449
150 Granby St Ste 150, Norfolk VA 23510
Tel (757) 351-7000 *SIC* 7374 2721 2741

LANDMARK MEDIA ENTERPRISES LLC p 843
150 Granby St, Norfolk VA 23510
Tel (757) 351-7000
SIC 2711 5045 2721 6531

CYGNUS BUSINESS MEDIA INC p 405
1233 Janesville Ave, Fort Atkinson WI 53538
Tel (920) 563-6388 *SIC* 2721 7389 7319

▲ QUAD/GRAPHICS INC p 1195
N61w23044 Harrys Way, Sussex WI 53089
Tel (414) 566-6000 *SIC* 2752 2754 2721

SIC 2731 Books: Publishing & Printing

▲ WALT DISNEY CO p 1574
500 S Buena Vista St, Burbank CA 91521
Tel (818) 560-1000
SIC 4833 4841 7011 7996 7812 2731

■ NEW INSPIRATION BROADCASTING CO INC p 1031
4880 Santa Rosa Rd, Camarillo CA 93012
Tel (805) 987-0400 *SIC* 4832 2731

▲ SALEM MEDIA GROUP INC p 1272
4880 Santa Rosa Rd, Camarillo CA 93012
Tel (818) 956-0400 *SIC* 4832 2731 4813

EDMUNDS.COM INC p 478
2401 Colorado Ave, Santa Monica CA 90404
Tel (310) 309-6300 *SIC* 2731

OREILLY MEDIA INC p 1094
1005 Gravenstein Hwy N, Sebastopol CA 95472
Tel (707) 827-7000 *SIC* 2731 2741

SAGE PUBLICATIONS INC p 1267
2455 Teller Rd, Thousand Oaks CA 91320
Tel (805) 499-0721 *SIC* 2731

■ JEPPESEN SANDERSON INC p 783
55 Inverness Dr E, Englewood CO 80112
Tel (303) 799-9090 *SIC* 2741 2731 8748

■ SCHOLASTIC LIBRARY PUBLISHING INC p 1288
90 Sherman Tpke, Danbury CT 06816
Tel (203) 797-3500
SIC 2731 5963 5192 2721 5961 7371

YALE UNIVERSITY p 1634
105 Wall St, New Haven CT 06511
Tel (203) 432-2550
SIC 8221 2731 2721 2741

TAUNTON INC p 1426
63 S Main St, Newtown CT 06470
Tel (203) 426-8171
SIC 2721 2731 7812 5963

DRAGON CLOUD INC p 455
1 Commerce St, Wilmington DE 19801
Tel (702) 508-2676 *SIC* 2731

TAYLOR & FRANCIS GROUP LLC p 1426
6000 Broken Sound Pkwy Nw # 300, Boca Raton FL 33487
Tel (800) 634-7064 *SIC* 2721 2731

TWINLAB CORP p 1495
2255 Glades Rd Ste 342w, Boca Raton FL 33431
Tel (212) 651-8500
SIC 2099 2834 2731 2721 2833

■ KAPLAN INC p 803
6301 Kaplan Univ Ave, Fort Lauderdale FL 33309
Tel (212) 492-5800
SIC 8299 7361 7372 2731

MORRIS COMMUNICATIONS CO LLC p 990
725 Broad St, Augusta GA 30901
Tel (706) 724-0851
SIC 2711 5199 2721 2731

SHIVERS TRADING & OPERATING CO p 1317
725 Broad St, Augusta GA 30901
Tel (706) 724-0851
SIC 2711 2721 2731 4832 7312 6512

NETWORK COMMUNICATIONS INC p 1028
2 Sun Ct Ste 300, Norcross GA 30092
Tel (678) 346-9300 *SIC* 2731 2721

AMERICAN BAR ASSOCIATION p 68
321 N Clark St Ste Ll2, Chicago IL 60654
Tel (312) 988-5000 *SIC* 8621 2721 2731

AMERICAN HOSPITAL ASSOCIATION p 74
155 N Wacker Dr Ste 400, Chicago IL 60606
Tel (312) 422-3000 *SIC* 2721 2731 8099

CHICAGO REVIEW PRESS INC p 297
814 N Franklin St Ste 100, Chicago IL 60610
Tel (312) 337-0747 *SIC* 5192 2731

ENCYCLOPAEDIA BRITANNICA INC p 496
325 N Lasalle St Ste 200, Chicago IL 60654
Tel (847) 777-2241 *SIC* 2731

MOODY BIBLE INSTITUTE OF CHICAGO p 987
820 N La Salle Dr, Chicago IL 60610
Tel (312) 329-4000
SIC 8661 8299 8221 4832 2731

PHOENIX INTERNATIONAL PUBLICATIONS INC p 1145
8501 W Higgins Rd Ste 300, Chicago IL 60631
Tel (312) 739-4400 *SIC* 5942 2731

PUBLICATIONS INTERNATIONAL LTD p 1190
8140 Lehigh Ave, Morton Grove IL 60053
Tel (847) 676-3470 *SIC* 2731 2721

CCH INC p 270
2700 Lake Cook Rd, Riverwoods IL 60015
Tel (847) 267-7000
SIC 2721 2731 7389 7338 8732 7371

WOLTERS KLUWER UNITED STATES INC p 1621
2700 Lake Cook Rd, Riverwoods IL 60015
Tel (847) 580-5000
SIC 2731 2721 2741 2759

WILTON BRANDS LLC p 1614
2240 75th St, Woodridge IL 60517
Tel (630) 963-7100
SIC 5023 2731 2721 7812 5199

WILTON HOLDINGS INC p 1614
2240 75th St, Woodridge IL 60517
Tel (630) 963-7100
SIC 5023 2731 2721 7812 5199

WILTON INDUSTRIES INC p 1614
2240 75th St, Woodridge IL 60517
Tel (630) 963-7100
SIC 5023 2731 2721 7812 5199

▲ MEREDITH CORP p 948
1716 Locust St, Des Moines IA 50309
Tel (515) 284-3000 *SIC* 2721 2731 4833

ROWMAN & LITTLEFIELD PUBLISHING GROUP INC p 1253
4501 Forbes Blvd Ste 200, Lanham MD 20706
Tel (301) 459-3366 *SIC* 2731 5192

CENGAGE LEARNING HOLDINGS II INC p 275
20 Channel Ctr St, Boston MA 02210
Tel (617) 289-7700 *SIC* 2731

CENGAGE LEARNING INC p 275
20 Channel Ctr St, Boston MA 02210
Tel (617) 289-7700 *SIC* 2731

HM PUBLISHING CORP p 697
222 Berkeley St, Boston MA 02116
Tel (617) 251-5000 *SIC* 2731

■ HMH PUBLISHERS LLC p 698
222 Berkeley St, Boston MA 02116
Tel (617) 351-5000 *SIC* 2731

▲ HOUGHTON MIFFLIN HARCOURT CO p 711
222 Berkeley St Fl 1-11, Boston MA 02116
Tel (617) 351-5000 *SIC* 3999 2731

■ HOUGHTON MIFFLIN HARCOURT PUBLISHERS INC p 711
222 Berkeley St Fl 1-11, Boston MA 02116
Tel (617) 351-5000 *SIC* 2731

■ HOUGHTON MIFFLIN HARCOURT PUBLISHING CO p 711
222 Berkeley St, Boston MA 02116
Tel (617) 351-5000 *SIC* 2731

HOUGHTON MIFFLIN HOLDING CO INC p 711
222 Berkeley St Fl 1-11, Boston MA 02116
Tel (617) 351-5000 *SIC* 2731

HOUGHTON MIFFLIN HOLDINGS INC p 711
222 Berkeley St Fl 1-11, Boston MA 02116
Tel (617) 351-5000 *SIC* 2731

HARVARD BUSINESS SCHOOL PUBLISHING CORP p 666
20 Guest St Ste 700, Brighton MA 02135
Tel (617) 783-7400 *SIC* 2721 2731 2741

IDG COMMUNICATIONS INC p 729
5 Speen St, Framingham MA 01701
Tel (508) 875-5000 *SIC* 2721 2731

EBSCO PUBLISHING INC p 474
10 Estes St, Ipswich MA 01938
Tel (978) 356-6500
SIC 2741 7375 2731 2721

COURIER CORP p 383
15 Wellman Ave, North Chelmsford MA 01863
Tel (978) 251-6000 *SIC* 2732 2731

■ **RAVEN VENTURES LLC** p 1209
15 Wellman Ave, North Chelmsford MA 01863
Tel (978) 251-6000 *SIC* 2731

■ **LANSING MPS INC** p 844
5800 W Grand River Ave, Lansing MI 48906
Tel (517) 323-9000
SIC 2759 2731 2761 3089 2671

HSP EPI ACQUISITION LLC p 715
1401 Crooks Rd Ste 150, Troy MI 48084
Tel (248) 404-1520 *SIC* 2731

HAZELDEN BETTY FORD FOUNDATION p 671
15251 Pleasant Valley Rd, Center City MN 55012
Tel (651) 213-4000 *SIC* 8361 2731

■ **THOMSON REUTERS (LEGAL) INC** p 1450
610 Opperman Dr, Eagan MN 55123
Tel (651) 687-7000 *SIC* 2731

CAPSTONE DIGITAL LLC p 251
1710 Roe Crest Dr, North Mankato MN 56003
Tel (507) 385-8280 *SIC* 2731

■ **BHSF INC** p 180
1440 Kiewit Plz, Omaha NE 68131
Tel (402) 346-1400
SIC 3635 3563 2731 3715

HUDSON GROUP (HG) INC p 716
1 Meadowlands Plz, East Rutherford NJ 07073
Tel (201) 939-5050 *SIC* 2731

▲ **JOHN WILEY & SONS INC** p 789
111 River St Ste 2000, Hoboken NJ 07030
Tel (201) 748-6000 *SIC* 2731 2721

■ **WILEY PUBLISHING INC** p 1609
111 River St, Hoboken NJ 07030
Tel (201) 748-6000 *SIC* 2731

MATTHEW BENDER & CO INC p 920
744 Broad St Fl 8, Newark NJ 07102
Tel (518) 487-3000 *SIC* 2731

AM BEST CO INC p 63
1 Ambest Rd, Oldwick NJ 08858
Tel (908) 439-2200 *SIC* 2731 2721 2732

BERLITZ LANGUAGES (UNITED STATES) INC p 175
7 Roszel Rd Fl 3, Princeton NJ 08540
Tel (609) 759-5371 *SIC* 8299 7389 2731

COLD SPRING HARBOR LABORATORY ASSOCIATION INC p 335
1 Bungtown Rd, Cold Spring Harbor NY 11724
Tel (516) 367-8446
SIC 8733 2731 2741 8249

CAMPUS COURSE PAKS INC p 246
1 South Ave Fl 1, Garden City NY 11530
Tel (516) 877-3967 *SIC* 2731

AI ENTERTAINMENT HOLDINGS LLC p 37
730 5th Ave Fl 20, New York NY 10019
Tel (212) 247-6400 *SIC* 2731

ALM MEDIA HOLDINGS INC p 59
120 Broadway Fl 5, New York NY 10271
Tel (212) 457-9400
SIC 2721 2711 2741 2731 7389

ALM MEDIA LLC p 59
120 Broadway Fl 5, New York NY 10271
Tel (212) 457-9400
SIC 2721 2711 2741 2731 7389

AMERICAN MANAGEMENT ASSOCIATION INTERNATIONAL p 75
1601 Broadway Fl 7, New York NY 10019
Tel (212) 586-8100
SIC 8299 2731 8621 7812 2721

BERTELSMANN INC p 176
1745 Broadway Fl 20, New York NY 10019
Tel (212) 782-1000
SIC 2731 2721 7819 3652 6512

BERTELSMANN PUBLISHING GROUP INC p 176
1540 Broadway Fl 24, New York NY 10036
Tel (212) 782-1000 *SIC* 2731 2721

■ **CBS CORP** p 269
51 W 52nd St Bsmt 1, New York NY 10019
Tel (212) 975-4321
SIC 4833 4832 7312 2731

CHURCH PENSION GROUP SERVICES CORP p 305
19 E 34th St Fl 3, New York NY 10016
Tel (212) 592-1800
SIC 6371 6321 6311 6331 2731

COURT SQUARE CAPITAL PARTNERS LP p 383
55 E 52nd St Rm 3400, New York NY 10055
Tel (212) 752-6110 *SIC* 6799 2731 2721

■ **DAVIS ZIFF PUBLISHING INC** p 416
28 E 28th St Fl 10, New York NY 10016
Tel (212) 503-3500 *SIC* 2721 2731 7371

FAIRCHILD PUBLICATIONS INC p 524
475 5th Ave, New York NY 10017
Tel (212) 630-4000 *SIC* 2721 2711 2731

HACHETTE BOOK GROUP INC p 652
1290 Ave Of The Americas, New York NY 10104
Tel (800) 759-0190 *SIC* 2731 5192

HAIGHTS CROSS COMMUNICATIONS INC p 653
136 Madison Ave Fl 8, New York NY 10016
Tel (212) 209-0500 *SIC* 2731

■ **HARPERCOLLINS PUBLISHERS LLC** p 663
195 Broadway Fl 2, New York NY 10007
Tel (212) 207-7000 *SIC* 5942 2731

HEARST CORP p 678
300 W 57th St Fl 42, New York NY 10019
Tel (212) 649-2000
SIC 2721 2731 2711 4832 4833 7383

HOLTZBRINCK PUBLISHERS LLC p 702
175 5th Ave, New York NY 10010
Tel (646) 307-5151 *SIC* 2731

MACANDREWS & FORBES INC p 891
38 E 63rd St, New York NY 10065
Tel (212) 688-9000
SIC 2844 2087 2121 7819 2721 2731

MACMILLAN HOLDINGS LLC p 892
175 5th Ave, New York NY 10010
Tel (646) 307-5151 *SIC* 2721 2731

MACMILLAN PUBLISHERS INC p 892
175 5th Ave Ste 400, New York NY 10010
Tel (646) 307-5151 *SIC* 2731 5192

MACMILLAN PUBLISHING GROUP LLC p 893
175 5th Ave, New York NY 10010
Tel (212) 674-5151 *SIC* 2731 5192

■ **MARTHA STEWART LIVING OMNIMEDIA INC** p 912
601 W 26th St Rm 900, New York NY 10001
Tel (212) 827-8000
SIC 2721 2731 4813 7812

MCGRAW-HILL GLOBAL EDUCATION HOLDINGS LLC p 929
2 Penn Plz Fl 20, New York NY 10121
Tel (646) 766-2000 *SIC* 2731

MCGRAW-HILL SCHOOL EDUCATION HOLDINGS LLC p 929
2 Penn Plz Fl 20, New York NY 10121
Tel (646) 766-2000 *SIC* 2731

MCGRAW-HILL SCHOOL EDUCATION LLC p 929
2 Penn Plz Fl 20, New York NY 10121
Tel (646) 766-2060 *SIC* 2731

■ **MULTI PACKAGING SOLUTIONS INC** p 999
150 E 52nd St Ste 2800, New York NY 10022
Tel (646) 885-0005
SIC 2759 2731 2761 3089 5092 2671

▲ **NEWS CORP** p 1039
1211 Ave Of The Americas, New York NY 10036
Tel (212) 416-3400 *SIC* 2711 2731 7375

OXFORD UNIVERSITY PRESS LLC p 1101
198 Madison Ave Fl 8, New York NY 10016
Tel (212) 726-6000 *SIC* 2731 5961

PEARSON EDUCATION HOLDINGS INC p 1126
330 Hudson St Fl 9, New York NY 10013
Tel (201) 236-6716 *SIC* 2731

PEARSON INC p 1126
1330 Hudson St, New York NY 10013
Tel (212) 641-2400 *SIC* 2711 2731

PENGUIN GROUP (USA) LLC p 1128
375 Hudson St Bsmt 1, New York NY 10014
Tel (212) 367-0200 *SIC* 2731

PENGUIN RANDOM HOUSE LLC p 1128
1745 Broadway, New York NY 10019
Tel (212) 782-9000 *SIC* 2731

RANDOM HOUSE LLC p 1208
1745 Broadway Frnt 3, New York NY 10019
Tel (212) 782-9000 *SIC* 5942 2731

RDA HOLDING CO p 1212
750 3rd Ave, New York NY 10017
Tel (914) 238-1000
SIC 2721 2731 5961 2741

RELX INC p 1222
230 Park Ave, New York NY 10169
Tel (212) 309-8100
SIC 2721 2731 7389 7374 8748

▲ **SCHOLASTIC CORP** p 1288
557 Broadway Lbby 1, New York NY 10012
Tel (212) 343-6100
SIC 2731 2721 7372 7812 6794 7311

■ **SCHOLASTIC INC** p 1288
557 Broadway Lbby 1, New York NY 10012
Tel (800) 724-6527
SIC 2731 2721 7372 7812

SESAME WORKSHOP p 1308
1 Lincoln Plz Fl 2, New York NY 10023
Tel (212) 595-3456 *SIC* 7812 2731

■ **SIMON & SCHUSTER INC** p 1324
1230 Ave Of The Americas, New York NY 10020
Tel (212) 698-7000
SIC 2731 2741 7372 8732

■ **STERLING PUBLISHING CO INC** p 1387
1166 Avenue Of The Flr 17, New York NY 10036
Tel (212) 532-7160 *SIC* 5192 2731

▲ **TIME WARNER INC** p 1454
1 Time Warner Ctr Bsmt B, New York NY 10019
Tel (212) 484-8000
SIC 4841 7812 2731 2721

TRUSTED MEDIA BRANDS INC p 1487
750 3rd Ave Fl 3, New York NY 10017
Tel (914) 238-1000
SIC 2721 2731 5961 2741

■ **VIACOM SONGS INC** p 1554
1515 Broadway Lbby, New York NY 10036
Tel (212) 258-6000
SIC 6531 6519 7359 7941 7812 2731

W W NORTON & CO INC p 1569
500 5th Ave Fl 6, New York NY 10110
Tel (212) 354-5500 *SIC* 2731 5192

WORKMAN PUBLISHING CO INC p 1624
225 Varick St Fl 9, New York NY 10014
Tel (212) 254-5900 *SIC* 2731

PEARSON LONGMAN LLC p 1126
10 Bank St Ste 1030, White Plains NY 10606
Tel (212) 641-2400 *SIC* 2731 2711

BAKER & TAYLOR ACQUISITIONS CORP p 145
2550 W Tyvola Rd Ste 300, Charlotte NC 28217
Tel (704) 998-3100 *SIC* 2731

CENTER FOR CREATIVE LEADERSHIP INC p 275
1 Leadership Pl, Greensboro NC 27410
Tel (336) 288-7210 *SIC* 8299 2731

F+W MEDIA INC p 523
10151 Carver Rd Ste 200, Blue Ash OH 45242
Tel (513) 531-2690 *SIC* 2731 2721

■ **GOLF GALAXY GOLFWORKS INC** p 622
4820 Jacksontown Rd, Newark OH 43056
Tel (740) 328-4193
SIC 5091 2731 3949 5941

PENNWELL CORP p 1131
1421 S Sheridan Rd, Tulsa OK 74112
Tel (918) 835-3161
SIC 2721 2731 2741 7389

OFFSET PAPERBACK MFRS INC p 1076
2211 Memorial Hwy, Dallas PA 18612
Tel (570) 675-5261 *SIC* 2731 2752

RODALE INC p 1246
400 S 10th St, Emmaus PA 18049
Tel (800) 848-4735 *SIC* 2721 2731

WOLTERS KLUWER HEALTH INC p 1621
2001 Market St Lbby 1, Philadelphia PA 19103
Tel (215) 521-8300
SIC 2721 2731 2741 7372 8748

AMERICAN BOOK CO p 69
10267 Kingston Pike, Knoxville TN 37922
Tel (865) 966-7454 *SIC* 5192 2731

■ **CHRISTIAN HARPERCOLLINS PUBLISHING INC** p 302
501 Nelson Pl, Nashville TN 37214
Tel (615) 889-9000 *SIC* 2731

LIFEWAY CHRISTIAN RESOURCES OF SOUTHERN BAPTIST CONVENTION p 865
1 Lifeway Plz, Nashville TN 37234
Tel (615) 251-2000
SIC 5942 5963 2731 5999 5735 5947

UNITED METHODIST PUBLISHING HOUSE p 1510
2222 Rosa L Parks Blvd, Nashville TN 37228
Tel (615) 749-6000
SIC 2731 5192 5942 2741 2721

■ **CAMBIUM LEARNING INC** p 244
17855 Dallas Pkwy Ste 400, Dallas TX 75287
Tel (214) 932-9500 *SIC* 2731

TAYLOR PUBLISHING CO p 1427
1550 W Mockingbird Ln, Dallas TX 75235
Tel (214) 819-8321 *SIC* 2731 2732

DESERET BOOK CO p 432
57 W South Temple, Salt Lake City UT 84101
Tel (801) 517-3294 *SIC* 5192 5942 2731

AIRLINE TARIFF PUBLISHING CO p 40
45005 Aviation Dr Ste 400, Dulles VA 20166
Tel (703) 661-7400 *SIC* 2721 7374 2731

ONE UP ENTERPRISES INC p 1086
7777 Lsburg Pike Ste 302s, Falls Church VA 22043
Tel (703) 448-7333
SIC 2731 2711 2092 6531

INTERNATIONAL MISSION BOARD OF SOUTHERN BAPTIST CONVENTION p 756
3806 Monument Ave, Richmond VA 23230
Tel (804) 353-0151 *SIC* 8661 2731 7812

INTERVARSITY CHRISTIAN FELLOWSHIP/USA p 759
635 Science Dr, Madison WI 53711
Tel (608) 274-9001 *SIC* 8661 2731 7032

■ **AMERICAN GIRL BRANDS LLC** p 73
8400 Fairway Pl, Middleton WI 53562
Tel (608) 836-4848 *SIC* 5945 2731

SIC 2732 Book Printing, Not Publishing

POST COMMUNITY MEDIA LLC p 1163
1301 K St Nw, Washington DC 20071
Tel (301) 670-2565 *SIC* 2711 2732 2721

▲ **RR DONNELLEY & SONS CO** p 1255
35 W Wacker Dr Ste 3650, Chicago IL 60601
Tel (312) 326-8000
SIC 2754 2759 2752 2732 7331 7336

■ **COURIER KENDALLVILLE INC** p 383
2500 Marion Dr, Kendallville IN 46755
Tel (260) 347-3044 *SIC* 2732

■ **PHOENIX COLOR CORP** p 1144
18249 Phoenix Rd, Hagerstown MD 21742
Tel (301) 733-0018 *SIC* 2732 3469 2796

SHERIDAN GROUP INC p 1315
11311 Mccormick Rd # 260, Hunt Valley MD 21031
Tel (410) 785-7277 *SIC* 2752 2732

COURIER CORP p 383
15 Wellman Ave, North Chelmsford MA 01863
Tel (978) 251-6000 *SIC* 2732 2731

EDWARDS BROTHERS INC p 480
5411 Jackson Rd, Ann Arbor MI 48103
Tel (800) 722-3231 *SIC* 2732 2789

EDWARDS BROTHERS MALLOY INC p 480
5411 Jackson Rd, Ann Arbor MI 48103
Tel (734) 665-6113 *SIC* 2732

■ **TWEDDLE GROUP INC** p 1494
24700 Maplehurst Dr, Clinton Township MI 48036
Tel (586) 307-3700
SIC 2732 2791 2752 2759 2741 7371

D & J PRINTING INC p 406
3323 Oak St, Brainerd MN 56401
Tel (218) 829-2877 *SIC* 2752 2789 2732

AM BEST CO INC p 63
1 Ambest Rd, Oldwick NJ 08858
Tel (908) 439-2200 *SIC* 2731 2721 2732

COMMAND WEB OFFSET CO INC p 344
100 Castle Rd, Secaucus NJ 07094
Tel (201) 863-8100 *SIC* 2752 2732

COLLEGE ENTRANCE EXAMINATION BOARD p 336
250 Vesey St, New York NY 10281
Tel (212) 713-8000 *SIC* 8299 8221 2732

TNC (US) HOLDINGS INC p 1458
770 Broadway Fl 8, New York NY 10003
Tel (646) 654-5500
SIC 8732 2721 2732 2741

HF GROUP LLC p 688
8844 Mayfield Rd, Chesterland OH 44026
Tel (440) 729-2445 *SIC* 2732

QUEBECOR WORLD JOHNSON & HARDIN CO p 1198
3600 Red Bank Rd, Cincinnati OH 45227
Tel (614) 326-0299 *SIC* 2759 2752 2732

MAPLE PRESS CO p 903
480 Willow Springs Ln, York PA 17406
Tel (717) 764-5911
SIC 2732 2791 2789 2752

TAYLOR PUBLISHING CO p 1427
1550 W Mockingbird Ln, Dallas TX 75235
Tel (214) 819-8321 *SIC* 2731 2732

BERRYVILLE GRAPHICS INC p 176
25 Jack Enders Blvd, Berryville VA 22611
Tel (540) 955-2750 *SIC* 2732 2752 2789

WORZALLA PUBLISHING CO p 1626
3535 Jefferson St, Stevens Point WI 54481
Tel (715) 344-9600 *SIC* 2732

SIC 2741 Misc Publishing

PENNYSAVER USA PUBLISHING LLC p 1131
2830 Orbiter St, Brea CA 92821
Tel (866) 640-3900 *SIC* 2741

1105 MEDIA INC p 1
9201 Oakdale Ave Ste 101, Chatsworth CA 91311
Tel (818) 814-5200
SIC 7313 7389 2721 2741 8748

AGI PUBLISHING INC p 35
1850 N Gateway Blvd # 152, Fresno CA 93727
Tel (559) 251-8888 *SIC* 2741

NATIONAL HOT ROD ASSOCIATION p 1013
2035 E Financial Way, Glendora CA 91741
Tel (626) 914-4761 *SIC* 7948 2711 2741

AUGE MEDIA CORP p 131
2029 Century Park E Fl 14, Los Angeles CA 90067
Tel (310) 739-8000 *SIC* 2741 7812

WARNER/CHAPPELL MUSIC INC p 1576
10585 Santa Monica Blvd # 300, Los Angeles CA 90025
Tel (310) 441-8600 *SIC* 2741

▲ **NETFLIX INC** p 1027
100 Winchester Cir, Los Gatos CA 95032
Tel (408) 540-3700 *SIC* 2741 7841

■ **UNIVERSAL STUDIOS INC** p 1517
100 Universal City Plz, North Hollywood CA 91608
Tel (818) 777-1000
SIC 7812 3652 2741 5947 5944 5961

TRANSWESTERN PUBLISHING CO LLC p 1473
8344 Clairemont Mesa Blvd, San Diego CA 92111
Tel (858) 467-2800 *SIC* 2741

PACIFIC BELL DIRECTORY p 1104
101 Spear St Fl 5, San Francisco CA 94105
Tel (800) 303-3000 *SIC* 2741

■ **PACIFIC BELL TELEPHONE CO** p 1104
430 Bush St Fl 3, San Francisco CA 94108
Tel (415) 542-9000 *SIC* 4813 2741 4822

2100 FREEDOM INC p 1
625 N Grand Ave, Santa Ana CA 92701
Tel (714) 796-7000
SIC 2711 2721 7313 2741 5963 4813

FREEDOM COMMUNICATIONS INC p 576
625 N Grand Ave, Santa Ana CA 92701
Tel (714) 796-7000
SIC 2711 2721 7313 2741 5963

UNIVERSAL MUSIC GROUP INC p 1517
2220 Colorado Ave, Santa Monica CA 90404
Tel (310) 865-4000 *SIC* 7389 2741

OREILLY MEDIA INC p 1094
1005 Gravenstein Hwy N, Sebastopol CA 95472
Tel (707) 827-7000 *SIC* 2731 2741

■ **UNIVERSAL CITY STUDIOS PRODUCTIONS LLLP LP** p 1516
100 Universal City Plz, Universal City CA 91608
Tel (818) 777-1000
SIC 7812 3652 2741 5947 5944 5961

AGI HOLDING CORP p 35
2575 Vista Del Mar Dr, Ventura CA 93001
Tel (805) 667-4100 *SIC* 7997 2741

■ **JEPPESEN SANDERSON INC** p 783
55 Inverness Dr E, Englewood CO 80112
Tel (303) 799-9090 *SIC* 2741 2731 8748

■ **SOUTHERN NEW ENGLAND TELECOMMUNICATIONS CORP** p 1349
2 Science Park, New Haven CT 06511
Tel (203) 771-5200
SIC 4813 4812 5065 6159 2741 4822

YALE UNIVERSITY p 1634
105 Wall St, New Haven CT 06511
Tel (203) 432-2550
SIC 8221 2731 2721 2741

STAMFORD CAPITAL GROUP INC p 1375
1266 E Main St Ste 700r, Stamford CT 06902
Tel (800) 977-7837 *SIC* 2741 6211

■ **VERIZON DELAWARE LLC** p 1550
901 N Tatnall St Fl 2, Wilmington DE 19801
Tel (302) 571-1571
SIC 4813 4812 7373 2741

BROOKINGS INSTITUTION p 218
1775 Massachusetts Ave Nw, Washington DC 20036
Tel (202) 797-6000 *SIC* 8733 2741 8621

AMERICAN MEDIA INC p 75
301 Yamato Rd Ste 4200, Boca Raton FL 33431
Tel (561) 997-7733 *SIC* 2711 2741

AMERICAN MEDIA OPERATIONS INC p 75
1000 American Media Way, Boca Raton FL 33464
Tel (561) 997-7733 *SIC* 2711 2741

NEWSMAX MEDIA INC p 1039
750 Park Of Commerce Dr # 100, Boca Raton FL 33487
Tel (561) 686-1165 *SIC* 2721 2741

IF MUSIC INC p 730
401 Orange St, Palm Harbor FL 34683
Tel (727) 515-3004 *SIC* 2741

QUANTUM SPATIAL INC p 1198
10033 Mlk St N Ste 200, Saint Petersburg FL 33716
Tel (920) 457-3631 *SIC* 2741 8713

▲ **NEENAH PAPER INC** p 1024
3460 Preston Ridge Rd # 150, Alpharetta GA 30005
Tel (678) 566-6500 *SIC* 2621 2741

■ **BELLSOUTH CORP** p 171
675 W Peach St Ste 4300, Atlanta GA 30375
Tel (404) 420-6126
SIC 4813 4812 2741 5065

■ **BELLSOUTH TELECOMMUNICATIONS INC** p 171
675 W Peach St Ne St Ne, Atlanta GA 30375
Tel (912) 526-3440
SIC 4813 4812 2741 5065

GEORGIA MUNICIPAL ASSOCIATION INC p 607
201 Pryor St Sw, Atlanta GA 30303
Tel (404) 688-0472 SIC 2711 2741 8611

CONSUMER SOURCE INC p 361
3585 Engrg Dr Ste 100, Norcross GA 30092
Tel (678) 421-3000 SIC 2741

■YP ADVERTISING & PUBLISHING LLC p 1639
2247 Northlake Pkwy, Tucker GA 30084
Tel (678) 406-5523 SIC 2741 7313 7311

■AT&T TELEHOLDINGS INC p 123
30 S Wacker Dr Fl 34, Chicago IL 60606
Tel (800) 257-0902
SIC 4813 4812 2741 5065 6159 7382

CISION US INC p 309
130 E Randolph St Fl 7, Chicago IL 60601
Tel (312) 922-2400 SIC 7389 2741 7331

QUINCY MEDIA INC p 1200
130 S 5th St, Quincy IL 62301
Tel (217) 223-5100
SIC 2711 4833 2752 2741

WOLTERS KLUWER UNITED STATES INC p 1621
2700 Lake Cook Rd, Riverwoods IL 60015
Tel (847) 580-5000
SIC 2731 2721 2741 2759

HERFF JONES LLC p 685
4501 W 62nd St, Indianapolis IN 46268
Tel (800) 837-4235 SIC 3911 2721 2741

WOODWARD COMMUNICATIONS INC p 1623
801 Bluff St, Dubuque IA 52001
Tel (563) 588-5611
SIC 2711 2741 4832 2752 7311

AGORA INC p 35
14 W Mount Vernon Pl, Baltimore MD 21201
Tel (410) 783-8499 SIC 2741 7331

ACCESS INTELLIGENCE LLC p 15
9211 Corp Blvd Fl 4, Rockville MD 20850
Tel (301) 354-2000 SIC 2741 2721

ABRY PARTNERS INC p 12
888 Boylston St Ste 1600, Boston MA 02199
Tel (617) 859-2959 SIC 4899 2741

HARVARD BUSINESS SCHOOL PUBLISHING CORP p 666
20 Guest St Ste 700, Brighton MA 02135
Tel (617) 783-7400 SIC 2721 2731 2741

LETS GO INC p 857
67 Mount Auburn St, Cambridge MA 02138
Tel (617) 495-9659 SIC 2741

EBSCO PUBLISHING INC p 474
10 Estes St, Ipswich MA 01938
Tel (978) 356-6500
SIC 2741 7375 2731 2721

EDUCATION DEVELOPMENT CENTER INC p 479
43 Foundry Ave, Waltham MA 02453
Tel (617) 969-7100 SIC 8732 2741

■TWEDDLE GROUP INC p 1494
24700 Maplehurst Dr, Clinton Township MI 48036
Tel (586) 307-3700
SIC 2732 2791 2752 2759 2741 7371

■AMERITECH PUBLISHING INC p 84
23500 Northwestern Hwy, Southfield MI 48075
Tel (800) 996-4609 SIC 2741

LIFETOUCH CHURCH DIRECTORIES AND PORTRAITS INC p 865
11000 Viking Dr Ste 400, Eden Prairie MN 55344
Tel (952) 826-4000 SIC 7221 2741

LIFETOUCH INC p 865
11000 Viking Dr, Eden Prairie MN 55344
Tel (952) 826-4000 SIC 7221 7812 2741

DOLAN LLC p 447
222 S 9th St Ste 2300, Minneapolis MN 55402
Tel (612) 317-9420
SIC 7375 2741 2711 2752

ECM PUBLISHERS INC p 475
4095 Coon Rapids Blvd Nw, Minneapolis MN 55433
Tel (763) 712-2400
SIC 2711 2741 7319 2789 2752

■JOSTENS INC p 794
3601 Minnesota Dr Ste 400, Minneapolis MN 55435
Tel (952) 830-3300 SIC 3911 2759 2741

■VISANT CORP p 1560
3601 Minnesota Dr Ste 400, Minneapolis MN 55435
Tel (914) 595-8200
SIC 3911 2741 2389 7221

■VISANT HOLDING CORP p 1561
3601 Minnesota Dr Ste 400, Minneapolis MN 55435
Tel (914) 595-8200
SIC 2741 2759 3911 6719

UNIVERSITY OF ST THOMAS p 1525
2115 Summit Ave, Saint Paul MN 55105
Tel (651) 962-5000 SIC 8221 2741 2721

WALSWORTH PUBLISHING CO INC p 1574
306 N Kansas Ave, Marceline MO 64658
Tel (660) 376-3543 SIC 2741 2752

ROMAN CATHOLIC BISHOP OF HELENA MONTANA p 1248
515 N Ewing St, Helena MT 59601
Tel (406) 442-5820
SIC 8661 8211 8221 2741

BOOKAZINE CO INC p 200
75 Hook Rd, Bayonne NJ 07002
Tel (201) 339-7777 SIC 5192 2741

■VISANT SECONDARY HOLDINGS CORP p 1561
357 Main St, Armonk NY 10504
Tel (914) 595-8200 SIC 2741

COLD SPRING HARBOR LABORATORY ASSOCIATION INC p 335
1 Bungtown Rd, Cold Spring Harbor NY 11724
Tel (516) 367-8446
SIC 8733 2731 2741 8249

HIBU INC p 690
90 Merrick Ave Ste 530, East Meadow NY 11554
Tel (516) 730-1900 SIC 2741

ALM MEDIA HOLDINGS INC p 59
120 Broadway Fl 5, New York NY 10271
Tel (212) 457-9400
SIC 2721 2711 2741 2731 7389

ALM MEDIA LLC p 59
120 Broadway Fl 5, New York NY 10271
Tel (212) 457-9400
SIC 2721 2711 2741 2731 7389

■BUCK CONSULTANTS LLC p 222
485 Lexington Ave Fl 10, New York NY 10017
Tel (212) 330-1000 SIC 8742 6282 2741

CAMBRIDGE INFORMATION GROUP INC p 244
888 7th Ave Ste 1701, New York NY 10106
Tel (301) 961-6700 SIC 2741

ELSEVIER INC p 489
230 Park Ave Fl 7, New York NY 10169
Tel (212) 633-3773 SIC 2741

■GTE CORP p 644
140 West St, New York NY 10007
Tel (212) 395-1000
SIC 4813 4812 3661 3663 4899 2741

■HISTORIC TW INC p 696
75 Rockefeller Plz, New York NY 10019
Tel (212) 484-8000
SIC 3652 6794 2741 7812 4841 2721

JOBSON MEDICAL INFORMATION LLC p 787
440 9th Ave Fl 14, New York NY 10001
Tel (212) 274-7000 SIC 2721 2741

MOSBY HOLDINGS CORP p 992
125 Park Ave, New York NY 10017
Tel (212) 309-8100 SIC 2741 8999

RDA HOLDING CO p 1212
750 3rd Ave, New York NY 10017
Tel (914) 238-1000
SIC 2721 2731 5961 2741

■SIMON & SCHUSTER INC p 1324
1230 Ave Of The Americas, New York NY 10020
Tel (212) 698-7000
SIC 2731 2741 7372 8732

SONY MUSIC HOLDINGS INC p 1341
550 Madison Ave Fl 16, New York NY 10022
Tel (212) 833-8000 SIC 3652 5099 2741

THOMAS PUBLISHING CO LLC p 1449
5 Penn Plz Fl 9, New York NY 10001
Tel (212) 695-0500
SIC 2741 2721 7374 7331

■THOMSON REUTERS CORP p 1450
3 Times Sq Lbby Mailroom, New York NY 10036
Tel (646) 223-4000
SIC 2741 8111 7372 7383

TNC (US) HOLDINGS INC p 1458
770 Broadway Fl 8, New York NY 10003
Tel (646) 654-5500
SIC 8732 2721 2732 2741

TRUSTED MEDIA BRANDS INC p 1487
750 3rd Ave Fl 3, New York NY 10017
Tel (914) 238-1000
SIC 2721 2731 5961 2741

UBM INC p 1498
2 Penn Plz, New York NY 10121
Tel (212) 600-3000
SIC 2721 2711 8732 2741

■VIVENDI UNIVERSAL ENTERTAINMENT LLLP p 1563
30 Rockefeller Plz, New York NY 10112
Tel (212) 664-4444
SIC 7812 3652 2741 5947 5944 5961

WARNER MUSIC INC p 1576
75 Rockefeller Plz Bsmt 1, New York NY 10019
Tel (212) 275-2000 SIC 3652 2741

WASSERSTEIN & CO LP p 1580
1185 Avenue Of The Americ, New York NY 10036
Tel (212) 702-5600 SIC 6799 2721 2741

WASSERSTEIN HOLDINGS LLC p 1580
1301 Avenue Of The Americ, New York NY 10019
Tel (212) 702-5600 SIC 6799 2721 2741

WMG ACQUISITION CORP p 1620
75 Rockefeller Plz, New York NY 10019
Tel (212) 275-2000 SIC 2782 2741 7929

WMG HOLDING CO INC p 1620
75 Rockefeller Plz, New York NY 10019
Tel (212) 275-2000 SIC 3652 2741

CONSUMERS UNION OF UNITED STATES INC p 362
101 Truman Ave, Yonkers NY 10703
Tel (914) 378-2000 SIC 2741 2721 7389

DEX ONE CORP p 434
1001 Winstead Dr Ste 100, Cary NC 27513
Tel (919) 297-1600 SIC 2741 8732

■NEWS AND OBSERVER PUBLISHING CO p 1039
215 S Mcdowell St, Raleigh NC 27601
Tel (919) 829-4500
SIC 2711 2741 2721 2752

PENTON BUSINESS MEDIA INC p 1132
1100 Superior Ave E Fl 8, Cleveland OH 44114
Tel (216) 696-7000 SIC 2741 7379

LEXISNEXIS GROUP p 859
9443 Springboro Pike, Miamisburg OH 45342
Tel (937) 865-6800 SIC 7375 2741

■L M BERRY AND CO p 834
3170 Kettering Blvd, Moraine OH 45439
Tel (937) 296-2121 SIC 7311 2741

■SNAP-ON BUSINESS SOLUTIONS INC p 1335
4025 Kinross Lakes Pkwy, Richfield OH 44286
Tel (330) 659-1600 SIC 2741

PENNWELL CORP p 1131
1421 S Sheridan Rd, Tulsa OK 74112
Tel (918) 835-3161
SIC 2721 2731 2741 7389

OREGON COMMUNITY FOUNDATION p 1093
1221 Sw Yamhill St Ste 100, Portland OR 97205
Tel (503) 227-6846 SIC 8399 2741

KAPPA MEDIA GROUP INC p 803
40 Skippack Pike, Fort Washington PA 19034
Tel (215) 643-5800 SIC 2721 2741 5111

AMERICAN FUTURE SYSTEMS INC p 73
370 Technology Dr, Malvern PA 19355
Tel (610) 695-8600 SIC 2741 8742

■THOMSON REUTERS (SCIENTIFIC) LLC p 1450
1500 Spring Garden St # 400, Philadelphia PA 19130
Tel (215) 386-0100 SIC 2741 7372

WOLTERS KLUWER HEALTH INC p 1621
2001 Market St Lbby 1, Philadelphia PA 19103
Tel (215) 521-8300
SIC 2721 2731 2741 7372 8748

MM USA HOLDINGS LLC p 979
780 Township Line Rd, Yardley PA 19067
Tel (267) 685-2300 SIC 2741 8732

UNITED METHODIST PUBLISHING HOUSE p 1510
2222 Rosa L Parks Blvd, Nashville TN 37228
Tel (615) 749-6000
SIC 2731 5192 5942 2741 2721

AMERICAN ACHIEVEMENT CORP p 67
7211 Circle S Rd, Austin TX 78745
Tel (512) 444-0571 SIC 3911 2741

▲AT&T INC p 123
208 S Akard St, Dallas TX 75202
Tel (210) 821-4105
SIC 4813 4812 3663 3661 2741

■VOYAGER LEARNING CO p 1566
17855 Dallas Pkwy Ste 400, Dallas TX 75287
Tel (214) 932-9500 SIC 2741 2759

DEX MEDIA INC p 434
2200 W Airfield Dr, Dfw Airport TX 75261
Tel (972) 453-7000 SIC 2741 7311

SUPERMEDIA INC p 1407
2200 W Airfield Dr, Dfw Airport TX 75261
Tel (972) 453-7000 SIC 2741

SUPERMEDIA LLC p 1407
2200 W Airfield Dr, Dfw Airport TX 75261
Tel (972) 453-7000 SIC 2741 6719

HARCOURT ASSESSMENT INC p 660
19500 Bulverde Rd, San Antonio TX 78259
Tel (210) 339-5000 SIC 8748 2741

USER FRIENDLY PHONE BOOK LLC p 1535
10200 Grogans Mill Rd # 440, The Woodlands TX 77380
Tel (281) 465-5400 SIC 2741

▲FRANKLIN COVEY CO p 575
2200 W Parkway Blvd, Salt Lake City UT 84119
Tel (801) 817-1776 SIC 8742 8331 2741

O C TANNER CO p 1070
1930 S State St, Salt Lake City UT 84115
Tel (801) 486-2430 SIC 3911 2759 2741

■CADMUS JOURNAL SERVICES INC p 236
2901 Byrdhill Rd, Henrico VA 23228
Tel (804) 287-5680 SIC 2752 2721 2741

■GANNETT RIVER STATES PUBLISHING CORP p 591
7950 Jones Branch Dr, Mc Lean VA 22102
Tel (703) 284-6000 SIC 2711 2741

DOMINION ENTERPRISES p 449
150 Granby St Ste 150, Norfolk VA 23510
Tel (757) 351-7000 SIC 7374 2721 2741

OGDEN NEWSPAPERS INC p 1076
1500 Main St, Wheeling WV 26003
Tel (304) 233-0100
SIC 2711 2754 2741 2791 2752

ALDRICH CHEMICAL CO LLC p 48
6000 N Teutonia Ave, Milwaukee WI 53209
Tel (414) 438-3850
SIC 2869 2819 3821 7371 2741

HAL LEONARD CORP p 653
7777 W Bluemound Rd, Milwaukee WI 53213
Tel (414) 774-3630 SIC 2741

J J KELLER & ASSOCIATES INC p 771
3003 Breezewood Ln, Neenah WI 54956
Tel (920) 722-2848 SIC 2741 8742

JOURNAL COMMUNITY PUBLISHING GROUP INC p 794
600 Industrial Dr, Waupaca WI 54981
Tel (715) 258-8450 SIC 2741 2711

SIC 2752 Commercial Printing: Lithographic

UPPER DECK CO LLC p 1529
2251 Rutherford Rd, Carlsbad CA 92008
Tel (800) 873-7332 SIC 2752 5947

SOUTHWEST OFFSET PRINTING CO INC p 1352
13650 Gramercy Pl, Gardena CA 90249
Tel (310) 965-9154 SIC 2752

LITHOGRAPHIX INC p 870
12250 Crenshaw Blvd, Hawthorne CA 90250
Tel (323) 770-1000 SIC 2752 2759

TREND OFFSET PRINTING SERVICES INC p 1476
3701 Catalina St, Los Alamitos CA 90720
Tel (562) 598-2446 SIC 2752

■MADISON/GRAHAM COLOR GRAPHICS INC p 894
150 N Myers St, Los Angeles CA 90033
Tel (323) 261-7171 SIC 2752 7336 2796

PACIFIC SOUTHWEST CONTAINER LLC p 1106
4530 Leckron Rd, Modesto CA 95357
Tel (209) 526-0444
SIC 2671 2657 3086 2653 2752

BREHM COMMUNICATIONS INC p 209
16644 W Bernardo Dr # 300, San Diego CA 92127
Tel (858) 451-6200 SIC 2752 2711

KP LLC p 828
13951 Washington Ave, San Leandro CA 94578
Tel (510) 346-0729
SIC 2752 7334 7331 7374 7389 8742

ALLIED PRINTING SERVICES INC p 56
1 Allied Way, Manchester CT 06042
Tel (860) 643-1101
SIC 2396 2752 2759 2789 2791

■WORLD COLOR (USA) HOLDING CO p 1625
291 State St, North Haven CT 06473
Tel (203) 288-2468 SIC 2752 2754

■CENVEO CORP p 283
200 First Stamford Pl # 200, Stamford CT 06902
Tel (303) 790-8023 SIC 2677 2752 2759

■MACDERMID INC p 892
245 Freight St, Waterbury CT 06702
Tel (203) 575-5700
SIC 2899 2842 2874 2992 2752 3577

WISE BUSINESS FORMS INC p 1619
555 Mcfarland 400 Dr, Alpharetta GA 30004
Tel (770) 442-1060 SIC 2761 2752

COMMUNITY NEWSPAPERS INC p 349
2365 Prince Ave A, Athens GA 30606
Tel (706) 548-0010 SIC 2752

ISD HOLDINGS INC p 766
4715 Frederick Dr Sw, Atlanta GA 30336
Tel (404) 691-7400
SIC 7389 2542 2759 2752

MILLER ZELL INC p 971
6100 Fulton Indus Blvd Sw, Atlanta GA 30336
Tel (404) 691-7400
SIC 7389 2542 2759 2752

MARKETING ALLIANCE GROUP INC p 908
2830 N Dug Gap Rd Sw, Dalton GA 30720
Tel (706) 277-9707 SIC 2752

JOHN H HARLAND CO p 788
2939 Miller Rd, Decatur GA 30035
Tel (770) 593-5050
SIC 2782 2752 2761 7371 7379

CURTIS 1000 INC p 402
1725 Breckinridge Park, Duluth GA 30096
Tel (770) 925-4500
SIC 2761 2759 2791 2789 2752

WALLE CORP p 1573
200 Hembree Park Dr Ste H, Roswell GA 30076
Tel (800) 942-6761 SIC 2759 2752 2671

MORRIS MULTIMEDIA INC p 990
27 Abercorn St, Savannah GA 31401
Tel (912) 233-1281 SIC 4833 2752

AMERICAN LITHO INC p 75
175 Mercedes Dr, Carol Stream IL 60188
Tel (630) 462-1700 SIC 2752

CHICAGO SUN-TIMES FEATURES INC p 297
350 N Orleans St Fl 10, Chicago IL 60654
Tel (312) 321-3000 SIC 2711 2752

COLOR COMMUNICATIONS INC p 338
4000 W Fillmore St, Chicago IL 60624
Tel (773) 638-1400 SIC 2752 3993

▲INNERWORKINGS INC p 744
600 W Chicago Ave Ste 850, Chicago IL 60654
Tel (312) 642-3700 SIC 2752 7374 7372

QST INDUSTRIES INC p 1195
550 W Adams St Ste 200, Chicago IL 60661
Tel (312) 930-9400 SIC 2396 2392 2752

▲RR DONNELLEY & SONS CO p 1255
35 W Wacker Dr Ste 3650, Chicago IL 60601
Tel (312) 326-8000
SIC 2754 2759 2752 2732 7331 7336

■RR DONNELLEY PRINTING CO LP p 1255
111 S Wacker Dr Ste 3500, Chicago IL 60606
Tel (312) 326-8000 SIC 2754 2752 5085

HOLDEN INDUSTRIES INC p 700
500 Lake Cook Rd Ste 400, Deerfield IL 60015
Tel (847) 940-1500
SIC 2752 2672 3545 3589 3541 3441

FORT DEARBORN CO p 568
1530 Morse Ave, Elk Grove Village IL 60007
Tel (847) 357-9500 SIC 2752 2759

SMALL NEWSPAPER GROUP p 1332
8 Dearborn Sq, Kankakee IL 60901
Tel (815) 937-3300 SIC 2711 2791 2752

VALID USA INC p 1540
1011 Warrenville Rd # 450, Lisle IL 60532
Tel (630) 852-8200 SIC 2752

MOLINE DISPATCH PUBLISHING CO p 983
1720 5th Ave, Moline IL 61265
Tel (309) 764-4344 SIC 2711 2752

SPECIALTY PROMOTIONS INC p 1356
6019 W Howard St, Niles IL 60714
Tel (847) 588-2580 SIC 2752

QUINCY MEDIA INC p 1200
130 S 5th St, Quincy IL 62301
Tel (217) 223-5100
SIC 2711 4833 2752 2741

THREE-Z PRINTING CO p 1451
902 W Main St, Teutopolis IL 62467
Tel (217) 857-3153 SIC 2752

NOSCO INC p 1062
651 S Ml King Jr Ave, Waukegan IL 60085
Tel (847) 336-4200 SIC 2752 2657

SEGERDAHL CORP p 1300
1351 Wheeling Rd, Wheeling IL 60090
Tel (847) 541-1080 SIC 2752

SEGERDAHL GRAPHICS INC p 1300
1351 Wheeling Rd, Wheeling IL 60090
Tel (847) 541-1080 SIC 2752 8742

MADDEN COMMUNICATIONS INC p 893
901 Mittel Dr, Wood Dale IL 60191
Tel (630) 787-2200 SIC 2752

■INDIANA NEWSPAPERS LLC p 738
130 S Meridian St, Indianapolis IN 46225
Tel (317) 444-4000 SIC 2711 2752

COLWELL INC p 343
2605 Marion Dr, Kendallville IN 46755
Tel (260) 347-1981 SIC 2752

GAZETTE CO p 594
500 3rd Ave Se, Cedar Rapids IA 52401
Tel (319) 398-8211 SIC 2711 2752 4833

MITTERA GROUP INC p 978
1312 Locust St Ste 202, Des Moines IA 50309
Tel (515) 343-5353 SIC 2752 7319

WOODWARD COMMUNICATIONS INC p 1623
801 Bluff St, Dubuque IA 52001
Tel (563) 588-5611
SIC 2711 2741 4832 2752 7311

■UNITED STATES PLAYING CARD CO p 1514
300 Gap Way, Erlanger KY 41018
Tel (859) 815-7300 SIC 2752 5092

■HENNEGAN CO p 683
7455 Empire Dr, Florence KY 41042
Tel (859) 282-3600 SIC 2752 2789

LANDMARK COMMUNITY NEWSPAPERS OF KENTUCKY LLC p 842
601 Taylorsville Rd, Shelbyville KY 40065
Tel (502) 633-4334 SIC 2711 2752

PUBLISHERS PRINTING CO LLC p 1190
100 Frank E Simon Ave, Shepherdsville KY 40165
Tel (502) 955-6526 SIC 2752 2791 2789

CAPITAL CITY PRESS LLC p 249
10705 Reiger Rd, Baton Rouge LA 70809
Tel (225) 383-1111 SIC 2711 2752

CHAMPION INDUSTRIES INC p 287
10848 Airline Hwy, Baton Rouge LA 70816
Tel (225) 291-9090
SIC 2542 2759 2791 2789 2752

GEIGER BROS p 597
70 Mount Hope Ave, Lewiston ME 04240
Tel (207) 755-2000
SIC 5199 3993 2752 2782 2789

SHERIDAN GROUP INC p 1315
11311 Mccormick Rd # 260, Hunt Valley MD 21031
Tel (410) 785-7277 SIC 2752 2732

WEBB-MASON INC p 1586
10830 Gilroy Rd, Hunt Valley MD 21031
Tel (410) 785-1111 SIC 2752

TRUSTEES OF TUFTS COLLEGE p 1488
169 Holland St Ste 318, Somerville MA 02144
Tel (617) 628-5000 SIC 8221 2791 2752

CIMPRESS USA INC p 307
275 Wyman St Ste 100, Waltham MA 02451
Tel (866) 614-8002 SIC 2752

UNIVERSAL WILDE INC p 1518
26 Dartmouth St Ste 1, Westwood MA 02090
Tel (781) 251-2700 SIC 2752

EPI PRINTERS INC p 505
5404 Wayne Rd, Battle Creek MI 49037
Tel (800) 562-9733 SIC 2752

■ TWEDDLE GROUP INC p 1494
24700 Maplehurst Dr, Clinton Township MI 48036
Tel (586) 307-3700
SIC 2732 2791 2752 2759 2741 7371

VALASSIS INTERNATIONAL INC p 1539
19975 Victor Pkwy, Livonia MI 48152
Tel (734) 591-3000
SIC 8743 3993 2759 2752

NTVB MEDIA INC p 1066
209 Park Dr, Troy MI 48083
Tel (248) 583-4190 SIC 2752

D & J PRINTING INC p 406
3323 Oak St, Brainerd MN 56401
Tel (218) 829-2877 SIC 2752 2789 2732

GLS COMPANIES p 618
6845 Winnetka Cir, Brooklyn Park MN 55428
Tel (763) 535-7277 SIC 2752

SCANTRON CORP p 1286
1313 Lone Oak Rd, Eagan MN 55121
Tel (651) 683-6000
SIC 3577 7372 2752 3575 2761

SMEAD MANUFACTURING CO INC p 1332
600 Smead Blvd, Hastings MN 55033
Tel (651) 437-4111
SIC 2675 7372 2789 2759 2752 2542

TRAVEL TAGS INC p 1473
5842 Carmen Ave, Inver Grove Heights MN 55076
Tel (651) 450-1201 SIC 2396 3999 2752

DATA RECOGNITION CORP p 413
13490 Bass Lake Rd, Maple Grove MN 55311
Tel (763) 268-2000 SIC 8732 2752

BUREAU OF ENGRAVING INC p 226
6465 Wayzata Blvd Ste 240, Minneapolis MN 55426
Tel (612) 788-1000 SIC 2752 8249

DOLAN LLC p 447
222 S 9th St Ste 2300, Minneapolis MN 55402
Tel (612) 317-9420
SIC 7375 2741 2711 2752

ECM PUBLISHERS INC p 475
4095 Coon Rapids Blvd Nw, Minneapolis MN 55433
Tel (763) 712-2400
SIC 2711 2741 7319 2789 2752

PROCESS DISPLAYS LLC p 1179
7108 31st Ave N, Minneapolis MN 55427
Tel (763) 541-1245
SIC 2541 2542 2599 2675 2752 2759

CORPORATE GRAPHICS INTERNATIONAL INC p 372
1885 Northway Dr, North Mankato MN 56003
Tel (507) 625-4400 SIC 2752

PRECISION PRESS INC p 1168
2020 Lookout Dr, North Mankato MN 56003
Tel (507) 625-7155 SIC 2678 2752

TAYLOR CORP p 1427
1725 Roe Crest Dr, North Mankato MN 56003
Tel (507) 625-2828
SIC 8742 2752 2677 2759

NAHAN PRINTING INC p 1006
7000 Saukview Dr, Saint Cloud MN 56303
Tel (320) 217-7700 SIC 2759 2752

COLWELL INDUSTRIES INC p 343
1611 County Road B W # 315, Saint Paul MN 55113
Tel (612) 340-0365 SIC 2752

GG MCGUIGGAN CORP p 610
1085 Snelling Ave N, Saint Paul MN 55108
Tel (651) 646-4544 SIC 2679 3993 2752

MERRILL/GLOBAL INC p 950
1 Merrill Cir Ste 1433, Saint Paul MN 55108
Tel (651) 646-4501 SIC 2759 2752 2791

SMYTH COMPANIES LLC p 1335
1085 Snelling Ave N, Saint Paul MN 55108
Tel (651) 646-4544
SIC 2679 2752 3993 7389 5084 7699

VOMELA SPECIALTY CO p 1565
274 Fillmore Ave E, Saint Paul MN 55107
Tel (651) 228-2200 SIC 7336 2396 2752

JAPS-OLSON CO p 778
7500 Excelsior Blvd, St Louis Park MN 55426
Tel (952) 932-9393
SIC 2752 7331 2791 2759

BURD & FLETCHER CO p 226
5151 E Geospace Dr, Independence MO 64056
Tel (816) 257-0291 SIC 2657 2752 6512

■ BROADRIDGE CUSTOMER COMMUNICATIONS LLC p 215
2600 Southwest Blvd, Kansas City MO 64108
Tel (816) 221-1234
SIC 7389 2759 7374 7331 2752 7336

WALSWORTH PUBLISHING CO INC p 1574
306 N Kansas Ave, Marceline MO 64658
Tel (660) 376-3543 SIC 2741 2752

HENRY WURST INC p 684
1331 Saline St, North Kansas City MO 64116
Tel (816) 701-0825 SIC 2752 7331

■ NIES/ARTCRAFT INC p 1043
3049 Chouteau Ave, Saint Louis MO 63103
Tel (314) 951-0400 SIC 2752

CREEL PRINTING & PUBLISHING CO INC p 391
6330 W Sunset Rd, Las Vegas NV 89118
Tel (702) 735-8161 SIC 2752

AMERICAN BANKNOTE CORP p 68
2200 Fletcher Ave Ste 501, Fort Lee NJ 07024
Tel (201) 592-3400 SIC 2759 2752 2621

DG3 GROUP AMERICA INC p 435
100 Burma Rd, Jersey City NJ 07305
Tel (201) 793-5000 SIC 2752

DG3 HOLDINGS LLC p 435
100 Burma Rd, Jersey City NJ 07305
Tel (201) 793-5000 SIC 2752

DG3 NORTH AMERICA INC p 435
100 Burma Rd, Jersey City NJ 07305
Tel (201) 793-5000 SIC 2752

■ ASBURY PARK PRESS INC p 115
3600 Route 66, Neptune NJ 07753
Tel (732) 922-6000 SIC 2711 2752

■ EARTHCOLOR INC p 469
249 Pomeroy Rd, Parsippany NJ 07054
Tel (973) 884-1300 SIC 2752 2759

COMMAND WEB OFFSET CO INC p 344
100 Castle Rd, Secaucus NJ 07094
Tel (201) 863-8100 SIC 2752 2732

HATTERAS PRESS INC p 668
56 Park Rd, Tinton Falls NJ 07724
Tel (732) 935-9800 SIC 2752 2796

PARIS CORP OF NEW JERSEY p 1115
800 Highland Dr, Westampton NJ 08060
Tel (609) 265-9200 SIC 5112 2752 5063

AMSTERDAM PRINTING & LITHO INC p 87
166 Wallins Corners Rd, Amsterdam NY 12010
Tel (518) 842-6000 SIC 3993 2752 2761

GRAPHIC CONTROLS ACQUISITION CORP p 631
400 Exchange St, Buffalo NY 14204
Tel (716) 853-7500 SIC 2752 2679

GRAPHIC CONTROLS HOLDINGS INC p 631
400 Exchange St, Buffalo NY 14204
Tel (716) 853-7500 SIC 2752 2679 6719

WEEKS-LERMAN GROUP LLC p 1587
5838 Page Pl, Maspeth NY 11378
Tel (718) 803-4700
SIC 5112 5021 2752 5044

■ 21ST CENTURY FOX AMERICA INC p 1
1211 Ave Of The Americas, New York NY 10036
Tel (212) 852-7000
SIC 2752 2721 4833 7812

■ ARCADE INC p 103
1700 Broadway Fl 25, New York NY 10019
Tel (212) 541-2600 SIC 2752

■ DONNELLEY FINANCIAL LLC p 451
55 Water St Lowr L1, New York NY 10041
Tel (212) 425-0298 SIC 2752

MDI HOLDINGS LLC p 933
399 Park Ave Fl 14, New York NY 10022
Tel (212) 559-1127
SIC 2899 2842 2874 2992 2752 3577

RUDER FINN INC p 1257
425 E 53rd St, New York NY 10022
Tel (212) 593-6400 SIC 8743 7311 2752

FLOWER CITY PRINTING INC p 560
1725 Mount Read Blvd, Rochester NY 14606
Tel (585) 663-9000 SIC 2657 2752

CLASSIC GRAPHICS LLC p 323
8335 Classic Dr, Charlotte NC 28262
Tel (704) 597-9015 SIC 2752

MCGRANN PAPER CORP p 929
3800 Arco Corprt Dr # 350, Charlotte NC 28273
Tel (800) 240-9455 SIC 5111 2752

REGULUS INTEGRATED SOLUTIONS LLC p 1220
9645-L Part Blvd, Charlotte NC 28216
Tel (704) 904-8759
SIC 2752 7389 3861 2759

MEASUREMENT INC p 934
423 Morris St, Durham NC 27701
Tel (919) 683-2413
SIC 2752 8748 2791 2789 2759

■ PBM GRAPHICS INC p 1123
3700 S Miami Blvd, Durham NC 27703
Tel (919) 544-6222 SIC 2752

FAYETTEVILLE PUBLISHING CO INC p 532
458 Whitfield St, Fayetteville NC 28306
Tel (910) 486-2741
SIC 2711 2791 2759 2752

■ NEWS AND OBSERVER PUBLISHING CO p 1039
215 S Mcdowell St, Raleigh NC 27601
Tel (919) 829-4500
SIC 2711 2741 2721 2752

QUEBECOR WORLD JOHNSON & HARDIN CO p 1198
3600 Red Bank Rd, Cincinnati OH 45227
Tel (614) 326-0299 SIC 2759 2752 2732

ANGSTROM GRAPHICS INC p 91
4437 E 49th St, Cleveland OH 44125
Tel (216) 271-5300 SIC 2721 2754 2752

WFSR HOLDINGS LLC p 1604
220 E Monument Ave, Dayton OH 45402
Tel (877) 735-4966
SIC 2752 2754 2759 2761 2789 2791

WORKFLOWONE LLC p 1624
220 E Monument Ave, Dayton OH 45402
Tel (877) 735-4966
SIC 2754 2791 4225 4731 2752 2759

■ CRABAR/GBF INC p 388
68 Vine St, Leipsic OH 45856
Tel (419) 943-2141 SIC 2752

D & S CREATIVE COMMUNICATIONS INC p 406
140 Park Ave E, Mansfield OH 44902
Tel (419) 524-6699
SIC 7311 2752 2791 2789

SANDUSKY NEWSPAPERS INC p 1278
314 W Market St, Sandusky OH 44870
Tel (419) 625-5500 SIC 4832 2711 2752

OKLAHOMA PUBLISHING CO OF OKLAHOMA p 1080
9000 N Brdwy, Oklahoma City OK 73114
Tel (405) 475-3311
SIC 2711 1311 6512 7375 2752

■ GRAPHIC ARTS CENTER INC p 631
2000 Nw Wilson St, Portland OR 97209
Tel (503) 224-7777 SIC 2752

■ MORNING CALL LLC p 989
101 N 6th St, Allentown PA 18101
Tel (610) 820-6500 SIC 2752 2711

NPC INC p 1064
13710 Dunnings Hwy, Claysburg PA 16625
Tel (814) 239-8787 SIC 2752 2789 2759

OFFSET PAPERBACK MFRS INC p 1076
2211 Memorial Hwy, Dallas PA 18612
Tel (570) 675-5261 SIC 2731 2752

LNP MEDIA GROUP INC p 872
8 W King St, Lancaster PA 17603
Tel (717) 291-8811 SIC 2711 2752

FRY COMMUNICATIONS INC p 582
800 W Church Rd, Mechanicsburg PA 17055
Tel (717) 766-0211 SIC 2752

CLONDALKIN HOLDINGS INC p 327
Crtis Centre Ste, Philadelphia PA 19106
Tel (215) 440-0570
SIC 2673 2621 2752 8741

■ IDL WORLDWIDE INC p 729
6515 Penn Ave, Pittsburgh PA 15206
Tel (412) 965-3954 SIC 3993 2752

READING EAGLE CO p 1213
345 Penn St, Reading PA 19601
Tel (610) 371-5000 SIC 2711 2752

BRODART CO p 216
500 Arch St, Williamsport PA 17701
Tel (570) 326-2461
SIC 5192 5942 2752 2782 2789 2531

MAPLE PRESS CO p 903
480 Willow Springs Ln, York PA 17406
Tel (717) 764-5911
SIC 2732 2791 2789 2752

PACE RESOURCES INC p 1103
140 E Market St Fl 2, York PA 17401
Tel (717) 852-1300
SIC 2752 5049 7334 2789

IGT GLOBAL SOLUTIONS CORP p 730
10 Memorial Blvd, Providence RI 02903
Tel (401) 392-1000
SIC 7999 3575 7372 7378 2752 7374

PIGGLY WIGGLY CAROLINA CO INC p 1147
176 Croghan Spur Ste 400, Charleston SC 29407
Tel (843) 554-9880
SIC 7311 5411 5148 5141 2752 1542

FUJIFILM MANUFACTURING USA INC p 583
215 Puckett Ferry Rd, Greenwood SC 29649
Tel (864) 223-2888 SIC 2796 2752 3861

OLAN MILLS INC p 1080
735 Broad St Ste 218, Chattanooga TN 37402
Tel (423) 622-5141 SIC 7221 2752

WESTROCK CONVERTING CO p 1602
2464 Amnicola Hwy, Chattanooga TN 37406
Tel (423) 622-2254 SIC 2752 2759

RESOURCE LABEL GROUP LLC p 1227
147 Seaboard Ln, Franklin TN 37067
Tel (615) 661-5900 SIC 2759 2752

BEACON PRINTING & GRAPHICS INC p 165
2748 Bingle Rd, Houston TX 77055
Tel (713) 464-8484 SIC 2752 2791 2789

■ CONSOLIDATED GRAPHICS INC p 360
5858 Westheimer Rd # 200, Houston TX 77057
Tel (713) 787-0977 SIC 2752

PREMIER GRAPHICS HOLDINGS INC p 1170
2500 West Loop S Ste 500, Houston TX 77027
Tel (713) 961-4700 SIC 2752

RTU INC p 1256
1445 Langham Creek Dr, Houston TX 77084
Tel (800) 247-4793 SIC 7319 2752

WINDWARD PRINT STAR INC p 1616
14950 Hethrw Frst Pkwy # 120, Houston TX 77032
Tel (281) 821-5522
SIC 2752 2791 2796 7335 7336 7331

HOV SERVICES INC p 712
2701 E Grauwyler Rd, Irving TX 75061
Tel (248) 837-7100
SIC 7374 7334 7389 2752 7331 7379

INTEGRACOLOR LLC p 748
3210 Innovative Way, Mesquite TX 75149
Tel (972) 289-0705 SIC 2752 2754

CLARKE AMERICAN CHECKS INC p 322
15955 La Cantera Pkwy, San Antonio TX 78256
Tel (210) 694-1492 SIC 2782 2759 2752

BERRYVILLE GRAPHICS INC p 176
25 Jack Enders Blvd, Berryville VA 22611
Tel (540) 955-2750 SIC 2732 2752 2789

■ CADMUS JOURNAL SERVICES INC p 236
2901 Byrdhill Rd, Henrico VA 23228
Tel (804) 287-5680 SIC 2752 2721 2741

■ CADMUS JOURNAL SERVICES INC p 236
2901 Byrdhill Rd, Richmond VA 23228
Tel (804) 264-2711 SIC 2752

OGDEN NEWSPAPERS INC p 1076
1500 Main St, Wheeling WV 26003
Tel (304) 233-0100
SIC 2711 2754 2741 2791 2752

W/S PACKAGING GROUP INC p 1569
2571 S Hemlock Rd, Green Bay WI 54229
Tel (920) 866-6300 SIC 2679 2752

ONETOUCHPOINT MIDWEST CORP p 1088
1225 Walnut Ridge Dr, Hartland WI 53029
Tel (262) 369-6000 SIC 2752

INLAND LABEL AND MARKETING SERVICES LLC p 743
2009 West Ave S, La Crosse WI 54601
Tel (608) 788-5800 SIC 2754 2752

ARANDELL CORP p 102
N82w13118 Leon Rd, Menomonee Falls WI 53051
Tel (262) 255-4400 SIC 2752

FGS-WI LLC p 539
1101 S Janesville St, Milton WI 53563
Tel (608) 373-6500 SIC 2752 7331

MBK-WI INC p 925
1101 S Janesville St, Milton WI 53563
Tel (608) 373-6500 SIC 2752

PAX HOLDINGS LLC p 1122
758 N Broadway Ste 910, Milwaukee WI 53202
Tel (414) 803-9983
SIC 5199 2759 2672 2671 2657 2752

TIMES PRINTING LLC p 1454
100 Industrial Dr, Random Lake WI 53075
Tel (920) 994-4396 SIC 2752

■ QG PRINTING CORP p 1195
N61w23044 Harrys Way, Sussex WI 53089
Tel (414) 566-6000 SIC 2752

■ QG PRINTING II CORP p 1195
N61w23044 Harrys Way, Sussex WI 53089
Tel (414) 566-6000 SIC 2752

▲ QUAD/GRAPHICS INC p 1195
N61w23044 Harrys Way, Sussex WI 53089
Tel (414) 566-6000 SIC 2752 2754 2721

SERIGRAPH INC p 1306
3801 Decorah Rd, West Bend WI 53095
Tel (262) 335-7200 SIC 2759 2752 2396

SIC 2754 Commercial Printing: Gravure

■ PRECISION DYNAMICS CORP p 1168
27770 N Entrmt Dr Ste 200, Valencia CA 91355
Tel (818) 897-1111
SIC 2672 2754 5047 3069

■ WORLD COLOR (USA) HOLDING CO p 1625
291 State St, North Haven CT 06473
Tel (203) 288-2468 SIC 2752 2754

■ DATAMAX-ONEIL CORP p 414
4501 Pkwy Commerce Blvd, Orlando FL 32808
Tel (407) 578-8007 SIC 3577 2754

SCIENTIFIC GAMES FINANCE CORP p 1292
1500 Bluegrass Lakes Pkwy, Alpharetta GA 30004
Tel (770) 664-3700 SIC 2754

▲ RR DONNELLEY & SONS CO p 1255
35 W Wacker Dr Ste 3650, Chicago IL 60601
Tel (312) 326-8000
SIC 2754 2759 2752 2732 7331 7336

■ RR DONNELLEY PRINTING CO LP p 1255
111 S Wacker Dr Ste 3500, Chicago IL 60606
Tel (312) 326-8000 SIC 2754 2752 5085

W/K HOLDING CO INC p 1569
2401 Cooper St, Fort Scott KS 66701
Tel (620) 223-5500 SIC 2754

■ NASHUA CORP p 1008
59 Daniel Webster Hwy A, Merrimack NH 03054
Tel (603) 880-1100
SIC 2672 2754 2679 2621 2782

GRUNER + JAHR USA GROUP INC p 642
1745 Broadway Fl 16, New York NY 10019
Tel (866) 323-9336 SIC 2721 2754

AMERICAN PACKAGING CORP p 77
777 Driving Park Ave, Rochester NY 14613
Tel (585) 254-9500
SIC 2673 3497 2671 2754 2674

ANGSTROM GRAPHICS INC p 91
4437 E 49th St, Cleveland OH 44125
Tel (216) 271-5300 SIC 2721 2754 2752

WFSR HOLDINGS LLC p 1604
220 E Monument Ave, Dayton OH 45402
Tel (877) 735-4966
SIC 2752 2754 2759 2761 2789 2791

WORKFLOWONE LLC p 1624
220 E Monument Ave, Dayton OH 45402
Tel (877) 735-4966
SIC 2754 2791 4225 4731 2752 2759

SHAMROCK COMPANIES INC p 1311
24090 Detroit Rd, Westlake OH 44145
Tel (440) 899-9510
SIC 5112 5199 7336 7389 2754 2395

INTEGRACOLOR LLC p 748
3210 Innovative Way, Mesquite TX 75149
Tel (972) 289-0705 SIC 2752 2754

HARLAND CLARKE CORP p 661
15955 La Cantera Pkwy, San Antonio TX 78256
Tel (830) 609-5500 SIC 2782 2754 7389

HARLAND CLARKE HOLDINGS CORP p 661
15955 La Cantera Pkwy, San Antonio TX 78256
Tel (210) 697-8888 SIC 2782 2754 7389

OGDEN NEWSPAPERS INC p 1076
1500 Main St, Wheeling WV 26003
Tel (304) 233-0100
SIC 2711 2754 2741 2791 2752

APPVION INC p 100
825 E Wisconsin Ave, Appleton WI 54911
Tel (920) 734-9841 SIC 2621 2754

■ FISERV SOLUTIONS LLC p 551
255 Fiserv Dr, Brookfield WI 53045
Tel (262) 879-5000 SIC 7374 2754 5084

INLAND LABEL AND MARKETING SERVICES LLC p 743
2009 West Ave S, La Crosse WI 54601
Tel (608) 788-5800 SIC 2754 2752

■ QG LLC p 1195
N61w23044 Harrys Way, Sussex WI 53089
Tel (414) 566-6000 SIC 2754

▲ QUAD/GRAPHICS INC p 1195
N61w23044 Harrys Way, Sussex WI 53089
Tel (414) 566-6000 SIC 2752 2754 2721

SIC 2759 Commercial Printing

MERCURY PLASTICS INC p 945
14825 Salt Lake Ave, City Of Industry CA 91746
Tel (626) 369-8457 SIC 2673 2759 3089

4 OVER LLC p 3
5900 San Fernando Rd D, Glendale CA 91202
Tel (818) 246-1170 SIC 2759 7336

LITHOGRAPHIX INC p 870
12250 Crenshaw Blvd, Hawthorne CA 90250
Tel (323) 770-1000 SIC 2752 2759

■ MCCLATCHY NEWSPAPERS INC p 926
2100 Q St, Sacramento CA 95816
Tel (916) 321-1000 SIC 2711 2759 7375

CIRCLE GRAPHICS INC p 308
120 9th Ave Ste B, Longmont CO 80501
Tel (303) 532-2370 SIC 2759 7374

PRIME RESOURCES CORP p 1175
1100 Boston Ave Bldg 1, Bridgeport CT 06610
Tel (203) 331-9100 SIC 3993 2759

ALLIED PRINTING SERVICES INC p 56
1 Allied Way, Manchester CT 06042
Tel (860) 643-1101
SIC 2396 2752 2759 2789 2791

OMEGA ENGINEERING INC p 1084
800 Connecticut Ave 5n01, Norwalk CT 06854
Tel (203) 359-1660
SIC 3823 3575 3577 3433 3826 2759

CCL INDUSTRIES CORP p 270
15 Controls Dr, Shelton CT 06484
Tel (203) 926-1253
SIC 2759 2992 3411 2819 2844

CCL LABEL (DELAWARE) INC p 270
15 Controls Dr, Shelton CT 06484
Tel (203) 926-1253 SIC 2759

■ CENVEO CORP p 283
200 First Stamford Pl # 200, Stamford CT 06902
Tel (303) 790-8023 SIC 2677 2752 2759

NAYLOR LLC p 1020
5950 Nw 1st Pl, Gainesville FL 32607
Tel (800) 369-6220 SIC 2759 7374

HIT PROMOTIONAL PRODUCTS INC p 696
7150 Bryan Dairy Rd, Largo FL 33777
Tel (727) 541-5561 SIC 2759 3993

WORLD COLOR INC p 1625
10 Sunshine Blvd, Ormond Beach FL 32174
Tel (386) 672-8388 SIC 2759

COX TARGET MEDIA INC p 386
1 Valpak Ave N, Saint Petersburg FL 33716
Tel (727) 399-3000
SIC 7331 8741 8742 2759

ISD HOLDINGS INC p 766
4715 Frederick Dr Sw, Atlanta GA 30336
Tel (404) 691-7400
SIC 7389 2542 2759 2752

MILLER ZELL INC p 971
6100 Fulton Indus Blvd Sw, Atlanta GA 30336
Tel (404) 691-7400
SIC 7389 2542 2759 2752

BROWN INDUSTRIES INC p 219
205 W Industrial Blvd, Dalton GA 30720
Tel (706) 277-1977
SIC 2759 5131 2273 3552 3315 2671

CURTIS 1000 INC p 402
1725 Breckinridge Park, Duluth GA 30096
Tel (770) 925-4500
SIC 2761 2759 2791 2789 2752

HARP BUSINESS SERVICES INC p 662
2725 Northwoods Pkwy A2, Peachtree Corners GA 30071
Tel (678) 482-0675 SIC 2759 4225 5699

WALLE CORP p 1573
200 Hembree Park Dr Ste H, Roswell GA 30076
Tel (800) 942-6761 SIC 2759 2752 2671

ARTCO (US) INC p 114
1 Stationery Pl, Rexburg ID 83441
Tel (208) 359-1000 SIC 5112 2759

FOX VALLEY PRESS INC p 573
495 N Commons Dr Ste 200, Aurora IL 60504
Tel (815) 439-5300 SIC 2759

BAGCRAFTPAPERCON I LLC p 144
3900 W 43rd St, Chicago IL 60632
Tel (620) 856-2800
SIC 2671 2674 2673 3497 2759

▲ RR DONNELLEY & SONS CO p 1255
35 W Wacker Dr Ste 3650, Chicago IL 60601
Tel (312) 326-8000
SIC 2754 2759 2752 2732 7331 7336

JORDAN INDUSTRIES INC p 793
1751 Lake Cook Rd Ste 550, Deerfield IL 60015
Tel (847) 945-5591
SIC 3621 3625 3714 3089 2759 5999

FORT DEARBORN CO p 568
1530 Morse Ave, Elk Grove Village IL 60007
Tel (847) 357-9500 SIC 2752 2759

MICHAEL LEWIS CO p 960
8900 W 50th St, Mc Cook IL 60525
Tel (708) 688-2200
SIC 5113 5141 5142 2782 2759 2621

WOLTERS KLUWER UNITED STATES INC p 1621
2700 Lake Cook Rd, Riverwoods IL 60015
Tel (847) 580-5000
SIC 2731 2721 2741 2759

SIMU LTD p 1326
201 Mittel Dr, Wood Dale IL 60191
Tel (630) 350-1060
SIC 5113 5141 5142 2782 2759 2621

STUMP PRINTING CO INC p 1395
101 Carroll Rd, South Whitley IN 46787
Tel (260) 723-5171
SIC 5199 2679 5961 2759

ITS GREEK TO ME INC p 768
520 Mccall Rd Ste A, Manhattan KS 66502
Tel (785) 537-8822
SIC 5136 5699 5137 5947 2759

CONTINENTAL AMERICAN CORP p 362
5000 E 29th St N, Wichita KS 67220
Tel (316) 685-2266 SIC 2759 3069

LANDMARK COMMUNITY NEWSPAPERS LLC p 842
601 Taylorsville Rd, Shelbyville KY 40065
Tel (502) 633-4334 SIC 2711 2759

CHAMPION INDUSTRIES INC p 287
10848 Airline Hwy, Baton Rouge LA 70816
Tel (225) 291-9090
SIC 2542 2759 2791 2789 2752

ENVELOPES UNLIMITED INC p 503
649 N Horners Ln, Rockville MD 20850
Tel (301) 424-3300 SIC 2759 7331

CCL LABEL INC p 270
161 Worcester Rd Ste 504, Framingham MA 01701
Tel (508) 872-4511 SIC 2759 3411 2671

■ NEW ENGLAND BUSINESS SERVICE INC p 1030
500 Main St, Groton MA 01471
Tel (978) 448-6111
SIC 2759 2771 5045 2653 3089 3069

CRANES PERSONAL DESIGN SERVICES p 389
1466 Curran Hwy, North Adams MA 01247
Tel (413) 664-4321 SIC 7389 2796 2759

■ TWEDDLE GROUP INC p 1494
24700 Maplehurst Dr, Clinton Township MI 48036
Tel (586) 307-3700
SIC 2732 2791 2752 2759 2741 7371

DISPLAY PACK INC p 443
1340 Monroe Ave Nw Ste 1, Grand Rapids MI 49505
Tel (616) 451-3061 SIC 3089 2759 7389

■ LANSING MPS INC p 844
5800 W Grand River Ave, Lansing MI 48906
Tel (517) 323-9000
SIC 2759 2731 2761 3089 2671

VALASSIS INTERNATIONAL INC p 1539
19975 Victor Pkwy, Livonia MI 48152
Tel (734) 591-3000
SIC 8743 3993 2759 2752

CENTURION MEDICAL PRODUCTS CORP p 281
100 Centurion Way, Williamston MI 48895
Tel (517) 546-5400 SIC 3842 2759 2671

VENTURE SOLUTIONS INC p 1548
1170 Grey Fox Rd, Arden Hills MN 55112
Tel (651) 494-1740 SIC 2759

UNITED MAILING INC p 1510
1001 Park Rd, Chanhassen MN 55317
Tel (952) 474-0961 SIC 7331 2759 8732

DOUGLAS CORP p 452
9650 Valley View Rd, Eden Prairie MN 55344
Tel (800) 806-6113 SIC 3089 2759

SMEAD MANUFACTURING CO INC p 1332
600 Smead Blvd, Hastings MN 55033
Tel (651) 437-4111
SIC 2675 7372 2789 2759 2752 2542

■ JOSTENS INC p 794
3601 Minnesota Dr Ste 400, Minneapolis MN 55435
Tel (952) 830-3300 SIC 3911 2759 2741

PROCESS DISPLAYS LLC p 1179
7108 31st Ave N, Minneapolis MN 55427
Tel (763) 541-1245
SIC 2541 2542 2599 2675 2752 2759

■ VISANT HOLDING CORP p 1561
3601 Minnesota Dr Ste 400, Minneapolis MN 55435
Tel (914) 595-8200
SIC 2741 2759 3911 6719

CARLSON CRAFT INC p 257
1750 Tower Blvd, North Mankato MN 56003
Tel (507) 625-5011 SIC 2759

NAVITOR INC p 1020
1725 Roe Crest Dr, North Mankato MN 56003
Tel (507) 625-2828 SIC 2759

OCCASIONS GROUP INC p 1072
1725 Roe Crest Dr, North Mankato MN 56003
Tel (208) 359-1000 SIC 2759

TAYLOR CORP p 1427
1725 Roe Crest Dr, North Mankato MN 56003
Tel (507) 625-2828
SIC 8742 2752 2677 2759

NAHAN PRINTING INC p 1006
7000 Saukview Dr, Saint Cloud MN 56303
Tel (320) 217-7700 SIC 2759 2752

BANYAN INCENTIVES p 153
4875 White Bear Pkwy, Saint Paul MN 55110
Tel (651) 426-1667 SIC 2759

COMPUTYPE INC p 353
2285 County Road C W, Saint Paul MN 55113
Tel (651) 633-0633
SIC 2759 2672 2679 3565 3577 2671

MERRILL/GLOBAL INC p 950
1 Merrill Cir Ste 1433, Saint Paul MN 55108
Tel (651) 646-4501 SIC 2759 2752 2791

IMAGINE PRINT SOLUTIONS INC p 733
1000 Valley Park Dr, Shakopee MN 55379
Tel (952) 903-4400 SIC 2759

JAPS-OLSON CO p 778
7500 Excelsior Blvd, St Louis Park MN 55426
Tel (952) 932-9393
SIC 2752 7331 2791 2759

BEDFORD INDUSTRIES INC p 168
1659 Rowe Ave, Worthington MN 56187
Tel (507) 376-4136 SIC 2671 2759

GRIMCO INC p 640
1585 Fencorp Dr, Fenton MO 63026
Tel (636) 305-0088
SIC 3469 2759 3993 3429 3312

■ BROADRIDGE CUSTOMER COMMUNICATIONS LLC p 215
2600 Southwest Blvd, Kansas City MO 64108
Tel (816) 221-1234
SIC 7389 2759 7374 7331 2752 7336

AMERICAN BANKNOTE CORP p 68
2200 Fletcher Ave Ste 501, Fort Lee NJ 07024
Tel (201) 592-3400 SIC 2759 2752 2621

■ EARTHCOLOR INC p 469
249 Pomeroy Rd, Parsippany NJ 07054
Tel (973) 884-1300 SIC 2752 2759

UNITED ENVELOPE LLC p 1508
65 Railroad Ave Ste 1a, Ridgefield NJ 07657
Tel (201) 699-5800 SIC 2759 2677

STEPHEN GOULD CORP p 1386
35 S Jefferson Rd, Whippany NJ 07981
Tel (973) 428-1500 SIC 2631 2759

BARD COLLEGE PUBLICATIONS p 155
Annandale Rd, Annandale On Hudson NY 12504
Tel (845) 758-7417 SIC 8999 2759 5311

GOULD PAPER CORP p 626
99 Park Ave Fl 10, New York NY 10016
Tel (212) 301-0000 SIC 5111 2759

MIMEO.COM INC p 972
3 Park Ave Fl 22, New York NY 10016
Tel (212) 847-3000 SIC 2759

■ MULTI PACKAGING SOLUTIONS INC p 999
150 E 52nd St Ste 2800, New York NY 10022
Tel (646) 885-0005
SIC 2759 2731 2761 3089 5092 2671

■ GATEHOUSE MEDIA LLC p 593
175 Sullys Trl Ste 300, Pittsford NY 14534
Tel (585) 598-0030 SIC 2711 7311 2759

HAMMER PACKAGING CORP p 656
200 Lucius Gordon Dr, West Henrietta NY 14586
Tel (585) 424-3880 SIC 2759

REGULUS INTEGRATED SOLUTIONS LLC p 1220
9645-L Part Blvd, Charlotte NC 28216
Tel (704) 904-8759
SIC 2752 7389 3861 2759

MEASUREMENT INC p 934
423 Morris St, Durham NC 27701
Tel (919) 683-2413
SIC 2752 8748 2791 2789 2759

FAYETTEVILLE PUBLISHING CO INC p 532
458 Whitfield St, Fayetteville NC 28306
Tel (910) 486-2741
SIC 2711 2791 2759 2752

NS FLEXIBLES LLC p 1064
2619 Phoenix Dr, Greensboro NC 27406
Tel (336) 292-9911 SIC 2671 7336 2759

▲ MULTI-COLOR CORP p 999
4053 Clough Woods Dr, Batavia OH 45103
Tel (513) 381-1480 SIC 2759 2679 2672

KDM SIGNS INC p 807
10450 Medallion Dr, Cincinnati OH 45241
Tel (513) 769-1932 SIC 2759 3993

QUEBECOR WORLD JOHNSON & HARDIN CO p 1198
3600 Red Bank Rd, Cincinnati OH 45227
Tel (614) 326-0299 SIC 2759 2752 2732

SRC LIQUIDATION LLC p 1363
600 Albany St, Dayton OH 45417
Tel (937) 221-1000
SIC 2761 2672 2677 2759

WFSR HOLDINGS LLC p 1604
220 E Monument Ave, Dayton OH 45402
Tel (877) 735-4966
SIC 2752 2754 2759 2761 2789 2791

WORKFLOWONE LLC p 1624
220 E Monument Ave, Dayton OH 45402
Tel (877) 735-4966
SIC 2754 2791 4225 4731 2752 2759

GBS CORP p 595
7233 Freedom Ave Nw, North Canton OH 44720
Tel (330) 494-5330
SIC 5045 5112 2675 2672 2761 2759

NPC INC p 1064
13710 Dunnings Hwy, Claysburg PA 16625
Tel (814) 239-8787 SIC 2752 2789 2759

NATIONAL LABEL CO p 1014
2025 Joshua Rd, Lafayette Hill PA 19444
Tel (610) 825-3250
SIC 2672 2679 2759 2671

MATLET GROUP LLC p 920
60 Delta Dr, Pawtucket RI 02860
Tel (401) 834-3007 SIC 2759

SPRINGS CREATIVE PRODUCTS GROUP LLC p 1361
300 Chatham Ave Ste 100, Rock Hill SC 29730
Tel (803) 324-6300 SIC 5949 2759

PRINCE GROUP LLC p 1176
3227 Sunset Blvd Ste E101, West Columbia SC 29169
Tel (803) 708-4789 SIC 2759 3479

WESTROCK CONVERTING CO p 1602
2464 Amnicola Hwy, Chattanooga TN 37406
Tel (423) 622-2254 SIC 2752 2759

RESOURCE LABEL GROUP LLC p 1227
147 Seaboard Ln, Franklin TN 37067
Tel (615) 661-5900 SIC 2759 2752

■ SAFEGUARD BUSINESS SYSTEMS INC p 1266
8585 N Stemmons Fwy, Dallas TX 75247
Tel (214) 640-3916
SIC 7374 2759 5112 5045

■ VOYAGER LEARNING CO p 1566
17855 Dallas Pkwy Ste 400, Dallas TX 75287
Tel (214) 932-9500 SIC 2741 2759

NATIONWIDE ARGOSY SOLUTIONS LLC p 1017
2764 Bingle Rd, Houston TX 77055
Tel (713) 961-4700 SIC 2759

▲ ENNIS INC p 500
2441 Presidential Pkwy, Midlothian TX 76065
Tel (972) 775-9801
SIC 2761 2759 2331 2329

CLARKE AMERICAN CHECKS INC p 322
15955 La Cantera Pkwy, San Antonio TX 78256
Tel (210) 694-1492 SIC 2782 2759 2752

■ DAHILL OFFICE TECHNOLOGY CORP p 408
8200 W Interstate 10 # 400, San Antonio TX 78230
Tel (210) 805-8200 SIC 5999 3861 2759

O C TANNER CO p 1070
1930 S State St, Salt Lake City UT 84115
Tel (801) 486-2430 SIC 3911 2759 2741

ABC IMAGING OF WASHINGTON INC p 10
5290 Shawnee Rd Ste 300, Alexandria VA 22312
Tel (202) 429-8870 SIC 2759

ON-SITE E DISCOVERY INC p 1086
806 N Henry St, Alexandria VA 22314
Tel (703) 683-9710 SIC 2759

CUSTOMINK LLC p 403
2910 District Ave Ste 100, Fairfax VA 22031
Tel (703) 891-2273 SIC 2759 5699 5941

■ INTERMEC TECHNOLOGIES CORP p 753
16201 25th Ave W, Lynnwood WA 98087
Tel (425) 348-2600 SIC 3577 2759

BELMARK INC p 171
600 Heritage Rd, De Pere WI 54115
Tel (920) 336-2848 SIC 2759 2657 2671

ONETOUCHPOINT CORP p 1088
1225 Walnut Ridge Dr, Hartland WI 53029
Tel (630) 586-9002 SIC 2759

■ BANTA CORP p 153
1457 Earl St, Menasha WI 54952
Tel (312) 326-8000 SIC 2759 8742

JOURNAL COMMUNICATIONS INC p 794
333 W State St, Milwaukee WI 53203
Tel (414) 224-2000
SIC 4832 4833 2711 2759 4813

PAX HOLDINGS LLC p 1122
758 N Broadway Ste 910, Milwaukee WI 53202
Tel (414) 803-9983
SIC 5199 2759 2672 2671 2657 2752

SERIGRAPH INC p 1306
3801 Decorah Rd, West Bend WI 53095
Tel (262) 335-7200 SIC 2759 2752 2396

SIC 2761 Manifold Business Forms

WISE BUSINESS FORMS INC p 1619
555 Mcfarland 400 Dr, Alpharetta GA 30004
Tel (770) 442-1060 SIC 2761 2752

JOHN H HARLAND CO p 788
2939 Miller Rd, Decatur GA 30035
Tel (770) 593-5050
SIC 2782 2752 2761 7371 7379

CURTIS 1000 INC p 402
1725 Breckinridge Park, Duluth GA 30096
Tel (770) 925-4500
SIC 2761 2759 2791 2789 2752

■ PRINTEGRA CORP p 1177
5040 Highlands Pkwy Se, Smyrna GA 30082
Tel (770) 487-5151
SIC 2761 2782 2677 2678 2679

▲ ACCO BRANDS CORP p 15
4 Corporate Dr, Lake Zurich IL 60047
Tel (847) 541-9500
SIC 2782 3083 2761 2672

■ ACCO BRANDS USA LLC p 15
4 Corporate Dr, Lake Zurich IL 60047
Tel (800) 222-6462
SIC 3089 2761 3496 2675

PROFESSIONAL OFFICE SERVICES INC p 1180
2757 Burton Ave, Waterloo IA 50703
Tel (319) 235-6777 SIC 2761

WARD-KRAFT INC p 1575
2401 Cooper St, Fort Scott KS 66701
Tel (800) 821-4021 SIC 2761 2672

■ LANSING MPS INC p 844
5800 W Grand River Ave, Lansing MI 48906
Tel (517) 323-9000
SIC 2759 2731 2761 3089 2671

SCANTRON CORP p 1286
1313 Lone Oak Rd, Eagan MN 55121
Tel (651) 683-6000
SIC 3577 7372 2752 3575 2761

▲ DELUXE CORP p 427
3680 Victoria St N, Shoreview MN 55126
Tel (651) 483-7111 SIC 2782 2761 7389

AMSTERDAM PRINTING & LITHO INC p 87
166 Wallins Corners Rd, Amsterdam NY 12010
Tel (518) 842-6000 SIC 3993 2752 2761

■ MULTI PACKAGING SOLUTIONS INC p 999
150 E 52nd St Ste 2800, New York NY 10022
Tel (646) 885-0005
SIC 2759 2731 2761 3089 5092 2671

SRC LIQUIDATION LLC p 1363
600 Albany St, Dayton OH 45417
Tel (937) 221-1000
SIC 2761 2672 2677 2759

WFSR HOLDINGS LLC p 1604
220 E Monument Ave, Dayton OH 45402
Tel (877) 735-4966
SIC 2752 2754 2759 2761 2789 2791

GBS CORP p 595
7233 Freedom Ave Nw, North Canton OH 44720
Tel (330) 494-5330
SIC 5045 5112 2675 2672 2761 2759

WRIGHT BUSINESS FORMS INC p 1627
18440 Ne San Rafael St, Portland OR 97230
Tel (503) 661-2525 SIC 2761

▲ IMPRESO INC p 735
652 Southwestern Blvd, Coppell TX 75019
Tel (972) 462-0100 SIC 2761 2679 2086

▲ ENNIS INC p 500
2441 Presidential Pkwy, Midlothian TX 76065
Tel (972) 775-9801
SIC 2761 2759 2331 2329

SIC 2771 Greeting Card Publishing

SCHURMAN FINE PAPERS p 1291
500 Chadbourne Rd, Fairfield CA 94534
Tel (707) 425-8006
SIC 5113 2679 2771 5947

C-USA INC p 234
1005 E Woodmen Rd, Colorado Springs CO 80920
Tel (719) 594-4100 SIC 5947 5961 2771

■ FLORISTS TRANSWORLD DELIVERY INC p 560
3113 Woodcreek Dr, Downers Grove IL 60515
Tel (630) 719-7800 SIC 5193 7389 2771

■ NEW ENGLAND BUSINESS SERVICE INC p 1030
500 Main St, Groton MA 01471
Tel (978) 448-6111
SIC 2759 2771 5045 2653 3089 3069

HALLMARK CARDS INC p 654
2501 Mcgee St, Kansas City MO 64108
Tel (816) 274-5111 SIC 2771

AMERICAN GREETINGS CORP p 73
1 American Rd, Cleveland OH 44144
Tel (216) 252-7300
SIC 2771 2679 2656 2678

CENTURY INTERMEDIATE HOLDING CO p 282
1 American Rd, Cleveland OH 44144
Tel (216) 252-7300
SIC 2771 2679 2656 2678

▲ CSS INDUSTRIES INC p 398
450 Plymouth Rd Ste 300, Plymouth Meeting PA 19462
Tel (610) 729-3959
SIC 2771 2679 2389 2396 2621 2865

SIC 2782 Blankbooks & Looseleaf Binders

EBSCO INDUSTRIES INC p 474
5724 Highway 280 E, Birmingham AL 35242
Tel (205) 991-6600
SIC 7389 2782 3949 7375 2721 6552

■ DIRECT CHECKS UNLIMITED LLC p 441
8245 N Union Blvd, Colorado Springs CO 80920
Tel (719) 531-3900 *SIC* 2782

JOHN H HARLAND CO p 788
2939 Miller Rd, Decatur GA 30035
Tel (770) 593-5050
SIC 2782 2752 2761 7371 7379

■ PRINTEGRA CORP p 1177
5040 Highlands Pkwy Se, Smyrna GA 30082
Tel (770) 487-5151
SIC 2761 2782 2677 2678 2679

▲ ACCO BRANDS CORP p 15
4 Corporate Dr, Lake Zurich IL 60047
Tel (847) 541-9500
SIC 2782 3083 2761 2672

GENERAL BINDING CORP p 599
4 Corporate Dr, Lake Zurich IL 60047
Tel (847) 541-9500
SIC 5044 2782 3559 3589 7629 3579

MICHAEL LEWIS CO p 960
8900 W 50th St, Mc Cook IL 60525
Tel (708) 688-2200
SIC 5113 5141 5142 2782 2759 2621

SIMU LTD p 1326
201 Mittel Dr, Wood Dale IL 60191
Tel (630) 350-1060
SIC 5113 5141 5142 2782 2759 2621

GEIGER BROS p 597
70 Mount Hope Ave, Lewiston ME 04240
Tel (207) 755-2000
SIC 5199 3993 2752 2782 2789

▲ DELUXE CORP p 427
3680 Victoria St N, Shoreview MN 55126
Tel (651) 483-7111 *SIC* 2782 2761 7389

■ NASHUA CORP p 1008
59 Daniel Webster Hwy A, Merrimack NH 03054
Tel (603) 880-1100
SIC 2672 2754 2679 2621 2782

ESSELTE HOLDINGS INC p 510
48 S Service Rd Ste 400, Melville NY 11747
Tel (631) 675-5700
SIC 2675 2782 3579 2672 3953 3596

M & F WORLDWIDE CORP p 888
35 E 62nd St, New York NY 10065
Tel (212) 572-8600 *SIC* 5149 8741 2782

WMG ACQUISITION CORP p 1620
75 Rockefeller Plz, New York NY 10019
Tel (212) 275-2000 *SIC* 2782 2741 7929

BRODART CO p 216
500 Arch St, Williamsport PA 17701
Tel (570) 326-2461
SIC 5192 5942 2752 2782 2789 2531

CLARKE AMERICAN CHECKS INC p 322
15955 La Cantera Pkwy, San Antonio TX 78256
Tel (210) 694-1492 *SIC* 2782 2759 2752

HARLAND CLARKE CORP p 661
15955 La Cantera Pkwy, San Antonio TX 78256
Tel (830) 609-5500 *SIC* 2782 2754 7389

HARLAND CLARKE HOLDINGS CORP p 661
15955 La Cantera Pkwy, San Antonio TX 78256
Tel (210) 697-8888 *SIC* 2782 2754 7389

SIC 2789 Bookbinding

ALLIED PRINTING SERVICES INC p 56
1 Allied Way, Manchester CT 06042
Tel (860) 643-1101
SIC 2396 2752 2759 2789 2791

CURTIS 1000 INC p 402
1725 Breckinridge Park, Duluth GA 30096
Tel (770) 925-4500
SIC 2761 2759 2791 2789 2752

■ HENNEGAN CO p 683
7455 Empire Dr, Florence KY 41042
Tel (859) 282-3600 *SIC* 2752 2789

PUBLISHERS PRINTING CO LLC p 1190
100 Frank E Simon Ave, Shepherdsville KY 40165
Tel (502) 955-6526 *SIC* 2752 2791 2789

CHAMPION INDUSTRIES INC p 287
10848 Airline Hwy, Baton Rouge LA 70816
Tel (225) 291-9090
SIC 2542 2759 2791 2789 2752

GEIGER BROS p 597
70 Mount Hope Ave, Lewiston ME 04240
Tel (207) 755-2000
SIC 5199 3993 2752 2782 2789

EDWARDS BROTHERS INC p 480
5411 Jackson Rd, Ann Arbor MI 48103
Tel (800) 722-3231 *SIC* 2732 2789

D & J PRINTING INC p 406
3323 Oak St, Brainerd MN 56401
Tel (218) 829-2877 *SIC* 2752 2789 2732

SMEAD MANUFACTURING CO INC p 1332
600 Smead Blvd, Hastings MN 55033
Tel (651) 437-4111
SIC 2675 7372 2789 2759 2752 2542

ECM PUBLISHERS INC p 475
4095 Coon Rapids Blvd Nw, Minneapolis MN 55433
Tel (763) 712-2400
SIC 2711 2741 7319 2789 2752

GL GROUP INC p 613
5111 Southwest Ave, Saint Louis MO 63110
Tel (314) 647-0600 *SIC* 5192 2789

SPIRAL BINDING CO INC p 1359
1 Maltese Dr, Totowa NJ 07512
Tel (973) 256-0666
SIC 2789 3083 5112 2891

MEASUREMENT INC p 934
423 Morris St, Durham NC 27701
Tel (919) 683-2413
SIC 2752 8748 2791 2789 2759

WFSR HOLDINGS LLC p 1604
220 E Monument Ave, Dayton OH 45402
Tel (877) 735-4966
SIC 2752 2754 2759 2761 2789 2791

D & S CREATIVE COMMUNICATIONS INC p 406
140 Park Ave E, Mansfield OH 44902
Tel (419) 524-6699
SIC 7311 2752 2791 2789

NPC INC p 1064
13710 Dunnings Hwy, Claysburg PA 16625
Tel (814) 239-8787 *SIC* 2752 2789 2759

BRODART CO p 216
500 Arch St, Williamsport PA 17701
Tel (570) 326-2461
SIC 5192 5942 2752 2782 2789 2531

MAPLE PRESS CO p 903
480 Willow Springs Ln, York PA 17406
Tel (717) 764-5911
SIC 2732 2791 2789 2752

PACE RESOURCES INC p 1103
140 E Market St Fl 2, York PA 17401
Tel (717) 852-1300
SIC 2752 5049 7334 2789

■ JARDEN ZINC PRODUCTS LLC p 778
2500 Old Stage Rd, Greeneville TN 37745
Tel (423) 639-8111
SIC 2796 3364 3356 1031 2789

BEACON PRINTING & GRAPHICS INC p 165
2748 Bingle Rd, Houston TX 77055
Tel (713) 464-8484 *SIC* 2752 2791 2789

BERRYVILLE GRAPHICS INC p 176
25 Jack Enders Blvd, Berryville VA 22611
Tel (540) 955-2750 *SIC* 2732 2752 2789

SIC 2791 Typesetting

ALLIED PRINTING SERVICES INC p 56
1 Allied Way, Manchester CT 06042
Tel (860) 643-1101
SIC 2396 2752 2759 2789 2791

HALIFAX MEDIA HOLDINGS LLC p 654
901 6th St, Daytona Beach FL 32117
Tel (386) 681-2404 *SIC* 2711 2791

CURTIS 1000 INC p 402
1725 Breckinridge Park, Duluth GA 30096
Tel (770) 925-4500
SIC 2761 2759 2791 2789 2752

SMALL NEWSPAPER GROUP p 1332
8 Dearborn Sq, Kankakee IL 60901
Tel (815) 937-3300 *SIC* 2711 2791 2752

LAKE COUNTY PRESS INC p 838
98 Noll St, Waukegan IL 60085
Tel (847) 336-4333 *SIC* 2791 7334

PUBLISHERS PRINTING CO LLC p 1190
100 Frank E Simon Ave, Shepherdsville KY 40165
Tel (502) 955-6526 *SIC* 2752 2791 2789

CHAMPION INDUSTRIES INC p 287
10848 Airline Hwy, Baton Rouge LA 70816
Tel (225) 291-9090
SIC 2542 2759 2791 2789 2752

TRUSTEES OF TUFTS COLLEGE p 1488
169 Holland St Ste 318, Somerville MA 02144
Tel (617) 628-5000 *SIC* 8221 2791 2752

■ TWEDDLE GROUP INC p 1494
24700 Maplehurst Dr, Clinton Township MI 48036
Tel (586) 307-3700
SIC 2732 2791 2752 2759 2741 7371

MERRILL/GLOBAL INC p 950
1 Merrill Cir Ste 1433, Saint Paul MN 55108
Tel (651) 646-4501 *SIC* 2759 2752 2791

JAPS-OLSON CO p 778
7500 Excelsior Blvd, St Louis Park MN 55426
Tel (952) 932-9393
SIC 2752 7331 2791 2759

MEASUREMENT INC p 934
423 Morris St, Durham NC 27701
Tel (919) 683-2413
SIC 2752 8748 2791 2789 2759

FAYETTEVILLE PUBLISHING CO INC p 532
458 Whitfield St, Fayetteville NC 28306
Tel (910) 486-2741
SIC 2711 2791 2759 2752

WFSR HOLDINGS LLC p 1604
220 E Monument Ave, Dayton OH 45402
Tel (877) 735-4966
SIC 2752 2754 2759 2761 2789 2791

WORKFLOWONE LLC p 1624
220 E Monument Ave, Dayton OH 45402
Tel (877) 735-4966
SIC 2754 2791 4225 4731 2752 2759

D & S CREATIVE COMMUNICATIONS INC p 406
140 Park Ave E, Mansfield OH 44902
Tel (419) 524-6699
SIC 7311 2752 2791 2789

MTM RECOGNITION CORP p 998
3201 Se 29th St, Oklahoma City OK 73115
Tel (405) 609-6900
SIC 3911 3873 2499 2389 3499 2791

REED TECHNOLOGY AND INFORMATION SERVICES INC p 1217
7 Walnut Grove Dr, Horsham PA 19044
Tel (215) 441-6400 *SIC* 2791

MAPLE PRESS CO p 903
480 Willow Springs Ln, York PA 17406
Tel (717) 764-5911
SIC 2732 2791 2789 2752

BEACON PRINTING & GRAPHICS INC p 165
2748 Bingle Rd, Houston TX 77055
Tel (713) 464-8484 *SIC* 2752 2791 2789

WINDWARD PRINT STAR INC p 1616
14950 Hethrw Frst Pkwy # 120, Houston TX 77032
Tel (281) 821-5522
SIC 2752 2791 2796 7335 7336 7331

OGDEN NEWSPAPERS INC p 1076
1500 Main St, Wheeling WV 26003
Tel (304) 233-0100
SIC 2711 2754 2741 2791 2752

SIC 2796 Platemaking & Related Svcs

■ MADISON/GRAHAM COLOR GRAPHICS INC p 894
150 N Myers St, Los Angeles CA 90033
Tel (323) 261-7171 *SIC* 2752 7336 2796

SOUTHERN GRAPHIC SYSTEMS LLC p 1348
626 W Main St Ste 500, Louisville KY 40202
Tel (502) 637-5443 *SIC* 2796

■ PHOENIX COLOR CORP p 1144
18249 Phoenix Rd, Hagerstown MD 21742
Tel (301) 733-0018 *SIC* 2732 3469 2796

CRANES PERSONAL DESIGN SERVICES p 389
1466 Curran Hwy, North Adams MA 01247
Tel (413) 664-4321 *SIC* 7389 2796 2759

HATTERAS PRESS INC p 668
56 Park Rd, Tinton Falls NJ 07724
Tel (732) 935-9800 *SIC* 2752 2796

▲ MATTHEWS INTERNATIONAL CORP p 920
2 N Shore Ctr Ste 200, Pittsburgh PA 15212
Tel (412) 442-8200
SIC 3366 1542 3569 3995 3953 2796

FUJIFILM MANUFACTURING USA INC p 583
215 Puckett Ferry Rd, Greenwood SC 29649
Tel (864) 223-2888 *SIC* 2796 2752 3861

■ JARDEN ZINC PRODUCTS LLC p 778
2500 Old Stage Rd, Greeneville TN 37745
Tel (423) 639-8111
SIC 2796 3364 3356 1031 2789

WINDWARD PRINT STAR INC p 1616
14950 Hethrw Frst Pkwy # 120, Houston TX 77032
Tel (281) 821-5522
SIC 2752 2791 2796 7335 7336 7331

SIC 2812 Alkalies & Chlorine

POOL WATER PRODUCTS p 1161
17872 Mitchell N Ste 250, Irvine CA 92614
Tel (949) 756-1666 *SIC* 5091 2899 2812

■ AXIALL CORP p 140
1000 Abernathy Rd # 1200, Atlanta GA 30328
Tel (770) 395-4500
SIC 2812 2821 2865 2861 2873

■ CINER ENTERPRISES INC p 308
5 Concourse Pkwy Ste 2500, Atlanta GA 30328
Tel (770) 375-2300 *SIC* 1474 2812

■ CINER RESOURCES CORP p 308
5 Concourse Pkwy, Atlanta GA 30328
Tel (770) 375-2300 *SIC* 1474 2812

■ CINER WYOMING HOLDING CO p 308
5 Concourse Pkwy, Atlanta GA 30328
Tel (770) 375-2300 *SIC* 1474 2812

■ EAGLE SPINCO INC p 468
115 Perimeter Center Pl, Atlanta GA 30346
Tel (770) 395-4500 *SIC* 2812 5169

BIO-LAB INC p 183
1725 N Brown Rd, Lawrenceville GA 30043
Tel (678) 502-4000 *SIC* 2812 2819 2899

CHAMPION PACKAGING & DISTRIBUTION INC p 287
1840 Internationale Pkwy, Woodridge IL 60517
Tel (630) 755-4220 *SIC* 2842 2812

▲ DOW CHEMICAL CO p 453
2030 Dow Ctr, Midland MI 48674
Tel (989) 636-1000
SIC 2821 3081 3086 2812 2879

▲ OLIN CORP p 1082
190 Carondelet Plz # 1530, Saint Louis MO 63105
Tel (314) 480-1400
SIC 2812 2819 2821 2842 2869 2891

■ OLIN SUNBELT II INC p 1082
190 Carondelet Plz # 1530, Saint Louis MO 63105
Tel (314) 480-1400 *SIC* 2812

SOLVAY HOLDING INC p 1339
8 Cedarbrook Dr, Cranbury NJ 08512
Tel (609) 860-4000
SIC 2819 2812 2865 2869

▲ CHURCH & DWIGHT CO INC p 305
500 Charles Ewing Blvd, Ewing NJ 08628
Tel (609) 806-1200
SIC 2841 2812 2842 2844 2819

KUEHNE CHEMICAL CO INC p 831
86 N Hackensack Ave, Kearny NJ 07032
Tel (973) 589-0700 *SIC* 2819 4226 2812

FORMOSA PLASTICS CORP USA p 568
9 Peach Tree Hill Rd, Livingston NJ 07039
Tel (973) 994-7674 *SIC* 2821 2812

PMC GROUP INC p 1157
1288 Route 73 Ste 401, Mount Laurel NJ 08054
Tel (856) 533-1866 *SIC* 3089 2812

CHEMTRADE CHEMICALS US LLC p 293
90 E Halsey Rd, Parsippany NJ 07054
Tel (973) 515-0900 *SIC* 2812

TATA CHEMICALS NORTH AMERICA INC p 1426
100 Enterprise Dr Ste 701, Rockaway NJ 07866
Tel (973) 599-5500 *SIC* 2812

▲ ALBEMARLE CORP p 46
4350 Congress St Ste 700, Charlotte NC 28209
Tel (980) 299-5700
SIC 2821 2834 2819 2899 2812 2869

ARKEMA DELAWARE INC p 110
900 First Ave, King Of Prussia PA 19406
Tel (610) 205-7000
SIC 2812 2819 2869 2891 2899 2992

ARKEMA INC p 110
900 First Ave, King Of Prussia PA 19406
Tel (610) 205-7000 *SIC* 2812

▲ FMC CORP p 562
2929 Walnut St, Philadelphia PA 19104
Tel (215) 299-6000 *SIC* 2812 2879 2869

TRONOX ALKALI CORP p 1484
1735 Market St, Philadelphia PA 19103
Tel (215) 299-6904 *SIC* 2812

▲ PPG INDUSTRIES INC p 1166
1 Ppg Pl, Pittsburgh PA 15272
Tel (412) 434-3131
SIC 2851 3211 3231 3229 2812 2821

■ OLIN CHLOR ALKALI LOGISTICS INC p 1082
490 Stuart Rd Ne, Cleveland TN 37312
Tel (423) 336-4850 *SIC* 2812

■ OCCIDENTAL CHEMICAL CORP p 1072
5005 Lyndon B Johnson Fwy # 2200, Dallas TX 75244
Tel (972) 404-3800 *SIC* 2812

■ WESTLAKE VINYLS CO LP p 1601
2801 Post Oak Blvd # 600, Houston TX 77056
Tel (713) 960-9111 *SIC* 2812 2869 2821

■ CINER WYOMING LLC p 308
254 County Rd 4/6, Green River WY 82935
Tel (307) 875-2600 *SIC* 2812

TRONOX ALKALI WYOMING CORP p 1484
580 Westvaco Rd, Green River WY 82935
Tel (307) 875-2580 *SIC* 2812

SIC 2813 Industrial Gases

AMERICAN AIR LIQUIDE INC p 67
46409 Landing Pkwy, Fremont CA 94538
Tel (510) 624-4000
SIC 2813 5084 3533 4931

■ PRAXAIR DISTRIBUTION INC p 1167
39 Old Ridgebury Rd, Danbury CT 06810
Tel (203) 837-2000 *SIC* 2813 5084 5999

▲ PRAXAIR INC p 1168
10 Riverview Dr, Danbury CT 06810
Tel (203) 837-2000
SIC 2813 3569 3471 3479

AIRGAS CARBONIC INC p 40
2530 Sever Rd Ste 300, Lawrenceville GA 30043
Tel (770) 717-2210 *SIC* 2813 7359 5088

NORCO INC p 1047
1125 W Amity Rd, Boise ID 83705
Tel (208) 336-1643
SIC 5084 5169 7352 5999 3548 2813

PLZ AEROSCIENCE CORP p 1157
1005 S Westgate St, Addison IL 60101
Tel (630) 334-9100 *SIC* 2813

DIVERSIFIED CPC INTERNATIONAL INC p 444
24338 W Durkee Rd, Channahon IL 60410
Tel (815) 423-5991 *SIC* 2813 5169

CONTINENTAL CARBONIC PRODUCTS INC p 363
3985 E Harrison Ave, Decatur IL 62526
Tel (217) 428-2068 *SIC* 2813

■ AIR PRODUCTS MANUFACTURING CORP p 39
6601 S Ridge Rd, Haysville KS 67060
Tel (316) 522-8181 *SIC* 2813 2819

KOCH FERTILIZER LLC p 825
4111 E 37th St N, Wichita KS 67220
Tel (316) 828-5010 *SIC* 2873 5169 2813

CARBIDE INDUSTRIES LLC p 252
4400 Bells Ln, Louisville KY 40211
Tel (502) 775-4100 *SIC* 2813 2819

MATHESON TRI-GAS INC p 919
150 Allen Rd Ste 302, Basking Ridge NJ 07920
Tel (908) 991-9200 *SIC* 2813 5084

LINDE GAS NORTH AMERICA LLC p 868
200 Somerset Corp Blvd # 7000, Bridgewater NJ 08807
Tel (908) 464-8100 *SIC* 2813

LINDE GAS USA LLC p 868
200 Somset Cor B Ste 7000, Bridgewater NJ 08807
Tel (908) 464-8100 *SIC* 2813 5084

LINDE LLC p 868
200 Somerset Corporate Bl, Bridgewater NJ 08807
Tel (908) 464-8100
SIC 2813 3569 3561 3823

LINDE NORTH AMERICA INC p 868
200 Somerset Corporate Bl, Bridgewater NJ 08807
Tel (908) 464-8100
SIC 2813 3569 3559 3561 3511 3823

BOC GROUP INC p 196
575 Mountain Ave, New Providence NJ 07974
Tel (908) 665-2400
SIC 2813 3569 3559 3561 3511 3823

■ PANENERGY CORP p 1111
526 S Church St, Charlotte NC 28202
Tel (704) 594-6200
SIC 4922 1321 2813 5172 4911 4613

ARC3 GASES INC p 103
1636 Us Highway 301 S, Dunn NC 28334
Tel (910) 892-4016
SIC 2813 5084 5169 7359 7692

▲ INVACARE CORP p 760
1 Invacare Way, Elyria OH 44035
Tel (440) 329-6000 *SIC* 3842 2514 2813

▲ AIR PRODUCTS AND CHEMICALS INC p 39
7201 Hamilton Blvd, Allentown PA 18195
Tel (610) 481-4911
SIC 2813 2842 2891 3569

GT&S INC p 644
5275 Tilghman St, Allentown PA 18104
Tel (610) 398-2211
SIC 4925 5169 5084 5085 2813 5172

■ AMERIGAS INC p 82
460 N Gulph Rd Ste 100, King Of Prussia PA 19406
Tel (610) 337-7000
SIC 5984 5172 5722 2911 2813

AIRGAS INC p 40
259 N Radnor Chester Rd # 100, Radnor PA 19087
Tel (610) 687-5253
SIC 5169 5084 5085 2813 2819

AIRGAS USA LLC p 40
259 N Radnor Chester Rd # 100, Radnor PA 19087
Tel (610) 687-5253
SIC 5169 5084 5085 2813 2819

HOLSTON GASES INC p 702
545 W Baxter Ave, Knoxville TN 37921
Tel (865) 573-1917 *SIC* 5169 5084 2813

WESTERN INTERNATIONAL GAS & CYLINDERS INC p 1598
7173 Highway 159 E, Bellville TX 77418
Tel (979) 865-5991 *SIC* 5169 2813

AIR LIQUIDE ELECTRONICS US LP p 39
9101 Lyndon B Johnson Fwy # 800, Dallas TX 75243
Tel (972) 301-5200
SIC 2813 3564 8631 2819

AIR LIQUIDE ADVANCED MATERIALS INC p 38
9811 Katy Fwy Ste 100, Houston TX 77024
Tel (713) 624-8000 *SIC* 2813

AIR LIQUIDE ADVANCED TECHNOLOGIES US LLC p 39
9807 Katy Fwy, Houston TX 77024
Tel (713) 624-8000 *SIC* 2813

AIR LIQUIDE AMERICA LP p 39
9811 Katy Fwy Ste 100, Houston TX 77024
Tel (713) 624-8000
SIC 5084 3533 2813 3569

AIR LIQUIDE AMERICA SPECIALTY GASES LLC p 39
2700 Post Oak Blvd, Houston TX 77056
Tel (800) 217-2688 *SIC* 2911 2813

AIR LIQUIDE INDUSTRIAL US LP p 39
2700 Post Oak Blvd # 1800, Houston TX 77056
Tel (713) 624-8000 *SIC* 2813

AIR LIQUIDE LARGE INDUSTRIES US LP p 39
9811 Katy Fwy Ste 100, Houston TX 77024
Tel (713) 624-8000 *SIC* 2813

AIR LIQUIDE USA LLC p 39
9811 Kepy Fwy Ste 100, Houston TX 77024
Tel (713) 402-2221 *SIC* 2813

AMERICAN AIR LIQUIDE HOLDINGS INC p 67
2700 Post Oak Blvd, Houston TX 77056
Tel (713) 624-8000 *SIC* 2813 6719

SIC 2816 Inorganic Pigments

PLASTIC SERVICES AND PRODUCTS p 1155
12243 Branford St, Sun Valley CA 91352
Tel (818) 896-1101
SIC 3086 3674 2865 2816 3296 2819

PMC GLOBAL INC p 1157
12243 Branford St, Sun Valley CA 91352
Tel (818) 896-1101
SIC 3086 3674 2865 2816 3296 2819

■ **CHEMOURS CO FC LLC** p 293
1007 Market St, Wilmington DE 19898
Tel (302) 774-1000 *SIC* 2879 2816

DSM FINANCE USA INC p 458
1408 Columbia Nitrogen Dr, Augusta GA 30901
Tel (706) 849-6515
SIC 2891 2816 3089 3083 5169

TRONOX LLC p 1484
1 Kerr Mcgee Rd, Savannah GA 31404
Tel (912) 652-1000 *SIC* 2816 2819 5198

STANDRIDGE COLOR CORP p 1376
1196 E Hightower Trl, Social Circle GA 30025
Tel (770) 464-3362 *SIC* 2865 2816 3083

AMERICAN CHEMET CORP p 70
740 Waukegan Rd Ste 202, Deerfield IL 60015
Tel (847) 948-0800 *SIC* 2819 2816

■ **RUST-OLEUM CORP** p 1260
11 E Hawthorn Pkwy, Vernon Hills IL 60061
Tel (847) 367-7700
SIC 2891 2899 2816 2842 2851

WH FERER CO LLC p 1604
2910 N 9th St, Carter Lake IA 51510
Tel (712) 847-0800 *SIC* 2816

■ **FLO KAY INDUSTRIES INC** p 557
1919 Grand Ave, Sioux City IA 51106
Tel (712) 277-2011 *SIC* 2873 2048 2816

■ **KRONOS LOUISIANA INC** p 830
3300 Bayou Dinde Rd, Westlake LA 70669
Tel (337) 882-1774 *SIC* 2816

LOUISIANA PIGMENT CO LP p 880
3300 Bayou Dinde Rd, Westlake LA 70669
Tel (337) 882-7000 *SIC* 2816

CRISTAL p 392
20 Wight Ave Ste 100, Hunt Valley MD 21030
Tel (410) 229-4440
SIC 1241 3531 2816 2869 1321 3631

CRISTAL USA INC p 393
20 Wight Ave Ste 150, Hunt Valley MD 21030
Tel (410) 229-4441 *SIC* 2816

■ **SENSIENT COLORS LLC** p 1304
2515 N Jefferson Ave, Saint Louis MO 63106
Tel (314) 889-7600 *SIC* 2816

ELEMENTIS SPECIALTIES INC p 486
469 Old Trenton Rd, East Windsor NJ 08512
Tel (609) 443-2000
SIC 2851 8731 2899 2865 2816

BASF CATALYSTS LLC p 158
25 Middlesex Tpke, Iselin NJ 08830
Tel (732) 205-5000
SIC 2819 2816 5094 3339

DSM HOLDING CO USA INC p 458
45 Waterview Blvd, Parsippany NJ 07054
Tel (973) 257-1063
SIC 2891 2816 3089 3083 5169

EVONIK CORP p 515
299 Jefferson Rd, Parsippany NJ 07054
Tel (973) 929-8000
SIC 2819 2869 2851 2816

■ **ROCKWOOD HOLDINGS INC** p 1245
100 Overlook Ctr Ste 101, Princeton NJ 08540
Tel (609) 514-0300 *SIC* 2819 2816

BRENNTAG SPECIALTIES INC p 210
1000 Coolidge St, South Plainfield NJ 07080
Tel (800) 732-0562 *SIC* 5169 2816 2899

AMERICHEM INC p 81
2000 Americhem Way, Cuyahoga Falls OH 44221
Tel (330) 929-4213
SIC 2865 2851 2819 2816

▲ **FERRO CORP** p 538
6060 Parkland Blvd # 250, Mayfield Heights OH 44124
Tel (216) 875-5600
SIC 3479 2816 2851 3399 2821 2834

THORWORKS INDUSTRIES INC p 1450
2520 Campbell St, Sandusky OH 44870
Tel (419) 626-4375
SIC 2851 3531 2952 2951 2891 2816

TRONOX LLC p 1484
3301 Nw 150th St, Oklahoma City OK 73134
Tel (405) 775-5000 *SIC* 2819 2816

TRONOX US HOLDINGS INC p 1484
3301 Nw 150th St, Oklahoma City OK 73134
Tel (405) 775-5000 *SIC* 2816 2819 5198

TRONOX WORLDWIDE LLC p 1484
3301 Nw 150th St, Oklahoma City OK 73134
Tel (405) 775-5000 *SIC* 2819 2816

PENN COLOR INC p 1129
400 Old Dublin Pike, Doylestown PA 18901
Tel (215) 345-6364 *SIC* 2865 2816

EMD PERFORMANCE MATERIALS CORP p 491
1 International Plz # 300, Philadelphia PA 19113
Tel (484) 652-5600 *SIC* 2819 2816

AMERICAN IRON OXIDE CO p 75
Fster Plz Ste 7 661 Adrsn, Pittsburgh PA 15220
Tel (412) 929-0177 *SIC* 4953 2816

LANXESS CORP p 844
111 Parkwest Dr, Pittsburgh PA 15275
Tel (800) 526-9377
SIC 2869 2821 2822 2816 2819

SILBERLINE MANUFACTURING CO INC p 1322
130 Lincoln Dr, Tamaqua PA 18252
Tel (570) 668-6050 *SIC* 2816 2819

■ **NUTRA-FLO CO** p 1067
200 S Derby Ln, North Sioux City SD 57049
Tel (712) 277-2011 *SIC* 2873 2816 2048

COLORTECH INC p 339
5712 Commerce Blvd, Morristown TN 37814
Tel (423) 587-0837 *SIC* 3087 2816

▲ **CONTRAN CORP** p 364
5430 Lyndon B Johnson Fwy, Dallas TX 75240
Tel (972) 233-1700 *SIC* 2816

■ **KRONOS INTERNATIONAL INC** p 830
5430 L B Johnson Fwy 1700, Dallas TX 75240
Tel (972) 233-1700 *SIC* 2816

▲ **KRONOS WORLDWIDE INC** p 830
5430 Lbj Fwy Ste 1700, Dallas TX 75240
Tel (972) 233-1700 *SIC* 2816

■ **VALHI HOLDING CO** p 1540
5430 Lyndon B Johnson Fwy # 1700, Dallas TX 75240
Tel (972) 233-1700 *SIC* 2816

■ **VALHI INC** p 1540
5430 Lbj Fwy Ste 1700, Dallas TX 75240
Tel (972) 233-1700
SIC 2816 2899 3429 4953

■ **KERR-MCGEE CORP** p 813
1201 Lake Robbins Dr, Spring TX 77380
Tel (832) 636-1000
SIC 2816 2819 1311 1221 1222

▲ **HUNTSMAN CORP** p 720
10003 Woodloch Forest Dr # 260, The Woodlands TX 77380
Tel (281) 719-6000
SIC 2821 3081 2869 2816 2865

■ **HUNTSMAN INTERNATIONAL LLC** p 720
1003 Woodloch Forest Dr, The Woodlands TX 77380
Tel (281) 719-6000
SIC 2821 3081 2869 2816 2865

SIC 2819 Indl Inorganic Chemicals, NEC

■ **VULCAN PERFORMANCE CHEMICALS** p 1567
1200 Urban Center Dr, Vestavia AL 35242
Tel (205) 298-3000 *SIC* 2819

■ **VENTANA MEDICAL SYSTEMS INC** p 1547
1910 E Innovation Park Dr, Oro Valley AZ 85755
Tel (520) 887-2155 *SIC* 3841 2819 3826

KENYON COMPANIES p 813
2602 N 35th Ave, Phoenix AZ 85009
Tel (602) 233-1191 *SIC* 1742 2819

APACHE NITROGEN PRODUCTS INC p 96
1436 S Apache Powder Rd, Saint David AZ 85630
Tel (520) 720-2217
SIC 2873 5169 2875 2819

■ **FUTUREFUEL CHEMICAL CO** p 586
2800 Gap Rd, Batesville AR 72501
Tel (870) 698-3000 *SIC* 2819

■ **DOW CHEMICAL CO** p 453
25500 Whitesell St, Hayward CA 94545
Tel (510) 786-0100 *SIC* 2819 2821

HILL BROTHERS CHEMICAL CO p 693
1675 N Main St, Orange CA 92867
Tel (714) 998-8800 *SIC* 5169 2819

GENERAL ATOMIC TECHNOLOGIES CORP p 599
3550 General Atomics Ct, San Diego CA 92121
Tel (858) 455-3000
SIC 8731 3829 3443 7374 3499 2819

PLASTIC SERVICES AND PRODUCTS p 1155
12243 Branford St, Sun Valley CA 91352
Tel (818) 896-1101
SIC 3086 3674 2865 2816 3296 2819

PMC GLOBAL INC p 1157
12243 Branford St, Sun Valley CA 91352
Tel (818) 896-1101
SIC 3086 3674 2865 2816 3296 2819

■ **DIONEX CORP** p 441
1228 Titan Way Ste 1002, Sunnyvale CA 94085
Tel (408) 737-0700
SIC 3826 2819 3087 3841

US BORAX INC p 1531
8051 E Maplewood Ave # 100, Greenwood Village CO 80111
Tel (303) 713-5000 *SIC* 1474 2819

THOMPSON CREEK MINING LTD p 1449
26 W Dry Creek Cir # 810, Littleton CO 80120
Tel (303) 761-8801 *SIC* 1061 2899 2819

■ **HACH CO** p 652
5600 Lindbergh Dr, Loveland CO 80538
Tel (970) 669-3050
SIC 3826 3823 3231 2819 2869

RT VANDERBILT CO INC p 1203
30 Winfield St, Norwalk CT 06855
Tel (203) 853-1400
SIC 5169 2869 2819 5052 1499 1459

RT VANDERBILT HOLDING CO INC p 1256
30 Winfield St, Norwalk CT 06855
Tel (203) 295-2141
SIC 5169 2869 2819 1499 1459

VANDERBILT CHEMICALS LLC p 1543
30 Winfield St, Norwalk CT 06855
Tel (203) 853-1400 *SIC* 2819 2869 5169

CCL INDUSTRIES CORP p 270
15 Controls Dr, Shelton CT 06484
Tel (203) 926-1253
SIC 2759 2992 3411 2819 2844

NORFALCO LLC p 1048
301 Tresser Blvd, Stamford CT 06901
Tel (416) 775-1400 *SIC* 2819

TRONOX INC p 1484
1 Stamford Plz, Stamford CT 06901
Tel (203) 705-3800 *SIC* 2819 2421

W L GORE & ASSOCIATES INC p 1568
555 Paper Mill Rd, Newark DE 19711
Tel (302) 738-4880
SIC 3357 2821 5131 3841 2819 3069

HOLTEC INTERNATIONAL p 702
1001 N Us Highway 1, Jupiter FL 33477
Tel (561) 745-7772 *SIC* 2819 8711

TRANS-RESOURCES INC p 1470
17780 Collins Ave, Sunny Isles Beach FL 33160
Tel (305) 933-8301 *SIC* 2873 2819 2879

ARCH CHEMICALS INC p 104
1200 Bluegrass Lakes Pkwy, Alpharetta GA 30004
Tel (678) 624-5800 *SIC* 2819 2899

KEMIRA CHEMICALS INC p 809
1000 Parkwood Cir Se # 500, Atlanta GA 30339
Tel (863) 533-5990 *SIC* 2869 2819

FIBRANT LLC p 540
1408 Columbia Nitrogen Dr, Augusta GA 30901
Tel (706) 849-6600 *SIC* 2819 2899

BIO-LAB INC p 183
1725 N Brown Rd, Lawrenceville GA 30043
Tel (678) 502-4000 *SIC* 2812 2819 2899

AKZO NOBEL PULP AND PERFORMANCE CHEMICALS INC p 43
1850 Parkway Pl Se # 1200, Marietta GA 30067
Tel (770) 578-0858 *SIC* 2899 2819

AMREP INC p 86
425 Franklin Gtwy Se # 530, Marietta GA 30067
Tel (770) 590-5960
SIC 2842 2079 2911 2869 2841 2819

IMERYS USA INC p 733
100 Mansell Ct E Ste 300, Roswell GA 30076
Tel (770) 645-3300
SIC 1455 1459 1429 1422 2819

TRONOX LLC p 1484
1 Kerr Mcgee Rd, Savannah GA 31404
Tel (912) 652-1000 *SIC* 2816 2819 5198

AKZO NOBEL INC p 42
525 W Van Buren St Fl 16, Chicago IL 60607
Tel (312) 544-7000
SIC 2869 2851 2834 3841 3826 2819

AMERICAN CHEMET CORP p 70
740 Waukegan Rd Ste 202, Deerfield IL 60015
Tel (847) 948-0800 *SIC* 2819 2816

■ **UOP LLC** p 1528
25 E Algonquin Rd, Des Plaines IL 60016
Tel (847) 391-2000
SIC 2819 8711 8731 8999 3823 3479

■ **PHOSPHATE RESOURCE PARTNERS LIMITED PARTNERSHIP** p 1145
100 Saunders Rd Ste 300, Lake Forest IL 60045
Tel (847) 739-1200
SIC 2874 1311 1475 2819 1094

BP AMOCO CHEMICAL CO p 205
150 W Warrenville Rd, Naperville IL 60563
Tel (630) 420-5111
SIC 2221 2821 2869 2819 2865

PCS PHOSPHATE CO INC p 1124
1101 Skokie Blvd Ste 400, Northbrook IL 60062
Tel (847) 849-4200
SIC 1475 1474 2874 2819

SCHOLLE IPN CORP p 1288
200 W North Ave, Northlake IL 60164
Tel (708) 562-7290
SIC 2819 3081 2821 3089

CARUS GROUP INC p 262
315 5th St, Peru IL 61354
Tel (815) 223-1500 *SIC* 2819

GEO SPECIALTY CHEMICALS INC p 605
401 S Earl Ave Ste 3, Lafayette IN 47904
Tel (765) 448-9412 *SIC* 2819

■ **AIR PRODUCTS MANUFACTURING CORP** p 39
6601 S Ridge Rd, Haysville KS 67060
Tel (316) 522-8181 *SIC* 2813 2819

CONSPEC MARKETING AND MFG CO p 360
636 S 66th Ter, Kansas City KS 66111
Tel (913) 287-1700 *SIC* 2819

CORBION AMERICA HOLDINGS INC p 368
7905 Quivira Rd, Lenexa KS 66215
Tel (913) 890-5500
SIC 2819 2869 2041 2023

■ **COMPASS MINERALS GROUP INC** p 351
9900 W 109th St Ste 600, Overland Park KS 66210
Tel (913) 344-9100 *SIC* 2819 2899

▲ **COMPASS MINERALS INTERNATIONAL INC** p 351
9900 W 109th St Ste 100, Overland Park KS 66210
Tel (913) 344-9200 *SIC* 1474 2899 2819

■ **WILD FLAVORS INC** p 1609
1261 Pacific Ave, Erlanger KY 41018
Tel (859) 342-3600 *SIC* 2869 2819

CARBIDE INDUSTRIES LLC p 252
4400 Bells Ln, Louisville KY 40211
Tel (502) 775-4100 *SIC* 2813 2819

CENTRAL CARBIDE LLC p 277
4400 Bells Ln, Louisville KY 40211
Tel (502) 775-4100 *SIC* 2819

SUD-CHEMIE INC p 1396
1600 W Hill St, Louisville KY 40210
Tel (502) 634-7361 *SIC* 2819

ALLTECH INC p 58
3031 Catnip Hill Rd, Nicholasville KY 40356
Tel (859) 885-9613
SIC 2869 2048 3821 2819

ALMATIS BURNSIDE LLC p 59
41237 Hwy 22, Burnside LA 70738
Tel (225) 474-1700 *SIC* 2819

COMILOG US INC p 344
610 Pittman Rd, Baltimore MD 21226
Tel (410) 789-8800 *SIC* 2819 3313 3356

UNITED STATES ENRICHMENT CORP p 1513
6903 Rockledge Dr, Bethesda MD 20817
Tel (301) 564-3200 *SIC* 2819 2869

CRISTAL INORGANIC CHEMICALS US INC p 393
20 Wight Ave Ste 150, Cockeysville MD 21030
Tel (410) 229-4400 *SIC* 2819

▲ **W R GRACE & CO** p 1569
7500 Grace Dr, Columbia MD 21044
Tel (410) 531-4000
SIC 2819 3531 2899 2891 3479

■ **W R GRACE & CO-CONN** p 1569
7500 Grace Dr, Columbia MD 21044
Tel (410) 531-4000
SIC 2819 3531 2899 2891 3479

INSTRUMENTATION LABORATORY CO p 747
180 Hartwell Rd, Bedford MA 01730
Tel (800) 955-9525
SIC 3841 2819 8731 2835

▲ **CABOT CORP** p 235
2 Seaport Ln Ste 1300, Boston MA 02210
Tel (617) 345-0100
SIC 2895 3081 3084 2819 3339

▲ **GCP APPLIED TECHNOLOGIES INC** p 595
62 Whittemore Ave, Cambridge MA 02140
Tel (617) 876-1400 *SIC* 2819 2899

■ **ROHM AND HAAS ELECTRONIC MATERIALS LLC** p 1247
455 Forest St, Marlborough MA 01752
Tel (508) 481-7950 *SIC* 2819 2869

PRESSURE VESSEL SERVICE INC p 1173
10900 Harper Ave, Detroit MI 48213
Tel (313) 921-1200
SIC 5169 2819 2899 4953 3535

HAVILAND PRODUCTS CO p 668
421 Ann St Nw, Grand Rapids MI 49504
Tel (616) 361-6691 *SIC* 5169 2819

■ **MOSAIC GLOBAL HOLDINGS INC** p 991
3033 Campus Dr Ste E490, Minneapolis MN 55441
Tel (763) 577-2700
SIC 2874 1474 1475 2875 2819

■ **MOS HOLDINGS INC** p 991
3033 Campus Dr Ste E490, Plymouth MN 55441
Tel (763) 577-2700
SIC 2874 1475 2819 1094 1481

SOUTHERN IONICS INC p 1349
180 W Broad St, West Point MS 39773
Tel (662) 494-3055 *SIC* 2819

PLAZE INC p 1156
105 Bolte Ln, Saint Clair MO 63077
Tel (630) 543-7600 *SIC* 5169 2819

▲ **FUTUREFUEL CORP** p 586
8235 Forsyth Blvd 4, Saint Louis MO 63105
Tel (314) 854-8385 *SIC* 2819

ICL NORTH AMERICA INC p 727
622 Emerson Rd Ste 500, Saint Louis MO 63141
Tel (314) 983-7500 *SIC* 2819

ICL PERFORMANCE PRODUCTS LP p 727
622 Emerson Rd Ste 500, Saint Louis MO 63141
Tel (314) 983-7500 *SIC* 2819

JOST CHEMICAL CO p 794
8150 Lackland Rd, Saint Louis MO 63114
Tel (314) 428-4300 *SIC* 2834 2819

MISSISSIPPI LIME CO p 975
3870 S Lindbergh Blvd # 200, Saint Louis MO 63127
Tel (314) 543-6300
SIC 3274 2819 2879 1422

▲ **OLIN CORP** p 1082
190 Carondelet Plz # 1530, Saint Louis MO 63105
Tel (314) 480-1400
SIC 2812 2819 2821 2842 2869 2891

VECTRA CO p 1546
120 S Central Ave Ste 200, Saint Louis MO 63105
Tel (314) 797-8600 *SIC* 2819

LONZA INC p 877
90 Boroline Rd Ste 1, Allendale NJ 07401
Tel (201) 316-9200 *SIC* 2899 2869 2819

▲ **INNOPHOS HOLDINGS INC** p 744
259 Prospect Plains Rd A, Cranbury NJ 08512
Tel (609) 495-2495 *SIC* 2874 2819

■ **INNOPHOS INC** p 744
259 Prospect Plains Rd A, Cranbury NJ 08512
Tel (609) 495-2495 *SIC* 2819

■ **INNOPHOS INVESTMENTS II INC** p 744
259 Prospect Plains Rd, Cranbury NJ 08512
Tel (609) 495-2495 *SIC* 2874 2819

SOLVAY HOLDING INC p 1339
8 Cedarbrook Dr, Cranbury NJ 08512
Tel (609) 860-4000
SIC 2819 2812 2865 2869

JM HUBER CORP p 786
499 Thornall St Ste 8, Edison NJ 08837
Tel (732) 603-3630
SIC 0811 1311 1455 2493 2819

▲ **CHURCH & DWIGHT CO INC** p 305
500 Charles Ewing Blvd, Ewing NJ 08628
Tel (609) 806-1200
SIC 2841 2812 2842 2844 2819

BASF CORP p 158
100 Park Ave, Florham Park NJ 07932
Tel (973) 245-6000
SIC 2869 2819 2899 2843 2834 2879

BASFIN CORP p 158
100 Campus Dr Ste 301, Florham Park NJ 07932
Tel (973) 245-6000
SIC 2869 2819 2899 2843 2879 2834

BASF CATALYSTS LLC p 158
25 Middlesex Tpke, Iselin NJ 08830
Tel (732) 205-5000
SIC 2819 2816 5094 3339

KUEHNE CHEMICAL CO INC p 831
86 N Hackensack Ave, Kearny NJ 07032
Tel (973) 589-0700 *SIC* 2819 4226 2812

CHEMTRADE CHEMICALS CORP p 293
90 E Halsey Rd Ste 301, Parsippany NJ 07054
Tel (973) 515-0900 *SIC* 2819

CHEMTRADE GCC HOLDING CO p 293
90 E Halsey Rd, Parsippany NJ 07054
Tel (973) 515-0900 *SIC* 6719 2819

CHEMTRADE SOLUTIONS LLC p 293
90 E Halsey Rd, Parsippany NJ 07054
Tel (973) 515-0900 *SIC* 5169 2819

EVONIK CORP p 515
299 Jefferson Rd, Parsippany NJ 07054
Tel (973) 929-8000
SIC 2819 2869 2851 2816

GENTEK INC p 604
90 E Halsey Rd Ste 301, Parsippany NJ 07054
Tel (973) 515-0900
SIC 2869 2819 2844 3714 3496

■ ROCKWOOD HOLDINGS INC p 1245
100 Overlook Ctr Ste 101, Princeton NJ 08540
Tel (609) 514-0300 *SIC* 2819 2816

REAGENT CHEMICAL & RESEARCH INC p 1213
115 Rte 202, Ringoes NJ 08551
Tel (908) 284-2800 *SIC* 3949 2819

■ PHIBRO ANIMAL HEALTH CORP p 1142
300 Frank W Burr Blvd, Teaneck NJ 07666
Tel (201) 329-7300
SIC 2819 5169 2899 2834

CYTEC INDUSTRIES INC p 406
5 Garret Mountain Plz, Woodland Park NJ 07424
Tel (973) 357-3100
SIC 2899 2821 2672 2851 2823 2819

MULTISORB TECHNOLOGIES INC p 1000
325 Harlem Rd, Buffalo NY 14224
Tel (716) 824-8900 *SIC* 2819

▲ ALCOA CORP p 47
390 Park Ave Fl 12, New York NY 10022
Tel (212) 518-5400
SIC 3355 3363 3297 2819

▲ MINERALS TECHNOLOGIES INC p 973
622 3rd Ave Fl 38, New York NY 10017
Tel (212) 878-1800
SIC 3295 2819 3274 1411 3281 5032

PRINCE MINERAL HOLDING CORP p 1176
21 W 46th St Fl 14th, New York NY 10036
Tel (646) 747-4222 *SIC* 2819

RESURGENCE ASSET MANAGEMENT LLC p 1228
1185 Av Of The Amer Fl 18, New York NY 10036
Tel (212) 710-5001
SIC 6282 2865 2821 2869 2861 2819

■ SPECIALTY MINERALS INC p 1356
622 3rd Ave Fl 38, New York NY 10017
Tel (212) 878-1800
SIC 2819 5032 1422 5169 2899

TAKEDA AMERICA HOLDINGS INC p 1422
767 3rd Ave, New York NY 10017
Tel (212) 421-6954 *SIC* 5122 5169 2819

TOSHIBA NUCLEAR ENERGY HOLDINGS (US) INC p 1462
1251 Ave Of Amrcs 400 Ste 4100, New York NY 10020
Tel (212) 596-0600
SIC 8711 3829 3823 2819

▲ ALBEMARLE CORP p 46
4350 Congress St Ste 700, Charlotte NC 28209
Tel (980) 299-5700
SIC 2821 2834 2819 2899 2812 2869

AREVA INC p 107
7207 Ibm Dr, Charlotte NC 28262
Tel (704) 805-2000
SIC 3823 3829 8711 5085 3561 2819

CLARIANT CORP p 321
4000 Monroe Rd, Charlotte NC 28205
Tel (704) 331-7000 *SIC* 2869 2819

CLARIANT PLASTICS & COATINGS USA INC p 321
4000 Monroe Rd, Charlotte NC 28205
Tel (704) 331-7000 *SIC* 2869 2819

■ ROCKWOOD LITHIUM INC p 1245
348 Holiday Inn Dr, Kings Mountain NC 28086
Tel (704) 739-2501 *SIC* 2819

■ GE-HITACHI NUCLEAR ENERGY AMERICA LLC p 597
3901 Castle Hayne Rd, Wilmington NC 28401
Tel (910) 819-5073 *SIC* 2819

▲ OMNOVA SOLUTIONS INC p 1085
25435 Harvard Rd, Beachwood OH 44122
Tel (216) 682-7000
SIC 2819 2211 3069 3081

OMYA INC p 1085
9987 Carver Rd Ste 300, Blue Ash OH 45242
Tel (513) 387-4600 *SIC* 2819

AMERICHEM INC p 81
2000 Americhem Way, Cuyahoga Falls OH 44221
Tel (330) 929-4213
SIC 2865 2851 2819 2816

DOVER CHEMICAL CORP p 453
3676 Davis Rd Nw, Dover OH 44622
Tel (330) 343-7711 *SIC* 2819 2869 2899

GLOBE METALLURGICAL INC p 618
County Road 32, Waterford OH 45786
Tel (740) 984-2361 *SIC* 3339 3313 2819

■ EL DORADO CHEMICAL CO INC p 482
16 S Pennsylvania Ave, Oklahoma City OK 73107
Tel (405) 235-4546 *SIC* 2819 2875 2892

■ LSB CHEMICAL LLC p 883
16 S Pennsylvania Ave, Oklahoma City OK 73107
Tel (405) 235-4546 *SIC* 2819 2873 2892

TRONOX LLC p 1484
3301 Nw 150th St, Oklahoma City OK 73134
Tel (405) 775-5000 *SIC* 2819 2816

TRONOX US HOLDINGS INC p 1484
3301 Nw 150th St, Oklahoma City OK 73134
Tel (405) 775-5000 *SIC* 2816 2819 5198

TRONOX WORLDWIDE LLC p 1484
3301 Nw 150th St, Oklahoma City OK 73134
Tel (405) 775-5000 *SIC* 2819 2816

PENN UNITED TECHNOLOGIES INC p 1129
799 N Pike Rd, Cabot PA 16023
Tel (724) 352-1507 *SIC* 3544 2819

AVANTOR PERFORMANCE MATERIALS HOLDINGS LLC p 136
3477 Corp Pkwy Ste 200, Center Valley PA 18034
Tel (610) 573-2600 *SIC* 2819

AVANTOR PERFORMANCE MATERIALS INC p 136
3477 Corp Pkwy Ste 200, Center Valley PA 18034
Tel (610) 573-2600 *SIC* 2819

WESTINGHOUSE ELECTRIC CO LLC p 1601
1000 Westinghouse Dr, Cranberry Township PA 16066
Tel (412) 374-2020
SIC 3829 8711 3823 2819

INTERSTATE CHEMICAL CO INC p 758
2797 Freedland Rd, Hermitage PA 16148
Tel (724) 981-3771 *SIC* 5169 2819

ARKEMA DELAWARE INC p 110
900 First Ave, King Of Prussia PA 19406
Tel (610) 205-7000
SIC 2812 2819 2869 2891 2899 2992

ALMATIS INC p 59
501 W Park Rd, Leetsdale PA 15056
Tel (412) 630-2800 *SIC* 2819

■ NIAGARA HOLDINGS INC p 1042
300 Lindenwood Dr, Malvern PA 19355
Tel (610) 651-4200 *SIC* 2819 3231

PQ CORP p 1166
300 Lindenwood Dr, Malvern PA 19355
Tel (610) 651-4429 *SIC* 2819 3231

PQ HOLDING INC p 1166
300 Lindenwood Dr, Malvern PA 19355
Tel (610) 651-4400 *SIC* 2819

ZEOLYST INTERNATIONAL p 1642
300 Lindenwood Dr, Malvern PA 19355
Tel (610) 651-4200 *SIC* 2819

▲ CALGON CARBON CORP p 238
3000 Gsk Dr, Moon Township PA 15108
Tel (412) 787-6700
SIC 2819 7699 3589 3564

■ INDSPEC CHEMICAL CORP p 739
133 Main St, Petrolia PA 16050
Tel (724) 756-2370 *SIC* 2865 2819

EMD PERFORMANCE MATERIALS CORP p 491
1 International Plz # 300, Philadelphia PA 19113
Tel (484) 652-5600 *SIC* 2819 2816

■ PEROXYCHEM LLC p 1137
1 Commerce Sq, Philadelphia PA 19103
Tel (267) 422-2400 *SIC* 5169 2819

■ ROHM AND HAAS CO p 1246
100 N Independence Mall W, Philadelphia PA 19106
Tel (215) 592-3000
SIC 2819 2851 2891 2899

BAYER CORP p 161
100 Bayer Rd, Pittsburgh PA 15205
Tel (412) 777-2000
SIC 2821 2879 2819 2834 3841

■ FISHER SCIENTIFIC CO LLC p 552
300 Industry Dr, Pittsburgh PA 15275
Tel (412) 490-8300
SIC 5049 5169 3821 3826 2869 2819

LANXESS CORP p 844
111 Parkwest Dr, Pittsburgh PA 15275
Tel (800) 526-9377
SIC 2869 2821 2822 2816 2819

AIRGAS INC p 40
259 N Radnor Chester Rd # 100, Radnor PA 19087
Tel (610) 687-5253
SIC 5169 5084 5085 2813 2819

AIRGAS USA LLC p 40
259 N Radnor Chester Rd # 100, Radnor PA 19087
Tel (610) 687-5253
SIC 5169 5084 5085 2813 2819

▲ VWR CORP p 1567
100 Matsonford Rd 1-200, Radnor PA 19087
Tel (610) 386-1700
SIC 2869 2819 3821 5047

SILBERLINE MANUFACTURING CO INC p 1322
130 Lincoln Dr, Tamaqua PA 18252
Tel (570) 668-6050 *SIC* 2816 2819

SAINT-GOBAIN CERAMICS & PLASTICS INC p 1271
750 E Swedesford Rd, Valley Forge PA 19482
Tel (610) 341-7000
SIC 2819 3679 3544 3297

DILMAR OIL CO INC p 440
1951 W Darlington St, Florence SC 29501
Tel (843) 662-4179 *SIC* 5172 2819

▲ INGEVITY CORP p 742
5255 Virginia Ave, North Charleston SC 29406
Tel (843) 740-2300 *SIC* 2819

HELENA CHEMICAL CO p 681
255 Schilling Blvd # 200, Collierville TN 38017
Tel (901) 761-0050 *SIC* 5191 2819

NORANDA ALUMINUM HOLDING CORP p 1047
801 Crescent Cntre Dr 6 Ste 600, Franklin TN 37067
Tel (615) 771-5700 *SIC* 3334 2819 3353

BUCKMAN LABORATORIES INC p 223
1256 N Mclean Blvd, Memphis TN 38108
Tel (901) 278-0330 *SIC* 2869 2819

BULAB HOLDINGS INC p 225
1256 N Mclean Blvd, Memphis TN 38108
Tel (901) 278-0330 *SIC* 2819 2869

AIR LIQUIDE ELECTRONICS US LP p 39
9101 Lyndon B Johnson Fwy # 800, Dallas TX 75243
Tel (972) 301-5200
SIC 2813 3564 8631 2819

■ CELANESE US HOLDINGS LLC p 273
1601 Lyndon B Johnson Fwy, Dallas TX 75234
Tel (972) 443-4000 *SIC* 2821 2879 2819

▲ N L INDUSTRIES INC p 1005
5430 Lbj Fwy Ste 1700, Dallas TX 75240
Tel (972) 233-1700 *SIC* 2819 3572 3699

■ OXY VINYLS LP p 1101
5005 Lbj Fwy Ste 2200, Dallas TX 75244
Tel (972) 720-7000
SIC 2821 2899 2819 1382

■ ROHM AND HAAS TEXAS INC p 1247
6600 La Porte Fwy, Deer Park TX 77536
Tel (281) 476-8304 *SIC* 2869 2899 2819

NASHTEC LLC p 1008
4633 Hwy 361, Gregory TX 78359
Tel (361) 777-2280 *SIC* 2819

CRITERION CATALYSTS & TECHNOLOGIES LP p 393
910 Louisiana St Ste 2900, Houston TX 77002
Tel (713) 241-3000 *SIC* 2819 2869

DX HOLDING CO INC p 464
300 Jackson Hill St, Houston TX 77007
Tel (713) 863-1947 *SIC* 2869 2819 5169

PERMIAN MUD SERVICE INC p 1136
3200 Southwest Fwy # 2700, Houston TX 77027
Tel (713) 627-1101 *SIC* 2819

SHELL CATALYST VENTURES INC p 1314
910 Louisiana St, Houston TX 77002
Tel (713) 241-5766 *SIC* 2819

SOLVAY AMERICA INC p 1339
3737 Buffalo Ste 800, Houston TX 77098
Tel (713) 525-4000 *SIC* 2819

SOLVAY CHEMICALS INC p 1339
3737 Buffalo Speedway, Houston TX 77098
Tel (713) 525-6800 *SIC* 1474 2819

SOLVAY INTEROX INC p 1339
3737 Buffalo Speedway, Houston TX 77098
Tel (713) 525-6500 *SIC* 2819 2899

TEXAS UNITED CORP p 1444
4800 San Felipe St, Houston TX 77056
Tel (713) 877-1793
SIC 1479 2819 4619 2899 3299 7353

■ CELANESE AMERICAS LLC p 273
222 Colinas Blvd W 900n, Irving TX 75039
Tel (972) 443-4000
SIC 2821 2819 2824 5169

▲ CELANESE CORP p 273
222 Las Colinas Blvd W # 900, Irving TX 75039
Tel (972) 443-4000 *SIC* 2819 2821 2869

■ CELANESE INTERNATIONAL CORP p 273
222 Las Colinas Blvd W, Irving TX 75039
Tel (972) 443-4000 *SIC* 2819 2869

■ CNA HOLDINGS LLC p 330
222 Las Colinas Blvd W, Irving TX 75039
Tel (972) 443-4000
SIC 2823 2821 2819 5169 8731

▲ MARTIN MIDSTREAM PARTNERS LP p 913
4200 Stone Rd, Kilgore TX 75662
Tel (903) 983-6200
SIC 5171 4226 1321 4424 2819 2875

■ ALBEMARLE CATALYSTS CO LP p 46
13000 Baypark Rd, Pasadena TX 77507
Tel (281) 474-2864 *SIC* 2819

ECO SERVICES OPERATIONS LLC p 475
2002 Timberloch Pl # 300, Spring TX 77380
Tel (800) 642-4200 *SIC* 2819

■ KERR-MCGEE CORP p 813
1201 Lake Robbins Dr, Spring TX 77380
Tel (832) 636-1000
SIC 2816 2819 1311 1221 1222

■ NALCO CHAMPION LLC p 1006
7705 Highway 90a, Sugar Land TX 77478
Tel (713) 627-3303 *SIC* 2819

▲ TETRA TECHNOLOGIES INC p 1441
24955 Interstate 45, The Woodlands TX 77380
Tel (281) 367-1983 *SIC* 2819 1389

G S L CORP p 587
765 N 10500 W, Ogden UT 84404
Tel (801) 731-3100 *SIC* 2819 2899 3339

THATCHER GROUP INC p 1446
1905 W Fortune Rd, Salt Lake City UT 84104
Tel (801) 972-4587 *SIC* 2819

US MAGNESIUM LLC p 1532
238 N 2200 W, Salt Lake City UT 84116
Tel (801) 532-2043 *SIC* 3356 2819

BNG AMERICA LLC p 194
1235 S Clark St Ste 700a, Arlington VA 22202
Tel (703) 412-2500
SIC 8711 8741 4953 2819

WVA MANUFACTURING LLC p 1628
Rr 60, Alloy WV 25002
Tel (304) 779-3200 *SIC* 3339 2819

HYDRITE CHEMICAL CO p 723
300 N Patrick Blvd Fl 2, Brookfield WI 53045
Tel (262) 792-1450
SIC 5169 2819 2841 2869

ALDRICH CHEMICAL CO LLC p 48
6000 N Teutonia Ave, Milwaukee WI 53209
Tel (414) 438-3850
SIC 2869 2819 3821 7371 2741

EMCO CHEMICAL DISTRIBUTORS INC p 491
8601 95th St, Pleasant Prairie WI 53158
Tel (262) 427-0400 *SIC* 5169 7389 2819

SIC 2821 Plastics, Mtrls & Nonvulcanizable Elastomers

ALPHAPET INC p 60
1301 Finley Island Rd, Decatur AL 35601
Tel (256) 308-1180 *SIC* 2821

HB&G BUILDING PRODUCTS INC p 671
1015 S Brundidge Blvd, Troy AL 36081
Tel (334) 566-5000 *SIC* 2431 2421 2821

CYTEC ENGINEERED MATERIALS INC p 406
2085 E Tech Cir Ste 300, Tempe AZ 85284
Tel (480) 730-2000 *SIC* 3769 5085 2821

TECHMER PM INC p 1431
18420 S Laurel Park Rd, Compton CA 90220
Tel (310) 632-9211 *SIC* 2821

TALCO PLASTICS INC p 1422
1000 W Rincon St, Corona CA 92880
Tel (951) 531-2000 *SIC* 4953 2821

HENRY CO LLC p 684
999 N Sepulveda Blvd, El Segundo CA 90245
Tel (310) 955-9200 *SIC* 2952 2821 2891

HNC PARENT INC p 698
999 N Sepulveda Blvd, El Segundo CA 90245
Tel (310) 955-9200 *SIC* 2952 2821 2891

GKN AEROSPACE TRANSPARENCY SYSTEMS INC p 613
12122 Western Ave, Garden Grove CA 92841
Tel (714) 893-7531
SIC 3089 3231 3827 3728 3081 2821

■ DOW CHEMICAL CO p 453
25500 Whitesell St, Hayward CA 94545
Tel (510) 786-0100 *SIC* 2819 2821

J-M MANUFACTURING CO INC p 772
5200 W Century Blvd, Los Angeles CA 90045
Tel (800) 621-4404 *SIC* 2821 3491 3084

BURKE INDUSTRIES INC p 227
2250 S 10th St, San Jose CA 95112
Tel (408) 297-3500
SIC 3069 2822 2821 3061

■ CHEVRON ORONITE CO LLC p 296
6001 Bollinger Canyon Rd, San Ramon CA 94583
Tel (713) 432-2500
SIC 2821 2899 2869 1311

REHRIG PACIFIC CO p 1220
4010 E 26th St, Vernon CA 90058
Tel (800) 421-6244 *SIC* 3089 2821

REHRIG PACIFIC HOLDINGS INC p 1220
4010 E 26th St, Vernon CA 90058
Tel (323) 262-5145 *SIC* 3089 2821

GEORGIA PACIFIC HOLDINGS INC p 607
13208 Hadley St Apt 1, Whittier CA 90601
Tel (626) 926-1474
SIC 2676 2656 2435 2821

CPI HOLDING CO p 387
10368 W Centennial Rd, Littleton CO 80127
Tel (303) 973-9311 *SIC* 2821

HENKEL CORP p 683
1 Henkel Way, Rocky Hill CT 06067
Tel (860) 571-5100
SIC 2843 2821 2833 2899 2891

HENKEL OF AMERICA INC p 683
1 Henkel Way, Rocky Hill CT 06067
Tel (860) 571-5100
SIC 2869 2843 2821 2833 2899 2891

▲ ROGERS CORP p 1246
1 Technology Dr, Rogers CT 06263
Tel (860) 774-9605 *SIC* 2891 2821 2824

▲ HEXCEL CORP p 688
281 Tresser Blvd Ste 1503, Stamford CT 06901
Tel (203) 969-0666
SIC 2821 3728 3089 3624 2891 3469

RESINALL CORP p 1227
3065 High Ridge Rd, Stamford CT 06903
Tel (203) 329-7100 *SIC* 2821

W L GORE & ASSOCIATES INC p 1568
555 Paper Mill Rd, Newark DE 19711
Tel (302) 738-4880
SIC 3357 2821 5131 3841 2819 3069

▲ E I DU PONT DE NEMOURS AND CO p 466
974 Centre Rd, Wilmington DE 19805
Tel (302) 774-1000
SIC 2879 2824 2865 2821 2834

▲ RAYONIER ADVANCED MATERIALS INC p 1210
1301 Riverplace Blvd # 2300, Jacksonville FL 32207
Tel (904) 357-4600 *SIC* 2821 2823

■ LINVATEC CORP p 869
11311 Concept Blvd, Largo FL 33773
Tel (727) 392-6464 *SIC* 3842 3841 2821

ALLNEX USA INC p 58
9005 Westside Pkwy, Alpharetta GA 30009
Tel (800) 433-2873 *SIC* 2821

■ AXIALL CORP p 140
1000 Abernathy Rd # 1200, Atlanta GA 30328
Tel (770) 395-4500
SIC 2812 2821 2865 2861 2873

■ AXIALL LLC p 140
1000 Abernathy Rd # 1200, Atlanta GA 30328
Tel (770) 395-4500 *SIC* 2821

GEORGIA-PACIFIC LLC p 608
133 Peachtree St Ne # 4810, Atlanta GA 30303
Tel (404) 652-4000
SIC 2676 2656 2653 2435 2821 3275

CELLOFOAM NORTH AMERICA INC p 274
1917 Rockdale Indstrl Blv, Conyers GA 30012
Tel (770) 929-3688 *SIC* 3089 2821

FIBERVISIONS MANUFACTURING CO p 539
7101 Alcovy Rd Ne, Covington GA 30014
Tel (770) 784-3402 *SIC* 2821 2823

TEXTILE RUBBER AND CHEMICAL CO INC p 1445
1300-1350 Tiarco Dr Sw, Dalton GA 30721
Tel (706) 277-1300 *SIC* 5169 2821

ARCLIN USA LLC p 105
1000 Holcomb Woods Pkwy, Roswell GA 30076
Tel (678) 999-2100 *SIC* 2821 2891

GEM INDUSTRIES INC p 598
Hwy 123 N, Toccoa GA 30577
Tel (706) 886-8431
SIC 3429 2531 2511 3446 2821 2515

SENIOR HOLDINGS INC p 1304
300 E Devon Ave, Bartlett IL 60103
Tel (630) 837-1811 *SIC* 3599 2821

POLYNT COMPOSITES USA INC p 1160
99 E Cottage Ave, Carpentersville IL 60110
Tel (847) 428-2657 *SIC* 2821

AMCOR FLEXIBLES LLC p 65
1919 S Butterfield Rd, Mundelein IL 60060
Tel (847) 362-9000
SIC 2671 2621 2821 3081 3466

BP AMOCO CHEMICAL CO p 205
150 W Warrenville Rd, Naperville IL 60563
Tel (630) 420-5111
SIC 2221 2821 2869 2819 2865

▲ STEPAN CO p 1386
22 W Frontage Rd, Northfield IL 60093
Tel (847) 446-7500
SIC 2843 2821 2087 2865

SCHOLLE IPN CORP p 1288
200 W North Ave, Northlake IL 60164
Tel (708) 562-7290
SIC 2819 3081 2821 3089

NOVIPAX LLC p 1063
2215 York Rd Ste 504, Oak Brook IL 60523
Tel (630) 686-2735 *SIC* 2821 2299

■ AMERI KART CORP p 67
17196 State Road 120, Bristol IN 46507
Tel (574) 848-7462
SIC 3089 3537 2821 5162

DSM ENGINEERING PLASTICS INC p 458
2267 W Mill Rd, Evansville IN 47720
Tel (812) 435-7500 *SIC* 2821 3087 3083

SABIC INNOVATIVE PLASTICS MT VERNON LLC p 1264
1 Lexan Ln, Mount Vernon IN 47620
Tel (812) 838-4385 *SIC* 2821 3087 3081

PRIMEX PLASTICS CORP p 1176
1235 N F St, Richmond IN 47374
Tel (765) 966-7774 *SIC* 3081 2821

CARAVAN INGREDIENTS INC p 252
7905 Quivira Rd, Lenexa KS 66215
Tel (913) 890-5500
SIC 2099 2821 5084 2087

■ ASHLAND LLC p 117
50 E Rivercenter Blvd # 1600, Covington KY 41011
Tel (859) 815-3333
SIC 2899 2851 2821 2911 5169 7549

MINOVA HOLDING INC p 974
150 Carley Ct, Georgetown KY 40324
Tel (502) 863-6800 *SIC* 2821 3564 2439

AMERICAN SYNTHETIC RUBBER CO LLC p 80
4500 Camp Ground Rd, Louisville KY 40216
Tel (502) 449-8300 *SIC* 2822 2821

REVSTONE INDUSTRIES LLC p 1229
2008 Cypress St Ste 100, Paris KY 40361
Tel (859) 294-5590 *SIC* 2821 3086 3341

CORNERSTONE CHEMICAL CO p 371
10800 River Rd, Westwego LA 70094
Tel (504) 431-9511 *SIC* 2822 2821

CCC ACQUISITION HOLDINGS INC p 269
200 Clarendon St Ste 4000, Boston MA 02116
Tel (617) 516-2000 *SIC* 6719 2821

ACUSHNET RUBBER CO INC p 20
744 Belleville Ave, New Bedford MA 02745
Tel (508) 998-4000 *SIC* 3053 3061 2821

SABIC US HOLDINGS LP p 1264
1 Plastics Ave, Pittsfield MA 01201
Tel (413) 448-7110 *SIC* 2821

■ DOW CORNING CORP p 453
2200 W Salzburg Rd, Auburn MI 48611
Tel (989) 496-4000 *SIC* 2821 2869

ASAHI KASEI PLASTICS (AMERICA) INC p 115
1 Thermofil Way, Fowlerville MI 48836
Tel (517) 223-2000 *SIC* 2821

ASAHI KASEI PLASTICS NORTH AMERICA INC p 115
1 Thermofil Way, Fowlerville MI 48836
Tel (517) 223-2000 *SIC* 2821

DART CONTAINER CORP OF KENTUCKY p 413
500 Hogsback Rd, Mason MI 48854
Tel (517) 676-3800 *SIC* 2821 3086

▲ DOW CHEMICAL CO p 453
2030 Dow Ctr, Midland MI 48674
Tel (989) 636-1000
SIC 2821 3081 3086 2812 2879

SUMITOMO BAKELITE NORTH AMERICA INC p 1398
46820 Magellan Dr Ste C, Novi MI 48377
Tel (248) 313-7000 *SIC* 2821

FREUDENBERG NORTH AMERICA LIMITED PARTNERSHIP p 579
47774 W Anchor Ct, Plymouth MI 48170
Tel (734) 354-5505
SIC 2821 3714 3053 3061

FREUDENBERG-NOK GENERAL PARTNERSHIP p 579
47690 E Anchor Ct, Plymouth MI 48170
Tel (734) 451-0020
SIC 2821 3714 3053 3061

VIBRACOUSTIC NORTH AMERICA L P p 1555
400 Aylworth Ave, South Haven MI 49090
Tel (269) 637-2116
SIC 2821 3714 3053 3061

INTERPLASTIC CORP p 757
1225 Willow Lake Blvd, Saint Paul MN 55110
Tel (651) 481-6860 *SIC* 2821

MILLER WASTE MILLS INC p 971
580 E Front St, Winona MN 55987
Tel (507) 454-6906 *SIC* 3087 2821

DASH MULTI-CORP INC p 413
2500 Adie Rd, Maryland Heights MO 63043
Tel (314) 432-3200
SIC 2821 3069 6512 5169 7359

▲ OLIN CORP p 1082
190 Carondelet Plz # 1530, Saint Louis MO 63105
Tel (314) 480-1400
SIC 2812 2819 2821 2842 2869 2891

■ PETROLITE CORP p 1139
369 Marshall Ave, Saint Louis MO 63119
Tel (314) 961-3500
SIC 3559 2999 2899 2821 2911

■ SOLUTIA INC p 1339
575 Maryville Centre Dr, Saint Louis MO 63141
Tel (423) 229-2000
SIC 2824 2821 3081 2869

SPARTECH CORP p 1355
120 S Central Ave # 1700, Saint Louis MO 63105
Tel (314) 721-4242 *SIC* 3081 2821 3089

REID PLASTICS INC p 1221
10861 Mill Valley Rd, Omaha NE 68154
Tel (402) 934-2400 *SIC* 3085 2821 3089

GLOBAL PLASTICS LP p 617
99 Middle St Ste 1, Manchester NH 03101
Tel (800) 417-4605 *SIC* 2821

ICI AMERICA INC p 727
10 Finderne Ave, Bridgewater NJ 08807
Tel (908) 203-2800
SIC 2821 3081 2869 2843 2865

ICI AMERICAN HOLDINGS LLC p 727
10 Finderne Ave, Bridgewater NJ 08807
Tel (908) 203-2800
SIC 2851 2821 3081 2869 2843 2865

INDOPCO INC p 739
10 Finderne Ave Ste A, Bridgewater NJ 08807
Tel (908) 685-5000
SIC 2891 2046 2821 2869 2899 2099

FORMOSA PLASTICS CORP USA p 568
9 Peach Tree Hill Rd, Livingston NJ 07039
Tel (973) 994-7674 *SIC* 2821 2812

SIKA CORP p 1322
201 Polito Ave, Lyndhurst NJ 07071
Tel (201) 933-8800
SIC 2891 2899 2851 2821 3272

ARC INTERNATIONAL NORTH AMERICA INC p 103
601 S Wade Blvd, Millville NJ 08332
Tel (856) 825-5620 *SIC* 5023 2821

▲ AEP INDUSTRIES INC p 29
95 Chestnut Ridge Rd, Montvale NJ 07645
Tel (201) 641-6600 *SIC* 3081 2821

▲ HONEYWELL INTERNATIONAL INC p 705
115 Tabor Rd, Morris Plains NJ 07950
Tel (973) 455-2000
SIC 3724 3812 3585 2824 2821 3714

EVONIK CYRO LLC p 515
299 Jefferson Rd, Parsippany NJ 07054
Tel (973) 929-8000 *SIC* 2821

SOLVAY USA INC p 1339
504 Carnegie Ctr, Princeton NJ 08540
Tel (609) 860-4000
SIC 2899 2869 2821 2087 2865

■ INTERNATIONAL SPECIALTY PRODUCTS INC p 757
1361 Alps Rd, Wayne NJ 07470
Tel (859) 815-3333
SIC 2869 2821 2843 2842 2899

CYTEC INDUSTRIES INC p 406
5 Garret Mountain Plz, Woodland Park NJ 07424
Tel (973) 357-3100
SIC 2899 2821 2672 2851 2823 2819

FOUGERA PHARMACEUTICALS INC p 571
60 Baylis Rd, Melville NY 11747
Tel (631) 454-7677
SIC 2834 2851 2821 3479 3829

ICC INDUSTRIES INC p 727
460 Park Ave Fl 7, New York NY 10022
Tel (212) 521-1700
SIC 2821 2869 2911 2899 3081 2834

RESURGENCE ASSET MANAGEMENT LLC p 1228
1185 Av Of The Amer Fl 18, New York NY 10036
Tel (212) 710-5001
SIC 6282 2865 2821 2869 2861 2819

TORAY HOLDING (USA) INC p 1461
461 5th Ave Fl 9, New York NY 10017
Tel (212) 697-8150 *SIC* 2821

DAIKIN AMERICA INC p 408
20 Olympic Dr, Orangeburg NY 10962
Tel (845) 365-9500 *SIC* 3081 2821

MITSUI CHEMICALS AMERICA INC p 978
800 Westchester Ave N607, Rye Brook NY 10573
Tel (914) 253-0777
SIC 2821 2865 3082 8731 5169 6159

▲ ALBEMARLE CORP p 46
4350 Congress St Ste 700, Charlotte NC 28209
Tel (980) 299-5700
SIC 2821 2834 2819 2899 2812 2869

CELGARD LLC p 273
13800 S Lakes Dr, Charlotte NC 28273
Tel (704) 588-5310 *SIC* 2821 3081

DAK AMERICAS LLC p 409
5925 Carnegie Blvd # 500, Charlotte NC 28209
Tel (704) 940-7500 *SIC* 2821

I KESTREL ACQUISITION CORP p 725
1035 Swabia Ct, Durham NC 27703
Tel (919) 990-7500
SIC 2821 2822 2869 2899 2891 2851

REICHHOLD HOLDINGS US INC p 1220
1035 Swabia Ct, Durham NC 27703
Tel (919) 990-7500
SIC 2821 2822 2891 3089 5169 5162

REICHHOLD INDUSTRIES INC p 1220
1035 Swabia Ct, Durham NC 27703
Tel (919) 990-7500 *SIC* 2821

REICHHOLD LIQUIDATION INC p 1220
1035 Swabia Ct, Durham NC 27703
Tel (919) 990-7500
SIC 2821 2822 2869 2899 2891 2851

REICHHOLD LLC 2 p 1220
1035 Swabia Ct, Durham NC 27703
Tel (919) 990-7500 *SIC* 2821 2851

TOTER LLC p 1463
841 Meacham Rd, Statesville NC 28677
Tel (800) 424-0422
SIC 3089 3536 3469 3412 2821

FREEMAN MANUFACTURING & SUPPLY CO p 577
1101 Moore Rd, Avon OH 44011
Tel (440) 934-1902
SIC 5084 3087 3543 2821

MEXICHEM SPECIALTY RESINS INC p 957
33653 Walker Rd, Avon Lake OH 44012
Tel (440) 930-1435 *SIC* 2822 2821

▲ POLYONE CORP p 1160
33587 Walker Rd, Avon Lake OH 44012
Tel (440) 930-1000
SIC 2821 3087 5162 3081

HEXPOL COMPOUNDING LLC p 688
14330 Kinsman Rd, Burton OH 44021
Tel (440) 834-4644 *SIC* 3087 2821

HFI LLC p 689
59 Gender Rd, Canal Winchester OH 43110
Tel (614) 491-0700
SIC 2396 2821 3714 3429 3086

EP BOLLINGER LLC p 504
2664 Saint Georges Ct, Cincinnati OH 45233
Tel (513) 941-1101 *SIC* 2821

■ HEXION INC p 688
180 E Broad St Fl 26, Columbus OH 43215
Tel (614) 225-4000 *SIC* 2821

■ HEXION LLC p 688
180 E Broad St Fl 26, Columbus OH 43215
Tel (614) 225-4000 *SIC* 2821 2899

MOMENTIVE PERFORMANCE MATERIALS INC p 983
180 E Broad St, Columbus OH 43215
Tel (614) 986-2495 *SIC* 2821 2869

PLASKOLITE LLC p 1155
1770 Joyce Ave, Columbus OH 43219
Tel (614) 294-3281 *SIC* 2821

ELYRIA FOUNDRY CO LLC p 490
120 Filbert St, Elyria OH 44035
Tel (440) 322-4657
SIC 3321 3369 3325 2821

▲ A SCHULMAN INC p 6
3637 Ridgewood Rd, Fairlawn OH 44333
Tel (330) 666-3751 *SIC* 2821

■ HPC HOLDINGS LLC p 714
3637 Ridgewood Rd, Fairlawn OH 44333
Tel (330) 666-3751 *SIC* 2821 2655

▲ FERRO CORP p 538
6060 Parkland Blvd # 250, Mayfield Heights OH 44124
Tel (216) 875-5600
SIC 3479 2816 2851 3399 2821 2834

■ PREMIX INC p 1171
3365 E Center St, North Kingsville OH 44068
Tel (440) 224-2181 *SIC* 3089 2821

AKZO NOBEL COATINGS INC p 42
8220 Mohawk Dr, Strongsville OH 44136
Tel (440) 297-5100 *SIC* 2851 5198 2821

PUROLITE CORP p 1193
150 Monument Rd Ste 202, Bala Cynwyd PA 19004
Tel (610) 668-9090 *SIC* 2821

S A TRINSEO p 1261
1000 Chesterbrook Blvd, Berwyn PA 19312
Tel (610) 240-3200 *SIC* 2821

TRINSEO LLC p 1482
1000 Chesterbrook Blvd # 300, Berwyn PA 19312
Tel (610) 240-3200 *SIC* 2821

SEKISUI POLYMER INNOVATIONS LLC p 1301
6685 Low St, Bloomsburg PA 17815
Tel (570) 387-6997 *SIC* 2821

NOVA CHEMICALS INC p 1062
400 Frankfort Rd, Monaca PA 15061
Tel (412) 490-4560 *SIC* 2821

BRASKEM AMERICA INC p 208
1735 Market St Fl 28, Philadelphia PA 19103
Tel (215) 841-3100 *SIC* 2821 2865 2869

▲ CHEMTURA CORP p 294
1818 Market St Ste 3700, Philadelphia PA 19103
Tel (215) 446-3911
SIC 2869 2843 2821 2911 2899 2842

ARLANXEO USA HOLDINGS CORP p 110
111 Ridc Park West Dr, Pittsburgh PA 15275
Tel (412) 809-1000 *SIC* 2821 2824

ARLANXEO USA LLC p 110
111 Ridc Park West Dr, Pittsburgh PA 15275
Tel (412) 809-1000 *SIC* 2821 2824

BAYER CORP p 161
100 Bayer Rd, Pittsburgh PA 15205
Tel (412) 777-2000
SIC 2821 2879 2819 2834 3841

COVESTRO LLC p 385
1 Covestro Cir, Pittsburgh PA 15205
Tel (412) 413-2000 *SIC* 2891 2821

LANXESS CORP p 844
111 Parkwest Dr, Pittsburgh PA 15275
Tel (800) 526-9377
SIC 2869 2821 2822 2816 2819

▲ PPG INDUSTRIES INC p 1166
1 Ppg Pl, Pittsburgh PA 15272
Tel (412) 434-3131
SIC 2851 3211 3231 3229 2812 2821

QUADRANT EPP USA INC p 1196
2120 Fairmont Ave, Reading PA 19605
Tel (610) 320-6600 *SIC* 2821

AUDIA INTERNATIONAL INC p 130
450 Racetrack Rd, Washington PA 15301
Tel (724) 228-1260 *SIC* 2821

ENSINGER INDUSTRIES INC p 501
365 Meadowlands Blvd, Washington PA 15301
Tel (724) 746-6050 *SIC* 2821

TEKNOR APEX CO p 1433
505 Central Ave, Pawtucket RI 02861
Tel (401) 725-8000
SIC 3087 3069 3052 2869 3081 2821

MOORE CO p 987
36 Beach St, Westerly RI 02891
Tel (401) 596-2816
SIC 2258 2241 3069 3061 2821

WELLMAN ADVANCED MATERIALS LLC p 1589
520 Kingsburg Hwy, Johnsonville SC 29555
Tel (843) 386-8152 *SIC* 2824 2821

AURIGA POLYMERS INC p 131
1550 Dewberry Rd, Spartanburg SC 29307
Tel (864) 579-5570 *SIC* 2821

MILLIKEN & CO p 971
920 Milliken Rd, Spartanburg SC 29303
Tel (864) 503-2020
SIC 2221 2211 2231 2273 2821 4911

TECHMER PM LLC p 1431
1 Quality Cir, Clinton TN 37716
Tel (865) 457-6700 *SIC* 2821

▲ EASTMAN CHEMICAL CO p 473
200 S Wilcox Dr, Kingsport TN 37660
Tel (423) 229-2000
SIC 2821 2869 2865 2823

■ CELANESE CHEMICALS INC p 273
1601 Lyndon B Johnson Fwy, Dallas TX 75234
Tel (972) 443-4000
SIC 2821 2824 2865 2869

■ CELANESE HOLDINGS LLC p 273
1601 Lyndon B Johnson Fwy, Dallas TX 75234
Tel (972) 443-4000 *SIC* 2821 2824

■ CELANESE US HOLDINGS LLC p 273
1601 Lyndon B Johnson Fwy, Dallas TX 75234
Tel (972) 443-4000 *SIC* 2821 2879 2819

■ OXY VINYLS LP p 1101
5005 Lbj Fwy Ste 2200, Dallas TX 75244
Tel (972) 720-7000
SIC 2821 2899 2819 1382

ASCEND PERFORMANCE MATERIALS OPERATIONS LLC p 116
1010 Travis St Ste 900, Houston TX 77002
Tel (713) 315-5700 *SIC* 2821 2284

▲ KRATON CORP p 829
15710 John F Kennedy Blvd # 300, Houston TX 77032
Tel (281) 504-4700 *SIC* 2821

KURARAY AMERICA INC p 832
2625 Bay Area Blvd # 600, Houston TX 77058
Tel (281) 474-1592 *SIC* 2821 3081 3843

KURARAY HOLDINGS USA INC p 832
2625 Bay Area Blvd, Houston TX 77058
Tel (713) 495-7311 *SIC* 5047 5049 2821

LYONDELLBASELL INDUSTRIES INC p 888
1221 Mckinney St Ste 700, Houston TX 77010
Tel (713) 309-7200 *SIC* 2821

MB BARTER (USA) INC p 924
3388 Sage Rd Unit 402e, Houston TX 77056
Tel (713) 505-1303 *SIC* 2821

SHELL OIL CO p 1314
910 Louisiana St Ste 1500, Houston TX 77002
Tel (713) 241-6161
SIC 5541 4612 1311 2821 2869 2911

SHINTECH INC p 1317
3 Greenway Plz Ste 1150, Houston TX 77046
Tel (713) 965-0713 *SIC* 2821

TRIBUTE ENERGY INC p 1479
2100 West Loop S Ste 1220, Houston TX 77027
Tel (281) 768-5300 *SIC* 5169 3295 2821

▲ TTWF LP p 1490
2801 Post Oak Blvd, Houston TX 77056
Tel (713) 960-9111 *SIC* 2821 2869 2865

■ UNION CARBIDE CORP p 1504
1254 Enclave Pkwy, Houston TX 77077
Tel (281) 966-2727 *SIC* 2869 2821

■ WESTLAKE CHEMICAL CORP p 1601
2801 Post Oak Blvd # 600, Houston TX 77056
Tel (713) 960-9111 *SIC* 2821

■ WESTLAKE VINYLS CO LP p 1601
2801 Post Oak Blvd # 600, Houston TX 77056
Tel (713) 960-9111 *SIC* 2812 2869 2821

■ CELANESE AMERICAS LLC p 273
222 Colinas Blvd W 900n, Irving TX 75039
Tel (972) 443-4000
SIC 2821 2819 2824 5169

▲ CELANESE CORP p 273
222 Las Colinas Blvd W # 900, Irving TX 75039
Tel (972) 443-4000 *SIC* 2819 2821 2869

■ CNA HOLDINGS LLC p 330
222 Las Colinas Blvd W, Irving TX 75039
Tel (972) 443-4000
SIC 2823 2821 2819 5169 8731

INEOS NITRILES USA LLC p 740
2600 S Shore Blvd Ste 250, League City TX 77573
Tel (281) 535-6600 *SIC* 2821

INEOS USA LLC p 740
2600 S Shore Blvd Ste 500, League City TX 77573
Tel (281) 535-6600 *SIC* 2821 3999

KANEKA NORTH AMERICA LLC p 802
6161 Underwood Rd, Pasadena TX 77507
Tel (281) 474-7084 *SIC* 2821 3081 2023

FORMOSA PLASTICS CORP TEXAS p 568
201 Formosa Dr, Point Comfort TX 77978
Tel (361) 987-7000 *SIC* 2821

■ EXXONMOBIL CHEMICAL CO p 521
22777 Sprngwoods Vlg Pkwy, Spring TX 77389
Tel (281) 834-5200 *SIC* 2821

■ ICO - SCHULMAN LLC p 727
24624 Interstate 45, Spring TX 77386
Tel (832) 663-3131 *SIC* 2821

■ WILSONART INTERNATIONAL INC p 1614
2501 Wilsonart Dr, Temple TX 76503
Tel (254) 207-7000 *SIC* 2821 2541

AMERICAS STYRENICS LLC p 81
24 Waterway Ave Ste 1200, The Woodlands TX 77380
Tel (832) 616-7800 *SIC* 2821 2865

CHEVRON PHILLIPS CHEMICAL CO LLC p 296
10001 Six Pines Dr, The Woodlands TX 77380
Tel (832) 813-4100 *SIC* 2821

▲ HUNTSMAN CORP p 720
10003 Woodloch Forest Dr # 260, The Woodlands TX 77380
Tel (281) 719-6000
SIC 2821 3081 2869 2816 2865

■ HUNTSMAN INTERNATIONAL LLC p 720
1003 Woodloch Forest Dr, The Woodlands TX 77380
Tel (281) 719-6000
SIC 2821 3081 2869 2816 2865

■ NEXEO SOLUTIONS LLC p 1040
3 Waterway Square Pl # 1000, The Woodlands TX 77380
Tel (281) 297-0700 *SIC* 5169 5162 2821

■ HUNTSMAN ADVANCED MATERIALS LLC p 720
500 S Huntsman Way, Salt Lake City UT 84108
Tel (801) 584-5700 *SIC* 2821 2891 3087

■ HUNTSMAN HOLDINGS LLC p 720
500 S Huntsman Way, Salt Lake City UT 84108
Tel (801) 584-5700
SIC 2821 2911 3081 2869

■ HUNTSMAN-COOPER LLC p 720
500 S Huntsman Way, Salt Lake City UT 84108
Tel (801) 584-5700 *SIC* 2821

CARPENTER CO p 260
5016 Monument Ave, Richmond VA 23230
Tel (804) 359-0800
SIC 3086 1311 2869 2297 2392 2821

PENROD CO p 1131
272 Bendix Rd Ste 550, Virginia Beach VA 23452
Tel (757) 498-0186 SIC 3429 5039 2821

EMERALD PERFORMANCE MATERIALS LLC p 491
1499 Se Tech Center Pl, Vancouver WA 98683
Tel (330) 916-6700 SIC 2821

STAR PLASTICS INC p 1378
326 Jack Burlingame Dr, Millwood WV 25262
Tel (304) 273-0352 SIC 5162 2821

MGS MFG GROUP INC p 958
W188n11707 Maple Rd, Germantown WI 53022
Tel (262) 255-5790 SIC 3089 5047 2821

SIC 2822 Synthetic Rubber (Vulcanizable Elastomers)

MOLDING ACQUISITION CORP p 982
2651 Cooper Ave, Merced CA 95348
Tel (209) 723-5000 SIC 2822

LTI HOLDINGS INC p 883
600 S Mcclure Rd, Modesto CA 95357
Tel (209) 236-1111 SIC 3069 2822

BURKE INDUSTRIES INC p 227
2250 S 10th St, San Jose CA 95112
Tel (408) 297-3500
SIC 3069 2822 2821 3061

■ CHEMTURA USA CORP p 294
199 Benson Rd, Middlebury CT 06762
Tel (203) 573-2000 SIC 2879 2869 2822

■ ARLON LLC p 110
1100 Governor Lea Rd, Bear DE 19701
Tel (302) 834-2100 SIC 2822

■ DUPONT PERFORMANCE ELASTOMERS LLC p 462
4417 Lancaster Pike, Wilmington DE 19805
Tel (302) 774-1000 SIC 2822

SNF HOLDING CO p 1335
1 Chemical Plant Rd, Riceboro GA 31323
Tel (912) 884-3366 SIC 2822 2899

SNF INC p 1335
1 Chemical Plant Rd, Riceboro GA 31323
Tel (912) 884-3366 SIC 2822

MORTON INTERNATIONAL LLC p 991
123 N Wacker Dr Ste 2400, Chicago IL 60606
Tel (312) 807-2696
SIC 2891 2851 2822 1479 2899

MORTON SALT INC p 991
123 N Wacker Dr Fl 24, Chicago IL 60606
Tel (800) 725-8847
SIC 2891 2851 2822 1479 2899

AMERICAN SYNTHETIC RUBBER CO LLC p 80
4500 Camp Ground Rd, Louisville KY 40216
Tel (502) 449-8300 SIC 2822 2821

EAST WEST COPOLYMER LLC p 471
5955 Scenic Hwy, Baton Rouge LA 70805
Tel (225) 267-3400 SIC 2822

LION ELASTOMER HOLDINGS LLC p 869
36191 Highway 30, Geismar LA 70734
Tel (225) 673-8871 SIC 2822

CORNERSTONE CHEMICAL CO p 371
10800 River Rd, Westwego LA 70094
Tel (504) 431-9511 SIC 2822 2821

FLEXFAB HORIZONS INTERNATIONAL INC p 556
102 Cook Rd, Hastings MI 49058
Tel (269) 945-4700
SIC 3599 3052 3053 2822

FLEXFAB LLC p 556
1699 W M 43 Hwy, Hastings MI 49058
Tel (269) 945-2433 SIC 3599 3052 2822

BERGQUIST CO p 174
18930 W 78th St, Chanhassen MN 55317
Tel (952) 835-2322
SIC 5731 5063 3645 3646 2822

ANSELL HEALTHCARE PRODUCTS LLC p 93
111 Wood Ave S Ste 210, Iselin NJ 08830
Tel (732) 345-5400
SIC 3069 3842 2822 2326

I KESTREL ACQUISITION CORP p 725
1035 Swabia Ct, Durham NC 27703
Tel (919) 990-7500
SIC 2821 2822 2869 2899 2891 2851

REICHHOLD HOLDINGS US INC p 1220
1035 Swabia Ct, Durham NC 27703
Tel (919) 990-7500
SIC 2821 2822 2891 3089 5169 5162

REICHHOLD LIQUIDATION INC p 1220
1035 Swabia Ct, Durham NC 27703
Tel (919) 990-7500
SIC 2821 2822 2869 2899 2891 2851

BRIDGESTONE PROCUREMENT HOLDINGS USA INC p 211
381 W Wilbeth Rd, Akron OH 44301
Tel (337) 882-1200 SIC 2822

MEXICHEM SPECIALTY RESINS INC p 957
33653 Walker Rd, Avon Lake OH 44012
Tel (440) 930-1435 SIC 2822 2821

LANXESS CORP p 844
111 Parkwest Dr, Pittsburgh PA 15275
Tel (800) 526-9377
SIC 2869 2821 2822 2816 2819

■ DRYVIT HOLDINGS INC p 457
1 Energy Way, Providence RI 02903
Tel (401) 822-4100 SIC 2822 2899

BRIDGESTONE AMERICAS INC p 211
535 Marriott Dr, Nashville TN 37214
Tel (615) 937-1000
SIC 3011 3493 2952 2822 3229

EQUISTAR CHEMICALS LP p 506
1221 Mckinney St Ste 700, Houston TX 77010
Tel (713) 309-7200 SIC 2869 2822

■ KRATON POLYMERS LLC p 829
15710 John F Kennedy Blvd # 300, Houston TX 77032
Tel (281) 504-4700 SIC 2822

■ KRATON POLYMERS US LLC p 829
15710 John F Kennedy Blvd # 300, Houston TX 77032
Tel (281) 504-4700 SIC 2822

■ WESTLAKE OLEFINS CORP p 1601
2801 Post Oak Blvd Fl 6, Houston TX 77056
Tel (713) 960-9111 SIC 2869 2822

LION ELASTOMERS LLC p 869
1615 Main St, Port Neches TX 77651
Tel (409) 722-8321 SIC 2822

SIC 2823 Cellulosic Man-Made Fibers

▲ RAYONIER ADVANCED MATERIALS INC p 1210
1301 Riverplace Blvd # 2300, Jacksonville FL 32207
Tel (904) 357-4600 SIC 2821 2823

FIBERVISIONS MANUFACTURING CO p 539
7101 Alcovy Rd Ne, Covington GA 30014
Tel (770) 784-3402 SIC 2821 2823

CYTEC SURFACE SPECIALTIES INC p 406
1950 Lake Park Dr Se, Smyrna GA 30080
Tel (770) 434-6188
SIC 3086 5169 5191 5162 3081 2823

FORMED FIBER TECHNOLOGIES INC p 567
125 Allied Rd, Auburn ME 04210
Tel (207) 784-1118 SIC 2824 3089 2823

CYTEC INDUSTRIES INC p 406
5 Garret Mountain Plz, Woodland Park NJ 07424
Tel (973) 357-3100
SIC 2899 2821 2672 2851 2823 2819

SOLVAIRA SPECIALTIES INC p 1339
50 Bridge St, North Tonawanda NY 14120
Tel (716) 693-4040 SIC 2823 2299

MORGAN ADHESIVES CO LLC p 988
4560 Darrow Rd, Stow OH 44224
Tel (330) 688-1111
SIC 2891 3565 2672 2823

WILLIAM BARNET & SON LLC p 1610
1300 Hayne St, Spartanburg SC 29301
Tel (864) 327-4620
SIC 5199 2823 2221 2824

▲ EASTMAN CHEMICAL CO p 473
200 S Wilcox Dr, Kingsport TN 37660
Tel (423) 229-2000
SIC 2821 2869 2865 2823

■ CNA HOLDINGS LLC p 330
222 Las Colinas Blvd W, Irving TX 75039
Tel (972) 443-4000
SIC 2823 2821 2819 5169 8731

ESSENTRA HOLDINGS CORP p 510
1625 Ashton Park Dr Ste A, South Chesterfield VA 23834
Tel (804) 518-0322
SIC 3081 3082 3999 3951 2823

ESSENTRA POROUS TECHNOLOGIES CORP p 510
1625 Ashton Park Dr Ste A, South Chesterfield VA 23834
Tel (804) 524-4983
SIC 3081 3951 3082 2823 3999

SIC 2824 Synthetic Organic Fibers, Exc Cellulosic

SANDERS INDUSTRIES p 1278
3701 E Conant St, Long Beach CA 90808
Tel (562) 354-2920 SIC 2824

▲ ROGERS CORP p 1246
1 Technology Dr, Rogers CT 06263
Tel (860) 774-9605 SIC 2891 2821 2824

SCAPA NORTH AMERICA INC p 1286
111 Great Pond Dr, Windsor CT 06095
Tel (860) 688-8000
SIC 2231 3069 2211 2824 2672

▲ E I DU PONT DE NEMOURS AND CO p 466
974 Centre Rd, Wilmington DE 19805
Tel (302) 774-1000
SIC 2879 2824 2865 2821 2834

▲ UNIROYAL GLOBAL ENGINEERED PRODUCTS INC p 1505
1800 2nd St Ste 970, Sarasota FL 34236
Tel (941) 906-8580 SIC 2824 2396

FORMED FIBER TECHNOLOGIES INC p 567
125 Allied Rd, Auburn ME 04210
Tel (207) 784-1118 SIC 2824 3089 2823

■ SOLUTIA INC p 1339
575 Maryville Centre Dr, Saint Louis MO 63141
Tel (423) 229-2000
SIC 2824 2821 3081 2869

NAN YA PLASTICS CORP AMERICA p 1007
9 Peach Tree Hill Rd, Livingston NJ 07039
Tel (973) 992-1775 SIC 2824 2869 3083

▲ HONEYWELL INTERNATIONAL INC p 705
115 Tabor Rd, Morris Plains NJ 07950
Tel (973) 455-2000
SIC 3724 3812 3585 2824 2821 3714

STEIN FIBERS LTD p 1385
4 Computer Dr W Ste 200, Albany NY 12205
Tel (518) 489-5700 SIC 2824

DURAFIBER TECHNOLOGIES (DFT) ENTERPRISES INC p 462
13620 Reese Blvd E # 400, Huntersville NC 28078
Tel (704) 912-3770 SIC 2824

DURAFIBER TECHNOLOGIES (DFT) HOLDINGS II LLC p 462
13620 Reese Blvd E # 400, Huntersville NC 28078
Tel (704) 912-3700 SIC 2824

DURAFIBER TECHNOLOGIES (DFT) INC p 462
13620 Reese Blvd E # 400, Huntersville NC 28078
Tel (704) 912-3700 SIC 2824

DURAFIBER TECHNOLOGIES (DFT) OPERATIONS LLC p 462
13620 Reese Blvd E # 400, Huntersville NC 28078
Tel (704) 912-3770 SIC 2824

PHARR YARNS LLC p 1141
100 Main St, Mc Adenville NC 28101
Tel (704) 824-3551 SIC 2281 2282 2824

ARLANXEO USA HOLDINGS CORP p 110
111 Ridc Park West Dr, Pittsburgh PA 15275
Tel (412) 809-1000 SIC 2821 2824

ARLANXEO USA LLC p 110
111 Ridc Park West Dr, Pittsburgh PA 15275
Tel (412) 809-1000 SIC 2821 2824

WELLMAN ADVANCED MATERIALS LLC p 1589
520 Kingsburg Hwy, Johnsonville SC 29555
Tel (843) 386-8152 SIC 2824 2821

WILLIAM BARNET & SON LLC p 1610
1300 Hayne St, Spartanburg SC 29301
Tel (864) 327-4620
SIC 5199 2823 2221 2824

■ CELANESE CHEMICALS INC p 273
1601 Lyndon B Johnson Fwy, Dallas TX 75234
Tel (972) 443-4000
SIC 2821 2824 2865 2869

■ CELANESE HOLDINGS LLC p 273
1601 Lyndon B Johnson Fwy, Dallas TX 75234
Tel (972) 443-4000 SIC 2821 2824

■ CELANESE AMERICAS LLC p 273
222 Colinas Blvd W 900n, Irving TX 75039
Tel (972) 443-4000
SIC 2821 2819 2824 5169

UNIVERSAL FIBERS INC p 1516
14401 Industrial Park Rd, Bristol VA 24202
Tel (276) 669-1161 SIC 2824 2281

SIC 2833 Medicinal Chemicals & Botanical Prdts

GLANBIA NUTRITIONALS (NA) INC p 614
2840 Loker Ave E Ste 100, Carlsbad CA 92010
Tel (760) 438-0089 SIC 5169 2833 8099

▲ NATURAL ALTERNATIVES INTERNATIONAL INC p 1018
1535 Faraday Ave, Carlsbad CA 92008
Tel (760) 744-7340 SIC 2833

HERBALIFE LTD INC p 685
800 W Olympic Blvd # 406, Los Angeles CA 90015
Tel (310) 410-9600 SIC 2833

PHARMAVITE LLC p 1141
8510 Balboa Blvd Ste 300, Northridge CA 91325
Tel (818) 221-6200 SIC 2833 2834

HONEST CO INC p 705
12130 Millennium Ste 500, Playa Vista CA 90094
Tel (310) 917-9199 SIC 2341 2833

OTSUKA AMERICA INC p 1097
1 Embarcadero Ctr # 2020, San Francisco CA 94111
Tel (415) 986-5300
SIC 3829 3499 5122 2833 2084 2086

THRESHOLD ENTERPRISES LTD p 1451
23 Janis Way, Scotts Valley CA 95066
Tel (831) 438-6851 SIC 2833

■ INTERNATIONAL MEDICATION SYSTEMS LTD p 756
1886 Santa Anita Ave, South El Monte CA 91733
Tel (626) 442-6757 SIC 2834 2833 3841

■ ROCHE HOLDINGS INC p 1243
1 Dna Way, South San Francisco CA 94080
Tel (625) 225-1000
SIC 2834 2833 2835 2869

CORDEN PHARMA COLORADO INC p 369
2075 55th St, Boulder CO 80301
Tel (303) 442-1926 SIC 2833 8748 2834

HENKEL CORP p 683
1 Henkel Way, Rocky Hill CT 06067
Tel (860) 571-5100
SIC 2843 2821 2833 2899 2891

HENKEL OF AMERICA INC p 683
1 Henkel Way, Rocky Hill CT 06067
Tel (860) 571-5100
SIC 2869 2843 2821 2833 2899 2891

GLAXOSMITHKLINE HOLDINGS (AMERICAS) INC p 614
1105 N Market St, Wilmington DE 19801
Tel (302) 656-5280
SIC 2834 2836 2833 2844 8071

TWINLAB CORP p 1495
2255 Glades Rd Ste 342w, Boca Raton FL 33431
Tel (212) 651-8500
SIC 2099 2834 2731 2721 2833

■ FDC VITAMINS LLC p 533
14620 Nw 60th Ave, Miami Lakes FL 33014
Tel (305) 468-1600 SIC 2833

MELALEUCA INC p 940
4609 W 65th S, Idaho Falls ID 83402
Tel (208) 522-0700
SIC 2833 5122 2844 2841 2834

■ GE HEALTHCARE HOLDINGS INC p 596
3350 N Ridge Ave, Arlington Heights IL 60004
Tel (847) 398-8400
SIC 2835 2833 5169 5122

GLANBIA PERFORMANCE NUTRITION INC p 614
3500 Lacey Rd, Downers Grove IL 60515
Tel (630) 236-0097 SIC 2833 5149 5122

■ GE HEALTHCARE INC p 596
100 Results Way, Marlborough MA 01752
Tel (800) 292-8514 SIC 5122 2833

NOVA BIOMEDICAL CORP p 1062
200 Prospect St, Waltham MA 02453
Tel (781) 894-0800 SIC 2833 3826

ACCESS BUSINESS GROUP LLC p 14
7575 Fulton St E, Ada MI 49355
Tel (616) 787-6000
SIC 5169 2842 5122 2833 5136 5137

ALTICOR GLOBAL HOLDINGS INC p 62
7575 Fulton St E, Ada MI 49301
Tel (616) 787-1000
SIC 5169 5122 2833 5136 5137 5021

ALTICOR INC p 62
7575 Fulton St E, Ada MI 49355
Tel (616) 787-1000
SIC 5169 5122 2833 5136 5137 5021

TWINLAB HOLDINGS INC p 1495
3133 Orchard Vista Dr Se, Grand Rapids MI 49546
Tel (616) 464-5000
SIC 2833 2834 5149 2721

■ RESEARCH AND DIAGNOSTIC SYSTEMS INC p 1226
614 Mckinley Pl Ne, Minneapolis MN 55413
Tel (612) 379-2956
SIC 8733 2833 8731 3829 3825

MALLINCKRODT LLC p 900
675 Jmes S Mcdonnell Blvd, Hazelwood MO 63042
Tel (314) 654-2000
SIC 3841 3829 2834 2833

■ ZOETIS PRODUCTS LLC p 1644
100 Campus Dr Ste 3, Florham Park NJ 07932
Tel (973) 660-5000 SIC 2833 2834

■ PHARMACIA & UPJOHN INC p 1141
100 Route 206 N, Peapack NJ 07977
Tel (908) 901-8000 SIC 2834 2833

NOVO-NORDISK OF NORTH AMERICA INC p 1063
800 Scudders Mill Rd, Plainsboro NJ 08536
Tel (609) 987-5800
SIC 8741 8733 5122 2833 2834

NATUREX INC p 1019
375 Huyler St, South Hackensack NJ 07606
Tel (201) 440-5000 SIC 2833

■ JANSSEN PHARMACEUTICALS INC p 777
1125 Trnton Harbourton Rd, Titusville NJ 08560
Tel (609) 730-2000 SIC 2833 2834

■ ALO ACQUISITION LLC p 59
26 Corporate Cir, Albany NY 12203
Tel (518) 464-0279 SIC 2833 5122 8733

■ REXALL SUNDOWN INC p 1230
110 Orville Dr, Bohemia NY 11716
Tel (631) 567-9500 SIC 5961 5122 2833

▲ PFIZER INC p 1140
235 E 42nd St, New York NY 10017
Tel (212) 733-2323 SIC 2834 2833

■ ALPHABET HOLDING CO INC p 60
2100 Smithtown Ave, Ronkonkoma NY 11779
Tel (631) 200-2000
SIC 2833 5122 5499 5961

■ NBTY INC p 1021
2100 Smithtown Ave, Ronkonkoma NY 11779
Tel (631) 200-2000
SIC 2833 5122 5499 5961

NOVO NORDISK PHARMACEUTICAL INDUSTRIES INC p 1063
3612 Powhatan Rd, Clayton NC 27527
Tel (919) 550-2200 SIC 2833

TEVA PHARMACEUTICALS USA INC p 1441
1090 Horsham Rd, North Wales PA 19454
Tel (215) 591-3000 SIC 2834 2833 5122

V L H INC p 1538
600 Boyce Rd, Pittsburgh PA 15205
Tel (800) 245-4440 SIC 2833 5122 2834

▲ MANNATECH INC p 902
600 S Royal Ln Ste 200, Coppell TX 75019
Tel (972) 471-7400 SIC 2833

SPFM LP p 1358
4310 West Ave, San Antonio TX 78213
Tel (210) 805-8931
SIC 5122 5149 2834 2833 2841 2844

▲ NUTRACEUTICAL INTERNATIONAL CORP p 1067
1400 Kearns Blvd Fl 2, Park City UT 84060
Tel (435) 655-6106 SIC 2833

▲ USANA HEALTH SCIENCES INC p 1534
3838 W Parkway Blvd, Salt Lake City UT 84120
Tel (801) 954-7100 SIC 2833

SCIENTIFIC PROTEIN LABORATORIES LLC p 1292
700 E Main St, Waunakee WI 53597
Tel (608) 849-5944 SIC 2834 2833

SIC 2834 Pharmaceuticals

APTALIS HOLDINGS INC p 101
22 Inverness Center Pkwy # 310, Birmingham AL 35242
Tel (205) 991-8085 SIC 2834

APTALIS MIDHOLDINGS LLC p 101
22 Inverness Center Pkwy, Birmingham AL 35242
Tel (205) 991-8085 SIC 2834

APTALIS PHARMA LLC p 101
22 Inverness Center Pkwy # 310, Birmingham AL 35242
Tel (205) 991-8085 SIC 2834

BOCA PHARMACAL LLC p 196
150 Vintage Dr Ne, Huntsville AL 35811
Tel (800) 444-4011 SIC 2834

GENERICS INTERNATIONAL (US) INC p 602
130 Vintage Dr Ne, Huntsville AL 35811
Tel (256) 859-2575 SIC 2834

ANS HOLDINGS INC p 93
210 S Beck Ave, Chandler AZ 85226
Tel (480) 966-9630 SIC 2834

ARIZONA NUTRITIONAL SUPPLEMENTS LLC p 109
210 S Beck Ave, Chandler AZ 85226
Tel (480) 966-9630 SIC 2834

▲ INSYS THERAPEUTICS INC p 748
1333 S Spectrum Blvd, Chandler AZ 85286
Tel (480) 500-3127 SIC 2836 2834

ISAGENIX INTERNATIONAL LLC p 766
155 E Rivulon Blvd, Gilbert AZ 85297
Tel (480) 889-5747 SIC 2834

AVANIR PHARMACEUTICALS INC p 136
30 Enterprise Ste 400, Aliso Viejo CA 92656
Tel (949) 389-6700 SIC 2834

ACCESS BUSINESS GROUP INTERNATIONAL LLC p 14
5600 Beach Blvd, Buena Park CA 90621
Tel (714) 521-2853 SIC 2834

▲ IONIS PHARMACEUTICALS INC p 762
2855 Gazelle Ct, Carlsbad CA 92010
Tel (760) 931-9200 SIC 2834 8731 3845

■ LEINER HEALTH PRODUCTS INC p 854
901 E 233rd St, Carson CA 90745
Tel (631) 200-2000 SIC 2834 5122

FRESENIUS USA INC p 578
4040 Nelson Ave, Concord CA 94520
Tel (925) 288-4218
SIC 2834 3841 2835 3842 2836

WATSON LABORATORIES INC p 1583
311 Bonnie Cir, Corona CA 92880
Tel (951) 493-5300 *SIC* 2834

▲ SCICLONE PHARMACEUTICALS INC p 1292
950 Tower Ln Ste 900, Foster City CA 94404
Tel (650) 358-3456 *SIC* 2834

■ MICROGENICS CORP p 962
46500 Kato Rd, Fremont CA 94538
Tel (510) 979-9147 *SIC* 2834

▲ IMPAX LABORATORIES INC p 734
30831 Huntwood Ave, Hayward CA 94544
Tel (510) 240-6000 *SIC* 2834

ALLERGAN SPECIALTY THERAPEUTICS INC p 53
2525 Dupont Dr, Irvine CA 92612
Tel (714) 264-4500 *SIC* 2834

ALLERGAN USA INC p 53
2525 Dupont Dr, Irvine CA 92612
Tel (714) 246-4500 *SIC* 2834

GENSIA SICOR INC p 604
19 Hughes, Irvine CA 92618
Tel (949) 455-4700 *SIC* 2834 8731

■ TALON THERAPEUTICS INC p 1423
157 Technology Dr, Irvine CA 92618
Tel (949) 788-6700 *SIC* 2834 8731

TEVA PARENTERAL MEDICINES INC p 1441
19 Hughes, Irvine CA 92618
Tel (949) 455-4700 *SIC* 2834

■ ABRAXIS BIOSCIENCE INC p 12
11755 Wilshire Blvd Fl 20, Los Angeles CA 90025
Tel (310) 883-1300 *SIC* 2834

■ ABRAXIS BIOSCIENCE LLC p 12
11755 Wilshire Blvd Fl 20, Los Angeles CA 90025
Tel (800) 564-0216 *SIC* 2834

GRIFOLS BIOLOGICALS INC p 640
5555 Valley Blvd, Los Angeles CA 90032
Tel (323) 227-7028 *SIC* 2836 2834

GRIFOLS SHARED SERVICES NORTH AMERICA INC p 640
2410 Lillyvale Ave, Los Angeles CA 90032
Tel (323) 225-2221 *SIC* 5122 2834

▲ VIVUS INC p 1563
351 E Evelyn Ave, Mountain View CA 94041
Tel (650) 934-5200 *SIC* 2834

▲ DEPOMED INC p 431
7999 Gateway Blvd Ste 300, Newark CA 94560
Tel (510) 744-8000 *SIC* 2834

■ ONYX PHARMACEUTICALS INC p 1088
1 Amgen Center Dr, Newbury Park CA 91320
Tel (650) 266-0000 *SIC* 2834 8049

PHARMAVITE LLC p 1141
8510 Balboa Blvd Ste 300, Northridge CA 91325
Tel (818) 221-6200 *SIC* 2833 2834

RAPTOR PHARMACEUTICAL CORP p 1209
7 Hamilton Landing # 100, Novato CA 94949
Tel (415) 408-6200 *SIC* 8733 2834

■ SYBRON DENTAL SPECIALTIES INC p 1413
1717 W Collins Ave, Orange CA 92867
Tel (714) 516-7400 *SIC* 3843 2834

JAZZ PHARMACEUTICALS INC p 779
3180 Porter Dr, Palo Alto CA 94304
Tel (650) 496-3777 *SIC* 2834

AMPAC FINE CHEMICALS LLC p 86
Highway 50 And Hazel Ave Bldg 5019, Rancho Cordova CA 95741
Tel (916) 357-6880 *SIC* 2834

▲ AMPHASTAR PHARMACEUTICALS INC p 86
11570 6th St, Rancho Cucamonga CA 91730
Tel (909) 980-9484 *SIC* 2834

■ AGOURON PHARMACEUTICALS INC p 35
10777 Science Center Dr, San Diego CA 92121
Tel (858) 622-3000 *SIC* 2834 5122 8731

AMYLIN OHIO LLC p 88
9360 Towne Centre Dr, San Diego CA 92121
Tel (858) 552-2200 *SIC* 2834

CARE FUSION p 254
10020 Pacific Mesa Blvd, San Diego CA 92121
Tel (858) 617-2000 *SIC* 2834

■ CAREFUSION 213 LLC p 255
3750 Torrey View Ct, San Diego CA 92130
Tel (800) 523-0502 *SIC* 2834

▲ HALOZYME THERAPEUTICS INC p 655
11388 Sorrento Valley Rd # 200, San Diego CA 92121
Tel (858) 794-8889 *SIC* 2834 2836

PROMETHEUS LABORATORIES INC p 1183
9410 Carroll Park Dr, San Diego CA 92121
Tel (858) 824-0895 *SIC* 2834 8011

▲ RETROPHIN INC p 1229
12255 El Camino Real # 250, San Diego CA 92130
Tel (760) 260-8600 *SIC* 2834 8731

▲ FIBROGEN INC p 540
409 Illinois St, San Francisco CA 94158
Tel (415) 978-1200 *SIC* 2834

■ MEDIVATION INC p 938
525 Market St Fl 36, San Francisco CA 94105
Tel (415) 543-3470 *SIC* 2834

▲ NEKTAR THERAPEUTICS p 1025
455 Mission Bay Blvd S, San Francisco CA 94158
Tel (415) 482-5300 *SIC* 2834

▲ BIOMARIN PHARMACEUTICAL INC p 184
770 Lindaro St, San Rafael CA 94901
Tel (415) 506-6700 *SIC* 2834 2835

ROBINSON PHARMA INC p 1242
3330 S Harbor Blvd, Santa Ana CA 92704
Tel (714) 241-0235 *SIC* 2834

HARMONY FOODS CORP p 662
2200 Delaware Ave, Santa Cruz CA 95060
Tel (831) 457-3200 *SIC* 2834 2064

■ INTERNATIONAL MEDICATION SYSTEMS LTD p 756
1886 Santa Anita Ave, South El Monte CA 91733
Tel (626) 442-6757 *SIC* 2834 2833 3841

FIVE PRIME THERAPEUTICS INC p 553
2 Corporate Dr, South San Francisco CA 94080
Tel (415) 365-5600 *SIC* 2834 8733

■ GENENTECH INC p 598
1 Dna Way, South San Francisco CA 94080
Tel (650) 225-1000 *SIC* 2834

■ GENENTECH USA INC p 599
1 Dna Way, South San Francisco CA 94080
Tel (650) 225-1000 *SIC* 2834

■ ROCHE HOLDINGS INC p 1243
1 Dna Way, South San Francisco CA 94080
Tel (625) 225-1000
SIC 2834 2833 2835 2869

PHARMACYCLICS INC p 1141
995 E Arques Ave, Sunnyvale CA 94085
Tel (408) 774-0330 *SIC* 2834

■ PHARMACYCLICS LLC p 1141
999 E Arques Ave, Sunnyvale CA 94085
Tel (408) 774-0330 *SIC* 2834

VITATECH NUTRITIONAL SCIENCES INC p 1563
2802 Dow Ave, Tustin CA 92780
Tel (714) 832-9700 *SIC* 2834

▲ ARRAY BIOPHARMA INC p 112
3200 Walnut St, Boulder CO 80301
Tel (303) 381-6600 *SIC* 2834

CORDEN PHARMA COLORADO INC p 369
2075 55th St, Boulder CO 80301
Tel (303) 442-1926 *SIC* 2833 8748 2834

TOLMAR HOLDING INC p 1459
701 Centre Ave, Fort Collins CO 80526
Tel (970) 212-4500 *SIC* 2834

TOLMAR INC p 1459
701 Centre Ave, Fort Collins CO 80526
Tel (970) 212-4500 *SIC* 2834

▲ HESKA CORP p 688
3760 Rocky Mountain Ave, Loveland CO 80538
Tel (970) 493-7272 *SIC* 2834 5122

■ ALLOS THERAPEUTICS INC p 58
11000 Westmoor Cir # 150, Westminster CO 80021
Tel (303) 426-6262 *SIC* 2834

APTUIT (SCIENTIFIC OPERATIONS) LLC p 101
2 Greenwich Office Park, Greenwich CT 06831
Tel (203) 422-6600 *SIC* 2834

▲ ALEXION PHARMACEUTICALS INC p 49
100 College St, New Haven CT 06510
Tel (203) 272-2596 *SIC* 2834 8733

BOEHRINGER INGELHEIM CORP p 197
900 Ridgebury Rd, Ridgefield CT 06877
Tel (203) 798-9988 *SIC* 2834 6221

BOEHRINGER INGELHEIM PHARMACEUTICALS INC p 197
900 Ridgebury Rd, Ridgefield CT 06877
Tel (203) 798-9988 *SIC* 2834

BOEHRINGER INGELHEIM USA CORP p 197
900 Ridgebury Rd, Ridgefield CT 06877
Tel (203) 798-9988 *SIC* 2834

PHARMACEUTICAL RESEARCH ASSOCIATES INC p 1141
1 Stamford Forum, Stamford CT 06901
Tel (203) 588-8000 *SIC* 2834 5122

PRA HOLDINGS INC p 1167
1 Stamford Forum, Stamford CT 06901
Tel (203) 853-0123 *SIC* 2834 5122 8742

PURDUE PHARMA LP p 1192
201 Tresser Blvd Fl 1, Stamford CT 06901
Tel (203) 588-8000 *SIC* 2834 5122

PURDUE PRODUCTS LP p 1192
1 Stamford Forum, Stamford CT 06901
Tel (203) 588-8000 *SIC* 2834

AMYLIN PHARMACEUTICALS LLC p 88
1800 Concord Pike, Wilmington DE 19897
Tel (858) 552-2200 *SIC* 2834 8731

ASTRAZENECA LP p 122
1800 Concord Pike, Wilmington DE 19803
Tel (302) 886-3000 *SIC* 2834

ASTRAZENECA PHARMACEUTICALS LP p 122
1800 Concord Pike, Wilmington DE 19803
Tel (302) 886-3000 *SIC* 2834 5122

▲ E I DU PONT DE NEMOURS AND CO p 466
974 Centre Rd, Wilmington DE 19805
Tel (302) 774-1000
SIC 2879 2824 2865 2821 2834

GB BIOSCIENCES LLC p 594
2200 Concord Pike, Wilmington DE 19803
Tel (336) 632-6000 *SIC* 2879 2834 2899

GLAXOSMITHKLINE HOLDINGS (AMERICAS) INC p 614
1105 N Market St, Wilmington DE 19801
Tel (302) 656-5280
SIC 2834 2836 2833 2844 8071

▲ INCYTE CORP p 735
1801 Augustine Cut Off, Wilmington DE 19803
Tel (302) 498-6700 *SIC* 2834

▲ VANDA PHARMACEUTICALS INC p 1543
2200 Penn Ave Nw Ste 300e, Washington DC 20037
Tel (202) 734-3400 *SIC* 2834 8731

BIOTEST PHARMACEUTICALS CORP p 184
5800 Pk Of Commerce Blvd, Boca Raton FL 33487
Tel (561) 989-5800 *SIC* 8731 2834

TWINLAB CORP p 1495
2255 Glades Rd Ste 342w, Boca Raton FL 33431
Tel (212) 651-8500
SIC 2099 2834 2731 2721 2833

ION LABS INC p 762
5355 115th Ave N, Clearwater FL 33760
Tel (727) 527-1072 *SIC* 5122 2834

ANDRX CORP p 91
4955 Orange Dr, Davie FL 33314
Tel (954) 585-1400 *SIC* 2834 5122

BAKER NORTON US INC p 146
74 Nw 176th St, Miami FL 33169
Tel (305) 575-6000 *SIC* 2834

IVAX CORP p 769
4400 Biscayne Blvd, Miami FL 33137
Tel (305) 329-3795 *SIC* 2834

IVAX PHARMACEUTICALS LLC p 769
74 Nw 176th St, Miami FL 33169
Tel (305) 575-6000 *SIC* 2834

NOVEN PHARMACEUTICALS INC p 1063
11960 Sw 144th St, Miami FL 33186
Tel (305) 964-3393 *SIC* 2834

▲ OPKO HEALTH INC p 1089
4400 Biscayne Blvd, Miami FL 33137
Tel (305) 575-4100 *SIC* 2834 2835 8731

■ CORDIS INTERNATIONAL CORP p 369
14201 Nw 60th Ave, Miami Lakes FL 33014
Tel (305) 824-2000 *SIC* 2834

AVEVA DRUG DELIVERY SYSTEMS INC p 137
3250 Commerce Pkwy, Miramar FL 33025
Tel (954) 430-3340 *SIC* 2834

NEPHRON PHARMACEUTICALS CORP p 1026
4121 Sw 34th St, Orlando FL 32811
Tel (407) 246-1389 *SIC* 2834

WELLSPRING PHARMACEUTICAL CORP p 1591
5911 N Honore Ave Ste 211, Sarasota FL 34243
Tel (941) 312-4727 *SIC* 5122 2834

THERAGENICS CORP p 1447
5203 Bristol Indus Way, Buford GA 30518
Tel (770) 271-0233 *SIC* 2834 3842

MERIAL UK LLC p 948
3239 Satellite Blvd, Duluth GA 30096
Tel (678) 638-3000 *SIC* 2836 2834 3841

■ MWI VETERINARY SUPPLY CO p 1004
3041 W Pasadena Dr, Boise ID 83705
Tel (208) 955-8930
SIC 5047 2834 2835 2836

MELALEUCA INC p 940
4609 W 65th S, Idaho Falls ID 83402
Tel (208) 522-0700
SIC 2833 5122 2844 2841 2834

▲ ABBOTT LABORATORIES p 9
100 Abbott Park Rd, Abbott Park IL 60064
Tel (224) 667-6100
SIC 2834 2835 3841 3826

■ ABBOTT LABORATORIES INC p 9
200 Abbott Park Rd, Abbott Park IL 60064
Tel (224) 668-2076 *SIC* 2834 3841

BAXALTA INC p 160
1200 Lakeside Dr, Bannockburn IL 60015
Tel (224) 940-2000 *SIC* 2834

NOW HEALTH GROUP INC p 1064
244 Knollwood Dr Ste 300, Bloomingdale IL 60108
Tel (630) 545-9098 *SIC* 2834

AKZO NOBEL INC p 42
525 W Van Buren St Fl 16, Chicago IL 60607
Tel (312) 544-7000
SIC 2869 2851 2834 3841 3826 2819

DANIELS SHARPSMART INC p 411
111 W Jackson Blvd # 720, Chicago IL 60604
Tel (312) 546-8900 *SIC* 4953 2834

▲ BAXTER INTERNATIONAL INC p 160
1 Baxter Pkwy, Deerfield IL 60015
Tel (224) 948-2000
SIC 2834 3841 2835 3842

■ BAXTER WORLD TRADE CORP p 160
1 Baxter Pkwy, Deerfield IL 60015
Tel (224) 948-2000 *SIC* 2834 3841

LUNDBECK LLC p 886
6 Parkway N Ste 400, Deerfield IL 60015
Tel (847) 282-1000 *SIC* 2834 5122

TAKEDA DEVELOPMENT CENTER AMERICAS INC p 1422
1 Takeda Pkwy, Deerfield IL 60015
Tel (224) 554-6500 *SIC* 2834

TAKEDA PHARMACEUTICALS AMERICA INC p 1422
1 Takeda Pkwy, Deerfield IL 60015
Tel (224) 554-6500 *SIC* 2834

TAKEDA PHARMACEUTICALS USA INC p 1422
1 Takeda Pkwy, Deerfield IL 60015
Tel (224) 554-6500 *SIC* 2834

▲ MEAD JOHNSON NUTRITION CO p 933
2701 Patriot Blvd, Glenview IL 60026
Tel (847) 832-2420 *SIC* 2023 2834

JEWEL OSCO INC p 784
150 E Pierce Rd Ste 200, Itasca IL 60143
Tel (630) 551-2672 *SIC* 5411 2834

▲ AKORN INC p 42
1925 W Field Ct Ste 300, Lake Forest IL 60045
Tel (847) 279-6100 *SIC* 2834 5047

HORIZON PHARMA INC p 707
150 Saunders Rd Ste 130, Lake Forest IL 60045
Tel (224) 383-3000 *SIC* 2834

HORIZON THERAPEUTICS INC p 707
150 Saunders Rd Ste 150, Lake Forest IL 60045
Tel (224) 383-3000 *SIC* 2834

■ HOSPIRA INC p 709
275 N Field Dr, Lake Forest IL 60045
Tel (224) 212-2000 *SIC* 2834 3841

RENAISSANCE SSP HOLDINGS INC p 1223
272 E Deerpath Ste 350, Lake Forest IL 60045
Tel (210) 476-8194 *SIC* 2834

ROUNDTABLE HEALTHCARE PARTNERS LP p 1253
272 E Deerpath Ste 350, Lake Forest IL 60045
Tel (847) 482-9275 *SIC* 6722 3699 2834

FRESENIUS KABI USA INC p 578
3 Corporate Dr Ste 300, Lake Zurich IL 60047
Tel (847) 969-2700 *SIC* 2834

FRESENIUS KABI USA LLC p 578
3 Corporate Dr Ste 300, Lake Zurich IL 60047
Tel (847) 550-2300 *SIC* 2834

MORTON GROVE PHARMACEUTICALS INC p 991
6451 Main St, Morton Grove IL 60053
Tel (847) 967-5600 *SIC* 2834

▲ ABBVIE INC p 10
1 N Waukegan Rd, North Chicago IL 60064
Tel (847) 932-7900 *SIC* 2834 2836

ASTELLAS US HOLDING INC p 122
1 Astellas Way, Northbrook IL 60062
Tel (224) 205-8800 *SIC* 2834

SAGENT PHARMACEUTICALS INC p 1268
1901 N Roselle Rd Ste 700, Schaumburg IL 60195
Tel (847) 908-1600 *SIC* 2834 5122

■ MEAD JOHNSON & CO LLC p 933
2400 W Lloyd Expy, Evansville IN 47712
Tel (812) 429-5000 *SIC* 2099 2834 2032

▲ ELI LILLY AND CO p 486
Lilly Corporate Center, Indianapolis IN 46285
Tel (317) 276-2000 *SIC* 2834

■ ELI LILLY INTERNATIONAL CORP p 487
893 S Delaware St, Indianapolis IN 46225
Tel (317) 276-2000
SIC 8742 2834 8731 3841 2879

■ KREMERS URBAN PHARMACEUTICALS INC p 829
1101 C Ave W, Seymour IN 47274
Tel (812) 523-5347 *SIC* 2834

■ CAMBREX CHARLES CITY INC p 244
1205 11th St, Charles City IA 50616
Tel (641) 257-1000
SIC 2834 2899 2865 2048

KEMIN INDUSTRIES INC p 809
2100 Maury St, Des Moines IA 50317
Tel (515) 559-5100 *SIC* 2834

TEVA NEUROSCIENCE INC p 1441
11100 Nall Ave, Leawood KS 66211
Tel (913) 777-3000 *SIC* 2834

▲ IDEXX LABORATORIES INC p 729
1 Idexx Dr, Westbrook ME 04092
Tel (207) 556-0300 *SIC* 3826 2834 5047

▲ EMERGENT BIOSOLUTIONS INC p 492
400 Professional Dr # 400, Gaithersburg MD 20879
Tel (240) 631-3200 *SIC* 2834 2836

MEDIMMUNE LLC p 938
1 Medimmune Way, Gaithersburg MD 20878
Tel (301) 398-1200 *SIC* 2834

PHARMACEUTICS INTERNATIONAL INC p 1141
10819 Gilroy Rd Ste 100, Hunt Valley MD 21031
Tel (410) 584-0001 *SIC* 2834 5122

HUMAN GENOME SCIENCES INC p 718
14200 Shady Grove Rd, Rockville MD 20850
Tel (301) 309-8504 *SIC* 8731 2834

▲ MACROGENICS INC p 893
9704 Medical Center Dr, Rockville MD 20850
Tel (301) 251-5172 *SIC* 2834

▲ SUCAMPO PHARMACEUTICALS INC p 1396
805 King Farm Blvd # 550, Rockville MD 20850
Tel (301) 961-3400 *SIC* 2834

SUPERNUS PHARMACEUTICALS INC p 1407
1550 E Gude Dr, Rockville MD 20850
Tel (301) 838-2500 *SIC* 2834

▲ UNITED THERAPEUTICS CORP p 1514
1040 Spring St, Silver Spring MD 20910
Tel (301) 608-9292 *SIC* 2834

▲ VERTEX PHARMACEUTICALS INC p 1552
50 Northern Ave, Boston MA 02210
Tel (617) 341-6100 *SIC* 2834 8731

▲ BIOGEN INC p 184
225 Binney St, Cambridge MA 02142
Tel (617) 679-2000 *SIC* 2834 2836 8731

GENZYME CORP p 605
500 Kendall St, Cambridge MA 02142
Tel (617) 252-7500
SIC 2835 2834 8071 3842 2836 5122

▲ INFINITY PHARMACEUTICALS INC p 741
784 Memorial Dr, Cambridge MA 02139
Tel (617) 453-1000 *SIC* 2834 8731

▲ IRONWOOD PHARMACEUTICALS INC p 765
301 Binney St, Cambridge MA 02142
Tel (617) 621-7722 *SIC* 2834 8731

MERRIMACK PHARMACEUTICALS INC p 950
1 Kendall Sq Ste B7201, Cambridge MA 02139
Tel (617) 441-1000 *SIC* 2834

▲ MOMENTA PHARMACEUTICALS INC p 983
675 W Kendall St, Cambridge MA 02142
Tel (617) 491-9700 *SIC* 2834

NOVARTIS VACCINES AND DIAGNOSTICS INC p 1063
350 Massachusetts Ave, Cambridge MA 02139
Tel (617) 871-7000 *SIC* 2834 2835 2836

NOVELION THERAPEUTICS INC p 1063
1 Main St 800, Cambridge MA 02142
Tel (877) 764-3131 *SIC* 2834

SHIRE-NPS PHARMACEUTICALS INC p 1317
300 Shire Way, Lexington MA 02421
Tel (617) 349-0200 *SIC* 2834

KAZ INC p 805
400 Donald Lynch Blvd # 300, Marlborough MA 01752
Tel (508) 490-7000 *SIC* 8082 2834 5047

SUNOVION PHARMACEUTICALS INC p 1403
84 Waterford Dr, Marlborough MA 01752
Tel (508) 481-6700 *SIC* 2834

▲ LANTHEUS HOLDINGS INC p 844
331 Treble Cove Rd, North Billerica MA 01862
Tel (978) 671-8001 *SIC* 2835 2834

LANTHEUS MEDICAL IMAGING INC p 844
331 Treble Cove Rd, North Billerica MA 01862
Tel (978) 671-8001 *SIC* 3841 2834

LANTHEUS MI INTERMEDIATE INC p 844
331 Treble Cove Rd, North Billerica MA 01862
Tel (978) 671-8001 *SIC* 3841 2834

EMD SERONO INC p 491
1 Technology Pl, Rockland MA 02370
Tel (781) 982-9000 *SIC* 2834

ALKERMES INC p 50
852 Winter St, Waltham MA 02451
Tel (781) 609-6000 *SIC* 2834 8731

▲ AMAG PHARMACEUTICALS INC p 64
1100 Winter St Fl 3, Waltham MA 02451
Tel (617) 498-3300 *SIC* 2834 2835

ENANTA PHARMACEUTICALS INC p 495
500 Arsenal St, Watertown MA 02472
Tel (617) 607-0800 *SIC* 2834 8731

L PERRIGO CO p 834
515 Eastern Ave, Allegan MI 49010
Tel (269) 673-8451 *SIC* 2834

PERRIGO CO p 1137
515 Eastern Ave, Allegan MI 49010
Tel (269) 673-8451 *SIC* 2834

TWINLAB HOLDINGS INC p 1495
3133 Orchard Vista Dr Se, Grand Rapids MI 49546
Tel (616) 464-5000
SIC 2833 2834 5149 2721

■ EMERGENT BIODEFENSE OPERATIONS LANSING LLC p 492
3500 N Martin Luther King, Lansing MI 48906
Tel (517) 327-1500 *SIC* 2836 2834

EP MANAGEMENT CORP p 504
801 W Ann Arbor Trl # 220, Plymouth MI 48170
Tel (313) 749-5500
SIC 3692 3661 2834 3674 3691

APOTHECARY PRODUCTS LLC p 97
11750 12th Ave S, Burnsville MN 55337
Tel (800) 328-2742 *SIC* 2834 5122 3069

PRIME THERAPEUTICS LLC p 1175
1305 Corporate Center Dr, Eagan MN 55121
Tel (612) 777-4000 *SIC* 8741 6411 2834

MILK SPECIALTIES CO p 969
7500 Flying Cloud Dr # 500, Eden Prairie MN 55344
Tel (952) 942-7310 *SIC* 2026 2834 5149

UPSHER-SMITH LABORATORIES INC p 1529
6701 Evenstad Dr N, Maple Grove MN 55369
Tel (763) 315-2000 *SIC* 2834

PADDOCK LABORATORIES LLC p 1107
3940 Quebec Ave N, Minneapolis MN 55427
Tel (763) 546-4676 *SIC* 2834

▲ PATTERSON COMPANIES INC p 1121
1031 Mendota Heights Rd, Saint Paul MN 55120
Tel (651) 686-1600
SIC 5047 5112 7372 7699 2834

NESHER PHARMACEUTICALS (USA) LLC p 1026
13910 St Charles Rock Rd, Bridgeton MO 63044
Tel (314) 209-4700 *SIC* 2834

ARD MALLINCKRODT INC p 106
675 Jmes S Mcdonnell Blvd, Hazelwood MO 63042
Tel (714) 786-4200 *SIC* 2834

MALLINCKRODT LLC p 900
675 Jmes S Mcdonnell Blvd, Hazelwood MO 63042
Tel (314) 654-2000
SIC 3841 3829 2834 2833

BOEHRINGER INGELHEIM VETMEDICA INC p 197
2621 N Belt Hwy, Saint Joseph MO 64506
Tel (800) 325-9167 *SIC* 2836 2834 5191

BUNGE NORTH AMERICA FOUNDATION p 226
11720 Borman Dr, Saint Louis MO 63146
Tel (314) 872-3030
SIC 2075 2079 2048 2834

JOST CHEMICAL CO p 794
8150 Lackland Rd, Saint Louis MO 63114
Tel (314) 428-4300 *SIC* 2834 2819

SERGEANTS PET CARE PRODUCTS INC p 1306
10077 S 134th St, Omaha NE 68138
Tel (402) 938-7000 *SIC* 2834 5199 2048

▲ SPECTRUM PHARMACEUTICALS INC p 1357
11500 S Estrn Ave Ste 240, Henderson NV 89052
Tel (702) 835-6300 *SIC* 2834

LONZA BIOLOGICS INC p 877
101 International Dr, Portsmouth NH 03801
Tel (603) 610-4500 *SIC* 2834

TORRENT PHARMA INC p 1462
150 Allen Rd Ste 102, Basking Ridge NJ 07920
Tel (269) 544-2299 *SIC* 2834

AMNEAL PHARMACEUTICALS LLC p 86
400 Crossing Blvd Fl 3, Bridgewater NJ 08807
Tel (631) 952-0214 *SIC* 2834 3999

AVENTIS INC p 136
55 Corporate Dr, Bridgewater NJ 08807
Tel (800) 981-2491 *SIC* 2834

DENDREON PHARMACEUTICALS INC p 428
400 Somerset Corp Blvd # 500, Bridgewater NJ 08807
Tel (908) 927-1400 *SIC* 2834

■ IMCLONE SYSTEMS LLC p 733
440 Us Highway 22, Bridgewater NJ 08807
Tel (908) 541-8000 *SIC* 2836 2834

MEDICIS PHARMACEUTICAL CORP p 937
700 Us Highway 202/206, Bridgewater NJ 08807
Tel (866) 246-8245 *SIC* 2834

SALIX PHARMACEUTICALS LTD p 1273
400 Somerset Corp Blvd, Bridgewater NJ 08807
Tel (919) 862-1000 *SIC* 2834

SANOFI US SERVICES INC p 1280
55 Corporate Dr, Bridgewater NJ 08807
Tel (336) 407-4994 *SIC* 2834

SANOFI-AVENTIS US LLC p 1280
55 Corporate Dr, Bridgewater NJ 08807
Tel (908) 981-5000 *SIC* 5122 2834

TRIGEN LABORATORIES LLC p 1480
400 Crossing Blvd, Bridgewater NJ 08807
Tel (732) 721-0070 *SIC* 2834

VALEANT PHARMACEUTICALS INTERNATIONAL CORP p 1539
400 Somerset Corp Blvd, Bridgewater NJ 08807
Tel (908) 927-1400 *SIC* 2834

■ KOS PHARMACEUTICALS INC p 828
1 Cedarbrook Dr, Cranbury NJ 08512
Tel (609) 495-0500 *SIC* 2834

SUN PHARMACEUTICAL INDUSTRIES INC p 1400
270 Prospect Plains Rd, Cranbury NJ 08512
Tel (609) 495-2800 *SIC* 2834

AKRIMAX PHARMACEUTICALS LLC p 42
11 Commerce Dr Ste 103, Cranford NJ 07016
Tel (908) 372-0506 *SIC* 2834

▲ CAMBREX CORP p 244
1 Meadowlands Plz # 1510, East Rutherford NJ 07073
Tel (201) 804-3000 *SIC* 2834

WEST-WARD PHARMACEUTICALS CORP p 1596
401 Industrial Way W, Eatontown NJ 07724
Tel (732) 542-1191 *SIC* 2834

ACTAVIS ELIZABETH LLC p 19
200 Elmora Ave, Elizabeth NJ 07202
Tel (908) 527-9100 *SIC* 2834

BASF CORP p 158
100 Park Ave, Florham Park NJ 07932
Tel (973) 245-6000
SIC 2869 2819 2899 2843 2834 2879

BASFIN CORP p 158
100 Campus Dr Ste 301, Florham Park NJ 07932
Tel (973) 245-6000
SIC 2869 2819 2899 2843 2879 2834

SHIONOGI PHARMA INC p 1317
300 Campus Dr Ste 300, Florham Park NJ 07932
Tel (678) 427-5359 *SIC* 2834

■ ZOETIS LLC p 1644
100 Campus Dr, Florham Park NJ 07932
Tel (800) 601-1357 *SIC* 2834

■ ZOETIS PRODUCTS LLC p 1644
100 Campus Dr Ste 3, Florham Park NJ 07932
Tel (973) 660-5000 *SIC* 2833 2834

DAINIPPON SUMITOMO PHARMA AMERICA HOLDINGS INC p 408
1 Bridge Plz N Ste 510, Fort Lee NJ 07024
Tel (201) 592-2050 *SIC* 2834

INTERNATIONAL VITAMIN CORP p 757
500 Halls Mill Rd, Freehold NJ 07728
Tel (951) 361-1120 *SIC* 2834 5149 8099

PHARMACHEM LABORATORIES INC p 1141
265 Harrison Tpke, Kearny NJ 07032
Tel (201) 246-1000 *SIC* 2099 2834

■ CUBIST PHARMACEUTICALS LLC p 399
2000 Galloping Hill Rd, Kenilworth NJ 07033
Tel (908) 740-4000 *SIC* 2834

▲ MERCK & CO INC p 945
2000 Galloping Hill Rd, Kenilworth NJ 07033
Tel (908) 740-4000
SIC 2834 2836 2844 5122

■ MERCK SHARP & DOHME CORP p 945
2000 Galloping Hill Rd, Kenilworth NJ 07033
Tel (908) 740-4000 *SIC* 2834 8741

RENAISSANCE LAKEWOOD LLC p 1223
1200 Paco Way, Lakewood NJ 08701
Tel (732) 367-9000 *SIC* 2834 2844 2675

■ WYETH HOLDINGS LLC p 1629
5 Giralda Farms, Madison NJ 07940
Tel (973) 660-5000 *SIC* 2834 2836

COREPHARMA LLC p 369
215 Wood Ave, Middlesex NJ 08846
Tel (732) 356-0318 *SIC* 2834

CAPSUGEL INC p 251
412 Mount Kemble Ave 200c, Morristown NJ 07960
Tel (862) 242-1700 *SIC* 2834

▲ PERNIX THERAPEUTICS HOLDINGS INC p 1136
10 N Park Pl Ste 201, Morristown NJ 07960
Tel (800) 793-2145 *SIC* 2834

▲ JOHNSON & JOHNSON p 790
1 Johnson And Johnson Plz, New Brunswick NJ 08933
Tel (732) 524-0400
SIC 2676 2844 3841 3842 2834

■ VS HERCULES LLC p 1566
2101 91st St, North Bergen NJ 07047
Tel (201) 868-5959 *SIC* 2834

■ HOFFMANN-LA ROCHE INC p 699
340 Kingsland St, Nutley NJ 07110
Tel (973) 235-5000 *SIC* 2834 8733

ACTAVIS LLC p 19
400 Interpace Pkwy, Parsippany NJ 07054
Tel (862) 261-7000 *SIC* 2834 5122

ACTAVIS PHARMA INC p 19
400 Interpace Pkwy Ste A1, Parsippany NJ 07054
Tel (862) 261-7000 *SIC* 2834

ALLERGAN INC p 53
400 Interpace Pkwy Bldg D, Parsippany NJ 07054
Tel (862) 261-7000 *SIC* 2834 3841

DPI NEWCO LLC p 454
45 Waterview Blvd, Parsippany NJ 07054
Tel (973) 257-8113 *SIC* 2834

FERRING PHARMACEUTICALS INC p 538
100 Interpace Pkwy, Parsippany NJ 07054
Tel (973) 796-1600 *SIC* 2834 5122

FOREST PHARMACEUTICALS INC p 567
400 Interpace Pkwy Ste A1, Parsippany NJ 07054
Tel (862) 261-7000 *SIC* 2834

▲ MEDICINES CO p 937
8 Sylvan Way, Parsippany NJ 07054
Tel (973) 290-6000 *SIC* 2834

▲ PACIRA PHARMACEUTICALS INC p 1106
5 Sylvan Way Ste 300, Parsippany NJ 07054
Tel (973) 254-3560 *SIC* 2834

WARNER CHILCOTT (US) LLC p 1576
400 Interpace Pkwy, Parsippany NJ 07054
Tel (862) 261-7000 *SIC* 2834

▲ ZOETIS INC p 1644
10 Sylvan Way Ste 105, Parsippany NJ 07054
Tel (973) 822-7000 *SIC* 2834 5122

■ PHARMACIA & UPJOHN INC p 1141
100 Route 206 N, Peapack NJ 07977
Tel (908) 901-8000 *SIC* 2834 2833

ZYDUS PHARMACEUTICALS USA INC p 1645
73 Route 31 N, Pennington NJ 08534
Tel (609) 730-1900 *SIC* 2834

SIEGFRIED USA HOLDING INC p 1320
33 Industrial Park Rd, Pennsville NJ 08070
Tel (856) 678-3601 *SIC* 2834

ALVOGEN GROUP INC p 63
10 Bloomfield Ave, Pine Brook NJ 07058
Tel (973) 796-3400 *SIC* 2834

ALVOGEN INC p 63
10 Bloomfield Ave Ste 3, Pine Brook NJ 07058
Tel (973) 796-3400 *SIC* 2834

NOVO NORDISK INC p 1063
800 Scudders Mill Rd, Plainsboro NJ 08536
Tel (609) 987-5800 *SIC* 2834

NOVO-NORDISK OF NORTH AMERICA INC p 1063
800 Scudders Mill Rd, Plainsboro NJ 08536
Tel (609) 987-5800
SIC 8741 8733 5122 2833 2834

▲ DERMA SCIENCES INC p 431
214 Carnegie Ctr Ste 300, Princeton NJ 08540
Tel (609) 514-4744 *SIC* 3842 2211 2834

RANBAXY PHARMACEUTICALS INC p 1207
600 College Rd E Ste 2100, Princeton NJ 08540
Tel (609) 720-9200 *SIC* 2834 5122

SANDOZ INC p 1278
100 College Rd W, Princeton NJ 08540
Tel (609) 627-8500 *SIC* 2834 5122

■ JANSSEN RESEARCH & DEVELOPMENT LLC p 777
920 Us Highway 202, Raritan NJ 08869
Tel (908) 704-4000 *SIC* 2834 8731

ORTHO-CLINICAL DIAGNOSTICS INC p 1096
1001 Us Highway 202, Raritan NJ 08869
Tel (908) 218-8000 *SIC* 2835 2834

WARNER CHILCOTT CORP p 1576
100 Enterprise Dr Ste 280, Rockaway NJ 07866
Tel (862) 261-7000 *SIC* 2834 6719

■ JOHNSON & JOHNSON CONSUMER INC p 790
199 Grandview Rd, Skillman NJ 08558
Tel (908) 874-1000 *SIC* 2834

■ CARDINAL HEALTH SYSTEMS INC p 253
14 Schoolhouse Rd, Somerset NJ 08873
Tel (732) 537-6544 *SIC* 7372 2834

▲ CATALENT INC p 264
14 Schoolhouse Rd, Somerset NJ 08873
Tel (732) 537-6200 *SIC* 2834

■ CATALENT PHARMA SOLUTIONS INC p 264
14 Schoolhouse Rd, Somerset NJ 08873
Tel (732) 537-6200 *SIC* 2834 3841

MEDA PHARMACEUTICALS INC p 935
265 Davidson Ave Ste 400, Somerset NJ 08873
Tel (732) 564-2200 *SIC* 2834

NOVEL LABORATORIES INC p 1063
400 Campus Dr, Somerset NJ 08873
Tel (908) 603-6000 *SIC* 2834

■ PTS INTERMEDIATE HOLDINGS LLC p 1189
14 Schoolhouse Rd, Somerset NJ 08873
Tel (732) 537-6200 *SIC* 2834

G & W LABORATORIES INC p 586
111 Coolidge St, South Plainfield NJ 07080
Tel (908) 753-2000 *SIC* 2834

▲ CELGENE CORP p 273
86 Morris Ave, Summit NJ 07901
Tel (908) 673-9000 *SIC* 2834

■ PHIBRO ANIMAL HEALTH CORP p 1142
300 Frank W Burr Blvd, Teaneck NJ 07666
Tel (201) 329-7300
SIC 2819 5169 2899 2834

■ JANSSEN PHARMACEUTICALS INC p 777
1125 Trnton Harbourton Rd, Titusville NJ 08560
Tel (609) 730-2000 *SIC* 2833 2834

GSK CONSUMER HEALTHCARE p 643
184 Liberty Corner Rd # 2, Warren NJ 07059
Tel (973) 503-8000 *SIC* 2834

LTS LOHMANN THERAPY SYSTEMS CORP p 883
21 Henderson Dr, West Caldwell NJ 07006
Tel (973) 575-5170 *SIC* 2834

VITAQUEST INTERNATIONAL LLC p 1563
8 Henderson Dr, West Caldwell NJ 07006
Tel (973) 575-9200
SIC 2834 5149 5122 8742

BAYER HEALTHCARE LLC p 161
100 Bayer Blvd, Whippany NJ 07981
Tel (862) 404-3000
SIC 2834 8731 3845 3841

BAYER HEALTHCARE PHARMACEUTICALS INC p 161
100 Bayer Blvd, Whippany NJ 07981
Tel (862) 404-3000 *SIC* 2834 3841

BERLIN SCHERING INC p 175
100 Bayer Blvd, Whippany NJ 07981
Tel (862) 404-3000 *SIC* 2834 3841

■ MERCK HOLDINGS LLC p 945
1 Merck Dr, Whitehouse Station NJ 08889
Tel (908) 423-1000 *SIC* 2834 6712

EISAI INC p 482
100 Tice Blvd, Woodcliff Lake NJ 07677
Tel (919) 941-6920 *SIC* 2834

■ OSO BIOPHARMACEUTICAL MANUFACTURING LLC p 1097
4401 Alexander Blvd Ne, Albuquerque NM 87107
Tel (505) 923-1500 *SIC* 2834

■ HI-TECH PHARMACAL CO INC p 689
369 Bayview Ave, Amityville NY 11701
Tel (631) 789-8228 *SIC* 2834

▲ ACORDA THERAPEUTICS INC p 18
420 Saw Mill River Rd, Ardsley NY 10502
Tel (914) 347-4300 *SIC* 2834 8731 2836

PERRIGO NEW YORK INC p 1137
1700 Bathgate Ave, Bronx NY 10457
Tel (718) 960-9900 *SIC* 2834

AMNEAL PHARMACEUTICALS OF NEW YORK LLC p 86
50 Horseblock Rd, Brookhaven NY 11719
Tel (631) 952-0214 *SIC* 2834 5122

PAR PHARMACEUTICAL COMPANIES INC p 1113
1 Ram Ridge Rd, Chestnut Ridge NY 10977
Tel (845) 573-5500 *SIC* 2834

PAR STERILE PRODUCTS LLC p 1113
1 Ram Ridge Rd, Chestnut Ridge NY 10977
Tel (845) 573-5500 *SIC* 2834

MARIETTA CORP p 906
37 Huntington St, Cortland NY 13045
Tel (607) 753-6746 *SIC* 2844 2834 2541

CONTRACT PHARMACAL CORP p 364
135 Adams Ave, Hauppauge NY 11788
Tel (631) 231-4610 *SIC* 2834

INVAGEN PHARMACEUTICALS INC p 760
7 Oser Ave Ste 4, Hauppauge NY 11788
Tel (631) 231-3233 *SIC* 2834 5122

FOUGERA PHARMACEUTICALS INC p 571
60 Baylis Rd, Melville NY 11747
Tel (631) 454-7677
SIC 2834 2851 2821 3479 3829

BAUSCH & LOMB HOLDINGS INC p 160
450 Lexington Ave, New York NY 10017
Tel (585) 338-6000 *SIC* 3851 2834

▲ BRISTOL-MYERS SQUIBB CO p 214
345 Park Ave Bsmt Lc3, New York NY 10154
Tel (212) 546-4000 *SIC* 2834

FOREST LABORATORIES LLC p 566
909 3rd Ave Fl 23, New York NY 10022
Tel (212) 421-7850 *SIC* 2834 5122

ICC INDUSTRIES INC p 727
460 Park Ave Fl 7, New York NY 10022
Tel (212) 521-1700
SIC 2821 2869 2911 2899 3081 2834

■ ORAL COLGATE PHARMACEUTICALS INC p 1091
300 Park Ave Fl 3, New York NY 10022
Tel (212) 310-2000 *SIC* 5122 2834

▲ PFIZER INC p 1140
235 E 42nd St, New York NY 10017
Tel (212) 733-2323 *SIC* 2834 2833

■ WYETH LLC p 1629
235 E 42nd St, New York NY 10017
Tel (973) 660-5000 *SIC* 2834 2836

KLG USA LLC p 823
20 W King St, Port Jervis NY 12771
Tel (845) 856-5311 *SIC* 2844 7389 2834

■ PALL CORP p 1108
25 Harbor Park Dr, Port Washington NY 11050
Tel (516) 484-5400
SIC 3569 3599 3714 2834 3841

BAUSCH & LOMB INC p 160
1400 N Goodman St, Rochester NY 14609
Tel (585) 338-6000 *SIC* 3851 2834 3841

■ NATURES BOUNTY INC p 1019
2100 Smithtown Ave, Ronkonkoma NY 11779
Tel (631) 580-6137 *SIC* 2834

DSM NUTRITIONAL PRODUCTS LLC p 458
2105 Technology Dr, Schenectady NY 12308
Tel (518) 372-5155 *SIC* 2834 2836

LUITPOLD PHARMACEUTICALS INC p 884
5 Ramsey Rd, Shirley NY 11967
Tel (631) 924-4000 *SIC* 2834

LIPTIS PHARMACEUTICALS USA INC p 870
110 Red Schoolhouse Rd, Spring Valley NY 10977
Tel (845) 627-0260 *SIC* 2834

PAR PHARMACEUTICAL COMPANIES INC p 1113
1 Ram Ridge Rd, Spring Valley NY 10977
Tel (201) 802-4000 *SIC* 2834

PAR PHARMACEUTICAL INC p 1113
1 Ram Ridge Rd, Spring Valley NY 10977
Tel (845) 425-7100 *SIC* 2834

NOVARTIS CORP p 1062
520 White Plains Rd, Tarrytown NY 10591
Tel (212) 307-1122
SIC 2834 2879 2032 2865

▲ PRESTIGE BRANDS HOLDINGS INC p 1173
660 White Plains Rd, Tarrytown NY 10591
Tel (914) 524-6800 *SIC* 2834 2841

▲ REGENERON PHARMACEUTICALS INC p 1219
777 Old Saw Mill River Rd # 10, Tarrytown NY 10591
Tel (914) 847-7000 *SIC* 2834

▲ NEW YORK HEALTH CARE INC p 1035
20 E Sunrise Hwy Ste 201, Valley Stream NY 11581
Tel (718) 375-6700 *SIC* 2834 8082

WAVODYNE THERAPEUTICS INC p 1584
150 Lucius Gordon Dr, West Henrietta NY 14586
Tel (954) 632-6630 *SIC* 2834

P & L DEVELOPMENT LLC p 1102
200 Hicks St, Westbury NY 11590
Tel (516) 986-1700 *SIC* 2834

COMBE INC p 343
1101 Westchester Ave, White Plains NY 10604
Tel (914) 694-5454 *SIC* 2841 2834

▲ ALBEMARLE CORP p 46
4350 Congress St Ste 700, Charlotte NC 28209
Tel (980) 299-5700
SIC 2821 2834 2819 2899 2812 2869

PATHEON INC p 1120
4815 Emperor Blvd Ste 300, Durham NC 27703
Tel (919) 226-3200 *SIC* 2834

STIEFEL LABORATORIES INC p 1389
20 Tw Alexander Dr, Durham NC 27709
Tel (888) 784-3335 *SIC* 5122 2834

■ ELANCO US INC p 483
3200 Northline Ave # 300, Greensboro NC 27408
Tel (877) 352-6261 *SIC* 2834

DPI NEWCO LLC p 454
5900 Martin Luther King, Greenville NC 27834
Tel (252) 758-3436 *SIC* 2834

DSM PHARMACEUTICALS INC p 458
5900 M L King Jr Hwy, Greenville NC 27834
Tel (252) 758-3436 *SIC* 2834

■ MAYNE PHARMA INC p 923
1240 Sugg Pkwy, Greenville NC 27834
Tel (252) 752-3800 *SIC* 5122 2834

PATHEON SOFTGELS INC p 1120
4125 Premier Dr, High Point NC 27265
Tel (336) 812-8700 *SIC* 2834

EI LLC p 481
2865 N Cannon Blvd, Kannapolis NC 28083
Tel (704) 939-4300 *SIC* 2834 2844

SALIX PHARMACEUTICALS INC p 1273
8540 Colonnade Center Dr # 401, Raleigh NC 27615
Tel (919) 862-1000 *SIC* 2834

ALCAMI CAROLINAS CORP p 47
2320 Scientific Park Dr, Wilmington NC 28405
Tel (910) 254-7000 *SIC* 2834 8734 8731

ALCAMI CORP p 47
2320 Scientific Park Dr, Wilmington NC 28405
Tel (910) 254-7000 *SIC* 2834

ALCAMI HOLDINGS LLC p 47
2320 Scientific Park Dr, Wilmington NC 28405
Tel (910) 254-7000 *SIC* 2834 8731 8734

PPD INTERNATIONAL HOLDINGS INC p 1166
929 N Front St, Wilmington NC 28401
Tel (910) 251-0081 *SIC* 2834

SWANSON HEALTH PRODUCTS INC p 1411
4075 40th Ave S, Fargo ND 58104
Tel (701) 356-2700 *SIC* 5499 2834

BEN VENUE LABORATORIES INC p 172
300 Northfield Rd, Bedford OH 44146
Tel (800) 989-3320 *SIC* 2834

■ LUBRIZOL ADVANCED MATERIALS INC p 884
9911 Brecksville Rd, Brecksville OH 44141
Tel (216) 447-5000
SIC 2899 2891 3088 2834 3629

■ BIORX LLC p 184
7167 E Kemper Rd, Cincinnati OH 45249
Tel (866) 442-4679
SIC 5122 8748 2834 5047 8051

▲ MEDPACE HOLDINGS INC p 938
5375 Medpace Way, Cincinnati OH 45227
Tel (513) 579-9911 SIC 2834 8731

▲ MERIDIAN BIOSCIENCE INC p 948
3471 River Hills Dr, Cincinnati OH 45244
Tel (513) 271-3700 SIC 2835 2834

WARNER CHILCOTT PHARMACEUTICALS INC p 1576
1 Procter And Gamble Plz, Cincinnati OH 45202
Tel (513) 983-1100 SIC 2834

COLUMBUS WEST-WARD INC p 342
1809 Wilson Rd, Columbus OH 43228
Tel (614) 276-4000 SIC 2834

ROXANE LABORATORIES INC p 1253
1809 Wilson Rd, Columbus OH 43228
Tel (614) 276-4000 SIC 2834

■ CARDINAL HEALTH 414 LLC p 253
7000 Cardinal Pl, Dublin OH 43017
Tel (614) 757-5000 SIC 2834 2835

▲ FERRO CORP p 538
6060 Parkland Blvd # 250, Mayfield Heights OH 44124
Tel (216) 875-5600
SIC 3479 2816 2851 3399 2821 2834

ALMAC PHARMA SERVICES LLC p 59
2661 Audubon Rd, Audubon PA 19403
Tel (610) 666-9500 SIC 2834

MYLAN INC p 1004
1000 Mylan Blvd, Canonsburg PA 15317
Tel (724) 514-1800 SIC 2834

■ COVANCE RESEARCH PRODUCTS INC p 384
310 Swamp Bridge Rd, Denver PA 17517
Tel (717) 336-4921 SIC 0279 2836 2834

LARON PHARMA INC p 845
500 Office Center Dr # 400, Fort Washington PA 19034
Tel (267) 575-1470 SIC 2834 5122

■ JANSSEN BIOTECH INC p 777
800 Ridgeview Dr, Horsham PA 19044
Tel (610) 651-6000 SIC 2834 2835

THEOREM CLINICAL RESEARCH INC p 1446
1016 W 9th Ave Ste 300, King Of Prussia PA 19406
Tel (484) 679-2400 SIC 8731 8071 2834

AUXILIUM PHARMACEUTICALS INC p 135
1400 Atwater Dr, Malvern PA 19355
Tel (484) 321-5900 SIC 2834

CEPHALON INC p 283
41 Moores Rd, Malvern PA 19355
Tel (610) 344-0200 SIC 2834

ENDO HEALTH SOLUTIONS INC p 496
1400 Atwater Dr, Malvern PA 19355
Tel (484) 216-0000 SIC 2834

ENDO PHARMACEUTICALS INC p 496
1400 Atwater Dr, Malvern PA 19355
Tel (484) 216-0000 SIC 2834

SLATE PHARMACEUTICALS INC p 1331
1400 Atwater Dr, Malvern PA 19355
Tel (484) 321-5900 SIC 2834

BARR LABORATORIES INC p 156
1090 Horsham Rd, North Wales PA 19454
Tel (215) 591-3000 SIC 2834

TEVA PHARMACEUTICALS USA INC p 1441
1090 Horsham Rd, North Wales PA 19454
Tel (215) 591-3000 SIC 2834 2833 5122

DELAVAU LLC p 423
10101 Roosevelt Blvd, Philadelphia PA 19154
Tel (215) 671-1400 SIC 2087 2834

GLAXOSMITHKLINE LLC p 614
5 Crescent Dr, Philadelphia PA 19112
Tel (215) 751-4000 SIC 2834 5122

▲ LANNETT CO INC p 844
9000 State Rd, Philadelphia PA 19136
Tel (215) 333-9000 SIC 2834

MUTUAL PHARMACEUTICAL CO INC p 1003
1100 Orthodox St, Philadelphia PA 19124
Tel (215) 288-6500 SIC 2834

BAYER CORP p 161
100 Bayer Rd, Pittsburgh PA 15205
Tel (412) 777-2000
SIC 2821 2879 2819 2834 3841

V L H INC p 1538
600 Boyce Rd, Pittsburgh PA 15205
Tel (800) 245-4440 SIC 2833 5122 2834

ALMAC GROUP INC p 59
25 Fretz Rd, Souderton PA 18964
Tel (215) 660-8500 SIC 2834

PENTEC HEALTH INC p 1132
4 Creek Pkwy Ste A, Upper Chichester PA 19061
Tel (610) 494-8700 SIC 2834 8082

MATTHEY JOHNSON HOLDINGS INC p 921
435 Devon Park Dr Ste 600, Wayne PA 19087
Tel (610) 971-3000
SIC 3341 3339 3356 2834 3399 3714

MATTHEY JOHNSON INC p 921
435 Devon Park Dr Ste 600, Wayne PA 19087
Tel (610) 971-3000
SIC 3341 3339 3356 2834 3399 3714

COLORCON INC p 339
420 Moyer Blvd, West Point PA 19486
Tel (215) 699-7733 SIC 2834

■ AMO PUERTO RICO MANUFACTURING INC p 86
Carr 402 Km 42 Zona Indus St Ca, Anasco PR 00610
Tel (787) 826-2727 SIC 2834

■ ABBVIE BIOTECHNOLOGY LTD p 10
Road No 2 Km 59 2, Barceloneta PR 00617
Tel (787) 846-3500
SIC 2834 2844 2835 3841 3826

■ PFIZER PHARMACEUTICALS INC p 1140
Km 58 Hm 2 Rr 2, Barceloneta PR 00617
Tel (787) 846-4300 SIC 2834

P R PATHEON LLC p 1102
2 Calle Aquamarina Villa, Caguas PR 00725
Tel (787) 746-8500 SIC 2834

I P R PHARMACEUTICAL INC p 725
San Isdro Indus Park Lot, Canovanas PR 00729
Tel (787) 957-1400 SIC 2834

■ ELI LILLY INDUSTRIES INC p 487
430 Calle Fabril, Carolina PR 00987
Tel (787) 257-5555 SIC 2834

■ BRISTOL-MYERS SQUIBB PUERTO RICO INC p 214
6 Calle Tabonuco, Guaynabo PR 00968
Tel (787) 774-2800 SIC 2834

PATHEON PUERTO RICO INC p 1120
State Rd 670 Km 2/7 # 27, Manati PR 00674
Tel (787) 746-8500 SIC 2834

RHODES PHARMACEUTICALS LP p 1232
498 Washington St, Coventry RI 02816
Tel (401) 262-9200 SIC 2834

■ KING PHARMACEUTICALS LLC p 820
501 5th St, Bristol TN 37620
Tel (423) 989-8000 SIC 2834

CHATTEM INC p 292
1715 W 38th St, Chattanooga TN 37409
Tel (423) 821-4571
SIC 2834 2844 2023 5963

APHENA PHARMA SOLUTIONS HOLDINGS INC p 96
1920 Fisk Rd, Cookeville TN 38506
Tel (215) 953-5100 SIC 7389 2834

ALCON LABORATORIES HOLDING CORP p 47
6201 South Fwy, Fort Worth TX 76134
Tel (817) 293-0450 SIC 2834 3841

ALCON LABORATORIES INC p 47
6201 South Fwy, Fort Worth TX 76134
Tel (817) 293-0450 SIC 3841 2834

ALCON MANUFACTURING LTD p 47
6201 South Fwy, Fort Worth TX 76134
Tel (817) 293-0450 SIC 2834 3841

ALCON RESEARCH LTD p 47
6201 South Fwy, Fort Worth TX 76134
Tel (817) 551-4555 SIC 8733 3841 2834

DFB PHARMACEUTICALS LLC p 435
3909 Hulen St, Fort Worth TX 76107
Tel (817) 900-4050 SIC 2834

FALCON PHARMACEUTICALS LTD p 526
6201 South Fwy, Fort Worth TX 76134
Tel (800) 343-2133 SIC 2834 3841

GALDERMA LABORATORIES LP p 589
14501 North Fwy, Fort Worth TX 76177
Tel (817) 961-5000 SIC 2834

VIRBAC CORP p 1558
3200 Meacham Blvd, Fort Worth TX 76137
Tel (800) 338-3659 SIC 2834 5122

PROGRESSIVE LABORATORIES INC p 1181
3131 Story Rd W, Irving TX 75038
Tel (972) 518-9660 SIC 2834

ACELITY LP INC p 17
12930 W Interstate 10, San Antonio TX 78249
Tel (210) 524-9000 SIC 3841 2834

DPT LABORATORIES LTD p 454
318 Mccullough Ave, San Antonio TX 78215
Tel (866) 225-5378 SIC 2834

MISSION PHARMACAL CO p 975
10999 W Interstate 10 # 1000, San Antonio TX 78230
Tel (210) 696-8400 SIC 2834

SPFM LP p 1358
4310 West Ave, San Antonio TX 78213
Tel (210) 805-8931
SIC 5122 5149 2834 2833 2841 2844

▲ LEXICON PHARMACEUTICALS INC p 859
8800 Technology Forest Pl, The Woodlands TX 77381
Tel (281) 863-3000 SIC 2834

▲ NATURES SUNSHINE PRODUCTS INC p 1019
2500 W Executive Pkwy # 100, Lehi UT 84043
Tel (801) 341-7900 SIC 2834

CORNERSTONE RESEARCH & DEVELOPMENT INC p 371
900 S Depot Dr, Ogden UT 84404
Tel (801) 337-9400 SIC 2834

■ NUTRACEUTICAL CORP p 1067
1400 Kearns Blvd Ste 200, Park City UT 84060
Tel (435) 655-6000 SIC 2834

▲ LIFEVANTAGE CORP p 865
9785 S Monroe St Ste 300, Sandy UT 84070
Tel (801) 432-9000 SIC 2834

C B FLEET CO INC p 232
4615 Murray Pl, Lynchburg VA 24502
Tel (434) 528-4000 SIC 2834

■ WYETH CONSUMER HEALTHCARE LLC p 1629
1405 Cummings Dr, Richmond VA 23220
Tel (804) 257-2000 SIC 2834

DENDREON CORP p 428
601 Union St Ste 4900, Seattle WA 98101
Tel (206) 256-4545 SIC 2834

■ IMMUNEX CORP p 734
51 University St, Seattle WA 98101
Tel (206) 551-5169 SIC 2834 8731 2836

JUBILANT HOLLISTERSTIER LLC p 796
3525 N Regal St, Spokane WA 99207
Tel (509) 482-4945 SIC 2834

GENOA A QOL HEALTHCARE CO LLC p 604
18300 Cascade Ave S, Tukwila WA 98188
Tel (253) 218-0830 SIC 2834

▲ KEY TECHNOLOGY INC p 814
150 Avery St, Walla Walla WA 99362
Tel (509) 529-2161 SIC 3556 2834

MYLAN PHARMACEUTICALS INC p 1004
781 Chestnut Ridge Rd, Morgantown WV 26505
Tel (304) 599-2595 SIC 2834

MYLAN SPECIALTY LP p 1004
781 Chestnut Ridge Rd, Morgantown WV 26505
Tel (304) 554-4519 SIC 2834 8731

ENZYMATIC THERAPY LLC p 504
825 Challenger Dr, Green Bay WI 54311
Tel (920) 469-1313 SIC 2834

SCHWABE NORTH AMERICA INC p 1291
825 Challenger Dr, Green Bay WI 54311
Tel (920) 469-1313 SIC 2834 2099

UNIVERSITY OF WISCONSIN MEDICAL FOUNDATION INC p 1527
7974 Uw Health Ct, Middleton WI 53562
Tel (608) 821-4223
SIC 8221 8011 2834 8299 8042 8043

SCIENTIFIC PROTEIN LABORATORIES LLC p 1292
700 E Main St, Waunakee WI 53597
Tel (608) 849-5944 SIC 2834 2833

SIC 2835 Diagnostic Substances

YAVAPAI REGIONAL MEDICAL CENTER FOUNDATION p 1635
1003 Willow Creek Rd, Prescott AZ 86301
Tel (928) 445-2700 SIC 8011 8082 2835

■ ABBOTT DIABETES CARE INC p 9
1360 S Loop Rd, Alameda CA 94502
Tel (510) 749-5400 SIC 2835 3845 3823

■ LIFE TECHNOLOGIES CORP p 864
5781 Van Allen Way, Carlsbad CA 92008
Tel (760) 603-7200 SIC 2836 2835

FRESENIUS USA INC p 578
4040 Nelson Ave, Concord CA 94520
Tel (925) 288-4218
SIC 2834 3841 2835 3842 2836

DIASORIN MOLECULAR LLC p 437
11331 Valley View St, Cypress CA 90630
Tel (562) 240-6500 SIC 2835 5047

▲ BIO-RAD LABORATORIES INC p 183
1000 Alfred Nobel Dr, Hercules CA 94547
Tel (510) 724-7000 SIC 3826 3845 2835

■ DANISCO US INC p 412
925 Page Mill Rd, Palo Alto CA 94304
Tel (650) 846-7500
SIC 2835 8731 2899 2869

▲ NATERA INC p 1009
201 Industrial Rd Ste 410, San Carlos CA 94070
Tel (650) 249-9090 SIC 8071 2835

■ ALERE SAN DIEGO INC p 48
9975 Summers Ridge Rd, San Diego CA 92121
Tel (858) 455-4808 SIC 2835

INOVA DIAGNOSTICS INC p 745
9900 Old Grove Rd, San Diego CA 92131
Tel (858) 586-9900 SIC 2835 8731

▲ QUIDEL CORP p 1199
12544 High Bluff Dr # 200, San Diego CA 92130
Tel (858) 552-1100 SIC 2835

▲ BIOMARIN PHARMACEUTICAL INC p 184
770 Lindaro St, San Rafael CA 94901
Tel (415) 506-6700 SIC 2834 2835

SCANTIBODIES LABORATORY INC p 1286
9336 Abraham Way, Santee CA 92071
Tel (619) 258-9300 SIC 2835

■ ROCHE HOLDINGS INC p 1243
1 Dna Way, South San Francisco CA 94080
Tel (625) 225-1000
SIC 2834 2833 2835 2869

▲ ABAXIS INC p 9
3240 Whipple Rd, Union City CA 94587
Tel (510) 675-6500 SIC 3829 2835

QIAGEN INC p 1195
27220 Turnberry Ln # 200, Valencia CA 91355
Tel (661) 702-3598
SIC 3826 5047 8731 2835

ANDWIN CORP p 91
6636 Variel Ave, Woodland Hills CA 91303
Tel (818) 999-2828
SIC 5113 3842 5199 5087 5047 2835

ENSIGN-BICKFORD INDUSTRIES INC p 501
125 Pwder Frest Dr Fl 3, Simsbury CT 06070
Tel (860) 843-2000
SIC 3764 2047 2835 3829 2499 6552

▲ OPKO HEALTH INC p 1089
4400 Biscayne Blvd, Miami FL 33137
Tel (305) 575-4100 SIC 2834 2835 8731

IMMUCOR INC p 734
3130 Gateway Dr, Peachtree Corners GA 30071
Tel (770) 441-2051 SIC 2835

IVD HOLDINGS INC p 769
3130 Gateway Dr, Peachtree Corners GA 30071
Tel (770) 441-2051 SIC 2835

IVD INTERMEDIATE HOLDINGS B INC p 769
3130 Gateway Dr, Peachtree Corners GA 30071
Tel (770) 441-2051 SIC 2835

■ MWI VETERINARY SUPPLY CO p 1004
3041 W Pasadena Dr, Boise ID 83705
Tel (208) 955-8930
SIC 5047 2834 2835 2836

▲ ABBOTT LABORATORIES p 9
100 Abbott Park Rd, Abbott Park IL 60064
Tel (224) 667-6100
SIC 2834 2835 3841 3826

■ GE HEALTHCARE HOLDINGS INC p 596
3350 N Ridge Ave, Arlington Heights IL 60004
Tel (847) 398-8400
SIC 2835 2833 5169 5122

■ BAXTER HEALTHCARE CORP p 160
1 Baxter Pkwy, Deerfield IL 60015
Tel (224) 948-2000
SIC 3841 2835 2389 3842 5047

▲ BAXTER INTERNATIONAL INC p 160
1 Baxter Pkwy, Deerfield IL 60015
Tel (224) 948-2000
SIC 2834 3841 2835 3842

■ ROCHE DIAGNOSTICS CORP p 1243
9115 Hague Rd, Indianapolis IN 46256
Tel (800) 428-5076 SIC 2835

INSTRUMENTATION LABORATORY CO p 747
180 Hartwell Rd, Bedford MA 01730
Tel (800) 955-9525
SIC 3841 2819 8731 2835

GENZYME CORP p 605
500 Kendall St, Cambridge MA 02142
Tel (617) 252-7500
SIC 2835 2834 8071 3842 2836 5122

NOVARTIS VACCINES AND DIAGNOSTICS INC p 1063
350 Massachusetts Ave, Cambridge MA 02139
Tel (617) 871-7000 SIC 2834 2835 2836

▲ LANTHEUS HOLDINGS INC p 844
331 Treble Cove Rd, North Billerica MA 01862
Tel (978) 671-8001 SIC 2835 2834

▲ ALERE INC p 48
51 Sawyer Rd Ste 200, Waltham MA 02453
Tel (781) 647-3900 SIC 2835 8071 8742

▲ AMAG PHARMACEUTICALS INC p 64
1100 Winter St Fl 3, Waltham MA 02451
Tel (617) 498-3300 SIC 2834 2835

■ ESOTERIX GENETIC LABORATORIES LLC p 509
3400 Computer Dr, Westborough MA 01581
Tel (508) 389-6650 SIC 8731 2835 8071

▲ NEOGEN CORP p 1025
620 Lesher Pl, Lansing MI 48912
Tel (517) 372-9200 SIC 2835 3841 2836

▲ BIO-TECHNE CORP p 183
614 Mckinley Pl Ne, Minneapolis MN 55413
Tel (612) 379-8854 SIC 2835 8731

DIASORIN INC p 437
1951 Northwestern Ave S, Stillwater MN 55082
Tel (651) 439-9710 SIC 2835 5047

▲ QUEST DIAGNOSTICS INC p 1199
3 Giralda Farms, Madison NJ 07940
Tel (973) 520-2700 SIC 8071 2835

MINDRAY DS USA INC p 972
800 Macarthur Blvd, Mahwah NJ 07430
Tel (201) 995-8000 SIC 3845 2835 3841

BRACCO DIAGNOSTICS INC p 206
259 Prospect Plains Rd, Monroe Township NJ 08831
Tel (609) 514-2200 SIC 2835

BRACCO USA INC p 206
259 Prospect Plains Rd, Monroe Township NJ 08831
Tel (609) 514-2200 SIC 2835

■ ASCENSIA DIABETES CARE US INC p 116
5 Woodhollow Rd, Parsippany NJ 07054
Tel (973) 560-6500 SIC 5047 2835 3841

■ ARMKEL LLC p 111
469 N Harrison St, Princeton NJ 08540
Tel (609) 683-5900 SIC 2844 2835

ORTHO-CLINICAL DIAGNOSTICS INC p 1096
1001 Us Highway 202, Raritan NJ 08869
Tel (908) 218-8000 SIC 2835 2834

■ WELCH ALLYN INC p 1588
4341 State Street Rd, Skaneateles Falls NY 13153
Tel (315) 685-4100 SIC 3841 2835 3827

▲ MERIDIAN BIOSCIENCE INC p 948
3471 River Hills Dr, Cincinnati OH 45244
Tel (513) 271-3700 SIC 2835 2834

■ CARDINAL HEALTH 414 LLC p 253
7000 Cardinal Pl, Dublin OH 43017
Tel (614) 757-5000 SIC 2834 2835

▲ ORASURE TECHNOLOGIES INC p 1092
220 E 1st St, Bethlehem PA 18015
Tel (610) 882-1820 SIC 2835

■ LIFESCAN INC p 864
965 Chesterbrook Blvd, Chesterbrook PA 19087
Tel (800) 227-8862 SIC 2835 3841

■ JANSSEN BIOTECH INC p 777
800 Ridgeview Dr, Horsham PA 19044
Tel (610) 651-6000 SIC 2834 2835

■ ABBVIE BIOTECHNOLOGY LTD p 10
Road No 2 Km 59 2, Barceloneta PR 00617
Tel (787) 846-3500
SIC 2834 2844 2835 3841 3826

■ ACCREDO HEALTH INC p 15
1640 Century Center Pkwy # 110, Memphis TN 38134
Tel (901) 373-8958 SIC 2835 8092

▲ MYRIAD GENETICS INC p 1005
320 S Wakara Way, Salt Lake City UT 84108
Tel (801) 584-3600 SIC 2835 8731

SIC 2836 Biological Prdts, Exc Diagnostic Substances

▲ INSYS THERAPEUTICS INC p 748
1333 S Spectrum Blvd, Chandler AZ 85286
Tel (480) 500-3127 SIC 2836 2834

■ LIFE TECHNOLOGIES CORP p 864
5781 Van Allen Way, Carlsbad CA 92008
Tel (760) 603-7200 SIC 2836 2835

FRESENIUS USA INC p 578
4040 Nelson Ave, Concord CA 94520
Tel (925) 288-4218
SIC 2834 3841 2835 3842 2836

▲ GILEAD SCIENCES INC p 612
333 Lakeside Dr, Foster City CA 94404
Tel (650) 574-3000 SIC 2836

GRIFOLS BIOLOGICALS INC p 640
5555 Valley Blvd, Los Angeles CA 90032
Tel (323) 227-7028 SIC 2836 2834

▲ HALOZYME THERAPEUTICS INC p 655
11388 Sorrento Valley Rd # 200, San Diego CA 92121
Tel (858) 794-8889 SIC 2834 2836

▲ AMGEN INC p 85
1 Amgen Center Dr, Thousand Oaks CA 91320
Tel (805) 447-1000 SIC 2836

■ INTERVET INC p 759
29160 Intervet Ln, Millsboro DE 19966
Tel (302) 934-4341 SIC 2836

GLAXOSMITHKLINE HOLDINGS (AMERICAS) INC p 614
1105 N Market St, Wilmington DE 19801
Tel (302) 656-5280
SIC 2834 2836 2833 2844 8071

MERIAL LIMITED p 948
3239 Satellite Blvd 500, Duluth GA 30096
Tel (678) 638-3000 SIC 2836

MERIAL UK LLC p 948
3239 Satellite Blvd, Duluth GA 30096
Tel (678) 638-3000 SIC 2836 2834 3841

MERIAL SELECT INC p 948
1168 Airport Pkwy, Gainesville GA 30501
Tel (770) 536-8787 *SIC* 5122 2836

■ **MWI VETERINARY SUPPLY CO** p 1004
3041 W Pasadena Dr, Boise ID 83705
Tel (208) 955-8930
SIC 5047 2834 2835 2836

▲ **ABBVIE INC** p 10
1 N Waukegan Rd, North Chicago IL 60064
Tel (847) 932-7900 *SIC* 2834 2836

■ **REMEL INC** p 1222
12076 Santa Fe Trail Dr, Lenexa KS 66215
Tel (800) 255-6730 *SIC* 2836

SAFC BIOSCIENCES INC p 1265
13804 W 107th St, Lenexa KS 66215
Tel (913) 469-5580 *SIC* 2836

▲ **EMERGENT BIOSOLUTIONS INC** p 492
400 Professional Dr # 400, Gaithersburg MD 20879
Tel (240) 631-3200 *SIC* 2834 2836

LONZA WALKERSVILLE INC p 877
8830 Biggs Ford Rd, Walkersville MD 21793
Tel (301) 898-7025 *SIC* 2836

▲ **ANIKA THERAPEUTICS INC** p 91
32 Wiggins Ave, Bedford MA 01730
Tel (781) 457-9000 *SIC* 2836

▲ **ARIAD PHARMACEUTICALS INC** p 108
26 Landsdowne St Ste 175, Cambridge MA 02139
Tel (617) 494-0400 *SIC* 2836 8731

▲ **BIOGEN INC** p 184
225 Binney St, Cambridge MA 02142
Tel (617) 679-2000 *SIC* 2834 2836 8731

GENZYME CORP p 605
500 Kendall St, Cambridge MA 02142
Tel (617) 252-7500
SIC 2835 2834 8071 3842 2836 5122

NOVARTIS VACCINES AND DIAGNOSTICS INC p 1063
350 Massachusetts Ave, Cambridge MA 02139
Tel (617) 871-7000 *SIC* 2834 2835 2836

ORGANOGENESIS INC p 1094
150 Dan Rd Ste 3, Canton MA 02021
Tel (781) 575-0198 *SIC* 2836

▲ **REPLIGEN CORP** p 1225
41 Seyon St Ste 100, Waltham MA 02453
Tel (781) 250-0111 *SIC* 2836

■ **BIOGEN MA INC** p 184
133 Boston Post Rd, Weston MA 02493
Tel (617) 679-2000 *SIC* 2836 8731

■ **EMERGENT BIODEFENSE OPERATIONS LANSING LLC** p 492
3500 N Martin Luther King, Lansing MI 48906
Tel (517) 327-1500 *SIC* 2836 2834

▲ **NEOGEN CORP** p 1025
620 Lesher Pl, Lansing MI 48912
Tel (517) 372-9200 *SIC* 2835 3841 2836

BOEHRINGER INGELHEIM VETMEDICA INC p 197
2621 N Belt Hwy, Saint Joseph MO 64506
Tel (800) 325-9167 *SIC* 2836 2834 5191

SIGMA CHEMICAL CORP p 1321
3050 Spruce St, Saint Louis MO 63103
Tel (314) 771-5765 *SIC* 2836 2869

▲ **PDL BIOPHARMA INC** p 1124
932 Southwood Blvd, Incline Village NV 89451
Tel (775) 832-8500 *SIC* 2836

LIFECELL CORP p 864
1 Millennium Way, Branchburg NJ 08876
Tel (908) 947-1100 *SIC* 2836

■ **IMCLONE SYSTEMS LLC** p 733
440 Us Highway 22, Bridgewater NJ 08807
Tel (908) 541-8000 *SIC* 2836 2834

▲ **MERCK & CO INC** p 945
2000 Galloping Hill Rd, Kenilworth NJ 07033
Tel (908) 740-4000
SIC 2834 2836 2844 5122

■ **WYETH HOLDINGS LLC** p 1629
5 Giralda Farms, Madison NJ 07940
Tel (973) 660-5000 *SIC* 2834 2836

▲ **INTEGRA LIFESCIENCES HOLDINGS CORP** p 748
311 Enterprise Dr, Plainsboro NJ 08536
Tel (609) 275-0500 *SIC* 3841 2836 3842

▲ **ALBANY MOLECULAR RESEARCH INC** p 45
26 Corporate Cir, Albany NY 12203
Tel (518) 512-2000 *SIC* 2836 8731

▲ **ACORDA THERAPEUTICS INC** p 18
420 Saw Mill River Rd, Ardsley NY 10502
Tel (914) 347-4300 *SIC* 2834 8731 2836

NEW YORK BLOOD CENTER INC p 1034
310 E 67th St, New York NY 10065
Tel (212) 570-3010 *SIC* 8099 2836

■ **WYETH LLC** p 1629
235 E 42nd St, New York NY 10017
Tel (973) 660-5000 *SIC* 2834 2836

DSM NUTRITIONAL PRODUCTS LLC p 458
2105 Technology Dr, Schenectady NY 12308
Tel (518) 372-5155 *SIC* 2834 2836

CAROLINA BIOLOGICAL SUPPLY CO p 259
2700 York Rd, Burlington NC 27215
Tel (336) 584-0381
SIC 5049 2836 3829 3826 3821

OCTAPHARMA PLASMA INC p 1074
10644 Westlake Dr, Charlotte NC 28273
Tel (704) 654-4600 *SIC* 2836

GRIFOLS THERAPEUTICS INC p 640
79 Tw Alexander Dr, Durham NC 27709
Tel (919) 316-6300 *SIC* 2836

FUJIFILM DIOSYNTH BIOTECHNOLOGIES USA INC p 583
101 J Morris Commons Ln # 300, Morrisville NC 27560
Tel (919) 337-4400 *SIC* 2836

■ **COVANCE RESEARCH PRODUCTS INC** p 384
310 Swamp Bridge Rd, Denver PA 17517
Tel (717) 336-4921 *SIC* 0279 2836 2834

CSL BEHRING LLC p 398
1020 1st Ave, King Of Prussia PA 19406
Tel (610) 878-4000 *SIC* 2836

SANOFI PASTEUR INC p 1280
1 Discovery Dr, Swiftwater PA 18370
Tel (570) 839-7187 *SIC* 2836

■ **AMGEN MANUFACTURING LIMITED** p 85
6 Carr 31 Km, Juncos PR 00777
Tel (787) 656-2000 *SIC* 2836

CARTER BLOODCARE p 261
2205 Highway 121, Bedford TX 76021
Tel (817) 412-5000 *SIC* 2836

QUALTEX LABORATORIES p 1198
6211 W Interstate 10, San Antonio TX 78201
Tel (210) 736-8952 *SIC* 2836

■ **HYCLONE LABORATORIES INC** p 723
925 W 1800 S, Logan UT 84321
Tel (435) 792-8000 *SIC* 2836 8071

▲ **SEATTLE GENETICS INC** p 1297
21823 30th Dr Se, Bothell WA 98021
Tel (425) 527-4000 *SIC* 2836

■ **IMMUNEX CORP** p 734
51 University St, Seattle WA 98101
Tel (206) 551-5169 *SIC* 2834 8731 2836

PROMEGA CORP p 1183
2800 Woods Hollow Rd, Fitchburg WI 53711
Tel (608) 274-4330 *SIC* 2836

SIC 2841 Soap & Detergents

DIAL CORP p 436
7201 E Henkel Way, Scottsdale AZ 85255
Tel (480) 754-3425
SIC 2841 2844 2842 2032 2013

HENKEL CONSUMER GOODS INC p 683
7201 E Henkel Way, Scottsdale AZ 85255
Tel (860) 571-5100 *SIC* 2841

IMPERIAL WESTERN PRODUCTS INC p 734
86600 Avenue 54, Coachella CA 92236
Tel (760) 398-0815 *SIC* 5159 2841 2869

ALL ONE GOD FAITH INC p 51
1335 Park Center Dr, Vista CA 92081
Tel (844) 937-2551 *SIC* 2841

BEIERSDORF NORTH AMERICA INC p 169
45 Danbury Rd, Wilton CT 06897
Tel (203) 563-5800
SIC 2844 5122 3842 2841 2672

SUN PRODUCTS CORP p 1400
60 Danbury Rd, Wilton CT 06897
Tel (203) 254-6700 *SIC* 2841

ACUITY SPECIALTY PRODUCTS INC p 20
1310 Sboard Indus Blvd Nw, Atlanta GA 30318
Tel (404) 352-1680
SIC 2841 2879 2842 5169

ZEP INC p 1642
3330 Cumberland Blvd Se # 700, Atlanta GA 30339
Tel (877) 428-9937 *SIC* 2841 2879 2842

AMREP INC p 86
425 Franklin Gtwy Se # 530, Marietta GA 30067
Tel (770) 590-5960
SIC 2842 2079 2911 2869 2841 2819

MELALEUCA INC p 940
4609 W 65th S, Idaho Falls ID 83402
Tel (208) 522-0700
SIC 2833 5122 2844 2841 2834

VENUS LABORATORIES INC p 1548
111 S Rohlwing Rd, Addison IL 60101
Tel (630) 595-1900 *SIC* 2842 2841

AKZO NOBEL CHEMICALS LLC p 42
525 W Van Buren St # 1600, Chicago IL 60607
Tel (312) 544-7000 *SIC* 2841

VANTAGE OLEOCHEMICALS INC p 1544
4650 S Racine Ave, Chicago IL 60609
Tel (773) 376-9000 *SIC* 2869 2841 5169

KIK CUSTOM PRODUCTS INC p 817
1 W Hegeler Ln, Danville IL 61832
Tel (217) 442-1400
SIC 2841 2842 2843 2844

VVF ILLINOIS SERVICES LLC p 1567
2000 Aucutt Rd, Montgomery IL 60538
Tel (630) 892-4381 *SIC* 2841

GEA FARM TECHNOLOGIES INC p 597
1880 Country Farm Dr, Naperville IL 60563
Tel (630) 548-8200
SIC 5083 3523 2841 2842

■ **CHEMTOOL INC** p 293
801 W Rockton Rd, Rockton IL 61072
Tel (815) 957-4140
SIC 2992 2899 2842 2841

DIVERSIFIED CHEMICAL TECHNOLOGIES INC p 444
15477 Woodrow Wilson St, Detroit MI 48238
Tel (313) 867-5444
SIC 2891 2992 2899 2842 2841

JACOBS INDUSTRIES INC p 775
8096 Excelsior Blvd, Hopkins MN 55343
Tel (612) 339-9500
SIC 2841 2087 2099 2844 5084 6794

▲ **ECOLAB INC** p 476
370 Wabasha St N, Saint Paul MN 55102
Tel (800) 232-6522 *SIC* 2841 2842 7342

WATKINS INC p 1582
150 Liberty St, Winona MN 55987
Tel (507) 457-3300 *SIC* 2087 2841

AKZO NOBEL SPG LLC p 43
10 Finderne Ave Ste A, Bridgewater NJ 08807
Tel (908) 685-5000 *SIC* 2841

CONOPCO INC p 358
700 Sylvan Ave, Englewood Cliffs NJ 07632
Tel (201) 894-2727
SIC 2035 2038 2086 2024 2844 2841

UNILEVER UNITED STATES INC p 1503
700 Sylvan Ave, Englewood Cliffs NJ 07632
Tel (201) 894-4000
SIC 2035 2086 2024 2038 2844 2841

▲ **CHURCH & DWIGHT CO INC** p 305
500 Charles Ewing Blvd, Ewing NJ 08628
Tel (609) 806-1200
SIC 2841 2812 2842 2844 2819

MARIETTA HOLDING CORP INC p 906
37 Huntington St, Cortland NY 13045
Tel (607) 753-6746 *SIC* 6719 2841

▲ **COLGATE-PALMOLIVE CO** p 336
300 Park Ave Fl 5, New York NY 10022
Tel (212) 310-2000
SIC 2844 3991 2841 2842 2047

■ **HFC PRESTIGE INTERNATIONAL US LLC** p 689
350 5th Ave, New York NY 10118
Tel (212) 389-7800
SIC 2844 2676 3421 2842 2841

MAYBELLINE INC p 923
575 5th Ave Bsmt Fl, New York NY 10017
Tel (212) 885-1310 *SIC* 2844 2841

NM Z PARENT INC p 1045
787 7th Ave Fl 49, New York NY 10019
Tel (212) 720-0300
SIC 6726 2841 2879 2842

▲ **PRESTIGE BRANDS HOLDINGS INC** p 1173
660 White Plains Rd, Tarrytown NY 10591
Tel (914) 524-6800 *SIC* 2834 2841

COMBE INC p 343
1101 Westchester Ave, White Plains NY 10604
Tel (914) 694-5454 *SIC* 2841 2834

PIEDMONT CHEMICAL INDUSTRIES INC p 1146
331 Burton Ave, High Point NC 27262
Tel (336) 885-5131 *SIC* 2841 2843

KAO USA INC p 803
2535 Spring Grove Ave, Cincinnati OH 45214
Tel (513) 421-1400 *SIC* 2844 2841

▲ **PROCTER & GAMBLE CO** p 1179
1 Procter And Gamble Plz, Cincinnati OH 45202
Tel (513) 983-1100
SIC 2844 2676 3421 2842 2841

■ **PROCTER & GAMBLE MANUFACTURING CO** p 1179
1 Procter And Gamble Plz, Cincinnati OH 45202
Tel (513) 983-1100
SIC 2841 2079 2099 2844 2045

ST BERNARD SOAP CO p 1365
5177 Spring Grove Ave, Cincinnati OH 45217
Tel (513) 242-2227 *SIC* 2841

STATE INDUSTRIAL PRODUCTS CORP p 1381
5915 Landerbrook Dr # 300, Cleveland OH 44124
Tel (877) 747-6986
SIC 2841 5072 2842 2992 2952 2899

WASHING SYSTEMS LLC p 1577
167 Commerce Dr, Loveland OH 45140
Tel (800) 272-1974 *SIC* 5169 2841

PLAZA PROVISION CO (PUERTO RICO) p 1156
Carretera 165 Esq, Guaynabo PR 00965
Tel (787) 781-2070 *SIC* 5182 4222 2841

BRADFORD SOAP INTERNATIONAL INC p 206
200 Providence St, West Warwick RI 02893
Tel (401) 821-2141 *SIC* 2841

ORIGINAL BRADFORD SOAP WORKS INC p 1094
200 Providence St, West Warwick RI 02893
Tel (401) 821-2141 *SIC* 2841

4E BRANDS NORTHAMERICA LLC p 3
17806 W Interstate 10 # 30, San Antonio TX 78257
Tel (210) 819-7385 *SIC* 2841

SPFM LP p 1358
4310 West Ave, San Antonio TX 78213
Tel (210) 805-8931
SIC 5122 5149 2834 2833 2841 2844

■ **ETHYL CORP** p 511
330 S 4th St, Richmond VA 23219
Tel (804) 788-5000
SIC 2869 5169 2899 2841 2865

▲ **NEWMARKET CORP** p 1038
330 S 4th St, Richmond VA 23219
Tel (804) 788-5000
SIC 2869 2899 2841 2865

C-TECH INDUSTRIES INC p 234
4275 Nw Pacific Rim Blvd, Camas WA 98607
Tel (360) 833-1600 *SIC* 3589 2841 3559

HYDRITE CHEMICAL CO p 723
300 N Patrick Blvd Fl 2, Brookfield WI 53045
Tel (262) 792-1450
SIC 5169 2819 2841 2869

NORTHERN LABS INC p 1056
5800 West Dr, Manitowoc WI 54220
Tel (920) 684-7137 *SIC* 2842 2841

SIC 2842 Spec Cleaning, Polishing & Sanitation Preparations

DIAL CORP p 436
7201 E Henkel Way, Scottsdale AZ 85255
Tel (480) 754-3425
SIC 2841 2844 2842 2032 2013

▲ **VERSUM MATERIALS INC** p 1552
8555 S River Pkwy, Tempe AZ 85284
Tel (610) 481-6697 *SIC* 2842 2891 3569

▲ **CLOROX CO** p 327
1221 Broadway Ste 1300, Oakland CA 94612
Tel (510) 271-7000
SIC 2842 2673 2035 2844 2879

■ **CLOROX INTERNATIONAL CO** p 327
1221 Broadway Ste 13, Oakland CA 94612
Tel (510) 271-7000 *SIC* 2842 2879

■ **CLOROX PRODUCTS MANUFACTURING CO** p 327
1221 Broadway Ste 51, Oakland CA 94612
Tel (510) 271-7000 *SIC* 2842

■ **GLAD PRODUCTS CO** p 614
1221 Broadway Ste A, Oakland CA 94612
Tel (510) 271-7000
SIC 3081 2673 2842 3295

KIK-SOCAL INC p 817
9028 Dice Rd, Santa Fe Springs CA 90670
Tel (562) 946-6427 *SIC* 2842

■ **ARMORED AUTOGROUP PARENT INC** p 111
44 Old Ridgebury Rd # 300, Danbury CT 06810
Tel (203) 205-2900 *SIC* 2842 2911 2899

■ **GREAT LAKES CHEMICAL CORP** p 633
199 Benson Rd, Middlebury CT 06762
Tel (203) 573-2000 *SIC* 2899 2842

■ **MACDERMID INC** p 892
245 Freight St, Waterbury CT 06702
Tel (203) 575-5700
SIC 2899 2842 2874 2992 2752 3577

■ **PLAYTEX MANUFACTURING INC** p 1155
50 N Dupont Hwy, Dover DE 19901
Tel (302) 678-6000 *SIC* 2676 3844 2842

JCI JONES CHEMICALS INC p 780
1765 Ringling Blvd, Sarasota FL 34236
Tel (941) 330-1537 *SIC* 5169 2842

ACUITY SPECIALTY PRODUCTS INC p 20
1310 Sboard Indus Blvd Nw, Atlanta GA 30318
Tel (404) 352-1680
SIC 2841 2879 2842 5169

ZEP INC p 1642
3330 Cumberland Blvd Se # 700, Atlanta GA 30339
Tel (877) 428-9937 *SIC* 2841 2879 2842

AMREP INC p 86
425 Franklin Gtwy Se # 530, Marietta GA 30067
Tel (770) 590-5960
SIC 2842 2079 2911 2869 2841 2819

■ **OIL-DRI CORP OF GEORGIA** p 1079
28990 Hwy 3, Ochlocknee GA 31773
Tel (229) 574-5131 *SIC* 3295 3564 2842

TURTLE WAX INC p 1493
2250 W Pinehurst Blvd # 150, Addison IL 60101
Tel (630) 455-3700 *SIC* 2842

VENUS LABORATORIES INC p 1548
111 S Rohlwing Rd, Addison IL 60101
Tel (630) 595-1900 *SIC* 2842 2841

▲ **CABOT MICROELECTRONICS CORP** p 235
870 N Commons Dr, Aurora IL 60504
Tel (630) 375-6631 *SIC* 2842

▲ **OIL-DRI CORP OF AMERICA** p 1079
410 N Michigan Ave # 400, Chicago IL 60611
Tel (312) 321-1515 *SIC* 2842 3295

KIK CUSTOM PRODUCTS INC p 817
1 W Hegeler Ln, Danville IL 61832
Tel (217) 442-1400
SIC 2841 2842 2843 2844

MAT HOLDINGS INC p 918
6700 Wildlife Way, Long Grove IL 60047
Tel (847) 821-9630 *SIC* 2842 3714 3563

GEA FARM TECHNOLOGIES INC p 597
1880 Country Farm Dr, Naperville IL 60563
Tel (630) 548-8200
SIC 5083 3523 2841 2842

■ **CHEMTOOL INC** p 293
801 W Rockton Rd, Rockton IL 61072
Tel (815) 957-4140
SIC 2992 2899 2842 2841

■ **RUST-OLEUM CORP** p 1260
11 E Hawthorn Pkwy, Vernon Hills IL 60061
Tel (847) 367-7700
SIC 2891 2899 2816 2842 2851

CHAMPION PACKAGING & DISTRIBUTION INC p 287
1840 Internationale Pkwy, Woodridge IL 60517
Tel (630) 755-4220 *SIC* 2842 2812

K2 INDUSTRIAL SERVICES INC p 799
4527 Columbia Ave 2, Hammond IN 46327
Tel (708) 928-4765 *SIC* 2842 1799

FULLER BRUSH CO INC p 584
1 Fuller Way, Great Bend KS 67530
Tel (620) 792-1711 *SIC* 2842 2844 3991

MONSON COMPANIES INC p 985
154 Pioneer Dr, Leominster MA 01453
Tel (978) 840-7007
SIC 5169 5172 2899 2842

ACCESS BUSINESS GROUP LLC p 14
7575 Fulton St E, Ada MI 49355
Tel (616) 787-6000
SIC 5169 2842 5122 2833 5136 5137

THETFORD CORP p 1447
7101 Jackson Rd, Ann Arbor MI 48103
Tel (734) 769-6000
SIC 3632 3089 2842 2621 3431 2899

DIVERSIFIED CHEMICAL TECHNOLOGIES INC p 444
15477 Woodrow Wilson St, Detroit MI 48238
Tel (313) 867-5444
SIC 2891 2992 2899 2842 2841

BISSELL INC p 185
2345 Walker Ave Nw, Grand Rapids MI 49544
Tel (616) 453-4451 *SIC* 3589 2842 3635

▲ **3M CO** p 2
3m Center Bldg 22011w02, Saint Paul MN 55144
Tel (651) 733-1110
SIC 3841 3842 3291 2842 2672 2891

▲ **ECOLAB INC** p 476
370 Wabasha St N, Saint Paul MN 55102
Tel (800) 232-6522 *SIC* 2841 2842 7342

DELAVAL INC p 423
11100 N Congress Ave, Kansas City MO 64153
Tel (816) 891-7700
SIC 5083 3523 2842 0241

BUCKEYE INTERNATIONAL INC p 223
2700 Wagner Pl, Maryland Heights MO 63043
Tel (314) 291-1900 *SIC* 2842

▲ **OLIN CORP** p 1082
190 Carondelet Plz # 1530, Saint Louis MO 63105
Tel (314) 480-1400
SIC 2812 2819 2821 2842 2869 2891

WILLERT HOME PRODUCTS INC p 1610
4044 Park Ave, Saint Louis MO 63110
Tel (314) 772-2822
SIC 3089 2869 2879 2842

ALBERTO-CULVER CO p 46
800 Sylvan Ave, Englewood Cliffs NJ 07632
Tel (708) 681-2668 *SIC* 2844 2842 2099

▲ **CHURCH & DWIGHT CO INC** p 305
500 Charles Ewing Blvd, Ewing NJ 08628
Tel (609) 806-1200
SIC 2841 2812 2842 2844 2819

■ **CHEMETALL US INC** p 293
675 Central Ave, New Providence NJ 07974
Tel (908) 464-6900 *SIC* 2842 2899 2851

RB MANUFACTURING LLC p 1211
399 Interpace Pkwy, Parsippany NJ 07054
Tel (973) 404-2600 *SIC* 2035 2842

RECKITT BENCKISER (NORTH AMERICA) INC p 1214
399 Interpace Pkwy # 101, Parsippany NJ 07054
Tel (973) 404-2600 SIC 2035 2842

RECKITT BENCKISER LLC p 1214
399 Interpace Pkwy # 101, Parsippany NJ 07054
Tel (973) 404-2600 SIC 2035 2842

AMANO USA HOLDINGS INC p 64
140 Harrison Ave, Roseland NJ 07068
Tel (973) 403-1900
SIC 3589 2842 3579 3559 5169 5087

RONELL INDUSTRIES INC p 1249
298 Cox St, Roselle NJ 07203
Tel (908) 245-5255 SIC 7349 2842

■ INTERNATIONAL SPECIALTY PRODUCTS INC p 757
1361 Alps Rd, Wayne NJ 07470
Tel (859) 815-3333
SIC 2869 2821 2843 2842 2899

US NONWOVENS CORP p 1532
100 Emjay Blvd, Brentwood NY 11717
Tel (631) 952-0100 SIC 2842

▲ COLGATE-PALMOLIVE CO p 336
300 Park Ave Fl 5, New York NY 10022
Tel (212) 310-2000
SIC 2844 3991 2841 2842 2047

■ HFC PRESTIGE INTERNATIONAL US LLC p 689
350 5th Ave, New York NY 10118
Tel (212) 389-7800
SIC 2844 2676 3421 2842 2841

MDI HOLDINGS LLC p 933
399 Park Ave Fl 14, New York NY 10022
Tel (212) 559-1127
SIC 2899 2842 2874 2992 2752 3577

NM Z PARENT INC p 1045
787 7th Ave Fl 49, New York NY 10019
Tel (212) 720-0300
SIC 6726 2841 2879 2842

ROCHESTER MIDLAND CORP p 1243
155 Paragon Dr, Rochester NY 14624
Tel (585) 336-2200 SIC 2842 2676 2899

■ DIVERSEY INC p 443
2415 Cascade Pointe Blvd, Charlotte NC 28208
Tel (262) 631-4001 SIC 2842

■ KAY CHEMICAL CO p 805
8300 Capital Dr, Greensboro NC 27409
Tel (336) 668-7290 SIC 2842

GOJO INDUSTRIES INC p 620
1 Gojo Plz Ste 500, Akron OH 44311
Tel (330) 255-6000 SIC 2842 3586 2844

■ TREMCO INC p 1476
3735 Green Rd, Beachwood OH 44122
Tel (216) 292-5000
SIC 2891 2952 1761 1752 2851 2842

DUBOIS CHEMICALS p 459
3630 E Kemper Rd, Cincinnati OH 45241
Tel (800) 438-2647 SIC 2842

▲ PROCTER & GAMBLE CO p 1179
1 Procter And Gamble Plz, Cincinnati OH 45202
Tel (513) 983-1100
SIC 2844 2676 3421 2842 2841

■ PROCTER & GAMBLE FAR EAST INC p 1179
1 Procter And Gamble Plz, Cincinnati OH 45202
Tel (513) 983-1100 SIC 2842 2844 2676

STATE INDUSTRIAL PRODUCTS CORP p 1381
5915 Landerbrook Dr # 300, Cleveland OH 44124
Tel (877) 747-6986
SIC 2841 5072 2842 2992 2952 2899

SPARTAN CHEMICAL CO INC p 1355
1110 Spartan Dr, Maumee OH 43537
Tel (419) 897-5551 SIC 2842

■ REPUBLIC POWDERED METALS INC p 1225
2628 Pearl Rd, Medina OH 44256
Tel (330) 225-3192
SIC 2851 2891 3069 2899 2865 2842

▲ RPM INTERNATIONAL INC p 1255
2628 Pearl Rd, Medina OH 44256
Tel (330) 273-5090
SIC 2851 2891 3069 2899 2865 2842

TRANZONIC COMPANIES p 1473
26301 Curtiss Wright Pkwy # 200, Richmond Heights OH 44143
Tel (216) 535-4300
SIC 2676 2211 2326 2842 2273 2262

TZ ACQUISITION CORP p 1496
26301 Curtiss Wright Pkwy, Richmond Heights OH 44143
Tel (216) 535-4300
SIC 2676 2211 2326 2842 2262

CANBERRA CORP p 246
3610 N Hiland Sylvania Rd, Toledo OH 43615
Tel (419) 724-4300 SIC 2842

▲ AIR PRODUCTS AND CHEMICALS INC p 39
7201 Hamilton Blvd, Allentown PA 18195
Tel (610) 481-4911
SIC 2813 2842 2891 3569

ALCO INDUSTRIES INC p 47
1275 Glenlivet Dr Ste 100, Allentown PA 18106
Tel (610) 666-0930
SIC 2879 2851 2842 2873

■ VERSUM MATERIALS US LLC p 1552
1919 Vultee St, Allentown PA 18103
Tel (610) 481-3706 SIC 2842 2891 3569

CRYSTAL INC - PMC p 397
601 W 8th St, Lansdale PA 19446
Tel (267) 649-7330 SIC 2899 2842

▲ CHEMTURA CORP p 294
1818 Market St Ste 3700, Philadelphia PA 19103
Tel (215) 446-3911
SIC 2869 2843 2821 2911 2899 2842

CRC INDUSTRIES INC p 390
885 Louis Dr, Warminster PA 18974
Tel (215) 674-4300
SIC 2992 3471 2899 2842

NCH CORP p 1022
2727 Chemsearch Blvd, Irving TX 75062
Tel (972) 438-0211
SIC 2842 2899 3432 3548 3429

RUG DOCTOR LLC p 1257
4701 Old Shepard Pl, Plano TX 75093
Tel (972) 673-1400 SIC 2842 3589 5087

NORTHERN LABS INC p 1056
5800 West Dr, Manitowoc WI 54220
Tel (920) 684-7137 SIC 2842 2841

KLEENTEST PRODUCTS CORP p 823
1611 S Sunset Rd, Port Washington WI 53074
Tel (262) 284-6600 SIC 2842 2675

S C JOHNSON & SON INC p 1262
1525 Howe St, Racine WI 53403
Tel (262) 260-2000
SIC 2842 2844 2879 2865 7342 7349

■ DIVERSEY HOLDINGS INC p 443
8310 16th St, Sturtevant WI 53177
Tel (262) 631-4001 SIC 2842

SIC 2843 Surface Active & Finishing Agents, Sulfonated Oils

HENKEL CORP p 683
1 Henkel Way, Rocky Hill CT 06067
Tel (860) 571-5100
SIC 2843 2821 2833 2899 2891

HENKEL OF AMERICA INC p 683
1 Henkel Way, Rocky Hill CT 06067
Tel (860) 571-5100
SIC 2869 2843 2821 2833 2899 2891

KIK CUSTOM PRODUCTS INC p 817
1 W Hegeler Ln, Danville IL 61832
Tel (217) 442-1400
SIC 2841 2842 2843 2844

▲ STEPAN CO p 1386
22 W Frontage Rd, Northfield IL 60093
Tel (847) 446-7500
SIC 2843 2821 2087 2865

METALWORKING LUBRICANTS CO p 953
25 W Silverdome Indus Par, Pontiac MI 48342
Tel (248) 332-3500
SIC 5172 2869 2843 2992

LANXESS SYBRON CHEMICALS INC p 844
200 Birmingham Rd, Birmingham NJ 08011
Tel (609) 893-1100 SIC 2843 2899 3589

ICI AMERICA INC p 727
10 Finderne Ave, Bridgewater NJ 08807
Tel (908) 203-2800
SIC 2821 3081 2869 2843 2865

ICI AMERICAN HOLDINGS LLC p 727
10 Finderne Ave, Bridgewater NJ 08807
Tel (908) 203-2800
SIC 2851 2821 3081 2869 2843 2865

BASF CORP p 158
100 Park Ave, Florham Park NJ 07932
Tel (973) 245-6000
SIC 2869 2819 2899 2843 2834 2879

BASFIN CORP p 158
100 Campus Dr Ste 301, Florham Park NJ 07932
Tel (973) 245-6000
SIC 2869 2819 2899 2843 2879 2834

G HOLDINGS INC p 587
1 Campus Dr, Parsippany NJ 07054
Tel (973) 628-3000 SIC 2869 2843 3295

G-I HOLDINGS INC p 587
1361 Alps Rd, Wayne NJ 07470
Tel (973) 628-3000 SIC 2869 2843 3295

■ INTERNATIONAL SPECIALTY PRODUCTS INC p 757
1361 Alps Rd, Wayne NJ 07470
Tel (859) 815-3333
SIC 2869 2821 2843 2842 2899

PIEDMONT CHEMICAL INDUSTRIES INC p 1146
331 Burton Ave, High Point NC 27262
Tel (336) 885-5131 SIC 2841 2843

▲ CHEMTURA CORP p 294
1818 Market St Ste 3700, Philadelphia PA 19103
Tel (215) 446-3911
SIC 2869 2843 2821 2911 2899 2842

MERIDIAN INDUSTRIES INC p 949
735 N Water St Ste 630, Milwaukee WI 53202
Tel (414) 224-0610
SIC 3069 2843 2269 7389

SIC 2844 Perfumes, Cosmetics & Toilet Preparations

DIAL CORP p 436
7201 E Henkel Way, Scottsdale AZ 85255
Tel (480) 754-3425
SIC 2841 2844 2842 2032 2013

HANNAS CANDLE CO p 658
2700 S Armstrong Ave, Fayetteville AR 72701
Tel (479) 443-5467 SIC 3999 2844 5999

DERMALOGICA LLC p 431
1535 Beachey Pl, Carson CA 90746
Tel (310) 900-4000 SIC 2844

THIBIANT INTERNATIONAL INC p 1447
20320 Prairie St, Chatsworth CA 91311
Tel (818) 709-1345 SIC 2844

AMERICAN INTERNATIONAL INDUSTRIES p 75
2220 Gaspar Ave, Commerce CA 90040
Tel (323) 728-2999 SIC 5122 2844

■ O P I PRODUCTS INC p 1070
13034 Saticoy St, North Hollywood CA 91605
Tel (818) 759-8688 SIC 5087 2844

▲ CLOROX CO p 327
1221 Broadway Ste 1300, Oakland CA 94612
Tel (510) 271-7000
SIC 2842 2673 2035 2844 2879

BEAUTY 21 COSMETICS INC p 166
2021 S Archibald Ave, Ontario CA 91761
Tel (909) 945-2220 SIC 5122 2844

DEN-MAT CORP p 428
236 S Broadway St, Orcutt CA 93455
Tel (805) 922-8491 SIC 2844 3843

JESSICA MCCLINTOCK INC p 783
2307 Broadway St, San Francisco CA 94115
Tel (415) 553-8200 SIC 2361 2335 2844

SHADOW HOLDINGS LLC p 1310
26455 Ruether Ave, Santa Clarita CA 91350
Tel (661) 252-3807 SIC 2844

MARKWINS INTERNATIONAL CORP p 909
22067 Ferrero, Walnut CA 91789
Tel (909) 595-8898 SIC 2844

■ WELLA CORP p 1589
6109 De Soto Ave, Woodland Hills CA 91367
Tel (818) 999-5112 SIC 2844

■ BEAUTYGE BRANDS USA INC p 166
1515 Wazee St Ste 200, Denver CO 80202
Tel (800) 598-2739 SIC 5122 2844

CCL INDUSTRIES CORP p 270
15 Controls Dr, Shelton CT 06484
Tel (203) 926-1253
SIC 2759 2992 3411 2819 2844

■ EDGEWELL PERSONAL CARE BRANDS LLC p 477
6 Research Dr, Shelton CT 06484
Tel (203) 944-5500 SIC 3421 2844 2676

■ PLAYTEX PRODUCTS LLC p 1155
6 Research Dr Ste 400, Shelton CT 06484
Tel (203) 944-5500
SIC 2676 3069 2844 3842

ALBEA THOMASTON INC p 46
60 Electric Ave, Thomaston CT 06787
Tel (860) 283-2000 SIC 2844

BEIERSDORF INC p 168
45 Danbury Rd, Wilton CT 06897
Tel (203) 563-5800 SIC 2844

BEIERSDORF NORTH AMERICA INC p 169
45 Danbury Rd, Wilton CT 06897
Tel (203) 563-5800
SIC 2844 5122 3842 2841 2672

CRABTREE & EVELYN LTD p 388
102 Peake Brook Rd, Woodstock CT 06281
Tel (800) 272-2873 SIC 5122 5149 2844

■ PLAYTEX MANUFACTURING INC p 1155
50 N Dupont Hwy, Dover DE 19901
Tel (302) 678-6000 SIC 2676 2844 2842

GLAXOSMITHKLINE HOLDINGS (AMERICAS) INC p 614
1105 N Market St, Wilmington DE 19801
Tel (302) 656-5280
SIC 2834 2836 2833 2844 8071

PRODUCT QUEST MANUFACTURING LLC p 1179
330 Carswell Ave, Daytona Beach FL 32117
Tel (386) 239-8787 SIC 2844

GREAT AMERICAN BEAUTY INC p 633
124 N Swinton Ave, Delray Beach FL 33444
Tel (561) 496-2730 SIC 5122 2844

ROUX LABORATORIES INC p 1253
5344 Overmyer Dr, Jacksonville FL 32254
Tel (904) 366-2602 SIC 2844

▲ TUPPERWARE BRANDS CORP p 1492
14901 S Orange Blossom Tr, Orlando FL 32837
Tel (407) 826-5050 SIC 3089 2844

■ ELIZABETH ARDEN INC p 487
880 Sw 145th Ave Ste 200, Pembroke Pines FL 33027
Tel (954) 364-6900 SIC 2844

MELALEUCA INC p 940
4609 W 65th S, Idaho Falls ID 83402
Tel (208) 522-0700
SIC 2833 5122 2844 2841 2834

NAMASTE LABORATORIES LLC p 1007
310 S Racine Ave Fl 8, Chicago IL 60607
Tel (708) 824-1393 SIC 2844

KIK CUSTOM PRODUCTS INC p 817
1 W Hegeler Ln, Danville IL 61832
Tel (217) 442-1400
SIC 2841 2842 2843 2844

▲ VERA BRADLEY INC p 1549
12420 Stonebridge Rd, Roanoke IN 46783
Tel (877) 708-8372
SIC 3171 3111 2392 2844

FULLER BRUSH CO INC p 584
1 Fuller Way, Great Bend KS 67530
Tel (620) 792-1711 SIC 2842 2844 3991

■ NOXELL CORP p 1064
11050 York Rd, Hunt Valley MD 21030
Tel (410) 785-7300 SIC 2844

■ GILLETTE CO p 612
1 Gillette Park, Boston MA 02127
Tel (617) 421-7000
SIC 3421 3634 2844 3951 2899

■ AVEDA CORP p 136
4000 Pheasant Ridge Dr Ne, Blaine MN 55449
Tel (763) 783-4250 SIC 2844 7231

APEX INTERNATIONAL MFG INC p 96
134 Columbia Ct, Chaska MN 55318
Tel (952) 227-3000 SIC 2844

JACOBS INDUSTRIES INC p 775
8096 Excelsior Blvd, Hopkins MN 55343
Tel (612) 339-9500
SIC 2841 2087 2099 2844 5084 6794

COLOPLAST CORP p 338
1601 W River Rd, Minneapolis MN 55411
Tel (612) 337-7800 SIC 3842 2844 5047

▲ EDGEWELL PERSONAL CARE CO p 477
1350 Timberlake Manor Pkwy, Chesterfield MO 63017
Tel (314) 594-1900
SIC 3421 2844 2676 3069

■ EDGEWELL PERSONAL CARE LLC p 478
1350 Timberlake Mano, Chesterfield MO 63017
Tel (314) 594-1900 SIC 2844

VI-JON INC p 1554
8515 Page Ave, Saint Louis MO 63114
Tel (314) 427-1000 SIC 2869 2844

VJCS HOLDINGS INC p 1563
8515 Page Ave, Saint Louis MO 63114
Tel (314) 427-1000 SIC 6719 2844

MARIANNA INDUSTRIES INC p 906
11222 I St Ste A, Omaha NE 68137
Tel (402) 593-0211 SIC 5122 2844 7231

NU-WORLD CORP p 1066
300 Milik St, Carteret NJ 07008
Tel (732) 541-6300 SIC 2844

SHISEIDO AMERICA INC p 1317
366 Prnicton Hightstown Rd, East Windsor NJ 08520
Tel (609) 371-5800 SIC 5122 2844

ALBERTO-CULVER CO p 46
800 Sylvan Ave, Englewood Cliffs NJ 07632
Tel (708) 681-2668 SIC 2844 2842 2099

CONOPCO INC p 358
700 Sylvan Ave, Englewood Cliffs NJ 07632
Tel (201) 894-2727
SIC 2035 2038 2086 2024 2844 2841

ET BROWNE DRUG CO INC p 511
440 Sylvan Ave, Englewood Cliffs NJ 07632
Tel (201) 894-9020 SIC 2844

UNILEVER MANUFACTURING (US) INC p 1503
800 Sylvan Ave, Englewood Cliffs NJ 07632
Tel (800) 298-5018 SIC 2844 2099

UNILEVER UNITED STATES INC p 1503
700 Sylvan Ave, Englewood Cliffs NJ 07632
Tel (201) 894-4000
SIC 2035 2086 2024 2038 2844 2841

▲ CHURCH & DWIGHT CO INC p 305
500 Charles Ewing Blvd, Ewing NJ 08628
Tel (609) 806-1200
SIC 2841 2812 2842 2844 2819

MYCONE DENTAL SUPPLY CO INC p 1004
480 S Democrat Rd, Gibbstown NJ 08027
Tel (856) 663-4700 SIC 5047 3843 2844

CEI HOLDINGS INC p 273
2182 State Route 35, Holmdel NJ 07733
Tel (732) 888-7788
SIC 2844 7389 4225 5122

COSMETIC ESSENCE LLC p 373
2182 Hwy 35, Holmdel NJ 07733
Tel (732) 888-7788 SIC 2844 7389 4225

▲ MERCK & CO INC p 945
2000 Galloping Hill Rd, Kenilworth NJ 07033
Tel (908) 740-4000
SIC 2834 2836 2844 5122

RENAISSANCE LAKEWOOD LLC p 1223
1200 Paco Way, Lakewood NJ 08701
Tel (732) 367-9000 SIC 2834 2844 2675

UNGERER INDUSTRIES INC p 1502
4 Bridgewater Ln, Lincoln Park NJ 07035
Tel (973) 628-0600 SIC 2899 2844 2087

■ SYSCO GUEST SUPPLY LLC p 1417
4301 Us Highway 1 Ste 300, Monmouth Junction NJ 08852
Tel (609) 514-9696
SIC 5122 2844 5131 5139 7011 8741

▲ JOHNSON & JOHNSON p 790
1 Johnson And Johnson Plz, New Brunswick NJ 08933
Tel (732) 524-0400
SIC 2676 2844 3841 3842 2834

GENTEK INC p 604
90 E Halsey Rd Ste 301, Parsippany NJ 07054
Tel (973) 515-0900
SIC 2869 2819 2844 3714 3496

■ ARMKEL LLC p 111
469 N Harrison St, Princeton NJ 08540
Tel (609) 683-5900 SIC 2844 2835

TAKASAGO INTERNATIONAL CORP (USA) p 1421
4 Volvo Dr, Rockleigh NJ 07647
Tel (201) 767-9001 SIC 2844

UNIVERSAL PACKAGING SYSTEMS INC p 1517
6080 Jericho Tpke, Commack NY 11725
Tel (631) 543-2277
SIC 2844 7389 3565 2671

MARIETTA CORP p 906
37 Huntington St, Cortland NY 13045
Tel (607) 753-6746 SIC 2844 2834 2541

MANA PRODUCTS INC p 900
3202 Queens Blvd Fl 6, Long Island City NY 11101
Tel (718) 361-2550 SIC 2844 5122

▲ HAIN CELESTIAL GROUP INC p 653
1111 Marcus Ave Ste 100, New Hyde Park NY 11042
Tel (516) 587-5000
SIC 2023 2034 2096 2086 2844

VERLA INTERNATIONAL LTD p 1551
463 Temple Hill Rd, New Windsor NY 12553
Tel (845) 561-2440 SIC 2844

■ ARAMIS INC p 102
767 5th Ave, New York NY 10153
Tel (212) 572-4200 SIC 5122 2844

▲ AVON PRODUCTS INC p 139
777 3rd Ave, New York NY 10017
Tel (212) 282-5000
SIC 2844 3961 5961 5023 5137

CHANEL INC p 288
9 W 57th St Fl 44, New York NY 10019
Tel (212) 688-5055
SIC 5632 2844 5122 5944 5961 5999

▲ COLGATE-PALMOLIVE CO p 336
300 Park Ave Fl 5, New York NY 10022
Tel (212) 310-2000
SIC 2844 3991 2841 2842 2047

■ COTY INC p 374
350 5th Ave Ste 2700, New York NY 10118
Tel (212) 389-7300 SIC 2844

■ COTY US LLC p 374
350 5th Ave Fl C1700, New York NY 10118
Tel (212) 389-7000 SIC 2844

▲ ESTEE LAUDER COMPANIES INC p 511
767 5th Ave Fl 37, New York NY 10153
Tel (212) 572-4200 SIC 2844

■ ESTEE LAUDER INC p 511
767 5th Ave Fl 37, New York NY 10153
Tel (212) 572-4200 SIC 2844 5999

■ ESTEE LAUDER INTERNATIONAL INC p 511
767 5th Ave Bsmt 1, New York NY 10153
Tel (212) 572-4200 SIC 2844

■ HFC PRESTIGE INTERNATIONAL US LLC p 689
350 5th Ave, New York NY 10118
Tel (212) 389-7800
SIC 2844 2676 3421 2842 2841

▲ **INTER PARFUMS INC** p 751
551 5th Ave, New York NY 10176
Tel (212) 983-2640 SIC 2844

▲ **INTERNATIONAL FLAVORS & FRAGRANCES INC** p 755
521 W 57th St, New York NY 10019
Tel (212) 765-5500 SIC 2869 2844 2087

LOREAL USA INC p 878
10 Hudson Yards Fl 30, New York NY 10001
Tel (212) 818-1500 SIC 5122 2844

MACANDREWS & FORBES INC p 891
38 E 63rd St, New York NY 10065
Tel (212) 688-9000
SIC 2844 2087 2121 7819 2721 2731

MAYBELLINE INC p 923
575 5th Ave Bsmt Fl, New York NY 10017
Tel (212) 885-1310 SIC 2844 2841

MOET HENNESSY USA INC p 982
85 10th Ave Fl 2, New York NY 10011
Tel (212) 888-7575
SIC 0172 2844 6153 5182 5122

■ **NEW AVON LLC** p 1029
777 3rd Ave Fl 8, New York NY 10017
Tel (212) 282-8500 SIC 2844 5122 5999

REV HOLDINGS INC p 1229
466 Lexington Ave Fl 21, New York NY 10017
Tel (212) 527-4000
SIC 2844 3421 5122 5199 5999

■ **REVLON CONSUMER PRODUCTS CORP** p 1229
1 New York Plz, New York NY 10004
Tel (212) 527-4000 SIC 2844 3421

REVLON HOLDINGS INC p 1229
237 Park Ave, New York NY 10017
Tel (212) 527-4000
SIC 2844 3421 5122 5199 5999

▲ **REVLON INC** p 1229
1 New York Plz, New York NY 10004
Tel (212) 527-4000 SIC 2844

■ **REVLON REAL ESTATE CORP** p 1229
466 Lexington Ave Fl 13, New York NY 10017
Tel (212) 527-4000
SIC 5122 2844 3421 5199 5999

RGI GROUP INC p 1231
625 Madison Ave Frnt 4, New York NY 10022
Tel (212) 527-4000
SIC 2844 3421 5122 5199 5999

SHISEIDO AMERICAS CORP p 1317
900 3rd Ave Fl 15, New York NY 10022
Tel (212) 805-2300 SIC 2844 5122

KLG USA LLC p 823
20 W King St, Port Jervis NY 12771
Tel (845) 856-5311 SIC 2844 7389 2834

KOLMAR LABORATORIES INC p 827
20 W King St, Port Jervis NY 12771
Tel (845) 856-5311 SIC 2844

AMERICAN FIBER & FINISHING INC p 72
225 N Depot St, Albemarle NC 28001
Tel (704) 983-6102
SIC 2211 3842 2844 2392

■ **BURTS BEES INC** p 229
210 W Pettigrew St, Durham NC 27701
Tel (919) 998-5200 SIC 2844 5122 5087

PARKDALE MILLS INC p 1116
531 Cotton Blossom Cir, Gastonia NC 28054
Tel (704) 864-8761 SIC 2281 2844 2241

US COTTON LLC p 1531
531 Cotton Blossom Cir, Gastonia NC 28054
Tel (216) 676-6400 SIC 2844 2241

EI LLC p 481
2865 N Cannon Blvd, Kannapolis NC 28083
Tel (704) 939-4300 SIC 2834 2844

ALBAAD USA INC p 45
129 S Technology Dr, Reidsville NC 27320
Tel (336) 634-0091 SIC 2844

■ **PHILOSOPHY INC** p 1144
1400 Broadway Rd, Sanford NC 27332
Tel (602) 794-8500 SIC 5122 2844

BODY SHOP INC p 197
5036 One World Way, Wake Forest NC 27587
Tel (919) 554-4900 SIC 5999 6794 2844

GOJO INDUSTRIES INC p 620
1 Gojo Plz Ste 500, Akron OH 44311
Tel (330) 255-6000 SIC 2842 3586 2844

LUMINEX HOME DECOR & FRAGRANCE HOLDING CORP p 885
10521 Millington Ct, Blue Ash OH 45242
Tel (513) 563-1113 SIC 5023 2844

KAO USA INC p 803
2535 Spring Grove Ave, Cincinnati OH 45214
Tel (513) 421-1400 SIC 2844 2841

▲ **PROCTER & GAMBLE CO** p 1179
1 Procter And Gamble Plz, Cincinnati OH 45202
Tel (513) 983-1100
SIC 2844 2676 3421 2842 2841

■ **PROCTER & GAMBLE FAR EAST INC** p 1179
1 Procter And Gamble Plz, Cincinnati OH 45202
Tel (513) 983-1100 SIC 2842 2844 2676

■ **PROCTER & GAMBLE MANUFACTURING CO** p 1179
1 Procter And Gamble Plz, Cincinnati OH 45202
Tel (513) 983-1100
SIC 2841 2079 2099 2844 2045

■ **BATH & BODY WORKS LLC** p 159
7 Limited Pkwy E, Reynoldsburg OH 43068
Tel (614) 856-6000 SIC 5999 2844

■ **ABBVIE BIOTECHNOLOGY LTD** p 10
Road No 2 Km 59 2, Barceloneta PR 00617
Tel (787) 846-3500
SIC 2834 2844 2835 3841 3826

OLAY CO INC p 1080
Km 2 Hm 3 Rr 735, Cayey PR 00736
Tel (787) 738-2191 SIC 2844

CHATTEM INC p 292
1715 W 38th St, Chattanooga TN 37409
Tel (423) 821-4571
SIC 2834 2844 2023 5963

TEAM TECHNOLOGIES INC p 1430
5949 Commerce Blvd, Morristown TN 37814
Tel (423) 587-2199
SIC 2844 5122 5719 3991

SCHWAN COSMETICS USA INC p 1291
3202 Elam Farms Pkwy, Murfreesboro TN 37127
Tel (931) 359-6253 SIC 2844

KIMBERLAND SWAN HOLDINGS INC p 818
1 Swan Dr, Smyrna TN 37167
Tel (615) 459-8900 SIC 2844

FRUIT OF EARTH INC p 582
3101 High Rver Rd Ste 175, Fort Worth TX 76155
Tel (817) 510-1600 SIC 5122 2844

FAROUK SYSTEMS INC p 530
880 E Richey Rd, Houston TX 77073
Tel (281) 876-2000 SIC 2844

SPFM LP p 1358
4310 West Ave, San Antonio TX 78213
Tel (210) 805-8931
SIC 5122 5149 2834 2833 2841 2844

▲ **NU SKIN ENTERPRISES INC** p 1066
75 W Center St, Provo UT 84601
Tel (801) 345-1000 SIC 2844 5122

■ **NU SKIN INTERNATIONAL INC** p 1066
75 W Center St, Provo UT 84601
Tel (801) 345-1000 SIC 2844

S C JOHNSON & SON INC p 1262
1525 Howe St, Racine WI 53403
Tel (262) 260-2000
SIC 2842 2844 2879 2865 7342 7349

SIC 2851 Paints, Varnishes, Lacquers, Enamels

MOBILE PAINT MANUFACTURING CO OF DELAWARE INC p 980
4775 Hamilton Blvd, Theodore AL 36582
Tel (251) 443-6110 SIC 2851 5198 5231

VISTA PAINT CORP p 1562
2020 E Orangethorpe Ave, Fullerton CA 92831
Tel (714) 680-3800 SIC 5231 2851

DURA COAT PRODUCTS INC p 462
5361 Via Ricardo, Riverside CA 92509
Tel (951) 341-6500 SIC 3479 2851

KELLY-MOORE PAINT CO INC p 809
987 Commercial St, San Carlos CA 94070
Tel (650) 592-8337 SIC 2851

▲ **WD-40 CO** p 1585
1061 Cudahy Pl, San Diego CA 92110
Tel (619) 275-1400 SIC 2992 2851

■ **BEHR PAINT CORP** p 168
3400 W Segerstrom Ave, Santa Ana CA 92704
Tel (714) 545-7101 SIC 2851

■ **BEHR PROCESS CORP** p 168
3400 W Segerstrom Ave, Santa Ana CA 92704
Tel (714) 545-7101 SIC 2851

■ **SIERRACIN CORP** p 1321
12780 San Fernando Rd, Sylmar CA 91342
Tel (818) 741-1656 SIC 2851

DUNN-EDWARDS CORP p 461
4885 E 52nd Pl, Vernon CA 90058
Tel (323) 771-3330 SIC 2851 5231

BONAKEMI USA INC p 199
2550 S Parker Rd Ste 600, Aurora CO 80014
Tel (303) 371-1411
SIC 5198 5169 5023 2851

BYK USA INC p 231
524 S Cherry St, Wallingford CT 06492
Tel (203) 265-2086 SIC 2851

GARDNER-GIBSON INC p 592
4161 E 7th Ave, Tampa FL 33605
Tel (813) 248-2101 SIC 2951 2851 2952

■ **TCI INC** p 1428
734 Dixon Dr, Ellaville GA 31806
Tel (229) 937-5411 SIC 2851

AKZO NOBEL INC p 42
525 W Van Buren St Fl 16, Chicago IL 60607
Tel (312) 544-7000
SIC 2869 2851 2834 3841 3826 2819

LAWTER INC p 848
200 N La Salle St # 2600, Chicago IL 60601
Tel (312) 662-5700 SIC 2899 2851

MORTON INTERNATIONAL LLC p 991
123 N Wacker Dr Ste 2400, Chicago IL 60606
Tel (312) 807-2696
SIC 2891 2851 2822 1479 2899

MORTON SALT INC p 991
123 N Wacker Dr Fl 24, Chicago IL 60606
Tel (800) 725-8847
SIC 2891 2851 2822 1479 2899

TRUE VALUE CO p 1486
8600 W Bryn Mawr Ave 100s, Chicago IL 60631
Tel (773) 695-5000 SIC 5072 2851 3991

NB COATINGS INC p 1021
2701 E 170th St, Lansing IL 60438
Tel (800) 323-3224 SIC 2851 2865

■ **RUST-OLEUM CORP** p 1260
11 E Hawthorn Pkwy, Vernon Hills IL 60061
Tel (847) 367-7700
SIC 2891 2899 2816 2842 2851

RED SPOT PAINT & VARNISH CO INC p 1216
1107 E Louisiana St, Evansville IN 47711
Tel (812) 428-9100 SIC 2851

DIAMOND-VOGEL PAINT CO p 437
1110 Albany Pl Se, Orange City IA 51041
Tel (712) 737-8880 SIC 2851 5231

VOGEL PAINT & WAX CO INC p 1564
1110 Albany Pl Se, Orange City IA 51041
Tel (712) 737-4993 SIC 2851 5198

VOGEL PAINT INC p 1564
1110 Albany Pl Se, Orange City IA 51041
Tel (712) 737-8880 SIC 2851 8741

■ **ASHLAND LLC** p 117
50 E Rivercenter Blvd # 1600, Covington KY 41011
Tel (859) 815-3333
SIC 2899 2851 2821 2911 5169 7549

A W CHESTERTON CO p 7
860 Salem St, Groveland MA 01834
Tel (781) 438-7000
SIC 3053 2851 2992 2891 5169

BEMIS ASSOCIATES INC p 171
1 Bemis Way, Shirley MA 01464
Tel (978) 425-6761 SIC 2891 2851 3479

ND INDUSTRIES INC p 1022
1000 N Crooks Rd, Clawson MI 48017
Tel (248) 288-0000
SIC 3452 2851 5072 2891 3479

EFTEC NORTH AMERICA LLC p 481
31601 Research Park Dr, Madison Heights MI 48071
Tel (248) 526-4565
SIC 2891 8731 3296 2899 2851

ROLLED ALLOYS INC p 1247
125 W Sterns Rd, Temperance MI 48182
Tel (800) 521-0332
SIC 5051 3369 3341 3317 2899 2851

HIRSHFIELDS INC p 696
725 2nd Ave N Ste 1, Minneapolis MN 55405
Tel (612) 377-3910 SIC 5198 5231 2851

▲ **VALSPAR CORP** p 1542
1101 S 3rd St, Minneapolis MN 55415
Tel (612) 851-7000 SIC 2851

TNEMEC CO INC p 1458
6800 Corporate Dr, Kansas City MO 64120
Tel (816) 483-3400 SIC 2851

■ **CARBOLINE CO** p 252
2150 Schuetz Rd, Saint Louis MO 63146
Tel (314) 644-1000 SIC 2851

ICI AMERICAN HOLDINGS LLC p 727
10 Finderne Ave, Bridgewater NJ 08807
Tel (908) 203-2800
SIC 2851 2821 3081 2869 2843 2865

ELEMENTIS SPECIALTIES INC p 486
469 Old Trenton Rd, East Windsor NJ 08512
Tel (609) 443-2000
SIC 2851 8731 2899 2865 2816

SIKA CORP p 1322
201 Polito Ave, Lyndhurst NJ 07071
Tel (201) 933-8800
SIC 2891 2899 2851 2821 3272

■ **STONCOR GROUP INC** p 1391
1000 E Park Ave, Maple Shade NJ 08052
Tel (800) 257-7953 SIC 2851

■ **BENJAMIN MOORE & CO** p 173
101 Paragon Dr, Montvale NJ 07645
Tel (201) 573-9600 SIC 2851 5231

GDB INTERNATIONAL INC p 595
1 Home News Row, New Brunswick NJ 08901
Tel (732) 246-3001
SIC 2851 5162 5111 5093

■ **CHEMETALL US INC** p 293
675 Central Ave, New Providence NJ 07974
Tel (908) 464-6900 SIC 2842 2899 2851

EVONIK CORP p 515
299 Jefferson Rd, Parsippany NJ 07054
Tel (973) 929-8000
SIC 2819 2869 2851 2816

NIPPON PAINT (USA) INC p 1044
300 Frank W Burr Blvd # 10, Teaneck NJ 07666
Tel (201) 692-1111 SIC 2851

SUPERIOR PRINTING INK CO INC p 1407
100 North St, Teterboro NJ 07608
Tel (201) 478-5600 SIC 2893 2851

MINWAX GROUP INC p 974
10 Montinview Rd Ste N300, Upper Saddle River NJ 07458
Tel (201) 818-7500 SIC 2851

CYTEC INDUSTRIES INC p 406
5 Garret Mountain Plz, Woodland Park NJ 07424
Tel (973) 357-3100
SIC 2899 2821 2672 2851 2823 2819

FOUGERA PHARMACEUTICALS INC p 571
60 Baylis Rd, Melville NY 11747
Tel (631) 454-7677
SIC 2834 2851 2821 3479 3829

SI GROUP INC p 1319
2750 Balltown Rd, Schenectady NY 12309
Tel (518) 347-4200 SIC 2865 3087 2851

LORD CORP p 878
111 Lord Dr, Cary NC 27511
Tel (877) 275-5673
SIC 2891 3724 3728 2851

I KESTREL ACQUISITION CORP p 725
1035 Swabia Ct, Durham NC 27703
Tel (919) 990-7500
SIC 2821 2822 2869 2899 2891 2851

REICHHOLD LIQUIDATION INC p 1220
1035 Swabia Ct, Durham NC 27703
Tel (919) 990-7500
SIC 2821 2822 2869 2899 2891 2851

REICHHOLD LLC 2 p 1220
1035 Swabia Ct, Durham NC 27703
Tel (919) 990-7500 SIC 2821 2851

■ **RPM WOOD FINISHES GROUP INC** p 1255
2220 Hwy 70 Se Ste 100, Hickory NC 28602
Tel (828) 261-0325 SIC 2851

TRIMACO LLC p 1480
2300 Gateway Centre Blvd # 200, Morrisville NC 27560
Tel (919) 674-3476
SIC 2851 2621 2672 2679 2394

ENNIS PAINT INC p 500
115 Todd Ct, Thomasville NC 27360
Tel (800) 331-8118 SIC 2851 3953

■ **TREMCO INC** p 1476
3735 Green Rd, Beachwood OH 44122
Tel (216) 292-5000
SIC 2891 2952 1761 1752 2851 2842

BASF CONSTRUCTION CHEMICALS LLC p 158
23700 Chagrin Blvd, Cleveland OH 44122
Tel (216) 831-5500 SIC 2899 2851 1799

■ **COMEX NORTH AMERICA INC** p 344
101 W Prospect Ave # 1020, Cleveland OH 44115
Tel (303) 307-2100
SIC 2851 8742 5198 5231

GARLAND CO INC p 592
3800 E 91st St, Cleveland OH 44105
Tel (216) 641-7500 SIC 2952 2851

■ **PPG INDUSTRIES OHIO INC** p 1166
3800 W 143rd St, Cleveland OH 44111
Tel (216) 671-0050 SIC 2851

■ **SHERWIN-WILLIAMS AUTOMOTIVE FINISHES CORP** p 1316
4440 Warrensville Ctr Rd, Cleveland OH 44128
Tel (216) 332-8330 SIC 5231 2851

▲ **SHERWIN-WILLIAMS CO** p 1316
101 W Prospect Ave # 1020, Cleveland OH 44115
Tel (216) 566-2000 SIC 5231 2851

AMERICHEM INC p 81
2000 Americhem Way, Cuyahoga Falls OH 44221
Tel (330) 929-4213
SIC 2865 2851 2819 2816

▲ **FERRO CORP** p 538
6060 Parkland Blvd # 250, Mayfield Heights OH 44124
Tel (216) 875-5600
SIC 3479 2816 2851 3399 2821 2834

■ **REPUBLIC POWDERED METALS INC** p 1225
2628 Pearl Rd, Medina OH 44256
Tel (330) 225-3192
SIC 2851 2891 3069 2899 2865 2842

▲ **RPM INTERNATIONAL INC** p 1255
2628 Pearl Rd, Medina OH 44256
Tel (330) 273-5090
SIC 2851 2891 3069 2899 2865 2842

THORWORKS INDUSTRIES INC p 1450
2520 Campbell St, Sandusky OH 44870
Tel (419) 626-4375
SIC 2851 3531 2952 2951 2891 2816

AKZO NOBEL COATINGS INC p 42
8220 Mohawk Dr, Strongsville OH 44136
Tel (440) 297-5100 SIC 2851 5198 2821

AKZO NOBEL PAINTS LLC p 42
8381 Pearl Rd, Strongsville OH 44136
Tel (440) 297-8000 SIC 2851 2891

WILLAMETTE VALLEY CO p 1609
1075 Arrowsmith St, Eugene OR 97402
Tel (541) 484-9621
SIC 5085 2851 2891 5169

MILLER PAINT CO INC p 971
12812 Ne Whitaker Way, Portland OR 97230
Tel (503) 255-0190 SIC 2851 5231

RODDA PAINT CO p 1246
6107 N Marine Dr Ste 3, Portland OR 97203
Tel (503) 521-4300
SIC 2851 5198 5023 5231 5719

ALCO INDUSTRIES INC p 47
1275 Glenlivet Dr Ste 100, Allentown PA 18106
Tel (610) 666-0930
SIC 2879 2851 2842 2873

■ **AXALTA COATING SYSTEMS LLC** p 139
2001 Market St Fl 36a, Philadelphia PA 19103
Tel (215) 255-7932 SIC 2851 3479

▲ **AXALTA COATING SYSTEMS LTD** p 139
2001 Market St Ste 3600, Philadelphia PA 19103
Tel (855) 547-1461 SIC 2851

■ **ROHM AND HAAS CO** p 1246
100 N Independence Mall W, Philadelphia PA 19106
Tel (215) 592-3000
SIC 2819 2851 2891 2899

■ **PPG ARCHITECTURAL FINISHES INC** p 1166
1 Ppg Pl, Pittsburgh PA 15272
Tel (412) 434-3131 SIC 2851 2891

▲ **PPG INDUSTRIES INC** p 1166
1 Ppg Pl, Pittsburgh PA 15272
Tel (412) 434-3131
SIC 2851 3211 3231 3229 2812 2821

QUEST SPECIALTY CHEMICALS INC p 1199
225 Sven Farms Dr Ste 204, Charleston SC 29492
Tel (800) 966-7580 SIC 2851

WIKOFF COLOR CORP p 1608
1886 Merritt Rd, Fort Mill SC 29715
Tel (803) 548-2210 SIC 2893 2851

WM BARR & CO INC p 1620
6750 Lenox Center Ct # 200, Memphis TN 38115
Tel (901) 775-0100 SIC 2851

HEMPEL (USA) INC p 682
600 Conroe Park North Dr, Conroe TX 77303
Tel (936) 523-6000 SIC 2851

■ **AXALTA POWDER COATING SYSTEMS USA INC** p 139
9800 Genard Rd, Houston TX 77041
Tel (800) 247-3886 SIC 2851

INTERNATIONAL PAINT LLC p 756
6001 Antoine Dr, Houston TX 77091
Tel (713) 682-1711 SIC 2851

SIC 2861 Gum & Wood Chemicals

■ **KINGSFORD PRODUCTS CO LLC** p 821
1221 Broadway Ste 1300, Oakland CA 94612
Tel (510) 271-7000
SIC 2861 2099 2035 2033 2879

ARIZONA CHEMICAL CO LLC p 108
4600 Touchton Rd E # 1500, Jacksonville FL 32246
Tel (904) 928-8700 SIC 2861 2911

■ **AXIALL CORP** p 140
1000 Abernathy Rd # 1200, Atlanta GA 30328
Tel (770) 395-4500
SIC 2812 2821 2865 2861 2873

PINOVA INC p 1150
2801 Cook St, Brunswick GA 31520
Tel (888) 807-2958 SIC 2861

LINCOLNWAY ENERGY LLC p 868
59511 Lincoln Hwy, Nevada IA 50201
Tel (515) 232-1010 SIC 2869 2861

▲ **OCIP HOLDING LLC** p 1074
660 Madison Ave Fl 19, New York NY 10065
Tel (646) 589-6180 SIC 2861 2873

RESURGENCE ASSET MANAGEMENT LLC p 1228
1185 Av Of The Amer Fl 18, New York NY 10036
Tel (212) 710-5001
SIC 6282 2865 2821 2869 2861 2819

■ **OCI PARTNERS LP** p 1073
5470 N Twin City Hwy, Nederland TX 77627
Tel (409) 723-1900 SIC 2861 2873

■ WESTROCK MWV LLC p 1603
501 S 5th St, Richmond VA 23219
Tel (804) 444-1000
SIC 2631 2671 2678 2677 2861 2611

SIC 2865 Cyclic-Crudes, Intermediates, Dyes & Org Pigments

INEOS AMERICAS LLC p 740
7770 Rangeline Rd, Theodore AL 36582
Tel (251) 443-3000 SIC 2869 2865

PLASTIC SERVICES AND PRODUCTS p 1155
12243 Branford St, Sun Valley CA 91352
Tel (818) 896-1101
SIC 3086 3674 2865 2816 3296 2819

PMC GLOBAL INC p 1157
12243 Branford St, Sun Valley CA 91352
Tel (818) 896-1101
SIC 3086 3674 2865 2816 3296 2819

▲ E I DU PONT DE NEMOURS AND CO p 466
974 Centre Rd, Wilmington DE 19805
Tel (302) 774-1000
SIC 2879 2824 2865 2821 2834

■ AXIALL CORP p 140
1000 Abernathy Rd # 1200, Atlanta GA 30328
Tel (770) 395-4500
SIC 2812 2821 2865 2861 2873

STANDRIDGE COLOR CORP p 1376
1196 E Hightower Trl, Social Circle GA 30025
Tel (770) 464-3362 SIC 2865 2816 3083

NB COATINGS INC p 1021
2701 E 170th St, Lansing IL 60438
Tel (800) 323-3224 SIC 2851 2865

BP AMOCO CHEMICAL CO p 205
150 W Warrenville Rd, Naperville IL 60563
Tel (630) 420-5111
SIC 2221 2821 2869 2819 2865

▲ STEPAN CO p 1386
22 W Frontage Rd, Northfield IL 60093
Tel (847) 446-7500
SIC 2843 2821 2087 2865

VERTELLUS HEALTH & SPECIALTY PRODUCTS LLC p 1552
201 N Illinois St # 1800, Indianapolis IN 46204
Tel (317) 247-8141 SIC 2865

VERTELLUS SPECIALTIES HOLDINGS CORP p 1552
201 N Illinois St # 1800, Indianapolis IN 46204
Tel (317) 247-8141 SIC 2865 6719

VSI LIQUIDATING INC p 1566
201 N Illinois St # 1800, Indianapolis IN 46204
Tel (317) 247-8141 SIC 2865

■ CAMBREX CHARLES CITY INC p 244
1205 11th St, Charles City IA 50616
Tel (641) 257-1000
SIC 2834 2899 2865 2048

FLINT GROUP US LLC p 557
14909 N Beck Rd, Plymouth MI 48170
Tel (734) 781-4600 SIC 2865 2893

ICI AMERICA INC p 727
10 Finderne Ave, Bridgewater NJ 08807
Tel (908) 203-2800
SIC 2821 3081 2869 2843 2865

ICI AMERICAN HOLDINGS LLC p 727
10 Finderne Ave, Bridgewater NJ 08807
Tel (908) 203-2800
SIC 2851 2821 3081 2869 2843 2865

SOLVAY HOLDING INC p 1339
8 Cedarbrook Dr, Cranbury NJ 08512
Tel (609) 860-4000
SIC 2819 2812 2865 2869

ELEMENTIS SPECIALTIES INC p 486
469 Old Trenton Rd, East Windsor NJ 08512
Tel (609) 443-2000
SIC 2851 8731 2899 2865 2816

SUN CHEMICAL CORP p 1400
35 Waterview Blvd Ste 100, Parsippany NJ 07054
Tel (973) 404-6000 SIC 2893 2865

CHEMICAL RESOURCES INC p 293
103 Carnegie Ctr Ste 100, Princeton NJ 08540
Tel (609) 520-0000 SIC 5162 5169 2865

SOLVAY USA INC p 1339
504 Carnegie Ctr, Princeton NJ 08540
Tel (609) 860-4000
SIC 2899 2869 2821 2087 2865

RESURGENCE ASSET MANAGEMENT LLC p 1228
1185 Av Of The Amer Fl 18, New York NY 10036
Tel (212) 710-5001
SIC 6282 2865 2821 2869 2861 2819

MITSUI CHEMICALS AMERICA INC p 978
800 Westchester Ave N607, Rye Brook NY 10573
Tel (914) 253-0777
SIC 2821 2865 3082 8731 5169 6159

SI GROUP INC p 1319
2750 Balltown Rd, Schenectady NY 12309
Tel (518) 347-4200 SIC 2865 3087 2851

NOVARTIS CORP p 1062
520 White Plains Rd, Tarrytown NY 10591
Tel (212) 307-1122
SIC 2834 2879 2032 2865

AMERICHEM INC p 81
2000 Americhem Way, Cuyahoga Falls OH 44221
Tel (330) 929-4213
SIC 2865 2851 2819 2816

■ MARATHON PETROLEUM CO LP p 904
539 S Main St, Findlay OH 45840
Tel (419) 422-2121 SIC 5172 2951 2865

■ REPUBLIC POWDERED METALS INC p 1225
2628 Pearl Rd, Medina OH 44256
Tel (330) 225-3192
SIC 2851 2891 3069 2899 2865 2842

▲ RPM INTERNATIONAL INC p 1255
2628 Pearl Rd, Medina OH 44256
Tel (330) 273-5090
SIC 2851 2891 3069 2899 2865 2842

PENN COLOR INC p 1129
400 Old Dublin Pike, Doylestown PA 18901
Tel (215) 345-6364 SIC 2865 2816

■ SUNOCO INC p 1403
3801 West Chester Pike, Newtown Square PA 19073
Tel (215) 977-3000
SIC 5541 2911 2869 2865 5171 5052

■ INDSPEC CHEMICAL CORP p 739
133 Main St, Petrolia PA 16050
Tel (724) 756-2370 SIC 2865 2819

BRASKEM AMERICA INC p 208
1735 Market St Fl 28, Philadelphia PA 19103
Tel (215) 841-3100 SIC 2821 2865 2869

▲ KOPPERS HOLDINGS INC p 827
436 7th Ave, Pittsburgh PA 15219
Tel (412) 227-2001
SIC 2865 2491 2895 3312 2899

■ KOPPERS INC p 828
436 7th Ave, Pittsburgh PA 15219
Tel (412) 227-2001
SIC 2865 2491 3312 2899

▲ CSS INDUSTRIES INC p 398
450 Plymouth Rd Ste 300, Plymouth Meeting PA 19462
Tel (610) 729-3959
SIC 2771 2679 2389 2396 2621 2865

ALPHA CORP OF TENNESSEE p 60
955 Highway 57, Collierville TN 38017
Tel (901) 854-2800 SIC 3089 2866

▲ EASTMAN CHEMICAL CO p 473
200 S Wilcox Dr, Kingsport TN 37660
Tel (423) 229-2000
SIC 2821 2869 2865 2823

■ CELANESE CHEMICALS INC p 273
1601 Lyndon B Johnson Fwy, Dallas TX 75234
Tel (972) 443-4000
SIC 2821 2824 2865 2869

M-I LLC p 890
5950 N Course Dr, Houston TX 77072
Tel (281) 561-1300
SIC 1389 2865 2869 8711 8741

▲ TTWF LP p 1490
2801 Post Oak Blvd, Houston TX 77056
Tel (713) 960-9111 SIC 2821 2869 2865

AMERICAS STYRENICS LLC p 81
24 Waterway Ave Ste 1200, The Woodlands TX 77380
Tel (832) 616-7800 SIC 2821 2865

▲ HUNTSMAN CORP p 720
10003 Woodloch Forest Dr # 260, The Woodlands TX 77380
Tel (281) 719-6000
SIC 2821 3081 2869 2816 2865

■ HUNTSMAN INTERNATIONAL LLC p 720
1003 Woodloch Forest Dr, The Woodlands TX 77380
Tel (281) 719-6000
SIC 2821 3081 2869 2816 2865

▲ SYNALLOY CORP p 1414
4510 Cox Rd Ste 201, Glen Allen VA 23060
Tel (864) 585-3605
SIC 3317 3443 2865 2899 2869

■ ETHYL CORP p 511
330 S 4th St, Richmond VA 23219
Tel (804) 788-5000
SIC 2869 5169 2899 2841 2865

▲ NEWMARKET CORP p 1038
330 S 4th St, Richmond VA 23219
Tel (804) 788-5000
SIC 2869 2899 2841 2865

S C JOHNSON & SON INC p 1262
1525 Howe St, Racine WI 53403
Tel (262) 260-2000
SIC 2842 2844 2879 2865 7342 7349

SIC 2869 Industrial Organic Chemicals, NEC

INEOS AMERICAS LLC p 740
7770 Rangeline Rd, Theodore AL 36582
Tel (251) 443-3000 SIC 2869 2865

■ INC AEROJET ROCKETDYNE OF DE p 735
8900 De Soto Ave, Canoga Park CA 91304
Tel (818) 586-1000 SIC 2869 3724

IMPERIAL WESTERN PRODUCTS INC p 734
86600 Avenue 54, Coachella CA 92236
Tel (760) 398-0815 SIC 5159 2841 2869

■ DANISCO US INC p 412
925 Page Mill Rd, Palo Alto CA 94304
Tel (650) 846-7500
SIC 2835 8731 2899 2869

■ PACIFIC AG PRODUCTS LLC p 1103
400 Capitol Mall Ste 2060, Sacramento CA 95814
Tel (916) 403-2123 SIC 2869

▲ PACIFIC ETHANOL INC p 1104
400 Capitol Mall Ste 2060, Sacramento CA 95814
Tel (916) 403-2123 SIC 2869

■ CHEVRON ORONITE CO LLC p 296
6001 Bollinger Canyon Rd, San Ramon CA 94583
Tel (713) 432-2500
SIC 2821 2899 2869 1311

■ VISHAY SILICONIX LLC p 1561
2201 Laurelwood Rd, Santa Clara CA 95054
Tel (408) 988-8000 SIC 2869

■ ROCHE HOLDINGS INC p 1243
1 Dna Way, South San Francisco CA 94080
Tel (625) 225-1000
SIC 2834 2833 2835 2869

▲ INNOSPEC INC p 744
8310 S Valley Hwy Ste 350, Englewood CO 80112
Tel (303) 792-5554 SIC 2911 2869

■ PENFORD CORP p 1128
345 Inverness Dr S # 200, Englewood CO 80112
Tel (303) 649-1900 SIC 2046 2869

■ HACH CO p 652
5600 Lindbergh Dr, Loveland CO 80538
Tel (970) 669-3050
SIC 3826 3823 3231 2819 2869

■ CHEMTURA USA CORP p 294
199 Benson Rd, Middlebury CT 06762
Tel (203) 573-2000 SIC 2879 2869 2822

RT VANDERBILT CO INC p 1203
30 Winfield St, Norwalk CT 06855
Tel (203) 853-1400
SIC 5169 2869 2819 5052 1499 1459

RT VANDERBILT HOLDING CO INC p 1256
30 Winfield St, Norwalk CT 06855
Tel (203) 295-2141
SIC 5169 2869 2819 1499 1459

VANDERBILT CHEMICALS LLC p 1543
30 Winfield St, Norwalk CT 06855
Tel (203) 853-1400 SIC 2819 2869 5169

HENKEL OF AMERICA INC p 683
1 Henkel Way, Rocky Hill CT 06067
Tel (860) 571-5100
SIC 2869 2843 2821 2833 2899 2891

■ ASHLAND SPECIALTY INGREDIENTS GP p 117
8145 Blazer Dr, Wilmington DE 19808
Tel (302) 594-5000 SIC 2869

■ HERCULES INC p 685
500 Hercules Rd, Wilmington DE 19808
Tel (302) 594-5000 SIC 2869 2891

INVISTA CAPITAL MANAGEMENT LLC p 762
2801 Centerville Rd, Wilmington DE 19808
Tel (302) 683-3000 SIC 2869

■ ST MARKS POWDER INC p 1370
7121 Coastal Hwy, Crawfordville FL 32327
Tel (850) 577-2824 SIC 2869

ARR-MAZ CUSTOM CHEMICALS INC p 112
4800 State Road 60 E, Mulberry FL 33860
Tel (863) 578-1206 SIC 2869

ARR-MAZ PRODUCTS LP p 112
4800 State Road 60 E, Mulberry FL 33860
Tel (863) 578-1206 SIC 2899 2869

▲ PLATFORM SPECIALTY PRODUCTS CORP p 1155
1450 Centrepark Blvd, West Palm Beach FL 33401
Tel (561) 207-9600 SIC 2869 2899

AGC AMERICA INC p 34
11175 Cicero Dr Ste 400, Alpharetta GA 30022
Tel (404) 446-4200
SIC 6719 3211 2869 5169 3229

KEMIRA CHEMICALS INC p 809
1000 Parkwood Cir Se # 500, Atlanta GA 30339
Tel (863) 533-5990 SIC 2869 2819

PINOVA HOLDINGS INC p 1150
2801 Cook St, Brunswick GA 31520
Tel (888) 807-2958 SIC 2869

AMREP INC p 86
425 Franklin Gtwy Se # 530, Marietta GA 30067
Tel (770) 590-5960
SIC 2842 2079 2911 2869 2841 2819

CHEMTALL INC p 293
1 Chemical Plant Rd, Riceboro GA 31323
Tel (912) 884-3366 SIC 2869

NUFARM AMERICAS INC p 1067
11901 S Austin Ave Ste A, Alsip IL 60803
Tel (708) 377-1330 SIC 2869 2879

INEOS STYROLUTION AMERICA LLC p 740
4245 Meridian Pkwy # 151, Aurora IL 60504
Tel (630) 820-9500 SIC 2869

ANGUS CHEMICAL CO p 91
1500 E Lake Cook Rd, Buffalo Grove IL 60089
Tel (847) 215-8600 SIC 2869 2899

AKZO NOBEL FUNCTIONAL CHEMICAL LLC p 42
525 W Van Buren St # 1600, Chicago IL 60607
Tel (312) 544-7000 SIC 2869

AKZO NOBEL INC p 42
525 W Van Buren St Fl 16, Chicago IL 60607
Tel (312) 544-7000
SIC 2869 2851 2834 3841 3826 2819

AKZO NOBEL POLYMER CHEM LLC p 42
525 W Van Buren St # 1600, Chicago IL 60607
Tel (312) 544-7000 SIC 2869

MERISANT CO p 949
125 S Wacker Dr Ste 3150, Chicago IL 60606
Tel (312) 840-6000 SIC 2869

MERISANT US INC p 949
125 S Wacker Dr Ste 3150, Chicago IL 60606
Tel (312) 840-6000 SIC 2869

VANTAGE OLEOCHEMICALS INC p 1544
4650 S Racine Ave, Chicago IL 60609
Tel (773) 376-9000 SIC 2869 2841 5169

BIG RIVER RESOURCES GALVA LLC p 181
1100 Se 2nd St, Galva IL 61434
Tel (309) 932-2033 SIC 2869

VANTAGE SPECIALTIES INC p 1544
3938 Porett Dr, Gurnee IL 60031
Tel (847) 244-3410 SIC 4925 2869

ONYX ENVIRONMENTAL SERVICES LLC p 1088
700 E Bttrfeld Rd Ste 201, Lombard IL 60148
Tel (630) 218-1500
SIC 8711 4953 2869 1799 1629

BP AMOCO CHEMICAL CO p 205
150 W Warrenville Rd, Naperville IL 60563
Tel (630) 420-5111
SIC 2221 2821 2869 2819 2865

PURECIRCLE USA INC p 1192
915 Harger Rd Ste 250, Oak Brook IL 60523
Tel (866) 960-8242 SIC 2869

■ AVENTINE RENEWABLE ENERGY HOLDINGS LLC p 136
1300 S 2nd St, Pekin IL 61554
Tel (309) 347-9200 SIC 2869

■ PACIFIC ETHANOL PEKIN INC p 1104
1300 S 2nd St, Pekin IL 61554
Tel (309) 347-9200 SIC 2869

HA-INTERNATIONAL LLC p 651
630 Oakmont Ln, Westmont IL 60559
Tel (630) 575-5700 SIC 2869

HA-USA INC p 651
630 Oakmont Ln, Westmont IL 60559
Tel (630) 575-5700 SIC 2869

CARDINAL ETHANOL LLC p 252
1554 N County Rd 600 E, Union City IN 47390
Tel (765) 964-3137 SIC 2869 2085

▲ RENEWABLE ENERGY GROUP INC p 1223
416 S Bell Ave, Ames IA 50010
Tel (515) 239-8000 SIC 2911 2869

SOUTHWEST IOWA RENEWABLE ENERGY LLC p 1352
10868 189th St, Council Bluffs IA 51503
Tel (712) 366-0392 SIC 2869 2085 2046

AMAIZING ENERGY HOLDING CO LLC p 64
2404 Highway 30, Denison IA 51442
Tel (712) 263-2676 SIC 2869

BIG RIVER UNITED ENERGY LLC p 181
3294 Vine Rd, Dyersville IA 52040
Tel (563) 875-5500 SIC 2869

CORN LP p 370
1303 Highway 3 E, Goldfield IA 50542
Tel (515) 825-3161 SIC 2869

ROQUETTE AMERICA INC p 1250
1003 S 5th St, Keokuk IA 52632
Tel (319) 524-5757 SIC 2046 2869

HOMELAND ENERGY SOLUTIONS LLC p 703
2779 Highway 24, Lawler IA 52154
Tel (563) 238-5555 SIC 2869 2085 2046

LITTLE SIOUX CORN PROCESSORS LLC p 871
4808 F Ave, Marcus IA 51035
Tel (712) 376-2800 SIC 2869

GOLDEN GRAIN ENERGY LLC p 621
1822 43rd St Sw, Mason City IA 50401
Tel (641) 423-8525 SIC 2869

GRAIN PROCESSING CORP p 629
1600 Oregon St, Muscatine IA 52761
Tel (563) 264-4265 SIC 2869 2085 2082

KENT CORP p 812
2905 N Highway 61, Muscatine IA 52761
Tel (563) 264-4211
SIC 2869 2085 2046 2048

LINCOLNWAY ENERGY LLC p 868
59511 Lincoln Hwy, Nevada IA 50201
Tel (515) 232-1010 SIC 2869 2861

BIG RIVER RESOURCES LLC p 181
15210 103rd St, West Burlington IA 52655
Tel (319) 753-1100 SIC 2869

BIG RIVER RESOURCES WEST BURLINGTON LLC p 181
15210 103rd St, West Burlington IA 52655
Tel (319) 753-1100 SIC 2869

HARCROS CHEMICALS INC p 660
5200 Speaker Rd, Kansas City KS 66106
Tel (913) 321-3131 SIC 5169 2869

CORBION AMERICA HOLDINGS INC p 368
7905 Quivira Rd, Lenexa KS 66215
Tel (913) 890-5500
SIC 2819 2869 2041 2023

PURAC AMERICA INC p 1192
7905 Quivira Rd, Lenexa KS 66215
Tel (847) 634-6330 SIC 2869

WESTERN PLAINS ENERGY LLC p 1599
3022 County Road 18, Oakley KS 67748
Tel (785) 672-8810 SIC 2869

■ ISP CHEMICALS LLC p 767
455 N Main St, Calvert City KY 42029
Tel (270) 395-4165 SIC 2869

■ WILD FLAVORS INC p 1609
1261 Pacific Ave, Erlanger KY 41018
Tel (859) 342-3600 SIC 2869 2819

ALLTECH INC p 58
3031 Catnip Hill Rd, Nicholasville KY 40356
Tel (859) 885-9613
SIC 2869 2048 3821 2819

■ CETCO ENERGY SERVICES CO LLC p 284
1001 Ochsner Blvd Ste 425, Covington LA 70433
Tel (985) 871-4700 SIC 1389 2869 3533

UNITED STATES ENRICHMENT CORP p 1513
6903 Rockledge Dr, Bethesda MD 20817
Tel (301) 564-3200 SIC 2819 2869

CRISTAL p 392
20 Wight Ave Ste 100, Hunt Valley MD 21030
Tel (410) 229-4440
SIC 1241 3531 2816 2869 1321 3631

■ ROHM AND HAAS ELECTRONIC MATERIALS LLC p 1247
455 Forest St, Marlborough MA 01752
Tel (508) 481-7950 SIC 2819 2869

■ FISHER SCIENTIFIC INTERNATIONAL LLC p 552
81 Wyman St, Waltham MA 02451
Tel (781) 622-1000
SIC 2869 3821 5169 5049

WACKER CHEMICAL CORP p 1570
3301 Sutton Rd, Adrian MI 49221
Tel (517) 264-8500 SIC 2869 5169

■ DOW CORNING CORP p 453
2200 W Salzburg Rd, Auburn MI 48611
Tel (989) 496-4000 SIC 2821 2869

METALWORKING LUBRICANTS CO p 953
25 W Silverdome Indus Par, Pontiac MI 48342
Tel (248) 332-3500
SIC 5172 2869 2843 2992

ADVANCED BIOENERGY LLC p 25
8000 Norman Center Dr # 610, Bloomington MN 55437
Tel (763) 226-2701 SIC 2869

OTTER TAIL AG ENTERPRISES LLC p 1098
24096 170th Ave, Fergus Falls MN 56537
Tel (218) 998-4301 SIC 2869

GRANITE FALLS ENERGY LLC p 631
15045 Highway 23 Se, Granite Falls MN 56241
Tel (320) 564-3100 SIC 2869 2085 2046

HERON LAKE BIOENERGY LLC p 687
91246 390th Ave, Heron Lake MN 56137
Tel (507) 793-0077 SIC 1321 2869

HIGHWATER ETHANOL LLC p 692
24500 Us Highway 14, Lamberton MN 56152
Tel (507) 752-6160 SIC 2869

ABENGOA BIOENERGY US HOLDING LLC p 11
16150 Main Circle Dr # 300, Chesterfield MO 63017
Tel (478) 254-7183 SIC 2869

MID-MISSOURI ENERGY LLC p 963
15311 N Saline 65 Hwy, Malta Bend MO 65339
Tel (660) 595-0144 SIC 2869

▲ **OLIN CORP** p 1082
190 Carondelet Plz # 1530, Saint Louis MO 63105
Tel (314) 480-1400
SIC 2812 2819 2821 2842 2869 2891

SIGMA CHEMICAL CORP p 1321
3050 Spruce St, Saint Louis MO 63103
Tel (314) 771-5765 *SIC* 2836 2869

■ **SOLUTIA INC** p 1339
575 Maryville Centre Dr, Saint Louis MO 63141
Tel (423) 229-2000
SIC 2824 2821 3081 2869

VI-JON INC p 1554
8515 Page Ave, Saint Louis MO 63114
Tel (314) 427-1000 *SIC* 2869 2844

WILLERT HOME PRODUCTS INC p 1610
4044 Park Ave, Saint Louis MO 63110
Tel (314) 772-2822
SIC 3089 2869 2879 2842

CHIEF INDUSTRIES INC p 298
3942 W Old Highway 30, Grand Island NE 68803
Tel (308) 389-7200
SIC 3448 2451 3523 2869 3442

SIOUXLAND ETHANOL LLC p 1326
1501 Knox Blvd, Jackson NE 68743
Tel (402) 632-2676 *SIC* 2869 2083

▲ **GREEN PLAINS INC** p 637
450 Regency Pkwy Ste 400, Omaha NE 68114
Tel (402) 884-8700 *SIC* 2869 2046

■ **GREEN PLAINS ATKINSON LLC** p 637
49131 Highway 20, Oneill NE 68763
Tel (402) 315-1658 *SIC* 2869

HUSKER AG LLC p 721
54048 Highway 20, Plainview NE 68769
Tel (402) 582-4446 *SIC* 2869

JUST LIKE SUGAR INC p 797
2020 Pama Ln, Las Vegas NV 89119
Tel (702) 483-6777 *SIC* 2869

LONZA INC p 877
90 Boroline Rd Ste 1, Allendale NJ 07401
Tel (201) 316-9200 *SIC* 2899 2869 2819

ICI AMERICA INC p 727
10 Finderne Ave, Bridgewater NJ 08807
Tel (908) 203-2800
SIC 2821 3081 2869 2843 2865

ICI AMERICAN HOLDINGS LLC p 727
10 Finderne Ave, Bridgewater NJ 08807
Tel (908) 203-2800
SIC 2851 2821 3081 2869 2843 2865

INDOPCO INC p 739
10 Finderne Ave Ste A, Bridgewater NJ 08807
Tel (908) 685-5000
SIC 2891 2046 2821 2869 2899 2099

■ **NATIONAL STARCH AND CHEMICAL HOLDING CORP** p 1016
10 Finderne Ave, Bridgewater NJ 08807
Tel (908) 685-5000 *SIC* 2891 2046 2869

BERJE INC p 174
700 Blair Rd, Carteret NJ 07008
Tel (973) 748-8980 *SIC* 5169 2869

■ **SCHER CHEMICALS INC** p 1286
Industrial West, Clifton NJ 07012
Tel (973) 471-1300 *SIC* 2869

SOLVAY HOLDING INC p 1339
8 Cedarbrook Dr, Cranbury NJ 08512
Tel (609) 860-4000
SIC 2819 2812 2865 2869

BASF CORP p 158
100 Park Ave, Florham Park NJ 07932
Tel (973) 245-6000
SIC 2869 2819 2899 2843 2834 2879

BASFIN CORP p 158
100 Campus Dr Ste 301, Florham Park NJ 07932
Tel (973) 245-6000
SIC 2869 2819 2899 2843 2879 2834

TROY CORP p 1485
8 Vreeland Rd, Florham Park NJ 07932
Tel (973) 443-4200 *SIC* 2869

AJINOMOTO NORTH AMERICA INC p 41
400 Kelby St, Fort Lee NJ 07024
Tel (201) 292-3200
SIC 5142 5169 2869 2899

NAN YA PLASTICS CORP AMERICA p 1007
9 Peach Tree Hill Rd, Livingston NJ 07039
Tel (973) 992-1775 *SIC* 2824 2869 3083

EVONIK CORP p 515
299 Jefferson Rd, Parsippany NJ 07054
Tel (973) 929-8000
SIC 2819 2869 2851 2816

G HOLDINGS INC p 587
1 Campus Dr, Parsippany NJ 07054
Tel (973) 628-3000 *SIC* 2869 2843 3295

GENTEK INC p 604
90 E Halsey Rd Ste 301, Parsippany NJ 07054
Tel (973) 515-0900
SIC 2869 2819 2844 3714 3496

FIRMENICH INC p 544
250 Plainsboro Rd, Plainsboro NJ 08536
Tel (609) 452-1000 *SIC* 2899 2869

SOLVAY USA INC p 1339
504 Carnegie Ctr, Princeton NJ 08540
Tel (609) 860-4000
SIC 2899 2869 2821 2087 2865

SYMRISE INC p 1414
300 North St, Teterboro NJ 07608
Tel (201) 462-5559 *SIC* 2869

G-I HOLDINGS INC p 587
1361 Alps Rd, Wayne NJ 07470
Tel (973) 628-3000 *SIC* 2869 2843 3295

■ **INTERNATIONAL SPECIALTY PRODUCTS INC** p 757
1361 Alps Rd, Wayne NJ 07470
Tel (859) 815-3333
SIC 2869 2821 2843 2842 2899

ISP CHEMICALS INC p 767
1361 Alps Rd, Wayne NJ 07470
Tel (973) 628-4000 *SIC* 2869

MANE USA INC p 901
60 Demarest Dr, Wayne NJ 07470
Tel (973) 633-5533 *SIC* 2869

MOMENTIVE PERFORMANCE MATERIALS HOLDINGS INC p 983
22 Corporate Woods Blvd, Albany NY 12211
Tel (518) 533-4600 *SIC* 2869 3479

CUMBERLAND PACKING CORP p 400
2 Cumberland St, Brooklyn NY 11205
Tel (718) 858-4200 *SIC* 2869

▲ **BALCHEM CORP** p 147
52 Sunrise Park Rd, New Hampton NY 10958
Tel (845) 326-5600 *SIC* 2869 2899

FLAVORS HOLDINGS INC p 555
35 E 62nd St, New York NY 10065
Tel (212) 572-8677 *SIC* 2869 6712

ICC INDUSTRIES INC p 727
460 Park Ave Fl 7, New York NY 10022
Tel (212) 521-1700
SIC 2821 2869 2911 2899 3081 2834

▲ **INTERNATIONAL FLAVORS & FRAGRANCES INC** p 755
521 W 57th St, New York NY 10019
Tel (212) 765-5500 *SIC* 2869 2844 2087

MAFCO CONSOLIDATED GROUP INC p 895
35 E 62nd St, New York NY 10065
Tel (212) 572-8600 *SIC* 2121 2131 2869

RESURGENCE ASSET MANAGEMENT LLC p 1228
1185 Av Of The Amer Fl 18, New York NY 10036
Tel (212) 710-5001
SIC 6282 2865 2821 2869 2861 2819

SUGAR FOODS CORP p 1397
950 3rd Ave Fl 21, New York NY 10022
Tel (212) 753-6900
SIC 2869 2023 2099 2068 7389

MOMENTIVE PERFORMANCE MATERIALS INC p 983
260 Hudson River Rd, Waterford NY 12188
Tel (518) 237-3330 *SIC* 2869 3479 3679

MPM HOLDINGS INC p 995
260 Hudson River Rd, Waterford NY 12188
Tel (518) 237-3330 *SIC* 2869 3479 3679

MPM INTERMEDIATE HOLDINGS INC p 995
260 Hudson River Rd, Waterford NY 12188
Tel (518) 237-3330 *SIC* 2869 3479 3679

MPM SILICONES LLC p 995
260 Hudson River Rd, Waterford NY 12188
Tel (518) 233-3330 *SIC* 2869

▲ **ALBEMARLE CORP** p 46
4350 Congress St Ste 700, Charlotte NC 28209
Tel (980) 299-5700
SIC 2821 2834 2819 2899 2812 2869

CLARIANT CORP p 321
4000 Monroe Rd, Charlotte NC 28205
Tel (704) 331-7000 *SIC* 2869 2819

CLARIANT PLASTICS & COATINGS USA INC p 321
4000 Monroe Rd, Charlotte NC 28205
Tel (704) 331-7000 *SIC* 2869 2819

I KESTREL ACQUISITION CORP p 725
1035 Swabia Ct, Durham NC 27703
Tel (919) 990-7500
SIC 2821 2822 2869 2899 2891 2851

REICHHOLD LIQUIDATION INC p 1220
1035 Swabia Ct, Durham NC 27703
Tel (919) 990-7500
SIC 2821 2822 2869 2899 2891 2851

NOVOZYMES NORTH AMERICA INC p 1063
77 Perry Chapel Church Rd, Franklinton NC 27525
Tel (919) 494-2014 *SIC* 2869

EVONIK STOCKHAUSEN LLC p 516
2401 Doyle St, Greensboro NC 27406
Tel (336) 333-3500 *SIC* 2869 2899

■ **HANKINSON RENEWABLE ENERGY LLC** p 658
9230 County Road 1, Hankinson ND 58041
Tel (701) 242-9420 *SIC* 2869

RED TRAIL ENERGY LLC p 1216
3682 Highway 8, Richardton ND 58652
Tel (701) 974-3308 *SIC* 2869 2085

■ **BADLANDS POWER FUELS LLC** p 144
3711 4th Ave Ne, Watford City ND 58854
Tel (701) 842-3618 *SIC* 2869

GIVAUDAN FLAVORS AND FRAGRANCES INC p 613
1199 Edison Dr, Cincinnati OH 45216
Tel (513) 948-8000 *SIC* 2869 2087

GIVAUDAN FLAVORS CORP p 613
1199 Edison Dr, Cincinnati OH 45216
Tel (513) 948-8000 *SIC* 2869 2087

GIVAUDAN FRAGRANCES CORP p 613
1199 Edison Dr Ste 1-2, Cincinnati OH 45216
Tel (513) 948-3428 *SIC* 2869

GIVAUDAN ROURE (UNITED STATES) INC p 613
1199 Edison Dr, Cincinnati OH 45216
Tel (513) 948-8000 *SIC* 2869 2087

MOMENTIVE PERFORMANCE MATERIALS INC p 983
180 E Broad St, Columbus OH 43215
Tel (614) 986-2495 *SIC* 2821 2869

▲ **REX AMERICAN RESOURCES CORP** p 1229
7720 Paragon Rd, Dayton OH 45459
Tel (937) 276-3931 *SIC* 2869 6531

DOVER CHEMICAL CORP p 453
3676 Davis Rd Nw, Dover OH 44622
Tel (330) 343-7711 *SIC* 2819 2869 2899

■ **SPEEDWAY LLC** p 1358
500 Speedway Dr, Enon OH 45323
Tel (937) 864-3000 *SIC* 5411 5541 2869

DUBOIS CHEMICALS INC p 459
3630 E Kemper Rd, Sharonville OH 45241
Tel (800) 438-2647 *SIC* 2869

■ **LUBRIZOL CORP** p 884
29400 Lakeland Blvd, Wickliffe OH 44092
Tel (440) 943-4200 *SIC* 2899 2869

■ **TAMINCO US LLC** p 1423
7540 Windsor Dr Ste 411, Allentown PA 18195
Tel (610) 366-6730 *SIC* 2869 5169

▲ **QUAKER CHEMICAL CORP** p 1196
901 E Hector St, Conshohocken PA 19428
Tel (610) 832-4000
SIC 2992 2899 2869 2891

VIGON INTERNATIONAL INC p 1556
127 Airport Rd, East Stroudsburg PA 18301
Tel (570) 476-4172 *SIC* 2869 5149 2077

ARKEMA DELAWARE INC p 110
900 First Ave, King Of Prussia PA 19406
Tel (610) 205-7000
SIC 2812 2819 2869 2891 2899 2992

■ **SUNOCO INC** p 1403
3801 West Chester Pike, Newtown Square PA 19073
Tel (215) 977-3000
SIC 5541 2911 2869 2865 5171 5052

■ **SUNOCO INC (R&M)** p 1403
3801 West Chester Pike, Newtown Square PA 19073
Tel (215) 977-3000
SIC 5541 2869 2911 5411

HOUGHTON INTERNATIONAL INC p 711
945 Madison Ave, Norristown PA 19403
Tel (610) 666-4000 *SIC* 2869 2992

BRASKEM AMERICA INC p 208
1735 Market St Fl 28, Philadelphia PA 19103
Tel (215) 841-3100 *SIC* 2821 2865 2869

▲ **CHEMTURA CORP** p 294
1818 Market St Ste 3700, Philadelphia PA 19103
Tel (215) 446-3911
SIC 2869 2843 2821 2911 2899 2842

▲ **FMC CORP** p 562
2929 Walnut St, Philadelphia PA 19104
Tel (215) 299-6000 *SIC* 2812 2879 2869

■ **FISHER SCIENTIFIC CO LLC** p 552
300 Industry Dr, Pittsburgh PA 15275
Tel (412) 490-8300
SIC 5049 5169 3821 3826 2869 2819

LANXESS CORP p 844
111 Parkwest Dr, Pittsburgh PA 15275
Tel (800) 526-9377
SIC 2869 2821 2822 2816 2819

▲ **VWR CORP** p 1567
100 Matsonford Rd 1-200, Radnor PA 19087
Tel (610) 386-1700
SIC 2869 2819 3821 5047

GH HOLDINGS INC p 610
Madison & Van Buren Ave, Valley Forge PA 19482
Tel (610) 666-4000 *SIC* 2869 2992

TEKNOR APEX CO p 1433
505 Central Ave, Pawtucket RI 02861
Tel (401) 725-8000
SIC 3087 3069 3052 2869 3081 2821

3V SIGMA USA INC p 3
888 Woodstock St, Georgetown SC 29440
Tel (843) 546-8556 *SIC* 2869 2899 8731

REDFIELD ENERGY LLC p 1216
38650 171st St, Redfield SD 57469
Tel (605) 302-0090 *SIC* 0723 2869

POET LLC p 1159
4615 N Lewis Ave, Sioux Falls SD 57104
Tel (605) 965-2200 *SIC* 2869

LAKE AREA CORN PROCESSORS CO-OPERATIVE p 838
46269 Sd Highway 34, Wentworth SD 57075
Tel (605) 483-2676 *SIC* 2869

▲ **EASTMAN CHEMICAL CO** p 473
200 S Wilcox Dr, Kingsport TN 37660
Tel (423) 229-2000
SIC 2821 2869 2865 2823

■ **TAMINCO CORP** p 1423
200 S Wilcox Dr, Kingsport TN 37660
Tel (423) 229-2000 *SIC* 2869

BUCKMAN LABORATORIES INC p 223
1256 N Mclean Blvd, Memphis TN 38108
Tel (901) 278-0330 *SIC* 2869 2819

BULAB HOLDINGS INC p 225
1256 N Mclean Blvd, Memphis TN 38108
Tel (901) 278-0330 *SIC* 2819 2869

SACHEM INC p 1264
821 Woodward St, Austin TX 78704
Tel (512) 421-4900 *SIC* 2869

■ **CELANESE CHEMICALS INC** p 273
1601 Lyndon B Johnson Fwy, Dallas TX 75234
Tel (972) 443-4000
SIC 2821 2824 2865 2869

OXEA CORP p 1100
1505 L B Johnson Fwy # 400, Dallas TX 75234
Tel (972) 481-2700 *SIC* 2869

OXY CHEMICAL CORP p 1101
5005 L B Johnson Fwy 2200, Dallas TX 75244
Tel (972) 404-3800
SIC 2869 2873 2874 2899 3089

■ **ROHM AND HAAS TEXAS INC** p 1247
6600 La Porte Fwy, Deer Park TX 77536
Tel (281) 476-8304 *SIC* 2869 2899 2819

■ **KMG-BERNUTH INC** p 824
300 Throckmorton St, Fort Worth TX 76102
Tel (817) 761-6100 *SIC* 5169 2869

ATLANTIC METHANOL PRODUCTION CO LLC p 127
16945 Northchase Dr # 1950, Houston TX 77060
Tel (281) 872-8324 *SIC* 2869

■ **CHEVRON MARINE PRODUCTS LLC** p 296
1500 Louisiana St, Houston TX 77002
Tel (832) 854-2767 *SIC* 5172 2992 2869

CRITERION CATALYSTS & TECHNOLOGIES LP p 393
910 Louisiana St Ste 2900, Houston TX 77002
Tel (713) 241-3000 *SIC* 2819 2869

DX HOLDING CO INC p 464
300 Jackson Hill St, Houston TX 77007
Tel (713) 863-1947 *SIC* 2869 2819 5169

ECONOMY MUD PRODUCTS CO p 476
435 E Anderson Rd, Houston TX 77047
Tel (800) 231-2066 *SIC* 2869 2899

EQUISTAR CHEMICALS LP p 506
1221 Mckinney St Ste 700, Houston TX 77010
Tel (713) 309-7200 *SIC* 2869 2822

▲ **FLOTEK INDUSTRIES INC** p 560
10603 W Sam Houston Pkwy, Houston TX 77064
Tel (713) 849-9911
SIC 2087 2869 2899 3533 3491

LYONDELL CHEMICAL CO p 888
1221 Mckinney St Ste 300, Houston TX 77010
Tel (713) 309-7200 *SIC* 2869 2911

LYONDELL CHEMICAL WORLDWIDE INC p 888
1221 Mckinney St Ste 1600, Houston TX 77010
Tel (713) 652-7200 *SIC* 2869

M-I LLC p 890
5950 N Course Dr, Houston TX 77072
Tel (281) 561-1300
SIC 1389 2865 2869 8711 8741

▲ **PHILLIPS 66** p 1144
2331 City West Blvd, Houston TX 77042
Tel (832) 765-3300 *SIC* 1311 2911 2869

SASOL CHEMICALS (USA) LLC p 1283
12120 Wickchester Ln, Houston TX 77079
Tel (281) 588-3000 *SIC* 2869 5169

SHELL CHEMICAL LP p 1314
910 Louisiana St, Houston TX 77002
Tel (855) 697-4355 *SIC* 2869

SHELL OIL CO p 1314
910 Louisiana St Ste 1500, Houston TX 77002
Tel (713) 241-6161
SIC 5541 4612 1311 2821 2869 2911

TEXAS PETROCHEMICALS LP p 1444
8600 Park Place Blvd, Houston TX 77017
Tel (713) 477-9211 *SIC* 2869

■ **TOTAL PETROCHEMICALS & REFINING USA INC** p 1463
1201 La St Ste 1800, Houston TX 77002
Tel (713) 483-5000 *SIC* 2911 2899 2869

TPC GROUP INC p 1467
1 Allen Ctr Ste 1000, Houston TX 77002
Tel (713) 627-7474 *SIC* 2869

TPC GROUP LLC p 1467
1 Allen Center 500, Houston TX 77002
Tel (713) 477-9211 *SIC* 2869

▲ **TTWF LP** p 1490
2801 Post Oak Blvd, Houston TX 77056
Tel (713) 960-9111 *SIC* 2821 2869 2865

■ **UNION CARBIDE CORP** p 1504
1254 Enclave Pkwy, Houston TX 77077
Tel (281) 966-2727 *SIC* 2869 2821

■ **WESTLAKE CHEMICAL PARTNERS LP** p 1601
2801 Post Oak Blvd # 600, Houston TX 77056
Tel (713) 585-2900 *SIC* 2869

■ **WESTLAKE OLEFINS CORP** p 1601
2801 Post Oak Blvd Fl 6, Houston TX 77056
Tel (713) 960-9111 *SIC* 2869 2822

■ **WESTLAKE POLYMERS LLC** p 1601
2801 Post Oak Blvd # 650, Houston TX 77056
Tel (713) 960-9111 *SIC* 2673 2869

■ **WESTLAKE VINYLS CO LP** p 1601
2801 Post Oak Blvd # 600, Houston TX 77056
Tel (713) 960-9111 *SIC* 2812 2869 2821

▲ **CELANESE CORP** p 273
222 Las Colinas Blvd W # 900, Irving TX 75039
Tel (972) 443-4000 *SIC* 2819 2821 2869

■ **CELANESE INTERNATIONAL CORP** p 273
222 Las Colinas Blvd W, Irving TX 75039
Tel (972) 443-4000 *SIC* 2819 2869

INEOS AMERICAS LLC p 740
2600 S Shore Blvd Ste 500, League City TX 77573
Tel (281) 535-6600 *SIC* 2873 2869

AMERICAN ACRYL LP p 67
4631 Old Highway 146 B, Pasadena TX 77507
Tel (281) 909-2600 *SIC* 2869

AMERICAN ACRYL NA LLC p 67
4631 Old Highway 146 B, Pasadena TX 77507
Tel (281) 909-2600 *SIC* 2869

WHITE ENERGY INC p 1606
2745 Dallas Pkwy Ste 670, Plano TX 75093
Tel (972) 715-6490 *SIC* 2869

▲ **VALERO ENERGY CORP** p 1539
1 Valero Way, San Antonio TX 78249
Tel (210) 345-2000 *SIC* 2911 2869

■ **BAKER PETROLITE LLC** p 146
12645 W Airport Blvd, Sugar Land TX 77478
Tel (281) 276-5400 *SIC* 2899 2869

▲ **HUNTSMAN CORP** p 720
10003 Woodloch Forest Dr # 260, The Woodlands TX 77380
Tel (281) 719-6000
SIC 2821 3081 2869 2816 2865

■ **HUNTSMAN INTERNATIONAL LLC** p 720
1003 Woodloch Forest Dr, The Woodlands TX 77380
Tel (281) 719-6000
SIC 2821 3081 2869 2816 2865

■ **HUNTSMAN HOLDINGS LLC** p 720
500 S Huntsman Way, Salt Lake City UT 84108
Tel (801) 584-5700
SIC 2821 2911 3081 2869

▲ **SYNALLOY CORP** p 1414
4510 Cox Rd Ste 201, Glen Allen VA 23060
Tel (864) 585-3605
SIC 3317 3443 2865 2899 2869

CARPENTER CO p 260
5016 Monument Ave, Richmond VA 23230
Tel (804) 359-0800
SIC 3086 1311 2869 2297 2392 2821

■ **ETHYL CORP** p 511
330 S 4th St, Richmond VA 23219
Tel (804) 788-5000
SIC 2869 5169 2899 2841 2865

▲ **NEWMARKET CORP** p 1038
330 S 4th St, Richmond VA 23219
Tel (804) 788-5000
SIC 2869 2899 2841 2865

HYDRITE CHEMICAL CO p 723
300 N Patrick Blvd Fl 2, Brookfield WI 53045
Tel (262) 792-1450
SIC 5169 2819 2841 2869

UNITED ETHANOL LLC p 1508
1250 Chicago St, Milton WI 53563
Tel (608) 868-5900 *SIC* 2869

ALDRICH CHEMICAL CO LLC p 48
6000 N Teutonia Ave, Milwaukee WI 53209
Tel (414) 438-3850
SIC 2869 2819 3821 7371 2741

SIC 2873 Nitrogenous Fertilizers

APACHE NITROGEN PRODUCTS INC p 96
1436 S Apache Powder Rd, Saint David AZ 85630
Tel (520) 720-2217
SIC 2873 5169 2875 2819

BAYOU GRAIN & CHEMICAL CORP p 162
P.O. Box 67, Parkdale AR 71661
Tel (870) 473-2281 SIC 4221 2873 5153

■ EAST DUBUQUE NITROGEN PARTNERS LP p 470
10877 Wilshire Blvd Fl 10, Los Angeles CA 90024
Tel (310) 571-9800 SIC 2873

▲ RENTECH INC p 1224
10880 Wilshire Blvd # 1101, Los Angeles CA 90024
Tel (310) 571-9800 SIC 2999 2873 6794

CLIPPER OIL p 327
2040 Harbor Island Dr # 203, San Diego CA 92101
Tel (619) 692-9701 SIC 5172 2873 5169

AGRIUM US INC p 36
4582 S Ulster St Ste 1700, Denver CO 80237
Tel (303) 804-4400 SIC 2873

AGRIUM ADVANCED TECHNOLOGIES (US) INC p 36
2915 Rocky Mountain Ave # 400, Loveland CO 80538
Tel (970) 292-9000 SIC 2873

TRANS-RESOURCES INC p 1470
17780 Collins Ave, Sunny Isles Beach FL 33160
Tel (305) 933-8301 SIC 2873 2819 2879

■ AXIALL CORP p 140
1000 Abernathy Rd # 1200, Atlanta GA 30328
Tel (770) 395-4500
SIC 2812 2821 2865 2861 2873

■ PENNINGTON SEED INC p 1130
1280 Atlanta Hwy, Madison GA 30650
Tel (706) 342-1234
SIC 5261 2873 5191 6799 0723

JR SIMPLOT CO p 795
999 W Main St Ste 1300, Boise ID 83702
Tel (208) 336-2110
SIC 0211 2879 2037 2874 2873

LAND VIEW INC p 842
20504 4th St, Rupert ID 83350
Tel (208) 531-4100
SIC 2879 2873 2874 5999 5261 5169

▲ CF INDUSTRIES HOLDINGS INC p 285
4 Parkway N Ste 400, Deerfield IL 60015
Tel (847) 405-2400 SIC 2873 2874

■ CF INDUSTRIES INC p 285
4 Parkway N Ste 400, Deerfield IL 60015
Tel (847) 405-2400 SIC 2873 2874

■ CF INDUSTRIES NITROGEN LLC p 285
4 Parkway N Ste 400, Deerfield IL 60015
Tel (847) 405-2400 SIC 2875 2873

■ CF INDUSTRIES SALES LLC p 285
4 Parkway N Ste 400, Deerfield IL 60015
Tel (847) 405-2400 SIC 2873

▲ TERRA NITROGEN CO LP p 1439
4 Parkway N Ste 400, Deerfield IL 60015
Tel (847) 405-2400 SIC 2873

PCS NITROGEN FERTILIZER OPERATIONS INC p 1124
1101 Skokie Blvd Ste 400, Northbrook IL 60062
Tel (847) 849-4200 SIC 2873

PCS NITROGEN INC p 1124
1101 Skokie Blvd Ste 400, Northbrook IL 60062
Tel (847) 849-4200 SIC 2873 2874

■ FLO KAY INDUSTRIES INC p 557
1919 Grand Ave, Sioux City IA 51106
Tel (712) 277-2011 SIC 2873 2048 2816

■ TERRA INDUSTRIES INC p 1439
600 4th St Terra Ctr, Sioux City IA 51102
Tel (712) 943-5501 SIC 2873

KOCH FERTILIZER LLC p 825
4111 E 37th St N, Wichita KS 67220
Tel (316) 828-5010 SIC 2873 5169 2813

PEABODY HOLDING CO LLC p 1125
701 Market St Ste 700, Saint Louis MO 63101
Tel (314) 342-3400
SIC 1221 1222 5052 2873 6719

▲ OCIP HOLDING LLC p 1074
660 Madison Ave Fl 19, New York NY 10065
Tel (646) 589-6180 SIC 2861 2873

HARVEY FERTILIZER AND GAS CO p 667
303 Bohannon Rd, Kinston NC 28501
Tel (252) 526-4150 SIC 5191 2873 2875

DAKOTA GASIFICATION CO INC p 409
1717 E Interstate Ave, Bismarck ND 58503
Tel (701) 223-0441 SIC 2873 5169 1311

TURF CARE SUPPLY CORP p 1492
50 Pearl Rd Ste 200, Brunswick OH 44212
Tel (877) 220-1014 SIC 2873

■ HYPONEX CORP p 724
14111 Scottslawn Rd, Marysville OH 43040
Tel (937) 644-0011 SIC 2873 2875

■ SCOTTS CO LLC p 1294
14111 Scottslawn Rd, Marysville OH 43040
Tel (937) 644-0011
SIC 2873 2874 2879 0782 2499 3524

■ LSB CHEMICAL LLC p 883
16 S Pennsylvania Ave, Oklahoma City OK 73107
Tel (405) 235-4546 SIC 2819 2873 2892

▲ LSB INDUSTRIES INC p 883
16 S Pennsylvania Ave, Oklahoma City OK 73107
Tel (405) 235-4546
SIC 3822 3585 3567 2873

■ PRYOR CHEMICAL CO p 1187
4463 Hunt St, Pryor OK 74361
Tel (918) 825-3383 SIC 2873

ALCO INDUSTRIES INC p 47
1275 Glenlivet Dr Ste 100, Allentown PA 18106
Tel (610) 666-0930
SIC 2879 2851 2842 2873

PEACH BOTTOM TRANSPORT LLC p 1125
2663 Robert Fulton Hwy, Peach Bottom PA 17563
Tel (717) 278-8055 SIC 2873

FREMAR LLC p 577
44608 273rd St, Marion SD 57043
Tel (605) 648-3941 SIC 5153 2873

■ NUTRA-FLO CO p 1067
200 S Derby Ln, North Sioux City SD 57049
Tel (712) 277-2011 SIC 2873 2816 2048

OXY CHEMICAL CORP p 1101
5005 L B Johnson Fwy 2200, Dallas TX 75244
Tel (972) 404-3800
SIC 2869 2873 2874 2899 3089

INEOS AMERICAS LLC p 740
2600 S Shore Blvd Ste 500, League City TX 77573
Tel (281) 535-6600 SIC 2873 2869

■ OCI PARTNERS LP p 1073
5470 N Twin City Hwy, Nederland TX 77627
Tel (409) 723-1900 SIC 2861 2873

▲ CVR ENERGY INC p 404
2277 Plaza Dr Ste 500, Sugar Land TX 77479
Tel (281) 207-3200 SIC 2911 2873

■ CVR PARTNERS LP p 404
2277 Plaza Dr Ste 500, Sugar Land TX 77479
Tel (281) 207-3200 SIC 2873

SOUTHERN STATES COOPERATIVE INC p 1350
6606 W Broad St Ste B, Richmond VA 23230
Tel (804) 281-1000
SIC 2048 0181 2873 2874 5191 5172

AMSOIL INC p 87
925 Tower Ave, Superior WI 54880
Tel (715) 392-7101
SIC 2992 3589 2873 3714

SIC 2874 Phosphatic Fertilizers

■ MACDERMID INC p 892
245 Freight St, Waterbury CT 06702
Tel (203) 575-5700
SIC 2899 2842 2874 2992 2752 3577

■ MOSAIC FERTILIZER LLC p 991
13830 Circa Crossing Dr, Lithia FL 33547
Tel (813) 500-6300 SIC 2874

JR SIMPLOT CO p 795
999 W Main St Ste 1300, Boise ID 83702
Tel (208) 336-2110
SIC 0211 2879 2037 2874 2873

SIMPLOT PHOSPHATES LLC p 1325
999 W Main St Ste 1300, Boise ID 83702
Tel (208) 336-2110 SIC 2874

LAND VIEW INC p 842
20504 4th St, Rupert ID 83350
Tel (208) 531-4100
SIC 2879 2873 2874 5999 5261 5169

NU-WEST INDUSTRIES INC p 1066
3010 Conda Rd, Soda Springs ID 83276
Tel (208) 547-4381 SIC 2874

▲ CF INDUSTRIES HOLDINGS INC p 285
4 Parkway N Ste 400, Deerfield IL 60015
Tel (847) 405-2400 SIC 2873 2874

■ CF INDUSTRIES INC p 285
4 Parkway N Ste 400, Deerfield IL 60015
Tel (847) 405-2400 SIC 2873 2874

■ PHOSPHATE RESOURCE PARTNERS LIMITED PARTNERSHIP p 1145
100 Saunders Rd Ste 300, Lake Forest IL 60045
Tel (847) 739-1200
SIC 2874 1311 1475 2819 1094

PCS NITROGEN INC p 1124
1101 Skokie Blvd Ste 400, Northbrook IL 60062
Tel (847) 849-4200 SIC 2873 2874

PCS PHOSPHATE CO INC p 1124
1101 Skokie Blvd Ste 400, Northbrook IL 60062
Tel (847) 849-4200
SIC 1475 1474 2874 2819

■ MOSAIC CROP NUTRITION LLC p 991
3033 Campus Dr, Minneapolis MN 55441
Tel (763) 577-2700 SIC 2874 1474

■ MOSAIC GLOBAL HOLDINGS INC p 991
3033 Campus Dr Ste E490, Minneapolis MN 55441
Tel (763) 577-2700
SIC 2874 1474 1475 2875 2819

■ MOS HOLDINGS INC p 991
3033 Campus Dr Ste E490, Plymouth MN 55441
Tel (763) 577-2700
SIC 2874 1475 2819 1094 1481

▲ MOSAIC CO p 991
3033 Campus Dr Ste E490, Plymouth MN 55441
Tel (800) 918-8270 SIC 2874 1475

MISSISSIPPI PHOSPHATES CORP p 975
601 Industrial Rd, Pascagoula MS 39581
Tel (228) 762-3210 SIC 2874

▲ INNOPHOS HOLDINGS INC p 744
259 Prospect Plains Rd A, Cranbury NJ 08512
Tel (609) 495-2495 SIC 2874 2819

■ INNOPHOS INVESTMENTS II INC p 744
259 Prospect Plains Rd, Cranbury NJ 08512
Tel (609) 495-2495 SIC 2874 2819

MDI HOLDINGS LLC p 933
399 Park Ave Fl 14, New York NY 10022
Tel (212) 559-1127
SIC 2899 2842 2874 2992 2752 3577

STEEL PARTNERS II LP p 1384
590 Madison Ave Rm 3202, New York NY 10022
Tel (212) 758-3232 SIC 5191 2874

■ SCOTTS CO LLC p 1294
14111 Scottslawn Rd, Marysville OH 43040
Tel (937) 644-0011
SIC 2873 2874 2879 0782 2499 3524

▲ ANDERSONS INC p 90
480 W Dussel Dr, Maumee OH 43537
Tel (419) 893-5050
SIC 5153 0723 5191 2874 4789 4741

OXY CHEMICAL CORP p 1101
5005 L B Johnson Fwy 2200, Dallas TX 75244
Tel (972) 404-3800
SIC 2869 2873 2874 2899 3089

SOUTHERN STATES COOPERATIVE INC p 1350
6606 W Broad St Ste B, Richmond VA 23230
Tel (804) 281-1000
SIC 2048 0181 2873 2874 5191 5172

MCGREGOR CO p 929
401 Colfax Airport Rd, Colfax WA 99111
Tel (509) 397-4355 SIC 5191 3523 2874

SIC 2875 Fertilizers, Mixing Only

APACHE NITROGEN PRODUCTS INC p 96
1436 S Apache Powder Rd, Saint David AZ 85630
Tel (520) 720-2217
SIC 2873 5169 2875 2819

L & L NURSERY SUPPLY INC p 833
2552 Shenandoah Way, San Bernardino CA 92407
Tel (909) 591-0461
SIC 5191 2875 2449 5193

BEN HILL GRIFFIN INC p 172
700 S Scenic Hwy, Frostproof FL 33843
Tel (863) 635-2281 SIC 2875 0174 2033

HARRELLS INC p 663
720 Kraft Rd, Lakeland FL 33815
Tel (863) 687-2774 SIC 2875 5191

HARRELLS LLC p 663
5105 New Tampa Hwy, Lakeland FL 33815
Tel (863) 687-2774 SIC 2875 5191

■ CF INDUSTRIES NITROGEN LLC p 285
4 Parkway N Ste 400, Deerfield IL 60015
Tel (847) 405-2400 SIC 2875 2873

SOUTH CENTRAL FS INC p 1343
405 S Banker St, Effingham IL 62401
Tel (217) 342-9231 SIC 5171 5191 2875

COUNTRY STONE INC p 375
6300 75th Ave Ste A, Milan IL 61264
Tel (309) 787-1744
SIC 2499 2875 3273 3281

BRANDT CONSOLIDATED INC p 208
2935 S Koke Mill Rd, Springfield IL 62711
Tel (217) 547-5800 SIC 2875 5191

CO-ALLIANCE LLP p 330
5250 E Us Hwy 3, Avon IN 46123
Tel (317) 745-4491
SIC 5191 5171 5153 2875

VAN DIEST SUPPLY CO p 1542
1434 220th St, Webster City IA 50595
Tel (515) 832-2366 SIC 5191 2875 2879

CONRAD FAFARD INC p 358
770 Silver St, Agawam MA 01001
Tel (413) 786-4343 SIC 5191 2875

SUN GRO HORTICULTURE DISTRIBUTION INC p 1400
770 Silver St, Agawam MA 01001
Tel (413) 786-4343 SIC 1499 2875

CENTRA SOTA COOPERATIVE p 277
805 Highway 55 E, Buffalo MN 55313
Tel (763) 682-2557
SIC 5191 2875 5171 5153

WESTERN CONSOLIDATED COOPERATIVE p 1597
520 County Road 9, Holloway MN 56249
Tel (320) 394-2171 SIC 5153 4221 2875

■ MOSAIC GLOBAL HOLDINGS INC p 991
3033 Campus Dr Ste E490, Minneapolis MN 55441
Tel (763) 577-2700
SIC 2874 1474 1475 2875 2819

NU WAY COOPERATIVE (INC) p 1066
440 Highway 4 S, Trimont MN 56176
Tel (507) 639-2311
SIC 5191 5171 5541 2875

MFA INC p 957
201 Ray Young Dr, Columbia MO 65201
Tel (573) 874-5111
SIC 2875 2048 5191 5153

CENTRAL MISSOURI AGRISERVICE LLC p 279
211 N Lyon Ave, Marshall MO 65340
Tel (660) 886-7880 SIC 2875 2048 5251

MOUNTAIN VIEW CO-OP p 994
2200 Old Havre Hwy, Black Eagle MT 59414
Tel (406) 453-5900
SIC 5541 5153 2875 5191

HARVEY FERTILIZER AND GAS CO p 667
303 Bohannon Rd, Kinston NC 28501
Tel (252) 526-4150 SIC 5191 2873 2875

LEGACY FARMERS COOPERATIVE p 852
6566 County Road 236, Findlay OH 45840
Tel (419) 423-2611
SIC 5153 5191 5984 2875 2048 2041

■ HYPONEX CORP p 724
14111 Scottslawn Rd, Marysville OH 43040
Tel (937) 644-0011 SIC 2873 2875

■ EL DORADO CHEMICAL CO INC p 482
16 S Pennsylvania Ave, Oklahoma City OK 73107
Tel (405) 235-4546 SIC 2819 2875 2892

J FRANK SCHMIDT & SON CO p 771
9500 Se 327th Ave, Boring OR 97009
Tel (503) 663-4128 SIC 0783 2875

LEBANON SEABOARD CORP p 850
1600 E Cumberland St, Lebanon PA 17042
Tel (717) 273-1685 SIC 5191 2875 2048

AGRICULTURAL COMMODITIES INC p 36
2224 Oxford Rd, New Oxford PA 17350
Tel (717) 624-8249
SIC 5191 2048 2041 0723 2875

MOYER & SON INC p 995
113 E Reliance Rd, Souderton PA 18964
Tel (215) 799-2000
SIC 5191 5983 2875 0782 1711

LETCO GROUP LLC p 857
1901 Cal Crossing Rd, Dallas TX 75220
Tel (972) 506-8575 SIC 2875

AMERICAN PLANT FOOD CORP p 77
903 Mayo Shell Rd, Galena Park TX 77547
Tel (713) 675-2231 SIC 2875

▲ MARTIN MIDSTREAM PARTNERS LP p 913
4200 Stone Rd, Kilgore TX 75662
Tel (903) 983-6200
SIC 5171 4226 1321 4424 2819 2875

UNITED AMERICAN ACQUISITION CORP p 1506
3022 Franklin Ave, Waco TX 76710
Tel (859) 987-5389
SIC 2211 0782 3423 2875

WILCOX FARMS INC p 1608
40400 Harts Lake Vly Rd, Roy WA 98580
Tel (360) 458-7774 SIC 0252 2015 2875

SIC 2879 Pesticides & Agricultural Chemicals, NEC

▲ AMERICAN VANGUARD CORP p 81
4695 Macarthur Ct, Newport Beach CA 92660
Tel (949) 260-1200 SIC 2879

▲ CLOROX CO p 327
1221 Broadway Ste 1300, Oakland CA 94612
Tel (510) 271-7000
SIC 2842 2673 2035 2844 2879

■ CLOROX INTERNATIONAL CO p 327
1221 Broadway Ste 13, Oakland CA 94612
Tel (510) 271-7000 SIC 2842 2879

■ KINGSFORD PRODUCTS CO LLC p 821
1221 Broadway Ste 1300, Oakland CA 94612
Tel (510) 271-7000
SIC 2861 2099 2035 2033 2879

■ YASHENG GROUP p 1635
805 Veterans Blvd Ste 228, Redwood City CA 94063
Tel (650) 363-8345
SIC 2879 0111 0115 0116 0112

VALENT USA CORP p 1539
1600 Riviera Ave Ste 200, Walnut Creek CA 94596
Tel (925) 256-2700 SIC 2879

AGU US HOLDINGS INC p 36
7251 W 4th St, Greeley CO 80634
Tel (970) 356-4400 SIC 2879 5191

PLATTE CHEMICAL CO p 1155
3005 Rocky Mountain Ave, Loveland CO 80538
Tel (970) 685-3300 SIC 2879

■ CHEMTURA USA CORP p 294
199 Benson Rd, Middlebury CT 06762
Tel (203) 573-2000 SIC 2879 2869 2822

▲ CHEMOURS CO p 293
1007 Market St, Wilmington DE 19898
Tel (302) 773-1000 SIC 2879

■ CHEMOURS CO FC LLC p 293
1007 Market St, Wilmington DE 19898
Tel (302) 774-1000 SIC 2879 2816

▲ E I DU PONT DE NEMOURS AND CO p 466
974 Centre Rd, Wilmington DE 19805
Tel (302) 774-1000
SIC 2879 2824 2865 2821 2834

GB BIOSCIENCES LLC p 594
2200 Concord Pike, Wilmington DE 19803
Tel (336) 632-6000 SIC 2879 2834 2899

SYNGENTA CORP p 1415
3411 Silverside Rd # 100, Wilmington DE 19810
Tel (302) 425-2000 SIC 2879 5191 8741

TRANS-RESOURCES INC p 1470
17780 Collins Ave, Sunny Isles Beach FL 33160
Tel (305) 933-8301 SIC 2873 2819 2879

ACUITY SPECIALTY PRODUCTS INC p 20
1310 Sboard Indus Blvd Nw, Atlanta GA 30318
Tel (404) 352-1680
SIC 2841 2879 2842 5169

ZEP INC p 1642
3330 Cumberland Blvd Se # 700, Atlanta GA 30339
Tel (877) 428-9937 SIC 2841 2879 2842

JR SIMPLOT CO p 795
999 W Main St Ste 1300, Boise ID 83702
Tel (208) 336-2110
SIC 0211 2879 2037 2874 2873

LAND VIEW INC p 842
20504 4th St, Rupert ID 83350
Tel (208) 531-4100
SIC 2879 2873 2874 5999 5261 5169

NUFARM AMERICAS INC p 1067
11901 S Austin Ave Ste A, Alsip IL 60803
Tel (708) 377-1330 SIC 2869 2879

MAPLEHURST FARMS INC p 904
936 S Moore Rd, Rochelle IL 61068
Tel (815) 562-8723 SIC 5153 2879 4212

■ DOW AGROSCIENCES LLC p 453
9330 Zionsville Rd, Indianapolis IN 46268
Tel (317) 337-3000
SIC 2879 5191 0721 8731

■ ELI LILLY INTERNATIONAL CORP p 487
893 S Delaware St, Indianapolis IN 46225
Tel (317) 276-2000
SIC 8742 2834 8731 3841 2879

■ MYCOGEN CORP p 1004
9330 Zionsville Rd, Indianapolis IN 46268
Tel (317) 337-3000
SIC 5191 2879 0721 8731

ALBAUGH LLC p 46
1525 Ne 36th St, Ankeny IA 50021
Tel (515) 964-9444 SIC 2879

VAN DIEST SUPPLY CO p 1542
1434 220th St, Webster City IA 50595
Tel (515) 832-2366 SIC 5191 2875 2879

CERTIS USA LLC p 284
9145 Guilford Rd Ste 175, Columbia MD 21046
Tel (301) 604-7340 SIC 5191 2879

▲ DOW CHEMICAL CO p 453
2030 Dow Ctr, Midland MI 48674
Tel (989) 636-1000
SIC 2821 3081 3086 2812 2879

LAND OLAKES INC p 842
4001 Lexington Ave N, Arden Hills MN 55126
Tel (651) 375-2222 SIC 2879

ROSENS DIVERSIFIED INC p 1251
1120 Lake Ave, Fairmont MN 56031
Tel (507) 238-4201
SIC 2011 8748 5149 2879

UNIVERSAL COOPERATIVES INC p 1516
1300 Corporate Ctr Curv, Saint Paul MN 55121
Tel (651) 239-1000 SIC 2879 5169 2298

■ UNITED INDUSTRIES CORP p 1509
1 Rider Trl Ste 300, Earth City MO 63045
Tel (314) 738-0375 SIC 2879 3691

MISSISSIPPI LIME CO p 975
3870 S Lindbergh Blvd # 200, Saint Louis MO 63127
Tel (314) 543-6300
SIC 3274 2819 2879 1422

▲ MONSANTO CO *p* 985
800 N Lindbergh Blvd, Saint Louis MO 63167
Tel (314) 694-1000 *SIC* 2879 0181

SCHAEFFER MFG CO *p* 1286
102 Barton St, Saint Louis MO 63104
Tel (314) 865-4100 *SIC* 2992 2879

WILLERT HOME PRODUCTS INC *p* 1610
4044 Park Ave, Saint Louis MO 63110
Tel (314) 772-2822
SIC 3089 2869 2879 2842

BASF CORP *p* 158
100 Park Ave, Florham Park NJ 07932
Tel (973) 245-6000
SIC 2869 2819 2899 2843 2834 2879

BASFIN CORP *p* 158
100 Campus Dr Ste 301, Florham Park NJ 07932
Tel (973) 245-6000
SIC 2869 2819 2899 2843 2879 2834

NM Z PARENT INC *p* 1045
787 7th Ave Fl 49, New York NY 10019
Tel (212) 720-0300
SIC 6726 2841 2879 2842

NOVARTIS CORP *p* 1062
520 White Plains Rd, Tarrytown NY 10591
Tel (212) 307-1122
SIC 2834 2879 2032 2865

BAYER CROPSCIENCE LP *p* 161
2 Tw Alexander Dr, Durham NC 27709
Tel (919) 549-2000 *SIC* 2879 5191

MAKHTESHIM AGAN OF NORTH AMERICA INC *p* 899
3120 Highwoods Blvd # 100, Raleigh NC 27604
Tel (919) 256-9300 *SIC* 2879

■ SCOTTS CO LLC *p* 1294
14111 Scottslawn Rd, Marysville OH 43040
Tel (937) 644-0011
SIC 2873 2874 2879 0782 2499 3524

ALCO INDUSTRIES INC *p* 47
1275 Glenlivet Dr Ste 100, Allentown PA 18106
Tel (610) 666-0930
SIC 2879 2851 2842 2873

▲ FMC CORP *p* 562
2929 Walnut St, Philadelphia PA 19104
Tel (215) 299-6000 *SIC* 2812 2879 2869

BAYER CORP *p* 161
100 Bayer Rd, Pittsburgh PA 15205
Tel (412) 777-2000
SIC 2821 2879 2819 2834 3841

HELENA INDUSTRIES INC *p* 681
225 Schilling Blvd # 400, Collierville TN 38017
Tel (901) 820-5700 *SIC* 2879

DREXEL CHEMICAL CO *p* 456
1700 Channel Ave, Memphis TN 38106
Tel (901) 774-4370 *SIC* 2879

■ CELANESE US HOLDINGS LLC *p* 273
1601 Lyndon B Johnson Fwy, Dallas TX 75234
Tel (972) 443-4000 *SIC* 2821 2879 2819

ZXP TECHNOLOGIES LTD *p* 1645
409 Wallisville Rd, Highlands TX 77562
Tel (281) 426-8800 *SIC* 2992 2879 7549

STOLLER INTERNATIONAL INC *p* 1390
9090 Katy Fwy Ste 400, Houston TX 77024
Tel (713) 461-1493 *SIC* 5191 2879

BELL LABORATORIES INC *p* 170
3699 Kinsman Blvd, Madison WI 53704
Tel (608) 241-0202 *SIC* 2879

■ SPECTRUM BRANDS HOLDINGS INC *p* 1357
3001 Deming Way, Middleton WI 53562
Tel (608) 275-3340
SIC 3692 2879 3999 3648

■ SPECTRUM BRANDS INC *p* 1357
3001 Deming Way, Middleton WI 53562
Tel (608) 275-3340
SIC 3692 3634 2879 3999 3648

S C JOHNSON & SON INC *p* 1262
1525 Howe St, Racine WI 53403
Tel (262) 260-2000
SIC 2842 2844 2879 2865 7342 7349

SIC 2891 Adhesives & Sealants

▲ VERSUM MATERIALS INC *p* 1552
8555 S River Pkwy, Tempe AZ 85284
Tel (610) 481-6697 *SIC* 2842 2891 3569

AVERY PRODUCTS CORP *p* 137
50 Pointe Dr, Brea CA 92821
Tel (714) 675-8500
SIC 2678 3951 2672 2891

IPS CORP *p* 763
455 W Victoria St, Compton CA 90220
Tel (310) 898-3300 *SIC* 2891

LEHIGH SOUTHWEST CEMENT CO *p* 854
2300 Clayton Rd Ste 300, Concord CA 94520
Tel (972) 653-5500
SIC 3241 2891 5032 5211

HENRY CO LLC *p* 684
999 N Sepulveda Blvd, El Segundo CA 90245
Tel (310) 955-9200 *SIC* 2952 2821 2891

HNC PARENT INC *p* 698
999 N Sepulveda Blvd, El Segundo CA 90245
Tel (310) 955-9200 *SIC* 2952 2821 2891

CUSTOM BUILDING PRODUCTS INC *p* 403
7711 Center Ave Fl 5, Huntington Beach CA 92647
Tel (800) 272-8786 *SIC* 2891

■ SIMPSON STRONG-TIE CO INC *p* 1325
5956 W Las Positas Blvd, Pleasanton CA 94588
Tel (925) 560-9000 *SIC* 3449 2891

■ PRC - DESOTO INTERNATIONAL INC *p* 1168
24811 Ave Rockefeller, Valencia CA 91355
Tel (661) 678-4209 *SIC* 2891 3089

LATICRETE INTERNATIONAL INC *p* 846
1 Laticrete Park N 91, Bethany CT 06524
Tel (203) 393-0010 *SIC* 2899 2891

HENKEL CORP *p* 683
1 Henkel Way, Rocky Hill CT 06067
Tel (860) 571-5100
SIC 2843 2821 2833 2899 2891

HENKEL OF AMERICA INC *p* 683
1 Henkel Way, Rocky Hill CT 06067
Tel (860) 571-5100
SIC 2869 2843 2821 2833 2899 2891

▲ ROGERS CORP *p* 1246
1 Technology Dr, Rogers CT 06263
Tel (860) 774-9605 *SIC* 2891 2821 2824

▲ HEXCEL CORP *p* 688
281 Tresser Blvd Ste 1503, Stamford CT 06901
Tel (203) 969-0666
SIC 2821 3728 3089 3624 2891 3469

■ HERCULES INC *p* 685
500 Hercules Rd, Wilmington DE 19808
Tel (302) 594-5000 *SIC* 2869 2891

▲ QEP CO INC *p* 1194
1001 Brkn Snd Pkwy Nw A, Boca Raton FL 33487
Tel (561) 994-5550 *SIC* 5072 5085 2891

MAPEI CORP *p* 903
1144 E Newport Center Dr, Deerfield Beach FL 33442
Tel (954) 246-8888 *SIC* 2891

GARDNER-GIBSON MANUFACTURING INC *p* 592
4161 E 7th Ave, Tampa FL 33605
Tel (813) 248-2101 *SIC* 2951 2891 2952

DSM FINANCE USA INC *p* 458
1408 Columbia Nitrogen Dr, Augusta GA 30901
Tel (706) 849-6515
SIC 2891 2816 3089 3083 5169

CW MATTHEWS CONTRACTING CO INC *p* 404
1600 Kenview Dr Nw, Marietta GA 30060
Tel (770) 422-7520 *SIC* 2891 2951

ARCLIN USA LLC *p* 105
1000 Holcomb Woods Pkwy, Roswell GA 30076
Tel (678) 999-2100 *SIC* 2821 2891

MORTON INTERNATIONAL LLC *p* 991
123 N Wacker Dr Ste 2400, Chicago IL 60606
Tel (312) 807-2696
SIC 2891 2851 2822 1479 2899

MORTON SALT INC *p* 991
123 N Wacker Dr Fl 24, Chicago IL 60606
Tel (800) 725-8847
SIC 2891 2851 2822 1479 2899

■ SANFORD LP *p* 1279
3500 Lacey Rd, Downers Grove IL 60515
Tel (770) 418-7000 *SIC* 2891 3951 3952

▲ ILLINOIS TOOL WORKS INC *p* 732
155 Harlem Ave, Glenview IL 60025
Tel (847) 724-7500
SIC 3089 3965 3499 2891 3585

ADCO GLOBAL INC *p* 21
100 Tri State Intl # 135, Lincolnshire IL 60069
Tel (847) 282-3485 *SIC* 2891

■ NALCO CO LLC *p* 1006
1601 W Diehl Rd, Naperville IL 60563
Tel (630) 305-1000
SIC 3559 2899 2992 2891

■ RUST-OLEUM CORP *p* 1260
11 E Hawthorn Pkwy, Vernon Hills IL 60061
Tel (847) 367-7700
SIC 2891 2899 2816 2842 2851

TYDEN GROUP HOLDINGS CORP *p* 1496
409 Hoosier Dr, Angola IN 46703
Tel (740) 420-6777 *SIC* 3953 2891

DEHCO INC *p* 422
3601 Charlotte Ave, Elkhart IN 46517
Tel (574) 294-2684
SIC 2891 5031 5074 5014 5084

▲ PATRICK INDUSTRIES INC *p* 1120
107 W Franklin St, Elkhart IN 46516
Tel (574) 294-7511
SIC 3275 2493 2435 5031 5033 2891

■ COVALENCE SPECIALTY ADHESIVES LLC *p* 383
101 Oakley St, Evansville IN 47710
Tel (812) 424-2904 *SIC* 2891

KOCH ENTERPRISES INC *p* 825
14 S 11th Ave, Evansville IN 47712
Tel (812) 465-9800
SIC 3363 5075 3559 5084 2891 3069

ROYAL ADHESIVES AND SEALANTS LLC *p* 1254
2001 W Washington St, South Bend IN 46628
Tel (574) 246-5000 *SIC* 2891 7389 8711

ROYAL HOLDINGS INC *p* 1254
2001 W Washington St, South Bend IN 46628
Tel (574) 246-5000 *SIC* 2891

LION COPOLYMER HOLDINGS LLC *p* 869
36191 Highway 30, Geismar LA 70734
Tel (225) 673-8871 *SIC* 2891

▲ W R GRACE & CO *p* 1569
7500 Grace Dr, Columbia MD 21044
Tel (410) 531-4000
SIC 2819 3531 2899 2891 3479

■ W R GRACE & CO-CONN *p* 1569
7500 Grace Dr, Columbia MD 21044
Tel (410) 531-4000
SIC 2819 3531 2899 2891 3479

A W CHESTERTON CO *p* 7
860 Salem St, Groveland MA 01834
Tel (781) 438-7000
SIC 3053 2851 2992 2891 5169

STAHL (USA) INC *p* 1374
13 Corwin St, Peabody MA 01960
Tel (978) 531-0371 *SIC* 2891

BEMIS ASSOCIATES INC *p* 171
1 Bemis Way, Shirley MA 01464
Tel (978) 425-6761 *SIC* 2891 2851 3479

FLEXCON CO INC *p* 556
1 Flexcon Industrial Park, Spencer MA 01562
Tel (508) 885-8200 *SIC* 3081 2891

SAINT-GOBAIN ABRASIVES INC *p* 1271
1 New Bond St, Worcester MA 01606
Tel (508) 795-5000
SIC 3291 3559 3545 3297 3082 2891

HENNIGES AUTOMOTIVE HOLDINGS INC *p* 683
2750 High Meadow Cir, Auburn Hills MI 48326
Tel (248) 340-4100 *SIC* 3069 2891 3714

HENNIGES AUTOMOTIVE SEALING SYSTEMS NORTH AMERICA INC *p* 683
2750 High Meadow Cir, Auburn Hills MI 48326
Tel (248) 340-4100 *SIC* 3053 2891 3714

LJ/HAH HOLDINGS CORP *p* 872
2750 High Meadow Cir, Auburn Hills MI 48326
Tel (248) 340-4100 *SIC* 2891 3714

ND INDUSTRIES INC *p* 1022
1000 N Crooks Rd, Clawson MI 48017
Tel (248) 288-0000
SIC 3452 2851 5072 2891 3479

GENOVA PRODUCTS INC *p* 604
7034 E Court St, Davison MI 48423
Tel (810) 744-4500
SIC 3089 2891 2911 3494 3084 2952

DIVERSIFIED CHEMICAL TECHNOLOGIES INC *p* 444
15477 Woodrow Wilson St, Detroit MI 48238
Tel (313) 867-5444
SIC 2891 2992 2899 2842 2841

EFTEC NORTH AMERICA LLC *p* 481
31601 Research Park Dr, Madison Heights MI 48071
Tel (248) 526-4565
SIC 2891 8731 3296 2899 2851

▲ TILE SHOP HOLDINGS INC *p* 1453
14000 Carlson Pkwy, Plymouth MN 55441
Tel (763) 852-2988 *SIC* 5211 5961 2891

▲ 3M CO *p* 2
3m Center Bldg 22011w02, Saint Paul MN 55144
Tel (651) 733-1110
SIC 3841 3842 3291 2842 2672 2891

▲ HB FULLER CO *p* 671
1200 Willow Lake Blvd, Saint Paul MN 55110
Tel (651) 236-5900 *SIC* 2891 2899

▲ OLIN CORP *p* 1082
190 Carondelet Plz # 1530, Saint Louis MO 63105
Tel (314) 480-1400
SIC 2812 2819 2821 2842 2869 2891

■ AUDUBON MATERIALS LLC *p* 131
15100 E Crtney Athrton Rd, Sugar Creek MO 64058
Tel (816) 257-4040 *SIC* 2891

INDOPCO INC *p* 739
10 Finderne Ave Ste A, Bridgewater NJ 08807
Tel (908) 685-5000
SIC 2891 2046 2821 2869 2899 2099

■ NATIONAL STARCH AND CHEMICAL HOLDING CORP *p* 1016
10 Finderne Ave, Bridgewater NJ 08807
Tel (908) 685-5000 *SIC* 2891 2046 2869

SIKA CORP *p* 1322
201 Polito Ave, Lyndhurst NJ 07071
Tel (201) 933-8800
SIC 2891 2899 2851 2821 3272

DSM HOLDING CO USA INC *p* 458
45 Waterview Blvd, Parsippany NJ 07054
Tel (973) 257-1063
SIC 2891 2816 3089 3083 5169

■ ARROW FASTENER CO LLC *p* 113
271 Mayhill St, Saddle Brook NJ 07663
Tel (201) 843-6900
SIC 3579 3315 3452 3542 2891 3586

SPIRAL BINDING CO INC *p* 1359
1 Maltese Dr, Totowa NJ 07512
Tel (973) 256-0666
SIC 2789 3083 5112 2891

SAINT GOBAIN GRAINS & POWDERS *p* 1269
6600 Walmore Rd, Niagara Falls NY 14304
Tel (716) 731-8200 *SIC* 3221 3269 2891

LORD CORP *p* 878
111 Lord Dr, Cary NC 27511
Tel (877) 275-5673
SIC 2891 3724 3728 2851

I KESTREL ACQUISITION CORP *p* 725
1035 Swabia Ct, Durham NC 27703
Tel (919) 990-7500
SIC 2821 2822 2869 2899 2891 2851

REICHHOLD HOLDINGS US INC *p* 1220
1035 Swabia Ct, Durham NC 27703
Tel (919) 990-7500
SIC 2821 2822 2891 3089 5169 5162

REICHHOLD LIQUIDATION INC *p* 1220
1035 Swabia Ct, Durham NC 27703
Tel (919) 990-7500
SIC 2821 2822 2869 2899 2891 2851

SENSUS USA INC *p* 1305
8601 Six Forks Rd Ste 700, Raleigh NC 27615
Tel (919) 845-4000
SIC 3824 3363 2891 3491

HEXPOL COMPOUNDING NC INC *p* 688
280 Crawford Rd, Statesville NC 28625
Tel (704) 872-1585 *SIC* 3069 3087 2891

■ TREMCO INC *p* 1476
3735 Green Rd, Beachwood OH 44122
Tel (216) 292-5000
SIC 2891 2952 1761 1752 2851 2842

■ LUBRIZOL ADVANCED MATERIALS INC *p* 884
9911 Brecksville Rd, Brecksville OH 44141
Tel (216) 447-5000
SIC 2899 2891 3088 2834 3629

FAIRMOUNT SANTROL INC *p* 525
8834 Mayfield Rd Ste A, Chesterland OH 44026
Tel (440) 214-3200 *SIC* 2891

TECHNICAL RUBBER CO INC *p* 1431
200 E Coshocton St, Johnstown OH 43031
Tel (740) 967-9015 *SIC* 3011 5014 2891

■ REPUBLIC POWDERED METALS INC *p* 1225
2628 Pearl Rd, Medina OH 44256
Tel (330) 225-3192
SIC 2851 2891 3069 2899 2865 2842

▲ RPM INTERNATIONAL INC *p* 1255
2628 Pearl Rd, Medina OH 44256
Tel (330) 273-5090
SIC 2851 2891 3069 2899 2865 2842

THORWORKS INDUSTRIES INC *p* 1450
2520 Campbell St, Sandusky OH 44870
Tel (419) 626-4375
SIC 2851 3531 2952 2951 2891 2816

MORGAN ADHESIVES CO LLC *p* 988
4560 Darrow Rd, Stow OH 44224
Tel (330) 688-1111
SIC 2891 3565 2672 2823

AKZO NOBEL PAINTS LLC *p* 42
8381 Pearl Rd, Strongsville OH 44136
Tel (440) 297-8000 *SIC* 2851 2891

WILLAMETTE VALLEY CO *p* 1609
1075 Arrowsmith St, Eugene OR 97402
Tel (541) 484-9621
SIC 5085 2851 2891 5169

▲ AIR PRODUCTS AND CHEMICALS INC *p* 39
7201 Hamilton Blvd, Allentown PA 18195
Tel (610) 481-4911
SIC 2813 2842 2891 3569

■ VERSUM MATERIALS US LLC *p* 1552
1919 Vultee St, Allentown PA 18103
Tel (610) 481-3706 *SIC* 2842 2891 3569

■ CARLISLE CONSTRUCTION MATERIALS LLC *p* 257
1285 Ritner Hwy, Carlisle PA 17013
Tel (717) 245-7000
SIC 2952 3069 5031 2899 2891

▲ QUAKER CHEMICAL CORP *p* 1196
901 E Hector St, Conshohocken PA 19428
Tel (610) 832-4000
SIC 2992 2899 2869 2891

WHITFORD WORLDWIDE CO *p* 1606
47 Park Ave, Elverson PA 19520
Tel (610) 286-3500 *SIC* 2891

ADHESIVES RESEARCH INC *p* 22
400 Seaks Run Rd, Glen Rock PA 17327
Tel (717) 235-7979 *SIC* 2891

ARKEMA DELAWARE INC *p* 110
900 First Ave, King Of Prussia PA 19406
Tel (610) 205-7000
SIC 2812 2819 2869 2891 2899 2992

SAINT-GOBAIN CORP *p* 1271
20 Moores Rd, Malvern PA 19355
Tel (610) 893-6000 *SIC* 2891 3269 3221

■ ROHM AND HAAS CO *p* 1246
100 N Independence Mall W, Philadelphia PA 19106
Tel (215) 592-3000
SIC 2819 2851 2891 2899

COVESTRO LLC *p* 385
1 Covestro Cir, Pittsburgh PA 15205
Tel (412) 413-2000 *SIC* 2891 2821

■ PPG ARCHITECTURAL FINISHES INC *p* 1166
1 Ppg Pl, Pittsburgh PA 15272
Tel (412) 434-3131 *SIC* 2851 2891

FRES-CO SYSTEMS USA INC *p* 578
3005 State Rd, Telford PA 18969
Tel (215) 721-4600 *SIC* 5084 3565 2891

SAINT-GOBAIN DELAWARE CORP *p* 1271
750 E Swedesford Rd, Valley Forge PA 19482
Tel (610) 341-7000
SIC 3291 3269 2891 3296 3084 3221

REX-HIDE INC *p* 1230
705 S Lyons Ave, Tyler TX 75702
Tel (903) 593-7387
SIC 3061 3069 2891 6799

■ HUNTSMAN ADVANCED MATERIALS LLC *p* 720
500 S Huntsman Way, Salt Lake City UT 84108
Tel (801) 584-5700 *SIC* 2821 2891 3087

HELLERMANNTYTON CORP *p* 681
7930 N Faulkner Rd, Milwaukee WI 53224
Tel (414) 355-1130 *SIC* 3089 2891

BOSTIK INC *p* 202
11320 W Wtertown Plank Rd, Wauwatosa WI 53226
Tel (414) 774-2250 *SIC* 2891

SIC 2892 Explosives

NELSON BROTHERS INC *p* 1025
820 Shades Creek Pkwy # 2000, Birmingham AL 35209
Tel (205) 414-2900 *SIC* 2892 5169

NELSON BROTHERS LLC *p* 1025
820 Shades Creek Pkwy # 2000, Birmingham AL 35209
Tel (205) 414-2900 *SIC* 2892

PACIFIC SCIENTIFIC ENERGETIC MATERIALS CO (CALIFORNIA) LLC *p* 1105
7073 W Willis Rd Ste 5002, Chandler AZ 85226
Tel (480) 763-3000
SIC 2892 2899 3483 3489 3699 3728

■ PACIFIC SCIENTIFIC ENERGETIC MATERIALS CO (CALIFORNIA) *p* 1105
3601 Union Rd, Hollister CA 95023
Tel (831) 637-3731
SIC 2892 2899 3489 3483 3699 3728

ORICA US SERVICES INC *p* 1094
33101 E Quincy Ave, Watkins CO 80137
Tel (303) 268-5000 *SIC* 2892 5169

ORICA USA INC *p* 1094
33101 E Quincy Ave, Watkins CO 80137
Tel (720) 870-1809 *SIC* 2892 5169

ENSIGN-BICKFORD AEROSPACE & DEFENSE CO *p* 501
640 Hopmeadow St, Simsbury CT 06070
Tel (860) 843-2289 *SIC* 2892

■ GENERAL DYNAMICS ORDNANCE AND TACTICAL SYSTEMS INC *p* 600
11399 16th Ct N Ste 200, Saint Petersburg FL 33716
Tel (727) 578-8100
SIC 3483 3482 2892 3489

EAGLEPICHER TECHNOLOGIES LLC *p* 468
C & Porter Sts, Joplin MO 64802
Tel (417) 623-8000
SIC 3691 3629 3599 2892

AUSTIN POWDER CO *p* 133
25800 Science Park Dr # 300, Cleveland OH 44122
Tel (216) 464-2400 *SIC* 2892

AUSTIN POWDER HOLDINGS CO *p* 133
25800 Science Park Dr # 300, Cleveland OH 44122
Tel (216) 464-2400 *SIC* 2892

■ EL DORADO CHEMICAL CO INC *p* 482
16 S Pennsylvania Ave, Oklahoma City OK 73107
Tel (405) 235-4546 *SIC* 2819 2875 2892

■ **LSB CHEMICAL LLC** p 883
16 S Pennsylvania Ave, Oklahoma City OK 73107
Tel (405) 235-4546 SIC 2819 2873 2892

OWEN OIL TOOLS INC p 1099
12001 County Road 1000, Godley TX 76044
Tel (817) 396-4570 SIC 2892 3533

GEODYNAMICS INC p 606
10500 W Interstate 20, Millsap TX 76066
Tel (817) 341-5300 SIC 2892 3533

DYNO NOBEL HOLDINGS USA INC p 465
2795 E Cottonwood Pkwy # 500, Salt Lake City UT 84121
Tel (801) 364-4800 SIC 2892

DYNO NOBEL INC p 465
2795 E Cottonwood Pkwy # 500, Salt Lake City UT 84121
Tel (801) 364-4800 SIC 2892

WESTERN EXPLOSIVES SYSTEMS CO p 1598
3135 S Richmond St, Salt Lake City UT 84106
Tel (801) 484-6557
SIC 5169 1629 1241 1081 1481 2892

DAVIS MINING & MANUFACTURING INC p 416
613 Front St E, Coeburn VA 24230
Tel (276) 395-3354
SIC 2892 5082 2426 1221 1222

■ **ALLIANT TECHSYSTEMS OPERATIONS LLC** p 55
Hc 114, Radford VA 24143
Tel (540) 831-4788 SIC 2892

SIC 2893 Printing Ink

THRALL ENTERPRISES INC p 1450
180 N Stetson Ave, Chicago IL 60601
Tel (312) 621-8200 SIC 2893

INX GROUP LTD p 762
150 N Martingale Rd # 700, Schaumburg IL 60173
Tel (630) 382-1800 SIC 2893

INX INTERNATIONAL INK CO p 762
150 N Martingale Rd # 700, Schaumburg IL 60173
Tel (630) 382-1800 SIC 2893

TOYO INK INTERNATIONAL CORP p 1466
1225 N Michael Dr, Wood Dale IL 60191
Tel (866) 969-8696 SIC 2893 5112

NAZDAR CO p 1021
8501 Hedge Lane Ter, Shawnee KS 66227
Tel (913) 422-1888 SIC 2893

FLINT GROUP NORTH AMERICA CORP p 557
14909 N Beck Rd, Plymouth MI 48170
Tel (734) 781-4600 SIC 2893

FLINT GROUP US LLC p 557
14909 N Beck Rd, Plymouth MI 48170
Tel (734) 781-4600 SIC 2865 2893

■ **MARKEM-IMAJE CORP** p 908
150 Congress St, Keene NH 03431
Tel (603) 352-1130 SIC 2893

SUN CHEMICAL CORP p 1400
35 Waterview Blvd Ste 100, Parsippany NJ 07054
Tel (973) 404-6000 SIC 2893 2865

SUPERIOR PRINTING INK CO INC p 1407
100 North St, Teterboro NJ 07608
Tel (201) 478-5600 SIC 2893 2851

WIKOFF COLOR CORP p 1608
1886 Merritt Rd, Fort Mill SC 29715
Tel (803) 548-2210 SIC 2893 2851

SIC 2895 Carbon Black

COLUMBIAN CHEMICALS CO p 342
1800 W Oak Commons Ct, Marietta GA 30062
Tel (770) 792-9400 SIC 2895

▲ **CABOT CORP** p 235
2 Seaport Ln Ste 1300, Boston MA 02210
Tel (617) 345-0100
SIC 2895 3081 3084 2819 3339

TOTAL AMERICAN SERVICES INC p 1462
100 Town Square Pl # 401, Jersey City NJ 07310
Tel (206) 626-3500
SIC 2911 4612 5172 5541 2895

▲ **KOPPERS HOLDINGS INC** p 827
436 7th Ave, Pittsburgh PA 15219
Tel (412) 227-2001
SIC 2865 2491 2895 3312 2899

■ **ALON USA LP** p 59
12700 Park Central Dr # 1600, Dallas TX 75251
Tel (972) 367-3600
SIC 2911 4612 5172 5541 2895

SID RICHARDSON CARBON & ENERGY CO p 1319
309 Main St, Fort Worth TX 76102
Tel (817) 336-0494 SIC 2895

CONTINENTAL CARBON CO p 363
16850 Park Row, Houston TX 77084
Tel (281) 647-3700 SIC 2895 3624

ORION ENGINEERED CARBONS LLC p 1094
4501 Magnolia Cove Dr, Kingwood TX 77345
Tel (832) 445-3300 SIC 2895

SIC 2899 Chemical Preparations, NEC

PACIFIC SCIENTIFIC ENERGETIC MATERIALS CO (CALIFORNIA) LLC p 1105
7073 W Willis Rd Ste 5002, Chandler AZ 85226
Tel (480) 763-3000
SIC 2892 2899 3483 3489 3699 3728

■ **STERNO PRODUCTS LLC** p 1388
1880 Compton Ave Ste 101, Corona CA 92881
Tel (951) 682-9600
SIC 3641 3645 3589 3634 2899

▲ **ELECTRONICS FOR IMAGING INC** p 486
6750 Dumbarton Cir, Fremont CA 94555
Tel (650) 357-3500 SIC 3577 2899

MORGAN ADVANCED CERAMICS INC p 988
2425 Whipple Rd, Hayward CA 94544
Tel (510) 491-1100 SIC 2899 3251 3264

■ **PACIFIC SCIENTIFIC ENERGETIC MATERIALS CO (CALIFORNIA)** p 1105
3601 Union Rd, Hollister CA 95023
Tel (831) 637-3731
SIC 2892 2899 3489 3483 3699 3728

POOL WATER PRODUCTS p 1161
17872 Mitchell N Ste 250, Irvine CA 92614
Tel (949) 756-1666 SIC 5091 2899 2812

HYDRANAUTICS p 723
401 Jones Rd, Oceanside CA 92058
Tel (760) 901-2597 SIC 2899 3589

■ **DANISCO US INC** p 412
925 Page Mill Rd, Palo Alto CA 94304
Tel (650) 846-7500
SIC 2835 8731 2899 2869

■ **CHEVRON ORONITE CO LLC** p 296
6001 Bollinger Canyon Rd, San Ramon CA 94583
Tel (713) 432-2500
SIC 2821 2899 2869 1311

HERAEUS PRECIOUS METALS NORTH AMERICA LLC p 685
15524 Carmenita Rd, Santa Fe Springs CA 90670
Tel (562) 921-7464 SIC 3341 2899

SUNKIST GROWERS INC p 1402
27770 N Entertainment Dr # 120, Valencia CA 91355
Tel (818) 986-4800
SIC 5148 2033 2037 2899 6794 5046

THOMPSON CREEK MINING CO p 1449
26 W Dry Creek Cir # 810, Littleton CO 80120
Tel (303) 783-6413 SIC 2899 1061

THOMPSON CREEK MINING LTD p 1449
26 W Dry Creek Cir # 810, Littleton CO 80120
Tel (303) 761-8801 SIC 1061 2899 2819

LATICRETE INTERNATIONAL INC p 846
1 Laticrete Park N 91, Bethany CT 06524
Tel (203) 393-0010 SIC 2899 2891

■ **ARMORED AUTOGROUP PARENT INC** p 111
44 Old Ridgebury Rd # 300, Danbury CT 06810
Tel (203) 205-2900 SIC 2842 2911 2899

▲ **LYDALL INC** p 887
1 Colonial Rd, Manchester CT 06042
Tel (860) 646-1233
SIC 2297 3053 2899 2631 3714 3564

■ **GREAT LAKES CHEMICAL CORP** p 633
199 Benson Rd, Middlebury CT 06762
Tel (203) 573-2000 SIC 2899 2842

HENKEL CORP p 683
1 Henkel Way, Rocky Hill CT 06067
Tel (860) 571-5100
SIC 2843 2821 2833 2899 2891

HENKEL OF AMERICA INC p 683
1 Henkel Way, Rocky Hill CT 06067
Tel (860) 571-5100
SIC 2869 2843 2821 2833 2899 2891

BIC CORP p 181
1 Bic Way Ste 1, Shelton CT 06484
Tel (203) 783-2000
SIC 3951 2899 3999 3421 5091 3952

BIC USA INC p 181
1 Bic Way Ste 1, Shelton CT 06484
Tel (203) 783-2000
SIC 3951 2899 3999 3421

■ **MACDERMID INC** p 892
245 Freight St, Waterbury CT 06702
Tel (203) 575-5700
SIC 2899 2842 2874 2992 2752 3577

GB BIOSCIENCES LLC p 594
2200 Concord Pike, Wilmington DE 19803
Tel (336) 632-6000 SIC 2879 2834 2899

SOLENIS LLC p 1338
3 Beaver Valley Rd # 500, Wilmington DE 19803
Tel (866) 337-1533 SIC 2899

ARR-MAZ PRODUCTS LP p 112
4800 State Road 60 E, Mulberry FL 33860
Tel (863) 578-1206 SIC 2899 2869

▲ **PLATFORM SPECIALTY PRODUCTS CORP** p 1155
1450 Centrepark Blvd, West Palm Beach FL 33401
Tel (561) 207-9600 SIC 2869 2899

ARCH CHEMICALS INC p 104
1200 Bluegrass Lakes Pkwy, Alpharetta GA 30004
Tel (678) 624-5800 SIC 2819 2899

CP KELCO US INC p 387
3100 Cumberland Blvd Se # 600, Atlanta GA 30339
Tel (678) 247-7300 SIC 2899

KEMIRA WATER SOLUTIONS INC p 809
1000 Parkwood Cir Se # 500, Atlanta GA 30339
Tel (770) 436-1542 SIC 2899

FIBRANT LLC p 540
1408 Columbia Nitrogen Dr, Augusta GA 30901
Tel (706) 849-6600 SIC 2819 2899

BRUNSWICK CELLULOSE LLC p 221
1400 9th St, Brunswick GA 31520
Tel (912) 265-5780
SIC 2611 2421 2899 2631

FIBERVISIONS CORP p 539
3700 Crestwood Pkwy Nw, Duluth GA 30096
Tel (678) 578-7240 SIC 2899

BIO-LAB INC p 183
1725 N Brown Rd, Lawrenceville GA 30043
Tel (678) 502-4000 SIC 2812 2819 2899

AKZO NOBEL PULP AND PERFORMANCE CHEMICALS INC p 43
1850 Parkway Pl Se # 1200, Marietta GA 30067
Tel (770) 578-0858 SIC 2899 2819

▲ **WESTROCK CO** p 1602
504 Thrasher St, Norcross GA 30071
Tel (678) 291-7456
SIC 2631 2899 3699 6531

SNF HOLDING CO p 1335
1 Chemical Plant Rd, Riceboro GA 31323
Tel (912) 884-3366 SIC 2822 2899

BORAL INDUSTRIES INC p 201
200 Mansell Ct E Ste 310, Roswell GA 30076
Tel (770) 645-4500
SIC 3251 3272 3275 5032 3271 2899

ROYAL OAK ENTERPRISES LLC p 1254
1 Royal Oak Ave, Roswell GA 30076
Tel (678) 461-3200 SIC 2999 2899

ANGUS CHEMICAL CO p 91
1500 E Lake Cook Rd, Buffalo Grove IL 60089
Tel (847) 215-8600 SIC 2869 2899

K+S MONTANA HOLDINGS LLC p 799
123 N Wacker Dr, Chicago IL 60606
Tel (312) 807-2000 SIC 2899

K+S SALT LLC p 799
123 N Wacker Dr Fl 6, Chicago IL 60606
Tel (844) 789-3991 SIC 2899 5149 5169

LAWTER INC p 848
200 N La Salle St # 2600, Chicago IL 60601
Tel (312) 662-5700 SIC 2899 2851

MORTON INTERNATIONAL LLC p 991
123 N Wacker Dr Ste 2400, Chicago IL 60606
Tel (312) 807-2696
SIC 2891 2851 2822 1479 2899

MORTON SALT INC p 991
123 N Wacker Dr Fl 24, Chicago IL 60606
Tel (800) 725-8847
SIC 2891 2851 2822 1479 2899

WM WRIGLEY JR CO p 1620
930 W Evergreen Ave, Chicago IL 60642
Tel (312) 280-4710
SIC 2067 2064 2087 2899

HOLLAND LP p 700
1000 Holland Dr, Crete IL 60417
Tel (708) 672-2300 SIC 2899 3743

FUCHS CORP p 583
17050 Lathrop Ave, Harvey IL 60426
Tel (800) 323-7755 SIC 2992 5172 2899

■ **AMERICAN COLLOID CO** p 70
2870 Forbs Ave, Hoffman Estates IL 60192
Tel (847) 851-1700 SIC 1459 2899

■ **COLLOID ENVIRONMENTAL TECHNOLOGIES CO LLC** p 337
2870 Forbs Ave, Hoffman Estates IL 60192
Tel (847) 851-1500 SIC 3259 2899

PRESTONE PRODUCTS CORP p 1173
1900 W Field Ct, Lake Forest IL 60045
Tel (847) 482-2045 SIC 2899

ALDRIDGE ELECTRIC INC p 48
844 E Rockland Rd, Libertyville IL 60048
Tel (847) 680-5200 SIC 2899 4789 3643

■ **NALCO CO LLC** p 1006
1601 W Diehl Rd, Naperville IL 60563
Tel (630) 305-1000
SIC 3559 2899 2992 2891

■ **NALCO HOLDING CO** p 1007
1601 W Diehl Rd, Naperville IL 60563
Tel (630) 305-1000 SIC 2899 2992

■ **NALCO HOLDINGS LLC** p 1007
1601 W Diehl Rd, Naperville IL 60563
Tel (630) 305-1000 SIC 2899 2992 3559

■ **CHEMTOOL INC** p 293
801 W Rockton Rd, Rockton IL 61072
Tel (815) 957-4140
SIC 2992 2899 2842 2841

■ **RUST-OLEUM CORP** p 1260
11 E Hawthorn Pkwy, Vernon Hills IL 60061
Tel (847) 367-7700
SIC 2891 2899 2816 2842 2851

■ **CAMBREX CHARLES CITY INC** p 244
1205 11th St, Charles City IA 50616
Tel (641) 257-1000
SIC 2834 2899 2865 2048

ROUSSELOT DUBUQUE INC p 1253
2350 Kerper Blvd, Dubuque IA 52001
Tel (262) 363-6050 SIC 2899

■ **COMPASS MINERALS AMERICA INC** p 351
9900 W 109th St Ste 600, Overland Park KS 66210
Tel (913) 344-9100 SIC 2899 1479

■ **COMPASS MINERALS GROUP INC** p 351
9900 W 109th St Ste 600, Overland Park KS 66210
Tel (913) 344-9100 SIC 2819 2899

▲ **COMPASS MINERALS INTERNATIONAL INC** p 351
9900 W 109th St Ste 100, Overland Park KS 66210
Tel (913) 344-9200 SIC 1474 2899 2819

■ **ASHLAND LLC** p 117
50 E Rivercenter Blvd # 1600, Covington KY 41011
Tel (859) 815-3333
SIC 2899 2851 2821 2911 5169 7549

▲ **W R GRACE & CO** p 1569
7500 Grace Dr, Columbia MD 21044
Tel (410) 531-4000
SIC 2819 3531 2899 2891 3479

■ **W R GRACE & CO-CONN** p 1569
7500 Grace Dr, Columbia MD 21044
Tel (410) 531-4000
SIC 2819 3531 2899 2891 3479

■ **GILLETTE CO** p 612
1 Gillette Park, Boston MA 02127
Tel (617) 421-7000
SIC 3421 3634 2844 3951 2899

■ **GE IONICS INC** p 596
3 Burlington Woods Dr # 200, Burlington MA 01803
Tel (781) 359-7000
SIC 3589 2086 4941 3559 2899 3823

▲ **GCP APPLIED TECHNOLOGIES INC** p 595
62 Whittemore Ave, Cambridge MA 02140
Tel (617) 876-1400 SIC 2819 2899

MEXICHEM SPECIALTY COMPOUNDS INC p 957
170 Pioneer Dr, Leominster MA 01453
Tel (978) 537-8071 SIC 3087 2899

MONSON COMPANIES INC p 985
154 Pioneer Dr, Leominster MA 01453
Tel (978) 840-7007
SIC 5169 5172 2899 2842

▲ **ASPEN AEROGELS INC** p 118
30 Forbes Rd Bldg B, Northborough MA 01532
Tel (508) 691-1111 SIC 2899

■ **YANKEE CANDLE CO INC** p 1634
16 Yankee Candle Way, South Deerfield MA 01373
Tel (413) 665-8306 SIC 3999 2899 5999

■ **YANKEE HOLDING CORP** p 1635
16 Yankee Candle Way, South Deerfield MA 01373
Tel (413) 665-8306 SIC 3999 2899

■ **YCC HOLDINGS LLC** p 1635
16 Yankee Candle Way, South Deerfield MA 01373
Tel (413) 665-8306 SIC 3999 2899 5999

WACKER BIOCHEM CORP p 1570
3301 Sutton Rd, Adrian MI 49221
Tel (517) 264-8500 SIC 2899

THETFORD CORP p 1447
7101 Jackson Rd, Ann Arbor MI 48103
Tel (734) 769-6000
SIC 3632 3089 2842 2621 3431 2899

MAGNI GROUP INC p 896
390 Park St Ste 300, Birmingham MI 48009
Tel (248) 647-4500 SIC 2899 3479

DIVERSIFIED CHEMICAL TECHNOLOGIES INC p 444
15477 Woodrow Wilson St, Detroit MI 48238
Tel (313) 867-5444
SIC 2891 2992 2899 2842 2841

PRESSURE VESSEL SERVICE INC p 1173
10900 Harper Ave, Detroit MI 48213
Tel (313) 921-1200
SIC 5169 2819 2899 4953 3535

EFTEC NORTH AMERICA LLC p 481
31601 Research Park Dr, Madison Heights MI 48071
Tel (248) 526-4565
SIC 2891 8731 3296 2899 2851

ROLLED ALLOYS INC p 1247
125 W Sterns Rd, Temperance MI 48182
Tel (800) 521-0332
SIC 5051 3369 3341 3317 2899 2851

▲ **HAWKINS INC** p 670
2381 Rosegate, Roseville MN 55113
Tel (612) 331-6910 SIC 5169 5074 2899

▲ **HB FULLER CO** p 671
1200 Willow Lake Blvd, Saint Paul MN 55110
Tel (651) 236-5900 SIC 2891 2899

FIKE CORP p 542
704 Sw 10th St, Blue Springs MO 64015
Tel (816) 229-3405
SIC 3494 3569 3444 2899

■ **PETROLITE CORP** p 1139
369 Marshall Ave, Saint Louis MO 63119
Tel (314) 961-3500
SIC 3559 2999 2899 2821 2911

SIGMA - ALDRICH CO LLC p 1321
3050 Spruce St, Saint Louis MO 63103
Tel (314) 771-5765 SIC 2899 5169

SIGMA-ALDRICH CORP p 1321
3050 Spruce St, Saint Louis MO 63103
Tel (314) 771-5765 SIC 2899 5169 8099

▲ **ALBANY INTERNATIONAL CORP** p 45
216 Airport Dr, Rochester NH 03867
Tel (518) 445-2200
SIC 2221 3496 2399 2899 3089

LONZA INC p 877
90 Boroline Rd Ste 1, Allendale NJ 07401
Tel (201) 316-9200 SIC 2899 2869 2819

LANXESS SYBRON CHEMICALS INC p 844
200 Birmingham Rd, Birmingham NJ 08011
Tel (609) 893-1100 SIC 2843 2899 3589

INDOPCO INC p 739
10 Finderne Ave Ste A, Bridgewater NJ 08807
Tel (908) 685-5000
SIC 2891 2046 2821 2869 2899 2099

ELEMENTIS GLOBAL LLC p 486
469 Old Trenton Rd, East Windsor NJ 08512
Tel (609) 443-2000 SIC 2899

ELEMENTIS SPECIALTIES INC p 486
469 Old Trenton Rd, East Windsor NJ 08512
Tel (609) 443-2000
SIC 2851 8731 2899 2865 2816

BASF CORP p 158
100 Park Ave, Florham Park NJ 07932
Tel (973) 245-6000
SIC 2869 2819 2899 2843 2834 2879

BASFIN CORP p 158
100 Campus Dr Ste 301, Florham Park NJ 07932
Tel (973) 245-6000
SIC 2869 2819 2899 2843 2879 2834

AJINOMOTO NORTH AMERICA INC p 41
400 Kelby St, Fort Lee NJ 07024
Tel (201) 292-3200
SIC 5142 5169 2869 2899

UNGERER INDUSTRIES INC p 1502
4 Bridgewater Ln, Lincoln Park NJ 07035
Tel (973) 628-0600 SIC 2899 2844 2087

SIKA CORP p 1322
201 Polito Ave, Lyndhurst NJ 07071
Tel (201) 933-8800
SIC 2891 2899 2851 2821 3272

■ **CHEMETALL US INC** p 293
675 Central Ave, New Providence NJ 07974
Tel (908) 464-6900 SIC 2842 2899 2851

FIRMENICH INC p 544
250 Plainsboro Rd, Plainsboro NJ 08536
Tel (609) 452-1000 SIC 2899 2869

■ **ROCKWOOD SPECIALTIES GROUP INC** p 1245
100 Overlook Ctr Ste 101, Princeton NJ 08540
Tel (609) 514-0300 SIC 5169 2899

SOLVAY USA INC p 1339
504 Carnegie Ctr, Princeton NJ 08540
Tel (609) 860-4000
SIC 2899 2869 2821 2087 2865

BRENNTAG SPECIALTIES INC p 210
1000 Coolidge St, South Plainfield NJ 07080
Tel (800) 732-0562 SIC 5169 2816 2899

■ **PHIBRO ANIMAL HEALTH CORP** p 1142
300 Frank W Burr Blvd, Teaneck NJ 07666
Tel (201) 329-7300
SIC 2819 5169 2899 2834

■ **INTERNATIONAL SPECIALTY PRODUCTS INC** p 757
1361 Alps Rd, Wayne NJ 07470
Tel (859) 815-3333
SIC 2869 2821 2843 2842 2899

CYTEC INDUSTRIES INC p 406
5 Garret Mountain Plz, Woodland Park NJ 07424
Tel (973) 357-3100
SIC 2899 2821 2672 2851 2823 2819

▲ **BALCHEM CORP** p 147
52 Sunrise Park Rd, New Hampton NY 10958
Tel (845) 326-5600 SIC 2869 2899

ICC INDUSTRIES INC p 727
460 Park Ave Fl 7, New York NY 10022
Tel (212) 521-1700
SIC 2821 2869 2911 2899 3081 2834

MDI HOLDINGS LLC p 933
399 Park Ave Fl 14, New York NY 10022
Tel (212) 559-1127
SIC 2899 2842 2874 2992 2752 3577

■ SPECIALTY MINERALS INC p 1356
622 3rd Ave Fl 38, New York NY 10017
Tel (212) 878-1800
SIC 2819 5032 1422 5169 2899

ROCHESTER MIDLAND CORP p 1243
155 Paragon Dr, Rochester NY 14624
Tel (585) 336-2200 *SIC* 2842 2676 2899

ALAMANCE FOODS INC p 43
840 Plantation Dr, Burlington NC 27215
Tel (336) 226-6392
SIC 2026 2899 2024 2086

▲ ALBEMARLE CORP p 46
4350 Congress St Ste 700, Charlotte NC 28209
Tel (980) 299-5700
SIC 2821 2834 2819 2899 2812 2869

BONSAL AMERICAN INC p 200
625 Griffith Rd Ste 100, Charlotte NC 28217
Tel (704) 525-1621
SIC 3272 1442 3253 2899

■ CARLISLE CORP p 257
11605 N Community Hse Rd, Charlotte NC 28277
Tel (704) 501-1100
SIC 2952 2899 3011 2295 3089 3577

I KESTREL ACQUISITION CORP p 725
1035 Swabia Ct, Durham NC 27703
Tel (919) 990-7500
SIC 2821 2822 2869 2899 2891 2851

REICHHOLD LIQUIDATION INC p 1220
1035 Swabia Ct, Durham NC 27703
Tel (919) 990-7500
SIC 2821 2822 2869 2899 2891 2851

LOW & BONAR INC p 881
1301 Sand Hill Rd, Enka NC 28728
Tel (828) 665-5000
SIC 5199 3296 2899 2297 2221

EVONIK STOCKHAUSEN LLC p 516
2401 Doyle St, Greensboro NC 27406
Tel (336) 333-3500 *SIC* 2869 2899

RADIATOR SPECIALTY CO INC p 1204
600 Radiator Rd, Indian Trail NC 28079
Tel (704) 688-2302 *SIC* 2899

FIBER COMPOSITES LLC p 539
181 Random Dr, New London NC 28127
Tel (704) 463-7120 *SIC* 2899

■ MILACRON LLC p 968
10200 Alliance Rd Ste 200, Blue Ash OH 45242
Tel (513) 487-5000 *SIC* 3549 2899

■ LUBRIZOL ADVANCED MATERIALS INC p 884
9911 Brecksville Rd, Brecksville OH 44141
Tel (216) 447-5000
SIC 2899 2891 3088 2834 3629

EMERY OLEOCHEMICALS LLC p 492
4900 Este Ave, Cincinnati OH 45232
Tel (513) 762-2500 *SIC* 2899

BASF CONSTRUCTION CHEMICALS LLC p 158
23700 Chagrin Blvd, Cleveland OH 44122
Tel (216) 831-5500 *SIC* 2899 2851 1799

■ EUCLID CHEMICAL CO p 512
19218 Redwood Rd, Cleveland OH 44110
Tel (800) 321-7628 *SIC* 2899 4213

PRINCE & IZANT CO p 1176
12999 Plaza Dr, Cleveland OH 44130
Tel (216) 362-7000
SIC 5051 3398 3351 3341 3339 2899

STATE INDUSTRIAL PRODUCTS CORP p 1381
5915 Landerbrook Dr # 300, Cleveland OH 44124
Tel (877) 747-6986
SIC 2841 5072 2842 2992 2952 2899

■ HEXION LLC p 688
180 E Broad St Fl 26, Columbus OH 43215
Tel (614) 225-4000 *SIC* 2821 2899

DOVER CHEMICAL CORP p 453
3676 Davis Rd Nw, Dover OH 44622
Tel (330) 343-7711 *SIC* 2819 2869 2899

ASK CHEMICALS LP p 118
495 Metro Pl S Ste 250, Dublin OH 43017
Tel (614) 763-0384 *SIC* 2899

POLYMER ADDITIVES HOLDINGS INC p 1160
7500 E Pleasant Valley Rd, Independence OH 44131
Tel (216) 875-7200 *SIC* 5169 2899

POLYMER ADDITIVES INC p 1160
7500 E Pleasant Valley Rd, Independence OH 44131
Tel (216) 875-7200 *SIC* 5169 2899

■ REPUBLIC POWDERED METALS INC p 1225
2628 Pearl Rd, Medina OH 44256
Tel (330) 225-3192
SIC 2851 2891 3069 2899 2865 2842

▲ RPM INTERNATIONAL INC p 1255
2628 Pearl Rd, Medina OH 44256
Tel (330) 273-5090
SIC 2851 2891 3069 2899 2865 2842

DAYTON SUPERIOR CORP p 418
1125 Byers Rd, Miamisburg OH 45342
Tel (937) 866-0711
SIC 3315 3452 3462 3089 2899

■ LUBRIZOL CORP p 884
29400 Lakeland Blvd, Wickliffe OH 44092
Tel (440) 943-4200 *SIC* 2899 2869

■ CARLISLE CONSTRUCTION MATERIALS LLC p 257
1285 Ritner Hwy, Carlisle PA 17013
Tel (717) 245-7000
SIC 2952 3069 5031 2899 2891

▲ QUAKER CHEMICAL CORP p 1196
901 E Hector St, Conshohocken PA 19428
Tel (610) 832-4000
SIC 2992 2899 2869 2891

■ GE INFRASTRUCTURE SENSING p 596
4636 Somerton Rd, Feasterville Trevose PA 19053
Tel (617) 926-1749
SIC 3589 2086 4941 3559 2899 3823

ARKEMA DELAWARE INC p 110
900 First Ave, King Of Prussia PA 19406
Tel (610) 205-7000
SIC 2812 2819 2869 2891 2899 2992

CRYSTAL INC - PMC p 397
601 W 8th St, Lansdale PA 19446
Tel (267) 649-7330 *SIC* 2899 2842

BERWIND CORP p 176
3000 Ctr Sq W 1500 Mkt St 1500 W, Philadelphia PA 19102
Tel (215) 563-2800
SIC 6519 5052 4789 3625 3669 2899

▲ CHEMTURA CORP p 294
1818 Market St Ste 3700, Philadelphia PA 19103
Tel (215) 446-3911
SIC 2869 2843 2821 2911 2899 2842

■ ROHM AND HAAS CO p 1246
100 N Independence Mall W, Philadelphia PA 19106
Tel (215) 592-3000
SIC 2819 2851 2891 2899

AXIALL LLC p 140
11 Stanwix St Ste 1900, Pittsburgh PA 15222
Tel (412) 515-8149 *SIC* 2899

▲ KOPPERS HOLDINGS INC p 827
436 7th Ave, Pittsburgh PA 15219
Tel (412) 227-2001
SIC 2865 2491 2895 3312 2899

■ KOPPERS INC p 828
436 7th Ave, Pittsburgh PA 15219
Tel (412) 227-2001
SIC 2865 2491 3312 2899

■ GE BETZ INC p 595
4636 Somerton Rd, Trevose PA 19053
Tel (215) 355-3300
SIC 2899 3826 5084 3823

CRC INDUSTRIES INC p 390
885 Louis Dr, Warminster PA 18974
Tel (215) 674-4300
SIC 2992 3471 2899 2842

CRANSTON PRINT WORKS CO INC p 389
1381 Cranston St, Cranston RI 02920
Tel (401) 943-4800 *SIC* 2261 2262 2899

TECHNIC INC p 1431
47 Molter St, Cranston RI 02910
Tel (401) 781-6100 *SIC* 2899 3559

■ DRYVIT HOLDINGS INC p 457
1 Energy Way, Providence RI 02903
Tel (401) 822-4100 *SIC* 2822 2899

■ DRYVIT SYSTEMS INC p 457
1 Energy Way, West Warwick RI 02893
Tel (401) 822-4100 *SIC* 2899

3V SIGMA USA INC p 3
888 Woodstock St, Georgetown SC 29440
Tel (843) 546-8556 *SIC* 2869 2899 8731

CAPSUGEL MANUFACTURING INC p 251
535 Emerald Rd N, Greenwood SC 29646
Tel (864) 223-2270 *SIC* 2899

■ MANUFACTURERS CHEMICALS LLC p 903
4325 Old Tasso Rd Ne, Cleveland TN 37312
Tel (423) 476-6666 *SIC* 2899

PMC BIOGENIX INC p 1157
1231 Pope St, Memphis TN 38108
Tel (901) 320-5800 *SIC* 2899

KILGORE FLARES CO LLC p 818
155 Kilgore Rd, Toone TN 38381
Tel (731) 228-5200 *SIC* 2899 3728

FLARE INDUSTRIES LLC p 554
16310 Bratton Ln Ste 350, Austin TX 78728
Tel (512) 836-9473
SIC 3822 7359 3694 2899 1711 3569

OXEA HOLDING CORP p 1100
1505 Lyndon B Johnson Fwy, Dallas TX 75234
Tel (972) 481-2700 *SIC* 2899

OXY CHEMICAL CORP p 1101
5005 L B Johnson Fwy 2200, Dallas TX 75244
Tel (972) 404-3800
SIC 2869 2873 2874 2899 3089

■ OXY VINYLS LP p 1101
5005 Lbj Fwy Ste 2200, Dallas TX 75244
Tel (972) 720-7000
SIC 2821 2899 2819 1382

SEKISUI SPECIALTY CHEMICALS AMERICA LLC p 1301
1501 Lyndo B Johns Fwy St Ste 530, Dallas TX 75234
Tel (972) 277-2900 *SIC* 2899

■ VALHI INC p 1540
5430 Lbj Fwy Ste 1700, Dallas TX 75240
Tel (972) 233-1700
SIC 2816 2899 3429 4953

■ ROHM AND HAAS TEXAS INC p 1247
6600 La Porte Fwy, Deer Park TX 77536
Tel (281) 476-8304 *SIC* 2869 2899 2819

■ ESAB GROUP INC p 509
2800 Airport Rd, Denton TX 76207
Tel (843) 669-4411 *SIC* 3548 2899

▲ KMG CHEMICALS INC p 824
300 Throckmorton St, Fort Worth TX 76102
Tel (817) 761-6100 *SIC* 2899

■ BAKER HUGHES OILFIELD OPERATIONS INC p 146
17021 Aldine Westfield Rd, Houston TX 77073
Tel (713) 439-8600
SIC 1381 1311 1389 2899

ECONOMY MUD PRODUCTS CO p 476
435 E Anderson Rd, Houston TX 77047
Tel (800) 231-2066 *SIC* 2869 2899

▲ FLOTEK INDUSTRIES INC p 560
10603 W Sam Houston Pkwy, Houston TX 77064
Tel (713) 849-9911
SIC 2087 2869 2899 3533 3491

HAVERHILL CHEMICALS LLC p 668
16800 Imperial Valley Dr # 499, Houston TX 77060
Tel (281) 885-8900 *SIC* 2899

SOLVAY INTEROX INC p 1339
3737 Buffalo Speedway, Houston TX 77098
Tel (713) 525-6500 *SIC* 2819 2899

TEXAS UNITED CORP p 1444
4800 San Felipe St, Houston TX 77056
Tel (713) 877-1793
SIC 1479 2819 4619 2899 3299 7353

■ TOTAL PETROCHEMICALS & REFINING USA INC p 1463
1201 La St Ste 1800, Houston TX 77002
Tel (713) 483-5000 *SIC* 2911 2899 2869

NCH CORP p 1022
2727 Chemsearch Blvd, Irving TX 75062
Tel (972) 438-0211
SIC 2842 2899 3432 3548 3429

FRITZ INDUSTRIES INC p 580
500 N Sam Houston Rd, Mesquite TX 75149
Tel (972) 285-5471 *SIC* 2899

THIRD COAST PACKAGING INC p 1448
1871 Mykawa Rd, Pearland TX 77581
Tel (281) 412-0275 *SIC* 5172 4783 2899

■ BAKER PETROLITE LLC p 146
12645 W Airport Blvd, Sugar Land TX 77478
Tel (281) 276-5400 *SIC* 2899 2869

■ NALCO ENERGY SERVICES LP p 1007
7705 Highway 90a, Sugar Land TX 77478
Tel (281) 263-7000 *SIC* 2899

■ HUNTSMAN ADVANCED MATERIALS AMERICAS LLC p 720
10003 Woodloch Forest Dr # 260, The Woodlands TX 77380
Tel (281) 719-6000 *SIC* 2899

■ INDEPENDENCE OILFIELD CHEMICALS LLC p 736
1450 Lake Robbins Dr # 400, The Woodlands TX 77380
Tel (713) 936-4340 *SIC* 2899 5169

MAGNABLEND INC p 896
326 N Grand Ave, Waxahachie TX 75165
Tel (972) 938-2028 *SIC* 2899

AMERICAN PACIFIC CORP p 77
10622 W 6400 N, Cedar City UT 84721
Tel (435) 865-5000 *SIC* 2899

G S L CORP p 587
765 N 10500 W, Ogden UT 84404
Tel (801) 731-3100 *SIC* 2819 2899 3339

DOTERRA INTERNATIONAL LLC p 452
389 S 1300 W, Pleasant Grove UT 84062
Tel (801) 615-7200 *SIC* 2899

■ CHEMTREAT INC p 293
5640 Cox Rd Ste 300, Glen Allen VA 23060
Tel (804) 935-2000 *SIC* 2899 3589

▲ SYNALLOY CORP p 1414
4510 Cox Rd Ste 201, Glen Allen VA 23060
Tel (864) 585-3605
SIC 3317 3443 2865 2899 2869

LUCK STONE CORP p 884
515 Stone Mill Dr, Manakin Sabot VA 23103
Tel (804) 784-3383
SIC 1423 2899 3281 5211 8741

■ AFTON CHEMICAL CORP p 33
500 Spring St, Richmond VA 23219
Tel (804) 788-5086 *SIC* 2899 2999 3999

■ ETHYL CORP p 511
330 S 4th St, Richmond VA 23219
Tel (804) 788-5000
SIC 2869 5169 2899 2841 2865

▲ NEWMARKET CORP p 1038
330 S 4th St, Richmond VA 23219
Tel (804) 788-5000
SIC 2869 2899 2841 2865

WIXON INDUSTRIES INC p 1619
1390 E Bolivar Ave, Milwaukee WI 53235
Tel (800) 841-5304 *SIC* 2099 2087 2899

SIC 2911 Petroleum Refining

INDORAMA VENTURES XYLENES & PTA LLC p 739
1401 Finley Island Rd, Decatur AL 35601
Tel (256) 340-5200 *SIC* 2911

ARCTIC SLOPE REGIONAL CORP p 106
3900 C St Ste 801, Anchorage AK 99503
Tel (907) 339-6000 *SIC* 1389 2911 1623

■ GIANT INDUSTRIES INC p 611
1250 W Washington St # 101, Tempe AZ 85281
Tel (915) 534-1400 *SIC* 2911 5541 5172

■ NORTHERN TIER ENERGY LP p 1057
1250 W Washington St # 101, Tempe AZ 85281
Tel (602) 302-5450 *SIC* 2911

■ WESTERN REFINING SOUTHWEST INC p 1599
1250 W Washington St # 101, Tempe AZ 85281
Tel (602) 286-1400
SIC 2911 5171 5411 5541

■ WESTERN REFINING WHOLESALE INC p 1599
1250 W Washington St # 101, Tempe AZ 85281
Tel (602) 286-1401 *SIC* 5171 2911 2992

▲ MURPHY OIL CORP p 1001
300 E Peach St, El Dorado AR 71730
Tel (870) 862-6411 *SIC* 1311 1382 2911

■ MURPHY OIL USA INC p 1001
200 E Peach St, El Dorado AR 71730
Tel (870) 862-6411
SIC 8742 2911 1311 4213

■ CALIFORNIA RESOURCES ELK HILLS LLC p 241
11109 River Run Blvd, Bakersfield CA 93311
Tel (661) 412-5000 *SIC* 2911

▲ AEMETIS INC p 29
20400 Stevens, Cupertino CA 95014
Tel (408) 213-0940 *SIC* 8731 2911

ATLANTIC RICHFIELD CO INC p 127
4 Centerpointe Dr Ste 200, La Palma CA 90623
Tel (800) 333-3991 *SIC* 5541 1321 2911

SHELL MARTINEZ REFINING CO p 1314
3485 Pacheco Blvd, Martinez CA 94553
Tel (925) 313-3000 *SIC* 2911

NEWTON BIOFUELS LLC p 1039
127 Crystal Ave, Newport Beach CA 92662
Tel (949) 697-3088 *SIC* 2911

■ PARAMOUNT PETROLEUM CORP p 1114
14700 Downey Ave, Paramount CA 90723
Tel (562) 531-2060 *SIC* 2911

APOLLO IDEMITSU CORP p 97
1831 16th St, Sacramento CA 95811
Tel (916) 443-0890 *SIC* 5172 2911

■ CHEVRON CAPTAIN CO LLC p 295
6001 Bollinger Canyon Rd, San Ramon CA 94583
Tel (925) 842-1000 *SIC* 2911

▲ CHEVRON CORP p 295
6001 Bollinger Canyon Rd, San Ramon CA 94583
Tel (925) 842-1000
SIC 2911 1311 1382 1321 5541

■ CHEVRON GLOBAL ENERGY INC p 296
6001 Bollinger Canyon Rd, San Ramon CA 94583
Tel (925) 842-1000 *SIC* 2911 4731 5172

■ CHEVRON USA INC p 296
6001 Bollinger Canyon Rd D1248, San Ramon CA 94583
Tel (925) 842-1000
SIC 5541 5511 2911 5171

WORLD OIL MARKETING CO p 1625
9302 Garfield Ave, South Gate CA 90280
Tel (562) 928-0100
SIC 2911 4953 2951 5541 4213 4212

DUQUESNE ENERGY SERVCES LLC p 462
4949 S Syracuse St # 550, Denver CO 80237
Tel (832) 278-5980 *SIC* 2911 5142

ENCANA OIL & GAS (USA) INC p 495
370 17th St Ste 1700, Denver CO 80202
Tel (303) 623-2300 *SIC* 2911 1311

■ FRONTIER REFINING & MARKETING LLC p 581
8055 E Tufts Ave, Denver CO 80237
Tel (303) 694-0025 *SIC* 2911

SUNCOR ENERGY (USA) INC p 1402
717 17th St Ste 2900, Denver CO 80202
Tel (303) 793-8000 *SIC* 2911

▲ INNOSPEC INC p 744
8310 S Valley Hwy Ste 350, Englewood CO 80112
Tel (303) 792-5554 *SIC* 2911 2869

■ ARMORED AUTOGROUP PARENT INC p 111
44 Old Ridgebury Rd # 300, Danbury CT 06810
Tel (203) 205-2900 *SIC* 2842 2911 2899

AEGEAN BUNKERING (USA) LLC p 29
20 Signal Rd, Stamford CT 06902
Tel (212) 430-1100 *SIC* 2911

AXEON REFINING LLC p 140
750 Wshngton Blvd Ste 600, Stamford CT 06901
Tel (210) 249-9988 *SIC* 2911

AXEON SPECIALTY PRODUCTS LLC p 140
750 Wshngton Blvd Ste 600, Stamford CT 06901
Tel (855) 378-4958 *SIC* 2911

MERCURY FUEL SERVICE INC p 945
43 Lafayette St, Waterbury CT 06708
Tel (203) 756-7284
SIC 5172 5541 5411 5983 1711 2911

SOLENIS INTERNATIONAL LP p 1338
500 Hercules Rd, Wilmington DE 19808
Tel (302) 994-1698 *SIC* 2911 2611 1382

UNITED ACQUISITION CORP p 1506
802 N West St, Wilmington DE 19801
Tel (302) 651-9856 *SIC* 2911 5541 2951

SEMINOLE TRIBE OF FLORIDA INC p 1302
6300 Stirling Rd, Hollywood FL 33024
Tel (954) 966-6300
SIC 7999 5194 2011 5182 2911

ARIZONA CHEMICAL CO LLC p 108
4600 Touchton Rd E # 1500, Jacksonville FL 32246
Tel (904) 928-8700 *SIC* 2861 2911

▲ KLX INC p 823
1300 Corporate Center Way # 200, Wellington FL 33414
Tel (561) 383-5100 *SIC* 3728 2911 1381

AMREP INC p 86
425 Franklin Gtwy Se # 530, Marietta GA 30067
Tel (770) 590-5960
SIC 2842 2079 2911 2869 2841 2819

HAWAII ENERGY RESOURCES INC p 669
733 Bishop St Fl 28, Honolulu HI 96813
Tel (808) 547-3111 *SIC* 5172 2911 5171

PDV MIDWEST REFINING LLC p 1125
135th St New Ave, Lemont IL 60439
Tel (630) 257-7761
SIC 2992 2911 5171 4213

BP AMERICA INC p 205
4101 Winfield Rd Ste 200, Warrenville IL 60555
Tel (630) 420-5111
SIC 2911 5171 4612 4613 4424

STANDARD OIL CO p 1376
4101 Winfield Rd Ste 100, Warrenville IL 60555
Tel (630) 836-5000 *SIC* 2911

▲ CALUMET SPECIALTY PRODUCTS PARTNERS LP p 243
2780 Waterfront Pkwy Ste 200 E, Indianapolis IN 46214
Tel (317) 328-5660 *SIC* 2911 2992

COUNTRYMARK COOPERATIVE HOLDING CORP p 375
225 S East St Ste 144, Indianapolis IN 46202
Tel (800) 808-3170
SIC 5172 2911 1382 1311 6719

■ REG BIOFUELS LLC p 1218
416 S Bell Ave, Ames IA 50010
Tel (515) 239-8000 *SIC* 2911

▲ RENEWABLE ENERGY GROUP INC p 1223
416 S Bell Ave, Ames IA 50010
Tel (515) 239-8000 *SIC* 2911 2869

■ HOLLYFRONTIER EL DORADO REFINING LLC p 701
1401 Douglas Rd, El Dorado KS 67042
Tel (316) 321-2200 *SIC* 2911

■ CHS MCPHERSON REFINERY INC p 304
2000 S Main St, Mcpherson KS 67460
Tel (620) 241-2340 *SIC* 2911 4612 4213

FLINT HILLS RESOURCES LP p 557
4111 E 37th St N, Wichita KS 67220
Tel (800) 292-3133
SIC 5172 4612 1382 2911

KOCH INDUSTRIES INC p 825
4111 E 37th St N, Wichita KS 67220
Tel (316) 828-5500 *SIC* 5172 2911 5169

KOCH RESOURCES LLC p 826
4111 E 37th St N, Wichita KS 67220
Tel (316) 828-5500 SIC 6221 2911

KOCH SUPPLY & TRADING LP p 826
4111 E 37th St N, Wichita KS 67220
Tel (316) 828-5500 SIC 2911

KS&T INTERNATIONAL HOLDINGS LP p 831
4111 E 37th St N, Wichita KS 67220
Tel (316) 828-5500 SIC 2911

MONUMENT CHEMICAL KENTUCKY LLC p 987
2450 Olin Rd, Brandenburg KY 40108
Tel (270) 422-2101 SIC 2911

■ CATLETTSBURG REFINING LLC p 267
11631 Us Route 23, Catlettsburg KY 41129
Tel (606) 921-3333 SIC 2911

■ ASHLAND LLC p 117
50 E Rivercenter Blvd # 1600, Covington KY 41011
Tel (859) 815-3333
SIC 2899 2851 2821 2911 5169 7549

■ CHALMETTE REFINING LLC p 287
500 W Saint Bernard Hwy, Chalmette LA 70043
Tel (504) 281-1212 SIC 2911

■ ALON REFINING KROTZ SPRINGS INC p 59
E I 20, Krotz Springs LA 70750
Tel (337) 594-5300 SIC 2911

CROWN CENTRAL PETROLEUM CORP p 395
1 N Charles St Ste 2100, Baltimore MD 21201
Tel (410) 539-7400 SIC 2911 5171 6794

ROSEMORE HOLDINGS INC p 1251
1 N Charles St Ste 2200, Baltimore MD 21201
Tel (410) 347-7090
SIC 2911 5171 5541 5411

MICHIGAN PAVING AND MATERIALS CO p 961
2575 S Haggerty Rd # 100, Canton MI 48188
Tel (734) 397-2050 SIC 1522 1541 2911

GENOVA PRODUCTS INC p 604
7034 E Court St, Davison MI 48423
Tel (810) 744-4500
SIC 3089 2891 2911 3494 3084 2952

CENEX INC p 275
5500 Cenex Dr, Inver Grove Heights MN 55077
Tel (800) 232-3639
SIC 1311 2911 4613 4922 4789 4213

▲ CHS INC p 304
5500 Cenex Dr, Inver Grove Heights MN 55077
Tel (651) 355-6000
SIC 5153 5191 2075 1311 2911 4613

ERGON INC p 507
2829 Lakeland Dr Ste 2000, Flowood MS 39232
Tel (601) 933-3000
SIC 2911 4213 4449 4613 5171 5172

■ PETROLITE CORP p 1139
369 Marshall Ave, Saint Louis MO 63119
Tel (314) 961-3500
SIC 3559 2999 2899 2821 2911

TOTAL AMERICAN SERVICES INC p 1462
100 Town Square Pl # 401, Jersey City NJ 07310
Tel (206) 626-3500
SIC 2911 4612 5541 2895

■ PBF ENERGY CO LLC p 1123
1 Sylvan Way Ste 2, Parsippany NJ 07054
Tel (973) 455-7500 SIC 2911

▲ PBF ENERGY INC p 1123
1 Sylvan Way Ste 2, Parsippany NJ 07054
Tel (973) 455-7500 SIC 2911

■ PBF HOLDING CO LLC p 1123
1 Sylvan Way Ste 2, Parsippany NJ 07054
Tel (888) 661-8949 SIC 2911 2992

■ MOBIL RESEARCH AND DEVELOPMENT CORP p 980
600 Billingsport Rd, Paulsboro NJ 08066
Tel (856) 224-2134 SIC 2911

■ PAULSBORO REFINING CO LLC p 1122
800 Jenkins Blvd, Paulsboro NJ 08066
Tel (973) 455-7500 SIC 2911

■ HOLLYFRONTIER NAVAJO REFINING LLC p 701
501 E Main St, Artesia NM 88210
Tel (575) 748-3311 SIC 2911 2951

MACK ENERGY CORP p 892
11344 Lovington Hwy, Artesia NM 88210
Tel (575) 748-1288 SIC 1311 2911

▲ HESS CORP p 688
1185 Ave Of The Americas, New York NY 10036
Tel (212) 997-8500
SIC 1311 2911 5171 5541 4911

■ HESS OIL VIRGIN ISLAND CORP p 688
1185 Ave Of The Amer 39, New York NY 10036
Tel (212) 997-8500 SIC 2911

ICC INDUSTRIES INC p 727
460 Park Ave Fl 7, New York NY 10022
Tel (212) 521-1700
SIC 2821 2869 2911 2899 3081 2834

WARREN OIL CO INC p 1577
2340 Us Highway 301 N, Dunn NC 28334
Tel (910) 892-6456
SIC 5172 5171 3826 2911

▲ MARATHON PETROLEUM CORP p 904
539 S Main St, Findlay OH 45840
Tel (419) 422-2121 SIC 2911 5172

■ MARATHON PETROLEUM SUPPLY LLC p 904
539 S Main St, Findlay OH 45840
Tel (419) 422-2121 SIC 2911

LIMA REFINING CO p 866
1150 S Metcalf St, Lima OH 45804
Tel (419) 226-2300 SIC 2911

■ DEVON ENERGY INTERNATIONAL CO p 434
20 N Broadway Ave # 1500, Oklahoma City OK 73102
Tel (405) 235-3611 SIC 2911

■ ENABLE OKLAHOMA INTRASTATE TRANSMISSION LLC p 495
211 N Robinson Ave N950, Oklahoma City OK 73102
Tel (405) 525-7788
SIC 4922 1321 4923 2911

CITGO INVESTMENT CO p 309
6100 S Yale Ave Ste 1200, Tulsa OK 74136
Tel (918) 254-6062 SIC 2911

PDV HOLDING INC p 1125
6100 S Yale Ave, Tulsa OK 74136
Tel (918) 495-4000
SIC 2911 2992 5171 4213

ROYAL MFG CO LP p 1254
516 S 25th West Ave, Tulsa OK 74127
Tel (918) 584-2671 SIC 2992 2911

SAMSON RESOURCES CO p 1274
2 W 2nd St Ste 1500, Tulsa OK 74103
Tel (918) 583-1791 SIC 1311 2911

AMERICAN REFINING GROUP INC p 78
77 N Kendall Ave, Bradford PA 16701
Tel (814) 368-1200 SIC 5171 2911

■ AMERIGAS INC p 82
460 N Gulph Rd Ste 100, King Of Prussia PA 19406
Tel (610) 337-7000
SIC 5984 5172 5722 2911 2813

■ SUNOCO INC p 1403
3801 West Chester Pike, Newtown Square PA 19073
Tel (215) 977-3000
SIC 5541 2911 2869 2865 5171 5052

■ SUNOCO INC (R&M) p 1403
3801 West Chester Pike, Newtown Square PA 19073
Tel (215) 977-3000
SIC 5541 2869 2911 5411

ATLANTIC PETROLEUM CORP p 127
1801 Market St Ste 1500, Philadelphia PA 19103
Tel (215) 977-3000
SIC 5541 5172 2911 4612

■ ATLANTIC REFINING & MARKETING CORP p 127
1801 Market St, Philadelphia PA 19103
Tel (215) 977-3000
SIC 2911 5171 5541 5411

▲ CHEMTURA CORP p 294
1818 Market St Ste 3700, Philadelphia PA 19103
Tel (215) 446-3911
SIC 2869 2843 2821 2911 2899 2842

PHILADELPHIA ENERGY SOLUTIONS LLC p 1142
1735 Market St Fl 10, Philadelphia PA 19103
Tel (267) 238-4300 SIC 2911

PHILADELPHIA ENERGY SOLUTIONS REFINING AND MARKETING LLC p 1142
1735 Market St Fl 11, Philadelphia PA 19103
Tel (267) 238-4300 SIC 2911

INTERNATIONAL GROUP INC p 755
1007 E Spring St, Titusville PA 16354
Tel (814) 827-4900 SIC 5169 2911

■ MONROE ENERGY LLC p 985
4101 Post Rd, Trainer PA 19061
Tel (610) 364-8000 SIC 2911

UNITED REFINING CO p 1511
15 Bradley St, Warren PA 16365
Tel (814) 723-1500 SIC 2911 5541 5411

UNITED REFINING INC p 1511
15 Bradley St, Warren PA 16365
Tel (814) 723-1500
SIC 2911 5541 5411 4612

■ DELEK REFINING LIMITED PARTNERSHIP p 424
7102 Commerce Way, Brentwood TN 37027
Tel (615) 771-6701 SIC 4612 2911

▲ DELEK US HOLDINGS INC p 424
7102 Commerce Way, Brentwood TN 37027
Tel (615) 771-6701
SIC 2911 4612 5541 5411

■ LION OIL CO p 869
7102 Commerce Way, Brentwood TN 37027
Tel (615) 771-6701 SIC 2911 4612 5172

■ EXXONMOBIL OIL CORP p 521
2805 Sycamore St, Beaumont TX 77701
Tel (409) 757-3763
SIC 2911 5171 4613 1311

OFFSHORE RENTAL LTD p 1076
1655 Louisiana St, Beaumont TX 77701
Tel (409) 833-2665 SIC 2911

BERRY CONTRACTING LP p 176
1414 Corn Product Rd, Corpus Christi TX 78409
Tel (361) 693-2100 SIC 2911 1611

▲ ALON USA ENERGY INC p 59
12700 Park Central Dr # 1600, Dallas TX 75251
Tel (972) 367-3600 SIC 2911 5171 5411

■ ALON USA INC p 59
12700 Park Central Dr # 1600, Dallas TX 75251
Tel (972) 367-3600 SIC 2911

■ ALON USA LP p 59
12700 Park Central Dr # 1600, Dallas TX 75251
Tel (972) 367-3600
SIC 2911 4612 5172 5541 2895

■ ALON USA PARTNERS LP p 59
12700 Park Central Dr # 1600, Dallas TX 75251
Tel (972) 367-3600 SIC 2911

▲ HOLLYFRONTIER CORP p 701
2828 N Harwood St # 1300, Dallas TX 75201
Tel (214) 871-3555 SIC 2911 4613

■ HOLLYFRONTIER REFINING & MARKETING LLC p 701
2828 N Harwood St # 1300, Dallas TX 75201
Tel (214) 871-3555 SIC 2911 4612

HUNT CONSOLIDATED INC p 718
1900 N Akard St, Dallas TX 75201
Tel (214) 978-8000
SIC 6799 1311 2911 1382 0212

HUNT OIL USA INC p 719
1900 N Akard St, Dallas TX 75201
Tel (214) 978-8000 SIC 1311 1382 2911

PLACID HOLDING CO p 1153
1601 Elm St Ste 3900, Dallas TX 75201
Tel (214) 880-8479 SIC 2911

RRH CORP p 1255
1900 N Akard St, Dallas TX 75201
Tel (214) 978-8000
SIC 1382 1311 2911 0212 6799

■ WESTERN REFINING CO LP p 1599
123 W Mills Ave Ste 200, El Paso TX 79901
Tel (915) 534-1400 SIC 2911

▲ WESTERN REFINING INC p 1599
123 W Mills Ave Ste 200, El Paso TX 79901
Tel (915) 534-1400 SIC 2911 5983

AIR LIQUIDE AMERICA SPECIALTY GASES LLC p 39
2700 Post Oak Blvd, Houston TX 77056
Tel (800) 217-2688 SIC 2911 2813

BP CORP NORTH AMERICA INC p 205
501 Westlake Park Blvd, Houston TX 77079
Tel (281) 366-2000
SIC 2911 5541 5171 1311 4613 4612

CITGO HOLDING INC p 309
1293 Eldridge Pkwy, Houston TX 77077
Tel (281) 531-0004
SIC 2911 2992 5171 4213

CITGO PETROLEUM CORP p 309
1293 Eldridge Pkwy, Houston TX 77077
Tel (832) 486-4000
SIC 2911 5171 4213 4612

■ CONOCOPHILLIPS HOLDING CO p 358
600 N Dairy Ashford Rd, Houston TX 77079
Tel (281) 293-1000 SIC 2911 5171 5541

■ EL PASO CGP CO LLC p 483
1001 Louisiana St, Houston TX 77002
Tel (713) 420-2600
SIC 2911 1311 4613 4612 5541 4922

ENRON CREDITORS RECOVERY CORP p 500
1221 Lamar St Ste 1325, Houston TX 77010
Tel (713) 853-6161
SIC 5172 4922 4911 1311 1321 2911

EP ENERGY RESALE CO LLC p 504
1001 Louisiana St, Houston TX 77002
Tel (713) 997-1000 SIC 2911

EQUILON ENTERPRISES LLC p 506
910 Louisiana St Ste 2, Houston TX 77002
Tel (713) 241-6161
SIC 2911 4612 2992 5172

■ EXXONMOBIL UPSTREAM RESEARCH CO p 522
3120 Buffalo Speedway, Houston TX 77098
Tel (713) 431-4222 SIC 2911

FRONTIER PETROLEUM RESOURCES INC p 581
6200 Savoy Dr Ste 650, Houston TX 77036
Tel (832) 242-1510 SIC 2911 5172

▲ LAZARUS ENERGY HOLDINGS LLC p 849
801 Travis St Ste 2100, Houston TX 77002
Tel (713) 850-0500 SIC 2911

LYONDELL CHEMICAL CO p 888
1221 Mckinney St Ste 300, Houston TX 77010
Tel (713) 309-7200 SIC 2869 2911

■ MARATHON OIL CO p 904
5555 San Felipe St # 2796, Houston TX 77056
Tel (713) 629-6600
SIC 2911 5171 5541 1311 4612 4613

▲ MARATHON OIL CORP p 904
5555 San Felipe St # 2796, Houston TX 77056
Tel (713) 629-6600
SIC 1311 2911 5171 5541

MERICHEM CO p 948
5455 Old Spanish Trl, Houston TX 77023
Tel (713) 428-5000 SIC 2911

MOTIVA ENTERPRISES LLC p 992
500 Dallas St, Houston TX 77002
Tel (713) 241-6161 SIC 2911 5541

■ PAR HAWAII REFINING LLC p 1113
800 Gessner Rd Ste 875, Houston TX 77024
Tel (281) 899-4800 SIC 5541 2911

▲ PAR PACIFIC HOLDINGS INC p 1113
800 Gessner Rd Ste 875, Houston TX 77024
Tel (713) 969-3293 SIC 1311 2911 4923

PETROBRAS AMERICA INC p 1139
10350 Richmond Ave, Houston TX 77042
Tel (713) 808-2000 SIC 5172 1382 2911

▲ PHILLIPS 66 p 1144
2331 City West Blvd, Houston TX 77042
Tel (832) 765-3300 SIC 1311 2911 2869

■ PHILLIPS 66 CO p 1144
1075 W Sam Houston Pkwy N # 200, Houston TX 77043
Tel (281) 293-6600 SIC 2911

■ PHILLIPS PETROLEUM CO p 1144
600 N Dairy Ashford Rd, Houston TX 77079
Tel (281) 293-1000
SIC 1382 2911 5171 5541

SHELL OIL CO p 1314
910 Louisiana St Ste 1500, Houston TX 77002
Tel (713) 241-6161
SIC 5541 4612 1311 2821 2869 2911

SHELL PETROLEUM INC p 1314
910 Louisiana St Ste 420, Houston TX 77002
Tel (713) 241-6161 SIC 2911 4613 5172

■ TOTAL PETROCHEMICALS & REFINING USA INC p 1463
1201 La St Ste 1800, Houston TX 77002
Tel (713) 483-5000 SIC 2911 2899 2869

TRICAN WELL SERVICE LP p 1479
5825 N Sam Houston Pkwy W # 600, Houston TX 77086
Tel (281) 716-9152 SIC 2911 1481 1389

▲ VERTEX ENERGY INC p 1552
1331 Gemini St Ste 250, Houston TX 77058
Tel (866) 660-8156 SIC 2911

▲ EXXON MOBIL CORP p 521
5959 Las Colinas Blvd, Irving TX 75039
Tel (972) 444-1000
SIC 2911 4612 5541 5171 4911

■ MOBIL CORP p 980
5959 Las Colinas Blvd, Irving TX 75039
Tel (972) 444-1000
SIC 2911 5171 4612 4613 1311

MARTIN RESOURCE MANAGEMENT CORP p 913
4200 Stone Rd, Kilgore TX 75662
Tel (903) 983-6200
SIC 2911 4924 5984 5172

PASADENA REFINING SYSTEM INC p 1119
111 Red Bluff Rd, Pasadena TX 77506
Tel (713) 920-1874 SIC 2911

■ DIAMOND SHAMROCK REFINING AND MARKETING CO p 437
6000 N Loop 1604 W, San Antonio TX 78249
Tel (210) 345-2000 SIC 5541 5171 2911

▲ TESORO CORP p 1440
19100 Ridgewood Pkwy, San Antonio TX 78259
Tel (210) 626-6000
SIC 2911 1311 5983 5984

■ TESORO REFINING & MARKETING CO LLC p 1440
19100 Ridgewood Pkwy, San Antonio TX 78259
Tel (210) 828-8484 SIC 2911 5541

■ TPI PETROLEUM INC p 1467
6000 N Loop 1604 W, San Antonio TX 78249
Tel (210) 592-2000
SIC 2911 5541 4612 4212 4213

■ ULTRAMAR INC p 1501
1 Valero Way, San Antonio TX 78249
Tel (210) 345-2000 SIC 2911 5172 5541

▲ VALERO ENERGY CORP p 1539
1 Valero Way, San Antonio TX 78249
Tel (210) 345-2000 SIC 2911 2869

■ VALERO REFINING CO (INC) p 1539
1 Valero Way, San Antonio TX 78249
Tel (210) 345-2000 SIC 2911

■ VALERO REFINING CO-CALIFORNIA p 1539
1 Valero Way, San Antonio TX 78249
Tel (210) 345-2000 SIC 2911

■ VALERO REFINING CO-NEW JERSEY p 1539
1 Valero Way, San Antonio TX 78249
Tel (210) 345-2000 SIC 2911 6163

■ VALERO REFINING-NEW ORLEANS LLC p 1539
1 Valero Way, San Antonio TX 78249
Tel (210) 345-2000 SIC 2911

■ VALERO REFINING-TEXAS LP p 1539
1 Valero Way, San Antonio TX 78249
Tel (210) 345-2000 SIC 2911

■ VALERO RENEWABLE FUELS CO LLC p 1539
1 Valero Way, San Antonio TX 78249
Tel (210) 345-2000 SIC 2911

VALERO SERVICES INC p 1539
1 Valero Way, San Antonio TX 78249
Tel (210) 345-2000 SIC 2911 5172 5411

INSIGHT EQUITY ACQUISITION CO LLC p 746
1400 Civic Pl Ste 250, Southlake TX 76092
Tel (817) 354-2715
SIC 2911 6722 3851 3441

INSIGHT EQUITY HOLDINGS LLC p 746
1400 Civic Pl Ste 250, Southlake TX 76092
Tel (817) 488-7775
SIC 6726 3851 2911 3441

■ EXXONMOBIL PIPELINE CO p 521
22777 Sprngwoods Vlg Pkwy, Spring TX 77389
Tel (713) 656-3636 SIC 4612 4613 2911

■ EXXONMOBIL SALES AND SUPPLY LLC p 521
22777 Sprngwoods Vlg Pkwy, Spring TX 77389
Tel (800) 243-9966 SIC 2911

■ MOBIL INTERNATIONAL PETROLEUM CORP p 980
22777 Sprngwoods Vlg Pkwy, Spring TX 77389
Tel (281) 288-4545 SIC 2911

■ MOBIL PETROLEUM CO INC p 980
22777 Sprngwoods Vlg Pkwy, Spring TX 77389
Tel (703) 846-3000 SIC 2911

■ COFFEYVILLE RESOURCES LLC p 334
2277 Plaza Dr Ste 500, Sugar Land TX 77479
Tel (281) 207-3200 SIC 2911

■ COFFEYVILLE RESOURCES REFINING & MARKETING LLC p 334
2277 Plaza Dr Ste 500, Sugar Land TX 77479
Tel (281) 207-3200 SIC 2911

▲ CVR ENERGY INC p 404
2277 Plaza Dr Ste 500, Sugar Land TX 77479
Tel (281) 207-3200 SIC 2911 2873

■ CVR REFINING HOLDINGS LLC p 404
2277 Plaza Dr Ste 500, Sugar Land TX 77479
Tel (281) 207-3200 SIC 2911 4612

■ CVR REFINING LLC p 404
2277 Plaza Dr Ste 500, Sugar Land TX 77479
Tel (281) 207-3200 SIC 2911

■ CVR REFINING LP p 404
2277 Plaza Dr Ste 500, Sugar Land TX 77479
Tel (281) 207-3200 SIC 2911 4612

▲ TRECORA RESOURCES p 1475
1650 Highway 6 Ste 190, Sugar Land TX 77478
Tel (409) 385-8300 SIC 2911

■ ANADARKO E&P ONSHORE LLC p 88
1201 Lake Robbins Dr, The Woodlands TX 77380
Tel (832) 636-1000 SIC 2911

CHEVRON PHILLIPS CHEMICAL CO LP p 296
10001 Six Pines Dr, The Woodlands TX 77380
Tel (832) 813-4100
SIC 5169 3292 3089 3084 3432 2911

BIG WEST OIL LLC p 182
333 W Center St, North Salt Lake UT 84054
Tel (801) 624-1000 SIC 2911 5172

FJ MANAGEMENT INC p 553
185 S State St Ste 201, Salt Lake City UT 84111
Tel (801) 624-1000
SIC 5541 2911 5411 1382 6022

■ HUNTSMAN HOLDINGS LLC p 720
500 S Huntsman Way, Salt Lake City UT 84108
Tel (801) 584-5700
SIC 2821 2911 3081 2869

■ HUNTSMAN PETROCHEMICAL LLC p 720
500 S Huntsman Way, Salt Lake City UT 84108
Tel (801) 584-5700 SIC 2911

SINCLAIR COMPANIES p 1326
550 E South Temple, Salt Lake City UT 84102
Tel (801) 363-5100
SIC 2911 4612 1382 5541 7011 0212

SINCLAIR OIL CORP p 1326
550 E South Temple, Salt Lake City UT 84102
Tel (801) 524-2700 SIC 2911 5172

EMERALD SERVICES INC p 491
7343 E Marginal Way S, Seattle WA 98108
Tel (206) 430-7795
SIC 4953 7699 2911 8748 7359

LAMPLIGHT FARMS INC p 841
W140n4900 Lilly Rd, Menomonee Falls WI 53051
Tel (262) 781-9590
SIC 3648 3999 3229 2911

■ FRONTIER REFINING LLC p 581
300 Morrie Ave, Cheyenne WY 82007
Tel (307) 634-3551 *SIC* 2951 2911

SINCLAIR WYOMING REFINING CO p 1326
100 E Lincoln Ave, Sinclair WY 82334
Tel (307) 328-3539 *SIC* 2911

SIC 2951 Paving Mixtures & Blocks

DUNN CONSTRUCTION CO INC p 461
3905 Airport Hwy, Birmingham AL 35222
Tel (205) 592-3866 *SIC* 1611 2951

WIREGRASS CONSTRUCTION CO INC p 1618
170 E Main St, Dothan AL 36301
Tel (334) 699-6800 *SIC* 1611 2951

■ LEGACY VULCAN LLC p 852
1200 Urban Center Dr, Shoal Creek AL 35242
Tel (205) 298-3000
SIC 1422 1423 1442 2951 3273

■ LEGACY VULCAN LLC p 852
1200 Urban Center Dr, Vestavia AL 35242
Tel (205) 298-3000
SIC 1422 1423 1442 2951 3273

▲ VULCAN MATERIALS CO p 1567
1200 Urban Center Dr, Vestavia AL 35242
Tel (205) 298-3000
SIC 1422 1423 2951 1442 3273 3272

CRAFCO INC p 388
6165 W Detroit St, Chandler AZ 85226
Tel (480) 505-8030 *SIC* 2951 3531

FNF CONSTRUCTION INC p 562
115 S 48th St, Tempe AZ 85281
Tel (480) 784-2910 *SIC* 1611 1794 2951

PINE BLUFF SAND AND GRAVEL CO p 1148
1501 Heartwood St, White Hall AR 71602
Tel (870) 534-7120
SIC 2951 3273 1442 5032 1629

ROBERTSONS READY MIX LTD A CALIFORNIA LIMITED PARTNERSHIP p 1242
200 S Main St Ste 200, Corona CA 92882
Tel (951) 493-6500
SIC 3273 3531 5032 2951 1442

■ CALMAT CO p 242
500 N Brand Blvd Ste 500, Glendale CA 91203
Tel (818) 553-8821
SIC 2951 1442 1429 3273 6512 6552

BASIC RESOURCES INC p 158
928 12th St Ste 700, Modesto CA 95354
Tel (209) 521-9771
SIC 1611 3273 2951 3532 3531

SYAR INDUSTRIES INC p 1413
2301 Napa Vallejo Hwy, Napa CA 94558
Tel (707) 252-8711
SIC 5032 2951 0762 7992 5932

SKANSKA USA CIVIL WEST CALIFORNIA DISTRICT INC p 1329
1995 Agua Mansa Rd, Riverside CA 92509
Tel (951) 684-5360
SIC 1611 1622 1629 8711 2951

WORLD OIL MARKETING CO p 1625
9302 Garfield Ave, South Gate CA 90280
Tel (562) 928-0100
SIC 2911 4953 2951 5541 4213 4212

GRANITE ROCK CO p 631
350 Technology Dr, Watsonville CA 95076
Tel (831) 768-2000
SIC 1442 3273 5032 2951 1611 3271

AGGREGATE INDUSTRIES-WCR INC p 35
1687 Cole Blvd Ste 300, Lakewood CO 80401
Tel (303) 716-5200
SIC 1611 1442 1499 2951

TILCON CONNECTICUT INC p 1453
642 Black Rock Ave, New Britain CT 06052
Tel (860) 224-6010
SIC 5032 1611 3273 2951

TILCON INC p 1453
301 Hartford Ave, Newington CT 06111
Tel (860) 223-3651
SIC 1611 5032 3273 2951

O & G INDUSTRIES INC p 1070
112 Wall St, Torrington CT 06790
Tel (860) 489-9261
SIC 1542 1541 1611 1623 5032 2951

UNITED ACQUISITION CORP p 1506
802 N West St, Wilmington DE 19801
Tel (302) 651-9856 *SIC* 2911 5541 2951

DEVCON INTERNATIONAL CORP p 433
595 S Federal Hwy Ste 500, Boca Raton FL 33432
Tel (954) 926-5200
SIC 3699 3273 3281 3271 2951 5032

MATCON TRADING CORP p 919
2020 Ponce De Leon Blvd # 1204, Coral Gables FL 33134
Tel (305) 442-6333 *SIC* 6792 2951

ANDERSON COLUMBIA CO INC p 89
871 Nw Guerdon St, Lake City FL 32055
Tel (386) 752-7585 *SIC* 1611 2951

COMMUNITY ASPHALT CORP p 347
9675 Nw 117th Ave Ste 108, Medley FL 33178
Tel (305) 884-9444 *SIC* 1611 2951

AJAX PAVING INDUSTRIES OF FLORIDA LLC p 41
1 Ajax Dr, North Venice FL 34275
Tel (941) 486-3600 *SIC* 1611 2951

GARDNER-GIBSON INC p 592
4161 E 7th Ave, Tampa FL 33605
Tel (813) 248-2101 *SIC* 2951 2851 2952

GARDNER-GIBSON MANUFACTURING INC p 592
4161 E 7th Ave, Tampa FL 33605
Tel (813) 248-2101 *SIC* 2951 2891 2952

GECOS INC p 597
1936 Lee Rd, Winter Park FL 32789
Tel (407) 645-5500 *SIC* 1611 2951 1623

HUBBARD CONSTRUCTION CO p 716
1936 Lee Rd Ste 101, Winter Park FL 32789
Tel (407) 645-5500 *SIC* 1611 2951 1623

HUBBARD GROUP INC p 716
1936 Lee Rd Ste 101, Winter Park FL 32789
Tel (407) 645-5500 *SIC* 1611 2951 1623

APAC-SOUTHEAST INC p 95
900 Ashwood Pkwy Ste 700, Atlanta GA 30338
Tel (770) 392-5300 *SIC* 1611 1622 2951

OLDCASTLE MATERIALS INC p 1082
900 Ashwood Pkwy Ste 700, Atlanta GA 30338
Tel (770) 522-5600
SIC 3272 1622 1611 2951 5032

BALDWIN PAVING CO INC p 147
1014 Kenmill Dr Nw, Marietta GA 30060
Tel (770) 425-9191 *SIC* 1611 2951

CW MATTHEWS CONTRACTING CO INC p 404
1600 Kenview Dr Nw, Marietta GA 30060
Tel (770) 422-7520 *SIC* 2891 2951

LAFARGE NORTH AMERICA INC p 837
8700 W Bryn Mawr Ave Ll, Chicago IL 60631
Tel (703) 480-3600
SIC 3241 3273 3272 3271 1442 2951

E & B PAVING INC p 465
286 W 300 N, Anderson IN 46012
Tel (765) 643-5358 *SIC* 1611 2951 1794

IRVING MATERIALS INC p 765
8032 N State Road 9, Greenfield IN 46140
Tel (317) 326-3101
SIC 3273 3271 5032 2951

ASPHALT MATERIALS INC p 118
5400 W 86th St, Indianapolis IN 46268
Tel (317) 872-6010 *SIC* 2951 1442

MANATTS INC p 900
1775 Old 6 Rd, Brooklyn IA 52211
Tel (641) 522-9206
SIC 1611 1442 2951 3273

HUSQVARNA CONSTRUCTION PRODUCTS NORTH AMERICA INC p 721
17400 W 119th St, Olathe KS 66061
Tel (913) 928-1000
SIC 3541 3291 5085 5082 3425 2951

APAC-KANSAS INC p 95
7415 W 130th St Ste 300, Overland Park KS 66213
Tel (913) 371-1003
SIC 1611 1771 2951 7353 1622

SCOTTYS CONTRACTING AND STONE LLC p 1294
2300 Barren River Rd, Bowling Green KY 42101
Tel (270) 781-3998 *SIC* 1629 1611 2951

ELMO GREER & SONS LLC p 489
3138 N Us Highway 25, East Bernstadt KY 40729
Tel (606) 862-4233 *SIC* 1611 2951

WALKER CO OF KENTUCKY INC p 1573
105 Apperson Hts, Mount Sterling KY 40353
Tel (859) 498-0092
SIC 1611 2951 1542 3273 1422

HINKLE CONTRACTING CORP p 695
395 N Middletown Rd, Paris KY 40361
Tel (859) 987-3670
SIC 1611 1422 3273 3272 3271 2951

MADDEN CONTRACTING CO LLC p 893
11288 Hwy 371, Minden LA 71055
Tel (318) 377-0927 *SIC* 1611 2951

BROX INDUSTRIES INC p 220
1471 Methuen St, Dracut MA 01826
Tel (978) 454-9105
SIC 1442 1499 1611 1629 1794 2951

EDW C LEVY CO p 479
9300 Dix, Dearborn MI 48120
Tel (313) 429-2200 *SIC* 3295 5032 2951

AGGREGATE INDUSTRIES p 34
6211 N Ann Arbor Rd, Dundee MI 48131
Tel (734) 529-5876
SIC 3273 2951 1442 1411 1771 5211

AJAX PAVING INDUSTRIES INC p 41
1957 Crooks Rd A, Troy MI 48084
Tel (248) 244-3300
SIC 1611 2951 3273 3272

HHJ HOLDINGS LIMITED p 689
1957 Crooks Rd A, Troy MI 48084
Tel (248) 652-9716 *SIC* 1611 2951

TILLER CORP p 1453
7200 Hemlock Ln N Ste 200, Maple Grove MN 55369
Tel (763) 424-5400 *SIC* 1442 2951

HARDRIVES INC p 661
14475 Quiram Dr Ste 1, Rogers MN 55374
Tel (763) 428-8886 *SIC* 1611 2951

■ KNIFE RIVER CORP - NORTH CENTRAL p 824
4787 Shadowwood Dr Ne, Sauk Rapids MN 56379
Tel (320) 251-9472
SIC 1611 1442 3273 2951

ERGON ASPHALT & EMULSIONS INC p 507
2829 Lakeland Dr Ste 2000, Flowood MS 39232
Tel (601) 933-3000 *SIC* 5172 2951

APAC-MISSISSIPPI INC p 95
101 Riverview Dr, Richland MS 39218
Tel (601) 376-4000
SIC 1611 1771 3531 5032 2951

DELTA COMPANIES INC p 426
114 S Silver Springs Rd, Cape Girardeau MO 63703
Tel (573) 334-5261 *SIC* 2951 1611

LIONMARK CONSTRUCTION COMPANIES LLC p 870
1620 Woodson Rd, Saint Louis MO 63114
Tel (314) 991-2180 *SIC* 1611 2951 1622

MISSOURI PETROLEUM PRODUCTS CO LLC p 976
1620 Woodson Rd, Saint Louis MO 63114
Tel (314) 219-7305 *SIC* 5033 1611 2951

PIKE INDUSTRIES INC p 1148
3 Eastgate Park Dr, Belmont NH 03220
Tel (603) 527-5100 *SIC* 1611 2951 3295

COLAS INC p 335
163 Madison Ave Ste 500, Morristown NJ 07960
Tel (973) 290-9082 *SIC* 1611 1622 2951

BARRETT INDUSTRIES CORP p 157
3 Becker Farm Rd Ste 307, Roseland NJ 07068
Tel (973) 533-1001
SIC 1611 2951 4213 1799 1794

BARRETT PAVING MATERIALS INC p 157
3 Becker Farm Rd Ste 307, Roseland NJ 07068
Tel (973) 533-1001
SIC 1611 2951 4213 1799 1794

HANSON AGGREGATES WRP INC p 659
1333 Campus Pkwy, Wall Township NJ 07753
Tel (972) 653-5500
SIC 3281 3272 2951 1442

■ HOLLYFRONTIER NAVAJO REFINING LLC p 701
501 E Main St, Artesia NM 88210
Tel (575) 748-3311 *SIC* 2911 2951

SUIT-KOTE CORP p 1397
1911 Lorings Crossing Rd, Cortland NY 13045
Tel (607) 753-1100 *SIC* 2951 1611

CALLANAN INDUSTRIES INC p 242
1245 Kings Rd Ste 1, Schenectady NY 12303
Tel (518) 374-2222 *SIC* 3272 2951

PECKHAM INDUSTRIES INC p 1126
20 Haarlem Ave Ste 200, White Plains NY 10603
Tel (914) 949-2000 *SIC* 2951

CAROLINA SUNROCK LLC p 259
1001 W B St, Butner NC 27509
Tel (919) 575-4502
SIC 1429 3273 2951 1411

BLYTHE CONSTRUCTION INC p 193
2911 N Graham St, Charlotte NC 28206
Tel (704) 375-8474 *SIC* 1611 1622 2951

SUNROCK GROUP HOLDINGS CORP p 1404
200 Horizon Dr Ste 100, Raleigh NC 27615
Tel (919) 747-6400
SIC 1429 3273 2951 1411

VALLEY ASPHALT CORP p 1540
11641 Mosteller Rd, Cincinnati OH 45241
Tel (513) 771-0820 *SIC* 1611 2951

■ MARATHON PETROLEUM CO LP p 904
539 S Main St, Findlay OH 45840
Tel (419) 422-2121 *SIC* 5172 2951 2865

THORWORKS INDUSTRIES INC p 1450
2520 Campbell St, Sandusky OH 44870
Tel (419) 626-4375
SIC 2851 3531 2952 2951 2891 2816

SHELLY MATERIALS INC p 1314
80 Park Dr, Thornville OH 43076
Tel (740) 246-6315
SIC 1422 1442 2951 4492

M & B ASPHALT CO INC p 888
1525 W Seneca Cnty Rd 42, Tiffin OH 44883
Tel (419) 992-4235
SIC 1429 2951 1611 2952 1771

SHELLY AND SANDS INC p 1314
3570 S River Rd, Zanesville OH 43701
Tel (740) 453-0721 *SIC* 1611 1442 2951

■ CMI TEREX CORP p 329
9528 W I 40 Service Rd, Oklahoma City OK 73128
Tel (405) 787-6020
SIC 3531 3715 3596 3541 3444 2951

HASKELL LEMON CONSTRUCTION CO p 667
3800 Sw 10th St, Oklahoma City OK 73108
Tel (405) 947-6069
SIC 5032 1611 3272 2951

EVANS & ASSOCIATES ENTERPRISES INC p 513
3320 N 14th St, Ponca City OK 74601
Tel (580) 765-6693
SIC 5032 2951 1442 1611 3273 1311

▲ SEMGROUP CORP p 1302
6120 S Yale Ave Ste 700, Tulsa OK 74136
Tel (918) 524-8100
SIC 1389 4612 5171 2951

HEMPT BROS INC p 682
205 Creek Rd, Camp Hill PA 17011
Tel (717) 774-2911
SIC 1611 3273 2951 1442 0212

IA CONSTRUCTION CORP p 725
24 Gibb Rd, Franklin PA 16323
Tel (814) 432-3184
SIC 1611 2951 1622 1623

GLASGOW INC p 614
104 Willow Grove Ave, Glenside PA 19038
Tel (215) 884-8800 *SIC* 2951 1611 1623

PENNSY SUPPLY INC p 1130
1001 Paxton St, Harrisburg PA 17104
Tel (717) 233-4511
SIC 1422 2951 3273 4212 5032

RUSSELL STANDARD CORP p 1259
285 Kappa Dr Ste 300, Pittsburgh PA 15238
Tel (412) 449-0700 *SIC* 1611 2951

HAINES & KIBBLEHOUSE INC p 653
2052 Lucon Rd, Skippack PA 19474
Tel (610) 584-8500
SIC 1794 1611 1422 2951

GLENN O HAWBAKER INC p 615
1952 Waddle Rd Ste 203, State College PA 16803
Tel (814) 237-1444
SIC 2951 3281 1622 1794 1611 1422

BETTEROADS ASPHALT CORP p 178
Edif Empresas Diaz, San Juan PR 00926
Tel (787) 760-1050 *SIC* 1611 2951

JH LYNCH & SONS INC p 785
50 Lynch Pl, Cumberland RI 02864
Tel (401) 333-4300 *SIC* 1611 2951

PALMETTO CORP OF CONWAY p 1109
3873 Highway 701 N, Conway SC 29526
Tel (843) 365-2156 *SIC* 2951

BOMAG AMERICAS INC p 199
125 Blue Granite Pkwy, Ridgeway SC 29130
Tel (803) 337-0700 *SIC* 3531 2951

APAC-ATLANTIC INC p 95
4817 Rutledge Pike, Knoxville TN 37914
Tel (865) 983-3100
SIC 5032 3531 3273 2951 1611

LEHMAN-ROBERTS CO p 854
1111 Wilson St, Memphis TN 38106
Tel (901) 774-4000 *SIC* 1611 2951

MAYMEAD INC p 923
1995 Roan Creek Rd, Mountain City TN 37683
Tel (423) 727-2000
SIC 1611 2951 5032 5191

CHARLES BLALOCK & SONS INC p 289
409 Robert Henderson Rd, Sevierville TN 37862
Tel (865) 429-5902
SIC 1611 7353 3271 3255 2951

DMG EQUIPMENT CO LTD p 446
1575 Fm 1485 Rd, Conroe TX 77301
Tel (936) 756-6960 *SIC* 1611 2951

CEMEX EL PASO INC p 274
1 Mckelligon Canyon Rd, El Paso TX 79930
Tel (915) 565-4681
SIC 3273 2951 5032 1442

TEXAS CRUSHED STONE CO INC p 1442
5300 S Interstate 35, Georgetown TX 78626
Tel (512) 255-4405 *SIC* 1422 2951 1442

HANSON AGGREGATES LLC p 658
8505 Freeport Pkwy Ste 500, Irving TX 75063
Tel (469) 417-1200 *SIC* 3273 2951 5032

HUNTER INDUSTRIES LTD p 719
5080 Fm 2439, New Braunfels TX 78132
Tel (512) 353-7757 *SIC* 1611 2951 1442

CAPITOL AGGREGATES INC p 250
11551 Nacogdoches Rd, San Antonio TX 78217
Tel (210) 655-3010
SIC 3241 1442 1422 2951 4011

■ MARTIN MARIETTA MATERIALS SOUTHWEST INC p 912
5710 W Hausman Rd Ste 121, San Antonio TX 78249
Tel (210) 208-4400
SIC 1422 3273 2951 3274 1442

STAKER & PARSON COMPANIES p 1374
2350 S 1900 W Ste 100, Ogden UT 84401
Tel (801) 298-7500
SIC 1611 5032 3273 4212 2951 1771

GRAYMONT INC p 632
301 S 700 E 3950, Salt Lake City UT 84102
Tel (801) 262-3942 *SIC* 1429 2951 3273

SLURRY PAVERS INC p 1331
3617 Nine Mile Rd, Richmond VA 23223
Tel (804) 264-0707 *SIC* 2951 1611

ADAMS CONSTRUCTION CO p 21
523 Rutherford Ave Ne, Roanoke VA 24016
Tel (540) 982-2366 *SIC* 1611 2951

LAKESIDE INDUSTRIES INC p 840
6505 226th Pl Se Ste 200, Issaquah WA 98027
Tel (425) 313-2600 *SIC* 1611 2951 5032

JF ALLEN CO INC p 785
U.S 33 W Red Rock Rd, Buckhannon WV 26201
Tel (304) 472-8890
SIC 3271 1611 3273 3281 2951

GREER INDUSTRIES INC p 639
570 Canyon Rd, Morgantown WV 26508
Tel (304) 296-2549
SIC 3316 3272 2951 1422 3274 1446

■ FRONTIER REFINING LLC p 581
300 Morrie Ave, Cheyenne WY 82007
Tel (307) 634-3551 *SIC* 2951 2911

SIC 2952 Asphalt Felts & Coatings

▲ CARLISLE COMPANIES INC p 257
16430 N Scottsdale Rd, Scottsdale AZ 85254
Tel (704) 501-1100
SIC 2952 3714 3312 3357 3263

HENRY CO LLC p 684
999 N Sepulveda Blvd, El Segundo CA 90245
Tel (310) 955-9200 *SIC* 2952 2821 2891

HNC PARENT INC p 698
999 N Sepulveda Blvd, El Segundo CA 90245
Tel (310) 955-9200 *SIC* 2952 2821 2891

PACIFIC COAST BUILDING PRODUCTS INC p 1104
10600 White Rock Rd # 100, Rancho Cordova CA 95670
Tel (916) 631-6500
SIC 3275 3271 5031 1761 2952 2426

■ JOHNS MANVILLE CORP p 790
717 17th St Ste 800, Denver CO 80202
Tel (303) 978-2000 *SIC* 2952 1761 1742

CELOTEX CORP p 274
10301 Dr Martn L Kng Jr S, Saint Petersburg FL 33716
Tel (727) 563-5100
SIC 3086 3275 3296 2493 2952

GARDNER-GIBSON INC p 592
4161 E 7th Ave, Tampa FL 33605
Tel (813) 248-2101 *SIC* 2951 2851 2952

GARDNER-GIBSON MANUFACTURING INC p 592
4161 E 7th Ave, Tampa FL 33605
Tel (813) 248-2101 *SIC* 2951 2891 2952

SPECTRA METAL SALES INC p 1357
6104 Boat Rock Blvd Sw, Atlanta GA 30336
Tel (404) 344-4305
SIC 5051 3354 3355 3479 3444 2952

PETRIN CORP p 1139
1405 Commercial Dr, Port Allen LA 70767
Tel (225) 343-0471 *SIC* 1799 2952

GENOVA PRODUCTS INC p 604
7034 E Court St, Davison MI 48423
Tel (810) 744-4500
SIC 3089 2891 2911 3494 3084 2952

HOOD COMPANIES INC p 705
623 N Main St Ste 300, Hattiesburg MS 39401
Tel (601) 582-1545 *SIC* 3086 2952 6719

ATLAS ROOFING CORP p 128
802 Highway 19 N Ste 190, Meridian MS 39307
Tel (601) 484-8900 *SIC* 3086 2952

TAMKO BUILDING PRODUCTS INC p 1423
220 W 4th St, Joplin MO 64801
Tel (417) 624-6644 *SIC* 2952

S & K DISTRIBUTION LLC p 1261
535 Old Tarrytown Rd, White Plains NY 10603
Tel (914) 948-6363 *SIC* 5031 2952 5033

▲ PLY GEM HOLDINGS INC p 1157
5020 Weston Pkwy Ste 400, Cary NC 27513
Tel (919) 677-3900 SIC 2431 2952

■ CARLISLE CORP p 257
11605 N Community Hse Rd, Charlotte NC 28277
Tel (704) 501-1100
SIC 2952 2899 3011 2295 3089 3577

■ TREMCO INC p 1476
3735 Green Rd, Beachwood OH 44122
Tel (216) 292-5000
SIC 2891 2952 1761 1752 2851 2842

GARLAND CO INC p 592
3800 E 91st St, Cleveland OH 44105
Tel (216) 641-7500 SIC 2952 2851

GARLAND INDUSTRIES INC p 592
3800 E 91st St, Cleveland OH 44105
Tel (216) 641-7500 SIC 2952 6512 8712

STATE INDUSTRIAL PRODUCTS CORP p 1381
5915 Landerbrook Dr # 300, Cleveland OH 44124
Tel (877) 747-6986
SIC 2841 5072 2842 2992 2952 2899

TRANSTAR HOLDING CO p 1473
5900 Landerbrook Dr Bsmt, Cleveland OH 44124
Tel (440) 684-1400 SIC 3444 3281 2952

THORWORKS INDUSTRIES INC p 1450
2520 Campbell St, Sandusky OH 44870
Tel (419) 626-4375
SIC 2851 3531 2952 2951 2891 2816

M & B ASPHALT CO INC p 888
1525 W Seneca Cnty Rd 42, Tiffin OH 44883
Tel (419) 992-4235
SIC 1429 2951 1611 2952 1771

▲ OWENS CORNING p 1100
1 Owens Corning Pkwy, Toledo OH 43659
Tel (419) 248-8000
SIC 3296 2952 3229 3089

■ OWENS CORNING SALES LLC p 1100
1 Owens Corning Pkwy, Toledo OH 43659
Tel (419) 248-8000
SIC 3296 2952 3229 3089 1761

HERBERT MALARKEY ROOFING CO p 685
3131 N Columbia Blvd, Portland OR 97217
Tel (503) 283-1191 SIC 2952

■ CARLISLE CONSTRUCTION MATERIALS LLC p 257
1285 Ritner Hwy, Carlisle PA 17013
Tel (717) 245-7000
SIC 2952 3069 5031 2899 2891

BRIDGESTONE AMERICAS INC p 211
535 Marriott Dr, Nashville TN 37214
Tel (615) 937-1000
SIC 3011 3493 2952 2822 3229

ELK PREMIUM BUILDING PRODUCTS INC p 487
14911 Quorum Dr Ste 600, Dallas TX 75254
Tel (972) 851-0400 SIC 2952 2273

ELKCORP p 488
14911 Quorum Dr Ste 600, Dallas TX 75254
Tel (972) 851-0500
SIC 2952 5033 2426 2431 3471

▲ HEADWATERS INC p 673
10701 S River Front Pkwy # 300, South Jordan UT 84095
Tel (801) 984-9400
SIC 3272 3271 3281 2952

SIC 2992 Lubricating Oils & Greases

■ WESTERN REFINING WHOLESALE INC p 1599
1250 W Washington St # 101, Tempe AZ 85281
Tel (602) 286-1401 SIC 5171 2911 2992

WARREN UNILUBE INC p 1577
915 E Jefferson Ave, West Memphis AR 72301
Tel (870) 735-1514 SIC 2992

▲ WD-40 CO p 1585
1061 Cudahy Pl, San Diego CA 92110
Tel (619) 275-1400 SIC 2992 2851

CCL INDUSTRIES CORP p 270
15 Controls Dr, Shelton CT 06484
Tel (203) 926-1253
SIC 2759 2992 3411 2819 2844

■ MACDERMID INC p 892
245 Freight St, Waterbury CT 06702
Tel (203) 575-5700
SIC 2899 2842 2874 2992 2752 3577

CLIFF BERRY INC p 326
851 Eller Dr, Fort Lauderdale FL 33316
Tel (954) 763-3390
SIC 4953 4959 4212 2992 4491

AMALIE OIL CO p 64
1601 Mcclosky Blvd, Tampa FL 33605
Tel (813) 248-1988 SIC 2992 3085

FUCHS CORP p 583
17050 Lathrop Ave, Harvey IL 60426
Tel (800) 323-7755 SIC 2992 5172 2899

PDV MIDWEST REFINING LLC p 1125
135th St New Ave, Lemont IL 60439
Tel (630) 257-7761
SIC 2992 2911 5171 4213

■ NALCO CO LLC p 1006
1601 W Diehl Rd, Naperville IL 60563
Tel (630) 305-1000
SIC 3559 2899 2992 2891

■ NALCO HOLDING CO p 1007
1601 W Diehl Rd, Naperville IL 60563
Tel (630) 305-1000 SIC 2899 2992

■ NALCO HOLDINGS LLC p 1007
1601 W Diehl Rd, Naperville IL 60563
Tel (630) 305-1000 SIC 2899 2992 3559

■ CHEMTOOL INC p 293
801 W Rockton Rd, Rockton IL 61072
Tel (815) 957-4140
SIC 2992 2899 2842 2841

■ CALUMET LUBRICANTS CO LIMITED PARTNERSHIP p 243
2780 Waterfront Pkwy Ste 200 E, Indianapolis IN 46214
Tel (317) 328-5660 SIC 2992

■ CALUMET OPERATING LLC p 243
2780 Waterfront Pkwy, Indianapolis IN 46214
Tel (317) 328-5660 SIC 2992

▲ CALUMET SPECIALTY PRODUCTS PARTNERS LP p 243
2780 Waterfront Pkwy Ste 200 E, Indianapolis IN 46214
Tel (317) 328-5660 SIC 2911 2992

PINNACLE OIL HOLDINGS LLC p 1150
5009 W 81st St, Indianapolis IN 46268
Tel (317) 875-9465 SIC 2992 5172 8742

IDEMITSU LUBRICANTS AMERICA CORP p 729
701 Port Rd, Jeffersonville IN 47130
Tel (812) 284-3300 SIC 2992

KCG INC p 806
15720 W 108th St Ste 100, Lenexa KS 66219
Tel (913) 438-4142 SIC 5032 2992

CLEAN HARBORS WICHITA LLC p 324
2824 N Ohio St, Wichita KS 67219
Tel (316) 832-0151 SIC 2992 5169 5172

UNIVERSAL COMPANIES INC p 1516
2824 N Ohio St, Wichita KS 67219
Tel (316) 832-0151
SIC 5171 5541 6512 8741 6099 2992

■ VALVOLINE INC p 1542
3499 Blazer Pkwy, Lexington KY 40509
Tel (859) 357-7777 SIC 2992

■ VALVOLINE LLC p 1542
3499 Blazer Pkwy, Lexington KY 40509
Tel (859) 357-7777 SIC 2992

■ VALVOLINE US LLC p 1542
3499 Blazer Pkwy, Lexington KY 40509
Tel (859) 357-7777 SIC 2992

A W CHESTERTON CO p 7
860 Salem St, Groveland MA 01834
Tel (781) 438-7000
SIC 3053 2851 2992 2891 5169

DIVERSIFIED CHEMICAL TECHNOLOGIES INC p 444
15477 Woodrow Wilson St, Detroit MI 48238
Tel (313) 867-5444
SIC 2891 2992 2899 2842 2841

METALWORKING LUBRICANTS CO p 953
25 W Silverdome Indus Par, Pontiac MI 48342
Tel (248) 332-3500
SIC 5172 2869 2843 2992

SCHAEFFER MFG CO p 1286
102 Barton St, Saint Louis MO 63104
Tel (314) 865-4100 SIC 2992 2879

WARREN DISTRIBUTION INC p 1577
727 S 13th St, Omaha NE 68102
Tel (402) 341-9397 SIC 2992

■ PBF HOLDING CO LLC p 1123
1 Sylvan Way Ste 2, Parsippany NJ 07054
Tel (888) 661-8949 SIC 2911 2992

BP LUBRICANTS USA INC p 205
1500 Valley Rd, Wayne NJ 07470
Tel (973) 633-2200 SIC 2992

BLASER SWISSLUBE HOLDING CORP p 189
31 Hatfield Ln, Goshen NY 10924
Tel (845) 294-3200 SIC 2992

MDI HOLDINGS LLC p 933
399 Park Ave Fl 14, New York NY 10022
Tel (212) 559-1127
SIC 2899 2842 2874 2992 2752 3577

NOCO INC p 1046
2440 Sheridan Dr Ste 202, Tonawanda NY 14150
Tel (716) 833-6626
SIC 2992 6719 5172 4924

RELADYNE INC p 1221
9395 Kenwood Rd Ste 104, Blue Ash OH 45242
Tel (513) 489-6000 SIC 2992

CHEMICAL SOLVENTS INC p 293
3751 Jennings Rd, Cleveland OH 44109
Tel (216) 741-9310
SIC 5169 7349 3471 2992

STATE INDUSTRIAL PRODUCTS CORP p 1381
5915 Landerbrook Dr # 300, Cleveland OH 44124
Tel (877) 747-6986
SIC 2841 5072 2842 2992 2952 2899

MASTER CHEMICAL CORP p 918
501 W Boundary St, Perrysburg OH 43551
Tel (419) 874-7902 SIC 2992 3559

PDV HOLDING INC p 1125
6100 S Yale Ave, Tulsa OK 74136
Tel (918) 495-4000
SIC 2911 2992 5171 4213

ROYAL MFG CO LP p 1254
516 S 25th West Ave, Tulsa OK 74127
Tel (918) 584-2671 SIC 2992 2911

▲ QUAKER CHEMICAL CORP p 1196
901 E Hector St, Conshohocken PA 19428
Tel (610) 832-4000
SIC 2992 2899 2869 2891

ARKEMA DELAWARE INC p 110
900 First Ave, King Of Prussia PA 19406
Tel (610) 205-7000
SIC 2812 2819 2869 2891 2899 2992

HOUGHTON INTERNATIONAL INC p 711
945 Madison Ave, Norristown PA 19403
Tel (610) 666-4000 SIC 2869 2992

GH HOLDINGS INC p 610
Madison & Van Buren Ave, Valley Forge PA 19482
Tel (610) 666-4000 SIC 2869 2992

CRC INDUSTRIES INC p 390
885 Louis Dr, Warminster PA 18974
Tel (215) 674-4300
SIC 2992 3471 2899 2842

TECHNICAL CHEMICAL CO p 1431
3327 Pipeline Rd, Cleburne TX 76033
Tel (817) 645-6088 SIC 2992

ZXP TECHNOLOGIES LTD p 1645
409 Wallisville Rd, Highlands TX 77562
Tel (281) 426-8800 SIC 2992 2879 7549

■ CHEVRON MARINE PRODUCTS LLC p 296
1500 Louisiana St, Houston TX 77002
Tel (832) 854-2767 SIC 5172 2992 2869

CITGO HOLDING INC p 309
1293 Eldridge Pkwy, Houston TX 77077
Tel (281) 531-0004
SIC 2911 2992 5171 4213

EQUILON ENTERPRISES LLC p 506
910 Louisiana St Ste 2, Houston TX 77002
Tel (713) 241-6161
SIC 2911 4612 2992 5172

PENNZOIL-QUAKER STATE CO p 1131
700 Milam St Ste 125, Houston TX 77002
Tel (713) 546-4000 SIC 2992

SUN COAST RESOURCES INC p 1400
6405 Cavalcade St Bldg 1, Houston TX 77026
Tel (713) 844-9600
SIC 5172 2992 5084 1389

AMSOIL INC p 87
925 Tower Ave, Superior WI 54880
Tel (715) 392-7101
SIC 2992 3589 2873 3714

■ CALUMET SUPERIOR LLC p 243
2407 Stinson Ave, Superior WI 54880
Tel (715) 398-3533 SIC 2992

SIC 2999 Products Of Petroleum & Coal, NEC

WALTER COKE INC p 1574
3500 35th Ave N, Birmingham AL 35207
Tel (205) 808-7803 SIC 2999

▲ RENTECH INC p 1224
10880 Wilshire Blvd # 1101, Los Angeles CA 90024
Tel (310) 571-9800 SIC 2999 2873 6794

OXBOW CARBON LLC p 1100
1601 Forum Pl Ste 1400, West Palm Beach FL 33401
Tel (561) 907-5400 SIC 1241 2999 5052

ROYAL OAK ENTERPRISES LLC p 1254
1 Royal Oak Ave, Roswell GA 30076
Tel (678) 461-3200 SIC 2999 2899

MAXYIELD COOPERATIVE p 923
313 3rd Ave Nw, West Bend IA 50597
Tel (515) 887-7211
SIC 5153 5191 2999 0723

■ PETROLITE CORP p 1139
369 Marshall Ave, Saint Louis MO 63119
Tel (314) 961-3500
SIC 3559 2999 2899 2821 2911

■ HONEYWELL SPECIALTY WAX & ADDITIVES INC p 705
101 Columbia Rd, Morristown NJ 07960
Tel (973) 455-2000 SIC 2999 5169

HH LIQUIDATING CORP p 689
110 E 59th St Fl 34, New York NY 10022
Tel (646) 282-2500
SIC 3624 2999 3356 3339

■ AFTON CHEMICAL CORP p 33
500 Spring St, Richmond VA 23219
Tel (804) 788-5086 SIC 2899 2999 3999

SIC 3011 Tires & Inner Tubes

TOYO TIRE HOLDINGS OF AMERICAS INC p 1466
5900 Katella Ave Ste 200a, Cypress CA 90630
Tel (562) 431-6502 SIC 3011

YOKOHAMA TIRE CORP p 1637
1 Macarthur Pl Ste 800, Santa Ana CA 92707
Tel (714) 870-3800 SIC 5014 3011

EUROTIRE INC p 513
200 S Biscayne Blvd # 5500, Miami FL 33131
Tel (212) 262-2251 SIC 3011

PIRELLI TIRE LLC p 1151
100 Pirelli Dr Se, Rome GA 30161
Tel (706) 368-5800 SIC 3011

TOYO TIRE NORTH AMERICA MANUFACTURING INC p 1466
3660 Highway 411 Ne, White GA 30184
Tel (678) 721-7200 SIC 3011

▲ TITAN INTERNATIONAL INC p 1456
2701 Spruce St, Quincy IL 62301
Tel (217) 228-6011 SIC 3312 3714 3011

■ TITAN TIRE CORP p 1456
2345 E Market St, Des Moines IA 50317
Tel (515) 265-9200 SIC 3011

BRIDGESTONE BANDAG LLC p 211
2000 Bandag Dr, Muscatine IA 52761
Tel (563) 262-2511
SIC 7534 3559 5014 3011 7549 6794

GPX INTERNATIONAL TIRE CORP p 628
124 Washington St Ste 101, Foxboro MA 02035
Tel (781) 321-3910 SIC 3011

■ HUTCHINSON CORP p 722
460 Fuller Ave Ne, Grand Rapids MI 49503
Tel (616) 459-4541 SIC 3069 3011

OMNI UNITED (USA) INC p 1085
5350 Birch Point Dr, Interlochen MI 49643
Tel (231) 943-9804 SIC 3011

▲ SPH GROUP HOLDINGS LLC p 1358
590 Madison Ave Fl 32, New York NY 10022
Tel (212) 520-2300 SIC 3339 3011 3312

■ HANDY & HARMAN LTD p 657
1133 Westchester Ave N-222, White Plains NY 10604
Tel (914) 461-1300 SIC 3339 3011 3312

■ CARLISLE CORP p 257
11605 N Community Hse Rd, Charlotte NC 28277
Tel (704) 501-1100
SIC 2952 2899 3011 2295 3089 3577

▲ GOODYEAR TIRE & RUBBER CO p 625
200 E Innovation Way, Akron OH 44316
Tel (330) 796-2121
SIC 3011 3052 7534 7538 7539 5013

▲ COOPER TIRE & RUBBER CO INC p 367
701 Lima Ave, Findlay OH 45840
Tel (419) 423-1321 SIC 3011

TECHNICAL RUBBER CO INC p 1431
200 E Coshocton St, Johnstown OH 43031
Tel (740) 967-9015 SIC 3011 5014 2891

SUPERIOR TIRE SERVICE INC p 1407
4230 27th Ct Se, Salem OR 97302
Tel (503) 585-1955 SIC 5014 7534 3011

POLYMER ENTERPRISES INC p 1160
4731 State Route 30 # 401, Greensburg PA 15601
Tel (724) 838-2340 SIC 3069 3011

CONTINENTAL AUTOMOTIVE INC p 362
1830 Macmillan Park Dr, Fort Mill SC 29707
Tel (704) 583-3900 SIC 3011 8711

CONTINENTAL TIRE AMERICAS LLC p 364
1830 Macmillan Park Dr, Fort Mill SC 29707
Tel (800) 450-3187 SIC 3011

CONTINENTAL TIRE HOLDING US LLC p 364
1830 Macmillan Park Dr, Fort Mill SC 29707
Tel (704) 588-5895 SIC 3011

MICHELIN NORTH AMERICA INC p 960
1 Parkway S, Greenville SC 29615
Tel (864) 458-5000 SIC 3011

BRIDGESTONE AMERICAS INC p 211
535 Marriott Dr, Nashville TN 37214
Tel (615) 937-1000
SIC 3011 3493 2952 2822 3229

BRIDGESTONE AMERICAS TIRE OPERATIONS LLC p 211
535 Marriott Dr, Nashville TN 37214
Tel (615) 937-1000 SIC 3011 5531

SCHRADER-BRIDGEPORT INTERNATIONAL INC p 1290
205 Frazier Rd, Altavista VA 24517
Tel (434) 369-4741
SIC 3492 3714 3491 3011

YOKOHAMA CORP OF NORTH AMERICA p 1637
1500 Indiana St, Salem VA 24153
Tel (540) 389-5426 SIC 3011 5014

YOKOHAMA TIRE MANUFACTURING VIRGINIA LLC p 1637
1500 Indiana St, Salem VA 24153
Tel (540) 389-5426 SIC 3011

SIC 3021 Rubber & Plastic Footwear

■ VANS INC p 1544
6550 Katella Ave, Cypress CA 90630
Tel (714) 889-6100
SIC 3021 2321 2329 2325 2353 2393

OAKLEY INC p 1071
1 Icon, Foothill Ranch CA 92610
Tel (949) 951-0991
SIC 3851 2331 2339 3021 3873 3143

▲ DECKERS OUTDOOR CORP p 421
250 Coromar Dr, Goleta CA 93117
Tel (805) 967-7611 SIC 3021 2389 2339

▲ SKECHERS USA INC p 1329
228 Manhattan Beach Blvd # 200, Manhattan Beach CA 90266
Tel (310) 318-3100 SIC 3021 3149

K-SWISS INC p 799
31248 Oak Crest Dr, Westlake Village CA 91361
Tel (818) 706-5100 SIC 3021 3911

K-SWISS SALES CORP p 799
31248 Oak Crest Dr # 150, Westlake Village CA 91361
Tel (818) 706-5100 SIC 3021

▲ CROCS INC p 393
7477 Dry Creek Pkwy, Niwot CO 80503
Tel (303) 848-7000
SIC 3021 5139 3069 5661 2389

▲ UNDER ARMOUR INC p 1502
1020 Hull St Ste 300, Baltimore MD 21230
Tel (410) 454-6428
SIC 2329 2353 2339 3021

RED WING SHOE CO INC p 1216
314 Main St, Red Wing MN 55066
Tel (651) 388-8211
SIC 3143 3149 3144 3111 5661 3021

HANDWEAR SALES INC p 657
74 Bleecker St, Gloversville NY 12078
Tel (518) 725-8641
SIC 3151 3949 2253 3021

WINSTON-SALEM INDUSTRIES FOR BLIND INC p 1617
7730 N Point Blvd, Winston Salem NC 27106
Tel (336) 759-0551
SIC 2515 3021 2392 2253 2394 3851

TOTES ISOTONER HOLDINGS CORP p 1463
9655 International Blvd, West Chester OH 45246
Tel (513) 682-8200
SIC 2381 3151 2211 3021 5699

▲ NIKE INC p 1043
1 Sw Bowerman Dr, Beaverton OR 97005
Tel (503) 671-6453
SIC 3021 2329 2339 5139 5661 5136

ADIDAS AMERICA INC p 22
5055 N Greeley Ave, Portland OR 97217
Tel (971) 234-2300
SIC 5139 5136 5137 3021 2339

▲ COLUMBIA SPORTSWEAR CO p 341
14375 Nw Science Park Dr, Portland OR 97229
Tel (503) 985-4000
SIC 2329 2339 3021 2353 3949

■ COLUMBIA SPORTSWEAR USA CORP p 341
14375 Nw Science Park Dr, Portland OR 97229
Tel (503) 985-4000
SIC 5137 5136 2329 2339 3021 2353

LACROSSE FOOTWEAR INC p 837
17634 Ne Airport Way, Portland OR 97230
Tel (503) 262-0110 SIC 3021

NORCROSS SAFETY PRODUCTS LLC p 1047
900 Douglas Pike Ste 100, Smithfield RI 02917
Tel (800) 430-5490 SIC 3842 3021 3469

BIO WORLD MERCHANDISING INC p 183
2111 W Walnut Hill Ln, Irving TX 75038
Tel (888) 831-2138
SIC 2353 3161 2253 5199 3021

SIC 3052 Rubber & Plastic Hose & Belting

GATES CORP p 593
1551 Wewatta St, Denver CO 80202
Tel (303) 744-1911
SIC 3052 3089 3568 5084 4789

OMAHA HOLDINGS LLC p 1083
1551 Wewatta St, Denver CO 80202
Tel (303) 744-1911
SIC 3052 3089 3568 5084 4789

OMAHA INTERMEDIATE HOLDING LLC p 1083
1551 Wewatta St, Denver CO 80202
Tel (303) 744-1911
SIC 3052 3089 3568 5084 4789

BBA US HOLDINGS INC p 163
201 S Orange Ave Ste 1425, Orlando FL 32801
Tel (407) 648-7230 SIC 3728 2399 3052

SUNCAST CORP p 1401
701 N Kirk Rd, Batavia IL 60510
Tel (630) 879-2050 SIC 2519 3052 3432

TIGERFLEX CORP p 1453
801 Estes Ave, Elk Grove Village IL 60007
Tel (847) 439-1766 SIC 3052

KURIYAMA OF AMERICA INC p 832
360 E State Pkwy, Schaumburg IL 60173
Tel (847) 755-0360 SIC 5085 3052

APACHE HOSE & BELTING CO INC p 96
4805 Bowling St Sw, Cedar Rapids IA 52404
Tel (319) 365-0471 SIC 3496 3052 5085

G T SALES & MANUFACTURING INC p 587
2202 S West St, Wichita KS 67213
Tel (316) 943-2171 SIC 5085 3053 3052

EMERSON POWER TRANSMISSION CORP p 492
7120 New Buffington Rd, Florence KY 41042
Tel (859) 342-7900
SIC 3429 3052 3568 3562 3566 3462

YOKOHAMA INDUSTRIES AMERICAS INC p 1637
105 Industry Dr, Versailles KY 40383
Tel (859) 873-2188
SIC 3714 3585 3492 3052

TITEFLEX CORP p 1456
603 Hendee St, Springfield MA 01104
Tel (413) 271-8170 SIC 3052 3599

TI AUTOMOTIVE LLC p 1452
2020 Taylor Rd, Auburn Hills MI 48326
Tel (248) 494-5000
SIC 3317 3312 3599 3052 3714 3585

TI GROUP AUTOMOTIVE SYSTEMS LLC p 1452
2020 Taylor Rd, Auburn Hills MI 48326
Tel (248) 296-8000
SIC 3317 3312 3599 3052 3714 3585

FLEXFAB HORIZONS INTERNATIONAL INC p 556
102 Cook Rd, Hastings MI 49058
Tel (269) 945-4700
SIC 3599 3052 3053 2822

FLEXFAB LLC p 556
1699 W M 43 Hwy, Hastings MI 49058
Tel (269) 945-2433 SIC 3599 3052 2822

■ JOHNSON KADANT INC p 791
805 Wood St, Three Rivers MI 49093
Tel (269) 278-1715
SIC 3494 8711 1389 3052 1099

EATON HYDRAULICS LLC p 473
14615 Lone Oak Rd, Eden Prairie MN 55344
Tel (952) 937-9800
SIC 3089 3052 3568 3492 3594 3728

■ BERKLEY RISK ADMINISTRATION CO LLC p 175
222 S 9th St Ste 2700, Minneapolis MN 55402
Tel (612) 766-3000 SIC 6411 3052 3432

BELTSERVICE CORP p 171
4143 Rider Trl N, Earth City MO 63045
Tel (314) 344-8500 SIC 3052

JASON INDUSTRIAL INC p 778
340 Kaplan Dr, Fairfield NJ 07004
Tel (973) 227-4904 SIC 5084 3052

US WIRE & CABLE CORP p 1533
1 Flexon Plz, Newark NJ 07114
Tel (973) 824-5530 SIC 3052 3315

JGB ENTERPRISES INC p 785
115 Metropolitan Dr, Liverpool NY 13088
Tel (315) 451-2770 SIC 3052 5085 3429

▲ STANDARD MOTOR PRODUCTS INC p 1376
3718 Northern Blvd # 600, Long Island City NY 11101
Tel (718) 392-0200
SIC 3714 3694 3585 3564 3052

HITACHI CABLE AMERICA INC p 696
2 Manhattanville Rd # 301, Purchase NY 10577
Tel (914) 694-9200 SIC 3052

FORBO SIEGLING LLC p 565
12201 Vanstory Dr, Huntersville NC 28078
Tel (704) 948-0800 SIC 3052 3535

▲ GOODYEAR TIRE & RUBBER CO p 625
200 E Innovation Way, Akron OH 44316
Tel (330) 796-2121
SIC 3011 3052 7534 7538 7539 5013

▲ MYERS INDUSTRIES INC p 1004
1293 S Main St, Akron OH 44301
Tel (330) 253-5592
SIC 3089 3086 3069 3052 5013 5014

DTR INDUSTRIES INC p 458
320 Snider Rd, Bluffton OH 45817
Tel (419) 358-2121
SIC 3052 3069 3829 3714

AEROQUIP-VICKERS INC p 30
1111 Superior Ave E, Cleveland OH 44114
Tel (216) 523-5000
SIC 3052 3492 3429 3069 3585 3728

EATON-AEROQUIP LLC p 474
1000 Eaton Blvd, Cleveland OH 44122
Tel (216) 523-5000
SIC 3052 3492 3429 3069 3585 3728

HBD INDUSTRIES INC p 671
5200 Upper Metro Pl # 110, Dublin OH 43017
Tel (614) 526-7000
SIC 3052 3621 3566 3564 3812

TEKNI-PLEX INC p 1433
460 E Swedesford Rd # 3000, Wayne PA 19087
Tel (484) 690-1520
SIC 2679 3462 3052 2672

TEKNOR APEX CO p 1433
505 Central Ave, Pawtucket RI 02861
Tel (401) 725-8000
SIC 3087 3069 3052 2869 3081 2821

FLEXIBLE TECHNOLOGIES INC p 556
528 Carwellyn Rd, Abbeville SC 29620
Tel (864) 366-5441 SIC 3052 3089

TEKNOR APEX TENNESSEE CO p 1433
751 N Dupree Ave, Brownsville TN 38012
Tel (731) 772-4842 SIC 3052

TENNESSEE DTR INC p 1438
199 Pottertown Rd, Midway TN 37809
Tel (423) 422-4454 SIC 3069 3052

GHX INDUSTRIAL LLC p 610
3430 S Sam Houston Pkwy E, Houston TX 77047
Tel (713) 222-2231 SIC 3053 3052 3061

FISKARS BRANDS INC p 552
7800 Discovery Dr, Middleton WI 53562
Tel (608) 259-1649
SIC 3052 3679 3421 3069 3423

SIC 3053 Gaskets, Packing & Sealing Devices

AMERICAN CAST IRON PIPE CO p 70
1501 31st Ave N, Birmingham AL 35207
Tel (205) 325-7856
SIC 3491 3369 3321 3053 3317

BOYD LTI p 205
600 S Mcclure Rd, Modesto CA 95357
Tel (800) 554-0200 SIC 3549 3053 8711

WEST AMERICAN RUBBER CO LLC p 1593
1337 W Braden Ct, Orange CA 92868
Tel (714) 532-3355 SIC 3069 3061 3053

COORSTEK LLC p 368
16000 Table Mountain Pkwy, Golden CO 80403
Tel (303) 271-7000
SIC 3264 3053 3081 3082 3545

▲ LYDALL INC p 887
1 Colonial Rd, Manchester CT 06042
Tel (860) 646-1233
SIC 2297 3053 2899 2631 3714 3564

KEYSTONE HOLDINGS LLC p 815
10 Nw 42nd Ave Ste 700, Miami FL 33126
Tel (305) 567-1577
SIC 8711 3053 3081 3082 3545

THERMAL CERAMICS INC p 1447
2102 Old Savannah Rd, Augusta GA 30906
Tel (706) 796-4200
SIC 3299 3255 5085 3296 3264 3053

WIKA INSTRUMENT LP p 1608
1000 Wiegand Blvd, Lawrenceville GA 30043
Tel (770) 513-8200 SIC 3053 3823

JOHN CRANE INC p 788
227 W Monroe St Ste 1800, Chicago IL 60606
Tel (312) 605-7800 SIC 3053

BRC RUBBER & PLASTICS INC p 209
1029a W State Blvd, Fort Wayne IN 46808
Tel (260) 693-2171 SIC 3061 3714 3053

ILPEA INDUSTRIES INC p 733
745 S Gardner St, Scottsburg IN 47170
Tel (812) 837-6616 SIC 3053 3089

G T SALES & MANUFACTURING INC p 587
2202 S West St, Wichita KS 67213
Tel (316) 943-2171 SIC 5085 3053 3052

MPD INC p 995
316 E 9th St, Owensboro KY 42303
Tel (270) 685-6200
SIC 3671 3829 3812 3663 3643 3053

AMESBURY GROUP INC p 84
57 S Hunt Rd, Amesbury MA 01913
Tel (978) 834-3233
SIC 3053 3442 3086 2221 3089

HOLLINGSWORTH & VOSE CO p 701
112 Washington St, East Walpole MA 02032
Tel (508) 850-2000
SIC 2621 3053 2297 2499

A W CHESTERTON CO p 7
860 Salem St, Groveland MA 01834
Tel (781) 438-7000
SIC 3053 2851 2992 2891 5169

ACUSHNET RUBBER CO INC p 20
744 Belleville Ave, New Bedford MA 02745
Tel (508) 998-4000 SIC 3053 3061 2821

ZD USA HOLDINGS INC p 1641
744 Belleville Ave, New Bedford MA 02745
Tel (508) 998-4000 SIC 3053

■ PERKINELMER HOLDINGS INC p 1136
940 Winter St, Wellesley MA 02481
Tel (781) 663-6900 SIC 3053

KAYDON CORP p 805
2723 S State St Ste 300, Ann Arbor MI 48104
Tel (734) 747-7025
SIC 3562 3569 3592 3053 3621 3679

HENNIGES AUTOMOTIVE SEALING SYSTEMS NORTH AMERICA INC p 683
2750 High Meadow Cir, Auburn Hills MI 48326
Tel (248) 340-4100 SIC 3053 2891 3714

▲ UNIQUE FABRICATING INC p 1505
800 Standard Pkwy, Auburn Hills MI 48326
Tel (248) 853-2333
SIC 3053 3086 3296 2671

L & L PRODUCTS INC p 833
160 Mclean, Bruce Twp MI 48065
Tel (586) 336-1600 SIC 3053

ZEPHYROS INC p 1642
160 Mclean, Bruce Twp MI 48065
Tel (586) 336-1600 SIC 3053

ROGER ZATKOFF CO p 1246
23230 Industrial Park Dr, Farmington Hills MI 48335
Tel (248) 478-2400 SIC 5085 5072 3053

CREATIVE FOAM CORP p 390
300 N Alloy Dr, Fenton MI 48430
Tel (574) 546-4238
SIC 3061 3089 3053 3086 3069

OLIVER PRODUCTS CO p 1082
445 6th St Nw, Grand Rapids MI 49504
Tel (616) 456-7711 SIC 5084 5199 3053

FLEXFAB HORIZONS INTERNATIONAL INC p 556
102 Cook Rd, Hastings MI 49058
Tel (269) 945-4700
SIC 3599 3052 3053 2822

■ FLOWSERVE FSD CORP p 560
2100 Factory St, Kalamazoo MI 49001
Tel (269) 226-3954 SIC 3053

FREUDENBERG NORTH AMERICA LIMITED PARTNERSHIP p 579
47774 W Anchor Ct, Plymouth MI 48170
Tel (734) 354-5505
SIC 2821 3714 3053 3061

FREUDENBERG-NOK GENERAL PARTNERSHIP p 579
47690 E Anchor Ct, Plymouth MI 48170
Tel (734) 451-0020
SIC 2821 3714 3053 3061

VIBRACOUSTIC NORTH AMERICA L P p 1555
400 Aylworth Ave, South Haven MI 49090
Tel (269) 637-2116
SIC 2821 3714 3053 3061

■ FEDERAL-MOGUL PISTON RINGS INC p 536
26555 Northwestern Hwy, Southfield MI 48033
Tel (248) 354-7700 SIC 3592 3053 3369

HOFFMAN ENCLOSURES INC p 699
2100 Hoffman Way, Anoka MN 55303
Tel (763) 421-2240
SIC 3444 3699 3613 3469 3053

NOTT CO p 1062
4480 Round Lake Rd W, Arden Hills MN 55112
Tel (651) 415-3400
SIC 5084 5085 3492 3053

SEALING DEVICES INC p 1296
4400 Walden Ave, Lancaster NY 14086
Tel (716) 684-7600 SIC 5085 3069 3053

■ GARLOCK SEALING TECHNOLOGIES LLC p 592
1666 Division St, Palmyra NY 14522
Tel (315) 597-4811 SIC 3053 3585 3714

SCHLEGEL SYSTEMS INC p 1287
1555 Jefferson Rd, Rochester NY 14623
Tel (585) 427-7200 SIC 3053 3089 3069

■ COLTEC INDUSTRIES INC p 339
5605 Carnegie Blvd # 500, Charlotte NC 28209
Tel (704) 731-1500 SIC 3053 3519 3089

▲ ENPRO INDUSTRIES INC p 500
5605 Carnegie Blvd # 500, Charlotte NC 28209
Tel (704) 731-1500 SIC 3053 3519 3089

■ TECHNETICS GROUP LLC p 1431
5605 Carnegie Blvd # 500, Charlotte NC 28209
Tel (704) 731-1500 SIC 3053 3351

UCHIYAMA MANUFACTURING AMERICA LLC p 1499
494 Arrington Bridge Rd, Goldsboro NC 27530
Tel (919) 731-2364 SIC 5085 3714 3053

CHESTNUT HOLDINGS INC p 295
670 W Market St, Akron OH 44303
Tel (330) 849-6503
SIC 3053 5014 5013 3714

▲ PARKER-HANNIFIN CORP p 1116
6035 Parkland Blvd, Cleveland OH 44124
Tel (216) 896-3000
SIC 3594 3593 3492 3569 3053 3829

▲ DANA INC p 410
3939 Technology Dr, Maumee OH 43537
Tel (419) 887-3000
SIC 3714 3053 3593 3492

■ DANA LIMITED p 410
3939 Technology Dr, Maumee OH 43537
Tel (630) 697-3783
SIC 3714 3053 3593 3492

SAINT-GOBAIN PERFORMANCE PLASTICS CORP p 1271
31500 Solon Rd, Solon OH 44139
Tel (440) 836-6900 SIC 3089 3053

FOREST CITY TECHNOLOGIES INC p 566
299 Clay St, Wellington OH 44090
Tel (440) 647-2115 SIC 3053

TWEED GREENE & CO INC p 1494
2075 Detwiler Rd, Kulpsville PA 19443
Tel (215) 256-9521 SIC 3053

INTERFACE PERFORMANCE MATERIALS INC p 752
216 Wohlsen Way, Lancaster PA 17603
Tel (717) 390-1886 SIC 3053

SKF USA INC p 1329
890 Forty Foot Rd, Lansdale PA 19446
Tel (267) 436-6000 SIC 3562 3053 3829

FLEXITALLIC GROUP INC p 556
201 Kingwood Med Dr B20 Ste B 200, Houston TX 77067
Tel (281) 604-2525
SIC 3053 3533 3463 3965

GHX INDUSTRIAL LLC p 610
3430 S Sam Houston Pkwy E, Houston TX 77047
Tel (713) 222-2231 SIC 3053 3052 3061

■ LAMONS GASKET CO p 841
7300 Airport Blvd, Houston TX 77061
Tel (713) 547-9527 SIC 3053 5085

▲ OIL STATES INTERNATIONAL INC p 1079
333 Clay St Ste 4620, Houston TX 77002
Tel (713) 652-0582
SIC 3353 3061 3053 3561 3491

UTEX INDUSTRIES INC p 1536
10810 Katy Fwy Ste 100, Houston TX 77043
Tel (713) 559-0203 SIC 3053 3061

CDI ENERGY PRODUCTS INC p 271
8103 Rankin Rd, Humble TX 77396
Tel (281) 446-6662 SIC 3053

FGI ACQUISITION CORP p 539
201 Kingwood Medical Dr B200, Kingwood TX 77339
Tel (281) 604-2525 SIC 3053

SIC 3061 Molded, Extruded & Lathe-Cut Rubber Mechanical Goods

WEST AMERICAN RUBBER CO LLC p 1593
1337 W Braden Ct, Orange CA 92868
Tel (714) 532-3355 SIC 3069 3061 3053

BURKE INDUSTRIES INC p 227
2250 S 10th St, San Jose CA 95112
Tel (408) 297-3500
SIC 3069 2822 2821 3061

MAC LEAN-FOGG CO p 891
1000 Allanson Rd, Mundelein IL 60060
Tel (847) 566-0010
SIC 3678 3452 3089 3061 3492 3451

BRC RUBBER & PLASTICS INC p 209
1029a W State Blvd, Fort Wayne IN 46808
Tel (260) 693-2171 SIC 3061 3714 3053

JASPER RUBBER PRODUCTS INC p 778
1010 1st Ave W, Jasper IN 47546
Tel (812) 482-3242 SIC 3061

■ HUTCHINSON AEROSPACE & INDUSTRY INC p 721
82 South St, Hopkinton MA 01748
Tel (508) 417-7000 SIC 3714 3061 3724

ACUSHNET RUBBER CO INC p 20
744 Belleville Ave, New Bedford MA 02745
Tel (508) 998-4000 SIC 3053 3061 2821

■ HUTCHINSON FTS INC p 722
1060 Centre Rd, Auburn Hills MI 48326
Tel (248) 589-7710
SIC 3714 3061 3567 3492 3443 3429

AVON AUTOMOTIVE HOLDINGS INC p 139
603 7th St, Cadillac MI 49601
Tel (231) 775-6571 SIC 3061 3089

AVON RUBBER & PLASTICS INC p 139
503 8th St, Cadillac MI 49601
Tel (231) 779-6290 SIC 3089 3061

CREATIVE FOAM CORP p 390
300 N Alloy Dr, Fenton MI 48430
Tel (574) 546-4238
SIC 3061 3089 3053 3086 3069

■ HUTCHINSON ANTIVIBRATION SYSTEMS INC p 722
460 Fuller Ave Ne, Grand Rapids MI 49503
Tel (616) 459-4541 SIC 3069 3061

■ PULLMAN CO p 1191
1 International Dr, Monroe MI 48161
Tel (734) 243-8000 SIC 3714 3715 3061

FREUDENBERG NORTH AMERICA LIMITED PARTNERSHIP p 579
47774 W Anchor Ct, Plymouth MI 48170
Tel (734) 354-5505
SIC 2821 3714 3053 3061

FREUDENBERG-NOK GENERAL PARTNERSHIP p 579
47690 E Anchor Ct, Plymouth MI 48170
Tel (734) 451-0020
SIC 2821 3714 3053 3061

TRELLEBORG AUTOMOTIVE USA INC p 1476
400 Aylworth Ave, South Haven MI 49090
Tel (269) 637-2116 SIC 3061 3625

VIBRACOUSTIC NORTH AMERICA L P p 1555
400 Aylworth Ave, South Haven MI 49090
Tel (269) 637-2116
SIC 2821 3714 3053 3061

HP PELZER AUTOMOTIVE SYSTEMS INC p 714
1175 Crooks Rd, Troy MI 48084
Tel (248) 280-1010 SIC 3061 2273

HYGENIC CORP p 723
1245 Home Ave, Akron OH 44310
Tel (330) 633-8460 SIC 3069 3061

BRIDGESTONE APM CO p 211
2030 Production Dr, Findlay OH 45840
Tel (419) 423-9552 SIC 3061

TIGERPOLY MANUFACTURING INC p 1453
6231 Enterprise Pkwy, Grove City OH 43123
Tel (614) 871-0045
SIC 3089 3714 3621 3061

Q HOLDING CO p 1194
1700 Highland Rd, Twinsburg OH 44087
Tel (330) 425-8472 SIC 3061

GRIFFITH RUBBER MILLS p 640
2625 Nw Indul St, Portland OR 97210
Tel (503) 226-6971 SIC 3061 3069

MOORE CO p 987
36 Beach St, Westerly RI 02891
Tel (401) 596-2816
SIC 2258 2241 3069 3061 2821

FENNER ADVANCED SEALING TECHNOLOGIES INC p 537
975 Market St Ste 201a, Fort Mill SC 29708
Tel (803) 547-8434 SIC 3061

SAARGUMMI TENNESSEE INC p 1263
200 Commerce Way, Pulaski TN 38478
Tel (931) 363-1363 SIC 3061

■ OIL STATES INDUSTRIES INC p 1079
7701 S Cooper St, Arlington TX 76001
Tel (817) 548-4200
SIC 1389 3061 3561 3533

GHX INDUSTRIAL LLC p 610
3430 S Sam Houston Pkwy E, Houston TX 77047
Tel (713) 222-2231 SIC 3053 3052 3061

▲ OIL STATES INTERNATIONAL INC p 1079
333 Clay St Ste 4620, Houston TX 77002
Tel (713) 652-0582
SIC 3353 3061 3053 3561 3491

UTEX INDUSTRIES INC p 1536
10810 Katy Fwy Ste 100, Houston TX 77043
Tel (713) 559-0203 SIC 3053 3061

REX-HIDE INC p 1230
705 S Lyons Ave, Tyler TX 75702
Tel (903) 593-7387
SIC 3061 3069 2891 6799

SIC 3069 Fabricated Rubber Prdts, NEC

HWASEUNG AUTOMOTIVE ALABAMA LLC p 722
100 Sonata Dr, Enterprise AL 36330
Tel (334) 348-9516 SIC 3714 3069

HWASEUNG AUTOMOTIVE AMERICA HOLDINGS INC p 722
100 Sonata Dr, Enterprise AL 36330
Tel (334) 348-9516 SIC 3069 5085

WEST COAST BEAUTY SUPPLY CO p 1594
5001 Industrial Way, Benicia CA 94510
Tel (707) 748-4800 SIC 5087 3069

■ KIRKHILL-TA CO p 822
300 E Cypress St, Brea CA 92821
Tel (714) 529-4901 SIC 3069

NUSIL TECHNOLOGY LLC p 1067
1050 Cindy Ln, Carpinteria CA 93013
Tel (805) 684-8780 SIC 3069

KRACO ENTERPRISES LLC p 829
505 E Euclid Ave, Compton CA 90222
Tel (310) 639-0666 SIC 5531 3069 5013

MCP INDUSTRIES INC p 932
708 S Temescal St Ste 101, Corona CA 92879
Tel (951) 736-1881 SIC 3069 3259 3089

A B BOYD CO p 4
600 S Mcclure Rd, Modesto CA 95357
Tel (800) 554-0200 SIC 3069

LTI HOLDINGS INC p 883
600 S Mcclure Rd, Modesto CA 95357
Tel (209) 236-1111 SIC 3069 2822

WEST AMERICAN RUBBER CO LLC p 1593
1337 W Braden Ct, Orange CA 92868
Tel (714) 532-3355 SIC 3069 3061 3053

BURKE INDUSTRIES INC p 227
2250 S 10th St, San Jose CA 95112
Tel (408) 297-3500
SIC 3069 2822 2821 3061

■ PRECISION DYNAMICS CORP p 1168
27770 N Entrmt Dr Ste 200, Valencia CA 91355
Tel (818) 897-1111
SIC 2672 2754 5047 3069

■ OUTDOOR SPORTS GEAR INC p 1098
2320 Cousteau Ct Ste 100, Vista CA 92081
Tel (914) 967-9400
SIC 3949 3069 2339 2329

▲ CROCS INC p 393
7477 Dry Creek Pkwy, Niwot CO 80503
Tel (303) 848-7000
SIC 3021 5139 3069 5661 2389

▲ ACME UNITED CORP p 18
55 Walls Dr Ste 201, Fairfield CT 06824
Tel (203) 254-6060
SIC 3421 2499 3842 3579 3069 3999

■ PLAYTEX PRODUCTS LLC p 1155
6 Research Dr Ste 400, Shelton CT 06484
Tel (203) 944-5500
SIC 2676 3069 2844 3842

SCAPA NORTH AMERICA INC p 1286
111 Great Pond Dr, Windsor CT 06095
Tel (860) 688-8000
SIC 2231 3069 2211 2824 2672

W L GORE & ASSOCIATES INC p 1568
555 Paper Mill Rd, Newark DE 19711
Tel (302) 738-4880
SIC 3357 2821 5131 3841 2819 3069

ASBURY CARBONS INC p 115
103 Foulk Rd Ste 202, Wilmington DE 19803
Tel (302) 652-0266
SIC 1499 3295 1241 5051 3952 3069

ENER1 GROUP INC p 497
550 W Cypress Creek Rd, Fort Lauderdale FL 33309
Tel (954) 202-4442 SIC 3577 3069

MAUI ACQUISITION CORP p 921
13386 International Pkwy, Jacksonville FL 32218
Tel (904) 741-5400 SIC 3069 2389

■ GOODY PRODUCTS INC p 625
3 Glenlake Pkwy, Atlanta GA 30328
Tel (770) 418-7300 SIC 3999 3089 3069

KLEEN-TEX INDUSTRIES INC p 823
101 N Greenwood St Ste C, Lagrange GA 30240
Tel (706) 882-0111 SIC 3069 2273 2392

ROTATION DYNAMICS CORP p 1252
8140 Cass Ave, Darien IL 60561
Tel (630) 769-9255 SIC 3069

FENWAL HOLDINGS INC p 537
3 Corporate Dr Ste 300, Lake Zurich IL 60047
Tel (847) 550-2300 SIC 3069 5047

FENWAL INC p 537
3 Corporate Dr Ste 300, Lake Zurich IL 60047
Tel (847) 550-2300 SIC 5047 3069

KELCO INDUSTRIES INC p 808
1425 Lake Ave, Woodstock IL 60098
Tel (815) 334-3600
SIC 3599 3069 3494 3585 3544 3625

VESTIL MANUFACTURING CORP p 1552
2999 N Wayne St, Angola IN 46703
Tel (260) 665-7586 SIC 3999 3535 3069

DOREL JUVENILE GROUP INC p 451
2525 State St, Columbus IN 47201
Tel (800) 457-5276
SIC 3089 3069 3429 3699 3648

PONTOON BOAT LLC p 1161
2805 Decio Dr, Elkhart IN 46514
Tel (574) 264-6336 SIC 3069

KOCH ENTERPRISES INC p 825
14 S 11th Ave, Evansville IN 47712
Tel (812) 465-9800
SIC 3363 5075 3559 5084 2891 3069

NISHIKAWA COOPER LLC p 1044
324 Morrow St, Topeka IN 46571
Tel (260) 593-2156 SIC 3069

NISHIKAWA OF AMERICA INC p 1044
324 Morrow St, Topeka IN 46571
Tel (260) 593-2156 SIC 3069

HENNIGES AUTOMOTIVE IOWA INC p 683
3200 Main St, Keokuk IA 52632
Tel (319) 524-4560
SIC 3069 3442 3429 2295

CONTINENTAL AMERICAN CORP p 362
5000 E 29th St N, Wichita KS 67220
Tel (316) 685-2266 SIC 2759 3069

DAICEL SAFETY SYSTEMS AMERICA LLC p 408
720 Old Liberty Church Rd, Beaver Dam KY 42320
Tel (270) 274-0062 SIC 3069

HAARTZ CORP p 651
87 Hayward Rd, Acton MA 01720
Tel (978) 264-2600 SIC 3069 2295

■ NEW ENGLAND BUSINESS SERVICE INC p 1030
500 Main St, Groton MA 01471
Tel (978) 448-6111
SIC 2759 2771 5045 2653 3089 3069

▲ AMERICAN BILTRITE INC p 69
57 River St Ste 302, Wellesley MA 02481
Tel (781) 237-6655
SIC 3069 2672 2241 3961 5094

AIRBOSS FLEXIBLE PRODUCTS CO p 39
2600 Auburn Ct, Auburn Hills MI 48326
Tel (248) 852-5500 SIC 3069 3714

HENNIGES AUTOMOTIVE HOLDINGS INC p 683
2750 High Meadow Cir, Auburn Hills MI 48326
Tel (248) 340-4100 SIC 3069 2891 3714

■ HUTCHINSON SEALING SYSTEMS INC p 722
1060 Centre Rd, Auburn Hills MI 48326
Tel (248) 375-3720 SIC 3069

CREATIVE FOAM CORP p 390
300 N Alloy Dr, Fenton MI 48430
Tel (574) 546-4238
SIC 3061 3089 3053 3086 3069

■ HUTCHINSON ANTIVIBRATION SYSTEMS INC p 722
460 Fuller Ave Ne, Grand Rapids MI 49503
Tel (616) 459-4541 SIC 3069 3061

■ HUTCHINSON CORP p 722
460 Fuller Ave Ne, Grand Rapids MI 49503
Tel (616) 459-4541 SIC 3069 3011

ZHONGDING SEALING PARTS (USA) INC p 1643
400 Detroit Ave, Monroe MI 48162
Tel (734) 241-8870 SIC 3069

DAY INTERNATIONAL GROUP INC p 417
14909 N Beck Rd, Plymouth MI 48170
Tel (734) 781-4600 SIC 3069

TRICO PRODUCTS CORP p 1479
3255 W Hamlin Rd, Rochester Hills MI 48309
Tel (248) 371-1700
SIC 3714 3069 3082 8734 8731

TOYODA GOSEI NORTH AMERICA CORP p 1466
1400 Stephenson Hwy, Troy MI 48083
Tel (248) 280-2100 SIC 3069 3089

■ VISTA OUTDOOR SALES LLC p 1562
1 Vista Way, Anoka MN 55303
Tel (763) 323-2414 SIC 3482 3069

APOTHECARY PRODUCTS LLC p 97
11750 12th Ave S, Burnsville MN 55337
Tel (800) 328-2742 SIC 2834 5122 3069

■ ANAGRAM INTERNATIONAL INC p 88
7700 Anagram Dr, Eden Prairie MN 55344
Tel (952) 949-5600 SIC 3069

AMERICAN PHOENIX INC p 77
5500 Wayzata Blvd # 1010, Golden Valley MN 55416
Tel (763) 591-5035 SIC 3069

QUADION HOLDINGS LLC p 1196
1100 Xenium Ln N Ste 1, Minneapolis MN 55441
Tel (952) 927-1400 SIC 3069 3089

■ QUADION LLC p 1196
1100 Xenium Ln N Ste 1, Minneapolis MN 55441
Tel (952) 927-1400 SIC 3069 3089

WINCRAFT INC p 1615
960 E Mark St, Winona MN 55987
Tel (507) 454-5510
SIC 3499 2399 3089 3961 3999 3069

▲ EDGEWELL PERSONAL CARE CO p 477
1350 Timberlake Manor Pkwy, Chesterfield MO 63017
Tel (314) 594-1900
SIC 3421 2844 2676 3069

DASH MULTI-CORP INC p 413
2500 Adie Rd, Maryland Heights MO 63043
Tel (314) 432-3200
SIC 2821 3069 6512 5169 7359

VENTION MEDICAL ADVANCED COMPONENTS INC p 1548
29 Northwestern Dr, Salem NH 03079
Tel (603) 327-0600 SIC 3082 3069 3083

ANSELL HEALTHCARE PRODUCTS LLC p 93
111 Wood Ave S Ste 210, Iselin NJ 08830
Tel (732) 345-5400
SIC 3069 3842 2822 2326

ANSELL PROTECTIVE PRODUCTS LLC p 93
111 Wood Ave S Ste 210, Iselin NJ 08830
Tel (732) 345-5400 SIC 3842 3069

INNOCOR INC p 744
200 Schulz Dr Ste 2, Red Bank NJ 07701
Tel (844) 824-9348 SIC 2515 2392 3069

PACIFIC DUNLOP HOLDINGS (USA) LLC p 1104
200 Schulz Dr, Red Bank NJ 07701
Tel (732) 345-5400 SIC 3069 3691

PACIFIC DUNLOP INVESTMENTS (USA) INC p 1104
200 Schulz Dr, Red Bank NJ 07701
Tel (732) 345-5400 SIC 3069 3842

■ HUTCHINSON INDUSTRIES INC p 722
460 Southard St, Trenton NJ 08638
Tel (609) 394-1010 SIC 3069

AIR CRUISERS CO LLC p 38
1747 State Route 34, Wall Township NJ 07727
Tel (732) 681-3527
SIC 2531 3069 3728 2399

■ AMSCAN HOLDINGS INC p 87
80 Grasslands Rd Ste 3, Elmsford NY 10523
Tel (914) 345-2020
SIC 5947 2679 3089 3069 6794

SEALING DEVICES INC p 1296
4400 Walden Ave, Lancaster NY 14086
Tel (716) 684-7600 SIC 5085 3069 3053

SCHLEGEL SYSTEMS INC p 1287
1555 Jefferson Rd, Rochester NY 14623
Tel (585) 427-7200 SIC 3053 3089 3069

GREAT AMERICAN INDUSTRIES INC p 633
300 Plaza Dr, Vestal NY 13850
Tel (607) 729-9331
SIC 3086 5031 5074 3442 3069 5091

PRESTIGE FABRICATORS INC p 1173
905 Nc Highway 49 S, Asheboro NC 27205
Tel (336) 626-4595 SIC 3069

DARAMIC LLC p 412
11430 N Cmnity Hse Rd # 350, Charlotte NC 28277
Tel (704) 587-8599 SIC 3069 2499 3269

HICKORY SPRINGS MANUFACTURING CO p 690
235 2nd Ave Nw, Hickory NC 28601
Tel (828) 328-2201
SIC 3069 3495 2514 5072 2399

COOPER CROUSE- HINDS LLC p 366
4758 Washington St, La Grange NC 28551
Tel (252) 566-3014 SIC 3069 3643

HEXPOL COMPOUNDING NC INC p 688
280 Crawford Rd, Statesville NC 28625
Tel (704) 872-1585 SIC 3069 3087 2891

▲ XERIUM TECHNOLOGIES INC p 1631
14101 Capital Blvd, Youngsville NC 27596
Tel (919) 526-1400 SIC 2221 3069

FIRESTONE POLYMERS LLC p 544
381 W Wilbeth Rd, Akron OH 44301
Tel (330) 379-7000 SIC 3069

HYGENIC CORP p 723
1245 Home Ave, Akron OH 44310
Tel (330) 633-8460 SIC 3069 3061

▲ MYERS INDUSTRIES INC p 1004
1293 S Main St, Akron OH 44301
Tel (330) 253-5592
SIC 3089 3086 3069 3052 5013 5014

PREFERRED COMPOUNDING CORP p 1169
1020 Lambert St, Barberton OH 44203
Tel (330) 798-4790 SIC 3069

▲ OMNOVA SOLUTIONS INC p 1085
25435 Harvard Rd, Beachwood OH 44122
Tel (216) 682-7000
SIC 2819 2211 3069 3081

DTR INDUSTRIES INC p 458
320 Snider Rd, Bluffton OH 45817
Tel (419) 358-2121
SIC 3052 3069 3829 3714

GREENTOKAI CO LTD p 637
55 Robert Wright Dr, Brookville OH 45309
Tel (937) 833-5444 SIC 3714 3069

TARKETT INC p 1425
16910 Munn Rd, Chagrin Falls OH 44023
Tel (800) 899-8916 SIC 3069

AEROQUIP-VICKERS INC p 30
1111 Superior Ave E, Cleveland OH 44114
Tel (216) 523-5000
SIC 3052 3492 3429 3069 3585 3728

EATON-AEROQUIP LLC p 474
1000 Eaton Blvd, Cleveland OH 44122
Tel (216) 523-5000
SIC 3052 3492 3429 3069 3585 3728

▲ PARK-OHIO HOLDINGS CORP p 1116
6065 Parkland Blvd Ste 1, Cleveland OH 44124
Tel (440) 947-2000
SIC 3462 3069 3567 3363 3631 3524

■ PARK-OHIO INDUSTRIES INC p 1116
6065 Parkland Blvd Ste 1, Cleveland OH 44124
Tel (440) 947-2000
SIC 3462 3069 3567 3363 3524

KOROSEAL INTERIOR PRODUCTS LLC p 828
3875 Embassy Pkwy Ste 110, Fairlawn OH 44333
Tel (330) 668-7600 SIC 3081 3089 3069

RJF INTERNATIONAL CORP p 1239
3875 Embassy Pkwy Ste 110, Fairlawn OH 44333
Tel (330) 668-2069 SIC 3081 3089 3069

ROPPE HOLDING CO p 1250
1602 N Union St, Fostoria OH 44830
Tel (419) 435-8546 SIC 3089 3069

■ REPUBLIC POWDERED METALS INC p 1225
2628 Pearl Rd, Medina OH 44256
Tel (330) 225-3192
SIC 2851 2891 3069 2899 2865 2842

▲ RPM INTERNATIONAL INC p 1255
2628 Pearl Rd, Medina OH 44256
Tel (330) 273-5090
SIC 2851 2891 3069 2899 2865 2842

LAUREN INTERNATIONAL LTD p 847
2228 Reiser Ave Se, New Philadelphia OH 44663
Tel (330) 339-3373 SIC 3069

LEXINGTON RUBBER GROUP INC p 859
1700 Highland Rd, Twinsburg OH 44087
Tel (330) 425-8472 SIC 3069

YUSA CORP p 1640
151 Jamison Rd Sw, Washington Court Hou OH 43160
Tel (740) 335-0335 SIC 3069

GRIFFITH RUBBER MILLS p 640
2625 Nw Indul St, Portland OR 97210
Tel (503) 226-6971 SIC 3061 3069

■ CARLISLE CONSTRUCTION MATERIALS LLC p 257
1285 Ritner Hwy, Carlisle PA 17013
Tel (717) 245-7000
SIC 2952 3069 5031 2899 2891

▲ WEST PHARMACEUTICAL SERVICES INC p 1595
530 Herman O West Dr, Exton PA 19341
Tel (610) 594-2900
SIC 3069 3466 2673 3085 3089

POLYMER ENTERPRISES INC p 1160
4731 State Route 30 # 401, Greensburg PA 15601
Tel (724) 838-2340 SIC 3069 3011

ADVANCED SCIENTIFICS INC p 26
163 Research Ln, Millersburg PA 17061
Tel (717) 692-2104 SIC 3069

COOLEY GROUP HOLDINGS INC p 366
50 Esten Ave, Pawtucket RI 02860
Tel (401) 724-0510 SIC 5211 3069

COOLEY INC p 366
50 Esten Ave, Pawtucket RI 02860
Tel (401) 724-9000 SIC 2295 3069 2262

▲ HASBRO INC p 667
1027 Newport Ave, Pawtucket RI 02861
Tel (401) 431-8697 SIC 3944 3942 3069

TEKNOR APEX CO p 1433
505 Central Ave, Pawtucket RI 02861
Tel (401) 725-8000
SIC 3087 3069 3052 2869 3081 2821

MOORE CO p 987
36 Beach St, Westerly RI 02891
Tel (401) 596-2816
SIC 2258 2241 3069 3061 2821

TENNESSEE DTR INC p 1438
199 Pottertown Rd, Midway TN 37809
Tel (423) 422-4454 SIC 3069 3052

FIRESTONE NATURAL RUBBER CO LLC p 544
535 Marriott Dr Fl 3, Nashville TN 37214
Tel (866) 900-3767 SIC 3069 2499

HYDRIL USA MANUFACTURING LLC p 723
3300 N Sam Houston Pkwy E, Houston TX 77032
Tel (281) 449-2000 SIC 3089

REX-HIDE INC p 1230
705 S Lyons Ave, Tyler TX 75702
Tel (903) 593-7387
SIC 3061 3069 2891 6799

FISKARS BRANDS INC p 552
7800 Discovery Dr, Middleton WI 53562
Tel (608) 259-1649
SIC 3052 3679 3421 3069 3423

MERIDIAN INDUSTRIES INC p 949
735 N Water St Ste 630, Milwaukee WI 53202
Tel (414) 224-0610
SIC 3069 2843 2269 7389

DYNATECT MANUFACTURING INC p 464
2300 S Calhoun Rd, New Berlin WI 53151
Tel (262) 786-1500
SIC 3069 3499 3714 3599

METSO MINERALS INDUSTRIES INC p 957
20965 Crossroads Cir, Waukesha WI 53186
Tel (262) 798-3994
SIC 3321 3069 3561 3535 3532

SIC 3081 Plastic Unsupported Sheet & Film

GKN AEROSPACE TRANSPARENCY SYSTEMS INC p 613
12122 Western Ave, Garden Grove CA 92841
Tel (714) 893-7531
SIC 3089 3231 3827 3728 3081 2821

▲ AVERY DENNISON CORP p 137
207 N Goode Ave Fl 6, Glendale CA 91203
Tel (626) 304-2000
SIC 2672 3081 3497 2678

INTEX RECREATION CORP p 759
4001 Via Oro Ave Ste 210, Long Beach CA 90810
Tel (310) 549-5400
SIC 5091 5092 5021 3081

■ GLAD PRODUCTS CO p 614
1221 Broadway Ste A, Oakland CA 94612
Tel (510) 271-7000
SIC 3081 2673 2842 3295

COORSTEK LLC p 368
16000 Table Mountain Pkwy, Golden CO 80403
Tel (303) 271-7000
SIC 3264 3053 3081 3082 3545

ENGINEERING SERVICES & PRODUCTS CO p 499
1395 John Fitch Blvd, South Windsor CT 06074
Tel (860) 528-1119 SIC 3523 5083 3081

■ DELSTAR TECHNOLOGIES INC p 425
601 Industrial Rd, Middletown DE 19709
Tel (302) 378-8888 SIC 3081

TAGHLEEF INDUSTRIES INC p 1421
500 Creek View Rd Ste 301, Newark DE 19711
Tel (302) 326-5500 SIC 3081

■ RAYONIER PERFORMANCE FIBERS LLC p 1210
1301 Riverplace Blvd, Jacksonville FL 32207
Tel (912) 427-5000 SIC 3081

KEYSTONE HOLDINGS LLC p 815
10 Nw 42nd Ave Ste 700, Miami FL 33126
Tel (305) 567-1577
SIC 8711 3053 3081 3082 3545

FLEXSOL HOLDING CORP p 556
1531 Nw 12th Ave, Pompano Beach FL 33069
Tel (954) 941-6333 SIC 2673 3082 3081

PRINTPACK INC p 1177
2800 Overlook Pkwy Ne, Atlanta GA 30339
Tel (404) 460-7000 SIC 2673 3081

■ WESTROCK CONVERTING CO p 1602
504 Thrasher St, Norcross GA 30071
Tel (770) 246-9982 SIC 2631 2653 3081

CYTEC SURFACE SPECIALTIES INC p 406
1950 Lake Park Dr Se, Smyrna GA 30080
Tel (770) 434-6188
SIC 3086 5169 5191 5162 3081 2823

MIDWEST CANVAS CORP p 967
4635 W Lake St, Chicago IL 60644
Tel (773) 287-4400 SIC 3081 3089

JORDAN SPECIALTY PLASTICS INC p 793
1751 Lake Cook Rd Ste 550, Deerfield IL 60015
Tel (847) 945-5591 SIC 3089 3081

TRANSCENDIA INC p 1471
9201 Belmont Ave, Franklin Park IL 60131
Tel (847) 678-1800 SIC 3081 5162

AMCOR FLEXIBLES LLC p 65
1919 S Butterfield Rd, Mundelein IL 60060
Tel (847) 362-9000
SIC 2671 2621 2821 3081 3466

SCHOLLE IPN CORP p 1288
200 W North Ave, Northlake IL 60164
Tel (708) 562-7290
SIC 2819 3081 2821 3089

■ PLIANT LLC p 1156
1701 Golf Rd Ste 2-900, Rolling Meadows IL 60008
Tel (812) 424-2904 SIC 3081 2673 3089

■ BERRY PLASTICS CORP p 176
101 Oakley St, Evansville IN 47710
Tel (812) 424-2904 SIC 3089 3081

▲ BERRY PLASTICS GROUP INC p 176
101 Oakley St, Evansville IN 47710
Tel (812) 424-2904
SIC 3089 3085 2673 3081 3083

SABIC INNOVATIVE PLASTICS MT VERNON LLC p 1264
1 Lexan Ln, Mount Vernon IN 47620
Tel (812) 838-4385 SIC 2821 3087 3081

PRIMEX PLASTICS CORP p 1176
1235 N F St, Richmond IN 47374
Tel (765) 966-7774 SIC 3081 2821

INDUSTRIAL LAMINATES/NORPLEX INC p 740
665 Lybrand St, Postville IA 52162
Tel (563) 864-7321 *SIC* 3089 3081

▲ ENTEGRIS INC p 501
129 Concord Rd, Billerica MA 01821
Tel (978) 436-6500 *SIC* 3089 3081 3674

▲ CABOT CORP p 235
2 Seaport Ln Ste 1300, Boston MA 02210
Tel (617) 345-0100
SIC 2895 3081 3084 2819 3339

FLEXCON CO INC p 556
1 Flexcon Industrial Park, Spencer MA 01562
Tel (508) 885-8200 *SIC* 3081 2891

▲ DOW CHEMICAL CO p 453
2030 Dow Ctr, Midland MI 48674
Tel (989) 636-1000
SIC 2821 3081 3086 2812 2879

CADILLAC PRODUCTS INC p 236
5800 Crooks Rd Ste 100, Troy MI 48098
Tel (248) 813-8200
SIC 3714 3081 2673 3089

CADILLAC PRODUCTS PACKAGING CO p 236
5800 Crooks Rd, Troy MI 48098
Tel (248) 879-5000 *SIC* 3081

■ MASTIC HOME EXTERIORS INC p 918
2600 Grand Blvd Ste 900, Kansas City MO 64108
Tel (816) 426-8200 *SIC* 3081 3089

■ SOLUTIA INC p 1339
575 Maryville Centre Dr, Saint Louis MO 63141
Tel (423) 229-2000
SIC 2824 2821 3081 2869

SPARTECH CORP p 1355
120 S Central Ave # 1700, Saint Louis MO 63105
Tel (314) 721-4242 *SIC* 3081 2821 3089

ICI AMERICA INC p 727
10 Finderne Ave, Bridgewater NJ 08807
Tel (908) 203-2800
SIC 2821 3081 2869 2843 2865

ICI AMERICAN HOLDINGS LLC p 727
10 Finderne Ave, Bridgewater NJ 08807
Tel (908) 203-2800
SIC 2851 2821 3081 2869 2843 2865

NAN YA PLASTICS CORP USA p 1007
9 Peach Tree Hill Rd, Livingston NJ 07039
Tel (973) 992-1775 *SIC* 3081

TRINITY PLASTICS INC p 1481
9 Peach Tree Hill Rd, Livingston NJ 07039
Tel (973) 994-8018 *SIC* 2673 3081

▲ AEP INDUSTRIES INC p 29
95 Chestnut Ridge Rd, Montvale NJ 07645
Tel (201) 641-6600 *SIC* 3081 2821

CONGOLEUM CORP p 356
3500 Quakerbridge Rd, Trenton NJ 08619
Tel (609) 584-3000 *SIC* 3081 5713 8741

LATHAM INTERNATIONAL INC p 846
787 Watervliet Shaker Rd, Latham NY 12110
Tel (518) 783-7776 *SIC* 3086 3081

LATHAM MANUFACTURING CORP p 846
787 Watervliet Shaker Rd, Latham NY 12110
Tel (518) 783-7776
SIC 3086 3081 3083 3949

ICC INDUSTRIES INC p 727
460 Park Ave Fl 7, New York NY 10022
Tel (212) 521-1700
SIC 2821 2869 2911 2899 3081 2834

API INDUSTRIES INC p 96
2 Glenshaw St, Orangeburg NY 10962
Tel (845) 365-2200 *SIC* 2673 3081

DAIKIN AMERICA INC p 408
20 Olympic Dr, Orangeburg NY 10962
Tel (845) 365-9500 *SIC* 3081 2821

BONSET AMERICA CORP p 200
6107 Corporate Park Dr, Browns Summit NC 27214
Tel (336) 375-0234 *SIC* 3081

CELGARD LLC p 273
13800 S Lakes Dr, Charlotte NC 28273
Tel (704) 588-5310 *SIC* 2821 3081

PIEDMONT PLASTICS INC p 1147
5010 W Wt Harris Blvd, Charlotte NC 28269
Tel (704) 597-8200 *SIC* 3081 3082 5162

PP HOLDING CORP p 1166
13800 S Lakes Dr, Charlotte NC 28273
Tel (704) 587-8409 *SIC* 3081 3089

ROCHLING ENGINEERED PLASTICS LIMITED PARTNERSHIP p 1243
903 Gastonia Tech Pkwy, Dallas NC 28034
Tel (704) 922-7814 *SIC* 3081 3082

3A COMPOSITES USA INC p 2
3480 Taylorsville Hwy, Statesville NC 28625
Tel (704) 872-8974
SIC 3334 2679 3081 3449

▲ POLYONE CORP p 1160
33587 Walker Rd, Avon Lake OH 44012
Tel (440) 930-1000
SIC 2821 3087 5162 3081

▲ OMNOVA SOLUTIONS INC p 1085
25435 Harvard Rd, Beachwood OH 44122
Tel (216) 682-7000
SIC 2819 2211 3069 3081

AMPAC HOLDINGS LLC p 86
12025 Tricon Rd, Cincinnati OH 45246
Tel (513) 671-1777
SIC 2673 2677 3081 2674 6719

LIQUI-BOX CORP p 870
480 Schrock Rd Ste G, Columbus OH 43229
Tel (804) 325-1400
SIC 2673 3585 3089 3081 5149

PLASTIC SUPPLIERS INC p 1155
2450 Marilyn Ln, Columbus OH 43219
Tel (614) 471-9100 *SIC* 3081

KOROSEAL INTERIOR PRODUCTS LLC p 828
3875 Embassy Pkwy Ste 110, Fairlawn OH 44333
Tel (330) 668-7600 *SIC* 3081 3089 3069

RJF INTERNATIONAL CORP p 1239
3875 Embassy Pkwy Ste 110, Fairlawn OH 44333
Tel (330) 668-2069 *SIC* 3081 3089 3069

■ CLOPAY CORP p 327
8585 Duke Blvd, Mason OH 45040
Tel (800) 282-2260
SIC 3081 3442 2431 1796

■ CLOPAY PLASTIC PRODUCTS CO INC p 327
8585 Duke Blvd, Mason OH 45040
Tel (513) 770-4800 *SIC* 3081

AUTOMATED PACKAGING SYSTEMS INC p 134
10175 Philipp Pkwy, Streetsboro OH 44241
Tel (330) 528-2000 *SIC* 3081 3565

CLARKWESTERN DIETRICH BUILDING SYSTEMS LLC p 322
9100 Centre Pointe Dr # 210, West Chester OH 45069
Tel (513) 870-1100 *SIC* 3444 8711 3081

WEXCO INC p 1603
3490 Board Rd, York PA 17406
Tel (717) 764-8585
SIC 3089 3949 3999 5091 3081

TORAY PLASTICS (AMERICA) INC p 1461
50 Belver Ave, North Kingstown RI 02852
Tel (401) 667-2426 *SIC* 3081

TEKNOR APEX CO p 1433
505 Central Ave, Pawtucket RI 02861
Tel (401) 725-8000
SIC 3087 3069 3052 2869 3081 2821

■ JPS INDUSTRIES INC p 795
2200 S Murray Ave, Anderson SC 29624
Tel (864) 239-3900 *SIC* 2221 3081

MITSUBISHI POLYESTER FILM INC p 978
2001 Hood Rd, Greer SC 29650
Tel (864) 879-5000 *SIC* 3081 2671

▲ RAVEN INDUSTRIES INC p 1209
205 E 6th St, Sioux Falls SD 57104
Tel (605) 336-2750
SIC 5065 3523 3081 3823 3083

PI INC p 1146
213 Dennis St, Athens TN 37303
Tel (423) 745-6213
SIC 2519 3949 3089 2499 3086 3081

BUCKEYE TECHNOLOGIES INC p 223
1001 Tillman St, Memphis TN 38112
Tel (901) 320-8100 *SIC* 2611 3081

MARCO DISPLAY SPECIALISTS LP p 905
3209 Marquita Dr, Fort Worth TX 76116
Tel (817) 244-8300
SIC 2521 2541 3993 3089 3081

POLY-AMERICA LP p 1160
2000 W Marshall Dr, Grand Prairie TX 75051
Tel (972) 337-7100 *SIC* 3081 2673

GSE ENVIRONMENTAL INC p 643
19103 Gundle Rd, Houston TX 77073
Tel (281) 443-8564 *SIC* 3081 1799

GSE ENVIRONMENTAL LLC p 643
19103 Gundle Rd, Houston TX 77073
Tel (281) 443-8564 *SIC* 3081

GSE HOLDING INC p 643
19103 Gundle Rd, Houston TX 77073
Tel (281) 443-8564 *SIC* 3081 6719

KURARAY AMERICA INC p 832
2625 Bay Area Blvd # 600, Houston TX 77058
Tel (281) 474-1592 *SIC* 2821 3081 3843

AMTOPP CORP p 87
101 Interplast Blvd, Lolita TX 77971
Tel (361) 874-3000 *SIC* 3081

INTEGRATED BAGGING SYSTEMS CORP p 749
101 Interplast Blvd, Lolita TX 77971
Tel (361) 874-3000 *SIC* 3081

KANEKA NORTH AMERICA LLC p 802
6161 Underwood Rd, Pasadena TX 77507
Tel (281) 474-7084 *SIC* 2821 3081 2023

HERCULES FILMS LLC p 685
12600 Cardinal Mdw, Sugar Land TX 77478
Tel (920) 284-0796 *SIC* 3081 5199

▲ HUNTSMAN CORP p 720
10003 Woodloch Forest Dr # 260, The Woodlands TX 77380
Tel (281) 719-6000
SIC 2821 3081 2869 2816 2865

■ HUNTSMAN INTERNATIONAL LLC p 720
1003 Woodloch Forest Dr, The Woodlands TX 77380
Tel (281) 719-6000
SIC 2821 3081 2869 2816 2865

■ HUNTSMAN HOLDINGS LLC p 720
500 S Huntsman Way, Salt Lake City UT 84108
Tel (801) 584-5700
SIC 2821 2911 3081 2869

DU PONT TEIJIN FILMS US LIMITED PARTNERSHIP p 459
3600 Discovery Dr, Chester VA 23836
Tel (804) 530-4076 *SIC* 3081

■ CPFILMS INC p 387
4210 The Great Rd, Fieldale VA 24089
Tel (276) 627-3000 *SIC* 3081

KLOCKNER PENTAPLAST OF AMERICA INC p 823
3585 Kloeckner Rd, Gordonsville VA 22942
Tel (540) 832-1400 *SIC* 3081 4213

KLOCKNER PENTAPLAST PARTICIPATION LLC p 823
3585 Kloeckner Rd, Gordonsville VA 22942
Tel (540) 832-3600 *SIC* 3081 4213

▲ TREDEGAR CORP p 1475
1100 Boulders Pkwy # 200, North Chesterfield VA 23225
Tel (804) 330-1000
SIC 3081 2671 3083 3354

■ TREDEGAR FILM PRODUCTS CORP p 1475
1100 Boulders Pkwy # 200, North Chesterfield VA 23225
Tel (804) 330-1000 *SIC* 3081

ESSENTRA HOLDINGS CORP p 510
1625 Ashton Park Dr Ste A, South Chesterfield VA 23834
Tel (804) 518-0322
SIC 3081 3082 3999 3951 2823

ESSENTRA POROUS TECHNOLOGIES CORP p 510
1625 Ashton Park Dr Ste A, South Chesterfield VA 23834
Tel (804) 524-4983
SIC 3081 3951 3082 2823 3999

OSULLIVAN FILMS INC p 1097
1944 Valley Ave, Winchester VA 22601
Tel (540) 667-6666 *SIC* 3081

PRENT CORP p 1171
2225 Kennedy Rd, Janesville WI 53545
Tel (608) 754-0276 *SIC* 3081

CHARTER NEX HOLDING CO p 291
1264 E High St, Milton WI 53563
Tel (608) 531-1405 *SIC* 3081

INPRO CORP p 745
S80w18766 Apollo Dr, Muskego WI 53150
Tel (262) 679-9010 *SIC* 3081

■ DUNSIRN INDUSTRIES INC p 461
2415 Industrial Dr, Neenah WI 54956
Tel (920) 725-3814
SIC 2671 5113 3081 2672 2621

SIC 3082 Plastic Unsupported Profile Shapes

ADVANCE PAPER BOX CO p 24
6100 S Gramercy Pl, Los Angeles CA 90047
Tel (323) 750-2550 *SIC* 2653 3082

KENNERLEY-SPRATLING INC p 811
2116 Farallon Dr, San Leandro CA 94577
Tel (510) 351-8230 *SIC* 3089 3082

COORSTEK LLC p 368
16000 Table Mountain Pkwy, Golden CO 80403
Tel (303) 271-7000
SIC 3264 3053 3081 3082 3545

ORAFOL AMERICAS INC p 1091
120 Darling Dr, Avon CT 06001
Tel (860) 223-9297 *SIC* 3082

CEBAL AMERICAS p 272
101 Merritt 7 Ste 2, Norwalk CT 06851
Tel (203) 845-6356 *SIC* 3082

KEYSTONE HOLDINGS LLC p 815
10 Nw 42nd Ave Ste 700, Miami FL 33126
Tel (305) 567-1577
SIC 8711 3053 3081 3082 3545

FLEXSOL HOLDING CORP p 556
1531 Nw 12th Ave, Pompano Beach FL 33069
Tel (954) 941-6333 *SIC* 2673 3082 3081

POREX CORP p 1161
500 Bohannon Rd, Fairburn GA 30213
Tel (800) 241-0195 *SIC* 3082 3842 3841

SAINT-GOBAIN ABRASIVES INC p 1271
1 New Bond St, Worcester MA 01606
Tel (508) 795-5000
SIC 3291 3559 3545 3297 3082 2891

TG FLUID SYSTEMS USA CORP p 1446
100 Brighton Interior Dr, Brighton MI 48116
Tel (810) 220-6161 *SIC* 3082 3089

TRICO PRODUCTS CORP p 1479
3255 W Hamlin Rd, Rochester Hills MI 48309
Tel (248) 371-1700
SIC 3714 3069 3082 8734 8731

VENTION MEDICAL ADVANCED COMPONENTS INC p 1548
29 Northwestern Dr, Salem NH 03079
Tel (603) 327-0600 *SIC* 3082 3069 3083

ALPHA WIRE CORP p 60
711 Lidgerwood Ave, Elizabeth NJ 07202
Tel (908) 259-2613 *SIC* 5063 3082 3357

MITSUI CHEMICALS AMERICA INC p 978
800 Westchester Ave N607, Rye Brook NY 10573
Tel (914) 253-0777
SIC 2821 2865 3082 8731 5169 6159

PIEDMONT PLASTICS INC p 1147
5010 W Wt Harris Blvd, Charlotte NC 28269
Tel (704) 597-8200 *SIC* 3081 3082 5162

ROCHLING ENGINEERED PLASTICS LIMITED PARTNERSHIP p 1243
903 Gastonia Tech Pkwy, Dallas NC 28034
Tel (704) 922-7814 *SIC* 3081 3082

DLHBOWLES INC p 445
2422 Leo Ave Sw, Canton OH 44706
Tel (330) 478-2503 *SIC* 8711 3089 3082

DECEUNINCK NORTH AMERICA LLC p 421
351 N Garver Rd, Monroe OH 45050
Tel (513) 539-5466 *SIC* 3082

■ SONOCO PLASTICS INC p 1340
1 N 2nd St, Hartsville SC 29550
Tel (843) 383-7000 *SIC* 3082

ZEUS INDUSTRIAL PRODUCTS INC p 1642
620 Magnolia St, Orangeburg SC 29115
Tel (803) 268-9500 *SIC* 3082 3083

ESSENTRA HOLDINGS CORP p 510
1625 Ashton Park Dr Ste A, South Chesterfield VA 23834
Tel (804) 518-0322
SIC 3081 3082 3999 3951 2823

ESSENTRA POROUS TECHNOLOGIES CORP p 510
1625 Ashton Park Dr Ste A, South Chesterfield VA 23834
Tel (804) 524-4983
SIC 3081 3951 3082 2823 3999

SIC 3083 Plastic Laminated Plate & Sheet

HANWHA L & C HOLDINGS USA LLC p 659
4400 N Park Dr, Opelika AL 36801
Tel (334) 741-7725 *SIC* 3083 3714

ISOLA USA CORP p 767
3100 W Ray Rd Ste 301, Chandler AZ 85226
Tel (480) 893-6527 *SIC* 3083

PANOLAM INDUSTRIES INC p 1111
20 Progress Dr, Shelton CT 06484
Tel (203) 925-1556 *SIC* 3089 3083

PIONEER PLASTICS CORP p 1151
20 Progress Dr, Shelton CT 06484
Tel (203) 925-1556 *SIC* 3083 3087

DSM FINANCE USA INC p 458
1408 Columbia Nitrogen Dr, Augusta GA 30901
Tel (706) 849-6515
SIC 2891 2816 3089 3083 5169

STANDRIDGE COLOR CORP p 1376
1196 E Hightower Trl, Social Circle GA 30025
Tel (770) 464-3362 *SIC* 2865 2816 3083

▲ ACCO BRANDS CORP p 15
4 Corporate Dr, Lake Zurich IL 60047
Tel (847) 541-9500
SIC 2782 3083 2761 2672

▲ BERRY PLASTICS GROUP INC p 176
101 Oakley St, Evansville IN 47710
Tel (812) 424-2904
SIC 3089 3085 2673 3081 3083

DSM ENGINEERING PLASTICS INC p 458
2267 W Mill Rd, Evansville IN 47720
Tel (812) 435-7500 *SIC* 2821 3087 3083

HARTSON-KENNEDY CABINET TOP CO INC p 666
522 W 22nd St, Marion IN 46953
Tel (765) 673-0451 *SIC* 3083

V-T INDUSTRIES INC p 1538
1000 Industrial Park, Holstein IA 51025
Tel (712) 368-4381
SIC 3089 3083 4213 2435 2434 2431

■ TPI IOWA LLC p 1467
2300 N 33rd E, Newton IA 50208
Tel (641) 791-3500 *SIC* 3083

AFCO INDUSTRIES INC p 32
3400 Roy Ave, Alexandria LA 71302
Tel (318) 448-1651 *SIC* 3354 3083 3442

TOTAL PLASTICS RESOURCES LLC p 1463
2810 N Burdick St Ste A, Kalamazoo MI 49004
Tel (269) 344-0009 *SIC* 3083 5162

NORTHERN CONTOURS INC p 1056
1355 Mendota Heights Rd # 100, Saint Paul MN 55120
Tel (651) 695-1698 *SIC* 3083 1751 2435

KALWALL CORP p 801
1111 Candia Rd, Manchester NH 03109
Tel (603) 627-3861 *SIC* 3089 3083

VENTION MEDICAL ADVANCED COMPONENTS INC p 1548
29 Northwestern Dr, Salem NH 03079
Tel (603) 327-0600 *SIC* 3082 3069 3083

STRATEGIC INDUSTRIES LLC p 1392
26 Main St Ste 200, Chatham NJ 07928
Tel (732) 512-0195
SIC 3724 3499 3451 3083 3111

NAN YA PLASTICS CORP AMERICA p 1007
9 Peach Tree Hill Rd, Livingston NJ 07039
Tel (973) 992-1775 *SIC* 2824 2869 3083

DSM HOLDING CO USA INC p 458
45 Waterview Blvd, Parsippany NJ 07054
Tel (973) 257-1063
SIC 2891 2816 3089 3083 5169

SPIRAL BINDING CO INC p 1359
1 Maltese Dr, Totowa NJ 07512
Tel (973) 256-0666
SIC 2789 3083 5112 2891

LATHAM MANUFACTURING CORP p 846
787 Watervliet Shaker Rd, Latham NY 12110
Tel (518) 783-7776
SIC 3086 3081 3083 3949

▲ GRIFFON CORP p 640
712 5th Ave Fl 18, New York NY 10019
Tel (212) 957-5000
SIC 3442 2431 1751 1799 3083 3663

■ NALGE NUNC INTERNATIONAL CORP p 1007
75 Panorama Creek Dr, Rochester NY 14625
Tel (585) 586-8800
SIC 3089 3949 3821 3085 3083

UPM RAFLATAC INC p 1528
400 Broadpointe Dr, Mills River NC 28759
Tel (828) 651-4800 *SIC* 2672 3083

TSTRIM INDUSTRIES INC p 1489
6380 Canal St, Canal Winchester OH 43110
Tel (614) 837-4114
SIC 5013 3465 3714 3083

■ HANCOR INC p 657
4640 Trueman Blvd, Hilliard OH 43026
Tel (614) 658-0050
SIC 3084 3088 3089 3083

WASHINGTON PENN PLASTIC CO INC p 1578
450 Racetrack Rd, Washington PA 15301
Tel (724) 228-1260 *SIC* 3083 3087

■ NEPTCO INC p 1026
30 Hamlet St, Pawtucket RI 02861
Tel (401) 722-5500 *SIC* 3496 3083 2672

PRECISION SOUTHEAST INC p 1169
4900 Highway 501, Myrtle Beach SC 29579
Tel (843) 347-4218 *SIC* 3089 8731 3083

ZEUS INDUSTRIAL PRODUCTS INC p 1642
620 Magnolia St, Orangeburg SC 29115
Tel (803) 268-9500 *SIC* 3082 3083

▲ RAVEN INDUSTRIES INC p 1209
205 E 6th St, Sioux Falls SD 57104
Tel (605) 336-2750
SIC 5065 3523 3081 3823 3083

ATCO RUBBER PRODUCTS INC p 124
7101 Atco Dr, Fort Worth TX 76118
Tel (817) 589-7035
SIC 3443 3084 3585 3444 3083

GENERAL PLASTICS & COMPOSITES LP p 601
6910 E Orem Dr, Houston TX 77075
Tel (713) 644-1449 *SIC* 3083

▲ TREDEGAR CORP p 1475
1100 Boulders Pkwy # 200, North Chesterfield VA 23225
Tel (804) 330-1000
SIC 3081 2671 3083 3354

EXTREME PLASTICS PLUS INC p 521
360 Epic Circle Dr, Fairmont WV 26554
Tel (304) 534-3600 *SIC* 3083

SIC 3084 Plastic Pipe

J-M MANUFACTURING CO INC p 772
5200 W Century Blvd, Los Angeles CA 90045
Tel (800) 621-4404 SIC 2821 3491 3084

PW EAGLE INC p 1193
5200 W Century Blvd, Los Angeles CA 90045
Tel (800) 621-4404 SIC 3084

■ AMERON INTERNATIONAL CORP p 84
245 S Los Robles Ave, Pasadena CA 91101
Tel (626) 683-4000
SIC 3272 3317 3273 1442 3084

HUNTER INDUSTRIES INC p 719
1940 Diamond St, San Marcos CA 92078
Tel (800) 383-4747 SIC 5087 3084

CRESLINE PLASTIC PIPE CO INC p 391
600 N Cross Pointe Blvd, Evansville IN 47715
Tel (812) 428-9300 SIC 3084

▲ CABOT CORP p 235
2 Seaport Ln Ste 1300, Boston MA 02210
Tel (617) 345-0100
SIC 2895 3081 3084 2819 3339

GENOVA PRODUCTS INC p 604
7034 E Court St, Davison MI 48423
Tel (810) 744-4500
SIC 3089 2891 2911 3494 3084 2952

▲ OTTER TAIL CORP p 1098
215 S Cascade St, Fergus Falls MN 56537
Tel (218) 739-8200
SIC 4911 3084 5047 2099 1731

■ TORO MANUFACTURING CORP p 1462
8111 Lyndale Ave S, Minneapolis MN 55420
Tel (952) 888-8801 SIC 3084

UPONOR INC p 1529
5925 148th St W, Saint Paul MN 55124
Tel (952) 891-2000 SIC 3084 3567 3433

PRINSCO INC p 1177
1717 16th St Ne Fl 3, Willmar MN 56201
Tel (320) 978-4116 SIC 3084

DIAMOND PLASTICS CORP p 437
1212 Johnstown Rd, Grand Island NE 68803
Tel (765) 287-9234 SIC 3084

NATIONAL PIPE & PLASTICS INC p 1015
3421 Vestal Rd, Vestal NY 13850
Tel (607) 729-9381 SIC 3084

SILVER-LINE PLASTICS CORP p 1324
900 Riverside Dr, Asheville NC 28804
Tel (828) 252-8755 SIC 3084

CHARLOTTE PIPE AND FOUNDRY CO p 290
2109 Randolph Rd, Charlotte NC 28207
Tel (704) 372-5030 SIC 3084 3089 3321

■ NORTHERN PIPE PRODUCTS INC p 1056
1302 39th St N, Fargo ND 58102
Tel (701) 282-7655 SIC 3084

■ HANCOR HOLDING CORP p 657
401 Olive St, Findlay OH 45840
Tel (419) 422-6521 SIC 3084

▲ ADVANCED DRAINAGE SYSTEMS INC p 25
4640 Trueman Blvd, Hilliard OH 43026
Tel (614) 658-0050 SIC 3084 3086

■ HANCOR INC p 657
4640 Trueman Blvd, Hilliard OH 43026
Tel (614) 658-0050
SIC 3084 3088 3089 3083

CONTECH ENGINEERED SOLUTIONS INC p 362
9025 Centre Pointe Dr # 400, West Chester OH 45069
Tel (513) 645-7000
SIC 3444 3084 3317 3441 3443

CONTECH ENGINEERED SOLUTIONS LLC p 362
9025 Ctr Pinte Dr Ste 400, West Chester OH 45069
Tel (513) 645-7000
SIC 3444 3084 3317 3441 3443

CERTAINTEED CORP p 284
20 Moores Rd, Malvern PA 19355
Tel (610) 893-5000
SIC 3221 3292 3259 3084 3089 3432

SAINT-GOBAIN DELAWARE CORP p 1271
750 E Swedesford Rd, Valley Forge PA 19482
Tel (610) 341-7000
SIC 3291 3269 2891 3296 3084 3221

ATCO RUBBER PRODUCTS INC p 124
7101 Atco Dr, Fort Worth TX 76118
Tel (817) 589-7035
SIC 3443 3084 3585 3444 3083

CANTEX INC p 247
301 Commerce St Ste 2700, Fort Worth TX 76102
Tel (817) 215-7000 SIC 3084 3089

WL PLASTICS CORP p 1620
575 Lone Star Cir Ste 300, Fort Worth TX 76177
Tel (682) 831-2701 SIC 3084

CHEVRON PHILLIPS CHEMICAL CO LP p 296
10001 Six Pines Dr, The Woodlands TX 77380
Tel (832) 813-4100
SIC 5169 3292 3089 3084 3432 2911

SIMPSON INVESTMENT CO INC p 1325
1301 5th Ave Ste 2700, Seattle WA 98101
Tel (253) 272-0158
SIC 2621 2611 2421 2431 3084

SIC 3085 Plastic Bottles

▲ BALL CORP p 148
10 Longs Peak Dr, Broomfield CO 80021
Tel (303) 469-3131
SIC 3411 3085 3812 3679

▲ SILGAN HOLDINGS INC p 1323
4 Landmark Sq Ste 400, Stamford CT 06901
Tel (203) 975-7110 SIC 3411 3085 3089

AMALIE OIL CO p 64
1601 Mcclosky Blvd, Tampa FL 33605
Tel (813) 248-1988 SIC 2992 3085

LOGOPLASTE USA INC p 875
14420 N Van Dyke Rd, Plainfield IL 60544
Tel (815) 230-6961 SIC 3085

▲ BERRY PLASTICS GROUP INC p 176
101 Oakley St, Evansville IN 47710
Tel (812) 424-2904
SIC 3089 3085 2673 3081 3083

WESTON PRESIDIO INC p 1602
200 Clarendon St Ste 5000, Boston MA 02116
Tel (617) 988-2500
SIC 6799 3944 2519 3085

AMCOR RIGID PLASTICS USA LLC p 66
10521 M 52, Manchester MI 48158
Tel (734) 428-9741 SIC 3085

INOAC USA INC p 745
1515 Equity Dr Ste 200, Troy MI 48084
Tel (248) 619-7031 SIC 3085 3714

■ SILGAN PLASTICS LLC p 1323
14515 North Outer 40 Rd # 210, Chesterfield MO 63017
Tel (800) 274-5426 SIC 3085 3089

ALPHA PACKAGING HOLDINGS INC p 60
1555 Page Industrial Blvd, Saint Louis MO 63132
Tel (314) 427-4300 SIC 3085

ALPHA PLASTICS INC p 60
1555 Page Industrial Blvd, Saint Louis MO 63132
Tel (314) 427-4300 SIC 3085

REID PLASTICS INC p 1221
10861 Mill Valley Rd, Omaha NE 68154
Tel (402) 934-2400 SIC 3085 2821 3089

AMCOR PHARMACEUTICAL PACKAGING USA LLC p 66
625 Sharp St N, Millville NJ 08332
Tel (856) 327-1540 SIC 3221 3085

■ NALGE NUNC INTERNATIONAL CORP p 1007
75 Panorama Creek Dr, Rochester NY 14625
Tel (585) 586-8800
SIC 3089 3949 3821 3085 3083

INTRAPAC INTERNATIONAL CORP p 760
136 Fairview Rd Ste 320, Mooresville NC 28117
Tel (704) 360-8910 SIC 3085 3221

DRUG PLASTICS AND GLASS CO INC p 457
1 Bottle Dr, Boyertown PA 19512
Tel (610) 367-5000 SIC 3085

▲ WEST PHARMACEUTICAL SERVICES INC p 1595
530 Herman O West Dr, Exton PA 19341
Tel (610) 594-2900
SIC 3069 3466 2673 3085 3089

CAPSULE PA INC p 252
1100 Northbrook Dr Fl 2, Trevose PA 19053
Tel (215) 552-3700 SIC 3089 3085

RING CONTAINER TECHNOLOGIES LLC p 1235
1 Industrial Park, Oakland TN 38060
Tel (901) 465-6333 SIC 3085

RINGWOOD CONTAINERS LP p 1235
1 Industrial Park, Oakland TN 38060
Tel (901) 465-3607 SIC 3085

■ WESTERN CONTAINER CORP p 1597
2150 Town Square Pl # 400, Sugar Land TX 77479
Tel (281) 302-4314 SIC 3085

SIC 3086 Plastic Foam Prdts

FOAM FABRICATORS INC p 562
8722 E San Alberto Dr # 200, Scottsdale AZ 85258
Tel (480) 607-7330 SIC 3086

SAYCO CONTAINER INC p 1285
13400 Nelson Ave, City Of Industry CA 91746
Tel (619) 440-4411 SIC 2653 3089 3086

DART CONTAINER CORP OF CALIFORNIA p 412
150 S Maple St, Corona CA 92880
Tel (951) 739-7791 SIC 3086

FREE-FLOW PACKAGING INTERNATIONAL INC p 576
34175 Ardenwood Blvd, Fremont CA 94555
Tel (650) 261-5300 SIC 3086

PACIFIC SOUTHWEST CONTAINER LLC p 1106
4530 Leckron Rd, Modesto CA 95357
Tel (209) 526-0444
SIC 2671 2657 3086 2653 2752

■ THARCO HOLDINGS INC p 1446
2222 Grant Ave, San Lorenzo CA 94580
Tel (303) 373-1860 SIC 2653 3086 2675

PLASTIC SERVICES AND PRODUCTS p 1155
12243 Branford St, Sun Valley CA 91352
Tel (818) 896-1101
SIC 3086 3674 2865 2816 3296 2819

PMC GLOBAL INC p 1157
12243 Branford St, Sun Valley CA 91352
Tel (818) 896-1101
SIC 3086 3674 2865 2816 3296 2819

ACH FOAM TECHNOLOGIES INC p 17
5250 Sherman St, Denver CO 80216
Tel (303) 297-3844 SIC 3086

■ COLEMAN CO INC p 336
1767 Denver West Blvd # 200, Golden CO 80401
Tel (316) 832-2653 SIC 3086 5941

CELOTEX CORP p 274
10301 Dr Martn L Kng Jr S, Saint Petersburg FL 33716
Tel (727) 563-5100
SIC 3086 3275 3296 2493 2952

CYTEC SURFACE SPECIALTIES INC p 406
1950 Lake Park Dr Se, Smyrna GA 30080
Tel (770) 434-6188
SIC 3086 5169 5191 5162 3081 2823

NEW WINCUP HOLDINGS INC p 1033
4640 Lewis Rd, Stone Mountain GA 30083
Tel (770) 938-5281 SIC 3086

WINCUP INC p 1615
4640 Lewis Rd, Stone Mountain GA 30083
Tel (770) 771-5861 SIC 3086 3089

PREGIS LLC p 1170
1650 Lake Cook Rd Ste 400, Deerfield IL 60015
Tel (847) 597-9330 SIC 3086

PREGIS LLC p 1170
1650 Lake Cook Rd Ste 400, Deerfield IL 60015
Tel (847) 597-2200 SIC 2671 2673 3086

SIMONTON HOLDINGS INC p 1325
520 Lake Cook Rd, Deerfield IL 60015
Tel (304) 428-8261
SIC 3089 5961 3086 5963

FUTURE FOAM INC p 585
1610 Avenue N, Council Bluffs IA 51501
Tel (712) 323-9122 SIC 3086

PREMIER PACKAGING LLC p 1170
3900 Produce Rd, Louisville KY 40218
Tel (502) 935-8786 SIC 5085 5113 3086

REVSTONE INDUSTRIES LLC p 1229
2008 Cypress St Ste 100, Paris KY 40361
Tel (859) 294-5590 SIC 2821 3086 3341

■ HUNTER PANELS LLC p 719
15 Franklin St Ste B2, Portland ME 04101
Tel (888) 746-1114 SIC 3086

WM T BURNETT HOLDING LLC p 1620
1500 Bush St, Baltimore MD 21230
Tel (410) 837-3000 SIC 2299 3086

■ LIFOAM INDUSTRIES LLC p 865
9999 E 121st, Belcamp MD 21017
Tel (866) 770-3626 SIC 3086

AMESBURY GROUP INC p 84
57 S Hunt Rd, Amesbury MA 01913
Tel (978) 834-3233
SIC 3053 3442 3086 2221 3089

▲ UFP TECHNOLOGIES INC p 1499
100 Hale St, Newburyport MA 01950
Tel (978) 352-2200 SIC 3086

ROGERS FOAM CORP p 1246
20 Vernon St Ste 1, Somerville MA 02145
Tel (617) 623-3010 SIC 3086

▲ UNIQUE FABRICATING INC p 1505
800 Standard Pkwy, Auburn Hills MI 48326
Tel (248) 853-2333
SIC 3053 3086 3296 2671

CREATIVE FOAM CORP p 390
300 N Alloy Dr, Fenton MI 48430
Tel (574) 546-4238
SIC 3061 3089 3053 3086 3069

JSJ CORP p 796
700 Robbins Rd, Grand Haven MI 49417
Tel (616) 842-6350
SIC 3465 3469 3366 3089 3086 2522

LEON INTERIORS INC p 856
88 E 48th St, Holland MI 49423
Tel (616) 531-7970 SIC 3089 3714 3086

DART CONTAINER OF MICHIGAN LLC p 413
3120 Sovereign Dr Ste 4b, Lansing MI 48911
Tel (888) 327-8001 SIC 3086

DART CONTAINER CORP p 412
500 Hogsback Rd, Mason MI 48854
Tel (800) 248-5960 SIC 3086

DART CONTAINER CORP OF KENTUCKY p 413
500 Hogsback Rd, Mason MI 48854
Tel (517) 676-3800 SIC 2821 3086

▲ DOW CHEMICAL CO p 453
2030 Dow Ctr, Midland MI 48674
Tel (989) 636-1000
SIC 2821 3081 3086 2812 2879

WOODBRIDGE HOLDINGS INC p 1622
1515 Equity Dr, Troy MI 48084
Tel (248) 288-0100 SIC 2531 3086

ENGINEERED POLYMERS CORP p 499
1020 Maple Ave E, Mora MN 55051
Tel (320) 679-3232 SIC 3086 3089

HOOD COMPANIES INC p 705
623 N Main St Ste 300, Hattiesburg MS 39401
Tel (601) 582-1545 SIC 3086 2952 6719

ATLAS ROOFING CORP p 128
802 Highway 19 N Ste 190, Meridian MS 39307
Tel (601) 484-8900 SIC 3086 2952

ANCHOR PACKAGING INC p 89
13515 Barrett Parkway Dr # 100, Ballwin MO 63021
Tel (314) 394-3701 SIC 3086

FEDERAL INTERNATIONAL INC p 535
7935 Clayton Rd Ste A, Saint Louis MO 63117
Tel (314) 721-3377 SIC 3086 7389

HERMANN COMPANIES INC p 687
7701 Forsyth Blvd # 1000, Saint Louis MO 63105
Tel (314) 863-9200 SIC 3086

■ SILGAN PLASTIC FOOD CONTAINERS CORP p 1323
710 W Park Rd, Union MO 63084
Tel (636) 583-5550 SIC 3086

■ CRYOVAC INC p 396
200 Riverfront Blvd, Elmwood Park NJ 07407
Tel (201) 791-7600 SIC 3086

■ SEALED AIR CORP (US) p 1296
200 Riverfront Blvd # 301, Elmwood Park NJ 07407
Tel (201) 791-7600
SIC 2673 2671 3087 3086 3089

INNOCOR FOAM TECHNOLOGIES LLC p 744
200 Schulz Dr Ste 2, Red Bank NJ 07701
Tel (732) 263-0800 SIC 3086

SEKISUI AMERICA CORP p 1301
666 5th St Fl 12t, Secaucus NJ 07094
Tel (201) 423-7960 SIC 3086

JAMESTOWN CONTAINER CORP p 777
14 Deming Dr, Falconer NY 14733
Tel (716) 665-4623 SIC 2653 3086

LATHAM INTERNATIONAL INC p 846
787 Watervliet Shaker Rd, Latham NY 12110
Tel (518) 783-7776 SIC 3086 3081

LATHAM MANUFACTURING CORP p 846
787 Watervliet Shaker Rd, Latham NY 12110
Tel (518) 783-7776
SIC 3086 3081 3083 3949

GREAT AMERICAN INDUSTRIES INC p 633
300 Plaza Dr, Vestal NY 13850
Tel (607) 729-9331
SIC 3086 5031 5074 3442 3069 5091

BARNHARDT MANUFACTURING CO p 156
1100 Hawthorne Ln, Charlotte NC 28205
Tel (704) 376-0380 SIC 0131 3086

▲ SEALED AIR CORP p 1296
8215 Forest Point Blvd # 100, Charlotte NC 28273
Tel (980) 221-3235
SIC 2673 2671 3087 3086 3089

■ SONOCO DISPLAY & PACKAGING LLC p 1340
555 Aureole St, Winston Salem NC 27107
Tel (336) 784-0445 SIC 3086

NOEL GROUP LLC p 1046
501 Nmc Dr, Zebulon NC 27597
Tel (919) 269-6500 SIC 3086

▲ MYERS INDUSTRIES INC p 1004
1293 S Main St, Akron OH 44301
Tel (330) 253-5592
SIC 3089 3086 3069 3052 5013 5014

HFI LLC p 689
59 Gender Rd, Canal Winchester OH 43110
Tel (614) 491-0700
SIC 2396 2821 3714 3429 3086

■ GREIF PACKAGING LLC p 639
366 Greif Pkwy, Delaware OH 43015
Tel (740) 549-6000 SIC 3086

▲ ADVANCED DRAINAGE SYSTEMS INC p 25
4640 Trueman Blvd, Hilliard OH 43026
Tel (614) 658-0050 SIC 3084 3086

OHIO DECORATIVE PRODUCTS LLC p 1077
220 S Elizabeth St, Spencerville OH 45887
Tel (419) 647-9033
SIC 3086 3369 3471 3363

ASTRO SHAPES INC p 122
65 Main St, Struthers OH 44471
Tel (330) 755-1414 SIC 3354 3086

STOROPACK INC p 1392
4758 Devitt Dr, West Chester OH 45246
Tel (513) 874-0314 SIC 5199 3086 2671

DART CONTAINER CORP OF PENNSYLVANIA p 413
60 E Main St, Leola PA 17540
Tel (717) 656-2236 SIC 3086

FOAMEX INTERNATIONAL INC p 562
1400 N Providence Rd, Media PA 19063
Tel (610) 744-2300 SIC 3086

FOAMEX LP p 562
1400 N Providence Rd # 2000, Media PA 19063
Tel (610) 565-2374 SIC 3086

FXI HOLDINGS INC p 586
1400 N Providence Rd # 2000, Media PA 19063
Tel (610) 744-2300 SIC 3086

FXI INC p 586
1400 N Providence Rd # 2000, Media PA 19063
Tel (610) 744-2300 SIC 3086

■ CARDINAL HEALTH 407 INC p 253
3001 Red Lion Rd Ste Ag, Philadelphia PA 19114
Tel (215) 501-1210 SIC 7389 3086 3089

SCA AMERICAS INC p 1285
2929 Arch St Ste 2600, Philadelphia PA 19104
Tel (610) 499-3700 SIC 2621 3086 2676

■ SONOCO PROTECTIVE SOLUTIONS INC p 1340
1 N 2nd St, Hartsville SC 29550
Tel (843) 383-7000 SIC 3086 2679

SOUTHLAND CONTAINER CORP p 1351
60 Fairview Church Rd, Spartanburg SC 29303
Tel (864) 578-0085 SIC 2653 3086

PI INC p 1146
213 Dennis St, Athens TN 37303
Tel (423) 745-6213
SIC 2519 3949 3089 2499 3086 3081

NU-FOAM PRODUCTS INC p 1066
1101 Wisdom St, Chattanooga TN 37406
Tel (423) 698-6911 SIC 3086

IDENTITY GROUP HOLDINGS CORP p 729
1480 Gould Dr, Cookeville TN 38506
Tel (931) 432-4000
SIC 3089 3086 3993 3953

INLAND PAPERBOARD AND PACKAGING INC p 743
1300 S Mo Pac Expy Fl 3, Austin TX 78746
Tel (512) 234-5001
SIC 2653 2631 3086 2679 2657

NPPI INTERMEDIATE INC p 1064
106 E 6th St Ste 300, Austin TX 78701
Tel (512) 476-7100 SIC 3086

HOUSTON FOAM PLASTICS INC p 712
2019 Brooks St, Houston TX 77026
Tel (713) 224-3484 SIC 3086

IGLOO PRODUCTS CORP p 730
777 Igloo Rd, Katy TX 77494
Tel (281) 394-6800 SIC 3086

CARPENTER CO p 260
5016 Monument Ave, Richmond VA 23230
Tel (804) 359-0800
SIC 3086 1311 2869 2297 2392 2821

CARPENTER HOLDINGS INC p 260
5016 Monument Ave, Richmond VA 23230
Tel (804) 359-0800 SIC 3086

BOX MAKER INC p 205
6412 S 190th St, Kent WA 98032
Tel (425) 251-0655
SIC 5113 2653 2672 3086 5199 2631

ALLIANCE PACKAGING LLC p 55
1000 Sw 43rd St, Renton WA 98057
Tel (425) 291-3500 SIC 2653 3086

RHEM LLC p 1231
700 Powell Ave Sw, Renton WA 98057
Tel (425) 228-4111 SIC 5033 3086 1742

MENASHA CORP p 943
1645 Bergstrom Rd, Neenah WI 54956
Tel (920) 751-1000
SIC 2631 2653 2679 3086 0811

SIC 3087 Custom Compounding Of Purchased Plastic Resins

■ DIONEX CORP p 441
1228 Titan Way Ste 1002, Sunnyvale CA 94085
Tel (408) 737-0700
SIC 3826 2819 3087 3841

PIONEER PLASTICS CORP p 1151
20 Progress Dr, Shelton CT 06484
Tel (203) 925-1556 SIC 3083 3087

■ BULK MOLDING COMPOUNDS INC p 225
1600 Powis Ct, West Chicago IL 60185
Tel (630) 377-1065 SIC 3087

DSM ENGINEERING PLASTICS INC p 458
2267 W Mill Rd, Evansville IN 47720
Tel (812) 435-7500 SIC 2821 3087 3083

SABIC INNOVATIVE PLASTICS MT VERNON LLC p 1264
1 Lexan Ln, Mount Vernon IN 47620
Tel (812) 838-4385 SIC 2821 3087 3081

MEXICHEM SPECIALTY COMPOUNDS INC p 957
170 Pioneer Dr, Leominster MA 01453
Tel (978) 537-8071 *SIC* 3087 2899

MILLER WASTE MILLS INC p 971
580 E Front St, Winona MN 55987
Tel (507) 454-6906 *SIC* 3087 2821

JOYCE LESLIE INC p 794
186 Paterson Ave Ste 102, East Rutherford NJ 07073
Tel (201) 804-7800 *SIC* 3087

■ **SEALED AIR CORP (US)** p 1296
200 Riverfront Blvd # 301, Elmwood Park NJ 07407
Tel (201) 791-7600
SIC 2673 2671 3087 3086 3089

■ **WASTE MANAGEMENT OF NEW JERSEY INC** p 1581
107 Silvia St, Ewing NJ 08628
Tel (609) 434-5200 *SIC* 3087

SI GROUP INC p 1319
2750 Balltown Rd, Schenectady NY 12309
Tel (518) 347-4200 *SIC* 2865 3087 2851

AMPACET CORP p 86
660 White Plains Rd # 360, Tarrytown NY 10591
Tel (914) 631-6600 *SIC* 3087

▲ **SEALED AIR CORP** p 1296
8215 Forest Point Blvd # 100, Charlotte NC 28273
Tel (980) 221-3235
SIC 2673 2671 3087 3086 3089

HEXPOL COMPOUNDING NC INC p 688
280 Crawford Rd, Statesville NC 28625
Tel (704) 872-1585 *SIC* 3069 3087 2891

FREEMAN MANUFACTURING & SUPPLY CO p 577
1101 Moore Rd, Avon OH 44011
Tel (440) 934-1902
SIC 5084 3087 3543 2821

▲ **POLYONE CORP** p 1160
33587 Walker Rd, Avon Lake OH 44012
Tel (440) 930-1000
SIC 2821 3087 5162 3081

HEXPOL COMPOUNDING LLC p 688
14330 Kinsman Rd, Burton OH 44021
Tel (440) 834-4644 *SIC* 3087 2821

WASHINGTON PENN PLASTIC CO INC p 1578
450 Racetrack Rd, Washington PA 15301
Tel (724) 228-1260 *SIC* 3083 3087

TEKNOR APEX CO p 1433
505 Central Ave, Pawtucket RI 02861
Tel (401) 725-8000
SIC 3087 3069 3052 2869 3081 2821

COLORTECH INC p 339
5712 Commerce Blvd, Morristown TN 37814
Tel (423) 587-0837 *SIC* 3087 2816

■ **TICONA POLYMERS INC** p 1452
222 Las Colinas Blvd W 900n, Irving TX 75039
Tel (972) 443-4000 *SIC* 3087

■ **HUNTSMAN ADVANCED MATERIALS LLC** p 720
500 S Huntsman Way, Salt Lake City UT 84108
Tel (801) 584-5700 *SIC* 2821 2891 3087

SIC 3088 Plastic Plumbing Fixtures

SHASTA INDUSTRIES INC p 1312
6031 N 16th St, Phoenix AZ 85016
Tel (602) 532-3750
SIC 1799 1771 5169 7389 3088 5091

AQUATIC CO p 101
8101 E Kaiser Blvd # 200, Anaheim CA 92808
Tel (714) 993-1220 *SIC* 3088

JACUZZI INC p 775
14525 Monte Vista Ave, Chino CA 91710
Tel (909) 606-7733 *SIC* 3088 3589

JACUZZI WHIRLPOOL BATH INC p 775
14525 Monte Vista Ave, Chino CA 91710
Tel (909) 606-1416 *SIC* 3088

TOTO USA HOLDINGS INC p 1463
1155 Southern Rd, Morrow GA 30260
Tel (770) 960-8531 *SIC* 3088 3431 3261

MASCO BATH CORP p 915
8445 Keystone Xing # 100, Indianapolis IN 46240
Tel (317) 254-5959 *SIC* 3088 3842

▲ **MASCO CORP** p 915
21001 Van Born Rd, Taylor MI 48180
Tel (313) 274-7400
SIC 2434 3432 3088 3429 1742

MAAX US CORP p 891
7767 Elm Creek Blvd N # 310, Maple Grove MN 55369
Tel (877) 438-6229 *SIC* 3088

XERXES CORP p 1631
7901 Xerxes Ave S Ste 201, Minneapolis MN 55431
Tel (952) 887-1890 *SIC* 3089 3443 3088

PCE INC p 1124
1711 Yolanda Ave, Lincoln NE 68521
Tel (402) 474-4690 *SIC* 3089 3644 3088

ITR INDUSTRIES INC p 768
441 Saw Mill River Rd, Yonkers NY 10701
Tel (914) 964-7063
SIC 3431 3429 3446 3088

■ **LUBRIZOL ADVANCED MATERIALS INC** p 884
9911 Brecksville Rd, Brecksville OH 44141
Tel (216) 447-5000
SIC 2899 2891 3088 2834 3629

AD INDUSTRIES INC p 21
6450 Poe Ave Ste 109, Dayton OH 45414
Tel (303) 744-1911
SIC 3634 3564 3535 3714 3088 3089

■ **HANCOR INC** p 657
4640 Trueman Blvd, Hilliard OH 43026
Tel (614) 658-0050
SIC 3084 3088 3089 3083

CRANE PLUMBING LLC p 389
41 Cairns Rd, Mansfield OH 44903
Tel (419) 522-4211 *SIC* 3261 3431 3088

MANSFIELD PLUMBING PRODUCTS LLC p 903
150 E 1st St, Perrysville OH 44864
Tel (419) 938-5211
SIC 3261 3463 3088 3431 3432 5074

PRAXIS COMPANIES LLC p 1168
435 Industrial Rd, Savannah TN 38372
Tel (731) 925-7656 *SIC* 3088

HF HOLDINGS INC p 688
1500 S 1000 W, Logan UT 84321
Tel (435) 750-5000 *SIC* 3949 3088

SIC 3089 Plastic Prdts

■ **ALABAMA METAL INDUSTRIES CORP** p 43
3245 Fayette Ave, Birmingham AL 35208
Tel (205) 787-2611
SIC 3446 3449 3089 3441 3316

SJA INC p 1328
274 Thweatt Indus Blvd, Dadeville AL 36853
Tel (256) 825-2290 *SIC* 3089

MID-SOUTH INDUSTRIES INC p 963
2620 E Meighan Blvd, Gadsden AL 35903
Tel (256) 492-8997
SIC 3672 3089 3824 3714

MFG GALILEO COMPOSITES p 958
18361 Galileo Dr, Opp AL 36467
Tel (334) 493-0014 *SIC* 5731 3089

RAINSVILLE TECHNOLOGY INC p 1206
189 Rti Dr, Rainsville AL 35986
Tel (256) 638-9760 *SIC* 3089

SEOYON E-HWA INTERIOR SYSTEMS ALABAMA LLC p 1306
200 Craig Industrial Park, Selma AL 36701
Tel (334) 410-7100 *SIC* 3089

■ **TECH GROUP INC** p 1430
14677 N 74th St, Scottsdale AZ 85260
Tel (480) 281-4500 *SIC* 3089

DENSO MANUFACTURING ARKANSAS INC p 428
100 Denso Rd, Osceola AR 72370
Tel (870) 622-9500 *SIC* 3089 7539

■ **HACKNEY LADISH INC** p 652
708 S Elmira Ave, Russellville AR 72802
Tel (479) 968-7555 *SIC* 3089 3463

BACE MANUFACTURING INC p 143
3125 E Coronado St, Anaheim CA 92806
Tel (714) 630-6002 *SIC* 3089

UPM INC p 1528
13245 Los Angeles St, Baldwin Park CA 91706
Tel (626) 962-4001 *SIC* 3544 3089

KING HOLDING CORP p 820
360 N Crescent Dr, Beverly Hills CA 90210
Tel (586) 254-3900
SIC 3452 3465 3469 3089 5072

EEP HOLDINGS LLC p 480
4626 Eucalyptus Ave, Chino CA 91710
Tel (909) 597-7861 *SIC* 3089 3544

TTL HOLDINGS LLC p 1489
4626 Eucalyptus Ave, Chino CA 91710
Tel (909) 597-7861 *SIC* 3089 3544

MERCURY PLASTICS INC p 945
14825 Salt Lake Ave, City Of Industry CA 91746
Tel (626) 369-8457 *SIC* 2673 2759 3089

SAYCO CONTAINER INC p 1285
13400 Nelson Ave, City Of Industry CA 91746
Tel (619) 440-4411 *SIC* 2653 3089 3086

MCP INDUSTRIES INC p 932
708 S Temescal St Ste 101, Corona CA 92879
Tel (951) 736-1881 *SIC* 3089 3259 3089

MERRICK ENGINEERING INC p 950
1275 Quarry St, Corona CA 92879
Tel (951) 737-6040 *SIC* 3089

WESTAR CAPITAL ASSOCIATES II LLC p 1596
949 S Coast Dr Ste 170, Costa Mesa CA 92626
Tel (714) 481-5160 *SIC* 6799 3089

AMS PLASTICS INC p 87
1530 Hilton Head Rd # 205, El Cajon CA 92019
Tel (619) 713-2000 *SIC* 3089

GILL CORP p 612
4056 Easy St, El Monte CA 91731
Tel (626) 443-6094 *SIC* 3089

ROPAK CORP p 1249
10540 Talbert Ave 200w, Fountain Valley CA 92708
Tel (714) 845-2845 *SIC* 3089

GKN AEROSPACE TRANSPARENCY SYSTEMS INC p 613
12122 Western Ave, Garden Grove CA 92841
Tel (714) 893-7531
SIC 3089 3231 3827 3728 3081 2821

PLASTIKON INDUSTRIES INC p 1155
688 Sandoval Way, Hayward CA 94544
Tel (510) 400-1010 *SIC* 3544 3089

CAMBRO MANUFACTURING CO INC p 244
5801 Skylab Rd, Huntington Beach CA 92647
Tel (714) 848-1555 *SIC* 3089

TRANS WESTERN POLYMERS INC p 1470
7539 Las Positas Rd, Livermore CA 94551
Tel (925) 449-7800 *SIC* 2673 5023 3089

PALPILOT INTERNATIONAL CORP p 1110
500 Yosemite Dr, Milpitas CA 95035
Tel (408) 855-8866 *SIC* 3672 3089

■ **MEDEGEN LLC** p 935
4501 E Wall St, Ontario CA 91761
Tel (909) 390-9080 *SIC* 3089

SKB CORP p 1329
434 W Levers Pl, Orange CA 92867
Tel (714) 637-1252 *SIC* 3089 3161

B & S PLASTICS INC p 141
2200 Sturgis Rd, Oxnard CA 93030
Tel (805) 981-0262 *SIC* 3089

AMA PLASTICS p 64
1100 Citrus St, Riverside CA 92507
Tel (951) 734-5600 *SIC* 3089 3544

OLDCASTLE PRECAST INC p 1082
2434 Rubidoux Blvd, Riverside CA 92509
Tel (951) 788-9720 *SIC* 3089

NISHIBA INDUSTRIES CORP p 1044
2360 Marconi Ct, San Diego CA 92154
Tel (619) 661-8866 *SIC* 3089 3544 5162

ASSOCIATED MATERIALS GROUP INC p 120
1 Maritime Plz Fl 12, San Francisco CA 94111
Tel (415) 788-5111
SIC 3089 5033 5031 3442

ASSOCIATED MATERIALS INC p 121
1 Maritime Plz Fl 12, San Francisco CA 94111
Tel (415) 788-5111
SIC 3089 5033 5031 3442

FLUIDMASTER INC p 561
30800 Rancho Viejo Rd, San Juan Capistrano CA 92675
Tel (949) 728-2000 *SIC* 3432 3089

KENNERLEY-SPRATLING INC p 811
2116 Farallon Dr, San Leandro CA 94577
Tel (510) 351-8230 *SIC* 3089 3082

VOLEX INC p 1564
3110 Coronado Dr, Santa Clara CA 95054
Tel (669) 444-1740 *SIC* 3089

■ **SIERRACIN/SYLMAR CORP** p 1321
12780 San Fernando Rd, Sylmar CA 91342
Tel (818) 362-6711
SIC 3089 3812 3621 3231

PELICAN PRODUCTS INC p 1128
23215 Early Ave, Torrance CA 90505
Tel (310) 326-4700 *SIC* 3648 3161 3089

■ **PRC - DESOTO INTERNATIONAL INC** p 1168
24811 Ave Rockefeller, Valencia CA 91355
Tel (661) 678-4209 *SIC* 2891 3089

STRATASYS DIRECT INC p 1392
28309 Avenue Crocker, Valencia CA 91355
Tel (661) 295-4400 *SIC* 3089

REHRIG PACIFIC CO p 1220
4010 E 26th St, Vernon CA 90058
Tel (800) 421-6244 *SIC* 3089 2821

REHRIG PACIFIC HOLDINGS INC p 1220
4010 E 26th St, Vernon CA 90058
Tel (323) 262-5145 *SIC* 3089 2821

NATIONAL DIVERSIFIED SALES INC p 1011
21300 Victory Blvd # 215, Woodland Hills CA 91367
Tel (559) 562-9888 *SIC* 3089

AD CORP p 21
1551 Wewatta St, Denver CO 80202
Tel (303) 744-1911
SIC 3634 3564 3822 3089 3714 3312

GATES CORP p 593
1551 Wewatta St, Denver CO 80202
Tel (303) 744-1911
SIC 3052 3089 3568 5084 4789

OMAHA HOLDINGS LLC p 1083
1551 Wewatta St, Denver CO 80202
Tel (303) 744-1911
SIC 3052 3089 3568 5084 4789

OMAHA INTERMEDIATE HOLDING LLC p 1083
1551 Wewatta St, Denver CO 80202
Tel (303) 744-1911
SIC 3052 3089 3568 5084 4789

OTTER PRODUCTS LLC p 1098
209 S Meldrum St, Fort Collins CO 80521
Tel (970) 493-8446 *SIC* 3089

CPI CARD GROUP - COLORADO INC p 387
10368 W Centennial Rd A, Littleton CO 80127
Tel (303) 973-9311 *SIC* 3089

FARREL CORP p 530
1 Farrell Blvd, Ansonia CT 06401
Tel (203) 736-5500 *SIC* 3559 1011 3089

LACEY MANUFACTURING CO LLC p 837
1146 Barnum Ave, Bridgeport CT 06610
Tel (203) 336-7427 *SIC* 3841 3089

BARDEN CORP p 155
200 Park Ave, Danbury CT 06810
Tel (203) 744-2211
SIC 3562 3469 3842 3089 3399

INFILTRATOR WATER TECHNOLOGIES LLC p 740
4 Business Park Rd, Old Saybrook CT 06475
Tel (860) 577-7000 *SIC* 3089

DAVIS-STANDARD LLC p 416
1 Extrusion Dr, Pawcatuck CT 06379
Tel (860) 599-1010 *SIC* 3089

NEVAMAR CO LLC p 1029
20 Progress Dr, Shelton CT 06484
Tel (203) 925-1556 *SIC* 3089 5162

PANOLAM INDUSTRIES INC p 1111
20 Progress Dr, Shelton CT 06484
Tel (203) 925-1556 *SIC* 3089 3083

PANOLAM INDUSTRIES INTERNATIONAL INC p 1111
20 Progress Dr, Shelton CT 06484
Tel (203) 925-1556 *SIC* 2493 3089

▲ **HEXCEL CORP** p 688
281 Tresser Blvd Ste 1503, Stamford CT 06901
Tel (203) 969-0666
SIC 2821 3728 3089 3624 2891 3469

▲ **SILGAN HOLDINGS INC** p 1323
4 Landmark Sq Ste 400, Stamford CT 06901
Tel (203) 975-7110 *SIC* 3411 3085 3089

TECHNICAL INDUSTRIES INC p 1431
336 Pinewoods Rd, Torrington CT 06790
Tel (860) 489-2160 *SIC* 3089

SIEMON CO p 1320
101 Siemon Company Dr, Watertown CT 06795
Tel (860) 945-4200
SIC 3643 3089 3679 3469 3613 3357

GRUPO PHOENIX CORPORATE SERVICES LLC p 643
18851 Ne 29th Ave Ste 601, Aventura FL 33180
Tel (954) 241-0023 *SIC* 3089

■ **JARDEN CORP** p 778
1800 N Military Trl # 210, Boca Raton FL 33431
Tel (561) 447-2520 *SIC* 3089 3634

J T WALKER INDUSTRIES INC p 772
861 N Hercules Ave, Clearwater FL 33765
Tel (727) 461-0501
SIC 3442 3089 3585 5193

TERVIS TUMBLER CO p 1440
201 Triple Diamond Blvd, North Venice FL 34275
Tel (941) 966-2114 *SIC* 3089

■ **DART INDUSTRIES INC** p 413
14901 S Orange Blossom Tr, Orlando FL 32837
Tel (407) 826-5050 *SIC* 3089

▲ **TUPPERWARE BRANDS CORP** p 1492
14901 S Orange Blossom Tr, Orlando FL 32837
Tel (407) 826-5050 *SIC* 3089 2844

■ **TUPPERWARE US INC** p 1492
14901 S Ornge Blossom Trl, Orlando FL 32837
Tel (407) 826-5050 *SIC* 3089

FLORIDA PRODUCTION ENGINEERING INC p 559
2 E Tower Cir, Ormond Beach FL 32174
Tel (386) 677-2566 *SIC* 3465 3089

FLEXSOL PACKAGING CORP OF POMPANO BEACH p 556
1531 Nw 12th Ave, Pompano Beach FL 33069
Tel (800) 325-7740 *SIC* 3089

■ **MTS MEDICATION TECHNOLOGIES INC** p 998
2003 Gandy Blvd N Ste 800, Saint Petersburg FL 33702
Tel (727) 576-6311 *SIC* 3565 3089

PEXCO LLC p 1140
2500 Northwinds Pkwy # 472, Alpharetta GA 30009
Tel (404) 564-8560 *SIC* 3089

SOLVAY SPECIALTY POLYMERS USA LLC p 1339
4500 Mcginnis Ferry Rd, Alpharetta GA 30005
Tel (770) 772-8200 *SIC* 3089

TENSAR CORP GEORGIA p 1438
2500 Northwinds Pkwy # 50, Alpharetta GA 30009
Tel (770) 344-2090 *SIC* 3089 8711

TENSAR INTERNATIONAL CORP p 1438
2500 Northwinds Pkwy # 500, Alpharetta GA 30009
Tel (770) 344-2090 *SIC* 8711 3089

PBR INC p 1123
335 Athena Dr, Athens GA 30601
Tel (706) 354-3700 *SIC* 2297 2221 3089

BWAY CORP p 230
8607 Roberts Dr Ste 250, Atlanta GA 30350
Tel (770) 645-4800 *SIC* 3411 3089

BWAY HOLDING CO p 231
8607 Roberts Dr Ste 250, Atlanta GA 30350
Tel (770) 645-4800 *SIC* 3411 3089

BWAY INTERMEDIATE CO INC p 231
8607 Roberts Dr Ste 250, Atlanta GA 30350
Tel (770) 645-4800 *SIC* 3411 3089

CKS PACKAGING INC p 320
350 Great Sw Pkwy Sw, Atlanta GA 30336
Tel (404) 691-8900 *SIC* 3089

CONSOLIDATED CONTAINER CO LLC p 359
3101 Towercreek Pkwy Se, Atlanta GA 30339
Tel (678) 742-4600 *SIC* 3089

CONSOLIDATED CONTAINER CO LP p 359
3101 Towercreek Pkwy Se, Atlanta GA 30339
Tel (678) 742-4600 *SIC* 3089 3999

■ **GOODY PRODUCTS INC** p 625
3 Glenlake Pkwy, Atlanta GA 30328
Tel (770) 418-7300 *SIC* 3999 3089 3069

■ **RUBBERMAID INC** p 1256
3 Glenlake Pkwy, Atlanta GA 30328
Tel (770) 418-7000
SIC 3089 2519 3944 2369 2392

DSM FINANCE USA INC p 458
1408 Columbia Nitrogen Dr, Augusta GA 30901
Tel (706) 849-6515
SIC 2891 2816 3089 3083 5169

CELLOFOAM NORTH AMERICA INC p 274
1917 Rockdale Indstrl Blv, Conyers GA 30012
Tel (770) 929-3688 *SIC* 3089 2821

HANIL E HWA INTERIOR SYSTEMS GEORGIA INC p 657
104 Wiley Rd, Lagrange GA 30240
Tel (706) 298-9701 *SIC* 3089

DIXIEN LLC p 445
5286 Circle Dr, Lake City GA 30260
Tel (478) 929-4121 *SIC* 3089

WINCUP INC p 1615
4640 Lewis Rd, Stone Mountain GA 30083
Tel (770) 771-5861 *SIC* 3086 3089

HONDA PRECISION PARTS OF GEORGIA LLC p 705
550 Honda Pkwy, Tallapoosa GA 30176
Tel (770) 574-3400 *SIC* 3089

THOMSON PLASTICS INC p 1449
130 Quality Dr, Thomson GA 30824
Tel (706) 828-7508 *SIC* 3949 3089

PRAIRIE PACKAGING INC p 1167
7200 S Mason Ave, Bedford Park IL 60638
Tel (708) 496-1172 *SIC* 3089 3421

MID OAKS INVESTMENTS LLC p 963
750 W Lake Cook Rd # 460, Buffalo Grove IL 60089
Tel (847) 215-3475 *SIC* 6726 3089

REVCOR INC p 1229
251 Edwards Ave, Carpentersville IL 60110
Tel (847) 428-4411 *SIC* 3564 3089

GILSTER-MARY LEE CORP p 612
1037 State St, Chester IL 62233
Tel (618) 826-2361
SIC 2043 2098 2099 2045 3089

BWAY PARENT CO INC p 231
3200 S Kilbourn Ave, Chicago IL 60623
Tel (773) 890-3300 *SIC* 3411 3089

HOME PRODUCTS INTERNATIONAL - NORTH AMERICA INC p 703
4501 W 47th St, Chicago IL 60632
Tel (773) 890-1010 *SIC* 3089 3499

LOGAN SQUARE ALUMINUM SUPPLY INC p 874
2500 N Pulaski Rd, Chicago IL 60639
Tel (773) 235-2500 *SIC* 5211 3089

MIDWEST CANVAS CORP p 967
4635 W Lake St, Chicago IL 60644
Tel (773) 287-4400 *SIC* 3081 3089

MOLD-RITE PLASTICS LLC p 982
30 N La Salle St Ste 2425, Chicago IL 60602
Tel (518) 561-1812 *SIC* 3089

WIND POINT PARTNERS LP p 1615
676 N Michigan Ave # 3700, Chicago IL 60611
Tel (312) 255-4800 *SIC* 6799 7363 3089

▲ **APTARGROUP INC** p 101
475 W Terra Cotta Ave E, Crystal Lake IL 60014
Tel (815) 477-0424 *SIC* 3089 3499

JORDAN INDUSTRIES INC p 793
1751 Lake Cook Rd Ste 550, Deerfield IL 60015
Tel (847) 945-5591
SIC 3621 3625 3714 3089 2759 5999

JORDAN SPECIALTY PLASTICS INC p 793
1751 Lake Cook Rd Ste 550, Deerfield IL 60015
Tel (847) 945-5591 SIC 3089 3081

SIMONTON HOLDINGS INC p 1325
520 Lake Cook Rd, Deerfield IL 60015
Tel (304) 428-8261
SIC 3089 5961 3086 5963

■ TEGRANT ALLOYD BRANDS INC p 1432
1401 Pleasant St, Dekalb IL 60115
Tel (815) 756-8451 SIC 3089 3565

■ TEGRANT HOLDING CORP p 1433
1401 Pleasant St, Dekalb IL 60115
Tel (815) 756-8451 SIC 3089 3565

SUBURBAN PLASTICS CO p 1396
340 Renner Dr, Elgin IL 60123
Tel (847) 741-4900 SIC 3089

D&W FINE PACK HOLDINGS LLC p 407
1900 Pratt Blvd, Elk Grove Village IL 60007
Tel (847) 378-1200 SIC 3089

D&W FINE PACK LLC p 407
1900 Pratt Blvd, Elk Grove Village IL 60007
Tel (847) 378-1200 SIC 3089

ESSENTRA COMPONENTS INC p 510
7400 Industrial Dr, Forest Park IL 60130
Tel (773) 539-4060 SIC 3089

■ NEWELL OPERATING CO p 1037
29 E Stephenson St, Freeport IL 61032
Tel (815) 235-4171
SIC 3365 3991 3089 2591 3965 3596

RUBBERMAID SPECIALTY PRODUCTS INC p 1256
29 E Stephenson St, Freeport IL 61032
Tel (815) 235-4171 SIC 3089

▲ ILLINOIS TOOL WORKS INC p 732
155 Harlem Ave, Glenview IL 60025
Tel (847) 724-7500
SIC 3089 3965 3499 2891 3585

■ FILTERTEK INC p 542
11411 Price Rd, Hebron IL 60034
Tel (815) 648-2410 SIC 3089 3564

SOLO CUP INVESTMENT CORP p 1338
1700 Old Deerfield Rd, Highland Park IL 60035
Tel (847) 831-4800 SIC 3089 2656 3421

ALLMETAL INC p 58
1 Pierce Pl Ste 900, Itasca IL 60143
Tel (630) 250-8090 SIC 3699 3089

INTERNATIONAL PRECISION COMPONENTS CORP p 756
28468 N Ballard Dr, Lake Forest IL 60045
Tel (847) 247-2050 SIC 3089

PACTIV LLC p 1107
1900 W Field Ct, Lake Forest IL 60045
Tel (847) 482-2000 SIC 5113 3089 2673

SCC HOLDING CO LLC p 1286
150 Saunders Rd Ste 150, Lake Forest IL 60045
Tel (847) 444-5000 SIC 3089 2656 3421

■ ACCO BRANDS USA LLC p 15
4 Corporate Dr, Lake Zurich IL 60047
Tel (800) 222-6462
SIC 3089 2761 3496 2675

SOLO CUP CO p 1338
300 Tri State Intl # 200, Lincolnshire IL 60069
Tel (847) 831-4800 SIC 3089 3421 2656

SOLO CUP CO LLC p 1338
300 Tri State Intl # 200, Lincolnshire IL 60069
Tel (847) 444-5000 SIC 3089 2656 3421

SOLO CUP OPERATING CORP p 1338
300 Tr State Intl Ste 200, Lincolnshire IL 60069
Tel (847) 444-5000 SIC 3089 2656 3556

■ VISKASE COMPANIES INC p 1561
333 E Butterfield Rd # 400, Lombard IL 60148
Tel (630) 874-0700 SIC 3089

■ VISKASE CORP p 1562
333 E Bttrfeld Rd Ste 400, Lombard IL 60148
Tel (630) 874-0700 SIC 3089

FABRIK INDUSTRIES INC p 523
5213 Prime Pkwy, Mchenry IL 60050
Tel (815) 385-9480 SIC 3089 3544

MAC LEAN-FOGG CO p 891
1000 Allanson Rd, Mundelein IL 60060
Tel (847) 566-0010
SIC 3678 3452 3089 3061 3492 3451

ALP LIGHTING & CEILING PRODUCTS INC p 60
6333 W Gross Point Rd, Niles IL 60714
Tel (773) 774-9550
SIC 3089 3354 5162 3496 3442 3229

SCHOLLE IPN CORP p 1288
200 W North Ave, Northlake IL 60164
Tel (708) 562-7290
SIC 2819 3081 2821 3089

SCHOLLE IPN PACKAGING INC p 1288
200 W North Ave, Northlake IL 60164
Tel (708) 562-7290 SIC 3089

NORTH AMERICA PACKAGING CORP p 1049
1515 W 22nd St Ste 550, Oak Brook IL 60523
Tel (630) 203-4100 SIC 3089

INTEC GROUP INC p 748
666 S Vermont St, Palatine IL 60067
Tel (847) 358-0088 SIC 3089

EAKAS CORP p 468
6251 State Route 251, Peru IL 61354
Tel (815) 223-8811 SIC 3089

■ PLIANT LLC p 1156
1701 Golf Rd Ste 2-900, Rolling Meadows IL 60008
Tel (812) 424-2904 SIC 3081 2673 3089

HOFFER PLASTICS CORP p 699
500 N Collins St, South Elgin IL 60177
Tel (847) 741-5740 SIC 3089

PLASTICS GROUP INC p 1155
7409 S Quincy St, Willowbrook IL 60527
Tel (630) 325-1210 SIC 3089

■ AMERI KART CORP p 67
17196 State Road 120, Bristol IN 46507
Tel (574) 848-7462
SIC 3089 3537 2821 5162

DOREL JUVENILE GROUP INC p 451
2525 State St, Columbus IN 47201
Tel (800) 457-5276
SIC 3089 3069 3429 3699 3648

BRISTOL LASALLE CORP p 214
601 County Road 17, Elkhart IN 46516
Tel (574) 295-4400
SIC 5023 5021 5051 5033 3645 3089

NIBCO INC p 1042
1516 Middlebury St, Elkhart IN 46516
Tel (574) 295-3000 SIC 3494 3491 3089

■ BERRY PLASTICS CORP p 176
101 Oakley St, Evansville IN 47710
Tel (812) 424-2904 SIC 3089 3081

▲ BERRY PLASTICS GROUP INC p 176
101 Oakley St, Evansville IN 47710
Tel (812) 424-2904
SIC 3089 3085 2673 3081 3083

■ BPREX CLOSURES LLC p 206
101 Oakley St, Evansville IN 47710
Tel (812) 424-2904 SIC 3089

■ CAPTIVE PLASTICS INC p 252
101 Oakley St, Evansville IN 47710
Tel (812) 424-2904 SIC 3089

■ POLY-SEAL LLC p 1160
101 Oakley St, Evansville IN 47710
Tel (812) 306-2573 SIC 3089

SRG GLOBAL TRIM INC p 1363
601 N Congress Ave, Evansville IN 47715
Tel (812) 473-6200 SIC 3089

MULLINIX PACKAGES INC p 999
3511 Engle Rd, Fort Wayne IN 46809
Tel (260) 747-3149 SIC 3089

TRELLEBORG SEALING SOLUTIONS US INC p 1476
2531 Bremer Rd, Fort Wayne IN 46803
Tel (260) 749-9631 SIC 3089

■ GROUP DEKKO INC p 641
2505 Dekko Dr, Garrett IN 46738
Tel (260) 357-3621
SIC 3479 3469 3643 3315 3089

EXO-S US LLC p 519
6505 N State Road 9, Howe IN 46746
Tel (260) 562-4100 SIC 3089

DEFLECTO LLC p 422
7035 E 86th St, Indianapolis IN 46250
Tel (317) 849-9555 SIC 3089

CPX INC p 388
410 E Kent St, Kentland IN 47951
Tel (219) 474-5280 SIC 3089 3694

SYNDICATE SALES INC p 1415
2025 N Wabash Ave, Kokomo IN 46901
Tel (765) 457-7277 SIC 3089

NYLONCRAFT INC p 1069
616 W Mckinley Ave, Mishawaka IN 46545
Tel (574) 256-1521 SIC 3089

BEACH MOLD & TOOL INC p 164
999 Progress Blvd, New Albany IN 47150
Tel (812) 945-2688 SIC 3089 3544

■ BETTER WAY PARTNERS LLC p 178
70891 County Road 23, New Paris IN 46553
Tel (574) 831-3340 SIC 3089

PARAGON MEDICAL INC p 1113
8 Matchett Dr, Pierceton IN 46562
Tel (574) 594-2140 SIC 3089 3841 7371

ILPEA INDUSTRIES INC p 733
745 S Gardner St, Scottsburg IN 47170
Tel (812) 837-6616 SIC 3053 3089

PK USA INC p 1153
600 Northridge Dr, Shelbyville IN 46176
Tel (317) 395-5500
SIC 3465 3089 3714 3429

ELKHART PLASTICS p 488
3300 N Kenmore St, South Bend IN 46628
Tel (574) 232-8066 SIC 3089

TEMPLETON COAL CO INC p 1436
701 Wabash Ave Ste 501, Terre Haute IN 47807
Tel (812) 232-7037
SIC 5074 3567 3961 5049 3089

FUTABA INDIANA OF AMERICA CORP p 585
3320 S Keller Rd, Vincennes IN 47591
Tel (812) 895-4700 SIC 3089 3465 2396

REVERE INDUSTRIES LLC p 1229
16855 Suthpark Dr Ste 100, Westfield IN 46074
Tel (317) 580-2420
SIC 3089 3399 3363 3497

CUSTOM-PAK INC p 403
86 16th Ave N, Clinton IA 52732
Tel (563) 659-2100 SIC 3089

ENGINEERED PLASTIC COMPONENTS INC p 499
1408 Zimmerman Dr, Grinnell IA 50112
Tel (641) 236-3100 SIC 3089

V-T INDUSTRIES INC p 1538
1000 Industrial Park, Holstein IA 51025
Tel (712) 368-4381
SIC 3089 3083 4213 2435 2434 2431

CENTRO INC p 281
950 N Bend Dr, North Liberty IA 52317
Tel (319) 626-3200 SIC 3089

INDUSTRIAL LAMINATES/NORPLEX INC p 740
665 Lybrand St, Postville IA 52162
Tel (563) 864-7321 SIC 3089 3081

HUHTAMAKI AMERICAS INC p 718
9201 Packaging Dr, De Soto KS 66018
Tel (913) 583-3025 SIC 3089

HUHTAMAKI FILMS INC p 718
9201 Packaging Dr, De Soto KS 66018
Tel (913) 583-3025 SIC 3089

■ PACKERWARE LLC p 1107
2330 Packer Rd, Lawrence KS 66049
Tel (785) 331-4236 SIC 3089

LEISURE TIME PRODUCTS LLC p 854
3001 N Rouse St, Pittsburg KS 66762
Tel (620) 232-2400 SIC 3089 3949 2452

■ BALCO INC p 147
2626 S Sheridan Ave, Wichita KS 67217
Tel (800) 767-0082
SIC 3441 3089 3496 3446 3443

MELROSE US 3 LLC p 941
2600 S Custer Ave, Wichita KS 67217
Tel (859) 887-6390 SIC 3089

■ WADDINGTON NORTH AMERICA INC p 1571
50 E Rivercenter Blvd # 650, Covington KY 41011
Tel (859) 292-8028 SIC 3089

MONTAPLAST OF NORTH AMERICA INC p 986
2011 Hoover Blvd, Frankfort KY 40601
Tel (502) 695-7766 SIC 3714 3089

DOMETIC CORP p 448
13551 Triton Park Blvd # 1000, Louisville KY 40223
Tel (502) 873-3524
SIC 3089 3443 3444 3822 3823 3999

ENOVAPREMIER LLC p 500
1630 Lyndon Farm Ct # 100, Louisville KY 40223
Tel (502) 412-4406 SIC 3089

JONES PLASTIC AND ENGINEERING CO LLC p 792
2410 Plantside Dr, Louisville KY 40299
Tel (502) 491-3785 SIC 3089

VENTRA PLASTICS (RUSSELLVILLE) INC p 1548
140 Progress Dr, Russellville KY 42276
Tel (270) 726-4767 SIC 3089

ABELL CORP p 11
2500 Sterlington Rd, Monroe LA 71203
Tel (318) 343-7565 SIC 5191 3089

FORMED FIBER TECHNOLOGIES INC p 567
125 Allied Rd, Auburn ME 04210
Tel (207) 784-1118 SIC 2824 3089 2823

■ K & R HOLDINGS INC p 798
400 Warren Ave, Portland ME 04103
Tel (207) 797-7950 SIC 5033 3089

AMESBURY GROUP INC p 84
57 S Hunt Rd, Amesbury MA 01913
Tel (978) 834-3233
SIC 3053 3442 3086 2221 3089

PEP INDUSTRIES LLC p 1133
110 Frank Mossberg Dr, Attleboro MA 02703
Tel (508) 226-5600
SIC 3089 3351 3469 3471 3643 3841

PRECISION ENGINEERED PRODUCTS LLC p 1168
110 Frank Mossberg Dr, Attleboro MA 02703
Tel (508) 226-5600
SIC 3643 3469 3841 3471 3089 3351

▲ ENTEGRIS INC p 501
129 Concord Rd, Billerica MA 01821
Tel (978) 436-6500 SIC 3089 3081 3674

■ NYPRO INC p 1069
101 Union St, Clinton MA 01510
Tel (978) 365-8100
SIC 3089 3559 7389 8711

■ NEW ENGLAND BUSINESS SERVICE INC p 1030
500 Main St, Groton MA 01471
Tel (978) 448-6111
SIC 2759 2771 5045 2653 3089 3069

WEB INDUSTRIES INC p 1586
377 Simarano Dr Ste 220, Marlborough MA 01752
Tel (508) 898-2988
SIC 2671 5162 3089 2269 3441

■ AXYGEN BIOSCIENCE INC p 140
836 North St, Tewksbury MA 01876
Tel (978) 442-2200 SIC 3089

STERILITE CORP p 1386
30 Scales Ln, Townsend MA 01469
Tel (978) 597-1000 SIC 3089 4226

ACCELLENT ACQUISITION CORP p 14
100 Fordham Rd Bldg C, Wilmington MA 01887
Tel (978) 570-6900
SIC 3841 3317 3679 3315 3552 3089

ACCELLENT HOLDINGS CORP p 14
100 Fordham Rd, Wilmington MA 01887
Tel (978) 570-6900
SIC 3841 3679 3315 3552 3317 3089

ETX HOLDINGS INC p 512
2000 Michigan Ave, Alma MI 48801
Tel (989) 463-1151
SIC 3585 3621 3714 5013 3089

THETFORD CORP p 1447
7101 Jackson Rd, Ann Arbor MI 48103
Tel (734) 769-6000
SIC 3632 3089 2842 2621 3431 2899

CONTINENTAL STRUCTURAL PLASTICS HOLDINGS CORP p 363
255 Rex Blvd, Auburn Hills MI 48326
Tel (248) 237-7800 SIC 3089

CONTINENTAL STRUCTURAL PLASTICS INC p 363
255 Rex Blvd, Auburn Hills MI 48326
Tel (248) 237-7800 SIC 3089

CSP HOLDING CORP p 398
255 Rex Blvd, Auburn Hills MI 48326
Tel (248) 237-7800 SIC 3089

GEMINI GROUP INC p 598
175 Thompson Rd Ste A, Bad Axe MI 48413
Tel (989) 269-6272 SIC 8741 3089

ASMO MAUNFACTURING INC p 118
500 Fritz Keiper Blvd, Battle Creek MI 49037
Tel (269) 441-2040 SIC 3621 3089

SYSTEX PRODUCTS CORP p 1419
300 Buckner Rd, Battle Creek MI 49037
Tel (269) 964-8800 SIC 3089

LEXAMAR CORP p 859
100 Lexamar Dr, Boyne City MI 49712
Tel (231) 582-3163 SIC 3089

TG FLUID SYSTEMS USA CORP p 1446
100 Brighton Interior Dr, Brighton MI 48116
Tel (810) 220-6161 SIC 3082 3089

PLASTIC SYSTEMS LLC p 1155
15055 32 Mile Rd, Bruce Twp MI 48065
Tel (586) 336-9696 SIC 3089

AVON AUTOMOTIVE HOLDINGS INC p 139
603 7th St, Cadillac MI 49601
Tel (231) 775-6571 SIC 3061 3089

AVON RUBBER & PLASTICS INC p 139
503 8th St, Cadillac MI 49601
Tel (231) 779-6290 SIC 3089 3061

GENOVA PRODUCTS INC p 604
7034 E Court St, Davison MI 48423
Tel (810) 744-4500
SIC 3089 2891 2911 3494 3084 2952

CREATIVE FOAM CORP p 390
300 N Alloy Dr, Fenton MI 48430
Tel (574) 546-4238
SIC 3061 3089 3053 3086 3069

JSJ CORP p 796
700 Robbins Rd, Grand Haven MI 49417
Tel (616) 842-6350
SIC 3465 3469 3366 3089 3086 2522

SHAPE CORP p 1311
1900 Hayes St, Grand Haven MI 49417
Tel (616) 846-8700 SIC 3449 3089

ADAC PLASTICS INC p 21
5920 Tahoe Dr Se, Grand Rapids MI 49546
Tel (616) 957-0311 SIC 3089

CASCADE ENGINEERING INC p 262
3400 Innovation Ct Se, Grand Rapids MI 49512
Tel (616) 975-4800 SIC 3089

DISPLAY PACK INC p 443
1340 Monroe Ave Nw Ste 1, Grand Rapids MI 49505
Tel (616) 451-3061 SIC 3089 2759 7389

LACKS ENTERPRISES INC p 837
5460 Cascade Rd Se, Grand Rapids MI 49546
Tel (616) 949-6570 SIC 3089

LACKS EXTERIOR SYSTEMS LLC p 837
5460 Cascade Rd Se, Grand Rapids MI 49546
Tel (616) 949-6570 SIC 3089

LACKS INDUSTRIES INC p 837
5460 Cascade Rd Se, Grand Rapids MI 49546
Tel (616) 949-6570 SIC 3089

HUMPHREY COMPANIES LLC p 718
2851 Prairie St Sw, Grandville MI 49418
Tel (616) 530-1717
SIC 3537 3714 3089 5023 5162

LEON INTERIORS INC p 856
88 E 48th St, Holland MI 49423
Tel (616) 531-7970 SIC 3089 3714 3086

ROYAL TECHNOLOGIES CORP p 1254
3765 Quincy St, Hudsonville MI 49426
Tel (616) 669-3393 SIC 3089

VENTRA IONIA MAIN LLC p 1548
14 Beardsley St, Ionia MI 48846
Tel (616) 597-3220 SIC 3469 3089 5198

NYLONCRAFT OF MICHIGAN INC p 1069
1640 E Chicago Rd, Jonesville MI 49250
Tel (517) 849-9911 SIC 3089

FABRI-KAL CORP p 523
600 Plastics Pl, Kalamazoo MI 49001
Tel (269) 385-5050 SIC 3089

■ LANSING MPS INC p 844
5800 W Grand River Ave, Lansing MI 48906
Tel (517) 323-9000
SIC 2759 2731 2761 3089 2671

ALBAR INDUSTRIES INC p 45
780 Whitney Dr, Lapeer MI 48446
Tel (810) 667-0150 SIC 3089

KEY PLASTICS LLC p 814
19575 Victor Pkwy Ste 400, Livonia MI 48152
Tel (248) 449-6100 SIC 3089 7389

NYX LLC p 1069
36111 Schoolcraft Rd, Livonia MI 48150
Tel (734) 462-2385
SIC 3089 3714 3565 2671

TRW AUTOMOTIVE US LLC p 1489
12001 Tech Center Dr, Livonia MI 48150
Tel (734) 855-2600 SIC 3679 3469 3089

UNIVERSAL TRIM INC p 1518
1451 E Lincoln Ave, Madison Heights MI 48071
Tel (248) 586-3300
SIC 3714 3199 3089 3429

MARTINREA INDUSTRIES INC p 913
10501 Mi State Road 52, Manchester MI 48158
Tel (734) 428-2400
SIC 3714 3317 3089 3544

DART CONTAINER CORP OF GEORGIA p 412
500 Hogsback Rd, Mason MI 48854
Tel (517) 676-3800 SIC 3089

TH PLASTICS INC p 1446
106 E Main St, Mendon MI 49072
Tel (269) 496-8495 SIC 3089

PORT CITY GROUP INC p 1162
1985 E Laketon Ave, Muskegon MI 49442
Tel (231) 777-3941 SIC 3542 3089

JCIM US LLC p 780
45000 Helm St Ste 200, Plymouth MI 48170
Tel (734) 254-3100 SIC 3089

PLASTIPAK HOLDINGS INC p 1155
41605 Ann Arbor Rd E, Plymouth MI 48170
Tel (734) 455-3600 SIC 3089

PLASTIPAK PACKAGING INC p 1155
41605 Ann Arbor Rd E, Plymouth MI 48170
Tel (734) 455-3600 SIC 3089

JAC HOLDING CORP p 773
3937 Campus Dr, Pontiac MI 48341
Tel (248) 874-1800 SIC 3089

JAC PRODUCTS INC p 773
3937 Campus Dr, Pontiac MI 48341
Tel (248) 874-1800 SIC 3089 3714

MANN + HUMMEL USA INC p 902
6400 S Sprinkle Rd, Portage MI 49002
Tel (269) 329-3900 SIC 3089 3714

SUMMIT POLYMERS INC p 1399
6715 S Sprinkle Rd, Portage MI 49002
Tel (269) 324-9330 SIC 3089

LETICA CORP p 857
52585 Dequindre Rd, Rochester Hills MI 48307
Tel (248) 652-0557 SIC 2656 3089

RCO ENGINEERING INC p 1212
29200 Calahan Rd, Roseville MI 48066
Tel (586) 774-0100
SIC 3714 3089 3365 7361 3325 2531

JVIS INTERNATIONAL LLC p 798
52048 Shelby Pkwy, Shelby Township MI 48315
Tel (586) 739-9542 SIC 3089

JVIS USA LLC p 798
52048 Shelby Pkwy, Shelby Township MI 48315
Tel (586) 884-5700 SIC 3089

US FARATHANE HOLDINGS CORP p 1531
11650 Park Ct, Shelby Township MI 48315
Tel (248) 754-7000 SIC 3089

■ ABC GROUP HOLDINGS INC p 10
24133 Northwestern Hwy, Southfield MI 48075
Tel (248) 352-3706 SIC 3089

INTERNATIONAL AUTOMOTIVE COMPONENTS GROUP NORTH AMERICA INC p 754
28333 Telegraph Rd, Southfield MI 48034
Tel (248) 455-7000 SIC 3089 5013

■ LEAR OPERATIONS CORP p 850
21557 Telegraph Rd, Southfield MI 48033
Tel (248) 447-1500 SIC 3089

MAYCO INTERNATIONAL LLC p 923
42400 Merrill Rd, Sterling Heights MI 48314
Tel (586) 803-6000 SIC 3089

STURGIS MOLDED PRODUCTS CO p 1395
70343 Clark Rd, Sturgis MI 49091
Tel (269) 651-9381 SIC 3089 3544

CADILLAC PRODUCTS INC p 236
5800 Crooks Rd Ste 100, Troy MI 48098
Tel (248) 813-8200
SIC 3714 3081 2673 3089

PLASTIC OMNIUM AUTO EXTERIORS LLC p 1155
2710 Bellingham Dr # 400, Troy MI 48083
Tel (248) 458-0700 SIC 3089

SRG GLOBAL INC p 1363
800 Stephenson Hwy, Troy MI 48083
Tel (586) 757-7800
SIC 3089 3571 3494 2522 3826 3825

TOYODA GOSEI NORTH AMERICA CORP p 1466
1400 Stephenson Hwy, Troy MI 48083
Tel (248) 280-2100 SIC 3069 3089

PEPRO ENTERPRISES INC p 1134
2147 Leppek Rd, Ubly MI 48475
Tel (989) 658-3200 SIC 3089

GUARDIAN AUTOMOTIVE CORP p 645
23751 Amber Ave, Warren MI 48089
Tel (586) 757-7800 SIC 3089 3465

PROPER GROUP INTERNATIONAL INC p 1183
13870 E 11 Mile Rd, Warren MI 48089
Tel (586) 779-8787 SIC 3089

GT TECHNOLOGIES INC p 644
5859 E Executive Dr, Westland MI 48185
Tel (734) 467-8371
SIC 8711 3714 3545 3089

WILLIAMSTON PRODUCTS INC p 1612
845 Progress Ct, Williamston MI 48895
Tel (517) 655-2131 SIC 3089

STONE PLASTICS AND MANUFACTURING INC p 1391
8245 Riley St Ste 100, Zeeland MI 49464
Tel (616) 748-9740 SIC 5162 3089

DOUGLAS CORP p 452
9650 Valley View Rd, Eden Prairie MN 55344
Tel (800) 806-6113 SIC 3089 2759

EATON HYDRAULICS LLC p 473
14615 Lone Oak Rd, Eden Prairie MN 55344
Tel (952) 937-9800
SIC 3089 3052 3568 3492 3594 3728

CRETEX COMPANIES INC p 392
311 Lowell Ave Nw, Elk River MN 55330
Tel (763) 441-2121 SIC 3272 3089 3841

OSMONICS INC p 1097
5951 Clearwater Dr, Hopkins MN 55343
Tel (952) 933-2277
SIC 3569 3589 3561 3824 3823 3089

IMPERIAL PLASTICS INC p 734
21320 Hamburg Ave, Lakeville MN 55044
Tel (952) 469-4951 SIC 3089

LE SUEUR INC p 850
1409 Vine St, Le Sueur MN 56058
Tel (507) 665-6204
SIC 3363 3089 3544 3369

PLASTIC PRODUCTS CO INC p 1155
30355 Akerson St, Lindstrom MN 55045
Tel (651) 257-5980 SIC 3089

▲ PROTO LABS INC p 1185
5540 Pioneer Creek Dr, Maple Plain MN 55359
Tel (763) 479-3680 SIC 3089

ACTIVAR INC p 19
7808 Creekridge Cir # 200, Minneapolis MN 55439
Tel (952) 944-3533
SIC 2542 3479 3442 3429 3089

■ CONWED PLASTICS LLC p 365
2810 Weeks Ave Se, Minneapolis MN 55414
Tel (612) 623-1700 SIC 3089

NORTHLAND ALUMINUM PRODUCTS INC p 1057
5005 Highway 7, Minneapolis MN 55416
Tel (952) 924-8505 SIC 3089 3479

QUADION HOLDINGS LLC p 1196
1100 Xenium Ln N Ste 1, Minneapolis MN 55441
Tel (952) 927-1400 SIC 3069 3089

■ QUADION LLC p 1196
1100 Xenium Ln N Ste 1, Minneapolis MN 55441
Tel (952) 927-1400 SIC 3069 3089

XERXES CORP p 1631
7901 Xerxes Ave S Ste 201, Minneapolis MN 55431
Tel (952) 887-1890 SIC 3089 3443 3088

ENGINEERED POLYMERS CORP p 499
1020 Maple Ave E, Mora MN 55051
Tel (320) 679-3232 SIC 3086 3089

LIBERTY DIVERSIFIED INTERNATIONAL INC p 861
5600 Highway 169 N, New Hope MN 55428
Tel (763) 536-6600
SIC 2653 2631 5112 2542 3089 5961

ENTRUST DATACARD CORP p 503
1187 Park Pl, Shakopee MN 55379
Tel (952) 933-1223
SIC 3579 3089 7373 7372

WINCRAFT INC p 1615
960 E Mark St, Winona MN 55987
Tel (507) 454-5510
SIC 3499 2399 3089 3961 3999 3069

AUTO PARTS MANUFACTURING MISSISSIPPI INC p 133
100 Tab Way, Guntown MS 38849
Tel (662) 365-3082 SIC 3089 3465

DIVERSITY-VUTEQ LLC p 444
2300 Munsford Dr, New Albany MS 38652
Tel (662) 534-9250 SIC 3089

SINCLAIR & RUSH INC p 1326
123 Manufacturers Dr, Arnold MO 63010
Tel (636) 282-6800 SIC 3089

SAFE FLEET HOLDINGS LLC p 1266
6800 E 163rd St, Belton MO 64012
Tel (816) 318-8000 SIC 3089 3448

HARBISON CORP p 659
15450 South Outer 40 Rd # 120, Chesterfield MO 63017
Tel (314) 727-8200 SIC 3089

PRETIUM PACKAGING LLC p 1173
15450 S Outer Forty Dr St Ste 120, Chesterfield MO 63017
Tel (314) 727-8200 SIC 3089

■ SILGAN PLASTICS LLC p 1323
14515 North Outer 40 Rd # 210, Chesterfield MO 63017
Tel (800) 274-5426 SIC 3085 3089

PETERSON MANUFACTURING CO p 1138
4200 E 135th St, Grandview MO 64030
Tel (816) 765-2000
SIC 3647 4111 3089 3714

■ WESTROCK DISPENSING SYSTEMS INC p 1602
11901 Grandview Rd, Grandview MO 64030
Tel (816) 986-6000 SIC 3089

■ MASTIC HOME EXTERIORS INC p 918
2600 Grand Blvd Ste 900, Kansas City MO 64108
Tel (816) 426-8200 SIC 3081 3089

■ VARIFORM INC p 1545
303 W Major St, Kearney MO 64060
Tel (919) 677-3900 SIC 3089 1521 3444

MEXICO PLASTIC CO p 957
2000 W Boulevard St, Mexico MO 65265
Tel (573) 581-4128 SIC 2673 3089 2655

MARY LEE PACKAGING CORP p 914
615 Saint Marys Rd, Perryville MO 63775
Tel (573) 547-1705
SIC 2043 2099 3089 2098

BUNZL INDUSTRIAL INC p 226
1 Cityplace Dr Ste 200, Saint Louis MO 63141
Tel (314) 997-5959 SIC 3089

SPARTECH CORP p 1355
120 S Central Ave # 1700, Saint Louis MO 63105
Tel (314) 721-4242 SIC 3081 2821 3089

WILLERT HOME PRODUCTS INC p 1610
4044 Park Ave, Saint Louis MO 63110
Tel (314) 772-2822
SIC 3089 2869 2879 2842

PCE INC p 1124
1711 Yolande Ave, Lincoln NE 68521
Tel (402) 474-4690 SIC 3089 3644 3088

SNYDER INDUSTRIES INC p 1336
6940 O St Ste 100, Lincoln NE 68510
Tel (402) 465-1206 SIC 3089

AIRLITE PLASTICS CO p 40
6110 Abbott Dr, Omaha NE 68110
Tel (402) 341-7300 SIC 3089

REID PLASTICS INC p 1221
10861 Mill Valley Rd, Omaha NE 68154
Tel (402) 934-2400 SIC 3085 2821 3089

KALWALL CORP p 801
1111 Candia Rd, Manchester NH 03109
Tel (603) 627-3861 SIC 3089 3083

SUMMIT PACKAGING SYSTEMS INC p 1399
400 Gay St, Manchester NH 03103
Tel (603) 669-5410 SIC 3499 3089

▲ ALBANY INTERNATIONAL CORP p 45
216 Airport Dr, Rochester NH 03867
Tel (518) 445-2200
SIC 2221 3496 2399 2899 3089

REVERE INDUSTRIES LLC p 1229
838 N Delsea Dr, Clayton NJ 08312
Tel (856) 881-3600 SIC 3497 3089

HAYWARD INDUSTRIES INC p 670
620 Division St, Elizabeth NJ 07201
Tel (908) 351-5400
SIC 3589 3561 3423 3494 3569 3089

EMDEON CORP p 491
669 River Dr Ste 240, Elmwood Park NJ 07407
Tel (201) 703-3400 SIC 7373 3089

■ SEALED AIR CORP (US) p 1296
200 Riverfront Blvd # 301, Elmwood Park NJ 07407
Tel (201) 791-7600
SIC 2673 2671 3087 3086 3089

▲ NEWELL BRANDS INC p 1037
221 River St, Hoboken NJ 07030
Tel (201) 610-6600
SIC 3089 3469 2591 3951 3999 3546

PMC GROUP INC p 1157
1288 Route 73 Ste 401, Mount Laurel NJ 08054
Tel (856) 533-1866 SIC 3089 2812

SILVER LINE BUILDING PRODUCTS LLC p 1324
1 Silverline Dr, North Brunswick NJ 08902
Tel (732) 435-1000 SIC 3089 3442

DSM HOLDING CO USA INC p 458
45 Waterview Blvd, Parsippany NJ 07054
Tel (973) 257-1063
SIC 2891 2816 3089 3083 5169

DR REDDYS LABORATORIES INC p 455
107 College Rd E Ste 100, Princeton NJ 08540
Tel (908) 203-4900 SIC 5122 3089

TINGUE BROWN & CO p 1455
535 N Midland Ave, Saddle Brook NJ 07663
Tel (201) 796-4490 SIC 5087 3089 2394

SABERT CORP p 1264
2288 Main St, Sayreville NJ 08872
Tel (800) 722-3781 SIC 3089

CV HOLDINGS LLC p 404
1030 Riverfront Ctr, Amsterdam NY 12010
Tel (518) 627-0051 SIC 5162 3089

FELCHAR MANUFACTURING CORP p 537
196 Corporate Dr, Binghamton NY 13904
Tel (607) 723-3106 SIC 3678 3089 3621

PII HOLDINGS INC p 1147
2150 Elmwood Ave, Buffalo NY 14207
Tel (716) 876-9951 SIC 3089 3822 6719

PROTECTIVE INDUSTRIES INC p 1185
2150 Elmwood Ave, Buffalo NY 14207
Tel (716) 876-9951 SIC 3089 3822

■ SONOCO-CRELLIN INTERNATIONAL INC p 1340
87 Center St, Chatham NY 12037
Tel (518) 392-2000 SIC 3089

KELTA INC p 809
141 Rodeo Dr, Edgewood NY 11717
Tel (631) 789-5000 SIC 3089 3643 3661

■ AMSCAN HOLDINGS INC p 87
80 Grasslands Rd Ste 3, Elmsford NY 10523
Tel (914) 345-2020
SIC 5947 2679 3089 3069 6794

■ AMSCAN INC p 87
80 Grasslands Rd Ste 3, Elmsford NY 10523
Tel (914) 345-2020
SIC 2656 3089 5113 2676

KASSON & KELLER INC p 804
60 School St, Fonda NY 12068
Tel (518) 853-3421
SIC 3442 3089 1521 3231

GREAT PACIFIC ENTERPRISES (US) INC p 634
68 Warren St, Glens Falls NY 12801
Tel (518) 761-2593 SIC 3089

SPOTLESS PLASTICS (USA) INC p 1360
100 Motor Pkwy Ste 155, Hauppauge NY 11788
Tel (631) 951-9000 SIC 3089

ACCESSORY CORP p 15
575 8th Ave Fl 16, New York NY 10018
Tel (212) 391-8607 SIC 3089 5199

ALBEA COSMETICS AMERICA INC p 46
595 Madison Ave Fl 10, New York NY 10022
Tel (212) 371-5100
SIC 3089 3911 5162 5051

BRAIFORM ENTERPRISES INC p 207
237 W 35th St Ste 504, New York NY 10001
Tel (800) 738-7396 SIC 3089

KOBE STEEL USA HOLDINGS INC p 825
535 Madison Ave Fl 5, New York NY 10022
Tel (212) 751-9400 SIC 3542 3089

■ MULTI PACKAGING SOLUTIONS INC p 999
150 E 52nd St Ste 2800, New York NY 10022
Tel (646) 885-0005
SIC 2759 2731 2761 3089 5092 2671

CENTURY MOLD CO INC p 282
25 Vantage Point Dr, Rochester NY 14624
Tel (585) 352-8600 SIC 3089 3544

■ NALGE NUNC INTERNATIONAL CORP p 1007
75 Panorama Creek Dr, Rochester NY 14625
Tel (585) 586-8800
SIC 3089 3949 3821 3085 3083

SCHLEGEL SYSTEMS INC p 1287
1555 Jefferson Rd, Rochester NY 14623
Tel (585) 427-7200 SIC 3053 3089 3069

■ QUOIN LLC p 1201
555 Theodore Fremd Ave B302, Rye NY 10580
Tel (914) 967-9400 SIC 3089

TESSY PLASTICS CORP p 1441
700 Visions Dr, Skaneateles NY 13152
Tel (315) 689-3924 SIC 3089 3549

TECHNIMARK LLC p 1431
180 Commerce Pl, Asheboro NC 27203
Tel (336) 498-4171 SIC 3089 5199

TECHNIMARK REYNOSA LLC p 1431
180 Commerce Pl, Asheboro NC 27203
Tel (336) 498-4171 SIC 3089

■ CARLISLE CORP p 257
11605 N Community Hse Rd, Charlotte NC 28277
Tel (704) 501-1100
SIC 2952 2899 3011 2295 3089 3577

CHARLOTTE PIPE AND FOUNDRY CO p 290
2109 Randolph Rd, Charlotte NC 28207
Tel (704) 372-5030 SIC 3084 3089 3321

COATS & CLARK INC p 332
3430 Toringdon Way # 301, Charlotte NC 28277
Tel (704) 329-5800
SIC 2284 2281 3364 3089 2241 3965

COATS NORTH AMERICA DE REPUBLICA DOMINICANA INC p 332
3430 Toringdon Way # 301, Charlotte NC 28277
Tel (800) 242-8095
SIC 2284 2281 3364 3089 2241 3965

■ COLTEC INDUSTRIES INC p 339
5605 Carnegie Blvd # 500, Charlotte NC 28209
Tel (704) 731-1500 SIC 3053 3519 3089

▲ ENPRO INDUSTRIES INC p 500
5605 Carnegie Blvd # 500, Charlotte NC 28209
Tel (704) 731-1500 SIC 3053 3519 3089

PP HOLDING CORP p 1166
13800 S Lakes Dr, Charlotte NC 28273
Tel (704) 587-8409 SIC 3081 3089

SCHAEFER SYSTEMS INTERNATIONAL INC p 1286
10021 Westlake Dr, Charlotte NC 28273
Tel (704) 944-4500
SIC 3089 5046 5084 5099 7372

▲ SEALED AIR CORP p 1296
8215 Forest Point Blvd # 100, Charlotte NC 28273
Tel (980) 221-3235
SIC 2673 2671 3087 3086 3089

REICHHOLD HOLDINGS US INC p 1220
1035 Swabia Ct, Durham NC 27703
Tel (919) 990-7500
SIC 2821 2822 2891 3089 5169 5162

ASMO NORTH AMERICA LLC p 118
470 Crawford Rd, Statesville NC 28625
Tel (704) 872-2319 SIC 3089 3621

TOTER LLC p 1463
841 Meacham Rd, Statesville NC 28677
Tel (800) 424-0422
SIC 3089 3536 3469 3412 2821

NOMACORC LLC p 1047
400 Vintage Park Dr, Zebulon NC 27597
Tel (919) 460-2200 SIC 3089

▲ MYERS INDUSTRIES INC p 1004
1293 S Main St, Akron OH 44301
Tel (330) 253-5592
SIC 3089 3086 3069 3052 5013 5014

BALL BOUNCE AND SPORT INC p 148
1 Hedstrom Dr, Ashland OH 44805
Tel (419) 759-3838 SIC 5092 5091 3089

MOLDED FIBER GLASS COMPANIES p 982
2925 Mfg Pl, Ashtabula OH 44004
Tel (440) 997-5851 SIC 3089

NIFCO AMERICA CORP p 1043
8015 Dove Pkwy, Canal Winchester OH 43110
Tel (614) 920-6800 SIC 3089

DLHBOWLES INC p 445
2422 Leo Ave Sw, Canton OH 44706
Tel (330) 478-2503 SIC 8711 3089 3082

CHAMPION OPCO LLC p 287
12121 Champion Way, Cincinnati OH 45241
Tel (513) 924-4858 SIC 3089 1761 3442

REVERE PLASTICS SYSTEMS GROUP LLC p 1229
401 Elm St, Clyde OH 43410
Tel (419) 547-6918 SIC 3089

REVERE PLASTICS SYSTEMS LLC p 1229
401 Elm St, Clyde OH 43410
Tel (419) 547-6918 SIC 3089

▲ CORE MOLDING TECHNOLOGIES INC p 369
800 Manor Park Dr, Columbus OH 43228
Tel (614) 870-5000 SIC 3089

CRANE GROUP COMPANIES LIMITED p 389
2141 Fairwood Ave, Columbus OH 43207
Tel (614) 443-4891 SIC 3089

ERNIE GREEN INDUSTRIES INC p 508
2030 Dividend Dr, Columbus OH 43228
Tel (614) 219-1423
SIC 3714 3089 3471 3469

LIQUI-BOX CORP p 870
480 Schrock Rd Ste G, Columbus OH 43229
Tel (804) 325-1400
SIC 2673 3585 3089 3081 5149

YACHIYO OF AMERICA INC p 1633
2285 Walcutt Rd, Columbus OH 43228
Tel (614) 876-3220 SIC 3089 3465 3714

ASSOCIATED MATERIALS HOLDINGS LLC p 120
3773 State Rd, Cuyahoga Falls OH 44223
Tel (330) 929-1811
SIC 3089 5033 5031 5063 3442

ASSOCIATED MATERIALS LLC p 121
3773 State Rd, Cuyahoga Falls OH 44223
Tel (330) 929-1811
SIC 3089 5033 5031 3442

GENTEK BUILDING PRODUCTS INC p 604
3773 State Rd, Cuyahoga Falls OH 44223
Tel (800) 548-4542 SIC 3444 3089

AD INDUSTRIES INC p 21
6450 Poe Ave Ste 109, Dayton OH 45414
Tel (303) 744-1911
SIC 3634 3564 3535 3714 3088 3089

▲ GREIF INC p 639
425 Winter Rd, Delaware OH 43015
Tel (740) 549-6000
SIC 2653 2449 2655 3412 3089 2674

KOROSEAL INTERIOR PRODUCTS LLC p 828
3875 Embassy Pkwy Ste 110, Fairlawn OH 44333
Tel (330) 668-7600 SIC 3081 3089 3069

RJF INTERNATIONAL CORP p 1239
3875 Embassy Pkwy Ste 110, Fairlawn OH 44333
Tel (330) 668-2069 SIC 3081 3089 3069

ROPPE HOLDING CO p 1250
1602 N Union St, Fostoria OH 44830
Tel (419) 435-8546 SIC 3089 3069

STYLE CREST ENTERPRISES INC p 1395
2450 Enterprise St, Fremont OH 43420
Tel (419) 355-8586 SIC 3089 5075

STYLE CREST INC p 1395
2450 Enterprise St, Fremont OH 43420
Tel (419) 332-7369 SIC 3089 5075

TIGERPOLY MANUFACTURING INC p 1453
6231 Enterprise Pkwy, Grove City OH 43123
Tel (614) 871-0045
SIC 3089 3714 3621 3061

■ HANCOR INC p 657
4640 Trueman Blvd, Hilliard OH 43026
Tel (614) 658-0050
SIC 3084 3088 3089 3083

ANCHOR HOCKING LLC p 89
519 N Pierce Ave, Lancaster OH 43130
Tel (740) 681-6478
SIC 3229 3089 3411 3221

EVERYWARE GLOBAL INC p 515
519 N Pierce Ave, Lancaster OH 43130
Tel (740) 687-2500 SIC 3469 3089

GHP II LLC p 610
1115 W 5th Ave, Lancaster OH 43130
Tel (740) 687-2500
SIC 3229 3089 3411 3221

STANLEY ELECTRIC US CO INC p 1377
420 E High St, London OH 43140
Tel (740) 852-5200 SIC 3647 3694 3089

JAY INDUSTRIES INC p 779
150 Longview Ave E, Mansfield OH 44903
Tel (419) 524-3778 SIC 2531 3089

DAYTON SUPERIOR CORP p 418
1125 Byers Rd, Miamisburg OH 45342
Tel (937) 866-0711
SIC 3315 3452 3462 3089 2899

■ BUCKHORN INC p 223
55 W Techne Center Dr A, Milford OH 45150
Tel (513) 831-4402 SIC 3089

CK TECHNOLOGIES LLC p 320
1701 Magda Dr, Montpelier OH 43543
Tel (419) 485-1110 SIC 3089 3999

AXIUM PLASTICS LLC p 140
9005 Smiths Mill Rd, New Albany OH 43054
Tel (614) 706-5955 SIC 3089

PENDAFORM CO p 1128
200 S Friendship Dr, New Concord OH 43762
Tel (740) 826-5000 *SIC* 3089

■ PREMIX INC p 1171
3365 E Center St, North Kingsville OH 44068
Tel (440) 224-2181 *SIC* 3089 2821

■ BPREX HEALTHCARE BROOKVILLE INC p 206
1899 N Wilkinson Way, Perrysburg OH 43551
Tel (847) 541-9700 *SIC* 3089

SAINT-GOBAIN PERFORMANCE PLASTICS CORP p 1271
31500 Solon Rd, Solon OH 44139
Tel (440) 836-6900 *SIC* 3089 3053

SOFT-LITE LLC p 1337
10250 Philipp Pkwy, Streetsboro OH 44241
Tel (330) 528-3400 *SIC* 3089

STEP2 CO LLC p 1386
10010 Aurora Hudson Rd, Streetsboro OH 44241
Tel (866) 429-5200 *SIC* 3089 3944 3423

■ BPREX PLASTIC PACKAGING INC p 206
1 Seagate Ste 10, Toledo OH 43604
Tel (419) 247-5000 *SIC* 3221 3089

GRAHAM PACKAGING PLASTIC PRODUCTS INC p 629
1 Seagate Ste 10, Toledo OH 43604
Tel (717) 849-8500 *SIC* 3089

■ IMPACT PRODUCTS LLC p 734
2840 Centennial Rd, Toledo OH 43617
Tel (419) 841-2891
SIC 5084 5087 2392 3089

▲ OWENS CORNING p 1100
1 Owens Corning Pkwy, Toledo OH 43659
Tel (419) 248-8000
SIC 3296 2952 3229 3089

■ OWENS CORNING SALES LLC p 1100
1 Owens Corning Pkwy, Toledo OH 43659
Tel (419) 248-8000
SIC 3296 2952 3229 3089 1761

TOLEDO MOLDING & DIE INC p 1459
1429 Coining Dr, Toledo OH 43612
Tel (419) 470-3950 *SIC* 3089 3544

ROHRER CORP p 1247
717 Seville Rd, Wadsworth OH 44281
Tel (330) 335-1541 *SIC* 3089 2675

■ GREAT LAKES WINDOW INC p 634
30499 Tracy Rd, Walbridge OH 43465
Tel (419) 666-5555 *SIC* 3089 5211

MODERN BUILDERS SUPPLY INC p 981
302 Mcclurg Rd, Youngstown OH 44512
Tel (330) 729-2690
SIC 5032 3089 3446 3442

■ CARLISLE FOODSERVICE PRODUCTS INC p 257
4711 E Hefner Rd, Oklahoma City OK 73131
Tel (405) 528-3011 *SIC* 3089 3269

GEORG FISCHER CENTRAL PLASTICS LLC p 606
39605 Independence St, Shawnee OK 74804
Tel (405) 273-6302 *SIC* 3089

AMERISTAR PERIMETER SECURITY USA INC p 83
1555 N Mingo Rd, Tulsa OK 74116
Tel (918) 835-0898 *SIC* 3089 3446 1799

■ PECO INC p 1127
11241 Se Highway 212, Clackamas OR 97015
Tel (503) 233-6401
SIC 3089 3822 3364 3363

ENTEK INTERNATIONAL LLC p 501
250 Hansard Ave, Lebanon OR 97355
Tel (541) 259-3901 *SIC* 3089

AMCOR PET PACKAGING USA INC p 66
6974 Schantz Rd, Allentown PA 18106
Tel (610) 871-9000 *SIC* 3089

NURSERY SUPPLIES INC p 1067
1415 Orchard Dr, Chambersburg PA 17201
Tel (717) 263-7780 *SIC* 3089

LA FRANCE CORP p 835
1 Lafrance Way, Concordville PA 19331
Tel (610) 361-4300
SIC 3089 3364 3993 5013 7389

DOPACO INC p 451
461 Boot Rd, Downingtown PA 19335
Tel (610) 269-6048
SIC 2657 2656 3089 3792

MCS INDUSTRIES INC p 932
2280 Newlins Mill Rd, Easton PA 18045
Tel (610) 253-6268
SIC 2499 3089 3499 3993 3231

PLASTEK INDUSTRIES INC p 1155
2425 W 23rd St, Erie PA 16506
Tel (814) 878-4400 *SIC* 3089

▲ WEST PHARMACEUTICAL SERVICES INC p 1595
530 Herman O West Dr, Exton PA 19341
Tel (610) 594-2900
SIC 3069 3466 2673 3085 3089

VEKA HOLDINGS INC p 1547
100 Veka Dr, Fombell PA 16123
Tel (724) 452-1000 *SIC* 3089

VEKA INC p 1547
100 Veka Dr, Fombell PA 16123
Tel (800) 654-5589 *SIC* 3089

MI WINDOWS AND DOORS INC p 959
650 W Market St, Gratz PA 17030
Tel (717) 365-3300 *SIC* 3089 3442

NEW WERNER HOLDING CO INC p 1033
93 Werner Rd, Greenville PA 16125
Tel (724) 588-2000
SIC 3499 3355 3089 3446 2499 6512

OLD LADDER CO p 1081
93 Werner Rd, Greenville PA 16125
Tel (888) 523-3371
SIC 3446 3089 3334 3444 3499

WERNER CO p 1592
93 Werner Rd, Greenville PA 16125
Tel (724) 588-2000
SIC 3499 3355 3089 3446 2499

WERNER HOLDING CO (PA) INC p 1593
93 Werner Rd, Greenville PA 16125
Tel (888) 523-3371
SIC 3499 3355 3089 3446 2499

STABLER COMPANIES INC p 1374
635 Lucknow Rd, Harrisburg PA 17110
Tel (717) 236-9307
SIC 5032 3089 7359 3531 1611 3648

GRAHAM PACKAGING CO INC p 629
700 Indian Springs Dr # 100, Lancaster PA 17601
Tel (717) 849-8500 *SIC* 5199 3089 5162

GRAHAM PACKAGING CO LP p 629
700 Indian Springs Dr # 100, Lancaster PA 17601
Tel (717) 849-8500 *SIC* 3089

GRAHAM PACKAGING HOLDINGS CO p 629
700 Indian Springs Dr # 100, Lancaster PA 17601
Tel (717) 849-8500 *SIC* 3089

■ KERR GROUP LLC p 813
1846 Charter Ln Ste 209, Lancaster PA 17601
Tel (812) 424-2904 *SIC* 3089

CERTAINTEED CORP p 284
20 Moores Rd, Malvern PA 19355
Tel (610) 893-5000
SIC 3221 3292 3259 3084 3089 3432

■ CARDINAL HEALTH 407 INC p 253
3001 Red Lion Rd Ste Ag, Philadelphia PA 19114
Tel (215) 501-1210 *SIC* 7389 3086 3089

BRENTWOOD INDUSTRIES INC p 210
500 Spring Ridge Dr, Reading PA 19610
Tel (610) 374-5109 *SIC* 3089

PHOENIX FORGE GROUP LLC p 1145
1020 Macarthur Rd, Reading PA 19605
Tel (800) 234-8665 *SIC* 3089

TRAY-PAK CORP p 1475
Tuckerton Rd And, Reading PA 19605
Tel (888) 926-1777 *SIC* 3089

M&Q HOLDINGS LLC p 890
3 Earl Ave, Schuylkill Haven PA 17972
Tel (570) 385-4991 *SIC* 3089 6719

■ CPG INTERNATIONAL INC p 387
888 N Keyser Ave, Scranton PA 18504
Tel (570) 558-8000 *SIC* 3089 3272

CAPSULE INTERNATIONAL LLC p 251
1100 Northbrook Dr, Trevose PA 19053
Tel (215) 552-3700 *SIC* 3089

CAPSULE PA INC p 252
1100 Northbrook Dr Fl 2, Trevose PA 19053
Tel (215) 552-3700 *SIC* 3089 3085

SAINT-GOBAIN VETROTEX AMERICA INC p 1271
20 Moores Rd, Valley Forge PA 19482
Tel (610) 893-6000 *SIC* 3089

WHIRLEY INDUSTRIES INC p 1605
618 4th Ave, Warren PA 16365
Tel (814) 723-7600 *SIC* 3089

■ DIAMOND MANUFACTURING CO p 437
243 W Eigth St, Wyoming PA 18644
Tel (570) 693-0300
SIC 3469 3471 3479 3089

GPC CAPITAL CORP II p 627
2401 Pleasant Valley Rd # 2, York PA 17402
Tel (717) 849-8500 *SIC* 3089

GRAHAM PACKAGING CO EUROPE LLC p 629
2401 Pleasant Valley Rd # 2, York PA 17402
Tel (717) 849-8500 *SIC* 3089

WEXCO INC p 1603
3490 Board Rd, York PA 17406
Tel (717) 764-8585
SIC 3089 3949 3999 5091 3081

■ NYPRO PUERTO RICO INC p 1069
15 Ave Luis Mnoz Rivera S, Cayey PR 00736
Tel (787) 738-4211 *SIC* 3089

INTERNATIONAL PACKAGING CORP p 756
517 Mineral Spring Ave, Pawtucket RI 02860
Tel (401) 724-1600 *SIC* 3499 3089

MARS 2000 INC p 910
40 Agnes St, Providence RI 02909
Tel (401) 421-5275 *SIC* 3089

FLEXIBLE TECHNOLOGIES INC p 556
528 Carwellyn Rd, Abbeville SC 29620
Tel (864) 366-5441 *SIC* 3052 3089

PLASTIC OMNIUM INDUSTRIES INC p 1155
5100 Old Pearman Dairy Rd, Anderson SC 29625
Tel (864) 260-0000 *SIC* 3089

AUGUSTA FIBERGLASS COATINGS INC p 131
86 Lake Cynthia Dr, Blackville SC 29817
Tel (803) 284-2246 *SIC* 3089

■ SHAKESPEARE CO LLC p 1310
6111 Shakespeare Rd, Columbia SC 29223
Tel (803) 754-7011
SIC 3089 3949 3679 3663

ROCHLING AUTOMOTIVE USA LLP p 1243
245 Parkway E, Duncan SC 29334
Tel (864) 486-0888 *SIC* 3089

COVERIS RIGID NA INC p 385
50 International Dr # 100, Greenville SC 29615
Tel (864) 225-9750 *SIC* 2671 3089

▲ SONOCO PRODUCTS CO p 1340
1 N 2nd St, Hartsville SC 29550
Tel (843) 383-7000
SIC 2631 2671 2653 2655 3089 2499

PRECISION SOUTHEAST INC p 1169
4900 Highway 501, Myrtle Beach SC 29579
Tel (843) 347-4218 *SIC* 3089 8731 3083

LOXCREEN CO INC p 882
1630 Old Dunbar Rd, West Columbia SC 29172
Tel (803) 822-1600 *SIC* 3354 3442 3089

PI INC p 1146
213 Dennis St, Athens TN 37303
Tel (423) 745-6213
SIC 2519 3949 3089 2499 3086 3081

CLARITY INDUSTRIES LLC p 322
9265 Hunterboro Dr, Brentwood TN 37027
Tel (330) 528-3400 *SIC* 3089

ALPHA CORP OF TENNESSEE p 60
955 Highway 57, Collierville TN 38017
Tel (901) 854-2800 *SIC* 3089 2865

IDENTITY GROUP HOLDINGS CORP p 729
1480 Gould Dr, Cookeville TN 38506
Tel (931) 432-4000
SIC 3089 3086 3993 3953

▲ CLARCOR INC p 321
840 Crescent Centre Dr # 600, Franklin TN 37067
Tel (615) 771-3100
SIC 3714 3599 3564 3569 3411 3089

AMERICA PLASTICS LLC p 67
2636 Byington Solway Rd, Knoxville TN 37931
Tel (865) 457-7000 *SIC* 3089

M-TEK INC p 890
1020 Volunteer Pkwy, Manchester TN 37355
Tel (931) 728-4122 *SIC* 3089 3714 3429

▲ MUELLER INDUSTRIES INC p 998
8285 Tournament Dr # 150, Memphis TN 38125
Tel (901) 753-3200 *SIC* 3463 3494 3089

TEKNI-PLEX MANAGEMENT LLC p 1433
260 N Denton Tap Rd, Coppell TX 75019
Tel (972) 304-5077 *SIC* 3089 2631 2656

ATRIUM WINDOWS AND DOORS INC p 129
3890 W Northwest Hwy # 500, Dallas TX 75220
Tel (214) 956-8031
SIC 3442 2431 3089 3354 7629

KRESTMARK INDUSTRIES LP p 830
3950 Bastille Rd Ste 100, Dallas TX 75212
Tel (214) 237-5055 *SIC* 3442 3089

OXY CHEMICAL CORP p 1101
5005 L B Johnson Fwy 2200, Dallas TX 75244
Tel (972) 404-3800
SIC 2869 2873 2874 2899 3089

PLASTICOS PROMEX USA INC p 1155
1220 Barranca Dr Ste 4c, El Paso TX 79935
Tel (915) 592-5447 *SIC* 3089

CANTEX INC p 247
301 Commerce St Ste 2700, Fort Worth TX 76102
Tel (817) 215-7000 *SIC* 3084 3089

KPS GLOBAL LLC p 829
4201 N Beach St, Fort Worth TX 76137
Tel (817) 281-5121 *SIC* 3089 3585

MARCO DISPLAY SPECIALISTS LP p 905
3209 Marquita Dr, Fort Worth TX 76116
Tel (817) 244-8300
SIC 2521 2541 3993 3089 3081

WELBILT WALK-INS LP p 1588
4201 N Beach St, Fort Worth TX 76137
Tel (817) 281-5121 *SIC* 3089 3585

DENALI INC p 428
550 Westcott St Ste 450, Houston TX 77007
Tel (713) 627-0933 *SIC* 3089

HOOVER GROUP INC p 706
2135 Highway 6 S, Houston TX 77077
Tel (800) 844-8683
SIC 3496 3412 3443 3089 7359 3411

HOOVER MATERIALS HANDLING GROUP INC p 706
2135 Highway 6 S, Houston TX 77077
Tel (800) 844-8683 *SIC* 5113 3089

MEDPLAST GROUP INC p 938
7865 Northcourt Rd # 100, Houston TX 77040
Tel (480) 553-6400 *SIC* 3089

LAIRD PLASTICS INC p 838
5800 Campus Circle Dr E, Irving TX 75063
Tel (469) 299-7000 *SIC* 5162 3089

CHEVRON PHILLIPS CHEMICAL CO LP p 296
10001 Six Pines Dr, The Woodlands TX 77380
Tel (832) 813-4100
SIC 5169 3292 3089 3084 3432 2911

LIFETIME LLC p 865
Freeport Ctr Bldg D-11, Clearfield UT 84016
Tel (801) 776-1532 *SIC* 3089

ENVIROTECH PUMPSYSTEMS INC p 504
440 W 800 S, Salt Lake City UT 84101
Tel (801) 359-8731 *SIC* 3561 3491 3089

MACK GROUP INC p 892
608 Warm Brook Rd, Arlington VT 05250
Tel (802) 375-2511 *SIC* 3089 3577 6719

MACK MOLDING CO INC p 892
608 Warm Brook Rd, Arlington VT 05250
Tel (802) 375-2511 *SIC* 3089 3577

G W PLASTICS INC p 587
239 Pleasant St, Bethel VT 05032
Tel (802) 234-9941 *SIC* 3089 3544

STRONGWELL CORP p 1394
400 Commonwealth Ave, Bristol VA 24201
Tel (276) 645-8000 *SIC* 3089

OBERTHUR TECHNOLOGIES OF AMERICA CORP p 1072
4250 Pleasant Valley Rd, Chantilly VA 20151
Tel (703) 263-0100
SIC 3089 7382 3953 3578 3499

GIESECKE & DEVRIENT MOBILE SECURITY AMERICA INC p 611
45925 Horseshoe Dr, Dulles VA 20166
Tel (703) 480-2100
SIC 7382 3089 5045 7374

REHAU INC p 1220
1501 Edwards Ferry Rd Ne, Leesburg VA 20176
Tel (703) 777-5255 *SIC* 3089

GENERAL FOAM PLASTICS CORP p 601
4429 Bonney Rd Ste 500, Virginia Beach VA 23462
Tel (757) 857-0153 *SIC* 3089

■ RUBBERMAID COMMERCIAL PRODUCTS LLC p 1256
3124 Valley Ave, Winchester VA 22601
Tel (540) 677-8700 *SIC* 3089 2673

■ MILGARD MANUFACTURING INC p 969
1010 54th Ave E, Fife WA 98424
Tel (253) 922-6030 *SIC* 3089 3442

MIKRON INDUSTRIES INC p 968
1034 6th Ave N, Kent WA 98032
Tel (253) 854-8020 *SIC* 3089

CASCADE DESIGNS INC p 262
4000 1st Ave S, Seattle WA 98134
Tel (206) 583-0583
SIC 2515 3089 3949 8733

VAUPELL INDUSTRIAL PLASTICS INC p 1545
1144 Nw 53rd St, Seattle WA 98107
Tel (206) 784-9050 *SIC* 3089

CONSOLIDATED METCO INC p 360
5701 Se Columbia Way, Vancouver WA 98661
Tel (360) 828-2599
SIC 3365 3363 3089 3714 3443 3312

SIMONTON BUILDING PRODUCTS INC p 1325
5300 Briscoe Rd, Parkersburg WV 26105
Tel (304) 659-2851 *SIC* 3089 3442 3231

FLAMBEAU INC p 554
801 Lynn Ave, Baraboo WI 53913
Tel (608) 356-5551 *SIC* 3089 3949 3944

PLASTIC INGENUITY INC p 1155
1017 Park St, Cross Plains WI 53528
Tel (608) 798-3071 *SIC* 3089

DON EVANS INC p 450
100 W North St, Deforest WI 53532
Tel (608) 846-6000 *SIC* 3089

■ MERCURY MARINE INC p 945
W6250 W Pioneer Rd, Fond Du Lac WI 54935
Tel (920) 929-5000 *SIC* 3089 3535

MGS GROUP NORTH AMERICA INC p 958
W190n11701 Moldmakers Way, Germantown WI 53022
Tel (262) 250-2950 *SIC* 3089

MGS MFG GROUP INC p 958
W188n11707 Maple Rd, Germantown WI 53022
Tel (262) 255-5790 *SIC* 3089 5047 2821

WENDORFF BROS CO INC p 1592
105 Steelcraft Dr, Hartford WI 53027
Tel (262) 673-6770
SIC 3469 3089 5013 3479

PHILLIPS-MEDISIZE CORP p 1144
1201 Hanley Rd, Hudson WI 54016
Tel (715) 386-4320 *SIC* 3089 3444 3544

CPT INC p 388
3706 Enterprise Dr, Janesville WI 53546
Tel (608) 314-2020 *SIC* 3089 5162

WEATHER SHIELD MFG INC p 1585
1 Weathershield Plz, Medford WI 54451
Tel (715) 748-2100 *SIC* 2431 3089 3442

GOSSEN CORP p 626
2030 W Bender Rd, Milwaukee WI 53209
Tel (800) 558-8984 *SIC* 2431 3089 2452

HELLERMANNTYTON CORP p 681
7930 N Faulkner Rd, Milwaukee WI 53224
Tel (414) 355-1130 *SIC* 3089 2891

TECHNIPLAS LLC p 1431
N44w33341 Wtrtwn Plnk Rd, Nashotah WI 53058
Tel (262) 369-5555 *SIC* 3089 3544

■ SENTRY SAFE INC p 1305
137 W Forest Hill Ave, Oak Creek WI 53154
Tel (585) 381-4900 *SIC* 3089 3499 2522

ORBIS CORP p 1092
1055 Corporate Center Dr, Oconomowoc WI 53066
Tel (262) 560-5000 *SIC* 3089

DUTCHLAND PLASTICS LLC p 463
54 Enterprise Ct, Oostburg WI 53070
Tel (920) 564-3633 *SIC* 3089 3544

IRIS USA INC p 764
11111 80th Ave, Pleasant Prairie WI 53158
Tel (262) 612-1000 *SIC* 3089

REHRIG PENN LOGISTICS INC p 1220
7800 100th St, Pleasant Prairie WI 53158
Tel (262) 947-0032 *SIC* 3089

TVCI HOLDING INC p 1494
1236 N 18th St, Sheboygan WI 53081
Tel (920) 457-4851 *SIC* 3914 3365 3089

VOLLRATH CO LLC p 1564
1236 N 18th St, Sheboygan WI 53081
Tel (920) 459-6568
SIC 3089 3365 3421 3556 3914

BEMIS MANUFACTURING CO INC p 171
300 Mill St, Sheboygan Falls WI 53085
Tel (920) 467-4621 *SIC* 3089

SCIENTIFIC MOLDING CORP LTD p 1292
330 Smc Dr, Somerset WI 54025
Tel (715) 247-3500 *SIC* 3089 3544

LAWRENCE HOLDING INC p 848
803 S Black River St, Sparta WI 54656
Tel (608) 269-6911 *SIC* 3469 3089 3544

NORTHERN ENGRAVING CORP p 1056
803 S Black River St, Sparta WI 54656
Tel (608) 269-6911 *SIC* 3469 3544 3089

SUSSEX IM INC p 1409
N65w24770 Main St, Sussex WI 53089
Tel (262) 246-8022 *SIC* 3089

MINIATURE PRECISION COMPONENTS INC p 973
820 Wisconsin St, Walworth WI 53184
Tel (262) 275-5791 *SIC* 3089

WESTERN INDUSTRIES INC p 1598
1141 S 10th St, Watertown WI 53094
Tel (920) 261-0660
SIC 3443 3469 3089 3444 1761 3491

CLACK CORP p 321
4462 Duraform Ln, Windsor WI 53598
Tel (608) 846-3010 *SIC* 3589 3089

SIC 3111 Leather Tanning & Finishing

▲ DIFFERENTIAL BRANDS GROUP INC p 438
1231 S Gerhart Ave, Commerce CA 90022
Tel (323) 890-1800
SIC 2337 2339 2311 2325 3111 2387

CHARMING TRIM & PACKAGING INC p 290
28 Brookside Ct, Novato CA 94947
Tel (415) 302-7021 *SIC* 5131 3111

▲ VERA BRADLEY INC p 1549
12420 Stonebridge Rd, Roanoke IN 46783
Tel (877) 708-8372
SIC 3171 3111 2392 2844

TASMAN INDUSTRIES INC p 1426
930 Geiger St, Louisville KY 40206
Tel (502) 785-7477 *SIC* 3111 5159

AFX INDUSTRIES LLC p 33
1411 3rd St Ste G, Port Huron MI 48060
Tel (810) 966-4650 *SIC* 3111 5531

▲ WOLVERINE WORLD WIDE INC p 1621
9341 Courtland Dr Ne, Rockford MI 49351
Tel (616) 866-5500
SIC 3143 3149 3144 3111

■ EAGLE OTTAWA LLC p 468
21557 Telegraph Rd, Southfield MI 48033
Tel (248) 364-7400 SIC 3111 2399 2396

GST AUTOLEATHER INC p 643
20 Oak Hollow St Ste 300, Southfield MI 48033
Tel (248) 436-2300 SIC 3111

RED WING SHOE CO INC p 1216
314 Main St, Red Wing MN 55066
Tel (651) 388-8211
SIC 3143 3149 3144 3111 5661 3021

■ NATIONAL BEEF LEATHERS LLC p 1010
205 Florence Rd, Saint Joseph MO 64504
Tel (816) 236-1603 SIC 3111

STRATEGIC INDUSTRIES LLC p 1392
26 Main St Ste 200, Chatham NJ 07928
Tel (732) 512-0195
SIC 3724 3499 3451 3083 3111

MYERS GROUP L L C p 1004
74 Blanchard Rd, South Orange NJ 07079
Tel (973) 761-6414 SIC 3111

SMITH GREENTECH TANNERY LLC p 1333
2233 Vantage St, Dallas TX 75207
Tel (214) 566-8392 SIC 3111

▲ TANDY LEATHER FACTORY INC p 1424
1900 Se Loop 820, Fort Worth TX 76140
Tel (817) 872-3200 SIC 5948 5199 3111

ALBERT TROSTEL & SONS CO p 46
800 N Marshall St, Milwaukee WI 53202
Tel (414) 223-1560 SIC 3111

EVERETT SMITH GROUP LTD p 514
330 E Kilbourn Ave # 1400, Milwaukee WI 53202
Tel (414) 223-1560 SIC 3111 6282

SIC 3131 Boot & Shoe Cut Stock & Findings

SAN ANTONIO SHOE INC p 1275
1717 Sas Dr, San Antonio TX 78224
Tel (877) 727-7463
SIC 3131 5661 5139 5632 3144

SIC 3142 House Slippers

PRINCIPLE BUSINESS ENTERPRISES INC p 1177
20189 Pine Lake Rd, Bowling Green OH 43402
Tel (419) 352-1551 SIC 2676 3142

SIC 3143 Men's Footwear, Exc Athletic

STRATEGIC PARTNERS INC p 1392
9800 De Soto Ave, Chatsworth CA 91311
Tel (818) 671-2100
SIC 3143 3144 5139 2339 2389 2329

OAKLEY INC p 1071
1 Icon, Foothill Ranch CA 92610
Tel (949) 951-0991
SIC 3851 2331 2339 3021 3873 3143

■ B H SHOE HOLDINGS INC p 142
124 W Putnam Ave Ste 1, Greenwich CT 06830
Tel (203) 661-2424 SIC 3143

■ HH BROWN SHOE CO INC p 689
124 W Putnam Ave Ste 1a, Greenwich CT 06830
Tel (203) 661-2424 SIC 3143 3144

BELLEVILLE BOOT CO p 170
100 Premier Dr, Belleville IL 62220
Tel (618) 233-5600 SIC 3143

REEBOK INTERNATIONAL LTD p 1217
1895 J W Foster Blvd, Canton MA 02021
Tel (781) 401-5000
SIC 3149 3143 3144 2329 2339 5661

C & J CLARK AMERICA INC p 231
60 Tower Rd, Waltham MA 02451
Tel (617) 964-1222 SIC 3143 5139 5661

▲ WOLVERINE WORLD WIDE INC p 1621
9341 Courtland Dr Ne, Rockford MI 49351
Tel (616) 866-5500
SIC 3143 3149 3144 3111

RED WING SHOE CO INC p 1216
314 Main St, Red Wing MN 55066
Tel (651) 388-8211
SIC 3143 3149 3144 3111 5661 3021

TIMBERLAND LLC p 1454
200 Domain Dr, Stratham NH 03885
Tel (603) 772-9500
SIC 3143 3144 2386 2329 2321 2325

▲ STEVEN MADDEN LTD p 1388
5216 Barnett Ave, Long Island City NY 11104
Tel (718) 446-1800
SIC 3143 3144 3149 5632

▲ COACH INC p 330
10 Hudson Yards, New York NY 10001
Tel (212) 594-1850
SIC 3171 3172 2387 3143 3144

■ GH BASS & CO p 610
200 Madison Ave, New York NY 10016
Tel (212) 381-3900
SIC 3144 3143 3149 5661

▲ ICONIX BRAND GROUP INC p 728
1450 Broadway Fl 3, New York NY 10018
Tel (212) 730-0030 SIC 6794 3143 3144

KCP HOLDCO INC p 806
603 W 50th St, New York NY 10019
Tel (212) 265-1500
SIC 3143 3171 5661 5632 5611

KENNETH COLE PRODUCTIONS INC p 811
603 W 50th St, New York NY 10019
Tel (212) 265-1500
SIC 3143 3144 3171 5661 5632 5611

▲ PVH CORP p 1193
200 Madison Ave Bsmt 1, New York NY 10016
Tel (212) 381-3500
SIC 2321 2331 2253 3143 5621 5611

▲ ROCKY BRANDS INC p 1245
39 E Canal St, Nelsonville OH 45764
Tel (740) 753-1951
SIC 3143 3144 2329 2331 2339 2389

IRON AGE HOLDINGS CORP p 764
3 Robinson Plz Ste 300, Pittsburgh PA 15205
Tel (412) 788-0888
SIC 5139 5661 3143 3144

■ JUSTIN BRANDS INC p 798
610 W Daggett Ave, Fort Worth TX 76104
Tel (817) 332-4385 SIC 3144 3143 3149

HAT BRANDS HOLDING CORP p 667
601 Marion Dr, Garland TX 75042
Tel (972) 494-7133
SIC 2353 3914 3144 3143

ALLEN EDMONDS CORP p 53
201 E Seven Hills Rd, Port Washington WI 53074
Tel (262) 235-6000 SIC 3143 5661

SIC 3144 Women's Footwear, Exc Athletic

MUNRO & CO INC p 1000
3770 Malvern Rd, Hot Springs AR 71901
Tel (501) 262-6000 SIC 3144 3149

STRATEGIC PARTNERS INC p 1392
9800 De Soto Ave, Chatsworth CA 91311
Tel (818) 671-2100
SIC 3143 3144 5139 2339 2389 2329

■ HH BROWN SHOE CO INC p 689
124 W Putnam Ave Ste 1a, Greenwich CT 06830
Tel (203) 661-2424 SIC 3143 3144

REEBOK INTERNATIONAL LTD p 1217
1895 J W Foster Blvd, Canton MA 02021
Tel (781) 401-5000
SIC 3149 3143 3144 2329 2339 5661

▲ WOLVERINE WORLD WIDE INC p 1621
9341 Courtland Dr Ne, Rockford MI 49351
Tel (616) 866-5500
SIC 3143 3149 3144 3111

RED WING SHOE CO INC p 1216
314 Main St, Red Wing MN 55066
Tel (651) 388-8211
SIC 3143 3149 3144 3111 5661 3021

TIMBERLAND LLC p 1454
200 Domain Dr, Stratham NH 03885
Tel (603) 772-9500
SIC 3143 3144 2386 2329 2321 2325

▲ STEVEN MADDEN LTD p 1388
5216 Barnett Ave, Long Island City NY 11104
Tel (718) 446-1800
SIC 3143 3144 3149 5632

▲ COACH INC p 330
10 Hudson Yards, New York NY 10001
Tel (212) 594-1850
SIC 3171 3172 2387 3143 3144

■ GH BASS & CO p 610
200 Madison Ave, New York NY 10016
Tel (212) 381-3900
SIC 3144 3143 3149 5661

▲ ICONIX BRAND GROUP INC p 728
1450 Broadway Fl 3, New York NY 10018
Tel (212) 730-0030 SIC 6794 3143 3144

KENNETH COLE PRODUCTIONS INC p 811
603 W 50th St, New York NY 10019
Tel (212) 265-1500
SIC 3143 3144 3171 5661 5632 5611

NINE WEST FOOTWEAR CORP p 1044
1411 Broadway Fl 20, New York NY 10018
Tel (800) 999-1877
SIC 3144 3171 5661 5632 5139

▲ ROCKY BRANDS INC p 1245
39 E Canal St, Nelsonville OH 45764
Tel (740) 753-1951
SIC 3143 3144 2329 2331 2339 2389

IRON AGE HOLDINGS CORP p 764
3 Robinson Plz Ste 300, Pittsburgh PA 15205
Tel (412) 788-0888
SIC 5139 5661 3143 3144

■ JUSTIN BRANDS INC p 798
610 W Daggett Ave, Fort Worth TX 76104
Tel (817) 332-4385 SIC 3144 3143 3149

HAT BRANDS HOLDING CORP p 667
601 Marion Dr, Garland TX 75042
Tel (972) 494-7133
SIC 2353 3914 3144 3143

SAN ANTONIO SHOE INC p 1275
1717 Sas Dr, San Antonio TX 78224
Tel (877) 727-7463
SIC 3131 5661 5139 5632 3144

SIC 3149 Footwear, NEC

MUNRO & CO INC p 1000
3770 Malvern Rd, Hot Springs AR 71901
Tel (501) 262-6000 SIC 3144 3149

▲ SKECHERS USA INC p 1329
228 Manhattan Beach Blvd # 200, Manhattan Beach CA 90266
Tel (310) 318-3100 SIC 3021 3149

REEBOK INTERNATIONAL LTD p 1217
1895 J W Foster Blvd, Canton MA 02021
Tel (781) 401-5000
SIC 3149 3143 3144 2329 2339 5661

■ ACUSHNET CO p 20
333 Bridge St, Fairhaven MA 02719
Tel (508) 979-2000 SIC 3949 3149 2381

■ STRIDE RITE CORP p 1393
500 Totten Pond Rd Ste 1, Waltham MA 02451
Tel (617) 824-6000 SIC 5139 5661 3149

▲ WOLVERINE WORLD WIDE INC p 1621
9341 Courtland Dr Ne, Rockford MI 49351
Tel (616) 866-5500
SIC 3143 3149 3144 3111

RED WING SHOE CO INC p 1216
314 Main St, Red Wing MN 55066
Tel (651) 388-8211
SIC 3143 3149 3144 3111 5661 3021

▲ STEVEN MADDEN LTD p 1388
5216 Barnett Ave, Long Island City NY 11104
Tel (718) 446-1800
SIC 3143 3144 3149 5632

■ GH BASS & CO p 610
200 Madison Ave, New York NY 10016
Tel (212) 381-3900
SIC 3144 3143 3149 5661

RADIAL INC p 1204
935 1st Ave, King Of Prussia PA 19406
Tel (610) 491-7000
SIC 3149 5139 5091 5136 5137 7375

■ JUSTIN BRANDS INC p 798
610 W Daggett Ave, Fort Worth TX 76104
Tel (817) 332-4385 SIC 3144 3143 3149

SIC 3151 Leather Gloves & Mittens

MAGID GLOVE & SAFETY MANUFACTURING CO LLC p 895
1300 Naperville Dr, Romeoville IL 60446
Tel (773) 384-2070
SIC 3151 2381 5699 3842 2326

MIDWEST QUALITY GLOVES INC p 967
835 Industrial Rd, Chillicothe MO 64601
Tel (660) 646-2165 SIC 5199 3151

HANDWEAR SALES INC p 657
74 Bleecker St, Gloversville NY 12078
Tel (518) 725-8641
SIC 3151 3949 2253 3021

FOWNES BROTHERS & CO INC p 572
16 E 34th St Fl 5, New York NY 10016
Tel (212) 683-0150
SIC 3151 2381 5136 5137 3949

TOTES ISOTONER HOLDINGS CORP p 1463
9655 International Blvd, West Chester OH 45246
Tel (513) 682-8200
SIC 2381 3151 2211 3021 5699

SIC 3161 Luggage

DAMAO LUGGAGE INTERNATIONAL INC p 410
1909 S Vineyard Ave, Ontario CA 91761
Tel (909) 923-6531 SIC 5099 3161

SKB CORP p 1329
434 W Levers Pl, Orange CA 92867
Tel (714) 637-1252 SIC 3089 3161

PELICAN PRODUCTS INC p 1128
23215 Early Ave, Torrance CA 90505
Tel (310) 326-4700 SIC 3648 3161 3089

TUMI HOLDINGS INC p 1491
1001 Durham Ave Ste 1b, South Plainfield NJ 07080
Tel (908) 756-4400 SIC 3161 3172 5948

TUMI INC p 1491
1001 Durham Ave Ste 1b, South Plainfield NJ 07080
Tel (908) 756-4400 SIC 5199 5948 3161

COACH STORES INC p 331
516 W 34th St Bsmt 5, New York NY 10001
Tel (212) 643-9727
SIC 3171 3161 3172 2387 5137 5099

LENOX HOLDINGS INC p 856
1414 Radcliffe St Fl 1, Bristol PA 19007
Tel (267) 525-7800
SIC 3229 3161 5719 5948

LEEDSWORLD INC p 852
400 Hunt Valley Rd, New Kensington PA 15068
Tel (724) 334-9000
SIC 5199 5111 5112 3172 3161 2394

POLYCONCEPT NORTH AMERICA INC p 1160
400 Hunt Valley Rd, New Kensington PA 15068
Tel (724) 334-9000
SIC 5199 5111 5112 3172 3161 2394

BIO WORLD MERCHANDISING INC p 183
2111 W Walnut Hill Ln, Irving TX 75038
Tel (888) 831-2138
SIC 2353 3161 2253 5199 3021

■ JANSPORT INC p 777
N850 County Road Cb, Appleton WI 54914
Tel (920) 734-5708
SIC 3949 3161 2339 2329 2321

SIC 3171 Handbags & Purses

FRANCES MARY ACCESSORIES INC p 573
3732 Mt Diablo Blvd # 260, Lafayette CA 94549
Tel (925) 962-2111 SIC 3171

BECARRO INTERNATIONAL CORP p 167
1730 Corporate Dr, Boynton Beach FL 33426
Tel (561) 737-5585 SIC 3171

VERA BRADLEY INC p 1549
3715 Courtwood Dr, Fort Wayne IN 46815
Tel (260) 482-3250 SIC 3171

▲ VERA BRADLEY INC p 1549
12420 Stonebridge Rd, Roanoke IN 46783
Tel (877) 708-8372
SIC 3171 3111 2392 2844

LOEHMANNS HOLDINGS INC p 874
2500 Halsey St Frnt 1, Bronx NY 10461
Tel (718) 409-2000 SIC 5621 5661 3171

▲ COACH INC p 330
10 Hudson Yards, New York NY 10001
Tel (212) 594-1850
SIC 3171 3172 2387 3143 3144

COACH STORES INC p 331
516 W 34th St Bsmt 5, New York NY 10001
Tel (212) 643-9727
SIC 3171 3161 3172 2387 5137 5099

KCP HOLDCO INC p 806
603 W 50th St, New York NY 10019
Tel (212) 265-1500
SIC 3143 3171 5661 5632 5611

KENNETH COLE PRODUCTIONS INC p 811
603 W 50th St, New York NY 10019
Tel (212) 265-1500
SIC 3143 3144 3171 5661 5632 5611

NINE WEST FOOTWEAR CORP p 1044
1411 Broadway Fl 20, New York NY 10018
Tel (800) 999-1877
SIC 3144 3171 5661 5632 5139

RENCO GROUP INC p 1223
1 Rockefeller Plz Fl 29, New York NY 10020
Tel (212) 541-6000
SIC 3312 3316 2514 2511 3171 3496

STUART WEITZMAN RETAIL STORES LLC p 1394
625 Madison Ave Frnt 3, New York NY 10022
Tel (212) 582-6388 SIC 7389 3171 5999

SIC 3172 Personal Leather Goods

RICO INDUSTRIES INC p 1233
7000 N Austin Ave, Niles IL 60714
Tel (312) 427-0313
SIC 5199 3172 2396 3993

RANDA ACCESSORIES LEATHER GOODS LLC p 1207
5600 N River Rd Ste 500, Rosemont IL 60018
Tel (847) 292-8300 SIC 5136 5948 3172

TUMI HOLDINGS INC p 1491
1001 Durham Ave Ste 1b, South Plainfield NJ 07080
Tel (908) 756-4400 SIC 3161 3172 5948

▲ COACH INC p 330
10 Hudson Yards, New York NY 10001
Tel (212) 594-1850
SIC 3171 3172 2387 3143 3144

COACH STORES INC p 331
516 W 34th St Bsmt 5, New York NY 10001
Tel (212) 643-9727
SIC 3171 3161 3172 2387 5137 5099

EXCELLED SHEEPSKIN & LEATHER COAT CORP p 516
1400 Brdwy Fl 31, New York NY 10018
Tel (212) 594-5843
SIC 2386 3172 2337 2311

ZIPPO MANUFACTURING CO INC p 1643
33 Barbour St, Bradford PA 16701
Tel (814) 368-2700
SIC 3914 3993 5172 3999 3421 3172

LEEDSWORLD INC p 852
400 Hunt Valley Rd, New Kensington PA 15068
Tel (724) 334-9000
SIC 5199 5111 5112 3172 3161 2394

POLYCONCEPT NORTH AMERICA INC p 1160
400 Hunt Valley Rd, New Kensington PA 15068
Tel (724) 334-9000
SIC 5199 5111 5112 3172 3161 2394

MARY KAY HOLDING CORP p 914
16251 Dallas Pkwy, Addison TX 75001
Tel (972) 687-6300
SIC 5963 3961 3172 4724

▲ TANDY BRANDS ACCESSORIES INC p 1424
501 N College St, Waxahachie TX 75165
Tel (214) 519-5200 SIC 3172 5961

SIC 3199 Leather Goods, NEC

ARIAT INTERNATIONAL INC p 108
3242 Whipple Rd, Union City CA 94587
Tel (510) 477-7000
SIC 3199 5139 5137 5136

SAFARILAND LLC p 1265
13386 International Pkwy, Jacksonville FL 32218
Tel (904) 741-5400 SIC 3842 3199

KLEIN TOOLS INC p 823
450 Bond St, Lincolnshire IL 60069
Tel (847) 821-5500 SIC 3423 3199

IPC INTERNATIONAL CORP p 763
10255 W Higgi, Rosemont IL 60018
Tel (847) 444-2000
SIC 7381 8742 2389 3199

UNIVERSAL TRIM INC p 1518
1451 E Lincoln Ave, Madison Heights MI 48071
Tel (248) 586-3300
SIC 3714 3199 3089 3429

■ AM RETAIL GROUP INC p 63
7401 Boone Ave N, Brooklyn Park MN 55428
Tel (763) 391-4000 SIC 3199

SIC 3211 Flat Glass

▲ PGT INC p 1140
1070 Technology Dr, North Venice FL 34275
Tel (941) 480-1600 SIC 3442 2431 3211

CWS HOLDING CO LLC p 404
1900 Sw 44th Ave, Ocala FL 34474
Tel (352) 368-6922 SIC 2431 3211

AGC AMERICA INC p 34
11175 Cicero Dr Ste 400, Alpharetta GA 30022
Tel (404) 446-4200
SIC 6719 3211 2869 5169 3229

AGC FLAT GLASS NORTH AMERICA INC p 34
11175 Cicero Dr Ste 400, Alpharetta GA 30022
Tel (404) 446-4200 SIC 3231 3211

GUARDIAN INDUSTRIES CORP p 645
2300 Harmon Rd, Auburn Hills MI 48326
Tel (248) 340-1800 SIC 3211

CARLEX GLASS OF INDIANA INC p 257
1209 E Big Beaver Rd, Troy MI 48083
Tel (586) 365-4900 SIC 3211

CARDINAL GLASS INDUSTRIES INC p 253
775 Pririe Ctr Dr Ste 200, Eden Prairie MN 55344
Tel (952) 229-2600 SIC 3231 3211

CHURCHILL COMPANIES p 305
333 S 7th St Ste 3100, Minneapolis MN 55402
Tel (612) 673-6700 SIC 3211 3824 5083

■ VIRACON INC p 1558
800 Park Dr, Owatonna MN 55060
Tel (507) 451-9555 SIC 3211

■ ERIE SCIENTIFIC LLC p 508
20 Post Rd, Portsmouth NH 03801
Tel (603) 430-6859
SIC 3231 3821 3229 3221 3211

EDMUND OPTICS INC p 478
101 E Gloucester Pike, Barrington NJ 08007
Tel (856) 547-3488 SIC 3211 5961

SCHOTT CORP p 1290
555 Taxter Rd Ste 470, Elmsford NY 10523
Tel (914) 831-2200
SIC 3211 3829 3221 3229

CRYSTAL WINDOW & DOOR SYSTEMS LTD p 397
3110 Whitestone Expy, Flushing NY 11354
Tel (718) 961-7300
SIC 5031 3442 3231 3211 2431 1751

PILKINGTON HOLDINGS INC p 1148
811 Madison Ave Fl 1, Toledo OH 43604
Tel (419) 247-3731 SIC 3211

PILKINGTON NORTH AMERICA INC p 1148
811 Madison Ave Fl 1, Toledo OH 43604
Tel (419) 247-4955 SIC 3211

■ BENSON INDUSTRIES INC p 173
1650 Nw Naito Pkwy # 250, Portland OR 97209
Tel (503) 226-7611
SIC 5031 1793 3231 3211

■TRACO DELAWARE INC p 1468
71 Progress Ave, Cranberry Township PA 16066
Tel (724) 776-7000
SIC 3442 3211 3444 3448 3354 7992

CONSOLIDATED GLASS HOLDINGS INC p 359
500 Grant Ave Ste 201, East Butler PA 16029
Tel (866) 412-6977
SIC 5039 3211 6719 1793

■ PITTSBURGH GLASS WORKS LLC p 1152
30 Isabella St Ste 500, Pittsburgh PA 15212
Tel (412) 995-6500 SIC 3211 5013

▲ PPG INDUSTRIES INC p 1166
1 Ppg Pl, Pittsburgh PA 15272
Tel (412) 434-3131
SIC 2851 3211 3231 3229 2812 2821

SCHOTT GEMTRON CORP p 1290
615 Highway 68, Sweetwater TN 37874
Tel (423) 337-3522 SIC 3211

SIC 3221 Glass Containers

PACIFIC VIAL MFG INC p 1106
2738 Supply Ave, Commerce CA 90040
Tel (323) 721-7004 SIC 3221

RENO JONES INC p 1224
2373 N Watney Way, Fairfield CA 94533
Tel (707) 422-4300 SIC 5199 5085 3221

GALLO GLASS CO p 590
605 S Santa Cruz Ave, Modesto CA 95354
Tel (209) 341-3710 SIC 3221

ANCHOR GLASS CONTAINER CORP p 89
401 E Jackson St Ste 1100, Tampa FL 33602
Tel (813) 884-0000 SIC 3221

■ SGD NORTH AMERICA INC p 1310
9141 Technology Dr, Covington GA 30014
Tel (770) 385-3800 SIC 3221

■ HEARTHMARK LLC p 678
9999 E 121st St, Fishers IN 46037
Tel (765) 557-3000 SIC 3221

ARDAGH GLASS INC p 106
1509 S Macedonia Ave, Muncie IN 47302
Tel (765) 741-7000 SIC 3221

■ ERIE SCIENTIFIC LLC p 508
20 Post Rd, Portsmouth NH 03801
Tel (603) 430-6859
SIC 3231 3821 3229 3221 3211

PIRAMAL GLASS - USA INC p 1151
329 Herrod Blvd, Dayton NJ 08810
Tel (856) 293-6400 SIC 3221

AMCOR PHARMACEUTICAL PACKAGING USA LLC p 66
625 Sharp St N, Millville NJ 08332
Tel (856) 327-1540 SIC 3221 3085

NIPRO PHARMAPACKAGING AMERICAS CORP p 1044
1200 N 10th St, Millville NJ 08332
Tel (856) 825-1400 SIC 3221

GERRESHEIMER GLASS INC p 609
537 Crystal Ave, Vineland NJ 08360
Tel (856) 692-3600 SIC 3221

SCHOTT CORP p 1290
555 Taxter Rd Ste 470, Elmsford NY 10523
Tel (914) 831-2200
SIC 3211 3829 3221 3229

LIDESTRI FOODS INC p 863
815 Whitney Rd W, Fairport NY 14450
Tel (585) 377-7700 SIC 3221 2033

SAINT GOBAIN GRAINS & POWDERS p 1269
6600 Walmore Rd, Niagara Falls NY 14304
Tel (716) 731-8200 SIC 3221 3269 2891

INTRAPAC INTERNATIONAL CORP p 760
136 Fairview Rd Ste 320, Mooresville NC 28117
Tel (704) 360-8910 SIC 3085 3221

ANCHOR HOCKING LLC p 89
519 N Pierce Ave, Lancaster OH 43130
Tel (740) 681-6478
SIC 3229 3089 3411 3221

GHP II LLC p 610
1115 W 5th Ave, Lancaster OH 43130
Tel (740) 687-2500
SIC 3229 3089 3411 3221

■ OWENS-BROCKWAY GLASS CONTAINER INC p 1100
1 Michael Owens Way, Perrysburg OH 43551
Tel (567) 336-8449 SIC 3221

■ OWENS-BROCKWAY PACKAGING INC p 1100
1 Michael Owens Way, Perrysburg OH 43551
Tel (567) 336-5000 SIC 3221

■ OWENS-ILLINOIS GROUP INC p 1100
1 Michael Owens Way, Perrysburg OH 43551
Tel (567) 336-5000 SIC 3221

▲ OWENS-ILLINOIS INC p 1100
1 Michael Owens Way, Perrysburg OH 43551
Tel (567) 336-5000 SIC 3221

■ BPREX PLASTIC PACKAGING INC p 206
1 Seagate Ste 10, Toledo OH 43604
Tel (419) 247-5000 SIC 3221 3089

CERTAINTEED CORP p 284
20 Moores Rd, Malvern PA 19355
Tel (610) 893-5000
SIC 3221 3292 3259 3084 3089 3432

SAINT-GOBAIN CORP p 1271
20 Moores Rd, Malvern PA 19355
Tel (610) 893-6000 SIC 2891 3269 3221

SAINT-GOBAIN DELAWARE CORP p 1271
750 E Swedesford Rd, Valley Forge PA 19482
Tel (610) 341-7000
SIC 3291 3269 2891 3296 3084 3221

VITRO PACKAGING LLC p 1563
13481 Resource, Laredo TX 78045
Tel (956) 717-4232 SIC 3221

SIC 3229 Pressed & Blown Glassware, NEC

TE CONNECTIVITY MOG INC p 1429
501 Oakside Ave, Redwood City CA 94063
Tel (650) 361-5292 SIC 3229

AURORA NETWORKS INC p 132
1764 Automation Pkwy, San Jose CA 95131
Tel (408) 428-9500 SIC 3229

ALLIANCE FIBER OPTIC PRODUCTS INC p 54
275 Gibraltar Dr, Sunnyvale CA 94089
Tel (408) 736-6900 SIC 3229 3661

TRANSITIONS OPTICAL INC p 1472
9251 Belcher Rd N, Pinellas Park FL 33782
Tel (727) 545-0400 SIC 3229 3851

AGC AMERICA INC p 34
11175 Cicero Dr Ste 400, Alpharetta GA 30022
Tel (404) 446-4200
SIC 6719 3211 2869 5169 3229

OFS BRIGHTWAVE LLC p 1076
2000 Northeast Expy, Norcross GA 30071
Tel (770) 798-3000 SIC 3357 3229

OFS FITEL LLC p 1076
2000 Northeast Expy, Norcross GA 30071
Tel (770) 798-2000 SIC 3229 3357

ALP LIGHTING & CEILING PRODUCTS INC p 60
6333 W Gross Point Rd, Niles IL 60714
Tel (773) 774-9550
SIC 3089 3354 5162 3496 3442 3229

HTS ACQUISITION INC p 715
915 Harger Rd, Oak Brook IL 60523
Tel (630) 368-0920 SIC 3646 3229 3645

WKI HOLDING CO INC p 1620
9525 Bryn Mawr Ave # 300, Rosemont IL 60018
Tel (847) 233-8600 SIC 3229 3469

WORLD KITCHEN LLC p 1625
9525 Bryn Mawr Ave # 300, Rosemont IL 60018
Tel (847) 233-8600
SIC 3229 3469 3365 3421 5719

KNAUF INSULATION INC p 824
1 Knauf Dr, Shelbyville IN 46176
Tel (317) 398-4434 SIC 3229

▲ IPG PHOTONICS CORP p 763
50 Old Webster Rd, Oxford MA 01540
Tel (508) 373-1100 SIC 3699 3229 3674

■APOGENT TECHNOLOGIES INC p 97
81 Wyman St, Waltham MA 02451
Tel (781) 622-1300 SIC 3821 3229 3843

■ ERIE SCIENTIFIC LLC p 508
20 Post Rd, Portsmouth NH 03801
Tel (603) 430-6859
SIC 3231 3821 3229 3221 3211

DURAND GLASS MANUFACTURING CO INC p 462
901 S Wade Blvd, Millville NJ 08332
Tel (856) 327-1850 SIC 3229 3269 5023

▲ CORNING INC p 371
1 Riverfront Plz, Corning NY 14831
Tel (607) 974-9000
SIC 3229 3357 3661 3674

■ CORNING INTERNATIONAL CORP p 371
1 Riverfront Plz, Corning NY 14831
Tel (607) 974-9000 SIC 3229 5945

■ CORNING VITRO CORP p 371
1 Riverfront Plz, Corning NY 14830
Tel (607) 974-8605 SIC 3229 3469

SCHOTT CORP p 1290
555 Taxter Rd Ste 470, Elmsford NY 10523
Tel (914) 831-2200
SIC 3211 3829 3221 3229

LIGHTING HOLDINGS INTERNATIONAL LLC p 865
4 Manhattanville Rd, Purchase NY 10577
Tel (845) 306-1850
SIC 3641 5719 5063 4225 3643 3229

■ PPG INDUSTRIES FIBER GLASS PRODUCTS INC p 1166
940 Washburn Switch Rd, Shelby NC 28150
Tel (704) 434-2261 SIC 3229

ANCHOR HOCKING LLC p 89
519 N Pierce Ave, Lancaster OH 43130
Tel (740) 681-6478
SIC 3229 3089 3411 3221

GHP II LLC p 610
1115 W 5th Ave, Lancaster OH 43130
Tel (740) 687-2500
SIC 3229 3089 3411 3221

■ LIBBEY GLASS INC p 861
300 Madison Ave Fl 4, Toledo OH 43604
Tel (419) 325-2100 SIC 3229 3231

▲ LIBBEY INC p 861
300 Madison Ave, Toledo OH 43604
Tel (419) 325-2100 SIC 3229 3262

▲ OWENS CORNING p 1100
1 Owens Corning Pkwy, Toledo OH 43659
Tel (419) 248-8000
SIC 3296 2952 3229 3089

■ OWENS CORNING SALES LLC p 1100
1 Owens Corning Pkwy, Toledo OH 43659
Tel (419) 248-8000
SIC 3296 2952 3229 3089 1761

LENOX HOLDINGS INC p 856
1414 Radcliffe St Fl 1, Bristol PA 19007
Tel (267) 525-7800
SIC 3229 3161 5719 5948

▲ PPG INDUSTRIES INC p 1166
1 Ppg Pl, Pittsburgh PA 15272
Tel (412) 434-3131
SIC 2851 3211 3231 3229 2812 2821

▲ II-VI INC p 731
375 Saxonburg Blvd, Saxonburg PA 16056
Tel (724) 352-4455
SIC 3827 3229 3674 3699

TE CONNECTIVITY SEACON PHOENIX INC p 1429
15 Gray Ln Ste 108, Ashaway RI 02804
Tel (401) 637-4952 SIC 3229

AFL TELECOMMUNICATIONS LLC p 33
170 Ridgeview Center Dr, Duncan SC 29334
Tel (864) 433-0333 SIC 3229 1731

BRIDGESTONE AMERICAS INC p 211
535 Marriott Dr, Nashville TN 37214
Tel (615) 937-1000
SIC 3011 3493 2952 2822 3229

LAMPLIGHT FARMS INC p 841
W140n4900 Lilly Rd, Menomonee Falls WI 53051
Tel (262) 781-9590
SIC 3648 3999 3229 2911

SIC 3231 Glass Prdts Made Of Purchased Glass

GKN AEROSPACE TRANSPARENCY SYSTEMS INC p 613
12122 Western Ave, Garden Grove CA 92841
Tel (714) 893-7531
SIC 3089 3231 3827 3728 3081 2821

AMERICAN BUILDING SUPPLY INC p 69
8360 Elder Creek Rd, Sacramento CA 95828
Tel (916) 503-4100 SIC 5031 3231

■ SIERRACIN/SYLMAR CORP p 1321
12780 San Fernando Rd, Sylmar CA 91342
Tel (818) 362-6711
SIC 3089 3812 3621 3231

■ HACH CO p 652
5600 Lindbergh Dr, Loveland CO 80538
Tel (970) 669-3050
SIC 3826 3823 3231 2819 2869

■ PGT INDUSTRIES INC p 1140
1070 Technology Dr, North Venice FL 34275
Tel (352) 335-5556 SIC 3442 2431 3231

AGC FLAT GLASS NORTH AMERICA INC p 34
11175 Cicero Dr Ste 400, Alpharetta GA 30022
Tel (404) 446-4200 SIC 3231 3211

GROTE INDUSTRIES INC p 641
2600 Lanier Dr, Madison IN 47250
Tel (812) 273-2121 SIC 3231 3647

GROTE INDUSTRIES LLC p 641
2600 Lanier Dr, Madison IN 47250
Tel (812) 265-8273 SIC 3647 3231

MURAKAMI MANUFACTURING USA INC p 1001
575 Watertower Byp, Campbellsville KY 42718
Tel (270) 469-3939 SIC 3231

MAGNA MIRRORS NORTH AMERICA LLC p 896
6151 Bancroft Ave Se, Alto MI 49302
Tel (616) 868-6122 SIC 3231 3442

MAGNA MIRRORS OF AMERICA INC p 896
5085 Kraft Ave Se, Grand Rapids MI 49512
Tel (616) 942-0163 SIC 3231 3647 3827

SMR AUTOMOTIVE MIRROR INTERNATIONAL USA INC p 1334
1855 Busha Hwy, Marysville MI 48040
Tel (810) 364-4141 SIC 3231

SMR AUTOMOTIVE SYSTEMS USA INC p 1334
1855 Busha Hwy, Marysville MI 48040
Tel (810) 364-4141 SIC 3231

SMR AUTOMOTIVE TECHNOLOGY HOLDINGS USA PARTNERS LLP p 1334
1855 Busha Hwy, Marysville MI 48040
Tel (810) 364-4141 SIC 3231

▲ GENTEX CORP p 604
600 N Centennial St, Zeeland MI 49464
Tel (616) 772-1800 SIC 3231 3714 3669

ANDERSEN CORP p 89
100 4th Ave N, Bayport MN 55003
Tel (651) 264-5150 SIC 2431 3231

CARDINAL GLASS INDUSTRIES INC p 253
775 Pririe Ctr Dr Ste 200, Eden Prairie MN 55344
Tel (952) 229-2600 SIC 3231 3211

▲ APOGEE ENTERPRISES INC p 97
4400 W 78th St Ste 520, Minneapolis MN 55435
Tel (952) 835-1874 SIC 3231

■ ERIE SCIENTIFIC LLC p 508
20 Post Rd, Portsmouth NH 03801
Tel (603) 430-6859
SIC 3231 3821 3229 3221 3211

KIMBLE CHASE LIFE SCIENCE AND RESEARCH PRODUCTS LLC p 818
1022 Spruce St, Vineland NJ 08360
Tel (865) 717-2600 SIC 3231

CRYSTAL WINDOW & DOOR SYSTEMS LTD p 397
3110 Whitestone Expy, Flushing NY 11354
Tel (718) 961-7300
SIC 5031 3442 3231 3211 2431 1751

KASSON & KELLER INC p 804
60 School St, Fonda NY 12068
Tel (518) 853-3421
SIC 3442 3089 1521 3231

TAYLOR MADE GROUP LLC p 1427
66 Kingsboro Ave, Gloversville NY 12078
Tel (518) 725-0681 SIC 3429 3231

GARDNER GLASS PRODUCTS INC p 592
301 Elkin Hwy, North Wilkesboro NC 28659
Tel (336) 651-9300 SIC 3231

SAFELITE GLASS CORP p 1266
7400 Safelite Way, Columbus OH 43235
Tel (614) 210-9000 SIC 3231

SAFELITE GROUP INC p 1266
7400 Safelite Way, Columbus OH 43235
Tel (614) 210-9000 SIC 7536 3231 6411

ANCHI INC p 89
1115 W 5th Ave, Lancaster OH 43130
Tel (740) 653-2527 SIC 3231

▲ COMMERCIAL VEHICLE GROUP INC p 345
7800 Walton Pkwy, New Albany OH 43054
Tel (614) 289-5360 SIC 3714 3231

■ LIBBEY GLASS INC p 861
300 Madison Ave Fl 4, Toledo OH 43604
Tel (419) 325-2100 SIC 3229 3231

■ BENSON INDUSTRIES INC p 173
1650 Nw Naito Pkwy # 250, Portland OR 97209
Tel (503) 226-7611
SIC 5031 1793 3231 3211

▲ DORMAN PRODUCTS INC p 451
3400 E Walnut St, Colmar PA 18915
Tel (215) 997-1800 SIC 3714 3231 3965

■ RB DISTRIBUTION INC p 1211
3400 E Walnut St, Colmar PA 18915
Tel (215) 997-1800 SIC 3714 3231

MCS INDUSTRIES INC p 932
2280 Newlins Mill Rd, Easton PA 18045
Tel (610) 253-6268
SIC 2499 3089 3499 3993 3231

■ NIAGARA HOLDINGS INC p 1042
300 Lindenwood Dr, Malvern PA 19355
Tel (610) 651-4200 SIC 2819 3231

POTTERS INDUSTRIES LLC p 1164
300 Lindenwood Dr, Malvern PA 19355
Tel (610) 651-4700 SIC 3231

PQ CORP p 1166
300 Lindenwood Dr, Malvern PA 19355
Tel (610) 651-4429 SIC 2819 3231

▲ PPG INDUSTRIES INC p 1166
1 Ppg Pl, Pittsburgh PA 15272
Tel (412) 434-3131
SIC 2851 3211 3231 3229 2812 2821

■ FERRO COLOR & GLASS CORP p 538
251 W Wylie Ave, Washington PA 15301
Tel (724) 223-5900 SIC 3231

SWAROVSKI NORTH AMERICA LIMITED p 1411
1 Kenney Dr, Cranston RI 02920
Tel (401) 463-6400 SIC 3961 5023 3231

SWAROVSKI US HOLDING LIMITED p 1411
1 Kenney Dr, Cranston RI 02920
Tel (401) 463-6400
SIC 3961 3231 5048 5099

■ JPS COMPOSITE MATERIALS CORP p 795
2200 S Murray Ave, Anderson SC 29624
Tel (864) 836-8011 SIC 3231

VVP HOLDINGS LLC p 1567
965 Ridge Lake Blvd # 300, Memphis TN 38120
Tel (901) 767-7111
SIC 5039 5013 1793 3231 3444 5719

CARLEX GLASS AMERICA LLC p 257
7200 Centennial Blvd, Nashville TN 37209
Tel (615) 350-7500 SIC 3231

MARVIN WINDOWS OF TENNESSEE INC p 914
101 Marvin Dr, Ripley TN 38063
Tel (731) 635-5190 SIC 2431 3231

■ CHASE SCIENTIFIC GLASS INC p 291
234 Cardiff Valley Rd, Rockwood TN 37854
Tel (865) 354-4206 SIC 3231

OLDCASTLE BUILDINGENVELOPE INC p 1082
5005 Lndn B Jnsn Fwy 10 Ste 1050, Dallas TX 75244
Tel (214) 273-3400 SIC 3231 5231

CONSOLIDATED GLASS & MIRROR CORP p 359
110 Jack Guynn Dr, Galax VA 24333
Tel (276) 236-5196 SIC 3231

BRENNER HOLDINGS INC p 210
2580 Broadway Ave Sw, Roanoke VA 24014
Tel (540) 981-1211
SIC 4953 5093 3341 3231

SIMONTON BUILDING PRODUCTS INC p 1325
5300 Briscoe Rd, Parkersburg WV 26105
Tel (304) 659-2851 SIC 3089 3442 3231

SIC 3241 Cement, Hydraulic

READY MIX USA LLC p 1213
2657 Ruffner Rd, Birmingham AL 35210
Tel (205) 967-5211 SIC 5211 3241

CEMEX CONSTRUCTION MATERIALS SOUTH LLC p 274
2088 E 20th St, Yuma AZ 85365
Tel (928) 343-4100 SIC 3241

LEHIGH SOUTHWEST CEMENT CO p 854
2300 Clayton Rd Ste 300, Concord CA 94520
Tel (972) 653-5500
SIC 3241 2891 5032 5211

NATIONAL CEMENT CO INC p 1010
15821 Ventura Blvd # 475, Encino CA 91436
Tel (818) 728-5200 SIC 3241 3273

CALPORTLAND CO p 243
2025 E Financial Way, Glendora CA 91741
Tel (626) 852-6200 SIC 3241 3273 5032

TAIHEIYO CEMENT USA INC p 1421
2025 E Fincl Way Ste 200, Glendora CA 91741
Tel (626) 852-6200 SIC 3241 3273

PAVESTONE LLC p 1122
3490 Piedmont Rd Ne # 1300, Atlanta GA 30305
Tel (404) 926-3167
SIC 3251 3241 3255 3272

QUIKRETE COMPANIES LLC p 1200
3490 Piedmont Rd Ne, Atlanta GA 30305
Tel (404) 634-9100
SIC 3272 3255 3251 3241

QUIKRETE HOLDINGS INC p 1200
3490 Piedmont Rd Ne # 1300, Atlanta GA 30305
Tel (404) 926-3167 SIC 3272 3241 3255

LAFARGE BUILDING MATERIALS INC p 837
8700 W Bryn Mawr Ave 300n, Chicago IL 60631
Tel (678) 746-2000
SIC 3241 3274 3273 3271

LAFARGE NORTH AMERICA INC p 837
8700 W Bryn Mawr Ave Ll, Chicago IL 60631
Tel (703) 480-3600
SIC 3241 3273 3272 3271 1442 2951

SOUTHFIELD CORP p 1351
8995 W 95th St, Palos Hills IL 60465
Tel (708) 344-1000
SIC 3273 1442 3241 4212 4213 5032

LONE STAR INDUSTRIES INC p 875
10401 N Meridian St # 400, Indianapolis IN 46290
Tel (317) 706-3314 SIC 3241 3273

▲ MONARCH CEMENT CO p 983
449 1200th St, Humboldt KS 66748
Tel (620) 473-2222 SIC 3241 3273

ASH GROVE CEMENT CO p 116
11011 Cody St Ste 300, Overland Park KS 66210
Tel (913) 451-8900
SIC 3241 3273 1422 3271

HOLCIM (US) INC p 700
6211 N Ann Arbor Rd, Dundee MI 48131
Tel (734) 529-4278 SIC 3241 3272

■ CONTINENTAL CEMENT CO LLC p 363
16100 Swingley Ridge Rd, Chesterfield MO 63017
Tel (636) 532-7440 SIC 3241 4953

MATERIAL PACKAGING CORP p 919
23018 S State Route 291, Harrisonville MO 64701
Tel (816) 380-4473 SIC 3241

BUZZI UNICEM USA INC p 230
100 Brodhead Rd Ste 230, Bethlehem PA 18017
Tel (610) 882-5000 SIC 3241

ESSROC CEMENT CORP p 510
3251 Bath Pike, Nazareth PA 18064
Tel (610) 837-6725 SIC 3241

ESSROC CORP p 511
3251 Bath Pike, Nazareth PA 18064
Tel (610) 837-6725 *SIC* 3241 5032 3273

CEMEX DE PUERTO RICO INC p 274
Km 2/7 Carr, Guaynabo PR 00968
Tel (787) 783-3000 *SIC* 3273 3241

▲ **EAGLE MATERIALS INC** p 468
3811 Turtle Creek Blvd # 1100, Dallas TX 75219
Tel (214) 432-2000 *SIC* 3241 3275 3273

■ **TEXAS INDUSTRIES INC** p 1443
1503 Lyndon B Johnson Fwy # 400, Dallas TX 75234
Tel (972) 647-6700
SIC 3241 3299 3281 3273

CEMEX CEMENT INC p 274
929 Gessner Rd Ste 1900, Houston TX 77024
Tel (713) 650-6200 *SIC* 3273 3241

LEHIGH CEMENT CO LLC p 853
300 E John Carpenter Fwy, Irving TX 75062
Tel (877) 534-4442 *SIC* 3241 3273 5032

CAPITOL AGGREGATES INC p 250
11551 Nacogdoches Rd, San Antonio TX 78217
Tel (210) 655-3010
SIC 3241 1442 1422 2951 4011

ZACHRY CONSOLIDATED LLC p 1640
527 Logwood Ave, San Antonio TX 78221
Tel (210) 871-2700
SIC 1611 1622 1623 1629 3241 1442

ZACHRY CONSTRUCTION & MATERIALS INC p 1640
2330 N Loop 1604 W, San Antonio TX 78248
Tel (210) 479-1027
SIC 1611 1622 1623 1629 1542 3241

GIANT CEMENT HOLDING INC p 610
1600 Duke St Ste 400, Alexandria VA 22314
Tel (571) 302-7150 *SIC* 3241 4953

TITAN AMERICA LLC p 1456
1151 Azalea Garden Rd, Norfolk VA 23502
Tel (757) 858-6500
SIC 3241 3273 3271 4213

SIC 3251 Brick & Structural Clay Tile

MORGAN ADVANCED CERAMICS INC p 988
2425 Whipple Rd, Hayward CA 94544
Tel (510) 491-1100 *SIC* 2899 3251 3264

PABCO BUILDING PRODUCTS LLC p 1103
10600 White Rock Rd # 100, Rancho Cordova CA 95670
Tel (510) 792-1577 *SIC* 3275 3251 3259

OLDCASTLE ARCHITECTURAL INC p 1081
900 Ashwood Pkwy Ste 600, Atlanta GA 30338
Tel (770) 804-3363 *SIC* 3251

PAVESTONE LLC p 1122
3490 Piedmont Rd Ne # 1300, Atlanta GA 30305
Tel (404) 926-3167
SIC 3251 3241 3255 3272

QUIKRETE COMPANIES LLC p 1200
3490 Piedmont Rd Ne, Atlanta GA 30305
Tel (404) 634-9100
SIC 3272 3255 3251 3241

BORAL BRICKS INC p 201
200 Mansell Ct E Ste 310, Roswell GA 30076
Tel (770) 645-4500 *SIC* 3251 5211 3271

BORAL INDUSTRIES INC p 201
200 Mansell Ct E Ste 310, Roswell GA 30076
Tel (770) 645-4500
SIC 3251 3272 3275 5032 3271 2899

FORTERRA BRICK LLC p 569
3820 Serr Rd, Corunna MI 48817
Tel (989) 743-3444 *SIC* 3251

FORTERRA BRICK LLC p 569
7400 Carmel Exec Park 2, Charlotte NC 28226
Tel (704) 341-8750 *SIC* 3251

PINE HALL BRICK CO INC p 1149
2701 Shorefair Dr, Winston Salem NC 27105
Tel (336) 721-7500 *SIC* 3251 5032

GLEN-GERY CORP p 614
1166 Spring St, Reading PA 19610
Tel (610) 374-4011 *SIC* 3251

■ **ACME BRICK CO** p 17
3024 Acme Brick Plz, Fort Worth TX 76109
Tel (817) 332-4101 *SIC* 3251 5032 5211

■ **JUSTIN INDUSTRIES INC** p 798
3024 Acme Brick Plz, Fort Worth TX 76109
Tel (817) 332-4101
SIC 3251 3271 5211 5032

SIC 3253 Ceramic Tile

■ **DAL-TILE SERVICES INC** p 409
160 S Industrial Blvd, Calhoun GA 30701
Tel (706) 629-7721 *SIC* 3253

▲ **MOHAWK INDUSTRIES INC** p 982
160 S Industrial Blvd, Calhoun GA 30701
Tel (706) 629-7721 *SIC* 2273 3253

CURRAN GROUP INC p 402
286 Memorial Ct, Crystal Lake IL 60014
Tel (815) 455-5100 *SIC* 1799 3253 1611

FLORIDA TILE INC p 559
998 Governors Ln Ste 300, Lexington KY 40513
Tel (859) 219-5200 *SIC* 3253

MANNINGTON MILLS INC p 902
75 Mannington Mills Rd, Salem NJ 08079
Tel (856) 935-3000
SIC 3996 3253 2273 2435

BONSAL AMERICAN INC p 200
625 Griffith Rd Ste 100, Charlotte NC 28217
Tel (704) 525-1621
SIC 3272 1442 3253 2899

TARKETT USA INC p 1425
30000 Aurora Rd, Solon OH 44139
Tel (440) 543-8916 *SIC* 3253

FLORIM USA INC p 560
300 International Blvd, Clarksville TN 37040
Tel (931) 553-7548 *SIC* 3253

CROSSVILLE INC p 394
346 Sweeney Dr, Crossville TN 38555
Tel (931) 484-2110 *SIC* 3253

■ **AMERICAN MARAZZI TILE INC** p 75
7834 C F Hawn Fwy, Dallas TX 75217
Tel (972) 232-3801 *SIC* 3253

■ **DAL-TILE CORP** p 409
7834 C F Hawn Fwy, Dallas TX 75217
Tel (214) 398-1411 *SIC* 3253

■ **DAL-TILE GROUP INC** p 409
7834 C F Hawn Fwy, Dallas TX 75217
Tel (214) 398-1411 *SIC* 3253

INTERCERAMIC INC p 751
2333 S Jupiter Rd, Garland TX 75041
Tel (214) 503-4967 *SIC* 3253 5032

EVERGREEN ENTERPRISES INC p 514
5915 Midlothian Tpke, Richmond VA 23225
Tel (804) 231-1800
SIC 3253 2399 5193 5999

SIC 3255 Clay Refractories

RHI REFRACTORIES HOLDING CO p 1231
1105 N Market St Ste 1300, Wilmington DE 19801
Tel (302) 655-6497
SIC 3297 3255 1459 3546 3272 3589

OLDCASTLE INC p 1082
900 Ashwood Pkwy Ste 600, Atlanta GA 30338
Tel (770) 804-3363
SIC 3273 3272 3271 3255

PAVESTONE LLC p 1122
3490 Piedmont Rd Ne # 1300, Atlanta GA 30305
Tel (404) 926-3167
SIC 3251 3241 3255 3272

QUIKRETE COMPANIES LLC p 1200
3490 Piedmont Rd Ne, Atlanta GA 30305
Tel (404) 634-9100
SIC 3272 3255 3251 3241

QUIKRETE HOLDINGS INC p 1200
3490 Piedmont Rd Ne # 1300, Atlanta GA 30305
Tel (404) 926-3167 *SIC* 3272 3241 3255

THERMAL CERAMICS INC p 1447
2102 Old Savannah Rd, Augusta GA 30906
Tel (706) 796-4200
SIC 3299 3255 5085 3296 3264 3053

CORHART REFRACTORIES CORP p 370
10300 Ormsby Park Pl # 450, Louisville KY 40223
Tel (502) 423-6324 *SIC* 3255 3297

TWIN CITY CONCRETE PRODUCTS CO INC p 1495
2025 Centre Pointe Blvd # 300, Mendota Heights MN 55120
Tel (651) 688-9116
SIC 5032 3273 3255 1442

SAINT-GOBAIN STRUCTURAL CERAMICS p 1271
23 Acheson Dr, Niagara Falls NY 14303
Tel (716) 278-6233 *SIC* 3255

MORGANITE INDUSTRIES INC p 989
4000 Westchase Blvd # 170, Raleigh NC 27607
Tel (919) 821-1253
SIC 3674 3255 3699 3264 3299 3624

GLOBAL INDUSTRIAL TECHNOLOGIES INC p 616
1305 Chrrington Pkwy Moon, Coraopolis PA 15108
Tel (412) 375-6600
SIC 3297 3255 1459 3546 3272 3589

HARBISON-WALKER REFRACTORIES CO p 659
1305 Cherrington Pkwy, Coraopolis PA 15108
Tel (412) 375-6600 *SIC* 3255 3297

NORTH AMERICAN REFRACTORIES CO p 1050
1305 Cherrington Pkwy # 100, Coraopolis PA 15108
Tel (412) 375-6600 *SIC* 3297 3255

RESCO PRODUCTS INC p 1226
1 Robinson Plz Ste 300, Pittsburgh PA 15205
Tel (412) 494-4491
SIC 3297 3255 1455 1499 5032

▲ **CARPENTER TECHNOLOGY CORP** p 260
2 Meridian Blvd, Wyomissing PA 19610
Tel (610) 208-2000
SIC 3312 3443 3255 3316 3315

CHARLES BLALOCK & SONS INC p 289
409 Robert Henderson Rd, Sevierville TN 37862
Tel (865) 429-5902
SIC 1611 7353 3271 3255 2951

SIC 3259 Structural Clay Prdts, NEC

MCP INDUSTRIES INC p 932
708 S Temescal St Ste 101, Corona CA 92879
Tel (951) 736-1881 *SIC* 3069 3259 3089

BORAL ROOFING LLC p 201
7575 Irvine Center Dr # 100, Irvine CA 92618
Tel (949) 756-1605 *SIC* 1761 3272 3259

PABCO BUILDING PRODUCTS LLC p 1103
10600 White Rock Rd # 100, Rancho Cordova CA 95670
Tel (510) 792-1577 *SIC* 3275 3251 3259

■ **COLLOID ENVIRONMENTAL TECHNOLOGIES CO LLC** p 337
2870 Forbs Ave, Hoffman Estates IL 60192
Tel (847) 851-1500 *SIC* 3259 2899

CERTAINTEED CORP p 284
20 Moores Rd, Malvern PA 19355
Tel (610) 893-5000
SIC 3221 3292 3259 3084 3089 3432

SIC 3261 China Plumbing Fixtures & Fittings

TOTO USA HOLDINGS INC p 1463
1155 Southern Rd, Morrow GA 30260
Tel (770) 960-8531 *SIC* 3088 3431 3261

GERBER PLUMBING FIXTURES LLC p 608
2500 Intrntonale Pkwy, Woodridge IL 60517
Tel (630) 679-1420 *SIC* 3261

GLOBE UNION GROUP INC p 618
2500 Internationale Pkwy, Woodridge IL 60517
Tel (630) 679-1420 *SIC* 3261 3432 7699

AS AMERICA INC p 115
1 Centennial Ave Ste 101, Piscataway NJ 08854
Tel (732) 980-3000 *SIC* 3261 3432

CRANE PLUMBING LLC p 389
41 Cairns Rd, Mansfield OH 44903
Tel (419) 522-4211 *SIC* 3261 3431 3088

MANSFIELD PLUMBING PRODUCTS LLC p 903
150 E 1st St, Perrysville OH 44864
Tel (419) 938-5211
SIC 3261 3463 3088 3431 3432 5074

KENNEY MANUFACTURING CO p 811
1000 Jefferson Blvd, Warwick RI 02886
Tel (401) 739-2200
SIC 2591 3261 2511 3699 3499 2541

▲ **SUMMER INFANT INC** p 1398
1275 Park East Dr, Woonsocket RI 02895
Tel (401) 671-6550
SIC 2514 2399 3842 3261

KOHLER CO p 826
444 Highland Dr, Kohler WI 53044
Tel (920) 457-4441
SIC 3431 3432 3261 2511 2521 3519

■ **RBS GLOBAL INC** p 1211
4701 W Greenfield Ave, Milwaukee WI 53214
Tel (414) 643-3000
SIC 3562 3566 3568 3272 3261

SIC 3262 China, Table & Kitchen Articles

▲ **LIBBEY INC** p 861
300 Madison Ave, Toledo OH 43604
Tel (419) 325-2100 *SIC* 3229 3262

HOMER LAUGHLIN CHINA CO p 704
672 Fiesta Dr, Newell WV 26050
Tel (304) 387-1300 *SIC* 3262 5719

SIC 3263 Earthenware, Whiteware, Table & Kitchen Articles

▲ **CARLISLE COMPANIES INC** p 257
16430 N Scottsdale Rd, Scottsdale AZ 85254
Tel (704) 501-1100
SIC 2952 3714 3312 3357 3263

CHINA LENOX INC p 301
1414 Radcliffe St, Bristol PA 19007
Tel (267) 525-7800 *SIC* 3263

SIC 3264 Porcelain Electrical Splys

■ **MATERION CERAMICS INC** p 919
6100 S Tucson Blvd, Tucson AZ 85706
Tel (520) 741-3411 *SIC* 3351 3264

MORGAN ADVANCED CERAMICS INC p 988
2425 Whipple Rd, Hayward CA 94544
Tel (510) 491-1100 *SIC* 2899 3251 3264

MARIN CLEAN ENERGY p 906
1125 Tamalpais Ave, San Rafael CA 94901
Tel (415) 464-6028 *SIC* 3264

ALTA PROPERTIES INC p 61
879 Ward Dr, Santa Barbara CA 93111
Tel (805) 967-0171
SIC 3264 3699 3823 3679

COORSTEK LLC p 368
16000 Table Mountain Pkwy, Golden CO 80403
Tel (303) 271-7000
SIC 3264 3053 3081 3082 3545

NGK NORTH AMERICA INC p 1041
1105 N Market St Ste 1300, Wilmington DE 19801
Tel (302) 654-1344
SIC 3714 5013 3264 5063

NGK SPARK PLUGS (USA) HOLDING INC p 1041
1011 Centre Rd, Wilmington DE 19805
Tel (302) 288-0131 *SIC* 3643 3264

THERMAL CERAMICS INC p 1447
2102 Old Savannah Rd, Augusta GA 30906
Tel (706) 796-4200
SIC 3299 3255 5085 3296 3264 3053

LECO CORP p 851
3000 Lakeview Ave, Saint Joseph MI 49085
Tel (269) 983-5531
SIC 4493 3821 3826 3825 3823 3264

NGK SPARK PLUGS (USA) INC p 1041
46929 Magellan, Wixom MI 48393
Tel (248) 926-6900 *SIC* 3643 3264

HITACHI METALS AMERICA LTD p 697
2 Manhattanville Rd # 301, Purchase NY 10577
Tel (914) 694-9200
SIC 3264 3577 3365 5051 3321 3559

■ **ARNOLD MAGNETIC TECHNOLOGIES CORP** p 112
770 Linden Ave, Rochester NY 14625
Tel (585) 385-9010 *SIC* 3264 3499

MORGANITE INDUSTRIES INC p 989
4000 Westchase Blvd # 170, Raleigh NC 27607
Tel (919) 821-1253
SIC 3674 3255 3699 3264 3299 3624

■ **MATERION BRUSH INC** p 919
6070 Parkland Blvd Ste 1, Mayfield Heights OH 44124
Tel (216) 486-4200
SIC 3351 3356 3264 3339 3341 3674

■ **SPS TECHNOLOGIES LLC** p 1362
301 Highland Ave, Jenkintown PA 19046
Tel (215) 572-3000
SIC 3452 3423 3499 3264 3679 3341

SIC 3269 Pottery Prdts, NEC

DURAND GLASS MANUFACTURING CO INC p 462
901 S Wade Blvd, Millville NJ 08332
Tel (856) 327-1850 *SIC* 3229 3269 5023

SAINT GOBAIN GRAINS & POWDERS p 1269
6600 Walmore Rd, Niagara Falls NY 14304
Tel (716) 731-8200 *SIC* 3221 3269 2891

DARAMIC LLC p 412
11430 N Cmnity Hse Rd # 350, Charlotte NC 28277
Tel (704) 587-8599 *SIC* 3069 2499 3269

■ **CARLISLE FOODSERVICE PRODUCTS INC** p 257
4711 E Hefner Rd, Oklahoma City OK 73131
Tel (405) 528-3011 *SIC* 3089 3269

SAINT-GOBAIN CORP p 1271
20 Moores Rd, Malvern PA 19355
Tel (610) 893-6000 *SIC* 2891 3269 3221

SAINT-GOBAIN DELAWARE CORP p 1271
750 E Swedesford Rd, Valley Forge PA 19482
Tel (610) 341-7000
SIC 3291 3269 2891 3296 3084 3221

■ **PFALTZGRAFF FACTORY STORES INC** p 1140
140 E Market St, York PA 17401
Tel (717) 848-5500 *SIC* 3269 5719

SIC 3271 Concrete Block & Brick

PACIFIC COAST BUILDING PRODUCTS INC p 1104
10600 White Rock Rd # 100, Rancho Cordova CA 95670
Tel (916) 631-6500
SIC 3275 3271 5031 1761 2952 2426

GRANITE ROCK CO p 631
350 Technology Dr, Watsonville CA 95076
Tel (831) 768-2000
SIC 1442 3273 5032 2951 1611 3271

DEVCON INTERNATIONAL CORP p 433
595 S Federal Hwy Ste 600, Boca Raton FL 33432
Tel (954) 926-5200
SIC 3699 3273 3281 3271 2951 5032

CEMEX MATERIALS LLC p 274
1501 Belvedere Rd, West Palm Beach FL 33406
Tel (561) 833-5555
SIC 3271 3273 3272 1422

OLDCASTLE INC p 1082
900 Ashwood Pkwy Ste 600, Atlanta GA 30338
Tel (770) 804-3363
SIC 3273 3272 3271 3255

BORAL BRICKS INC p 201
200 Mansell Ct E Ste 310, Roswell GA 30076
Tel (770) 645-4500 *SIC* 3251 5211 3271

BORAL INDUSTRIES INC p 201
200 Mansell Ct E Ste 310, Roswell GA 30076
Tel (770) 645-4500
SIC 3251 3272 3275 5032 3271 2899

LAFARGE BUILDING MATERIALS INC p 837
8700 W Bryn Mawr Ave 300n, Chicago IL 60631
Tel (678) 746-2000
SIC 3241 3274 3273 3271

LAFARGE NORTH AMERICA INC p 837
8700 W Bryn Mawr Ave Ll, Chicago IL 60631
Tel (703) 480-3600
SIC 3241 3273 3272 3271 1442 2951

IRVING MATERIALS INC p 765
8032 N State Road 9, Greenfield IN 46140
Tel (317) 326-3101
SIC 3273 3271 5032 2951

ASH GROVE CEMENT CO p 116
11011 Cody St Ste 300, Overland Park KS 66210
Tel (913) 451-8900
SIC 3241 3273 1422 3271

HINKLE CONTRACTING CORP p 695
395 N Middletown Rd, Paris KY 40361
Tel (859) 987-3670
SIC 1611 1422 3273 3272 3271 2951

CONSUMERS CONCRETE CORP p 362
3508 S Sprinkle Rd, Kalamazoo MI 49001
Tel (269) 342-0136 *SIC* 3273 3271 5032

NEBCO INC p 1023
1815 Y St, Lincoln NE 68508
Tel (402) 434-1212
SIC 5999 3273 3272 3271 1442 4013

LYMAN-RICHEY CORP p 887
4315 Cuming St, Omaha NE 68131
Tel (402) 556-3600
SIC 3273 1442 3271 5211 5032

FORT MILLER SERVICE CORP p 569
688 Wilbur Ave, Greenwich NY 12834
Tel (518) 695-5000
SIC 3272 3271 5211 1799

MARTIN LIMESTONE INC p 912
3580 Division Hwy, East Earl PA 17519
Tel (717) 335-4500
SIC 3273 3271 1611 1422 8741 5211

CHARLES BLALOCK & SONS INC p 289
409 Robert Henderson Rd, Sevierville TN 37862
Tel (865) 429-5902
SIC 1611 7353 3271 3255 2951

TRNLWB LLC p 1483
1112 E Cpeland Rd Ste 500, Arlington TX 76011
Tel (800) 581-3117 *SIC* 3271

■ **TXI OPERATIONS LP** p 1495
1341 W Mockingbird Ln 700w, Dallas TX 75247
Tel (972) 647-6700
SIC 3273 3271 3272 1442

■ **JUSTIN INDUSTRIES INC** p 798
3024 Acme Brick Plz, Fort Worth TX 76109
Tel (817) 332-4101
SIC 3251 3271 5211 5032

CEMEX CONSTRUCTION MATERIALS SOUTH LLC p 274
920 Mmrial Cy Way Ste 100, Houston TX 77024
Tel (713) 650-6200
SIC 3271 3273 3272 1422

CEMEX INC p 274
929 Gessner Rd Ste 1900, Houston TX 77024
Tel (713) 650-6200
SIC 3273 3271 3272 5032

RMC USA INC p 1239
920 Memorial City Way, Houston TX 77024
Tel (713) 650-6200
SIC 3273 3272 3271 5031

▲ **HEADWATERS INC** p 673
10701 S River Front Pkwy # 300, South Jordan UT 84095
Tel (801) 984-9400
SIC 3272 3271 3281 2952

SUNROC CORP p 1404
3657 S River Rd, St George UT 84790
Tel (435) 634-2200
SIC 5031 3273 5032 3271 1442

EAGLE CORP p 468
1020 Harris St, Charlottesville VA 22903
Tel (434) 971-2686 *SIC* 3272 3271 3273

TARMAC MID-ATLANTIC INC p 1425
1151 Azalea Garden Rd, Norfolk VA 23502
Tel (757) 858-6500
SIC 3273 1442 3272 3271

TITAN AMERICA LLC p 1456
1151 Azalea Garden Rd, Norfolk VA 23502
Tel (757) 858-6500
SIC 3241 3273 3271 4213

JF ALLEN CO INC p 785
U.S 33 W Red Rock Rd, Buckhannon WV 26201
Tel (304) 472-8890
SIC 3271 1611 3273 3281 2951

COUNTY MATERIALS CORP p 375
205 North St, Marathon WI 54448
Tel (715) 443-2434
SIC 3271 5211 3273 3272 1442

SIC 3272 Concrete Prdts

■VALMONT NEWMARK INC p 1542
2 Perimeter Park S 475w, Birmingham AL 35243
Tel (205) 968-7200 *SIC* 3272 1731 3317

▲VULCAN MATERIALS CO p 1567
1200 Urban Center Dr, Vestavia AL 35242
Tel (205) 298-3000
SIC 1422 1423 2951 1442 3273 3272

APAC-CENTRAL INC p 95
755 E Millsap Rd, Fayetteville AR 72703
Tel (417) 226-4833 *SIC* 3272 1611

BOND MANUFACTURING CO INC p 200
1700 W 4th St, Antioch CA 94509
Tel (925) 252-1135 *SIC* 5083 3272

BASALITE CONCRETE PRODUCTS LLC p 158
605 Industrial Way, Dixon CA 95620
Tel (707) 678-1901 *SIC* 3272

BORAL ROOFING LLC p 201
7575 Irvine Center Dr # 100, Irvine CA 92618
Tel (949) 756-1605 *SIC* 1761 3272 3259

A & A STEPPING STONE MFG INC p 4
10291 Ophir Rd, Newcastle CA 95658
Tel (530) 885-7481 *SIC* 5211 3272

■AMERON INTERNATIONAL CORP p 84
245 S Los Robles Ave, Pasadena CA 91101
Tel (626) 683-4000
SIC 3272 3317 3273 1442 3084

■ELDORADO STONE LLC p 484
1370 Grand Ave Bldg B, San Marcos CA 92078
Tel (800) 925-1491 *SIC* 3272

CLARK - PACIFIC CORP p 322
1980 S River Rd, West Sacramento CA 95691
Tel (916) 371-0305 *SIC* 3272 5032

LANE CONSTRUCTION CORP p 843
90 Fieldstone Ct, Cheshire CT 06410
Tel (203) 235-3351
SIC 1622 1611 1629 3272 5032

LANE INDUSTRIES INC p 843
90 Fieldstone Ct, Cheshire CT 06410
Tel (203) 235-3351
SIC 1629 1611 5032 3272 1622

RHI REFRACTORIES HOLDING CO p 1231
1105 N Market St Ste 1300, Wilmington DE 19801
Tel (302) 655-6497
SIC 3297 3255 1459 3546 3272 3589

■METALS USA HOLDINGS CORP p 952
2400 E Coml Blvd Ste 905, Fort Lauderdale FL 33308
Tel (954) 202-4000 *SIC* 5051 3272 3354

GATE PETROLEUM CO p 593
9540 San Jose Blvd, Jacksonville FL 32257
Tel (904) 730-3470
SIC 5541 3272 5411 7997

GATE PRECAST CO p 593
9540 San Jose Blvd, Jacksonville FL 32257
Tel (904) 732-7668 *SIC* 3272

HASKELL CO p 667
111 Riverside Ave, Jacksonville FL 32202
Tel (904) 791-4500
SIC 1541 1542 1522 1623 8712 3272

HASKELL CO INC p 667
111 Riverside Ave, Jacksonville FL 32202
Tel (904) 791-4500
SIC 1541 1542 1522 1623 8712 3272

CEMEX CONSTRUCTION MATERIALS ATLANTIC LLC p 274
1501 Belvedere Rd, West Palm Beach FL 33406
Tel (561) 833-5555 *SIC* 3272

CEMEX CONSTRUCTION MATERIALS PACIFIC LLC p 274
1501 Belvedere Rd, West Palm Beach FL 33406
Tel (561) 833-5555 *SIC* 3272

CEMEX MATERIALS LLC p 274
1501 Belvedere Rd, West Palm Beach FL 33406
Tel (561) 833-5555
SIC 3271 3273 3272 1422

ARGOS USA LLC p 107
3015 Windward Plz, Alpharetta GA 30005
Tel (678) 368-4300 *SIC* 3272

ARGOS USA LLC p 107
3015 Windward Plz Ste 300, Alpharetta GA 30005
Tel (678) 368-4300 *SIC* 3272 5032

CRH AMERICA INC p 392
900 Ashwood Pkwy Ste 600, Atlanta GA 30338
Tel (770) 804-3363 *SIC* 3272

INTERFACE FLOORING SYSTEMS INC p 752
2859 Paces Ferry Rd Se, Atlanta GA 30339
Tel (800) 336-0225 *SIC* 3272 1771 3999

OLDCASTLE INC p 1082
900 Ashwood Pkwy Ste 600, Atlanta GA 30338
Tel (770) 804-3363
SIC 3273 3272 3271 3255

OLDCASTLE MATERIALS INC p 1082
900 Ashwood Pkwy Ste 700, Atlanta GA 30338
Tel (770) 522-5600
SIC 3272 1622 1611 2951 5032

PAVESTONE LLC p 1122
3490 Piedmont Rd Ne # 1300, Atlanta GA 30305
Tel (404) 926-3167
SIC 3251 3241 3255 3272

QUIKRETE COMPANIES LLC p 1200
3490 Piedmont Rd Ne, Atlanta GA 30305
Tel (404) 634-9100
SIC 3272 3255 3251 3241

QUIKRETE HOLDINGS INC p 1200
3490 Piedmont Rd Ne # 1300, Atlanta GA 30305
Tel (404) 926-3167 *SIC* 3272 3241 3255

CONCRETE CO p 355
1030 1st Ave, Columbus GA 31901
Tel (706) 256-5700 *SIC* 1442 3272

FOLEY PRODUCTS CO p 563
1030 1st Ave, Columbus GA 31901
Tel (706) 563-7882 *SIC* 3272

STANDARD CONCRETE PRODUCTS INC p 1376
945 Broadway Ste 300, Columbus GA 31901
Tel (706) 322-3274 *SIC* 3272

DIVERSITECH CORP p 444
6650 Sugarloaf Pkwy # 100, Duluth GA 30097
Tel (678) 542-3600 *SIC* 3272

CORESLAB STRUCTURES (ATLANTA) INC p 370
1655 Noahs Ark Rd, Jonesboro GA 30236
Tel (770) 471-1150 *SIC* 3272 1771

BORAL INDUSTRIES INC p 201
200 Mansell Ct E Ste 310, Roswell GA 30076
Tel (770) 645-4500
SIC 3251 3272 3275 5032 3271 2899

ATLANTIC WOOD INDUSTRIES INC p 127
405 E Perry St, Savannah GA 31401
Tel (912) 966-7008 *SIC* 2491 3272

GRACE PACIFIC LLC p 628
949 Kamokila Blvd Ste 200, Kapolei HI 96707
Tel (808) 674-8383 *SIC* 1611 1429 3272

LAFARGE NORTH AMERICA INC p 837
8700 W Bryn Mawr Ave Ll, Chicago IL 60631
Tel (703) 480-3600
SIC 3241 3273 3272 3271 1442 2951

ELMHURST-CHICAGO STONE CO p 489
400 W 1st St, Elmhurst IL 60126
Tel (630) 832-4000 *SIC* 1442 3273 3272

FORTERRA PRESSURE PIPE INC p 569
4416 Prairie Hill Rd, South Beloit IL 61080
Tel (815) 389-4800 *SIC* 3272 3317

RASMUSSEN GROUP INC p 1209
5550 Ne 22nd St, Des Moines IA 50313
Tel (515) 266-5173 *SIC* 1622 1611 3272

ASH GROVE MATERIALS CORP p 117
11011 Cody St Ste 300, Overland Park KS 66210
Tel (913) 345-2030
SIC 3273 3272 1411 7389 4212

WILBERT FUNERAL SERVICES INC p 1608
10965 Granada Ln Ste 300, Overland Park KS 66211
Tel (913) 345-2120 *SIC* 3272

HINKLE CONTRACTING CORP p 695
395 N Middletown Rd, Paris KY 40361
Tel (859) 987-3670
SIC 1611 1422 3273 3272 3271 2951

FIBREBOND CORP p 540
1300 Davenport Dr, Minden LA 71055
Tel (318) 377-1030 *SIC* 3272

PETRICCA INDUSTRIES INC p 1139
550 Cheshire Rd, Pittsfield MA 01201
Tel (413) 499-1441
SIC 1611 1623 3273 3272 1442

HOLCIM (US) INC p 700
6211 N Ann Arbor Rd, Dundee MI 48131
Tel (734) 529-4278 *SIC* 3241 3272

CHAMPION INC p 287
180 Traders Mine Rd, Iron Mountain MI 49801
Tel (906) 779-2300
SIC 8741 1542 5063 5082 3273 3272

STRESS CON INDUSTRIES INC p 1393
50500 Design Ln, Shelby Township MI 48315
Tel (586) 731-1628 *SIC* 3272

AJAX PAVING INDUSTRIES INC p 41
1957 Crooks Rd A, Troy MI 48084
Tel (248) 244-3300
SIC 1611 2951 3273 3272

WELLS CONCRETE PRODUCTS CO p 1589
210 Inspiration Ln, Albany MN 56307
Tel (800) 658-7049 *SIC* 3272 3273

■MCNEILUS TRUCK AND MANUFACTURING INC p 932
524 County Rd 34 E, Dodge Center MN 55927
Tel (614) 868-0760
SIC 3713 3531 3537 3272

CRETEX COMPANIES INC p 392
311 Lowell Ave Nw, Elk River MN 55330
Tel (763) 441-2121 *SIC* 3272 3089 3841

FABCON COMPANIES LLC p 523
6111 Highway 13 W, Savage MN 55378
Tel (952) 890-4444 *SIC* 3272 1771

FABCON INC p 523
6111 Highway 13 W, Savage MN 55378
Tel (952) 890-4444 *SIC* 3272 1771

PLY GEM SIDING GROUP p 1157
2600 Grand Blvd, Kansas City MO 64108
Tel (816) 426-8200 *SIC* 3272

FRED WEBER INC p 576
2320 Creve Coeur Mill Rd, Maryland Heights MO 63043
Tel (314) 344-0070
SIC 1611 1442 3272 1622 1542

NEBCO INC p 1023
1815 Y St, Lincoln NE 68508
Tel (402) 434-1212
SIC 5999 3273 3272 3271 1442 4013

JENSEN ENTERPRISES INC p 782
825 Steneri Way, Sparks NV 89431
Tel (775) 352-2700 *SIC* 3272

KUIKEN BROTHERS CO INC p 831
6-02 Fair Lawn Ave, Fair Lawn NJ 07410
Tel (201) 796-2082 *SIC* 5211 5031 3272

TRAP ROCK INDUSTRIES INC p 1473
460 River Rd, Kingston NJ 08528
Tel (609) 924-0300
SIC 3273 3272 1429 1611

CONSTRUCTION SPECIALTIES INC p 361
3 Werner Way Ste 100, Lebanon NJ 08833
Tel (908) 236-0800
SIC 3446 3354 3443 3272 3585

SIKA CORP p 1322
201 Polito Ave, Lyndhurst NJ 07071
Tel (201) 933-8800
SIC 2891 2899 2851 2821 3272

HANSON AGGREGATES WRP INC p 659
1333 Campus Pkwy, Wall Township NJ 07753
Tel (972) 653-5500
SIC 3281 3272 2951 1442

FORT MILLER GROUP INC p 569
688 Wilbur Ave, Greenwich NY 12834
Tel (518) 695-5000 *SIC* 3272 3441

FORT MILLER SERVICE CORP p 569
688 Wilbur Ave, Greenwich NY 12834
Tel (518) 695-5000
SIC 3272 3271 5211 1799

SOLVATION INC p 1339
885 3rd Ave Fl 34, New York NY 10022
Tel (212) 888-5500 *SIC* 6153 1611 3272

APOLLO MANAGEMENT V LP p 97
1 Manhattanville Rd # 201, Purchase NY 10577
Tel (914) 467-6510 *SIC* 5051 3272 3354

CALLANAN INDUSTRIES INC p 242
1245 Kings Rd Ste 1, Schenectady NY 12303
Tel (518) 374-2222 *SIC* 3272 2951

WILBERT INC p 1608
2001 Oaks Pkwy, Belmont NC 28012
Tel (704) 247-3850 *SIC* 5162 3272

BONSAL AMERICAN INC p 200
625 Griffith Rd Ste 100, Charlotte NC 28217
Tel (704) 525-1621
SIC 3272 1442 3253 2899

HOG SLAT INC p 699
206 Fayetteville St, Newton Grove NC 28366
Tel (866) 464-7528
SIC 1542 3272 3523 0213

AMESBURY ACQUISITION HOLDINGS (2) INC p 84
2061 Sherrill Dr, Statesville NC 28625
Tel (704) 924-8586 *SIC* 3272

AMERICAN SPRING WIRE CORP p 79
26300 Miles Rd, Bedford Heights OH 44146
Tel (216) 292-4620
SIC 3272 3315 3316 3339 3624

MACK INDUSTRIES INC p 892
1321 Industrial Pkwy N # 500, Brunswick OH 44212
Tel (330) 460-7005 *SIC* 3272 1771

PRESTRESS SERVICES INDUSTRIES LLC p 1173
250 N Hartford Ave, Columbus OH 43222
Tel (859) 299-0461 *SIC* 3272

HASKELL LEMON CONSTRUCTION CO p 667
3800 Sw 10th St, Oklahoma City OK 73108
Tel (405) 947-6069
SIC 5032 1611 3272 2951

GLOBAL INDUSTRIAL TECHNOLOGIES INC p 616
1305 Chrrington Pkwy Moon, Coraopolis PA 15108
Tel (412) 375-6600
SIC 3297 3255 1459 3546 3272 3589

HIGH CONCRETE GROUP LLC p 690
125 Denver Rd, Denver PA 17517
Tel (717) 336-9300 *SIC* 1791 3272

HIGH INDUSTRIES INC p 690
1853 William Penn Way, Lancaster PA 17601
Tel (717) 293-4444
SIC 1791 3272 5051 3441

HARBISONWALKER INTERNATIONAL INC p 659
1305 Cherrington Pkwy # 100, Moon Township PA 15108
Tel (412) 375-6600 *SIC* 3297 3272 1459

▲L B FOSTER CO p 833
415 Holiday Dr Ste 1, Pittsburgh PA 15220
Tel (412) 928-3417 *SIC* 3312 3272 3317

■CPG INTERNATIONAL INC p 387
888 N Keyser Ave, Scranton PA 18504
Tel (570) 558-8000 *SIC* 3089 3272

METROMONT CORP p 955
2802 White Horse Rd, Greenville SC 29611
Tel (864) 222-6770 *SIC* 3272

TINDALL CORP p 1455
3076 N Blackstock Rd, Spartanburg SC 29301
Tel (864) 576-3230 *SIC* 3272

ALAMO CONCRETE PRODUCTS LTD p 44
6055 W Green Mountain Rd, Austin TX 78744
Tel (512) 444-2464 *SIC* 3272

JD ABRAMS LP p 780
5811 Trade Center Dr # 1, Austin TX 78744
Tel (512) 322-4000
SIC 1611 1622 1629 3272

■TXI OPERATIONS LP p 1495
1341 W Mockingbird Ln 700w, Dallas TX 75247
Tel (972) 647-6700
SIC 3273 3271 3272 1442

JOBE MATERIALS LP p 787
1150 Southview Dr Ste A, El Paso TX 79928
Tel (915) 298-9900 *SIC* 3272

▲US CONCRETE INC p 1531
331 N Main St, Euless TX 76039
Tel (817) 835-4105 *SIC* 3273 3272

HANSON PRESSURE PIPE INC p 659
1003 Macarthur Blvd, Grand Prairie TX 75050
Tel (972) 262-3600 *SIC* 3317 3272 3999

CEMEX CONSTRUCTION MATERIALS SOUTH LLC p 274
920 Mmrial Cy Way Ste 100, Houston TX 77024
Tel (713) 650-6200
SIC 3271 3273 3272 1422

CEMEX INC p 274
929 Gessner Rd Ste 1900, Houston TX 77024
Tel (713) 650-6200
SIC 3273 3271 3272 5032

▲QUANEX BUILDING PRODUCTS CORP p 1198
1800 West Loop S Ste 1500, Houston TX 77027
Tel (713) 961-4600 *SIC* 3272 3353

RMC USA INC p 1239
920 Memorial City Way, Houston TX 77024
Tel (713) 650-6200
SIC 3273 3272 3271 5031

■FORTERRA INC p 569
511 E John Carpenter Fwy, Irving TX 75062
Tel (469) 284-8678 *SIC* 3272 3569

FORTERRA PIPE & PRECAST LLC p 569
511 E John Carpenter Fwy, Irving TX 75062
Tel (469) 458-7973 *SIC* 3272 1771

HANSON LEHIGH INC p 659
300 E John Carpenter Fwy, Irving TX 75062
Tel (972) 653-5500
SIC 1442 1422 1423 3297 3273 3272

▲HEADWATERS INC p 673
10701 S River Front Pkwy # 300, South Jordan UT 84095
Tel (801) 984-9400
SIC 3272 3271 3281 2952

CONCRETE PIPE & PRECAST LLC p 355
11352 Virginia Precast Rd, Ashland VA 23005
Tel (804) 798-6068 *SIC* 3272

EAGLE CORP p 468
1020 Harris St, Charlottesville VA 22903
Tel (434) 971-2686 *SIC* 3272 3271 3273

TARMAC MID-ATLANTIC INC p 1425
1151 Azalea Garden Rd, Norfolk VA 23502
Tel (757) 858-6500
SIC 3273 1442 3272 3271

SKANSKA USA CIVIL SOUTHEAST INC p 1329
295 Bendix Rd Ste 400, Virginia Beach VA 23452
Tel (757) 420-4140
SIC 1622 1629 3272 1541

OLDCASTLE PRECAST INC p 1082
1002 15th St Sw Ste 110, Auburn WA 98001
Tel (253) 833-2777 *SIC* 3272 3446

NORTHWEST CASCADE INC p 1059
10412 John Bananola Way E, Puyallup WA 98374
Tel (253) 848-2371
SIC 1623 7359 7699 3272 1711

CPM DEVELOPMENT CORP p 387
5111 E Broadway Ave, Spokane Valley WA 99212
Tel (509) 534-6221 *SIC* 3273 1771 3272

GREER INDUSTRIES INC p 639
570 Canyon Rd, Morgantown WV 26508
Tel (304) 296-2549
SIC 3316 3272 2951 1422 3274 1446

COUNTY MATERIALS CORP p 375
205 North St, Marathon WI 54448
Tel (715) 443-2434
SIC 3271 5211 3273 3272 1442

BRADLEY CORP p 206
W142n9101 Fountain Blvd, Menomonee Falls WI 53051
Tel (262) 251-6000 *SIC* 3431 3272

■RBS GLOBAL INC p 1211
4701 W Greenfield Ave, Milwaukee WI 53214
Tel (414) 643-3000
SIC 3562 3566 3568 3272 3261

▲NEENAH ENTERPRISES INC p 1024
2121 Brooks Ave, Neenah WI 54956
Tel (920) 725-7000 *SIC* 3272 3312

WAUSAU TILE INC p 1583
9001 Business Highway 51, Rothschild WI 54474
Tel (715) 359-3121 *SIC* 3272

SPANCRETE GROUP INC p 1354
N16W 23415 Stone Rdge Dr St N 16, Waukesha WI 53188
Tel (414) 290-9000 *SIC* 3272 3531

SIC 3273 Ready-Mixed Concrete

DUNN INVESTMENT CO p 461
3900 Messer Airport Hwy, Birmingham AL 35222
Tel (205) 592-3866 *SIC* 1542 1611 3273

■LEGACY VULCAN LLC p 852
1200 Urban Center Dr, Shoal Creek AL 35242
Tel (205) 298-3000
SIC 1422 1423 1442 2951 3273

■LEGACY VULCAN LLC p 852
1200 Urban Center Dr, Vestavia AL 35242
Tel (205) 298-3000
SIC 1422 1423 1442 2951 3273

▲VULCAN MATERIALS CO p 1567
1200 Urban Center Dr, Vestavia AL 35242
Tel (205) 298-3000
SIC 1422 1423 2951 1442 3273 3272

CEMEX CORP p 274
4646 E Van Buren St # 250, Phoenix AZ 85008
Tel (602) 416-2600 *SIC* 5032 3273

PINE BLUFF SAND AND GRAVEL CO p 1148
1501 Heartwood St, White Hall AR 71602
Tel (870) 534-7120
SIC 2951 3273 1442 5032 1629

ROBERTSONS READY MIX LTD A CALIFORNIA LIMITED PARTNERSHIP p 1242
200 S Main St Ste 200, Corona CA 92882
Tel (951) 493-6500
SIC 3273 3531 5032 2951 1442

NATIONAL CEMENT CO INC p 1010
15821 Ventura Blvd # 475, Encino CA 91436
Tel (818) 728-5200 *SIC* 3241 3273

SUPERIOR READY MIX CONCRETE LP p 1407
1508 Mission Rd, Escondido CA 92029
Tel (760) 745-0556 *SIC* 3273 1611 5032

■CALMAT CO p 242
500 N Brand Blvd Ste 500, Glendale CA 91203
Tel (818) 553-8821
SIC 2951 1442 1429 3273 6512 6552

CALPORTLAND CO p 243
2025 E Financial Way, Glendora CA 91741
Tel (626) 852-6200 *SIC* 3241 3273 5032

TAIHEIYO CEMENT USA INC p 1421
2025 E Fincl Way Ste 200, Glendora CA 91741
Tel (626) 852-6200 *SIC* 3241 3273

BASIC RESOURCES INC p 158
928 12th St Ste 700, Modesto CA 95354
Tel (209) 521-9771
SIC 1611 3273 2951 3532 3531

■AMERON INTERNATIONAL CORP p 84
245 S Los Robles Ave, Pasadena CA 91101
Tel (626) 683-4000
SIC 3272 3317 3273 1442 3084

A TEICHERT & SON INC p 6
3500 American River Dr, Sacramento CA 95864
Tel (916) 484-3011
SIC 5032 3273 1611 1442 1521

TEICHERT INC p 1433
3500 American River Dr, Sacramento CA 95864
Tel (916) 484-3011
SIC 3273 5032 1611 1442 1521 5039

J F SHEA CO INC p 771
655 Brea Canyon Rd, Walnut CA 91789
Tel (909) 594-9500 *SIC* 3273

GRANITE ROCK CO p 631
350 Technology Dr, Watsonville CA 95076
Tel (831) 768-2000
SIC 1442 3273 5032 2951 1611 3271

OLDCASTLE SW GROUP INC p 1082
2273 River Rd, Grand Junction CO 81505
Tel (970) 243-4900 *SIC* 1611 3273 5032

LAFARGE WEST INC p 837
10170 Church Ranch Way # 200, Westminster CO 80021
Tel (303) 657-4355 *SIC* 5032 1611 3273

TILCON CONNECTICUT INC p 1453
642 Black Rock Ave, New Britain CT 06052
Tel (860) 224-6010
SIC 5032 1611 3273 2951

TILCON INC p 1453
301 Hartford Ave, Newington CT 06111
Tel (860) 223-3651
SIC 1611 5032 3273 2951

DEVCON INTERNATIONAL CORP p 433
595 S Federal Hwy Ste 500, Boca Raton FL 33432
Tel (954) 926-5200
SIC 3699 3273 3281 3271 2951 5032

CEMEX MATERIALS LLC p 274
1501 Belvedere Rd, West Palm Beach FL 33406
Tel (561) 833-5555
SIC 3271 3273 3272 1422

ARGOS READY MIX (SOUTH CENTRAL) CORP p 107
3015 Wndward Pl Dr Ste 30, Alpharetta GA 30005
Tel (678) 368-4300 *SIC* 3273

OLDCASTLE INC p 1082
900 Ashwood Pkwy Ste 600, Atlanta GA 30338
Tel (770) 804-3363
SIC 3273 3272 3271 3255

THOMAS CONCRETE INDUSTRIES INC p 1448
2500 Cumberland Pkwy Se # 200, Atlanta GA 30339
Tel (770) 431-3300 *SIC* 3273 5032

THOMAS CONCRETE OF GEORGIA INC p 1448
2500 Cumbrld Pkwy Se 20 Ste 200, Atlanta GA 30339
Tel (770) 969-8545 *SIC* 3273

VCNA PRAIRIE INC p 1545
7601 W 79th St Ste 1, Bridgeview IL 60455
Tel (708) 458-0400 *SIC* 3273

▲ CONTINENTAL MATERIALS CORP p 363
440 S La Salle St # 3100, Chicago IL 60605
Tel (312) 541-7200 *SIC* 3585 3273 5031

LAFARGE BUILDING MATERIALS INC p 837
8700 W Bryn Mawr Ave 300n, Chicago IL 60631
Tel (678) 746-2000
SIC 3241 3274 3273 3271

LAFARGE NORTH AMERICA INC p 837
8700 W Bryn Mawr Ave Ll, Chicago IL 60631
Tel (703) 480-3600
SIC 3241 3273 3272 3271 1442 2951

ELMHURST-CHICAGO STONE CO p 489
400 W 1st St, Elmhurst IL 60126
Tel (630) 832-4000 *SIC* 1442 3273 3272

COUNTRY STONE INC p 375
6300 75th Ave Ste A, Milan IL 61264
Tel (309) 787-1744
SIC 2499 2875 3273 3281

OZINGA BROS INC p 1102
19001 Old Lagrange Rd # 30, Mokena IL 60448
Tel (708) 326-4200 *SIC* 3273 5032

SOUTHFIELD CORP p 1351
8995 W 95th St, Palos Hills IL 60465
Tel (708) 344-1000
SIC 3273 1442 3241 4212 4213 5032

IRVING MATERIALS INC p 765
8032 N State Road 9, Greenfield IN 46140
Tel (317) 326-3101
SIC 3273 3271 5032 2951

LONE STAR INDUSTRIES INC p 875
10401 N Meridian St # 400, Indianapolis IN 46290
Tel (317) 706-3314 *SIC* 3241 3273

MULZER CRUSHED STONE INC p 1000
534 Mozart St, Tell City IN 47586
Tel (812) 547-7921
SIC 1422 3273 5191 5085

MANATTS INC p 900
1775 Old 6 Rd, Brooklyn IA 52211
Tel (641) 522-9206
SIC 1611 1442 2951 3273

▲ MONARCH CEMENT CO p 983
449 1200th St, Humboldt KS 66748
Tel (620) 473-2222 *SIC* 3241 3273

ASH GROVE CEMENT CO p 116
11011 Cody St Ste 300, Overland Park KS 66210
Tel (913) 451-8900
SIC 3241 3273 1422 3271

ASH GROVE MATERIALS CORP p 117
11011 Cody St Ste 300, Overland Park KS 66210
Tel (913) 345-2030
SIC 3273 3272 1411 7389 4212

IMI SOUTH LLC p 734
1440 Selinda Ave, Louisville KY 40213
Tel (502) 456-6930 *SIC* 3273

WALKER CO OF KENTUCKY INC p 1573
105 Apperson Hts, Mount Sterling KY 40353
Tel (859) 498-0092
SIC 1611 2951 1542 3273 1422

YAGER MATERIALS LLC p 1633
5001 Highway 2830, Owensboro KY 42303
Tel (270) 926-0893
SIC 1442 1422 1611 3273 4491 3731

HARPER INDUSTRIES INC p 663
960 N Hc Mathis Dr, Paducah KY 42001
Tel (270) 442-2753
SIC 3273 1711 1611 1542

HINKLE CONTRACTING CORP p 695
395 N Middletown Rd, Paris KY 40361
Tel (859) 987-3670
SIC 1611 1422 3273 3272 3271 2951

PORT AGGREGATES INC p 1161
314 N Main St, Jennings LA 70546
Tel (337) 656-3224 *SIC* 5032 3273

LAFARGE MID-ATLANTIC LLC p 837
300 E Joppa Rd Ste 200, Baltimore MD 21286
Tel (410) 847-9445 *SIC* 3273 1422

CHANEY ENTERPRISES LIMITED PARTNERSHIP p 288
2410 Evergreen Rd Ste 201, Gambrills MD 21054
Tel (410) 451-0197
SIC 3273 1442 5032 3429

BOSTON SAND & GRAVEL CO INC p 203
100 N Washington St Fl 2, Boston MA 02114
Tel (617) 227-9000 *SIC* 3273 1442

PETRICCA INDUSTRIES INC p 1139
550 Cheshire Rd, Pittsfield MA 01201
Tel (413) 499-1441
SIC 1611 1623 3273 3272 1442

AGGREGATE INDUSTRIES p 34
6211 N Ann Arbor Rd, Dundee MI 48131
Tel (734) 529-5876
SIC 3273 2951 1442 1411 1771 5211

CHAMPION INC p 287
180 Traders Mine Rd, Iron Mountain MI 49801
Tel (906) 779-2300
SIC 8741 1542 5063 5082 3273 3272

CONSUMERS CONCRETE CORP p 362
3508 S Sprinkle Rd, Kalamazoo MI 49001
Tel (269) 342-0136 *SIC* 3273 3271 5032

AJAX PAVING INDUSTRIES INC p 41
1957 Crooks Rd A, Troy MI 48084
Tel (248) 244-3300
SIC 1611 2951 3273 3272

WELLS CONCRETE PRODUCTS CO p 1589
210 Inspiration Ln, Albany MN 56307
Tel (800) 658-7049 *SIC* 3272 3273

CEMSTONE PRODUCTS CO p 274
2025 Centr Poin Blvd Ste 300, Mendota Heights MN 55120
Tel (651) 688-9292 *SIC* 3273 5032 1442

TWIN CITY CONCRETE PRODUCTS CO INC p 1495
2025 Centre Pointe Blvd # 300, Mendota Heights MN 55120
Tel (651) 688-9116
SIC 5032 3273 3255 1442

■ KNIFE RIVER CORP - NORTH CENTRAL p 824
4787 Shadowwood Dr Ne, Sauk Rapids MN 56379
Tel (320) 251-9472
SIC 1611 1442 3273 2951

MMC MATERIALS INC p 979
1052 Highland Colony Pkwy # 201, Ridgeland MS 39157
Tel (601) 898-4000 *SIC* 3273

OFTEDAL CONSTRUCTION INC p 1076
434 Highway 59 N 59n, Miles City MT 59301
Tel (406) 232-5911 *SIC* 1629 3273 1611

MITCHELLS OILFIELD SERVICE INC p 977
409 N Central Ave, Sidney MT 59270
Tel (406) 482-4927 *SIC* 1389 3273

PAULSEN INC p 1122
1116 E Highway 30, Cozad NE 69130
Tel (308) 784-3333 *SIC* 1611 1542 3273

NEBCO INC p 1023
1815 Y St, Lincoln NE 68508
Tel (402) 434-1212
SIC 5999 3273 3272 3271 1442 4013

LYMAN-RICHEY CORP p 887
4315 Cuming St, Omaha NE 68131
Tel (402) 556-3600
SIC 3273 1442 3271 5211 5032

TRAP ROCK INDUSTRIES INC p 1473
460 River Rd, Kingston NJ 08528
Tel (609) 924-0300
SIC 3273 3272 1429 1611

DALRYMPLE HOLDING CORP p 410
2105 S Broadway, Pine City NY 14871
Tel (607) 737-6200
SIC 3273 1611 1442 1622 3281

CHANDLER CONCRETE INC p 288
1006 S Church St, Burlington NC 27215
Tel (336) 272-6127 *SIC* 3273

CAROLINA SUNROCK LLC p 259
1001 W B St, Butner NC 27509
Tel (919) 575-4502
SIC 1429 3273 2951 1411

CONCRETE SUPPLY HOLDINGS INC p 355
3823 Raleigh St, Charlotte NC 28206
Tel (704) 372-2930 *SIC* 3273

ARGOS READY MIX (CAROLINAS) CORP p 107
3610 Bush St, Raleigh NC 27609
Tel (919) 790-1520 *SIC* 3273

SUNROCK GROUP HOLDINGS CORP p 1404
200 Horizon Dr Ste 100, Raleigh NC 27615
Tel (919) 747-6400
SIC 1429 3273 2951 1411

B V HEDRICK GRAVEL & SAND CO p 142
120 1/2 N Church St, Salisbury NC 28144
Tel (704) 633-5982
SIC 1442 7359 6512 3273 1541 1542

S T WOOTEN CORP p 1263
3801 Black Creek Rd Se, Wilson NC 27893
Tel (252) 637-4294 *SIC* 1611 3273 1623

■ KNIFE RIVER CORP p 824
1150 W Century Ave, Bismarck ND 58503
Tel (701) 530-1400 *SIC* 1442 3273 1221

STRATA CORP p 1392
1600 N 48th St, Grand Forks ND 58203
Tel (701) 775-4205
SIC 1611 3273 1442 5032

HILLTOP BASIC RESOURCES INC p 694
1 W 4th St Ste 1100, Cincinnati OH 45202
Tel (513) 651-5000 *SIC* 1442 3273

ERNST ENTERPRISES INC p 508
3361 Successful Way, Dayton OH 45414
Tel (937) 233-5555 *SIC* 3273

NATIONAL LIME AND STONE CO p 1014
551 Lake Cascade Pkwy, Findlay OH 45840
Tel (419) 422-4341
SIC 1422 1442 3273 1423 1499

DOLESE BROS CO p 448
20 Nw 13th St, Oklahoma City OK 73103
Tel (405) 235-2311 *SIC* 3273 1422 1442

EVANS & ASSOCIATES ENTERPRISES INC p 513
3320 N 14th St, Ponca City OK 74601
Tel (580) 765-6693
SIC 5032 2951 1442 1611 3273 1311

■ KNIFE RIVER CORP - NORTHWEST p 824
32260 Old Highway 34, Tangent OR 97389
Tel (541) 928-6491 *SIC* 1611 3273

HEMPT BROS INC p 682
205 Creek Rd, Camp Hill PA 17011
Tel (717) 774-2911
SIC 1611 3273 2951 1442 0212

MARTIN LIMESTONE INC p 912
3580 Division Hwy, East Earl PA 17519
Tel (717) 335-4500
SIC 3273 3271 1611 1422 8741 5211

PENNSY SUPPLY INC p 1130
1001 Paxton St, Harrisburg PA 17104
Tel (717) 233-4511
SIC 1422 2951 3273 4212 5032

BERKS PRODUCTS CORP p 175
167 Berks Products Dr, Leesport PA 19533
Tel (610) 374-5131
SIC 5031 3273 5983 5172 2439 1711

ESSROC CORP p 511
3251 Bath Pike, Nazareth PA 18064
Tel (610) 837-6725 *SIC* 3241 5032 3273

EASTERN INDUSTRIES INC p 472
3724 Crescent Ct W 200, Whitehall PA 18052
Tel (610) 866-0932 *SIC* 5032 3273 1611

CEMEX DE PUERTO RICO INC p 274
Km 2/7 Carr, Guaynabo PR 00968
Tel (787) 783-3000 *SIC* 3273 3241

PETE LIEN & SONS INC p 1138
3401 Universal Dr, Rapid City SD 57702
Tel (605) 342-7224
SIC 3273 3441 1422 3274

SUMMERS-TAYLOR INC p 1398
300 W Elk Ave, Elizabethton TN 37643
Tel (423) 543-3181 *SIC* 1611 1794 3273

APAC-ATLANTIC INC p 95
4817 Rutledge Pike, Knoxville TN 37914
Tel (865) 983-3100
SIC 5032 3531 3273 2951 1611

LATTIMORE MATERIALS CO LP p 846
15900 Dooley Rd, Addison TX 75001
Tel (972) 221-4646 *SIC* 3273 1422 1442

TRANSIT MIX CONCRETE & MATERIALS CO p 1472
850 Pine St, Beaumont TX 77701
Tel (409) 835-4934 *SIC* 3273

■ ALBERTA INVESTMENTS INC p 46
1445 Mac Arthur Dr Ste 13, Carrollton TX 75007
Tel (972) 242-4550 *SIC* 3273

CUSTOM CRETE INC p 403
2624 Joe Field Rd, Dallas TX 75229
Tel (972) 243-4466 *SIC* 5032 3273

▲ EAGLE MATERIALS INC p 468
3811 Turtle Creek Blvd # 1100, Dallas TX 75219
Tel (214) 432-2000 *SIC* 3241 3275 3273

■ TEXAS INDUSTRIES INC p 1443
1503 Lyndon B Johnson Fwy # 400, Dallas TX 75234
Tel (972) 647-6700
SIC 3241 3299 3281 3273

■ TXI OPERATIONS LP p 1495
1341 W Mockingbird Ln 700w, Dallas TX 75247
Tel (972) 647-6700
SIC 3273 3271 3272 1442

CEMEX EL PASO INC p 274
1 Mckelligon Canyon Rd, El Paso TX 79930
Tel (915) 565-4681
SIC 3273 2951 5032 1442

▲ US CONCRETE INC p 1531
331 N Main St, Euless TX 76039
Tel (817) 835-4105 *SIC* 3273 3272

TRINITY MATERIALS INC p 1481
401 N Interstate Hwy 45, Ferris TX 75125
Tel (972) 544-5900 *SIC* 3273

ARGOS USA CORP p 107
757 N Eldridge Pkwy # 525, Houston TX 77079
Tel (281) 759-7392 *SIC* 3273

CAMPBELL CONCRETE & MATERIALS LP p 245
16155 Park Row Ste 120, Houston TX 77084
Tel (281) 592-5201 *SIC* 3273

CEMEX CEMENT INC p 274
929 Gessner Rd Ste 1900, Houston TX 77024
Tel (713) 650-6200 *SIC* 3273 3241

CEMEX CONSTRUCTION MATERIALS LP p 274
929 Gessner Rd Ste 1900, Houston TX 77024
Tel (713) 650-6200 *SIC* 3273

CEMEX CONSTRUCTION MATERIALS SOUTH LLC p 274
920 Mmrial Cy Way Ste 100, Houston TX 77024
Tel (713) 650-6200
SIC 3271 3273 3272 1422

CEMEX INC p 274
929 Gessner Rd Ste 1900, Houston TX 77024
Tel (713) 650-6200
SIC 3273 3271 3272 5032

RMC USA INC p 1239
920 Memorial City Way, Houston TX 77024
Tel (713) 650-6200
SIC 3273 3272 3271 5031

HANSON AGGREGATES LLC p 658
8505 Freport Pkwy Ste 500, Irving TX 75063
Tel (469) 417-1200 *SIC* 3273 2951 5032

HANSON LEHIGH INC p 659
300 E John Carpenter Fwy, Irving TX 75062
Tel (972) 653-5500
SIC 1442 1422 1423 3297 3273 3272

LEHIGH CEMENT CO LLC p 853
300 E John Carpenter Fwy, Irving TX 75062
Tel (877) 534-4442 *SIC* 3241 3273 5032

INGRAM READYMIX INC p 743
3580 Farm Market 482, New Braunfels TX 78132
Tel (830) 625-9156 *SIC* 3273

■ MARTIN MARIETTA MATERIALS SOUTHWEST INC p 912
5710 W Hausman Rd Ste 121, San Antonio TX 78249
Tel (210) 208-4400
SIC 1422 3273 2951 3274 1442

STAKER & PARSON COMPANIES p 1374
2350 S 1900 W Ste 100, Ogden UT 84401
Tel (801) 298-7500
SIC 1611 5032 3273 4212 2951 1771

GRAYMONT INC p 632
301 S 700 E 3950, Salt Lake City UT 84102
Tel (801) 262-3942 *SIC* 1429 2951 3273

SUNROC CORP p 1404
3657 S River Rd, St George UT 84790
Tel (435) 634-2200
SIC 5031 3273 5032 3271 1442

EAGLE CORP p 468
1020 Harris St, Charlottesville VA 22903
Tel (434) 971-2686 *SIC* 3272 3271 3273

TARMAC MID-ATLANTIC INC p 1425
1151 Azalea Garden Rd, Norfolk VA 23502
Tel (757) 858-6500
SIC 3273 1442 3272 3271

TITAN AMERICA LLC p 1456
1151 Azalea Garden Rd, Norfolk VA 23502
Tel (757) 858-6500
SIC 3241 3273 3271 4213

TITAN FLORIDA LLC p 1456
1151 Azalea Garden Rd, Norfolk VA 23502
Tel (757) 858-2095 *SIC* 3273

MILES SAND & GRAVEL CO p 969
400 Valley Ave Ne, Puyallup WA 98372
Tel (253) 833-3705 *SIC* 3273 5032

CADMAN INC p 236
7554 185th Ave Ne Ste 100, Redmond WA 98052
Tel (425) 867-1234 *SIC* 3273

GARY MERLINO CONSTRUCTION CO INC p 593
9125 10th Ave S, Seattle WA 98108
Tel (206) 763-9552 *SIC* 1611 1623 3273

CPM DEVELOPMENT CORP p 387
5111 E Broadway Ave, Spokane Valley WA 99212
Tel (509) 534-6221 *SIC* 3273 1771 3272

JF ALLEN CO INC p 785
U.S 33 W Red Rock Rd, Buckhannon WV 26201
Tel (304) 472-8890
SIC 3271 1611 3273 3281 2951

MCC INC p 926
2600 N Roemer Rd, Appleton WI 54911
Tel (920) 749-3360 *SIC* 3273 1442 1611

COUNTY MATERIALS CORP p 375
205 North St, Marathon WI 54448
Tel (715) 443-2434
SIC 3271 5211 3273 3272 1442

SIC 3274 Lime

LAFARGE BUILDING MATERIALS INC p 837
8700 W Bryn Mawr Ave 300n, Chicago IL 60631
Tel (678) 746-2000
SIC 3241 3274 3273 3271

MISSISSIPPI LIME CO p 975
3870 S Lindbergh Blvd # 200, Saint Louis MO 63127
Tel (314) 543-6300
SIC 3274 2819 2879 1422

▲ MINERALS TECHNOLOGIES INC p 973
622 3rd Ave Fl 38, New York NY 10017
Tel (212) 878-1800
SIC 3295 2819 3274 1411 3281 5032

DAKOTA COAL CO p 409
1717 E Interstate Ave, Bismarck ND 58503
Tel (701) 223-0441 *SIC* 6519 7353 3274

CARMEUSE LIME INC p 258
11 Stanwix St Fl 21, Pittsburgh PA 15222
Tel (412) 995-5500 *SIC* 1422 3274

MAGNESITA REFRACTORIES CO p 896
425 S Salem Church Rd, York PA 17408
Tel (717) 792-3611 *SIC* 3297 3274 1422

PETE LIEN & SONS INC p 1138
3401 Universal Dr, Rapid City SD 57702
Tel (605) 342-7224
SIC 3273 3441 1422 3274

■ UNITED STATES LIME & MINERALS INC p 1513
5429 Lbj Fwy Ste 230, Dallas TX 75240
Tel (972) 991-8400 *SIC* 1422 3274 6289

KDM HOLDING INC p 807
3700 Hulen St, Fort Worth TX 76107
Tel (817) 732-8164 *SIC* 3274

LHOIST NORTH AMERICA INC p 861
3700 Hulen St, Fort Worth TX 76107
Tel (817) 732-8164 *SIC* 3274

LIME HOLDING INC p 866
3700 Hulen St, Fort Worth TX 76107
Tel (817) 732-8164 *SIC* 3274

■ MARTIN MARIETTA MATERIALS SOUTHWEST INC p 912
5710 W Hausman Rd Ste 121, San Antonio TX 78249
Tel (210) 208-4400
SIC 1422 3273 2951 3274 1442

GREER INDUSTRIES INC p 639
570 Canyon Rd, Morgantown WV 26508
Tel (304) 296-2549
SIC 3316 3272 2951 1422 3274 1446

GRAYMONT (WI) LLC p 632
800 Hill Ave, Superior WI 54880
Tel (715) 392-5146 *SIC* 3274

SIC 3275 Gypsum Prdts

JAMES HARDIE TRANSITION CO INC p 776
26300 La Alameda Ste 400, Mission Viejo CA 92691
Tel (949) 348-1800
SIC 3275 3523 3494 5072

PABCO BUILDING PRODUCTS LLC p 1103
10600 White Rock Rd # 100, Rancho Cordova CA 95670
Tel (510) 792-1577 *SIC* 3275 3251 3259

PACIFIC COAST BUILDING PRODUCTS INC p 1104
10600 White Rock Rd # 100, Rancho Cordova CA 95670
Tel (916) 631-6500
SIC 3275 3271 5031 1761 2952 2426

CELOTEX CORP p 274
10301 Dr Martn L Kng Jr S, Saint Petersburg FL 33716
Tel (727) 563-5100
SIC 3086 3275 3296 2493 2952

GEORGIA-PACIFIC LLC p 608
133 Peachtree St Ne # 4810, Atlanta GA 30303
Tel (404) 652-4000
SIC 2676 2656 2653 2435 2821 3275

BORAL INDUSTRIES INC p 201
200 Mansell Ct E Ste 310, Roswell GA 30076
Tel (770) 645-4500
SIC 3251 3272 3275 5032 3271 2899

▲ GMS INC p 619
100 Crescent Center Pkwy, Tucker GA 30084
Tel (800) 392-4619 *SIC* 3275 5031 5039

■ UNITED STATES GYPSUM CO INC p 1513
550 W Adams St Ste 1300, Chicago IL 60661
Tel (312) 606-4000 *SIC* 3275

▲ USG CORP p 1535
550 W Adams St, Chicago IL 60661
Tel (312) 436-4000 *SIC* 3275 3296

▲ PATRICK INDUSTRIES INC p 1120
107 W Franklin St, Elkhart IN 46516
Tel (574) 294-7511
SIC 3275 2493 2435 5031 5033 2891

CERTAINTEED GYPSUM INC p 284
750 E Swedesford Rd, Wayne PA 19087
Tel (813) 286-3900 *SIC* 3275

■ AMERICAN GYPSUM CO LLC p 73
3811 Turtle Creek Blvd # 1200, Dallas TX 75219
Tel (214) 530-5500 *SIC* 3275 5031

▲ EAGLE MATERIALS INC p 468
3811 Turtle Creek Blvd # 1100, Dallas TX 75219
Tel (214) 432-2000 *SIC* 3241 3275 3273

▲ CONTINENTAL BUILDING PRODUCTS INC p 363
12950 Worldgate Dr # 700, Herndon VA 20170
Tel (703) 480-3800 *SIC* 3275

SIC 3281 Cut Stone Prdts

RSI HOME PRODUCTS INC p 1256
400 E Orangethorpe Ave, Anaheim CA 92801
Tel (714) 449-2200
SIC 2514 2541 3281 2434

HALABI INC p 653
2100 Huntington Dr, Fairfield CA 94533
Tel (707) 402-1600 *SIC* 3281 1799

ENVIRONMENTAL MATERIALS LLC p 503
7306 S Alton Way Ste B, Centennial CO 80112
Tel (303) 309-6610 *SIC* 3281

DEVCON INTERNATIONAL CORP p 433
595 S Federal Hwy Ste 500, Boca Raton FL 33432
Tel (954) 926-5200
SIC 3699 3273 3281 3271 2951 5032

■ POLYVISION CORP p 1160
10700 Abbotts Bridge Rd # 100, Johns Creek GA 30097
Tel (678) 542-3100 *SIC* 3281 3993

COUNTRY STONE INC p 375
6300 75th Ave Ste A, Milan IL 61264
Tel (309) 787-1744
SIC 2499 2875 3273 3281

COLD SPRING GRANITE CO INC p 335
17482 Granite West Rd, Cold Spring MN 56320
Tel (320) 685-3621 *SIC* 3281 1741 3366

HANSON AGGREGATES WRP INC p 659
1333 Campus Pkwy, Wall Township NJ 07753
Tel (972) 653-5500
SIC 3281 3272 2951 1442

▲ MINERALS TECHNOLOGIES INC p 973
622 3rd Ave Fl 38, New York NY 10017
Tel (212) 878-1800
SIC 3295 2819 3274 1411 3281 5032

DALRYMPLE HOLDING CORP p 410
2105 S Broadway, Pine City NY 14871
Tel (607) 737-6200
SIC 3273 1611 1442 1622 3281

TRANSTAR HOLDING CO p 1473
5900 Landerbrook Dr Bsmt, Cleveland OH 44124
Tel (440) 684-1400 *SIC* 3444 3281 2952

SNYDER ASSOCIATED COMPANIES INC p 1336
1 Glade Park Dr, Kittanning PA 16201
Tel (724) 548-8101 *SIC* 1442 3281 1222

GLENN O HAWBAKER INC p 615
1952 Waddle Rd Ste 203, State College PA 16803
Tel (814) 237-1444
SIC 2951 3281 1622 1794 1611 1422

ALLAN MYERS INC p 51
1805 Berks Rd, Worcester PA 19490
Tel (610) 222-8800
SIC 1629 1794 1611 1622 3281 5032

■ TEXAS INDUSTRIES INC p 1443
1503 Lyndon B Johnson Fwy # 400, Dallas TX 75234
Tel (972) 647-6700
SIC 3241 3299 3281 3273

ROYAL BATHS MANUFACTURING CO LTD p 1254
14635 Chrisman Rd, Houston TX 77039
Tel (281) 442-3400
SIC 3842 3949 3432 3281

▲ HEADWATERS INC p 673
10701 S River Front Pkwy # 300, South Jordan UT 84095
Tel (801) 984-9400
SIC 3272 3271 3281 2952

LUCK STONE CORP p 884
515 Stone Mill Dr, Manakin Sabot VA 23103
Tel (804) 784-3383
SIC 1423 2899 3281 5211 8741

JF ALLEN CO INC p 785
U.S 33 W Red Rock Rd, Buckhannon WV 26201
Tel (304) 472-8890
SIC 3271 1611 3273 3281 2951

SIC 3291 Abrasive Prdts

GLOBAL MATERIAL TECHNOLOGIES INC p 617
750 W Lake Cook Rd # 480, Buffalo Grove IL 60089
Tel (847) 495-4700 *SIC* 3291

SEVERSTAL US HOLDINGS II INC p 1309
907 N Elm St Ste 100, Hinsdale IL 60521
Tel (708) 756-0400 *SIC* 3291

RADIAC ABRASIVES INC p 1204
1015 S College St, Salem IL 62881
Tel (618) 548-4200 *SIC* 3291

HUSQVARNA CONSTRUCTION PRODUCTS NORTH AMERICA INC p 721
17400 W 119th St, Olathe KS 66061
Tel (913) 928-1000
SIC 3541 3291 5085 5082 3425 2951

■ CAMBRIDGE INTERNATIONAL HOLDINGS CORP p 244
105 Goodwill Rd, Cambridge MD 21613
Tel (410) 901-4979 *SIC* 3291

WASHINGTON MILLS GROUP INC p 1578
20 N Main St, North Grafton MA 01536
Tel (508) 839-6511 *SIC* 3291

SAINT-GOBAIN ABRASIVES INC p 1271
1 New Bond St, Worcester MA 01606
Tel (508) 795-5000
SIC 3291 3559 3545 3297 3082 2891

ERVIN INDUSTRIES INC p 508
3893 Research Park Dr, Ann Arbor MI 48108
Tel (734) 769-4600 *SIC* 3291 6159

▲ 3M CO p 2
3m Center Bldg 22011w02, Saint Paul MN 55144
Tel (651) 733-1110
SIC 3841 3842 3291 2842 2672 2891

BARTON MINES CO LLC p 158
6 Warren St, Glens Falls NY 12801
Tel (518) 798-5462 *SIC* 1499 3291 5085

NYCO MINERALS INC p 1069
803 Mountain View Dr, Willsboro NY 12996
Tel (518) 963-4262
SIC 1499 5052 3295 3291

DIAMOND INNOVATIONS INC p 437
6325 Huntley Rd, Columbus OH 43229
Tel (614) 438-2000 *SIC* 3291

ALI INDUSTRIES INC p 50
747 E Xenia Dr, Fairborn OH 45324
Tel (937) 878-3946 *SIC* 3291

ABRASIVE TECHNOLOGY INC p 12
8400 Green Meadows Dr N, Lewis Center OH 43035
Tel (740) 548-4100 *SIC* 3291

GLOBAL TUNGSTEN & POWDERS CORP p 617
1 Hawes St, Towanda PA 18848
Tel (570) 268-5000 *SIC* 3313 3291

SAINT-GOBAIN DELAWARE CORP p 1271
750 E Swedesford Rd, Valley Forge PA 19482
Tel (610) 341-7000
SIC 3291 3269 2891 3296 3084 3221

AIM SPECIALTY MATERIALS USA p 38
25 Kenney Dr, Cranston RI 02920
Tel (401) 463-5605 *SIC* 3291

ACS INDUSTRIES INC p 19
1 New England Way Unit 1, Lincoln RI 02865
Tel (401) 769-4700
SIC 3291 3496 3312 3315 3569 3991

▲ CARBO CERAMICS INC p 252
575 N Dairy Ashford Rd # 30, Houston TX 77079
Tel (281) 921-6400
SIC 3291 5945 8742 7371

■ JW WILLIAMS INC p 798
2180 W Renauna Ave, Casper WY 82601
Tel (307) 237-8345
SIC 3533 3443 3547 1761 3291

SIC 3292 Asbestos products

CERTAINTEED CORP p 284
20 Moores Rd, Malvern PA 19355
Tel (610) 893-5000
SIC 3221 3292 3259 3084 3089 3432

CHEVRON PHILLIPS CHEMICAL CO LP p 296
10001 Six Pines Dr, The Woodlands TX 77380
Tel (832) 813-4100
SIC 5169 3292 3089 3084 3432 2911

SIC 3295 Minerals & Earths: Ground Or Treated

IMERYS MINERALS CALIFORNIA INC p 733
2500 San Miguelito Rd, Lompoc CA 93436
Tel (805) 736-1221 *SIC* 1499 3295

■ GLAD PRODUCTS CO p 614
1221 Broadway Ste A, Oakland CA 94612
Tel (510) 271-7000
SIC 3081 2673 2842 3295

IMERYS TALC AMERICA INC p 733
1732 N 1st St Ste 450, San Jose CA 95112
Tel (805) 562-0260 *SIC* 3295 1499

ASBURY CARBONS INC p 115
103 Foulk Rd Ste 202, Wilmington DE 19803
Tel (302) 652-0266
SIC 1499 3295 1241 5051 3952 3069

KAMIN LLC p 802
822 Huber Rd, Macon GA 31217
Tel (478) 750-5410 *SIC* 3295

■ OIL-DRI CORP OF GEORGIA p 1079
28990 Hwy 3, Ochlocknee GA 31773
Tel (229) 574-5131 *SIC* 3295 3564 2842

C-E MINERALS INC p 234
100 Mansell Ct E Ste 615, Roswell GA 30076
Tel (770) 225-7900
SIC 1099 1446 3295 6512

▲ OIL-DRI CORP OF AMERICA p 1079
410 N Michigan Ave # 400, Chicago IL 60611
Tel (312) 321-1515 *SIC* 2842 3295

SUPERIOR GRAPHITE CO p 1406
10 S Riverside Plz # 1470, Chicago IL 60606
Tel (312) 559-2999 *SIC* 3295

CC METALS AND ALLOYS LLC p 269
1542 N Main St, Calvert City KY 42029
Tel (270) 395-7631 *SIC* 3313 3341 3295

EDW C LEVY CO p 479
9300 Dix, Dearborn MI 48120
Tel (313) 429-2200 *SIC* 3295 5032 2951

■ HEMLOCK SEMICONDUCTOR OPERATIONS LLC p 682
12334 Geddes Rd, Hemlock MI 48626
Tel (989) 642-5201 *SIC* 3295

MIX HOLDINGS INC p 978
2501 Mc Gee Traffic Way, Kansas City MO 64108
Tel (816) 274-5111
SIC 3952 3951 3295 3944

PIKE INDUSTRIES INC p 1148
3 Eastgate Park Dr, Belmont NH 03220
Tel (603) 527-5100 *SIC* 1611 2951 3295

G HOLDINGS INC p 587
1 Campus Dr, Parsippany NJ 07054
Tel (973) 628-3000 *SIC* 2869 2843 3295

G-I HOLDINGS INC p 587
1361 Alps Rd, Wayne NJ 07470
Tel (973) 628-3000 *SIC* 2869 2843 3295

▲ MINERALS TECHNOLOGIES INC p 973
622 3rd Ave Fl 38, New York NY 10017
Tel (212) 878-1800
SIC 3295 2819 3274 1411 3281 5032

PRINCE MINERALS LLC p 1176
21 W 46th St Fl 14, New York NY 10036
Tel (646) 747-4222 *SIC* 3295 3356

NYCO MINERALS INC p 1069
803 Mountain View Dr, Willsboro NY 12996
Tel (518) 963-4262
SIC 1499 5052 3295 3291

▲ MARTIN MARIETTA MATERIALS INC p 912
2710 Wycliff Rd, Raleigh NC 27607
Tel (919) 781-4550
SIC 1423 1422 1442 3295 3297

CRAYOLA LLC p 389
1100 Church Ln, Easton PA 18040
Tel (610) 253-6271
SIC 3952 3951 3295 3944

MILL SERVICES CORP p 969
12 Monongahela Ave, Glassport PA 15045
Tel (412) 678-6141
SIC 3295 1422 8742 3341

INTERNATIONAL MILL SERVICE INC p 756
1155 Bus Ctr Dr Ste 200, Horsham PA 19044
Tel (215) 956-5500
SIC 3295 3341 1422 8742

BYK ADDITIVES INC p 231
1212 Church St, Gonzales TX 78629
Tel (830) 672-2891 *SIC* 1459 3295 3297

TRIBUTE ENERGY INC p 1479
2100 West Loop S Ste 1220, Houston TX 77027
Tel (281) 768-5300 *SIC* 5169 3295 2821

SIC 3296 Mineral Wool

PLASTIC SERVICES AND PRODUCTS p 1155
12243 Branford St, Sun Valley CA 91352
Tel (818) 896-1101
SIC 3086 3674 2865 2816 3296 2819

PMC GLOBAL INC p 1157
12243 Branford St, Sun Valley CA 91352
Tel (818) 896-1101
SIC 3086 3674 2865 2816 3296 2819

CELOTEX CORP p 274
10301 Dr Martn L Kng Jr S, Saint Petersburg FL 33716
Tel (727) 563-5100
SIC 3086 3275 3296 2493 2952

THERMAL CERAMICS INC p 1447
2102 Old Savannah Rd, Augusta GA 30906
Tel (706) 796-4200
SIC 3299 3255 5085 3296 3264 3053

TRANSCO INC p 1471
200 N La Salle St # 1550, Chicago IL 60601
Tel (312) 896-8527
SIC 4789 3743 3296 1742

▲ USG CORP p 1535
550 W Adams St, Chicago IL 60661
Tel (312) 436-4000 *SIC* 3275 3296

▲ UNIQUE FABRICATING INC p 1505
800 Standard Pkwy, Auburn Hills MI 48326
Tel (248) 853-2333
SIC 3053 3086 3296 2671

EFTEC NORTH AMERICA LLC p 481
31601 Research Park Dr, Madison Heights MI 48071
Tel (248) 526-4565
SIC 2891 8731 3296 2899 2851

PASSAIC METAL & BUILDING SUPPLIES CO p 1119
5 Central Ave Ste 1, Clifton NJ 07011
Tel (973) 546-9000
SIC 5033 5031 5051 5075 3444 3296

LOW & BONAR INC p 881
1301 Sand Hill Rd, Enka NC 28728
Tel (828) 665-5000
SIC 5199 3296 2899 2297 2221

▲ OWENS CORNING p 1100
1 Owens Corning Pkwy, Toledo OH 43659
Tel (419) 248-8000
SIC 3296 2952 3229 3089

■ OWENS CORNING SALES LLC p 1100
1 Owens Corning Pkwy, Toledo OH 43659
Tel (419) 248-8000
SIC 3296 2952 3229 3089 1761

MOLDED ACOUSTICAL PRODUCTS OF EASTON INC p 982
3 Danforth Dr, Easton PA 18045
Tel (610) 253-7135 *SIC* 3296

▲ ARMSTRONG WORLD INDUSTRIES INC p 111
2500 Columbia Ave Bldg 5b, Lancaster PA 17603
Tel (717) 397-0611 *SIC* 3646 3296

PITTSBURGH CORNING CORP p 1152
800 Presque Isle Dr, Pittsburgh PA 15239
Tel (724) 327-6100 *SIC* 3296

SAINT-GOBAIN DELAWARE CORP p 1271
750 E Swedesford Rd, Valley Forge PA 19482
Tel (610) 341-7000
SIC 3291 3269 2891 3296 3084 3221

GUARDIAN BUILDING PRODUCTS INC p 645
979 Batesville Rd Ste A, Greer SC 29651
Tel (864) 297-6101 *SIC* 3296 2452 8741

KNAUF INSULATION LLC p 824
979 Batesville Rd Ste B, Greer SC 29651
Tel (517) 629-9464 *SIC* 3296

SIC 3297 Nonclay Refractories

ALDILA INC p 48
14145 Danielson St Ste B, Poway CA 92064
Tel (858) 513-1801 *SIC* 3949 3297

RHI REFRACTORIES HOLDING CO p 1231
1105 N Market St Ste 1300, Wilmington DE 19801
Tel (302) 655-6497
SIC 3297 3255 1459 3546 3272 3589

VESUVIUS CRUCIBLE CO p 1552
1404 Newton Dr, Champaign IL 61822
Tel (217) 351-5000 *SIC* 3297 5051

VESUVIUS U S A CORP p 1552
1404 Newton Dr, Champaign IL 61822
Tel (217) 402-9204 *SIC* 3297 5085

CORHART REFRACTORIES CORP p 370
10300 Ormsby Park Pl # 450, Louisville KY 40223
Tel (502) 423-6324 *SIC* 3255 3297

OSRAM SYLVANIA INC p 1097
200 Ballardvale St # 305, Wilmington MA 01887
Tel (978) 570-3000
SIC 3646 3641 3647 3643 3297

SAINT-GOBAIN ABRASIVES INC p 1271
1 New Bond St, Worcester MA 01606
Tel (508) 795-5000
SIC 3291 3559 3545 3297 3082 2891

MITSUBISHI CEMENT CORP p 977
151 Cassia Way, Henderson NV 89014
Tel (702) 932-3900 *SIC* 3297 5032

▲ ALCOA CORP p 47
390 Park Ave Fl 12, New York NY 10022
Tel (212) 518-5400
SIC 3355 3363 3297 2819

▲ MARTIN MARIETTA MATERIALS INC p 912
2710 Wycliff Rd, Raleigh NC 27607
Tel (919) 781-4550
SIC 1423 1422 1442 3295 3297

ALLIED MINERAL PRODUCTS INC p 56
2700 Scioto Pkwy, Columbus OH 43221
Tel (614) 876-0244 *SIC* 3297

ORMET PRIMARY ALUMINUM CORP p 1095
43840 State Rt 7, Hannibal OH 43931
Tel (740) 483-1381 *SIC* 3334 3297

■ MINTEQ INTERNATIONAL INC p 974
35 Highland Ave, Bethlehem PA 18017
Tel (724) 794-3000 *SIC* 3297

GLOBAL INDUSTRIAL TECHNOLOGIES INC p 616
1305 Chrrington Pkwy Moon, Coraopolis PA 15108
Tel (412) 375-6600
SIC 3297 3255 1459 3546 3272 3589

HARBISON-WALKER REFRACTORIES CO p 659
1305 Cherrington Pkwy, Coraopolis PA 15108
Tel (412) 375-6600 *SIC* 3255 3297

NORTH AMERICAN REFRACTORIES CO p 1050
1305 Cherrington Pkwy # 100, Coraopolis PA 15108
Tel (412) 375-6600 *SIC* 3297 3255

HARBISONWALKER INTERNATIONAL INC p 659
1305 Cherrington Pkwy # 100, Moon Township PA 15108
Tel (412) 375-6600 *SIC* 3297 3272 1459

RESCO PRODUCTS INC p 1226
1 Robinson Plz Ste 300, Pittsburgh PA 15205
Tel (412) 494-4491
SIC 3297 3255 1455 1499 5032

SAINT-GOBAIN CERAMICS & PLASTICS INC p 1271
750 E Swedesford Rd, Valley Forge PA 19482
Tel (610) 341-7000
SIC 2819 3679 3544 3297

MAGNESITA REFRACTORIES CO p 896
425 S Salem Church Rd, York PA 17408
Tel (717) 792-3611 *SIC* 3297 3274 1422

BYK ADDITIVES INC p 231
1212 Church St, Gonzales TX 78629
Tel (830) 672-2891 *SIC* 1459 3295 3297

HANSON LEHIGH INC p 659
300 E John Carpenter Fwy, Irving TX 75062
Tel (972) 653-5500
SIC 1442 1422 1423 3297 3273 3272

SIC 3299 Nonmetallic Mineral Prdts, NEC

PAREX USA INC p 1114
4125 E La Palma Ave, Anaheim CA 92807
Tel (714) 778-2266 *SIC* 3299 5031

■ CERADYNE INC p 283
1922 Barranca Pkwy, Irvine CA 92606
Tel (714) 549-0421 *SIC* 3299 3671

APPROVED NETWORKS INC p 100
717 Lakefield Rd Ste A, Westlake Village CA 91361
Tel (800) 590-9535 *SIC* 3299

THERMAL CERAMICS INC p 1447
2102 Old Savannah Rd, Augusta GA 30906
Tel (706) 796-4200
SIC 3299 3255 5085 3296 3264 3053

UFX HOLDING I CORP p 1499
55 E 52nd St Fl 35, New York NY 10055
Tel (212) 644-5900 *SIC* 3299

UFX HOLDING II CORP p 1499
55 E 52nd St Fl 35, New York NY 10055
Tel (212) 644-5900 SIC 3299

UNIFRAX HOLDING CO p 1503
55 E 52nd St Fl 35, New York NY 10055
Tel (212) 644-5900 SIC 3299

■ UNIFRAX I LLC p 1503
600 Rverwalk Pkwy Ste 120, Tonawanda NY 14150
Tel (716) 768-6500 SIC 3299

MORGANITE INDUSTRIES INC p 989
4000 Westchase Blvd # 170, Raleigh NC 27607
Tel (919) 821-1253
SIC 3674 3255 3699 3264 3299 3624

R W SIDLEY INC p 1203
436 Casement Ave, Painesville OH 44077
Tel (440) 352-9343 SIC 1771 3299

■ TEXAS INDUSTRIES INC p 1443
1503 Lyndon B Johnson Fwy # 400, Dallas TX 75234
Tel (972) 647-6700
SIC 3241 3299 3281 3273

TEXAS UNITED CORP p 1444
4800 San Felipe St, Houston TX 77056
Tel (713) 877-1793
SIC 1479 2819 4619 2899 3299 7353

R D WING CO INC p 1202
517 6th St S, Kirkland WA 98033
Tel (425) 821-7222 SIC 3299

SIC 3312 Blast Furnaces, Coke Ovens, Steel & Rolling Mills

MCWANE INC p 933
2900 Highway 280 S # 300, Birmingham AL 35223
Tel (205) 414-3100
SIC 3491 1221 3321 3312 3494

■ NUCOR STEEL BIRMINGHAM INC p 1066
2301 Fl Shuttlesworth Dr, Birmingham AL 35234
Tel (866) 862-4796 SIC 3312

■ SMI STEEL LLC p 1333
101 50th St S, Birmingham AL 35212
Tel (205) 592-8981 SIC 3312

AM/NS CALVERT LLC p 64
1 Am Ns Way, Calvert AL 36513
Tel (251) 289-3000 SIC 3312 3449

OUTOKUMPU STAINLESS USA LLC p 1099
1 Steel Dr, Calvert AL 36513
Tel (251) 829-3600 SIC 3312 3399

■ NUCOR STEEL DECATUR LLC p 1066
4301 Iverson Blvd, Trinity AL 35673
Tel (256) 301-3500 SIC 3312

■ NUCOR STEEL TUSCALOOSA INC p 1067
1700 Holt Rd Ne, Tuscaloosa AL 35404
Tel (205) 556-1310 SIC 3312

DRUMMOND CO INC p 457
1000 Urban Center Dr # 300, Vestavia AL 35242
Tel (205) 945-6500
SIC 1221 1222 3312 5052 5085 5172

■ FREEPORT MINERALS CORP p 577
333 N Central Ave, Phoenix AZ 85004
Tel (602) 366-8100
SIC 1061 1021 3312 3351

▲ CARLISLE COMPANIES INC p 257
16430 N Scottsdale Rd, Scottsdale AZ 85254
Tel (704) 501-1100
SIC 2952 3714 3312 3357 3263

■ NUCOR-YAMATO STEEL CO (LIMITED PARTNERSHIP) p 1067
5929 E State Highway 18, Blytheville AR 72315
Tel (870) 762-5500 SIC 3312 3441

KPI INTERMEDIATE HOLDINGS INC p 828
481 S Shiloh Dr, Fayetteville AR 72704
Tel (479) 443-1455 SIC 3363 3312

ARKANSAS STEEL ASSOCIATES LLC p 110
2803 Van Dyke Rd, Newport AR 72112
Tel (870) 523-3693 SIC 3312 3547

KISWIRE PINE BLUFF INC p 822
5100 Industrial Dr S, Pine Bluff AR 71602
Tel (870) 247-2444 SIC 3312 2296

■ ARKGALV INC p 110
998 Escue Dr, Prairie Grove AR 72753
Tel (479) 846-4500 SIC 3312

CALIFORNIA STEEL INDUSTRIES INC p 241
14000 San Bernardino Ave, Fontana CA 92335
Tel (909) 350-6300 SIC 3312 3317

RENT-A-TIRE LP p 1224
11726 San Vicente Blvd # 400, Los Angeles CA 90049
Tel (818) 786-7906 SIC 5531 3312

USS-POSCO INDUSTRIES A CALIFORNIA JOINT VENTURE p 1535
900 Loveridge Rd, Pittsburg CA 94565
Tel (800) 877-7672 SIC 3312

AD CORP p 21
1551 Wewatta St, Denver CO 80202
Tel (303) 744-1911
SIC 3634 3564 3822 3089 3714 3312

CF&I STEEL LP p 285
1612 E Abriendo Ave, Pueblo CO 81004
Tel (719) 561-6000 SIC 3441 3317 3312

ULBRICH STAINLESS STEELS & SPECIAL METALS INC p 1500
153 Washington Ave, North Haven CT 06473
Tel (203) 239-4481
SIC 3316 3356 5051 3341 3312

■ CMC STEEL HOLDING CO p 329
802 N West St Ste 302, Wilmington DE 19801
Tel (302) 691-6200 SIC 3441 3312

BAE SYSTEMS AH INC p 144
13386 International Pkwy, Jacksonville FL 32218
Tel (904) 741-5400
SIC 3711 3842 3312 3728

GERDAU AMERISTEEL CORP p 608
4221 W Boy Scout Blvd # 600, Tampa FL 33607
Tel (813) 286-8383 SIC 3312

GERDAU AMERISTEEL US INC p 608
4221 W Boy Scout Blvd # 600, Tampa FL 33607
Tel (813) 286-8383 SIC 3312 3449 3315

GERDAU USA INC p 608
4221 W Boy Scout Blvd, Tampa FL 33607
Tel (813) 286-8383 SIC 3312 3449 3315

PRIMETALS TECHNOLOGIES USA LLC p 1175
5895 Windward Pkwy Fl 2, Alpharetta GA 30005
Tel (770) 740-3800 SIC 3312

ALTON STEEL INC p 62
5 Cut St, Alton IL 62002
Tel (618) 463-4490 SIC 3312

■ NUCOR STEEL KANKAKEE INC p 1066
1 Nucor Way, Bourbonnais IL 60914
Tel (815) 937-3131 SIC 3312 3547 3449

A FINKL & SONS CO p 5
1355 E 93rd St, Chicago IL 60619
Tel (773) 975-2510 SIC 3312

ARCELORMITTAL USA LLC p 104
1 S Dearborn St Ste 1800, Chicago IL 60603
Tel (312) 346-0300
SIC 3312 3325 3356 3316

EVRAZ INC NA p 516
200 E Randolph St # 7800, Chicago IL 60601
Tel (312) 533-3621 SIC 3312 3317 3325

■ FERALLOY CORP p 537
8755 W Higgins Rd Ste 970, Chicago IL 60631
Tel (503) 286-8869
SIC 5051 3471 3444 3312

CHS ACQUISITION CORP p 304
211 E Main St, Chicago Heights IL 60411
Tel (708) 756-5648 SIC 3312

MAIN STEEL LLC p 897
2200 Pratt Blvd, Elk Grove Village IL 60007
Tel (847) 916-1220 SIC 3312

MATERIAL SCIENCES CORP p 919
2250 Pratt Blvd, Elk Grove Village IL 60007
Tel (888) 603-1553 SIC 3312 5051

SSAB ENTERPRISES LLC p 1363
801 Warrenville Rd # 800, Lisle IL 60532
Tel (630) 810-4800 SIC 3312

SSAB US HOLDING INC p 1363
801 Warrenville Rd # 800, Lisle IL 60532
Tel (630) 810-4800 SIC 3312

▲ SUNCOKE ENERGY INC p 1402
1011 Warrenville Rd # 600, Lisle IL 60532
Tel (630) 824-1000 SIC 3312 1241

■ SUNCOKE ENERGY PARTNERS LP p 1402
1011 Warrenville Rd # 600, Lisle IL 60532
Tel (630) 824-1000 SIC 3312

▲ TITAN INTERNATIONAL INC p 1456
2701 Spruce St, Quincy IL 62301
Tel (217) 228-6011 SIC 3312 3714 3011

■ STERLING STEEL CO LLC p 1387
101 Avenue K, Sterling IL 61081
Tel (815) 548-7000 SIC 3312

ARCELORMITTAL BURNS HARBOR LLC p 104
250 W Us Highway 12, Burns Harbor IN 46304
Tel (219) 787-2120 SIC 3312

ARCELORMITTAL HOLDINGS LLC p 104
3210 Watling St, East Chicago IN 46312
Tel (219) 399-1200 SIC 3312 1011

INDIANA ARCELORMITTAL HARBOR LLC p 738
3210 Watling St, East Chicago IN 46312
Tel (219) 399-1200 SIC 3312

▲ STEEL DYNAMICS INC p 1384
7575 W Jefferson Blvd, Fort Wayne IN 46804
Tel (260) 969-3500 SIC 3312 3316 7389

NLMK INDIANA LLC p 1045
6500 S Boundary Rd, Portage IN 46368
Tel (219) 787-8200 SIC 3312

SEYMOUR TUBING INC p 1309
1515 E 4th Street Rd, Seymour IN 47274
Tel (812) 523-0842 SIC 3312

COMPANHIA SIDERURGICA NACIONAL LLC p 350
455 W Industrial Dr, Terre Haute IN 47802
Tel (812) 299-4157 SIC 3316 3312

AVIS INDUSTRIAL CORP p 138
1909 S Main St, Upland IN 46989
Tel (765) 998-8100
SIC 3429 3462 3312 3531 3714 3569

SSAB IOWA INC p 1363
1770 Bill Sharp Blvd, Muscatine IA 52761
Tel (563) 381-5300 SIC 3312

C&M TIRE INC p 234
401 S 42nd St, Kansas City KS 66106
Tel (913) 321-3003
SIC 5531 7534 5014 3312

MUBEA INC p 998
6800 Industrial Rd, Florence KY 41042
Tel (859) 746-5300
SIC 3493 3312 3495 3429 3714

NORTH AMERICAN STAINLESS p 1050
6870 Us Highway 42 E, Ghent KY 41045
Tel (502) 347-6000 SIC 3316 3312

STEEL TECHNOLOGIES LLC p 1384
700 N Hurstbourne Pkwy, Louisville KY 40222
Tel (502) 245-2110 SIC 3312 3316

BD LAPLACE LLC p 164
138 Highway 3217, La Place LA 70068
Tel (985) 652-4900 SIC 3312

MICROGROUP INC p 962
7 Industrial Park Rd, Medway MA 02053
Tel (508) 533-4925
SIC 5051 3312 3498 3494 3492 3317

TI AUTOMOTIVE LLC p 1452
2020 Taylor Rd, Auburn Hills MI 48326
Tel (248) 494-5000
SIC 3317 3312 3599 3052 3714 3585

TI GROUP AUTOMOTIVE SYSTEMS LLC p 1452
2020 Taylor Rd, Auburn Hills MI 48326
Tel (248) 296-8000
SIC 3317 3312 3599 3052 3714 3585

GILL CORP p 612
706 Bond Ave Nw, Grand Rapids MI 49503
Tel (859) 625-5284
SIC 3469 3312 3495 3493 3496 3465

GERDAU MACSTEEL INC p 608
5591 Morrill Rd, Jackson MI 49201
Tel (517) 782-0415 SIC 3316 3312

NATIONAL GALVANIZING LP p 1012
1500 Telb St, Monroe MI 48162
Tel (734) 243-1882
SIC 3312 3316 3471 3341 5051

■ CANNON-MUSKEGON CORP p 247
2875 Lincoln St, Norton Shores MI 49441
Tel (231) 759-2831
SIC 3313 3341 3339 3312

EATON STEEL CORP p 473
10221 Capital St, Oak Park MI 48237
Tel (248) 398-3434 SIC 5051 3312

SET ENTERPRISES INC p 1308
30500 Van Dyke Ave # 701, Warren MI 48093
Tel (586) 573-3600
SIC 7389 3465 3544 3312

UPONOR NORTH AMERICA INC p 1529
5925 148th St W, Apple Valley MN 55124
Tel (952) 891-2000 SIC 8742 3312

■ KEYSTONE AUTOMOTIVE INDUSTRIES MN INC p 815
3615 Marshall St Ne, Minneapolis MN 55418
Tel (612) 789-1919 SIC 5013 3312 3465

MILLERBERND MANUFACTURING CO p 971
622 6th St S, Winsted MN 55395
Tel (320) 485-2111 SIC 3312

PSL-NORTH AMERICA LLC p 1188
13092 Sea Plane Road Bay, Bay St Louis MS 39520
Tel (228) 533-7779 SIC 3312

■ NUCOR STEEL JACKSON INC p 1066
3630 Fourth St, Flowood MS 39232
Tel (601) 939-1623 SIC 3312

ROTO-DIE CO INC p 1252
800 Howerton Ln, Eureka MO 63025
Tel (636) 587-3600 SIC 3544 3555 3312

GRIMCO INC p 640
1585 Fencorp Dr, Fenton MO 63026
Tel (636) 305-0088
SIC 3469 2759 3993 3429 3312

BRADKEN INC p 206
12200 N Ambassador Dr # 647, Kansas City MO 64163
Tel (816) 270-0700 SIC 3325 3321 3312

HOEGANAES CORP p 699
1001 Taylors Ln, Cinnaminson NJ 08077
Tel (856) 303-0366 SIC 3312 3399

ATLAS COPCO NORTH AMERICA LLC p 128
7 Campus Dr Ste 200, Parsippany NJ 07054
Tel (973) 397-3400 SIC 3312

GERDAU AMERISTEEL SAYREVILLE INC p 608
N Crossman Rd, Sayreville NJ 08872
Tel (732) 721-6600 SIC 3312

ALBEA AMERICAS INC p 46
191 State Route 31 N, Washington NJ 07882
Tel (908) 689-3000 SIC 3312

■ NUCOR STEEL AUBURN INC p 1066
25 Quarry Rd, Auburn NY 13021
Tel (315) 253-4561 SIC 3312

CHINA INDUSTRIAL STEEL INC p 301
110 Wall St Fl 11, New York NY 10005
Tel (646) 328-1502 SIC 3312

KPI CAPITAL HOLDINGS INC p 828
437 Madison Ave Fl 36, New York NY 10022
Tel (479) 443-1455 SIC 6719 3363 3312

KPI HOLDINGS INC p 828
437 Madison Ave Fl 36, New York NY 10022
Tel (479) 443-1455 SIC 6719 3363 3312

RENCO GROUP INC p 1223
1 Rockefeller Plz Fl 29, New York NY 10020
Tel (212) 541-6000
SIC 3312 3316 2514 2511 3171 3496

▲ SPH GROUP HOLDINGS LLC p 1358
590 Madison Ave Fl 32, New York NY 10022
Tel (212) 520-2300 SIC 3339 3011 3312

CRUCIBLE INDUSTRIES LLC p 396
575 State Fair Blvd, Syracuse NY 13209
Tel (800) 365-1180 SIC 3312

■ HANDY & HARMAN LTD p 657
1133 Westchester Ave N-222, White Plains NY 10604
Tel (914) 461-1300 SIC 3339 3011 3312

▲ NUCOR CORP p 1066
1915 Rexford Rd Ste 400, Charlotte NC 28211
Tel (704) 366-7000
SIC 3312 3441 3448 3452 5093

KIRTLAND CAPITAL PARTNERS LP p 822
3201 Entp Pkwy Ste 200, Beachwood OH 44122
Tel (216) 593-0100
SIC 5051 3312 3498 3494 3492 3317

CANTON DROP FORGE INC p 247
4575 Southway St Sw, Canton OH 44706
Tel (330) 477-4511
SIC 3462 3463 3356 3312

OHIO GRATINGS INC p 1077
5299 Southway St Sw, Canton OH 44706
Tel (330) 477-6707
SIC 3446 3444 3441 3312

REPUBLIC STEEL INC p 1225
2633 8th St Ne, Canton OH 44704
Tel (330) 438-5435 SIC 3312

▲ TIMKENSTEEL CORP p 1455
1835 Dueber Ave Sw, Canton OH 44706
Tel (330) 471-7000 SIC 3312

XTEK INC p 1633
11451 Reading Rd, Cincinnati OH 45241
Tel (513) 733-7800
SIC 3568 3547 3398 3312

ARCELORMITTAL CLEVELAND LLC p 104
3060 Eggers Ave, Cleveland OH 44105
Tel (216) 429-6000 SIC 3312

STEIN INC p 1385
1929 E Royalton Rd Ste C, Cleveland OH 44147
Tel (440) 526-9301 SIC 3399 3312 5084

MATANDY STEEL & METAL PRODUCTS LLC p 919
1200 Central Ave, Hamilton OH 45011
Tel (513) 887-5274
SIC 5051 3312 3444 3399

PIONEER PIPE INC p 1151
2021 Hanna Rd, Marietta OH 45750
Tel (740) 376-2400
SIC 3498 1711 3443 3441 3312

COHEN BROTHERS INC p 335
1723 Woodlawn Ave, Middletown OH 45044
Tel (513) 422-3696
SIC 5093 3441 3341 3312

CENTAUR INC p 275
2401 Front St, Toledo OH 43605
Tel (419) 469-8000 SIC 3312 3316 3999

HEIDTMAN STEEL PRODUCTS INC p 681
2401 Front St, Toledo OH 43605
Tel (419) 691-4646 SIC 3316 3312

■ LATROBE SPECIALTY METALS DISTRIBUTION INC p 846
1551 Vienna Pkwy, Vienna OH 44473
Tel (330) 609-5137 SIC 5051 3312

■ AK STEEL CORP p 41
9227 Centre Pointe Dr, West Chester OH 45069
Tel (513) 425-4200 SIC 3312

▲ AK STEEL HOLDING CORP p 41
9227 Centre Pointe Dr, West Chester OH 45069
Tel (513) 425-5000 SIC 3312

SHEFFIELD STEEL CORP p 1314
2300 S State Highway 97, Sand Springs OK 74063
Tel (918) 245-1335 SIC 3312

▲ WEBCO INDUSTRIES INC p 1586
9101 W 21st St, Sand Springs OK 74063
Tel (918) 245-2211 SIC 3312 5051

■ CASCADE STEEL ROLLING MILLS INC p 262
3200 Ne Highway 99w, Mcminnville OR 97128
Tel (503) 472-4181 SIC 3312

▲ SCHNITZER STEEL INDUSTRIES INC p 1288
299 Sw Clay St Ste 350, Portland OR 97201
Tel (503) 224-9900
SIC 5093 3312 3449 3441 3433 5015

CRONIMET CORP p 393
1 Pilarsky Way, Aliquippa PA 15001
Tel (724) 375-5004 SIC 5093 5051 3312

▲ UNIVERSAL STAINLESS & ALLOY PRODUCTS INC p 1517
600 Mayer St Ste 2, Bridgeville PA 15017
Tel (412) 257-7600 SIC 3312

STANDARD STEEL LLC p 1376
500 N Walnut St, Burnham PA 17009
Tel (717) 242-4615 SIC 3312 3462

▲ AMPCO-PITTSBURGH CORP p 86
726 Bell Ave Ste 301, Carnegie PA 15106
Tel (412) 456-4400
SIC 3312 3561 3351 3353

■ UNION ELECTRIC STEEL CORP p 1504
726 Bell Ave, Carnegie PA 15106
Tel (412) 429-7655 SIC 3325 3398 3312

ARCELORMITTAL PLATE LLC p 104
139 Modena Rd, Coatesville PA 19320
Tel (610) 383-2000 SIC 3312

ELLWOOD GROUP INC p 489
600 Commercial Ave, Ellwood City PA 16117
Tel (724) 752-3680 SIC 3312 3462

NLMK PENNSYLVANIA LLC p 1045
15 Roemer Blvd, Farrell PA 16121
Tel (724) 983-6464 SIC 3316 3356 3312

TMS INTERNATIONAL CORP p 1457
12 Monongahela Ave, Glassport PA 15045
Tel (412) 678-6141
SIC 3312 4731 3399 7359 4213

TMS INTERNATIONAL HOLDING CORP p 1457
12 Monongahela Ave, Glassport PA 15045
Tel (412) 678-6141
SIC 3312 4731 3399 7359 4213

TMS INTERNATIONAL LLC p 1458
12 Monongahela Ave, Glassport PA 15045
Tel (412) 678-6141
SIC 3312 4731 3399 7359 4213

JERSEY SHORE STEEL CO p 783
70 Maryland Ave, Jersey Shore PA 17740
Tel (570) 753-3000 SIC 3312

IPSCO KOPPEL TUBULARS LLC p 764
6403 6th Ave, Koppel PA 16136
Tel (724) 847-6389 SIC 3312

■ LATROBE SPECIALTY METALS CO LLC p 846
2626 Ligonier St, Latrobe PA 15650
Tel (724) 537-7711 SIC 3312 3369

MARCEGAGLIA USA INC p 905
1001 E Waterfront Dr, Munhall PA 15120
Tel (412) 462-2185 SIC 3317 3312

ELLWOOD QUALITY STEELS CO p 489
700 Moravia St Ste 7, New Castle PA 16101
Tel (724) 658-6502 SIC 3312

■ ALLEGHENY LUDLUM LLC p 52
1000 Six Ppg Pl, Pittsburgh PA 15222
Tel (412) 394-2800 SIC 3312

▲ ALLEGHENY TECHNOLOGIES INC p 52
1000 Six Ppg Pl, Pittsburgh PA 15222
Tel (412) 394-2800 SIC 3312 3339 3545

▲ KOPPERS HOLDINGS INC p 827
436 7th Ave, Pittsburgh PA 15219
Tel (412) 227-2001
SIC 2865 2491 2895 3312 2899

■ KOPPERS INC p 828
436 7th Ave, Pittsburgh PA 15219
Tel (412) 227-2001
SIC 2865 2491 3312 2899

▲ L B FOSTER CO p 833
415 Holiday Dr Ste 1, Pittsburgh PA 15220
Tel (412) 928-3417 SIC 3312 3272 3317

SPANG & CO p 1354
110 Delta Dr, Pittsburgh PA 15238
Tel (412) 963-9363
SIC 3672 3944 3612 3613 3312

■ TDY INDUSTRIES LLC p 1429
1000 Six Ppg Pl, Pittsburgh PA 15222
Tel (412) 394-2896
SIC 3356 3312 3316 3339 3369

▲ UNITED STATES STEEL CORP p 1514
600 Grant St Ste 468, Pittsburgh PA 15219
Tel (412) 433-1121 SIC 3312 3317 3356

WHEMCO INC p 1605
5 Hot Metal St Ste 300, Pittsburgh PA 15203
Tel (412) 390-2700
SIC 3312 3462 3731 3325 3441 3369

ARCELORMITTAL STEELTON LLC p 104
215 S Front St, Steelton PA 17113
Tel (717) 986-2000 SIC 3312

SSSI INC p 1364
2755a Park Ave, Washington PA 15301
Tel (724) 743-5815 SIC 1611 3312 4925

▲ CARPENTER TECHNOLOGY CORP p 260
2 Meridian Blvd, Wyomissing PA 19610
Tel (610) 208-2000
SIC 3312 3443 3255 3316 3315

ACS INDUSTRIES INC p 19
1 New England Way Unit 1, Lincoln RI 02865
Tel (401) 769-4700
SIC 3291 3496 3312 3315 3569 3991

■ BRISTOL METALS LLC p 214
390 Bristol Metals Rd, Bristol TN 37620
Tel (423) 968-2151 SIC 3312

■ SISKIN STEEL & SUPPLY CO INC p 1327
1901 Riverfront Pkwy, Chattanooga TN 37408
Tel (423) 756-3671 SIC 3312 5051

■ NUCOR STEEL MEMPHIS INC p 1066
3601 Paul R Lowry Rd, Memphis TN 38109
Tel (901) 786-5837
SIC 3312 3441 3448 3452

THOMAS & BETTS CORP p 1448
8155 T&B Blvd, Memphis TN 38125
Tel (901) 252-5000 SIC 3643 3312 3567

JSW STEEL (USA) INC p 796
5200 E Mckinney Rd # 110, Baytown TX 77523
Tel (281) 383-2525 SIC 3317 3312

■ BELLVILLE TUBE CO LP p 171
141 Miller Rd E, Bellville TX 77418
Tel (979) 865-9111 SIC 3312

SOUTHEAST TEXAS INDUSTRIES INC p 1346
35911 Us Highway 96 S, Buna TX 77612
Tel (409) 994-3570 SIC 3312 3443

BD VINTON LLC p 164
I-10 Vinton Rd, Canutillo TX 79835
Tel (915) 886-2000
SIC 5051 3312 3449 3316

■ KEYSTONE CONSOLIDATED INDUSTRIES INC p 815
5430 Lyndon B Johnson Fwy # 1740, Dallas TX 75240
Tel (800) 441-0308 SIC 3312 3315

■ LONE STAR TECHNOLOGIES INC p 876
15660 Dallas Pkwy Ste 500, Dallas TX 75248
Tel (972) 770-6401 SIC 3317 3312

ENNIS STEEL INDUSTRIES INC p 500
204 Metro Park Blvd, Ennis TX 75119
Tel (972) 878-0400 SIC 3312 3441 1791

▲ AZZ INC p 141
3100 W 7th St Ste 500, Fort Worth TX 76107
Tel (817) 810-0095
SIC 3699 3613 3494 3312

■ NORTH AMERICAN GALVANIZING & COATINGS INC p 1050
3100 W 7th St Ste 500, Fort Worth TX 76107
Tel (817) 810-0095 SIC 7539 3312

FLEXSTEEL PIPELINE TECHNOLOGIES INC p 556
1201 La St Ste 2700, Houston TX 77002
Tel (832) 531-8555 SIC 3312

INTSEL STEEL DISTRIBUTORS LLC p 760
11310 W Little York Rd, Houston TX 77041
Tel (713) 937-9500 SIC 5051 3312 3444

▲ COMMERCIAL METALS CO p 345
6565 N Mcarthur Blvd # 800, Irving TX 75039
Tel (214) 689-4300
SIC 3312 3441 5051 5093

■ JOY GLOBAL LONGVIEW OPERATIONS LLC p 794
2400 S Macarthur Dr, Longview TX 75602
Tel (903) 237-7000
SIC 3532 3533 3312 3531

GERDAU AMERISTEEL US INC p 608
300 Ward Rd, Midlothian TX 76065
Tel (972) 775-8241 SIC 3312

GULF COPPER & MANUFACTURING CORP p 646
5700 Procter Ext, Port Arthur TX 77642
Tel (409) 989-0300
SIC 3731 3599 3312 3732 3498 3441

■ C M C STEEL FABRICATORS INC p 233
1 Steel Mill Dr, Seguin TX 78155
Tel (830) 372-8200 SIC 3312 3441

■ STRUCTURAL METALS INC p 1394
1 Steel Mill Dr, Seguin TX 78155
Tel (830) 372-8200 SIC 3312 3441 3462

CB&I LLC p 268
2103 Research Forest Dr, The Woodlands TX 77380
Tel (832) 513-1000 SIC 1791 3443 3312

W SILVER INC p 1569
9059 Doniphan Dr, Vinton TX 79821
Tel (915) 886-3553 SIC 3312 3462

VIRGINIA CHAPARRAL INC p 1558
25801 Hofheimer Way, North Dinwiddie VA 23803
Tel (804) 520-0286 SIC 3312

■ ROANOKE ELECTRIC STEEL CORP p 1240
102 Westside Blvd Nw, Roanoke VA 24017
Tel (540) 342-1831 SIC 3312

CONSOLIDATED METCO INC p 360
5701 Se Columbia Way, Vancouver WA 98661
Tel (360) 828-2599
SIC 3365 3363 3089 3714 3443 3312

WHEELING-NISSHIN INC p 1605
400 Penn St, Follansbee WV 26037
Tel (304) 527-2800 SIC 3312

■ SWVA INC p 1413
17th St & Second Ave, Huntington WV 25703
Tel (304) 696-8200 SIC 3441 3312

WEIRTON STEEL CORP p 1588
400 Three Springs Dr, Weirton WV 26062
Tel (304) 797-2000 SIC 3312 3316

RG STEEL WHEELING STEEL GROUP LLC p 1231
1134 Market St, Wheeling WV 26003
Tel (304) 234-2400 SIC 3312 3444

CHARTER MANUFACTURING CO INC p 291
1212 W Glen Oaks Ln, Mequon WI 53092
Tel (262) 243-4700 SIC 3312 3496

UNITED P&H SUPPLY CO p 1510
9947 W Carmen Ave, Milwaukee WI 53225
Tel (414) 393-6600
SIC 5085 5074 3312 3463

▲ NEENAH ENTERPRISES INC p 1024
2121 Brooks Ave, Neenah WI 54956
Tel (920) 725-7000 SIC 3272 3312

SIC 3313 Electrometallurgical Prdts

■ CLIMAX MOLYBDENUM MARKETING CORP p 326
333 N Central Ave Ste 100, Phoenix AZ 85004
Tel (602) 366-8100 SIC 1061 3313

GLOBE SPECIALTY METALS INC p 618
600 Brickell Ave Ste 3100, Miami FL 33131
Tel (786) 509-6900 SIC 3339 3313

TEMPEL STEEL CO p 1436
5500 N Wolcott Ave, Chicago IL 60640
Tel (773) 250-8000
SIC 3469 3313 3316 3398 5051

CC METALS AND ALLOYS LLC p 269
1542 N Main St, Calvert City KY 42029
Tel (270) 395-7631 SIC 3313 3341 3295

COMILOG US INC p 344
610 Pittman Rd, Baltimore MD 21226
Tel (410) 789-8800 SIC 2819 3313 3356

H C STARCK INC p 649
45 Industrial Pl, Newton MA 02461
Tel (617) 630-5800 SIC 3339 3356 3313

■ CANNON-MUSKEGON CORP p 247
2875 Lincoln St, Norton Shores MI 49441
Tel (231) 759-2831
SIC 3313 3341 3339 3312

VDM METALS USA LLC p 1546
306 Columbia Tpke, Florham Park NJ 07932
Tel (973) 437-1664 SIC 3313

MEDIMA LLC p 938
5727 Strickler Rd, Clarence NY 14031
Tel (716) 741-0400 SIC 3339 3313

■ SIRONA DENTAL SYSTEMS INC p 1327
3030 47th Ave Ste 500, Long Island City NY 11101
Tel (718) 482-2011
SIC 8021 3313 3843 3841

■ REAL ALLOY HOLDING INC p 1213
3700 Park East Dr Ste 300, Beachwood OH 44122
Tel (216) 755-8800 SIC 3341 3313 3334

MARIETTA ERAMET INC p 906
16705 State Route 7, Marietta OH 45750
Tel (740) 374-1000 SIC 3313

GLOBE METALLURGICAL INC p 618
County Road 32, Waterford OH 45786
Tel (740) 984-2361 SIC 3339 3313 2819

ELKEM HOLDING INC p 488
Airport Office Park Bldg, Coraopolis PA 15108
Tel (412) 299-7200 SIC 3313

NEH INC p 1024
Airport Ofc Pk Bl 2 400 R, Coraopolis PA 15108
Tel (412) 299-7200 SIC 3313 6719

▲ KENNAMETAL INC p 810
600 Grant St Ste 5100, Pittsburgh PA 15219
Tel (412) 248-8200
SIC 3545 3532 3531 3313 3399

■ READING ALLOYS INC p 1213
220 Old West Penn Ave, Robesonia PA 19551
Tel (610) 693-5822 SIC 3313 3341

GLOBAL TUNGSTEN & POWDERS CORP p 617
1 Hawes St, Towanda PA 18848
Tel (570) 268-5000 SIC 3313 3291

METALLURG HOLDINGS INC p 952
435 Devon Park Dr Ste 200, Wayne PA 19087
Tel (610) 293-0838 SIC 3313 1081

METALLURG INC p 952
435 Devon Park Dr Ste 200, Wayne PA 19087
Tel (610) 293-2501 SIC 3313 1081

TRAVIS PATTERN & FOUNDRY INC p 1475
1413 E Hawthorne Rd, Spokane WA 99218
Tel (509) 466-1798
SIC 3523 3369 3313 3321 3625

SIC 3315 Steel Wire Drawing & Nails & Spikes

TREE ISLAND WIRE (USA) INC p 1475
3880 Valley Blvd, Walnut CA 91789
Tel (909) 594-7511 SIC 3315

■ RSCC WIRE & CABLE LLC p 1255
20 Bradley Park Rd, East Granby CT 06026
Tel (860) 653-8300 SIC 3357 3315

WIREMOLD CO p 1618
60 Woodlawn St, West Hartford CT 06110
Tel (860) 233-6251
SIC 3644 3643 3496 3315

■ PHELPS DODGE INTERNATIONAL CORP p 1141
9850 Nw 41st St Ste 200, Doral FL 33178
Tel (305) 648-7888 SIC 8742 3357 3315

■ FLAG INTERMEDIATE HOLDINGS CORP p 554
2400 E Coml Blvd Ste 905, Fort Lauderdale FL 33308
Tel (954) 202-4000 SIC 5051 3354 3315

GERDAU AMERISTEEL US INC p 608
4221 W Boy Scout Blvd # 600, Tampa FL 33607
Tel (813) 286-8383 SIC 3312 3449 3315

GERDAU USA INC p 608
4221 W Boy Scout Blvd, Tampa FL 33607
Tel (813) 286-8383 SIC 3312 3449 3315

BROWN INDUSTRIES INC p 219
205 W Industrial Blvd, Dalton GA 30720
Tel (706) 277-1977
SIC 2759 5131 2273 3552 3315 2671

HEICO COMPANIES L L C p 680
5600 Three First Nat Plz, Chicago IL 60602
Tel (312) 419-8220
SIC 3315 3589 3448 3531 1731 3663

FORT WAYNE METALS RESEARCH PRODUCTS CORP p 569
9609 Ardmore Ave, Fort Wayne IN 46809
Tel (260) 747-4154 SIC 3315

■ GROUP DEKKO INC p 641
2505 Dekko Dr, Garrett IN 46738
Tel (260) 357-3621
SIC 3479 3469 3643 3315 3089

■ G K TECHNOLOGIES INC p 587
4 Tesseneer Dr, Highland Heights KY 41076
Tel (859) 572-8000 SIC 3357 3315

■ GENERAL CABLE INDUSTRIES INC p 599
4 Tesseneer Dr, Highland Heights KY 41076
Tel (859) 572-8000 SIC 3351 3315 3357

STEPHENS PIPE & STEEL LLC p 1386
2224 E Highway 619, Russell Springs KY 42642
Tel (270) 866-3331 SIC 5051 3315

ACCELLENT ACQUISITION CORP p 14
100 Fordham Rd Bldg C, Wilmington MA 01887
Tel (978) 570-6900
SIC 3841 3317 3679 3315 3552 3089

ACCELLENT HOLDINGS CORP p 14
100 Fordham Rd, Wilmington MA 01887
Tel (978) 570-6900
SIC 3841 3679 3315 3552 3317 3089

NATIONAL-STANDARD LLC p 1017
1631 Lake St, Niles MI 49120
Tel (269) 683-9902 SIC 3315 3496

SANDVIK INC p 1279
17-02 Nevins Rd, Fair Lawn NJ 07410
Tel (201) 794-5000
SIC 3316 3317 3356 3315 3545 3533

US WIRE & CABLE CORP p 1533
1 Flexon Plz, Newark NJ 07114
Tel (973) 824-5530 SIC 3052 3315

QUALITY COMPUTER ACCESSORIES INC p 1196
70 Ethel Rd W Ste 1, Piscataway NJ 08854
Tel (732) 572-2719
SIC 5063 5051 3315 3644

OKONITE CO p 1080
102 Hilltop Rd, Ramsey NJ 07446
Tel (201) 825-0300 SIC 3357 3315 3355

■ ARROW FASTENER CO LLC p 113
271 Mayhill St, Saddle Brook NJ 07663
Tel (201) 843-6900
SIC 3579 3315 3452 3542 2891 3586

■ HANDY & HARMAN p 657
1133 Westchester Ave N-222, White Plains NY 10604
Tel (914) 461-1300
SIC 3356 3399 3341 3317 3315

BLUE RIDGE METALS CORP p 192
180 Mills Gap Rd, Fletcher NC 28732
Tel (828) 687-2525 SIC 3399 3315

▲ INSTEEL INDUSTRIES INC p 747
1373 Boggs Dr, Mount Airy NC 27030
Tel (336) 786-2141 SIC 3315

■ INSTEEL WIRE PRODUCTS CO p 747
1373 Boggs Dr, Mount Airy NC 27030
Tel (336) 719-9000 SIC 3315

▲ WILLIAMS INDUSTRIES INC p 1611
1128 Tyler Farms Dr, Raleigh NC 27603
Tel (919) 604-1746
SIC 3441 1531 1541 3315 1791

AMERICAN SPRING WIRE CORP p 79
26300 Miles Rd, Bedford Heights OH 44146
Tel (216) 292-4620
SIC 3272 3315 3316 3339 3624

BEKAERT CORP p 169
3200 W Market St Ste 303, Fairlawn OH 44333
Tel (330) 867-3325 SIC 3315

BEKAERT NORTH AMERICA MANAGEMENT CORP p 169
3200 W Market St Ste 303, Fairlawn OH 44333
Tel (330) 867-3325 SIC 3315

DAYTON SUPERIOR CORP p 418
1125 Byers Rd, Miamisburg OH 45342
Tel (937) 866-0711
SIC 3315 3452 3462 3089 2899

BARRETTE OUTDOOR LIVING INC p 157
7830 Freeway Cir, Middleburg Heights OH 44130
Tel (440) 891-0790 SIC 3315

DW-NATIONAL STANDARD-STILLWATER LLC p 463
3602 N Perkins Rd, Stillwater OK 74075
Tel (405) 377-5050 SIC 3315

GAFP INC p 589
1555 N Mingo Rd, Tulsa OK 74116
Tel (918) 835-0898 SIC 3315

DRS LAUREL TECHNOLOGIES p 457
246 Airport Rd, Johnstown PA 15904
Tel (814) 534-8900 SIC 3672 3315

BOMBARDIER TRANSPORTATION (HOLDINGS) USA INC p 199
1501 Lebanon Church Rd, Pittsburgh PA 15236
Tel (412) 655-5700 SIC 3743 3315 3823

INTERMETRO INDUSTRIES CORP p 753
651 N Washington St, Wilkes Barre PA 18705
Tel (570) 825-2741
SIC 3496 2542 3537 3411 3315 2441

WIREROPE WORKS INC p 1618
100 Maynard St, Williamsport PA 17701
Tel (570) 327-4229 SIC 3496 2298 3315

▲ CARPENTER TECHNOLOGY CORP p 260
2 Meridian Blvd, Wyomissing PA 19610
Tel (610) 208-2000
SIC 3312 3443 3255 3316 3315

ACS INDUSTRIES INC p 19
1 New England Way Unit 1, Lincoln RI 02865
Tel (401) 769-4700
SIC 3291 3496 3312 3315 3569 3991

■ KEYSTONE CONSOLIDATED INDUSTRIES INC p 815
5430 Lyndon B Johnson Fwy # 1740, Dallas TX 75240
Tel (800) 441-0308 SIC 3312 3315

MASTER-HALCO INC p 918
3010 Lbj Fwy Ste 800, Dallas TX 75234
Tel (972) 714-7300
SIC 3315 5039 3496 3446 5031 1799

SUNCOAST POST-TENSION LTD p 1402
509 N Sam Houston Pkwy E # 300, Houston TX 77060
Tel (281) 445-8886
SIC 3315 3316 3496 3449

■ NEENAH FOUNDRY CO p 1024
2121 Brooks Ave, Neenah WI 54956
Tel (920) 725-7000 SIC 3321 3315

SIC 3316 Cold Rolled Steel Sheet, Strip & Bars

■ ALABAMA METAL INDUSTRIES CORP p 43
3245 Fayette Ave, Birmingham AL 35208
Tel (205) 787-2611
SIC 3446 3449 3089 3441 3316

▲ EASTERN CO p 472
112 Bridge St, Naugatuck CT 06770
Tel (203) 729-2255
SIC 3429 3452 3316 2439

ULBRICH STAINLESS STEELS & SPECIAL METALS INC p 1500
153 Washington Ave, North Haven CT 06473
Tel (203) 239-4481
SIC 3316 3356 5051 3341 3312

ARCELORMITTAL USA LLC p 104
1 S Dearborn St Ste 1800, Chicago IL 60603
Tel (312) 346-0300
SIC 3312 3325 3356 3316

LAPHAM-HICKEY STEEL CORP p 845
5500 W 73rd St, Chicago IL 60638
Tel (708) 496-6111
SIC 5051 3398 3355 3317 3316

MADISON INDUSTRIES HOLDINGS LLC p 894
500 W Madison St Ste 3890, Chicago IL 60661
Tel (312) 277-0156
SIC 6719 5051 3443 3316

TEMPEL STEEL CO p 1436
5500 N Wolcott Ave, Chicago IL 60640
Tel (773) 250-8000
SIC 3469 3313 3316 3398 5051

COREY STEEL CO p 370
2800 S 61st Ct, Cicero IL 60804
Tel (800) 323-2750 SIC 3316 5051

ARCELORMITTAL RIVERDALE INC p 104
13500 S Perry Ave, Riverdale IL 60827
Tel (708) 849-8803 SIC 3316

DERINGER-NEY INC p 431
616 Atrium Dr Ste 100, Vernon Hills IL 60061
Tel (847) 566-4100
SIC 3643 3542 3469 3452 3316

S&S STEEL SERVICES INC p 1263
444 E 29th St, Anderson IN 46016
Tel (765) 622-4545 SIC 5051 3316

▲ STEEL DYNAMICS INC p 1384
7575 W Jefferson Blvd, Fort Wayne IN 46804
Tel (260) 969-3500 SIC 3312 3316 7389

NIAGARA LASALLE CORP p 1042
1412 150th St, Hammond IN 46327
Tel (219) 853-6000 SIC 3316

I/N TEK LP p 725
30755 Edison Rd, New Carlisle IN 46552
Tel (574) 654-1000 SIC 3316

COMPANHIA SIDERURGICA NACIONAL LLC p 350
455 W Industrial Dr, Terre Haute IN 47802
Tel (812) 299-4157 SIC 3316 3312

SIOUX CITY FOUNDRY CO p 1326
801 Division St, Sioux City IA 51105
Tel (712) 252-4181
SIC 5051 3443 3321 3316 3444 3441

NORTH AMERICAN STAINLESS p 1050
6870 Us Highway 42 E, Ghent KY 41045
Tel (502) 347-6000 SIC 3316 3312

NUMIT LLC p 1067
15415 Shelbyville Rd, Louisville KY 40245
Tel (502) 245-2110 SIC 3316

STEEL TECHNOLOGIES LLC p 1384
700 N Hurstbourne Pkwy, Louisville KY 40222
Tel (502) 245-2110 SIC 3312 3316

BHS CORRUGATED - NORTH AMERICA INC p 180
9103 Yellow Brick Rd N, Baltimore MD 21237
Tel (410) 574-1550 SIC 5084 7699 3316

THOMPSON STEEL CO INC p 1449
120 Royall St Ste 2, Canton MA 02021
Tel (781) 828-8800 SIC 5051 3316

■ ATI ALLEGHENY LUDLUM INC p 124
1357 E Rodney French Blvd, New Bedford MA 02744
Tel (508) 992-4067 SIC 3316

GERDAU MACSTEEL INC p 608
5591 Morrill Rd, Jackson MI 49201
Tel (517) 782-0415 SIC 3316 3312

NATIONAL GALVANIZING LP p 1012
1500 Telb St, Monroe MI 48162
Tel (734) 243-1882
SIC 3312 3316 3471 3341 5051

SANDVIK INC p 1279
17-02 Nevins Rd, Fair Lawn NJ 07410
Tel (201) 794-5000
SIC 3316 3317 3356 3315 3545 3533

▲ GIBRALTAR INDUSTRIES INC p 611
3556 Lake Shore Rd # 100, Buffalo NY 14219
Tel (716) 826-6500
SIC 3499 3316 3441 3398

■ SUNLIGHT US CO INC p 1403
3556 Lake Shore Rd # 100, Buffalo NY 14219
Tel (716) 826-6500
SIC 3499 3316 3441 3398

RENCO GROUP INC p 1223
1 Rockefeller Plz Fl 29, New York NY 10020
Tel (212) 541-6000
SIC 3312 3316 2514 2511 3171 3496

AMERICAN SPRING WIRE CORP p 79
26300 Miles Rd, Bedford Heights OH 44146
Tel (216) 292-4620
SIC 3272 3315 3316 3339 3624

CENTAUR INC p 275
2401 Front St, Toledo OH 43605
Tel (419) 469-8000 SIC 3312 3316 3999

HEIDTMAN STEEL PRODUCTS INC p 681
2401 Front St, Toledo OH 43605
Tel (419) 691-4646 SIC 3316 3312

▲WORTHINGTON INDUSTRIES INC p 1626
200 W Old Wlson Bridge Rd, Worthington OH 43085
Tel (614) 438-3210
SIC 3316 3449 3443 3325

■WORTHINGTON INDUSTRIES INC p 1626
200 W Old Wlson Bridge Rd, Worthington OH 43085
Tel (614) 438-3077 SIC 3316

NLMK PENNSYLVANIA LLC p 1045
15 Roemer Blvd, Farrell PA 16121
Tel (724) 983-6464 SIC 3316 3356 3312

■TDY INDUSTRIES LLC p 1429
1000 Six Ppg Pl, Pittsburgh PA 15222
Tel (412) 394-2896
SIC 3356 3312 3316 3339 3369

▲ CARPENTER TECHNOLOGY CORP p 260
2 Meridian Blvd, Wyomissing PA 19610
Tel (610) 208-2000
SIC 3312 3443 3255 3316 3315

BD VINTON LLC p 164
I-10 Vinton Rd, Canutillo TX 79835
Tel (915) 886-2000
SIC 5051 3312 3449 3316

SUNCOAST POST-TENSION LTD p 1402
509 N Sam Houston Pkwy E # 300, Houston TX 77060
Tel (281) 445-8886
SIC 3315 3316 3496 3449

■ RICHARDSON TRIDENT CO LLC p 1233
405 N Plano Rd, Richardson TX 75081
Tel (972) 231-5176
SIC 5051 5085 5063 5065 3316

GREER INDUSTRIES INC p 639
570 Canyon Rd, Morgantown WV 26508
Tel (304) 296-2549
SIC 3316 3272 2951 1422 3274 1446

ARCELORMITTAL WEIRTON INC p 104
100 Pennsylvania Ave, Weirton WV 26062
Tel (304) 797-2000 SIC 3316

WEIRTON STEEL CORP p 1588
400 Three Springs Dr, Weirton WV 26062
Tel (304) 797-2000 SIC 3312 3316

SIC 3317 Steel Pipe & Tubes

AMERICAN CAST IRON PIPE CO p 70
1501 31st Ave N, Birmingham AL 35207
Tel (205) 325-7856
SIC 3491 3369 3321 3053 3317

SOUTHLAND TUBE INC p 1351
3525 Richard Arringt, Birmingham AL 35234
Tel (205) 251-1884 SIC 3317

TUBULAR PRODUCTS CO p 1490
1400 Red Hollow Rd, Birmingham AL 35215
Tel (205) 856-1300 SIC 3317

■VALMONT NEWMARK INC p 1542
2 Perimeter Park S 475w, Birmingham AL 35243
Tel (205) 968-7200 SIC 3272 1731 3317

BERG SPIRAL PIPE CORP p 174
900 Paper Mill Rd, Mobile AL 36610
Tel (251) 330-2900 SIC 3317

WELSPUN TUBULAR LLC p 1591
9301 Frazier Pike, Little Rock AR 72206
Tel (501) 301-8800 SIC 3317

PRIMROSE ALLOYS INC p 1176
330 Primrose Rd Ste 205, Burlingame CA 94010
Tel (650) 678-5781 SIC 3317

CALIFORNIA STEEL INDUSTRIES INC p 241
14000 San Bernardino Ave, Fontana CA 92335
Tel (909) 350-6300 SIC 3312 3317

■AMERON INTERNATIONAL CORP p 84
245 S Los Robles Ave, Pasadena CA 91101
Tel (626) 683-4000
SIC 3272 3317 3273 1442 3084

SHAPCO INC p 1311
1666 20th St Ste 100, Santa Monica CA 90404
Tel (310) 264-1666 SIC 5051 3317 6799

CF&I STEEL LP p 285
1612 E Abriendo Ave, Pueblo CO 81004
Tel (719) 561-6000 SIC 3441 3317 3312

OPTIMA SPECIALTY STEEL INC p 1090
200 S Biscayne Blvd # 5500, Miami FL 33131
Tel (877) 289-2277 SIC 3317

■ CHATHAM STEEL CORP p 291
501 W Boundary St, Savannah GA 31401
Tel (912) 233-4182 SIC 5051 3317

ATLAS HOLDING INC p 128
1855 E 122nd St, Chicago IL 60633
Tel (773) 646-4500 SIC 3317

ATLAS TUBE (CHICAGO) LLC p 128
1855 E 122nd St, Chicago IL 60633
Tel (773) 646-4500 SIC 3317 3644

EVRAZ INC NA p 516
200 E Randolph St # 7800, Chicago IL 60601
Tel (312) 533-3621 SIC 3312 3317 3325

HARRIS WILLIAM & CO INC p 664
191 N Wacker Dr Ste 1500, Chicago IL 60606
Tel (312) 621-0590 SIC 6799 3317

LAPHAM-HICKEY STEEL CORP p 845
5500 W 73rd St, Chicago IL 60638
Tel (708) 496-6111
SIC 5051 3398 3355 3317 3316

WHEATLAND TUBE LLC p 1604
227 W Monroe St Ste 2600, Chicago IL 60606
Tel (312) 275-1600 SIC 3317 3644

WHI CAPITAL PARTNERS p 1605
191 N Wacker Dr Ste 1500, Chicago IL 60606
Tel (312) 621-0590 SIC 6799 3317

ZEKELMAN INDUSTRIES INC p 1641
227 W Monroe St Fl 26, Chicago IL 60606
Tel (312) 275-1600 SIC 3317

■ALLIED TUBE & CONDUIT CORP p 57
16100 Lathrop Ave, Harvey IL 60426
Tel (708) 339-1610 SIC 3317

■ATKORE INTERNATIONAL INC p 125
16100 Lathrop Ave, Harvey IL 60426
Tel (708) 339-1610 SIC 3317

D D G INC p 407
1955 Shermer Rd Ste 300, Northbrook IL 60062
Tel (847) 412-0277 SIC 3317 2511 6512

FORTERRA PRESSURE PIPE INC p 569
4416 Prairie Hill Rd, South Beloit IL 61080
Tel (815) 389-4800 SIC 3272 3317

PLYMOUTH TUBE CO p 1157
29w 150 Warrenville Rd, Warrenville IL 60555
Tel (630) 393-3550 SIC 3317 3354

GEORGETOWN METAL PROCESSING LLC p 607
650 Triport Rd, Georgetown KY 40324
Tel (502) 868-3450 SIC 3317

MICROGROUP INC p 962
7 Industrial Park Rd, Medway MA 02053
Tel (508) 533-4925
SIC 5051 3312 3498 3494 3492 3317

■WYMAN-GORDON CO p 1629
244 Worcester St, North Grafton MA 01536
Tel (508) 839-8252
SIC 3463 3462 3324 3728 3317

ACCELLENT ACQUISITION CORP p 14
100 Fordham Rd Bldg C, Wilmington MA 01887
Tel (978) 570-6900
SIC 3841 3317 3679 3315 3552 3089

ACCELLENT HOLDINGS CORP p 14
100 Fordham Rd, Wilmington MA 01887
Tel (978) 570-6900
SIC 3841 3679 3315 3552 3317 3089

TI AUTOMOTIVE LLC p 1452
2020 Taylor Rd, Auburn Hills MI 48326
Tel (248) 494-5000
SIC 3317 3312 3599 3052 3714 3585

TI GROUP AUTOMOTIVE SYSTEMS LLC p 1452
2020 Taylor Rd, Auburn Hills MI 48326
Tel (248) 296-8000
SIC 3317 3312 3599 3052 3714 3585

MARTINREA INDUSTRIES INC p 913
10501 Mi State Road 52, Manchester MI 48158
Tel (734) 428-2400
SIC 3714 3317 3089 3544

MICHIGAN SEAMLESS TUBE LLC p 961
400 Mcmunn St, South Lyon MI 48178
Tel (248) 486-0100 SIC 3317

ROLLED ALLOYS INC p 1247
125 W Sterns Rd, Temperance MI 48182
Tel (800) 521-0332
SIC 5051 3369 3341 3317 2899 2851

METAL-MATIC INC p 952
629 2nd St Se, Minneapolis MN 55414
Tel (612) 928-2856 SIC 3317

BOOMERANG TUBE LLC p 200
14567 North Outer 40 Rd # 500, Chesterfield MO 63017
Tel (636) 534-5555 SIC 3317

BULL MOOSE TUBE CO p 225
1819 Clarkson Rd Ste 100, Chesterfield MO 63017
Tel (636) 537-1249 SIC 3317

STUPP BROS INC p 1395
3800 Weber Rd, Saint Louis MO 63125
Tel (314) 638-5000 SIC 3441 3317 6022

▲VALMONT INDUSTRIES INC p 1541
1 Valmont Plz Ste 500, Omaha NE 68154
Tel (402) 963-1000
SIC 3441 3399 3317 3523 3612

■ ANVIL INTERNATIONAL LLC p 94
2 Holland Way, Exeter NH 03833
Tel (603) 418-2800
SIC 3498 3321 3317 3494 3429

■ RATHGIBSON NORTH BRANCH LLC p 1209
100 Aspen Hill Rd, Branchburg NJ 08876
Tel (908) 253-3260 SIC 3317

SANDVIK INC p 1279
17-02 Nevins Rd, Fair Lawn NJ 07410
Tel (201) 794-5000
SIC 3316 3317 3356 3315 3545 3533

■ SKYLINE STEEL LLC p 1330
8 Woodhollow Rd Ste 102, Parsippany NJ 07054
Tel (973) 428-6100 SIC 3317 5051

VASS PIPE & STEEL CO INC p 1545
158 3rd St Ste 2, Mineola NY 11501
Tel (516) 741-8398 SIC 5051 3317

■ HANDY & HARMAN p 657
1133 Westchester Ave N-222, White Plains NY 10604
Tel (914) 461-1300
SIC 3356 3399 3341 3317 3315

FORTILINE LLC p 569
7025 Northwinds Dr Nw, Concord NC 28027
Tel (704) 788-9800 SIC 3317 5085

AMERICAN STAINLESS TUBING INC p 79
129 Honeycutt Rd, Troutman NC 28166
Tel (704) 878-8823 SIC 3317

KIRTLAND CAPITAL PARTNERS LP p 822
3201 Entp Pkwy Ste 200, Beachwood OH 44122
Tel (216) 593-0100
SIC 5051 3312 3498 3494 3492 3317

ARCELORMITTAL TUBULAR PRODUCTS SHELBY LLC p 104
132 W Main St, Shelby OH 44875
Tel (419) 347-2424 SIC 3317 3321

CONTECH ENGINEERED SOLUTIONS INC p 362
9025 Centre Pointe Dr # 400, West Chester OH 45069
Tel (513) 645-7000
SIC 3444 3084 3317 3441 3443

CONTECH ENGINEERED SOLUTIONS LLC p 362
9025 Ctr Pinte Dr Ste 400, West Chester OH 45069
Tel (513) 645-7000
SIC 3444 3084 3317 3441 3443

VALLOUREC STAR LP p 1541
2669 M L K J Blvd, Youngstown OH 44510
Tel (330) 742-6300 SIC 3317

PARAGON INDUSTRIES INC p 1113
3378 W Highway 117, Sapulpa OK 74066
Tel (918) 291-4459 SIC 3317

PIPING AND EQUIPMENT p 1151
1001 Consol Energy Dr, Canonsburg PA 15317
Tel (724) 514-3990 SIC 3317

■ SUPERIOR TUBE CO INC p 1407
3900 Germantown Pike, Collegeville PA 19426
Tel (610) 489-5200 SIC 3317 3498

SUPERIOR GROUP INC p 1406
100 Front St Ste 525, Conshohocken PA 19428
Tel (610) 397-2040
SIC 5051 3357 3317 3491 3469 7389

MARCEGAGLIA USA INC p 905
1001 E Waterfront Dr, Munhall PA 15120
Tel (412) 462-2185 SIC 3317 3312

ARCELORMITTAL TUBULAR PRODUCTS USA LLC p 104
4 Gateway Ctr, Pittsburgh PA 15222
Tel (419) 342-1200 SIC 3317

▲ L B FOSTER CO p 833
415 Holiday Dr Ste 1, Pittsburgh PA 15220
Tel (412) 928-3417 SIC 3312 3272 3317

▲ UNITED STATES STEEL CORP p 1514
600 Grant St Ste 468, Pittsburgh PA 15219
Tel (412) 433-1121 SIC 3312 3317 3356

PTC GROUP HOLDINGS CORP p 1189
6051 Wallace Road Ext # 2, Wexford PA 15090
Tel (412) 299-7900 SIC 3317

STEEL AND PIPES INC p 1384
Road 1rio, Caguas PR 00725
Tel (787) 747-9415
SIC 5051 3446 3317 5085

JSW STEEL (USA) INC p 796
5200 E Mckinney Rd # 110, Baytown TX 77523
Tel (281) 383-2525 SIC 3317 3312

■ LONE STAR TECHNOLOGIES INC p 876
15660 Dallas Pkwy Ste 500, Dallas TX 75248
Tel (972) 770-6401 SIC 3317 3312

HANSON PRESSURE PIPE INC p 659
1003 Macarthur Blvd, Grand Prairie TX 75050
Tel (972) 262-3600 SIC 3317 3272 3999

BORUSAN MANNESMANN PIPE US INC p 201
363 N Sam H Pkwy E Ste 63, Houston TX 77060
Tel (832) 399-6000 SIC 3317

MAVERICK TUBE CORP p 921
2200 West Loop S Ste 800, Houston TX 77027
Tel (713) 767-4400 SIC 3317

TEJAS TUBULAR PRODUCTS INC p 1433
8799 North Loop E Ste 300, Houston TX 77029
Tel (281) 822-3400 SIC 3317 3498

TENARIS GLOBAL SERVICES (USA) CORP p 1437
2200 West Loop S Ste 800, Houston TX 77027
Tel (713) 767-4400 SIC 3317

V&M STAR A PARTNERSHIP WITH GENERAL AND LIMITED PARTNERS LP p 1538
8603 Sheldon Rd, Houston TX 77049
Tel (281) 456-6000 SIC 3317

AMERICAN BULK PIPE & STEEL LLC p 69
607 Oyster Shell Ct, Missouri City TX 77459
Tel (281) 431-3473 SIC 3317

PRIEFERT MFG CO INC p 1174
2630 S Jefferson Ave, Mount Pleasant TX 75455
Tel (903) 572-1741
SIC 3523 3446 3444 3317 3449

BOURLAND & LEVERICH SUPPLY CO LLC p 204
11707 Highway 152, Pampa TX 79065
Tel (806) 665-0061 SIC 3317

SDB TRADE INTERNATIONAL LP p 1295
817 Southmore Ave Ste 301, Pasadena TX 77502
Tel (713) 475-0048 SIC 3317

▲ SYNALLOY CORP p 1414
4510 Cox Rd Ste 201, Glen Allen VA 23060
Tel (864) 585-3605
SIC 3317 3443 2865 2899 2869

GRIFFIN PIPE PRODUCTS CO INC p 640
10 Adams St, Lynchburg VA 24504
Tel (434) 845-8021 SIC 3317

▲ NORTHWEST PIPE CO p 1060
5721 Se Columbia Way # 200, Vancouver WA 98661
Tel (360) 397-6250 SIC 3317 3443

UNITED STARS INC p 1512
1546 Henry Ave, Beloit WI 53511
Tel (608) 368-4625
SIC 3317 3351 3463 3613 3621

■ RATHGIBSON HOLDING CO LLC p 1209
2505 Foster Ave, Janesville WI 53545
Tel (608) 754-2222 SIC 3317 5051

■ RATHGIBSON LLC p 1209
2505 Foster Ave, Janesville WI 53545
Tel (608) 754-2222 SIC 3317

NELSON GLOBAL PRODUCTS INC p 1025
1560 Williams Dr, Stoughton WI 53589
Tel (608) 719-1800 SIC 3714 3317

SIC 3321 Gray Iron Foundries

AMERICAN CAST IRON PIPE CO p 70
1501 31st Ave N, Birmingham AL 35207
Tel (205) 325-7856
SIC 3491 3369 3321 3053 3317

MCWANE INC p 933
2900 Highway 280 S # 300, Birmingham AL 35223
Tel (205) 414-3100
SIC 3491 1221 3321 3312 3494

UNITED STATES PIPE AND FOUNDRY CO LLC p 1514
2 Chase Corporate Dr # 200, Hoover AL 35244
Tel (205) 263-8540 SIC 3321

U S HOLDINGS INC p 1497
3200 W 84th St, Hialeah FL 33018
Tel (305) 885-0301 SIC 3321 3543

UNITED STATES FOUNDRY & MANUFACTURING CORP p 1513
8351 Nw 93rd St, Medley FL 33166
Tel (305) 885-0301 SIC 3321 3441 3322

■ MUELLER GROUP LLC p 998
1200 Abernathy Rd, Atlanta GA 30328
Tel (770) 206-4200
SIC 3823 3321 3533 7699

▲ MUELLER WATER PRODUCTS INC p 998
1200 Abernathy Rd # 1200, Atlanta GA 30328
Tel (770) 206-4200
SIC 3491 3492 3494 3443 3321 3823

AMSTED INDUSTRIES INC p 87
180 N Stetson Ave, Chicago IL 60601
Tel (312) 645-1700
SIC 3443 3325 3585 3321 3743

USP HOLDINGS INC p 1535
6250 N Rver Rd Ste 10100, Des Plaines IL 60018
Tel (847) 604-6100 SIC 3321 3491

■ STANDARD CAR TRUCK CO INC p 1375
6400 Shafer Ct Ste 450, Rosemont IL 60018
Tel (847) 692-6050 SIC 3743 3321

METAL TECHNOLOGIES OF INDIANA INC p 952
1401 S Grandstaff Dr, Auburn IN 46706
Tel (260) 925-4717 SIC 3321 3443

BREMEN CASTINGS INC p 209
500 N Baltimore St, Bremen IN 46506
Tel (574) 546-2411 SIC 3321

TRANSPORTATION TECHNOLOGIES INDUSTRIES INC p 1473
7140 Office Cir, Evansville IN 47715
Tel (812) 962-5000
SIC 2531 3714 3321 4741 3471

ROCHESTER METAL PRODUCTS CORP p 1243
616 Indiana Ave, Rochester IN 46975
Tel (574) 223-3164 SIC 3321

INTAT PRECISION INC p 748
2148 N State Road 3, Rushville IN 46173
Tel (765) 932-5323 SIC 3321

DALTON CORP p 410
1900 E Jefferson St, Warsaw IN 46580
Tel (574) 267-8111 SIC 3321

NEW DALTON FOUNDRY LLC p 1029
1900 E Jefferson St, Warsaw IN 46580
Tel (574) 267-8111 SIC 3321

DEXTER APACHE HOLDINGS INC p 434
2211 W Grimes Ave, Fairfield IA 52556
Tel (641) 472-5131 SIC 3321 3592

SIOUX CITY FOUNDRY CO p 1326
801 Division St, Sioux City IA 51105
Tel (712) 252-4181
SIC 5051 3443 3321 3316 3444 3441

DVCC INC p 463
800 High St, Chestertown MD 21620
Tel (410) 778-2000
SIC 3492 5085 3535 3321 3364

▲ KADANT INC p 800
1 Technology Park Dr # 210, Westford MA 01886
Tel (978) 776-2000 SIC 3554 3321 2621

EJ AMERICAS LLC p 482
301 Spring St, East Jordan MI 49727
Tel (231) 536-2261 SIC 6719 3321

EJ GROUP INC p 482
301 Spring St, East Jordan MI 49727
Tel (231) 536-2261 SIC 3321

EJ USA INC p 482
301 Spring St, East Jordan MI 49727
Tel (800) 874-4100 SIC 3321

GREDE FOUNDRIES INC p 636
4000 Town Ctr Ste 500, Southfield MI 48075
Tel (248) 440-9500 SIC 3321

■ GREDE HOLDINGS LLC p 636
1 Towne Sq Ste 550, Southfield MI 48076
Tel (248) 440-9500 SIC 3321

■ GREDE II LLC p 636
4000 Town Ctr Ste 500, Southfield MI 48075
Tel (248) 522-4500 SIC 3321

■ GREDE LLC p 636
1 Towne Sq Ste 550, Southfield MI 48076
Tel (248) 440-9500 SIC 3321

WATEROUS CO p 1582
125 Hardman Ave S, South Saint Paul MN 55075
Tel (651) 450-5000
SIC 3491 3561 3494 3321

BRADKEN INC p 206
12200 N Ambassador Dr # 647, Kansas City MO 64163
Tel (816) 270-0700 SIC 3325 3321 3312

■ANVIL INTERNATIONAL LLC p 94
2 Holland Way, Exeter NH 03833
Tel (603) 418-2800
SIC 3498 3321 3317 3494 3429

ALSTOM USA INC p 61
1 Transit Dr, Hornell NY 14843
Tel (607) 324-4595 SIC 3321 7699

HITACHI METALS AMERICA LTD p 697
2 Manhattanville Rd # 301, Purchase NY 10577
Tel (914) 694-9200
SIC 3264 3577 3365 5051 3321 3559

CHARLOTTE PIPE AND FOUNDRY CO p 290
2109 Randolph Rd, Charlotte NC 28207
Tel (704) 372-5030 SIC 3084 3089 3321

ELYRIA FOUNDRY CO LLC p 490
120 Filbert St, Elyria OH 44035
Tel (440) 322-4657
SIC 3321 3369 3325 2821

OSCO INDUSTRIES INC p 1096
734 11th St, Portsmouth OH 45662
Tel (740) 354-3183 SIC 3321

ARCELORMITTAL TUBULAR PRODUCTS SHELBY LLC p 104
132 W Main St, Shelby OH 44875
Tel (419) 347-2424 SIC 3317 3321

■ HOBART CORP p 698
701 S Ridge Ave, Troy OH 45374
Tel (937) 332-3000
SIC 3589 3556 3596 3585 3321

BENTON FOUNDRY INC p 173
5297 State Route 487, Benton PA 17814
Tel (570) 925-6711 SIC 3321

WARD MANUFACTURING LLC p 1575
117 Gulick St, Blossburg PA 16912
Tel (570) 638-2131 SIC 3321 3322 3498

VICTAULIC CO p 1555
4901 Kesslersville Rd, Easton PA 18040
Tel (610) 559-3300
SIC 3321 3491 3494 5085

R H SHEPPARD CO INC p 1202
101 Philadelphia St, Hanover PA 17331
Tel (717) 637-3751 *SIC* 3714 3321 3594

MCLANAHAN CORP p 930
200 Wall St, Hollidaysburg PA 16648
Tel (814) 695-9807
SIC 3532 3321 3599 3523

TYCO FIRE PRODUCTS LP p 1496
1400 Pennbrook Pkwy, Lansdale PA 19446
Tel (215) 362-0700
SIC 3569 3494 3321 5085

HITACHI METALS AUTOMOTIVE COMPONENTS USA LLC p 697
18986 Route 287, Tioga PA 16946
Tel (217) 347-0600 *SIC* 3465 3321 3559

DONSCO INC p 451
124 N Front St, Wrightsville PA 17368
Tel (717) 252-0690 *SIC* 3398 3321

MARTIN SPROCKET & GEAR INC p 913
3100 Sprocket Dr, Arlington TX 76015
Tel (817) 258-3000
SIC 3566 3568 3535 3321 3462 3429

GAS EQUIPMENT CO INC p 593
11616 Harry Hines Blvd, Dallas TX 75229
Tel (972) 241-2333 *SIC* 5084 5085 3321

INTERMET CORP p 753
301 Commerce St Ste 2901, Fort Worth TX 76102
Tel (817) 348-9190
SIC 3321 3714 3462 3365 3364

▲ FLOWSERVE CORP p 560
5215 N Oconnor Blvd Connor, Irving TX 75039
Tel (972) 443-6500
SIC 3561 3491 3621 3494 3463 3321

■ LUFKIN INDUSTRIES LLC p 884
601 S Raguet St, Lufkin TX 75904
Tel (936) 634-2211 *SIC* 3561 3321 3462

MCWANE INC p 933
11910 County Road 492, Tyler TX 75706
Tel (800) 527-8478 *SIC* 3321

H D FOWLER CO INC p 649
13440 Se 30th St, Bellevue WA 98005
Tel (425) 746-8400
SIC 5084 5083 5085 3321

TRAVIS PATTERN & FOUNDRY INC p 1475
1413 E Hawthorne Rd, Spokane WA 99218
Tel (509) 466-1798
SIC 3523 3369 3313 3321 3625

■ BRILLION IRON WORKS INC p 213
200 Park Ave, Brillion WI 54110
Tel (920) 756-2121 *SIC* 3321

■ NEENAH FOUNDRY CO p 1024
2121 Brooks Ave, Neenah WI 54956
Tel (920) 725-7000 *SIC* 3321 3315

■ NFC CASTINGS INC p 1041
2121 Brooks Ave, Neenah WI 54956
Tel (920) 725-7000 *SIC* 3325 3321

METSO MINERALS INDUSTRIES INC p 957
20965 Crossroads Cir, Waukesha WI 53186
Tel (262) 798-3994
SIC 3321 3069 3561 3535 3532

HITACHI METALS FOUNDRY AMERICA INC p 697
1955 Brunner Dr, Waupaca WI 54981
Tel (715) 258-6600 *SIC* 3321

WAUPACA FOUNDRY INC p 1583
1955 Brunner Dr, Waupaca WI 54981
Tel (715) 258-6611 *SIC* 3321

SIC 3322 Malleable Iron Foundries

UNITED STATES FOUNDRY & MANUFACTURING CORP p 1513
8351 Nw 93rd St, Medley FL 33166
Tel (305) 885-0301 *SIC* 3321 3441 3322

WARD MANUFACTURING LLC p 1575
117 Gulick St, Blossburg PA 16912
Tel (570) 638-2131 *SIC* 3321 3322 3498

SIC 3324 Steel Investment Foundries

ALIGN AEROSPACE HOLDING INC p 50
21123 Nordhoff St, Chatsworth CA 91311
Tel (818) 727-7800 *SIC* 3324

▲ STURM RUGER & CO INC p 1395
1 Lacey Pl, Southport CT 06890
Tel (203) 259-7843 *SIC* 3484 3324

HAMILTON SUNDSTRAND SERVICE CORP p 655
1 Hamilton Rd, Windsor Locks CT 06096
Tel (860) 654-6000 *SIC* 3324

AE INDUSTRIAL PARTNERS LLC p 28
2500 N Military Trl # 470, Boca Raton FL 33431
Tel (561) 372-7820 *SIC* 3369 3324

■ WYMAN-GORDON CO p 1629
244 Worcester St, North Grafton MA 01536
Tel (508) 839-8252
SIC 3463 3462 3324 3728 3317

■ HOWMET HOLDINGS CORP p 713
1 Misco Dr, Whitehall MI 49461
Tel (231) 894-5686
SIC 3324 3542 5051 3479

HITCHINER MANUFACTURING CO INC p 697
594 Elm St, Milford NH 03055
Tel (603) 673-1100 *SIC* 3324

UNIMET METAL SUPPLY INC p 1503
150 Lackawanna Ave, Parsippany NJ 07054
Tel (973) 673-5700 *SIC* 3324

CPP-SYRACUSE INC p 387
901 E Genesee St, Chittenango NY 13037
Tel (315) 687-0014 *SIC* 3324 3369 3356

CONSOLIDATED PRECISION PRODUCTS CORP p 360
1621 Euclid Ave Ste 1850, Cleveland OH 44115
Tel (909) 595-2252 *SIC* 3365 3324

■ HOWMET CASTINGS & SERVICES INC p 713
1616 Harvard Ave, Newburgh Heights OH 44105
Tel (216) 641-4400 *SIC* 3324

■ HOWMET CORP p 713
1616 Harvard Ave, Newburgh Heights OH 44105
Tel (800) 242-9898
SIC 3324 3542 5051 3479

■ PRECISION CASTPARTS CORP p 1168
4650 Sw Mcdam Ave Ste 300, Portland OR 97239
Tel (503) 946-4800
SIC 3324 3369 3724 3511 3519

TRIUMPH STRUCTURES - EAST TEXAS p 1483
899 Cassatt Rd Ste 210, Berwyn PA 19312
Tel (610) 251-1000 *SIC* 3324

ESMARK INC p 509
100 Hazel Ln Ste 300, Sewickley PA 15143
Tel (412) 259-8868 *SIC* 1382 3324

CONSOLIDATED CASTING CORP p 359
1501 S Interstate 45, Hutchins TX 75141
Tel (972) 225-7305 *SIC* 3324 3369

SIGNICAST LLC p 1322
1800 Innovation Way, Hartford WI 53027
Tel (262) 673-2700 *SIC* 3324

SIC 3325 Steel Foundries, NEC

LIGON INDUSTRIES LLC p 866
1927 1st Ave N Ste 500, Birmingham AL 35203
Tel (205) 322-3302
SIC 3365 3593 3325 3471 3714 3446

KARSTEN MANUFACTURING CORP p 804
2201 W Desert Cove Ave, Phoenix AZ 85029
Tel (602) 870-5000
SIC 3949 3398 3363 3325 8711 7997

EDELBROCK FOUNDRY CORP p 477
1320 S Buena Vista St, San Jacinto CA 92583
Tel (951) 654-6677 *SIC* 3363 3365 3325

AMSTED INDUSTRIES INC p 87
180 N Stetson Ave, Chicago IL 60601
Tel (312) 645-1700
SIC 3443 3325 3585 3321 3743

ARCELORMITTAL USA LLC p 104
1 S Dearborn St Ste 1800, Chicago IL 60603
Tel (312) 346-0300
SIC 3312 3325 3356 3316

EVRAZ INC NA p 516
200 E Randolph St # 7800, Chicago IL 60601
Tel (312) 533-3621 *SIC* 3312 3317 3325

US TSUBAKI POWER TRANSMISSION LLC p 1533
301 E Marquardt Dr, Wheeling IL 60090
Tel (847) 459-9500
SIC 3568 5085 5063 3714 3462 3325

HARRISON STEEL CASTINGS CO p 664
900 S Mound St, Attica IN 47918
Tel (765) 762-2481 *SIC* 3325

SIVYER STEEL CORP p 1328
225 33rd St, Bettendorf IA 52722
Tel (563) 355-1811 *SIC* 3325

BRADKEN - ATCHISON/ST JOSEPH INC p 206
400 S 4th St, Atchison KS 66002
Tel (913) 367-2121 *SIC* 3325

E2 ACQUISITION CORP p 467
1430 Sparrows Point Blvd, Baltimore MD 21219
Tel (410) 388-3000 *SIC* 3325

HURON CASTING INC p 721
7050 Hartley St, Pigeon MI 48755
Tel (989) 453-3933 *SIC* 3325 3369

RCO ENGINEERING INC p 1212
29200 Calahan Rd, Roseville MI 48066
Tel (586) 774-0100
SIC 3714 3089 3365 7361 3325 2531

■ STEEL DYNAMICS COLUMBUS LLC p 1384
1945 Airport Rd, Columbus MS 39701
Tel (662) 245-4200 *SIC* 3325

BRADKEN INC p 206
12200 N Ambassador Dr # 647, Kansas City MO 64163
Tel (816) 270-0700 *SIC* 3325 3321 3312

▲ HC2 HOLDINGS INC p 671
450 Park Ave Fl 30, New York NY 10022
Tel (212) 235-2690 *SIC* 4813 3325 8731

COLUMBUS STEEL CASTINGS CO p 342
2211 Parsons Ave, Columbus OH 43207
Tel (614) 444-2121 *SIC* 3325

JMAC INC p 786
200 W Nationwide Blvd # 1, Columbus OH 43215
Tel (614) 436-2418
SIC 3325 5198 7999 5511 8741

ELYRIA FOUNDRY CO LLC p 490
120 Filbert St, Elyria OH 44035
Tel (440) 322-4657
SIC 3321 3369 3325 2821

▲ WORTHINGTON INDUSTRIES INC p 1626
200 W Old Wilson Bridge Rd, Worthington OH 43085
Tel (614) 438-3210
SIC 3316 3449 3443 3325

COLUMBIA STEEL CASTING CO INC p 342
10425 N Bloss Ave, Portland OR 97203
Tel (503) 286-0685 *SIC* 3325

ESCO CORP p 509
2141 Nw 25th Ave, Portland OR 97210
Tel (360) 690-0074
SIC 3535 3545 3325 3531

■ UNION ELECTRIC STEEL CORP p 1504
726 Bell Ave, Carnegie PA 15106
Tel (412) 429-7655 *SIC* 3325 3398 3312

WHEMCO INC p 1605
5 Hot Metal St Ste 300, Pittsburgh PA 15203
Tel (412) 390-2700
SIC 3312 3462 3731 3325 3441 3369

HENSLEY INDUSTRIES INC p 685
2108 Joe Field Rd, Dallas TX 75229
Tel (972) 241-2321 *SIC* 3325

■ SFI-GRAY STEEL LLC p 1310
3511 W 12th St, Houston TX 77008
Tel (713) 864-6450 *SIC* 3325 5051

MATRIX METALS HOLDINGS INC p 920
126 Collins Rd, Richmond TX 77469
Tel (281) 633-4263 *SIC* 3325

MATRIX METALS LLC p 920
126 Collins Rd, Richmond TX 77469
Tel (281) 342-5511 *SIC* 3325

DELTA CENTRIFUGAL CORP p 426
3402 Center St, Temple TX 76504
Tel (254) 773-9055 *SIC* 5051 3325 3369

CHICAGO BRIDGE & IRON CO (DELAWARE) p 297
2103 Research Forest Dr, The Woodlands TX 77380
Tel (832) 513-1000 *SIC* 8711 3325 3462

■ REXNORD LLC p 1230
3001 W Canal St, Milwaukee WI 53208
Tel (414) 342-3131 *SIC* 3566 3325 3599

■ NFC CASTINGS INC p 1041
2121 Brooks Ave, Neenah WI 54956
Tel (920) 725-7000 *SIC* 3325 3321

SIC 3331 Primary Smelting & Refining Of Copper

■ SOUTHERN COPPER CORP p 1348
1440 E Missouri Ave # 160, Phoenix AZ 85014
Tel (602) 264-1375
SIC 1021 3331 1031 1061 1044

▲ AMERICAS MINING CORP p 81
1150 N 7th Ave, Tucson AZ 85705
Tel (520) 798-7500
SIC 1021 1044 1031 1041 3331

■ AR SILVER BELL INC p 102
5285 E Williams Cir, Tucson AZ 85711
Tel (520) 798-7500
SIC 1021 1044 1031 1041 3331 3339

■ ASARCO LLC p 115
5285 E Williams Cir # 2000, Tucson AZ 85711
Tel (520) 798-7500
SIC 1021 1044 1031 1041 3331 3339

■ CERRO FLOW PRODUCTS LLC p 284
3000 Mississippi Ave, Sauget IL 62206
Tel (618) 337-6000
SIC 3351 3331 3498 3585 5051

PMX INDUSTRIES INC p 1158
5300 Willow Creek Dr Sw, Cedar Rapids IA 52404
Tel (319) 368-7700
SIC 3366 5051 3444 3364 3351 3331

IMC-METALSAMERICA LLC p 733
135 Old Boiling Sprng Rd, Shelby NC 28152
Tel (704) 482-8200 *SIC* 3331

■ MATERION TECHNICAL MATERIALS INC p 919
5 Wellington Rd, Lincoln RI 02865
Tel (401) 333-1700 *SIC* 3331 3339 3423

SIC 3334 Primary Production Of Aluminum

▲ KAISER ALUMINUM CORP p 800
27422 Portola Pkwy # 200, Foothill Ranch CA 92610
Tel (949) 614-1740
SIC 3334 3353 3354 3355

■ KAISER ALUMINUM FABRICATED PRODUCTS LLC p 800
27422 Portola Pkwy # 200, Foothill Ranch CA 92610
Tel (949) 614-1740
SIC 3353 3334 3354 3355

■ KAISER ALUMINUM INVESTMENTS CO p 800
27422 Portola Pkwy # 350, Foothill Ranch CA 92610
Tel (949) 614-1740
SIC 3353 3334 3354 3355

▲ CENTURY ALUMINUM CO p 281
1 S Wacker Dr Ste 1000, Chicago IL 60606
Tel (312) 696-3101 *SIC* 3334

CLOSURE SYSTEMS INTERNATIONAL INC p 327
7702 Woodland Dr Ste 200, Indianapolis IN 46278
Tel (317) 390-5000 *SIC* 3334 3565

■ CENTURY ALUMINUM SEBREE LLC p 282
9404 State Route 2096, Robards KY 42452
Tel (270) 521-7811 *SIC* 3334

NORANDA ALUMINA LLC p 1047
1111 E Airline Hwy Us61, Gramercy LA 70052
Tel (225) 869-2100 *SIC* 3334

NORANDA ALUMINUM INC p 1047
St Jude Industrial Park, New Madrid MO 63869
Tel (573) 643-2361
SIC 3353 3354 3334 3714

METAL EXCHANGE CORP p 952
111 West Port Plz Ste 350, Saint Louis MO 63146
Tel (314) 542-7250 *SIC* 3334 5093

▲ ARCONIC INC p 106
390 Park Ave, New York NY 10022
Tel (212) 836-2674 *SIC* 3334 3353 1099

3A COMPOSITES USA INC p 2
3480 Taylorsville Hwy, Statesville NC 28625
Tel (704) 872-8974
SIC 3334 2679 3081 3449

■ REAL ALLOY HOLDING INC p 1213
3700 Park East Dr Ste 300, Beachwood OH 44122
Tel (216) 755-8800 *SIC* 3341 3313 3334

ORMET CORP p 1095
43840 State Rte 7, Hannibal OH 43931
Tel (740) 483-1381 *SIC* 3334

ORMET PRIMARY ALUMINUM CORP p 1095
43840 State Rt 7, Hannibal OH 43931
Tel (740) 483-1381 *SIC* 3334 3297

ALCAN PRIMARY PRODUCTS CORP p 47
6055 Rockside Woods Blvd, Independence OH 44131
Tel (440) 460-3300 *SIC* 3334

OLD LADDER CO p 1081
93 Werner Rd, Greenville PA 16125
Tel (888) 523-3371
SIC 3446 3089 3334 3444 3499

■ ALCOA MEXICO HOLDINGS LLC p 47
201 Isabella St, Pittsburgh PA 15212
Tel (412) 553-4545 *SIC* 3334

■ ALUMAX LLC p 63
201 Isabella St, Pittsburgh PA 15212
Tel (412) 553-4545
SIC 3334 3353 3354 3449 3442 3446

NORANDA ALUMINUM HOLDING CORP p 1047
801 Crescent Cntre Dr 6 Ste 600, Franklin TN 37067
Tel (615) 771-5700 *SIC* 3334 2819 3353

NORANDA INTERMEDIATE HOLDING CORP p 1047
801 Crescent Centre Dr, Franklin TN 37067
Tel (615) 771-5700
SIC 3353 3334 3714 3354

■ INTALCO ALUMINUM LLC p 748
4050 Mountain View Rd, Ferndale WA 98248
Tel (360) 384-7061 *SIC* 3334

SIC 3339 Primary Nonferrous Metals, NEC

■ AR SILVER BELL INC p 102
5285 E Williams Cir, Tucson AZ 85711
Tel (520) 798-7500
SIC 1021 1044 1031 1041 3331 3339

■ ASARCO LLC p 115
5285 E Williams Cir # 2000, Tucson AZ 85711
Tel (520) 798-7500
SIC 1021 1044 1031 1041 3331 3339

GLOBE SPECIALTY METALS INC p 618
600 Brickell Ave Ste 3100, Miami FL 33131
Tel (786) 509-6900 *SIC* 3339 3313

NETSHAPE TECHNOLOGIES INC p 1027
3620 Paoli Pike Ste 8, Floyds Knobs IN 47119
Tel (812) 248-9273 *SIC* 3339

▲ CABOT CORP p 235
2 Seaport Ln Ste 1300, Boston MA 02210
Tel (617) 345-0100
SIC 2895 3081 3084 2819 3339

H C STARCK INC p 649
45 Industrial Pl, Newton MA 02461
Tel (617) 630-5800 *SIC* 3339 3356 3313

■ CANNON-MUSKEGON CORP p 247
2875 Lincoln St, Norton Shores MI 49441
Tel (231) 759-2831
SIC 3313 3341 3339 3312

MISSISSIPPI SILICON LLC p 976
80 County Road 210, Burnsville MS 38833
Tel (662) 696-2600 *SIC* 3339

DOE RUN RESOURCES CORP p 447
1801 Park 270 Dr Ste 300, Saint Louis MO 63146
Tel (314) 453-7100 *SIC* 1031 1021 3339

REC ADVANCED SILICON MATERIALS LLC p 1214
119140 Rick Jones Way, Butte MT 59750
Tel (406) 496-9898 *SIC* 3339

BASF CATALYSTS LLC p 158
25 Middlesex Tpke, Iselin NJ 08830
Tel (732) 205-5000
SIC 2819 2816 5094 3339

METALLIX REFINING INC p 952
59 Avenue At The Cmn # 201, Shrewsbury NJ 07702
Tel (732) 936-0050 *SIC* 3339

AURAMET TRADING LLC p 131
300 Frank W Burr Blvd # 24, Teaneck NJ 07666
Tel (201) 905-5000 *SIC* 3339

■ MATERION ADVANCED MATERIALS TECHNOLOGIES AND SERVICES INC p 919
2978 Main St, Buffalo NY 14214
Tel (800) 327-1355 *SIC* 3339

MEDIMA LLC p 938
5727 Strickler Rd, Clarence NY 14031
Tel (716) 741-0400 *SIC* 3339 3313

HH LIQUIDATING CORP p 689
110 E 59th St Fl 34, New York NY 10022
Tel (646) 282-2500
SIC 3624 2999 3356 3339

▲ SPH GROUP HOLDINGS LLC p 1358
590 Madison Ave Fl 32, New York NY 10022
Tel (212) 520-2300 *SIC* 3339 3011 3312

■ HANDY & HARMAN LTD p 657
1133 Westchester Ave N-222, White Plains NY 10604
Tel (914) 461-1300 *SIC* 3339 3011 3312

UMICORE USA INC p 1501
3600 Glenwood Ave Ste 250, Raleigh NC 27612
Tel (919) 874-7171
SIC 5052 5051 5093 5169 3339

AMERICAN SPRING WIRE CORP p 79
26300 Miles Rd, Bedford Heights OH 44146
Tel (216) 292-4620
SIC 3272 3315 3316 3339 3624

PRINCE & IZANT CO p 1176
12999 Plaza Dr, Cleveland OH 44130
Tel (216) 362-7000
SIC 5051 3398 3351 3341 3339 2899

■ MATERION BRUSH INC p 919
6070 Parkland Blvd Ste 1, Mayfield Heights OH 44124
Tel (216) 486-4200
SIC 3351 3356 3264 3339 3341 3674

▲ MATERION CORP p 919
6070 Parkland Blvd Ste 1, Mayfield Heights OH 44124
Tel (216) 486-4200
SIC 3339 3351 3356 3341 3674

GLOBE METALLURGICAL INC p 618
County Road 32, Waterford OH 45786
Tel (740) 984-2361 *SIC* 3339 3313 2819

ABINGTON RELDAN METALS LLC p 11
550 Old Bordentown Rd, Fairless Hills PA 19030
Tel (267) 316-2000 *SIC* 3339

▲ ALLEGHENY TECHNOLOGIES INC p 52
1000 Six Ppg Pl, Pittsburgh PA 15222
Tel (412) 394-2800 *SIC* 3312 3339 3545

HORSEHEAD CORP p 708
4955 Steubenville Pike, Pittsburgh PA 15205
Tel (724) 774-1020 *SIC* 3339 3629

HORSEHEAD HOLDING CORP p 708
4955 Steubenville Pike, Pittsburgh PA 15205
Tel (724) 774-1020 *SIC* 3339

■ TDY INDUSTRIES LLC p 1429
1000 Six Ppg Pl, Pittsburgh PA 15222
Tel (412) 394-2896
SIC 3356 3312 3316 3339 3369

MATTHEY JOHNSON HOLDINGS INC p 921
435 Devon Park Dr Ste 600, Wayne PA 19087
Tel (610) 971-3000
SIC 3341 3339 3356 2834 3399 3714

MATTHEY JOHNSON INC p 921
435 Devon Park Dr Ste 600, Wayne PA 19087
Tel (610) 971-3000
SIC 3341 3339 3356 2834 3399 3714

HERAEUS INC HIC p 685
770 Township Line Rd, Yardley PA 19067
Tel (212) 752-2180
SIC 3399 3823 3339 3469

■ **MATERION TECHNICAL MATERIALS INC** p 919
5 Wellington Rd, Lincoln RI 02865
Tel (401) 333-1700 SIC 3331 3339 3423

ELEMETAL LLC p 486
15850 Dallas Pkwy, Dallas TX 75248
Tel (214) 956-7600 SIC 3341 3356 3339

REC SILICON INC p 1214
3700 Buffalo Speedway # 620, Houston TX 77098
Tel (281) 325-3800 SIC 3339

■ **MATERION NATURAL RESOURCES INC** p 919
10 Miles North Hwy 6, Delta UT 84624
Tel (435) 864-2701 SIC 1099 3339

G S L CORP p 587
765 N 10500 W, Ogden UT 84404
Tel (801) 731-3100 SIC 2819 2899 3339

WVA MANUFACTURING LLC p 1628
Rr 60, Alloy WV 25002
Tel (304) 779-3200 SIC 3339 2819

SIC 3341 Secondary Smelting & Refining Of Nonferrous Metals

SANDERS LEAD CO INC p 1278
1 Sanders Rd, Troy AL 36079
Tel (334) 566-1563 SIC 3341

CUSTOM ALLOY SALES INC p 403
13191 Crssrds Pkwy N 37, City Of Industry CA 91746
Tel (626) 369-3641 SIC 3341 5051

HERAEUS PRECIOUS METALS NORTH AMERICA LLC p 685
15524 Carmenita Rd, Santa Fe Springs CA 90670
Tel (562) 921-7464 SIC 3341 2899

ULBRICH STAINLESS STEELS & SPECIAL METALS INC p 1500
153 Washington Ave, North Haven CT 06473
Tel (203) 239-4481
SIC 3316 3356 5051 3341 3312

■ **GBC METALS LLC** p 594
427 N Shamrock St, East Alton IL 62024
Tel (618) 258-2350 SIC 3351 3341 3469

■ **GLOBAL BRASS AND COPPER INC** p 615
305 Lewis And Clark Blvd, East Alton IL 62024
Tel (618) 258-5000
SIC 3351 3341 3469 1542

▲ **GLOBAL BRASS AND COPPER HOLDINGS INC** p 615
475 N Marti Rd Ste 1050, Schaumburg IL 60173
Tel (847) 240-4700 SIC 3351 3341 3469

VERSATILE PROCESSING GROUP INC p 1551
9820 Westpoint Dr Ste 300, Indianapolis IN 46256
Tel (317) 577-8930 SIC 3341

SHINE BROS CORP p 1317
225 10th Ave Se, Spencer IA 51301
Tel (712) 262-5579 SIC 5093 3341

CC METALS AND ALLOYS LLC p 269
1542 N Main St, Calvert City KY 42029
Tel (270) 395-7631 SIC 3313 3341 3295

■ **RIVER METALS RECYCLING LLC** p 1237
334 Beechwood Rd Ste 401, Fort Mitchell KY 41017
Tel (859) 292-8400 SIC 5093 3341

AUDUBON METALS LLC p 131
3055 Ohio Dr, Henderson KY 42420
Tel (270) 830-6622 SIC 3341

INTERLOCK INDUSTRIES INC p 753
545 S 3rd St Ste 310, Louisville KY 40202
Tel (502) 569-2007
SIC 3341 4121 3444 3354 2653

REVSTONE INDUSTRIES LLC p 1229
2008 Cypress St Ste 100, Paris KY 40361
Tel (859) 294-5590 SIC 2821 3086 3341

OHIO VALLEY ALUMINUM CO II LLC p 1078
1100 Brooks Industrial Rd, Shelbyville KY 40065
Tel (502) 633-2783 SIC 3341

CONNELL LIMITED PARTNERSHIP p 358
1 International Pl Fl 31, Boston MA 02110
Tel (617) 737-2700
SIC 3443 3444 3341 3544 6719

SCHUPAN & SONS INC p 1291
2619 Miller Rd, Kalamazoo MI 49001
Tel (269) 382-0000 SIC 5093 5051 3341

NATIONAL GALVANIZING LP p 1012
1500 Telb St, Monroe MI 48162
Tel (734) 243-1882
SIC 3312 3316 3471 3341 5051

■ **CANNON-MUSKEGON CORP** p 247
2875 Lincoln St, Norton Shores MI 49441
Tel (231) 759-2831
SIC 3313 3341 3339 3312

TRELLEBORG CORP p 1476
200 Veterans Blvd Ste 3, South Haven MI 49090
Tel (269) 639-9891
SIC 3341 1021 1044 1031 4226 1041

ROLLED ALLOYS INC p 1247
125 W Sterns Rd, Temperance MI 48182
Tel (800) 521-0332
SIC 5051 3369 3341 3317 2899 2851

HURON VALLEY STEEL CORP p 721
1650 W Jefferson Ave, Trenton MI 48183
Tel (734) 479-3500 SIC 5093 3341 3559

BEN WEITSMAN AND SON INC p 172
15 W Main St, Owego NY 13827
Tel (607) 687-2780 SIC 5051 5093 3341

■ **HANDY & HARMAN** p 657
1133 Westchester Ave N-222, White Plains NY 10604
Tel (914) 461-1300
SIC 3356 3399 3341 3317 3315

ALERIS ROLLED PRODUCTS INC p 48
25825 Science Park Dr # 400, Beachwood OH 44122
Tel (216) 910-3400 SIC 3341

■ **REAL ALLOY HOLDING INC** p 1213
3700 Park East Dr Ste 300, Beachwood OH 44122
Tel (216) 755-8800 SIC 3341 3313 3334

■ **REAL ALLOY RECYCLING INC** p 1213
3700 Park East Dr Ste 300, Beachwood OH 44122
Tel (216) 755-8900 SIC 3341

PRINCE & IZANT CO p 1176
12999 Plaza Dr, Cleveland OH 44130
Tel (216) 362-7000
SIC 5051 3398 3351 3341 3339 2899

■ **MATERION BRUSH INC** p 919
6070 Parkland Blvd Ste 1, Mayfield Heights OH 44124
Tel (216) 486-4200
SIC 3351 3356 3264 3339 3341 3674

▲ **MATERION CORP** p 919
6070 Parkland Blvd Ste 1, Mayfield Heights OH 44124
Tel (216) 486-4200
SIC 3339 3351 3356 3341 3674

COHEN BROTHERS INC p 335
1723 Woodlawn Ave, Middletown OH 45044
Tel (513) 422-3696
SIC 5093 3441 3341 3312

MILL SERVICES CORP p 969
12 Monongahela Ave, Glassport PA 15045
Tel (412) 678-6141
SIC 3295 1422 8742 3341

INTERNATIONAL MILL SERVICE INC p 756
1155 Bus Ctr Dr Ste 200, Horsham PA 19044
Tel (215) 956-5500
SIC 3295 3341 1422 8742

■ **SPS TECHNOLOGIES LLC** p 1362
301 Highland Ave, Jenkintown PA 19046
Tel (215) 572-3000
SIC 3452 3423 3499 3264 3679 3341

ELG METALS INC p 486
369 River Rd, Mckeesport PA 15132
Tel (412) 672-9200 SIC 5093 3341

■ **READING ALLOYS INC** p 1213
220 Old West Penn Ave, Robesonia PA 19551
Tel (610) 693-5822 SIC 3313 3341

MATTHEY JOHNSON HOLDINGS INC p 921
435 Devon Park Dr Ste 600, Wayne PA 19087
Tel (610) 971-3000
SIC 3341 3339 3356 2834 3399 3714

MATTHEY JOHNSON INC p 921
435 Devon Park Dr Ste 600, Wayne PA 19087
Tel (610) 971-3000
SIC 3341 3339 3356 2834 3399 3714

■ **CENTURY ALUMINUM OF SOUTH CAROLINA INC** p 282
3575 U S Hwy 52, Goose Creek SC 29445
Tel (843) 572-3700 SIC 3341

ELEMETAL LLC p 486
15850 Dallas Pkwy, Dallas TX 75248
Tel (214) 956-7600 SIC 3341 3356 3339

QUEMETCO INC p 1198
2777 N Stemmons Fwy, Dallas TX 75207
Tel (317) 247-1303 SIC 3341 4953

QUEXCO INC p 1199
2777 N Stemmons Fwy, Dallas TX 75207
Tel (214) 688-4000 SIC 3341

RSR CORP p 1256
2777 N Stemmons Fwy, Dallas TX 75207
Tel (317) 247-1303 SIC 3341

LOPEZ SCRAP METAL INC p 878
351 N Nevarez Rd, El Paso TX 79927
Tel (915) 859-0770 SIC 5093 3341

BHP COPPER INC p 180
1360 Post Oak Blvd # 150, Houston TX 77056
Tel (713) 961-8500 SIC 1021 3341 1041

BHP HOLDINGS (RESOURCES) INC p 180
1360 Post Oak Blvd # 150, Houston TX 77056
Tel (713) 961-8500 SIC 1021 3341 1041

BRENNER HOLDINGS INC p 210
2580 Broadway Ave Sw, Roanoke VA 24014
Tel (540) 981-1211
SIC 4953 5093 3341 3231

FRENCH HOLDINGS LLC p 578
3101 S Taylor Dr, Sheboygan WI 53081
Tel (920) 458-7724 SIC 3363 3341 8711

NEMAK AUTOMOTIVE CASTINGS INC p 1025
3101 S Taylor Dr, Sheboygan WI 53081
Tel (920) 458-7724 SIC 3341 3363 8711

SIC 3351 Rolling, Drawing & Extruding Of Copper

WOLVERINE TUBE INC p 1621
2100 Market St Ne, Decatur AL 35601
Tel (256) 353-1310 SIC 3351

■ **CERRO WIRE LLC** p 284
1099 Thompson Rd Se, Hartselle AL 35640
Tel (256) 773-2522 SIC 3351

GD COPPER (USA) INC p 595
405 Gd Copper Dr, Pine Hill AL 36769
Tel (334) 637-0200 SIC 3351 3999

■ **FREEPORT MINERALS CORP** p 577
333 N Central Ave, Phoenix AZ 85004
Tel (602) 366-8100
SIC 1061 1021 3312 3351

■ **MATERION CERAMICS INC** p 919
6100 S Tucson Blvd, Tucson AZ 85706
Tel (520) 741-3411 SIC 3351 3264

SOUTHWIRE CO LLC p 1353
1 Southwire Dr, Carrollton GA 30119
Tel (770) 832-4242
SIC 3351 3355 3357 3599

■ **MARMON HOLDINGS INC** p 909
181 W Madison St Ste 2600, Chicago IL 60602
Tel (312) 372-9500
SIC 5051 3351 3743 4741 3423 3589

■ **GBC METALS LLC** p 594
427 N Shamrock St, East Alton IL 62024
Tel (618) 258-2350 SIC 3351 3341 3469

■ **GLOBAL BRASS AND COPPER INC** p 615
305 Lewis And Clark Blvd, East Alton IL 62024
Tel (618) 258-5000
SIC 3351 3341 3469 1542

■ **CERRO FLOW PRODUCTS LLC** p 284
3000 Mississippi Ave, Sauget IL 62206
Tel (618) 337-6000
SIC 3351 3331 3498 3585 5051

▲ **GLOBAL BRASS AND COPPER HOLDINGS INC** p 615
475 N Marti Rd Ste 1050, Schaumburg IL 60173
Tel (847) 240-4700 SIC 3351 3341 3469

■ **MARMON RETAIL PRODUCTS INC** p 909
1002 Industrial Way, Crothersville IN 47229
Tel (812) 793-2929 SIC 3357 3351

PMX INDUSTRIES INC p 1158
5300 Willow Creek Dr Sw, Cedar Rapids IA 52404
Tel (319) 368-7700
SIC 3366 5051 3444 3364 3351 3331

▲ **GENERAL CABLE CORP** p 599
4 Tesseneer Dr, Highland Heights KY 41076
Tel (859) 572-8000 SIC 3351 3357

■ **GENERAL CABLE INDUSTRIES INC** p 599
4 Tesseneer Dr, Highland Heights KY 41076
Tel (859) 572-8000 SIC 3351 3315 3357

EMS ENGINEERED MATERIALS SOLUTIONS LLC p 495
39 Perry Ave, Attleboro MA 02703
Tel (508) 342-2100 SIC 3351

PEP INDUSTRIES LLC p 1133
110 Frank Mossberg Dr, Attleboro MA 02703
Tel (508) 226-5600
SIC 3089 3351 3469 3471 3643 3841

PRECISION ENGINEERED PRODUCTS LLC p 1168
110 Frank Mossberg Dr, Attleboro MA 02703
Tel (508) 226-5600
SIC 3643 3469 3841 3471 3089 3351

HEYCO PRODUCTS INC p 688
1800 Industrial Way, Toms River NJ 08755
Tel (732) 286-4336 SIC 3351 3679

AURUBIS BUFFALO INC p 132
70 Sayre St, Buffalo NY 14207
Tel (716) 879-6700 SIC 3351

CAMDEN WIRE CO INC p 245
12 Masonic Ave, Camden NY 13316
Tel (315) 245-3800 SIC 3351 3357

INTERNATIONAL WIRE GROUP p 757
12 Masonic Ave, Camden NY 13316
Tel (315) 245-3800 SIC 3351

OMEGA WIRE INC p 1084
12 Masonic Ave, Camden NY 13316
Tel (315) 245-3800 SIC 3351

■ **TECHNETICS GROUP LLC** p 1431
5605 Carnegie Blvd # 500, Charlotte NC 28209
Tel (704) 731-1500 SIC 3053 3351

WIELAND COPPER PRODUCTS LLC p 1608
3990 Us 311 Hwy N, Pine Hall NC 27042
Tel (336) 445-4500 SIC 3351

ALCAN CORP p 47
6060 Parkland Blvd, Cleveland OH 44124
Tel (440) 460-3307
SIC 3351 3355 3496 3357

PRINCE & IZANT CO p 1176
12999 Plaza Dr, Cleveland OH 44130
Tel (216) 362-7000
SIC 5051 3398 3351 3341 3339 2899

■ **MATERION BRUSH INC** p 919
6070 Parkland Blvd Ste 1, Mayfield Heights OH 44124
Tel (216) 486-4200
SIC 3351 3356 3264 3339 3341 3674

▲ **MATERION CORP** p 919
6070 Parkland Blvd Ste 1, Mayfield Heights OH 44124
Tel (216) 486-4200
SIC 3339 3351 3356 3341 3674

■ **CHASE BRASS AND COPPER CO LLC** p 291
14212 Selwyn Dr, Montpelier OH 43543
Tel (419) 485-3193 SIC 3351

▲ **AMPCO-PITTSBURGH CORP** p 86
726 Bell Ave Ste 301, Carnegie PA 15106
Tel (412) 456-4400
SIC 3312 3561 3351 3353

ST PRODUCTS LLC p 1372
200 Oliphant Dr, Duncansville PA 16635
Tel (814) 693-6000 SIC 3351

HCL LIQUIDATION LTD p 672
100 Washington St, Leetsdale PA 15056
Tel (724) 251-4200 SIC 3351

LIBERTAS COPPER LLC p 861
100 Washington St, Leetsdale PA 15056
Tel (724) 251-4200 SIC 3366 3351

CAMBRIDGE-LEE HOLDINGS INC p 244
86 Tube Dr, Reading PA 19605
Tel (610) 926-4141 SIC 5051 3351 5084

■ **MUELLER BRASS CO** p 998
8285 Tournament Dr # 150, Memphis TN 38125
Tel (901) 753-3200
SIC 3351 3463 3354 3494

■ **MUELLER BRASS HOLDING CO INC** p 998
8285 Tournament Dr # 150, Memphis TN 38125
Tel (901) 753-3200 SIC 3351 3463 3494

■ **MUELLER COPPER TUBE PRODUCTS INC** p 998
8285 Tournament Dr # 150, Memphis TN 38125
Tel (901) 753-3200 SIC 3351

BAE SYSTEMS RESOLUTION INC p 144
1000 La St Ste 4950, Houston TX 77002
Tel (713) 868-7700
SIC 3713 5084 3711 7699 3351 3829

UNITED STARS INC p 1512
1546 Henry Ave, Beloit WI 53511
Tel (608) 368-4625
SIC 3317 3351 3463 3613 3621

SIC 3353 Aluminum Sheet, Plate & Foil

WISE ALLOYS LLC p 1619
4805 2nd St, Muscle Shoals AL 35661
Tel (256) 386-6000 SIC 3353

WISE METALS GROUP LLC p 1619
4805 2nd St, Muscle Shoals AL 35661
Tel (256) 386-6000 SIC 3353 3356

CENTRAL STATES MANUFACTURING INC p 280
302 Jane Pl, Lowell AR 72745
Tel (479) 770-0188 SIC 3353 3448 7389

■ **FORGED METALS INC** p 567
10685 Beech Ave, Fontana CA 92337
Tel (909) 350-9260 SIC 3353

▲ **KAISER ALUMINUM CORP** p 800
27422 Portola Pkwy # 200, Foothill Ranch CA 92610
Tel (949) 614-1740
SIC 3334 3353 3354 3355

■ **KAISER ALUMINUM FABRICATED PRODUCTS LLC** p 800
27422 Portola Pkwy # 200, Foothill Ranch CA 92610
Tel (949) 614-1740
SIC 3353 3334 3354 3355

■ **KAISER ALUMINUM INVESTMENTS CO** p 800
27422 Portola Pkwy # 350, Foothill Ranch CA 92610
Tel (949) 614-1740
SIC 3353 3334 3354 3355

GOLDEN ALUMINUM INC p 620
1405 14th St, Fort Lupton CO 80621
Tel (800) 838-1004 SIC 3353

LUPTON VENTURES INC p 886
1405 14th St, Fort Lupton CO 80621
Tel (303) 659-9767 SIC 3353

UNITED ALUMINUM CORP p 1506
100 United Dr, North Haven CT 06473
Tel (203) 575-9771 SIC 3353

NOVELIS CORP p 1063
3560 Lenox Rd Ne Ste 2000, Atlanta GA 30326
Tel (404) 760-4000 SIC 3353

REYNOLDS CONSUMER PRODUCTS LLC p 1230
1900 W Field Ct, Lake Forest IL 60045
Tel (847) 482-3500 SIC 3353

BRAZEWAY INC p 209
2711 E Maumee St, Adrian MI 49221
Tel (517) 265-2121 SIC 3354 3353

NORANDA ALUMINUM INC p 1047
St Jude Industrial Park, New Madrid MO 63869
Tel (573) 643-2361
SIC 3353 3354 3334 3714

▲ **ARCONIC INC** p 106
390 Park Ave, New York NY 10022
Tel (212) 836-2674 SIC 3334 3353 1099

▲ **AMPCO-PITTSBURGH CORP** p 86
726 Bell Ave Ste 301, Carnegie PA 15106
Tel (412) 456-4400
SIC 3312 3561 3351 3353

■ **ALUMAX LLC** p 63
201 Isabella St, Pittsburgh PA 15212
Tel (412) 553-4545
SIC 3334 3353 3354 3449 3442 3446

■ **JW ALUMINUM HOLDING CORP** p 798
435 Old Mount Holly Rd, Goose Creek SC 29445
Tel (843) 572-1100 SIC 3353 3497

GRANGES AMERICAS INC p 631
801 Crescent Centre Dr, Franklin TN 37067
Tel (615) 778-2004 SIC 3353

NORANDA ALUMINUM HOLDING CORP p 1047
801 Crescent Cntre Dr 6 Ste 600, Franklin TN 37067
Tel (615) 771-5700 SIC 3334 2819 3353

NORANDA INTERMEDIATE HOLDING CORP p 1047
801 Crescent Centre Dr, Franklin TN 37067
Tel (615) 771-5700
SIC 3353 3334 3714 3354

NORANDAL USA INC p 1047
801 Crescent Centre Dr # 600, Franklin TN 37067
Tel (615) 778-2000 SIC 3353

▲ **OIL STATES INTERNATIONAL INC** p 1079
333 Clay St Ste 4620, Houston TX 77002
Tel (713) 652-0582
SIC 3353 3061 3053 3561 3491

▲ **QUANEX BUILDING PRODUCTS CORP** p 1198
1800 West Loop S Ste 1500, Houston TX 77027
Tel (713) 961-4600 SIC 3272 3353

■ **ARCONIC SECURITIES LLC** p 106
101 Cherry St Ste 400, Burlington VT 05401
Tel (802) 658-2661 SIC 3353

■ **CONSTELLIUM ROLLED PRODUCTS RAVENSWOOD LLC** p 361
859 Century Rd, Ravenswood WV 26164
Tel (304) 273-7000 SIC 3353

SIC 3354 Aluminum Extruded Prdts

PHIFER INC p 1142
4400 Kauloosa Ave, Tuscaloosa AL 35401
Tel (205) 345-2120
SIC 3496 2221 3357 2295 3442 3354

CLARIDGE PRODUCTS AND EQUIPMENT INC p 321
601 Highway 62 65 S, Harrison AR 72601
Tel (870) 743-2200
SIC 2531 3354 2541 2542

▲ **KAISER ALUMINUM CORP** p 800
27422 Portola Pkwy # 200, Foothill Ranch CA 92610
Tel (949) 614-1740
SIC 3334 3353 3354 3355

■ **KAISER ALUMINUM FABRICATED PRODUCTS LLC** p 800
27422 Portola Pkwy # 200, Foothill Ranch CA 92610
Tel (949) 614-1740
SIC 3353 3334 3354 3355

■ **KAISER ALUMINUM INVESTMENTS CO** p 800
27422 Portola Pkwy # 350, Foothill Ranch CA 92610
Tel (949) 614-1740
SIC 3353 3334 3354 3355

LUXFER INC p 887
3016 Kansas Ave Bldg 1, Riverside CA 92507
Tel (336) 578-4515 SIC 3728 3354

BRYNWOOD PARTNERS V LIMITED PARTNERSHIP p 222
8 Sound Shore Dr Ste 265, Greenwich CT 06830
Tel (203) 622-1790
SIC 6282 1751 3442 5031 3354

■ **FLAG INTERMEDIATE HOLDINGS CORP** p 554
2400 E Coml Blvd Ste 905, Fort Lauderdale FL 33308
Tel (954) 202-4000 SIC 5051 3354 3315

■ **METALS USA HOLDINGS CORP** p 952
2400 E Coml Blvd Ste 905, Fort Lauderdale FL 33308
Tel (954) 202-4000 SIC 5051 3272 3354

STYLE-VIEW PRODUCTS INC p 1395
1800 N Bayshore Dr # 4001, Miami FL 33132
Tel (305) 634-9688
SIC 3442 3444 3443 3354

SPECTRA METAL SALES INC p 1357
6104 Boat Rock Blvd Sw, Atlanta GA 30336
Tel (404) 344-4305
SIC 5051 3354 3355 3479 3444 2952

FRANKLIN ALUMINUM CO INC p 574
266 Mary Johnson Dr, Franklin GA 30217
Tel (706) 675-3341 SIC 3354

YKK CORP OF AMERICA p 1636
1850 Parkway Pl Se # 300, Marietta GA 30067
Tel (770) 261-6120 SIC 3965 3354

■ **BON L MANUFACTURING CO** p 199
25 Bonnell St, Newnan GA 30263
Tel (770) 253-2020 SIC 3354

■ **WILLIAM L BONNELL CO INC** p 1610
25 Bonnell St, Newnan GA 30263
Tel (770) 253-2020 SIC 3354

TRULITE GLASS & ALUMINUM SOLUTIONS LLC p 1486
403 Westpark Ct Ste 201, Peachtree City GA 30269
Tel (678) 593-9200 SIC 3354 3449

FUTURE FOUNDATION INC p 585
380 E Parkcenter Blvd # 230, Boise ID 83706
Tel (208) 336-0150 SIC 3354 5013 6361

NATIONAL MATERIAL LP p 1014
1965 Pratt Blvd, Elk Grove Village IL 60007
Tel (847) 806-7200
SIC 5051 3469 3354 5093 4911 4924

ALP LIGHTING & CEILING PRODUCTS INC p 60
6333 W Gross Point Rd, Niles IL 60714
Tel (773) 774-9550
SIC 3089 3354 5162 3496 3442 3229

SAPA EXTRUSIONS INC p 1281
6250 N River Rd Ste 5000, Rosemont IL 60018
Tel (877) 710-7272 SIC 3354

PLYMOUTH TUBE CO p 1157
29w 150 Warrenville Rd, Warrenville IL 60555
Tel (630) 393-3550 SIC 3317 3354

DURABLE INC p 462
750 Northgate Pkwy, Wheeling IL 60090
Tel (847) 541-4400 SIC 3497 3354

80/20 INC p 4
1701 S 400 E, Columbia City IN 46725
Tel (260) 248-8030 SIC 3354

■ **CENTURY ALUMINUM OF KENTUCKY LLC** p 281
1627 State Rte 271 N, Hawesville KY 42348
Tel (270) 685-2493 SIC 3354

INTERLOCK INDUSTRIES INC p 753
545 S 3rd St Ste 310, Louisville KY 40202
Tel (502) 569-2007
SIC 3341 4121 3444 3354 2653

AFCO INDUSTRIES INC p 32
3400 Roy Ave, Alexandria LA 71302
Tel (318) 448-1651 SIC 3354 3083 3442

SAPA EXTRUSIONS NORTH AMERICA LLC p 1281
999 Corporate Blvd # 100, Linthicum Heights MD 21090
Tel (410) 487-4500 SIC 3354

MESTEK INC p 951
260 N Elm St, Westfield MA 01085
Tel (413) 568-9571
SIC 3585 3634 3549 3542 3354

BRAZEWAY INC p 209
2711 E Maumee St, Adrian MI 49221
Tel (517) 265-2121 SIC 3354 3353

SRS INDUSTRIES LLC p 1363
5175 W 6th St, Ludington MI 49431
Tel (231) 845-5101 SIC 3354

AACOA EXTRUSIONS INC p 8
2005 Mayflower Rd, Niles MI 49120
Tel (269) 697-6063 SIC 3354

ALEXANDRIA EXTRUSION CO p 49
401 County Road 22 Nw, Alexandria MN 56308
Tel (320) 762-7657 SIC 3354

NORANDA ALUMINUM INC p 1047
St Jude Industrial Park, New Madrid MO 63869
Tel (573) 643-2361
SIC 3363 3354 3334 3714

WAKEFIELD THERMAL SOLUTIONS INC p 1572
33 Bridge St, Pelham NH 03076
Tel (603) 635-2800 SIC 3354

SHAPES/ARCH HOLDINGS LLC p 1311
9000 River Rd, Delair NJ 08110
Tel (856) 662-5500 SIC 3354 3365

CONSTRUCTION SPECIALTIES INC p 361
3 Werner Way Ste 100, Lebanon NJ 08833
Tel (908) 236-0800
SIC 3446 3354 3443 3272 3585

KEYMARK CORP p 815
1188 Cayadutta St, Fonda NY 12068
Tel (518) 853-3421 SIC 3354 3479 3471

APOLLO MANAGEMENT V LP p 97
1 Manhattanville Rd # 201, Purchase NY 10577
Tel (914) 467-6510 SIC 5051 3272 3354

ALERIS INTERNATIONAL INC p 48
25825 Science Park Dr # 400, Beachwood OH 44122
Tel (216) 910-3400 SIC 3355 3354

NICHOLS ALUMINUM LLC p 1042
25825 Science Park Dr # 400, Beachwood OH 44122
Tel (216) 910-3400 SIC 3355 3354

ALERIS CORP p 48
25825 Science Park Dr # 400, Cleveland OH 44122
Tel (216) 910-3400 SIC 3355 3354

ASTRO SHAPES INC p 122
65 Main St, Struthers OH 44471
Tel (330) 755-1414 SIC 3354 3086

EXAL CORP p 516
1 Performance Pl, Youngstown OH 44502
Tel (330) 744-9505 SIC 3411 3354

SAPA PROFILES INC p 1281
7933 Ne 21st Ave, Portland OR 97211
Tel (503) 285-0404 SIC 3354 3471

■ **TRACO DELAWARE INC** p 1468
71 Progress Ave, Cranberry Township PA 16066
Tel (724) 776-7000
SIC 3442 3211 3444 3448 3354 7992

■ **TRI CITY ALUMINUM CO** p 1476
71 Progress Ave, Cranberry Township PA 16066
Tel (724) 799-8917 SIC 3442 3354 7992

SAPA EXTRUDER INC p 1281
Airport Offc Park, Moon Township PA 15108
Tel (412) 299-7600 SIC 3354

SAPA NORTH AMERICA INC p 1281
400 Rouser Rd Ste 300, Moon Township PA 15108
Tel (877) 922-7272 SIC 3354

■ **ALUMAX LLC** p 63
201 Isabella St, Pittsburgh PA 15212
Tel (412) 553-4545
SIC 3334 3353 3354 3449 3442 3446

FENIX MANUFACTURING SOLUTIONS LLC p 537
2063 University Pkwy, Aiken SC 29801
Tel (803) 649-1381
SIC 3694 3825 3625 3354

LOXCREEN CO INC p 882
1630 Old Dunbar Rd, West Columbia SC 29172
Tel (803) 822-1600 SIC 3354 3442 3089

NORANDA INTERMEDIATE HOLDING CORP p 1047
801 Crescent Centre Dr, Franklin TN 37067
Tel (615) 771-5700
SIC 3353 3334 3714 3354

■ **MUELLER BRASS CO** p 998
8285 Tournament Dr # 150, Memphis TN 38125
Tel (901) 753-3200
SIC 3351 3463 3354 3494

ATRIUM WINDOWS AND DOORS INC p 129
3890 W Northwest Hwy # 500, Dallas TX 75220
Tel (214) 956-8031
SIC 3442 2431 3089 3354 7629

ELECTRO-MECHANICAL CORP p 485
329 Williams St, Bristol VA 24201
Tel (276) 669-9428
SIC 3612 5063 3829 3822 3613 3354

▲ **TREDEGAR CORP** p 1475
1100 Boulders Pkwy # 200, North Chesterfield VA 23225
Tel (804) 330-1000
SIC 3081 2671 3083 3354

WILLIAM L BONNELL CO INC p 1610
1100 Boulders Pkwy, North Chesterfield VA 23225
Tel (804) 330-1147 SIC 3354

SIC 3355 Aluminum Rolling & Drawing, NEC

■ **METALS USA BUILDING PRODUCTS LP** p 952
955 Columbia St, Brea CA 92821
Tel (713) 946-9000 SIC 3355 5031 1542

▲ **KAISER ALUMINUM CORP** p 800
27422 Portola Pkwy # 200, Foothill Ranch CA 92610
Tel (949) 614-1740
SIC 3334 3353 3354 3355

■ **KAISER ALUMINUM FABRICATED PRODUCTS LLC** p 800
27422 Portola Pkwy # 200, Foothill Ranch CA 92610
Tel (949) 614-1740
SIC 3353 3334 3354 3355

■ **KAISER ALUMINUM INVESTMENTS CO** p 800
27422 Portola Pkwy # 350, Foothill Ranch CA 92610
Tel (949) 614-1740
SIC 3353 3334 3354 3355

ARCADIA INC p 103
2301 E Vernon Ave, Vernon CA 90058
Tel (323) 269-7300 SIC 3355

NOVELIS INC p 1063
3560 Lenox Rd Ne Ste 2000, Atlanta GA 30326
Tel (404) 760-4000 SIC 3355

SPECTRA METAL SALES INC p 1357
6104 Boat Rock Blvd Sw, Atlanta GA 30336
Tel (404) 344-4305
SIC 5051 3354 3355 3479 3444 2952

SOUTHWIRE CO LLC p 1353
1 Southwire Dr, Carrollton GA 30119
Tel (770) 832-4242
SIC 3351 3355 3357 3599

LAPHAM-HICKEY STEEL CORP p 845
5500 W 73rd St, Chicago IL 60638
Tel (708) 496-6111
SIC 5051 3398 3355 3317 3316

ROLLER DIE AND FORMING CO INC p 1247
1172 Industrial Blvd, Louisville KY 40219
Tel (502) 969-1327 SIC 3355 3544

LOGAN ALUMINUM INC p 874
200 Gate Two Rd, Russellville KY 42276
Tel (270) 755-6000 SIC 3355

LAPP HOLDING NA INC p 845
29 Hanover Rd, Florham Park NJ 07932
Tel (973) 660-9700 SIC 3355

OKONITE CO p 1080
102 Hilltop Rd, Ramsey NJ 07446
Tel (201) 825-0300 SIC 3357 3315 3355

▲ **ALCOA CORP** p 47
390 Park Ave Fl 12, New York NY 10022
Tel (212) 518-5400
SIC 3355 3363 3297 2819

ALERIS INTERNATIONAL INC p 48
25825 Science Park Dr # 400, Beachwood OH 44122
Tel (216) 910-3400 SIC 3355 3354

NICHOLS ALUMINUM LLC p 1042
25825 Science Park Dr # 400, Beachwood OH 44122
Tel (216) 910-3400 SIC 3355 3354

■ **REAL ALLOY SPECIALTY PRODUCTS INC** p 1213
3700 Park East Dr Ste 300, Beachwood OH 44122
Tel (216) 755-8836 SIC 3355

ALCAN CORP p 47
6060 Parkland Blvd, Cleveland OH 44124
Tel (440) 460-3307
SIC 3351 3355 3496 3357

ALERIS CORP p 48
25825 Science Park Dr # 400, Cleveland OH 44122
Tel (216) 910-3400 SIC 3355 3354

ALERIS ROLLED PRODUCTS LLC p 48
25825 Science Park Dr # 400, Cleveland OH 44122
Tel (216) 910-3400 SIC 3355

AMH HOLDINGS II INC p 85
3773 State Rd, Cuyahoga Falls OH 44223
Tel (330) 929-1811 SIC 3355

AMH HOLDINGS LLC p 85
3773 State Rd, Cuyahoga Falls OH 44223
Tel (330) 929-1811 SIC 3355 3444

NEW WERNER HOLDING CO INC p 1033
93 Werner Rd, Greenville PA 16125
Tel (724) 588-2000
SIC 3499 3355 3089 3446 2499 6512

WERNER CO p 1592
93 Werner Rd, Greenville PA 16125
Tel (724) 588-2000
SIC 3499 3355 3089 3446 2499

WERNER HOLDING CO (PA) INC p 1593
93 Werner Rd, Greenville PA 16125
Tel (888) 523-3371
SIC 3499 3355 3089 3446 2499

ALERIS RECYCLING BENS RUN LLC p 48
4203 S State Route 2, Friendly WV 26146
Tel (304) 652-1415 SIC 3355

SIC 3356 Rolling, Drawing-Extruding Of Nonferrous Metals

WISE METALS GROUP LLC p 1619
4805 2nd St, Muscle Shoals AL 35661
Tel (256) 386-6000 SIC 3353 3356

DONCASTERS INC p 450
36 Spring Ln, Farmington CT 06032
Tel (860) 677-1376
SIC 3511 3356 3728 7699

ULBRICH STAINLESS STEELS & SPECIAL METALS INC p 1500
153 Washington Ave, North Haven CT 06473
Tel (203) 239-4481
SIC 3316 3356 5051 3341 3312

ARCELORMITTAL USA LLC p 104
1 S Dearborn St Ste 1800, Chicago IL 60603
Tel (312) 346-0300
SIC 3312 3325 3356 3316

COOPER B-LINE INC p 366
509 W Monroe St, Highland IL 62249
Tel (618) 654-2184
SIC 3441 3443 3452 3444 3429 3356

■ **KESTER INC** p 814
800 W Thorndale Ave, Itasca IL 60143
Tel (630) 616-4000 SIC 3356

TUBE PROCESSING CORP p 1490
604 E Legrande Ave, Indianapolis IN 46203
Tel (317) 787-1321
SIC 3498 3356 3469 7692 3444 3728

▲ **HAYNES INTERNATIONAL INC** p 670
1020 W Park Ave, Kokomo IN 46901
Tel (765) 456-6000 SIC 3356

COMILOG US INC p 344
610 Pittman Rd, Baltimore MD 21226
Tel (410) 789-8800 SIC 2819 3313 3356

H C STARCK INC p 649
45 Industrial Pl, Newton MA 02461
Tel (617) 630-5800 SIC 3339 3356 3313

U S MANUFACTURING CORP p 1497
28201 Van Dyke Ave, Warren MI 48093
Tel (586) 467-1600 SIC 3714 3462 3356

SANDVIK INC p 1279
17-02 Nevins Rd, Fair Lawn NJ 07410
Tel (201) 794-5000
SIC 3316 3317 3356 3315 3545 3533

CPP-SYRACUSE INC p 387
901 E Genesee St, Chittenango NY 13037
Tel (315) 687-0014 SIC 3324 3369 3356

INDIUM CORP OF AMERICA p 739
34 Robinson Rd, Clinton NY 13323
Tel (800) 446-3486 SIC 3356

HH LIQUIDATING CORP p 689
110 E 59th St Fl 34, New York NY 10022
Tel (646) 282-2500
SIC 3624 2999 3356 3339

PRINCE MINERALS LLC p 1176
21 W 46th St Fl 14, New York NY 10036
Tel (646) 747-4222 SIC 3295 3356

NATIONWIDE PRECISION PRODUCTS CORP p 1018
200 Tech Park Dr, Rochester NY 14623
Tel (585) 272-7100 SIC 3356

■ **HANDY & HARMAN** p 657
1133 Westchester Ave N-222, White Plains NY 10604
Tel (914) 461-1300
SIC 3356 3399 3341 3317 3315

CANTON DROP FORGE INC p 247
4575 Southway St Sw, Canton OH 44706
Tel (330) 477-4511
SIC 3462 3463 3356 3312

■ **MATERION BRUSH INC** p 919
6070 Parkland Blvd Ste 1, Mayfield Heights OH 44124
Tel (216) 486-4200
SIC 3351 3356 3264 3339 3341 3674

▲ **MATERION CORP** p 919
6070 Parkland Blvd Ste 1, Mayfield Heights OH 44124
Tel (216) 486-4200
SIC 3339 3351 3356 3341 3674

■ **RMI TITANIUM CO LLC** p 1239
1000 Warren Ave, Niles OH 44446
Tel (330) 652-9952
SIC 3399 3356 1741 3533

TAILWIND TECHNOLOGIES INC p 1421
1 Propeller Pl, Piqua OH 45356
Tel (937) 778-4200 SIC 3356

■ **SPECIAL METALS CORP** p 1356
4832 Richmond Rd Ste 100, Warrensville Heights OH 44128
Tel (216) 755-3030 SIC 3356

■ **RTI INTERNATIONAL METALS INC** p 1256
5th Fl 1550 Crplis Hts Rd, Coraopolis PA 15108
Tel (412) 893-0026 SIC 3356 3441

■ **TITANIUM METALS CORP** p 1456
224 Valley Creek Blvd # 200, Exton PA 19341
Tel (610) 968-1300 SIC 3356

NLMK PENNSYLVANIA LLC p 1045
15 Roemer Blvd, Farrell PA 16121
Tel (724) 983-6464 SIC 3316 3356 3312

■ **TDY INDUSTRIES LLC** p 1429
1000 Six Ppg Pl, Pittsburgh PA 15222
Tel (412) 394-2896
SIC 3356 3312 3316 3339 3369

▲ **UNITED STATES STEEL CORP** p 1514
600 Grant St Ste 468, Pittsburgh PA 15219
Tel (412) 433-1121 SIC 3312 3317 3356

MATTHEY JOHNSON HOLDINGS INC p 921
435 Devon Park Dr Ste 600, Wayne PA 19087
Tel (610) 971-3000
SIC 3341 3339 3356 2834 3399 3714

MATTHEY JOHNSON INC p 921
435 Devon Park Dr Ste 600, Wayne PA 19087
Tel (610) 971-3000
SIC 3341 3339 3356 2834 3399 3714

■ **JARDEN ZINC PRODUCTS LLC** p 778
2500 Old Stage Rd, Greeneville TN 37745
Tel (423) 639-8111
SIC 2796 3364 3356 1031 2789

ECO-BAT AMERICA LLC p 476
2777 N Stemmons Fwy, Dallas TX 75207
Tel (214) 688-4000 SIC 3356

ELEMETAL LLC p 486
15850 Dallas Pkwy, Dallas TX 75248
Tel (214) 956-7600 SIC 3341 3356 3339

US ZINC CORP p 1533
2727 Allen Pkwy Ste 800, Houston TX 77019
Tel (713) 514-0037 SIC 3356

VOTORANTIM METAIS NORTH AMERICA INC p 1566
6020 Navigation Blvd, Houston TX 77011
Tel (713) 926-1705 SIC 3356

US MAGNESIUM LLC p 1532
238 N 2200 W, Salt Lake City UT 84116
Tel (801) 532-2043 SIC 3356 2819

■ **HUNTINGTON ALLOYS CORP** p 719
3200 Riverside Dr, Huntington WV 25705
Tel (304) 526-5100 SIC 3356

■ **LUCAS-MILHAUPT INC** p 884
5656 S Pennsylvania Ave, Cudahy WI 53110
Tel (414) 769-6000 SIC 3356

SIC 3357 Nonferrous Wire Drawing

PHIFER INC p 1142
4400 Kauloosa Ave, Tuscaloosa AL 35401
Tel (205) 345-2120
SIC 3496 2221 3357 2295 3442 3354

▲ **CARLISLE COMPANIES INC** p 257
16430 N Scottsdale Rd, Scottsdale AZ 85254
Tel (704) 501-1100
SIC 2952 3714 3312 3357 3263

GLENAIR INC p 615
1211 Air Way, Glendale CA 91201
Tel (818) 247-6000 SIC 3643 3825 3357

AOC TECHNOLOGIES INC p 94
5960 Inglewood Dr, Pleasanton CA 94588
Tel (925) 875-0808 SIC 5051 3357

LYNN PRODUCTS INC p 888
2645 W 237th St, Torrance CA 90505
Tel (310) 530-5966 SIC 3577 3357

GORES ENT HOLDINGS INC p 626
6260 Lookout Rd, Boulder CO 80301
Tel (303) 531-3100 SIC 3577 7373 3357

■ **RSCC WIRE & CABLE LLC** p 1255
20 Bradley Park Rd, East Granby CT 06026
Tel (860) 653-8300 SIC 3357 3315

■ **TIMES FIBER COMMUNICATIONS INC** p 1454
358 Hall Ave, Wallingford CT 06492
Tel (203) 265-8500 SIC 3357

SIEMON CO p 1320
101 Siemon Company Dr, Watertown CT 06795
Tel (860) 945-4200
SIC 3643 3089 3679 3469 3613 3357

W L GORE & ASSOCIATES INC p 1568
555 Paper Mill Rd, Newark DE 19711
Tel (302) 738-4880
SIC 3357 2821 5131 3841 2819 3069

SIEMENS CORP p 1320
300 New Jersey Ave Nw # 10, Washington DC 20001
Tel (202) 434-4800
SIC 3661 3641 3844 3612 3357

■ **PHELPS DODGE INTERNATIONAL CORP** p 1141
9850 Nw 41st St Ste 200, Doral FL 33178
Tel (305) 648-7888 SIC 8742 3357 3315

■ **CARLISLE INTERCONNECT TECHNOLOGIES INC** p 257
100 Tensolite Dr, Saint Augustine FL 32092
Tel (904) 829-5600
SIC 3679 3399 3678 3357 3643 5063

■ **TENSOLITE LLC** p 1438
100 Tensolite Dr, Saint Augustine FL 32092
Tel (904) 829-5600 SIC 3357 3643 3679

SUPERIOR ESSEX HOLDING CORP p 1406
150 Interstate N Pkwy, Atlanta GA 30339
Tel (770) 657-6000 SIC 3357

SUPERIOR ESSEX INC p 1406
6120 Powers Ferry Rd # 150, Atlanta GA 30339
Tel (770) 657-6000 SIC 3357

SUPERIOR ESSEX INTERNATIONAL LP p 1406
6120 Powers Ferry Rd # 150, Atlanta GA 30339
Tel (770) 657-6000 SIC 3357

CUBS ACQUISITION CORP p 400
1 Southwire Dr, Carrollton GA 30119
Tel (770) 832-4242 SIC 3357 3661 3643

SOUTHWIRE CO LLC p 1353
1 Southwire Dr, Carrollton GA 30119
Tel (770) 832-4242
SIC 3351 3355 3357 3599

OFS BRIGHTWAVE LLC p 1076
2000 Northeast Expy, Norcross GA 30071
Tel (770) 798-3000 SIC 3357 3229

OFS FITEL LLC p 1076
2000 Northeast Expy, Norcross GA 30071
Tel (770) 798-2000 SIC 3229 3357

ARRIS GROUP INC p 112
3871 Lakefield Dr Ste 300, Suwanee GA 30024
Tel (678) 473-2907
SIC 7372 3663 3357 7373 3661

ARRIS SOLUTIONS INC p 112
3871 Lakefield Dr Ste 300, Suwanee GA 30024
Tel (678) 473-2000 SIC 3661 3663 3357

WOODHEAD INDUSTRIES LLC p 1623
333 Knightsbridge Pkwy # 200, Lincolnshire IL 60069
Tel (847) 353-2500
SIC 3678 3679 3643 3357

MOLEX LLC p 982
2222 Wellington Ct, Lisle IL 60532
Tel (630) 969-4550 SIC 3679 3643 3357

MOLEX PREMISE NETWORKS INC p 982
2222 Wellington Ct, Lisle IL 60532
Tel (866) 733-6659 SIC 3679 3643 3357

MOLEX U S INC p 982
2222 Wellington Ct, Lisle IL 60532
Tel (630) 969-4550
SIC 3678 3679 3643 3357

COLEMAN CABLE LLC p 336
1530 S Shields Dr, Waukegan IL 60085
Tel (847) 672-2300 SIC 3661 3357 3643

■ COMMSCOPE TECHNOLOGIES LLC p 346
4 Westbrook Corporate Ctr, Westchester IL 60154
Tel (708) 236-6000
SIC 3663 3357 3679 3812 3699

TELAMON CORP p 1433
1000 E 116th St, Carmel IN 46032
Tel (317) 818-6888 SIC 4813 8711 3357

■ MARMON RETAIL PRODUCTS INC p 909
1002 Industrial Way, Crothersville IN 47229
Tel (812) 793-2929 SIC 3357 3351

ESSEX GROUP INC p 510
1601 Wall St, Fort Wayne IN 46802
Tel (260) 461-4000 SIC 3357

REA MAGNET WIRE CO INC p 1213
3600 E Pontiac St, Fort Wayne IN 46803
Tel (260) 421-7321 SIC 3357

WIRE AMERICA INC p 1618
1613 E Wallace St, Fort Wayne IN 46803
Tel (260) 969-1700 SIC 4226 3357

■ BELDEN WIRE & CABLE CO LLC p 169
2200 Us Highway 27 S, Richmond IN 47374
Tel (765) 983-5200 SIC 3357

ACK CONTROLS INC p 17
2600 Happy Valley Rd, Glasgow KY 42141
Tel (270) 678-6200 SIC 5013 3625 3357

■ G K TECHNOLOGIES INC p 587
4 Tesseneer Dr, Highland Heights KY 41076
Tel (859) 572-8000 SIC 3357 3315

▲ GENERAL CABLE CORP p 599
4 Tesseneer Dr, Highland Heights KY 41076
Tel (859) 572-8000 SIC 3351 3357

■ GENERAL CABLE INDUSTRIES INC p 599
4 Tesseneer Dr, Highland Heights KY 41076
Tel (859) 572-8000 SIC 3351 3315 3357

■ GENERAL CABLE TECHNOLOGIES CORP p 599
4 Tesseneer Dr, Highland Heights KY 41076
Tel (859) 572-8000 SIC 3357

L-COM INC p 835
50 High St Fl 3, North Andover MA 01845
Tel (800) 343-1455 SIC 3678 3577 3357

DRAKA CABLETEQ USA INC p 455
22 Joseph E Warner Blvd, North Dighton MA 02764
Tel (508) 822-5444 SIC 3357

MORRELL INC p 990
3333 Bald Mountain Rd, Auburn Hills MI 48326
Tel (248) 373-1600
SIC 5084 5065 3621 3643 3559 3357

HI-LEX AMERICA INC p 689
5200 Wayne Rd, Battle Creek MI 49037
Tel (269) 968-0781 SIC 3496 3357

TSK OF AMERICA INC p 1489
5200 Wayne Rd, Battle Creek MI 49037
Tel (269) 968-0781 SIC 3357

■ BELDEN 1993 LLC p 169
1 N Brentwood Blvd # 1500, Saint Louis MO 63105
Tel (314) 854-8000 SIC 3357

▲ BELDEN INC p 169
1 N Brentwood Blvd # 1500, Saint Louis MO 63105
Tel (314) 854-8000 SIC 3357

■ MARMON UTILITY LLC p 909
53 Old Wilton Rd, Milford NH 03055
Tel (603) 673-2040 SIC 3357

■ AMPHENOL PRINTED CIRCUITS INC p 86
91 Northeastern Blvd, Nashua NH 03062
Tel (603) 324-4500
SIC 3679 3678 3672 3357

TYCO ELECTRONICS INTEGRATED CABLE SYSTEMS LLC p 1496
100 Piscataqua Dr, Newington NH 03801
Tel (603) 436-6100 SIC 3357

■ ENTERASYS NETWORKS INC p 501
9 Northstern Blvd Ste 300, Salem NH 03079
Tel (603) 952-5000
SIC 3577 7373 3357 5045

ALPHA WIRE CORP p 60
711 Lidgerwood Ave, Elizabeth NJ 07202
Tel (908) 259-2613 SIC 5063 3082 3357

OKONITE CO p 1080
102 Hilltop Rd, Ramsey NJ 07446
Tel (201) 825-0300 SIC 3357 3315 3355

CAMDEN WIRE CO INC p 245
12 Masonic Ave, Camden NY 13316
Tel (315) 245-3800 SIC 3351 3357

INTERNATIONAL WIRE GROUP INC p 757
12 Masonic Ave, Camden NY 13316
Tel (315) 245-2000 SIC 3357

▲ CORNING INC p 371
1 Riverfront Plz, Corning NY 14831
Tel (607) 974-9000
SIC 3229 3357 3661 3674

LEVITON MANUFACTURING CO INC p 858
201 N Service Rd, Melville NY 11747
Tel (631) 812-6000
SIC 3643 3613 3357 3674 3694 3678

HUBER + SUHNER INC p 716
8530 Steele Creek Place D, Charlotte NC 28273
Tel (704) 790-7300
SIC 3679 3678 3357 5065

DRAKA HOLDINGS USA INC p 455
2512 Penny Rd, Claremont NC 28610
Tel (828) 459-8550 SIC 3357

■ COMMSCOPE CONNECTIVITY SOLUTIONS LLC p 346
1100 Commscope Pl Se, Hickory NC 28602
Tel (828) 324-2200
SIC 3661 3357 3643 8999

■ COMMSCOPE INC OF NORTH CAROLINA p 346
1100 Commscope Pl Se, Hickory NC 28602
Tel (828) 324-2200
SIC 3663 3357 3679 3812 3699

NEXANS USA INC p 1039
39 2nd St Nw, Hickory NC 28601
Tel (828) 323-2660 SIC 3357 3661 3678

ALCAN CORP p 47
6060 Parkland Blvd, Cleveland OH 44124
Tel (440) 460-3307
SIC 3351 3355 3496 3357

SUPERIOR GROUP INC p 1406
100 Front St Ste 525, Conshohocken PA 19428
Tel (610) 397-2040
SIC 5051 3357 3317 3491 3469 7389

KALAS MFG INC p 801
167 Greenfield Rd, Lancaster PA 17601
Tel (717) 335-2360 SIC 3357 3694

BERK-TEK LLC p 174
132 White Oak Rd, New Holland PA 17557
Tel (717) 354-6200 SIC 3357

PRETTL INTERNATIONAL INC p 1173
1721 White Horse Rd, Greenville SC 29605
Tel (864) 220-1010 SIC 3357

PRYSMIAN CABLES AND SYSTEMS USA LLC p 1187
700 Industrial Dr, Lexington SC 29072
Tel (803) 951-4800 SIC 3357

UCI HOLDINGS LLC p 1499
2727 Geesling Rd, Denton TX 76208
Tel (940) 243-7676 SIC 3357

UNITED COPPER INDUSTRIES INC p 1507
2727 Geesling Rd, Denton TX 76208
Tel (940) 243-8200 SIC 3357

▲ ENCORE WIRE CORP p 496
1329 Millwood Rd, Mckinney TX 75069
Tel (972) 562-9473 SIC 3357

CUSTOM COMPUTER CABLES OF AMERICA INC p 403
2901 Summit Ave Ste 400, Plano TX 75074
Tel (972) 638-9309 SIC 5051 3357

STATE ELECTRIC SUPPLY CO p 1380
2010 2nd Ave, Huntington WV 25703
Tel (304) 523-7491 SIC 5063 3357

STATE ELECTRIC SUPPLY CO p 1380
2010 2nd Ave, Huntington WV 25703
Tel (304) 523-7491 SIC 5063 3357

WELLS VEHICLE ELECTRONICS LP p 1591
385 W Rolling Meadows Dr, Fond Du Lac WI 54937
Tel (920) 922-5900
SIC 3714 3694 3644 3357

SIC 3363 Aluminum Die Castings

KARSTEN MANUFACTURING CORP p 804
2201 W Desert Cove Ave, Phoenix AZ 85029
Tel (602) 870-5000
SIC 3949 3398 3363 3325 8711 7997

KPI INTERMEDIATE HOLDINGS INC p 828
481 S Shiloh Dr, Fayetteville AR 72704
Tel (479) 443-1455 SIC 3363 3312

PACE INDUSTRIES LLC p 1103
481 S Shiloh Dr, Fayetteville AR 72704
Tel (479) 443-1455 SIC 3363

EDELBROCK FOUNDRY CORP p 477
1320 S Buena Vista St, San Jacinto CA 92583
Tel (951) 654-6677 SIC 3363 3365 3325

RCM INDUSTRIES INC p 1212
3021 Cullerton St, Franklin Park IL 60131
Tel (847) 455-1950 SIC 3363

SPARTAN LIGHT METAL PRODUCTS INC p 1355
510 E Mcclurken Ave, Sparta IL 62286
Tel (618) 443-4346
SIC 3363 3364 3369 3365

KOCH ENTERPRISES INC p 825
14 S 11th Ave, Evansville IN 47712
Tel (812) 465-9800
SIC 3363 5075 3559 5084 2891 3069

MADISON PRECISION PRODUCTS INC p 894
94 E 400 N, Madison IN 47250
Tel (812) 273-4702 SIC 3363 3365

RYOBI DIE CASTING (USA) INC p 1261
800 W Mausoleum Rd, Shelbyville IN 46176
Tel (317) 398-3398
SIC 3714 3444 3365 3363

REVERE INDUSTRIES LLC p 1229
16855 Suthpark Dr Ste 100, Westfield IN 46074
Tel (317) 580-2420
SIC 3089 3399 3363 3497

TRACE DIE CAST INC p 1468
140 Graham Ave, Bowling Green KY 42101
Tel (270) 781-0049 SIC 3363

GIBBS DIE CASTING CORP p 611
369 Community Dr, Henderson KY 42420
Tel (270) 827-1801 SIC 3364 3363 3542

AISIN AUTOMOTIVE CASTING LLC p 41
4870 E Highway 552, London KY 40744
Tel (606) 878-6523 SIC 3363

LE SUEUR INC p 850
1409 Vine St, Le Sueur MN 56058
Tel (507) 665-6204
SIC 3363 3089 3544 3369

KURT MANUFACTURING CO INC p 832
5280 Main St Ne, Minneapolis MN 55421
Tel (763) 572-1500
SIC 3499 3545 3363 3728 3842 3365

▲ LEGGETT & PLATT INC p 853
1 Leggett Rd, Carthage MO 64836
Tel (417) 358-8131
SIC 2515 2514 3495 2392 2542 3363

SPARTAN LIGHT METAL PRODUCTS LLC p 1355
2510 Lakeview Rd, Mexico MO 65265
Tel (573) 581-2272
SIC 3363 3364 3369 3365

BODINE ALUMINUM INC p 197
2100 Walton Rd, Saint Louis MO 63114
Tel (314) 423-8200 SIC 3363

▲ ALCOA CORP p 47
390 Park Ave Fl 12, New York NY 10022
Tel (212) 518-5400
SIC 3355 3363 3297 2819

KPI CAPITAL HOLDINGS INC p 828
437 Madison Ave Fl 36, New York NY 10022
Tel (479) 443-1455 SIC 6719 3363 3312

KPI HOLDINGS INC p 828
437 Madison Ave Fl 36, New York NY 10022
Tel (479) 443-1455 SIC 6719 3363 3312

SENSUS (BERMUDA 2) LTD p 1305
8601 Six Forks Rd, Raleigh NC 27615
Tel (919) 845-4000 SIC 3824 3363 3491

SENSUS USA INC p 1305
8601 Six Forks Rd Ste 700, Raleigh NC 27615
Tel (919) 845-4000
SIC 3824 3363 2891 3491

▲ PARK-OHIO HOLDINGS CORP p 1116
6065 Parkland Blvd Ste 1, Cleveland OH 44124
Tel (440) 947-2000
SIC 3462 3069 3567 3363 3631 3524

■ PARK-OHIO INDUSTRIES INC p 1116
6065 Parkland Blvd Ste 1, Cleveland OH 44124
Tel (440) 947-2000
SIC 3462 3069 3567 3363 3524

OHIO DECORATIVE PRODUCTS LLC p 1077
220 S Elizabeth St, Spencerville OH 45887
Tel (419) 647-9033
SIC 3086 3369 3471 3363

■ PECO INC p 1127
11241 Se Highway 212, Clackamas OR 97015
Tel (503) 233-6401
SIC 3089 3822 3364 3363

PURE POWER TECHNOLOGIES INC p 1192
1410 Northpoint Blvd, Blythewood SC 29016
Tel (803) 744-7020 SIC 3363

NEMAK USA INC p 1025
1635 Old Columbia Rd, Dickson TN 37055
Tel (615) 446-8110 SIC 3363 3714

WALKER DIE CASTING INC p 1573
1125 Higgs Rd, Lewisburg TN 37091
Tel (931) 359-6206 SIC 3363

CONSOLIDATED METCO INC p 360
5701 Se Columbia Way, Vancouver WA 98661
Tel (360) 828-2599
SIC 3365 3363 3089 3714 3443 3312

MADISON-KIPP CORP p 894
201 Waubesa St, Madison WI 53704
Tel (608) 244-3511 SIC 3363

■ ALBANY-CHICAGO CO LLC p 45
8200 100th St, Pleasant Prairie WI 53158
Tel (262) 947-7600 SIC 3363

FRENCH HOLDINGS LLC p 578
3101 S Taylor Dr, Sheboygan WI 53081
Tel (920) 458-7724 SIC 3363 3341 8711

JL FRENCH LLC p 786
3101 S Taylor Dr, Sheboygan WI 53081
Tel (920) 458-7724 SIC 3363

NEMAK AUTOMOTIVE CASTINGS INC p 1025
3101 S Taylor Dr, Sheboygan WI 53081
Tel (920) 458-7724 SIC 3341 3363 8711

SIC 3364 Nonferrous Die Castings, Exc Aluminum

■ PCC STRUCTURALS GROTON p 1123
839 Poquonnock Rd, Groton CT 06340
Tel (860) 405-3700 SIC 3364

SPARTAN LIGHT METAL PRODUCTS INC p 1355
510 E Mcclurken Ave, Sparta IL 62286
Tel (618) 443-4346
SIC 3363 3364 3369 3365

PMX INDUSTRIES INC p 1158
5300 Willow Creek Dr Sw, Cedar Rapids IA 52404
Tel (319) 368-7700
SIC 3366 5051 3444 3364 3351 3331

GIBBS DIE CASTING CORP p 611
369 Community Dr, Henderson KY 42420
Tel (270) 827-1801 SIC 3364 3363 3542

DVCC INC p 463
800 High St, Chestertown MD 21620
Tel (410) 778-2000
SIC 3492 5085 3535 3321 3364

HITCHCOCK INDUSTRIES INC p 697
8701 Harriet Ave S, Minneapolis MN 55420
Tel (952) 881-1000
SIC 3365 3364 3544 3369

SPARTAN LIGHT METAL PRODUCTS LLC p 1355
2510 Lakeview Rd, Mexico MO 65265
Tel (573) 581-2272
SIC 3363 3364 3369 3365

CERTECH INC p 284
1 Park Pl W, Wood Ridge NJ 07075
Tel (201) 842-6800 SIC 3364

COATS & CLARK INC p 332
3430 Toringdon Way # 301, Charlotte NC 28277
Tel (704) 329-5800
SIC 2284 2281 3364 3089 2241 3965

COATS NORTH AMERICA DE REPUBLICA DOMINICANA INC p 332
3430 Toringdon Way # 301, Charlotte NC 28277
Tel (800) 242-8095
SIC 2284 2281 3364 3089 2241 3965

DYNACAST INTERNATIONAL INC p 464
14045 Ballantyne Ste 400, Charlotte NC 28277
Tel (704) 927-2790 SIC 3364

■ PECO INC p 1127
11241 Se Highway 212, Clackamas OR 97015
Tel (503) 233-6401
SIC 3089 3822 3364 3363

LA FRANCE CORP p 835
1 Lafrance Way, Concordville PA 19331
Tel (610) 361-4300
SIC 3089 3364 3993 5013 7389

■ JARDEN ZINC PRODUCTS LLC p 778
2500 Old Stage Rd, Greeneville TN 37745
Tel (423) 639-8111
SIC 2796 3364 3356 1031 2789

INTERMET CORP p 753
301 Commerce St Ste 2901, Fort Worth TX 76102
Tel (817) 348-9190
SIC 3321 3714 3462 3365 3364

WAGSTAFF INC p 1571
3910 N Flora Rd, Spokane Valley WA 99216
Tel (509) 922-1404 SIC 3542 3364

▲ STRATTEC SECURITY CORP p 1393
3333 W Good Hope Rd, Milwaukee WI 53209
Tel (414) 247-3333 SIC 3714 3364 3429

METALTEK INTERNATIONAL INC p 953
905 E Saint Paul Ave, Waukesha WI 53188
Tel (262) 544-7777 SIC 3366 3443 3364

SIC 3365 Aluminum Foundries

LIGON INDUSTRIES LLC p 866
1927 1st Ave N Ste 500, Birmingham AL 35203
Tel (205) 322-3302
SIC 3365 3593 3325 3471 3714 3446

GRISWOLD INDUSTRIES p 641
1701 Placentia Ave, Costa Mesa CA 92627
Tel (949) 722-4800 SIC 3492 3365 3366

EDELBROCK FOUNDRY CORP p 477
1320 S Buena Vista St, San Jacinto CA 92583
Tel (951) 654-6677 SIC 3363 3365 3325

■ CALPHALON CORP p 242
3 Glenlake Pkwy, Atlanta GA 30328
Tel (770) 418-7100 SIC 3365 3469

■ NEWELL OPERATING CO p 1037
29 E Stephenson St, Freeport IL 61032
Tel (815) 235-4171
SIC 3365 3991 3089 2591 3965 3596

WORLD KITCHEN LLC p 1625
9525 Bryn Mawr Ave # 300, Rosemont IL 60018
Tel (847) 233-8600
SIC 3229 3469 3365 3421 5719

SPARTAN LIGHT METAL PRODUCTS INC p 1355
510 E Mcclurken Ave, Sparta IL 62286
Tel (618) 443-4346
SIC 3363 3364 3369 3365

ENKEI AMERICA INC p 499
2900 Inwood Dr, Columbus IN 47201
Tel (812) 373-7000 SIC 3714 3365

SHIPSTON ALUMINUM TECHNOLOGIES INTERNATIONAL LLC p 1317
1450 Commerce Pkwy, Franklin IN 46131
Tel (317) 738-0282 SIC 3365

MADISON PRECISION PRODUCTS INC p 894
94 E 400 N, Madison IN 47250
Tel (812) 273-4702 SIC 3363 3365

RYOBI DIE CASTING (USA) INC p 1261
800 W Mausoleum Rd, Shelbyville IN 46176
Tel (317) 398-3398
SIC 3714 3444 3365 3363

HARVEY INDUSTRIES LLC p 667
3837 Mill St, Wabash IN 46992
Tel (260) 563-8371 SIC 3463 3365

FANSTEEL INC p 527
1746 Commerce Rd, Creston IA 50801
Tel (641) 782-8521
SIC 3463 3728 3365 3369 3769 3545

WELLMAN DYNAMICS CORP p 1589
1746 Commerce Rd, Creston IA 50801
Tel (641) 782-8521 SIC 3369 3365

RCO ENGINEERING INC p 1212
29200 Calahan Rd, Roseville MI 48066
Tel (586) 774-0100
SIC 3714 3089 3365 7361 3325 2531

HITCHCOCK INDUSTRIES INC p 697
8701 Harriet Ave S, Minneapolis MN 55420
Tel (952) 881-1000
SIC 3365 3364 3544 3369

KURT MANUFACTURING CO INC p 832
5280 Main St Ne, Minneapolis MN 55421
Tel (763) 572-1500
SIC 3499 3545 3363 3728 3842 3365

STAHL SPECIALTY CO p 1374
111 E Pacific St, Kingsville MO 64061
Tel (816) 597-3322
SIC 5051 3544 3365 3567 3369

SPARTAN LIGHT METAL PRODUCTS LLC p 1355
2510 Lakeview Rd, Mexico MO 65265
Tel (573) 581-2272
SIC 3363 3364 3369 3365

SHAPES/ARCH HOLDINGS LLC p 1311
9000 River Rd, Delair NJ 08110
Tel (856) 662-5500 SIC 3354 3365

HITACHI METALS AMERICA LTD p 697
2 Manhattanville Rd # 301, Purchase NY 10577
Tel (914) 694-9200
SIC 3264 3577 3365 5051 3321 3559

CONSOLIDATED PRECISION PRODUCTS CORP p 360
1621 Euclid Ave Ste 1850, Cleveland OH 44115
Tel (909) 595-2252 SIC 3365 3324

■ GENERAL ALUMINUM MFG CO p 599
6065 Parkland Blvd, Cleveland OH 44124
Tel (440) 947-2000 SIC 3365 3369

ALUMINUM LINE PRODUCTS CO p 63
24460 Sperry Cir, Westlake OH 44145
Tel (440) 835-8880 *SIC* 5051 3365 3999

INTERMET CORP p 753
301 Commerce St Ste 2901, Fort Worth TX 76102
Tel (817) 348-9190
SIC 3321 3714 3462 3365 3364

PYROTEK INC p 1194
705 W 1st Ave, Spokane WA 99201
Tel (509) 926-6212 *SIC* 3365

CONSOLIDATED METCO INC p 360
5701 Se Columbia Way, Vancouver WA 98661
Tel (360) 828-2599
SIC 3365 3363 3089 3714 3443 3312

TVCI HOLDING INC p 1494
1236 N 18th St, Sheboygan WI 53081
Tel (920) 457-4851 *SIC* 3914 3365 3089

VOLLRATH CO LLC p 1564
1236 N 18th St, Sheboygan WI 53081
Tel (920) 459-6568
SIC 3089 3365 3421 3556 3914

SIC 3366 Copper Foundries

BALDOR ELECTRIC CO p 147
5711 Rs Boreham Jr St, Fort Smith AR 72901
Tel (479) 646-4711
SIC 3621 3566 3463 3366

GRISWOLD INDUSTRIES p 641
1701 Placentia Ave, Costa Mesa CA 92627
Tel (949) 722-4800 *SIC* 3492 3365 3366

PMX INDUSTRIES INC p 1158
5300 Willow Creek Dr Sw, Cedar Rapids IA 52404
Tel (319) 368-7700
SIC 3366 5051 3444 3364 3351 3331

GKN SINTER METALS LLC p 613
2200 N Opdyke Rd, Auburn Hills MI 48326
Tel (248) 296-7832
SIC 3714 3568 3369 3366

JSJ CORP p 796
700 Robbins Rd, Grand Haven MI 49417
Tel (616) 842-6350
SIC 3465 3469 3366 3089 3086 2522

COLD SPRING GRANITE CO INC p 335
17482 Granite West Rd, Cold Spring MN 56320
Tel (320) 685-3621 *SIC* 3281 1741 3366

LIBERTAS COPPER LLC p 861
100 Washington St, Leetsdale PA 15056
Tel (724) 251-4200 *SIC* 3366 3351

▲ MATTHEWS INTERNATIONAL CORP p 920
2 N Shore Ctr Ste 200, Pittsburgh PA 15212
Tel (412) 442-8200
SIC 3366 1542 3569 3995 3953 2796

METALTEK INTERNATIONAL INC p 953
905 E Saint Paul Ave, Waukesha WI 53188
Tel (262) 544-7777 *SIC* 3366 3443 3364

SIC 3369 Nonferrous Foundries: Castings, NEC

AMERICAN CAST IRON PIPE CO p 70
1501 31st Ave N, Birmingham AL 35207
Tel (205) 325-7856
SIC 3491 3369 3321 3053 3317

AE INDUSTRIAL PARTNERS LLC p 28
2500 N Military Trl # 470, Boca Raton FL 33431
Tel (561) 372-7820 *SIC* 3369 3324

SPARTAN LIGHT METAL PRODUCTS INC p 1355
510 E Mcclurken Ave, Sparta IL 62286
Tel (618) 443-4346
SIC 3363 3364 3369 3365

TEMPCO ELECTRIC HEATER CORP p 1436
607 N Central Ave, Wood Dale IL 60191
Tel (630) 350-2252 *SIC* 3567 3369 3829

FANSTEEL INC p 527
1746 Commerce Rd, Creston IA 50801
Tel (641) 782-8521
SIC 3463 3728 3365 3369 3769 3545

WELLMAN DYNAMICS CORP p 1589
1746 Commerce Rd, Creston IA 50801
Tel (641) 782-8521 *SIC* 3369 3365

MEGGITT (ERLANGER) LLC p 940
1400 Jamike Ave, Erlanger KY 41018
Tel (859) 525-8040 *SIC* 3369

GKN SINTER METALS LLC p 613
2200 N Opdyke Rd, Auburn Hills MI 48326
Tel (248) 296-7832
SIC 3714 3568 3369 3366

HURON CASTING INC p 721
7050 Hartley St, Pigeon MI 48755
Tel (989) 453-3933 *SIC* 3325 3369

■ FEDERAL-MOGUL PISTON RINGS INC p 536
26555 Northwestern Hwy, Southfield MI 48033
Tel (248) 354-7700 *SIC* 3592 3053 3369

ROLLED ALLOYS INC p 1247
125 W Sterns Rd, Temperance MI 48182
Tel (800) 521-0332
SIC 5051 3369 3341 3317 2899 2851

LE SUEUR INC p 850
1409 Vine St, Le Sueur MN 56058
Tel (507) 665-6204
SIC 3363 3089 3544 3369

HITCHCOCK INDUSTRIES INC p 697
8701 Harriet Ave S, Minneapolis MN 55420
Tel (952) 881-1000
SIC 3365 3364 3544 3369

STAHL SPECIALTY CO p 1374
111 E Pacific St, Kingsville MO 64061
Tel (816) 597-3322
SIC 5051 3544 3365 3567 3369

SPARTAN LIGHT METAL PRODUCTS LLC p 1355
2510 Lakeview Rd, Mexico MO 65265
Tel (573) 581-2272
SIC 3363 3364 3369 3365

CPP-SYRACUSE INC p 387
901 E Genesee St, Chittenango NY 13037
Tel (315) 687-0014 *SIC* 3324 3369 3356

■ PCC AIRFOILS LLC p 1123
3401 Entp Pkwy Ste 200, Beachwood OH 44122
Tel (216) 831-3590 *SIC* 3369

ILSCO CORP p 733
4730 Madison Rd, Cincinnati OH 45227
Tel (513) 533-6200
SIC 3643 3369 3451 3678 3544 3469

■ GENERAL ALUMINUM MFG CO p 599
6065 Parkland Blvd, Cleveland OH 44124
Tel (440) 947-2000 *SIC* 3365 3369

ELYRIA FOUNDRY CO LLC p 490
120 Filbert St, Elyria OH 44035
Tel (440) 322-4657
SIC 3321 3369 3325 2821

OHIO DECORATIVE PRODUCTS LLC p 1077
220 S Elizabeth St, Spencerville OH 45887
Tel (419) 647-9033
SIC 3086 3369 3471 3363

■ PRECISION CASTPARTS CORP p 1168
4650 Sw Mcdam Ave Ste 300, Portland OR 97239
Tel (503) 946-4800
SIC 3324 3369 3724 3511 3519

■ LATROBE SPECIALTY METALS CO LLC p 846
2626 Ligonier St, Latrobe PA 15650
Tel (724) 537-7711 *SIC* 3312 3369

■ TDY INDUSTRIES LLC p 1429
1000 Six Ppg Pl, Pittsburgh PA 15222
Tel (412) 394-2896
SIC 3356 3312 3316 3339 3369

WHEMCO INC p 1605
5 Hot Metal St Ste 300, Pittsburgh PA 15203
Tel (412) 390-2700
SIC 3312 3462 3731 3325 3441 3369

■ HAAS GROUP p 651
1475 Phoenixville Pike, West Chester PA 19380
Tel (484) 564-4500 *SIC* 8741 3369

MAGOTTEAUX INC p 897
725 Cool Springs Blvd # 200, Franklin TN 37067
Tel (615) 385-3055 *SIC* 3369

CONSOLIDATED CASTING CORP p 359
1501 S Interstate 45, Hutchins TX 75141
Tel (972) 225-7305 *SIC* 3324 3369

DELTA CENTRIFUGAL CORP p 426
3402 Center St, Temple TX 76504
Tel (254) 773-9055 *SIC* 5051 3325 3369

TRAVIS PATTERN & FOUNDRY INC p 1475
1413 E Hawthorne Rd, Spokane WA 99218
Tel (509) 466-1798
SIC 3523 3369 3313 3321 3625

SIC 3398 Metal Heat Treating

KARSTEN MANUFACTURING CORP p 804
2201 W Desert Cove Ave, Phoenix AZ 85029
Tel (602) 870-5000
SIC 3949 3398 3363 3325 8711 7997

LAPHAM-HICKEY STEEL CORP p 845
5500 W 73rd St, Chicago IL 60638
Tel (708) 496-6111
SIC 5051 3398 3355 3317 3316

TEMPEL STEEL CO p 1436
5500 N Wolcott Ave, Chicago IL 60640
Tel (773) 250-8000
SIC 3469 3313 3316 3398 5051

TC INDUSTRIES INC p 1428
3703 S Il Route 31, Crystal Lake IL 60012
Tel (815) 459-2401 *SIC* 3499 3398

TERRA COTTA HOLDINGS CO p 1439
3703 S Il Route 31, Crystal Lake IL 60012
Tel (815) 459-2400 *SIC* 3499 3398 6531

IONBOND LLC p 762
1823 E Whitcomb Ave, Madison Heights MI 48071
Tel (248) 398-9100 *SIC* 3398 3479

GESTAMP MASON LLC p 609
200 E Kipp Rd, Mason MI 48854
Tel (517) 244-8800
SIC 3398 5013 3714 3711 3465

PAULO PRODUCTS CO p 1121
5711 W Park Ave, Saint Louis MO 63110
Tel (314) 647-7500
SIC 3471 3398 8734 3567

■ TSI GROUP INC p 1489
94 Tide Mill Rd, Hampton NH 03842
Tel (603) 964-0296
SIC 3599 3398 3443 3444

SMITHS TUBULAR SYSTEMS-LACONIA INC p 1334
93 Lexington Dr, Laconia NH 03246
Tel (603) 524-2064
SIC 3463 3498 8734 7692 3441 3398

■ METAL IMPROVEMENT CO LLC p 952
80 E State Rt 4 Ste 310, Paramus NJ 07652
Tel (201) 843-7800 *SIC* 3398

▲ GIBRALTAR INDUSTRIES INC p 611
3556 Lake Shore Rd # 100, Buffalo NY 14219
Tel (716) 826-6500
SIC 3499 3316 3441 3398

■ SUNLIGHT US CO INC p 1403
3556 Lake Shore Rd # 100, Buffalo NY 14219
Tel (716) 826-6500
SIC 3499 3316 3441 3398

ATERIAN INVESTMENT PARTNERS LP p 124
11 E 44th St Rm 1803, New York NY 10017
Tel (212) 547-2806 *SIC* 3398

GRAYWOOD COMPANIES INC p 633
1390 Mount Read Blvd, Rochester NY 14606
Tel (585) 254-7000
SIC 3541 3545 3544 3398

XTEK INC p 1633
11451 Reading Rd, Cincinnati OH 45241
Tel (513) 733-7800
SIC 3568 3547 3398 3312

PRINCE & IZANT CO p 1176
12999 Plaza Dr, Cleveland OH 44130
Tel (216) 362-7000
SIC 5051 3398 3351 3341 3339 2899

■ UNION ELECTRIC STEEL CORP p 1504
726 Bell Ave, Carnegie PA 15106
Tel (412) 429-7655 *SIC* 3325 3398 3312

DONSCO INC p 451
124 N Front St, Wrightsville PA 17368
Tel (717) 252-0690 *SIC* 3398 3321

BWT LLC p 231
201 Brookfield Pkwy, Greenville SC 29607
Tel (864) 990-0050 *SIC* 3398

BODYCOTE THERMAL PROCESSING INC p 197
12700 Park Central Dr # 700, Dallas TX 75251
Tel (214) 904-2420 *SIC* 3398

STIHL INC p 1389
536 Viking Dr, Virginia Beach VA 23452
Tel (757) 486-9100 *SIC* 3546 3398

WT WALKER GROUP INC p 1628
222 E Erie St Ste 300, Milwaukee WI 53202
Tel (414) 223-2000 *SIC* 3462 3398

SIC 3399 Primary Metal Prdts, NEC

OUTOKUMPU STAINLESS USA LLC p 1099
1 Steel Dr, Calvert AL 36513
Tel (251) 829-3600 *SIC* 3312 3399

MPG GEAR TECHNOLOGIES p 995
7800 Ball Rd, Fort Smith AR 72908
Tel (479) 646-1662 *SIC* 3714 3568 3399

▲ SIMPSON MANUFACTURING CO INC p 1325
5956 W Las Positas Blvd, Pleasanton CA 94588
Tel (925) 560-9000 *SIC* 3441 3399

▲ DMC GLOBAL INC p 446
5405 Spine Rd, Boulder CO 80301
Tel (303) 665-5700 *SIC* 3399

GERALD H PHIPPS INC p 608
5995 Greenwood Ste 100, Greenwood Village CO 80111
Tel (303) 571-5377 *SIC* 1542 3399

BARDEN CORP p 155
200 Park Ave, Danbury CT 06810
Tel (203) 744-2211
SIC 3562 3469 3842 3089 3399

■ CARLISLE INTERCONNECT TECHNOLOGIES INC p 257
100 Tensolite Dr, Saint Augustine FL 32092
Tel (904) 829-5600
SIC 3679 3399 3678 3357 3643 5063

HOOVER PRECISION PRODUCTS INC p 706
2200 Pendley Rd, Cumming GA 30041
Tel (770) 889-9223 *SIC* 3399

BURGESS-NORTON MFG CO INC p 227
737 Peyton St, Geneva IL 60134
Tel (630) 232-4100 *SIC* 3399 3592 3452

■ OMNISOURCE CORP p 1085
7575 W Jefferson Blvd, Fort Wayne IN 46804
Tel (260) 422-5541 *SIC* 5093 3462 3399

REVERE INDUSTRIES LLC p 1229
16855 Suthpark Dr Ste 100, Westfield IN 46074
Tel (317) 580-2420
SIC 3089 3399 3363 3497

ARCH GLOBAL PRECISION LLC p 104
12955 Inkster Rd, Livonia MI 48150
Tel (734) 266-6900 *SIC* 5049 3399

▲ VALMONT INDUSTRIES INC p 1541
1 Valmont Plz Ste 500, Omaha NE 68154
Tel (402) 963-1000
SIC 3441 3399 3317 3523 3612

HOEGANAES CORP p 699
1001 Taylors Ln, Cinnaminson NJ 08077
Tel (856) 303-0366 *SIC* 3312 3399

OERLIKON METCO (US) INC p 1075
1101 Prospect Ave, Westbury NY 11590
Tel (516) 334-1300 *SIC* 3399 5084 3479

■ HANDY & HARMAN p 657
1133 Westchester Ave N-222, White Plains NY 10604
Tel (914) 461-1300
SIC 3356 3399 3341 3317 3315

BLUE RIDGE METALS CORP p 192
180 Mills Gap Rd, Fletcher NC 28732
Tel (828) 687-2525 *SIC* 3399 3315

ELGIN FASTENER GROUP LLC p 486
10217 Brecksville Rd, Brecksville OH 44141
Tel (812) 717-2544 *SIC* 3399 3452

STEIN INC p 1385
1929 E Royalton Rd Ste C, Cleveland OH 44147
Tel (440) 526-9301 *SIC* 3399 3312 5084

MIDWEST MOTOR SUPPLY CO p 967
4800 Roberts Rd, Columbus OH 43228
Tel (800) 233-1294 *SIC* 3965 3399 8742

MATANDY STEEL & METAL PRODUCTS LLC p 919
1200 Central Ave, Hamilton OH 45011
Tel (513) 887-5274
SIC 5051 3312 3444 3399

▲ FERRO CORP p 538
6060 Parkland Blvd # 250, Mayfield Heights OH 44124
Tel (216) 875-5600
SIC 3479 2816 2851 3399 2821 2834

■ RMI TITANIUM CO LLC p 1239
1000 Warren Ave, Niles OH 44446
Tel (330) 652-9952
SIC 3399 3356 1741 3533

TMS INTERNATIONAL CORP p 1457
12 Monongahela Ave, Glassport PA 15045
Tel (412) 678-6141
SIC 3312 4731 3399 7359 4213

TMS INTERNATIONAL HOLDING CORP p 1457
12 Monongahela Ave, Glassport PA 15045
Tel (412) 678-6141
SIC 3312 4731 3399 7359 4213

TMS INTERNATIONAL LLC p 1458
12 Monongahela Ave, Glassport PA 15045
Tel (412) 678-6141
SIC 3312 4731 3399 7359 4213

NORTH AMERICAN HOGANAS CO p 1050
111 Hoganas Way, Hollsopple PA 15935
Tel (814) 479-3500 *SIC* 3399

▲ KENNAMETAL INC p 810
600 Grant St Ste 5100, Pittsburgh PA 15219
Tel (412) 248-8200
SIC 3545 3532 3531 3313 3399

■ METALDYNE SINTERED RIDGWAY LLC p 952
1149 Rocky Rd, Ridgway PA 15853
Tel (814) 776-1141 *SIC* 3399 3441 3462

MATTHEY JOHNSON HOLDINGS INC p 921
435 Devon Park Dr Ste 600, Wayne PA 19087
Tel (610) 971-3000
SIC 3341 3339 3356 2834 3399 3714

MATTHEY JOHNSON INC p 921
435 Devon Park Dr Ste 600, Wayne PA 19087
Tel (610) 971-3000
SIC 3341 3339 3356 2834 3399 3714

HERAEUS INC HIC p 685
770 Township Line Rd, Yardley PA 19067
Tel (212) 752-2180
SIC 3399 3823 3339 3469

■ STANLEY FASTENING SYSTEMS LP p 1377
2 Briggs Dr, East Greenwich RI 02818
Tel (401) 884-2500 *SIC* 3399 3579

SSI TECHNOLOGIES INC p 1364
3200 Palmer Dr, Janesville WI 53546
Tel (608) 758-1500 *SIC* 3399 3825

SIC 3411 Metal Cans

■ SILGAN CONTAINERS CORP p 1323
21800 Oxnard St Ste 600, Woodland Hills CA 91367
Tel (818) 348-3700 *SIC* 3411

■ SILGAN CONTAINERS LLC p 1323
21800 Oxnard St Ste 600, Woodland Hills CA 91367
Tel (818) 710-3700 *SIC* 3411

■ SILGAN CONTAINERS MANUFACTURING CORP p 1323
21800 Oxnard St Ste 600, Woodland Hills CA 91367
Tel (818) 710-3700 *SIC* 3411

▲ BALL CORP p 148
10 Longs Peak Dr, Broomfield CO 80021
Tel (303) 469-3131
SIC 3411 3085 3812 3679

■ BALL METAL BEVERAGE CONTAINER CORP p 148
9300 W 108th Cir, Westminster CO 80021
Tel (303) 469-5511 *SIC* 3411

■ BALL METAL FOOD CONTAINER LLC p 148
9300 W 108th Cir, Westminster CO 80021
Tel (303) 469-3131 *SIC* 3411

■ BALL PACKAGING LLC p 148
9300 W 108th Cir, Westminster CO 80021
Tel (303) 469-5511 *SIC* 3411

CCL INDUSTRIES CORP p 270
15 Controls Dr, Shelton CT 06484
Tel (203) 926-1253
SIC 2759 2992 3411 2819 2844

▲ SILGAN HOLDINGS INC p 1323
4 Landmark Sq Ste 400, Stamford CT 06901
Tel (203) 975-7110 *SIC* 3411 3085 3089

■ SILGAN WHITE CAP CORP p 1323
4 Landmark Sq Ste 400, Stamford CT 06901
Tel (630) 515-8383 *SIC* 3411

INDUSTRIAL CONTAINER SERVICES LLC p 739
2400 Maitland Center Pkwy, Maitland FL 32751
Tel (800) 273-3786 *SIC* 3443 3411 3412

BWAY CORP p 230
8607 Roberts Dr Ste 250, Atlanta GA 30350
Tel (770) 645-4800 *SIC* 3411 3089

BWAY HOLDING CO p 231
8607 Roberts Dr Ste 250, Atlanta GA 30350
Tel (770) 645-4800 *SIC* 3411 3089

BWAY INTERMEDIATE CO INC p 231
8607 Roberts Dr Ste 250, Atlanta GA 30350
Tel (770) 645-4800 *SIC* 3411 3089

ARDAGH METAL BEVERAGE USA INC p 106
8770 W Bryn Mawr Ave # 175, Chicago IL 60631
Tel (773) 399-3000 *SIC* 3411

BWAY PARENT CO INC p 231
3200 S Kilbourn Ave, Chicago IL 60623
Tel (773) 890-3300 *SIC* 3411 3089

REXAM BEVERAGE CAN CO p 1230
8770 W Bryn Mawr Ave Fl 8, Chicago IL 60631
Tel (773) 399-3000 *SIC* 3411

KRAFT FOODS GROUP INC p 829
3 Lakes Dr, Northfield IL 60093
Tel (847) 646-2000
SIC 2022 3411 2095 2043 2035 2087

PSC INDUSTRIES INC p 1188
1100 W Market St, Louisville KY 40203
Tel (502) 625-7700 *SIC* 3411

CCL LABEL INC p 270
161 Worcester Rd Ste 504, Framingham MA 01701
Tel (508) 872-4511 *SIC* 2759 3411 2671

ANHEUSER-BUSCH COMPANIES LLC p 91
1 Busch Pl, Saint Louis MO 63118
Tel (314) 632-6777 *SIC* 2082 3411 7996

METAL CONTAINER CORP p 952
3636 S Geyer Rd Ste 400, Saint Louis MO 63127
Tel (314) 577-2000 *SIC* 3411

PENNY PLATE LLC p 1131
14000 Horizon Way Ste 300, Mount Laurel NJ 08054
Tel (856) 429-7583 *SIC* 3411 3556

FOULKROD ASSOCIATES p 571
8275 N Crescent Blvd, Pennsauken NJ 08110
Tel (856) 662-6767 *SIC* 3411 5149

PERK-UP INC p 1136
399 Knollwood Rd Ste 309, White Plains NY 10603
Tel (914) 580-3200
SIC 5113 5149 2673 3411 2674 2035

BALL INC p 148
4201 Congress St Ste 340, Charlotte NC 28209
Tel (704) 551-1500 *SIC* 3411

ANCHOR HOCKING LLC p 89
519 N Pierce Ave, Lancaster OH 43130
Tel (740) 681-6478
SIC 3229 3089 3411 3221

GHP II LLC p 610
1115 W 5th Ave, Lancaster OH 43130
Tel (740) 687-2500
SIC 3229 3089 3411 3221

EXAL CORP p 516
1 Performance Pl, Youngstown OH 44502
Tel (330) 744-9505 *SIC* 3411 3354

■ CROWN CORK & SEAL CO INC p 395
1 Crown Way, Philadelphia PA 19154
Tel (215) 698-5100 *SIC* 3411

■ **CROWN CORK & SEAL USA INC** p 395
1 Crown Way, Philadelphia PA 19154
Tel (215) 698-5100 *SIC* 3411 3466

▲ **CROWN HOLDINGS INC** p 395
1 Crown Way, Philadelphia PA 19154
Tel (215) 698-5100 *SIC* 3411 3466 3499

INTERMETRO INDUSTRIES CORP p 753
651 N Washington St, Wilkes Barre PA 18705
Tel (570) 825-2741
SIC 3496 2542 3537 3411 3315 2441

SPARTANBURG AUTOMOTIVE INC p 1355
1290 New Cut Rd, Spartanburg SC 29303
Tel (864) 585-5211 *SIC* 3465 3412 3411

▲ **CLARCOR INC** p 321
840 Crescent Centre Dr # 600, Franklin TN 37067
Tel (615) 771-3100
SIC 3714 3599 3564 3569 3411 3089

HOOVER GROUP INC p 706
2135 Highway 6 S, Houston TX 77077
Tel (800) 844-8683
SIC 3496 3412 3443 3089 7359 3411

■ **REYNOLDS METALS CO LLC** p 1230
6603 W Broad St, Richmond VA 23230
Tel (804) 281-2000 *SIC* 3411

SIC 3412 Metal Barrels, Drums, Kegs & Pails

▲ **MOBILE MINI INC** p 980
4646 E Van Buren St # 400, Phoenix AZ 85008
Tel (480) 894-6311
SIC 4225 3448 3441 3412 7359

HYUNDAI TRANSLEAD p 724
8880 Rio San Diego Dr # 600, San Diego CA 92108
Tel (619) 574-1500 *SIC* 3443 3715 3412

WG GLOBAL LLC p 1604
603 Park Point Dr Ste 200, Golden CO 80401
Tel (303) 395-2100
SIC 3569 3559 3629 3625 3443 3412

RIO TINTO AMERICA INC p 1236
8051 E Maplewood Ave # 100, Greenwood Village CO 80111
Tel (303) 713-5000 *SIC* 3412 5082 1044

CONNECTICUT CONTAINER CORP p 356
455 Sackett Point Rd, North Haven CT 06473
Tel (203) 248-2161
SIC 2653 3993 3412 2631

INDUSTRIAL CONTAINER SERVICES LLC p 739
2400 Maitland Center Pkwy, Maitland FL 32751
Tel (800) 273-3786 *SIC* 3443 3411 3412

ANTHONY WAYNE REHABILITATION CENTER FOR HANDICAPPED AND BLIND INC p 94
8515 Bluffton Rd, Fort Wayne IN 46809
Tel (260) 744-6145
SIC 8331 7331 3441 3412 2449 2448

ADVANCE PACKAGING CORP p 24
4459 40th St Se, Grand Rapids MI 49512
Tel (616) 949-6610 *SIC* 2653 3412

MAUSER USA LLC p 921
35 Cotters Ln, East Brunswick NJ 08816
Tel (732) 353-7100 *SIC* 3412 2655

TOTER LLC p 1463
841 Meacham Rd, Statesville NC 28677
Tel (800) 424-0422
SIC 3089 3536 3469 3412 2821

BERENFIELD CONTAINERS INC p 174
4555 Lake Forest Dr # 205, Blue Ash OH 45242
Tel (513) 618-3780 *SIC* 3412 2655

▲ **GREIF INC** p 639
425 Winter Rd, Delaware OH 43015
Tel (740) 549-6000
SIC 2653 2449 2655 3412 3089 2674

CLEVELAND STEEL CONTAINER CORP p 326
30310 Emerald Valley Pkwy, Solon OH 44139
Tel (440) 349-8000 *SIC* 3412

SPARTANBURG AUTOMOTIVE INC p 1355
1290 New Cut Rd, Spartanburg SC 29303
Tel (864) 585-5211 *SIC* 3465 3412 3411

HOOVER GROUP INC p 706
2135 Highway 6 S, Houston TX 77077
Tel (800) 844-8683
SIC 3496 3412 3443 3089 7359 3411

STEEL KING INDUSTRIES INC p 1384
2700 Chamber St, Stevens Point WI 54481
Tel (715) 341-3120
SIC 3441 3537 3412 2542

SIC 3421 Cutlery

▲ **ACME UNITED CORP** p 18
55 Walls Dr Ste 201, Fairfield CT 06824
Tel (203) 254-6060
SIC 3421 2499 3842 3579 3069 3999

■ **SCHICK MANUFACTURING INC** p 1287
10 Leighton Rd, Milford CT 06460
Tel (203) 882-2100 *SIC* 3421

BIC CORP p 181
1 Bic Way Ste 1, Shelton CT 06484
Tel (203) 783-2000
SIC 3951 2899 3999 3421 5091 3952

BIC USA INC p 181
1 Bic Way Ste 1, Shelton CT 06484
Tel (203) 783-2000
SIC 3951 2899 3999 3421

■ **EDGEWELL PERSONAL CARE BRANDS LLC** p 477
6 Research Dr, Shelton CT 06484
Tel (203) 944-5500 *SIC* 3421 2844 2676

■ **AMERICAN HOUSEHOLD INC** p 74
2381 Nw Executive Ctr Dr, Boca Raton FL 33431
Tel (561) 912-4100
SIC 3631 2514 3421 3634 3829 3841

■ **SUNBEAM AMERICAS HOLDINGS LLC** p 1401
2381 Nw Executive Ctr Dr, Boca Raton FL 33431
Tel (561) 912-4100
SIC 3631 2514 3421 3634 3829 3841

PRAIRIE PACKAGING INC p 1167
7200 S Mason Ave, Bedford Park IL 60638
Tel (708) 496-1172 *SIC* 3089 3421

SOLO CUP INVESTMENT CORP p 1338
1700 Old Deerfield Rd, Highland Park IL 60035
Tel (847) 831-4800 *SIC* 3089 2656 3421

SCC HOLDING CO LLC p 1286
150 Saunders Rd Ste 150, Lake Forest IL 60045
Tel (847) 444-5000 *SIC* 3089 2656 3421

SOLO CUP CO p 1338
300 Tri State Intl # 200, Lincolnshire IL 60069
Tel (847) 831-4800 *SIC* 3089 3421 2656

SOLO CUP CO LLC p 1338
300 Tri State Intl # 200, Lincolnshire IL 60069
Tel (847) 444-5000 *SIC* 3089 2656 3421

ESTWING MANUFACTURING CO INC p 511
2647 8th St, Rockford IL 61109
Tel (815) 397-9521
SIC 3423 3546 3545 3429 3421 3425

WORLD KITCHEN LLC p 1625
9525 Bryn Mawr Ave # 300, Rosemont IL 60018
Tel (847) 233-8600
SIC 3229 3469 3365 3421 5719

■ **GILLETTE CO** p 612
1 Gillette Park, Boston MA 02127
Tel (617) 421-7000
SIC 3421 3634 2844 3951 2899

▲ **EDGEWELL PERSONAL CARE CO** p 477
1350 Timberlake Manor Pkwy, Chesterfield MO 63017
Tel (314) 594-1900
SIC 3421 2844 2676 3069

OLD RAZOR CO LLC p 1081
240 Cedar Knolls Rd, Cedar Knolls NJ 07927
Tel (973) 753-3000 *SIC* 3421

▲ **LIFETIME BRANDS INC** p 864
1000 Stewart Ave, Garden City NY 11530
Tel (516) 683-6000 *SIC* 3421 5023 5719

■ **HFC PRESTIGE INTERNATIONAL US LLC** p 689
350 5th Ave, New York NY 10118
Tel (212) 389-7800
SIC 2844 2676 3421 2842 2841

REV HOLDINGS INC p 1229
466 Lexington Ave Fl 21, New York NY 10017
Tel (212) 527-4000
SIC 2844 3421 5122 5199 5999

■ **REVLON CONSUMER PRODUCTS CORP** p 1229
1 New York Plz, New York NY 10004
Tel (212) 527-4000 *SIC* 2844 3421

REVLON HOLDINGS INC p 1229
237 Park Ave, New York NY 10017
Tel (212) 527-4000
SIC 2844 3421 5122 5199 5999

■ **REVLON REAL ESTATE CORP** p 1229
466 Lexington Ave Fl 13, New York NY 10017
Tel (212) 527-4000
SIC 5122 2844 3421 5199 5999

RGI GROUP INC p 1231
625 Madison Ave Frnt 4, New York NY 10022
Tel (212) 527-4000
SIC 2844 3421 5122 5199 5999

CUTCO CORP p 403
1116 E State St, Olean NY 14760
Tel (716) 372-3111 *SIC* 5963 3421

■ **IRWIN INDUSTRIAL TOOL CO** p 765
8935 N Pointe Exec Pk Dr, Huntersville NC 28078
Tel (704) 987-4555 *SIC* 3423 3545 3421

▲ **PROCTER & GAMBLE CO** p 1179
1 Procter And Gamble Plz, Cincinnati OH 45202
Tel (513) 983-1100
SIC 2844 2676 3421 2842 2841

LEATHERMAN TOOL GROUP INC p 850
12106 Ne Ainsworth Cir, Portland OR 97220
Tel (503) 253-7826 *SIC* 3421

KAI USA LTD p 800
18600 Sw Teton Ave, Tualatin OR 97062
Tel (503) 682-1966 *SIC* 3421

W R CASE & SONS CUTLERY CO p 1569
50 Owens Way, Bradford PA 16701
Tel (800) 523-6350 *SIC* 3421

ZIPPO MANUFACTURING CO INC p 1643
33 Barbour St, Bradford PA 16701
Tel (814) 368-2700
SIC 3914 3993 5172 3999 3421 3172

FISKARS BRANDS INC p 552
7800 Discovery Dr, Middleton WI 53562
Tel (608) 259-1649
SIC 3052 3679 3421 3069 3423

VOLLRATH CO LLC p 1564
1236 N 18th St, Sheboygan WI 53081
Tel (920) 459-6568
SIC 3089 3365 3421 3556 3914

SIC 3423 Hand & Edge Tools

MTD SOUTHWEST INC p 997
9235 S Mckemy St, Tempe AZ 85284
Tel (480) 961-1002 *SIC* 3524 3546 3423

GARDEN PALS INC p 591
1300 Valley Vista Dr # 209, Diamond Bar CA 91765
Tel (909) 605-0200 *SIC* 3423

BUFFINGTON & ASSOCIATES INC p 224
5775 Las Positas Rd, Livermore CA 94551
Tel (925) 583-1600 *SIC* 3423

WESTERN FORGE INC p 1598
4607 Forge Rd, Colorado Springs CO 80907
Tel (719) 598-5070 *SIC* 3423 3545

TRUMPF INC p 1487
111 Hyde Rd, Farmington CT 06032
Tel (860) 255-6000 *SIC* 3542 3423 3546

▲ **STANLEY BLACK & DECKER INC** p 1377
1000 Stanley Dr, New Britain CT 06053
Tel (860) 225-5111
SIC 3429 3546 3423 3452 3699

EASCO HAND TOOLS INC p 469
125 Powder Forest Dr, Simsbury CT 06070
Tel (860) 843-7351 *SIC* 3423

■ **BLACK & DECKER INC** p 186
1423 Kirkwood Hwy, Newark DE 19711
Tel (302) 738-0250
SIC 3429 3452 3579 3423 3949

■ **MARMON HOLDINGS INC** p 909
181 W Madison St Ste 2600, Chicago IL 60602
Tel (312) 372-9500
SIC 5051 3351 3743 4741 3423 3589

KLEIN TOOLS INC p 823
450 Bond St, Lincolnshire IL 60069
Tel (847) 821-5500 *SIC* 3423 3199

ESTWING MANUFACTURING CO INC p 511
2647 8th St, Rockford IL 61109
Tel (815) 397-9521
SIC 3423 3546 3545 3429 3421 3425

MUSCO CORP p 1002
100 1st Ave W, Oskaloosa IA 52577
Tel (641) 676-1746
SIC 7359 3648 3646 3641 3545 3423

APEX TOOL GROUP LLC p 96
14600 York Rd Ste A, Sparks MD 21152
Tel (410) 773-7800 *SIC* 3423

BC MOUNTAIN HOLDINGS INC p 163
14600 York Rd Ste A, Sparks MD 21152
Tel (800) 763-1233 *SIC* 3423

▲ **L S STARRETT CO** p 834
121 Crescent St, Athol MA 01331
Tel (978) 249-3551
SIC 3545 3423 3999 3425 3823

■ **VICTOR TECHNOLOGIES GROUP INC** p 1555
16253 Swingley Ridge Rd # 200, Chesterfield MO 63017
Tel (636) 728-3000
SIC 3541 3423 3613 3443 3621 3548

HAYWARD INDUSTRIES INC p 670
620 Division St, Elizabeth NJ 07201
Tel (908) 351-5400
SIC 3589 3561 3423 3494 3569 3089

■ **CLOPAY AMES TRUE TEMPER HOLDING CORP** p 327
100 Jericho Quadrangle # 224, Jericho NY 11753
Tel (516) 938-5544 *SIC* 3423 3799 3524

■ **IRWIN INDUSTRIAL TOOL CO** p 765
8935 N Pointe Exec Pk Dr, Huntersville NC 28078
Tel (704) 987-4555 *SIC* 3423 3545 3421

MCKENZIE SPORTS PRODUCTS LLC p 930
1910 Saint Luke Church Rd, Salisbury NC 28146
Tel (704) 279-7985 *SIC* 3949 3423

■ **RIDGE TOOL CO** p 1234
400 Clark St, Elyria OH 44035
Tel (440) 323-5581
SIC 3541 3423 3547 3546

■ **RIDGE TOOL MANUFACTURING CO** p 1234
400 Clark St, Elyria OH 44035
Tel (440) 323-5581
SIC 3541 3423 3547 3546 3545 3469

STERLING JEWELERS INC p 1387
375 Ghent Rd, Fairlawn OH 44333
Tel (330) 668-5000 *SIC* 3423

■ **MATCO TOOLS CORP** p 919
4403 Allen Rd, Stow OH 44224
Tel (330) 929-4949
SIC 5251 5072 3469 3423 5013

STEP2 CO LLC p 1386
10010 Aurora Hudson Rd, Streetsboro OH 44241
Tel (866) 429-5200 *SIC* 3089 3944 3423

CORNWELL QUALITY TOOLS CO p 371
667 Seville Rd, Wadsworth OH 44281
Tel (330) 336-3506 *SIC* 5085 3423 6794

■ **STANLEY INDUSTRIAL & AUTOMOTIVE LLC** p 1377
505 N Cleveland Ave, Westerville OH 43082
Tel (614) 755-7000
SIC 3429 3546 3423 3452

■ **AMES COMPANIES INC** p 84
465 Railroad Ave, Camp Hill PA 17011
Tel (717) 737-1500 *SIC* 3423 3799 3524

■ **SPS TECHNOLOGIES LLC** p 1362
301 Highland Ave, Jenkintown PA 19046
Tel (215) 572-3000
SIC 3452 3423 3499 3264 3679 3341

BOLTTECH MANNINGS INC p 199
501 Mosside Blvd, North Versailles PA 15137
Tel (724) 872-4873
SIC 3546 5072 3599 7359 3545 3423

■ **MATERION TECHNICAL MATERIALS INC** p 919
5 Wellington Rd, Lincoln RI 02865
Tel (401) 333-1700 *SIC* 3331 3339 3423

ROSEWOOD PRIVATE INVESTMENTS INC p 1251
2101 Cedar Springs Rd # 1600, Dallas TX 75201
Tel (214) 849-9000 *SIC* 6799 3423

COOPER INDUSTRIES LLC p 366
600 Travis St Ste 5400, Houston TX 77002
Tel (713) 209-8400
SIC 3646 3612 3613 3644 3546 3423

EATON ELECTRIC HOLDINGS LLC p 473
600 Travis St Ste 5600, Houston TX 77002
Tel (713) 209-8400
SIC 3646 3612 3613 3644 3536 3423

UNITED AMERICAN ACQUISITION CORP p 1506
3022 Franklin Ave, Waco TX 76710
Tel (859) 987-5389
SIC 2211 0782 3423 2875

■ **IDSC HOLDINGS LLC** p 729
2801 80th St, Kenosha WI 53143
Tel (262) 656-5200
SIC 3423 3559 7372 6794 5013 3546

WACKER NEUSON CORP p 1570
N92w15000 Anthony Ave, Menomonee Falls WI 53051
Tel (262) 255-0500
SIC 3531 3621 3561 3546 3423

FISKARS BRANDS INC p 552
7800 Discovery Dr, Middleton WI 53562
Tel (608) 259-1649
SIC 3052 3679 3421 3069 3423

SIC 3425 Hand Saws & Saw Blades

ESTWING MANUFACTURING CO INC p 511
2647 8th St, Rockford IL 61109
Tel (815) 397-9521
SIC 3423 3546 3545 3429 3421 3425

WOOD-MIZER HOLDINGS INC p 1622
8180 W 10th St, Indianapolis IN 46214
Tel (317) 271-1542
SIC 3553 3524 3425 2431

HUSQVARNA CONSTRUCTION PRODUCTS NORTH AMERICA INC p 721
17400 W 119th St, Olathe KS 66061
Tel (913) 928-1000
SIC 3541 3291 5085 5082 3425 2951

▲ **L S STARRETT CO** p 834
121 Crescent St, Athol MA 01331
Tel (978) 249-3551
SIC 3545 3423 3999 3425 3823

M K MORSE CO p 889
1101 11th St Se, Canton OH 44707
Tel (330) 453-8187 *SIC* 3425

MILWAUKEE ELECTRIC TOOL CORP p 972
13135 W Lisbon Rd, Brookfield WI 53005
Tel (800) 729-3878 *SIC* 3546 3425

SIC 3429 Hardware, NEC

RADIANCE TECHNOLOGIES INC p 1204
350 Wynn Dr Nw, Huntsville AL 35805
Tel (256) 704-3400
SIC 3721 8711 3429 3812

T - H MARINE SUPPLIES INC p 1419
200 Finney Dr Sw, Huntsville AL 35824
Tel (256) 772-0164 *SIC* 5551 3999 3429

HILLMAN GROUP INC p 694
8990 S Kyrene Rd, Tempe AZ 85284
Tel (800) 800-4900 *SIC* 3429 5162 3599

■ **HUCK INTERNATIONAL INC** p 716
3724 E Columbia St, Tucson AZ 85714
Tel (520) 519-7400 *SIC* 3429 3452

CRIMSON CAPITAL SILICON VALLEY p 392
1000 Marina Blvd Ste 105, Brisbane CA 94005
Tel (650) 325-8673 *SIC* 6799 3429

EMTEK PRODUCTS INC p 495
15250 Stafford St, City Of Industry CA 91744
Tel (626) 961-0413 *SIC* 3429

■ **BALDWIN HARDWARE CORP** p 147
19701 Da Vinci, Foothill Ranch CA 92610
Tel (949) 672-4000 *SIC* 3429

KWIKSET CORP p 833
19701 Da Vinci, Foothill Ranch CA 92610
Tel (949) 672-4000 *SIC* 3429

■ **NATIONAL MANUFACTURING CO** p 1014
19701 Da Vinci, Foothill Ranch CA 92610
Tel (800) 346-9445 *SIC* 3429

DIGIPAS TECHNOLOGIES INC p 439
200 Spectrum Center Dr, Irvine CA 92618
Tel (949) 558-0160 *SIC* 3429 3499 3699

GCX CORP p 595
3875 Cypress Dr, Petaluma CA 94954
Tel (707) 773-1100 *SIC* 3429

■ **HARTWELL CORP** p 666
900 Richfield Rd, Placentia CA 92870
Tel (714) 993-2752 *SIC* 3429

ACCURIDE INTERNATIONAL INC p 16
12311 Shoemaker Ave, Santa Fe Springs CA 90670
Tel (562) 903-0200 *SIC* 3429

HI-SHEAR CORP p 689
2600 Skypark Dr, Torrance CA 90505
Tel (310) 784-4025 *SIC* 3452 3429

CORBIN RUSSWIN INC p 368
225 Episcopal Rd, Berlin CT 06037
Tel (860) 225-7411 *SIC* 3429

▲ **EASTERN CO** p 472
112 Bridge St, Naugatuck CT 06770
Tel (203) 729-2255
SIC 3429 3452 3316 2439

▲ **STANLEY BLACK & DECKER INC** p 1377
1000 Stanley Dr, New Britain CT 06053
Tel (860) 225-5111
SIC 3429 3546 3423 3452 3699

ASSA ABLOY INC p 119
110 Sargent Dr, New Haven CT 06511
Tel (203) 624-5225
SIC 5065 5072 3699 3429

SARGENT MANUFACTURING CO p 1282
100 Sargent Dr, New Haven CT 06511
Tel (203) 562-2151 *SIC* 3429

■ **BLACK & DECKER INC** p 186
1423 Kirkwood Hwy, Newark DE 19711
Tel (302) 738-0250
SIC 3429 3452 3579 3423 3949

PERKO INC p 1136
16490 Nw 13th Ave, Miami FL 33169
Tel (305) 621-7525 *SIC* 3429

HL-A CO p 697
101 Thomas B Mur Ind Blvd, Bremen GA 30110
Tel (678) 309-2000 *SIC* 3429 3714

GEM INDUSTRIES INC p 598
Hwy 123 N, Toccoa GA 30577
Tel (706) 886-8431
SIC 3429 2531 2511 3446 2821 2515

COLSON GROUP INC p 339
1 N Franklin St Ste 2420, Chicago IL 60606
Tel (312) 980-1100 *SIC* 3429

WIND POINT PARTNERS VI LP p 1615
676 N Michigan Ave # 3700, Chicago IL 60611
Tel (312) 255-4800
SIC 6799 2542 2541 3429

▲ **FORTUNE BRANDS HOME & SECURITY INC** p 570
520 Lake Cook Rd, Deerfield IL 60015
Tel (847) 484-4400
SIC 2531 2599 3429 3469

NEISEWANDER ENTERPRISES INC p 1025
1101 E River Rd, Dixon IL 61021
Tel (815) 288-1431 *SIC* 3442 2431 3429

FLEXIBLE STEEL LACING CO INC p 556
2525 Wisconsin Ave, Downers Grove IL 60515
Tel (630) 971-0150 *SIC* 3429

■ **AFC CABLE SYSTEMS INC** p 32
16100 Lathrop Ave, Harvey IL 60426
Tel (508) 998-1131
SIC 3429 3444 3599 5085

■ UNISTRUT INTERNATIONAL CORP p 1505
16100 Lathrop Ave, Harvey IL 60426
Tel (800) 882-5543
SIC 3441 1791 3446 3448 3496 3429

COOPER B-LINE INC p 366
509 W Monroe St, Highland IL 62249
Tel (618) 654-2184
SIC 3441 3443 3452 3444 3429 3356

ESTWING MANUFACTURING CO INC p 511
2647 8th St, Rockford IL 61109
Tel (815) 397-9521
SIC 3423 3546 3545 3429 3421 3425

AGRI-FAB INC p 36
809 S Hamilton St, Sullivan IL 61951
Tel (217) 728-8388 *SIC* 3469 3429 5083

ALLEGION S&S US HOLDING CO INC p 53
11819 N Pennsylvania St, Carmel IN 46032
Tel (317) 810-3700 *SIC* 3429

SCHLAGE LOCK CO LLC p 1287
11819 N Pennsylvania St, Carmel IN 46032
Tel (317) 810-3700 *SIC* 3429

DOREL JUVENILE GROUP INC p 451
2525 State St, Columbus IN 47201
Tel (800) 457-5276
SIC 3089 3069 3429 3699 3648

VON DUPRIN LLC p 1565
2720 Tobey Dr, Indianapolis IN 46219
Tel (317) 429-2866 *SIC* 3429

FKI SECURITY GROUP LLC p 554
101 Security Pkwy, New Albany IN 47150
Tel (812) 948-8400
SIC 2522 5044 3499 3429

PK USA INC p 1153
600 Northridge Dr, Shelbyville IN 46176
Tel (317) 395-5500
SIC 3465 3089 3714 3429

AVIS INDUSTRIAL CORP p 138
1909 S Main St, Upland IN 46989
Tel (765) 998-8100
SIC 3429 3462 3312 3531 3714 3569

HENNIGES AUTOMOTIVE IOWA INC p 683
3200 Main St, Keokuk IA 52632
Tel (319) 524-4560
SIC 3069 3442 3429 2295

▲ HNI CORP p 698
408 E 2nd St, Muscatine IA 52761
Tel (563) 272-7400
SIC 2522 2542 2521 2541 3433 3429

PRECISION INC p 1168
300 Se 14th St, Pella IA 50219
Tel (641) 628-3115 *SIC* 2499 3429

EMERSON POWER TRANSMISSION CORP p 492
7120 New Buffington Rd, Florence KY 41042
Tel (859) 342-7900
SIC 3429 3052 3568 3562 3566 3462

MUBEA INC p 998
6800 Industrial Rd, Florence KY 41042
Tel (859) 746-5300
SIC 3493 3312 3495 3429 3714

TOYOTETSU AMERICA INC p 1467
100 Pin Oak Dr, Somerset KY 42503
Tel (606) 274-9005 *SIC* 3465 3714 3429

CHANEY ENTERPRISES LIMITED PARTNERSHIP p 288
2410 Evergreen Rd Ste 201, Gambrills MD 21054
Tel (410) 451-0197
SIC 3273 1442 5032 3429

▲ XCERRA CORP p 1631
825 University Ave, Norwood MA 02062
Tel (781) 461-1000 *SIC* 3825 3429

■ SMITH & WESSON CORP p 1333
2100 Roosevelt Ave, Springfield MA 01104
Tel (413) 781-8300
SIC 3484 3429 3999 5091

ROLLS-ROYCE MARINE NORTH AMERICA INC p 1247
110 Norfolk St, Walpole MA 02081
Tel (508) 668-9610 *SIC* 3599 3446 3429

■ DOVER ENERGY INC p 453
15 Corporate Dr, Auburn Hills MI 48326
Tel (248) 836-6700 *SIC* 3429

DURA OPERATING LLC p 462
1780 Pond Run, Auburn Hills MI 48326
Tel (248) 299-7500 *SIC* 3429 3714

■ HUTCHINSON FTS INC p 722
1060 Centre Rd, Auburn Hills MI 48326
Tel (248) 589-7710
SIC 3714 3061 3567 3492 3443 3429

KNAPE & VOGT MANUFACTURING CO p 824
2700 Oak Industrial Dr Ne, Grand Rapids MI 49505
Tel (616) 459-3311 *SIC* 2542 2541 3429

UNIVERSAL TRIM INC p 1518
1451 E Lincoln Ave, Madison Heights MI 48071
Tel (248) 586-3300
SIC 3714 3199 3089 3429

■ ANCHOR COUPLING INC p 89
5520 13th St, Menominee MI 49858
Tel (906) 863-2672 *SIC* 3429

L & W INC p 833
17757 Woodland Dr, New Boston MI 48164
Tel (734) 397-6300
SIC 3469 3465 3441 3429

HELLA CORPORATE CENTER USA INC p 681
43811 Plymouth Oaks Blvd, Plymouth MI 48170
Tel (586) 232-4788
SIC 3625 5013 5088 3822 3585 3429

IRVIN AUTOMOTIVE PRODUCTS INC p 765
2600 Centerpoint Pkwy, Pontiac MI 48341
Tel (248) 451-4100 *SIC* 3429 2396

■ MASCO BUILDING PRODUCTS CORP p 915
21001 Van Born Rd, Taylor MI 48180
Tel (313) 274-7400 *SIC* 3429 3639 3644

▲ MASCO CORP p 915
21001 Van Born Rd, Taylor MI 48180
Tel (313) 274-7400
SIC 2434 3432 3088 3429 1742

■ HEARTH & HOME TECHNOLOGIES LLC p 678
7571 215th St W, Lakeville MN 55044
Tel (952) 985-6000 *SIC* 3429 4925

CAMBRIA CO LLC p 244
31496 Cambria Ave, Le Sueur MN 56058
Tel (507) 665-5003 *SIC* 5211 3429

ACTIVAR INC p 19
7808 Creekridge Cir # 200, Minneapolis MN 55439
Tel (952) 944-3533
SIC 2542 3479 3442 3429 3089

TRUTH HARDWARE CORP p 1489
700 W Bridge St, Owatonna MN 55060
Tel (507) 451-5620 *SIC* 2431 3442 3429

■ MITEK USA INC p 977
16023 Swingley Ridge Rd, Chesterfield MO 63017
Tel (314) 434-1200
SIC 3443 3429 3542 8711 5051 5085

GRIMCO INC p 640
1585 Fencorp Dr, Fenton MO 63026
Tel (636) 305-0088
SIC 3469 2759 3993 3429 3312

C HAGER & SONS HINGE MANUFACTURING CO p 232
139 Victor St, Saint Louis MO 63104
Tel (314) 772-4400 *SIC* 3429

WATERLOO HOLDINGS INC p 1582
1500 Waterloo Dr, Sedalia MO 65301
Tel (660) 826-0960 *SIC* 3429 6719

WATERLOO INDUSTRIES INC p 1582
1500 Waterloo Dr, Sedalia MO 65301
Tel (660) 826-0960 *SIC* 3429

■ ANVIL INTERNATIONAL LLC p 94
2 Holland Way, Exeter NH 03833
Tel (603) 418-2800
SIC 3498 3321 3317 3494 3429

WORLD AND MAIN LLC p 1624
324a Half Acre Rd, Cranbury NJ 08512
Tel (609) 860-9990 *SIC* 1711 3429

■ AIRBORNE SYSTEMS NORTH AMERICA INC p 39
5800 Magnolia Ave, Pennsauken NJ 08109
Tel (856) 663-1275 *SIC* 2426 3429

ROTOR CLIP CO INC p 1252
187 Davidson Ave, Somerset NJ 08873
Tel (732) 469-7707 *SIC* 3429

▲ NAPCO SECURITY TECHNOLOGIES INC p 1007
333 Bayview Ave, Amityville NY 11701
Tel (631) 842-9400
SIC 3669 3699 3429 1731 7373

TAYLOR MADE GROUP HOLDINGS INC p 1427
66 Kingsboro Ave, Gloversville NY 12078
Tel (518) 725-0681 *SIC* 3429

TAYLOR MADE GROUP LLC p 1427
66 Kingsboro Ave, Gloversville NY 12078
Tel (518) 725-0681 *SIC* 3429 3231

JGB ENTERPRISES INC p 785
115 Metropolitan Dr, Liverpool NY 13088
Tel (315) 451-2770 *SIC* 3052 5085 3429

PEM HOLDING CO INC p 1128
800 3rd Ave Fl 40, New York NY 10022
Tel (212) 446-9300 *SIC* 6211 3429 3621

SAFE SKIES LLC p 1266
954 3rd Ave Ste 504, New York NY 10022
Tel (888) 632-5027 *SIC* 3429

TINICUM CAPITAL PARTNERS II LP p 1455
800 3rd Ave Fl 40, New York NY 10022
Tel (212) 446-9300 *SIC* 6211 3429 3621

TURBINE ENGINE COMPONENTS TECHNOLOGIES - UTICA CORP p 1492
2 Halsey Rd, Whitesboro NY 13492
Tel (315) 768-8070
SIC 3724 3511 3429 3842 3769

ITR INDUSTRIES INC p 768
441 Saw Mill River Rd, Yonkers NY 10701
Tel (914) 964-7063
SIC 3431 3429 3446 3088

ENDURA PRODUCTS INC p 496
8817 W Market St, Colfax NC 27235
Tel (336) 668-2472 *SIC* 3429

INGERSOLL-RAND CO p 742
800 Beaty St Ste B, Davidson NC 28036
Tel (704) 655-4000
SIC 3561 3429 3546 3563 3531

GRASS AMERICA INC p 632
1202 Nc Highway 66 S, Kernersville NC 27284
Tel (336) 996-4041 *SIC* 3429

YALE SECURITY INC p 1634
1902 Airport Rd, Monroe NC 28110
Tel (704) 283-2101 *SIC* 3429 3466

ILCO UNICAN HOLDING CORP p 731
400 Jeffreys Rd, Rocky Mount NC 27804
Tel (252) 446-3321 *SIC* 3429

KABA ILCO CORP p 799
400 Jeffreys Rd, Rocky Mount NC 27804
Tel (252) 446-3321 *SIC* 3429

BLUM INC p 193
7733 Old Plank Rd, Stanley NC 28164
Tel (704) 827-1345 *SIC* 3429

HFI LLC p 689
59 Gender Rd, Canal Winchester OH 43110
Tel (614) 491-0700
SIC 2396 2821 3714 3429 3086

AEROQUIP-VICKERS INC p 30
1111 Superior Ave E, Cleveland OH 44114
Tel (216) 523-5000
SIC 3052 3492 3429 3069 3585 3728

EATON-AEROQUIP LLC p 474
1000 Eaton Blvd, Cleveland OH 44122
Tel (216) 523-5000
SIC 3052 3492 3429 3069 3585 3728

SUPERIOR METAL PRODUCTS INC p 1406
1005 W Grand Ave, Lima OH 45801
Tel (419) 228-1145 *SIC* 3469 3429

DESCO CORP p 432
7795 Walton Pkwy Ste 175, New Albany OH 43054
Tel (614) 888-8855
SIC 3442 3825 3643 3531 3429

■ ELEMENT14 US HOLDINGS INC p 486
4180 Highlander Pkwy, Richfield OH 44286
Tel (330) 523-4280 *SIC* 5065 3429

■ PREMIER FARNELL HOLDING INC p 1170
4180 Highlander Pkwy, Richfield OH 44286
Tel (330) 523-4273 *SIC* 5065 3429

■ STANLEY INDUSTRIAL & AUTOMOTIVE LLC p 1377
505 N Cleveland Ave, Westerville OH 43082
Tel (614) 755-7000
SIC 3429 3546 3423 3452

CROSBY GROUP LLC p 393
2801 Dawson Rd, Tulsa OK 74110
Tel (918) 834-4611 *SIC* 3462 3429

FKI INDUSTRIES INC p 554
2801 Dawson Rd, Tulsa OK 74110
Tel (918) 834-4611
SIC 3429 3536 3535 3496 3569 3823

PENN ENGINEERING & MANUFACTURING CORP p 1129
5190 Old Easton Rd, Danboro PA 18916
Tel (215) 766-8853 *SIC* 3429 3549 8711

▲ OMEGA FLEX INC p 1084
451 Creamery Way, Exton PA 19341
Tel (610) 524-7272 *SIC* 3599 3429

DORMA USA INC p 451
1 Dorma Dr, Reamstown PA 17567
Tel (717) 336-3881 *SIC* 3429

NORMA PENNSYLVANIA INC p 1048
3582 Tunnelton Rd, Saltsburg PA 15681
Tel (724) 639-3571 *SIC* 3429

■ COMPX SECURITY PRODUCTS INC p 353
26 Old Mill Rd, Greenville SC 29607
Tel (864) 286-1122 *SIC* 3429

M-TEK INC p 890
1020 Volunteer Pkwy, Manchester TN 37355
Tel (931) 728-4122 *SIC* 3089 3714 3429

IDEAL CLAMP PRODUCTS INC p 729
8100 Tridon Dr, Smyrna TN 37167
Tel (615) 459-5800 *SIC* 3429

MARTIN SPROCKET & GEAR INC p 913
3100 Sprocket Dr, Arlington TX 76015
Tel (817) 258-3000
SIC 3566 3568 3535 3321 3462 3429

■ VALHI INC p 1540
5430 Lbj Fwy Ste 1700, Dallas TX 75240
Tel (972) 233-1700
SIC 2816 2899 3429 4953

AMERICAN BLOCK CO p 69
6311 Breen Dr, Houston TX 77086
Tel (800) 572-9087
SIC 3441 3599 3533 3496 3444 3429

NCH CORP p 1022
2727 Chemsearch Blvd, Irving TX 75062
Tel (972) 438-0211
SIC 2842 2899 3432 3548 3429

■ US HOME SYSTEMS INC p 1532
2951 Kinwest Pkwy, Irving TX 75063
Tel (214) 488-6300 *SIC* 3429 5031 1751

FAIRFIELD INDUSTRIES INC p 525
1111 Gillingham Ln, Sugar Land TX 77478
Tel (281) 275-7627
SIC 7374 3829 1382 3429

PENROD CO p 1131
272 Bendix Rd Ste 550, Virginia Beach VA 23452
Tel (757) 498-0186 *SIC* 3429 5039 2821

▲ ESTERLINE TECHNOLOGIES CORP p 511
500 108th Ave Ne Ste 1500, Bellevue WA 98004
Tel (425) 453-9400 *SIC* 3728 3812 3429

▲ STRATTEC SECURITY CORP p 1393
3333 W Good Hope Rd, Milwaukee WI 53209
Tel (414) 247-3333 *SIC* 3714 3364 3429

■ MASTER LOCK CO LLC p 918
137 W Forest Hill Ave, Oak Creek WI 53154
Tel (414) 444-2800 *SIC* 3429 3462

TREK BICYCLE CORP p 1476
801 W Madison St, Waterloo WI 53594
Tel (920) 478-2191 *SIC* 5941 3429

SIC 3431 Enameled Iron & Metal Sanitary Ware

MAG AEROSPACE INDUSTRIES INC p 895
1500 Glenn Curtiss St, Carson CA 90746
Tel (310) 631-3800 *SIC* 3431 3728

ACORN ENGINEERING CO p 18
15125 Proctor Ave, City Of Industry CA 91746
Tel (800) 488-8999 *SIC* 3448 3431 3442

■ HANSGROHE INC p 658
1490 Bluegrass Lakes Pkwy, Alpharetta GA 30004
Tel (770) 360-9880 *SIC* 3432 5074 3431

TOTO USA HOLDINGS INC p 1463
1155 Southern Rd, Morrow GA 30260
Tel (770) 960-8531 *SIC* 3088 3431 3261

ELKAY MANUFACTURING CO INC p 487
2222 Camden Ct, Oak Brook IL 60523
Tel (630) 574-8484
SIC 3431 3585 3432 2434

ELKAY PLUMBING PRODUCTS CO p 487
2222 Camden Ct, Oak Brook IL 60523
Tel (630) 574-8484 *SIC* 3431

▲ DREW INDUSTRIES INC p 455
3501 County Road 6 E, Elkhart IN 46514
Tel (574) 535-1125
SIC 3711 3714 3715 3442 3431

PARAGON INTERNATIONAL INC p 1113
731 W 18th St, Nevada IA 50201
Tel (515) 382-8000 *SIC* 3589 3556 3431

THETFORD CORP p 1447
7101 Jackson Rd, Ann Arbor MI 48103
Tel (734) 769-6000
SIC 3632 3089 2842 2621 3431 2899

SWAN SURFACES LLC p 1411
515 Olive St Ste 900, Saint Louis MO 63101
Tel (314) 231-8148 *SIC* 2541 5722 3431

ITR INDUSTRIES INC p 768
441 Saw Mill River Rd, Yonkers NY 10701
Tel (914) 964-7063
SIC 3431 3429 3446 3088

CROSCILL HOME LLC p 393
1500 N Carolina St, Goldsboro NC 27530
Tel (919) 735-7111 *SIC* 5023 3431

CRANE PLUMBING LLC p 389
41 Cairns Rd, Mansfield OH 44903
Tel (419) 522-4211 *SIC* 3261 3431 3088

MANSFIELD PLUMBING PRODUCTS LLC p 903
150 E 1st St, Perrysville OH 44864
Tel (419) 938-5211
SIC 3261 3463 3088 3431 3432 5074

WOLVERINE BRASS INC p 1621
2951 E Highway 501, Conway SC 29526
Tel (843) 347-3121 *SIC* 5074 3432 3431

FRANKE KITCHEN SYSTEMS LLC p 574
800 Aviation Pkwy, Smyrna TN 37167
Tel (800) 637-6485 *SIC* 3431 5074

KOHLER CO p 826
444 Highland Dr, Kohler WI 53044
Tel (920) 457-4441
SIC 3431 3432 3261 2511 2521 3519

BRADLEY CORP p 206
W142n9101 Fountain Blvd, Menomonee Falls WI 53051
Tel (262) 251-6000 *SIC* 3431 3272

SIC 3432 Plumbing Fixture Fittings & Trim, Brass

RAIN BIRD CORP p 1205
1000 W Sierra Madre Ave, Azusa CA 91702
Tel (626) 812-3400 *SIC* 3494 3432 3523

■ PRICE PFISTER INC p 1174
19701 Da Vinci, Foothill Ranch CA 92610
Tel (949) 672-4000 *SIC* 3432

ANTHONY MANUFACTURING CORP p 94
145 N Grand Ave, Glendora CA 91741
Tel (626) 963-9311 *SIC* 3432

FLUIDMASTER INC p 561
30800 Rancho Viejo Rd, San Juan Capistrano CA 92675
Tel (949) 728-2000 *SIC* 3432 3089

■ BRASSTECH INC p 208
2001 Carnegie Ave, Santa Ana CA 92705
Tel (949) 417-5207 *SIC* 3432

WATER PIK INC p 1581
1730 E Prospect Rd, Fort Collins CO 80525
Tel (800) 525-2774 *SIC* 3432 3843

KEENEY MANUFACTURING CO p 807
1170 Main St, Newington CT 06111
Tel (603) 239-6371 *SIC* 3432 5074

■ HANSGROHE INC p 658
1490 Bluegrass Lakes Pkwy, Alpharetta GA 30004
Tel (770) 360-9880 *SIC* 3432 5074 3431

SUNCAST CORP p 1401
701 N Kirk Rd, Batavia IL 60510
Tel (630) 879-2050 *SIC* 2519 3052 3432

CHICAGO FAUCET CO p 297
2100 Clearwater Dr, Des Plaines IL 60018
Tel (847) 803-5000 *SIC* 3432

SLOAN VALVE CO p 1331
10500 Seymour Ave, Franklin Park IL 60131
Tel (847) 671-4300 *SIC* 3494 3432

ELKAY MANUFACTURING CO INC p 487
2222 Camden Ct, Oak Brook IL 60523
Tel (630) 574-8484
SIC 3431 3585 3432 2434

GLOBE UNION GROUP INC p 618
2500 Internationale Pkwy, Woodridge IL 60517
Tel (630) 679-1420 *SIC* 3261 3432 7699

■ MASCO CORP OF INDIANA p 915
55 E 111th St, Indianapolis IN 46280
Tel (317) 848-1812 *SIC* 3432

A Y MCDONALD INDUSTRIES INC p 7
4800 Chavenelle Rd, Dubuque IA 52002
Tel (800) 292-2737
SIC 3432 3561 3494 5074 5075 5031

ZOELLER CO p 1644
3649 Cane Run Rd, Louisville KY 40211
Tel (502) 778-2731
SIC 3561 5251 3432 3491

■ BRASSCRAFT MANUFACTURING CO p 208
39600 Orchard Hill Pl, Novi MI 48375
Tel (248) 305-6000 *SIC* 3432

▲ MASCO CORP p 915
21001 Van Born Rd, Taylor MI 48180
Tel (313) 274-7400
SIC 2434 3432 3088 3429 1742

■ BERKLEY RISK ADMINISTRATION CO LLC p 175
222 S 9th St Ste 2700, Minneapolis MN 55402
Tel (612) 766-3000 *SIC* 6411 3052 3432

AS AMERICA INC p 115
1 Centennial Ave Ste 101, Piscataway NJ 08854
Tel (732) 980-3000 *SIC* 3261 3432

WAXMAN INDUSTRIES INC p 1584
24460 Aurora Rd, Cleveland OH 44146
Tel (440) 439-1830
SIC 5072 5074 3494 3491 3432

MANSFIELD PLUMBING PRODUCTS LLC p 903
150 E 1st St, Perrysville OH 44864
Tel (419) 938-5211
SIC 3261 3463 3088 3431 3432 5074

CERTAINTEED CORP p 284
20 Moores Rd, Malvern PA 19355
Tel (610) 893-5000
SIC 3221 3292 3259 3084 3089 3432

PROFESSIONAL PLUMBING GROUP INC p 1180
2951 E Highway 501, Conway SC 29526
Tel (415) 124-5678 *SIC* 3432

WOLVERINE BRASS INC p 1621
2951 E Highway 501, Conway SC 29526
Tel (843) 347-3121 *SIC* 5074 3432 3431

■ FLOWTRONEX PSI LLC p 560
10661 Newkirk St, Dallas TX 75220
Tel (469) 221-1200
SIC 3561 3949 3523 3432

ROYAL BATHS MANUFACTURING CO LTD p 1254
14635 Chrisman Rd, Houston TX 77039
Tel (281) 442-3400
SIC 3842 3949 3432 3281

NCH CORP p 1022
2727 Chemsearch Blvd, Irving TX 75062
Tel (972) 438-0211
SIC 2842 2899 3432 3548 3429

CHEVRON PHILLIPS CHEMICAL CO LP p 296
10001 Six Pines Dr, The Woodlands TX 77380
Tel (832) 813-4100
SIC 5169 3292 3089 3084 3432 2911

KOHLER CO p 826
444 Highland Dr, Kohler WI 53044
Tel (920) 457-4441
SIC 3431 3432 3261 2511 2521 3519

MILWAUKEE VALVE CO INC p 972
16550 W Stratton Dr, New Berlin WI 53151
Tel (262) 432-2800 SIC 3494 3492 3432

SIC 3433 Heating Eqpt

TEYMA USA & ABENER ENGINEERING AND CONSTRUCTION SERVICES PARTNERSHIP p 1445
57750 S Painted Rock Rd, Phoenix AZ 85012
Tel (303) 928-8500 SIC 3433

▲ FIRST SOLAR INC p 549
350 W Washington St # 600, Tempe AZ 85281
Tel (602) 414-9300 SIC 3674 3433

RAYPAK INC p 1210
2151 Eastman Ave, Oxnard CA 93030
Tel (805) 278-5300 SIC 3433

SPI SOLAR INC p 1358
3500 Douglas Blvd Ste 240, Roseville CA 95661
Tel (916) 770-8100 SIC 3433

IHP OPERATIONS LLC p 731
2701 S Harbor Blvd, Santa Ana CA 92704
Tel (714) 549-7782 SIC 3433

SMA AMERICA PRODUCTION LLC p 1331
3801 Havana St, Denver CO 80239
Tel (720) 347-6000 SIC 3433

OMEGA ENGINEERING INC p 1084
800 Connecticut Ave 5n01, Norwalk CT 06854
Tel (203) 359-1660
SIC 3823 3575 3577 3433 3826 2759

RHEEM MANUFACTURING CO INC p 1231
1100 Abernathy Rd # 1700, Atlanta GA 30328
Tel (770) 351-3000 SIC 3585 3433

SUNIVA INC p 1402
5765 Peachtree Indus Blvd, Norcross GA 30092
Tel (404) 477-2700 SIC 3674 3433

CLEAVER-BROOKS INC p 325
221 Law St, Thomasville GA 31792
Tel (229) 226-3024
SIC 3589 3569 3561 3433 3443

FILTRAN HOLDINGS LLC p 542
875 Seegers Rd, Des Plaines IL 60016
Tel (847) 635-6670 SIC 3433

FILTRAN LLC p 542
875 Seegers Rd, Des Plaines IL 60016
Tel (847) 635-6670 SIC 3433

■ ECLIPSE COMBUSTION INC p 475
1665 Elmwood Rd, Rockford IL 61103
Tel (815) 877-3031 SIC 3433

■ ECLIPSE INC p 475
1665 Elmwood Rd, Rockford IL 61103
Tel (815) 877-3031
SIC 3564 3433 3822 3823 3443 3494

■ PUROLATOR PRODUCTS AIR FILTRATION CO p 1192
100 River Ridge Cir, Jeffersonville IN 47130
Tel (866) 925-2247 SIC 3564 3433

▲ HNI CORP p 698
408 E 2nd St, Muscatine IA 52761
Tel (563) 272-7400
SIC 2522 2542 2521 2541 3433 3429

AIRTEX MANUFACTURING LLLP p 40
32050 W 83rd St, De Soto KS 66018
Tel (913) 583-3181
SIC 3585 5075 3564 3433

TRAD NORTH AMERICA INC p 1468
750 Frank Yost Ln, Hopkinsville KY 42240
Tel (270) 885-9116 SIC 3433

■ MONESSEN HEARTH SYSTEMS CO p 984
149 Cleveland Dr, Paris KY 40361
Tel (859) 987-0740 SIC 3433

BABCOCK POWER INC p 143
6 Kimball Ln Ste 210, Lynnfield MA 01940
Tel (978) 646-3300 SIC 3443 3569 3433

RILEY POWER INC p 1235
5 Neponset St, Worcester MA 01606
Tel (508) 852-7100
SIC 3569 3443 3433 1711 3564 3511

UPONOR INC p 1529
5925 148th St W, Saint Paul MN 55124
Tel (952) 891-2000 SIC 3084 3567 3433

NORTEK GLOBAL HVAC LLC p 1049
8000 Phoenix Pkwy, O Fallon MO 63368
Tel (636) 561-7300 SIC 3585 3567 3433

AMEC FOSTER WHEELER NORTH AMERICA CORP p 66
Perryville Corporate Pk 5, Hampton NJ 08827
Tel (908) 713-2891
SIC 3433 3443 3532 3569

ROBERTS-GORDON LLC p 1242
1250 William St, Buffalo NY 14206
Tel (716) 852-4400 SIC 3675 3433

SLANT/FIN CORP p 1331
100 Forest Dr, Greenvale NY 11548
Tel (516) 484-2600 SIC 3433 3443

DYSON-KISSNER-MORAN CORP p 465
2515 South Rd Ste 5, Poughkeepsie NY 12601
Tel (212) 661-4600 SIC 3433 3625 3699

ECR INTERNATIONAL INC p 476
2201 Dwyer Ave, Utica NY 13501
Tel (315) 797-1310 SIC 3433 3443

■ MARLEY CO LLC p 909
13515 Balntyn Corp Pl, Charlotte NC 28277
Tel (704) 752-4400
SIC 3443 3433 3586 3561 3634

HUNTER DEFENSE TECHNOLOGIES INC p 719
30500 Aurora Rd Ste 100, Solon OH 44139
Tel (216) 438-6111
SIC 3433 3569 3822 8331 8711 3549

ZEECO USA LLC p 1641
22151 E 91st St S, Broken Arrow OK 74014
Tel (918) 258-8551 SIC 3433

▲ SCHNITZER STEEL INDUSTRIES INC p 1288
299 Sw Clay St Ste 350, Portland OR 97201
Tel (503) 224-9900
SIC 5093 3312 3449 3441 3433 5015

BRADFORD-WHITE CORP p 206
725 Talamore Dr, Ambler PA 19002
Tel (215) 641-9400 SIC 3433 1711

BURNHAM HOLDINGS INC p 228
1241 Harrisburg Ave, Lancaster PA 17603
Tel (717) 390-7800 SIC 3433

TACO INC p 1421
1160 Cranston St, Cranston RI 02920
Tel (401) 942-8000
SIC 3433 3561 3443 3822

■ ALLIED AIR ENTERPRISES LLC p 56
215 Metropolitan Dr, West Columbia SC 29170
Tel (803) 738-4000 SIC 3585 3433 5075

■ ASTEC INC p 122
4101 Jerome Ave, Chattanooga TN 37407
Tel (423) 867-4210 SIC 3531 3433 3443

▲ ASTEC INDUSTRIES INC p 122
1725 Shepherd Rd, Chattanooga TN 37421
Tel (423) 899-5898 SIC 3531 3433 3533

INNOVATIVE HEARTH HOLDINGS LLC p 744
1508 Elm Hill Pike # 108, Nashville TN 37210
Tel (714) 549-7782 SIC 3433

INNOVATIVE HEARTH PRODUCTS LLC p 744
1508 Elm Hill Pike # 108, Nashville TN 37210
Tel (615) 925-3417 SIC 3634 3433

MORTEX PRODUCTS INC p 991
501 Terminal Rd, Fort Worth TX 76106
Tel (817) 624-0820
SIC 3585 3433 1711 3999

M+W AMERICAS INC p 890
1001 Klein Rd Ste 400, Plano TX 75074
Tel (972) 535-7300
SIC 3433 8712 8711 8741

ALFA LAVAL INC p 49
5400 Intl Trade Dr, Richmond VA 23231
Tel (804) 222-5300
SIC 3491 3433 3585 3569 3821

▲ A O SMITH CORP p 6
11270 W Park Pl Ste 1200, Milwaukee WI 53224
Tel (414) 359-4000 SIC 3639 3433

▲ MODINE MANUFACTURING CO INC p 981
1500 Dekoven Ave, Racine WI 53403
Tel (262) 636-1200
SIC 3443 3714 3433 3585

SIC 3441 Fabricated Structural Steel

■ ALABAMA METAL INDUSTRIES CORP p 43
3245 Fayette Ave, Birmingham AL 35208
Tel (205) 787-2611
SIC 3446 3449 3089 3441 3316

FABARC STEEL SUPPLY INC p 523
111 Meadow Ln, Oxford AL 36203
Tel (256) 831-8770 SIC 3441

PROCESS EQUIPMENT INC p 1179
2770 Welborn St, Pelham AL 35124
Tel (205) 663-5330
SIC 3564 3535 3441 3443

WOLF CREEK FEDERAL SERVICES INC p 1620
3800 Cntrpint Dr Ste 1200, Anchorage AK 99503
Tel (907) 563-8866 SIC 3441

WOLF CREEK FEDERAL SERVICES INC p 1621
3800 Cntrpint Dr Ste 1200, Anchorage AK 99503
Tel (907) 563-8866 SIC 3441

■ DBM GLOBAL INC p 418
3020 E Camelback Rd # 100, Phoenix AZ 85016
Tel (602) 252-7787 SIC 3441 1791

▲ MOBILE MINI INC p 980
4646 E Van Buren St # 400, Phoenix AZ 85008
Tel (480) 894-6311
SIC 4225 3448 3441 3412 7359

■ SCHUFF STEEL CO p 1290
1841 W Buchanan St, Phoenix AZ 85007
Tel (602) 252-7787 SIC 3441

■ NUCOR-YAMATO STEEL CO (LIMITED PARTNERSHIP) p 1067
5929 E State Highway 18, Blytheville AR 72315
Tel (870) 762-5500 SIC 3312 3441

LEXICON INC p 859
8900 Fourche Dam Pike, Little Rock AR 72206
Tel (501) 490-4200 SIC 1629 3441

MULTI-CRAFT CONTRACTORS INC p 999
2300 N Lowell Rd, Springdale AR 72764
Tel (479) 751-4330 SIC 1711 3441 1731

HYSPAN PRECISION PRODUCTS INC p 724
1685 Brandywine Ave, Chula Vista CA 91911
Tel (619) 421-1355 SIC 3568 3496 3441

EAGLEBURGMANN KE INC p 468
10038 Marathon Pkwy, Lakeside CA 92040
Tel (619) 562-6083 SIC 3441

JOHN S FREY ENTERPRISES p 789
1900 E 64th St, Los Angeles CA 90001
Tel (323) 583-4061 SIC 3441 3444 6719

▲ SIMPSON MANUFACTURING CO INC p 1325
5956 W Las Positas Blvd, Pleasanton CA 94588
Tel (925) 560-9000 SIC 3441 3399

HERRICK CORP p 687
3003 E Hammer Ln, Stockton CA 95212
Tel (209) 956-4751 SIC 3441

NORMAN INDUSTRIAL MATERIALS INC p 1049
8300 San Fernando Rd, Sun Valley CA 91352
Tel (818) 729-3333 SIC 5051 3441 3449

GAYLE MANUFACTURING CO INC p 594
1455 E Kentucky Ave, Woodland CA 95776
Tel (707) 226-9136 SIC 3441 1541

RK MECHANICAL INC p 1239
3800 Xanthia St, Denver CO 80238
Tel (303) 576-9696 SIC 1711 3498 3441

CF&I STEEL LP p 285
1612 E Abriendo Ave, Pueblo CO 81004
Tel (719) 561-6000 SIC 3441 3317 3312

■ CMC STEEL HOLDING CO p 329
802 N West St Ste 302, Wilmington DE 19801
Tel (302) 691-6200 SIC 3441 3312

■ METALS USA INC p 953
2400 E Coml Blvd Ste 905, Fort Lauderdale FL 33308
Tel (954) 202-4000 SIC 3441

UNITED STATES FOUNDRY & MANUFACTURING CORP p 1513
8351 Nw 93rd St, Medley FL 33166
Tel (305) 885-0301 SIC 3321 3441 3322

CIVES CORP p 320
3700 Mansell Rd Ste 500, Alpharetta GA 30022
Tel (770) 993-4424 SIC 3441 3713 3443

HOLDEN INDUSTRIES INC p 700
500 Lake Cook Rd Ste 400, Deerfield IL 60015
Tel (847) 940-1500
SIC 2752 2672 3545 3589 3541 3441

■ DOVER ENGINEERED SYSTEMS INC p 453
3005 Highland Pkwy # 200, Downers Grove IL 60515
Tel (630) 743-2505
SIC 3568 3443 3441 3561 3491 3492

▲ ATKORE INTERNATIONAL GROUP INC p 125
16100 Lathrop Ave, Harvey IL 60426
Tel (708) 339-1610
SIC 3441 1791 3446 3448 3496

■ ATKORE INTERNATIONAL HOLDINGS INC p 125
16100 Lathrop Ave, Harvey IL 60426
Tel (708) 225-2051
SIC 6719 3441 1791 3446 3448 3496

■ UNISTRUT INTERNATIONAL CORP p 1505
16100 Lathrop Ave, Harvey IL 60426
Tel (800) 882-5543
SIC 3441 1791 3446 3448 3496 3429

COOPER B-LINE INC p 366
509 W Monroe St, Highland IL 62249
Tel (618) 654-2184
SIC 3441 3443 3452 3444 3429 3356

VERITAS STEEL LLC p 1550
2300 Cabot Dr Ste 148, Lisle IL 60532
Tel (630) 423-8708 SIC 3441

■ CHICAGO TUBE AND IRON CO p 298
1 Chicago Tube Dr, Romeoville IL 60446
Tel (815) 834-2500 SIC 5051 3441

ANTHONY WAYNE REHABILITATION CENTER FOR HANDICAPPED AND BLIND INC p 94
8515 Bluffton Rd, Fort Wayne IN 46809
Tel (260) 744-6145
SIC 8331 7331 3441 3412 2449 2448

■ ZIEMAN MANUFACTURING CO INC p 1643
2703 College Ave, Goshen IN 46528
Tel (574) 535-1125
SIC 3715 3441 2451 3799

OWEN INDUSTRIES INC p 1099
501 Avenue H, Carter Lake IA 51510
Tel (800) 831-9252 SIC 5051 3441

SABRE COMMUNICATIONS CORP p 1264
7101 Southbridge Dr, Sioux City IA 51111
Tel (712) 258-6690 SIC 3663 3441 1731

SIOUX CITY FOUNDRY CO p 1326
801 Division St, Sioux City IA 51105
Tel (712) 252-4181
SIC 5051 3443 3321 3316 3444 3441

PTMW INC p 1189
5040 Nw Us Highway 24, Topeka KS 66618
Tel (785) 232-7792 SIC 3441

■ BALCO INC p 147
2626 S Sheridan Ave, Wichita KS 67217
Tel (800) 767-0082
SIC 3441 3089 3496 3446 3443

CALDWELL TANKS INC p 238
4000 Tower Rd, Louisville KY 40219
Tel (502) 964-3361 SIC 3443 5084 3441

MODERN WELDING CO INC p 981
2880 New Hartford Rd, Owensboro KY 42303
Tel (270) 685-4400
SIC 3443 5051 3441 5085

CELLXION LLC p 274
5031 Hazel Jones Rd, Bossier City LA 71111
Tel (318) 213-2900
SIC 4812 1623 3448 3441

SEMCO LLC p 1302
186 Jean Lafitte Blvd, Lafitte LA 70067
Tel (504) 689-2054 SIC 3441 3731

DYNAMIC INDUSTRIES INC p 464
400 Poydras St Ste 1800, New Orleans LA 70130
Tel (504) 684-1305 SIC 3441

CREST INDUSTRIES p 392
4725 Highway 28 E, Pineville LA 71360
Tel (318) 767-5530
SIC 3699 3612 3441 5063 2439

CREST OPERATIONS LLC p 392
4725 Highway 28 E, Pineville LA 71360
Tel (318) 448-0274
SIC 3441 2439 3699 5063 3612

WAHLCOMETROFLEX INC p 1571
29 Lexington St, Lewiston ME 04240
Tel (207) 784-2338 SIC 3441 3822 8711

CANAM STEEL CORP p 246
4010 Clay St, Point Of Rocks MD 21777
Tel (301) 874-5141 SIC 3441 5051

WEB INDUSTRIES INC p 1586
377 Simarano Dr Ste 220, Marlborough MA 01752
Tel (508) 898-2988
SIC 2671 5162 3089 2269 3441

CENTER MANUFACTURING INC p 276
990 84th St Sw, Byron Center MI 49315
Tel (616) 878-3324 SIC 3499 3441

MIDWEST STEEL INC p 968
2525 E Grand Blvd, Detroit MI 48211
Tel (313) 873-2220 SIC 3441 1791

DEMMER CORP p 428
1600 N Larch St Ste 1, Lansing MI 48906
Tel (517) 321-3600
SIC 3795 3812 3544 3465 3441

▲ TOWER INTERNATIONAL INC p 1464
17672 N Laurel Park Dr, Livonia MI 48152
Tel (248) 675-6000 SIC 3465 3441

L & W INC p 833
17757 Woodland Dr, New Boston MI 48164
Tel (734) 397-6300
SIC 3469 3465 3441 3429

WEBASTO ROOF SYSTEMS INC p 1586
1757 Northfield Dr, Rochester Hills MI 48309
Tel (800) 860-7866 SIC 3714 3441 3469

LE JEUNE STEEL CO p 849
118 W 60th St, Minneapolis MN 55419
Tel (612) 861-3321 SIC 3441

STEEL SERVICE CORP p 1384
2260 Flowood Dr, Jackson MS 39232
Tel (601) 939-9222
SIC 3441 1791 3496 3443

STRUCTURAL STEEL HOLDING INC p 1394
6210 Saint Louis St, Meridian MS 39307
Tel (601) 483-5381 SIC 3441 3443 4213

SIGNAL INTERNATIONAL LLC p 1322
601 Bayou Casotte Pkwy, Pascagoula MS 39581
Tel (228) 762-0010 SIC 7699 3731 3441

BEN HUR CONSTRUCTION CO p 172
3783 Rider Trl S, Earth City MO 63045
Tel (314) 298-8007
SIC 1542 1791 1541 3441

STUPP BROS INC p 1395
3800 Weber Rd, Saint Louis MO 63125
Tel (314) 638-5000 SIC 3441 3317 6022

LINCOLN INDUSTRIES INC p 867
600 W E St, Lincoln NE 68522
Tel (402) 475-3671 SIC 3471 3441

KIEWIT OFFSHORE SERVICES LTD p 817
Kiewit Plz, Omaha NE 68131
Tel (402) 342-2052 SIC 3441

▲ VALMONT INDUSTRIES INC p 1541
1 Valmont Plz Ste 500, Omaha NE 68154
Tel (402) 963-1000
SIC 3441 3399 3317 3523 3612

SMITHS TUBULAR SYSTEMS-LACONIA INC p 1334
93 Lexington Dr, Laconia NH 03246
Tel (603) 524-2064
SIC 3463 3498 8734 7692 3441 3398

FRAZIER INDUSTRIAL CO p 575
91 Fairview Ave, Long Valley NJ 07853
Tel (908) 876-3001 SIC 3441 2542

▲ GIBRALTAR INDUSTRIES INC p 611
3556 Lake Shore Rd # 100, Buffalo NY 14219
Tel (716) 826-6500
SIC 3499 3316 3441 3398

■ SUNLIGHT US CO INC p 1403
3556 Lake Shore Rd # 100, Buffalo NY 14219
Tel (716) 826-6500
SIC 3499 3316 3441 3398

FORT MILLER GROUP INC p 569
688 Wilbur Ave, Greenwich NY 12834
Tel (518) 695-5000 SIC 3272 3441

ALBANY STEEL INC p 45
566 Broadway Ste 2, Menands NY 12204
Tel (518) 436-4851 SIC 5051 3441

▲ NUCOR CORP p 1066
1915 Rexford Rd Ste 400, Charlotte NC 28211
Tel (704) 366-7000
SIC 3312 3441 3448 3452 5093

STEELFAB INC p 1384
8623 Old Dowd Rd, Charlotte NC 28214
Tel (704) 394-5376 SIC 3441 3449

BOB BARKER CO INC p 196
134 N Main St, Fuquay Varina NC 27526
Tel (800) 235-8586
SIC 5131 5122 2392 5136 3441

INDUSTRIAL FABRICATORS INC p 740
4328 York Hwy, Gastonia NC 28052
Tel (704) 864-5026 SIC 3441

■ LYDALL THERMAL/ACOUSTICAL INC p 887
1243 Buck Shoals Rd, Hamptonville NC 27020
Tel (336) 468-8522 SIC 3441

▲ WILLIAMS INDUSTRIES INC p 1611
1128 Tyler Farms Dr, Raleigh NC 27603
Tel (919) 604-1746
SIC 3441 1531 1541 3315 1791

SCHLETTER INC p 1287
1001 Commerce Center Dr, Shelby NC 28150
Tel (704) 595-4200 SIC 3441 3999

TRUENORTH STEEL INC p 1486
702 13th Ave E, West Fargo ND 58078
Tel (701) 373-7781 SIC 3443 3444 3441

OHIO GRATINGS INC p 1077
5299 Southway St Sw, Canton OH 44706
Tel (330) 477-6707
SIC 3446 3444 3441 3312

REPUBLIC STORAGE SYSTEMS LLC p 1226
1038 Belden Ave Ne, Canton OH 44705
Tel (330) 438-5800 SIC 2542 3441

PIONEER PIPE INC p 1151
2021 Hanna Rd, Marietta OH 45750
Tel (740) 376-2400
SIC 3498 1711 3443 3441 3312

COHEN BROTHERS INC p 335
1723 Woodlawn Ave, Middletown OH 45044
Tel (513) 422-3696
SIC 5093 3441 3341 3312

ERICO INTERNATIONAL CORP p 507
31700 Solon Rd, Solon OH 44139
Tel (440) 349-2630 SIC 3441

WARREN FABRICATING CORP p 1577
3240 Mahoning Ave Nw, Warren OH 44483
Tel (330) 847-0596
SIC 3441 3599 3547 3532 3444 3443

CONTECH ENGINEERED SOLUTIONS INC p 362
9025 Centre Pointe Dr # 400, West Chester OH 45069
Tel (513) 645-7000
SIC 3444 3084 3317 3441 3443

CONTECH ENGINEERED SOLUTIONS LLC p 362
9025 Ctr Pinte Dr Ste 400, West Chester OH 45069
Tel (513) 645-7000
SIC 3444 3084 3317 3441 3443

■ **UNITED HOLDINGS LLC** p 1509
5 N Mccormick St Ste 200, Oklahoma City OK 73127
Tel (405) 947-3321
SIC 5084 5013 7538 7537 3441

WWSC HOLDINGS LLC p 1629
1730 W Reno Ave, Oklahoma City OK 73106
Tel (405) 235-3621 SIC 3441

VIGOR WORKS LLC p 1556
9700 Se Lawnfield Rd, Clackamas OR 97015
Tel (503) 653-6300 SIC 3441

▲ **SCHNITZER STEEL INDUSTRIES INC** p 1288
299 Sw Clay St Ste 350, Portland OR 97201
Tel (503) 224-9900
SIC 5093 3312 3449 3441 3433 5015

HAMILTON CONSTRUCTION CO p 655
2213 S F St, Springfield OR 97477
Tel (541) 746-2426 SIC 1622 3441

ROSBORO LLC p 1250
2509 Main St, Springfield OR 97477
Tel (541) 746-8411
SIC 2436 2421 2439 3441 2435

■ **RTI INTERNATIONAL METALS INC** p 1256
5th Fl 1550 Crplis Hts Rd, Coraopolis PA 15108
Tel (412) 893-0026 SIC 3356 3441

AMTHOR STEEL INC p 87
1717 Gaskell Ave, Erie PA 16503
Tel (814) 452-4700 SIC 3441

DURA-BOND INDUSTRIES INC p 462
2658 Puckety Dr, Export PA 15632
Tel (724) 327-0280 SIC 3441 3479

HIGH INDUSTRIES INC p 690
1853 William Penn Way, Lancaster PA 17601
Tel (717) 293-4444
SIC 1791 3272 5051 3441

WHEMCO INC p 1605
5 Hot Metal St Ste 300, Pittsburgh PA 15203
Tel (412) 390-2700
SIC 3312 3462 3731 3325 3441 3369

■ **METALDYNE SINTERED RIDGWAY LLC** p 952
1149 Rocky Rd, Ridgway PA 15853
Tel (814) 776-1141 SIC 3399 3441 3462

RIGGS INDUSTRIES INC p 1234
2478 Lincoln Hwy, Stoystown PA 15563
Tel (814) 629-5621 SIC 3713 3441

OWEN STEEL CO INC p 1100
727 Mauney Dr, Columbia SC 29201
Tel (803) 251-7680 SIC 3441

PETE LIEN & SONS INC p 1138
3401 Universal Dr, Rapid City SD 57702
Tel (605) 342-7224
SIC 3273 3441 1422 3274

■ **NUCOR STEEL MEMPHIS INC** p 1066
3601 Paul R Lowry Rd, Memphis TN 38109
Tel (901) 786-5837
SIC 3312 3441 3448 3452

ENOVATE MEDICAL LLC p 500
1152 Park Ave, Murfreesboro TN 37129
Tel (615) 896-1652 SIC 3441

COOPERS STEEL FABRICATORS INC () p 367
503 N Hillcrest Dr, Shelbyville TN 37160
Tel (931) 684-7962 SIC 3441 1791

SABRE INDUSTRIES INC p 1264
8653 E Highway 67, Alvarado TX 76009
Tel (817) 852-1700 SIC 3441

J M DAVIDSON INC p 771
2564 County Road 1960, Aransas Pass TX 78336
Tel (361) 883-0983 SIC 1541 1731 3441

MODERN GROUP LTD p 981
1655 Louisiana St, Beaumont TX 77701
Tel (800) 231-8198 SIC 7359 3441

ORIZON INDUSTRIES INC p 1095
7007 Fm 362 Rd, Brookshire TX 77423
Tel (281) 375-7700 SIC 3441

DELTA FABRICATION AND MACHINE INC p 427
1379 County Road 2110, Daingerfield TX 75638
Tel (903) 645-3994 SIC 1541 3599 3441

▲ **TRINITY INDUSTRIES INC** p 1481
2525 N Stemmons Fwy, Dallas TX 75207
Tel (214) 631-4420
SIC 3743 3731 3531 3444 3441 3443

ENNIS STEEL INDUSTRIES INC p 500
204 Metro Park Blvd, Ennis TX 75119
Tel (972) 878-0400 SIC 3312 3441 1791

AMERICAN BLOCK CO p 69
6311 Breen Dr, Houston TX 77086
Tel (800) 572-9087
SIC 3441 3599 3533 3496 3444 3429

FABCO LLC p 523
13835 Beaumont Hwy, Houston TX 77049
Tel (713) 633-6500 SIC 3441 8741 8711

▲ **GULF ISLAND FABRICATION INC** p 646
16225 Park Ten Pl Ste 280, Houston TX 77084
Tel (713) 714-6100 SIC 3441 1389

NORTH SHORE SUPPLY CO INC p 1053
1566 Miles St, Houston TX 77015
Tel (713) 453-3533 SIC 5051 5085 3441

PIPING TECHNOLOGY & PRODUCTS INC p 1151
3701 Holmes Rd, Houston TX 77051
Tel (800) 787-5914 SIC 3494 8711 3441

▲ **COMMERCIAL METALS CO** p 345
6565 N Mcarthr Blvd # 800, Irving TX 75039
Tel (214) 689-4300
SIC 3312 3441 5051 5093

JV INDUSTRIAL COMPANIES LTD p 798
4040 Red Bluff Rd, Pasadena TX 77503
Tel (713) 568-2600 SIC 7692 3441 8711

GULF COPPER & MANUFACTURING CORP p 646
5700 Procter Ext, Port Arthur TX 77642
Tel (409) 989-0300
SIC 3731 3599 3312 3732 3498 3441

HIRSCHFELD HOLDINGS LP p 696
112 W 29th St, San Angelo TX 76903
Tel (325) 486-4201 SIC 1622 3441

HIRSCHFELD STEEL GROUP LP p 696
112 W 29th St, San Angelo TX 76903
Tel (325) 486-4201 SIC 3441

■ **C M C STEEL FABRICATORS INC** p 233
1 Steel Mill Dr, Seguin TX 78155
Tel (830) 372-8200 SIC 3312 3441

■ **STRUCTURAL METALS INC** p 1394
1 Steel Mill Dr, Seguin TX 78155
Tel (830) 372-8200 SIC 3312 3441 3462

INSIGHT EQUITY A P X L P p 746
1400 Civic Pl Ste 250, Southlake TX 76092
Tel (817) 488-7775
SIC 6722 3441 3443 3556 3714 5171

INSIGHT EQUITY ACQUISITION CO LLC p 746
1400 Civic Pl Ste 250, Southlake TX 76092
Tel (817) 354-2715
SIC 2911 6722 3851 3441

INSIGHT EQUITY HOLDINGS LLC p 746
1400 Civic Pl Ste 250, Southlake TX 76092
Tel (817) 488-7775
SIC 6726 3851 2911 3441

INSIGHT EQUITY LP p 746
1400 Civic Pl Ste 250, Southlake TX 76092
Tel (817) 488-7775
SIC 6722 3441 3443 3556 3714 5171

NRG MANUFACTURING INC p 1064
11311 Holderrieth Rd # 100, Tomball TX 77375
Tel (281) 320-2525 SIC 3449 3441

MOUNTAIN STATES STEEL INC p 994
325 S Geneva Rd Ste 1, Lindon UT 84042
Tel (801) 785-5085 SIC 3441

PETERSEN INC p 1138
1527 N 2000 W, Ogden UT 84404
Tel (801) 731-1366
SIC 5084 3441 7692 3444

SME INDUSTRIES INC p 1332
5801 W Wells Park Rd, West Jordan UT 84081
Tel (801) 280-3960 SIC 1791 3441

TECNICO CORP p 1432
831 Industrial Ave, Chesapeake VA 23324
Tel (757) 545-4013
SIC 3446 3443 3441 3444 3731

ELECTRONIC WARFARE ASSOCIATES INC p 486
13873 Park Center Rd # 500, Herndon VA 20171
Tel (703) 904-5700
SIC 7373 7374 3672 3699 3643 3441

GREENBERRY INDUSTRIAL LLC p 637
600 Se Maritime Ave # 190, Vancouver WA 98661
Tel (360) 567-0006
SIC 1711 1541 3443 3441

■ **STEEL OF WEST VIRGINIA INC** p 1384
17th St & 2nd Ave, Huntington WV 25703
Tel (304) 696-8200 SIC 3441

■ **SWVA INC** p 1413
17th St & Second Ave, Huntington WV 25703
Tel (304) 696-8200 SIC 3441 3312

RALEIGH MINE AND INDUSTRIAL SUPPLY INC p 1206
1500 Mill Creek Rd, Mount Hope WV 25880
Tel (304) 877-5503
SIC 5085 1629 3532 3441

KALKREUTH ROOFING & SHEET METAL INC p 801
53 14th St Ste 100, Wheeling WV 26003
Tel (304) 232-8540
SIC 1761 3446 3444 3441

MANITOWOC TOOL AND MACHINING LLC p 902
4211 Clipper Dr, Manitowoc WI 54220
Tel (920) 682-8825 SIC 3441

SUPER STEEL LLC p 1406
7900 W Tower Ave, Milwaukee WI 53223
Tel (414) 362-9114
SIC 3443 3444 3441 3446

MONROE TRUCK EQUIPMENT INC p 985
1051 W 7th St, Monroe WI 53566
Tel (608) 328-8127 SIC 5013 3441 3599

STEEL KING INDUSTRIES INC p 1384
2700 Chamber St, Stevens Point WI 54481
Tel (715) 341-3120
SIC 3441 3537 3412 2542

UNIVERSAL ACOUSTIC & EMISSION TECHNOLOGIES INC p 1516
1925 Us Highway 51 & 138, Stoughton WI 53589
Tel (608) 873-4272 SIC 3569 3441

SIC 3442 Metal Doors, Sash, Frames, Molding & Trim

PHIFER INC p 1142
4400 Kauloosa Ave, Tuscaloosa AL 35401
Tel (205) 345-2120
SIC 3496 2221 3357 2295 3442 3354

ARCH ALUMINUM & GLASS CO OF ARIZONA INC p 104
1825 S 43rd Ave Ste A, Phoenix AZ 85009
Tel (602) 484-9777 SIC 3442 1793

ACORN ENGINEERING CO p 18
15125 Proctor Ave, City Of Industry CA 91746
Tel (800) 488-8999 SIC 3448 3431 3442

FLEETWOOD ALUMINUM PRODUCTS INC p 555
1 Fleetwood Way, Corona CA 92879
Tel (800) 736-7363 SIC 5031 3442

ARCHITECTURAL GLASS & ALUMINUM CO INC p 105
6400 Brisa St, Livermore CA 94550
Tel (925) 583-2460
SIC 5051 1793 1791 3442

HEHR INTERNATIONAL INC p 680
3333 Casitas Ave, Los Angeles CA 90039
Tel (323) 663-1261 SIC 3442

T M COBB CO p 1419
500 Palmyrita Ave, Riverside CA 92507
Tel (951) 248-2400 SIC 2431 3442

ARCHITECTURAL BLOMBERG LLC p 105
1453 Blair Ave, Sacramento CA 95822
Tel (916) 428-8060 SIC 3442

ASSOCIATED MATERIALS GROUP INC p 120
1 Maritime Plz Fl 12, San Francisco CA 94111
Tel (415) 788-5111
SIC 3089 5033 5031 3442

ASSOCIATED MATERIALS INC p 121
1 Maritime Plz Fl 12, San Francisco CA 94111
Tel (415) 788-5111
SIC 3089 5033 5031 3442

BRYNWOOD PARTNERS V LIMITED PARTNERSHIP p 222
8 Sound Shore Dr Ste 265, Greenwich CT 06830
Tel (203) 622-1790
SIC 6282 1751 3442 5031 3354

J T WALKER INDUSTRIES INC p 772
861 N Hercules Ave, Clearwater FL 33765
Tel (727) 461-0501
SIC 3442 3089 3585 5193

RAYMOND BUILDING SUPPLY p 1210
7751 Bayshore Rd, Fort Myers FL 33917
Tel (941) 429-1212
SIC 5211 2439 2431 3442 2434 3634

RC ALUMINUM INDUSTRIES INC p 1211
2805 Nw 75th Ave, Miami FL 33122
Tel (305) 592-1515 SIC 3442 1751

STYLE-VIEW PRODUCTS INC p 1395
1800 N Bayshore Dr # 4001, Miami FL 33132
Tel (305) 634-9688
SIC 3442 3444 3443 3354

▲ **PGT INC** p 1140
1070 Technology Dr, North Venice FL 34275
Tel (941) 480-1600 SIC 3442 2431 3211

■ **PGT INDUSTRIES INC** p 1140
1070 Technology Dr, North Venice FL 34275
Tel (352) 335-5556 SIC 3442 2431 3231

CUSTOM WINDOW SYSTEMS INC p 403
1900 Sw 44th Ave, Ocala FL 34474
Tel (352) 368-6922 SIC 3442

FLORIDA A&G CO INC p 557
10200 Nw 67th St, Tamarac FL 33321
Tel (800) 432-8132 SIC 3442 5039

MASONITE HOLDINGS INC p 916
201 N Franklin St Ste 300, Tampa FL 33602
Tel (813) 877-2726 SIC 2431 3442

▲ **MASONITE INTERNATIONAL CORP** p 916
201 N Franklin St, Tampa FL 33602
Tel (813) 877-2726 SIC 2431 3442

■ **MAGNATRAX CORP** p 896
1220 Old Alpharetta Rd # 310, Alpharetta GA 30005
Tel (678) 455-3360
SIC 3448 3442 3479 4213 3444

YKK AP AMERICA INC p 1636
270 Riverside Pkwy Ste A, Austell GA 30168
Tel (678) 838-6000 SIC 3442 3449

■ **KAWNEER CO INC** p 805
555 Guthridge Ct Tech, Norcross GA 30092
Tel (770) 449-5555 SIC 3442 3446

JANUS INTERNATIONAL GROUP LLC p 778
135 Janus Intl Blvd, Temple GA 30179
Tel (770) 562-2850 SIC 3442

■ **C H I OVERHEAD DOORS INC** p 232
1485 Sunrise Dr, Arthur IL 61911
Tel (217) 543-2135 SIC 3442

■ **CHI DOORS HOLDINGS INC** p 296
1485 Sunrise Dr, Arthur IL 61911
Tel (217) 543-2135 SIC 3442

NEISEWANDER ENTERPRISES INC p 1025
1101 E River Rd, Dixon IL 61021
Tel (815) 288-1431 SIC 3442 2431 3429

RAYNOR MFG CO p 1210
1101 E River Rd, Dixon IL 61021
Tel (815) 288-1431
SIC 3442 7011 3699 2431

ALP LIGHTING & CEILING PRODUCTS INC p 60
6333 W Gross Point Rd, Niles IL 60714
Tel (773) 774-9550
SIC 3089 3354 5162 3496 3442 3229

▲ **DREW INDUSTRIES INC** p 455
3501 County Road 6 E, Elkhart IN 46514
Tel (574) 535-1125
SIC 3711 3714 3715 3442 3431

■ **KINRO MANUFACTURING INC** p 821
3501 County Road 6 E, Elkhart IN 46514
Tel (574) 535-1125 SIC 3442

HENNIGES AUTOMOTIVE IOWA INC p 683
3200 Main St, Keokuk IA 52632
Tel (319) 524-4560
SIC 3069 3442 3429 2295

AADG INC p 8
1502 12th St Nw, Mason City IA 50401
Tel (641) 423-1334 SIC 3442

GARAGE DOOR GROUP INC p 591
3800 Greenway Cir, Lawrence KS 66046
Tel (800) 503-3667 SIC 3442

MANKO WINDOW SYSTEMS INC p 902
800 Hayes Dr, Manhattan KS 66502
Tel (785) 776-9643 SIC 3442 1799 5039

AFCO INDUSTRIES INC p 32
3400 Roy Ave, Alexandria LA 71302
Tel (318) 448-1651 SIC 3354 3083 3442

AMESBURY GROUP INC p 84
57 S Hunt Rd, Amesbury MA 01913
Tel (978) 834-3233
SIC 3053 3442 3086 2221 3089

HARVEY INDUSTRIES INC p 667
1400 Main St Fl 3, Waltham MA 02451
Tel (781) 899-3500
SIC 5031 5033 3442 2431

MAGNA MIRRORS NORTH AMERICA LLC p 896
6151 Bancroft Ave Se, Alto MI 49302
Tel (616) 868-6122 SIC 3231 3442

ACTIVAR INC p 19
7808 Creekridge Cir # 200, Minneapolis MN 55439
Tel (952) 944-3533
SIC 2542 3479 3442 3429 3089

TRUTH HARDWARE CORP p 1489
700 W Bridge St, Owatonna MN 55060
Tel (507) 451-5620 SIC 2431 3442 3429

QUAKER WINDOW PRODUCTS CO p 1196
504 Highway 63 S, Freeburg MO 65582
Tel (800) 347-0438 SIC 3442

EFCO CORP p 480
1000 County Rd, Monett MO 65708
Tel (800) 221-4169 SIC 3442 3449

CHIEF INDUSTRIES INC p 298
3942 W Old Highway 30, Grand Island NE 68803
Tel (308) 389-7200
SIC 3448 2451 3523 2869 3442

THERMWELL PRODUCTS CO INC p 1447
420 State Rt 17, Mahwah NJ 07430
Tel (201) 684-4400 SIC 3442

SILVER LINE BUILDING PRODUCTS LLC p 1324
1 Silverline Dr, North Brunswick NJ 08902
Tel (732) 435-1000 SIC 3089 3442

A G M DECO INC p 5
741 Myrtle Ave, Brooklyn NY 11205
Tel (718) 624-6200 SIC 3442

CRYSTAL WINDOW & DOOR SYSTEMS LTD p 397
3110 Whitestone Expy, Flushing NY 11354
Tel (718) 961-7300
SIC 5031 3442 3231 3211 2431 1751

KASSON & KELLER INC p 804
60 School St, Fonda NY 12068
Tel (518) 853-3421
SIC 3442 3089 1521 3231

▲ **GRIFFON CORP** p 640
712 5th Ave Fl 18, New York NY 10019
Tel (212) 957-5000
SIC 3442 2431 1751 1799 3083 3663

GREAT AMERICAN INDUSTRIES INC p 633
300 Plaza Dr, Vestal NY 13850
Tel (607) 729-9331
SIC 3086 5031 5074 3442 3069 5091

■ **KINRO MANUFACTURING INC** p 821
200 Mmaroneck Ave Ste 301, White Plains NY 10601
Tel (817) 483-7791 SIC 3442

JELD-WEN INC p 782
440 S Church St Ste 400, Charlotte NC 28202
Tel (800) 535-3936 SIC 3442 5031 2421

MOSS SUPPLY CO p 992
5001 N Graham St, Charlotte NC 28269
Tel (704) 596-8717 SIC 3442

ASSA ABLOY ENTRANCE SYSTEMS US INC p 119
1900 Airport Rd, Monroe NC 28110
Tel (704) 290-5520 SIC 3699 1796 3442

AMARR CO p 64
165 Carriage Ct, Winston Salem NC 27105
Tel (336) 744-5100
SIC 2431 3442 5031 5211

CHAMPION OPCO LLC p 287
12121 Champion Way, Cincinnati OH 45241
Tel (513) 924-4858 SIC 3089 1761 3442

CASCADE OHIO INC p 262
1209 Maple Ave, Conneaut OH 44030
Tel (440) 593-5800 SIC 2431 3442

ASSOCIATED MATERIALS HOLDINGS LLC p 120
3773 State Rd, Cuyahoga Falls OH 44223
Tel (330) 929-1811
SIC 3089 5033 5031 5063 3442

ASSOCIATED MATERIALS LLC p 121
3773 State Rd, Cuyahoga Falls OH 44223
Tel (330) 929-1811
SIC 3089 5033 5031 3442

■ **CLOPAY BUILDING PRODUCTS CO INC** p 327
8585 Duke Blvd, Mason OH 45040
Tel (513) 770-4800 SIC 2431 3442 2436

■ **CLOPAY CORP** p 327
8585 Duke Blvd, Mason OH 45040
Tel (800) 282-2260
SIC 3081 3442 2431 1796

■ **THERMA-TRU CORP** p 1447
1750 Indian Wood Cir # 100, Maumee OH 43537
Tel (419) 891-7400 SIC 3442

HRH DOOR CORP p 714
1 Door Dr, Mount Hope OH 44660
Tel (850) 208-3400 SIC 3442 2431

DESCO CORP p 432
7795 Walton Pkwy Ste 175, New Albany OH 43054
Tel (614) 888-8855
SIC 3442 3825 3643 3531 3429

PROVIA DOOR INC p 1185
2150 State Route 39, Sugarcreek OH 44681
Tel (330) 852-4711 SIC 3442 5031

CHASE INDUSTRIES INC p 291
10021 Commerce Park Dr, West Chester OH 45246
Tel (513) 860-5565 SIC 3442

MODERN BUILDERS SUPPLY INC p 981
302 Mcclurg Rd, Youngstown OH 44512
Tel (330) 729-2690
SIC 5032 3089 3446 3442

M-D BUILDING PRODUCTS INC p 890
4041 N Santa Fe Ave, Oklahoma City OK 73118
Tel (405) 528-4411 SIC 3442

MILL CREEK LUMBER & SUPPLY CO INC p 969
6974 E 38th St, Tulsa OK 74145
Tel (405) 671-3540
SIC 3442 1771 5031 5211

■ **TRACO DELAWARE INC** p 1468
71 Progress Ave, Cranberry Township PA 16066
Tel (724) 776-7000
SIC 3442 3211 3444 3448 3354 7992

■ **TRI CITY ALUMINUM CO** p 1476
71 Progress Ave, Cranberry Township PA 16066
Tel (724) 799-8917 SIC 3442 3354 7992

RITESCREEN CO LLC p 1237
4314 State Route 209, Elizabethville PA 17023
Tel (717) 362-7483 SIC 3442 2431

MI WINDOWS AND DOORS INC p 959
650 W Market St, Gratz PA 17030
Tel (717) 365-3300 SIC 3089 3442

CIW ENTERPRISES INC p 320
24 Elmwood Ave, Mountain Top PA 18707
Tel (800) 233-8366 SIC 3442 3446 2431

CORNELLCOOKSON INC p 370
24 Elmwood Ave, Mountain Top PA 18707
Tel (570) 474-6773 SIC 3442

■ ALUMAX LLC p 63
201 Isabella St, Pittsburgh PA 15212
Tel (412) 553-4545
SIC 3334 3353 3354 3449 3442 3446

GRAHAM ARCHITECTURAL PRODUCTS CORP p 628
1551 Mount Rose Ave, York PA 17403
Tel (717) 849-8100 SIC 3442

VELUX GREENWOOD INC p 1547
450 Old Brickyard Rd, Greenwood SC 29649
Tel (864) 941-4700 SIC 3442

LOXCREEN CO INC p 882
1630 Old Dunbar Rd, West Columbia SC 29172
Tel (803) 822-1600 SIC 3354 3442 3089

LARSON MANUFACTURING CO OF SOUTH DAKOTA INC p 845
2333 Eastbrook Dr, Brookings SD 57006
Tel (605) 692-6115 SIC 3442

■ ALENCO HOLDING CORP p 48
615 W Carson St, Bryan TX 77801
Tel (979) 779-1051 SIC 3442

ATRIUM CORP p 129
13355 Noel Rd Ste 1250, Dallas TX 75240
Tel (214) 583-1543 SIC 3442

ATRIUM WINDOWS AND DOORS INC p 129
3890 W Northwest Hwy # 500, Dallas TX 75220
Tel (214) 956-8031
SIC 3442 2431 3089 3354 7629

KRESTMARK INDUSTRIES LP p 830
3950 Bastille Rd Ste 100, Dallas TX 75212
Tel (214) 237-5055 SIC 3442 3089

SANWA USA INC p 1281
4020 Mcewen Rd Ste 118, Dallas TX 75244
Tel (972) 503-3031
SIC 3442 2431 3699 3537

GENERAL ALUMINUM CO OF TEXAS LP p 599
1900 Lakeside Pkwy, Flower Mound TX 75028
Tel (972) 242-5271 SIC 3442 5031

CHAMPION WINDOW INC p 287
12427 Duncan Rd, Houston TX 77066
Tel (281) 440-7000 SIC 3442

▲ NCI BUILDING SYSTEMS INC p 1022
10943 N Sam Huston Pkwy W, Houston TX 77064
Tel (281) 897-7788
SIC 3448 3444 3442 1542 1541 7389

OVERHEAD DOOR CORP p 1099
2501 S State Hwy 121 Ste, Lewisville TX 75067
Tel (469) 549-7100
SIC 3442 2431 3699 3537 3589

AMSCO WINDOWS p 87
1880 S 1045 W, Salt Lake City UT 84104
Tel (801) 972-6444 SIC 3442

■ MILGARD MANUFACTURING INC p 969
1010 54th Ave E, Fife WA 98424
Tel (253) 922-6030 SIC 3089 3442

WINDOW PRODUCTS INC p 1615
10507 E Montgomery Dr, Spokane Valley WA 99206
Tel (800) 442-8544 SIC 3442 5211

SIMONTON BUILDING PRODUCTS INC p 1325
5300 Briscoe Rd, Parkersburg WV 26105
Tel (304) 659-2851 SIC 3089 3442 3231

AWS/GB CORP p 139
2929 Walker Dr, Green Bay WI 54311
Tel (920) 406-4000
SIC 5031 2431 3442 5033 1542 1541

LA FORCE INC p 835
1060 W Mason St, Green Bay WI 54303
Tel (920) 497-7100 SIC 5072 5031 3442

HUFCOR INC p 717
2101 Kennedy Rd, Janesville WI 53545
Tel (608) 756-1241 SIC 2542 3442

■ MARSHFIELD DOORSYSTEMS INC p 911
1401 E 4th St, Marshfield WI 54449
Tel (715) 384-2141 SIC 2431 3442

PEACHTREE COMPANIES INC p 1125
1 Weathershield Plz, Medford WI 54451
Tel (715) 748-6555 SIC 3442 2431

WEATHER SHIELD MFG INC p 1585
1 Weathershield Plz, Medford WI 54451
Tel (715) 748-2100 SIC 2431 3089 3442

■ APOGEE WAUSAU GROUP INC p 97
7800 International Dr, Wausau WI 54401
Tel (715) 845-2161
SIC 3479 3442 3471 3449

■ LINETEC p 869
7500 Stewart Ave, Wausau WI 54401
Tel (715) 843-4100 SIC 3442

SIC 3443 Fabricated Plate Work

DONGHEE ALABAMA LLC p 450
2550 Innovation Dr, Auburn AL 36832
Tel (334) 321-2756 SIC 3443

THERMASYS GROUP HOLDING CO p 1447
2776 Gunter Park Dr E, Montgomery AL 36109
Tel (334) 244-9240 SIC 3714 3443

PROCESS EQUIPMENT INC p 1179
2770 Welborn St, Pelham AL 35124
Tel (205) 663-5330
SIC 3564 3535 3441 3443

TW CRYOGENICS LLC p 1494
4075 Hamilton Blvd, Theodore AL 36582
Tel (251) 443-8680 SIC 3443

MCABEE CONSTRUCTION INC p 925
5724 21st St, Tuscaloosa AL 35401
Tel (205) 349-2212
SIC 1629 1791 1796 3443 3498

WALBRO LLC p 1572
2015 W River Rd 202, Tucson AZ 85704
Tel (520) 229-5642
SIC 3592 3594 3694 3443

DEFIANCE METAL PRODUCTS OF ARKANSAS INC p 422
944 By Pass Rd, Heber Springs AR 72543
Tel (501) 362-1919
SIC 3465 3443 3544 3469

■ ATK SPACE SYSTEMS INC p 125
6033 Bandini Blvd, Commerce CA 90040
Tel (323) 722-0222 SIC 3443

COMBUSTION ASSOCIATES INC p 343
555 Monica Cir, Corona CA 92880
Tel (951) 272-6999 SIC 4911 3443

BA HOLDINGS p 143
3016 Kansas Ave Bldg 1, Riverside CA 92507
Tel (951) 684-5110 SIC 3443 3728

GENERAL ATOMIC TECHNOLOGIES CORP p 599
3550 General Atomics Ct, San Diego CA 92121
Tel (858) 455-3000
SIC 8731 3829 3443 7374 3499 2819

HYUNDAI TRANSLEAD p 724
8880 Rio San Diego Dr # 600, San Diego CA 92108
Tel (619) 574-1500 SIC 3443 3715 3412

THERMAL ENGINEERING INTERNATIONAL (USA) INC p 1447
10375 Slusher Dr, Santa Fe Springs CA 90670
Tel (323) 726-0641 SIC 3443 8711

CONSOLIDATED FABRICATORS CORP p 359
14620 Arminta St, Van Nuys CA 91402
Tel (818) 901-1005 SIC 3443 5051 3444

WG GLOBAL LLC p 1604
603 Park Point Dr Ste 200, Golden CO 80401
Tel (303) 395-2100
SIC 3569 3559 3629 3625 3443 3412

VESTAS TOWERS AMERICA INC p 1552
100 Tower Rd, Pueblo CO 81004
Tel (719) 288-2200 SIC 3443

WHITCRAFT LLC p 1605
76 County Rd, Eastford CT 06242
Tel (860) 974-0786 SIC 3443 3444 3728

■ ALSTOM POWER INC p 61
200 Great Pond Dr, Windsor CT 06095
Tel (866) 257-8664
SIC 3443 3564 3621 3823 8711

■ ANDERSON GROUP INC p 90
3411 Silverside Rd # 103, Wilmington DE 19810
Tel (302) 478-6160
SIC 5047 5063 5099 7699 3443

CENTRAL MAINTENANCE AND WELDING INC p 279
2620 E Keysville Rd, Lithia FL 33547
Tel (813) 229-0012 SIC 3443 1791 7692

INDUSTRIAL CONTAINER SERVICES LLC p 739
2400 Maitland Center Pkwy, Maitland FL 32751
Tel (800) 273-3786 SIC 3443 3411 3412

STYLE-VIEW PRODUCTS INC p 1395
1800 N Bayshore Dr # 4001, Miami FL 33132
Tel (305) 634-9688
SIC 3442 3444 3443 3354

MCKENZIE TANK LINES INC p 930
1966 Commonwealth Ln, Tallahassee FL 32303
Tel (850) 576-1221 SIC 4213 3715 3443

CIVES CORP p 320
3700 Mansell Rd Ste 500, Alpharetta GA 30022
Tel (770) 993-4424 SIC 3441 3713 3443

LOR INC p 878
2170 Piedmont Rd Ne, Atlanta GA 30324
Tel (404) 486-5600 SIC 6799 5084 3443

MARINER HEALTH CARE INC p 907
1 Ravinia Dr Ste 1500, Atlanta GA 30346
Tel (678) 443-7000
SIC 5912 8051 8093 8741 8062 3443

▲ MUELLER WATER PRODUCTS INC p 998
1200 Abernathy Rd # 1200, Atlanta GA 30328
Tel (770) 206-4200
SIC 3491 3492 3494 3443 3321 3823

NATIONAL SENIOR CARE INC p 1016
1 Ravinia Dr Ste 1500, Atlanta GA 30346
Tel (678) 443-7000
SIC 5912 8051 8093 8741 8062 3443

NORTH AMERICAN CONTAINER CORP p 1050
1811 W Oak Pkwy Ste D, Marietta GA 30062
Tel (770) 431-4858 SIC 3443

CLEAVER-BROOKS INC p 325
221 Law St, Thomasville GA 31792
Tel (229) 226-3024
SIC 3589 3569 3561 3433 3443

AMSTED INDUSTRIES INC p 87
180 N Stetson Ave, Chicago IL 60601
Tel (312) 645-1700
SIC 3443 3325 3585 3321 3743

MADISON INDUSTRIES HOLDINGS LLC p 894
500 W Madison St Ste 3890, Chicago IL 60661
Tel (312) 277-0156
SIC 6719 5051 3443 3316

■ DOVER ENGINEERED SYSTEMS INC p 453
3005 Highland Pkwy # 200, Downers Grove IL 60515
Tel (630) 743-2505
SIC 3568 3443 3441 3561 3491 3492

COOPER B-LINE INC p 366
509 W Monroe St, Highland IL 62249
Tel (618) 654-2184
SIC 3441 3443 3452 3444 3429 3356

CABLOFIL INC p 235
8319 State Route 4, Mascoutah IL 62258
Tel (618) 566-3230 SIC 3443

G K ENTERPRISES INC p 587
26000 S Whiting Way Ste 2, Monee IL 60449
Tel (708) 587-2150
SIC 3743 3443 3559 3556 3536

■ ECLIPSE INC p 475
1665 Elmwood Rd, Rockford IL 61103
Tel (815) 877-3031
SIC 3564 3433 3822 3823 3443 3494

AEC INC p 28
1100 E Wdfield Rd Ste 588, Schaumburg IL 60173
Tel (847) 273-7700
SIC 3585 3823 3559 3443 3535

UCC HOLDINGS CORP p 1499
2100 Norman Dr, Waukegan IL 60085
Tel (847) 473-5900 SIC 3443 8711

METAL TECHNOLOGIES OF INDIANA INC p 952
1401 S Grandstaff Dr, Auburn IN 46706
Tel (260) 925-4717 SIC 3321 3443

STERLING BOILER AND MECHANICAL INC p 1387
1420 Kimber Ln, Evansville IN 47715
Tel (812) 479-5447 SIC 1711 3443

ROLLS-ROYCE CORP p 1247
450 S Meridian St, Indianapolis IN 46225
Tel (317) 230-2000
SIC 3724 3443 3462 3731 3743 3732

SMALL PARTS INC p 1332
600 Humphrey St, Logansport IN 46947
Tel (574) 753-6323 SIC 3443

■ CTB INC p 399
410 N Higbee St, Milford IN 46542
Tel (574) 658-4191 SIC 3443 3523

SIOUX CITY FOUNDRY CO p 1326
801 Division St, Sioux City IA 51105
Tel (712) 252-4181
SIC 5051 3443 3321 3316 3444 3441

■ SPX COOLING TECHNOLOGIES INC p 1362
7401 W 129th St, Overland Park KS 66213
Tel (913) 664-7400 SIC 3443

TANK CONNECTION LLC p 1424
3609 N 16th St, Parsons KS 67357
Tel (620) 423-0251 SIC 5084 3443

WALL-TIES & FORMS INC p 1573
4000 Bonner Industrial Dr, Shawnee KS 66226
Tel (913) 441-0073 SIC 5082 3444 3443

■ BALCO INC p 147
2626 S Sheridan Ave, Wichita KS 67217
Tel (800) 767-0082
SIC 3441 3089 3496 3446 3443

KOCH CHEMICAL TECHNOLOGY GROUP LLC p 825
4111 E 37th St N, Wichita KS 67220
Tel (316) 828-8515 SIC 3443

KOCH-GLITSCH LP p 826
4111 E 37th St N, Wichita KS 67220
Tel (316) 828-5110 SIC 3443

CALDWELL GROUP LLC p 238
4000 Tower Rd, Louisville KY 40219
Tel (502) 964-3361 SIC 3443

CALDWELL TANKS INC p 238
4000 Tower Rd, Louisville KY 40219
Tel (502) 964-3361 SIC 3443 5084 3441

DOMETIC CORP p 448
13551 Triton Park Blvd # 1000, Louisville KY 40223
Tel (502) 873-3524
SIC 3089 3443 3444 3822 3823 3999

MODERN WELDING CO INC p 981
2880 New Hartford Rd, Owensboro KY 42303
Tel (270) 685-4400
SIC 3443 5051 3441 5085

BALTIMORE AIRCOIL CO INC p 149
7600 Dorsey Run Rd, Jessup MD 20794
Tel (410) 799-6200 SIC 3585 3443

EVAPCO INC p 513
5151 Allendale Ln, Taneytown MD 21787
Tel (410) 756-2600 SIC 3443 3585

CONNELL LIMITED PARTNERSHIP p 358
1 International Pl Fl 31, Boston MA 02110
Tel (617) 737-2700
SIC 3443 3444 3341 3544 6719

BABCOCK POWER INC p 143
6 Kimball Ln Ste 210, Lynnfield MA 01940
Tel (978) 646-3300 SIC 3443 3569 3433

HTP INC p 715
272 Duchaine Blvd, New Bedford MA 02745
Tel (508) 763-8071 SIC 5084 3443

RILEY POWER INC p 1235
5 Neponset St, Worcester MA 01606
Tel (508) 852-7100
SIC 3569 3443 3433 1711 3564 3511

BESSER CO p 177
801 Johnson St, Alpena MI 49707
Tel (989) 354-4508
SIC 3531 3559 3564 3443

■ HUTCHINSON FTS INC p 722
1060 Centre Rd, Auburn Hills MI 48326
Tel (248) 589-7710
SIC 3714 3061 3567 3492 3443 3429

▲ TRIMAS CORP p 1480
39400 Woodward Ave # 130, Bloomfield Hills MI 48304
Tel (248) 631-5450
SIC 3799 3714 3443 2672 3452 3545

HINES CORP p 695
1218 E Pontaluna Rd Ste B, Norton Shores MI 49456
Tel (231) 799-6240
SIC 3443 3823 3589 3531 3535 5082

MERRILL TOOL HOLDING CO p 950
400 Florence St, Saginaw MI 48602
Tel (989) 791-6676
SIC 3443 3599 8734 8711 3724

PENTAIR TECHNICAL PRODUCTS p 1132
2100 Hoffman Way, Anoka MN 55303
Tel (763) 323-8200 SIC 3585 3443

POLAR TANK TRAILERS p 1159
12810 County Road 17, Holdingford MN 56340
Tel (417) 862-5526 SIC 3443 3715

POLAR CORP p 1159
1015 W St Germain St 42 Ste 420, Hopkins MN 55305
Tel (612) 430-6401 SIC 3443 5012 7699

XERXES CORP p 1631
7901 Xerxes Ave S Ste 201, Minneapolis MN 55431
Tel (952) 887-1890 SIC 3089 3443 3088

TAYLOR-WHARTON INTERNATIONAL LLC p 1427
5600 Rowland Rd Ste 170, Minnetonka MN 55343
Tel (717) 763-5060 SIC 3443 3491

■ CHART INC p 290
407 7th St Nw, New Prague MN 56071
Tel (952) 758-4484 SIC 3443 3842

TATUM DEVELOPMENT CORP p 1426
11 Parkway Blvd, Hattiesburg MS 39401
Tel (601) 544-6043
SIC 5141 5084 4924 3443

STEEL SERVICE CORP p 1384
2260 Flowood Dr, Jackson MS 39232
Tel (601) 939-9222
SIC 3441 1791 3496 3443

STRUCTURAL STEEL HOLDING INC p 1394
6210 Saint Louis St, Meridian MS 39307
Tel (601) 483-5381 SIC 3441 3443 4213

■ MITEK USA INC p 977
16023 Swingley Ridge Rd, Chesterfield MO 63017
Tel (314) 434-1200
SIC 3443 3429 3542 8711 5051 5085

■ VICTOR TECHNOLOGIES GROUP INC p 1555
16253 Swingley Ridge Rd # 200, Chesterfield MO 63017
Tel (636) 728-3000
SIC 3541 3423 3613 3443 3621 3548

CST INDUSTRIES INC p 398
903 E 104th St Ste 900, Kansas City MO 64131
Tel (913) 621-3700 SIC 3443

NOOTER CORP p 1047
1500 S 2nd St, Saint Louis MO 63104
Tel (314) 421-7200
SIC 3443 3479 1796 8711 7699 1542

▲ PAUL MUELLER CO p 1121
1600 W Phelps St, Springfield MO 65802
Tel (417) 831-3000 SIC 3443 3556 3523

BEHLEN MFG CO p 168
4025 E 23rd St, Columbus NE 68601
Tel (402) 564-3111
SIC 3523 3448 4213 3556 3496 3443

▲ LINDSAY CORP p 868
2222 N 111th St, Omaha NE 68164
Tel (402) 829-6800 SIC 3523 3599 3443

■ LINDSAY MANUFACTURING LLC p 868
2222 N 111th St, Omaha NE 68164
Tel (402) 829-6800
SIC 3523 3599 3499 3443

■ TSI GROUP INC p 1489
94 Tide Mill Rd, Hampton NH 03842
Tel (603) 964-0296
SIC 3599 3398 3443 3444

CORBAN ENERGY GROUP CORP p 368
418 Falmouth Ave, Elmwood Park NJ 07407
Tel (201) 509-8555 SIC 1623 3443 5085

■ ASCO VALVE INC p 116
50-60 Hanover Rd, Florham Park NJ 07932
Tel (973) 966-2437
SIC 3443 3491 3492 3625 5063

AMEC FOSTER WHEELER NORTH AMERICA CORP p 66
Perryville Corporate Pk 5, Hampton NJ 08827
Tel (908) 713-2891
SIC 3433 3443 3532 3569

CONSTRUCTION SPECIALTIES INC p 361
3 Werner Way Ste 100, Lebanon NJ 08833
Tel (908) 236-0800
SIC 3446 3354 3443 3272 3585

PROCESS EQUIPMENT & SERVICE CO INC p 1179
5680 Us 64, Farmington NM 87401
Tel (505) 327-2222
SIC 3443 5084 7699 3533

■ AMERICAN PRECISION INDUSTRIES INC p 77
45 Hazelwood Dr, Amherst NY 14228
Tel (716) 691-9100
SIC 3677 3621 3625 3443

▲ GRAHAM CORP p 629
20 Florence Ave, Batavia NY 14020
Tel (585) 343-2216 SIC 3563 3585 3443

API HEAT TRANSFER CO p 96
2777 Walden Ave Ste 1, Buffalo NY 14225
Tel (716) 684-6700 SIC 3443

SLANT/FIN CORP p 1331
100 Forest Dr, Greenvale NY 11548
Tel (516) 484-2600 SIC 3433 3443

FULTON BOILER WORKS INC p 584
3981 Port St, Pulaski NY 13142
Tel (315) 298-5121 SIC 3443

FELDMEIER EQUIPMENT INC p 537
6800 Townline Rd, Syracuse NY 13211
Tel (315) 823-2000 SIC 3443

ECR INTERNATIONAL INC p 476
2201 Dwyer Ave, Utica NY 13501
Tel (315) 797-1310 SIC 3433 3443

STEBBINS ENGINEERING AND MANUFACTURING CO p 1384
363 Eastern Blvd, Watertown NY 13601
Tel (315) 782-3000 SIC 1799 3443

ARVOS INC p 115
3020 Truax Rd, Wellsville NY 14895
Tel (585) 593-2700 SIC 3443

■ BWXT INVESTMENT CO p 231
11525 N Community House, Charlotte NC 28277
Tel (704) 625-4900
SIC 3511 3443 3564 1629 1541 7699

■ MARLEY CO LLC p 909
13515 Balntyn Corp Pl, Charlotte NC 28277
Tel (704) 752-4400
SIC 3443 3433 3586 3561 3634

▲ SPX CORP p 1362
13320a Balntyn Corp Pl, Charlotte NC 28277
Tel (980) 474-3700
SIC 3443 3599 3829 3559 3545

TOSHIBA AMERICA NUCLEAR ENERGY CORP p 1462
3545 Whitehall Park Dr # 500, Charlotte NC 28273
Tel (704) 548-7777 SIC 3443 5211

WASTEQUIP LLC p 1581
6525 Morrison Blvd # 300, Charlotte NC 28211
Tel (704) 366-7140 SIC 3443 3537

WASTEQUIP MANUFACTURING CO LLC p 1581
1901 Roxborough Rd # 300, Charlotte NC 28211
Tel (704) 366-7140 SIC 3443

WASTE INDUSTRIES USA INC p 1580
3301 Benson Dr Ste 601, Raleigh NC 27609
Tel (919) 325-3000 SIC 4953 3443

NORDFAB LLC p 1048
150 Transit Ave, Thomasville NC 27360
Tel (336) 821-0829 SIC 3443

MISSOURI VALLEY PETROLEUM INC p 976
1722 Mandan Ave, Mandan ND 58554
Tel (701) 663-5091 SIC 5172 3443

TRUENORTH STEEL INC p 1486
702 13th Ave E, West Fargo ND 58078
Tel (701) 373-7781 SIC 3443 3444 3441

■ BABCOCK & WILCOX CO p 143
20 S Van Buren Ave, Barberton OH 44203
Tel (330) 753-4511
SIC 1629 1711 3443 7699 8741 3822

■ CECO GROUP INC p 272
4625 Red Bank Rd Ste 200, Cincinnati OH 45227
Tel (513) 458-2600
SIC 8711 3564 8734 3443 3444 1761

ENERFAB INC p 497
4955 Spring Grove Ave, Cincinnati OH 45232
Tel (513) 641-0500
SIC 3443 1629 1541 1711 3479

▲ CHART INDUSTRIES INC p 290
1 Infinity Corp Ctr Dr # 300, Cleveland OH 44125
Tel (440) 753-1490 SIC 3559 3569 3443

PARK CORP p 1115
6200 Riverside Dr, Cleveland OH 44135
Tel (216) 267-4870
SIC 3547 1711 3443 5084 6512 7999

DEFIANCE METAL PRODUCTS CO p 422
21 Seneca St, Defiance OH 43512
Tel (419) 784-5332 SIC 3465 3443 3544

BI-CON SERVICES INC p 180
10901 Clay Pike Rd, Derwent OH 43733
Tel (740) 685-2542 SIC 1623 3498 3443

PIONEER PIPE INC p 1151
2021 Hanna Rd, Marietta OH 45750
Tel (740) 376-2400
SIC 3498 1711 3443 3441 3312

SHELBURNE CORP p 1314
20001 Shelburne Rd, Shaker Heights OH 44118
Tel (216) 321-9177
SIC 3443 3823 3544 3769

MORRIS MATERIAL HANDLING INC p 990
4401 Gateway Blvd, Springfield OH 45502
Tel (937) 525-5520 SIC 3625 3443 7699

WARREN FABRICATING CORP p 1577
3240 Mahoning Ave Nw, Warren OH 44483
Tel (330) 847-0596
SIC 3441 3599 3547 3532 3444 3443

CONTECH ENGINEERED SOLUTIONS INC p 362
9025 Centre Pointe Dr # 400, West Chester OH 45069
Tel (513) 645-7000
SIC 3444 3084 3317 3441 3443

CONTECH ENGINEERED SOLUTIONS LLC p 362
9025 Ctr Pinte Dr Ste 400, West Chester OH 45069
Tel (513) 645-7000
SIC 3444 3084 3317 3441 3443

■ WORTHINGTON CYLINDER CORP p 1626
200 W Old Wlson Bridge Rd, Worthington OH 43085
Tel (614) 840-3210 SIC 3443

▲ WORTHINGTON INDUSTRIES INC p 1626
200 W Old Wlson Bridge Rd, Worthington OH 43085
Tel (614) 438-3210
SIC 3316 3449 3443 3325

AXH AIR-COOLERS LLC p 140
401 E Lowry Rd, Claremore OK 74017
Tel (918) 283-9200 SIC 3443

▲ HARSCO CORP p 664
350 Poplar Church Rd, Camp Hill PA 17011
Tel (717) 763-7064
SIC 7359 7353 5082 3443 3585 4789

PENN STAINLESS PRODUCTS INC p 1129
190 Kelly Rd, Quakertown PA 18951
Tel (215) 536-3053 SIC 5051 3443 3471

▲ CARPENTER TECHNOLOGY CORP p 260
2 Meridian Blvd, Wyomissing PA 19610
Tel (610) 208-2000
SIC 3312 3443 3255 3316 3315

PRECISION CUSTOM COMPONENTS LLC p 1168
500 Lincoln St, York PA 17401
Tel (717) 848-1126 SIC 3443 3699

TACO INC p 1421
1160 Cranston St, Cranston RI 02920
Tel (401) 942-8000
SIC 3433 3561 3443 3822

AMTROL HOLDINGS INC p 87
1400 Division Rd, West Warwick RI 02893
Tel (401) 884-6300 SIC 3822 3585 3443

AMTROL INC p 87
1400 Division Rd, West Warwick RI 02893
Tel (401) 884-6300 SIC 3443 3585

AME INC p 66
2467 Coltharp Rd, Fort Mill SC 29715
Tel (803) 548-7766 SIC 1541 7353 3443

■ JACOBS APPLIED TECHNOLOGY INC p 775
2040 Bushy Park Rd, Goose Creek SC 29445
Tel (843) 824-1100
SIC 3559 3443 8711 1629

■ STATE INDUSTRIES INC p 1381
500 Tennessee Waltz Pkwy, Ashland City TN 37015
Tel (615) 792-4371 SIC 3639 3443

■ ASTEC INC p 122
4101 Jerome Ave, Chattanooga TN 37407
Tel (423) 867-4210 SIC 3531 3433 3443

MANCHESTER TANK & EQUIPMENT CO INC p 901
1000 Corporate Centre Dr # 300, Franklin TN 37067
Tel (615) 370-6104 SIC 3443

■ LOCHINVAR LLC p 873
300 Maddox Simpson Pkwy, Lebanon TN 37090
Tel (615) 889-8900 SIC 3639 3443 5074

MAHLE ENGINE COMPONENTS USA INC p 897
1 Mahle Dr, Morristown TN 37815
Tel (423) 581-6603 SIC 3592 3443

HUDSON PRODUCTS CORP p 717
9660 Grunwald Rd, Beasley TX 77417
Tel (281) 396-8195 SIC 3443

HUDSON PRODUCTS HOLDINGS INC p 717
9660 Grunwald Rd, Beasley TX 77417
Tel (281) 396-8100 SIC 3443

DRAGON PRODUCTS LTD p 455
1655 Louisiana St, Beaumont TX 77701
Tel (409) 833-2665 SIC 3443

■ OHMSTEDE LTD p 1078
895 N Main St, Beaumont TX 77701
Tel (409) 833-6375 SIC 5075 3443

KEPPEL AMFELS LLC p 813
20000 State Highway 48, Brownsville TX 78521
Tel (956) 831-8220
SIC 1629 3731 1389 3449 3546 3443

SOUTHEAST TEXAS INDUSTRIES INC p 1346
35911 Us Highway 96 S, Buna TX 77612
Tel (409) 994-3570 SIC 3312 3443

■ HARBISON-FISCHER INC p 659
901 N Crowley Rd, Crowley TX 76036
Tel (817) 297-2211 SIC 3533 3443

▲ TRINITY INDUSTRIES INC p 1481
2525 N Stemmons Fwy, Dallas TX 75207
Tel (214) 631-4420
SIC 3743 3731 3531 3444 3441 3443

ATCO RUBBER PRODUCTS INC p 124
7101 Atco Dr, Fort Worth TX 76118
Tel (817) 589-7035
SIC 3443 3084 3585 3444 3083

AMEC FOSTER WHEELER USA CORP p 66
585 N Dairy Ashford Rd, Houston TX 77079
Tel (713) 929-5000 SIC 8711 3443 1629

AMERICAN ALLOY STEEL INC p 67
6230 N Houston Rosslyn Rd, Houston TX 77091
Tel (713) 462-8081 SIC 3443

HOOVER GROUP INC p 706
2135 Highway 6 S, Houston TX 77077
Tel (800) 844-8683
SIC 3496 3412 3443 3089 7359 3411

J D FIELDS & CO INC p 770
55 Waugh Dr Ste 1250, Houston TX 77007
Tel (281) 558-7199 SIC 5051 7359 3443

PERMIAN TANK & MANUFACTURING INC p 1136
2701 W Interstate 20, Odessa TX 79766
Tel (432) 580-1050 SIC 3443

■ VICEROY INC p 1555
3225 Pasadena Blvd, Pasadena TX 77503
Tel (713) 475-4518
SIC 1629 3443 1796 8742 8748 7363

INSIGHT EQUITY A P X L P p 746
1400 Civic Pl Ste 250, Southlake TX 76092
Tel (817) 488-7775
SIC 6722 3441 3443 3556 3714 5171

INSIGHT EQUITY LP p 746
1400 Civic Pl Ste 250, Southlake TX 76092
Tel (817) 488-7775
SIC 6722 3441 3443 3556 3714 5171

TEXAS HYDRAULICS INC p 1443
3410 Range Rd, Temple TX 76504
Tel (254) 778-4701 SIC 3593 3443

CB&I LLC p 268
2103 Research Forest Dr, The Woodlands TX 77380
Tel (832) 513-1000 SIC 1791 3443 3312

■ CHART ENERGY & CHEMICALS INC p 290
8665 New Trils Dr Ste 100, The Woodlands TX 77381
Tel (281) 364-8700 SIC 3443

HMT INC p 698
24 Waterway Ave Ste 400, The Woodlands TX 77380
Tel (281) 681-7000
SIC 7699 3443 7389 1791

■ ROBBINS & MYERS INC p 1241
10586 N Highway 75, Willis TX 77378
Tel (936) 890-1064
SIC 3533 3443 3823 5084

GREAT BASIN INDUSTRIAL LLC p 633
1284 Flint Meadow Dr A, Kaysville UT 84037
Tel (801) 543-2100 SIC 3443 7699 1731

ROCKY MOUNTAIN FABRICATION INC p 1245
1125 W 2300 N, Salt Lake City UT 84116
Tel (801) 532-5400 SIC 3443

TECNICO CORP p 1432
831 Industrial Ave, Chesapeake VA 23324
Tel (757) 545-4013
SIC 3446 3443 3441 3444 3731

▲ SYNALLOY CORP p 1414
4510 Cox Rd Ste 201, Glen Allen VA 23060
Tel (864) 585-3605
SIC 3317 3443 2865 2899 2869

■ BWXT GOVERNMENT GROUP INC p 231
2016 Mount Athos Rd, Lynchburg VA 24504
Tel (434) 522-6000 SIC 3443

■ BWXT NUCLEAR OPERATIONS GROUP INC p 231
2016 Mount Athos Rd, Lynchburg VA 24504
Tel (434) 522-6000 SIC 3443

SHIP COLONNAS YARD INC p 1317
400 E Indian River Rd, Norfolk VA 23523
Tel (757) 545-2414 SIC 3731 3443 3499

ALFA LAVAL USA INC p 49
5400 Intl Trade Dr, Richmond VA 23231
Tel (804) 222-5300 SIC 3443 3585

ALASKAN COPPER COMPANIES INC p 45
27402 72nd Ave S, Kent WA 98032
Tel (206) 623-5800 SIC 5051 3498 3443

ALCO INVESTMENT CO p 47
27402 72nd Ave S, Kent WA 98032
Tel (206) 623-5800 SIC 5051 3498 3443

CONSOLIDATED METCO INC p 360
5701 Se Columbia Way, Vancouver WA 98661
Tel (360) 828-2599
SIC 3365 3363 3089 3714 3443 3312

GREENBERRY INDUSTRIAL LLC p 637
600 Se Maritime Ave # 190, Vancouver WA 98661
Tel (360) 567-0006
SIC 1711 1541 3443 3441

▲ NORTHWEST PIPE CO p 1060
5721 Se Columbia Way # 200, Vancouver WA 98661
Tel (360) 397-6250 SIC 3317 3443

WELLONS INC p 1589
2525 W Firestone Ln, Vancouver WA 98660
Tel (360) 750-3500 SIC 3559 3443

ROBINSON METAL INC p 1242
1740 Eisenhower Rd, De Pere WI 54115
Tel (920) 494-7411 SIC 3444 3443 3599

■ BRENNER TANK LLC p 210
450 Arlington Ave, Fond Du Lac WI 54935
Tel (920) 922-4530 SIC 3715 3714 3443

HELGESEN INDUSTRIES INC p 681
7261 State Road 60, Hartford WI 53027
Tel (262) 709-4444 SIC 3443

SAMUEL PRESSURE VESSEL GROUP INC p 1275
2121 Cleveland Ave, Marinette WI 54143
Tel (715) 735-9311 SIC 3443

JASON HOLDINGS INC p 778
411 E Wisconsin Ave # 2120, Milwaukee WI 53202
Tel (414) 277-9300
SIC 2297 3465 3469 3844 3443

■ JASON INC p 778
411 E Wisconsin Ave, Milwaukee WI 53202
Tel (414) 277-9300
SIC 3465 2297 3625 3469 3844 3443

▲ JASON INDUSTRIES INC p 778
833 E Michigan St Ste 900, Milwaukee WI 53202
Tel (414) 277-9300
SIC 3465 2297 3625 3469 3844 3443

■ JPHI HOLDINGS INC p 795
411 E Wisconsin Ave, Milwaukee WI 53202
Tel (414) 277-9445
SIC 3465 2297 3625 3469 3844 3443

SUPER STEEL LLC p 1406
7900 W Tower Ave, Milwaukee WI 53223
Tel (414) 362-9114
SIC 3443 3444 3441 3446

■ WALKER GROUP HOLDINGS LLC p 1573
625 W State St, New Lisbon WI 53950
Tel (608) 562-7500 SIC 3443

■ WALKER STAINLESS EQUIPMENT CO LLC p 1573
625 W State St, New Lisbon WI 53950
Tel (608) 562-7500 SIC 3443 3556 3715

SUPERIOR DIE SET CORP p 1406
900 W Drexel Ave, Oak Creek WI 53154
Tel (414) 764-4900 SIC 3544 3443 3599

▲ MODINE MANUFACTURING CO INC p 981
1500 Dekoven Ave, Racine WI 53403
Tel (262) 636-1200
SIC 3443 3714 3433 3585

■ A & B PROCESS SYSTEMS CORP p 4
201 S Wisconsin Ave, Stratford WI 54484
Tel (715) 687-4332 SIC 3443 1799 8711

R G REZIN INC p 1202
1602 Rezin Rd, Tomah WI 54660
Tel (608) 372-5956
SIC 1623 3443 3613 3561 3523 3599

B-G WESTERN INC p 142
1141 S 10th St, Watertown WI 53094
Tel (920) 261-0660 SIC 3443 3469 3444

WESTERN INDUSTRIES INC p 1598
1141 S 10th St, Watertown WI 53094
Tel (920) 261-0660
SIC 3443 3469 3089 3444 1761 3491

METALTEK INTERNATIONAL INC p 953
905 E Saint Paul Ave, Waukesha WI 53188
Tel (262) 544-7777 SIC 3366 3443 3364

■ JW WILLIAMS INC p 798
2180 W Renauna Ave, Casper WY 82601
Tel (307) 237-8345
SIC 3533 3443 3547 1761 3291

SIC 3444 Sheet Metal Work

WHITESELL CORP p 1606
2703 Avalon Ave, Muscle Shoals AL 35661
Tel (256) 248-8500
SIC 3965 5085 3444 3452 3451

TREND TECHNOLOGIES LLC p 1476
4626 Eucalyptus Ave, Chino CA 91710
Tel (909) 597-7861 SIC 3444 3469 3499

MATERIAL SUPPLY INC p 919
11700 Industry Ave, Fontana CA 92337
Tel (951) 727-2200
SIC 3444 5075 7623 1711

IMPRESA AEROSPACE LLC p 735
344 W 157th St, Gardena CA 90248
Tel (310) 354-1200 SIC 3728 3444

JOHN S FREY ENTERPRISES p 789
1900 E 64th St, Los Angeles CA 90001
Tel (323) 583-4061 SIC 3441 3444 6719

FLEXTRONICS INTERNATIONAL PA INC p 556
847 Gibraltar Dr, Milpitas CA 95035
Tel (408) 576-7000 SIC 3444

THERMA CORP p 1447
1601 Las Plumas Ave, San Jose CA 95133
Tel (408) 347-3400 SIC 3444 3448

VANDER-BEND MANUFACTURING LLC p 1543
2701 Orchard Pkwy, San Jose CA 95134
Tel (408) 245-5150 SIC 3679 3444 3549

M&G DURAVENT INC p 890
877 Cotting Ct, Vacaville CA 95688
Tel (707) 446-1786 SIC 3444

CONSOLIDATED FABRICATORS CORP p 359
14620 Arminta St, Van Nuys CA 91402
Tel (818) 901-1005 SIC 3443 5051 3444

MCCAIN INC p 926
2365 Oak Ridge Way, Vista CA 92081
Tel (760) 727-8100 SIC 5084 3444 3669

WHITCRAFT LLC p 1605
76 County Rd, Eastford CT 06242
Tel (860) 974-0786 SIC 3443 3444 3728

HIGHWAY SAFETY CORP p 692
239 Commerce St Ste C, Glastonbury CT 06033
Tel (860) 659-4330 SIC 3444 3479

BCH MECHANICAL INC p 164
6354 118th Ave, Largo FL 33773
Tel (727) 546-3561 SIC 1711 3444

STYLE-VIEW PRODUCTS INC p 1395
1800 N Bayshore Dr # 4001, Miami FL 33132
Tel (305) 634-9688
SIC 3442 3444 3443 3354

DYNAMIC PRECISION GROUP INC p 464
3651 Se Commerce Ave, Stuart FL 34997
Tel (772) 287-7770 SIC 3724 3444

TURBOCOMBUSTOR TECHNOLOGY INC p 1492
3651 Se Commerce Ave, Stuart FL 34997
Tel (772) 287-7770 SIC 3724 3728 3444

■ MAGNATRAX CORP p 896
1220 Old Alpharetta Rd # 310, Alpharetta GA 30005
Tel (678) 455-3360
SIC 3448 3442 3479 4213 3444

SPECTRA METAL SALES INC p 1357
6104 Boat Rock Blvd Sw, Atlanta GA 30336
Tel (404) 344-4305
SIC 5051 3354 3355 3479 3444 2952

MADISON INDUSTRIES INC OF GEORGIA p 894
1035 Iris Dr Sw, Conyers GA 30094
Tel (770) 483-4401 SIC 1541 3444

EURAMAX HOLDINGS INC p 512
303 Research Dr Ste 400, Norcross GA 30092
Tel (770) 449-7066 SIC 3444

PRICE INDUSTRIES INC p 1174
2975 Shawnee Ridge Ct, Suwanee GA 30024
Tel (770) 623-8050 SIC 3444

■ FERALLOY CORP p 537
8755 W Higgins Rd Ste 970, Chicago IL 60631
Tel (503) 286-8869
SIC 5051 3471 3444 3312

IMS COMPANIES LLC p 735
1 Innovation Dr, Des Plaines IL 60016
Tel (847) 391-8100
SIC 3469 8711 3679 3714 3444

DAYTON SUPERIOR CORP p 418
2400 Arthur Ave, Elk Grove Village IL 60007
Tel (847) 391-4700 SIC 3444

ROLLEX CORP p 1247
800 Chase Ave, Elk Grove Village IL 60007
Tel (847) 437-3000 SIC 3444

■ AFC CABLE SYSTEMS INC p 32
16100 Lathrop Ave, Harvey IL 60426
Tel (508) 998-1131
SIC 3429 3444 3599 5085

COOPER B-LINE INC p 366
509 W Monroe St, Highland IL 62249
Tel (618) 654-2184
SIC 3441 3443 3452 3444 3429 3356

WOZNIAK INDUSTRIES INC p 1627
2 Mid America Plz Ste 700, Oakbrook Terrace IL 60181
Tel (630) 954-3400 SIC 3469 3444 3462

■ LIPPERT COMPONENTS INC p 870
3501 County Road 6 E, Elkhart IN 46514
Tel (800) 551-9149
SIC 3711 3469 3444 3714

CENTURION INDUSTRIES INC p 281
1107 N Taylor Rd, Garrett IN 46738
Tel (260) 357-6665 SIC 3444 1796

MICRO METL CORP p 961
3035 N Shadeland Ave # 300, Indianapolis IN 46226
Tel (800) 662-4822 SIC 3444

TUBE PROCESSING CORP p 1490
604 E Legrande Ave, Indianapolis IN 46203
Tel (317) 787-1321
SIC 3498 3356 3469 7692 3444 3728

RYOBI DIE CASTING (USA) INC p 1261
800 W Mausoleum Rd, Shelbyville IN 46176
Tel (317) 398-3398
SIC 3714 3444 3365 3363

■ OLYMPIC STEEL IOWA INC p 1083
6425 State St, Bettendorf IA 52722
Tel (563) 332-7785 SIC 5051 3444

PMX INDUSTRIES INC p 1158
5300 Willow Creek Dr Sw, Cedar Rapids IA 52404
Tel (319) 368-7700
SIC 3366 5051 3444 3364 3351 3331

BAKER MECHANICAL INC p 146
4224 Hubbell Ave, Des Moines IA 50317
Tel (515) 262-4000 SIC 1711 3444

WILIAN HOLDING CO p 1609
1800 Ne Broadway Ave, Des Moines IA 50313
Tel (515) 313-4350 SIC 3444

SIOUX CITY FOUNDRY CO p 1326
801 Division St, Sioux City IA 51105
Tel (712) 252-4181
SIC 5051 3443 3321 3316 3444 3441

WALL-TIES & FORMS INC p 1573
4000 Bonner Industrial Dr, Shawnee KS 66226
Tel (913) 441-0073 SIC 5082 3444 3443

AHI HOLDINGS INC p 36
3050 N Saint Francis St, Wichita KS 67219
Tel (316) 832-3484 SIC 3585 3444

CORKEN STEEL PRODUCTS CO p 370
7920 Kentucky Dr, Florence KY 41042
Tel (859) 291-4664
SIC 5075 3444 5051 8742 6411

DOMETIC CORP p 448
13551 Triton Park Blvd # 1000, Louisville KY 40223
Tel (502) 873-3524
SIC 3089 3443 3444 3822 3823 3999

INTERLOCK INDUSTRIES INC p 753
545 S 3rd St Ste 310, Louisville KY 40202
Tel (502) 569-2007
SIC 3341 4121 3444 3354 2653

HINES PRECISION INC p 695
5680 Old Highway 54, Philpot KY 42366
Tel (270) 729-4242 SIC 3469 3444

CONNELL LIMITED PARTNERSHIP p 358
1 International Pl Fl 31, Boston MA 02110
Tel (617) 737-2700
SIC 3443 3444 3341 3544 6719

LEE THOMAS H EQUITY FUND V LIMITED PARTNERSHIP p 852
100 Federal St Ste 3500, Boston MA 02110
Tel (617) 737-3261
SIC 3585 3444 3634 2431 3699

THL-NORTEK INVESTORS LLC p 1448
100 Federal St Ste 3100, Boston MA 02110
Tel (617) 227-1050
SIC 3585 3444 3634 2431

TECOMET INC p 1432
115 Eames St, Wilmington MA 01887
Tel (978) 642-2400 *SIC* 3841 3444

BELCO INDUSTRIES INC p 169
9138 W Belding Rd, Belding MI 48809
Tel (616) 794-0410
SIC 3567 5084 3541 3535 3444

SCHULER INC p 1290
7145 Commerce Blvd, Canton MI 48187
Tel (734) 207-7200 *SIC* 5084 3444 3599

SELKIRK CORP p 1302
5030 Corp Exch Blvd Se, Grand Rapids MI 49512
Tel (616) 656-8200 *SIC* 3444

QUALITY METALCRAFT INC p 1197
33355 Glendale St, Livonia MI 48150
Tel (734) 261-6700
SIC 3544 3465 3469 3444

W SOULE & CO p 1569
7125 S Sprinkle Rd, Portage MI 49002
Tel (269) 324-7001 *SIC* 1711 3444

SAGINAW CONTROL & ENGINEERING INC p 1268
95 Midland Rd, Saginaw MI 48638
Tel (989) 799-6871 *SIC* 3699 3444

THYSSENKRUPP MATERIALS NA INC p 1451
22355 W 11 Mile Rd, Southfield MI 48033
Tel (248) 233-5600
SIC 5051 5162 3444 8741

HOFFMAN ENCLOSURES INC p 699
2100 Hoffman Way, Anoka MN 55303
Tel (763) 421-2240
SIC 3444 3699 3613 3469 3053

EGAN CO p 481
7625 Boone Ave N, Brooklyn Park MN 55428
Tel (763) 595-4358
SIC 1711 1731 3444 7623 1793

JAMAR CO p 776
4701 Mike Colalillo Dr, Duluth MN 55807
Tel (218) 628-1027
SIC 1711 1761 1742 5033 7699 3444

GRIFFITHS CORP p 640
2717 Niagara Ln N, Minneapolis MN 55447
Tel (763) 557-8935
SIC 3544 3469 3444 3451

SPELL CAPITAL PARTNERS LLC p 1358
222 S 9th St Ste 2880, Minneapolis MN 55402
Tel (612) 371-9650 *SIC* 3599 3469 3444

CRENLO CAB PRODUCTS INC p 391
1600 4th Ave Nw, Rochester MN 55901
Tel (507) 289-3371
SIC 2522 3531 2542 3713 3469 3444

AEGIS CORP p 29
614 Dartmouth Terrace Ct, Ballwin MO 63011
Tel (636) 273-1011
SIC 3699 4812 3812 3444 2326

FIKE CORP p 542
704 Sw 10th St, Blue Springs MO 64015
Tel (816) 229-3405
SIC 3494 3569 3444 2899

MILBANK MANUFACTURING CO p 968
4801 Deramus Ave, Kansas City MO 64120
Tel (816) 483-5314 *SIC* 3825 3444

■ **VARIFORM INC** p 1545
303 W Major St, Kearney MO 64060
Tel (919) 677-3900 *SIC* 3089 1521 3444

DETROIT TOOL METAL PRODUCTS CO p 433
949 Bethel Rd, Lebanon MO 65536
Tel (417) 532-2142 *SIC* 3469 3444

GLOBAL INDUSTRIES INC p 617
1804 E 4th St, Grand Island NE 68801
Tel (800) 247-6621
SIC 7992 3589 3444 5084 5083 3535

■ **TSI GROUP INC** p 1489
94 Tide Mill Rd, Hampton NH 03842
Tel (603) 964-0296
SIC 3599 3398 3443 3444

ALLENTOWN INC p 53
165 Route 526, Allentown NJ 08501
Tel (609) 259-7951 *SIC* 3444 3496 5162

PASSAIC METAL & BUILDING SUPPLIES CO p 1119
5 Central Ave Ste 1, Clifton NJ 07011
Tel (973) 546-9000
SIC 5033 5031 5051 5075 3444 3296

MIDDLE ATLANTIC PRODUCTS INC p 964
300 Fairfield Rd, Fairfield NJ 07004
Tel (973) 839-1011 *SIC* 3444

GAF CORP p 589
1 Campus Dr, Parsippany NJ 07054
Tel (973) 628-3000 *SIC* 3444 3634

ENGLERT INC p 499
1200 Amboy Ave, Perth Amboy NJ 08861
Tel (800) 364-5378 *SIC* 3444 5033

PEMBERTON FABRICATORS INC p 1128
30 Indel Ave, Rancocas NJ 08073
Tel (609) 267-0922 *SIC* 3444 3824

WARE INDUSTRIES INC p 1575
400 Metuchen Rd, South Plainfield NJ 07080
Tel (908) 757-9000 *SIC* 3444

S & J SHEET METAL SUPPLY INC p 1261
608 E 133rd St, Bronx NY 10454
Tel (718) 993-0460 *SIC* 5033 3444

MERCURY AIRCRAFT INC p 945
8126 County Route 88, Hammondsport NY 14840
Tel (607) 569-4200 *SIC* 3469 3444

HUNTER DOUGLAS INC p 719
1 Blue Hill Plz Ste 1569, Pearl River NY 10965
Tel (845) 664-7000 *SIC* 2591 3444 5084

ENVIRONMENTAL FILTRATION TECHNOLOGIES LLC p 503
4404a Chesapeake Dr, Charlotte NC 28216
Tel (704) 399-7441
SIC 3569 5085 3564 3444 3469 3561

CAPTIVE-AIRE SYSTEMS INC p 252
4641 Paragon Park Rd # 104, Raleigh NC 27616
Tel (919) 882-2410 *SIC* 3444

SPC MECHANICAL CORP p 1355
1908 Baldree Rd S, Wilson NC 27893
Tel (252) 237-9035 *SIC* 3494 1711 3444

TRUENORTH STEEL INC p 1486
702 13th Ave E, West Fargo ND 58078
Tel (701) 373-7781 *SIC* 3443 3444 3441

FAMOUS INDUSTRIES INC p 527
2620 Ridgewood Rd Ste 200, Akron OH 44313
Tel (330) 535-1811 *SIC* 5074 3444 5065

OHIO GRATINGS INC p 1077
5299 Southway St Sw, Canton OH 44706
Tel (330) 477-6707
SIC 3446 3444 3441 3312

■ **CECO GROUP INC** p 272
4625 Red Bank Rd Ste 200, Cincinnati OH 45227
Tel (513) 458-2600
SIC 8711 3564 8734 3443 3444 1761

OATEY CO p 1072
4700 W 160th St, Cleveland OH 44135
Tel (216) 267-7100 *SIC* 3444

TRANSTAR HOLDING CO p 1473
5900 Landerbrook Dr Bsmt, Cleveland OH 44124
Tel (440) 684-1400 *SIC* 3444 3281 2952

N WASSERSTROM & SONS INC p 1005
2300 Lockbourne Rd, Columbus OH 43207
Tel (614) 737-8543 *SIC* 3556 5046 3444

AMH HOLDINGS LLC p 85
3773 State Rd, Cuyahoga Falls OH 44223
Tel (330) 929-1811 *SIC* 3355 3444

GENTEK BUILDING PRODUCTS INC p 604
3773 State Rd, Cuyahoga Falls OH 44223
Tel (800) 548-4542 *SIC* 3444 3089

MATANDY STEEL & METAL PRODUCTS LLC p 919
1200 Central Ave, Hamilton OH 45011
Tel (513) 887-5274
SIC 5051 3312 3444 3399

WARREN FABRICATING CORP p 1577
3240 Mahoning Ave Nw, Warren OH 44483
Tel (330) 847-0596
SIC 3441 3599 3547 3532 3444 3443

CLARKWESTERN DIETRICH BUILDING SYSTEMS LLC p 322
9100 Centre Pointe Dr # 210, West Chester OH 45069
Tel (513) 870-1100 *SIC* 3444 8711 3081

CONTECH ENGINEERED SOLUTIONS INC p 362
9025 Centre Pointe Dr # 400, West Chester OH 45069
Tel (513) 645-7000
SIC 3444 3084 3317 3441 3443

CONTECH ENGINEERED SOLUTIONS LLC p 362
9025 Ctr Pinte Dr Ste 400, West Chester OH 45069
Tel (513) 645-7000
SIC 3444 3084 3317 3441 3443

■ **CMI TEREX CORP** p 329
9528 W I 40 Service Rd, Oklahoma City OK 73128
Tel (405) 787-6020
SIC 3531 3715 3596 3541 3444 2951

LINDE PROCESS PLANTS INC p 868
6100 S Yale Ave Ste 1200, Tulsa OK 74136
Tel (918) 477-1200 *SIC* 3444 8711 1629

TEMP-CONTROL MECHANICAL CORP p 1436
4800 N Channel Ave, Portland OR 97217
Tel (503) 285-9851 *SIC* 1711 3444 1731

■ **CENTRIA INC** p 281
1005 Beaver Grade Rd # 2, Coraopolis PA 15108
Tel (412) 299-8000
SIC 3444 1761 3564 3449

■ **TRACO DELAWARE INC** p 1468
71 Progress Ave, Cranberry Township PA 16066
Tel (724) 776-7000
SIC 3442 3211 3444 3448 3354 7992

OLD LADDER CO p 1081
93 Werner Rd, Greenville PA 16125
Tel (888) 523-3371
SIC 3446 3089 3334 3444 3499

SOUTHWARK METAL MANUFACTURING CO p 1351
2800 Red Lion Rd, Philadelphia PA 19114
Tel (215) 735-3401 *SIC* 3444

NORTEK INC p 1049
500 Exchange St, Providence RI 02903
Tel (401) 751-1600
SIC 3585 3444 3634 3699 2434

CONSOLIDATED SYSTEMS INC p 360
650 Rosewood Dr, Columbia SC 29201
Tel (803) 771-7920 *SIC* 3444 3479 4213

VVP HOLDINGS LLC p 1567
965 Ridge Lake Blvd # 300, Memphis TN 38120
Tel (901) 767-7111
SIC 5039 5013 1793 3231 3444 5719

C H INDUSTRIES INC p 232
1700 Columbian Club Dr, Carrollton TX 75006
Tel (972) 416-1304 *SIC* 2599 3444 3469

HUMANETICS II LTD p 718
1700 Columbian Club Dr, Carrollton TX 75006
Tel (972) 416-1304 *SIC* 3444 3599

▲ **TRINITY INDUSTRIES INC** p 1481
2525 N Stemmons Fwy, Dallas TX 75207
Tel (214) 631-4420
SIC 3743 3731 3531 3444 3441 3443

ATCO RUBBER PRODUCTS INC p 124
7101 Atco Dr, Fort Worth TX 76118
Tel (817) 589-7035
SIC 3443 3084 3585 3444 3083

■ **M&M MANUFACTURING INC** p 890
4001 Mark Iv Pkwy, Fort Worth TX 76106
Tel (817) 336-2311 *SIC* 3444

POLK MECHANICAL CO LLC p 1159
2425 Dillard St, Grand Prairie TX 75051
Tel (972) 339-1200
SIC 1711 3444 3498 3599 3999

JENISYS ENGINEERED PRODUCTS INC p 782
404 E Dallas Rd, Grapevine TX 76051
Tel (817) 481-3521 *SIC* 3444

AMERICAN BLOCK CO p 69
6311 Breen Dr, Houston TX 77086
Tel (800) 572-9087
SIC 3441 3599 3533 3496 3444 3429

INTSEL STEEL DISTRIBUTORS LLC p 760
11310 W Little York Rd, Houston TX 77041
Tel (713) 937-9500 *SIC* 5051 3312 3444

MCCORVEY SHEET METAL WORKS LP p 927
8610 Wallisville Rd, Houston TX 77029
Tel (713) 672-7545 *SIC* 3444

▲ **NCI BUILDING SYSTEMS INC** p 1022
10943 N Sam Huston Pkwy W, Houston TX 77064
Tel (281) 897-7788
SIC 3448 3444 3442 1542 1541 7389

QUIETFLEX MANUFACTURING CO LP p 1199
4518 Brittmoore Rd, Houston TX 77041
Tel (713) 849-2163 *SIC* 3444 1799 3599

PRIEFERT MFG CO INC p 1174
2630 S Jefferson Ave, Mount Pleasant TX 75455
Tel (903) 572-1741
SIC 3523 3446 3444 3317 3449

PETERSEN INC p 1138
1527 N 2000 W, Ogden UT 84404
Tel (801) 731-1366
SIC 5084 3441 7692 3444

NSA INDUSTRIES LLC p 1064
210 Pierce Rd, Saint Johnsbury VT 05819
Tel (802) 748-5007 *SIC* 3444 1799 1796

TECNICO CORP p 1432
831 Industrial Ave, Chesapeake VA 23324
Tel (757) 545-4013
SIC 3446 3443 3441 3444 3731

■ **RIDDLEBERGER BROTHERS INC** p 1234
6127 S Valley Pike, Mount Crawford VA 22841
Tel (540) 434-1731 *SIC* 3444 1711

ATLANTIC CONSTRUCTORS INC p 126
1401 Battery Brooke Pkwy, North Chesterfield VA 23237
Tel (804) 222-3400 *SIC* 1796 1711 3444

GENSCO INC p 604
4402 20th St E, Fife WA 98424
Tel (253) 620-8203 *SIC* 5074 3444

APOLLO SHEET METAL INC p 97
1201 W Columbia Dr, Kennewick WA 99336
Tel (509) 586-1104 *SIC* 1711 3444

MCKINSTRY CO LLC p 930
5005 3rd Ave S, Seattle WA 98134
Tel (206) 762-3311
SIC 1711 1623 3446 3444

SCAFCO CORP p 1285
2800 E Main Ave, Spokane WA 99202
Tel (509) 343-9000
SIC 3523 5065 6531 3444

NATIONAL INDUSTRIAL CONCEPTS INC p 1013
23518 63rd Ave Se, Woodinville WA 98072
Tel (425) 489-4300 *SIC* 3444

KALKREUTH ROOFING & SHEET METAL INC p 801
53 14th St Ste 100, Wheeling WV 26003
Tel (304) 232-8540
SIC 1761 3446 3444 3441

RG STEEL WHEELING STEEL GROUP LLC p 1231
1134 Market St, Wheeling WV 26003
Tel (304) 234-2400 *SIC* 3312 3444

ROBINSON METAL INC p 1242
1740 Eisenhower Rd, De Pere WI 54115
Tel (920) 494-7411 *SIC* 3444 3443 3599

TWEET-GAROT MECHANICAL INC p 1494
2545 Larsen Rd, Green Bay WI 54303
Tel (920) 498-0400 *SIC* 1711 3444

PHILLIPS-MEDISIZE CORP p 1144
1201 Hanley Rd, Hudson WI 54016
Tel (715) 386-4320 *SIC* 3089 3444 3544

METALCRAFT OF MAYVILLE INC p 952
1000 Metalcraft Dr, Mayville WI 53050
Tel (920) 387-3150 *SIC* 3523 3444

SUPER STEEL LLC p 1406
7900 W Tower Ave, Milwaukee WI 53223
Tel (414) 362-9114
SIC 3443 3444 3441 3446

TRAFFIC AND PARKING CONTROL CO INC p 1469
5100 W Brown Deer Rd, Milwaukee WI 53223
Tel (262) 814-7000 *SIC* 5063 3444 3646

GLOBAL FINISHING SOLUTIONS LLC p 616
12731 Norway Rd, Osseo WI 54758
Tel (715) 597-8007 *SIC* 3444

CARNES CO INC p 258
600 College Ave, Pewaukee WI 53072
Tel (262) 691-9900
SIC 3822 3444 3585 3669

GREENHECK FAN CORP p 638
1100 Greenheck Dr, Schofield WI 54476
Tel (715) 359-6171 *SIC* 3564 3444

B-G WESTERN INC p 142
1141 S 10th St, Watertown WI 53094
Tel (920) 261-0660 *SIC* 3443 3469 3444

WESTERN INDUSTRIES INC p 1598
1141 S 10th St, Watertown WI 53094
Tel (920) 261-0660
SIC 3443 3469 3089 3444 1761 3491

SIC 3446 Architectural & Ornamental Metal Work

■ **ALABAMA METAL INDUSTRIES CORP** p 43
3245 Fayette Ave, Birmingham AL 35208
Tel (205) 787-2611
SIC 3446 3449 3089 3441 3316

LIGON INDUSTRIES LLC p 866
1927 1st Ave N Ste 500, Birmingham AL 35203
Tel (205) 322-3302
SIC 3365 3593 3325 3471 3714 3446

DMB ASSOCIATES INC p 445
7600 E Doubletree Ste 300, Scottsdale AZ 85258
Tel (480) 367-6874
SIC 5999 6512 5961 1542 3446

KAJIMA INTERNATIONAL INC p 801
3475 Piedmont Rd Ne # 1600, Atlanta GA 30305
Tel (404) 564-3900 *SIC* 1541 3446 1542

MERCHANTS METALS LLC p 945
211 Perimeter Center Pkwy, Atlanta GA 30346
Tel (770) 741-0300 *SIC* 3496 3446 5031

■ **KAWNEER CO INC** p 805
555 Guthridge Ct Tech, Norcross GA 30092
Tel (770) 449-5555 *SIC* 3442 3446

GEM INDUSTRIES INC p 598
Hwy 123 N, Toccoa GA 30577
Tel (706) 886-8431
SIC 3429 2531 2511 3446 2821 2515

■ **FIRST ALERT INC** p 544
3901 Liberty St, Aurora IL 60504
Tel (630) 851-7330
SIC 3669 3999 3446 3499 3829 3648

CHICAGO METALLIC CO LLC p 297
4849 S Austin Ave, Chicago IL 60638
Tel (708) 563-4600 *SIC* 3446 5033

CHICAGO METALLIC CORP p 297
4849 S Austin Ave, Chicago IL 60638
Tel (708) 563-4600 *SIC* 3446 5033

▲ **ATKORE INTERNATIONAL GROUP INC** p 125
16100 Lathrop Ave, Harvey IL 60426
Tel (708) 339-1610
SIC 3441 1791 3446 3448 3496

■ **ATKORE INTERNATIONAL HOLDINGS INC** p 125
16100 Lathrop Ave, Harvey IL 60426
Tel (708) 225-2051
SIC 6719 3441 1791 3446 3448 3496

■ **UNISTRUT INTERNATIONAL CORP** p 1505
16100 Lathrop Ave, Harvey IL 60426
Tel (800) 882-5543
SIC 3441 1791 3446 3448 3496 3429

■ **BALCO INC** p 147
2626 S Sheridan Ave, Wichita KS 67217
Tel (800) 767-0082
SIC 3441 3089 3496 3446 3443

TARTER GATE CO LLC p 1425
10739 S Us 127, Dunnville KY 42528
Tel (435) 744-0770 *SIC* 3446 0219

TARTER GATE WOOD PRODUCTS INC p 1425
10739 S Us 127, Dunnville KY 42528
Tel (606) 787-2081
SIC 3446 2448 2499 2426 2421

LAITRAM LLC p 838
220 Laitram Ln, Harahan LA 70123
Tel (504) 733-6000
SIC 3535 3556 7359 3446 6719

ROLLS-ROYCE MARINE NORTH AMERICA INC p 1247
110 Norfolk St, Walpole MA 02081
Tel (508) 668-9610 *SIC* 3599 3446 3429

HART & COOLEY INC p 664
5030 Corp Exch Blvd Se, Grand Rapids MI 49512
Tel (616) 656-8200 *SIC* 3446 3822

WENGER CORP p 1592
555 Park Dr, Owatonna MN 55060
Tel (507) 455-4100 *SIC* 2541 3446

RUSKIN CO p 1259
3900 Doctor Greaves Rd, Grandview MO 64030
Tel (816) 761-7476 *SIC* 3822 3446 3585

■ **APPLE JV HOLDING CORP** p 98
8000 W Florissant Ave, Saint Louis MO 63136
Tel (314) 553-2000
SIC 3644 3643 3613 3446 3699

CONSTRUCTION SPECIALTIES INC p 361
3 Werner Way Ste 100, Lebanon NJ 08833
Tel (908) 236-0800
SIC 3446 3354 3443 3272 3585

ITR INDUSTRIES INC p 768
441 Saw Mill River Rd, Yonkers NY 10701
Tel (914) 964-7063
SIC 3431 3429 3446 3088

OHIO GRATINGS INC p 1077
5299 Southway St Sw, Canton OH 44706
Tel (330) 477-6707
SIC 3446 3444 3441 3312

MODERN BUILDERS SUPPLY INC p 981
302 Mcclurg Rd, Youngstown OH 44512
Tel (330) 729-2690
SIC 5032 3089 3446 3442

AMERISTAR PERIMETER SECURITY USA INC p 83
1555 N Mingo Rd, Tulsa OK 74116
Tel (918) 835-0898 *SIC* 3089 3446 1799

NEW WERNER HOLDING CO INC p 1033
93 Werner Rd, Greenville PA 16125
Tel (724) 588-2000
SIC 3499 3355 3089 3446 2499 6512

OLD LADDER CO p 1081
93 Werner Rd, Greenville PA 16125
Tel (888) 523-3371
SIC 3446 3089 3334 3444 3499

WERNER CO p 1592
93 Werner Rd, Greenville PA 16125
Tel (724) 588-2000
SIC 3499 3355 3089 3446 2499

WERNER HOLDING CO (PA) INC p 1593
93 Werner Rd, Greenville PA 16125
Tel (888) 523-3371
SIC 3499 3355 3089 3446 2499

ARMSTRONG WORTHINGTON VENTURE p 112
101 Lindenwood Dr Ste 350, Malvern PA 19355
Tel (610) 722-1200 *SIC* 3446 5051

CIW ENTERPRISES INC p 320
24 Elmwood Ave, Mountain Top PA 18707
Tel (800) 233-8366 *SIC* 3442 3446 2431

■ **ALUMAX LLC** p 63
201 Isabella St, Pittsburgh PA 15212
Tel (412) 553-4545
SIC 3334 3353 3354 3449 3442 3446

FORMS AND SURFACES INC p 568
30 Pine St, Pittsburgh PA 15223
Tel (412) 781-9003 *SIC* 3446

STEEL AND PIPES INC p 1384
Road 1rio, Caguas PR 00725
Tel (787) 747-9415
SIC 5051 3446 3317 5085

MASTER-HALCO INC p 918
3010 Lbj Fwy Ste 800, Dallas TX 75234
Tel (972) 714-7300
SIC 3315 5039 3496 3446 5031 1799

■ **NCI GROUP INC** p 1022
10943 N Sam Huston Pkwy W, Houston TX 77064
Tel (281) 897-7500 *SIC* 3448 3446

PRIEFERT MFG CO INC p 1174
2630 S Jefferson Ave, Mount Pleasant TX 75455
Tel (903) 572-1741
SIC 3523 3446 3444 3317 3449

TECNICO CORP p 1432
831 Industrial Ave, Chesapeake VA 23324
Tel (757) 545-4013
SIC 3446 3443 3441 3444 3731

OLDCASTLE PRECAST INC p 1082
1002 15th St Sw Ste 110, Auburn WA 98001
Tel (253) 833-2777 *SIC* 3272 3446

MCKINSTRY CO LLC p 930
5005 3rd Ave S, Seattle WA 98134
Tel (206) 762-3311
SIC 1711 1623 3446 3444

SAFEWORKS LLC p 1267
365 Upland Dr, Tukwila WA 98188
Tel (206) 575-6445
SIC 3536 3531 3446 5082

KALKREUTH ROOFING & SHEET METAL INC p 801
53 14th St Ste 100, Wheeling WV 26003
Tel (304) 232-8540
SIC 1761 3446 3444 3441

SUPER STEEL LLC p 1406
7900 W Tower Ave, Milwaukee WI 53223
Tel (414) 362-9114
SIC 3443 3444 3441 3446

SIC 3448 Prefabricated Metal Buildings & Cmpnts

■ **AMERICAN BUILDINGS CO** p 69
1150 State Docks Rd, Eufaula AL 36027
Tel (888) 307-4338 *SIC* 3448

▲ **MOBILE MINI INC** p 980
4646 E Van Buren St # 400, Phoenix AZ 85008
Tel (480) 894-6311
SIC 4225 3448 3441 3412 7359

CENTRAL STATES MANUFACTURING INC p 280
302 Jane Pl, Lowell AR 72745
Tel (479) 770-0188 *SIC* 3353 3448 7389

ACORN ENGINEERING CO p 18
15125 Proctor Ave, City Of Industry CA 91746
Tel (800) 488-8999 *SIC* 3448 3431 3442

THERMA CORP p 1447
1601 Las Plumas Ave, San Jose CA 95133
Tel (408) 347-3400 *SIC* 3444 3448

KINGSPAN INSULATED PANELS INC p 821
726 Summerhill Dr, Deland FL 32724
Tel (386) 626-6789 *SIC* 3448

■ **MAGNATRAX CORP** p 896
1220 Old Alpharetta Rd # 310, Alpharetta GA 30005
Tel (678) 455-3360
SIC 3448 3442 3479 4213 3444

ASSOCIATED GROUP HOLDINGS LLC p 120
30 S Wacker Dr Ste 1600, Chicago IL 60606
Tel (312) 662-5488 *SIC* 3448

HEICO COMPANIES L L C p 680
5600 Three First Nat Plz, Chicago IL 60602
Tel (312) 419-8220
SIC 3315 3589 3448 3531 1731 3663

▲ **ATKORE INTERNATIONAL GROUP INC** p 125
16100 Lathrop Ave, Harvey IL 60426
Tel (708) 339-1610
SIC 3441 1791 3446 3448 3496

■ **ATKORE INTERNATIONAL HOLDINGS INC** p 125
16100 Lathrop Ave, Harvey IL 60426
Tel (708) 225-2051
SIC 6719 3441 1791 3446 3448 3496

■ **UNISTRUT INTERNATIONAL CORP** p 1505
16100 Lathrop Ave, Harvey IL 60426
Tel (800) 882-5543
SIC 3441 1791 3446 3448 3496 3429

CELLXION LLC p 274
5031 Hazel Jones Rd, Bossier City LA 71111
Tel (318) 213-2900
SIC 4812 1623 3448 3441

MCELROY METAL MILL INC p 928
1500 Hamilton Rd, Bossier City LA 71111
Tel (318) 747-8000 *SIC* 3448

MAC ARTHUR CO p 891
2400 Wycliff St, Saint Paul MN 55114
Tel (651) 646-2773 *SIC* 5033 3448

SAFE FLEET HOLDINGS LLC p 1266
6800 E 163rd St, Belton MO 64012
Tel (816) 318-8000 *SIC* 3089 3448

BLUESCOPE STEEL NORTH AMERICA CORP p 193
1540 Genessee St, Kansas City MO 64102
Tel (816) 968-1700 *SIC* 1542 3448

BEHLEN MFG CO p 168
4025 E 23rd St, Columbus NE 68601
Tel (402) 564-3111
SIC 3523 3448 4213 3556 3496 3443

BEHLEN MKTG CO p 168
4025 E 23rd St, Columbus NE 68601
Tel (402) 564-3111 *SIC* 3523 3448 4213

CHIEF INDUSTRIES INC p 298
3942 W Old Highway 30, Grand Island NE 68803
Tel (308) 389-7200
SIC 3448 2451 3523 2869 3442

INDUSTRIAL ACOUSTICS CO INC p 739
233 S 13th St Ste 1100, Lincoln NE 68508
Tel (718) 931-8000 *SIC* 3448 1742

▲ **NUCOR CORP** p 1066
1915 Rexford Rd Ste 400, Charlotte NC 28211
Tel (704) 366-7000
SIC 3312 3441 3448 3452 5093

ALLIANCE STEEL INC p 55
3333 S Council Rd, Oklahoma City OK 73179
Tel (405) 745-7500 *SIC* 3448

MARCON & BOYER INC p 905
645 Hamilton St Ste 300, Allentown PA 18101
Tel (610) 866-5959
SIC 3448 1742 1743 1799

■ **TRACO DELAWARE INC** p 1468
71 Progress Ave, Cranberry Township PA 16066
Tel (724) 776-7000
SIC 3442 3211 3444 3448 3354 7992

BONITZ INC p 200
645 Rosewood Dr, Columbia SC 29201
Tel (803) 799-0181
SIC 3448 1542 1742 1541 1761 1752

SIOUX STEEL CO p 1326
196 1/2 E 6th St, Sioux Falls SD 57104
Tel (605) 336-1750 *SIC* 3523 3448 2221

PLAYCORE HOLDINGS LLC p 1155
401 Chestnut St Ste 410, Chattanooga TN 37402
Tel (877) 762-7563 *SIC* 2452 3949 3448

■ **NUCOR STEEL MEMPHIS INC** p 1066
3601 Paul R Lowry Rd, Memphis TN 38109
Tel (901) 786-5837
SIC 3312 3441 3448 3452

VARCO PRUDEN HOLDING INC p 1544
3200 Players Club Cir, Memphis TN 38125
Tel (901) 748-8000 *SIC* 3448

■ **KMT REFRIGERATION INC** p 824
2915 Tennessee Ave N, Parsons TN 38363
Tel (731) 847-6361 *SIC* 3585 3448 1711

■ **KIRBY BUILDING SYSTEMS LLC** p 821
124 Kirby Dr, Portland TN 37148
Tel (615) 325-4165 *SIC* 3448

MUELLER SUPPLY CO INC p 998
1913 Hutchins Ave, Ballinger TX 76821
Tel (325) 365-3555 *SIC* 3448 3496 5039

4FRONT HOLDINGS INC p 3
1612 Hutton Dr Ste 140, Carrollton TX 75006
Tel (972) 466-0707 *SIC* 3537 3999 3448

GHM CORP p 610
12700 Hillcrest Rd # 291, Dallas TX 75230
Tel (972) 840-1200
SIC 3448 1799 5999 5561

WINGATE PARTNERS V LP p 1616
750 N Saint Paul St # 1200, Dallas TX 75201
Tel (214) 720-1313 *SIC* 6726 3448

SCHULTE BUILDING SYSTEMS INC p 1290
17600 Badtke Rd, Hockley TX 77447
Tel (281) 304-6111 *SIC* 3448

▲ **NCI BUILDING SYSTEMS INC** p 1022
10943 N Sam Huston Pkwy W, Houston TX 77064
Tel (281) 897-7788
SIC 3448 3444 3442 1542 1541 7389

■ **NCI GROUP INC** p 1022
10943 N Sam Huston Pkwy W, Houston TX 77064
Tel (281) 897-7500 *SIC* 3448 3446

■ **ROBERTSON-CECO II CORP** p 1242
10943 N Sam Huston Pkwy W, Houston TX 77064
Tel (281) 897-7788 *SIC* 3448

UNITED STRUCTURES OF AMERICA INC p 1514
1912 Buschong St, Houston TX 77039
Tel (281) 442-8247 *SIC* 3448

WHIRLWIND HOLDING CO INC p 1605
8234 Hansen Rd, Houston TX 77075
Tel (713) 946-7140 *SIC* 3448

WHIRLWIND STEEL BUILDINGS INC p 1605
8234 Hansen Rd, Houston TX 77075
Tel (713) 946-7140 *SIC* 3448

WACO INC p 1570
5450 Lewis Rd, Sandston VA 23150
Tel (804) 222-8440
SIC 1711 1799 3448 5033

RITE-HITE CO LLC p 1236
8900 N Arbon Dr, Milwaukee WI 53223
Tel (414) 355-2600 *SIC* 5084 3842 3448

■ **QUANEX HOMESHIELD LLC** p 1198
311 W Coleman St, Rice Lake WI 54868
Tel (715) 234-9061 *SIC* 3448

CLEARY BUILDING CORP p 324
190 Paoli St, Verona WI 53593
Tel (608) 845-9700 *SIC* 1541 3448

SIC 3449 Misc Structural Metal Work

■ **ALABAMA METAL INDUSTRIES CORP** p 43
3245 Fayette Ave, Birmingham AL 35208
Tel (205) 787-2611
SIC 3446 3449 3089 3441 3316

AM/NS CALVERT LLC p 64
1 Am Ns Way, Calvert AL 36513
Tel (251) 289-3000 *SIC* 3312 3449

■ **SIMPSON STRONG-TIE CO INC** p 1325
5956 W Las Positas Blvd, Pleasanton CA 94588
Tel (925) 560-9000 *SIC* 3449 2891

TAMCO INC p 1423
12459 Arrow Rte, Rancho Cucamonga CA 91739
Tel (909) 899-0660 *SIC* 3449

NORMAN INDUSTRIAL MATERIALS INC p 1049
8300 San Fernando Rd, Sun Valley CA 91352
Tel (818) 729-3333 *SIC* 5051 3441 3449

GERDAU AMERISTEEL US INC p 608
4221 W Boy Scout Blvd # 600, Tampa FL 33607
Tel (813) 286-8383 *SIC* 3312 3449 3315

GERDAU USA INC p 608
4221 W Boy Scout Blvd, Tampa FL 33607
Tel (813) 286-8383 *SIC* 3312 3449 3315

YKK AP AMERICA INC p 1636
270 Riverside Pkwy Ste A, Austell GA 30168
Tel (678) 838-6000 *SIC* 3442 3449

TRULITE GLASS & ALUMINUM SOLUTIONS LLC p 1486
403 Westpark Ct Ste 201, Peachtree City GA 30269
Tel (678) 593-9200 *SIC* 3354 3449

■ **NUCOR STEEL KANKAKEE INC** p 1066
1 Nucor Way, Bourbonnais IL 60914
Tel (815) 937-3131 *SIC* 3312 3547 3449

MMC PRECISION HOLDINGS CORP p 979
1021 W Birchwood St, Morton IL 61550
Tel (309) 266-7176 *SIC* 3449

MORTON INDUSTRIAL GROUP INC p 991
1021 W Birchwood St, Morton IL 61550
Tel (309) 266-7176 *SIC* 3449

MCLEAN CONTRACTING CO p 931
6700 Mclean Way, Glen Burnie MD 21060
Tel (410) 553-6700
SIC 1622 1623 1629 3449

BARKER STEEL LLC p 155
55 Sumner St Ste 1, Milford MA 01757
Tel (508) 473-8484 *SIC* 3449

SHAPE CORP p 1311
1900 Hayes St, Grand Haven MI 49417
Tel (616) 846-8700 *SIC* 3449 3089

EFCO CORP p 480
1000 County Rd, Monett MO 65708
Tel (800) 221-4169 *SIC* 3442 3449

METALICO INC p 952
135 Dermody St, Cranford NJ 07016
Tel (908) 497-9610 *SIC* 3449

STEELFAB INC p 1384
8623 Old Dowd Rd, Charlotte NC 28214
Tel (704) 394-5376 *SIC* 3441 3449

3A COMPOSITES USA INC p 2
3480 Taylorsville Hwy, Statesville NC 28625
Tel (704) 872-8974
SIC 3334 2679 3081 3449

▲ **WORTHINGTON INDUSTRIES INC** p 1626
200 W Old Wilson Bridge Rd, Worthington OH 43085
Tel (614) 438-3210
SIC 3316 3449 3443 3325

▲ **SCHNITZER STEEL INDUSTRIES INC** p 1288
299 Sw Clay St Ste 350, Portland OR 97201
Tel (503) 224-9900
SIC 5093 3312 3449 3441 3433 5015

■ **CENTRIA INC** p 281
1005 Beaver Grade Rd # 2, Coraopolis PA 15108
Tel (412) 299-8000
SIC 3444 1761 3564 3449

■ **ALUMAX LLC** p 63
201 Isabella St, Pittsburgh PA 15212
Tel (412) 553-4545
SIC 3334 3353 3354 3449 3442 3446

KEPPEL AMFELS LLC p 813
20000 State Highway 48, Brownsville TX 78521
Tel (956) 831-8220
SIC 1629 3731 1389 3449 3546 3443

BD VINTON LLC p 164
I-10 Vinton Rd, Canutillo TX 79835
Tel (915) 886-2000
SIC 5051 3312 3449 3316

WILLBANKS METALS INC p 1610
1155 Ne 28th St, Fort Worth TX 76106
Tel (817) 625-6161 *SIC* 5051 3449

SUNCOAST POST-TENSION LTD p 1402
509 N Sam Houston Pkwy E # 300, Houston TX 77060
Tel (281) 445-8886
SIC 3315 3316 3496 3449

PRIEFERT MFG CO INC p 1174
2630 S Jefferson Ave, Mount Pleasant TX 75455
Tel (903) 572-1741
SIC 3523 3446 3444 3317 3449

NRG MANUFACTURING INC p 1064
11311 Holderrieth Rd # 100, Tomball TX 77375
Tel (281) 320-2525 *SIC* 3449 3441

RITE-HITE HOLDING CORP p 1237
8900 N Arbon Dr, Milwaukee WI 53223
Tel (414) 355-2600 *SIC* 5084 3449 3537

■ **APOGEE WAUSAU GROUP INC** p 97
7800 International Dr, Wausau WI 54401
Tel (715) 845-2161
SIC 3479 3442 3471 3449

SIC 3451 Screw Machine Prdts

WHITESELL CORP p 1606
2703 Avalon Ave, Muscle Shoals AL 35661
Tel (256) 248-8500
SIC 3965 5085 3444 3452 3451

■ **DESIGNED METAL CONNECTIONS INC** p 432
14800 S Figueroa St, Gardena CA 90248
Tel (310) 323-6200 *SIC* 3451

■ **KAMATICS CORP** p 801
1330 Blue Hills Ave, Bloomfield CT 06002
Tel (860) 243-9704
SIC 3451 3562 3724 3728

MAC LEAN-FOGG CO p 891
1000 Allanson Rd, Mundelein IL 60060
Tel (847) 566-0010
SIC 3678 3452 3089 3061 3492 3451

MELLING TOOL CO p 941
2620 Saradan Dr, Jackson MI 49202
Tel (517) 787-8172
SIC 3451 3714 3625 3568 3561 3494

STONEBRIDGE INDUSTRIES INC p 1391
42400 Merrill Rd, Sterling Heights MI 48314
Tel (586) 323-0348 *SIC* 3496 3462 3451

GRIFFITHS CORP p 640
2717 Niagara Ln N, Minneapolis MN 55447
Tel (763) 557-8935
SIC 3544 3469 3444 3451

■ **TIMKEN SMO LLC** p 1455
2601 W Battlefield St, Springfield MO 65807
Tel (866) 773-2926 *SIC* 3451 3714

STRATEGIC INDUSTRIES LLC p 1392
26 Main St Ste 200, Chatham NJ 07928
Tel (732) 512-0195
SIC 3724 3499 3451 3083 3111

STANDBY SCREW MACHINE PRODUCTS CO p 1376
1122 W Bagley Rd, Berea OH 44017
Tel (440) 243-8200 *SIC* 3451

ILSCO CORP p 733
4730 Madison Rd, Cincinnati OH 45227
Tel (513) 533-6200
SIC 3643 3369 3451 3678 3544 3469

■ **PREMIER FARNELL CORP** p 1170
4180 Highlander Pkwy, Richfield OH 44286
Tel (216) 525-4300 *SIC* 3451

SIC 3452 Bolts, Nuts, Screws, Rivets & Washers

BIRMINGHAM FASTENER & SUPPLY INC p 185
931 Avenue W, Birmingham AL 35214
Tel (205) 595-3511 *SIC* 5085 3452

WHITESELL CORP p 1606
2703 Avalon Ave, Muscle Shoals AL 35661
Tel (256) 248-8500
SIC 3965 5085 3444 3452 3451

COPPER STATE BOLT & NUT CO INC p 368
3602 N 35th Ave, Phoenix AZ 85017
Tel (602) 272-2384 *SIC* 5072 3452

■ **HUCK INTERNATIONAL INC** p 716
3724 E Columbia St, Tucson AZ 85714
Tel (520) 519-7400 *SIC* 3429 3452

KING HOLDING CORP p 820
360 N Crescent Dr, Beverly Hills CA 90210
Tel (586) 254-3900
SIC 3452 3465 3469 3089 5072

PAUL R BRILES INC p 1121
1700 W 132nd St, Gardena CA 90249
Tel (310) 323-6222 *SIC* 3452

TA CHEN INTERNATIONAL INC p 1420
5855 Obispo Ave, Long Beach CA 90805
Tel (562) 808-8000 *SIC* 3452 5051

■ **AVIBANK MFG INC** p 138
11500 Sherman Way, North Hollywood CA 91605
Tel (818) 392-2100 *SIC* 3452

MS AEROSPACE INC p 996
13928 Balboa Blvd, Sylmar CA 91342
Tel (818) 833-9095 *SIC* 3452 3728

HI-SHEAR CORP p 689
2600 Skypark Dr, Torrance CA 90505
Tel (310) 784-4025 *SIC* 3452 3429

LEWIS BOLT & NUT CO p 858
30105 6th Ave, La Junta CO 81050
Tel (719) 384-5400 *SIC* 3452

▲ **EASTERN CO** p 472
112 Bridge St, Naugatuck CT 06770
Tel (203) 729-2255
SIC 3429 3452 3316 2439

▲ **STANLEY BLACK & DECKER INC** p 1377
1000 Stanley Dr, New Britain CT 06053
Tel (860) 225-5111
SIC 3429 3546 3423 3452 3699

■ **BLACK & DECKER INC** p 186
1423 Kirkwood Hwy, Newark DE 19711
Tel (302) 738-0250
SIC 3429 3452 3579 3423 3949

EDWIN B STIMPSON CO INC p 480
1515 Sw 13th Ct, Pompano Beach FL 33069
Tel (954) 946-3500 *SIC* 3452 3469

YKK (USA) INC p 1636
1300 Cobb Industrial Dr, Marietta GA 30066
Tel (770) 427-5521 *SIC* 3452 3965

■ **LEHIGH CONSUMER PRODUCTS LLC** p 853
3901 Liberty St, Aurora IL 60504
Tel (630) 851-7330
SIC 3965 2298 3462 3452 8742

■ **MARMON GROUP LLC** p 909
181 W Madison St Ste 2600, Chicago IL 60602
Tel (312) 372-9500 *SIC* 3452 5072

■ **MEDALIST INDUSTRIES INC** p 935
2700 Elmhurst Rd, Elk Grove Village IL 60007
Tel (847) 766-9000 *SIC* 3452

BURGESS-NORTON MFG CO INC p 227
737 Peyton St, Geneva IL 60134
Tel (630) 232-4100 *SIC* 3399 3592 3452

COOPER B-LINE INC p 366
509 W Monroe St, Highland IL 62249
Tel (618) 654-2184
SIC 3441 3443 3452 3444 3429 3356

MAC LEAN-FOGG CO p 891
1000 Allanson Rd, Mundelein IL 60060
Tel (847) 566-0010
SIC 3678 3452 3089 3061 3492 3451

CONTINENTAL/MIDLAND LLC p 364
24000 S Western Ave, Park Forest IL 60466
Tel (708) 747-1200 *SIC* 3452

DERINGER-NEY INC p 431
616 Atrium Dr Ste 100, Vernon Hills IL 60061
Tel (847) 566-4100
SIC 3643 3542 3469 3452 3316

■ **AWW 10 INC** p 139
1441 N Wood Dale Rd, Wood Dale IL 60191
Tel (630) 595-0000 *SIC* 3452 5072

INDIANA AUTOMOTIVE FASTENERS INC p 738
1300 Anderson Blvd, Greenfield IN 46140
Tel (317) 467-0100 *SIC* 3452 3714

■ **INFASTECH DECORAH LLC** p 740
1304 Kerr Dr, Decorah IA 52101
Tel (563) 382-4216 *SIC* 3452 3965

■ **BLACK & DECKER CORP** p 186
701 E Joppa Rd, Towson MD 21286
Tel (410) 716-3900
SIC 3546 3553 3541 3634 3452

▲ **TRIMAS CORP** p 1480
39400 Woodward Ave # 130, Bloomfield Hills MI 48304
Tel (248) 631-5450
SIC 3799 3714 3443 2672 3452 3545

ND INDUSTRIES INC p 1022
1000 N Crooks Rd, Clawson MI 48017
Tel (248) 288-0000
SIC 3452 2851 5072 2891 3479

SHANNON PRECISION FASTENER LLC p 1311
31600 Stephenson Hwy, Madison Heights MI 48071
Tel (248) 589-9670 *SIC* 3452

SAF-HOLLAND INC *p* 1265
1950 Industrial Blvd, Muskegon MI 49442
Tel (231) 773-3271
SIC 3714 3715 3568 3537 3452

KAMAX LP *p* 801
500 W Long Lake Rd, Troy MI 48098
Tel (248) 879-0200 *SIC* 3452

MNP CORP *p* 980
44225 Utica Rd, Utica MI 48317
Tel (586) 254-1320
SIC 3452 5051 5072 3714

COLD HEADING CO *p* 335
21777 Hoover Rd, Warren MI 48089
Tel (586) 497-7000 *SIC* 3452 8711

FASTENTECH INC *p* 531
8500 Normandale Lake Blvd, Minneapolis MN 55437
Tel (952) 921-2090 *SIC* 3452

■ **ARROW FASTENER CO LLC** *p* 113
271 Mayhill St, Saddle Brook NJ 07663
Tel (201) 843-6900
SIC 3579 3315 3452 3542 2891 3586

▲ **NUCOR CORP** *p* 1066
1915 Rexford Rd Ste 400, Charlotte NC 28211
Tel (704) 366-7000
SIC 3312 3441 3448 3452 5093

EFG HOLDINGS INC *p* 480
10217 Brecksville Rd, Brecksville OH 44141
Tel (812) 717-2544 *SIC* 3452

ELGIN FASTENER GROUP LLC *p* 486
10217 Brecksville Rd, Brecksville OH 44141
Tel (812) 717-2544 *SIC* 3399 3452

■ **SUPPLY TECHNOLOGIES LLC** *p* 1407
6065 Parkland Blvd Ste 1, Cleveland OH 44124
Tel (440) 947-2100 *SIC* 5085 3452 3469

NELSON STUD WELDING INC *p* 1025
7900 W Ridge Rd, Elyria OH 44035
Tel (440) 329-0400 *SIC* 3452 3548

FERRY CAP & SET SCREW CO *p* 538
13300 Bramley Ave, Lakewood OH 44107
Tel (216) 649-7400 *SIC* 3452

DAYTON SUPERIOR CORP *p* 418
1125 Byers Rd, Miamisburg OH 45342
Tel (937) 866-0711
SIC 3315 3452 3462 3089 2899

OHASHI TECHNICA USA INC *p* 1077
111 Burrer Dr, Sunbury OH 43074
Tel (740) 965-5115 *SIC* 5013 5072 3452

FACIL NORTH AMERICA INC *p* 523
2242 Pinnacle Pkwy # 100, Twinsburg OH 44087
Tel (330) 487-2500 *SIC* 5072 3452 5085

■ **STANLEY INDUSTRIAL & AUTOMOTIVE LLC** *p* 1377
505 N Cleveland Ave, Westerville OH 43082
Tel (614) 755-7000
SIC 3429 3546 3423 3452

TOUCHPOINT INC *p* 1463
210 N Brinton Lake Rd, Concordville PA 19331
Tel (610) 459-4000 *SIC* 6512 3452

■ **SPS TECHNOLOGIES LLC** *p* 1362
301 Highland Ave, Jenkintown PA 19046
Tel (215) 572-3000
SIC 3452 3423 3499 3264 3679 3341

■ **NUCOR STEEL MEMPHIS INC** *p* 1066
3601 Paul R Lowry Rd, Memphis TN 38109
Tel (901) 786-5837
SIC 3312 3441 3448 3452

WINZER CORP *p* 1617
4060 E Plano Pkwy, Plano TX 75074
Tel (800) 527-4126
SIC 5072 3452 5251 5169

MATENAER CORP *p* 919
810 Schoenhaar Dr, West Bend WI 53090
Tel (262) 338-0700 *SIC* 5051 3452

SIC 3462 Iron & Steel Forgings

ARMORWORKS INC *p* 111
7071 W Frye Rd, Chandler AZ 85226
Tel (480) 517-1150 *SIC* 3462

SCHLOSSER FORGE CO *p* 1287
11711 Arrow Rte, Rancho Cucamonga CA 91730
Tel (909) 987-4760 *SIC* 3463 3462

■ **SHULTZ STEEL CO** *p* 1319
5321 Firestone Blvd, South Gate CA 90280
Tel (323) 357-3200 *SIC* 3463 3462

GENEVE HOLDINGS INC *p* 603
96 Cummings Point Rd, Stamford CT 06902
Tel (203) 358-8000 *SIC* 3462 6331

■ **A T I FUNDING CORP** *p* 6
801 N West St Fl 2, Wilmington DE 19801
Tel (302) 656-8937 *SIC* 3462

■ **TDY HOLDINGS LLC** *p* 1429
1403 Foulk Rd Ste 200, Wilmington DE 19803
Tel (302) 254-4172 *SIC* 3462

▲ **ARC GROUP WORLDWIDE INC** *p* 103
810 Flight Line Blvd, Deland FL 32724
Tel (303) 467-5236 *SIC* 3499 3462 3812

POINT BLANK ENTERPRISES INC *p* 1159
2102 Sw 2nd St, Pompano Beach FL 33069
Tel (954) 630-0900
SIC 3842 3462 3728 8711

WELDBEND CORP *p* 1589
6600 S Harlem Ave, Argo IL 60501
Tel (708) 594-1700 *SIC* 3462

■ **LEHIGH CONSUMER PRODUCTS LLC** *p* 853
3901 Liberty St, Aurora IL 60504
Tel (630) 851-7330
SIC 3965 2298 3462 3452 8742

GENERAL ELECTRIC RAILCAR SERVICES CORP *p* 600
161 N Clark St Fl 7, Chicago IL 60601
Tel (312) 853-5000
SIC 7359 3743 4789 3462

■ **JERNBERG INDUSTRIES LLC** *p* 783
328 W 40th Pl, Chicago IL 60609
Tel (773) 268-3004 *SIC* 3462 3463

THYSSENKRUPP CRANKSHAFT CO LLC *p* 1451
1000 Lynch Rd, Danville IL 61834
Tel (217) 431-0060 *SIC* 3714 3462

WOZNIAK INDUSTRIES INC *p* 1627
2 Mid America Plz Ste 700, Oakbrook Terrace IL 60181
Tel (630) 954-3400 *SIC* 3469 3444 3462

ROCKFORD PRODUCTS LLC *p* 1244
707 Harrison Ave, Rockford IL 61104
Tel (815) 397-6000 *SIC* 3462

SCOT FORGE CO *p* 1293
8001 Winn Rd, Spring Grove IL 60081
Tel (815) 675-1000 *SIC* 3462

US TSUBAKI POWER TRANSMISSION LLC *p* 1533
301 E Marquardt Dr, Wheeling IL 60090
Tel (847) 459-9500
SIC 3568 5085 5063 3714 3462 3325

IMPACT FORGE GROUP LLC *p* 734
2805 Norcross Dr, Columbus IN 47201
Tel (812) 342-4437 *SIC* 3462 3463

■ **OMNISOURCE CORP** *p* 1085
7575 W Jefferson Blvd, Fort Wayne IN 46804
Tel (260) 422-5541 *SIC* 5093 3462 3399

ROLLS-ROYCE CORP *p* 1247
450 S Meridian St, Indianapolis IN 46225
Tel (317) 230-2000
SIC 3724 3443 3462 3731 3743 3732

FAIRFIELD MANUFACTURING CO INC *p* 525
2400 Sagamore Pkwy S, Lafayette IN 47905
Tel (765) 772-4000 *SIC* 3462 3714 5085

AVIS INDUSTRIAL CORP *p* 138
1909 S Main St, Upland IN 46989
Tel (765) 998-8100
SIC 3429 3462 3312 3531 3714 3569

EMERSON POWER TRANSMISSION CORP *p* 492
7120 New Buffington Rd, Florence KY 41042
Tel (859) 342-7900
SIC 3429 3052 3568 3562 3566 3462

▲ **SYPRIS SOLUTIONS INC** *p* 1416
101 Bullitt Ln Ste 450, Louisville KY 40222
Tel (502) 329-2000
SIC 3672 3679 3812 3674 3462

■ **SYPRIS TECHNOLOGIES INC** *p* 1416
2820 W Broadway, Louisville KY 40211
Tel (502) 774-6011 *SIC* 3462

■ **WYMAN-GORDON CO** *p* 1629
244 Worcester St, North Grafton MA 01536
Tel (508) 839-8252
SIC 3463 3462 3324 3728 3317

JERVIS B WEBB CO *p* 783
34375 W 12 Mile Rd, Farmington Hills MI 48331
Tel (248) 553-1000
SIC 3535 3536 3462 3537 3613

HEPHAESTUS HOLDINGS INC *p* 685
39475 W 13 Mile Rd # 105, Novi MI 48377
Tel (248) 479-2700 *SIC* 3462 3463

M P I INTERNATIONAL INC *p* 889
2129 Austin Ave, Rochester Hills MI 48309
Tel (608) 764-5416 *SIC* 3462 3714 3469

ASP HHI HOLDINGS INC *p* 118
2727 W 14 Mile Rd, Royal Oak MI 48073
Tel (248) 597-3800 *SIC* 3462

FORM HHI TECH LLC *p* 567
2727 W 14 Mile Rd, Royal Oak MI 48073
Tel (248) 597-3800 *SIC* 3462

■ **HHI FORGING LLC** *p* 689
2727 W 14 Mile Rd, Royal Oak MI 48073
Tel (248) 284-2900 *SIC* 3462

■ **FEDERAL-MOGUL CORP** *p* 536
27300 W 11 Mile Rd, Southfield MI 48034
Tel (248) 354-7700
SIC 3559 3462 3812 3674 3694

■ **FEDERAL-MOGUL HOLDINGS CORP** *p* 536
27300 W 11 Mile Rd, Southfield MI 48034
Tel (248) 354-7700
SIC 3462 3559 3694 3812 3674 3714

STONEBRIDGE INDUSTRIES INC *p* 1391
42400 Merrill Rd, Sterling Heights MI 48314
Tel (586) 323-0348 *SIC* 3496 3462 3451

U S MANUFACTURING CORP *p* 1497
28201 Van Dyke Ave, Warren MI 48093
Tel (586) 467-1600 *SIC* 3714 3462 3356

COLUMBIA GEAR CORP *p* 340
530 County Road 50, Avon MN 56310
Tel (440) 838-4700 *SIC* 3566 3462

■ **PSEG NUCLEAR LLC** *p* 1188
80 Park Plz, Hancocks Bridge NJ 08038
Tel (856) 339-1002 *SIC* 3462

TITANIUM INDUSTRIES INC *p* 1456
18 Green Pond Rd Ste 1, Rockaway NJ 07866
Tel (973) 983-1185 *SIC* 5051 3542 3462

■ **BORGWARNER MORSE TEC INC** *p* 201
800 Warren Rd, Ithaca NY 14850
Tel (607) 257-6700 *SIC* 3714 3462 3568

DESIGNATRONICS INC *p* 432
2101 Jericho Tpke Ste 1, New Hyde Park NY 11040
Tel (516) 328-3300
SIC 3824 3559 3545 3625 3462

■ **IEH FM HOLDINGS LLC** *p* 730
767 5th Ave Ste 4700, New York NY 10153
Tel (212) 702-4300
SIC 3462 3559 3694 3812 3674

FIRTH RIXSON INC *p* 551
181 Mckee Rd, Rochester NY 14611
Tel (585) 328-1383 *SIC* 3462

■ **HANDY & HARMAN GROUP LTD** *p* 657
1133 Westchester Ave N-222, White Plains NY 10604
Tel (914) 461-1300 *SIC* 3462

GKN DRIVELINE NEWTON LLC *p* 613
1848 Gkn Way, Newton NC 28658
Tel (828) 428-1591 *SIC* 3462 3714

CANTON DROP FORGE INC *p* 247
4575 Southway St Sw, Canton OH 44706
Tel (330) 477-4511
SIC 3462 3463 3356 3312

CORDIER GROUP HOLDINGS INC *p* 369
4575 Southway St Sw, Canton OH 44706
Tel (330) 477-4511 *SIC* 3462

▲ **PARK-OHIO HOLDINGS CORP** *p* 1116
6065 Parkland Blvd Ste 1, Cleveland OH 44124
Tel (440) 947-2000
SIC 3462 3069 3567 3363 3631 3524

■ **PARK-OHIO INDUSTRIES INC** *p* 1116
6065 Parkland Blvd Ste 1, Cleveland OH 44124
Tel (440) 947-2000
SIC 3462 3069 3567 3363 3524

PRESRITE CORP *p* 1172
3665 E 78th St, Cleveland OH 44105
Tel (216) 441-5990 *SIC* 3462

▲ **SIFCO INDUSTRIES INC** *p* 1321
970 E 64th St, Cleveland OH 44103
Tel (216) 881-8600 *SIC* 3724 3462 3471

SUMMA HOLDINGS INC *p* 1398
8223 Brecksville Rd # 100, Cleveland OH 44141
Tel (440) 838-4700
SIC 2542 3462 3569 7359 3728

■ **COLFOR MANUFACTURING INC** *p* 336
3255 Alliance Rd Nw, Malvern OH 44644
Tel (330) 863-0404 *SIC* 3462 3599 3463

DAYTON SUPERIOR CORP *p* 418
1125 Byers Rd, Miamisburg OH 45342
Tel (937) 866-0711
SIC 3315 3452 3462 3089 2899

TEKFOR INC *p* 1433
3690 Long Rd, Wooster OH 44691
Tel (330) 202-7420 *SIC* 3462

CROSBY GROUP LLC *p* 393
2801 Dawson Rd, Tulsa OK 74110
Tel (918) 834-4611 *SIC* 3462 3429

STANDARD STEEL LLC *p* 1376
500 N Walnut St, Burnham PA 17009
Tel (717) 242-4615 *SIC* 3312 3462

ELLWOOD GROUP INC *p* 489
600 Commercial Ave, Ellwood City PA 16117
Tel (724) 752-3680 *SIC* 3312 3462

NORTH AMERICAN HOGANAS HOLDINGS INC *p* 1050
111 Hoganas Way, Hollsopple PA 15935
Tel (814) 479-2551 *SIC* 3462

■ **ATI OPERATING HOLDINGS LLC** *p* 124
1000 Six Ppg Pl, Pittsburgh PA 15222
Tel (412) 394-2800 *SIC* 3462

WHEMCO INC *p* 1605
5 Hot Metal St Ste 300, Pittsburgh PA 15203
Tel (412) 390-2700
SIC 3312 3462 3731 3325 3441 3369

■ **METALDYNE SINTERED RIDGWAY LLC** *p* 952
1149 Rocky Rd, Ridgway PA 15853
Tel (814) 776-1141 *SIC* 3399 3441 3462

TEKNI-PLEX INC *p* 1433
460 E Swedesford Rd # 3000, Wayne PA 19087
Tel (484) 690-1520
SIC 2679 3462 3052 2672

MARTIN SPROCKET & GEAR INC *p* 913
3100 Sprocket Dr, Arlington TX 76015
Tel (817) 258-3000
SIC 3566 3568 3535 3321 3462 3429

INTERMET CORP *p* 753
301 Commerce St Ste 2901, Fort Worth TX 76102
Tel (817) 348-9190
SIC 3321 3714 3462 3365 3364

AMERIFORGE CORP *p* 82
13770 Industrial Rd, Houston TX 77015
Tel (713) 393-4200 *SIC* 3462

AMERIFORGE GROUP INC *p* 82
945 Bunker Hill Rd # 500, Houston TX 77024
Tel (713) 688-9705 *SIC* 3462

■ **WYMAN-GORDON FORGINGS INC** *p* 1629
10825 Telge Rd, Houston TX 77095
Tel (281) 897-2400 *SIC* 3462

■ **LUFKIN INDUSTRIES LLC** *p* 884
601 S Raguet St, Lufkin TX 75904
Tel (936) 634-2211 *SIC* 3561 3321 3462

ELLWOOD TEXAS FORGE NAVASOTA LLC *p* 489
10908 County Road 419, Navasota TX 77868
Tel (936) 825-7531 *SIC* 3462

■ **STRUCTURAL METALS INC** *p* 1394
1 Steel Mill Dr, Seguin TX 78155
Tel (830) 372-8200 *SIC* 3312 3441 3462

CHICAGO BRIDGE & IRON CO (DELAWARE) *p* 297
2103 Research Forest Dr, The Woodlands TX 77380
Tel (832) 513-1000 *SIC* 8711 3325 3462

W SILVER INC *p* 1569
9059 Doniphan Dr, Vinton TX 79821
Tel (915) 886-3553 *SIC* 3312 3462

■ **ATI TITANIUM LLC** *p* 124
12633 N Rowley Rd, Grantsville UT 84029
Tel (801) 443-9958 *SIC* 3462

■ **ATI LADISH LLC** *p* 124
5481 S Packard Ave, Cudahy WI 53110
Tel (414) 747-2611 *SIC* 3462 3463

■ **JOY GLOBAL SURFACE MINING INC** *p* 794
4400 W National Ave, Milwaukee WI 53214
Tel (414) 671-4400 *SIC* 3462

WT WALKER GROUP INC *p* 1628
222 E Erie St Ste 300, Milwaukee WI 53202
Tel (414) 223-2000 *SIC* 3462 3398

■ **MASTER LOCK CO LLC** *p* 918
137 W Forest Hill Ave, Oak Creek WI 53154
Tel (414) 444-2800 *SIC* 3429 3462

SIC 3463 Nonferrous Forgings

BALDOR ELECTRIC CO *p* 147
5711 Rs Boreham Jr St, Fort Smith AR 72901
Tel (479) 646-4711
SIC 3621 3566 3463 3366

■ **HACKNEY LADISH INC** *p* 652
708 S Elmira Ave, Russellville AR 72802
Tel (479) 968-7555 *SIC* 3089 3463

WEBER METALS INC *p* 1586
16706 Garfield Ave, Paramount CA 90723
Tel (562) 602-0260 *SIC* 3463

SCHLOSSER FORGE CO *p* 1287
11711 Arrow Rte, Rancho Cucamonga CA 91730
Tel (909) 987-4760 *SIC* 3463 3462

ALUMINUM PRECISION PRODUCTS INC *p* 63
3333 W Warner Ave, Santa Ana CA 92704
Tel (714) 546-8125 *SIC* 3463

■ **SHULTZ STEEL CO** *p* 1319
5321 Firestone Blvd, South Gate CA 90280
Tel (323) 357-3200 *SIC* 3463 3462

■ **DELAWARE CAPITAL FORMATION INC** *p* 423
501 Silverside Rd Ste 5, Wilmington DE 19809
Tel (302) 793-4921
SIC 5084 3463 3542 3823

POWER SYSTEMS MFG LLC *p* 1165
1440 W Indiantown Rd # 200, Jupiter FL 33458
Tel (561) 354-1100 *SIC* 3463

TURBINE ENGINE COMPONENTS TECHNOLOGIES CORP *p* 1492
1211 Old Albany Rd, Thomasville GA 31792
Tel (229) 228-2600
SIC 3463 3724 3714 3469

■ **JERNBERG INDUSTRIES LLC** *p* 783
328 W 40th Pl, Chicago IL 60609
Tel (773) 268-3004 *SIC* 3462 3463

IMPACT FORGE GROUP LLC *p* 734
2805 Norcross Dr, Columbus IN 47201
Tel (812) 342-4437 *SIC* 3462 3463

HARVEY INDUSTRIES LLC *p* 667
3837 Mill St, Wabash IN 46992
Tel (260) 563-8371 *SIC* 3463 3365

FANSTEEL INC *p* 527
1746 Commerce Rd, Creston IA 50801
Tel (641) 782-8521
SIC 3463 3728 3365 3369 3769 3545

■ **WESTPORT AXLE CORP** *p* 1602
12740 Westport Rd Ste H, Louisville KY 40245
Tel (502) 425-2103 *SIC* 5051 3463 3714

■ **WYMAN-GORDON CO** *p* 1629
244 Worcester St, North Grafton MA 01536
Tel (508) 839-8252
SIC 3463 3462 3324 3728 3317

HEPHAESTUS HOLDINGS INC *p* 685
39475 W 13 Mile Rd # 105, Novi MI 48377
Tel (248) 479-2700 *SIC* 3462 3463

HHI FORMTECH INDUSTRIES LLC *p* 689
2727 W 14 Mile Rd, Royal Oak MI 48073
Tel (248) 597-3800 *SIC* 3463

SMITHS TUBULAR SYSTEMS-LACONIA INC *p* 1334
93 Lexington Dr, Laconia NH 03246
Tel (603) 524-2064
SIC 3463 3498 8734 7692 3441 3398

CANTON DROP FORGE INC *p* 247
4575 Southway St Sw, Canton OH 44706
Tel (330) 477-4511
SIC 3462 3463 3356 3312

■ **COLFOR MANUFACTURING INC** *p* 336
3255 Alliance Rd Nw, Malvern OH 44644
Tel (330) 863-0404 *SIC* 3462 3599 3463

MANSFIELD PLUMBING PRODUCTS LLC *p* 903
150 E 1st St, Perrysville OH 44864
Tel (419) 938-5211
SIC 3261 3463 3088 3431 3432 5074

■ **MUELLER BRASS CO** *p* 998
8285 Tournament Dr # 150, Memphis TN 38125
Tel (901) 753-3200
SIC 3351 3463 3354 3494

■ **MUELLER BRASS HOLDING CO INC** *p* 998
8285 Tournament Dr # 150, Memphis TN 38125
Tel (901) 753-3200 *SIC* 3351 3463 3494

▲ **MUELLER INDUSTRIES INC** *p* 998
8285 Tournament Dr # 150, Memphis TN 38125
Tel (901) 753-3200 *SIC* 3463 3494 3089

ACCUDYNE INDUSTRIES LLC *p* 16
2728 N Harwood St Ste 200, Dallas TX 75201
Tel (469) 518-4777 *SIC* 3463

FLEXITALLIC GROUP INC *p* 556
201 Kingwood Med Dr B200 Ste B 200, Houston TX 77067
Tel (281) 604-2525
SIC 3053 3533 3463 3965

▲ **FLOWSERVE CORP** *p* 560
5215 N Oconnor Blvd Connor, Irving TX 75039
Tel (972) 443-6500
SIC 3561 3491 3621 3494 3463 3321

UNITED STARS INC *p* 1512
1546 Henry Ave, Beloit WI 53511
Tel (608) 368-4625
SIC 3317 3351 3463 3613 3621

■ **ATI LADISH LLC** *p* 124
5481 S Packard Ave, Cudahy WI 53110
Tel (414) 747-2611 *SIC* 3462 3463

UNITED P&H SUPPLY CO *p* 1510
9947 W Carmen Ave, Milwaukee WI 53225
Tel (414) 393-6600
SIC 5085 5074 3312 3463

SIC 3465 Automotive Stampings

JOON LLC *p* 793
1500 County Road 177, Cusseta AL 36852
Tel (334) 756-8601 *SIC* 3465 4214

DONGWON AUTOPART TECHNOLOGY ALABAMA LLC *p* 450
12970 Montgomery Hwy, Luverne AL 36049
Tel (334) 537-5000 *SIC* 3465

DONGWON AUTOPART TECHNOLOGY INC *p* 450
12970 Montgomery Hwy, Luverne AL 36049
Tel (706) 637-9735 *SIC* 3465

SMART ALABAMA LLC *p* 1332
121 Shin Young Dr, Luverne AL 36049
Tel (334) 335-5800 *SIC* 3469 3465

GESTAMP ALABAMA LLC *p* 609
7000 Jefferson Metro Pkwy, Mc Calla AL 35111
Tel (205) 477-1412 *SIC* 3465

UNIPRES ALABAMA INC *p* 1505
990 Duncan Farms Rd, Steele AL 35987
Tel (256) 538-1974 *SIC* 3465

DEFIANCE METAL PRODUCTS OF ARKANSAS INC *p* 422
944 By Pass Rd, Heber Springs AR 72543
Tel (501) 362-1919
SIC 3465 3443 3544 3469

KING HOLDING CORP p 820
360 N Crescent Dr, Beverly Hills CA 90210
Tel (586) 254-3900
SIC 3452 3465 3469 3089 5072

FLORIDA PRODUCTION ENGINEERING INC p 559
2 E Tower Cir, Ormond Beach FL 32174
Tel (386) 677-2566 SIC 3465 3089

HUTCHINGS AUTOMOTIVE PRODUCTS INC p 721
2041 Nw 15th Ave, Pompano Beach FL 33069
Tel (954) 958-9866 SIC 3465

DMI COLUMBUS LLC p 446
1600 Northside Indus Blvd, Columbus GA 31904
Tel (248) 728-8642 SIC 3465

MERCURY PRODUCTS CORP p 945
1201 Mercury Dr, Schaumburg IL 60193
Tel (847) 524-4400 SIC 3465 3469 3714

DIVERSIFIED MACHINE BRISTOL LLC p 444
51650 County Road 133, Bristol IN 46507
Tel (248) 728-8642 SIC 3465

INDIANA MULTIMATIC MFG INC p 738
201 Re Jones Rd, Butler IN 46721
Tel (260) 868-1000 SIC 3465

HERITAGE PRODUCTS INC p 686
2000 Smith Ave, Crawfordsville IN 47933
Tel (765) 364-9002 SIC 3465

PK USA INC p 1153
600 Northridge Dr, Shelbyville IN 46176
Tel (317) 395-5500
SIC 3465 3089 3714 3429

FUTABA INDIANA OF AMERICA CORP p 585
3320 S Keller Rd, Vincennes IN 47591
Tel (812) 895-4700 SIC 3089 3465 2396

TG AUTOMOTIVE SEALING KENTUCKY LLC p 1445
501 Frank Yost Ln, Hopkinsville KY 42240
Tel (270) 475-1400 SIC 3465

TOYOTETSU AMERICA INC p 1467
100 Pin Oak Dr, Somerset KY 42503
Tel (606) 274-9005 SIC 3465 3714 3429

BENTELER AUTOMOTIVE CORP p 173
2650 N Opdyke Rd Ste B, Auburn Hills MI 48326
Tel (248) 364-7190 SIC 3714 3465 3999

WELLINGTON INDUSTRIES INC p 1589
39555 S I 94 Servce Dr, Belleville MI 48111
Tel (734) 942-1060 SIC 3465

SODECIA USA AUTOMOTIVE CORP p 1336
24331 Sherwood, Center Line MI 48015
Tel (586) 759-2200 SIC 3465

TRIANON INDUSTRIES CORP p 1478
24331 Sherwood, Center Line MI 48015
Tel (586) 759-2200 SIC 3465 3544

HATCH STAMPING CO LLC p 667
635 E Industrial Dr, Chelsea MI 48118
Tel (734) 475-8628 SIC 3465 3544

PLASTIC TRIM INTERNATIONAL INC p 1155
935 Aulerich Rd, East Tawas MI 48730
Tel (248) 259-7468 SIC 3465

P & C GROUP I INC p 1102
37000 W 12 Mile Rd, Farmington Hills MI 48331
Tel (248) 442-6800 SIC 3499 3465

JSJ CORP p 796
700 Robbins Rd, Grand Haven MI 49417
Tel (616) 842-6350
SIC 3465 3469 3366 3089 3086 2522

CHALLENGE MFG CO p 287
3200 Fruit Ridge Ave Nw, Grand Rapids MI 49544
Tel (616) 735-6500 SIC 3465

GILL CORP p 612
706 Bond Ave Nw, Grand Rapids MI 49503
Tel (859) 625-5284
SIC 3469 3312 3495 3493 3496 3465

GILL HOLDING CO INC p 612
5271 Plainfield Ave Ne, Grand Rapids MI 49525
Tel (616) 559-2700 SIC 3465 3544

GILL INDUSTRIES INC p 612
5271 Plainfield Ave Ne, Grand Rapids MI 49525
Tel (616) 559-2700 SIC 3465 3544

PRIDGEON & CLAY INC p 1174
50 Cottage Grove St Sw, Grand Rapids MI 49507
Tel (616) 241-5675 SIC 3714 3465

VENTRA GRAND RAPIDS 5 LLC p 1548
3075 Breton Rd Se, Grand Rapids MI 49512
Tel (616) 949-6303 SIC 3465

MOTUS LLC p 993
88 E 48th St, Holland MI 49423
Tel (616) 422-7479 SIC 3465

THAI SUMMIT AMERICA CORP p 1446
1480 Mcpherson Park Dr, Howell MI 48843
Tel (517) 548-4900 SIC 3465

MARTINREA JONESVILLE LLC p 913
260 Gaige St, Jonesville MI 49250
Tel (517) 849-2195 SIC 3465

DEMMER CORP p 428
1600 N Larch St Ste 1, Lansing MI 48906
Tel (517) 321-3600
SIC 3795 3812 3544 3465 3441

QUALITY METALCRAFT INC p 1197
33355 Glendale St, Livonia MI 48150
Tel (734) 261-6700
SIC 3544 3465 3469 3444

■ STEMCO PRODUCTS INC p 1385
37770 Amrhein Rd, Livonia MI 48150
Tel (734) 416-8911 SIC 3714 3465

■ TOWER AUTOMOTIVE HOLDINGS USA LLC p 1464
17672 N Laurel Park Dr 400e, Livonia MI 48152
Tel (248) 675-6000 SIC 3465

■ TOWER AUTOMOTIVE OPERATIONS USA I LLC p 1464
17672 N Laurel Park Dr 400e, Livonia MI 48152
Tel (248) 675-6000 SIC 3465

▲ TOWER INTERNATIONAL INC p 1464
17672 N Laurel Park Dr, Livonia MI 48152
Tel (248) 675-6000 SIC 3465 3441

GESTAMP MASON LLC p 609
200 E Kipp Rd, Mason MI 48854
Tel (517) 244-8800
SIC 3398 5013 3714 3711 3465

■ TWB CO LLC p 1494
1600 Nadeau Rd, Monroe MI 48162
Tel (734) 289-6400 SIC 3465

L & W INC p 833
17757 Woodland Dr, New Boston MI 48164
Tel (734) 397-6300
SIC 3469 3465 3441 3429

■ TROY DESIGN & MANUFACTURING CO p 1485
12675 Berwyn, Redford MI 48239
Tel (313) 592-2300 SIC 3465

PRECISION PARTS HOLDINGS INC p 1168
2129 Austin Ave, Rochester Hills MI 48309
Tel (248) 853-9010 SIC 3465 3469 3544

MEANS INDUSTRIES INC p 934
3715 E Washington Rd, Saginaw MI 48601
Tel (989) 754-1433 SIC 3714 3465

CONCORD INTERNATIONAL INC p 354
300 Galleria Officentre # 501, Southfield MI 48034
Tel (248) 728-8642 SIC 3465

DIVERSIFIED MACHINE INC p 444
300 Galleria Officentre # 501, Southfield MI 48034
Tel (248) 728-8642 SIC 3465

UC HOLDINGS INC p 1498
300 Galleria Officentre, Southfield MI 48034
Tel (248) 728-8642 SIC 3465 3714

ST JAMES INC p 1367
18500 Walnut St, Southgate MI 48195
Tel (734) 285-4911 SIC 3714 3711 3465

LENAWEE STAMPING CORP p 855
1200 E Chicago Blvd, Tecumseh MI 49286
Tel (517) 423-2400 SIC 3465

▲ MERITOR INC p 949
2135 W Maple Rd, Troy MI 48084
Tel (248) 435-1000
SIC 3714 3493 3625 3465

GUARDIAN AUTOMOTIVE CORP p 645
23751 Amber Ave, Warren MI 48089
Tel (586) 757-7800 SIC 3089 3465

SET ENTERPRISES INC p 1308
30500 Van Dyke Ave # 701, Warren MI 48093
Tel (586) 573-3600
SIC 7389 3465 3544 3312

■ KEYSTONE AUTOMOTIVE INDUSTRIES MN INC p 815
3615 Marshall St Ne, Minneapolis MN 55418
Tel (612) 789-1919 SIC 5013 3312 3465

AUTO PARTS MANUFACTURING MISSISSIPPI INC p 133
100 Tab Way, Guntown MS 38849
Tel (662) 365-3082 SIC 3089 3465

MARTINREA RIVERSIDE LLC p 913
5233 Nw 41st St, Riverside MO 64150
Tel (816) 587-0875 SIC 3465

A J ROSE MFGCO p 5
38000 Chester Rd, Avon OH 44011
Tel (216) 631-4645 SIC 3465 3568 3469

FEINTOOL US OPERATIONS INC p 537
11280 Cornell Park Dr, Blue Ash OH 45242
Tel (513) 247-0110 SIC 3469 3465

TS TRIM INDUSTRIES INC p 1489
6380 Canal St, Canal Winchester OH 43110
Tel (614) 837-4114
SIC 5013 3465 3714 3083

NORTHERN STAMPING CO p 1056
6600 Chapek Pkwy, Cleveland OH 44125
Tel (216) 883-8888 SIC 3465 3469

YACHIYO OF AMERICA INC p 1633
2285 Walcutt Rd, Columbus OH 43228
Tel (614) 876-3220 SIC 3089 3465 3714

DEFIANCE METAL PRODUCTS CO p 422
21 Seneca St, Defiance OH 43512
Tel (419) 784-5332 SIC 3465 3443 3544

▲ SHILOH INDUSTRIES INC p 1316
880 Steel Dr, Valley City OH 44280
Tel (330) 558-2600 SIC 3465 3469 3544

■ ARTIFLEX MANUFACTURING LLC p 114
1425 E Bowman St, Wooster OH 44691
Tel (330) 262-2015 SIC 3465 3469

CARDONE INDUSTRIES INC p 253
5501 Whitaker Ave, Philadelphia PA 19124
Tel (215) 912-3000 SIC 3465 3714

HITACHI METALS AUTOMOTIVE COMPONENTS USA LLC p 697
18986 Route 287, Tioga PA 16946
Tel (217) 347-0600 SIC 3465 3321 3559

NEW STANDARD CORP p 1033
74 Commerce Way, York PA 17406
Tel (717) 757-9450 SIC 3469 3465

DRIVE AUTOMOTIVE INDUSTRIES OF AMERICA INC p 456
120 Moon Acres Rd, Piedmont SC 29673
Tel (864) 299-1349
SIC 3465 3714 3711 3469

SPARTANBURG AUTOMOTIVE INC p 1355
1290 New Cut Rd, Spartanburg SC 29303
Tel (864) 585-5211 SIC 3465 3412 3411

SPARTANBURG AUTOMOTIVE STEEL INC p 1355
1290 New Cut Rd, Spartanburg SC 29303
Tel (864) 585-5211 SIC 3465

GESTAMP SOUTH CAROLINA LLC p 609
1 Lsp Dr, Union SC 29379
Tel (864) 466-3960 SIC 3465

GESTAMP CHATTANOOGA LLC p 609
3063 Hickory Valley Rd, Chattanooga TN 37421
Tel (423) 305-6300 SIC 3465

EAGLE BEND MFG INC p 467
1000 Jd Yrnell Indus Pkwy, Clinton TN 37716
Tel (865) 457-3800 SIC 3465 3714

YOROZU AUTOMOTIVE TENNESSEE INC p 1637
395 Mt View Industrial Dr, Morrison TN 37357
Tel (931) 668-7700 SIC 3465

NASG TENNESSEE NORTH 2 LLC p 1008
160 Kirby Dr, Portland TN 37148
Tel (615) 323-0500 SIC 3465

UNIPRES USA INC p 1505
201 Kirby Dr, Portland TN 37148
Tel (615) 325-7311 SIC 3465

TST NA TRIM LLC p 1489
401 E Olmos Ave, Hidalgo TX 78557
Tel (956) 843-3500 SIC 3465

ANDERTON CASTINGS LLC p 90
222 Lely Dr, Troy TX 76579
Tel (254) 938-2541 SIC 3465

JASON HOLDINGS INC p 778
411 E Wisconsin Ave # 2120, Milwaukee WI 53202
Tel (414) 277-9300
SIC 2297 3465 3469 3844 3443

■ JASON INC p 778
411 E Wisconsin Ave, Milwaukee WI 53202
Tel (414) 277-9300
SIC 3465 2297 3625 3469 3844 3443

▲ JASON INDUSTRIES INC p 778
833 E Michigan St Ste 900, Milwaukee WI 53202
Tel (414) 277-9300
SIC 3465 2297 3625 3469 3844 3443

■ JPHI HOLDINGS INC p 795
411 E Wisconsin Ave, Milwaukee WI 53202
Tel (414) 277-9445
SIC 3465 2297 3625 3469 3844 3443

JL FRENCH AUTOMOTIVE LLC p 786
3101 S Taylor Dr, Sheboygan WI 53081
Tel (920) 458-7724 SIC 3465

SIC 3466 Crowns & Closures

AMCOR FLEXIBLES LLC p 65
1919 S Butterfield Rd, Mundelein IL 60060
Tel (847) 362-9000
SIC 2671 2621 2821 3081 3466

YALE SECURITY INC p 1634
1902 Airport Rd, Monroe NC 28110
Tel (704) 283-2101 SIC 3429 3466

▲ WEST PHARMACEUTICAL SERVICES INC p 1595
530 Herman O West Dr, Exton PA 19341
Tel (610) 594-2900
SIC 3069 3466 2673 3085 3089

■ CROWN CORK & SEAL USA INC p 395
1 Crown Way, Philadelphia PA 19154
Tel (215) 698-5100 SIC 3411 3466

▲ CROWN HOLDINGS INC p 395
1 Crown Way, Philadelphia PA 19154
Tel (215) 698-5100 SIC 3411 3466 3499

SIC 3469 Metal Stampings, NEC

VULCAN INC p 1567
410 E Berry Ave, Foley AL 36535
Tel (251) 943-7000 SIC 3469 3993

SMART ALABAMA LLC p 1332
121 Shin Young Dr, Luverne AL 36049
Tel (334) 335-5800 SIC 3469 3465

STAMPED METAL AMERICAN RESEARCH TECHNOLOGY INC p 1375
121 Shin Young Dr, Luverne AL 36049
Tel (334) 296-5126 SIC 3469

DEFIANCE METAL PRODUCTS OF ARKANSAS INC p 422
944 By Pass Rd, Heber Springs AR 72543
Tel (501) 362-1919
SIC 3465 3443 3544 3469

KING HOLDING CORP p 820
360 N Crescent Dr, Beverly Hills CA 90210
Tel (586) 254-3900
SIC 3452 3465 3469 3089 5072

TREND TECHNOLOGIES LLC p 1476
4626 Eucalyptus Ave, Chino CA 91710
Tel (909) 597-7861 SIC 3444 3469 3499

■ AHF-DUCOMMUN INC p 36
268 E Gardena Blvd, Gardena CA 90248
Tel (310) 380-5390
SIC 3728 3812 3769 3469

TABC INC p 1420
6375 N Paramount Blvd, Long Beach CA 90805
Tel (562) 984-3305 SIC 3714 3713 3469

▲ BARNES GROUP INC p 156
123 Main St, Bristol CT 06010
Tel (860) 583-7070 SIC 3724 3495 3469

BARDEN CORP p 155
200 Park Ave, Danbury CT 06810
Tel (203) 744-2211
SIC 3562 3469 3842 3089 3399

CONNECTICUT SPRING AND STAMPING CORP p 357
48 Spring Ln, Farmington CT 06032
Tel (860) 677-1341 SIC 3469 3495 3493

PRECISION RESOURCE INC p 1168
25 Forest Pkwy, Shelton CT 06484
Tel (203) 925-0012 SIC 3469

▲ HEXCEL CORP p 688
281 Tresser Blvd Ste 1503, Stamford CT 06901
Tel (203) 969-0666
SIC 2821 3728 3089 3624 2891 3469

SIEMON CO p 1320
101 Siemon Company Dr, Watertown CT 06795
Tel (860) 945-4200
SIC 3643 3089 3679 3469 3613 3357

EDWIN B STIMPSON CO INC p 480
1515 Sw 13th Ct, Pompano Beach FL 33069
Tel (954) 946-3500 SIC 3452 3469

■ MASONITE CORP p 916
1 Tampa City Center 20, Tampa FL 33602
Tel (813) 877-2726 SIC 2431 3469

■ CALPHALON CORP p 242
3 Glenlake Pkwy, Atlanta GA 30328
Tel (770) 418-7100 SIC 3365 3469

■ UNIFIED BRANDS INC p 1503
2016 Gees Mill Rd Ne, Conyers GA 30013
Tel (601) 372-3903 SIC 3469

ROTARY CORP p 1252
801 W Barnard St, Glennville GA 30427
Tel (912) 654-3433 SIC 5083 3469 5013

TURBINE ENGINE COMPONENTS TECHNOLOGIES CORP p 1492
1211 Old Albany Rd, Thomasville GA 31792
Tel (229) 228-2600
SIC 3463 3724 3714 3469

JD NORMAN INDUSTRIES INC p 780
787 W Belden Ave, Addison IL 60101
Tel (630) 458-3700 SIC 3469 3496 3495

PRINCIPAL MANUFACTURING CORP p 1177
2800 S 19th Ave, Broadview IL 60155
Tel (708) 865-7500 SIC 3469

FIC AMERICA CORP p 540
485 E Lies Rd, Carol Stream IL 60188
Tel (630) 871-7609 SIC 3469

TEMPEL STEEL CO p 1436
5500 N Wolcott Ave, Chicago IL 60640
Tel (773) 250-8000
SIC 3469 3313 3316 3398 5051

▲ FORTUNE BRANDS HOME & SECURITY INC p 570
520 Lake Cook Rd, Deerfield IL 60015
Tel (847) 484-4400
SIC 2531 2599 3429 3469

IMS COMPANIES LLC p 735
1 Innovation Dr, Des Plaines IL 60016
Tel (847) 391-8100
SIC 3469 8711 3679 3714 3444

■ GBC METALS LLC p 594
427 N Shamrock St, East Alton IL 62024
Tel (618) 258-2350 SIC 3351 3341 3469

■ GLOBAL BRASS AND COPPER INC p 615
305 Lewis And Clark Blvd, East Alton IL 62024
Tel (618) 258-5000
SIC 3351 3341 3469 1542

NATIONAL MATERIAL LP p 1014
1965 Pratt Blvd, Elk Grove Village IL 60007
Tel (847) 806-7200
SIC 5051 3469 3354 5093 4911 4924

WOZNIAK INDUSTRIES INC p 1627
2 Mid America Plz Ste 700, Oakbrook Terrace IL 60181
Tel (630) 954-3400 SIC 3469 3444 3462

WKI HOLDING CO INC p 1620
9525 Bryn Mawr Ave # 300, Rosemont IL 60018
Tel (847) 233-8600 SIC 3229 3469

WORLD KITCHEN LLC p 1625
9525 Bryn Mawr Ave # 300, Rosemont IL 60018
Tel (847) 233-8600
SIC 3229 3469 3365 3421 5719

▲ GLOBAL BRASS AND COPPER HOLDINGS INC p 615
475 N Marti Rd Ste 1050, Schaumburg IL 60173
Tel (847) 240-4700 SIC 3351 3341 3469

MERCURY PRODUCTS CORP p 945
1201 Mercury Dr, Schaumburg IL 60193
Tel (847) 524-4400 SIC 3465 3469 3714

RITTAL CORP p 1237
425 N Martingale Rd # 400, Schaumburg IL 60173
Tel (847) 240-4600 SIC 3469 5065

AGRI-FAB INC p 36
809 S Hamilton St, Sullivan IL 61951
Tel (217) 728-8388 SIC 3469 3429 5083

DERINGER-NEY INC p 431
616 Atrium Dr Ste 100, Vernon Hills IL 60061
Tel (847) 566-4100
SIC 3643 3542 3469 3452 3316

BATESVILLE TOOL & DIE INC p 159
177 Six Pine Ranch Rd, Batesville IN 47006
Tel (812) 934-5616 SIC 3469 3544

BTD MANUFACTURING INC p 222
177 Six Pine Ranch Rd, Batesville IN 47006
Tel (812) 934-5616 SIC 3469 3544

■ LIPPERT COMPONENTS INC p 870
3501 County Road 6 E, Elkhart IN 46514
Tel (800) 551-9149
SIC 3711 3469 3444 3714

■ GROUP DEKKO INC p 641
2505 Dekko Dr, Garrett IN 46738
Tel (260) 357-3621
SIC 3479 3469 3643 3315 3089

FIRESTONE INDUSTRIAL PRODUCTS CO LLC p 544
250 W 96th St Ste 150, Indianapolis IN 46260
Tel (317) 818-8600
SIC 5531 3469 3714 3495

TUBE PROCESSING CORP p 1490
604 E Legrande Ave, Indianapolis IN 46203
Tel (317) 787-1321
SIC 3498 3356 3469 7692 3444 3728

MILLENNIUM INDUSTRIES CORP p 970
925 N Main St, Ligonier IN 46767
Tel (260) 894-3163 SIC 3469

HINES PRECISION INC p 695
5680 Old Highway 54, Philpot KY 42366
Tel (270) 729-4242 SIC 3469 3444

■ PHOENIX COLOR CORP p 1144
18249 Phoenix Rd, Hagerstown MD 21742
Tel (301) 733-0018 SIC 2732 3469 2796

PEP INDUSTRIES LLC p 1133
110 Frank Mossberg Dr, Attleboro MA 02703
Tel (508) 226-5600
SIC 3089 3351 3469 3471 3643 3841

PRECISION ENGINEERED PRODUCTS LLC p 1168
110 Frank Mossberg Dr, Attleboro MA 02703
Tel (508) 226-5600
SIC 3643 3469 3841 3471 3089 3351

TECH-ETCH INC p 1431
45 Aldrin Rd, Plymouth MA 02360
Tel (508) 747-0300 SIC 3469 3672 3479

ADRIAN STEEL CO p 24
906 James St, Adrian MI 49221
Tel (517) 265-6194 SIC 3496 3469

GLOBAL AUTOMOTIVE SYSTEMS LLC p 615
1780 Pond Run, Auburn Hills MI 48326
Tel (248) 299-7230 SIC 3469

OAKWOOD METAL FABRICATING CO p 1071
1100 Oakwood Blvd, Dearborn MI 48124
Tel (313) 561-7740 SIC 5199 3714 3469

JSJ CORP p 796
700 Robbins Rd, Grand Haven MI 49417
Tel (616) 842-6350
SIC 3465 3469 3366 3089 3086 2522

GILL CORP p 612
706 Bond Ave Nw, Grand Rapids MI 49503
Tel (859) 625-5284
SIC 3469 3312 3495 3493 3496 3465

RIDGEVIEW INDUSTRIES INC p 1234
3093 Northridge Dr Nw, Grand Rapids MI 49544
Tel (616) 453-8636 *SIC* 3469 7692

VENTRA IONIA MAIN LLC p 1548
14 Beardsley St, Ionia MI 48846
Tel (616) 597-3220 *SIC* 3469 3089 5198

QUALITY METALCRAFT INC p 1197
33355 Glendale St, Livonia MI 48150
Tel (734) 261-6700
SIC 3544 3465 3469 3444

TRW AUTOMOTIVE US LLC p 1489
12001 Tech Center Dr, Livonia MI 48150
Tel (734) 855-2600 *SIC* 3679 3469 3089

MIDWAY PRODUCTS GROUP INC p 967
1 Lyman E Hoyt Dr, Monroe MI 48161
Tel (734) 241-7242 *SIC* 8741 3469

L & W INC p 833
17757 Woodland Dr, New Boston MI 48164
Tel (734) 397-6300
SIC 3469 3465 3441 3429

MODINEER CO p 981
2190 Industrial Dr, Niles MI 49120
Tel (269) 683-2550 *SIC* 3469 3599 3544

TA DELAWARE INC p 1420
17672 N Laure Park Dr Ste, Novi MI 48377
Tel (248) 675-6000 *SIC* 3469

A RAYMOND CORPORATE NORTH AMERICA INC p 6
2350 Austin Ave Ste 200, Rochester Hills MI 48309
Tel (248) 853-2500 *SIC* 5085 3469 6719

A RAYMOND TINNERMAN AUTOMOTIVE INC p 6
3091 Research Dr, Rochester Hills MI 48309
Tel (248) 260-2121 *SIC* 5085 3469

M P I INTERNATIONAL INC p 889
2129 Austin Ave, Rochester Hills MI 48309
Tel (608) 764-5416 *SIC* 3462 3714 3469

PRECISION PARTS HOLDINGS INC p 1168
2129 Austin Ave, Rochester Hills MI 48309
Tel (248) 853-9010 *SIC* 3465 3469 3544

WEBASTO ROOF SYSTEMS INC p 1586
1757 Northfield Dr, Rochester Hills MI 48309
Tel (800) 860-7866 *SIC* 3714 3441 3469

HOFFMAN ENCLOSURES INC p 699
2100 Hoffman Way, Anoka MN 55303
Tel (763) 421-2240
SIC 3444 3699 3613 3469 3053

■ **BTD MANUFACTURING INC** p 222
1111 13th Ave Se, Detroit Lakes MN 56501
Tel (218) 847-4446 *SIC* 3469 3544

GRIFFITHS CORP p 640
2717 Niagara Ln N, Minneapolis MN 55447
Tel (763) 557-8935
SIC 3544 3469 3444 3451

GRIFFITHS HOLDING CORP p 640
2717 Niagara Ln N, Minneapolis MN 55447
Tel (763) 557-8935 *SIC* 3544 3469

SPELL CAPITAL PARTNERS LLC p 1358
222 S 9th St Ste 2880, Minneapolis MN 55402
Tel (612) 371-9650 *SIC* 3599 3469 3444

CRENLO CAB PRODUCTS INC p 391
1600 4th Ave Nw, Rochester MN 55901
Tel (507) 289-3371
SIC 2522 3531 2542 3713 3469 3444

LAIRD TECHNOLOGIES INC p 838
3481 Rider Trl S, Earth City MO 63045
Tel (636) 898-6000 *SIC* 3469 3663

GRIMCO INC p 640
1585 Fencorp Dr, Fenton MO 63026
Tel (636) 305-0088
SIC 3469 2759 3993 3429 3312

BLOUNT INTERNATIONAL INC p 190
10331 Nw Transcon Dr, Kansas City MO 64153
Tel (816) 231-5007 *SIC* 5083 3524 3469

DETROIT TOOL METAL PRODUCTS CO p 433
949 Bethel Rd, Lebanon MO 65536
Tel (417) 532-2142 *SIC* 3469 3444

WAINWRIGHT INDUSTRIES INC p 1571
114 Piper Hill Dr Ste 201, Saint Peters MO 63376
Tel (636) 327-8292 *SIC* 3469 3728 3544

▲ **NEWELL BRANDS INC** p 1037
221 River St, Hoboken NJ 07030
Tel (201) 610-6600
SIC 3089 3469 2591 3951 3999 3546

INTERPLEX INDUSTRIES INC p 757
1434 110th St Ste 301, College Point NY 11356
Tel (718) 961-6212
SIC 3471 3825 3674 3469

■ **CORNING VITRO CORP** p 371
1 Riverfront Plz, Corning NY 14830
Tel (607) 974-8605 *SIC* 3229 3469

MERCURY AIRCRAFT INC p 945
8126 County Route 88, Hammondsport NY 14840
Tel (607) 569-4200 *SIC* 3469 3444

GLEASON WORKS p 614
1000 University Ave, Rochester NY 14607
Tel (585) 473-1000
SIC 3714 3728 3566 3541 3829 3469

ENVIRONMENTAL FILTRATION TECHNOLOGIES LLC p 503
4404a Chesapeake Dr, Charlotte NC 28216
Tel (704) 399-7441
SIC 3569 5085 3564 3444 3469 3561

VRUSH INDUSTRIES INC p 1566
118 N Wrenn St, High Point NC 27260
Tel (336) 886-7700
SIC 5045 5021 7379 3469 5712 7375

TOTER LLC p 1463
841 Meacham Rd, Statesville NC 28677
Tel (800) 424-0422
SIC 3089 3536 3469 3412 2821

A J ROSE MFGCO p 5
38000 Chester Rd, Avon OH 44011
Tel (216) 631-4645 *SIC* 3465 3568 3469

FEINTOOL US OPERATIONS INC p 537
11280 Cornell Park Dr, Blue Ash OH 45242
Tel (513) 247-0110 *SIC* 3469 3465

ILSCO CORP p 733
4730 Madison Rd, Cincinnati OH 45227
Tel (513) 533-6200
SIC 3643 3369 3451 3678 3544 3469

NORTHERN STAMPING CO p 1056
6600 Chapek Pkwy, Cleveland OH 44125
Tel (216) 883-8888 *SIC* 3465 3469

■ **SUPPLY TECHNOLOGIES LLC** p 1407
6065 Parkland Blvd Ste 1, Cleveland OH 44124
Tel (440) 947-2100 *SIC* 5085 3452 3469

ERNIE GREEN INDUSTRIES INC p 508
2030 Dividend Dr, Columbus OH 43228
Tel (614) 219-1423
SIC 3714 3089 3471 3469

■ **RIDGE TOOL MANUFACTURING CO** p 1234
400 Clark St, Elyria OH 44035
Tel (440) 323-5581
SIC 3541 3423 3547 3546 3545 3469

PACIFIC MANUFACTURING OHIO INC p 1105
8955 Seward Rd, Fairfield OH 45011
Tel (513) 860-3900 *SIC* 3714 3469

TAKUMI STAMPING INC p 1422
8585 Seward Rd, Fairfield OH 45011
Tel (513) 642-0081 *SIC* 3469

EVERYWARE GLOBAL INC p 515
519 N Pierce Ave, Lancaster OH 43130
Tel (740) 687-2500 *SIC* 3469 3089

AMERICAN TRIM LLC p 80
1005 W Grand Ave, Lima OH 45801
Tel (419) 228-1145 *SIC* 3469

SUPERIOR METAL PRODUCTS INC p 1406
1005 W Grand Ave, Lima OH 45801
Tel (419) 228-1145 *SIC* 3469 3429

ANOMATIC CORP p 92
1650 Tamarack Rd, Newark OH 43055
Tel (740) 522-2203 *SIC* 3471 3469 2396

NORPLAS INDUSTRIES INC p 1049
7825 Caple Blvd, Northwood OH 43619
Tel (419) 662-3317 *SIC* 3469

■ **MATCO TOOLS CORP** p 919
4403 Allen Rd, Stow OH 44224
Tel (330) 929-4949
SIC 5251 5072 3469 3423 5013

ATLANTIC TOOL & DIE CO INC p 127
19963 Progress Dr, Strongsville OH 44149
Tel (440) 238-6931 *SIC* 3469 3544

ICE INDUSTRIES INC p 727
3810 Herr Rd, Sylvania OH 43560
Tel (419) 842-3612 *SIC* 3469

MTD HOLDINGS INC p 997
5965 Grafton Rd, Valley City OH 44280
Tel (330) 225-2600
SIC 3524 3544 3469 6141

■ **SHILOH CORP** p 1316
880 Steel Dr, Valley City OH 44280
Tel (330) 558-2600 *SIC* 3469 3544

▲ **SHILOH INDUSTRIES INC** p 1316
880 Steel Dr, Valley City OH 44280
Tel (330) 558-2600 *SIC* 3465 3469 3544

■ **ARTIFLEX MANUFACTURING LLC** p 114
1425 E Bowman St, Wooster OH 44691
Tel (330) 262-2015 *SIC* 3465 3469

SUPERIOR GROUP INC p 1406
100 Front St Ste 525, Conshohocken PA 19428
Tel (610) 397-2040
SIC 5051 3357 3317 3491 3469 7389

OBERG INDUSTRIES INC p 1072
2301 Silverville Rd, Freeport PA 16229
Tel (724) 295-2121 *SIC* 3469 3545

READING TRUCK BODY LLC p 1213
201 Hancock Blvd, Reading PA 19611
Tel (610) 775-3301 *SIC* 3713 3792 3469

TRG WIND DOWN LLC p 1476
201 Hancock Blvd, Reading PA 19611
Tel (610) 775-3301
SIC 3713 3792 3469 5531 7532

■ **DIAMOND MANUFACTURING CO** p 437
243 W Eigth St, Wyoming PA 18644
Tel (570) 693-0300
SIC 3469 3471 3479 3089

HERAEUS INC HIC p 685
770 Township Line Rd, Yardley PA 19067
Tel (212) 752-2180
SIC 3399 3823 3339 3469

NEW STANDARD CORP p 1033
74 Commerce Way, York PA 17406
Tel (717) 757-9450 *SIC* 3469 3465

NORCROSS SAFETY PRODUCTS LLC p 1047
900 Douglas Pike Ste 100, Smithfield RI 02917
Tel (800) 430-5490 *SIC* 3842 3021 3469

DRIVE AUTOMOTIVE INDUSTRIES OF AMERICA INC p 456
120 Moon Acres Rd, Piedmont SC 29673
Tel (864) 299-1349
SIC 3465 3714 3711 3469

UNAKA CO INC p 1502
1500 Industrial Rd, Greeneville TN 37745
Tel (423) 639-1171
SIC 2099 3469 2514 2253 4226

NORTH AMERICAN STAMPING GROUP LLC p 1050
119 Kirby Dr, Portland TN 37148
Tel (615) 323-0500 *SIC* 3469 6719

■ **ASSOCIATED AMERICAN INDUSTRIES INC** p 119
1307 N Watters Rd, Allen TX 75013
Tel (214) 421-7366
SIC 3914 3634 3469 3639

C H INDUSTRIES INC p 232
1700 Columbian Club Dr, Carrollton TX 75006
Tel (972) 416-1304 *SIC* 2599 3444 3469

NEW PROCESS STEEL LP p 1033
1322 N Post Oak Rd, Houston TX 77055
Tel (713) 686-9631 *SIC* 5051 3469

GESTAMP WEST VIRGINIA LLC p 609
3100 Maccorkle Ave Sw, South Charleston WV 25303
Tel (304) 744-4601 *SIC* 3469

VULCAN INDUSTRIES CORP p 1567
N113w18830 Carnegie Dr, Germantown WI 53022
Tel (262) 255-1090 *SIC* 3469 3498

WENDORFF BROS CO INC p 1592
105 Steelcraft Dr, Hartford WI 53027
Tel (262) 673-6770
SIC 3469 3089 5013 3479

REGAL WARE INC p 1218
1675 Reigle Dr, Kewaskum WI 53040
Tel (262) 626-2121 *SIC* 3634 3469

MAYVILLE ENGINEERING CO INC p 924
715 South St, Mayville WI 53050
Tel (920) 387-4500 *SIC* 3469

JASON HOLDINGS INC p 778
411 E Wisconsin Ave # 2120, Milwaukee WI 53202
Tel (414) 277-9300
SIC 2297 3465 3469 3844 3443

■ **JASON INC** p 778
411 E Wisconsin Ave, Milwaukee WI 53202
Tel (414) 277-9445
SIC 3465 2297 3625 3469 3844 3443

▲ **JASON INDUSTRIES INC** p 778
833 E Michigan St Ste 900, Milwaukee WI 53202
Tel (414) 277-9300
SIC 3465 2297 3625 3469 3844 3443

■ **JPHI HOLDINGS INC** p 795
411 E Wisconsin Ave, Milwaukee WI 53202
Tel (414) 277-9445
SIC 3465 2297 3625 3469 3844 3443

WINDWAY CAPITAL CORP p 1616
630 Riverfront Dr Ste 200, Sheboygan WI 53081
Tel (920) 457-8600
SIC 3469 2394 3624 3732

LAWRENCE HOLDING INC p 848
803 S Black River St, Sparta WI 54656
Tel (608) 269-6911 *SIC* 3469 3089 3544

NORTHERN ENGRAVING CORP p 1056
803 S Black River St, Sparta WI 54656
Tel (608) 269-6911 *SIC* 3469 3544 3089

B-G WESTERN INC p 142
1141 S 10th St, Watertown WI 53094
Tel (920) 261-0660 *SIC* 3443 3469 3444

WESTERN INDUSTRIES INC p 1598
1141 S 10th St, Watertown WI 53094
Tel (920) 261-0660
SIC 3443 3469 3089 3444 1761 3491

SIC 3471 Electroplating, Plating, Polishing, Anodizing & Coloring

LIGON INDUSTRIES LLC p 866
1927 1st Ave N Ste 500, Birmingham AL 35203
Tel (205) 322-3302
SIC 3365 3593 3325 3471 3714 3446

▲ **PRAXAIR INC** p 1168
10 Riverview Dr, Danbury CT 06810
Tel (203) 837-2000
SIC 2813 3569 3471 3479

EURAMAX INTERNATIONAL INC p 512
303 Research Dr Ste 400, Norcross GA 30092
Tel (770) 449-7066 *SIC* 3471

■ **FERALLOY CORP** p 537
8755 W Higgins Rd Ste 970, Chicago IL 60631
Tel (503) 286-8869
SIC 5051 3471 3444 3312

OERLIKON BALZERS COATING USA INC p 1075
1475 E Wdfield Rd Ste 201, Schaumburg IL 60173
Tel (847) 619-5541 *SIC* 3479 3471

AACOA INC p 8
2551 County Road 10 W, Elkhart IN 46514
Tel (574) 262-4685 *SIC* 3471

TRANSPORTATION TECHNOLOGIES INDUSTRIES INC p 1473
7140 Office Cir, Evansville IN 47715
Tel (812) 962-5000
SIC 2531 3714 3321 4741 3471

PEP INDUSTRIES LLC p 1133
110 Frank Mossberg Dr, Attleboro MA 02703
Tel (508) 226-5600
SIC 3089 3351 3469 3471 3643 3841

PRECISION ENGINEERED PRODUCTS LLC p 1168
110 Frank Mossberg Dr, Attleboro MA 02703
Tel (508) 226-5600
SIC 3643 3469 3841 3471 3089 3351

MATERIAL SCIENCES CORP p 919
6855 Commerce Blvd, Canton MI 48187
Tel (734) 207-4444 *SIC* 3479 3471

NATIONAL GALVANIZING LP p 1012
1500 Telb St, Monroe MI 48162
Tel (734) 243-1882
SIC 3312 3316 3471 3341 5051

CG LIQUIDATION INC p 285
2111 Walter P Reuther Dr, Warren MI 48091
Tel (586) 575-9800 *SIC* 3479 3471

PAULO PRODUCTS CO p 1121
5711 W Park Ave, Saint Louis MO 63110
Tel (314) 647-7500
SIC 3471 3398 8734 3567

LINCOLN INDUSTRIES INC p 867
600 W E St, Lincoln NE 68522
Tel (402) 475-3671 *SIC* 3471 3441

INTERPLEX INDUSTRIES INC p 757
1434 110th St Ste 301, College Point NY 11356
Tel (718) 961-6212
SIC 3471 3825 3674 3469

KEYMARK CORP p 815
1188 Cayadutta St, Fonda NY 12068
Tel (518) 853-3421 *SIC* 3354 3479 3471

CHEMICAL SOLVENTS INC p 293
3751 Jennings Rd, Cleveland OH 44109
Tel (216) 741-9310
SIC 5169 7349 3471 2992

▲ **SIFCO INDUSTRIES INC** p 1321
970 E 64th St, Cleveland OH 44103
Tel (216) 881-8600 *SIC* 3724 3462 3471

ERNIE GREEN INDUSTRIES INC p 508
2030 Dividend Dr, Columbus OH 43228
Tel (614) 219-1423
SIC 3714 3089 3471 3469

ANOMATIC CORP p 92
1650 Tamarack Rd, Newark OH 43055
Tel (740) 522-2203 *SIC* 3471 3469 2396

OHIO DECORATIVE PRODUCTS LLC p 1077
220 S Elizabeth St, Spencerville OH 45887
Tel (419) 647-9033
SIC 3086 3369 3471 3363

SAPA PROFILES INC p 1281
7933 Ne 21st Ave, Portland OR 97211
Tel (503) 285-0404 *SIC* 3354 3471

PENN STAINLESS PRODUCTS INC p 1129
190 Kelly Rd, Quakertown PA 18951
Tel (215) 536-3053 *SIC* 5051 3443 3471

CRC INDUSTRIES INC p 390
885 Louis Dr, Warminster PA 18974
Tel (215) 674-4300
SIC 2992 3471 2899 2842

■ **DIAMOND MANUFACTURING CO** p 437
243 W Eigth St, Wyoming PA 18644
Tel (570) 693-0300
SIC 3469 3471 3479 3089

NASHVILLE WIRE PRODUCTS MFG CO p 1008
199 Polk Ave, Nashville TN 37210
Tel (615) 743-2500 *SIC* 3496 3471 3643

ELKCORP p 488
14911 Quorum Dr Ste 600, Dallas TX 75254
Tel (972) 851-0500
SIC 2952 5033 2426 2431 3471

SCOT INDUSTRIES INC p 1293
3756 Fm 250 N, Lone Star TX 75668
Tel (903) 639-2551
SIC 7389 5051 3498 3471

PANASONIC INDUSTRIAL DEVICES CORP OF AMERICA p 1111
4900 Gorge Mcvay Dr Ste C, Mcallen TX 78503
Tel (956) 984-3700 *SIC* 3651 3675 3471

SWANSON INDUSTRIES INC p 1411
2608 Smithtown Rd, Morgantown WV 26508
Tel (304) 292-0021
SIC 3593 3471 7629 5084

PIONEER METAL FINISHING LLC p 1151
480 Pilgrim Way Ste 1400, Green Bay WI 54304
Tel (920) 499-6996 *SIC* 3471

■ **APOGEE WAUSAU GROUP INC** p 97
7800 International Dr, Wausau WI 54401
Tel (715) 845-2161
SIC 3479 3442 3471 3449

SIC 3479 Coating & Engraving, NEC

DURA COAT PRODUCTS INC p 462
5361 Via Ricardo, Riverside CA 92509
Tel (951) 341-6500 *SIC* 3479 2851

■ **OPTICAL COATING LABORATORY LLC** p 1090
2789 Northpoint Pkwy, Santa Rosa CA 95407
Tel (707) 545-6440 *SIC* 3479 3577 3827

■ **TRICOR DIRECT INC** p 1479
20 Thompson Rd, Branford CT 06405
Tel (203) 488-8059 *SIC* 3479

▲ **PRAXAIR INC** p 1168
10 Riverview Dr, Danbury CT 06810
Tel (203) 837-2000
SIC 2813 3569 3471 3479

HIGHWAY SAFETY CORP p 692
239 Commerce St Ste C, Glastonbury CT 06033
Tel (860) 659-4330 *SIC* 3444 3479

■ **MAGNATRAX CORP** p 896
1220 Old Alpharetta Rd # 310, Alpharetta GA 30005
Tel (678) 455-3360
SIC 3448 3442 3479 4213 3444

SPECTRA METAL SALES INC p 1357
6104 Boat Rock Blvd Sw, Atlanta GA 30336
Tel (404) 344-4305
SIC 5051 3354 3355 3479 3444 2952

FIRST AMERICAN RESOURCES CO LLC p 544
2030 Rverview Indus Dr Se, Mableton GA 30126
Tel (404) 505-3499 *SIC* 5051 3479

■ **UOP LLC** p 1528
25 E Algonquin Rd, Des Plaines IL 60016
Tel (847) 391-2000
SIC 2819 8711 8731 8999 3823 3479

R & O SPECIALTIES INC p 1201
120 4th Ave E, Milan IL 61264
Tel (309) 736-8660 *SIC* 5085 5013 3479

WILLIS STEIN & PARTNERS MANAGEMENT III LLC p 1612
1033 Skokie Blvd Ste 360, Northbrook IL 60062
Tel (312) 422-2400
SIC 6799 3479 2721 8721

OERLIKON BALZERS COATING USA INC p 1075
1475 E Wdfield Rd Ste 201, Schaumburg IL 60173
Tel (847) 619-5541 *SIC* 3479 3471

■ **GROUP DEKKO INC** p 641
2505 Dekko Dr, Garrett IN 46738
Tel (260) 357-3621
SIC 3479 3469 3643 3315 3089

DELORO STELLITE HOLDINGS CORP p 425
1201 Eisenhower Dr N, Goshen IN 46526
Tel (574) 534-2585 *SIC* 3479

■ **PRECOAT METALS CORP** p 1169
1950 E Main St, Greenfield IN 46140
Tel (317) 462-7761 *SIC* 3479

■ **PRAXAIR SURFACE TECHNOLOGIES INC** p 1168
1500 Polco St, Indianapolis IN 46222
Tel (317) 240-2500 *SIC* 3479 3548 3563

▲ **W R GRACE & CO** p 1569
7500 Grace Dr, Columbia MD 21044
Tel (410) 531-4000
SIC 2819 3531 2899 2891 3479

■ W R GRACE & CO-CONN p 1569
7500 Grace Dr, Columbia MD 21044
Tel (410) 531-4000
SIC 2819 3531 2899 2891 3479

▲ CHASE CORP p 291
26 Summer St, Bridgewater MA 02324
Tel (508) 819-4200 SIC 3644 3479 3672

TECH-ETCH INC p 1431
45 Aldrin Rd, Plymouth MA 02360
Tel (508) 747-0300 SIC 3469 3672 3479

BEMIS ASSOCIATES INC p 171
1 Bemis Way, Shirley MA 01464
Tel (978) 425-6761 SIC 2891 2851 3479

MAGNI GROUP INC p 896
390 Park St Ste 300, Birmingham MI 48009
Tel (248) 647-4500 SIC 2899 3479

MATERIAL SCIENCES CORP p 919
6855 Commerce Blvd, Canton MI 48187
Tel (734) 207-4444 SIC 3479 3471

ND INDUSTRIES INC p 1022
1000 N Crooks Rd, Clawson MI 48017
Tel (248) 288-0000
SIC 3452 2851 5072 2891 3479

STAR CUTTER CO p 1378
23461 Industrial Park Dr, Farmington Hills MI 48335
Tel (248) 474-8200
SIC 3545 3479 3546 3541

IONBOND LLC p 762
1823 E Whitcomb Ave, Madison Heights MI 48071
Tel (248) 398-9100 SIC 3398 3479

CG LIQUIDATION INC p 285
2111 Walter P Reuther Dr, Warren MI 48091
Tel (586) 575-9800 SIC 3479 3471

CROWN GROUP CO p 395
2111 Walter Reuther Dr, Warren MI 48091
Tel (586) 575-9800 SIC 3479

■ HOWMET HOLDINGS CORP p 713
1 Misco Dr, Whitehall MI 49461
Tel (231) 894-5686
SIC 3324 3542 5051 3479

ACTIVAR INC p 19
7808 Creekridge Cir # 200, Minneapolis MN 55439
Tel (952) 944-3533
SIC 2542 3479 3442 3429 3089

NORTHLAND ALUMINUM PRODUCTS INC p 1057
5005 Highway 7, Minneapolis MN 55416
Tel (952) 924-8505 SIC 3089 3479

SYSTEMS ELECTRO COATING LLC p 1419
253 Old Jackson Rd, Madison MS 39110
Tel (601) 407-2340 SIC 3479

NOOTER CORP p 1047
1500 S 2nd St, Saint Louis MO 63104
Tel (314) 421-7200
SIC 3443 3479 1796 8711 7699 1542

■ PRECOAT METALS p 1169
1310 Papin St Ste 300, Saint Louis MO 63103
Tel (314) 436-7010 SIC 3479

T-L IRRIGATION CO p 1420
151 E Hwy 6 And Ab Rd, Hastings NE 68901
Tel (402) 462-4128
SIC 3523 3561 3479 7359

MOMENTIVE PERFORMANCE MATERIALS HOLDINGS INC p 983
22 Corporate Woods Blvd, Albany NY 12211
Tel (518) 533-4600 SIC 2869 3479

KEYMARK CORP p 815
1188 Cayadutta St, Fonda NY 12068
Tel (518) 853-3421 SIC 3354 3479 3471

FOUGERA PHARMACEUTICALS INC p 571
60 Baylis Rd, Melville NY 11747
Tel (631) 454-7677
SIC 2834 2851 2821 3479 3829

▲ STEEL PARTNERS HOLDINGS LP p 1384
590 Madison Ave Rm 3202, New York NY 10022
Tel (212) 520-2300
SIC 3479 3497 1381 6141

MOMENTIVE PERFORMANCE MATERIALS INC p 983
260 Hudson River Rd, Waterford NY 12188
Tel (518) 237-3330 SIC 2869 3479 3679

MPM HOLDINGS INC p 995
260 Hudson River Rd, Waterford NY 12188
Tel (518) 237-3330 SIC 2869 3479 3679

MPM INTERMEDIATE HOLDINGS INC p 995
260 Hudson River Rd, Waterford NY 12188
Tel (518) 237-3330 SIC 2869 3479 3679

OERLIKON METCO (US) INC p 1075
1101 Prospect Ave, Westbury NY 11590
Tel (516) 334-1300 SIC 3399 5084 3479

ENERFAB INC p 497
4955 Spring Grove Ave, Cincinnati OH 45232
Tel (513) 641-0500
SIC 3443 1629 1541 1711 3479

VOIGT & SCHWEIZER LLC p 1564
987 Buckeye Park Rd, Columbus OH 43207
Tel (614) 449-8281 SIC 3479

■ METOKOTE CORP p 954
1340 Neubrecht Rd, Lima OH 45801
Tel (419) 996-7800 SIC 3479

▲ FERRO CORP p 538
6060 Parkland Blvd # 250, Mayfield Heights OH 44124
Tel (216) 875-5600
SIC 3479 2816 2851 3399 2821 2834

■ HOWMET CORP p 713
1616 Harvard Ave, Newburgh Heights OH 44105
Tel (800) 242-9898
SIC 3324 3542 5051 3479

DURA-BOND INDUSTRIES INC p 462
2658 Puckety Dr, Export PA 15632
Tel (724) 327-0280 SIC 3441 3479

OERLIKON USA HOLDING INC p 1075
5700 Mellon Rd, Export PA 15632
Tel (303) 273-9700
SIC 3563 3823 3699 3479 3599 5084

■ AXALTA COATING SYSTEMS LLC p 139
2001 Market St Fl 36a, Philadelphia PA 19103
Tel (215) 255-7932 SIC 2851 3479

■ DIAMOND MANUFACTURING CO p 437
243 W Eigth St, Wyoming PA 18644
Tel (570) 693-0300
SIC 3469 3471 3479 3089

CONSOLIDATED SYSTEMS INC p 360
650 Rosewood Dr, Columbia SC 29201
Tel (803) 771-7920 SIC 3444 3479 4213

PRINCE GROUP LLC p 1176
3227 Sunset Blvd Ste E101, West Columbia SC 29169
Tel (803) 708-4789 SIC 2759 3479

SHAWCOR PIPE PROTECTION LLC p 1313
3838 N Sam Houston Pkwy E # 300, Houston TX 77032
Tel (281) 886-2350 SIC 3479

■ VARCO LP p 1544
2835 Holmes Rd, Houston TX 77051
Tel (713) 799-5272 SIC 1389 3479

WOMBLE CO INC p 1621
12821 Industrial Rd, Houston TX 77015
Tel (713) 636-8700 SIC 3479

PRINCE GROUP OF VIRGINIA LLC p 1176
901 N Glebe Rd Ste 901, Arlington VA 22203
Tel (703) 953-0577 SIC 3479

STEELSCAPE LLC p 1385
222 W Kalama River Rd, Kalama WA 98625
Tel (360) 673-8200 SIC 3479

GM NAMEPLATE INC p 618
2040 15th Ave W, Seattle WA 98119
Tel (206) 284-2200 SIC 3479 2679 3679

WENDORFF BROS CO INC p 1592
105 Steelcraft Dr, Hartford WI 53027
Tel (262) 673-6770
SIC 3469 3089 5013 3479

CRYSTAL FINISHING SYSTEMS INC p 396
4704 Bayberry St, Schofield WI 54476
Tel (715) 355-5351 SIC 3479

■ APOGEE WAUSAU GROUP INC p 97
7800 International Dr, Wausau WI 54401
Tel (715) 845-2161
SIC 3479 3442 3471 3449

SIC 3482 Small Arms Ammunition

■ GENERAL DYNAMICS ORDNANCE AND TACTICAL SYSTEMS INC p 600
11399 16th Ct N Ste 200, Saint Petersburg FL 33716
Tel (727) 578-8100
SIC 3483 3482 2892 3489

▲ SMITH & WESSON HOLDING CORP p 1333
2100 Roosevelt Ave, Springfield MA 01104
Tel (800) 331-0852 SIC 3482

■ VISTA OUTDOOR SALES LLC p 1562
1 Vista Way, Anoka MN 55303
Tel (763) 323-2414 SIC 3482 3069

■ ALLIANT HOLDINGS LLC p 55
7480 Flying Cloud Dr, Eden Prairie MN 55344
Tel (952) 351-3000
SIC 3764 3812 3483 3482 3489

HORNADY MANUFACTURING CO p 708
3625 W Old Potash Hwy, Grand Island NE 68803
Tel (308) 382-1390 SIC 3482 3559 3483

■ FGI OPERATING CO LLC p 539
870 Remington Dr, Madison NC 27025
Tel (336) 548-8700 SIC 3484 3482

■ REMINGTON ARMS CO LLC p 1222
870 Remington Dr, Madison NC 27025
Tel (336) 548-8700 SIC 3482 3484

▲ VISTA OUTDOOR INC p 1562
262 N University Ave, Farmington UT 84025
Tel (801) 447-3000
SIC 3482 3483 3827 3949 3484 3812

▲ ORBITAL ATK INC p 1092
45101 Warp Dr, Dulles VA 20166
Tel (703) 406-5000
SIC 3764 3812 3483 3482 3489

SIC 3483 Ammunition, Large

PACIFIC SCIENTIFIC ENERGETIC MATERIALS CO (CALIFORNIA) LLC p 1105
7073 W Willis Rd Ste 5002, Chandler AZ 85226
Tel (480) 763-3000
SIC 2892 2899 3483 3489 3699 3728

■ PACIFIC SCIENTIFIC ENERGETIC MATERIALS CO (CALIFORNIA) p 1105
3601 Union Rd, Hollister CA 95023
Tel (831) 637-3731
SIC 2892 2899 3489 3483 3699 3728

GENEVE CORP p 603
96 Cummings Point Rd, Stamford CT 06902
Tel (203) 358-8000 SIC 5961 3483 6282

■ GENERAL DYNAMICS ORDNANCE AND TACTICAL SYSTEMS INC p 600
11399 16th Ct N Ste 200, Saint Petersburg FL 33716
Tel (727) 578-8100
SIC 3483 3482 2892 3489

AMERICAN ORDNANCE LLC p 77
17575 Hwy 79, Middletown IA 52638
Tel (319) 753-7004 SIC 3483

■ TEXTRON SYSTEMS CORP p 1445
201 Lowell St, Wilmington MA 01887
Tel (978) 657-5111 SIC 3483 5088

■ ALLIANT HOLDINGS LLC p 55
7480 Flying Cloud Dr, Eden Prairie MN 55344
Tel (952) 351-3000
SIC 3764 3812 3483 3482 3489

HORNADY MANUFACTURING CO p 708
3625 W Old Potash Hwy, Grand Island NE 68803
Tel (308) 382-1390 SIC 3482 3559 3483

■ L-3 FUZING AND ORDNANCE SYSTEMS INC p 835
3975 Mcmann Rd, Cincinnati OH 45245
Tel (513) 943-2000 SIC 3483

DAY AND ZIMMERMANN INC p 417
1500 Spring Garden St # 900, Philadelphia PA 19130
Tel (215) 299-8000
SIC 8744 8712 8711 3559 3483

BAE SYSTEMS ORDNANCE SYSTEMS INC p 144
4509 W Stone Dr, Kingsport TN 37660
Tel (423) 578-6000 SIC 3483

■ BABCOCK & WILCOX TECHNICAL SERVICES Y-12 LLC p 143
301 Bear Creek Rd, Oak Ridge TN 37830
Tel (865) 574-1000 SIC 3483 3761

▲ VISTA OUTDOOR INC p 1562
262 N University Ave, Farmington UT 84025
Tel (801) 447-3000
SIC 3482 3483 3827 3949 3484 3812

▲ ORBITAL ATK INC p 1092
45101 Warp Dr, Dulles VA 20166
Tel (703) 406-5000
SIC 3764 3812 3483 3482 3489

▲ NATIONAL PRESTO INDUSTRIES INC p 1015
3925 N Hastings Way, Eau Claire WI 54703
Tel (715) 839-2121 SIC 2211 3483 3634

■ AMTEC CORP p 87
4230 Capital Cir, Janesville WI 53546
Tel (608) 752-2699 SIC 3483

SIC 3484 Small Arms

SUREFIRE LLC p 1408
18300 Mount Baldy Cir, Fountain Valley CA 92708
Tel (714) 545-9444 SIC 3648 3842 3484

▲ STURM RUGER & CO INC p 1395
1 Lacey Pl, Southport CT 06890
Tel (203) 259-7843 SIC 3484 3324

COLT DEFENSE HOLDING LLC p 339
547 New Park Ave, West Hartford CT 06110
Tel (860) 232-4489 SIC 3484

COLT DEFENSE LLC p 339
547 New Park Ave, West Hartford CT 06110
Tel (860) 232-4489 SIC 3484

STAR OF DAVID ARMS INDUSTRIES INC p 1378
304 Se 2nd St Apt B, Grimes IA 50111
Tel (888) 491-0307 SIC 3484 7389

BERETTA USA CORP p 174
17601 Beretta Dr, Accokeek MD 20607
Tel (301) 283-2191 SIC 5091 3484

■ SMITH & WESSON CORP p 1333
2100 Roosevelt Ave, Springfield MA 01104
Tel (413) 781-8300
SIC 3484 3429 3999 5091

■ CALIBER CO p 239
100 Springdale Rd, Westfield MA 01085
Tel (413) 642-4260 SIC 3484

■ SAVAGE ARMS INC p 1283
140 Apremont Way, Westfield MA 01085
Tel (413) 642-4135 SIC 3484

■ SAVAGE SPORTS CORP p 1284
100 Springdale Rd, Westfield MA 01085
Tel (413) 568-7001 SIC 3484

■ ALLIANT TECHSYSTEMS OPERATIONS LLC p 55
4700 Nathan Ln N, Plymouth MN 55442
Tel (952) 351-3000 SIC 3484

SIG SAUER INC p 1321
72 Pease Blvd, Newington NH 03801
Tel (603) 610-3000 SIC 3484 7999

■ FGI OPERATING CO LLC p 539
870 Remington Dr, Madison NC 27025
Tel (336) 548-8700 SIC 3484 3482

■ REMINGTON ARMS CO LLC p 1222
870 Remington Dr, Madison NC 27025
Tel (336) 548-8700 SIC 3482 3484

▲ VISTA OUTDOOR INC p 1562
262 N University Ave, Farmington UT 84025
Tel (801) 447-3000
SIC 3482 3483 3827 3949 3484 3812

FN AMERICA LLC p 562
7918 Jones Branch Dr # 400, Mc Lean VA 22102
Tel (703) 288-3500 SIC 3484

SIC 3489 Ordnance & Access, NEC

PACIFIC SCIENTIFIC ENERGETIC MATERIALS CO (CALIFORNIA) LLC p 1105
7073 W Willis Rd Ste 5002, Chandler AZ 85226
Tel (480) 763-3000
SIC 2892 2899 3483 3489 3699 3728

▲ TASER INTERNATIONAL INC p 1426
17800 N 85th St, Scottsdale AZ 85255
Tel (480) 991-0797 SIC 3489

■ PACIFIC SCIENTIFIC ENERGETIC MATERIALS CO (CALIFORNIA) p 1105
3601 Union Rd, Hollister CA 95023
Tel (831) 637-3731
SIC 2892 2899 3489 3483 3699 3728

■ GENERAL DYNAMICS ORDNANCE AND TACTICAL SYSTEMS INC p 600
11399 16th Ct N Ste 200, Saint Petersburg FL 33716
Tel (727) 578-8100
SIC 3483 3482 2892 3489

■ ALLIANT HOLDINGS LLC p 55
7480 Flying Cloud Dr, Eden Prairie MN 55344
Tel (952) 351-3000
SIC 3764 3812 3483 3482 3489

DAY & ZIMMERMANN GROUP INC p 417
1500 Spring Garden St # 900, Philadelphia PA 19130
Tel (215) 299-8000
SIC 8711 8712 8741 7381 7382 3489

▲ ORBITAL ATK INC p 1092
45101 Warp Dr, Dulles VA 20166
Tel (703) 406-5000
SIC 3764 3812 3483 3482 3489

■ ITT DEFENSE & ELECTRONICS INC p 768
1650 Tysons Blvd Ste 1700, Mc Lean VA 22102
Tel (703) 790-6300
SIC 3679 3678 3674 3769 3489

SIC 3491 Industrial Valves

AMERICAN CAST IRON PIPE CO p 70
1501 31st Ave N, Birmingham AL 35207
Tel (205) 325-7856
SIC 3491 3369 3321 3053 3317

MCWANE INC p 933
2900 Highway 280 S # 300, Birmingham AL 35223
Tel (205) 414-3100
SIC 3491 1221 3321 3312 3494

J-M MANUFACTURING CO INC p 772
5200 W Century Blvd, Los Angeles CA 90045
Tel (800) 621-4404 SIC 2821 3491 3084

CONTROL COMPONENTS INC p 364
22591 Avenida Empresa, Rcho Sta Marg CA 92688
Tel (949) 858-1877 SIC 3491

■ KAMAN INDUSTRIAL TECHNOLOGIES CORP p 801
1 Vision Way, Bloomfield CT 06002
Tel (860) 687-5000 SIC 3491 5085

■ EECO INC p 480
850 Library Ave Ste 204c, Newark DE 19711
Tel (302) 456-1448
SIC 3823 3491 3621 3585 3546 3679

TYCO SIMPLEXGRINNELL p 1496
1501 Nw 51st St, Boca Raton FL 33431
Tel (561) 988-3658 SIC 3569 3491

HOERBIGER CORP OF AMERICA INC p 699
3350 Gateway Dr, Pompano Beach FL 33069
Tel (954) 974-5700 SIC 3491

▲ ROPER TECHNOLOGIES INC p 1250
6901 Prof Pkwy E Ste 200, Sarasota FL 34240
Tel (941) 556-2601
SIC 3823 3563 3491 3826 3829

▲ MUELLER WATER PRODUCTS INC p 998
1200 Abernathy Rd # 1200, Atlanta GA 30328
Tel (770) 206-4200
SIC 3491 3492 3494 3443 3321 3823

■ HENRY PRATT CO LLC p 684
401 S Highland Ave, Aurora IL 60506
Tel (630) 844-4000 SIC 3491

HENRY TECHNOLOGIES INC p 684
701 S Main St, Chatham IL 62629
Tel (217) 483-2406
SIC 3491 3585 3567 3564 3545 3494

USP HOLDINGS INC p 1535
6250 N River Rd Ste 10100, Des Plaines IL 60018
Tel (847) 604-6100 SIC 3321 3491

■ DOVER ENGINEERED SYSTEMS INC p 453
3005 Highland Pkwy # 200, Downers Grove IL 60515
Tel (630) 743-2505
SIC 3568 3443 3441 3561 3491 3492

■ HONEYWELL ANALYTICS INC p 705
405 Barclay Blvd, Lincolnshire IL 60069
Tel (847) 955-8200 SIC 3491 3829

STANT MANUFACTURING INC p 1377
1620 Columbia Ave, Connersville IN 47331
Tel (870) 247-5480 SIC 3491

NIBCO INC p 1042
1516 Middlebury St, Elkhart IN 46516
Tel (574) 295-3000 SIC 3494 3491 3089

DWYER INSTRUMENTS INC p 464
102 Indiana Highway 212, Michigan City IN 46360
Tel (219) 879-8868
SIC 3823 3824 3822 3829 3491 3625

■ FISHER CONTROLS INTERNATIONAL LLC p 552
205 S Center St, Marshalltown IA 50158
Tel (641) 754-3011
SIC 3491 3823 3625 3612 3494

ZOELLER CO p 1644
3649 Cane Run Rd, Louisville KY 40211
Tel (502) 778-2731
SIC 3561 5251 3432 3491

▲ MKS INSTRUMENTS INC p 979
2 Tech Dr Ste 201, Andover MA 01810
Tel (978) 645-5500 SIC 3823 3491 3494

■ WATTS REGULATOR CO p 1583
815 Chestnut St, North Andover MA 01845
Tel (978) 689-6000 SIC 3491 3494

▲ WATTS WATER TECHNOLOGIES INC p 1583
815 Chestnut St, North Andover MA 01845
Tel (978) 688-1811 SIC 3491 3494

ARMSTRONG INTERNATIONAL INC p 111
816 Maple St, Three Rivers MI 49093
Tel (269) 273-1415 SIC 3491

MAC VALVES INC p 891
30569 Beck Rd, Wixom MI 48393
Tel (248) 624-7700 SIC 3492 3494 3491

■ TESCOM CORP p 1440
12616 Industrial Blvd Nw, Elk River MN 55330
Tel (763) 441-6330 SIC 3491 3625 3494

▲ GRACO INC p 628
88 11th Ave Ne, Minneapolis MN 55413
Tel (612) 623-6000
SIC 3561 3594 3563 3491 3823 3569

PENTAIR INC p 1132
5500 Wayzata Blvd Ste 600, Minneapolis MN 55416
Tel (763) 545-1730
SIC 3491 3559 4971 3589

TAYLOR-WHARTON INTERNATIONAL LLC p 1427
5600 Rowland Rd Ste 170, Minnetonka MN 55343
Tel (717) 763-5060 SIC 3443 3491

DEZURIK INC p 435
250 Riverside Ave N, Sartell MN 56377
Tel (320) 259-2000 SIC 3491

WATEROUS CO p 1582
125 Hardman Ave S, South Saint Paul MN 55075
Tel (651) 450-5000
SIC 3491 3561 3494 3321

CONTINENTAL DISC CORP p 363
3160 W Heartland Dr, Liberty MO 64068
Tel (816) 792-1500
SIC 3491 3498 7699 3494

▲ EMERSON ELECTRIC CO p 492
8000 W Florissant Ave, Saint Louis MO 63136
Tel (314) 553-2000
SIC 3823 3491 3621 3585 3679

ROBERT FAMILY HOLDINGS INC p 1241
12430 Tesson Ferry Rd, Saint Louis MO 63128
Tel (314) 821-5665
SIC 2671 3572 3491 3498 7699 3494

■ **ASCO VALVE INC** p 116
50-60 Hanover Rd, Florham Park NJ 07932
Tel (973) 966-2437
SIC 3443 3491 3492 3625 5063

■ **AUTOMATIC SWITCH CO** p 134
50-60 Hanover Rd, Florham Park NJ 07932
Tel (973) 966-2000
SIC 3491 3625 3677 3674 3613 3492

■ **HONEYWELL INC** p 705
115 Tabor Rd, Morris Plains NJ 07950
Tel (973) 455-2000
SIC 3823 3812 3669 3491 3699 3822

TYCO INTERNATIONAL MANAGEMENT CO LLC p 1496
9 Roszel Rd Ste 2, Princeton NJ 08540
Tel (609) 720-4200
SIC 3999 1711 1731 3669 3491

■ **CURTISS-WRIGHT FLOW CONTROL CORP** p 402
1966 Broadhollow Rd Ste E, Farmingdale NY 11735
Tel (631) 293-3800 *SIC* 3491 3494

▲ **CURTISS-WRIGHT CORP** p 402
13925 Balntyn Corp Pl, Charlotte NC 28277
Tel (704) 869-4600 *SIC* 3491 3621 3812

ENGINEERED CONTROLS INTERNATIONAL LLC p 499
100 Rego Dr, Elon NC 27244
Tel (336) 449-7707 *SIC* 3491

SENSUS (BERMUDA 2) LTD p 1305
8601 Six Forks Rd, Raleigh NC 27615
Tel (919) 845-4000 *SIC* 3824 3363 3491

SENSUS USA INC p 1305
8601 Six Forks Rd Ste 700, Raleigh NC 27615
Tel (919) 845-4000
SIC 3824 3363 2891 3491

■ **TRANSDIGM INC** p 1471
4223 Monticello Blvd, Cleveland OH 44121
Tel (216) 706-2939
SIC 5088 3563 3625 3492 3691 3491

WAXMAN INDUSTRIES INC p 1584
24460 Aurora Rd, Cleveland OH 44146
Tel (440) 439-1830
SIC 5072 5074 3494 3491 3432

SWAGELOK CO p 1411
29500 Solon Rd, Solon OH 44139
Tel (440) 248-4600 *SIC* 3494 3491 3599

BALON CORP p 149
3245 S Hattie Ave, Oklahoma City OK 73129
Tel (405) 677-3321 *SIC* 3491 3494 5085

SUPERIOR GROUP INC p 1406
100 Front St Ste 525, Conshohocken PA 19428
Tel (610) 397-2040
SIC 5051 3357 3317 3491 3469 7389

VICTAULIC CO p 1555
4901 Kesslersville Rd, Easton PA 18040
Tel (610) 559-3300
SIC 3321 3491 3494 5085

GAS BREAKER INC p 593
17 Lee Blvd Ste D, Malvern PA 19355
Tel (610) 407-7200 *SIC* 3491

■ **APCOM INC** p 96
125 Se Parkway, Franklin TN 37064
Tel (615) 794-5574 *SIC* 3491 5064

TAPCOENPRO LLC p 1424
16315 Market St, Channelview TX 77530
Tel (281) 247-8100 *SIC* 3491

NOVATECH HOLDINGS CORP p 1063
8388 C F Hawn Fwy, Dallas TX 75217
Tel (214) 398-1491 *SIC* 3491

BRAY INTERNATIONAL INC p 209
13333 Westland East Blvd, Houston TX 77041
Tel (281) 894-7979 *SIC* 3491

CAMERON INTERNATIONAL CORP p 245
4646 W Sam Houston Pkwy N, Houston TX 77041
Tel (713) 513-3300 *SIC* 3533 3563 3491

■ **DANIEL MEASUREMENT AND CONTROL INC** p 411
11100 Brittmoore Park Dr, Houston TX 77041
Tel (713) 467-6000
SIC 3824 3498 3499 3823 3571 3491

▲ **FLOTEK INDUSTRIES INC** p 560
10603 W Sam Houston Pkwy, Houston TX 77064
Tel (713) 849-9911
SIC 2087 2869 2899 3533 3491

■ **GE OIL & GAS PRESSURE CONTROL LP** p 596
4424 W Sam Houston Pkwy N # 100, Houston TX 77041
Tel (281) 398-8901 *SIC* 3491

▲ **OIL STATES INTERNATIONAL INC** p 1079
333 Clay St Ste 4620, Houston TX 77002
Tel (713) 652-0582
SIC 3353 3061 3053 3561 3491

ONESUBSEA LLC p 1088
4646 W Sam Houston Pkwy N, Houston TX 77041
Tel (713) 939-2211 *SIC* 3533 3563 3491

PENTAIR VALVES & CONTROLS LLC p 1132
10707 Clay Rd Ste 200, Houston TX 77041
Tel (713) 986-4665 *SIC* 3491

PENTAIR VALVES & CONTROLS US LP p 1132
10707 Clay Rd Ste 200, Houston TX 77041
Tel (713) 986-4665 *SIC* 3491 3625 3494

■ **T-3 ENERGY SERVICES INC** p 1420
140 Cypress Station Dr # 225, Houston TX 77090
Tel (713) 944-5950 *SIC* 5211 3491 7699

TYCO ENGINEERED PRODUCTS & SERVICES p 1496
9600 W Gulf Bank Rd, Houston TX 77040
Tel (609) 720-4200 *SIC* 3491 3625 3621

▲ **FLOWSERVE CORP** p 560
5215 N Oconnor Blvd Connor, Irving TX 75039
Tel (972) 443-6500
SIC 3561 3491 3621 3494 3463 3321

■ **FLOWSERVE US INC** p 560
5215 N Oconnor Blvd Ste, Irving TX 75039
Tel (972) 443-6500 *SIC* 3561 3491

EPRODUCTION SOLUTIONS LLC p 505
22001 Northpark Dr, Kingwood TX 77339
Tel (281) 348-1000 *SIC* 3491 5084 1389

■ **EMERSON PROCESS MANAGEMENT REGULATOR TECHNOLOGIES INC** p 492
3200 Emerson Way, Mckinney TX 75069
Tel (972) 548-3585 *SIC* 3491

VENTECH INC p 1548
1149 Ellsworth Dr Ofc, Pasadena TX 77506
Tel (713) 477-0201
SIC 8711 3491 5084 6512

■ **DRESSER INC** p 455
601 Shiloh Rd, Plano TX 75074
Tel (262) 549-2626
SIC 3491 3825 3594 3593 3561 3494

■ **MCC HOLDINGS INC** p 926
4526 Res Frest Dr Ste 400, The Woodlands TX 77381
Tel (936) 271-6500 *SIC* 3491 7699

■ **XOMOX CORP** p 1632
4526 Res Frest Dr Ste 400, The Woodlands TX 77381
Tel (936) 271-6500 *SIC* 3491 3593 3494

■ **ROBBIN & MEYERS ENERGY SYSTEMS LP** p 1240
10586 N Highway 75, Willis TX 77378
Tel (936) 890-1064 *SIC* 3491 3533

ENVIROTECH PUMPSYSTEMS INC p 504
440 W 800 S, Salt Lake City UT 84101
Tel (801) 359-8731 *SIC* 3561 3491 3089

■ **FLOWSERVE FCD CORP** p 560
1350 N Mtn Spring Pkwy, Springville UT 84663
Tel (801) 489-8611 *SIC* 3491

VELAN VALVE CORP p 1547
94 Avenue C, Williston VT 05495
Tel (802) 863-2561 *SIC* 3491

SCHRADER-BRIDGEPORT INTERNATIONAL INC p 1290
205 Frazier Rd, Altavista VA 24517
Tel (434) 369-4741
SIC 3492 3714 3491 3011

ALFA LAVAL INC p 49
5400 Intl Trade Dr, Richmond VA 23231
Tel (804) 222-5300
SIC 3491 3433 3585 3569 3821

▲ **BADGER METER INC** p 144
4545 W Brown Deer Rd, Milwaukee WI 53223
Tel (414) 355-0400 *SIC* 3824 3491 3823

▲ **REXNORD CORP** p 1230
4701 W Greenfield Ave, Milwaukee WI 53214
Tel (414) 643-3739 *SIC* 3491

WESTERN INDUSTRIES INC p 1598
1141 S 10th St, Watertown WI 53094
Tel (920) 261-0660
SIC 3443 3469 3089 3444 1761 3491

SIC 3492 Fluid Power Valves & Hose Fittings

■ **SARGENT AEROSPACE & DEFENSE LLC** p 1282
5675 W Burlingame Rd, Tucson AZ 85743
Tel (520) 744-1000
SIC 3728 3724 3568 3492

GRISWOLD INDUSTRIES p 641
1701 Placentia Ave, Costa Mesa CA 92627
Tel (949) 722-4800 *SIC* 3492 3365 3366

EBARA AMERICA CORP p 474
809 Walker Ave Apt 1, Oakland CA 94610
Tel (510) 251-0500 *SIC* 3492

■ **WOODWARD HRT INC** p 1623
25200 Rye Canyon Rd, Santa Clarita CA 91355
Tel (661) 294-6000 *SIC* 3625 3492

▲ **WOODWARD INC** p 1623
1081 Woodward Way, Fort Collins CO 80524
Tel (970) 482-5811
SIC 3625 3629 3492 3519

NORGREN INC p 1048
5400 S Delaware St, Littleton CO 80120
Tel (303) 794-5000 *SIC* 3492

■ **EM CLARCOR HOLDINGS INC** p 490
60 Prestige Park Rd, East Hartford CT 06108
Tel (860) 920-4200 *SIC* 3714 3492

■ **CRANE AEROSPACE INC** p 388
100 Stamford Pl, Stamford CT 06902
Tel (203) 363-7300 *SIC* 3492

▲ **CRANE CO** p 388
100 1st Stamford Pl # 300, Stamford CT 06902
Tel (203) 363-7300
SIC 3492 3494 3594 3589 3728 5031

■ **CRANE INTERNATIONAL HOLDINGS INC** p 389
100 Stamford Pl, Stamford CT 06902
Tel (203) 363-7300 *SIC* 3492

STANADYNE INTERMEDIATE HOLDINGS LLC p 1375
92 Deerfield Rd, Windsor CT 06095
Tel (860) 525-0821 *SIC* 3714 3492

▲ **SUN HYDRAULICS CORP** p 1400
1500 W University Pkwy, Sarasota FL 34243
Tel (941) 362-1200 *SIC* 3492

▲ **MUELLER WATER PRODUCTS INC** p 998
1200 Abernathy Rd # 1200, Atlanta GA 30328
Tel (770) 206-4200
SIC 3491 3492 3494 3443 3321 3823

VERNAY LABORATORIES INC p 1551
2077 Cnvntion Ctr Cncurse, Atlanta GA 30337
Tel (404) 994-2000 *SIC* 3492

■ **MARMON INDUSTRIAL LLC** p 909
181 W Madison St Fl 26, Chicago IL 60602
Tel (312) 372-9500
SIC 3743 4741 3589 6159 3965 3492

■ **DOVER ENGINEERED SYSTEMS INC** p 453
3005 Highland Pkwy # 200, Downers Grove IL 60515
Tel (630) 743-2505
SIC 3568 3443 3441 3561 3491 3492

ROBERTSHAW CONTROLS CO p 1242
1222 Hamilton Pkwy, Itasca IL 60143
Tel (630) 260-3400 *SIC* 3823 3822 3492

HYDRAFORCE INC p 723
500 Barclay Blvd, Lincolnshire IL 60069
Tel (847) 793-2300 *SIC* 3492

MAC LEAN-FOGG CO p 891
1000 Allanson Rd, Mundelein IL 60060
Tel (847) 566-0010
SIC 3678 3452 3089 3061 3492 3451

DEUBLIN CO p 433
2050 Norman Dr, Waukegan IL 60085
Tel (847) 689-8600
SIC 3498 3492 3568 3494

ROSENBOOM MACHINE & TOOL INC p 1251
1530 Western Ave, Sheldon IA 51201
Tel (712) 324-4854 *SIC* 3593 3492 3594

YOKOHAMA INDUSTRIES AMERICAS INC p 1637
105 Industry Dr, Versailles KY 40383
Tel (859) 873-2188
SIC 3714 3585 3492 3052

DIXON VALVE & COUPLING CO p 445
800 High St, Chestertown MD 21620
Tel (410) 778-2000 *SIC* 3492 5085

DVCC INC p 463
800 High St, Chestertown MD 21620
Tel (410) 778-2000
SIC 3492 5085 3535 3321 3364

▲ **CIRCOR INTERNATIONAL INC** p 308
30 Corporate Dr Ste 200, Burlington MA 01803
Tel (781) 270-1200 *SIC* 3492

MICROGROUP INC p 962
7 Industrial Park Rd, Medway MA 02053
Tel (508) 533-4925
SIC 5051 3312 3498 3494 3492 3317

■ **HUTCHINSON FTS INC** p 722
1060 Centre Rd, Auburn Hills MI 48326
Tel (248) 589-7710
SIC 3714 3061 3567 3492 3443 3429

OILGEAR CO p 1079
1424 International Dr, Traverse City MI 49686
Tel (231) 929-1660 *SIC* 3594 3492 3593

MAC VALVES INC p 891
30569 Beck Rd, Wixom MI 48393
Tel (248) 624-7700 *SIC* 3492 3494 3491

NOTT CO p 1062
4480 Round Lake Rd W, Arden Hills MN 55112
Tel (651) 415-3400
SIC 5084 5085 3492 3053

EATON HYDRAULICS LLC p 473
14615 Lone Oak Rd, Eden Prairie MN 55344
Tel (952) 937-9800
SIC 3089 3052 3568 3492 3594 3728

■ **ESCO TECHNOLOGIES HOLDING LLC** p 509
9900 Clayton Rd Ste A, Saint Louis MO 63124
Tel (314) 213-7200
SIC 3825 3492 3812 3711 3663

■ **ASCO VALVE INC** p 116
50-60 Hanover Rd, Florham Park NJ 07932
Tel (973) 966-2437
SIC 3443 3491 3492 3625 5063

■ **AUTOMATIC SWITCH CO** p 134
50-60 Hanover Rd, Florham Park NJ 07932
Tel (973) 966-2000
SIC 3491 3625 3677 3674 3613 3492

■ **BW ELLIOTT MANUFACTURING CO LLC** p 230
11 Beckwith Ave, Binghamton NY 13901
Tel (607) 772-0404 *SIC* 3568 3492 3531

GW LISK CO INC p 648
2 South St, Clifton Springs NY 14432
Tel (315) 462-2611 *SIC* 3679 4119 3492

▲ **MOOG INC** p 987
400 Jamison Rd Plant26, Elma NY 14059
Tel (716) 652-2000
SIC 3812 3492 3625 3769 3728 3841

FESTO CORP p 539
395 Moreland Rd, Hauppauge NY 11788
Tel (800) 993-3786
SIC 5085 3593 3566 3492

CROSS TECHNOLOGIES INC p 394
4400 Piedmont Pkwy, Greensboro NC 27410
Tel (336) 856-6000 *SIC* 5084 3492

KIRTLAND CAPITAL PARTNERS LP p 822
3201 Entp Pkwy Ste 200, Beachwood OH 44122
Tel (216) 593-0100
SIC 5051 3312 3498 3494 3492 3317

AEROQUIP-VICKERS INC p 30
1111 Superior Ave E, Cleveland OH 44114
Tel (216) 523-5000
SIC 3052 3492 3429 3069 3585 3728

EATON-AEROQUIP LLC p 474
1000 Eaton Blvd, Cleveland OH 44122
Tel (216) 523-5000
SIC 3052 3492 3429 3069 3585 3728

▲ **PARKER-HANNIFIN CORP** p 1116
6035 Parkland Blvd, Cleveland OH 44124
Tel (216) 896-3000
SIC 3594 3593 3492 3569 3053 3829

■ **TRANSDIGM INC** p 1471
4223 Monticello Blvd, Cleveland OH 44121
Tel (216) 706-2939
SIC 5088 3563 3625 3492 3691 3491

▲ **DANA INC** p 410
3939 Technology Dr, Maumee OH 43537
Tel (419) 887-3000
SIC 3714 3053 3593 3492

■ **DANA LIMITED** p 410
3939 Technology Dr, Maumee OH 43537
Tel (630) 697-3783
SIC 3714 3053 3593 3492

NATIONAL MACHINE CO p 1014
4880 Hudson Dr, Stow OH 44224
Tel (330) 688-6494 *SIC* 3599 3492

HYDAC TECHNOLOGY CORP p 723
2260 City Line Rd 2280, Bethlehem PA 18017
Tel (205) 520-1220 *SIC* 3492

PRINCE MANUFACTURING CORP p 1176
612 N Derby Ln, North Sioux City SD 57049
Tel (605) 235-1220 *SIC* 3593 3492 3594

TUBULAR MACHINED PRODUCTS p 1490
90 Campbell Acres Rd, Cleveland TX 77328
Tel (713) 504-8932 *SIC* 5051 3492 7389

SCHLUMBERGER INTERNATIONAL INC p 1287
7030 Ardmore St, Houston TX 77054
Tel (713) 747-4000
SIC 1389 3561 3492 3533

SCHRADER-BRIDGEPORT INTERNATIONAL INC p 1290
205 Frazier Rd, Altavista VA 24517
Tel (434) 369-4741
SIC 3492 3714 3491 3011

▲ **ACTUANT CORP** p 20
N86w12500 Westbrook Xing, Menomonee Falls WI 53051
Tel (262) 293-1500
SIC 3593 3492 3594 3625 7359

MASON WELLS BUYOUT FUND II LIMITED PARTNERSHIP p 916
411 E Wisconsin Ave, Milwaukee WI 53202
Tel (414) 727-6400
SIC 3594 3492 3593 6211

MILWAUKEE VALVE CO INC p 972
16550 W Stratton Dr, New Berlin WI 53151
Tel (262) 432-2800 *SIC* 3494 3492 3432

HUSCO INTERNATIONAL INC p 721
2239 Pewaukee Rd, Waukesha WI 53188
Tel (262) 513-4200 *SIC* 3492

SIC 3493 Steel Springs, Except Wire

DAEWON AMERICA INC p 408
4600 N Park Dr, Opelika AL 36801
Tel (334) 364-1600 *SIC* 3493

CONNECTICUT SPRING AND STAMPING CORP p 357
48 Spring Ln, Farmington CT 06032
Tel (860) 677-1341 *SIC* 3469 3495 3493

BOLER CO p 198
500 Park Blvd Ste 1010, Itasca IL 60143
Tel (630) 773-9111 *SIC* 3714 3493

MATTHEW WARREN INC p 920
9501 Tech Blvd Ste 401, Rosemont IL 60018
Tel (847) 349-5760 *SIC* 3493

MUBEA INC p 998
6800 Industrial Rd, Florence KY 41042
Tel (859) 746-5300
SIC 3493 3312 3495 3429 3714

GILL CORP p 612
706 Bond Ave Nw, Grand Rapids MI 49503
Tel (859) 625-5284
SIC 3469 3312 3495 3493 3496 3465

▲ **MERITOR INC** p 949
2135 W Maple Rd, Troy MI 48084
Tel (248) 435-1000
SIC 3714 3493 3625 3465

STABILUS INC p 1374
1201 Tulip Dr, Gastonia NC 28052
Tel (704) 865-7444 *SIC* 3493

STABLE HOLDCO INC p 1374
1201 Tulip Dr, Gastonia NC 28052
Tel (704) 866-7140 *SIC* 3493

DAYTON PROGRESS CORP p 418
500 Progress Rd, Dayton OH 45449
Tel (937) 859-5111
SIC 3544 3545 3495 3493

MACLEAN POWER LLC p 892
481 Munn Rd E Ste 300, Fort Mill SC 29715
Tel (847) 455-0014 *SIC* 3493

BRIDGESTONE AMERICAS INC p 211
535 Marriott Dr, Nashville TN 37214
Tel (615) 937-1000
SIC 3011 3493 2952 2822 3229

SIC 3494 Valves & Pipe Fittings, NEC

CONSOLIDATED PIPE & SUPPLY CO INC p 360
1205 Hilltop Pkwy, Birmingham AL 35204
Tel (205) 323-7261 *SIC* 3494

MCWANE INC p 933
2900 Highway 280 S # 300, Birmingham AL 35223
Tel (205) 414-3100
SIC 3491 1221 3321 3312 3494

WELSPUN PIPES INC p 1591
9301 Frazier Pike, Little Rock AR 72206
Tel (501) 301-8800 *SIC* 1799 3494

RAIN BIRD CORP p 1205
1000 W Sierra Madre Ave, Azusa CA 91702
Tel (626) 812-3400 *SIC* 3494 3432 3523

SMITH COOPER INTERNATIONAL INC p 1333
2867 Vail Ave, Commerce CA 90040
Tel (323) 890-4455 *SIC* 5085 3494

JAMES HARDIE TRANSITION CO INC p 776
26300 La Alameda Ste 400, Mission Viejo CA 92691
Tel (949) 348-1800
SIC 3275 3523 3494 5072

■ **IDEX HEALTH & SCIENCE LLC** p 729
600 Park Ct, Rohnert Park CA 94928
Tel (707) 588-2000
SIC 3821 3829 3826 3823 3494

SPEARS MANUFACTURING CO p 1355
15853 Olden St, Sylmar CA 91342
Tel (818) 364-7306 *SIC* 3494 5083

▲ **CRANE CO** p 388
100 1st Stamford Pl # 300, Stamford CT 06902
Tel (203) 363-7300
SIC 3492 3494 3594 3589 3728 5031

HOERBIGER COMPRESSION TECHNOLOGY AMERICA HOLDING INC p 699
3350 Gateway Dr, Pompano Beach FL 33069
Tel (954) 974-5700 *SIC* 3494 7699

▲ **MUELLER WATER PRODUCTS INC** p 998
1200 Abernathy Rd # 1200, Atlanta GA 30328
Tel (770) 206-4200
SIC 3491 3492 3494 3443 3321 3823

AMERICAN BOA INC p 69
1420 Redi Rd, Cumming GA 30040
Tel (678) 513-3348 *SIC* 3494

HENRY TECHNOLOGIES INC p 684
701 S Main St, Chatham IL 62629
Tel (217) 483-2406
SIC 3491 3585 3567 3564 3545 3494

SLOAN VALVE CO p 1331
10500 Seymour Ave, Franklin Park IL 60131
Tel (847) 671-4300 SIC 3494 3432

■ ECLIPSE INC p 475
1665 Elmwood Rd, Rockford IL 61103
Tel (815) 877-3031
SIC 3564 3433 3822 3823 3443 3494

DEUBLIN CO p 433
2050 Norman Dr, Waukegan IL 60085
Tel (847) 689-8600
SIC 3498 3492 3568 3494

KELCO INDUSTRIES INC p 808
1425 Lake Ave, Woodstock IL 60098
Tel (815) 334-3600
SIC 3599 3069 3494 3585 3544 3625

NIBCO INC p 1042
1516 Middlebury St, Elkhart IN 46516
Tel (574) 295-3000 SIC 3494 3491 3089

FORD METER BOX CO INC p 565
775 Manchester Ave, Wabash IN 46992
Tel (260) 563-3171 SIC 3494

A Y MCDONALD INDUSTRIES INC p 7
4800 Chavenelle Rd, Dubuque IA 52002
Tel (800) 292-2737
SIC 3432 3561 3494 5074 5075 5031

■ FISHER CONTROLS INTERNATIONAL LLC p 552
205 S Center St, Marshalltown IA 50158
Tel (641) 754-3011
SIC 3491 3823 3625 3612 3494

■ INSTRUMENT & VALVE SERVICES CO p 747
205 S Center St, Marshalltown IA 50158
Tel (641) 754-3011 SIC 3494 3825 7699

▲ MKS INSTRUMENTS INC p 979
2 Tech Dr Ste 201, Andover MA 01810
Tel (978) 645-5500 SIC 3823 3491 3494

MICROGROUP INC p 962
7 Industrial Park Rd, Medway MA 02053
Tel (508) 533-4925
SIC 5051 3312 3498 3494 3492 3317

■ WATTS REGULATOR CO p 1583
815 Chestnut St, North Andover MA 01845
Tel (978) 689-6000 SIC 3491 3494

▲ WATTS WATER TECHNOLOGIES INC p 1583
815 Chestnut St, North Andover MA 01845
Tel (978) 688-1811 SIC 3491 3494

THG CORP p 1447
70 Bearfoot Rd, Northborough MA 01532
Tel (508) 393-7660
SIC 5085 5084 3569 3728 3625 3494

GENOVA PRODUCTS INC p 604
7034 E Court St, Davison MI 48423
Tel (810) 744-4500
SIC 3089 2891 2911 3494 3084 2952

MELLING TOOL CO p 941
2620 Saradan Dr, Jackson MI 49202
Tel (517) 787-8172
SIC 3451 3714 3625 3568 3561 3494

■ JOHNSON KADANT INC p 791
805 Wood St, Three Rivers MI 49093
Tel (269) 278-1715
SIC 3494 8711 1389 3052 1099

SRG GLOBAL INC p 1363
800 Stephenson Hwy, Troy MI 48083
Tel (586) 757-7800
SIC 3089 3571 3494 2522 3826 3825

MAC VALVES INC p 891
30569 Beck Rd, Wixom MI 48393
Tel (248) 624-7700 SIC 3492 3494 3491

▲ TORO CO p 1461
8111 Lyndale Ave S, Bloomington MN 55420
Tel (952) 888-8801
SIC 3523 3524 3494 3645

■ TESCOM CORP p 1440
12616 Industrial Blvd Nw, Elk River MN 55330
Tel (763) 441-6330 SIC 3491 3625 3494

SPECIALTY MFG CO p 1356
5858 Centerville Rd, Saint Paul MN 55127
Tel (651) 653-0599 SIC 3494

WATEROUS CO p 1582
125 Hardman Ave S, South Saint Paul MN 55075
Tel (651) 450-5000
SIC 3491 3561 3494 3321

FIKE CORP p 542
704 Sw 10th St, Blue Springs MO 64015
Tel (816) 229-3405
SIC 3494 3569 3444 2899

CONTINENTAL DISC CORP p 363
3160 W Heartland Dr, Liberty MO 64068
Tel (816) 792-1500
SIC 3491 3498 7699 3494

ROBERT FAMILY HOLDINGS INC p 1241
12430 Tesson Ferry Rd, Saint Louis MO 63128
Tel (314) 821-5665
SIC 2671 3572 3491 3498 7699 3494

■ ANVIL INTERNATIONAL LLC p 94
2 Holland Way, Exeter NH 03833
Tel (603) 418-2800
SIC 3498 3321 3317 3494 3429

SIGMA INTERNATIONAL GROUP INC p 1321
700 Goldman Dr, Cream Ridge NJ 08514
Tel (609) 758-0800 SIC 3494

HAYWARD INDUSTRIES INC p 670
620 Division St, Elizabeth NJ 07201
Tel (908) 351-5400
SIC 3589 3561 3423 3494 3569 3089

■ CURTISS-WRIGHT FLOW CONTROL CORP p 402
1966 Broadhollow Rd Ste E, Farmingdale NY 11735
Tel (631) 293-3800 SIC 3491 3494

ARVOS HOLDING LLC p 114
3020 Truax Rd, Wellsville NY 14895
Tel (585) 596-2501 SIC 3494

ITT FLUID TECHNOLOGY CORP p 768
1133 Westcstr Ave N100 Ste N, White Plains NY 10604
Tel (914) 641-2000 SIC 3494 3594 3561

JAMES M PLEASANTS CO INC p 776
603 Diamond Hill Ct, Greensboro NC 27406
Tel (336) 275-3152
SIC 5075 3585 3561 3494

CONBRACO INDUSTRIES INC p 354
701 Matthews Mint Hill Rd, Matthews NC 28105
Tel (704) 841-6000 SIC 3625 3494

SPC MECHANICAL CORP p 1355
1908 Baldree Rd S, Wilson NC 27893
Tel (252) 237-9035 SIC 3494 1711 3444

KIRTLAND CAPITAL PARTNERS LP p 822
3201 Entp Pkwy Ste 200, Beachwood OH 44122
Tel (216) 593-0100
SIC 5051 3312 3498 3494 3492 3317

WAXMAN INDUSTRIES INC p 1584
24460 Aurora Rd, Cleveland OH 44146
Tel (440) 439-1830
SIC 5072 5074 3494 3491 3432

FCX PERFORMANCE INC p 533
3000 E 14th Ave, Columbus OH 43219
Tel (614) 324-6050 SIC 5084 5085 3494

SWAGELOK CO p 1411
29500 Solon Rd, Solon OH 44139
Tel (440) 248-4600 SIC 3494 3491 3599

BALON CORP p 149
3245 S Hattie Ave, Oklahoma City OK 73129
Tel (405) 677-3321 SIC 3491 3494 5085

VICTAULIC CO p 1555
4901 Kesslersville Rd, Easton PA 18040
Tel (610) 559-3300
SIC 3321 3491 3494 5085

TYCO FIRE PRODUCTS LP p 1496
1400 Pennbrook Pkwy, Lansdale PA 19446
Tel (215) 362-0700
SIC 3569 3494 3321 5085

LASCO FITTINGS INC p 846
414 Morgan St, Brownsville TN 38012
Tel (800) 776-2756 SIC 3494

■ MUELLER BRASS CO p 998
8285 Tournament Dr # 150, Memphis TN 38125
Tel (901) 753-3200
SIC 3351 3463 3354 3494

■ MUELLER BRASS HOLDING CO INC p 998
8285 Tournament Dr # 150, Memphis TN 38125
Tel (901) 753-3200 SIC 3351 3463 3494

▲ MUELLER INDUSTRIES INC p 998
8285 Tournament Dr # 150, Memphis TN 38125
Tel (901) 753-3200 SIC 3463 3494 3089

▲ AZZ INC p 141
3100 W 7th St Ste 500, Fort Worth TX 76107
Tel (817) 810-0095
SIC 3699 3613 3494 3312

■ DANIEL INDUSTRIES INC p 411
11100 Brittmoore Park Dr, Houston TX 77041
Tel (713) 467-6000
SIC 3823 3824 3494 3829 3826 3571

PENTAIR VALVES & CONTROLS US LP p 1132
10707 Clay Rd Ste 200, Houston TX 77041
Tel (713) 986-4665 SIC 3491 3625 3494

PIPING TECHNOLOGY & PRODUCTS INC p 1151
3701 Holmes Rd, Houston TX 77051
Tel (800) 787-5914 SIC 3494 8711 3441

▲ FLOWSERVE CORP p 560
5215 N Oconnor Blvd Connor, Irving TX 75039
Tel (972) 443-6500
SIC 3561 3491 3621 3494 3463 3321

W CSE INDUSTRIES INC p 1568
11500 Charles Rd, Jersey Village TX 77041
Tel (713) 466-9463
SIC 3625 3613 3594 3494

■ DRESSER INC p 455
601 Shiloh Rd, Plano TX 75074
Tel (262) 549-2626
SIC 3491 3825 3594 3593 3561 3494

■ XOMOX CORP p 1632
4526 Res Frest Dr Ste 400, The Woodlands TX 77381
Tel (936) 271-6500 SIC 3491 3593 3494

VSC FIRE & SECURITY INC p 1566
10343b Kings Acres Rd, Ashland VA 23005
Tel (804) 459-2200 SIC 1711 3494

KSB AMERICA CORP p 831
4415 Sarellen Rd, Richmond VA 23231
Tel (804) 222-1818
SIC 3561 3494 3625 5084

MILWAUKEE VALVE CO INC p 972
16550 W Stratton Dr, New Berlin WI 53151
Tel (262) 432-2800 SIC 3494 3492 3432

SIC 3495 Wire Springs

BAL SEAL ENGINEERING INC p 147
19650 Pauling, Foothill Ranch CA 92610
Tel (949) 334-8500 SIC 3495

▲ BARNES GROUP INC p 156
123 Main St, Bristol CT 06010
Tel (860) 583-7070 SIC 3724 3495 3469

CONNECTICUT SPRING AND STAMPING CORP p 357
48 Spring Ln, Farmington CT 06032
Tel (860) 677-1341 SIC 3469 3495 3493

JD NORMAN INDUSTRIES INC p 780
787 W Belden Ave, Addison IL 60101
Tel (630) 458-3700 SIC 3469 3496 3495

FIRESTONE INDUSTRIAL PRODUCTS CO LLC p 544
250 W 96th St Ste 150, Indianapolis IN 46260
Tel (317) 818-8600
SIC 5531 3469 3714 3495

MUBEA INC p 998
6800 Industrial Rd, Florence KY 41042
Tel (859) 746-5300
SIC 3493 3312 3495 3429 3714

GILL CORP p 612
706 Bond Ave Nw, Grand Rapids MI 49503
Tel (859) 625-5284
SIC 3469 3312 3495 3493 3496 3465

PETERSON AMERICAN CORP p 1138
21200 Telegraph Rd, Southfield MI 48033
Tel (248) 799-5400 SIC 3495

▲ LEGGETT & PLATT INC p 853
1 Leggett Rd, Carthage MO 64836
Tel (417) 358-8131
SIC 2515 2514 3495 2392 2542 3363

HICKORY SPRINGS MANUFACTURING CO p 690
235 2nd Ave Nw, Hickory NC 28601
Tel (828) 328-2201
SIC 3069 3495 2514 5072 2399

DAYTON PROGRESS CORP p 418
500 Progress Rd, Dayton OH 45449
Tel (937) 859-5111
SIC 3544 3545 3495 3493

BLOUNT INC p 190
4909 Se International Way, Portland OR 97222
Tel (503) 653-8881
SIC 3546 3568 7699 3495

SIC 3496 Misc Fabricated Wire Prdts

PHIFER INC p 1142
4400 Kauloosa Ave, Tuscaloosa AL 35401
Tel (205) 345-2120
SIC 3496 2221 3357 2295 3442 3354

SSW HOLDING CO INC p 1364
3501 Tulsa St, Fort Smith AR 72903
Tel (479) 646-1651 SIC 3496 6719

HYSPAN PRECISION PRODUCTS INC p 724
1685 Brandywine Ave, Chula Vista CA 91911
Tel (619) 421-1355 SIC 3568 3496 3441

NATIONAL BUSINESS GROUP INC p 1010
15319 Chatsworth St, Mission Hills CA 91345
Tel (818) 221-6000
SIC 7353 5039 7359 3496 7519

WIREMOLD CO p 1618
60 Woodlawn St, West Hartford CT 06110
Tel (860) 233-6251
SIC 3644 3643 3496 3315

BIO MEDIC CORP p 183
742 Sussex Ave, Seaford DE 19973
Tel (302) 628-4300
SIC 5049 3821 3496 3914 3661

MERCHANTS METALS LLC p 945
211 Perimeter Center Pkwy, Atlanta GA 30346
Tel (770) 741-0300 SIC 3496 3446 5031

JD NORMAN INDUSTRIES INC p 780
787 W Belden Ave, Addison IL 60101
Tel (630) 458-3700 SIC 3469 3496 3495

▲ ATKORE INTERNATIONAL GROUP INC p 125
16100 Lathrop Ave, Harvey IL 60426
Tel (708) 339-1610
SIC 3441 1791 3446 3448 3496

■ ATKORE INTERNATIONAL HOLDINGS INC p 125
16100 Lathrop Ave, Harvey IL 60426
Tel (708) 225-2051
SIC 6719 3441 1791 3446 3448 3496

■ UNISTRUT INTERNATIONAL CORP p 1505
16100 Lathrop Ave, Harvey IL 60426
Tel (800) 882-5543
SIC 3441 1791 3446 3448 3496 3429

■ ACCO BRANDS USA LLC p 15
4 Corporate Dr, Lake Zurich IL 60047
Tel (800) 222-6462
SIC 3089 2761 3496 2675

ALP LIGHTING & CEILING PRODUCTS INC p 60
6333 W Gross Point Rd, Niles IL 60714
Tel (773) 774-9550
SIC 3089 3354 5162 3496 3442 3229

GROUP DEKKO HOLDINGS INC p 641
2505 Dekko Dr, Garrett IN 46738
Tel (260) 347-0700 SIC 3496

DEKKO ACQUISITION PARENT INC p 423
6928 N 400 E, Kendallville IN 46755
Tel (260) 347-0700 SIC 3496

APACHE HOSE & BELTING CO INC p 96
4805 Bowling St Sw, Cedar Rapids IA 52404
Tel (319) 365-0471 SIC 3496 3052 5085

WIRECO WORLDGROUP INC p 1618
2400 W 75th St, Prairie Village KS 66208
Tel (816) 270-4700 SIC 3496

WIRECO WORLDGROUP US HOLDINGS INC p 1618
2400 W 75th St, Prairie Village KS 66208
Tel (816) 270-4700 SIC 3496

■ BALCO INC p 147
2626 S Sheridan Ave, Wichita KS 67217
Tel (800) 767-0082
SIC 3441 3089 3496 3446 3443

CAMBRIDGE INTERNATIONAL INC p 244
105 Goodwill Rd, Cambridge MD 21613
Tel (410) 228-3000 SIC 3496

ADRIAN STEEL CO p 24
906 James St, Adrian MI 49221
Tel (517) 265-6194 SIC 3496 3469

HI-LEX AMERICA INC p 689
5200 Wayne Rd, Battle Creek MI 49037
Tel (269) 968-0781 SIC 3496 3357

GILL CORP p 612
706 Bond Ave Nw, Grand Rapids MI 49503
Tel (859) 625-5284
SIC 3469 3312 3495 3493 3496 3465

NATIONAL-STANDARD LLC p 1017
1631 Lake St, Niles MI 49120
Tel (269) 683-9902 SIC 3315 3496

STONEBRIDGE INDUSTRIES INC p 1391
42400 Merrill Rd, Sterling Heights MI 48314
Tel (586) 323-0348 SIC 3496 3462 3451

COMMERCIAL GROUP INC p 345
12801 Universal Dr, Taylor MI 48180
Tel (313) 931-6100
SIC 5085 5051 3496 3537 3534

PEERLESS INDUSTRIAL GROUP INC p 1127
1416 E Sanborn St, Winona MN 55987
Tel (507) 457-9100 SIC 3496

STEEL SERVICE CORP p 1384
2260 Flowood Dr, Jackson MS 39232
Tel (601) 939-9222
SIC 3441 1791 3496 3443

BEHLEN MFG CO p 168
4025 E 23rd St, Columbus NE 68601
Tel (402) 564-3111
SIC 3523 3448 4213 3556 3496 3443

▲ ALBANY INTERNATIONAL CORP p 45
216 Airport Dr, Rochester NH 03867
Tel (518) 445-2200
SIC 2221 3496 2399 2899 3089

ALLENTOWN INC p 53
165 Route 526, Allentown NJ 08501
Tel (609) 259-7951 SIC 3444 3496 5162

GENTEK INC p 604
90 E Halsey Rd Ste 301, Parsippany NJ 07054
Tel (973) 515-0900
SIC 2869 2819 2844 3714 3496

HANES SUPPLY INC p 657
55 James E Casey Dr, Buffalo NY 14206
Tel (716) 826-2636
SIC 5085 5082 3496 1799

SEFAR INC p 1300
111 Calumet St, Depew NY 14043
Tel (716) 683-4050
SIC 5131 5051 5084 3496 2297 2221

▲ COLUMBUS MCKINNON CORP p 342
205 Crosspoint Pkwy, Getzville NY 14068
Tel (716) 689-5400
SIC 3536 3496 3535 3537

EASTERN WHOLESALE FENCE CO INC p 473
274 Middle Island Rd, Medford NY 11763
Tel (631) 698-0900
SIC 5039 5031 5051 3496

RENCO GROUP INC p 1223
1 Rockefeller Plz Fl 29, New York NY 10020
Tel (212) 541-6000
SIC 3312 3316 2514 2511 3171 3496

AEROFLEX INC p 30
35 S Service Rd, Plainview NY 11803
Tel (516) 694-6700
SIC 3812 3621 3677 3674 3496 3827

INTERNATIONAL TEXTILE GROUP INC p 757
804 Green Valley Rd # 300, Greensboro NC 27408
Tel (336) 379-6299
SIC 3714 3496 2211 2231 2221 2273

ALCAN CORP p 47
6060 Parkland Blvd, Cleveland OH 44124
Tel (440) 460-3307
SIC 3351 3355 3496 3357

OKLAHOMA STEEL & WIRE CO INC p 1080
Hwy 70 S, Madill OK 73446
Tel (580) 795-7311 SIC 3496

FKI INDUSTRIES INC p 554
2801 Dawson Rd, Tulsa OK 74110
Tel (918) 834-4611
SIC 3429 3536 3535 3496 3569 3823

■ UNARCO INDUSTRIES LLC p 1502
400 Se 15th St, Wagoner OK 74467
Tel (918) 485-9531 SIC 3496

TRI-BORO CONSTRUCTION SUPPLIES INC p 1477
465 E Locust St, Dallastown PA 17313
Tel (717) 246-3095 SIC 5082 3496 5251

WOODSTREAM CORP p 1623
69 N Locust St, Lititz PA 17543
Tel (717) 626-2125 SIC 3496

FENNER DUNLOP AMERICAS INC p 537
1000 Omega Dr Ste 1400, Pittsburgh PA 15205
Tel (412) 249-0700 SIC 3496

INTERMETRO INDUSTRIES CORP p 753
651 N Washington St, Wilkes Barre PA 18705
Tel (570) 825-2741
SIC 3496 2542 3537 3411 3315 2441

WIREROPE WORKS INC p 1618
100 Maynard St, Williamsport PA 17701
Tel (570) 327-4229 SIC 3496 2298 3315

ACS INDUSTRIES INC p 19
1 New England Way Unit 1, Lincoln RI 02865
Tel (401) 769-4700
SIC 3291 3496 3312 3315 3569 3991

■ NEPTCO INC p 1026
30 Hamlet St, Pawtucket RI 02861
Tel (401) 722-5500 SIC 3496 3083 2672

NASHVILLE WIRE PRODUCTS MFG CO p 1008
199 Polk Ave, Nashville TN 37210
Tel (615) 743-2500 SIC 3496 3471 3643

MUELLER SUPPLY CO INC p 998
1913 Hutchins Ave, Ballinger TX 76821
Tel (325) 365-3555 SIC 3448 3496 5039

MASTER-HALCO INC p 918
3010 Lbj Fwy Ste 800, Dallas TX 75234
Tel (972) 714-7300
SIC 3315 5039 3496 3446 5031 1799

AMERICAN BLOCK CO p 69
6311 Breen Dr, Houston TX 77086
Tel (800) 572-9087
SIC 3441 3599 3533 3496 3444 3429

BLP SETTLEMENT CO p 190
125 Mccarty St, Houston TX 77029
Tel (713) 674-2266 SIC 5085 3496

DELTA RIGGING & TOOLS INC p 427
125 Mccarty St, Houston TX 77029
Tel (713) 512-1700 SIC 7359 2298 3496

HOOVER GROUP INC p 706
2135 Highway 6 S, Houston TX 77077
Tel (800) 844-8683
SIC 3496 3412 3443 3089 7359 3411

SBP HOLDING LP p 1285
125 Mccarty St, Houston TX 77029
Tel (713) 953-1113 SIC 5085 3496

SUNCOAST POST-TENSION LTD p 1402
509 N Sam Houston Pkwy E # 300, Houston TX 77060
Tel (281) 445-8886
SIC 3315 3316 3496 3449

KASPAR WIRE WORKS INC p 804
959 State Highway 95 N, Shiner TX 77984
Tel (361) 594-3327 SIC 3496

GLOBAL SAFETY TEXTILES LLC p 617
1556 Montgomery St, South Hill VA 23970
Tel (434) 447-7629 SIC 3714 2211 3496

CHARTER MANUFACTURING CO INC p 291
1212 W Glen Oaks Ln, Mequon WI 53092
Tel (262) 243-4700 SIC 3312 3496

SIC 3497 Metal Foil & Leaf

▲ AVERY DENNISON CORP p 137
207 N Goode Ave Fl 6, Glendale CA 91203
Tel (626) 304-2000
SIC 2672 3081 3497 2678

BAGCRAFTPAPERCON I LLC p 144
3900 W 43rd St, Chicago IL 60632
Tel (620) 856-2800
SIC 2671 2674 2673 3497 2759

DURABLE INC p 462
750 Northgate Pkwy, Wheeling IL 60090
Tel (847) 541-4400 SIC 3497 3354

HANDI-FOIL CORP p 657
135 E Hintz Rd, Wheeling IL 60090
Tel (847) 520-1000 SIC 3497

HFA INC p 689
135 E Hintz Rd, Wheeling IL 60090
Tel (847) 520-1000 SIC 3497

REVERE INDUSTRIES LLC p 1229
16855 Suthpark Dr Ste 100, Westfield IN 46074
Tel (317) 580-2420
SIC 3089 3399 3363 3497

REVERE INDUSTRIES LLC p 1229
838 N Delsea Dr, Clayton NJ 08312
Tel (856) 881-3600 SIC 3497 3089

▲ STEEL PARTNERS HOLDINGS LP p 1384
590 Madison Ave Rm 3202, New York NY 10022
Tel (212) 520-2300
SIC 3479 3497 1381 6141

AMERICAN PACKAGING CORP p 77
777 Driving Park Ave, Rochester NY 14613
Tel (585) 254-9500
SIC 2673 3497 2671 2754 2674

GOULD ELECTRONICS INC p 626
34929 Curtis Blvd Ste 100, Eastlake OH 44095
Tel (440) 953-5000
SIC 3825 3497 3613 3691 3674

■ JW ALUMINUM HOLDING CORP p 798
435 Old Mount Holly Rd, Goose Creek SC 29445
Tel (843) 572-1100 SIC 3353 3497

SIC 3498 Fabricated Pipe & Pipe Fittings

MCABEE CONSTRUCTION INC p 925
5724 21st St, Tuscaloosa AL 35401
Tel (205) 349-2212
SIC 1629 1791 1796 3443 3498

RK MECHANICAL INC p 1239
3800 Xanthia St, Denver CO 80238
Tel (303) 576-9696 SIC 1711 3498 3441

MORTON INDUSTRIES LLC p 991
70 Commerce Dr, Morton IL 61550
Tel (309) 263-2590 SIC 3498

■ PERMA-PIPE INC p 1136
7720 N Lehigh Ave, Niles IL 60714
Tel (847) 966-2190 SIC 3498

■ CERRO FLOW PRODUCTS LLC p 284
3000 Mississippi Ave, Sauget IL 62206
Tel (618) 337-6000
SIC 3351 3331 3498 3585 5051

DEUBLIN CO p 433
2050 Norman Dr, Waukegan IL 60085
Tel (847) 689-8600
SIC 3498 3492 3568 3494

ELKHART PRODUCTS CORP p 488
1255 Oak St, Elkhart IN 46514
Tel (574) 264-3181 SIC 3498

TUBE PROCESSING CORP p 1490
604 E Legrande Ave, Indianapolis IN 46203
Tel (317) 787-1321
SIC 3498 3356 3469 7692 3444 3728

SCHIMBERG CO p 1287
1106 Shaver Rd Ne, Cedar Rapids IA 52402
Tel (319) 365-9421 SIC 5074 3498

CURTIS-MARUYASU AMERICA INC p 402
665 Metts Dr, Lebanon KY 40033
Tel (270) 692-2109 SIC 3714 3498

PERFORMANCE CONTRACTORS INC p 1135
9901 Pecue Ln, Baton Rouge LA 70810
Tel (225) 490-2000 SIC 1541 3498

SHAW GROUP INC p 1312
4171 Essen Ln, Baton Rouge LA 70809
Tel (225) 932-2500
SIC 8711 8734 1629 3498

CHET MORRISON CONTRACTORS LLC p 295
9 Bayou Dularge Rd, Houma LA 70363
Tel (985) 868-1950
SIC 1623 3498 1629 1389

MICROGROUP INC p 962
7 Industrial Park Rd, Medway MA 02053
Tel (508) 533-4925
SIC 5051 3312 3498 3494 3492 3317

DENSO AIR SYSTEMS MICHIGAN INC p 428
300 Fritz Keiper Blvd, Battle Creek MI 49037
Tel (269) 962-9676 SIC 3714 3498

SPS COMPANIES INC p 1362
6363 Highway 7, Minneapolis MN 55416
Tel (952) 929-1377 SIC 5074 5075 3498

CONTINENTAL DISC CORP p 363
3160 W Heartland Dr, Liberty MO 64068
Tel (816) 792-1500
SIC 3491 3498 7699 3494

ROBERT FAMILY HOLDINGS INC p 1241
12430 Tesson Ferry Rd, Saint Louis MO 63128
Tel (314) 821-5665
SIC 2671 3572 3491 3498 7699 3494

■ ANVIL INTERNATIONAL LLC p 94
2 Holland Way, Exeter NH 03833
Tel (603) 418-2800
SIC 3498 3321 3317 3494 3429

SMITHS TUBULAR SYSTEMS-LACONIA INC p 1334
93 Lexington Dr, Laconia NH 03246
Tel (603) 524-2064
SIC 3463 3498 8734 7692 3441 3398

WESTCON INC p 1597
7401 Yukon Dr, Bismarck ND 58503
Tel (701) 222-0076 SIC 1541 3498 8741

KIRTLAND CAPITAL PARTNERS LP p 822
3201 Entp Pkwy Ste 200, Beachwood OH 44122
Tel (216) 593-0100
SIC 5051 3312 3498 3494 3492 3317

ATLAS INDUSTRIAL CONTRACTORS LLC p 128
5275 Sinclair Rd, Columbus OH 43229
Tel (614) 841-4500 SIC 1731 3498 1796

BI-CON SERVICES INC p 180
10901 Clay Pike Rd, Derwent OH 43733
Tel (740) 685-2542 SIC 1623 3498 3443

SANOH AMERICA INC p 1280
1849 Industrial Dr, Findlay OH 45840
Tel (419) 425-2600 SIC 3498

SCOTT PROCESS SYSTEMS INC p 1293
1160 Sunnyside St Sw, Hartville OH 44632
Tel (330) 877-2350 SIC 3498

PIONEER PIPE INC p 1151
2021 Hanna Rd, Marietta OH 45750
Tel (740) 376-2400
SIC 3498 1711 3443 3441 3312

PANHANDLE OILFIELD SERVICE COMPANIES INC p 1111
14000 Quail Springs Pkwy # 300, Oklahoma City OK 73134
Tel (405) 608-5330
SIC 1389 7389 3498 4212 5082 1794

WARD MANUFACTURING LLC p 1575
117 Gulick St, Blossburg PA 16912
Tel (570) 638-2131 SIC 3321 3322 3498

■ SUPERIOR TUBE CO INC p 1407
3900 Germantown Pike, Collegeville PA 19426
Tel (610) 489-5200 SIC 3317 3498

ATW COMPANIES INC p 130
125 Metro Center Blvd # 3001, Warwick RI 02886
Tel (401) 244-1002 SIC 3674 3498

BERRY GP INC p 176
1414 Corn Product Rd, Corpus Christi TX 78409
Tel (361) 693-2100 SIC 1541 1611 3498

BERRY HOLDINGS LP p 176
1414 Corn Product Rd, Corpus Christi TX 78409
Tel (361) 693-2100 SIC 1541 1611 3498

POLK MECHANICAL CO LLC p 1159
2425 Dillard St, Grand Prairie TX 75051
Tel (972) 339-1200
SIC 1711 3444 3498 3599 3999

BOCCARD PIPE FABRICATORS INC p 197
2500 Galveston Rd, Houston TX 77017
Tel (713) 643-0681 SIC 3498

■ DANIEL MEASUREMENT AND CONTROL INC p 411
11100 Brittmoore Park Dr, Houston TX 77041
Tel (713) 467-6000
SIC 3824 3498 3499 3823 3571 3491

IPSCO TUBULARS INC p 764
10120 Houston Oaks Dr, Houston TX 77064
Tel (281) 949-1023 SIC 3498

J D RUSH CORP p 770
2 Northpoint Dr Ste 150, Houston TX 77060
Tel (281) 558-8004 SIC 3498 5051

SOUTHWEST STAINLESS LP p 1352
515 Post Oak Blvd Ste 800, Houston TX 77027
Tel (713) 943-3544 SIC 3498 5051 5085

TEJAS TUBULAR PRODUCTS INC p 1433
8799 North Loop E Ste 300, Houston TX 77029
Tel (281) 822-3400 SIC 3317 3498

TEXAS STEEL CONVERSION INC p 1444
3101 Holmes Rd, Houston TX 77051
Tel (713) 733-6013 SIC 3498

U S WEATHERFORD L P p 1497
2000 Saint James Pl, Houston TX 77056
Tel (713) 693-4000 SIC 3498 3533

VALLOUREC INDUSTRIES INC p 1541
19210 E Hardy Rd, Houston TX 77073
Tel (281) 821-5510 SIC 3498

VAM USA LLC p 1542
4424 W S Houston N 150, Houston TX 77041
Tel (281) 821-5510 SIC 3498

VINSON PROCESS CONTROLS CO LP p 1558
2747 Highpoint Oaks Dr, Lewisville TX 75067
Tel (972) 459-8200 SIC 5084 3533 3498

SCOT INDUSTRIES INC p 1293
3756 Fm 250 N, Lone Star TX 75668
Tel (903) 639-2551
SIC 7389 5051 3498 3471

ECHO MAINTENANCE LLC p 475
6711 N Twin City Hwy, Port Arthur TX 77642
Tel (409) 724-0456 SIC 1541 3498 1623

GULF COPPER & MANUFACTURING CORP p 646
5700 Procter Ext, Port Arthur TX 77642
Tel (409) 989-0300
SIC 3731 3599 3312 3732 3498 3441

ATLAS TUBULAR LLC p 128
1710 S Highway 77, Robstown TX 78380
Tel (361) 387-7505 SIC 5051 3498

■ RTI ENERGY SYSTEMS INC p 1256
7211 Spring Cypress Rd, Spring TX 77379
Tel (281) 379-4289 SIC 3533 3498

ALASKAN COPPER COMPANIES INC p 45
27402 72nd Ave S, Kent WA 98032
Tel (206) 623-5800 SIC 5051 3498 3443

ALCO INVESTMENT CO p 47
27402 72nd Ave S, Kent WA 98032
Tel (206) 623-5800 SIC 5051 3498 3443

MICHELS CORP p 960
817 W Main St, Brownsville WI 53006
Tel (920) 583-3132
SIC 1623 1771 1381 1629 3498 1794

VULCAN INDUSTRIES CORP p 1567
N113w18830 Carnegie Dr, Germantown WI 53022
Tel (262) 255-1090 SIC 3469 3498

SIC 3499 Fabricated Metal Prdts, NEC

CHATSWORTH PRODUCTS INC p 292
29899 Agoura Rd Ste 120, Agoura Hills CA 91301
Tel (818) 735-6100 SIC 3499 2542

TREND TECHNOLOGIES LLC p 1476
4626 Eucalyptus Ave, Chino CA 91710
Tel (909) 597-7861 SIC 3444 3469 3499

CAPSTAN CALIFORNIA INC p 251
16100 S Figueroa St, Gardena CA 90248
Tel (310) 366-5999 SIC 3499

DIGIPAS TECHNOLOGIES INC p 439
200 Spectrum Center Dr, Irvine CA 92618
Tel (949) 558-0160 SIC 3429 3499 3699

GENERAL ATOMIC TECHNOLOGIES CORP p 599
3550 General Atomics Ct, San Diego CA 92121
Tel (858) 455-3000
SIC 8731 3829 3443 7374 3499 2819

OTSUKA AMERICA INC p 1097
1 Embarcadero Ctr # 2020, San Francisco CA 94111
Tel (415) 986-5300
SIC 3829 3499 5122 2833 2084 2086

■ YARDE METALS INC p 1635
45 Newell St, Southington CT 06489
Tel (860) 406-6061 SIC 5051 3499

▲ ARC GROUP WORLDWIDE INC p 103
810 Flight Line Blvd, Deland FL 32724
Tel (303) 467-5236 SIC 3499 3462 3812

■ ALBECCA INC p 46
3900 Steve Reynolds Blvd, Norcross GA 30093
Tel (770) 279-5210 SIC 2499 3499

■ LARSON-JUHL US LLC p 845
3900 Steve Reynolds Blvd, Norcross GA 30093
Tel (770) 279-5200 SIC 2499 3499 2431

■ FIRST ALERT INC p 544
3901 Liberty St, Aurora IL 60504
Tel (630) 851-7330
SIC 3669 3999 3446 3499 3829 3648

HOME PRODUCTS INTERNATIONAL - NORTH AMERICA INC p 703
4501 W 47th St, Chicago IL 60632
Tel (773) 890-1010 SIC 3089 3499

▲ APTARGROUP INC p 101
475 W Terra Cotta Ave E, Crystal Lake IL 60014
Tel (815) 477-0424 SIC 3089 3499

TC INDUSTRIES INC p 1428
3703 S Il Route 31, Crystal Lake IL 60012
Tel (815) 459-2401 SIC 3499 3398

TERRA COTTA HOLDINGS CO p 1439
3703 S Il Route 31, Crystal Lake IL 60012
Tel (815) 459-2400 SIC 3499 3398 6531

SPRAYING SYSTEMS CO p 1360
200 W North Ave, Glendale Heights IL 60139
Tel (630) 665-5000 SIC 3499

▲ ILLINOIS TOOL WORKS INC p 732
155 Harlem Ave, Glenview IL 60025
Tel (847) 724-7500
SIC 3089 3965 3499 2891 3585

■ SIGNODE CORP p 1322
3600 W Lake Ave, Glenview IL 60026
Tel (800) 527-1499 SIC 3565 3499

TALARIS INC p 1422
3333 Warrenville Rd # 310, Lisle IL 60532
Tel (630) 577-1000 SIC 3578 3499

■ TITAN WHEEL CORP OF ILLINOIS p 1456
2701 Spruce St, Quincy IL 62301
Tel (217) 228-6023 SIC 3499

SAMUEL STRAPPING SYSTEMS INC p 1275
1401 Davey Rd Ste 300, Woodridge IL 60517
Tel (630) 783-8900 SIC 3499 5085

FKI SECURITY GROUP LLC p 554
101 Security Pkwy, New Albany IN 47150
Tel (812) 948-8400
SIC 2522 5044 3499 3429

■ MAGNEQUENCH INC p 896
237 S Pendleton Ave Ste C, Pendleton IN 46064
Tel (765) 778-7809 SIC 3499

BOWLING GREEN METALFORMING LLC p 204
111 Cosma Dr, Bowling Green KY 42101
Tel (270) 901-1555 SIC 3499 3715

PLANSEE USA LLC p 1154
115 Constitution Blvd, Franklin MA 02038
Tel (508) 553-3800 SIC 3499

■ LOCKHEED MARTIN SIPPICAN INC p 873
7 Barnabas Rd, Marion MA 02738
Tel (508) 748-3399
SIC 3812 3826 3499 3672 3829 3845

CENTER MANUFACTURING INC p 276
990 84th St Sw, Byron Center MI 49315
Tel (616) 878-3324 SIC 3499 3441

CAMACO LLC p 243
37000 W 12 Mile Rd, Farmington Hills MI 48331
Tel (248) 442-6800 SIC 3565 3499

P & C GROUP I INC p 1102
37000 W 12 Mile Rd, Farmington Hills MI 48331
Tel (248) 442-6800 SIC 3499 3465

VIKING CORP p 1556
210 Industrial Park Dr, Hastings MI 49058
Tel (269) 945-9501 SIC 3499

MPG p 995
47659 Halyard Dr, Plymouth MI 48170
Tel (734) 207-6200 SIC 3499

KURT MANUFACTURING CO INC p 832
5280 Main St Ne, Minneapolis MN 55421
Tel (763) 572-1500
SIC 3499 3545 3363 3728 3842 3365

WINCRAFT INC p 1615
960 E Mark St, Winona MN 55987
Tel (507) 454-5510
SIC 3499 2399 3089 3961 3999 3069

■ LINDSAY MANUFACTURING LLC p 868
2222 N 111th St, Omaha NE 68164
Tel (402) 829-6800
SIC 3523 3599 3499 3443

SUMMIT PACKAGING SYSTEMS INC p 1399
400 Gay St, Manchester NH 03103
Tel (603) 669-5410 SIC 3499 3089

STRATEGIC INDUSTRIES LLC p 1392
26 Main St Ste 200, Chatham NJ 07928
Tel (732) 512-0195
SIC 3724 3499 3451 3083 3111

FAPS INC p 528
371 Craneway St, Newark NJ 07114
Tel (973) 589-5656 SIC 3499 3711 7538

CRESTRON ELECTRONICS INC p 392
15 Volvo Dr, Rockleigh NJ 07647
Tel (201) 767-3400
SIC 3571 3651 1731 3663 3499 3669

HAMON CORP p 656
58 E Main St, Somerville NJ 08876
Tel (908) 333-2000
SIC 1629 3564 3499 5084

▲ GIBRALTAR INDUSTRIES INC p 611
3556 Lake Shore Rd # 100, Buffalo NY 14219
Tel (716) 826-6500
SIC 3499 3316 3441 3398

■ SUNLIGHT US CO INC p 1403
3556 Lake Shore Rd # 100, Buffalo NY 14219
Tel (716) 826-6500
SIC 3499 3316 3441 3398

RAYTECH CORP ASBESTOS PERSONAL INJURY SETTLEMENT TRUST p 1210
190 Willis Ave, Mineola NY 11501
Tel (516) 747-0300 SIC 3499

■ ARNOLD MAGNETIC TECHNOLOGIES CORP p 112
770 Linden Ave, Rochester NY 14625
Tel (585) 385-9010 SIC 3264 3499

PRECISION VALVE CORP p 1169
800 Westchester Ave, Rye Brook NY 10573
Tel (914) 969-6500 SIC 3499 0273 5085

RAYTECH CORP p 1210
97 Froehlich Farm Blvd, Woodbury NY 11797
Tel (718) 259-7388 SIC 3499

▲ DIEBOLD INC p 438
5995 Mayfair Rd, North Canton OH 44720
Tel (330) 490-4000 SIC 3578 3699 3499

MTM RECOGNITION CORP p 998
3201 Se 29th St, Oklahoma City OK 73115
Tel (405) 609-6900
SIC 3911 3873 2499 2389 3499 2791

MCS INDUSTRIES INC p 932
2280 Newlins Mill Rd, Easton PA 18045
Tel (610) 253-6268
SIC 2499 3089 3499 3993 3231

NEW WERNER HOLDING CO INC p 1033
93 Werner Rd, Greenville PA 16125
Tel (724) 588-2000
SIC 3499 3355 3089 3446 2499 6512

OLD LADDER CO p 1081
93 Werner Rd, Greenville PA 16125
Tel (888) 523-3371
SIC 3446 3089 3334 3444 3499

WERNER CO p 1592
93 Werner Rd, Greenville PA 16125
Tel (724) 588-2000
SIC 3499 3355 3089 3446 2499

WERNER HOLDING CO (PA) INC p 1593
93 Werner Rd, Greenville PA 16125
Tel (888) 523-3371
SIC 3499 3355 3089 3446 2499

■ SPS TECHNOLOGIES LLC p 1362
301 Highland Ave, Jenkintown PA 19046
Tel (215) 572-3000
SIC 3452 3423 3499 3264 3679 3341

▲ CROWN HOLDINGS INC p 395
1 Crown Way, Philadelphia PA 19154
Tel (215) 698-5100 SIC 3411 3466 3499

KEYSTONE POWDERED METAL CO p 816
251 State St, Saint Marys PA 15857
Tel (814) 781-1591 SIC 3499

INTERNATIONAL PACKAGING CORP p 756
517 Mineral Spring Ave, Pawtucket RI 02860
Tel (401) 724-1600 SIC 3499 3089

KENNEY MANUFACTURING CO p 811
1000 Jefferson Blvd, Warwick RI 02886
Tel (401) 739-2200
SIC 2591 3261 2511 3699 3499 2541

CARLSTAR GROUP LLC p 258
725 Cool Springs Blvd, Franklin TN 37067
Tel (615) 503-0220
SIC 3714 5014 3499 5013 2296

MANUFACTURERS INDUSTRIAL GROUP LLC p 903
659 Natchez Trace Dr, Lexington TN 38351
Tel (731) 968-3601 SIC 3499 2531

■ DANIEL MEASUREMENT AND CONTROL INC p 411
11100 Brittmoore Park Dr, Houston TX 77041
Tel (713) 467-6000
SIC 3824 3498 3499 3823 3571 3491

■ LIBERTY SAFE AND SECURITY PRODUCTS INC p 862
1199 W Utah Ave, Payson UT 84651
Tel (801) 925-1000 SIC 3499

OBERTHUR TECHNOLOGIES OF AMERICA CORP p 1072
4250 Pleasant Valley Rd, Chantilly VA 20151
Tel (703) 263-0100
SIC 3089 7382 3953 3578 3499

AMFAB INC p 85
1424 Campostella Rd, Chesapeake VA 23320
Tel (757) 543-1485 SIC 3499

SHIP COLONNAS YARD INC p 1317
400 E Indian River Rd, Norfolk VA 23523
Tel (757) 545-2414 SIC 3731 3443 3499

▲ AVISTA CORP p 138
1411 E Mission Ave, Spokane WA 99202
Tel (509) 489-0500 SIC 4911 4924 3499

DYNATECT MANUFACTURING INC p 464
2300 S Calhoun Rd, New Berlin WI 53151
Tel (262) 786-1500
SIC 3069 3499 3714 3599

■ SENTRY SAFE INC p 1305
137 W Forest Hill Ave, Oak Creek WI 53154
Tel (585) 381-4900 SIC 3089 3499 2522

SIC 3511 Steam, Gas & Hydraulic Turbines & Engines

▲ CAPSTONE TURBINE CORP p 251
21211 Nordhoff St, Chatsworth CA 91311
Tel (818) 734-5300 SIC 3511

CLAYTON MANUFACTURING CO p 323
17477 Hurley St, City Of Industry CA 91744
Tel (626) 443-9381 SIC 3569 3829 3511

■ **SOLAR TURBINES INC** p 1338
2200 Pacific Hwy, San Diego CA 92101
Tel (619) 544-5000 SIC 3511

■ **GE WIND ENERGY LLC** p 597
13000 Jameson Rd, Tehachapi CA 93561
Tel (661) 823-6700 SIC 3511

■ **ALSTOM RENEWABLE US LLC** p 61
7901 Suthpark Plz Ste 110, Littleton CO 80120
Tel (303) 730-4000 SIC 3621 3511

DONCASTERS INC p 450
36 Spring Ln, Farmington CT 06032
Tel (860) 677-1376
SIC 3511 3356 3728 7699

ASEA BROWN BOVERI INC p 116
501 Merritt 7, Norwalk CT 06851
Tel (203) 750-2200
SIC 3612 3613 5063 3511 3625 8711

SIEMENS ENERGY INC p 1320
4400 N Alafaya Trl, Orlando FL 32826
Tel (407) 736-5183 SIC 3511

■ **PATTERSON PUMP CO** p 1121
2129 Ayersville Rd, Toccoa GA 30577
Tel (706) 886-2101 SIC 3561 3511 3559

SUZLON WIND ENERGY CORP p 1410
8750 W Bryn Mawr Ave # 900, Chicago IL 60631
Tel (773) 328-5073 SIC 3511

▲ **BROADWIND ENERGY INC** p 216
3240 S Central Ave, Cicero IL 60804
Tel (708) 780-4800 SIC 3511

▲ **CATERPILLAR INC** p 265
100 Ne Adams St, Peoria IL 61629
Tel (309) 675-1000
SIC 3531 3519 3511 6531 6321 6331

▲ **GENERAL ELECTRIC CO** p 600
41 Farnsworth St, Boston MA 02210
Tel (617) 443-3000
SIC 3511 3724 3632 3845

RILEY POWER INC p 1235
5 Neponset St, Worcester MA 01606
Tel (508) 852-7100
SIC 3569 3443 3433 1711 3564 3511

▲ **ORMAT TECHNOLOGIES INC** p 1095
6225 Neil Rd, Reno NV 89511
Tel (775) 356-9029 SIC 4911 3511

LINDE NORTH AMERICA INC p 868
200 Somerset Corporate Bl, Bridgewater NJ 08807
Tel (908) 464-8100
SIC 2813 3569 3559 3561 3511 3823

BOC GROUP INC p 196
575 Mountain Ave, New Providence NJ 07974
Tel (908) 665-2400
SIC 2813 3569 3559 3561 3511 3823

DRESSER-RAND CO p 455
500 Paul Clark Dr, Olean NY 14760
Tel (716) 375-3000 SIC 3563 3511 3621

TURBINE ENGINE COMPONENTS TECHNOLOGIES - UTICA CORP p 1492
2 Halsey Rd, Whitesboro NY 13492
Tel (315) 768-8070
SIC 3724 3511 3429 3842 3769

ABB INC p 9
12040 Regency Pkwy # 200, Cary NC 27518
Tel (919) 856-2360
SIC 8711 3612 3511 5063 3613 3625

■ **BWXT INVESTMENT CO** p 231
11525 N Community House, Charlotte NC 28277
Tel (704) 625-4900
SIC 3511 3443 3564 1629 1541 7699

LM WIND POWER BLADES (ND) INC p 872
1580 S 48th St, Grand Forks ND 58201
Tel (701) 780-9910 SIC 3511 3621

ROLLS-ROYCE ENERGY SYSTEMS INC p 1247
105 N Sandusky St, Mount Vernon OH 43050
Tel (740) 393-8888 SIC 3511 5084 8711

■ **PCC STRUCTURALS INC** p 1123
4600 Se Harney Dr, Portland OR 97206
Tel (503) 777-3881
SIC 3728 3842 3511 3824

■ **PRECISION CASTPARTS CORP** p 1168
4650 Sw Mcdam Ave Ste 300, Portland OR 97239
Tel (503) 946-4800
SIC 3324 3369 3724 3511 3519

VESTAS-AMERICAN WIND TECHNOLOGY INC p 1552
1417 Sw Naito Pkwy # 100, Portland OR 97201
Tel (503) 327-2000 SIC 3523 3511 5084

■ **CURTISS-WRIGHT ELECTRO-MECHANICAL CORP** p 402
1000 Wright Way, Cheswick PA 15024
Tel (724) 275-5000 SIC 3561 3621 3511

ELLIOTT CO p 488
901 N 4th St, Jeannette PA 15644
Tel (724) 527-2811 SIC 3563 3511

VOITH HYDRO INC p 1564
760 E Berlin Rd, York PA 17408
Tel (717) 792-7000 SIC 3511 7699

DRESSER-RAND GROUP INC p 455
10205 Westheimer Rd # 1000, Houston TX 77042
Tel (713) 354-6100 SIC 3563 3511

■ **GE PACKAGED POWER INC** p 596
1330 West Loop S Ste 1000, Houston TX 77027
Tel (713) 803-0900 SIC 3511

■ **GE PACKAGED POWER LP** p 596
16415 Jacintoport Blvd, Houston TX 77015
Tel (281) 452-3610 SIC 3511

■ **BROADWIND TOWERS INC** p 216
101 S 16th St, Manitowoc WI 54220
Tel (920) 684-5531 SIC 3511

SIC 3519 Internal Combustion Engines, NEC

QUINCY COMPRESSOR LLC p 1200
701 N Dobson Ave, Bay Minette AL 36507
Tel (251) 937-5900 SIC 3519 3563 3561

SUZUKI MOTOR OF AMERICA INC p 1410
3251 E Imperial Hwy, Brea CA 92821
Tel (714) 996-7040 SIC 3751 3519 3799

TRACY INDUSTRIES INC p 1468
3737 Capitol Ave, City Of Industry CA 90601
Tel (562) 692-9034 SIC 3519 7538

VALLEY POWER SYSTEMS INC p 1541
425 S Hacienda Blvd, City Of Industry CA 91745
Tel (626) 333-1243 SIC 3519 5082

■ **CUMMINS PACIFIC LLC** p 401
1939 Deere Ave, Irvine CA 92606
Tel (949) 253-6000 SIC 3519 5063 7538

▲ **TELEDYNE TECHNOLOGIES INC** p 1434
1049 Camino Dos Rios, Thousand Oaks CA 91360
Tel (805) 373-4545
SIC 3679 3761 3519 3724 3812 3674

■ **CUMMINS ROCKY MOUNTAIN LLC** p 401
390 Interlocken Cres # 200, Broomfield CO 80021
Tel (800) 927-7201 SIC 5084 3519

▲ **WOODWARD INC** p 1623
1081 Woodward Way, Fort Collins CO 80524
Tel (970) 482-5811
SIC 3625 3629 3492 3519

■ **JACOBS VEHICLE SYSTEMS INC** p 775
22 E Dudley Town Rd, Bloomfield CT 06002
Tel (860) 243-5222 SIC 3519

▲ **WORLD FUEL SERVICES CORP** p 1625
9800 Nw 41st St Ste 400, Doral FL 33178
Tel (305) 428-8000 SIC 5172 3519 5541

YANMAR AMERICA CORP p 1635
101 International Pkwy, Adairsville GA 30103
Tel (770) 877-9894
SIC 5084 7699 5083 3519

ILLINOIS AUTO ELECTRIC CO p 732
700 Enterprise St, Aurora IL 60504
Tel (630) 862-3300
SIC 5084 5013 5083 5078 7699 3519

▲ **BRUNSWICK CORP** p 221
1 N Field Ct, Lake Forest IL 60045
Tel (847) 735-4700
SIC 3519 3732 3949 7933 5091

■ **NAVISTAR INC** p 1020
2701 Navistar Dr, Lisle IL 60532
Tel (331) 332-5000
SIC 3711 3714 3519 6153 6159 6331

▲ **NAVISTAR INTERNATIONAL CORP** p 1020
2701 Navistar Dr, Lisle IL 60532
Tel (331) 332-5000
SIC 3711 3714 3713 3519 6159

SIERRA INTERNATIONAL INC p 1320
1 Sierra Pl, Litchfield IL 62056
Tel (217) 324-9400 SIC 5088 3519

UNICARRIERS AMERICAS CORP p 1502
240 N Prospect St, Marengo IL 60152
Tel (800) 871-5438 SIC 3537 3519 5084

■ **PROGRESS RAIL LOCOMOTIVE INC** p 1181
9301 W 55th St, Mc Cook IL 60525
Tel (800) 255-5355 SIC 3621 3519 3647

CUMMINS - ALLISON CORP p 401
852 Feehanville Dr, Mount Prospect IL 60056
Tel (847) 759-6403 SIC 3578 3519

▲ **CATERPILLAR INC** p 265
100 Ne Adams St, Peoria IL 61629
Tel (309) 675-1000
SIC 3531 3519 3511 6531 6321 6331

▲ **CUMMINS INC** p 401
500 Jackson St, Columbus IN 47201
Tel (812) 377-5000
SIC 3519 3714 3694 3621

■ **CUMMINS CROSSPOINT LLC** p 401
2601 Fortune Cir E Ste 30, Indianapolis IN 46241
Tel (317) 243-7979 SIC 5084 7538 3519

■ **CUMMINS CROSSPOINT LLC** p 401
2601 Fortune Cir E 300c, Indianapolis IN 46241
Tel (317) 243-7979
SIC 5084 7538 5063 3519

DETROIT DIESEL CORP p 433
13400 W Outer Dr, Detroit MI 48239
Tel (313) 592-5000 SIC 3519 3714 7538

DETROIT DIESEL REMANUFACTURING CORP p 433
13400 W Outer Dr, Detroit MI 48239
Tel (313) 592-5000 SIC 3519

ENGINEERED MACHINED PRODUCTS INC p 499
3111 N 28th St, Escanaba MI 49829
Tel (906) 786-8404
SIC 3519 3714 3568 3599 3561

■ **CUMMINS BRIDGEWAY LLC** p 401
21810 Clessie Ct, New Hudson MI 48165
Tel (248) 573-1600 SIC 5084 7538 3519

K & S PROPERTY INC p 798
21810 Clessie Ct, New Hudson MI 48165
Tel (248) 573-1600 SIC 5084 3519

MTU AMERICA INC p 998
39525 Mackenzie Dr, Novi MI 48377
Tel (248) 560-8000 SIC 3519

■ **CUMMINS POWER GENERATION INC** p 401
1400 73rd Ave Ne, Minneapolis MN 55432
Tel (763) 574-5000 SIC 3621 3519

■ **CUMMINS NPOWER LLC** p 401
1600 Buerkle Rd, White Bear Lake MN 55110
Tel (800) 642-0085
SIC 5084 5063 7538 3519

SPRINGFIELD REMANUFACTURING CORP p 1361
650 N Broadview Pl, Springfield MO 65802
Tel (417) 862-3501
SIC 3519 3714 3713 3561

SRC HOLDINGS CORP p 1363
531 S Union Ave, Springfield MO 65802
Tel (417) 862-2337 SIC 3519 3714

■ **CUMMINS CENTRAL POWER LLC** p 401
10088 S 136th St, Omaha NE 68138
Tel (402) 551-7678
SIC 5084 7538 5999 3519

■ **COLTEC INDUSTRIES INC** p 339
5605 Carnegie Blvd # 500, Charlotte NC 28209
Tel (704) 731-1500 SIC 3053 3519 3089

▲ **ENPRO INDUSTRIES INC** p 500
5605 Carnegie Blvd # 500, Charlotte NC 28209
Tel (704) 731-1500 SIC 3053 3519 3089

ASMO NORTH CAROLINA INC p 118
470 Crawford Rd, Statesville NC 28625
Tel (704) 878-6663 SIC 3519 3621

■ **CONSOLIDATED DIESEL INC** p 359
9377 N Us Highway 301, Whitakers NC 27891
Tel (252) 437-6611 SIC 3519

DETROIT DIESEL REMANUFACTURING-EAST INC p 433
60703 Country Club Rd, Byesville OH 43723
Tel (740) 439-7701 SIC 3519

■ **DMAX LTD** p 445
3100 Dryden Rd, Moraine OH 45439
Tel (937) 425-9700 SIC 3519

■ **PRECISION CASTPARTS CORP** p 1168
4650 Sw Mcdam Ave Ste 300, Portland OR 97239
Tel (503) 946-4800
SIC 3324 3369 3724 3511 3519

■ **CUMMINS POWER SYSTEMS LLC** p 401
2727 Ford Rd, Bristol PA 19007
Tel (215) 785-6005
SIC 5084 5063 7538 7629 3519

■ **CUMMINS SOUTHERN PLAINS LLC** p 401
600 N Watson Rd, Arlington TX 76011
Tel (817) 640-6801 SIC 5084 3519

DETROIT DIESEL REMANUFACTURING-WEST INC p 433
100 Lodestone Way, Tooele UT 84074
Tel (435) 843-6000 SIC 3519 3714 5013

KENWORTH SALES CO p 813
2125 S Constitution Blvd, West Valley City UT 84119
Tel (801) 487-4161
SIC 5012 5013 7538 3519

VOLVO PENTA OF AMERICAS LLC p 1565
1300 Volvo Penta Dr, Chesapeake VA 23320
Tel (757) 436-2800
SIC 5088 3519 5091 5063

PACIFIC POWER GROUP LLC p 1105
805 Broadway St Ste 700, Vancouver WA 98660
Tel (360) 887-7400
SIC 5088 3621 5063 3519 5084

TOYOTA MOTOR MANUFACTURING WEST VIRGINIA INC p 1467
1 Sugar Maple Ln, Buffalo WV 25033
Tel (304) 937-7000 SIC 3714 3519

■ **COLTEC INDUSTRIES INC** p 340
701 White Ave, Beloit WI 53511
Tel (608) 364-4411 SIC 3519

KOHLER CO p 826
444 Highland Dr, Kohler WI 53044
Tel (920) 457-4441
SIC 3431 3432 3261 2511 2521 3519

■ **NELSON INDUSTRIES INC** p 1025
1801 Us Highway 51 & 138, Stoughton WI 53589
Tel (608) 873-4200 SIC 3714 3519 3569

▲ **BRIGGS & STRATTON CORP** p 212
12301 W Wirth St, Wauwatosa WI 53222
Tel (414) 259-5333 SIC 3519 3524

SIC 3523 Farm Machinery & Eqpt

BAJAJ CONEAGLE LLC p 145
1900 Market St, Millbrook AL 36054
Tel (334) 517-6139 SIC 3523

■ **BUSH HOG INC** p 229
2501 Griffin Ave, Selma AL 36703
Tel (800) 363-6096 SIC 3523

RAIN BIRD CORP p 1205
1000 W Sierra Madre Ave, Azusa CA 91702
Tel (626) 812-3400 SIC 3494 3432 3523

JAMES HARDIE TRANSITION CO INC p 776
26300 La Alameda Ste 400, Mission Viejo CA 92691
Tel (949) 348-1800
SIC 3275 3523 3494 5072

RIVULIS IRRIGATION INC p 1239
7545 Carroll Rd, San Diego CA 92121
Tel (858) 578-1860 SIC 3523

ENGINEERING SERVICES & PRODUCTS CO p 499
1395 John Fitch Blvd, South Windsor CT 06074
Tel (860) 528-1119 SIC 3523 5083 3081

TAYLOR FARMS FLORIDA INC p 1427
7492 Chancellor Dr, Orlando FL 32809
Tel (407) 515-8436 SIC 3523

ANDRITZ (USA) INC p 91
5405 Windward Pkwy 100, Alpharetta GA 30004
Tel (770) 640-2500 SIC 3554 3523

AG-PRO LLC p 34
19595 Us Hwy 84, Boston GA 31626
Tel (229) 498-8833 SIC 3523 5082

▲ **AGCO CORP** p 34
4205 River Green Pkwy, Duluth GA 30096
Tel (770) 813-9200 SIC 3523 6159

■ **GSI HOLDINGS CORP** p 643
1004 E Illinois St, Assumption IL 62510
Tel (217) 226-4421 SIC 3523

▲ **DEERE & CO** p 422
1 John Deere Pl, Moline IL 61265
Tel (309) 765-8000
SIC 3523 3531 3524 6159

GEA FARM TECHNOLOGIES INC p 597
1880 Country Farm Dr, Naperville IL 60563
Tel (630) 548-8200
SIC 5083 3523 2841 2842

GENWOODS HOLDCO LLC p 605
2606 S Il Route 2, Oregon IL 61061
Tel (815) 732-2141 SIC 3523

WOODS EQUIPMENT CO p 1623
2606 S Il Route 2, Oregon IL 61061
Tel (815) 732-2141 SIC 3523 3524 3531

■ **CATERPILLAR BRAZIL LLC** p 265
100 Ne Adams St, Peoria IL 61629
Tel (309) 675-1000 SIC 3523

■ **CTB INC** p 399
410 N Higbee St, Milford IN 46542
Tel (574) 658-4191 SIC 3443 3523

HAGIE HOLDING CO p 653
721 Central Ave W, Clarion IA 50525
Tel (515) 532-2861 SIC 3523

EFCO CORP p 480
1800 Ne 46th Ave, Des Moines IA 50313
Tel (515) 266-1141 SIC 3523

ELDON C STUTSMAN INC p 484
121 Lassie, Hills IA 52235
Tel (319) 679-2281 SIC 5191 3523

VERMEER MANUFACTURING CO p 1551
1210 E Vermeer Rd, Pella IA 50219
Tel (641) 628-3141 SIC 3531 3523

SUKUP MANUFACTURING CO p 1397
1555 255th St, Sheffield IA 50475
Tel (641) 892-4222 SIC 3523

CPM ACQUISITION CORP p 387
2975 Airline Cir, Waterloo IA 50703
Tel (319) 232-8444 SIC 3523

KINZE MANUFACTURING INC p 821
2172 M Ave, Williamsburg IA 52361
Tel (319) 668-1300 SIC 3523

SUNFLOWER MANUFACTURING CO INC p 1402
3154 Hallie Trl, Beloit KS 67420
Tel (785) 738-2261 SIC 3523

LANDOLL CORP p 843
1900 North St, Marysville KS 66508
Tel (785) 562-5381
SIC 3728 3715 3523 3537

MORIDGE MANUFACTURING INC p 989
105 Old Us Highway 81, Moundridge KS 67107
Tel (620) 345-6301 SIC 3524 3523

GREAT PLAINS MANUFACTURING INC p 634
1525 E North St, Salina KS 67401
Tel (785) 823-3276 SIC 3523

MORBARK LLC p 988
8507 S Winn Rd, Winn MI 48896
Tel (989) 866-2381
SIC 3599 3553 3549 3523

▲ **TORO CO** p 1461
8111 Lyndale Ave S, Bloomington MN 55420
Tel (952) 888-8801
SIC 3523 3524 3494 3645

FAST GLOBAL SOLUTIONS INC p 531
20631 State Highway 55, Glenwood MN 56334
Tel (320) 634-5126 SIC 3537 3565 3523

DELAVAL INC p 423
11100 N Congress Ave, Kansas City MO 64153
Tel (816) 891-7700
SIC 5083 3523 2842 0241

▲ **PAUL MUELLER CO** p 1121
1600 W Phelps St, Springfield MO 65802
Tel (417) 831-3000 SIC 3443 3556 3523

BEHLEN MFG CO p 168
4025 E 23rd St, Columbus NE 68601
Tel (402) 564-3111
SIC 3523 3448 4213 3556 3496 3443

BEHLEN MKTG CO p 168
4025 E 23rd St, Columbus NE 68601
Tel (402) 564-3111 SIC 3523 3448 4213

CHIEF INDUSTRIES INC p 298
3942 W Old Highway 30, Grand Island NE 68803
Tel (308) 389-7200
SIC 3448 2451 3523 2869 3442

T-L IRRIGATION CO p 1420
151 E Hwy 6 And Ab Rd, Hastings NE 68901
Tel (402) 462-4128
SIC 3523 3561 3479 7359

▲ **LINDSAY CORP** p 868
2222 N 111th St, Omaha NE 68164
Tel (402) 829-6800 SIC 3523 3599 3443

■ **LINDSAY MANUFACTURING LLC** p 868
2222 N 111th St, Omaha NE 68164
Tel (402) 829-6800
SIC 3523 3599 3499 3443

▲ **VALMONT INDUSTRIES INC** p 1541
1 Valmont Plz Ste 500, Omaha NE 68154
Tel (402) 963-1000
SIC 3441 3399 3317 3523 3612

VALMONT INDUSTRIES INC p 1542
7002 N 288th St, Valley NE 68064
Tel (402) 359-2201 SIC 3523

GEA WESTFALIA SEPARATOR INC p 597
100 Fairway Ct, Northvale NJ 07647
Tel (201) 767-3900 SIC 5083 5084 3523

ASP BLADE INTERMEDIATE HOLDINGS INC p 118
299 Park Ave Fl 34, New York NY 10171
Tel (212) 476-8000 SIC 3531 3523 6719

GOULD PAPER CORP p 626
99 Park Ave Fl 10, New York NY 10016
Tel (212) 301-0000 SIC 5113 5111 3523

COASTAL AGROBUSINESS INC p 331
3702 Evans St, Greenville NC 27834
Tel (252) 756-1126 SIC 5191 3523

HOG SLAT INC p 699
206 Fayetteville St, Newton Grove NC 28366
Tel (866) 464-7528
SIC 1542 3272 3523 0213

UNVERFERTH MANUFACTURING CO INC p 1528
601 S Broad St, Kalida OH 45853
Tel (419) 532-3121 SIC 3523

CREAMER METAL PRODUCTS INC p 390
77 S Madison Rd, London OH 43140
Tel (740) 852-1752 SIC 3523

BLOUNT INTERNATIONAL INC p 190
4909 Se International Way, Portland OR 97222
Tel (503) 653-8881 SIC 3531 3523

VESTAS-AMERICAN WIND TECHNOLOGY INC p 1552
1417 Sw Naito Pkwy # 100, Portland OR 97201
Tel (503) 327-2000 SIC 3523 3511 5084

MCLANAHAN CORP p 930
200 Wall St, Hollidaysburg PA 16648
Tel (814) 695-9807
SIC 3532 3321 3599 3523

CNH INC p 330
500 Diller Ave, New Holland PA 17557
Tel (717) 355-1121 SIC 3523

NEW HOLLAND NORTH AMERICA INC p 1030
300 Diller Ave, New Holland PA 17557
Tel (717) 355-1121 SIC 3523

FIMCO INC p 542
800 Stevens Port Dr, Dakota Dunes SD 57049
Tel (605) 232-6800 SIC 3523 3524

▲ RAVEN INDUSTRIES INC p 1209
205 E 6th St, Sioux Falls SD 57104
Tel (605) 336-2750
SIC 5065 3523 3081 3823 3083

SIOUX STEEL CO p 1326
196 1/2 E 6th St, Sioux Falls SD 57104
Tel (605) 336-1750 SIC 3523 3448 2221

■ FLOWTRONEX PSI LLC p 560
10661 Newkirk St, Dallas TX 75220
Tel (469) 221-1200
SIC 3561 3949 3523 3432

BIG TEX TRAILER MANUFACTURING INC p 182
950 Interstate Hwy 30 E, Mount Pleasant TX 75455
Tel (903) 575-0300 SIC 3523 5013 5599

PRIEFERT MFG CO INC p 1174
2630 S Jefferson Ave, Mount Pleasant TX 75455
Tel (903) 572-1741
SIC 3523 3446 3444 3317 3449

■ ALAMO GROUP (USA) INC p 44
1627 E Walnut St, Seguin TX 78155
Tel (830) 379-1480 SIC 3523

▲ ALAMO GROUP INC p 44
1627 E Walnut St, Seguin TX 78155
Tel (830) 379-1480 SIC 3523 3531

ORBIT IRRIGATION PRODUCTS INC p 1092
845 Overland St, North Salt Lake UT 84054
Tel (801) 299-5555 SIC 3523

MCGREGOR CO p 929
401 Colfax Airport Rd, Colfax WA 99111
Tel (509) 397-4355 SIC 5191 3523 2874

SCAFCO CORP p 1285
2800 E Main Ave, Spokane WA 99202
Tel (509) 343-9000
SIC 3523 5065 6531 3444

TRAVIS PATTERN & FOUNDRY INC p 1475
1413 E Hawthorne Rd, Spokane WA 99218
Tel (509) 466-1798
SIC 3523 3369 3313 3321 3625

WASHINGTON TRACTOR INC p 1579
2700 136th Avenue Ct E, Sumner WA 98390
Tel (253) 863-4436
SIC 3523 5083 5261 7699 7353

KUHN NORTH AMERICA INC p 831
1501 W 7th Ave, Brodhead WI 53520
Tel (608) 897-4508 SIC 3523 3531

MADISON ONE HOLDINGS LLC p 894
2001 S Stoughton Rd, Madison WI 53716
Tel (608) 222-3484 SIC 3523

METALCRAFT OF MAYVILLE INC p 952
1000 Metalcraft Dr, Mayville WI 53050
Tel (920) 387-3150 SIC 3523 3444

CASE CONSTRUCTION EQUIPMENT INC p 263
700 State St, Racine WI 53404
Tel (262) 636-6011 SIC 6159 3531 3523

CASE NEW HOLLAND INDUSTRIAL INC p 263
700 State St, Racine WI 53404
Tel (262) 636-6011 SIC 3523 3531

CNH INDUSTRIAL AMERICA LLC p 330
700 St St, Racine WI 53404
Tel (262) 636-6011 SIC 3523 3531 6159

R G REZIN INC p 1202
1602 Rezin Rd, Tomah WI 54660
Tel (608) 372-5956
SIC 1623 3443 3613 3561 3523 3599

MANITOU AMERICAS INC p 902
1 Gehl Way, West Bend WI 53095
Tel (262) 334-9461 SIC 3531 3523

SIC 3524 Garden, Lawn Tractors & Eqpt

MTD SOUTHWEST INC p 997
9235 S Mckemy St, Tempe AZ 85284
Tel (480) 961-1002 SIC 3524 3546 3423

HUSQVARNA OUTDOOR PRODUCTS INC p 721
1 Poulan Dr, Nashville AR 71852
Tel (870) 845-1234 SIC 3524

KUBOTA MANUFACTURING OF AMERICA CORP p 831
2715 Ramsey Rd, Gainesville GA 30501
Tel (770) 532-0038 SIC 3524 3537

TUTHILL CORP p 1493
8500 S Madison St, Burr Ridge IL 60527
Tel (630) 382-4900 SIC 3561 3586 3524

ECHO INC p 475
400 Oakwood Rd, Lake Zurich IL 60047
Tel (847) 540-8400 SIC 3524

▲ DEERE & CO p 422
1 John Deere Pl, Moline IL 61265
Tel (309) 765-8000
SIC 3523 3531 3524 6159

WOODS EQUIPMENT CO p 1623
2606 S Il Route 2, Oregon IL 61061
Tel (815) 732-2141 SIC 3523 3524 3531

WOOD-MIZER HOLDINGS INC p 1622
8180 W 10th St, Indianapolis IN 46214
Tel (317) 271-1542
SIC 3553 3524 3425 2431

NOVAE CORP p 1062
1 Novae Pkwy, Markle IN 46770
Tel (260) 758-9800 SIC 5084 3524

MORIDGE MANUFACTURING INC p 989
105 Old Us Highway 81, Moundridge KS 67107
Tel (620) 345-6301 SIC 3524 3523

▲ TORO CO p 1461
8111 Lyndale Ave S, Bloomington MN 55420
Tel (952) 888-8801
SIC 3523 3524 3494 3645

■ TORO LLC p 1462
8111 Lyndale Ave S, Bloomington MN 55420
Tel (952) 887-8041 SIC 3524 5083

BLOUNT INTERNATIONAL INC p 190
10331 Nw Transcon Dr, Kansas City MO 64153
Tel (816) 231-5007 SIC 5083 3524 3469

■ CLOPAY AMES TRUE TEMPER HOLDING CORP p 327
100 Jericho Quadrangle # 224, Jericho NY 11753
Tel (516) 938-5544 SIC 3423 3799 3524

HUSQVARNA CONSUMER OUTDOOR PRODUCTS NA INC p 721
9335 Harris Corners Pkwy P, Charlotte NC 28269
Tel (704) 597-5000 SIC 3524

HONDA POWER EQUIPMENT MFG INC p 704
3721 Nc Hwy 119, Swepsonville NC 27359
Tel (336) 578-5300 SIC 3524

▲ PARK-OHIO HOLDINGS CORP p 1116
6065 Parkland Blvd Ste 1, Cleveland OH 44124
Tel (440) 947-2000
SIC 3462 3069 3567 3363 3631 3524

■ PARK-OHIO INDUSTRIES INC p 1116
6065 Parkland Blvd Ste 1, Cleveland OH 44124
Tel (440) 947-2000
SIC 3462 3069 3567 3363 3524

■ SCOTTS CO LLC p 1294
14111 Scottslawn Rd, Marysville OH 43040
Tel (937) 644-0011
SIC 2873 2874 2879 0782 2499 3524

MTD CONSUMER GROUP INC p 997
5965 Grafton Rd, Valley City OH 44280
Tel (330) 225-2600 SIC 3524

MTD HOLDINGS INC p 997
5965 Grafton Rd, Valley City OH 44280
Tel (330) 225-2600
SIC 3524 3544 3469 6141

MTD PRODUCTS INC p 997
5965 Grafton Rd, Valley City OH 44280
Tel (330) 225-2600 SIC 3524

■ AMES COMPANIES INC p 84
465 Railroad Ave, Camp Hill PA 17011
Tel (717) 737-1500 SIC 3423 3799 3524

FIMCO INC p 542
800 Stevens Port Dr, Dakota Dunes SD 57049
Tel (605) 232-6800 SIC 3523 3524

TUFF TORQ CORP p 1491
5943 Commerce Blvd, Morristown TN 37814
Tel (423) 585-2000 SIC 3679 3524

SUNLIGHT SUPPLY INC p 1403
5408 Ne 88th St Ste A101, Vancouver WA 98665
Tel (360) 883-8846 SIC 3524 5191

ARIENS CO p 108
655 W Ryan St, Brillion WI 54110
Tel (920) 756-2141 SIC 3524

▲ BRIGGS & STRATTON CORP p 212
12301 W Wirth St, Wauwatosa WI 53222
Tel (414) 259-5333 SIC 3519 3524

SIC 3531 Construction Machinery & Eqpt

ALTEC INC p 62
210 Inverness Center Dr, Birmingham AL 35242
Tel (205) 991-7733 SIC 3531 3713 3536

ALTEC INDUSTRIES INC p 62
210 Inverness Center Dr, Birmingham AL 35242
Tel (205) 991-7733 SIC 3531 3536 3713

PREFERRED MATERIALS INC p 1169
500 Rvrhills Bus Park, Birmingham AL 35242
Tel (205) 995-5900
SIC 1611 1771 3531 5032

CRAFCO INC p 388
6165 W Detroit St, Chandler AZ 85226
Tel (480) 505-8030 SIC 2951 3531

HUGG AND HALL EQUIPMENT CO p 717
7201 Scott Hamilton Dr, Little Rock AR 72209
Tel (501) 562-1262
SIC 5084 5082 7353 7699 5083 3531

ROBERTSONS READY MIX LTD A CALIFORNIA LIMITED PARTNERSHIP p 1242
200 S Main St Ste 200, Corona CA 92882
Tel (951) 493-6500
SIC 3273 3531 5032 2951 1442

BNS HOLDING INC p 194
61 E Main St Ste B, Los Gatos CA 95030
Tel (408) 399-6498 SIC 3711 3713 3531

BASIC RESOURCES INC p 158
928 12th St Ste 700, Modesto CA 95354
Tel (209) 521-9771
SIC 1611 3273 2951 3532 3531

POWERPLUS GROUP INC USA p 1166
1521 E Grand Ave, Pomona CA 91766
Tel (909) 622-5888 SIC 3531

KUBOTA TRACTOR CORP p 831
3401 Del Amo Blvd, Torrance CA 90503
Tel (310) 370-3370 SIC 5083 3531 3799

KUBOTA USA INC p 831
3401 Del Amo Blvd, Torrance CA 90503
Tel (310) 370-3370
SIC 5083 3577 5051 3531 3571

BAE SYSTEMS POWER INC p 144
5840 Dahlia St, Commerce City CO 80022
Tel (303) 287-7441
SIC 5084 3531 3999 3569

▲ TEREX CORP p 1439
200 Nyala Farms Rd Ste 2, Westport CT 06880
Tel (203) 222-7170 SIC 3531 3537

WHITE CONSTRUCTION CO INC p 1606
2811 N Young Blvd, Chiefland FL 32626
Tel (352) 493-1444 SIC 1611 0241 3531

GENERAL ASPHALT CO INC p 599
4850 Nw 72nd Ave, Miami FL 33166
Tel (305) 592-6005 SIC 3531

GARDNER ASPHALT CORP p 592
4161 E 7th Ave, Tampa FL 33605
Tel (813) 248-2441 SIC 3531

APAC HOLDINGS INC p 95
900 Ashwood Pkwy Ste 700, Atlanta GA 30338
Tel (770) 392-5300 SIC 1611 3531 5032

JCB INC p 780
2000 Bamford Blvd, Pooler GA 31322
Tel (912) 447-2000
SIC 5082 5084 3531 3537

DOOSAN INFRACORE INTERNATIONAL INC p 451
2905 Shawnee Industrial W, Suwanee GA 30024
Tel (770) 831-2200 SIC 3531

MAGBEE BROS LUMBER AND SUPPLY CO INC p 895
1065 Bankhead Hwy, Winder GA 30680
Tel (678) 425-2600
SIC 2431 5211 3531 2439

HEICO COMPANIES L L C p 680
5600 Three First Nat Plz, Chicago IL 60602
Tel (312) 419-8220
SIC 3315 3589 3448 3531 1731 3663

LANCO INTERNATIONAL INC p 842
3111 167th St, Hazel Crest IL 60429
Tel (708) 596-5200
SIC 3531 8711 5084 3536 7353 3537

MI-JACK PRODUCTS INC p 959
3111 167th St, Hazel Crest IL 60429
Tel (708) 596-5200 SIC 3531 8711

▲ DEERE & CO p 422
1 John Deere Pl, Moline IL 61265
Tel (309) 765-8000
SIC 3523 3531 3524 6159

INTERNATIONAL EQUIPMENT SOLUTIONS LLC p 755
2211 York Rd Ste 320, Oak Brook IL 60523
Tel (630) 570-6880 SIC 3531

E D ETNYRE & CO p 466
1333 S Daysville Rd, Oregon IL 61061
Tel (815) 732-2116 SIC 3531

WOODS EQUIPMENT CO p 1623
2606 S Il Route 2, Oregon IL 61061
Tel (815) 732-2141 SIC 3523 3524 3531

▲ CATERPILLAR INC p 265
100 Ne Adams St, Peoria IL 61629
Tel (309) 675-1000
SIC 3531 3519 3511 6531 6321 6331

BERGSTROM INC p 174
2390 Blackhawk Rd, Rockford IL 61109
Tel (815) 874-7821 SIC 3531

KOMATSU AMERICA CORP p 827
1701 Golf Rd Ste 1-100, Rolling Meadows IL 60008
Tel (847) 437-5800 SIC 5082 3532 3531

APL LOGISTICS AMERICAS LTD p 97
2649 Internationale Pkwy, Woodridge IL 60517
Tel (630) 783-0200 SIC 3531

AVIS INDUSTRIAL CORP p 138
1909 S Main St, Upland IN 46989
Tel (765) 998-8100
SIC 3429 3462 3312 3531 3714 3569

■ IOWA MOLD TOOLING CO INC p 763
500 W Us Highway 18, Garner IA 50438
Tel (641) 923-3711 SIC 3531 3713 3563

GODBERSEN-SMITH CONSTRUCTION CO INC p 619
121 E State Highway 175, Ida Grove IA 51445
Tel (712) 364-3388 SIC 3531 1622

VERMEER MANUFACTURING CO p 1551
1210 E Vermeer Rd, Pella IA 50219
Tel (641) 628-3141 SIC 3531 3523

■ CATERPILLAR WORK TOOLS INC p 265
400 Work Tool Rd, Wamego KS 66547
Tel (904) 786-8700 SIC 3531

LINK-BELT CONSTRUCTION EQUIPMENT CO LP LLLP p 869
2651 Palumbo Dr, Lexington KY 40509
Tel (859) 263-5200 SIC 3531

▲ W R GRACE & CO p 1569
7500 Grace Dr, Columbia MD 21044
Tel (410) 531-4000
SIC 2819 3531 2899 2891 3479

■ W R GRACE & CO-CONN p 1569
7500 Grace Dr, Columbia MD 21044
Tel (410) 531-4000
SIC 2819 3531 2899 2891 3479

CRISTAL p 392
20 Wight Ave Ste 100, Hunt Valley MD 21030
Tel (410) 229-4440
SIC 1241 3531 2816 2869 1321 3631

BOSTON AND MAINE CORP p 202
1700 Iron Horse Park, North Billerica MA 01862
Tel (978) 663-1130 SIC 3531

BESSER CO p 177
801 Johnson St, Alpena MI 49707
Tel (989) 354-4508
SIC 3531 3559 3564 3443

PALADIN BRANDS GROUP INC p 1108
2800 Zeeb Rd, Dexter MI 48130
Tel (319) 378-3696 SIC 3531

HINES CORP p 695
1218 E Pontaluna Rd Ste B, Norton Shores MI 49456
Tel (231) 799-6240
SIC 3443 3823 3589 3531 3535 5082

BANDIT INDUSTRIES INC p 150
6750 W Millbrook Rd, Remus MI 49340
Tel (989) 561-2270 SIC 3531 5082

■ MCNEILUS TRUCK AND MANUFACTURING INC p 932
524 County Rd 34 E, Dodge Center MN 55927
Tel (614) 868-0760
SIC 3713 3531 3537 3272

■ CATERPILLAR PAVING PRODUCTS INC p 265
9401 85th Ave N, Minneapolis MN 55445
Tel (763) 425-4100 SIC 3531

CRENLO CAB PRODUCTS INC p 391
1600 4th Ave Nw, Rochester MN 55901
Tel (507) 289-3371
SIC 2522 3531 2542 3713 3469 3444

SCHWING AMERICA INC p 1291
5900 Centerville Rd, Saint Paul MN 55127
Tel (651) 429-0999 SIC 3531 3561 3999

APAC-MISSISSIPPI INC p 95
101 Riverview Dr, Richland MS 39218
Tel (601) 376-4000
SIC 1611 1771 3531 5032 2951

DUTTON-LAINSON CO p 463
451 W 2nd St, Hastings NE 68901
Tel (402) 463-6702
SIC 3531 5999 5083 5074

ELLIOTT EQUIPMENT CO p 488
4427 S 76th Cir, Omaha NE 68127
Tel (402) 592-4500 SIC 3531

■ BREEZE-EASTERN LLC p 209
35 Melanie Ln, Whippany NJ 07981
Tel (973) 602-1001 SIC 3728 3563 3531

■ BW ELLIOTT MANUFACTURING CO LLC p 230
11 Beckwith Ave, Binghamton NY 13901
Tel (607) 772-0404 SIC 3568 3492 3531

FERRANDINO & SON INC p 538
71 Carolyn Blvd, Farmingdale NY 11735
Tel (866) 571-4609
SIC 1542 0781 3531 7299

ASP BLADE INTERMEDIATE HOLDINGS INC p 118
299 Park Ave Fl 34, New York NY 10171
Tel (212) 476-8000 SIC 3531 3523 6719

INGERSOLL-RAND CO p 742
800 Beaty St Ste B, Davidson NC 28036
Tel (704) 655-4000
SIC 3561 3429 3546 3563 3531

APAC-ATLANTIC INC p 95
300 S Benbow Rd, Greensboro NC 27401
Tel (336) 412-6800
SIC 1611 1771 3531 5032

DEERE-HITACHI CONSTRUCTION MACHINERY CORP p 422
1000 Deere Hitachi Rd, Kernersville NC 27284
Tel (336) 996-8100 SIC 3531

HANSON AGGREGATES EAST LLC p 658
3131 Rdu Center Dr, Morrisville NC 27560
Tel (919) 380-2500 SIC 3531 5032

CLARK EQUIPMENT CO p 322
250 E Beaton Dr, West Fargo ND 58078
Tel (701) 241-8700 SIC 3599 3531

PUBCO CORP p 1189
3830 Kelley Ave, Cleveland OH 44114
Tel (216) 881-5300 SIC 3531 6512 3955

INDY EQUIPMENT INDEPENDENCE RECYCLING INC p 740
6220 E Schaaf Rd, Independence OH 44131
Tel (216) 524-0999 SIC 3531

DESCO CORP p 432
7795 Walton Pkwy Ste 175, New Albany OH 43054
Tel (614) 888-8855
SIC 3442 3825 3643 3531 3429

■ GRADALL INDUSTRIES INC p 628
406 Mill Ave Sw, New Philadelphia OH 44663
Tel (330) 339-2211 SIC 3537 3531

THORWORKS INDUSTRIES INC p 1450
2520 Campbell St, Sandusky OH 44870
Tel (419) 626-4375
SIC 2851 3531 2952 2951 2891 2816

ROBBINS CO p 1241
29100 Hall St Ste 100, Solon OH 44139
Tel (440) 248-3303 SIC 3535 3541 3531

FORGE INDUSTRIES INC p 567
4450 Market St, Youngstown OH 44512
Tel (330) 782-8301
SIC 5085 3566 3599 3531 6411 7699

■ TULSA WINCH INC p 1491
11135 S James Ave, Jenks OK 74037
Tel (918) 298-8300 SIC 5084 3566 3531

■ CMI TEREX CORP p 329
9528 W I 40 Service Rd, Oklahoma City OK 73128
Tel (405) 787-6020
SIC 3531 3715 3596 3541 3444 2951

CHARLES MACHINE WORKS INC p 289
1959 W Fir St, Perry OK 73077
Tel (580) 572-3344
SIC 3531 3541 3829 3546

RAMSEY INDUSTRIES INC p 1207
4707 N Mingo Rd, Tulsa OK 74117
Tel (918) 438-2760 SIC 3531 3536

■ WARN INDUSTRIES INC p 1575
12900 Se Capps Rd, Clackamas OR 97015
Tel (503) 722-1200 SIC 3714 3531

CASCADE CORP p 262
2201 Ne 201st Ave, Fairview OR 97024
Tel (503) 669-6300 SIC 3537 3531

BLOUNT INTERNATIONAL INC p 190
4909 Se International Way, Portland OR 97222
Tel (503) 653-8881 SIC 3531 3523

ESCO CORP p 509
2141 Nw 25th Ave, Portland OR 97210
Tel (360) 690-0074
SIC 3535 3545 3325 3531

ALLIED SYSTEMS CO p 57
21433 Sw Oregon St, Sherwood OR 97140
Tel (503) 625-2560 SIC 3531 3537 3536

ROCKLAND INC p 1244
152 Weber Ln, Bedford PA 15522
Tel (814) 623-1115 SIC 3531

GROVE INVESTORS INC p 642
1542 Buchanan Trl E, Greencastle PA 17225
Tel (717) 597-8121 SIC 3531

STABLER COMPANIES INC p 1374
635 Lucknow Rd, Harrisburg PA 17110
Tel (717) 236-9307
SIC 5032 3089 7359 3531 1611 3648

■ MARINE ACQUISITION (US) INC p 906
640 N Lewis Rd, Limerick PA 19468
Tel (610) 495-7011 SIC 3531 5551

■ JLG INDUSTRIES INC p 786
1 J L G Dr, Mc Connellsburg PA 17233
Tel (717) 485-5161 SIC 3531

▲ KENNAMETAL INC p 810
600 Grant St Ste 5100, Pittsburgh PA 15219
Tel (412) 248-8200
SIC 3545 3532 3531 3313 3399

STELLA-JONES CORP p 1385
2 Gateway Ctr Ste 1000, Pittsburgh PA 15222
Tel (412) 894-2846 SIC 2491 2421 3531

■ GROVE US LLC p 642
1565 Buchanan Trl E, Shady Grove PA 17256
Tel (717) 597-8121 SIC 3531 3537

ER EQUIPMENT INC p 507
Calle Sur Num 10 Mariani St Calle Sur N, Ponce PR 00730
Tel (787) 841-2743 SIC 3531

BOMAG AMERICAS INC p 199
125 Blue Granite Pkwy, Ridgeway SC 29130
Tel (803) 337-0700 SIC 3531 2951

■ CRANE MERCHANDISING SYSTEMS INC p 389
3330 Crane Way, Williston SC 29853
Tel (803) 266-5000 SIC 3581 3531

■ TEREX UTILITIES INC p 1439
500 Oakwood Rd, Watertown SD 57201
Tel (605) 882-4000 SIC 3531 3537

GEHL POWER PRODUCTS INC p 597
900 Ferdig St, Yankton SD 57078
Tel (605) 665-6500 SIC 3537 3531 3535

■ KOLBERG-PIONEER INC p 826
700 W 21st St, Yankton SD 57078
Tel (605) 665-9311 SIC 3532 3531 3535

■ ASTEC INC p 122
4101 Jerome Ave, Chattanooga TN 37407
Tel (423) 867-4210 SIC 3531 3433 3443

▲ ASTEC INDUSTRIES INC p 122
1725 Shepherd Rd, Chattanooga TN 37421
Tel (423) 899-5898 SIC 3531 3433 3533

■ ROADTEC INC p 1240
800 Manufacturers Rd, Chattanooga TN 37405
Tel (423) 265-0600 SIC 3531

APAC-ATLANTIC INC p 95
4817 Rutledge Pike, Knoxville TN 37914
Tel (865) 983-3100
SIC 5032 3531 3273 2951 1611

POWER EQUIPMENT CO p 1165
3300 Alcoa Hwy, Knoxville TN 37920
Tel (865) 577-5563 SIC 5082 3531 7353

HEAVY MACHINES INC p 680
3926 E Raines Rd, Memphis TN 38118
Tel (901) 260-2200
SIC 5082 7699 7353 3531 5063

▲ TRINITY INDUSTRIES INC p 1481
2525 N Stemmons Fwy, Dallas TX 75207
Tel (214) 631-4420
SIC 3743 3731 3531 3444 3441 3443

BISHOP LIFTING PRODUCTS INC p 185
125 Mccarty St, Houston TX 77029
Tel (713) 674-2266 SIC 1799 3531

ROWAN COMPANIES INC p 1253
2800 Post Oak Blvd # 5450, Houston TX 77056
Tel (713) 621-7800 SIC 1381 3531 3533

SEATRAX INC p 1297
13223 Fm 529 Rd, Houston TX 77041
Tel (713) 896-6500 SIC 3531 3536

THRUSTMASTER OF TEXAS INC p 1451
6900 Thrustmaster Dr, Houston TX 77041
Tel (713) 937-6295 SIC 3531

■ JOY GLOBAL LONGVIEW OPERATIONS LLC p 794
2400 S Macarthur Dr, Longview TX 75602
Tel (903) 237-7000
SIC 3532 3533 3312 3531

WARREN POWER & MACHINERY INC p 1577
10325 Younger Rd, Midland TX 79706
Tel (432) 571-4200 SIC 3531

HOLT TEXAS LTD p 702
5665 Se Loop 410, San Antonio TX 78222
Tel (210) 648-1111
SIC 3531 5082 7353 7699

PSP INDUSTRIES INC p 1188
9885 Doerr Ln, Schertz TX 78154
Tel (210) 651-9595
SIC 3533 3531 3564 3532 3559

▲ ALAMO GROUP INC p 44
1627 E Walnut St, Seguin TX 78155
Tel (830) 379-1480 SIC 3523 3531

VISION TECHNOLOGIES SYSTEMS INC p 1561
99 Canal Center Plz # 220, Alexandria VA 22314
Tel (703) 739-2610 SIC 3731 3531

PLASSER AMERICAN CORP p 1155
2001 Myers Rd, Chesapeake VA 23324
Tel (757) 543-3526 SIC 3531

CARTER MACHINERY CO INC p 262
1330 Lynchburg Tpke, Salem VA 24153
Tel (540) 387-1111 SIC 5082 3531

■ GENIE MANUFACTURING INC p 604
18340 Ne 76th St, Redmond WA 98052
Tel (425) 881-1800 SIC 3531

SAFEWORKS LLC p 1267
365 Upland Dr, Tukwila WA 98188
Tel (206) 575-6445
SIC 3536 3531 3446 5082

KUHN NORTH AMERICA INC p 831
1501 W 7th Ave, Brodhead WI 53520
Tel (608) 897-4508 SIC 3523 3531

▲ MANITOWOC CO INC p 902
2400 S 44th St, Manitowoc WI 54220
Tel (920) 684-4410
SIC 3536 3537 3531 3585

■ MANITOWOC CRANES LLC p 902
2401 S 30th St, Manitowoc WI 54220
Tel (920) 684-6621 SIC 3531

WACKER NEUSON CORP p 1570
N92w15000 Anthony Ave, Menomonee Falls WI 53051
Tel (262) 255-0500
SIC 3531 3621 3561 3546 3423

■ TELSMITH INC p 1435
10910 N Industrial Dr, Mequon WI 53092
Tel (262) 242-6600 SIC 3531 3532

▲ DOUGLAS DYNAMICS INC p 452
7777 N 73rd St, Milwaukee WI 53223
Tel (414) 354-2310 SIC 3531

■ DOUGLAS DYNAMICS LLC p 452
7777 N 73rd St, Milwaukee WI 53223
Tel (414) 354-2310 SIC 3531

▲ OSHKOSH CORP p 1096
2307 Oregon St, Oshkosh WI 54902
Tel (920) 235-9151 SIC 3711 3531 3715

■ OSHKOSH DEFENSE LLC p 1096
2307 Oregon St, Oshkosh WI 54902
Tel (920) 235-9151 SIC 3711 3531 3715

■ TOTAL MIXER TECHNOLOGIES LLC p 1463
2307 Oregon St, Oshkosh WI 54902
Tel (920) 235-9150 SIC 3531

CASE CONSTRUCTION EQUIPMENT INC p 263
700 State St, Racine WI 53404
Tel (262) 636-6011 SIC 6159 3531 3523

CASE NEW HOLLAND INDUSTRIAL INC p 263
700 State St, Racine WI 53404
Tel (262) 636-6011 SIC 3523 3531

CNH INDUSTRIAL AMERICA LLC p 330
700 St St, Racine WI 53404
Tel (262) 636-6011 SIC 3523 3531 6159

■ CATERPILLAR GLOBAL MINING LLC p 265
1100 Milwaukee Ave, South Milwaukee WI 53172
Tel (414) 762-0376 SIC 3531 3532 3599

SPANCRETE GROUP INC p 1354
N16W 23415 Stone Rdge Dr St N 16, Waukesha WI 53188
Tel (414) 290-9000 SIC 3272 3531

MANITOU AMERICAS INC p 902
1 Gehl Way, West Bend WI 53095
Tel (262) 334-9461 SIC 3531 3523

SIC 3532 Mining Machinery & Eqpt

RAIN BIRD CORP p 1205
6991 E Suthpoint Rd Ste 1, Tucson AZ 85756
Tel (520) 806-5635 SIC 3532

BASIC RESOURCES INC p 158
928 12th St Ste 700, Modesto CA 95354
Tel (209) 521-9771
SIC 1611 3273 2951 3532 3531

■ TEREX USA LLC p 1439
200 Nyala Farms Rd, Westport CT 06880
Tel (203) 222-7170 SIC 3532

ELGIN EQUIPMENT GROUP LLC p 486
2001 Bttrfeld Rd Ste 1020, Downers Grove IL 60515
Tel (630) 434-7200 SIC 3532

ELGIN NATIONAL INDUSTRIES INC p 486
2001 Bttrfeld Rd Ste 1020, Downers Grove IL 60515
Tel (630) 434-7200 SIC 3532 8711

MARTIN ENGINEERING CO p 912
1 Martin Pl, Neponset IL 61345
Tel (309) 852-2384 SIC 3829 3532

KOMATSU AMERICA CORP p 827
1701 Golf Rd Ste 1-100, Rolling Meadows IL 60008
Tel (847) 437-5800 SIC 5082 3532 3531

BRAKE SUPPLY CO INC p 207
5501 Foundation Blvd, Evansville IN 47725
Tel (812) 467-1000
SIC 5082 5084 5088 5013 3532

SYNTRON MATERIAL HANDLING LLC p 1416
2730 Highway 145, Saltillo MS 38866
Tel (662) 869-5711 SIC 3532

AMEC FOSTER WHEELER NORTH AMERICA CORP p 66
Perryville Corporate Pk 5, Hampton NJ 08827
Tel (908) 713-2891
SIC 3433 3443 3532 3569

■ K-TRON INTERNATIONAL INC p 799
590 Woodbury Glassboro Rd, Sewell NJ 08080
Tel (856) 589-0500 SIC 3532 3535

FISHER SAND & GRAVEL CO p 552
3020 Energy Dr, Dickinson ND 58601
Tel (701) 456-9184 SIC 1442 3532 5084

WARREN FABRICATING CORP p 1577
3240 Mahoning Ave Nw, Warren OH 44483
Tel (330) 847-0596
SIC 3441 3599 3547 3532 3444 3443

FLS US HOLDINGS INC p 561
2040 Avenue C, Bethlehem PA 18017
Tel (610) 264-6011
SIC 3559 3554 3549 3532 3535

MCLANAHAN CORP p 930
200 Wall St, Hollidaysburg PA 16648
Tel (814) 695-9807
SIC 3532 3321 3599 3523

■ CATERPILLAR GLOBAL MINING AMERICA LLC p 265
2045 W Pike St, Houston PA 15342
Tel (724) 743-1200 SIC 3532 7629

JENNMAR CORP p 782
258 Kappa Dr, Pittsburgh PA 15238
Tel (412) 963-9071 SIC 3532

▲ KENNAMETAL INC p 810
600 Grant St Ste 5100, Pittsburgh PA 15219
Tel (412) 248-8200
SIC 3545 3532 3531 3313 3399

■ JOY GLOBAL UNDERGROUND MINING LLC p 794
40 Pennwood Pl Ste 100, Warrendale PA 15086
Tel (724) 779-4500 SIC 3535 3532

BRIDON-AMERICAN CORP p 212
C280 New Commerce Blvd, Wilkes Barre PA 18706
Tel (570) 822-3349 SIC 3533 3532 5084

■ KOLBERG-PIONEER INC p 826
700 W 21st St, Yankton SD 57078
Tel (605) 665-9311 SIC 3532 3531 3535

VAREL INTERNATIONAL IND LP p 1544
1625 W Crosby Rd Ste 124, Carrollton TX 75006
Tel (972) 242-1160 SIC 3545 3532 1381

CANRIG DRILLING TECH LTD p 247
515 W Greens Rd Ste 1200, Houston TX 77067
Tel (281) 774-5600 SIC 3532

SMITH INTERNATIONAL INC p 1333
1310 Rankin Rd, Houston TX 77073
Tel (281) 443-3370 SIC 3532 3533

■ JOY GLOBAL LONGVIEW OPERATIONS LLC p 794
2400 S Macarthur Dr, Longview TX 75602
Tel (903) 237-7000
SIC 3532 3533 3312 3531

PSP INDUSTRIES INC p 1188
9885 Doerr Ln, Schertz TX 78154
Tel (210) 651-9595
SIC 3533 3531 3564 3532 3559

BOART LONGYEAR CO p 196
2570 W 1700 S, Salt Lake City UT 84104
Tel (801) 972-6430
SIC 1481 3532 3559 1771

LONGYEAR HOLDINGS INC p 877
2340 W 1700 S, Salt Lake City UT 84104
Tel (801) 972-6430 SIC 1481 3532 3559

LIEBHERR MINING & CONSTRUCTION EQUIPMENT INC p 863
4100 Chestnut Ave, Newport News VA 23607
Tel (757) 245-5251 SIC 5082 5084 3532

J H FLETCHER & CO p 771
402 High St, Huntington WV 25705
Tel (304) 525-7811
SIC 5082 3532 3743 3546 3541

RALEIGH MINE AND INDUSTRIAL SUPPLY INC p 1206
1500 Mill Creek Rd, Mount Hope WV 25880
Tel (304) 877-5503
SIC 5085 1629 3532 3441

■ TELSMITH INC p 1435
10910 N Industrial Dr, Mequon WI 53092
Tel (262) 242-6600 SIC 3531 3532

▲ JOY GLOBAL INC p 794
100 E Wisconsin Ave # 2780, Milwaukee WI 53202
Tel (414) 319-8500 SIC 3532

OLDENBURG GROUP INC p 1082
1717 W Civic Dr, Milwaukee WI 53209
Tel (414) 354-6600 SIC 3537 3532 3646

■ CATERPILLAR GLOBAL MINING LLC p 265
1100 Milwaukee Ave, South Milwaukee WI 53172
Tel (414) 762-0376 SIC 3531 3532 3599

METSO MINERALS INDUSTRIES INC p 957
20965 Crossroads Cir, Waukesha WI 53186
Tel (262) 798-3994
SIC 3321 3069 3561 3535 3532

SIC 3533 Oil Field Machinery & Eqpt

AMERICAN AIR LIQUIDE INC p 67
46409 Landing Pkwy, Fremont CA 94538
Tel (510) 624-4000
SIC 2813 5084 3533 4931

FTT HOLDINGS INC p 583
3020 Old Ranch Pkwy, Seal Beach CA 90740
Tel (562) 430-6262 SIC 3533

DESCO ACQUISITION LLC p 431
230 Commerce Rd, Berthoud CO 80513
Tel (970) 532-0600 SIC 1796 3533 1389

■ PCS FERGUSON INC p 1124
3771 Eureka Way, Frederick CO 80516
Tel (720) 407-3550 SIC 3533 5084

WGH HOLDING CORP p 1604
350 Indiana St Ste 610, Golden CO 80401
Tel (706) 884-6884 SIC 3533

■ DELAWARE CAPITAL HOLDINGS INC p 423
501 Silverside Rd Ste 5, Wilmington DE 19809
Tel (302) 793-4921 SIC 5084 3533 7699

CARIB ENERGY (USA) LLC p 256
9487 Regency Square Blvd, Jacksonville FL 32225
Tel (904) 727-2559 SIC 3533

■ CHROMALLOY GAS TURBINE LLC p 304
3999 Rca Blvd, Palm Beach Gardens FL 33410
Tel (561) 935-3571
SIC 3724 7699 4581 3764 3769 3533

■ MUELLER GROUP LLC p 998
1200 Abernathy Rd, Atlanta GA 30328
Tel (770) 206-4200
SIC 3823 3321 3533 7699

■ U O P EQUITEC SERVICES INC p 1497
25 E Algonquin Rd, Des Plaines IL 60016
Tel (847) 391-2000 SIC 3533

■ DOVER ARTIFICIAL LIFT INTERNATIONAL LLC p 453
3005 Highland Pkwy, Downers Grove IL 60515
Tel (630) 743-2563
SIC 3559 3535 3533 3561

▲ DOVER CORP p 453
3005 Highland Pkwy # 200, Downers Grove IL 60515
Tel (630) 541-1540
SIC 3632 3586 3533 3577 3674

■ CETCO ENERGY SERVICES CO LLC p 284
1001 Ochsner Blvd Ste 425, Covington LA 70433
Tel (985) 871-4700 SIC 1389 2869 3533

ASRC ENERGY SERVICES OMEGA LLC p 119
4418 Pesson Rd, New Iberia LA 70560
Tel (337) 365-6028 SIC 1389 3533

SPARTAN OFFSHORE DRILLING LLC p 1355
516 J F Smith Ave, Slidell LA 70460
Tel (504) 885-7449 SIC 3533

SPARTAN OFFSHORE INTERMEDIATE LLC p 1355
516 J F Smith Ave, Slidell LA 70460
Tel (504) 885-7449 SIC 3533

CUMING CORP p 400
225 Bodwell St, Avon MA 02322
Tel (508) 580-2660 SIC 3533 3679

SANDVIK INC p 1279
17-02 Nevins Rd, Fair Lawn NJ 07410
Tel (201) 794-5000
SIC 3316 3317 3356 3315 3545 3533

PROCESS EQUIPMENT & SERVICE CO INC p 1179
5680 Us 64, Farmington NM 87401
Tel (505) 327-2222
SIC 3443 5084 7699 3533

DERRICK CORP p 431
590 Duke Rd, Buffalo NY 14225
Tel (716) 683-9010 SIC 3533

BASIN HOLDINGS US LLC p 159
200 Park Ave Fl 58, New York NY 10166
Tel (212) 695-7376 SIC 3533

BLUE TEE CORP p 192
387 Park Ave S Fl 5, New York NY 10016
Tel (212) 598-0880
SIC 3533 3589 5093 3715 3823 5051

■ RMI TITANIUM CO LLC p 1239
1000 Warren Ave, Niles OH 44446
Tel (330) 652-9952
SIC 3399 3356 1741 3533

WILCO MACHINE & FAB INC p 1608
1326 S Broadway St, Marlow OK 73055
Tel (580) 658-6993 SIC 3533

■ COMPRESSCO INC p 352
1313 Se 25th St, Oklahoma City OK 73129
Tel (405) 677-0221 SIC 3533

SEVENTY SEVEN OPERATING LLC p 1309
777 Nw 63rd St, Oklahoma City OK 73116
Tel (405) 608-7777 SIC 3533 1389

SERVICE KING MANUFACTURING INC p 1307
2100 W Hgwy 66, Stroud OK 74079
Tel (918) 968-2899 SIC 3533

BORETS US INC p 201
1600 N Garnett Rd, Tulsa OK 74116
Tel (918) 439-7000 SIC 3533

BRIDON-AMERICAN CORP p 212
C280 New Commerce Blvd, Wilkes Barre PA 18706
Tel (570) 822-3349 SIC 3533 3532 5084

▲ ASTEC INDUSTRIES INC p 122
1725 Shepherd Rd, Chattanooga TN 37421
Tel (423) 899-5898 SIC 3531 3433 3533

■ MUELLER CO LLC p 998
633 Chestnut St Ste 1200, Chattanooga TN 37450
Tel (423) 209-4800 SIC 3823 3533 7699

J-W ENERGY CO p 772
15505 Wright Brothers Dr, Addison TX 75001
Tel (972) 233-8191
SIC 1311 7353 3533 1381

■ OIL STATES INDUSTRIES INC p 1079
7701 S Cooper St, Arlington TX 76001
Tel (817) 548-4200
SIC 1389 3061 3561 3533

LOADCRAFT INDUSTRIES LTD p 872
3811 N Bridge St, Brady TX 76825
Tel (325) 597-2911 SIC 3533

■ HARBISON-FISCHER INC p 659
901 N Crowley Rd, Crowley TX 76036
Tel (817) 297-2211 SIC 3533 3443

PREFERRED PUMP & EQUIPMENT LP p 1169
2201 Scott Ave Ste 100, Fort Worth TX 76103
Tel (817) 536-9800
SIC 5084 5083 5074 3533 5082

SPM FLOW CONTROL INC p 1359
601 Weir Way, Fort Worth TX 76108
Tel (817) 246-2461 SIC 3533 3599

■ ULTERRA DRILLING TECHNOLOGIES LP p 1500
420 Throckmorton St # 1110, Fort Worth TX 76102
Tel (817) 293-7555 SIC 5084 3533

OWEN OIL TOOLS INC p 1099
12001 County Road 1000, Godley TX 76044
Tel (817) 396-4570 SIC 2892 3533

TOTAL EQUIPMENT AND SERVICE p 1462
4801 Glen Rose Hwy, Granbury TX 76048
Tel (817) 573-3550 SIC 3533

AIR LIQUIDE AMERICA LP p 39
9811 Katy Fwy Ste 100, Houston TX 77024
Tel (713) 624-8000
SIC 5084 3533 2813 3569

AKER SUBSEA INC p 42
3010 Briarpark Dr, Houston TX 77042
Tel (713) 685-5700 SIC 3533 1389 8711

AMERICAN BLOCK CO p 69
6311 Breen Dr, Houston TX 77086
Tel (800) 572-9087
SIC 3441 3599 3533 3496 3444 3429

ANTELOPE OIL TOOL & MFG CO LLC p 93
8807 W Sam Houston Pkwy N # 200, Houston TX 77040
Tel (832) 756-2300 SIC 3533

▲ BAKER HUGHES INC p 146
17021 Aldine Westfield Rd, Houston TX 77073
Tel (713) 439-8600 SIC 3533 3561

CACTUS WELLHEAD LLC p 236
1 Greenway Plz Ste 200, Houston TX 77046
Tel (713) 626-8800 SIC 3533

CAMERON INTERNATIONAL CORP p 245
4646 W Sam Houston Pkwy N, Houston TX 77041
Tel (713) 513-3300 SIC 3533 3563 3491

CAMERON SOLUTIONS INC p 245
11210 Equity Dr Ste 100, Houston TX 77041
Tel (713) 849-7500 SIC 3533 1389 3569

CAMERON TECHNOLOGIES INC p 245
4646 W Sam Houston Pkwy N, Houston TX 77041
Tel (713) 513-3300 SIC 5084 3533

■ DNOW LP p 446
7402 N Eldridge Pkwy, Houston TX 77041
Tel (281) 823-4700 SIC 5084 7353 3533

▲ DRIL-QUIP INC p 456
6401 N Eldridge Pkwy, Houston TX 77041
Tel (713) 939-7711 SIC 3533

DRILLMEC INC p 456
18320 Imperial Valley Dr, Houston TX 77060
Tel (281) 885-0777 SIC 3533

EAGLE PIPE LLC p 468
9525 Katy Fwy Ste 306, Houston TX 77024
Tel (713) 464-7473 SIC 3533 5082

■ EXLP FINANCE CORP p 519
16666 Northchase Dr, Houston TX 77060
Tel (281) 836-7000 SIC 3533

FLEXITALLIC GROUP INC p 556
201 Kingwood Med Dr B20 Ste B 200, Houston TX 77067
Tel (281) 604-2525
SIC 3053 3533 3463 3965

▲ FLOTEK INDUSTRIES INC p 560
10603 W Sam Houston Pkwy, Houston TX 77064
Tel (713) 849-9911
SIC 2087 2869 2899 3533 3491

▲ FMC TECHNOLOGIES INC p 562
5875 N Sam Houston Pkwy W, Houston TX 77086
Tel (281) 591-4000 SIC 3533

▲ FORUM ENERGY TECHNOLOGIES INC p 570
920 Memorial City Way # 1000, Houston TX 77024
Tel (281) 949-2500 SIC 3533

Section III Businesses by Industry Classification

GLOBAL ENERGY SERVICES INC p 616
10307 Wallisville Rd, Houston TX 77013
Tel (281) 447-9000 SIC 3533

■ **GRANT PRIDECO INC** p 631
10100 Houston Oaks Dr, Houston TX 77064
Tel (281) 878-8000 SIC 3533

HYDRIL CO p 723
302 Mccarty St, Houston TX 77029
Tel (713) 670-3500 SIC 3533

■ **HYDRIL USA DISTRIBUTION LLC** p 723
3300 N Sam Houston Pkwy E, Houston TX 77032
Tel (281) 449-2000 SIC 3533

KW INTERNATIONAL LLC p 832
10880 Alcott Dr, Houston TX 77043
Tel (713) 468-9581 SIC 3533

NATCO GROUP INC p 1009
11210 Equity Dr Ste 100, Houston TX 77041
Tel (713) 849-7500 SIC 3533 1389

▲ **NATIONAL OILWELL VARCO INC** p 1014
7909 Parkwood Circle Dr, Houston TX 77036
Tel (713) 346-7500 SIC 3533 3594 5084

■ **NATIONAL OILWELL VARCO LP** p 1014
1530 W Sam Houston Pkwy N, Houston TX 77043
Tel (713) 960-5100 SIC 3533 5082 5084

■ **OIL STATES ENERGY SERVICES LLC** p 1079
333 Clay St Ste 2100, Houston TX 77002
Tel (713) 425-2400 SIC 3533 5082

ONESUBSEA LLC p 1088
4646 W Sam Houston Pkwy N, Houston TX 77041
Tel (713) 939-2211 SIC 3533 3563 3491

PEARCE INDUSTRIES INC p 1126
12320 Main St, Houston TX 77035
Tel (713) 723-1050 SIC 5084 3533 5082

PRECISION ENERGY SERVICES INC p 1168
2000 Saint James Pl, Houston TX 77056
Tel (713) 693-4000 SIC 3533 1389

REEF SERVICES LLC p 1217
515 Post Oak Blvd Ste 600, Houston TX 77027
Tel (432) 560-5600 SIC 3533

ROWAN COMPANIES INC p 1253
2800 Post Oak Blvd # 5450, Houston TX 77056
Tel (713) 621-7800 SIC 1381 3531 3533

SCHLUMBERGER INTERNATIONAL INC p 1287
7030 Ardmore St, Houston TX 77054
Tel (713) 747-4000
SIC 1389 3561 3492 3533

SMITH INTERNATIONAL INC p 1333
1310 Rankin Rd, Houston TX 77073
Tel (281) 443-3370 SIC 3532 3533

SOFEC INC p 1337
15011 Katy Fwy Ste 500, Houston TX 77094
Tel (713) 510-6600 SIC 3533 8742

SOUTHWEST OILFIELD PRODUCTS INC p 1352
10340 Wallisville Rd, Houston TX 77013
Tel (713) 675-7541 SIC 3533 3561

STEWART & STEVENSON LLC p 1389
1000 La St Ste 5900, Houston TX 77002
Tel (713) 751-2600
SIC 5084 5082 3533 7353

STEWART & STEVENSON POWER PRODUCTS LLC p 1389
1000 La St Ste 5900, Houston TX 77002
Tel (713) 751-2600
SIC 1389 5084 5082 3533 7353

▲ **SUPERIOR ENERGY SERVICES INC** p 1406
1001 La St Ste 2900, Houston TX 77002
Tel (713) 654-2200 SIC 1389 3533 7353

TAM INTERNATIONAL INC p 1423
4620 Southerland Rd, Houston TX 77092
Tel (713) 462-7617 SIC 3533

▲ **TESCO CORP** p 1440
11330 Clay Rd Ste 350, Houston TX 77041
Tel (713) 359-7000 SIC 3533

■ **TIW CORP** p 1457
12300 Main St, Houston TX 77035
Tel (713) 729-2110 SIC 3533

TRELLEBORG OFFSHORE US INC p 1476
1902 Rankin Rd, Houston TX 77073
Tel (281) 774-2600 SIC 3533

TSC OFFSHORE CORP p 1489
7611 Railhead Ln, Houston TX 77086
Tel (832) 456-3900 SIC 3533

TUCKER ENERGY SERVICES INC p 1490
411 N Sam Houston Pkwy E # 300, Houston TX 77060
Tel (281) 442-9095 SIC 1389 3533

U S WEATHERFORD L P p 1497
2000 Saint James Pl, Houston TX 77056
Tel (713) 693-4000 SIC 3498 3533

■ **VETCO GRAY INC** p 1552
4424 W Sam Houston Pkwy N, Houston TX 77041
Tel (713) 683-2400 SIC 3533

VINSON PROCESS CONTROLS CO LP p 1558
2747 Highpoint Oaks Dr, Lewisville TX 75067
Tel (972) 459-8200 SIC 5084 3533 3498

■ **JOY GLOBAL LONGVIEW OPERATIONS LLC** p 794
2400 S Macarthur Dr, Longview TX 75602
Tel (903) 237-7000
SIC 3532 3533 3312 3531

LINCOLN MANUFACTURING INC p 867
31209 Fm 2978 Rd, Magnolia TX 77354
Tel (281) 252-9494 SIC 3533 5082

▲ **CSI COMPRESSCO LP** p 397
3809 S Fm 1788, Midland TX 79706
Tel (432) 563-1170 SIC 1389 3533

GEODYNAMICS INC p 606
10500 W Interstate 20, Millsap TX 76066
Tel (817) 341-5300 SIC 2892 3533

RUSH SALES CO p 1258
2700 E I 20 Service Rd, Odessa TX 79766
Tel (432) 337-2397 SIC 3533 5511

■ **NUSTAR GP LLC** p 1067
19003 W Interstate 10, San Antonio TX 78257
Tel (210) 370-2000 SIC 3533

PSP INDUSTRIES INC p 1188
9885 Doerr Ln, Schertz TX 78154
Tel (210) 651-9595
SIC 3533 3531 3564 3532 3559

APPLIED MACHINERY CORP p 99
20105 Krahn Rd, Spring TX 77388
Tel (281) 821-0700 SIC 3533

▲ **INTEGRATED DRILLING EQUIPMENT HOLDINGS CORP** p 749
25311 I 45 N Bldg 6, Spring TX 77380
Tel (281) 465-9393 SIC 3533 7539 5084

■ **RTI ENERGY SYSTEMS INC** p 1256
7211 Spring Cypress Rd, Spring TX 77379
Tel (281) 379-4289 SIC 3533 3498

SCHLUMBERGER TECHNOLOGY CORP p 1287
100 Gillingham Ln, Sugar Land TX 77478
Tel (281) 285-8500
SIC 1382 1389 3825 3824 3533 3586

■ **ROBBIN & MEYERS ENERGY SYSTEMS LP** p 1240
10586 N Highway 75, Willis TX 77378
Tel (936) 890-1064 SIC 3491 3533

■ **ROBBINS & MYERS INC** p 1241
10586 N Highway 75, Willis TX 77378
Tel (936) 890-1064
SIC 3533 3443 3823 5084

BOART LONGYEAR MANUFACTURING AND DISTRIBUTION INC p 196
2640 W 1700 S, Salt Lake City UT 84104
Tel (801) 972-6430 SIC 1381 5084 3533

■ **JW WILLIAMS INC** p 798
2180 W Renauna Ave, Casper WY 82601
Tel (307) 237-8345
SIC 3533 3443 3547 1761 3291

SIC 3534 Elevators & Moving Stairways

ESSICK AIR PRODUCTS INC p 510
5800 Murray St, Little Rock AR 72209
Tel (501) 562-1094 SIC 3534 3585 3634

MITSUBISHI ELECTRIC US INC p 977
5900 Katella Ave Ste A, Cypress CA 90630
Tel (714) 220-2500
SIC 5065 5045 1796 3534

MAXON LIFT CORP p 922
11921 Slauson Ave, Santa Fe Springs CA 90670
Tel (562) 464-0099 SIC 5084 3537 3534

■ **OTIS ELEVATOR CO** p 1097
10 Farm Springs Rd, Farmington CT 06032
Tel (860) 676-6000 SIC 3534 1796 7699

▲ **UNITED TECHNOLOGIES CORP** p 1514
10 Farm Springs Rd, Farmington CT 06032
Tel (860) 728-7000
SIC 3724 3585 3721 3534 3669 3699

THYSSENKRUPP ELEVATOR AMERICAS CORP p 1451
11605 Haynes Bridge Rd, Alpharetta GA 30009
Tel (678) 319-3240 SIC 7699 3534 1796

THYSSENKRUPP ELEVATOR CORP p 1451
11605 Haynes Bridge Rd # 650, Alpharetta GA 30009
Tel (678) 319-3240 SIC 3534 1796 7699

KONE ELEVATOR p 827
1 Kone Ct, Moline IL 61265
Tel (309) 764-6771 SIC 7699 3534

KONE INC p 827
1 Kone Ct, Moline IL 61265
Tel (309) 764-6771 SIC 7699 3534 1796

HOLLISTER-WHITNEY ELEVATOR CORP p 701
2603 N 24th St, Quincy IL 62305
Tel (217) 222-0466 SIC 3534

COMMERCIAL GROUP INC p 345
12801 Universal Dr, Taylor MI 48180
Tel (313) 931-6100
SIC 5085 5051 3496 3537 3534

SCHINDLER ELEVATOR CORP p 1287
20 Whippany Rd, Morristown NJ 07960
Tel (973) 397-6500 SIC 3534 7699 1796

SCHINDLER ENTERPRISES INC p 1287
20 Whippany Rd, Morristown NJ 07960
Tel (973) 397-6500 SIC 3534 7699 1796

FUJITEC AMERICA INC p 583
7258 Innovation Way, Mason OH 45040
Tel (513) 755-6100 SIC 3534

THYSSENKRUPP ELEVATOR MANUFACTURING INC p 1451
9280 Crestwyn Hills Dr, Memphis TN 38125
Tel (901) 261-1800 SIC 3534

ALIMAK HEK INC p 50
12552 Galveston Rd Ste A 160, Webster TX 77598
Tel (713) 640-8500
SIC 5084 7699 3535 3534

SIC 3535 Conveyors & Eqpt

PROCESS EQUIPMENT INC p 1179
2770 Welborn St, Pelham AL 35124
Tel (205) 663-5330
SIC 3564 3535 3441 3443

■ **CONTINENTAL GLOBAL GROUP INC** p 363
438 Industrial Dr, Winfield AL 35594
Tel (205) 487-6492 SIC 3535

ROACH MANUFACTURING CORP p 1240
808 Highway 463 N, Trumann AR 72472
Tel (870) 483-7631 SIC 3535

TRANSLOGIC CORP p 1472
10825 E 47th Ave, Denver CO 80239
Tel (303) 371-7770 SIC 3535

ALVEST (USA) INC p 63
812 Bloomfield Ave, Windsor CT 06095
Tel (860) 602-3400 SIC 3585 3535

MAREL STORK POULTRY PROCESSING INC p 905
1024 Airport Pkwy, Gainesville GA 30501
Tel (770) 532-7041 SIC 3556 3535

VANDERLANDE INDUSTRIES INC p 1543
1975 W Oak Cir, Marietta GA 30062
Tel (770) 250-2800 SIC 8711 3535

■ **DOVER ARTIFICIAL LIFT INTERNATIONAL LLC** p 453
3005 Highland Pkwy, Downers Grove IL 60515
Tel (630) 743-2563
SIC 3559 3535 3533 3561

WYNRIGHT CORP p 1630
2500 Elmhurst Rd, Elk Grove Village IL 60007
Tel (847) 595-9400 SIC 5084 3535 8711

BARRY-WEHMILLER CONTAINER SYSTEMS INC p 157
1305 Lakeview Dr, Romeoville IL 60446
Tel (630) 759-6800 SIC 3535

AEC INC p 28
1100 E Wdfield Rd Ste 588, Schaumburg IL 60173
Tel (847) 273-7700
SIC 3585 3823 3559 3443 3535

UNITED CONVEYOR CORP p 1507
2100 Norman Dr, Waukegan IL 60085
Tel (847) 473-5900 SIC 3535

VESTIL MANUFACTURING CORP p 1552
2999 N Wayne St, Angola IN 46703
Tel (260) 665-7586 SIC 3999 3535 3069

▲ **HILLENBRAND INC** p 693
1 Batesville Blvd, Batesville IN 47006
Tel (812) 934-7500 SIC 3535 3995

HALO LLC p 655
10585 N Meridian St Fl 3, Indianapolis IN 46290
Tel (317) 575-9992 SIC 8711 3535

HIRATA CORP OF AMERICA p 695
5625 Decatur Blvd, Indianapolis IN 46241
Tel (317) 856-8600 SIC 3535 3537 8711

CARDINAL CARRYOR INC p 252
1055 Grade Ln, Louisville KY 40213
Tel (502) 363-6641
SIC 5084 7699 7359 5085 3535

INTRALOX LLC p 760
301 Plantation Rd, Harahan LA 70123
Tel (504) 733-6739 SIC 3535

LAITRAM LLC p 838
220 Laitram Ln, Harahan LA 70123
Tel (504) 733-6000
SIC 3535 3556 7359 3446 6719

DVCC INC p 463
800 High St, Chestertown MD 21620
Tel (410) 778-2000
SIC 3492 5085 3535 3321 3364

BELCO INDUSTRIES INC p 169
9138 W Belding Rd, Belding MI 48809
Tel (616) 794-0410
SIC 3567 5084 3541 3535 3444

PRESSURE VESSEL SERVICE INC p 1173
10900 Harper Ave, Detroit MI 48213
Tel (313) 921-1200
SIC 5169 2819 2899 4953 3535

JERVIS B WEBB CO p 783
34375 W 12 Mile Rd, Farmington Hills MI 48331
Tel (248) 553-1000
SIC 3535 3536 3462 3537 3613

DEMATIC CORP p 428
507 Plymouth Ave Ne, Grand Rapids MI 49505
Tel (678) 695-4500 SIC 3535 1796 8711

HINES CORP p 695
1218 E Pontaluna Rd Ste B, Norton Shores MI 49456
Tel (231) 799-6240
SIC 3443 3823 3589 3531 3535 5082

DEARBORN MID-WEST CO LLC p 420
20334 Superior Rd, Taylor MI 48180
Tel (734) 288-4400 SIC 3535

SUPERIOR INDUSTRIES INC p 1406
315 State Highway 28, Morris MN 56267
Tel (320) 589-2406 SIC 3535

BUHLER INC p 224
13105 12th Ave N, Plymouth MN 55441
Tel (763) 847-9900
SIC 3556 3542 3535 3564

BARRY-WEHMILLER COMPANIES INC p 157
8020 Forsyth Blvd, Saint Louis MO 63105
Tel (314) 862-8000
SIC 3565 3535 3554 8711

BARRY-WEHMILLER GROUP INC p 157
8020 Forsyth Blvd, Saint Louis MO 63105
Tel (314) 862-8000
SIC 3565 3535 3554 8711

GLOBAL INDUSTRIES INC p 617
1804 E 4th St, Grand Island NE 68801
Tel (800) 247-6621
SIC 7992 3589 3444 5084 5083 3535

KENECO INC p 810
123 N 8th St, Kenilworth NJ 07033
Tel (908) 241-3700 SIC 3535

■ **K-TRON INTERNATIONAL INC** p 799
590 Woodbury Glassboro Rd, Sewell NJ 08080
Tel (856) 589-0500 SIC 3532 3535

▲ **COLUMBUS MCKINNON CORP** p 342
205 Crosspoint Pkwy, Getzville NY 14068
Tel (716) 689-5400
SIC 3536 3496 3535 3537

RAYMOND CORP p 1210
22 S Canal St, Greene NY 13778
Tel (607) 656-2311 SIC 3537 3535 7359

FIAT USA INC p 539
375 Park Ave Ste 2703, New York NY 10152
Tel (212) 355-2600
SIC 3714 8741 3535 5012 5013 5082

AC CORP p 13
301 Creek Ridge Rd, Greensboro NC 27406
Tel (336) 273-4472
SIC 1711 1731 3556 3823 3625 3535

FORBO SIEGLING LLC p 565
12201 Vanstory Dr, Huntersville NC 28078
Tel (704) 948-0800 SIC 3052 3535

GROB SYSTEMS INC p 641
1070 Navajo Dr, Bluffton OH 45817
Tel (419) 358-9015 SIC 3535 7699

NESCO INC p 1026
6140 Parkland Blvd # 110, Cleveland OH 44124
Tel (440) 461-6000
SIC 3535 3541 3644 8711 6531

PNEUMATIC SCALE CORP p 1158
10 Ascot Pkwy, Cuyahoga Falls OH 44223
Tel (330) 923-0491 SIC 3565 3569 3535

AD INDUSTRIES INC p 21
6450 Poe Ave Ste 109, Dayton OH 45414
Tel (303) 744-1911
SIC 3634 3564 3535 3714 3088 3089

INTELLIGRATED INC p 750
7901 Innovation Way, Mason OH 45040
Tel (866) 936-7300 SIC 3535

■ **INTELLIGRATED SYSTEMS INC** p 750
7901 Innovation Way, Mason OH 45040
Tel (866) 936-7300 SIC 3535 5084 7371

■ **INTELLIGRATED SYSTEMS LLC** p 750
7901 Innovation Way, Mason OH 45040
Tel (513) 701-7300 SIC 3535 5084 7371

■ **INTELLIGRATED SYSTEMS OF OHIO LLC** p 750
7901 Innovation Way, Mason OH 45040
Tel (513) 701-7300 SIC 3535 5084 3537

ROBBINS CO p 1241
29100 Hall St Ste 100, Solon OH 44139
Tel (440) 248-3303 SIC 3535 3541 3531

FKI INDUSTRIES INC p 554
2801 Dawson Rd, Tulsa OK 74110
Tel (918) 834-4611
SIC 3429 3536 3535 3496 3569 3823

EMERGING ACQUISITIONS LLC p 492
3592 W 5th Ave, Eugene OR 97402
Tel (541) 485-0999 SIC 3535

WESTERN PNEUMATICS INC p 1599
110 N Seneca Rd, Eugene OR 97402
Tel (541) 461-2600 SIC 3535 3553 5099

ESCO CORP p 509
2141 Nw 25th Ave, Portland OR 97210
Tel (360) 690-0074
SIC 3535 3545 3325 3531

FLS US HOLDINGS INC p 561
2040 Avenue C, Bethlehem PA 18017
Tel (610) 264-6011
SIC 3559 3554 3549 3532 3535

■ **JOY GLOBAL UNDERGROUND MINING LLC** p 794
40 Pennwood Pl Ste 100, Warrendale PA 15086
Tel (724) 779-4500 SIC 3535 3532

PTERIS GLOBAL (USA) INC p 1189
208 Shoreline Pkwy, Fort Mill SC 29708
Tel (980) 253-3267 SIC 3535

GOWER CORP p 627
355 Woodruff Rd Ste 101, Greenville SC 29607
Tel (864) 458-3114 SIC 3535 5051 7373

GEHL POWER PRODUCTS INC p 597
900 Ferdig St, Yankton SD 57078
Tel (605) 665-6500 SIC 3537 3531 3535

■ **KOLBERG-PIONEER INC** p 826
700 W 21st St, Yankton SD 57078
Tel (605) 665-9311 SIC 3532 3531 3535

MARTIN SPROCKET & GEAR INC p 913
3100 Sprocket Dr, Arlington TX 76015
Tel (817) 258-3000
SIC 3566 3568 3535 3321 3462 3429

ALIMAK HEK INC p 50
12552 Galveston Rd Ste A 160, Webster TX 77598
Tel (713) 640-8500
SIC 5084 7699 3535 3534

■ **MERCURY MARINE INC** p 945
W6250 W Pioneer Rd, Fond Du Lac WI 54935
Tel (920) 929-5000 SIC 3089 3535

METSO MINERALS INDUSTRIES INC p 957
20965 Crossroads Cir, Waukesha WI 53186
Tel (262) 798-3994
SIC 3321 3069 3561 3535 3532

SIC 3536 Hoists, Cranes & Monorails

DESHAZO LLC p 432
190 Airpark Industrial Rd, Alabaster AL 35007
Tel (205) 664-2006 SIC 3536

ALTEC INC p 62
210 Inverness Center Dr, Birmingham AL 35242
Tel (205) 991-7733 SIC 3531 3713 3536

ALTEC INDUSTRIES INC p 62
210 Inverness Center Dr, Birmingham AL 35242
Tel (205) 991-7733 SIC 3531 3536 3713

■ **TIMKEN MOTOR & CRANE SERVICES LLC** p 1455
4850 Moline St, Denver CO 80239
Tel (303) 623-8658
SIC 5063 1731 7694 3613 3536

▲ **MANITEX INTERNATIONAL INC** p 901
9725 Industrial Dr, Bridgeview IL 60455
Tel (708) 430-7500 SIC 3537 3536

LANCO INTERNATIONAL INC p 842
3111 167th St, Hazel Crest IL 60429
Tel (708) 596-5200
SIC 3531 8711 5084 3536 7353 3537

G K ENTERPRISES INC p 587
26000 S Whiting Way Ste 2, Monee IL 60449
Tel (708) 587-2150
SIC 3743 3443 3559 3556 3536

OMAHA STANDARD LLC p 1083
3501 S 11th St Ste 1, Council Bluffs IA 51501
Tel (712) 328-7444 SIC 3713 3536 3537

CONSTRUCTION PRODUCTS INC p 361
1800 Ne 46th Ave, Des Moines IA 50313
Tel (515) 313-4253 SIC 3536 3544

■ **TEREX MHPS CORP** p 1439
106 12th St Se, Waverly IA 50677
Tel (877) 794-5284 SIC 3536

JERVIS B WEBB CO p 783
34375 W 12 Mile Rd, Farmington Hills MI 48331
Tel (248) 553-1000
SIC 3535 3536 3462 3537 3613

▲ **COLUMBUS MCKINNON CORP** p 342
205 Crosspoint Pkwy, Getzville NY 14068
Tel (716) 689-5400
SIC 3536 3496 3535 3537

TOTER LLC p 1463
841 Meacham Rd, Statesville NC 28677
Tel (800) 424-0422
SIC 3089 3536 3469 3412 2821

KCI HOLDING USA INC p 806
4401 Gateway Blvd, Springfield OH 45502
Tel (937) 525-5533 *SIC* 3536

KONECRANES INC p 827
4401 Gateway Blvd, Springfield OH 45502
Tel (937) 525-5533 *SIC* 3536

MMH AMERICAS INC p 979
4401 Gateway Blvd, Springfield OH 45502
Tel (414) 764-6200 *SIC* 3536 5084 6719

MMH HOLDINGS INC p 979
4401 Gateway Blvd, Springfield OH 45502
Tel (937) 525-5533 *SIC* 3536 5084

FKI INDUSTRIES INC p 554
2801 Dawson Rd, Tulsa OK 74110
Tel (918) 834-4611
SIC 3429 3536 3535 3496 3569 3823

RAMSEY INDUSTRIES INC p 1207
4707 N Mingo Rd, Tulsa OK 74117
Tel (918) 438-2760 *SIC* 3531 3536

ALLIED SYSTEMS CO p 57
21433 Sw Oregon St, Sherwood OR 97140
Tel (503) 625-2560 *SIC* 3531 3537 3536

EATON ELECTRIC HOLDINGS LLC p 473
600 Travis St Ste 5600, Houston TX 77002
Tel (713) 209-8400
SIC 3646 3612 3613 3644 3536 3423

SEATRAX INC p 1297
13223 Fm 529 Rd, Houston TX 77041
Tel (713) 896-6500 *SIC* 3531 3536

■ **GENIE HOLDINGS INC** p 604
18340 Ne 76th St, Redmond WA 98052
Tel (425) 881-1800 *SIC* 3536

■ **GENIE INDUSTRIES INC** p 604
18340 Ne 76th St, Redmond WA 98052
Tel (425) 881-1800 *SIC* 3536

SAFEWORKS LLC p 1267
365 Upland Dr, Tukwila WA 98188
Tel (206) 575-6445
SIC 3536 3531 3446 5082

▲ **MANITOWOC CO INC** p 902
2400 S 44th St, Manitowoc WI 54220
Tel (920) 684-4410
SIC 3536 3537 3531 3585

SIC 3537 Indl Trucks, Tractors, Trailers & Stackers

PS LOGISTICS LLC p 1187
1810 Avenue C, Birmingham AL 35218
Tel (205) 788-4000 *SIC* 4214 3537

MAXON LIFT CORP p 922
11921 Slauson Ave, Santa Fe Springs CA 90670
Tel (562) 464-0099 *SIC* 5084 3537 3534

▲ **TEREX CORP** p 1439
200 Nyala Farms Rd Ste 2, Westport CT 06880
Tel (203) 222-7170 *SIC* 3531 3537

KUBOTA MANUFACTURING OF AMERICA CORP p 831
2715 Ramsey Rd, Gainesville GA 30501
Tel (770) 532-0038 *SIC* 3524 3537

■ **TUG MANUFACTURING CORP** p 1491
2652 S Main St Nw, Kennesaw GA 30144
Tel (770) 422-7230 *SIC* 3537

■ **TUG TECHNOLOGIES CORP** p 1491
1995 Duncan Dr Nw, Kennesaw GA 30144
Tel (770) 422-7230 *SIC* 3537

JCB INC p 780
2000 Bamford Blvd, Pooler GA 31322
Tel (912) 447-2000
SIC 5082 5084 3531 3537

▲ **MANITEX INTERNATIONAL INC** p 901
9725 Industrial Dr, Bridgeview IL 60455
Tel (708) 430-7500 *SIC* 3537 3536

▲ **JOHN BEAN TECHNOLOGIES CORP** p 787
70 W Madison St Ste 4400, Chicago IL 60602
Tel (312) 861-5900 *SIC* 3556 3585 3537

LANCO INTERNATIONAL INC p 842
3111 167th St, Hazel Crest IL 60429
Tel (708) 596-5200
SIC 3531 8711 5084 3536 7353 3537

HENDRICKSON USA LLC p 683
500 Park Blvd Ste 450, Itasca IL 60143
Tel (630) 874-9700 *SIC* 3537

UNICARRIERS AMERICAS CORP p 1502
240 N Prospect St, Marengo IL 60152
Tel (800) 871-5438 *SIC* 3537 3519 5084

■ **VACTOR MANUFACTURING INC** p 1538
1621 S Illinois St, Streator IL 61364
Tel (815) 672-3171 *SIC* 3537

▲ **AAR CORP** p 8
1100 N Wood Dale Rd, Wood Dale IL 60191
Tel (630) 227-2000
SIC 3724 4581 3537 5599 7359

VESTIL MANUFACTURING CO p 1552
201 Growth Pkwy, Angola IN 46703
Tel (260) 665-2867 *SIC* 3537

■ **AMERI KART CORP** p 67
17196 State Road 120, Bristol IN 46507
Tel (574) 848-7462
SIC 3089 3537 2821 5162

TOYOTA INDUSTRIAL EQUIPMENT MFG INC p 1466
5555 Inwood Dr, Columbus IN 47201
Tel (812) 342-0060 *SIC* 3537

▲ **SUPREME INDUSTRIES INC** p 1408
2581 Kercher Rd, Goshen IN 46528
Tel (574) 642-3070 *SIC* 3537 3713 3799

HIRATA CORP OF AMERICA p 695
5625 Decatur Blvd, Indianapolis IN 46241
Tel (317) 856-8600 *SIC* 3535 3537 8711

OMAHA STANDARD LLC p 1083
3501 S 11th St Ste 1, Council Bluffs IA 51501
Tel (712) 328-7444 *SIC* 3713 3536 3537

■ **HENDERSON PRODUCTS INC** p 682
1085 S 3rd St, Manchester IA 52057
Tel (563) 927-2828 *SIC* 3537

RAYMOND-MUSCATINE INC p 1210
3305 N Highway 38, Muscatine IA 52761
Tel (563) 262-7700 *SIC* 3537

SNORKEL INTERNATIONAL INC p 1336
2009 Roseport Rd, Elwood KS 66024
Tel (785) 989-3000 *SIC* 3537

LANDOLL CORP p 843
1900 North St, Marysville KS 66508
Tel (785) 562-5381
SIC 3728 3715 3523 3537

CARGOTEC HOLDING INC p 255
415 E Dundee St, Ottawa KS 66067
Tel (785) 242-2200 *SIC* 3593 3537

KALMAR SOLUTIONS LLC p 801
415 E Dundee St, Ottawa KS 66067
Tel (785) 242-2200
SIC 3537 3714 3713 3643

JERVIS B WEBB CO p 783
34375 W 12 Mile Rd, Farmington Hills MI 48331
Tel (248) 553-1000
SIC 3535 3536 3462 3537 3613

HUMPHREY COMPANIES LLC p 718
2851 Prairie St Sw, Grandville MI 49418
Tel (616) 530-1717
SIC 3537 3714 3089 5023 5162

ALTA EQUIPMENT CO INC p 61
13211 Merriman Rd, Livonia MI 48150
Tel (248) 449-6700 *SIC* 3537 5084

SAF-HOLLAND INC p 1265
1950 Industrial Blvd, Muskegon MI 49442
Tel (231) 773-3271
SIC 3714 3715 3568 3537 3452

COMMERCIAL GROUP INC p 345
12801 Universal Dr, Taylor MI 48180
Tel (313) 931-6100
SIC 5085 5051 3496 3537 3534

■ **MCNEILUS TRUCK AND MANUFACTURING INC** p 932
524 County Rd 34 E, Dodge Center MN 55927
Tel (614) 868-0760
SIC 3713 3531 3537 3272

FAST GLOBAL SOLUTIONS INC p 531
20631 State Highway 55, Glenwood MN 56334
Tel (320) 634-5126 *SIC* 3537 3565 3523

TAYLOR MACHINE WORKS INC p 1427
650 N Church Ave, Louisville MS 39339
Tel (662) 773-3421 *SIC* 3537

SYSTEMS DRS SUSTAINMENT INC p 1418
201 Evans Ln, Saint Louis MO 63121
Tel (314) 553-4000
SIC 3715 3537 3812 3829 3769

▲ **COLUMBUS MCKINNON CORP** p 342
205 Crosspoint Pkwy, Getzville NY 14068
Tel (716) 689-5400
SIC 3536 3496 3535 3537

RAYMOND CONSOLIDATED CORP p 1210
22 S Canal St, Greene NY 13778
Tel (800) 235-7200 *SIC* 3537

RAYMOND CORP p 1210
22 S Canal St, Greene NY 13778
Tel (607) 656-2311 *SIC* 3537 3535 7359

SAGE PARTS PLUS INC p 1267
30 Hub Dr Ste 1, Melville NY 11747
Tel (631) 501-1300 *SIC* 5088 3812 3537

DUCON TECHNOLOGIES INC p 459
5 Penn Plz Ste 2403, New York NY 10001
Tel (631) 694-1700 *SIC* 3537 3564

OTTO ENVIRONMENTAL SYSTEMS (NC) LLC p 1098
12700 General Dr, Charlotte NC 28273
Tel (704) 588-9191 *SIC* 3537

OTTO INDUSTRIES NORTH AMERICA INC p 1098
12700 General Dr, Charlotte NC 28273
Tel (704) 588-9191 *SIC* 3537

WASTEQUIP LLC p 1581
6525 Morrison Blvd # 300, Charlotte NC 28211
Tel (704) 366-7140 *SIC* 3443 3537

■ **HYSTER-YALE GROUP INC** p 724
1400 Sullivan Dr, Greenville NC 27834
Tel (252) 931-5100 *SIC* 3537

KINSTON NEUSE CORP p 821
2000 Dobbs Farm Rd, Kinston NC 28504
Tel (252) 522-3088 *SIC* 3537

▲ **HYSTER-YALE MATERIALS HANDLING INC** p 724
5875 Landerbrook Dr # 300, Cleveland OH 44124
Tel (440) 449-9600 *SIC* 3537

■ **INTELLIGRATED SYSTEMS OF OHIO LLC** p 750
7901 Innovation Way, Mason OH 45040
Tel (513) 701-7300 *SIC* 3535 5084 3537

■ **GRADALL INDUSTRIES INC** p 628
406 Mill Ave Sw, New Philadelphia OH 44663
Tel (330) 339-2211 *SIC* 3537 3531

■ **HOBART BROTHERS CO** p 698
101 Trade Sq E, Troy OH 45373
Tel (937) 332-5439 *SIC* 3548 3537

CASCADE CORP p 262
2201 Ne 201st Ave, Fairview OR 97024
Tel (503) 669-6300 *SIC* 3537 3531

NMHG HOLDING CO p 1045
650 Ne Holladay St # 1600, Portland OR 97232
Tel (503) 721-6000 *SIC* 3537 5084

ALLIED SYSTEMS CO p 57
21433 Sw Oregon St, Sherwood OR 97140
Tel (503) 625-2560 *SIC* 3531 3537 3536

STRICK CORP p 1393
225 Lincoln Hwy, Fairless Hills PA 19030
Tel (215) 949-3600
SIC 3715 2426 3713 3537

TEAM BIONDI LLC p 1429
248 Easton Tpke, Lake Ariel PA 18436
Tel (570) 503-7087 *SIC* 3537

■ **GROVE US LLC** p 642
1565 Buchanan Trl E, Shady Grove PA 17256
Tel (717) 597-8121 *SIC* 3531 3537

INTERMETRO INDUSTRIES CORP p 753
651 N Washington St, Wilkes Barre PA 18705
Tel (570) 825-2741
SIC 3496 2542 3537 3411 3315 2441

■ **TEREX UTILITIES INC** p 1439
500 Oakwood Rd, Watertown SD 57201
Tel (605) 882-4000 *SIC* 3531 3537

■ **WORTHINGTON INDUSTRIES ENGINEERED CABS INC** p 1626
315 Airport Dr, Watertown SD 57201
Tel (605) 886-5681 *SIC* 3537

GEHL POWER PRODUCTS INC p 597
900 Ferdig St, Yankton SD 57078
Tel (605) 665-6500 *SIC* 3537 3531 3535

4FRONT ENGINEERED SOLUTIONS INC p 3
1612 Hutton Dr Ste 140, Carrollton TX 75006
Tel (972) 466-0707 *SIC* 3537

4FRONT HOLDINGS INC p 3
1612 Hutton Dr Ste 140, Carrollton TX 75006
Tel (972) 466-0707 *SIC* 3537 3999 3448

SANWA USA INC p 1281
4020 Mcewen Rd Ste 118, Dallas TX 75244
Tel (972) 503-3031
SIC 3442 2431 3699 3537

MITSUBISHI CATERPILLAR FORKLIFT AMERICA INC p 977
2121 W Sam Houston Pkwy N, Houston TX 77043
Tel (713) 365-1000 *SIC* 3537 5084

STEWART & STEVENSON CAPITAL CORP p 1388
601 W 38th St, Houston TX 77018
Tel (713) 868-7700
SIC 5084 5013 5078 5082 3711 3537

OVERHEAD DOOR CORP p 1099
2501 S State Hwy 121 Ste, Lewisville TX 75067
Tel (469) 549-7100
SIC 3442 2431 3699 3537 3589

CAPACITY OF TEXAS INC p 248
401 Capacity Dr, Longview TX 75604
Tel (903) 759-0610 *SIC* 3537

▲ **PACCAR INC** p 1103
777 106th Ave Ne, Bellevue WA 98004
Tel (425) 468-7400
SIC 3711 3714 3713 3537 5013 6153

▲ **MANITOWOC CO INC** p 902
2400 S 44th St, Manitowoc WI 54220
Tel (920) 684-4410
SIC 3536 3537 3531 3585

OLDENBURG GROUP INC p 1082
1717 W Civic Dr, Milwaukee WI 53209
Tel (414) 354-6600 *SIC* 3537 3532 3646

RITE-HITE HOLDING CORP p 1237
8900 N Arbor Dr, Milwaukee WI 53223
Tel (414) 355-2600 *SIC* 5084 3449 3537

STEEL KING INDUSTRIES INC p 1384
2700 Chamber St, Stevens Point WI 54481
Tel (715) 341-3120
SIC 3441 3537 3412 2542

SIC 3541 Machine Tools: Cutting

US UNION TOOL INC p 1533
1260 N Fee Ana St, Anaheim CA 92807
Tel (714) 521-6242 *SIC* 3541

HAAS AUTOMATION INC p 651
2800 Sturgis Rd, Oxnard CA 93030
Tel (805) 278-1800 *SIC* 3541

EDAC TECHNOLOGIES LLC p 477
5 Mckee Pl, Cheshire CT 06410
Tel (203) 806-2090 *SIC* 3769 3541 3724

■ **BRANSON ULTRASONICS CORP** p 208
41 Eagle Rd Ste 1, Danbury CT 06810
Tel (203) 796-0400 *SIC* 3699 3548 3541

EMHART TEKNOLOGIES LLC p 492
480 Myrtle St, New Britain CT 06053
Tel (800) 783-6427 *SIC* 8711 3541

MAGNETROL INTERNATIONAL INC p 896
705 Enterprise St, Aurora IL 60504
Tel (630) 723-6600
SIC 3823 3699 3643 3625 3541

PEDDINGHAUS CORP p 1127
300 N Washington Ave, Bradley IL 60915
Tel (815) 937-3800 *SIC* 3541

ROBERT BOSCH LLC p 1241
2800 S 25th Ave, Broadview IL 60155
Tel (248) 876-1000
SIC 3714 3694 5013 5064 3565 3541

HOLDEN INDUSTRIES INC p 700
500 Lake Cook Rd Ste 400, Deerfield IL 60015
Tel (847) 940-1500
SIC 2752 2672 3545 3589 3541 3441

DMG MORI USA INC p 446
2400 Huntington Blvd, Hoffman Estates IL 60192
Tel (847) 593-5400 *SIC* 3541 3545

■ **GREENLEE TEXTRON INC** p 638
4455 Boeing Dr, Rockford IL 61109
Tel (815) 397-7070 *SIC* 3549 3541 3546

ANGIOTECH PHARMACEUTICALS (US) INC p 91
241 W Palatine Rd, Wheeling IL 60090
Tel (847) 637-3333
SIC 3841 3541 3842 8731

MANAN TOOL & MANUFACTURING INC p 900
241 W Palatine Rd, Wheeling IL 60090
Tel (847) 637-3333 *SIC* 3541 3841

MOSEY MANUFACTURING CO INC p 992
262 Fort Wayne Ave, Richmond IN 47374
Tel (765) 983-8800 *SIC* 3541

HUSQVARNA CONSTRUCTION PRODUCTS NORTH AMERICA INC p 721
17400 W 119th St, Olathe KS 66061
Tel (913) 928-1000
SIC 3541 3291 5085 5082 3425 2951

MAZAK CORP p 924
8025 Production Dr, Florence KY 41042
Tel (859) 342-1700 *SIC* 3541 5084

FIVES LANDIS CORP p 553
16778 Halfway Blvd, Hagerstown MD 21740
Tel (301) 797-3400 *SIC* 3541

■ **BLACK & DECKER CORP** p 186
701 E Joppa Rd, Towson MD 21286
Tel (410) 716-3900
SIC 3546 3553 3541 3634 3452

BELCO INDUSTRIES INC p 169
9138 W Belding Rd, Belding MI 48809
Tel (616) 794-0410
SIC 3567 5084 3541 3535 3444

STAR CUTTER CO p 1378
23461 Industrial Park Dr, Farmington Hills MI 48335
Tel (248) 474-8200
SIC 3545 3479 3546 3541

LOC PERFORMANCE PRODUCTS INC p 872
13505 N Haggerty Rd, Plymouth MI 48170
Tel (734) 453-2300 *SIC* 3541

HOUGEN MANUFACTURING INC p 711
3001 Hougen Dr, Swartz Creek MI 48473
Tel (810) 635-7111
SIC 5084 3545 3546 3541

UTICA ENTERPRISES INC p 1537
5750 New King Dr Ste 200, Troy MI 48098
Tel (586) 726-4300
SIC 3548 3549 3545 8711 3541 3544

■ **VICTOR TECHNOLOGIES GROUP INC** p 1555
16253 Swingley Ridge Rd # 200, Chesterfield MO 63017
Tel (636) 728-3000
SIC 3541 3423 3613 3443 3621 3548

■ **VICTOR TECHNOLOGIES HOLDINGS INC** p 1555
16052 Swingley Ridge Rd # 300, Chesterfield MO 63017
Tel (636) 728-3000 *SIC* 3541

U S TOOL GRINDING INC p 1497
2000 Progress Dr, Farmington MO 63640
Tel (573) 431-3856 *SIC* 3541 3545

SUNNEN PRODUCTS CO p 1403
7910 Manchester Rd, Saint Louis MO 63143
Tel (314) 781-2100 *SIC* 3549 3541

HYPERTHERM INC p 724
21 Great Hollow Rd, Hanover NH 03755
Tel (603) 643-3441 *SIC* 3541

INDEL INC p 736
10 Indel Ave, Rancocas NJ 08073
Tel (609) 267-9000
SIC 3567 3548 3822 3541 3563

▲ **HARDINGE INC** p 661
1 Hardinge Dr, Elmira NY 14902
Tel (607) 734-2281
SIC 3541 3545 3553 3549

IPC/RAZOR LLC p 763
277 Park Ave Fl 39, New York NY 10172
Tel (212) 551-4500 *SIC* 3541

KPS CAPITAL PARTNERS LP p 829
485 Lexington Ave Fl 31, New York NY 10017
Tel (212) 338-5100
SIC 3541 6722 3545 5084

GLEASON CORP p 614
1000 University Ave, Rochester NY 14607
Tel (585) 473-1000 *SIC* 3541 3829

GLEASON WORKS p 614
1000 University Ave, Rochester NY 14607
Tel (585) 473-1000
SIC 3714 3728 3566 3541 3829 3469

GRAYWOOD COMPANIES INC p 633
1390 Mount Read Blvd, Rochester NY 14606
Tel (585) 254-7000
SIC 3541 3545 3544 3398

■ **MILACRON MARKETING CO LLC** p 968
4165 Half Acre Rd, Batavia OH 45103
Tel (513) 536-2000 *SIC* 3541

NESCO INC p 1026
6140 Parkland Blvd # 110, Cleveland OH 44124
Tel (440) 461-6000
SIC 3535 3541 3544 8711 6531

■ **RIDGE TOOL CO** p 1234
400 Clark St, Elyria OH 44035
Tel (440) 323-5581
SIC 3541 3423 3547 3546

■ **RIDGE TOOL MANUFACTURING CO** p 1234
400 Clark St, Elyria OH 44035
Tel (440) 323-5581
SIC 3541 3423 3547 3546 3545 3469

MAKINO INC p 899
7680 Innovation Way, Mason OH 45040
Tel (513) 573-7200 *SIC* 3541

ROBBINS CO p 1241
29100 Hall St Ste 100, Solon OH 44139
Tel (440) 248-3303 *SIC* 3535 3541 3531

■ **CMI TEREX CORP** p 329
9528 W I 40 Service Rd, Oklahoma City OK 73128
Tel (405) 787-6020
SIC 3531 3715 3596 3541 3444 2951

CHARLES MACHINE WORKS INC p 289
1959 W Fir St, Perry OK 73077
Tel (580) 572-3344
SIC 3531 3541 3829 3546

GREENLEAF CORP p 638
18695 Greenleaf Dr, Saegertown PA 16433
Tel (814) 763-2915 *SIC* 3545 3541

■ **VICTOR EQUIPMENT CO** p 1555
2800 Airport Rd, Denton TX 76207
Tel (940) 566-2000 *SIC* 5088 3541 3548

■ **VICTOR TECHNOLOGIES INTERNATIONAL INC** p 1555
2800 Airport Rd, Denton TX 76207
Tel (940) 381-1353 *SIC* 3541 3548

ATLAS COPCO DRILLING SOLUTIONS LLC p 127
2100 N 1st St, Garland TX 75040
Tel (972) 496-7258 *SIC* 3541

NOBLE DRILLING SERVICES INC p 1046
13135 Dairy Ashford Rd # 800, Sugar Land TX 77478
Tel (281) 276-6100 *SIC* 3541

J H FLETCHER & CO p 771
402 High St, Huntington WV 25705
Tel (304) 525-7811
SIC 5082 3532 3743 3546 3541

SIC 3542 Machine Tools: Forming

STOLLE MACHINERY CO LLC p 1390
6949 S Potomac St, Centennial CO 80112
Tel (303) 708-9044 *SIC* 3542

TRUMPF INC p 1487
111 Hyde Rd, Farmington CT 06032
Tel (860) 255-6000 *SIC* 3542 3423 3546

■ DELAWARE CAPITAL FORMATION INC p 423
501 Silverside Rd Ste 5, Wilmington DE 19809
Tel (302) 793-4921
SIC 5084 3463 3542 3823

HYDRAPOWER INTERNATIONAL INC p 723
950 N Collier Blvd # 202, Marco Island FL 34145
Tel (239) 642-5379 *SIC* 3542

BRIDGESTONE HOSEPOWER LLC p 211
50 Industrial Loop N, Orange Park FL 32073
Tel (904) 264-1267 *SIC* 5085 3542

■ SEQUA CORP p 1306
3999 Rca Blvd, Palm Beach Gardens FL 33410
Tel (201) 343-1122
SIC 3724 3764 3812 3699 3845 3542

MADISON CAPITAL PARTNERS CORP p 894
500 W Madison St Ste 3890, Chicago IL 60661
Tel (312) 277-0323 *SIC* 3542 8741

STERLING PRODUCTS INC p 1387
1100 E Woodfield Rd # 550, Schaumburg IL 60173
Tel (847) 273-7700 *SIC* 3559 3823 3542

DERINGER-NEY INC p 431
616 Atrium Dr Ste 100, Vernon Hills IL 60061
Tel (847) 566-4100
SIC 3643 3542 3469 3452 3316

GIBBS DIE CASTING CORP p 611
369 Community Dr, Henderson KY 42420
Tel (270) 827-1801 *SIC* 3364 3363 3542

PHILLIPS CORP p 1144
7390 Coca Cola Dr Ste 200, Hanover MD 21076
Tel (800) 878-4747 *SIC* 5084 7373 3542

▲ ALTRA INDUSTRIAL MOTION CORP p 62
300 Granite St Ste 201, Braintree MA 02184
Tel (781) 917-0600
SIC 3568 5085 3542 3625

MESTEK INC p 951
260 N Elm St, Westfield MA 01085
Tel (413) 568-9571
SIC 3585 3634 3549 3542 3354

PORT CITY GROUP INC p 1162
1985 E Laketon Ave, Muskegon MI 49442
Tel (231) 777-3941 *SIC* 3542 3089

FANUC AMERICA CORP p 527
3900 W Hamlin Rd, Rochester Hills MI 48309
Tel (248) 377-7000
SIC 3559 3548 3569 3542

■ HOWMET HOLDINGS CORP p 713
1 Misco Dr, Whitehall MI 49461
Tel (231) 894-5686
SIC 3324 3542 5051 3479

BUHLER INC p 224
13105 12th Ave N, Plymouth MN 55441
Tel (763) 847-9900
SIC 3556 3542 3535 3564

WILSON TOOL INTERNATIONAL INC p 1614
12912 Farnham Ave N, White Bear Lake MN 55110
Tel (651) 286-6000 *SIC* 3542 3544

■ MITEK USA INC p 977
16023 Swingley Ridge Rd, Chesterfield MO 63017
Tel (314) 434-1200
SIC 3443 3429 3542 8711 5051 5085

CIC GROUP INC p 306
530 Maryville Centre Dr, Saint Louis MO 63141
Tel (314) 682-2900 *SIC* 7692 3542 8741

TITANIUM INDUSTRIES INC p 1456
18 Green Pond Rd Ste 1, Rockaway NJ 07866
Tel (973) 983-1185 *SIC* 5051 3542 3462

■ ARROW FASTENER CO LLC p 113
271 Mayhill St, Saddle Brook NJ 07663
Tel (201) 843-6900
SIC 3579 3315 3452 3542 2891 3586

KOBE STEEL USA HOLDINGS INC p 825
535 Madison Ave Fl 5, New York NY 10022
Tel (212) 751-9400 *SIC* 3542 3089

MURATA MACHINERY USA HOLDINGS INC p 1001
2120 Queen City Dr, Charlotte NC 28208
Tel (704) 394-8331 *SIC* 3542 3552 5065

MURATA MACHINERY USA INC p 1001
2120 Queen City Dr, Charlotte NC 28208
Tel (704) 875-9280 *SIC* 5084 5085 3542

▲ SCOTTS MIRACLE-GRO CO p 1294
14111 Scottslawn Rd, Marysville OH 43040
Tel (937) 644-0011 *SIC* 3542 0782 7342

NIDEC MINSTER CORP p 1043
240 W 5th St, Minster OH 45865
Tel (419) 628-2331 *SIC* 3542 3568

■ HOWMET CORP p 713
1616 Harvard Ave, Newburgh Heights OH 44105
Tel (800) 242-9898
SIC 3324 3542 5051 3479

NATIONAL MACHINERY LLC p 1014
161 Greenfield St, Tiffin OH 44883
Tel (419) 447-5211 *SIC* 3542

NM GROUP GLOBAL LLC p 1045
161 Greenfield St, Tiffin OH 44883
Tel (419) 447-5211 *SIC* 3542 3599 6799

GASBARRE PRODUCTS INC p 593
590 Division St, Du Bois PA 15801
Tel (814) 371-3015 *SIC* 3542 3567 3544

SMS USA LLC p 1334
100 Sandusky St, Pittsburgh PA 15212
Tel (412) 231-1200 *SIC* 3547 3542

ELECTROIMPACT INC p 485
4413 Chennault Beach Rd, Mukilteo WA 98275
Tel (425) 348-8090 *SIC* 3542

WAGSTAFF INC p 1571
3910 N Flora Rd, Spokane Valley WA 99216
Tel (509) 922-1404 *SIC* 3542 3364

STERLING INC p 1387
2900 S 160th St, New Berlin WI 53151
Tel (414) 354-0970 *SIC* 3823 3542 3559

SIC 3543 Industrial Patterns

U S HOLDINGS INC p 1497
3200 W 84th St, Hialeah FL 33018
Tel (305) 885-0301 *SIC* 3321 3543

COMPLETE PROTOTYPE SERVICES INC p 351
44783 Morley Dr, Clinton Township MI 48036
Tel (586) 690-8897 *SIC* 3543 3714

FREEMAN MANUFACTURING & SUPPLY CO p 577
1101 Moore Rd, Avon OH 44011
Tel (440) 934-1902
SIC 5084 3087 3543 2821

AIM AEROSPACE SUMNER INC p 38
1502 20th St Nw, Auburn WA 98001
Tel (253) 804-3355 *SIC* 3728 3543

SIC 3544 Dies, Tools, Jigs, Fixtures & Indl Molds

DEFIANCE METAL PRODUCTS OF ARKANSAS INC p 422
944 By Pass Rd, Heber Springs AR 72543
Tel (501) 362-1919
SIC 3465 3443 3544 3469

UPM INC p 1528
13245 Los Angeles St, Baldwin Park CA 91706
Tel (626) 962-4001 *SIC* 3544 3089

EEP HOLDINGS LLC p 480
4626 Eucalyptus Ave, Chino CA 91710
Tel (909) 597-7861 *SIC* 3089 3544

TTL HOLDINGS LLC p 1489
4626 Eucalyptus Ave, Chino CA 91710
Tel (909) 597-7861 *SIC* 3089 3544

PLASTIKON INDUSTRIES INC p 1155
688 Sandoval Way, Hayward CA 94544
Tel (510) 400-1010 *SIC* 3544 3089

AMA PLASTICS p 64
1100 Citrus St, Riverside CA 92507
Tel (951) 734-5600 *SIC* 3089 3544

NISHIBA INDUSTRIES CORP p 1044
2360 Marconi Ct, San Diego CA 92154
Tel (619) 661-8866 *SIC* 3089 3544 5162

ASCENT AEROSPACE LLC p 116
1395 S Lyon St, Santa Ana CA 92705
Tel (949) 455-0665 *SIC* 3544

VOTAW PRECISION TECHNOLOGIES INC p 1566
13153 Lakeland Rd, Santa Fe Springs CA 90670
Tel (562) 666-2138 *SIC* 3544 3812

MENNIES MACHINE CO p 943
Mennie Dr Rr 71, Mark IL 61340
Tel (815) 339-2226 *SIC* 3544 8742

FABRIK INDUSTRIES INC p 523
5213 Prime Pkwy, Mchenry IL 60050
Tel (815) 385-9480 *SIC* 3089 3544

▲ FEDERAL SIGNAL CORP p 536
1415 W 22nd St Ste 1100, Oak Brook IL 60523
Tel (630) 954-2000
SIC 3711 3647 3669 3559 3544 3545

KELCO INDUSTRIES INC p 808
1425 Lake Ave, Woodstock IL 60098
Tel (815) 334-3600
SIC 3599 3069 3494 3585 3544 3625

BATESVILLE TOOL & DIE INC p 159
177 Six Pine Ranch Rd, Batesville IN 47006
Tel (812) 934-5616 *SIC* 3469 3544

BTD MANUFACTURING INC p 222
177 Six Pine Ranch Rd, Batesville IN 47006
Tel (812) 934-5616 *SIC* 3469 3544

C & A TOOL ENGINEERING INC p 231
4100 N Us 33 N, Churubusco IN 46723
Tel (260) 693-2167 *SIC* 3544 3545

BEACH MOLD & TOOL INC p 164
999 Progress Blvd, New Albany IN 47150
Tel (812) 945-2688 *SIC* 3089 3544

CONSTRUCTION PRODUCTS INC p 361
1800 Ne 46th Ave, Des Moines IA 50313
Tel (515) 313-4253 *SIC* 3536 3544

ROLLER DIE AND FORMING CO INC p 1247
1172 Industrial Blvd, Louisville KY 40219
Tel (502) 969-1327 *SIC* 3355 3544

SEURAT HOLDINGS INC p 1309
5 Fortune Dr, Billerica MA 01821
Tel (877) 489-9449 *SIC* 3544 5084

CONNELL LIMITED PARTNERSHIP p 358
1 International Pl Fl 31, Boston MA 02110
Tel (617) 737-2700
SIC 3443 3444 3341 3544 6719

TRIANON INDUSTRIES CORP p 1478
24331 Sherwood, Center Line MI 48015
Tel (586) 759-2200 *SIC* 3465 3544

HATCH STAMPING CO LLC p 667
635 E Industrial Dr, Chelsea MI 48118
Tel (734) 475-8628 *SIC* 3465 3544

GILL HOLDING CO INC p 612
5271 Plainfield Ave Ne, Grand Rapids MI 49525
Tel (616) 559-2700 *SIC* 3465 3544

GILL INDUSTRIES INC p 612
5271 Plainfield Ave Ne, Grand Rapids MI 49525
Tel (616) 559-2700 *SIC* 3465 3544

DEMMER CORP p 428
1600 N Larch St Ste 1, Lansing MI 48906
Tel (517) 321-3600
SIC 3795 3812 3544 3465 3441

QUALITY METALCRAFT INC p 1197
33355 Glendale St, Livonia MI 48150
Tel (734) 261-6700
SIC 3544 3465 3469 3444

BAKER INDUSTRIES INC p 146
16936 Enterprise Dr, Macomb MI 48044
Tel (586) 286-4900 *SIC* 3544

MARTINREA INDUSTRIES INC p 913
10501 Mi State Road 52, Manchester MI 48158
Tel (734) 428-2400
SIC 3714 3317 3089 3544

MODINEER CO p 981
2190 Industrial Dr, Niles MI 49120
Tel (269) 683-2550 *SIC* 3469 3599 3544

PRECISION PARTS HOLDINGS INC p 1168
2129 Austin Ave, Rochester Hills MI 48309
Tel (248) 853-9010 *SIC* 3465 3469 3544

STURGIS MOLDED PRODUCTS CO p 1395
70343 Clark Rd, Sturgis MI 49091
Tel (269) 651-9381 *SIC* 3089 3544

MAGNA EXTERIORS OF AMERICA INC p 896
750 Tower Dr, Troy MI 48098
Tel (248) 631-1100 *SIC* 3714 3544 8711

UTICA ENTERPRISES INC p 1537
5750 New King Dr Ste 200, Troy MI 48098
Tel (586) 726-4300
SIC 3548 3549 3545 8711 3541 3544

PASLIN CO p 1119
25303 Ryan Rd, Warren MI 48091
Tel (586) 758-0200 *SIC* 3548 3544 3545

SET ENTERPRISES INC p 1308
30500 Van Dyke Ave # 701, Warren MI 48093
Tel (586) 573-3600
SIC 7389 3465 3544 3312

■ BTD MANUFACTURING INC p 222
1111 13th Ave Se, Detroit Lakes MN 56501
Tel (218) 847-4446 *SIC* 3469 3544

LE SUEUR INC p 850
1409 Vine St, Le Sueur MN 56058
Tel (507) 665-6204
SIC 3363 3089 3544 3369

GRIFFITHS CORP p 640
2717 Niagara Ln N, Minneapolis MN 55447
Tel (763) 557-8935
SIC 3544 3469 3444 3451

GRIFFITHS HOLDING CORP p 640
2717 Niagara Ln N, Minneapolis MN 55447
Tel (763) 557-8935 *SIC* 3544 3469

HITCHCOCK INDUSTRIES INC p 697
8701 Harriet Ave S, Minneapolis MN 55420
Tel (952) 881-1000
SIC 3365 3364 3544 3369

WILSON TOOL INTERNATIONAL INC p 1614
12912 Farnham Ave N, White Bear Lake MN 55110
Tel (651) 286-6000 *SIC* 3542 3544

ROTO-DIE CO INC p 1252
800 Howerton Ln, Eureka MO 63025
Tel (636) 587-3600 *SIC* 3544 3555 3312

STAHL SPECIALTY CO p 1374
111 E Pacific St, Kingsville MO 64061
Tel (816) 597-3322
SIC 5051 3544 3365 3567 3369

WAINWRIGHT INDUSTRIES INC p 1571
114 Piper Hill Dr Ste 201, Saint Peters MO 63376
Tel (636) 327-8292 *SIC* 3469 3728 3544

CENTURY MOLD CO INC p 282
25 Vantage Point Dr, Rochester NY 14624
Tel (585) 352-8600 *SIC* 3089 3544

GRAYWOOD COMPANIES INC p 633
1390 Mount Read Blvd, Rochester NY 14606
Tel (585) 254-7000
SIC 3541 3545 3544 3398

QUALITY MOLD INC p 1197
2200 Massillon Rd, Akron OH 44312
Tel (330) 645-6653 *SIC* 3544

■ MILACRON PLASTICS TECHNOLOGIES GROUP LLC p 968
4165 Half Acre Rd, Batavia OH 45103
Tel (513) 536-2000 *SIC* 3544

▲ MILACRON HOLDINGS CORP p 968
10200 Alliance Rd Ste 200, Blue Ash OH 45242
Tel (513) 487-5000 *SIC* 3544

ILSCO CORP p 733
4730 Madison Rd, Cincinnati OH 45227
Tel (513) 533-6200
SIC 3643 3369 3451 3678 3544 3469

NESCO INC p 1026
6140 Parkland Blvd # 110, Cleveland OH 44124
Tel (440) 461-6000
SIC 3535 3541 3544 8711 6531

PROSPECT MOLD & DIE CO p 1184
1100 Main St, Cuyahoga Falls OH 44221
Tel (330) 929-3311 *SIC* 5084 3544

DAYTON LAMINA CORP p 417
500 Progress Rd, Dayton OH 45449
Tel (937) 859-5111 *SIC* 3544 6719

DAYTON PROGRESS CORP p 418
500 Progress Rd, Dayton OH 45449
Tel (937) 859-5111
SIC 3544 3545 3495 3493

MISUMI INVESTMENT USA CORP p 976
500 Progress Rd, Dayton OH 45449
Tel (937) 859-5111 *SIC* 6719 3544

DEFIANCE METAL PRODUCTS CO p 422
21 Seneca St, Defiance OH 43512
Tel (419) 784-5332 *SIC* 3465 3443 3544

HONDA ENGINEERING NORTH AMERICA INC p 704
24000 Honda Pkwy, Marysville OH 43040
Tel (937) 642-5000 *SIC* 3544

SHELBURNE CORP p 1314
20001 Shelburne Rd, Shaker Heights OH 44118
Tel (216) 321-9177
SIC 3443 3823 3544 3769

ATLANTIC TOOL & DIE CO INC p 127
19963 Progress Dr, Strongsville OH 44149
Tel (440) 238-6931 *SIC* 3469 3544

TOLEDO MOLDING & DIE INC p 1459
1429 Coining Dr, Toledo OH 43612
Tel (419) 470-3950 *SIC* 3089 3544

MTD HOLDINGS INC p 997
5965 Grafton Rd, Valley City OH 44280
Tel (330) 225-2600
SIC 3524 3544 3469 6141

■ SHILOH CORP p 1316
880 Steel Dr, Valley City OH 44280
Tel (330) 558-2600 *SIC* 3469 3544

▲ SHILOH INDUSTRIES INC p 1316
880 Steel Dr, Valley City OH 44280
Tel (330) 558-2600 *SIC* 3465 3469 3544

PENN UNITED TECHNOLOGIES INC p 1129
799 N Pike Rd, Cabot PA 16023
Tel (724) 352-1507 *SIC* 3544 2819

GASBARRE PRODUCTS INC p 593
590 Division St, Du Bois PA 15801
Tel (814) 371-3015 *SIC* 3542 3567 3544

■ NORDSON XALOY INC p 1048
1399 County Line Rd, New Castle PA 16101
Tel (724) 656-5600 *SIC* 3544

SAINT-GOBAIN CERAMICS & PLASTICS INC p 1271
750 E Swedesford Rd, Valley Forge PA 19482
Tel (610) 341-7000
SIC 2819 3679 3544 3297

ADVANCED INTEGRATION TECHNOLOGY LP p 26
2805 E Plano Pkwy Ste 300, Plano TX 75074
Tel (972) 423-8354 *SIC* 3728 3544

G W PLASTICS INC p 587
239 Pleasant St, Bethel VT 05032
Tel (802) 234-9941 *SIC* 3089 3544

PHILLIPS-MEDISIZE CORP p 1144
1201 Hanley Rd, Hudson WI 54016
Tel (715) 386-4320 *SIC* 3089 3444 3544

TECHNIPLAS LLC p 1431
N44w33341 Wtrtwn Plnk Rd, Nashotah WI 53058
Tel (262) 369-5555 *SIC* 3089 3544

SUPERIOR DIE SET CORP p 1406
900 W Drexel Ave, Oak Creek WI 53154
Tel (414) 764-4900 *SIC* 3544 3443 3599

DUTCHLAND PLASTICS LLC p 463
54 Enterprise Ct, Oostburg WI 53070
Tel (920) 564-3633 *SIC* 3089 3544

SCIENTIFIC MOLDING CORP LTD p 1292
330 Smc Dr, Somerset WI 54025
Tel (715) 247-3500 *SIC* 3089 3544

LAWRENCE HOLDING INC p 848
803 S Black River St, Sparta WI 54656
Tel (608) 269-6911 *SIC* 3469 3089 3544

NORTHERN ENGRAVING CORP p 1056
803 S Black River St, Sparta WI 54656
Tel (608) 269-6911 *SIC* 3469 3544 3089

SIC 3545 Machine Tool Access

■ ATMEL CORP p 128
1600 Technology Dr, San Jose CA 95110
Tel (408) 441-0311 *SIC* 3674 3714 3545

WESTERN FORGE INC p 1598
4607 Forge Rd, Colorado Springs CO 80907
Tel (719) 598-5070 *SIC* 3423 3545

COORSTEK LLC p 368
16000 Table Mountain Pkwy, Golden CO 80403
Tel (303) 271-7000
SIC 3264 3053 3081 3082 3545

COORSTEK INC p 368
14143 Denver West Pkwy # 400, Lakewood CO 80401
Tel (303) 271-7000 *SIC* 3545

■ DH HOLDINGS CORP p 435
1250 24th St Nw, Washington DC 20037
Tel (202) 828-0850 *SIC* 3545

KEYSTONE HOLDINGS LLC p 815
10 Nw 42nd Ave Ste 700, Miami FL 33126
Tel (305) 567-1577
SIC 8711 3053 3081 3082 3545

HENRY TECHNOLOGIES INC p 684
701 S Main St, Chatham IL 62629
Tel (217) 483-2406
SIC 3491 3585 3567 3564 3545 3494

HOLDEN INDUSTRIES INC p 700
500 Lake Cook Rd Ste 400, Deerfield IL 60015
Tel (847) 940-1500
SIC 2752 2672 3545 3589 3541 3441

DMG MORI USA INC p 446
2400 Huntington Blvd, Hoffman Estates IL 60192
Tel (847) 593-5400 *SIC* 3541 3545

▲ FEDERAL SIGNAL CORP p 536
1415 W 22nd St Ste 1100, Oak Brook IL 60523
Tel (630) 954-2000
SIC 3711 3647 3669 3559 3544 3545

ESTWING MANUFACTURING CO INC p 511
2647 8th St, Rockford IL 61109
Tel (815) 397-9521
SIC 3423 3546 3545 3429 3421 3425

C & A TOOL ENGINEERING INC p 231
4100 N Us 33 N, Churubusco IN 46723
Tel (260) 693-2167 *SIC* 3544 3545

FANSTEEL INC p 527
1746 Commerce Rd, Creston IA 50801
Tel (641) 782-8521
SIC 3463 3728 3365 3369 3769 3545

MUSCO CORP p 1002
100 1st Ave W, Oskaloosa IA 52577
Tel (641) 676-1746
SIC 7359 3648 3646 3641 3545 3423

▲ L S STARRETT CO p 834
121 Crescent St, Athol MA 01331
Tel (978) 249-3551
SIC 3545 3423 3999 3425 3823

SAINT-GOBAIN ABRASIVES INC p 1271
1 New Bond St, Worcester MA 01606
Tel (508) 795-5000
SIC 3291 3559 3545 3297 3082 2891

▲ TRIMAS CORP p 1480
39400 Woodward Ave # 130, Bloomfield Hills MI 48304
Tel (248) 631-5450
SIC 3799 3714 3443 2672 3452 3545

STAR CUTTER CO p 1378
23461 Industrial Park Dr, Farmington Hills MI 48335
Tel (248) 474-8200
SIC 3545 3479 3546 3541

L E JONES CO p 834
1200 34th Ave, Menominee MI 49858
Tel (906) 863-1043 *SIC* 3592 3545

COMAU LLC p 343
21000 Telegraph Rd, Southfield MI 48033
Tel (248) 353-8888 *SIC* 3548 3829 3545

HOUGEN MANUFACTURING INC p 711
3001 Hougen Dr, Swartz Creek MI 48473
Tel (810) 635-7111
SIC 5084 3545 3546 3541

SECO HOLDING CO INC p 1298
2805 Bellingham Dr, Troy MI 48083
Tel (248) 528-5200 *SIC* 3545

SECO TOOLS LLC p 1298
2805 Bellingham Dr, Troy MI 48083
Tel (248) 528-5200 *SIC* 5084 3545

UTICA ENTERPRISES INC p 1537
5750 New King Dr Ste 200, Troy MI 48098
Tel (586) 726-4300
SIC 3548 3549 3545 8711 3541 3544

PASLIN CO p 1119
25303 Ryan Rd, Warren MI 48091
Tel (586) 758-0200 *SIC* 3548 3544 3545

GT TECHNOLOGIES INC p 644
5859 E Executive Dr, Westland MI 48185
Tel (734) 467-8371
SIC 8711 3714 3545 3089

■ ROSEMOUNT INC p 1251
8200 Market Blvd, Chanhassen MN 55317
Tel (952) 906-8888
SIC 3823 3824 3545 5084 3829

CARL ZEISS INDUSTRIAL METROLOGY LLC p 256
6250 Sycamore Ln N, Maple Grove MN 55369
Tel (763) 533-9990 *SIC* 3545 3825

KURT MANUFACTURING CO INC p 832
5280 Main St Ne, Minneapolis MN 55421
Tel (763) 572-1500
SIC 3499 3545 3363 3728 3842 3365

U S TOOL GRINDING INC p 1497
2000 Progress Dr, Farmington MO 63640
Tel (573) 431-3856 *SIC* 3541 3545

MSS LIQUIDATION CORP p 997
1716 Guinotte Ave, Kansas City MO 64120
Tel (816) 842-4290 *SIC* 5085 3545

SANDVIK INC p 1279
17-02 Nevins Rd, Fair Lawn NJ 07410
Tel (201) 794-5000
SIC 3316 3317 3356 3315 3545 3533

▲ HARDINGE INC p 661
1 Hardinge Dr, Elmira NY 14902
Tel (607) 734-2281
SIC 3541 3545 3553 3549

DESIGNATRONICS INC p 432
2101 Jericho Tpke Ste 1, New Hyde Park NY 11040
Tel (516) 328-3300
SIC 3824 3559 3545 3625 3462

KPS CAPITAL PARTNERS LP p 829
485 Lexington Ave Fl 31, New York NY 10017
Tel (212) 338-5100
SIC 3541 6722 3545 5084

GRAYWOOD COMPANIES INC p 633
1390 Mount Read Blvd, Rochester NY 14606
Tel (585) 254-7000
SIC 3541 3545 3544 3398

▲ SPX CORP p 1362
13320a Balntyn Corp Pl, Charlotte NC 28277
Tel (980) 474-3700
SIC 3443 3599 3829 3559 3545

■ IRWIN INDUSTRIAL TOOL CO p 765
8935 N Pointe Exec Pk Dr, Huntersville NC 28078
Tel (704) 987-4555 *SIC* 3423 3545 3421

BETA LASERMIKE INC p 177
8001 Technology Blvd, Dayton OH 45424
Tel (937) 233-9935 *SIC* 3545

DAYTON PROGRESS CORP p 418
500 Progress Rd, Dayton OH 45449
Tel (937) 859-5111
SIC 3544 3545 3495 3493

■ RIDGE TOOL MANUFACTURING CO p 1234
400 Clark St, Elyria OH 44035
Tel (440) 323-5581
SIC 3541 3423 3547 3546 3545 3469

ESCO CORP p 509
2141 Nw 25th Ave, Portland OR 97210
Tel (360) 690-0074
SIC 3535 3545 3325 3531

OBERG INDUSTRIES INC p 1072
2301 Silverville Rd, Freeport PA 16229
Tel (724) 295-2121 *SIC* 3469 3545

BOLTTECH MANNINGS INC p 199
501 Mosside Blvd, North Versailles PA 15137
Tel (724) 872-4873
SIC 3546 5072 3599 7359 3545 3423

▲ ALLEGHENY TECHNOLOGIES INC p 52
1000 Six Ppg Pl, Pittsburgh PA 15222
Tel (412) 394-2800 *SIC* 3312 3339 3545

▲ KENNAMETAL INC p 810
600 Grant St Ste 5100, Pittsburgh PA 15219
Tel (412) 248-8200
SIC 3545 3532 3531 3313 3399

GREENLEAF CORP p 638
18695 Greenleaf Dr, Saegertown PA 16433
Tel (814) 763-2915 *SIC* 3545 3541

HEXAGON METROLOGY INC p 688
250 Circuit Dr, North Kingstown RI 02852
Tel (401) 886-2000 *SIC* 3823 3545

VAREL INTERNATIONAL ENERGY SERVICES INC p 1544
1625 W Crosby Rd Ste 124, Carrollton TX 75006
Tel (800) 827-3526 *SIC* 1381 3545

VAREL INTERNATIONAL IND LP p 1544
1625 W Crosby Rd Ste 124, Carrollton TX 75006
Tel (972) 242-1160 *SIC* 3545 3532 1381

■ POLLOK INC p 1160
6 Butterfield Trail Blvd, El Paso TX 79906
Tel (915) 592-5700
SIC 5065 3823 3714 3545

OMAX CORP p 1084
21409 72nd Ave S, Kent WA 98032
Tel (253) 872-2300 *SIC* 3545 3561

GUHRING INC p 645
1445 Commerce Ave, Brookfield WI 53045
Tel (262) 784-6730 *SIC* 3545

RICE LAKE WEIGHING SYSTEMS INC p 1232
230 W Coleman St, Rice Lake WI 54868
Tel (715) 234-9171 *SIC* 3596 3545

WALTER USA LLC p 1574
N22 W 23855 Rdg St N 22, Waukesha WI 53188
Tel (800) 945-5554 *SIC* 3545

SIC 3546 Power Hand Tools

MTD SOUTHWEST INC p 997
9235 S Mckemy St, Tempe AZ 85284
Tel (480) 961-1002 *SIC* 3524 3546 3423

TRUMPF INC p 1487
111 Hyde Rd, Farmington CT 06032
Tel (860) 255-6000 *SIC* 3542 3423 3546

■ BLACK & DECKER (US) INC p 186
1000 Stanley Dr, New Britain CT 06053
Tel (410) 716-3900 *SIC* 3546 3634

▲ STANLEY BLACK & DECKER INC p 1377
1000 Stanley Dr, New Britain CT 06053
Tel (860) 225-5111
SIC 3429 3546 3423 3452 3699

■ EECO INC p 480
850 Library Ave Ste 204c, Newark DE 19711
Tel (302) 456-1448
SIC 3823 3491 3621 3585 3546 3679

RHI REFRACTORIES HOLDING CO p 1231
1105 N Market St Ste 1300, Wilmington DE 19801
Tel (302) 655-6497
SIC 3297 3255 1459 3546 3272 3589

MAKITA CORP OF AMERICA p 899
2650 Buford Hwy, Buford GA 30518
Tel (770) 932-2901 *SIC* 3546

ROBERT BOSCH TOOL CORP p 1241
1800 W Central Rd, Mount Prospect IL 60056
Tel (224) 232-2000 *SIC* 3546

ESTWING MANUFACTURING CO INC p 511
2647 8th St, Rockford IL 61109
Tel (815) 397-9521
SIC 3423 3546 3545 3429 3421 3425

■ GREENLEE TEXTRON INC p 638
4455 Boeing Dr, Rockford IL 61109
Tel (815) 397-7070 *SIC* 3549 3541 3546

■ BLACK & DECKER CORP p 186
701 E Joppa Rd, Towson MD 21286
Tel (410) 716-3900
SIC 3546 3553 3541 3634 3452

STAR CUTTER CO p 1378
23461 Industrial Park Dr, Farmington Hills MI 48335
Tel (248) 474-8200
SIC 3545 3479 3546 3541

HOUGEN MANUFACTURING INC p 711
3001 Hougen Dr, Swartz Creek MI 48473
Tel (810) 635-7111
SIC 5084 3545 3546 3541

▲ NEWELL BRANDS INC p 1037
221 River St, Hoboken NJ 07030
Tel (201) 610-6600
SIC 3089 3469 2591 3951 3999 3546

EPCOS INC p 504
485b Route 1 S Ste 200, Iselin NJ 08830
Tel (732) 906-4300
SIC 3679 3546 5065 3671

INGERSOLL-RAND CO p 742
800 Beaty St Ste B, Davidson NC 28036
Tel (704) 655-4000
SIC 3561 3429 3546 3563 3531

SENCO BRANDS INC p 1303
4270 Ivy Pointe Blvd # 300, Cincinnati OH 45245
Tel (513) 388-2000 *SIC* 3546

■ RIDGE TOOL CO p 1234
400 Clark St, Elyria OH 44035
Tel (440) 323-5581
SIC 3541 3423 3547 3546

■ RIDGE TOOL MANUFACTURING CO p 1234
400 Clark St, Elyria OH 44035
Tel (440) 323-5581
SIC 3541 3423 3547 3546 3545 3469

■ CAMPBELL HAUSFELD LLC p 245
100 Production Dr, Harrison OH 45030
Tel (513) 367-4811 *SIC* 3563 3546 3548

■ STANLEY INDUSTRIAL & AUTOMOTIVE LLC p 1377
505 N Cleveland Ave, Westerville OH 43082
Tel (614) 755-7000
SIC 3429 3546 3423 3452

CHARLES MACHINE WORKS INC p 289
1959 W Fir St, Perry OK 73077
Tel (580) 572-3344
SIC 3531 3541 3829 3546

BLOUNT INC p 190
4909 Se International Way, Portland OR 97222
Tel (503) 653-8881
SIC 3546 3568 7699 3495

GLOBAL INDUSTRIAL TECHNOLOGIES INC p 616
1305 Chrrington Pkwy Moon, Coraopolis PA 15108
Tel (412) 375-6600
SIC 3297 3255 1459 3546 3272 3589

BOLTTECH MANNINGS INC p 199
501 Mosside Blvd, North Versailles PA 15137
Tel (724) 872-4873
SIC 3546 5072 3599 7359 3545 3423

▲ TEXTRON INC p 1445
40 Westminster St, Providence RI 02903
Tel (401) 421-2800
SIC 3721 3724 3728 3799 3829 3546

COOPER TOOLS INC p 367
670 Industrial Dr, Lexington SC 29072
Tel (803) 359-1200 *SIC* 3546

■ PORTER-CABLE CORP p 1162
4825 Highway 45 N Ste 880, Jackson TN 38305
Tel (731) 660-5986 *SIC* 3546

KEPPEL AMFELS LLC p 813
20000 State Highway 48, Brownsville TX 78521
Tel (956) 831-8220
SIC 1629 3731 1389 3449 3546 3443

COOPER INDUSTRIES LLC p 366
600 Travis St Ste 5400, Houston TX 77002
Tel (713) 209-8400
SIC 3646 3612 3613 3644 3546 3423

HILTI OF AMERICA INC p 694
7250 Dallas Pkwy Ste 1000, Plano TX 75024
Tel (800) 879-8000 *SIC* 5084 3546 3825

STIHL INC p 1389
536 Viking Dr, Virginia Beach VA 23452
Tel (757) 486-9100 *SIC* 3546 3398

J H FLETCHER & CO p 771
402 High St, Huntington WV 25705
Tel (304) 525-7811
SIC 5082 3532 3743 3546 3541

MILWAUKEE ELECTRIC TOOL CORP p 972
13135 W Lisbon Rd, Brookfield WI 53005
Tel (800) 729-3878 *SIC* 3546 3425

■ IDSC HOLDINGS LLC p 729
2801 80th St, Kenosha WI 53143
Tel (262) 656-5200
SIC 3423 3559 7372 6794 5013 3546

▲ SNAP-ON INC p 1335
2801 80th St, Kenosha WI 53143
Tel (262) 656-5200 *SIC* 3546 3559 3825

WACKER NEUSON CORP p 1570
N92w15000 Anthony Ave, Menomonee Falls WI 53051
Tel (262) 255-0500
SIC 3531 3621 3561 3546 3423

SIC 3547 Rolling Mill Machinery & Eqpt

ARKANSAS STEEL ASSOCIATES LLC p 110
2803 Van Dyke Rd, Newport AR 72112
Tel (870) 523-3693 *SIC* 3312 3547

■ NUCOR STEEL KANKAKEE INC p 1066
1 Nucor Way, Bourbonnais IL 60914
Tel (815) 937-3131 *SIC* 3312 3547 3449

XTEK INC p 1633
11451 Reading Rd, Cincinnati OH 45241
Tel (513) 733-7800
SIC 3568 3547 3398 3312

PARK CORP p 1115
6200 Riverside Dr, Cleveland OH 44135
Tel (216) 267-4870
SIC 3547 1711 3443 5084 6512 7999

■ RIDGE TOOL CO p 1234
400 Clark St, Elyria OH 44035
Tel (440) 323-5581
SIC 3541 3423 3547 3546

■ RIDGE TOOL MANUFACTURING CO p 1234
400 Clark St, Elyria OH 44035
Tel (440) 323-5581
SIC 3541 3423 3547 3546 3545 3469

WARREN FABRICATING CORP p 1577
3240 Mahoning Ave Nw, Warren OH 44483
Tel (330) 847-0596
SIC 3441 3599 3547 3532 3444 3443

SMS USA LLC p 1334
100 Sandusky St, Pittsburgh PA 15212
Tel (412) 231-1200 *SIC* 3547 3542

■ JW WILLIAMS INC p 798
2180 W Renauna Ave, Casper WY 82601
Tel (307) 237-8345
SIC 3533 3443 3547 1761 3291

SIC 3548 Welding Apparatus

■ BRANSON ULTRASONICS CORP p 208
41 Eagle Rd Ste 1, Danbury CT 06810
Tel (203) 796-0400 *SIC* 3699 3548 3541

NORCO INC p 1047
1125 W Amity Rd, Boise ID 83705
Tel (208) 336-1643
SIC 5084 5169 7352 5999 3548 2813

■ PRAXAIR SURFACE TECHNOLOGIES INC p 1168
1500 Polco St, Indianapolis IN 46222
Tel (317) 240-2500 *SIC* 3479 3548 3563

FANUC AMERICA CORP p 527
3900 W Hamlin Rd, Rochester Hills MI 48309
Tel (248) 377-7000
SIC 3559 3548 3569 3542

COMAU LLC p 343
21000 Telegraph Rd, Southfield MI 48033
Tel (248) 353-8888 *SIC* 3548 3829 3545

UTICA ENTERPRISES INC p 1537
5750 New King Dr Ste 200, Troy MI 48098
Tel (586) 726-4300
SIC 3548 3549 3545 8711 3541 3544

PASLIN CO p 1119
25303 Ryan Rd, Warren MI 48091
Tel (586) 758-0200 *SIC* 3548 3544 3545

■ VICTOR TECHNOLOGIES GROUP INC p 1555
16253 Swingley Ridge Rd # 200, Chesterfield MO 63017
Tel (636) 728-3000
SIC 3541 3423 3613 3443 3621 3548

INDEL INC p 736
10 Indel Ave, Rancocas NJ 08073
Tel (609) 267-9000
SIC 3567 3548 3822 3541 3563

AMERICAN WELDING & GAS INC p 81
4900 Falls Of Neuse Rd, Raleigh NC 27609
Tel (406) 969-1444 *SIC* 3548

▲ LINCOLN ELECTRIC HOLDINGS INC p 867
22801 Saint Clair Ave, Cleveland OH 44117
Tel (216) 481-8100 *SIC* 3548

NELSON STUD WELDING INC p 1025
7900 W Ridge Rd, Elyria OH 44035
Tel (440) 329-0400 *SIC* 3452 3548

■ LINCOLN ELECTRIC CO p 866
22801 Saint Clair Ave, Euclid OH 44117
Tel (216) 481-8100 *SIC* 3548

■ LINCOLN ELECTRIC INTERNATIONAL HOLDING CO p 867
22801 Saint Clair Ave, Euclid OH 44117
Tel (216) 481-8100 *SIC* 3548

■ CAMPBELL HAUSFELD LLC p 245
100 Production Dr, Harrison OH 45030
Tel (513) 367-4811 *SIC* 3563 3546 3548

■ HOBART BROTHERS CO p 698
101 Trade Sq E, Troy OH 45373
Tel (937) 332-5439 *SIC* 3548 3537

■ PRAXAIR DISTRIBUTION MID-ATLANTIC LLC p 1167
5275 Tilghman St, Allentown PA 18104
Tel (610) 398-2211 *SIC* 4925 3548

■ NORDSON EFD LLC p 1048
40 Catamore Blvd, East Providence RI 02914
Tel (401) 434-1680 *SIC* 3548 3586 3699

■ ESAB GROUP INC p 509
2800 Airport Rd, Denton TX 76207
Tel (843) 669-4411 *SIC* 3548 2899

■ VICTOR EQUIPMENT CO p 1555
2800 Airport Rd, Denton TX 76207
Tel (940) 566-2000 *SIC* 5088 3541 3548

■ VICTOR TECHNOLOGIES INTERNATIONAL INC p 1555
2800 Airport Rd, Denton TX 76207
Tel (940) 381-1353 *SIC* 3541 3548

NCH CORP p 1022
2727 Chemsearch Blvd, Irving TX 75062
Tel (972) 438-0211
SIC 2842 2899 3432 3548 3429

■ MILLER ELECTRIC MFG CO p 970
1635 W Spencer St, Appleton WI 54914
Tel (920) 734-9821 *SIC* 3548 3621

AMERICAN ROLLER CO LLC p 78
1440 13th Ave, Union Grove WI 53182
Tel (262) 878-8665 *SIC* 3549 3548

SIC 3549 Metalworking Machinery, NEC

BOYD LTI p 205
600 S Mcclure Rd, Modesto CA 95357
Tel (800) 554-0200 *SIC* 3549 3053 8711

VANDER-BEND MANUFACTURING LLC p 1543
2701 Orchard Pkwy, San Jose CA 95134
Tel (408) 245-5150 *SIC* 3679 3444 3549

▲ SIGMATRON INTERNATIONAL INC p 1321
2201 Landmeier Rd, Elk Grove Village IL 60007
Tel (847) 956-8000
SIC 3672 3677 3679 3549 3825

■ GREENLEE TEXTRON INC p 638
4455 Boeing Dr, Rockford IL 61109
Tel (815) 397-7070 *SIC* 3549 3541 3546

MESTEK INC p 951
260 N Elm St, Westfield MA 01085
Tel (413) 568-9571
SIC 3585 3634 3549 3542 3354

CASEPICK SYSTEMS LLC p 263
200 Research Dr, Wilmington MA 01887
Tel (978) 284-2800 *SIC* 3549

FIVES INC p 553
23400 Halsted Rd, Farmington Hills MI 48335
Tel (248) 477-0800 *SIC* 3549

JR AUTOMATION TECHNOLOGIES LLC p 795
13365 Tyler St, Holland MI 49424
Tel (616) 399-2168 *SIC* 3549

JR TECHNOLOGY GROUP LLC p 795
13365 Tyler St, Holland MI 49424
Tel (616) 399-2168 *SIC* 3549

IWKA HOLDING CORP p 769
6600 Center Dr, Sterling Heights MI 48312
Tel (586) 795-2000
SIC 3549 5084 7371 8711

KUKA SYSTEMS NORTH AMERICA LLC p 831
6600 Center Dr, Sterling Heights MI 48312
Tel (586) 795-2000 *SIC* 3549

UTICA ENTERPRISES INC p 1537
5750 New King Dr Ste 200, Troy MI 48098
Tel (586) 726-4300
SIC 3548 3549 3545 8711 3541 3544

MORBARK LLC p 988
8507 S Winn Rd, Winn MI 48896
Tel (989) 866-2381
SIC 3599 3553 3549 3523

SUNNEN PRODUCTS CO p 1403
7910 Manchester Rd, Saint Louis MO 63143
Tel (314) 781-2100 *SIC* 3549 3541

▲ STANDEX INTERNATIONAL CORP p 1376
11 Keewaydin Dr, Salem NH 03079
Tel (603) 893-9701 *SIC* 3585 3549 3675

▲ HARDINGE INC p 661
1 Hardinge Dr, Elmira NY 14902
Tel (607) 734-2281
SIC 3541 3545 3553 3549

TESSY PLASTICS CORP p 1441
700 Visions Dr, Skaneateles NY 13152
Tel (315) 689-3924 *SIC* 3089 3549

■ MILACRON LLC p 968
10200 Alliance Rd Ste 200, Blue Ash OH 45242
Tel (513) 487-5000 *SIC* 3549 2899

CINCINNATI INC p 307
7420 Kilby Rd, Harrison OH 45030
Tel (513) 367-7100 *SIC* 3549

HUNTER DEFENSE TECHNOLOGIES INC p 719
30500 Aurora Rd Ste 100, Solon OH 44139
Tel (216) 438-6111
SIC 3433 3569 3822 8331 8711 3549

FLS US HOLDINGS INC p 561
2040 Avenue C, Bethlehem PA 18017
Tel (610) 264-6011
SIC 3559 3554 3549 3532 3535

PENN ENGINEERING & MANUFACTURING CORP p 1129
5190 Old Easton Rd, Danboro PA 18916
Tel (215) 766-8853 *SIC* 3429 3549 8711

AMERICAN ROLLER CO LLC p 78
1440 13th Ave, Union Grove WI 53182
Tel (262) 878-8665 *SIC* 3549 3548

SIC 3552 Textile Machinery

BROWN INDUSTRIES INC p 219
205 W Industrial Blvd, Dalton GA 30720
Tel (706) 277-1977
SIC 2759 5131 2273 3552 3315 2671

M & R PRINTING EQUIPMENT INC p 889
440 Medinah Rd, Roselle IL 60172
Tel (800) 736-6431 *SIC* 3555 3552 5084

M&R HOLDINGS INC p 890
440 Medinah Rd, Roselle IL 60172
Tel (630) 858-6101 *SIC* 3552

ACCELLENT ACQUISITION CORP p 14
100 Fordham Rd Bldg C, Wilmington MA 01887
Tel (978) 570-6900
SIC 3841 3317 3679 3315 3552 3089

ACCELLENT HOLDINGS CORP p 14
100 Fordham Rd, Wilmington MA 01887
Tel (978) 570-6900
SIC 3841 3679 3315 3552 3317 3089

MURATA MACHINERY USA HOLDINGS INC p 1001
2120 Queen City Dr, Charlotte NC 28208
Tel (704) 394-8331 SIC 3542 3552 5065

STORK UNITED CORP p 1392
3201 Rotary Dr, Charlotte NC 28269
Tel (704) 598-7171 SIC 5084 3552 3556

TUFTCO CORP p 1491
2318 S Holtzclaw Ave, Chattanooga TN 37408
Tel (423) 648-3869 SIC 3552

SIC 3553 Woodworking Machinery

WESTERVELT CO p 1600
1400 Jack Warner Pkwy Ne, Tuscaloosa AL 35404
Tel (205) 562-5295 SIC 3553 2421

WOOD-MIZER HOLDINGS INC p 1622
8180 W 10th St, Indianapolis IN 46214
Tel (317) 271-1542
SIC 3553 3524 3425 2431

■ **BLACK & DECKER CORP** p 186
701 E Joppa Rd, Towson MD 21286
Tel (410) 716-3900
SIC 3546 3553 3541 3634 3452

SIMONDS INTERNATIONAL LLC p 1325
135 Intervale Rd, Fitchburg MA 01420
Tel (978) 343-3731 SIC 3553

MORBARK LLC p 988
8507 S Winn Rd, Winn MI 48896
Tel (989) 866-2381
SIC 3599 3553 3549 3523

▲ **HARDINGE INC** p 661
1 Hardinge Dr, Elmira NY 14902
Tel (607) 734-2281
SIC 3541 3545 3553 3549

WESTERN PNEUMATICS INC p 1599
110 N Seneca Rd, Eugene OR 97402
Tel (541) 461-2600 SIC 3535 3553 5099

USNR LLC p 1535
1981 Schurman Way, Woodland WA 98674
Tel (360) 225-8267
SIC 3585 3553 3625 1221 5084

SIC 3554 Paper Inds Machinery

MAXCO SUPPLY INC p 922
605 S Zediker Ave, Parlier CA 93648
Tel (559) 646-8449 SIC 5113 2436 3554

ANDRITZ (USA) INC p 91
5405 Windward Pkwy 100, Alpharetta GA 30004
Tel (770) 640-2500 SIC 3554 3523

VALMET INC p 1541
2425 Commerce Ave Ste 100, Duluth GA 30096
Tel (770) 263-7863 SIC 3554 5084

WARD MACHINERY CO p 1575
10615 Beaver Dam Rd, Cockeysville MD 21030
Tel (410) 584-7700 SIC 3554

METSO USA INC p 957
133 Federal St Ste 302, Boston MA 02110
Tel (617) 369-7850 SIC 3554 5084

JEN-COAT INC p 782
132 N Elm St, Westfield MA 01085
Tel (413) 875-9861 SIC 3554

▲ **KADANT INC** p 800
1 Technology Park Dr # 210, Westford MA 01886
Tel (978) 776-2000 SIC 3554 3321 2621

BARRY-WEHMILLER COMPANIES INC p 157
8020 Forsyth Blvd, Saint Louis MO 63105
Tel (314) 862-8000
SIC 3565 3535 3554 8711

BARRY-WEHMILLER GROUP INC p 157
8020 Forsyth Blvd, Saint Louis MO 63105
Tel (314) 862-8000
SIC 3565 3535 3554 8711

MAXCESS INTERNATIONAL CORP p 922
222 W Memorial Rd, Oklahoma City OK 73114
Tel (405) 755-1600 SIC 3554 3565 6719

MAXCESS INTERNATIONAL HOLDING CORP p 922
222 W Memorial Rd, Oklahoma City OK 73114
Tel (405) 755-1600 SIC 3554 3565 6719

FLS US HOLDINGS INC p 561
2040 Avenue C, Bethlehem PA 18017
Tel (610) 264-6011
SIC 3559 3554 3549 3532 3535

ANDRITZ INC p 91
500 Technology Dr, Canonsburg PA 15317
Tel (724) 597-7801 SIC 3554 8711 7389

NORTH PACIFIC PAPER CO LLC p 1053
3001 Indl Way, Longview WA 98632
Tel (360) 636-6400 SIC 2621 5084 3554

ALLIANCE MACHINE SYSTEMS INTERNATIONAL LLC p 54
5303 E Desmet Ave, Spokane Valley WA 99212
Tel (509) 842-5104 SIC 3554

VOITH HOLDING INC p 1564
2200 N Roemer Rd, Appleton WI 54911
Tel (920) 731-7724
SIC 5131 3554 2221 6719

VOITH PAPER INC p 1564
2200 N Roemer Rd, Appleton WI 54911
Tel (920) 731-0769 SIC 3554

CG BRETTING MANUFACTURING CO INC p 285
3401 Lake Park Rd, Ashland WI 54806
Tel (715) 682-5231
SIC 3554 3599 3565 3555

PAPER CONVERTING MACHINE CO p 1112
2300 S Ashland Ave, Green Bay WI 54304
Tel (920) 494-5601 SIC 3554

BARRY-WEHMILLER PAPERSYSTEMS INC p 157
1300 N Airport Rd, Phillips WI 54555
Tel (314) 862-8000 SIC 3554

MARQUIP LLC p 910
1300 N Airport Rd, Phillips WI 54555
Tel (715) 339-2191 SIC 3554

CURT G JOA INC p 402
100 Crocker Ave, Sheboygan Falls WI 53085
Tel (920) 467-6136 SIC 3554

WAUSAU COATED PRODUCTS INC p 1583
7801 Stewart Ave, Wausau WI 54401
Tel (715) 848-2741 SIC 2672 3554

SIC 3555 Printing Trades Machinery & Eqpt

■ **MACDERMID PRINTING SOLUTIONS LLC** p 892
5210 Phillip Lee Dr Sw, Atlanta GA 30336
Tel (404) 472-0072 SIC 3555

HEIDELBERG USA INC p 680
1000 Gutenberg Dr Nw, Kennesaw GA 30144
Tel (770) 419-6500 SIC 5084 3555

WEBER MARKING SYSTEMS INC p 1586
711 W Algonquin Rd, Arlington Heights IL 60005
Tel (847) 364-8500 SIC 3555 2672 2675

4L TECHNOLOGIES INC p 3
4200 Columbus St, Ottawa IL 61350
Tel (815) 431-8100 SIC 3555

M & R PRINTING EQUIPMENT INC p 889
440 Medinah Rd, Roselle IL 60172
Tel (800) 736-6431 SIC 3555 3552 5084

GOSS INTERNATIONAL CORP p 626
9018 Heritage Pkwy # 1200, Woodridge IL 60517
Tel (630) 796-7560 SIC 3555 5084

SHPS FULFILLMENT SERVICES p 1319
3900 Collins Ln, Louisville KY 40245
Tel (502) 267-3423 SIC 3555

ANDY MARK INC p 91
18081 Chstrfld Aprt Rd, Chesterfield MO 63005
Tel (636) 532-4433 SIC 3555 3565

ROTO-DIE CO INC p 1252
800 Howerton Ln, Eureka MO 63025
Tel (636) 587-3600 SIC 3544 3555 3312

BALDWIN TECHNOLOGY CO INC p 147
8040 Forsyth Blvd, Saint Louis MO 63105
Tel (314) 726-2152 SIC 3555

GOSS INTERNATIONAL AMERICAS LLC p 626
121 Technology Dr, Durham NH 03824
Tel (603) 749-6600 SIC 7699 3555

PRESSTEK LLC p 1173
55 Executive Dr, Hudson NH 03051
Tel (603) 595-7000 SIC 3555 3577 3861

PAMARCO TECHNOLOGIES LLC p 1110
235 E 11th Ave, Roselle NJ 07203
Tel (908) 241-1200 SIC 3555

INTERNATIONAL IMAGING MATERIALS INC p 755
310 Commerce Dr, Amherst NY 14228
Tel (716) 691-6333 SIC 3955 3555

CANON VIRGINIA INC p 247
12000 Canon Blvd, Newport News VA 23606
Tel (757) 881-6000
SIC 3861 3577 3555 4953

CG BRETTING MANUFACTURING CO INC p 285
3401 Lake Park Rd, Ashland WI 54806
Tel (715) 682-5231
SIC 3554 3599 3565 3555

■ **MEGTEC SYSTEMS INC** p 940
830 Prosper St, De Pere WI 54115
Tel (920) 336-5715
SIC 3822 3555 3567 3823

SIC 3556 Food Prdts Machinery

HEAT AND CONTROL INC p 679
21121 Cabot Blvd, Hayward CA 94545
Tel (510) 259-0500 SIC 3556 7699

STATCO ENGINEERING & FABRICATORS INC p 1380
7595 Reynolds Cir, Huntington Beach CA 92647
Tel (714) 375-6300 SIC 5084 3556

CFP GROUP INC p 285
1117 W Olympic Blvd, Montebello CA 90640
Tel (323) 727-0900 SIC 3556

BAKEMARK USA LLC p 145
7351 Crider Ave, Pico Rivera CA 90660
Tel (562) 949-1054
SIC 2045 5149 3556 2099

SUNNYGEM LLC p 1403
500 N F St, Wasco CA 93280
Tel (661) 758-0491 SIC 2033 3556

■ **CARRIER COMMERCIAL REFRIGERATION INC** p 260
3 Farm Glen Blvd Ste 301, Farmington CT 06032
Tel (336) 245-6400
SIC 3556 3631 3585 3589 3634

METAL MASTERS FOODSERVICE EQUIPMENT CO INC p 952
100 Industrial Blvd, Clayton DE 19938
Tel (302) 653-3000 SIC 3589 3556

MAREL STORK POULTRY PROCESSING INC p 905
1024 Airport Pkwy, Gainesville GA 30501
Tel (770) 532-7041 SIC 3556 3535

▲ **JOHN BEAN TECHNOLOGIES CORP** p 787
70 W Madison St Ste 4400, Chicago IL 60602
Tel (312) 861-5900 SIC 3556 3585 3537

■ **DOVER PRINTING & IDENTIFICATION INC** p 453
3005 Highland Pkwy # 200, Downers Grove IL 60515
Tel (630) 541-1540
SIC 3556 3565 3593 7699

■ **MARSHALL MIDDLEBY INC** p 911
1400 Toastmaster Dr, Elgin IL 60120
Tel (847) 289-0204 SIC 3556 3585 3631

▲ **MIDDLEBY CORP** p 965
1400 Toastmaster Dr, Elgin IL 60120
Tel (847) 741-3300 SIC 3556 3589

■ **CORNELIUS INC** p 370
101 Regency Dr, Glendale Heights IL 60139
Tel (630) 539-6850 SIC 3585 3556 3586

SOLO CUP OPERATING CORP p 1338
300 Tr State Intl Ste 200, Lincolnshire IL 60069
Tel (847) 444-5000 SIC 3089 2656 3556

ARMOUR-ECKRICH MEATS LLC p 111
4225 Naperville Rd # 600, Lisle IL 60532
Tel (630) 281-5000 SIC 3556

G K ENTERPRISES INC p 587
26000 S Whiting Way Ste 2, Monee IL 60449
Tel (708) 587-2150
SIC 3743 3443 3559 3556 3536

URSCHEL LABORATORIES INC p 1530
1200 Cutting Edge Dr, Chesterton IN 46304
Tel (219) 464-4811 SIC 3556 7374

SHAMBAUGH & SON LP p 1311
7614 Opportunity Dr, Fort Wayne IN 46825
Tel (260) 487-7814 SIC 8711 3556 5122

PARAGON INTERNATIONAL INC p 1113
731 W 18th St, Nevada IA 50201
Tel (515) 382-8000 SIC 3589 3556 3431

REMBRANDT ENTERPRISES INC p 1222
1521 18th St, Spirit Lake IA 51360
Tel (712) 759-1800 SIC 2015 3556

LAITRAM LLC p 838
220 Laitram Ln, Harahan LA 70123
Tel (504) 733-6000
SIC 3535 3556 7359 3446 6719

PERDUE AGRIBUSINESS LLC p 1134
6906 Zion Church Rd, Salisbury MD 21804
Tel (410) 543-3000 SIC 5159 3556

DAWN EQUIPMENT CO INC p 416
2021 Micor Dr, Jackson MI 49203
Tel (517) 789-4500 SIC 5046 3556

DAWN FOOD PRODUCTS INC p 416
3333 Sargent Rd, Jackson MI 49201
Tel (517) 789-4400 SIC 2045 5046 3556

DAWN FOODS INC p 416
3333 Sargent Rd, Jackson MI 49201
Tel (517) 789-4400
SIC 2053 2045 3556 5046 6719

BUHLER INC p 224
13105 12th Ave N, Plymouth MN 55441
Tel (763) 847-9900
SIC 3556 3542 3535 3564

SOUTHERN HENS INC p 1348
327 Moselle Seminary Rd, Moselle MS 39459
Tel (601) 582-2262 SIC 3556

DUKE MFG PROPERTIES LLC p 460
2224 N 10th St, Saint Louis MO 63102
Tel (800) 735-3853 SIC 3589 3556

▲ **PAUL MUELLER CO** p 1121
1600 W Phelps St, Springfield MO 65802
Tel (417) 831-3000 SIC 3443 3556 3523

BEHLEN MFG CO p 168
4025 E 23rd St, Columbus NE 68601
Tel (402) 564-3111
SIC 3523 3448 4213 3556 3496 3443

PENNY PLATE LLC p 1131
14000 Horizon Way Ste 300, Mount Laurel NJ 08054
Tel (856) 429-7583 SIC 3411 3556

■ **SPX FLOW TECHNOLOGY SYSTEMS INC** p 1362
105 Crosspoint Pkwy, Getzville NY 14068
Tel (716) 692-3000 SIC 3556 8742

BUHLER AEROGLIDE CORP p 224
100 Aeroglide Dr, Cary NC 27511
Tel (919) 278-2925 SIC 3556 3585 3567

▲ **SPX FLOW INC** p 1362
13320 Balntyn Corp Pl, Charlotte NC 28277
Tel (704) 752-4400 SIC 3556

STORK UNITED CORP p 1392
3201 Rotary Dr, Charlotte NC 28269
Tel (704) 598-7171 SIC 5084 3552 3556

AC CORP p 13
301 Creek Ridge Rd, Greensboro NC 27406
Tel (336) 273-4472
SIC 1711 1731 3556 3823 3625 3535

GOLD MEDAL PRODUCTS CO p 620
10700 Medallion Dr, Cincinnati OH 45241
Tel (513) 769-7676
SIC 3556 3589 5145 3581

N WASSERSTROM & SONS INC p 1005
2300 Lockbourne Rd, Columbus OH 43207
Tel (614) 737-8543 SIC 3556 5046 3444

VITA-MIX CORP p 1562
8615 Usher Rd, Olmsted Twp OH 44138
Tel (440) 235-4840 SIC 5961 3556

■ **HOBART CORP** p 698
701 S Ridge Ave, Troy OH 45374
Tel (937) 332-3000
SIC 3589 3556 3596 3585 3321

■ **ITW FOOD EQUIPMENT GROUP LLC** p 769
701 S Ridge Ave, Troy OH 45374
Tel (937) 332-3000 SIC 5046 3556

TRUITT BROS INC p 1486
1105 Front St Ne, Salem OR 97301
Tel (503) 365-2837 SIC 3556

INSIGHT EQUITY A P X L P p 746
1400 Civic Pl Ste 250, Southlake TX 76092
Tel (817) 488-7775
SIC 6722 3441 3443 3556 3714 5171

INSIGHT EQUITY LP p 746
1400 Civic Pl Ste 250, Southlake TX 76092
Tel (817) 488-7775
SIC 6722 3441 3443 3556 3714 5171

AMF AUTOMATION TECHNOLOGIES LLC p 84
2115 W Laburnum Ave, Richmond VA 23227
Tel (804) 355-7961 SIC 3556

▲ **KEY TECHNOLOGY INC** p 814
150 Avery St, Walla Walla WA 99362
Tel (509) 529-2161 SIC 3556 2834

SCHREIBER FOODS INC p 1290
400 N Washington St, Green Bay WI 54301
Tel (920) 437-7601 SIC 2022 3556 3565

■ **WALKER STAINLESS EQUIPMENT CO LLC** p 1573
625 W State St, New Lisbon WI 53950
Tel (608) 562-7500 SIC 3443 3556 3715

VOLLRATH CO LLC p 1564
1236 N 18th St, Sheboygan WI 53081
Tel (920) 459-6568
SIC 3089 3365 3421 3556 3914

KHS USA INC p 816
880 Bahcall Ct, Waukesha WI 53186
Tel (262) 797-7200 SIC 3556

SIC 3559 Special Ind Machinery, NEC

SEOHAN-NTN DRIVESHAFT USA CORP p 1305
246 Teague Ct, Auburn AL 36832
Tel (334) 707-6863 SIC 3559

ASM AMERICA INC p 118
3440 E University Dr, Phoenix AZ 85034
Tel (602) 470-5700 SIC 3559

VANTAGE MOBILITY INTERNATIONAL LLC p 1544
5202 S 28th Pl, Phoenix AZ 85040
Tel (602) 243-2700 SIC 5012 3559

▲ **AMTECH SYSTEMS INC** p 87
131 S Clark Dr, Tempe AZ 85281
Tel (480) 967-5146 SIC 3559

▲ **EMCORE CORP** p 491
2015 Chestnut St, Alhambra CA 91803
Tel (626) 293-3400 SIC 3674 3559

GEORGE FISCHER INC p 606
3401 Aero Jet Ave, El Monte CA 91731
Tel (626) 571-2770
SIC 3599 5074 3829 3559

■ **CROSSING AUTOMATION INC** p 394
46702 Bayside Pkwy, Fremont CA 94538
Tel (510) 661-5000 SIC 3559

MATTSON TECHNOLOGY INC p 921
47131 Bayside Pkwy, Fremont CA 94538
Tel (510) 657-5900 SIC 3559

▲ **NANOMETRICS INC** p 1007
1550 Buckeye Dr, Milpitas CA 95035
Tel (408) 545-6000 SIC 3829 3559

■ **ICEE CO** p 727
1205 S Dupont Ave, Ontario CA 91761
Tel (800) 426-4233
SIC 2038 5145 3559 2087

NOVELLUS SYSTEMS INC p 1063
4000 N 1st St, San Jose CA 95134
Tel (408) 943-9700 SIC 3559

▲ **ULTRATECH INC** p 1501
3050 Zanker Rd, San Jose CA 95134
Tel (408) 321-8835 SIC 3559

▲ **APPLIED MATERIALS INC** p 99
3050 Bowers Ave, Santa Clara CA 95054
Tel (408) 727-5555 SIC 3559 3674

GLOBALFOUNDRIES US INC p 617
2600 Great America Way, Santa Clara CA 95054
Tel (408) 462-3900 SIC 3559 3825 5065

WG GLOBAL LLC p 1604
603 Park Point Dr Ste 200, Golden CO 80401
Tel (303) 395-2100
SIC 3569 3559 3629 3625 3443 3412

FARREL CORP p 530
1 Farrell Blvd, Ansonia CT 06401
Tel (203) 736-5500 SIC 3559 1011 3089

DAVIS-STANDARD HOLDINGS INC p 416
1 Extrusion Dr, Pawcatuck CT 06379
Tel (860) 599-1010 SIC 3559

GERBER TECHNOLOGY LLC p 608
24 Industrial Park Rd W, Tolland CT 06084
Tel (860) 871-8082 SIC 3559 7371

CAE(US) INC p 236
1011 Ct Rd Ste 322, Wilmington DE 19805
Tel (813) 885-7481 SIC 3559

SEWICKLEY CAPITAL INC p 1309
501 Silverside Rd Ste 67, Wilmington DE 19809
Tel (302) 793-4964 SIC 3559 3822

GIW INDUSTRIES INC p 613
5000 Wrightsboro Rd, Grovetown GA 30813
Tel (706) 863-1011 SIC 3561 3559

KNAPP LOGISTICS AUTOMATION INC p 824
2124 Barrett Park Dr Nw # 100, Kennesaw GA 30144
Tel (678) 388-2880 SIC 3559

■ **PATTERSON PUMP CO** p 1121
2129 Ayersville Rd, Toccoa GA 30577
Tel (706) 886-2101 SIC 3561 3511 3559

PLASTICS COLOR CORP p 1155
14201 Paxton Ave, Calumet City IL 60409
Tel (708) 868-3800 SIC 3559

■ **DOVER ARTIFICIAL LIFT INTERNATIONAL LLC** p 453
3005 Highland Pkwy, Downers Grove IL 60515
Tel (630) 743-2563
SIC 3559 3535 3533 3561

GENERAL BINDING CORP p 599
4 Corporate Dr, Lake Zurich IL 60047
Tel (847) 541-9500
SIC 5044 2782 3559 3589 7629 3579

G K ENTERPRISES INC p 587
26000 S Whiting Way Ste 2, Monee IL 60449
Tel (708) 587-2150
SIC 3743 3443 3559 3556 3536

■ **NALCO CO LLC** p 1006
1601 W Diehl Rd, Naperville IL 60563
Tel (630) 305-1000
SIC 3559 2899 2992 2891

■ **NALCO HOLDINGS LLC** p 1007
1601 W Diehl Rd, Naperville IL 60563
Tel (630) 305-1000 SIC 2899 2992 3559

▲ **FEDERAL SIGNAL CORP** p 536
1415 W 22nd St Ste 1100, Oak Brook IL 60523
Tel (630) 954-2000
SIC 3711 3647 3669 3559 3544 3545

AEC INC p 28
1100 E Wdfield Rd Ste 588, Schaumburg IL 60173
Tel (847) 273-7700
SIC 3585 3823 3559 3443 3535

STERLING PRODUCTS INC p 1387
1100 E Woodfield Rd # 550, Schaumburg IL 60173
Tel (847) 273-7700 SIC 3559 3823 3542

■ **FLUID MANAGEMENT INC** p 561
1023 Wheeling Rd, Wheeling IL 60090
Tel (847) 537-0880 SIC 3559

KOCH ENTERPRISES INC p 825
14 S 11th Ave, Evansville IN 47712
Tel (812) 465-9800
SIC 3363 5075 3559 5084 2891 3069

BRIDGESTONE BANDAG LLC p 211
2000 Bandag Dr, Muscatine IA 52761
Tel (563) 262-2511
SIC 7534 3559 5014 3011 7549 6794

SCRIPTPRO LLC p 1295
5828 Reeds Rd, Shawnee Mission KS 66202
Tel (913) 384-1008 *SIC* 3559 3586

KRAUSS-MAFFEI CORP p 829
7095 Industrial Rd, Florence KY 41042
Tel (859) 283-0200 *SIC* 5084 3559

FIVES MACHINING SYSTEMS INC p 553
2200 Litton Ln, Hebron KY 41048
Tel (859) 534-4600 *SIC* 3559

GRUPO ANTOLIN KENTUCKY INC p 643
208 Commerce Ct, Hopkinsville KY 42240
Tel (270) 885-2703 *SIC* 3559 2399

■ OAO CORP p 1071
700 N Frederick Ave, Gaithersburg MD 20879
Tel (301) 240-7000
SIC 7371 8711 3823 3559

▲ AXCELIS TECHNOLOGIES INC p 140
108 Cherry Hill Dr, Beverly MA 01915
Tel (978) 787-4000 *SIC* 3559 3829

EMD MILLIPORE CORP p 491
290 Concord Rd, Billerica MA 01821
Tel (781) 533-6000 *SIC* 3559 1541 3999

■ GE IONICS INC p 596
3 Burlington Woods Dr # 200, Burlington MA 01803
Tel (781) 359-7000
SIC 3589 2086 4941 3559 2899 3823

▲ BROOKS AUTOMATION INC p 218
15 Elizabeth Dr, Chelmsford MA 01824
Tel (978) 262-2400
SIC 3559 3563 3823 7699

■ NYPRO INC p 1069
101 Union St, Clinton MA 01510
Tel (978) 365-8100
SIC 3089 3559 7389 8711

■ FEI CO MEPD PEABODY p 537
1 Corporation Way Ste 2, Peabody MA 01960
Tel (978) 538-6700 *SIC* 3559 3827 3699

SAINT-GOBAIN ABRASIVES INC p 1271
1 New Bond St, Worcester MA 01606
Tel (508) 795-5000
SIC 3291 3559 3545 3297 3082 2891

BESSER CO p 177
801 Johnson St, Alpena MI 49707
Tel (989) 354-4508
SIC 3531 3559 3564 3443

MORRELL INC p 990
3333 Bald Mountain Rd, Auburn Hills MI 48326
Tel (248) 373-1600
SIC 5084 5065 3621 3643 3559 3357

SYNCREON HOLDINGS INC p 1415
2851 High Meadow Cir # 250, Auburn Hills MI 48326
Tel (248) 377-4700 *SIC* 3559

WILLAN INC p 1610
2851 High Meadow Cir # 250, Auburn Hills MI 48326
Tel (248) 377-4700 *SIC* 3559

■ WOLVERINE ADVANCED MATERIALS LLC p 1621
5850 Mercury Dr Ste 250, Dearborn MI 48126
Tel (313) 749-6100 *SIC* 3559 3694

AUTO-WARES GROUP INC p 133
440 Kirtland St Sw, Grand Rapids MI 49507
Tel (616) 243-2125 *SIC* 3559

FIRSTRONIC LLC p 551
1655 Michigan St Ne, Grand Rapids MI 49503
Tel (616) 456-9220 *SIC* 3559

CORVAC COMPOSITES LLC p 373
4450 36th St Se, Kentwood MI 49512
Tel (616) 281-4026 *SIC* 3559

MANN + HUMMEL INC p 902
6400 S Sprinkle Rd, Portage MI 49002
Tel (269) 329-3900 *SIC* 3559 3585

FANUC AMERICA CORP p 527
3900 W Hamlin Rd, Rochester Hills MI 48309
Tel (248) 377-7000
SIC 3559 3548 3569 3542

DURR SYSTEMS INC p 463
26801 Northwestern Hwy, Southfield MI 48033
Tel (248) 450-2000 *SIC* 3559 3567

DURR – INC p 463
26801 Northwestern Hwy, Southfield MI 48033
Tel (734) 459-6800 *SIC* 3559 3567

■ FEDERAL-MOGUL CORP p 536
27300 W 11 Mile Rd, Southfield MI 48034
Tel (248) 354-7700
SIC 3559 3462 3812 3674 3694

■ FEDERAL-MOGUL HOLDINGS CORP p 536
27300 W 11 Mile Rd, Southfield MI 48034
Tel (248) 354-7700
SIC 3462 3559 3694 3812 3674 3714

HURON VALLEY STEEL CORP p 721
1650 W Jefferson Ave, Trenton MI 48183
Tel (734) 479-3500 *SIC* 5093 3341 3559

PENTAIR INC p 1132
5500 Wayzata Blvd Ste 600, Minneapolis MN 55416
Tel (763) 545-1730
SIC 3491 3559 4971 3589

WAGNER HOLDINGS INC p 1571
1770 Fernbrook Ln N, Minneapolis MN 55447
Tel (763) 553-7000 *SIC* 3563 3559

JT SHANNON LUMBER CO INC p 796
2200 Cole Rd, Horn Lake MS 38637
Tel (662) 393-3765 *SIC* 5031 3559 2421

HUNTER ENGINEERING CO INC p 719
11250 Hunter Dr, Bridgeton MO 63044
Tel (314) 731-3020 *SIC* 3559

LINCOLN INDUSTRIAL CORP p 867
5148 N Hanley Rd, Saint Louis MO 63134
Tel (314) 679-4200
SIC 3569 3559 3561 3714

■ PETROLITE CORP p 1139
369 Marshall Ave, Saint Louis MO 63119
Tel (314) 961-3500
SIC 3559 2999 2899 2821 2911

SUNEDISON INTERNATIONAL INC p 1402
501 Pearl Dr, Saint Peters MO 63376
Tel (636) 474-5000 *SIC* 3559

■ SEMITOOL INC p 1303
655 W Reserve Dr, Kalispell MT 59901
Tel (406) 752-2107 *SIC* 3559

HORNADY MANUFACTURING CO p 708
3625 W Old Potash Hwy, Grand Island NE 68803
Tel (308) 382-1390 *SIC* 3482 3559 3483

BROTHER INTERNATIONAL CORP p 219
200 Crossing Blvd, Bridgewater NJ 08807
Tel (908) 704-1700
SIC 5044 3579 3559 5084 5064 5065

LINDE NORTH AMERICA INC p 868
200 Somerset Corporate Bl, Bridgewater NJ 08807
Tel (908) 464-8100
SIC 2813 3569 3559 3561 3511 3823

BOC GROUP INC p 196
575 Mountain Ave, New Providence NJ 07974
Tel (908) 665-2400
SIC 2813 3569 3559 3561 3511 3823

ALVOGEN PHARMA US INC p 63
10 Bloomfield Ave, Pine Brook NJ 07058
Tel (973) 796-3400 *SIC* 3559

AMANO USA HOLDINGS INC p 64
140 Harrison Ave, Roseland NJ 07068
Tel (973) 403-1900
SIC 3589 2842 3579 3559 5169 5087

HOSOKAWA MICRON INTERNATIONAL INC p 708
10 Chatham Rd, Summit NJ 07901
Tel (908) 273-6360 *SIC* 3559

UI ACQUISITION HOLDING CO p 1500
33 Broome Corporate Pkwy, Conklin NY 13748
Tel (607) 779-7522 *SIC* 3559

UI HOLDING CO p 1500
33 Broome Corporate Pkwy, Conklin NY 13748
Tel (607) 779-7522 *SIC* 3559

UNIVERSAL INSTRUMENTS CORP p 1517
33 Broome Corporate Pkwy, Conklin NY 13748
Tel (800) 842-9732 *SIC* 3559

DESIGNATRONICS INC p 432
2101 Jericho Tpke Ste 1, New Hyde Park NY 11040
Tel (516) 328-3300
SIC 3824 3559 3545 3625 3462

■ IEH FM HOLDINGS LLC p 730
767 5th Ave Ste 4700, New York NY 10153
Tel (212) 702-4300
SIC 3462 3559 3694 3812 3674

▲ VEECO INSTRUMENTS INC p 1546
1 Terminal Dr, Plainview NY 11803
Tel (516) 677-0200 *SIC* 3559

HITACHI METALS AMERICA LTD p 697
2 Manhattanville Rd # 301, Purchase NY 10577
Tel (914) 694-9200
SIC 3264 3577 3365 5051 3321 3559

■ PFAUDLER INC p 1140
1000 West Ave, Rochester NY 14611
Tel (585) 464-5663 *SIC* 3559

▲ SPX CORP p 1362
13320a Balntyn Corp Pl, Charlotte NC 28277
Tel (980) 474-3700
SIC 3443 3599 3829 3559 3545

MI 2009 INC p 959
4165 Half Acre Rd, Batavia OH 45103
Tel (513) 536-2000 *SIC* 3559

▲ CHART INDUSTRIES INC p 290
1 Infinity Corp Ctr Dr # 300, Cleveland OH 44125
Tel (440) 753-1490 *SIC* 3559 3569 3443

CROWNE GROUP LLC p 396
127 Public Sq Ste 5110, Cleveland OH 44114
Tel (216) 589-0198 *SIC* 3559 8711

EATON CORP p 473
1000 Eaton Blvd, Cleveland OH 44122
Tel (216) 523-5000
SIC 3625 3714 3594 3559 3571

PEERLESS-WINSMITH INC p 1127
5200 Upper Metro Pl # 110, Dublin OH 43017
Tel (614) 526-7000
SIC 3621 3566 3634 3812 3559

MASTER CHEMICAL CORP p 918
501 W Boundary St, Perrysburg OH 43551
Tel (419) 874-7902 *SIC* 2992 3559

VESTA CORP p 1552
11950 Sw Garden Pl, Portland OR 97223
Tel (503) 639-0235 *SIC* 3559 3578

ICHOR SYSTEMS INC p 727
9660 Sw Herman Rd, Tualatin OR 97062
Tel (503) 625-2251 *SIC* 3559 5984

FLS US HOLDINGS INC p 561
2040 Avenue C, Bethlehem PA 18017
Tel (610) 264-6011
SIC 3559 3554 3549 3532 3535

IPEG INC p 763
200 W Kensinger Dr # 100, Cranberry Township PA 16066
Tel (724) 584-5500 *SIC* 3559

TSB NUCLEAR ENERGY USA GROUP INC p 1489
1000 Westinghouse Dr, Cranberry Township PA 16066
Tel (412) 374-4111 *SIC* 3823 3559

ERIEZ MANUFACTURING CO p 508
2200 Asbury Rd, Erie PA 16506
Tel (814) 835-6000 *SIC* 3559

■ GE INFRASTRUCTURE SENSING p 596
4636 Somerton Rd, Feasterville Trevose PA 19053
Tel (617) 926-1749
SIC 3589 2086 4941 3559 2899 3823

DAY AND ZIMMERMANN INC p 417
1500 Spring Garden St # 900, Philadelphia PA 19130
Tel (215) 299-8000
SIC 8744 8712 8711 3559 3483

HITACHI METALS AUTOMOTIVE COMPONENTS USA LLC p 697
18986 Route 287, Tioga PA 16946
Tel (217) 347-0600 *SIC* 3465 3321 3559

TECHNIC INC p 1431
47 Molter St, Cranston RI 02910
Tel (401) 781-6100 *SIC* 2899 3559

■ JACOBS APPLIED TECHNOLOGY INC p 775
2040 Bushy Park Rd, Goose Creek SC 29445
Tel (843) 824-1100
SIC 3559 3443 8711 1629

TOKYO ELECTRON AMERICA INC p 1458
2400 Grove Blvd, Austin TX 78741
Tel (512) 424-1000 *SIC* 3559 8711

CRYOGENIC VESSEL ALTERNATIVES INC p 396
1301 Transport Dr, Baytown TX 77523
Tel (281) 738-2863 *SIC* 3559

VENTECH ENGINEERS INTERNATIONAL CORP p 1548
1149 Ellsworth Dr Ofc, Pasadena TX 77506
Tel (713) 477-0201
SIC 1629 8711 3559 5084

■ SAFETY-KLEEN INC p 1266
2600 N Central Expy # 400, Richardson TX 75080
Tel (800) 669-5740
SIC 4953 3559 4212 5172 5085 7389

■ SAFETY-KLEEN SYSTEMS INC p 1266
2600 N Central Expy # 400, Richardson TX 75080
Tel (972) 265-2000
SIC 3559 7359 5172 4212 7389 5085

TOPPAN PHOTOMASKS INC p 1461
131 E Old Settlers Blvd, Round Rock TX 78664
Tel (512) 310-6500 *SIC* 3559

AVANZAR INTERIOR TECHNOLOGIES LTD p 136
1 Lone Star Pass Bldg 41, San Antonio TX 78264
Tel (210) 271-2300 *SIC* 3559

PSP INDUSTRIES INC p 1188
9885 Doerr Ln, Schertz TX 78154
Tel (210) 651-9595
SIC 3533 3531 3564 3532 3559

BOART LONGYEAR CO p 196
2570 W 1700 S, Salt Lake City UT 84104
Tel (801) 972-6430
SIC 1481 3532 3559 1771

LONGYEAR HOLDINGS INC p 877
2340 W 1700 S, Salt Lake City UT 84104
Tel (801) 972-6430 *SIC* 1481 3532 3559

C-TECH INDUSTRIES INC p 234
4275 Nw Pacific Rim Blvd, Camas WA 98607
Tel (360) 833-1600 *SIC* 3589 2841 3559

WHITTEN GROUP INTERNATIONAL CORP p 1607
2622 Lilac St, Longview WA 98632
Tel (360) 560-3319 *SIC* 5172 3559

WELLONS INC p 1589
2525 W Firestone Ln, Vancouver WA 98660
Tel (360) 750-3500 *SIC* 3559 3443

■ IDSC HOLDINGS LLC p 729
2801 80th St, Kenosha WI 53143
Tel (262) 656-5200
SIC 3423 3559 7372 6794 5013 3546

▲ SNAP-ON INC p 1335
2801 80th St, Kenosha WI 53143
Tel (262) 656-5200 *SIC* 3546 3559 3825

STERLING INC p 1387
2900 S 160th St, New Berlin WI 53151
Tel (414) 354-0970 *SIC* 3823 3542 3559

SIC 3561 Pumps & Pumping Eqpt

QUINCY COMPRESSOR LLC p 1200
701 N Dobson Ave, Bay Minette AL 36507
Tel (251) 937-5900 *SIC* 3519 3563 3561

HASKEL INTERNATIONAL LLC p 667
100 E Graham Pl, Burbank CA 91502
Tel (818) 843-4000
SIC 3561 3594 5084 5085 3699

SUNDYNE LLC p 1402
14845 W 64th Ave, Arvada CO 80007
Tel (303) 425-0800 *SIC* 3563 3561

GARDNER DENVER NASH LLC p 592
2 Trefoil Dr, Trumbull CT 06611
Tel (203) 459-3923
SIC 5084 3563 8711 3561

HORNERXPRESS INC p 708
5755 Powerline Rd, Fort Lauderdale FL 33309
Tel (954) 772-6966 *SIC* 5091 3949 3561

■ ROPER PUMP CO p 1250
3475 Old Maysville Rd, Commerce GA 30529
Tel (706) 336-3459 *SIC* 3823 3561

GIW INDUSTRIES INC p 613
5000 Wrightsboro Rd, Grovetown GA 30813
Tel (706) 863-1011 *SIC* 3561 3559

CLEAVER-BROOKS INC p 325
221 Law St, Thomasville GA 31792
Tel (229) 226-3024
SIC 3589 3569 3561 3433 3443

■ PATTERSON PUMP CO p 1121
2129 Ayersville Rd, Toccoa GA 30577
Tel (706) 886-2101 *SIC* 3561 3511 3559

TUTHILL CORP p 1493
8500 S Madison St, Burr Ridge IL 60527
Tel (630) 382-4900 *SIC* 3561 3586 3524

■ DOVER ARTIFICIAL LIFT INTERNATIONAL LLC p 453
3005 Highland Pkwy, Downers Grove IL 60515
Tel (630) 743-2563
SIC 3559 3535 3533 3561

■ DOVER ENGINEERED SYSTEMS INC p 453
3005 Highland Pkwy # 200, Downers Grove IL 60515
Tel (630) 743-2505
SIC 3568 3443 3441 3561 3491 3492

W S DARLEY & CO p 1569
325 Spring Lake Dr, Itasca IL 60143
Tel (630) 735-3500
SIC 3561 5087 5099 3569 3812

▲ IDEX CORP p 729
1925 W Field Ct Ste 200, Lake Forest IL 60045
Tel (847) 498-7070 *SIC* 3561 3563 3594

■ PUMP SOLUTIONS GROUP p 1192
1815 S Meyers Rd Ste 670, Oakbrook Terrace IL 60181
Tel (630) 487-2240 *SIC* 3561

▲ FRANKLIN ELECTRIC CO INC p 575
9255 Coverdale Rd, Fort Wayne IN 46809
Tel (260) 824-2900 *SIC* 3621 3561

STERLING FLUID SYSTEMS (USA) LLC p 1387
2005 Dr Mrtn Lthr Kng Jr, Indianapolis IN 46202
Tel (317) 925-9661 *SIC* 3561

FLINT & WALLING INC p 557
95 N Oak St, Kendallville IN 46755
Tel (260) 347-1781 *SIC* 3561

■ VIKING PUMP INC p 1557
406 State St, Cedar Falls IA 50613
Tel (319) 266-1741 *SIC* 3561

A Y MCDONALD INDUSTRIES INC p 7
4800 Chavenelle Rd, Dubuque IA 52002
Tel (800) 292-2737
SIC 3432 3561 3494 5074 5075 5031

ZOELLER CO p 1644
3649 Cane Run Rd, Louisville KY 40211
Tel (502) 778-2731
SIC 3561 5251 3432 3491

▲ COLFAX CORP p 336
420 Natl Bus Pkwy Fl 5, Annapolis Junction MD 20701
Tel (301) 323-9000 *SIC* 3561 3829 3625

HAYES PUMP INC p 670
66 Old Powder Mill Rd I, Concord MA 01742
Tel (978) 369-8800 *SIC* 5084 3561

■ GAST MANUFACTURING INC p 593
2300 M 139, Benton Harbor MI 49022
Tel (269) 926-6171
SIC 3563 3594 3621 3566 3561

ENGINEERED MACHINED PRODUCTS INC p 499
3111 N 28th St, Escanaba MI 49829
Tel (906) 786-8404
SIC 3519 3714 3568 3599 3561

MELLING TOOL CO p 941
2620 Saradan Dr, Jackson MI 49202
Tel (517) 787-8172
SIC 3451 3714 3625 3568 3561 3494

OSMONICS INC p 1097
5951 Clearwater Dr, Hopkins MN 55343
Tel (952) 933-2277
SIC 3569 3589 3561 3824 3823 3089

DESIGN READY CONTROLS INC p 432
9325 Winnetka Ave N, Minneapolis MN 55445
Tel (763) 565-3000 *SIC* 5084 3613 3561

FLOW CONTROL US HOLDING CORP p 560
5500 Wayzata Blvd, Minneapolis MN 55416
Tel (763) 545-1730 *SIC* 3561

▲ GRACO INC p 628
88 11th Ave Ne, Minneapolis MN 55413
Tel (612) 623-6000
SIC 3561 3594 3563 3491 3823 3569

SMITHS MEDICAL MD INC p 1334
6000 Nathan Ln N Ste 100, Minneapolis MN 55442
Tel (651) 633-2556 *SIC* 3841 3586 3561

SCHWING AMERICA INC p 1291
5900 Centerville Rd, Saint Paul MN 55127
Tel (651) 429-0999 *SIC* 3531 3561 3999

WATEROUS CO p 1582
125 Hardman Ave S, South Saint Paul MN 55075
Tel (651) 450-5000
SIC 3491 3561 3494 3321

LINCOLN INDUSTRIAL CORP p 867
5148 N Hanley Rd, Saint Louis MO 63134
Tel (314) 679-4200
SIC 3569 3559 3561 3714

SPRINGFIELD REMANUFACTURING CORP p 1361
650 N Broadview Pl, Springfield MO 65802
Tel (417) 862-3501
SIC 3519 3714 3713 3561

T-L IRRIGATION CO p 1420
151 E Hwy 6 And Ab Rd, Hastings NE 68901
Tel (402) 462-4128
SIC 3523 3561 3479 7359

PFEIFFER VACUUM INC p 1140
24 Trafalgar Sq, Nashua NH 03063
Tel (603) 578-6500 *SIC* 3561

■ XYLEM DEWATERING SOLUTIONS INC p 1633
84 Floodgate Rd, Bridgeport NJ 08014
Tel (410) 243-4900 *SIC* 7353 3561 5084

LINDE LLC p 868
200 Somerset Corporate Bl, Bridgewater NJ 08807
Tel (908) 464-8100
SIC 2813 3569 3561 3823

LINDE NORTH AMERICA INC p 868
200 Somerset Corporate Bl, Bridgewater NJ 08807
Tel (908) 464-8100
SIC 2813 3569 3559 3561 3511 3823

HAYWARD INDUSTRIES INC p 670
620 Division St, Elizabeth NJ 07201
Tel (908) 351-5400
SIC 3589 3561 3423 3494 3569 3089

BOC GROUP INC p 196
575 Mountain Ave, New Providence NJ 07974
Tel (908) 665-2400
SIC 2813 3569 3559 3561 3511 3823

LIBERTY PUMPS INC p 862
7000 Appletree Ave, Bergen NY 14416
Tel (800) 543-2550 *SIC* 3561

■ FLUID HANDLING LLC p 561
175 Standard Pkwy, Cheektowaga NY 14227
Tel (716) 897-2800 *SIC* 3561

▲ XYLEM INC p 1633
1 International Dr, Rye Brook NY 10573
Tel (914) 323-5700 *SIC* 3561

■ GOULDS PUMPS INC p 627
240 Fall St, Seneca Falls NY 13148
Tel (315) 568-2811 *SIC* 3561 5084

■ ITT GOULDS PUMPS INC p 768
240 Fall St, Seneca Falls NY 13148
Tel (914) 641-2129 *SIC* 3561 5084

ITT FLUID TECHNOLOGY CORP p 768
1133 Westcstr Ave N100 Ste N, White Plains NY 10604
Tel (914) 641-2000 *SIC* 3494 3594 3561

AREVA INC p 107
7207 Ibm Dr, Charlotte NC 28262
Tel (704) 805-2000
SIC 3823 3829 8711 5085 3561 2819

ENVIRONMENTAL FILTRATION TECHNOLOGIES LLC p 503
4404a Chesapeake Dr, Charlotte NC 28216
Tel (704) 399-7441
SIC 3569 5085 3564 3444 3469 3561

■ **MARLEY CO LLC** p 909
13515 Balntyn Corp Pl, Charlotte NC 28277
Tel (704) 752-4400
SIC 3443 3433 3586 3561 3634

INGERSOLL-RAND CO p 742
800 Beaty St Ste B, Davidson NC 28036
Tel (704) 655-4000
SIC 3561 3429 3546 3563 3531

JAMES M PLEASANTS CO INC p 776
603 Diamond Hill Ct, Greensboro NC 27406
Tel (336) 275-3152
SIC 5075 3585 3561 3494

■ **IMO INDUSTRIES INC** p 734
1710 Airport Rd, Monroe NC 28110
Tel (704) 289-6511 SIC 3561 3714 3829

PENTAIR WATER POOL AND SPA INC p 1132
1620 Hawkins Ave, Sanford NC 27330
Tel (919) 774-4151
SIC 3589 3561 3569 3648

■ **HURST JAWS OF LIFE INC** p 721
711 N Post Rd, Shelby NC 28150
Tel (704) 487-6961 SIC 3569 3561 3594

PENTAIR FLOW TECHNOLOGIES LLC p 1132
1101 Myers Pkwy, Ashland OH 44805
Tel (419) 289-1144 SIC 3561

RUMPKE TRANSPORTATION CO LLC p 1258
10795 Hughes Rd, Cincinnati OH 45251
Tel (513) 851-0122
SIC 3561 5084 7537 4953

▲ **GORMAN-RUPP CO** p 626
600 S Airport Rd, Mansfield OH 44903
Tel (419) 755-1011 SIC 3561 3594

■ **CRANE PUMPS & SYSTEMS INC** p 389
420 3rd St, Piqua OH 45356
Tel (937) 773-2442 SIC 3561

BLACKHAWK INDUSTRIAL DISTRIBUTION INC p 187
1501 Sw Expressway Dr, Broken Arrow OK 74012
Tel (918) 663-3252 SIC 5085 3561 5084

■ **LITTLE GIANT PUMP CO LLC** p 871
301 N Macarthur Blvd, Oklahoma City OK 73127
Tel (405) 947-2511 SIC 3561

▲ **AMPCO-PITTSBURGH CORP** p 86
726 Bell Ave Ste 301, Carnegie PA 15106
Tel (412) 456-4400
SIC 3312 3561 3351 3353

■ **CURTISS-WRIGHT ELECTRO-MECHANICAL CORP** p 402
1000 Wright Way, Cheswick PA 15024
Tel (724) 275-5000 SIC 3561 3621 3511

MILTON ROY LLC p 972
201 Ivyland Rd, Ivyland PA 18974
Tel (215) 441-0800 SIC 3561 3586 3826

AIRGAS SAFETY INC p 40
2501 Green Ln, Levittown PA 19057
Tel (215) 826-9000
SIC 5084 5085 3561 3841

TACO INC p 1421
1160 Cranston St, Cranston RI 02920
Tel (401) 942-8000
SIC 3433 3561 3443 3822

ASSOCIATED FUEL PUMP SYSTEMS CORP p 120
1100 Scotts Bridge Rd, Anderson SC 29621
Tel (864) 224-0012 SIC 3714 3561

■ **OIL STATES INDUSTRIES INC** p 1079
7701 S Cooper St, Arlington TX 76001
Tel (817) 548-4200
SIC 1389 3061 3561 3533

CS&P TECHNOLOGIES LP p 397
18119 Telge Rd, Cypress TX 77429
Tel (713) 467-0869 SIC 3561

■ **FLOWTRONEX PSI LLC** p 560
10661 Newkirk St, Dallas TX 75220
Tel (469) 221-1200
SIC 3561 3949 3523 3432

FTS INTERNATIONAL SERVICES LLC p 583
777 Main St Ste 2900, Fort Worth TX 76102
Tel (817) 850-1008
SIC 3561 8711 7353 4225

WEIR GROUP INC p 1588
7601 Wyatt Dr, Fort Worth TX 76108
Tel (817) 246-2461 SIC 3561 8711

▲ **BAKER HUGHES INC** p 146
17021 Aldine Westfield Rd, Houston TX 77073
Tel (713) 439-8600 SIC 3533 3561

▲ **OIL STATES INTERNATIONAL INC** p 1079
333 Clay St Ste 4620, Houston TX 77002
Tel (713) 652-0582
SIC 3353 3061 3053 3561 3491

SCHLUMBERGER INTERNATIONAL INC p 1287
7030 Ardmore St, Houston TX 77054
Tel (713) 747-4000
SIC 1389 3561 3492 3533

SOUTHWEST OILFIELD PRODUCTS INC p 1352
10340 Wallisville Rd, Houston TX 77013
Tel (713) 675-7541 SIC 3533 3561

WEATHERFORD ARTIFICIAL LIFT SYSTEMS LLC p 1586
2000 Saint James Pl, Houston TX 77056
Tel (713) 836-4000 SIC 3561 5084

▲ **FLOWSERVE CORP** p 560
5215 N Oconnor Blvd Connor, Irving TX 75039
Tel (972) 443-6500
SIC 3561 3491 3621 3494 3463 3321

■ **FLOWSERVE US INC** p 560
5215 N Oconnor Blvd Ste, Irving TX 75039
Tel (972) 443-6500 SIC 3561 3491

■ **LUFKIN INDUSTRIES LLC** p 884
601 S Raguet St, Lufkin TX 75904
Tel (936) 634-2211 SIC 3561 3321 3462

DON-NAN PUMP AND SUPPLY CO INC p 450
3427 E Garden Cy Hwy 158, Midland TX 79706
Tel (432) 682-7742 SIC 1389 3599 3561

■ **DRESSER INC** p 455
601 Shiloh Rd, Plano TX 75074
Tel (262) 549-2626
SIC 3491 3825 3594 3593 3561 3494

ENVIROTECH PUMPSYSTEMS INC p 504
440 W 800 S, Salt Lake City UT 84101
Tel (801) 359-8731 SIC 3561 3491 3089

WEIR GROUP LP p 1588
440 W 800 S, Salt Lake City UT 84101
Tel (801) 530-7937 SIC 3561

■ **CONSTELLATION PUMPS CORP** p 361
10571 Telg Rd Ste 201, Glen Allen VA 23059
Tel (804) 327-5664 SIC 3561

KSB AMERICA CORP p 831
4415 Sarellen Rd, Richmond VA 23231
Tel (804) 222-1818
SIC 3561 3494 3625 5084

FLOW INTERNATIONAL CORP p 560
23500 64th Ave S, Kent WA 98032
Tel (253) 850-3500 SIC 3561

OMAX CORP p 1084
21409 72nd Ave S, Kent WA 98032
Tel (253) 872-2300 SIC 3545 3561

STA-RITE INDUSTRIES LLC p 1374
293 S Wright St, Delavan WI 53115
Tel (888) 782-7483 SIC 3561 5084 5251

WACKER NEUSON CORP p 1570
N92w15000 Anthony Ave, Menomonee Falls WI 53051
Tel (262) 255-0500
SIC 3531 3621 3561 3546 3423

GARDNER DENVER INC p 592
222 E Erie St Ste 500, Milwaukee WI 53202
Tel (414) 212-4700 SIC 3564 3561 3563

PENTAIR FILTRATION INC p 1131
5730 N Glen Park Rd, Milwaukee WI 53209
Tel (800) 645-0267 SIC 3561

PUTZMEISTER AMERICA INC p 1193
1733 90th St, Sturtevant WI 53177
Tel (262) 886-3200 SIC 3561

R G REZIN INC p 1202
1602 Rezin Rd, Tomah WI 54660
Tel (608) 372-5956
SIC 1623 3443 3613 3561 3523 3599

METSO MINERALS INDUSTRIES INC p 957
20965 Crossroads Cir, Waukesha WI 53186
Tel (262) 798-3994
SIC 3321 3069 3561 3535 3532

SIC 3562 Ball & Roller Bearings

NMB (USA) INC p 1045
9730 Independence Ave, Chatsworth CA 91311
Tel (818) 709-1770
SIC 3562 5063 5084 3728 5065

■ **KAMATICS CORP** p 801
1330 Blue Hills Ave, Bloomfield CT 06002
Tel (860) 243-9704
SIC 3451 3562 3724 3728

BARDEN CORP p 155
200 Park Ave, Danbury CT 06810
Tel (203) 744-2211
SIC 3562 3469 3842 3089 3399

FAG HOLDING CORP p 524
200 Park Ave, Danbury CT 06810
Tel (203) 790-5474 SIC 3562

▲ **RBC BEARINGS INC** p 1211
102 Willenbrock Rd Bldg B, Oxford CT 06478
Tel (203) 267-7001 SIC 3562

■ **ROLLER BEARING CO OF AMERICA INC** p 1247
102 Willenbrock Rd, Oxford CT 06478
Tel (203) 267-7001 SIC 3562

NAKANISHI MANUFACTURING CORP p 1006
1225 Voyles Rd, Winterville GA 30683
Tel (706) 353-0006 SIC 5085 3562

AMERICAN NTN BEARING MANUFACTURING CORP p 77
1525 Holmes Rd, Elgin IL 60123
Tel (847) 741-4545 SIC 3562

NTN-BOWER CORP p 1065
711 Bower Rd, Macomb IL 61455
Tel (309) 837-0440 SIC 3562

NTN USA CORP p 1065
1600 Bishop Ct, Mount Prospect IL 60056
Tel (847) 298-4652 SIC 5085 3562 3568

■ **MCGILL MANUFACTURING CO INC** p 929
2300 Evans Ave, Valparaiso IN 46383
Tel (219) 465-2200 SIC 3562

EMERSON POWER TRANSMISSION CORP p 492
7120 New Buffington Rd, Florence KY 41042
Tel (859) 342-7900
SIC 3429 3052 3568 3562 3566 3462

KAYDON CORP p 805
2723 S State St Ste 300, Ann Arbor MI 48104
Tel (734) 747-7025
SIC 3562 3569 3592 3053 3621 3679

NSK CORP p 1065
4200 Goss Rd, Ann Arbor MI 48105
Tel (734) 913-7500
SIC 3714 5013 3594 3568 3562

■ **MPB CORP** p 995
7 Optical Ave, Keene NH 03431
Tel (603) 352-0310 SIC 3562 6061

■ **TIMKEN US LLC** p 1455
336 Mechanic St, Lebanon NH 03766
Tel (603) 443-5217 SIC 3562

NEW HAMPSHIRE BALL BEARINGS INC p 1030
175 Jaffrey Rd, Peterborough NH 03458
Tel (603) 924-3311 SIC 3562

MRC BEARINGS INC p 996
1 Maroco St, Falconer NY 14733
Tel (716) 661-2600 SIC 3562

GENERAL BEARING CORP p 599
44 High St, West Nyack NY 10994
Tel (845) 358-6000 SIC 3562

KOYO BEARINGS NORTH AMERICA LLC p 828
4895 Dressler Rd Nw Ste B, Canton OH 44718
Tel (330) 994-0890 SIC 3562

▲ **TIMKEN CO** p 1454
4500 Mount Pleasant St Nw, North Canton OH 44720
Tel (234) 262-3000 SIC 3562

JTEKT NORTH AMERICA CORP p 796
29570 Clemens Rd, Westlake OH 44145
Tel (440) 835-1000 SIC 5085 3562

SKF USA INC p 1329
890 Forty Foot Rd, Lansdale PA 19446
Tel (267) 436-6000 SIC 3562 3053 3829

SCHAEFFLER GROUP USA INC p 1286
308 Springhill Farm Rd, Fort Mill SC 29715
Tel (803) 548-8500 SIC 3562

▲ **NN INC** p 1045
207 Mockingbird Ln Ste 10, Johnson City TN 37604
Tel (423) 743-9151 SIC 3562

■ **RBS GLOBAL INC** p 1211
4701 W Greenfield Ave, Milwaukee WI 53214
Tel (414) 643-3000
SIC 3562 3566 3568 3272 3261

SIC 3563 Air & Gas Compressors

QUINCY COMPRESSOR LLC p 1200
701 N Dobson Ave, Bay Minette AL 36507
Tel (251) 937-5900 SIC 3519 3563 3561

DANFOSS SCROLL TECHNOLOGIES LLC p 411
1 Scroll Dr, Arkadelphia AR 71923
Tel (870) 246-0700 SIC 3679 3563

KOBELCO COMPRESSORS AMERICA INC p 825
1450 W Rincon St, Corona CA 92880
Tel (951) 739-3030 SIC 1623 3563

SUNDYNE LLC p 1402
14845 W 64th Ave, Arvada CO 80007
Tel (303) 425-0800 SIC 3563 3561

GARDNER DENVER NASH LLC p 592
2 Trefoil Dr, Trumbull CT 06611
Tel (203) 459-3923
SIC 5084 3563 8711 3561

▲ **ROPER TECHNOLOGIES INC** p 1250
6901 Prof Pkwy E Ste 200, Sarasota FL 34240
Tel (941) 556-2601
SIC 3823 3563 3491 3826 3829

▲ **IDEX CORP** p 729
1925 W Field Ct Ste 200, Lake Forest IL 60045
Tel (847) 498-7070 SIC 3561 3563 3594

MAT HOLDINGS INC p 918
6700 Wildlife Way, Long Grove IL 60047
Tel (847) 821-9630 SIC 2842 3714 3563

MAT INDUSTRIES LLC p 918
6700 Wildlife Way, Long Grove IL 60047
Tel (847) 821-9630 SIC 3563

GARDNER DENVER HOLDINGS INC p 592
1800 Gardner Expy, Quincy IL 62305
Tel (217) 222-5400 SIC 3564 3563

■ **PRAXAIR SURFACE TECHNOLOGIES INC** p 1168
1500 Polco St, Indianapolis IN 46222
Tel (317) 240-2500 SIC 3479 3548 3563

SULLAIR LLC p 1397
3700 E Michigan Blvd, Michigan City IN 46360
Tel (219) 879-5451 SIC 3569 3563

■ **IOWA MOLD TOOLING CO INC** p 763
500 W Us Highway 18, Garner IA 50438
Tel (641) 923-3711 SIC 3531 3713 3563

▲ **BROOKS AUTOMATION INC** p 218
15 Elizabeth Dr, Chelmsford MA 01824
Tel (978) 262-2400
SIC 3559 3563 3823 7699

■ **GAST MANUFACTURING INC** p 593
2300 M 139, Benton Harbor MI 49022
Tel (269) 926-6171
SIC 3563 3594 3621 3566 3561

MICHIGAN AUTOMOTIVE COMPRESSOR INC p 960
2400 N Dearing Rd, Parma MI 49269
Tel (517) 622-7000
SIC 3585 3714 3568 3563

▲ **GRACO INC** p 628
88 11th Ave Ne, Minneapolis MN 55413
Tel (612) 623-6000
SIC 3561 3594 3563 3491 3823 3569

WAGNER HOLDINGS INC p 1571
1770 Fernbrook Ln N, Minneapolis MN 55447
Tel (763) 553-7000 SIC 3563 3559

■ **BHSF INC** p 180
1440 Kiewit Plz, Omaha NE 68131
Tel (402) 346-1400
SIC 3635 3563 2731 3715

INDEL INC p 736
10 Indel Ave, Rancocas NJ 08073
Tel (609) 267-9000
SIC 3567 3548 3822 3541 3563

■ **BREEZE-EASTERN LLC** p 209
35 Melanie Ln, Whippany NJ 07981
Tel (973) 602-1001 SIC 3728 3563 3531

▲ **GRAHAM CORP** p 629
20 Florence Ave, Batavia NY 14020
Tel (585) 343-2216 SIC 3563 3585 3443

DRESSER-RAND CO p 455
500 Paul Clark Dr, Olean NY 14760
Tel (716) 375-3000 SIC 3563 3511 3621

EDWARDS VACUUM LLC p 480
6416 Inducon Dr W, Sanborn NY 14132
Tel (800) 848-9800 SIC 3563

ATLAS COPCO COMPTEC LLC p 127
46 School Rd, Voorheesville NY 12186
Tel (518) 765-3344 SIC 3563

INGERSOLL-RAND CO p 742
800 Beaty St Ste B, Davidson NC 28036
Tel (704) 655-4000
SIC 3561 3429 3546 3563 3531

■ **TRANSDIGM INC** p 1471
4223 Monticello Blvd, Cleveland OH 44121
Tel (216) 706-2939
SIC 5088 3563 3625 3492 3691 3491

■ **CAMPBELL HAUSFELD LLC** p 245
100 Production Dr, Harrison OH 45030
Tel (513) 367-4811 SIC 3563 3546 3548

ARIEL CORP p 108
35 Blackjack Road Ext, Mount Vernon OH 43050
Tel (740) 397-0311 SIC 3563

▲ **NORDSON CORP** p 1048
28601 Clemens Rd, Westlake OH 44145
Tel (440) 892-1580 SIC 3563

A G EQUIPMENT CO p 5
3401 W Albany St, Broken Arrow OK 74012
Tel (918) 250-7386 SIC 3563 5084

FS-ELLIOTT CO LLC p 582
5710 Mellon Rd, Export PA 15632
Tel (724) 387-3200 SIC 3563

OERLIKON USA HOLDING INC p 1075
5700 Mellon Rd, Export PA 15632
Tel (303) 273-9700
SIC 3563 3823 3699 3479 3599 5084

ELLIOTT CO p 488
901 N 4th St, Jeannette PA 15644
Tel (724) 527-2811 SIC 3563 3511

ATLAS COPCO COMPRESSORS LLC p 127
1800 Overview Dr, Rock Hill SC 29730
Tel (803) 817-7000 SIC 3563 3999

■ **DEVILBISS AIR POWER CO** p 434
4825 Highway 45 N, Jackson TN 38305
Tel (800) 888-2468 SIC 3563 3621 3589

CAMERON INTERNATIONAL CORP p 245
4646 W Sam Houston Pkwy N, Houston TX 77041
Tel (713) 513-3300 SIC 3533 3563 3491

DRESSER-RAND GROUP INC p 455
10205 Westheimer Rd # 1000, Houston TX 77042
Tel (713) 354-6100 SIC 3563 3511

DRESSER-RAND LLC p 455
1200 W Sam Houston Pkwy N, Houston TX 77043
Tel (713) 354-6100 SIC 3563

ENERFLEX ENERGY SYSTEMS INC p 497
10815 Telge Rd, Houston TX 77095
Tel (281) 345-9300
SIC 3585 7623 7699 3563

ONESUBSEA LLC p 1088
4646 W Sam Houston Pkwy N, Houston TX 77041
Tel (713) 939-2211 SIC 3533 3563 3491

■ **SEC ENERGY PRODUCTS & SERVICES LP** p 1298
9523 Frbanks N Houston Rd, Houston TX 77064
Tel (281) 890-9977 SIC 3563

TEXAS AIRSYSTEMS LLC p 1442
6029 Campus Circle Dr W, Irving TX 75063
Tel (210) 499-0004 SIC 3563

■ **COMPRESSOR SYSTEMS INC** p 352
3809 S Fm 1788, Midland TX 79706
Tel (432) 563-1170 SIC 7359 7699 3563

▲ **NATURAL GAS SERVICES GROUP INC** p 1018
508 W Wall St Ste 550, Midland TX 79701
Tel (432) 262-2700 SIC 7353 3563

WARREN EQUIPMENT CO p 1577
10325 Younger Rd, Midland TX 79706
Tel (432) 571-8462
SIC 5082 5084 7699 3563 7359

PACKAGING SERVICE CO INC p 1107
1904 Mykawa Rd, Pearland TX 77581
Tel (281) 485-1458 SIC 3563

SANDEN INTERNATIONAL (USA) INC p 1278
601 Sanden Blvd, Wylie TX 75098
Tel (972) 442-8941
SIC 3714 1711 3585 3563

■ **AUTOLIV ASP INC** p 134
3350 Airport Rd, Ogden UT 84405
Tel (801) 625-4800 SIC 3714 3563

BUSCH CONSOLIDATED INC p 229
516 Viking Dr, Virginia Beach VA 23452
Tel (757) 463-7800 SIC 5084 3563

GARDNER DENVER INC p 592
222 E Erie St Ste 500, Milwaukee WI 53202
Tel (414) 212-4700 SIC 3564 3561 3563

GARDNER DENVER THOMAS INC p 592
1419 Illinois Ave, Sheboygan WI 53081
Tel (920) 457-4891 SIC 3563

SIC 3564 Blowers & Fans

PROCESS EQUIPMENT INC p 1179
2770 Welborn St, Pelham AL 35124
Tel (205) 663-5330
SIC 3564 3535 3441 3443

RESOURCE COLLECTION INC p 1227
3771 W 242nd St Ste 205, Torrance CA 90505
Tel (310) 219-3272
SIC 7349 7381 0782 3564

AD CORP p 21
1551 Wewatta St, Denver CO 80202
Tel (303) 744-1911
SIC 3634 3564 3822 3089 3714 3312

EBM-PAPST INC p 474
100 Hyde Rd, Farmington CT 06032
Tel (860) 674-1515 SIC 5084 3564

▲ **LYDALL INC** p 887
1 Colonial Rd, Manchester CT 06042
Tel (860) 646-1233
SIC 2297 3053 2899 2631 3714 3564

■ **ALSTOM POWER INC** p 61
200 Great Pond Dr, Windsor CT 06095
Tel (866) 257-8664
SIC 3443 3564 3621 3823 8711

■ **OIL-DRI CORP OF GEORGIA** p 1079
28990 Hwy 3, Ochlocknee GA 31773
Tel (229) 574-5131 SIC 3295 3564 2842

REVCOR INC p 1229
251 Edwards Ave, Carpentersville IL 60110
Tel (847) 428-4411 SIC 3564 3089

HENRY TECHNOLOGIES INC p 684
701 S Main St, Chatham IL 62629
Tel (217) 483-2406
SIC 3491 3585 3567 3564 3545 3494

CHICAGO BLOWER CORP p 297
1675 Glen Ellyn Rd, Glendale Heights IL 60139
Tel (630) 858-2600 SIC 3564 1711

■ FILTERTEK INC p 542
11411 Price Rd, Hebron IL 60034
Tel (815) 648-2410 SIC 3089 3564

FILTRATION GROUP CORP p 542
912 E Washington St Ste 1, Joliet IL 60433
Tel (815) 726-4600 SIC 3564

FILTRATION GROUP LLC p 542
912 E Washington St Ste 1, Joliet IL 60433
Tel (815) 726-4600 SIC 3564

▲ MFRI INC p 958
6410 W Howard St, Niles IL 60714
Tel (847) 966-1000 SIC 3677 3564 3569

GARDNER DENVER HOLDINGS INC p 592
1800 Gardner Expy, Quincy IL 62305
Tel (217) 222-5400 SIC 3564 3563

■ ECLIPSE INC p 475
1665 Elmwood Rd, Rockford IL 61103
Tel (815) 877-3031
SIC 3564 3433 3822 3823 3443 3494

NEW YORK BLOWER CO p 1034
7660 S Quincy St, Willowbrook IL 60527
Tel (630) 794-5700 SIC 3564

■ CLARCOR AIR FILTRATION PRODUCTS INC p 321
100 River Ridge Cir, Jeffersonville IN 47130
Tel (502) 969-2304 SIC 3564

■ PUROLATOR PRODUCTS AIR FILTRATION CO p 1192
100 River Ridge Cir, Jeffersonville IN 47130
Tel (866) 925-2247 SIC 3564 3433

AIRTEX MANUFACTURING LLLP p 40
32050 W 83rd St, De Soto KS 66018
Tel (913) 583-3181
SIC 3585 5075 3564 3433

■ BHA ALTAIR LLC p 180
11501 Outlook St Ste 100, Overland Park KS 66211
Tel (816) 356-8400 SIC 3564

MINOVA HOLDING INC p 974
150 Carley Ct, Georgetown KY 40324
Tel (502) 863-6800 SIC 2821 3564 2439

ORICA GROUND SUPPORT INC p 1094
150 Summer Ct, Georgetown KY 40324
Tel (502) 863-6800
SIC 5082 3564 2439 7699

AAF-MCQUAY GROUP INC p 8
9920 Corporate Campus Dr # 2200, Louisville KY 40223
Tel (502) 637-0111
SIC 5075 3585 3564 7623

AMERICAN AIR FILTER CO INC p 67
9920 Corporate Campus Dr # 2200, Louisville KY 40223
Tel (502) 637-0011 SIC 3564

MUNTERS CORP p 1001
79 Monroe St, Amesbury MA 01913
Tel (978) 241-1100
SIC 3585 3822 3569 3564

KOCH MEMBRANE SYSTEMS INC p 825
850 Main St, Wilmington MA 01887
Tel (978) 694-7000 SIC 3569 3564

RILEY POWER INC p 1235
5 Neponset St, Worcester MA 01606
Tel (508) 852-7100
SIC 3569 3443 3433 1711 3564 3511

BESSER CO p 177
801 Johnson St, Alpena MI 49707
Tel (989) 354-4508
SIC 3531 3559 3564 3443

■ GELMAN SCIENCES INC p 598
674 S Wagner Rd, Ann Arbor MI 48103
Tel (734) 665-0651
SIC 3821 3569 3564 3841 3845 3699

▲ DONALDSON CO INC p 450
1400 W 94th St, Minneapolis MN 55431
Tel (952) 887-3131
SIC 3599 3569 3714 3564

TWIN CITY FAN COMPANIES LTD p 1495
5959 Trenton Ln N, Minneapolis MN 55442
Tel (763) 551-7500 SIC 3564 5084

BUHLER INC p 224
13105 12th Ave N, Plymouth MN 55441
Tel (763) 847-9900
SIC 3556 3542 3535 3564

LOREN COOK CO p 878
2015 E Dale St, Springfield MO 65803
Tel (417) 869-6474 SIC 3564

■ BALDWIN FILTERS INC p 147
4400 Highway 30 E, Kearney NE 68847
Tel (800) 822-5394 SIC 3714 3564

CAMFIL USA INC p 245
1 N Corporate Dr, Riverdale NJ 07457
Tel (973) 616-7300 SIC 3564 3569

HAMON CORP p 656
58 E Main St, Somerville NJ 08876
Tel (908) 333-2000
SIC 1629 3564 3499 5084

■ HOWDEN NORTH AMERICA INC p 713
2475 George Urban Blvd # 100, Depew NY 14043
Tel (803) 741-2700 SIC 3564 3568

HILLIARD CORP p 693
100 W 4th St, Elmira NY 14901
Tel (607) 733-7121 SIC 3564 3569 3823

▲ STANDARD MOTOR PRODUCTS INC p 1376
3718 Northern Blvd # 600, Long Island City NY 11101
Tel (718) 392-0200
SIC 3714 3694 3585 3564 3052

DUCON TECHNOLOGIES INC p 459
5 Penn Plz Ste 2403, New York NY 10001
Tel (631) 694-1700 SIC 3537 3564

■ ROTRON INC p 1252
55 Hasbrouck Ln, Woodstock NY 12498
Tel (845) 679-2401 SIC 3564

■ BWXT INVESTMENT CO p 231
11525 N Community House, Charlotte NC 28277
Tel (704) 625-4900
SIC 3511 3443 3564 1629 1541 7699

ENVIRONMENTAL FILTRATION TECHNOLOGIES LLC p 503
4404a Chesapeake Dr, Charlotte NC 28216
Tel (704) 399-7441
SIC 3569 5085 3564 3444 3469 3561

■ BAHNSON HOLDINGS INC p 145
4731 Commercial Park Ct, Clemmons NC 27012
Tel (336) 760-3111
SIC 8711 1711 3585 3564

FLANDERS CORP p 554
531 Flanders Filter Rd, Washington NC 27889
Tel (252) 946-8081 SIC 3564

PRECISIONAIRE INC p 1169
531 Flanders Filter Rd, Washington NC 27889
Tel (252) 946-8081 SIC 3564

▲ CECO ENVIRONMENTAL CORP p 272
4625 Red Bank Rd Ste 200, Cincinnati OH 45227
Tel (513) 458-2600 SIC 3564

■ CECO GROUP INC p 272
4625 Red Bank Rd Ste 200, Cincinnati OH 45227
Tel (513) 458-2600
SIC 8711 3564 8734 3443 3444 1761

MORRISON PRODUCTS INC p 990
16900 S Waterloo Rd, Cleveland OH 44110
Tel (216) 486-4000 SIC 3564

AD INDUSTRIES INC p 21
6450 Poe Ave Ste 109, Dayton OH 45414
Tel (303) 744-1911
SIC 3634 3564 3535 3714 3088 3089

LAU INDUSTRIES INC p 846
4509 Springfield St, Dayton OH 45431
Tel (937) 476-6500 SIC 3564

HBD INDUSTRIES INC p 671
5200 Upper Metro Pl # 110, Dublin OH 43017
Tel (614) 526-7000
SIC 3052 3621 3566 3564 3812

TOSOH AMERICA INC p 1462
3600 Gantz Rd, Grove City OH 43123
Tel (614) 539-8622
SIC 5169 3564 5047 5052

■ DIAMOND POWER INTERNATIONAL INC p 437
2600 E Main St, Lancaster OH 43130
Tel (740) 687-6500 SIC 3564

ACME ENGINEERING AND MANUFACTURING CORP p 18
1820 N York St, Muskogee OK 74403
Tel (918) 682-7791 SIC 3564

■ CENTRIA INC p 281
1005 Beaver Grade Rd # 2, Coraopolis PA 15108
Tel (412) 299-8000
SIC 3444 1761 3564 3449

RAF INDUSTRIES INC p 1205
165 Township Line Rd # 2100, Jenkintown PA 19046
Tel (215) 572-0738 SIC 8742 3564

■ CLARK FILTER INC p 322
3649 Hempland Rd, Lancaster PA 17601
Tel (717) 285-5941 SIC 3564 3714

▲ CALGON CARBON CORP p 238
3000 Gsk Dr, Moon Township PA 15108
Tel (412) 787-6700
SIC 2819 7699 3589 3564

RESPIRONICS INC p 1227
1010 Murry Ridge Ln, Murrysville PA 15668
Tel (724) 387-5200
SIC 3641 3845 3841 3564 8351

■ MET-PRO TECHNOLOGIES LLC p 952
460 E Swedesford Rd # 2030, Wayne PA 19087
Tel (215) 717-7909 SIC 3564

LASKO PRODUCTS INC p 846
820 Lincoln Ave, West Chester PA 19380
Tel (610) 692-7400 SIC 4789 3585 3564

ORECK CORP p 1093
1400 Salem Rd, Cookeville TN 38506
Tel (800) 219-2044
SIC 3589 3564 5064 5087

▲ CLARCOR INC p 321
840 Crescent Centre Dr # 600, Franklin TN 37067
Tel (615) 771-3100
SIC 3714 3599 3564 3569 3411 3089

TPI CORP p 1467
114 Roscoe Fitz Rd, Johnson City TN 37615
Tel (800) 682-3398 SIC 3567 3564

AIR LIQUIDE ELECTRONICS US LP p 39
9101 Lyndon B Johnson Fwy # 800, Dallas TX 75243
Tel (972) 301-5200
SIC 2813 3564 8631 2819

FEDDERS CORP p 533
13455 Noel Rd Ste 2200, Dallas TX 75240
Tel (604) 908-8686
SIC 3585 3674 3634 3564

JONES INDUSTRIAL HOLDINGS INC p 792
806 Seaco Ct, Deer Park TX 77536
Tel (281) 479-6000 SIC 3564

GOODMAN GLOBAL HOLDINGS INC p 624
5151 San Felipe St # 500, Houston TX 77056
Tel (713) 861-2500 SIC 3585 3564

GOODMAN GLOBAL INC p 624
5151 San Felipe St # 500, Houston TX 77056
Tel (713) 861-2500 SIC 3585 3564

PSP INDUSTRIES INC p 1188
9885 Doerr Ln, Schertz TX 78154
Tel (210) 651-9595
SIC 3533 3531 3564 3532 3559

TRI-DIM FILTER CORP p 1477
93 Industrial Dr, Louisa VA 23093
Tel (540) 967-2600 SIC 3564

RESEARCH PRODUCTS CORP p 1226
1015 E Washington Ave, Madison WI 53703
Tel (608) 257-8801 SIC 5075 3564 3569

GARDNER DENVER INC p 592
222 E Erie St Ste 500, Milwaukee WI 53202
Tel (414) 212-4700 SIC 3564 3561 3563

GREENHECK FAN CORP p 638
1100 Greenheck Dr, Schofield WI 54476
Tel (715) 359-6171 SIC 3564 3444

SIC 3565 Packaging Machinery

■ MTS MEDICATION TECHNOLOGIES INC p 998
2003 Gandy Blvd N Ste 800, Saint Petersburg FL 33702
Tel (727) 576-6311 SIC 3565 3089

ROBERT BOSCH LLC p 1241
2800 S 25th Ave, Broadview IL 60155
Tel (248) 876-1000
SIC 3714 3694 5013 5064 3565 3541

■ BPREX HEALTHCARE PACKAGING INC p 206
600 Deerfield Pkwy, Buffalo Grove IL 60089
Tel (800) 537-0178 SIC 3565

■ TEGRANT ALLOYD BRANDS INC p 1432
1401 Pleasant St, Dekalb IL 60115
Tel (815) 756-8451 SIC 3089 3565

■ TEGRANT HOLDING CORP p 1433
1401 Pleasant St, Dekalb IL 60115
Tel (815) 756-8451 SIC 3089 3565

■ DOVER PRINTING & IDENTIFICATION INC p 453
3005 Highland Pkwy # 200, Downers Grove IL 60515
Tel (630) 541-1540
SIC 3556 3565 3593 7699

■ SIGNODE CORP p 1322
3600 W Lake Ave, Glenview IL 60026
Tel (800) 527-1499 SIC 3565 3499

CLOSURE SYSTEMS INTERNATIONAL INC p 327
7702 Woodland Dr Ste 200, Indianapolis IN 46278
Tel (317) 390-5000 SIC 3334 3565

HUHTAMAKI INC p 718
9201 Packaging Dr, De Soto KS 66018
Tel (913) 583-3025 SIC 2656 3565

PRO MACH INC p 1178
50 E Rivercntr Blvd 180 Ste 1800, Covington KY 41011
Tel (513) 831-8778 SIC 3565

RA JONES & CO p 1203
2701 Crescent Springs Rd, Covington KY 41017
Tel (859) 341-0400 SIC 3565 3823

LANTECH.COM LLC p 844
11000 Bluegrass Pkwy, Louisville KY 40299
Tel (502) 267-4200 SIC 3565

SPEEDLINE TECHNOLOGIES INC p 1358
16 Forge Pkwy, Franklin MA 02038
Tel (508) 541-4867 SIC 3565 3569

CAMACO LLC p 243
37000 W 12 Mile Rd, Farmington Hills MI 48331
Tel (248) 442-6800 SIC 3565 3499

NYX LLC p 1069
36111 Schoolcraft Rd, Livonia MI 48150
Tel (734) 462-2385
SIC 3089 3714 3565 2671

DOUGLAS MACHINE INC p 452
3404 Iowa St, Alexandria MN 56308
Tel (320) 763-6587 SIC 3565

FAST GLOBAL SOLUTIONS INC p 531
20631 State Highway 55, Glenwood MN 56334
Tel (320) 634-5126 SIC 3537 3565 3523

RYT-WAY ACQUISITION CO LLC p 1261
21850 Grenada Ave, Lakeville MN 55044
Tel (952) 469-1417 SIC 7389 2023 3565

RYT-WAY MIDCO LLC p 1261
21850 Grenada Ave, Lakeville MN 55044
Tel (952) 469-1417 SIC 7389 2023 3565

THIELE TECHNOLOGIES INC p 1448
315 27th Ave Ne, Minneapolis MN 55418
Tel (612) 782-1200 SIC 3565

COMPUTYPE INC p 353
2285 County Road C W, Saint Paul MN 55113
Tel (651) 633-0633
SIC 2759 2672 2679 3565 3577 2671

ANDY MARK INC p 91
18081 Chstrfld Aprt Rd, Chesterfield MO 63005
Tel (636) 532-4433 SIC 3555 3565

VC999 PACKAGING SYSTEMS INC p 1545
419 E 11th Ave, Kansas City MO 64116
Tel (816) 472-8999 SIC 5084 3565

BARRY-WEHMILLER COMPANIES INC p 157
8020 Forsyth Blvd, Saint Louis MO 63105
Tel (314) 862-8000
SIC 3565 3535 3554 8711

BARRY-WEHMILLER GROUP INC p 157
8020 Forsyth Blvd, Saint Louis MO 63105
Tel (314) 862-8000
SIC 3565 3535 3554 8711

QUALITY PACKAGING SPECIALISTS INTERNATIONAL LLC p 1197
5 Cooper St, Burlington NJ 08016
Tel (609) 239-0503 SIC 7389 3565

UNIVERSAL PACKAGING SYSTEMS INC p 1517
6080 Jericho Tpke, Commack NY 11725
Tel (631) 543-2277
SIC 2844 7389 3565 2671

INTRAPAC (PLATTSBURGH) INC p 760
4 Plant St, Plattsburgh NY 12901
Tel (518) 561-2030 SIC 5199 3565

PNEUMATIC SCALE CORP p 1158
10 Ascot Pkwy, Cuyahoga Falls OH 44223
Tel (330) 923-0491 SIC 3565 3569 3535

MORGAN ADHESIVES CO LLC p 988
4560 Darrow Rd, Stow OH 44224
Tel (330) 688-1111
SIC 2891 3565 2672 2823

AUTOMATED PACKAGING SYSTEMS INC p 134
10175 Philipp Pkwy, Streetsboro OH 44241
Tel (330) 528-2000 SIC 3081 3565

MILLWOOD INC p 971
3708 International Blvd, Vienna OH 44473
Tel (330) 393-4400 SIC 3565 4731

MAXCESS INTERNATIONAL CORP p 922
222 W Memorial Rd, Oklahoma City OK 73114
Tel (405) 755-1600 SIC 3554 3565 6719

MAXCESS INTERNATIONAL HOLDING CORP p 922
222 W Memorial Rd, Oklahoma City OK 73114
Tel (405) 755-1600 SIC 3554 3565 6719

TELSTAR NORTH AMERICA INC p 1435
1504 Grundy Ln, Bristol PA 19007
Tel (215) 826-0770 SIC 3565

ARDAGH METAL PACKAGING USA INC p 106
600 N Bell Ave Ste 200, Carnegie PA 15106
Tel (412) 923-1080 SIC 3565

WINPAK PORTION PACKAGING INC p 1617
828a Newtown Yardley Rd # 101, Newtown PA 18940
Tel (267) 685-8200 SIC 3565 2671

FRES-CO SYSTEMS USA INC p 578
3005 State Rd, Telford PA 18969
Tel (215) 721-4600 SIC 5084 3565 2891

TETRA PAK INC p 1441
3300 Airport Rd, Denton TX 76207
Tel (940) 565-8800 SIC 2671 3565 5084

■ BELVAC PRODUCTION MACHINERY INC p 171
237 Graves Mill Rd, Lynchburg VA 24502
Tel (434) 239-0358 SIC 3565

VOLM COMPANIES INC p 1564
1804 Edison St, Antigo WI 54409
Tel (715) 627-4826 SIC 5113 5199 3565

CG BRETTING MANUFACTURING CO INC p 285
3401 Lake Park Rd, Ashland WI 54806
Tel (715) 682-5231
SIC 3554 3599 3565 3555

KRONES INC p 830
9600 S 58th St, Franklin WI 53132
Tel (414) 409-4000 SIC 3565

SCHREIBER FOODS INC p 1290
400 N Washington St, Green Bay WI 54301
Tel (920) 437-7601 SIC 2022 3556 3565

BOSCH PACKAGING TECHNOLOGY INC p 202
869 S Knowles Ave, New Richmond WI 54017
Tel (715) 246-6511 SIC 3565

■ BEMIS HEALTHCARE PACKAGING INC p 171
3500 N Main St, Oshkosh WI 54901
Tel (920) 527-7464 SIC 2671 3565

SIC 3566 Speed Changers, Drives & Gears

BALDOR ELECTRIC CO p 147
5711 Rs Boreham Jr St, Fort Smith AR 72901
Tel (479) 646-4711
SIC 3621 3566 3463 3366

THUNDER BASIN CORP p 1451
103 Foulk Rd Ste 151, Wilmington DE 19803
Tel (610) 962-3770 SIC 3566 2298

HABASIT AMERICA INC p 651
805 Satellite Blvd Nw, Suwanee GA 30024
Tel (678) 288-3600 SIC 3566

KINETEK INC p 819
25 Northwest Point Blvd # 900, Elk Grove Village IL 60007
Tel (224) 265-1290 SIC 3621 3566 3613

YASKAWA AMERICA INC p 1635
2121 Norman Dr, Waukegan IL 60085
Tel (847) 887-7000
SIC 3621 7694 5063 3566 3823 3625

EMERSON POWER TRANSMISSION CORP p 492
7120 New Buffington Rd, Florence KY 41042
Tel (859) 342-7900
SIC 3429 3052 3568 3562 3566 3462

■ GAST MANUFACTURING INC p 593
2300 M 139, Benton Harbor MI 49022
Tel (269) 926-6171
SIC 3563 3594 3621 3566 3561

COLUMBIA GEAR CORP p 340
530 County Road 50, Avon MN 56310
Tel (440) 838-4700 SIC 3566 3462

FESTO CORP p 539
395 Moreland Rd, Hauppauge NY 11788
Tel (800) 993-3786
SIC 5085 3593 3566 3492

GLEASON WORKS p 614
1000 University Ave, Rochester NY 14607
Tel (585) 473-1000
SIC 3714 3728 3566 3541 3829 3469

INDUSTRIAL MANUFACTURING CO LLC p 740
8223 Brecksville Rd Ste 1, Brecksville OH 44141
Tel (440) 838-4700 SIC 2542 3728 3566

WASSERSTROM CO p 1580
477 S Front St, Columbus OH 43215
Tel (614) 737-8472
SIC 5087 3566 5021 5046 5112 5719

HBD INDUSTRIES INC p 671
5200 Upper Metro Pl # 110, Dublin OH 43017
Tel (614) 526-7000
SIC 3052 3621 3566 3564 3812

PEERLESS-WINSMITH INC p 1127
5200 Upper Metro Pl # 110, Dublin OH 43017
Tel (614) 526-7000
SIC 3621 3566 3634 3812 3559

■ AMETEK TECHNICAL & INDUSTRIAL PRODUCTS INC p 84
100 E Erie St Ste 130, Kent OH 44240
Tel (330) 677-3754 SIC 3621 5063 3566

LUK CLUTCH SYSTEMS LLC p 884
3401 Old Airport Rd, Wooster OH 44691
Tel (330) 264-4383 SIC 3714 3568 3566

LUK TRANSMISSION SYSTEMS LLC p 885
3401 Old Airport Rd, Wooster OH 44691
Tel (330) 264-4383 SIC 3714 3566

FORGE INDUSTRIES INC p 567
4450 Market St, Youngstown OH 44512
Tel (330) 782-8301
SIC 5085 3566 3599 3531 6411 7699

■ TULSA WINCH INC p 1491
11135 S James Ave, Jenks OK 74037
Tel (918) 298-8300 SIC 5084 3566 3531

SEW-EURODRIVE INC p 1309
1295 Old Spartanburg Hwy, Lyman SC 29365
Tel (864) 439-7537 SIC 3566

MARTIN SPROCKET & GEAR INC p 913
3100 Sprocket Dr, Arlington TX 76015
Tel (817) 258-3000
SIC 3566 3568 3535 3321 3462 3429

▲ REGAL BELOIT CORP p 1218
200 State St, Beloit WI 53511
Tel (608) 364-8800 SIC 3621 3714 3566

■ RBS GLOBAL INC p 1211
4701 W Greenfield Ave, Milwaukee WI 53214
Tel (414) 643-3000
SIC 3562 3566 3568 3272 3261

■ REXNORD INDUSTRIES LLC p 1230
247 W Freshwater Way # 200, Milwaukee WI 53204
Tel (414) 643-3000
SIC 3568 3566 3625 3714

■ REXNORD LLC p 1230
3001 W Canal St, Milwaukee WI 53208
Tel (414) 342-3131 SIC 3566 3325 3599

■ REXNORD-ZURN HOLDINGS INC p 1230
4701 W Greenfield Ave, Milwaukee WI 53214
Tel (414) 643-3000
SIC 3568 3566 3625 3714

▲ ROCKWELL AUTOMATION INC p 1245
1201 S 2nd St, Milwaukee WI 53204
Tel (414) 382-2000
SIC 3625 3621 3566 3661

■ WAUKESHA BEARINGS CORP p 1583
W231n2811 Roundy Cir E, Pewaukee WI 53072
Tel (262) 506-3000 SIC 3568 3566

▲ TWIN DISC INC p 1495
1328 Racine St, Racine WI 53403
Tel (262) 638-4000 SIC 3568 3566 3714

SIC 3567 Indl Process Furnaces & Ovens

HKF INC p 697
5983 Smithway St, Commerce CA 90040
Tel (323) 225-1318
SIC 5075 3873 5064 3567 3643

SEASONS-4 INC p 1297
4500 Industrial Access Rd, Douglasville GA 30134
Tel (770) 489-0716 SIC 3585 3567

HENRY TECHNOLOGIES INC p 684
701 S Main St, Chatham IL 62629
Tel (217) 483-2406
SIC 3491 3585 3567 3564 3545 3494

TEMPCO ELECTRIC HEATER CORP p 1436
607 N Central Ave, Wood Dale IL 60191
Tel (630) 350-2252 SIC 3567 3369 3829

TEMPLETON COAL CO INC p 1436
701 Wabash Ave Ste 501, Terre Haute IN 47807
Tel (812) 232-7037
SIC 5074 3567 3961 5049 3089

HEATRON INC p 679
3000 Wilson Ave, Leavenworth KS 66048
Tel (913) 651-4420 SIC 3567 3634

■ HUTCHINSON FTS INC p 722
1060 Centre Rd, Auburn Hills MI 48326
Tel (248) 589-7710
SIC 3714 3061 3567 3492 3443 3429

BELCO INDUSTRIES INC p 169
9138 W Belding Rd, Belding MI 48809
Tel (616) 794-0410
SIC 3567 5084 3541 3535 3444

DURR SYSTEMS INC p 463
26801 Northwestern Hwy, Southfield MI 48033
Tel (248) 450-2000 SIC 3559 3567

DURR—INC p 463
26801 Northwestern Hwy, Southfield MI 48033
Tel (734) 459-6800 SIC 3559 3567

■ VERDUN LLC p 1549
8860 207th St W, Lakeville MN 55044
Tel (952) 469-5424 SIC 3567

UPONOR INC p 1529
5925 148th St W, Saint Paul MN 55124
Tel (952) 891-2000 SIC 3084 3567 3433

STAHL SPECIALTY CO p 1374
111 E Pacific St, Kingsville MO 64061
Tel (816) 597-3322
SIC 5051 3544 3365 3567 3369

NORTEK GLOBAL HVAC LLC p 1049
8000 Phoenix Pkwy, O Fallon MO 63368
Tel (636) 561-7300 SIC 3585 3567 3433

PAULO PRODUCTS CO p 1121
5711 W Park Ave, Saint Louis MO 63110
Tel (314) 647-7500
SIC 3471 3398 8734 3567

GTAT CORP p 644
243 Daniel Webster Hwy, Merrimack NH 03054
Tel (603) 883-5200 SIC 3674 3567

INDEL INC p 736
10 Indel Ave, Rancocas NJ 08073
Tel (609) 267-9000
SIC 3567 3548 3822 3541 3563

BUHLER AEROGLIDE CORP p 224
100 Aeroglide Dr, Cary NC 27511
Tel (919) 278-2925 SIC 3556 3585 3567

FIVES NORTH AMERICAN COMBUSTION INC p 553
4455 E 71st St, Cleveland OH 44105
Tel (216) 271-6000 SIC 3567

▲ PARK-OHIO HOLDINGS CORP p 1116
6065 Parkland Blvd Ste 1, Cleveland OH 44124
Tel (440) 947-2000
SIC 3462 3069 3567 3363 3631 3524

■ PARK-OHIO INDUSTRIES INC p 1116
6065 Parkland Blvd Ste 1, Cleveland OH 44124
Tel (440) 947-2000
SIC 3462 3069 3567 3363 3524

WARREN STEEL HOLDINGS LLC p 1577
4000 Mahoning Ave Nw, Warren OH 44483
Tel (330) 847-0487 SIC 3567

▲ LSB INDUSTRIES INC p 883
16 S Pennsylvania Ave, Oklahoma City OK 73107
Tel (405) 235-4546
SIC 3822 3585 3567 2873

LINDE ENGINEERING NORTH AMERICA INC p 868
6100 S Yale Ave Ste 1200, Tulsa OK 74136
Tel (918) 477-1200 SIC 3567 8711

GASBARRE PRODUCTS INC p 593
590 Division St, Du Bois PA 15801
Tel (814) 371-3015 SIC 3542 3567 3544

CHROMALOX INC p 304
103 Gamma Dr Ste 2, Pittsburgh PA 15238
Tel (412) 967-3800 SIC 3567

TPI CORP p 1467
114 Roscoe Fitz Rd, Johnson City TN 37615
Tel (800) 682-3398 SIC 3567 3564

THOMAS & BETTS CORP p 1448
8155 T&B Blvd, Memphis TN 38125
Tel (901) 252-5000 SIC 3643 3312 3567

BACKER EHP INC p 143
4700 John Bragg Hwy, Murfreesboro TN 37127
Tel (615) 907-6900 SIC 3567 3585

■ MEGTEC SYSTEMS INC p 940
830 Prosper St, De Pere WI 54115
Tel (920) 336-5715
SIC 3822 3555 3567 3823

INFRATROL MANUFACTURING CORP p 742
2500 S 162nd St, New Berlin WI 53151
Tel (262) 797-8140 SIC 3567

SIC 3568 Mechanical Power Transmission Eqpt, NEC

■ SARGENT AEROSPACE & DEFENSE LLC p 1282
5675 W Burlingame Rd, Tucson AZ 85743
Tel (520) 744-1000
SIC 3728 3724 3568 3492

MPG GEAR TECHNOLOGIES p 995
7800 Ball Rd, Fort Smith AR 72908
Tel (479) 646-1662 SIC 3714 3568 3399

HYSPAN PRECISION PRODUCTS INC p 724
1685 Brandywine Ave, Chula Vista CA 91911
Tel (619) 421-1355 SIC 3568 3496 3441

GATES CORP p 593
1551 Wewatta St, Denver CO 80202
Tel (303) 744-1911
SIC 3052 3089 3568 5084 4789

OMAHA HOLDINGS LLC p 1083
1551 Wewatta St, Denver CO 80202
Tel (303) 744-1911
SIC 3052 3089 3568 5084 4789

OMAHA INTERMEDIATE HOLDING LLC p 1083
1551 Wewatta St, Denver CO 80202
Tel (303) 744-1911
SIC 3052 3089 3568 5084 4789

■ DOVER ENGINEERED SYSTEMS INC p 453
3005 Highland Pkwy # 200, Downers Grove IL 60515
Tel (630) 743-2505
SIC 3568 3443 3441 3561 3491 3492

AURORA BEARING CO p 131
901 Aucutt Rd, Montgomery IL 60538
Tel (630) 897-8941 SIC 3568

NTN USA CORP p 1065
1600 Bishop Ct, Mount Prospect IL 60056
Tel (847) 298-4652 SIC 5085 3562 3568

DEUBLIN CO p 433
2050 Norman Dr, Waukegan IL 60085
Tel (847) 689-8600
SIC 3498 3492 3568 3494

US TSUBAKI HOLDINGS INC p 1533
301 E Marquardt Dr, Wheeling IL 60090
Tel (847) 459-9500 SIC 5085 3568

US TSUBAKI POWER TRANSMISSION LLC p 1533
301 E Marquardt Dr, Wheeling IL 60090
Tel (847) 459-9500
SIC 3568 5085 5063 3714 3462 3325

NTN DRIVESHAFT INC p 1065
8251 S International Dr, Columbus IN 47201
Tel (812) 342-5414 SIC 3568

EMERSON POWER TRANSMISSION CORP p 492
7120 New Buffington Rd, Florence KY 41042
Tel (859) 342-7900
SIC 3429 3052 3568 3562 3566 3462

UNIVANCE INC p 1516
3400 Corporate Dr, Winchester KY 40391
Tel (859) 737-2306 SIC 3568 3714 5012

▲ ALTRA INDUSTRIAL MOTION CORP p 62
300 Granite St Ste 201, Braintree MA 02184
Tel (781) 917-0600
SIC 3568 5085 3542 3625

NSK CORP p 1065
4200 Goss Rd, Ann Arbor MI 48105
Tel (734) 913-7500
SIC 3714 5013 3594 3568 3562

GKN SINTER METALS LLC p 613
2200 N Opdyke Rd, Auburn Hills MI 48326
Tel (248) 296-7832
SIC 3714 3568 3369 3366

NEAPCO HOLDINGS LLC p 1023
6735 Haggerty Rd, Belleville MI 48111
Tel (734) 447-1380
SIC 3568 3714 6719 6799

ENGINEERED MACHINED PRODUCTS INC p 499
3111 N 28th St, Escanaba MI 49829
Tel (906) 786-8404
SIC 3519 3714 3568 3599 3561

MELLING TOOL CO p 941
2620 Saradan Dr, Jackson MI 49202
Tel (517) 787-8172
SIC 3451 3714 3625 3568 3561 3494

SAF-HOLLAND INC p 1265
1950 Industrial Blvd, Muskegon MI 49442
Tel (231) 773-3271
SIC 3714 3715 3568 3537 3452

MICHIGAN AUTOMOTIVE COMPRESSOR INC p 960
2400 N Dearing Rd, Parma MI 49269
Tel (517) 622-7000
SIC 3585 3714 3568 3563

DAYCO PRODUCTS LLC p 417
1650 Research Dr Ste 200, Troy MI 48083
Tel (248) 404-6500 SIC 3568

FORCE AMERICA INC p 565
501 Cliff Rd E Ste 100, Burnsville MN 55337
Tel (952) 707-1300 SIC 5084 3568

EATON HYDRAULICS LLC p 473
14615 Lone Oak Rd, Eden Prairie MN 55344
Tel (952) 937-9800
SIC 3089 3052 3568 3492 3594 3728

■ BW ELLIOTT MANUFACTURING CO LLC p 230
11 Beckwith Ave, Binghamton NY 13901
Tel (607) 772-0404 SIC 3568 3492 3531

■ HOWDEN NORTH AMERICA INC p 713
2475 George Urban Blvd # 100, Depew NY 14043
Tel (803) 741-2700 SIC 3564 3568

■ BORGWARNER MORSETEC INC p 201
800 Warren Rd, Ithaca NY 14850
Tel (607) 257-6700 SIC 3714 3462 3568

COBHAM MANAGEMENT SERVICES INC p 332
10 Cobham Dr, Orchard Park NY 14127
Tel (716) 662-0006 SIC 3568

A J ROSE MFG CO p 5
38000 Chester Rd, Avon OH 44011
Tel (216) 631-4645 SIC 3465 3568 3469

XTEK INC p 1633
11451 Reading Rd, Cincinnati OH 45241
Tel (513) 733-7800
SIC 3568 3547 3398 3312

NIDEC MINSTER CORP p 1043
240 W 5th St, Minster OH 45865
Tel (419) 628-2331 SIC 3542 3568

LUK CLUTCH SYSTEMS LLC p 884
3401 Old Airport Rd, Wooster OH 44691
Tel (330) 264-4383 SIC 3714 3568 3566

BLOUNT INC p 190
4909 Se International Way, Portland OR 97222
Tel (503) 653-8881
SIC 3546 3568 7699 3495

NEAPCO COMPONENTS LLC p 1023
740 Queen St, Pottstown PA 19464
Tel (610) 323-6000 SIC 3714 3568

MARTIN SPROCKET & GEAR INC p 913
3100 Sprocket Dr, Arlington TX 76015
Tel (817) 258-3000
SIC 3566 3568 3535 3321 3462 3429

■ GE ENERGY MANUFACTURING INC p 596
1333 West Loop S Ste 700, Houston TX 77027
Tel (713) 803-0900 SIC 3621 3568 5084

▲ GLOBAL POWER EQUIPMENT GROUP INC p 617
400 Las Colinas Blvd E, Irving TX 75039
Tel (214) 574-2000 SIC 3568 1796 7699

SUMITOMO MACHINERY CORP OF AMERICA p 1398
4200 Holland Blvd, Chesapeake VA 23323
Tel (757) 485-3355 SIC 5063 3568

■ RBS GLOBAL INC p 1211
4701 W Greenfield Ave, Milwaukee WI 53214
Tel (414) 643-3000
SIC 3562 3566 3568 3272 3261

■ REXNORD INDUSTRIES LLC p 1230
247 W Freshwater Way # 200, Milwaukee WI 53204
Tel (414) 643-3000
SIC 3568 3566 3625 3714

■ REXNORD-ZURN HOLDINGS INC p 1230
4701 W Greenfield Ave, Milwaukee WI 53214
Tel (414) 643-3000
SIC 3568 3566 3625 3714

VENTUREDYNE LTD p 1548
600 College Ave, Pewaukee WI 53072
Tel (262) 691-9900
SIC 3568 3829 3826 3823 3625

■ WAUKESHA BEARINGS CORP p 1583
W231n2811 Roundy Cir E, Pewaukee WI 53072
Tel (262) 506-3000 SIC 3568 3566

▲ TWIN DISC INC p 1495
1328 Racine St, Racine WI 53403
Tel (262) 638-4000 SIC 3568 3566 3714

SIC 3569 Indl Machinery & Eqpt, NEC

▲ VERSUM MATERIALS INC p 1552
8555 S River Pkwy, Tempe AZ 85284
Tel (610) 481-6697 SIC 2842 2891 3569

CLAYTON MANUFACTURING CO p 323
17477 Hurley St, City Of Industry CA 91744
Tel (626) 443-9381 SIC 3569 3829 3511

■ DELTA DESIGN INC p 426
12367 Crosthwaite Cir, Poway CA 92064
Tel (858) 848-8000 SIC 3569 3825 3674

BAE SYSTEMS POWER INC p 144
5840 Dahlia St, Commerce City CO 80022
Tel (303) 287-7441
SIC 5084 3531 3999 3569

WG GLOBAL LLC p 1604
603 Park Point Dr Ste 200, Golden CO 80401
Tel (303) 395-2100
SIC 3569 3559 3629 3625 3443 3412

▲ PRAXAIR INC p 1168
10 Riverview Dr, Danbury CT 06810
Tel (203) 837-2000
SIC 2813 3569 3471 3479

■ 3M PURIFICATION INC p 3
400 Research Pkwy, Meriden CT 06450
Tel (203) 237-5541 SIC 3589 3569

SUEZ NORTH AMERICA INC p 1396
2000 First State Blvd, Wilmington DE 19804
Tel (302) 633-5670 SIC 4941 3569 3589

TYCO SIMPLEXGRINNELL p 1496
1501 Nw 51st St, Boca Raton FL 33431
Tel (561) 988-3658 SIC 3569 3491

■ PALL AEROPOWER CORP p 1108
10540 Ridge Rd Ste 100, New Port Richey FL 34654
Tel (727) 849-9999 SIC 3569

■ SPX FLOW TECHNOLOGY USA INC p 1362
4647 Se 40th Ave, Ocala FL 34474
Tel (352) 237-1220 SIC 3569

CLEAVER-BROOKS INC p 325
221 Law St, Thomasville GA 31792
Tel (229) 226-3024
SIC 3589 3569 3561 3433 3443

W S DARLEY & CO p 1569
325 Spring Lake Dr, Itasca IL 60143
Tel (630) 735-3500
SIC 3561 5087 5099 3569 3812

■ ATLAS MATERIAL TESTING TECHNOLOGY LLC p 128
1500 Bishop Ct, Mount Prospect IL 60056
Tel (773) 327-4520
SIC 3823 3569 3599 8734 3825 3821

▲ MFRI INC p 958
6410 W Howard St, Niles IL 60714
Tel (847) 966-1000 SIC 3677 3564 3569

■ PALL FILTER SPECIALISTS INC p 1108
100 Anchor Rd, Michigan City IN 46360
Tel (219) 879-3307 SIC 3569

SULLAIR LLC p 1397
3700 E Michigan Blvd, Michigan City IN 46360
Tel (219) 879-5451 SIC 3569 3563

AVIS INDUSTRIAL CORP p 138
1909 S Main St, Upland IN 46989
Tel (765) 998-8100
SIC 3429 3462 3312 3531 3714 3569

MI-T-M CORP p 959
50 Mitm Dr, Peosta IA 52068
Tel (563) 556-7484 SIC 3569

■ PALL FILTRATION AND SEPARATIONS GROUP INC p 1108
2118 Greenspring Dr, Lutherville Timonium MD 21093
Tel (410) 252-0800 SIC 3569

MUNTERS CORP p 1001
79 Monroe St, Amesbury MA 01913
Tel (978) 241-1100
SIC 3585 3822 3569 3564

▲ IROBOT CORP p 764
8 Crosby Dr, Bedford MA 01730
Tel (781) 430-3000 SIC 3569 3731

SPEEDLINE TECHNOLOGIES INC p 1358
16 Forge Pkwy, Franklin MA 02038
Tel (508) 541-4867 SIC 3565 3569

BABCOCK POWER INC p 143
6 Kimball Ln Ste 210, Lynnfield MA 01940
Tel (978) 646-3300 SIC 3443 3569 3433

THG CORP p 1447
70 Bearfoot Rd, Northborough MA 01532
Tel (508) 393-7660
SIC 5085 5084 3569 3728 3625 3494

KOCH MEMBRANE SYSTEMS INC p 825
850 Main St, Wilmington MA 01887
Tel (978) 694-7000 SIC 3569 3564

RILEY POWER INC p 1235
5 Neponset St, Worcester MA 01606
Tel (508) 852-7100
SIC 3569 3443 3433 1711 3564 3511

■ GELMAN SCIENCES INC p 598
674 S Wagner Rd, Ann Arbor MI 48103
Tel (734) 665-0651
SIC 3821 3569 3564 3841 3845 3699

KAYDON CORP p 805
2723 S State St Ste 300, Ann Arbor MI 48104
Tel (734) 747-7025
SIC 3562 3569 3592 3053 3621 3679

HIROTEC AMERICA INC p 695
3000 High Meadow Cir, Auburn Hills MI 48326
Tel (248) 836-5100 SIC 3569

THERMOTRON INDUSTRIES INC p 1447
291 Kollen Park Dr, Holland MI 49423
Tel (616) 392-1491 SIC 3569

FANUC AMERICA CORP p 527
3900 W Hamlin Rd, Rochester Hills MI 48309
Tel (248) 377-7000
SIC 3559 3548 3569 3542

OSMONICS INC p 1097
5951 Clearwater Dr, Hopkins MN 55343
Tel (952) 933-2277
SIC 3569 3589 3561 3824 3823 3089

▲ DONALDSON CO INC p 450
1400 W 94th St, Minneapolis MN 55431
Tel (952) 887-3131
SIC 3599 3569 3714 3564

▲ GRACO INC p 628
88 11th Ave Ne, Minneapolis MN 55413
Tel (612) 623-6000
SIC 3561 3594 3563 3491 3823 3569

■ RTI REMMELE ENGINEERING INC p 1256
10 Old Highway 8 Sw, Saint Paul MN 55112
Tel (651) 635-4100
SIC 3728 3569 3812 3761 3842

FIKE CORP p 542
704 Sw 10th St, Blue Springs MO 64015
Tel (816) 229-3405
SIC 3494 3569 3444 2899

▲ ESCO TECHNOLOGIES INC p 509
9900 Clayton Rd Ste A, Saint Louis MO 63124
Tel (314) 213-7200 SIC 3669 3569 3825

LINCOLN INDUSTRIAL CORP p 867
5148 N Hanley Rd, Saint Louis MO 63134
Tel (314) 679-4200
SIC 3569 3559 3561 3714

LINDE LLC p 868
200 Somerset Corporate Bl, Bridgewater NJ 08807
Tel (908) 464-8100
SIC 2813 3569 3561 3823

LINDE NORTH AMERICA INC p 868
200 Somerset Corporate Bl, Bridgewater NJ 08807
Tel (908) 464-8100
SIC 2813 3569 3559 3561 3511 3823

HAYWARD INDUSTRIES INC p 670
620 Division St, Elizabeth NJ 07201
Tel (908) 351-5400
SIC 3589 3561 3423 3494 3569 3089

AMEC FOSTER WHEELER NORTH AMERICA CORP p 66
Perryville Corporate Pk 5, Hampton NJ 08827
Tel (908) 713-2891
SIC 3433 3443 3532 3569

FOSTER WHEELER ZACK INC p 571
53 Frontage Rd, Hampton NJ 08827
Tel (908) 730-4000
SIC 8711 1629 3569 4931

BOC GROUP INC p 196
575 Mountain Ave, New Providence NJ 07974
Tel (908) 665-2400
SIC 2813 3569 3559 3561 3511 3823

CAMFIL USA INC p 245
1 N Corporate Dr, Riverdale NJ 07457
Tel (973) 616-7300 SIC 3564 3569

HILLIARD CORP p 693
100 W 4th St, Elmira NY 14901
Tel (607) 733-7121 SIC 3564 3569 3823

RELIABLE AUTOMATIC SPRINKLER CO INC p 1221
103 Fairview Pk Dr Ste 1, Elmsford NY 10523
Tel (914) 829-2042 SIC 3569

■ VEECO PROCESS EQUIPMENT INC p 1546
1 Terminal Dr, Plainview NY 11803
Tel (516) 677-0200 SIC 3569

■ PALL CORP p 1108
25 Harbor Park Dr, Port Washington NY 11050
Tel (516) 484-5400
SIC 3569 3599 3714 2834 3841

ENVIRONMENTAL FILTRATION TECHNOLOGIES LLC p 503
4404a Chesapeake Dr, Charlotte NC 28216
Tel (704) 399-7441
SIC 3569 5085 3564 3444 3469 3561

INDUSTRIAL PIPING INC p 740
212 S Tryon St Ste 1050, Charlotte NC 28281
Tel (704) 588-1100 SIC 3599 3569

MANN+HUMMEL PUROLATOR FILTERS LLC p 902
3200 Natal St, Fayetteville NC 28306
Tel (910) 425-4181 SIC 3569

BUCKEYE FIRE EQUIPMENT CO p 223
110 Kings Rd, Kings Mountain NC 28086
Tel (704) 739-7415 SIC 3569

SCOTT TECHNOLOGIES INC p 1294
4320 Goldmine Rd, Monroe NC 28110
Tel (800) 247-7257 SIC 3842 3728 3569

PENTAIR WATER POOL AND SPA INC p 1132
1620 Hawkins Ave, Sanford NC 27330
Tel (919) 774-4151
SIC 3589 3561 3569 3648

■ HURST JAWS OF LIFE INC p 721
711 N Post Rd, Shelby NC 28150
Tel (704) 487-6961 SIC 3569 3561 3594

COLUMBUS INDUSTRIES INC p 342
2938 State Route 752, Ashville OH 43103
Tel (740) 983-2552 SIC 3569

▲ CHART INDUSTRIES INC p 290
1 Infinity Corp Ctr Dr # 300, Cleveland OH 44125
Tel (440) 753-1490 SIC 3559 3569 3443

▲ PARKER-HANNIFIN CORP p 1116
6035 Parkland Blvd, Cleveland OH 44124
Tel (216) 896-3000
SIC 3594 3593 3492 3569 3053 3829

SUMMA HOLDINGS INC p 1398
8223 Brecksville Rd # 100, Cleveland OH 44141
Tel (440) 838-4700
SIC 2542 3462 3569 7359 3728

PNEUMATIC SCALE CORP p 1158
10 Ascot Pkwy, Cuyahoga Falls OH 44223
Tel (330) 923-0491 SIC 3565 3569 3535

KUSS FILTRATION INC p 832
2150 Industrial Dr, Findlay OH 45840
Tel (419) 423-9040 SIC 3569

MAC LTT INC p 891
1400 Fairchild Ave, Kent OH 44240
Tel (330) 474-3795 SIC 3569

ATS SYSTEMS OREGON INC p 129
425 Enterprise Dr, Lewis Center OH 43035
Tel (541) 738-0932 SIC 3569 5084

AUTOMATION TOOLING SYSTEMS INC p 134
425 Enterprise Dr, Lewis Center OH 43035
Tel (614) 781-8063 SIC 3569

HUNTER DEFENSE TECHNOLOGIES INC p 719
30500 Aurora Rd Ste 100, Solon OH 44139
Tel (216) 438-6111
SIC 3433 3569 3822 8331 8711 3549

FKI INDUSTRIES INC p 554
2801 Dawson Rd, Tulsa OK 74110
Tel (918) 834-4611
SIC 3429 3536 3535 3496 3569 3823

▲ AIR PRODUCTS AND CHEMICALS INC p 39
7201 Hamilton Blvd, Allentown PA 18195
Tel (610) 481-4911
SIC 2813 2842 2891 3569

■ VERSUM MATERIALS US LLC p 1552
1919 Vultee St, Allentown PA 18103
Tel (610) 481-3706 SIC 2842 2891 3569

SMS TECHNICAL SERVICES LLC p 1334
210 W Kensinger Dr # 300, Cranberry Township PA 16066
Tel (724) 553-3420 SIC 3569 7539

TYCO FIRE PRODUCTS LP p 1496
1400 Pennbrook Pkwy, Lansdale PA 19446
Tel (215) 362-0700
SIC 3569 3494 3321 5085

▲ MATTHEWS INTERNATIONAL CORP p 920
2 N Shore Ctr Ste 200, Pittsburgh PA 15212
Tel (412) 442-8200
SIC 3366 1542 3569 3995 3953 2796

■ MAR COR PURIFICATION INC p 904
4450 Township Line Rd, Skippack PA 19474
Tel (800) 633-3080 SIC 3569 3677

EVOQUA WATER TECHNOLOGIES LLC p 516
181 Thorn Hill Rd, Warrendale PA 15086
Tel (724) 772-0044
SIC 3589 3569 3823 3826 4941

■ PALL PUERTO RICO INC p 1108
Km 0 Hm 4 Rr 194, Fajardo PR 00738
Tel (787) 863-1124 SIC 3569

SARTORIUS STEDIM FILTERS INC p 1282
Intersection 376 Rr 128, Yauco PR 00698
Tel (787) 856-5020 SIC 3569

ACS INDUSTRIES INC p 19
1 New England Way Unit 1, Lincoln RI 02865
Tel (401) 769-4700
SIC 3291 3496 3312 3315 3569 3991

▲ CLARCOR INC p 321
840 Crescent Centre Dr # 600, Franklin TN 37067
Tel (615) 771-3100
SIC 3714 3599 3564 3569 3411 3089

FLARE INDUSTRIES LLC p 554
16310 Bratton Ln Ste 350, Austin TX 78728
Tel (512) 836-9473
SIC 3822 7359 3694 2899 1711 3569

▲ CSW INDUSTRIALS INC p 398
5400 Lyndon B Johnson Fwy, Dallas TX 75240
Tel (972) 233-8242 SIC 3569

PMFG INC p 1157
14651 Dallas Pkwy Ste 500, Dallas TX 75254
Tel (214) 357-6181 SIC 3569

AIR LIQUIDE AMERICA LP p 39
9811 Katy Fwy Ste 100, Houston TX 77024
Tel (713) 624-8000
SIC 5084 3533 2813 3569

CAMERON SOLUTIONS INC p 245
11210 Equity Dr Ste 100, Houston TX 77041
Tel (713) 849-7500 SIC 3533 1389 3569

■ FORTERRA INC p 569
511 E John Carpenter Fwy, Irving TX 75062
Tel (469) 284-8678 SIC 3272 3569

SUPERIOR FIBERS INC p 1406
1333 Corporate Dr Ste 350, Irving TX 75038
Tel (972) 600-9953 SIC 3677 3569

SULZER TURBO SERVICES HOUSTON INC p 1397
11518 Old La Porte Rd, La Porte TX 77571
Tel (713) 567-2700 SIC 3569

TYCO FIRE PRODUCTS LP p 1496
8902 N Interstate 27, Lubbock TX 79403
Tel (806) 472-2400 SIC 3569

ALFA LAVAL INC p 49
5400 Intl Trade Dr, Richmond VA 23231
Tel (804) 222-5300
SIC 3491 3433 3585 3569 3821

ALFA LAVAL US HOLDING INC p 49
5400 Intl Trade Dr, Richmond VA 23231
Tel (804) 222-5300 SIC 3569 5085

RESEARCH PRODUCTS CORP p 1226
1015 E Washington Ave, Madison WI 53703
Tel (608) 257-8801 SIC 5075 3564 3569

■ NELSON INDUSTRIES INC p 1025
1801 Us Highway 51 & 138, Stoughton WI 53589
Tel (608) 873-4200 SIC 3714 3519 3569

UNIVERSAL ACOUSTIC & EMISSION TECHNOLOGIES INC p 1516
1925 Us Highway 51 & 138, Stoughton WI 53589
Tel (608) 873-4272 SIC 3569 3441

SIC 3571 Electronic Computers

ABACO SYSTEMS INC p 9
12090 S Memorial Pkwy, Huntsville AL 35803
Tel (256) 382-8200 SIC 3571 3672 3577

SCI SYSTEMS INC p 1292
13000 Memorial Pkwy Sw, Huntsville AL 35803
Tel (256) 882-4800 SIC 3571

ENGHOUSE INTERACTIVE INC p 498
2095 W Pinnacle Peak Rd, Phoenix AZ 85027
Tel (602) 789-2800
SIC 3571 3661 3663 7372 7374

■ INSIGHT DIRECT USA INC p 746
201 N Central Ave, Phoenix AZ 85004
Tel (480) 333-3000 SIC 5045 3571

ARTESYN EMBEDDED TECHNOLOGIES INC p 114
2900 S Diablo Way Ste 190, Tempe AZ 85282
Tel (800) 759-1107
SIC 3679 3577 3571 7629 5045

FLEXTRONICS CORP p 556
6201 America Center Dr, Alviso CA 95002
Tel (803) 936-5200 SIC 3679 3577 3571

▲ APPLE INC p 98
1 Infinite Loop, Cupertino CA 95014
Tel (408) 996-1010
SIC 3663 3571 3575 3577 3651 7372

CYBERNET MANUFACTURING INC p 404
5 Holland Ste 201, Irvine CA 92618
Tel (949) 600-8000 SIC 3571 3577

GATEWAY INC p 594
7565 Irvine Center Dr # 150, Irvine CA 92618
Tel (949) 471-7000 SIC 3571 3577

▲ OMNICELL INC p 1085
590 E Middlefield Rd, Mountain View CA 94043
Tel (650) 251-6100 SIC 3571

■ HEWLETT-PACKARD ENTERPRISES LLC p 688
3000 Hanover St, Palo Alto CA 94304
Tel (650) 857-1501 SIC 3571

▲ HP INC p 714
1501 Page Mill Rd, Palo Alto CA 94304
Tel (650) 857-1501
SIC 3571 7372 3861 3577 3572 3575

■ ORACLE AMERICA INC p 1091
500 Oracle Pkwy, Redwood City CA 94065
Tel (650) 506-7000
SIC 3571 7379 7373 7372 3674

▲ ORACLE CORP p 1091
500 Oracle Pkwy, Redwood City CA 94065
Tel (650) 506-7000
SIC 7372 7379 8243 3571 3674

ACER AMERICAN HOLDINGS CORP p 17
333 W San Carlos St # 1500, San Jose CA 95110
Tel (408) 533-7700 SIC 3577 3571

▲ SUPER MICRO COMPUTER INC p 1405
980 Rock Ave, San Jose CA 95131
Tel (408) 503-8000 SIC 3571 3572 7372

HITACHI DATA SYSTEMS CORP p 696
2845 Lafayette St, Santa Clara CA 95050
Tel (408) 970-1000
SIC 5045 7378 7379 5734 4225 3571

MATERIAL IN MOTION INC p 919
726 Palomar Ave, Sunnyvale CA 94085
Tel (650) 967-3300 SIC 3571

KUBOTA USA INC p 831
3401 Del Amo Blvd, Torrance CA 90503
Tel (310) 370-3370
SIC 5083 3577 5051 3531 3571

UNITED WIRELESS TECHNOLOGIES INC p 1515
300 Se 5th Ave Apt 8180, Boca Raton FL 33432
Tel (561) 302-9350 SIC 3571 3663

■ KIMBALL ELECTRONICS GROUP LLC p 818
1205 Kimball Blvd, Jasper IN 47546
Tel (812) 634-4000 SIC 3571

FORCE 3 LLC p 565
2151 Priest Bridge Dr # 7, Crofton MD 21114
Tel (301) 261-0204 SIC 7373 5045 3571

BULL DATA SYSTEMS INC p 225
285 Billerica Rd Ste 200, Chelmsford MA 01824
Tel (978) 294-6000 SIC 3571 3577 7378

MANUFACTURERS SERVICES LIMITED p 903
300 Baker Ave Ste 106, Concord MA 01742
Tel (978) 287-5630
SIC 3571 3577 3572 3661 3663

MACK TECHNOLOGIES INC p 892
27 Carlisle Rd, Westford MA 01886
Tel (978) 392-5500 SIC 3577 3571

SRG GLOBAL INC p 1363
800 Stephenson Hwy, Troy MI 48083
Tel (586) 757-7800
SIC 3089 3571 3494 2522 3826 3825

■ COMPELLENT TECHNOLOGIES INC p 351
12982 Valley View Rd, Eden Prairie MN 55344
Tel (952) 294-3300 SIC 3571 3695

EQUUS COMPUTER SYSTEMS INC p 507
7725 Washington Ave S, Edina MN 55439
Tel (612) 617-6200 SIC 3571

CRESTRON ELECTRONICS INC p 392
15 Volvo Dr, Rockleigh NJ 07647
Tel (201) 767-3400
SIC 3571 3651 1731 3663 3499 3669

■ IBM WORLD TRADE CORP p 726
1 New Orchard Rd Ste 1, Armonk NY 10504
Tel (914) 765-1900
SIC 3571 3577 7377 7379

▲ INTERNATIONAL BUSINESS MACHINES CORP p 754
1 New Orchard Rd Ste 1, Armonk NY 10504
Tel (914) 499-1900
SIC 7379 7371 3571 3572 3674

■ TELXON CORP p 1435
1 Zebra Plz, Holtsville NY 11742
Tel (631) 738-2400 SIC 3571 7373 3663

TOSHIBA AMERICA INC p 1462
1251 Ave Of Ameri Ste 4100, New York NY 10020
Tel (212) 596-0600
SIC 3651 3631 5064 5075 3571 3661

TOSHIBA AMERICA INFORMATION SYSTEMS INC p 1462
1251 Ave Of The Ste 4110, New York NY 10020
Tel (949) 583-3000
SIC 3571 3577 3572 3661 5045

■ HAND HELD PRODUCTS INC p 657
700 Visions Dr, Skaneateles Falls NY 13153
Tel (315) 554-6000
SIC 3577 3571 3663 3578

LENOVO (UNITED STATES) INC p 856
1009 Think Pl, Morrisville NC 27560
Tel (919) 294-2500 SIC 3571

LENOVO HOLDING CO INC p 856
1009 Think Pl, Morrisville NC 27560
Tel (919) 294-0600 SIC 3571

WALKER AND ASSOCIATES INC p 1573
7129 Old Hwy 52, Welcome NC 27374
Tel (336) 731-6391
SIC 4813 5065 8731 8711 3572 3571

LENOVO US FULFILLMENT CENTER LLC p 856
6540 Franz Warner Pkwy, Whitsett NC 27377
Tel (919) 294-0477 SIC 3571

EATON CORP p 473
1000 Eaton Blvd, Cleveland OH 44122
Tel (216) 523-5000
SIC 3625 3714 3594 3559 3571

▲ TERADATA CORP p 1439
10000 Innovation Dr, Miamisburg OH 45342
Tel (866) 548-8348
SIC 3571 3572 7372 7371

■ TERADATA OPERATIONS INC p 1439
10000 Innovation Dr, Miamisburg OH 45342
Tel (937) 242-4030 SIC 3571

■ GRIMES AEROSPACE CO p 640
550 State Route 55, Urbana OH 43078
Tel (937) 484-2000
SIC 3728 3647 3646 3645 3577 3571

▲ UNISYS CORP p 1506
801 Lakeview Dr Ste 100, Blue Bell PA 19422
Tel (215) 986-4011
SIC 7373 7378 7379 3571 3572

■ VOCOLLECT INC p 1564
703 Rodi Rd, Pittsburgh PA 15235
Tel (412) 829-8145 SIC 3577 3571 7372

■ 3D SYSTEMS INC p 2
333 Three D Systems Cir, Rock Hill SC 29730
Tel (803) 326-3900 SIC 3571

■ DANIEL INDUSTRIES INC p 411
11100 Brittmoore Park Dr, Houston TX 77041
Tel (713) 467-6000
SIC 3823 3824 3494 3829 3826 3571

■ DANIEL MEASUREMENT AND CONTROL INC p 411
11100 Brittmoore Park Dr, Houston TX 77041
Tel (713) 467-6000
SIC 3824 3498 3499 3823 3571 3491

■ DELL INC p 425
1 Dell Way, Round Rock TX 78682
Tel (512) 338-4400
SIC 3571 3572 3575 3577 7372 7379

■ DELL INTERNATIONAL INC p 425
1 Dell Way, Round Rock TX 78682
Tel (512) 728-3500 SIC 3571

■ DELL PRODUCTS LP p 425
1 Dell Way, Round Rock TX 78682
Tel (512) 338-4400 SIC 3571

■ DENALI INTERMEDIATE INC p 428
1 Dell Way, Round Rock TX 78682
Tel (713) 627-0933
SIC 3571 3572 3577 7372

INTELLIGENT DECISIONS INC p 750
21445 Beaumeade Cir, Ashburn VA 20147
Tel (703) 554-1600 SIC 3571 5045

IRON BOW TECHNOLOGIES LLC p 764
4800 Westfields Blvd # 300, Chantilly VA 20151
Tel (703) 279-3000 SIC 3571

■ GENERAL DYNAMICS MISSION SYSTEMS INC p 600
12450 Fair Lakes Cir # 800, Fairfax VA 22033
Tel (703) 263-2800 SIC 3571

TVAR SOLUTIONS LLC p 1494
1320 Old Chain Bridge Rd # 445, Mc Lean VA 22101
Tel (703) 635-3900 SIC 5045 7379 3571

SLAIT PARTNERS INC p 1331
100 Landmark Sq, Virginia Beach VA 23452
Tel (757) 313-6500
SIC 5045 3571 8748 7373

▲ CRAY INC p 389
901 5th Ave Ste 1000, Seattle WA 98164
Tel (206) 701-2000 SIC 3571 7379

ASTRONAUTICS CORP OF AMERICA p 122
4115 N Teutonia Ave, Milwaukee WI 53209
Tel (414) 449-4000
SIC 3812 3571 3572 3769

DEDICATED COMPUTING LLC p 421
N26w23880 Commerce Cir B, Waukesha WI 53188
Tel (262) 951-7200 SIC 3571 3577 5045

SIC 3572 Computer Storage Devices

DATADIRECT NETWORKS INC p 414
9351 Deering Ave, Chatsworth CA 91311
Tel (818) 700-7600 SIC 3572 7374

COMPUCASE CORP p 352
16720 Chestnut St Ste C, City Of Industry CA 91748
Tel (626) 336-6588 SIC 3572

SEAGATE TECHNOLOGY (US) HOLDINGS INC p 1296
10200 S De Anza Blvd, Cupertino CA 95014
Tel (831) 438-6550 SIC 3572

SEAGATE TECHNOLOGY LLC p 1296
10200 S De Anza Blvd, Cupertino CA 95014
Tel (408) 658-1000 SIC 3572

PHIHONG USA CORP p 1142
47800 Fremont Blvd, Fremont CA 94538
Tel (510) 445-0100 SIC 5045 3572

UNIGEN CORP p 1503
45388 Warm Springs Blvd, Fremont CA 94539
Tel (510) 668-2088 SIC 3674 3572

■ CERTANCE LLC p 284
141 Innovation Dr, Irvine CA 92617
Tel (949) 856-7800 SIC 3572

▲ WESTERN DIGITAL CORP p 1598
3355 Michelson Dr Ste 100, Irvine CA 92612
Tel (949) 672-7000 SIC 3572

■ WESTERN DIGITAL TECHNOLOGIES INC p 1598
3355 Michelson Dr Ste 100, Irvine CA 92612
Tel (949) 672-7000 SIC 3572

US CRITICAL LLC p 1531
6 Orchard Ste 150, Lake Forest CA 92630
Tel (800) 884-8945 SIC 3572

HEADWAY TECHNOLOGIES INC p 673
682 S Hillview Dr, Milpitas CA 95035
Tel (408) 934-5300 SIC 3572

■ SANDISK CORP p 1278
951 Sandisk Dr, Milpitas CA 95035
Tel (408) 801-1000 SIC 3572

▲ PURE STORAGE INC p 1192
650 Castro St Ste 400, Mountain View CA 94041
Tel (800) 379-7873 SIC 3572

WINTEC INDUSTRIES INC p 1617
8674 Thornton Ave, Newark CA 94560
Tel (408) 856-0500 SIC 3577 3674 3572

▲ HEWLETT PACKARD ENTERPRISE CO p 688
3000 Hanover St, Palo Alto CA 94304
Tel (650) 857-5817 SIC 7372 7379 3572

▲ HP INC p 714
1501 Page Mill Rd, Palo Alto CA 94304
Tel (650) 857-1501
SIC 3571 7372 3861 3577 3572 3575

▲ GUIDANCE SOFTWARE INC p 645
1055 E Colo Blvd Ste 400, Pasadena CA 91106
Tel (626) 229-9191 SIC 7372 3572

SONY ELECTRONICS INC p 1341
16535 Via Esprillo Bldg 1, San Diego CA 92127
Tel (858) 942-2400
SIC 3651 5064 3695 3671 3572 3674

VIGOBYTE TAPE CORP p 1556
2498 Roll Dr Ste 916, San Diego CA 92154
Tel (866) 803-8446 SIC 3572

■ SYPRIS DATA SYSTEMS INC p 1416
160 Via Verde, San Dimas CA 91773
Tel (909) 962-9400 SIC 3572 3651

■ HGST INC p 689
3403 Yerba Buena Rd, San Jose CA 95135
Tel (800) 801-4618 SIC 3572

▲ NIMBLE STORAGE INC p 1043
211 River Oaks Pkwy, San Jose CA 95134
Tel (408) 432-9600 SIC 3572

▲ QUANTUM CORP p 1198
224 Airport Pkwy Ste 300, San Jose CA 95110
Tel (408) 944-4000 SIC 3572 8731

▲ SUPER MICRO COMPUTER INC p 1405
980 Rock Ave, San Jose CA 95131
Tel (408) 503-8000 SIC 3571 3572 7372

ZCO LIQUIDATING CORP p 1641
6373 San Ignacio Ave, San Jose CA 95119
Tel (408) 733-8400 SIC 3572

■ STEC INC p 1384
3001 Daimler St, Santa Ana CA 92705
Tel (415) 222-9996 SIC 3572 3674 3577

MAXTOR CORP p 923
4575 Scotts Valley Dr, Scotts Valley CA 95066
Tel (831) 438-6550 SIC 3572

▲ NETAPP INC p 1027
495 E Java Dr, Sunnyvale CA 94089
Tel (408) 822-6000 *SIC* 3572 7373 7372

■ MCDATA SERVICES CORP p 927
4 Brocade Pkwy, Broomfield CO 80021
Tel (720) 558-8000 *SIC* 7373 3572

XIOTECH CORP p 1631
9950 Federal Dr Unit 100, Colorado Springs CO 80921
Tel (719) 388-5500 *SIC* 3572 4226

DOT HILL SYSTEMS CORP p 452
1351 S Sunset St, Longmont CO 80501
Tel (303) 845-3200 *SIC* 3572 7371

AMERICAN MEGATRENDS INC p 76
5555 Okbrook Pkwy Ste 200, Norcross GA 30093
Tel (770) 246-8600 *SIC* 3572

FELLOWES INC p 537
1789 Norwood Ave, Itasca IL 60143
Tel (630) 893-1600
SIC 2522 3589 2653 3577 3572 3579

SONY DADC US INC p 1341
1800 N Fruitridge Ave, Terre Haute IN 47804
Tel (812) 462-8100
SIC 3695 3652 3651 3577 3572

UNICOM ENGINEERING INC p 1502
25 Dan Rd, Canton MA 02021
Tel (781) 332-1000 *SIC* 3572 7372

MANUFACTURERS SERVICES LIMITED p 903
300 Baker Ave Ste 106, Concord MA 01742
Tel (978) 287-5630
SIC 3571 3577 3572 3661 3663

■ EMC CORP p 490
176 South St, Hopkinton MA 01748
Tel (508) 435-1000
SIC 3572 7372 7371 3577

■ EMC INTERNATIONAL HOLDINGS INC p 490
176 South St, Hopkinton MA 01748
Tel (508) 435-1000 *SIC* 3572 3577

■ AUTOCAM CORP p 134
4180 40th St Se, Kentwood MI 49512
Tel (616) 698-0707
SIC 3714 3572 3841 5084

▲ IMATION CORP p 733
1099 Helmo Ave N Ste 250, Oakdale MN 55128
Tel (651) 704-4000 *SIC* 3695 3572

ROBERT FAMILY HOLDINGS INC p 1241
12430 Tesson Ferry Rd, Saint Louis MO 63128
Tel (314) 821-5665
SIC 2671 3572 3491 3498 7699 3494

PNY TECHNOLOGIES INC p 1158
100 Jefferson Rd, Parsippany NJ 07054
Tel (973) 515-9700 *SIC* 3572

▲ INTERNATIONAL BUSINESS MACHINES CORP p 754
1 New Orchard Rd Ste 1, Armonk NY 10504
Tel (914) 499-1900
SIC 7379 7371 3571 3572 3674

SONY CORP OF AMERICA p 1341
25 Madison Ave Fl 27, New York NY 10010
Tel (212) 833-8000
SIC 3695 3652 3651 3577 3572

TOSHIBA AMERICA INFORMATION SYSTEMS INC p 1462
1251 Ave Of The Ste 4110, New York NY 10020
Tel (949) 583-3000
SIC 3571 3577 3572 3661 5045

WALKER AND ASSOCIATES INC p 1573
7129 Old Hwy 52, Welcome NC 27374
Tel (336) 731-6391
SIC 4813 5065 8731 8711 3572 3571

▲ TERADATA CORP p 1439
10000 Innovation Dr, Miamisburg OH 45342
Tel (866) 548-8348
SIC 3571 3572 7372 7371

HITACHI COMPUTER PRODUCTS (AMERICA) INC p 696
1800 E Imhoff Rd, Norman OK 73071
Tel (405) 360-5500 *SIC* 3577 3572 7379

▲ UNISYS CORP p 1506
801 Lakeview Dr Ste 100, Blue Bell PA 19422
Tel (215) 986-4011
SIC 7373 7378 7379 3571 3572

OLYMPUS AMERICA INC p 1083
3500 Corporate Pkwy, Center Valley PA 18034
Tel (484) 896-5000
SIC 5047 5043 5064 3827 3695 3572

OLYMPUS CORP OF AMERICAS p 1083
3500 Corp Pkwy, Center Valley PA 18034
Tel (484) 896-5000
SIC 5047 5043 5064 3827 3695 3572

AUTOMATED TELECOMMUNICATION SERVICES LP p 134
13355 Noel Rd Ste 2100, Dallas TX 75240
Tel (972) 233-9614 *SIC* 3572

▲ N L INDUSTRIES INC p 1005
5430 Lbj Fwy Ste 1700, Dallas TX 75240
Tel (972) 233-1700 *SIC* 2819 3572 3699

TOSHIBA INTERNATIONAL CORP p 1462
13131 W Little York Rd, Houston TX 77041
Tel (713) 466-0277
SIC 3621 5084 5063 3613 3594 3572

VCE CO LLC p 1545
1500 N Greenville Ave, Richardson TX 75081
Tel (972) 656-5300 *SIC* 3572

■ DELL INC p 425
1 Dell Way, Round Rock TX 78682
Tel (512) 338-4400
SIC 3571 3572 3575 3577 7372 7379

■ DENALI INTERMEDIATE INC p 428
1 Dell Way, Round Rock TX 78682
Tel (713) 627-0933
SIC 3571 3572 3577 7372

■ FUSION-IO INC p 585
2855 E Cottonwood Pkwy # 200, Salt Lake City UT 84121
Tel (801) 424-5569 *SIC* 3572

DRS TECHNOLOGIES INC p 457
2345 Crystal Dr Ste 1000, Arlington VA 22202
Tel (973) 898-1500
SIC 3812 3699 3572 3669 3679 8741

■ ADVANCED DIGITAL INFORMATION CORP p 25
11431 Willows Rd Ne, Redmond WA 98052
Tel (425) 881-8004 *SIC* 3572

ASTRONAUTICS CORP OF AMERICA p 122
4115 N Teutonia Ave, Milwaukee WI 53209
Tel (414) 449-4000
SIC 3812 3571 3572 3769

SIC 3575 Computer Terminals

AVOCENT CORP p 138
4991 Corporate Dr Nw, Huntsville AL 35805
Tel (256) 430-4000 *SIC* 3575 3577 7373

▲ APPLE INC p 98
1 Infinite Loop, Cupertino CA 95014
Tel (408) 996-1010
SIC 3663 3571 3575 3577 3651 7372

ELO TOUCH SOLUTIONS INC p 489
1033 Mccarthy Blvd, Milpitas CA 95035
Tel (408) 597-8000 *SIC* 3575

▲ HP INC p 714
1501 Page Mill Rd, Palo Alto CA 94304
Tel (650) 857-1501
SIC 3571 7372 3861 3577 3572 3575

■ VERIFONE INC p 1549
88 W Plumeria Dr, San Jose CA 95134
Tel (408) 232-7800
SIC 3578 7372 3577 3575 8711 3643

OMEGA ENGINEERING INC p 1084
800 Connecticut Ave 5n01, Norwalk CT 06854
Tel (203) 359-1660
SIC 3823 3575 3577 3433 3826 2759

BARCO INC p 155
3059 Premiere Pkwy # 400, Duluth GA 30097
Tel (408) 400-4100 *SIC* 3575 3669

▲ NCR CORP p 1022
3097 Satellite Blvd # 100, Duluth GA 30096
Tel (937) 445-5000
SIC 3575 3578 7379 7374 7371

GRAYHILL INC p 632
561 W Hillgrove Ave, La Grange IL 60525
Tel (708) 354-1040
SIC 3613 3625 3679 3643 3575

SCANTRON CORP p 1286
1313 Lone Oak Rd, Eagan MN 55121
Tel (651) 683-6000
SIC 3577 7372 2752 3575 2761

▲ DIGI INTERNATIONAL INC p 438
11001 Bren Rd E, Minnetonka MN 55343
Tel (952) 912-3444
SIC 3577 3575 7374 7371

CLAYTON DUBILIER & RICE FUND V LIMITED PARTNERSHIP p 323
375 Park Ave Fl 18, New York NY 10152
Tel (212) 407-5200
SIC 3825 3661 3812 3577 3575 7372

IGT GLOBAL SOLUTIONS CORP p 730
10 Memorial Blvd, Providence RI 02903
Tel (401) 392-1000
SIC 7999 3575 7372 7378 2752 7374

TOUCH INTERNATIONAL INC p 1463
2222 W Rundberg Ln # 200, Austin TX 78758
Tel (512) 832-8292 *SIC* 3575 3577

EMS ASSEMBLY LLC p 495
8807 Fallbrook Dr, Houston TX 77064
Tel (281) 668-1551 *SIC* 3575

TELCO INTERCONTINENTAL CORP p 1433
9812 Whithorn Dr, Houston TX 77095
Tel (281) 500-8270 *SIC* 5063 5065 3575

■ RAYTHEON E-SYSTEMS INC p 1211
1727 Cityline Dr, Richardson TX 75082
Tel (972) 205-9374
SIC 3663 3812 7373 3575 4581 3721

■ DELL INC p 425
1 Dell Way, Round Rock TX 78682
Tel (512) 338-4400
SIC 3571 3572 3575 3577 7372 7379

■ SPACELABS HEALTHCARE (WASHINGTON) INC p 1354
35301 Se Center St, Snoqualmie WA 98065
Tel (425) 396-3300
SIC 3845 3841 3575 7699 7378

■ SPACELABS HEALTHCARE INC p 1354
35301 Se Center St, Snoqualmie WA 98065
Tel (425) 396-3302
SIC 3841 3845 3575 7699 7378

SIC 3577 Computer Peripheral Eqpt, NEC

ABACO SYSTEMS INC p 9
12090 S Memorial Pkwy, Huntsville AL 35803
Tel (256) 382-8200 *SIC* 3571 3672 3577

AVOCENT CORP p 138
4991 Corporate Dr Nw, Huntsville AL 35805
Tel (256) 430-4000 *SIC* 3575 3577 7373

AVOCENT HUNTSVILLE CORP p 138
4991 Corporate Dr Nw, Huntsville AL 35805
Tel (256) 430-4000 *SIC* 3577

INTER-TEL TECHNOLOGIES INC p 751
1146 N Alma School Rd, Mesa AZ 85201
Tel (480) 858-9600
SIC 5999 1731 5065 3661 3577

■ BENCHMARK ELECTRONICS PHOENIX INC p 172
2222 W Pinnacle Pk Rd # 310, Phoenix AZ 85027
Tel (619) 397-2400 *SIC* 3577 3672

ARTESYN EMBEDDED TECHNOLOGIES INC p 114
2900 S Diablo Way Ste 190, Tempe AZ 85282
Tel (800) 759-1107
SIC 3679 3577 3571 7629 5045

FLEXTRONICS CORP p 556
6201 America Center Dr, Alviso CA 95002
Tel (803) 936-5200 *SIC* 3679 3577 3571

RGB SYSTEMS INC p 1231
1025 E Ball Rd, Anaheim CA 92805
Tel (714) 491-1500 *SIC* 3577

VIEWSONIC CORP p 1556
10 Pointe Dr Ste 200, Brea CA 92821
Tel (909) 444-8888 *SIC* 3577

LEEMAH CORP p 852
155 S Hill Dr, Brisbane CA 94005
Tel (415) 394-1288
SIC 3671 3672 3669 3663 3577

EPIC TECHNOLOGIES LLC p 505
9340 Owensmouth Ave, Chatsworth CA 91311
Tel (818) 734-6500 *SIC* 3661 3577 3679

EMULEX CORP p 495
3333 Susan St, Costa Mesa CA 92626
Tel (714) 662-5600 *SIC* 3577 3661

▲ APPLE INC p 98
1 Infinite Loop, Cupertino CA 95014
Tel (408) 996-1010
SIC 3663 3571 3575 3577 3651 7372

D-LINK SYSTEMS INC p 407
17595 Mount Herrmann St, Fountain Valley CA 92708
Tel (714) 885-6000 *SIC* 5045 3577

KINGSTON TECHNOLOGY CO INC p 821
17600 Newhope St, Fountain Valley CA 92708
Tel (714) 435-2600 *SIC* 3577

ASI COMPUTER TECHNOLOGIES INC p 117
48289 Fremont Blvd, Fremont CA 94538
Tel (510) 226-8000 *SIC* 5045 3577

ASUS COMPUTER INTERNATIONAL INC p 123
800 Corp Way, Fremont CA 94539
Tel (510) 739-3777 *SIC* 5045 3577

DELTA PRODUCTS CORP p 427
46101 Fremont Blvd, Fremont CA 94538
Tel (510) 668-5100
SIC 5065 5045 8741 5063 3577

▲ ELECTRONICS FOR IMAGING INC p 486
6750 Dumbarton Cir, Fremont CA 94555
Tel (650) 357-3500 *SIC* 3577 2899

CYBERNET MANUFACTURING INC p 404
5 Holland Ste 201, Irvine CA 92618
Tel (949) 600-8000 *SIC* 3571 3577

GATEWAY INC p 594
7565 Irvine Center Dr # 150, Irvine CA 92618
Tel (949) 471-7000 *SIC* 3571 3577

KOFAX INC p 826
15211 Laguna Canyon Rd, Irvine CA 92618
Tel (949) 783-1000 *SIC* 3577 7371

PRINTRONIX LLC p 1177
15345 Barranca Pkwy, Irvine CA 92618
Tel (714) 368-2300 *SIC* 3577

EPSON AMERICA INC p 506
3840 Kilroy Airport Way, Long Beach CA 90806
Tel (800) 463-7766 *SIC* 3577

US EPSON INC p 1531
3840 Kilroy Airport Way, Long Beach CA 90806
Tel (562) 290-5678 *SIC* 5045 3577

CREATIVE HOLDINGS INC p 390
1901 Mccarthy Blvd, Milpitas CA 95035
Tel (408) 428-6600
SIC 5045 3577 3931 3674 8711 3651

CREATIVE LABS INC p 390
1901 Mccarthy Blvd, Milpitas CA 95035
Tel (408) 428-6600 *SIC* 5045 5734 3577

■ SILICON GRAPHICS INTERNATIONAL CORP p 1323
900 N Mccarthy Blvd, Milpitas CA 95035
Tel (669) 900-8000 *SIC* 3577 7371

LOGITECH INC p 875
7700 Gateway Blvd, Newark CA 94560
Tel (510) 795-8500 *SIC* 3577

SMART MODULAR TECHNOLOGIES (WWH) INC p 1332
39870 Eureka Dr, Newark CA 94560
Tel (510) 623-1231 *SIC* 3674 3577 3679

WINTEC INDUSTRIES INC p 1617
8674 Thornton Ave, Newark CA 94560
Tel (408) 856-0500 *SIC* 3577 3674 3572

▲ HP INC p 714
1501 Page Mill Rd, Palo Alto CA 94304
Tel (650) 857-1501
SIC 3571 7372 3861 3577 3572 3575

AL SHELLCO LLC p 43
9330 Scranton Rd Ste 600, San Diego CA 92121
Tel (570) 296-6444 *SIC* 3651 3577

RIVERBED TECHNOLOGY INC p 1237
680 Folsom St Ste 500, San Francisco CA 94107
Tel (415) 247-8800 *SIC* 3577 5045

ACER AMERICAN HOLDINGS CORP p 17
333 W San Carlos St # 1500, San Jose CA 95110
Tel (408) 533-7700 *SIC* 3577 3571

▲ BROCADE COMMUNICATIONS SYSTEMS INC p 216
130 Holger Way, San Jose CA 95134
Tel (408) 333-8000 *SIC* 3577 4813

▲ CISCO SYSTEMS INC p 309
170 W Tasman Dr, San Jose CA 95134
Tel (408) 526-4000 *SIC* 3577 7379

DIAMOND MULTIMEDIA SYSTEMS INC p 437
2880 Junction Ave, San Jose CA 95134
Tel (408) 868-9613 *SIC* 3672 3577 3661

▲ NETGEAR INC p 1027
350 E Plumeria Dr, San Jose CA 95134
Tel (408) 907-8000 *SIC* 3661 3577

▲ SYNAPTICS INC p 1414
1251 Mckay Dr, San Jose CA 95131
Tel (408) 904-1100 *SIC* 3577 7372

■ VERIFONE INC p 1549
88 W Plumeria Dr, San Jose CA 95134
Tel (408) 232-7800
SIC 3578 7372 3577 3575 8711 3643

■ STEC INC p 1384
3001 Daimler St, Santa Ana CA 92705
Tel (415) 222-9996 *SIC* 3572 3674 3577

▲ ARISTA NETWORKS INC p 108
5453 Great America Pkwy, Santa Clara CA 95054
Tel (408) 547-5500 *SIC* 3577

▲ GIGAMON INC p 611
3300 Olcott St, Santa Clara CA 95054
Tel (408) 831-4000 *SIC* 7372 3577

▲ INTEL CORP p 750
2200 Mission College Blvd, Santa Clara CA 95054
Tel (408) 765-8080 *SIC* 3674 3577 7372

▲ PALO ALTO NETWORKS INC p 1110
4401 Great America Pkwy, Santa Clara CA 95054
Tel (408) 753-4000 *SIC* 3577 7371

■ OPTICAL COATING LABORATORY LLC p 1090
2789 Northpoint Pkwy, Santa Rosa CA 95407
Tel (707) 545-6440 *SIC* 3479 3577 3827

■ ARUBA NETWORKS INC p 114
1344 Crossman Ave, Sunnyvale CA 94089
Tel (408) 227-4500 *SIC* 3577 3663 7371

JUNIPER NETWORKS (US) INC p 797
1133 Innovation Way, Sunnyvale CA 94089
Tel (408) 745-2000 *SIC* 3577

▲ JUNIPER NETWORKS INC p 797
1133 Innovation Way, Sunnyvale CA 94089
Tel (408) 745-2000 *SIC* 3577 7372

NOKIA INC p 1046
200 S Mathilda Ave, Sunnyvale CA 94086
Tel (408) 530-7600
SIC 3663 5065 3661 3577

KUBOTA USA INC p 831
3401 Del Amo Blvd, Torrance CA 90503
Tel (310) 370-3370
SIC 5083 3577 5051 3531 3571

LYNN PRODUCTS INC p 888
2645 W 237th St, Torrance CA 90505
Tel (310) 530-5966 *SIC* 3577 3357

GORES ENT HOLDINGS INC p 626
6260 Lookout Rd, Boulder CO 80301
Tel (303) 531-3100 *SIC* 3577 7373 3357

■ MCDATA CORP p 927
4 Brocade Pkwy, Broomfield CO 80021
Tel (720) 558-8000
SIC 3679 5045 3825 3577

FLO-TECH LLC p 557
699 Middle St, Middletown CT 06457
Tel (860) 613-3333 *SIC* 5045 3577

OMEGA ENGINEERING INC p 1084
800 Connecticut Ave 5n01, Norwalk CT 06854
Tel (203) 359-1660
SIC 3823 3575 3577 3433 3826 2759

▲ XEROX CORP p 1631
45 Glover Ave Ste 700, Norwalk CT 06850
Tel (203) 968-3000
SIC 3861 3579 3577 7629 7378 7374

■ DICTAPHONE CORP p 438
3191 Broadbridge Ave, Stratford CT 06614
Tel (203) 381-7000
SIC 3579 3825 3695 3577

GERBER SCIENTIFIC LLC p 608
24 Indl Pk Rd W, Tolland CT 06084
Tel (860) 871-8082
SIC 3993 7336 3851 7372 3577

■ MACDERMID INC p 892
245 Freight St, Waterbury CT 06702
Tel (203) 575-5700
SIC 2899 2842 2874 2992 2752 3577

▲ DANAHER CORP p 411
2200 Penn Ave Nw Ste 800w, Washington DC 20037
Tel (202) 828-0850
SIC 3845 3829 3577 3823 3843

THAYER-BLUM FUNDING III LLC p 1446
1455 Penn Ave Nw Ste 350, Washington DC 20004
Tel (202) 371-0150 *SIC* 6722 3672 3577

ENER1 GROUP INC p 497
550 W Cypress Creek Rd, Fort Lauderdale FL 33309
Tel (954) 202-4442 *SIC* 3577 3069

■ DATAMAX-ONEIL CORP p 414
4501 Pkwy Commerce Blvd, Orlando FL 32808
Tel (407) 578-8007 *SIC* 3577 2754

INGENICO CORP (DELAWARE) p 742
3025 Windward Plz Ste 600, Alpharetta GA 30005
Tel (678) 456-1200 *SIC* 3577

■ SCIENTIFIC-ATLANTA LLC p 1292
5030 Sugarloaf Pkwy, Lawrenceville GA 30044
Tel (678) 277-1000
SIC 3663 3661 3577 3825

TRIPPE MANUFACTURING CO p 1482
1111 W 35th St Fl 12, Chicago IL 60609
Tel (773) 869-1111 *SIC* 3577

▲ DOVER CORP p 453
3005 Highland Pkwy # 200, Downers Grove IL 60515
Tel (630) 541-1540
SIC 3632 3586 3533 3577 3674

FELLOWES INC p 537
1789 Norwood Ave, Itasca IL 60143
Tel (630) 893-1600
SIC 2522 3589 2653 3577 3572 3579

▲ ZEBRA TECHNOLOGIES CORP p 1641
3 Overlook Pt, Lincolnshire IL 60069
Tel (847) 634-6700
SIC 3577 2672 2679 5045

CDS OFFICE SYSTEMS INC p 271
612 S Dirksen Pkwy, Springfield IL 62703
Tel (800) 367-1508
SIC 5044 5999 7629 7378 3861 3577

SONY DADC US INC p 1341
1800 N Fruitridge Ave, Terre Haute IN 47804
Tel (812) 462-8100
SIC 3695 3652 3651 3577 3572

ALEXANDER OPEN SYSTEMS INC p 49
12980 Foster St Ste 300, Overland Park KS 66213
Tel (913) 307-2300
SIC 5045 7373 8748 7376 3577 1731

LEXMARK INTERNATIONAL INC p 860
740 W New Circle Rd, Lexington KY 40511
Tel (859) 232-2000 *SIC* 3577

LOGO HOLDINGS I CORP p 875
626 W Main St, Louisville KY 40202
Tel (502) 637-5443 *SIC* 3577

■ **MICROS SYSTEMS INC** p 962
7031 Columbia Gateway Dr # 1, Columbia MD 21046
Tel (443) 285-6000
SIC 7373 7372 3577 3578

CGI INFORMATION SYSTEMS & MANAGEMENT CONSULTANTS INC p 286
600 Federal St, Andover MA 01810
Tel (978) 946-3000 SIC 7374 3577 7373

■ **RSA SECURITY LLC** p 1255
174 Middlesex Tpke, Bedford MA 01730
Tel (781) 515-5000 SIC 3577 7372 7373

BULL DATA SYSTEMS INC p 225
285 Billerica Rd Ste 200, Chelmsford MA 01824
Tel (978) 294-6000 SIC 3571 3577 7378

MANUFACTURERS SERVICES LIMITED p 903
300 Baker Ave Ste 106, Concord MA 01742
Tel (978) 287-5630
SIC 3571 3577 3572 3661 3663

■ **EMC CORP** p 490
176 South St, Hopkinton MA 01748
Tel (508) 435-1000
SIC 3572 7372 7371 3577

■ **EMC INTERNATIONAL HOLDINGS INC** p 490
176 South St, Hopkinton MA 01748
Tel (508) 435-1000 SIC 3572 3577

▲ **CSP INC** p 398
175 Cabot St Ste 210, Lowell MA 01854
Tel (978) 663-7598 SIC 3577 7372 7373

■ **3M TOUCH SYSTEMS INC** p 3
501 Griffin Brook Dr, Methuen MA 01844
Tel (978) 659-0053 SIC 3577

L-COM INC p 835
50 High St Fl 3, North Andover MA 01845
Tel (800) 343-1455 SIC 3678 3577 3357

MACK TECHNOLOGIES INC p 892
27 Carlisle Rd, Westford MA 01886
Tel (978) 392-5500 SIC 3577 3571

▲ **NETSCOUT SYSTEMS INC** p 1027
310 Littleton Rd, Westford MA 01886
Tel (978) 614-4000 SIC 7373 3577

VISIONIT SUPPLIES AND SERVICES INC p 1561
3031 W Grand Blvd Ste 600, Detroit MI 48202
Tel (313) 664-5650 SIC 3577 3955 5734

SCANTRON CORP p 1286
1313 Lone Oak Rd, Eagan MN 55121
Tel (651) 683-6000
SIC 3577 7372 2752 3575 2761

STRATASYS INC p 1392
7665 Commerce Way, Eden Prairie MN 55344
Tel (800) 801-6491 SIC 3577

NCS PEARSON INC p 1022
5601 Green Valley Dr # 220, Minneapolis MN 55437
Tel (952) 681-3000
SIC 3577 7372 7374 8748 7379

▲ **COMMUNICATIONS SYSTEMS INC** p 347
10900 Red Circle Dr, Minnetonka MN 55343
Tel (952) 996-1674
SIC 3661 3577 3663 8748

▲ **DIGI INTERNATIONAL INC** p 438
11001 Bren Rd E, Minnetonka MN 55343
Tel (952) 912-3444
SIC 3577 3575 7374 7371

COMPUTYPE INC p 353
2285 County Road C W, Saint Paul MN 55113
Tel (651) 633-0633
SIC 2759 2672 2679 3565 3577 2671

ERGOTRON INC p 507
1181 Trapp Rd Ste 100, Saint Paul MN 55121
Tel (651) 681-7600 SIC 7373 3577

ELECTION SYSTEMS & SOFTWARE LLC p 484
11208 John Galt Blvd, Omaha NE 68137
Tel (402) 593-0101 SIC 3577

PRESSTEK LLC p 1173
55 Executive Dr, Hudson NH 03051
Tel (603) 595-7000 SIC 3555 3577 3861

■ **ENTERASYS NETWORKS INC** p 501
9 Northeastern Blvd Ste 300, Salem NH 03079
Tel (603) 952-5000
SIC 3577 7373 3357 5045

■ **METROLOGIC INSTRUMENTS INC** p 955
534 Fellowship Rd, Mount Laurel NJ 08054
Tel (856) 228-8100 SIC 3577 3699

DIALOGIC INC p 436
4 Gatehall Dr, Parsippany NJ 07054
Tel (973) 967-6000 SIC 3661 3577 7371

RARITAN INC p 1209
400 Cottontail Ln, Somerset NJ 08873
Tel (732) 764-8886 SIC 3612 3577

■ **IBM WORLD TRADE CORP** p 726
1 New Orchard Rd Ste 1, Armonk NY 10504
Tel (914) 765-1900
SIC 3571 3577 7377 7379

■ **DATA DEVICE CORP** p 413
105 Wilbur Pl, Bohemia NY 11716
Tel (631) 567-5600 SIC 3577 3674 3677

CANON USA INC p 247
1 Canon Park, Melville NY 11747
Tel (516) 328-5000
SIC 5044 5065 5045 3861 3577 5043

CLAYTON DUBILIER & RICE FUND V LIMITED PARTNERSHIP p 323
375 Park Ave Fl 18, New York NY 10152
Tel (212) 407-5200
SIC 3825 3661 3812 3577 3575 7372

HUMANSCALE CORP p 718
11 E 26th St Fl 8, New York NY 10010
Tel (212) 725-4749 SIC 3577 2521

MDI HOLDINGS LLC p 933
399 Park Ave Fl 14, New York NY 10022
Tel (212) 559-1127
SIC 2899 2842 2874 2992 2752 3577

SONY CORP OF AMERICA p 1341
25 Madison Ave Fl 27, New York NY 10010
Tel (212) 833-8000
SIC 3695 3652 3651 3577 3572

TOSHIBA AMERICA INFORMATION SYSTEMS INC p 1462
1251 Ave Of The Ste 4110, New York NY 10020
Tel (949) 583-3000
SIC 3571 3577 3572 3661 5045

HITACHI METALS AMERICA LTD p 697
2 Manhattanville Rd # 301, Purchase NY 10577
Tel (914) 694-9200
SIC 3264 3577 3365 5051 3321 3559

■ **EASTMAN KODAK CO** p 473
343 State St, Rochester NY 14650
Tel (585) 724-4000 SIC 3861 3577 7384

ODYSSEY GROUP OF COMPANIES p 1075
11 Overlook Way, Setauket NY 11733
Tel (631) 751-8400
SIC 7373 3577 7371 1731

■ **HAND HELD PRODUCTS INC** p 657
700 Visions Dr, Skaneateles Falls NY 13153
Tel (315) 554-6000
SIC 3577 3571 3663 3578

HITACHI AMERICA LTD p 696
50 Prospect Ave, Tarrytown NY 10591
Tel (914) 332-5800
SIC 5084 5065 3577 5063 5045 3651

■ **CARLISLE CORP** p 257
11605 N Community Hse Rd, Charlotte NC 28277
Tel (704) 501-1100
SIC 2952 2899 3011 2295 3089 3577

■ **GRIMES AEROSPACE CO** p 640
550 State Route 55, Urbana OH 43078
Tel (937) 484-2000
SIC 3728 3647 3646 3645 3577 3571

HITACHI COMPUTER PRODUCTS (AMERICA) INC p 696
1800 E Imhoff Rd, Norman OK 73071
Tel (405) 360-5500 SIC 3577 3572 7379

DATALOGIC ADC INC p 414
959 Terry St, Eugene OR 97402
Tel (541) 683-5700 SIC 3577

DATALOGIC HOLDINGS INC p 414
959 Terry St, Eugene OR 97402
Tel (541) 683-5700 SIC 3577

EPSON PORTLAND INC p 506
3950 Nw Aloclek Pl, Hillsboro OR 97124
Tel (503) 645-1118 SIC 3577

▲ **BLACK BOX CORP** p 186
1000 Park Dr, Lawrence PA 15055
Tel (724) 746-5500
SIC 3577 3679 3661 5045 5065 5063

■ **BLACK BOX CORP OF PENNSYLVANIA** p 186
1000 Park Dr, Lawrence PA 15055
Tel (724) 746-5500
SIC 5045 5063 5065 3577 3679 3661

■ **VOCOLLECT INC** p 1564
703 Rodi Rd, Pittsburgh PA 15235
Tel (412) 829-8145 SIC 3577 3571 7372

DATALOGIC AUTOMATION INC p 414
511 School House Rd, Telford PA 18969
Tel (215) 723-0981 SIC 3577

▲ **ASTRONOVA INC** p 123
600 E Greenwich Ave, West Warwick RI 02893
Tel (401) 828-4000 SIC 3577 3829

▲ **3D SYSTEMS CORP** p 2
333 Three D Systems Cir, Rock Hill SC 29730
Tel (803) 326-3900 SIC 3577 7372

QCH NASHVILLE LLC p 1194
1621 Heil Quaker Blvd, La Vergne TN 37086
Tel (615) 501-7500 SIC 5045 3577

QUANTA SERVICE NASHVILLE LLC p 1198
1621 Heil Quaker Blvd, La Vergne TN 37086
Tel (615) 501-7500 SIC 3577

GUNZE ELECTRONICS USA CORP p 648
2113 Wells Branch Pkwy # 54, Austin TX 78728
Tel (512) 990-3400 SIC 3577

TOUCH INTERNATIONAL INC p 1463
2222 W Rundberg Ln # 200, Austin TX 78758
Tel (512) 832-8292 SIC 3575 3577

▲ **XPLORE TECHNOLOGIES CORP** p 1632
8601 Ranch Road 2222 Ii, Austin TX 78730
Tel (512) 336-7797 SIC 3577

■ **DELL INC** p 425
1 Dell Way, Round Rock TX 78682
Tel (512) 338-4400
SIC 3571 3572 3575 3577 7372 7379

■ **DENALI INTERMEDIATE INC** p 428
1 Dell Way, Round Rock TX 78682
Tel (713) 627-0933
SIC 3571 3572 3577 7372

MACK GROUP INC p 892
608 Warm Brook Rd, Arlington VT 05250
Tel (802) 375-2511 SIC 3089 3577 6719

MACK MOLDING CO INC p 892
608 Warm Brook Rd, Arlington VT 05250
Tel (802) 375-2511 SIC 3089 3577

SYBASE 365 INC p 1413
4511 Singer Ct Ste 300, Chantilly VA 20151
Tel (925) 236-5000 SIC 3577

HARRIS TECHNICAL SERVICES CORP p 664
21000 Atl Blvd Ste 300, Dulles VA 20166
Tel (703) 610-4200
SIC 7371 7379 8711 3577

CANON VIRGINIA INC p 247
12000 Canon Blvd, Newport News VA 23606
Tel (757) 881-6000
SIC 3861 3577 3555 4953

CORNET TECHNOLOGY INC p 371
6800 Versar Ctr, Springfield VA 22151
Tel (703) 658-3400 SIC 5065 3669 3577

■ **INTERMEC INC** p 753
16201 25th Ave W, Lynnwood WA 98087
Tel (425) 348-2600 SIC 3577

■ **INTERMEC TECHNOLOGIES CORP** p 753
16201 25th Ave W, Lynnwood WA 98087
Tel (425) 348-2600 SIC 3577 2759

▲ **MICROSOFT CORP** p 962
1 Microsoft Way, Redmond WA 98052
Tel (425) 882-8080
SIC 7372 7371 3577 7375

▲ **KEYTRONIC CORP** p 815
4424 N Sullivan Rd, Spokane Valley WA 99216
Tel (509) 928-8000 SIC 3577

▲ **BRADY CORP** p 207
6555 W Good Hope Rd, Milwaukee WI 53223
Tel (414) 358-6600
SIC 3993 2672 3695 3577

■ **BANTA GLOBAL TURNKEY LTD** p 153
1600 Disk Dr, Plover WI 54467
Tel (715) 341-0544 SIC 3577

DEDICATED COMPUTING LLC p 421
N26w23880 Commerce Cir B, Waukesha WI 53188
Tel (262) 951-7200 SIC 3571 3577 5045

SIC 3578 Calculating & Accounting Eqpt

■ **HYPERCOM CORP** p 724
8888 E Raintree Dr # 300, Scottsdale AZ 85260
Tel (480) 642-5000
SIC 3578 7372 7299 5065

■ **VERIFONE INC** p 1549
88 W Plumeria Dr, San Jose CA 95134
Tel (408) 232-7800
SIC 3578 7372 3577 3575 8711 3643

▲ **VERIFONE SYSTEMS INC** p 1549
88 W Plumeria Dr, San Jose CA 95134
Tel (408) 232-7800 SIC 3578 7372

■ **METAVANTE HOLDINGS LLC** p 953
601 Riverside Ave, Jacksonville FL 32204
Tel (904) 438-6000 SIC 3578 5049 7374

■ **AUTOTOTE SYSTEMS INC** p 135
1500 Bluegrass Lakes Pkwy, Alpharetta GA 30004
Tel (770) 664-3700
SIC 3578 7373 7359 8711

▲ **NCR CORP** p 1022
3097 Satellite Blvd # 100, Duluth GA 30096
Tel (937) 445-5000
SIC 3575 3578 7379 7374 7371

PFINGSTEN PARTNERS LLC p 1140
300 N Lasalle St 5400, Chicago IL 60654
Tel (312) 222-8707
SIC 5065 6211 3679 3578

TALARIS INC p 1422
3333 Warrenville Rd # 310, Lisle IL 60532
Tel (630) 577-1000 SIC 3578 3499

CUMMINS - ALLISON CORP p 401
852 Feehanville Dr, Mount Prospect IL 60056
Tel (847) 759-6403 SIC 3578 3519

▲ **CHURCHILL DOWNS INC** p 305
600 N Hurstbourne Pkwy, Louisville KY 40222
Tel (502) 636-4400 SIC 7948 7993 3578

■ **MICROS SYSTEMS INC** p 962
7031 Columbia Gateway Dr # 1, Columbia MD 21046
Tel (443) 285-6000
SIC 7373 7372 3577 3578

DUMAC BUSINESS SYSTEMS INC p 461
19 Corporate Cir Ste 1, East Syracuse NY 13057
Tel (315) 463-1010 SIC 5045 7699 3578

■ **HAND HELD PRODUCTS INC** p 657
700 Visions Dr, Skaneateles Falls NY 13153
Tel (315) 554-6000
SIC 3577 3571 3663 3578

DIEBOLD SELF SERVICE SYSTEMS p 438
5995 Mayfair Rd, Canton OH 44720
Tel (330) 490-5099 SIC 3578

▲ **DIEBOLD INC** p 438
5995 Mayfair Rd, North Canton OH 44720
Tel (330) 490-4000 SIC 3578 3699 3499

VESTA CORP p 1552
11950 Sw Garden Pl, Portland OR 97223
Tel (503) 639-0235 SIC 3559 3578

SICOM SYSTEMS INC p 1319
4434 Progress Meadow Dr, Doylestown PA 18902
Tel (215) 489-2500 SIC 5045 3578 7379

■ **CRANE PAYMENT INNOVATIONS INC** p 389
3222 Phoenixville Pike # 200, Malvern PA 19355
Tel (610) 430-2700 SIC 3578

▲ **TEXAS INSTRUMENTS INC** p 1443
12500 Ti Blvd, Dallas TX 75243
Tel (214) 479-3773
SIC 3674 3613 3822 3578

OBERTHUR TECHNOLOGIES OF AMERICA CORP p 1072
4250 Pleasant Valley Rd, Chantilly VA 20151
Tel (703) 263-0100
SIC 3089 7382 3953 3578 3499

SIC 3579 Office Machines, NEC

▲ **ACME UNITED CORP** p 18
55 Walls Dr Ste 201, Fairfield CT 06824
Tel (203) 254-6060
SIC 3421 2499 3842 3579 3069 3999

NEOPOST USA INC p 1026
478 Wheelers Farms Rd, Milford CT 06461
Tel (203) 301-3400 SIC 3579 7359 7629

▲ **XEROX CORP** p 1631
45 Glover Ave Ste 700, Norwalk CT 06850
Tel (203) 968-3000
SIC 3861 3579 3577 7629 7378 7374

▲ **PITNEY BOWES INC** p 1152
3001 Summer St Ste 3, Stamford CT 06905
Tel (203) 356-5000
SIC 3579 7359 3661 8744 7372

■ **DICTAPHONE CORP** p 438
3191 Broadbridge Ave, Stratford CT 06614
Tel (203) 381-7000
SIC 3579 3825 3695 3577

■ **BLACK & DECKER INC** p 186
1423 Kirkwood Hwy, Newark DE 19711
Tel (302) 738-0250
SIC 3429 3452 3579 3423 3949

■ **B WILLIAMS HOLDING CORP** p 142
1403 Foulk Rd Ste 200, Wilmington DE 19803
Tel (302) 656-8596
SIC 3579 3661 3861 7359 7629 6159

SIMPLEXGRINNELL HOLDINGS LLC p 1325
1501 Nw 51st St, Boca Raton FL 33431
Tel (561) 988-7200
SIC 3579 3669 3699 3822

FELLOWES INC p 537
1789 Norwood Ave, Itasca IL 60143
Tel (630) 893-1600
SIC 2522 3589 2653 3577 3572 3579

GENERAL BINDING CORP p 599
4 Corporate Dr, Lake Zurich IL 60047
Tel (847) 541-9500
SIC 5044 2782 3559 3589 7629 3579

BOWE BELL + HOWELL HOLDINGS INC p 204
760 S Wolf Rd, Wheeling IL 60090
Tel (312) 541-9300 SIC 3579

■ **VIDEOJET TECHNOLOGIES INC** p 1556
1500 N Mittel Blvd, Wood Dale IL 60191
Tel (630) 860-7300 SIC 3579

▲ **ESCALADE INC** p 509
817 Maxwell Ave, Evansville IN 47711
Tel (812) 467-4449 SIC 3949 3579

BASTIAN AUTOMATION ENGINEERING LLC p 159
2155 Fields Blvd, Greenfield IN 46140
Tel (317) 467-2583 SIC 3579 7699

TSI INC p 1489
500 Cardigan Rd, Saint Paul MN 55126
Tel (651) 483-0900
SIC 3579 3829 3823 3845 3825

ENTRUST DATACARD CORP p 503
1187 Park Pl, Shakopee MN 55379
Tel (952) 933-1223
SIC 3579 3089 7373 7372

BROTHER INTERNATIONAL CORP p 219
200 Crossing Blvd, Bridgewater NJ 08807
Tel (908) 704-1700
SIC 5044 3579 3559 5084 5064 5065

OPEX CORP p 1089
305 Commerce Dr, Moorestown NJ 08057
Tel (856) 727-1100 SIC 3579

AMANO USA HOLDINGS INC p 64
140 Harrison Ave, Roseland NJ 07068
Tel (973) 403-1900
SIC 3589 2842 3579 3559 5169 5087

■ **ARROW FASTENER CO LLC** p 113
271 Mayhill St, Saddle Brook NJ 07663
Tel (201) 843-6900
SIC 3579 3315 3452 3542 2891 3586

ESSELTE HOLDINGS INC p 510
48 S Service Rd Ste 400, Melville NY 11747
Tel (631) 675-5700
SIC 2675 2782 3579 2672 3953 3596

BELL AND HOWELL LLC p 169
3791 S Alston Ave, Durham NC 27713
Tel (919) 767-4401 SIC 3579

CONTRADO BBH HOLDINGS LLC p 364
2929 Arch St Fl 27, Philadelphia PA 19104
Tel (215) 609-3400 SIC 3579

■ **STANLEY FASTENING SYSTEMS LP** p 1377
2 Briggs Dr, East Greenwich RI 02818
Tel (401) 884-2500 SIC 3399 3579

BROTHER INDUSTRIES (USA) INC p 219
7819 N Brother Blvd, Memphis TN 38133
Tel (901) 377-7777 SIC 3579

SIC 3581 Automatic Vending Machines

■ **MAYTAG CORP** p 924
2000 N M 63, Benton Harbor MI 49022
Tel (269) 923-5000
SIC 3633 3631 3632 3639 3635 3581

COIN ACCEPTORS INC p 335
300 Hunter Ave, Saint Louis MO 63124
Tel (314) 725-0100 SIC 3581

ROYAL VENDORS INC p 1254
300 Hunter Ave Fl 2, Saint Louis MO 63124
Tel (304) 728-7056 SIC 3581

GOLD MEDAL PRODUCTS CO p 620
10700 Medallion Dr, Cincinnati OH 45241
Tel (513) 769-7676
SIC 3556 3589 5145 3581

■ **CRANE MERCHANDISING SYSTEMS INC** p 389
3330 Crane Way, Williston SC 29853
Tel (803) 266-5000 SIC 3581 3531

■ **DIXIE-NARCO INC** p 445
3330 Dixie Narco Blvd, Williston SC 29853
Tel (803) 266-5000 SIC 3581

SANDENVENDO AMERICA INC p 1278
10710 Sanden Dr, Dallas TX 75238
Tel (800) 344-7216 SIC 3581

SANDEN OF AMERICA INC p 1278
601 Sanden Blvd, Wylie TX 75098
Tel (972) 442-8400 SIC 3585 3581

SIC 3582 Commercial Laundry, Dry Clean & Pressing Mchs

DEXTER APACHE HOLDINGS INC p 434
2211 W Grimes Ave, Fairfield IA 52556
Tel (641) 472-5131 SIC 3321 3582

■ **AMERICAN DRYER CORP** p 71
88 Currant Rd, Fall River MA 02720
Tel (508) 678-9000 SIC 3582

HUSQVARNA US HOLDING INC p 721
20445 Emerald Pkwy, Cleveland OH 44135
Tel (216) 898-1800 SIC 3582

ALLIANCE LAUNDRY HOLDINGS LLC p 54
221 Shepard St, Ripon WI 54971
Tel (920) 748-3121 SIC 3582 3633

ALLIANCE LAUNDRY SYSTEMS LLC p 54
221 Shepard St, Ripon WI 54971
Tel (920) 748-3121 SIC 3582 3633

SIC 3585 Air Conditioning & Heating Eqpt

ESSICK AIR PRODUCTS INC p 510
5800 Murray St, Little Rock AR 72209
Tel (501) 562-1094 SIC 3534 3585 3634

ENERGY LABS INC p 497
1695 Cactus Rd, San Diego CA 92154
Tel (619) 671-0100 SIC 3585

■ **ANTHONY DOORS INC** p 94
12391 Montero Ave, Sylmar CA 91342
Tel (818) 365-9451 SIC 3585

MILE HIGH EQUIPMENT LLC p 969
11100 E 45th Ave, Denver CO 80239
Tel (303) 576-2940 *SIC* 3585

■ CARRIER COMMERCIAL REFRIGERATION INC p 260
1 Carrier Pl, Farmington CT 06032
Tel (860) 674-3000 *SIC* 3585

■ CARRIER COMMERCIAL REFRIGERATION INC p 260
3 Farm Glen Blvd Ste 301, Farmington CT 06032
Tel (336) 245-6400
SIC 3556 3631 3585 3589 3634

▲ UNITED TECHNOLOGIES CORP p 1514
10 Farm Springs Rd, Farmington CT 06032
Tel (860) 728-7000
SIC 3724 3585 3721 3534 3669 3699

ALVEST (USA) INC p 63
812 Bloomfield Ave, Windsor CT 06095
Tel (860) 602-3400 *SIC* 3585 3535

■ EECO INC p 480
850 Library Ave Ste 204c, Newark DE 19711
Tel (302) 456-1448
SIC 3823 3491 3621 3585 3546 3679

J T WALKER INDUSTRIES INC p 772
861 N Hercules Ave, Clearwater FL 33765
Tel (727) 461-0501
SIC 3442 3089 3585 5193

METAL INDUSTRIES INC p 952
1985 Carroll St, Clearwater FL 33765
Tel (727) 441-2651 *SIC* 3585

FHP MANUFACTURING CO p 539
601 Nw 65th Ct, Fort Lauderdale FL 33309
Tel (954) 776-5471 *SIC* 3585

■ CARRIER CORP p 260
17900 Bee Line Hwy, Jupiter FL 33478
Tel (561) 796-2000 *SIC* 3585

BEAM ASSOCIATES LLC p 165
301 Commerce Blvd Ste 2, Oldsmar FL 34677
Tel (813) 855-5695 *SIC* 3585

MI METALS INC p 959
301 Commerce Blvd, Oldsmar FL 34677
Tel (813) 855-5695 *SIC* 3585

■ KYSOR INDUSTRIAL CORP p 833
2227 Welbilt Blvd, Trinity FL 34655
Tel (727) 376-8600 *SIC* 3585 3714

▲ MANITOWOC FOODSERVICE INC p 902
2227 Welbilt Blvd, Trinity FL 34655
Tel (727) 375-7010 *SIC* 3585 3589

RHEEM MANUFACTURING CO INC p 1231
1100 Abernathy Rd # 1700, Atlanta GA 30328
Tel (770) 351-3000 *SIC* 3585 3433

RHEEM SALES CO INC p 1231
1100 Abernathy Rd # 1400, Atlanta GA 30328
Tel (770) 351-3016 *SIC* 3585

SIMS ENTERPRISES OF GEORGIA LLC p 1325
205 Creekview Blvd, Covington GA 30016
Tel (770) 385-3461 *SIC* 3585

SEASONS-4 INC p 1297
4500 Industrial Access Rd, Douglasville GA 30134
Tel (770) 489-0716 *SIC* 3585 3567

HOSHIZAKI AMERICA INC p 708
618 Highway 74 S, Peachtree City GA 30269
Tel (770) 487-2331 *SIC* 3585 5078

■ HEATCRAFT REFRIGERATION PRODUCTS LLC p 679
2175 W Park Place Blvd, Stone Mountain GA 30087
Tel (770) 465-5600 *SIC* 3585

HENRY TECHNOLOGIES INC p 684
701 S Main St, Chatham IL 62629
Tel (217) 483-2406
SIC 3491 3585 3567 3564 3545 3494

AMSTED INDUSTRIES INC p 87
180 N Stetson Ave, Chicago IL 60601
Tel (312) 645-1700
SIC 3443 3325 3585 3321 3743

▲ CONTINENTAL MATERIALS CORP p 363
440 S La Salle St # 3100, Chicago IL 60605
Tel (312) 541-7200 *SIC* 3585 3273 5031

▲ JOHN BEAN TECHNOLOGIES CORP p 787
70 W Madison St Ste 4400, Chicago IL 60602
Tel (312) 861-5900 *SIC* 3556 3585 3537

■ MARSHALL MIDDLEBY INC p 911
1400 Toastmaster Dr, Elgin IL 60120
Tel (847) 289-0204 *SIC* 3556 3585 3631

■ CORNELIUS INC p 370
101 Regency Dr, Glendale Heights IL 60139
Tel (630) 539-6850 *SIC* 3585 3556 3586

▲ ILLINOIS TOOL WORKS INC p 732
155 Harlem Ave, Glenview IL 60025
Tel (847) 724-7500
SIC 3089 3965 3499 2891 3585

ELKAY MANUFACTURING CO INC p 487
2222 Camden Ct, Oak Brook IL 60523
Tel (630) 574-8484
SIC 3431 3585 3432 2434

BERGSTROM CLIMATE SYSTEMS LLC p 174
2390 Blackhawk Rd, Rockford IL 61109
Tel (815) 874-7821 *SIC* 3585

■ CERRO FLOW PRODUCTS LLC p 284
3000 Mississippi Ave, Sauget IL 62206
Tel (618) 337-6000
SIC 3351 3331 3498 3585 5051

AEC INC p 28
1100 E Wdfield Rd Ste 588, Schaumburg IL 60173
Tel (847) 273-7700
SIC 3585 3823 3559 3443 3535

SCOTSMAN INDUSTRIES INC p 1293
101 Corporate Woods Pkwy, Vernon Hills IL 60061
Tel (847) 215-4501 *SIC* 3585 3632

KELCO INDUSTRIES INC p 808
1425 Lake Ave, Woodstock IL 60098
Tel (815) 334-3600
SIC 3599 3069 3494 3585 3544 3625

TOYOTA INDUSTRIES NORTH AMERICA INC p 1466
3030 Barker Dr, Columbus IN 47201
Tel (812) 341-3810 *SIC* 3585 5084

■ SUPREME CORP p 1408
2581 Kercher Rd, Goshen IN 46528
Tel (574) 642-4888 *SIC* 3713 3792 3585

■ MANITOWOC BEVERAGE SYSTEMS INC p 902
2100 Future Dr, Sellersburg IN 47172
Tel (419) 861-0800 *SIC* 3585

AIRTEX MANUFACTURING LLLP p 40
32050 W 83rd St, De Soto KS 66018
Tel (913) 583-3181
SIC 3585 5075 3564 3433

AHI HOLDINGS INC p 36
3050 N Saint Francis St, Wichita KS 67219
Tel (316) 832-3484 *SIC* 3585 3444

AIRXCEL INC p 41
3050 N Saint Francis St, Wichita KS 67219
Tel (316) 832-3400 *SIC* 3585

AAF-MCQUAY GROUP INC p 8
9920 Corporate Campus Dr # 2200, Louisville KY 40223
Tel (502) 637-0111
SIC 5075 3585 3564 7623

YOKOHAMA INDUSTRIES AMERICAS INC p 1637
105 Industry Dr, Versailles KY 40383
Tel (859) 873-2188
SIC 3714 3585 3492 3052

DANFOSS LLC p 411
11655 Crossroads Cir A, Baltimore MD 21220
Tel (410) 931-8250 *SIC* 3585 3625 3822

STULZ AIR TECHNOLOGY SYSTEM INC p 1395
1572 Tilco Dr, Frederick MD 21704
Tel (301) 620-2033 *SIC* 3585

BALTIMORE AIRCOIL CO INC p 149
7600 Dorsey Run Rd, Jessup MD 20794
Tel (410) 799-6200 *SIC* 3585 3443

EVAPCO INC p 513
5151 Allendale Ln, Taneytown MD 21787
Tel (410) 756-2600 *SIC* 3443 3585

MUNTERS CORP p 1001
79 Monroe St, Amesbury MA 01913
Tel (978) 241-1100
SIC 3585 3822 3569 3564

MUNTERS USA INC p 1001
79 Monroe St, Amesbury MA 01913
Tel (978) 241-1100 *SIC* 3585

LEE THOMAS H EQUITY FUND V LIMITED PARTNERSHIP p 852
100 Federal St Ste 3500, Boston MA 02110
Tel (617) 737-3261
SIC 3585 3444 3634 2431 3699

THL-NORTEK INVESTORS LLC p 1448
100 Federal St Ste 3100, Boston MA 02110
Tel (617) 227-1050
SIC 3585 3444 3634 2431

MESTEK INC p 951
260 N Elm St, Westfield MA 01085
Tel (413) 568-9571
SIC 3585 3634 3549 3542 3354

ETX HOLDINGS INC p 512
2000 Michigan Ave, Alma MI 48801
Tel (989) 463-1151
SIC 3585 3621 3714 5013 3089

MA INDUSTRIAL JV LLC p 891
5683 Hines Dr, Ann Arbor MI 48108
Tel (734) 585-9500 *SIC* 3585 3679 6719

TECUMSEH PRODUCTS CO p 1432
5683 Hines Dr, Ann Arbor MI 48108
Tel (734) 585-9500 *SIC* 3585 3679

TI AUTOMOTIVE LLC p 1452
2020 Taylor Rd, Auburn Hills MI 48326
Tel (248) 494-5000
SIC 3317 3312 3599 3052 3714 3585

TI GROUP AUTOMOTIVE SYSTEMS LLC p 1452
2020 Taylor Rd, Auburn Hills MI 48326
Tel (248) 296-8000
SIC 3317 3312 3599 3052 3714 3585

▲ WHIRLPOOL CORP p 1605
2000 N M 63, Benton Harbor MI 49022
Tel (269) 923-5000
SIC 3633 3585 3632 3635

MICHIGAN AUTOMOTIVE COMPRESSOR INC p 960
2400 N Dearing Rd, Parma MI 49269
Tel (517) 622-7000
SIC 3585 3714 3568 3563

HELLA CORPORATE CENTER USA INC p 681
43811 Plymouth Oaks Blvd, Plymouth MI 48170
Tel (586) 232-4788
SIC 3625 5013 5088 3822 3585 3429

MANN + HUMMEL INC p 902
6400 S Sprinkle Rd, Portage MI 49002
Tel (269) 329-3900 *SIC* 3559 3585

HANON SYSTEMS USA LLC p 658
1 Village Center Dr, Van Buren Twp MI 48111
Tel (734) 710-5000 *SIC* 3714 3585 3699

PENTAIR TECHNICAL PRODUCTS p 1132
2100 Hoffman Way, Anoka MN 55303
Tel (763) 323-8200 *SIC* 3585 3443

NORTEK AIR SOLUTIONS LLC p 1049
13200 Pioneer Trl Ste 150, Eden Prairie MN 55347
Tel (952) 358-6600 *SIC* 3585

DAIKIN APPLIED AMERICAS INC p 408
13600 Industrial Pk Blvd, Minneapolis MN 55441
Tel (763) 553-5330 *SIC* 5075 3585

THERMO KING CORP p 1447
314 W 90th St, Minneapolis MN 55420
Tel (952) 887-2200 *SIC* 3585

■ ADVANCED DISTRIBUTOR PRODUCTS LLC p 25
1995 Air Industrial Pk Rd, Grenada MS 38901
Tel (662) 229-3000 *SIC* 3585

LUVATA GRENADA LLC p 887
3984 Highway 51 S, Grenada MS 38901
Tel (662) 226-3421 *SIC* 3621 3585

HUSSMANN CORP p 721
12999 St Charles Rock Rd, Bridgeton MO 63044
Tel (314) 291-2000 *SIC* 3585

HUSSMANN INTERNATIONAL INC p 721
12999 St Charles Rock Rd, Bridgeton MO 63044
Tel (314) 291-2000 *SIC* 3585 5963

RUSKIN CO p 1259
3900 Doctor Greaves Rd, Grandview MO 64030
Tel (816) 761-7476 *SIC* 3822 3446 3585

ARIZON COMPANIES INC p 108
11880 Dorsett Rd, Maryland Heights MO 63043
Tel (314) 739-0037
SIC 3585 1711 2394 1541 1542 8611

NORTEK GLOBAL HVAC LLC p 1049
8000 Phoenix Pkwy, O Fallon MO 63368
Tel (636) 561-7300 *SIC* 3585 3567 3433

TRUE MANUFACTURING CO INC p 1486
2001 E Terra Ln, O Fallon MO 63366
Tel (636) 240-2400 *SIC* 3585

▲ EMERSON ELECTRIC CO p 492
8000 W Florissant Ave, Saint Louis MO 63136
Tel (314) 553-2000
SIC 3823 3491 3621 3585 3679

▲ STANDEX INTERNATIONAL CORP p 1376
11 Keewaydin Dr, Salem NH 03079
Tel (603) 893-9701 *SIC* 3585 3549 3675

FUJITSU GENERAL AMERICA INC p 584
353 Us Highway 46, Fairfield NJ 07004
Tel (973) 575-0380 *SIC* 3585

CONSTRUCTION SPECIALTIES INC p 361
3 Werner Way Ste 100, Lebanon NJ 08833
Tel (908) 236-0800
SIC 3446 3354 3443 3272 3585

▲ HONEYWELL INTERNATIONAL INC p 705
115 Tabor Rd, Morris Plains NJ 07950
Tel (973) 455-2000
SIC 3724 3812 3585 2824 2821 3714

SODASTREAM USA INC p 1336
200 E Park Dr Ste 600, Mount Laurel NJ 08054
Tel (800) 763-2258 *SIC* 2087 3585

INGERSOLL-RAND US TRANE HOLDINGS CORP p 742
1 Centennial Ave Ste 101, Piscataway NJ 08854
Tel (732) 652-7100 *SIC* 3585

TRANE INC p 1469
1 Centennial Ave Ste 101, Piscataway NJ 08854
Tel (732) 652-7100 *SIC* 3585

TRANE US INC p 1469
1 Centennial Ave Ste 101, Piscataway NJ 08854
Tel (732) 652-7100 *SIC* 3585

▲ GRAHAM CORP p 629
20 Florence Ave, Batavia NY 14020
Tel (585) 343-2216 *SIC* 3563 3585 3443

DYNE DURO NATIONAL CORP p 465
81 Spence St, Bay Shore NY 11706
Tel (631) 249-9000 *SIC* 3585

▲ STANDARD MOTOR PRODUCTS INC p 1376
3718 Northern Blvd # 600, Long Island City NY 11101
Tel (718) 392-0200
SIC 3714 3694 3585 3564 3052

■ GARLOCK SEALING TECHNOLOGIES LLC p 592
1666 Division St, Palmyra NY 14522
Tel (315) 597-4811 *SIC* 3053 3585 3714

■ THERMO FISHER SCIENTIFIC (ASHVILLE) LLC p 1447
28 Schenck Pkwy Ste 400, Asheville NC 28803
Tel (828) 658-2711
SIC 3585 3826 3821 3829

BUHLER AEROGLIDE CORP p 224
100 Aeroglide Dr, Cary NC 27511
Tel (919) 278-2925 *SIC* 3556 3585 3567

ELECTROLUX NORTH AMERICA INC p 485
10200 David Taylor Dr, Charlotte NC 28262
Tel (980) 236-2000
SIC 3631 3585 3632 3633 3635 3639

■ BAHNSON HOLDINGS INC p 145
4731 Commercial Park Ct, Clemmons NC 27012
Tel (336) 760-3111
SIC 8711 1711 3585 3564

JAMES M PLEASANTS CO INC p 776
603 Diamond Hill Ct, Greensboro NC 27406
Tel (336) 275-3152
SIC 5075 3585 3561 3494

▲ PRIMO WATER CORP p 1176
101 N Cherry St Ste 501, Winston Salem NC 27101
Tel (336) 331-4000 *SIC* 5149 3585 5141

AEROQUIP-VICKERS INC p 30
1111 Superior Ave E, Cleveland OH 44114
Tel (216) 523-5000
SIC 3052 3492 3429 3069 3585 3728

EATON-AEROQUIP LLC p 474
1000 Eaton Blvd, Cleveland OH 44122
Tel (216) 523-5000
SIC 3052 3492 3429 3069 3585 3728

CORTES NP ACQUISITION CORP p 373
1050 Dearborn Dr, Columbus OH 43085
Tel (614) 888-0246 *SIC* 3679 3585

LIEBERT CORP p 863
1050 Dearborn Dr, Columbus OH 43085
Tel (614) 888-0246 *SIC* 3585 3613 7629

LIEBERT NORTH AMERICA INC p 863
1050 Dearborn Dr, Columbus OH 43085
Tel (614) 888-0246 *SIC* 3699 3585

LIQUI-BOX CORP p 870
480 Schrock Rd Ste G, Columbus OH 43229
Tel (804) 325-1400
SIC 2673 3585 3089 3081 5149

■ EMERSON CLIMATE TECHNOLOGIES INC p 492
1675 Campbell Rd, Sidney OH 45365
Tel (937) 498-3011 *SIC* 3585

■ HOBART CORP p 698
701 S Ridge Ave, Troy OH 45374
Tel (937) 332-3000
SIC 3589 3556 3596 3585 3321

■ CLIMATE MASTER INC p 326
7300 Sw 44th St, Oklahoma City OK 73179
Tel (405) 745-6000 *SIC* 3585

▲ LSB INDUSTRIES INC p 883
16 S Pennsylvania Ave, Oklahoma City OK 73107
Tel (405) 235-4546
SIC 3822 3585 3567 2873

RAE CORP p 1205
4492 Hunt St, Pryor OK 74361
Tel (918) 825-7222 *SIC* 3585

▲ AAON INC p 8
2425 S Yukon Ave, Tulsa OK 74107
Tel (918) 583-2266 *SIC* 3585

HUNTAIR INC p 719
19855 Sw 124th Ave, Tualatin OR 97062
Tel (503) 639-0113 *SIC* 3585

NATIONAL REFRIGERATION & AIR CONDITIONING PRODUCTS INC p 1015
539 Dunksferry Rd, Bensalem PA 19020
Tel (215) 244-1400 *SIC* 3585 5075

▲ HARSCO CORP p 664
350 Poplar Church Rd, Camp Hill PA 17011
Tel (717) 763-7064
SIC 7359 7353 5082 3443 3585 4789

FOLLETT CORP p 563
801 Church Ln, Easton PA 18040
Tel (610) 252-7301 *SIC* 3585

S P INDUSTRIES INC p 1262
935 Mearns Rd, Warminster PA 18974
Tel (215) 672-7800
SIC 3826 3585 7699 3821

LASKO PRODUCTS INC p 846
820 Lincoln Ave, West Chester PA 19380
Tel (610) 692-7400 *SIC* 4789 3585 3564

GEA REFRIGERATION NORTH AMERICA INC p 597
3475 Board Rd, York PA 17406
Tel (717) 767-6411 *SIC* 3585

YORK INTERNATIONAL CORP p 1637
631 S Richland Ave, York PA 17403
Tel (717) 771-7890 *SIC* 3585

THERMO KING DE PUERTO RICO INC p 1447
517 Zona Industrial, Arecibo PR 00612
Tel (787) 878-1690 *SIC* 3585

NORTEK INC p 1049
500 Exchange St, Providence RI 02903
Tel (401) 751-1600
SIC 3585 3444 3634 3699 2434

SCHNEIDER ELECTRIC IT CORP p 1287
132 Fairgrounds Rd, West Kingston RI 02892
Tel (401) 789-5735
SIC 3629 3612 3677 3585 7372 2542

AMTROL HOLDINGS INC p 87
1400 Division Rd, West Warwick RI 02893
Tel (401) 884-6300 *SIC* 3822 3585 3443

AMTROL INC p 87
1400 Division Rd, West Warwick RI 02893
Tel (401) 884-6300 *SIC* 3443 3585

■ ALLIED AIR ENTERPRISES LLC p 56
215 Metropolitan Dr, West Columbia SC 29170
Tel (803) 738-4000 *SIC* 3585 3433 5075

■ ARMSTRONG AIR CONDITIONING INC p 111
215 Metropolitan Dr, West Columbia SC 29170
Tel (803) 738-4000 *SIC* 3585

SUBURBAN MANUFACTURING CO p 1396
676 Broadway St, Dayton TN 37321
Tel (423) 775-2131 *SIC* 3585

BACKER EHP INC p 143
4700 John Bragg Hwy, Murfreesboro TN 37127
Tel (615) 907-6900 *SIC* 3567 3585

■ KMT REFRIGERATION INC p 824
2915 Tennessee Ave N, Parsons TN 38363
Tel (731) 847-6361 *SIC* 3585 3448 1711

CALSONICKANSEI NORTH AMERICA INC p 243
1 Calsonic Way, Shelbyville TN 37160
Tel (931) 684-4490 *SIC* 3585

CNA INC p 330
1 Calsonic Way, Shelbyville TN 37160
Tel (931) 684-4490 *SIC* 3585

FEDDERS CORP p 533
13455 Noel Rd Ste 2200, Dallas TX 75240
Tel (604) 908-8686
SIC 3585 3674 3634 3564

ATCO RUBBER PRODUCTS INC p 124
7101 Atco Dr, Fort Worth TX 76118
Tel (817) 589-7035
SIC 3443 3084 3585 3444 3083

KPS GLOBAL LLC p 829
4201 N Beach St, Fort Worth TX 76137
Tel (817) 281-5121 *SIC* 3089 3585

MORTEX PRODUCTS INC p 991
501 Terminal Rd, Fort Worth TX 76106
Tel (817) 624-0820
SIC 3585 3433 1711 3999

■ TRAULSEN & CO INC p 1473
4401 Blue Mound Rd, Fort Worth TX 76106
Tel (817) 625-9671 *SIC* 3585

WELBILT WALK-INS LP p 1588
4201 N Beach St, Fort Worth TX 76137
Tel (817) 281-5121 *SIC* 3089 3585

■ IDQ ACQUISITION CORP p 729
2901 W Kingsley Rd, Garland TX 75041
Tel (214) 778-4600 *SIC* 3585

CHILL HOLDINGS INC p 300
5151 San Felipe St # 500, Houston TX 77056
Tel (713) 861-2500 *SIC* 3585

DAIKIN MANUFACTURING CO LP p 408
5151 San Felipe St # 500, Houston TX 77056
Tel (972) 245-1510 *SIC* 3585

ENERFLEX ENERGY SYSTEMS INC p 497
10815 Telge Rd, Houston TX 77095
Tel (281) 345-9300
SIC 3585 7623 7699 3563

GOODMAN GLOBAL HOLDINGS INC p 624
5151 San Felipe St # 500, Houston TX 77056
Tel (713) 861-2500 *SIC* 3585 3564

GOODMAN GLOBAL INC p 624
5151 San Felipe St # 500, Houston TX 77056
Tel (713) 861-2500 *SIC* 3585 3564

GOODMAN MANUFACTURING CO LP p 624
5151 San Felipe St # 500, Houston TX 77056
Tel (877) 254-4729 *SIC* 3585

TURBINE AIR SYSTEMS LTD p 1492
6110 Cullen Blvd, Houston TX 77021
Tel (713) 877-8700 SIC 3585

AUTO AIR EXPORT INC p 133
1401 Valley View Ln # 100, Irving TX 75061
Tel (972) 812-7000 SIC 5075 3585 5531

■ AAON COIL PRODUCTS INC p 8
203 Gum Springs Rd, Longview TX 75602
Tel (903) 236-4403 SIC 3585

AIR DISTRIBUTION TECHNOLOGIES INC p 38
605 Shiloh Rd, Plano TX 75074
Tel (972) 943-6100 SIC 3585

AIR SYSTEM COMPONENTS INC p 39
605 Shiloh Rd, Plano TX 75074
Tel (972) 212-4888 SIC 3585

▲ LENNOX INTERNATIONAL INC p 855
2140 Lake Park Blvd, Richardson TX 75080
Tel (972) 497-5350 SIC 3585 3621

FRIEDRICH AIR CONDITIONING CO LTD p 579
10001 Reunion Pl Ste 500, San Antonio TX 78216
Tel (210) 546-0500 SIC 3585 5722

LANCER CORP p 841
6655 Lancer Blvd, San Antonio TX 78219
Tel (210) 661-6964 SIC 3585

UNITED ELECTRIC CO LP p 1508
501 Galveston St, Wichita Falls TX 76301
Tel (940) 397-2100 SIC 3585

SANDEN INTERNATIONAL (USA) INC p 1278
601 Sanden Blvd, Wylie TX 75098
Tel (972) 442-8941
SIC 3714 1711 3585 3563

SANDEN OF AMERICA INC p 1278
601 Sanden Blvd, Wylie TX 75098
Tel (972) 442-8400 SIC 3585 3581

BRISTOL COMPRESSORS INTERNATIONAL LLC p 214
15185 Industrial Park Rd, Bristol VA 24202
Tel (276) 466-4121 SIC 3585

ALFA LAVAL INC p 49
5400 Intl Trade Dr, Richmond VA 23231
Tel (804) 222-5300
SIC 3491 3433 3585 3569 3821

ALFA LAVAL USA INC p 49
5400 Intl Trade Dr, Richmond VA 23231
Tel (804) 222-5300 SIC 3443 3585

RED DOT CORP p 1215
495 Andover Park E, Tukwila WA 98188
Tel (206) 151-3840 SIC 3714 3585

USNR LLC p 1535
1981 Schurman Way, Woodland WA 98674
Tel (360) 225-8267
SIC 3585 3553 3625 1221 5084

TRANE CO p 1469
3600 Pammel Creek Rd, La Crosse WI 54601
Tel (608) 787-2000 SIC 3585

▲ MANITOWOC CO INC p 902
2400 S 44th St, Manitowoc WI 54220
Tel (920) 684-4410
SIC 3536 3537 3531 3585

CARNES CO INC p 258
600 College Ave, Pewaukee WI 53072
Tel (262) 691-9900
SIC 3822 3444 3585 3669

▲ MODINE MANUFACTURING CO INC p 981
1500 Dekoven Ave, Racine WI 53403
Tel (262) 636-1200
SIC 3443 3714 3433 3585

SIC 3586 Measuring & Dispensing Pumps

VITALITY FOODSERVICE INC p 1562
400 N Tampa St Ste 1700, Tampa FL 33602
Tel (813) 301-4600 SIC 5149 3586

TUTHILL CORP p 1493
8500 S Madison St, Burr Ridge IL 60527
Tel (630) 382-4900 SIC 3561 3586 3524

▲ DOVER CORP p 453
3005 Highland Pkwy # 200, Downers Grove IL 60515
Tel (630) 541-1540
SIC 3632 3586 3533 3577 3674

■ CORNELIUS INC p 370
101 Regency Dr, Glendale Heights IL 60139
Tel (630) 539-6850 SIC 3585 3556 3586

SCRIPTPRO LLC p 1295
5828 Reeds Rd, Shawnee Mission KS 66202
Tel (913) 384-1008 SIC 3559 3586

SMITHS MEDICAL MD INC p 1334
6000 Nathan Ln N Ste 100, Minneapolis MN 55442
Tel (651) 633-2556 SIC 3841 3586 3561

■ ARROW FASTENER CO LLC p 113
271 Mayhill St, Saddle Brook NJ 07663
Tel (201) 843-6900
SIC 3579 3315 3452 3542 2891 3586

■ MARLEY CO LLC p 909
13515 Balntyn Corp Pl, Charlotte NC 28277
Tel (704) 752-4400
SIC 3443 3433 3586 3561 3634

■ GILBARCO INC p 612
7300 W Friendly Ave, Greensboro NC 27410
Tel (336) 547-5000 SIC 3586

GOJO INDUSTRIES INC p 620
1 Gojo Plz Ste 500, Akron OH 44311
Tel (330) 255-6000 SIC 2842 3586 2844

MILTON ROY LLC p 972
201 Ivyland Rd, Ivyland PA 18974
Tel (215) 441-0800 SIC 3561 3586 3826

■ NORDSON EFD LLC p 1048
40 Catamore Blvd, East Providence RI 02914
Tel (401) 434-1680 SIC 3548 3586 3699

SCHLUMBERGER TECHNOLOGY CORP p 1287
100 Gillingham Ln, Sugar Land TX 77478
Tel (281) 285-8500
SIC 1382 1389 3825 3824 3533 3586

SIC 3589 Service Ind Machines, NEC

■ MARATHON EQUIPMENT CO (DELAWARE) p 904
Highway 9 S, Vernon AL 35592
Tel (205) 695-9105 SIC 3589

JACUZZI INC p 775
14525 Monte Vista Ave, Chino CA 91710
Tel (909) 606-7733 SIC 3088 3589

■ STERNO PRODUCTS LLC p 1388
1880 Compton Ave Ste 101, Corona CA 92881
Tel (951) 682-9600
SIC 3641 3645 3589 3634 2899

DYNAMIC COOKING SYSTEMS INC p 464
695 Town Center Dr # 180, Costa Mesa CA 92626
Tel (714) 372-7000 SIC 3589

NITTO AMERICAS INC p 1045
48500 Fremont Blvd, Fremont CA 94538
Tel (510) 445-5400
SIC 2672 3589 5162 5065

WILBUR CURTIS CO INC p 1608
6913 W Acco St, Montebello CA 90640
Tel (323) 837-2300 SIC 3589

HYDRANAUTICS p 723
401 Jones Rd, Oceanside CA 92058
Tel (760) 901-2597 SIC 2899 3589

TECHKO INC p 1431
27301 Calle De La Rosa, San Juan Capistrano CA 92675
Tel (949) 486-0678 SIC 3699 3589

COMPASS WATER SOLUTIONS INC p 351
15542 Mosher Ave, Tustin CA 92780
Tel (949) 222-5777 SIC 3589

■ ZODIAC POOL SOLUTIONS NORTH AMERICA INC p 1644
2620 Commerce Way, Vista CA 92081
Tel (760) 599-9600 SIC 3589

■ ZODIAC POOL SYSTEMS INC p 1644
2620 Commerce Way, Vista CA 92081
Tel (760) 599-9600 SIC 3589 3999

BSI HOLDINGS INC p 222
2495 Uravan St, Aurora CO 80011
Tel (303) 371-2200
SIC 6719 3589 5093 3715 3823 5051

■ CARRIER COMMERCIAL REFRIGERATION INC p 260
3 Farm Glen Blvd Ste 301, Farmington CT 06032
Tel (336) 245-6400
SIC 3556 3631 3585 3589 3634

■ 3M PURIFICATION INC p 3
400 Research Pkwy, Meriden CT 06450
Tel (203) 237-5541 SIC 3589 3569

▲ CRANE CO p 388
100 1st Stamford Pl # 300, Stamford CT 06902
Tel (203) 363-7300
SIC 3492 3494 3594 3589 3728 5031

EAGLE GROUP INC p 468
100 Industrial Blvd, Clayton DE 19938
Tel (302) 653-3000 SIC 3589 8099

METAL MASTERS FOODSERVICE EQUIPMENT CO INC p 952
100 Industrial Blvd, Clayton DE 19938
Tel (302) 653-3000 SIC 3589 3556

FRANKE USA HOLDING INC p 574
1105 N Market St Ste 1300, Wilmington DE 19801
Tel (615) 462-4000 SIC 3589 5023 5084

RHI REFRACTORIES HOLDING CO p 1231
1105 N Market St Ste 1300, Wilmington DE 19801
Tel (302) 655-6497
SIC 3297 3255 1459 3546 3272 3589

SEVERN TRENT (DEL) INC p 1309
1011 Centre Rd Ste 320, Wilmington DE 19805
Tel (302) 427-5990 SIC 3589 7371 8741

SUEZ NORTH AMERICA INC p 1396
2000 First State Blvd, Wilmington DE 19804
Tel (302) 633-5670 SIC 4941 3569 3589

ESD WASTE2WATER INC p 509
495 Oak Rd, Ocala FL 34472
Tel (800) 277-3279 SIC 3589

SONNYS ENTERPRISES INC p 1340
5605 Hiatus Rd, Tamarac FL 33321
Tel (954) 720-4100 SIC 5087 3589

▲ MANITOWOC FOODSERVICE INC p 902
2227 Welbilt Blvd, Trinity FL 34655
Tel (727) 375-7010 SIC 3585 3589

KASON INDUSTRIES INC p 804
57 Amlajack Blvd, Newnan GA 30265
Tel (770) 251-1422 SIC 3589

KIMBERLY-CLARK PROFESSIONAL p 818
1400 Holcomb Bridge Rd, Roswell GA 30076
Tel (800) 241-3146 SIC 3589

COMPASS CHEMICAL INTERNATIONAL LLC p 351
5544 Oakdale Rd Se, Smyrna GA 30082
Tel (404) 696-6711 SIC 5169 3589

CLEAVER-BROOKS INC p 325
221 Law St, Thomasville GA 31792
Tel (229) 226-3024
SIC 3589 3569 3561 3433 3443

■ PRINCE CASTLE LLC p 1176
355 Kehoe Blvd, Carol Stream IL 60188
Tel (630) 462-8800 SIC 3589

HEICO COMPANIES L L C p 680
5600 Three First Nat Plz, Chicago IL 60602
Tel (312) 419-8220
SIC 3315 3589 3448 3531 1731 3663

■ MARMON HOLDINGS INC p 909
181 W Madison St Ste 2600, Chicago IL 60602
Tel (312) 372-9500
SIC 5051 3351 3743 4741 3423 3589

■ MARMON INDUSTRIAL LLC p 909
181 W Madison St Fl 26, Chicago IL 60602
Tel (312) 372-9500
SIC 3743 4741 3589 6159 3965 3492

HOLDEN INDUSTRIES INC p 700
500 Lake Cook Rd Ste 400, Deerfield IL 60015
Tel (847) 940-1500
SIC 2752 2672 3545 3589 3541 3441

▲ MIDDLEBY CORP p 965
1400 Toastmaster Dr, Elgin IL 60120
Tel (847) 741-3300 SIC 3556 3589

FELLOWES INC p 537
1789 Norwood Ave, Itasca IL 60143
Tel (630) 893-1600
SIC 2522 3589 2653 3577 3572 3579

GENERAL BINDING CORP p 599
4 Corporate Dr, Lake Zurich IL 60047
Tel (847) 541-9500
SIC 5044 2782 3559 3589 7629 3579

CULLIGAN INTERNATIONAL CO p 400
9399 W Higgins Rd # 1100, Rosemont IL 60018
Tel (847) 430-2800 SIC 3589

BUNN-O-MATIC CORP p 226
5020 Ash Grove Dr, Springfield IL 62711
Tel (217) 529-6601 SIC 3589

ALI GROUP NORTH AMERICA CORP p 50
101 Corporate Woods Pkwy, Vernon Hills IL 60061
Tel (847) 215-6565 SIC 3589

RYKO SOLUTIONS INC p 1261
1500 Se 37th St, Grimes IA 50111
Tel (515) 986-3700 SIC 3589 1796 7699

PARAGON INTERNATIONAL INC p 1113
731 W 18th St, Nevada IA 50201
Tel (515) 382-8000 SIC 3589 3556 3431

SMITH AND LOVELESS INC p 1333
14040 Santa Fe Trail Dr, Shawnee Mission KS 66215
Tel (913) 888-5201 SIC 3589 5074

■ FRYMASTER LLC p 582
8700 Line Ave, Shreveport LA 71106
Tel (318) 865-1711 SIC 3589 5046

■ GE IONICS INC p 596
3 Burlington Woods Dr # 200, Burlington MA 01803
Tel (781) 359-7000
SIC 3589 2086 4941 3559 2899 3823

SWEEPSTER ATTACHMENTS LLC p 1411
2800 Zeeb Rd, Dexter MI 48130
Tel (734) 996-9116 SIC 3589 3991

BISSELL INC p 185
2345 Walker Ave Nw, Grand Rapids MI 49544
Tel (616) 453-4451 SIC 3589 2842 3635

■ DELFIELD CO LLC p 424
980 S Isabella Rd, Mount Pleasant MI 48858
Tel (989) 773-7981 SIC 3589

HINES CORP p 695
1218 E Pontaluna Rd Ste B, Norton Shores MI 49456
Tel (231) 799-6240
SIC 3443 3823 3589 3531 3535 5082

NILFISK INC p 1043
9435 Winnetka Ave N, Brooklyn Park MN 55445
Tel (800) 334-1083 SIC 3589 5087

OSMONICS INC p 1097
5951 Clearwater Dr, Hopkins MN 55343
Tel (952) 933-2277
SIC 3569 3589 3561 3824 3823 3089

■ MEDIVATORS INC p 938
14605 28th Ave N, Minneapolis MN 55447
Tel (763) 553-3300
SIC 3841 3842 3845 3589

PENTAIR INC p 1132
5500 Wayzata Blvd Ste 600, Minneapolis MN 55416
Tel (763) 545-1730
SIC 3491 3559 4971 3589

▲ TENNANT CO p 1437
701 Lilac Dr N, Minneapolis MN 55422
Tel (763) 540-1200 SIC 3589 3635

■ ECOWATER SYSTEMS LLC p 476
1890 Woodlane Dr, Saint Paul MN 55125
Tel (651) 731-7401 SIC 5074 3589

■ CRANE MERCHANDISING SYSTEMS INC p 389
2043 Wdlnd Pkwy Ste 102, Saint Louis MO 63146
Tel (314) 298-3500 SIC 3589 5087

DUKE MFG PROPERTIES LLC p 460
2224 N 10th St, Saint Louis MO 63102
Tel (800) 735-3853 SIC 3589 3556

▲ KATY INDUSTRIES INC p 805
11840 Westline Industrial, Saint Louis MO 63146
Tel (314) 656-4321 SIC 3589 2673

■ NEW STAR HOLDINGS INTERNATIONAL INC p 1033
10 Sunnen Dr, Saint Louis MO 63143
Tel (800) 264-7827 SIC 3589

■ STAR INTERNATIONAL HOLDINGS INC p 1378
10 Sunnen Dr, Saint Louis MO 63143
Tel (314) 781-2777 SIC 3589

GLOBAL INDUSTRIES INC p 617
1804 E 4th St, Grand Island NE 68801
Tel (800) 247-6621
SIC 7992 3589 3444 5084 5083 3535

■ PITCO FRIALATOR INC p 1152
553 Route 3a, Bow NH 03304
Tel (603) 225-6684 SIC 3589

LANXESS SYBRON CHEMICALS INC p 844
200 Birmingham Rd, Birmingham NJ 08011
Tel (609) 893-1100 SIC 2843 2899 3589

HAYWARD INDUSTRIES INC p 670
620 Division St, Elizabeth NJ 07201
Tel (908) 351-5400
SIC 3589 3561 3423 3494 3569 3089

▲ CANTEL MEDICAL CORP p 247
150 Clove Rd Ste 36, Little Falls NJ 07424
Tel (973) 890-7220 SIC 3841 3589

SUEZ TREATMENT SOLUTIONS INC p 1396
461 From Rd Ste 400, Paramus NJ 07652
Tel (804) 756-7600 SIC 3589

AMANO USA HOLDINGS INC p 64
140 Harrison Ave, Roseland NJ 07068
Tel (973) 403-1900
SIC 3589 2842 2579 3559 5169 5087

KINPLEX CORP p 821
200 Heartland Blvd, Edgewood NY 11717
Tel (631) 242-4800 SIC 3589

BLUE TEE CORP p 192
387 Park Ave S Fl 5, New York NY 10016
Tel (212) 598-0880
SIC 3533 3589 5093 3715 3823 5051

CLAYTON DUBILIER & RICE INC p 323
375 Park Ave Fl 18, New York NY 10152
Tel (212) 407-5200 SIC 6799 3589 5812

EWT HOLDINGS III CORP p 516
666 5th Ave Fl 36, New York NY 10103
Tel (212) 644-5900
SIC 3589 3823 3826 4941 5051

PENTAIR WATER POOL AND SPA INC p 1132
1620 Hawkins Ave, Sanford NC 27330
Tel (919) 774-4151
SIC 3589 3561 3569 3648

■ SHRED-IT USA LLC p 1319
11311 Cornell Park Dr # 125, Blue Ash OH 45242
Tel (513) 699-0845 SIC 3589

GOLD MEDAL PRODUCTS CO p 620
10700 Medallion Dr, Cincinnati OH 45241
Tel (513) 769-7676
SIC 3556 3589 5145 3581

HENNY PENNY CORP p 683
1219 Us Route 35, Eaton OH 45320
Tel (937) 456-8400 SIC 3589

MPW INDUSTRIAL SERVICES GROUP INC p 996
9711 Lancaster Rd, Hebron OH 43025
Tel (740) 927-8790 SIC 7349 8744 3589

KINETICO INC p 820
10845 Kinsman Rd, Newbury OH 44065
Tel (440) 564-9111 SIC 3589 5074

■ HOBART CORP p 698
701 S Ridge Ave, Troy OH 45374
Tel (937) 332-3000
SIC 3589 3556 3596 3585 3321

AQUATECH INTERNATIONAL LLC p 101
1 Four Coins Dr, Canonsburg PA 15317
Tel (724) 746-5300 SIC 3589

GLOBAL INDUSTRIAL TECHNOLOGIES INC p 616
1305 Chrrington Pkwy Moon, Coraopolis PA 15108
Tel (412) 375-6600
SIC 3297 3255 1459 3546 3272 3589

■ GE INFRASTRUCTURE SENSING p 596
4636 Somerton Rd, Feasterville Trevose PA 19053
Tel (617) 926-1749
SIC 3589 2086 4941 3559 2899 3823

SEVERN TRENT SERVICES INC p 1309
220 Gibraltar Rd Ste 200, Fort Washington PA 19034
Tel (215) 646-9201 SIC 8748 3589

▲ CALGON CARBON CORP p 238
3000 Gsk Dr, Moon Township PA 15108
Tel (412) 787-6700
SIC 2819 7699 3589 3564

EVOQUA WATER TECHNOLOGIES LLC p 516
181 Thorn Hill Rd, Warrendale PA 15086
Tel (724) 772-0044
SIC 3589 3569 3823 3826 4941

SHOP VAC CORP p 1318
2323 Reach Rd, Williamsport PA 17701
Tel (570) 326-0502 SIC 3589

ORECK CORP p 1093
1400 Salem Rd, Cookeville TN 38506
Tel (800) 219-2044
SIC 3589 3564 5064 5087

■ DEVILBISS AIR POWER CO p 434
4825 Highway 45 N, Jackson TN 38305
Tel (800) 888-2468 SIC 3563 3621 3589

TRENT SEVERN ENVIRONMENTAL SERVICES INC p 1476
2002 W Grand Pkwy N, Katy TX 77449
Tel (281) 578-4200 SIC 8741 3589

OVERHEAD DOOR CORP p 1099
2501 S State Hwy 121 Ste, Lewisville TX 75067
Tel (469) 549-7100
SIC 3442 2431 3699 3537 3589

RUG DOCTOR LLC p 1257
4701 Old Shepard Pl, Plano TX 75093
Tel (972) 673-1400 SIC 2842 3589 5087

WESTECH ENGINEERING INC p 1597
3665 S West Temple, Salt Lake City UT 84115
Tel (801) 265-1000 SIC 3589

■ CHEMTREAT INC p 293
5640 Cox Rd Ste 300, Glen Allen VA 23060
Tel (804) 935-2000 SIC 2890 3589

■ GE MOBILE WATER INC p 596
4545 Patent Rd, Norfolk VA 23502
Tel (757) 855-9000 SIC 3589

C-TECH INDUSTRIES INC p 234
4275 Nw Pacific Rim Blvd, Camas WA 98607
Tel (360) 833-1600 SIC 3589 2841 3559

HATCO CORP p 668
635 S 28th St, Milwaukee WI 53215
Tel (414) 671-6350 SIC 3589

AMSOIL INC p 87
925 Tower Ave, Superior WI 54880
Tel (715) 392-7101
SIC 2992 3589 2873 3714

CLACK CORP p 321
4462 Duraform Ln, Windsor WI 53598
Tel (608) 846-3010 SIC 3589 3089

SIC 3592 Carburetors, Pistons, Rings & Valves

WALBRO LLC p 1572
2015 W River Rd 202, Tucson AZ 85704
Tel (520) 229-5642
SIC 3592 3594 3694 3443

IMPCO TECHNOLOGIES INC p 734
3030 S Susan St, Santa Ana CA 92704
Tel (714) 656-1200 SIC 3714 3592 7363

BURGESS-NORTON MFG CO INC p 227
737 Peyton St, Geneva IL 60134
Tel (630) 232-4100 SIC 3399 3592 3452

HIGH PERFORMANCE INDUSTRIES HOLDINGS INC p 690
1801 Russellville Rd, Bowling Green KY 42101
Tel (270) 782-2900 SIC 3592 3714

HOLLEY PERFORMANCE PRODUCTS INC p 700
1801 Russellville Rd, Bowling Green KY 42101
Tel (270) 782-2900 SIC 3714 3592

VOGT POWER INTERNATIONAL INC p 1564
13551 Triton Ste 2000, Louisville KY 40223
Tel (502) 899-4500 SIC 3592

METSO FLOW CONTROL USA INC p 957
44 Bowditch Dr, Shrewsbury MA 01545
Tel (508) 852-0200 SIC 3592

KAYDON CORP p 805
2723 S State St Ste 300, Ann Arbor MI 48104
Tel (734) 747-7025
SIC 3562 3569 3592 3053 3621 3679

L E JONES CO p 834
1200 34th Ave, Menominee MI 49858
Tel (906) 863-1043 *SIC* 3592 3545

■ **FEDERAL-MOGUL PISTON RINGS INC** p 536
26555 Northwestern Hwy, Southfield MI 48033
Tel (248) 354-7700 *SIC* 3592 3053 3369

TYDE GROUP WORLDWIDE LLC p 1496
5700 Crooks Rd Ste 207, Troy MI 48098
Tel (248) 879-7656 *SIC* 3592

FUEL SYSTEMS SOLUTIONS INC p 583
780 3rd Ave Fl 25, New York NY 10017
Tel (646) 502-7170 *SIC* 3714 3592 7363

MAGNETI MARELLI POWERTRAIN USA LLC p 896
2101 Nash St, Sanford NC 27330
Tel (919) 776-4111 *SIC* 3714 3592

CELINA ALUMINUM PRECISION TECHNOLOGY INC p 273
7059 Staeger Rd, Celina OH 45822
Tel (419) 586-2278 *SIC* 3592

EATON USEV HOLDING CO INC p 473
1111 Suprr Eatn Ctr 173, Cleveland OH 44114
Tel (216) 523-5000 *SIC* 3592

US ENGINE VALVE CORP p 1531
7039 S Highway 11, Westminster SC 29693
Tel (864) 647-2061 *SIC* 3592

MAHLE ENGINE COMPONENTS USA INC p 897
1 Mahle Dr, Morristown TN 37815
Tel (423) 581-6603 *SIC* 3592 3443

KS KOLBENSCHMIDT US INC p 831
1731 Industrial Pkwy N, Marinette WI 54143
Tel (715) 732-0181 *SIC* 3592

KSPG HOLDING USA INC p 831
1731 Industrial Pkwy N, Marinette WI 54143
Tel (715) 732-0181 *SIC* 3592 3714 6719

KSPG NORTH AMERICA INC p 831
1731 Industrial Pkwy N, Marinette WI 54143
Tel (715) 732-0181 *SIC* 3592

SIC 3593 Fluid Power Cylinders & Actuators

LIGON INDUSTRIES LLC p 866
1927 1st Ave N Ste 500, Birmingham AL 35203
Tel (205) 322-3302
SIC 3365 3593 3325 3471 3714 3446

■ **DOVER PRINTING & IDENTIFICATION INC** p 453
3005 Highland Pkwy # 200, Downers Grove IL 60515
Tel (630) 541-1540
SIC 3556 3565 3593 7699

BIMBA MANUFACTURING CO INC p 183
25150 S Governors Hwy, University Park IL 60484
Tel (708) 534-8544 *SIC* 3593

ROSENBOOM MACHINE & TOOL INC p 1251
1530 Western Ave, Sheldon IA 51201
Tel (712) 324-4854 *SIC* 3593 3492 3594

CARGOTEC HOLDING INC p 255
415 E Dundee St, Ottawa KS 66067
Tel (785) 242-2200 *SIC* 3593 3537

POWCO OF LOUISIANA LLC p 1164
208 Gunther Ln, Belle Chasse LA 70037
Tel (504) 394-6005 *SIC* 3593

OILGEAR CO p 1079
1424 International Dr, Traverse City MI 49686
Tel (231) 929-1660 *SIC* 3594 3492 3593

■ **EMERSON PROCESS MANAGEMENT VALVE AUTOMATION INC** p 492
8000 W Florissant Ave, Saint Louis MO 63136
Tel (314) 553-2000 *SIC* 3594 3593

FESTO CORP p 539
395 Moreland Rd, Hauppauge NY 11788
Tel (800) 993-3786
SIC 5085 3593 3566 3492

■ **ITT ENIDINE INC** p 768
7 Centre Dr, Orchard Park NY 14127
Tel (716) 662-1900 *SIC* 3724 3714 3593

▲ **PARKER-HANNIFIN CORP** p 1116
6035 Parkland Blvd, Cleveland OH 44124
Tel (216) 896-3000
SIC 3594 3593 3492 3569 3053 3829

▲ **DANA INC** p 410
3939 Technology Dr, Maumee OH 43537
Tel (419) 887-3000
SIC 3714 3053 3593 3492

■ **DANA LIMITED** p 410
3939 Technology Dr, Maumee OH 43537
Tel (630) 697-3783
SIC 3714 3053 3593 3492

PRINCE MANUFACTURING CORP p 1176
612 N Derby Ln, North Sioux City SD 57049
Tel (605) 235-1220 *SIC* 3593 3492 3594

■ **DRESSER INC** p 455
601 Shiloh Rd, Plano TX 75074
Tel (262) 549-2626
SIC 3491 3825 3594 3593 3561 3494

TEXAS HYDRAULICS INC p 1443
3410 Range Rd, Temple TX 76504
Tel (254) 778-4701 *SIC* 3593 3443

■ **XOMOX CORP** p 1632
4526 Res Frest Dr Ste 400, The Woodlands TX 77381
Tel (936) 271-6500 *SIC* 3491 3593 3494

■ **TRIUMPH GEAR SYSTEMS INC** p 1483
6125 Silver Creek Dr, Park City UT 84098
Tel (435) 649-1900 *SIC* 3593 3728 3812

NABTESCO AEROSPACE INC p 1006
12413 Willows Rd Ne, Kirkland WA 98034
Tel (425) 602-8400 *SIC* 3728 3812 3593

SWANSON INDUSTRIES INC p 1411
2608 Smithtown Rd, Morgantown WV 26508
Tel (304) 292-0021
SIC 3593 3471 7629 5084

▲ **ACTUANT CORP** p 20
N86w12500 Westbrook Xing, Menomonee Falls WI 53051
Tel (262) 293-1500
SIC 3593 3492 3594 3625 7359

MASON WELLS BUYOUT FUND II LIMITED PARTNERSHIP p 916
411 E Wisconsin Ave, Milwaukee WI 53202
Tel (414) 727-6400
SIC 3594 3492 3593 6211

SIC 3594 Fluid Power Pumps & Motors

WALBRO LLC p 1572
2015 W River Rd 202, Tucson AZ 85704
Tel (520) 229-5642
SIC 3592 3594 3694 3443

HASKEL INTERNATIONAL LLC p 667
100 E Graham Pl, Burbank CA 91502
Tel (818) 843-4000
SIC 3561 3594 5084 5085 3699

■ **FLINT ENERGY SERVICES INC** p 557
6901 S Havana St, Centennial CO 80112
Tel (918) 294-3030 *SIC* 1389 3594 1623

▲ **CRANE CO** p 388
100 1st Stamford Pl # 300, Stamford CT 06902
Tel (203) 363-7300
SIC 3492 3494 3594 3589 3728 5031

■ **HAMILTON SUNDSTRAND CORP** p 655
1 Hamilton Rd, Windsor Locks CT 06096
Tel (860) 654-6000
SIC 3621 3594 3728 3625 3823 3822

▲ **IDEX CORP** p 729
1925 W Field Ct Ste 200, Lake Forest IL 60045
Tel (847) 498-7070 *SIC* 3561 3563 3594

ROCKFORD CONCENTRIC INC p 1244
2222 15th St, Rockford IL 61104
Tel (815) 398-4400 *SIC* 3594 3629

HYDRO-GEAR INC p 723
1411 S Hamilton St, Sullivan IL 61951
Tel (217) 728-2581 *SIC* 3594

DANFOSS POWER SOLUTIONS (US) CO p 411
2800 E 13th St, Ames IA 50010
Tel (515) 239-6000 *SIC* 3594

ROSENBOOM MACHINE & TOOL INC p 1251
1530 Western Ave, Sheldon IA 51201
Tel (712) 324-4854 *SIC* 3593 3492 3594

NSK CORP p 1065
4200 Goss Rd, Ann Arbor MI 48105
Tel (734) 913-7500
SIC 3714 5013 3594 3568 3562

■ **GAST MANUFACTURING INC** p 593
2300 M 139, Benton Harbor MI 49022
Tel (269) 926-6171
SIC 3563 3594 3621 3566 3561

OILGEAR CO p 1079
1424 International Dr, Traverse City MI 49686
Tel (231) 929-1660 *SIC* 3594 3492 3593

EATON HYDRAULICS LLC p 473
14615 Lone Oak Rd, Eden Prairie MN 55344
Tel (952) 937-9800
SIC 3089 3052 3568 3492 3594 3728

▲ **GRACO INC** p 628
88 11th Ave Ne, Minneapolis MN 55413
Tel (612) 623-6000
SIC 3561 3594 3563 3491 3823 3569

HALDEX INC p 653
10930 N Pomona Ave, Kansas City MO 64153
Tel (816) 891-2470 *SIC* 3714 3594

■ **EMERSON PROCESS MANAGEMENT VALVE AUTOMATION INC** p 492
8000 W Florissant Ave, Saint Louis MO 63136
Tel (314) 553-2000 *SIC* 3594 3593

NIDEC AMERICAS HOLDING CORP p 1043
8050 W Florissant Ave, Saint Louis MO 63136
Tel (314) 595-8000 *SIC* 3625 3594 6719

NIDEC MOTOR CORP p 1043
8050 W Florissant Ave, Saint Louis MO 63136
Tel (314) 595-8000 *SIC* 3625 3594

ITT FLUID TECHNOLOGY CORP p 768
1133 Westcstr Ave N100 Ste N, White Plains NY 10604
Tel (914) 641-2000 *SIC* 3494 3594 3561

▲ **ITT INC** p 768
1133 Westchester Ave N-100, White Plains NY 10604
Tel (914) 641-2000
SIC 3594 3625 3823 3812

■ **ITT LLC** p 768
1133 Westchester Ave N-100, White Plains NY 10604
Tel (914) 641-2000
SIC 3594 3625 3823 3812

BOSCH REXROTH CORP p 202
14001 S Lakes Dr, Charlotte NC 28273
Tel (847) 645-3600 *SIC* 3594

ASMO GREENVILLE OF NORTH CAROLINA INC p 118
1125 Sugg Pkwy, Greenville NC 27834
Tel (252) 754-1000 *SIC* 3594

■ **HURST JAWS OF LIFE INC** p 721
711 N Post Rd, Shelby NC 28150
Tel (704) 487-6961 *SIC* 3569 3561 3594

EATON CORP p 473
1000 Eaton Blvd, Cleveland OH 44122
Tel (216) 523-5000
SIC 3625 3714 3594 3559 3571

▲ **PARKER-HANNIFIN CORP** p 1116
6035 Parkland Blvd, Cleveland OH 44124
Tel (216) 896-3000
SIC 3594 3593 3492 3569 3053 3829

▲ **GORMAN-RUPP CO** p 626
600 S Airport Rd, Mansfield OH 44903
Tel (419) 755-1011 *SIC* 3561 3594

R H SHEPPARD CO INC p 1202
101 Philadelphia St, Hanover PA 17331
Tel (717) 637-3751 *SIC* 3714 3321 3594

PRINCE MANUFACTURING CORP p 1176
612 N Derby Ln, North Sioux City SD 57049
Tel (605) 235-1220 *SIC* 3593 3492 3594

▲ **NATIONAL OILWELL VARCO INC** p 1014
7909 Parkwood Circle Dr, Houston TX 77036
Tel (713) 346-7500 *SIC* 3533 3594 5084

SULZER PUMPS (US) INC p 1397
1255 Enclave Pkwy 300, Houston TX 77077
Tel (281) 934-6014 *SIC* 3594

TOSHIBA INTERNATIONAL CORP p 1462
13131 W Little York Rd, Houston TX 77041
Tel (713) 466-0277
SIC 3621 5084 5063 3613 3594 3572

W CSE INDUSTRIES INC p 1568
11500 Charles Rd, Jersey Village TX 77041
Tel (713) 466-9463
SIC 3625 3613 3594 3494

■ **DRESSER INC** p 455
601 Shiloh Rd, Plano TX 75074
Tel (262) 549-2626
SIC 3491 3825 3594 3593 3561 3494

SULZER US HOLDING INC p 1397
2277 Plaza Dr Ste 600, Sugar Land TX 77479
Tel (832) 886-2299 *SIC* 7699 3594

▲ **ACTUANT CORP** p 20
N86w12500 Westbrook Xing, Menomonee Falls WI 53051
Tel (262) 293-1500
SIC 3593 3492 3594 3625 7359

MASON WELLS BUYOUT FUND II LIMITED PARTNERSHIP p 916
411 E Wisconsin Ave, Milwaukee WI 53202
Tel (414) 727-6400
SIC 3594 3492 3593 6211

SIC 3596 Scales & Balances, Exc Laboratory

■ **NEWELL OPERATING CO** p 1037
29 E Stephenson St, Freeport IL 61032
Tel (815) 235-4171
SIC 3365 3991 3089 2591 3965 3596

MEDELA INC p 935
1101 Corporate Dr, Mchenry IL 60050
Tel (800) 435-8316 *SIC* 5047 3596

■ **AVERY WEIGH-TRONIX LLC** p 137
1000 Armstrong Dr, Fairmont MN 56031
Tel (507) 238-4461 *SIC* 3596 5083

FAIRBANKS SCALES INC p 524
821 Locust St, Kansas City MO 64106
Tel (816) 471-0231 *SIC* 3596

FANCOR INC p 527
821 Locust St, Kansas City MO 64106
Tel (816) 471-0231 *SIC* 3596 7699 5046

CARDINAL SCALE MANUFACTURING CO p 253
203 E Daugherty St, Webb City MO 64870
Tel (417) 673-4631 *SIC* 3596

ESSELTE HOLDINGS INC p 510
48 S Service Rd Ste 400, Melville NY 11747
Tel (631) 675-5700
SIC 2675 2782 3579 2672 3953 3596

▲ **METTLER-TOLEDO INTERNATIONAL INC** p 957
1900 Polaris Pkwy Fl 6, Columbus OH 43240
Tel (614) 438-4511
SIC 3596 3821 3826 3823

■ **METTLER-TOLEDO LLC** p 957
1900 Polaris Pkwy Fl 6, Columbus OH 43240
Tel (614) 438-4511
SIC 3596 5049 7699 3821 3823 3826

■ **HOBART CORP** p 698
701 S Ridge Ave, Troy OH 45374
Tel (937) 332-3000
SIC 3589 3556 3596 3585 3321

■ **CMI TEREX CORP** p 329
9528 W I 40 Service Rd, Oklahoma City OK 73128
Tel (405) 787-6020
SIC 3531 3715 3596 3541 3444 2951

RICE LAKE WEIGHING SYSTEMS INC p 1232
230 W Coleman St, Rice Lake WI 54868
Tel (715) 234-9171 *SIC* 3596 3545

SIC 3599 Machinery & Eqpt, Indl & Commercial, NEC

MODERN INDUSTRIES INC p 981
4747 E Beautiful Ln, Phoenix AZ 85044
Tel (602) 267-7248 *SIC* 3599 3769

HILLMAN GROUP INC p 694
8990 S Kyrene Rd, Tempe AZ 85284
Tel (800) 800-4900 *SIC* 3429 5162 3599

EVAERO INC p 513
3807 E Kleindale Rd, Tucson AZ 85716
Tel (520) 327-0053 *SIC* 3599

■ **TRIUMPH STRUCTURES-LOS ANGELES INC** p 1483
17055 Gale Ave, City Of Industry CA 91745
Tel (626) 965-1642 *SIC* 3599

GEORGE FISCHER INC p 606
3401 Aero Jet Ave, El Monte CA 91731
Tel (626) 571-2770
SIC 3599 5074 3829 3559

K & N ENGINEERING INC p 798
1455 Citrus St, Riverside CA 92507
Tel (951) 826-4000 *SIC* 3751 3599 3714

COAST COMPOSITES LLC p 331
1395 S Lyon St, Santa Ana CA 92705
Tel (949) 455-0665 *SIC* 3599

BROCKWAY MORAN & PARTNERS INC p 216
225 Ne Mizner Blvd # 700, Boca Raton FL 33432
Tel (561) 750-2000 *SIC* 5812 3599 3728

SOUTHWIRE CO LLC p 1353
1 Southwire Dr, Carrollton GA 30119
Tel (770) 832-4242
SIC 3351 3355 3357 3599

COPE PLASTICS INC p 368
4441 Indl Dr, Alton IL 62002
Tel (618) 466-0221 *SIC* 5162 3599

SENIOR HOLDINGS INC p 1304
300 E Devon Ave, Bartlett IL 60103
Tel (630) 837-1811 *SIC* 3599 2821

SENIOR OPERATIONS LLC p 1304
300 E Devon Ave, Bartlett IL 60103
Tel (630) 837-1811 *SIC* 3599

HEADCO INDUSTRIES INC p 673
2601 Parkes Dr, Broadview IL 60155
Tel (708) 681-4400 *SIC* 5085 3599 5084

■ **AFC CABLE SYSTEMS INC** p 32
16100 Lathrop Ave, Harvey IL 60426
Tel (508) 998-1131
SIC 3429 3444 3599 5085

LB STEEL LLC p 849
15700 Lathrop Ave, Harvey IL 60426
Tel (708) 331-2600 *SIC* 3599

■ **ATLAS MATERIAL TESTING TECHNOLOGY LLC** p 128
1500 Bishop Ct, Mount Prospect IL 60056
Tel (773) 327-4520
SIC 3823 3569 3599 8734 3825 3821

GOELLNER INC p 619
2500 Latham St, Rockford IL 61103
Tel (815) 962-6076 *SIC* 3599

KELCO INDUSTRIES INC p 808
1425 Lake Ave, Woodstock IL 60098
Tel (815) 334-3600
SIC 3599 3069 3494 3585 3644 3625

BUSCHE PERFORMANCE GROUP INC p 229
1563 E State Road 8, Albion IN 46701
Tel (260) 636-7030 *SIC* 3599

KIRBY RISK CORP p 821
1815 Sagamore Pkwy N, Lafayette IN 47904
Tel (765) 448-4567
SIC 5063 7694 3599 3679 3629

WORLD CLASS INDUSTRIES INC p 1625
925 N 15th Ave, Hiawatha IA 52233
Tel (319) 378-1766 *SIC* 3599

BABEN MANAGEMENT LLC p 143
3400 Industrial Park, Houma LA 70363
Tel (985) 879-2487 *SIC* 5084 3599

BOLLINGER SHIPYARDS LLC p 198
8365 Highway 308, Lockport LA 70374
Tel (985) 532-2554 *SIC* 3731 3599

K&B MACHINE WORKS LLC p 799
208 Rebeccas Pond Rd, Schriever LA 70395
Tel (985) 868-6730 *SIC* 3599

TITEFLEX CORP p 1456
603 Hendee St, Springfield MA 01104
Tel (413) 271-8170 *SIC* 3052 3599

ROLLS-ROYCE MARINE NORTH AMERICA INC p 1247
110 Norfolk St, Walpole MA 02081
Tel (508) 668-9610 *SIC* 3599 3446 3429

TI AUTOMOTIVE LLC p 1452
2020 Taylor Rd, Auburn Hills MI 48326
Tel (248) 494-5000
SIC 3317 3312 3599 3052 3714 3585

TI GROUP AUTOMOTIVE SYSTEMS LLC p 1452
2020 Taylor Rd, Auburn Hills MI 48326
Tel (248) 296-8000
SIC 3317 3312 3599 3052 3714 3585

SCHULER INC p 1290
7145 Commerce Blvd, Canton MI 48187
Tel (734) 207-7200 *SIC* 5084 3444 3599

ENGINEERED MACHINED PRODUCTS INC p 499
3111 N 28th St, Escanaba MI 49829
Tel (906) 786-8404
SIC 3519 3714 3568 3599 3561

■ **AMPHENOL BORISCH TECHNOLOGIES INC** p 86
4511 East Paris Ave Se, Grand Rapids MI 49512
Tel (616) 554-9820 *SIC* 3679 3599

FLEXFAB HORIZONS INTERNATIONAL INC p 556
102 Cook Rd, Hastings MI 49058
Tel (269) 945-4700
SIC 3599 3052 3053 2822

FLEXFAB LLC p 556
1699 W M 43 Hwy, Hastings MI 49058
Tel (269) 945-2433 *SIC* 3599 3052 2822

LOUIS PADNOS IRON AND METAL CO p 879
185 W 8th St, Holland MI 49423
Tel (616) 396-6521 *SIC* 5093 4491 3599

MODINEER CO p 981
2190 Industrial Dr, Niles MI 49120
Tel (269) 683-2550 *SIC* 3469 3599 3544

MERRILL TOOL HOLDING CO p 950
400 Florence St, Saginaw MI 48602
Tel (989) 791-6676
SIC 3443 3599 8734 8711 3724

MORBARK LLC p 988
8507 S Winn Rd, Winn MI 48896
Tel (989) 866-2381
SIC 3599 3553 3549 3523

TEAM INDUSTRIES BAGLEY-AUDUBON INC p 1430
105 Park Ave Nw, Bagley MN 56621
Tel (218) 694-3550 *SIC* 3599 8711 3714

TEAM INDUSTRIES INC p 1430
105 Park Ave Nw, Bagley MN 56621
Tel (218) 694-3550 *SIC* 3599 8711 3714

ELK RIVER MACHINE CO p 487
828 4th St Nw, Elk River MN 55330
Tel (763) 441-1581 *SIC* 3599

▲ **DONALDSON CO INC** p 450
1400 W 94th St, Minneapolis MN 55431
Tel (952) 887-3131
SIC 3599 3569 3714 3564

SPELL CAPITAL PARTNERS LLC p 1358
222 S 9th St Ste 2880, Minneapolis MN 55402
Tel (612) 371-9650 *SIC* 3599 3469 3444

EAGLEPICHER TECHNOLOGIES LLC p 468
C & Porter Sts, Joplin MO 64802
Tel (417) 623-8000
SIC 3691 3629 3599 2892

▲ **LINDSAY CORP** p 868
2222 N 111th St, Omaha NE 68164
Tel (402) 829-6800 *SIC* 3523 3599 3443

■ LINDSAY MANUFACTURING LLC p 868
2222 N 111th St, Omaha NE 68164
Tel (402) 829-6800
SIC 3523 3599 3499 3443

TURBOCAM INC p 1492
607 Calef Hwy, Barrington NH 03825
Tel (603) 749-6066 SIC 3599

■ TSI GROUP INC p 1489
94 Tide Mill Rd, Hampton NH 03842
Tel (603) 964-0296
SIC 3599 3398 3443 3444

LINCOLNSHIRE MANAGEMENT INC p 868
780 3rd Ave Rm 4000, New York NY 10017
Tel (212) 319-3633 SIC 6211 7389 3599

■ PALL CORP p 1108
25 Harbor Park Dr, Port Washington NY 11050
Tel (516) 484-5400
SIC 3569 3599 3714 2834 3841

KIMBER MFG INC p 818
1 Lawton St, Yonkers NY 10705
Tel (914) 964-0771 SIC 3599

INDUSTRIAL PIPING INC p 740
212 S Tryon St Ste 1050, Charlotte NC 28281
Tel (704) 588-1100 SIC 3599 3569

▲ SPX CORP p 1362
13320a Balntyn Corp Pl, Charlotte NC 28277
Tel (980) 474-3700
SIC 3443 3599 3829 3559 3545

CLARK EQUIPMENT CO p 322
250 E Beaton Dr, West Fargo ND 58078
Tel (701) 241-8700 SIC 3599 3531

MEYER TOOL INC p 957
3055 Colerain Ave, Cincinnati OH 45225
Tel (513) 681-7362 SIC 3724 3599

ATS ASSEMBLY AND TEST INC p 129
313 Mound St, Dayton OH 45402
Tel (937) 222-3030 SIC 3599

ATLAS INDUSTRIES INC p 128
1750 E State St, Fremont OH 43420
Tel (419) 355-1000 SIC 3599

NORMAN NOBLE INC p 1049
5507 Avion Park Dr, Highland Heights OH 44143
Tel (216) 761-5387 SIC 3599

■ COLFOR MANUFACTURING INC p 336
3255 Alliance Rd Nw, Malvern OH 44644
Tel (330) 863-0404 SIC 3462 3599 3463

ALEX PRODUCTS INC p 49
19911 County Rd T, Ridgeville Corners OH 43555
Tel (419) 267-5240 SIC 3599

SWAGELOK CO p 1411
29500 Solon Rd, Solon OH 44139
Tel (440) 248-4600 SIC 3494 3491 3599

NATIONAL MACHINE CO p 1014
4880 Hudson Dr, Stow OH 44224
Tel (330) 688-6494 SIC 3599 3492

NM GROUP GLOBAL LLC p 1045
161 Greenfield St, Tiffin OH 44883
Tel (419) 447-5211 SIC 3542 3599 6799

WARREN FABRICATING CORP p 1577
3240 Mahoning Ave Nw, Warren OH 44483
Tel (330) 847-0596
SIC 3441 3599 3547 3532 3444 3443

FLOTURN INC p 560
4236 Thunderbird Ln, West Chester OH 45014
Tel (513) 860-8040 SIC 3599

TSS TECHNOLOGIES INC p 1489
8800 Global Way, West Chester OH 45069
Tel (513) 772-7000 SIC 3599 8711

FORGE INDUSTRIES INC p 567
4450 Market St, Youngstown OH 44512
Tel (330) 782-8301
SIC 5085 3566 3599 3531 6411 7699

VIGOR INDUSTRIAL LLC p 1556
5555 N Channel Ave # 71, Portland OR 97217
Tel (503) 247-1777 SIC 3731 3599 6531

OERLIKON USA HOLDING INC p 1075
5700 Mellon Rd, Export PA 15632
Tel (303) 273-9700
SIC 3563 3823 3699 3479 3599 5084

▲ OMEGA FLEX INC p 1084
451 Creamery Way, Exton PA 19341
Tel (610) 524-7272 SIC 3599 3429

MCLANAHAN CORP p 930
200 Wall St, Hollidaysburg PA 16648
Tel (814) 695-9807
SIC 3532 3321 3599 3523

LAUREL HOLDINGS INC p 847
111 Roosevelt Blvd, Johnstown PA 15906
Tel (814) 533-5777
SIC 4941 5063 3599 4724 7349

BOLTTECH MANNINGS INC p 199
501 Mosside Blvd, North Versailles PA 15137
Tel (724) 872-4873
SIC 3546 5072 3599 7359 3545 3423

BALDOR ELECTRIC CO p 147
6040 Ponders Ct, Greenville SC 29615
Tel (864) 991-8492 SIC 3599

D M G INC p 407
809 W Russell St, Sioux Falls SD 57104
Tel (605) 336-3693
SIC 5063 7694 3599 1731

▲ CLARCOR INC p 321
840 Crescent Centre Dr # 600, Franklin TN 37067
Tel (615) 771-3100
SIC 3714 3599 3564 3569 3411 3089

HUMANETICS II LTD p 718
1700 Columbian Club Dr, Carrollton TX 75006
Tel (972) 416-1304 SIC 3444 3599

DELTA FABRICATION AND MACHINE INC p 427
1379 County Road 2110, Daingerfield TX 75638
Tel (903) 645-3994 SIC 1541 3599 3441

H M DUNN CO INC p 650
3301 House Anderson Rd, Euless TX 76040
Tel (817) 283-3722 SIC 3724 3599 3728

SPM FLOW CONTROL INC p 1359
601 Weir Way, Fort Worth TX 76108
Tel (817) 246-2461 SIC 3533 3599

POLK MECHANICAL CO LLC p 1159
2425 Dillard St, Grand Prairie TX 75051
Tel (972) 339-1200
SIC 1711 3444 3498 3599 3999

AMERICAN BLOCK CO p 69
6311 Breen Dr, Houston TX 77086
Tel (800) 572-9087
SIC 3441 3599 3533 3496 3444 3429

■ FURMANITE WORLDWIDE INC p 585
10370 Richmond Ave # 600, Houston TX 77042
Tel (972) 699-4000 SIC 7699 3599 7389

■ INTEGRATED PRODUCTION SERVICES INC p 749
16800 Greenspt Pk Dr 200s, Houston TX 77060
Tel (281) 774-6700 SIC 1389 3599

OLD GES INC p 1080
11757 Katy Fwy Ste 700, Houston TX 77079
Tel (281) 598-6830
SIC 1389 7353 3599 7359 1382

QUIETFLEX MANUFACTURING CO LP p 1199
4518 Brittmoore Rd, Houston TX 77041
Tel (713) 849-2163 SIC 3444 1799 3599

DON-NAN PUMP AND SUPPLY CO INC p 450
3427 E Garden Cy Hwy 158, Midland TX 79706
Tel (432) 682-7742 SIC 1389 3599 3561

GULF COPPER & MANUFACTURING CORP p 646
5700 Procter Ext, Port Arthur TX 77642
Tel (409) 989-0300
SIC 3731 3599 3312 3732 3498 3441

CG BRETTING MANUFACTURING CO INC p 285
3401 Lake Park Rd, Ashland WI 54806
Tel (715) 682-5231
SIC 3554 3599 3565 3555

ROBINSON METAL INC p 1242
1740 Eisenhower Rd, De Pere WI 54115
Tel (920) 494-7411 SIC 3444 3443 3599

■ REXNORD LLC p 1230
3001 W Canal St, Milwaukee WI 53208
Tel (414) 342-3131 SIC 3566 3325 3599

MONROE TRUCK EQUIPMENT INC p 985
1051 W 7th St, Monroe WI 53566
Tel (608) 328-8127 SIC 5013 3441 3599

DYNATECT MANUFACTURING INC p 464
2300 S Calhoun Rd, New Berlin WI 53151
Tel (262) 786-1500
SIC 3069 3499 3714 3599

SUPERIOR DIE SET CORP p 1406
900 W Drexel Ave, Oak Creek WI 53154
Tel (414) 764-4900 SIC 3544 3443 3599

■ CATERPILLAR GLOBAL MINING LLC p 265
1100 Milwaukee Ave, South Milwaukee WI 53172
Tel (414) 762-0376 SIC 3531 3532 3599

R G REZIN INC p 1202
1602 Rezin Rd, Tomah WI 54660
Tel (608) 372-5956
SIC 1623 3443 3613 3561 3523 3599

HYPRO INC p 724
600 S Jefferson St, Waterford WI 53185
Tel (608) 348-4810 SIC 3599

OEM FABRICATORS INC p 1075
300 Mcmillan Rd, Woodville WI 54028
Tel (715) 698-2111 SIC 3599

SIC 3612 Power, Distribution & Specialty Transformers

CENTRAL MOLONEY INC p 279
2400 W 6th Ave, Pine Bluff AR 71601
Tel (870) 534-5332 SIC 3612

■ POWER PARAGON INC p 1165
901 E Ball Rd, Anaheim CA 92805
Tel (714) 956-9200
SIC 3612 3613 3621 3643

CALIFORNIA NATURAL PRODUCTS p 240
15789 Mckinley Ave, Lathrop CA 95330
Tel (209) 249-1616 SIC 2099 8731 3612

OCM PE HOLDINGS LP p 1074
333 S Grand Ave Fl 28, Los Angeles CA 90071
Tel (213) 830-6213 SIC 3679 3612 3663

PULSE ELECTRONICS CORP p 1191
12220 World Trade Dr, San Diego CA 92128
Tel (858) 674-8100 SIC 3679 3612 3663

PULSE ELECTRONICS INC p 1191
12220 World Trade Dr, San Diego CA 92128
Tel (858) 674-8100 SIC 3612 3674 3677

ASEA BROWN BOVERI INC p 116
501 Merritt 7, Norwalk CT 06851
Tel (203) 750-2200
SIC 3612 3613 5063 3511 3625 8711

CARLING TECHNOLOGIES INC p 257
60 Johnson Ave, Plainville CT 06062
Tel (860) 793-9281 SIC 3643 3613 3612

■ CARLYLE PARTNERS II LP p 258
1001 Pennsylvania Ave Nw, Washington DC 20004
Tel (202) 347-2626 SIC 3612

SIEMENS CORP p 1320
300 New Jersey Ave Nw # 10, Washington DC 20001
Tel (202) 434-4800
SIC 3661 3641 3844 3612 3357

■ INSTRUMENT TRANSFORMERS LLC p 747
1907 Calumet St, Clearwater FL 33765
Tel (727) 461-9413 SIC 3612

POWER PARTNERS INC p 1165
200 Newton Bridge Rd, Athens GA 30607
Tel (706) 548-3121 SIC 3612

■ GE ENERGY PARTS INC p 596
4200 Wildwood Pkwy, Atlanta GA 30339
Tel (678) 844-6000 SIC 5065 3612

■ GE GRID SOLUTIONS LLC p 596
4200 Wildwood Pkwy, Atlanta GA 30339
Tel (877) 605-6777 SIC 3612

WEG ELECTRIC CORP p 1587
6655 Sugarloaf Pkwy, Duluth GA 30097
Tel (678) 249-2000
SIC 3612 3621 3613 3625

BASLER ELECTRIC CO p 159
12570 State Route 143, Highland IL 62249
Tel (618) 654-2341 SIC 3679 3612 3672

INTERMATIC INC p 753
7777 Winn Rd, Spring Grove IL 60081
Tel (815) 675-2321 SIC 3612 3645

XFMRS INC p 1631
7570 E Landersdale Rd, Camby IN 46113
Tel (317) 834-1066 SIC 3677 5065 3612

■ FISHER CONTROLS INTERNATIONAL LLC p 552
205 S Center St, Marshalltown IA 50158
Tel (641) 754-3011
SIC 3491 3823 3625 3612 3494

SOLOMON TRANSFORMERS LLC p 1338
103 W Main St, Solomon KS 67480
Tel (785) 655-2191 SIC 3612 5093

KENTUCKY ASSOCIATION OF ELECTRIC COOPERATIVES INC p 812
4515 Bishop Ln, Louisville KY 40218
Tel (502) 451-2430
SIC 3612 2721 7629 5063

CREST INDUSTRIES p 392
4725 Highway 28 E, Pineville LA 71360
Tel (318) 767-5530
SIC 3699 3612 3441 5063 2439

CREST OPERATIONS LLC p 392
4725 Highway 28 E, Pineville LA 71360
Tel (318) 448-0274
SIC 3441 3699 5063 3612

SCHNEIDER ELECTRIC USA INC p 1288
800 Federal St, Andover MA 01810
Tel (978) 975-9600
SIC 3613 3643 3612 3823 3625 5063

CG POWER SYSTEMS USA INC p 285
1 Pauwels Dr, Washington MO 63090
Tel (636) 239-6783 SIC 3612

▲ VALMONT INDUSTRIES INC p 1541
1 Valmont Plz Ste 500, Omaha NE 68154
Tel (402) 963-1000
SIC 3441 3399 3317 3523 3612

STERNSCHNUPPE LLC p 1388
3325 W Sunset Rd Ste E, Las Vegas NV 89118
Tel (702) 458-6797 SIC 3612

▲ PIONEER POWER SOLUTIONS INC p 1151
400 Kelby St Ste 12, Fort Lee NJ 07024
Tel (212) 867-0700 SIC 3612

TRANSISTOR DEVICES INC p 1471
36 Newburgh Rd, Hackettstown NJ 07840
Tel (908) 850-1595
SIC 3612 3625 3672 3812 3829

RARITAN INC p 1209
400 Cottontail Ln, Somerset NJ 08873
Tel (732) 764-8886 SIC 3612 3577

SPELLMAN HIGH VOLTAGE ELECTRONICS CORP p 1358
475 Wireless Blvd, Hauppauge NY 11788
Tel (631) 630-3000 SIC 3612

ABB HOLDINGS INC p 9
12040 Regency Pkwy # 200, Cary NC 27518
Tel (919) 856-2360 SIC 3612

ABB INC p 9
12040 Regency Pkwy # 200, Cary NC 27518
Tel (919) 856-2360
SIC 8711 3612 3511 5063 3613 3625

ABB POWER T & D CO INC p 9
940 Main Campus Dr # 400, Raleigh NC 27606
Tel (919) 856-3806 SIC 3612

SOUTHWEST ELECTRIC CO p 1351
6503 Se 74th St, Oklahoma City OK 73135
Tel (800) 364-4445 SIC 3825 3612

C&D TECHNOLOGIES INC p 233
1400 Union Meeting Rd # 110, Blue Bell PA 19422
Tel (215) 619-7815
SIC 3612 3691 3613 3692 3674

PENNSYLVANIA TRANSFORMER TECHNOLOGY INC p 1130
30 Curry Ave Ste 2, Canonsburg PA 15317
Tel (724) 873-2100 SIC 3612 5063 3677

SPECTRUM CONTROL INC p 1357
8061 Avonia Rd, Fairview PA 16415
Tel (814) 474-2207
SIC 3677 3663 3612 3676

▲ VISHAY INTERTECHNOLOGY INC p 1561
63 Lancaster Ave, Malvern PA 19355
Tel (610) 644-1300
SIC 3676 3677 3675 3674 3613 3612

■ SPD ELECTRICAL SYSTEMS INC p 1355
13500 Roosevelt Blvd, Philadelphia PA 19116
Tel (215) 698-6426 SIC 3612 3699 3613

SPANG & CO p 1354
110 Delta Dr, Pittsburgh PA 15238
Tel (412) 963-9363
SIC 3672 3944 3612 3613 3312

SCHNEIDER ELECTRIC IT CORP p 1287
132 Fairgrounds Rd, West Kingston RI 02892
Tel (401) 789-5735
SIC 3629 3612 3677 3585 7372 2542

■ ITRON ELECTRICITY METERING INC p 768
313 N Highway 11, West Union SC 29696
Tel (864) 638-8300
SIC 3825 3823 3824 3679 3829 3612

HOLIEN INC p 700
312 9th Ave Se Ste B, Watertown SD 57201
Tel (605) 886-3889 SIC 3612 3672 3993

ELECTRIC RESEARCH AND MANUFACTURING COOPERATIVE INC p 484
2225 Industrial Rd, Dyersburg TN 38024
Tel (731) 285-9121 SIC 3612

UNIVERSAL LIGHTING TECHNOLOGIES INC p 1517
51 Century Blvd Ste 230, Nashville TN 37214
Tel (615) 316-5100 SIC 3612

TEXAS ELECTRIC COOPERATIVES INC p 1443
1122 Colorado St Ste 2400, Austin TX 78701
Tel (512) 454-0311 SIC 2491 3612 8621

COOPER INDUSTRIES LLC p 366
600 Travis St Ste 5400, Houston TX 77002
Tel (713) 209-8400
SIC 3646 3612 3613 3644 3546 3423

EATON ELECTRIC HOLDINGS LLC p 473
600 Travis St Ste 5600, Houston TX 77002
Tel (713) 209-8400
SIC 3646 3612 3613 3644 3536 3423

▲ POWELL INDUSTRIES INC p 1165
8550 Mosley Rd, Houston TX 77075
Tel (713) 944-6900
SIC 3612 3613 3625 3643 3823

■ THERMON MANUFACTURING CO INC p 1447
100 Thermon Dr, San Marcos TX 78666
Tel (512) 396-5801 SIC 3643 3612

ELECTRO-MECHANICAL CORP p 485
329 Williams St, Bristol VA 24201
Tel (276) 669-9428
SIC 3612 5063 3829 3822 3613 3354

DELTA STAR INC p 427
3550 Mayflower Dr, Lynchburg VA 24501
Tel (434) 845-0921 SIC 3612

■ GE DRIVES & CONTROLS INC p 596
1501 Roanoke Blvd, Salem VA 24153
Tel (540) 387-7000 SIC 3612

BELLOFRAM CORP p 171
8019 Ohio River Blvd, Newell WV 26050
Tel (304) 387-1200 SIC 3612 3829 3625

COOPER POWER SYSTEMS LLC p 367
2300 Badger Dr, Waukesha WI 53188
Tel (262) 524-4227
SIC 3612 3613 3644 3643 3629 3679

■ SPX TRANSFORMER SOLUTIONS INC p 1362
400 S Prairie Ave, Waukesha WI 53186
Tel (262) 547-0121 SIC 7629 3612

SIC 3613 Switchgear & Switchboard Apparatus

■ POWER PARAGON INC p 1165
901 E Ball Rd, Anaheim CA 92805
Tel (714) 956-9200
SIC 3612 3613 3621 3643

ALE USA INC p 48
26801 Agoura Rd, Calabasas CA 91301
Tel (818) 878-4816 SIC 3663 3613

■ TIMKEN MOTOR & CRANE SERVICES LLC p 1455
4850 Moline St, Denver CO 80239
Tel (303) 623-8658
SIC 5063 1731 7694 3613 3536

ASEA BROWN BOVERI INC p 116
501 Merritt 7, Norwalk CT 06851
Tel (203) 750-2200
SIC 3612 3613 5063 3511 3625 8711

CARLING TECHNOLOGIES INC p 257
60 Johnson Ave, Plainville CT 06062
Tel (860) 793-9281 SIC 3643 3613 3612

■ GEMS SENSORS INC p 598
1 Cowles Rd, Plainville CT 06062
Tel (860) 747-3000
SIC 3824 5084 3812 3625 3613

SIEMON CO p 1320
101 Siemon Company Dr, Watertown CT 06795
Tel (860) 945-4200
SIC 3643 3089 3679 3469 3613 3357

TECHNOLOGY RESEARCH LLC p 1432
4525 140th Ave N Ste 900, Clearwater FL 33762
Tel (727) 535-0572 SIC 3613

TAMPA ARMATURE WORKS INC p 1423
6312 S 78th St, Riverview FL 33578
Tel (813) 621-5661 SIC 5063 3613 3621

WEG ELECTRIC CORP p 1587
6655 Sugarloaf Pkwy, Duluth GA 30097
Tel (678) 249-2000
SIC 3612 3621 3613 3625

SOUTHERN STATES LLC p 1350
30 Georgia Ave, Hampton GA 30228
Tel (770) 946-4562 SIC 3613 4013 1731

COOPER WIRING DEVICES INC p 367
203 Cooper Cir, Peachtree City GA 30269
Tel (770) 631-2100 SIC 3643 3613

G & W ELECTRIC CO p 586
305 W Crossroads Pkwy, Bolingbrook IL 60440
Tel (708) 388-5010 SIC 3613 3643

▲ LITTELFUSE INC p 870
8755 W Higgins Rd Ste 500, Chicago IL 60631
Tel (773) 628-1000 SIC 3613 3679

S & C ELECTRIC CO p 1261
6601 N Ridge Blvd, Chicago IL 60626
Tel (773) 338-1000
SIC 3613 3643 3625 8711

KINETEK INC p 819
25 Northwest Point Blvd # 900, Elk Grove Village IL 60007
Tel (224) 265-1290 SIC 3621 3566 3613

GRAYHILL INC p 632
561 W Hillgrove Ave, La Grange IL 60525
Tel (708) 354-1040
SIC 3613 3625 3679 3643 3575

■ APPLETON GRP LLC p 99
9377 W Higgins Rd, Rosemont IL 60018
Tel (847) 268-6000
SIC 3644 3643 3613 3646 3699

■ HUBBELL INC (DELAWARE) p 716
3902 W Sample St, South Bend IN 46619
Tel (574) 234-7151 SIC 3644 3699 3613

SCHNEIDER ELECTRIC USA INC p 1288
800 Federal St, Andover MA 01810
Tel (978) 975-9600
SIC 3613 3643 3612 3823 3625 5063

▲ VICOR CORP p 1555
25 Frontage Rd, Andover MA 01810
Tel (978) 470-2900 SIC 3679 3613

RUSSELECTRIC INC p 1259
S Shore Park, Hingham MA 02043
Tel (781) 749-6000 SIC 3613

COGHLIN COMPANIES INC p 334
27 Otis St Ste 300, Westborough MA 01581
Tel (508) 753-2354 SIC 3613

COLUMBIA ELECTRICAL CONTRACTORS INC p 340
27 Otis St Ste 300, Westborough MA 01581
Tel (508) 366-8297 SIC 3613

ELECTRO SWITCH CORP p 485
775 Pleasant St Ste 1, Weymouth MA 02189
Tel (781) 335-1195 SIC 3613 3625

JERVIS B WEBB CO p 783
34375 W 12 Mile Rd, Farmington Hills MI 48331
Tel (248) 553-1000
SIC 3535 3536 3462 3537 3613

PRINCE MANUFACTURING CORP p 1176
36 W 8th St Ste 250, Holland MI 49423
Tel (616) 494-5374 SIC 1611 3613 5013

DAYCO INC p 417
1650 Research Dr Ste 200, Troy MI 48083
Tel (716) 689-4972
SIC 3641 3646 3643 3625 3613

HOFFMAN ENCLOSURES INC p 699
2100 Hoffman Way, Anoka MN 55303
Tel (763) 421-2240
SIC 3444 3699 3613 3469 3053

DESIGN READY CONTROLS INC p 432
9325 Winnetka Ave N, Minneapolis MN 55445
Tel (763) 565-3000 SIC 5084 3613 3561

■ VICTOR TECHNOLOGIES GROUP INC p 1555
16253 Swingley Ridge Rd # 200, Chesterfield MO 63017
Tel (636) 728-3000
SIC 3541 3423 3613 3443 3621 3548

COOPER BUSSMANN LLC p 366
114 Old State Rd, Ellisville MO 63021
Tel (636) 527-1324 SIC 3613 3699 3643

DURHAM CO p 462
722 Durham Rd, Lebanon MO 65536
Tel (417) 532-7121 SIC 3644 3643 3613

■ APPLE JV HOLDING CORP p 98
8000 W Florissant Ave, Saint Louis MO 63136
Tel (314) 553-2000
SIC 3644 3643 3613 3446 3699

■ AUTOMATIC SWITCH CO p 134
50-60 Hanover Rd, Florham Park NJ 07932
Tel (973) 966-2000
SIC 3491 3625 3677 3674 3613 3492

ASTRODYNE CORP p 122
36 Newburgh Rd, Hackettstown NJ 07840
Tel (908) 850-5088 SIC 3625 3621 3613

▲ BEL FUSE INC p 169
206 Van Vorst St, Jersey City NJ 07302
Tel (201) 432-0463
SIC 3679 3674 3613 3677

MARQUARDT SWITCHES INC p 910
2711 Us Route 20, Cazenovia NY 13035
Tel (315) 655-8050 SIC 3625 3613

LEVITON MANUFACTURING CO INC p 858
201 N Service Rd, Melville NY 11747
Tel (631) 812-6000
SIC 3643 3613 3357 3674 3694 3678

ABB INC p 9
12040 Regency Pkwy # 200, Cary NC 27518
Tel (919) 856-2360
SIC 8711 3612 3511 5063 3613 3625

SIEMENS POWER TRANSMISSION & DISTRIBUTION INC p 1320
110 Macalyson Ct, Cary NC 27511
Tel (919) 463-8702 SIC 3613 3625

■ ELSTER AMERICAN METER CO LLC p 489
208 S Rogers Ln, Raleigh NC 27610
Tel (800) 257-9754 SIC 3824 3613

LIEBERT CORP p 863
1050 Dearborn Dr, Columbus OH 43085
Tel (614) 888-0246 SIC 3585 3613 7629

GOULD ELECTRONICS INC p 626
34929 Curtis Blvd Ste 100, Eastlake OH 44095
Tel (440) 953-5000
SIC 3825 3497 3613 3691 3674

DELTA SYSTEMS INC p 427
1734 Frost Rd, Streetsboro OH 44241
Tel (330) 626-2811 SIC 3613 3625

■ ON ELECTRIC GROUP INC p 1086
1709 Se 3rd Ave, Portland OR 97214
Tel (503) 234-9900 SIC 1731 3613

C&D TECHNOLOGIES INC p 233
1400 Union Meeting Rd # 110, Blue Bell PA 19422
Tel (215) 619-7815
SIC 3612 3691 3613 3692 3674

▲ VISHAY INTERTECHNOLOGY INC p 1561
63 Lancaster Ave, Malvern PA 19355
Tel (610) 644-1300
SIC 3676 3677 3675 3674 3613 3612

ALSTOM GRID INC p 61
2 International Plz # 325, Philadelphia PA 19113
Tel (724) 483-7816 SIC 3613

■ SPD ELECTRICAL SYSTEMS INC p 1355
13500 Roosevelt Blvd, Philadelphia PA 19116
Tel (215) 698-6426 SIC 3612 3699 3613

SPANG & CO p 1354
110 Delta Dr, Pittsburgh PA 15238
Tel (412) 963-9363
SIC 3672 3944 3612 3613 3312

MITSUBISHI ELECTRIC POWER PRODUCTS INC p 977
530 Keystone Dr, Warrendale PA 15086
Tel (724) 772-2555 SIC 3613

■ CARIBE GE INTERNATIONAL OF PUERTO RICO INC p 256
980 Ave San Luis, Arecibo PR 00612
Tel (787) 878-1420 SIC 3613

CUTLER-HAMMER DE PUERTO RICO INC p 403
Carr 2 Km 67 6 Santana In St Ca, Arecibo PR 00612
Tel (787) 881-3640 SIC 3613

▲ TEXAS INSTRUMENTS INC p 1443
12500 Ti Blvd, Dallas TX 75243
Tel (214) 479-3773
SIC 3674 3613 3822 3578

▲ AZZ INC p 141
3100 W 7th St Ste 500, Fort Worth TX 76107
Tel (817) 810-0095
SIC 3699 3613 3494 3312

COOPER INDUSTRIES LLC p 366
600 Travis St Ste 5400, Houston TX 77002
Tel (713) 209-8400
SIC 3646 3612 3613 3644 3546 3423

EATON ELECTRIC HOLDINGS LLC p 473
600 Travis St Ste 5600, Houston TX 77002
Tel (713) 209-8400
SIC 3646 3612 3613 3644 3536 3423

HUNTING INNOVA INC p 719
8383 N Sam Houston Pkwy W, Houston TX 77064
Tel (281) 653-5500 SIC 3672 3613 8711

MCGRAW-EDISON CO p 929
600 Travis St Ste 5400, Houston TX 77002
Tel (713) 209-8400
SIC 3613 3641 3645 3646

▲ POWELL INDUSTRIES INC p 1165
8550 Mosley Rd, Houston TX 77075
Tel (713) 944-6900
SIC 3612 3613 3625 3643 3823

TOSHIBA INTERNATIONAL CORP p 1462
13131 W Little York Rd, Houston TX 77041
Tel (713) 466-0277
SIC 3621 5084 5063 3613 3594 3572

W CSE INDUSTRIES INC p 1568
11500 Charles Rd, Jersey Village TX 77041
Tel (713) 466-9463
SIC 3625 3613 3594 3494

■ GE ZENITH CONTROLS INC p 597
601 Shiloh Rd, Plano TX 75074
Tel (903) 436-1503 SIC 3613

LUMINATOR TECHNOLOGY GROUP LLC p 885
900 Klein Rd, Plano TX 75074
Tel (972) 424-6511
SIC 3613 3643 3646 3647

ELECTRO-MECHANICAL CORP p 485
329 Williams St, Bristol VA 24201
Tel (276) 669-9428
SIC 3612 5063 3829 3822 3613 3354

■ KORRY ELECTRONICS CO p 828
11910 Beverly Park Rd, Everett WA 98204
Tel (425) 297-9700 SIC 3613

■ ELDEC CORP p 484
16700 13th Ave W, Lynnwood WA 98037
Tel (425) 743-8362
SIC 3812 3728 3824 3769 3674 3613

UNITED STARS INC p 1512
1546 Henry Ave, Beloit WI 53511
Tel (608) 368-4625
SIC 3317 3351 3463 3613 3621

L & S ELECTRIC INC p 833
5101 Mesker St, Schofield WI 54476
Tel (715) 359-3155
SIC 7694 5063 8711 3613

R G REZIN INC p 1202
1602 Rezin Rd, Tomah WI 54660
Tel (608) 372-5956
SIC 1623 3443 3613 3561 3523 3599

COOPER POWER SYSTEMS LLC p 367
2300 Badger Dr, Waukesha WI 53188
Tel (262) 524-4227
SIC 3612 3613 3644 3643 3629 3679

SIC 3621 Motors & Generators

ASTEC AMERICA LLC p 122
2900 S Diablo Way Ste 190, Tempe AZ 85282
Tel (602) 438-5720 SIC 3679 3629 3621

BALDOR ELECTRIC CO p 147
5711 Rs Boreham Jr St, Fort Smith AR 72901
Tel (479) 646-4711
SIC 3621 3566 3463 3366

■ POWER PARAGON INC p 1165
901 E Ball Rd, Anaheim CA 92805
Tel (714) 956-9200
SIC 3612 3613 3621 3643

AIH LLC p 38
5810 Van Allen Way, Carlsbad CA 92008
Tel (760) 930-4600 SIC 3629 3621 3679

LEOCH BATTERY CORP p 856
19751 Descartes Unit A, Foothill Ranch CA 92610
Tel (949) 588-5853 SIC 3621

■ AES ALAMITOS LLC p 31
690 N Studebaker Rd, Long Beach CA 90803
Tel (562) 493-7891 SIC 3621

PACIFIC SCIENTIFIC CO INC p 1105
1785 Voyager Ave Ste 101, Simi Valley CA 93063
Tel (805) 526-5700
SIC 3812 3669 3621 3694 3823 3625

■ SIERRACIN/SYLMAR CORP p 1321
12780 San Fernando Rd, Sylmar CA 91342
Tel (818) 362-6711
SIC 3089 3812 3621 3231

VESTAS BLADES AMERICA INC p 1552
1500 E Crown Prince Blvd, Brighton CO 80603
Tel (303) 655-5800 SIC 3621

■ ALSTOM RENEWABLE US LLC p 61
7901 Suthpark Plz Ste 110, Littleton CO 80120
Tel (303) 730-4000 SIC 3621 3511

■ ALSTOM POWER INC p 61
200 Great Pond Dr, Windsor CT 06095
Tel (866) 257-8664
SIC 3443 3564 3621 3823 8711

■ HAMILTON SUNDSTRAND CORP p 655
1 Hamilton Rd, Windsor Locks CT 06096
Tel (860) 654-6000
SIC 3621 3594 3728 3625 3823 3822

■ EECO INC p 480
850 Library Ave Ste 204c, Newark DE 19711
Tel (302) 456-1448
SIC 3823 3491 3621 3585 3546 3679

TAMPA ARMATURE WORKS INC p 1423
6312 S 78th St, Riverview FL 33578
Tel (813) 621-5661 SIC 5063 3613 3621

WEG ELECTRIC CORP p 1587
6655 Sugarloaf Pkwy, Duluth GA 30097
Tel (678) 249-2000
SIC 3612 3621 3613 3625

JORDAN INDUSTRIES INC p 793
1751 Lake Cook Rd Ste 550, Deerfield IL 60015
Tel (847) 945-5591
SIC 3621 3625 3714 3089 2759 5999

KINETEK INC p 819
25 Northwest Point Blvd # 900, Elk Grove Village IL 60007
Tel (224) 265-1290 SIC 3621 3566 3613

■ PROGRESS RAIL LOCOMOTIVE INC p 1181
9301 W 55th St, Mc Cook IL 60525
Tel (800) 255-5355 SIC 3621 3519 3647

■ MPC PRODUCTS CORP p 995
6300 W Howard St, Niles IL 60714
Tel (847) 673-8300
SIC 3728 3621 3676 3812 3625

BODINE ELECTRIC CO p 197
201 Northfield Rd, Northfield IL 60093
Tel (773) 478-3515 SIC 5063 3625 3621

L & H CO INC p 833
2215 York Rd Ste 304, Oak Brook IL 60523
Tel (630) 571-7200
SIC 1731 1611 1623 3621

SCHNEIDER ELECTRIC BUILDINGS LLC p 1287
839 N Perryville Rd, Rockford IL 61107
Tel (815) 381-5000
SIC 3822 1711 3625 3823 3621

SCHNEIDER ELECTRIC HOLDINGS INC p 1287
200 N Martingale Rd # 100, Schaumburg IL 60173
Tel (717) 944-5460
SIC 3822 1711 3625 3823 3621

YASKAWA AMERICA INC p 1635
2121 Norman Dr, Waukegan IL 60085
Tel (847) 887-7000
SIC 3621 7694 5063 3566 3823 3625

▲ CUMMINS INC p 401
500 Jackson St, Columbus IN 47201
Tel (812) 377-5000
SIC 3519 3714 3694 3621

▲ FRANKLIN ELECTRIC CO INC p 575
9255 Coverdale Rd, Fort Wayne IN 46809
Tel (260) 824-2900 SIC 3621 3561

■ REMY INC p 1223
600 Corporation Dr, Pendleton IN 46064
Tel (765) 778-6499
SIC 3714 3694 3625 3621 5013

■ REMY POWER PRODUCTS LLC p 1223
600 Corporation Dr, Pendleton IN 46064
Tel (765) 778-6499 SIC 3625 3694 3621

▲ ATLANTIC POWER CORP p 127
3 Allied Dr Ste 220, Dedham MA 02026
Tel (617) 977-2400 SIC 4911 3621

▲ AMERICAN SUPERCONDUCTOR CORP p 80
64 Jackson Rd, Devens MA 01434
Tel (978) 842-3000 SIC 3674 3621

ETX HOLDINGS INC p 512
2000 Michigan Ave, Alma MI 48801
Tel (989) 463-1151
SIC 3585 3621 3714 5013 3089

KAYDON CORP p 805
2723 S State St Ste 300, Ann Arbor MI 48104
Tel (734) 747-7025
SIC 3562 3569 3592 3053 3621 3679

MORRELL INC p 990
3333 Bald Mountain Rd, Auburn Hills MI 48326
Tel (248) 373-1600
SIC 5084 5065 3621 3643 3559 3357

ASMO MAUNFACTURING INC p 118
500 Fritz Keiper Blvd, Battle Creek MI 49037
Tel (269) 441-2040 SIC 3621 3089

■ GAST MANUFACTURING INC p 593
2300 M 139, Benton Harbor MI 49022
Tel (269) 926-6171
SIC 3563 3594 3621 3566 3561

BALLARD POWER SYSTEMS CORP p 148
15001 N Commerce Dr, Dearborn MI 48120
Tel (313) 583-5980 SIC 3621

PRESTOLITE ELECTRIC HOLDING INC p 1173
30120 Hudson Dr, Novi MI 48377
Tel (248) 313-3807 SIC 3621 3694

PRESTOLITE ELECTRIC INC p 1173
30120 Hudson Dr, Novi MI 48377
Tel (585) 492-1700 SIC 3621 3694

PRESTOLITE ELECTRIC LLC p 1173
30120 Hudson Dr, Novi MI 48377
Tel (248) 313-3807
SIC 3643 3824 3621 3625 3694

MTU ONSITE ENERGY CORP p 998
100 Power Dr, Mankato MN 56001
Tel (507) 625-7973 SIC 3621

■ CUMMINS POWER GENERATION INC p 401
1400 73rd Ave Ne, Minneapolis MN 55432
Tel (763) 574-5000 SIC 3621 3519

ELECTRIC MACHINERY CO INC p 484
800 Central Ave Ne, Minneapolis MN 55413
Tel (612) 378-8000 SIC 3621

■ KATO ENGINEERING INC p 804
2075 Howard Dr W, North Mankato MN 56003
Tel (507) 345-2716 SIC 3621 3643 3625

LUVATA GRENADA LLC p 887
3984 Highway 51 S, Grenada MS 38901
Tel (662) 226-3421 SIC 3621 3585

■ VICTOR TECHNOLOGIES GROUP INC p 1555
16253 Swingley Ridge Rd # 200, Chesterfield MO 63017
Tel (636) 728-3000
SIC 3541 3423 3613 3443 3621 3548

▲ EMERSON ELECTRIC CO p 492
8000 W Florissant Ave, Saint Louis MO 63136
Tel (314) 553-2000
SIC 3823 3491 3621 3585 3679

■ CALENERGY OPERATING CORP p 238
1111 S 103rd St Fl 4, Omaha NE 68124
Tel (402) 398-7200 SIC 3621

EXX INC p 521
1350 E Flamingo Rd 689, Las Vegas NV 89119
Tel (248) 409-1070
SIC 3621 3669 3714 3944

DMI TECHNOLOGY CORP p 446
1 Progress Dr, Dover NH 03820
Tel (603) 742-3330 SIC 3625 3621

ELECTROCRAFT INC p 485
1 Progress Dr, Dover NH 03820
Tel (603) 742-3330 SIC 3625 3621

BILLOWS ELECTRIC SUPPLY CO INC p 182
1813 Underwood Blvd, Delran NJ 08075
Tel (215) 332-9700
SIC 5063 3679 3621 3643 3644

ASTRODYNE CORP p 122
36 Newburgh Rd, Hackettstown NJ 07840
Tel (908) 850-5088 SIC 3625 3621 3613

▲ ALLIED MOTION TECHNOLOGIES INC p 56
495 Commerce Dr Ste 3, Amherst NY 14228
Tel (716) 242-8634 SIC 3621 3825

■ AMERICAN PRECISION INDUSTRIES INC p 77
45 Hazelwood Dr, Amherst NY 14228
Tel (716) 691-9100
SIC 3677 3621 3625 3443

FELCHAR MANUFACTURING CORP p 537
196 Corporate Dr, Binghamton NY 13904
Tel (607) 723-3106 SIC 3678 3089 3621

MAKERBOT INDUSTRIES LLC p 899
1 Metrotech Ctr Fl 21, Brooklyn NY 11201
Tel (347) 334-6800 SIC 3621 3625 5084

PEM HOLDING CO INC p 1128
800 3rd Ave Fl 40, New York NY 10022
Tel (212) 446-9300 SIC 6211 3429 3621

TINICUM CAPITAL PARTNERS II LP p 1455
800 3rd Ave Fl 40, New York NY 10022
Tel (212) 446-9300 SIC 6211 3429 3621

DRESSER-RAND CO p 455
500 Paul Clark Dr, Olean NY 14760
Tel (716) 375-3000 SIC 3563 3511 3621

AEROFLEX INC p 30
35 S Service Rd, Plainview NY 11803
Tel (516) 694-6700
SIC 3812 3621 3677 3674 3496 3827

AEROFLEX PLAINVIEW INC p 30
35 S Service Rd, Plainview NY 11803
Tel (516) 694-6700
SIC 3679 3621 3674 3827

▲ BABCOCK & WILCOX ENTERPRISES INC p 143
13024 Ballantyne Corporat, Charlotte NC 28277
Tel (704) 625-4900 SIC 3621 3829

▲ CURTISS-WRIGHT CORP p 402
13925 Balntyn Corp Pl, Charlotte NC 28277
Tel (704) 869-4600 SIC 3491 3621 3812

ASMO NORTH AMERICA LLC p 118
470 Crawford Rd, Statesville NC 28625
Tel (704) 872-2319 SIC 3089 3621

ASMO NORTH CAROLINA INC p 118
470 Crawford Rd, Statesville NC 28625
Tel (704) 878-6663 SIC 3519 3621

LM WIND POWER BLADES (ND) INC p 872
1580 S 48th St, Grand Forks ND 58201
Tel (701) 780-9910 SIC 3511 3621

SWIGER COIL SYSTEMS LTD p 1412
4677 Manufacturing Ave, Cleveland OH 44135
Tel (216) 362-7500 SIC 3621 3677

DAYTON-PHOENIX GROUP INC p 418
1619 Kuntz Rd, Dayton OH 45404
Tel (937) 496-3900 SIC 3621 3743

■ GLOBE MOTORS INC p 618
2275 Stanley Ave, Dayton OH 45404
Tel (334) 983-3542 SIC 3621

HBD INDUSTRIES INC p 671
5200 Upper Metro Pl # 110, Dublin OH 43017
Tel (614) 526-7000
SIC 3052 3621 3566 3564 3812

PEERLESS-WINSMITH INC p 1127
5200 Upper Metro Pl # 110, Dublin OH 43017
Tel (614) 526-7000
SIC 3621 3566 3634 3812 3559

TIGERPOLY MANUFACTURING INC p 1453
6231 Enterprise Pkwy, Grove City OH 43123
Tel (614) 871-0045
SIC 3089 3714 3621 3061

■ AMETEK TECHNICAL & INDUSTRIAL PRODUCTS INC p 84
100 E Erie St Ste 130, Kent OH 44240
Tel (330) 677-3754 SIC 3621 5063 3566

OECO LLC p 1075
4607 Se International Way, Milwaukie OR 97222
Tel (503) 659-5999
SIC 3679 5065 4911 3621 3694

▲ AMETEK INC p 84
1100 Cassatt Rd, Berwyn PA 19312
Tel (610) 647-2121
SIC 3621 3823 3824 3825

■ CURTISS-WRIGHT ELECTRO-MECHANICAL CORP p 402
1000 Wright Way, Cheswick PA 15024
Tel (724) 275-5000 SIC 3561 3621 3511

GAMESA TECHNOLOGY CORP INC p 590
1150 Northbrook Dr # 300, Feasterville Trevose PA 19053
Tel (215) 710-3100 SIC 6719 3621

RELIANCE ELECTRIC CO p 1221
6040 Ponders Ct, Greenville SC 29615
Tel (864) 297-4800 SIC 3714 3621

■ DEVILBISS AIR POWER CO p 434
4825 Highway 45 N, Jackson TN 38305
Tel (800) 888-2468 SIC 3563 3621 3589

■ LEROY-SOMER INC p 857
669 Natchez Trace Dr, Lexington TN 38351
Tel (731) 967-3000 SIC 3621

LUMINANT GENERATION CO LLC p 885
1601 Bryan St, Dallas TX 75201
Tel (214) 812-4600 SIC 4911 3621

■ GE ENERGY MANUFACTURING INC p 596
1333 West Loop S Ste 700, Houston TX 77027
Tel (713) 803-0900 SIC 3621 3568 5084

JUST ENERGY (US) CORP p 797
5251 Westheimr Rd # 1000, Houston TX 77056
Tel (713) 850-6784 SIC 3621 4924

■ NRG TEXAS POWER LLC p 1064
1301 Mckinney St Ste 2300, Houston TX 77010
Tel (713) 537-3000 SIC 3621

TOSHIBA INTERNATIONAL CORP p 1462
13131 W Little York Rd, Houston TX 77041
Tel (713) 466-0277
SIC 3621 5084 5063 3613 3594 3572

TYCO ENGINEERED PRODUCTS & SERVICES p 1496
9600 W Gulf Bank Rd, Houston TX 77040
Tel (609) 720-4200 *SIC* 3491 3625 3621

WAUKESHA-PEARCE INDUSTRIES INC p 1583
12320 Main St, Houston TX 77035
Tel (713) 723-1050 *SIC* 5084 5082 3621

▲ FLOWSERVE CORP p 560
5215 N Oconnor Blvd Connor, Irving TX 75039
Tel (972) 443-6500
SIC 3561 3491 3621 3494 3463 3321

▲ LENNOX INTERNATIONAL INC p 855
2140 Lake Park Blvd, Richardson TX 75080
Tel (972) 497-5350 *SIC* 3585 3621

■ FISHER-ROSEMOUNT SYSTEMS INC p 552
1100 W Louis Henna Blvd, Round Rock TX 78681
Tel (512) 835-2190 *SIC* 3625 3621 7699

TECO HOLDINGS USA INC p 1432
5100 N Interstate 35, Round Rock TX 78681
Tel (512) 255-4141 *SIC* 3621

TECO-WESTINGHOUSE MOTOR CO p 1432
5100 N Interstate 35 A, Round Rock TX 78681
Tel (512) 218-7448 *SIC* 3621

SAFRAN USA INC p 1267
700 S Washington St # 320, Alexandria VA 22314
Tel (703) 351-9898
SIC 3643 3621 7699 3724 5013 5088

▲ BWX TECHNOLOGIES INC p 231
800 Main St Ste 4, Lynchburg VA 24504
Tel (980) 365-4300 *SIC* 3621 3829

■ KOLLMORGEN CORP p 826
203a W Rock Rd, Radford VA 24141
Tel (540) 639-2495
SIC 3621 3825 3827 3861

PACIFIC POWER GROUP LLC p 1105
805 Broadway St Ste 700, Vancouver WA 98660
Tel (360) 887-7400
SIC 5088 3621 5063 3519 5084

■ MILLER ELECTRIC MFG CO p 970
1635 W Spencer St, Appleton WI 54914
Tel (920) 734-9821 *SIC* 3548 3621

■ REGAL BELOIT AMERICA INC p 1218
200 State St, Beloit WI 53511
Tel (608) 364-8800 *SIC* 3644 3621

▲ REGAL BELOIT CORP p 1218
200 State St, Beloit WI 53511
Tel (608) 364-8800 *SIC* 3621 3714 3566

UNITED STARS INC p 1512
1546 Henry Ave, Beloit WI 53511
Tel (608) 368-4625
SIC 3317 3351 3463 3613 3621

■ LEESON ELECTRIC CORP p 852
1051 Cheyenne Ave, Grafton WI 53024
Tel (262) 377-8810 *SIC* 3621

WACKER NEUSON CORP p 1570
N92w15000 Anthony Ave, Menomonee Falls WI 53051
Tel (262) 255-0500
SIC 3531 3621 3561 3546 3423

▲ ROCKWELL AUTOMATION INC p 1245
1201 S 2nd St, Milwaukee WI 53204
Tel (414) 382-2000
SIC 3625 3621 3566 3661

GENERAC POWER SYSTEMS INC p 599
3815 Oregon St, Oshkosh WI 54902
Tel (262) 544-4811 *SIC* 3621

▲ GENERAC HOLDINGS INC p 599
S45w29290 Hwy 59, Waukesha WI 53189
Tel (262) 544-4811 *SIC* 3621

■ GENERAC POWER SYSTEMS INC p 599
S45w29290 Wisconsin 59 St S 45, Waukesha WI 53189
Tel (262) 544-4811 *SIC* 3621

■ BRIGGS & STRATTON POWER PRODUCTS GROUP LLC p 212
12301 W Wirth St, Wauwatosa WI 53222
Tel (414) 259-5333 *SIC* 3621

SIC 3624 Carbon & Graphite Prdts

▲ HEXCEL CORP p 688
281 Tresser Blvd Ste 1503, Stamford CT 06901
Tel (203) 969-0666
SIC 2821 3728 3089 3624 2891 3469

ZOLTEK COMPANIES INC p 1644
3101 Mckelvey Rd, Bridgeton MO 63044
Tel (314) 291-5110 *SIC* 3624

MERSEN USA BN CORP p 951
400 Myrtle Ave, Boonton NJ 07005
Tel (973) 334-0700 *SIC* 3624

HH LIQUIDATING CORP p 689
110 E 59th St Fl 34, New York NY 10022
Tel (646) 282-2500
SIC 3624 2999 3356 3339

SGL CARBON LLC p 1310
10130 Perimeter Pkwy # 500, Charlotte NC 28216
Tel (704) 593-5100 *SIC* 3624

BGF INDUSTRIES INC p 180
3802 Robert Porcher Way, Greensboro NC 27410
Tel (843) 537-3172
SIC 2221 3624 2241 2295

NOUVEAU VERRE HOLDINGS INC p 1062
3802 Robert Porcher Way, Greensboro NC 27410
Tel (336) 545-0011
SIC 2221 3624 2241 2295

NVH INC p 1068
3802 Robert Porcher Way, Greensboro NC 27410
Tel (336) 545-0011
SIC 2221 3624 2241 2295

MORGANITE INDUSTRIES INC p 989
4000 Westchase Blvd # 170, Raleigh NC 27607
Tel (919) 821-1253
SIC 3674 3255 3699 3264 3299 3624

AMERICAN SPRING WIRE CORP p 79
26300 Miles Rd, Bedford Heights OH 44146
Tel (216) 292-4620
SIC 3272 3315 3316 3339 3624

GRAFTECH HOLDINGS INC p 628
6100 Oak Tree Blvd # 300, Independence OH 44131
Tel (216) 676-2000 *SIC* 1499 3624

GRAFTECH INTERNATIONAL HOLDINGS INC p 628
6100 Oak Tree Blvd # 300, Independence OH 44131
Tel (216) 676-2000 *SIC* 3624

GRAFTECH INTERNATIONAL LTD p 628
6100 Oak Tree Blvd # 300, Independence OH 44131
Tel (216) 676-2000 *SIC* 3624

SHOWA DENKO CARBON INC p 1318
478 Ridge Rd, Ridgeville SC 29472
Tel (843) 875-3200 *SIC* 3624

CONTINENTAL CARBON CO p 363
16850 Park Row, Houston TX 77084
Tel (281) 647-3700 *SIC* 2895 3624

TORAY COMPOSITES (AMERICA) INC p 1461
19002 50th Ave E, Tacoma WA 98446
Tel (253) 846-1777 *SIC* 3624

WINDWAY CAPITAL CORP p 1616
630 Riverfront Dr Ste 200, Sheboygan WI 53081
Tel (920) 457-8600
SIC 3469 2394 3624 3732

SIC 3625 Relays & Indl Controls

SYNCRO CORP p 1415
1030 Sundown Dr Nw, Arab AL 35016
Tel (256) 586-6045
SIC 3714 3625 3694 3823 3643

DAEHAN SOLUTION ALABAMA LLC p 408
9101 County Road 26, Hope Hull AL 36043
Tel (334) 404-5000 *SIC* 3625 2273

TOPCON POSITIONING SYSTEMS INC p 1461
7400 National Dr, Livermore CA 94550
Tel (925) 245-8300
SIC 3829 3625 3823 3699 8713 1794

CAL-COMP ELECTRONICS (USA) CO LTD p 237
9877 Waples St, San Diego CA 92121
Tel (858) 587-6900 *SIC* 3625

CRYDOM INC p 396
2320 Paseo Delas Amer 2 Ste 201, San Diego CA 92154
Tel (619) 210-1600
SIC 3625 5065 3674 3643

■ MICROSEMI FREQUENCY AND TIME CORP p 962
3870 N 1st St, San Jose CA 95134
Tel (408) 428-6993 *SIC* 3625 7372

▲ UNIVERSAL ELECTRONICS INC p 1516
201 Sandpointe Ave # 800, Santa Ana CA 92707
Tel (714) 918-9500 *SIC* 3651 3625 7372

■ WOODWARD HRT INC p 1623
25200 Rye Canyon Rd, Santa Clarita CA 91355
Tel (661) 294-6000 *SIC* 3625 3492

PACIFIC SCIENTIFIC CO INC p 1105
1785 Voyager Ave Ste 101, Simi Valley CA 93063
Tel (805) 526-5700
SIC 3812 3669 3621 3694 3823 3625

▲ MOTORCAR PARTS OF AMERICA INC p 993
2929 California St, Torrance CA 90503
Tel (310) 212-7910
SIC 3714 3694 3625 5013

▲ ADVANCED ENERGY INDUSTRIES INC p 25
1625 Sharp Point Dr, Fort Collins CO 80525
Tel (970) 221-4670 *SIC* 3679 3629 3625

▲ WOODWARD INC p 1623
1081 Woodward Way, Fort Collins CO 80524
Tel (970) 482-5811
SIC 3625 3629 3492 3519

WG GLOBAL LLC p 1604
603 Park Point Dr Ste 200, Golden CO 80401
Tel (303) 395-2100
SIC 3569 3559 3629 3625 3443 3412

ASEA BROWN BOVERI INC p 116
501 Merritt 7, Norwalk CT 06851
Tel (203) 750-2200
SIC 3612 3613 5063 3511 3625 8711

■ GEMS SENSORS INC p 598
1 Cowles Rd, Plainville CT 06062
Tel (860) 747-3000
SIC 3824 5084 3812 3625 3613

ULTRA ELECTRONICS AIRPORT SYSTEMS INC p 1501
107 Church Hill Rd Ste G2, Sandy Hook CT 06482
Tel (203) 270-3696 *SIC* 3625

ASHCROFT INC p 117
250 E Main St, Stratford CT 06614
Tel (203) 378-8281
SIC 3823 3679 3663 3625

ASHCROFT-NAGANO KEIKI HOLDINGS INC p 117
250 E Main St, Stratford CT 06614
Tel (203) 378-8281
SIC 3823 3679 3663 3625

■ HAMILTON SUNDSTRAND CORP p 655
1 Hamilton Rd, Windsor Locks CT 06096
Tel (860) 654-6000
SIC 3621 3594 3728 3625 3823 3822

WEG ELECTRIC CORP p 1587
6655 Sugarloaf Pkwy, Duluth GA 30097
Tel (678) 249-2000
SIC 3612 3621 3613 3625

MAGNETROL INTERNATIONAL INC p 896
705 Enterprise St, Aurora IL 60504
Tel (630) 723-6600
SIC 3823 3699 3643 3625 3541

SIEMENS INDUSTRY INC p 1320
1000 Deerfield Pkwy, Buffalo Grove IL 60089
Tel (847) 215-1000
SIC 3822 5063 3669 1731 7382 3625

AVG ADVANCED TECHNOLOGIES LP p 137
343 Saint Paul Blvd, Carol Stream IL 60188
Tel (630) 668-3900
SIC 3672 3661 3824 3822 3625

S & C ELECTRIC CO p 1261
6601 N Ridge Blvd, Chicago IL 60626
Tel (773) 338-1000
SIC 3613 3643 3625 8711

JORDAN INDUSTRIES INC p 793
1751 Lake Cook Rd Ste 550, Deerfield IL 60015
Tel (847) 945-5591
SIC 3621 3625 3714 3089 2759 5999

CAPSONIC AUTOMOTIVE INC p 251
460 2nd St, Elgin IL 60123
Tel (847) 888-7300 *SIC* 3625 3679 3674

CHAMBERLAIN MANUFACTURING CORP p 287
845 N Larch Ave, Elmhurst IL 60126
Tel (630) 279-3600 *SIC* 3651 3625 3699

■ KNOWLES ELECTRONICS HOLDINGS INC p 825
1151 Maplewood Dr, Itasca IL 60143
Tel (630) 250-5100
SIC 3679 3625 3651 8731 6159

GRAYHILL INC p 632
561 W Hillgrove Ave, La Grange IL 60525
Tel (708) 354-1040
SIC 3613 3625 3679 3643 3575

■ MPC PRODUCTS CORP p 995
6300 W Howard St, Niles IL 60714
Tel (847) 673-8300
SIC 3728 3621 3676 3812 3625

BODINE ELECTRIC CO p 197
201 Northfield Rd, Northfield IL 60093
Tel (773) 478-3515 *SIC* 5063 3625 3621

SCHNEIDER ELECTRIC BUILDINGS LLC p 1287
839 N Perryville Rd, Rockford IL 61107
Tel (815) 381-5000
SIC 3822 1711 3625 3823 3621

OMRON AUTOMOTIVE ELECTRONICS INC p 1085
3709 Ohio Ave, Saint Charles IL 60174
Tel (630) 443-6800
SIC 5065 3625 3714 8742

SCHNEIDER ELECTRIC HOLDINGS INC p 1287
200 N Martingale Rd # 100, Schaumburg IL 60173
Tel (717) 944-5460
SIC 3822 1711 3625 3823 3621

OHMITE HOLDING LLC p 1078
27501 Bella Vista Pkwy, Warrenville IL 60555
Tel (847) 258-0300 *SIC* 3625 5065

YASKAWA AMERICA INC p 1635
2121 Norman Dr, Waukegan IL 60085
Tel (847) 887-7000
SIC 3621 7694 5063 3566 3823 3625

KELCO INDUSTRIES INC p 808
1425 Lake Ave, Woodstock IL 60098
Tel (815) 334-3600
SIC 3599 3069 3494 3585 3544 3625

DWYER INSTRUMENTS INC p 464
102 Indiana Highway 212, Michigan City IN 46360
Tel (219) 879-8868
SIC 3823 3824 3822 3829 3491 3625

■ REMY INC p 1223
600 Corporation Dr, Pendleton IN 46064
Tel (765) 778-6499
SIC 3714 3694 3625 3621 5013

■ REMY POWER PRODUCTS LLC p 1223
600 Corporation Dr, Pendleton IN 46064
Tel (765) 778-6499 *SIC* 3625 3694 3621

■ FISHER CONTROLS INTERNATIONAL LLC p 552
205 S Center St, Marshalltown IA 50158
Tel (641) 754-3011
SIC 3491 3823 3625 3612 3494

SHELL TOPCO LP p 1314
2533 S West St, Wichita KS 67217
Tel (316) 942-7266 *SIC* 3625 1711

ACK CONTROLS INC p 17
2600 Happy Valley Rd, Glasgow KY 42141
Tel (270) 678-6200 *SIC* 5013 3625 3357

HITACHI AUTOMOTIVE SYSTEMS AMERICAS INC p 696
955 Warwick Rd, Harrodsburg KY 40330
Tel (859) 734-9451
SIC 3694 3714 3699 3625

▲ COLFAX CORP p 336
420 Natl Bus Pkwy Fl 5, Annapolis Junction MD 20701
Tel (301) 323-9000 *SIC* 3561 3829 3625

DANFOSS LLC p 411
11655 Crossroads Cir A, Baltimore MD 21220
Tel (410) 931-8250 *SIC* 3585 3625 3822

SCHNEIDER ELECTRIC USA INC p 1288
800 Federal St, Andover MA 01810
Tel (978) 975-9600
SIC 3613 3643 3612 3823 3625 5063

■ KIDDE-FENWAL INC p 817
400 Main St, Ashland MA 01721
Tel (508) 881-2000
SIC 3669 3823 3825 3822 3643 3625

SENSATA TECHNOLOGIES INDIANA INC p 1304
529 Pleasant St, Attleboro MA 02703
Tel (508) 236-3245 *SIC* 3676 3625

WABASH TECHNOLOGIES INC p 1570
529 Pleasant St, Attleboro MA 02703
Tel (260) 355-4100 *SIC* 3625 3676

■ GE INFRASTRUCTURE SENSING INC p 596
1100 Technology Park Dr # 100, Billerica MA 01821
Tel (978) 437-1000
SIC 3823 5084 3699 3674 3663 3625

▲ ALTRA INDUSTRIAL MOTION CORP p 62
300 Granite St Ste 201, Braintree MA 02184
Tel (781) 917-0600
SIC 3568 5085 3542 3625

THG CORP p 1447
70 Bearfoot Rd, Northborough MA 01532
Tel (508) 393-7660
SIC 5085 5084 3569 3728 3625 3494

■ GENERAL DYNAMICS DEFENSE SYSTEMS INC p 600
100 Plastics Ave, Pittsfield MA 01201
Tel (413) 494-1110 *SIC* 3812 3795 3625

ELECTRO SWITCH CORP p 485
775 Pleasant St Ste 1, Weymouth MA 02189
Tel (781) 335-1195 *SIC* 3613 3625

MELLING TOOL CO p 941
2620 Saradan Dr, Jackson MI 49202
Tel (517) 787-8172
SIC 3451 3714 3625 3568 3561 3494

TAC MANUFACTURING INC p 1421
4111 County Farm Rd, Jackson MI 49201
Tel (517) 789-7000 *SIC* 3714 3625

■ BORGWARNER THERMAL SYSTEMS INC p 201
1507 S Kalamazoo Ave, Marshall MI 49068
Tel (269) 781-1228 *SIC* 3625

PRESTOLITE ELECTRIC LLC p 1173
30120 Hudson Dr, Novi MI 48377
Tel (248) 313-3807
SIC 3643 3824 3621 3625 3694

▲ STONERIDGE INC p 1391
39675 Mackenzie Dr # 400, Novi MI 48377
Tel (330) 856-2443 *SIC* 3714 3679 3625

HELLA CORPORATE CENTER USA INC p 681
43811 Plymouth Oaks Blvd, Plymouth MI 48170
Tel (586) 232-4788
SIC 3625 5013 5088 3822 3585 3429

HELLA ELECTRONICS CORP p 681
43811 Plymouth Oaks Blvd, Plymouth MI 48170
Tel (734) 414-0900 *SIC* 3625 3714

JOHNSON ELECTRIC NORTH AMERICA INC p 791
47660 Halyard Dr, Plymouth MI 48170
Tel (734) 392-5300
SIC 5063 3625 3674 8711

FLEXTRONICS AUTOMOTIVE USA INC p 556
2120 Austin Ave, Rochester Hills MI 48309
Tel (248) 853-5724 *SIC* 3625 3714 3643

TRELLEBORG AUTOMOTIVE USA INC p 1476
400 Aylworth Ave, South Haven MI 49090
Tel (269) 637-2116 *SIC* 3061 3625

DAYCO INC p 417
1650 Research Dr Ste 200, Troy MI 48083
Tel (716) 689-4972
SIC 3641 3646 3643 3625 3613

▲ MERITOR INC p 949
2135 W Maple Rd, Troy MI 48084
Tel (248) 435-1000
SIC 3714 3493 3625 3465

■ TESCOM CORP p 1440
12616 Industrial Blvd Nw, Elk River MN 55330
Tel (763) 441-6330 *SIC* 3491 3625 3494

■ RESEARCH AND DIAGNOSTIC SYSTEMS INC p 1226
614 Mckinley Pl Ne, Minneapolis MN 55413
Tel (612) 379-2956
SIC 8733 2833 8731 3829 3625

■ SL-MONTEVIDEO TECHNOLOGY INC p 1331
2002 Black Oak Ave, Montevideo MN 56265
Tel (320) 269-5583 *SIC* 3625

■ KATO ENGINEERING INC p 804
2075 Howard Dr W, North Mankato MN 56003
Tel (507) 345-2716 *SIC* 3621 3643 3625

TURCK INC p 1492
3000 Campus Dr, Plymouth MN 55441
Tel (763) 553-9224 *SIC* 3625

NIDEC AMERICAS HOLDING CORP p 1043
8050 W Florissant Ave, Saint Louis MO 63136
Tel (314) 595-8000 *SIC* 3625 3594 6719

NIDEC MOTOR CORP p 1043
8050 W Florissant Ave, Saint Louis MO 63136
Tel (314) 595-8000 *SIC* 3625 3594

DMI TECHNOLOGY CORP p 446
1 Progress Dr, Dover NH 03820
Tel (603) 742-3330 *SIC* 3625 3621

ELECTROCRAFT INC p 485
1 Progress Dr, Dover NH 03820
Tel (603) 742-3330 *SIC* 3625 3621

■ ASCO VALVE INC p 116
50-60 Hanover Rd, Florham Park NJ 07932
Tel (973) 966-2437
SIC 3443 3491 3492 3625 5063

■ AUTOMATIC SWITCH CO p 134
50-60 Hanover Rd, Florham Park NJ 07932
Tel (973) 966-2000
SIC 3491 3625 3677 3674 3613 3492

ASTRODYNE CORP p 122
36 Newburgh Rd, Hackettstown NJ 07840
Tel (908) 850-5088 *SIC* 3625 3621 3613

TRANSISTOR DEVICES INC p 1471
36 Newburgh Rd, Hackettstown NJ 07840
Tel (908) 850-1595
SIC 3612 3625 3672 3812 3829

SWATCH GROUP U S INC p 1411
1200 Harbor Blvd Fl 7, Weehawken NJ 07086
Tel (201) 271-1400
SIC 5063 3625 5094 3873

■ WHIPPANY ACTUATION SYSTEMS LLC p 1605
110 Algonquin Pkwy, Whippany NJ 07981
Tel (973) 428-9898 *SIC* 3625 3728

■ AMERICAN PRECISION INDUSTRIES INC p 77
45 Hazelwood Dr, Amherst NY 14228
Tel (716) 691-9100
SIC 3677 3621 3625 3443

MAKERBOT INDUSTRIES LLC p 899
1 Metrotech Ctr Fl 21, Brooklyn NY 11201
Tel (347) 334-6800 *SIC* 3621 3625 5084

MARQUARDT SWITCHES INC p 910
2711 Us Route 20, Cazenovia NY 13035
Tel (315) 655-8050 *SIC* 3625 3613

▲ MOOG INC p 987
400 Jamison Rd Plant26, Elma NY 14059
Tel (716) 652-2000
SIC 3812 3492 3625 3769 3728 3841

BOSCH SECURITY SYSTEMS INC p 202
130 Perinton Pkwy, Fairport NY 14450
Tel (585) 223-4060
SIC 3669 3699 3826 3825 3823 3625

DESIGNATRONICS INC p 432
2101 Jericho Tpke Ste 1, New Hyde Park NY 11040
Tel (516) 328-3300
SIC 3824 3559 3545 3625 3462

KEARNEY-NATIONAL INC p 807
565 5th Ave Fl 4, New York NY 10017
Tel (212) 661-4600
SIC 3679 3694 3714 3625

DYSON-KISSNER-MORAN CORP p 465
2515 South Rd Ste 5, Poughkeepsie NY 12601
Tel (212) 661-4600 *SIC* 3433 3625 3699

▲ ITT INC p 768
1133 Westchester Ave N-100, White Plains NY 10604
Tel (914) 641-2000
SIC 3594 3625 3823 3812

■ ITT LLC p 768
1133 Westchester Ave N-100, White Plains NY 10604
Tel (914) 641-2000
SIC 3594 3625 3823 3812

■ HUBBELL INDUSTRIAL CONTROLS INC p 716
4301 Cheyenne Dr, Archdale NC 27263
Tel (336) 434-2800 *SIC* 3625

ABB INC p 9
12040 Regency Pkwy # 200, Cary NC 27518
Tel (919) 856-2360
SIC 8711 3612 3511 5063 3613 3625

SIEMENS POWER TRANSMISSION & DISTRIBUTION INC p 1320
110 Macalyson Ct, Cary NC 27511
Tel (919) 463-8702 *SIC* 3613 3625

AC CORP p 13
301 Creek Ridge Rd, Greensboro NC 27406
Tel (336) 273-4472
SIC 1711 1731 3556 3823 3625 3535

CONBRACO INDUSTRIES INC p 354
701 Matthews Mint Hill Rd, Matthews NC 28105
Tel (704) 841-6000 *SIC* 3625 3494

KEIHIN CAROLINA SYSTEM TECHNOLOGY LLC p 807
4047 Mcnair Rd, Tarboro NC 27886
Tel (252) 641-6750 *SIC* 3694 3625 3714

EATON CORP p 473
1000 Eaton Blvd, Cleveland OH 44122
Tel (216) 523-5000
SIC 3625 3714 3594 3559 3571

■ TRANSDIGM INC p 1471
4223 Monticello Blvd, Cleveland OH 44121
Tel (216) 706-2939
SIC 5088 3563 3625 3492 3691 3491

MORRIS MATERIAL HANDLING INC p 990
4401 Gateway Blvd, Springfield OH 45502
Tel (937) 525-5520 *SIC* 3625 3443 7699

DELTA SYSTEMS INC p 427
1734 Frost Rd, Streetsboro OH 44241
Tel (330) 626-2811 *SIC* 3613 3625

PEPPERL + FUCHS INC p 1134
1600 Enterprise Pkwy, Twinsburg OH 44087
Tel (330) 425-3555
SIC 5065 3625 3822 3674

ENOVATION CONTROLS LLC p 500
5311 S 122nd East Ave, Tulsa OK 74146
Tel (918) 317-4100
SIC 3625 3714 3694 8711

TALEN ENERGY SERVICES HOLDINGS LLC p 1422
835 Hamilton St, Allentown PA 18101
Tel (610) 774-5151 *SIC* 4911 1711 3625

LUTRON ELECTRONICS CO INC p 886
7200 Suter Rd, Coopersburg PA 18036
Tel (610) 282-3800 *SIC* 3625

BERWIND CORP p 176
3000 Ctr Sq W 1500 Mkt St 1500 W, Philadelphia PA 19102
Tel (215) 563-2800
SIC 6519 5052 4789 3625 3669 2899

FENIX MANUFACTURING SOLUTIONS LLC p 537
2063 University Pkwy, Aiken SC 29801
Tel (803) 649-1381
SIC 3694 3825 3625 3354

AMERIMEX MOTOR & CONTROLS LLC p 82
610 N Milby St, Houston TX 77003
Tel (713) 225-4300 *SIC* 5063 3625 7694

PENTAIR VALVES & CONTROLS US LP p 1132
10707 Clay Rd Ste 200, Houston TX 77041
Tel (713) 986-4665 *SIC* 3491 3625 3494

■ POWELL ELECTRICAL SYSTEMS INC p 1165
8550 Mosley Rd, Houston TX 77075
Tel (708) 409-1200 *SIC* 3625

▲ POWELL INDUSTRIES INC p 1165
8550 Mosley Rd, Houston TX 77075
Tel (713) 944-6900
SIC 3612 3613 3625 3643 3823

TYCO ENGINEERED PRODUCTS & SERVICES p 1496
9600 W Gulf Bank Rd, Houston TX 77040
Tel (609) 720-4200 *SIC* 3491 3625 3621

W CSE INDUSTRIES INC p 1568
11500 Charles Rd, Jersey Village TX 77041
Tel (713) 466-9463
SIC 3625 3613 3594 3494

■ AMX LLC p 88
3000 Research Dr, Richardson TX 75082
Tel (469) 624-8740 *SIC* 3625

■ FISHER-ROSEMOUNT SYSTEMS INC p 552
1100 W Louis Henna Blvd, Round Rock TX 78681
Tel (512) 835-2190 *SIC* 3625 3621 7699

■ GE INTELLIGENT PLATFORMS INC p 596
2500 Austin Dr, Charlottesville VA 22911
Tel (434) 978-5000 *SIC* 3625 3674 7371

KSB AMERICA CORP p 831
4415 Sarellen Rd, Richmond VA 23231
Tel (804) 222-1818
SIC 3561 3494 3625 5084

TRAVIS PATTERN & FOUNDRY INC p 1475
1413 E Hawthorne Rd, Spokane WA 99218
Tel (509) 466-1798
SIC 3523 3369 3313 3321 3625

USNR LLC p 1535
1981 Schurman Way, Woodland WA 98674
Tel (360) 225-8267
SIC 3585 3553 3625 1221 5084

BELLOFRAM CORP p 171
8019 Ohio River Blvd, Newell WV 26050
Tel (304) 387-1200 *SIC* 3612 3829 3625

▲ ACTUANT CORP p 20
N86w12500 Westbrook Xing, Menomonee Falls WI 53051
Tel (262) 293-1500
SIC 3593 3492 3594 3625 7359

■ MAGNETEK INC p 896
N49w13650 Campbell Dr, Menomonee Falls WI 53051
Tel (262) 783-3500 *SIC* 3625

■ JASON INC p 778
411 E Wisconsin Ave, Milwaukee WI 53202
Tel (414) 277-9300
SIC 3465 2297 3625 3469 3844 3443

▲ JASON INDUSTRIES INC p 778
833 E Michigan St Ste 900, Milwaukee WI 53202
Tel (414) 277-9300
SIC 3465 2297 3625 3469 3844 3443

■ JPHI HOLDINGS INC p 795
411 E Wisconsin Ave, Milwaukee WI 53202
Tel (414) 277-9445
SIC 3465 2297 3625 3469 3844 3443

■ REXNORD INDUSTRIES LLC p 1230
247 W Freshwater Way # 200, Milwaukee WI 53204
Tel (414) 643-3000
SIC 3568 3566 3625 3714

■ REXNORD-ZURN HOLDINGS INC p 1230
4701 W Greenfield Ave, Milwaukee WI 53214
Tel (414) 643-3000
SIC 3568 3566 3625 3714

▲ ROCKWELL AUTOMATION INC p 1245
1201 S 2nd St, Milwaukee WI 53204
Tel (414) 382-2000
SIC 3625 3621 3566 3661

PHMH HOLDING CO p 1144
315 W Forest Hill Ave, Oak Creek WI 53154
Tel (414) 764-6200 *SIC* 3625 6719

VENTUREDYNE LTD p 1548
600 College Ave, Pewaukee WI 53072
Tel (262) 691-9900
SIC 3568 3829 3826 3823 3625

SIC 3629 Electrical Indl Apparatus, NEC

CHENEGA CORP p 294
3000 C St Ste 301, Anchorage AK 99503
Tel (907) 277-5706
SIC 8744 7379 7376 3629 8742

ASTEC AMERICA LLC p 122
2900 S Diablo Way Ste 190, Tempe AZ 85282
Tel (602) 438-5720 *SIC* 3679 3629 3621

AIH LLC p 38
5810 Van Allen Way, Carlsbad CA 92008
Tel (760) 930-4600 *SIC* 3629 3621 3679

SOLAREDGE TECHNOLOGIES INC p 1338
47505 Seabridge Dr, Fremont CA 94538
Tel (877) 360-5292 *SIC* 3629

MYERS POWER PRODUCTS INC p 1004
2950 E Philadelphia St, Ontario CA 91761
Tel (909) 923-1800 *SIC* 3629

▲ MAXWELL TECHNOLOGIES INC p 923
3888 Calle Fortunada, San Diego CA 92123
Tel (858) 503-3200 *SIC* 3629

▲ ADVANCED ENERGY INDUSTRIES INC p 25
1625 Sharp Point Dr, Fort Collins CO 80525
Tel (970) 221-4670 *SIC* 3679 3629 3625

▲ WOODWARD INC p 1623
1081 Woodward Way, Fort Collins CO 80524
Tel (970) 482-5811
SIC 3625 3629 3492 3519

WG GLOBAL LLC p 1604
603 Park Point Dr Ste 200, Golden CO 80401
Tel (303) 395-2100
SIC 3569 3559 3629 3625 3443 3412

SCHUMACHER ELECTRIC CORP p 1291
801 E Business Center Dr, Mount Prospect IL 60056
Tel (847) 385-1600 *SIC* 3629 3677

ROCKFORD CONCENTRIC INC p 1244
2222 15th St, Rockford IL 61104
Tel (815) 398-4400 *SIC* 3594 3629

CHARLES INDUSTRIES LTD p 289
5600 Apollo Dr, Rolling Meadows IL 60008
Tel (847) 806-6300 *SIC* 3661 3629 3677

INVENTUS POWER INC p 761
1200 Internationale Pkwy, Woodridge IL 60517
Tel (630) 410-7900 *SIC* 3629

KIRBY RISK CORP p 821
1815 Sagamore Pkwy N, Lafayette IN 47904
Tel (765) 448-4567
SIC 5063 7694 3599 3679 3629

INTERSTATES CONSTRUCTION SERVICES INC p 758
1520 N Main Ave, Sioux Center IA 51250
Tel (712) 722-1662 *SIC* 1731 3629

ASSURANCE TECHNOLOGY CORP p 121
84 South St, Carlisle MA 01741
Tel (978) 369-8848 *SIC* 8711 3629

AEROVOX INC p 31
167 John Vertente Blvd, New Bedford MA 02745
Tel (508) 994-9661 *SIC* 3629 3675

▲ THERMO FISHER SCIENTIFIC INC p 1447
168 3rd Ave, Waltham MA 02451
Tel (781) 622-1000
SIC 3826 3845 3823 3629

EAGLEPICHER TECHNOLOGIES LLC p 468
C & Porter Sts, Joplin MO 64802
Tel (417) 623-8000
SIC 3691 3629 3599 2892

KOLLSMAN INC p 826
220 Daniel Webster Hwy, Merrimack NH 03054
Tel (603) 889-2500 *SIC* 3812 3629

TDK-LAMBDA AMERICAS INC p 1429
405 Essex Rd, Tinton Falls NJ 07753
Tel (732) 922-9300 *SIC* 3629

CURTIS INSTRUMENTS INC p 402
200 Kisco Ave, Mount Kisco NY 10549
Tel (914) 666-2971 *SIC* 3825 3824 3629

TONOGA INC p 1460
136 Coon Brook Rd, Petersburg NY 12138
Tel (518) 658-3202 *SIC* 2295 3629

STATIC CONTROL COMPONENTS INC p 1383
3010 Lee Ave, Sanford NC 27332
Tel (919) 774-3808 *SIC* 3629

■ POWERSECURE INTERNATIONAL INC p 1166
1609 Heritage Commerce Ct, Wake Forest NC 27587
Tel (919) 556-3056 *SIC* 3629 4931

■ LUBRIZOL ADVANCED MATERIALS INC p 884
9911 Brecksville Rd, Brecksville OH 44141
Tel (216) 447-5000
SIC 2899 2891 3088 2834 3629

CROSBY US ACQUISITION CORP p 393
2801 Dawson Rd, Tulsa OK 74110
Tel (918) 834-4611 *SIC* 3629

■ GE ENERGY POWER CONVERSION USA INC p 596
610 Epsilon Dr, Pittsburgh PA 15238
Tel (412) 967-0765 *SIC* 3629

HORSEHEAD CORP p 708
4955 Steubenville Pike, Pittsburgh PA 15205
Tel (724) 774-1020 *SIC* 3339 3629

■ SPRAGUE VISHAY INC p 1360
111 Gilbane St, Warwick RI 02886
Tel (401) 738-9150 *SIC* 3629

SCHNEIDER ELECTRIC IT CORP p 1287
132 Fairgrounds Rd, West Kingston RI 02892
Tel (401) 789-5735
SIC 3629 3612 3677 3585 7372 2542

■ ARBOR-CROWLEY INC p 103
3100 W 7th St Ste 500, Fort Worth TX 76107
Tel (817) 810-0095 *SIC* 3629

THOMAS & BETTS POWER SOLUTIONS LLC p 1448
5900 Eastport Blvd Bldg 5, Richmond VA 23231
Tel (804) 236-3300 *SIC* 3629

COOPER POWER SYSTEMS LLC p 367
2300 Badger Dr, Waukesha WI 53188
Tel (262) 524-4227
SIC 3612 3613 3644 3643 3629 3679

SIC 3631 Household Cooking Eqpt

TOSHIBA AMERICA ELECTRONIC COMPONENTS INC p 1462
9740 Irvine Blvd Ste D700, Irvine CA 92618
Tel (949) 462-7700
SIC 3651 3631 3674 3679 5065 5064

■ CARRIER COMMERCIAL REFRIGERATION INC p 260
3 Farm Glen Blvd Ste 301, Farmington CT 06032
Tel (336) 245-6400
SIC 3556 3631 3585 3589 3634

CONAIR CORP p 354
1 Cummings Point Rd, Stamford CT 06902
Tel (203) 351-9000
SIC 3634 3631 3639 3999

■ AMERICAN HOUSEHOLD INC p 74
2381 Nw Executive Ctr Dr, Boca Raton FL 33431
Tel (561) 912-4100
SIC 3631 2514 3421 3634 3829 3841

■ SUNBEAM AMERICAS HOLDINGS LLC p 1401
2381 Nw Executive Ctr Dr, Boca Raton FL 33431
Tel (561) 912-4100
SIC 3631 2514 3421 3634 3829 3841

■ SUNBEAM PRODUCTS INC p 1401
2381 Nw Executive Ctr Dr, Boca Raton FL 33431
Tel (561) 912-4100 *SIC* 3631 3634

MASTERBUILT MANUFACTURING LLC p 918
1 Masterbuilt Ct, Columbus GA 31907
Tel (706) 327-5622 *SIC* 3631 3714

W C BRADLEY CO p 1568
1017 Front Ave, Columbus GA 31901
Tel (706) 571-7000 *SIC* 3631 3949 3999

■ ROPER CORP p 1250
1507 Broomtown Rd, La Fayette GA 30728
Tel (706) 638-3559 *SIC* 3631 3634

■ MARSHALL MIDDLEBY INC p 911
1400 Toastmaster Dr, Elgin IL 60120
Tel (847) 289-0204 *SIC* 3556 3585 3631

WEBER-STEPHEN PRODUCTS LLC p 1586
1415 S Roselle Rd, Palatine IL 60067
Tel (847) 934-5700 *SIC* 3631

CRISTAL p 392
20 Wight Ave Ste 100, Hunt Valley MD 21030
Tel (410) 229-4440
SIC 1241 3531 2816 2869 1321 3631

■ MAYTAG CORP p 924
2000 N M 63, Benton Harbor MI 49022
Tel (269) 923-5000
SIC 3633 3631 3632 3639 3635 3581

RESTAURANT TECHNOLOGIES INC p 1228
2250 Pilot Knob Rd # 100, Mendota Heights MN 55120
Tel (651) 796-1600 *SIC* 5149 3631

■ VIKING RANGE LLC p 1557
111 W Front St, Greenwood MS 38930
Tel (662) 455-1200 *SIC* 3631 5064

SHARP ELECTRONICS CORP p 1312
1 Sharp Plz Ste 1, Mahwah NJ 07495
Tel (201) 529-8200
SIC 5044 5064 3651 3631 3861 3674

TOSHIBA AMERICA INC p 1462
1251 Ave Of Ameri Ste 4100, New York NY 10020
Tel (212) 596-0600
SIC 3651 3631 5064 5075 3571 3661

ELECTROLUX NORTH AMERICA INC p 485
10200 David Taylor Dr, Charlotte NC 28262
Tel (980) 236-2000
SIC 3631 3585 3632 3633 3635 3639

▲ NACCO INDUSTRIES INC p 1006
5875 Landerbrook Dr # 300, Cleveland OH 44124
Tel (440) 229-5151
SIC 3634 1221 5719 3631

▲ PARK-OHIO HOLDINGS CORP p 1116
6065 Parkland Blvd Ste 1, Cleveland OH 44124
Tel (440) 947-2000
SIC 3462 3069 3567 3363 3631 3524

J BAXTER BRINKMANN INTERNATIONAL CORP p 770
4099 Mcewen Rd Ste 375, Dallas TX 75244
Tel (972) 387-4939 *SIC* 3648 3631

TRAEGER PELLET GRILLS LLC p 1469
1215 E Wilmington Ave # 200, Salt Lake City UT 84106
Tel (855) 382-2560 *SIC* 3631

APPLICA CONSUMER PRODUCTS INC p 99
601 Ray O Vac Dr, Madison WI 53711
Tel (608) 275-4562 *SIC* 3634 3631

SIC 3632 Household Refrigerators & Freezers

■ HILL PHOENIX INC p 693
2016 Gees Mill Rd Ne, Conyers GA 30013
Tel (770) 285-3264 *SIC* 3632

▲ DOVER CORP p 453
3005 Highland Pkwy # 200, Downers Grove IL 60515
Tel (630) 541-1540
SIC 3632 3586 3533 3577 3674

SCOTSMAN INDUSTRIES INC p 1293
101 Corporate Woods Pkwy, Vernon Hills IL 60061
Tel (847) 215-4501 *SIC* 3585 3632

▲ GENERAL ELECTRIC CO p 600
41 Farnsworth St, Boston MA 02210
Tel (617) 443-3000
SIC 3511 3724 3632 3845

THETFORD CORP p 1447
7101 Jackson Rd, Ann Arbor MI 48103
Tel (734) 769-6000
SIC 3632 3089 2842 2621 3431 2899

■ MAYTAG CORP p 924
2000 N M 63, Benton Harbor MI 49022
Tel (269) 923-5000
SIC 3633 3631 3632 3639 3635 3581

▲ WHIRLPOOL CORP p 1605
2000 N M 63, Benton Harbor MI 49022
Tel (269) 923-5000
SIC 3633 3585 3632 3635

ELECTROLUX NORTH AMERICA INC p 485
10200 David Taylor Dr, Charlotte NC 28262
Tel (980) 236-2000
SIC 3631 3585 3632 3633 3635 3639

NORCOLD INC p 1047
600 S Kuther Rd, Sidney OH 45365
Tel (937) 497-3080 *SIC* 3632

SUB-ZERO GROUP INC p 1395
4717 Hammersley Rd, Madison WI 53711
Tel (608) 271-2233 *SIC* 3632

SUB-ZERO INC p 1395
4717 Hammersley Rd, Madison WI 53711
Tel (608) 271-2233 *SIC* 3632

SIC 3633 Household Laundry Eqpt

■ MAYTAG CORP p 924
2000 N M 63, Benton Harbor MI 49022
Tel (269) 923-5000
SIC 3633 3631 3632 3639 3635 3581

▲ WHIRLPOOL CORP p 1605
2000 N M 63, Benton Harbor MI 49022
Tel (269) 923-5000
SIC 3633 3585 3632 3635

COINMACH SERVICE CORP p 335
303 Sunnyside Blvd # 70, Plainview NY 11803
Tel (516) 349-8555 *SIC* 3633 5087

CSC SERVICEWORKS HOLDINGS INC p 397
303 Sunnyside Blvd # 70, Plainview NY 11803
Tel (516) 349-8555 *SIC* 3633 5087

CSC SERVICEWORKS INC p 397
303 Sunnyside Blvd # 70, Plainview NY 11803
Tel (516) 349-8555 *SIC* 3633 5087

SPIN HOLDCO INC p 1358
303 Sunnyside Blvd # 70, Plainview NY 11803
Tel (516) 349-8555 *SIC* 3633 5087

ELECTROLUX NORTH AMERICA INC p 485
10200 David Taylor Dr, Charlotte NC 28262
Tel (980) 236-2000
SIC 3631 3585 3632 3633 3635 3639

ALLIANCE LAUNDRY HOLDINGS LLC p 54
221 Shepard St, Ripon WI 54971
Tel (920) 748-3121 *SIC* 3582 3633

ALLIANCE LAUNDRY SYSTEMS LLC p 54
221 Shepard St, Ripon WI 54971
Tel (920) 748-3121 *SIC* 3582 3633

SIC 3634 Electric Household Appliances

ESSICK AIR PRODUCTS INC p 510
5800 Murray St, Little Rock AR 72209
Tel (501) 562-1094 *SIC* 3534 3585 3634

■ STERNO PRODUCTS LLC p 1388
1880 Compton Ave Ste 101, Corona CA 92881
Tel (951) 682-9600
SIC 3641 3645 3589 3634 2899

AD CORP p 21
1551 Wewatta St, Denver CO 80202
Tel (303) 744-1911
SIC 3634 3564 3822 3089 3714 3312

■ CARRIER COMMERCIAL REFRIGERATION INC p 260
3 Farm Glen Blvd Ste 301, Farmington CT 06032
Tel (336) 245-6400
SIC 3556 3631 3585 3589 3634

■ BLACK & DECKER (US) INC p 186
1000 Stanley Dr, New Britain CT 06053
Tel (410) 716-3900 *SIC* 3546 3634

CONAIR CORP p 354
1 Cummings Point Rd, Stamford CT 06902
Tel (203) 351-9000
SIC 3634 3631 3639 3999

■ AMERICAN HOUSEHOLD INC p 74
2381 Nw Executive Ctr Dr, Boca Raton FL 33431
Tel (561) 912-4100
SIC 3631 2514 3421 3634 3829 3841

■ JARDEN CORP p 778
1800 N Military Trl # 210, Boca Raton FL 33431
Tel (561) 447-2520 *SIC* 3089 3634

■ **SUNBEAM AMERICAS HOLDINGS LLC** p 1401
2381 Nw Executive Ctr Dr, Boca Raton FL 33431
Tel (561) 912-4100
SIC 3631 2514 3421 3634 3829 3841

■ **SUNBEAM PRODUCTS INC** p 1401
2381 Nw Executive Ctr Dr, Boca Raton FL 33431
Tel (561) 912-4100 SIC 3631 3634

RAYMOND BUILDING SUPPLY p 1210
7751 Bayshore Rd, Fort Myers FL 33917
Tel (941) 429-1212
SIC 5211 2439 2431 3442 2434 3634

■ **ROPER CORP** p 1250
1507 Broomtown Rd, La Fayette GA 30728
Tel (706) 638-3559 SIC 3631 3634

EGO NORTH AMERICA INC p 481
83 Hillwood Cir, Newnan GA 30263
Tel (770) 251-3980 SIC 3634 5065

HEATRON INC p 679
3000 Wilson Ave, Leavenworth KS 66048
Tel (913) 651-4420 SIC 3567 3634

■ **BLACK & DECKER CORP** p 186
701 E Joppa Rd, Towson MD 21286
Tel (410) 716-3900
SIC 3546 3553 3541 3634 3452

■ **GILLETTE CO** p 612
1 Gillette Park, Boston MA 02127
Tel (617) 421-7000
SIC 3421 3634 2844 3951 2899

■ **GILLETTE DE MEXICO INC** p 612
800 Boylston St, Boston MA 02199
Tel (617) 421-7000 SIC 3634

LEE THOMAS H EQUITY FUND V LIMITED PARTNERSHIP p 852
100 Federal St Ste 3500, Boston MA 02110
Tel (617) 737-3261
SIC 3585 3444 3634 2431 3699

THL-NORTEK INVESTORS LLC p 1448
100 Federal St Ste 3100, Boston MA 02110
Tel (617) 227-1050
SIC 3585 3444 3634 2431

MESTEK INC p 951
260 N Elm St, Westfield MA 01085
Tel (413) 568-9571
SIC 3585 3634 3549 3542 3354

FKA DISTRIBUTING CO LLC p 553
3000 N Pontiac Trl, Commerce Township MI 48390
Tel (248) 863-3000 SIC 3679 3634

TACONY CORP p 1421
1760 Gilsinn Ln, Fenton MO 63026
Tel (636) 349-3000 SIC 3634

GAF CORP p 589
1 Campus Dr, Parsippany NJ 07054
Tel (973) 628-3000 SIC 3444 3634

▲ **HRG GROUP INC** p 714
450 Park Ave Fl 29, New York NY 10022
Tel (212) 906-8555
SIC 3691 3634 3999 6311

■ **MARLEY CO LLC** p 909
13515 Balntyn Corp Pl, Charlotte NC 28277
Tel (704) 752-4400
SIC 3443 3433 3586 3561 3634

▲ **NACCO INDUSTRIES INC** p 1006
5875 Landerbrook Dr # 300, Cleveland OH 44124
Tel (440) 229-5151
SIC 3634 1221 5719 3631

AD INDUSTRIES INC p 21
6450 Poe Ave Ste 109, Dayton OH 45414
Tel (303) 744-1911
SIC 3634 3564 3535 3714 3088 3089

PEERLESS-WINSMITH INC p 1127
5200 Upper Metro Pl # 110, Dublin OH 43017
Tel (614) 526-7000
SIC 3621 3566 3634 3812 3559

BOYD COFFEE CO p 205
19730 Ne Sandy Blvd, Portland OR 97230
Tel (503) 666-4545
SIC 2095 5499 5141 3634 2099

LASKO GROUP INC p 846
820 Lincoln Ave, West Chester PA 19380
Tel (610) 692-7400 SIC 4789 3634

NORTEK INC p 1049
500 Exchange St, Providence RI 02903
Tel (401) 751-1600
SIC 3585 3444 3634 3699 2434

■ **MARLEY ENGINEERED PRODUCTS LLC** p 909
470 Beauty Spot Rd E, Bennettsville SC 29512
Tel (843) 479-4006 SIC 3634

TUTCO INC p 1493
500 Gould Dr, Cookeville TN 38506
Tel (931) 432-4141 SIC 3634

HUNTER FAN CO p 719
7130 Goodlett Farms Pkwy Ste 400, Memphis TN 38103
Tel (901) 743-1360 SIC 5064 3634 3645

INNOVATIVE HEARTH PRODUCTS LLC p 744
1508 Elm Hill Pike # 108, Nashville TN 37210
Tel (615) 925-3417 SIC 3634 3433

■ **ASSOCIATED AMERICAN INDUSTRIES INC** p 119
1307 N Watters Rd, Allen TX 75013
Tel (214) 421-7366
SIC 3914 3634 3469 3639

FEDDERS CORP p 533
13455 Noel Rd Ste 2200, Dallas TX 75240
Tel (604) 908-8686
SIC 3585 3674 3634 3564

■ **HOUSEWARES HOLDING CO INC** p 711
14785 Preston Rd Ste 1100, Dallas TX 75254
Tel (440) 449-9600 SIC 3634 5719

HELEN OF TROY LP p 681
1 Helen Of Troy Plz, El Paso TX 79912
Tel (915) 225-8000 SIC 3999 3634

■ **HAMILTON BEACH BRANDS INC** p 655
4421 Waterfront Dr, Glen Allen VA 23060
Tel (804) 273-9777 SIC 3634

▲ **NATIONAL PRESTO INDUSTRIES INC** p 1015
3925 N Hastings Way, Eau Claire WI 54703
Tel (715) 839-2121 SIC 2211 3483 3634

BROAN-NUTONE LLC p 216
926 W State St, Hartford WI 53027
Tel (262) 673-4340
SIC 3634 3699 3635 3639 2514 3669

REGAL WARE INC p 1218
1675 Reigle Dr, Kewaskum WI 53040
Tel (262) 626-2121 SIC 3634 3469

APPLICA CONSUMER PRODUCTS INC p 99
601 Ray O Vac Dr, Madison WI 53711
Tel (608) 275-4562 SIC 3634 3631

■ **SPECTRUM BRANDS INC** p 1357
3001 Deming Way, Middleton WI 53562
Tel (608) 275-3340
SIC 3692 3634 2879 3999 3648

SIC 3635 Household Vacuum Cleaners

KARCHER NORTH AMERICA INC p 804
4555 Airport Way Fl 4, Denver CO 80239
Tel (303) 762-1800 SIC 3635 5084

■ **MAYTAG CORP** p 924
2000 N M 63, Benton Harbor MI 49022
Tel (269) 923-5000
SIC 3633 3631 3632 3639 3635 3581

▲ **WHIRLPOOL CORP** p 1605
2000 N M 63, Benton Harbor MI 49022
Tel (269) 923-5000
SIC 3633 3585 3632 3635

BISSELL HOMECARE INC p 185
2345 Walker Ave Nw, Grand Rapids MI 49544
Tel (616) 453-4451 SIC 3635

BISSELL INC p 185
2345 Walker Ave Nw, Grand Rapids MI 49544
Tel (616) 453-4451 SIC 3589 2842 3635

■ **REXAIR HOLDINGS INC** p 1230
50 W Big Beavr Rd Ste 350, Troy MI 48084
Tel (248) 643-7222 SIC 3635

■ **REXAIR LLC** p 1230
50 W Big Beaver Rd # 350, Troy MI 48084
Tel (248) 643-7222 SIC 3635

▲ **TENNANT CO** p 1437
701 Lilac Dr N, Minneapolis MN 55422
Tel (763) 540-1200 SIC 3589 3635

■ **BHSF INC** p 180
1440 Kiewit Plz, Omaha NE 68131
Tel (402) 346-1400
SIC 3635 3563 2731 3715

ELECTROLUX NORTH AMERICA INC p 485
10200 David Taylor Dr, Charlotte NC 28262
Tel (980) 236-2000
SIC 3631 3585 3632 3633 3635 3639

KIRBY SALES CO INC p 821
1920 W 114th St, Cleveland OH 44102
Tel (216) 228-2400 SIC 3635

STANLEY STEEMER INTERNATIONAL INC p 1377
5800 Innovation Dr, Dublin OH 43016
Tel (614) 764-2007
SIC 7217 3635 6794 5713

GMI HOLDINGS INC p 619
1 Door Dr, Mount Hope OH 44660
Tel (330) 821-5360 SIC 3699 3635

BROAN-NUTONE LLC p 216
926 W State St, Hartford WI 53027
Tel (262) 673-4340
SIC 3634 3699 3635 3639 2514 3669

SIC 3639 Household Appliances, NEC

BSH HOME APPLIANCES CORP p 222
1901 Main St Ste 600, Irvine CA 92614
Tel (949) 440-7100 SIC 3639

BOURNS INC p 204
1200 Columbia Ave, Riverside CA 92507
Tel (951) 781-5500
SIC 3677 3676 3661 3639 3679

CONAIR CORP p 354
1 Cummings Point Rd, Stamford CT 06902
Tel (203) 351-9000
SIC 3634 3631 3639 3999

HAIER US APPLIANCE SOLUTIONS INC p 653
4000 Buechel Bank Rd, Louisville KY 40225
Tel (502) 452-4666 SIC 3639

■ **MAYTAG CORP** p 924
2000 N M 63, Benton Harbor MI 49022
Tel (269) 923-5000
SIC 3633 3631 3632 3639 3635 3581

■ **MASCO BUILDING PRODUCTS CORP** p 915
21001 Van Born Rd, Taylor MI 48180
Tel (313) 274-7400 SIC 3429 3639 3644

ELECTROLUX NORTH AMERICA INC p 485
10200 David Taylor Dr, Charlotte NC 28262
Tel (980) 236-2000
SIC 3631 3585 3632 3633 3635 3639

CE CARIBE LLC p 271
Carretera 14 Km 25 3 St Carrete, Coamo PR 00769
Tel (787) 825-6000 SIC 3639 5064

■ **STATE INDUSTRIES INC** p 1381
500 Tennessee Waltz Pkwy, Ashland City TN 37015
Tel (615) 792-4371 SIC 3639 3443

■ **AMERICAN WATER HEATER CO** p 81
500 Princeton Rd, Johnson City TN 37601
Tel (423) 283-8000 SIC 3639

■ **LOCHINVAR LLC** p 873
300 Maddox Simpson Pkwy, Lebanon TN 37090
Tel (615) 889-8900 SIC 3639 3443 5074

■ **ASSOCIATED AMERICAN INDUSTRIES INC** p 119
1307 N Watters Rd, Allen TX 75013
Tel (214) 421-7366
SIC 3914 3634 3469 3639

BROAN-NUTONE LLC p 216
926 W State St, Hartford WI 53027
Tel (262) 673-4340
SIC 3634 3699 3635 3639 2514 3669

▲ **A O SMITH CORP** p 6
11270 W Park Pl Ste 1200, Milwaukee WI 53224
Tel (414) 359-4000 SIC 3639 3433

SIC 3641 Electric Lamps

■ **STERNO PRODUCTS LLC** p 1388
1880 Compton Ave Ste 101, Corona CA 92881
Tel (951) 682-9600
SIC 3641 3645 3589 3634 2899

LIGHTS OF AMERICA INC p 865
611 Reyes Dr, Walnut CA 91789
Tel (909) 594-7883
SIC 3645 3646 7629 3641

WHELEN ENGINEERING CO INC p 1605
51 Winthrop Rd, Chester CT 06412
Tel (860) 526-9504
SIC 3647 3646 3671 3651 3648 3641

▲ **REVOLUTION LIGHTING TECHNOLOGIES INC** p 1229
177 Broad St Fl 12, Stamford CT 06901
Tel (203) 504-1111 SIC 3674 3641 3993

SIEMENS CORP p 1320
300 New Jersey Ave Nw # 10, Washington DC 20001
Tel (202) 434-4800
SIC 3661 3641 3844 3612 3357

■ **ACUITY BRANDS LIGHTING INC** p 20
1 Acuity Way, Conyers GA 30012
Tel (800) 922-9641 SIC 3646 3645 3641

ANIXTER INC p 92
2301 Patriot Blvd, Glenview IL 60026
Tel (800) 323-8167 SIC 3641

VALEO LIGHTING SYSTEMS NORTH AMERICA LLC p 1539
1231 A Ave N, Seymour IN 47274
Tel (812) 524-5021 SIC 3641 3714

MUSCO CORP p 1002
100 1st Ave W, Oskaloosa IA 52577
Tel (641) 676-1746
SIC 7359 3648 3646 3641 3545 3423

PHILIPS ELECTRONICS NORTH AMERICA CORP p 1143
3000 Minuteman Rd Ms1203, Andover MA 01810
Tel (978) 687-1501
SIC 5064 3651 3674 3641 3645 5047

PHILIPS HOLDING USA INC p 1143
3000 Minuteman Rd Ste 109, Andover MA 01810
Tel (978) 687-1501
SIC 5064 3674 5045 5047 3641

■ **PARTYLITE INC** p 1119
59 Armstrong Rd, Plymouth MA 02360
Tel (203) 661-1926
SIC 2023 3999 3641 5199 5023

OSRAM SYLVANIA INC p 1097
200 Ballardvale St # 305, Wilmington MA 01887
Tel (978) 570-3000
SIC 3646 3641 3647 3643 3297

CHICL LLC p 298
1708 Northwood Dr, Troy MI 48084
Tel (859) 294-5590 SIC 3641

DAYCO INC p 417
1650 Research Dr Ste 200, Troy MI 48083
Tel (716) 689-4972
SIC 3641 3646 3643 3625 3613

SARATOGA LIGHTING HOLDINGS LLC p 1282
535 Madison Ave Fl 4, New York NY 10022
Tel (212) 906-7800
SIC 3641 3645 3646 3648

LIGHTING HOLDINGS INTERNATIONAL LLC p 865
4 Manhattanville Rd, Purchase NY 10577
Tel (845) 306-1850
SIC 3641 5719 5063 4225 3643 3229

L D KICHLER CO p 834
7711 E Pleasant Valley Rd, Cleveland OH 44131
Tel (216) 573-1000 SIC 3645 3648 3641

ADVANCED LIGHTING TECHNOLOGIES INC p 26
7905 Cochran Rd Ste 300, Solon OH 44139
Tel (440) 519-0500
SIC 3641 3645 3646 3648

RESPIRONICS INC p 1227
1010 Murry Ridge Ln, Murrysville PA 15668
Tel (724) 387-5200
SIC 3641 3845 3841 3564 8351

WESTINGHOUSE LIGHTING CORP p 1601
12401 Mcnulty Rd Ofc, Philadelphia PA 19154
Tel (215) 671-2000 SIC 5063 3641 3645

MCGRAW-EDISON CO p 929
600 Travis St Ste 5400, Houston TX 77002
Tel (713) 209-8400
SIC 3613 3641 3645 3646

SIC 3643 Current-Carrying Wiring Devices

SYNCRO CORP p 1415
1030 Sundown Dr Nw, Arab AL 35016
Tel (256) 586-6045
SIC 3714 3625 3694 3823 3643

ANDES INDUSTRIES INC p 90
2260 W Broadway Rd # 101, Mesa AZ 85202
Tel (480) 813-0925 SIC 5063 3663 3643

■ **AMPHENOL OPTIMIZE MANUFACTURING CO** p 86
180 N Freeport Dr 10, Nogales AZ 85621
Tel (520) 397-7015 SIC 3678 3643

RADIALL USA INC p 1204
8950 S 52nd St Ste 401, Tempe AZ 85284
Tel (480) 682-9400 SIC 3643

LEONI WIRING SYSTEMS INC p 856
3100 N Campbell Ave # 101, Tucson AZ 85719
Tel (520) 741-0895 SIC 3643 8741 5063

■ **POWER PARAGON INC** p 1165
901 E Ball Rd, Anaheim CA 92805
Tel (714) 956-9200
SIC 3612 3613 3621 3643

HKF INC p 697
5983 Smithway St, Commerce CA 90040
Tel (323) 225-1318
SIC 5075 3873 5064 3567 3643

■ **TRI-STAR ELECTRONICS INTERNATIONAL INC** p 1477
2201 Rosecrans Ave, El Segundo CA 90245
Tel (310) 536-0444 SIC 3643

GLENAIR INC p 615
1211 Air Way, Glendale CA 91201
Tel (818) 247-6000 SIC 3643 3825 3357

■ **JOSLYN SUNBANK CO LLC** p 794
1740 Commerce Way, Paso Robles CA 93446
Tel (805) 238-2840 SIC 3678 3643 5065

AUTOSPLICE INC p 135
10431 Wtridge Cir Ste 110, San Diego CA 92121
Tel (858) 535-0077 SIC 3643

CRYDOM INC p 396
2320 Paseo Delas Amer 2 Ste 201, San Diego CA 92154
Tel (619) 210-1600
SIC 3625 5065 3674 3643

■ **VERIFONE INC** p 1549
88 W Plumeria Dr, San Jose CA 95134
Tel (408) 232-7800
SIC 3578 7372 3577 3575 8711 3643

XMULTIPLE TECHNOLOGIES INC p 1632
1060 E Los Angeles Ave, Simi Valley CA 93065
Tel (805) 579-1100 SIC 3643

CARLING TECHNOLOGIES INC p 257
60 Johnson Ave, Plainville CT 06062
Tel (860) 793-9281 SIC 3643 3613 3612

▲ **HUBBELL INC** p 716
40 Waterview Dr, Shelton CT 06484
Tel (475) 882-4000 SIC 3643

▲ **AMPHENOL CORP** p 86
358 Hall Ave, Wallingford CT 06492
Tel (203) 265-8900 SIC 3678 3643 3661

SIEMON CO p 1320
101 Siemon Company Dr, Watertown CT 06795
Tel (860) 945-4200
SIC 3643 3089 3679 3469 3613 3357

LEGRAND HOLDING INC p 853
60 Woodlawn St, West Hartford CT 06110
Tel (860) 233-6251 SIC 3643 6719

WIREMOLD CO p 1618
60 Woodlawn St, West Hartford CT 06110
Tel (860) 233-6251
SIC 3644 3643 3496 3315

NGK SPARK PLUGS (USA) HOLDING INC p 1041
1011 Centre Rd, Wilmington DE 19805
Tel (302) 288-0131 SIC 3643 3264

TE CONNECTIVITY INC p 1429
607 14th St Nw Ste 250, Washington DC 20005
Tel (202) 471-3400 SIC 3678 3643

■ **CARLISLE INTERCONNECT TECHNOLOGIES INC** p 257
100 Tensolite Dr, Saint Augustine FL 32092
Tel (904) 829-5600
SIC 3679 3399 3678 3357 3643 5063

■ **TENSOLITE LLC** p 1438
100 Tensolite Dr, Saint Augustine FL 32092
Tel (904) 829-5600 SIC 3357 3643 3679

AUBREY SILVEY ENTERPRISES INC p 130
371 Hamp Jones Rd, Carrollton GA 30117
Tel (770) 834-0738
SIC 1629 1541 3643 7389 3699 5063

CUBS ACQUISITION CORP p 400
1 Southwire Dr, Carrollton GA 30119
Tel (770) 832-4242 SIC 3357 3661 3643

COOPER WIRING DEVICES INC p 367
203 Cooper Cir, Peachtree City GA 30269
Tel (770) 631-2100 SIC 3643 3613

RAYCAP INC p 1210
806 S Clearwater Loop, Post Falls ID 83854
Tel (208) 457-0895 SIC 3643 5063

MAGNETROL INTERNATIONAL INC p 896
705 Enterprise St, Aurora IL 60504
Tel (630) 723-6600
SIC 3823 3699 3643 3625 3541

G & W ELECTRIC CO p 586
305 W Crossroads Pkwy, Bolingbrook IL 60440
Tel (708) 388-5010 SIC 3613 3643

OTTO ENGINEERING INC p 1098
2 E Main St, Carpentersville IL 60110
Tel (847) 428-7171 SIC 3643

▲ **METHODE ELECTRONICS INC** p 953
7401 W Wilson Ave, Chicago IL 60706
Tel (708) 867-6777
SIC 3678 3674 3676 3672 3825 3643

S & C ELECTRIC CO p 1261
6601 N Ridge Blvd, Chicago IL 60626
Tel (773) 338-1000
SIC 3613 3643 3625 8711

GRAYHILL INC p 632
561 W Hillgrove Ave, La Grange IL 60525
Tel (708) 354-1040
SIC 3613 3625 3679 3643 3575

ALDRIDGE ELECTRIC INC p 48
844 E Rockland Rd, Libertyville IL 60048
Tel (847) 680-5200 SIC 2899 4789 3643

WOODHEAD INDUSTRIES LLC p 1623
333 Knightsbridge Pkwy # 200, Lincolnshire IL 60069
Tel (847) 353-2500
SIC 3678 3679 3643 3357

MOLEX LLC p 982
2222 Wellington Ct, Lisle IL 60532
Tel (630) 969-4550 SIC 3679 3643 3357

MOLEX PREMISE NETWORKS INC p 982
2222 Wellington Ct, Lisle IL 60532
Tel (866) 733-6659 SIC 3679 3643 3357

MOLEX U S INC p 982
2222 Wellington Ct, Lisle IL 60532
Tel (630) 969-4550
SIC 3678 3679 3643 3357

■ **CINCH CONNECTORS INC** p 307
1700 S Finley Rd, Lombard IL 60148
Tel (630) 705-6001 SIC 3643 3678

■ **APPLETON GRP LLC** p 99
9377 W Higgins Rd, Rosemont IL 60018
Tel (847) 268-6000
SIC 3644 3643 3613 3646 3699

CHICAGO FREIGHT CAR LEASING CO p 297
425 N Martingale Rd Fl 6, Schaumburg IL 60173
Tel (847) 318-8000 SIC 4741 3643

IDEAL INDUSTRIES INC p 729
1375 Park Ave, Sycamore IL 60178
Tel (815) 895-5181 SIC 3825 3643

DERINGER-NEY INC p 431
616 Atrium Dr Ste 100, Vernon Hills IL 60061
Tel (847) 566-4100
SIC 3643 3542 3469 3452 3316

COLEMAN CABLE LLC p 336
1530 S Shields Dr, Waukegan IL 60085
Tel (847) 672-2300 SIC 3661 3357 3643

■ GROUP DEKKO INC p 641
2505 Dekko Dr, Garrett IN 46738
Tel (260) 357-3621
SIC 3479 3469 3643 3315 3089

■ AEARO TECHNOLOGIES LLC p 28
5457 W 79th St, Indianapolis IN 46268
Tel (317) 692-6666 SIC 3842 3851 3643

KALMAR SOLUTIONS LLC p 801
415 E Dundee St, Ottawa KS 66067
Tel (785) 242-2200
SIC 3537 3714 3713 3643

MPD INC p 995
316 E 9th St, Owensboro KY 42303
Tel (270) 685-6200
SIC 3671 3829 3812 3663 3643 3053

SCHNEIDER ELECTRIC USA INC p 1288
800 Federal St, Andover MA 01810
Tel (978) 975-9600
SIC 3613 3643 3612 3823 3625 5063

■ KIDDE-FENWAL INC p 817
400 Main St, Ashland MA 01721
Tel (508) 881-2000
SIC 3669 3823 3825 3822 3643 3625

PEP INDUSTRIES LLC p 1133
110 Frank Mossberg Dr, Attleboro MA 02703
Tel (508) 226-5600
SIC 3089 3351 3469 3471 3643 3841

PRECISION ENGINEERED PRODUCTS LLC p 1168
110 Frank Mossberg Dr, Attleboro MA 02703
Tel (508) 226-5600
SIC 3643 3469 3841 3471 3089 3351

▲ TERADYNE INC p 1439
600 Riverpark Dr, North Reading MA 01864
Tel (978) 370-2700 SIC 3825 3643 3674

TRU CORP p 1485
245 Lynnfield St, Peabody MA 01960
Tel (978) 532-0775 SIC 3643 3678

■ ITW ARK-LES CORP p 769
95 Mill St, Stoughton MA 02072
Tel (781) 297-6000 SIC 3643 3644

OSRAM SYLVANIA INC p 1097
200 Ballardvale St # 305, Wilmington MA 01887
Tel (978) 570-3000
SIC 3646 3641 3647 3643 3297

MORRELL INC p 990
3333 Bald Mountain Rd, Auburn Hills MI 48326
Tel (248) 373-1600
SIC 5084 5065 3621 3643 3559 3357

TRMI INC p 1483
100 Hill Brady Rd, Battle Creek MI 49037
Tel (269) 966-0800 SIC 3714 3643

YAZAKI INTERNATIONAL CORP p 1635
6801 N Haggerty Rd 4707e, Canton MI 48187
Tel (734) 983-1000 SIC 5013 3643

PRESTOLITE ELECTRIC LLC p 1173
30120 Hudson Dr, Novi MI 48377
Tel (248) 313-3807
SIC 3643 3824 3621 3625 3694

TRAM INC p 1469
47200 Port St, Plymouth MI 48170
Tel (734) 254-8500 SIC 3714 3643

FLEXTRONICS AUTOMOTIVE USA INC p 556
2120 Austin Ave, Rochester Hills MI 48309
Tel (248) 853-5724 SIC 3625 3714 3643

▲ LEAR CORP p 850
21557 Telegraph Rd, Southfield MI 48033
Tel (248) 447-1500
SIC 3714 2531 2396 3643

DAYCO INC p 417
1650 Research Dr Ste 200, Troy MI 48083
Tel (716) 689-4972
SIC 3641 3646 3643 3625 3613

NGK SPARK PLUGS (USA) INC p 1041
46929 Magellan, Wixom MI 48393
Tel (248) 926-6900 SIC 3643 3264

■ KATO ENGINEERING INC p 804
2075 Howard Dr W, North Mankato MN 56003
Tel (507) 345-2716 SIC 3621 3643 3625

COOPER BUSSMANN LLC p 366
114 Old State Rd, Ellisville MO 63021
Tel (636) 527-1324 SIC 3613 3699 3643

DURHAM CO p 462
722 Durham Rd, Lebanon MO 65536
Tel (417) 532-7121 SIC 3644 3643 3613

■ APPLE JV HOLDING CORP p 98
8000 W Florissant Ave, Saint Louis MO 63136
Tel (314) 553-2000
SIC 3644 3643 3613 3446 3699

ECI HOLDING INC p 475
1 Cityplace Dr Ste 450, Saint Louis MO 63141
Tel (314) 692-4204 SIC 3643

■ BURNDY AMERICAS INC p 228
47 E Industrial Pk Dr, Manchester NH 03109
Tel (603) 647-5000 SIC 3643 5063

■ BURNDY LLC p 228
47 E Industrial Park Dr, Manchester NH 03109
Tel (603) 626-3730 SIC 3643 5063

BILLOWS ELECTRIC SUPPLY CO INC p 182
1813 Underwood Blvd, Delran NJ 08075
Tel (215) 332-9700
SIC 5063 3679 3621 3643 3644

TYCOM LIMITED p 1496
10 Park Ave, Morristown NJ 07960
Tel (973) 753-3040 SIC 3643 1623

■ SL INDUSTRIES INC p 1330
520 Fellowship Rd A114, Mount Laural NJ 08054
Tel (856) 727-1500 SIC 3679 3643

ROXBORO HOLDINGS INC p 1254
1501 State Route 34, Wall Township NJ 07727
Tel (732) 919-3119
SIC 3643 3679 3993 3823 3674

DELTA GROUP ELECTRONICS INC p 427
4521a Osuna Rd Ne, Albuquerque NM 87109
Tel (505) 883-7674 SIC 3643 3679

KELTA INC p 809
141 Rodeo Dr, Edgewood NY 11717
Tel (631) 789-5000 SIC 3089 3643 3661

LEVITON MANUFACTURING CO INC p 858
201 N Service Rd, Melville NY 11747
Tel (631) 812-6000
SIC 3643 3613 3357 3674 3694 3678

LIGHTING HOLDINGS INTERNATIONAL LLC p 865
4 Manhattanville Rd, Purchase NY 10577
Tel (845) 306-1850
SIC 3641 5719 5063 4225 3643 3229

PASS & SEYMOUR INC p 1119
50 Boyd Ave, Syracuse NY 13209
Tel (315) 468-6211 SIC 3643 5731

■ COMMSCOPE CONNECTIVITY SOLUTIONS LLC p 346
1100 Commscope Pl Se, Hickory NC 28602
Tel (828) 324-2200
SIC 3661 3357 3643 8999

COOPER CROUSE- HINDS LLC p 366
4758 Washington St, La Grange NC 28551
Tel (252) 566-3014 SIC 3069 3643

FARGO ASSEMBLY CO p 528
3300 7th Ave N, Fargo ND 58102
Tel (701) 298-3803 SIC 3643

BARDES CORP p 155
4730 Madison Rd, Cincinnati OH 45227
Tel (513) 533-6200 SIC 3643

ILSCO CORP p 733
4730 Madison Rd, Cincinnati OH 45227
Tel (513) 533-6200
SIC 3643 3369 3451 3678 3544 3469

■ AVIATION TECHNOLOGIES INC p 138
1301 E 9th St Ste 3000, Cleveland OH 44114
Tel (216) 706-2960
SIC 3643 3678 3679 3728 3812 3648

DESCO CORP p 432
7795 Walton Pkwy Ste 175, New Albany OH 43054
Tel (614) 888-8855
SIC 3442 3825 3643 3531 3429

TYCO ELECTRONICS CORP p 1496
1050 Westlakes Dr, Berwyn PA 19312
Tel (717) 986-7275 SIC 3678 3643

PHOENIX CONTACT SERVICES INC p 1144
586 Fulling Mill Rd, Middletown PA 17057
Tel (717) 944-1300 SIC 5063 3678 3643

■ HARVEY HUBBELL CARIBE INC p 667
Km 17 Hm 3 Rr 686, Vega Baja PR 00693
Tel (787) 855-1075 SIC 3643

■ HUBBELL POWER SYSTEMS INC p 716
200 Center Point Cir # 200, Columbia SC 29210
Tel (803) 216-2600 SIC 3643

THOMAS & BETTS CORP p 1448
8155 T&B Blvd, Memphis TN 38125
Tel (901) 252-5000 SIC 3643 3312 3567

NASHVILLE WIRE PRODUCTS MFG CO p 1008
199 Polk Ave, Nashville TN 37210
Tel (615) 743-2500 SIC 3496 3471 3643

OPTEK TECHNOLOGY INC p 1090
1645 Wallace Dr, Carrollton TX 75006
Tel (972) 323-2200
SIC 3674 3825 3812 3661 3643

▲ POWELL INDUSTRIES INC p 1165
8550 Mosley Rd, Houston TX 77075
Tel (713) 944-6900
SIC 3612 3613 3625 3643 3823

LUMINATOR TECHNOLOGY GROUP LLC p 885
900 Klein Rd, Plano TX 75074
Tel (972) 424-6511
SIC 3613 3643 3646 3647

■ THERMON INDUSTRIES INC p 1447
100 Thermon Dr, San Marcos TX 78666
Tel (512) 396-5801 SIC 3643

■ THERMON MANUFACTURING CO INC p 1447
100 Thermon Dr, San Marcos TX 78666
Tel (512) 396-5801 SIC 3643 3612

SAFRAN USA INC p 1267
700 S Washington St # 320, Alexandria VA 22314
Tel (703) 351-9898
SIC 3643 3621 7699 3724 5013 5088

ELECTRONIC WARFARE ASSOCIATES INC p 486
13873 Park Center Rd # 500, Herndon VA 20171
Tel (703) 904-5700
SIC 7373 7374 3672 3699 3643 3441

CARLISLE INC p 257
7911 S 188th St Ste 100, Kent WA 98032
Tel (425) 251-0700 SIC 3643 5065 5063

CARLYLE HOLDINGS INC p 258
7911 S 188th St Ste 100, Kent WA 98032
Tel (425) 251-0700 SIC 3643 5065 5063

■ HONEYWELL ELECTRONIC MATERIALS INC p 705
15128 E Euclid Ave, Spokane Valley WA 99216
Tel (509) 252-2200 SIC 3679 3674 3643

WAGO CORP p 1571
N120 W 19129 Freistadt Rd N 120 W, Germantown WI 53022
Tel (262) 255-6333 SIC 5063 3643 3678

COOPER POWER SYSTEMS LLC p 367
2300 Badger Dr, Waukesha WI 53188
Tel (262) 524-4227
SIC 3612 3613 3644 3643 3629 3679

SIC 3644 Noncurrent-Carrying Wiring Devices

WIREMOLD CO p 1618
60 Woodlawn St, West Hartford CT 06110
Tel (860) 233-6251
SIC 3644 3643 3496 3315

ATLAS TUBE (CHICAGO) LLC p 128
1855 E 122nd St, Chicago IL 60633
Tel (773) 646-4500 SIC 3317 3644

WHEATLAND TUBE LLC p 1604
227 W Monroe St Ste 2600, Chicago IL 60606
Tel (312) 275-1600 SIC 3317 3644

■ APPLETON GRP LLC p 99
9377 W Higgins Rd, Rosemont IL 60018
Tel (847) 268-6000
SIC 3644 3643 3613 3646 3699

PANDUIT CORP p 1111
18900 Panduit Dr, Tinley Park IL 60487
Tel (708) 532-1800 SIC 3699 3644 5063

INDUSTRIAL DIELECTRICS HOLDINGS INC p 740
407 S 7th St, Noblesville IN 46060
Tel (317) 773-1766 SIC 3644

■ HUBBELL INC (DELAWARE) p 716
3902 W Sample St, South Bend IN 46619
Tel (574) 234-7151 SIC 3644 3699 3613

▲ CHASE CORP p 291
26 Summer St, Bridgewater MA 02324
Tel (508) 819-4200 SIC 3644 3479 3672

■ ITW ARK-LES CORP p 769
95 Mill St, Stoughton MA 02072
Tel (781) 297-6000 SIC 3643 3644

■ MASCO BUILDING PRODUCTS CORP p 915
21001 Van Born Rd, Taylor MI 48180
Tel (313) 274-7400 SIC 3429 3639 3644

DURHAM CO p 462
722 Durham Rd, Lebanon MO 65536
Tel (417) 532-7121 SIC 3644 3643 3613

■ APPLE JV HOLDING CORP p 98
8000 W Florissant Ave, Saint Louis MO 63136
Tel (314) 553-2000
SIC 3644 3643 3613 3446 3699

PCE INC p 1124
1711 Yolande Ave, Lincoln NE 68521
Tel (402) 474-4690 SIC 3089 3644 3088

BILLOWS ELECTRIC SUPPLY CO INC p 182
1813 Underwood Blvd, Delran NJ 08075
Tel (215) 332-9700
SIC 5063 3679 3621 3643 3644

QUALITY COMPUTER ACCESSORIES INC p 1196
70 Ethel Rd W Ste 1, Piscataway NJ 08854
Tel (732) 572-2719
SIC 5063 5051 3315 3644

EMERSON NETWORK POWER ENERGY SYSTEMS NORTH AMERICA INC p 492
1510 Kansas Ave, Lorain OH 44052
Tel (440) 288-1122 SIC 3661 3644 7629

▲ PREFORMED LINE PRODUCTS CO p 1169
660 Beta Dr, Mayfield Village OH 44143
Tel (440) 461-5200 SIC 3644 3661

DURA-LINE CORP p 462
11400 Parkside Dr Ste 300, Knoxville TN 37934
Tel (865) 218-3460 SIC 3644

COOPER INDUSTRIES LLC p 366
600 Travis St Ste 5400, Houston TX 77002
Tel (713) 209-8400
SIC 3646 3612 3613 3644 3546 3423

EATON ELECTRIC HOLDINGS LLC p 473
600 Travis St Ste 5600, Houston TX 77002
Tel (713) 209-8400
SIC 3646 3612 3613 3644 3536 3423

■ REGAL BELOIT AMERICA INC p 1218
200 State St, Beloit WI 53511
Tel (608) 364-8800 SIC 3644 3621

WELLS VEHICLE ELECTRONICS LP p 1591
385 W Rolling Meadows Dr, Fond Du Lac WI 54937
Tel (920) 922-5900
SIC 3714 3694 3644 3357

COOPER POWER SYSTEMS LLC p 367
2300 Badger Dr, Waukesha WI 53188
Tel (262) 524-4227
SIC 3612 3613 3644 3643 3629 3679

WESTERN POWER PRODUCTS INC p 1599
2300 Badger Dr, Waukesha WI 53188
Tel (262) 896-2400 SIC 3644

SIC 3645 Residential Lighting Fixtures

MULTIQUIP INC p 1000
18910 Wilmington Ave, Carson CA 90746
Tel (310) 537-3700 SIC 5063 5082 3645

■ STERNO PRODUCTS LLC p 1388
1880 Compton Ave Ste 101, Corona CA 92881
Tel (951) 682-9600
SIC 3641 3645 3589 3634 2899

■ AEE SOLAR INC p 29
775 Fiero Ln Ste 200, San Luis Obispo CA 93401
Tel (800) 777-6609 SIC 5063 3645

LIGHTS OF AMERICA INC p 865
611 Reyes Dr, Walnut CA 91789
Tel (909) 594-7883
SIC 3645 3646 7629 3641

BLUMBERG INDUSTRIES INC p 193
5770 Miami Lakes Dr E, Miami Lakes FL 33014
Tel (305) 821-3850 SIC 3645 3646

▲ ACUITY BRANDS INC p 20
1170 Peachtree St Ne, Atlanta GA 30309
Tel (404) 853-1400 SIC 3648 3646 3645

■ ACUITY BRANDS LIGHTING INC p 20
1 Acuity Way, Conyers GA 30012
Tel (800) 922-9641 SIC 3646 3645 3641

JUNO LIGHTING LLC p 797
1300 S Wolf Rd, Des Plaines IL 60018
Tel (847) 827-9880 SIC 3646 3645

JJI LIGHTING GROUP INC p 786
11500 Melrose Ave, Franklin Park IL 60131
Tel (847) 451-3258 SIC 3646 3648 3645

HTS ACQUISITION INC p 715
915 Harger Rd, Oak Brook IL 60523
Tel (630) 368-0920 SIC 3646 3229 3645

INTERMATIC INC p 753
7777 Winn Rd, Spring Grove IL 60081
Tel (815) 675-2321 SIC 3612 3645

BRISTOL LASALLE CORP p 214
601 County Road 17, Elkhart IN 46516
Tel (574) 295-4400
SIC 5023 5021 5051 5033 3645 3089

GENLYTE GROUP INC p 604
3000 Minuteman Rd, Andover MA 01810
Tel (781) 418-7900 SIC 3646 3645 3648

PHILIPS ELECTRONICS NORTH AMERICA CORP p 1143
3000 Minuteman Rd Ms1203, Andover MA 01810
Tel (978) 687-1501
SIC 5064 3651 3674 3641 3645 5047

▲ TORO CO p 1461
8111 Lyndale Ave S, Bloomington MN 55420
Tel (952) 888-8801
SIC 3523 3524 3494 3645

BERGQUIST CO p 174
18930 W 78th St, Chanhassen MN 55317
Tel (952) 835-2322
SIC 5731 5063 3645 3646 2822

SEA GULL LIGHTING PRODUCTS LLC p 1295
1829 Underwood Blvd Ste 2, Delran NJ 08075
Tel (856) 764-0500 SIC 3645

QUALITY HOME BRANDS HOLDINGS LLC p 1197
125 Rose Feiss Blvd, Bronx NY 10454
Tel (718) 292-2024 SIC 3645 5063

SARATOGA LIGHTING HOLDINGS LLC p 1282
535 Madison Ave Fl 4, New York NY 10022
Tel (212) 906-7800
SIC 3641 3645 3646 3648

L D KICHLER CO p 834
7711 E Pleasant Valley Rd, Cleveland OH 44131
Tel (216) 573-1000 SIC 3645 3648 3641

ADVANCED LIGHTING TECHNOLOGIES INC p 26
7905 Cochran Rd Ste 300, Solon OH 44139
Tel (440) 519-0500
SIC 3641 3645 3646 3648

■ GRIMES AEROSPACE CO p 640
550 State Route 55, Urbana OH 43078
Tel (937) 484-2000
SIC 3728 3647 3646 3645 3577 3571

WESTINGHOUSE LIGHTING CORP p 1601
12401 Mcnulty Rd Ofc, Philadelphia PA 19154
Tel (215) 671-2000 SIC 5063 3641 3645

■ PROGRESS LIGHTING INC p 1181
701 Millennium Blvd, Greenville SC 29607
Tel (864) 678-1000 SIC 3645 3646

HUNTER FAN CO p 719
7130 Goodlett Farms Pkwy Ste 400, Memphis TN 38103
Tel (901) 743-1360 SIC 5064 3634 3645

WINGATE PARTNERS LP p 1616
750 N Saint Paul St # 1200, Dallas TX 75201
Tel (214) 720-1313
SIC 2621 2672 3645 2519 5021 2521

MCGRAW-EDISON CO p 929
600 Travis St Ste 5400, Houston TX 77002
Tel (713) 209-8400
SIC 3613 3641 3645 3646

SIC 3646 Commercial, Indl & Institutional Lighting Fixtures

LIGHTS OF AMERICA INC p 865
611 Reyes Dr, Walnut CA 91789
Tel (909) 594-7883
SIC 3645 3646 7629 3641

WHELEN ENGINEERING CO INC p 1605
51 Winthrop Rd, Chester CT 06412
Tel (860) 526-9504
SIC 3647 3646 3671 3651 3648 3641

BLUMBERG INDUSTRIES INC p 193
5770 Miami Lakes Dr E, Miami Lakes FL 33014
Tel (305) 821-3850 SIC 3645 3646

▲ ACUITY BRANDS INC p 20
1170 Peachtree St Ne, Atlanta GA 30309
Tel (404) 853-1400 SIC 3648 3646 3645

■ ACUITY BRANDS LIGHTING INC p 20
1 Acuity Way, Conyers GA 30012
Tel (800) 922-9641 SIC 3646 3645 3641

COOPER LIGHTING LLC p 367
1121 Highway 74 S, Peachtree City GA 30269
Tel (770) 486-4800 SIC 3648 3646

JUNO LIGHTING LLC p 797
1300 S Wolf Rd, Des Plaines IL 60018
Tel (847) 827-9880 SIC 3646 3645

JJI LIGHTING GROUP INC p 786
11500 Melrose Ave, Franklin Park IL 60131
Tel (847) 451-3258 SIC 3646 3648 3645

HTS ACQUISITION INC p 715
915 Harger Rd, Oak Brook IL 60523
Tel (630) 368-0920 SIC 3646 3229 3645

■ APPLETON GRP LLC p 99
9377 W Higgins Rd, Rosemont IL 60018
Tel (847) 268-6000
SIC 3644 3643 3613 3646 3699

MUSCO CORP p 1002
100 1st Ave W, Oskaloosa IA 52577
Tel (641) 676-1746
SIC 7359 3648 3646 3641 3545 3423

GENLYTE GROUP INC p 604
3000 Minuteman Rd, Andover MA 01810
Tel (781) 418-7900 SIC 3646 3645 3648

AUDAX GROUP LP p 130
101 Huntington Ave # 2450, Boston MA 02199
Tel (617) 859-1500 SIC 6726 3646

PHILIPS LIGHTING NORTH AMERICA CORP p 1143
3 Burlington Woods Dr # 4, Burlington MA 01803
Tel (617) 423-9999 SIC 3646

OSRAM SYLVANIA INC p 1097
200 Ballardvale St # 305, Wilmington MA 01887
Tel (978) 570-3000
SIC 3646 3641 3647 3643 3297

DAYCO INC p 417
1650 Research Dr Ste 200, Troy MI 48083
Tel (716) 689-4972
SIC 3641 3646 3643 3625 3613

BERGQUIST CO p 174
18930 W 78th St, Chanhassen MN 55317
Tel (952) 835-2322
SIC 5731 5063 3645 3646 2822

H E WILLIAMS INC p 650
831 W Fairview Ave, Carthage MO 64836
Tel (417) 358-4065 SIC 3646

AMERLUX LLC p 84
178 Bauer Dr, Oakland NJ 07436
Tel (973) 882-5010 SIC 3646

GENLYTE THOMAS GROUP LLC p 604
200 Franklin Pk Sq Dr, Somerset NJ 08875
Tel (800) 825-5844 SIC 3646

■ LSI LIGHTRON INC p 883
500 Hudson Valley Ave, New Windsor NY 12553
Tel (845) 562-5500 SIC 3646 5063

SARATOGA LIGHTING HOLDINGS LLC p 1282
535 Madison Ave Fl 4, New York NY 10022
Tel (212) 906-7800
SIC 3641 3645 3646 3648

■ HOLOPHANE CORP p 702
3825 Columbus Rd Bldg A, Granville OH 43023
Tel (866) 759-1577 SIC 3646 3648

ADVANCED LIGHTING TECHNOLOGIES INC p 26
7905 Cochran Rd Ste 300, Solon OH 44139
Tel (440) 519-0500
SIC 3641 3645 3646 3648

■ GRIMES AEROSPACE CO p 640
550 State Route 55, Urbana OH 43078
Tel (937) 484-2000
SIC 3728 3647 3646 3645 3577 3571

▲ ARMSTRONG WORLD INDUSTRIES INC p 111
2500 Columbia Ave Bldg 5b, Lancaster PA 17603
Tel (717) 397-0611 SIC 3646 3296

■ PROGRESS LIGHTING INC p 1181
701 Millennium Blvd, Greenville SC 29607
Tel (864) 678-1000 SIC 3645 3646

■ COLUMBIA LIGHTING INC p 341
101 Corporate Dr Ste L, Spartanburg SC 29303
Tel (864) 678-1000 SIC 3646

COOPER INDUSTRIES LLC p 366
600 Travis St Ste 5400, Houston TX 77002
Tel (713) 209-8400
SIC 3646 3612 3613 3644 3546 3423

EATON ELECTRIC HOLDINGS LLC p 473
600 Travis St Ste 5600, Houston TX 77002
Tel (713) 209-8400
SIC 3646 3612 3613 3644 3536 3423

MCGRAW-EDISON CO p 929
600 Travis St Ste 5400, Houston TX 77002
Tel (713) 209-8400
SIC 3613 3641 3645 3646

LUMINATOR TECHNOLOGY GROUP LLC p 885
900 Klein Rd, Plano TX 75074
Tel (972) 424-6511
SIC 3613 3643 3646 3647

OLDENBURG GROUP INC p 1082
1717 W Civic Dr, Milwaukee WI 53209
Tel (414) 354-6600 SIC 3537 3532 3646

TRAFFIC AND PARKING CONTROL CO INC p 1469
5100 W Brown Deer Rd, Milwaukee WI 53223
Tel (262) 814-7000 SIC 5063 3444 3646

SIC 3647 Vehicular Lighting Eqpt

WHELEN ENGINEERING CO INC p 1605
51 Winthrop Rd, Chester CT 06412
Tel (860) 526-9504
SIC 3647 3646 3671 3651 3648 3641

▲ B/E AEROSPACE INC p 142
1400 Corporate Center Way, Wellington FL 33414
Tel (561) 791-5000 SIC 2531 3728 3647

■ PROGRESS RAIL LOCOMOTIVE INC p 1181
9301 W 55th St, Mc Cook IL 60525
Tel (800) 255-5355 SIC 3621 3519 3647

▲ FEDERAL SIGNAL CORP p 536
1415 W 22nd St Ste 1100, Oak Brook IL 60523
Tel (630) 954-2000
SIC 3711 3647 3669 3559 3544 3545

NORTH AMERICAN LIGHTING INC p 1050
2275 S Main St, Paris IL 61944
Tel (217) 465-6600 SIC 3647

GROTE INDUSTRIES INC p 641
2600 Lanier Dr, Madison IN 47250
Tel (812) 273-2121 SIC 3231 3647

GROTE INDUSTRIES LLC p 641
2600 Lanier Dr, Madison IN 47250
Tel (812) 265-8273 SIC 3647 3231

OSRAM SYLVANIA INC p 1097
200 Ballardvale St # 305, Wilmington MA 01887
Tel (978) 570-3000
SIC 3646 3641 3647 3643 3297

AUTOMOTIVE LIGHTING LLC p 134
3900 Automation Ave, Auburn Hills MI 48326
Tel (248) 418-3000 SIC 8711 3647

PENSKE CO LLC p 1131
2555 S Telegraph Rd, Bloomfield Hills MI 48302
Tel (248) 648-2000 SIC 3647

MAGNA MIRRORS OF AMERICA INC p 896
5085 Kraft Ave Se, Grand Rapids MI 49512
Tel (616) 942-0163 SIC 3231 3647 3827

PETERSON MANUFACTURING CO p 1138
4200 E 135th St, Grandview MO 64030
Tel (816) 765-2000
SIC 3647 4111 3089 3714

PUBLIC SAFETY EQUIPMENT INC p 1189
10986 N Warson Rd, Saint Louis MO 63114
Tel (314) 426-2700 SIC 3647 3669

▲ ASTRONICS CORP p 122
130 Commerce Way, East Aurora NY 14052
Tel (716) 805-1599 SIC 3728 3647

TRUCK-LITE CO INC p 1485
310 E Elmwood Ave, Falconer NY 14733
Tel (716) 665-6214 SIC 3648 3647

TRUCK-LITE CO LLC p 1485
310 E Elmwood Ave, Falconer NY 14733
Tel (716) 665-6214 SIC 3647

STANLEY ELECTRIC US CO INC p 1377
420 E High St, London OH 43140
Tel (740) 852-5200 SIC 3647 3694 3089

■ GRIMES AEROSPACE CO p 640
550 State Route 55, Urbana OH 43078
Tel (937) 484-2000
SIC 3728 3647 3646 3645 3577 3571

■ AKRON BRASS CO p 42
343 Venture Blvd, Wooster OH 44691
Tel (330) 264-5678 SIC 3647 3699

■ AKRON BRASS HOLDING CORP p 42
343 Venture Blvd, Wooster OH 44691
Tel (330) 264-5678 SIC 3647 3699 6719

LUMINATOR TECHNOLOGY GROUP LLC p 885
900 Klein Rd, Plano TX 75074
Tel (972) 424-6511
SIC 3613 3643 3646 3647

SIC 3648 Lighting Eqpt, NEC

SUREFIRE LLC p 1408
18300 Mount Baldy Cir, Fountain Valley CA 92708
Tel (714) 545-9444 SIC 3648 3842 3484

MAG INSTRUMENT INC p 895
2001 S Hellman Ave, Ontario CA 91761
Tel (909) 947-1006 SIC 3648

US POLE CO INC p 1533
660 W Avenue O, Palmdale CA 93551
Tel (800) 877-6537 SIC 3648

PELICAN PRODUCTS INC p 1128
23215 Early Ave, Torrance CA 90505
Tel (310) 326-4700 SIC 3648 3161 3089

PANAVISION INC p 1111
6101 Variel Ave, Woodland Hills CA 91367
Tel (818) 316-1000
SIC 7359 3861 3648 5063

WHELEN ENGINEERING CO INC p 1605
51 Winthrop Rd, Chester CT 06412
Tel (860) 526-9504
SIC 3647 3646 3671 3651 3648 3641

▲ ACUITY BRANDS INC p 20
1170 Peachtree St Ne, Atlanta GA 30309
Tel (404) 853-1400 SIC 3648 3646 3645

COOPER LIGHTING LLC p 367
1121 Highway 74 S, Peachtree City GA 30269
Tel (770) 486-4800 SIC 3648 3646

■ FIRST ALERT INC p 544
3901 Liberty St, Aurora IL 60504
Tel (630) 851-7330
SIC 3669 3999 3446 3499 3829 3648

JJI LIGHTING GROUP INC p 786
11500 Melrose Ave, Franklin Park IL 60131
Tel (847) 451-3258 SIC 3646 3648 3645

DOREL JUVENILE GROUP INC p 451
2525 State St, Columbus IN 47201
Tel (800) 457-5276
SIC 3089 3069 3429 3699 3648

MUSCO CORP p 1002
100 1st Ave W, Oskaloosa IA 52577
Tel (641) 676-1746
SIC 7359 3648 3646 3641 3545 3423

MUSCO SPORTS LIGHTING LLC p 1002
100 1st Ave W, Oskaloosa IA 52577
Tel (641) 673-0411 SIC 3648

GENLYTE GROUP INC p 604
3000 Minuteman Rd, Andover MA 01810
Tel (781) 418-7900 SIC 3646 3645 3648

■ NEEDHAM ELECTRIC SUPPLY CORP p 1024
5 Shawmut Rd, Canton MA 02021
Tel (781) 828-9494 SIC 5063 3648

EXCELITAS TECHNOLOGIES CORP p 516
200 West St, Waltham MA 02451
Tel (781) 522-5910 SIC 3648 3845

EXCELITAS TECHNOLOGIES HOLDING CORP p 516
200 West St Ste E403, Waltham MA 02451
Tel (781) 522-5914 SIC 3648 3845

EXCELITAS TECHNOLOGIES HOLDINGS LLC p 516
200 West St Ste E403, Waltham MA 02451
Tel (781) 522-5900 SIC 3648

▲ STEELCASE INC p 1384
901 44th St Se, Grand Rapids MI 49508
Tel (616) 247-2710
SIC 2522 2521 3648 8748

LANDSCAPE FORMS INC p 843
7800 E Michigan Ave, Kalamazoo MI 49048
Tel (269) 381-0396
SIC 2531 2522 2511 2449 3648

CODE 3 INC p 333
10986 N Warson Rd, Saint Louis MO 63114
Tel (314) 996-2721 SIC 3669 3648

▲ BALLANTYNE STRONG INC p 148
11422 Miracle Hills Dr # 300, Omaha NE 68154
Tel (402) 453-4444 SIC 3861 3648

TRUCK-LITE CO INC p 1485
310 E Elmwood Ave, Falconer NY 14733
Tel (716) 665-6214 SIC 3648 3647

PX HOLDING CORP p 1193
35 E 62nd St, New York NY 10065
Tel (212) 688-9000 SIC 7359 3861 3648

SARATOGA LIGHTING HOLDINGS LLC p 1282
535 Madison Ave Fl 4, New York NY 10022
Tel (212) 906-7800
SIC 3641 3645 3646 3648

PENTAIR WATER POOL AND SPA INC p 1132
1620 Hawkins Ave, Sanford NC 27330
Tel (919) 774-4151
SIC 3589 3561 3569 3648

▲ LSI INDUSTRIES INC p 883
10000 Alliance Rd, Blue Ash OH 45242
Tel (513) 793-3200 SIC 3648 3993 3663

■ AVIATION TECHNOLOGIES INC p 138
1301 E 9th St Ste 3000, Cleveland OH 44114
Tel (216) 706-2960
SIC 3643 3678 3679 3728 3812 3648

L D KICHLER CO p 834
7711 E Pleasant Valley Rd, Cleveland OH 44131
Tel (216) 573-1000 SIC 3645 3648 3641

ADB SAFEGATE AMERICAS LLC p 21
977 Gahanna Pkwy, Columbus OH 43230
Tel (614) 861-1304 SIC 3648 3812

■ HOLOPHANE CORP p 702
3825 Columbus Rd Bldg A, Granville OH 43023
Tel (866) 759-1577 SIC 3646 3648

ADVANCED LIGHTING TECHNOLOGIES INC p 26
7905 Cochran Rd Ste 300, Solon OH 44139
Tel (440) 519-0500
SIC 3641 3645 3646 3648

MIDMARK CORP p 966
60 Vista Dr, Versailles OH 45380
Tel (937) 526-3662
SIC 3648 3842 3843 2542 3841

■ MINE SAFETY APPLIANCES CO LLC p 973
1000 Cranberry Woods Dr, Cranberry Township PA 16066
Tel (724) 776-8600
SIC 3842 3826 3823 3648 3829

▲ MSA SAFETY INC p 996
1000 Cranberry Woods Dr, Cranberry Township PA 16066
Tel (724) 776-8600
SIC 3842 3826 3823 3648 3829

STREAMLIGHT INC p 1393
30 Eagleville Rd Ste 1, Eagleville PA 19403
Tel (610) 631-0600 SIC 3648

STABLER COMPANIES INC p 1374
635 Lucknow Rd, Harrisburg PA 17110
Tel (717) 236-9307
SIC 5032 3089 7359 3531 1611 3648

■ HUBBELL LIGHTING INC p 716
701 Millennium Blvd, Greenville SC 29607
Tel (864) 678-1000 SIC 3648

J BAXTER BRINKMANN INTERNATIONAL CORP p 770
4099 Mcewen Rd Ste 375, Dallas TX 75244
Tel (972) 387-4939 SIC 3648 3631

■ AVTECHTYEE INC p 139
6500 Merrill Creek Pkwy, Everett WA 98203
Tel (206) 695-8000 SIC 3728 3648 3812

LAMPLIGHT FARMS INC p 841
W140n4900 Lilly Rd, Menomonee Falls WI 53051
Tel (262) 781-9590
SIC 3648 3999 3229 2911

■ SPECTRUM BRANDS HOLDINGS INC p 1357
3001 Deming Way, Middleton WI 53562
Tel (608) 275-3340
SIC 3692 2879 3999 3648

■ SPECTRUM BRANDS INC p 1357
3001 Deming Way, Middleton WI 53562
Tel (608) 275-3340
SIC 3692 3634 2879 3999 3648

SIC 3651 Household Audio & Video Eqpt

LG ELECTRONICS ALABAMA INC p 860
201 James Record Rd Sw, Huntsville AL 35824
Tel (256) 772-0623
SIC 3651 3695 5064 5085 5065 4225

▲ ON SEMICONDUCTOR CORP p 1086
5005 E Mcdowell Rd, Phoenix AZ 85008
Tel (602) 244-6600 SIC 3674 3825 3651

FENDER MUSICAL INSTRUMENTS CORP p 537
17600 N Perimeter Dr # 100, Scottsdale AZ 85255
Tel (480) 596-7195 SIC 3651 3931

ROCKFORD CORP p 1244
600 S Rockford Dr, Tempe AZ 85281
Tel (480) 967-3565 SIC 3651

■ WARNER BROS HOME ENTERTAINMENT INC p 1576
4000 Warner Blvd Bldg 160, Burbank CA 91522
Tel (818) 954-6000 SIC 3651

■ DTS INC p 458
5220 Las Virgenes Rd, Calabasas CA 91302
Tel (818) 436-1000 SIC 7819 3651

QSC LLC p 1195
1675 Macarthur Blvd, Costa Mesa CA 92626
Tel (714) 754-6175 SIC 3651

■ BEATS ELECTRONICS LLC p 166
8600 Hayden Pl, Culver City CA 90232
Tel (424) 326-4679 SIC 3651 3679

▲ APPLE INC p 98
1 Infinite Loop, Cupertino CA 95014
Tel (408) 996-1010
SIC 3663 3571 3575 3577 3651 7372

MITSUBISHI ELECTRIC US HOLDINGS INC p 977
5900 Katella Ave Ste A, Cypress CA 90630
Tel (714) 220-2500
SIC 5065 5045 3651 3663

■ GRASS VALLEY USA LLC p 632
125 Crown Point Ct, Grass Valley CA 95945
Tel (800) 547-8949 SIC 3651 3661 3663

TOSHIBA AMERICA ELECTRONIC COMPONENTS INC p 1462
9740 Irvine Blvd Ste D700, Irvine CA 92618
Tel (949) 462-7700
SIC 3651 3631 3674 3679 5065 5064

VIZIO INC p 1563
39 Tesla, Irvine CA 92618
Tel (949) 428-2525 SIC 3651

PIONEER NORTH AMERICA INC p 1151
2265 E 220th St, Long Beach CA 90810
Tel (213) 746-6337 SIC 5064 3651

CREATIVE HOLDINGS INC p 390
1901 Mccarthy Blvd, Milpitas CA 95035
Tel (408) 428-6600
SIC 5045 3577 3931 3674 8711 3651

■ HARMAN PROFESSIONAL INC p 662
8500 Balboa Blvd, Northridge CA 91329
Tel (818) 894-8850 SIC 3651

AL SHELLCO LLC p 43
9330 Scranton Rd Ste 600, San Diego CA 92121
Tel (570) 296-6444 SIC 3651 3577

INZI DISPLAY AMERICA INC p 762
7880 Airway Rd Ste B6e, San Diego CA 92154
Tel (619) 929-3501 SIC 3651

SONY ELECTRONICS INC p 1341
16535 Via Esprillo Bldg 1, San Diego CA 92127
Tel (858) 942-2400
SIC 3651 5064 3695 3671 3572 3674

■ SYPRIS DATA SYSTEMS INC p 1416
160 Via Verde, San Dimas CA 91773
Tel (909) 962-9400 SIC 3572 3651

▲ UNIVERSAL ELECTRONICS INC p 1516
201 Sandpointe Ave # 800, Santa Ana CA 92707
Tel (714) 918-9500 SIC 3651 3625 7372

ALPINE ELECTRONICS OF AMERICA INC p 60
19145 Gramercy Pl, Torrance CA 90501
Tel (310) 326-8000 SIC 5064 3651 3679

VECTOR RESOURCES INC p 1546
3530 Voyager St, Torrance CA 90503
Tel (310) 436-1000 SIC 1731 3651 7373

DEI HOLDINGS INC p 422
1 Viper Way Ste 3, Vista CA 92081
Tel (760) 598-6200 SIC 3669 3651

WHELEN ENGINEERING CO INC p 1605
51 Winthrop Rd, Chester CT 06412
Tel (860) 526-9504
SIC 3647 3646 3671 3651 3648 3641

▲ HARMAN INTERNATIONAL INDUSTRIES INC p 662
400 Atlantic St Ste 15, Stamford CT 06901
Tel (203) 328-3500 SIC 3651

■ HARMAN KG HOLDING LLC p 662
400 Atlantic St Ste 1500, Stamford CT 06901
Tel (203) 328-3500 SIC 3651

SUN MACKIE LLC p 1400
5200 Town Center Cir # 470, Boca Raton FL 33486
Tel (561) 394-0550 SIC 3651

METRA ELECTRONICS CORP p 954
460 Walker St, Holly Hill FL 32117
Tel (386) 257-1186 SIC 3651

▲ VOXX INTERNATIONAL CORP p 1566
2351 J Lawson Blvd, Orlando FL 32824
Tel (800) 645-7750 SIC 3711 3651 3663

ALLIANCE ENTERTAINMENT LLC p 54
1401 Nw 136th Ave Ste 100, Sunrise FL 33323
Tel (954) 255-4403 SIC 5199 3651

AUDIO VISUAL INNOVATIONS INC p 130
6301 Benjamin Rd Ste 101, Tampa FL 33634
Tel (813) 884-7168
SIC 3669 5064 3861 3663 3651 5043

AVI-SPL EMPLOYEE EMERGENCY RELIEF FUND INC p 137
6301 Benjamin Rd Ste 101, Tampa FL 33634
Tel (813) 884-7168
SIC 3669 3861 3663 3651 5043 5064

AVI-SPL HOLDINGS INC p 137
6301 Benjamin Rd Ste 101, Tampa FL 33634
Tel (866) 708-5034
SIC 3669 3861 3663 3651 1731 5064

CHAMBERLAIN MANUFACTURING CORP p 287
845 N Larch Ave, Elmhurst IL 60126
Tel (630) 279-3600 SIC 3651 3625 3699

▲ KNOWLES CORP p 825
1151 Maplewood Dr, Itasca IL 60143
Tel (630) 250-5100 SIC 3651 3675

■ KNOWLES ELECTRONICS HOLDINGS INC p 825
1151 Maplewood Dr, Itasca IL 60143
Tel (630) 250-5100
SIC 3679 3625 3651 8731 6159

ZENITH ELECTRONICS CORP p 1642
2000 Millbrook Dr, Lincolnshire IL 60069
Tel (847) 941-8000
SIC 3651 3671 3663 3674 2517 2519

SHURE INC p 1319
5800 W Touhy Ave, Niles IL 60714
Tel (847) 600-2000 SIC 3651 3679 3661

DRAPER INC p 455
411 S Pearl St, Spiceland IN 47385
Tel (765) 987-7999 SIC 3861 2591 3651

SONY DADC US INC p 1341
1800 N Fruitridge Ave, Terre Haute IN 47804
Tel (812) 462-8100
SIC 3695 3652 3651 3577 3572

PHILIPS ELECTRONICS NORTH AMERICA CORP p 1143
3000 Minuteman Rd Ms1203, Andover MA 01810
Tel (978) 687-1501
SIC 5064 3651 3674 3641 3645 5047

VIPER HOLDINGS CORP p 1558
200 Clarendon St Fl 54, Boston MA 02116
Tel (617) 619-5400 SIC 3669 3651

BOSE CORP p 202
100 The Mountain, Framingham MA 01701
Tel (508) 879-7330 SIC 3651 5731

LOTUS INTERNATIONAL CO p 879
6880 Commerce Blvd, Canton MI 48187
Tel (734) 245-0140 SIC 8711 3651 1221

TIERNEY BROTHERS INC p 1453
1771 Energy Park Dr, Saint Paul MN 55108
Tel (612) 331-5500 SIC 5049 5043 3651

YORK TELECOM CORP p 1637
81 Corbett Way, Eatontown NJ 07724
Tel (732) 413-6000 SIC 3669 3651

LG ELECTRONICS USA INC p 860
1000 Sylvan Ave, Englewood Cliffs NJ 07632
Tel (201) 816-2000 SIC 5064 3651

D & M HOLDINGS US INC p 406
100 Corporate Dr, Mahwah NJ 07430
Tel (201) 762-6500 SIC 5065 3651

SHARP ELECTRONICS CORP p 1312
1 Sharp Plz Ste 1, Mahwah NJ 07495
Tel (201) 529-8200
SIC 5044 5064 3651 3631 3861 3674

AUDIO AND VIDEO LABS INC p 130
7905 N Crescent Blvd, Pennsauken NJ 08110
Tel (856) 663-9030
SIC 3652 5099 7389 3651

TECHNICOLOR USA INC p 1431
4 Research Way, Princeton NJ 08540
Tel (317) 587-3000 SIC 3651 3861 3661

CRESTRON ELECTRONICS INC p 392
15 Volvo Dr, Rockleigh NJ 07647
Tel (201) 767-3400
SIC 3571 3651 1731 3663 3499 3669

JAZZY ELECTRONICS CORP p 779
1600 63rd St, Brooklyn NY 11204
Tel (718) 236-8000 SIC 6512 5064 3651

SONY CORP OF AMERICA p 1341
25 Madison Ave Fl 27, New York NY 10010
Tel (212) 833-8000
SIC 3695 3652 3651 3577 3572

TOSHIBA AMERICA INC p 1462
1251 Ave Of Ameri Ste 4100, New York NY 10020
Tel (212) 596-0600
SIC 3651 3631 5064 5075 3571 3661

HITACHI AMERICA LTD p 696
50 Prospect Ave, Tarrytown NY 10591
Tel (914) 332-5800
SIC 5084 5065 3577 5063 5045 3651

■ **VTB HOLDINGS INC** p 1567
100 Summit Lake Dr, Valhalla NY 10595
Tel (914) 345-2255 SIC 3651

MITSUBISHI ELECTRIC AUTOMOTIVE AMERICA INC p 977
4773 Bethany Rd, Mason OH 45040
Tel (513) 573-6614 SIC 3694 3651 3714

PIONEER AUTOMOTIVE TECHNOLOGIES INC p 1150
100 S Pioneer Blvd, Springboro OH 45066
Tel (937) 746-2293 SIC 5013 3714 3651

PANASONIC INDUSTRIAL DEVICES CORP OF AMERICA p 1111
4900 Gorge Mcvay Dr Ste C, Mcallen TX 78503
Tel (956) 984-3700 SIC 3651 3675 3471

INRIX INC p 745
10210 Ne Pints Dr Ste 400, Kirkland WA 98033
Tel (425) 284-3800 SIC 3651

LOUD TECHNOLOGIES INC p 879
16220 Wood Red Rd Ne, Woodinville WA 98072
Tel (425) 892-6500 SIC 3651

SIC 3652 Phonograph Records & Magnetic Tape

CAPITOL-EMI MUSIC INC p 251
1750b Vine St, Los Angeles CA 90028
Tel (323) 462-6252 SIC 3652

■ **UNIVERSAL STUDIOS INC** p 1517
100 Universal City Plz, North Hollywood CA 91608
Tel (818) 777-1000
SIC 7812 3652 2741 5947 5944 5961

■ **UNIVERSAL CITY STUDIOS PRODUCTIONS LLLP LP** p 1516
100 Universal City Plz, Universal City CA 91608
Tel (818) 777-1000
SIC 7812 3652 2741 5947 5944 5961

COMVEST INVESTMENT PARTNERS III LP p 353
525 Okeechobee Blvd # 1050, West Palm Beach FL 33401
Tel (561) 727-2000
SIC 4731 5912 5999 3652 8742 1731

CINRAM INC p 308
1600 Rich Rd, Richmond IN 47374
Tel (416) 298-8190 SIC 3652 3695

SONY DADC US INC p 1341
1800 N Fruitridge Ave, Terre Haute IN 47804
Tel (812) 462-8100
SIC 3695 3652 3651 3577 3572

AUDIO AND VIDEO LABS INC p 130
7905 N Crescent Blvd, Pennsauken NJ 08110
Tel (856) 663-9030
SIC 3652 5099 7389 3651

BERTELSMANN INC p 176
1745 Broadway Fl 20, New York NY 10019
Tel (212) 782-1000
SIC 2731 2721 7819 3652 6512

■ **HISTORIC TW INC** p 696
75 Rockefeller Plz, New York NY 10019
Tel (212) 484-8000
SIC 3652 6794 2741 7812 4841 2721

SONY BROADBAND ENTERTAINMENT CORP p 1340
550 Madison Ave Fl 6, New York NY 10022
Tel (212) 833-6800
SIC 3652 7812 5734 7832 5735

SONY CORP OF AMERICA p 1341
25 Madison Ave Fl 27, New York NY 10010
Tel (212) 833-8000
SIC 3695 3652 3651 3577 3572

SONY MUSIC ENTERTAINMENT INC p 1341
25 Madison Ave Fl 19, New York NY 10010
Tel (212) 833-8500 SIC 3652 5064

SONY MUSIC HOLDINGS INC p 1341
550 Madison Ave Fl 16, New York NY 10022
Tel (212) 833-8000 SIC 3652 5099 2741

■ **VIVENDI UNIVERSAL ENTERTAINMENT LLLP** p 1563
30 Rockefeller Plz, New York NY 10112
Tel (212) 664-4444
SIC 7812 3652 2741 5947 5944 5961

WARNER MUSIC GROUP CORP p 1576
1633 Broadway, New York NY 10019
Tel (212) 275-2000 SIC 3652 6794

WARNER MUSIC INC p 1576
75 Rockefeller Plz Bsmt 1, New York NY 10019
Tel (212) 275-2000 SIC 3652 2741

WEA INTERNATIONAL INC p 1585
75 Rockefeller Plz, New York NY 10019
Tel (212) 275-1300 SIC 3652

WMG HOLDING CO INC p 1620
75 Rockefeller Plz, New York NY 10019
Tel (212) 275-2000 SIC 3652 2741

CDA INC p 270
8500 S Tryon St, Charlotte NC 28273
Tel (704) 504-1877 SIC 5099 3652

CINRAM MANUFACTURING INC p 308
1400 E Lackawanna St, Olyphant PA 18448
Tel (570) 383-3291 SIC 3652

TECHNICOLOR HOME ENTERTAINMENT p 1431
437 New Sanford Rd, La Vergne TN 37086
Tel (615) 372-9258 SIC 3652

SIC 3661 Telephone & Telegraph Apparatus

▲ **ADTRAN INC** p 24
901 Explorer Blvd Nw, Huntsville AL 35806
Tel (256) 963-8000 SIC 3661 3663 4813

GTEL HOLDINGS INC p 644
2609 Cameron St, Mobile AL 36607
Tel (251) 479-4500 SIC 3661 7389

INTER-TEL TECHNOLOGIES INC p 751
1146 N Alma School Rd, Mesa AZ 85201
Tel (480) 858-9600
SIC 5999 1731 5065 3661 3577

MITEL (DELAWARE) INC p 977
1146 N Alma School Rd, Mesa AZ 85201
Tel (480) 449-8900
SIC 3661 5045 4813 5065 1731 7359

MITEL NETWORKS INC p 977
1146 N Alma School Rd, Mesa AZ 85201
Tel (480) 961-9000
SIC 3661 7359 1731 7373

ENGHOUSE INTERACTIVE INC p 498
2095 W Pinnacle Peak Rd, Phoenix AZ 85027
Tel (602) 789-2800
SIC 3571 3661 3663 7372 7374

■ **XETA TECHNOLOGIES INC** p 1631
4001 N Rodney Parham Rd, Little Rock AR 72212
Tel (800) 697-8153 SIC 3661 5999 7389

EPIC TECHNOLOGIES LLC p 505
9340 Owensmouth Ave, Chatsworth CA 91311
Tel (818) 734-6500 SIC 3661 3577 3679

EMULEX CORP p 495
3333 Susan St, Costa Mesa CA 92626
Tel (714) 662-5600 SIC 3577 3661

OPLINK COMMUNICATIONS LLC p 1089
46335 Landing Pkwy, Fremont CA 94538
Tel (510) 933-7200 SIC 3661 4899

■ **GRASS VALLEY USA LLC** p 632
125 Crown Point Ct, Grass Valley CA 95945
Tel (800) 547-8949 SIC 3651 3661 3663

■ **AVIAT US INC** p 138
860 N Mccarthy Blvd, Milpitas CA 95035
Tel (408) 941-7100 SIC 3663 3661

■ **DASAN ZHONE SOLUTIONS INC** p 413
7195 Oakport St, Oakland CA 94621
Tel (510) 777-7000 SIC 3661

BOURNS INC p 204
1200 Columbia Ave, Riverside CA 92507
Tel (951) 781-5500
SIC 3677 3676 3661 3639 3679

▲ **NOVATEL WIRELESS INC** p 1063
9645 Scranton Rd Ste 205, San Diego CA 92121
Tel (858) 812-3400 SIC 3661 7371

DIAMOND MULTIMEDIA SYSTEMS INC p 437
2880 Junction Ave, San Jose CA 95134
Tel (408) 868-9613 SIC 3672 3577 3661

▲ **EXTREME NETWORKS INC** p 521
145 Rio Robles, San Jose CA 95134
Tel (408) 579-2800 SIC 3661 7373 7372

FORCE10 NETWORKS INC p 565
350 Holger Way, San Jose CA 95134
Tel (707) 665-4400 SIC 3661

▲ **NETGEAR INC** p 1027
350 E Plumeria Dr, San Jose CA 95134
Tel (408) 907-8000 SIC 3661 3577

■ **NORTHROP GRUMMAN SPACE & MISSION SYSTEMS CORP** p 1058
6377 San Ignacio Ave, San Jose CA 95119
Tel (703) 280-2900
SIC 7373 3663 3661 3812 3761

BLACKBERRY CORP p 187
3001 Bishop Dr, San Ramon CA 94583
Tel (972) 650-6126 SIC 5999 3661 4812

BUTLER SERVICE GROUP INC p 230
3820 State St Ste A, Santa Barbara CA 93105
Tel (201) 891-5312
SIC 7363 8711 8748 3661 7538

AVAYA HOLDINGS CORP p 136
4655 Great America Pkwy, Santa Clara CA 95054
Tel (908) 953-6000 SIC 3661 7372

AVAYA INC p 136
4655 Great America Pkwy, Santa Clara CA 95054
Tel (908) 953-6000 SIC 3661 7372 7371

▲ **PLANTRONICS INC** p 1154
345 Encinal St, Santa Cruz CA 95060
Tel (831) 426-5858 SIC 3661 3679

ALLIANCE FIBER OPTIC PRODUCTS INC p 54
275 Gibraltar Dr, Sunnyvale CA 94089
Tel (408) 736-6900 SIC 3229 3661

▲ **FINISAR CORP** p 543
1389 Moffett Park Dr, Sunnyvale CA 94089
Tel (408) 548-1000 SIC 3661 3663

▲ **INFINERA CORP** p 740
140 Caspian Ct, Sunnyvale CA 94089
Tel (408) 572-5200 SIC 3661 7372

NOKIA INC p 1046
200 S Mathilda Ave, Sunnyvale CA 94086
Tel (408) 530-7600
SIC 3663 5065 3661 3577

▲ **SHORETEL INC** p 1318
960 Stewart Dr, Sunnyvale CA 94085
Tel (408) 331-3300 SIC 3661 3663 7372

AIRBUS DS COMMUNICATIONS INC p 40
42505 Rio Nedo, Temecula CA 92590
Tel (951) 719-2100 SIC 3661

▲ **ZAYO GROUP HOLDINGS INC** p 1641
1805 29th St Unit 2050, Boulder CO 80301
Tel (303) 381-4683 SIC 4813 3661

■ **ZAYO GROUP LLC** p 1641
1805 29th St Unit 2050, Boulder CO 80301
Tel (303) 381-4683 SIC 4813 3661

RADIO FREQUENCY SYSTEMS INC p 1204
200 Pond View Dr, Meriden CT 06450
Tel (203) 630-3311
SIC 3663 3661 5045 5065

▲ **PITNEY BOWES INC** p 1152
3001 Summer St Ste 3, Stamford CT 06905
Tel (203) 356-5000
SIC 3579 7359 3661 8744 7372

▲ **AMPHENOL CORP** p 86
358 Hall Ave, Wallingford CT 06492
Tel (203) 265-8900 SIC 3678 3643 3661

BIO MEDIC CORP p 183
742 Sussex Ave, Seaford DE 19973
Tel (302) 628-4300
SIC 5049 3821 3496 3914 3661

■ **B WILLIAMS HOLDING CORP** p 142
1403 Foulk Rd Ste 200, Wilmington DE 19803
Tel (302) 656-8596
SIC 3579 3661 3861 7359 7629 6159

SIEMENS CORP p 1320
300 New Jersey Ave Nw # 10, Washington DC 20001
Tel (202) 434-4800
SIC 3661 3641 3844 3612 3357

▲ **HARRIS CORP** p 663
1025 W Nasa Blvd, Melbourne FL 32919
Tel (321) 727-9100
SIC 3812 3663 3699 3661 3674

NOBLE SYSTEMS CORP p 1046
1200 Ashwood Pkwy Ste 300, Atlanta GA 30338
Tel (404) 851-1331 SIC 3661

CUBS ACQUISITION CORP p 400
1 Southwire Dr, Carrollton GA 30119
Tel (770) 832-4242 SIC 3357 3661 3643

■ **SCIENTIFIC-ATLANTA LLC** p 1292
5030 Sugarloaf Pkwy, Lawrenceville GA 30044
Tel (678) 277-1000
SIC 3663 3661 3577 3825

ARRIS GROUP INC p 112
3871 Lakefield Dr Ste 300, Suwanee GA 30024
Tel (678) 473-2907
SIC 7372 3663 3357 7373 3661

ARRIS SOLUTIONS INC p 112
3871 Lakefield Dr Ste 300, Suwanee GA 30024
Tel (678) 473-2000 SIC 3661 3663 3357

▲ **WESTELL TECHNOLOGIES INC** p 1597
750 N Commons Dr, Aurora IL 60504
Tel (630) 898-2500 SIC 3661 4813 7389

AVG ADVANCED TECHNOLOGIES LP p 137
343 Saint Paul Blvd, Carol Stream IL 60188
Tel (630) 668-3900
SIC 3672 3661 3824 3822 3625

▲ **MOTOROLA SOLUTIONS INC** p 993
500 W Monroe St, Chicago IL 60661
Tel (847) 576-5000 SIC 3663 3661

RAULAND-BORG CORP p 1209
1802 W Central Rd, Mount Prospect IL 60056
Tel (847) 590-7100 SIC 3661 3663

CORIANT OPERATIONS INC p 370
1415 W Diehl Rd, Naperville IL 60563
Tel (847) 382-8817 SIC 3661

TELLABS INC p 1435
1415 W Diehl Rd, Naperville IL 60563
Tel (630) 798-8800 SIC 3661 1731

SHURE INC p 1319
5800 W Touhy Ave, Niles IL 60714
Tel (847) 600-2000 SIC 3651 3679 3661

CHARLES INDUSTRIES LTD p 289
5600 Apollo Dr, Rolling Meadows IL 60008
Tel (847) 806-6300 SIC 3661 3629 3677

COLEMAN CABLE LLC p 336
1530 S Shields Dr, Waukegan IL 60085
Tel (847) 672-2300 SIC 3661 3357 3643

TELAMON TECHNOLOGIES CORP p 1433
1000 E 116th St, Carmel IN 46032
Tel (317) 818-6888 SIC 3661

KGP PRODUCTS INC p 816
600 New Century Pkwy, New Century KS 66031
Tel (800) 755-1950 SIC 3661

▲ **CIENA CORP** p 306
7035 Ridge Rd, Hanover MD 21076
Tel (410) 694-5700 SIC 3661 7373

LTS GROUP HOLDINGS LLC p 883
80 Central St Ste 240, Boxborough MA 01719
Tel (978) 264-6001 SIC 3661

MANUFACTURERS SERVICES LIMITED p 903
300 Baker Ave Ste 106, Concord MA 01742
Tel (978) 287-5630
SIC 3571 3577 3572 3661 3663

GN NETCOM INC p 619
900 Chelmsford St # 313, Lowell MA 01851
Tel (800) 826-4656 SIC 3661

EP MANAGEMENT CORP p 504
801 W Ann Arbor Trl # 220, Plymouth MI 48170
Tel (313) 749-5500
SIC 3692 3661 2834 3674 3691

■ **NORSTAN INC** p 1049
5050 Lincoln Dr Ste 300, Minneapolis MN 55436
Tel (952) 352-4000
SIC 7389 3661 8748 7379

▲ **COMMUNICATIONS SYSTEMS INC** p 347
10900 Red Circle Dr, Minnetonka MN 55343
Tel (952) 996-1674
SIC 3661 3577 3663 8748

TYCO ELECTRONICS SUBSEA COMMUNICATIONS LLC p 1496
250 Industrial Way W, Eatontown NJ 07724
Tel (732) 578-7000
SIC 3661 5063 7373 1731 8999

IPC SYSTEMS INC p 763
Harborside Fincl 2nd St, Jersey City NJ 07311
Tel (201) 253-2000 SIC 3661

DIALOGIC INC p 436
4 Gatehall Dr, Parsippany NJ 07054
Tel (973) 967-6000 SIC 3661 3577 7371

TECHNICOLOR USA INC p 1431
4 Research Way, Princeton NJ 08540
Tel (317) 587-3000 SIC 3651 3861 3661

▲ **CORNING INC** p 371
1 Riverfront Plz, Corning NY 14831
Tel (607) 974-9000
SIC 3229 3357 3661 3674

KELTA INC p 809
141 Rodeo Dr, Edgewood NY 11717
Tel (631) 789-5000 SIC 3089 3643 3661

■ **TELEPHONICS CORP** p 1435
815 Broadhollow Rd, Farmingdale NY 11735
Tel (631) 755-7000
SIC 3669 3661 3679 3812 3663

CLAYTON DUBILIER & RICE FUND V LIMITED PARTNERSHIP p 323
375 Park Ave Fl 18, New York NY 10152
Tel (212) 407-5200
SIC 3825 3661 3812 3577 3575 7372

■ **GTE CORP** p 644
140 West St, New York NY 10007
Tel (212) 395-1000
SIC 4813 4812 3661 3663 4899 2741

TOSHIBA AMERICA INC p 1462
1251 Ave Of Ameri Ste 4100, New York NY 10020
Tel (212) 596-0600
SIC 3651 3631 5064 5075 3571 3661

TOSHIBA AMERICA INFORMATION SYSTEMS INC p 1462
1251 Ave Of The Ste 4110, New York NY 10020
Tel (949) 583-3000
SIC 3571 3577 3572 3661 5045

■ **SPECTRASITE COMMUNICATIONS LLC** p 1357
400 Regency Forest Dr # 300, Cary NC 27518
Tel (919) 468-0112
SIC 4812 8748 1623 3661 4813 4899

■ **COMMSCOPE CONNECTIVITY SOLUTIONS LLC** p 346
1100 Commscope Pl Se, Hickory NC 28602
Tel (828) 324-2200
SIC 3661 3357 3643 8999

■ **CORNING OPTICAL COMMUNICATIONS LLC** p 371
800 17th St Nw, Hickory NC 28601
Tel (828) 901-5000 SIC 3661

NEXANS USA INC p 1039
39 2nd St Nw, Hickory NC 28601
Tel (828) 323-2660 SIC 3357 3661 3678

TEKELEC GLOBAL INC p 1433
5200 Paramount Pkwy, Morrisville NC 27560
Tel (919) 460-5500 SIC 3661 3825 7371

TITAN PRIVATE HOLDINGS I LLC p 1456
5200 Paramount Pkwy, Morrisville NC 27560
Tel (919) 460-5500 SIC 3661 3825 7371

EMERSON NETWORK POWER ENERGY SYSTEMS NORTH AMERICA INC p 492
1510 Kansas Ave, Lorain OH 44052
Tel (440) 288-1122 SIC 3661 3644 7629

▲ **PREFORMED LINE PRODUCTS CO** p 1169
660 Beta Dr, Mayfield Village OH 44143
Tel (440) 461-5200 SIC 3644 3661

▲ **BLACK BOX CORP** p 186
1000 Park Dr, Lawrence PA 15055
Tel (724) 746-5500
SIC 3577 3679 3661 5045 5065 5063

■ **BLACK BOX CORP OF PENNSYLVANIA** p 186
1000 Park Dr, Lawrence PA 15055
Tel (724) 746-5500
SIC 5045 5063 5065 3577 3679 3661

RICOH AMERICAS CORP p 1233
70 Valley Stream Pkwy, Malvern PA 19355
Tel (610) 296-8000
SIC 5044 5065 5045 5043 3861 3661

AMERICA FUJIKURA LTD p 67
170 Ridgeview Cir, Duncan SC 29334
Tel (864) 433-8281 SIC 3661

NORTEL NETWORKS HPOCS INC p 1049
725 Cool Springs Blvd # 600, Franklin TN 37067
Tel (800) 684-2228 SIC 3661

OPTEK TECHNOLOGY INC p 1090
1645 Wallace Dr, Carrollton TX 75006
Tel (972) 323-2200
SIC 3674 3825 3812 3661 3643

▲ **AT&T INC** p 123
208 S Akard St, Dallas TX 75202
Tel (210) 821-4105
SIC 4813 4812 3663 3661 2741

■ **INTERVOICE LLC** p 759
17787 Waterview Pkwy, Dallas TX 75252
Tel (972) 454-8000 SIC 3661

GENBAND US LLC p 598
2801 Network Blvd Ste 300, Frisco TX 75034
Tel (972) 521-5800 SIC 3661

■ **CONTEL FEDERAL SYSTEMS INC** p 362
600 Hidden Rdg, Irving TX 75038
Tel (972) 718-5600 SIC 3661 4813

ALCATEL-LUCENT HOLDINGS INC p 47
601 Data Dr, Plano TX 75075
Tel (972) 477-2000 SIC 3661

■ **GE POWER ELECTRONICS INC** p 596
601 Shiloh Rd, Plano TX 75074
Tel (972) 244-9288 SIC 3661

FUJITSU NETWORK COMMUNICATIONS INC p 584
2801 Telecom Pkwy, Richardson TX 75082
Tel (972) 479-6000 SIC 3661 3663

■ **BROADWING CORP** p 216
1122 Capital Of Texas Hwy, West Lake Hills TX 78746
Tel (512) 742-3700 SIC 3661

TELECT INC p 1434
22245 E Appleway Blvd Ste, Liberty Lake WA 99019
Tel (509) 926-6000 SIC 3661

▲ **ROCKWELL AUTOMATION INC** p 1245
1201 S 2nd St, Milwaukee WI 53204
Tel (414) 382-2000
SIC 3625 3621 3566 3661

SIC 3663 Radio & TV Communications, Systs & Eqpt, Broadcast/Studio

▲ **ADTRAN INC** p 24
901 Explorer Blvd Nw, Huntsville AL 35806
Tel (256) 963-8000 SIC 3661 3663 4813

■ SCITECHNOLOGY INC p 1292
13000 Memorial Pkwy Sw, Huntsville AL 35803
Tel (256) 882-4800
SIC 3672 3829 8711 3663

ANDES INDUSTRIES INC p 90
2260 W Broadway Rd # 101, Mesa AZ 85202
Tel (480) 813-0925 SIC 5063 3663 3643

PCT INTERNATIONAL INC p 1124
2260 W Broadway Rd # 101, Mesa AZ 85202
Tel (480) 813-0925 SIC 3663

ENGHOUSE INTERACTIVE INC p 498
2095 W Pinnacle Peak Rd, Phoenix AZ 85027
Tel (602) 789-2800
SIC 3571 3661 3663 7372 7374

LEEMAH CORP p 852
155 S Hill Dr, Brisbane CA 94005
Tel (415) 394-1288
SIC 3671 3672 3669 3663 3577

ALE USA INC p 48
26801 Agoura Rd, Calabasas CA 91301
Tel (818) 878-4816 SIC 3663 3613

SPIRENT COMMUNICATIONS INC p 1359
27349 Agoura Rd, Calabasas CA 91301
Tel (818) 676-2300 SIC 3663 3829 3825

▲ VIASAT INC p 1554
6155 El Camino Real, Carlsbad CA 92009
Tel (760) 476-2200 SIC 3663

PELCO INC p 1128
3500 Pelco Way, Clovis CA 93612
Tel (559) 292-1981 SIC 3663 7382

SEATEL INC p 1297
4030 Nelson Ave, Concord CA 94520
Tel (925) 798-7979 SIC 3663

▲ APPLE INC p 98
1 Infinite Loop, Cupertino CA 95014
Tel (408) 996-1010
SIC 3663 3571 3575 3577 3651 7372

MITSUBISHI ELECTRIC US HOLDINGS INC p 977
5900 Katella Ave Ste A, Cypress CA 90630
Tel (714) 220-2500
SIC 5065 5045 3651 3663

■ BOEING SATELLITE SYSTEMS INC p 197
900 N Sepulveda Blvd, El Segundo CA 90245
Tel (310) 791-7450 SIC 3663

GRASS VALLEY INC p 632
125 Crown Point Ct, Grass Valley CA 95945
Tel (530) 478-3000 SIC 3663

■ GRASS VALLEY USA LLC p 632
125 Crown Point Ct, Grass Valley CA 95945
Tel (800) 547-8949 SIC 3651 3661 3663

▲ CALAMP CORP p 238
15635 Alton Pkwy Ste 250, Irvine CA 92618
Tel (949) 600-5600 SIC 3663

HBC SOLUTIONS HOLDINGS LLC p 671
10877 Wilshire Blvd Fl 18, Los Angeles CA 90024
Tel (321) 727-9100 SIC 3663

OCM PE HOLDINGS LP p 1074
333 S Grand Ave Fl 28, Los Angeles CA 90071
Tel (213) 830-6213 SIC 3679 3612 3663

▲ AVIAT NETWORKS INC p 138
860 N Mccarthy Blvd, Milpitas CA 95035
Tel (408) 941-7000 SIC 3663

■ AVIAT US INC p 138
860 N Mccarthy Blvd, Milpitas CA 95035
Tel (408) 941-7100 SIC 3663 3661

ANRITSU CO p 92
490 Jarvis Dr, Morgan Hill CA 95037
Tel (408) 201-1551 SIC 5065 3825 3663

ANRITSU US HOLDING INC p 93
490 Jarvis Dr, Morgan Hill CA 95037
Tel (408) 778-2000 SIC 3825 3663 5065

COMMUNICATIONS & POWER INDUSTRIES LLC p 347
607 Hansen Way, Palo Alto CA 94304
Tel (650) 846-2900
SIC 3671 3679 3699 3663

MDA COMMUNICATIONS HOLDINGS LLC p 933
3825 Fabian Way, Palo Alto CA 94303
Tel (650) 852-4000 SIC 3663

SPACE SYSTEMS/LORAL LLC p 1354
3825 Fabian Way, Palo Alto CA 94303
Tel (650) 852-7320 SIC 4899 3663

▲ CALIX INC p 242
1035 N Mcdowell Blvd, Petaluma CA 94954
Tel (707) 766-3000 SIC 3663 4899 4813

▲ COHU INC p 335
12367 Crosthwaite Cir, Poway CA 92064
Tel (858) 848-8100 SIC 3825 3663 3699

■ CUBIC DEFENSE APPLICATIONS INC p 399
9333 Balboa Ave, San Diego CA 92123
Tel (858) 277-6780 SIC 3699 3663 3812

LG ELECTRONICS MOBILECOMM USA INC p 860
10225 Willow Creek Rd, San Diego CA 92131
Tel (858) 635-5300 SIC 5065 3663

PULSE ELECTRONICS CORP p 1191
12220 World Trade Dr, San Diego CA 92128
Tel (858) 674-8100 SIC 3679 3612 3663

▲ DOLBY LABORATORIES INC p 447
1275 Market St, San Francisco CA 94103
Tel (415) 558-0200 SIC 3663 6794

▲ HARMONIC INC p 662
4300 N 1st St, San Jose CA 95134
Tel (408) 542-2500 SIC 3663 3823

■ NORTHROP GRUMMAN SPACE & MISSION SYSTEMS CORP p 1058
6377 San Ignacio Ave, San Jose CA 95119
Tel (703) 280-2900
SIC 7373 3663 3661 3812 3761

TCOMT INC p 1428
111 N Market St Ste 670, San Jose CA 95113
Tel (408) 351-3340 SIC 3663

SONY MOBILE COMMUNICATIONS (USA) INC p 1341
2207 Bridgepoint Pkwy, San Mateo CA 94404
Tel (866) 766-9374 SIC 3663 5999

MOSELEY ASSOCIATES INC p 992
82 Coromar Dr, Santa Barbara CA 93117
Tel (805) 968-9621 SIC 3663

■ ARUBA NETWORKS INC p 114
1344 Crossman Ave, Sunnyvale CA 94089
Tel (408) 227-4500 SIC 3577 3663 7371

▲ FINISAR CORP p 543
1389 Moffett Park Dr, Sunnyvale CA 94089
Tel (408) 548-1000 SIC 3661 3663

NOKIA INC p 1046
200 S Mathilda Ave, Sunnyvale CA 94086
Tel (408) 530-7600
SIC 3663 5065 3661 3577

PALM INC p 1109
950 W Maude Ave, Sunnyvale CA 94085
Tel (408) 617-7000 SIC 3663

▲ SHORETEL INC p 1318
960 Stewart Dr, Sunnyvale CA 94085
Tel (408) 331-3300 SIC 3661 3663 7372

SPECTRALINK CORP p 1357
2560 55th St, Boulder CO 80301
Tel (303) 441-7500 SIC 3663

■ DISH ORBITAL CORP p 442
9601 S Meridian Blvd, Englewood CO 80112
Tel (303) 723-1000 SIC 3663 4841

▲ ECHOSTAR CORP p 475
100 Inverness Ter E, Englewood CO 80112
Tel (303) 706-4000 SIC 3663 4841

RADIO FREQUENCY SYSTEMS INC p 1204
200 Pond View Dr, Meriden CT 06450
Tel (203) 630-3311
SIC 3663 3661 5045 5065

ASHCROFT INC p 117
250 E Main St, Stratford CT 06614
Tel (203) 378-8281
SIC 3823 3679 3663 3625

ASHCROFT-NAGANO KEIKI HOLDINGS INC p 117
250 E Main St, Stratford CT 06614
Tel (203) 378-8281
SIC 3823 3679 3663 3625

▲ INTERDIGITAL INC p 752
200 Bellevue Pkwy Ste 300, Wilmington DE 19809
Tel (302) 281-3600 SIC 3663 5999 6794

INMARSAT INC p 744
1101 Conn Ave Nw Ste 1200, Washington DC 20036
Tel (202) 248-5150 SIC 3663

UNITED WIRELESS TECHNOLOGIES INC p 1515
300 Se 5th Ave Apt 8180, Boca Raton FL 33432
Tel (561) 302-9350 SIC 3571 3663

▲ HARRIS CORP p 663
1025 W Nasa Blvd, Melbourne FL 32919
Tel (321) 727-9100
SIC 3812 3663 3699 3661 3674

SATCOM DIRECT INC p 1283
1050 Satcom Ln, Melbourne FL 32940
Tel (321) 777-3000 SIC 3663

▲ VOXX INTERNATIONAL CORP p 1566
2351 J Lawson Blvd, Orlando FL 32824
Tel (800) 645-7750 SIC 3711 3651 3663

AUDIO VISUAL INNOVATIONS INC p 130
6301 Benjamin Rd Ste 101, Tampa FL 33634
Tel (813) 884-7168
SIC 3669 3861 3663 3651 5043

AVI-SPL EMPLOYEE EMERGENCY RELIEF FUND INC p 137
6301 Benjamin Rd Ste 101, Tampa FL 33634
Tel (813) 884-7168
SIC 3669 3861 3663 3651 5043 5064

AVI-SPL HOLDINGS INC p 137
6301 Benjamin Rd Ste 101, Tampa FL 33634
Tel (866) 708-5034
SIC 3669 3861 3663 3651 1731 5064

SYNIVERSE HOLDINGS INC p 1415
8125 Highwoods Palm Way, Tampa FL 33647
Tel (813) 637-5000 SIC 4812 3663

SYNIVERSE TECHNOLOGIES LLC p 1415
8125 Highwoods Palm Way, Tampa FL 33647
Tel (813) 637-5000 SIC 4812 3663

DATAPATH INC p 414
2205 Northmont Pkwy 100, Duluth GA 30096
Tel (678) 597-0300 SIC 3663

■ SCIENTIFIC-ATLANTA LLC p 1292
5030 Sugarloaf Pkwy, Lawrenceville GA 30044
Tel (678) 277-1000
SIC 3663 3661 3577 3825

■ EMS TECHNOLOGIES INC p 495
660 Engineering Dr, Norcross GA 30092
Tel (770) 263-9200 SIC 3663 7373

ARRIS GROUP INC p 112
3871 Lakefield Dr Ste 300, Suwanee GA 30024
Tel (678) 473-2907
SIC 7372 3663 3357 7373 3661

ARRIS INTERNATIONAL INC p 112
3871 Lakefield Dr Ste 300, Suwanee GA 30024
Tel (678) 473-2000 SIC 3663

ARRIS SOLUTIONS INC p 112
3871 Lakefield Dr Ste 300, Suwanee GA 30024
Tel (678) 473-2000 SIC 3661 3663 3357

▲ BOEING CO p 197
100 N Riverside Plz, Chicago IL 60606
Tel (312) 544-2000
SIC 3721 3663 3761 3764 3812 3728

■ BOEING IRVING CO p 197
100 N Riverside Plz Fl 35, Chicago IL 60606
Tel (312) 544-2000 SIC 3663

■ GOGO LLC p 620
111 N Canal St Fl 15, Chicago IL 60606
Tel (630) 647-1400
SIC 3663 4812 4813 4899

HEICO COMPANIES L L C p 680
5600 Three First Nat Plz, Chicago IL 60602
Tel (312) 419-8220
SIC 3315 3589 3448 3531 1731 3663

MOTOROLA MOBILITY HOLDINGS LLC p 993
222 Merchandise Mart Plz, Chicago IL 60654
Tel (800) 668-6765 SIC 3663

MOTOROLA MOBILITY LLC p 993
222 Merchandise Mart Plz, Chicago IL 60654
Tel (800) 866-6765 SIC 3663 4812

▲ MOTOROLA SOLUTIONS INC p 993
500 W Monroe St, Chicago IL 60661
Tel (847) 576-5000 SIC 3663 3661

■ GOGO INTERMEDIATE HOLDINGS LLC p 620
1250 N Arlington Rd, Itasca IL 60143
Tel (630) 647-1400 SIC 3663

■ ANDREW INTERNATIONAL SERVICES CORP p 90
2700 Ellis Rd, Joliet IL 60433
Tel (779) 435-6000 SIC 3663

ZENITH ELECTRONICS CORP p 1642
2000 Millbrook Dr, Lincolnshire IL 60069
Tel (847) 941-8000
SIC 3651 3671 3663 3674 2517 2519

RAULAND-BORG CORP p 1209
1802 W Central Rd, Mount Prospect IL 60056
Tel (847) 590-7100 SIC 3661 3663

■ COMMSCOPE TECHNOLOGIES LLC p 346
4 Westbrook Corporate Ctr, Westchester IL 60154
Tel (708) 236-6000
SIC 3663 3357 3679 3812 3699

FURRION LLC p 585
2612 Glenview Dr, Elkhart IN 46514
Tel (888) 354-5792 SIC 3663

▲ ROCKWELL COLLINS INC p 1245
400 Collins Rd Ne, Cedar Rapids IA 52498
Tel (319) 295-1000 SIC 3812 3663

SABRE COMMUNICATIONS CORP p 1264
7101 Southbridge Dr, Sioux City IA 51111
Tel (712) 258-6690 SIC 3663 3441 1731

MPD INC p 995
316 E 9th St, Owensboro KY 42303
Tel (270) 685-6200
SIC 3671 3829 3812 3663 3643 3053

▲ LOCKHEED MARTIN CORP p 873
6801 Rockledge Dr, Bethesda MD 20817
Tel (301) 897-6000
SIC 3761 3721 3663 3764 3812 3728

THALES DEFENSE & SECURITY INC p 1446
22605 Gateway Center Dr, Clarksburg MD 20871
Tel (240) 864-7000 SIC 3663

■ HUGHES COMMUNICATIONS INC p 717
11717 Exploration Ln, Germantown MD 20876
Tel (301) 428-5500 SIC 4813 4899 3663

▲ SEACHANGE INTERNATIONAL INC p 1296
50 Nagog Park, Acton MA 01720
Tel (978) 897-0100 SIC 3663 7822 7371

■ GE INFRASTRUCTURE SENSING INC p 596
1100 Technology Park Dr # 100, Billerica MA 01821
Tel (978) 437-1000
SIC 3823 5084 3699 3674 3663 3625

▲ AMERICAN TOWER CORP p 80
116 Huntington Ave # 1100, Boston MA 02116
Tel (617) 375-7500 SIC 4813 3663

■ ATC TOWER SERVICES LLC p 124
116 Huntington Ave # 1100, Boston MA 02116
Tel (617) 375-7500 SIC 4813 3663

MANUFACTURERS SERVICES LIMITED p 903
300 Baker Ave Ste 106, Concord MA 01742
Tel (978) 287-5630
SIC 3571 3577 3572 3661 3663

■ MACOM TECHNOLOGY SOLUTIONS INC p 893
100 Chelmsford St, Lowell MA 01851
Tel (978) 656-2500 SIC 3663 3679

SINOHUB INC p 1326
3 Kensington Way, Upton MA 01568
Tel (508) 603-1085 SIC 3663

▲ RAYTHEON CO p 1211
870 Winter St, Waltham MA 02451
Tel (781) 522-3000 SIC 3812 3663 3761

TELEX COMMUNICATIONS HOLDINGS INC p 1435
12000 Portland Ave, Burnsville MN 55337
Tel (877) 863-4166 SIC 3663 3669 3679

▲ COMMUNICATIONS SYSTEMS INC p 347
10900 Red Circle Dr, Minnetonka MN 55343
Tel (952) 996-1674
SIC 3661 3577 3663 8748

■ PEOPLENET COMMUNICATIONS CORP p 1132
4400 Baker Rd, Minnetonka MN 55343
Tel (952) 908-6200 SIC 7373 3663 4812

LAIRD TECHNOLOGIES INC p 838
3481 Rider Trl S, Earth City MO 63045
Tel (636) 898-6000 SIC 3469 3663

■ ESCO TECHNOLOGIES HOLDING LLC p 509
9900 Clayton Rd Ste A, Saint Louis MO 63124
Tel (314) 213-7200
SIC 3825 3492 3812 3711 3663

ANTRONIX INC p 94
440 Forsgate Dr, Cranbury NJ 08512
Tel (609) 860-0160 SIC 3663 5063

CRESTRON ELECTRONICS INC p 392
15 Volvo Dr, Rockleigh NJ 07647
Tel (201) 767-3400
SIC 3571 3651 1731 3663 3499 3669

CHECKPOINT SYSTEMS INC p 292
101 Wolf Dr, West Deptford NJ 08086
Tel (856) 848-1800 SIC 3699 3812 3663

■ EDO LLC p 478
1500 New Horizons Blvd, Amityville NY 11701
Tel (631) 630-4000
SIC 3812 3728 3663 3679

■ TELEPHONICS CORP p 1435
815 Broadhollow Rd, Farmingdale NY 11735
Tel (631) 755-7000
SIC 3669 3661 3679 3812 3663

GLOBECOMM SYSTEMS INC p 618
45 Oser Ave, Hauppauge NY 11788
Tel (631) 231-9800 SIC 3663 4813

■ TELXON CORP p 1435
1 Zebra Plz, Holtsville NY 11742
Tel (631) 738-2400 SIC 3571 7373 3663

▲ COMTECH TELECOMMUNICATIONS CORP p 353
68 S Service Rd Ste 230, Melville NY 11747
Tel (631) 962-7000 SIC 3663

ANAREN HOLDING CORP p 88
590 Madison Ave Fl 41, New York NY 10022
Tel (212) 415-6700 SIC 3663

▲ GRIFFON CORP p 640
712 5th Ave Fl 18, New York NY 10019
Tel (212) 957-5000
SIC 3442 2431 1751 1799 3083 3663

■ GTE CORP p 644
140 West St, New York NY 10007
Tel (212) 395-1000
SIC 4813 4812 3661 3663 4899 2741

■ L-3 COMMUNICATIONS CORP p 834
600 3rd Ave, New York NY 10016
Tel (212) 697-1111
SIC 3812 3663 3669 3679 3769

▲ L-3 COMMUNICATIONS HOLDINGS INC p 835
600 3rd Ave, New York NY 10016
Tel (212) 697-1111
SIC 3663 3669 3679 3812 3769

▲ LORAL SPACE & COMMUNICATIONS INC p 878
565 5th Ave, New York NY 10017
Tel (212) 697-1105 SIC 3663 4899

■ LORAL SPACECOM CORP p 878
565 5th Ave Fl 19, New York NY 10017
Tel (212) 697-1105 SIC 3663

■ HAND HELD PRODUCTS INC p 657
700 Visions Dr, Skaneateles Falls NY 13153
Tel (315) 554-6000
SIC 3577 3571 3663 3578

■ GENERAL DYNAMICS SATCOM TECHNOLOGIES INC p 600
1700 Cable Dr Ne, Conover NC 28613
Tel (704) 462-7330 SIC 3663

▲ COMMSCOPE HOLDING CO INC p 346
1100 Commscope Pl Se, Hickory NC 28602
Tel (828) 324-2200 SIC 3663 4899

■ COMMSCOPE INC OF NORTH CAROLINA p 346
1100 Commscope Pl Se, Hickory NC 28602
Tel (828) 324-2200
SIC 3663 3357 3679 3812 3699

▲ LSI INDUSTRIES INC p 883
10000 Alliance Rd, Blue Ash OH 45242
Tel (513) 793-3200 SIC 3648 3993 3663

AGERE SYSTEMS INC p 34
1110 American Pkwy Ne, Allentown PA 18109
Tel (610) 712-1000 SIC 3663

■ TVC COMMUNICATIONS LLC p 1494
800 Airport Rd, Annville PA 17003
Tel (717) 838-3790 SIC 3663 2298

ALSTOM SIGNALING OPERATION LLC p 61
2901 E Lake Rd Bldg 122, Erie PA 16531
Tel (800) 825-3178
SIC 3669 5088 3672 3663

SPECTRUM CONTROL INC p 1357
8061 Avonia Rd, Fairview PA 16415
Tel (814) 474-2207
SIC 3677 3663 3612 3676

▲ KVH INDUSTRIES INC p 832
50 Enterprise Ctr, Middletown RI 02842
Tel (401) 847-3327 SIC 3663 3812

CORDILLERA COMMUNICATIONS LLC p 369
134 Columbus St, Charleston SC 29403
Tel (843) 577-7111 SIC 2711 3663

■ SHAKESPEARE CO LLC p 1310
6111 Shakespeare Rd, Columbia SC 29223
Tel (803) 754-7011
SIC 3089 3949 3679 3663

CVE TECHNOLOGY GROUP INC p 404
915 Enterprise Blvd, Allen TX 75013
Tel (972) 424-6606 SIC 3663

▲ AT&T INC p 123
208 S Akard St, Dallas TX 75202
Tel (210) 821-4105
SIC 4813 4812 3663 3661 2741

PHILIPS CONSUMER ELECTRONIC CO p 1143
12430 Mercantile Ave, El Paso TX 79928
Tel (915) 298-4111 SIC 3663

IMAGINE COMMUNICATIONS CORP p 733
3001 Dallas Pkwy Ste 300, Frisco TX 75034
Tel (469) 803-4900 SIC 4899 3663

NOKIA INC p 1046
6363 N State Highway 161 # 800, Irving TX 75038
Tel (214) 496-0329 SIC 3663

NOKIA SOLUTIONS AND NETWORKS US LLC p 1046
6000 Connection Dr, Irving TX 75039
Tel (972) 374-3000 SIC 3663 5999 4813

VERTEX COMMUNICATIONS CORP p 1552
2600 N Longview St, Kilgore TX 75662
Tel (903) 984-0555 SIC 3663

ERICSSON HOLDING II INC p 507
6300 Legacy Dr, Plano TX 75024
Tel (972) 398-0183 SIC 3663

HUAWEI DEVICE USA INC p 715
5700 Tennyson Pkwy # 600, Plano TX 75024
Tel (214) 919-6688 SIC 3663

FUJITSU NETWORK COMMUNICATIONS INC p 584
2801 Telecom Pkwy, Richardson TX 75082
Tel (972) 479-6000 SIC 3661 3663

QORVO INC p 1195
500 W Renner Rd, Richardson TX 75080
Tel (972) 994-8200 SIC 3663 3674 3679

■ RADIATION SYSTEMS PRECISION CONTROLS INC p 1204
1219 Digital Dr Ste 101, Richardson TX 75081
Tel (972) 907-9599 SIC 3663

■ RAYTHEON E-SYSTEMS INC p 1211
1727 Cityline Dr, Richardson TX 75082
Tel (972) 205-9374
SIC 3663 3812 3573 3575 4581 3721

AMERICAN SMARTPHONE INC p 79
10421 S Jordan Gtwy # 500, South Jordan UT 84095
Tel (801) 748-1780 SIC 3663

■ **GENERAL DYNAMICS GOVERNMENT SYSTEMS OVERSEAS CORP** p 600
3211 Jermantown Rd, Fairfax VA 22030
Tel (703) 995-8666 *SIC* 3663

■ **HARRIS IT SERVICES CORP** p 663
2235 Monroe St, Herndon VA 20171
Tel (703) 673-1400 *SIC* 8711 3663 3674

VT IDIRECT INC p 1567
13861 Sunrise Valley Dr, Herndon VA 20171
Tel (703) 648-8002 *SIC* 3663

SES GOVERNMENT SOLUTIONS INC p 1308
11790 Sunrise Valley Dr # 300, Reston VA 20191
Tel (703) 610-1000 *SIC* 7389 3663

DESIGN HOMES INC p 432
600 N Marquette Rd, Prairie Du Chien WI 53821
Tel (608) 326-8406 *SIC* 2452 3663 5211

CS ESTATE INC p 397
N7w22025 Johnson Dr, Waukesha WI 53186
Tel (262) 953-3500 *SIC* 3841 3663 7374

SIC 3669 Communications Eqpt, NEC

ECONOLITE CONTROL PRODUCTS INC p 476
3360 E La Palma Ave, Anaheim CA 92806
Tel (714) 630-3700 *SIC* 3669

LEEMAH CORP p 852
155 S Hill Dr, Brisbane CA 94005
Tel (415) 394-1288
SIC 3671 3672 3669 3663 3577

▲ **LUMENTUM HOLDINGS INC** p 885
400 N Mccarthy Blvd, Milpitas CA 95035
Tel (408) 546-5483 *SIC* 3669 3674 3826

H M ELECTRONICS INC p 650
14110 Stowe Dr, Poway CA 92064
Tel (858) 535-6000 *SIC* 3669

▲ **VOCERA COMMUNICATIONS INC** p 1564
525 Race St Ste 150, San Jose CA 95126
Tel (408) 882-5100 *SIC* 3669

PACIFIC SCIENTIFIC CO INC p 1105
1785 Voyager Ave Ste 101, Simi Valley CA 93063
Tel (805) 526-5700
SIC 3812 3669 3621 3694 3823 3625

■ **MERU NETWORKS INC** p 951
894 Ross Dr, Sunnyvale CA 94089
Tel (408) 215-5300 *SIC* 3669

■ **RAYTHEON APPLIED SIGNAL TECHNOLOGY INC** p 1210
460 W California Ave, Sunnyvale CA 94086
Tel (408) 749-1888 *SIC* 3669

DEI HOLDINGS INC p 422
1 Viper Way Ste 3, Vista CA 92081
Tel (760) 598-6200 *SIC* 3669 3651

MCCAIN INC p 926
2365 Oak Ridge Way, Vista CA 92081
Tel (760) 727-8100 *SIC* 5084 3444 3669

▲ **UNITED TECHNOLOGIES CORP** p 1514
10 Farm Springs Rd, Farmington CT 06032
Tel (860) 728-7000
SIC 3724 3585 3721 3534 3669 3699

SIMPLEXGRINNELL HOLDINGS LLC p 1325
1501 Nw 51st St, Boca Raton FL 33431
Tel (561) 988-7200
SIC 3579 3669 3699 3822

SIMPLEXGRINNELL LP p 1325
4700 Exchange Ct, Boca Raton FL 33431
Tel (561) 988-7200
SIC 5087 1711 3669 7382

■ **UTC FIRE & SECURITY AMERICAS CORP INC** p 1536
8985 Town Center Pkwy, Lakewood Ranch FL 34202
Tel (941) 739-4200 *SIC* 3669 5065

AUDIO VISUAL INNOVATIONS INC p 130
6301 Benjamin Rd Ste 101, Tampa FL 33634
Tel (813) 884-7168
SIC 3669 5064 3861 3663 3651 5043

AVI-SPL EMPLOYEE EMERGENCY RELIEF FUND INC p 137
6301 Benjamin Rd Ste 101, Tampa FL 33634
Tel (813) 884-7168
SIC 3669 3861 3663 3651 5043 5064

AVI-SPL HOLDINGS INC p 137
6301 Benjamin Rd Ste 101, Tampa FL 33634
Tel (866) 708-5034
SIC 3669 3861 3663 3651 1731 5064

▲ **NUMEREX CORP** p 1067
400 Interstate North Pkwy, Atlanta GA 30339
Tel (770) 693-5950 *SIC* 3669 7371

BARCO INC p 155
3059 Premiere Pkwy # 400, Duluth GA 30097
Tel (408) 400-4100 *SIC* 3575 3669

■ **BRK BRANDS INC** p 215
3901 Liberty St, Aurora IL 60504
Tel (630) 851-7330 *SIC* 3669

■ **FIRST ALERT INC** p 544
3901 Liberty St, Aurora IL 60504
Tel (630) 851-7330
SIC 3669 3999 3446 3499 3829 3648

SIEMENS INDUSTRY INC p 1320
1000 Deerfield Pkwy, Buffalo Grove IL 60089
Tel (847) 215-1000
SIC 3822 5063 3669 1731 7382 3625

▲ **FEDERAL SIGNAL CORP** p 536
1415 W 22nd St Ste 1100, Oak Brook IL 60523
Tel (630) 954-2000
SIC 3711 3647 3669 3559 3544 3545

SYSTEM SENSOR LTD p 1418
3825 Ohio Ave, Saint Charles IL 60174
Tel (630) 377-6674 *SIC* 3669

GARMIN INTERNATIONAL INC p 592
1200 E 151st St, Olathe KS 66062
Tel (913) 397-8200 *SIC* 3812 3669 8713

SIEMENS RAIL AUTOMATION CORP p 1320
2400 Nelson Miller Pkwy, Louisville KY 40223
Tel (502) 244-7400 *SIC* 3743 3669

■ **ACTERNA LLC** p 19
20250 Century Blvd # 100, Germantown MD 20874
Tel (301) 353-1550
SIC 3669 7379 3825 5065 3679 8734

■ **KIDDE-FENWAL INC** p 817
400 Main St, Ashland MA 01721
Tel (508) 881-2000
SIC 3669 3823 3825 3822 3643 3625

VIPER HOLDINGS CORP p 1558
200 Clarendon St Fl 54, Boston MA 02116
Tel (617) 619-5400 *SIC* 3669 3651

LIFELINE SYSTEMS CO p 864
111 Lawrence St, Framingham MA 01702
Tel (508) 988-1000 *SIC* 3669

SIMPLEX TIME RECORDER LLC p 1325
50 Technology Dr, Westminster MA 01441
Tel (978) 731-2500 *SIC* 7382 3669 1711

▲ **GENTEX CORP** p 604
600 N Centennial St, Zeeland MI 49464
Tel (616) 772-1800 *SIC* 3231 3714 3669

BOSCH SECURITY SYSTEMS INC p 202
12000 Portland Ave, Burnsville MN 55337
Tel (952) 884-4051 *SIC* 1731 3669 3679

TELEX COMMUNICATIONS HOLDINGS INC p 1435
12000 Portland Ave, Burnsville MN 55337
Tel (877) 863-4166 *SIC* 3663 3669 3679

MILESTONE AV TECHNOLOGIES LLC p 969
6436 City West Pkwy, Eden Prairie MN 55344
Tel (952) 236-7231 *SIC* 3669

■ **Q3 CONTRACTING INC** p 1194
3066 Spruce St, Saint Paul MN 55117
Tel (651) 224-2424 *SIC* 1623 7699 3669

CODE 3 INC p 333
10986 N Warson Rd, Saint Louis MO 63114
Tel (314) 996-2721 *SIC* 3669 3648

▲ **ESCO TECHNOLOGIES INC** p 509
9900 Clayton Rd Ste A, Saint Louis MO 63124
Tel (314) 213-7200 *SIC* 3669 3569 3825

PUBLIC SAFETY EQUIPMENT INC p 1189
10986 N Warson Rd, Saint Louis MO 63114
Tel (314) 426-2700 *SIC* 3647 3669

DIGITAL MONITORING PRODUCTS INC p 439
2500 N Partnership Blvd, Springfield MO 65803
Tel (417) 831-9362 *SIC* 3669

EXX INC p 521
1350 E Flamingo Rd 689, Las Vegas NV 89119
Tel (248) 409-1070
SIC 3621 3669 3714 3944

YORK TELECOM CORP p 1637
81 Corbett Way, Eatontown NJ 07724
Tel (732) 413-6000 *SIC* 3669 3651

■ **AT&T SERVICES INC** p 123
200 S Laurel Ave, Middletown NJ 07748
Tel (732) 420-3131 *SIC* 3669

■ **HONEYWELL INC** p 705
115 Tabor Rd, Morris Plains NJ 07950
Tel (973) 455-2000
SIC 3823 3812 3669 3491 3699 3822

TYCO INTERNATIONAL MANAGEMENT CO LLC p 1496
9 Roszel Rd Ste 2, Princeton NJ 08540
Tel (609) 720-4200
SIC 3999 1711 1731 3669 3491

CRESTRON ELECTRONICS INC p 392
15 Volvo Dr, Rockleigh NJ 07647
Tel (201) 767-3400
SIC 3571 3651 1731 3663 3499 3669

▲ **NAPCO SECURITY TECHNOLOGIES INC** p 1007
333 Bayview Ave, Amityville NY 11701
Tel (631) 842-9400
SIC 3669 3699 3429 1731 7373

BOSCH SECURITY SYSTEMS INC p 202
130 Perinton Pkwy, Fairport NY 14450
Tel (585) 223-4060
SIC 3669 3699 3826 3825 3823 3625

■ **TELEPHONICS CORP** p 1435
815 Broadhollow Rd, Farmingdale NY 11735
Tel (631) 755-7000
SIC 3669 3661 3679 3812 3663

■ **L-3 COMMUNICATIONS CORP** p 834
600 3rd Ave, New York NY 10016
Tel (212) 697-1111
SIC 3812 3663 3669 3679 3769

▲ **L-3 COMMUNICATIONS HOLDINGS INC** p 835
600 3rd Ave, New York NY 10016
Tel (212) 697-1111
SIC 3663 3669 3679 3812 3769

■ **MCDOWELL RESEARCH CO INC** p 928
2000 Technology Pkwy, Newark NY 14513
Tel (315) 332-7100 *SIC* 3669

CURBELL INC p 402
7 Cobham Dr, Orchard Park NY 14127
Tel (716) 667-3377 *SIC* 5162 3669 3842

AREA WIDE PROTECTIVE INC p 106
826 Overholt Rd, Kent OH 44240
Tel (330) 644-0655 *SIC* 3669

BIRD TECHNOLOGIES GROUP INC p 185
30303 Aurora Rd, Solon OH 44139
Tel (440) 248-1200 *SIC* 3825 3669

ALSTOM SIGNALING OPERATION LLC p 61
2901 E Lake Rd Bldg 122, Erie PA 16531
Tel (800) 825-3178
SIC 3669 5088 3672 3663

BERWIND CORP p 176
3000 Ctr Sq W 1500 Mkt St 1500 W, Philadelphia PA 19102
Tel (215) 563-2800
SIC 6519 5052 4789 3625 3669 2899

ANSALDO STS USA INC p 93
1000 Technology Dr, Pittsburgh PA 15219
Tel (412) 688-2400 *SIC* 3669

■ **KIDDE FIRE PROTECTION INC** p 817
350 E Union St, West Chester PA 19382
Tel (610) 363-1400 *SIC* 3669 3999 3823

DRS TECHNOLOGIES INC p 457
2345 Crystal Dr Ste 1000, Arlington VA 22202
Tel (973) 898-1500
SIC 3812 3699 3572 3669 3679 8741

EXELIS INC p 518
2235 Monroe St, Herndon VA 20171
Tel (703) 790-6300 *SIC* 3669 3823 3812

CORNET TECHNOLOGY INC p 371
6800 Versar Ctr, Springfield VA 22151
Tel (703) 658-3400 *SIC* 5065 3669 3577

BROAN-NUTONE LLC p 216
926 W State St, Hartford WI 53027
Tel (262) 673-4340
SIC 3634 3699 3635 3639 2514 3669

CARNES CO INC p 258
600 College Ave, Pewaukee WI 53072
Tel (262) 691-9900
SIC 3822 3444 3585 3669

SIC 3671 Radio & T V Receiving Electron Tubes

LEEMAH CORP p 852
155 S Hill Dr, Brisbane CA 94005
Tel (415) 394-1288
SIC 3671 3672 3669 3663 3577

■ **CERADYNE INC** p 283
1922 Barranca Pkwy, Irvine CA 92606
Tel (714) 549-0421 *SIC* 3299 3671

DCX-CHOL ENTERPRISES INC p 419
12831 S Figueroa St, Los Angeles CA 90061
Tel (310) 516-1692 *SIC* 3671

COMMUNICATIONS & POWER INDUSTRIES LLC p 347
607 Hansen Way, Palo Alto CA 94304
Tel (650) 846-2900
SIC 3671 3679 3699 3663

CPI INTERNATIONAL INC p 387
811 Hansen Way, Palo Alto CA 94304
Tel (650) 846-2801
SIC 3671 3679 3699 3825

SONY ELECTRONICS INC p 1341
16535 Via Esprillo Bldg 1, San Diego CA 92127
Tel (858) 942-2400
SIC 3651 5084 3695 3671 3572 3674

■ **L-3 COMMUNICATIONS ELECTRON TECHNOLOGIES INC** p 834
3100 Lomita Blvd, Torrance CA 90505
Tel (310) 517-6000 *SIC* 3671 3764

■ **INTERMOUNTAIN ELECTRIC INC** p 753
5050 Osage St Ste 500, Denver CO 80221
Tel (303) 733-7248 *SIC* 1542 8742 3671

WHELEN ENGINEERING CO INC p 1605
51 Winthrop Rd, Chester CT 06412
Tel (860) 526-9504
SIC 3647 3646 3671 3651 3648 3641

▲ **RICHARDSON ELECTRONICS LTD** p 1232
40w267 Keslinger Rd, Lafox IL 60147
Tel (630) 208-2316 *SIC* 5065 7373 3671

ZENITH ELECTRONICS CORP p 1642
2000 Millbrook Dr, Lincolnshire IL 60069
Tel (847) 941-8000
SIC 3651 3671 3663 3674 2517 2519

MPD INC p 995
316 E 9th St, Owensboro KY 42303
Tel (270) 685-6200
SIC 3671 3829 3812 3663 3643 3053

■ **VECTRON INTERNATIONAL INC** p 1546
267 Lowell Rd Ste B, Hudson NH 03051
Tel (603) 598-0070 *SIC* 3671

EPCOS INC p 504
485b Route 1 S Ste 200, Iselin NJ 08830
Tel (732) 906-4300
SIC 3679 3546 5065 3671

PETRA SYSTEMS INC p 1139
1 Cragwood Rd Ste 303, South Plainfield NJ 07080
Tel (908) 462-5200 *SIC* 5074 3671

SIC 3672 Printed Circuit Boards

MID-SOUTH INDUSTRIES INC p 963
2620 E Meighan Blvd, Gadsden AL 35903
Tel (256) 492-8997
SIC 3672 3089 3824 3714

ABACO SYSTEMS INC p 9
12090 S Memorial Pkwy, Huntsville AL 35803
Tel (256) 382-8200 *SIC* 3571 3672 3577

■ **SCI TECHNOLOGY INC** p 1292
13000 Memorial Pkwy Sw, Huntsville AL 35803
Tel (256) 882-4800
SIC 3672 3829 8711 3663

SOUTH BAY CIRCUITS INC p 1342
99 N Mckemy Ave, Chandler AZ 85226
Tel (480) 940-3125 *SIC* 3672

TOOH DINEH INDUSTRIES INC p 1460
Leupp School Rd Bldg 4, Leupp AZ 86035
Tel (928) 686-6477 *SIC* 3679 3672

■ **BENCHMARK ELECTRONICS PHOENIX INC** p 172
2222 W Pinnacle Pk Rd # 310, Phoenix AZ 85027
Tel (619) 397-2400 *SIC* 3577 3672

■ **SMART ELECTRONICS AND ASSEMBLY INC** p 1332
2000 W Corporate Way, Anaheim CA 92801
Tel (714) 772-2651 *SIC* 3672

LEEMAH CORP p 852
155 S Hill Dr, Brisbane CA 94005
Tel (415) 394-1288
SIC 3671 3672 3669 3663 3577

ONCORE MANUFACTURING LLC p 1086
9340 Owensmouth Ave, Chatsworth CA 91311
Tel (818) 734-6500 *SIC* 3672 8711

ONCORE MANUFACTURING SERVICES INC p 1086
9340 Owensmouth Ave, Chatsworth CA 91311
Tel (510) 360-2222 *SIC* 3672

▲ **TTM TECHNOLOGIES INC** p 1490
1665 Scenic Ave Ste 250, Costa Mesa CA 92626
Tel (714) 327-3000 *SIC* 3672

ASTEELFLASH USA CORP p 122
4211 Starboard Dr, Fremont CA 94538
Tel (510) 440-2840 *SIC* 3672 3679

SONIC MANUFACTURING TECHNOLOGIES INC p 1340
47951 Westinghouse Dr, Fremont CA 94539
Tel (510) 580-8500 *SIC* 3672

■ **OSI OPTOELECTRONICS INC** p 1096
12525 Chadron Ave, Hawthorne CA 90250
Tel (310) 978-0516
SIC 3674 3827 3812 3672

MULTI-FINELINE ELECTRONIX INC p 999
8659 Research Dr, Irvine CA 92618
Tel (949) 453-6800 *SIC* 3672

PALPILOT INTERNATIONAL CORP p 1110
500 Yosemite Dr, Milpitas CA 95035
Tel (408) 855-8866 *SIC* 3672 3089

■ **BENCHMARK ELECTRONICS MANUFACTURING SOLUTIONS INC** p 172
5550 Hellyer Ave, San Jose CA 95138
Tel (408) 754-9800 *SIC* 3672

DIAMOND MULTIMEDIA SYSTEMS INC p 437
2880 Junction Ave, San Jose CA 95134
Tel (408) 868-9613 *SIC* 3672 3577 3661

FLEXTRONICS AMERICA LLC p 556
6201 America Center Dr, San Jose CA 95002
Tel (408) 576-7000 *SIC* 3672

FLEXTRONICS HOLDING USA INC p 556
2090 Fortune Dr, San Jose CA 95131
Tel (408) 576-7000
SIC 3672 3679 7371 3825

FLEXTRONICS INTERNATIONAL USA INC p 556
6201 America Center Dr, San Jose CA 95002
Tel (408) 576-7000 *SIC* 3672

▲ **SANMINA CORP** p 1280
2700 N 1st St, San Jose CA 95134
Tel (408) 964-3500 *SIC* 3672 3674

SMTC MANUFACTURING CORP OF CALIFORNIA p 1335
2302 Trade Zone Blvd, San Jose CA 95131
Tel (408) 934-7100 *SIC* 3672

▲ **XILINX INC** p 1631
2100 Logic Dr, San Jose CA 95124
Tel (408) 559-7778 *SIC* 3672 3674 7372

EXPRESS MANUFACTURING INC p 520
3519 W Warner Ave, Santa Ana CA 92704
Tel (714) 979-2228 *SIC* 3672 3679

■ **TTM PRINTED CIRCUIT GROUP INC** p 1490
2630 S Harbor Blvd, Santa Ana CA 92704
Tel (714) 327-3000 *SIC* 3672

■ **HADCO SANTA CLARA INC** p 652
500 El Camino Real, Santa Clara CA 95050
Tel (408) 241-9900 *SIC* 3672 3679

■ **ADVANCED CIRCUITS INC** p 25
21101 E 32nd Pkwy, Aurora CO 80011
Tel (303) 576-6610 *SIC* 3672

THAYER-BLUM FUNDING III LLC p 1446
1455 Penn Ave Nw Ste 350, Washington DC 20004
Tel (202) 371-0150 *SIC* 6722 3672 3577

M C TEST SERVICE INC p 889
425 North Dr, Melbourne FL 32934
Tel (321) 956-3052 *SIC* 3672 8734

MC ASSEMBLY HOLDINGS INC p 925
425 North Dr, Melbourne FL 32934
Tel (321) 253-0541 *SIC* 8734 3672

▲ **JABIL CIRCUIT INC** p 773
10560 Dr Martin Luther, Saint Petersburg FL 33716
Tel (727) 577-9749 *SIC* 3672

■ **JABIL CIRCUIT LLC** p 773
10560 Dr Martin, Saint Petersburg FL 33716
Tel (727) 577-9749 *SIC* 3672

■ **SYPRIS ELECTRONICS LLC** p 1416
10421 Univ Ctr Dr Ste 100, Tampa FL 33612
Tel (813) 972-6000 *SIC* 3672 3679

AVG ADVANCED TECHNOLOGIES LP p 137
343 Saint Paul Blvd, Carol Stream IL 60188
Tel (630) 668-3900
SIC 3672 3661 3824 3822 3625

▲ **METHODE ELECTRONICS INC** p 953
7401 W Wilson Ave, Chicago IL 60706
Tel (708) 867-6777
SIC 3678 3674 3676 3672 3825 3643

▲ **SIGMATRON INTERNATIONAL INC** p 1321
2201 Landmeier Rd, Elk Grove Village IL 60007
Tel (847) 956-8000
SIC 3672 3677 3679 3549 3825

BASLER ELECTRIC CO p 159
12570 State Route 143, Highland IL 62249
Tel (618) 654-2341 *SIC* 3679 3612 3672

▲ **SPARTON CORP** p 1355
425 N Martingale Rd, Schaumburg IL 60173
Tel (847) 762-5800 *SIC* 3674 3672

▲ **KIMBALL ELECTRONICS INC** p 818
1205 Kimball Blvd, Jasper IN 47546
Tel (812) 634-4000 *SIC* 3672

■ **KIMBALL ELECTRONICS TAMPA INC** p 818
1205 Kimball Blvd, Jasper IN 47546
Tel (812) 634-4000 *SIC* 3679 3672

CAL-COMP USA (INDIANA) INC p 237
1 Technology Way, Logansport IN 46947
Tel (574) 739-2929 *SIC* 3672

■ **CDR MANUFACTURING INC** p 271
10200 Forest Green Blvd, Louisville KY 40223
Tel (502) 625-0760 *SIC* 3679 3672 3699

▲ **SYPRIS SOLUTIONS INC** p 1416
101 Bullitt Ln Ste 450, Louisville KY 40222
Tel (502) 329-2000
SIC 3672 3679 3812 3674 3462

■ **WABTEC RAILWAY ELECTRONICS INC** p 1570
21200 Dorsey Mill Rd, Germantown MD 20876
Tel (301) 515-2000
SIC 3825 3679 3743 3672

▲ **CHASE CORP** p 291
26 Summer St, Bridgewater MA 02324
Tel (508) 819-4200 *SIC* 3644 3479 3672

▲ **MERCURY SYSTEMS INC** p 945
201 Riverneck Rd, Chelmsford MA 01824
Tel (978) 256-1300 *SIC* 3672 7372

■ **LOCKHEED MARTIN SIPPICAN INC** p 873
7 Barnabas Rd, Marion MA 02738
Tel (508) 748-3399
SIC 3812 3826 3499 3672 3829 3845

TECH-ETCH INC p 1431
45 Aldrin Rd, Plymouth MA 02360
Tel (508) 747-0300 *SIC* 3469 3672 3479

MAGNA ELECTRONICS INC p 896
10410 N Holly Rd, Holly MI 48442
Tel (810) 606-0444 SIC 3672 3679

LOGIC PD INC p 874
6201 Bury Dr, Eden Prairie MN 55346
Tel (952) 646-1191 SIC 3672 8711

MINCO PRODUCTS INC p 972
7300 Commerce Ln Ne, Minneapolis MN 55432
Tel (763) 571-3121 SIC 3672 3823 3829

MULTEK FLEXIBLE CIRCUITS INC p 999
1150 Sheldahl Rd, Northfield MN 55057
Tel (507) 663-8000 SIC 3672

■ VIASYSTEMS GROUP INC p 1554
101 S Hanley Rd Ste 400, Saint Louis MO 63105
Tel (314) 727-2087 SIC 3672 3694

■ VIASYSTEMS INC p 1554
520 Maryville Centre Dr # 400, Saint Louis MO 63141
Tel (314) 727-2087 SIC 3672

■ AMPHENOL PRINTED CIRCUITS INC p 86
91 Northeastern Blvd, Nashua NH 03062
Tel (603) 324-4500
SIC 3679 3678 3672 3357

■ HADCO CORP p 652
12a Manor Pkwy, Salem NH 03079
Tel (603) 421-3400 SIC 3672

TRANSISTOR DEVICES INC p 1471
36 Newburgh Rd, Hackettstown NJ 07840
Tel (908) 850-1595
SIC 3612 3625 3672 3812 3829

I3 ELECTRONICS INC p 725
100 Eldredge St, Binghamton NY 13901
Tel (607) 238-7077 SIC 3672

■ AMERICAN TECHNICAL CERAMICS CORP p 80
1 Norden Ln, Huntington Station NY 11746
Tel (631) 622-4700 SIC 3672 3675

▲ PARK ELECTROCHEMICAL CORP p 1115
48 S Service Rd Ste 300, Melville NY 11747
Tel (631) 465-3600 SIC 3672 3674

▲ IEC ELECTRONICS CORP p 730
105 Norton St, Newark NY 14513
Tel (315) 331-7742 SIC 3672 3679

ANSEN CORP p 93
100 Chimney Point Dr, Ogdensburg NY 13669
Tel (315) 393-3573 SIC 3672

▲ CREE INC p 391
4600 Silicon Dr, Durham NC 27703
Tel (919) 407-5300 SIC 3674 3672

STACI CORP p 1374
110 Commerce Dr, Lagrange OH 44050
Tel (440) 355-5102 SIC 3672

VANGUARD EMS INC p 1543
3725 Sw Hocken Ave, Beaverton OR 97005
Tel (503) 644-4808 SIC 3672 3679

ALSTOM SIGNALING OPERATION LLC p 61
2901 E Lake Rd Bldg 122, Erie PA 16531
Tel (800) 825-3178
SIC 3669 5088 3672 3663

DRS LAUREL TECHNOLOGIES p 457
246 Airport Rd, Johnstown PA 15904
Tel (814) 534-8900 SIC 3672 3315

SPANG & CO p 1354
110 Delta Dr, Pittsburgh PA 15238
Tel (412) 963-9363
SIC 3672 3944 3612 3613 3312

PRIMUS TECHNOLOGIES CORP p 1176
2333 Reach Rd, Williamsport PA 17701
Tel (570) 326-6591 SIC 3672

HOLIEN INC p 700
312 9th Ave Se Ste B, Watertown SD 57201
Tel (605) 886-3889 SIC 3612 3672 3993

▲ BENCHMARK ELECTRONICS INC p 172
3000 Technology Rd, Angleton TX 77515
Tel (979) 849-6550 SIC 3672 3679

VG HOLDINGS LLC p 1553
200 Crescent Ct Ste 1600, Dallas TX 75201
Tel (314) 727-2087 SIC 3672

HUNTING INNOVA INC p 719
8383 N Sam Houston Pkwy W, Houston TX 77064
Tel (281) 653-5500 SIC 3672 3613 8711

AM-MEX PRODUCTS INC p 63
3801 W Military Hwy, Mcallen TX 78503
Tel (956) 631-7916 SIC 3714 7361 3672

CREATION TECHNOLOGIES KENTUCKY INC p 390
1001 Klein Rd Ste 100, Plano TX 75074
Tel (859) 253-3066 SIC 3679 3672

ELECTRONIC WARFARE ASSOCIATES INC p 486
13873 Park Center Rd # 500, Herndon VA 20171
Tel (703) 904-5700
SIC 7373 7374 3672 3699 3643 3441

■ VIASYSTEMS NORTH AMERICA INC p 1554
1200 Severn Way, Sterling VA 20166
Tel (703) 450-2600 SIC 3672

APPLIED TECHNICAL SERVICES CORP p 100
6300 Merrill Creek Pkwy A100, Everett WA 98203
Tel (425) 249-5555 SIC 3672

TEKNETIX INC p 1433
2501 Garfield Ave, Parkersburg WV 26101
Tel (304) 489-3600 SIC 3672 7371

■ TTM ADVANCED CIRCUITS INC p 1490
234 Cashman Dr, Chippewa Falls WI 54729
Tel (715) 720-5000 SIC 3672 3674

■ ELECTRONIC ASSEMBLY CORP p 485
55 Jewelers Park Dr, Neenah WI 54956
Tel (920) 722-3451
SIC 3672 3679 3825 3841

▲ PLEXUS CORP p 1156
1 Plexus Way, Neenah WI 54956
Tel (920) 969-6000 SIC 3672 3825

CREATION TECHNOLOGIES WISCONSIN INC p 390
2250 W South Branch Blvd, Oak Creek WI 53154
Tel (414) 761-0400 SIC 3672

SIC 3674 Semiconductors

■ MICREL LLC p 961
2355 W Chandler Blvd, Chandler AZ 85224
Tel (480) 792-7200 SIC 3674

▲ MICROCHIP TECHNOLOGY INC p 962
2355 W Chandler Blvd, Chandler AZ 85224
Tel (480) 792-7200 SIC 3674

▲ ON SEMICONDUCTOR CORP p 1086
5005 E Mcdowell Rd, Phoenix AZ 85008
Tel (602) 244-6600 SIC 3674 3825 3651

■ SEMICONDUCTOR COMPONENTS INDUSTRIES LLC p 1302
5005 E Mcdowell Rd, Phoenix AZ 85008
Tel (602) 244-6600 SIC 3674 3823

SUMCO PHOENIX CORP p 1397
19801 N Tatum Blvd, Phoenix AZ 85050
Tel (480) 473-6000 SIC 3674

SUMCO SOUTHWEST CORP p 1397
19801 N Tatum Blvd, Phoenix AZ 85050
Tel (480) 473-6000 SIC 3674

▲ AMKOR TECHNOLOGY INC p 85
2045 E Innovation Cir, Tempe AZ 85284
Tel (480) 821-5000 SIC 3674 3825

▲ FIRST SOLAR INC p 549
350 W Washington St # 600, Tempe AZ 85281
Tel (602) 414-9300 SIC 3674 3433

MOTOROLA SATELLITE COMMUNICATIONS INC p 993
2900 S Diablo Way, Tempe AZ 85282
Tel (480) 732-2000 SIC 3674

▲ EMCORE CORP p 491
2015 Chestnut St, Alhambra CA 91803
Tel (626) 293-3400 SIC 3674 3559

■ CNT ACQUISITION CORP p 330
1 Enterprise, Aliso Viejo CA 92656
Tel (949) 380-6100 SIC 3674

▲ MICROSEMI CORP p 962
1 Enterprise, Aliso Viejo CA 92656
Tel (949) 380-6100 SIC 3674

■ QLOGIC CORP p 1195
26650 Aliso Viejo Pkwy, Aliso Viejo CA 92656
Tel (949) 389-6000 SIC 3674

▲ SEMTECH CORP p 1303
200 Flynn Rd, Camarillo CA 93012
Tel (805) 498-2111 SIC 3674

■ ENTROPIC COMMUNICATIONS LLC p 503
5966 La Place Ct Ste 100, Carlsbad CA 92008
Tel (858) 768-3600 SIC 3674 7372

▲ MAXLINEAR INC p 922
5966 La Place Ct Ste 100, Carlsbad CA 92008
Tel (760) 692-0711 SIC 3674

▲ MRV COMMUNICATIONS INC p 996
20520 Nordhoff St, Chatsworth CA 91311
Tel (818) 773-0900 SIC 3674

NATEL ENGINEERING CO INC p 1009
9340 Owensmouth Ave, Chatsworth CA 91311
Tel (818) 734-6523 SIC 3674 3679

INFINEON TECHNOLOGIES AMERICAS CORP p 740
101 N Sepulveda Blvd, El Segundo CA 90245
Tel (310) 726-8000 SIC 3674

KINGSTON TECHNOLOGY CORP p 821
17600 Newhope St, Fountain Valley CA 92708
Tel (714) 445-3495 SIC 3674

■ ASYST TECHNOLOGIES INC p 123
46897 Bayside Pkwy, Fremont CA 94538
Tel (408) 329-6661 SIC 3674

▲ AXT INC p 140
4281 Technology Dr, Fremont CA 94538
Tel (510) 438-4700 SIC 3674

▲ EXAR CORP p 516
48720 Kato Rd, Fremont CA 94538
Tel (510) 668-7000 SIC 3674

▲ LAM RESEARCH CORP p 841
4650 Cushing Pkwy, Fremont CA 94538
Tel (510) 572-0200 SIC 3674

▲ QUANTENNA COMMUNICATIONS INC p 1198
3450 W Warren Ave, Fremont CA 94538
Tel (510) 743-2260 SIC 3674

▲ SIGMA DESIGNS INC p 1321
47467 Fremont Blvd, Fremont CA 94538
Tel (510) 897-0200 SIC 3674

UNIGEN CORP p 1503
45388 Warm Springs Blvd, Fremont CA 94539
Tel (510) 668-2088 SIC 3674 3572

■ MICROSEMI CORP - ANALOG MIXED SIGNAL GROUP p 962
11861 Western Ave, Garden Grove CA 92841
Tel (714) 898-8121 SIC 3674

■ OSI OPTOELECTRONICS INC p 1096
12525 Chadron Ave, Hawthorne CA 90250
Tel (310) 978-0516
SIC 3674 3827 3812 3672

▲ OSI SYSTEMS INC p 1097
12525 Chadron Ave, Hawthorne CA 90250
Tel (310) 978-0516 SIC 3674 3845

▲ ULTRA CLEAN HOLDINGS INC p 1501
26462 Corporate Ave, Hayward CA 94545
Tel (510) 576-4400 SIC 3674

BROADCOM CORP p 215
5300 California Ave, Irvine CA 92617
Tel (949) 926-5000 SIC 3674

TOSHIBA AMERICA ELECTRONIC COMPONENTS INC p 1462
9740 Irvine Blvd Ste D700, Irvine CA 92618
Tel (949) 462-7700
SIC 3651 3631 3674 3679 5065 5064

▲ FORMFACTOR INC p 567
7005 Southfront Rd, Livermore CA 94551
Tel (925) 290-4000 SIC 3674

▲ DSP GROUP INC p 458
161 S San Antonio Rd # 10, Los Altos CA 94022
Tel (408) 986-4300 SIC 3674 7371

CREATIVE HOLDINGS INC p 390
1901 Mccarthy Blvd, Milpitas CA 95035
Tel (408) 428-6600
SIC 5045 3577 3931 3674 8711 3651

INFINEON TECHNOLOGIES NORTH AMERICA CORP p 740
640 N Mccarthy Blvd, Milpitas CA 95035
Tel (866) 951-9519 SIC 3674

INFINEON TECHNOLOGIES US HOLDCO INC p 740
640 N Mccarthy Blvd, Milpitas CA 95035
Tel (408) 956-8960 SIC 3674

INTEGRATED SILICON SOLUTION INC p 749
1623 Buckeye Dr, Milpitas CA 95035
Tel (408) 969-6600 SIC 3674

■ INTERSIL COMMUNICATIONS LLC p 757
1001 Murphy Ranch Rd, Milpitas CA 95035
Tel (408) 432-8888 SIC 3674

▲ INTERSIL CORP p 758
1001 Murphy Ranch Rd, Milpitas CA 95035
Tel (408) 432-8888 SIC 3674 3679

▲ IXYS CORP p 769
1590 Buckeye Dr, Milpitas CA 95035
Tel (408) 457-9000 SIC 3674

▲ LINEAR TECHNOLOGY CORP p 869
1630 Mccarthy Blvd, Milpitas CA 95035
Tel (408) 432-1900 SIC 3674

▲ LUMENTUM HOLDINGS INC p 885
400 N Mccarthy Blvd, Milpitas CA 95035
Tel (408) 546-5483 SIC 3669 3674 3826

■ PERICOM SEMICONDUCTOR CORP p 1136
1545 Barber Ln, Milpitas CA 95035
Tel (408) 232-9100 SIC 3674 3825

▲ VIAVI SOLUTIONS INC p 1554
430 N Mccarthy Blvd, Milpitas CA 95035
Tel (408) 404-3600 SIC 3674 3826

■ XICOR LLC p 1631
1001 Murphy Ranch Rd, Milpitas CA 95035
Tel (408) 432-8888 SIC 3674

■ AUDIENCE INC p 130
331 Fairchild Dr, Mountain View CA 94043
Tel (650) 254-2800 SIC 3674

SMART MODULAR TECHNOLOGIES (WWH) INC p 1332
39870 Eureka Dr, Newark CA 94560
Tel (510) 623-1231 SIC 3674 3577 3679

WINTEC INDUSTRIES INC p 1617
8674 Thornton Ave, Newark CA 94560
Tel (408) 856-0500 SIC 3577 3674 3572

JAZZ SEMICONDUCTOR INC p 779
4321 Jamboree Rd, Newport Beach CA 92660
Tel (949) 435-8000 SIC 3674

■ MINDSPEED TECHNOLOGIES INC p 972
4000 Macarthur Blvd, Newport Beach CA 92660
Tel (949) 579-3000 SIC 3674

TOWER US HOLDINGS INC p 1464
4321 Jamboree Rd, Newport Beach CA 92660
Tel (949) 435-8000 SIC 3674

▲ ENPHASE ENERGY INC p 500
1420 N Mcdowell Blvd, Petaluma CA 94954
Tel (707) 774-7000 SIC 3674

■ DELTA DESIGN INC p 426
12367 Crosthwaite Cir, Poway CA 92064
Tel (858) 848-8000 SIC 3569 3825 3674

■ ORACLE AMERICA INC p 1091
500 Oracle Pkwy, Redwood City CA 94065
Tel (650) 506-7000
SIC 3571 7379 7373 7372 3674

▲ ORACLE CORP p 1091
500 Oracle Pkwy, Redwood City CA 94065
Tel (650) 506-7000
SIC 7372 7379 8243 3571 3674

CRYDOM INC p 396
2320 Paseo Delas Amer 2 Ste 201, San Diego CA 92154
Tel (619) 210-1600
SIC 3625 5065 3674 3643

KYOCERA AMERICA INC p 833
8611 Balboa Ave, San Diego CA 92123
Tel (858) 576-2600 SIC 3674

PEREGRINE SEMICONDUCTOR CORP p 1134
9380 Carroll Park Dr, San Diego CA 92121
Tel (858) 731-9400 SIC 3674

PULSE ELECTRONICS INC p 1191
12220 World Trade Dr, San Diego CA 92128
Tel (858) 674-8100 SIC 3612 3674 3677

▲ QUALCOMM INC p 1196
5775 Morehouse Dr, San Diego CA 92121
Tel (858) 587-1121 SIC 3674 7372 6794

■ QUALCOMM TECHNOLOGIES INC p 1196
5775 Morehouse Dr, San Diego CA 92121
Tel (858) 587-1121 SIC 3674 7372 6794

SONY ELECTRONICS INC p 1341
16535 Via Esprillo Bldg 1, San Diego CA 92127
Tel (858) 942-2400
SIC 3651 5064 3695 3671 3572 3674

▲ SUNRUN INC p 1404
595 Market St Fl 29, San Francisco CA 94105
Tel (415) 580-6900 SIC 3674

■ ALTERA CORP p 62
101 Innovation Dr, San Jose CA 95134
Tel (408) 544-7000 SIC 3674 7371

ARM INC p 110
150 Rose Orchard Way, San Jose CA 95134
Tel (408) 576-1500 SIC 3674

■ ATMEL CORP p 128
1600 Technology Dr, San Jose CA 95110
Tel (408) 441-0311 SIC 3674 3714 3545

AVAGO TECHNOLOGIES US INC p 135
1320 Ridder Park Dr, San Jose CA 95131
Tel (800) 433-8778 SIC 3674

BROADCOM LIMITED p 215
1320 Ridder Park Dr, San Jose CA 95131
Tel (408) 433-8000 SIC 3674

▲ CAVIUM INC p 267
2315 N 1st St, San Jose CA 95131
Tel (408) 943-7100 SIC 3674

CM MANUFACTURING INC p 328
6321 San Ignacio Ave, San Jose CA 95119
Tel (408) 284-7200 SIC 3674

■ CSR TECHNOLOGY INC p 398
1060 Rincon Cir, San Jose CA 95131
Tel (408) 523-6500 SIC 3679 3812 3674

▲ CYPRESS SEMICONDUCTOR CORP p 405
5883 Rue Ferrari Ste 100, San Jose CA 95138
Tel (408) 943-2600 SIC 3674

▲ INTEGRATED DEVICE TECHNOLOGY INC p 749
6024 Silver Creek Vly Rd, San Jose CA 95138
Tel (408) 284-8200 SIC 3674

KSM CORP p 831
1959 Concourse Dr, San Jose CA 95131
Tel (408) 514-2400 SIC 3674

LSI CORP p 883
1320 Ridder Park Dr, San Jose CA 95131
Tel (408) 433-8000 SIC 3674

▲ MAXIM INTEGRATED PRODUCTS INC p 922
160 Rio Robles, San Jose CA 95134
Tel (408) 601-1000 SIC 3674

MICREL INC p 961
2180 Fortune Dr, San Jose CA 95131
Tel (408) 944-0800 SIC 3674

■ MICROSEMI SOC CORP p 962
3870 N 1st St, San Jose CA 95134
Tel (408) 643-6000 SIC 3674 7371

▲ MONOLITHIC POWER SYSTEMS INC p 984
79 Great Oaks Blvd, San Jose CA 95119
Tel (408) 826-0600 SIC 3674 8711

■ MPS INTERNATIONAL LTD p 996
79 Great Oaks Blvd, San Jose CA 95119
Tel (408) 826-0660 SIC 3674

▲ NEOPHOTONICS CORP p 1026
2911 Zanker Rd, San Jose CA 95134
Tel (408) 232-9200 SIC 3674

NXP SEMICONDUCTORS USA INC p 1068
411 E Plumeria Dr, San Jose CA 95134
Tel (408) 518-5500 SIC 3674

▲ OCLARO INC p 1074
225 Charcot Ave, San Jose CA 95131
Tel (408) 383-1400 SIC 3674 3826 3827

▲ POWER INTEGRATIONS INC p 1165
5245 Hellyer Ave, San Jose CA 95138
Tel (408) 414-9200 SIC 3674

■ QUALCOMM ATHEROS INC p 1196
1700 Technology Dr, San Jose CA 95110
Tel (408) 773-5200 SIC 3674 4899

▲ SANMINA CORP p 1280
2700 N 1st St, San Jose CA 95134
Tel (408) 964-3500 SIC 3672 3674

■ SILICON IMAGE INC p 1323
2115 Onel Dr, San Jose CA 95131
Tel (408) 616-4000 SIC 3674 7371

■ SPANSION INC p 1354
198 Champion Ct, San Jose CA 95134
Tel (408) 962-2500 SIC 3674

STION CORP p 1390
6321 San Ignacio Ave, San Jose CA 95119
Tel (408) 284-7200 SIC 3674

SUMCO USA SALES CORP p 1398
2099 Gateway Pl Ste 400, San Jose CA 95110
Tel (408) 352-3880 SIC 3674

■ SUNPOWER CORP p 1403
77 Rio Robles, San Jose CA 95134
Tel (408) 240-5550 SIC 3674 3679

▲ TESSERA HOLDING CORP p 1441
3025 Orchard Pkwy, San Jose CA 95134
Tel (408) 321-6000 SIC 3674

■ TESSERA TECHNOLOGIES INC p 1441
3025 Orchard Pkwy, San Jose CA 95134
Tel (408) 321-6000 SIC 6794 3674

▲ XILINX INC p 1631
2100 Logic Dr, San Jose CA 95124
Tel (408) 559-7778 SIC 3672 3674 7372

■ ZORAN CORP p 1644
1060 Rincon Cir, San Jose CA 95131
Tel (972) 673-1600 SIC 3674

■ STEC INC p 1384
3001 Daimler St, Santa Ana CA 92705
Tel (415) 222-9996 SIC 3572 3674 3577

AMBARELLA INC p 65
3101 Jay St, Santa Clara CA 95054
Tel (408) 734-8888 SIC 3674

▲ APPLIED MATERIALS INC p 99
3050 Bowers Ave, Santa Clara CA 95054
Tel (408) 727-5555 SIC 3559 3674

▲ APPLIED MICRO CIRCUITS CORP p 100
4555 Great America Pkwy # 601, Santa Clara CA 95054
Tel (408) 542-8600 SIC 3674

▲ INPHI CORP p 745
2953 Bunker Hill Ln # 300, Santa Clara CA 95054
Tel (408) 217-7300 SIC 3674

▲ INTEL CORP p 750
2200 Mission College Blvd, Santa Clara CA 95054
Tel (408) 765-8080 SIC 3674 3577 7372

MARVELL SEMICONDUCTOR INC p 914
5488 Marvell Ln, Santa Clara CA 95054
Tel (408) 222-2500 SIC 3674

MIASOLE p 959
2590 Walsh Ave, Santa Clara CA 95051
Tel (408) 919-5700 SIC 3674

NETLOGIC MICROSYSTEMS LLC p 1027
3975 Freedom Cir Ste 900, Santa Clara CA 95054
Tel (408) 454-3000 SIC 3674

▲ NVIDIA CORP p 1068
2701 San Tomas Expy, Santa Clara CA 95050
Tel (408) 486-2000 SIC 3674

OMNIVISION TECHNOLOGIES INC p 1085
4275 Burton Dr, Santa Clara CA 95054
Tel (408) 567-3000 SIC 3674

■ SILICONIX INC p 1323
2201 Laurelwood Rd, Santa Clara CA 95054
Tel (408) 988-8000 SIC 3674

PLASTIC SERVICES AND PRODUCTS p 1155
12243 Branford St, Sun Valley CA 91352
Tel (818) 896-1101
SIC 3086 3674 2865 2816 3296 2819

PMC GLOBAL INC p 1157
12243 Branford St, Sun Valley CA 91352
Tel (818) 896-1101
SIC 3086 3674 2865 2816 3296 2819

▲ ADVANCED MICRO DEVICES INC p 26
1 Amd Pl, Sunnyvale CA 94085
Tel (408) 749-4000 SIC 3674

BLOOM ENERGY CORP p 189
1299 Orleans Dr, Sunnyvale CA 94089
Tel (408) 543-1500 SIC 3674

■ FAIRCHILD SEMICONDUCTOR INTERNATIONAL INC p 524
1272 Borregas Ave, Sunnyvale CA 94089
Tel (408) 822-2000 SIC 3674

MELLANOX TECHNOLOGIES INC p 940
350 Oakmead Pkwy, Sunnyvale CA 94085
Tel (408) 970-3400 SIC 3674

■ MICROSEMI STORAGE SOLUTIONS INC p 962
1380 Bordeaux Dr, Sunnyvale CA 94089
Tel (408) 239-8000 SIC 3674

▲ RAMBUS INC p 1207
1050 Entp Way Ste 700, Sunnyvale CA 94089
Tel (408) 462-8000 SIC 3674 6794

TRIDENT MICROSYSTEMS INC p 1479
1170 Kifer Rd, Sunnyvale CA 94086
Tel (408) 962-5000 SIC 3674

■ SPECTROLAB INC p 1357
12500 Gladstone Ave, Sylmar CA 91342
Tel (818) 365-4611 SIC 3674 3679

▲ TELEDYNE TECHNOLOGIES INC p 1434
1049 Camino Dos Rios, Thousand Oaks CA 91360
Tel (805) 373-4545
SIC 3679 3761 3519 3724 3812 3674

SEAKR ENGINEERING INC p 1296
6221 S Racine Cir, Centennial CO 80111
Tel (303) 662-1449 SIC 3674 8711

AEROFLEX COLORADO SPRINGS INC p 30
4350 Centennial Blvd, Colorado Springs CO 80907
Tel (719) 594-8000 SIC 3674

AVAGO TECHNOLOGIES WIRELESS (USA) INC p 135
4380 Ziegler Rd, Fort Collins CO 80525
Tel (970) 288-2575 SIC 3674

▲ PHOTRONICS INC p 1145
15 Secor Rd, Brookfield CT 06804
Tel (203) 775-9000 SIC 3674

■ ATMI INC p 128
7 Commerce Dr, Danbury CT 06810
Tel (952) 942-0855 SIC 3674

▲ REVOLUTION LIGHTING TECHNOLOGIES INC p 1229
177 Broad St Fl 12, Stamford CT 06901
Tel (203) 504-1111 SIC 3674 3641 3993

■ QORVO FLORIDA INC p 1195
1818 S Orange Blossom Trl, Apopka FL 32703
Tel (407) 886-8860 SIC 3674

DRS NETWORK & IMAGING SYSTEMS LLC p 457
100 N Babcock St, Melbourne FL 32935
Tel (321) 309-1500 SIC 3674

▲ HARRIS CORP p 663
1025 W Nasa Blvd, Melbourne FL 32919
Tel (321) 727-9100
SIC 3812 3663 3699 3661 3674

■ TEKTRONIX SERVICE SOLUTIONS INC p 1433
6120 Hanging Moss Rd, Orlando FL 32807
Tel (407) 678-6900
SIC 3812 3674 8734 7699

SUNIVA INC p 1402
5765 Peachtree Indus Blvd, Norcross GA 30092
Tel (404) 477-2700 SIC 3674 3433

▲ MICRON TECHNOLOGY INC p 962
8000 S Federal Way, Boise ID 83716
Tel (208) 368-4000 SIC 3674

AMI SEMICONDUCTOR INC p 85
2300 W Buckskin Rd, Pocatello ID 83201
Tel (208) 233-4690 SIC 3674 8711

▲ METHODE ELECTRONICS INC p 953
7401 W Wilson Ave, Chicago IL 60706
Tel (708) 867-6777
SIC 3678 3674 3676 3672 3825 3643

▲ DOVER CORP p 453
3005 Highland Pkwy # 200, Downers Grove IL 60515
Tel (630) 541-1540
SIC 3632 3586 3533 3577 3674

CAPSONIC AUTOMOTIVE INC p 251
460 2nd St, Elgin IL 60123
Tel (847) 888-7300 SIC 3625 3679 3674

ZENITH ELECTRONICS CORP p 1642
2000 Millbrook Dr, Lincolnshire IL 60069
Tel (847) 941-8000
SIC 3651 3671 3663 3674 2517 2519

▲ CTS CORP p 399
2375 Cabot Dr, Lisle IL 60532
Tel (630) 577-8800
SIC 3678 3829 3676 3679 3674

▲ SPARTON CORP p 1355
425 N Martingale Rd, Schaumburg IL 60173
Tel (847) 762-5800 SIC 3674 3672

■ SPARTON EMT LLC p 1355
425 N Martingale Rd Ste 2, Schaumburg IL 60173
Tel (800) 772-7866 SIC 3674

■ TOUCHSENSOR TECHNOLOGIES LLC p 1463
203 N Gables Blvd, Wheaton IL 60187
Tel (630) 221-9000 SIC 5065 3674

▲ SYPRIS SOLUTIONS INC p 1416
101 Bullitt Ln Ste 450, Louisville KY 40222
Tel (502) 329-2000
SIC 3672 3679 3812 3674 3462

■ FAIRCHILD SEMICONDUCTOR CORP p 524
82 Running Hill Rd, South Portland ME 04106
Tel (207) 775-8100 SIC 3674

PHILIPS ELECTRONICS NORTH AMERICA CORP p 1143
3000 Minuteman Rd Ms1203, Andover MA 01810
Tel (978) 687-1501
SIC 5064 3651 3674 3641 3645 5047

PHILIPS HOLDING USA INC p 1143
3000 Minuteman Rd Ste 109, Andover MA 01810
Tel (978) 687-1501
SIC 5064 3674 5045 5047 3641

▲ ENTEGRIS INC p 501
129 Concord Rd, Billerica MA 01821
Tel (978) 436-6500 SIC 3089 3081 3674

■ GE INFRASTRUCTURE SENSING INC p 596
1100 Technology Park Dr # 100, Billerica MA 01821
Tel (978) 437-1000
SIC 3823 5084 3699 3674 3663 3625

ORBOTECH INC p 1093
44 Manning Rd, Billerica MA 01821
Tel (978) 667-6037 SIC 5065 3823 3674

■ HITTITE MICROWAVE LLC p 697
2 Elizabeth Dr, Chelmsford MA 01824
Tel (978) 250-3343 SIC 3674

▲ AMERICAN SUPERCONDUCTOR CORP p 80
64 Jackson Rd, Devens MA 01434
Tel (978) 842-3000 SIC 3674 3621

■ VARIAN SEMICONDUCTOR EQUIPMENT ASSOCIATES INC p 1544
35 Dory Rd, Gloucester MA 01930
Tel (978) 282-2000 SIC 5065 3674

■ INTEL MASSACHUSETTS INC p 750
75 Reed Rd, Hudson MA 01749
Tel (978) 553-4000 SIC 3674

▲ MACOM TECHNOLOGY SOLUTIONS HOLDINGS INC p 893
100 Chelmsford St, Lowell MA 01851
Tel (978) 656-2500 SIC 3674

API TECHNOLOGIES CORP p 96
400 Nickerson Rd, Marlborough MA 01752
Tel (855) 294-3800 SIC 3674

RF1 HOLDING CO p 1231
400 Nickerson Rd, Marlborough MA 01752
Tel (855) 294-3800 SIC 3674 6719

▲ ACACIA COMMUNICATIONS INC p 13
3 Mill And Main Pl # 400, Maynard MA 01754
Tel (978) 938-4896 SIC 3674 8999

▲ TERADYNE INC p 1439
600 Riverpark Dr, North Reading MA 01864
Tel (978) 370-2700 SIC 3825 3643 3674

▲ ANALOG DEVICES INC p 88
1 Technology Way, Norwood MA 02062
Tel (781) 329-4700 SIC 3674

▲ IPG PHOTONICS CORP p 763
50 Old Webster Rd, Oxford MA 01540
Tel (508) 373-1100 SIC 3699 3229 3674

SPECTRIS INC p 1357
117 Flanders Rd, Westborough MA 01581
Tel (508) 768-6400
SIC 3674 3829 3826 3821

▲ SKYWORKS SOLUTIONS INC p 1330
20 Sylvan Rd, Woburn MA 01801
Tel (781) 376-3000 SIC 3674

ALLEGRO MICROSYSTEMS LLC p 53
115 Ne Cutoff, Worcester MA 01606
Tel (508) 853-5000 SIC 3674

UNITED SOLAR OVONIC LLC p 1511
3800 Lapeer Rd, Auburn Hills MI 48326
Tel (248) 475-0100 SIC 3674

ELECTRO-MATIC VENTURES INC p 485
23409 Industrial Park Ct, Farmington Hills MI 48335
Tel (248) 478-1182 SIC 5063 3674

EP MANAGEMENT CORP p 504
801 W Ann Arbor Trl # 220, Plymouth MI 48170
Tel (313) 749-5500
SIC 3692 3661 2834 3674 3691

JOHNSON ELECTRIC NORTH AMERICA INC p 791
47660 Halyard Dr, Plymouth MI 48170
Tel (734) 392-5300
SIC 5063 3625 3674 8711

■ FEDERAL-MOGUL CORP p 536
27300 W 11 Mile Rd, Southfield MI 48034
Tel (248) 354-7700
SIC 3559 3462 3812 3674 3694

■ FEDERAL-MOGUL HOLDINGS CORP p 536
27300 W 11 Mile Rd, Southfield MI 48034
Tel (248) 354-7700
SIC 3462 3559 3694 3812 3674 3714

KEY SAFETY RESTRAINT SYSTEMS INC p 814
7000 19 Mile Rd, Sterling Heights MI 48314
Tel (586) 726-3800 SIC 3714 3674 3679

ENERGY CONVERSION DEVICES INC p 497
1441 E Maple Rd Ste 301, Troy MI 48083
Tel (248) 293-8772 SIC 3674

■ CYPRESS SEMICONDUCTOR (MINNESOTA) INC p 405
2401 E 86th St, Bloomington MN 55425
Tel (952) 851-5200 SIC 3674

POLAR SEMICONDUCTOR LLC p 1159
2800 E Old Shakopee Rd, Bloomington MN 55425
Tel (952) 876-3000 SIC 3674

▲ NORTECH SYSTEMS INC p 1049
7550 Meridian Cir N # 150, Maple Grove MN 55369
Tel (952) 345-2244 SIC 3674 3679

BANNER ENGINEERING CORP p 153
9714 10th Ave N, Minneapolis MN 55441
Tel (763) 544-3164 SIC 3674

▲ SUNEDISON INC p 1402
13736 Rverport Dr Ste 180, Maryland Heights MO 63043
Tel (314) 770-7300 SIC 3674

■ SUN EDISON p 1400
501 Pearl Dr, Saint Peters MO 63376
Tel (636) 474-5000 SIC 3674

VAOPTO LLC p 1544
5178 W Patrick Ln, Las Vegas NV 89118
Tel (702) 979-3582 SIC 3674

GT ADVANCED TECHNOLOGIES INC p 644
243 Daniel Webster Hwy, Merrimack NH 03054
Tel (603) 883-5200 SIC 3674

GTAT CORP p 644
243 Daniel Webster Hwy, Merrimack NH 03054
Tel (603) 883-5200 SIC 3674 3567

KEYENCE CORP OF AMERICA p 815
669 River Dr Ste 403, Elmwood Park NJ 07407
Tel (201) 930-0100 SIC 3825 5084 3674

▲ UNIVERSAL DISPLAY CORP p 1516
375 Phillips Blvd Ste 1, Ewing NJ 08618
Tel (609) 671-0980 SIC 3674

■ AUTOMATIC SWITCH CO p 134
50-60 Hanover Rd, Florham Park NJ 07932
Tel (973) 966-2000
SIC 3491 3625 3677 3674 3613 3492

▲ BEL FUSE INC p 169
206 Van Vorst St, Jersey City NJ 07302
Tel (201) 432-0463
SIC 3679 3674 3613 3677

SHARP ELECTRONICS CORP p 1312
1 Sharp Plz Ste 1, Mahwah NJ 07495
Tel (201) 529-8200
SIC 5044 5064 3651 3631 3861 3674

ALCATEL-LUCENT USA INC p 47
600 Mountain Ave Ste 700, New Providence NJ 07974
Tel (908) 582-3275 SIC 7372 3674

DIALIGHT CORP p 436
1501 State Route 34, Wall Township NJ 07727
Tel (732) 919-3119 SIC 3679 3674

ROXBORO HOLDINGS INC p 1254
1501 State Route 34, Wall Township NJ 07727
Tel (732) 919-3119
SIC 3643 3679 3993 3823 3674

SOLAERO TECHNOLOGIES CORP p 1338
10420 Res Rd Se Bldg 1, Albuquerque NM 87123
Tel (505) 332-5000 SIC 3679 3674

▲ INTERNATIONAL BUSINESS MACHINES CORP p 754
1 New Orchard Rd Ste 1, Armonk NY 10504
Tel (914) 499-1900
SIC 7379 7371 3571 3572 3674

■ DATA DEVICE CORP p 413
105 Wilbur Pl, Bohemia NY 11716
Tel (631) 567-5600 SIC 3577 3674 3677

■ ILC HOLDINGS INC p 731
105 Wilbur Pl, Bohemia NY 11716
Tel (631) 567-5600 SIC 3674

■ ILC INDUSTRIES LLC p 731
105 Wilbur Pl, Bohemia NY 11716
Tel (631) 567-5600 SIC 3674

INTERPLEX INDUSTRIES INC p 757
1434 110th St Ste 301, College Point NY 11356
Tel (718) 961-6212
SIC 3471 3825 3674 3469

▲ CORNING INC p 371
1 Riverfront Plz, Corning NY 14831
Tel (607) 974-9000
SIC 3229 3357 3661 3674

■ STANDARD MICROSYSTEMS CORP p 1376
80 Arkay Dr Ste 100, Hauppauge NY 11788
Tel (631) 435-6000 SIC 3674

GLOBALFOUNDRIES US 2 LLC p 617
2070 Route 52, Hopewell Junction NY 12533
Tel (408) 582-8140 SIC 3674

PHILIPS MEDICAL SYSTEMS MR INC p 1143
450 Old Niskayuna Rd, Latham NY 12110
Tel (518) 782-1122 SIC 3845 3674 3679

LEVITON MANUFACTURING CO INC p 858
201 N Service Rd, Melville NY 11747
Tel (631) 812-6000
SIC 3643 3613 3357 3674 3694 3678

▲ PARK ELECTROCHEMICAL CORP p 1115
48 S Service Rd Ste 300, Melville NY 11747
Tel (631) 465-3600 SIC 3672 3674

■ IEH FM HOLDINGS LLC p 730
767 5th Ave Ste 4700, New York NY 10153
Tel (212) 702-4300
SIC 3462 3559 3694 3812 3674

AEROFLEX HOLDING CORP p 30
35 S Service Rd, Plainview NY 11803
Tel (516) 694-6700 SIC 3674

AEROFLEX INC p 30
35 S Service Rd, Plainview NY 11803
Tel (516) 694-6700
SIC 3812 3621 3677 3674 3496 3827

AEROFLEX PLAINVIEW INC p 30
35 S Service Rd, Plainview NY 11803
Tel (516) 694-6700
SIC 3679 3621 3674 3827

TOSHIBA AMERICA ENERGY SYSTEMS CORP p 1462
3545 Whitehall Park Dr # 500, Charlotte NC 28273
Tel (704) 548-7777 SIC 3674

▲ CREE INC p 391
4600 Silicon Dr, Durham NC 27703
Tel (919) 407-5300 SIC 3674 3672

▲ QORVO INC p 1195
7628 Thorndike Rd, Greensboro NC 27409
Tel (336) 664-1233 SIC 3825 3674

■ QORVO US INC p 1195
7628 Thorndike Rd, Greensboro NC 27409
Tel (336) 664-1233 SIC 3674

RF MICRO DEVICES INC p 1231
7628 Thorndike Rd, Greensboro NC 27409
Tel (336) 664-1233 SIC 3674

MORGANITE INDUSTRIES INC p 989
4000 Westchase Blvd # 170, Raleigh NC 27607
Tel (919) 821-1253
SIC 3674 3255 3699 3264 3299 3624

SANTRONICS INC p 1281
3010 Lee Ave, Sanford NC 27332
Tel (919) 775-1223 SIC 3679 3674

GOULD ELECTRONICS INC p 626
34929 Curtis Blvd Ste 100, Eastlake OH 44095
Tel (440) 953-5000
SIC 3825 3497 3613 3691 3674

■ MATERION BRUSH INC p 919
6070 Parkland Blvd Ste 1, Mayfield Heights OH 44124
Tel (216) 486-4200
SIC 3351 3356 3264 3339 3341 3674

▲ MATERION CORP p 919
6070 Parkland Blvd Ste 1, Mayfield Heights OH 44124
Tel (216) 486-4200
SIC 3339 3351 3356 3341 3674

PEPPERL + FUCHS INC p 1134
1600 Enterprise Pkwy, Twinsburg OH 44087
Tel (330) 425-3555
SIC 5065 3625 3822 3674

■ CASCADE MICROTECH INC p 262
9100 Sw Gemini Dr, Beaverton OR 97008
Tel (503) 601-1000 SIC 3825 3674 7372

■ AE SOLAR ENERGY INC p 28
20720 Brinson Blvd, Bend OR 97701
Tel (541) 312-3832 SIC 3674

SOLARWORLD AMERICAS INC p 1338
25300 Nw Evergreen Rd, Hillsboro OR 97124
Tel (503) 844-3400 SIC 3674

SOLARWORLD INDUSTRIES AMERICA LP p 1338
25300 Nw Evergreen Rd, Hillsboro OR 97124
Tel (805) 482-6800 SIC 3674

▲ LATTICE SEMICONDUCTOR CORP p 846
111 Sw 5th Ave Ste 700, Portland OR 97204
Tel (503) 268-8000 SIC 3674

SILTRONIC CORP p 1323
7200 Nw Front Ave, Portland OR 97210
Tel (503) 243-2020 SIC 3674

C&D TECHNOLOGIES INC p 233
1400 Union Meeting Rd # 110, Blue Bell PA 19422
Tel (215) 619-7815
SIC 3612 3691 3613 3692 3674

▲ KULICKE AND SOFFA INDUSTRIES INC p 832
1005 Virginia Dr, Fort Washington PA 19034
Tel (215) 784-6000 SIC 3674

▲ VISHAY INTERTECHNOLOGY INC p 1561
63 Lancaster Ave, Malvern PA 19355
Tel (610) 644-1300
SIC 3676 3677 3675 3674 3613 3612

▲ II-VI INC p 731
375 Saxonburg Blvd, Saxonburg PA 16056
Tel (724) 352-4455
SIC 3827 3229 3674 3699

ATW COMPANIES INC p 130
125 Metro Center Blvd # 3001, Warwick RI 02886
Tel (401) 244-1002 SIC 3674 3498

▲ CIRRUS LOGIC INC p 309
800 W 6th St, Austin TX 78701
Tel (512) 851-4000 SIC 3674

FREESCALE SEMICONDUCTOR HOLDINGS V INC p 577
6501 W William Cannon Dr, Austin TX 78735
Tel (512) 895-2000 SIC 3674

FREESCALE SEMICONDUCTOR LTD p 577
6501 W William Cannon Dr, Austin TX 78735
Tel (512) 895-2000 SIC 3674

NXP USA INC p 1068
6501 W William Cannon Dr, Austin TX 78735
Tel (512) 933-8214 SIC 3674

SAMSUNG AUSTIN SEMICONDUCTOR LLC p 1275
12100 Samsung Blvd, Austin TX 78754
Tel (512) 672-1000 SIC 3674

▲ SILICON LABORATORIES INC p 1323
400 W Cesar Chavez St, Austin TX 78701
Tel (512) 416-8500 SIC 3674

TOKYO ELECTRON US HOLDINGS INC p 1458
2400 Grove Blvd, Austin TX 78741
Tel (512) 424-1000 SIC 3674

■ ATMI MATERIALS LTD p 128
706 Houston Clinton Dr, Burnet TX 78611
Tel (512) 715-5343 SIC 3674

OPTEK TECHNOLOGY INC p 1090
1645 Wallace Dr, Carrollton TX 75006
Tel (972) 323-2200
SIC 3674 3825 3812 3661 3643

STMICROELECTRONICS (NORTH AMERICA) HOLDING INC p 1390
1310 Electronics Dr, Carrollton TX 75006
Tel (972) 466-6000 SIC 3674

STMICROELECTRONICS INC p 1390
750 Canyon Dr Ste 300, Coppell TX 75019
Tel (972) 466-6000 SIC 3674

FEDDERS CORP p 533
13455 Noel Rd Ste 2200, Dallas TX 75240
Tel (604) 908-8686
SIC 3585 3674 3634 3564

▲ TEXAS INSTRUMENTS INC p 1443
12500 Ti Blvd, Dallas TX 75243
Tel (214) 479-3773
SIC 3674 3613 3822 3578

TPG ASIA ADVISORS II INC p 1467
301 Commerce St Ste 3300, Fort Worth TX 76102
Tel (817) 871-4000 SIC 3674

TPG CAPITAL MANAGEMENT LP p 1467
301 Commerce St Ste 3300, Fort Worth TX 76102
Tel (817) 871-4000
SIC 6726 3674 6799 3993 6719

▲ DIODES INC p 441
4949 Hedgcoxe Rd Ste 200, Plano TX 75024
Tel (972) 987-3900 SIC 3674

QORVO INC p 1195
500 W Renner Rd, Richardson TX 75080
Tel (972) 994-8200 SIC 3663 3674 3679

■ QORVO TEXAS LLC p 1195
500 W Renner Rd, Richardson TX 75080
Tel (972) 994-8200 SIC 3674

■ MEMC SOUTHWEST INC p 941
6416 S Us Highway 75, Sherman TX 75090
Tel (903) 891-5000 SIC 3674

▲ APPLIED OPTOELECTRONICS INC p 100
13139 Jess Pirtle Blvd, Sugar Land TX 77478
Tel (281) 295-1800 SIC 3674 3827 3699

■ IM FLASH TECHNOLOGIES LLC p 733
4000 N Flash Dr, Lehi UT 84043
Tel (801) 767-4000 SIC 3674

■ GE INTELLIGENT PLATFORMS INC p 596
2500 Austin Dr, Charlottesville VA 22911
Tel (434) 978-5000 SIC 3625 3674 7371

■ HARRIS IT SERVICES CORP p 663
2235 Monroe St, Herndon VA 20171
Tel (703) 673-1400 SIC 8711 3663 3674

■ **ITT DEFENSE & ELECTRONICS INC** p 768
1650 Tysons Blvd Ste 1700, Mc Lean VA 22102
Tel (703) 790-6300
SIC 3679 3678 3674 3769 3489

▲ **LEIDOS HOLDINGS INC** p 854
11951 Freedom Dr Ste 500, Reston VA 20190
Tel (571) 526-6000
SIC 8731 7371 7373 8742 3674

TSMC DEVELOPMENT INC p 1489
5509 Nw Parker St, Camas WA 98607
Tel (360) 817-3000 SIC 3674

WAFERTECH LLC p 1571
5509 Nw Parker St, Camas WA 98607
Tel (360) 817-3000 SIC 3674 7361

■ **ELDEC CORP** p 484
16700 13th Ave W, Lynnwood WA 98037
Tel (425) 743-8362
SIC 3812 3728 3824 3769 3674 3613

■ **HONEYWELL ELECTRONIC MATERIALS INC** p 705
15128 E Euclid Ave, Spokane Valley WA 99216
Tel (509) 252-2200 SIC 3679 3674 3643

NLIGHT INC p 1045
5408 Ne 88th St Ste E, Vancouver WA 98665
Tel (360) 566-4460 SIC 3674 3699

SHIN-ETSU HANDOTAI AMERICA INC p 1316
4111 Ne 112th Ave, Vancouver WA 98682
Tel (360) 883-7000 SIC 3674 5065

■ **TTM ADVANCED CIRCUITS INC** p 1490
234 Cashman Dr, Chippewa Falls WI 54729
Tel (715) 720-5000 SIC 3672 3674

SIC 3675 Electronic Capacitors

■ **NOVACAP LLC** p 1062
25111 Anza Dr, Valencia CA 91355
Tel (661) 295-5920 SIC 3675

MURATA ELECTRONICS NORTH AMERICA INC p 1001
2200 Lake Park Dr Se, Smyrna GA 30080
Tel (770) 436-1300 SIC 5065 3675 3679

▲ **KNOWLES CORP** p 825
1151 Maplewood Dr, Itasca IL 60143
Tel (630) 250-5100 SIC 3651 3675

PHILIPS MEDICAL SYSTEMS HSG p 1143
3000 Minuteman Rd, Andover MA 01810
Tel (978) 687-1501 SIC 3675 3676

AEROVOX INC p 31
167 John Vertente Blvd, New Bedford MA 02745
Tel (508) 994-9661 SIC 3629 3675

▲ **STANDEX INTERNATIONAL CORP** p 1376
11 Keewaydin Dr, Salem NH 03079
Tel (603) 893-9701 SIC 3585 3549 3675

ROBERTS-GORDON LLC p 1242
1250 William St, Buffalo NY 14206
Tel (716) 852-4400 SIC 3675 3433

■ **AMERICAN TECHNICAL CERAMICS CORP** p 80
1 Norden Ln, Huntington Station NY 11746
Tel (631) 622-4700 SIC 3672 3675

▲ **VISHAY INTERTECHNOLOGY INC** p 1561
63 Lancaster Ave, Malvern PA 19355
Tel (610) 644-1300
SIC 3676 3677 3675 3674 3613 3612

■ **AVX CORP** p 139
1 Avx Blvd, Fountain Inn SC 29644
Tel (864) 967-2150 SIC 3675 5065 3678

CORNELL-DUBILIER ELECTRONICS INC p 370
140 Technology Pl, Liberty SC 29657
Tel (864) 843-2277 SIC 3675 3677

▲ **KEMET CORP** p 809
2835 Kemet Way, Simpsonville SC 29681
Tel (864) 963-6300 SIC 3675

▲ **INTEGER HOLDINGS CORP** p 748
2595 Dallas Pkwy Ste 310, Frisco TX 75034
Tel (716) 759-5600 SIC 3675 3692 3691

PANASONIC INDUSTRIAL DEVICES CORP OF AMERICA p 1111
4900 Gorge Mcvay Dr Ste C, Mcallen TX 78503
Tel (956) 984-3700 SIC 3651 3675 3471

SIC 3676 Electronic Resistors

BOURNS INC p 204
1200 Columbia Ave, Riverside CA 92507
Tel (951) 781-5500
SIC 3677 3676 3661 3639 3679

▲ **METHODE ELECTRONICS INC** p 953
7401 W Wilson Ave, Chicago IL 60706
Tel (708) 867-6777
SIC 3678 3674 3676 3672 3825 3643

▲ **CTS CORP** p 399
2375 Cabot Dr, Lisle IL 60532
Tel (630) 577-8800
SIC 3678 3829 3676 3679 3674

■ **MPC PRODUCTS CORP** p 995
6300 W Howard St, Niles IL 60714
Tel (847) 673-8300
SIC 3728 3621 3676 3812 3625

PHILIPS MEDICAL SYSTEMS HSG p 1143
3000 Minuteman Rd, Andover MA 01810
Tel (978) 687-1501 SIC 3675 3676

SENSATA TECHNOLOGIES INDIANA INC p 1304
529 Pleasant St, Attleboro MA 02703
Tel (508) 236-3245 SIC 3676 3625

WABASH TECHNOLOGIES INC p 1570
529 Pleasant St, Attleboro MA 02703
Tel (260) 355-4100 SIC 3625 3676

■ **DALE VISHAY ELECTRONICS LLC** p 409
1122 23rd St, Columbus NE 68601
Tel (605) 665-9301
SIC 3676 3679 3677 3678

DAHUA ELECTRONICS CORP p 408
13412 59th Ave, Flushing NY 11355
Tel (718) 886-2188 SIC 3676

SPECTRUM CONTROL INC p 1357
8061 Avonia Rd, Fairview PA 16415
Tel (814) 474-2207
SIC 3677 3663 3612 3676

▲ **VISHAY INTERTECHNOLOGY INC** p 1561
63 Lancaster Ave, Malvern PA 19355
Tel (610) 644-1300
SIC 3676 3677 3675 3674 3613 3612

■ **VISHAY PRECISION FOIL INC** p 1561
3 Great Valley Pkwy # 150, Malvern PA 19355
Tel (484) 321-5300 SIC 3676

▲ **VISHAY PRECISION GROUP INC** p 1561
3 Great Valley Pkwy # 150, Malvern PA 19355
Tel (484) 321-5300 SIC 3676 3823

SIC 3677 Electronic Coils & Transformers

BOURNS INC p 204
1200 Columbia Ave, Riverside CA 92507
Tel (951) 781-5500
SIC 3677 3676 3661 3639 3679

PULSE ELECTRONICS INC p 1191
12220 World Trade Dr, San Diego CA 92128
Tel (858) 674-8100 SIC 3612 3674 3677

RENCO ELECTRONICS INC p 1223
595 International Pl, Rockledge FL 32955
Tel (321) 637-1000 SIC 5065 3677

▲ **SIGMATRON INTERNATIONAL INC** p 1321
2201 Landmeier Rd, Elk Grove Village IL 60007
Tel (847) 956-8000
SIC 3672 3677 3679 3549 3825

SCHUMACHER ELECTRIC CORP p 1291
801 E Business Center Dr, Mount Prospect IL 60056
Tel (847) 385-1600 SIC 3629 3677

▲ **MFRI INC** p 958
6410 W Howard St, Niles IL 60714
Tel (847) 966-1000 SIC 3677 3564 3569

CHARLES INDUSTRIES LTD p 289
5600 Apollo Dr, Rolling Meadows IL 60008
Tel (847) 806-6300 SIC 3661 3629 3677

XFMRS INC p 1631
7570 E Landersdale Rd, Camby IN 46113
Tel (317) 834-1066 SIC 3677 5065 3612

■ **DALE VISHAY ELECTRONICS LLC** p 409
1122 23rd St, Columbus NE 68601
Tel (605) 665-9301
SIC 3676 3679 3677 3678

■ **AUTOMATIC SWITCH CO** p 134
50-60 Hanover Rd, Florham Park NJ 07932
Tel (973) 966-2000
SIC 3491 3625 3677 3674 3613 3492

▲ **BEL FUSE INC** p 169
206 Van Vorst St, Jersey City NJ 07302
Tel (201) 432-0463
SIC 3679 3674 3613 3677

■ **AMERICAN PRECISION INDUSTRIES INC** p 77
45 Hazelwood Dr, Amherst NY 14228
Tel (716) 691-9100
SIC 3677 3621 3625 3443

■ **DATA DEVICE CORP** p 413
105 Wilbur Pl, Bohemia NY 11716
Tel (631) 567-5600 SIC 3577 3674 3677

■ **PALL TRINITY MICRO CORP** p 1108
3643 State Route 281, Cortland NY 13045
Tel (607) 753-6041 SIC 3677

AEROFLEX INC p 30
35 S Service Rd, Plainview NY 11803
Tel (516) 694-6700
SIC 3812 3621 3677 3674 3496 3827

SWIGER COIL SYSTEMS LTD p 1412
4677 Manufacturing Ave, Cleveland OH 44135
Tel (216) 362-7500 SIC 3621 3677

ELECTROMOTIVE INC p 485
4880 Hudson Dr, Stow OH 44224
Tel (330) 688-6494 SIC 3679 3677

PENNSYLVANIA TRANSFORMER TECHNOLOGY INC p 1130
30 Curry Ave Ste 2, Canonsburg PA 15317
Tel (724) 873-2100 SIC 3612 5063 3677

SPECTRUM CONTROL INC p 1357
8061 Avonia Rd, Fairview PA 16415
Tel (814) 474-2207
SIC 3677 3663 3612 3676

▲ **VISHAY INTERTECHNOLOGY INC** p 1561
63 Lancaster Ave, Malvern PA 19355
Tel (610) 644-1300
SIC 3676 3677 3675 3674 3613 3612

PEI/GENESIS INC p 1128
2180 Hornig Rd Ste 2, Philadelphia PA 19116
Tel (215) 464-1410 SIC 3678 3677

■ **MAR COR PURIFICATION INC** p 904
4450 Township Line Rd, Skippack PA 19474
Tel (800) 633-3080 SIC 3569 3677

SCHNEIDER ELECTRIC IT CORP p 1287
132 Fairgrounds Rd, West Kingston RI 02892
Tel (401) 789-5735
SIC 3629 3612 3677 3585 7372 2542

CORNELL-DUBILIER ELECTRONICS INC p 370
140 Technology Pl, Liberty SC 29657
Tel (864) 843-2277 SIC 3675 3677

SUPERIOR FIBERS INC p 1406
1333 Corporate Dr Ste 350, Irving TX 75038
Tel (972) 600-9953 SIC 3677 3569

HATFIELD AND CO INC p 668
2475 Discovery Blvd, Rockwall TX 75032
Tel (972) 288-7625 SIC 5084 3677 5074

SIC 3678 Electronic Connectors

■ **AMPHENOL OPTIMIZE MANUFACTURING CO** p 86
180 N Freeport Dr 10, Nogales AZ 85621
Tel (520) 397-7015 SIC 3678 3643

JAE ELECTRONICS INC p 775
142 Technology Dr Ste 100, Irvine CA 92618
Tel (949) 753-2600
SIC 5065 5088 3679 3829 3678

■ **JOSLYN SUNBANK CO LLC** p 794
1740 Commerce Way, Paso Robles CA 93446
Tel (805) 238-2840 SIC 3678 3643 5065

BRANTNER HOLDING CO p 208
501 Oakside Ave, Redwood City CA 94063
Tel (650) 361-5292 SIC 3678

LEMO USA INC p 855
635 Park Ct, Rohnert Park CA 94928
Tel (707) 206-3700 SIC 5065 3678

I O INTERCONNECT LTD p 725
1202 E Wakeham Ave, Santa Ana CA 92705
Tel (714) 564-1111 SIC 3678 3679

WINCHESTER ELECTRONICS CORP p 1614
199 Park Rad Ext Ste 104, Middlebury CT 06762
Tel (203) 741-5400 SIC 3678

▲ **AMPHENOL CORP** p 86
358 Hall Ave, Wallingford CT 06492
Tel (203) 265-8900 SIC 3678 3643 3661

TE CONNECTIVITY INC p 1429
607 14th St Nw Ste 250, Washington DC 20005
Tel (202) 471-3400 SIC 3678 3643

■ **TELEDYNE ODI INC** p 1434
1026 N Williamson Blvd, Daytona Beach FL 32114
Tel (386) 236-0780 SIC 3678

■ **CARLISLE INTERCONNECT TECHNOLOGIES INC** p 257
100 Tensolite Dr, Saint Augustine FL 32092
Tel (904) 829-5600
SIC 3679 3399 3678 3357 3643 5063

A A G STUCCHI NORTH AMERICA INC p 4
3400 Peachtree Rd Ne # 945, Atlanta GA 30326
Tel (404) 806-5399 SIC 3678

▲ **METHODE ELECTRONICS INC** p 953
7401 W Wilson Ave, Chicago IL 60706
Tel (708) 867-6777
SIC 3678 3674 3676 3672 3825 3643

WOODHEAD INDUSTRIES LLC p 1623
333 Knightsbridge Pkwy # 200, Lincolnshire IL 60069
Tel (847) 353-2500
SIC 3678 3679 3643 3357

▲ **CTS CORP** p 399
2375 Cabot Dr, Lisle IL 60532
Tel (630) 577-8800
SIC 3678 3829 3676 3679 3674

MOLEX U S INC p 982
2222 Wellington Ct, Lisle IL 60532
Tel (630) 969-4550
SIC 3678 3679 3643 3357

■ **CINCH CONNECTIVITY SOLUTIONS INC** p 307
1700 S Finley Rd, Lombard IL 60148
Tel (847) 739-0300 SIC 3678 3679

■ **CINCH CONNECTORS INC** p 307
1700 S Finley Rd, Lombard IL 60148
Tel (630) 705-6001 SIC 3643 3678

MAC LEAN-FOGG CO p 891
1000 Allanson Rd, Mundelein IL 60060
Tel (847) 566-0010
SIC 3678 3452 3089 3061 3492 3451

L-COM INC p 835
50 High St Fl 3, North Andover MA 01845
Tel (800) 343-1455 SIC 3678 3577 3357

TRU CORP p 1485
245 Lynnfield St, Peabody MA 01960
Tel (978) 532-0775 SIC 3643 3678

POSITRONIC INDUSTRIES INC p 1163
423 N Campbell Ave, Springfield MO 65806
Tel (417) 866-2322 SIC 3678

■ **DALE VISHAY ELECTRONICS LLC** p 409
1122 23rd St, Columbus NE 68601
Tel (605) 665-9301
SIC 3676 3679 3677 3678

■ **AMPHENOL PRINTED CIRCUITS INC** p 86
91 Northeastern Blvd, Nashua NH 03062
Tel (603) 324-4500
SIC 3679 3678 3672 3357

LAPP USA LLC p 845
29 Hanover Rd, Florham Park NJ 07932
Tel (973) 660-9700 SIC 5063 3678

POWELL ELECTRONICS INC p 1165
200 Commodore Dr, Swedesboro NJ 08085
Tel (856) 241-8000 SIC 3678

FELCHAR MANUFACTURING CORP p 537
196 Corporate Dr, Binghamton NY 13904
Tel (607) 723-3106 SIC 3678 3089 3621

LEVITON MANUFACTURING CO INC p 858
201 N Service Rd, Melville NY 11747
Tel (631) 812-6000
SIC 3643 3613 3357 3674 3694 3678

HUBER + SUHNER INC p 716
8530 Steele Creek Place D, Charlotte NC 28273
Tel (704) 790-7300
SIC 3679 3678 3357 5065

NEXANS USA INC p 1039
39 2nd St Nw, Hickory NC 28601
Tel (828) 323-2660 SIC 3357 3661 3678

ILSCO CORP p 733
4730 Madison Rd, Cincinnati OH 45227
Tel (513) 533-6200
SIC 3643 3369 3451 3678 3544 3469

■ **AVIATION TECHNOLOGIES INC** p 138
1301 E 9th St Ste 3000, Cleveland OH 44114
Tel (216) 706-2960
SIC 3643 3678 3679 3728 3812 3648

LASTAR INC p 846
3555 Kettering Blvd, Moraine OH 45439
Tel (937) 224-0639 SIC 3678

TYCO ELECTRONICS CORP p 1496
1050 Westlakes Dr, Berwyn PA 19312
Tel (717) 986-7275 SIC 3678 3643

PHOENIX CONTACT SERVICES INC p 1144
586 Fulling Mill Rd, Middletown PA 17057
Tel (717) 944-1300 SIC 5063 3678 3643

PEI/GENESIS INC p 1128
2180 Hornig Rd Ste 2, Philadelphia PA 19116
Tel (215) 464-1410 SIC 3678 3677

■ **AVX CORP** p 139
1 Avx Blvd, Fountain Inn SC 29644
Tel (864) 967-2150 SIC 3675 5065 3678

THOMAS & BETTS INTERNATIONAL INC p 1448
8155 T And B Blvd, Memphis TN 38125
Tel (901) 682-7766 SIC 3699 3678

AIRBORN INTERCONNECT INC p 39
3500 Airborn Cir, Georgetown TX 78626
Tel (512) 863-5585 SIC 3678 3679

■ **ITT DEFENSE & ELECTRONICS INC** p 768
1650 Tysons Blvd Ste 1700, Mc Lean VA 22102
Tel (703) 790-6300
SIC 3679 3678 3674 3769 3489

WAGO CORP p 1571
N120 W 19129 Freistadt Rd N 120 W, Germantown WI 53022
Tel (262) 255-6333 SIC 5063 3643 3678

SIC 3679 Electronic Components, NEC

TOOH DINEH INDUSTRIES INC p 1460
Leupp School Rd Bldg 4, Leupp AZ 86035
Tel (928) 686-6477 SIC 3679 3672

EDS MANUFACTURING INC p 479
765 N Target Range Rd, Nogales AZ 85621
Tel (520) 287-9711 SIC 3679

POWER-ONE INC p 1165
2626 S 7th St, Phoenix AZ 85034
Tel (805) 987-8741 SIC 3679

NAI GROUP LLC p 1006
7975 N Hayden Rd Ste D105, Scottsdale AZ 85258
Tel (480) 556-6066 SIC 3679

ARTESYN EMBEDDED TECHNOLOGIES INC p 114
2900 S Diablo Way Ste 190, Tempe AZ 85282
Tel (800) 759-1107
SIC 3679 3577 3571 7629 5045

ASTEC AMERICA LLC p 122
2900 S Diablo Way Ste 190, Tempe AZ 85282
Tel (602) 438-5720 SIC 3679 3629 3621

LEONISCHE HOLDING INC p 856
2861 N Flowing Wells Rd, Tucson AZ 85705
Tel (520) 741-0895 SIC 3679

DANFOSS SCROLL TECHNOLOGIES LLC p 411
1 Scroll Dr, Arkadelphia AR 71923
Tel (870) 246-0700 SIC 3679 3563

ACTRONIX INC p 20
476 W Industrial Prk Rd, Flippin AR 72634
Tel (870) 453-8871 SIC 3679

PERFECTVISION MANUFACTURING INC p 1135
16101 La Grande Dr, Little Rock AR 72223
Tel (501) 955-0033 SIC 3679

FLEXTRONICS CORP p 556
6201 America Center Dr, Alviso CA 95002
Tel (803) 936-5200 SIC 3679 3577 3571

■ **INTERSTATE ELECTRONICS CORP** p 758
602 E Vermont Ave, Anaheim CA 92805
Tel (714) 758-0500 SIC 3825 3812 3679

MONSTER INC p 985
455 Valley Dr, Brisbane CA 94005
Tel (415) 840-2000 SIC 5099 4841 3679

■ **LEACH INTERNATIONAL CORP** p 850
6900 Orangethorpe Ave, Buena Park CA 90620
Tel (714) 736-7537 SIC 3679

AIH LLC p 38
5810 Van Allen Way, Carlsbad CA 92008
Tel (760) 930-4600 SIC 3629 3621 3679

▲ **DUCOMMUN INC** p 459
23301 Wilmington Ave, Carson CA 90745
Tel (310) 513-7200 SIC 3728 3679

EPIC TECHNOLOGIES LLC p 505
9340 Owensmouth Ave, Chatsworth CA 91311
Tel (818) 734-6500 SIC 3661 3577 3679

NATEL ENGINEERING CO INC p 1009
9340 Owensmouth Ave, Chatsworth CA 91311
Tel (818) 734-6523 SIC 3674 3679

■ **BEATS ELECTRONICS LLC** p 166
8600 Hayden Pl, Culver City CA 90232
Tel (424) 326-4679 SIC 3651 3679

ASTEELFLASH USA CORP p 122
4211 Starboard Dr, Fremont CA 94538
Tel (510) 440-2840 SIC 3672 3679

DELTA AMERICA LTD p 426
46101 Fremont Blvd, Fremont CA 94538
Tel (510) 668-5100 SIC 5065 3679 8731

BI TECHNOLOGIES CORP p 180
4200 Bonita Pl, Fullerton CA 92835
Tel (714) 447-2300 SIC 3679 5065 8711

JAE ELECTRONICS INC p 775
142 Technology Dr Ste 100, Irvine CA 92618
Tel (949) 753-2600
SIC 5065 5088 3679 3829 3678

TOSHIBA AMERICA ELECTRONIC COMPONENTS INC p 1462
9740 Irvine Blvd Ste D700, Irvine CA 92618
Tel (949) 462-7700
SIC 3651 3631 3674 3679 5065 5064

OCM PE HOLDINGS LP p 1074
333 S Grand Ave Fl 28, Los Angeles CA 90071
Tel (213) 830-6213 SIC 3679 3612 3663

▲ **INTERSIL CORP** p 758
1001 Murphy Ranch Rd, Milpitas CA 95035
Tel (408) 432-8888 SIC 3674 3679

■ **BENCHMARK ELECTRONICS MANUFACTURING SOLUTIONS (MOORPARK) INC** p 172
200 Science Dr, Moorpark CA 93021
Tel (805) 532-2800 SIC 3679

CUSTOM SENSORS & TECHNOLOGIES INC p 403
14401 Princeton Ave, Moorpark CA 93021
Tel (805) 523-2000 SIC 3679

■ **TELEDYNE WIRELESS LLC** p 1434
1274 Terra Bella Ave, Mountain View CA 94043
Tel (650) 691-9800 SIC 3679

PIONEER SPEAKERS INC p 1151
2427 Transportation Ave, National City CA 91950
Tel (619) 477-0850 SIC 3679

SMART MODULAR TECHNOLOGIES (WWH) INC p 1332
39870 Eureka Dr, Newark CA 94560
Tel (510) 623-1231 SIC 3674 3577 3679

COMMUNICATIONS & POWER INDUSTRIES LLC p 347
607 Hansen Way, Palo Alto CA 94304
Tel (650) 846-2900
SIC 3671 3679 3699 3683

CPI INTERNATIONAL HOLDING CORP p 387
811 Hansen Way, Palo Alto CA 94304
Tel (650) 846-2900 *SIC* 3679

CPI INTERNATIONAL INC p 387
811 Hansen Way, Palo Alto CA 94304
Tel (650) 846-2801
SIC 3671 3679 3699 3825

BOURNS INC p 204
1200 Columbia Ave, Riverside CA 92507
Tel (951) 781-5500
SIC 3677 3676 3661 3639 3679

■ HCC INDUSTRIES INC p 672
4232 Temple City Blvd, Rosemead CA 91770
Tel (626) 443-8933 *SIC* 3679

NEW VISION DISPLAY INC p 1033
1430 Blue Oaks Blvd # 100, Roseville CA 95747
Tel (916) 786-8111 *SIC* 3679

PRIDE INDUSTRIES p 1174
10030 Foothills Blvd, Roseville CA 95747
Tel (916) 788-2100 *SIC* 4226 7349 3679

■ AMETEK PROGRAMMABLE POWER INC p 84
9250 Brown Deer Rd, San Diego CA 92121
Tel (858) 450-0085 *SIC* 3679

■ NYPRO HEALTHCARE BAJA INC p 1069
2195 Britannia Blvd # 107, San Diego CA 92154
Tel (619) 498-9250 *SIC* 3841 3679

PULSE ELECTRONICS CORP p 1191
12220 World Trade Dr, San Diego CA 92128
Tel (858) 674-8100 *SIC* 3679 3612 3663

▲ TURTLE BEACH CORP p 1493
12220 Scripps Summit Dr # 100, San Diego CA 92131
Tel (914) 345-2255 *SIC* 3679

■ CSR TECHNOLOGY INC p 398
1060 Rincon Cir, San Jose CA 95131
Tel (408) 523-6500 *SIC* 3679 3812 3674

FLEXTRONICS HOLDING USA INC p 556
2090 Fortune Dr, San Jose CA 95131
Tel (408) 576-7000
SIC 3672 3679 7371 3825

■ SUNPOWER CORP p 1403
77 Rio Robles, San Jose CA 95134
Tel (408) 240-5500 *SIC* 3674 3679

VANDER-BEND MANUFACTURING LLC p 1543
2701 Orchard Pkwy, San Jose CA 95134
Tel (408) 245-5150 *SIC* 3679 3444 3549

EXPRESS MANUFACTURING INC p 520
3519 W Warner Ave, Santa Ana CA 92704
Tel (714) 979-2228 *SIC* 3672 3679

I O INTERCONNECT LTD p 725
1202 E Wakeham Ave, Santa Ana CA 92705
Tel (714) 564-1111 *SIC* 3678 3679

ALTA PROPERTIES INC p 61
879 Ward Dr, Santa Barbara CA 93111
Tel (805) 967-0171
SIC 3264 3699 3823 3679

■ HADCO SANTA CLARA INC p 652
500 El Camino Real, Santa Clara CA 95050
Tel (408) 241-9900 *SIC* 3672 3679

▲ PLANTRONICS INC p 1154
345 Encinal St, Santa Cruz CA 95060
Tel (831) 426-5858 *SIC* 3661 3679

MEGGITT-USA INC p 940
1955 Surveyor Ave, Simi Valley CA 93063
Tel (805) 526-5700 *SIC* 3728 3829 3679

■ SPECTROLAB INC p 1357
12500 Gladstone Ave, Sylmar CA 91342
Tel (818) 365-4611 *SIC* 3674 3679

BEI SENSORS & SYSTEMS CO LLC p 168
1461 Lawrence Dr, Thousand Oaks CA 91320
Tel (805) 968-0782 *SIC* 3679

KAVLICO CORP p 805
1461 Lawrence Dr, Thousand Oaks CA 91320
Tel (805) 523-2000 *SIC* 3679 3829 3823

▲ TELEDYNE TECHNOLOGIES INC p 1434
1049 Camino Dos Rios, Thousand Oaks CA 91360
Tel (805) 373-4545
SIC 3679 3761 3519 3724 3812 3674

ALPINE ELECTRONICS OF AMERICA INC p 60
19145 Gramercy Pl, Torrance CA 90501
Tel (310) 326-8000 *SIC* 5064 3651 3679

■ SL POWER ELECTRONICS CORP p 1330
6050 King Dr Ste A, Ventura CA 93003
Tel (805) 228-3400 *SIC* 3679

▲ BALL CORP p 148
10 Longs Peak Dr, Broomfield CO 80021
Tel (303) 469-3131
SIC 3411 3085 3812 3679

■ MCDATA CORP p 927
4 Brocade Pkwy, Broomfield CO 80021
Tel (720) 558-8000
SIC 3679 5045 3825 3577

▲ ADVANCED ENERGY INDUSTRIES INC p 25
1625 Sharp Point Dr, Fort Collins CO 80525
Tel (970) 221-4670 *SIC* 3679 3629 3625

VALIDUS DC SYSTEMS LLC p 1540
50 Pocono Rd, Brookfield CT 06804
Tel (203) 448-3600 *SIC* 3679

ASHCROFT INC p 117
250 E Main St, Stratford CT 06614
Tel (203) 378-8281
SIC 3823 3679 3663 3625

ASHCROFT-NAGANO KEIKI HOLDINGS INC p 117
250 E Main St, Stratford CT 06614
Tel (203) 378-8281
SIC 3823 3679 3663 3625

SIEMON CO p 1320
101 Siemon Company Dr, Watertown CT 06795
Tel (860) 945-4200
SIC 3643 3089 3679 3469 3613 3357

■ EECO INC p 480
850 Library Ave Ste 204c, Newark DE 19711
Tel (302) 456-1448
SIC 3823 3491 3621 3585 3546 3679

GABLES ENGINEERING INC p 588
247 Greco Ave, Coral Gables FL 33146
Tel (305) 774-4400 *SIC* 3679

■ CARLISLE INTERCONNECT TECHNOLOGIES INC p 257
100 Tensolite Dr, Saint Augustine FL 32092
Tel (904) 829-5600
SIC 3679 3399 3678 3357 3643 5063

■ TENSOLITE LLC p 1438
100 Tensolite Dr, Saint Augustine FL 32092
Tel (904) 829-5600 *SIC* 3357 3643 3679

COMPULINK CORP p 352
1205 Gandy Blvd N, Saint Petersburg FL 33702
Tel (727) 579-1065 *SIC* 3679

SMITHS INTERCONNECT INC p 1334
4726 Eisenhower Blvd, Tampa FL 33634
Tel (813) 901-7200 *SIC* 3679

■ SYPRIS ELECTRONICS LLC p 1416
10421 Univ Ctr Dr Ste 100, Tampa FL 33612
Tel (813) 972-6000 *SIC* 3672 3679

MURATA ELECTRONICS NORTH AMERICA INC p 1001
2200 Lake Park Dr Se, Smyrna GA 30080
Tel (770) 436-1300 *SIC* 5065 3675 3679

▲ LITTELFUSE INC p 870
8755 W Higgins Rd Ste 500, Chicago IL 60631
Tel (773) 628-1000 *SIC* 3613 3679

PFINGSTEN PARTNERS LLC p 1140
300 N Lasalle St 5400, Chicago IL 60654
Tel (312) 222-8707
SIC 5065 6211 3679 3578

IMS COMPANIES LLC p 735
1 Innovation Dr, Des Plaines IL 60016
Tel (847) 391-8100
SIC 3469 8711 3679 3714 3444

CAPSONIC AUTOMOTIVE INC p 251
460 2nd St, Elgin IL 60123
Tel (847) 888-7300 *SIC* 3625 3679 3674

▲ SIGMATRON INTERNATIONAL INC p 1321
2201 Landmeier Rd, Elk Grove Village IL 60007
Tel (847) 956-8000
SIC 3672 3677 3679 3549 3825

BASLER ELECTRIC CO p 159
12570 State Route 143, Highland IL 62249
Tel (618) 654-2341 *SIC* 3679 3612 3672

■ KNOWLES ELECTRONICS HOLDINGS INC p 825
1151 Maplewood Dr, Itasca IL 60143
Tel (630) 250-5100
SIC 3679 3625 3651 8731 6159

■ KNOWLES ELECTRONICS LLC p 825
1151 Maplewood Dr, Itasca IL 60143
Tel (630) 250-5100 *SIC* 3679 3842

GRAYHILL INC p 632
561 W Hillgrove Ave, La Grange IL 60525
Tel (708) 354-1040
SIC 3613 3625 3679 3643 3575

WOODHEAD INDUSTRIES LLC p 1623
333 Knightsbridge Pkwy # 200, Lincolnshire IL 60069
Tel (847) 353-2500
SIC 3678 3679 3643 3357

▲ CTS CORP p 399
2375 Cabot Dr, Lisle IL 60532
Tel (630) 577-8800
SIC 3678 3829 3676 3679 3674

MOLEX LLC p 982
2222 Wellington Ct, Lisle IL 60532
Tel (630) 969-4550 *SIC* 3679 3643 3357

MOLEX PREMISE NETWORKS INC p 982
2222 Wellington Ct, Lisle IL 60532
Tel (866) 733-6659 *SIC* 3679 3643 3357

MOLEX U S INC p 982
2222 Wellington Ct, Lisle IL 60532
Tel (630) 969-4550
SIC 3678 3679 3643 3357

■ CINCH CONNECTIVITY SOLUTIONS INC p 307
1700 S Finley Rd, Lombard IL 60148
Tel (847) 739-0300 *SIC* 3678 3679

SHURE INC p 1319
5800 W Touhy Ave, Niles IL 60714
Tel (847) 600-2000 *SIC* 3651 3679 3661

■ COMMSCOPE TECHNOLOGIES LLC p 346
4 Westbrook Corporate Ctr, Westchester IL 60154
Tel (708) 236-6000
SIC 3663 3357 3679 3812 3699

EJ BROOKS CO p 482
409 Hoosier Dr, Angola IN 46703
Tel (800) 348-4777 *SIC* 3679

■ KIMBALL ELECTRONICS MANUFACTURING INC p 818
1600 Royal St, Jasper IN 47549
Tel (812) 482-1600 *SIC* 3679

■ KIMBALL ELECTRONICS TAMPA INC p 818
1205 Kimball Blvd, Jasper IN 47546
Tel (812) 634-4000 *SIC* 3679 3672

KIRBY RISK CORP p 821
1815 Sagamore Pkwy N, Lafayette IN 47904
Tel (765) 448-4567
SIC 5063 7694 3599 3679 3629

SAMTEC INC p 1275
520 Park East Blvd, New Albany IN 47150
Tel (812) 944-6733 *SIC* 3679

CARLETON LIFE SUPPORT SYSTEMS INC p 257
2734 Hickory Grove Rd, Davenport IA 52804
Tel (563) 383-6000 *SIC* 3679

■ MONONA WIRE CORP p 984
301 W Spruce St, Monona IA 52159
Tel (563) 539-2012 *SIC* 3679 3694

CELLTRON INC p 274
1110 W 7th St, Galena KS 66739
Tel (620) 783-1333 *SIC* 3679

■ CDR MANUFACTURING INC p 271
10200 Forest Green Blvd, Louisville KY 40223
Tel (502) 625-0760 *SIC* 3679 3672 3699

▲ SYPRIS SOLUTIONS INC p 1416
101 Bullitt Ln Ste 450, Louisville KY 40222
Tel (502) 329-2000
SIC 3672 3679 3812 3674 3462

■ ACTERNA LLC p 19
20250 Century Blvd # 100, Germantown MD 20874
Tel (301) 353-1550
SIC 3669 7379 3825 5065 3679 8734

■ WABTEC RAILWAY ELECTRONICS INC p 1570
21200 Dorsey Mill Rd, Germantown MD 20876
Tel (301) 515-2000
SIC 3825 3679 3743 3672

▲ VICOR CORP p 1555
25 Frontage Rd, Andover MA 01810
Tel (978) 470-2900 *SIC* 3679 3613

SENSATA TECHNOLOGIES INC p 1304
529 Pleasant St, Attleboro MA 02703
Tel (508) 236-3800 *SIC* 3679

CUMING CORP p 400
225 Bodwell St, Avon MA 02322
Tel (508) 580-2660 *SIC* 3533 3679

■ MACOM TECHNOLOGY SOLUTIONS INC p 893
100 Chelmsford St, Lowell MA 01851
Tel (978) 656-2500 *SIC* 3663 3679

ACCELLENT ACQUISITION CORP p 14
100 Fordham Rd Bldg C, Wilmington MA 01887
Tel (978) 570-6900
SIC 3841 3317 3679 3315 3552 3089

ACCELLENT HOLDINGS CORP p 14
100 Fordham Rd, Wilmington MA 01887
Tel (978) 570-6900
SIC 3841 3679 3315 3552 3317 3089

HEILIND ELECTRONICS INC p 681
58 Jonspin Rd, Wilmington MA 01887
Tel (978) 658-7000 *SIC* 5065 3679 5063

KAYDON CORP p 805
2723 S State St Ste 300, Ann Arbor MI 48104
Tel (734) 747-7025
SIC 3562 3569 3592 3053 3621 3679

MA INDUSTRIAL JV LLC p 891
5683 Hines Dr, Ann Arbor MI 48108
Tel (734) 585-9500 *SIC* 3585 3679 6719

TECUMSEH PRODUCTS CO p 1432
5683 Hines Dr, Ann Arbor MI 48108
Tel (734) 585-9500 *SIC* 3585 3679

FKA DISTRIBUTING CO LLC p 553
3000 N Pontiac Trl, Commerce Township MI 48390
Tel (248) 863-3000 *SIC* 3679 3634

AEES INC p 29
36555 Corp Dr Ste 300, Farmington Hills MI 48331
Tel (248) 489-4700 *SIC* 3679

■ AMPHENOL BORISCH TECHNOLOGIES INC p 86
4511 East Paris Ave Se, Grand Rapids MI 49512
Tel (616) 554-9820 *SIC* 3679 3599

MAGNA ELECTRONICS INC p 896
10410 N Holly Rd, Holly MI 48442
Tel (810) 606-0444 *SIC* 3672 3679

TRW AUTOMOTIVE US LLC p 1489
12001 Tech Center Dr, Livonia MI 48150
Tel (734) 855-2600 *SIC* 3679 3469 3089

▲ STONERIDGE INC p 1391
39675 Mackenzie Dr # 400, Novi MI 48377
Tel (330) 856-2443 *SIC* 3714 3679 3625

KEY SAFETY RESTRAINT SYSTEMS INC p 814
7000 19 Mile Rd, Sterling Heights MI 48314
Tel (586) 726-3800 *SIC* 3714 3674 3679

EMPIRE ELECTRONICS INC p 493
214 E Maple Rd, Troy MI 48083
Tel (248) 585-8130 *SIC* 3679

MADISON ELECTRIC CO p 894
31855 Van Dyke Ave, Warren MI 48093
Tel (586) 825-0200 *SIC* 5063 3679

BOSCH SECURITY SYSTEMS INC p 202
12000 Portland Ave, Burnsville MN 55337
Tel (952) 884-4051 *SIC* 1731 3669 3679

TELEX COMMUNICATIONS HOLDINGS INC p 1435
12000 Portland Ave, Burnsville MN 55337
Tel (877) 863-4166 *SIC* 3663 3669 3679

ARTESYN NORTH AMERICA LLC p 114
7575 Market Place Dr, Eden Prairie MN 55344
Tel (952) 392-6500 *SIC* 3679 7629

HUTCHINSON TECHNOLOGY INC p 722
40 W Highland Park Dr Ne, Hutchinson MN 55350
Tel (320) 587-3797 *SIC* 3679 8731

▲ NORTECH SYSTEMS INC p 1049
7550 Meridian Cir N # 150, Maple Grove MN 55369
Tel (952) 345-2244 *SIC* 3674 3679

CYBERPOWER SYSTEMS (USA) INC p 405
4241 12th Ave E Ste 400, Shakopee MN 55379
Tel (952) 403-9500 *SIC* 3679

ELECTRICAL COMPONENTS INTERNATIONAL INC p 485
1 Cityplace Dr Ste 450, Saint Louis MO 63141
Tel (314) 692-4204 *SIC* 3679

▲ EMERSON ELECTRIC CO p 492
8000 W Florissant Ave, Saint Louis MO 63136
Tel (314) 553-2000
SIC 3823 3491 3621 3585 3679

■ DALE VISHAY ELECTRONICS LLC p 409
1122 23rd St, Columbus NE 68601
Tel (605) 665-9301
SIC 3676 3679 3677 3678

CONTINENTAL MICROWAVE AND TOOL CO INC p 363
11 Continental Dr, Exeter NH 03833
Tel (603) 775-5200 *SIC* 3679

AAVID CORP p 9
1 Aavid Cir, Laconia NH 03246
Tel (603) 528-3400 *SIC* 3679

AAVID THERMALLOY LLC p 9
1 Aavid Cir, Laconia NH 03246
Tel (603) 528-3400 *SIC* 3679

CELESTICA LLC p 273
11 Continental Blvd # 103, Merrimack NH 03054
Tel (603) 657-3001 *SIC* 3679

■ AMPHENOL PRINTED CIRCUITS INC p 86
91 Northeastern Blvd, Nashua NH 03062
Tel (603) 324-4500
SIC 3679 3678 3672 3357

BILLOWS ELECTRIC SUPPLY CO INC p 182
1813 Underwood Blvd, Delran NJ 08075
Tel (215) 332-9700
SIC 5063 3679 3621 3643 3644

EPCOS INC p 504
485b Route 1 S Ste 200, Iselin NJ 08830
Tel (732) 906-4300
SIC 3679 3546 5065 3671

▲ BEL FUSE INC p 169
206 Van Vorst St, Jersey City NJ 07302
Tel (201) 432-0463
SIC 3679 3674 3613 3677

■ SL INDUSTRIES INC p 1330
520 Fellowship Rd A114, Mount Laurel NJ 08054
Tel (856) 727-1500 *SIC* 3679 3643

HEYCO PRODUCTS INC p 688
1800 Industrial Way, Toms River NJ 08755
Tel (732) 286-4336 *SIC* 3351 3679

DIALIGHT CORP p 436
1501 State Route 34, Wall Township NJ 07727
Tel (732) 919-3119 *SIC* 3679 3674

ROXBORO HOLDINGS INC p 1254
1501 State Route 34, Wall Township NJ 07727
Tel (732) 919-3119
SIC 3643 3679 3993 3823 3674

HERLEY-CTI INC p 686
9 Whippany Rd, Whippany NJ 07981
Tel (973) 884-2580 *SIC* 3679

DELTA GROUP ELECTRONICS INC p 427
4521a Osuna Rd Ne, Albuquerque NM 87109
Tel (505) 883-7674 *SIC* 3643 3679

SOLAERO TECHNOLOGIES CORP p 1338
10420 Res Rd Se Bldg 1, Albuquerque NM 87123
Tel (505) 332-5000 *SIC* 3679 3674

■ EDO LLC p 478
1500 New Horizons Blvd, Amityville NY 11701
Tel (631) 630-4000
SIC 3812 3728 3663 3679

SCIENTIFIC COMPONENTS CORP p 1292
13 Neptune Ave, Brooklyn NY 11235
Tel (718) 934-4500 *SIC* 3679

GW LISK CO INC p 648
2 South St, Clifton Springs NY 14432
Tel (315) 462-2611 *SIC* 3679 4119 3492

■ PCB GROUP INC p 1123
3425 Walden Ave, Depew NY 14043
Tel (716) 684-0001 *SIC* 3679 3823

■ PCB PIEZOTRONICS INC p 1123
3425 Walden Ave, Depew NY 14043
Tel (716) 684-0001 *SIC* 3829 3679

ANAREN INC p 88
6635 Kirkville Rd, East Syracuse NY 13057
Tel (315) 432-8909 *SIC* 3679

■ AMPHENOL INTERCONNECT PRODUCTS CORP p 86
20 Valley St, Endicott NY 13760
Tel (607) 754-4444 *SIC* 3679

■ TELEPHONICS CORP p 1435
815 Broadhollow Rd, Farmingdale NY 11735
Tel (631) 755-7000
SIC 3669 3661 3679 3812 3663

PHILIPS MEDICAL SYSTEMS MR INC p 1143
450 Old Niskayuna Rd, Latham NY 12110
Tel (518) 782-1122 *SIC* 3845 3674 3679

KEARNEY-NATIONAL INC p 807
565 5th Ave Fl 4, New York NY 10017
Tel (212) 661-4600
SIC 3679 3694 3714 3625

■ L-3 COMMUNICATIONS CORP p 834
600 3rd Ave, New York NY 10016
Tel (212) 697-1111
SIC 3812 3663 3669 3679 3769

▲ L-3 COMMUNICATIONS HOLDINGS INC p 835
600 3rd Ave, New York NY 10016
Tel (212) 697-1111
SIC 3663 3669 3679 3812 3769

▲ IEC ELECTRONICS CORP p 730
105 Norton St, Newark NY 14513
Tel (315) 331-7742 *SIC* 3672 3679

COBHAM HOLDINGS (US) INC p 332
10 Cobham Dr, Orchard Park NY 14127
Tel (716) 662-0006 *SIC* 3679 3812

COBHAM HOLDINGS INC p 332
10 Orchard Park Dr, Orchard Park NY 14127
Tel (716) 662-0006 *SIC* 3679 3812

AEROFLEX PLAINVIEW INC p 30
35 S Service Rd, Plainview NY 11803
Tel (516) 694-6700
SIC 3679 3621 3674 3827

TDK USA CORP p 1429
455 Rxr Plz, Uniondale NY 11556
Tel (516) 535-2600 *SIC* 3679 8741

MOMENTIVE PERFORMANCE MATERIALS INC p 983
260 Hudson River Rd, Waterford NY 12188
Tel (518) 237-3330 *SIC* 2869 3479 3679

MPM HOLDINGS INC p 995
260 Hudson River Rd, Waterford NY 12188
Tel (518) 237-3330 *SIC* 2869 3479 3679

MPM INTERMEDIATE HOLDINGS INC p 995
260 Hudson River Rd, Waterford NY 12188
Tel (518) 237-3330 *SIC* 2869 3479 3679

HUBER + SUHNER INC p 716
8530 Steele Creek Place D, Charlotte NC 28273
Tel (704) 790-7300
SIC 3679 3678 3357 5065

■ COMMSCOPE INC OF NORTH CAROLINA p 346
1100 Commscope Pl Se, Hickory NC 28602
Tel (828) 324-2200
SIC 3663 3357 3679 3812 3699

SANTRONICS INC p 1281
3010 Lee Ave, Sanford NC 27332
Tel (919) 775-1223 *SIC* 3679 3674

■ AVIATION TECHNOLOGIES INC p 138
1301 E 9th St Ste 3000, Cleveland OH 44114
Tel (216) 706-2960
SIC 3643 3678 3679 3728 3812 3648

CORTES NP ACQUISITION CORP p 373
1050 Dearborn Dr, Columbus OH 43085
Tel (614) 888-0246 SIC 3679 3585

ELECTROMOTIVE INC p 485
4880 Hudson Dr, Stow OH 44224
Tel (330) 688-6494 SIC 3679 3677

PLANAR SYSTEMS INC p 1154
1195 Nw Compton Way, Beaverton OR 97006
Tel (503) 748-1100 SIC 3679

VANGUARD EMS INC p 1543
3725 Sw Hocken Ave, Beaverton OR 97005
Tel (503) 644-4808 SIC 3672 3679

OECO HOLDINGS LLC p 1075
4607 Se International Way, Milwaukie OR 97222
Tel (503) 659-5999 SIC 3679 5065

OECO LLC p 1075
4607 Se International Way, Milwaukie OR 97222
Tel (503) 659-5999
SIC 3679 5065 4911 3621 3694

PRECISION INTERCONNECT LLC p 1168
10025 Sw Freeman Dr, Wilsonville OR 97070
Tel (503) 620-9400 SIC 3679

SPECTRUM MICROWAVE INC p 1357
8061 Avonia Rd, Fairview PA 16415
Tel (814) 474-4300 SIC 3679

■ SPS TECHNOLOGIES LLC p 1362
301 Highland Ave, Jenkintown PA 19046
Tel (215) 572-3000
SIC 3452 3423 3499 3264 3679 3341

▲ BLACK BOX CORP p 186
1000 Park Dr, Lawrence PA 15055
Tel (724) 746-5500
SIC 3577 3679 3661 5045 5065 5063

■ BLACK BOX CORP OF PENNSYLVANIA p 186
1000 Park Dr, Lawrence PA 15055
Tel (724) 746-5500
SIC 5045 5063 5065 3577 3679 3661

SMITHS GROUP NORTH AMERICA INC p 1334
101 Lindenwood Dr Ste 125, Malvern PA 19355
Tel (772) 286-9300 SIC 3812 3841 3679

FARGO ASSEMBLY OF PA INC p 528
800 W Washington St, Norristown PA 19401
Tel (610) 272-6850 SIC 3679

GLOBAL HARNESS SYSTEMS INC p 616
3304 Danley Rd, Philadelphia PA 19154
Tel (609) 815-2100 SIC 3679

SAINT-GOBAIN CERAMICS & PLASTICS INC p 1271
750 E Swedesford Rd, Valley Forge PA 19482
Tel (610) 341-7000
SIC 2819 3679 3544 3297

SCHNEIDER ELECTRIC IT USA INC p 1288
132 Fairgrounds Rd, West Kingston RI 02892
Tel (401) 789-5735 SIC 3679

■ SHAKESPEARE CO LLC p 1310
6111 Shakespeare Rd, Columbia SC 29223
Tel (803) 754-7011
SIC 3089 3949 3679 3663

■ ITRON ELECTRICITY METERING INC p 768
313 N Highway 11, West Union SC 29696
Tel (864) 638-8300
SIC 3825 3823 3824 3679 3829 3612

TUFFTORQ CORP p 1491
5943 Commerce Blvd, Morristown TN 37814
Tel (423) 585-2000 SIC 3679 3524

MACLEAN POWER TN LLC p 892
1465 Industrial Park Dr, Trenton TN 38382
Tel (847) 566-0010 SIC 3679

▲ BENCHMARK ELECTRONICS INC p 172
3000 Technology Rd, Angleton TX 77515
Tel (979) 849-6550 SIC 3672 3679

JEWELRY CHANNEL INC p 784
100 Mchl Agl Way Ste 400d, Austin TX 78728
Tel (512) 852-7000 SIC 3679

HICKS HOLDINGS LLC p 690
2200 Ross Ave Ste 5000, Dallas TX 75201
Tel (214) 615-2300 SIC 3679

OCULAR LCD INC p 1074
12700 Park Central Dr # 750, Dallas TX 75251
Tel (972) 437-3888 SIC 3679

TXU ENERGY SERVICES CO LLC p 1495
1601 Bryan St, Dallas TX 75201
Tel (214) 812-4600 SIC 3679

ELCOM INC p 484
20 Butterfield Trail Blvd, El Paso TX 79906
Tel (915) 298-2000 SIC 3679 3694

■ STONERIDGE ELECTRONICS INC p 1391
21 Butterfield Trail Blvd A, El Paso TX 79906
Tel (915) 593-2011 SIC 3679 3714

AIRBORN INTERCONNECT INC p 39
3500 Airborn Cir, Georgetown TX 78626
Tel (512) 863-5585 SIC 3678 3679

CREATION TECHNOLOGIES KENTUCKY INC p 390
1001 Klein Rd Ste 100, Plano TX 75074
Tel (859) 253-3066 SIC 3679 3672

MACH SPEED HOLDINGS LLC p 892
7200 Bishop Rd Ste 280, Plano TX 75024
Tel (214) 978-3800 SIC 5091 5065 3679

QORVO INC p 1195
500 W Renner Rd, Richardson TX 75080
Tel (972) 994-8200 SIC 3663 3674 3679

▲ CONTROL4 CORP p 364
11734 S Election Rd, Draper UT 84020
Tel (801) 523-3100 SIC 3679 7372

SKULLCANDY INC p 1330
1441 Ute Blvd Ste 250, Park City UT 84098
Tel (435) 940-1545 SIC 3679

COBHAM AES HOLDINGS INC p 332
2121 Crystal Dr Ste 625, Arlington VA 22202
Tel (703) 414-5300 SIC 3679 3812

DRS TECHNOLOGIES INC p 457
2345 Crystal Dr Ste 1000, Arlington VA 22202
Tel (973) 898-1500
SIC 3812 3699 3572 3669 3679 8741

THALES USA INC p 1446
2733 Crystal Dr, Arlington VA 22202
Tel (703) 413-6029
SIC 5065 3699 3679 3841 8711 7371

■ ITT DEFENSE & ELECTRONICS INC p 768
1650 Tysons Blvd Ste 1700, Mc Lean VA 22102
Tel (703) 790-6300
SIC 3679 3678 3674 3769 3489

QUALITEL CORP p 1196
11831 Beverly Park Rd A, Everett WA 98204
Tel (425) 423-8388 SIC 3679

■ CRANE ELECTRONICS INC p 388
10301 Willows Rd Ne, Redmond WA 98052
Tel (425) 882-3100 SIC 3679

GM NAMEPLATE INC p 618
2040 15th Ave W, Seattle WA 98119
Tel (206) 284-2200 SIC 3479 2679 3679

■ HONEYWELL ELECTRONIC MATERIALS INC p 705
15128 E Euclid Ave, Spokane Valley WA 99216
Tel (509) 252-2200 SIC 3679 3674 3643

POWER PRODUCTS LLC p 1165
N85w12545 Westbrook Xing, Menomonee Falls WI 53051
Tel (262) 293-0600 SIC 3679 3699 3691

FISKARS BRANDS INC p 552
7800 Discovery Dr, Middleton WI 53562
Tel (608) 259-1649
SIC 3052 3679 3421 3069 3423

■ ELECTRONIC ASSEMBLY CORP p 485
55 Jewelers Park Dr, Neenah WI 54956
Tel (920) 722-3451
SIC 3672 3679 3825 3841

COOPER POWER SYSTEMS LLC p 367
2300 Badger Dr, Waukesha WI 53188
Tel (262) 524-4227
SIC 3612 3613 3644 3643 3629 3679

SIC 3691 Storage Batteries

A & A MANUFACTURING CO INC p 4
1675 Sampson Ave, Corona CA 92879
Tel (951) 371-8090 SIC 3691

TROJAN BATTERY CO LLC p 1483
12380 Clark St, Santa Fe Springs CA 90670
Tel (800) 423-6569 SIC 3691 3692

■ DURACELL INC p 462
14 Research Dr, Bethel CT 06801
Tel (203) 796-4000 SIC 3691

■ DURACELL INTERNATIONAL INC p 462
14 Research Dr, Bethel CT 06801
Tel (203) 796-4000 SIC 3691

■ SAFT AMERICA INC p 1267
13575 Waterworks St, Jacksonville FL 32221
Tel (904) 861-1501 SIC 3691 5063

PANASONIC ENERGY CORP OF AMERICA p 1111
1 Panasonic Dr, Columbus GA 31907
Tel (706) 561-7730 SIC 3691 5531

EXIDE TECHNOLOGIES p 519
13000 Deerfield Pkwy # 200, Milton GA 30004
Tel (678) 566-9000 SIC 3691

B456 SYSTEMS INC p 143
200 West St, Waltham MA 02451
Tel (617) 778-5700 SIC 3691

▲ AROTECH CORP p 112
1229 Oak Valley Dr, Ann Arbor MI 48108
Tel (800) 281-0356 SIC 3691 3694

A123 SYSTEMS LLC p 7
39000 7 Mile Rd, Livonia MI 48152
Tel (734) 772-0300 SIC 5063 3691

EP MANAGEMENT CORP p 504
801 W Ann Arbor Trl # 220, Plymouth MI 48170
Tel (313) 749-5500
SIC 3692 3661 2834 3674 3691

■ UNITED INDUSTRIES CORP p 1509
1 Rider Trl Ste 300, Earth City MO 63045
Tel (314) 738-0375 SIC 2879 3691

EAGLEPICHER TECHNOLOGIES LLC p 468
C & Porter Sts, Joplin MO 64802
Tel (417) 623-8000
SIC 3691 3629 3599 2892

■ ENERGIZER BATTERY INC p 497
533 Maryville Univ Dr, Saint Louis MO 63141
Tel (314) 985-2000 SIC 3691

▲ ENERGIZER HOLDINGS INC p 497
533 Maryville Univ Dr, Saint Louis MO 63141
Tel (314) 985-2000 SIC 3691

PACIFIC DUNLOP HOLDINGS (USA) LLC p 1104
200 Schulz Dr, Red Bank NJ 07701
Tel (732) 345-5400 SIC 3069 3691

ENER1 INC p 497
1540 Broadway Fl 25c, New York NY 10036
Tel (212) 920-3500 SIC 3691

▲ HRG GROUP INC p 714
450 Park Ave Fl 29, New York NY 10022
Tel (212) 906-8555
SIC 3691 3634 3999 6311

POLYPORE INTERNATIONAL LP p 1160
11430 N Community House R, Charlotte NC 28277
Tel (704) 587-8409 SIC 3691

■ TRANSDIGM INC p 1471
4223 Monticello Blvd, Cleveland OH 44121
Tel (216) 706-2939
SIC 5088 3563 3625 3492 3691 3491

GOULD ELECTRONICS INC p 626
34929 Curtis Blvd Ste 100, Eastlake OH 44095
Tel (440) 953-5000
SIC 3825 3497 3613 3691 3674

CROWN BATTERY MANUFACTURING CO p 395
1445 Majestic Dr, Fremont OH 43420
Tel (419) 332-0563 SIC 3691

■ ENERGIZER MANUFACTURING INC p 497
25225 Detroit Rd, Westlake OH 44145
Tel (440) 835-7866 SIC 3691

C&D TECHNOLOGIES INC p 233
1400 Union Meeting Rd # 110, Blue Bell PA 19422
Tel (215) 619-7815
SIC 3612 3691 3613 3692 3674

EAST PENN MANUFACTURING CO p 470
102 Deka Rd, Lyon Station PA 19536
Tel (610) 682-6361
SIC 3694 3691 5063 4225

▲ ENERSYS p 498
2366 Bernville Rd, Reading PA 19605
Tel (610) 208-1991 SIC 3691 3699

■ ENERSYS DELAWARE INC p 498
2366 Bernville Rd, Reading PA 19605
Tel (214) 324-8990 SIC 3691 5063

▲ INTEGER HOLDINGS CORP p 748
2595 Dallas Pkwy Ste 310, Frisco TX 75034
Tel (716) 759-5600 SIC 3675 3692 3691

POWER PRODUCTS LLC p 1165
N85w12545 Westbrook Xing, Menomonee Falls WI 53051
Tel (262) 293-0600 SIC 3679 3699 3691

JOHNSON CONTROLS BATTERY GROUP INC p 791
5757 N Green Bay Ave, Milwaukee WI 53209
Tel (414) 524-1200 SIC 3691

JOHNSON CONTROLS INC p 791
5757 N Green Bay Ave, Milwaukee WI 53209
Tel (414) 524-1200
SIC 2531 3714 3691 3822 8744

SIC 3692 Primary Batteries: Dry & Wet

TROJAN BATTERY CO LLC p 1483
12380 Clark St, Santa Fe Springs CA 90670
Tel (800) 423-6569 SIC 3691 3692

EP MANAGEMENT CORP p 504
801 W Ann Arbor Trl # 220, Plymouth MI 48170
Tel (313) 749-5500
SIC 3692 3661 2834 3674 3691

NORTHSTAR BATTERY CO LLC p 1058
4000 E Continental Way, Springfield MO 65803
Tel (417) 575-8200 SIC 3692

C&D TECHNOLOGIES INC p 233
1400 Union Meeting Rd # 110, Blue Bell PA 19422
Tel (215) 619-7815
SIC 3612 3691 3613 3692 3674

▲ INTEGER HOLDINGS CORP p 748
2595 Dallas Pkwy Ste 310, Frisco TX 75034
Tel (716) 759-5600 SIC 3675 3692 3691

■ SPECTRUM BRANDS HOLDINGS INC p 1357
3001 Deming Way, Middleton WI 53562
Tel (608) 275-3340
SIC 3692 2879 3999 3648

■ SPECTRUM BRANDS INC p 1357
3001 Deming Way, Middleton WI 53562
Tel (608) 275-3340
SIC 3692 3634 2879 3999 3648

SIC 3694 Electrical Eqpt For Internal Combustion Engines

SYNCRO CORP p 1415
1030 Sundown Dr Nw, Arab AL 35016
Tel (256) 586-6045
SIC 3714 3625 3694 3823 3643

BBB INDUSTRIES LLC p 163
29627 Renaissance Blvd, Daphne AL 36526
Tel (800) 280-2737 SIC 3694 3714

WALBRO LLC p 1572
2015 W River Rd 202, Tucson AZ 85704
Tel (520) 229-5642
SIC 3592 3594 3694 3443

▲ AEROVIRONMENT INC p 31
800 Royal Oaks Dr Ste 210, Monrovia CA 91016
Tel (626) 357-9983 SIC 3721 8711 3694

PACIFIC SCIENTIFIC CO INC p 1105
1785 Voyager Ave Ste 101, Simi Valley CA 93063
Tel (805) 526-5700
SIC 3812 3669 3621 3694 3823 3625

▲ MOTORCAR PARTS OF AMERICA INC p 993
2929 California St, Torrance CA 90503
Tel (310) 212-7910
SIC 3714 3694 3625 5013

■ UNISON INDUSTRIES LLC p 1505
7575 Baymeadows Way, Jacksonville FL 32256
Tel (904) 739-4000 SIC 3694

ROBERT BOSCH LLC p 1241
2800 S 25th Ave, Broadview IL 60155
Tel (248) 876-1000
SIC 3714 3694 5013 5064 3565 3541

FRAM GROUP OPERATIONS LLC p 573
1900 W Field Ct, Lake Forest IL 60045
Tel (800) 890-2075 SIC 3694 3714

■ MONONA HOLDINGS LLC p 984
1952 Mc Dowell Rd Ste 207, Naperville IL 60563
Tel (630) 946-0630 SIC 3694 5063

▲ CUMMINS INC p 401
500 Jackson St, Columbus IN 47201
Tel (812) 377-5000
SIC 3519 3714 3694 3621

CPX INC p 388
410 E Kent St, Kentland IN 47951
Tel (219) 474-5280 SIC 3089 3694

■ BALLANTRAE INC p 148
600 Corporation Dr, Pendleton IN 46064
Tel (800) 372-3555 SIC 3714 3694

■ BORGWARNER PDS (INDIANA) INC p 201
600 Corporation Dr, Pendleton IN 46064
Tel (800) 372-3555 SIC 3694 3714

■ NEW PDS CORP p 1032
600 Corporation Dr, Pendleton IN 46064
Tel (800) 372-3555 SIC 3694 3714

■ REMAN HOLDINGS LLC p 1222
600 Corporation Dr, Pendleton IN 46064
Tel (800) 372-5131 SIC 3714 3694

■ REMY HOLDINGS INC p 1223
600 Corporation Dr, Pendleton IN 46064
Tel (765) 778-6499 SIC 3694 3714

■ REMY INC p 1223
600 Corporation Dr, Pendleton IN 46064
Tel (765) 778-6499
SIC 3714 3694 3625 3621 5013

■ REMY POWER PRODUCTS LLC p 1223
600 Corporation Dr, Pendleton IN 46064
Tel (765) 778-6499 SIC 3625 3694 3621

■ MONONA WIRE CORP p 984
301 W Spruce St, Monona IA 52159
Tel (563) 539-2012 SIC 3679 3694

SUMITOMO ELECTRIC WIRING SYSTEMS INC p 1398
1018 Ashley St, Bowling Green KY 42103
Tel (270) 782-7397 SIC 3714 5063 3694

HITACHI AUTOMOTIVE SYSTEMS AMERICAS INC p 696
955 Warwick Rd, Harrodsburg KY 40330
Tel (859) 734-9451
SIC 3694 3714 3699 3625

AEES POWER SYSTEMS LIMITED PARTNERSHIP p 29
999 Republic Dr, Allen Park MI 48101
Tel (248) 489-4900 SIC 3694

▲ AROTECH CORP p 112
1229 Oak Valley Dr, Ann Arbor MI 48108
Tel (800) 281-0356 SIC 3691 3694

■ WOLVERINE ADVANCED MATERIALS LLC p 1621
5850 Mercury Dr Ste 250, Dearborn MI 48126
Tel (313) 749-6100 SIC 3559 3694

PRESTOLITE ELECTRIC HOLDING INC p 1173
30120 Hudson Dr, Novi MI 48377
Tel (248) 313-3807 SIC 3621 3694

PRESTOLITE ELECTRIC INC p 1173
30120 Hudson Dr, Novi MI 48377
Tel (585) 492-1700 SIC 3621 3694

PRESTOLITE ELECTRIC LLC p 1173
30120 Hudson Dr, Novi MI 48377
Tel (248) 313-3807
SIC 3643 3824 3621 3625 3694

■ FEDERAL-MOGUL CORP p 536
27300 W 11 Mile Rd, Southfield MI 48034
Tel (248) 354-7700
SIC 3559 3462 3812 3674 3694

■ FEDERAL-MOGUL HOLDINGS CORP p 536
27300 W 11 Mile Rd, Southfield MI 48034
Tel (248) 354-7700
SIC 3462 3559 3694 3812 3674 3714

■ PRESTOLITE WIRE LLC p 1173
200 Galleria Officentre, Southfield MI 48034
Tel (248) 355-4422 SIC 3694

■ VIASYSTEMS GROUP INC p 1554
101 S Hanley Rd Ste 400, Saint Louis MO 63105
Tel (314) 727-2087 SIC 3672 3694

▲ STANDARD MOTOR PRODUCTS INC p 1376
3718 Northern Blvd # 600, Long Island City NY 11101
Tel (718) 392-0200
SIC 3714 3694 3585 3564 3052

LEVITON MANUFACTURING CO INC p 858
201 N Service Rd, Melville NY 11747
Tel (631) 812-6000
SIC 3643 3613 3357 3674 3694 3678

■ IEH FM HOLDINGS LLC p 730
767 5th Ave Ste 4700, New York NY 10153
Tel (212) 702-4300
SIC 3462 3559 3694 3812 3674

KEARNEY-NATIONAL INC p 807
565 5th Ave Fl 4, New York NY 10017
Tel (212) 661-4600
SIC 3679 3694 3714 3625

KEIHIN CAROLINA SYSTEM TECHNOLOGY LLC p 807
4047 Mcnair Rd, Tarboro NC 27886
Tel (252) 641-6750 SIC 3694 3625 3714

TRI-W GROUP INC p 1478
835 Goodale Blvd, Columbus OH 43212
Tel (614) 228-5000 SIC 3694 7538 7537

GSW MANUFACTURING INC p 644
1801 Production Dr, Findlay OH 45840
Tel (419) 423-7111 SIC 3714 3694

STANLEY ELECTRIC US CO INC p 1377
420 E High St, London OH 43140
Tel (740) 852-5200 SIC 3647 3694 3089

MITSUBISHI ELECTRIC AUTOMOTIVE AMERICA INC p 977
4773 Bethany Rd, Mason OH 45040
Tel (513) 573-6614 SIC 3694 3651 3714

ENOVATION CONTROLS LLC p 500
5311 S 122nd East Ave, Tulsa OK 74146
Tel (918) 317-4100
SIC 3625 3714 3694 8711

OECO LLC p 1075
4607 Se International Way, Milwaukie OR 97222
Tel (503) 659-5999
SIC 3679 5065 4911 3621 3694

KALAS MFG INC p 801
167 Greenfield Rd, Lancaster PA 17601
Tel (717) 335-2360 SIC 3357 3694

EAST PENN MANUFACTURING CO p 470
102 Deka Rd, Lyon Station PA 19536
Tel (610) 682-6361
SIC 3694 3691 5063 4225

■ ATC TECHNOLOGY CORP p 124
100 Papercraft Park, Pittsburgh PA 15238
Tel (412) 820-3700 SIC 1541 3694 4225

FENIX MANUFACTURING SOLUTIONS LLC p 537
2063 University Pkwy, Aiken SC 29801
Tel (803) 649-1381
SIC 3694 3825 3625 3354

DENSO MANUFACTURING ATHENS TENNESSEE INC p 428
2400 Denso Dr, Athens TN 37303
Tel (423) 746-0000 SIC 3694 3714

DENSO MANUFACTURING TENNESSEE INC p 429
1720 Robert C Jackson Dr, Maryville TN 37801
Tel (865) 982-7000 SIC 3694 3714

FLARE INDUSTRIES LLC p 554
16310 Bratton Ln Ste 350, Austin TX 78728
Tel (512) 836-9473
SIC 3822 7359 3694 2899 1711 3569

INTERSTATE BATTERIES INC p 758
12770 Merit Dr Ste 400, Dallas TX 75251
Tel (972) 991-1444 SIC 5531 3694

DELPHI AUTOMOTIVE SYSTEMS CORP p 425
12170 Rojas Dr, El Paso TX 79936
Tel (915) 612-2855 SIC 3694

ELAMEX USA CORP p 483
1800 Northwestern Dr, El Paso TX 79912
Tel (915) 298-3061 SIC 3694 2068 2064

ELCOM INC p 484
20 Butterfield Trail Blvd, El Paso TX 79906
Tel (915) 298-2000 SIC 3679 3694

MSDP GROUP LLC p 997
1350 Pullman Dr Dr14, El Paso TX 79936
Tel (915) 857-5200 SIC 3694

■ ATC LOGISTICS & ELECTRONICS INC p 124
13500 Independence Pkwy, Fort Worth TX 76177
Tel (817) 491-7700 SIC 4225 3714 3694

■ SIMMONDS PRECISION PRODUCTS INC p 1324
100 Panton Rd, Vergennes VT 05491
Tel (802) 877-4000
SIC 3829 3694 3724 3728

■ ATLANTIC RESEARCH CORP p 127
5945 Wellington Rd, Gainesville VA 20155
Tel (703) 754-5000 SIC 3764 3694

DIAMOND ELECTRIC MFG CORP p 436
Hc 62, Eleanor WV 25070
Tel (304) 586-0070 SIC 3694

NGK SPARK PLUGS (USA) INC p 1041
1 Ngk Dr, Sissonville WV 25320
Tel (304) 988-0060 SIC 5013 3694

WELLS VEHICLE ELECTRONICS LP p 1591
385 W Rolling Meadows Dr, Fond Du Lac WI 54937
Tel (920) 922-5900
SIC 3714 3694 3644 3357

SIC 3695 Recording Media

LG ELECTRONICS ALABAMA INC p 860
201 James Record Rd Sw, Huntsville AL 35824
Tel (256) 772-0623
SIC 3651 3695 5064 5085 5065 4225

NAJAFI COMPANIES LLC p 1006
2525 E Camelback Rd, Phoenix AZ 85016
Tel (602) 476-0600 SIC 3695

■ ELECTRONIC ARTS REDWOOD INC p 485
209 Redwood Shores Pkwy, Redwood City CA 94065
Tel (650) 628-1500 SIC 3695

SONY ELECTRONICS INC p 1341
16535 Via Esprillo Bldg 1, San Diego CA 92127
Tel (858) 942-2400
SIC 3651 5064 3695 3671 3572 3674

■ WD MEDIA LLC p 1585
1710 Automation Pkwy, San Jose CA 95131
Tel (408) 576-2000 SIC 3695

RICOH ELECTRONICS INC p 1233
1100 Valencia Ave, Tustin CA 92780
Tel (714) 566-2500 SIC 3861 3695

■ DICTAPHONE CORP p 438
3191 Broadbridge Ave, Stratford CT 06614
Tel (203) 381-7000
SIC 3579 3825 3695 3577

CINRAM INC p 308
1600 Rich Rd, Richmond IN 47374
Tel (416) 298-8190 SIC 3652 3695

SONY DADC US INC p 1341
1800 N Fruitridge Ave, Terre Haute IN 47804
Tel (812) 462-8100
SIC 3695 3652 3651 3577 3572

DAIFUKU WEBB HOLDING CO p 408
34375 W 12 Mile Rd, Farmington Hills MI 48331
Tel (248) 553-1000 SIC 3695

■ COMPELLENT TECHNOLOGIES INC p 351
12982 Valley View Rd, Eden Prairie MN 55344
Tel (952) 294-3300 SIC 3571 3695

▲ IMATION CORP p 733
1099 Helmo Ave N Ste 250, Oakdale MN 55128
Tel (651) 704-4000 SIC 3695 3572

■ IMATION ENTERPRISES CORP p 733
1099 Helmo Ave N Ste 250, Saint Paul MN 55128
Tel (651) 704-4000 SIC 3695 3845 5112

SONY CORP OF AMERICA p 1341
25 Madison Ave Fl 27, New York NY 10010
Tel (212) 833-8000
SIC 3695 3652 3651 3577 3572

FUJIFILM NORTH AMERICA CORP p 583
200 Summit Lake Dr Fl 2, Valhalla NY 10595
Tel (914) 789-8100
SIC 7384 5043 5065 3695 2673 3861

OLYMPUS AMERICA INC p 1083
3500 Corporate Pkwy, Center Valley PA 18034
Tel (484) 896-5000
SIC 5047 5043 5064 3827 3695 3572

OLYMPUS CORP OF AMERICAS p 1083
3500 Corp Pkwy, Center Valley PA 18034
Tel (484) 896-5000
SIC 5047 5043 5064 3827 3695 3572

CINRAM GROUP INC p 308
437 New Sanford Rd, La Vergne TN 37086
Tel (615) 287-3800 SIC 3695

▲ BRADY CORP p 207
6555 W Good Hope Rd, Milwaukee WI 53223
Tel (414) 358-6600
SIC 3993 2672 3695 3577

SIC 3699 Electrical Machinery, Eqpt & Splys, NEC

■ BENCHMARK ELECTRONICS HUNTSVILLE INC p 172
4807 Bradford Dr Nw, Huntsville AL 35805
Tel (256) 722-6000 SIC 3699

PACIFIC SCIENTIFIC ENERGETIC MATERIALS CO (CALIFORNIA) LLC p 1105
7073 W Willis Rd Ste 5002, Chandler AZ 85226
Tel (480) 763-3000
SIC 2892 2899 3483 3489 3699 3728

HASKEL INTERNATIONAL LLC p 667
100 E Graham Pl, Burbank CA 91502
Tel (818) 843-4000
SIC 3561 3594 5084 5085 3699

LORENZ INC p 878
280 Campillo St Ste G, Calexico CA 92231
Tel (760) 356-1019 SIC 3699

■ TR MANUFACTURING LLC p 1468
45757 Northport Loop W, Fremont CA 94538
Tel (510) 657-3850 SIC 3699

MITSUBISHI KAGAKU IMAGING CORP p 978
655 N Central Ave # 1550, Glendale CA 91203
Tel (818) 837-8100 SIC 5044 3699

■ FLIR COMMERCIAL SYSTEMS INC p 557
6769 Hollister Ave # 100, Goleta CA 93117
Tel (805) 690-6685 SIC 5065 3699

■ PACIFIC SCIENTIFIC ENERGETIC MATERIALS CO (CALIFORNIA) p 1105
3601 Union Rd, Hollister CA 95023
Tel (831) 637-3731
SIC 2892 2899 3489 3483 3699 3728

DIGIPAS TECHNOLOGIES INC p 439
200 Spectrum Center Dr, Irvine CA 92618
Tel (949) 558-0160 SIC 3429 3499 3699

■ NEWPORT CORP p 1038
1791 Deere Ave, Irvine CA 92606
Tel (949) 863-3144
SIC 3821 3699 3827 3826

TOPCON POSITIONING SYSTEMS INC p 1461
7400 National Dr, Livermore CA 94550
Tel (925) 245-8300
SIC 3829 3625 3823 3699 8713 1794

GORES RADIO HOLDINGS LLC p 626
10877 Wilshire Blvd # 1805, Los Angeles CA 90024
Tel (310) 209-3010 SIC 3699 7382

ONESOURCE DISTRIBUTORS LLC p 1088
3951 Oceanic Dr, Oceanside CA 92056
Tel (760) 966-4500 SIC 5063 3699

COMMUNICATIONS & POWER INDUSTRIES LLC p 347
607 Hansen Way, Palo Alto CA 94304
Tel (650) 846-2900
SIC 3671 3679 3699 3663

CPI INTERNATIONAL INC p 387
811 Hansen Way, Palo Alto CA 94304
Tel (650) 846-2801
SIC 3671 3679 3699 3825

▲ COHU INC p 335
12367 Crosthwaite Cir, Poway CA 92064
Tel (858) 848-8100 SIC 3825 3663 3699

▲ CUBIC CORP p 399
9333 Balboa Ave, San Diego CA 92123
Tel (858) 277-6780 SIC 3812 3699 7372

■ CUBIC DEFENSE APPLICATIONS INC p 399
9333 Balboa Ave, San Diego CA 92123
Tel (858) 277-6780 SIC 3699 3663 3812

CYMER INC p 405
17075 Thornmint Ct, San Diego CA 92127
Tel (858) 385-7300 SIC 3699 3827

CYMER LLC p 405
17075 Thornmint Ct, San Diego CA 92127
Tel (858) 385-7300 SIC 3699 3827

O & S CALIFORNIA INC p 1070
9731 Siempre Viva Rd E, San Diego CA 92154
Tel (619) 661-1800 SIC 3699

■ RAE SYSTEMS INC p 1205
3775 N 1st St, San Jose CA 95134
Tel (408) 952-8200 SIC 3829 3812 3699

TECHKO INC p 1431
27301 Calle De La Rosa, San Juan Capistrano CA 92675
Tel (949) 486-0678 SIC 3699 3589

ALTA PROPERTIES INC p 61
879 Ward Dr, Santa Barbara CA 93111
Tel (805) 967-0171
SIC 3264 3699 3823 3679

■ AKT AMERICA INC p 42
3101 Scott Blvd Bldg 91, Santa Clara CA 95054
Tel (408) 563-5455 SIC 3699

▲ COHERENT INC p 335
5100 Patrick Henry Dr, Santa Clara CA 95054
Tel (408) 764-4000 SIC 3826 3845 3699

■ SPECTRA-PHYSICS INC p 1357
3635 Peterson Way, Santa Clara CA 95054
Tel (650) 961-2550 SIC 3699 8731

WALTERS WHOLESALE ELECTRIC CO p 1574
2825 Temple Ave, Signal Hill CA 90755
Tel (562) 988-3100 SIC 5063 3699 1731

MEGGITT SAFETY SYSTEMS INC p 940
1785 Voyager Ave Ste 100, Simi Valley CA 93063
Tel (805) 584-4100 SIC 3699 3724 3728

■ BRANSON ULTRASONICS CORP p 208
41 Eagle Rd Ste 1, Danbury CT 06810
Tel (203) 796-0400 SIC 3699 3548 3541

▲ UNITED TECHNOLOGIES CORP p 1514
10 Farm Springs Rd, Farmington CT 06032
Tel (860) 728-7000
SIC 3724 3585 3721 3534 3669 3699

▲ STANLEY BLACK & DECKER INC p 1377
1000 Stanley Dr, New Britain CT 06053
Tel (860) 225-5111
SIC 3429 3546 3423 3452 3699

ASSA ABLOY INC p 119
110 Sargent Dr, New Haven CT 06511
Tel (203) 624-5225
SIC 5065 5072 3699 3429

ADT CORP p 24
1501 Yamato Rd, Boca Raton FL 33431
Tel (561) 988-3600 SIC 7381 7382 3699

DEVCON INTERNATIONAL CORP p 433
595 S Federal Hwy Ste 500, Boca Raton FL 33432
Tel (954) 926-5200
SIC 3699 3273 3281 3271 2951 5032

RED HAWK FIRE & SECURITY LLC p 1215
5100 Town Center Cir # 350, Boca Raton FL 33486
Tel (561) 672-3737 SIC 3699 7382

SIMPLEXGRINNELL HOLDINGS LLC p 1325
1501 Nw 51st St, Boca Raton FL 33431
Tel (561) 988-7200
SIC 3579 3669 3699 3822

INTERBOND HOLDING CORP p 751
3200 Sw 42nd St, Fort Lauderdale FL 33312
Tel (954) 797-4000 SIC 7629 3699 5722

▲ FIDELITY NATIONAL FINANCIAL INC p 540
601 Riverside Ave Fl 4, Jacksonville FL 32204
Tel (904) 854-8100
SIC 6361 6331 6531 8741 3699

■ SERVICELINK HOLDINGS LLC p 1307
601 Riverside Ave Bldg 5, Jacksonville FL 32204
Tel (904) 854-8100
SIC 6361 6331 6531 8741 3699

▲ HARRIS CORP p 663
1025 W Nasa Blvd, Melbourne FL 32919
Tel (321) 727-9100
SIC 3812 3663 3699 3661 3674

■ SEQUA CORP p 1306
3999 Rca Blvd, Palm Beach Gardens FL 33410
Tel (201) 343-1122
SIC 3724 3764 3812 3699 3845 3542

CAE USA INC p 236
4908 Tampa West Blvd, Tampa FL 33634
Tel (813) 885-7481
SIC 3699 7373 8299 8249 8711

■ AQUILEX SPECIALTY REPAIR AND OVERHAUL LLC p 102
3344 Peachtree Rd Ne, Atlanta GA 30326
Tel (800) 868-9353 SIC 3699

AUBREY SILVEY ENTERPRISES INC p 130
371 Hamp Jones Rd, Carrollton GA 30117
Tel (770) 834-0738
SIC 1629 1541 3643 7389 3699 5063

▲ WESTROCK CO p 1602
504 Thrasher St, Norcross GA 30071
Tel (678) 291-7456
SIC 2631 2899 3699 6531

MEGGITT TRAINING SYSTEMS INC p 940
296 Brogdon Rd, Suwanee GA 30024
Tel (678) 288-1090 SIC 3699

MAGNETROL INTERNATIONAL INC p 896
705 Enterprise St, Aurora IL 60504
Tel (630) 723-6600
SIC 3823 3699 3643 3625 3541

RAYNOR MFG CO p 1210
1101 E River Rd, Dixon IL 61021
Tel (815) 288-1431
SIC 3442 7011 3699 2431

CHAMBERLAIN GROUP INC p 287
845 N Larch Ave, Elmhurst IL 60126
Tel (630) 279-3600 SIC 3699

CHAMBERLAIN MANUFACTURING CORP p 287
845 N Larch Ave, Elmhurst IL 60126
Tel (630) 279-3600 SIC 3651 3625 3699

DUCHOSSOIS GROUP INC p 459
845 N Larch Ave, Elmhurst IL 60126
Tel (630) 279-3600 SIC 3699

OMRON ELECTRONICS LLC p 1085
2895 Greenspt Pkwy 200, Hoffman Estates IL 60169
Tel (847) 843-7900 SIC 5065 3699

ALLMETAL INC p 58
1 Pierce Pl Ste 900, Itasca IL 60143
Tel (630) 250-8090 SIC 3699 3089

ROUNDTABLE HEALTHCARE PARTNERS LP p 1253
272 E Deerpath Ste 350, Lake Forest IL 60045
Tel (847) 482-9275 SIC 6722 3699 2834

■ TENNECO AUTOMOTIVE OPERATING CO INC p 1437
500 N Field Dr, Lake Forest IL 60045
Tel (847) 482-5000 SIC 3714 3699

■ APPLETON GRP LLC p 99
9377 W Higgins Rd, Rosemont IL 60018
Tel (847) 268-6000
SIC 3644 3643 3613 3646 3699

PANDUIT CORP p 1111
18900 Panduit Dr, Tinley Park IL 60487
Tel (708) 532-1800 SIC 3699 3644 5063

■ COMMSCOPE TECHNOLOGIES LLC p 346
4 Westbrook Corporate Ctr, Westchester IL 60154
Tel (708) 236-6000
SIC 3663 3357 3679 3812 3699

XFMRS HOLDINGS INC p 1631
7570 E Landersdale Rd, Camby IN 46113
Tel (317) 834-1066 SIC 3699

DOREL JUVENILE GROUP INC p 451
2525 State St, Columbus IN 47201
Tel (800) 457-5276
SIC 3089 3069 3429 3699 3648

■ STANLEY SECURITY SOLUTIONS INC p 1377
9998 Crosspoint Blvd # 3, Indianapolis IN 46256
Tel (317) 849-2255 SIC 3699

MARIAN INC p 906
2787 S Freeman Rd, Monticello IN 47960
Tel (574) 583-3464 SIC 3699

■ HUBBELL INC (DELAWARE) p 716
3902 W Sample St, South Bend IN 46619
Tel (574) 234-7151 SIC 3644 3699 3613

■ ROCKWELL COLLINS SIMULATION & TRAINING SOLUTIONS LLC p 1245
400 Collins Rd Ne, Cedar Rapids IA 52498
Tel (319) 295-1000 SIC 3699 8744

HITACHI AUTOMOTIVE SYSTEMS AMERICAS INC p 696
955 Warwick Rd, Harrodsburg KY 40330
Tel (859) 734-9451
SIC 3694 3714 3699 3625

■ CDR MANUFACTURING INC p 271
10200 Forest Green Blvd, Louisville KY 40223
Tel (502) 625-0760 SIC 3679 3672 3699

CREST INDUSTRIES p 392
4725 Highway 28 E, Pineville LA 71360
Tel (318) 767-5530
SIC 3699 3612 3441 5063 2439

CREST OPERATIONS LLC p 392
4725 Highway 28 E, Pineville LA 71360
Tel (318) 448-0274
SIC 3441 2439 3699 5063 3612

■ NOVANTA CORP p 1062
125 Middlesex Tpke, Bedford MA 01730
Tel (781) 266-5700 SIC 3699

▲ NOVANTA INC p 1062
125 Middlesex Tpke, Bedford MA 01730
Tel (781) 266-5700 SIC 3699 3845

■ GE INFRASTRUCTURE SENSING INC p 596
1100 Technology Park Dr # 100, Billerica MA 01821
Tel (978) 437-1000
SIC 3823 5084 3699 3674 3663 3625

LEE THOMAS H EQUITY FUND V LIMITED PARTNERSHIP p 852
100 Federal St Ste 3500, Boston MA 02110
Tel (617) 737-3261
SIC 3585 3444 3634 2431 3699

■ LOJACK CORP p 875
40 Pequot Way, Canton MA 02021
Tel (781) 302-4200 SIC 3699

SHANGHAI FOXBORO CO p 1311
33 Commercial St, Foxboro MA 02035
Tel (508) 543-8750 SIC 3699

▲ IPG PHOTONICS CORP p 763
50 Old Webster Rd, Oxford MA 01540
Tel (508) 373-1100 SIC 3699 3229 3674

■ FEI CO MEPD PEABODY p 537
1 Corporation Way Ste 2, Peabody MA 01960
Tel (978) 538-6700 SIC 3559 3827 3699

■ GELMAN SCIENCES INC p 598
674 S Wagner Rd, Ann Arbor MI 48103
Tel (734) 665-0651
SIC 3821 3569 3564 3841 3845 3699

■ ROFIN-SINAR TECHNOLOGIES INC p 1246
40984 Concept Dr, Plymouth MI 48170
Tel (734) 416-0206 SIC 3699

SAGINAW CONTROL & ENGINEERING INC p 1268
95 Midland Rd, Saginaw MI 48638
Tel (989) 799-6871 SIC 3699 3444

HANON SYSTEMS USA LLC p 658
1 Village Center Dr, Van Buren Twp MI 48111
Tel (734) 710-5000 SIC 3714 3585 3699

HOFFMAN ENCLOSURES INC p 699
2100 Hoffman Way, Anoka MN 55303
Tel (763) 421-2240
SIC 3444 3699 3613 3469 3053

■ OTTER TAIL POWER CO p 1098
215 S Cascade St, Fergus Falls MN 56537
Tel (218) 739-8200 SIC 3699 4953 6531

AEGIS CORP p 29
614 Dartmouth Terrace Ct, Ballwin MO 63011
Tel (636) 273-1011
SIC 3699 4812 3812 3444 2326

CAPE ELECTRICAL SUPPLY LLC p 248
489 Kell Farm Dr, Cape Girardeau MO 63701
Tel (573) 431-1838 SIC 3699 5063

COOPER BUSSMANN LLC p 366
114 Old State Rd, Ellisville MO 63021
Tel (636) 527-1324 SIC 3813 3699 3643

■ APPLE JV HOLDING CORP p 98
8000 W Florissant Ave, Saint Louis MO 63136
Tel (314) 553-2000
SIC 3644 3643 3613 3446 3699

■ DUCOMMUN LABARGE TECHNOLOGIES INC p 459
689 Craig Rd 200, Saint Louis MO 63141
Tel (314) 997-0800 SIC 3812 3699

WATLOW ELECTRIC MANUFACTURING CO p 1582
12001 Lackland Rd, Saint Louis MO 63146
Tel (314) 878-4600 SIC 3699

ASCO POWER TECHNOLOGIES LP p 116
50-60 Hanover Rd, Florham Park NJ 07932
Tel (973) 966-2000 SIC 3699

■ HONEYWELL INC p 705
115 Tabor Rd, Morris Plains NJ 07950
Tel (973) 455-2000
SIC 3823 3812 3669 3491 3699 3822

■ METROLOGIC INSTRUMENTS INC p 955
534 Fellowship Rd, Mount Laurel NJ 08054
Tel (856) 228-8100 SIC 3577 3699

PAIGE ELECTRIC CO LP p 1108
1160 Springfield Rd, Union NJ 07083
Tel (908) 687-7810 SIC 5063 3699

CHECKPOINT SYSTEMS INC p 292
101 Wolf Dr, West Deptford NJ 08086
Tel (856) 848-1800 SIC 3699 3812 3663

▲ NAPCO SECURITY TECHNOLOGIES INC p 1007
333 Bayview Ave, Amityville NY 11701
Tel (631) 842-9400
SIC 3669 3699 3429 1731 7373

SAAB SENSIS CORP p 1263
85 Collamer Crossings, East Syracuse NY 13057
Tel (315) 445-0550 SIC 3699 7371 3728

BOSCH SECURITY SYSTEMS INC p 202
130 Perinton Pkwy, Fairport NY 14450
Tel (585) 223-4060
SIC 3669 3699 3826 3825 3823 3625

PRIME SECURITY SERVICES BORROWER LLC p 1175
9 W 57th St Fl 43, New York NY 10019
Tel (212) 515-3200
SIC 6799 7382 3699 7381

DYSON-KISSNER-MORAN CORP p 465
2515 South Rd Ste 5, Poughkeepsie NY 12601
Tel (212) 661-4600 SIC 3433 3625 3699

SPIRENT INC p 1359
303 Griffing Ave, Riverhead NY 11901
Tel (631) 208-0680 SIC 3699

COOPER CROUSE-HINDS LLC p 366
1201 Wolf St, Syracuse NY 13208
Tel (315) 477-7000 SIC 3699

■ COMMSCOPE INC OF NORTH CAROLINA p 346
1100 Commscope Pl Se, Hickory NC 28602
Tel (828) 324-2200
SIC 3663 3357 3679 3812 3699

ASSA ABLOY ENTRANCE SYSTEMS US INC p 119
1900 Airport Rd, Monroe NC 28110
Tel (704) 290-5520 SIC 3699 1796 3442

MORGANITE INDUSTRIES INC p 989
4000 Westchase Blvd # 170, Raleigh NC 27607
Tel (919) 821-1253
SIC 3674 3255 3699 3264 3299 3624

PHILIPS MEDICAL SYSTEMS (CLEVELAND) INC p 1143
595 Miner Rd, Cleveland OH 44143
Tel (440) 247-2652
SIC 3844 5047 5137 3842 3821 3699

LIEBERT NORTH AMERICA INC p 863
1050 Dearborn Dr, Columbus OH 43085
Tel (614) 888-0246 SIC 3699 3585

■ CORRPRO COMPANIES INC p 373
1055 W Smith Rd, Medina OH 44256
Tel (330) 723-5082 SIC 3699 8711

GMI HOLDINGS INC p 619
1 Door Dr, Mount Hope OH 44660
Tel (330) 821-5360 SIC 3699 3635

▲ DIEBOLD INC p 438
5995 Mayfair Rd, North Canton OH 44720
Tel (330) 490-4000 SIC 3578 3699 3499

■ AKRON BRASS CO p 42
343 Venture Blvd, Wooster OH 44691
Tel (330) 264-5678 SIC 3647 3699

■ AKRON BRASS HOLDING CORP p 42
343 Venture Blvd, Wooster OH 44691
Tel (330) 264-5678 SIC 3647 3699 6719

CYMSTAR LLC p 405
1700 W Albany St Ste 500, Broken Arrow OK 74012
Tel (918) 251-8100 SIC 3699 3728

MATHENA INC p 919
3900 S Hwy 81 Service Rd, El Reno OK 73036
Tel (405) 422-3600 SIC 3699 3822

CAPP INC p 251
201 Marple Ave, Clifton Heights PA 19018
Tel (610) 394-1100 SIC 5084 3699

OERLIKON USA HOLDING INC p 1075
5700 Mellon Rd, Export PA 15632
Tel (303) 273-9700
SIC 3563 3823 3699 3479 3599 5084

■ SPD ELECTRICAL SYSTEMS INC p 1355
13500 Roosevelt Blvd, Philadelphia PA 19116
Tel (215) 698-6426 SIC 3612 3699 3613

AEROTECH INC p 31
100 Zeta Dr, Pittsburgh PA 15238
Tel (412) 963-7470 SIC 3699 3825

▲ ENERSYS p 498
2366 Bernville Rd, Reading PA 19605
Tel (610) 208-1991 SIC 3691 3699

▲ II-VI INC p 731
375 Saxonburg Blvd, Saxonburg PA 16056
Tel (724) 352-4455
SIC 3827 3229 3674 3699

PRECISION CUSTOM COMPONENTS LLC p 1168
500 Lincoln St, York PA 17401
Tel (717) 848-1126 SIC 3443 3699

■ NORDSON EFD LLC p 1048
40 Catamore Blvd, East Providence RI 02914
Tel (401) 434-1680 SIC 3548 3586 3699

NORTEK INC p 1049
500 Exchange St, Providence RI 02903
Tel (401) 751-1600
SIC 3585 3444 3634 3699 2434

KENNEY MANUFACTURING CO p 811
1000 Jefferson Blvd, Warwick RI 02886
Tel (401) 739-2200
SIC 2591 3261 2511 3699 3499 2541

THOMAS & BETTS INTERNATIONAL INC p 1448
8155 T And B Blvd, Memphis TN 38125
Tel (901) 682-7766 SIC 3699 3678

INNOVATIVE IDM LLC p 745
1625 Wallace Dr Ste 110, Carrollton TX 75006
Tel (214) 574-9500 SIC 5063 7622 3699

■ COMPX INTERNATIONAL INC p 353
5430 Lbj Fwy Ste 1700, Dallas TX 75240
Tel (972) 448-1400 SIC 3699 3714

▲ N L INDUSTRIES INC p 1005
5430 Lbj Fwy Ste 1700, Dallas TX 75240
Tel (972) 233-1700 SIC 2819 3572 3699

SANWA USA INC p 1281
4020 Mcewen Rd Ste 118, Dallas TX 75244
Tel (972) 503-3031
SIC 3442 2431 3699 3537

FRL INC p 580
1465 Henry Brennan Dr H, El Paso TX 79936
Tel (915) 225-0333 SIC 3699

▲ AZZ INC p 141
3100 W 7th St Ste 500, Fort Worth TX 76107
Tel (817) 810-0095
SIC 3699 3613 3494 3312

OVERHEAD DOOR CORP p 1099
2501 S State Hwy 121 Ste, Lewisville TX 75067
Tel (469) 549-7100
SIC 3442 2431 3699 3537 3589

▲ APPLIED OPTOELECTRONICS INC p 100
13139 Jess Pirtle Blvd, Sugar Land TX 77478
Tel (281) 295-1800 SIC 3674 3827 3699

INTERMOUNTAIN ELECTRONICS INC OF PRICE UTAH p 753
1511 S Highway 6, Price UT 84501
Tel (435) 637-7160 SIC 3699 5063

BAE SYSTEMS HOLDINGS INC p 144
1101 Wilson Blvd Ste 2000, Arlington VA 22209
Tel (703) 312-6100 SIC 3699 3728 3812

DRS TECHNOLOGIES INC p 457
2345 Crystal Dr Ste 1000, Arlington VA 22202
Tel (973) 898-1500
SIC 3812 3699 3572 3669 3679 8741

THALES USA INC p 1446
2733 Crystal Dr, Arlington VA 22202
Tel (703) 413-6029
SIC 5065 3699 3679 3841 8711 7371

SAAB NORTH AMERICA INC p 1263
20700 Loudoun County Pkwy # 152, Ashburn VA 20147
Tel (703) 406-7277 SIC 5088 3699 7371

ELECTRONIC WARFARE ASSOCIATES INC p 486
13873 Park Center Rd # 500, Herndon VA 20171
Tel (703) 904-5700
SIC 7373 7374 3672 3699 3643 3441

NLIGHT INC p 1045
5408 Ne 88th St Ste E, Vancouver WA 98665
Tel (360) 566-4460 SIC 3674 3699

BROAN-NUTONE LLC p 216
926 W State St, Hartford WI 53027
Tel (262) 673-4340
SIC 3634 3699 3635 3639 2514 3669

POWER PRODUCTS LLC p 1165
N85w12545 Westbrook Xing, Menomonee Falls WI 53051
Tel (262) 293-0600 SIC 3679 3699 3691

SIC 3711 Motor Vehicles & Car Bodies

INNOVATIVE XCESSORIES & SERVICES LLC p 745
1862 Sparkman Dr Nw, Huntsville AL 35816
Tel (877) 330-1331 SIC 5012 3711

MERCEDES-BENZ US INTERNATIONAL INC p 944
1 Mercedes Dr, Vance AL 35490
Tel (205) 507-2252 SIC 3711 3714

■ IC BUS LLC p 726
600 Bayford Dr, Conway AR 72034
Tel (501) 327-7761 SIC 3713 3711

KARMA AUTOMOTIVE LLC p 804
3080 Airway Ave, Costa Mesa CA 92626
Tel (714) 723-3247 SIC 3711

NEW UNITED MOTOR MANUFACTURING INC p 1033
45500 Fremont Blvd, Fremont CA 94538
Tel (510) 498-5500 SIC 3714 3711

BNS HOLDING INC p 194
61 E Main St Ste B, Los Gatos CA 95030
Tel (408) 399-6498 SIC 3711 3713 3531

▲ TESLA MOTORS INC p 1440
3500 Deer Creek Rd, Palo Alto CA 94304
Tel (650) 681-5000 SIC 3711 3714

ELDORADO NATIONAL (CALIFORNIA) INC p 484
9670 Galena St, Riverside CA 92509
Tel (951) 727-9300 SIC 3711

HONDA NORTH AMERICA INC p 704
700 Van Ness Ave, Torrance CA 90501
Tel (310) 781-4961 SIC 3711 8748

TOYOTA MOTOR SALES USA INC p 1467
19001 S Western Ave, Torrance CA 90501
Tel (310) 468-4000 SIC 6159 5012 3711

VEHICLE PRODUCTION GROUP LLC p 1547
101 Ne 3rd Ave Ste 1500, Fort Lauderdale FL 33301
Tel (877) 681-3678 SIC 3711

BAE SYSTEMS AH INC p 144
13386 International Pkwy, Jacksonville FL 32218
Tel (904) 741-5400
SIC 3711 3842 3312 3728

E-ONE INC p 467
1601 Sw 37th Ave, Ocala FL 34474
Tel (352) 237-1122 SIC 3711

▲ VOXX INTERNATIONAL CORP p 1566
2351 J Lawson Blvd, Orlando FL 32824
Tel (800) 645-7750 SIC 3711 3651 3663

BENNETT AUTO SUPPLY INC p 173
3141 Sw 10th St, Pompano Beach FL 33069
Tel (954) 335-8700 SIC 5531 5013 3711

REV AMBULANCE GROUP ORLANDO INC p 1229
2737 Forsyth Rd, Winter Park FL 32792
Tel (407) 677-7777 SIC 3711

BLUE BIRD GLOBAL CORP p 190
402 Bluebird Blvd, Fort Valley GA 31030
Tel (478) 822-2811 SIC 3713 3711

PEACH COUNTY HOLDINGS INC p 1125
402 Bluebird Blvd, Fort Valley GA 31030
Tel (478) 825-2021 SIC 3713 3711

SEWON AMERICA INC p 1309
1000 Sewon Blvd, Lagrange GA 30240
Tel (706) 298-5800 SIC 3711

MOTOR COACH INDUSTRIES INTERNATIONAL INC p 993
200 E Oakton St, Des Plaines IL 60018
Tel (847) 285-2000 SIC 3713 3711 3714

■ ELGIN SWEEPER CO p 486
1300 W Bartlett Rd, Elgin IL 60120
Tel (847) 741-5370 SIC 3711

■ NAVISTAR INC p 1020
2701 Navistar Dr, Lisle IL 60532
Tel (331) 332-5000
SIC 3711 3714 3519 6153 6159 6331

▲ NAVISTAR INTERNATIONAL CORP p 1020
2701 Navistar Dr, Lisle IL 60532
Tel (331) 332-5000
SIC 3711 3714 3713 3519 6159

▲ FEDERAL SIGNAL CORP p 536
1415 W 22nd St Ste 1100, Oak Brook IL 60523
Tel (630) 954-2000
SIC 3711 3647 3669 3559 3544 3545

▲ DREW INDUSTRIES INC p 455
3501 County Road 6 E, Elkhart IN 46514
Tel (574) 535-1125
SIC 3711 3714 3715 3442 3431

■ LIPPERT COMPONENTS INC p 870
3501 County Road 6 E, Elkhart IN 46514
Tel (800) 551-9149
SIC 3711 3469 3444 3714

▲ THOR INDUSTRIES INC p 1450
601 E Beardsley Ave, Elkhart IN 46514
Tel (574) 970-7460 SIC 3799 3711

HONDA MANUFACTURING OF INDIANA LLC p 704
2755 N Michigan Ave, Greensburg IN 47240
Tel (812) 222-6000 SIC 3711

SUBARU OF INDIANA AUTOMOTIVE INC p 1395
5500 State Road 38 E, Lafayette IN 47905
Tel (765) 449-1111 SIC 3711

■ VEHICLE SERVICE GROUP LLC p 1547
2700 Lanier Dr, Madison IN 47250
Tel (800) 640-5438 SIC 3711

TOYOTA MOTOR MANUFACTURING INDIANA INC p 1466
4000 S Tulip Tree Dr, Princeton IN 47670
Tel (812) 387-2000 SIC 3711

AM GENERAL HOLDINGS LLC p 63
105 N Niles Ave, South Bend IN 46617
Tel (574) 237-6222 SIC 3714 3711 8711

AM GENERAL LLC p 63
105 N Niles Ave, South Bend IN 46617
Tel (574) 237-6222 SIC 3711 3714 8711

■ CROSSROADS RV INC p 394
305 Hawpatch Dr, Topeka IN 46571
Tel (260) 593-3850 SIC 3711

COLLINS BUS CORP p 337
415 W 6th Ave, Hutchinson KS 67505
Tel (620) 662-9000 SIC 3711

TOYOTA BOSHOKU AMERICA INC p 1466
1360 Dolwick Rd Ste 125, Erlanger KY 41018
Tel (859) 817-4000 SIC 3711 5013

TOYOTA MOTOR ENGINEERING & MANUFACTURING NORTH AMERICA INC p 1466
25 Atlantic Ave, Erlanger KY 41018
Tel (469) 292-1074 SIC 3711 3713 8741

FERRARA FIRE APPARATUS INC p 538
27855 James Chapel Rd N, Holden LA 70744
Tel (225) 567-7100 SIC 3711

FCA NORTH AMERICA HOLDINGS LLC p 532
1000 Chrysler Dr, Auburn Hills MI 48326
Tel (248) 512-2950 SIC 3711 3714

FCA US LLC p 532
1000 Chrysler Dr, Auburn Hills MI 48326
Tel (248) 512-2950 SIC 3711 3714

▲ SPARTAN MOTORS INC p 1355
1541 Reynolds Rd, Charlotte MI 48813
Tel (517) 543-6400 SIC 3711 3714 7519

▲ FORD MOTOR CO p 565
1 American Rd, Dearborn MI 48126
Tel (313) 322-3000
SIC 3711 3713 3714 6153 6141 7515

▲ AMERICAN AXLE & MANUFACTURING HOLDINGS INC p 68
1 Dauch Dr, Detroit MI 48211
Tel (313) 758-2000 SIC 3714 3711

▲ GENERAL MOTORS CO p 601
300 Renaissance Ctr L1, Detroit MI 48243
Tel (313) 556-5000 SIC 3711 3714

■ GENERAL MOTORS HOLDINGS LLC p 601
300 Renaissance Ctr L1, Detroit MI 48243
Tel (313) 556-5000 SIC 3711 3714

■ GENERAL MOTORS LLC p 601
300 Renaissance Ctr L1, Detroit MI 48243
Tel (313) 556-5000 SIC 3711 3714

■ GM COMPONENTS HOLDINGS LLC p 618
300 Renaissance Ctr, Detroit MI 48243
Tel (313) 556-5000 SIC 3711 3714

AUTOALLIANCE MANAGEMENT CO p 133
1 International Dr, Flat Rock MI 48134
Tel (734) 782-7800 SIC 3711

■ FORD FLAT ROCK ASSEMBLY PLANT p 565
1 International Dr, Flat Rock MI 48134
Tel (734) 782-7800 SIC 5013 3711

WGS GLOBAL SERVICES LC p 1604
6350 Taylor Dr, Flint MI 48507
Tel (810) 239-4947 SIC 3711

DAKKOTA INTEGRATED SYSTEMS LLC p 409
1875 Holloway Dr, Holt MI 48842
Tel (517) 694-6500 SIC 3711

ZF TRW AUTOMOTIVE HOLDINGS CORP p 1642
12001 Tech Center Dr, Livonia MI 48150
Tel (734) 855-2600 SIC 3714 3711

ZF AXLE DRIVES MARYSVILLE LLC p 1642
2900 Busha Hwy, Marysville MI 48040
Tel (810) 989-8702 SIC 3711

GESTAMP MASON LLC p 609
200 E Kipp Rd, Mason MI 48854
Tel (517) 244-8800
SIC 3398 5013 3714 3711 3465

ST JAMES INC p 1367
18500 Walnut St, Southgate MI 48195
Tel (734) 285-4911 SIC 3714 3711 3465

▲ HORIZON GLOBAL CORP p 707
2600 W Big Beaver Rd # 555, Troy MI 48084
Tel (248) 593-8820 SIC 3714 3711 5531

NEW FLYER OF AMERICA INC p 1030
6200 Glenn Carlson Dr, Saint Cloud MN 56301
Tel (320) 203-0576 SIC 3713 3711

ROSENBAUER MINNESOTA LLC p 1251
5181 260th St, Wyoming MN 55092
Tel (651) 462-1000 SIC 3713 7699 3711

■ ESCO TECHNOLOGIES HOLDING LLC p 509
9900 Clayton Rd Ste A, Saint Louis MO 63124
Tel (314) 213-7200
SIC 3825 3492 3812 3711 3663

SMEAL FIRE APPARATUS CO p 1332
610 W 4th St, Snyder NE 68664
Tel (402) 568-2224 SIC 3711

FAPS INC p 528
371 Craneway St, Newark NJ 07114
Tel (973) 589-5656 SIC 3499 3711 7538

BMW OF NORTH AMERICA LLC p 194
300 Chestnut Ridge Rd, Woodcliff Lake NJ 07677
Tel (201) 307-4000
SIC 5013 3751 5012 3711

ROLLS-ROYCE MOTOR CARS NA LLC p 1247
300 Chestnut Ridge Rd, Woodcliff Lake NJ 07677
Tel (201) 307-4117 SIC 3711

TOYOTA MOTOR NORTH AMERICA INC p 1467
601 Lexington Ave Fl 49, New York NY 10022
Tel (212) 751-3053 SIC 5511 5012 3711

PREVOST CAR US INC p 1173
260 Banker Rd, Plattsburgh NY 12901
Tel (518) 957-2052 SIC 3711

MACK TRUCKS INC p 892
7825 National Service Rd, Greensboro NC 27409
Tel (336) 291-9001
SIC 3711 3714 5012 6141 6153 7538

MICKEY TRUCK BODIES INC p 961
1305 Trinity Ave, High Point NC 27260
Tel (336) 882-6806
SIC 3713 7532 3711 3715

THOMAS BUILT BUSES INC p 1448
1408 Courtesy Rd, High Point NC 27260
Tel (336) 889-4871 SIC 3711 3713

MOTOR COACH INDUSTRIES INC p 992
552 W Stutsman St, Pembina ND 58271
Tel (701) 825-6234 SIC 3711

■ AIRSTREAM INC p 40
419 W Pike St, Jackson Center OH 45334
Tel (937) 596-6111
SIC 3716 3792 3714 3713 3711

HONDA OF AMERICA MFG INC p 704
24000 Honda Pkwy, Marysville OH 43040
Tel (937) 642-5000 SIC 3711

JEFFERSON INDUSTRIES CORP p 781
6670 State Route 29, West Jefferson OH 43162
Tel (614) 879-5300 SIC 3711

■ IC BUS OF OKLAHOMA LLC p 726
2322 N Mingo Rd, Tulsa OK 74116
Tel (918) 833-4000 SIC 3711 3713

DAIMLER TRUCKS NORTH AMERICA LLC p 408
4747 N Channel Ave, Portland OR 97217
Tel (503) 745-8011 SIC 3711 4789

SERVICE STEEL INC p 1307
5555 N Channel Ave Bldg 2, Portland OR 97217
Tel (503) 224-9500 SIC 5051 3711

WOLFINGTON BODY CO INC p 1621
N Off Pa Tpk Exit Rr 100, Exton PA 19341
Tel (610) 458-8501 SIC 3711 3713 5012

KOVATCH MOBILE EQUIPMENT CORP p 828
1 Industrial Complex, Nesquehoning PA 18240
Tel (570) 669-9461 SIC 3711

FREIGHTLINER CUSTOM CHASSIS CORP p 577
552 Hyatt St, Gaffney SC 29341
Tel (864) 487-1700 SIC 3711

■ FORCE PROTECTION INC p 565
9801 Highway 78 Bldg 1, Ladson SC 29456
Tel (843) 569-8716 SIC 3711

DRIVE AUTOMOTIVE INDUSTRIES OF AMERICA INC p 456
120 Moon Acres Rd, Piedmont SC 29673
Tel (864) 299-1349
SIC 3465 3714 3711 3469

ROSENBAUER AMERICA LLC p 1251
100 3rd St, Lyons SD 57041
Tel (605) 543-5591 SIC 3711

ROSENBAUER SOUTH DAKOTA LLC p 1251
100 3rd St, Lyons SD 57041
Tel (605) 543-5591 SIC 3711

NISSAN NORTH AMERICA INC p 1044
1 Nissan Way, Franklin TN 37067
Tel (615) 725-1000
SIC 5012 8711 8734 6141 8741 3711

SHIROKI NORTH AMERICA INC p 1317
1111 W Broad St, Smithville TN 37166
Tel (615) 597-8870 SIC 3711

BAE SYSTEMS RESOLUTION INC p 144
1000 La St Ste 4950, Houston TX 77002
Tel (713) 868-7700
SIC 3713 5084 3711 7699 3351 3829

STEWART & STEVENSON CAPITAL CORP p 1388
601 W 38th St, Houston TX 77018
Tel (713) 868-7700
SIC 5084 5013 5078 5082 3711 3537

TOYODA GOSEI BROWNSVILLE TEXAS LLC p 1466
107 Joaquin Cavazos Rd, Los Indios TX 78567
Tel (956) 290-8802 SIC 3711

PADFIELD INC p 1107
1335 W 2100 S, Salt Lake City UT 84119
Tel (801) 972-1944 SIC 5014 5531 3711

▲ GENERAL DYNAMICS CORP p 600
2941 Frview Pk Dr Ste 100, Falls Church VA 22042
Tel (703) 876-3000
SIC 3721 3731 3795 3711 3812

▲ PACCAR INC p 1103
777 106th Ave Ne, Bellevue WA 98004
Tel (425) 468-7400
SIC 3711 3714 3713 3537 5013 6153

■ PIERCE MANUFACTURING INC p 1147
2600 American Dr, Appleton WI 54914
Tel (920) 832-3000 SIC 3711

FWD SEAGRAVE HOLDINGS LP p 586
105 E 12th St, Clintonville WI 54929
Tel (715) 823-2141 SIC 3711

REV GROUP INC p 1229
111 E Kilbourn Ave # 2600, Milwaukee WI 53202
Tel (414) 290-0190 SIC 3711

▲ OSHKOSH CORP p 1096
2307 Oregon St, Oshkosh WI 54902
Tel (920) 235-9151 SIC 3711 3531 3715

■ OSHKOSH DEFENSE LLC p 1096
2307 Oregon St, Oshkosh WI 54902
Tel (920) 235-9151 SIC 3711 3531 3715

SIC 3713 Truck & Bus Bodies

NABI BUS LLC p 1006
106 National Dr, Anniston AL 36207
Tel (888) 452-7871 SIC 3713 5012

ALTEC INC p 62
210 Inverness Center Dr, Birmingham AL 35242
Tel (205) 991-7733 SIC 3531 3713 3536

ALTEC INDUSTRIES INC p 62
210 Inverness Center Dr, Birmingham AL 35242
Tel (205) 991-7733 SIC 3531 3536 3713

■ IC BUS LLC p 726
600 Bayford Dr, Conway AR 72034
Tel (501) 327-7761 SIC 3713 3711

GILLIG LLC p 612
25800 Clawiter Rd, Hayward CA 94545
Tel (510) 785-1500 SIC 3713

TABC INC p 1420
6375 N Paramount Blvd, Long Beach CA 90805
Tel (562) 984-3305 SIC 3714 3713 3469

BNS HOLDING INC p 194
61 E Main St Ste B, Los Gatos CA 95030
Tel (408) 399-6498 SIC 3711 3713 3531

CIVES CORP p 320
3700 Mansell Rd Ste 500, Alpharetta GA 30022
Tel (770) 993-4424 SIC 3441 3713 3443

LUND INTERNATIONAL HOLDING CO p 886
4325 Hamilton Mill Rd, Buford GA 30518
Tel (678) 804-3767 SIC 3714 3713

HORTON VANS INC p 708
130 Coleman Dr, Eatonton GA 31024
Tel (706) 923-2900 SIC 3713 3792

■ BIRD BLUE CORP p 185
402 Bluebird Blvd, Fort Valley GA 31030
Tel (478) 822-2801 SIC 3713

BLUE BIRD GLOBAL CORP p 190
402 Bluebird Blvd, Fort Valley GA 31030
Tel (478) 822-2811 SIC 3713 3711

PEACH COUNTY HOLDINGS INC p 1125
402 Bluebird Blvd, Fort Valley GA 31030
Tel (478) 825-2021 SIC 3713 3711

■ COTTRELL INC p 374
2125 Candler Rd, Gainesville GA 30507
Tel (770) 532-7251 SIC 3713

AUTO TRUCK GROUP LLC p 133
1420 Brewster Creek Blvd, Bartlett IL 60103
Tel (630) 860-5600 SIC 3713 1541

MOTOR COACH INDUSTRIES INTERNATIONAL INC p 993
200 E Oakton St, Des Plaines IL 60018
Tel (847) 285-2000 SIC 3713 3711 3714

GVW GROUP LLC p 648
625 Roger Williams Ave, Highland Park IL 60035
Tel (847) 681-8417 SIC 3713

▲ NAVISTAR INTERNATIONAL CORP p 1020
2701 Navistar Dr, Lisle IL 60532
Tel (331) 332-5000
SIC 3711 3714 3713 3519 6159

TRUCK ACCESSORIES GROUP LLC p 1485
28858 Ventura Dr, Elkhart IN 46517
Tel (574) 522-5337 SIC 3713

ACCURIDE CORP p 16
7140 Office Cir, Evansville IN 47715
Tel (812) 962-5000 SIC 3714 3713

■ SUPREME CORP p 1408
2581 Kercher Rd, Goshen IN 46528
Tel (574) 642-4888 SIC 3713 3792 3585

▲ SUPREME INDUSTRIES INC p 1408
2581 Kercher Rd, Goshen IN 46528
Tel (574) 642-3070 SIC 3537 3713 3799

AUTOCAR LLC p 134
551 S Washington St, Hagerstown IN 47346
Tel (765) 489-5499 SIC 3713

VANGUARD NATIONAL TRAILER CORP p 1543
289 Water Tower Dr, Monon IN 47959
Tel (219) 253-2000 SIC 3715 3713

INTERNATIONAL BRAKE INDUSTRIES INC p 754
4300 Quality Dr, South Bend IN 46628
Tel (419) 905-7468 SIC 3713 3714

OMAHA STANDARD LLC p 1083
3501 S 11th St Ste 1, Council Bluffs IA 51501
Tel (712) 328-7444 SIC 3713 3536 3537

■ IOWA MOLD TOOLING CO INC p 763
500 W Us Highway 18, Garner IA 50438
Tel (641) 923-3711 SIC 3531 3713 3563

KALMAR SOLUTIONS LLC p 801
415 E Dundee St, Ottawa KS 66067
Tel (785) 242-2200
SIC 3537 3714 3713 3643

TOYOTA MOTOR ENGINEERING & MANUFACTURING NORTH AMERICA INC p 1466
25 Atlantic Ave, Erlanger KY 41018
Tel (469) 292-1074 SIC 3711 3713 8741

▲ FORD MOTOR CO p 565
1 American Rd, Dearborn MI 48126
Tel (313) 322-3000
SIC 3713 3711 3714 6153 6141 7515

MORGAN OLSON LLC p 988
1801 S Nottawa St, Sturgis MI 49091
Tel (269) 659-0200 SIC 3713

■ MCNEILUS COMPANIES INC p 932
524 E Highway St, Dodge Center MN 55927
Tel (507) 374-6321 SIC 3713

■ MCNEILUS TRUCK AND MANUFACTURING INC p 932
524 County Rd 34 E, Dodge Center MN 55927
Tel (614) 868-0760
SIC 3713 3531 3537 3272

TRUCK BODIES & EQUIPMENT INTERNATIONAL INC p 1485
52182 Ember Rd, Lake Crystal MN 56055
Tel (507) 726-2728 SIC 3713 4953

CRENLO CAB PRODUCTS INC p 391
1600 4th Ave Nw, Rochester MN 55901
Tel (507) 289-3371
SIC 2522 3531 2542 3713 3469 3444

NEW FLYER OF AMERICA INC p 1030
6200 Glenn Carlson Dr, Saint Cloud MN 56301
Tel (320) 203-0576 SIC 3713 3711

ROSENBAUER MINNESOTA LLC p 1251
5181 260th St, Wyoming MN 55092
Tel (651) 462-1000 SIC 3713 7699 3711

CUSTOM TRUCK & EQUIPMENT LLC p 403
7701 Independence Ave, Kansas City MO 64125
Tel (816) 241-4888 SIC 3713

UTILITY ONE SOURCE LP p 1537
7701 Independence Ave, Kansas City MO 64125
Tel (312) 316-9520 SIC 3713

SPRINGFIELD REMANUFACTURING CORP p 1361
650 N Broadview Pl, Springfield MO 65802
Tel (417) 862-3501
SIC 3519 3714 3713 3561

LARSON GROUP p 845
3026 N Mulroy Rd, Strafford MO 65757
Tel (417) 865-5355 SIC 3713

JID TRANSPORTATION INC p 785
158 61st St Apt 2, West New York NJ 07093
Tel (201) 362-0841 SIC 3713 4212 7363

VNA HOLDING INC p 1563
7825 National Service Rd, Greensboro NC 27409
Tel (336) 393-4890
SIC 6159 3713 5012 5013

VOLVO GROUP NORTH AMERICA LLC p 1565
7900 National Service Rd, Greensboro NC 27409
Tel (336) 393-2000 SIC 3713 5012 5013

VOLVO TRUCKS NORTH AMERICA INC p 1565
7900 National Service Rd, Greensboro NC 27409
Tel (336) 393-2000 SIC 3713 5012 5013

MICKEY TRUCK BODIES INC p 961
1305 Trinity Ave, High Point NC 27260
Tel (336) 882-6806
SIC 3713 7532 3711 3715

THOMAS BUILT BUSES INC p 1448
1408 Courtesy Rd, High Point NC 27260
Tel (336) 889-4871 SIC 3711 3713

VT HACKNEY INC p 1567
911 W 5th St, Washington NC 27889
Tel (252) 946-6521 SIC 3713

■ AIRSTREAM INC p 40
419 W Pike St, Jackson Center OH 45334
Tel (937) 596-6111
SIC 3716 3792 3714 3713 3711

ARE ACCESSORIES LLC p 106
400 Nave Rd Se, Massillon OH 44646
Tel (330) 830-7800 SIC 3713

ARE INC p 106
400 Nave Rd Sw, Massillon OH 44646
Tel (330) 830-7800
SIC 3713 3714 3792 5013

■ IC BUS OF OKLAHOMA LLC p 726
2322 N Mingo Rd, Tulsa OK 74116
Tel (918) 833-4000 SIC 3711 3713

ROBERTS TRUCK CENTER OF OKLAHOMA LLC p 1242
1023 N Garnett Rd, Tulsa OK 74116
Tel (918) 438-2000 SIC 3713

M H EBY INC p 889
1194 Main St, Blue Ball PA 17506
Tel (800) 292-4752 SIC 3713 5012

WOLFINGTON BODY CO INC p 1621
N Off Pa Tpk Exit Rr 100, Exton PA 19341
Tel (610) 458-8501 SIC 3711 3713 5012

STRICK CORP p 1393
225 Lincoln Hwy, Fairless Hills PA 19030
Tel (215) 949-3600
SIC 3715 2426 3713 3537

MORGAN TRUCK BODY LLC p 989
111 Morgan Way, Morgantown PA 19543
Tel (610) 286-5025
SIC 3713 7532 5013 5084

READING TRUCK BODY LLC p 1213
201 Hancock Blvd, Reading PA 19611
Tel (610) 775-3301 SIC 3713 3792 3469

TRG WIND DOWN LLC p 1476
201 Hancock Blvd, Reading PA 19611
Tel (610) 775-3301
SIC 3713 3792 3469 5531 7532

RIGGS INDUSTRIES INC p 1234
2478 Lincoln Hwy, Stoystown PA 15563
Tel (814) 629-5621 SIC 3713 3441

TRAIL KING INDUSTRIES INC p 1469
300 E Norway Ave, Mitchell SD 57301
Tel (605) 996-2562 SIC 3715 3713

■ CENTURY HOLDINGS INC p 282
8503 Hilltop Dr, Ooltewah TN 37363
Tel (423) 238-4171 SIC 3713

▲ MILLER INDUSTRIES INC p 970
8503 Hilltop Dr, Ooltewah TN 37363
Tel (423) 238-4171 SIC 3713

BAE SYSTEMS RESOLUTION INC p 144
1000 La St Ste 4950, Houston TX 77002
Tel (713) 868-7700
SIC 3713 5084 3711 7699 3351 3829

J B POINDEXTER & CO INC p 770
600 Travis St Ste 200, Houston TX 77002
Tel (713) 655-9800 SIC 3713

METALSA-ROANOKE INC p 953
184 Vista Dr, Roanoke VA 24019
Tel (540) 966-5300 SIC 3713

▲ PACCAR INC p 1103
777 106th Ave Ne, Bellevue WA 98004
Tel (425) 468-7400
SIC 3711 3714 3713 3537 5013 6153

SEAGRAVE FIRE APPARATUS LLC p 1296
105 E 12th St, Clintonville WI 54929
Tel (715) 823-2141 SIC 5012 3713 8711

PENDA CORP p 1128
2344 W Wisconsin St, Portage WI 53901
Tel (608) 742-5301
SIC 5013 3714 3792 3713 2273

SIC 3714 Motor Vehicle Parts & Access

SL ALABAMA LLC p 1330
2481 Airport Blvd, Alexander City AL 35010
Tel (256) 397-8140 SIC 3714

SYNCRO CORP p 1415
1030 Sundown Dr Nw, Arab AL 35016
Tel (256) 586-6045
SIC 3714 3625 3694 3823 3643

BORBET ALABAMA INC p 201
979 W Veterans Blvd, Auburn AL 36832
Tel (334) 502-9400 SIC 3714

KAMTEK INC p 802
1595 Sterilite Dr, Birmingham AL 35215
Tel (205) 327-7000 SIC 3714

LIGON INDUSTRIES LLC p 866
1927 1st Ave N Ste 500, Birmingham AL 35203
Tel (205) 322-3302
SIC 3365 3593 3325 3471 3714 3446

ALABAMA CULLMAN YUTAKA TECHNOLOGIES LLC p 43
460 Al Highway 157, Cullman AL 35058
Tel (256) 739-3533 SIC 3714

■ WEBB WHEEL PRODUCTS INC p 1586
2310 Industrial Dr Sw, Cullman AL 35055
Tel (256) 739-6660 SIC 3714

BBB INDUSTRIES LLC p 163
29627 Renaissance Blvd, Daphne AL 36526
Tel (800) 280-2737 SIC 3694 3714

HWASEUNG AUTOMOTIVE ALABAMA LLC p 722
100 Sonata Dr, Enterprise AL 36330
Tel (334) 348-9516 SIC 3714 3069

HWASEUNG AUTOMOTIVE USA LLC p 722
101 Development Ln, Enterprise AL 36330
Tel (334) 348-9516 SIC 3714

SEJONG ALABAMA LLC p 1301
450 Old Fort Rd E, Fort Deposit AL 36032
Tel (334) 227-0821 SIC 3714

MID-SOUTH INDUSTRIES INC p 963
2620 E Meighan Blvd, Gadsden AL 35903
Tel (256) 492-8997
SIC 3672 3089 3824 3714

VISION TECHNOLOGIES KINETICS INC p 1561
3800 Richardson Rd, Hope Hull AL 36043
Tel (334) 284-8665 SIC 3714 3795

KYUNGSHIN-LEAR SALES AND ENGINEERING LLC p 833
100 Smothers Rd, Montgomery AL 36117
Tel (334) 413-0575 SIC 3714

MOBIS ALABAMA LLC p 980
1395 Mitchell Young Rd, Montgomery AL 36108
Tel (334) 387-4800 SIC 3714

MOBIS AMERICA INC p 980
1395 Mitchell Young Rd, Montgomery AL 36108
Tel (334) 387-4840 SIC 3714

THERMASYS GROUP HOLDING CO p 1447
2776 Gunter Park Dr E, Montgomery AL 36109
Tel (334) 244-9240 SIC 3714 3443

HANWHA ADVANCED MATERIALS AMERICA LLC p 659
4400 N Park Dr, Opelika AL 36801
Tel (334) 741-7725 SIC 3714

HANWHA L & C HOLDINGS USA LLC p 659
4400 N Park Dr, Opelika AL 36801
Tel (334) 741-7725 SIC 3083 3714

MANDO AMERICA CORP p 901
4201 N Park Dr, Opelika AL 36801
Tel (334) 364-3600 SIC 3714

WKW ERBSLOEH NORTH AMERICA LLC p 1620
103 Parkway E, Pell City AL 35125
Tel (205) 338-4242 SIC 3714

MERCEDES-BENZ US INTERNATIONAL INC p 944
1 Mercedes Dr, Vance AL 35490
Tel (205) 507-2252 SIC 3711 3714

▲ CARLISLE COMPANIES INC p 257
16430 N Scottsdale Rd, Scottsdale AZ 85254
Tel (704) 501-1100
SIC 2952 3714 3312 3357 3263

MPG GEAR TECHNOLOGIES p 995
7800 Ball Rd, Fort Smith AR 72908
Tel (479) 646-1662 SIC 3714 3568 3399

CWD LLC p 404
21046 Figueroa St Ste B, Carson CA 90745
Tel (310) 218-1082 SIC 3714

NEW UNITED MOTOR MANUFACTURING INC p 1033
45500 Fremont Blvd, Fremont CA 94538
Tel (510) 498-5500 SIC 3714 3711

PRIME WHEEL CORP p 1175
17705 S Main St, Gardena CA 90248
Tel (310) 516-9126 SIC 3714

DELPHI CONNECTION SYSTEMS LLC p 425
30 Corporate Park Ste 303, Irvine CA 92606
Tel (949) 458-3100 SIC 3714

FABCO AUTOMOTIVE CORP p 523
151 Lawrence Dr, Livermore CA 94551
Tel (925) 245-4100 SIC 3714

FABCO AUTOMOTIVE CORP p 523
151 Lawrence Dr, Livermore CA 94551
Tel (925) 454-9500 SIC 3714

DENSO PRODUCTS AND SERVICES AMERICAS INC p 429
3900 Via Oro Ave, Long Beach CA 90810
Tel (310) 834-6352
SIC 5013 7361 5075 3714

TABC INC p 1420
6375 N Paramount Blvd, Long Beach CA 90805
Tel (562) 984-3305 SIC 3714 3713 3469

▲ TESLA MOTORS INC p 1440
3500 Deer Creek Rd, Palo Alto CA 94304
Tel (650) 681-5000 SIC 3711 3714

K & N ENGINEERING INC p 798
1455 Citrus St, Riverside CA 92507
Tel (951) 826-4000 SIC 3751 3599 3714

GST AUTOMOTIVE SAFETY COMPONENTS INTERNATIONAL INC p 643
2155 Pseo De Las Americas, San Diego CA 92154
Tel (619) 661-9347 SIC 3714

■ ATMEL CORP p 128
1600 Technology Dr, San Jose CA 95110
Tel (408) 441-0311 SIC 3674 3714 3545

IMPCO TECHNOLOGIES INC p 734
3030 S Susan St, Santa Ana CA 92704
Tel (714) 656-1200 SIC 3714 3592 7363

SPECIAL DEVICES INC p 1356
2655 1st St Ste 300, Simi Valley CA 93065
Tel (805) 387-1000 SIC 3714

EDELBROCK HOLDINGS INC p 477
2700 California St, Torrance CA 90503
Tel (310) 781-2222 SIC 3714 3751

EDELBROCK LLC p 477
2700 California St, Torrance CA 90503
Tel (310) 781-2222 SIC 3714 3751

▲ MOTORCAR PARTS OF AMERICA INC p 993
2929 California St, Torrance CA 90503
Tel (310) 212-7910
SIC 3714 3694 3625 5013

CR LAURENCE CO INC p 388
2503 E Vernon Ave, Vernon CA 90058
Tel (323) 588-1281 SIC 3714 5072 5039

CHECKERS INDUSTRIAL PRODUCTS LLC p 292
620 Compton St, Broomfield CO 80020
Tel (720) 890-1187 SIC 3714 3965

AD CORP p 21
1551 Wewatta St, Denver CO 80202
Tel (303) 744-1911
SIC 3634 3564 3822 3089 3714 3312

BESTOP INC p 177
333 Centennial Pkwy B, Louisville CO 80027
Tel (303) 465-1755 SIC 2394 3714

ARMORED AUTOGROUP INC p 111
44 Old Ridgebury Rd # 300, Danbury CT 06810
Tel (203) 205-2900 SIC 3714

■ EM CLARCOR HOLDINGS INC p 490
60 Prestige Park Rd, East Hartford CT 06108
Tel (860) 920-4200 SIC 3714 3492

▲ LYDALL INC p 887
1 Colonial Rd, Manchester CT 06042
Tel (860) 646-1233
SIC 2297 3053 2899 2631 3714 3564

THULE HOLDING INC p 1451
42 Silvermine Rd, Seymour CT 06483
Tel (203) 881-9600 SIC 3792 3714

THULE INC p 1451
42 Silvermine Rd, Seymour CT 06483
Tel (203) 881-9600 SIC 3714 5021

LEE CO p 851
2 Pettipaug Rd, Westbrook CT 06498
Tel (860) 399-6281
SIC 3823 3841 3812 3728 3714

STANADYNE INTERMEDIATE HOLDINGS LLC p 1375
92 Deerfield Rd, Windsor CT 06095
Tel (860) 525-0821 SIC 3714 3492

STANADYNE LLC p 1375
92 Deerfield Rd, Windsor CT 06095
Tel (860) 525-0821 SIC 3714

STANADYNE PARENT HOLDINGS INC p 1375
92 Deerfield Rd, Windsor CT 06095
Tel (860) 525-0821 SIC 3714

NGK NORTH AMERICA INC p 1041
1105 N Market St Ste 1300, Wilmington DE 19801
Tel (302) 654-1344
SIC 3714 5013 3264 5063

■ SMART CHOICE AUTOMOTIVE GROUP INC p 1332
5130 S Washington Ave, Titusville FL 32780
Tel (321) 269-9680 SIC 5521 3714 6141

■ KYSOR INDUSTRIAL CORP p 833
2227 Welbilt Blvd, Trinity FL 34655
Tel (727) 376-8600 SIC 3585 3714

▲ GENUINE PARTS CO p 605
2999 Wildwood Pkwy, Atlanta GA 30339
Tel (770) 953-1700
SIC 5013 5531 3714 5084 5085 5021

HL-A CO p 697
101 Thomas B Mur Ind Blvd, Bremen GA 30110
Tel (678) 309-2000 SIC 3429 3714

LUND INC p 886
4325 Hamilton Mill Rd # 400, Buford GA 30518
Tel (678) 804-3767 SIC 3714

LUND INTERNATIONAL HOLDING CO p 886
4325 Hamilton Mill Rd, Buford GA 30518
Tel (678) 804-3767 SIC 3714 3713

DECOSTAR INDUSTRIES INC p 421
1 Decoma Dr, Carrollton GA 30117
Tel (770) 801-2900 SIC 3714

MASTERBUILT MANUFACTURING LLC p 918
1 Masterbuilt Ct, Columbus GA 31907
Tel (706) 327-5622 SIC 3631 3714

GEORGIA L SEJONG L C p 607
1641 Lukken Indl Dr W, Lagrange GA 30240
Tel (706) 845-7091 SIC 3714

PAI INDUSTRIES INC p 1107
950 Northbrook Pkwy, Suwanee GA 30024
Tel (770) 822-1000 SIC 3714 5013

TURBINE ENGINE COMPONENTS TECHNOLOGIES CORP p 1492
1211 Old Albany Rd, Thomasville GA 31792
Tel (229) 228-2600
SIC 3463 3724 3714 3469

DAEHAN SOLUTION GEORGIA LLC p 408
791 S Progress Pkwy, West Point GA 31833
Tel (706) 902-5200 SIC 5013 8711 3714

KYUNGSHIN AMERICA CORP p 833
1201 Og Skinner Dr, West Point GA 31833
Tel (706) 645-1595 SIC 3714

POWERTECH AMERICA INC p 1166
6801 Kia Pkwy, West Point GA 31833
Tel (706) 902-6800 SIC 5012 3714

CHAMPION LABORATORIES INC p 287
200 S 4th St, Albion IL 62806
Tel (618) 445-6011 SIC 3714

ROBERT BOSCH LLC p 1241
2800 S 25th Ave, Broadview IL 60155
Tel (248) 876-1000
SIC 3714 3694 5013 5064 3565 3541

MORSE AUTOMOTIVE CORP p 990
750 W Lake Cook Rd # 480, Buffalo Grove IL 60089
Tel (773) 843-9000 SIC 3714

NTA PRECISION AXLE CORP p 1065
795 Kimberly Dr, Carol Stream IL 60188
Tel (630) 690-6300 SIC 3714

THYSSENKRUPP NORTH AMERICA INC p 1451
111 W Jackson Blvd # 2400, Chicago IL 60604
Tel (312) 525-2800 SIC 6719 3714

THYSSENKRUPP CRANKSHAFT CO LLC p 1451
1000 Lynch Rd, Danville IL 61834
Tel (217) 431-0060 SIC 3714 3462

THYSSENKRUPP PRESTA DANVILLE LLC p 1451
75 Walz Crk, Danville IL 61834
Tel (217) 444-5500 SIC 3714

JORDAN INDUSTRIES INC p 793
1751 Lake Cook Rd Ste 550, Deerfield IL 60015
Tel (847) 945-5591
SIC 3621 3625 3714 3089 2759 5999

IMS COMPANIES LLC p 735
1 Innovation Dr, Des Plaines IL 60016
Tel (847) 391-8100
SIC 3469 8711 3679 3714 3444

MOTOR COACH INDUSTRIES INTERNATIONAL INC p 993
200 E Oakton St, Des Plaines IL 60018
Tel (847) 285-2000 SIC 3713 3711 3714

BOLER CO p 198
500 Park Blvd Ste 1010, Itasca IL 60143
Tel (630) 773-9111 SIC 3714 3493

AUTOPARTS HOLDINGS LTD p 135
1900 W Field Ct, Lake Forest IL 60045
Tel (203) 830-7800 SIC 3714

FRAM GROUP OPERATIONS LLC p 573
1900 W Field Ct, Lake Forest IL 60045
Tel (800) 890-2075 SIC 3694 3714

■TENNECO AUTOMOTIVE OPERATING CO INC p 1437
500 N Field Dr, Lake Forest IL 60045
Tel (847) 482-5000 SIC 3714 3699

▲TENNECO INC p 1437
500 N Field Dr, Lake Forest IL 60045
Tel (847) 482-5000 SIC 3714

UCI INTERNATIONAL INC p 1499
1900 W Field Ct, Lake Forest IL 60045
Tel (812) 867-4156 SIC 3714

UNITED COMPONENTS LLC p 1507
1900 W Field Ct, Lake Forest IL 60045
Tel (812) 867-4516 SIC 5013 3714

TOYOTA BOSHOKU ILLINOIS LLC p 1466
100 Trim Masters Dr, Lawrenceville IL 62439
Tel (618) 943-5300 SIC 3714

■ NAVISTAR INC p 1020
2701 Navistar Dr, Lisle IL 60532
Tel (331) 332-5000
SIC 3711 3714 3519 6153 6159 6331

▲ NAVISTAR INTERNATIONAL CORP p 1020
2701 Navistar Dr, Lisle IL 60532
Tel (331) 332-5000
SIC 3711 3714 3713 3519 6159

MAT HOLDINGS INC p 918
6700 Wildlife Way, Long Grove IL 60047
Tel (847) 821-9630 SIC 2842 3714 3563

AISIN MFG ILLINOIS LLC p 41
11000 Redco Dr, Marion IL 62959
Tel (618) 998-8333 SIC 3714

BPI HOLDINGS INTERNATIONAL INC p 206
4400 Prime Pkwy, Mchenry IL 60050
Tel (815) 363-9000 SIC 3714

BRAKE PARTS INC LLC p 207
4400 Prime Pkwy, Mchenry IL 60050
Tel (815) 363-9000 SIC 3714

DYNAMIC MANUFACTURING INC p 464
1930 N Mannheim Rd, Melrose Park IL 60160
Tel (708) 343-8753 SIC 3714

CERTIFIED POWER INC p 284
970 Campus Dr, Mundelein IL 60060
Tel (847) 573-3800 SIC 3714 7539 5013

NASCOTE INDUSTRIES INC p 1008
18310 Enterprise Ave, Nashville IL 62263
Tel (618) 327-3286 SIC 3714

▲TITAN INTERNATIONAL INC p 1456
2701 Spruce St, Quincy IL 62301
Tel (217) 228-6011 SIC 3312 3714 3011

GUNITE CORP p 647
302 Peoples Ave, Rockford IL 61104
Tel (815) 964-3301 SIC 3714

OMRON AUTOMOTIVE ELECTRONICS INC p 1085
3709 Ohio Ave, Saint Charles IL 60174
Tel (630) 443-6800
SIC 5065 3625 3714 8742

MERCURY PRODUCTS CORP p 945
1201 Mercury Dr, Schaumburg IL 60193
Tel (847) 524-4400 SIC 3465 3469 3714

■WARNER ELECTRIC LLC p 1576
449 Gardner St, South Beloit IL 61080
Tel (815) 389-4300 SIC 3714

UGN INC p 1499
18410 Crossing Dr Ste C, Tinley Park IL 60487
Tel (773) 437-2400 SIC 3714

FLEX-N-GATE CORP p 555
1306 E University Ave, Urbana IL 61802
Tel (217) 384-6600 SIC 3714

US TSUBAKI POWER TRANSMISSION LLC p 1533
301 E Marquardt Dr, Wheeling IL 60090
Tel (847) 459-9500
SIC 3568 5085 5063 3714 3462 3325

GKN AMERICA CORP p 613
2715 Davey Rd Ste 300, Woodridge IL 60517
Tel (630) 972-9300 SIC 3714

GKN NORTH AMERICA SERVICES INC p 613
2715 Davey Rd Ste 300, Woodridge IL 60517
Tel (630) 972-9300 SIC 3714 5013 7359

KEIHIN NORTH AMERICA INC p 808
2701 Enterprise Dr # 100, Anderson IN 46013
Tel (765) 298-6030 SIC 3714

COUPLED PRODUCTS LLC p 383
2651 S 600 E, Columbia City IN 46725
Tel (260) 248-3200 SIC 3714

▲ CUMMINS INC p 401
500 Jackson St, Columbus IN 47201
Tel (812) 377-5000
SIC 3519 3714 3694 3621

ENKEI AMERICA INC p 499
2900 Inwood Dr, Columbus IN 47201
Tel (812) 373-7000 SIC 3714 3365

FAURECIA EMISSIONS CONTROL TECHNOLOGIES USA LLC p 531
950 W 450 S, Columbus IN 47201
Tel (812) 341-2000 SIC 3714

STANT CORP p 1377
1620 Columbia Ave, Connersville IN 47331
Tel (765) 825-3121 SIC 3714

STANT USA CORP p 1377
1620 Columbia Ave, Connersville IN 47331
Tel (765) 825-3121 SIC 3714

VAPOR ACQUISITION CORP p 1544
1620 Columbia Ave, Connersville IN 47331
Tel (765) 825-3121 SIC 3714

RAYTECH COMPOSITES INC p 1210
1204 Darlington Ave, Crawfordsville IN 47933
Tel (765) 362-3500 SIC 3714

ALL AMERICAN GROUP INC p 51
2831 Dexter Dr, Elkhart IN 46514
Tel (574) 262-0123
SIC 3716 3792 2452 3714 1521

ATWOOD MOBILE PRODUCTS INC p 130
1120 N Main St, Elkhart IN 46514
Tel (574) 264-2131 SIC 3714

ATWOOD MOBILE PRODUCTS LLC p 130
1120 N Main St, Elkhart IN 46514
Tel (574) 264-2131 SIC 3714

DEXTER AXLE CO p 434
2900 Industrial Pkwy, Elkhart IN 46516
Tel (574) 295-7888 SIC 3714

▲ DREW INDUSTRIES INC p 455
3501 County Road 6 E, Elkhart IN 46514
Tel (574) 535-1125
SIC 3711 3714 3715 3442 3431

■ LIPPERT COMPONENTS INC p 870
3501 County Road 6 E, Elkhart IN 46514
Tel (800) 551-9149
SIC 3711 3469 3444 3714

ELSA CORP p 489
1240 S State Road 37, Elwood IN 46036
Tel (765) 552-5200 SIC 3714

ACCURIDE CORP p 16
7140 Office Cir, Evansville IN 47715
Tel (812) 962-5000 SIC 3714 3713

TRANSPORTATION TECHNOLOGIES INDUSTRIES INC p 1473
7140 Office Cir, Evansville IN 47715
Tel (812) 962-5000
SIC 2531 3714 3321 4741 3471

UCI ACQUISITION HOLDINGS (NO 1) CORP p 1499
14601 Highway 41 N, Evansville IN 47725
Tel (812) 867-4156 SIC 3714

BRC RUBBER & PLASTICS INC p 209
1029a W State Blvd, Fort Wayne IN 46808
Tel (260) 693-2171 SIC 3061 3714 3053

■ DANA LIGHT AXLE PRODUCTS LLC p 410
2100 W State Blvd, Fort Wayne IN 46808
Tel (260) 483-7174 SIC 3714

RIVERSIDE MFG LLC p 1238
14510 Lima Rd, Fort Wayne IN 46818
Tel (260) 637-4470 SIC 3714

KYB AMERICAS CORP p 833
2625 N Morton St, Franklin IN 46131
Tel (317) 736-7774 SIC 3714 8711

MOBILE CLIMATE CONTROL CORP p 980
17103 State Road 4, Goshen IN 46528
Tel (574) 534-1516 SIC 5075 3714

HEARTLAND AUTOMOTIVE INC p 679
300 S Warren Dr, Greencastle IN 46135
Tel (765) 653-4263 SIC 3714

INDIANA AUTOMOTIVE FASTENERS INC p 738
1300 Anderson Blvd, Greenfield IN 46140
Tel (317) 467-0100 SIC 3452 3714

KEIHIN IPT MFG LLC p 808
400 W New Rd, Greenfield IN 46140
Tel (317) 462-3015 SIC 3714

G E C O M CORP p 586
1025 Barachel Ln, Greensburg IN 47240
Tel (812) 663-2270 SIC 3714

VALEO ENGINE COOLING INC p 1539
1100 Barachel Ln, Greensburg IN 47240
Tel (812) 663-8541 SIC 3714

▲ ALLISON TRANSMISSION HOLDINGS INC p 58
1 Allison Way, Indianapolis IN 46222
Tel (317) 242-5000 SIC 3714

■ ALLISON TRANSMISSION INC p 58
1 Allison Way, Indianapolis IN 46222
Tel (317) 242-5000 SIC 3714

FIRESTONE INDUSTRIAL PRODUCTS CO LLC p 544
250 W 96th St Ste 150, Indianapolis IN 46260
Tel (317) 818-8600
SIC 5531 3469 3714 3495

MAHOMED SALES & WAREHOUSING LLC p 897
8258 Zionsville Rd, Indianapolis IN 46268
Tel (317) 472-5800 SIC 4225 3714

JASPER ENGINE EXCHANGE INC p 778
815 Wernsing Rd, Jasper IN 47546
Tel (812) 482-1041 SIC 3714 7538 6512

FAIRFIELD MANUFACTURING CO INC p 525
2400 Sagamore Pkwy S, Lafayette IN 47905
Tel (765) 772-4000 SIC 3462 3714 5085

▲ WABASH NATIONAL CORP p 1570
1000 Sagamore Pkwy S, Lafayette IN 47905
Tel (765) 771-5310 SIC 3715 3714 5012

CARTER FUEL SYSTEMS LLC p 262
101 E Industrial Blvd, Logansport IN 46947
Tel (800) 342-6125 SIC 3714 5989

ARVIN SANGO INC p 114
2905 Wilson Ave, Madison IN 47250
Tel (812) 265-2888 SIC 3714

TOA (USA) LLC p 1458
2000 Pleiades Dr, Mooresville IN 46158
Tel (317) 834-0522 SIC 3714

GULF STREAM COACH INC p 647
503 S Oakland Ave, Nappanee IN 46550
Tel (574) 773-7761
SIC 3716 3792 3714 2451

■ BALLANTRAE INC p 148
600 Corporation Dr, Pendleton IN 46064
Tel (800) 372-3555 SIC 3714 3694

■ BORGWARNER PDS (INDIANA) INC p 201
600 Corporation Dr, Pendleton IN 46064
Tel (800) 372-3555 SIC 3694 3714

■ NEW PDS CORP p 1032
600 Corporation Dr, Pendleton IN 46064
Tel (800) 372-3555 SIC 3694 3714

■ REMAN HOLDINGS LLC p 1222
600 Corporation Dr, Pendleton IN 46064
Tel (800) 372-5131 SIC 3714 3694

■ REMY HOLDINGS INC p 1223
600 Corporation Dr, Pendleton IN 46064
Tel (765) 778-6499 SIC 3694 3714

■ REMY INC p 1223
600 Corporation Dr, Pendleton IN 46064
Tel (765) 778-6499
SIC 3714 3694 3625 3621 5013

INDIANA FCC INC p 738
555 Industrial Dr, Portland IN 47371
Tel (260) 726-8023 SIC 3714

AISIN USA MFG INC p 41
1700 E 4th Street Rd, Seymour IN 47274
Tel (812) 523-1969 SIC 3714

VALEO LIGHTING SYSTEMS NORTH AMERICA LLC p 1539
1231 A Ave N, Seymour IN 47274
Tel (812) 524-5021 SIC 3641 3714

PK USA INC p 1153
600 Northridge Dr, Shelbyville IN 46176
Tel (317) 395-5500
SIC 3465 3089 3714 3429

RYOBI DIE CASTING (USA) INC p 1261
800 W Mausoleum Rd, Shelbyville IN 46176
Tel (317) 398-3398
SIC 3714 3444 3365 3363

AM GENERAL HOLDINGS LLC p 63
105 N Niles Ave, South Bend IN 46617
Tel (574) 237-6222 SIC 3714 3711 8711

AM GENERAL LLC p 63
105 N Niles Ave, South Bend IN 46617
Tel (574) 237-6222 SIC 3711 3714 8711

INTERNATIONAL BRAKE INDUSTRIES INC p 754
4300 Quality Dr, South Bend IN 46628
Tel (419) 905-7468 SIC 3713 3714

TIRE RACK INC p 1455
7101 Vorden Pkwy, South Bend IN 46628
Tel (888) 541-1777 SIC 5014 3714

INDIANA LLC ADVICS MANUFACTURING p 738
10550 James Adams St, Terre Haute IN 47802
Tel (812) 298-1617 SIC 3714

AVIS INDUSTRIAL CORP p 138
1909 S Main St, Upland IN 46989
Tel (765) 998-8100
SIC 3429 3462 3312 3531 3714 3569

PIERCE CO INC p 1147
35 N 8th St, Upland IN 46989
Tel (765) 998-8100 SIC 3714

INDIANA MILLS & MANUFACTURING INC p 738
18881 Immi Way, Westfield IN 46074
Tel (317) 896-9531 SIC 3714

FEATHERLITE INC p 533
13380 Highways 63 & 9, Cresco IA 52136
Tel (563) 547-6000 SIC 3716 3799 3714

DEE ZEE INC p 421
1572 Ne 58th Ave, Des Moines IA 50313
Tel (515) 265-7331 SIC 3714

▲WINNEBAGO INDUSTRIES INC p 1616
605 W Crystal Lake Rd, Forest City IA 50436
Tel (641) 585-3535 SIC 3716 3714

HOPKINS MANUFACTURING CORP p 706
428 Peyton St, Emporia KS 66801
Tel (620) 342-7320 SIC 3714

KALMAR SOLUTIONS LLC p 801
415 E Dundee St, Ottawa KS 66067
Tel (785) 242-2200
SIC 3537 3714 3713 3643

MITSUBA BARDSTOWN INC p 977
901 Withrow Ct, Bardstown KY 40004
Tel (502) 348-1409 SIC 3714

HIGH PERFORMANCE INDUSTRIES HOLDINGS INC p 690
1801 Russellville Rd, Bowling Green KY 42101
Tel (270) 782-2900 SIC 3592 3714

HOLLEY PERFORMANCE PRODUCTS INC p 700
1801 Russellville Rd, Bowling Green KY 42101
Tel (270) 782-2900 SIC 3714 3592

SUMITOMO ELECTRIC WIRING SYSTEMS INC p 1398
1018 Ashley St, Bowling Green KY 42103
Tel (270) 782-7397 SIC 3714 5063 3694

AKEBONO BRAKE ELIZABETHTOWN PLANT p 42
300 Ring Rd, Elizabethtown KY 42701
Tel (270) 737-4906 SIC 3714

AMBRAKE MANUFACTURING LTD p 65
300 Ring Rd, Elizabethtown KY 42701
Tel (270) 737-4906 SIC 3714

MUBEA INC p 998
6800 Industrial Rd, Florence KY 41042
Tel (859) 746-5300
SIC 3493 3312 3495 3429 3714

ROBERT BOSCH AUTOMOTIVE STEERING LLC p 1241
15 Spiral Dr, Florence KY 41042
Tel (859) 568-1143 SIC 3714

MONTAPLAST OF NORTH AMERICA INC p 986
2011 Hoover Blvd, Frankfort KY 40601
Tel (502) 695-7766 SIC 3714 3089

TOPY AMERICA INC p 1461
980 Chenault Rd, Frankfort KY 40601
Tel (502) 783-1250 SIC 3714

FRANKLIN PRECISION INDUSTRY INC p 575
3220 Bowling Green Rd, Franklin KY 42134
Tel (270) 598-4300 SIC 3714

INTERNATIONAL CRANKSHAFT INC p 755
101 Carley Ct, Georgetown KY 40324
Tel (502) 868-0003 SIC 3714

AMAK BRAKE LLC p 64
1765 Cleveland Ave, Glasgow KY 42141
Tel (270) 678-1765 SIC 3714

HITACHI AUTOMOTIVE SYSTEMS AMERICAS INC p 696
955 Warwick Rd, Harrodsburg KY 40330
Tel (859) 734-9451
SIC 3694 3714 3699 3625

CURTIS-MARUYASU AMERICA INC p 402
665 Metts Dr, Lebanon KY 40033
Tel (270) 692-2109 SIC 3714 3498

■WESTPORT AXLE CORP p 1602
12740 Westport Rd Ste H, Louisville KY 40245
Tel (502) 425-2103 SIC 5051 3463 3714

CENTRAL MOTOR WHEEL OF AMERICA INC p 279
150 Wheat Dr, Paris KY 40361
Tel (859) 987-0500 SIC 3714

TOYOTETSU AMERICA INC p 1467
100 Pin Oak Dr, Somerset KY 42503
Tel (606) 274-9005 SIC 3465 3714 3429

YOKOHAMA INDUSTRIES AMERICAS INC p 1637
105 Industry Dr, Versailles KY 40383
Tel (859) 873-2188
SIC 3714 3585 3492 3052

UNIVANCE INC p 1516
3400 Corporate Dr, Winchester KY 40391
Tel (859) 737-2306 SIC 3568 3714 5012

NICHOLS PORTLAND LLC p 1042
2400 Congress St, Portland ME 04102
Tel (207) 774-6121 SIC 3714 8711

■ HUTCHINSON AEROSPACE & INDUSTRY INC p 721
82 South St, Hopkinton MA 01748
Tel (508) 417-7000 SIC 3714 3061 3724

ETX HOLDINGS INC p 512
2000 Michigan Ave, Alma MI 48801
Tel (989) 463-1151
SIC 3585 3621 3714 5013 3089

NSK AMERICAS INC p 1065
4200 Goss Rd, Ann Arbor MI 48105
Tel (734) 913-7500 SIC 3714 5013 5085

NSK CORP p 1065
4200 Goss Rd, Ann Arbor MI 48105
Tel (734) 913-7500
SIC 3714 5013 3594 3568 3562

NSK STEERING SYSTEMS AMERICA INC p 1065
4200 Goss Rd, Ann Arbor MI 48105
Tel (734) 913-7500 SIC 3714

TRUCK HERO INC p 1485
5400 S State Rd, Ann Arbor MI 48108
Tel (734) 677-0444 SIC 3714

AIRBOSS FLEXIBLE PRODUCTS CO p 39
2600 Auburn Ct, Auburn Hills MI 48326
Tel (248) 852-5500 SIC 3069 3714

ANTOLIN INTERIORS USA INC p 94
1700 Atlantic Blvd, Auburn Hills MI 48326
Tel (248) 373-1749 SIC 3714

BENTELER AUTOMOTIVE CORP p 173
2650 N Opdyke Rd Ste B, Auburn Hills MI 48326
Tel (248) 364-7190 SIC 3714 3465 3999

■ BORGWARNER EMISSIONS SYSTEMS OF MICHIGAN INC p 201
3800 Automation Ave # 200, Auburn Hills MI 48326
Tel (248) 754-9600 SIC 3714

▲ BORGWARNER INC p 201
3850 Hamlin Rd, Auburn Hills MI 48326
Tel (248) 754-9200 SIC 3714

■ BORGWARNER TORQTRANSFER SYSTEMS INC p 201
3850 Hamlin Rd, Auburn Hills MI 48326
Tel (248) 754-9600 SIC 3714

■ BORGWARNER TRANSMISSION SYSTEMS INC p 201
3800 Automation Ave # 500, Auburn Hills MI 48326
Tel (248) 754-0200 SIC 3714

CONTINENTAL AUTOMOTIVE SYSTEMS INC p 363
1 Continental Dr, Auburn Hills MI 48326
Tel (248) 393-5300 SIC 3714

CONTINENTAL TEVES INC p 363
1 Continental Dr, Auburn Hills MI 48326
Tel (248) 393-5300 SIC 3714

DURA AUTOMOTIVE SYSTEMS LLC p 462
1780 Pond Run, Auburn Hills MI 48326
Tel (248) 299-7500 SIC 3714

DURA OPERATING LLC p 462
1780 Pond Run, Auburn Hills MI 48326
Tel (248) 299-7500 SIC 3429 3714

FAURECIA USA HOLDINGS INC p 531
2800 High Meadow Cir, Auburn Hills MI 48326
Tel (248) 724-5100 SIC 3714

FCA NORTH AMERICA HOLDINGS LLC p 532
1000 Chrysler Dr, Auburn Hills MI 48326
Tel (248) 512-2950 SIC 3711 3714

FCA US LLC p 532
1000 Chrysler Dr, Auburn Hills MI 48326
Tel (248) 512-2950 SIC 3711 3714

GKN DRIVELINE NORTH AMERICA INC p 613
2200 N Opdyke Rd, Auburn Hills MI 48326
Tel (248) 296-7000 SIC 3714 5013

GKN NORTH AMERICA INC p 613
2200 N Opdyke Rd, Auburn Hills MI 48326
Tel (248) 296-7200 SIC 3714 5013 7359

GKN SINTER METALS LLC p 613
2200 N Opdyke Rd, Auburn Hills MI 48326
Tel (248) 296-7832
SIC 3714 3568 3369 3366

HENNIGES AUTOMOTIVE HOLDINGS INC p 683
2750 High Meadow Cir, Auburn Hills MI 48326
Tel (248) 340-4100 SIC 3069 2891 3714

HENNIGES AUTOMOTIVE SEALING SYSTEMS NORTH AMERICA INC p 683
2750 High Meadow Cir, Auburn Hills MI 48326
Tel (248) 340-4100 SIC 3053 2891 3714

■ HUTCHINSON FTS INC p 722
1060 Centre Rd, Auburn Hills MI 48326
Tel (248) 589-7710
SIC 3714 3061 3567 3492 3443 3429

INALFA ROOF SYSTEMS INC p 735
1370 Pacific Dr, Auburn Hills MI 48326
Tel (248) 371-3060 SIC 3714

LJ/HAH HOLDINGS CORP p 872
2750 High Meadow Cir, Auburn Hills MI 48326
Tel (248) 340-4100 SIC 2891 3714

NEXTEER AUTOMOTIVE CORP p 1040
1272 Doris Rd, Auburn Hills MI 48326
Tel (989) 757-5000 SIC 3714

TI AUTOMOTIVE LLC p 1452
2020 Taylor Rd, Auburn Hills MI 48326
Tel (248) 494-5000
SIC 3317 3312 3599 3052 3714 3585

TI GROUP AUTOMOTIVE SYSTEMS LLC p 1452
2020 Taylor Rd, Auburn Hills MI 48326
Tel (248) 296-8000
SIC 3317 3312 3599 3052 3714 3585

TK HOLDINGS INC p 1457
2500 Takata Dr, Auburn Hills MI 48326
Tel (248) 373-8040
SIC 2221 2399 2396 3714

DENSO AIR SYSTEMS MICHIGAN INC p 428
300 Fritz Keiper Blvd, Battle Creek MI 49037
Tel (269) 962-9676 *SIC* 3714 3498

MUSASHI AUTO PARTS MICHIGAN INC p 1002
195 Brydges Dr, Battle Creek MI 49037
Tel (269) 965-0057 *SIC* 3714

TRMI INC p 1483
100 Hill Brady Rd, Battle Creek MI 49037
Tel (269) 966-0800 *SIC* 3714 3643

NEAPCO HOLDINGS LLC p 1023
6735 Haggerty Rd, Belleville MI 48111
Tel (734) 447-1380
SIC 3568 3714 6719 6799

DETROIT TECHNOLOGIES INC p 433
32500 Telg Rd Ste 207, Bingham Farms MI 48025
Tel (248) 647-0400 *SIC* 3714

▲TRIMAS CORP p 1480
39400 Woodward Ave # 130, Bloomfield Hills MI 48304
Tel (248) 631-5450
SIC 3799 3714 3443 2672 3452 3545

CADILLAC CASTING INC p 236
1500 4th Ave, Cadillac MI 49601
Tel (231) 779-9600 *SIC* 3714

▲ SPARTAN MOTORS INC p 1355
1541 Reynolds Rd, Charlotte MI 48813
Tel (517) 543-6400 *SIC* 3711 3714 7519

COMPLETE PROTOTYPE SERVICES INC p 351
44783 Morley Dr, Clinton Township MI 48036
Tel (586) 690-8897 *SIC* 3543 3714

ASAMA COLDWATER MANUFACTURING INC p 115
180 Asama Pkwy, Coldwater MI 49036
Tel (517) 279-1090 *SIC* 3714

▲ FORD MOTOR CO p 565
1 American Rd, Dearborn MI 48126
Tel (313) 322-3000
SIC 3711 3713 3714 6153 6141 7515

OAKWOOD METAL FABRICATING CO p 1071
1100 Oakwood Blvd, Dearborn MI 48124
Tel (313) 561-7740 *SIC* 5199 3714 3469

▲AMERICAN AXLE & MANUFACTURING HOLDINGS INC p 68
1 Dauch Dr, Detroit MI 48211
Tel (313) 758-2000 *SIC* 3714 3711

■AMERICAN AXLE & MANUFACTURING INC p 68
1 Dauch Dr, Detroit MI 48211
Tel (313) 758-3600 *SIC* 3714

DETROIT DIESEL CORP p 433
13400 W Outer Dr, Detroit MI 48239
Tel (313) 592-5000 *SIC* 3519 3714 7538

■ GENERAL MOTORS CHINA INC p 601
300 Renaissance Ctr L1, Detroit MI 48243
Tel (313) 556-5000 *SIC* 3714

▲ GENERAL MOTORS CO p 601
300 Renaissance Ctr L1, Detroit MI 48243
Tel (313) 556-5000 *SIC* 3711 3714

■ GENERAL MOTORS HOLDINGS LLC p 601
300 Renaissance Ctr L1, Detroit MI 48243
Tel (313) 556-5000 *SIC* 3711 3714

■ GENERAL MOTORS LLC p 601
300 Renaissance Ctr L1, Detroit MI 48243
Tel (313) 556-5000 *SIC* 3711 3714

■ GM COMPONENTS HOLDINGS LLC p 618
300 Renaissance Ctr, Detroit MI 48243
Tel (313) 556-5000 *SIC* 3711 3714

ENGINEERED MACHINED PRODUCTS INC p 499
3111 N 28th St, Escanaba MI 49829
Tel (906) 786-8404
SIC 3519 3714 3568 3599 3561

AKEBONO BRAKE CORP p 42
34385 W 12 Mile Rd, Farmington Hills MI 48331
Tel (248) 489-7400 *SIC* 3714

AUTONEUM NORTH AMERICA INC p 135
38555 Hills Tech Dr, Farmington Hills MI 48331
Tel (570) 784-4100 *SIC* 3714

BOSCH AUTOMOTIVE MOTOR SYSTEMS CORP p 202
38000 Hills Tech Dr, Farmington Hills MI 48331
Tel (248) 553-9000 *SIC* 3714

MAHLE INDUSTRIES INC p 897
23030 Mahle Dr, Farmington Hills MI 48335
Tel (248) 305-8200 *SIC* 3714

RIDE CONTROL LLC p 1234
39300 Country Club Dr, Farmington Hills MI 48331
Tel (248) 247-7600 *SIC* 3714

A I FLINT LLC p 5
4444 W Maple Ave, Flint MI 48507
Tel (810) 732-8760 *SIC* 3714

OAKLEY INDUSTRIES SUB ASSEMBLY DIVISION INC p 1071
4333 Matthew, Flint MI 48507
Tel (810) 720-4444 *SIC* 3714

GHSP INC p 610
1250 S Beechtree St, Grand Haven MI 49417
Tel (248) 588-5095 *SIC* 3714

PRIDGEON & CLAY INC p 1174
50 Cottage Grove St Sw, Grand Rapids MI 49507
Tel (616) 241-5675 *SIC* 3714 3465

HUMPHREY COMPANIES LLC p 718
2851 Prairie St Sw, Grandville MI 49418
Tel (616) 530-1717
SIC 3537 3714 3089 5023 5162

LEON INTERIORS INC p 856
88 E 48th St, Holland MI 49423
Tel (616) 531-7970 *SIC* 3089 3714 3086

MELLING TOOL CO p 941
2620 Saradan Dr, Jackson MI 49202
Tel (517) 787-8172
SIC 3451 3714 3625 3568 3561 3494

TAC MANUFACTURING INC p 1421
4111 County Farm Rd, Jackson MI 49201
Tel (517) 789-7000 *SIC* 3714 3625

■AUTOCAM CORP p 134
4180 40th St Se, Kentwood MI 49512
Tel (616) 698-0707
SIC 3714 3572 3841 5084

MICRON HOLDINGS INC p 962
4436 Broadmoor Ave Se, Kentwood MI 49512
Tel (616) 698-0707 *SIC* 3714

TITAN HOLDINGS INC p 1456
4436 Broadmoor Ave Se, Kentwood MI 49512
Tel (616) 698-0707 *SIC* 3714

LANSING L MPT L C p 844
3140 Spanish Oak Dr Ste A, Lansing MI 48911
Tel (517) 316-1013 *SIC* 3714

ZF CHASSIS COMPONENTS LLC p 1642
3300 John Conley Dr, Lapeer MI 48446
Tel (810) 245-2000 *SIC* 3714

KELSEY-HAYES CO p 809
12001 Tech Center Dr, Livonia MI 48150
Tel (734) 812-6979 *SIC* 3714

LUCASVARITY AUTOMOTIVE HOLDING CO p 884
12001 Tech Center Dr, Livonia MI 48150
Tel (734) 855-2600 *SIC* 3714

NYX LLC p 1069
36111 Schoolcraft Rd, Livonia MI 48150
Tel (734) 462-2385
SIC 3089 3714 3565 2671

ROUSH ENTERPRISES INC p 1253
12447 Levan Rd, Livonia MI 48150
Tel (734) 779-7006
SIC 8711 3714 7948 8734

■ STEMCO PRODUCTS INC p 1385
37770 Amrhein Rd, Livonia MI 48150
Tel (734) 416-8911 *SIC* 3714 3465

TRW AUTOMOTIVE INC p 1489
12025 Tech Center Dr, Livonia MI 48150
Tel (734) 266-2600 *SIC* 3714

ZF TRW AUTOMOTIVE HOLDINGS CORP p 1642
12001 Tech Center Dr, Livonia MI 48150
Tel (734) 855-2600 *SIC* 3714 3711

CTA ACOUSTICS INC p 399
25211 Dequindre Rd, Madison Heights MI 48071
Tel (248) 544-2580 *SIC* 3714

UNIVERSAL TRIM INC p 1518
1451 E Lincoln Ave, Madison Heights MI 48071
Tel (248) 586-3300
SIC 3714 3199 3089 3429

MARTINREA INDUSTRIES INC p 913
10501 Mi State Road 52, Manchester MI 48158
Tel (734) 428-2400
SIC 3714 3317 3089 3544

GESTAMP MASON LLC p 609
200 E Kipp Rd, Mason MI 48854
Tel (517) 244-8800
SIC 3398 5013 3714 3711 3465

■ PULLMAN CO p 1191
1 International Dr, Monroe MI 48161
Tel (734) 243-8000 *SIC* 3714 3715 3061

AMERICAN MITSUBA CORP p 76
2945 Three Leaves Dr, Mount Pleasant MI 48858
Tel (989) 779-4962 *SIC* 3714

SAF-HOLLAND INC p 1265
1950 Industrial Blvd, Muskegon MI 49442
Tel (231) 773-3271
SIC 3714 3715 3568 3537 3452

▲ GENTHERM INC p 605
21680 Haggerty Rd Ste 101, Northville MI 48167
Tel (248) 504-0500 *SIC* 3714

ZF NORTH AMERICA INC p 1642
15811 Centennial Dr, Northville MI 48168
Tel (734) 416-6200 *SIC* 3714 5013

■ COOPER-STANDARD AUTOMOTIVE INC p 367
39550 Orchard Hill Pl, Novi MI 48375
Tel (248) 596-5900 *SIC* 3714

▲ COOPER-STANDARD HOLDINGS INC p 367
39550 Orchard Hill Pl, Novi MI 48375
Tel (248) 596-5900 *SIC* 3714

EBERSPAECHER NORTH AMERICA INC p 474
29101 Haggerty Rd, Novi MI 48377
Tel (248) 994-7010 *SIC* 3714

IOCHPE HOLDINGS LLC p 762
39500 Orchard Hill Pl # 500, Novi MI 48375
Tel (734) 737-5000 *SIC* 3714

KONGSBERG AUTOMOTIVE INC p 827
27275 Haggerty Rd Ste 610, Novi MI 48377
Tel (248) 468-1300 *SIC* 3714

KONGSBERG HOLDING III INC p 827
27275 Haggerty Rd Ste 610, Novi MI 48377
Tel (248) 468-1300 *SIC* 3714

MAGNA SEATING OF AMERICA INC p 896
39600 Lewis Dr Ste 216, Novi MI 48377
Tel (248) 553-8094 *SIC* 3714

MAXION WHEELS p 922
39500 Orchard Hill Pl # 500, Novi MI 48375
Tel (734) 737-5000 *SIC* 3714

MAXION WHEELS USA LLC p 922
39500 Orchard Hill Pl # 500, Novi MI 48375
Tel (734) 737-5000 *SIC* 3714

METALSA STRUCTURAL PRODUCTS INC p 953
29545 Hudson Dr, Novi MI 48377
Tel (248) 669-3704 *SIC* 3714

▲ STONERIDGE INC p 1391
39675 Mackenzie Dr # 400, Novi MI 48377
Tel (330) 856-2443 *SIC* 3714 3679 3625

MICHIGAN AUTOMOTIVE COMPRESSOR INC p 960
2400 N Dearing Rd, Parma MI 49269
Tel (517) 622-7000
SIC 3585 3714 3568 3563

ADIENT US LLC p 22
49200 Halyard Dr, Plymouth MI 48170
Tel (734) 254-5000 *SIC* 3714

BREMBO NORTH AMERICA INC p 209
47765 Halyard Dr, Plymouth MI 48170
Tel (734) 416-1275 *SIC* 3714 5013

■ CEQUENT PERFORMANCE PRODUCTS INC p 283
47912 Halyard Dr Ste 100, Plymouth MI 48170
Tel (734) 656-3000 *SIC* 3799 3714

FREUDENBERG NORTH AMERICA LIMITED PARTNERSHIP p 579
47774 W Anchor Ct, Plymouth MI 48170
Tel (734) 354-5505
SIC 2821 3714 3053 3061

FREUDENBERG-NOK GENERAL PARTNERSHIP p 579
47690 E Anchor Ct, Plymouth MI 48170
Tel (734) 451-0020
SIC 2821 3714 3053 3061

HELLA ELECTRONICS CORP p 681
43811 Plymouth Oaks Blvd, Plymouth MI 48170
Tel (734) 414-0900 *SIC* 3625 3714

INTERTEC SYSTEMS LLC p 759
45000 Helm St Ste 200, Plymouth MI 48170
Tel (734) 254-3268 *SIC* 3714

■ METALDYNE LLC p 952
47659 Halyard Dr, Plymouth MI 48170
Tel (734) 207-6200 *SIC* 3714

TRAM INC p 1469
47200 Port St, Plymouth MI 48170
Tel (734) 254-8500 *SIC* 3714 3643

JAC PRODUCTS INC p 773
3937 Campus Dr, Pontiac MI 48341
Tel (248) 874-1800 *SIC* 3089 3714

MANN + HUMMEL USA INC p 902
6400 S Sprinkle Rd, Portage MI 49002
Tel (269) 329-3900 *SIC* 3089 3714

PISTON AUTOMOTIVE LLC p 1152
12723 Telegraph Rd Ste 1, Redford MI 48239
Tel (313) 541-8674 *SIC* 3714

FLEXTRONICS AUTOMOTIVE USA INC p 556
2120 Austin Ave, Rochester Hills MI 48309
Tel (248) 853-5724 *SIC* 3625 3714 3643

M P I INTERNATIONAL INC p 889
2129 Austin Ave, Rochester Hills MI 48309
Tel (608) 764-5416 *SIC* 3462 3714 3469

NEWCOR INC p 1037
715 South Blvd E Ste 101, Rochester Hills MI 48307
Tel (248) 537-0014 *SIC* 3714

TRICO PRODUCTS CORP p 1479
3255 W Hamlin Rd, Rochester Hills MI 48309
Tel (248) 371-1700
SIC 3714 3069 3082 8734 8731

▲WABCO HOLDINGS INC p 1570
2770 Research Dr Fl 1, Rochester Hills MI 48309
Tel (248) 270-9299 *SIC* 3714

WEBASTO ROOF SYSTEMS INC p 1586
1757 Northfield Dr, Rochester Hills MI 48309
Tel (800) 860-7866 *SIC* 3714 3441 3469

RCO ENGINEERING INC p 1212
29200 Calahan Rd, Roseville MI 48066
Tel (586) 774-0100
SIC 3714 3089 3365 7361 3325 2531

MEANS INDUSTRIES INC p 934
3715 E Washington Rd, Saginaw MI 48601
Tel (989) 754-1433 *SIC* 3714 3465

VIBRACOUSTIC NORTH AMERICA L P p 1555
400 Aylworth Ave, South Haven MI 49090
Tel (269) 637-2116
SIC 2821 3714 3053 3061

CHASSIX INC p 291
300 Galleria Officentre, Southfield MI 48034
Tel (248) 728-8642 *SIC* 3714

DENSO INTERNATIONAL AMERICA INC p 428
24777 Denso Dr, Southfield MI 48033
Tel (248) 350-7500 *SIC* 3714 5013

■ FEDERAL-MOGUL HOLDINGS CORP p 536
27300 W 11 Mile Rd, Southfield MI 48034
Tel (248) 354-7700
SIC 3462 3559 3694 3812 3674 3714

■ FEDERAL-MOGUL PRODUCTS INC p 536
26555 Northwestern Hwy, Southfield MI 48033
Tel (248) 354-7700 *SIC* 3714

▲ LEAR CORP p 850
21557 Telegraph Rd, Southfield MI 48033
Tel (248) 447-1500
SIC 3714 2531 2396 3643

▲ METALDYNE PERFORMANCE GROUP INC p 952
1 Towne Sq Ste 550, Southfield MI 48076
Tel (248) 727-1800 *SIC* 3714

▲ SUPERIOR INDUSTRIES INTERNATIONAL INC p 1406
26600 Telg Rd Ste 400, Southfield MI 48033
Tel (248) 352-7300 *SIC* 3714

UC HOLDINGS INC p 1498
300 Galleria Officentre, Southfield MI 48034
Tel (248) 728-8642 *SIC* 3465 3714

ST JAMES INC p 1367
18500 Walnut St, Southgate MI 48195
Tel (734) 285-4911 *SIC* 3714 3711 3465

KEY SAFETY RESTRAINT SYSTEMS INC p 814
7000 19 Mile Rd, Sterling Heights MI 48314
Tel (586) 726-3800 *SIC* 3714 3674 3679

KEY SAFETY SYSTEMS INC p 814
7000 19 Mile Rd, Sterling Heights MI 48314
Tel (586) 726-3800 *SIC* 2399 3714

■ARVINMERITOR OE LLC p 114
2135 W Maple Rd, Troy MI 48084
Tel (248) 435-1000 *SIC* 3714

CADILLAC PRODUCTS INC p 236
5800 Crooks Rd Ste 100, Troy MI 48098
Tel (248) 813-8200
SIC 3714 3081 2673 3089

COSMA AMERICA HOLDINGS INC p 373
750 Tower Dr, Troy MI 48098
Tel (248) 524-5300 *SIC* 3714

COSMA INTERNATIONAL OF AMERICA INC p 373
750 Tower Dr, Troy MI 48098
Tel (248) 631-1100 *SIC* 3714

DELPHI AUTOMOTIVE SYSTEMS LLC p 425
5725 Delphi Dr, Troy MI 48098
Tel (248) 813-2000 *SIC* 3714

DELPHI CORP p 425
5725 Delphi Dr, Troy MI 48098
Tel (248) 813-2000 *SIC* 3714

DELPHI HOLDINGS LLC p 425
5725 Delphi Dr, Troy MI 48098
Tel (248) 813-2000 *SIC* 3714

DIEOMATIC INC p 438
750 Tower Dr Mail 7000 Mail Code, Troy MI 48098
Tel (319) 668-2031 *SIC* 3714

DPH HOLDINGS CORP p 454
5725 Delphi Dr, Troy MI 48098
Tel (248) 813-2000 *SIC* 3714

DPH LLC p 454
5725 Delphi Dr, Troy MI 48098
Tel (248) 813-2000 *SIC* 3714

DPH-DAS GLOBAL (HOLDINGS) LLC p 454
5725 Delphi Dr, Troy MI 48098
Tel (248) 813-2000 *SIC* 3714

DPH-DAS LLC p 454
5725 Delphi Dr, Troy MI 48098
Tel (248) 813-2000 *SIC* 3714

▲ HORIZON GLOBAL CORP p 707
2600 W Big Beaver Rd # 555, Troy MI 48084
Tel (248) 593-8820 *SIC* 3714 3711 5531

INERGY AUTOMOTIVE SYSTEMS (USA) LLC p 740
2710 Bellingham Dr # 400, Troy MI 48083
Tel (248) 743-5700 *SIC* 3714

INOAC USA INC p 745
1515 Equity Dr Ste 200, Troy MI 48084
Tel (248) 619-7031 *SIC* 3085 3714

INTEVA PRODUCTS LLC p 759
1401 Crooks Rd, Troy MI 48084
Tel (248) 655-8886 *SIC* 3714 5085

■ KAUTEX INC p 805
750 Stephenson Hwy, Troy MI 48083
Tel (248) 616-5100 *SIC* 3714

MAGNA EXTERIORS OF AMERICA INC p 896
750 Tower Dr, Troy MI 48098
Tel (248) 631-1100 *SIC* 3714 3544 8711

MAGNA INTERNATIONAL OF AMERICA INC p 896
750 Tower Dr 7000, Troy MI 48098
Tel (248) 729-2400 *SIC* 3714

MAGNA POWERTRAIN USA INC p 896
1870 Technology Dr, Troy MI 48083
Tel (248) 680-4900 *SIC* 3714

MAHLE BEHR MANUFACTURING MANAGEMENT INC p 897
2700 Daley Dr, Troy MI 48083
Tel (248) 735-3623 *SIC* 5013 3714

MAHLE BEHR USA INC p 897
2700 Daley Dr, Troy MI 48083
Tel (248) 743-3700 *SIC* 3714

MARTINREA AUTOMOTIVE-STRUCTURES (USA) INC p 913
2800 Livernois Rd Ste 450, Troy MI 48083
Tel (248) 823-5700 *SIC* 3714

▲ MERITOR INC p 949
2135 W Maple Rd, Troy MI 48084
Tel (248) 435-1000
SIC 3714 3493 3625 3465

METAVATION LLC p 953
900 Wilshire Dr Ste 270, Troy MI 48084
Tel (248) 351-1000 *SIC* 3714

NOBLE INTERNATIONAL LTD p 1046
840 W Long Lake Rd # 601, Troy MI 48098
Tel (248) 519-0700 *SIC* 3714

THYSSENKRUPP AUTOMOTIVE SALES & TECHNICAL CENTER INC p 1451
3155 W Big Beaver Rd # 260, Troy MI 48084
Tel (248) 530-2902 *SIC* 5013 3714

VALEO INC p 1539
150 Stephenson Hwy, Troy MI 48083
Tel (248) 619-8300 *SIC* 3714

VALEO NORTH AMERICA INC p 1539
150 Stephenson Hwy, Troy MI 48083
Tel (248) 619-8300 *SIC* 3714

VALEO RADAR SYSTEMS INC p 1539
150 Stephenson Hwy, Troy MI 48083
Tel (248) 619-8300 *SIC* 5731 3714

VALEO SWITCHES & DETECTION SYSTEMS INC p 1539
150 Stephenson Hwy, Troy MI 48083
Tel (248) 619-8300 *SIC* 3714

MNP CORP p 980
44225 Utica Rd, Utica MI 48317
Tel (586) 254-1320
SIC 3452 5051 5072 3714

HANON SYSTEMS USA LLC p 658
1 Village Center Dr, Van Buren Twp MI 48111
Tel (734) 710-5000 *SIC* 3714 3585 3699

▲VISTEON CORP p 1562
1 Village Center Dr, Van Buren Twp MI 48111
Tel (800) 847-8366 *SIC* 3714

U S MANUFACTURING CORP p 1497
28201 Van Dyke Ave, Warren MI 48093
Tel (586) 467-1600 *SIC* 3714 3482 3356

TRW VEHICLE SAFETY SYSTEMS INC p 1489
4505 26 Mile Rd, Washington MI 48094
Tel (734) 855-2600 *SIC* 3714

GT TECHNOLOGIES INC p 644
5859 E Executive Dr, Westland MI 48185
Tel (734) 467-8371
SIC 8711 3714 3545 3089

KIEKERT USA INC p 817
46941 Liberty Dr, Wixom MI 48393
Tel (248) 960-4100 *SIC* 3714

BOSAL INDUSTRIES-GEORGIA INC p 201
1476 Seaver Way, Ypsilanti MI 48197
Tel (734) 547-7022 *SIC* 3714

▲ GENTEX CORP p 604
600 N Centennial St, Zeeland MI 49464
Tel (616) 772-1800 *SIC* 3231 3714 3669

TEAM INDUSTRIES BAGLEY-AUDUBON INC p 1430
105 Park Ave Nw, Bagley MN 56621
Tel (218) 694-3550 *SIC* 3599 8711 3714

TEAM INDUSTRIES INC p 1430
105 Park Ave Nw, Bagley MN 56621
Tel (218) 694-3550 *SIC* 3599 8711 3714

PHILLIPS & TEMRO INDUSTRIES INC p 1143
9700 W 74th St, Eden Prairie MN 55344
Tel (952) 941-9700 SIC 3714

▲ POLARIS INDUSTRIES INC p 1159
2100 Highway 55, Medina MN 55340
Tel (763) 542-0500
SIC 3799 3751 3714 5699

▲ DONALDSON CO INC p 450
1400 W 94th St, Minneapolis MN 55431
Tel (952) 887-3131
SIC 3599 3569 3714 3564

■ REMY REMAN LLC p 1223
214 Fellowship Rd, Taylorsville MS 39168
Tel (601) 785-9504 SIC 3714

PETERSON MANUFACTURING CO p 1138
4200 E 135th St, Grandview MO 64030
Tel (816) 765-2000
SIC 3647 4111 3089 3714

HALDEX BRAKE PRODUCTS CORP p 653
10930 N Pomona Ave, Kansas City MO 64153
Tel (816) 891-2470 SIC 3714

HALDEX INC p 653
10930 N Pomona Ave, Kansas City MO 64153
Tel (816) 891-2470 SIC 3714 3594

NORANDA ALUMINUM INC p 1047
St Jude Industrial Park, New Madrid MO 63869
Tel (573) 643-2361
SIC 3353 3354 3334 3714

LINCOLN INDUSTRIAL CORP p 867
5148 N Hanley Rd, Saint Louis MO 63134
Tel (314) 679-4200
SIC 3569 3559 3561 3714

HUTCHENS INDUSTRIES INC p 721
215 N Patterson Ave, Springfield MO 65802
Tel (417) 862-5012 SIC 3714

SPRINGFIELD REMANUFACTURING CORP p 1361
650 N Broadview Pl, Springfield MO 65802
Tel (417) 862-3501
SIC 3519 3714 3713 3561

SRC HOLDINGS CORP p 1363
531 S Union Ave, Springfield MO 65802
Tel (417) 862-2337 SIC 3519 3714

■ TIMKEN SMO LLC p 1455
2601 W Battlefield St, Springfield MO 65807
Tel (866) 773-2926 SIC 3451 3714

■ BALDWIN FILTERS INC p 147
4400 Highway 30 E, Kearney NE 68847
Tel (800) 822-5394 SIC 3714 3564

LINCOLN HEXAGON INC p 867
5150 Nw 40th St, Lincoln NE 68524
Tel (402) 470-5000 SIC 3714

EXX INC p 521
1350 E Flamingo Rd 689, Las Vegas NV 89119
Tel (248) 409-1070
SIC 3621 3669 3714 3944

■ CEQUENT UK LTD p 283
123 Town Square Pl, Jersey City NJ 07310
Tel (734) 656-3078 SIC 4789 3714 5531

▲ HONEYWELL INTERNATIONAL INC p 705
115 Tabor Rd, Morris Plains NJ 07950
Tel (973) 455-2000
SIC 3724 3812 3585 2824 2821 3714

GENTEK INC p 604
90 E Halsey Rd Ste 301, Parsippany NJ 07054
Tel (973) 515-0900
SIC 2869 2819 2844 3714 3496

VOLVO CARS OF NORTH AMERICA LLC p 1565
1 Volvo Dr, Rockleigh NJ 07647
Tel (201) 768-7300
SIC 5511 5013 6159 7515 3714

WHITING DOOR MFG CORP p 1607
113 Cedar St, Akron NY 14001
Tel (716) 542-5427 SIC 3714

■ BORGWARNER MORSE TEC INC p 201
800 Warren Rd, Ithaca NY 14850
Tel (607) 257-6700 SIC 3714 3462 3568

TITANX ENGINE COOLING INC p 1456
2258 Allen Street Ext, Jamestown NY 14701
Tel (716) 665-7129 SIC 3714

▲ STANDARD MOTOR PRODUCTS INC p 1376
3718 Northern Blvd # 600, Long Island City NY 11101
Tel (718) 392-0200
SIC 3714 3694 3585 3564 3052

FIAT USA INC p 539
375 Park Ave Ste 2703, New York NY 10152
Tel (212) 355-2600
SIC 3714 8741 3535 5012 5013 5082

FUEL SYSTEMS SOLUTIONS INC p 583
780 3rd Ave Fl 25, New York NY 10017
Tel (646) 502-7170 SIC 3714 3592 7363

▲ ICAHN ENTERPRISES LP p 726
767 5th Ave Ste 4700, New York NY 10153
Tel (212) 702-4300
SIC 6722 3714 7999 3743 5093 6531

KEARNEY-NATIONAL INC p 807
565 5th Ave Fl 4, New York NY 10017
Tel (212) 661-4600
SIC 3679 3694 3714 3625

WLR RECOVERY FUND II LP p 1620
1166 6th Ave, New York NY 10036
Tel (212) 278-9821 SIC 6719 3714

■ ITT ENIDINE INC p 768
7 Centre Dr, Orchard Park NY 14127
Tel (716) 662-1900 SIC 3724 3714 3593

■ GARLOCK SEALING TECHNOLOGIES LLC p 592
1666 Division St, Palmyra NY 14522
Tel (315) 597-4811 SIC 3053 3585 3714

■ PALL CORP p 1108
25 Harbor Park Dr, Port Washington NY 11050
Tel (516) 484-5400
SIC 3569 3599 3714 2834 3841

GLEASON WORKS p 614
1000 University Ave, Rochester NY 14607
Tel (585) 473-1000
SIC 3714 3728 3566 3541 3829 3469

AW NORTH CAROLINA INC p 139
4112 Old Oxford Rd, Durham NC 27712
Tel (919) 620-5500 SIC 3714

MANN+HUMMEL FILTRATION TECHNOLOGY GROUP INC p 902
1 Wix Way, Gastonia NC 28054
Tel (704) 869-3300 SIC 3714 5013

MANN+HUMMEL FILTRATION TECHNOLOGY HOLDINGS INC p 902
1 Wix Way, Gastonia NC 28054
Tel (704) 869-3300 SIC 3714

MANN+HUMMEL FILTRATION TECHNOLOGY INTERMEDIATE HOLDINGS INC p 902
1 Wix Way, Gastonia NC 28054
Tel (704) 869-3300 SIC 3714

MANN+HUMMEL FILTRATION TECHNOLOGY US LLC p 902
1 Wix Way, Gastonia NC 28054
Tel (704) 869-3300 SIC 3714

AP EMISSIONS TECHNOLOGIES LLC p 95
300 Dixie Trl, Goldsboro NC 27530
Tel (919) 580-2000 SIC 3714

UCHIYAMA MANUFACTURING AMERICA LLC p 1499
494 Arrington Bridge Rd, Goldsboro NC 27530
Tel (919) 731-2364 SIC 5085 3714 3053

INTERNATIONAL TEXTILE GROUP INC p 757
804 Green Valley Rd # 300, Greensboro NC 27408
Tel (336) 379-6299
SIC 3714 3496 2211 2231 2221 2273

MACK TRUCKS INC p 892
7825 National Service Rd, Greensboro NC 27409
Tel (336) 291-9001
SIC 3711 3714 5012 6141 6153 7538

■ IMO INDUSTRIES INC p 734
1710 Airport Rd, Monroe NC 28110
Tel (704) 289-6511 SIC 3561 3714 3829

GKN DRIVELINE NEWTON LLC p 613
1848 Gkn Way, Newton NC 28658
Tel (828) 428-1591 SIC 3462 3714

MAGNETI MARELLI POWERTRAIN USA LLC p 896
2101 Nash St, Sanford NC 27330
Tel (919) 776-4111 SIC 3714 3592

KEIHIN CAROLINA SYSTEM TECHNOLOGY LLC p 807
4047 Mcnair Rd, Tarboro NC 27886
Tel (252) 641-6750 SIC 3694 3625 3714

CHESTNUT HOLDINGS INC p 295
670 W Market St, Akron OH 44303
Tel (330) 849-6503
SIC 3053 5014 5013 3714

VIUS SERVICES CORP p 1563
9395 Kenwood Rd Ste 200, Blue Ash OH 45242
Tel (513) 731-3590 SIC 7349 8741 3714

DTR INDUSTRIES INC p 458
320 Snider Rd, Bluffton OH 45817
Tel (419) 358-2121
SIC 3052 3069 3829 3714

GREEN TOKAI CO LTD p 637
55 Robert Wright Dr, Brookville OH 45309
Tel (937) 833-5444 SIC 3714 3069

HFI LLC p 689
59 Gender Rd, Canal Winchester OH 43110
Tel (614) 491-0700
SIC 2396 2821 3714 3429 3086

TS TRIM INDUSTRIES INC p 1489
6380 Canal St, Canal Winchester OH 43110
Tel (614) 837-4114
SIC 5013 3465 3714 3083

CARDINGTON YUTAKA TECHNOLOGIES INC p 253
575 W Main St, Cardington OH 43315
Tel (419) 864-8777 SIC 3714

EATON CORP p 473
1000 Eaton Blvd, Cleveland OH 44122
Tel (216) 523-5000
SIC 3625 3714 3594 3559 3571

INTERSTATE DIESEL SERVICE INC p 758
5300 Lakeside Ave E, Cleveland OH 44114
Tel (216) 881-0015 SIC 5013 3714

■ CORE AUTOMOTIVE TECHNOLOGIES LLC p 369
800 Manor Park Dr, Columbus OH 43228
Tel (614) 870-5000 SIC 3714 5521

ERNIE GREEN INDUSTRIES INC p 508
2030 Dividend Dr, Columbus OH 43228
Tel (614) 219-1423
SIC 3714 3089 3471 3469

YACHIYO OF AMERICA INC p 1633
2285 Walcutt Rd, Columbus OH 43228
Tel (614) 876-3220 SIC 3089 3465 3714

AD INDUSTRIES INC p 21
6450 Poe Ave Ste 109, Dayton OH 45414
Tel (303) 744-1911
SIC 3634 3564 3535 3714 3088 3089

MAHLE BEHR DAYTON LLC p 897
1600 Webster St, Dayton OH 45404
Tel (937) 369-2900 SIC 3714

NEATON AUTO PRODUCTS MANUFACTURING INC p 1023
975 S Franklin St, Eaton OH 45320
Tel (937) 456-7103 SIC 3714

PACIFIC MANUFACTURING OHIO INC p 1105
8955 Seward Rd, Fairfield OH 45011
Tel (513) 860-3900 SIC 3714 3469

■ AUTOLIV NISSIN BRAKE SYSTEMS AMERICA LLC p 134
2001 Industrial Dr, Findlay OH 45840
Tel (419) 425-6725 SIC 3714

G S WIRING SYSTEMS INC p 587
1801 Production Dr, Findlay OH 45840
Tel (419) 423-7111 SIC 3714 5013

GSW MANUFACTURING INC p 644
1801 Production Dr, Findlay OH 45840
Tel (419) 423-7111 SIC 3714 3694

NISSIN BRAKE OHIO INC p 1044
1901 Industrial Dr, Findlay OH 45840
Tel (419) 420-3800 SIC 3714

ROKI AMERICA CO LTD p 1247
2001 Production Dr, Findlay OH 45840
Tel (419) 424-9713 SIC 3714

FT PRECISION INC p 582
9731 Mount Gilead Rd, Fredericktown OH 43019
Tel (740) 694-1500 SIC 3714

TIGERPOLY MANUFACTURING INC p 1453
6231 Enterprise Pkwy, Grove City OH 43123
Tel (614) 871-0045
SIC 3089 3714 3621 3061

■ AIRSTREAM INC p 40
419 W Pike St, Jackson Center OH 45334
Tel (937) 596-6111
SIC 3716 3792 3714 3713 3711

ADVICS MANUFACTURING OHIO INC p 28
1650 Kingsview Dr, Lebanon OH 45036
Tel (513) 934-0023 SIC 3714

QUALITOR INC p 1196
1840 Mccullough St, Lima OH 45801
Tel (248) 204-8600 SIC 3714 5013

LORAIN COUNTY AUTOMOTIVE SYSTEMS INC p 878
7470 Industrial Pkwy Dr, Lorain OH 44053
Tel (440) 960-7470 SIC 3714

NEWMAN TECHNOLOGY INC p 1038
100 Cairns Rd, Mansfield OH 44903
Tel (419) 525-1856 SIC 3714 3751

MARION INDUSTRIES INC p 907
999 Kellogg Pkwy, Marion OH 43302
Tel (740) 223-0075 SIC 3714

MITSUBISHI ELECTRIC AUTOMOTIVE AMERICA INC p 977
4773 Bethany Rd, Mason OH 45040
Tel (513) 573-6614 SIC 3694 3651 3714

ARE INC p 106
400 Nave Rd Sw, Massillon OH 44646
Tel (330) 830-7800
SIC 3713 3714 3792 5013

■ DANA AUTOMOTIVE SYSTEMS GROUP LLC p 410
3939 Technology Dr, Maumee OH 43537
Tel (419) 887-3000 SIC 3714

■ DANA DRIVESHAFT PRODUCTS LLC p 410
3939 Technology Dr, Maumee OH 43537
Tel (419) 887-3000 SIC 3714

■ DANA HEAVY VEHICLE SYSTEMS GROUP LLC p 410
3939 Technology Rd, Maumee OH 43537
Tel (419) 887-3000 SIC 3714

▲ DANA INC p 410
3939 Technology Dr, Maumee OH 43537
Tel (419) 887-3000
SIC 3714 3053 3593 3492

■ DANA LIGHT AXLE MANUFACTURING LLC p 410
3939 Technology Dr, Maumee OH 43537
Tel (419) 887-3000 SIC 3714

■ DANA LIMITED p 410
3939 Technology Dr, Maumee OH 43537
Tel (630) 697-3783
SIC 3714 3053 3593 3492

■ DANA SEALING PRODUCTS LLC p 411
3939 Technology Dr, Maumee OH 43537
Tel (419) 887-3000 SIC 3714

■ FRICTION PRODUCTS CO p 579
920 Lake Rd, Medina OH 44256
Tel (330) 725-4941 SIC 3728 3714

BUYERS PRODUCTS CO p 230
9049 Tyler Blvd, Mentor OH 44060
Tel (440) 974-8888 SIC 5013 3714

KEIHIN THERMAL TECHNOLOGY OF AMERICA INC p 808
10500 Oday Harrison Rd, Mount Sterling OH 43143
Tel (740) 869-3000 SIC 5013 3714

▲ COMMERCIAL VEHICLE GROUP INC p 345
7800 Walton Pkwy, New Albany OH 43054
Tel (614) 289-5360 SIC 3714 3231

■ TRIM SYSTEMS OPERATING CORP p 1480
7800 Walton Pkwy, New Albany OH 43054
Tel (614) 289-5360 SIC 3714

ASC INDUSTRIES INC p 115
2100 International Pkwy, North Canton OH 44720
Tel (330) 899-0340 SIC 3714

TS TECH USA CORP p 1489
8400 E Broad St, Reynoldsburg OH 43068
Tel (614) 577-1088 SIC 3714

HONDA TRANSMISSION MANUFACTURING OF AMERICA INC p 705
6964 State Route 235 N, Russells Point OH 43348
Tel (937) 843-5555 SIC 3714

NEW SABINA INDUSTRIES INC p 1033
12555 Us Highway 22 And 3, Sabina OH 45169
Tel (937) 584-2433 SIC 3714

AAP ST MARYS CORP p 8
1100 Mckinley Rd, Saint Marys OH 45885
Tel (419) 394-7840 SIC 3714

KTH PARTS INDUSTRIES INC p 831
1111 State Route 235 N, Saint Paris OH 43072
Tel (937) 663-5941 SIC 3714

KYKLOS BEARING INTERNATIONAL LLC p 833
2509 Hayes Ave, Sandusky OH 44870
Tel (419) 627-7000 SIC 3714

■ CEQUENT CONSUMER PRODUCTS INC p 283
29000 Aurora Rd Ste 2, Solon OH 44139
Tel (440) 498-0001 SIC 5531 3714

YAMADA NORTH AMERICA INC p 1634
9000 Clmbus Cincinnati Rd, South Charleston OH 45368
Tel (937) 462-7111 SIC 3714

PIONEER AUTOMOTIVE TECHNOLOGIES INC p 1150
100 S Pioneer Blvd, Springboro OH 45066
Tel (937) 746-2293 SIC 5013 3714 3651

AMERICAN SHOWA INC p 79
707 W Cherry St, Sunbury OH 43074
Tel (740) 965-1133 SIC 3714

FAURECIA AUTOMOTIVE HOLDINGS INC p 531
543 Matzinger Rd, Toledo OH 43612
Tel (419) 727-5000 SIC 3714

FAURECIA EXHAUST SYSTEMS LLC p 531
543 Matzinger Rd, Toledo OH 43612
Tel (419) 727-5000 SIC 3714 5013

MAGNA MODULAR SYSTEMS INC p 896
1800 Nathan Dr, Toledo OH 43611
Tel (419) 324-3387 SIC 3714

F&P AMERICA MFG INC p 522
2101 Corporate Dr, Troy OH 45373
Tel (937) 339-0212 SIC 3714

LUK CLUTCH SYSTEMS LLC p 884
3401 Old Airport Rd, Wooster OH 44691
Tel (330) 264-4383 SIC 3714 3568 3566

LUK TRANSMISSION SYSTEMS LLC p 885
3401 Old Airport Rd, Wooster OH 44691
Tel (330) 264-4383 SIC 3714 3566

LUK USA LLC p 885
3401 Old Airport Rd, Wooster OH 44691
Tel (330) 264-4383 SIC 3714

FLEX-N-GATE OKLAHOMA LLC p 556
1 General St, Ada OK 74820
Tel (580) 272-6700 SIC 3714

■ ATC DRIVETRAIN LLC p 124
9901 W Reno Ave, Oklahoma City OK 73127
Tel (405) 350-3600 SIC 3714 4731

ENOVATION CONTROLS LLC p 500
5311 S 122nd East Ave, Tulsa OK 74146
Tel (918) 317-4100
SIC 3625 3714 3694 8711

■ WARN INDUSTRIES INC p 1575
12900 Se Capps Rd, Clackamas OR 97015
Tel (503) 722-1200 SIC 3714 3531

▲ DORMAN PRODUCTS INC p 451
3400 E Walnut St, Colmar PA 18915
Tel (215) 997-1800 SIC 3714 3231 3965

■ RB DISTRIBUTION INC p 1211
3400 E Walnut St, Colmar PA 18915
Tel (215) 997-1800 SIC 3714 3231

R H SHEPPARD CO INC p 1202
101 Philadelphia St, Hanover PA 17331
Tel (717) 637-3751 SIC 3714 3321 3594

■ CLARK FILTER INC p 322
3649 Hempland Rd, Lancaster PA 17601
Tel (717) 285-5941 SIC 3564 3714

CARDONE INDUSTRIES INC p 253
5501 Whitaker Ave, Philadelphia PA 19124
Tel (215) 912-3000 SIC 3465 3714

NEAPCO COMPONENTS LLC p 1023
740 Queen St, Pottstown PA 19464
Tel (610) 323-6000 SIC 3714 3568

MATTHEY JOHNSON HOLDINGS INC p 921
435 Devon Park Dr Ste 600, Wayne PA 19087
Tel (610) 971-3000
SIC 3341 3339 3356 2834 3399 3714

MATTHEY JOHNSON INC p 921
435 Devon Park Dr Ste 600, Wayne PA 19087
Tel (610) 971-3000
SIC 3341 3339 3356 2834 3399 3714

ASSOCIATED FUEL PUMP SYSTEMS CORP p 120
1100 Scotts Bridge Rd, Anderson SC 29621
Tel (864) 224-0012 SIC 3714 3561

HENGST OF NORTH AMERICA INC p 683
29 Hengst Blvd, Camden SC 29020
Tel (803) 432-5992 SIC 3714

HENGST USA INC p 683
29 Hengst Blvd, Camden SC 29020
Tel (803) 432-5992 SIC 3714

MAHLE BEHR CHARLESTON INC p 897
4500 Leeds Ave Ste 101, Charleston SC 29405
Tel (843) 745-1233 SIC 3714

DAA DRAEXLMAIER AUTOMOTIVE OF AMERICA LLC p 407
1751 E Main St, Duncan SC 29334
Tel (864) 433-8910 SIC 3714

ZF TRANSMISSIONS GRAY COURT LLC p 1642
2846 N Old Laurens Rd, Gray Court SC 29645
Tel (864) 601-2500 SIC 3714

ASCI HOLDINGS UK (DE) INC p 116
40 Emery St, Greenville SC 29605
Tel (864) 240-2600 SIC 3714

RELIANCE ELECTRIC CO p 1221
6040 Ponders Ct, Greenville SC 29615
Tel (864) 297-4800 SIC 3714 3621

AVM INDUSTRIES LLC p 138
3108 W Highway 76, Marion SC 29571
Tel (843) 464-5406 SIC 3714

DRIVE AUTOMOTIVE INDUSTRIES OF AMERICA INC p 456
120 Moon Acres Rd, Piedmont SC 29673
Tel (864) 299-1349
SIC 3465 3714 3711 3469

TRANSAXLE MANUFACTURING OF AMERICA CORP p 1471
240 Waterford Park Dr, Rock Hill SC 29730
Tel (803) 329-8900 SIC 3714

ADAMS THERMAL SYSTEMS INC p 21
47920 W 5th St, Canton SD 57013
Tel (605) 764-1260 SIC 3714

DENSO MANUFACTURING ATHENS TENNESSEE INC p 428
2400 Denso Dr, Athens TN 37303
Tel (423) 746-0000 SIC 3694 3714

EAGLE BEND MFG INC p 467
1000 Jd Yrnell Indus Pkwy, Clinton TN 37716
Tel (865) 457-3800 SIC 3465 3714

SL AMERICA CORP p 1330
312 Frank L Diggs Dr, Clinton TN 37716
Tel (865) 457-8511 SIC 3714

SL TENNESSEE LLC p 1330
312 Frank Diggs Dr, Clinton TN 37716
Tel (865) 457-8511 SIC 3714

DACCO INC p 407
741 Dacco Dr, Cookeville TN 38506
Tel (931) 303-0112 SIC 3714 5013

NEMAK USA INC p 1025
1635 Old Columbia Rd, Dickson TN 37055
Tel (615) 446-8110 *SIC* 3363 3714

CARLSTAR GROUP LLC p 258
725 Cool Springs Blvd, Franklin TN 37067
Tel (615) 503-0220
SIC 3714 5014 3499 5013 2296

▲ CLARCOR INC p 321
840 Crescent Centre Dr # 600, Franklin TN 37067
Tel (615) 771-3100
SIC 3714 3599 3564 3569 3411 3089

NORANDA INTERMEDIATE HOLDING CORP p 1047
801 Crescent Centre Dr, Franklin TN 37067
Tel (615) 771-5700
SIC 3353 3334 3714 3354

TENNESSEE TBDN CO p 1438
1410 Us Highway 70 Byp, Jackson TN 38301
Tel (731) 421-4800 *SIC* 3714

ARC AUTOMOTIVE INC p 103
1729 Midpark Rd Ste 100, Knoxville TN 37921
Tel (865) 583-7600 *SIC* 3714

■ HENNESSY INDUSTRIES INC p 683
1601 Jp Hennessy Dr, La Vergne TN 37086
Tel (615) 641-7533 *SIC* 3714 5013

M-TEK INC p 890
1020 Volunteer Pkwy, Manchester TN 37355
Tel (931) 728-4122 *SIC* 3089 3714 3429

DENSO MANUFACTURING TENNESSEE INC p 429
1720 Robert C Jackson Dr, Maryville TN 37801
Tel (865) 982-7000 *SIC* 3694 3714

EXEDY AMERICA CORP p 518
2121 Holston Bend Dr, Mascot TN 37806
Tel (865) 932-3700 *SIC* 3714

JTEKT AUTOMOTIVE TENNESSEE-MORRISTOWN INC p 796
5932 Commerce Blvd, Morristown TN 37814
Tel (423) 585-2544 *SIC* 3714

MAHLE FILTER SYSTEMS NORTH AMERICA INC p 897
906 Butler Dr, Murfreesboro TN 37127
Tel (615) 895-5572 *SIC* 3714

■ CUMMINS FILTRATION INC p 401
26 Century Blvd Ste 500, Nashville TN 37214
Tel (615) 367-0040 *SIC* 3714

■ KEYSTONE AUTOMOTIVE INDUSTRIES INC p 815
655 Grassmere Park, Nashville TN 37211
Tel (615) 781-5200 *SIC* 5013 5531 3714

THERMAL SOLUTIONS MANUFACTURING INC p 1447
15 Century Blvd Ste 102, Nashville TN 37214
Tel (615) 806-7907 *SIC* 3714

VISTA-PRO AUTOMOTIVE LLC p 1562
22 Century Blvd Ste 410, Nashville TN 37214
Tel (615) 622-2200 *SIC* 3714

■ FEDERAL-MOGUL FAP INC p 536
1 Grizzly Ln, Smithville TN 37166
Tel (615) 597-6700 *SIC* 3714

QUALITY TRAILER PRODUCTS LP p 1197
604 W Main St, Azle TX 76020
Tel (817) 444-4518 *SIC* 3714 5013

TRICO TECHNOLOGIES CORP p 1479
1995 Billy Mitchell Blvd, Brownsville TX 78521
Tel (956) 544-2722 *SIC* 3714

AER MANUFACTURING LP p 30
1605 Surveyor Blvd, Carrollton TX 75006
Tel (972) 418-6499 *SIC* 3714

■ COMPX INTERNATIONAL INC p 353
5430 Lbj Fwy Ste 1700, Dallas TX 75240
Tel (972) 448-1400 *SIC* 3699 3714

■ POLLOK INC p 1160
6 Butterfield Trail Blvd, El Paso TX 79906
Tel (915) 592-5700
SIC 5065 3823 3714 3545

■ STONERIDGE ELECTRONICS INC p 1391
21 Butterfield Trail Blvd A, El Paso TX 79906
Tel (915) 593-2011 *SIC* 3679 3714

JTEKT AUTOMOTIVE TEXAS LP p 796
4400 Sterilite Dr, Ennis TX 75119
Tel (972) 878-1800 *SIC* 3714

■ ATC LOGISTICS & ELECTRONICS INC p 124
13500 Independence Pkwy, Fort Worth TX 76177
Tel (817) 491-7700 *SIC* 4225 3714 3694

INTERMET CORP p 753
301 Commerce St Ste 2901, Fort Worth TX 76102
Tel (817) 348-9190
SIC 3321 3714 3462 3365 3364

■ STEMCO LP p 1385
300 Industrial Dr, Longview TX 75602
Tel (903) 232-3500 *SIC* 3714

AM-MEX PRODUCTS INC p 63
3801 W Military Hwy, Mcallen TX 78503
Tel (956) 631-7916 *SIC* 3714 7361 3672

INSIGHT EQUITY A P X L P p 746
1400 Civic Pl Ste 250, Southlake TX 76092
Tel (817) 488-7775
SIC 6722 3441 3443 3556 3714 5171

INSIGHT EQUITY LP p 746
1400 Civic Pl Ste 250, Southlake TX 76092
Tel (817) 488-7775
SIC 6722 3441 3443 3556 3714 5171

KONGSBERG POWER PRODUCTS SYSTEMS I INC p 827
300 S Cochran St, Willis TX 77378
Tel (936) 856-2971 *SIC* 3714

SANDEN INTERNATIONAL (USA) INC p 1278
601 Sanden Blvd, Wylie TX 75098
Tel (972) 442-8941
SIC 3714 1711 3585 3563

■ AUTOLIV ASP INC p 134
3350 Airport Rd, Ogden UT 84405
Tel (801) 625-4800 *SIC* 3714 3563

▲ AUTOLIV INC p 134
3350 Airport Rd, Ogden UT 84405
Tel (801) 629-9800 *SIC* 3714

SMITH POWER PRODUCTS INC p 1333
3065 W California Ave, Salt Lake City UT 84104
Tel (801) 262-2631
SIC 5084 7538 3714 5063

DETROIT DIESEL REMANUFACTURING-WEST INC p 433
100 Lodestone Way, Tooele UT 84074
Tel (435) 843-6000 *SIC* 3519 3714 5013

SCHRADER-BRIDGEPORT INTERNATIONAL INC p 1290
205 Frazier Rd, Altavista VA 24517
Tel (434) 369-4741
SIC 3492 3714 3491 3011

DYNAX AMERICA CORP p 464
568 Eastpark Dr, Roanoke VA 24019
Tel (540) 966-6010 *SIC* 3714

GLOBAL SAFETY TEXTILES LLC p 617
1556 Montgomery St, South Hill VA 23970
Tel (434) 447-7629 *SIC* 3714 2211 3496

▲ PACCAR INC p 1103
777 106th Ave Ne, Bellevue WA 98004
Tel (425) 468-7400
SIC 3711 3714 3713 3537 5013 6153

RED DOT CORP p 1215
495 Andover Park E, Tukwila WA 98188
Tel (206) 151-3840 *SIC* 3714 3585

CONSOLIDATED METCO INC p 360
5701 Se Columbia Way, Vancouver WA 98661
Tel (360) 828-2599
SIC 3365 3363 3089 3714 3443 3312

TOYOTA MOTOR MANUFACTURING WEST VIRGINIA INC p 1467
1 Sugar Maple Ln, Buffalo WV 25033
Tel (304) 937-7000 *SIC* 3714 3519

▲ REGAL BELOIT CORP p 1218
200 State St, Beloit WI 53511
Tel (608) 364-8800 *SIC* 3621 3714 3566

■ BRENNER TANK LLC p 210
450 Arlington Ave, Fond Du Lac WI 54935
Tel (920) 922-4530 *SIC* 3715 3714 3443

WELLS VEHICLE ELECTRONICS LP p 1591
385 W Rolling Meadows Dr, Fond Du Lac WI 54937
Tel (920) 922-5900
SIC 3714 3694 3644 3357

SENIOR FLEXONICS GA PRECISION p 1304
5215 W Airways Ave, Franklin WI 53132
Tel (414) 817-5300 *SIC* 3714

KSPG HOLDING USA INC p 831
1731 Industrial Pkwy N, Marinette WI 54143
Tel (715) 732-0181 *SIC* 3592 3714 6719

HB PERFORMANCE SYSTEMS INC p 671
5800 W Donges Bay Rd, Mequon WI 53092
Tel (262) 242-4300 *SIC* 3714 3751

HUF NORTH AMERICA AUTOMOTIVE PARTS MANUFACTURING CORP p 717
9020 W Dean Rd, Milwaukee WI 53224
Tel (414) 365-4950 *SIC* 3714

JOHNSON CONTROLS INC p 791
5757 N Green Bay Ave, Milwaukee WI 53209
Tel (414) 524-1200
SIC 2531 3714 3691 3822 8744

■ REXNORD INDUSTRIES LLC p 1230
247 W Freshwater Way # 200, Milwaukee WI 53204
Tel (414) 643-3000
SIC 3568 3566 3625 3714

■ REXNORD-ZURN HOLDINGS INC p 1230
4701 W Greenfield Ave, Milwaukee WI 53214
Tel (414) 643-3000
SIC 3568 3566 3625 3714

▲ STRATTEC SECURITY CORP p 1393
3333 W Good Hope Rd, Milwaukee WI 53209
Tel (414) 247-3333 *SIC* 3714 3364 3429

DYNATECT MANUFACTURING INC p 464
2300 S Calhoun Rd, New Berlin WI 53151
Tel (262) 786-1500
SIC 3069 3499 3714 3599

PENDA CORP p 1128
2344 W Wisconsin St, Portage WI 53901
Tel (608) 742-5301
SIC 5013 3714 3792 3713 2273

▲ MODINE MANUFACTURING CO INC p 981
1500 Dekoven Ave, Racine WI 53403
Tel (262) 636-1200
SIC 3443 3714 3433 3585

▲ TWIN DISC INC p 1495
1328 Racine St, Racine WI 53403
Tel (262) 638-4000 *SIC* 3568 3566 3714

NELSON GLOBAL PRODUCTS INC p 1025
1560 Williams Dr, Stoughton WI 53589
Tel (608) 719-1800 *SIC* 3714 3317

■ NELSON INDUSTRIES INC p 1025
1801 Us Highway 51 & 138, Stoughton WI 53589
Tel (608) 873-4200 *SIC* 3714 3519 3569

AMSOIL INC p 87
925 Tower Ave, Superior WI 54880
Tel (715) 392-7101
SIC 2992 3589 2873 3714

SIC 3715 Truck Trailers

UTILITY TRAILER MANUFACTURING CO p 1537
17295 Railroad St Ste A, City Of Industry CA 91748
Tel (626) 964-7319 *SIC* 3715

HYUNDAI TRANSLEAD p 724
8880 Rio San Diego Dr # 600, San Diego CA 92108
Tel (619) 574-1500 *SIC* 3443 3715 3412

BSI HOLDINGS INC p 222
2495 Uravan St, Aurora CO 80011
Tel (303) 371-2200
SIC 6719 3589 5093 3715 3823 5051

UNIVERSAL TRAILER CARGO GROUP p 1518
12800 University Dr # 300, Fort Myers FL 33907
Tel (513) 671-3880 *SIC* 3715

MCKENZIE TANK LINES INC p 930
1966 Commonwealth Ln, Tallahassee FL 32303
Tel (850) 576-1221 *SIC* 4213 3715 3443

GREAT DANE LIMITED PARTNERSHIP p 633
222 N Lasalle St Ste 920, Chicago IL 60601
Tel (773) 254-5533 *SIC* 3715

UNIVERSAL TRAILER CARGO GROUP INC p 1518
14054 C R 4, Bristol IN 46507
Tel (574) 264-9661 *SIC* 3715

▲ DREW INDUSTRIES INC p 455
3501 County Road 6 E, Elkhart IN 46514
Tel (574) 535-1125
SIC 3711 3714 3715 3442 3431

■ FOREST RIVER INC p 567
900 County Road 1 N, Elkhart IN 46514
Tel (574) 389-4600 *SIC* 5561 3715

■ ZIEMAN MANUFACTURING CO INC p 1643
2703 College Ave, Goshen IN 46528
Tel (574) 535-1125
SIC 3715 3441 2451 3799

▲ WABASH NATIONAL CORP p 1570
1000 Sagamore Pkwy S, Lafayette IN 47905
Tel (765) 771-5310 *SIC* 3715 3714 5012

VANGUARD NATIONAL TRAILER CORP p 1543
289 Water Tower Dr, Monon IN 47959
Tel (219) 253-2000 *SIC* 3715 3713

XL SPECIALIZED TRAILERS INC p 1632
1086 S 3rd St, Manchester IA 52057
Tel (563) 927-4900 *SIC* 3715

WILSON TRAILER CO p 1614
4400 S Lewis Blvd, Sioux City IA 51106
Tel (712) 252-6500 *SIC* 3715

LANDOLL CORP p 843
1900 North St, Marysville KS 66508
Tel (785) 562-5381
SIC 3728 3715 3523 3537

BOWLING GREEN METALFORMING LLC p 204
111 Cosma Dr, Bowling Green KY 42101
Tel (270) 901-1555 *SIC* 3499 3715

■ XPO CNW INC p 1632
2211 Old Earhart Rd, Ann Arbor MI 48105
Tel (253) 926-2251 *SIC* 4213 4731 3715

JOST INTERNATIONAL CORP p 794
1770 Hayes St, Grand Haven MI 49417
Tel (616) 846-7700 *SIC* 3715

■ PULLMAN CO p 1191
1 International Dr, Monroe MI 48161
Tel (734) 243-8000 *SIC* 3714 3715 3061

SAF-HOLLAND INC p 1265
1950 Industrial Blvd, Muskegon MI 49442
Tel (231) 773-3271
SIC 3714 3715 3568 3537 3452

POLAR TANK TRAILERS p 1159
12810 County Road 17, Holdingford MN 56340
Tel (417) 862-5526 *SIC* 3443 3715

SYSTEMS DRS SUSTAINMENT INC p 1418
201 Evans Ln, Saint Louis MO 63121
Tel (314) 553-4000
SIC 3715 3537 3812 3829 3769

■ BHSF INC p 180
1440 Kiewit Plz, Omaha NE 68131
Tel (402) 346-1400
SIC 3635 3563 2731 3715

TRAC INTERMODAL LLC p 1468
750 College Rd E, Princeton NJ 08540
Tel (609) 452-8900 *SIC* 7359 3715 5012

AUTOMANN INC p 134
850 Randolph Rd, Somerset NJ 08873
Tel (201) 529-4996 *SIC* 5013 3715

BLUE TEE CORP p 192
387 Park Ave S Fl 5, New York NY 10016
Tel (212) 598-0880
SIC 3533 3589 5093 3715 3823 5051

MICKEY TRUCK BODIES INC p 961
1305 Trinity Ave, High Point NC 27260
Tel (336) 882-6806
SIC 3713 7532 3711 3715

MAC MANUFACTURING INC p 891
14599 Commerce St Ne, Alliance OH 44601
Tel (330) 823-9900 *SIC* 3715 5012

MAC TRAILER MANUFACTURING INC p 891
14599 Commerce St Ne, Alliance OH 44601
Tel (330) 823-9900
SIC 3715 5012 5013 5015 7539

CONTAINERPORT GROUP INC p 362
1340 Depot St Ste 103, Cleveland OH 44116
Tel (440) 333-2009 *SIC* 3715

SUNDOWNER TRAILERS INC p 1402
9805 Ok Highway 48 S, Coleman OK 73432
Tel (580) 937-4255 *SIC* 3715

■ CMI TEREX CORP p 329
9528 W I 40 Service Rd, Oklahoma City OK 73128
Tel (405) 787-6020
SIC 3531 3715 3596 3541 3444 2951

STRICK CORP p 1393
225 Lincoln Hwy, Fairless Hills PA 19030
Tel (215) 949-3600
SIC 3715 2426 3713 3537

TRAIL KING INDUSTRIES INC p 1469
300 E Norway Ave, Mitchell SD 57301
Tel (605) 996-2562 *SIC* 3715 3713

■ HEIL CO p 681
2030 Hamilton Place Blvd # 200, Chattanooga TN 37421
Tel (866) 367-4345 *SIC* 3715

IMPERIAL GROUP MANUFACTURING INC p 734
4545 Airport Rd, Denton TX 76207
Tel (940) 565-8505 *SIC* 3715

AMERICAN TRAILER WORKS INC p 80
180 State St Ste 230, Southlake TX 76092
Tel (817) 328-3686 *SIC* 3715

PJ TRAILERS INC p 1153
1807 Farm Road 2352, Sumner TX 75486
Tel (903) 785-6879 *SIC* 3715

■ BRENNER TANK LLC p 210
450 Arlington Ave, Fond Du Lac WI 54935
Tel (920) 922-4530 *SIC* 3715 3714 3443

■ WALKER STAINLESS EQUIPMENT CO LLC p 1573
625 W State St, New Lisbon WI 53950
Tel (608) 562-7500 *SIC* 3443 3556 3715

▲ OSHKOSH CORP p 1096
2307 Oregon St, Oshkosh WI 54902
Tel (920) 235-9151 *SIC* 3711 3531 3715

■ OSHKOSH DEFENSE LLC p 1096
2307 Oregon St, Oshkosh WI 54902
Tel (920) 235-9151 *SIC* 3711 3531 3715

STOUGHTON TRAILERS LLC p 1392
416 S Academy St, Stoughton WI 53589
Tel (608) 873-2500 *SIC* 3715

SIC 3716 Motor Homes

TIFFIN MOTOR HOMES INC p 1453
105 2nd St Nw, Red Bay AL 35582
Tel (256) 356-8661 *SIC* 3716

FLEETWOOD MOTOR HOMES-CALIFINC p 555
3125 Myers St, Riverside CA 92503
Tel (951) 354-3000 *SIC* 3716

AIP/FW FUNDING INC p 38
1031 E Us Highway 224, Decatur IN 46733
Tel (212) 627-2360 *SIC* 3716

ALLIED RECREATION GROUP INC p 56
1031 E Us Highway 224, Decatur IN 46733
Tel (260) 728-2121 *SIC* 3716

ALL AMERICAN GROUP INC p 51
2831 Dexter Dr, Elkhart IN 46514
Tel (574) 262-0123
SIC 3716 3792 2452 3714 1521

■ THOR MOTOR COACH INC p 1450
520 County Road 15, Elkhart IN 46516
Tel (574) 266-1111 *SIC* 3716 3792

■ JAYCO INC p 779
903 S Main St, Middlebury IN 46540
Tel (574) 825-5861 *SIC* 5013 3716 3792

GULF STREAM COACH INC p 647
503 S Oakland Ave, Nappanee IN 46550
Tel (574) 773-7761
SIC 3716 3792 3714 2451

NEWMAR CORP p 1038
355 Delaware St, Nappanee IN 46550
Tel (574) 773-7791 *SIC* 3716 3792

FEATHERLITE INC p 533
13380 Highways 63 & 9, Cresco IA 52136
Tel (563) 547-6000 *SIC* 3716 3799 3714

▲ WINNEBAGO INDUSTRIES INC p 1616
605 W Crystal Lake Rd, Forest City IA 50436
Tel (641) 585-3535 *SIC* 3716 3714

■ AIRSTREAM INC p 40
419 W Pike St, Jackson Center OH 45334
Tel (937) 596-6111
SIC 3716 3792 3714 3713 3711

SIC 3721 Aircraft

RADIANCE TECHNOLOGIES INC p 1204
350 Wynn Dr Nw, Huntsville AL 35805
Tel (256) 704-3400
SIC 3721 8711 3429 3812

STANDARDAERO AVIATION HOLDINGS INC p 1376
6710 N Scottsdale Rd # 250, Paradise Valley AZ 85253
Tel (480) 377-3100 *SIC* 3721

BAE SYSTEMS PROTECTION SYSTEMS INC p 144
7822 S 46th St, Phoenix AZ 85044
Tel (602) 643-7233
SIC 3721 2353 3795 3842

AERCAP US GLOBAL AVIATION LLC p 30
10250 Constellation Blvd, Los Angeles CA 90067
Tel (310) 788-1999 *SIC* 3721 4581 6159

■ SCALED COMPOSITES LLC p 1285
1624 Flight Line, Mojave CA 93501
Tel (661) 824-4541 *SIC* 3721 3999 8711

▲ AEROVIRONMENT INC p 31
800 Royal Oaks Dr Ste 210, Monrovia CA 91016
Tel (626) 357-9983 *SIC* 3721 8711 3694

GENERAL ATOMICS AERONAUTICAL SYSTEMS INC p 599
14200 Kirkham Way, Poway CA 92064
Tel (858) 312-2810 *SIC* 3721

AERONAUTICAL SYSTEMS INC p 30
16761 Via Del Campo Ct, San Diego CA 92127
Tel (858) 455-2810 *SIC* 3721

ROBINSON HELICOPTER CO INC p 1242
2901 Airport Dr, Torrance CA 90505
Tel (310) 539-0508 *SIC* 3721

■ KAMAN AEROSPACE CORP p 801
30 Old Windsor Rd, Bloomfield CT 06002
Tel (860) 242-4461 *SIC* 3721 3728

■ KAMAN AEROSPACE GROUP INC p 801
1332 Blue Hills Ave, Bloomfield CT 06002
Tel (860) 243-7100
SIC 3721 3724 3728 3769

▲ KAMAN CORP p 801
1332 Blue Hills Ave, Bloomfield CT 06002
Tel (860) 243-7100 *SIC* 5085 3721 3728

▲ UNITED TECHNOLOGIES CORP p 1514
10 Farm Springs Rd, Farmington CT 06032
Tel (860) 728-7000
SIC 3724 3585 3721 3534 3669 3699

■ SIKORSKY AIRCRAFT CORP p 1322
6900 Main St, Stratford CT 06614
Tel (203) 386-4000 *SIC* 3721 4581 5599

ILC DOVER LP p 731
1 Moonwalker Rd, Frederica DE 19946
Tel (302) 335-3911 *SIC* 3842 3721 7389

EMBRAER SERVICES INC p 490
276 Sw 34th St, Fort Lauderdale FL 33315
Tel (954) 359-3700 *SIC* 3721

SOUTHEAST AEROSPACE INC p 1345
1399 General Aviation Dr, Melbourne FL 32935
Tel (321) 255-9877
SIC 5088 3812 3728 3721 4581

PIPER AIRCRAFT INC p 1151
2926 Piper Dr, Vero Beach FL 32960
Tel (772) 567-4361 *SIC* 3721 3728

■ LOCKHEED MARTIN AERONAUTICAL CO p 873
86 S Cobb Dr Se, Marietta GA 30063
Tel (770) 494-4411
SIC 3721 3812 7699 3769

■ **GULFSTREAM AEROSPACE CORP** p 647
500 Gulfstream Rd, Savannah GA 31408
Tel (912) 965-3000 SIC 3721 4581

■ **GULFSTREAM AEROSPACE CORP (GEORGIA)** p 647
500 Gulfstream Rd, Savannah GA 31408
Tel (912) 965-3000 SIC 3721

■ **GULFSTREAM DELAWARE CORP** p 647
500 Gulfstream Rd, Savannah GA 31408
Tel (912) 965-3000 SIC 3721 5088

▲ **BOEING CO** p 197
100 N Riverside Plz, Chicago IL 60606
Tel (312) 544-2000
SIC 3721 3663 3761 3764 3812 3728

■ **BEECHCRAFT CORP** p 168
10511 E Central Ave, Wichita KS 67206
Tel (316) 676-7111 SIC 3728 3721

■ **BEECHCRAFT HOLDINGS LLC** p 168
10511 E Central Ave, Wichita KS 67206
Tel (316) 676-7111 SIC 3721 3728 6719

BOMBARDIER LEARJET INC p 199
1 Learjet Way, Wichita KS 67209
Tel (316) 946-2000 SIC 3721

■ **CESSNA AIRCRAFT CO** p 284
1 Cessna Blvd, Wichita KS 67215
Tel (316) 517-6000 SIC 3721

LEARJET INC p 850
1 Learjet Way, Wichita KS 67209
Tel (316) 946-2000 SIC 3721 3812

▲ **LOCKHEED MARTIN CORP** p 873
6801 Rockledge Dr, Bethesda MD 20817
Tel (301) 897-6000
SIC 3761 3721 3663 3764 3812 3728

CIRRUS DESIGN CORP p 308
4515 Taylor Cir, Hermantown MN 55811
Tel (218) 727-2737 SIC 3721

CIRRUS INDUSTRIES INC p 309
4515 Taylor Cir, Hermantown MN 55811
Tel (218) 727-2737 SIC 3721

DASSAULT FALCON JET CORP p 413
200 Riser Rd, Little Ferry NJ 07643
Tel (201) 440-6700 SIC 5088 3721

AIP/AEROSPACE HOLDINGS LLC p 38
330 Madison Ave Fl 28, New York NY 10017
Tel (212) 916-8142 SIC 3721 6799

ERICKSON INC p 507
5550 Sw Mcdam Ave Ste 200, Portland OR 97239
Tel (503) 505-5800
SIC 7363 4581 3721 7359 5599 3728

SIKORSKY GLOBAL HELICOPTERS INC p 1322
110 Stewart Huston Dr, Coatesville PA 19320
Tel (610) 644-4430 SIC 3721

PHILADELPHIA AGUSTAWESTLAND CORP p 1142
3050 Red Lion Rd, Philadelphia PA 19114
Tel (215) 281-1400 SIC 3721 5088

ALLIANCE AIRCRAFT LTD p 53
4906 Penn Ave, Reading PA 19608
Tel (888) 233-1503 SIC 3721

▲ **TEXTRON INC** p 1445
40 Westminster St, Providence RI 02903
Tel (401) 421-2800
SIC 3721 3724 3728 3799 3829 3546

■ **LOCKHEED MARTIN AIRCRAFT CENTER** p 873
244 Terminal Rd, Greenville SC 29605
Tel (864) 422-6262 SIC 3721 4581

■ **AEROSTRUCTURES CORP** p 31
1431 Vultee Blvd, Nashville TN 37217
Tel (615) 361-2000
SIC 3721 3728 3812 3769

■ **BELL HELICOPTER TEXTRON INC** p 170
3255 Bell Helicopter Blvd, Fort Worth TX 76118
Tel (817) 280-2011 SIC 3728 5088 3721

AIRBUS HELICOPTERS INC p 40
2701 N Forum Dr, Grand Prairie TX 75052
Tel (972) 641-0000 SIC 5088 7699 3721

■ **TRIUMPH AEROSTRUCTURES LLC** p 1483
300 Austin Blvd, Red Oak TX 75154
Tel (972) 515-8276
SIC 3721 3728 3812 3769

BOMBARDIER AEROSPACE CORP p 199
3400 Waterview Pkwy # 400, Richardson TX 75080
Tel (972) 960-3810 SIC 5088 3721

■ **RAYTHEON E-SYSTEMS INC** p 1211
1727 Cityline Dr, Richardson TX 75082
Tel (972) 205-9374
SIC 3663 3812 7373 3575 4581 3721

DEE HOWARD CO p 421
9610 John Saunders Rd, San Antonio TX 78216
Tel (210) 828-1341 SIC 3721 3724 4581

BAE SYSTEMS LAND & ARMAMENTS INC p 144
2000 15th Nw, Arlington VA 22201
Tel (703) 907-8200 SIC 3721 3795

▲ **GENERAL DYNAMICS CORP** p 600
2941 Frview Pk Dr Ste 100, Falls Church VA 22042
Tel (703) 876-3000
SIC 3721 3731 3795 3711 3812

■ **NORTHROP GRUMMAN SYSTEMS CORP** p 1058
2980 Fairview Park Dr, Falls Church VA 22042
Tel (703) 280-2900
SIC 3721 3761 3728 3812 3825 4581

AIRBUS AMERICAS INC p 39
2550 Wasser Ter Ste 9100, Herndon VA 20171
Tel (703) 834-3400 SIC 3721

AIRBUS DEFENSE AND SPACE HOLDINGS INC p 39
2550 Wasser Ter Ste 9000, Herndon VA 20171
Tel (703) 466-5600 SIC 3721

AIRBUS DEFENSE AND SPACE INC p 39
2550 Wasser Ter Ste 9000, Herndon VA 20171
Tel (703) 466-5600 SIC 3721

AURORA FLIGHT SCIENCES CORP p 132
9950 Wakeman Dr, Manassas VA 20110
Tel (703) 369-3633 SIC 3721

■ **TITAN II INC** p 1456
4101 Washington Ave, Newport News VA 23607
Tel (757) 380-2000
SIC 3728 3761 7373 3721 4581 3812

SIC 3724 Aircraft Engines & Engine Parts

YULISTA AVIATION INC p 1640
631 Discovery Dr Nw, Huntsville AL 35806
Tel (256) 319-4621 SIC 3724

CONTINENTAL MOTORS INC p 363
2039 S Broad St, Mobile AL 36615
Tel (251) 438-3411 SIC 3724

■ **SARGENT AEROSPACE & DEFENSE LLC** p 1282
5675 W Burlingame Rd, Tucson AZ 85743
Tel (520) 744-1000
SIC 3728 3724 3568 3492

■ **INC AEROJET ROCKETDYNE OF DE** p 735
8900 De Soto Ave, Canoga Park CA 91304
Tel (818) 586-1000 SIC 2869 3724

■ **THERMAL STRUCTURES INC** p 1447
2362 Railroad St, Corona CA 92880
Tel (951) 736-9911 SIC 3724

GKN AEROSPACE CHEM-TRONICS INC p 613
1150 W Bradley Ave, El Cajon CA 92020
Tel (619) 448-2320 SIC 3724 7699

■ **DUCOMMUN AEROSTRUCTURES INC** p 459
268 E Gardena Blvd, Gardena CA 90248
Tel (310) 380-5390 SIC 3724 3812 3728

■ **CONTINENTAL GRAPHICS CORP** p 363
4060 N Lakewood Blvd, Long Beach CA 90808
Tel (714) 503-4200
SIC 3724 7371 7372 7374

MEGGITT SAFETY SYSTEMS INC p 940
1785 Voyager Ave Ste 100, Simi Valley CA 93063
Tel (805) 584-4100 SIC 3699 3724 3728

▲ **TELEDYNE TECHNOLOGIES INC** p 1434
1049 Camino Dos Rios, Thousand Oaks CA 91360
Tel (805) 373-4545
SIC 3679 3761 3519 3724 3812 3674

■ **KAMAN AEROSPACE GROUP INC** p 801
1332 Blue Hills Ave, Bloomfield CT 06002
Tel (860) 243-7100
SIC 3721 3724 3728 3769

■ **KAMATICS CORP** p 801
1330 Blue Hills Ave, Bloomfield CT 06002
Tel (860) 243-9704
SIC 3451 3562 3724 3728

▲ **BARNES GROUP INC** p 156
123 Main St, Bristol CT 06010
Tel (860) 583-7070 SIC 3724 3495 3469

EDAC TECHNOLOGIES LLC p 477
5 Mckee Pl, Cheshire CT 06410
Tel (203) 806-2090 SIC 3769 3541 3724

▲ **UNITED TECHNOLOGIES CORP** p 1514
10 Farm Springs Rd, Farmington CT 06032
Tel (860) 728-7000
SIC 3724 3585 3721 3534 3669 3699

■ **TRIUMPH ENGINE CONTROL SYSTEMS LLC** p 1483
1 Charter Oak Blvd, West Hartford CT 06110
Tel (860) 236-0651 SIC 3728 3724 3812

GA TELESIS LLC p 588
1850 Nw 49th St, Fort Lauderdale FL 33309
Tel (954) 676-3111 SIC 5088 3724

■ **HEICO AEROSPACE CORP** p 680
3000 Taft St, Hollywood FL 33021
Tel (954) 987-6101 SIC 3724 3812

■ **HEICO AEROSPACE HOLDINGS CORP** p 680
3000 Taft St, Hollywood FL 33021
Tel (954) 987-4000 SIC 3724

▲ **HEICO CORP** p 680
3000 Taft St, Hollywood FL 33021
Tel (954) 987-4000 SIC 3724 3728 7699

■ **CHROMALLOY GAS TURBINE LLC** p 304
3999 Rca Blvd, Palm Beach Gardens FL 33410
Tel (561) 935-3571
SIC 3724 7699 4581 3764 3769 3533

■ **SEQUA CORP** p 1306
3999 Rca Blvd, Palm Beach Gardens FL 33410
Tel (201) 343-1122
SIC 3724 3764 3812 3699 3845 3542

DYNAMIC PRECISION GROUP INC p 464
3651 Se Commerce Ave, Stuart FL 34997
Tel (772) 287-7770 SIC 3724 3444

TURBOCOMBUSTOR TECHNOLOGY INC p 1492
3651 Se Commerce Ave, Stuart FL 34997
Tel (772) 287-7770 SIC 3724 3728 3444

PRECISION COMPONENTS INTERNATIONAL INC p 1168
8801 Macon Rd, Midland GA 31820
Tel (706) 568-5900 SIC 3728 5088 3724

TURBINE ENGINE COMPONENTS TECHNOLOGIES CORP p 1492
1211 Old Albany Rd, Thomasville GA 31792
Tel (229) 228-2600
SIC 3463 3724 3714 3469

HELIGEAR ACQUISITION CO p 681
6006 W 73rd St, Bedford Park IL 60638
Tel (708) 728-2000 SIC 3724 7699

■ **CTS ELECTRONIC COMPONENTS INC** p 399
2375 Cabot Dr, Lisle IL 60532
Tel (630) 577-8800 SIC 3724

▲ **AAR CORP** p 8
1100 N Wood Dale Rd, Wood Dale IL 60191
Tel (630) 227-2000
SIC 3724 4581 3537 5599 7359

ROLLS-ROYCE CORP p 1247
450 S Meridian St, Indianapolis IN 46225
Tel (317) 230-2000
SIC 3724 3443 3462 3731 3743 3732

■ **VALENT AEROSTRUCTURES LLC** p 1539
11064 Strang Line Rd, Lenexa KS 66215
Tel (816) 423-5600 SIC 3724

▲ **SPIRIT AEROSYSTEMS HOLDINGS INC** p 1359
3801 S Oliver St, Wichita KS 67210
Tel (316) 526-9000 SIC 3728 3724

▲ **GENERAL ELECTRIC CO** p 600
41 Farnsworth St, Boston MA 02210
Tel (617) 443-3000
SIC 3511 3724 3632 3845

■ **HUTCHINSON AEROSPACE & INDUSTRY INC** p 721
82 South St, Hopkinton MA 01748
Tel (508) 417-7000 SIC 3714 3061 3724

WILLIAMS INTERNATIONAL CO LLC p 1611
2280 E West Maple Rd, Commerce Township MI 48390
Tel (248) 624-5200 SIC 3724 3764

■ **GE AVIATION MUSKEGON** p 595
2034 Latimer Dr, Muskegon MI 49442
Tel (231) 777-2685 SIC 3724

MERRILL TOOL HOLDING CO p 950
400 Florence St, Saginaw MI 48602
Tel (989) 791-6676
SIC 3443 3599 8734 8711 3724

MOELLER MFG CO LLC p 982
30100 Beck Rd, Wixom MI 48393
Tel (248) 960-3999 SIC 3724 3728

STRATEGIC INDUSTRIES LLC p 1392
26 Main St Ste 200, Chatham NJ 07928
Tel (732) 512-0195
SIC 3724 3499 3451 3083 3111

AVIO INC p 138
270 Sylvan Ave Ste 130, Englewood Cliffs NJ 07632
Tel (201) 816-2720 SIC 3724

▲ **HONEYWELL INTERNATIONAL INC** p 705
115 Tabor Rd, Morris Plains NJ 07950
Tel (973) 455-2000
SIC 3724 3812 3585 2824 2821 3714

■ **ADVANCED ATOMIZATION TECHNOLOGIES LLC** p 25
124 Columbia St, Clyde NY 14433
Tel (315) 923-2341 SIC 3724

SOS INTERNATIONAL LLC p 1341
40 Fulton St Fl 26, New York NY 10038
Tel (212) 742-2410
SIC 3724 8711 7389 8732

■ **ITT ENIDINE INC** p 768
7 Centre Dr, Orchard Park NY 14127
Tel (716) 662-1900 SIC 3724 3714 3593

TURBINE ENGINE COMPONENTS TECHNOLOGIES - UTICA CORP p 1492
2 Halsey Rd, Whitesboro NY 13492
Tel (315) 768-8070
SIC 3724 3511 3429 3842 3769

LORD CORP p 878
111 Lord Dr, Cary NC 27511
Tel (877) 275-5673
SIC 2891 3724 3728 2851

■ **GOODRICH CORP** p 624
4 Coliseum Ctr 2730 W, Charlotte NC 28217
Tel (704) 423-7000 SIC 7372 3724 3728

MEYER TOOL INC p 957
3055 Colerain Ave, Cincinnati OH 45225
Tel (513) 681-7362 SIC 3724 3599

AT HOLDINGS CORP p 123
23555 Euclid Ave, Cleveland OH 44117
Tel (216) 692-6000 SIC 3724 3728 6512

EATON INDUSTRIAL CORP p 473
23555 Euclid Ave, Cleveland OH 44117
Tel (216) 692-5456 SIC 3724 3728

▲ **SIFCO INDUSTRIES INC** p 1321
970 E 64th St, Cleveland OH 44103
Tel (216) 881-8600 SIC 3724 3462 3471

NORDAM GROUP INC p 1047
6911 Whirlpool Dr, Tulsa OK 74117
Tel (918) 878-4000 SIC 3728 3724

■ **PRECISION CASTPARTS CORP** p 1168
4650 Sw Mcdam Ave Ste 300, Portland OR 97239
Tel (503) 946-4800
SIC 3324 3369 3724 3511 3519

▲ **TRIUMPH GROUP INC** p 1483
899 Cassatt Rd Ste 210, Berwyn PA 19312
Tel (610) 251-1000 SIC 3728 3724 3812

▲ **TEXTRON INC** p 1445
40 Westminster St, Providence RI 02903
Tel (401) 421-2800
SIC 3721 3724 3728 3799 3829 3546

■ **TEXTRON LYCOMING CORP** p 1445
40 Westminster St, Providence RI 02903
Tel (401) 421-2800 SIC 3728 3724

STANDARD AERO (ALLIANCE) INC p 1375
1029 Ross Dr, Maryville TN 37801
Tel (865) 983-2992 SIC 3724

H M DUNN CO INC p 650
3301 House Anderson Rd, Euless TX 76040
Tel (817) 283-3722 SIC 3724 3599 3728

HM DUNN AEROSYSTEMS INC p 697
3301 House Anderson Rd, Euless TX 76040
Tel (817) 283-3722 SIC 3724

INTERNATIONAL AIRMOTIVE HOLDING CO INC p 754
900 Nolen Dr Ste 100, Grapevine TX 76051
Tel (214) 956-3000 SIC 7699 3724

■ **GE ENGINE SERVICES - MCALLEN L P** p 596
6200 S 42nd St, Mcallen TX 78503
Tel (956) 971-5200 SIC 3724

■ **CHROMALLOY COMPONENT SERVICES INC** p 304
303 Industrial Park Rd, San Antonio TX 78226
Tel (210) 331-2300 SIC 7699 3724

DEE HOWARD CO p 421
9610 John Saunders Rd, San Antonio TX 78216
Tel (210) 828-1341 SIC 3721 3724 4581

CFAN CO p 285
1000 Technology Way, San Marcos TX 78666
Tel (512) 754-3005 SIC 3724

■ **SIMMONDS PRECISION PRODUCTS INC** p 1324
100 Panton Rd, Vergennes VT 05491
Tel (802) 877-4000
SIC 3829 3694 3724 3728

SAFRAN USA INC p 1267
700 S Washington St # 320, Alexandria VA 22314
Tel (703) 351-9898
SIC 3643 3621 7699 3724 5013 5088

ROLLS-ROYCE NORTH AMERICA (USA) HOLDINGS CO p 1247
1875 Explorer St Ste 200, Reston VA 20190
Tel (703) 834-1700
SIC 5088 8741 6159 3724

EXOTIC METALS FORMING CO LLC p 519
5411 S 226th St, Kent WA 98032
Tel (253) 220-5900 SIC 3728 3724

■ **TRIUMPH COMPOSITE SYSTEMS INC** p 1483
1514 S Flint Rd, Spokane WA 99224
Tel (509) 623-8536 SIC 3724 3728

■ **PRATT & WHITNEY ENGINE SERVICES INC** p 1167
1525 Midway Park Rd, Bridgeport WV 26330
Tel (860) 565-4321 SIC 7699 3724 4581

SIC 3728 Aircraft Parts & Eqpt, NEC

GKN WESTLAND AEROSPACE INC p 613
3951 Al Highway 229 S, Tallassee AL 36078
Tel (334) 283-9200 SIC 3728

PACIFIC SCIENTIFIC ENERGETIC MATERIALS CO (CALIFORNIA) LLC p 1105
7073 W Willis Rd Ste 5002, Chandler AZ 85226
Tel (480) 763-3000
SIC 2892 2899 3483 3489 3699 3728

▲ **TPI COMPOSITES INC** p 1467
8501 N Scottsdale Rd # 280, Scottsdale AZ 85253
Tel (480) 305-8910 SIC 3728

■ **TRIUMPH INSULATION SYSTEMS LLC** p 1483
2925 S Roosevelt St 2, Tempe AZ 85282
Tel (949) 250-4999 SIC 3728

■ **SARGENT AEROSPACE & DEFENSE LLC** p 1282
5675 W Burlingame Rd, Tucson AZ 85743
Tel (520) 744-1000
SIC 3728 3724 3568 3492

KIRKHILL AIRCRAFT PARTS CO p 821
3120 Enterprise St, Brea CA 92821
Tel (714) 223-5400 SIC 5088 3728

■ **HYDRO-AIRE INC** p 723
3000 Winona Ave, Burbank CA 91504
Tel (818) 526-2600 SIC 3728

▲ **DUCOMMUN INC** p 459
23301 Wilmington Ave, Carson CA 90745
Tel (310) 513-7200 SIC 3728 3679

MAG AEROSPACE INDUSTRIES INC p 895
1500 Glenn Curtiss St, Carson CA 90746
Tel (310) 631-3800 SIC 3431 3728

HYDRAULICS INTERNATIONAL INC p 723
9201 Independence Ave, Chatsworth CA 91311
Tel (818) 998-1231 SIC 3728

NMB (USA) INC p 1045
9730 Independence Ave, Chatsworth CA 91311
Tel (818) 709-1770
SIC 3562 5063 5084 3728 5065

ONTIC ENGINEERING AND MANUFACTURING INC p 1088
20400 Plummer St, Chatsworth CA 91311
Tel (818) 678-6555 SIC 5088 3728 3812

■ **ROHR INC** p 1247
850 Lagoon Dr, Chula Vista CA 91910
Tel (619) 691-4111 SIC 3728

GKN AEROSPACE TRANSPARENCY SYSTEMS INC p 613
12122 Western Ave, Garden Grove CA 92841
Tel (714) 893-7531
SIC 3089 3231 3827 3728 3081 2821

■ **AHF-DUCOMMUN INC** p 36
268 E Gardena Blvd, Gardena CA 90248
Tel (310) 380-5390
SIC 3728 3812 3769 3469

■ **DUCOMMUN AEROSTRUCTURES INC** p 459
268 E Gardena Blvd, Gardena CA 90248
Tel (310) 380-5390 SIC 3724 3812 3728

IMPRESA AEROSPACE LLC p 735
344 W 157th St, Gardena CA 90248
Tel (310) 354-1200 SIC 3728 3444

■ **PACIFIC SCIENTIFIC ENERGETIC MATERIALS CO (CALIFORNIA)** p 1105
3601 Union Rd, Hollister CA 95023
Tel (831) 637-3731
SIC 2892 2899 3489 3483 3699 3728

C&D ZODIAC INC p 234
5701 Bolsa Ave, Huntington Beach CA 92647
Tel (714) 934-0000 SIC 3728

DRIESSEN AIRCRAFT INTERIOR SYSTEMS INC p 456
17311 Nichols Ln, Huntington Beach CA 92647
Tel (714) 861-7300 SIC 3728

MARVIN ENGINEERING CO INC p 914
261 W Beach Ave, Inglewood CA 90302
Tel (310) 674-5030 SIC 3728

ARROWHEAD PRODUCTS CORP p 113
4411 Katella Ave, Los Alamitos CA 90720
Tel (714) 828-7770 SIC 3728

CADENCE AEROSPACE LLC p 236
610 Nwport Ctr Dr Ste 950, Newport Beach CA 92660
Tel (949) 877-3630 SIC 3728

■ **KLUNE HOLDINGS INC** p 823
7323 Coldwater Canyon Ave, North Hollywood CA 91605
Tel (818) 503-8100 SIC 3728

■ **KLUNE INDUSTRIES INC** p 823
7323 Coldwater Canyon Ave, North Hollywood CA 91605
Tel (818) 503-8100 SIC 3728

■ **AEROJET ROCKETDYNE INC** p 30
2001 Aerojet Rd, Rancho Cordova CA 95742
Tel (916) 355-4000
SIC 3728 3764 3769 3761

BA HOLDINGS p 143
3016 Kansas Ave Bldg 1, Riverside CA 92507
Tel (951) 684-5110 SIC 3443 3728

LUXFER INC p 887
3016 Kansas Ave Bldg 1, Riverside CA 92507
Tel (336) 578-4515 SIC 3728 3354

KAISER AEROSPACE & ELECTRONICS CORP p 800
2701 Orchard Pkwy Ste 100, San Jose CA 95134
Tel (949) 250-1015 *SIC* 3728

MEGGITT SAFETY SYSTEMS INC p 940
1785 Voyager Ave Ste 100, Simi Valley CA 93063
Tel (805) 584-4100 *SIC* 3699 3724 3728

MEGGITT-USA INC p 940
1955 Surveyor Ave, Simi Valley CA 93063
Tel (805) 526-5700 *SIC* 3728 3829 3679

MS AEROSPACE INC p 996
13928 Balboa Blvd, Sylmar CA 91342
Tel (818) 833-9095 *SIC* 3452 3728

■ AEROSPACE DYNAMICS INTERNATIONAL INC p 31
25540 Rye Canyon Rd, Valencia CA 91355
Tel (661) 257-3535 *SIC* 3728

■ KAMAN AEROSPACE CORP p 801
30 Old Windsor Rd, Bloomfield CT 06002
Tel (860) 242-4461 *SIC* 3721 3728

■ KAMAN AEROSPACE GROUP INC p 801
1332 Blue Hills Ave, Bloomfield CT 06002
Tel (860) 243-7100
SIC 3721 3724 3728 3769

▲ KAMAN CORP p 801
1332 Blue Hills Ave, Bloomfield CT 06002
Tel (860) 243-7100 *SIC* 5085 3721 3728

■ KAMATICS CORP p 801
1330 Blue Hills Ave, Bloomfield CT 06002
Tel (860) 243-9704
SIC 3451 3562 3724 3728

WHITCRAFT LLC p 1605
76 County Rd, Eastford CT 06242
Tel (860) 974-0786 *SIC* 3443 3444 3728

DONCASTERS INC p 450
36 Spring Ln, Farmington CT 06032
Tel (860) 677-1376
SIC 3511 3356 3728 7699

■ MANCHESTER PARADIGM INC p 901
967 Parker St, Manchester CT 06042
Tel (860) 646-4048 *SIC* 3728

PCX AEROSTRUCTURES LLC p 1124
300 Fenn Rd, Newington CT 06111
Tel (860) 666-2471 *SIC* 3728

▲ CRANE CO p 388
100 1st Stamford Pl # 300, Stamford CT 06902
Tel (203) 363-7300
SIC 3492 3494 3594 3589 3728 5031

▲ HEXCEL CORP p 688
281 Tresser Blvd Ste 1503, Stamford CT 06901
Tel (203) 969-0666
SIC 2821 3728 3089 3624 2891 3489

■ HELICOPTER SUPPORT INC p 681
124 Quarry Rd, Trumbull CT 06611
Tel (203) 416-4000 *SIC* 5088 4581 3728

■ TRIUMPH ENGINE CONTROL SYSTEMS LLC p 1483
1 Charter Oak Blvd, West Hartford CT 06110
Tel (860) 236-0651 *SIC* 3728 3724 3812

LEE CO p 851
2 Pettipaug Rd, Westbrook CT 06498
Tel (860) 399-6281
SIC 3823 3841 3812 3728 3714

TLD AMERICA CORP p 1457
812 Bloomfield Ave, Windsor CT 06095
Tel (860) 602-3400 *SIC* 5088 3728 7629

■ HAMILTON SUNDSTRAND CORP p 655
1 Hamilton Rd, Windsor Locks CT 06096
Tel (860) 654-6000
SIC 3621 3594 3728 3625 3823 3822

BROCKWAY MORAN & PARTNERS INC p 216
225 Ne Mizner Blvd # 700, Boca Raton FL 33432
Tel (561) 750-2000 *SIC* 5812 3599 3728

▲ HEICO CORP p 680
3000 Taft St, Hollywood FL 33021
Tel (954) 987-4000 *SIC* 3724 3728 7699

■ HEICO ELECTRONIC TECHNOLOGIES CORP p 680
3000 Taft St, Hollywood FL 33021
Tel (954) 987-6101 *SIC* 3728

BAE SYSTEMS AH INC p 144
13386 International Pkwy, Jacksonville FL 32218
Tel (904) 741-5400
SIC 3711 3842 3312 3728

FLIGHTSTAR AIRCRAFT SERVICES LLC p 557
6025 Flightline Dr, Jacksonville FL 32221
Tel (904) 741-0300 *SIC* 4581 3728

SOUTHEAST AEROSPACE INC p 1345
1399 General Aviation Dr, Melbourne FL 32935
Tel (321) 255-9877
SIC 5088 3812 3728 3721 4581

BBA US HOLDINGS INC p 163
201 S Orange Ave Ste 1425, Orlando FL 32801
Tel (407) 648-7230 *SIC* 3728 2399 3052

■ LOCKHEED MARTIN TRAINING SOLUTIONS p 873
100 Global Innovation Cir, Orlando FL 32825
Tel (407) 306-4000 *SIC* 3728

POINT BLANK ENTERPRISES INC p 1159
2102 Sw 2nd St, Pompano Beach FL 33069
Tel (954) 630-0900
SIC 3842 3462 3728 8711

■ GENERAL DYNAMICS-OTS INC p 600
11399 16th Ct N Ste 200, Saint Petersburg FL 33716
Tel (727) 578-8100 *SIC* 3728 3812

TURBOCOMBUSTOR TECHNOLOGY INC p 1492
3651 Se Commerce Ave, Stuart FL 34997
Tel (772) 287-7770 *SIC* 3724 3728 3444

PEMCO WORLD AIR SERVICES INC p 1128
4102 N West Shore Blvd, Tampa FL 33614
Tel (813) 322-9600 *SIC* 4581 3728

PIPER AIRCRAFT INC p 1151
2926 Piper Dr, Vero Beach FL 32960
Tel (772) 567-4361 *SIC* 3721 3728

▲ B/E AEROSPACE INC p 142
1400 Corporate Center Way, Wellington FL 33414
Tel (561) 791-5000 *SIC* 2531 3728 3647

▲ KLX INC p 823
1300 Corporate Center Way # 200, Wellington FL 33414
Tel (561) 383-5100 *SIC* 3728 2911 1381

BLADES TECHNOLOGY INTERNATIONAL INC p 188
8801 Macon Rd, Columbus GA 31908
Tel (706) 568-5900 *SIC* 3728

PRECISION COMPONENTS INTERNATIONAL INC p 1168
8801 Macon Rd, Midland GA 31820
Tel (706) 568-5900 *SIC* 3728 5088 3724

WENCOR GROUP LLC p 1591
416 Dividend Dr, Peachtree City GA 30269
Tel (678) 490-0140 *SIC* 3728 4581

MEGGITT (ROCKMART) INC p 940
669 Goodyear Ave, Rockmart GA 30153
Tel (770) 684-7855 *SIC* 3728

▲ BOEING CO p 197
100 N Riverside Plz, Chicago IL 60606
Tel (312) 544-2000
SIC 3721 3663 3761 3764 3812 3728

■ MPC PRODUCTS CORP p 995
6300 W Howard St, Niles IL 60714
Tel (847) 673-8300
SIC 3728 3621 3676 3812 3625

■ AAR SUPPLY CHAIN INC p 8
1100 N Wood Dale Rd, Wood Dale IL 60191
Tel (630) 227-2000 *SIC* 5088 3728

TUBE PROCESSING CORP p 1490
604 E Legrande Ave, Indianapolis IN 46203
Tel (317) 787-1321
SIC 3498 3356 3469 7692 3444 3728

FANSTEEL INC p 527
1746 Commerce Rd, Creston IA 50801
Tel (641) 782-8521
SIC 3463 3728 3365 3369 3769 3545

LANDOLL CORP p 843
1900 North St, Marysville KS 66508
Tel (785) 562-5381
SIC 3728 3715 3523 3537

■ BEECHCRAFT CORP p 168
10511 E Central Ave, Wichita KS 67206
Tel (316) 676-7111 *SIC* 3728 3721

■ BEECHCRAFT HOLDINGS LLC p 168
10511 E Central Ave, Wichita KS 67206
Tel (316) 676-7111 *SIC* 3721 3728 6719

▲ SPIRIT AEROSYSTEMS HOLDINGS INC p 1359
3801 S Oliver St, Wichita KS 67210
Tel (316) 526-9000 *SIC* 3728 3724

■ SPIRIT AEROSYSTEMS INC p 1359
3801 S Oliver St, Wichita KS 67210
Tel (316) 526-9000 *SIC* 3728

■ MRA SYSTEMS INC p 996
103 Chesapeake Park Plz, Baltimore MD 21220
Tel (410) 682-1500 *SIC* 3728

▲ LOCKHEED MARTIN CORP p 873
6801 Rockledge Dr, Bethesda MD 20817
Tel (301) 897-6000
SIC 3761 3721 3663 3764 3812 3728

■ AAI CORP p 8
124 Industry Ln, Hunt Valley MD 21030
Tel (410) 666-1400
SIC 3728 3769 7699 8711

LABINAL SALISBURY LLC p 836
600 Glen Ave, Salisbury MD 21804
Tel (410) 548-7800 *SIC* 3728

■ WYMAN-GORDON CO p 1629
244 Worcester St, North Grafton MA 01536
Tel (508) 839-8252
SIC 3463 3462 3324 3728 3317

THG CORP p 1447
70 Bearfoot Rd, Northborough MA 01532
Tel (508) 393-7660
SIC 5085 5084 3569 3728 3625 3494

MOELLER MFG CO LLC p 982
30100 Beck Rd, Wixom MI 48393
Tel (248) 960-3999 *SIC* 3724 3728

EATON HYDRAULICS LLC p 473
14615 Lone Oak Rd, Eden Prairie MN 55344
Tel (952) 937-9800
SIC 3089 3052 3568 3492 3594 3728

KURT MANUFACTURING CO INC p 832
5280 Main St Ne, Minneapolis MN 55421
Tel (763) 572-1500
SIC 3499 3545 3363 3728 3842 3365

■ RTI REMMELE ENGINEERING INC p 1256
10 Old Highway 8 Sw, Saint Paul MN 55112
Tel (651) 635-4100
SIC 3728 3569 3812 3761 3842

▲ LMI AEROSPACE INC p 872
411 Fountain Lakes Blvd, Saint Charles MO 63301
Tel (636) 946-6525 *SIC* 3728

G K N AEROSPACE NORTH AMERICA INC p 587
142 Js Mcdonnell Blvd, Saint Louis MO 63135
Tel (314) 264-3000 *SIC* 3812 3728

WAINWRIGHT INDUSTRIES INC p 1571
114 Piper Hill Dr Ste 201, Saint Peters MO 63376
Tel (636) 327-8292 *SIC* 3469 3728 3544

SIERRA NEVADA CORP p 1320
444 Salomon Cir, Sparks NV 89434
Tel (775) 331-0222 *SIC* 3728 3812

INTEGRATED DEICING SERVICES LLC p 749
175 Ammon Dr, Manchester NH 03103
Tel (603) 647-1717 *SIC* 3728 4581

KULITE SEMICONDUCTOR PRODUCTS INC p 832
1 Willow Tree Rd, Leonia NJ 07605
Tel (201) 461-0900 *SIC* 3728 3829

AIR CRUISERS CO LLC p 38
1747 State Route 34, Wall Township NJ 07727
Tel (732) 681-3527
SIC 2531 3069 3728 2399

ZODIAC US CORP p 1644
1747 State Route 34, Wall Township NJ 07727
Tel (732) 681-3527 *SIC* 3728

■ BREEZE-EASTERN LLC p 209
35 Melanie Ln, Whippany NJ 07981
Tel (973) 602-1001 *SIC* 3728 3563 3531

■ WHIPPANY ACTUATION SYSTEMS LLC p 1605
110 Algonquin Pkwy, Whippany NJ 07981
Tel (973) 428-9898 *SIC* 3625 3728

■ EDO LLC p 478
1500 New Horizons Blvd, Amityville NY 11701
Tel (631) 630-4000
SIC 3812 3728 3663 3679

GKN AEROSPACE MONITOR INC p 613
1000 New Horizons Blvd, Amityville NY 11701
Tel (562) 619-8558 *SIC* 3728 3769

▲ ASTRONICS CORP p 122
130 Commerce Way, East Aurora NY 14052
Tel (716) 805-1599 *SIC* 3728 3647

SAAB SENSIS CORP p 1263
85 Collamer Crossings, East Syracuse NY 13057
Tel (315) 445-0550 *SIC* 3699 7371 3728

CPI AEROSTRUCTURES INC p 387
91 Heartland Blvd, Edgewood NY 11717
Tel (631) 586-5200 *SIC* 3728

▲ MOOG INC p 987
400 Jamison Rd Plant26, Elma NY 14059
Tel (716) 652-2000
SIC 3812 3492 3625 3769 3728 3841

ENLIGHTEN AIR INC p 500
23 E 81st St Apt 10, New York NY 10028
Tel (917) 656-1248 *SIC* 3728

CARLETON TECHNOLOGIES INC p 257
10 Cobham Dr, Orchard Park NY 14127
Tel (716) 662-0006 *SIC* 3728

GLEASON WORKS p 614
1000 University Ave, Rochester NY 14607
Tel (585) 473-1000
SIC 3714 3728 3566 3541 3829 3469

LORD CORP p 878
111 Lord Dr, Cary NC 27511
Tel (877) 275-5673
SIC 2891 3724 3728 2851

■ CURTISS-WRIGHT CONTROLS INC p 402
15801 Brixham Hill Ave # 200, Charlotte NC 28277
Tel (704) 869-4600 *SIC* 3728

■ GOODRICH CORP p 624
4 Coliseum Ctr 2730 W, Charlotte NC 28217
Tel (704) 423-7000 *SIC* 7372 3724 3728

HONDA AIRCRAFT CO INC p 704
6430 Ballinger Rd, Greensboro NC 27410
Tel (336) 662-0246 *SIC* 3728

▲ T AIR INC p 1419
3524 Airport Rd, Maiden NC 28650
Tel (828) 464-8741 *SIC* 4512 3728 7699

SCOTT TECHNOLOGIES INC p 1294
4320 Goldmine Rd, Monroe NC 28110
Tel (800) 247-7257 *SIC* 3842 3728 3569

■ KIDDE TECHNOLOGIES INC p 817
4200 Airport Dr Nw, Wilson NC 27896
Tel (252) 237-7004 *SIC* 3728

MEGGITT AIRCRAFT BRAKING SYSTEMS CORP p 940
1204 Massillon Rd, Akron OH 44306
Tel (330) 796-4400 *SIC* 3728

INDUSTRIAL MANUFACTURING CO LLC p 740
8223 Brecksville Rd Ste 1, Brecksville OH 44141
Tel (440) 838-4700 *SIC* 2542 3728 3566

AEROQUIP-VICKERS INC p 30
1111 Superior Ave E, Cleveland OH 44114
Tel (216) 523-5000
SIC 3052 3492 3429 3069 3585 3728

AT HOLDINGS CORP p 123
23555 Euclid Ave, Cleveland OH 44117
Tel (216) 692-6000 *SIC* 3724 3728 6512

■ AVIATION TECHNOLOGIES INC p 138
1301 E 9th St Ste 3000, Cleveland OH 44114
Tel (216) 706-2960
SIC 3643 3678 3679 3728 3812 3648

EATON INDUSTRIAL CORP p 473
23555 Euclid Ave, Cleveland OH 44117
Tel (216) 692-5456 *SIC* 3724 3728

EATON-AEROQUIP LLC p 474
1000 Eaton Blvd, Cleveland OH 44122
Tel (216) 523-5000
SIC 3052 3492 3429 3069 3585 3728

SUMMA HOLDINGS INC p 1398
8223 Brecksville Rd # 100, Cleveland OH 44141
Tel (440) 838-4700
SIC 2542 3462 3569 7359 3728

▲ TRANSDIGM GROUP INC p 1471
1301 E 9th St Ste 3000, Cleveland OH 44114
Tel (216) 706-2960 *SIC* 3728 5088

■ FRICTION PRODUCTS CO p 579
920 Lake Rd, Medina OH 44256
Tel (330) 725-4941 *SIC* 3728 3714

■ GRIMES AEROSPACE CO p 640
550 State Route 55, Urbana OH 43078
Tel (937) 484-2000
SIC 3728 3647 3646 3645 3577 3571

CYMSTAR LLC p 405
1700 W Albany St Ste 500, Broken Arrow OK 74012
Tel (918) 251-8100 *SIC* 3699 3728

CHEROKEE NATION BUSINESSES LLC p 294
777 W Cherokee St Bldg 2, Catoosa OK 74015
Tel (918) 384-7474 *SIC* 3728 5085 5088

NORDAM GROUP INC p 1047
6911 Whirlpool Dr, Tulsa OK 74117
Tel (918) 878-4000 *SIC* 3728 3724

PRECISE MACHINING & MANUFACTURING LLC p 1168
12716 E Pine St, Tulsa OK 74116
Tel (918) 438-3121 *SIC* 3728

■ TRIUMPH AEROSTRUCTURES - TULSA LLC p 1483
3330 N Mingo Rd, Tulsa OK 74116
Tel (615) 361-2061 *SIC* 3728 3999

ERICKSON INC p 507
5550 Sw Mcdam Ave Ste 200, Portland OR 97239
Tel (503) 505-5800
SIC 7363 4581 3721 7359 5599 3728

■ PCC STRUCTURALS INC p 1123
4600 Se Harney Dr, Portland OR 97206
Tel (503) 777-3881
SIC 3728 3842 3511 3824

■ TRIUMPH AEROSPACE SYSTEMS GROUP INC p 1483
899 Cassatt Rd Ste 210, Berwyn PA 19312
Tel (610) 251-1000 *SIC* 3728

▲ TRIUMPH GROUP INC p 1483
899 Cassatt Rd Ste 210, Berwyn PA 19312
Tel (610) 251-1000 *SIC* 3728 3724 3812

▲ ENVIRONMENTAL TECTONICS CORP p 503
125 James Way, Southampton PA 18966
Tel (215) 355-9100
SIC 3728 3842 3826 3823 3841

▲ TEXTRON INC p 1445
40 Westminster St, Providence RI 02903
Tel (401) 421-2800
SIC 3721 3724 3728 3799 3829 3546

■ TEXTRON LYCOMING CORP p 1445
40 Westminster St, Providence RI 02903
Tel (401) 421-2800 *SIC* 3728 3724

■ AEROSTRUCTURES CORP p 31
1431 Vultee Blvd, Nashville TN 37217
Tel (615) 361-2000
SIC 3721 3728 3812 3769

KILGORE FLARES CO LLC p 818
155 Kilgore Rd, Toone TN 38381
Tel (731) 228-5200 *SIC* 2899 3728

LABINAL LLC p 836
3790 Russell Newman Blvd # 100, Denton TX 76208
Tel (940) 272-5700 *SIC* 3728

H M DUNN CO INC p 650
3301 House Anderson Rd, Euless TX 76040
Tel (817) 283-3722 *SIC* 3724 3599 3728

■ BELL HELICOPTER TEXTRON INC p 170
3255 Bell Helicopter Blvd, Fort Worth TX 76118
Tel (817) 280-2011 *SIC* 3728 5088 3721

ZODIAC SEATS US LLC p 1644
2000 Zodiac Dr, Gainesville TX 76240
Tel (940) 668-8541 *SIC* 5088 3728

ACCURUS AEROSPACE CORP p 16
222 Las Colinas Blvd W, Irving TX 75039
Tel (469) 317-6140 *SIC* 3728

ADVANCED INTEGRATION TECHNOLOGY LP p 26
2805 E Plano Pkwy Ste 300, Plano TX 75074
Tel (972) 423-8354 *SIC* 3728 3544

■ TRIUMPH AEROSTRUCTURES LLC p 1483
300 Austin Blvd, Red Oak TX 75154
Tel (972) 515-8276
SIC 3721 3728 3812 3769

■ ATK SPACE SYSTEMS INC p 125
Freeport Ctr Bldg A15, Clearfield UT 84016
Tel (801) 775-1141 *SIC* 3728 3769

■ TRIUMPH GEAR SYSTEMS INC p 1483
6125 Silver Creek Dr, Park City UT 84098
Tel (435) 649-1900 *SIC* 3593 3728 3812

G S PRECISION INC p 587
101 John Seitz Dr, Brattleboro VT 05301
Tel (802) 257-5200 *SIC* 3728

■ SIMMONDS PRECISION PRODUCTS INC p 1324
100 Panton Rd, Vergennes VT 05491
Tel (802) 877-4000
SIC 3829 3694 3724 3728

BAE SYSTEMS HOLDINGS INC p 144
1101 Wilson Blvd Ste 2000, Arlington VA 22209
Tel (703) 312-6100 *SIC* 3699 3728 3812

BAE SYSTEMS INC p 144
1101 Wilson Blvd Ste 2000, Arlington VA 22209
Tel (703) 312-6100 *SIC* 3812 3728

PAE AVIATION AND TECHNICAL SERVICES LLC p 1107
1320 N Courthouse Rd # 800, Arlington VA 22201
Tel (856) 866-2200 *SIC* 4581 3728 8742

■ NORTHROP GRUMMAN SYSTEMS CORP p 1058
2980 Fairview Park Dr, Falls Church VA 22042
Tel (703) 280-2900
SIC 3721 3761 3728 3812 3825 4581

■ TITAN II INC p 1456
4101 Washington Ave, Newport News VA 23607
Tel (757) 380-2000
SIC 3728 3761 7373 3721 4581 3812

AIM AEROSPACE SUMNER INC p 38
1502 20th St Nw, Auburn WA 98001
Tel (253) 804-3355 *SIC* 3728 3543

■ PRIMUS INTERNATIONAL INC p 1176
610 Bllvue Way Ne Ste 200, Auburn WA 98001
Tel (425) 688-0444 *SIC* 3728

▲ ESTERLINE TECHNOLOGIES CORP p 511
500 108th Ave Ne Ste 1500, Bellevue WA 98004
Tel (425) 453-9400 *SIC* 3728 3812 3429

HEATH TECNA INC p 679
3225 Woburn St, Bellingham WA 98226
Tel (360) 738-2005 *SIC* 3728 5088

■ AVTECH TYEE INC p 139
6500 Merrill Creek Pkwy, Everett WA 98203
Tel (206) 695-8000 *SIC* 3728 3648 3812

JAMCO AMERICA INC p 776
1018 80th St Sw, Everett WA 98203
Tel (425) 347-4735 *SIC* 3728

EXOTIC METALS FORMING CO LLC p 519
5411 S 226th St, Kent WA 98032
Tel (253) 220-5900 *SIC* 3728 3724

NABTESCO AEROSPACE INC p 1006
12413 Willows Rd Ne, Kirkland WA 98034
Tel (425) 602-8400 *SIC* 3728 3812 3593

■ ELDEC CORP p 484
16700 13th Ave W, Lynnwood WA 98037
Tel (425) 743-8362
SIC 3812 3728 3824 3769 3674 3613

AIM GROUP USA INC p 38
705 Sw 7th St, Renton WA 98057
Tel (425) 235-2750 *SIC* 3728

JANICKI INDUSTRIES INC p 777
719 Metcalf St, Sedro Woolley WA 98284
Tel (360) 856-5143 *SIC* 3728

■ TRIUMPH COMPOSITE SYSTEMS INC p 1483
1514 S Flint Rd, Spokane WA 99224
Tel (509) 623-8536 *SIC* 3724 3728

SIC 3731 Shipbuilding & Repairing

AUSTAL USA LLC p 132
1 Dunlap Dr, Mobile AL 36602
Tel (251) 434-8000 SIC 3731

BAE SYSTEMS SOUTHEAST SHIPYARDS ALABAMA LLC p 144
Mn Gate Dunlap Dr, Mobile AL 36652
Tel (251) 690-7100 SIC 3731

FINN HOLDING CORP p 543
360 N Crescent Dr, Beverly Hills CA 90210
Tel (310) 712-1850 SIC 4449 3731 4491

BAE SYSTEMS SAN DIEGO SHIP REPAIR INC p 144
2205 E Belt St Foot Of S, San Diego CA 92113
Tel (619) 238-1000 SIC 3731

■ **NASSCO HOLDINGS INC** p 1009
2798 Harbor Dr, San Diego CA 92113
Tel (619) 544-3400 SIC 3731

■ **NATIONAL STEEL & SHIPBUILDING CO** p 1016
2798 Harbor Dr, San Diego CA 92113
Tel (619) 544-3400 SIC 3731

■ **ELECTRIC BOAT CORP** p 484
75 Eastern Point Rd, Groton CT 06340
Tel (860) 433-3000 SIC 3731 8711

BAE SYSTEMS SOUTHEAST SHIPYARDS AMHC INC p 144
8500 Heckscher Dr, Jacksonville FL 32226
Tel (904) 251-3111 SIC 3731

EASTERN SHIPBUILDING GROUP INC p 472
2200 Nelson Ave, Panama City FL 32401
Tel (850) 763-1900 SIC 3731

SHIP L TAMPA L C p 1317
1130 Mcclosky Blvd, Tampa FL 33605
Tel (813) 248-9310 SIC 3731

ROLLS-ROYCE CORP p 1247
450 S Meridian St, Indianapolis IN 46225
Tel (317) 230-2000
SIC 3724 3443 3462 3731 3743 3732

AMERICAN BARGE LINE CO p 68
1701 E Market St, Jeffersonville IN 47130
Tel (812) 288-0100 SIC 4449 3731 4491

AMERICAN COMMERCIAL BARGE LINE p 70
1701 E Market St, Jeffersonville IN 47130
Tel (812) 288-0100 SIC 4449 3731 4491

AMERICAN COMMERCIAL LINES INC p 70
1701 E Market St, Jeffersonville IN 47130
Tel (812) 288-0100 SIC 4449 3731 4491

COMMERCIAL BARGE LINE CO p 345
1701 E Market St, Jeffersonville IN 47130
Tel (812) 288-0100 SIC 3731 4449 4491

SMOKER CRAFT INC p 1334
68143 Clunette St, New Paris IN 46553
Tel (574) 831-2103 SIC 3732 5551 3731

YAGER MATERIALS LLC p 1633
5001 Highway 2830, Owensboro KY 42303
Tel (270) 926-0893
SIC 1442 1422 1611 3273 4491 3731

JAMES MARINE INC p 776
4500 Clarks River Rd, Paducah KY 42003
Tel (270) 898-7392
SIC 3731 4492 5541 3732

BOLLINGER MARINE FABRICATORS INC p 198
816 Bollinger Ln, Amelia LA 70340
Tel (985) 631-5300 SIC 3731

■ **AVONDALE INDUSTRIES OF NEW YORK INC** p 139
5100 River Rd, Avondale LA 70094
Tel (504) 654-5254 SIC 3731

CARI INVESTMENT CO LLC p 256
222 N Vermont St, Covington LA 70433
Tel (985) 635-6009
SIC 6211 4424 3731 5146

NORTH AMERICAN FABRICATORS LLC p 1050
367 Dickson Rd, Houma LA 70363
Tel (985) 917-2000 SIC 3731

LEEVAC SHIPYARDS JENNINGS LLC p 852
111 Bunge St, Jennings LA 70546
Tel (337) 824-2210 SIC 3731

SEMCO LLC p 1302
186 Jean Lafitte Blvd, Lafitte LA 70067
Tel (504) 689-2054 SIC 3441 3731

NORTH AMERICAN SHIPBUILDING LLC p 1050
800 Industrial Park Rd, Larose LA 70373
Tel (985) 693-4072 SIC 3731

BOLLINGER SHIPYARDS LLC p 198
8365 Highway 308, Lockport LA 70374
Tel (985) 532-2554 SIC 3731 3599

BOLLINGER SHIPYARDS LOCKPORT LLC p 198
8365 Highway 308, Lockport LA 70374
Tel (985) 532-2554 SIC 3731

▲ **CONRAD INDUSTRIES INC** p 358
1100 Brashear Ave Ste 200, Morgan City LA 70380
Tel (985) 702-0195 SIC 3731

BOLLINGER CALCASIEU LLC p 198
8086 Global Dr, Sulphur LA 70665
Tel (337) 583-7383 SIC 3731

■ **BATH IRON WORKS CORP** p 159
700 Washington St Stop 1, Bath ME 04530
Tel (207) 443-3311 SIC 3731 8711

■ **ELLICOTT DREDGE ENTERPRISES LLC** p 488
1611 Bush St, Baltimore MD 21230
Tel (410) 625-0808 SIC 3731

■ **ELLICOTT DREDGES LLC** p 488
1611 Bush St, Baltimore MD 21230
Tel (410) 625-0808 SIC 3731

▲ **IROBOT CORP** p 764
8 Crosby Dr, Bedford MA 01730
Tel (781) 430-3000 SIC 3569 3731

GULF COAST SHIPYARD GROUP INC p 646
13085 Seaway Rd, Gulfport MS 39503
Tel (228) 276-1051 SIC 3731

■ **HUNTINGTON INGALLS INDUSTRIES INTERNATIONAL SHIPBUILDING INC** p 720
1000 Access Rd, Pascagoula MS 39567
Tel (228) 935-1122 SIC 3731

SIGNAL INTERNATIONAL LLC p 1322
601 Bayou Casotte Pkwy, Pascagoula MS 39581
Tel (228) 762-0010 SIC 7699 3731 3441

VT HALTER MARINE INC p 1567
900 Bayou Casotte Pkwy, Pascagoula MS 39581
Tel (228) 696-6888 SIC 3731

GEORGE G SHARP INC p 606
160 Broadway, New York NY 10038
Tel (212) 732-2800 SIC 3731 4225 8712

MCNATIONAL INC p 932
502 2nd St E, South Point OH 45680
Tel (740) 377-4391 SIC 3731 7699 4491

MILES MARINE INC p 969
5555 N Channel Ave, Portland OR 97217
Tel (503) 247-1777 SIC 3731

VIGOR FAB LLC p 1556
5555 N Channel Ave, Portland OR 97217
Tel (503) 247-1777 SIC 3731

VIGOR INDUSTRIAL LLC p 1556
5555 N Channel Ave # 71, Portland OR 97217
Tel (503) 247-1777 SIC 3731 3599 6531

VIGOR MARINE LLC p 1556
5555 N Channel Ave # 71, Portland OR 97217
Tel (503) 247-1804 SIC 3731

WHEMCO INC p 1605
5 Hot Metal St Ste 300, Pittsburgh PA 15203
Tel (412) 390-2700
SIC 3312 3462 3731 3325 3441 3369

SENESCO MARINE LLC p 1303
10 Macnaught St, North Kingstown RI 02852
Tel (401) 295-0373 SIC 3731

MIDLAND ENTERPRISES INC p 965
4400 Harding Pike, Nashville TN 37205
Tel (615) 298-8200
SIC 4449 4492 3731 4491

KEPPEL AMFELS LLC p 813
20000 State Highway 48, Brownsville TX 78521
Tel (956) 831-8220
SIC 1629 3731 1389 3449 3546 3443

▲ **TRINITY INDUSTRIES INC** p 1481
2525 N Stemmons Fwy, Dallas TX 75207
Tel (214) 631-4420
SIC 3743 3731 3531 3444 3441 3443

MODEC INTERNATIONAL INC p 980
15011 Katy Fwy Ste 500, Houston TX 77094
Tel (281) 529-8100 SIC 8711 2499 3731

▲ **OCEANEERING INTERNATIONAL INC** p 1073
11911 Fm 529 Rd, Houston TX 77041
Tel (713) 329-4500 SIC 1389 3731 8711

SUBSEA 7 (US) LLC p 1396
10787 Clay Rd, Houston TX 77041
Tel (281) 966-7600 SIC 1629 3731

WARTSILA NORTH AMERICA INC p 1577
11710 N Gessner Rd Ste A, Houston TX 77064
Tel (281) 233-6200
SIC 1629 5084 1382 4789 3731

BEACON MARITIME INC p 165
96 W Front St, Orange TX 77630
Tel (409) 670-1060 SIC 1629 3731

GULF COPPER & MANUFACTURING CORP p 646
5700 Procter Ext, Port Arthur TX 77642
Tel (409) 989-0300
SIC 3731 3599 3312 3732 3498 3441

VISIONTECHNOLOGIES SYSTEMS INC p 1561
99 Canal Center Plz # 220, Alexandria VA 22314
Tel (703) 739-2610 SIC 3731 3531

AMERICAN MARITIME HOLDINGS INC p 75
813 Industrial Ave, Chesapeake VA 23324
Tel (757) 961-9311 SIC 3731 7929

TECNICO CORP p 1432
831 Industrial Ave, Chesapeake VA 23324
Tel (757) 545-4013
SIC 3446 3443 3441 3444 3731

▲ **GENERAL DYNAMICS CORP** p 600
2941 Frview Pk Dr Ste 100, Falls Church VA 22042
Tel (703) 876-3000
SIC 3721 3731 3795 3711 3812

■ **HUNTINGTON INGALLS INC** p 720
4101 Washington Ave, Newport News VA 23607
Tel (757) 380-2000 SIC 3731

▲ **HUNTINGTON INGALLS INDUSTRIES INC** p 720
4101 Washington Ave, Newport News VA 23607
Tel (757) 380-2000 SIC 3731

■ **NORTHROP GRUMMAN NEWPORT NEWS INC** p 1058
4101 Washington Ave, Newport News VA 23607
Tel (757) 380-2000 SIC 3731

BAE SYSTEMS NORFOLK SHIP REPAIR INC p 144
750 W Berkley Ave, Norfolk VA 23523
Tel (757) 494-4000 SIC 3731 3732 7699

BAE SYSTEMS SHIP REPAIR INC p 144
750 W Berkley Ave, Norfolk VA 23523
Tel (757) 494-4000 SIC 3731 3732

■ **CDI MARINE CO LLC** p 271
4600 Village Ave, Norfolk VA 23502
Tel (757) 763-6666
SIC 8711 8712 3732 3731

■ **METRO MACHINE CORP** p 955
200 Ligon St, Norfolk VA 23523
Tel (757) 543-6801 SIC 3731

SHIP COLONNAS YARD INC p 1317
400 E Indian River Rd, Norfolk VA 23523
Tel (757) 545-2414 SIC 3731 3443 3499

QED SYSTEMS INC p 1194
4646 N Witchduck Rd, Virginia Beach VA 23455
Tel (757) 490-5000 SIC 8711 3731

DAKOTA CREEK INDUSTRIES INC p 409
820 4th St, Anacortes WA 98221
Tel (360) 293-9575 SIC 3732 3731

FOSS MARITIME CO p 570
1151 Fairview Ave N, Seattle WA 98109
Tel (206) 281-4001
SIC 4412 4424 4492 4491 3731 4959

PUGET SOUND COMMERCE CENTER INC p 1191
1801 16th Ave Sw, Seattle WA 98134
Tel (206) 623-1635 SIC 3731

VIGOR SHIPYARDS INC p 1556
1801 16th Ave Sw, Seattle WA 98134
Tel (206) 623-1635 SIC 3731

FINCANTIERI MARINE GROUP HOLDINGS INC p 543
605 N 3rd Ave, Sturgeon Bay WI 54235
Tel (920) 743-3406 SIC 3731

FINCANTIERI MARINE GROUP LLC p 543
605 N 3rd Ave, Sturgeon Bay WI 54235
Tel (920) 743-3406 SIC 3731

SIC 3732 Boat Building & Repairing

FISHING HOLDINGS LLC p 552
927 Highway 178 N, Flippin AR 72634
Tel (870) 453-2222 SIC 3732 5699

AMERICAN HONDA MOTOR CO INC p 74
1919 Torrance Blvd, Torrance CA 90501
Tel (310) 783-2000 SIC 5012 3732

■ **BOSTON WHALER INC** p 203
100 Whaler Way, Edgewater FL 32141
Tel (386) 428-0057 SIC 3732

NAUTIQUE BOAT CO INC p 1019
14700 Aerospace Pkwy, Orlando FL 32832
Tel (407) 855-4141 SIC 3799 3732

REGAL MARINE INDUSTRIES INC p 1218
2300 Jetport Dr, Orlando FL 32809
Tel (407) 851-4360 SIC 3732

SEABRING MARINE INDUSTRIES INC p 1296
1579 Sw 18th St, Williston FL 32696
Tel (352) 529-9161 SIC 5091 3732

▲ **MARINE PRODUCTS CORP** p 906
2801 Buford Hwy Ne # 520, Brookhaven GA 30329
Tel (404) 321-7910 SIC 3732

■ **CHAPARRAL BOATS INC** p 288
300 Industrial Park Blvd, Nashville GA 31639
Tel (229) 686-7481 SIC 3732

CAROLINA SKIFF LLC p 259
3231 Fulford Rd, Waycross GA 31503
Tel (912) 287-0547 SIC 5091 3732

▲ **BRUNSWICK CORP** p 221
1 N Field Ct, Lake Forest IL 60045
Tel (847) 735-4700
SIC 3519 3732 3949 7933 5091

LEISURE PROPERTIES LLC p 854
11884 Country Club Rd, West Frankfort IL 62896
Tel (618) 937-6426 SIC 3732

ROLLS-ROYCE CORP p 1247
450 S Meridian St, Indianapolis IN 46225
Tel (317) 230-2000
SIC 3724 3443 3462 3731 3743 3732

SMOKER CRAFT INC p 1334
68143 Clunette St, New Paris IN 46553
Tel (574) 831-2103 SIC 3732 5551 3731

COBALT BOATS LLC p 332
1715 N 8th St, Neodesha KS 66757
Tel (620) 325-2653 SIC 3732

JAMES MARINE INC p 776
4500 Clarks River Rd, Paducah KY 42003
Tel (270) 898-7392
SIC 3731 4492 5541 3732

REC BOAT HOLDINGS LLC p 1214
925 Frisbie St, Cadillac MI 49601
Tel (231) 775-1351 SIC 3732

▲ **ARCTIC CAT INC** p 106
500 N 3rd St, Minneapolis MN 55401
Tel (763) 354-1800
SIC 3799 2329 2339 3732

TRACKER MARINE LLC p 1468
2500 E Kearney St, Springfield MO 65898
Tel (417) 873-5900 SIC 3732

VIKING YACHT CO p 1557
On The Bass Riv Rr 9, New Gretna NJ 08224
Tel (609) 296-6000 SIC 3732

HATTERAS YACHTS INC p 668
110 N Glenburnie Rd, New Bern NC 28560
Tel (252) 633-3101 SIC 3732

TALARIA CO LLC p 1422
1 Lil Hrbr Landing Prt, Portsmouth RI 02871
Tel (401) 683-7100 SIC 3732

BENETEAU INC p 173
1313 W Highway 76, Marion SC 29571
Tel (843) 629-5300 SIC 3732

■ **SEA RAY BOATS INC** p 1295
800 S Gay St Ste 1200, Knoxville TN 37929
Tel (865) 522-4181 SIC 3732

▲ **MALIBU BOATS INC** p 899
5075 Kimberly Way, Loudon TN 37774
Tel (865) 458-5478 SIC 3732

■ **MALIBU BOATS LLC** p 899
5075 Kimberly Way, Loudon TN 37774
Tel (865) 458-5478 SIC 3732

■ **MCBC HOLDINGS INC** p 926
100 Cherokee Cove Dr, Vonore TN 37885
Tel (423) 884-2221 SIC 3732 3799

NATIONAL CONSUMER OUTDOORS CORP p 1011
4215 Mcewen Rd, Dallas TX 75244
Tel (972) 716-4200
SIC 3999 2399 2394 3732

GULF COPPER & MANUFACTURING CORP p 646
5700 Procter Ext, Port Arthur TX 77642
Tel (409) 989-0300
SIC 3731 3599 3312 3732 3498 3441

BAE SYSTEMS NORFOLK SHIP REPAIR INC p 144
750 W Berkley Ave, Norfolk VA 23523
Tel (757) 494-4000 SIC 3731 3732 7699

BAE SYSTEMS SHIP REPAIR INC p 144
750 W Berkley Ave, Norfolk VA 23523
Tel (757) 494-4000 SIC 3731 3732

■ **CDI MARINE CO LLC** p 271
4600 Village Ave, Norfolk VA 23502
Tel (757) 763-6666
SIC 8711 8712 3732 3731

DAKOTA CREEK INDUSTRIES INC p 409
820 4th St, Anacortes WA 98221
Tel (360) 293-9575 SIC 3732 3731

BRUNSWICK FAMILY BOAT CO INC p 221
17825 59th Ave Ne, Arlington WA 98223
Tel (360) 435-5571 SIC 3732

DELTA MARINE INDUSTRIES INC p 427
1608 S 96th St, Seattle WA 98108
Tel (206) 763-0760 SIC 3732

KCS INTERNATIONAL INC p 806
804 Pecor St, Oconto WI 54153
Tel (920) 834-2211 SIC 3732

▲ **JOHNSON OUTDOORS INC** p 791
555 Main St, Racine WI 53403
Tel (262) 631-6600 SIC 3949 3732 3812

WINDWAY CAPITAL CORP p 1616
630 Riverfront Dr Ste 200, Sheboygan WI 53081
Tel (920) 457-8600
SIC 3469 2394 3624 3732

PALMER JOHNSON ENTERPRISES INC p 1109
128 Kentucky St, Sturgeon Bay WI 54235
Tel (920) 746-6342 SIC 5085 4493 3732

PALMER JOHNSON YACHTS LLC p 1109
128 Kentucky St, Sturgeon Bay WI 54235
Tel (920) 743-4412 SIC 3732

BRP US INC p 220
10101 Science Dr, Sturtevant WI 53177
Tel (715) 842-8886 SIC 3732

SIC 3743 Railroad Eqpt

■ **MOTIVEPOWER INC** p 992
4600 S Apple St, Boise ID 83716
Tel (208) 947-4800 SIC 3743

AMSTED INDUSTRIES INC p 87
180 N Stetson Ave, Chicago IL 60601
Tel (312) 645-1700
SIC 3443 3325 3585 3321 3743

AMSTED RAIL CO INC p 87
311 S Wacker Dr Ste 5300, Chicago IL 60606
Tel (312) 922-4501 SIC 3743

▲ **FREIGHTCAR AMERICA INC** p 577
2 N Rverside Plz Ste 1300, Chicago IL 60606
Tel (800) 458-2235 SIC 3743

GENERAL ELECTRIC RAILCAR SERVICES CORP p 600
161 N Clark St Fl 7, Chicago IL 60601
Tel (312) 853-5000
SIC 7359 3743 4789 3462

■ **MARMON HOLDINGS INC** p 909
181 W Madison St Ste 2600, Chicago IL 60602
Tel (312) 372-9500
SIC 5051 3351 3743 4741 3423 3589

■ **MARMON INDUSTRIAL LLC** p 909
181 W Madison St Fl 26, Chicago IL 60602
Tel (312) 372-9500
SIC 3743 4741 3589 6159 3965 3492

TRANSCO INC p 1471
200 N La Salle St # 1550, Chicago IL 60601
Tel (312) 896-8527
SIC 4789 3743 3296 1742

■ **UNION TANK CAR CO** p 1505
175 W Jackson Blvd # 2100, Chicago IL 60604
Tel (312) 431-3111
SIC 3743 4741 4789 5051

HOLLAND LP p 700
1000 Holland Dr, Crete IL 60417
Tel (708) 672-2300 SIC 2899 3743

RESCAR INDUSTRIES INC p 1226
1101 31st St Ste 250, Downers Grove IL 60515
Tel (630) 963-1114 SIC 3743

G K ENTERPRISES INC p 587
26000 S Whiting Way Ste 2, Monee IL 60449
Tel (708) 587-2150
SIC 3743 3443 3559 3556 3536

NATIONAL RAILWAY EQUIPMENT CO p 1015
1100 Shawnee St, Mount Vernon IL 62864
Tel (618) 242-6590 SIC 5088 3743

■ **STANDARD CAR TRUCK CO INC** p 1375
6400 Shafer Ct Ste 450, Rosemont IL 60018
Tel (847) 692-6050 SIC 3743 3321

CONGLOBAL INDUSTRIES LLC p 356
8200 185th St Ste A, Tinley Park IL 60487
Tel (925) 543-0977
SIC 3743 4213 4231 1799 7699

ROLLS-ROYCE CORP p 1247
450 S Meridian St, Indianapolis IN 46225
Tel (317) 230-2000
SIC 3724 3443 3462 3731 3743 3732

SIEMENS RAIL AUTOMATION CORP p 1320
2400 Nelson Miller Pkwy, Louisville KY 40223
Tel (502) 244-7400 SIC 3743 3669

NATIONAL RAILWAY EQUIPMENT CO p 1015
1300 Kentucky Ave, Paducah KY 42003
Tel (270) 444-4555 SIC 3743

■ **WABTEC RAILWAY ELECTRONICS INC** p 1570
21200 Dorsey Mill Rd, Germantown MD 20876
Tel (301) 515-2000
SIC 3825 3679 3743 3672

LORAM MAINTENANCE OF WAY INC p 878
3900 Arrowhead Dr, Hamel MN 55340
Tel (763) 478-6014 SIC 3743

▲ **AMERICAN RAILCAR INDUSTRIES INC** p 78
100 Clark St, Saint Charles MO 63301
Tel (636) 940-6000 SIC 3743 8742

ACF INDUSTRIES HOLDING CORP p 17
767 5th Ave, New York NY 10153
Tel (212) 702-4363
SIC 3743 4741 4789 6799

BUFFALO INVESTORS CORP p 224
1 Wall Street Ct Apt 980, New York NY 10005
Tel (212) 702-4363 SIC 3743 4741

HIGHCREST INVESTORS LLC p 691
Icahn Associates Corp 767, New York NY 10153
Tel (212) 702-4323
SIC 3743 4741 4789 4813

▲ **ICAHN ENTERPRISES LP** p 726
767 5th Ave Ste 4700, New York NY 10153
Tel (212) 702-4300
SIC 6722 3714 7999 3743 5093 6531

ORIENT EXPRESS HOTELS INC p 1094
441 Lexington Ave Rm 504, New York NY 10017
Tel (212) 302-5055
SIC 7011 3743 5947 6552

KNORR BRAKE HOLDING CORP p 825
748 Starbuck Ave, Watertown NY 13601
Tel (315) 786-5356 *SIC* 3743 5013

KNORR BRAKE TRUCK SYSTEMS CO p 825
748 Starbuck Ave, Watertown NY 13601
Tel (315) 786-5200 *SIC* 3743

STARFIRE HOLDING CORP p 1379
445 Hamilton Ave Ste 1210, White Plains NY 10601
Tel (914) 614-7000 *SIC* 3743 4741 4789

DAYTON-PHOENIX GROUP INC p 418
1619 Kuntz Rd, Dayton OH 45404
Tel (937) 496-3900 *SIC* 3621 3743

▲ GREENBRIER COMPANIES INC p 637
1 Centerpointe Dr Ste 200, Lake Oswego OR 97035
Tel (503) 684-7000 *SIC* 3743 4789

■ GUNDERSON RAIL SERVICES LLC p 647
1 Centerpointe Dr Ste 200, Lake Oswego OR 97035
Tel (503) 684-7000 *SIC* 3743

■ GUNDERSON LLC p 647
4350 Nw Front Ave, Portland OR 97210
Tel (503) 972-5700 *SIC* 3743

■ JOHNSTOWN AMERICA CORP p 791
17 Johns St, Johnstown PA 15901
Tel (814) 533-5000 *SIC* 3743

BOMBARDIER TRANSPORTATION (HOLDINGS) USA INC p 199
1501 Lebanon Church Rd, Pittsburgh PA 15236
Tel (412) 655-5700 *SIC* 3743 3315 3823

■ WABTEC CORP p 1570
1001 Airbrake Ave, Wilmerding PA 15148
Tel (412) 825-1543 *SIC* 3743

▲ WESTINGHOUSE AIR BRAKE TECHNOLOGIES CORP p 1601
1001 Airbrake Ave, Wilmerding PA 15148
Tel (412) 825-1000 *SIC* 3743

■ YOUNG TOUCHSTONE CO p 1639
200 Smith Ln, Jackson TN 38301
Tel (731) 424-5045 *SIC* 4911 3743

▲ TRINITY INDUSTRIES INC p 1481
2525 N Stemmons Fwy, Dallas TX 75207
Tel (214) 631-4420
SIC 3743 3731 3531 3444 3441 3443

■ TRINITY RAIL GROUP LLC p 1481
2525 N Stemmons Fwy, Dallas TX 75207
Tel (214) 631-4420 *SIC* 3743

J H FLETCHER & CO p 771
402 High St, Huntington WV 25705
Tel (304) 525-7811
SIC 5082 3532 3743 3546 3541

SIC 3751 Motorcycles, Bicycles & Parts

SUZUKI MOTOR OF AMERICA INC p 1410
3251 E Imperial Hwy, Brea CA 92821
Tel (714) 996-7040 *SIC* 3751 3519 3799

MOTORSPORT AFTERMARKET GROUP INC p 993
17771 Mitchell N Ste A, Irvine CA 92614
Tel (949) 440-5500 *SIC* 3751

K & N ENGINEERING INC p 798
1455 Citrus St, Riverside CA 92507
Tel (951) 826-4000 *SIC* 3751 3599 3714

▲ FOX FACTORY HOLDING CORP p 572
915 Disc Dr, Scotts Valley CA 95066
Tel (831) 274-6500 *SIC* 3751

EDELBROCK HOLDINGS INC p 477
2700 California St, Torrance CA 90503
Tel (310) 781-2222 *SIC* 3714 3751

EDELBROCK LLC p 477
2700 California St, Torrance CA 90503
Tel (310) 781-2222 *SIC* 3714 3751

RBG HOLDINGS CORP p 1211
7855 Haskell Ave Ste 350, Van Nuys CA 91406
Tel (818) 782-6445 *SIC* 3949 5091 3751

SRAM LLC p 1362
1000 W Fulton Market # 400, Chicago IL 60607
Tel (312) 664-8800 *SIC* 3751

BRG SPORTS INC p 211
9801 W Higgins Rd, Rosemont IL 60018
Tel (831) 461-7500 *SIC* 3949 3751

VARROC LIGHTING SYSTEMS INC p 1545
47828 Halyard Dr, Plymouth MI 48170
Tel (734) 446-4400 *SIC* 3751

▲ POLARIS INDUSTRIES INC p 1159
2100 Highway 55, Medina MN 55340
Tel (763) 542-0500
SIC 3799 3751 3714 5699

KAWASAKI MOTORS MANUFACTURING CORP USA p 805
6600 Nw 27th St, Lincoln NE 68524
Tel (402) 476-6600 *SIC* 3751 5571

BMW OF NORTH AMERICA LLC p 194
300 Chestnut Ridge Rd, Woodcliff Lake NJ 07677
Tel (201) 307-4000
SIC 5013 3751 5012 3711

NEWMAN TECHNOLOGY INC p 1038
100 Cairns Rd, Mansfield OH 44903
Tel (419) 525-1856 *SIC* 3714 3751

■ CARLISLE BRAKE & FRICTION INC p 257
6180 Cochran Rd, Solon OH 44139
Tel (440) 528-4000 *SIC* 3751

CYCLING SPORTS GROUP INC p 405
16 Trowbridge Dr, Bedford PA 15522
Tel (203) 749-7000 *SIC* 3751 2329

PRIDE MOBILITY PRODUCTS CORP p 1174
182 Susquehanna Ave, Exeter PA 18643
Tel (570) 655-5574 *SIC* 3842 3799 3751

BELL SPORTS CORP p 170
6333 N State Highway 161 # 300, Irving TX 75038
Tel (469) 417-6600 *SIC* 3949 3751 5091

BELL SPORTS INC p 170
6333 N State Highway 161 # 300, Irving TX 75038
Tel (469) 417-6600 *SIC* 3949 3751

HB PERFORMANCE SYSTEMS INC p 671
5800 W Donges Bay Rd, Mequon WI 53092
Tel (262) 242-4300 *SIC* 3714 3751

▲ HARLEY-DAVIDSON INC p 661
3700 W Juneau Ave, Milwaukee WI 53208
Tel (414) 342-4680
SIC 3751 6153 6141 6411 6399

■ HARLEY-DAVIDSON MOTOR CO INC p 662
3700 W Juneau Ave 3800, Milwaukee WI 53208
Tel (414) 343-4056 *SIC* 3751

SIC 3761 Guided Missiles & Space Vehicles

SYSTEM STUDIES & SIMULATION INC p 1418
615 Discovery Dr Nw, Huntsville AL 35806
Tel (256) 539-1700 *SIC* 3761 7379 8711

■ RAYTHEON MISSILE SYSTEMS CO p 1211
1151 E Hermans Rd, Tucson AZ 85756
Tel (520) 794-3000 *SIC* 3761

SPACE EXPLORATION TECHNOLOGIES CORP p 1354
Rocket Rd, Hawthorne CA 90250
Tel (310) 363-6000 *SIC* 3761

■ AEROJET ROCKETDYNE INC p 30
2001 Aerojet Rd, Rancho Cordova CA 95742
Tel (916) 355-4000
SIC 3728 3764 3769 3761

▲ KRATOS DEFENSE & SECURITY SOLUTIONS INC p 829
4820 Estgate Mall Ste 200, San Diego CA 92121
Tel (858) 812-7300
SIC 3761 8711 8744 7382

■ NORTHROP GRUMMAN SPACE & MISSION SYSTEMS CORP p 1058
6377 San Ignacio Ave, San Jose CA 95119
Tel (703) 280-2900
SIC 7373 3663 3661 3812 3761

▲ TELEDYNE TECHNOLOGIES INC p 1434
1049 Camino Dos Rios, Thousand Oaks CA 91360
Tel (805) 373-4545
SIC 3679 3761 3519 3724 3812 3674

UNITED LAUNCH ALLIANCE LLC p 1509
9501 E Panorama Cir, Centennial CO 80112
Tel (720) 922-7100 *SIC* 3761

RD AMROSS LLC p 1212
3000 N Atl Ave Ste 207, Cocoa Beach FL 32931
Tel (321) 613-3902 *SIC* 3761

▲ BOEING CO p 197
100 N Riverside Plz, Chicago IL 60606
Tel (312) 544-2000
SIC 3721 3663 3761 3764 3812 3728

▲ LOCKHEED MARTIN CORP p 873
6801 Rockledge Dr, Bethesda MD 20817
Tel (301) 897-6000
SIC 3761 3721 3663 3764 3812 3728

■ RAYTHEON LOGISTICS SUPPORT & TRAINING CO p 1211
180 Hartwell Rd, Bedford MA 01730
Tel (310) 647-9438 *SIC* 3761

▲ RAYTHEON CO p 1211
870 Winter St, Waltham MA 02451
Tel (781) 522-3000 *SIC* 3812 3663 3761

■ RTI REMMELE ENGINEERING INC p 1256
10 Old Highway 8 Sw, Saint Paul MN 55112
Tel (651) 635-4100
SIC 3728 3569 3812 3761 3842

LAKE ATK CITY AMMUNITION p 838
101 N M 7 Hwy, Independence MO 64056
Tel (816) 796-7101 *SIC* 3761

■ BABCOCK & WILCOX TECHNICAL SERVICES Y-12 LLC p 143
301 Bear Creek Rd, Oak Ridge TN 37830
Tel (865) 574-1000 *SIC* 3483 3761

■ NORTHROP GRUMMAN SYSTEMS CORP p 1058
2980 Fairview Park Dr, Falls Church VA 22042
Tel (703) 280-2900
SIC 3721 3761 3728 3812 3825 4581

■ TITAN II INC p 1456
4101 Washington Ave, Newport News VA 23607
Tel (757) 380-2000
SIC 3728 3761 7373 3721 4581 3812

SIC 3764 Guided Missile/Space Vehicle Propulsion Units & parts

▲ AEROJET ROCKETDYNE HOLDINGS INC p 30
2001 Aerojet Rd, Rancho Cordova CA 95742
Tel (916) 355-4000
SIC 3812 3764 3769 6552 6519

■ AEROJET ROCKETDYNE INC p 30
2001 Aerojet Rd, Rancho Cordova CA 95742
Tel (916) 355-4000
SIC 3728 3764 3769 3761

■ L-3 COMMUNICATIONS ELECTRON TECHNOLOGIES INC p 834
3100 Lomita Blvd, Torrance CA 90505
Tel (310) 517-6000 *SIC* 3671 3764

ENSIGN-BICKFORD INDUSTRIES INC p 501
125 Powder Frest Dr Fl 3, Simsbury CT 06070
Tel (860) 843-2000
SIC 3764 2047 2835 3829 2499 6552

■ CHROMALLOY GAS TURBINE LLC p 304
3999 Rca Blvd, Palm Beach Gardens FL 33410
Tel (561) 935-3571
SIC 3724 7699 4581 3764 3769 3533

■ SEQUA CORP p 1306
3999 Rca Blvd, Palm Beach Gardens FL 33410
Tel (201) 343-1122
SIC 3724 3764 3812 3699 3845 3542

▲ BOEING CO p 197
100 N Riverside Plz, Chicago IL 60606
Tel (312) 544-2000
SIC 3721 3663 3761 3764 3812 3728

▲ LOCKHEED MARTIN CORP p 873
6801 Rockledge Dr, Bethesda MD 20817
Tel (301) 897-6000
SIC 3761 3721 3663 3764 3812 3728

■ ATK ELKTON LLC p 125
55 Thiokol Rd, Elkton MD 21921
Tel (410) 392-6890 *SIC* 3764

WILLIAMS INTERNATIONAL CO LLC p 1611
2280 E West Maple Rd, Commerce Township MI 48390
Tel (248) 624-5200 *SIC* 3724 3764

■ ALLIANT HOLDINGS LLC p 55
7480 Flying Cloud Dr, Eden Prairie MN 55344
Tel (952) 351-3000
SIC 3764 3812 3483 3482 3489

■ ATK LAUNCH SYSTEMS INC p 125
9160 N Highway 83, Corinne UT 84307
Tel (801) 251-2512 *SIC* 3764

▲ ORBITAL ATK INC p 1092
45101 Warp Dr, Dulles VA 20166
Tel (703) 406-5000
SIC 3764 3812 3483 3482 3489

■ ATLANTIC RESEARCH CORP p 127
5945 Wellington Rd, Gainesville VA 20155
Tel (703) 754-5000 *SIC* 3764 3694

SIC 3769 Guided Missile/Space Vehicle Parts & Eqpt, NEC

MODERN INDUSTRIES INC p 981
4747 E Beautiful Ln, Phoenix AZ 85044
Tel (602) 267-7248 *SIC* 3599 3769

CYTEC ENGINEERED MATERIALS INC p 406
2085 E Tech Cir Ste 300, Tempe AZ 85284
Tel (480) 730-2000 *SIC* 3769 5085 2821

■ AHF-DUCOMMUN INC p 36
268 E Gardena Blvd, Gardena CA 90248
Tel (310) 380-5390
SIC 3728 3812 3769 3469

▲ AEROJET ROCKETDYNE HOLDINGS INC p 30
2001 Aerojet Rd, Rancho Cordova CA 95742
Tel (916) 355-4000
SIC 3812 3764 3769 6552 6519

■ AEROJET ROCKETDYNE INC p 30
2001 Aerojet Rd, Rancho Cordova CA 95742
Tel (916) 355-4000
SIC 3728 3764 3769 3761

■ ATK SPACE SYSTEMS INC p 125
7130 Miramar Rd Ste 100b, San Diego CA 92121
Tel (937) 490-4145 *SIC* 3769

■ KAMAN AEROSPACE GROUP INC p 801
1332 Blue Hills Ave, Bloomfield CT 06002
Tel (860) 243-7100
SIC 3721 3724 3728 3769

EDAC TECHNOLOGIES LLC p 477
5 Mckee Pl, Cheshire CT 06410
Tel (203) 806-2090 *SIC* 3769 3541 3724

■ CHROMALLOY GAS TURBINE LLC p 304
3999 Rca Blvd, Palm Beach Gardens FL 33410
Tel (561) 935-3571
SIC 3724 7699 4581 3764 3769 3533

■ LOCKHEED MARTIN AERONAUTICAL CO p 873
86 S Cobb Dr Se, Marietta GA 30063
Tel (770) 494-4411
SIC 3721 3812 7699 3769

FANSTEEL INC p 527
1746 Commerce Rd, Creston IA 50801
Tel (641) 782-8521
SIC 3463 3728 3365 3369 3769 3545

■ AAI CORP p 8
124 Industry Ln, Hunt Valley MD 21030
Tel (410) 666-1400
SIC 3728 3769 7699 8711

SYSTEMS DRS SUSTAINMENT INC p 1418
201 Evans Ln, Saint Louis MO 63121
Tel (314) 553-4000
SIC 3715 3537 3812 3829 3769

GKN AEROSPACE MONITOR INC p 613
1000 New Horizons Blvd, Amityville NY 11701
Tel (562) 619-8558 *SIC* 3728 3769

▲ MOOG INC p 987
400 Jamison Rd Plant26, Elma NY 14059
Tel (716) 652-2000
SIC 3812 3492 3625 3769 3728 3841

■ L-3 COMMUNICATIONS CORP p 834
600 3rd Ave, New York NY 10016
Tel (212) 697-1111
SIC 3812 3663 3669 3679 3769

▲ L-3 COMMUNICATIONS HOLDINGS INC p 835
600 3rd Ave, New York NY 10016
Tel (212) 697-1111
SIC 3663 3669 3679 3812 3769

TURBINE ENGINE COMPONENTS TECHNOLOGIES - UTICA CORP p 1492
2 Halsey Rd, Whitesboro NY 13492
Tel (315) 768-8070
SIC 3724 3511 3429 3842 3769

■ L-3 COMMUNICATIONS CINCINNATI ELECTRONICS CORP p 834
7500 Innovation Way, Mason OH 45040
Tel (513) 573-6100 *SIC* 3812 3769 3823

SHELBURNE CORP p 1314
20001 Shelburne Rd, Shaker Heights OH 44118
Tel (216) 321-9177
SIC 3443 3823 3544 3769

■ AEROSTRUCTURES CORP p 31
1431 Vultee Blvd, Nashville TN 37217
Tel (615) 361-2000
SIC 3721 3728 3812 3769

■ TRIUMPH AEROSTRUCTURES LLC p 1483
300 Austin Blvd, Red Oak TX 75154
Tel (972) 515-8276
SIC 3721 3728 3812 3769

■ ATK SPACE SYSTEMS INC p 125
Freeport Ctr Bldg A15, Clearfield UT 84016
Tel (801) 775-1141 *SIC* 3728 3769

■ ITT DEFENSE & ELECTRONICS INC p 768
1650 Tysons Blvd Ste 1700, Mc Lean VA 22102
Tel (703) 790-6300
SIC 3679 3678 3674 3769 3489

■ ELDEC CORP p 484
16700 13th Ave W, Lynnwood WA 98037
Tel (425) 743-8362
SIC 3812 3728 3824 3769 3674 3613

ASTRONAUTICS CORP OF AMERICA p 122
4115 N Teutonia Ave, Milwaukee WI 53209
Tel (414) 449-4000
SIC 3812 3571 3572 3769

SIC 3792 Travel Trailers & Campers

THULE HOLDING INC p 1451
42 Silvermine Rd, Seymour CT 06483
Tel (203) 881-9600 *SIC* 3792 3714

HORTON VANS INC p 708
130 Coleman Dr, Eatonton GA 31024
Tel (706) 923-2900 *SIC* 3713 3792

ALL AMERICAN GROUP INC p 51
2831 Dexter Dr, Elkhart IN 46514
Tel (574) 262-0123
SIC 3716 3792 2452 3714 1521

■ HOMETTE CORP p 704
2520 Bypass Rd, Elkhart IN 46514
Tel (574) 294-6521 *SIC* 2452 3792

▲ SKYLINE CORP p 1330
2520 Bypass Rd, Elkhart IN 46514
Tel (574) 294-6521 *SIC* 2451 2452 3792

■ SKYLINE HOMES INC p 1330
2520 Bypass Rd, Elkhart IN 46514
Tel (574) 294-6521 *SIC* 2451 3792

■ THOR MOTOR COACH INC p 1450
520 County Road 15, Elkhart IN 46516
Tel (574) 266-1111 *SIC* 3716 3792

■ DMI HOLDING CORP p 446
2164 Caragana Ct, Goshen IN 46526
Tel (574) 534-1224 *SIC* 3792 5012

■ KEYSTONE RV CO p 816
2642 Hackberry Dr, Goshen IN 46526
Tel (574) 534-9430 *SIC* 3792

■ SUPREME CORP p 1408
2581 Kercher Rd, Goshen IN 46528
Tel (574) 642-4888 *SIC* 3713 3792 3585

■ JAYCO INC p 779
903 S Main St, Middlebury IN 46540
Tel (574) 825-5861 *SIC* 5013 3716 3792

GULF STREAM COACH INC p 647
503 S Oakland Ave, Nappanee IN 46550
Tel (574) 773-7761
SIC 3716 3792 3714 2451

NEWMAR CORP p 1038
355 Delaware St, Nappanee IN 46550
Tel (574) 773-7791 *SIC* 3716 3792

■ AIRSTREAM INC p 40
419 W Pike St, Jackson Center OH 45334
Tel (937) 596-6111
SIC 3716 3792 3714 3713 3711

ARE INC p 106
400 Nave Rd Sw, Massillon OH 44646
Tel (330) 830-7800
SIC 3713 3714 3792 5013

NORTHWOOD INVESTMENTS CORP p 1061
59948 Downs Rd, La Grande OR 97850
Tel (541) 962-6274 *SIC* 3792

NORTHWOOD MANUFACTURING INC p 1061
59948 Downs Rd, La Grande OR 97850
Tel (541) 962-6274 *SIC* 3792

DOPACO INC p 451
461 Boot Rd, Downingtown PA 19335
Tel (610) 269-6048
SIC 2657 2656 3089 3792

READING TRUCK BODY LLC p 1213
201 Hancock Blvd, Reading PA 19611
Tel (610) 775-3301 *SIC* 3713 3792 3469

TRG WIND DOWN LLC p 1476
201 Hancock Blvd, Reading PA 19611
Tel (610) 775-3301
SIC 3713 3792 3469 5531 7532

PENDA CORP p 1128
2344 W Wisconsin St, Portage WI 53901
Tel (608) 742-5301
SIC 5013 3714 3792 3713 2273

SIC 3795 Tanks & Tank Components

VISION TECHNOLOGIES KINETICS INC p 1561
3800 Richardson Rd, Hope Hull AL 36043
Tel (334) 284-8665 *SIC* 3714 3795

BAE SYSTEMS PROTECTION SYSTEMS INC p 144
7822 S 46th St, Phoenix AZ 85044
Tel (602) 643-7233
SIC 3721 2353 3795 3842

■ GENERAL DYNAMICS DEFENSE SYSTEMS INC p 600
100 Plastics Ave, Pittsfield MA 01201
Tel (413) 494-1110 *SIC* 3812 3795 3625

DEMMER CORP p 428
1600 N Larch St Ste 1, Lansing MI 48906
Tel (517) 321-3600
SIC 3795 3812 3544 3465 3441

US YACHIYO INC p 1533
1177 Kellogg Pkwy, Marion OH 43302
Tel (740) 223-3134 *SIC* 3795

■ GICHNER SYSTEMS GROUP INC p 611
490 E Locust St, Dallastown PA 17313
Tel (717) 246-5430 *SIC* 3795

■ UTLX MANUFACTURING LLC p 1537
16923 Old Beaumont 90, Houston TX 77049
Tel (281) 847-8200 *SIC* 3795

BAE SYSTEMS LAND & ARMAMENTS INC p 144
2000 15th Nw, Arlington VA 22201
Tel (703) 907-8200 *SIC* 3721 3795

BAE SYSTEMS LAND & ARMAMENTS LP p 144
2000 15th Nw Fl 11, Arlington VA 22201
Tel (703) 312-6100 *SIC* 3795 3812

▲ GENERAL DYNAMICS CORP p 600
2941 Frview Pk Dr Ste 100, Falls Church VA 22042
Tel (703) 876-3000
SIC 3721 3731 3795 3711 3812

SIC 3799 Transportation Eqpt, NEC

SUZUKI MOTOR OF AMERICA INC p 1410
3251 E Imperial Hwy, Brea CA 92821
Tel (714) 996-7040 *SIC* 3751 3519 3799

FLEETWOOD ENTERPRISES INC p 555
1351 Pomona Rd Ste 230, Corona CA 92882
Tel (951) 354-3000 SIC 3799 2451 5561

KUBOTA TRACTOR CORP p 831
3401 Del Amo Blvd, Torrance CA 90503
Tel (310) 370-3370 SIC 5083 3531 3799

NAUTIQUE BOAT CO INC p 1019
14700 Aerospace Pkwy, Orlando FL 32832
Tel (407) 855-4141 SIC 3799 3732

CLUB CAR LLC p 328
4125 Washington Rd, Evans GA 30809
Tel (706) 863-3000 SIC 3799

CARRY-ON TRAILER INC p 261
101 Joe Harvey St, Lavonia GA 30553
Tel (706) 356-5379 SIC 3799

■ HEARTLAND RECREATIONAL VEHICLES LLC p 679
2831 Dexter Dr, Elkhart IN 46514
Tel (574) 266-8726 SIC 3799

▲ THOR INDUSTRIES INC p 1450
601 E Beardsley Ave, Elkhart IN 46514
Tel (574) 970-7460 SIC 3799 3711

▲ SUPREME INDUSTRIES INC p 1408
2581 Karcher Rd, Goshen IN 46528
Tel (574) 642-3070 SIC 3537 3713 3799

■ ZIEMAN MANUFACTURING CO INC p 1643
2703 College Ave, Goshen IN 46528
Tel (574) 535-1125
SIC 3715 3441 2451 3799

FEATHERLITE INC p 533
13380 Highways 63 & 9, Cresco IA 52136
Tel (563) 547-6000 SIC 3716 3799 3714

▲ TRIMAS CORP p 1480
39400 Woodward Ave # 130, Bloomfield Hills MI 48304
Tel (248) 631-5450
SIC 3799 3714 3443 2672 3452 3545

■ CEQUENT PERFORMANCE PRODUCTS INC p 283
47912 Halyard Dr Ste 100, Plymouth MI 48170
Tel (734) 656-3000 SIC 3799 3714

▲ POLARIS INDUSTRIES INC p 1159
2100 Highway 55, Medina MN 55340
Tel (763) 542-0500
SIC 3799 3751 3714 5699

▲ ARCTIC CAT INC p 106
500 N 3rd St, Minneapolis MN 55401
Tel (763) 354-1800
SIC 3799 2329 2339 3732

SAVINO DEL BENE USA INC p 1284
34 Engelhard Ave, Avenel NJ 07001
Tel (347) 960-5568 SIC 3799 4731

■ CLOPAY AMES TRUE TEMPER HOLDING CORP p 327
100 Jericho Quadrangle # 224, Jericho NY 11753
Tel (516) 938-5544 SIC 3423 3799 3524

MIBA BEARINGS US LLC p 959
5037 N State Route 60 Nw, Mcconnelsville OH 43756
Tel (740) 962-4242 SIC 3799

■ AMES COMPANIES INC p 84
465 Railroad Ave, Camp Hill PA 17011
Tel (717) 737-1500 SIC 3423 3799 3524

PRIDE MOBILITY PRODUCTS CORP p 1174
182 Susquehanna Ave, Exeter PA 18643
Tel (570) 655-5574 SIC 3842 3799 3751

▲ TEXTRON INC p 1445
40 Westminster St, Providence RI 02903
Tel (401) 421-2800
SIC 3721 3724 3728 3799 3829 3546

WABCO PASSENGER TRANSPORTATION DIVISION p 1570
130 Ridgeview Center Dr, Duncan SC 29334
Tel (864) 433-5900 SIC 3799

HONDA OF SOUTH CAROLINA MFG INC p 704
1111 Honda Way, Timmonsville SC 29161
Tel (843) 346-8000 SIC 3799

■ MILLER INDUSTRIES TOWING EQUIPMENT INC p 970
8503 Hilltop Dr, Ooltewah TN 37363
Tel (423) 238-4171 SIC 3799

■ MASTERCRAFT BOAT CO LLC p 918
100 Cherokee Cove Dr, Vonore TN 37885
Tel (423) 884-2221 SIC 3799

■ MCBC HOLDINGS INC p 926
100 Cherokee Cove Dr, Vonore TN 37885
Tel (423) 884-2221 SIC 3732 3799

LOAD TRAIL LLC p 872
220 Farm Road 2216, Sumner TX 75486
Tel (903) 783-3900 SIC 3799

PJ TRAILERS MANUFACTURING INC p 1153
1807 Farm Road 2352, Sumner TX 75486
Tel (903) 785-6879 SIC 3799

CURT MANUFACTURING LLC p 402
6208 Industrial Dr, Eau Claire WI 54701
Tel (715) 831-8713 SIC 3799

SIC 3812 Search, Detection, Navigation & Guidance Systs & Instrs

RADIANCE TECHNOLOGIES INC p 1204
350 Wynn Dr Nw, Huntsville AL 35805
Tel (256) 704-3400
SIC 3721 8711 3429 3812

KATMAI GOVERNMENT SERVICES LLC p 804
11001 Omalley Centre Dr # 204, Anchorage AK 99515
Tel (907) 333-7000 SIC 3812

■ HONEYWELL AEROSPACE INC p 705
1944 E Sky Harbor Cir N, Phoenix AZ 85034
Tel (602) 365-3099 SIC 3812 7363 7699

CHELTON AVIONICS INC p 293
6400 Wilkinson Dr, Prescott AZ 86301
Tel (928) 708-1500 SIC 3812

UNIVERSAL AVIONICS SYSTEMS CORP p 1516
3260 E Universal Way, Tucson AZ 85756
Tel (520) 295-2300 SIC 3812 3829

■ INTERSTATE ELECTRONICS CORP p 758
602 E Vermont Ave, Anaheim CA 92805
Tel (714) 758-0500 SIC 3825 3812 3679

NORTH AMERICAN VIDEO CORP p 1050
1041 N Pacificenter Dr, Anaheim CA 92806
Tel (714) 779-7499 SIC 5065 3812

ONTIC ENGINEERING AND MANUFACTURING INC p 1088
20400 Plummer St, Chatsworth CA 91311
Tel (818) 678-6555 SIC 5088 3728 3812

CONSOLIDATED AEROSPACE MANUFACTURING LLC p 359
1425 S Acacia Ave, Fullerton CA 92831
Tel (714) 521-5060 SIC 3812

■ AHF-DUCOMMUN INC p 36
268 E Gardena Blvd, Gardena CA 90248
Tel (310) 380-5390
SIC 3728 3812 3769 3469

■ DUCOMMUN AEROSTRUCTURES INC p 459
268 E Gardena Blvd, Gardena CA 90248
Tel (310) 380-5390 SIC 3724 3812 3728

■ OSI OPTOELECTRONICS INC p 1096
12525 Chadron Ave, Hawthorne CA 90250
Tel (310) 978-0516
SIC 3674 3827 3812 3672

MORPHO DETECTION LLC p 989
7151 Gateway Blvd, Newark CA 94560
Tel (510) 739-2400 SIC 3812

▲ AEROJET ROCKETDYNE HOLDINGS INC p 30
2001 Aerojet Rd, Rancho Cordova CA 95742
Tel (916) 355-4000
SIC 3812 3764 3769 6552 6519

BAE SYSTEMS NATIONAL SECURITY SOLUTIONS INC p 144
10920 Technology Pl, San Diego CA 92127
Tel (858) 592-5000 SIC 3825 7373 3812

▲ CUBIC CORP p 399
9333 Balboa Ave, San Diego CA 92123
Tel (858) 277-6780 SIC 3812 3699 7372

■ CUBIC DEFENSE APPLICATIONS INC p 399
9333 Balboa Ave, San Diego CA 92123
Tel (858) 277-6780 SIC 3699 3663 3812

LYTX INC p 888
9785 Towne Centre Dr, San Diego CA 92121
Tel (858) 430-4000 SIC 3812

REMEC DEFENSE & SPACE INC p 1222
9404 Chesapeake Dr, San Diego CA 92123
Tel (858) 560-1301 SIC 3812

■ CSR TECHNOLOGY INC p 398
1060 Rincon Cir, San Jose CA 95131
Tel (408) 523-6500 SIC 3679 3812 3674

▲ INVENSENSE INC p 760
1745 Tech Dr Ste 200, San Jose CA 95110
Tel (408) 501-2200 SIC 3812

■ NORTHROP GRUMMAN SPACE & MISSION SYSTEMS CORP p 1058
6377 San Ignacio Ave, San Jose CA 95119
Tel (703) 280-2900
SIC 7373 3663 3661 3812 3761

■ RAE SYSTEMS INC p 1205
3775 N 1st St, San Jose CA 95134
Tel (408) 952-8200 SIC 3829 3812 3699

ASCENT TOOLING GROUP LLC p 116
1395 S Lyon St, Santa Ana CA 92705
Tel (949) 455-0665 SIC 3812

CHANNEL TECHNOLOGIES GROUP LLC p 288
879 Ward Dr, Santa Barbara CA 93111
Tel (805) 967-0171 SIC 3812

▲ TELENAV INC p 1434
4655 Great America Pkwy, Santa Clara CA 95054
Tel (408) 245-3800 SIC 3812

VOTAW PRECISION TECHNOLOGIES INC p 1566
13153 Lakeland Rd, Santa Fe Springs CA 90670
Tel (562) 666-2138 SIC 3544 3812

PACIFIC SCIENTIFIC CO INC p 1105
1785 Voyager Ave Ste 101, Simi Valley CA 93063
Tel (805) 526-5700
SIC 3812 3669 3621 3694 3823 3625

AEDAN INC p 29
27447, Sun City CA 92586
Tel (888) 272-5505
SIC 7371 7381 8733 3812 7382

▲ TRIMBLE INC p 1480
935 Stewart Dr, Sunnyvale CA 94085
Tel (408) 481-8000 SIC 3812 3829

■ SIERRACIN/SYLMAR CORP p 1321
12780 San Fernando Rd, Sylmar CA 91342
Tel (818) 362-6711
SIC 3089 3812 3621 3231

▲ TELEDYNE TECHNOLOGIES INC p 1434
1049 Camino Dos Rios, Thousand Oaks CA 91360
Tel (805) 373-4545
SIC 3679 3761 3519 3724 3812 3674

SANDEL AVIONICS INC p 1278
2401 Dogwood Way, Vista CA 92081
Tel (760) 727-4900 SIC 3812

■ BALL AEROSPACE & TECHNOLOGIES CORP p 148
1600 Commerce St, Boulder CO 80301
Tel (303) 939-4000 SIC 3812

▲ BALL CORP p 148
10 Longs Peak Dr, Broomfield CO 80021
Tel (303) 469-3131
SIC 3411 3085 3812 3679

■ ATLANTIC INERTIAL SYSTEMS INC p 126
250 Knotter Dr, Cheshire CT 06410
Tel (203) 250-3500 SIC 3812

■ GEMS SENSORS INC p 598
1 Cowles Rd, Plainville CT 06062
Tel (860) 747-3000
SIC 3824 5084 3812 3625 3613

■ TRIUMPH ENGINE CONTROL SYSTEMS LLC p 1483
1 Charter Oak Blvd, West Hartford CT 06110
Tel (860) 236-0651 SIC 3728 3724 3812

LEE CO p 851
2 Pettipaug Rd, Westbrook CT 06498
Tel (860) 399-6281
SIC 3823 3841 3812 3728 3714

▲ ARC GROUP WORLDWIDE INC p 103
810 Flight Line Blvd, Deland FL 32724
Tel (303) 467-5236 SIC 3499 3462 3812

DRS TRAINING & CONTROL SYSTEMS LLC p 457
645 Anchors St Nw, Fort Walton Beach FL 32548
Tel (850) 302-3000 SIC 3812 8713

■ HEICO AEROSPACE CORP p 680
3000 Taft St, Hollywood FL 33021
Tel (954) 987-6101 SIC 3724 3812

▲ HARRIS CORP p 663
1025 W Nasa Blvd, Melbourne FL 32919
Tel (321) 727-9100
SIC 3812 3663 3699 3661 3674

SOUTHEAST AEROSPACE INC p 1345
1399 General Aviation Dr, Melbourne FL 32935
Tel (321) 255-9877
SIC 5088 3812 3728 3721 4581

■ TEKTRONIX SERVICE SOLUTIONS INC p 1433
6120 Hanging Moss Rd, Orlando FL 32807
Tel (407) 678-6900
SIC 3812 3674 8734 7699

■ SEQUA CORP p 1306
3999 Rca Blvd, Palm Beach Gardens FL 33410
Tel (201) 343-1122
SIC 3724 3764 3812 3699 3845 3542

■ GENERAL DYNAMICS-OTS INC p 600
11399 16th Ct N Ste 200, Saint Petersburg FL 33716
Tel (727) 578-8100 SIC 3728 3812

■ UTILIQUEST LLC p 1537
2575 Westside Pkwy # 100, Alpharetta GA 30004
Tel (678) 461-3900 SIC 1623 3812

■ LOCKHEED MARTIN AERONAUTICAL CO p 873
86 S Cobb Dr Se, Marietta GA 30063
Tel (770) 494-4411
SIC 3721 3812 7699 3769

▲ BOEING CO p 197
100 N Riverside Plz, Chicago IL 60606
Tel (312) 544-2000
SIC 3721 3663 3761 3764 3812 3728

W S DARLEY & CO p 1569
325 Spring Lake Dr, Itasca IL 60143
Tel (630) 735-3500
SIC 3561 5087 5099 3569 3812

■ MPC PRODUCTS CORP p 995
6300 W Howard St, Niles IL 60714
Tel (847) 673-8300
SIC 3728 3621 3676 3812 3625

■ COMMSCOPE TECHNOLOGIES LLC p 346
4 Westbrook Corporate Ctr, Westchester IL 60154
Tel (708) 236-6000
SIC 3663 3357 3679 3812 3699

UNDERSEA SENSOR SYSTEMS INC p 1502
4868 E Park 30 Dr, Columbia City IN 46725
Tel (260) 244-3500 SIC 3812

DATA LINK SOLUTIONS LLC p 413
350 Collins Rd Ne, Cedar Rapids IA 52498
Tel (319) 295-8144 SIC 3812

▲ ROCKWELL COLLINS INC p 1245
400 Collins Rd Ne, Cedar Rapids IA 52498
Tel (319) 295-1000 SIC 3812 3663

GARMIN INTERNATIONAL INC p 592
1200 E 151st St, Olathe KS 66062
Tel (913) 397-8200 SIC 3812 3669 8713

LEARJET INC p 850
1 Learjet Way, Wichita KS 67209
Tel (316) 946-2000 SIC 3721 3812

▲ SYPRIS SOLUTIONS INC p 1416
101 Bullitt Ln Ste 450, Louisville KY 40222
Tel (502) 329-2000
SIC 3672 3679 3812 3674 3462

MPD INC p 995
316 E 9th St, Owensboro KY 42303
Tel (270) 685-6200
SIC 3671 3829 3812 3663 3643 3053

ASRC AEROSPACE CORP p 119
7000 Muirkirk Meadows Dr # 100, Beltsville MD 20705
Tel (301) 837-5500
SIC 3812 7371 7373 5088

▲ LOCKHEED MARTIN CORP p 873
6801 Rockledge Dr, Bethesda MD 20817
Tel (301) 897-6000
SIC 3761 3721 3663 3764 3812 3728

■ LOCKHEED MARTIN INTEGRATED SYSTEMS INC p 873
6801 Rockledge Dr, Bethesda MD 20817
Tel (856) 486-5000 SIC 3812

DRS DEFENSE SOLUTIONS LLC p 457
1 Milestone Center Ct, Germantown MD 20876
Tel (240) 238-3900 SIC 3812

COBHAM DEFENSE ELECTRONIC SYSTEMS CORP p 332
1001 Pawtucket Blvd, Lowell MA 01854
Tel (978) 779-7000 SIC 3812

COBHAM ELECTRONIC SYSTEMS INC p 332
1001 Pawtucket Blvd, Lowell MA 01854
Tel (978) 442-4700 SIC 3812

■ LOCKHEED MARTIN SIPPICAN INC p 873
7 Barnabas Rd, Marion MA 02738
Tel (508) 748-3399
SIC 3812 3826 3499 3672 3829 3845

■ POLARIS CONTRACT MANUFACTURING INC p 1159
15 Barnabas Rd, Marion MA 02738
Tel (508) 748-3399 SIC 3812

▲ ANALOGIC CORP p 88
8 Centennial Dr, Peabody MA 01960
Tel (978) 326-4000 SIC 3825 3812

■ GENERAL DYNAMICS DEFENSE SYSTEMS INC p 600
100 Plastics Ave, Pittsfield MA 01201
Tel (413) 494-1110 SIC 3812 3795 3625

QINETIQ NORTH AMERICA INC p 1195
350 2nd Ave Bldg 1, Waltham MA 02451
Tel (781) 684-4000 SIC 3812 8731

▲ RAYTHEON CO p 1211
870 Winter St, Waltham MA 02451
Tel (781) 522-3000 SIC 3812 3663 3761

BURTEK HOLDINGS INC p 229
50325 Patricia St, Chesterfield MI 48051
Tel (586) 421-8000 SIC 7371 3812 8711

■ L-3 COMMUNICATIONS AVIONICS SYSTEMS INC p 834
5353 52nd St Se, Grand Rapids MI 49512
Tel (616) 977-6837 SIC 3812

DEMMER CORP p 428
1600 N Larch St Ste 1, Lansing MI 48906
Tel (517) 321-3600
SIC 3795 3812 3544 3465 3441

■ HARMAN BECKER AUTOMOTIVE SYSTEMS INC p 662
30001 Cabot Dr, Novi MI 48377
Tel (248) 785-2361 SIC 3931 3812

■ FEDERAL-MOGUL CORP p 536
27300 W 11 Mile Rd, Southfield MI 48034
Tel (248) 354-7700
SIC 3559 3462 3812 3674 3694

■ FEDERAL-MOGUL HOLDINGS CORP p 536
27300 W 11 Mile Rd, Southfield MI 48034
Tel (248) 354-7700
SIC 3462 3559 3694 3812 3674 3714

■ ROSEMOUNT AEROSPACE INC p 1251
14300 Judicial Rd, Burnsville MN 55306
Tel (952) 892-4000 SIC 3812

■ ALLIANT HOLDINGS LLC p 55
7480 Flying Cloud Dr, Eden Prairie MN 55344
Tel (952) 351-3000
SIC 3764 3812 3483 3482 3489

■ RTI REMMELE ENGINEERING INC p 1256
10 Old Highway 8 Sw, Saint Paul MN 55112
Tel (651) 635-4100
SIC 3728 3569 3812 3761 3842

AEGIS CORP p 29
614 Dartmouth Terrace Ct, Ballwin MO 63011
Tel (636) 273-1011
SIC 3699 4812 3812 3444 2326

■ DUCOMMUN LABARGE TECHNOLOGIES INC p 459
689 Craig Rd 200, Saint Louis MO 63141
Tel (314) 997-0800 SIC 3812 3699

■ ESCO TECHNOLOGIES HOLDING LLC p 509
9900 Clayton Rd Ste A, Saint Louis MO 63124
Tel (314) 213-7200
SIC 3825 3492 3812 3711 3663

G K N AEROSPACE NORTH AMERICA INC p 587
142 Js Mcdonnell Blvd, Saint Louis MO 63135
Tel (314) 264-3000 SIC 3812 3728

SYSTEMS DRS SUSTAINMENT INC p 1418
201 Evans Ln, Saint Louis MO 63121
Tel (314) 553-4000
SIC 3715 3537 3812 3829 3769

SIERRA NEVADA CORP p 1320
444 Salomon Cir, Sparks NV 89434
Tel (775) 331-0222 SIC 3728 3812

KOLLSMAN INC p 826
220 Daniel Webster Hwy, Merrimack NH 03054
Tel (603) 889-2500 SIC 3812 3629

BAE SYSTEMS INFORMATION AND ELECTRONIC SYSTEMS INTEGRATION INC p 144
65 Spit Brook Rd, Nashua NH 03060
Tel (603) 885-4321 SIC 3812

■ ITT CORP p 768
77 River Rd, Clifton NJ 07014
Tel (973) 284-0123 SIC 3812

TRANSISTOR DEVICES INC p 1471
36 Newburgh Rd, Hackettstown NJ 07840
Tel (908) 850-1595
SIC 3612 3625 3672 3812 3829

■ HONEYWELL INC p 705
115 Tabor Rd, Morris Plains NJ 07950
Tel (973) 455-2000
SIC 3823 3812 3669 3491 3699 3822

▲ HONEYWELL INTERNATIONAL INC p 705
115 Tabor Rd, Morris Plains NJ 07950
Tel (973) 455-2000
SIC 3724 3812 3585 2824 2821 3714

CHECKPOINT SYSTEMS INC p 292
101 Wolf Dr, West Deptford NJ 08086
Tel (856) 848-1800 SIC 3699 3812 3663

KEARFOTT CORP p 807
1150 Mcbride Ave Ste 1, Woodland Park NJ 07424
Tel (973) 785-6000 SIC 3812

■ EDO LLC p 478
1500 New Horizons Blvd, Amityville NY 11701
Tel (631) 630-4000
SIC 3812 3728 3663 3679

INFICON INC p 740
2 Technology Pl, East Syracuse NY 13057
Tel (315) 434-1149 SIC 3823 3812

▲ MOOG INC p 987
400 Jamison Rd Plant26, Elma NY 14059
Tel (716) 652-2000
SIC 3812 3492 3625 3769 3728 3841

BAE SYSTEMS CONTROLS INC p 144
1098 Clark St, Endicott NY 13760
Tel (607) 770-2000 SIC 3812

■ TELEPHONICS CORP p 1435
815 Broadhollow Rd, Farmingdale NY 11735
Tel (631) 755-7000
SIC 3669 3661 3679 3812 3663

■ LOCKHEED MARTIN GLOBAL INC p 873
497 Electronics Pkwy # 5, Liverpool NY 13088
Tel (315) 456-2982 SIC 3812

SAGE PARTS PLUS INC p 1267
30 Hub Dr Ste 1, Melville NY 11747
Tel (631) 501-1300 SIC 5088 3812 3537

CLAYTON DUBILIER & RICE FUND V LIMITED PARTNERSHIP p 323
375 Park Ave Fl 18, New York NY 10152
Tel (212) 407-5200
SIC 3825 3661 3812 3577 3575 7372

FALCONHEAD CAPITAL LLC p 526
645 Madison Ave Fl 9, New York NY 10022
Tel (212) 634-3304 SIC 6722 3812

■ **IEH FM HOLDINGS LLC** *p* 730
767 5th Ave Ste 4700, New York NY 10153
Tel (212) 702-4300
SIC 3462 3559 3694 3812 3674

■ **L-3 COMMUNICATIONS CORP** *p* 834
600 3rd Ave, New York NY 10016
Tel (212) 697-1111
SIC 3812 3663 3669 3679 3769

▲ **L-3 COMMUNICATIONS HOLDINGS INC** *p* 835
600 3rd Ave, New York NY 10016
Tel (212) 697-1111
SIC 3663 3669 3679 3812 3769

COBHAM HOLDINGS (US) INC *p* 332
10 Cobham Dr, Orchard Park NY 14127
Tel (716) 662-0006 *SIC* 3679 3812

COBHAM HOLDINGS INC *p* 332
10 Orchard Park Dr, Orchard Park NY 14127
Tel (716) 662-0006 *SIC* 3679 3812

AEROFLEX INC *p* 30
35 S Service Rd, Plainview NY 11803
Tel (516) 694-6700
SIC 3812 3621 3677 3674 3496 3827

▲ **ITT INC** *p* 768
1133 Westchester Ave N-100, White Plains NY 10604
Tel (914) 641-2000
SIC 3594 3625 3823 3812

■ **ITT LLC** *p* 768
1133 Westchester Ave N-100, White Plains NY 10604
Tel (914) 641-2000
SIC 3594 3625 3823 3812

▲ **CURTISS-WRIGHT CORP** *p* 402
13925 Ballntyn Corp Pl, Charlotte NC 28277
Tel (704) 869-4600 *SIC* 3491 3621 3812

■ **COMMSCOPE INC OF NORTH CAROLINA** *p* 346
1100 Commscope Pl Se, Hickory NC 28602
Tel (828) 324-2200
SIC 3663 3357 3679 3812 3699

DRS ICAS LLC *p* 457
2601 Mission Point Blvd, Beavercreek OH 45431
Tel (937) 429-7408 *SIC* 3812

■ **GE AVIATION SYSTEMS LLC** *p* 595
1 Neumann Way, Cincinnati OH 45215
Tel (513) 243-2000 *SIC* 3812

■ **AVIATION TECHNOLOGIES INC** *p* 138
1301 E 9th St Ste 3000, Cleveland OH 44114
Tel (216) 706-2960
SIC 3643 3678 3679 3728 3812 3648

EATON AEROSPACE LLC *p* 473
1000 Eaton Blvd, Cleveland OH 44122
Tel (216) 523-5000 *SIC* 3812

ADB SAFEGATE AMERICAS LLC *p* 21
977 Gahanna Pkwy, Columbus OH 43230
Tel (614) 861-1304 *SIC* 3648 3812

HBD INDUSTRIES INC *p* 671
5200 Upper Metro Pl # 110, Dublin OH 43017
Tel (614) 526-7000
SIC 3052 3621 3566 3564 3812

PEERLESS-WINSMITH INC *p* 1127
5200 Upper Metro Pl # 110, Dublin OH 43017
Tel (614) 526-7000
SIC 3621 3566 3634 3812 3559

■ **L-3 COMMUNICATIONS CINCINNATI ELECTRONICS CORP** *p* 834
7500 Innovation Way, Mason OH 45040
Tel (513) 573-6100 *SIC* 3812 3769 3823

CEDAR ELECTRONICS HOLDINGS CORP *p* 272
5440 W Chester Rd, West Chester OH 45069
Tel (513) 870-8500 *SIC* 3812 5088

NAVICO INC *p* 1020
4500 S 129th East Ave # 200, Tulsa OK 74134
Tel (918) 437-6881 *SIC* 3812

▲ **FLIR SYSTEMS INC** *p* 557
27700 Sw Parkway Ave, Wilsonville OR 97070
Tel (503) 498-3547 *SIC* 3812 3826

▲ **TRIUMPH GROUP INC** *p* 1483
899 Cassatt Rd Ste 210, Berwyn PA 19312
Tel (610) 251-1000 *SIC* 3728 3724 3812

COBHAM ADVANCED ELECTRONIC SOLUTIONS INC *p* 332
305 Richardson Rd, Lansdale PA 19446
Tel (215) 996-2000 *SIC* 3812

SMITHS GROUP NORTH AMERICA INC *p* 1334
101 Lindenwood Dr Ste 125, Malvern PA 19355
Tel (772) 286-9300 *SIC* 3812 3841 3679

HERAEUS ELECTRO-NITE CO LLC *p* 685
770 Township Line Rd # 300, Yardley PA 19067
Tel (215) 944-9000 *SIC* 3812 3823

▲ **KVH INDUSTRIES INC** *p* 832
50 Enterprise Ctr, Middletown RI 02842
Tel (401) 847-3327 *SIC* 3663 3812

■ **AEROSTRUCTURES CORP** *p* 31
1431 Vultee Blvd, Nashville TN 37217
Tel (615) 361-2000
SIC 3721 3728 3812 3769

ULTRA ELECTRONICS DEFENSE INC *p* 1501
4101 Smith School Rd, Austin TX 78744
Tel (512) 327-6795 *SIC* 3812 3825

OPTEK TECHNOLOGY INC *p* 1090
1645 Wallace Dr, Carrollton TX 75006
Tel (972) 323-2200
SIC 3674 3825 3812 3661 3643

FIRST TEXAS HOLDING CORP *p* 549
1465 Henry Brennan Dr H, El Paso TX 79936
Tel (915) 633-8354 *SIC* 3812

FIRST TEXAS PRODUCTS LLC *p* 550
1465 Henry Brennan Dr H, El Paso TX 79936
Tel (915) 633-8354 *SIC* 3812

EFW INC *p* 481
4700 Marine Creek Pkwy, Fort Worth TX 76179
Tel (817) 916-1359 *SIC* 3812

HEATH CONSULTANTS INC *p* 679
9030 W Monroe Rd, Houston TX 77061
Tel (713) 844-1300 *SIC* 8711 3828 3812

USA (UNITED SPACE ALLIANCE PENSION) *p* 1533
600 Gemini St, Houston TX 77058
Tel (281) 212-6200 *SIC* 3812

■ **TRIUMPH AEROSTRUCTURES LLC** *p* 1483
300 Austin Blvd, Red Oak TX 75154
Tel (972) 515-8276
SIC 3721 3728 3812 3769

■ **RAYTHEON E-SYSTEMS INC** *p* 1211
1727 Cityline Dr, Richardson TX 75082
Tel (972) 205-9374
SIC 3663 3812 7373 3575 4581 3721

▲ **VISTA OUTDOOR INC** *p* 1562
262 N University Ave, Farmington UT 84025
Tel (801) 447-3000
SIC 3482 3483 3827 3949 3484 3812

■ **TRIUMPH GEAR SYSTEMS INC** *p* 1483
6125 Silver Creek Dr, Park City UT 84098
Tel (435) 649-1900 *SIC* 3593 3728 3812

L-3 COMMUNICATIONS CORP *p* 834
322 N 2200 W, Salt Lake City UT 84116
Tel (801) 594-2000 *SIC* 3812

BAE SYSTEMS HOLDINGS INC *p* 144
1101 Wilson Blvd Ste 2000, Arlington VA 22209
Tel (703) 312-6100 *SIC* 3699 3728 3812

BAE SYSTEMS INC *p* 144
1101 Wilson Blvd Ste 2000, Arlington VA 22209
Tel (703) 312-6100 *SIC* 3812 3728

BAE SYSTEMS LAND & ARMAMENTS LP *p* 144
2000 15th Nw Fl 11, Arlington VA 22201
Tel (703) 312-6100 *SIC* 3795 3812

COBHAM AES HOLDINGS INC *p* 332
2121 Crystal Dr Ste 625, Arlington VA 22202
Tel (703) 414-5300 *SIC* 3679 3812

DRS TECHNOLOGIES INC *p* 457
2345 Crystal Dr Ste 1000, Arlington VA 22202
Tel (973) 898-1500
SIC 3812 3699 3572 3669 3679 8741

QINETIQ US HOLDINGS INC *p* 1195
5885 Trinity Pkwy Ste 130, Centreville VA 20120
Tel (202) 429-6630 *SIC* 3812

VENCORE HOLDING CORP *p* 1547
15052 Conference Ctr Dr, Chantilly VA 20151
Tel (571) 313-6000
SIC 6719 8711 8733 3812 7372

VENCORE INC *p* 1547
15052 Conference Ctr Dr, Chantilly VA 20151
Tel (571) 313-6000
SIC 8711 8733 3812 7372

▲ **ORBITAL ATK INC** *p* 1092
45101 Warp Dr, Dulles VA 20166
Tel (703) 406-5000
SIC 3764 3812 3483 3482 3489

■ **ORBITAL SCIENCES CORP** *p* 1092
45101 Warp Dr, Dulles VA 20166
Tel (703) 406-5000 *SIC* 3812 4899 7372

■ **ARGON ST INC** *p* 107
12701 Fair Lakes Cir # 800, Fairfax VA 22033
Tel (703) 322-0881 *SIC* 3812

▲ **GENERAL DYNAMICS CORP** *p* 600
2941 Frview Pk Dr Ste 100, Falls Church VA 22042
Tel (703) 876-3000
SIC 3721 3731 3795 3711 3812

▲ **NORTHROP GRUMMAN CORP** *p* 1058
2980 Fairview Park Dr, Falls Church VA 22042
Tel (703) 280-2900 *SIC* 3812

■ **NORTHROP GRUMMAN SYSTEMS CORP** *p* 1058
2980 Fairview Park Dr, Falls Church VA 22042
Tel (703) 280-2900
SIC 3721 3761 3728 3812 3825 4581

EXELIS INC *p* 518
2235 Monroe St, Herndon VA 20171
Tel (703) 790-6300 *SIC* 3669 3823 3812

■ **TITAN II INC** *p* 1456
4101 Washington Ave, Newport News VA 23607
Tel (757) 380-2000
SIC 3728 3761 7373 3721 4581 3812

VENCORE SERVICES AND SOLUTIONS INC *p* 1547
1835 Alexander Bell Dr, Reston VA 20191
Tel (703) 391-7017 *SIC* 7379 7373 3812

▲ **ESTERLINE TECHNOLOGIES CORP** *p* 511
500 108th Ave Ne Ste 1500, Bellevue WA 98004
Tel (425) 453-9400 *SIC* 3728 3812 3429

■ **AVTECHTYEE INC** *p* 139
6500 Merrill Creek Pkwy, Everett WA 98203
Tel (206) 695-8000 *SIC* 3728 3648 3812

NABTESCO AEROSPACE INC *p* 1006
12413 Willows Rd Ne, Kirkland WA 98034
Tel (425) 602-8400 *SIC* 3728 3812 3593

■ **ELDEC CORP** *p* 484
16700 13th Ave W, Lynnwood WA 98037
Tel (425) 743-8362
SIC 3812 3728 3824 3769 3674 3613

ASTRONAUTICS CORP OF AMERICA *p* 122
4115 N Teutonia Ave, Milwaukee WI 53209
Tel (414) 449-4000
SIC 3812 3571 3572 3769

DRS POWER & CONTROL TECHNOLOGIES INC *p* 457
4265 N 30th St, Milwaukee WI 53216
Tel (414) 875-4314 *SIC* 3812

▲ **JOHNSON OUTDOORS INC** *p* 791
555 Main St, Racine WI 53403
Tel (262) 631-6600 *SIC* 3949 3732 3812

SIC 3821 Laboratory Apparatus & Furniture

■ **BECKMAN COULTER INC** *p* 167
250 S Kraemer Blvd, Brea CA 92821
Tel (714) 993-5321 *SIC* 3826 3841 3821

■ **NEWPORT CORP** *p* 1038
1791 Deere Ave, Irvine CA 92606
Tel (949) 863-3144
SIC 3821 3699 3827 3826

■ **METTLER-TOLEDO RAININ LLC** *p* 957
7500 Edgewater Dr, Oakland CA 94621
Tel (510) 564-1600 *SIC* 3821 3829

■ **IDEX HEALTH & SCIENCE LLC** *p* 729
600 Park Ct, Rohnert Park CA 94928
Tel (707) 588-2000
SIC 3821 3829 3826 3823 3494

▲ **ILLUMINA INC** *p* 733
5200 Illumina Way, San Diego CA 92122
Tel (858) 202-4500 *SIC* 3826 3821

TOTAL SOURCE MANUFACTURING *p* 1463
1445 Engineer St, Vista CA 92081
Tel (760) 598-2146 *SIC* 3821

EPPENDORF HOLDING INC *p* 505
175 Freshwater Blvd, Enfield CT 06082
Tel (860) 253-3417 *SIC* 3821

BIO MEDIC CORP *p* 183
742 Sussex Ave, Seaford DE 19973
Tel (302) 628-4300
SIC 5049 3821 3496 3914 3661

FLINN SCIENTIFIC INC *p* 557
770 N Raddant Rd, Batavia IL 60510
Tel (800) 452-1261 *SIC* 3821 5049

■ **LEICA MICROSYSTEMS INC** *p* 854
1700 Leider Ln, Buffalo Grove IL 60089
Tel (847) 405-0123 *SIC* 3827 3841 3821

■ **ATLAS MATERIAL TESTING TECHNOLOGY LLC** *p* 128
1500 Bishop Ct, Mount Prospect IL 60056
Tel (773) 327-4520
SIC 3823 3669 3599 8734 3825 3821

COOK GROUP INC *p* 365
750 N Daniels Way, Bloomington IN 47404
Tel (812) 339-2235
SIC 3841 3821 3845 6411 6512 6211

ALLTECH INC *p* 58
3031 Catnip Hill Rd, Nicholasville KY 40356
Tel (859) 885-9613
SIC 2869 2048 3821 2819

▲ **HARVARD BIOSCIENCE INC** *p* 666
84 October Hill Rd Ste 10, Holliston MA 01746
Tel (508) 893-8999 *SIC* 3821 3826

■ **APOGENT TECHNOLOGIES INC** *p* 97
81 Wyman St, Waltham MA 02451
Tel (781) 622-1300 *SIC* 3821 3229 3843

■ **FISHER SCIENTIFIC INTERNATIONAL LLC** *p* 552
81 Wyman St, Waltham MA 02451
Tel (781) 622-1000
SIC 2869 3821 5169 5049

■ **PERKINELMER HEALTH SCIENCES INC** *p* 1136
940 Winter St, Waltham MA 02451
Tel (617) 482-9595 *SIC* 3821

SPECTRIS INC *p* 1357
117 Flanders Rd, Westborough MA 01581
Tel (508) 768-6400
SIC 3674 3829 3826 3821

■ **GELMAN SCIENCES INC** *p* 598
674 S Wagner Rd, Ann Arbor MI 48103
Tel (734) 665-0651
SIC 3821 3569 3564 3841 3845 3699

LECO CORP *p* 851
3000 Lakeview Ave, Saint Joseph MI 49085
Tel (269) 983-5531
SIC 4493 3821 3826 3825 3823 3264

■ **ERIE SCIENTIFIC LLC** *p* 508
20 Post Rd, Portsmouth NH 03801
Tel (603) 430-6859
SIC 3231 3821 3229 3221 3211

▲ **BECTON DICKINSON AND CO** *p* 167
1 Becton Dr, Franklin Lakes NJ 07417
Tel (201) 847-6800
SIC 3841 3842 3829 3826 3821

ARTHUR H THOMAS CO *p* 114
1654 High Hill Rd, Swedesboro NJ 08085
Tel (856) 467-2000 *SIC* 3821 5049

■ **NALGE NUNC INTERNATIONAL CORP** *p* 1007
75 Panorama Creek Dr, Rochester NY 14625
Tel (585) 586-8800
SIC 3089 3949 3821 3085 3083

■ **THERMO FISHER SCIENTIFIC (ASHVILLE) LLC** *p* 1447
28 Schenck Pkwy Ste 400, Asheville NC 28803
Tel (828) 658-2711
SIC 3585 3826 3821 3829

CAROLINA BIOLOGICAL SUPPLY CO *p* 259
2700 York Rd, Burlington NC 27215
Tel (336) 584-0381
SIC 5049 2836 3829 3826 3821

▲ **KEWAUNEE SCIENTIFIC CORP** *p* 814
2700 W Front St, Statesville NC 28677
Tel (704) 873-7202 *SIC* 3821 2599

PHILIPS MEDICAL SYSTEMS (CLEVELAND) INC *p* 1143
595 Miner Rd, Cleveland OH 44143
Tel (440) 247-2652
SIC 3844 5047 5137 3842 3821 3699

▲ **METTLER-TOLEDO INTERNATIONAL INC** *p* 957
1900 Polaris Pkwy Fl 6, Columbus OH 43240
Tel (614) 438-4511
SIC 3596 3821 3826 3823

■ **METTLER-TOLEDO LLC** *p* 957
1900 Polaris Pkwy Fl 6, Columbus OH 43240
Tel (614) 438-4511
SIC 3596 5049 7699 3821 3823 3826

■ **FISHER SCIENTIFIC CO LLC** *p* 552
300 Industry Dr, Pittsburgh PA 15275
Tel (412) 490-8300
SIC 5049 5169 3821 3826 2869 2819

▲ **VWR CORP** *p* 1567
100 Matsonford Rd 1-200, Radnor PA 19087
Tel (610) 386-1700
SIC 2869 2819 3821 5047

S P INDUSTRIES INC *p* 1262
935 Mearns Rd, Warminster PA 18974
Tel (215) 672-7800
SIC 3826 3585 7699 3821

ALFA LAVAL INC *p* 49
5400 Intl Trade Dr, Richmond VA 23231
Tel (804) 222-5300
SIC 3491 3433 3585 3569 3821

HAMILTON L FISHER L C *p* 655
1716 Lawrence Dr Ste 1, De Pere WI 54115
Tel (920) 793-1121 *SIC* 3821

ALDRICH CHEMICAL CO LLC *p* 48
6000 N Teutonia Ave, Milwaukee WI 53209
Tel (414) 438-3850
SIC 2869 2819 3821 7371 2741

SIC 3822 Automatic Temperature Controls

PENTAIR THERMAL MANAGEMENT LLC *p* 1132
899 Broadway St, Redwood City CA 94063
Tel (650) 474-7414 *SIC* 1711 3822

AD CORP *p* 21
1551 Wewatta St, Denver CO 80202
Tel (303) 744-1911
SIC 3634 3564 3822 3089 3714 3312

▲ **ASCENT CAPITAL GROUP INC** *p* 116
5251 Dtc Pkwy Ste 1000, Greenwood Village CO 80111
Tel (303) 628-5600 *SIC* 3822 7392

LEXA INTERNATIONAL CORP *p* 859
1 Landmark Sq Ste 407, Stamford CT 06901
Tel (203) 326-5200 *SIC* 5171 3822

■ **HAMILTON SUNDSTRAND CORP** *p* 655
1 Hamilton Rd, Windsor Locks CT 06096
Tel (860) 654-6000
SIC 3621 3594 3728 3625 3823 3822

SEWICKLEY CAPITAL INC *p* 1309
501 Silverside Rd Ste 67, Wilmington DE 19809
Tel (302) 793-4964 *SIC* 3559 3822

SIMPLEXGRINNELL HOLDINGS LLC *p* 1325
1501 Nw 51st St, Boca Raton FL 33431
Tel (561) 988-7200
SIC 3579 3669 3699 3822

SOUTHERN ENVIRONMENTAL INC *p* 1348
6690 W Nine Mile Rd, Pensacola FL 32526
Tel (850) 944-4475 *SIC* 3822

■ **AUTOMATED LOGIC CORP** *p* 134
1150 Roberts Blvd Nw, Kennesaw GA 30144
Tel (770) 429-3000 *SIC* 3822

COMVERGE INC *p* 353
5390 Triangle Pkwy # 300, Norcross GA 30092
Tel (678) 802-8011 *SIC* 3822

SIEMENS INDUSTRY INC *p* 1320
1000 Deerfield Pkwy, Buffalo Grove IL 60089
Tel (847) 215-1000
SIC 3822 5063 3669 1731 7382 3625

AVG ADVANCED TECHNOLOGIES LP *p* 137
343 Saint Paul Blvd, Carol Stream IL 60188
Tel (630) 668-3900
SIC 3672 3661 3824 3822 3625

ROBERTSHAW CONTROLS CO *p* 1242
1222 Hamilton Pkwy, Itasca IL 60143
Tel (630) 260-3400 *SIC* 3823 3822 3492

VANGUARD ENERGY SERVICES LLC *p* 1543
850 E Diehl Rd Ste 142, Naperville IL 60563
Tel (630) 955-1500 *SIC* 3822

■ **ECLIPSE INC** *p* 475
1665 Elmwood Rd, Rockford IL 61103
Tel (815) 877-3031
SIC 3564 3433 3822 3823 3443 3494

SCHNEIDER ELECTRIC BUILDINGS LLC *p* 1287
839 N Perryville Rd, Rockford IL 61107
Tel (815) 381-5000
SIC 3822 1711 3625 3823 3621

SCHNEIDER ELECTRIC HOLDINGS INC *p* 1287
200 N Martingale Rd # 100, Schaumburg IL 60173
Tel (717) 944-5460
SIC 3822 1711 3625 3823 3621

■ **UNITED TECHNOLOGIES ELECTRONIC CONTROLS INC** *p* 1514
3650 W 200 N, Huntington IN 46750
Tel (260) 359-3514 *SIC* 3822

DWYER INSTRUMENTS INC *p* 464
102 Indiana Highway 212, Michigan City IN 46360
Tel (219) 879-8868
SIC 3823 3824 3822 3829 3491 3625

DOMETIC CORP *p* 448
13551 Triton Park Blvd # 1000, Louisville KY 40223
Tel (502) 873-3524
SIC 3089 3443 3444 3822 3823 3999

AGGREKO LLC *p* 35
4610 W Admiral Doyle Dr, New Iberia LA 70560
Tel (337) 367-7884 *SIC* 5064 3822

WAHLCOMETROFLEX INC *p* 1571
29 Lexington St, Lewiston ME 04240
Tel (207) 784-2338 *SIC* 3441 3822 8711

DANFOSS LLC *p* 411
11655 Crossroads Cir A, Baltimore MD 21220
Tel (410) 931-8250 *SIC* 3585 3625 3822

STULZ INVESTMENT CORP OF AMERICA *p* 1395
1572 Tilco Dr, Frederick MD 21704
Tel (301) 620-2033 *SIC* 3822

MUNTERS CORP *p* 1001
79 Monroe St, Amesbury MA 01913
Tel (978) 241-1100
SIC 3585 3822 3569 3564

SCHNEIDER AUTOMATION INC *p* 1287
800 Federal St Ste 1, Andover MA 01810
Tel (978) 794-0800 *SIC* 3822

TAC INC *p* 1421
1 High St, Andover MA 01810
Tel (978) 470-0555 *SIC* 3822

■ **KIDDE-FENWAL INC** *p* 817
400 Main St, Ashland MA 01721
Tel (508) 881-2000
SIC 3669 3823 3825 3822 3843 3625

■ **SENSITECH INC** *p* 1305
800 Cummings Ctr Ste 258x, Beverly MA 01915
Tel (978) 927-7033 *SIC* 3826 3823 3822

HART & COOLEY INC *p* 664
5030 Corp Exch Blvd Se, Grand Rapids MI 49512
Tel (616) 656-8200 *SIC* 3446 3822

HELLA CORPORATE CENTER USA INC *p* 681
43811 Plymouth Oaks Blvd, Plymouth MI 48170
Tel (586) 232-4788
SIC 3625 5013 5088 3822 3585 3429

RUSKIN CO *p* 1259
3900 Doctor Greaves Rd, Grandview MO 64030
Tel (816) 761-7476 *SIC* 3822 3446 3585

■ **HONEYWELL INC** p 705
115 Tabor Rd, Morris Plains NJ 07950
Tel (973) 455-2000
SIC 3823 3812 3669 3491 3699 3822

INDEL INC p 736
10 Indel Ave, Rancocas NJ 08073
Tel (609) 267-9000
SIC 3567 3548 3822 3541 3563

PII HOLDINGS INC p 1147
2150 Elmwood Ave, Buffalo NY 14207
Tel (716) 876-9951 *SIC* 3089 3822 6719

PROTECTIVE INDUSTRIES INC p 1185
2150 Elmwood Ave, Buffalo NY 14207
Tel (716) 876-9951 *SIC* 3089 3822

■ **BABCOCK & WILCOX CO** p 143
20 S Van Buren Ave, Barberton OH 44203
Tel (330) 753-4511
SIC 1629 1711 3443 7699 8741 3822

■ **THERM-O-DISC INC** p 1447
1320 S Main St, Mansfield OH 44907
Tel (419) 525-8500 *SIC* 3822 3823

HUNTER DEFENSE TECHNOLOGIES INC p 719
30500 Aurora Rd Ste 100, Solon OH 44139
Tel (216) 438-6111
SIC 3433 3569 3822 8331 8711 3549

PEPPERL + FUCHS INC p 1134
1600 Enterprise Pkwy, Twinsburg OH 44087
Tel (330) 425-3555
SIC 5065 3625 3822 3674

MATHENA INC p 919
3900 S Hwy 81 Service Rd, El Reno OK 73036
Tel (405) 422-3600 *SIC* 3699 3822

▲ **LSB INDUSTRIES INC** p 883
16 S Pennsylvania Ave, Oklahoma City OK 73107
Tel (405) 235-4546
SIC 3822 3585 3567 2873

■ **PECO INC** p 1127
11241 Se Highway 212, Clackamas OR 97015
Tel (503) 233-6401
SIC 3089 3822 3364 3363

FIRST QUALITY RETAIL SERVICES LLC p 549
601 Allendale Rd, King Of Prussia PA 19406
Tel (610) 265-5000 *SIC* 3822

TACO INC p 1421
1160 Cranston St, Cranston RI 02920
Tel (401) 942-8000
SIC 3433 3561 3443 3822

AMTROL HOLDINGS INC p 87
1400 Division Rd, West Warwick RI 02893
Tel (401) 884-6300 *SIC* 3822 3585 3443

KELE INC p 808
3300 Brother Blvd, Memphis TN 38133
Tel (901) 382-6084 *SIC* 5075 3822 3829

FLARE INDUSTRIES LLC p 554
16310 Bratton Ln Ste 350, Austin TX 78728
Tel (512) 836-9473
SIC 3822 7359 3694 2899 1711 3569

SCHNEIDER ELECTRIC BUILDINGS AMERICAS INC p 1287
1650 W Crosby Rd, Carrollton TX 75006
Tel (972) 323-1111 *SIC* 3822 1731

PURVIS INDUSTRIES LTD p 1193
10500 N Stemmons Fwy, Dallas TX 75220
Tel (214) 358-5500 *SIC* 5013 5085 3822

▲ **TEXAS INSTRUMENTS INC** p 1443
12500 Ti Blvd, Dallas TX 75243
Tel (214) 479-3773
SIC 3674 3613 3822 3578

INVENSYS PROCESSS SYSTEMS INC p 761
10900 Equity Dr, Houston TX 77041
Tel (713) 329-1600 *SIC* 3822

APX GROUP HOLDINGS INC p 101
4931 N 300 W, Provo UT 84604
Tel (801) 377-9111
SIC 7382 5065 3822 1711

APX GROUP INC p 101
4931 N 300 W, Provo UT 84604
Tel (801) 377-9111
SIC 8711 3822 1711 5065

APX PARENT HOLDCO INC p 101
4931 N 300 W, Provo UT 84604
Tel (801) 377-9111
SIC 6719 3822 1711 8711 5065 5074

VIVINT INC p 1563
4931 N 300 W, Provo UT 84604
Tel (801) 705-6253 *SIC* 3822

ELECTRO-MECHANICAL CORP p 485
329 Williams St, Bristol VA 24201
Tel (276) 669-9428
SIC 3612 5063 3829 3822 3613 3354

■ **MEGTEC SYSTEMS INC** p 940
830 Prosper St, De Pere WI 54115
Tel (920) 336-5715
SIC 3822 3555 3567 3823

JOHNSON CONTROLS INC p 791
5757 N Green Bay Ave, Milwaukee WI 53209
Tel (414) 524-1200
SIC 2531 3714 3691 3822 8744

CARNES CO INC p 258
600 College Ave, Pewaukee WI 53072
Tel (262) 691-9900
SIC 3822 3444 3585 3669

SIC 3823 Indl Instruments For Meas, Display & Control

SYNCRO CORP p 1415
1030 Sundown Dr Nw, Arab AL 35016
Tel (256) 586-6045
SIC 3714 3625 3694 3823 3643

■ **SEMICONDUCTOR COMPONENTS INDUSTRIES LLC** p 1302
5005 E Mcdowell Rd, Phoenix AZ 85008
Tel (602) 244-6600 *SIC* 3674 3823

■ **ABBOTT DIABETES CARE INC** p 9
1360 S Loop Rd, Alameda CA 94502
Tel (510) 749-5400 *SIC* 2835 3845 3823

■ **TELEDYNE INSTRUMENTS INC** p 1434
16830 Chestnut St, City Of Industry CA 91748
Tel (626) 961-9221 *SIC* 3829 3823

■ **ULTRA CLEAN TECHNOLOGY SYSTEMS AND SERVICE INC** p 1501
26462 Corporate Ave, Hayward CA 94545
Tel (510) 576-4400 *SIC* 3823

TOPCON POSITIONING SYSTEMS INC p 1461
7400 National Dr, Livermore CA 94550
Tel (925) 245-8300
SIC 3829 3625 3823 3699 8713 1794

■ **IDEX HEALTH & SCIENCE LLC** p 729
600 Park Ct, Rohnert Park CA 94928
Tel (707) 588-2000
SIC 3821 3829 3826 3823 3494

▲ **HARMONIC INC** p 662
4300 N 1st St, San Jose CA 95134
Tel (408) 542-2500 *SIC* 3663 3823

■ **THERMOQUEST CORP** p 1447
355 River Oaks Pkwy, San Jose CA 95134
Tel (408) 965-6000 *SIC* 3826 3823

ALTA PROPERTIES INC p 61
879 Ward Dr, Santa Barbara CA 93111
Tel (805) 967-0171
SIC 3264 3699 3823 3679

LUMASENSE TECHNOLOGIES INC p 885
3301 Leonard Ct, Santa Clara CA 95054
Tel (408) 727-1600
SIC 3823 3845 3829 3825

PACIFIC SCIENTIFIC CO INC p 1105
1785 Voyager Ave Ste 101, Simi Valley CA 93063
Tel (805) 526-5700
SIC 3812 3669 3621 3694 3823 3625

KAVLICO CORP p 805
1461 Lawrence Dr, Thousand Oaks CA 91320
Tel (805) 523-2000 *SIC* 3679 3829 3823

■ **TRIUMPH ACTUATION SYSTEMS - VALENCIA INC** p 1483
28150 Harrison Pkwy, Valencia CA 91355
Tel (661) 295-1015 *SIC* 3823

BSI HOLDINGS INC p 222
2495 Uravan St, Aurora CO 80011
Tel (303) 371-2200
SIC 6719 3589 5093 3715 3823 5051

▲ **MESA LABORATORIES INC** p 951
12100 W 6th Ave, Lakewood CO 80228
Tel (303) 987-8000 *SIC* 3823 3841

■ **HACH CO** p 652
5600 Lindbergh Dr, Loveland CO 80538
Tel (970) 669-3050
SIC 3826 3823 3231 2819 2869

DRS CONSOLIDATED CONTROLS INC p 457
21 South St, Danbury CT 06810
Tel (203) 798-3000 *SIC* 3823

OMEGA ENGINEERING INC p 1084
800 Connecticut Ave 5n01, Norwalk CT 06854
Tel (203) 359-1660
SIC 3823 3575 3577 3433 3826 2759

ASHCROFT INC p 117
250 E Main St, Stratford CT 06614
Tel (203) 378-8281
SIC 3823 3679 3663 3625

ASHCROFT-NAGANO KEIKI HOLDINGS INC p 117
250 E Main St, Stratford CT 06614
Tel (203) 378-8281
SIC 3823 3679 3663 3625

■ **BRISTOL INC** p 214
1100 Buckingham St, Watertown CT 06795
Tel (860) 945-2200 *SIC* 3823

■ **VEEDER-ROOT CO** p 1546
125 Powder Forest Dr, Weatogue CT 06089
Tel (860) 651-2700 *SIC* 3823 3824

LEE CO p 851
2 Pettipaug Rd, Westbrook CT 06498
Tel (860) 399-6281
SIC 3823 3841 3812 3728 3714

■ **ALSTOM POWER INC** p 61
200 Great Pond Dr, Windsor CT 06095
Tel (866) 257-8664
SIC 3443 3564 3621 3823 8711

■ **HAMILTON SUNDSTRAND CORP** p 655
1 Hamilton Rd, Windsor Locks CT 06096
Tel (860) 654-6000
SIC 3621 3594 3728 3625 3823 3822

■ **EECO INC** p 480
850 Library Ave Ste 204c, Newark DE 19711
Tel (302) 456-1448
SIC 3823 3491 3621 3585 3546 3679

■ **AMERICAN METER HOLDINGS CORP** p 76
1105 N Market St Ste 1300, Wilmington DE 19801
Tel (302) 477-0208 *SIC* 3824 3823

■ **DELAWARE CAPITAL FORMATION INC** p 423
501 Silverside Rd Ste 5, Wilmington DE 19809
Tel (302) 793-4921
SIC 5084 3463 3542 3823

■ **K-TRON INVESTMENT CO** p 799
300 Delaware Ave Ste 900, Wilmington DE 19801
Tel (856) 589-0500 *SIC* 3823

▲ **DANAHER CORP** p 411
2200 Penn Ave Nw Ste 800w, Washington DC 20037
Tel (202) 828-0850
SIC 3845 3829 3577 3823 3843

■ **POTOMAC HOLDING LLC** p 1164
2200 Penn Ave Nw Ste 800w, Washington DC 20037
Tel (202) 828-0850 *SIC* 3823

▲ **ROPER TECHNOLOGIES INC** p 1250
6901 Prof Pkwy E Ste 200, Sarasota FL 34240
Tel (941) 556-2601
SIC 3823 3563 3491 3826 3829

■ **MUELLER GROUP LLC** p 998
1200 Abernathy Rd, Atlanta GA 30328
Tel (770) 206-4200
SIC 3823 3321 3533 7699

▲ **MUELLER WATER PRODUCTS INC** p 998
1200 Abernathy Rd # 1200, Atlanta GA 30328
Tel (770) 206-4200
SIC 3491 3492 3494 3443 3321 3823

■ **ROPER PUMP CO** p 1250
3475 Old Maysville Rd, Commerce GA 30529
Tel (706) 336-3459 *SIC* 3823 3561

WIKA HOLDING L P p 1608
1000 Wiegand Blvd, Lawrenceville GA 30043
Tel (770) 513-8200 *SIC* 3823

WIKA INSTRUMENT LP p 1608
1000 Wiegand Blvd, Lawrenceville GA 30043
Tel (770) 513-8200 *SIC* 3053 3823

MAGNETROL INTERNATIONAL INC p 896
705 Enterprise St, Aurora IL 60504
Tel (630) 723-6600
SIC 3823 3699 3643 3625 3541

■ **UOP LLC** p 1528
25 E Algonquin Rd, Des Plaines IL 60016
Tel (847) 391-2000
SIC 2819 8711 8731 8999 3823 3479

ROBERTSHAW CONTROLS CO p 1242
1222 Hamilton Pkwy, Itasca IL 60143
Tel (630) 260-3400 *SIC* 3823 3822 3492

■ **ATLAS MATERIAL TESTING TECHNOLOGY LLC** p 128
1500 Bishop Ct, Mount Prospect IL 60056
Tel (773) 327-4520
SIC 3823 3569 3599 8734 3825 3821

■ **ECLIPSE INC** p 475
1665 Elmwood Rd, Rockford IL 61103
Tel (815) 877-3031
SIC 3564 3433 3822 3823 3443 3494

SCHNEIDER ELECTRIC BUILDINGS LLC p 1287
839 N Perryville Rd, Rockford IL 61107
Tel (815) 381-5000
SIC 3822 1711 3625 3823 3621

AEC INC p 28
1100 E Wdfield Rd Ste 588, Schaumburg IL 60173
Tel (847) 273-7700
SIC 3585 3823 3559 3443 3535

SCHNEIDER ELECTRIC HOLDINGS INC p 1287
200 N Martingale Rd # 100, Schaumburg IL 60173
Tel (717) 944-5460
SIC 3822 1711 3625 3823 3621

STERLING PRODUCTS INC p 1387
1100 E Woodfield Rd # 550, Schaumburg IL 60173
Tel (847) 273-7700 *SIC* 3559 3823 3542

YASKAWA AMERICA INC p 1635
2121 Norman Dr, Waukegan IL 60085
Tel (847) 887-7000
SIC 3621 7694 5063 3566 3823 3625

ENDRESS + HAUSER FLOWTEC AG INC p 496
2330 Endress Pl, Greenwood IN 46143
Tel (317) 535-7138 *SIC* 3823

▲ **HURCO COMPANIES INC** p 721
1 Technology Way, Indianapolis IN 46268
Tel (317) 293-5309 *SIC* 3823 7372

DWYER INSTRUMENTS INC p 464
102 Indiana Highway 212, Michigan City IN 46360
Tel (219) 879-8868
SIC 3823 3824 3822 3829 3491 3625

■ **FISHER CONTROLS INTERNATIONAL LLC** p 552
205 S Center St, Marshalltown IA 50158
Tel (641) 754-3011
SIC 3491 3823 3625 3612 3494

RA JONES & CO p 1203
2701 Crescent Springs Rd, Covington KY 41017
Tel (859) 341-0400 *SIC* 3565 3823

DOMETIC CORP p 448
13551 Triton Park Blvd # 1000, Louisville KY 40223
Tel (502) 873-3524
SIC 3089 3443 3444 3822 3823 3999

REV-A-SHELF CO LLC p 1229
12400 Earl Jones Way, Louisville KY 40299
Tel (502) 499-5835 *SIC* 3823 5063

ORION INSTRUMENTS LLC p 1095
2105 Oak Villa Blvd, Baton Rouge LA 70815
Tel (225) 906-2343 *SIC* 3823

SMITHS DETECTION INC p 1334
2202 Lakeside Blvd, Edgewood MD 21040
Tel (410) 510-9100
SIC 3824 3823 3829 8731

■ **OAO CORP** p 1071
700 N Frederick Ave, Gaithersburg MD 20879
Tel (301) 240-7000
SIC 7371 8711 3823 3559

▲ **MKS INSTRUMENTS INC** p 979
2 Tech Dr Ste 201, Andover MA 01810
Tel (978) 645-5500 *SIC* 3823 3491 3494

SCHNEIDER ELECTRIC USA INC p 1288
800 Federal St, Andover MA 01810
Tel (978) 975-9600
SIC 3613 3643 3612 3823 3625 5063

■ **KIDDE-FENWAL INC** p 817
400 Main St, Ashland MA 01721
Tel (508) 881-2000
SIC 3669 3823 3825 3822 3643 3625

▲ **L S STARRETT CO** p 834
121 Crescent St, Athol MA 01331
Tel (978) 249-3551
SIC 3545 3423 3999 3425 3823

■ **SENSITECH INC** p 1305
800 Cummings Ctr Ste 258x, Beverly MA 01915
Tel (978) 927-7033 *SIC* 3826 3823 3822

■ **GE INFRASTRUCTURE SENSING INC** p 596
1100 Technology Park Dr # 100, Billerica MA 01821
Tel (978) 437-1000
SIC 3823 5084 3699 3674 3663 3625

ORBOTECH INC p 1093
44 Manning Rd, Billerica MA 01821
Tel (978) 667-6037 *SIC* 5065 3823 3674

■ **GE IONICS INC** p 596
3 Burlington Woods Dr # 200, Burlington MA 01803
Tel (781) 359-7000
SIC 3589 2086 4941 3559 2899 3823

▲ **BROOKS AUTOMATION INC** p 218
15 Elizabeth Dr, Chelmsford MA 01824
Tel (978) 262-2400
SIC 3559 3563 3823 7699

■ **THERMO OPTEK CORP** p 1447
27 Forge Pkwy, Franklin MA 02038
Tel (508) 553-5100 *SIC* 3823

▲ **COGNEX CORP** p 334
1 Vision Dr, Natick MA 01760
Tel (508) 650-3000 *SIC* 3823

MATHWORKS INC p 920
3 Apple Hill Dr, Natick MA 01760
Tel (508) 647-7000 *SIC* 7371 3823 8222

▲ **THERMO FISHER SCIENTIFIC INC** p 1447
168 3rd Ave, Waltham MA 02451
Tel (781) 622-1000
SIC 3826 3845 3823 3629

▲ **RUDOLPH TECHNOLOGIES INC** p 1257
16 Jonspin Rd, Wilmington MA 01887
Tel (973) 691-1300 *SIC* 3823 3827

HINES CORP p 695
1218 E Pontaluna Rd Ste B, Norton Shores MI 49456
Tel (231) 799-6240
SIC 3443 3823 3589 3531 3535 5082

LECO CORP p 851
3000 Lakeview Ave, Saint Joseph MI 49085
Tel (269) 983-5531
SIC 4493 3821 3826 3825 3823 3264

HOWARD MILLER CO p 713
860 E Main Ave, Zeeland MI 49464
Tel (616) 772-9131 *SIC* 3873 3829 3823

■ **ROSEMOUNT INC** p 1251
8200 Market Blvd, Chanhassen MN 55317
Tel (952) 906-8888
SIC 3823 3824 3545 5084 3829

OSMONICS INC p 1097
5951 Clearwater Dr, Hopkins MN 55343
Tel (952) 933-2277
SIC 3569 3589 3561 3824 3823 3089

▲ **GRACO INC** p 628
88 11th Ave Ne, Minneapolis MN 55413
Tel (612) 623-6000
SIC 3561 3594 3563 3491 3823 3569

MINCO PRODUCTS INC p 972
7300 Commerce Ln Ne, Minneapolis MN 55432
Tel (763) 571-3121 *SIC* 3672 3823 3829

TSI INC p 1489
500 Cardigan Rd, Saint Paul MN 55126
Tel (651) 483-0900
SIC 3579 3829 3823 3845 3825

▲ **EMERSON ELECTRIC CO** p 492
8000 W Florissant Ave, Saint Louis MO 63136
Tel (314) 553-2000
SIC 3823 3491 3621 3585 3679

■ **EMERSUB 14 LLC** p 492
8000 W Florissant Ave, Saint Louis MO 63136
Tel (314) 553-2000 *SIC* 3823

HARBOUR GROUP LTD p 660
7701 Forsyth Blvd Ste 600, Saint Louis MO 63105
Tel (314) 727-5550 *SIC* 3823

■ **TELEDYNE ISCO INC** p 1434
4700 Superior St, Lincoln NE 68504
Tel (402) 464-0231 *SIC* 3823 3826

LINDE LLC p 868
200 Somerset Corporate Bl, Bridgewater NJ 08807
Tel (908) 464-8100
SIC 2813 3569 3561 3823

LINDE NORTH AMERICA INC p 868
200 Somerset Corporate Bl, Bridgewater NJ 08807
Tel (908) 464-8100
SIC 2813 3569 3559 3561 3511 3823

■ **HONEYWELL INC** p 705
115 Tabor Rd, Morris Plains NJ 07950
Tel (973) 455-2000
SIC 3823 3812 3669 3491 3699 3822

BOC GROUP INC p 196
575 Mountain Ave, New Providence NJ 07974
Tel (908) 665-2400
SIC 2813 3569 3559 3561 3511 3823

ROXBORO HOLDINGS INC p 1254
1501 State Route 34, Wall Township NJ 07727
Tel (732) 919-3119
SIC 3643 3679 3993 3823 3674

■ **PCB GROUP INC** p 1123
3425 Walden Ave, Depew NY 14043
Tel (716) 684-0001 *SIC* 3679 3823

INFICON INC p 740
2 Technology Pl, East Syracuse NY 13057
Tel (315) 434-1149 *SIC* 3823 3812

HILLIARD CORP p 693
100 W 4th St, Elmira NY 14901
Tel (607) 733-7121 *SIC* 3564 3569 3823

BOSCH SECURITY SYSTEMS INC p 202
130 Perinton Pkwy, Fairport NY 14450
Tel (585) 223-4060
SIC 3669 3699 3826 3825 3823 3625

BLUETEE CORP p 192
387 Park Ave S Fl 5, New York NY 10016
Tel (212) 598-0880
SIC 3533 3589 5093 3715 3823 5051

EWT HOLDINGS III CORP p 516
666 5th Ave Fl 36, New York NY 10103
Tel (212) 644-5900
SIC 3589 3823 3826 4941 5051

TOSHIBA NUCLEAR ENERGY HOLDINGS (US) INC p 1462
1251 Ave Of Amrcs 400 Ste 4100, New York NY 10020
Tel (212) 596-0600
SIC 8711 3829 3823 2819

▲ **ITT INC** p 768
1133 Westchester Ave N-100, White Plains NY 10604
Tel (914) 641-2000
SIC 3594 3625 3823 3812

■ **ITT LLC** p 768
1133 Westchester Ave N-100, White Plains NY 10604
Tel (914) 641-2000
SIC 3594 3625 3823 3812

AREVA INC p 107
7207 Ibm Dr, Charlotte NC 28262
Tel (704) 805-2000
SIC 3823 3829 8711 5085 3561 2819

AC CORP p 13
301 Creek Ridge Rd, Greensboro NC 27406
Tel (336) 273-4472
SIC 1711 1731 3556 3823 3625 3535

VEGA AMERICAS INC p 1546
4170 Rosslyn Dr Ste A, Cincinnati OH 45209
Tel (513) 272-0131 SIC 3823

▲ METTLER-TOLEDO INTERNATIONAL INC p 957
1900 Polaris Pkwy Fl 6, Columbus OH 43240
Tel (614) 438-4511
SIC 3596 3821 3826 3823

■ METTLER-TOLEDO LLC p 957
1900 Polaris Pkwy Fl 6, Columbus OH 43240
Tel (614) 438-4511
SIC 3596 5049 7699 3821 3823 3826

■ THERM-O-DISC INC p 1447
1320 S Main St, Mansfield OH 44907
Tel (419) 525-8500 SIC 3822 3823

■ L-3 COMMUNICATIONS CINCINNATI ELECTRONICS CORP p 834
7500 Innovation Way, Mason OH 45040
Tel (513) 573-6100 SIC 3812 3769 3823

SHELBURNE CORP p 1314
20001 Shelburne Rd, Shaker Heights OH 44118
Tel (216) 321-9177
SIC 3443 3823 3544 3769

■ KEITHLEY INSTRUMENTS INC p 808
28775 Aurora Rd, Solon OH 44139
Tel (440) 248-0400 SIC 3825 3823 7371

FKI INDUSTRIES INC p 554
2801 Dawson Rd, Tulsa OK 74110
Tel (918) 834-4611
SIC 3429 3536 3535 3496 3569 3823

JOHN ZINK CO LLC p 790
11920 E Apache St, Tulsa OK 74116
Tel (918) 234-1800 SIC 3823

▲ AMETEK INC p 84
1100 Cassatt Rd, Berwyn PA 19312
Tel (610) 647-2121
SIC 3621 3823 3824 3825

■ MINE SAFETY APPLIANCES CO LLC p 973
1000 Cranberry Woods Dr, Cranberry Township PA 16066
Tel (724) 776-8600
SIC 3842 3826 3823 3648 3829

▲ MSA SAFETY INC p 996
1000 Cranberry Woods Dr, Cranberry Township PA 16066
Tel (724) 776-8600
SIC 3842 3826 3823 3648 3829

TSB NUCLEAR ENERGY USA GROUP INC p 1489
1000 Westinghouse Dr, Cranberry Township PA 16066
Tel (412) 374-4111 SIC 3823 3559

WESTINGHOUSE ELECTRIC CO LLC p 1601
1000 Westinghouse Dr, Cranberry Township PA 16066
Tel (412) 374-2020
SIC 3829 8711 3823 2819

OERLIKON USA HOLDING INC p 1075
5700 Mellon Rd, Export PA 15632
Tel (303) 273-9700
SIC 3563 3823 3699 3479 3599 5084

■ GE INFRASTRUCTURE SENSING p 596
4636 Somerton Rd, Feasterville Trevose PA 19053
Tel (617) 926-1749
SIC 3589 2086 4941 3559 2899 3823

▲ VISHAY PRECISION GROUP INC p 1561
3 Great Valley Pkwy # 150, Malvern PA 19355
Tel (484) 321-5300 SIC 3676 3823

BOMBARDIER TRANSPORTATION (HOLDINGS) USA INC p 199
1501 Lebanon Church Rd, Pittsburgh PA 15236
Tel (412) 655-5700 SIC 3743 3315 3823

■ EMERSON PROCESS MANAGEMENT POWER & WATER SOLUTIONS INC p 492
200 Beta Dr, Pittsburgh PA 15238
Tel (412) 963-4000 SIC 3823 5063

■ AMPHENOL THERMOMETRICS INC p 86
967 Windfall Rd, Saint Marys PA 15857
Tel (814) 834-9140 SIC 3823

▲ ENVIRONMENTAL TECTONICS CORP p 503
125 James Way, Southampton PA 18966
Tel (215) 355-9100
SIC 3728 3842 3826 3823 3841

■ GE BETZ INC p 595
4636 Somerton Rd, Trevose PA 19053
Tel (215) 355-3300
SIC 2899 3826 5084 3823

EVOQUA WATER TECHNOLOGIES LLC p 516
181 Thorn Hill Rd, Warrendale PA 15086
Tel (724) 772-0044
SIC 3589 3569 3823 3826 4941

■ KIDDE FIRE PROTECTION INC p 817
350 E Union St, West Chester PA 19382
Tel (610) 363-1400 SIC 3669 3999 3823

HERAEUS ELECTRO-NITE CO LLC p 685
770 Township Line Rd # 300, Yardley PA 19067
Tel (215) 944-9000 SIC 3812 3823

HERAEUS INC HIC p 685
770 Township Line Rd, Yardley PA 19067
Tel (212) 752-2180
SIC 3399 3823 3339 3469

HEXAGON METROLOGY INC p 688
250 Circuit Dr, North Kingstown RI 02852
Tel (401) 886-2000 SIC 3823 3545

■ ITRON ELECTRICITY METERING INC p 768
313 N Highway 11, West Union SC 29696
Tel (864) 638-8300
SIC 3825 3823 3824 3679 3829 3612

▲ RAVEN INDUSTRIES INC p 1209
205 E 6th St, Sioux Falls SD 57104
Tel (605) 336-2750
SIC 5065 3523 3081 3823 3083

■ MUELLER CO LLC p 998
633 Chestnut St Ste 1200, Chattanooga TN 37450
Tel (423) 209-4800 SIC 3823 3533 7699

■ POLLOK INC p 1160
6 Butterfield Trail Blvd, El Paso TX 79906
Tel (915) 592-5700
SIC 5065 3823 3714 3545

CAMERON CO p 245
4646 W Sam Houston Pkwy N, Houston TX 77041
Tel (713) 513-3300 SIC 3823

■ DANIEL INDUSTRIES INC p 411
11100 Brittmoore Park Dr, Houston TX 77041
Tel (713) 467-6000
SIC 3823 3824 3494 3829 3826 3571

■ DANIEL MEASUREMENT AND CONTROL INC p 411
11100 Brittmoore Park Dr, Houston TX 77041
Tel (713) 467-6000
SIC 3823 3498 3499 3823 3571 3491

INVENSYS SYSTEMS INC p 761
10900 Equity Dr, Houston TX 77041
Tel (713) 329-1600 SIC 3823 8711 8741

▲ POWELL INDUSTRIES INC p 1165
8550 Mosley Rd, Houston TX 77075
Tel (713) 944-6900
SIC 3812 3613 3625 3643 3823

SCHLUMBERGER LIMITED p 1287
5599 San Felipe St Fl 17, Houston TX 77056
Tel (713) 513-2000
SIC 1381 1389 1382 3825 3824 3823

■ PECOFACET (US) INC p 1127
118 Washington Ave, Mineral Wells TX 76067
Tel (940) 325-2575 SIC 3823 5082

LUDLUM MEASUREMENTS INC p 884
501 Oak St, Sweetwater TX 79556
Tel (325) 235-5494
SIC 3829 3826 3824 3823

■ ROBBINS & MYERS INC p 1241
10586 N Highway 75, Willis TX 77378
Tel (936) 890-1064
SIC 3533 3443 3823 5084

EXELIS INC p 518
2235 Monroe St, Herndon VA 20171
Tel (703) 790-6300 SIC 3669 3823 3812

■ FLUKE CORP p 561
6920 Seaway Blvd, Everett WA 98203
Tel (425) 446-5400 SIC 3823 5065 7629

■ FLUKE ELECTRONICS CORP p 561
6920 Seaway Blvd, Everett WA 98203
Tel (425) 446-5610 SIC 3825 3823

▲ FORTIVE CORP p 570
6920 Seaway Blvd, Everett WA 98203
Tel (425) 446-5000 SIC 3823

■ MEGTEC SYSTEMS INC p 940
830 Prosper St, De Pere WI 54115
Tel (920) 336-5715
SIC 3822 3555 3567 3823

▲ BADGER METER INC p 144
4545 W Brown Deer Rd, Milwaukee WI 53223
Tel (414) 355-0400 SIC 3824 3491 3823

STERLING INC p 1387
2900 S 160th St, New Berlin WI 53151
Tel (414) 354-0970 SIC 3823 3542 3559

TOTAL MECHANICAL INC p 1463
W234n2830 Paul Rd, Pewaukee WI 53072
Tel (262) 523-2510 SIC 1711 1791 3823

VENTUREDYNE LTD p 1548
600 College Ave, Pewaukee WI 53072
Tel (262) 691-9900
SIC 3568 3829 3826 3823 3625

SIC 3824 Fluid Meters & Counters

MID-SOUTH INDUSTRIES INC p 963
2620 E Meighan Blvd, Gadsden AL 35903
Tel (256) 492-8997
SIC 3672 3089 3824 3714

■ NEPTUNE TECHNOLOGY GROUP INC p 1026
1600 Al Highway 229 S, Tallassee AL 36078
Tel (334) 283-6555 SIC 3824

■ MICRO MOTION INC p 961
7070 Winchester Cir, Boulder CO 80301
Tel (303) 530-8400 SIC 3824 5084

■ GEMS SENSORS INC p 598
1 Cowles Rd, Plainville CT 06062
Tel (860) 747-3000
SIC 3824 5084 3812 3625 3613

■ VEEDER-ROOT CO p 1546
125 Powder Forest Dr, Weatogue CT 06089
Tel (860) 651-2700 SIC 3823 3824

■ AMERICAN METER HOLDINGS CORP p 76
1105 N Market St Ste 1300, Wilmington DE 19801
Tel (302) 477-0208 SIC 3824 3823

AVG ADVANCED TECHNOLOGIES LP p 137
343 Saint Paul Blvd, Carol Stream IL 60188
Tel (630) 668-3900
SIC 3672 3661 3824 3822 3625

■ DYNAPAR CORP p 464
1675 N Delany Rd, Gurnee IL 60031
Tel (847) 662-2666 SIC 3824

DWYER INSTRUMENTS INC p 464
102 Indiana Highway 212, Michigan City IN 46360
Tel (219) 879-8868
SIC 3823 3824 3822 3829 3491 3625

SMITHS DETECTION INC p 1334
2202 Lakeside Blvd, Edgewood MD 21040
Tel (410) 510-9100
SIC 3824 3823 3829 8731

PRESTOLITE ELECTRIC LLC p 1173
30120 Hudson Dr, Novi MI 48377
Tel (248) 313-3807
SIC 3643 3824 3621 3625 3694

■ ROSEMOUNT INC p 1251
8200 Market Blvd, Chanhassen MN 55317
Tel (952) 906-8888
SIC 3823 3824 3545 5084 3829

OSMONICS INC p 1097
5951 Clearwater Dr, Hopkins MN 55343
Tel (952) 933-2277
SIC 3569 3589 3561 3824 3823 3089

CHURCHILL COMPANIES p 305
333 S 7th St Ste 3100, Minneapolis MN 55402
Tel (612) 673-6700 SIC 3211 3824 5083

ACLARA TECHNOLOGIES LLC p 17
945 Hornet Dr, Hazelwood MO 63042
Tel (314) 895-6400
SIC 3824 3825 3829 7371 7373

METER READINGS HOLDING LLC p 953
945 Hornet Dr, Hazelwood MO 63042
Tel (561) 394-0550
SIC 3824 3825 3829 7371 7373

■ EMERSON ELECTRIC (US) HOLDING CORP p 492
850 Library Ave Ste 204c, Saint Louis MO 63136
Tel (314) 553-2000 SIC 3824

PEMBERTON FABRICATORS INC p 1128
30 Indel Ave, Rancocas NJ 08073
Tel (609) 267-0922 SIC 3444 3824

CURTIS INSTRUMENTS INC p 402
200 Kisco Ave, Mount Kisco NY 10549
Tel (914) 666-2971 SIC 3825 3824 3629

DESIGNATRONICS INC p 432
2101 Jericho Tpke Ste 1, New Hyde Park NY 11040
Tel (516) 328-3300
SIC 3824 3559 3545 3625 3462

■ ELSTER AMERICAN METER CO LLC p 489
208 S Rogers Ln, Raleigh NC 27610
Tel (800) 257-9754 SIC 3824 3613

SENSUS (BERMUDA 2) LTD p 1305
8601 Six Forks Rd, Raleigh NC 27615
Tel (919) 845-4000 SIC 3824 3363 3491

SENSUS USA INC p 1305
8601 Six Forks Rd Ste 700, Raleigh NC 27615
Tel (919) 845-4000
SIC 3824 3363 2891 3491

■ PCC STRUCTURALS INC p 1123
4600 Se Harney Dr, Portland OR 97206
Tel (503) 777-3881
SIC 3728 3842 3511 3824

▲ CUI GLOBAL INC p 400
20050 Sw 112th Ave, Tualatin OR 97062
Tel (503) 612-2300 SIC 3824 8711

▲ AMETEK INC p 84
1100 Cassatt Rd, Berwyn PA 19312
Tel (610) 647-2121
SIC 3621 3823 3824 3825

SENSUS METERING SYSTEMS-NORTH AMERICA INC p 1305
450 N Gallatin Ave, Uniontown PA 15401
Tel (724) 439-7700 SIC 3824

■ ITRON ELECTRICITY METERING INC p 768
313 N Highway 11, West Union SC 29696
Tel (864) 638-8300
SIC 3825 3823 3824 3679 3829 3612

■ DANIEL INDUSTRIES INC p 411
11100 Brittmoore Park Dr, Houston TX 77041
Tel (713) 467-6000
SIC 3823 3824 3494 3829 3826 3571

■ DANIEL MEASUREMENT AND CONTROL INC p 411
11100 Brittmoore Park Dr, Houston TX 77041
Tel (713) 467-6000
SIC 3824 3498 3499 3823 3571 3491

SCHLUMBERGER LIMITED p 1287
5599 San Felipe St Fl 17, Houston TX 77056
Tel (713) 513-2000
SIC 1381 1389 1382 3825 3824 3823

SCHLUMBERGER TECHNOLOGY CORP p 1287
100 Gillingham Ln, Sugar Land TX 77478
Tel (281) 285-8500
SIC 1382 1389 3825 3824 3533 3586

LUDLUM MEASUREMENTS INC p 884
501 Oak St, Sweetwater TX 79556
Tel (325) 235-5494
SIC 3829 3826 3824 3823

■ ELDEC CORP p 484
16700 13th Ave W, Lynnwood WA 98037
Tel (425) 743-8362
SIC 3812 3728 3824 3769 3674 3613

▲ BADGER METER INC p 144
4545 W Brown Deer Rd, Milwaukee WI 53223
Tel (414) 355-0400 SIC 3824 3491 3823

SIC 3825 Instrs For Measuring & Testing Electricity

▲ ON SEMICONDUCTOR CORP p 1086
5005 E Mcdowell Rd, Phoenix AZ 85008
Tel (602) 244-6600 SIC 3674 3825 3651

▲ AMKOR TECHNOLOGY INC p 85
2045 E Innovation Cir, Tempe AZ 85284
Tel (480) 821-5000 SIC 3674 3825

SV PROBE INC p 1410
9185 S Farmer Ave Ste 105, Tempe AZ 85284
Tel (480) 635-4700 SIC 3825

■ INTERSTATE ELECTRONICS CORP p 758
602 E Vermont Ave, Anaheim CA 92805
Tel (714) 758-0500 SIC 3825 3812 3679

▲ IXIA p 769
26601 Agoura Rd, Calabasas CA 91302
Tel (818) 871-1800 SIC 3825 7371

SPIRENT COMMUNICATIONS INC p 1359
27349 Agoura Rd, Calabasas CA 91301
Tel (818) 676-2300 SIC 3663 3829 3825

GLENAIR INC p 615
1211 Air Way, Glendale CA 91201
Tel (818) 247-6000 SIC 3643 3825 3357

METRIC EQUIPMENT SALES INC p 954
25841 Industrial Blvd # 200, Hayward CA 94545
Tel (510) 264-0887
SIC 5065 5084 7359 3825

■ ASTRONICS TEST SYSTEMS INC p 122
4 Goodyear, Irvine CA 92618
Tel (800) 722-2528 SIC 3825

CYLANCE INC p 405
18201 Von Karman Ave # 700, Irvine CA 92612
Tel (949) 375-3380 SIC 3825 7379

HOYA HOLDINGS INC p 714
680 N Mccarthy Blvd # 120, Milpitas CA 95035
Tel (408) 654-2300 SIC 3861 3825 3827

▲ KLA-TENCOR CORP p 822
1 Technology Dr, Milpitas CA 95035
Tel (408) 875-3000
SIC 3827 3825 7699 7629

■ PERICOM SEMICONDUCTOR CORP p 1136
1545 Barber Ln, Milpitas CA 95035
Tel (408) 232-9100 SIC 3674 3825

ANRITSU CO p 92
490 Jarvis Dr, Morgan Hill CA 95037
Tel (408) 201-1551 SIC 5065 3825 3663

ANRITSU US HOLDING INC p 93
490 Jarvis Dr, Morgan Hill CA 95037
Tel (408) 778-2000 SIC 3825 3663 5065

CPI INTERNATIONAL INC p 387
811 Hansen Way, Palo Alto CA 94304
Tel (650) 846-2801
SIC 3671 3679 3699 3825

▲ COHU INC p 335
12367 Crosthwaite Cir, Poway CA 92064
Tel (858) 848-8100 SIC 3825 3663 3699

■ DELTA DESIGN INC p 426
12367 Crosthwaite Cir, Poway CA 92064
Tel (858) 848-8000 SIC 3569 3825 3674

BAE SYSTEMS NATIONAL SECURITY SOLUTIONS INC p 144
10920 Technology Pl, San Diego CA 92127
Tel (858) 592-5000 SIC 3825 7373 3812

FLEXTRONICS HOLDING USA INC p 556
2090 Fortune Dr, San Jose CA 95131
Tel (408) 576-7000
SIC 3672 3679 7371 3825

LUMILEDS LLC p 885
370 W Trimble Rd, San Jose CA 95131
Tel (408) 964-2900 SIC 3825

▲ AGILENT TECHNOLOGIES INC p 35
5301 Stevens Creek Blvd, Santa Clara CA 95051
Tel (408) 345-8886 SIC 3825 3826 7372

GLOBALFOUNDRIES US INC p 617
2600 Great America Way, Santa Clara CA 95054
Tel (408) 462-3900 SIC 3559 3825 5065

LUMASENSE TECHNOLOGIES INC p 885
3301 Leonard Ct, Santa Clara CA 95054
Tel (408) 727-1600
SIC 3823 3845 3829 3825

▲ KEYSIGHT TECHNOLOGIES INC p 815
1400 Fountaingrove Pkwy, Santa Rosa CA 95403
Tel (707) 577-5030 SIC 3825

■ MCDATA CORP p 927
4 Brocade Pkwy, Broomfield CO 80021
Tel (720) 558-8000
SIC 3679 5045 3825 3577

ALCOHOL MONITORING SYSTEMS INC p 47
1241 W Mineral Ave # 200, Littleton CO 80120
Tel (303) 785-7813 SIC 5169 3825

■ DICTAPHONE CORP p 438
3191 Broadbridge Ave, Stratford CT 06614
Tel (203) 381-7000
SIC 3579 3825 3695 3577

MC ASSEMBLY INTERNATIONAL LLC p 925
425 North Dr, Melbourne FL 32934
Tel (321) 253-0541 SIC 3825 1389

LANDIS+GYR INC p 842
30000 Mill Creek Ave, Alpharetta GA 30022
Tel (678) 258-1500 SIC 3825

■ SCIENTIFIC-ATLANTA LLC p 1292
5030 Sugarloaf Pkwy, Lawrenceville GA 30044
Tel (678) 277-1000
SIC 3663 3661 3577 3825

ARRIS TECHNOLOGY INC p 113
3871 Lakefield Dr, Suwanee GA 30024
Tel (678) 473-2907 SIC 7372 3825

▲ METHODE ELECTRONICS INC p 953
7401 W Wilson Ave, Chicago IL 60706
Tel (708) 867-6777
SIC 3678 3674 3676 3672 3825 3643

▲ SIGMATRON INTERNATIONAL INC p 1321
2201 Landmeier Rd, Elk Grove Village IL 60007
Tel (847) 956-8000
SIC 3672 3677 3679 3549 3825

■ ATLAS MATERIAL TESTING TECHNOLOGY LLC p 128
1500 Bishop Ct, Mount Prospect IL 60056
Tel (773) 327-4520
SIC 3823 3569 3599 8734 3825 3821

IDEAL INDUSTRIES INC p 729
1375 Park Ave, Sycamore IL 60178
Tel (815) 895-5181 SIC 3825 3643

■ INSTRUMENT & VALVE SERVICES CO p 747
205 S Center St, Marshalltown IA 50158
Tel (641) 754-3011 SIC 3494 3825 7699

■ ACTERNA LLC p 19
20250 Century Blvd # 100, Germantown MD 20874
Tel (301) 353-1550
SIC 3669 7379 3825 5065 3679 8734

■ JDSU ACTERNA HOLDINGS LLC p 781
1 Milestone Center Ct, Germantown MD 20876
Tel (240) 404-1550 SIC 3825

■ WABTEC RAILWAY ELECTRONICS INC p 1570
21200 Dorsey Mill Rd, Germantown MD 20876
Tel (301) 515-2000
SIC 3825 3679 3743 3672

■ KIDDE-FENWAL INC p 817
400 Main St, Ashland MA 01721
Tel (508) 881-2000
SIC 3669 3823 3825 3822 3643 3625

▲ TERADYNE INC p 1439
600 Riverpark Dr, North Reading MA 01864
Tel (978) 370-2700 SIC 3825 3643 3674

▲ XCERRA CORP p 1631
825 University Ave, Norwood MA 02062
Tel (781) 461-1000 SIC 3825 3429

▲ ANALOGIC CORP p 88
8 Centennial Dr, Peabody MA 01960
Tel (978) 326-4000 SIC 3825 3812

■ DOBLE ENGINEERING CO p 447
85 Walnut St, Watertown MA 02472
Tel (617) 926-4900
SIC 3825 7359 3829 3826

LECO CORP p 851
3000 Lakeview Ave, Saint Joseph MI 49085
Tel (269) 983-5531
SIC 4493 3821 3826 3825 3823 3264

SRG GLOBAL INC p 1363
800 Stephenson Hwy, Troy MI 48083
Tel (586) 757-7800
SIC 3089 3571 3494 2522 3826 3825

▲ MTS SYSTEMS CORP p 998
14000 Technology Dr, Eden Prairie MN 55344
Tel (952) 937-4000 SIC 3829 3825

CARL ZEISS INDUSTRIAL METROLOGY LLC p 256
6250 Sycamore Ln N, Maple Grove MN 55369
Tel (763) 533-9990 SIC 3545 3825

TSI INC p 1489
500 Cardigan Rd, Saint Paul MN 55126
Tel (651) 483-0900
SIC 3579 3829 3823 3845 3825

ACLARA TECHNOLOGIES LLC p 17
945 Hornet Dr, Hazelwood MO 63042
Tel (314) 895-6400
SIC 3824 3825 3829 7371 7373

METER READINGS HOLDING LLC p 953
945 Hornet Dr, Hazelwood MO 63042
Tel (561) 394-0550
SIC 3824 3825 3829 7371 7373

MILBANK MANUFACTURING CO p 968
4801 Deramus Ave, Kansas City MO 64120
Tel (816) 483-5314 SIC 3825 3444

■ ESCO TECHNOLOGIES HOLDING LLC p 509
9900 Clayton Rd Ste A, Saint Louis MO 63124
Tel (314) 213-7200
SIC 3825 3492 3812 3711 3663

▲ ESCO TECHNOLOGIES INC p 509
9900 Clayton Rd Ste A, Saint Louis MO 63124
Tel (314) 213-7200 SIC 3669 3569 3825

KEYENCE CORP OF AMERICA p 815
669 River Dr Ste 403, Elmwood Park NJ 07407
Tel (201) 930-0100 SIC 3825 5084 3674

▲ MISTRAS GROUP INC p 976
195 Clarksville Rd Ste 2, Princeton Junction NJ 08550
Tel (609) 716-4000
SIC 8711 7372 3829 3825

▲ ALLIED MOTION TECHNOLOGIES INC p 56
495 Commerce Dr Ste 3, Amherst NY 14228
Tel (716) 242-8634 SIC 3621 3825

■ TELEDYNE LECROY INC p 1434
700 Chestnut Ridge Rd, Chestnut Ridge NY 10977
Tel (845) 425-2000 SIC 3825 3829

INTERPLEX INDUSTRIES INC p 757
1434 110th St Ste 301, College Point NY 11356
Tel (718) 961-6212
SIC 3471 3825 3674 3469

BOSCH SECURITY SYSTEMS INC p 202
130 Perinton Pkwy, Fairport NY 14450
Tel (585) 223-4060
SIC 3669 3699 3826 3825 3823 3625

■ QUALITROL CO LLC p 1196
1385 Fairport Rd, Fairport NY 14450
Tel (586) 643-3717 SIC 3825

CURTIS INSTRUMENTS INC p 402
200 Kisco Ave, Mount Kisco NY 10549
Tel (914) 666-2971 SIC 3825 3824 3629

CLAYTON DUBILIER & RICE FUND V LIMITED PARTNERSHIP p 323
375 Park Ave Fl 18, New York NY 10152
Tel (212) 407-5200
SIC 3825 3661 3812 3577 3575 7372

▲ QORVO INC p 1195
7628 Thorndike Rd, Greensboro NC 27409
Tel (336) 664-1233 SIC 3825 3674

TEKELEC GLOBAL INC p 1433
5200 Paramount Pkwy, Morrisville NC 27560
Tel (919) 460-5500 SIC 3661 3825 7371

TITAN PRIVATE HOLDINGS I LLC p 1456
5200 Paramount Pkwy, Morrisville NC 27560
Tel (919) 460-5500 SIC 3661 3825 7371

■ ELSTER SOLUTIONS LLC p 489
208 S Rogers Ln, Raleigh NC 27610
Tel (919) 212-4800 SIC 3825

GOULD ELECTRONICS INC p 626
34929 Curtis Blvd Ste 100, Eastlake OH 44095
Tel (440) 953-5000
SIC 3825 3497 3613 3691 3674

DESCO CORP p 432
7795 Walton Pkwy Ste 175, New Albany OH 43054
Tel (614) 888-8855
SIC 3442 3825 3643 3531 3429

BIRD TECHNOLOGIES GROUP INC p 185
30303 Aurora Rd, Solon OH 44139
Tel (440) 248-1200 SIC 3825 3669

■ KEITHLEY INSTRUMENTS INC p 808
28775 Aurora Rd, Solon OH 44139
Tel (440) 248-0400 SIC 3825 3823 7371

TTI FLOOR CARE NORTH AMERICA INC p 1489
7005 Cochran Rd, Solon OH 44139
Tel (440) 996-2000 SIC 5072 3825

SOUTHWEST ELECTRIC CO p 1351
6503 Se 74th St, Oklahoma City OK 73135
Tel (800) 364-4445 SIC 3825 3612

■ CASCADE MICROTECH INC p 262
9100 Sw Gemini Dr, Beaverton OR 97008
Tel (503) 601-1000 SIC 3825 3674 7372

■ TEKTRONIX INC p 1433
14150 Sw Karl Braun Dr, Beaverton OR 97005
Tel (800) 833-9200 SIC 3825

▲ RADISYS CORP p 1204
5435 Ne Dawson Creek Dr, Hillsboro OR 97124
Tel (503) 615-1100 SIC 3825 7374 7372

■ TRIQUINT SALES & DESIGN INC p 1482
2300 Ne Brookwood Pkwy, Hillsboro OR 97124
Tel (503) 615-9000 SIC 3825

▲ AMETEK INC p 84
1100 Cassatt Rd, Berwyn PA 19312
Tel (610) 647-2121
SIC 3621 3823 3824 3825

AEROTECH INC p 31
100 Zeta Dr, Pittsburgh PA 15238
Tel (412) 963-7470 SIC 3699 3825

FENIX MANUFACTURING SOLUTIONS LLC p 537
2063 University Pkwy, Aiken SC 29801
Tel (803) 649-1381
SIC 3694 3825 3625 3354

■ ITRON ELECTRICITY METERING INC p 768
313 N Highway 11, West Union SC 29696
Tel (864) 638-8300
SIC 3825 3823 3824 3679 3829 3612

HID GLOBAL CORP p 690
611 Center Ridge Dr, Austin TX 78753
Tel (800) 237-7769 SIC 3825 1731 8741

ULTRA ELECTRONICS DEFENSE INC p 1501
4101 Smith School Rd, Austin TX 78744
Tel (512) 327-6795 SIC 3812 3825

OPTEK TECHNOLOGY INC p 1090
1645 Wallace Dr, Carrollton TX 75006
Tel (972) 323-2200
SIC 3674 3825 3812 3661 3643

SCHLUMBERGER LIMITED p 1287
5599 San Felipe St Fl 17, Houston TX 77056
Tel (713) 513-2000
SIC 1381 1389 1382 3825 3824 3823

■ DRESSER INC p 455
601 Shiloh Rd, Plano TX 75074
Tel (262) 549-2626
SIC 3491 3825 3594 3593 3561 3494

HILTI OF AMERICA INC p 694
7250 Dallas Pkwy Ste 1000, Plano TX 75024
Tel (800) 879-8000 SIC 5084 3546 3825

EXFO AMERICA INC p 519
3400 Waterview Pkwy # 100, Richardson TX 75080
Tel (972) 761-9271 SIC 3825 8734

SCHLUMBERGER TECHNOLOGY CORP p 1287
100 Gillingham Ln, Sugar Land TX 77478
Tel (281) 285-8500
SIC 1382 1389 3825 3824 3533 3586

■ SIX3 ADVANCED SYSTEMS INC p 1328
45200 Business Ct Ste 100, Dulles VA 20166
Tel (703) 742-7660
SIC 3825 4899 8099 4789

■ NORTHROP GRUMMAN SYSTEMS CORP p 1058
2980 Fairview Park Dr, Falls Church VA 22042
Tel (703) 280-2900
SIC 3721 3761 3728 3812 3825 4581

■ KOLLMORGEN CORP p 826
203a W Rock Rd, Radford VA 24141
Tel (540) 639-2495
SIC 3621 3825 3827 3861

■ FLUKE ELECTRONICS CORP p 561
6920 Seaway Blvd, Everett WA 98203
Tel (425) 446-5610 SIC 3825 3823

ASTRONICS ADVANCED ELECTRONIC SYSTEMS CORP p 122
12950 Willows Rd Ne, Kirkland WA 98034
Tel (425) 881-1700 SIC 3825

SSI TECHNOLOGIES INC p 1364
3200 Palmer Dr, Janesville WI 53546
Tel (608) 758-1500 SIC 3399 3825

▲ SNAP-ON INC p 1335
2801 80th St, Kenosha WI 53143
Tel (262) 656-5200 SIC 3546 3559 3825

■ ELECTRONIC ASSEMBLY CORP p 485
55 Jewelers Park Dr, Neenah WI 54956
Tel (920) 722-3451
SIC 3672 3679 3825 3841

▲ PLEXUS CORP p 1156
1 Plexus Way, Neenah WI 54956
Tel (920) 969-6000 SIC 3672 3825

SIC 3826 Analytical Instruments

■ VENTANA MEDICAL SYSTEMS INC p 1547
1910 E Innovation Park Dr, Oro Valley AZ 85755
Tel (520) 887-2155 SIC 3841 2819 3826

CLARIENT DIAGNOSTIC SERVICES INC p 321
31 Columbia, Aliso Viejo CA 92656
Tel (949) 425-5700 SIC 3841 3826 8071

■ BECKMAN COULTER INC p 167
250 S Kraemer Blvd, Brea CA 92821
Tel (714) 993-5321 SIC 3826 3841 3821

■ APPLIED BIOSYSTEMS LLC p 99
5791 Van Allen Way, Carlsbad CA 92008
Tel (650) 638-5000 SIC 3826 7372

■ ALZA CORP p 63
6500 Paseo Padre Pkwy, Fremont CA 94555
Tel (650) 564-5000 SIC 3826

■ MARCHI THERMAL SYSTEMS INC p 905
3108 Diablo Ave, Hayward CA 94545
Tel (510) 300-1500 SIC 3826

▲ BIO-RAD LABORATORIES INC p 183
1000 Alfred Nobel Dr, Hercules CA 94547
Tel (510) 724-7000 SIC 3826 3845 2835

■ NEWPORT CORP p 1038
1791 Deere Ave, Irvine CA 92606
Tel (949) 863-3144
SIC 3821 3699 3827 3826

▲ PACIFIC BIOSCIENCES OF CALIFORNIA INC p 1104
1380 Willow Rd, Menlo Park CA 94025
Tel (650) 521-8000 SIC 3826

▲ LUMENTUM HOLDINGS INC p 885
400 N Mccarthy Blvd, Milpitas CA 95035
Tel (408) 546-5483 SIC 3669 3674 3826

▲ VIAVI SOLUTIONS INC p 1554
430 N Mccarthy Blvd, Milpitas CA 95035
Tel (408) 404-3600 SIC 3674 3826

■ VARIAN INC p 1544
3100 Hansen Way, Palo Alto CA 94304
Tel (650) 213-8000
SIC 3826 3845 3829 3827

■ IDEX HEALTH & SCIENCE LLC p 729
600 Park Ct, Rohnert Park CA 94928
Tel (707) 588-2000
SIC 3821 3829 3826 3823 3494

▲ ILLUMINA INC p 733
5200 Illumina Way, San Diego CA 92122
Tel (858) 202-4500 SIC 3826 3821

▲ OCLARO INC p 1074
225 Charcot Ave, San Jose CA 95131
Tel (408) 383-1400 SIC 3674 3826 3827

■ THERMO FINNIGAN LLC p 1447
355 River Oaks Pkwy, San Jose CA 95134
Tel (408) 965-6000 SIC 3826

■ THERMOQUEST CORP p 1447
355 River Oaks Pkwy, San Jose CA 95134
Tel (408) 965-6000 SIC 3826 3823

■ QUEST DIAGNOSTICS NICHOLS INSTITUTE p 1199
33608 Ortega Hwy, San Juan Capistrano CA 92675
Tel (949) 728-4000 SIC 3826 8071

■ AFFYMETRIX INC p 33
3420 Central Expy, Santa Clara CA 95051
Tel (408) 731-5000 SIC 3826

▲ AGILENT TECHNOLOGIES INC p 35
5301 Stevens Creek Blvd, Santa Clara CA 95051
Tel (408) 345-8886 SIC 3825 3826 7372

▲ COHERENT INC p 335
5100 Patrick Henry Dr, Santa Clara CA 95054
Tel (408) 764-4000 SIC 3826 3845 3699

▲ FLUIDIGM CORP p 561
7000 Shoreline Ct Ste 100, South San Francisco CA 94080
Tel (650) 266-6000 SIC 3826

■ CEPHEID p 283
904 E Caribbean Dr, Sunnyvale CA 94089
Tel (408) 541-4191 SIC 3826 3841

■ DIONEX CORP p 441
1228 Titan Way Ste 1002, Sunnyvale CA 94085
Tel (408) 737-0700
SIC 3826 2819 3087 3841

■ MOLECULAR DEVICES LLC p 982
1311 Orleans Dr, Sunnyvale CA 94089
Tel (408) 747-1700 SIC 3826 3841

PHENOMENEX INC p 1142
411 Madrid Ave, Torrance CA 90501
Tel (310) 212-0555 SIC 3826

QIAGEN INC p 1195
27220 Turnberry Ln # 200, Valencia CA 91355
Tel (661) 702-3598
SIC 3826 5047 8731 2835

■ HACH CO p 652
5600 Lindbergh Dr, Loveland CO 80538
Tel (970) 669-3050
SIC 3826 3823 3231 2819 2869

OMEGA ENGINEERING INC p 1084
800 Connecticut Ave 5n01, Norwalk CT 06854
Tel (203) 359-1660
SIC 3823 3575 3577 3433 3826 2759

HAMILTON SUNDSTRAND SPACE SYSTEMS INTERNATIONAL INC p 655
1 Hamilton Rd, Windsor Locks CT 06096
Tel (860) 654-6000 SIC 3841 3826

■ TA INSTRUMENTS - WATERS LLC p 1420
159 Lukens Dr, New Castle DE 19720
Tel (302) 777-0712 SIC 3826

ANDRX PHARMACEUTICALS INC p 91
4955 Orange Dr, Davie FL 33314
Tel (954) 581-7500 SIC 3826

▲ ROPER TECHNOLOGIES INC p 1250
6901 Prof Pkwy E Ste 200, Sarasota FL 34240
Tel (941) 556-2601
SIC 3823 3563 3491 3826 3829

■ THERMO ELECTRON NORTH AMERICA LLC p 1447
770 Northpoint Pkwy # 100, West Palm Beach FL 33407
Tel (561) 688-8700 SIC 3826

▲ ABBOTT LABORATORIES p 9
100 Abbott Park Rd, Abbott Park IL 60064
Tel (224) 667-6100
SIC 2834 2835 3841 3826

AKZO NOBEL INC p 42
525 W Van Buren St Fl 16, Chicago IL 60607
Tel (312) 544-7000
SIC 2869 2851 2834 3841 3826 2819

▲ IDEXX LABORATORIES INC p 729
1 Idexx Dr, Westbrook ME 04092
Tel (207) 556-0300 SIC 3826 2834 5047

SCIENCE AND ENGINEERING SERVICES LLC p 1292
6992 Columbia Gateway Dr # 200, Columbia MD 21046
Tel (443) 539-0139 SIC 8711 8731 3826

MESO SCALE DISCOVERY LLC p 951
1601 Research Blvd, Rockville MD 20850
Tel (240) 314-2600 SIC 3826

■ SENSITECH INC p 1305
800 Cummings Ctr Ste 258x, Beverly MA 01915
Tel (978) 927-7033 SIC 3826 3823 3822

▲ BRUKER CORP p 220
40 Manning Rd, Billerica MA 01821
Tel (978) 663-3660 SIC 3826 3844

■ BRUKER DALTONICS INC p 221
40 Manning Rd, Billerica MA 01821
Tel (978) 667-9580 SIC 3826 5049

▲ HARVARD BIOSCIENCE INC p 666
84 October Hill Rd Ste 10, Holliston MA 01746
Tel (508) 893-8999 SIC 3821 3826

■ CALIPER LIFE SCIENCES INC p 242
68 Elm St, Hopkinton MA 01748
Tel (508) 435-9500 SIC 3826

■ LOCKHEED MARTIN SIPPICAN INC p 873
7 Barnabas Rd, Marion MA 02738
Tel (508) 748-3399
SIC 3812 3826 3499 3672 3829 3845

▲ WATERS CORP p 1582
34 Maple St, Milford MA 01757
Tel (508) 478-2000
SIC 3826 3829 7371 7372

■ WATERS TECHNOLOGIES CORP p 1582
34 Maple St, Milford MA 01757
Tel (508) 478-2000 SIC 3826 3829

CARL ZEISS MICROSCOPY LLC p 256
1 Corporate Pl Ste 3, Peabody MA 01960
Tel (978) 826-1500 SIC 5047 3826

NOVA BIOMEDICAL CORP p 1062
200 Prospect St, Waltham MA 02453
Tel (781) 894-0800 SIC 2833 3826

▲ PERKINELMER INC p 1136
940 Winter St, Waltham MA 02451
Tel (781) 663-6900 SIC 3826 3845

▲ THERMO FISHER SCIENTIFIC INC p 1447
168 3rd Ave, Waltham MA 02451
Tel (781) 622-1000
SIC 3826 3845 3823 3629

■ THERMO FISHER SCIENTIFIC WEST PALM HOLDINGS LLC p 1447
168 3rd Ave, Waltham MA 02451
Tel (781) 622-1000 SIC 3826

■ DOBLE ENGINEERING CO p 447
85 Walnut St, Watertown MA 02472
Tel (617) 926-4900
SIC 3825 7359 3829 3826

SPECTRIS INC p 1357
117 Flanders Rd, Westborough MA 01581
Tel (508) 768-6400
SIC 3674 3829 3826 3821

LECO CORP p 851
3000 Lakeview Ave, Saint Joseph MI 49085
Tel (269) 983-5531
SIC 4493 3821 3826 3825 3823 3264

SRG GLOBAL INC p 1363
800 Stephenson Hwy, Troy MI 48083
Tel (586) 757-7800
SIC 3089 3571 3494 2522 3826 3825

LI-COR INC p 861
4647 Superior St, Lincoln NE 68504
Tel (402) 467-3576 SIC 3826

■ TELEDYNE ISCO INC p 1434
4700 Superior St, Lincoln NE 68504
Tel (402) 464-0231 SIC 3823 3826

■ CORNING NETOPTIX p 371
69 Island St Ste T, Keene NH 03431
Tel (603) 357-7662 SIC 3827 3851 3826

NOVARTIS PHARMACEUTICALS CORP p 1062
1 Health Plz, East Hanover NJ 07936
Tel (862) 778-8300 SIC 3826

SIEMENS MEDICAL SOLUTIONS DIAGNOSTICS p 1320
62 Flanders Bartley Rd, Flanders NJ 07836
Tel (973) 927-2828 SIC 3826

▲ BECTON DICKINSON AND CO p 167
1 Becton Dr, Franklin Lakes NJ 07417
Tel (201) 847-6800
SIC 3841 3842 3829 3826 3821

THORLABS INC p 1450
56 Sparta Ave, Newton NJ 07860
Tel (973) 579-7227 SIC 3826

TOPCON MEDICAL SYSTEMS INC p 1461
111 Bauer Dr, Oakland NJ 07436
Tel (201) 599-5100
SIC 3841 3826 3827 3829 3851 5049

■ CVI LASER LLC p 404
200 Dorado Pl Se, Albuquerque NM 87123
Tel (505) 296-9541 SIC 3827 3851 3826

BOSCH SECURITY SYSTEMS INC p 202
130 Perinton Pkwy, Fairport NY 14450
Tel (585) 223-4060
SIC 3669 3699 3826 3825 3823 3625

EWT HOLDINGS III CORP p 516
666 5th Ave Fl 36, New York NY 10103
Tel (212) 644-5900
SIC 3589 3823 3826 4941 5051

CARL ZEISS INC p 256
1 Zeiss Dr, Thornwood NY 10594
Tel (914) 747-1800
SIC 3827 5049 3829 5084 3826

■ THERMO FISHER SCIENTIFIC (ASHVILLE) LLC p 1447
28 Schenck Pkwy Ste 400, Asheville NC 28803
Tel (828) 658-2711
SIC 3585 3826 3821 3829

CAROLINA BIOLOGICAL SUPPLY CO p 259
2700 York Rd, Burlington NC 27215
Tel (336) 584-0381
SIC 5049 2836 3829 3826 3821

WARREN OIL CO INC p 1577
2340 Us Highway 301 N, Dunn NC 28334
Tel (910) 892-6456
SIC 5172 5171 3826 2911

BIOMERIEUX INC p 184
100 Rodolphe St, Durham NC 27712
Tel (919) 620-2000
SIC 3845 8071 3841 3826

PARATA SYSTEMS LLC p 1114
2600 Meridian Pkwy, Durham NC 27713
Tel (919) 433-4400 SIC 3826 8733

HALMA HOLDINGS INC p 655
11500 Northlake Dr # 306, Cincinnati OH 45249
Tel (513) 772-5501 SIC 3826

▲ METTLER-TOLEDO INTERNATIONAL INC p 957
1900 Polaris Pkwy Fl 6, Columbus OH 43240
Tel (614) 438-4511
SIC 3596 3821 3826 3823

■ METTLER-TOLEDO LLC p 957
1900 Polaris Pkwy Fl 6, Columbus OH 43240
Tel (614) 438-4511
SIC 3596 5049 7699 3821 3823 3826

■ FLIR DETECTION INC p 557
1024 S Innovation Way, Stillwater OK 74074
Tel (703) 678-2111 SIC 3826

■ FEI CO p 537
5350 Ne Dawson Creek Dr, Hillsboro OR 97124
Tel (503) 726-7500 SIC 3826

▲ ELECTRO SCIENTIFIC INDUSTRIES INC p 485
13900 Nw Science Park Dr, Portland OR 97229
Tel (503) 641-4141 SIC 3826

▲ FLIR SYSTEMS INC p 557
27700 Sw Parkway Ave, Wilsonville OR 97070
Tel (503) 498-3547 SIC 3812 3826

SHIRE PHARMACEUTICALS LLC p 1317
1200 Morris Dr, Chesterbrook PA 19087
Tel (484) 595-8800 *SIC* 3826

■ MINE SAFETY APPLIANCES CO LLC p 973
1000 Cranberry Woods Dr, Cranberry Township PA 16066
Tel (724) 776-8600
SIC 3842 3826 3823 3648 3829

▲ MSA SAFETY INC p 996
1000 Cranberry Woods Dr, Cranberry Township PA 16066
Tel (724) 776-8600
SIC 3842 3826 3823 3648 3829

MILTON ROY LLC p 972
201 Ivyland Rd, Ivyland PA 18974
Tel (215) 441-0800 *SIC* 3561 3586 3826

■ FISHER SCIENTIFIC CO LLC p 552
300 Industry Dr, Pittsburgh PA 15275
Tel (412) 490-8300
SIC 5049 5169 3821 3826 2869 2819

▲ ENVIRONMENTAL TECTONICS CORP p 503
125 James Way, Southampton PA 18966
Tel (215) 355-9100
SIC 3728 3842 3826 3823 3841

■ GE BETZ INC p 595
4636 Somerton Rd, Trevose PA 19053
Tel (215) 355-3300
SIC 2899 3826 5084 3823

S P INDUSTRIES INC p 1262
935 Mearns Rd, Warminster PA 18974
Tel (215) 672-7800
SIC 3826 3585 7699 3821

EVOQUA WATER TECHNOLOGIES LLC p 516
181 Thorn Hill Rd, Warrendale PA 15086
Tel (724) 772-0044
SIC 3589 3569 3823 3826 4941

■ ABBVIE BIOTECHNOLOGY LTD p 10
Road No 2 Km 59 2, Barceloneta PR 00617
Tel (787) 846-3500
SIC 2834 2844 2835 3841 3826

HELENA LABORATORIES CORP p 681
1530 Lindbergh Dr, Beaumont TX 77707
Tel (409) 842-3714 *SIC* 3841 3826

■ OI CORP p 1078
151 Graham Rd, College Station TX 77845
Tel (979) 690-1711 *SIC* 3826

■ DANIEL INDUSTRIES INC p 411
11100 Brittmoore Park Dr, Houston TX 77041
Tel (713) 467-6000
SIC 3823 3824 3494 3829 3826 3571

HEATH CONSULTANTS INC p 679
9030 W Monroe Rd, Houston TX 77061
Tel (713) 844-1300 *SIC* 8711 3826 3812

LUDLUM MEASUREMENTS INC p 884
501 Oak St, Sweetwater TX 79556
Tel (325) 235-5494
SIC 3829 3826 3824 3823

BIOFIRE DEFENSE LLC p 183
79 W 4500 S Ste 14, Salt Lake City UT 84107
Tel (801) 262-3592 *SIC* 3829 3826 6794

VENTUREDYNE LTD p 1548
600 College Ave, Pewaukee WI 53072
Tel (262) 691-9900
SIC 3568 3829 3826 3823 3625

SIC 3827 Optical Instruments

CARL ZEISS MEDITEC INC p 256
5160 Hacienda Dr, Dublin CA 94568
Tel (925) 557-4100 *SIC* 3827

GKN AEROSPACE TRANSPARENCY SYSTEMS INC p 613
12122 Western Ave, Garden Grove CA 92841
Tel (714) 893-7531
SIC 3089 3231 3827 3728 3081 2821

■ OSI OPTOELECTRONICS INC p 1096
12525 Chadron Ave, Hawthorne CA 90250
Tel (310) 978-0516
SIC 3674 3827 3812 3672

■ NEWPORT CORP p 1038
1791 Deere Ave, Irvine CA 92606
Tel (949) 863-3144
SIC 3821 3699 3827 3826

HOYA HOLDINGS INC p 714
680 N Mccarthy Blvd # 120, Milpitas CA 95035
Tel (408) 654-2300 *SIC* 3861 3825 3827

▲ KLA-TENCOR CORP p 822
1 Technology Dr, Milpitas CA 95035
Tel (408) 875-3000
SIC 3827 3825 7699 7629

■ VARIAN INC p 1544
3100 Hansen Way, Palo Alto CA 94304
Tel (650) 213-8000
SIC 3826 3845 3829 3827

CARL ZEISS VISION INC p 256
12121 Scripps Summit Dr, San Diego CA 92131
Tel (858) 790-7700 *SIC* 3827 3851

CYMER INC p 405
17075 Thornmint Ct, San Diego CA 92127
Tel (858) 385-7300 *SIC* 3699 3827

CYMER LLC p 405
17075 Thornmint Ct, San Diego CA 92127
Tel (858) 385-7300 *SIC* 3699 3827

▲ OCLARO INC p 1074
225 Charcot Ave, San Jose CA 95131
Tel (408) 383-1400 *SIC* 3674 3826 3827

■ OPTICAL COATING LABORATORY LLC p 1090
2789 Northpoint Pkwy, Santa Rosa CA 95407
Tel (707) 545-6440 *SIC* 3479 3577 3827

■ ZYGO CORP p 1645
21 Laurel Brook Rd, Middlefield CT 06455
Tel (860) 347-8506 *SIC* 3827

JENOPTIK NORTH AMERICA INC p 782
16490 Innovation Dr, Jupiter FL 33478
Tel (561) 881-7400 *SIC* 3827

■ LEICA MICROSYSTEMS INC p 854
1700 Leider Ln, Buffalo Grove IL 60089
Tel (847) 405-0123 *SIC* 3827 3841 3821

■ BUSHNELL INC p 229
9200 Cody St, Overland Park KS 66214
Tel (913) 752-3400 *SIC* 3827

■ FEI CO MEPD PEABODY p 537
1 Corporation Way Ste 2, Peabody MA 01960
Tel (978) 538-6700 *SIC* 3559 3827 3699

▲ RUDOLPH TECHNOLOGIES INC p 1257
16 Jonspin Rd, Wilmington MA 01887
Tel (973) 691-1300 *SIC* 3823 3827

MAGNA MIRRORS OF AMERICA INC p 896
5085 Kraft Ave Se, Grand Rapids MI 49512
Tel (616) 942-0163 *SIC* 3231 3647 3827

■ CORNING NETOPTIX p 371
69 Island St SteT, Keene NH 03431
Tel (603) 357-7662 *SIC* 3827 3851 3826

■ L-3 COMMUNICATIONS CORP p 834
9 Akira Way, Londonderry NH 03053
Tel (603) 626-4800 *SIC* 3827

■ GENERAL DYNAMICS GLOBAL IMAGING TECHNOLOGIES INC p 600
24 Simon St, Nashua NH 03060
Tel (603) 864-6300 *SIC* 3827 3861

REFAC OPTICAL GROUP p 1217
1 Harmon Dr, Blackwood NJ 08012
Tel (856) 228-1000 *SIC* 3827

US VISION INC p 1533
1 Harmon Dr, Glendora NJ 08029
Tel (856) 227-8339 *SIC* 5995 3827

TOPCON MEDICAL SYSTEMS INC p 1461
111 Bauer Dr, Oakland NJ 07436
Tel (201) 599-5100
SIC 3841 3826 3827 3829 3851 5049

■ CVI LASER LLC p 404
200 Dorado Pl Se, Albuquerque NM 87123
Tel (505) 296-9541 *SIC* 3827 3851 3826

AEROFLEX INC p 30
35 S Service Rd, Plainview NY 11803
Tel (516) 694-6700
SIC 3812 3621 3677 3674 3496 3827

AEROFLEX PLAINVIEW INC p 30
35 S Service Rd, Plainview NY 11803
Tel (516) 694-6700
SIC 3679 3621 3674 3827

QUALITY VISION INTERNATIONAL INC p 1197
850 Hudson Ave, Rochester NY 14621
Tel (585) 544-0400 *SIC* 3827

■ WELCH ALLYN INC p 1588
4341 State Street Rd, Skaneateles Falls NY 13153
Tel (315) 685-4100 *SIC* 3841 2835 3827

CARL ZEISS INC p 256
1 Zeiss Dr, Thornwood NY 10594
Tel (914) 747-1800
SIC 3827 5049 3829 5084 3826

LEUPOLD & STEVENS INC p 858
14400 Nw Greenbrier Pkwy, Beaverton OR 97006
Tel (503) 526-1400 *SIC* 3827

CYOPTICS INC p 405
9999 Hamilton Blvd # 250, Breinigsville PA 18031
Tel (484) 397-2000 *SIC* 3827

OLYMPUS AMERICA INC p 1083
3500 Corporate Pkwy, Center Valley PA 18034
Tel (484) 896-5000
SIC 5047 5043 5064 3827 3695 3572

OLYMPUS CORP OF AMERICAS p 1083
3500 Corp Pkwy, Center Valley PA 18034
Tel (484) 896-5000
SIC 5047 5043 5064 3827 3695 3572

▲ II-VI INC p 731
375 Saxonburg Blvd, Saxonburg PA 16056
Tel (724) 352-4455
SIC 3827 3229 3674 3699

ELBIT SYSTEMS OF AMERICA LLC p 483
4700 Marine Creek Pkwy, Fort Worth TX 76179
Tel (817) 234-6600 *SIC* 3827

PETROLEUM GEO-SERVICES INC p 1139
15375 Memorial Dr Ste 100, Houston TX 77079
Tel (281) 509-8000 *SIC* 3827 8713 1382

▲ APPLIED OPTOELECTRONICS INC p 100
13139 Jess Pirtle Blvd, Sugar Land TX 77478
Tel (281) 295-1800 *SIC* 3674 3827 3699

▲ VISTA OUTDOOR INC p 1562
262 N University Ave, Farmington UT 84025
Tel (801) 447-3000
SIC 3482 3483 3827 3949 3484 3812

■ KOLLMORGEN CORP p 826
203a W Rock Rd, Radford VA 24141
Tel (540) 639-2495
SIC 3621 3825 3827 3861

SIC 3829 Measuring & Controlling Devices, NEC

■ SCI TECHNOLOGY INC p 1292
13000 Memorial Pkwy Sw, Huntsville AL 35803
Tel (256) 882-4800
SIC 3672 3829 8711 3663

ARTESYN EMBEDDED COMPUTING INC p 114
2900 S Diablo Way Ste 190, Tempe AZ 85282
Tel (602) 438-5720 *SIC* 3829

UNIVERSAL AVIONICS SYSTEMS CORP p 1516
3260 E Universal Way, Tucson AZ 85756
Tel (520) 295-2300 *SIC* 3812 3829

SPIRENT COMMUNICATIONS INC p 1359
27349 Agoura Rd, Calabasas CA 91301
Tel (818) 676-2300 *SIC* 3663 3829 3825

CLAYTON MANUFACTURING CO p 323
17477 Hurley St, City Of Industry CA 91744
Tel (626) 443-9381 *SIC* 3569 3829 3511

■ TELEDYNE INSTRUMENTS INC p 1434
16830 Chestnut St, City Of Industry CA 91748
Tel (626) 961-9221 *SIC* 3829 3823

GEORGE FISCHER INC p 606
3401 Aero Jet Ave, El Monte CA 91731
Tel (626) 571-2770
SIC 3599 5074 3829 3559

HORIBA INTERNATIONAL CORP p 706
9755 Research Dr, Irvine CA 92618
Tel (949) 250-4811 *SIC* 3829

JAE ELECTRONICS INC p 775
142 Technology Dr Ste 100, Irvine CA 92618
Tel (949) 753-2600
SIC 5065 5088 3679 3829 3678

TOPCON POSITIONING SYSTEMS INC p 1461
7400 National Dr, Livermore CA 94550
Tel (925) 245-8300
SIC 3829 3625 3823 3699 8713 1794

▲ NANOMETRICS INC p 1007
1550 Buckeye Dr, Milpitas CA 95035
Tel (408) 545-6000 *SIC* 3829 3559

■ METTLER-TOLEDO RAININ LLC p 957
7500 Edgewater Dr, Oakland CA 94621
Tel (510) 564-1600 *SIC* 3821 3829

■ VARIAN INC p 1544
3100 Hansen Way, Palo Alto CA 94304
Tel (650) 213-8000
SIC 3826 3845 3829 3827

■ IDEX HEALTH & SCIENCE LLC p 729
600 Park Ct, Rohnert Park CA 94928
Tel (707) 588-2000
SIC 3821 3829 3826 3823 3494

■ CUBIC TRANSPORTATION SYSTEMS INC p 399
5650 Kearny Mesa Rd, San Diego CA 92111
Tel (858) 268-3100 *SIC* 3829 1731

GENERAL ATOMIC TECHNOLOGIES CORP p 599
3550 General Atomics Ct, San Diego CA 92121
Tel (858) 455-3000
SIC 8731 3829 3443 7374 3499 2819

INTERNATIONAL TECHNIDYNE CORP p 757
6260 Sequence Dr, San Diego CA 92121
Tel (858) 263-2300 *SIC* 3841 3829

▲ FITBIT INC p 552
405 Howard St Ste 550, San Francisco CA 94105
Tel (415) 513-1000 *SIC* 3829

OTSUKA AMERICA INC p 1097
1 Embarcadero Ctr # 2020, San Francisco CA 94111
Tel (415) 986-5300
SIC 3829 3499 5122 2833 2084 2086

■ RAE SYSTEMS INC p 1205
3775 N 1st St, San Jose CA 95134
Tel (408) 952-8200 *SIC* 3829 3812 3699

MIRION TECHNOLOGIES INC p 974
3000 Executive Pkwy # 518, San Ramon CA 94583
Tel (925) 543-0800 *SIC* 3829

LUMASENSE TECHNOLOGIES INC p 885
3301 Leonard Ct, Santa Clara CA 95054
Tel (408) 727-1600
SIC 3823 3845 3829 3825

MEGGITT-USA INC p 940
1955 Surveyor Ave, Simi Valley CA 93063
Tel (805) 526-5700 *SIC* 3728 3829 3679

▲ TRIMBLE INC p 1480
935 Stewart Dr, Sunnyvale CA 94085
Tel (408) 481-8000 *SIC* 3812 3829

KAVLICO CORP p 805
1461 Lawrence Dr, Thousand Oaks CA 91320
Tel (805) 523-2000 *SIC* 3679 3829 3823

CITIZEN WATCH CO OF AMERICA INC p 310
1000 W 190th St, Torrance CA 90502
Tel (310) 532-8463 *SIC* 5094 3829

▲ ABAXIS INC p 9
3240 Whipple Rd, Union City CA 94587
Tel (510) 675-6500 *SIC* 3829 2835

■ SEMCO INSTRUMENTS INC p 1302
25700 Rye Canyon Rd, Valencia CA 91355
Tel (661) 257-2000 *SIC* 3829

CANBERRA INDUSTRIES INC p 246
800 Research Pkwy, Meriden CT 06450
Tel (203) 238-2351 *SIC* 3829 4813

ENSIGN-BICKFORD INDUSTRIES INC p 501
125 Pwder Frest Dr Fl 3, Simsbury CT 06070
Tel (860) 843-2000
SIC 3764 2047 2835 3829 2499 6552

▲ DANAHER CORP p 411
2200 Penn Ave Nw Ste 800w, Washington DC 20037
Tel (202) 828-0850
SIC 3845 3829 3577 3823 3843

■ AMERICAN HOUSEHOLD INC p 74
2381 Nw Executive Ctr Dr, Boca Raton FL 33431
Tel (561) 912-4100
SIC 3631 2514 3421 3634 3829 3841

■ SUNBEAM AMERICAS HOLDINGS LLC p 1401
2381 Nw Executive Ctr Dr, Boca Raton FL 33431
Tel (561) 912-4100
SIC 3631 2514 3421 3634 3829 3841

▲ FARO TECHNOLOGIES INC p 530
250 Technology Park, Lake Mary FL 32746
Tel (407) 333-9911 *SIC* 3829

▲ ROPER TECHNOLOGIES INC p 1250
6901 Prof Pkwy E Ste 200, Sarasota FL 34240
Tel (941) 556-2601
SIC 3823 3563 3491 3826 3829

■ FIRST ALERT INC p 544
3901 Liberty St, Aurora IL 60504
Tel (630) 851-7330
SIC 3669 3999 3446 3499 3829 3648

▲ LANDAUER INC p 842
2 Science Rd, Glenwood IL 60425
Tel (708) 755-7000 *SIC* 8734 5047 3829

■ HONEYWELL ANALYTICS INC p 705
405 Barclay Blvd, Lincolnshire IL 60069
Tel (847) 955-8200 *SIC* 3491 3829

▲ CTS CORP p 399
2375 Cabot Dr, Lisle IL 60532
Tel (630) 577-8800
SIC 3678 3829 3676 3679 3674

MARTIN ENGINEERING CO p 912
1 Martin Pl, Neponset IL 61345
Tel (309) 852-2384 *SIC* 3829 3532

TEMPCO ELECTRIC HEATER CORP p 1436
607 N Central Ave, Wood Dale IL 60191
Tel (630) 350-2252 *SIC* 3567 3369 3829

DWYER INSTRUMENTS INC p 464
102 Indiana Highway 212, Michigan City IN 46360
Tel (219) 879-8868
SIC 3823 3824 3822 3829 3491 3625

MPD INC p 995
316 E 9th St, Owensboro KY 42303
Tel (270) 685-6200
SIC 3671 3829 3812 3663 3643 3053

▲ COLFAX CORP p 336
420 Natl Bus Pkwy Fl 5, Annapolis Junction MD 20701
Tel (301) 323-9000 *SIC* 3561 3829 3625

SMITHS DETECTION INC p 1334
2202 Lakeside Blvd, Edgewood MD 21040
Tel (410) 510-9100
SIC 3824 3823 3829 8731

▲ AXCELIS TECHNOLOGIES INC p 140
108 Cherry Hill Dr, Beverly MA 01915
Tel (978) 787-4000 *SIC* 3559 3829

■ LOCKHEED MARTIN SIPPICAN INC p 873
7 Barnabas Rd, Marion MA 02738
Tel (508) 748-3399
SIC 3812 3826 3499 3672 3829 3845

▲ WATERS CORP p 1582
34 Maple St, Milford MA 01757
Tel (508) 478-2000
SIC 3826 3829 7371 7372

■ WATERS TECHNOLOGIES CORP p 1582
34 Maple St, Milford MA 01757
Tel (508) 478-2000 *SIC* 3826 3829

■ DOBLE ENGINEERING CO p 447
85 Walnut St, Watertown MA 02472
Tel (617) 926-4900
SIC 3825 7359 3829 3826

SPECTRIS INC p 1357
117 Flanders Rd, Westborough MA 01581
Tel (508) 768-6400
SIC 3674 3829 3826 3821

COMAU LLC p 343
21000 Telegraph Rd, Southfield MI 48033
Tel (248) 353-8888 *SIC* 3548 3829 3545

HOWARD MILLER CO p 713
860 E Main Ave, Zeeland MI 49464
Tel (616) 772-9131 *SIC* 3873 3829 3823

■ ROSEMOUNT INC p 1251
8200 Market Blvd, Chanhassen MN 55317
Tel (952) 906-8888
SIC 3823 3824 3545 5084 3829

▲ MTS SYSTEMS CORP p 998
14000 Technology Dr, Eden Prairie MN 55344
Tel (952) 937-4000 *SIC* 3829 3825

MINCO PRODUCTS INC p 972
7300 Commerce Ln Ne, Minneapolis MN 55432
Tel (763) 571-3121 *SIC* 3672 3823 3829

■ RESEARCH AND DIAGNOSTIC SYSTEMS INC p 1226
614 Mckinley Pl Ne, Minneapolis MN 55413
Tel (612) 379-2956
SIC 8733 2833 8731 3829 3625

TSI INC p 1489
500 Cardigan Rd, Saint Paul MN 55126
Tel (651) 483-0900
SIC 3579 3829 3823 3845 3825

ACLARA TECHNOLOGIES LLC p 17
945 Hornet Dr, Hazelwood MO 63042
Tel (314) 895-6400
SIC 3824 3825 3829 7371 7373

MALLINCKRODT LLC p 900
675 Jmes S Mcdonnell Blvd, Hazelwood MO 63042
Tel (314) 654-2000
SIC 3841 3829 2834 2833

METER READINGS HOLDING LLC p 953
945 Hornet Dr, Hazelwood MO 63042
Tel (561) 394-0550
SIC 3824 3825 3829 7371 7373

■ COMPUTATIONAL SYSTEMS INC p 352
8000 W Florissant Ave, Saint Louis MO 63136
Tel (314) 553-2000 *SIC* 3829

SYSTEMS DRS SUSTAINMENT INC p 1418
201 Evans Ln, Saint Louis MO 63121
Tel (314) 553-4000
SIC 3715 3537 3812 3829 3769

■ ELSTER AMERICAN METER CO LLC p 489
2221 Industrial Rd, Nebraska City NE 68410
Tel (402) 873-8200 *SIC* 3829

■ BENTLY NEVADA INC p 173
1631 Bently Pkwy S, Minden NV 89423
Tel (775) 782-3611 *SIC* 3829

▲ BECTON DICKINSON AND CO p 167
1 Becton Dr, Franklin Lakes NJ 07417
Tel (201) 847-6800
SIC 3841 3842 3829 3826 3821

TRANSISTOR DEVICES INC p 1471
36 Newburgh Rd, Hackettstown NJ 07840
Tel (908) 850-1595
SIC 3612 3625 3672 3812 3829

KULITE SEMICONDUCTOR PRODUCTS INC p 832
1 Willow Tree Rd, Leonia NJ 07605
Tel (201) 461-0900 *SIC* 3728 3829

TOPCON MEDICAL SYSTEMS INC p 1461
111 Bauer Dr, Oakland NJ 07436
Tel (201) 599-5100
SIC 3841 3826 3827 3829 3851 5049

▲ MISTRAS GROUP INC p 976
195 Clarksville Rd Ste 2, Princeton Junction NJ 08550
Tel (609) 716-4000
SIC 8711 7372 3829 3825

■ TELEDYNE LECROY INC p 1434
700 Chestnut Ridge Rd, Chestnut Ridge NY 10977
Tel (845) 425-2000 *SIC* 3825 3829

■ PCB PIEZOTRONICS INC p 1123
3425 Walden Ave, Depew NY 14043
Tel (716) 684-0001 *SIC* 3829 3679

SCHOTT CORP p 1290
555 Taxter Rd Ste 470, Elmsford NY 10523
Tel (914) 831-2200
SIC 3211 3829 3221 3229

FOUGERA PHARMACEUTICALS INC p 571
60 Baylis Rd, Melville NY 11747
Tel (631) 454-7677
SIC 2834 2851 2821 3479 3829

TOSHIBA NUCLEAR ENERGY HOLDINGS (US) INC p 1462
1251 Ave Of Amrcs 400 Ste 4100, New York NY 10020
Tel (212) 596-0600
SIC 8711 3829 3823 2819

GLEASON CORP p 614
1000 University Ave, Rochester NY 14607
Tel (585) 473-1000 SIC 3541 3829

GLEASON WORKS p 614
1000 University Ave, Rochester NY 14607
Tel (585) 473-1000
SIC 3714 3728 3566 3541 3829 3469

CARL ZEISS INC p 256
1 Zeiss Dr, Thornwood NY 10594
Tel (914) 747-1800
SIC 3827 5049 3829 5084 3826

■THERMO FISHER SCIENTIFIC (ASHVILLE) LLC p 1447
28 Schenck Pkwy Ste 400, Asheville NC 28803
Tel (828) 658-2711
SIC 3585 3826 3821 3829

CAROLINA BIOLOGICAL SUPPLY CO p 259
2700 York Rd, Burlington NC 27215
Tel (336) 584-0381
SIC 5049 2836 3829 3826 3821

AREVA INC p 107
7207 Ibm Dr, Charlotte NC 28262
Tel (704) 805-2000
SIC 3823 3829 8711 5085 3561 2819

▲ BABCOCK & WILCOX ENTERPRISES INC p 143
13024 Ballantyne Corporat, Charlotte NC 28277
Tel (704) 625-4900 SIC 3621 3829

▲ SPX CORP p 1362
13320a Balntyn Corp Pl, Charlotte NC 28277
Tel (980) 474-3700
SIC 3443 3599 3829 3559 3545

■ IMO INDUSTRIES INC p 734
1710 Airport Rd, Monroe NC 28110
Tel (704) 289-6511 SIC 3561 3714 3829

DTR INDUSTRIES INC p 458
320 Snider Rd, Bluffton OH 45817
Tel (419) 358-2121
SIC 3052 3069 3829 3714

▲ PARKER-HANNIFIN CORP p 1116
6035 Parkland Blvd, Cleveland OH 44124
Tel (216) 896-3000
SIC 3594 3593 3492 3569 3053 3829

MULTILINK INC p 999
580 Ternes Ln, Elyria OH 44035
Tel (440) 366-6966 SIC 5063 3829

CHARLES MACHINE WORKS INC p 289
1959 W Fir St, Perry OK 73077
Tel (580) 572-3344
SIC 3531 3541 3829 3546

■ MINE SAFETY APPLIANCES CO LLC p 973
1000 Cranberry Woods Dr, Cranberry Township PA 16066
Tel (724) 776-8600
SIC 3842 3826 3823 3648 3829

▲ MSA SAFETY INC p 996
1000 Cranberry Woods Dr, Cranberry Township PA 16066
Tel (724) 776-8600
SIC 3842 3826 3823 3648 3829

WESTINGHOUSE ELECTRIC CO LLC p 1601
1000 Westinghouse Dr, Cranberry Township PA 16066
Tel (412) 374-2020
SIC 3829 8711 3823 2819

SKF USA INC p 1329
890 Forty Foot Rd, Lansdale PA 19446
Tel (267) 436-6000 SIC 3562 3053 3829

▲ TEXTRON INC p 1445
40 Westminster St, Providence RI 02903
Tel (401) 421-2800
SIC 3721 3724 3728 3799 3829 3546

▲ ASTRONOVA INC p 123
600 E Greenwich Ave, West Warwick RI 02893
Tel (401) 828-4000 SIC 3577 3829

■ ITRON ELECTRICITY METERING INC p 768
313 N Highway 11, West Union SC 29696
Tel (864) 638-8300
SIC 3825 3823 3824 3679 3829 3612

KELE INC p 808
3300 Brother Blvd, Memphis TN 38133
Tel (901) 382-6084 SIC 5075 3822 3829

BAE SYSTEMS RESOLUTION INC p 144
1000 La St Ste 4950, Houston TX 77002
Tel (713) 868-7700
SIC 3713 5084 3711 7699 3351 3829

■ DANIEL INDUSTRIES INC p 411
11100 Brittmoore Park Dr, Houston TX 77041
Tel (713) 467-6000
SIC 3823 3824 3494 3829 3826 3571

▲ ION GEOPHYSICAL CORP p 762
2105 Citywest Blvd # 900, Houston TX 77042
Tel (281) 933-3339 SIC 7372 3829

SERCEL INC p 1306
17200 Park Row, Houston TX 77084
Tel (281) 492-6688 SIC 3829

FAIRFIELD INDUSTRIES INC p 525
1111 Gillingham Ln, Sugar Land TX 77478
Tel (281) 275-7627
SIC 7374 3829 1382 3429

LUDLUM MEASUREMENTS INC p 884
501 Oak St, Sweetwater TX 79556
Tel (325) 235-5494
SIC 3829 3826 3824 3823

BIOFIRE DEFENSE LLC p 183
79 W 4500 S Ste 14, Salt Lake City UT 84107
Tel (801) 262-3592 SIC 3829 3826 6794

■ SIMMONDS PRECISION PRODUCTS INC p 1324
100 Panton Rd, Vergennes VT 05491
Tel (802) 877-4000
SIC 3829 3694 3724 3728

ELECTRO-MECHANICAL CORP p 485
329 Williams St, Bristol VA 24201
Tel (276) 669-9428
SIC 3612 5063 3829 3822 3613 3354

MEASUREMENT SPECIALTIES INC p 934
1000 Lucas Way, Hampton VA 23666
Tel (757) 766-1500 SIC 3829

▲ BWX TECHNOLOGIES INC p 231
800 Main St Ste 4, Lynchburg VA 24504
Tel (980) 365-4300 SIC 3621 3829

▲ ITRON INC p 768
2111 N Molter Rd, Liberty Lake WA 99019
Tel (509) 924-9900 SIC 3829 7371

BELLOFRAM CORP p 171
8019 Ohio River Blvd, Newell WV 26050
Tel (304) 387-1200 SIC 3612 3829 3625

■TOMOTHERAPY INC p 1459
1240 Deming Way, Madison WI 53717
Tel (608) 824-2800 SIC 3829

VENTUREDYNE LTD p 1548
600 College Ave, Pewaukee WI 53072
Tel (262) 691-9900
SIC 3568 3829 3826 3823 3625

SIC 3841 Surgical & Medical Instrs & Apparatus

INTEGRATED MEDICAL SYSTEMS INTERNATIONAL INC p 749
3316 2nd Ave N, Birmingham AL 35222
Tel (205) 879-3840 SIC 3841 7699

■VENTANA MEDICAL SYSTEMS INC p 1547
1910 E Innovation Park Dr, Oro Valley AZ 85755
Tel (520) 887-2155 SIC 3841 2819 3826

■ STRYKER SUSTAINABILITY SOLUTIONS INC p 1394
1810 W Drake Dr Ste 101, Tempe AZ 85283
Tel (888) 888-3433
SIC 5084 5047 7699 3842 3841

PENUMBRA INC p 1132
1351 Harbor Bay Pkwy, Alameda CA 94502
Tel (510) 748-3200 SIC 3841

CLARIENT DIAGNOSTIC SERVICES INC p 321
31 Columbia, Aliso Viejo CA 92656
Tel (949) 425-5700 SIC 3841 3826 8071

■ BECKMAN COULTER INC p 167
250 S Kraemer Blvd, Brea CA 92821
Tel (714) 993-5321 SIC 3826 3841 3821

▲ ALPHATEC HOLDINGS INC p 60
5818 El Camino Real, Carlsbad CA 92008
Tel (760) 431-9286 SIC 3841

▲ SEASPINE HOLDINGS CORP p 1297
5770 Armada Dr, Carlsbad CA 92008
Tel (760) 727-8399 SIC 3841

DAKO NORTH AMERICA INC p 409
6392 Via Real, Carpinteria CA 93013
Tel (805) 566-6655 SIC 5122 3841

FRESENIUS USA INC p 578
4040 Nelson Ave, Concord CA 94520
Tel (925) 288-4218
SIC 2834 3841 2835 3842 2836

■ BIOSENSE WEBSTER INC p 184
3333 S Diamond Canyon Rd, Diamond Bar CA 91765
Tel (909) 839-8500 SIC 3845 3841

KARL STORZ ENDOSCOPY-AMERICA INC p 804
2151 E Grand Ave, El Segundo CA 90245
Tel (424) 218-8100 SIC 3841 5047

■ CORDIS CORP p 369
6500 Paseo Padre Pkwy, Fremont CA 94555
Tel (510) 248-2500 SIC 3841 3842

NITINOL DEVICES AND COMPONENTS INC p 1045
47533 Westinghouse Dr, Fremont CA 94539
Tel (510) 683-2000 SIC 3841 5047

▲ INOGEN INC p 745
326 Bollay Dr, Goleta CA 93117
Tel (805) 562-0500 SIC 3841 3842

KARL STORZ IMAGING INC p 804
175 Cremona Dr, Goleta CA 93117
Tel (805) 845-3617 SIC 3841

■ACCLARENT INC p 15
33 Technology Dr, Irvine CA 92618
Tel (650) 687-5888 SIC 3841

ALLIANCE MEDICAL PRODUCTS INC p 54
9342 Jeronimo Rd, Irvine CA 92618
Tel (949) 768-4690 SIC 3841 7819

▲ ENDOLOGIX INC p 496
2 Musick, Irvine CA 92618
Tel (949) 595-7200 SIC 3841

■ I-FLOW CORP p 725
43 Discovery Ste 100, Irvine CA 92618
Tel (800) 448-3569 SIC 3841

■ MENTOR WORLDWIDE LLC p 943
33 Technology Dr, Irvine CA 92618
Tel (800) 636-8678 SIC 3842 3845 3841

PARAMIT CORP p 1114
18735 Madrone Pkwy, Morgan Hill CA 95037
Tel (408) 782-5600 SIC 3841

■THORATEC CORP p 1450
6035 Stoneridge Dr, Pleasanton CA 94588
Tel (925) 847-8600 SIC 3845 3841

▲ ZELTIQ AESTHETICS INC p 1642
4410 Rosewood Dr, Pleasanton CA 94588
Tel (925) 474-2500 SIC 3841

APPLIED MEDICAL CORP p 100
22872 Avenida Empresa, Rcho Sta Marg CA 92688
Tel (949) 713-8000 SIC 3841

APPLIED MEDICAL RESOURCES CORP p 100
22872 Avenida Empresa, Rcho Sta Marg CA 92688
Tel (949) 635-9153 SIC 3841

▲ ICU MEDICAL INC p 728
951 Calle Amanecer, San Clemente CA 92673
Tel (949) 366-2183 SIC 3841 3845

■ CAREFUSION 303 INC p 255
10020 Pacific Mesa Blvd, San Diego CA 92121
Tel (858) 617-2000 SIC 3841

■ CAREFUSION CORP p 255
3750 Torrey View Ct, San Diego CA 92130
Tel (858) 617-2000 SIC 3841 3845 8742

▲ DEXCOM INC p 434
6340 Sequence Dr, San Diego CA 92121
Tel (858) 200-0200 SIC 3841

INTERNATIONAL TECHNIDYNE CORP p 757
6260 Sequence Dr, San Diego CA 92121
Tel (858) 263-2300 SIC 3841 3829

NEXUS DX INC p 1041
6759 Mesa Ridge Rd, San Diego CA 92121
Tel (858) 410-4600 SIC 3841

▲ NUVASIVE INC p 1068
7475 Lusk Blvd, San Diego CA 92121
Tel (858) 909-1800 SIC 3841

■ NYPRO HEALTHCARE BAJA INC p 1069
2195 Britannia Blvd # 107, San Diego CA 92154
Tel (619) 498-9250 SIC 3841 3679

▲ RESMED INC p 1227
9001 Spectrum Center Blvd, San Diego CA 92123
Tel (858) 836-5000 SIC 3841

■ ABBOTT MEDICAL OPTICS INC p 9
1700 E Saint Andrew Pl, Santa Ana CA 92705
Tel (714) 247-8200 SIC 3841 3845

■ AMO USA INC p 86
1700 E Saint Andrew Pl, Santa Ana CA 92705
Tel (714) 247-8200 SIC 3841 3845

MEDTRONIC CARDIOVASCULAR p 939
3576 Unocal Pl, Santa Rosa CA 95403
Tel (707) 545-1156 SIC 3841

■ INTERNATIONAL MEDICATION SYSTEMS LTD p 756
1886 Santa Anita Ave, South El Monte CA 91733
Tel (626) 442-6757 SIC 2834 2833 3841

▲ ACCURAY INC p 16
1310 Chesapeake Ter, Sunnyvale CA 94089
Tel (408) 716-4600 SIC 3841

■ CEPHEID p 283
904 E Caribbean Dr, Sunnyvale CA 94089
Tel (408) 541-4191 SIC 3826 3841

■ DIONEX CORP p 441
1228 Titan Way Ste 1002, Sunnyvale CA 94085
Tel (408) 737-0700
SIC 3826 2819 3087 3841

▲ INTUITIVE SURGICAL INC p 760
1020 Kifer Rd, Sunnyvale CA 94086
Tel (408) 523-2100 SIC 3841

MEDTRONIC SPINE LLC p 939
1221 Crossman Ave, Sunnyvale CA 94089
Tel (408) 548-6500 SIC 3841

■ MOLECULAR DEVICES LLC p 982
1311 Orleans Dr, Sunnyvale CA 94089
Tel (408) 747-1700 SIC 3826 3841

MICROVENTION INC p 962
1311 Valencia Ave, Tustin CA 92780
Tel (714) 258-8001 SIC 3841

VCP MOBILITY INC p 1545
6899 Winchester Cir # 200, Boulder CO 80301
Tel (303) 218-4500
SIC 3842 2599 2515 5047 3841

ALLOSOURCE p 58
6278 S Troy Cir, Centennial CO 80111
Tel (720) 873-0213 SIC 3841

▲ MESA LABORATORIES INC p 951
12100 W 6th Ave, Lakewood CO 80228
Tel (303) 987-8000 SIC 3823 3841

TERUMO BCT HOLDING CORP p 1440
10811 W Collins Ave, Lakewood CO 80215
Tel (303) 232-6800 SIC 3841 6719

LACEY MANUFACTURING CO LLC p 837
1146 Barnum Ave, Bridgeport CT 06610
Tel (203) 336-7427 SIC 3841 3089

UNITED STATES SURGICAL CORP p 1514
555 Long Wharf Dr Fl 4, New Haven CT 06511
Tel (203) 845-1000 SIC 3841 3845 3842

■ COOPERSURGICAL INC p 367
95 Corporate Dr, Trumbull CT 06611
Tel (203) 601-5200
SIC 5047 3842 3841 3845

LEE CO p 851
2 Pettipaug Rd, Westbrook CT 06498
Tel (860) 399-6281
SIC 3823 3841 3812 3728 3714

HAMILTON SUNDSTRAND SPACE SYSTEMS INTERNATIONAL INC p 655
1 Hamilton Rd, Windsor Locks CT 06096
Tel (860) 654-6000 SIC 3841 3826

W L GORE & ASSOCIATES INC p 1568
555 Paper Mill Rd, Newark DE 19711
Tel (302) 738-4880
SIC 3357 2821 5131 3841 2819 3069

SMITH & NEPHEW HOLDINGS INC p 1333
1201 N Orange St Ste 788, Wilmington DE 19801
Tel (302) 884-6720 SIC 5047 3841

■ AMERICAN HOUSEHOLD INC p 74
2381 Nw Executive Ctr Dr, Boca Raton FL 33431
Tel (561) 912-4100
SIC 3631 2514 3421 3634 3829 3841

■ SUNBEAM AMERICAS HOLDINGS LLC p 1401
2381 Nw Executive Ctr Dr, Boca Raton FL 33431
Tel (561) 912-4100
SIC 3631 2514 3421 3634 3829 3841

■ BOSTON SCIENTIFIC MIAMI CORP p 203
8600 Nw 41st St, Doral FL 33166
Tel (305) 597-4000 SIC 3841

MEDTRONIC XOMED INC p 939
6743 Southpoint Dr N, Jacksonville FL 32216
Tel (904) 296-9600 SIC 3842 3841

■ LINVATEC CORP p 869
11311 Concept Blvd, Largo FL 33773
Tel (727) 392-6464 SIC 3842 3841 2821

ARTHREX INC p 114
1370 Creekside Blvd, Naples FL 34108
Tel (239) 643-5553 SIC 3841

▲ HALYARD HEALTH INC p 655
5405 Windward Pkwy, Alpharetta GA 30004
Tel (678) 425-9273 SIC 3842 3841 3845

■ HALYARD SALES LLC p 655
5405 Windward Pkwy # 100, Alpharetta GA 30004
Tel (678) 425-9273 SIC 3845 3841

ELEKTA HOLDINGS US INC p 486
400 Perimeter Center Ter, Atlanta GA 30346
Tel (770) 300-9725 SIC 5047 3841

MERIAL UK LLC p 948
3239 Satellite Blvd, Duluth GA 30096
Tel (678) 638-3000 SIC 2836 2834 3841

POREX CORP p 1161
500 Bohannon Rd, Fairburn GA 30213
Tel (800) 241-0195 SIC 3082 3842 3841

▲ CRYOLIFE INC p 396
1655 Roberts Blvd Nw, Kennesaw GA 30144
Tel (770) 419-3355 SIC 3841

▲ MIMEDX GROUP INC p 972
1775 W Oak Commons Ct, Marietta GA 30062
Tel (770) 651-9100 SIC 3842 3841

PETER BRASSELER HOLDINGS LLC p 1138
1 Brasseler Blvd, Savannah GA 31419
Tel (912) 925-8525 SIC 5047 3841 3843

▲ ABBOTT LABORATORIES p 9
100 Abbott Park Rd, Abbott Park IL 60064
Tel (224) 667-6100
SIC 2834 2835 3841 3826

■ ABBOTT LABORATORIES INC p 9
200 Abbott Park Rd, Abbott Park IL 60064
Tel (224) 668-2076 SIC 2834 3841

■ LEICA MICROSYSTEMS INC p 854
1700 Leider Ln, Buffalo Grove IL 60089
Tel (847) 405-0123 SIC 3827 3841 3821

NEMERA BUFFALO GROVE LLC p 1025
600 Deerfield Pkwy, Buffalo Grove IL 60089
Tel (847) 541-7900 SIC 3841

NEMERA US HOLDING INC p 1025
600 Deerfield Pkwy, Buffalo Grove IL 60089
Tel (847) 325-3620 SIC 3841

AKZO NOBEL INC p 42
525 W Van Buren St Fl 16, Chicago IL 60607
Tel (312) 544-7000
SIC 2869 2851 2834 3841 3826 2819

BEECKEN PETTY OKEEFE & CO LLC p 168
131 S Dearborn St Ste 122, Chicago IL 60603
Tel (312) 435-0300 SIC 6799 3841

▲ HILL-ROM HOLDINGS INC p 693
2 Prudential Plz Ste 4100, Chicago IL 60601
Tel (312) 819-7200 SIC 3841 7352

■ MERGE HEALTHCARE INC p 948
71 S Wacker Dr Ste 2, Chicago IL 60606
Tel (312) 565-6868 SIC 7373 3841

■ BAXTER HEALTHCARE CORP p 160
1 Baxter Pkwy, Deerfield IL 60015
Tel (224) 948-2000
SIC 3841 2835 2389 3842 5047

▲ BAXTER INTERNATIONAL INC p 160
1 Baxter Pkwy, Deerfield IL 60015
Tel (224) 948-2000
SIC 2834 3841 2835 3842

■ BAXTER WORLD TRADE CORP p 160
1 Baxter Pkwy, Deerfield IL 60015
Tel (224) 948-2000 SIC 2834 3841

■ HOSPIRA INC p 709
275 N Field Dr, Lake Forest IL 60045
Tel (224) 212-2000 SIC 2834 3841

HOLLISTER INC p 701
2000 Hollister Dr, Libertyville IL 60048
Tel (847) 680-1000 SIC 3841 3842

SYSMEX AMERICA INC p 1418
577 Aptakisic Rd, Lincolnshire IL 60069
Tel (847) 996-4500 SIC 5047 3841

MEDLINE INDUSTRIES INC p 938
3 Lakes Dr, Northfield IL 60093
Tel (847) 949-5500 SIC 3841 5047 5999

RICHARD WOLF MEDICAL INSTRUMENTS CORP p 1232
353 Corporate Woods Pkwy, Vernon Hills IL 60061
Tel (847) 913-1113 SIC 5047 3841

■ PATTERSON MEDICAL PRODUCTS INC p 1121
28100 Torch Pkwy, Warrenville IL 60555
Tel (630) 393-6671 SIC 3841

BRAINLAB INC p 207
5 Westbrook Corp Ctr, Westchester IL 60154
Tel (800) 784-7700 SIC 5047 3841

ANGIOTECH PHARMACEUTICALS (US) INC p 91
241 W Palatine Rd, Wheeling IL 60090
Tel (847) 637-3333
SIC 3841 3541 3842 8731

MANAN TOOL & MANUFACTURING INC p 900
241 W Palatine Rd, Wheeling IL 60090
Tel (847) 637-3333 SIC 3541 3841

COOK GROUP INC p 365
750 N Daniels Way, Bloomington IN 47404
Tel (812) 339-2235
SIC 3841 3821 3845 6411 6512 6211

COOK INC p 366
750 N Daniels Way, Bloomington IN 47404
Tel (812) 339-2235 SIC 3841

■ ELI LILLY INTERNATIONAL CORP p 487
893 S Delaware St, Indianapolis IN 46225
Tel (317) 276-2000
SIC 8742 2834 8731 3841 2879

AMBU INC p 65
15011 Herriman Blvd, Noblesville IN 46060
Tel (317) 776-6823 SIC 3841

PARAGON MEDICAL INC p 1113
8 Matchett Dr, Pierceton IN 46562
Tel (574) 594-2140 SIC 3089 3841 7371

■ BIOMET INC p 184
56 E Bell Dr, Warsaw IN 46582
Tel (574) 267-6639 SIC 3842 3841 3845

LVB ACQUISITION HOLDING LLC p 887
56 E Bell Dr, Warsaw IN 46582
Tel (574) 267-6639 SIC 3842 3841 3845

■ LVB ACQUISITION INC p 887
56 E Bell Dr, Warsaw IN 46582
Tel (574) 267-6639 SIC 3842 3841 3845

SYMMETRY MEDICAL INC p 1414
3724 N State Road 15, Warsaw IN 46582
Tel (574) 268-2252 SIC 3841 3842

■ MERIDIAN MEDICAL TECHNOLOGIES INC p 949
6350 Stevens Forest Rd, Columbia MD 21046
Tel (443) 259-7800 *SIC* 3841

PEP INDUSTRIES LLC p 1133
110 Frank Mossberg Dr, Attleboro MA 02703
Tel (508) 226-5600
SIC 3089 3351 3469 3471 3643 3841

PRECISION ENGINEERED PRODUCTS LLC p 1168
110 Frank Mossberg Dr, Attleboro MA 02703
Tel (508) 226-5600
SIC 3643 3469 3841 3471 3089 3351

INSTRUMENTATION LABORATORY CO p 747
180 Hartwell Rd, Bedford MA 01730
Tel (800) 955-9525
SIC 3841 2819 8731 2835

▲ INSULET CORP p 747
600 Technology Park Dr # 200, Billerica MA 01821
Tel (978) 600-7000 *SIC* 3841

▲ HAEMONETICS CORP p 652
400 Wood Rd, Braintree MA 02184
Tel (781) 848-7100 *SIC* 3841 3845

KARL STORZ ENDOVISION INC p 804
91 Carpenter Hill Rd, Charlton MA 01507
Tel (508) 248-9011 *SIC* 3841

MEDTRONIC INTERVENTIONAL VASCULAR INC p 939
37a Cherry Hill Dr, Danvers MA 01923
Tel (978) 777-0042 *SIC* 3841

HEARTWARE INTERNATIONAL INC p 679
500 Old Connecticut Path, Framingham MA 01701
Tel (508) 739-0950 *SIC* 3841

TEGRA MEDICAL LLC p 1432
9 Forge Pkwy, Franklin MA 02038
Tel (508) 541-4200 *SIC* 3841

SEKISUI DIAGNOSTICS LLC p 1301
4 Hartwell Pl, Lexington MA 02421
Tel (781) 652-7800 *SIC* 3841

COVIDIEN LP p 385
15 Hampshire St, Mansfield MA 02048
Tel (508) 261-8000
SIC 3842 3841 3845 5122

NELLCOR PURITAN BENNETT LLC p 1025
15 Hampshire St, Mansfield MA 02048
Tel (508) 261-8000 *SIC* 3845 3841

▲ BOSTON SCIENTIFIC CORP p 203
300 Boston Scientific Way, Marlborough MA 01752
Tel (508) 683-4000 *SIC* 3841 3842 3845

■ CYTYC CORP p 406
250 Campus Dr, Marlborough MA 01752
Tel (508) 263-2900 *SIC* 3841

▲ HOLOGIC INC p 702
250 Campus Dr, Marlborough MA 01752
Tel (508) 263-2900 *SIC* 3845 3844 3841

LANTHEUS MEDICAL IMAGING INC p 844
331 Treble Cove Rd, North Billerica MA 01862
Tel (978) 671-8001 *SIC* 3841 2834

LANTHEUS MI INTERMEDIATE INC p 844
331 Treble Cove Rd, North Billerica MA 01862
Tel (978) 671-8001 *SIC* 3841 2834

GYRUS ACMI LLC p 649
136 Turnpike Rd Ste 300, Southborough MA 01772
Tel (508) 804-2600 *SIC* 3841 5047

FRESENIUS MEDICAL CARE HOLDINGS INC p 578
920 Winter St, Waltham MA 02451
Tel (781) 699-9000 *SIC* 3841 8092

FRESENIUS MEDICAL CARE NORTH AMERICA HOLDINGS LIMITED PARTNERSHIP p 578
920 Winter St Ste A, Waltham MA 02451
Tel (781) 699-9000 *SIC* 3841

ACCELLENT ACQUISITION CORP p 14
100 Fordham Rd Bldg C, Wilmington MA 01887
Tel (978) 570-6900
SIC 3841 3317 3679 3315 3552 3089

ACCELLENT HOLDINGS CORP p 14
100 Fordham Rd, Wilmington MA 01887
Tel (978) 570-6900
SIC 3841 3679 3315 3552 3317 3089

■ ACCELLENT LLC p 14
100 Fordham Rd Bldg C, Wilmington MA 01887
Tel (978) 570-6900 *SIC* 3841 8711

■ LAKE REGION MANUFACTURING INC p 839
100 Fordham Rd, Wilmington MA 01887
Tel (952) 361-2515 *SIC* 3841 3845

■ LAKE REGION MEDICAL INC p 839
100 Fordham Rd, Wilmington MA 01887
Tel (978) 570-6900 *SIC* 3841

■ MEDSOURCE TECHNOLOGIES HOLDINGS LLC p 939
100 Fordham Rd Bldg C, Wilmington MA 01887
Tel (978) 570-6900 *SIC* 3841 8711

TECOMET INC p 1432
115 Eames St, Wilmington MA 01887
Tel (978) 642-2400 *SIC* 3841 3444

■ GELMAN SCIENCES INC p 598
674 S Wagner Rd, Ann Arbor MI 48103
Tel (734) 665-0651
SIC 3821 3569 3564 3841 3845 3699

TERUMO CARDIOVASCULAR SYSTEMS CORP p 1440
6200 Jackson Rd, Ann Arbor MI 48103
Tel (734) 663-4145 *SIC* 3845 3841

■ AUTOCAM CORP p 134
4180 40th St Se, Kentwood MI 49512
Tel (616) 698-0707
SIC 3714 3572 3841 5084

▲ NEOGEN CORP p 1025
620 Lesher Pl, Lansing MI 48912
Tel (517) 372-9200 *SIC* 2835 3841 2836

▲ STRYKER CORP p 1394
2825 Airview Blvd, Portage MI 49002
Tel (269) 385-2600 *SIC* 3841 3842 2599

CRETEX COMPANIES INC p 392
311 Lowell Ave Nw, Elk River MN 55330
Tel (763) 441-2121 *SIC* 3272 3089 3841

▲ VASCULAR SOLUTIONS INC p 1545
6464 Sycamore Ct N, Maple Grove MN 55369
Tel (763) 656-4300 *SIC* 3841

GYRUS ACMI LP p 649
9600 Louisiana Ave N, Minneapolis MN 55445
Tel (763) 416-3000 *SIC* 3841

■ MEDIVATORS INC p 938
14605 28th Ave N, Minneapolis MN 55447
Tel (763) 553-3300
SIC 3841 3842 3845 3589

MEDTRONIC INC p 939
710 Medtronic Pkwy, Minneapolis MN 55432
Tel (763) 514-4000 *SIC* 3845 3842 3841

MEDTRONIC USA INC p 939
710 Medtronic Pkwy, Minneapolis MN 55432
Tel (763) 514-4000 *SIC* 3841 5047

RMS CO p 1239
8600 Evergreen Blvd Nw, Minneapolis MN 55433
Tel (763) 786-1520 *SIC* 3841

SMITHS MEDICAL MD INC p 1334
6000 Nathan Ln N Ste 100, Minneapolis MN 55442
Tel (651) 633-2556 *SIC* 3841 3586 3561

■ AMERICAN MEDICAL SYSTEMS LLC p 76
10700 Bren Rd W, Minnetonka MN 55343
Tel (952) 930-6000 *SIC* 3842 3841

■ ST JUDE MEDICAL CARDIOVASCULAR DIVISION p 1369
14901 Deveau Pl, Minnetonka MN 55345
Tel (952) 933-4700 *SIC* 3841 3842

EV3 ENDOVASCULAR INC p 513
3033 Campus Dr Ste W550, Plymouth MN 55441
Tel (763) 398-7000 *SIC* 3841

▲ 3M CO p 2
3m Center Bldg 22011w02, Saint Paul MN 55144
Tel (651) 733-1110
SIC 3841 3842 3291 2842 2672 2891

▲ CARDIOVASCULAR SYSTEMS INC p 253
1225 Old Highway 8 Nw, Saint Paul MN 55112
Tel (651) 259-1600 *SIC* 3841

■ GUIDANT SALES LLC p 645
4100 Hamline Ave N, Saint Paul MN 55112
Tel (800) 949-9459
SIC 3841 3845 5047 8733

▲ ST JUDE MEDICAL INC p 1369
1 Saint Jude Medical Dr, Saint Paul MN 55117
Tel (651) 756-2000 *SIC* 3845 3842 3841

ROCHESTER MEDICAL CORP p 1243
1 Rochester Medical Dr Nw, Stewartville MN 55976
Tel (507) 533-9600 *SIC* 3841

■ MICROTEK MEDICAL INC p 962
512 N Lehmberg Rd, Columbus MS 39702
Tel (662) 327-1863 *SIC* 3841

MALLINCKRODT LLC p 900
675 Jmes S Mcdonnell Blvd, Hazelwood MO 63042
Tel (314) 654-2000
SIC 3841 3829 2834 2833

ATRIUM MEDICAL CORP p 129
5 Wentworth Dr, Hudson NH 03051
Tel (603) 880-1433 *SIC* 3842 3841

CONVATEC INC p 364
1160 Rte 22 Ste 201, Bridgewater NJ 08807
Tel (908) 904-2500 *SIC* 3841

▲ BECTON DICKINSON AND CO p 167
1 Becton Dr, Franklin Lakes NJ 07417
Tel (201) 847-6800
SIC 3841 3842 3829 3826 3821

▲ CANTEL MEDICAL CORP p 247
150 Clove Rd Ste 36, Little Falls NJ 07424
Tel (973) 890-7220 *SIC* 3841 3589

MINDRAY DS USA INC p 972
800 Macarthur Blvd, Mahwah NJ 07430
Tel (201) 995-8000 *SIC* 3845 2835 3841

▲ JOHNSON & JOHNSON p 790
1 Johnson And Johnson Plz, New Brunswick NJ 08933
Tel (732) 524-0400
SIC 2676 2844 3841 3842 2834

▲ C R BARD INC p 233
730 Central Ave, New Providence NJ 07974
Tel (908) 277-8000 *SIC* 3841 3845 3842

TOPCON MEDICAL SYSTEMS INC p 1461
111 Bauer Dr, Oakland NJ 07436
Tel (201) 599-5100
SIC 3841 3826 3827 3829 3851 5049

ALLERGAN INC p 53
400 Interpace Pkwy Bldg D, Parsippany NJ 07054
Tel (862) 261-7000 *SIC* 2834 3841

■ ASCENSIA DIABETES CARE US INC p 116
5 Woodhollow Rd, Parsippany NJ 07054
Tel (973) 560-6500 *SIC* 5047 2835 3841

■ ELECTRO-BIOLOGY INC p 485
100 Interpace Pkwy Ste 1, Parsippany NJ 07054
Tel (973) 299-9022 *SIC* 3841

DATWYLER PHARMA PACKAGING USA REALTY INC p 414
9012 Pennsauken Hwy, Pennsauken NJ 08110
Tel (856) 663-2202 *SIC* 5047 3841

■ INTEGRA LIFESCIENCES CORP p 748
311 Enterprise Dr, Plainsboro NJ 08536
Tel (609) 275-2700 *SIC* 3841

▲ INTEGRA LIFESCIENCES HOLDINGS CORP p 748
311 Enterprise Dr, Plainsboro NJ 08536
Tel (609) 275-0500 *SIC* 3841 2836 3842

■ ABBOTT POINT OF CARE INC p 9
400 College Rd E, Princeton NJ 08540
Tel (609) 454-9000 *SIC* 3841

■ CATALENT PHARMA SOLUTIONS INC p 264
14 Schoolhouse Rd, Somerset NJ 08873
Tel (732) 537-6200 *SIC* 2834 3841

TERUMO AMERICAS HOLDING INC p 1440
2101 Cottontail Ln, Somerset NJ 08873
Tel (732) 302-4900 *SIC* 3841

VENTION MEDICAL INC p 1548
6 Century Ln, South Plainfield NJ 07080
Tel (908) 561-0717 *SIC* 3841

BAYER HEALTHCARE LLC p 161
100 Bayer Blvd, Whippany NJ 07981
Tel (862) 404-3000
SIC 2834 8731 3845 3841

BAYER HEALTHCARE PHARMACEUTICALS INC p 161
100 Bayer Blvd, Whippany NJ 07981
Tel (862) 404-3000 *SIC* 2834 3841

BERLIN SCHERING INC p 175
100 Bayer Blvd, Whippany NJ 07981
Tel (862) 404-3000 *SIC* 2834 3841

▲ MOOG INC p 987
400 Jamison Rd Plant26, Elma NY 14059
Tel (716) 652-2000
SIC 3812 3492 3625 3769 3728 3841

■ NAVILYST MEDICAL INC p 1020
10 Glens Fls Technical Pa, Glens Falls NY 12801
Tel (800) 833-9973 *SIC* 3841

▲ ANGIODYNAMICS INC p 91
14 Plaza Dr, Latham NY 12110
Tel (518) 795-1400 *SIC* 3841

■ SIRONA DENTAL SYSTEMS INC p 1327
3030 47th Ave Ste 500, Long Island City NY 11101
Tel (718) 482-2011
SIC 8021 3313 3843 3841

■ SIGMA INTERNATIONAL GENERAL MEDICAL APPARATUS LLC p 1321
711 Park Ave, Medina NY 14103
Tel (585) 798-3901 *SIC* 3841

■ PALL CORP p 1108
25 Harbor Park Dr, Port Washington NY 11050
Tel (516) 484-5400
SIC 3569 3599 3714 2834 3841

BAUSCH & LOMB INC p 160
1400 N Goodman St, Rochester NY 14609
Tel (585) 338-6000 *SIC* 3851 2834 3841

GETINGE USA INC p 609
1777 E Henrietta Rd, Rochester NY 14623
Tel (585) 475-1400 *SIC* 3842 3841

ALLYN WELCH HOLDINGS INC p 59
4341 State Street Rd, Skaneateles Falls NY 13153
Tel (315) 685-4100 *SIC* 3841

■ WELCH ALLYN INC p 1588
4341 State Street Rd, Skaneateles Falls NY 13153
Tel (315) 685-4100 *SIC* 3841 2835 3827

▲ CONMED CORP p 356
525 French Rd Ste 3, Utica NY 13502
Tel (315) 797-8375 *SIC* 3845 3841

LAERDAL MEDICAL CORP p 837
167 Myers Corners Rd, Wappingers Falls NY 12590
Tel (845) 297-7770 *SIC* 5047 3845 3841

BIOMERIEUX INC p 184
100 Rodolphe St, Durham NC 27712
Tel (919) 620-2000
SIC 3845 8071 3841 3826

ACCUMED CORP p 16
155 Boyce Dr, Mocksville NC 27028
Tel (800) 278-6796 *SIC* 3841

TECAN US GROUP INC p 1430
9401 Globe Center Dr # 140, Morrisville NC 27560
Tel (919) 361-5200 *SIC* 5047 3841

MERZ NORTH AMERICA INC p 951
6501 Six Forks Rd, Raleigh NC 27615
Tel (919) 582-8000 *SIC* 3841

■ ETHICON ENDO-SURGERY INC p 511
4545 Creek Rd, Blue Ash OH 45242
Tel (513) 337-7000 *SIC* 3841

DEVICOR MEDICAL PRODUCTS INC p 434
300 E Business Way Fl 5, Cincinnati OH 45241
Tel (513) 864-9000 *SIC* 3841

▲ ATRICURE INC p 129
7555 Innovation Way, Mason OH 45040
Tel (513) 755-4100 *SIC* 3841

STERIS CORP p 1386
5960 Heisley Rd, Mentor OH 44060
Tel (440) 354-2600 *SIC* 3841 3842 3845

MIDMARK CORP p 966
60 Vista Dr, Versailles OH 45380
Tel (937) 526-3662
SIC 3648 3842 3843 2542 3841

▲ GLOBUS MEDICAL INC p 618
2560 Gen Armistead Ave, Audubon PA 19403
Tel (610) 930-1800 *SIC* 3841

B BRAUN MEDICAL INC p 141
824 12th Ave, Bethlehem PA 18018
Tel (610) 691-5400 *SIC* 3841

B BRAUN OF AMERICA INC p 141
824 12th Ave, Bethlehem PA 18018
Tel (610) 691-5400 *SIC* 6719 3841

■ LIFESCAN INC p 864
965 Chesterbrook Blvd, Chesterbrook PA 19087
Tel (800) 227-8862 *SIC* 2835 3841

NASH KENSEY CORP p 1008
735 Pennsylvania Dr, Exton PA 19341
Tel (484) 713-2100 *SIC* 3841

BAYER MEDICAL CARE INC p 161
1 Bayer Dr, Indianola PA 15051
Tel (724) 940-6800 *SIC* 3841

AIRGAS SAFETY INC p 40
2501 Green Ln, Levittown PA 19057
Tel (215) 826-9000
SIC 5084 5085 3561 3841

SMITHS GROUP NORTH AMERICA INC p 1334
101 Lindenwood Dr Ste 125, Malvern PA 19355
Tel (772) 286-9300 *SIC* 3812 3841 3679

RESPIRONICS INC p 1227
1010 Murry Ridge Ln, Murrysville PA 15668
Tel (724) 387-5200
SIC 3641 3845 3841 3564 8351

BAYER CORP p 161
100 Bayer Rd, Pittsburgh PA 15205
Tel (412) 777-2000
SIC 2821 2879 2819 2834 3841

▲ ENVIRONMENTAL TECTONICS CORP p 503
125 James Way, Southampton PA 18966
Tel (215) 355-9100
SIC 3728 3842 3826 3823 3841

DRAEGER INC p 455
3135 Quarry Rd, Telford PA 18969
Tel (215) 721-5400 *SIC* 3841

■ ARROW INTERNATIONAL INC p 113
550 E Swedesford Rd # 400, Wayne PA 19087
Tel (610) 225-6800 *SIC* 3841 3844

▲ TELEFLEX INC p 1434
550 E Swedesford Rd # 400, Wayne PA 19087
Tel (610) 225-6800 *SIC* 3841 3842

■ DEPUY SYNTHES INC p 431
1302 Wrights Ln E, West Chester PA 19380
Tel (610) 719-5000 *SIC* 3841

SYNTHES (USA) LP p 1416
1302 Wrights Ln E, West Chester PA 19380
Tel (610) 719-5000 *SIC* 3842 3841

■ SYNTHES INC p 1416
1302 Wrights Ln E, West Chester PA 19380
Tel (610) 647-9700 *SIC* 3841 3842 6719

■ STRYKER PUERTO RICO LIMITED p 1394
Hwy 3 Km 131 2 Las Guasim, Arroyo PR 00714
Tel (787) 839-7688 *SIC* 3841

■ ABBVIE BIOTECHNOLOGY LTD p 10
Road No 2 Km 59 2, Barceloneta PR 00617
Tel (787) 846-3500
SIC 2834 2844 2835 3841 3826

MEDTECH PUERTO RICO INC p 939
Parque Industrial Carr Ca Que Industrial, Juncos PR 00777
Tel (787) 561-2200 *SIC* 3841

MEDTRONIC p 939
201 Sabanetas Ind Pk, Ponce PR 00716
Tel (787) 844-4526 *SIC* 3841

MEDTRONIC PUERTO RICO INC p 939
3 Carr 149 Km, Villalba PR 00766
Tel (787) 847-3500 *SIC* 3841

DEROYAL INDUSTRIES INC p 431
200 Debusk Ln, Powell TN 37849
Tel (865) 938-7828 *SIC* 3841

OSTEOMED LLC p 1097
3885 Arapaho Rd, Addison TX 75001
Tel (972) 677-4600 *SIC* 3841

▲ ATRION CORP p 129
1 Allentown Pkwy, Allen TX 75002
Tel (972) 390-9800 *SIC* 3841

ARTHROCARE CORP p 114
7000 W William Cannon Dr # 1, Austin TX 78735
Tel (512) 391-3900 *SIC* 3841

■ LDR HOLDING CORP p 849
13785 Res Blvd Ste 200, Austin TX 78750
Tel (512) 344-3333 *SIC* 3841

▲ LUMINEX CORP p 885
12212 Technology Blvd, Austin TX 78727
Tel (512) 219-8020 *SIC* 3841 8731

HELENA LABORATORIES CORP p 681
1530 Lindbergh Dr, Beaumont TX 77707
Tel (409) 842-3714 *SIC* 3841 3826

SEISA MEDICAL INC p 1301
9005 Montana Ave, El Paso TX 79925
Tel (915) 774-4321 *SIC* 3841

ALCON LABORATORIES HOLDING CORP p 47
6201 South Fwy, Fort Worth TX 76134
Tel (817) 293-0450 *SIC* 2834 3841

ALCON LABORATORIES INC p 47
6201 South Fwy, Fort Worth TX 76134
Tel (817) 293-0450 *SIC* 3841 2834

ALCON MANUFACTURING LTD p 47
6201 South Fwy, Fort Worth TX 76134
Tel (817) 293-0450 *SIC* 2834 3841

ALCON RESEARCH LTD p 47
6201 South Fwy, Fort Worth TX 76134
Tel (817) 551-4555 *SIC* 8733 3841 2834

ALCON SURGICAL INC p 47
6201 South Fwy, Fort Worth TX 76134
Tel (817) 293-0450 *SIC* 3841

FALCON PHARMACEUTICALS LTD p 526
6201 South Fwy, Fort Worth TX 76134
Tel (800) 343-2133 *SIC* 2834 3841

ORTHOFIX INC p 1096
3451 Plano Pkwy, Lewisville TX 75056
Tel (214) 937-2000 *SIC* 3841

ARGON MEDICAL DEVICES INC p 107
5151 Hdqtr Dr Ste 210, Plano TX 75024
Tel (903) 675-9321 *SIC* 3845 3842 3841

ACELITY LP INC p 17
12930 W Interstate 10, San Antonio TX 78249
Tel (210) 524-9000 *SIC* 3841 2834

CHIRON GUERNSEY HOLDINGS LP INC p 301
12930 W Interstate 10, San Antonio TX 78249
Tel (210) 524-9000 *SIC* 3841

■ VITAL SIGNS MN INC p 1562
5859 Farinon Dr Ste 200, San Antonio TX 78249
Tel (952) 894-7523 *SIC* 3841

■ BARD ACCESS SYSTEMS INC p 155
605 N 5600 W, Salt Lake City UT 84116
Tel (801) 522-5000 *SIC* 3841

■ BECTON DICKINSON INFUSION THERAPY HOLDINGS INC p 167
9450 S State St, Sandy UT 84070
Tel (801) 565-2300 *SIC* 3841 3842

■ BECTON DICKINSON INFUSION THERAPY SYSTEMS INC p 167
9450 S State St, Sandy UT 84070
Tel (801) 565-2300 *SIC* 3841 3842

▲ MERIT MEDICAL SYSTEMS INC p 949
1600 W Merit Pkwy, South Jordan UT 84095
Tel (801) 253-1600 *SIC* 3841

THALES USA INC p 1446
2733 Crystal Dr, Arlington VA 22202
Tel (703) 413-6029
SIC 5065 3699 3679 3841 8711 7371

PHYSIO-CONTROL INC p 1146
11811 Willows Rd Ne, Redmond WA 98052
Tel (425) 867-4000
SIC 3841 3845 7699 7372

■ SPACELABS HEALTHCARE (WASHINGTON) INC p 1354
35301 Se Center St, Snoqualmie WA 98065
Tel (425) 396-3300
SIC 3845 3841 3575 7699 7378

■ **SPACELABS HEALTHCARE INC** p 1354
35301 Se Center St, Snoqualmie WA 98065
Tel (425) 396-3302
SIC 3841 3845 3575 7699 7378

■ **ELECTRONIC ASSEMBLY CORP** p 485
55 Jewelers Park Dr, Neenah WI 54956
Tel (920) 722-3451
SIC 3672 3679 3825 3841

TIDI PRODUCTS LLC p 1452
570 Enterprise Dr, Neenah WI 54956
Tel (920) 751-4300 SIC 3843 3841 5047

CS ESTATE INC p 397
N7w22025 Johnson Dr, Waukesha WI 53186
Tel (262) 953-3500 SIC 3841 3663 7374

SIC 3842 Orthopedic, Prosthetic & Surgical Appliances/Splys

BAE SYSTEMS PROTECTION SYSTEMS INC p 144
7822 S 46th St, Phoenix AZ 85044
Tel (602) 643-7233
SIC 3721 2353 3795 3842

■ **BARD PERIPHERAL VASCULAR INC** p 155
1625 W 3rd St, Tempe AZ 85281
Tel (480) 894-9515 SIC 3842

■ **STRYKER SUSTAINABILITY SOLUTIONS INC** p 1394
1810 W Drake Dr Ste 101, Tempe AZ 85283
Tel (888) 888-3433
SIC 5084 5047 7699 3842 3841

■ **ALPHATEC SPINE INC** p 60
5818 El Camino Real, Carlsbad CA 92008
Tel (760) 494-6610 SIC 3842 8711 5047

FREUDENBERG MEDICAL LLC p 579
1110 Mark Ave, Carpinteria CA 93013
Tel (805) 684-3304 SIC 3842

JACUZZI BRANDS LLC p 775
13925 City Center Dr # 200, Chino Hills CA 91709
Tel (909) 606-1416 SIC 3842

FRESENIUS USA INC p 578
4040 Nelson Ave, Concord CA 94520
Tel (925) 288-4218
SIC 2834 3841 2835 3842 2836

MOLDEX-METRIC INC p 982
10111 Jefferson Blvd, Culver City CA 90232
Tel (310) 837-6500 SIC 3842

OSSUR AMERICAS INC p 1097
27051 Towne Centre Dr, Foothill Ranch CA 92610
Tel (949) 362-3883 SIC 3842

SUREFIRE LLC p 1408
18300 Mount Baldy Cir, Fountain Valley CA 92708
Tel (714) 545-9444 SIC 3648 3842 3484

■ **CORDIS CORP** p 369
6500 Paseo Padre Pkwy, Fremont CA 94555
Tel (510) 248-2500 SIC 3841 3842

▲ **INOGEN INC** p 745
326 Bollay Dr, Goleta CA 93117
Tel (805) 562-0500 SIC 3841 3842

▲ **EDWARDS LIFESCIENCES CORP** p 480
1 Edwards Way, Irvine CA 92614
Tel (949) 250-2500 SIC 3842

■ **MENTOR WORLDWIDE LLC** p 943
33 Technology Dr, Irvine CA 92618
Tel (800) 636-8678 SIC 3842 3845 3841

▲ **COOPER COMPANIES INC** p 366
6140 Stoneridge Mall Rd # 590, Pleasanton CA 94588
Tel (925) 460-3600 SIC 3851 3842

ADVANCED BIONICS LLC p 25
12740 San Fernando Rd, Sylmar CA 91342
Tel (661) 362-1400 SIC 3842

ADVANCED BIONICS CORP p 25
28515 Westinghouse Pl, Valencia CA 91355
Tel (661) 362-1400 SIC 3842

■ **DJO FINANCE LLC** p 445
1430 Decision St, Vista CA 92081
Tel (760) 727-1280 SIC 3842

■ **DJO GLOBAL INC** p 445
1430 Decision St, Vista CA 92081
Tel (760) 727-1280 SIC 3842

■ **DJO HOLDINGS LLC** p 445
1430 Decision St, Vista CA 92081
Tel (760) 727-1280 SIC 3842

■ **DJO LLC** p 445
1430 Decision St, Vista CA 92081
Tel (760) 727-1280 SIC 3842

ANDWIN CORP p 91
6636 Variel Ave, Woodland Hills CA 91303
Tel (818) 999-2828
SIC 5113 3842 5199 5087 5047 2835

VCP MOBILITY INC p 1545
6899 Winchester Cir # 200, Boulder CO 80301
Tel (303) 218-4500
SIC 3842 2599 2515 5047 3841

■ **GAMBRO RENAL PRODUCTS INC** p 590
9540 Maroon Cir Unit 400, Englewood CO 80112
Tel (303) 222-6500 SIC 3842

TERUMO BCT INC p 1440
10811 W Collins Ave, Lakewood CO 80215
Tel (303) 232-6800
SIC 8733 3842 3845 5047 7352 7699

SUNRISE MEDICAL HHG INC p 1404
7477 Dry Creek Pkwy, Niwot CO 80503
Tel (303) 218-4600 SIC 3842 3844

SUNRISE MEDICAL HOLDINGS INC p 1404
7477 Dry Creek Pkwy, Niwot CO 80503
Tel (303) 218-4600 SIC 3842

BARDEN CORP p 155
200 Park Ave, Danbury CT 06810
Tel (203) 744-2211
SIC 3562 3469 3842 3089 3399

■ **CELLU TISSUE CORP** p 274
2 Forbes St, East Hartford CT 06108
Tel (860) 289-7496 SIC 2621 3842 2676

▲ **ACME UNITED CORP** p 18
55 Walls Dr Ste 201, Fairfield CT 06824
Tel (203) 254-6060
SIC 3421 2499 3842 3579 3069 3999

UNITED STATES SURGICAL CORP p 1514
555 Long Wharf Dr Fl 4, New Haven CT 06511
Tel (203) 845-1000 SIC 3841 3845 3842

■ **PLAYTEX PRODUCTS LLC** p 1155
6 Research Dr Ste 400, Shelton CT 06484
Tel (203) 944-5500
SIC 2676 3069 2844 3842

■ **COOPERSURGICAL INC** p 367
95 Corporate Dr, Trumbull CT 06611
Tel (203) 601-5200
SIC 5047 3842 3841 3845

BEIERSDORF NORTH AMERICA INC p 169
45 Danbury Rd, Wilton CT 06897
Tel (203) 563-5800
SIC 2844 5122 3842 2841 2672

ILC DOVER LP p 731
1 Moonwalker Rd, Frederica DE 19946
Tel (302) 335-3911 SIC 3842 3721 7389

NEW ILC DOVER INC p 1031
1 Moonwalker Rd, Frederica DE 19946
Tel (302) 335-3911 SIC 3842

▲ **RTI SURGICAL INC** p 1256
11621 Research Cir, Alachua FL 32615
Tel (386) 418-8888 SIC 3842

■ **MAKO SURGICAL CORP** p 899
2555 Davie Rd, Davie FL 33317
Tel (866) 647-6256 SIC 3842

▲ **EXACTECH INC** p 516
2320 Nw 66th Ct, Gainesville FL 32653
Tel (352) 377-1140 SIC 3842

BAE SYSTEMS AH INC p 144
13386 International Pkwy, Jacksonville FL 32218
Tel (904) 741-5400
SIC 3711 3842 3312 3728

MEDTRONIC XOMED INC p 939
6743 Southpoint Dr N, Jacksonville FL 32216
Tel (904) 296-9600 SIC 3842 3841

SAFARILAND LLC p 1265
13386 International Pkwy, Jacksonville FL 32218
Tel (904) 741-5400 SIC 3842 3199

■ **LINVATEC CORP** p 869
11311 Concept Blvd, Largo FL 33773
Tel (727) 392-6464 SIC 3842 3841 2821

HIG CAPITAL PARTNERS III LP p 690
1450 Brickell Ave # 3100, Miami FL 33131
Tel (305) 379-2322
SIC 6211 5084 7352 7699 8748 3842

POINT BLANK ENTERPRISES INC p 1159
2102 Sw 2nd St, Pompano Beach FL 33069
Tel (954) 630-0900
SIC 3842 3462 3728 8711

POINT BLANK SOLUTIONS INC p 1159
2101 Sw 2nd St, Pompano Beach FL 33069
Tel (800) 413-5155 SIC 3842

■ **HALKEY-ROBERTS CORP** p 654
2700 Halkey Roberts Pl N, Saint Petersburg FL 33716
Tel (727) 471-4200 SIC 3842

HOVEROUND CORP p 713
6010 Cattleridge Dr, Sarasota FL 34232
Tel (941) 739-6200 SIC 3842

▲ **HALYARD HEALTH INC** p 655
5405 Windward Pkwy, Alpharetta GA 30004
Tel (678) 425-9273 SIC 3842 3841 3845

■ **MICROTEK MEDICAL HOLDINGS INC** p 962
13000 Drfeld Pkwy Ste 300, Alpharetta GA 30004
Tel (678) 896-4400 SIC 3842

THERAGENICS CORP p 1447
5203 Bristol Indus Way, Buford GA 30518
Tel (770) 271-0233 SIC 2834 3842

POREX CORP p 1161
500 Bohannon Rd, Fairburn GA 30213
Tel (800) 241-0195 SIC 3082 3842 3841

▲ **MIMEDX GROUP INC** p 972
1775 W Oak Commons Ct, Marietta GA 30062
Tel (770) 651-9100 SIC 3842 3841

■ **SALISBURY ELECTRICAL SAFETY LLC** p 1272
101 E Crssrads Pkwy Ste A, Bolingbrook IL 60440
Tel (877) 406-4501 SIC 3842

■ **SAGE PRODUCTS LLC** p 1267
3909 3 Oaks Rd, Cary IL 60013
Tel (815) 455-4700 SIC 3842 5047

■ **BAXTER HEALTHCARE CORP** p 160
1 Baxter Pkwy, Deerfield IL 60015
Tel (224) 948-2000
SIC 3841 2835 2389 3842 5047

▲ **BAXTER INTERNATIONAL INC** p 160
1 Baxter Pkwy, Deerfield IL 60015
Tel (224) 948-2000
SIC 2834 3841 2835 3842

■ **KNOWLES ELECTRONICS LLC** p 825
1151 Maplewood Dr, Itasca IL 60143
Tel (630) 250-5100 SIC 3679 3842

HOLLISTER INC p 701
2000 Hollister Dr, Libertyville IL 60048
Tel (847) 680-1000 SIC 3841 3842

LEICA BIOSYSTEMS RICHMOND INC p 854
5205 Rte 12, Richmond IL 60071
Tel (815) 678-2000 SIC 3842

MAGID GLOVE & SAFETY MANUFACTURING CO LLC p 895
1300 Naperville Dr, Romeoville IL 60446
Tel (773) 384-2070
SIC 3151 2381 5699 3842 2326

PHONAK LLC p 1145
4520 Weaver Pkwy Ste 1, Warrenville IL 60555
Tel (630) 821-5000 SIC 3842 5999

ANGIOTECH PHARMACEUTICALS (US) INC p 91
241 W Palatine Rd, Wheeling IL 60090
Tel (847) 637-3333
SIC 3841 3541 3842 8731

■ **AEARO TECHNOLOGIES LLC** p 28
5457 W 79th St, Indianapolis IN 46268
Tel (317) 692-6666 SIC 3842 3851 3643

MASCO BATH CORP p 915
8445 Keystone Xing # 100, Indianapolis IN 46240
Tel (317) 254-5959 SIC 3088 3842

■ **BIOMET INC** p 184
56 E Bell Dr, Warsaw IN 46582
Tel (574) 267-6639 SIC 3842 3841 3845

■ **BIOMET ORTHOPEDICS LLC** p 184
56 E Bell Dr, Warsaw IN 46582
Tel (574) 267-6639 SIC 3842

■ **DEPUY ORTHOPAEDICS INC** p 431
700 Orthopaedic Dr, Warsaw IN 46582
Tel (574) 267-8143 SIC 3842

■ **DEPUY PRODUCTS INC** p 431
700 Orthopaedic Dr, Warsaw IN 46582
Tel (574) 267-8143 SIC 3842

LVB ACQUISITION HOLDING LLC p 887
56 E Bell Dr, Warsaw IN 46582
Tel (574) 267-6639 SIC 3842 3841 3845

■ **LVB ACQUISITION INC** p 887
56 E Bell Dr, Warsaw IN 46582
Tel (574) 267-6639 SIC 3842 3841 3845

SYMMETRY MEDICAL INC p 1414
3724 N State Road 15, Warsaw IN 46582
Tel (574) 268-2252 SIC 3841 3842

▲ **ZIMMER BIOMET HOLDINGS INC** p 1643
345 E Main St, Warsaw IN 46580
Tel (574) 267-6131 SIC 3842

■ **ZIMMER INC** p 1643
1800 W Center St, Warsaw IN 46580
Tel (330) 343-8801 SIC 3842

BLAUER MANUFACTURING CO INC p 189
20 Aberdeen St, Boston MA 02215
Tel (617) 536-6606 SIC 5099 3842 2337

GENZYME CORP p 605
500 Kendall St, Cambridge MA 02142
Tel (617) 252-7500
SIC 2835 2834 8071 3842 2836 5122

GENTEX OPTICS INC p 605
183 W Main St, Dudley MA 01571
Tel (570) 282-8531 SIC 3851 3842

COVIDIEN LP p 385
15 Hampshire St, Mansfield MA 02048
Tel (508) 261-8000
SIC 3842 3841 3845 5122

▲ **BOSTON SCIENTIFIC CORP** p 203
300 Boston Scientific Way, Marlborough MA 01752
Tel (508) 683-4000 SIC 3841 3842 3845

TULIP US HOLDINGS INC p 1491
1489 Cedar St, Holt MI 48842
Tel (517) 694-2300 SIC 3842

▲ **STRYKER CORP** p 1394
2825 Airview Blvd, Portage MI 49002
Tel (269) 385-2600 SIC 3841 3842 2599

CENTURION MEDICAL PRODUCTS CORP p 281
100 Centurion Way, Williamston MI 48895
Tel (517) 546-5400 SIC 3842 2759 2671

■ **CAPITAL SAFETY INC** p 250
7900 Intl Dr Ste 405, Bloomington MN 55425
Tel (612) 216-5800 SIC 3842

GN HEARING CARE CORP p 619
8001 E Bloomington Fwy, Bloomington MN 55420
Tel (800) 248-4327 SIC 3842

STARKEY LABORATORIES INC p 1379
6600 Washington Ave S, Eden Prairie MN 55344
Tel (952) 941-6401 SIC 3842

AMERICAN MEDICAL SYSTEMS HOLDINGS INC p 76
10700 Bren Rd W, Hopkins MN 55343
Tel (952) 930-6000 SIC 3842

COLOPLAST CORP p 338
1601 W River Rd, Minneapolis MN 55411
Tel (612) 337-7800 SIC 3842 2844 5047

COVIDIEN HOLDING INC p 385
710 Medtronic Pkwy, Minneapolis MN 55432
Tel (508) 261-8000 SIC 3842

GN US HOLDINGS INC p 619
8001 E Bloomington Fwy, Minneapolis MN 55420
Tel (952) 769-8000 SIC 3842

KURT MANUFACTURING CO INC p 832
5280 Main St Ne, Minneapolis MN 55421
Tel (763) 572-1500
SIC 3499 3545 3363 3728 3842 3365

■ **MEDIVATORS INC** p 938
14605 28th Ave N, Minneapolis MN 55447
Tel (763) 553-3300
SIC 3841 3842 3845 3589

MEDTRONIC INC p 939
710 Medtronic Pkwy, Minneapolis MN 55432
Tel (763) 514-4000 SIC 3845 3842 3841

■ **AMERICAN MEDICAL SYSTEMS LLC** p 76
10700 Bren Rd W, Minnetonka MN 55343
Tel (952) 930-6000 SIC 3842 3841

■ **ST JUDE MEDICAL CARDIOVASCULAR DIVISION** p 1369
14901 Deveau Pl, Minnetonka MN 55345
Tel (952) 933-4700 SIC 3841 3842

■ **CHART INC** p 290
407 7th St Nw, New Prague MN 56071
Tel (952) 758-4484 SIC 3443 3842

AMPLIFON (USA) INC p 86
5000 Cheshire Pkwy N, Plymouth MN 55446
Tel (763) 268-4000 SIC 3842

SMITHS MEDICAL ASD INC p 1334
6000 Nathan Ln N Ste 100, Plymouth MN 55442
Tel (763) 383-3000 SIC 3842

UNITRON HEARING INC p 1515
14755 27th Ave N, Plymouth MN 55447
Tel (763) 744-3300 SIC 3842

▲ **3M CO** p 2
3m Center Bldg 22011w02, Saint Paul MN 55144
Tel (651) 733-1110
SIC 3841 3842 3291 2842 2672 2891

■ **RTI REMMELE ENGINEERING INC** p 1256
10 Old Highway 8 Sw, Saint Paul MN 55112
Tel (651) 635-4100
SIC 3728 3569 3812 3761 3842

■ **ST JUDE MEDICAL ATG INC** p 1369
1 Lillehei Plz, Saint Paul MN 55117
Tel (651) 756-2000 SIC 3842

▲ **ST JUDE MEDICAL INC** p 1369
1 Saint Jude Medical Dr, Saint Paul MN 55117
Tel (651) 756-2000 SIC 3845 3842 3841

ATRIUM MEDICAL CORP p 129
5 Wentworth Dr, Hudson NH 03051
Tel (603) 880-1433 SIC 3842 3841

GLOBE MANUFACTURING CO-OK LLC p 618
37 Loudon Rd, Pittsfield NH 03263
Tel (603) 435-8323 SIC 3842

▲ **BECTON DICKINSON AND CO** p 167
1 Becton Dr, Franklin Lakes NJ 07417
Tel (201) 847-6800
SIC 3841 3842 3829 3826 3821

ANSELL HEALTHCARE PRODUCTS LLC p 93
111 Wood Ave S Ste 210, Iselin NJ 08830
Tel (732) 345-5400
SIC 3069 3842 2822 2326

ANSELL PROTECTIVE PRODUCTS LLC p 93
111 Wood Ave S Ste 210, Iselin NJ 08830
Tel (732) 345-5400 SIC 3842 3069

■ **HOWMEDICA OSTEONICS CORP** p 713
325 Corporate Dr, Mahwah NJ 07430
Tel (201) 831-5000 SIC 3842 5047

DEPUY INC p 431
1 Johnson And Johnson Plz, New Brunswick NJ 08901
Tel (732) 524-0400 SIC 3842

▲ **JOHNSON & JOHNSON** p 790
1 Johnson And Johnson Plz, New Brunswick NJ 08933
Tel (732) 524-0400
SIC 2676 2844 3841 3842 2834

▲ **C R BARD INC** p 233
730 Central Ave, New Providence NJ 07974
Tel (908) 277-8000 SIC 3841 3845 3842

SIVANTOS INC p 1328
10 Constitution Ave, Piscataway NJ 08854
Tel (732) 562-6600 SIC 3842

▲ **INTEGRA LIFESCIENCES HOLDINGS CORP** p 748
311 Enterprise Dr, Plainsboro NJ 08536
Tel (609) 275-0500 SIC 3841 2836 3842

▲ **DERMA SCIENCES INC** p 431
214 Carnegie Ctr Ste 300, Princeton NJ 08540
Tel (609) 514-4744 SIC 3842 2211 2834

PACIFIC DUNLOP INVESTMENTS (USA) INC p 1104
200 Schulz Dr, Red Bank NJ 07701
Tel (732) 345-5400 SIC 3069 3842

■ **ETHICON INC** p 511
Us Route 22, Somerville NJ 08876
Tel (732) 524-0400 SIC 3842

■ **JOHNSON & JOHNSON MEDICAL INC** p 790
Us Rt 22, Somerville NJ 08876
Tel (908) 218-0707 SIC 3842

■ **SUNBRIDGE RETIREMENT CARE ASSOCIATES INC** p 1401
101 Sun Ave Ne, Albuquerque NM 87109
Tel (505) 821-3355 SIC 6513 3842

CREATIVE ORTHOTICS & PROSTHETICS INC p 390
1300 College Ave Ste 1, Elmira NY 14901
Tel (607) 734-7215 SIC 3842 5999 5047

■ **GRAND SLAM HOLDINGS LLC** p 630
345 Park Ave Bsmt Lb4, New York NY 10154
Tel (212) 583-5000 SIC 3842

VSM INVESTORS LLC p 1566
245 Park Ave Fl 41, New York NY 10167
Tel (212) 351-1600 SIC 3842 2599 2515

CURBELL INC p 402
7 Cobham Dr, Orchard Park NY 14127
Tel (716) 667-3377 SIC 5162 3669 3842

COMMUNITY PRODUCTS LLC p 350
2032 Route 213 St, Rifton NY 12471
Tel (845) 658-8799 SIC 3842 2511 3844

GETINGE USA INC p 609
1777 E Henrietta Rd, Rochester NY 14623
Tel (585) 475-1400 SIC 3842 3841

▲ **LAKELAND INDUSTRIES INC** p 840
3555 Vtrans Mem Hwy Ste C, Ronkonkoma NY 11779
Tel (631) 981-9700 SIC 3842 2389

TURBINE ENGINE COMPONENTS TECHNOLOGIES - UTICA CORP p 1492
2 Halsey Rd, Whitesboro NY 13492
Tel (315) 768-8070
SIC 3724 3511 3429 3842 3769

AMERICAN FIBER & FINISHING INC p 72
225 N Depot St, Albemarle NC 28001
Tel (704) 983-6102
SIC 2211 3842 2844 2392

■ **MEDICAL ACTION INDUSTRIES INC** p 936
25 Heywood Rd, Arden NC 28704
Tel (631) 231-4600 SIC 3842

KAYSER-ROTH CORP p 805
102 Corporate Center Blvd, Greensboro NC 27408
Tel (336) 852-2030
SIC 2252 2251 5961 8741 3842

SCOTT TECHNOLOGIES INC p 1294
4320 Goldmine Rd, Monroe NC 28110
Tel (800) 247-7257 SIC 3842 3728 3569

■ **TELEFLEX MEDICAL INC** p 1434
3015 Carrington Mill Blvd, Morrisville NC 27560
Tel (919) 544-8000 SIC 3842

WCM HOLDINGS INC p 1585
1150 Canal Rd, Cincinnati OH 45241
Tel (513) 705-2100 SIC 5099 2381 3842

PHILIPS MEDICAL SYSTEMS (CLEVELAND) INC p 1143
595 Miner Rd, Cleveland OH 44143
Tel (440) 247-2652
SIC 3844 5047 5137 3842 3821 3699

■ **MORNING PRIDE MFG LLC** p 989
1 Innovation Ct, Dayton OH 45414
Tel (937) 264-2662 SIC 3842 2326

▲ **CARDINAL HEALTH INC** p 253
7000 Cardinal Pl, Dublin OH 43017
Tel (614) 757-5000
SIC 5122 5047 8741 3842

▲ **INVACARE CORP** p 760
1 Invacare Way, Elyria OH 44035
Tel (440) 329-6000 SIC 3842 2514 2813

STERIS CORP p 1386
5960 Heisley Rd, Mentor OH 44060
Tel (440) 354-2600 *SIC* 3841 3842 3845
INVACARE CORP (TW) p 760
39400 Taylor Pkwy, North Ridgeville OH 44035
Tel (440) 329-6000 *SIC* 3842
CHESTER WEST HOLDINGS INC p 295
11500 Canal Rd, Sharonville OH 45241
Tel (800) 647-1900
SIC 3842 5136 5099 5137 2381
MIDMARK CORP p 966
60 Vista Dr, Versailles OH 45380
Tel (937) 526-3662
SIC 3648 3842 3843 2542 3841
■ **PCC STRUCTURALS INC** p 1123
4600 Se Harney Dr, Portland OR 97206
Tel (503) 777-3881
SIC 3728 3842 3511 3824
■ **MINE SAFETY APPLIANCES CO LLC** p 973
1000 Cranberry Woods Dr, Cranberry Township PA 16066
Tel (724) 776-8600
SIC 3842 3826 3823 3648 3829
▲ **MSA SAFETY INC** p 996
1000 Cranberry Woods Dr, Cranberry Township PA 16066
Tel (724) 776-8600
SIC 3842 3826 3823 3648 3829
PRIDE MOBILITY PRODUCTS CORP p 1174
182 Susquehanna Ave, Exeter PA 18643
Tel (570) 655-5574 *SIC* 3842 3799 3751
SIEMENS MEDICAL SOLUTIONS USA INC p 1320
40 Liberty Blvd, Malvern PA 19355
Tel (610) 219-6300
SIC 5047 3845 3842 3843
MUTUAL INDUSTRIES NORTH INC p 1003
707 W Grange Ave Ste 1, Philadelphia PA 19120
Tel (215) 927-6000 *SIC* 3842 2221
GENTEX CORP p 604
324 Main St, Simpson PA 18407
Tel (570) 282-3550 *SIC* 3842 8731 2295
▲ **ENVIRONMENTAL TECTONICS CORP** p 503
125 James Way, Southampton PA 18966
Tel (215) 355-9100
SIC 3728 3842 3826 3823 3841
▲ **TELEFLEX INC** p 1434
550 E Swedesford Rd # 400, Wayne PA 19087
Tel (610) 225-6800 *SIC* 3841 3842
SYNTHES (USA) LP p 1416
1302 Wrights Ln E, West Chester PA 19380
Tel (610) 719-5000 *SIC* 3842 3841
■ **SYNTHES INC** p 1416
1302 Wrights Ln E, West Chester PA 19380
Tel (610) 647-9700 *SIC* 3841 3842 6719
BLUEWATER DEFENSE INC p 193
Corozal Ind Pk Carr 159, Corozal PR 00783
Tel (787) 746-5020
SIC 2393 2326 3842 2325
■ **PALL LIFE SCIENCES PUERTO RICO LLC** p 1108
Carr 194 Pall Blvd 98, Fajardo PR 00738
Tel (787) 863-1124 *SIC* 3842
■ **ZIMMER CARIBE INC** p 1643
Road 1 Km 123 Hm 4 Bldg 1, Mercedita PR 00715
Tel (787) 259-5959 *SIC* 3842
NORTH SAFETY PRODUCTS LLC p 1053
2000 Plainfield Pike, Cranston RI 02921
Tel (401) 943-4400 *SIC* 3842
NORCROSS SAFETY PRODUCTS LLC p 1047
900 Douglas Pike Ste 100, Smithfield RI 02917
Tel (800) 430-5490 *SIC* 3842 3021 3469
■ **SPERIAN PROTECTION USA INC** p 1358
900 Douglas Pike, Smithfield RI 02917
Tel (401) 232-1200
SIC 3851 3842 2311 7218 5999
▲ **SUMMER INFANT INC** p 1398
1275 Park East Dr, Woonsocket RI 02895
Tel (401) 671-6550
SIC 2514 2399 3842 3261
HEART HOSPITAL OF SOUTH DAKOTA LLC p 678
4500 W 69th St, Sioux Falls SD 57108
Tel (605) 977-7000 *SIC* 8062 3842
SHELBY GROUP INTERNATIONAL INC p 1314
1255 W Schilling Blvd, Collierville TN 38017
Tel (901) 795-5810
SIC 3842 2381 3851 5137
NATIONAL SEATING & MOBILITY INC p 1016
320 Premier Ct S Ste 220, Franklin TN 37067
Tel (615) 595-1115 *SIC* 3842 5999
MEDTRONIC SOFAMOR DANEK USA INC p 939
1800 Pyramid Pl, Memphis TN 38132
Tel (901) 396-3133 *SIC* 3842 8099
SMITH & NEPHEW INC p 1333
1450 E Brooks Rd, Memphis TN 38116
Tel (901) 396-2121 *SIC* 3842 5047
WRIGHT MEDICAL GROUP INC p 1627
1023 Cherry Rd, Memphis TN 38117
Tel (800) 238-7117 *SIC* 3842
WRIGHT MEDICAL TECHNOLOGY INC p 1627
1023 Cherry Rd, Memphis TN 38117
Tel (901) 867-9971 *SIC* 3842 3845
■ **ENCORE MEDICAL LP** p 496
9800 Metric Blvd, Austin TX 78758
Tel (512) 832-9500 *SIC* 3842 5047
HANGER INC p 657
10910 Domain Dr Ste 300, Austin TX 78758
Tel (512) 777-3800 *SIC* 8093 5047 3842
ROYAL BATHS MANUFACTURING CO LTD p 1254
14635 Chrisman Rd, Houston TX 77039
Tel (281) 442-3400
SIC 3842 3949 3432 3281
CENTREX PRECISION PLASTICS p 281
7700 Bent Dr Ste 100, Irving TX 75063
Tel (972) 929-4804 *SIC* 3842

ARGON MEDICAL DEVICES INC p 107
5151 Hdqtr Dr Ste 210, Plano TX 75024
Tel (903) 675-9321 *SIC* 3845 3842 3841
KCI USA INC p 806
12930 W Interstate 10, San Antonio TX 78249
Tel (800) 275-4524 *SIC* 7352 3842 5047
KINETIC CONCEPTS INC p 819
12930 W Interstate 10, San Antonio TX 78249
Tel (800) 531-5346 *SIC* 3842
■ **BECTON DICKINSON INFUSION THERAPY HOLDINGS INC** p 167
9450 S State St, Sandy UT 84070
Tel (801) 565-2300 *SIC* 3841 3842
■ **BECTON DICKINSON INFUSION THERAPY SYSTEMS INC** p 167
9450 S State St, Sandy UT 84070
Tel (801) 565-2300 *SIC* 3841 3842
K2M GROUP HOLDINGS INC p 799
600 Hope Pkwy Se, Leesburg VA 20175
Tel (703) 777-3155 *SIC* 3842
■ **EAGLE INDUSTRIES UNLIMITED INC** p 468
2645 Intl Pkwy Ste 102, Virginia Beach VA 23454
Tel (888) 343-7547 *SIC* 3842
REYNOLDS PRESTO PRODUCTS INC p 1231
670 N Perkins St, Appleton WI 54914
Tel (800) 558-3525 *SIC* 2671 2673 3842
CAPTEL INC p 252
450 Science Dr, Madison WI 53711
Tel (608) 238-5400 *SIC* 3842
RITE-HITE CO LLC p 1236
8900 N Arbor Dr, Milwaukee WI 53223
Tel (414) 355-2600 *SIC* 5084 3842 3448
BRUNO INDEPENDENT LIVING AIDS INC p 221
1780 Executive Dr, Oconomowoc WI 53066
Tel (262) 953-5405 *SIC* 3842

SIC 3843 Dental Eqpt & Splys

DR FRESH LLC p 454
6645 Caballero Blvd, Buena Park CA 90620
Tel (714) 690-1573 *SIC* 5047 3843
DEN-MAT HOLDINGS LLC p 428
1017 W Central Ave, Lompoc CA 93436
Tel (805) 346-3700 *SIC* 3843
■ **3M UNITEK CORP** p 3
2724 Peck Rd, Monrovia CA 91016
Tel (626) 445-7960 *SIC* 3843
■ **KERR CORP** p 813
1717 W Collins Ave, Orange CA 92867
Tel (714) 516-7400 *SIC* 3843
■ **ORMCO CORP** p 1095
1717 W Collins Ave, Orange CA 92867
Tel (714) 516-7400 *SIC* 3843
■ **SYBRON DENTAL SPECIALTIES INC** p 1413
1717 W Collins Ave, Orange CA 92867
Tel (714) 516-7400 *SIC* 3843 2834
DEN-MAT CORP p 428
236 S Broadway St, Orcutt CA 93455
Tel (805) 922-8491 *SIC* 2844 3843
▲ **ALIGN TECHNOLOGY INC** p 50
2560 Orchard Pkwy, San Jose CA 95131
Tel (408) 470-1000 *SIC* 3843
CP DENTAL LLC p 387
2727 Skyway Dr, Santa Maria CA 93455
Tel (800) 433-6628 *SIC* 3843
■ **NOBEL BIOCARE USA LLC** p 1046
22715 Savi Ranch Pkwy, Yorba Linda CA 92887
Tel (714) 282-4800 *SIC* 3843
WATER PIK INC p 1581
1730 E Prospect Rd, Fort Collins CO 80525
Tel (800) 525-2774 *SIC* 3432 3843
▲ **DANAHER CORP** p 411
2200 Penn Ave Nw Ste 800w, Washington DC 20037
Tel (202) 828-0850
SIC 3845 3829 3577 3823 3843
■ **BIOMET 3I LLC** p 184
4555 Riverside Dr, Palm Beach Gardens FL 33410
Tel (561) 775-9928 *SIC* 3843
PETER BRASSELER HOLDINGS LLC p 1138
1 Brasseler Blvd, Savannah GA 31419
Tel (912) 925-8525 *SIC* 5047 3841 3843
YOUNG INNOVATIONS INC p 1638
2260 Wendt St, Algonquin IL 60102
Tel (847) 458-5400 *SIC* 3843
HU-FRIEDY MFG CO LLC p 715
3232 N Rockwell St, Chicago IL 60618
Tel (773) 975-3975 *SIC* 3843
YOUNG INNOVATIONS HOLDINGS LLC p 1638
111 S Wacker Dr, Chicago IL 60606
Tel (312) 506-5600 *SIC* 3843
SUNSTAR AMERICAS INC p 1404
301 E Central Rd, Schaumburg IL 60195
Tel (773) 777-4000 *SIC* 3843
■ **APOGENT TECHNOLOGIES INC** p 97
81 Wyman St, Waltham MA 02451
Tel (781) 622-1300 *SIC* 3821 3229 3843
RANIR LLC p 1208
4701 East Paris Ave Se, Grand Rapids MI 49512
Tel (616) 698-8880 *SIC* 3843 3991
MYCONE DENTAL SUPPLY CO INC p 1004
480 S Democrat Rd, Gibbstown NJ 08027
Tel (856) 663-4700 *SIC* 5047 3843 2844
■ **SIRONA DENTAL SYSTEMS INC** p 1327
3030 47th Ave Ste 500, Long Island City NY 11101
Tel (718) 482-2011
SIC 8021 3313 3843 3841
WBC GROUP LLC p 1585
6333 Hudson Crossing Pkwy, Hudson OH 44236
Tel (800) 472-4221 *SIC* 5122 5047 3843
MIDMARK CORP p 966
60 Vista Dr, Versailles OH 45380
Tel (937) 526-3662
SIC 3648 3842 3843 2542 3841
A-DEC INC p 7
2601 Crestview Dr, Newberg OR 97132
Tel (503) 538-9471 *SIC* 3843
DENTAL IMAGING TECHNOLOGIES CORP p 429
2800 Crystal Dr, Hatfield PA 19440
Tel (215) 997-5666 *SIC* 3843 5047

SIEMENS MEDICAL SOLUTIONS USA INC p 1320
40 Liberty Blvd, Malvern PA 19355
Tel (610) 219-6300
SIC 5047 3845 3842 3843
▲ **DENTSPLY SIRONA INC** p 429
221 W Philadelphia St, York PA 17401
Tel (717) 845-7511 *SIC* 3843
KURARAY AMERICA INC p 832
2625 Bay Area Blvd # 600, Houston TX 77058
Tel (281) 474-1592 *SIC* 2821 3081 3843
ULTRADENT PRODUCTS INC p 1501
505 W 10200 S, South Jordan UT 84095
Tel (801) 572-4200 *SIC* 3843
PHILIPS ORAL HEALTHCARE LLC p 1143
22100 Bothell Everett Hwy, Bothell WA 98021
Tel (425) 487-7000 *SIC* 3843
TIDI PRODUCTS LLC p 1452
570 Enterprise Dr, Neenah WI 54956
Tel (920) 751-4300 *SIC* 3843 3841 5047
AMERICAN ORTHODONTICS CORP p 77
3524 Washington Ave, Sheboygan WI 53081
Tel (920) 457-5051 *SIC* 3843 8021

SIC 3844 X-ray Apparatus & Tubes

▲ **VARIAN MEDICAL SYSTEMS INC** p 1544
3100 Hansen Way, Palo Alto CA 94304
Tel (650) 493-4000 *SIC* 3845 3844 7372
SUNRISE MEDICAL HHG INC p 1404
7477 Dry Creek Pkwy, Niwot CO 80503
Tel (303) 218-4600 *SIC* 3842 3844
SIEMENS CORP p 1320
300 New Jersey Ave Nw # 10, Washington DC 20001
Tel (202) 434-4800
SIC 3661 3641 3844 3612 3357
▲ **BRUKER CORP** p 220
40 Manning Rd, Billerica MA 01821
Tel (978) 663-3660 *SIC* 3826 3844
▲ **HOLOGIC INC** p 702
250 Campus Dr, Marlborough MA 01752
Tel (508) 263-2900 *SIC* 3845 3844 3841
COMMUNITY PRODUCTS LLC p 350
2032 Route 213 St, Rifton NY 12471
Tel (845) 658-8799 *SIC* 3842 2511 3844
PHILIPS MEDICAL SYSTEMS (CLEVELAND) INC p 1143
595 Miner Rd, Cleveland OH 44143
Tel (440) 247-2652
SIC 3844 5047 5137 3842 3821 3699
■ **ARROW INTERNATIONAL INC** p 113
550 E Swedesford Rd # 400, Wayne PA 19087
Tel (610) 225-6800 *SIC* 3841 3844
■ **OEC MEDICAL SYSTEMS INC** p 1075
384 N Wright Brothers Dr, Salt Lake City UT 84116
Tel (801) 328-9300 *SIC* 3844 7699
JASON HOLDINGS INC p 778
411 E Wisconsin Ave # 2120, Milwaukee WI 53202
Tel (414) 277-9300
SIC 2297 3465 3469 3844 3443
■ **JASON INC** p 778
411 E Wisconsin Ave, Milwaukee WI 53202
Tel (414) 277-9300
SIC 3465 2297 3625 3469 3844 3443
▲ **JASON INDUSTRIES INC** p 778
833 E Michigan St Ste 900, Milwaukee WI 53202
Tel (414) 277-9300
SIC 3465 2297 3625 3469 3844 3443
■ **JPHI HOLDINGS INC** p 795
411 E Wisconsin Ave, Milwaukee WI 53202
Tel (414) 277-9445
SIC 3465 2297 3625 3469 3844 3443

SIC 3845 Electromedical & Electrotherapeutic Apparatus

■ **ABBOTT DIABETES CARE INC** p 9
1360 S Loop Rd, Alameda CA 94502
Tel (510) 749-5400 *SIC* 2835 3845 3823
▲ **CUTERA INC** p 403
3240 Bayshore Blvd, Brisbane CA 94005
Tel (415) 657-5500 *SIC* 3845
▲ **IONIS PHARMACEUTICALS INC** p 762
2855 Gazelle Ct, Carlsbad CA 92010
Tel (760) 931-9200 *SIC* 2834 8731 3845
■ **BIOSENSE WEBSTER INC** p 184
3333 S Diamond Canyon Rd, Diamond Bar CA 91765
Tel (909) 839-8500 *SIC* 3845 3841
▲ **OSI SYSTEMS INC** p 1097
12525 Chadron Ave, Hawthorne CA 90250
Tel (310) 978-0516 *SIC* 3674 3845
SOLTA MEDICAL INC p 1339
25881 Industrial Blvd, Hayward CA 94545
Tel (510) 786-6946 *SIC* 3845
▲ **BIO-RAD LABORATORIES INC** p 183
1000 Alfred Nobel Dr, Hercules CA 94547
Tel (510) 724-7000 *SIC* 3826 3845 2835
▲ **MASIMO CORP** p 915
52 Discovery, Irvine CA 92618
Tel (949) 297-7000 *SIC* 3845
■ **MENTOR WORLDWIDE LLC** p 943
33 Technology Dr, Irvine CA 92618
Tel (800) 636-8678 *SIC* 3842 3845 3841
SYNERON INC p 1415
3 Goodyear Ste A, Irvine CA 92618
Tel (949) 716-6670 *SIC* 3845
MEDTRONIC MINIMED INC p 939
18000 Devonshire St, Northridge CA 91325
Tel (800) 646-4633 *SIC* 3845
■ **VARIAN INC** p 1544
3100 Hansen Way, Palo Alto CA 94304
Tel (650) 213-8000
SIC 3826 3845 3829 3827
▲ **VARIAN MEDICAL SYSTEMS INC** p 1544
3100 Hansen Way, Palo Alto CA 94304
Tel (650) 493-4000 *SIC* 3845 3844 7372
▲ **NATUS MEDICAL INC** p 1019
6701 Koll Center Pkwy # 150, Pleasanton CA 94566
Tel (925) 223-6700 *SIC* 3845

■ **THORATEC CORP** p 1450
6035 Stoneridge Dr, Pleasanton CA 94588
Tel (925) 847-8600 *SIC* 3845 3841
▲ **ICU MEDICAL INC** p 728
951 Calle Amanecer, San Clemente CA 92673
Tel (949) 366-2183 *SIC* 3841 3845
■ **CAREFUSION CORP** p 255
3750 Torrey View Ct, San Diego CA 92130
Tel (858) 617-2000 *SIC* 3841 3845 8742
VOLCANO CORP p 1564
3721 Vly Cntre Dr Ste 500, San Diego CA 92130
Tel (800) 228-4728 *SIC* 3845
■ **ABBOTT MEDICAL OPTICS INC** p 9
1700 E Saint Andrew Pl, Santa Ana CA 92705
Tel (714) 247-8200 *SIC* 3841 3845
■ **AMO USA INC** p 86
1700 E Saint Andrew Pl, Santa Ana CA 92705
Tel (714) 247-8200 *SIC* 3841 3845
■ **ABBOTT VASCULAR INC** p 10
3200 Lakeside Dr, Santa Clara CA 95054
Tel (650) 474-3000 *SIC* 3845
▲ **COHERENT INC** p 335
5100 Patrick Henry Dr, Santa Clara CA 95054
Tel (408) 764-4000 *SIC* 3826 3845 3699
LUMASENSE TECHNOLOGIES INC p 885
3301 Leonard Ct, Santa Clara CA 95054
Tel (408) 727-1600
SIC 3823 3845 3829 3825
TOSHIBA AMERICA MRI INC p 1462
280 Utah Ave Ste 200, South San Francisco CA 94080
Tel (650) 737-6686 *SIC* 3845 8731
■ **PACESETTER INC** p 1103
15900 Valley View Ct, Sylmar CA 91342
Tel (818) 362-6822 *SIC* 3845
SORIN GROUP USA INC p 1341
14401 W 65th Way, Arvada CO 80004
Tel (303) 425-5508 *SIC* 3845
▲ **SPECTRANETICS CORP** p 1357
9965 Federal Dr Ste 100, Colorado Springs CO 80921
Tel (719) 633-8333 *SIC* 3845
TERUMO BCT INC p 1440
10811 W Collins Ave, Lakewood CO 80215
Tel (303) 232-6800
SIC 8733 3842 3845 5047 7352 7699
UNITED STATES SURGICAL CORP p 1514
555 Long Wharf Dr Fl 4, New Haven CT 06511
Tel (203) 845-1000 *SIC* 3841 3845 3842
■ **COOPERSURGICAL INC** p 367
95 Corporate Dr, Trumbull CT 06611
Tel (203) 601-5200
SIC 5047 3842 3841 3845
▲ **DANAHER CORP** p 411
2200 Penn Ave Nw Ste 800w, Washington DC 20037
Tel (202) 828-0850
SIC 3845 3829 3577 3823 3843
■ **SEQUA CORP** p 1306
3999 Rca Blvd, Palm Beach Gardens FL 33410
Tel (201) 343-1122
SIC 3724 3764 3812 3699 3845 3542
▲ **HALYARD HEALTH INC** p 655
5405 Windward Pkwy, Alpharetta GA 30004
Tel (678) 425-9273 *SIC* 3842 3841 3845
■ **HALYARD SALES LLC** p 655
5405 Windward Pkwy # 100, Alpharetta GA 30004
Tel (678) 425-9273 *SIC* 3845 3841
LIFEWATCH CORP p 865
10255 W Higgins Rd # 100, Rosemont IL 60018
Tel (847) 720-2100 *SIC* 8099 5047 3845
LIFEWATCH SERVICES INC p 865
10255 W Higgins Rd # 100, Rosemont IL 60018
Tel (847) 720-2100
SIC 5047 8099 3845 8071
COOK GROUP INC p 365
750 N Daniels Way, Bloomington IN 47404
Tel (812) 339-2235
SIC 3841 3821 3845 6411 6512 6211
■ **BIOMET INC** p 184
56 E Bell Dr, Warsaw IN 46582
Tel (574) 267-6639 *SIC* 3842 3841 3845
LVB ACQUISITION HOLDING LLC p 887
56 E Bell Dr, Warsaw IN 46582
Tel (574) 267-6639 *SIC* 3842 3841 3845
■ **LVB ACQUISITION INC** p 887
56 E Bell Dr, Warsaw IN 46582
Tel (574) 267-6639 *SIC* 3842 3841 3845
▲ **NOVANTA INC** p 1062
125 Middlesex Tpke, Bedford MA 01730
Tel (781) 266-5700 *SIC* 3699 3845
▲ **GENERAL ELECTRIC CO** p 600
41 Farnsworth St, Boston MA 02210
Tel (617) 443-3000
SIC 3511 3724 3632 3845
▲ **HAEMONETICS CORP** p 652
400 Wood Rd, Braintree MA 02184
Tel (781) 848-7100 *SIC* 3841 3845
ZOLL MEDICAL CORP p 1644
269 Mill Rd, Chelmsford MA 01824
Tel (978) 421-9100 *SIC* 3845 7372
▲ **ABIOMED INC** p 11
22 Cherry Hill Dr, Danvers MA 01923
Tel (978) 646-1400 *SIC* 3845
▲ **NXSTAGE MEDICAL INC** p 1068
350 Merrimack St, Lawrence MA 01843
Tel (978) 687-4700 *SIC* 3845
COVIDIEN LP p 385
15 Hampshire St, Mansfield MA 02048
Tel (508) 261-8000
SIC 3842 3841 3845 5122
NELLCOR PURITAN BENNETT LLC p 1025
15 Hampshire St, Mansfield MA 02048
Tel (508) 261-8000 *SIC* 3845 3841
■ **LOCKHEED MARTIN SIPPICAN INC** p 873
7 Barnabas Rd, Marion MA 02738
Tel (508) 748-3399
SIC 3812 3826 3499 3672 3829 3845

▲ BOSTON SCIENTIFIC CORP p 203
300 Boston Scientific Way, Marlborough MA 01752
Tel (508) 683-4000 *SIC* 3841 3842 3845

▲ HOLOGIC INC p 702
250 Campus Dr, Marlborough MA 01752
Tel (508) 263-2900 *SIC* 3845 3844 3841

EXCELITAS TECHNOLOGIES CORP p 516
200 West St, Waltham MA 02451
Tel (781) 522-5910 *SIC* 3648 3845

EXCELITAS TECHNOLOGIES HOLDING CORP p 516
200 West St Ste E403, Waltham MA 02451
Tel (781) 522-5914 *SIC* 3648 3845

▲ PERKINELMER INC p 1136
940 Winter St, Waltham MA 02451
Tel (781) 663-6900 *SIC* 3826 3845

▲ THERMO FISHER SCIENTIFIC INC p 1447
168 3rd Ave, Waltham MA 02451
Tel (781) 622-1000
SIC 3826 3845 3823 3629

CANDELA CORP p 247
530 Boston Post Rd, Wayland MA 01778
Tel (949) 716-6670 *SIC* 3845

▲ CYNOSURE INC p 405
5 Carlisle Rd, Westford MA 01886
Tel (978) 256-4200 *SIC* 3845

■ LAKE REGION MANUFACTURING INC p 839
100 Fordham Rd, Wilmington MA 01887
Tel (952) 361-2515 *SIC* 3841 3845

■ GELMAN SCIENCES INC p 598
674 S Wagner Rd, Ann Arbor MI 48103
Tel (734) 665-0651
SIC 3821 3569 3564 3841 3845 3699

TERUMO CARDIOVASCULAR SYSTEMS CORP p 1440
6200 Jackson Rd, Ann Arbor MI 48103
Tel (734) 663-4145 *SIC* 3845 3841

■ MEDIVATORS INC p 938
14605 28th Ave N, Minneapolis MN 55447
Tel (763) 553-3300
SIC 3841 3842 3845 3589

MEDTRONIC INC p 939
710 Medtronic Pkwy, Minneapolis MN 55432
Tel (763) 514-4000 *SIC* 3845 3842 3841

■ CARDIAC PACEMAKERS INC p 252
4100 Hamline Ave N, Saint Paul MN 55112
Tel (651) 638-4000 *SIC* 3845

EMPI INC p 493
599 Cardigan Rd, Saint Paul MN 55126
Tel (651) 415-9000 *SIC* 3845

■ GUIDANT SALES LLC p 645
4100 Hamline Ave N, Saint Paul MN 55112
Tel (800) 949-9459
SIC 3841 3845 5047 8733

■ IMATION ENTERPRISES CORP p 733
1099 Helmo Ave N Ste 250, Saint Paul MN 55128
Tel (651) 704-4000 *SIC* 3695 3845 5112

▲ ST JUDE MEDICAL INC p 1369
1 Saint Jude Medical Dr, Saint Paul MN 55117
Tel (651) 756-2000 *SIC* 3845 3842 3841

TSI INC p 1489
500 Cardigan Rd, Saint Paul MN 55126
Tel (651) 483-0900
SIC 3579 3829 3823 3845 3825

DATASCOPE CORP p 414
15 Law Dr, Fairfield NJ 07004
Tel (973) 244-6100 *SIC* 3845

MINDRAY DS USA INC p 972
800 Macarthur Blvd, Mahwah NJ 07430
Tel (201) 995-8000 *SIC* 3845 2835 3841

▲ C R BARD INC p 233
730 Central Ave, New Providence NJ 07974
Tel (908) 277-8000 *SIC* 3841 3845 3842

TOPCON AMERICA CORP p 1461
111 Bauer Dr, Oakland NJ 07436
Tel (201) 599-5117 *SIC* 3845

KONICA MINOLTA HEALTHCARE AMERICAS INC p 827
411 Newark Pompton Tpke, Wayne NJ 07470
Tel (973) 633-1500 *SIC* 5047 3861 3845

BAYER HEALTHCARE LLC p 161
100 Bayer Blvd, Whippany NJ 07981
Tel (862) 404-3000
SIC 2834 8731 3845 3841

MED SERVICES INC p 935
100 Knickerbocker Ave C, Bohemia NY 11716
Tel (631) 218-6450 *SIC* 3845 7699

PHILIPS MEDICAL SYSTEMS MR INC p 1143
450 Old Niskayuna Rd, Latham NY 12110
Tel (518) 782-1122 *SIC* 3845 3674 3679

▲ CONMED CORP p 356
525 French Rd Ste 3, Utica NY 13502
Tel (315) 797-8375 *SIC* 3845 3841

LAERDAL MEDICAL CORP p 837
167 Myers Corners Rd, Wappingers Falls NY 12590
Tel (845) 297-7770 *SIC* 5047 3845 3841

BIOMERIEUX INC p 184
100 Rodolphe St, Durham NC 27712
Tel (919) 620-2000
SIC 3845 8071 3841 3826

EVOKE NEUROSCIENCE INC p 515
200 Valencia Dr Ste 109, Jacksonville NC 28546
Tel (910) 353-1760 *SIC* 3845

STERIS CORP p 1386
5960 Heisley Rd, Mentor OH 44060
Tel (440) 354-2600 *SIC* 3841 3842 3845

▲ BIOTELEMETRY INC p 184
1000 Cedar Hollow Rd, Malvern PA 19355
Tel (610) 729-7000 *SIC* 3845 8093

■ CARDIONET LLC p 253
1000 Cedar Hollow Rd, Malvern PA 19355
Tel (610) 729-5060 *SIC* 3845

SIEMENS MEDICAL SOLUTIONS USA INC p 1320
40 Liberty Blvd, Malvern PA 19355
Tel (610) 219-6300
SIC 5047 3845 3842 3843

RESPIRONICS INC p 1227
1010 Murry Ridge Ln, Murrysville PA 15668
Tel (724) 387-5200
SIC 3641 3845 3841 3564 8351

ZOLL SERVICES LLC p 1644
121 Gamma Dr, Pittsburgh PA 15238
Tel (412) 968-3333 *SIC* 3845

DEVILBISS HEALTHCARE LLC p 434
100 Devilbiss Dr, Somerset PA 15501
Tel (814) 443-4881 *SIC* 3845

■ GUIDANT PUERTO RICO BV p 645
12 Carr 698 Ste 171, Dorado PR 00646
Tel (787) 796-2115 *SIC* 3845

WRIGHT MEDICAL TECHNOLOGY INC p 1627
1023 Cherry Rd, Memphis TN 38117
Tel (901) 867-9971 *SIC* 3842 3845

HEALTHTRONICS INC p 678
9825 Spectrum Dr Bldg 3, Austin TX 78717
Tel (512) 328-2892 *SIC* 3845

HT INTERMEDIATE CO LLC p 715
9825 Spectrum Dr Bldg 3, Austin TX 78717
Tel (512) 328-2892 *SIC* 3845

CYBERONICS INC p 405
100 Cyberonics Blvd # 600, Houston TX 77058
Tel (281) 228-7200 *SIC* 3845

■ ADVANCED NEUROMODULATION SYSTEMS INC p 26
6901 Preston Rd, Plano TX 75024
Tel (972) 309-8000 *SIC* 3845

ARGON MEDICAL DEVICES INC p 107
5151 Hdqtr Dr Ste 210, Plano TX 75024
Tel (903) 675-9321 *SIC* 3845 3842 3841

FUJIFILM SONOSITE INC p 583
21919 30th Dr Se, Bothell WA 98021
Tel (425) 951-1200 *SIC* 3845

PHILIPS ULTRASOUND INC p 1143
22100 Bothell Everett Hwy, Bothell WA 98021
Tel (800) 982-2011 *SIC* 3845

■ VERATHON INC p 1549
20001 North Creek Pkwy, Bothell WA 98011
Tel (425) 867-1348 *SIC* 3845

PHYSIO-CONTROL INC p 1146
11811 Willows Rd Ne, Redmond WA 98052
Tel (425) 867-4000
SIC 3841 3845 7699 7372

■ PHYSIO-CONTROL INTERNATIONAL INC p 1146
11811 Willows Rd Ne, Redmond WA 98052
Tel (425) 867-4000 *SIC* 3845

■ SPACELABS HEALTHCARE (WASHINGTON) INC p 1354
35301 Se Center St, Snoqualmie WA 98065
Tel (425) 396-3300
SIC 3845 3841 3575 7699 7378

■ SPACELABS HEALTHCARE INC p 1354
35301 Se Center St, Snoqualmie WA 98065
Tel (425) 396-3302
SIC 3841 3845 3575 7699 7378

■ DATEX-OHMEDA INC p 414
3030 Ohmeda Dr, Madison WI 53718
Tel (608) 221-1551 *SIC* 3845

MORTARA INSTRUMENT INC p 991
7865 N 86th St, Milwaukee WI 53224
Tel (414) 354-1600 *SIC* 8731 3845

SIC 3851 Ophthalmic Goods

OAKLEY INC p 1071
1 Icon, Foothill Ranch CA 92610
Tel (949) 951-0991
SIC 3851 2331 2339 3021 3873 3143

▲ COOPER COMPANIES INC p 366
6140 Stoneridge Mall Rd # 590, Pleasanton CA 94588
Tel (925) 460-3600 *SIC* 3851 3842

CARL ZEISS VISION INC p 256
12121 Scripps Summit Dr, San Diego CA 92131
Tel (858) 790-7700 *SIC* 3827 3851

YOUNGER MFG CO p 1639
2925 California St, Torrance CA 90503
Tel (310) 783-1533 *SIC* 3851

GERBER SCIENTIFIC LLC p 608
24 Indl Pk Rd W, Tolland CT 06084
Tel (860) 871-8082
SIC 3993 7336 3851 7372 3577

ABB/CON-CISE OPTICAL GROUP LLC p 9
12301 Nw 39th St, Coral Springs FL 33065
Tel (800) 852-8089 *SIC* 5048 3851 8741

COSTA INC p 374
2361 Mason Ave Ste 100, Daytona Beach FL 32117
Tel (386) 274-4000 *SIC* 3851

FOR EYES OPTICAL CO OF COCONUT GROVE INC p 565
285 W 74th Pl, Hialeah FL 33014
Tel (305) 557-9004 *SIC* 3851 5995

■ JOHNSON & JOHNSON VISION CARE INC p 790
7500 Centurion Pkwy, Jacksonville FL 32256
Tel (904) 443-1000 *SIC* 3851

▲ HIG SURGERY CENTERS LLC p 690
1450 Brickell Ave Fl 31, Miami FL 33131
Tel (305) 379-2322 *SIC* 8062 3851

TRANSITIONS OPTICAL INC p 1472
9251 Belcher Rd N, Pinellas Park FL 33782
Tel (727) 545-0400 *SIC* 3229 3851

CIBA VISION INC p 305
333 Howard Ave, Des Plaines IL 60018
Tel (847) 294-3000 *SIC* 3851

WESLEY-JESSEN CORP (DEL) p 1593
333 Howard Ave, Des Plaines IL 60018
Tel (847) 294-3000 *SIC* 3851

MAUI JIM USA INC p 921
1 Aloha Ln, Peoria IL 61615
Tel (309) 589-6158 *SIC* 5099 3851

■ AEARO TECHNOLOGIES LLC p 28
5457 W 79th St, Indianapolis IN 46268
Tel (317) 692-6666 *SIC* 3842 3851 3643

■ BUSHNELL HOLDINGS INC p 229
9200 Cody St, Overland Park KS 66214
Tel (913) 752-3400 *SIC* 3851 5049 5091

GENTEX OPTICS INC p 605
183 W Main St, Dudley MA 01571
Tel (570) 282-8531 *SIC* 3851 3842

WALMAN OPTICAL CO p 1573
801 12th Ave N Ste 1, Minneapolis MN 55411
Tel (612) 520-6000 *SIC* 5048 3851

LENS VISION-EASE CORP p 856
7000 Sunwood Dr Nw, Ramsey MN 55303
Tel (763) 576-3930 *SIC* 3851

■ CORNING NETOPTIX p 371
69 Island St Ste T, Keene NH 03431
Tel (603) 357-7662 *SIC* 3827 3851 3826

USV OPTICAL INC p 1536
1 Harmon Dr Glen Oaks, Glendora NJ 08029
Tel (856) 228-1000 *SIC* 5995 3851

TOPCON MEDICAL SYSTEMS INC p 1461
111 Bauer Dr, Oakland NJ 07436
Tel (201) 599-5100
SIC 3841 3826 3827 3829 3851 5049

■ CVI LASER LLC p 404
200 Dorado Pl Se, Albuquerque NM 87123
Tel (505) 296-9541 *SIC* 3827 3851 3826

BAUSCH & LOMB HOLDINGS INC p 160
450 Lexington Ave, New York NY 10017
Tel (585) 338-6000 *SIC* 3851 2834

BAUSCH & LOMB INC p 160
1400 N Goodman St, Rochester NY 14609
Tel (585) 338-6000 *SIC* 3851 2834 3841

■ COOPERVISION INC p 367
209 High Point Dr, Victor NY 14564
Tel (585) 385-6810 *SIC* 3851

WINSTON-SALEM INDUSTRIES FOR BLIND INC p 1617
7730 N Point Blvd, Winston Salem NC 27106
Tel (336) 759-0551
SIC 2515 3021 2392 2253 2394 3851

■ OCULAR SCIENCES PUERTO RICO INC p 1074
500 Carr 584, Juana Diaz PR 00795
Tel (787) 260-0555 *SIC* 3851

FGX INTERNATIONAL HOLDINGS LIMITED p 539
500 Washington Hwy, Smithfield RI 02917
Tel (401) 231-3800 *SIC* 5099 3851

FGX INTERNATIONAL INC p 539
500 George Washington Hwy, Smithfield RI 02917
Tel (401) 231-3800 *SIC* 5099 3851

■ SPERIAN PROTECTION USA INC p 1358
900 Douglas Pike, Smithfield RI 02917
Tel (401) 232-1200
SIC 3851 3842 2311 7218 5999

SHELBY GROUP INTERNATIONAL INC p 1314
1255 W Schilling Blvd, Collierville TN 38017
Tel (901) 795-5810
SIC 3842 2381 3851 5137

■ SURGERY PARTNERS INC p 1409
40 Burton Hills Blvd # 500, Nashville TN 37215
Tel (615) 234-5900 *SIC* 8062 3851

ESSILOR LABORATORIES OF AMERICA INC p 510
13515 N Stemmons Fwy, Dallas TX 75234
Tel (972) 241-4141 *SIC* 3851 5048

ESSILOR OF AMERICA INC p 510
13555 N Stemmons Fwy, Dallas TX 75234
Tel (214) 496-4000 *SIC* 3851 5048

CIBA VISION CORP p 305
6201 South Fwy, Fort Worth TX 76134
Tel (817) 551-6881 *SIC* 3851

HOYA CORP p 714
651 E Corporate Dr, Lewisville TX 75057
Tel (972) 221-4141 *SIC* 3851

ECCA HOLDINGS CORP p 475
175 E Houston St Fl 6, San Antonio TX 78205
Tel (210) 340-3531 *SIC* 5995 3851

INSIGHT EQUITY ACQUISITION CO LLC p 746
1400 Civic Pl Ste 250, Southlake TX 76092
Tel (817) 354-2715
SIC 2911 6722 3851 3441

INSIGHT EQUITY HOLDINGS LLC p 746
1400 Civic Pl Ste 250, Southlake TX 76092
Tel (817) 488-7775
SIC 6726 3851 2911 3441

1-800 CONTACTS INC p 1
261 W Data Dr, Draper UT 84020
Tel (801) 316-5000 *SIC* 5961 3851

SIC 3861 Photographic Eqpt & Splys

LASERMASTERS LLC p 846
4857 W Van Buren St, Phoenix AZ 85043
Tel (602) 278-5234 *SIC* 3861

CHRISTIE DIGITAL SYSTEMS INC p 303
10550 Camden Dr, Cypress CA 90630
Tel (714) 236-8610 *SIC* 3861 6719

RED.COM INC p 1216
34 Parker, Irvine CA 92618
Tel (949) 206-7900 *SIC* 3861

HOYA HOLDINGS INC p 714
680 N Mccarthy Blvd # 120, Milpitas CA 95035
Tel (408) 654-2300 *SIC* 3861 3825 3827

▲ HP INC p 714
1501 Page Mill Rd, Palo Alto CA 94304
Tel (650) 857-1501
SIC 3571 7372 3861 3577 3572 3575

▲ GOPRO INC p 625
3000 Clearview Way, San Mateo CA 94402
Tel (650) 332-7600 *SIC* 3861 7372

RICOH ELECTRONICS INC p 1233
1100 Valencia Ave, Tustin CA 92780
Tel (714) 566-2500 *SIC* 3861 3695

WBI INC p 1585
8201 Woodley Ave, Van Nuys CA 91406
Tel (800) 673-4968 *SIC* 3861

PANAVISION INC p 1111
6101 Variel Ave, Woodland Hills CA 91367
Tel (818) 316-1000
SIC 7359 3861 3648 5063

PANAVISION INTERNATIONAL LP p 1111
6101 Variel Ave, Woodland Hills CA 91367
Tel (818) 316-1080 *SIC* 3861

▲ XEROX CORP p 1631
45 Glover Ave Ste 700, Norwalk CT 06850
Tel (203) 968-3000
SIC 3861 3579 3577 7629 7378 7374

FUJIFILM MEDICAL SYSTEMS USA INC p 583
419 West Ave, Stamford CT 06902
Tel (203) 324-2000 *SIC* 5047 5043 3861

OCE-USA HOLDING INC p 1072
100 Oakview Dr, Trumbull CT 06611
Tel (773) 714-8500 *SIC* 3861 5044

■ B WILLIAMS HOLDING CORP p 142
1403 Foulk Rd Ste 200, Wilmington DE 19803
Tel (302) 656-8596
SIC 3579 3661 3861 7359 7629 6159

AUDIO VISUAL INNOVATIONS INC p 130
6301 Benjamin Rd Ste 101, Tampa FL 33634
Tel (813) 884-7168
SIC 3669 5064 3861 3663 3651 5043

AVI-SPL EMPLOYEE EMERGENCY RELIEF FUND INC p 137
6301 Benjamin Rd Ste 101, Tampa FL 33634
Tel (813) 884-7168
SIC 3669 3861 3663 3651 5043 5064

AVI-SPL HOLDINGS INC p 137
6301 Benjamin Rd Ste 101, Tampa FL 33634
Tel (866) 708-5034
SIC 3669 3861 3663 3651 1731 5064

CLOVER TECHNOLOGIES GROUP LLC p 328
4200 Columbus St, Ottawa IL 61350
Tel (815) 431-8100 *SIC* 5943 3861

CDS OFFICE SYSTEMS INC p 271
612 S Dirksen Pkwy, Springfield IL 62703
Tel (800) 367-1508
SIC 5044 5999 7629 7378 3861 3577

DRAPER INC p 455
411 S Pearl St, Spiceland IN 47385
Tel (765) 987-7999 *SIC* 3861 2591 3651

▲ AVID TECHNOLOGY INC p 138
75 Network Dr, Burlington MA 01803
Tel (978) 640-6789 *SIC* 3861 7372

▲ BALLANTYNE STRONG INC p 148
11422 Miracle Hills Dr # 300, Omaha NE 68154
Tel (402) 453-4444 *SIC* 3861 3648

PRESSTEK LLC p 1173
55 Executive Dr, Hudson NH 03051
Tel (603) 595-7000 *SIC* 3555 3577 3861

■ GENERAL DYNAMICS GLOBAL IMAGING TECHNOLOGIES INC p 600
24 Simon St, Nashua NH 03060
Tel (603) 864-6300 *SIC* 3827 3861

BEACH TRADING CO INC p 164
80 Carter Dr, Edison NJ 08817
Tel (800) 572-3224 *SIC* 3861 5731

SHARP ELECTRONICS CORP p 1312
1 Sharp Plz Ste 1, Mahwah NJ 07495
Tel (201) 529-8200
SIC 5044 5064 3651 3631 3861 3674

TECHNICOLOR USA INC p 1431
4 Research Way, Princeton NJ 08540
Tel (317) 587-3000 *SIC* 3651 3861 3661

SAMSUNG OPTO-ELECTRONICS AMERICA INC p 1275
100 Challenger Rd Ste 700, Ridgefield Park NJ 07660
Tel (201) 325-2612 *SIC* 5043 7699 3861

KONICA MINOLTA HEALTHCARE AMERICAS INC p 827
411 Newark Pompton Tpke, Wayne NJ 07470
Tel (973) 633-1500 *SIC* 5047 3861 3845

KONICA MINOLTA SUPPLIES MANUFACTURING USA INC p 827
51 Hatfield Ln, Goshen NY 10924
Tel (845) 294-8400 *SIC* 3861

CANON USA INC p 247
1 Canon Park, Melville NY 11747
Tel (516) 328-5000
SIC 5044 5065 5045 3861 3577 5043

PX HOLDING CORP p 1193
35 E 62nd St, New York NY 10065
Tel (212) 688-9000 *SIC* 7359 3861 3648

■ EASTMAN KODAK CO p 473
343 State St, Rochester NY 14650
Tel (585) 724-4000 *SIC* 3861 3577 7384

KODAK ALARIS INC p 826
2400 Mount Read Blvd # 1175, Rochester NY 14615
Tel (585) 290-2891 *SIC* 3861

FUJIFILM NORTH AMERICA CORP p 583
200 Summit Lake Dr Fl 2, Valhalla NY 10595
Tel (914) 789-8100
SIC 7384 5043 5065 3695 2673 3861

REGULUS INTEGRATED SOLUTIONS LLC p 1220
9645-L Part Blvd, Charlotte NC 28216
Tel (704) 904-8759
SIC 2752 7389 3861 2759

OWEN STEPHENS PRODUCTIONS LLC p 1100
1304 Sw 176th Ter, Beaverton OR 97003
Tel (503) 810-0812 *SIC* 3861

RICOH AMERICAS CORP p 1233
70 Valley Stream Pkwy, Malvern PA 19355
Tel (610) 296-8000
SIC 5044 5065 5045 5043 3861 3661

AGFA CORP p 34
10 S Academy St, Greenville SC 29601
Tel (800) 526-5441 *SIC* 3861

FUJIFILM MANUFACTURING USA INC p 583
215 Puckett Ferry Rd, Greenwood SC 29649
Tel (864) 223-2888 *SIC* 2796 2752 3861

BLACK CREEK HOLDINGS LTD p 186
2400 Dallas Pkwy Ste 230, Plano TX 75093
Tel (972) 398-7100 *SIC* 3955 3861

NUKOTE INC p 1067
2400 Dallas Pkwy Ste 230, Plano TX 75093
Tel (972) 398-7100 *SIC* 3955 3861

■ DAHILL OFFICE TECHNOLOGY CORP p 408
8200 W Interstate 10 # 400, San Antonio TX 78230
Tel (210) 805-8200 *SIC* 5999 3861 2759

CANON VIRGINIA INC p 247
12000 Canon Blvd, Newport News VA 23606
Tel (757) 881-6000
SIC 3861 3577 3555 4953

■ KOLLMORGEN CORP p 826
203a W Rock Rd, Radford VA 24141
Tel (540) 639-2495
SIC 3621 3825 3827 3861

SIC 3873 Watch & Clock Devices & Parts

HKF INC p 697
5983 Smithway St, Commerce CA 90040
Tel (323) 225-1318
SIC 5075 3873 5064 3567 3643

OAKLEY INC p 1071
1 Icon, Foothill Ranch CA 92610
Tel (949) 951-0991
SIC 3851 2331 2339 3021 3873 3143

TIMEX GROUP USA INC p 1454
555 Christian Rd, Middlebury CT 06762
Tel (203) 346-5000 *SIC* 3873

HOWARD MILLER CO p 713
860 E Main Ave, Zeeland MI 49464
Tel (616) 772-9131 *SIC* 3873 3829 3823

▲ MOVADO GROUP INC p 995
650 From Rd Ste 375, Paramus NJ 07652
Tel (201) 267-8000 *SIC* 3873 3915 7631

SWATCH GROUP U S INC p 1411
1200 Harbor Blvd Fl 7, Weehawken NJ 07086
Tel (201) 271-1400
SIC 5063 3625 5094 3873

E GLUCK CORP p 466
6015 Little Neck Pkwy, Little Neck NY 11362
Tel (718) 784-0700 *SIC* 3873 5094

MZ BERGER & CO INC p 1005
2976 Northern Blvd Fl 4, Long Island City NY 11101
Tel (718) 472-7500 *SIC* 5094 3873

AWC LIQUIDATING CO p 139
1407 Brdwy Ste 400, New York NY 10018
Tel (212) 221-1177
SIC 5112 5199 3873 5094

MTM RECOGNITION CORP p 998
3201 Se 29th St, Oklahoma City OK 73115
Tel (405) 609-6900
SIC 3911 3873 2499 2389 3499 2791

RIDDLES GROUP INC p 1234
2707 Mount Rushmore Rd, Rapid City SD 57701
Tel (605) 343-7099 *SIC* 3873 3911

▲ FOSSIL GROUP INC p 570
901 S Central Expy, Richardson TX 75080
Tel (972) 234-2525
SIC 3873 5944 5094 5651 5632

SIC 3911 Jewelry: Precious Metal

K-SWISS INC p 799
31248 Oak Crest Dr, Westlake Village CA 91361
Tel (818) 706-5100 *SIC* 3021 3911

MAUI DIVERS OF HAWAII LIMITED p 921
1520 Liona St, Honolulu HI 96814
Tel (808) 946-7979 *SIC* 3911 5944 5094

HERFF JONES LLC p 685
4501 W 62nd St, Indianapolis IN 46268
Tel (800) 837-4235 *SIC* 3911 2721 2741

STULLER INC p 1394
302 Rue Louis Xiv, Lafayette LA 70508
Tel (337) 262-7700 *SIC* 5094 3911

■ JOSTENS INC p 794
3601 Minnesota Dr Ste 400, Minneapolis MN 55435
Tel (952) 830-3300 *SIC* 3911 2759 2741

■ VISANT CORP p 1560
3601 Minnesota Dr Ste 400, Minneapolis MN 55435
Tel (914) 595-8200
SIC 3911 2741 2389 7221

■ VISANT HOLDING CORP p 1561
3601 Minnesota Dr Ste 400, Minneapolis MN 55435
Tel (914) 595-8200
SIC 2741 2759 3911 6719

ANAYA GEMS INC p 88
3100 47th Ave Unit 5, Long Island City NY 11101
Tel (718) 391-7400 *SIC* 5094 3911

ALBEA COSMETICS AMERICA INC p 46
595 Madison Ave Fl 10, New York NY 10022
Tel (212) 371-5100
SIC 3089 3911 5162 5051

DAVID YURMAN ENTERPRISES LLC p 415
24 Vestry St, New York NY 10013
Tel (212) 896-1550 *SIC* 3911

JACMEL JEWELRY INC p 775
1385 Broadway Fl 8, New York NY 10018
Tel (718) 349-4300 *SIC* 3911

■ JOTALY INC p 794
1385 Broadway Fl 12, New York NY 10018
Tel (212) 886-6000 *SIC* 3911

LOUIS GLICK DIAMOND CORP p 879
810 7th Ave Fl 28, New York NY 10019
Tel (212) 259-0300 *SIC* 5094 3911

■ RICHLINE GROUP INC p 1233
1385 Broadway Fl 12, New York NY 10018
Tel (212) 886-6000 *SIC* 5094 3911

ALMOND JEWELERS INC p 59
16 S Maryland Ave, Port Washington NY 11050
Tel (516) 933-6000 *SIC* 3911

THARPEROBBINS CO INC p 1446
149 Crawford Rd, Statesville NC 28625
Tel (704) 872-5231 *SIC* 3911

MTM RECOGNITION CORP p 998
3201 Se 29th St, Oklahoma City OK 73115
Tel (405) 609-6900
SIC 3911 3873 2499 2389 3499 2791

RIDDLES GROUP INC p 1234
2707 Mount Rushmore Rd, Rapid City SD 57701
Tel (605) 343-7099 *SIC* 3873 3911

AAC GROUP HOLDING CORP p 8
7211 Circle S Rd, Austin TX 78745
Tel (512) 444-0571 *SIC* 3911

AMERICAN ACHIEVEMENT CORP p 67
7211 Circle S Rd, Austin TX 78745
Tel (512) 444-0571 *SIC* 3911 2741

COMMEMORATIVE BRANDS INC p 344
7211 Circle S Rd, Austin TX 78745
Tel (512) 444-0571 *SIC* 3911 5944 3961

JAMES AVERY CRAFTSMAN INC p 776
145 Avery Rd, Kerrville TX 78028
Tel (830) 895-6800 *SIC* 3911

O C TANNER CO p 1070
1930 S State St, Salt Lake City UT 84115
Tel (801) 486-2430 *SIC* 3911 2759 2741

O C TANNER MANUFACTURING p 1070
1930 S State St, Salt Lake City UT 84115
Tel (801) 486-2430 *SIC* 3911

SIC 3914 Silverware, Plated & Stainless Steel Ware

BIO MEDIC CORP p 183
742 Sussex Ave, Seaford DE 19973
Tel (302) 628-4300
SIC 5049 3821 3496 3914 3661

ZIPPO MANUFACTURING CO INC p 1643
33 Barbour St, Bradford PA 16701
Tel (814) 368-2700
SIC 3914 3993 5172 3999 3421 3172

■ ASSOCIATED AMERICAN INDUSTRIES INC p 119
1307 N Watters Rd, Allen TX 75013
Tel (214) 421-7366
SIC 3914 3634 3469 3639

HAT BRANDS HOLDING CORP p 667
601 Marion Dr, Garland TX 75042
Tel (972) 494-7133
SIC 2353 3914 3144 3143

TVCI HOLDING INC p 1494
1236 N 18th St, Sheboygan WI 53081
Tel (920) 457-4851 *SIC* 3914 3365 3089

VOLLRATH CO LLC p 1564
1236 N 18th St, Sheboygan WI 53081
Tel (920) 459-6568
SIC 3089 3365 3421 3556 3914

SIC 3915 Jewelers Findings & Lapidary Work

▲ MOVADO GROUP INC p 995
650 From Rd Ste 375, Paramus NJ 07652
Tel (201) 267-8000 *SIC* 3873 3915 7631

RIO GRANDE INC p 1235
7500 Bluewater Rd Nw, Albuquerque NM 87121
Tel (505) 839-3550 *SIC* 5094 5049 3915

ALEX AND ANI LLC p 48
2000 Chapel View Blvd # 360, Cranston RI 02920
Tel (401) 633-1486 *SIC* 3915 5944

■ US SYNTHETIC CORP p 1533
1260 S 1600 W, Orem UT 84058
Tel (801) 235-9001 *SIC* 3915

SIC 3931 Musical Instruments

FENDER MUSICAL INSTRUMENTS CORP p 537
17600 N Perimeter Dr # 100, Scottsdale AZ 85255
Tel (480) 596-7195 *SIC* 3651 3931

YAMAHA CORP OF AMERICA INC p 1634
6600 Orangethorpe Ave, Buena Park CA 90620
Tel (714) 522-9011
SIC 5099 5065 5091 3931

TAYLOR-LISTUG INC p 1427
1980 Gillespie Way, El Cajon CA 92020
Tel (619) 258-6957 *SIC* 3931

ROLAND CORP US p 1247
5100 S Eastern Ave, Los Angeles CA 90040
Tel (323) 890-3700 *SIC* 5099 5045 3931

CREATIVE HOLDINGS INC p 390
1901 Mccarthy Blvd, Milpitas CA 95035
Tel (408) 428-6600
SIC 5045 3577 3931 3674 8711 3651

ROKR DISTRIBUTION US INC p 1247
310 W Newberry Rd, Bloomfield CT 06002
Tel (860) 509-8888 *SIC* 5099 3931

CONN-SELMER INC p 356
600 Industrial Pkwy, Elkhart IN 46516
Tel (574) 522-1675 *SIC* 3931 5736

STEINWAY PIANO CO INC p 1385
600 Industrial Pkwy, Elkhart IN 46516
Tel (574) 522-1675 *SIC* 3931

■ HARMAN BECKER AUTOMOTIVE SYSTEMS INC p 662
30001 Cabot Dr, Novi MI 48377
Tel (248) 785-2361 *SIC* 3931 3812

PEAVEY ELECTRONICS CORP p 1126
5022 Hartley Peavey Dr, Meridian MS 39305
Tel (601) 486-1383 *SIC* 3931

DADDARIO & CO INC p 408
595 Smith St, Farmingdale NY 11735
Tel (631) 439-3300 *SIC* 3931

STEINWAY AND SONS p 1385
1 Steinway Pl, Long Island City NY 11105
Tel (718) 721-2600 *SIC* 3931 5736

STEINWAY INC p 1385
1 Steinway Pl, Long Island City NY 11105
Tel (718) 721-2600 *SIC* 3931 5736

STEINWAY MUSICAL INSTRUMENTS INC p 1385
1133 Ave Of The Am Fl 33, New York NY 10036
Tel (781) 894-9770 *SIC* 3931

C F MARTIN & CO INC p 232
510 Sycamore St, Nazareth PA 18064
Tel (610) 759-2837 *SIC* 3931

BALDWIN PIANO INC p 147
309 Plus Park Blvd, Nashville TN 37217
Tel (615) 277-2190 *SIC* 3931

GIBSON BRANDS INC p 611
309 Plus Park Blvd, Nashville TN 37217
Tel (615) 871-4500 *SIC* 3931

SIC 3942 Dolls & Stuffed Toys

▲ MATTEL INC p 920
333 Continental Blvd, El Segundo CA 90245
Tel (310) 252-2000 *SIC* 3944 3942

▲ HASBRO INC p 667
1027 Newport Ave, Pawtucket RI 02861
Tel (401) 431-8697 *SIC* 3944 3942 3069

SIC 3944 Games, Toys & Children's Vehicles

▲ MATTEL INC p 920
333 Continental Blvd, El Segundo CA 90245
Tel (310) 252-2000 *SIC* 3944 3942

LEAPFROG ENTERPRISES INC p 850
6401 Hollis St Ste 100, Emeryville CA 94608
Tel (510) 420-5000 *SIC* 3944

■ MEGA BRANDS AMERICA INC p 939
3 Ada Ste 200, Irvine CA 92618
Tel (949) 727-9009 *SIC* 3944

EXCELLIGENCE LEARNING CORP p 516
2 Lower Ragsda Dr Ste 200, Monterey CA 93940
Tel (831) 333-2000 *SIC* 3944 5999

IMPERIAL TOY LLC p 734
16641 Roscoe Pl, North Hills CA 91343
Tel (818) 536-6500 *SIC* 3944

▲ GLU MOBILE INC p 618
500 Howard St Ste 300, San Francisco CA 94105
Tel (415) 800-6100 *SIC* 7371 3944

▲ JAKKS PACIFIC INC p 776
2951 28th St Ste 51, Santa Monica CA 90405
Tel (424) 268-9444 *SIC* 3944

S & S WORLDWIDE INC p 1261
75 Mill St, Colchester CT 06415
Tel (860) 537-3451 *SIC* 5199 5049 3944

LEGO SYSTEMS INC p 853
555 Taylor Rd, Enfield CT 06082
Tel (860) 749-2291 *SIC* 3944 5092

■ RUBBERMAID INC p 1256
3 Glenlake Pkwy, Atlanta GA 30328
Tel (770) 418-7000
SIC 3089 2519 3944 2369 2392

RAPID DISPLAYS INC p 1208
4300 W 47th St, Chicago IL 60632
Tel (773) 927-5000 *SIC* 2675 3944

COSCO INC p 373
2525 State St, Columbus IN 47201
Tel (812) 372-0141 *SIC* 3944 2511 2514

DOREL USA INC p 451
2525 State St, Columbus IN 47201
Tel (812) 372-0141 *SIC* 3944 2511 2514

WESTON PRESIDIO INC p 1602
200 Clarendon St Ste 5000, Boston MA 02116
Tel (617) 988-2500
SIC 6799 3944 2519 3085

CARTAMUNDI EAST LONGMEADOW LLC p 261
443 Shaker Rd, East Longmeadow MA 01028
Tel (413) 526-2000 *SIC* 3944 3999

MIX HOLDINGS INC p 978
2501 Mc Gee Traffic Way, Kansas City MO 64108
Tel (816) 274-5111
SIC 3952 3951 3295 3944

EXX INC p 521
1350 E Flamingo Rd 689, Las Vegas NV 89119
Tel (248) 409-1070
SIC 3621 3669 3714 3944

■ SHFL ENTERTAINMENT INC p 1316
6650 El Camino Rd, Las Vegas NV 89118
Tel (702) 897-7150 *SIC* 3999 3949 3944

KID BRANDS INC p 817
1 Meadowlands Plz Ste 803, East Rutherford NJ 07073
Tel (201) 405-2400 *SIC* 2399 3944

■ FISHER-PRICE INC p 552
636 Girard Ave, East Aurora NY 14052
Tel (716) 687-3000 *SIC* 5092 5945 3944

■ ALLEGHANY CAPITAL CORP p 52
7 Times Square Tower, New York NY 10036
Tel (212) 752-1356 *SIC* 3944

■ MARVEL ENTERTAINMENT LLC p 913
135 W 50th St Fl 7, New York NY 10020
Tel (212) 576-4000
SIC 2721 6794 3944 7929

ARROW INTERNATIONAL INC p 113
9900 Clinton Rd, Cleveland OH 44144
Tel (216) 961-3500 *SIC* 3944

LITTLE TIKES CO p 871
2180 Barlow Rd, Hudson OH 44236
Tel (330) 650-3000 *SIC* 3944 2519

EVENFLO CO INC p 513
225 Byers Rd, Miamisburg OH 45342
Tel (937) 415-3300 *SIC* 3944 2519

STEP2 CO LLC p 1386
10010 Aurora Hudson Rd, Streetsboro OH 44241
Tel (866) 429-5200 *SIC* 3089 3944 3423

CRAYOLA LLC p 389
1100 Church Ln, Easton PA 18040
Tel (610) 253-6271
SIC 3952 3951 3295 3944

SPANG & CO p 1354
110 Delta Dr, Pittsburgh PA 15238
Tel (412) 963-9363
SIC 3672 3944 3612 3613 3312

▲ HASBRO INC p 667
1027 Newport Ave, Pawtucket RI 02861
Tel (401) 431-8697 *SIC* 3944 3942 3069

■ HASBRO INTERNATIONAL INC p 667
1027 Newport Ave, Pawtucket RI 02861
Tel (401) 431-8697 *SIC* 3944

■ EVERI GAMES HOLDING INC p 515
206 Wild Basin Rd, West Lake Hills TX 78746
Tel (512) 334-7500 *SIC* 3944

■ WIZARDS OF COAST LLC p 1619
1600 Lind Ave Sw Ste 400, Renton WA 98057
Tel (425) 226-6500 *SIC* 3944

FLAMBEAU INC p 554
801 Lynn Ave, Baraboo WI 53913
Tel (608) 356-5551 *SIC* 3089 3949 3944

SIC 3949 Sporting & Athletic Goods, NEC

EBSCO INDUSTRIES INC p 474
5724 Highway 280 E, Birmingham AL 35242
Tel (205) 991-6600
SIC 7389 2782 3949 7375 2721 6552

KARSTEN MANUFACTURING CORP p 804
2201 W Desert Cove Ave, Phoenix AZ 85029
Tel (602) 870-5000
SIC 3949 3398 3363 3325 8711 7997

■ VF OUTDOOR LLC p 1553
2701 Harbor Bay Pkwy, Alameda CA 94502
Tel (510) 618-3500
SIC 2329 2339 3949 2394 2399 5941

▲ CALLAWAY GOLF CO p 242
2180 Rutherford Rd, Carlsbad CA 92008
Tel (760) 931-1771
SIC 3949 2329 2339 6794

TAYLORMADE GOLF CO INC p 1427
5545 Fermi Ct, Carlsbad CA 92008
Tel (877) 860-8624 *SIC* 3949

■ QUIKSILVER INC p 1200
5600 Argosy Ave Ste 100, Huntington Beach CA 92649
Tel (714) 889-2200
SIC 2329 2339 3949 5136 5137

ALDILA INC p 48
14145 Danielson St Ste B, Poway CA 92064
Tel (858) 513-1801 *SIC* 3949 3297

ROAD RUNNER SPORTS INC p 1240
5549 Copley Dr, San Diego CA 92111
Tel (858) 974-4200 *SIC* 5961 3949 5661

LUCKY STRIKE ENTERTAINMENT INC p 884
15260 Ventura Blvd # 1110, Sherman Oaks CA 91403
Tel (818) 933-3752 *SIC* 3949 5812 5813

RBG HOLDINGS CORP p 1211
7855 Haskell Ave Ste 350, Van Nuys CA 91406
Tel (818) 782-6445 *SIC* 3949 5091 3751

■ OUTDOOR SPORTS GEAR INC p 1098
2320 Cousteau Ct Ste 100, Vista CA 92081
Tel (914) 967-9400
SIC 3949 3069 2339 2329

HTM USA HOLDINGS INC p 715
3125 Sterling Cir Ste 101, Boulder CO 80301
Tel (800) 874-3235 *SIC* 5091 5139 3949

■ BLACK & DECKER INC p 186
1423 Kirkwood Hwy, Newark DE 19711
Tel (302) 738-0250
SIC 3429 3452 3579 3423 3949

HORNERXPRESS INC p 708
5755 Powerline Rd, Fort Lauderdale FL 33309
Tel (954) 772-6966 *SIC* 5091 3949 3561

W C BRADLEY CO p 1568
1017 Front Ave, Columbus GA 31901
Tel (706) 571-7000 *SIC* 3631 3949 3999

BRIDGESTONE GOLF INC p 211
15320 Indsrial Pk Blvd Ne, Covington GA 30014
Tel (770) 787-7400 *SIC* 5091 3949

THOMSON PLASTICS INC p 1449
130 Quality Dr, Thomson GA 30824
Tel (706) 828-7508 *SIC* 3949 3089

AMER SPORTS CO p 66
8750 W Bryn Mawr Ave, Chicago IL 60631
Tel (773) 714-6400 *SIC* 3949

WILSON SPORTING GOODS CO p 1614
8750 W Bryn Mawr Ave Fl 2, Chicago IL 60631
Tel (773) 714-6400 *SIC* 5091 3949

▲ BRUNSWICK CORP p 221
1 N Field Ct, Lake Forest IL 60045
Tel (847) 735-4700
SIC 3519 3732 3949 7933 5091

BRG SPORTS INC p 211
9801 W Higgins Rd, Rosemont IL 60018
Tel (831) 461-7500 *SIC* 3949 3751

■ LIFE FITNESS INC p 863
9525 Bryn Mawr Ave Fl 6, Rosemont IL 60018
Tel (847) 288-3300 *SIC* 3949

RIDDELL INC p 1234
9801 W Higgins Rd Ste 800, Rosemont IL 60018
Tel (847) 292-1472 *SIC* 5091 3949

▲ ESCALADE INC p 509
817 Maxwell Ave, Evansville IN 47711
Tel (812) 467-4449 *SIC* 3949 3579

■ INDIAN INDUSTRIES INC p 737
817 Maxwell Ave, Evansville IN 47711
Tel (812) 467-1200 *SIC* 3949

■ FORT WAYNE POOLS p 569
6930 Gettysburg Pike, Fort Wayne IN 46804
Tel (260) 459-4100 *SIC* 5091 3949

LEISURE TIME PRODUCTS LLC p 854
3001 N Rouse St, Pittsburg KS 66762
Tel (620) 232-2400 *SIC* 3089 3949 2452

■ RUSSELL BRANDS LLC p 1259
1 Fruit Of The Loom Dr, Bowling Green KY 42103
Tel (270) 781-6400
SIC 2253 2211 2329 2339 3949 5091

LOUISVILLE BEDDING CO INC p 880
10400 Bunsen Way, Louisville KY 40299
Tel (502) 491-3370 *SIC* 2392 3949

BATON ROUGE GENERAL MEDICAL CENTER p 159
8490 Picardy Ave Ste 200, Baton Rouge LA 70809
Tel (225) 237-1547 *SIC* 3949

PRIDE MANUFACTURING CO LLC p 1174
10 N Main St, Burnham ME 04922
Tel (207) 487-3322 *SIC* 2411 3949

■ ACUSHNET CO p 20
333 Bridge St, Fairhaven MA 02719
Tel (508) 979-2000 *SIC* 3949 3149 2381

■ ACUSHNET HOLDINGS CORP p 20
333 Bridge St, Fairhaven MA 02719
Tel (800) 225-8500 *SIC* 3949

■ CYBEX INTERNATIONAL INC p 405
10 Trotter Dr, Medway MA 02053
Tel (508) 533-4300 *SIC* 3949

FRANKLIN SPORTS INC p 575
17 Campanelli Pkwy, Stoughton MA 02072
Tel (781) 344-1111 *SIC* 3949

BRUNSWICK BOWLING PRODUCTS LLC p 221
525 W Laketon Ave, Muskegon MI 49441
Tel (231) 725-3300 *SIC* 3949

LANDSCAPE STRUCTURES INC p 843
601 7th St S, Delano MN 55328
Tel (763) 972-3391 *SIC* 3949 2531

■ RAWLINGS SPORTING GOODS CO INC p 1209
510 Maryville University, Saint Louis MO 63141
Tel (866) 678-4327 SIC 3949 5091

■ SHFL ENTERTAINMENT INC p 1316
6650 El Camino Rd, Las Vegas NV 89118
Tel (702) 897-7150 SIC 3999 3949 3944

BAUER HOCKEY INC p 160
100 Domain Dr Ste 1, Exeter NH 03833
Tel (603) 430-2111 SIC 3949

PERFORMANCE SPORTS GROUP LTD p 1135
100 Domain Dr, Exeter NH 03833
Tel (603) 610-5802 SIC 3949

REAGENT CHEMICAL & RESEARCH INC p 1213
115 Rte 202, Ringoes NJ 08551
Tel (908) 284-2800 SIC 3949 2819

HANDWEAR SALES INC p 657
74 Bleecker St, Gloversville NY 12078
Tel (518) 725-8641
SIC 3151 3949 2253 3021

LATHAM MANUFACTURING CORP p 846
787 Watervliet Shaker Rd, Latham NY 12110
Tel (518) 783-7776
SIC 3086 3081 3083 3949

LATHAM POOL PRODUCTS INC p 846
787 Watervliet Shaker Rd, Latham NY 12110
Tel (518) 951-1000 SIC 3949

KOHLBERG SPORTS GROUP INC p 826
111 Radio Circle Dr, Mount Kisco NY 10549
Tel (914) 241-7430 SIC 3949

FOWNES BROTHERS & CO INC p 572
16 E 34th St Fl 5, New York NY 10016
Tel (212) 683-0150
SIC 3151 2381 5136 5137 3949

MAVERIK LACROSSE LLC p 922
535 W 24th St Fl 5, New York NY 10011
Tel (516) 213-3050 SIC 3949

■ NALGE NUNC INTERNATIONAL CORP p 1007
75 Panorama Creek Dr, Rochester NY 14625
Tel (585) 586-8800
SIC 3089 3949 3821 3085 3083

CAMCO MANUFACTURING INC p 244
121 Landmark Dr, Greensboro NC 27409
Tel (336) 668-7661 SIC 3949

PLAYPOWER INC p 1155
11515 Vanstory Dr Ste 100, Huntersville NC 28078
Tel (704) 875-6550 SIC 3949

■ REMINGTON OUTDOOR CO INC p 1222
870 Remington Dr, Madison NC 27025
Tel (336) 548-8700 SIC 5099 3949

MCKENZIE SPORTS PRODUCTS LLC p 930
1910 Saint Luke Church Rd, Salisbury NC 28146
Tel (704) 279-7985 SIC 3949 3423

KENT SPORTING GOODS CO INC p 812
433 Park Ave, New London OH 44851
Tel (419) 929-7021 SIC 3949

■ GOLF GALAXY GOLFWORKS INC p 622
4820 Jacksontown Rd, Newark OH 43056
Tel (740) 328-4193
SIC 5091 2731 3949 5941

CENTURY LLC p 282
1000 Century Blvd, Oklahoma City OK 73110
Tel (405) 732-2226 SIC 5091 3949

▲ COLUMBIA SPORTSWEAR CO p 341
14375 Nw Science Park Dr, Portland OR 97229
Tel (503) 985-4000
SIC 2329 2339 3021 2353 3949

WEXCO INC p 1603
3490 Board Rd, York PA 17406
Tel (717) 764-8585
SIC 3089 3949 3999 5091 3081

ELLETT BROTHERS LLC p 488
267 Columbia Ave, Chapin SC 29036
Tel (803) 345-3751
SIC 5091 3949 2499 2541

■ PURE FISHING INC p 1192
7 Science Ct, Columbia SC 29203
Tel (803) 754-7000 SIC 3949

■ SHAKESPEARE CO LLC p 1310
6111 Shakespeare Rd, Columbia SC 29223
Tel (803) 754-7011
SIC 3089 3949 3679 3663

INTERTECH GROUP INC p 759
4838 Jenkins Ave, North Charleston SC 29405
Tel (843) 744-5174 SIC 3949

PI INC p 1146
213 Dennis St, Athens TN 37303
Tel (423) 745-6213
SIC 2519 3949 3089 2499 3086 3081

PLAYCORE HOLDINGS INC p 1155
401 Chestnut St Ste 410, Chattanooga TN 37402
Tel (423) 756-0015 SIC 3949

PLAYCORE HOLDINGS LLC p 1155
401 Chestnut St Ste 410, Chattanooga TN 37402
Tel (877) 762-7563 SIC 2452 3949 3448

PLAYCORE WISCONSIN INC p 1155
401 Chestnut St Ste 410, Chattanooga TN 37402
Tel (423) 265-7529 SIC 3949

TRUE TEMPER SPORTS INC p 1486
8275 Tournament Dr # 200, Memphis TN 38125
Tel (901) 746-2000 SIC 5091 3949

■ FLOWTRONEX PSI LLC p 560
10661 Newkirk St, Dallas TX 75220
Tel (469) 221-1200
SIC 3561 3949 3523 3432

TOPGOLF INTERNATIONAL INC p 1461
8750 N Cntl Expy Ste 1200, Dallas TX 75231
Tel (214) 377-0615 SIC 3949

ROYAL BATHS MANUFACTURING CO LTD p 1254
14635 Chrisman Rd, Houston TX 77039
Tel (281) 442-3400
SIC 3842 3949 3432 3281

BELL SPORTS CORP p 170
6333 N State Highway 161 # 300, Irving TX 75038
Tel (469) 417-6600 SIC 3949 3751 5091

BELL SPORTS INC p 170
6333 N State Highway 161 # 300, Irving TX 75038
Tel (469) 417-6600 SIC 3949 3751

LIFETIME PRODUCTS INC p 865
Freeport Ctr Bldg D-11, Clearfield UT 84016
Tel (801) 776-1532
SIC 2519 3949 2531 2511

▲ VISTA OUTDOOR INC p 1562
262 N University Ave, Farmington UT 84025
Tel (801) 447-3000
SIC 3482 3483 3827 3949 3484 3812

HF HOLDINGS INC p 688
1500 S 1000 W, Logan UT 84321
Tel (435) 750-5000 SIC 3949 3088

ICON HEALTH & FITNESS INC p 727
1500 S 1000 W, Logan UT 84321
Tel (435) 750-5000 SIC 3949

▲ DIAMOND BLACK INC p 436
2084 E 3900 S, Salt Lake City UT 84124
Tel (801) 278-5552 SIC 3949 2329 2339

JAS D EASTON INC p 778
5215 W Wiley Post Way # 130, Salt Lake City UT 84116
Tel (801) 526-6211 SIC 3949 5091 6552

BURTON CORP p 229
80 Industrial Pkwy, Burlington VT 05401
Tel (802) 862-4500 SIC 3949

ORVIS CO INC p 1096
178 Conservation Way, Sunderland VT 05250
Tel (802) 362-3622 SIC 5961 5941 3949

AMF BOWLING WORLDWIDE INC p 84
7313 Bell Creek Rd, Mechanicsville VA 23111
Tel (804) 730-4000 SIC 3949 7933

QUBICAAMF WORLDWIDE LLC p 1198
8100 Amf Dr, Mechanicsville VA 23111
Tel (804) 569-1000 SIC 3949 7933

RECREATIONAL EQUIPMENT INC p 1215
6750 S 228th St, Kent WA 98032
Tel (253) 395-3780
SIC 2329 3949 2399 5941 5961 5699

CASCADE DESIGNS INC p 262
4000 1st Ave S, Seattle WA 98134
Tel (206) 583-0583
SIC 2515 3089 3949 8733

▲ NAUTILUS INC p 1019
17750 Se 6th Way, Vancouver WA 98683
Tel (360) 859-2900 SIC 3949

PRECOR INC p 1169
20031 142nd Ave Ne, Woodinville WA 98072
Tel (425) 486-9292 SIC 3949

■ JANSPORT INC p 777
N850 County Road Cb, Appleton WI 54914
Tel (920) 734-5708
SIC 3949 3161 2339 2329 2321

FLAMBEAU INC p 554
801 Lynn Ave, Baraboo WI 53913
Tel (608) 356-5551 SIC 3089 3949 3944

▲ JOHNSON OUTDOORS INC p 791
555 Main St, Racine WI 53403
Tel (262) 631-6600 SIC 3949 3732 3812

SIC 3951 Pens & Mechanical Pencils

AVERY PRODUCTS CORP p 137
50 Pointe Dr, Brea CA 92821
Tel (714) 675-8500
SIC 2678 3951 2672 2891

NATIONAL PEN CO LLC p 1015
12121 Scripps Summit Dr # 200, San Diego CA 92131
Tel (866) 388-9850 SIC 3951 3993

BIC CORP p 181
1 Bic Way Ste 1, Shelton CT 06484
Tel (203) 783-2000
SIC 3951 2899 3999 3421 5091 3952

BIC USA INC p 181
1 Bic Way Ste 1, Shelton CT 06484
Tel (203) 783-2000
SIC 3951 2899 3999 3421

PILOT CORP OF AMERICA p 1148
3855 Regent Blvd, Jacksonville FL 32224
Tel (904) 645-9999 SIC 5112 3951

■ SANFORD LP p 1279
3500 Lacey Rd, Downers Grove IL 60515
Tel (770) 418-7000 SIC 2891 3951 3952

■ GILLETTE CO p 612
1 Gillette Park, Boston MA 02127
Tel (617) 421-7000
SIC 3421 3634 2844 3951 2899

MIX HOLDINGS INC p 978
2501 Mc Gee Traffic Way, Kansas City MO 64108
Tel (816) 274-5111
SIC 3952 3951 3295 3944

▲ NEWELL BRANDS INC p 1037
221 River St, Hoboken NJ 07030
Tel (201) 610-6600
SIC 3089 3469 2591 3951 3999 3546

CRAYOLA LLC p 389
1100 Church Ln, Easton PA 18040
Tel (610) 253-6271
SIC 3952 3951 3295 3944

ESSENTRA HOLDINGS CORP p 510
1625 Ashton Park Dr Ste A, South Chesterfield VA 23834
Tel (804) 518-0322
SIC 3081 3082 3999 3951 2823

ESSENTRA POROUS TECHNOLOGIES CORP p 510
1625 Ashton Park Dr Ste A, South Chesterfield VA 23834
Tel (804) 524-4983
SIC 3081 3951 3082 2823 3999

SIC 3952 Lead Pencils, Crayons & Artist's Mtrls

BIC CORP p 181
1 Bic Way Ste 1, Shelton CT 06484
Tel (203) 783-2000
SIC 3951 2899 3999 3421 5091 3952

ASBURY CARBONS INC p 115
103 Foulk Rd Ste 202, Wilmington DE 19803
Tel (302) 652-0266
SIC 1499 3295 1241 5051 3952 3069

■ SANFORD LP p 1279
3500 Lacey Rd, Downers Grove IL 60515
Tel (770) 418-7000 SIC 2891 3951 3952

MIX HOLDINGS INC p 978
2501 Mc Gee Traffic Way, Kansas City MO 64108
Tel (816) 274-5111
SIC 3952 3951 3295 3944

CRAYOLA LLC p 389
1100 Church Ln, Easton PA 18040
Tel (610) 253-6271
SIC 3952 3951 3295 3944

SIC 3953 Marking Devices

IPG (US) HOLDINGS INC p 763
100 Paramount Dr Ste 300, Sarasota FL 34232
Tel (941) 727-5788 SIC 2672 3953

IPG (US) INC p 763
100 Paramount Dr Ste 300, Sarasota FL 34232
Tel (941) 727-5788 SIC 2672 3953

TYDEN GROUP HOLDINGS CORP p 1496
409 Hoosier Dr, Angola IN 46703
Tel (740) 420-6777 SIC 3953 2891

ESSELTE HOLDINGS INC p 510
48 S Service Rd Ste 400, Melville NY 11747
Tel (631) 675-5700
SIC 2675 2782 3579 2672 3953 3596

ENNIS PAINT INC p 500
115 Todd Ct, Thomasville NC 27360
Tel (800) 331-8118 SIC 2851 3953

▲ MATTHEWS INTERNATIONAL CORP p 920
2 N Shore Ctr Ste 200, Pittsburgh PA 15212
Tel (412) 442-8200
SIC 3366 1542 3569 3995 3953 2796

IDENTITY GROUP HOLDINGS CORP p 729
1480 Gould Dr, Cookeville TN 38506
Tel (931) 432-4000
SIC 3089 3086 3993 3953

IDENTITY GROUP HOLDINGS LLC p 729
1480 Gould Dr, Cookeville TN 38506
Tel (931) 432-4000 SIC 3953

IDENTITY HOLDING CO LLC p 729
1480 Gould Dr, Cookeville TN 38506
Tel (931) 432-4000 SIC 3953 2672

STAMPIN UP INC p 1375
12907 S 3600 W, Riverton UT 84065
Tel (801) 257-5400 SIC 3953

OBERTHUR TECHNOLOGIES OF AMERICA CORP p 1072
4250 Pleasant Valley Rd, Chantilly VA 20151
Tel (703) 263-0100
SIC 3089 7382 3953 3578 3499

SIC 3955 Carbon Paper & Inked Ribbons

INKCYCLE INC p 743
11100 W 82nd St, Lenexa KS 66214
Tel (913) 894-8387
SIC 3955 7699 7378 5045 8249 5734

VISIONIT SUPPLIES AND SERVICES INC p 1561
3031 W Grand Blvd Ste 600, Detroit MI 48202
Tel (313) 664-5650 SIC 3577 3955 5734

INTERNATIONAL IMAGING MATERIALS INC p 755
310 Commerce Dr, Amherst NY 14228
Tel (716) 691-6333 SIC 3955 3555

DNP IMAGINGCOMM AMERICA CORP p 446
4524 Enterprise Dr Nw, Concord NC 28027
Tel (704) 784-8100 SIC 3955

PUBCO CORP p 1189
3830 Kelley Ave, Cleveland OH 44114
Tel (216) 881-5300 SIC 3531 6512 3955

BLACK CREEK HOLDINGS LTD p 186
2400 Dallas Pkwy Ste 230, Plano TX 75093
Tel (972) 398-7100 SIC 3955 3861

NUKOTE INC p 1067
2400 Dallas Pkwy Ste 230, Plano TX 75093
Tel (972) 398-7100 SIC 3955 3861

SIC 3961 Costume Jewelry & Novelties

GRAY VESTAR INVESTORS LLC p 632
17622 Armstrong Ave, Irvine CA 92614
Tel (949) 863-1171
SIC 2253 2339 2335 2337 3961 2387

TEMPLETON COAL CO INC p 1436
701 Wabash Ave Ste 501, Terre Haute IN 47807
Tel (812) 232-7037
SIC 5074 3567 3961 5049 3089

▲ AMERICAN BILTRITE INC p 69
57 River St Ste 302, Wellesley MA 02481
Tel (781) 237-6655
SIC 3069 2672 2241 3961 5094

WINCRAFT INC p 1615
960 E Mark St, Winona MN 55987
Tel (507) 454-5510
SIC 3499 2399 3089 3961 3999 3069

▲ AVON PRODUCTS INC p 139
777 3rd Ave, New York NY 10017
Tel (212) 282-5000
SIC 2844 3961 5961 5023 5137

SWAROVSKI NORTH AMERICA LIMITED p 1411
1 Kenney Dr, Cranston RI 02920
Tel (401) 463-6400 SIC 3961 5023 3231

SWAROVSKI US HOLDING LIMITED p 1411
1 Kenney Dr, Cranston RI 02920
Tel (401) 463-6400
SIC 3961 3231 5048 5099

MARY KAY HOLDING CORP p 914
16251 Dallas Pkwy, Addison TX 75001
Tel (972) 687-6300
SIC 5963 3961 3172 4724

COMMEMORATIVE BRANDS INC p 344
7211 Circle S Rd, Austin TX 78745
Tel (512) 444-0571 SIC 3911 5944 3961

SIC 3965 Fasteners, Buttons, Needles & Pins

WHITESELL CORP p 1606
2703 Avalon Ave, Muscle Shoals AL 35661
Tel (256) 248-8500
SIC 3965 5085 3444 3452 3451

MICRO PLASTICS INC p 961
111 Industry Ln, Flippin AR 72634
Tel (870) 453-8861 SIC 3965

CHECKERS INDUSTRIAL PRODUCTS LLC p 292
620 Compton St, Broomfield CO 80020
Tel (720) 890-1187 SIC 3714 3965

YKK (USA) INC p 1636
1300 Cobb Industrial Dr, Marietta GA 30066
Tel (770) 427-5521 SIC 3452 3965

YKK CORP OF AMERICA p 1636
1850 Parkway Pl Se # 300, Marietta GA 30067
Tel (770) 261-6120 SIC 3965 3354

■ LEHIGH CONSUMER PRODUCTS LLC p 853
3901 Liberty St, Aurora IL 60504
Tel (630) 851-7330
SIC 3965 2298 3462 3452 8742

■ MARMON INDUSTRIAL LLC p 909
181 W Madison St Fl 26, Chicago IL 60602
Tel (312) 372-9500
SIC 3743 4741 3589 6159 3965 3492

■ NEWELL OPERATING CO p 1037
29 E Stephenson St, Freeport IL 61032
Tel (815) 235-4171
SIC 3365 3991 3089 2591 3965 3596

▲ ILLINOIS TOOL WORKS INC p 732
155 Harlem Ave, Glenview IL 60025
Tel (847) 724-7500
SIC 3089 3965 3499 2891 3585

■ INFASTECH DECORAH LLC p 740
1304 Kerr Dr, Decorah IA 52101
Tel (563) 382-4216 SIC 3452 3965

ACUMENT GLOBAL TECHNOLOGIES INC p 20
6125 18 Mile Rd, Sterling Heights MI 48314
Tel (586) 254-3900 SIC 3965 5072

VELCRO USA INC p 1547
95 Sundial Ave, Manchester NH 03103
Tel (603) 669-4880 SIC 2241 3965

COATS & CLARK INC p 332
3430 Toringdon Way # 301, Charlotte NC 28277
Tel (704) 329-5800
SIC 2284 2281 3364 3089 2241 3965

COATS NORTH AMERICA DE REPUBLICA DOMINICANA INC p 332
3430 Toringdon Way # 301, Charlotte NC 28277
Tel (800) 242-8095
SIC 2284 2281 3364 3089 2241 3965

MIDWEST MOTOR SUPPLY CO p 967
4800 Roberts Rd, Columbus OH 43228
Tel (800) 233-1294 SIC 3965 3399 8742

▲ DORMAN PRODUCTS INC p 451
3400 E Walnut St, Colmar PA 18915
Tel (215) 997-1800 SIC 3714 3231 3965

SOUTHCO INC p 1345
210 N Brinton Lake Rd, Concordville PA 19331
Tel (610) 459-4000 SIC 3965

FLEXITALLIC GROUP INC p 556
201 Kingwood Med Dr B20 Ste B 200, Houston TX 77067
Tel (281) 604-2525
SIC 3053 3533 3463 3965

MIDWEST MANUFACTURING INC p 967
5311 Kane Rd, Eau Claire WI 54703
Tel (715) 876-5555 SIC 5033 5031 3965

SIC 3991 Brooms & Brushes

AHI INVESTMENT INC p 36
675 Glenoaks Blvd, San Fernando CA 91340
Tel (818) 979-0030 SIC 5199 3991

EVERCARE CO p 513
3885 Crestwd Pkwy Nw # 175, Duluth GA 30096
Tel (770) 570-5000 SIC 3991

TRUE VALUE CO p 1486
8600 W Bryn Mawr Ave 100s, Chicago IL 60631
Tel (773) 695-5000 SIC 5072 2851 3991

■ NEWELL OPERATING CO p 1037
29 E Stephenson St, Freeport IL 61032
Tel (815) 235-4171
SIC 3365 3991 3089 2591 3965 3596

FULLER BRUSH CO INC p 584
1 Fuller Way, Great Bend KS 67530
Tel (620) 792-1711 SIC 2842 2844 3991

SWEEPSTER ATTACHMENTS LLC p 1411
2800 Zeeb Rd, Dexter MI 48130
Tel (734) 996-9116 SIC 3589 3991

RANIR LLC p 1208
4701 East Paris Ave Se, Grand Rapids MI 49512
Tel (616) 698-8880 SIC 3843 3991

■ QUICKIE MANUFACTURING CORP p 1199
1150 Taylors Ln Ste 2, Cinnaminson NJ 08077
Tel (856) 829-7900 SIC 2392 3991

▲ COLGATE-PALMOLIVE CO p 336
300 Park Ave Fl 5, New York NY 10022
Tel (212) 310-2000
SIC 2844 3991 2841 2842 2047

LINZER PRODUCTS CORP p 869
248 Wyandanch Ave, West Babylon NY 11704
Tel (631) 253-3333 SIC 5198 3991

ACS INDUSTRIES INC p 19
1 New England Way Unit 1, Lincoln RI 02865
Tel (401) 769-4700
SIC 3291 3496 3312 3315 3569 3991

TEAM TECHNOLOGIES INC p 1430
5949 Commerce Blvd, Morristown TN 37814
Tel (423) 587-2199
SIC 2844 5122 5719 3991

SIC 3993 Signs & Advertising Displays

VULCAN INC p 1567
410 E Berry Ave, Foley AL 36535
Tel (251) 943-7000 SIC 3469 3993

ANTIGUA GROUP INC p 94
16651 N 84th Ave, Peoria AZ 85382
Tel (623) 523-6000
SIC 5137 5136 2395 2339 3993

PACKAGING INNOVATORS CORP p 1106
6650 National Dr, Livermore CA 94550
Tel (925) 371-2000 SIC 5113 2653 3993

FEDERAL HEATH SIGN CO LLC p 534
4602 North Ave, Oceanside CA 92056
Tel (760) 941-0715 *SIC* 3993

NATIONAL PEN CO LLC p 1015
12121 Scripps Summit Dr # 200, San Diego CA 92131
Tel (866) 388-9850 *SIC* 3951 3993

RACKS INC p 1203
7565 Siempre Viva Rd, San Diego CA 92154
Tel (619) 661-0987 *SIC* 2542 3993 2541

PRIME RESOURCES CORP p 1175
1100 Boston Ave Bldg 1, Bridgeport CT 06610
Tel (203) 331-9100 *SIC* 3993 2759

CONNECTICUT CONTAINER CORP p 356
455 Sackett Point Rd, North Haven CT 06473
Tel (203) 248-2161
SIC 2653 3993 3412 2631

▲ REVOLUTION LIGHTING TECHNOLOGIES INC p 1229
177 Broad St Fl 12, Stamford CT 06901
Tel (203) 504-1111 *SIC* 3674 3641 3993

GERBER SCIENTIFIC LLC p 608
24 Indl Pk Rd W, Tolland CT 06084
Tel (860) 871-8082
SIC 3993 7336 3851 7372 3577

SONALYSTS INC p 1339
215 Parkway N, Waterford CT 06385
Tel (860) 442-4355
SIC 8711 7373 8748 8732 3993

ACQUINITY INTERACTIVE LLC p 18
2200 Sw 10th St, Deerfield Beach FL 33442
Tel (954) 312-4733 *SIC* 3993

HIT PROMOTIONAL PRODUCTS INC p 696
7150 Bryan Dairy Rd, Largo FL 33777
Tel (727) 541-5561 *SIC* 2759 3993

ROARK CAPITAL GROUP INC p 1240
1180 Peachtree St Ne # 2500, Atlanta GA 30309
Tel (404) 591-5200
SIC 6726 3993 7331 6794 5261

■ POLYVISION CORP p 1160
10700 Abbotts Bridge Rd # 100, Johns Creek GA 30097
Tel (678) 542-3100 *SIC* 3281 3993

COLOR COMMUNICATIONS INC p 338
4000 W Fillmore St, Chicago IL 60624
Tel (773) 638-1400 *SIC* 2752 3993

LEO BURNETT CO INC p 856
35 W Wacker Dr Fl 21, Chicago IL 60601
Tel (312) 220-5959 *SIC* 7311 3993

WATCHFIRE ENTERPRISES INC p 1581
1015 Maple St, Danville IL 61832
Tel (217) 442-0611 *SIC* 3993

WATCHFIRE SIGNS LLC p 1581
1015 Maple St, Danville IL 61832
Tel (217) 442-0611 *SIC* 3993

WATCHFIRE TECHNOLOGIES HOLDINGS I INC p 1581
1015 Maple St, Danville IL 61832
Tel (217) 442-6971 *SIC* 3993

WATCHFIRE TECHNOLOGIES HOLDINGS II INC p 1581
1015 Maple St, Danville IL 61832
Tel (217) 442-0611 *SIC* 3993

ICON IDENTITY SOLUTIONS INC p 727
1418 Elmhurst Rd, Elk Grove Village IL 60007
Tel (847) 364-2250 *SIC* 3993

RICO INDUSTRIES INC p 1233
7000 N Austin Ave, Niles IL 60714
Tel (312) 427-0313
SIC 5199 3172 2396 3993

WHITECO INDUSTRIES INC p 1606
1000 E 80th Pl Ste 700n, Merrillville IN 46410
Tel (219) 769-6601
SIC 7312 7011 7922 6552 7374 3993

GEIGER BROS p 597
70 Mount Hope Ave, Lewiston ME 04240
Tel (207) 755-2000
SIC 5199 3993 2752 2782 2789

GEORGE P JOHNSON CO p 606
3600 Giddings Rd, Auburn Hills MI 48326
Tel (248) 475-2500 *SIC* 3993 7389

HARBOR INDUSTRIES INC p 659
14130 172nd Ave, Grand Haven MI 49417
Tel (616) 842-5330 *SIC* 2541 3993

VALASSIS INTERNATIONAL INC p 1539
19975 Victor Pkwy, Livonia MI 48152
Tel (734) 591-3000
SIC 8743 3993 2759 2752

GG MCGUIGGAN CORP p 610
1085 Snelling Ave N, Saint Paul MN 55108
Tel (651) 646-4544 *SIC* 2679 3993 2752

SMYTH COMPANIES LLC p 1335
1085 Snelling Ave N, Saint Paul MN 55108
Tel (651) 646-4544
SIC 2679 2752 3993 7389 5084 7699

GRIMCO INC p 640
1585 Fencorp Dr, Fenton MO 63026
Tel (636) 305-0088
SIC 3469 2759 3993 3429 3312

ROXBORO HOLDINGS INC p 1254
1501 State Route 34, Wall Township NJ 07727
Tel (732) 919-3119
SIC 3643 3679 3993 3823 3674

AMSTERDAM PRINTING & LITHO INC p 87
166 Wallins Corners Rd, Amsterdam NY 12010
Tel (518) 842-6000 *SIC* 3993 2752 2761

■ GABELLI FUNDS LLC p 588
1 Corporate Ctr, Rye NY 10580
Tel (914) 921-5105 *SIC* 6726 3993

CREATIVE SOLUTIONS GROUP INC p 390
555 Tuckahoe Rd, Yonkers NY 10710
Tel (914) 771-4200 *SIC* 3993

▲ LSI INDUSTRIES INC p 883
10000 Alliance Rd, Blue Ash OH 45242
Tel (513) 793-3200 *SIC* 3648 3993 3663

KDM SIGNS INC p 807
10450 Medallion Dr, Cincinnati OH 45241
Tel (513) 769-1932 *SIC* 2759 3993

ZIPPO MANUFACTURING CO INC p 1643
33 Barbour St, Bradford PA 16701
Tel (814) 368-2700
SIC 3914 3993 5172 3999 3421 3172

LA FRANCE CORP p 835
1 Lafrance Way, Concordville PA 19331
Tel (610) 361-4300
SIC 3089 3364 3993 5013 7389

MCS INDUSTRIES INC p 932
2280 Newlins Mill Rd, Easton PA 18045
Tel (610) 253-6268
SIC 2499 3089 3499 3993 3231

■ IDL WORLDWIDE INC p 729
6515 Penn Ave, Pittsburgh PA 15206
Tel (412) 965-3954 *SIC* 3993 2752

BEISTLE CO p 169
1 Beistle Plz, Shippensburg PA 17257
Tel (717) 532-2131
SIC 2679 3993 2675 2657 2631 2621

▲ DAKTRONICS INC p 409
201 Daktronics Dr, Brookings SD 57006
Tel (605) 692-0200 *SIC* 3993 7372

HOLIEN INC p 700
312 9th Ave Se Ste B, Watertown SD 57201
Tel (605) 886-3889 *SIC* 3612 3672 3993

IDENTITY GROUP HOLDINGS CORP p 729
1480 Gould Dr, Cookeville TN 38506
Tel (931) 432-4000
SIC 3089 3086 3993 3953

MARCO DISPLAY SPECIALISTS LP p 905
3209 Marquita Dr, Fort Worth TX 76116
Tel (817) 244-8300 *SIC* 2541 3993

MARCO DISPLAY SPECIALISTS LP p 905
3209 Marquita Dr, Fort Worth TX 76116
Tel (817) 244-8300
SIC 2521 2541 3993 3089 3081

TPG CAPITAL MANAGEMENT LP p 1467
301 Commerce St Ste 3300, Fort Worth TX 76102
Tel (817) 871-4000
SIC 6726 3674 6799 3993 6719

UNIVERSAL DISPLAY AND FIXTURE CO p 1516
726 E Hwy 121, Lewisville TX 75057
Tel (972) 434-8067 *SIC* 2542 3993

YOUNG ELECTRIC SIGN CO INC p 1638
2401 S Foothill Dr, Salt Lake City UT 84109
Tel (801) 464-4600
SIC 3993 7359 1799 6794

ARCHITECTURAL GRAPHICS INC p 105
2655 International Pkwy, Virginia Beach VA 23452
Tel (757) 427-1900 *SIC* 3993

EVERBRITE LLC p 513
4949 S 110th St, Greenfield WI 53228
Tel (414) 529-3500 *SIC* 3993

▲ BRADY CORP p 207
6555 W Good Hope Rd, Milwaukee WI 53223
Tel (414) 358-6600
SIC 3993 2672 3695 3577

DERSE INC p 431
3800 W Canal St, Milwaukee WI 53208
Tel (414) 257-2000 *SIC* 3993 7312

SIC 3995 Burial Caskets

■ BATESVILLE CASKET CO INC p 159
1 Batesville Blvd, Batesville IN 47006
Tel (812) 934-7500 *SIC* 3995

■ BATESVILLE SERVICES INC p 159
1 Batesville Blvd, Batesville IN 47006
Tel (812) 934-7000 *SIC* 3995

▲ HILLENBRAND INC p 693
1 Batesville Blvd, Batesville IN 47006
Tel (812) 934-7500 *SIC* 3535 3995

▲ MATTHEWS INTERNATIONAL CORP p 920
2 N Shore Ctr Ste 200, Pittsburgh PA 15212
Tel (412) 442-8200
SIC 3366 1542 3569 3995 3953 2796

SIC 3996 Linoleum & Hard Surface Floor Coverings, NEC

MANNINGTON MILLS INC p 902
75 Mannington Mills Rd, Salem NJ 08079
Tel (856) 935-3000
SIC 3996 3253 2273 2435

▲ ARMSTRONG FLOORING INC p 111
2500 Columbia Ave, Lancaster PA 17603
Tel (717) 672-9611 *SIC* 3996 2426

NATCO PRODUCTS CORP p 1009
155 Brookside Ave, West Warwick RI 02893
Tel (401) 828-0300 *SIC* 3996 2273 5023

SIC 3999 Manufacturing Industries, NEC

T - H MARINE SUPPLIES INC p 1419
200 Finney Dr Sw, Huntsville AL 35824
Tel (256) 772-0164 *SIC* 5551 3999 3429

GD COPPER (USA) INC p 595
405 Gd Copper Dr, Pine Hill AL 36769
Tel (334) 637-0200 *SIC* 3351 3999

GLYNLYON INC p 618
300 N Mckemy Ave, Chandler AZ 85226
Tel (480) 940-0801 *SIC* 3999

HANNAS CANDLE CO p 658
2700 S Armstrong Ave, Fayetteville AR 72701
Tel (479) 443-5467 *SIC* 3999 2844 5999

SEGA HOLDINGS USA INC p 1300
9737 Lurline Ave, Chatsworth CA 91311
Tel (415) 701-6000 *SIC* 3999 5045

ELITE ONE SOURCE NUTRISCIENCES INC p 487
13840 Magnolia Ave, Chino CA 91710
Tel (909) 902-5005 *SIC* 8049 8099 3999

BANDAI NAMCO HOLDINGS USA INC p 150
2120 Park Pl Ste 120, El Segundo CA 90245
Tel (714) 816-9500 *SIC* 3999 7993

SEGA OF AMERICA INC p 1300
6400 Oak Cyn Ste 100, Irvine CA 92618
Tel (415) 806-0169 *SIC* 3999 5092

■ SCALED COMPOSITES LLC p 1285
1624 Flight Line, Mojave CA 93501
Tel (661) 824-4541 *SIC* 3721 3999 8711

PRIDE INDUSTRIES ONE INC p 1174
10030 Foothills Blvd, Roseville CA 95747
Tel (916) 788-2100 *SIC* 3999

ALTMAN SPECIALTY PLANTS INC p 62
3742 Blue Bird Canyon Rd, Vista CA 92084
Tel (760) 744-8191 *SIC* 5193 3999

■ WATKINS MANUFACTURING CORP p 1582
1280 Park Center Dr, Vista CA 92081
Tel (760) 598-6464 *SIC* 3999

■ ZODIAC POOL SYSTEMS INC p 1644
2620 Commerce Way, Vista CA 92081
Tel (760) 599-9600 *SIC* 3589 3999

BAE SYSTEMS POWER INC p 144
5840 Dahlia St, Commerce City CO 80022
Tel (303) 287-7441
SIC 5084 3531 3999 3569

▲ ACME UNITED CORP p 18
55 Walls Dr Ste 201, Fairfield CT 06824
Tel (203) 254-6060
SIC 3421 2499 3842 3579 3069 3999

BIC CORP p 181
1 Bic Way Ste 1, Shelton CT 06484
Tel (203) 783-2000
SIC 3951 2899 3999 3421 5091 3952

BIC USA INC p 181
1 Bic Way Ste 1, Shelton CT 06484
Tel (203) 783-2000
SIC 3951 2899 3999 3421

GALATA CHEMICALS LLC p 589
464 Heritage Rd Ste A1, Southbury CT 06488
Tel (203) 236-9000 *SIC* 5169 3999

CONAIR CORP p 354
1 Cummings Point Rd, Stamford CT 06902
Tel (203) 351-9000
SIC 3634 3631 3639 3999

UST LLC p 1536
6 High Ridge Park Bldg A, Stamford CT 06905
Tel (203) 817-3000
SIC 2131 2084 2621 3999

WORLD INDUSTRIAL RESOURCES CORP p 1625
13100 56th Ct Ste 710, Clearwater FL 33760
Tel (727) 572-9991
SIC 3999 2542 5113 2671

CROSS MATCH TECHNOLOGIES INC p 393
3950 Rca Blvd Ste 5001, Palm Beach Gardens FL 33410
Tel (561) 622-1650 *SIC* 3999

▲ SUPERIOR UNIFORM GROUP INC p 1407
10055 Seminole Blvd, Seminole FL 33772
Tel (727) 397-9611 *SIC* 2389 3999 7389

PET SUPERMARKET INC p 1137
1100 International Pkwy # 200, Sunrise FL 33323
Tel (866) 434-1990 *SIC* 5999 3999 5199

CONSOLIDATED CONTAINER CO LP p 359
3101 Towercreek Pkwy Se, Atlanta GA 30339
Tel (678) 742-4600 *SIC* 3089 3999

■ GOODY PRODUCTS INC p 625
3 Glenlake Pkwy, Atlanta GA 30328
Tel (770) 418-7300 *SIC* 3999 3089 3069

INTERFACE FLOORING SYSTEMS INC p 752
2859 Paces Ferry Rd Se, Atlanta GA 30339
Tel (800) 336-0225 *SIC* 3272 1771 3999

FIELDTURF USA INC p 541
175 N Industrial Blvd Ne, Calhoun GA 30701
Tel (706) 625-6533 *SIC* 3999

W C BRADLEY CO p 1568
1017 Front Ave, Columbus GA 31901
Tel (706) 571-7000 *SIC* 3631 3949 3999

SCENTSY INC p 1286
2701 E Pine Ave, Meridian ID 83642
Tel (208) 472-0800 *SIC* 3999

■ FIRST ALERT INC p 544
3901 Liberty St, Aurora IL 60504
Tel (630) 851-7330
SIC 3669 3999 3446 3499 3829 3648

■ WMS GAMING INC p 1620
3401 N California Ave, Chicago IL 60618
Tel (773) 961-1000 *SIC* 3999

■ WMS INDUSTRIES INC p 1620
3401 N California Ave, Chicago IL 60618
Tel (847) 785-3000 *SIC* 3999 7999

■ MONDELEZ GLOBAL LLC p 983
3 Parkway N Ste 300, Deerfield IL 60015
Tel (847) 943-4000
SIC 2052 2066 3999 2067 2022 2087

CAROLINA DESIGNS LTD p 259
999 E Touhy Ave Ste 500, Des Plaines IL 60018
Tel (847) 294-1100 *SIC* 3999

WAHL CLIPPER CORP p 1571
2900 Locust St, Sterling IL 61081
Tel (815) 625-6525 *SIC* 3999

ORBUS LLC p 1093
9033 Murphy Rd, Woodridge IL 60517
Tel (630) 226-1155 *SIC* 3999

VESTIL MANUFACTURING CORP p 1552
2999 N Wayne St, Angola IN 46703
Tel (260) 665-7586 *SIC* 3999 3535 3069

WILLIAMS BROS HEALTH CARE PHARMACY INC p 1611
10 Williams Brothers Dr, Washington IN 47501
Tel (812) 254-2497
SIC 5047 7352 5999 5169 3999

BRAUN CORP p 208
631 W 11th St, Winamac IN 46996
Tel (574) 946-6153 *SIC* 3999

FAIRVIEW MILLS LLC p 525
604 Nemaha St, Seneca KS 66538
Tel (785) 336-2148 *SIC* 3999

DOMETIC CORP p 448
13551 Triton Park Blvd # 1000, Louisville KY 40223
Tel (502) 873-3524
SIC 3089 3443 3444 3822 3823 3999

TREES N TRENDS INC p 1475
3229 Benton Rd, Paducah KY 42003
Tel (270) 443-5100
SIC 5999 3999 5947 5193

▲ L S STARRETT CO p 834
121 Crescent St, Athol MA 01331
Tel (978) 249-3551
SIC 3545 3423 3999 3425 3823

EMD MILLIPORE CORP p 491
290 Concord Rd, Billerica MA 01821
Tel (781) 533-6000 *SIC* 3559 1541 3999

▲ HOUGHTON MIFFLIN HARCOURT CO p 711
222 Berkeley St Fl 1-11, Boston MA 02116
Tel (617) 351-5000 *SIC* 3999 2731

CARTAMUNDI EAST LONGMEADOW LLC p 261
443 Shaker Rd, East Longmeadow MA 01028
Tel (413) 526-2000 *SIC* 3944 3999

■ PARTYLITE INC p 1119
59 Armstrong Rd, Plymouth MA 02360
Tel (203) 661-1926
SIC 2023 3999 3641 5199 5023

■ YANKEE CANDLE CO INC p 1634
16 Yankee Candle Way, South Deerfield MA 01373
Tel (413) 665-8306 *SIC* 3999 2899 5999

■ YANKEE CANDLE INVESTMENTS LLC p 1634
16 Yankee Candle Way, South Deerfield MA 01373
Tel (413) 665-8306 *SIC* 3999 5999

■ YANKEE HOLDING CORP p 1635
16 Yankee Candle Way, South Deerfield MA 01373
Tel (413) 665-8306 *SIC* 3999 2899

■ YCC HOLDINGS LLC p 1635
16 Yankee Candle Way, South Deerfield MA 01373
Tel (413) 665-8306 *SIC* 3999 2899 5999

■ SMITH & WESSON CORP p 1333
2100 Roosevelt Ave, Springfield MA 01104
Tel (413) 781-8300
SIC 3484 3429 3999 5091

BENTELER AUTOMOTIVE CORP p 173
2650 N Opdyke Rd Ste B, Auburn Hills MI 48326
Tel (248) 364-7190 *SIC* 3714 3465 3999

FAURECIA INTERIOR SYSTEMS INC p 531
2500 Executive Hills Dr, Auburn Hills MI 48326
Tel (248) 409-3500 *SIC* 5013 3999

TRAVEL TAGS INC p 1473
5842 Carmen Ave, Inver Grove Heights MN 55076
Tel (651) 450-1201 *SIC* 2396 3999 2752

SCHWING AMERICA INC p 1291
5900 Centerville Rd, Saint Paul MN 55127
Tel (651) 429-0999 *SIC* 3531 3561 3999

WINCRAFT INC p 1615
960 E Mark St, Winona MN 55987
Tel (507) 454-5510
SIC 3499 2399 3089 3961 3999 3069

■ BALLY GAMING INC p 148
6601 Bermuda Rd, Las Vegas NV 89119
Tel (702) 532-7700 *SIC* 3999

■ BALLY GAMING INTERNATIONAL INC p 148
6601 Bermuda Rd, Las Vegas NV 89119
Tel (702) 584-7700 *SIC* 3999

■ BALLY TECHNOLOGIES INC p 148
6601 Bermuda Rd, Las Vegas NV 89119
Tel (770) 420-2388
SIC 3999 7999 7993 7372

KONAMI GAMING INC p 827
585 Konami Cir, Las Vegas NV 89119
Tel (702) 616-1400 *SIC* 5092 3999

■ MERILLAT INDUSTRIES INC p 949
865 Pilot Rd, Las Vegas NV 89119
Tel (702) 897-9800 *SIC* 3999

■ SHFL ENTERTAINMENT INC p 1316
6650 El Camino Rd, Las Vegas NV 89118
Tel (702) 897-7150 *SIC* 3999 3949 3944

INTERNATIONAL GAME TECHNOLOGY p 755
9295 Prototype Dr, Reno NV 89521
Tel (775) 448-7777 *SIC* 3999 5099

AMNEAL PHARMACEUTICALS LLC p 86
400 Crossing Blvd Fl 3, Bridgewater NJ 08807
Tel (631) 952-0214 *SIC* 2834 3999

SUNSHINE BOUQUET CO p 1404
3 Chris Ct Ste A, Dayton NJ 08810
Tel (732) 274-2900 *SIC* 5193 3999

▲ NEWELL BRANDS INC p 1037
221 River St, Hoboken NJ 07030
Tel (201) 610-6600
SIC 3089 3469 2591 3951 3999 3546

TYCO INTERNATIONAL MANAGEMENT CO LLC p 1496
9 Roszel Rd Ste 2, Princeton NJ 08540
Tel (609) 720-4200
SIC 3999 1711 1731 3669 3491

HARTZ MOUNTAIN CORP p 666
400 Plaza Dr Ste 400, Secaucus NJ 07094
Tel (201) 271-4800 *SIC* 5199 3999

PRODUCTION RESOURCE GROUP LLC p 1179
200 Business Park Dr # 109, Armonk NY 10504
Tel (212) 589-5400 *SIC* 3999 7922

▲ HRG GROUP INC p 714
450 Park Ave Fl 29, New York NY 10022
Tel (212) 906-8555
SIC 3691 3634 3999 6311

SHAKE-N-GO FASHION INC p 1310
85 Harbor Rd, Port Washington NY 11050
Tel (516) 944-7777 *SIC* 3999

■ WALTER KIDDE PORTABLE EQUIPMENT INC p 1574
1016 Corporate Park Dr, Mebane NC 27302
Tel (919) 563-5911 *SIC* 3999

SCHLETTER INC p 1287
1001 Commerce Center Dr, Shelby NC 28150
Tel (704) 595-4200 *SIC* 3441 3999

CANDLE-LITE CO LLC p 247
10521 Millington Ct Ste B, Blue Ash OH 45242
Tel (513) 563-1113 *SIC* 3999

CK TECHNOLOGIES LLC p 320
1701 Magda Dr, Montpelier OH 43543
Tel (419) 485-1110 *SIC* 3089 3999

CENTAUR INC p 275
2401 Front St, Toledo OH 43605
Tel (419) 469-8000 *SIC* 3312 3316 3999

ALUMINUM LINE PRODUCTS CO p 63
24460 Sperry Cir, Westlake OH 44145
Tel (440) 835-8880 *SIC* 5051 3365 3999

■TRIUMPH AEROSTRUCTURES - TULSA LLC p 1483
3330 N Mingo Rd, Tulsa OK 74116
Tel (615) 361-2061 SIC 3728 3999

■MARLETTE HOMES p 909
400 W Elm Ave, Hermiston OR 97838
Tel (541) 567-5546 SIC 3999

ZIPCORP INC p 1643
33 Barbour St, Bradford PA 16701
Tel (814) 368-2700 SIC 3999 5172

ZIPPO MANUFACTURING CO INC p 1643
33 Barbour St, Bradford PA 16701
Tel (814) 368-2700
SIC 3914 3993 5172 3999 3421 3172

■KIDDE FIRE PROTECTION INC p 817
350 E Union St, West Chester PA 19382
Tel (610) 363-1400 SIC 3669 3999 3823

WEXCO INC p 1603
3490 Board Rd, York PA 17406
Tel (717) 764-8585
SIC 3089 3949 3999 5091 3081

MVP GROUP INTERNATIONAL INC p 1003
1031 Legrand Blvd, Charleston SC 29492
Tel (843) 216-8380 SIC 3999 5122

ATLAS COPCO COMPRESSORS LLC p 127
1800 Overview Dr, Rock Hill SC 29730
Tel (803) 817-7000 SIC 3563 3999

VIDEO GAMING TECHNOLOGIES INC p 1556
308 Mallory Station Rd, Franklin TN 37067
Tel (615) 372-1000 SIC 3999 7993

DOSKOCIL MANUFACTURING CO INC p 451
2300 E Randol Mill Rd, Arlington TX 76011
Tel (877) 738-6283 SIC 3999 5999

PETMATE HOLDINGS CO p 1138
2300 E Randol Mill Rd, Arlington TX 76011
Tel (817) 467-5116 SIC 3999 5999

4FRONT HOLDINGS INC p 3
1612 Hutton Dr Ste 140, Carrollton TX 75006
Tel (972) 466-0707 SIC 3537 3999 3448

NATIONAL CONSUMER OUTDOORS CORP p 1011
4215 Mcewen Rd, Dallas TX 75244
Tel (972) 716-4200
SIC 3999 2399 2394 3732

HELEN OF TROY LP p 681
1 Helen Of Troy Plz, El Paso TX 79912
Tel (915) 225-8000 SIC 3999 3634

HELEN OF TROY TEXAS CORP p 681
1 Helen Of Troy Plz, El Paso TX 79912
Tel (915) 225-8000 SIC 3999

ALLIED ELECTRONICS INC p 56
7151 Jack Newell Blvd S, Fort Worth TX 76118
Tel (817) 595-3500 SIC 5065 7389 3999

MORTEX PRODUCTS INC p 991
501 Terminal Rd, Fort Worth TX 76106
Tel (817) 624-0820
SIC 3585 3433 1711 3999

HANSON PRESSURE PIPE INC p 659
1003 Macarthur Blvd, Grand Prairie TX 75050
Tel (972) 262-3600 SIC 3317 3272 3999

POLK MECHANICAL CO LLC p 1159
2425 Dillard St, Grand Prairie TX 75051
Tel (972) 339-1200
SIC 1711 3444 3498 3599 3999

C&C INDUSTRIES INC p 233
10350 Clay Rd Ste 250, Houston TX 77041
Tel (713) 466-1644 SIC 3999 5085

HOWCO METALS MANAGEMENT LLC p 713
9611 Telge Rd, Houston TX 77095
Tel (281) 649-8800 SIC 5051 3999 8741

▲MICHAELS COMPANIES INC p 960
8000 Bent Branch Dr, Irving TX 75063
Tel (972) 409-1300 SIC 5945 3999 2273

INEOS USA LLC p 740
2600 S Shore Blvd Ste 500, League City TX 77573
Tel (281) 535-6600 SIC 2821 3999

MORINDA HOLDINGS INC p 989
737 E 1180 S, American Fork UT 84003
Tel (801) 234-1000 SIC 5149 8099 3999

■AFTON CHEMICAL CORP p 33
500 Spring St, Richmond VA 23219
Tel (804) 788-5086 SIC 2899 2999 3999

ESSENTRA HOLDINGS CORP p 510
1625 Ashton Park Dr Ste A, South Chesterfield VA 23834
Tel (804) 518-0322
SIC 3081 3082 3999 3951 2823

ESSENTRA POROUS TECHNOLOGIES CORP p 510
1625 Ashton Park Dr Ste A, South Chesterfield VA 23834
Tel (804) 524-4983
SIC 3081 3951 3082 2823 3999

■INSITU INC p 746
118 Columbia River Way, Bingen WA 98605
Tel (509) 493-8600 SIC 8711 3999

NW CENTER INDUSTRIES 5307 p 1068
7272 W Marginal Way S, Seattle WA 98108
Tel (206) 285-9140 SIC 3999

NASCO HEALTHCARE INC p 1008
901 Janesville Ave, Fort Atkinson WI 53538
Tel (920) 568-5600 SIC 3999

LAMPLIGHT FARMS INC p 841
W140n4900 Lilly Rd, Menomonee Falls WI 53051
Tel (262) 781-9590
SIC 3648 3999 3229 2911

■SPECTRUM BRANDS HOLDINGS INC p 1357
3001 Deming Way, Middleton WI 53562
Tel (608) 275-3340
SIC 3692 2879 3999 3648

■SPECTRUM BRANDS INC p 1357
3001 Deming Way, Middleton WI 53562
Tel (608) 275-3340
SIC 3692 3634 2879 3999 3648

■BRADY WORLDWIDE INC p 207
6555 W Good Hope Rd, Milwaukee WI 53223
Tel (414) 358-6600 SIC 3999

SIC 4011 Railroads, Line-Hauling Operations

ALASKA RAILROAD CORP p 45
327 W Ship Creek Ave, Anchorage AK 99501
Tel (907) 265-2494 SIC 4011 6531

APL LOGISTICS LTD p 97
16220 N Scottsdale Rd # 300, Scottsdale AZ 85254
Tel (602) 586-4800
SIC 4412 4731 4491 4011

▲GENESEE & WYOMING INC p 602
20 West Ave, Darien CT 06820
Tel (203) 202-8900 SIC 4011 4013

■RAILAMERICA INC p 1205
20 West Ave, Darien CT 06820
Tel (203) 656-1092 SIC 4011

UNIMIN CORP p 1504
258 Elm St, New Canaan CT 06840
Tel (203) 966-8880
SIC 1446 1499 1422 1459 4011 1442

■NATIONAL RAILROAD PASSENGER CORP p 1015
60 Massachusetts Ave Ne, Washington DC 20002
Tel (202) 906-3741 SIC 4011 4013

▲CSX CORP p 398
500 Water St Fl 15, Jacksonville FL 32202
Tel (904) 359-3200 SIC 4011

■CSX INTERMODAL INC p 398
500 Water St, Jacksonville FL 32202
Tel (904) 633-1000 SIC 4213 4011 4225

■CSX TRANSPORTATION INC p 398
500 Water St, Jacksonville FL 32202
Tel (904) 359-3100 SIC 4011

FECR RAIL CORP p 533
7411 Fullerton St Ste 100, Jacksonville FL 32256
Tel (800) 342-1131 SIC 4011

FLORIDA EAST COAST RAILWAY LLC p 558
7411 Fullerton St Ste 300, Jacksonville FL 32256
Tel (904) 538-6100 SIC 4011

■RAILAMERICA TRANSPORTATION CORP p 1205
7411 Fullerton St Ste 300, Jacksonville FL 32256
Tel (904) 538-6100 SIC 4011

IOWA PACIFIC HOLDINGS LLC p 763
118 S Clinton St Ste 400, Chicago IL 60661
Tel (312) 466-0900 SIC 4011

NORTHEAST ILLINOIS REGIONAL COMMUTER RAILROAD CORP p 1055
547 W Jackson Blvd Ste 1, Chicago IL 60661
Tel (312) 322-6900 SIC 4111 4011

GRAND TRUNK CORP p 630
17641 Ashland Ave, Homewood IL 60430
Tel (708) 332-3500 SIC 4011

GRAND TRUNK WESTERN RAILROAD CO p 630
17641 Ashland Ave, Homewood IL 60430
Tel (708) 332-3500 SIC 4011

ILLINOIS CENTRAL RAILROAD CO p 732
17641 Ashland Ave, Homewood IL 60430
Tel (708) 332-3500 SIC 4011

WISCONSIN CENTRAL LTD p 1618
17641 Ashland Ave, Homewood IL 60430
Tel (708) 332-3500 SIC 4011

PROFESSIONAL TRANSPORTATION INC p 1180
3700 E Morgan Ave, Evansville IN 47715
Tel (812) 471-2440 SIC 4011

■TRANSWORKS OF INDIANA INC p 1473
9910 Dupont Circle Dr E, Fort Wayne IN 46825
Tel (260) 487-4400 SIC 4011

INDIANA HARBOR BELT RAILROAD CO p 738
2721 161st St, Hammond IN 46323
Tel (219) 989-4703 SIC 4013 4011

■ALLIANT INDUSTRIES INC p 55
200 1st St Se, Cedar Rapids IA 52401
Tel (398) 786-4268
SIC 4011 4741 4911 4924

■B N S F INC p 142
616 S Boyd Ave, Newton KS 67114
Tel (316) 284-3260 SIC 4011

WATCO COMPANIES LLC p 1581
315 W 3rd St, Pittsburg KS 66762
Tel (620) 231-2230 SIC 4011 7538

R J CORMAN RAILROAD GROUP LLC p 1202
1 Jay Station Rd, Nicholasville KY 40356
Tel (859) 881-7521 SIC 4011

MASSACHUSETTS BAY COMMUTER RAILROAD CO LLC p 916
89 South St, Boston MA 02111
Tel (617) 222-8080 SIC 4011 4111

PAN AM RAILWAYS INC p 1110
1700 Iron Horse Park, North Billerica MA 01862
Tel (978) 663-1129 SIC 4011

SPRINGFIELD TERMINAL RAILWAY CO INC p 1361
1700 Iron Horse Park, North Billerica MA 01862
Tel (978) 663-1050 SIC 4011

SOO LINE RAILROAD CO p 1341
120 S 6th St Ste 900, Minneapolis MN 55402
Tel (800) 234-0013 SIC 4011

SOO LINE CORP p 1341
14327 Huntington Ave, Savage MN 55378
Tel (952) 895-5277 SIC 4011

▲KANSAS CITY SOUTHERN p 802
427 W 12th St, Kansas City MO 64105
Tel (816) 983-1303 SIC 4011

■KANSAS CITY SOUTHERN RAILWAY CO p 802
427 W 12th St, Kansas City MO 64105
Tel (816) 983-1303 SIC 4011 4213

MONTANA RAIL LINK INC p 986
101 International Dr, Missoula MT 59808
Tel (406) 523-1500 SIC 4011

▲UNION PACIFIC CORP p 1504
1400 Douglas St, Omaha NE 68179
Tel (402) 544-5000 SIC 4011

■UNION PACIFIC RAILROAD CO INC p 1504
1400 Douglas St, Omaha NE 68179
Tel (402) 544-5000 SIC 4011

NYK GROUP AMERICAS INC p 1069
300 Lighting Way Ste 500, Secaucus NJ 07094
Tel (201) 330-3000
SIC 4412 4731 4011 4491 7519

NYK LINE (NORTH AMERICA) INC p 1069
300 Lighting Way 4th, Secaucus NJ 07094
Tel (201) 330-3000
SIC 4412 4731 4213 4011 7519 4491

RR ACQUISITION HOLDING LLC p 1255
1345 Avenue Of The Americ, New York NY 10105
Tel (212) 479-7116 SIC 4011

■FLORIDA PROGRESS CORP p 559
410 S Wilmington St, Raleigh NC 27601
Tel (919) 546-6111
SIC 1221 4911 4011 4449

WHEELING & LAKE ERIE RAILWAY CO p 1605
100 1st St Se, Brewster OH 44613
Tel (330) 767-3401 SIC 4011

WHEELING CORP p 1605
100 1st St Se, Brewster OH 44613
Tel (330) 767-3401 SIC 1629 4011

RAILNET DR INC p 1205
100 School St Apt B, Glen Rock PA 17327
Tel (717) 817-1472 SIC 4011

■KINDER MORGAN MATERIALS SERVICES LLC p 819
333 Rouser Rd Ste 4601, Moon Township PA 15108
Tel (412) 264-6068 SIC 4011

CONRAIL INC p 358
1717 Arch St Ste 1310, Philadelphia PA 19103
Tel (215) 209-5027 SIC 4011

CONSOLIDATED RAIL CORP p 360
1717 Arch St Ste 1310, Philadelphia PA 19103
Tel (800) 456-7509 SIC 4011

CRR HOLDINGS LLC p 396
1717 Arch St Fl 13, Philadelphia PA 19103
Tel (215) 209-2000 SIC 4011

GREEN ACQUISITION CORP p 636
2001 Market St, Philadelphia PA 19103
Tel (215) 209-2000 SIC 4011

■BNSF RAILWAY CO p 194
2650 Lou Menk Dr, Fort Worth TX 76131
Tel (800) 795-2673 SIC 4731 4011

■BURLINGTON NORTHERN SANTA FE LLC p 228
2650 Lou Menk Dr, Fort Worth TX 76131
Tel (800) 795-2673 SIC 4731 4011

CAPITOL AGGREGATES INC p 250
11551 Nacogdoches Rd, San Antonio TX 78217
Tel (210) 655-3010
SIC 3241 1442 1422 2951 4011

■ALABAMA GREAT SOUTHERN RAILROAD CO p 43
3 Commercial Pl, Norfolk VA 23510
Tel (540) 981-4049 SIC 4011

■CAROLINA NORTH MIDLAND RAILROAD CO p 259
3 Commercial Pl, Norfolk VA 23510
Tel (757) 629-2645 SIC 4011

■LIVE OAK PERRY AND SOUTH GEORGIA RAILWAY CO p 871
3 Commercial Pl, Norfolk VA 23510
Tel (757) 629-2600 SIC 4011

■NORFOLK AND WESTERN RAILWAY CO (INC) p 1048
3 Commercial Pl, Norfolk VA 23510
Tel (757) 629-2600 SIC 4011

▲NORFOLK SOUTHERN CORP p 1048
3 Commercial Pl Ste 1a, Norfolk VA 23510
Tel (757) 629-2680 SIC 4011

■NORFOLK SOUTHERN RAILWAY CO p 1048
3 Commercial Pl Ste 1a, Norfolk VA 23510
Tel (757) 629-2680 SIC 4011

■VIRGINIA & SOUTHWESTERN RAILWAY CO p 1558
3 Commercial Pl, Norfolk VA 23510
Tel (757) 629-2645 SIC 4011

SIC 4013 Switching & Terminal Svcs

OMNITRAX INC p 1085
252 Clayton St Fl 4, Denver CO 80206
Tel (303) 398-4500 SIC 4013

▲GENESEE & WYOMING INC p 602
20 West Ave, Darien CT 06820
Tel (203) 202-8900 SIC 4011 4013

■NATIONAL RAILROAD PASSENGER CORP p 1015
60 Massachusetts Ave Ne, Washington DC 20002
Tel (202) 906-3741 SIC 4011 4013

■RAILSERVE INC p 1205
1691 Phoenix Blvd Ste 250, Atlanta GA 30349
Tel (770) 996-6838 SIC 4013

SOUTHERN STATES LLC p 1350
30 Georgia Ave, Hampton GA 30228
Tel (770) 946-4562 SIC 3613 4013 1731

INDIANA HARBOR BELT RAILROAD CO p 738
2721 161st St, Hammond IN 46323
Tel (219) 989-4703 SIC 4013 4011

WATCO INC p 1581
315 W 3rd St, Pittsburg KS 66762
Tel (208) 734-4644 SIC 4013 4741 4789

ROAD & RAIL SERVICES INC p 1240
4233 Bardstown Rd Ste 200, Louisville KY 40218
Tel (502) 365-5361 SIC 4789 4013

NEBCO INC p 1023
1815 Y St, Lincoln NE 68508
Tel (402) 434-1212
SIC 5999 3273 3272 3271 1442 4013

METRO-NORTH COMMUTER RAILROAD CO INC p 955
420 Lexington Ave, New York NY 10170
Tel (212) 878-7000 SIC 4013 4111

COLLINS PINE CO p 337
29190 Sw Town Center Loop, Wilsonville OR 97070
Tel (503) 227-1219
SIC 2421 2426 5211 4911 4013

M SIMON ZOOK CO p 890
4960 Horseshoe Pike, Honey Brook PA 19344
Tel (800) 327-4406 SIC 5149 2048 4013

TRANS-GLOBAL SOLUTIONS INC p 1470
11811 East Fwy Ste 630, Houston TX 77029
Tel (713) 453-0341 SIC 4491 4013 4789

CITY OF TACOMA DEPARTMENT OF PUBLIC UTILITIES p 319
3628 S 35th St, Tacoma WA 98409
Tel (253) 502-8900
SIC 4911 4941 4899 4013 4841

SIC 4111 Local & Suburban Transit

SUPERSHUTTLE INTERNATIONAL INC p 1407
14500 N Northsight Blvd # 329, Scottsdale AZ 85260
Tel (480) 609-3000 SIC 4111

TRANSDEV ON DEMAND INC p 1471
14500 N Northsight Blvd, Scottsdale AZ 85260
Tel (480) 609-3000 SIC 4111

ACCESS SERVICES p 15
3449 Santa Anita Ave, El Monte CA 91731
Tel (213) 270-6000 SIC 4111

LOS ANGELES COUNTY METROPOLITAN TRANSPORTATION AUTHORITY p 878
1 Gateway Plz Fl 25, Los Angeles CA 90012
Tel (323) 466-3876 SIC 4111

ALAMEDA-CONTRA COSTA TRANSIT DISTRICT p 44
1600 Franklin St, Oakland CA 94612
Tel (510) 891-4777 SIC 4111

SAN FRANCISCO BAY AREA RAPID TRANSIT DISTRICT p 1276
300 Lakeside Dr, Oakland CA 94604
Tel (510) 464-6000 SIC 4111

ORANGE COUNTY TRANSPORTATION AUTHORITY p 1092
550 S Main St, Orange CA 92868
Tel (714) 636-7433 SIC 4111 8711

SACRAMENTO REGIONAL TRANSIT DIST p 1265
1400 29th St, Sacramento CA 95816
Tel (916) 726-2877 SIC 4111

PENINSULA CORRIDOR JOINT POWERS BOARD p 1129
1250 San Carlos Ave, San Carlos CA 94070
Tel (650) 508-6200 SIC 4111

SAN DIEGO METROPOLITAN TRANSIT SYSTEM p 1276
1255 Imperial Ave # 1000, San Diego CA 92101
Tel (619) 231-1466 SIC 4111

METROPOLITAN TRANSPORTATION COMMISSION p 956
375 Beale St, San Francisco CA 94105
Tel (510) 817-5700 SIC 4111

REGIONAL TRANSPORTATION DISTRICT p 1219
1600 Blake St, Denver CO 80202
Tel (303) 628-9000 SIC 4111

FIRST TRANSIT INC p 550
249 Wawarme Ave, Hartford CT 06114
Tel (860) 247-0050 SIC 4111

WASHINGTON METROPOLITAN AREA TRANSIT AUTHORITY p 1578
600 5th St Nw, Washington DC 20001
Tel (202) 962-1000 SIC 4111

CENTRAL FLORIDA REGIONAL TRANSPORTATION AUTHORITY p 278
455 N Garland Ave, Orlando FL 32801
Tel (407) 841-2279 SIC 4111

■AIR SERV CORP p 39
3399 Peachtree Rd Ne, Atlanta GA 30326
Tel (404) 926-4200 SIC 4581 4111

METROPOLITAN ATLANTA RAPID TRANSIT AUTHORITY p 955
2424 Piedmont Rd Ne, Atlanta GA 30324
Tel (404) 848-5000 SIC 4111

CONSOLIDATED GOVERMENT OF GA INC p 359
814 Linwood Blvd, Columbus GA 31901
Tel (706) 653-4410 SIC 4111

BLUE BIRD BODY CO p 190
402 Bluebird Blvd, Fort Valley GA 31030
Tel (478) 825-2021 SIC 4111

SEA ISLAND SERVICES INC p 1295
100 Hudson Pl, Sea Island GA 31561
Tel (912) 638-3611 SIC 4111 4941

■HA 3049 UALENA STREET LLC p 651
3375 Koapaka St Ste G350, Honolulu HI 96819
Tel (808) 835-3700 SIC 4111

OAHU TRANSIT SERVICES INC p 1070
811 Middle St Rm 225, Honolulu HI 96819
Tel (808) 848-4400 SIC 4111

PACE SUBURBAN BUS DIVISION OF REGIONAL TRANSPORTATION AUTHORITY p 1103
550 W Algonquin Rd, Arlington Heights IL 60005
Tel (847) 364-7223 SIC 4111

CHICAGO TRANSIT AUTHORITY p 298
567 W Lake St Ste Cta, Chicago IL 60661
Tel (312) 664-7200 SIC 4111 4789

GO GROUP LLC p 619
1200 W 35th St, Chicago IL 60609
Tel (844) 787-1670 SIC 4111

NORTHEAST ILLINOIS REGIONAL COMMUTER RAILROAD CORP p 1055
547 W Jackson Blvd Ste 1, Chicago IL 60661
Tel (312) 322-6900 SIC 4111 4011

REGIONAL TRANSPORTATION AUTHORITY p 1219
175 W Jackson Blvd # 1650, Chicago IL 60604
Tel (312) 913-3200 SIC 4111

TRANSDEV NORTH AMERICA INC p 1471
720 E Bttrfeld Rd Ste 300, Lombard IL 60148
Tel (630) 571-7070 SIC 4111 4131 4173

VEOLIA TRANSPORTATION SERVICES INC p 1548
2015 Spring Rd Ste 750, Oak Brook IL 60523
Tel (630) 571-7070 SIC 4111 4141

ALL ABOARD AMERICA HOLDINGS INC p 50
2838 Touro St, New Orleans LA 70122
Tel (800) 356-6831
SIC 6719 4141 4131 4119 4111

MASSACHUSETTS BAY COMMUTER RAILROAD CO LLC p 916
89 South St, Boston MA 02111
Tel (617) 222-8080 *SIC* 4011 4111

FTM CORP p 583
69 Norman St Ste 13, Everett MA 02149
Tel (800) 672-7676 *SIC* 4111

SUBURBAN MOBILITY AUTHORITY FOR REGIONAL TRANSPORATION p 1396
535 Griswold St Ste 600, Detroit MI 48226
Tel (313) 223-2100 *SIC* 4111

PETERSON MANUFACTURING CO p 1138
4200 E 135th St, Grandview MO 64030
Tel (816) 765-2000
SIC 3647 4111 3089 3714

BI-STATE DEVELOPMENT AGENCY OF MISSOURI-ILLINOIS METROPOLITAN DISTRICT (INC) p 181
211 N Broadway Ste 700, Saint Louis MO 63102
Tel (314) 982-1400 *SIC* 4111 4581

DELAWARE RIVER PORT AUTHORITY p 424
2 Riverside Dr Ste 603, Camden NJ 08103
Tel (856) 968-2000 *SIC* 4111 4785

PORT AUTHORITY TRANS-HUDSON CORP p 1162
1 Path Plz, Jersey City NJ 07306
Tel (201) 239-3500 *SIC* 4111

NEW JERSEY TRANSIT BUS OPERATIONS INC p 1031
1 Penn Plz E, Newark NJ 07105
Tel (973) 491-7000 *SIC* 4131 4111

NEW JERSEY TRANSIT CORP p 1031
1 Penn Plz E, Newark NJ 07105
Tel (973) 491-7000 *SIC* 4111 4131

COACH USA INC p 331
160 S Route 17 N, Paramus NJ 07652
Tel (201) 225-7500 *SIC* 4725 4111 4121

NIAGARA FRONTIER TRANSPORTATION AUTHORITY p 1042
181 Ellicott St Ste 1, Buffalo NY 14203
Tel (716) 855-7300 *SIC* 4111 4581

LONG ISLAND RAIL ROAD CO p 876
9027 Sutphin Blvd, Jamaica NY 11435
Tel (718) 558-4704 *SIC* 4111

MANHATTAN AND BRONX SURFACE TRANSIT OPERATING AUTHORITY p 901
2 Broadway, New York NY 10004
Tel (718) 694-1000 *SIC* 4111

METRO-NORTH COMMUTER RAILROAD CO INC p 955
420 Lexington Ave, New York NY 10170
Tel (212) 878-7000 *SIC* 4013 4111

METROPOLITAN TRANSPORTATION AUTHORITY p 956
2 Broadway Bsmt B, New York NY 10004
Tel (212) 878-7000 *SIC* 4111

NEW YORK CITY TRANSIT AUTHORITY p 1034
2 Broadway, New York NY 10004
Tel (718) 330-1234 *SIC* 4111

PORT AUTHORITY OF NEW YORK & NEW JERSEY p 1162
4 World Trade Ctr 150, New York NY 10007
Tel (212) 435-7000
SIC 4581 4785 6512 4491 4111

ROCHESTER-GENESEE REGIONAL TRANSPORTATION AUTHORITY p 1243
1372 E Main St, Rochester NY 14609
Tel (585) 654-0200 *SIC* 4111

BIRNIE BUS SERVICE INC p 185
248 Otis St, Rome NY 13441
Tel (315) 336-3950
SIC 4151 4119 4141 4111

FIRST GROUP INVESTMENT PARTNERSHIP p 547
600 Vine St Ste 1200, Cincinnati OH 45202
Tel (513) 241-2200
SIC 7513 4212 4213 4225 4151 4111

FIRSTGROUP AMERICA INC p 550
600 Vine St Ste 1400, Cincinnati OH 45202
Tel (513) 241-2200
SIC 4151 4111 4119 4131 4141 8744

FIRSTGROUP USA INC p 550
600 Vine St Ste 1400, Cincinnati OH 45202
Tel (513) 241-2200
SIC 7513 4212 4213 4225 4151 4111

SOUTHWEST OHIO REGIONAL TRANSIT AUTHORITY p 1352
602 Main St Ste 1100, Cincinnati OH 45202
Tel (513) 621-4455 *SIC* 4111

GREATER CLEVELAND REGIONAL TRANSIT AUTHORITY p 635
1240 W 6th St, Cleveland OH 44113
Tel (216) 566-5100 *SIC* 4111

TRI-COUNTY METROPOLITAN TRANSPORTATION DISTRICT OF OREGON p 1477
1800 Sw 1st Ave Ste 300, Portland OR 97201
Tel (503) 238-7433 *SIC* 4111

SOUTHEASTERN PENNSYLVANIA TRANSPORTATION AUTHORITY p 1347
1234 Market St Fl 4, Philadelphia PA 19107
Tel (215) 580-7800 *SIC* 4111

■ **GENCO TRANSPORTATION MANAGEMENT LLC** p 598
100 Papercraft Park, Pittsburgh PA 15238
Tel (412) 820-3700
SIC 4225 4111 5045 4789

■ **I GENCO INC** p 725
100 Papercraft Park, Pittsburgh PA 15238
Tel (800) 677-3110 *SIC* 4225 4111 5045

AUTORIDAD METROPOLITANA DE AUTOBUSES p 135
Bo Monacillos 37 Ave De D 37th, San Juan PR 00919
Tel (787) 767-7979 *SIC* 4111

CAPITAL METROPOLITAN TRANSPORTATION AUTHORITY p 250
2910 E 5th St, Austin TX 78702
Tel (512) 389-7400 *SIC* 4111

DALLAS AREA RAPID TRANSIT p 410
1401 Pacific Ave, Dallas TX 75202
Tel (214) 979-1111 *SIC* 4111

GREYHOUND LINES INC p 639
350 N Saint Paul St # 300, Dallas TX 75201
Tel (214) 849-8000 *SIC* 4111 4215 4142

MV TRANSPORTATION INC p 1003
5910 N Cntrl Expy # 1145, Dallas TX 75206
Tel (972) 391-4600 *SIC* 4111

VIA METROPOLITAN TRANSIT p 1554
800 W Myrtle St, San Antonio TX 78212
Tel (210) 362-2000 *SIC* 4111

UTAH TRANSIT AUTHORITY (UTA) p 1536
669 W 200 S Bldg 1, Salt Lake City UT 84101
Tel (801) 262-5626 *SIC* 4111

KEOLIS AMERICA INC p 813
3003 Washington Blvd, Arlington VA 22201
Tel (301) 251-5612 *SIC* 4111

NORTHERN VIRGINIA TRANSPORTATION COMMISSION p 1057
2300 Wilson Blvd Ste 620, Arlington VA 22201
Tel (703) 524-3322 *SIC* 4111

TRANSPORTATION DIST COMMISION OF HAMPTON ROADS p 1472
3400 Victoria Blvd, Hampton VA 23661
Tel (757) 222-6000 *SIC* 4111

SIC 4119 Local Passenger Transportation: NEC

NORTHERN ARIZONA HEALTHCARE CORP p 1055
1200 N Beaver St, Flagstaff AZ 86001
Tel (928) 779-3366
SIC 8741 8062 8399 4119

■ **METRO CARE CORP** p 954
8465 N Pima Rd, Scottsdale AZ 85258
Tel (800) 352-2309 *SIC* 4119

■ **RURAL/METRO CORP** p 1258
8465 N Pima Rd, Scottsdale AZ 85258
Tel (480) 606-3886 *SIC* 4119 7389

■ **RURAL/METRO CORP** p 1258
8465 N Pima Rd, Scottsdale AZ 85258
Tel (480) 606-3345 *SIC* 4119 7389

■ **RURAL/METRO OPERATING CO LLC** p 1258
8465 N Pima Rd, Scottsdale AZ 85258
Tel (480) 606-3886 *SIC* 4119

■ **WP ROCKET HOLDINGS INC** p 1627
8465 N Pima Rd, Scottsdale AZ 85258
Tel (800) 352-2309 *SIC* 4119 7389

■ **AMERICAN MEDICAL RESPONSE OF SOUTHERN CALIFORNIA** p 76
1055 W Avenue J, Lancaster CA 93534
Tel (661) 945-9310 *SIC* 4119

KEOLIS TRANSIT AMERICA INC p 813
6053 W Century Blvd # 900, Los Angeles CA 90045
Tel (310) 981-9500 *SIC* 4119 7699

MIDWAY RENT A CAR INC p 967
4751 Wilshire Blvd # 120, Los Angeles CA 90010
Tel (323) 692-4000
SIC 5511 7515 5521 4119 7513

■ **SOUTHWEST HEALTHCARE SYSTEM AUXILIARY** p 1352
25500 Medical Center Dr, Murrieta CA 92562
Tel (951) 696-6000
SIC 8062 8051 8059 4119

■ **AMERICAN MEDICAL RESPONSE** p 76
879 Marlborough Ave, Riverside CA 92507
Tel (951) 782-5200 *SIC* 4119

■ **AMERICAN MEDICAL RESPONSE AMBULANCE SERVICE INC** p 76
879 Marlborough Ave, Riverside CA 92507
Tel (303) 495-1217 *SIC* 4119

■ **AMERICAN MEDICAL RESPONSE WEST** p 76
400 S Fresno St, Stockton CA 95203
Tel (209) 948-5136 *SIC* 4119

■ **AMERICAN MEDICAL RESPONSE INC** p 76
6363 S Fiddlers Green Cir # 1400, Greenwood Village CO 80111
Tel (303) 495-1200 *SIC* 4119

■ **ENVISION HEALTHCARE CORP** p 504
6363 S Fiddlers Green Cir # 1400, Greenwood Village CO 80111
Tel (303) 495-1200 *SIC* 4119 7363

▲ **ENVISION HEALTHCARE HOLDINGS INC** p 504
6200 S Syracuse Way, Greenwood Village CO 80111
Tel (303) 495-1200 *SIC* 8062 4119

CAREY INTERNATIONAL INC p 255
4530 Wscnsin Ave Nw Ste 5, Washington DC 20016
Tel (202) 895-1200 *SIC* 4119 6794

METRO PARKING CORP p 955
8300 Nw 7th Ave, North Miami Beach FL 33160
Tel (305) 579-5300 *SIC* 7521 4119

SEVEN-ONE-SEVEN PARKING SERVICES INC p 1309
1410 N Florida Ave, Tampa FL 33602
Tel (813) 228-7722
SIC 7299 6519 7521 4119 8742

PROVIDENT HEALTH SERVICES INC p 1186
4700 Waters Ave, Savannah GA 31404
Tel (912) 350-8000 *SIC* 8082 4119

ROBERTS HAWAII INC p 1242
680 Iwilei Rd Ste 700, Honolulu HI 96817
Tel (808) 523-7750
SIC 4119 4724 7011 4489

ROBERTS TOURS AND TRANSPORTATION INC p 1242
680 Iwilei Rd Ste 700, Honolulu HI 96817
Tel (808) 523-7750 *SIC* 4119

HARBORQUEST INC p 660
14 E Jackson Blvd # 1210, Chicago IL 60604
Tel (312) 612-7600 *SIC* 7363 4119 7361

TRANSDEV SERVICES INC p 1471
720 E Bttrfeld Rd Ste 300, Lombard IL 60148
Tel (630) 571-7070 *SIC* 4119 4121

NATIONAL EXPRESS LLC p 1011
4300 Weaver Pkwy Ste 100, Warrenville IL 60555
Tel (800) 950-0485 *SIC* 4119

WHEATLAND ENTERPRISES INC p 1604
2017 W 104th St, Leawood KS 66206
Tel (913) 381-3504 *SIC* 4119

RENZENBERGER INC p 1224
14325 W 95th St, Lenexa KS 66215
Tel (913) 631-0450 *SIC* 4131 4119

ACADIAN AMBULANCE SERVICE INC p 14
130 E Kaliste Saloom Rd, Lafayette LA 70508
Tel (337) 291-3333 *SIC* 4119

ALL ABOARD AMERICA HOLDINGS INC p 50
2838 Touro St, New Orleans LA 70122
Tel (800) 356-6831
SIC 6719 4141 4131 4119 4111

TOWNE PARK LLC p 1466
1 Park Pl Ste 200, Annapolis MD 21401
Tel (410) 267-6111 *SIC* 7521 4119

BROADWAY SERVICES INC p 216
3709 E Monument St, Baltimore MD 21205
Tel (410) 563-6900
SIC 7349 7381 7521 6512 4119

LIFESTAR RESPONSE CORP p 864
3710 Commerce Dr Ste 1006, Halethorpe MD 21227
Tel (631) 289-1100 *SIC* 4119

BOSTON COACH CORP p 202
69 Norman St Ste 13, Everett MA 02149
Tel (800) 672-7676 *SIC* 4119 8741

■ **AMERICAN MEDICAL RESPONSE OF MASSACHUSETTS INC** p 76
4 Tech Cir, Natick MA 01760
Tel (508) 650-5600 *SIC* 4119

HARRISON GLOBAL LLC p 664
224 Calvary St, Waltham MA 02453
Tel (781) 863-2626 *SIC* 4119

MEDICAL TRANSPORTATION MANAGEMENT INC p 937
16 Hawk Ridge Cir Ste 120, Lake Saint Louis MO 63367
Tel (636) 561-5686 *SIC* 4119

MOUNTAINVIEW HOSPITAL INC p 994
3100 N Tenaya Way, Las Vegas NV 89128
Tel (702) 255-5000 *SIC* 8062 8011 4119

EASTER SEAL NEW HAMPSHIRE INC p 471
555 Auburn St, Manchester NH 03103
Tel (603) 623-8863
SIC 8331 8399 4119 8322

KENNEDY HEALTH CARE FOUNDATION INC p 811
18 E Laurel Rd, Stratford NJ 08084
Tel (856) 661-5100
SIC 6733 4119 8051 6531 7361 8721

TRANSCARE CORP p 1471
1 Metrotech Ctr Fl 20, Brooklyn NY 11201
Tel (718) 251-4600 *SIC* 4119

GW LISK CO INC p 648
2 South St, Clifton Springs NY 14432
Tel (315) 462-2611 *SIC* 3679 4119 3492

WCA GROUP INC p 1585
207 Foote Ave, Jamestown NY 14701
Tel (716) 487-0141 *SIC* 8062 4119

BIRNIE BUS SERVICE INC p 185
248 Otis St, Rome NY 13441
Tel (315) 336-3950
SIC 4151 4119 4141 4111

TRANSCARE NEW YORK INC p 1471
3305 Jerusalem Ave # 201, Wantagh NY 11793
Tel (718) 763-8888 *SIC* 4119

FIRSTGROUP AMERICA INC p 550
600 Vine St Ste 1400, Cincinnati OH 45202
Tel (513) 241-2200
SIC 4151 4111 4119 4131 4141 8744

PORT AUTHORITY OF ALLEGHENY COUNTY p 1162
345 6th Ave Fl 3, Pittsburgh PA 15222
Tel (412) 566-5500 *SIC* 4119

FIRST CALL AMBULANCE SERVICE LLC p 545
1930 Air Lane Dr, Nashville TN 37210
Tel (615) 277-0900 *SIC* 4119

METROPOLITAN TRANSIT AUTHORITY OF HARRIS COUNTY p 956
1900 Main St, Houston TX 77002
Tel (713) 635-4000 *SIC* 4119

BOSTON COACH-WASHINGTON CORP p 202
5775c General Wash Dr, Alexandria VA 22312
Tel (703) 813-6280 *SIC* 4119

FALCK USA INC p 526
21540 30th Dr Se Ste 250, Bothell WA 98021
Tel (425) 892-1180 *SIC* 4119

EAGLE GROUP SYSTEMS INC p 468
230 Grant Rd, East Wenatchee WA 98802
Tel (509) 665-0319
SIC 4214 4119 4522 7373 7374 8741

LAMERS BUS LINES INC p 841
2407 S Point Rd, Green Bay WI 54313
Tel (920) 496-3600
SIC 4151 4142 4119 4725 4141

SIC 4121 Taxi Cabs

TRANSDEV SERVICES INC p 1471
720 E Bttrfeld Rd Ste 300, Lombard IL 60148
Tel (630) 571-7070 *SIC* 4119 4121

INTERLOCK INDUSTRIES INC p 753
545 S 3rd St Ste 310, Louisville KY 40202
Tel (502) 569-2007
SIC 3341 4121 3444 3354 2653

NEVADA YELLOW CAB CORP p 1029
5225 W Post Rd, Las Vegas NV 89118
Tel (702) 873-8012 *SIC* 4121

WHITTLESEA BLUE CAB CO p 1607
2000 Industrial Rd, Las Vegas NV 89102
Tel (702) 384-6111 *SIC* 4121

COACH USA INC p 331
160 S Route 17 N, Paramus NJ 07652
Tel (201) 225-7500 *SIC* 4725 4111 4121

SIC 4131 Intercity & Rural Bus Transportation

TRANSDEV NORTH AMERICA INC p 1471
720 E Bttrfeld Rd Ste 300, Lombard IL 60148
Tel (630) 571-7070 *SIC* 4111 4131 4173

LAIDLAW INTERNATIONAL INC p 838
55 Shuman Blvd Ste 400, Naperville IL 60563
Tel (214) 849-8100 *SIC* 4151 4131

RAILCREW XPRESS LLC p 1205
9867 Widmer Rd, Lenexa KS 66215
Tel (913) 928-5000 *SIC* 4131

RENZENBERGER INC p 1224
14325 W 95th St, Lenexa KS 66215
Tel (913) 631-0450 *SIC* 4131 4119

ALL ABOARD AMERICA HOLDINGS INC p 50
2838 Touro St, New Orleans LA 70122
Tel (800) 356-6831
SIC 6719 4141 4131 4119 4111

PETER PAN BUS LINES INC p 1138
1776 Main St Ste 1, Springfield MA 01103
Tel (413) 781-2900 *SIC* 4131

NEW JERSEY TRANSIT BUS OPERATIONS INC p 1031
1 Penn Plz E, Newark NJ 07105
Tel (973) 491-7000 *SIC* 4131 4111

NEW JERSEY TRANSIT CORP p 1031
1 Penn Plz E, Newark NJ 07105
Tel (973) 491-7000 *SIC* 4111 4131

FIRSTGROUP AMERICA INC p 550
600 Vine St Ste 1400, Cincinnati OH 45202
Tel (513) 241-2200
SIC 4151 4111 4119 4131 4141 8744

LAIDLAW TRANSIT SERVICES INC p 838
600 Vine St Ste 1400, Cincinnati OH 45202
Tel (513) 241-2200 *SIC* 4131

PORT AUTHORITY OF ALLEGHENY COUNTY p 1162
345 6th Ave Fl 3, Pittsburgh PA 15222
Tel (412) 566-5500 *SIC* 4131

MILWAUKEE TRANSPORT SERVICES INC p 972
1942 N 17th St, Milwaukee WI 53205
Tel (414) 344-6711 *SIC* 4131

SIC 4141 Local Bus Charter Svc

SANTA BARBARA TRANSPORTATION CORP p 1280
6414 Hollister Ave, Goleta CA 93117
Tel (805) 681-8355 *SIC* 4151 4141

VEOLIA TRANSPORTATION SERVICES INC p 1548
2015 Spring Rd Ste 750, Oak Brook IL 60523
Tel (630) 571-7070 *SIC* 4111 4141

ALL ABOARD AMERICA HOLDINGS INC p 50
2838 Touro St, New Orleans LA 70122
Tel (800) 356-6831
SIC 6719 4141 4131 4119 4111

HORIZON COACH LINES p 707
17810 Meeting House Rd # 200, Sandy Spring MD 20860
Tel (301) 260-2060 *SIC* 4141

BIRNIE BUS SERVICE INC p 185
248 Otis St, Rome NY 13441
Tel (315) 336-3950
SIC 4151 4119 4141 4111

ATLANTIC EXPRESS TRANSPORTATION GROUP INC p 126
7 North St, Staten Island NY 10302
Tel (718) 442-7000 *SIC* 4151 4141 5012

FIRSTGROUP AMERICA INC p 550
600 Vine St Ste 1400, Cincinnati OH 45202
Tel (513) 241-2200
SIC 4151 4111 4119 4131 4141 8744

SCHOOL SERVICES AND LEASING INC p 1290
9011 Mtn Rdg Dr Ste 200, Austin TX 78759
Tel (512) 241-7050 *SIC* 4151 4141

COACH AMERICA GROUP INC p 330
8150 N Central Expy # 1000, Dallas TX 75206
Tel (972) 354-3500 *SIC* 4141

■ **WHITE PASS & YOKON MOTOR COACHES INC** p 1606
300 Elliott Ave W, Seattle WA 98119
Tel (206) 281-3535 *SIC* 4141

LAMERS BUS LINES INC p 841
2407 S Point Rd, Green Bay WI 54313
Tel (920) 496-3600
SIC 4151 4142 4119 4725 4141

RITEWAY BUS SERVICE INC p 1237
W201 N13900 Fond Du Lac, Richfield WI 53076
Tel (262) 677-3282 *SIC* 4151 4142 4141

SIC 4142 Bus Charter Service, Except Local

ATLANTIC EXPRESS OF PENNSYLVANIA INC p 126
7 North St, Staten Island NY 10302
Tel (718) 442-7000 *SIC* 4151 4142

GREYHOUND LINES INC p 639
350 N Saint Paul St # 300, Dallas TX 75201
Tel (214) 849-8000 *SIC* 4111 4215 4142

LAMERS BUS LINES INC p 841
2407 S Point Rd, Green Bay WI 54313
Tel (920) 496-3600
SIC 4151 4142 4119 4725 4141

RITEWAY BUS SERVICE INC p 1237
W201 N13900 Fond Du Lac, Richfield WI 53076
Tel (262) 677-3282 *SIC* 4151 4142 4141

SIC 4151 School Buses

SANTA BARBARA TRANSPORTATION CORP p 1280
6414 Hollister Ave, Goleta CA 93117
Tel (805) 681-8355 *SIC* 4151 4141

ILLINOIS CENTRAL SCHOOL BUS LLC p 732
78 N Chicago St 2, Joliet IL 60432
Tel (815) 744-4800 *SIC* 4151

LAIDLAW INTERNATIONAL INC p 838
55 Shuman Blvd Ste 400, Naperville IL 60563
Tel (214) 849-8100 SIC 4151 4131

COOK-ILLINOIS CORP p 366
2100 Clearwater Dr # 250, Oak Brook IL 60523
Tel (708) 560-9840 SIC 4151

DURHAM SCHOOL SERVICES L P p 463
4300 Weaver Pkwy Ste 100, Warrenville IL 60555
Tel (630) 836-0292 SIC 4151

NRT BUS INC p 1064
55 Hampshire Rd, Methuen MA 01844
Tel (978) 681-4100 SIC 4151

STUDENT TRANSPORTATION OF AMERICA INC p 1394
3349 Hwy 138, Wall Township NJ 07719
Tel (732) 280-4200 SIC 4151

RATP DEV USA LLC p 1209
295 Madison Ave Fl 29, New York NY 10017
Tel (646) 927-0201 SIC 4151

WE TRANSPORT INC p 1585
75 Commercial St, Plainview NY 11803
Tel (516) 349-8200 SIC 4151

BIRNIE BUS SERVICE INC p 185
248 Otis St, Rome NY 13441
Tel (315) 336-3950
SIC 4151 4119 4141 4111

ACME BUS CORP p 17
3355 Vtrans Mem Hwy Ste C, Ronkonkoma NY 11779
Tel (631) 471-4600 SIC 4151

AMBOY BUS CO INC p 65
7 North St, Staten Island NY 10302
Tel (718) 442-7000 SIC 4151

ATLANTIC EXPRESS OF PENNSYLVANIA INC p 126
7 North St, Staten Island NY 10302
Tel (718) 442-7000 SIC 4151 4142

ATLANTIC EXPRESS TRANSPORTATION GROUP INC p 126
7 North St, Staten Island NY 10302
Tel (718) 442-7000 SIC 4151 4141 5012

FIRST GROUP INVESTMENT PARTNERSHIP p 547
600 Vine St Ste 1200, Cincinnati OH 45202
Tel (513) 241-2200
SIC 7513 4212 4213 4225 4151 4111

FIRST STUDENT INC p 549
600 Vine St Ste 1400, Cincinnati OH 45202
Tel (513) 241-2200 SIC 4151

FIRSTGROUP AMERICA INC p 550
600 Vine St Ste 1400, Cincinnati OH 45202
Tel (513) 241-2200
SIC 4151 4111 4119 4131 4141 8744

FIRSTGROUP USA INC p 550
600 Vine St Ste 1400, Cincinnati OH 45202
Tel (513) 241-2200
SIC 7513 4212 4213 4225 4151 4111

SCHOOL SERVICES AND LEASING INC p 1290
9011 Mtn Rdg Dr Ste 200, Austin TX 78759
Tel (512) 241-7050 SIC 4151 4141

MARION COUNTY SCHOOL TRANSPORTATION p 907
614 Virginia Ave, Fairmont WV 26554
Tel (304) 367-2161 SIC 4151

LAMERS BUS LINES INC p 841
2407 S Point Rd, Green Bay WI 54313
Tel (920) 496-3600
SIC 4151 4142 4119 4725 4141

RITEWAY BUS SERVICE INC p 1237
W201 N13900 Fond Du Lac, Richfield WI 53076
Tel (262) 677-3282 SIC 4151 4142 4141

SIC 4173 Bus Terminal & Svc Facilities

TRANSDEV NORTH AMERICA INC p 1471
720 E Bttrfeld Rd Ste 300, Lombard IL 60148
Tel (630) 571-7070 SIC 4111 4131 4173

■ AECOM GOVERNMENT SERVICES INC p 28
20501 Seneca Meadows Pkwy, Germantown MD 20876
Tel (703) 921-1600
SIC 4959 4173 4581 7299

ABC BUS COMPANIES INC p 10
1506 30th St Nw, Faribault MN 55021
Tel (507) 334-1871 SIC 5012 4173 5599

ABC BUS INC p 10
1506 30th St Nw, Faribault MN 55021
Tel (507) 334-1871 SIC 5012 4173

SIC 4212 Local Trucking Without Storage

ACTION RESOURCES INC p 19
40 County Road 517, Hanceville AL 35077
Tel (256) 352-2689 SIC 4212 4213 1794

CARLILE TRANSPORTATION SYSTEMS INC p 257
1800 E 1st Ave, Anchorage AK 99501
Tel (907) 276-7797 SIC 4212 4213 4731

▲ KNIGHT TRANSPORTATION INC p 824
20002 N 19th Ave, Phoenix AZ 85027
Tel (602) 269-2000 SIC 4213 4212

■ WASTE MANAGEMENT OF ARIZONA INC p 1580
1580 E Elwood St, Phoenix AZ 85040
Tel (480) 457-4700 SIC 4212

MACH 1 GLOBAL SERVICES INC p 892
1530 W Broadway Rd, Tempe AZ 85282
Tel (480) 921-3900 SIC 4731 4212

MAIL CONTRACTORS OF AMERICA INC p 897
3800 N Rodney Parham Rd # 301, Little Rock AR 72212
Tel (501) 280-0500 SIC 4212

■ TERRA RENEWAL SERVICES INC p 1439
201 S Denver Ave Ste B, Russellville AR 72801
Tel (479) 498-0500 SIC 4953 4212

BURRTEC WASTE INDUSTRIES INC p 229
9890 Cherry Ave, Fontana CA 92335
Tel (909) 429-4200 SIC 4953 4212

FOSTER POULTRY FARMS p 570
1000 Davis St, Livingston CA 95334
Tel (209) 394-6914
SIC 0254 2015 5812 0173 5191 4212

SAVE MART SUPERMARKETS p 1284
1800 Standiford Ave, Modesto CA 95350
Tel (209) 577-1600
SIC 5411 5141 4213 4212

DELANCEY STREET FOUNDATION p 423
600 The Embarcadero, San Francisco CA 94107
Tel (415) 957-9800
SIC 8361 5199 8322 4212 5812

FEDEX FREIGHT WEST INC p 536
6411 Guadalupe Mines Rd, San Jose CA 95120
Tel (775) 356-7600 SIC 4213 4731 4212

EDCO WASTE & RECYCLING SERVICES INC p 477
224 S Las Posas Rd, San Marcos CA 92078
Tel (760) 744-2700 SIC 4953 4212

MARBORG INDUSTRIES p 904
728 E Yanonali St, Santa Barbara CA 93103
Tel (805) 963-1852
SIC 4953 7359 7699 4212

WORLD OIL MARKETING CO p 1625
9302 Garfield Ave, South Gate CA 90280
Tel (562) 928-0100
SIC 2911 4953 2951 5541 4213 4212

CR&R INC p 388
11292 Western Ave, Stanton CA 90680
Tel (714) 826-9049 SIC 4953 4212 7359

■ COORS DISTRIBUTING CO p 368
5400 Pecos St, Denver CO 80221
Tel (303) 433-6541 SIC 5181 4212

ABE ORLANDO BUSTAMANTE p 10
7859 Diagonal Hwy, Longmont CO 80503
Tel (303) 652-3394 SIC 5099 4789 4212

TRADEBE TREATMENT AND RECYCLING NORTHEAST LLC p 1468
47 Gracey Ave, Meriden CT 06451
Tel (203) 238-8102 SIC 4953 1442 4212

J R C TRANSPORTATION INC p 772
47 Maple Ave, Thomaston CT 06787
Tel (860) 283-0207 SIC 4213 4212

■ SENTINEL TRANSPORTATION LLC p 1305
3521 Silverside Rd Ste 2a, Wilmington DE 19810
Tel (302) 477-1640 SIC 4212

COMCAR INDUSTRIES INC p 343
502 E Bridgers Ave, Auburndale FL 33823
Tel (863) 967-1101
SIC 4213 5521 5013 4212

CLIFF BERRY INC p 326
851 Eller Dr, Fort Lauderdale FL 33316
Tel (954) 763-3390
SIC 4953 4959 4212 2992 4491

EXPERIENCED MAIL TRANSPORT INC p 520
1072 Leeda Dr, Jacksonville FL 32254
Tel (904) 354-4855 SIC 4212

■ FLORIDA ROCK & TANK LINES INC p 559
200 W Forsyth St 7th, Jacksonville FL 32202
Tel (904) 396-5733 SIC 4213 4212

▲ PATRIOT TRANSPORTATION HOLDING INC p 1121
200 W Forsyth St Fl 7, Jacksonville FL 32202
Tel (904) 858-9100 SIC 4212

▲ RYDER SYSTEM INC p 1260
11690 Nw 105th St, Medley FL 33178
Tel (305) 500-3726 SIC 7513 4212

TRANSPORTATION AMERICA INC p 1472
2766 Nw 62nd St, Miami FL 33147
Tel (305) 308-8110 SIC 4212

BAGGAGE AIRLINE GUEST SERVICES INC p 145
6751 Forum Dr Ste 200, Orlando FL 32821
Tel (407) 447-5547 SIC 4212

N E WHERE TRANSPORT INC p 1005
3808 E Dr M L King Jr Blv Martin Luther, Tampa FL 33610
Tel (813) 363-0959 SIC 4212

QUALITY DISTRIBUTION LLC p 1197
4041 Park Oaks Blvd # 200, Tampa FL 33610
Tel (813) 630-5826 SIC 4213 7699 4212

FSA NETWORK INC p 582
1545 N Park Dr Ste 101, Weston FL 33326
Tel (954) 745-2120 SIC 4212 7641

LAZER SPOT INC p 849
6525 Shiloh Rd Ste 900, Alpharetta GA 30005
Tel (770) 886-6851 SIC 0762 4212

MANSFIELD ENERGY CORP p 903
1025 Airport Pkwy, Gainesville GA 30501
Tel (678) 450-2000 SIC 5172 4212 1796

BENNETT MOTOR EXPRESS LLC p 173
1001 Industrial Pkwy, Mcdonough GA 30253
Tel (770) 957-1866 SIC 4213 4212 4215

BRAMBLES USA INC (DEL) p 207
180 Technology Pkwy # 600, Norcross GA 30092
Tel (770) 776-1900
SIC 4953 4212 7353 8741 7359

DILLON TRANSPORT INC p 440
901 Mcclintock Dr Ste 300, Burr Ridge IL 60527
Tel (630) 281-7093 SIC 4212

BLACK HORSE CARRIERS INC p 187
150 Village Ct, Carol Stream IL 60188
Tel (630) 690-8900 SIC 4212 5159

CIM TRUCKING INC p 307
2232 S Blue Island Ave, Chicago IL 60608
Tel (773) 927-6611 SIC 4212

K R DRENTH TRUCKING INC p 799
20340 Stoney Island Ave, Chicago Heights IL 60411
Tel (708) 757-3333 SIC 4212

DSC LOGISTICS INC p 457
1750 S Wolf Rd, Des Plaines IL 60018
Tel (847) 390-6800
SIC 4225 4213 4212 4731

FEDERAL WAREHOUSE CO p 536
200 National St, East Peoria IL 61611
Tel (309) 694-4500 SIC 4225 4213 4212

EAGLE EXPRESS LINES INC p 468
925 175th St, Homewood IL 60430
Tel (708) 333-8401 SIC 4213 4215 4212

■ HUB GROUP TRUCKING INC p 716
2000 Clearwater Dr, Oak Brook IL 60523
Tel (630) 271-3600 SIC 4212

SOUTHFIELD CORP p 1351
8995 W 95th St, Palos Hills IL 60465
Tel (708) 344-1000
SIC 3273 1442 3241 4212 4213 5032

MAPLEHURST FARMS INC p 904
936 S Moore Rd, Rochelle IL 61068
Tel (815) 562-8723 SIC 5153 2879 4212

TRANSCARGOBG INC p 1471
812 Oregon Trl, Roselle IL 60172
Tel (847) 980-3779 SIC 4212

CARTER EXPRESS INC p 262
4020 W 73rd St, Anderson IN 46011
Tel (765) 778-6961 SIC 4213 4212

ALLIED DOMESTIC FORWARDING LLC p 56
5001 Us Highway 30 W, Fort Wayne IN 46818
Tel (260) 429-2511 SIC 4212

BUCHANAN HAULING & RIGGING INC p 222
4625 Industrial Rd, Fort Wayne IN 46825
Tel (260) 471-1877 SIC 4212

NORTH AMERICAN VAN LINES INC p 1050
5001 Us Highway 30 W, Fort Wayne IN 46818
Tel (260) 429-1682
SIC 4213 4731 4214 6331 7389 4212

BULKMATIC TRANSPORT CO INC p 225
2001 N Cline Ave, Griffith IN 46319
Tel (219) 972-7630 SIC 4213 4731 4212

▲ CELADON GROUP INC p 273
9503 E 33rd St, Indianapolis IN 46235
Tel (317) 972-7000 SIC 4212 4225

■ CELADON TRUCKING SERVICES INC p 273
9503 E 33rd St, Indianapolis IN 46235
Tel (317) 972-7000 SIC 4213 4212

■ DEFFENBAUGH INDUSTRIES INC p 422
2601 Midwest Dr, Kansas City KS 66111
Tel (913) 631-3300 SIC 4212 4953

RIVERSIDE TRANSPORT INC p 1238
5400 Kansas Ave, Kansas City KS 66106
Tel (913) 233-5500 SIC 4212 4213

ASH GROVE MATERIALS CORP p 117
11011 Cody St Ste 300, Overland Park KS 66210
Tel (913) 345-2030
SIC 3273 3272 1411 7389 4212

SLEDHEAD TRUCKING LLC p 1331
115 Denver Br, Hagerhill KY 41222
Tel (606) 297-5391 SIC 4212

CASTELLINI CO LLC p 264
2 Plum St, Highland Heights KY 41076
Tel (800) 233-8560 SIC 5148 4212 4213

ACME TRUCK LINE INC p 18
200 Westbank Expy, Gretna LA 70053
Tel (504) 368-2510 SIC 4213 4212

DUPRE INVESTMENTS INC p 462
201 Energy Pkwy Ste 500, Lafayette LA 70508
Tel (337) 237-8471 SIC 4212 4213 4731

DUPRE LOGISTICS LLC p 462
201 Energy Pkwy Ste 500, Lafayette LA 70508
Tel (337) 237-8471 SIC 4213 4212

CROWN ENTERPRISES LLC p 395
52410 Clarke Rd, White Castle LA 70788
Tel (225) 545-3040 SIC 1541 1791 4212

■ WASTE MANAGEMENT OF MARYLAND INC p 1580
6994 Columbia Gateway Dr # 200, Columbia MD 21046
Tel (410) 796-7010 SIC 4953 4212

KANE CO p 802
6500 Kane Way, Elkridge MD 21075
Tel (410) 799-3200 SIC 4212

IESI MD CORP p 730
2911 52nd Ave Ste A, Hyattsville MD 20781
Tel (410) 768-1900 SIC 4953 4212

LILY TRANSPORTATION CORP p 866
145 Rosemary St Ste D3, Needham MA 02494
Tel (781) 247-1300 SIC 4213 4212

ROADLINK USA INC p 1240
1 Kelleway Dr, Randolph MA 02368
Tel (888) 622-6076 SIC 4212

TRIUMVIRATE ENVIRONMENTAL INC p 1483
200 Innerbelt Rd 4, Somerville MA 02143
Tel (617) 623-0109 SIC 4212

M & M TRANSPORT SERVICES INC p 888
643 Manley St, West Bridgewater MA 02379
Tel (508) 521-6201 SIC 4213 4212

■ DTE COAL SERVICES INC p 458
414 S Main St Ste 600, Ann Arbor MI 48104
Tel (734) 913-2080 SIC 5052 4212

M & K TRUCK AND TRAILER INC p 888
8800 Byron Commerce Dr Sw, Byron Center MI 49315
Tel (616) 583-2100 SIC 5511 4212

MARTIN TRANSPORTATION SYSTEMS INC p 913
7300 Clyde Park Ave Sw, Byron Center MI 49315
Tel (616) 455-8850 SIC 4212

AD TRANSPORT EXPRESS INC p 21
5601 Belleville Rd, Canton MI 48188
Tel (734) 397-7100 SIC 4213 4212

E L HOLLINGSWORTH & CO p 466
3039 Airpark Dr N, Flint MI 48507
Tel (810) 233-7331 SIC 4212 4213

BRENNER OIL CO p 210
12948 Quincy St, Holland MI 49424
Tel (616) 399-9742 SIC 5172 4212

CENTRAL TRANSPORT INTERNATIONAL INC p 280
12225 Stephens Rd, Warren MI 48089
Tel (586) 467-0100 SIC 4212 4213

CENTURION p 281
12225 Stephens Rd, Warren MI 48089
Tel (586) 939-7000 SIC 4213 4212 4581

OMNI WORKSPACE CO LLC p 1085
1300 Washington Ave N # 200, Minneapolis MN 55411
Tel (612) 627-1600 SIC 7641 4212 4226

DEDICATED LOGISTICS INC p 421
2900 Granada Ln N, Oakdale MN 55128
Tel (651) 631-5918 SIC 4213 4212 4225

BAY & BAY TRANSFER CO INC p 160
3686 140th St E, Rosemount MN 55068
Tel (800) 273-0366 SIC 4213 4212

CERNX MN LLC p 284
2355 Highway 36 W Ste 400, Roseville MN 55113
Tel (320) 372-7400
SIC 4212 7389 4731 4222

DEE SPEE DELIVERY SERVICE INC p 421
4101 Clearwater Rd, Saint Cloud MN 56301
Tel (320) 251-6697 SIC 4212

TL WALLACE CONSTRUCTION INC p 1457
4025 Highway 35 N, Columbia MS 39429
Tel (601) 736-4525 SIC 1611 4212 8322

BUFFALO SERVICES INC p 224
747 S Broadway St, Mccomb MS 39648
Tel (601) 684-7702
SIC 5172 5411 6519 4212

B&C HOLDING CO LLC p 142
351 Peabody Ave, Cabool MO 65689
Tel (417) 962-2300 SIC 4212 4213

MILK TRANSPORT SERVICES LP p 969
910 Shelton Dr, Cabool MO 65689
Tel (417) 962-2373 SIC 4213 4212

WESTERN DAIRY TRANSPORT LLC p 1598
910 Shelton Dr, Cabool MO 65689
Tel (417) 962-2300 SIC 4213 4212

BUCHHEIT ENTERPRISES INC p 222
33 Pcr 540, Perryville MO 63775
Tel (573) 547-1010
SIC 4213 4212 5251 4225

GREGORY LOGISTICS INC p 639
2844 Fair St, Poplar Bluff MO 63901
Tel (573) 785-1088 SIC 4213 4212

JIH TRUCKING LLC p 785
1041 Camelot Gardens Dr, Saint Louis MO 63125
Tel (314) 487-7159 SIC 4212 4213

TRANSYSTEMS LLC p 1473
1901 Benefis Ct, Great Falls MT 59405
Tel (406) 727-7500 SIC 4212

CRETE CARRIER CORP p 392
400 Nw 56th St, Lincoln NE 68528
Tel (402) 475-9521 SIC 4213 4212 6512

TRANSWOOD CARRIERS INC p 1473
2565 Saint Marys Ave, Omaha NE 68105
Tel (402) 346-8092 SIC 4213 4212 7513

TRANSWOOD INC p 1473
2565 Saint Marys Ave, Omaha NE 68105
Tel (402) 346-8092 SIC 4212 4213

MCCOLLISTERS TRANSPORTATION GROUP INC p 927
1800 N Route 130, Burlington NJ 08016
Tel (609) 386-0600 SIC 4213 4212

NFI INDUSTRIES INC p 1041
1515 Burnt Mill Rd, Cherry Hill NJ 08003
Tel (856) 691-7000
SIC 4213 4212 8741 4225 4214 4783

CLEAN VENTURE INC p 324
201 S 1st St, Elizabeth NJ 07206
Tel (908) 355-5800
SIC 4225 4212 4953 8748

JERSEY CITY INCINERATOR AUTHORITY p 783
501 State Rt 440, Jersey City NJ 07305
Tel (201) 432-4645 SIC 4953 0782 4212

CORY JOSEPH HOLDING LLC p 373
150 Mdwlands Pkwy Fl 3, Secaucus NJ 07094
Tel (201) 795-1000 SIC 4212

MIDJERSEY DISPOSAL INC p 965
1298 Industrial Way, Toms River NJ 08755
Tel (732) 341-6100 SIC 4212 4953

JID TRANSPORTATION LLC p 785
158 61st St Apt 2, West New York NJ 07093
Tel (201) 362-0841 SIC 3713 4212 7363

GYPSUM EXPRESS LTD p 649
8280 Sixty Rd, Baldwinsville NY 13027
Tel (315) 638-2201 SIC 4212 4213

UTF TRUCKING INC p 1536
2330 Borden Ave, Long Island City NY 11101
Tel (718) 928-1000 SIC 4212

TRANSERVICE LEASE CORP p 1471
5 Dakota Dr, New Hyde Park NY 11042
Tel (800) 645-8018
SIC 7699 7539 4212 7353

TRANSERVICE LOGISTICS INC p 1471
5 Dakota Dr Ste 209, New Hyde Park NY 11042
Tel (800) 645-8018 SIC 4212

WADHAMS ENTERPRISES INC p 1571
369 Bostwick Rd, Phelps NY 14532
Tel (800) 334-1314 SIC 4212 4213

■ NORTHEAST RECYCLING CORP p 1055
1198 Prospect Ave, Westbury NY 11590
Tel (516) 937-0900 SIC 4953 4212

SHAMROCK ENVIRONMENTAL CORP p 1311
6106 Corporate Park Dr, Browns Summit NC 27214
Tel (336) 375-1989
SIC 4953 4212 8748 7699

KENAN TRANSPORT LLC p 810
100 Europa Dr Ste 170, Chapel Hill NC 27517
Tel (919) 967-8221 SIC 4212 4213

CARDINAL LOGISTICS MANAGEMENT INC p 253
5333 Davidson Hwy, Concord NC 28027
Tel (704) 786-6125 SIC 4212 4213 1541

CA PERRY & SON TRANSIT INC p 234
4033 Virginia Rd, Hobbsville NC 27946
Tel (252) 221-4463 SIC 4213 4212

COASTAL AUTO TRANSPORT LLC p 331
4928 Us Highway 301 S, Hope Mills NC 28348
Tel (910) 429-9902 SIC 4212

CHAMBERS EXPRESS TRUCKING INC p 287
2132 Bluebonnet Ln, Matthews NC 28104
Tel (704) 292-2916 SIC 4212

▲ OLD DOMINION FREIGHT LINE INC p 1080
500 Old Dominion Way, Thomasville NC 27360
Tel (336) 889-5000 SIC 4213 4212 4731

SALEM CARRIERS INC p 1272
175 Charlois Blvd, Winston Salem NC 27103
Tel (336) 768-6800 *SIC* 4213 4212

MIDWEST MOTOR EXPRESS INC p 967
5015 E Main Ave, Bismarck ND 58501
Tel (701) 223-1880 *SIC* 4212

MIDWEST LOGISTICS SYSTEMS LTD p 967
7021 State Route 703, Celina OH 45822
Tel (419) 584-1414 *SIC* 4213 4212

FIRST GROUP INVESTMENT PARTNERSHIP p 547
600 Vine St Ste 1200, Cincinnati OH 45202
Tel (513) 241-2200
SIC 7513 4212 4213 4225 4151 4111

FIRSTGROUP USA INC p 550
600 Vine St Ste 1400, Cincinnati OH 45202
Tel (513) 241-2200
SIC 7513 4212 4213 4225 4151 4111

RUMPKE OF OHIO INC p 1258
3800 Struble Rd, Cincinnati OH 45251
Tel (513) 851-0122 *SIC* 4953 4212

TRANSPORTATION UNLIMITED INC p 1473
3740 Carnegie Ave Ste 101, Cleveland OH 44115
Tel (216) 426-0088 *SIC* 7363 4213 4212

FST LOGISTICS INC p 582
1727 Georgesville Rd, Columbus OH 43228
Tel (614) 529-7900 *SIC* 4212

DAYTON FREIGHT LINES INC p 417
6450 Poe Ave Ste 311, Dayton OH 45414
Tel (937) 264-4060 *SIC* 4213 4212

AIM LEASING CO p 38
1500 Trumbull Ave, Girard OH 44420
Tel (330) 759-0438
SIC 7513 7538 4212 5983

■ PANTHER PREMIUM LOGISTICS INC p 1111
84 Medina Rd, Medina OH 44256
Tel (800) 685-0657 *SIC* 4213 4212

KUHNLE BROTHERS INC p 831
14905 Cross Creek Pkwy, Newbury OH 44065
Tel (440) 564-7168 *SIC* 4213 4212

KENAN ADVANTAGE GROUP INC p 810
4366 Mount Pleasant St Nw, North Canton OH 44720
Tel (877) 999-2524 *SIC* 4213 4212

INTERNATIONAL TRUCK AND ENGINE CORP p 757
6125 Urbana Rd, Springfield OH 45502
Tel (937) 390-4045 *SIC* 4212

SANTMYER OIL CO INC p 1281
3000 Old Airport Rd, Wooster OH 44691
Tel (330) 262-6501
SIC 5172 5983 4212 5531

AMERICAN BULK COMMODITIES INC p 69
8063 Southern Blvd, Youngstown OH 44512
Tel (330) 758-0841
SIC 4212 7532 6531 7363

OKLAHOMA ROOF MASTERS INC p 1080
601 Evergreen Dr, Guthrie OK 73044
Tel (405) 814-6440
SIC 1761 1541 4731 4212 4213

■ CHESAPEAKE OPERATING LLC p 295
6100 N Western Ave, Oklahoma City OK 73118
Tel (405) 848-8000 *SIC* 1311 1389 4212

PANHANDLE OILFIELD SERVICE COMPANIES INC p 1111
14000 Quail Springs Pkwy # 300, Oklahoma City OK 73134
Tel (405) 608-5330
SIC 1389 7389 3498 4212 5082 1794

DUCK DELIVERY PRODUCE INC p 459
8448 Ne 33rd Dr Ste 120, Portland OR 97211
Tel (503) 288-9380 *SIC* 5148 4212

ROADLINK USA NATIONAL LLC p 1240
1240 Win Dr, Bethlehem PA 18017
Tel (215) 333-4444 *SIC* 4212

PENNSY SUPPLY INC p 1130
1001 Paxton St, Harrisburg PA 17104
Tel (717) 233-4511
SIC 1422 2951 3273 4212 5032

■ EXECUTIVE AIR LINES INC p 517
Lmm Int Airport Central, Carolina PR 00983
Tel (787) 253-6401 *SIC* 4512 4212

CONSOLIDATED WASTE SERVICES CORP p 360
Km 9 Rr 189, Gurabo PR 00778
Tel (787) 273-7649 *SIC* 4212

DEARYBURY OIL & GAS INC p 420
2560 Southport Rd, Spartanburg SC 29302
Tel (864) 585-6226 *SIC* 5172 5983 4212

■ WASTE MANAGEMENT OF SOUTH CAROLINA INC p 1581
390 Innovation Way, Wellford SC 29385
Tel (864) 232-1537 *SIC* 4953 4212

GARDNER TRUCKING INC p 592
331 Premier Ct S, Franklin TN 37067
Tel (909) 563-5606 *SIC* 4213 4212

ANDERSON SERVICES LLC p 90
6016 Brookvale Ln 110b, Knoxville TN 37919
Tel (865) 584-6714 *SIC* 4212

PROLOGIC DISTRIBUTION SERVICES (EAST) LLC p 1182
6016 Brookvale Ln 110b, Knoxville TN 37919
Tel (865) 584-9765 *SIC* 4212 4213

QUICKWAY DISTRIBUTION SERVICES INC p 1199
1116 Polk Ave, Nashville TN 37210
Tel (615) 834-9470 *SIC* 4213 4212

DASEKE LONE STAR INC p 413
15455 Dallas Pkwy, Addison TX 75001
Tel (972) 248-0412 *SIC* 4212

LONE STAR HOLDINGS LLC p 875
6500 River Place Blvd # 2, Austin TX 78730
Tel (512) 873-8067 *SIC* 4215 4513 4212

GLENN THURMAN INC p 615
3180 S Belt Line Rd, Balch Springs TX 75181
Tel (972) 286-6333 *SIC* 1611 4212

TUTLE & TUTLE TRUCKING INC p 1493
3672 W Highway 67, Cleburne TX 76033
Tel (817) 556-2131 *SIC* 4212

GRAEBEL VANLINES HOLDINGS LLC p 628
12790 Merit Dr Bldg 9, Dallas TX 75251
Tel (972) 694-0400 *SIC* 4213 4214 4212

NATURAL GAS SUPPLY LLC p 1018
9233 Denton Dr Ste 300, Dallas TX 75235
Tel (469) 305-1508 *SIC* 4212

ABIBOW RECYCLING LLC p 11
14950 Hathrow Forest Pkwy, Houston TX 77032
Tel (800) 874-1301 *SIC* 4212

▲ ADAMS RESOURCES & ENERGY INC p 21
17 S Briar Hollow Ln, Houston TX 77027
Tel (713) 881-3600
SIC 5172 4212 1382 1311

BUCKEYE GP HOLDINGS LP p 223
1 Greenway Plz Ste 600, Houston TX 77046
Tel (832) 615-8600
SIC 4789 4213 4226 4212

■ CEVA GROUND US LP p 284
15390 Vickery Dr, Houston TX 77032
Tel (281) 227-5000 *SIC* 4212 4213

▲ GENESIS ENERGY LP p 602
919 Milam St Ste 2100, Houston TX 77002
Tel (713) 860-2500 *SIC* 4612 5171 4212

KEANE GROUP HOLDINGS LLC p 807
11200 Westheimer Rd # 900, Houston TX 77042
Tel (713) 960-0381 *SIC* 1381 7353 4212

■ KIRBY OFFSHORE MARINE LLC p 821
55 Waugh Dr Ste 1000, Houston TX 77007
Tel (713) 435-1000 *SIC* 5172 4212 4213

PSC HOLDINGS I LP p 1188
5151 San Felipe St # 1600, Houston TX 77056
Tel (713) 623-8777 *SIC* 4212

■ SAFETY-KLEEN INC p 1266
2600 N Central Expy # 400, Richardson TX 75080
Tel (800) 669-5740
SIC 4953 3559 4212 5172 5085 7389

■ SAFETY-KLEEN SYSTEMS INC p 1266
2600 N Central Expy # 400, Richardson TX 75080
Tel (972) 265-2000
SIC 3559 7359 5172 4212 7389 5085

COASTAL TRANSPORT CO INC p 332
1603 Ackerman Rd, San Antonio TX 78219
Tel (210) 661-4287 *SIC* 4212 4213

MG BUILDING MATERIALS LTD p 958
2651 Sw Military Dr, San Antonio TX 78224
Tel (210) 924-8604 *SIC* 2421 4212 5211

■ TPI PETROLEUM INC p 1467
6000 N Loop 1604 W, San Antonio TX 78249
Tel (210) 592-2000
SIC 2911 5541 4612 4212 4213

CENTRAL FREIGHT LINES INC p 278
5601 W Waco Dr, Waco TX 76710
Tel (254) 772-2120 *SIC* 4212

DATS TRUCKING INC p 414
321 N Old Highway 91, Hurricane UT 84737
Tel (435) 673-1886 *SIC* 4212 4213 5171

SAVAGE COMPANIES p 1283
901 W Legacy Center Way, Midvale UT 84047
Tel (801) 944-6600 *SIC* 4212 4213

SAVAGE SERVICES CORP p 1284
901 W Legacy Center Way, Midvale UT 84047
Tel (801) 944-6600 *SIC* 4212

STAKER & PARSON COMPANIES p 1374
2350 S 1900 W Ste 100, Ogden UT 84401
Tel (801) 298-7500
SIC 1611 5032 3273 4212 2951 1771

WOLF TRANSPORTATION LLC p 1621
5204 S Redwood Rd Ste B1, Taylorsville UT 84123
Tel (801) 759-9465 *SIC* 4212

■ CASELLA WASTE MANAGEMENT INC p 263
25 Green Hill Ln, Rutland VT 05701
Tel (802) 775-0325 *SIC* 4953 4212

ABILENE MOTOR EXPRESS p 11
1700 Willis Rd, North Chesterfield VA 23237
Tel (804) 275-0224 *SIC* 4213 6221 4212

LAWRENCE TRANSPORTATION SYSTEMS INC p 848
872 Lee Hwy, Roanoke VA 24019
Tel (540) 966-4000 *SIC* 4225 4213 4212

HILLDRUP COMPANIES INC p 693
4022 Jefferson Davis Hwy, Stafford VA 22554
Tel (703) 221-7155 *SIC* 4212

SMOKEY POINT DISTRIBUTING INC p 1334
19201 63rd Ave Ne, Arlington WA 98223
Tel (360) 435-5737 *SIC* 4213 4212 4214

POWELL - CHRISTENSEN INC p 1164
501 E Wine Country Rd, Grandview WA 98930
Tel (509) 882-2115 *SIC* 5171 4212

NOEL CORP p 1046
1001 S 1st St, Yakima WA 98901
Tel (509) 248-4545
SIC 2086 7389 4212 6512 4225 5962

MILLIS TRANSFER INC p 971
121 Gebhardt Rd, Black River Falls WI 54615
Tel (715) 284-4384 *SIC* 4213 4231 4212

■ WASTE MANAGEMENT OF WISCONSIN INC p 1581
N96 W 13600 Cnty Line Rd St N 96, Germantown WI 53022
Tel (262) 251-4000 *SIC* 4953 4212

SCHNEIDER LOGISTICS INC p 1288
3101 Packerland Dr, Green Bay WI 54313
Tel (920) 592-0000
SIC 4731 4225 4789 4212

■ VEOLIA ENVIRONMENTAL SERVICES NORTH AMERICA LLC p 1548
125 S 84th St Ste 200, Milwaukee WI 53214
Tel (414) 479-7800 *SIC* 4953 4212

SIC 4213 Trucking, Except Local

P&S TRANSPORTATION LLC p 1102
1810 Avenue C, Birmingham AL 35218
Tel (205) 788-4000 *SIC* 4213 4789

BOYD BROS TRANSPORTATION INC p 205
3275 Highway 30, Clayton AL 36016
Tel (800) 633-1502 *SIC* 4213

DANA TRANSPORT INC p 411
10837 Highway 43, Creola AL 36525
Tel (732) 750-9100 *SIC* 4213

AAA COOPER TRANSPORTATION p 7
1751 Kinsey Rd, Dothan AL 36303
Tel (334) 793-2284 *SIC* 4213

ACTION RESOURCES INC p 19
40 County Road 517, Hanceville AL 35077
Tel (256) 352-2689 *SIC* 4212 4213 1794

B R WILLIAMS TRUCKING INC p 142
2339 Al Highway 21 S, Oxford AL 36203
Tel (256) 831-5580 *SIC* 4213 4225

WILEY SANDERS TRUCK LINES INC p 1609
100 Sanders Rd, Troy AL 36079
Tel (334) 566-5184 *SIC* 4213

RE GARRISON TRUCKING INC p 1212
1103 County Road 1194, Vinemont AL 35179
Tel (888) 640-8482 *SIC* 4213

CARLILE TRANSPORTATION SYSTEMS INC p 257
1800 E 1st Ave, Anchorage AK 99501
Tel (907) 276-7797 *SIC* 4212 4213 4731

▲ KNIGHT TRANSPORTATION INC p 824
20002 N 19th Ave, Phoenix AZ 85027
Tel (602) 269-2000 *SIC* 4213 4212

▲ SWIFT TRANSPORTATION CO p 1412
2200 S 75th Ave, Phoenix AZ 85043
Tel (602) 269-9700 *SIC* 4213 4231

SWIFT TRANSPORTATION CO INC p 1412
2200 S 75th Ave, Phoenix AZ 85043
Tel (602) 269-9700 *SIC* 4213 4225

APL LOGISTICS WAREHOUSE MANAGEMENT SERVICES INC p 97
16220 N Scottsdale Rd # 300, Scottsdale AZ 85254
Tel (480) 483-0886 *SIC* 4213 4225

■ MURPHY OIL USA INC p 1001
200 E Peach St, El Dorado AR 71730
Tel (870) 862-6411
SIC 8742 2911 1311 4213

WILLIS SHAW EXPRESS INC p 1612
201 N Elm St, Elm Springs AR 72728
Tel (479) 248-7261 *SIC* 4213

■ ABF FREIGHT SYSTEM INC p 11
3801 Old Greenwood Rd, Fort Smith AR 72903
Tel (479) 785-8700 *SIC* 4213

▲ ARCBEST CORP p 104
3801 Old Greenwood Rd, Fort Smith AR 72903
Tel (479) 785-6000 *SIC* 4213 4731

■ FEDEX FREIGHT INC p 536
2200 Forward Dr, Harrison AR 72601
Tel (870) 741-9000 *SIC* 4213

■ J B HUNT TRANSPORT INC p 770
615 J B Hunt Corporate Dr, Lowell AR 72745
Tel (479) 820-0000 *SIC* 4213

▲ JB HUNT TRANSPORT SERVICES INC p 779
615 Jb Hunt Corp Dr, Lowell AR 72745
Tel (479) 820-0000 *SIC* 4213 4731

BRUCE OAKLEY INC p 220
3700 Lincoln Ave, North Little Rock AR 72114
Tel (501) 945-0875
SIC 4449 5153 5261 5191 4213

MAVERICK TRANSPORTATION LLC p 921
13301 Valentine Rd, North Little Rock AR 72117
Tel (501) 955-1222 *SIC* 4213

MAVERICK USA INC p 921
13301 Valentine Rd, North Little Rock AR 72117
Tel (501) 945-6130 *SIC* 4213

PAT SALMON & SONS INC p 1120
3809 Roundtop Dr, North Little Rock AR 72117
Tel (501) 945-0778 *SIC* 4213

TRANSCO LINES INC p 1471
60 Transco Park Dr, Russellville AR 72802
Tel (479) 967-5700 *SIC* 4213

■ PAM TRANSPORT INC p 1110
297 W Henri De Tonti Blvd, Tontitown AR 72770
Tel (479) 361-9111 *SIC* 4213

▲ PAM TRANSPORTATION SERVICES INC p 1110
297 W Henri De Tonti Blvd, Tontitown AR 72770
Tel (479) 361-9111 *SIC* 4213 4731

▲ USA TRUCK INC p 1534
3200 Industrial Park Rd, Van Buren AR 72956
Tel (479) 471-2500 *SIC* 4213

MP ENVIRONMENTAL SERVICES INC p 995
3400 Manor St, Bakersfield CA 93308
Tel (800) 458-3036
SIC 4953 4213 8748 7699

MIKE CAMPBELL & ASSOCIATES LTD p 968
13031 Temple Ave, City Of Industry CA 91746
Tel (626) 369-3981
SIC 4222 4225 4214 4213

PERFORMANCE TEAM FREIGHT SYS INC p 1135
2240 E Maple Ave, El Segundo CA 90245
Tel (562) 345-2200 *SIC* 4731 4225 4213

HENRY AVOCADO CORP p 684
2355 E Lincoln Ave, Escondido CA 92027
Tel (760) 745-6632 *SIC* 0179 4213

ROYALTY CAPITAL INC p 1254
1010 N Central Ave, Glendale CA 91202
Tel (888) 210-0332 *SIC* 4213

AGILITY HOLDINGS INC p 35
310 Commerce Ste 250, Irvine CA 92602
Tel (714) 617-6300 *SIC* 4731 4213 4214

HANSEN AUTO TRANSPORT INC p 658
3552 Green Ave Ste 201, Los Alamitos CA 90720
Tel (562) 430-4100 *SIC* 4213

DEPENDABLE HIGHWAY EXPRESS INC p 430
2555 E Olympic Blvd, Los Angeles CA 90023
Tel (323) 526-2200 *SIC* 4213 4225

URS GORES HOLDINGS CORP p 1530
10877 Wilshire Blvd Ste 1, Los Angeles CA 90024
Tel (310) 209-3010 *SIC* 4213

SAVE MART SUPERMARKETS p 1284
1800 Standiford Ave, Modesto CA 95350
Tel (209) 577-1600
SIC 5411 5141 4213 4212

BIAGI BROS INC p 181
787 Airpark Rd, Napa CA 94558
Tel (707) 745-8115 *SIC* 4213 4225

MATHESON TRUCKING INC p 920
9785 Goethe Rd, Sacramento CA 95827
Tel (916) 685-2330 *SIC* 4213 4731

■ XPO LOGISTICS WORLDWIDE INC p 1633
560 Mission St Ste 2950, San Francisco CA 94105
Tel (415) 486-2660
SIC 4731 4225 4213 8741

FEDEX FREIGHT WEST INC p 536
6411 Guadalupe Mines Rd, San Jose CA 95120
Tel (775) 356-7600 *SIC* 4213 4731 4212

TORRANCE VAN & STORAGE CO p 1462
12128 Burke St, Santa Fe Springs CA 90670
Tel (562) 567-2100 *SIC* 4214 4213

WORLD OIL MARKETING CO p 1625
9302 Garfield Ave, South Gate CA 90280
Tel (562) 928-0100
SIC 2911 4953 2951 5541 4213 4212

AEROGROUND INC p 30
270 Lawrence Ave, South San Francisco CA 94080
Tel (650) 266-6965 *SIC* 4581 4213

GRAEBEL HOLDINGS INC p 628
16346 Airport Cir, Aurora CO 80011
Tel (303) 214-6683 *SIC* 4213 4225 6719

GRAEBEL MOVERS INC p 628
16346 Airport Cir, Aurora CO 80011
Tel (303) 214-6683 *SIC* 4213 4214

JOHNSON STORAGE & MOVING CO HOLDINGS LLC p 791
7009 S Jordan Rd, Centennial CO 80112
Tel (303) 785-4300 *SIC* 4213 4214

FLEET-CAR LEASE INC p 555
7563 Dahlia St Unit A, Commerce City CO 80022
Tel (800) 624-3256 *SIC* 4213

FREIGHT ALL KINDS INC p 577
10885 E 51st Ave, Denver CO 80239
Tel (800) 321-7182 *SIC* 4731 4213

HVH TRANSPORTATION INC p 722
181 E 56th Ave Ste 200, Denver CO 80216
Tel (303) 292-3656 *SIC* 4213

NAVAJO EXPRESS INC p 1019
1400 W 64th Ave, Denver CO 80221
Tel (303) 287-3800 *SIC* 4213

NAVAJO SHIPPERS INC p 1019
1400 W 64th Ave, Denver CO 80221
Tel (303) 287-3800 *SIC* 4213

JBS CARRIERS INC p 779
2401 2nd Ave, Greeley CO 80631
Tel (866) 298-4573 *SIC* 4213

PACKERLAND HOLDINGS INC p 1107
1770 Promontory Cir, Greeley CO 80634
Tel (970) 506-8000 *SIC* 2011 4213

STOLT-NIELSEN TRANSPORTATION GROUP LTD p 1390
800 Connecticut Ave 4e, Norwalk CT 06854
Tel (203) 299-3600 *SIC* 4499 4213

J R C TRANSPORTATION INC p 772
47 Maple Ave, Thomaston CT 06787
Tel (860) 283-0207 *SIC* 4213 4212

BURRIS LOGISTICS p 228
501 Se 5th St, Milford DE 19963
Tel (302) 839-4531 *SIC* 5142 4222 4213

SECURITY STORAGE CO OF WASHINGTON p 1299
1701 Florida Ave Nw, Washington DC 20009
Tel (202) 797-5659
SIC 4213 4226 4214 4731

COMCAR INDUSTRIES INC p 343
502 E Bridgers Ave, Auburndale FL 33823
Tel (863) 967-1101
SIC 4213 5521 5013 4212

COMMERCIAL CARRIER CORP p 345
502 E Brdgs Ave, Auburndale FL 33823
Tel (863) 967-1101 *SIC* 4213

■ CEVA LOGISTICS US GROUP INC p 285
10751 Deerwood Park Blvd, Jacksonville FL 32256
Tel (904) 928-1400 *SIC* 4213 4226

■ CEVA LOGISTICS US HOLDINGS INC p 285
10751 Deerwood Park Blvd # 201, Jacksonville FL 32256
Tel (904) 928-1400 *SIC* 4213 4226

■ CSX INTERMODAL INC p 398
500 Water St, Jacksonville FL 32202
Tel (904) 633-1000 *SIC* 4213 4011 4225

CYPRESS TRUCK LINES INC p 405
1414 Lindrose St, Jacksonville FL 32206
Tel (904) 353-8641 *SIC* 4213

■ FLORIDA ROCK & TANK LINES INC p 559
200 W Forsyth St 7th, Jacksonville FL 32202
Tel (904) 396-5733 *SIC* 4213 4212

■ LANDSTAR LIGON INC p 843
13410 Sutton Park Dr S, Jacksonville FL 32224
Tel (904) 398-9400 *SIC* 4213

■ LANDSTAR SYSTEM HOLDINGS INC p 843
13410 Sutton Park Dr S, Jacksonville FL 32224
Tel (904) 398-9400 *SIC* 4213

■ PATRIOT TRANSPORTATION INC p 1121
200 W Forsyth St Ste 700, Jacksonville FL 32202
Tel (904) 356-6110 *SIC* 4213 6531 6519

■ RANGER LANDSTAR INC p 1208
13410 Sutton Park Dr S, Jacksonville FL 32224
Tel (800) 872-9400 *SIC* 4213

RAVEN TRANSPORT CO INC p 1209
6800 Broadway Ave, Jacksonville FL 32254
Tel (904) 880-1515 *SIC* 4213

SUDDATH VAN LINES INC p 1396
815 S Main St Ste 400, Jacksonville FL 32207
Tel (904) 390-7100 *SIC* 4213 4731 4214

DARNGAVIL ENTERPRISES LLC p 412
3103 Riachuelo Ln, Kissimmee FL 34744
Tel (407) 288-2776 *SIC* 4213

OAKLEY TRANSPORT INC p 1071
101 Abc Rd, Lake Wales FL 33859
Tel (863) 638-1435 *SIC* 4213 6531

AMERIJET HOLDINGS INC p 82
3401 Nw 72nd Ave Ste A, Miami FL 33122
Tel (800) 927-6059
SIC 4512 8741 4581 4213

ARMELLINI INDUSTRIES INC p 111
3446 Sw Armellini Ave, Palm City FL 34990
Tel (772) 287-0575 *SIC* 4213 5193 4731

MCKENZIE TANK LINES INC p 930
1966 Commonwealth Ln, Tallahassee FL 32303
Tel (850) 576-1221 SIC 4213 3715 3443

GRUDEN ACQUISITION INC p 642
4041 Park Oaks Blvd # 200, Tampa FL 33610
Tel (800) 282-2031 SIC 4213

QUALITY CARRIERS INC p 1196
4041 Park Oaks Blvd # 200, Tampa FL 33610
Tel (800) 282-2031 SIC 4213

QUALITY DISTRIBUTION INC p 1197
4041 Park Oaks Blvd # 200, Tampa FL 33610
Tel (813) 630-5826 SIC 4213

QUALITY DISTRIBUTION LLC p 1197
4041 Park Oaks Blvd # 200, Tampa FL 33610
Tel (813) 630-5826 SIC 4213 7699 4212

INDIAN RIVER TRANSPORT CO p 738
2580 Executive Rd, Winter Haven FL 33884
Tel (863) 324-2430 SIC 4213

■ **MAGNATRAX CORP** p 896
1220 Old Alpharetta Rd # 310, Alpharetta GA 30005
Tel (678) 455-3360
SIC 3448 3442 3479 4213 3444

ALLIED AUTOMOTIVE GROUP INC p 56
2302 Parklake Dr Ne # 600, Atlanta GA 30345
Tel (404) 373-4285 SIC 4213

ALLIED SYSTEMS HOLDINGS INC p 57
2302 Parkl Dr Bldg 15ste, Atlanta GA 30345
Tel (404) 373-4285 SIC 4213

BENTON GLOBAL LLC p 173
1045 S Rver Indus Blvd Se, Atlanta GA 30315
Tel (404) 267-2200 SIC 4213

PROGRESSIVE LOGISTICS SERVICES LLC p 1181
6 Piedmont Ctr Ne Ste 606, Atlanta GA 30305
Tel (404) 495-5300 SIC 4213

WATKINS ASSOCIATED INDUSTRIES INC p 1582
1958 Monroe Dr Ne, Atlanta GA 30324
Tel (404) 872-3841 SIC 4213 6552

■ **SAIA MOTOR FREIGHT LINE LLC** p 1268
11465 Johns Creek Pkwy # 400, Duluth GA 30097
Tel (770) 232-5067 SIC 4213

▲ **SAIA INC** p 1268
11465 Johns Creek Pkwy # 400, Johns Creek GA 30097
Tel (770) 232-5067 SIC 4213

BROWN INTEGRATED LOGISTICS INC p 219
6908 Chapman Rd, Lithonia GA 30058
Tel (770) 482-6521
SIC 4225 4213 4731 7359

JAMES BROWN CO p 776
6908 Chapman Rd, Lithonia GA 30058
Tel (770) 482-6521 SIC 4213

BENNETT INTERNATIONAL GROUP LLC p 173
1001 Industrial Pkwy, Mcdonough GA 30253
Tel (770) 957-1866 SIC 4213

BENNETT MOTOR EXPRESS LLC p 173
1001 Industrial Pkwy, Mcdonough GA 30253
Tel (770) 957-1866 SIC 4213 4212 4215

■ **MORGAN SOUTHERN INC** p 988
700 Westpark Dr Ste 250, Peachtree City GA 30269
Tel (404) 366-1345 SIC 4213

DSL XPRESS LLC p 458
2006 Karl Dr Apt 1602, Warner Robins GA 31088
Tel (706) 945-9542 SIC 4213

DOUG ANDRUS DISTRIBUTING LLC p 452
6300 S 45th W, Idaho Falls ID 83402
Tel (208) 523-1034 SIC 4213

GREAT LAKES SYNERGY CORP p 634
85 W Algonquin Rd Ste 600, Arlington Heights IL 60005
Tel (847) 437-0200 SIC 5084 4226 4213

A MICHAEL OWENS INC p 6
814 W Chestnut St, Bloomington IL 61701
Tel (309) 828-7750 SIC 5541 4213

NEW WORLD VAN LINES INC p 1033
5875 N Rogers Ave, Chicago IL 60646
Tel (773) 685-3399 SIC 4213

■ **ADM TRUCKING INC** p 23
2501 N Brush College Rd, Decatur IL 62526
Tel (217) 424-5200 SIC 4213

MCLEOD EXPRESS LLC p 931
5002 Cundiff Ct, Decatur IL 62526
Tel (217) 706-5045 SIC 4213

DSC LOGISTICS INC p 457
1750 S Wolf Rd, Des Plaines IL 60018
Tel (847) 390-6800
SIC 4225 4213 4212 4731

FEDERAL WAREHOUSE CO p 536
200 National St, East Peoria IL 61611
Tel (309) 694-4500 SIC 4225 4213 4212

CASSENS TRANSPORT CO p 263
145 N Kansas St, Edwardsville IL 62025
Tel (618) 656-3006 SIC 4213 4231

MULTI GROUP LOGISTICS INC p 999
10900 Belmont Ave Ste 400, Franklin Park IL 60131
Tel (847) 621-3333 SIC 4213

■ **AMCOL INTERNATIONAL CORP** p 65
2870 Forbs Ave, Hoffman Estates IL 60192
Tel (847) 851-1500
SIC 1459 5032 4213 4731

EAGLE EXPRESS LINES INC p 468
925 175th St, Homewood IL 60430
Tel (708) 333-8401 SIC 4213 4215 4212

PDV MIDWEST REFINING LLC p 1125
135th St New Ave, Lemont IL 60439
Tel (630) 257-7761
SIC 2992 2911 5171 4213

CHAS LEVY CIRCULATING CO p 291
1930 George St Ste 4, Melrose Park IL 60160
Tel (708) 356-3600 SIC 4213 4214 5192

■ **CAT LOGISTICS INC** p 264
500 N Morton Ave, Morton IL 61550
Tel (309) 675-1000 SIC 4225 5045 4213

G&D INTEGRATED TRANSPORTATION INC p 587
50 Commerce Dr, Morton IL 61550
Tel (309) 284-6700 SIC 4213

STAR TRANSPORT INC p 1378
240 W Ashland St, Morton IL 61550
Tel (309) 266-7613 SIC 4213 4731

HENIFF TRANSPORTATION SYSTEMS LLC p 683
2015 Spring Rd Ste 780, Oak Brook IL 60523
Tel (630) 230-2100 SIC 4213

SUPERIOR BULK LOGISTICS INC p 1406
711 Jorie Blvd Ste 101n, Oak Brook IL 60523
Tel (630) 573-2555 SIC 4213

TRANSPORT SERVICE CO p 1472
2001 Spring Rd Ste 400, Oak Brook IL 60523
Tel (630) 472-5900 SIC 4213 4731

SIRVA INC p 1327
1 Parkview Plz, Oakbrook Terrace IL 60181
Tel (630) 570-3047
SIC 4213 4214 4731 7513 6331

SIRVA WORLDWIDE INC p 1327
1 Parkview Plz Ste 300, Oakbrook Terrace IL 60181
Tel (630) 570-3047
SIC 4213 4214 4731 7513 6331

JEVIC TRANSPORTATION INC p 784
1540 E Dundee Rd Ste 240, Palatine IL 60074
Tel (856) 764-1909 SIC 4213

SOUTHFIELD CORP p 1351
8995 W 95th St, Palos Hills IL 60465
Tel (708) 344-1000
SIC 3273 1442 3241 4212 4213 5032

SHARKEY TRANSPORT SERVICES INC p 1312
3803 Dye Rd, Quincy IL 62305
Tel (217) 228-6555 SIC 4213

MIDWEST TRANSPORT INC p 968
11385 N Trimble Rd, Robinson IL 62454
Tel (618) 544-3399 SIC 4213

CONGLOBAL INDUSTRIES LLC p 356
8200 185th St Ste A, Tinley Park IL 60487
Tel (925) 543-0977
SIC 3743 4213 4231 1799 7699

CARTER EXPRESS INC p 262
4020 W 73rd St, Anderson IN 46011
Tel (765) 778-6961 SIC 4213 4212

JP HOLDING CO INC p 794
4020 W 73rd St, Anderson IN 46011
Tel (765) 778-6960 SIC 4213

ATLAS WORLD GROUP INC p 128
1212 Saint George Rd, Evansville IN 47711
Tel (812) 424-2222 SIC 4213 4731

VAN ATLAS LINES INC p 1542
1212 Saint George Rd, Evansville IN 47711
Tel (812) 424-4326 SIC 4213 4731

NORTH AMERICAN VAN LINES INC p 1050
5001 Us Highway 30 W, Fort Wayne IN 46818
Tel (260) 429-1682
SIC 4213 4731 4214 6331 7389 4212

TF INTER-HOLDINGS INC p 1445
17141 State Road 4, Goshen IN 46528
Tel (574) 533-0302 SIC 5147 4213 5144

ONLINE TRANSPORT INC p 1088
6311 W Stoner Dr, Greenfield IN 46140
Tel (317) 894-6860 SIC 4213

BULKMATIC TRANSPORT CO INC p 225
2001 N Cline Ave, Griffith IN 46319
Tel (219) 972-7630 SIC 4213 4731 4212

■ **CELADON TRUCKING SERVICES INC** p 273
9503 E 33rd St, Indianapolis IN 46235
Tel (317) 972-7000 SIC 4213 4212

HERITAGE ENVIRONMENTAL SERVICES INC p 686
7901 W Morris St, Indianapolis IN 46231
Tel (317) 243-0811
SIC 5093 4213 8731 7389 1799 8711

HERITAGE ENVIRONMENTAL SERVICES LLC p 686
7901 W Morris St, Indianapolis IN 46231
Tel (317) 243-0811
SIC 5093 4213 8731 7389 1799 8711

LIQUID TRANSPORT CORP p 870
8470 Allison Pointe Blvd # 400, Indianapolis IN 46250
Tel (317) 841-4200 SIC 4213

VITRAN EXPRESS INC p 1563
6500 E 30th St, Indianapolis IN 46219
Tel (317) 803-6400 SIC 4213

WHEATON VAN LINES INC p 1604
8010 Castleton Rd, Indianapolis IN 46250
Tel (317) 849-7900 SIC 4213 4731 4214

TOWNE HOLDINGS INC p 1466
24805 Us Highway 20, South Bend IN 46628
Tel (574) 233-3183 SIC 4213

US 1 INDUSTRIES INC p 1530
336 W Us Highway 30 # 201, Valparaiso IN 46385
Tel (219) 476-1300 SIC 4213 4731

FRICK SERVICES INC p 579
3154 Depot St, Wawaka IN 46794
Tel (260) 761-3311
SIC 5191 5153 5261 4221 2048 4213

WEAVER POPCORN CO INC p 1586
4485 S Perry Worth Rd, Whitestown IN 46075
Tel (765) 934-2101 SIC 5145 4213

CRST EXPEDITED INC p 396
1332 Edgewood Rd Sw, Cedar Rapids IA 52404
Tel (319) 396-4400 SIC 4213

CRST INTERNATIONAL INC p 396
3930 16th Ave Sw, Cedar Rapids IA 52404
Tel (319) 396-4400 SIC 4213

WEST SIDE TRANSPORT INC p 1595
4201 16th Ave Sw, Cedar Rapids IA 52404
Tel (319) 390-4466 SIC 4213

WEST SIDE UNLIMITED CORP p 1595
4201 16th Ave Sw, Cedar Rapids IA 52404
Tel (319) 390-4466 SIC 4213 7389

JACOBSON TRANSPORTATION CO INC p 775
1275 Nw 128th St, Clive IA 50325
Tel (515) 262-1236 SIC 4213 4731

ANNETT HOLDINGS INC p 92
6115 Leland Ave, Des Moines IA 50321
Tel (515) 287-6380 SIC 4213

RUAN TRANSPORT CORP p 1256
666 Grand Ave Ste 3100, Des Moines IA 50309
Tel (515) 245-2500 SIC 4213

RUAN TRANSPORTATION MANAGEMENT SYSTEMS INC p 1256
666 Grand Ave Ste 3100, Des Moines IA 50309
Tel (515) 245-2500 SIC 4213 7513

FOODLINER INC p 564
2099 Southpark Ct Ste 1, Dubuque IA 52003
Tel (563) 584-2670 SIC 4213

MCCOY GROUP INC p 927
2099 Southpark Ct, Dubuque IA 52003
Tel (563) 556-3773 SIC 5012 7538 4213

DECKER COMPANIES p 421
4000 5th Ave S, Fort Dodge IA 50501
Tel (515) 576-4141 SIC 4213

V-T INDUSTRIES INC p 1538
1000 Industrial Park, Holstein IA 51025
Tel (712) 368-4381
SIC 3089 3083 4213 2435 2434 2431

▲ **HEARTLAND EXPRESS INC** p 679
901 N Kansas Ave, North Liberty IA 52317
Tel (319) 626-3600 SIC 4213

■ **HEARTLAND EXPRESS INC OF IOWA** p 679
901 N Kansas Ave, North Liberty IA 52317
Tel (319) 626-3600 SIC 4213

RIVERSIDE TRANSPORT INC p 1238
5400 Kansas Ave, Kansas City KS 66106
Tel (913) 233-5500 SIC 4212 4213

■ **CHS MCPHERSON REFINERY INC** p 304
2000 S Main St, Mcpherson KS 67460
Tel (620) 241-2340 SIC 2911 4612 4213

TRANSAM TRUCKING INC p 1470
15910 S Us 169 Hwy, Olathe KS 66062
Tel (913) 782-5300 SIC 4213

■ **ROADWAY LLC** p 1240
10990 Roe Ave, Overland Park KS 66211
Tel (913) 344-3000 SIC 4213

■ **YRC INC** p 1639
10990 Roe Ave, Overland Park KS 66211
Tel (913) 696-6100 SIC 4213

■ **YRC REGIONAL TRANSPORTATION INC** p 1640
10990 Roe Ave, Overland Park KS 66211
Tel (913) 344-5220 SIC 4213 4231

▲ **YRC WORLDWIDE INC** p 1640
10990 Roe Ave, Overland Park KS 66211
Tel (913) 696-6100 SIC 4213

CARGILL MEAT SOLUTIONS CORP p 255
151 N Main St Ste 900, Wichita KS 67202
Tel (316) 291-2500 SIC 2011 5147 4213

PRATT (LOVE BOX) LLC p 1167
700 E 37th St N, Wichita KS 67219
Tel (316) 838-0851 SIC 2653 2448 4213

TRANSFREIGHT LLC p 1471
3940 Olympic Blvd Ste 500, Erlanger KY 41018
Tel (859) 372-5930 SIC 4213 8742

CASTELLINI CO LLC p 264
2 Plum St, Highland Heights KY 41076
Tel (800) 233-8560 SIC 5148 4212 4213

MERCER TRANSPORTATION CO INC p 944
1128 W Main St, Louisville KY 40203
Tel (502) 584-2301 SIC 4213

INTERSTATE PERSONNEL SERVICES INC p 758
3443 Us Highway 641 S, Murray KY 42071
Tel (270) 753-1717 SIC 4213

PASCHALL TRUCK LINES INC p 1119
3443 Us Highway 641 S, Murray KY 42071
Tel (270) 753-1717 SIC 4213

ACME TRUCK LINE INC p 18
200 Westbank Expy, Gretna LA 70053
Tel (504) 368-2510 SIC 4213 4212

DUPRE INVESTMENTS INC p 462
201 Energy Pkwy Ste 500, Lafayette LA 70508
Tel (337) 237-8471 SIC 4212 4213 4731

DUPRE LOGISTICS LLC p 462
201 Energy Pkwy Ste 500, Lafayette LA 70508
Tel (337) 237-8471 SIC 4213 4212

UV LOGISTICS ACQUISITION HOLDING CORP p 1537
4021 Abr Csy Py S 200 B A, Lafayette LA 70503
Tel (337) 291-6700 SIC 4213

UV LOGISTICS LLC p 1537
4021 Ambssdor Cffery Pkwy, Lafayette LA 70503
Tel (337) 837-4757 SIC 4213 1389

HARTT TRANSPORTATION SYSTEMS INC p 666
262 Bomarc Rd, Bangor ME 04401
Tel (207) 947-1106 SIC 4213

■ **SARGENT TRUCKING INC** p 1282
64 Main St, Mars Hill ME 04758
Tel (207) 429-8106 SIC 4213

COWAN SYSTEMS LLC p 385
4555 Hollins Ferry Rd, Baltimore MD 21227
Tel (410) 247-0800 SIC 4213

PERDUE FARMS INC p 1134
31149 Old Ocean City Rd, Salisbury MD 21804
Tel (410) 543-3000 SIC 2015 2075 4213

LILY TRANSPORTATION CORP p 866
145 Rosemary St Ste D3, Needham MA 02494
Tel (781) 247-1300 SIC 4213 4212

AMERICAN HOLDCO LLC p 74
448 Boston St, Topsfield MA 01983
Tel (978) 561-3800 SIC 5146 4213

M & M TRANSPORT SERVICES INC p 888
643 Manley St, West Bridgewater MA 02379
Tel (508) 521-6201 SIC 4213 4212

■ **XPO CNW INC** p 1632
2211 Old Earhart Rd, Ann Arbor MI 48105
Tel (253) 926-2251 SIC 4213 4731 3715

■ **XPO ENTERPRISE SERVICES INC** p 1632
2211 Old Earhart Rd # 100, Ann Arbor MI 48105
Tel (734) 998-4200 SIC 4213

AD TRANSPORT EXPRESS INC p 21
5601 Belleville Rd, Canton MI 48188
Tel (734) 397-7100 SIC 4213 4212

E L HOLLINGSWORTH & CO p 466
3039 Airpark Dr N, Flint MI 48507
Tel (810) 233-7331 SIC 4212 4213

SUPER SERVICE HOLDINGS LLC p 1405
6000 Clay Ave Sw, Grand Rapids MI 49548
Tel (616) 530-8551 SIC 4213

SUPER SERVICE LLC p 1405
6000 Clay Ave Sw, Grand Rapids MI 49548
Tel (616) 530-8558 SIC 4213

■ **USF HOLLAND LLC** p 1535
700 S Waverly Rd, Holland MI 49423
Tel (616) 395-5000 SIC 4213

INDIAN SUMMER COOPERATIVE INC p 738
3958 W Chauvez Rd Ste 1, Ludington MI 49431
Tel (231) 845-6248
SIC 2033 0723 4213 2035

TRANSPORTATION SERVICES INC p 1473
18165 Telegraph Rd, Romulus MI 48174
Tel (734) 282-4444 SIC 4213

UNITED ROAD SERVICES INC p 1511
10701 Middlebelt Rd, Romulus MI 48174
Tel (734) 946-3232 SIC 4213

CENTRAL TRANSPORT INTERNATIONAL INC p 280
12225 Stephens Rd, Warren MI 48089
Tel (586) 467-0100 SIC 4212 4213

CENTURION p 281
12225 Stephens Rd, Warren MI 48089
Tel (586) 939-7000 SIC 4213 4212 4581

▲ **UNIVERSAL LOGISTICS HOLDINGS INC** p 1517
12755 E 9 Mile Rd, Warren MI 48089
Tel (586) 920-0100 SIC 4213

VITRAN EXPRESS INC p 1563
12225 Stephens Rd, Warren MI 48089
Tel (317) 803-4000 SIC 4213

RUSH TRUCKING CORP p 1259
35160 E Michigan Ave, Wayne MI 48184
Tel (734) 641-1711 SIC 4213

TRANSPORT CORP OF AMERICA INC p 1472
1715 Yankee Doodle Rd # 100, Eagan MN 55121
Tel (651) 686-2500 SIC 4213

■ **SUPERVALU TRANSPORTATION INC** p 1407
11840 Valley View Rd, Eden Prairie MN 55344
Tel (952) 828-4000 SIC 4213

CENEX INC p 275
5500 Cenex Dr, Inver Grove Heights MN 55077
Tel (800) 232-3639
SIC 1311 2911 4613 4922 4789 4213

STAN KOCH & SONS TRUCKING INC p 1375
4200 Dahlberg Dr Ste 100, Minneapolis MN 55422
Tel (763) 302-5400 SIC 4213 4731

J & R SCHUGEL TRUCKING INC p 770
2026 N Broadway St, New Ulm MN 56073
Tel (800) 359-2900 SIC 4213

DEDICATED LOGISTICS INC p 421
2900 Granada Ln N, Oakdale MN 55128
Tel (651) 631-5918 SIC 4213 4212 4225

LTX INC p 883
1515 Industrial Dr Nw, Rochester MN 55901
Tel (507) 282-6715 SIC 4213

BAY & BAY TRANSFER CO INC p 160
3686 140th St E, Rosemount MN 55068
Tel (800) 273-0366 SIC 4213 4212

ANDERSON TRUCKING SERVICE INC p 90
725 Opportunity Dr, Saint Cloud MN 56301
Tel (320) 255-7400 SIC 4213

BELTMANN GROUP INC p 171
2480 Long Lake Rd, Saint Paul MN 55113
Tel (651) 639-2800 SIC 4213 4214

BERGER TRANSFER & STORAGE INC p 174
2950 Long Lake Rd, Saint Paul MN 55113
Tel (651) 639-2260 SIC 4731 4213 4214

BUCKLEY TRANSPORT LOGISTICS INC p 223
197 Airport Rd, Columbia MS 39429
Tel (601) 731-6309 SIC 4213

ERGON INC p 507
2829 Lakeland Dr Ste 2000, Flowood MS 39232
Tel (601) 933-3000
SIC 2911 4213 4449 4613 5171 5172

DEWEY CORP p 434
5500 Highway 80 W, Jackson MS 39209
Tel (601) 922-8331 SIC 4213 6719

KLLM TRANSPORT SERVICES LLC p 823
135 Riverview Dr, Jackson MS 39218
Tel (601) 939-2545 SIC 4213

STRUCTURAL STEEL HOLDING INC p 1394
6210 Saint Louis St, Meridian MS 39307
Tel (601) 483-5381 SIC 3441 3443 4213

JORDAN CARRIERS INC p 793
170 Highway 61 S, Natchez MS 39120
Tel (601) 446-8899 SIC 4213

KLLM INC p 823
135 Riverview Dr, Richland MS 39218
Tel (601) 932-8616 SIC 4213

TOTAL TRANSPORTATION OF MISSISSIPPI LLC p 1463
125 Riverview Dr, Richland MS 39218
Tel (601) 936-2104 SIC 4213

B&C HOLDING CO LLC p 142
351 Peabody Ave, Cabool MO 65689
Tel (417) 962-2300 SIC 4212 4213

MILK TRANSPORT SERVICES LP p 969
910 Shelton Dr, Cabool MO 65689
Tel (417) 962-2373 SIC 4213 4212

WESTERN DAIRY TRANSPORT LLC p 1598
910 Shelton Dr, Cabool MO 65689
Tel (417) 962-2300 SIC 4212 4213

UNIGROUP INC p 1503
1 Premier Dr, Fenton MO 63026
Tel (636) 305-5000 SIC 4213 7513 5087

CONTRACT FREIGHTERS INC p 364
4701 E 32nd St, Joplin MO 64804
Tel (417) 623-5229 SIC 4213

TRI-STATE MOTOR TRANSIT CO INC p 1478
8141 E 7th St, Joplin MO 64801
Tel (800) 234-8768 SIC 4213 4731

JACK COOPER TRANSPORT CO INC p 773
1100 Walnut St Ste 2400, Kansas City MO 64106
Tel (816) 983-4000 SIC 4213 7389

■ **KANSAS CITY SOUTHERN RAILWAY CO** p 802
427 W 12th St, Kansas City MO 64105
Tel (816) 983-1303 SIC 4011 4213

PROFFER WHOLESALE PRODUCE INC p 1180
920 5th St, Park Hills MO 63601
Tel (573) 431-0625 SIC 5148 4213

BUCHHEIT ENTERPRISES INC p 222
33 Pcr 540, Perryville MO 63775
Tel (573) 547-1010
SIC 4213 4212 5251 4225

GREGORY LOGISTICS INC p 639
2844 Fair St, Poplar Bluff MO 63901
Tel (573) 785-1088 SIC 4213 4212

CENTRAL FREIGHT MANAGEMENT LLC p 278
11500 Olive Blvd Ste 276, Saint Louis MO 63141
Tel (314) 428-9900 SIC 4213

JIH TRUCKING LLC p 785
1041 Camelot Gardens Dr, Saint Louis MO 63125
Tel (314) 487-7159 SIC 4212 4213

SLAY TRANSPORTATION CO INC p 1331
1441 Hampton Ave, Saint Louis MO 63139
Tel (314) 647-7529 SIC 4213

NEW PRIME INC p 1033
2740 N Mayfair Ave, Springfield MO 65803
Tel (800) 321-4552 SIC 4213

TCSI-TRANSLAND INC p 1428
1601 W Old Route 66, Strafford MO 65757
Tel (417) 864-5710 SIC 4213

WAGGONERS TRUCKING p 1571
5220 Midland Rd, Billings MT 59101
Tel (406) 248-1919 SIC 4213

MERGENTHALER TRANSFER & STORAGE CO INC p 948
1414 N Montana Ave, Helena MT 59601
Tel (406) 442-9470 SIC 4213 4214 7538

WASHINGTON CORPS p 1577
101 International Dr, Missoula MT 59808
Tel (406) 523-1300
SIC 5082 7353 4213 8741

WATKINS AND SHEPARD TRUCKING INC p 1582
N6400 Hwy 10W, Missoula MT 59801
Tel (406) 532-6121 SIC 4213 8299

BEHLEN MFG CO p 168
4025 E 23rd St, Columbus NE 68601
Tel (402) 564-3111
SIC 3523 3448 4213 3556 3496 3443

BEHLEN MKTG CO p 168
4025 E 23rd St, Columbus NE 68601
Tel (402) 564-3111 SIC 3523 3448 4213

CRETE CARRIER CORP p 392
400 Nw 56th St, Lincoln NE 68528
Tel (402) 475-9521 SIC 4213 4212 6512

TRANSWOOD CARRIERS INC p 1473
2565 Saint Marys Ave, Omaha NE 68105
Tel (402) 346-8092 SIC 4213 4212 7513

TRANSWOOD INC p 1473
2565 Saint Marys Ave, Omaha NE 68105
Tel (402) 346-8092 SIC 4212 4213

▲ WERNER ENTERPRISES INC p 1592
14507 Frontier Rd, Omaha NE 68138
Tel (402) 895-6640 SIC 4213

STARVING STUDENTS INC p 1379
6220 Kimberly Ave Ste 2, Las Vegas NV 89122
Tel (702) 900-4002 SIC 4214 4213

XPRESS HOLDINGS INC p 1633
3993 Howard Hughes Pkwy # 250, Las Vegas NV 89169
Tel (702) 866-6001 SIC 6719 4213

DANA TRANSPORT SYSTEM INC p 411
210 Essex Ave E, Avenel NJ 07001
Tel (732) 750-9100 SIC 4213 7513

MCCOLLISTERS TRANSPORTATION GROUP INC p 927
1800 N Route 130, Burlington NJ 08016
Tel (609) 386-0600 SIC 4213 4212

NATIONAL FREIGHT INC p 1012
1515 Burnt Mill Rd, Cherry Hill NJ 08003
Tel (856) 691-7000 SIC 7513 4213

NFI INDUSTRIES INC p 1041
1515 Burnt Mill Rd, Cherry Hill NJ 08003
Tel (856) 691-7000
SIC 4213 4212 8741 4225 4214 4783

NEW ENGLAND MOTOR FREIGHT INC p 1030
1-71 North Ave E, Elizabeth NJ 07201
Tel (908) 965-0100 SIC 4213

ARGIX DIRECT INC p 107
100 Middlesex Center Blvd, Jamesburg NJ 08831
Tel (732) 536-9173 SIC 4213 4225

WAKEFERN FOOD CORP p 1572
5000 Riverside Dr, Keasbey NJ 08832
Tel (908) 527-3300
SIC 5141 5149 5411 4213 2026

NEW CENTURY TRANSPORTATION INC p 1029
45 E Park Dr, Mount Holly NJ 08060
Tel (609) 265-1110 SIC 4213

SALSON LOGISTICS INC p 1273
888 Doremus Ave, Newark NJ 07114
Tel (973) 986-0200 SIC 4213

NATIONAL RETAIL TRANSPORTATION INC p 1016
2820 16th St, North Bergen NJ 07047
Tel (201) 866-0462 SIC 4213

FARREN INTERNATIONAL LLC p 530
1578 Sussex Tpke, Randolph NJ 07869
Tel (800) 253-3203 SIC 4213 1796 6719

BARRETT INDUSTRIES CORP p 157
3 Becker Farm Rd Ste 307, Roseland NJ 07068
Tel (973) 533-1001
SIC 1611 2951 4213 1799 1794

BARRETT PAVING MATERIALS INC p 157
3 Becker Farm Rd Ste 307, Roseland NJ 07068
Tel (973) 533-1001
SIC 1611 2951 4213 1799 1794

NYK LINE (NORTH AMERICA) INC p 1069
300 Lighting Way 4th, Secaucus NJ 07094
Tel (201) 330-3000
SIC 4412 4731 4213 4011 7519 4491

DELAWARE VALLEY FLORAL GROUP INC p 424
520 Mantua Blvd, Sewell NJ 08080
Tel (800) 676-1212 SIC 5193 4213 4214

MCCOLLISTERS TRANSPORTATION SYSTEMS OF NEW JERSEY p 927
1344 N West Blvd, Vineland NJ 08360
Tel (800) 257-9595 SIC 4213 4225 4214

AZTEC WELL SERVICING CO p 140
300 Legion Rd, Aztec NM 87410
Tel (505) 334-6194 SIC 1381 4213

MVT SERVICES LLC p 1003
3590 W Picacho Ave, Las Cruces NM 88007
Tel (915) 791-4000 SIC 4213

GYPSUM EXPRESS LTD p 649
8280 Sixty Rd, Baldwinsville NY 13027
Tel (315) 638-2201 SIC 4212 4213

RICCELLI ENTERPRISES INC p 1232
6131 E Taft Rd, North Syracuse NY 13212
Tel (315) 433-5115 SIC 4213

WADHAMS ENTERPRISES INC p 1571
369 Bostwick Rd, Phelps NY 14532
Tel (800) 334-1314 SIC 4212 4213

KENAN TRANSPORT LLC p 810
100 Europa Dr Ste 170, Chapel Hill NC 27517
Tel (919) 967-8221 SIC 4212 4213

CARDINAL LOGISTICS HOLDINGS LLC p 253
5333 Davidson Hwy, Concord NC 28027
Tel (972) 228-7300 SIC 4213 4731

CARDINAL LOGISTICS MANAGEMENT CORP p 253
5333 Davidson Hwy, Concord NC 28027
Tel (704) 786-6125 SIC 4213

CARDINAL LOGISTICS MANAGEMENT INC p 253
5333 Davidson Hwy, Concord NC 28027
Tel (704) 786-6125 SIC 4212 4213 1541

EPES CARRIERS INC p 504
3400 Edgefield Ct, Greensboro NC 27409
Tel (336) 668-3358 SIC 4213

EPES TRANSPORT SYSTEM INC p 504
3400 Edgefield Ct, Greensboro NC 27409
Tel (336) 668-3358 SIC 4213

■ XPO LOGISTICS WORLDWIDE GOVERNMENT SERVICES LLC p 1633
4035 Piedmont Pkwy, High Point NC 27265
Tel (844) 742-5976
SIC 4731 4225 4213 8741

■ XPO LOGISTICS WORLDWIDE LLC p 1633
4035 Piedmont Pkwy, High Point NC 27265
Tel (415) 486-2660 SIC 4731 4512 4213

CA PERRY & SON TRANSIT INC p 234
4033 Virginia Rd, Hobbsville NC 27946
Tel (252) 221-4463 SIC 4213 4212

EAGLE TRANSPORT CORP p 468
300 S Wesleyan Blvd # 200, Rocky Mount NC 27804
Tel (252) 937-2464 SIC 4213

▲ OLD DOMINION FREIGHT LINE INC p 1080
500 Old Dominion Way, Thomasville NC 27360
Tel (336) 889-5000 SIC 4213 4212 4731

SALEM CARRIERS INC p 1272
175 Charlois Blvd, Winston Salem NC 27103
Tel (336) 768-6800 SIC 4213 4212

SALEM HOLDING CO p 1272
175 Charlois Blvd, Winston Salem NC 27103
Tel (336) 768-6800 SIC 7513 4213

MISSOURI BASIN WELL SERVICE INC p 976
12980 35th St Sw, Belfield ND 58622
Tel (701) 575-8242 SIC 4213 1389

■ VARISTAR CORP p 1545
4334 18th Ave S Ste 200, Fargo ND 58103
Tel (701) 232-6414
SIC 6719 4899 1623 5047 1731 4213

E W WYLIE CORP p 467
1520 2nd Ave Nw, West Fargo ND 58078
Tel (701) 277-7540 SIC 4213

MIDWEST LOGISTICS SYSTEMS LTD p 967
7021 State Route 703, Celina OH 45822
Tel (419) 584-1414 SIC 4213 4212

FIRST GROUP INVESTMENT PARTNERSHIP p 547
600 Vine St Ste 1200, Cincinnati OH 45202
Tel (513) 241-2200
SIC 7513 4212 4213 4225 4151 4111

FIRSTGROUP USA INC p 550
600 Vine St Ste 1400, Cincinnati OH 45202
Tel (513) 241-2200
SIC 7513 4212 4213 4225 4151 4111

■ EUCLID CHEMICAL CO p 512
19218 Redwood Rd, Cleveland OH 44110
Tel (800) 321-7628 SIC 2899 4213

TRANSPORTATION UNLIMITED INC p 1473
3740 Carnegie Ave Ste 101, Cleveland OH 44115
Tel (216) 426-0088 SIC 7363 4213 4212

WORLD SHIPPING INC p 1625
1340 Depot St Ste 200, Cleveland OH 44116
Tel (440) 356-7676 SIC 4213 4731

DAYTON FREIGHT LINES INC p 417
6450 Poe Ave Ste 311, Dayton OH 45414
Tel (937) 264-4060 SIC 4213 4212

■ FEDEX SUPPLY CHAIN SERVICES INC p 537
5455 Darrow Rd, Hudson OH 44236
Tel (800) 588-3020
SIC 8742 4213 8741 4731

■ PANTHER PREMIUM LOGISTICS INC p 1111
84 Medina Rd, Medina OH 44256
Tel (800) 685-0657 SIC 4213 4212

LYKINS COMPANIES INC p 887
5163 Wlfpn Plsnt Hl Rd, Milford OH 45150
Tel (513) 831-8820 SIC 5172 4213 5411

MXD GROUP INC p 1004
7795 Walton Pkwy Ste 400, New Albany OH 43054
Tel (614) 895-1959 SIC 4214 4213

KUHNLE BROTHERS INC p 831
14905 Cross Creek Pkwy, Newbury OH 44065
Tel (440) 564-7168 SIC 4213 4212

DISTTECH INC p 443
4366 Mount Pleasant St Nw, North Canton OH 44720
Tel (800) 969-5419 SIC 4213

KENAN ADVANTAGE GROUP INC p 810
4366 Mount Pleasant St Nw, North Canton OH 44720
Tel (877) 999-2524 SIC 4213 4212

■ FEDEX CUSTOM CRITICAL INC p 536
1475 Boettler Rd, Uniontown OH 44685
Tel (234) 310-4090 SIC 4213

EXEL HOLDINGS (USA) INC p 518
570 Polaris Pkwy Ste 110, Westerville OH 43082
Tel (614) 865-8500 SIC 4226 4213

EXEL INC p 518
570 Polaris Pkwy, Westerville OH 43082
Tel (614) 865-8500 SIC 4213 4225 4581

R & L CARRIERS INC p 1201
600 Gilliam Rd, Wilmington OH 45177
Tel (937) 382-1494 SIC 4213

R & L TRANSFER INC p 1201
600 Gilliam Rd, Wilmington OH 45177
Tel (937) 382-1494 SIC 4213

FALCON TRANSPORT CO p 526
4944 Belmont Ave, Youngstown OH 44505
Tel (330) 793-1345 SIC 4213

GROENDYKE TRANSPORT INC p 641
2510 Rock Island Blvd, Enid OK 73701
Tel (580) 234-4663 SIC 4213

W B JOHNSTON GRAIN CO p 1568
411 W Chestnut Ave, Enid OK 73701
Tel (580) 233-5800
SIC 5153 5191 4491 4213 0111 0211

OKLAHOMA ROOF MASTERS INC p 1080
601 Evergreen Dr, Guthrie OK 73044
Tel (405) 814-6440
SIC 1761 1541 4731 4212 4213

HARRISON GYPSUM LLC p 664
1550 Double C Dr, Norman OK 73069
Tel (405) 366-9500 SIC 1499 4213

D & M CARRIERS LLC p 406
8125 Sw 15th St, Oklahoma City OK 73128
Tel (405) 491-2800 SIC 4213

JCT HOLDING CO LLC p 780
19007 W Highway 33, Sapulpa OK 74066
Tel (918) 227-1600 SIC 4213

JOHN CHRISTNER TRUCKING LLC p 788
19007 W Highway 33, Sapulpa OK 74066
Tel (918) 248-3300 SIC 4213

MELTON TRUCK LINES INC p 941
808 N 161st East Ave, Tulsa OK 74116
Tel (918) 234-1000 SIC 4213

PDV HOLDING INC p 1125
6100 S Yale Ave, Tulsa OK 74136
Tel (918) 495-4000
SIC 2911 2992 5171 4213

BEAVER EXPRESS SERVICE LLC p 166
4310 Oklahoma Ave, Woodward OK 73801
Tel (580) 256-6460 SIC 4213

S B INC p 1262
32921 Diamond Hill Dr, Harrisburg OR 97446
Tel (541) 995-7751 SIC 4213 4731

MORGAN INDUSTRIAL INC p 988
23810 Nw Huffman St, Hillsboro OR 97124
Tel (503) 647-7474 SIC 1796 4213

ENDEAVOUR CAPITAL FUND LIMITED PARTNERSHIP p 496
920 Sw 6th Ave Ste 1400, Portland OR 97204
Tel (503) 223-2721 SIC 4213 4731 6799

MARKET INDUSTRIES LTD p 908
110 N Marine Dr, Portland OR 97217
Tel (503) 283-2405 SIC 4731 4213

MARKET TRANSPORT LTD p 908
110 N Marine Dr, Portland OR 97217
Tel (503) 283-3279 SIC 4213

MAY TRUCKING CO p 923
4185 Brooklake Rd Ne, Salem OR 97303
Tel (503) 393-7030 SIC 4213

■ USF REDDAWAY INC p 1535
7720 Sw Mohawk St Bldg H, Tualatin OR 97062
Tel (503) 650-1286 SIC 4213

WARD TRUCKING LLC p 1575
1436 Ward Trucking Dr, Altoona PA 16602
Tel (814) 944-0803 SIC 4213 4214

■ MARMON DISTRIBUTION SERVICES INC p 909
225 E Cunningham St, Butler PA 16001
Tel (724) 283-3000 SIC 5051 4213

■ MARMON/KEYSTONE LLC p 909
225 E Cunningham St, Butler PA 16001
Tel (724) 283-3000 SIC 5051 4213

DAILY EXPRESS INC p 408
1072 Harrisburg Pike, Carlisle PA 17013
Tel (717) 243-5757 SIC 4213

KEEN TRANSPORT INC p 807
1951 Harrisburg Pike, Carlisle PA 17015
Tel (717) 243-6885 SIC 4213

PENN TANK LINES INC p 1129
300 Lionville Station Rd, Chester Springs PA 19425
Tel (484) 713-1500 SIC 4213

ECM TRANSPORT LLC p 475
1 Rich Hill Rd, Cheswick PA 15024
Tel (724) 339-8800 SIC 4214 4213

■ FEDEX GROUND PACKAGE SYSTEM INC p 536
1000 Fed Ex Dr, Coraopolis PA 15108
Tel (412) 269-1000 SIC 4213

TMS INTERNATIONAL CORP p 1457
12 Monongahela Ave, Glassport PA 15045
Tel (412) 678-6141
SIC 3312 4731 3399 7359 4213

TMS INTERNATIONAL HOLDING CORP p 1457
12 Monongahela Ave, Glassport PA 15045
Tel (412) 678-6141
SIC 3312 4731 3399 7359 4213

TMS INTERNATIONAL LLC p 1458
12 Monongahela Ave, Glassport PA 15045
Tel (412) 678-6141
SIC 3312 4731 3399 7359 4213

BEKINS A-1 MOVERS INC p 169
125 Stewart Rd, Hanover Township PA 18706
Tel (570) 793-2586 SIC 4213

■ NEW PENN MOTOR EXPRESS LLC p 1032
625 S 5th Ave, Lebanon PA 17042
Tel (800) 285-5000 SIC 4213 4231

PGT TRUCKING INC p 1141
1 Pgt Way, Monaca PA 15061
Tel (724) 728-3500 SIC 4213 4731

PITT-OHIO EXPRESS LLC p 1152
15 27th St, Pittsburgh PA 15222
Tel (412) 232-3015 SIC 4213

PENSKE LOGISTICS LLC p 1131
Green Hls Rr 10, Reading PA 19603
Tel (800) 529-6531 SIC 7513 4213

SMITH TRANSPORT INC p 1333
153 Smith Transport Rd, Roaring Spring PA 16673
Tel (814) 224-5155 SIC 4213

EVANS DELIVERY CO INC p 513
100 W Columbia St Ste 110, Schuylkill Haven PA 17972
Tel (570) 385-9048 SIC 4213

KANE IS ABLE INC p 802
3 Stauffer Industrial Par, Taylor PA 18517
Tel (570) 344-9801
SIC 4213 4222 4225 4214

ARPIN GROUP INC p 112
99 James P Murphy Ind Hwy, West Warwick RI 02893
Tel (401) 828-8111 SIC 4213

CONSOLIDATED SYSTEMS INC p 360
650 Rosewood Dr, Columbia SC 29201
Tel (803) 771-7920 SIC 3444 3479 4213

UTI INTEGRATED LOGISTICS LLC p 1536
700 Gervais St Ste 100, Columbia SC 29201
Tel (803) 771-6785 SIC 4226 4213

G&P TRUCKING CO INC p 587
126 Access Rd, Gaston SC 29053
Tel (803) 791-5500 SIC 4213

SOUTHEASTERN FREIGHT LINES INC p 1346
420 Davega Dr, Lexington SC 29073
Tel (803) 794-7300 SIC 4213

PICTSWEET CO p 1146
10 Pictsweet Dr, Bells TN 38006
Tel (731) 663-7600 SIC 2037 4213

PICTSWEET LLC p 1146
10 Pictsweet Dr, Bells TN 38006
Tel (731) 422-7600 SIC 4213 2037

■ COVENANT TRANSPORT INC p 384
400 Birmingham Hwy, Chattanooga TN 37419
Tel (423) 821-1212 SIC 4213

▲ COVENANT TRANSPORTATION GROUP INC p 384
400 Birmingham Hwy, Chattanooga TN 37419
Tel (423) 821-1212 SIC 4213

NEW MOUNTAIN LAKE HOLDINGS LLC p 1032
4080 Jenkins Rd, Chattanooga TN 37421
Tel (423) 510-3000 SIC 4213 4731

U S XPRESS INC p 1497
4080 Jenkins Rd, Chattanooga TN 37421
Tel (866) 266-7270 SIC 4213

US XPRESS ENTERPRISES INC p 1533
4080 Jenkins Rd, Chattanooga TN 37421
Tel (423) 510-3000 SIC 4213 4731

XPRESS GLOBAL SYSTEMS LLC p 1633
6137 Shallowford Rd # 102, Chattanooga TN 37421
Tel (706) 673-6551 SIC 4213

AVERITT EXPRESS INC p 137
1415 Neal St, Cookeville TN 38501
Tel (931) 526-3306 SIC 4214 4213

AVERITT INC p 137
1415 Neal St, Cookeville TN 38501
Tel (931) 526-3306 SIC 4213

GARDNER TRUCKING INC p 592
331 Premier Ct S, Franklin TN 37067
Tel (909) 563-5606 SIC 4213 4212

LANDAIR TRANSPORT INC p 842
1 Landair Way, Greeneville TN 37743
Tel (423) 783-1300 SIC 4213 4225

PROLOGIC DISTRIBUTION SERVICES (EAST) LLC p 1182
6016 Brookvale Ln 110b, Knoxville TN 37919
Tel (865) 584-9765 SIC 4212 4213

VENTURE EXPRESS INC p 1548
131 Industrial Blvd, La Vergne TN 37086
Tel (615) 793-9500 SIC 4213

ARMSTRONG TRANSFER AND STORAGE CO INC/ARMSTRONG RELOCATION CO MEMPHIS p 111
3927 Winchester Rd, Memphis TN 38118
Tel (901) 363-1914 SIC 4213

BARNHART CRANE AND RIGGING CO p 156
2163 Airways Blvd, Memphis TN 38114
Tel (901) 775-3000 SIC 7353 4213 1796

EMPIRE EXPRESS INC p 493
999 Channel Ave, Memphis TN 38106
Tel (901) 942-3300 SIC 4213

■ FEDERAL EXPRESS CORP p 534
3610 Hacks Cross Rd, Memphis TN 38125
Tel (901) 369-3600
SIC 4513 4512 4215 4213

▲ FEDEX CORP p 536
942 Shady Grove Rd S, Memphis TN 38120
Tel (901) 818-7500
SIC 4513 4512 4213 4215 7334

■ FEDEX FREIGHT CORP p 536
1715 Aaron Brenner Dr, Memphis TN 38120
Tel (901) 434-3100 SIC 4213 7513

KEITH DAVIS p 808
3574 Boxtown Rd, Memphis TN 38109
Tel (901) 496-6477 SIC 4213

■ MS CARRIERS INC p 996
1940 E Brooks Rd Ste 20, Memphis TN 38116
Tel (901) 332-2500 SIC 4213

OZARK MOTOR LINES INC p 1101
3934 Homewood Rd, Memphis TN 38118
Tel (901) 251-9711 SIC 4213

FIRST ENTERPRISES INC p 550
202 Heritage Park Dr, Murfreesboro TN 37129
Tel (615) 890-9229 SIC 4213

FIRSTFLEET INC p 550
202 Heritage Park Dr, Murfreesboro TN 37129
Tel (615) 890-9229 SIC 4213

QUICKWAY DISTRIBUTION SERVICES INC p 1199
1116 Polk Ave, Nashville TN 37210
Tel (615) 834-9470 SIC 4213 4212

WESTERN EXPRESS HOLDINGS INC p 1598
7135 Centennial Pl, Nashville TN 37209
Tel (615) 259-9920 SIC 4213

WESTERN EXPRESS INC p 1598
7135 Centennial Pl, Nashville TN 37209
Tel (615) 259-9920 SIC 4213

FLEETWOOD TRANSPORTATION SERVICES INC p 555
7632 S Us Highway 59, Burke TX 75941
Tel (936) 829-4735 SIC 4213

GRAEBEL VANLINES HOLDINGS LLC p 628
12790 Merit Dr Bldg 9, Dallas TX 75251
Tel (972) 694-0400 SIC 4213 4214 4212

GREATWIDE DEDICATED TRANSPORT LLC p 636
12404 Park Central Dr # 300, Dallas TX 75251
Tel (972) 228-7344 SIC 4213 4731

GREATWIDE LOGISTICS SERVICES LLC p 636
12404 Park Central Dr # 300, Dallas TX 75251
Tel (972) 228-7389 SIC 4213 4731

STEVENS TRANSPORT INC p 1388
9757 Military Pkwy, Dallas TX 75227
Tel (972) 216-9000 SIC 4213

TRANSPORTATION 100 LLC p 1472
12404 Park Central Dr 300s, Dallas TX 75251
Tel (972) 228-7300 SIC 4213 4731

LONE STAR TRANSPORTATION LLC p 876
1100 Northway Dr, Fort Worth TX 76131
Tel (817) 306-1000 SIC 4213

TEX ROBBINS TRANSPORTATION LLC p 1441
1100 Northway Dr, Fort Worth TX 76131
Tel (817) 306-1000 SIC 4213

TANGO TRANSPORT LLC p 1424
2933 Belclaire Dr, Frisco TX 75034
Tel (318) 683-6700 SIC 4213

ARNOLD TRANSPORTATION SERVICES INC p 112
3375 High Prairie Rd, Grand Prairie TX 75050
Tel (972) 986-3154 SIC 4213

BUCKEYE GP HOLDINGS LP p 223
1 Greenway Plz Ste 600, Houston TX 77046
Tel (832) 615-8600
SIC 4789 4213 4226 4212

▲ BUCKEYE PARTNERS LP p 223
1 Greenway Plz Ste 600, Houston TX 77046
Tel (832) 615-8600
SIC 4612 4789 4226 4213

■ CEVA GROUND US LP p 284
15390 Vickery Dr, Houston TX 77032
Tel (281) 227-5000 SIC 4212 4213

CITGO HOLDING INC p 309
1293 Eldridge Pkwy, Houston TX 77077
Tel (281) 531-0004
SIC 2911 2992 5171 4213

CITGO PETROLEUM CORP p 309
1293 Eldridge Pkwy, Houston TX 77077
Tel (832) 486-4000
SIC 2911 5171 4213 4612

■ KIRBY OFFSHORE MARINE LLC p 821
55 Waugh Dr Ste 1000, Houston TX 77007
Tel (713) 435-1000 SIC 5172 4212 4213

■ PLAINS MARKETING LP p 1153
333 Clay St Ste 1600, Houston TX 77002
Tel (713) 646-4100 SIC 5172 4213

TRIMAC ACTIVE INC p 1480
15333 John F Kennedy Blvd # 800, Houston TX 77032
Tel (281) 985-0000 SIC 4213

MARTIN TRANSPORT INC p 913
4200 Stone Rd, Kilgore TX 75662
Tel (281) 860-4313 SIC 4213

FFE TRANSPORTATION SERVICES INC p 539
3400 Stonewall St, Lancaster TX 75134
Tel (800) 569-9200 SIC 4213

FROZEN FOOD EXPRESS INDUSTRIES INC p 582
3400 Stonewall St, Lancaster TX 75134
Tel (800) 569-9200 SIC 4731 4213

AMERICAN HOMESTAR CORP p 74
2450 S Shore Blvd Ste 300, League City TX 77573
Tel (281) 334-9700
SIC 2451 4213 5271 6351 6515

TA SERVICES INC p 1420
241 Regency Pkwy, Mansfield TX 76063
Tel (800) 626-2185 SIC 4731 4213

DEPENDABLE AUTO SHIPPERS INC p 430
3020 U S 80 Frontage Rd, Mesquite TX 75149
Tel (214) 381-0181 SIC 4213

TFORCE ENERGY SERVICES INC p 1445
3800 E 42nd St Ste 417, Odessa TX 79762
Tel (303) 770-6511 SIC 4213

COASTAL TRANSPORT CO INC p 332
1603 Ackerman Rd, San Antonio TX 78219
Tel (210) 661-4287 SIC 4212 4213

TETCO INC p 1441
1100 Ne Loop 410 Ste 900, San Antonio TX 78209
Tel (210) 821-5900
SIC 4213 5411 1611 5193

■ TPI PETROLEUM INC p 1467
6000 N Loop 1604 W, San Antonio TX 78249
Tel (210) 592-2000
SIC 2911 5541 4612 4212 4213

■ EXXONMOBIL SAUDI ARABIA INC p 522
22777 Springwoods Vlg Pkwy, Spring TX 77389
Tel (281) 288-4545 SIC 4213

■ TRANSCO INC p 1471
4747 Mclane Pkwy, Temple TX 76504
Tel (254) 771-7500 SIC 4213

ALAN RITCHEY INC p 44
740 S Frontage Rd, Valley View TX 76272
Tel (940) 726-3276
SIC 7389 4213 2048 0291

CENTRAL FREIGHT LINES INC p 278
5601 W Waco Dr, Waco TX 76710
Tel (254) 772-2120 SIC 6719 4213

DATS TRUCKING INC p 414
321 N Old Highway 91, Hurricane UT 84737
Tel (435) 673-1886 SIC 4212 4213 5171

SAVAGE COMPANIES p 1283
901 W Legacy Center Way, Midvale UT 84047
Tel (801) 944-6600 SIC 4212 4213

■ MOTOR CARGO p 992
845 W Center St, North Salt Lake UT 84054
Tel (801) 936-1111 SIC 4213

MORRELL INTERNATIONAL INC p 990
14901 S Heritagecrest Way, Riverton UT 84065
Tel (801) 495-3111 SIC 4213 4226 5039

CR ENGLAND INC p 388
4701 W 2100 S, Salt Lake City UT 84120
Tel (800) 421-9004 SIC 4213

PRIDE TRANSPORT INC p 1174
5499 W 2455 S, Salt Lake City UT 84120
Tel (801) 972-8890 SIC 4213

TURNER GAS CO INC p 1492
2825 W 500 S, Salt Lake City UT 84104
Tel (801) 973-6886 SIC 5172 4213

CENTRAL REFRIGERATED SERVICE LLC p 280
5175 W 2100 S, West Valley City UT 84120
Tel (801) 924-7000 SIC 4213

WILSON TRUCKING CORP p 1614
137 Wilson Blvd, Fishersville VA 22939
Tel (540) 949-3200 SIC 4213

KLOCKNER PENTAPLAST OF AMERICA INC p 823
3585 Kloeckner Rd, Gordonsville VA 22942
Tel (540) 832-1400 SIC 3081 4213

KLOCKNER PENTAPLAST PARTICIPATION LLC p 823
3585 Kloeckner Rd, Gordonsville VA 22942
Tel (540) 832-3600 SIC 3081 4213

TITAN AMERICA LLC p 1456
1151 Azalea Garden Rd, Norfolk VA 23502
Tel (757) 858-6500
SIC 3241 3273 3271 4213

VIRGINIA INTERNATIONAL TERMINALS LLC p 1559
601 World Trade Ctr, Norfolk VA 23510
Tel (757) 440-7120 SIC 4491 4213

ABILENE MOTOR EXPRESS p 11
1700 Willis Rd, North Chesterfield VA 23237
Tel (804) 275-0224 SIC 4213 6221 4212

EASTERN SLEEP PRODUCTS CO p 472
4901 Fitzhugh Ave, Richmond VA 23230
Tel (804) 254-1711
SIC 2515 2512 7641 4213

ESTES EXPRESS LINES INC p 511
3901 W Broad St, Richmond VA 23230
Tel (804) 353-1900 SIC 4213

■ UPS GROUND FREIGHT INC p 1529
1000 Semmes Ave, Richmond VA 23224
Tel (866) 372-5619 SIC 4213

LAWRENCE TRANSPORTATION SYSTEMS INC p 848
872 Lee Hwy, Roanoke VA 24019
Tel (540) 966-4000 SIC 4225 4213 4212

SMOKEY POINT DISTRIBUTING INC p 1334
19201 63rd Ave Ne, Arlington WA 98223
Tel (360) 435-5737 SIC 4213 4212 4214

OAK HARBOR FREIGHT LINES INC p 1070
1339 W Valley Hwy N, Auburn WA 98001
Tel (206) 246-2600 SIC 4213 4214

TRANS-SYSTEM INC p 1470
7405 S Hayford Rd, Cheney WA 99004
Tel (509) 623-4001 SIC 4213 4731

AFF INC p 32
7400 45th Street Ct E, Fife WA 98424
Tel (253) 926-5000 SIC 4731 4213 7389

AMERICAN FAST FREIGHT INC p 72
7400 45th Street Ct E, Fife WA 98424
Tel (253) 926-5000
SIC 4731 4213 7389 4214

■ GORDON TRUCKING INC p 626
151 Stewart Rd Sw, Pacific WA 98047
Tel (253) 863-7777 SIC 4213

LYNDEN INC p 888
18000 Intl Blvd Ste 800, Seatac WA 98188
Tel (206) 241-8778 SIC 4213 4731 4424

INTERSTATE DISTRIBUTOR CO p 758
11707 21st Avenue Ct S, Tacoma WA 98444
Tel (253) 537-9455 SIC 4213

H O WOLDING INC p 650
9642 Western Way, Amherst WI 54406
Tel (715) 824-5513 SIC 4213

ASHLEY DISTRIBUTION SERVICES LTD p 117
1 Ashley Way, Arcadia WI 54612
Tel (608) 323-3377 SIC 4213

MILLIS TRANSFER INC p 971
121 Gebhardt Rd, Black River Falls WI 54615
Tel (715) 284-4384 SIC 4213 4231 4212

WEL COMPANIES INC p 1588
1625 S Broadway, De Pere WI 54115
Tel (800) 333-4415 SIC 4213

JBS PACKERLAND INC p 779
1330 Lime Kiln Rd, Green Bay WI 54311
Tel (920) 468-4000 SIC 2011 4213

PAPER TRANSPORT INC p 1112
2701 Executive Dr, Green Bay WI 54304
Tel (920) 497-6222 SIC 4213

SCHNEIDER NATIONAL INC p 1288
3101 Packerland Dr, Green Bay WI 54313
Tel (920) 592-2000 SIC 8742 4213

SCHNEIDER RESOURCES INC p 1288
3101 Packerland Dr, Green Bay WI 54313
Tel (920) 592-2000 SIC 4213

ROEHL TRANSPORT INC p 1246
1916 E 29th St, Marshfield WI 54449
Tel (715) 591-3795 SIC 4213

SCHWERMAN TRUCKING CO p 1291
611 S 28th St, Milwaukee WI 53215
Tel (414) 671-1600 SIC 4213

TANKSTAR USA INC p 1424
611 S 28th St, Milwaukee WI 53215
Tel (414) 671-3039 SIC 4213

▲ MARTEN TRANSPORT LTD p 912
129 Marten St, Mondovi WI 54755
Tel (715) 926-4216 SIC 4213

ACTIVE TRUCK TRANSPORT LLC p 20
10801 Corporate Dr, Pleasant Prairie WI 53158
Tel (800) 558-3271 SIC 4213

JHT HOLDINGS INC p 785
10801 Corporate Dr, Pleasant Prairie WI 53158
Tel (800) 558-3271 SIC 4213

HALVOR LINES INC p 655
217 Grand Ave, Superior WI 54880
Tel (715) 392-8161 SIC 4213

SIC 4214 Local Trucking With Storage

PS LOGISTICS LLC p 1187
1810 Avenue C, Birmingham AL 35218
Tel (205) 788-4000 SIC 4214 3537

JOON LLC p 793
1500 County Road 177, Cusseta AL 36852
Tel (334) 756-8601 SIC 3465 4214

COLEMAN WORLD GROUP LLC p 336
1 Eagle Ridge Dr, Midland City AL 36350
Tel (334) 803-8888 SIC 4214

MIKE CAMPBELL & ASSOCIATES LTD p 968
13031 Temple Ave, City Of Industry CA 91746
Tel (626) 369-3981
SIC 4222 4225 4214 4213

AGILITY HOLDINGS INC p 35
310 Commerce Ste 250, Irvine CA 92602
Tel (714) 617-6300 SIC 4731 4213 4214

L A HEARNE CO p 833
512 Metz Rd, King City CA 93930
Tel (831) 385-5441
SIC 5191 0723 5699 4214 2048 5261

TEOCAL TRANSPORT INC p 1439
2101 Carden St, San Leandro CA 94577
Tel (510) 569-3485 SIC 4214

TORRANCE VAN & STORAGE CO p 1462
12128 Burke St, Santa Fe Springs CA 90670
Tel (562) 567-2100 SIC 4214 4213

WEBER DISTRIBUTION WAREHOUSES p 1586
13530 Rosecrans Ave, Santa Fe Springs CA 90670
Tel (562) 356-6300 SIC 4214 4225

PORT LOGISTICS GROUP INC p 1162
288 S Mayo Ave, Walnut CA 91789
Tel (713) 439-1010 SIC 4214

GRAEBEL MOVERS INC p 628
16346 Airport Cir, Aurora CO 80011
Tel (303) 214-6683 SIC 4213 4214

JOHNSON STORAGE & MOVING CO HOLDINGS LLC p 791
7009 S Jordan Rd, Centennial CO 80112
Tel (303) 785-4300 SIC 4213 4214

SECURITY STORAGE CO OF WASHINGTON p 1299
1701 Florida Ave Nw, Washington DC 20009
Tel (202) 797-5659
SIC 4213 4226 4214 4731

SUDDATH COMPANIES p 1396
815 S Main St Ste 400, Jacksonville FL 32207
Tel (904) 390-7100 SIC 4214 4731

SUDDATH VAN LINES INC p 1396
815 S Main St Ste 400, Jacksonville FL 32207
Tel (904) 390-7100 SIC 4213 4731 4214

POSTAL FLEET SERVICES INC p 1164
2808 N 5th St Ste 501, Saint Augustine FL 32084
Tel (904) 824-2007 SIC 4214

STCHARLES TRUCKING INC p 1383
650 N Raddant Rd, Batavia IL 60510
Tel (630) 584-4285 SIC 4214

BEELMAN TRUCK CO p 168
1 Racehorse Dr, East Saint Louis IL 62205
Tel (618) 646-5300 SIC 4214

CHAS LEVY CIRCULATING CO p 291
1930 George St Ste 4, Melrose Park IL 60160
Tel (708) 356-3600 SIC 4213 4214 5192

CUSTOM COMPANIES INC p 403
317 W Lake St, Northlake IL 60164
Tel (708) 344-5555 SIC 4731 4214

SIRVA INC p 1327
1 Parkview Plz, Oakbrook Terrace IL 60181
Tel (630) 570-3047
SIC 4213 4214 4731 7513 6331

SIRVA WORLDWIDE INC p 1327
1 Parkview Plz Ste 300, Oakbrook Terrace IL 60181
Tel (630) 570-3047
SIC 4213 4214 4731 7513 6331

FIDELITONE INC p 540
1260 Karl Ct, Wauconda IL 60084
Tel (847) 487-3300 SIC 4214

NORTH AMERICAN VAN LINES INC p 1050
5001 Us Highway 30 W, Fort Wayne IN 46818
Tel (260) 429-1682
SIC 4213 4731 4214 6331 7389 4212

WHEATON VAN LINES INC p 1604
8010 Castleton Rd, Indianapolis IN 46250
Tel (317) 849-7900 SIC 4213 4731 4214

COASTAL SUNBELT INC p 332
9001 Whiskey Bottom Rd, Laurel MD 20723
Tel (410) 799-8000
SIC 5148 4214 0723 2099

■ UNIVERSAL DEDICATED INC p 1516
12755 E 9 Mile Rd, Warren MI 48089
Tel (800) 233-9445 SIC 4214

BATTMANN HOLDINGS INC p 160
2480 Long Lake Rd, Saint Paul MN 55113
Tel (651) 639-2800 SIC 4214

BELTMANN GROUP INC p 171
2480 Long Lake Rd, Saint Paul MN 55113
Tel (651) 639-2800 SIC 4213 4214

BERGER TRANSFER & STORAGE INC p 174
2950 Long Lake Rd, Saint Paul MN 55113
Tel (651) 639-2260 SIC 4731 4213 4214

WAGNER INDUSTRIES INC p 1571
1201 E 12th Ave, North Kansas City MO 64116
Tel (816) 421-3520 SIC 4225 4214 4731

MERGENTHALER TRANSFER & STORAGE CO INC p 948
1414 N Montana Ave, Helena MT 59601
Tel (406) 442-9470 SIC 4213 4214 7538

STARVING STUDENTS INC p 1379
6220 Kimberly Ave Ste 2, Las Vegas NV 89122
Tel (702) 900-4002 SIC 4214 4213

NFI INDUSTRIES INC p 1041
1515 Burnt Mill Rd, Cherry Hill NJ 08003
Tel (856) 691-7000
SIC 4213 4212 8741 4225 4214 4783

DAMCO DISTRIBUTION SERVICES INC p 410
180 Park Ave Ste 105, Florham Park NJ 07932
Tel (973) 514-5000 SIC 4214 4225

DYNAMIC INTERNATIONAL USA INC p 464
2501 71st St, North Bergen NJ 07047
Tel (973) 344-6300 SIC 4214

DELAWARE VALLEY FLORAL GROUP INC p 424
520 Mantua Blvd, Sewell NJ 08080
Tel (800) 676-1212 SIC 5193 4213 4214

MCCOLLISTERS TRANSPORTATION SYSTEMS OF NEW JERSEY p 927
1344 N West Blvd, Vineland NJ 08360
Tel (800) 257-9595 SIC 4213 4225 4214

MXD GROUP INC p 1004
7795 Walton Pkwy Ste 400, New Albany OH 43054
Tel (614) 895-1959 SIC 4214 4213

WARD TRANSPORT & LOGISTICS CORP p 1575
1436 Ward Trucking Dr, Altoona PA 16602
Tel (814) 944-0803 SIC 4214

WARD TRUCKING LLC p 1575
1436 Ward Trucking Dr, Altoona PA 16602
Tel (814) 944-0803 SIC 4213 4214

ECM TRANSPORT LLC p 475
1 Rich Hill Rd, Cheswick PA 15024
Tel (724) 339-8800 SIC 4214 4213

KANE IS ABLE INC p 802
3 Stauffer Industrial Par, Taylor PA 18517
Tel (570) 344-9801
SIC 4213 4222 4225 4214

A DUIE PYLE INC p 5
650 Westtown Rd, West Chester PA 19382
Tel (610) 696-5800 SIC 4214 4225 7519

■ A&S SERVICES GROUP LLC p 7
310 N Zarfoss Dr, York PA 17404
Tel (717) 235-2456 SIC 4214 4225

BONNIE BERSCHEID p 200
800 N Lewis Ave, Sioux Falls SD 57103
Tel (605) 359-8208 SIC 4214

AVERITT EXPRESS INC p 137
1415 Neal St, Cookeville TN 38501
Tel (931) 526-3306 SIC 4214 4213

GRAEBEL VANLINES HOLDINGS LLC p 628
12790 Merit Dr Bldg 9, Dallas TX 75251
Tel (972) 694-0400 SIC 4213 4214 4212

OMNITRACS LLC p 1085
717 N Harwood St Ste 1300, Dallas TX 75201
Tel (888) 627-2716 SIC 8741 4214

TTS LLC p 1490
11000 Frisco St Ste 100, Frisco TX 75033
Tel (214) 778-0800 SIC 4214

■ CEVA FREIGHT LLC p 284
15350 Vickery Dr, Houston TX 77032
Tel (281) 618-3100
SIC 4214 4225 4412 4512 4522 4731

PLG HOLDINGS INC p 1156
1 Greenway Plz Ste 400, Houston TX 77046
Tel (713) 439-1010 SIC 4214

FITE DISTRIBUTION SERVICES CO LP p 552
1001 Donaldson Ave, San Antonio TX 78228
Tel (210) 736-3141 SIC 4214 4225

LAND-AIR EXPRESS OF NEW ENGLAND LTD p 842
59 Avenue C, Williston VT 05495
Tel (800) 639-3095 SIC 4214

SMOKEY POINT DISTRIBUTING INC p 1334
19201 63rd Ave Ne, Arlington WA 98223
Tel (360) 435-5737 SIC 4213 4212 4214

OAK HARBOR FREIGHT LINES INC p 1070
1339 W Valley Hwy N, Auburn WA 98001
Tel (206) 246-2600 SIC 4213 4214

EAGLE GROUP SYSTEMS INC p 468
230 Grant Rd, East Wenatchee WA 98802
Tel (509) 665-0319
SIC 4214 4119 4522 7373 7374 8741

AMERICAN FAST FREIGHT INC p 72
7400 45th Street Ct E, Fife WA 98424
Tel (253) 926-5000
SIC 4731 4213 7389 4214

SIC 4215 Courier Svcs, Except Air

EXPRESS MESSENGER SYSTEMS INC p 520
2501 S Price Rd Ste 201, Chandler AZ 85286
Tel (800) 334-5000 SIC 4215

GOLDEN STATE OVERNIGHT DELIVERY SERVICE INC p 621
7901 Stoneridge Dr Ste 400, Pleasanton CA 94588
Tel (800) 322-5555 SIC 4215

■ MENLO WORLDWIDE FORWARDING INC p 943
1 Lagoon Dr Ste 400, Redwood City CA 94065
Tel (650) 596-9600
SIC 4513 4215 4522 4731 6159 6351

ATI SYSTEMS INTERNATIONAL INC p 124
2000 Nw Corp Blvd Ste 101, Boca Raton FL 33431
Tel (561) 939-7000 SIC 7381 4513 4215

BEAVEX INC p 166
2120 Powers Ferry Rd Se, Atlanta GA 30339
Tel (404) 260-0961 SIC 4215 4513

UNITED PARCEL SERVICE INC p 1510
55 Glenlake Pkwy, Atlanta GA 30328
Tel (404) 828-6000 SIC 4215

▲ UNITED PARCEL SERVICE INC p 1510
55 Glenlake Pkwy, Atlanta GA 30328
Tel (404) 828-6000 SIC 4215 4513 4522

■ UPS SUPPLY CHAIN SOLUTIONS GENERAL SERVICES INC p 1529
55 Glenlake Pkwy, Atlanta GA 30328
Tel (404) 828-6000 SIC 4215

BENNETT MOTOR EXPRESS LLC p 173
1001 Industrial Pkwy, Mcdonough GA 30253
Tel (770) 957-1866 SIC 4213 4212 4215

EAGLE EXPRESS LINES INC p 468
925 175th St, Homewood IL 60430
Tel (708) 333-8401 SIC 4213 4215 4212

EASTERN CONNECTION OPERATING INC p 472
60 Olympia Ave Ste 2, Woburn MA 01801
Tel (800) 795-2872 SIC 4215

EVERGREEN HOLDINGS INC p 514
3850 Ne Three Mile Ln, Mcminnville OR 97128
Tel (503) 472-0011 SIC 4522 4513 4215

EVERGREEN INTERNATIONAL AVIATION INC p 514
3850 Ne Three Mile Ln, Mcminnville OR 97128
Tel (503) 472-0011 SIC 4522 4513 4215

AMERICAN EXPEDITING CO p 72
801 Primos Ave, Folcroft PA 19032
Tel (484) 540-8180 SIC 4215 4513

■ **FEDERAL EXPRESS CORP** p 534
3610 Hacks Cross Rd, Memphis TN 38125
Tel (901) 369-3600
SIC 4513 4512 4215 4213

▲ **FEDEX CORP** p 536
942 Shady Grove Rd S, Memphis TN 38120
Tel (901) 818-7500
SIC 4513 4512 4213 4215 7334

LONE STAR HOLDINGS LLC p 875
6500 River Place Blvd # 2, Austin TX 78730
Tel (512) 873-8067 SIC 4215 4513 4212

GREYHOUND LINES INC p 639
350 N Saint Paul St # 300, Dallas TX 75201
Tel (214) 849-8000 SIC 4111 4215 4142

TF COURIER INC p 1445
5429 Lyndon B Johnson Fwy, Dallas TX 75240
Tel (214) 560-9000 SIC 4513 4215 8741

TF FINAL MILE LLC p 1445
5429 Lbj Fwy Ste 900, Dallas TX 75240
Tel (214) 560-9000 SIC 4215 4513

TFI HOLDINGS USA INC p 1445
5429 L B Johnson Fwy 10 Ste 1000, Dallas TX 75240
Tel (877) 396-2639 SIC 4215 8741 4513

■ **UPS FREIGHT SERVICES INC** p 1529
1000 Semmes Ave, Richmond VA 23224
Tel (804) 231-8000 SIC 4215

SIC 4221 Farm Product Warehousing & Storage

BAYOU GRAIN & CHEMICAL CORP p 162
P.O. Box 67, Parkdale AR 71661
Tel (870) 473-2281 SIC 4221 2873 5153

GRAINLAND COOPERATIVE p 629
421 S Colorado Ave, Haxtun CO 80731
Tel (970) 774-6166
SIC 5191 4221 5531 5541

TOP FLIGHT GRAIN MONTICELLO CO p 1460
420 W Marion St, Monticello IL 61856
Tel (217) 762-2163 SIC 5153 5191 4221

CONSOLIDATED GRAIN & BARGE CO p 359
Washington & Water St, Wayne City IL 62895
Tel (618) 895-2181
SIC 4221 5153 4449 4491

FRICK SERVICES INC p 579
3154 Depot St, Wawaka IN 46794
Tel (260) 761-3311
SIC 5191 5153 5261 4221 2048 4213

JHCI HOLDINGS INC p 785
1275 Nw 128th St, Clive IA 50325
Tel (515) 265-6171 SIC 4226 4221 4225

JACOBSON WAREHOUSE CO INC p 775
3811 Dixon St, Des Moines IA 50313
Tel (515) 265-6171
SIC 4226 4221 4225 8741 6552 4783

AGMARK LLC p 35
118 W Main St, Beloit KS 67420
Tel (785) 738-9641 SIC 4221

GREAT BEND COOPERATIVE ASSOCIATION p 633
606 Main St, Great Bend KS 67530
Tel (620) 793-3531
SIC 5153 5191 5171 4221

MIDLAND MARKETING CO-OP INC p 966
219 E 9th St, Hays KS 67601
Tel (785) 625-5138
SIC 5153 5191 5541 5171 4221

KANZA COOPERATIVE ASSOCIATION p 803
102 N Main St, Iuka KS 67066
Tel (620) 546-2231
SIC 5153 5191 5541 4221

SCOTT COOPERATIVE ASSOCIATION INC p 1293
410 E 1st St, Scott City KS 67871
Tel (620) 872-5823
SIC 5153 5541 5191 4221

CGB ENTERPRISES INC p 285
1127 Hwy 190 E Service Rd, Covington LA 70433
Tel (985) 867-3500 SIC 4221 5191 4491

WESTERN CONSOLIDATED COOPERATIVE p 1597
520 County Road 9, Holloway MN 56249
Tel (320) 394-2171 SIC 5153 4221 2875

■ **GENERAL MILLS OPERATIONS LLC** p 601
1 General Mills Blvd, Minneapolis MN 55426
Tel (763) 764-7600 SIC 4221

RIVERLAND AG CORP p 1237
1660 Highway 100 S # 350, Minneapolis MN 55416
Tel (952) 746-6800 SIC 5153 4221

STAPLE COTTON CO-OPERATIVE ASSOCIATION p 1377
214 W Market St, Greenwood MS 38930
Tel (662) 453-6231 SIC 5159 4221 6159

WEST PLAINS LLC p 1595
11500 N Ambassador Dr # 250, Kansas City MO 64153
Tel (816) 270-4000 SIC 5153 4221

AG PROCESSING INC p 33
12700 W Dodge Rd, Omaha NE 68154
Tel (402) 496-7809 SIC 4221

GAVILON GRAIN LLC p 594
1331 Capitol Ave, Omaha NE 68102
Tel (402) 889-4000
SIC 6221 5153 4221 4226

WATERTOWN COOPERATIVE ELEVATOR ASSOCIATION p 1582
811 Burlington Northern D, Watertown SD 57201
Tel (605) 886-8333 SIC 5153 5191 4221

DUNAVANT ENTERPRISES INC p 461
959 Ridg Loop Rd Ste 200, Memphis TN 38120
Tel (901) 369-1500
SIC 5159 4221 4731 0131

UNITED AGRICULTURAL COOPERATIVE INC p 1506
911 S Wharton St, El Campo TX 77437
Tel (979) 543-6284
SIC 5251 0724 5083 4221 5153

PLAINS COTTON COOPERATIVE ASSOCIATION p 1153
3301 E 50th St, Lubbock TX 79404
Tel (806) 763-8011 SIC 5159 4221

RITZVILLE WAREHOUSE CO p 1237
201 E 1st Ave, Ritzville WA 99169
Tel (509) 659-0130 SIC 5153 4221

LANDMARK SERVICES COOPERATIVE p 843
1401 Landmark Dr, Cottage Grove WI 53527
Tel (608) 819-3115
SIC 4221 5171 5191 1711

SIC 4222 Refrigerated Warehousing & Storage

MIKE CAMPBELL & ASSOCIATES LTD p 968
13031 Temple Ave, City Of Industry CA 91746
Tel (626) 369-3981
SIC 4222 4225 4214 4213

AMERICOLD LOGISTICS LLC p 82
19840 S Rancho Way, Compton CA 90220
Tel (310) 635-4993 SIC 4222

VERSACOLD US INC p 1551
19840 S Rancho Way, Compton CA 90220
Tel (310) 632-6265 SIC 4222

LINEAGE LOGISTICS HOLDINGS LLC p 868
17911 Von Karman Ave # 400, Irvine CA 92614
Tel (800) 678-7271 SIC 4222

LINEAGE LOGISTICS LLC p 868
17911 Von Karman Ave # 400, Irvine CA 92614
Tel (800) 678-7271 SIC 4222

CANTON FOOD CO INC p 247
750 S Alameda St, Los Angeles CA 90021
Tel (213) 688-7707
SIC 5141 5146 5411 5421 5149 4222

R W ZANT CO p 1203
1470 E 4th St, Los Angeles CA 90033
Tel (323) 980-5457
SIC 5147 5146 5144 4222

PACIFIC COAST CONTAINER INC p 1104
432 Estudillo Ave Ste 1, San Leandro CA 94577
Tel (510) 346-6100 SIC 4789 4225 4222

COASTAL PACIFIC FOOD DISTRIBUTORS INC p 332
1015 Performance Dr, Stockton CA 95206
Tel (909) 947-2066
SIC 5141 4225 7519 4222

RED CHAMBER CO p 1215
1912 E Vernon Ave, Vernon CA 90058
Tel (323) 234-9000 SIC 5146 4222

BURRIS LOGISTICS p 228
501 Se 5th St, Milford DE 19963
Tel (302) 839-4531 SIC 5142 4222 4213

SOUTHEAST FROZEN FOODS CO LP p 1345
3261 Executive Way, Miramar FL 33025
Tel (954) 882-1044 SIC 5142 4222 5411

AMERICOLD LOGISTICS LLC p 82
10 Glenlake Pkwy Ste 324, Atlanta GA 30328
Tel (678) 441-1400
SIC 4222 4899 8742 7389

AMERICOLD REALTY TRUST p 82
10 Glenlk Pkwy Ste 600, Atlanta GA 30328
Tel (404) 394-1312 SIC 4222

NORDIC LOGISTICS AND WAREHOUSING LLC p 1048
4300 Pleasantdale Rd, Atlanta GA 30340
Tel (770) 448-7400 SIC 4222

SYNCREON TECHNOLOGY (USA) LLC p 1415
1200 N Greenbriar Dr, Addison IL 60101
Tel (630) 261-3100 SIC 7389 4222

INTERSTATE WAREHOUSING OF VIRGINIA LLC p 758
9009 Coldwater Rd Ste 300, Fort Wayne IN 46825
Tel (260) 490-3000 SIC 4222

DERBY INDUSTRIES LLC p 431
4451 Robards Ln, Louisville KY 40218
Tel (502) 451-7373
SIC 4225 7389 4222 4226

LUIGINOS INC p 884
1325 Port Terminal Rd, Duluth MN 55802
Tel (218) 722-1427 SIC 4222 4225

CERNX MN LLC p 284
2355 Highway 36 W Ste 400, Roseville MN 55113
Tel (320) 372-7400
SIC 4212 7389 4731 4222

MILLARD REFRIGERATED SERVICES LLC p 970
13030 Pierce St, Omaha NE 68144
Tel (402) 896-6600 SIC 4222

PREFERRED FREEZER SERVICES INC p 1169
1 Main St Fl 3, Chatham NJ 07928
Tel (973) 820-4040 SIC 4222

UNITED STATES COLD STORAGE INC p 1512
201 Laurel Rd Ste 400, Voorhees NJ 08043
Tel (856) 354-8181 SIC 2097 4222

G & C FOOD DISTRIBUTORS & BROKERS INC p 586
3407 Walters Rd, Syracuse NY 13209
Tel (315) 422-3191 SIC 5147 5146 4222

WINN-DIXIE CHARLOTTE INC p 1616
2401 Nevada Blvd, Charlotte NC 28273
Tel (704) 587-4000
SIC 5411 8741 5141 4226 4222

NAUMES INC p 1019
2 W Barnett St, Medford OR 97501
Tel (541) 772-6268 SIC 0175 0723 4222

CLEMENS FAMILY CORP p 325
2700 Clemens Rd, Hatfield PA 19440
Tel (800) 523-5291
SIC 0213 2011 4222 8661

KANE IS ABLE INC p 802
3 Stauffer Industrial Par, Taylor PA 18517
Tel (570) 344-9801
SIC 4213 4222 4225 4214

PLAZA PROVISION CO (PUERTO RICO) p 1156
Carretera 165 Esq, Guaynabo PR 00965
Tel (787) 781-2070 SIC 5182 4222 2841

TROUT-BLUE CHELAN-MAGI INC p 1484
8 Howser Rd, Chelan WA 98816
Tel (509) 682-2591 SIC 0723 0175 4222

ZIRKLE FRUIT CO p 1643
352 Harrison Rd, Selah WA 98942
Tel (509) 697-6101 SIC 0175 0723 4222

HOLTZINGER FRUIT CO INC p 702
1312 N 6th Ave, Yakima WA 98902
Tel (509) 457-5115 SIC 5148 4222

SIC 4225 General Warehousing & Storage

LG ELECTRONICS ALABAMA INC p 860
201 James Record Rd Sw, Huntsville AL 35824
Tel (256) 772-0623
SIC 3651 3695 5064 5085 5065 4225

B R WILLIAMS TRUCKING INC p 142
2339 Al Highway 21 S, Oxford AL 36203
Tel (256) 831-5580 SIC 4213 4225

▲ **MOBILE MINI INC** p 980
4646 E Van Buren St # 400, Phoenix AZ 85008
Tel (480) 894-6311
SIC 4225 3448 3441 3412 7359

SWIFT TRANSPORTATION CO INC p 1412
2200 S 75th Ave, Phoenix AZ 85043
Tel (602) 269-9700 SIC 4213 4225

APL LOGISTICS WAREHOUSE MANAGEMENT SERVICES INC p 97
16220 N Scottsdale Rd # 300, Scottsdale AZ 85254
Tel (480) 483-0886 SIC 4213 4225

MIKE CAMPBELL & ASSOCIATES LTD p 968
13031 Temple Ave, City Of Industry CA 91746
Tel (626) 369-3981
SIC 4222 4225 4214 4213

PERFORMANCE TEAM FREIGHT SYS INC p 1135
2240 E Maple Ave, El Segundo CA 90245
Tel (562) 345-2200 SIC 4731 4225 4213

WORLD CLASS DISTRIBUTION INC p 1625
10288 Calabash Ave, Fontana CA 92335
Tel (909) 574-4140 SIC 4225

▲ **PUBLIC STORAGE** p 1190
701 Western Ave, Glendale CA 91201
Tel (818) 244-8080 SIC 6798 4225

DAHN CORP p 408
18552 Macarthur Blvd # 495, Irvine CA 92612
Tel (949) 752-1282 SIC 1531 6531 4225

DEPENDABLE HIGHWAY EXPRESS INC p 430
2555 E Olympic Blvd, Los Angeles CA 90023
Tel (323) 526-2200 SIC 4213 4225

BIAGI BROS INC p 181
787 Airpark Rd, Napa CA 94558
Tel (707) 745-8115 SIC 4213 4225

CJ KOREA EXPRESS USA CORP p 320
18805 S Laurel Park Rd, Rancho Dominguez CA 90220
Tel (714) 994-1200 SIC 4731 4783 4225

■ **XPO LOGISTICS WORLDWIDE INC** p 1633
560 Mission St Ste 2950, San Francisco CA 94105
Tel (415) 486-2660
SIC 4731 4225 4213 8741

PACIFIC COAST CONTAINER INC p 1104
432 Estudillo Ave Ste 1, San Leandro CA 94577
Tel (510) 346-6100 SIC 4789 4225 4222

HITACHI DATA SYSTEMS CORP p 696
2845 Lafayette St, Santa Clara CA 95050
Tel (408) 970-1000
SIC 5045 7378 7379 5734 4225 3571

WEBER DISTRIBUTION WAREHOUSES p 1586
13530 Rosecrans Ave, Santa Fe Springs CA 90670
Tel (562) 356-6300 SIC 4214 4225

COASTAL PACIFIC FOOD DISTRIBUTORS INC p 332
1015 Performance Dr, Stockton CA 95206
Tel (909) 947-2066
SIC 5141 4225 7519 4222

GRAEBEL HOLDINGS INC p 628
16346 Airport Cir, Aurora CO 80011
Tel (303) 214-6683 SIC 4213 4225 6719

PODS ENTERPRISES LLC p 1158
5585 Rio Vista Dr, Clearwater FL 33760
Tel (727) 538-6300 SIC 4225 6794

■ **CSX INTERMODAL INC** p 398
500 Water St, Jacksonville FL 32202
Tel (904) 633-1000 SIC 4213 4011 4225

SADDLE CREEK CORP p 1265
3010 Saddle Creek Rd, Lakeland FL 33801
Tel (863) 665-0966 SIC 4225

BROWN INTEGRATED LOGISTICS INC p 219
6908 Chapman Rd, Lithonia GA 30058
Tel (770) 482-6521
SIC 4225 4213 4731 7359

LMS INTELLIBOUND INC p 872
6525 The Corners Pkwy, Norcross GA 30092
Tel (770) 724-0564 SIC 4225

HARP BUSINESS SERVICES INC p 662
2725 Northwoods Pkwy A2, Peachtree Corners GA 30071
Tel (678) 482-0675 SIC 2759 4225 5699

■ **AMERITECH SERVICES INC** p 84
208 S Lasalle St Ste 814, Chicago IL 60604
Tel (847) 248-2000
SIC 7389 4225 8742 8721

VIRONEX INC p 1560
4350 W Ohio St, Chicago IL 60624
Tel (773) 265-0403 SIC 4225

JDM STEEL SERVICE INC p 781
330 E Joe Orr Rd Unit 3, Chicago Heights IL 60411
Tel (708) 757-2092 SIC 5051 4225

DSC LOGISTICS INC p 457
1750 S Wolf Rd, Des Plaines IL 60018
Tel (847) 390-6800
SIC 4225 4213 4212 4731

FEDERAL WAREHOUSE CO p 536
200 National St, East Peoria IL 61611
Tel (309) 694-4500 SIC 4225 4213 4212

■ **CAT LOGISTICS INC** p 264
500 N Morton Ave, Morton IL 61550
Tel (309) 675-1000 SIC 4225 5045 4213

■ **CATERPILLAR LOGISTICS INC** p 265
500 N Morton Ave, Morton IL 61550
Tel (309) 266-3591 SIC 4225

SCHWARZ PAPER CO LLC p 1291
8338 Austin Ave, Morton Grove IL 60053
Tel (847) 966-2550 SIC 2621 5199 4225

LESAINT LOGISTICS LLC p 857
868 W Crossroads Pkwy, Romeoville IL 60446
Tel (630) 243-5950 SIC 4731 4225 8742

■ **CH ROBINSON FREIGHT SERVICES LTD** p 286
1501 N Mittel Blvd Ste A, Wood Dale IL 60191
Tel (630) 766-4445 SIC 4731 4225

KEM KREST LLC p 809
3221 Magnum Dr, Elkhart IN 46516
Tel (574) 389-2650
SIC 5169 5013 5085 4783 4225

▲ **CELADON GROUP INC** p 273
9503 E 33rd St, Indianapolis IN 46235
Tel (317) 972-7000 SIC 4212 4225

MAHOMED SALES & WAREHOUSING LLC p 897
8258 Zionsville Rd, Indianapolis IN 46268
Tel (317) 472-5800 SIC 4225 3714

JHCI HOLDINGS INC p 785
1275 Nw 128th St, Clive IA 50325
Tel (515) 265-6171 SIC 4226 4221 4225

NETWORK IMAGING SOLUTIONS INC p 1028
242 E 90th St, Davenport IA 52806
Tel (563) 285-6123 SIC 4225

JACOBSON WAREHOUSE CO INC p 775
3811 Dixon St, Des Moines IA 50313
Tel (515) 265-6171
SIC 4226 4221 4225 8741 6552 4783

JHCI ACQUISITION INC p 785
3811 Dixon St, Des Moines IA 50313
Tel (515) 265-6171 SIC 4225

MIQ HOLDINGS INC p 974
11501 Outlook St Ste 500, Overland Park KS 66211
Tel (913) 696-7363 SIC 4225 4731 8741

DERBY INDUSTRIES LLC p 431
4451 Robards Ln, Louisville KY 40218
Tel (502) 451-7373
SIC 4225 7389 4222 4226

VERST GROUP LOGISTICS INC p 1552
300 Shorland Dr, Walton KY 41094
Tel (859) 485-1212 SIC 4225 7389

WILLIAMS SCOTSMAN INTERNATIONAL INC p 1611
901 S Bond St Ste 600, Baltimore MD 21231
Tel (800) 782-1500 SIC 4225

L B & B ASSOCIATES INC p 833
9891 Broken Land Pkwy # 400, Columbia MD 21046
Tel (301) 621-3944
SIC 8744 7338 4225 8742 8748 4581

BARRETT DISTRIBUTION CENTERS INC p 157
15 Freedom Way, Franklin MA 02038
Tel (508) 528-1747 SIC 4225

HOLLINGSWORTH LOGISTICS MANAGEMENT LLC p 701
14225 W Warren Ave, Dearborn MI 48126
Tel (313) 768-1400 SIC 4225 4783

BENORE LOGISTIC SYSTEMS INC p 173
2500 E Erie Rd, Erie MI 48133
Tel (734) 848-2046 SIC 4225

THYSSENKRUPP INDUSTRIAL SERVICES NA INC p 1451
22355 W 11 Mile Rd, Southfield MI 48033
Tel (248) 233-5600 SIC 4225 4731

LUIGINOS INC p 884
1325 Port Terminal Rd, Duluth MN 55802
Tel (218) 722-1427 SIC 4222 4225

■ **SUPERMARKET OPERATORS OF AMERICA INC** p 1407
11840 Valley View Rd, Eden Prairie MN 55344
Tel (952) 828-4000 SIC 5411 4225

DEDICATED LOGISTICS INC p 421
2900 Granada Ln N, Oakdale MN 55128
Tel (651) 631-5918 SIC 4213 4212 4225

ARCHWAY MARKETING SERVICES INC p 105
19850 S Diamond Lake Rd, Rogers MN 55374
Tel (763) 428-3300 SIC 8742 4225

WESTERN OIL INC p 1599
3553 Rider Trl S, Earth City MO 63045
Tel (314) 738-9900
SIC 5541 5411 7542 4225

WAGNER INDUSTRIES INC p 1571
1201 E 12th Ave, North Kansas City MO 64116
Tel (816) 421-3520 SIC 4225 4214 4731

BUCHHEIT ENTERPRISES INC p 222
33 Pcr 540, Perryville MO 63775
Tel (573) 547-1010
SIC 4213 4212 5251 4225

SPORTSMANS DISTRIBUTION CO p 1360
2500 E Kearney St, Springfield MO 65898
Tel (417) 873-5000 SIC 4225

ITS LOGISTICS LLC p 768
620 Spice Islands Dr, Reno NV 89501
Tel (775) 358-5300 SIC 4731 4225

NATIONAL DISTRIBUTION CENTERS LP p 1011
1515 Burnt Mill Rd, Cherry Hill NJ 08003
Tel (856) 691-7000 SIC 4225

NFI INDUSTRIES INC p 1041
1515 Burnt Mill Rd, Cherry Hill NJ 08003
Tel (856) 691-7000
SIC 4213 4212 8741 4225 4214 4783

ARGENT ASSOCIATES INC p 107
140 Fieldcrest Ave, Edison NJ 08837
Tel (732) 512-9009 *SIC* 4225

CLEAN VENTURE INC p 324
201 S 1st St, Elizabeth NJ 07206
Tel (908) 355-5800
SIC 4225 4212 4953 8748

KMM TELECOMMUNICATIONS INC p 824
9 Law Dr Ste 13, Fairfield NJ 07004
Tel (844) 566-8488 *SIC* 7629 4225

DAMCO DISTRIBUTION SERVICES INC p 410
180 Park Ave Ste 105, Florham Park NJ 07932
Tel (973) 514-5000 *SIC* 4214 4225

UNIMAVEN INC p 1503
74 Green St, Hackensack NJ 07601
Tel (201) 500-8050 *SIC* 4225

CEI HOLDINGS INC p 273
2182 State Route 35, Holmdel NJ 07733
Tel (732) 888-7788
SIC 2844 7389 4225 5122

COSMETIC ESSENCE LLC p 373
2182 Hwy 35, Holmdel NJ 07733
Tel (732) 888-7788 *SIC* 2844 7389 4225

GEODIS WILSON USA INC p 605
485c Us Highway 1 S # 410, Iselin NJ 08830
Tel (732) 362-0600 *SIC* 4731 4412 4225

H & M INTERNATIONAL TRANSPORTATION INC p 649
485b Us Highway 1 S # 110, Iselin NJ 08830
Tel (732) 510-4640 *SIC* 4731 8741 4225

ARGIX DIRECT INC p 107
100 Middlesex Center Blvd, Jamesburg NJ 08831
Tel (732) 536-9173 *SIC* 4213 4225

MCCOLLISTERS TRANSPORTATION SYSTEMS OF NEW JERSEY p 927
1344 N West Blvd, Vineland NJ 08360
Tel (800) 257-9595 *SIC* 4213 4225 4214

ROMARK LOGISTICS LLC p 1249
822 South Ave W, Westfield NJ 07090
Tel (908) 789-2800 *SIC* 4225 4789 2631

CUSTOMIZED DISTRIBUTION SERVICES INC p 403
20 Harry Shupe Blvd, Wharton NJ 07885
Tel (973) 366-5090 *SIC* 4225

WWL VEHICLE SERVICES AMERICAS INC p 1629
188 Broadway Ste 1, Woodcliff Lake NJ 07677
Tel (201) 505-5100 *SIC* 4225 5531 7549

RINCHEM CO INC p 1235
5131 Masthead St Ne, Albuquerque NM 87109
Tel (505) 998-4300 *SIC* 4789 4225

BOGOPA SERVICE CORP p 197
650 Fountain Ave, Brooklyn NY 11208
Tel (718) 257-7801 *SIC* 5411 4225 5149

SCHENKER INC p 1286
150 Albany Ave, Freeport NY 11520
Tel (516) 377-3000 *SIC* 4731 4225

NIPPON EXPRESS USA INC p 1044
2401 44th Rd Fl 14, Long Island City NY 11101
Tel (212) 758-6100 *SIC* 4731 4225

GEORGE G SHARP INC p 606
160 Broadway, New York NY 10038
Tel (212) 732-2800 *SIC* 3731 4225 8712

TOYOTA TSUSHO AMERICA INC p 1467
805 3rd Ave Fl 17, New York NY 10022
Tel (212) 355-3600
SIC 5051 5013 4225 6331 5153

LIGHTING HOLDINGS INTERNATIONAL LLC p 865
4 Manhattanville Rd, Purchase NY 10577
Tel (845) 306-1850
SIC 3641 5719 5063 4225 3643 3229

■ **XPO LOGISTICS WORLDWIDE GOVERNMENT SERVICES LLC** p 1633
4035 Piedmont Pkwy, High Point NC 27265
Tel (844) 742-5976
SIC 4731 4225 4213 8741

FIRST GROUP INVESTMENT PARTNERSHIP p 547
600 Vine St Ste 1200, Cincinnati OH 45202
Tel (513) 241-2200
SIC 7513 4212 4213 4225 4151 4111

FIRSTGROUP USA INC p 550
600 Vine St Ste 1400, Cincinnati OH 45202
Tel (513) 241-2200
SIC 7513 4212 4213 4225 4151 4111

ODW LOGISTICS INC p 1074
1580 Williams Rd, Columbus OH 43207
Tel (614) 497-1660 *SIC* 4225 4226

WORKFLOWONE LLC p 1624
220 E Monument Ave, Dayton OH 45402
Tel (877) 735-4966
SIC 2754 2791 4225 4731 2752 2759

BIG SANDY DISTRIBUTION INC p 182
8375 Gallia Pike, Franklin Furnace OH 45629
Tel (740) 574-2113 *SIC* 4225

FALCON PACKAGING LLC p 526
1359 Sater St, Greenville OH 45331
Tel (937) 547-9800 *SIC* 7389 4225

FARO SERVICES INC p 530
7070 Pontius Rd, Groveport OH 43125
Tel (614) 497-1700 *SIC* 4225 4731

EXEL INC p 518
570 Polaris Pkwy, Westerville OH 43082
Tel (614) 865-8500 *SIC* 4213 4225 4581

COMPREHENSIVE LOGISTICS CO INC p 352
4944 Belmont Ave Ste 202, Youngstown OH 44505
Tel (800) 734-0372 *SIC* 4225 4731

EAST PENN MANUFACTURING CO p 470
102 Deka Rd, Lyon Station PA 19536
Tel (610) 682-6361
SIC 3694 3691 5063 4225

CUBESMART LP p 399
5 Old Lancaster Rd, Malvern PA 19355
Tel (610) 535-5700 *SIC* 4225 6798

■ **ATC TECHNOLOGY CORP** p 124
100 Papercraft Park, Pittsburgh PA 15238
Tel (412) 820-3700 *SIC* 1541 3694 4225

■ **GENCO DISTRIBUTION SYSTEM INC** p 598
100 Papercraft Park, Pittsburgh PA 15238
Tel (412) 820-3700 *SIC* 4225 4731

■ **GENCO TRANSPORTATION MANAGEMENT LLC** p 598
100 Papercraft Park, Pittsburgh PA 15238
Tel (412) 820-3700
SIC 4225 4111 5045 4789

■ **I GENCO INC** p 725
100 Papercraft Park, Pittsburgh PA 15238
Tel (800) 677-3110 *SIC* 4225 4111 5045

KANE IS ABLE INC p 802
3 Stauffer Industrial Par, Taylor PA 18517
Tel (570) 344-9801
SIC 4213 4222 4225 4214

A DUIE PYLE INC p 5
650 Westtown Rd, West Chester PA 19382
Tel (610) 696-5800 *SIC* 4214 4225 7519

■ **A&S SERVICES GROUP LLC** p 7
310 N Zarfoss Dr, York PA 17404
Tel (717) 235-2456 *SIC* 4214 4225

WAREHOUSE SERVICES INC p 1575
58 S Burty Rd, Piedmont SC 29673
Tel (812) 831-4053 *SIC* 1541 4225

GEODIS LOGISTICS LLC p 605
7101 Executive Center Dr # 333, Brentwood TN 37027
Tel (615) 401-6400
SIC 4225 8742 4226 4731

OZBURN-HESSEY HOLDING CO LLC p 1101
7101 Executive Center Dr # 333, Brentwood TN 37027
Tel (615) 401-6400 *SIC* 4225 8742

KENCO GROUP INC p 810
2001 Rverside Dr Ste 3100, Chattanooga TN 37406
Tel (423) 622-1113 *SIC* 4225 6512

KENCO LOGISTIC SERVICES INC p 810
520 W 31st St, Chattanooga TN 37410
Tel (423) 756-5552 *SIC* 4225 4783

LANDAIR TRANSPORT INC p 842
1 Landair Way, Greeneville TN 37743
Tel (423) 783-1300 *SIC* 4213 4225

MALLORY ALEXANDER INTERNATIONAL LOGISTICS LLC p 900
4294 Swinnea Rd, Memphis TN 38118
Tel (901) 367-9400 *SIC* 4731 4225 4789

■ **SUSA PARTNERSHIP LP** p 1409
175 Toyota Plz, Memphis TN 38103
Tel (901) 252-2000 *SIC* 4225

TCW INC p 1428
22 Stanley St, Nashville TN 37210
Tel (615) 255-1122 *SIC* 4731 4225

■ **ATC LOGISTICS & ELECTRONICS INC** p 124
13500 Independence Pkwy, Fort Worth TX 76177
Tel (817) 491-7700 *SIC* 4225 3714 3694

FTS INTERNATIONAL SERVICES LLC p 583
777 Main St Ste 2900, Fort Worth TX 76102
Tel (817) 850-1008
SIC 3561 8711 7353 4225

MAALT LP p 891
4413 Carey St, Fort Worth TX 76119
Tel (817) 205-0460 *SIC* 4225 4731

AGILITY PROJECT LOGISTICS INC p 35
15600 Morales Rd, Houston TX 77032
Tel (504) 465-1000 *SIC* 4731 4225

■ **CEVA FREIGHT LLC** p 284
15350 Vickery Dr, Houston TX 77032
Tel (281) 618-3100
SIC 4214 4225 4412 4512 4522 4731

GULF WINDS INTERNATIONAL INC p 647
411 Brisbane St, Houston TX 77061
Tel (713) 747-4909 *SIC* 4225 4731

FITE DISTRIBUTION SERVICES CO LP p 552
1001 Donaldson Ave, San Antonio TX 78228
Tel (210) 736-3141 *SIC* 4214 4225

SAN ANTONIO FOOD BANK p 1275
5200 Enrique M Barrera Pa, San Antonio TX 78227
Tel (210) 337-3663 *SIC* 4225 8322

THOMAS PETROLEUM LLC p 1449
9701 Us Highway 59 N, Victoria TX 77905
Tel (361) 582-5100 *SIC* 5171 4225

■ **EXTRA SPACE MANAGEMENT INC** p 521
2795 E Cottonwood Pkwy # 400, Salt Lake City UT 84121
Tel (801) 562-5556 *SIC* 4225

LIMETREE BAY TERMINALS LLC p 866
1 Estate Hope, Christiansted VI 00820
Tel (340) 692-3000 *SIC* 4225

■ **DOLLAR TREE DISTRIBUTION INC** p 448
500 Volvo Pkwy, Chesapeake VA 23320
Tel (757) 321-5000 *SIC* 4225

LAWRENCE TRANSPORTATION SYSTEMS INC p 848
872 Lee Hwy, Roanoke VA 24019
Tel (540) 966-4000 *SIC* 4225 4213 4212

FISHER AUTO PARTS INC p 552
512 Greenville Ave, Staunton VA 24401
Tel (540) 885-8901 *SIC* 5013 5531 4225

EXEL GLOBAL LOGISTICS INC p 518
22879 Glenn Dr Ste 100, Sterling VA 20164
Tel (703) 350-1298 *SIC* 4731 4225

NOEL CORP p 1046
1001 S 1st St, Yakima WA 98901
Tel (509) 248-4545
SIC 2086 7389 4212 6512 4225 5962

MATERIAL LOGISTICS & SERVICES LLC p 919
1160 N Mayflower Dr, Appleton WI 54913
Tel (920) 830-5000 *SIC* 4225

VAN HOOF CORP p 1542
1160 N Mayflower Dr, Appleton WI 54913
Tel (920) 830-5000 *SIC* 4225

WAREHOUSE SPECIALISTS LLC p 1575
1160 N Mayflower Dr, Appleton WI 54913
Tel (920) 830-5000 *SIC* 4225

WOW LOGISTICS CO p 1627
3040 W Wisconsin Ave, Appleton WI 54914
Tel (800) 236-3565 *SIC* 4225

SCHNEIDER LOGISTICS INC p 1288
3101 Packerland Dr, Green Bay WI 54313
Tel (920) 592-0000
SIC 4731 4225 4789 4212

SIC 4226 Special Warehousing & Storage, NEC

■ **U-HAUL INTERNATIONAL INC** p 1498
2727 N Central Ave, Phoenix AZ 85004
Tel (602) 263-6011
SIC 7513 7519 7359 5531 4226 8741

KW INTERNATIONAL INC p 832
18655 Bishop Ave, Carson CA 90746
Tel (310) 747-1380 *SIC* 4731 4226 8744

■ **U-HAUL CO OF CALIFORNIA** p 1497
44511 S Grimmer Blvd, Fremont CA 94538
Tel (800) 528-0463 *SIC* 7513 7519 4226

RETRIEVEX ACQUISITION CORP II p 1229
6818 Patterson Pass Rd, Livermore CA 94550
Tel (925) 583-0100 *SIC* 4226 7375

CALIFORNIA CARTAGE CO LLC p 239
2931 Redondo Ave, Long Beach CA 90806
Tel (562) 427-1143 *SIC* 4226 8741 8721

PRIDE INDUSTRIES p 1174
10030 Foothills Blvd, Roseville CA 95747
Tel (916) 788-2100 *SIC* 4226 7349 3679

XIOTECH CORP p 1631
9950 Federal Dr Unit 100, Colorado Springs CO 80921
Tel (719) 388-5500 *SIC* 3572 4226

SECURITY STORAGE CO OF WASHINGTON p 1299
1701 Florida Ave Nw, Washington DC 20009
Tel (202) 797-5659
SIC 4213 4226 4214 4731

■ **CEVA LOGISTICS US GROUP INC** p 285
10751 Deerwood Park Blvd, Jacksonville FL 32256
Tel (904) 928-1400 *SIC* 4213 4226

■ **CEVA LOGISTICS US HOLDINGS INC** p 285
10751 Deerwood Park Blvd # 201, Jacksonville FL 32256
Tel (904) 928-1400 *SIC* 4213 4226

COLONIAL PIPELINE CO p 338
1185 Sanctuary Pkwy # 100, Alpharetta GA 30009
Tel (678) 762-2200
SIC 4613 4612 4226 1389 5171

COLONIAL GROUP INC p 337
101 N Lathrop Ave, Savannah GA 31415
Tel (800) 944-3835
SIC 5171 5169 5172 4924 4492 4226

■ **WASHINGTON CLOSURE CO LLC** p 1577
720 E Park Blvd Bsmt, Boise ID 83712
Tel (208) 386-5000
SIC 4959 1799 1795 4226

GREAT LAKES SYNERGY CORP p 634
85 W Algonquin Rd Ste 600, Arlington Heights IL 60005
Tel (847) 437-0200 *SIC* 5084 4226 4213

GROUP O INC p 642
4905 77th Ave E, Milan IL 61264
Tel (309) 736-8100
SIC 8742 7389 4226 5085

WIRE AMERICA INC p 1618
1613 E Wallace St, Fort Wayne IN 46803
Tel (260) 969-1700 *SIC* 4226 3357

STRACK AND VAN TIL SUPER MARKET INC p 1392
9632 Cline Ave, Highland IN 46322
Tel (219) 924-6932 *SIC* 5411 8741 4226

JHCI HOLDINGS INC p 785
1275 Nw 128th St, Clive IA 50325
Tel (515) 265-6171 *SIC* 4226 4221 4225

JACOBSON WAREHOUSE CO INC p 775
3811 Dixon St, Des Moines IA 50313
Tel (515) 265-6171
SIC 4226 4221 4225 8741 6552 4783

■ **AMAZON.COMKYDC LLC** p 65
1850 Mercer Rd, Lexington KY 40511
Tel (859) 381-2102 *SIC* 4226

DERBY INDUSTRIES LLC p 431
4451 Robards Ln, Louisville KY 40218
Tel (502) 451-7373
SIC 4225 7389 4222 4226

CONTANDA LLC p 362
365 Canal St Ste 2900, New Orleans LA 70130
Tel (504) 525-9741 *SIC* 4226 2048

■ **INTERNATIONAL-MATEX TANK TERMINALS** p 757
321 Saint Charles Ave, New Orleans LA 70130
Tel (504) 586-8300 *SIC* 4226 1799

SURE WINNER FOODS INC p 1408
2 Lehner Rd, Saco ME 04072
Tel (207) 282-1258 *SIC* 5143 4226 2024

▲ **IRON MOUNTAIN INC** p 764
1 Federal St Fl 7, Boston MA 02110
Tel (617) 535-4766
SIC 4226 8741 7375 6798

■ **IRON MOUNTAIN INFORMATION MANAGEMENT LLC** p 765
1 Federal St, Boston MA 02110
Tel (617) 357-4455 *SIC* 4226

STERILITE CORP p 1386
30 Scales Ln, Townsend MA 01469
Tel (978) 597-1000 *SIC* 3089 4226

TRELLEBORG CORP p 1476
200 Veterans Blvd Ste 3, South Haven MI 49090
Tel (269) 639-9891
SIC 3341 1021 1044 1031 4226 1041

OMNI WORKSPACE CO LLC p 1085
1300 Washington Ave N # 200, Minneapolis MN 55411
Tel (612) 627-1600 *SIC* 7641 4212 4226

GOODWILL INDUSTRIES INC p 624
553 Fairview Ave N, Saint Paul MN 55104
Tel (651) 379-5800
SIC 4953 8331 8322 5932 4226

APEX HOLDING CO p 96
8235 Forsyth Blvd Ste 400, Saint Louis MO 63105
Tel (314) 889-9600 *SIC* 6792 4412 4226

GAVILON GRAIN LLC p 594
1331 Capitol Ave, Omaha NE 68102
Tel (402) 889-4000
SIC 6221 5153 4221 4226

■ **NORTHERN NATURAL GAS CO** p 1056
1111 S 103rd St, Omaha NE 68124
Tel (877) 654-0646
SIC 4226 4922 4923 4925

▲ **AMERCO** p 66
5555 Kietzke Ln Ste 100, Reno NV 89511
Tel (775) 688-6300 *SIC* 7513 7519 4226

KUEHNE CHEMICAL CO INC p 831
86 N Hackensack Ave, Kearny NJ 07032
Tel (973) 589-0700 *SIC* 2819 4226 2812

HELM AMERICA CORP p 682
1110 Centennial Ave Ste 2, Piscataway NJ 08854
Tel (732) 981-1160
SIC 5169 5122 5191 4231 4226

A & E STORES INC p 4
1000 Huyler St, Teterboro NJ 07608
Tel (201) 393-0600
SIC 5621 8721 4226 7389

WINN-DIXIE CHARLOTTE INC p 1616
2401 Nevada Blvd, Charlotte NC 28273
Tel (704) 587-4000
SIC 5411 8741 5141 4226 4222

AMERIMARK DIRECT LLC p 82
6864 Engle Rd, Cleveland OH 44130
Tel (440) 826-1900 *SIC* 4226 5961 7331

AMERIMARK HOLDINGS LLC p 82
6864 Engle Rd, Cleveland OH 44130
Tel (440) 325-2000 *SIC* 5961 4226 7331

ODW LOGISTICS INC p 1074
1580 Williams Rd, Columbus OH 43207
Tel (614) 497-1660 *SIC* 4225 4226

HONDA LOGISTICS NORTH AMERICA INC p 704
11590 Township Road 298, East Liberty OH 43319
Tel (937) 642-0335 *SIC* 4226

MIDWEST EXPRESS INC p 967
11590 Township Road 298, East Liberty OH 43319
Tel (937) 642-0335 *SIC* 4226

EXEL HOLDINGS (USA) INC p 518
570 Polaris Pkwy Ste 110, Westerville OH 43082
Tel (614) 865-8500 *SIC* 4226 4213

CHOCTAW ARCHIVING ENTERPRISE p 301
2101 W Arkansas St, Durant OK 74701
Tel (580) 920-1501 *SIC* 8711 4226

▲ **BLUEKNIGHT ENERGY PARTNERS LP** p 193
201 Nw 10th St Ste 200, Oklahoma City OK 73103
Tel (405) 278-6400 *SIC* 4612 4226

EDM AMERICAS INC p 478
10 Ed Preate Dr, Moosic PA 18507
Tel (800) 852-9809
SIC 4226 7389 7334 8741

UTI INTEGRATED LOGISTICS LLC p 1536
700 Gervais St Ste 100, Columbia SC 29201
Tel (803) 771-6785 *SIC* 4226 4213

SO-PAK-CO INC p 1336
118 S Cypress St, Mullins SC 29574
Tel (423) 639-1163 *SIC* 2099 4226

GEODIS LOGISTICS LLC p 605
7101 Executive Center Dr # 333, Brentwood TN 37027
Tel (615) 401-6400
SIC 4225 8742 4226 4731

UNAKA CO INC p 1502
1500 Industrial Rd, Greeneville TN 37745
Tel (423) 639-1171
SIC 2099 3469 2514 2253 4226

BUCKEYE GP HOLDINGS LP p 223
1 Greenway Plz Ste 600, Houston TX 77046
Tel (832) 615-8600
SIC 4789 4213 4226 4212

▲ **BUCKEYE PARTNERS LP** p 223
1 Greenway Plz Ste 600, Houston TX 77046
Tel (832) 615-8600
SIC 4612 4789 4226 4213

■ **KINDER MORGAN ENERGY PARTNERS LP** p 819
1001 La St Ste 1000, Houston TX 77002
Tel (713) 369-9000
SIC 4613 4925 4922 4226 4619 5171

■ **KINDER MORGAN LIQUIDS TERMINALS LLC** p 819
500 Dallas St Ste 1000, Houston TX 77002
Tel (713) 369-8758 *SIC* 4226

VOPAK NORTH AMERICA INC p 1565
2000 West Loop S Ste 1550, Houston TX 77027
Tel (713) 561-7200
SIC 4491 4226 4953 4789

▲ **MARTIN MIDSTREAM PARTNERS LP** p 913
4200 Stone Rd, Kilgore TX 75662
Tel (903) 983-6200
SIC 5171 4226 1321 4424 2819 2875

▲ **NUSTAR ENERGY LP** p 1067
19003 W Ih 10, San Antonio TX 78257
Tel (210) 918-2000 *SIC* 4612 4613 4226

MORRELL INTERNATIONAL INC p 990
14901 S Heritagecrest Way, Riverton UT 84065
Tel (801) 495-3111 *SIC* 4213 4226 5039

J K MOVING & STORAGE INC p 771
44112 Mercure Cir Ste 1, Sterling VA 20166
Tel (703) 260-4282 *SIC* 4226

AUTO WAREHOUSING CO INC p 133
2810 Marshall Ave Ste B, Tacoma WA 98421
Tel (253) 719-1700 *SIC* 4226

GOODWILL RETAIL SERVICES INC p 625
5400 S 60th St, Greendale WI 53129
Tel (414) 847-4200 *SIC* 5651 4226

SIC 4231 Terminal & Joint Terminal Maint Facilities

▲ **SWIFT TRANSPORTATION CO** p 1412
2200 S 75th Ave, Phoenix AZ 85043
Tel (602) 269-9700 *SIC* 4213 4231

SEASIDE TRANSPORTATION SERVICES LLC p 1297
389 Terminal Way, San Pedro CA 90731
Tel (310) 241-1760 *SIC* 4231

CASSENS TRANSPORT CO p 263
145 N Kansas St, Edwardsville IL 62025
Tel (618) 656-3006 SIC 4213 4231

CONGLOBAL INDUSTRIES LLC p 356
8200 185th St Ste A, Tinley Park IL 60487
Tel (925) 543-0977
SIC 3743 4213 4231 1799 7699

VENTURE LOGISTICS LLC p 1548
1101 Harding Ct, Indianapolis IN 46217
Tel (888) 561-4449 SIC 4231

■YRC REGIONAL TRANSPORTATION INC p 1640
10990 Roe Ave, Overland Park KS 66211
Tel (913) 344-5220 SIC 4213 4231

RSI LOGISTICS INC p 1256
2419 Science Pkwy, Okemos MI 48864
Tel (517) 349-7713 SIC 8742 4231

MILLER TRANSPORTATION SERVICES INC p 971
5500 Highway 80 W, Jackson MS 39209
Tel (601) 856-6526 SIC 4231

HELM AMERICA CORP p 682
1110 Centennial Ave Ste 2, Piscataway NJ 08854
Tel (732) 981-1160
SIC 5169 5122 5191 4231 4226

WESTERN FLYER EXPRESS LLC p 1598
5204 W I 40 Service Rd, Oklahoma City OK 73128
Tel (405) 946-7289 SIC 4231

■ NEW PENN MOTOR EXPRESS LLC p 1032
625 S 5th Ave, Lebanon PA 17042
Tel (800) 285-5000 SIC 4213 4231

MILLIS TRANSFER INC p 971
121 Gebhardt Rd, Black River Falls WI 54615
Tel (715) 284-4384 SIC 4213 4231 4212

SIC 4311 Postal Service

UNITED STATES POSTAL SERVICE p 1514
475 Lenfant Plz Sw # 4012, Washington DC 20260
Tel (202) 268-2000 SIC 4311

SIC 4412 Deep Sea Foreign Transportation Of Freight

INTERNATIONAL SHIPHOLDING CORP p 756
29000 Us Highway 98 C201, Daphne AL 36526
Tel (251) 243-9100 SIC 4412 4424

AMERICAN PRESIDENT LINES LTD p 77
16220 N Scottsdale Rd, Scottsdale AZ 85254
Tel (602) 586-4894 SIC 4412 4424 4491

APL LOGISTICS LTD p 97
16220 N Scottsdale Rd # 300, Scottsdale AZ 85254
Tel (602) 586-4800
SIC 4412 4731 4491 4011

■TEXACO INC p 1441
6001 Bollinger Canyon Rd, San Ramon CA 94583
Tel (925) 842-1000
SIC 5541 5511 1321 4612 4613 4412

▲ EAGLE BULK SHIPPING INC p 467
300 Frst Stamford Pl Fl 5, Stamford CT 06902
Tel (203) 276-8100 SIC 4412

RESOLVE MARINE GROUP INC p 1227
1510 Se 17th St Ste 400, Fort Lauderdale FL 33316
Tel (954) 764-8700
SIC 4499 4492 4491 4412 7389

▲ SEACOR HOLDINGS INC p 1296
2200 Eller Dr, Fort Lauderdale FL 33316
Tel (954) 523-2200
SIC 4412 4424 4449 4959 8748

CROWLEY HOLDINGS INC p 394
9487 Regency Square Blvd # 101, Jacksonville FL 32225
Tel (904) 727-2200
SIC 4412 4424 5171 5172 5541 4492

CROWLEY MARITIME CORP p 395
9487 Regency Square Blvd, Jacksonville FL 32225
Tel (904) 727-2200
SIC 4412 4424 5171 5172 5541 4492

CROWLEY PETROLEUM SERVICES INC p 395
9487 Regency Square Blvd, Jacksonville FL 32225
Tel (904) 727-2200 SIC 4412 4424

■ SEABOARD MARINE LTD INC p 1295
8001 Nw 79th Ave, Medley FL 33166
Tel (305) 863-4444 SIC 4412

■ BIRDSALL INC p 185
5 E 11th St, Riviera Beach FL 33404
Tel (561) 881-3900 SIC 4412

TROPICAL SHIPPING USA LLC p 1484
501 Avenue P, Riviera Beach FL 33404
Tel (561) 863-5737 SIC 4412 4789

MOL (AMERICA) INC p 982
700 E Bttrfeld Rd Ste 250, Lombard IL 60148
Tel (630) 424-3480 SIC 4731 7373 4412

▲ SEABOARD CORP p 1295
9000 W 67th St, Merriam KS 66202
Tel (913) 676-8800
SIC 2011 0133 4412 6221 0723 0213

APEX HOLDING CO p 96
8235 Forsyth Blvd Ste 400, Saint Louis MO 63105
Tel (314) 889-9600 SIC 6792 4412 4226

APEX OIL CO INC p 96
8235 Forsyth Blvd Ste 400, Saint Louis MO 63105
Tel (314) 889-9600 SIC 4412 5084

DAMCO USA INC p 410
180 Park Ave Ste 105, Florham Park NJ 07932
Tel (973) 514-5000 SIC 4412 4491 4731

MAERSK INC p 894
180 Park Ave Ste 105, Florham Park NJ 07932
Tel (973) 514-5000 SIC 4731 4491 4412

GEODIS WILSON USA INC p 605
485c Us Highway 1 S # 410, Iselin NJ 08830
Tel (732) 362-0600 SIC 4731 4412 4225

NYK GROUP AMERICAS INC p 1069
300 Lighting Way Ste 500, Secaucus NJ 07094
Tel (201) 330-3000
SIC 4412 4731 4011 4491 7519

NYK LINE (NORTH AMERICA) INC p 1069
300 Lighting Way 4th, Secaucus NJ 07094
Tel (201) 330-3000
SIC 4412 4731 4213 4011 7519 4491

ATLANTIC CONTAINER LINE AB p 126
50 Cardinal Dr, Westfield NJ 07090
Tel (908) 518-5300 SIC 4412

WALLENIUS WILHELMSEN LOGISTICS AMERICAS LLC p 1573
188 Broadway Ste 1, Woodcliff Lake NJ 07677
Tel (201) 307-1300 SIC 4412

FAIRFIELD-MAXWELL LTD p 525
60 E 42nd St Fl 55, New York NY 10165
Tel (212) 297-9030
SIC 8741 4731 5172 4412

▲ GENCO SHIPPING & TRADING LTD p 598
299 Park Ave Rm 1200, New York NY 10171
Tel (646) 443-8550 SIC 4412

GENER8 MARITIME INC p 599
299 Park Ave Fl 2, New York NY 10171
Tel (212) 763-5600 SIC 4412

▲ OVERSEAS SHIPHOLDING GROUP INC p 1099
600 3rd Ave, New York NY 10016
Tel (212) 953-4100 SIC 4412 4424

TAL INTERNATIONAL GROUP INC p 1422
100 Manhattanville Rd # 13, Purchase NY 10577
Tel (914) 251-9000 SIC 7359 5085 4412

HORIZON LINES LLC p 707
2550 W Tyvola Rd Ste 530, Charlotte NC 28217
Tel (877) 678-7447
SIC 4424 4783 4731 4412

■ MATSON ALASKA INC p 920
2550 W Tyvola Rd, Charlotte NC 28217
Tel (704) 973-7000 SIC 4424 4731 4412

KEYSTONE SHIPPING CO p 816
1 Bala Plz Ste 600, Bala Cynwyd PA 19004
Tel (610) 617-6800 SIC 4731 4412 4424

PANGAEA LOGISTICS SOLUTIONS LTD p 1111
109 Long Wharf, Newport RI 02840
Tel (401) 846-7790 SIC 4412

■ CEVA FREIGHT LLC p 284
15350 Vickery Dr, Houston TX 77032
Tel (281) 618-3100
SIC 4214 4225 4412 4512 4522 4731

▲ GULFMARK OFFSHORE INC p 647
842 W Sam Houston Pkwy N, Houston TX 77024
Tel (713) 963-9522 SIC 4412

TRICO MARINE SERVICES INC p 1479
3200 Southwest Fwy # 2950, Houston TX 77027
Tel (888) 369-8929 SIC 4412

UTC OVERSEAS INC p 1536
2 Northpoint Dr Ste 213, Houston TX 77060
Tel (713) 422-2850 SIC 4412 4581

PERIMETER INTERNATIONAL p 1136
2700 Story Rd W Ste 150, Irving TX 75038
Tel (877) 701-1919
SIC 7389 4412 4731 4581 4449

K LINE AMERICA INC p 799
8730 Stony Point Pkwy # 400, Richmond VA 23235
Tel (804) 560-3600 SIC 4412 4491

FOSS MARITIME CO p 570
1151 Fairview Ave N, Seattle WA 98109
Tel (206) 281-4001
SIC 4412 4424 4492 4491 3731 4959

SALTCHUK RESOURCES INC p 1273
1111 Fairview Ave N, Seattle WA 98109
Tel (206) 652-1111 SIC 4492 4412 4499

SIC 4424 Deep Sea Domestic Transportation Of Freight

INTERNATIONAL SHIPHOLDING CORP p 756
29000 Us Highway 98 C201, Daphne AL 36526
Tel (251) 243-9100 SIC 4412 4424

AMERICAN PRESIDENT LINES LTD p 77
16220 N Scottsdale Rd, Scottsdale AZ 85254
Tel (602) 586-4894 SIC 4412 4424 4491

■ MATSON NAVIGATION CO INC p 920
555 12th St, Oakland CA 94607
Tel (510) 628-4000 SIC 4424 4491 4492

■ SEABULK INTERNATIONAL INC p 1296
2200 Eller Dr, Fort Lauderdale FL 33316
Tel (954) 828-1701 SIC 4424 4492

▲ SEACOR HOLDINGS INC p 1296
2200 Eller Dr, Fort Lauderdale FL 33316
Tel (954) 523-2200
SIC 4412 4424 4449 4959 8748

CROWLEY AMERICAN TRANSPORT INC p 394
9487 Regency Square Blvd, Jacksonville FL 32225
Tel (904) 727-2200 SIC 4424

CROWLEY HOLDINGS INC p 394
9487 Regency Square Blvd # 101, Jacksonville FL 32225
Tel (904) 727-2200
SIC 4412 4424 5171 5172 5541 4492

CROWLEY LINER SERVICES INC p 395
9487 Regency Square Blvd # 101, Jacksonville FL 32225
Tel (904) 727-2200 SIC 4424

CROWLEY MARITIME CORP p 395
9487 Regency Square Blvd, Jacksonville FL 32225
Tel (904) 727-2200
SIC 4412 4424 5171 5172 5541 4492

CROWLEY PETROLEUM SERVICES INC p 395
9487 Regency Square Blvd, Jacksonville FL 32225
Tel (904) 727-2200 SIC 4412 4424

TECO ENERGY INC p 1432
702 N Franklin St, Tampa FL 33602
Tel (813) 228-1111
SIC 4911 4924 4424 1221 1222

UNITED MARITIME GROUP LLC p 1510
601 S Harbour Island Blvd, Tampa FL 33602
Tel (813) 209-4200 SIC 4449 4424

BP AMERICA INC p 205
4101 Winfield Rd Ste 200, Warrenville IL 60555
Tel (630) 420-5111
SIC 2911 5171 4612 4613 4424

CARI INVESTMENT CO LLC p 256
222 N Vermont St, Covington LA 70433
Tel (985) 635-6009
SIC 6211 4424 3731 5146

■ SEACOR MARINE LLC p 1296
7910 Main St Ste 200, Houma LA 70360
Tel (985) 858-6427 SIC 4424

CANAL BARGE CO INC p 246
835 Union St Ste 300, New Orleans LA 70112
Tel (504) 581-2424 SIC 4449 4424 5171

▲ TIDEWATER INC p 1452
601 Poydras St Ste 1500, New Orleans LA 70130
Tel (504) 568-1010 SIC 4424 4493 4492

MCALLISTER BROTHERS INC p 925
17 Battery Pl Ste 1200, New York NY 10004
Tel (212) 269-3200 SIC 4424

▲ OVERSEAS SHIPHOLDING GROUP INC p 1099
600 3rd Ave, New York NY 10016
Tel (212) 953-4100 SIC 4412 4424

HORIZON LINES LLC p 707
2550 W Tyvola Rd Ste 530, Charlotte NC 28217
Tel (877) 678-7447
SIC 4424 4783 4731 4412

■ MATSON ALASKA INC p 920
2550 W Tyvola Rd, Charlotte NC 28217
Tel (704) 973-7000 SIC 4424 4731 4412

KEYSTONE SHIPPING CO p 816
1 Bala Plz Ste 600, Bala Cynwyd PA 19004
Tel (610) 617-6800 SIC 4731 4412 4424

■ AMERICAN PETROLEUM TANKERS PARENT LLC p 77
1777 Sentry Pkwy W, Blue Bell PA 19422
Tel (215) 367-1804 SIC 4491 4424

ED BELL INVESTMENTS INC p 476
10605 Harry Hines Blvd, Dallas TX 75220
Tel (214) 358-3414 SIC 1611 5082 4424

ENERGY XXI GULF COAST INC p 498
1021 Main St Ste 2626, Houston TX 77002
Tel (713) 351-3000 SIC 4424 1311

▲ MARTIN MIDSTREAM PARTNERS LP p 913
4200 Stone Rd, Kilgore TX 75662
Tel (903) 983-6200
SIC 5171 4226 1321 4424 2819 2875

LYNDEN INC p 888
18000 Intl Blvd Ste 800, Seatac WA 98188
Tel (206) 241-8778 SIC 4213 4731 4424

FOSS MARITIME CO p 570
1151 Fairview Ave N, Seattle WA 98109
Tel (206) 281-4001
SIC 4412 4424 4492 4491 3731 4959

SIC 4432 Freight Transportation On The Great Lakes

INTERLAKE STEAMSHIP CO p 753
7300 Engle Rd, Middleburg Heights OH 44130
Tel (440) 260-6900 SIC 4432

SIC 4449 Water Transportation Of Freight, NEC

UKPEAGVIK INUPIAT CORP p 1500
1250 Agvik St, Barrow AK 99723
Tel (907) 852-4460
SIC 1542 6512 6331 1389 4449

MCDONOUGH HOLDINGS INC (FN) p 928
21050 N Pima Rd Ste 100, Scottsdale AZ 85255
Tel (602) 544-5900
SIC 2431 4449 2426 2421

BRUCE OAKLEY INC p 220
3700 Lincoln Ave, North Little Rock AR 72114
Tel (501) 945-0875
SIC 4449 5153 5261 5191 4213

FINN HOLDING CORP p 543
360 N Crescent Dr, Beverly Hills CA 90210
Tel (310) 712-1850 SIC 4449 3731 4491

INTERLAKE HOLDING CO p 753
1 Landmark Sq Ste 710, Stamford CT 06901
Tel (203) 977-8900 SIC 4449 4499

■ PRESTIGE CRUISES INTERNATIONAL INC p 1173
8300 Nw 33rd St Ste 100, Doral FL 33122
Tel (305) 514-2300 SIC 4449

▲ SEACOR HOLDINGS INC p 1296
2200 Eller Dr, Fort Lauderdale FL 33316
Tel (954) 523-2200
SIC 4412 4424 4449 4959 8748

UNITED MARITIME GROUP LLC p 1510
601 S Harbour Island Blvd, Tampa FL 33602
Tel (813) 209-4200 SIC 4449 4424

■AMERICAN RIVER TRANSPORTATION CO LLC p 78
4666 E Faries Pkwy, Decatur IL 62526
Tel (217) 424-5200 SIC 4449

CONSOLIDATED GRAIN & BARGE CO p 359
Washington & Water St, Wayne City IL 62895
Tel (618) 895-2181
SIC 4221 5153 4449 4491

ACBL RIVER OPERATIONS LLC p 14
1701 E Market St, Jeffersonville IN 47130
Tel (636) 530-2100 SIC 4449

ACL TRANSPORTATION SERVICES LLC p 17
1701 E Market St, Jeffersonville IN 47130
Tel (800) 899-7195 SIC 4449

AMERICAN BARGE LINE CO p 68
1701 E Market St, Jeffersonville IN 47130
Tel (812) 288-0100 SIC 4449 3731 4491

AMERICAN COMMERCIAL BARGE LINE p 70
1701 E Market St, Jeffersonville IN 47130
Tel (812) 288-0100 SIC 4449 3731 4491

AMERICAN COMMERCIAL LINES INC p 70
1701 E Market St, Jeffersonville IN 47130
Tel (812) 288-0100 SIC 4449 3731 4491

AMERICAN COMMERCIAL LINES INTERNATIONAL LLC p 70
1701 E Market St, Jeffersonville IN 47130
Tel (800) 899-7195 SIC 4449

COMMERCIAL BARGE LINE CO p 345
1701 E Market St, Jeffersonville IN 47130
Tel (812) 288-0100 SIC 3731 4449 4491

BLESSEY ENTERPRISES INC p 189
1515 River Oaks Rd E, Harahan LA 70123
Tel (504) 734-1156 SIC 4449

CANAL BARGE CO INC p 246
835 Union St Ste 300, New Orleans LA 70112
Tel (504) 581-2424 SIC 4449 4424 5171

ERGON INC p 507
2829 Lakeland Dr Ste 2000, Flowood MS 39232
Tel (601) 933-3000
SIC 2911 4213 4449 4613 5171 5172

FORNAZOR INTERNATIONAL INC A NEW JERSEY CORP p 568
455 Hillsdale Ave, Hillsdale NJ 07642
Tel (201) 664-4000
SIC 0119 2034 2044 2045 2075 4449

HANJIN SHIPPING AMERICA LLC p 657
80 E State Rt 4 Ste 490, Paramus NJ 07652
Tel (201) 291-4600 SIC 4449

REINAUER TRANSPORTATION COMPANIES LLC p 1221
1983 Richmond Ter, Staten Island NY 10302
Tel (718) 816-8167 SIC 4449 4492

■ FLORIDA PROGRESS CORP p 559
410 S Wilmington St, Raleigh NC 27601
Tel (919) 546-6111
SIC 1221 4911 4011 4449

■ MIDLAND CO p 965
7000 Midland Blvd, Amelia OH 45102
Tel (513) 947-5503 SIC 6331 4449

■TRANSTAR INC p 1473
1200 Penn Ave Ste 300, Pittsburgh PA 15222
Tel (412) 433-4644 SIC 4449 4731

INGRAM BARGE CO p 743
4400 Harding Pike, Nashville TN 37205
Tel (615) 298-8200 SIC 4449

INGRAM INDUSTRIES INC p 743
4400 Harding Pike Ste 310, Nashville TN 37205
Tel (615) 298-8200 SIC 5192 4449

MIDLAND ENTERPRISES INC p 965
4400 Harding Pike, Nashville TN 37205
Tel (615) 298-8200
SIC 4449 4492 3731 4491

▲ KIRBY CORP p 821
55 Waugh Dr Ste 1000, Houston TX 77007
Tel (713) 435-1000 SIC 4449 7699

■ KIRBY INLAND MARINE LP p 821
55 Waugh Dr Ste 1000, Houston TX 77007
Tel (713) 435-1000 SIC 4449

PERIMETER INTERNATIONAL p 1136
2700 Story Rd W Ste 150, Irving TX 75038
Tel (877) 701-1919
SIC 7389 4412 4731 4581 4449

HARLEY MARINE SERVICES INC p 661
910 Sw Spokane St, Seattle WA 98134
Tel (206) 628-0051 SIC 4449 4492

SIC 4481 Deep Sea Transportation Of Passengers

PRINCESS CRUISE LINES LTD p 1176
24305 Town Center Dr, Santa Clarita CA 91355
Tel (661) 753-0000 SIC 4481 4725 7011

■ CARNIVAL CELEBRATION INC p 258
3655 Nw 87th Ave, Doral FL 33178
Tel (305) 599-2600 SIC 4481

▲ CARNIVAL CORP p 259
3655 Nw 87th Ave, Doral FL 33178
Tel (305) 599-2600 SIC 4481 4725 7011

■ REGENT SEVEN SEAS CRUISES INC p 1219
8300 Nw 33rd St Ste 100, Doral FL 33122
Tel (305) 514-4920 SIC 4481

■ NCL CORP LTD p 1022
7665 Corporate Center Dr, Miami FL 33126
Tel (305) 436-4000 SIC 4481

▲ NORWEGIAN CRUISE LINE HOLDINGS LTD p 1061
7665 Corp Ctr Dr, Miami FL 33126
Tel (305) 436-4000 SIC 4481

■ OCEANIA CRUISES INC p 1073
7665 Nw 19th St, Miami FL 33126
Tel (305) 514-2300 SIC 4481

■ PRESTIGE CRUISE HOLDINGS INC p 1173
7665 Nw 19th St, Miami FL 33126
Tel (305) 514-2300 SIC 4481

▲ ROYAL CARIBBEAN CRUISES LTD p 1254
1050 Caribbean Way, Miami FL 33132
Tel (305) 539-6000 SIC 4481

■ SEABOURN CRUISE LINE LIMITED p 1296
300 Elliott Ave W Ste 100, Seattle WA 98119
Tel (206) 626-9179 SIC 4481

SIC 4482 Ferries

WOODS HOLE MARTHAS VINEYARD AND NANTUCKET STEAMSHIP AUTHORITY p 1623
1 Cowdry Rd, Woods Hole MA 02543
Tel (508) 548-5011 SIC 4482

SIC 4489 Water Transport Of Passengers, NEC

GOLDBELT INC p 620
3025 Clinton Dr Ste 100, Juneau AK 99801
Tel (907) 790-4990 SIC 4489 6512

HORNBLOWER YACHTS LLC p 708
On The Embarcadero Pier 3 St Pier, San Francisco CA 94111
Tel (415) 788-8866 SIC 4489

MICCOSUKEE TRIBE OF INDIANS OF FLORIDA p 959
Sw 8th St & Us Hwy 41, Miami FL 33194
Tel (305) 223-8380
SIC 5812 5331 8412 5947 4489

ROBERTS HAWAII INC p 1242
680 Iwilei Rd Ste 700, Honolulu HI 96817
Tel (808) 523-7750
SIC 4119 4724 7011 4489

ENTERTAINMENT CRUISES INC p 502
455 N Ctyfrnt Plz Dr # 2600, Chicago IL 60611
Tel (312) 321-7600 SIC 4489

HOLLAND AMERICA LINE NV DBA HOLLAND AMERICA LINE NV LLC p 700
300 Elliott Ave W Ste 100, Seattle WA 98119
Tel (206) 281-3535 SIC 4489

SIC 4491 Marine Cargo Handling

COOPER/T SMITH STEVEDORING CO INC p 367
118 N Royal St Ste 1100, Mobile AL 36602
Tel (251) 431-6100 SIC 4491

SMITH COOPER/T CORP p 1333
118 N Royal St Ste 1000, Mobile AL 36602
Tel (251) 431-6100
SIC 4499 4492 2421 7692 4491

AMERICAN PRESIDENT LINES LTD p 77
16220 N Scottsdale Rd, Scottsdale AZ 85254
Tel (602) 586-4894 *SIC* 4412 4424 4491

APL LOGISTICS LTD p 97
16220 N Scottsdale Rd # 300, Scottsdale AZ 85254
Tel (602) 586-4800
SIC 4412 4731 4491 4011

FINN HOLDING CORP p 543
360 N Crescent Dr, Beverly Hills CA 90210
Tel (310) 712-1850 *SIC* 4449 3731 4491

■ MATSON NAVIGATION CO INC p 920
555 12th St, Oakland CA 94607
Tel (510) 628-4000 *SIC* 4424 4491 4492

SAN DIEGO UNIFIED PORT DISTRICT p 1276
3165 Pacific Hwy, San Diego CA 92101
Tel (619) 686-6200 *SIC* 4491

CLIFF BERRY INC p 326
851 Eller Dr, Fort Lauderdale FL 33316
Tel (954) 763-3390
SIC 4953 4959 4212 2992 4491

RESOLVE MARINE GROUP INC p 1227
1510 Se 17th St Ste 400, Fort Lauderdale FL 33316
Tel (954) 764-8700
SIC 4499 4492 4491 4412 7389

AMPORTS INC p 86
10201 Centurion Pkwy N # 401, Jacksonville FL 32256
Tel (904) 652-2962 *SIC* 4491

ELLER-ITO STEVEDORING CO LLC p 488
1007 N America Way # 501, Miami FL 33132
Tel (305) 379-3700 *SIC* 7999 4491

▲ GATX CORP p 594
222 W Adams St, Chicago IL 60606
Tel (312) 621-6200 *SIC* 4741 7359 4491

CONSOLIDATED GRAIN & BARGE CO p 359
Washington & Water St, Wayne City IL 62895
Tel (618) 895-2181
SIC 4221 5153 4449 4491

AMERICAN BARGE LINE CO p 68
1701 E Market St, Jeffersonville IN 47130
Tel (812) 288-0100 *SIC* 4449 3731 4491

AMERICAN COMMERCIAL BARGE LINE p 70
1701 E Market St, Jeffersonville IN 47130
Tel (812) 288-0100 *SIC* 4449 3731 4491

AMERICAN COMMERCIAL LINES INC p 70
1701 E Market St, Jeffersonville IN 47130
Tel (812) 288-0100 *SIC* 4449 3731 4491

COMMERCIAL BARGE LINE CO p 345
1701 E Market St, Jeffersonville IN 47130
Tel (812) 288-0100 *SIC* 3731 4449 4491

YAGER MATERIALS LLC p 1633
5001 Highway 2830, Owensboro KY 42303
Tel (270) 926-0893
SIC 1442 1422 1611 3273 4491 3731

CGB ENTERPRISES INC p 285
1127 Hwy 190 E Service Rd, Covington LA 70433
Tel (985) 867-3500 *SIC* 4221 5191 4491

OFFSHORE SERVICE VESSELS LLC p 1076
16201 E Main St, Cut Off LA 70345
Tel (985) 601-4444 *SIC* 4491

MASSACHUSETTS PORT AUTHORITY p 917
1 Harborside Dr Ste 200s, Boston MA 02128
Tel (617) 561-1600
SIC 4581 4491 6799 6512 4785

LOUIS PADNOS IRON AND METAL CO p 879
185 W 8th St, Holland MI 49423
Tel (616) 396-6521 *SIC* 5093 4491 3599

DAMCO USA INC p 410
180 Park Ave Ste 105, Florham Park NJ 07932
Tel (973) 514-5000 *SIC* 4412 4491 4731

MAERSK INC p 894
180 Park Ave Ste 105, Florham Park NJ 07932
Tel (973) 514-5000 *SIC* 4731 4491 4412

■ PORTS AMERICA INC p 1163
525 Washington Blvd, Jersey City NJ 07310
Tel (732) 635-3899 *SIC* 4491

■ PORT NEWARK CONTAINER TERMINAL LLC p 1162
241 Calcutta St, Newark NJ 07114
Tel (973) 522-2200 *SIC* 4491

NYK GROUP AMERICAS INC p 1069
300 Lighting Way Ste 500, Secaucus NJ 07094
Tel (201) 330-3000
SIC 4412 4731 4011 4491 7519

NYK LINE (NORTH AMERICA) INC p 1069
300 Lighting Way 4th, Secaucus NJ 07094
Tel (201) 330-3000
SIC 4412 4731 4213 4011 7519 4491

■ AIG HIGHSTAR CAPITAL LP p 38
277 Park Ave Fl 45, New York NY 10172
Tel (646) 857-8700 *SIC* 6722 4491

PORT AUTHORITY OF NEW YORK & NEW JERSEY p 1162
4 World Trade Ctr 150, New York NY 10007
Tel (212) 435-7000
SIC 4581 4785 6512 4491 4111

APM TERMINALS NORTH AMERICA INC p 97
9300 Arrowpoint Blvd, Charlotte NC 28273
Tel (704) 571-2768 *SIC* 4491

UNIVERSAL MARITIME SERVICE CORP p 1517
9300 Arrowpoint Blvd, Charlotte NC 28273
Tel (704) 571-2768 *SIC* 4491

MCNATIONAL INC p 932
502 2nd St E, South Point OH 45680
Tel (740) 377-4391 *SIC* 3731 7699 4491

W B JOHNSTON GRAIN CO p 1568
411 W Chestnut Ave, Enid OK 73701
Tel (580) 233-5800
SIC 5153 5191 4491 4213 0111 0211

PORT OF PORTLAND p 1162
7200 Ne Airport Way, Portland OR 97218
Tel (503) 944-7000 *SIC* 4491 4512

■ AMERICAN PETROLEUM TANKERS PARENT LLC p 77
1777 Sentry Pkwy W, Blue Bell PA 19422
Tel (215) 367-1804 *SIC* 4491 4424

INTERNATIONAL SHIPPING AGENCY INC p 756
500 Paseo Monaco Apt 55, Bayamon PR 00956
Tel (787) 778-2355 *SIC* 4491 4731

SOUTH CAROLINA STATE PORTS AUTHORITY p 1343
176 Concord St, Charleston SC 29401
Tel (843) 723-8651 *SIC* 4491 8111 2721

MIDLAND ENTERPRISES INC p 965
4400 Harding Pike, Nashville TN 37205
Tel (615) 298-8200
SIC 4449 4492 3731 4491

■ BUCKEYE TEXAS PARTNERS LLC p 223
1 Greenway Plz Ste 600, Houston TX 77046
Tel (832) 615-8600 *SIC* 6719 4491

■ JACINTOPORT INTERNATIONAL LLC p 773
16398 Jacintoport Blvd, Houston TX 77015
Tel (281) 457-2415 *SIC* 4491

■ KINDER MORGAN BULK TERMINALS LLC p 819
1001 Louisiana St # 1000, Houston TX 77002
Tel (713) 369-9000 *SIC* 4491

PORT OF HOUSTON AUTHORITY p 1162
111 East Loop N, Houston TX 77029
Tel (713) 670-2662 *SIC* 4491

■ TRAFIGURA TERMINALS LLC p 1469
1401 Mckinney St Ste 1375, Houston TX 77010
Tel (832) 203-6400 *SIC* 4491

TRANS-GLOBAL SOLUTIONS INC p 1470
11811 East Fwy Ste 630, Houston TX 77029
Tel (713) 453-0341 *SIC* 4491 4013 4789

UNI-CHARTERING USA LLC p 1502
840 Gessner Rd Ste 210, Houston TX 77024
Tel (281) 833-7271 *SIC* 4491

VOPAK NORTH AMERICA INC p 1565
2000 West Loop S Ste 1550, Houston TX 77027
Tel (713) 561-7200
SIC 4491 4226 4953 4789

VIRGINIA INTERNATIONAL TERMINALS LLC p 1559
601 World Trade Ctr, Norfolk VA 23510
Tel (757) 440-7120 *SIC* 4491 4213

K LINE AMERICA INC p 799
8730 Stony Point Pkwy # 400, Richmond VA 23235
Tel (804) 560-3600 *SIC* 4412 4491

CARRIX INC p 261
1131 Sw Klickitat Way, Seattle WA 98134
Tel (206) 623-0304 *SIC* 4491

FOSS MARITIME CO p 570
1151 Fairview Ave N, Seattle WA 98109
Tel (206) 281-4001
SIC 4412 4424 4492 4491 3731 4959

FRS CAPITAL CORP p 582
1131 Sw Klickitat Way, Seattle WA 98134
Tel (206) 623-0304 *SIC* 4491

PORT OF SEATTLE p 1162
2711 Alaskan Way Pier 69, Seattle WA 98121
Tel (206) 728-3000 *SIC* 4491

SSA MARINE INC p 1363
1131 Sw Klickitat Way, Seattle WA 98134
Tel (206) 623-0304 *SIC* 4491 4731

PORT OF TACOMA p 1162
1 Sitcum Way, Tacoma WA 98421
Tel (253) 383-5841 *SIC* 4491

SIC 4492 Towing & Tugboat Svcs

SMITH COOPER/T CORP p 1333
118 N Royal St Ste 1000, Mobile AL 36602
Tel (251) 431-6100
SIC 4499 4492 2421 7692 4491

■ MATSON NAVIGATION CO INC p 920
555 12th St, Oakland CA 94607
Tel (510) 628-4000 *SIC* 4424 4491 4492

RESOLVE MARINE GROUP INC p 1227
1510 Se 17th St Ste 400, Fort Lauderdale FL 33316
Tel (954) 764-8700
SIC 4499 4492 4491 4412 7389

■ SEABULK INTERNATIONAL INC p 1296
2200 Eller Dr, Fort Lauderdale FL 33316
Tel (954) 828-1701 *SIC* 4424 4492

CROWLEY HOLDINGS INC p 394
9487 Regency Square Blvd # 101, Jacksonville FL 32225
Tel (904) 727-2200
SIC 4412 4424 5171 5172 5541 4492

CROWLEY MARITIME CORP p 395
9487 Regency Square Blvd, Jacksonville FL 32225
Tel (904) 727-2200
SIC 4412 4424 5171 5172 5541 4492

COLONIAL GROUP INC p 337
101 N Lathrop Ave, Savannah GA 31415
Tel (800) 944-3835
SIC 5171 5169 5172 4924 4492 4226

JAMES MARINE INC p 776
4500 Clarks River Rd, Paducah KY 42003
Tel (270) 898-7392
SIC 3731 4492 5541 3732

CROSBY TUGS LLC p 393
17771 Highway 3235, Galliano LA 70354
Tel (985) 632-7575 *SIC* 4492

BLESSEY MARINE SERVICE INC p 189
1515 River Oaks Rd E, Harahan LA 70123
Tel (504) 734-1156 *SIC* 4492

CENAC MARINE SERVICES LLC p 274
742 Highway 182, Houma LA 70364
Tel (985) 872-2413 *SIC* 4492

▲ TIDEWATER INC p 1452
601 Poydras St Ste 1500, New Orleans LA 70130
Tel (504) 568-1010 *SIC* 4424 4493 4492

▲ RAND LOGISTICS INC p 1207
333 Washington St Ste 201, Jersey City NJ 07302
Tel (212) 863-9427 *SIC* 4789 4492

MCALLISTER TOWING AND TRANSPORTATION CO INC p 925
17 Battery Pl Ste 1200, New York NY 10004
Tel (212) 269-3200 *SIC* 4492

REINAUER TRANSPORTATION COMPANIES LLC p 1221
1983 Richmond Ter, Staten Island NY 10302
Tel (718) 816-8167 *SIC* 4449 4492

SHELLY MATERIALS INC p 1314
80 Park Dr, Thornville OH 43076
Tel (740) 246-6315
SIC 1422 1442 2951 4492

MIDLAND ENTERPRISES INC p 965
4400 Harding Pike, Nashville TN 37205
Tel (615) 298-8200
SIC 4449 4492 3731 4491

MARTIN ENERGY SERVICES LLC p 912
3 Riverway Ste 400, Houston TX 77056
Tel (713) 350-6800
SIC 5171 4492 5172 5551

FOSS MARITIME CO p 570
1151 Fairview Ave N, Seattle WA 98109
Tel (206) 281-4001
SIC 4412 4424 4492 4491 3731 4959

HARLEY MARINE SERVICES INC p 661
910 Sw Spokane St, Seattle WA 98134
Tel (206) 628-0051 *SIC* 4449 4492

SALTCHUK RESOURCES INC p 1273
1111 Fairview Ave N, Seattle WA 98109
Tel (206) 652-1111 *SIC* 4492 4412 4499

SIC 4493 Marinas

RUSSELL LANDS INC p 1259
2544 Willow Point Rd, Alexander City AL 35010
Tel (256) 329-0835
SIC 5211 6514 4493 7997 7011

GALATI YACHT SALES LLC p 589
902 Bay Blvd, Anna Maria FL 34216
Tel (941) 778-0755 *SIC* 5551 4493

▲ TIDEWATER INC p 1452
601 Poydras St Ste 1500, New Orleans LA 70130
Tel (504) 568-1010 *SIC* 4424 4493 4492

LECO CORP p 851
3000 Lakeview Ave, Saint Joseph MI 49085
Tel (269) 983-5531
SIC 4493 3821 3826 3825 3823 3264

DOCKWISE USA LLC p 447
16340 Park Ten Pl Ste 200, Houston TX 77084
Tel (713) 934-7300 *SIC* 4493

PALMER JOHNSON ENTERPRISES INC p 1109
128 Kentucky St, Sturgeon Bay WI 54235
Tel (920) 746-6342 *SIC* 5085 4493 3732

SIC 4499 Water Transportation Svcs, NEC

SMITH COOPER/T CORP p 1333
118 N Royal St Ste 1000, Mobile AL 36602
Tel (251) 431-6100
SIC 4499 4492 2421 7692 4491

STOLT-NIELSEN TRANSPORTATION GROUP LTD p 1390
800 Connecticut Ave 4e, Norwalk CT 06854
Tel (203) 299-3600 *SIC* 4499 4213

INTERLAKE HOLDING CO p 753
1 Landmark Sq Ste 710, Stamford CT 06901
Tel (203) 977-8900 *SIC* 4449 4499

RESOLVE MARINE GROUP INC p 1227
1510 Se 17th St Ste 400, Fort Lauderdale FL 33316
Tel (954) 764-8700
SIC 4499 4492 4491 4412 7389

▲ MATSON INC p 920
1411 Sand Island Pkwy, Honolulu HI 96819
Tel (808) 848-1211 *SIC* 4499

▲ HORNBECK OFFSHORE SERVICES INC p 708
103 Northpark Blvd # 300, Covington LA 70433
Tel (985) 727-2000 *SIC* 4499

ABDON CALLAIS OFFSHORE LLC p 10
1300 N Alex Plisance Blvd, Golden Meadow LA 70357
Tel (985) 475-7111 *SIC* 4499

■ GRAHAM MARINE INC p 629
7910 Main St Ste 200, Houma LA 70360
Tel (985) 876-5400 *SIC* 4499

HANJIN SHIPPING CO LTD p 657
80 E Rte 4 Ste 490, Paramus NJ 07652
Tel (201) 291-4600 *SIC* 4499

SGS NORTH AMERICA INC p 1310
301 Route 17, Rutherford NJ 07070
Tel (201) 508-3000
SIC 8734 7389 8071 4499 4785

THRUWAY AUTHORITY OF NEW YORK STATE p 1451
200 Southern Blvd, Albany NY 12209
Tel (518) 436-2700 *SIC* 4785 4499

DETYENS SHIPYARDS INC p 433
1670 Dry Dock Ave # 236, North Charleston SC 29405
Tel (843) 746-1603 *SIC* 4499

DAWSON MARINE INC p 417
4230 College St, Beaumont TX 77707
Tel (409) 840-4111 *SIC* 4499

ESCO MARINE INC p 509
16200 Jose Garza Rd, Brownsville TX 78521
Tel (956) 554-5300 *SIC* 4499 5093 7389

■ TRINITY INDUSTRIES LEASING CO p 1481
2525 N Stemmons Fwy, Dallas TX 75207
Tel (800) 227-8844 *SIC* 4741 4499

MAERSK LINE LIMITED p 895
1 Commercial Pl Fl 20, Norfolk VA 23510
Tel (757) 857-4800 *SIC* 4499

CROWLEY MARINE SERVICES INC p 395
1102 Sw Massachusetts St, Seattle WA 98134
Tel (206) 332-8000 *SIC* 4499

SALTCHUK RESOURCES INC p 1273
1111 Fairview Ave N, Seattle WA 98109
Tel (206) 652-1111 *SIC* 4492 4412 4499

SIC 4512 Air Transportation, Scheduled

HOTH INC p 710
4700 Old Intl Airport Rd, Anchorage AK 99502
Tel (907) 266-8300 *SIC* 4522 4512

PENINSULA AIRWAYS INC p 1129
6200 Boeing Ave Ste 300, Anchorage AK 99502
Tel (907) 771-2500 *SIC* 4512

FRONTIER ALASKA p 581
5245 Airport Indus Rd, Fairbanks AK 99709
Tel (907) 450-7250 *SIC* 4512

■ AMERICA WEST AIRLINES INC p 67
4000 E Sky Harbor Blvd, Phoenix AZ 85034
Tel (480) 693-0800 *SIC* 4512

MESA AIR GROUP INC p 951
410 N 44th St Ste 700, Phoenix AZ 85008
Tel (602) 685-4000 *SIC* 4512 4522

MESA AIRLINES INC p 951
410 N 44th St Ste 700, Phoenix AZ 85008
Tel (602) 685-4000 *SIC* 4512 4522 4581

US AIRWAYS INC p 1531
111 W Rio Salado Pkwy # 175, Tempe AZ 85281
Tel (480) 693-0800 *SIC* 4512

▲ VIRGIN AMERICA INC p 1558
555 Airport Blvd Ste 400, Burlingame CA 94010
Tel (877) 359-8474 *SIC* 4512

AERO CALIFORNIA AIRLINES p 30
1960 E Grand Ave Ste 1200, El Segundo CA 90245
Tel (800) 237-6225 *SIC* 4512

FRONTIER AIRLINES HOLDINGS INC p 580
7001 Tower Rd, Denver CO 80249
Tel (720) 374-4200 *SIC* 4512

FRONTIER AIRLINES INC p 581
7001 Tower Rd, Denver CO 80249
Tel (720) 374-4200 *SIC* 4512

AMERIJET HOLDINGS INC p 82
3401 Nw 72nd Ave Ste A, Miami FL 33122
Tel (800) 927-6059
SIC 4512 8741 4581 4213

LATAM AIRLINES GROUP SA INC p 846
6500 Nw 22nd St, Miami FL 33122
Tel (786) 265-6050 *SIC* 4512

▲ SPIRIT AIRLINES INC p 1359
2800 Executive Way, Miramar FL 33025
Tel (954) 447-7920 *SIC* 4512

■ AIRTRAN HOLDINGS INC p 41
9955 Airtran Blvd, Orlando FL 32827
Tel (407) 318-5600 *SIC* 4512

SOUTH AFRICAN AIRWAYS SOC LIMITED INC p 1342
1200 S Pine Isl Rd 650, Plantation FL 33324
Tel (800) 722-9675 *SIC* 4512

■ A S A HOLDINGS INC p 6
100 Hartsfield Ctr Pkwy, Atlanta GA 30354
Tel (404) 766-1400 *SIC* 4512

▲ DELTA AIR LINES INC p 426
1030 Delta Blvd, Atlanta GA 30354
Tel (404) 715-2600 *SIC* 4512

■ EXPRESSJET AIRLINES INC p 520
100 Hartsfield Ctr 700, Atlanta GA 30354
Tel (404) 856-1000 *SIC* 4512

■ UNITED PARCEL SERVICE CO p 1510
55 Glenlake Pkwy, Atlanta GA 30328
Tel (404) 828-6000 *SIC* 4512

■ HAWAIIAN AIRLINES INC p 669
3375 Koapaka St Ste G350, Honolulu HI 96819
Tel (808) 835-3700 *SIC* 4512

▲ HAWAIIAN HOLDINGS INC p 669
3375 Koapaka St Ste G350, Honolulu HI 96819
Tel (808) 835-3700 *SIC* 4512

H GROUP HOLDING INC p 650
222 W Adams St Ste 250, Chicago IL 60606
Tel (312) 750-1234
SIC 4512 7011 5812 5813

■ UNITED AIRLINES INC p 1506
233 S Wacker Dr Ste 430, Chicago IL 60606
Tel (872) 825-4000 *SIC* 4512 4513 4729

▲ UNITED CONTINENTAL HOLDINGS INC p 1507
233 S Wacker Dr, Chicago IL 60606
Tel (872) 825-4000 *SIC* 4512

TIGERS (USA) GLOBAL LOGISTICS INC p 1453
25 Northwest Point Blvd # 1025, Elk Grove Village IL 60007
Tel (516) 825-4774
SIC 4731 4581 4522 4512

CHAUTAUQUA AIRLINES INC p 292
8909 Purdue Rd Ste 300, Indianapolis IN 46268
Tel (317) 484-6000 *SIC* 4512 4522

■ REPUBLIC AIRLINE INC p 1225
8909 Purdue Rd Ste 300, Indianapolis IN 46268
Tel (317) 484-6000 *SIC* 4512

▲ REPUBLIC AIRWAYS HOLDINGS INC p 1225
8909 Purdue Rd Ste 300, Indianapolis IN 46268
Tel (317) 484-6000 *SIC* 4512

■ COMAIR HOLDINGS LLC p 343
82 Comair Blvd, Erlanger KY 41018
Tel (859) 767-2550 *SIC* 4512

▲ PHI INC p 1142
2001 Se Evangeline Trwy, Lafayette LA 70508
Tel (337) 235-2452 *SIC* 4512 4522 4581

■ PIEDMONT AIRLINES INC p 1146
5443 Airport Terminal Rd, Salisbury MD 21804
Tel (410) 742-2996 *SIC* 4512

■ MESABA AVIATION INC p 951
1000 Blue Gentian Rd # 200, Eagan MN 55121
Tel (651) 367-5000 *SIC* 4512

MN AIRLINES LLC p 979
1300 Corporate Ctr Curv, Eagan MN 55121
Tel (651) 681-3900 *SIC* 4512

■ ENDEAVOR AIR INC p 496
7500 Airline Dr, Minneapolis MN 55450
Tel (901) 348-4100 *SIC* 4512

NORTHWEST AIRLINES INC p 1059
7500 Airline Dr, Minneapolis MN 55450
Tel (404) 715-2600 *SIC* 4512 4513 4522

PINNACLE AIRLINES CORP p 1149
7500 Airline Dr, Minneapolis MN 55450
Tel (800) 603-4594 *SIC* 4512

TRANS STATES AIRLINES INC p 1470
11495 Navaid Rd 340, Bridgeton MO 63044
Tel (314) 222-4300 *SIC* 4512

DUNCAN AVIATION INC p 461
3701 Aviation Rd, Lincoln NE 68524
Tel (402) 479-1616
SIC 7699 5088 4522 4512

■ **ALLEGIANT AIR LLC** p 53
1201 N Town Center Dr # 110, Las Vegas NV 89144
Tel (702) 505-8888 SIC 4512

▲ **ALLEGIANT TRAVEL CO** p 53
1201 N Town Center Dr, Las Vegas NV 89144
Tel (702) 851-7300 SIC 4512 4724

FLIGHT CENTRE TRAVEL GROUP (USA) INC p 556
5 Paragon Dr Ste 200, Montvale NJ 07645
Tel (201) 934-3500 SIC 4512

■ **CHARTERX INC** p 291
18 W Piper Ave, Trenton NJ 08628
Tel (800) 579-1694 SIC 4512

▲ **JETBLUE AIRWAYS CORP** p 784
2701 Queens Plz N, Long Island City NY 11101
Tel (718) 286-7900 SIC 4512

TURKISH AIRLINES INC p 1492
350 5th Ave Ste 7510, New York NY 10118
Tel (800) 874-8875 SIC 4512

■ **ATLAS AIR INC** p 127
2000 Westchester Ave, Purchase NY 10577
Tel (914) 701-8000 SIC 4512

▲ **ATLAS AIR WORLDWIDE HOLDINGS INC** p 127
2000 Westchester Ave, Purchase NY 10577
Tel (914) 701-8000 SIC 4522 4512 7359

■ **XPO LOGISTICS WORLDWIDE LLC** p 1633
4035 Piedmont Pkwy, High Point NC 27265
Tel (415) 486-2660 SIC 4731 4512 4213

▲ **T AIR INC** p 1419
3524 Airport Rd, Maiden NC 28650
Tel (828) 464-8741 SIC 4512 3728 7699

■ **PSA AIRLINES INC** p 1188
3400 Terminal Rd, Vandalia OH 45377
Tel (937) 454-1116 SIC 4512

PORT OF PORTLAND p 1162
7200 Ne Airport Way, Portland OR 97218
Tel (503) 944-7000 SIC 4491 4512

■ **PIEDMONT AIRLINES INC** p 1146
1000 Rosedale Ave, Middletown PA 17057
Tel (410) 742-2996 SIC 4512

■ **EXECUTIVE AIR LINES INC** p 517
Lmm Int Airport Central, Carolina PR 00983
Tel (787) 253-6401 SIC 4512 4212

■ **FEDERAL EXPRESS CORP** p 534
3610 Hacks Cross Rd, Memphis TN 38125
Tel (901) 369-3600
SIC 4513 4512 4215 4213

▲ **FEDEX CORP** p 536
942 Shady Grove Rd S, Memphis TN 38120
Tel (901) 818-7500
SIC 4513 4512 4213 4215 7334

■ **AIRTRAN AIRWAYS INC** p 41
2702 Love Field Dr, Dallas TX 75235
Tel (407) 318-5600 SIC 4512

MENZIES AVIATION (TEXAS) INC p 943
2520 W Airfield Dr, Dallas TX 75261
Tel (972) 929-1020 SIC 4512

▲ **SOUTHWEST AIRLINES CO** p 1351
2702 Love Field Dr, Dallas TX 75235
Tel (214) 792-4000 SIC 4512

▲ **AMERICAN AIRLINES GROUP INC** p 67
4333 Amon Carter Blvd, Fort Worth TX 76155
Tel (817) 963-1234 SIC 4512 4581

■ **AMERICAN AIRLINES INC** p 67
4333 Amon Carter Blvd, Fort Worth TX 76155
Tel (817) 963-1234 SIC 4512 4513

■ **AMR EAGLE INC** p 86
4333 Amon Carter Blvd, Fort Worth TX 76155
Tel (214) 927-6016 SIC 4512

■ **TWA AIRLINES LLC** p 1494
4333 Amon Carter Blvd, Fort Worth TX 76155
Tel (817) 963-1234 SIC 4512 4522 4581

US AIRWAYS GROUP INC p 1531
4333 Amon Carter Blvd, Fort Worth TX 76155
Tel (480) 693-0800 SIC 4512

■ **CEVA FREIGHT LLC** p 284
15350 Vickery Dr, Houston TX 77032
Tel (281) 618-3100
SIC 4214 4225 4412 4512 4522 4731

▲ **ERA GROUP INC** p 507
818 Town And Country Blvd, Houston TX 77024
Tel (713) 369-4700 SIC 4512

■ **EXPRESSJET HOLDINGS INC** p 521
700 N Sam Hous Pkwy W # 200, Houston TX 77067
Tel (832) 353-1000 SIC 4512

■ **XJT HOLDINGS INC** p 1632
1600 Smith St, Houston TX 77002
Tel (713) 324-5236 SIC 4512

■ **ENVOY AIR INC** p 504
4301 Regent Blvd, Irving TX 75063
Tel (972) 374-5200 SIC 4512

■ **SKYWEST AIRLINES INC** p 1330
444 S River Rd, St George UT 84790
Tel (435) 634-3000 SIC 4512

▲ **SKYWEST INC** p 1330
444 S River Rd, St George UT 84790
Tel (435) 634-3000 SIC 4512

▲ **ALASKA AIR GROUP INC** p 44
19300 International Blvd, Seatac WA 98188
Tel (206) 392-5040 SIC 4512 4731

ALASKA AIRLINES p 44
20833 International Blvd, Seatac WA 98198
Tel (206) 392-5885 SIC 4512

■ **ALASKA AIRLINES INC** p 44
19300 International Blvd, Seatac WA 98188
Tel (206) 433-3200 SIC 4512

■ **HORIZON AIR INDUSTRIES INC** p 706
19521 International Blvd, Seatac WA 98188
Tel (206) 241-6757 SIC 4512 4522

AIR WISCONSIN AIRLINES CORP p 39
W6390 Challenger Dr # 203, Appleton WI 54914
Tel (920) 739-5123 SIC 4512

SIC 4513 Air Courier Svcs

MIDNITE AIR CORP p 966
2132 Michelson Dr, Irvine CA 92612
Tel (310) 330-2300 SIC 4513

■ **MENLO WORLDWIDE FORWARDING INC** p 943
1 Lagoon Dr Ste 400, Redwood City CA 94065
Tel (650) 596-9600
SIC 4513 4215 4522 4731 6159 6351

TRICOR AMERICA INC p 1479
717 Airport Blvd, South San Francisco CA 94080
Tel (650) 877-3650 SIC 4513

BINEX LINE CORP p 183
19515 S Vermont Ave, Torrance CA 90502
Tel (310) 416-8600 SIC 4731 4513

■ **WORLD COURIER GROUP INC** p 1625
4 High Ridge Park Ste 102, Stamford CT 06905
Tel (203) 595-0900 SIC 4513

FEDERAL EXPRESS PACIFIC INC p 534
1209 N Orange St, Wilmington DE 19801
Tel (901) 369-3600 SIC 4513

ATI SYSTEMS INTERNATIONAL INC p 124
2000 Nw Corp Blvd Ste 101, Boca Raton FL 33431
Tel (561) 939-7000 SIC 7381 4513 4215

AIR EXPRESS INTERNATIONAL USA INC p 38
1801 Nw 82nd Ave, Doral FL 33126
Tel (786) 264-3500 SIC 4731 4513

DHL EXPRESS (USA) INC p 435
1210 S Pine Island Rd, Plantation FL 33324
Tel (954) 888-7000 SIC 4513 7389 4731

DPWN HOLDINGS (USA) INC p 454
1210 S Pine Island Rd, Plantation FL 33324
Tel (954) 888-7000 SIC 4513 4731

GLOBAL MAIL INC p 617
2700 S Comm Pkwy Ste 300, Weston FL 33331
Tel (800) 805-9306 SIC 4513

BEAVEX INC p 166
2120 Powers Ferry Rd Se, Atlanta GA 30339
Tel (404) 260-0961 SIC 4215 4513

▲ **UNITED PARCEL SERVICE INC** p 1510
55 Glenlake Pkwy, Atlanta GA 30328
Tel (404) 828-6000 SIC 4215 4513 4522

■ **UPS LOGISTICS GROUP INC** p 1529
55 Glenlake Pkwy, Atlanta GA 30328
Tel (678) 746-4100
SIC 7389 7513 4731 4513

■ **UNITED AIRLINES INC** p 1506
233 S Wacker Dr Ste 430, Chicago IL 60606
Tel (872) 825-4000 SIC 4512 4513 4729

KALITTA AIR LLC p 801
818 Willow Run Airport, Ypsilanti MI 48198
Tel (734) 484-0088 SIC 4513

NORTHWEST AIRLINES INC p 1059
7500 Airline Dr, Minneapolis MN 55450
Tel (404) 715-2600 SIC 4512 4513 4522

■ **TNT USA INC** p 1458
68 S Service Rd Ste 340, Melville NY 11747
Tel (631) 712-6700 SIC 4513

UTAIR - HELICOPTER SERVICES LTD p 1536
420 Lexington Ave Rm 300, New York NY 10170
Tel (212) 297-6207 SIC 4513

ARAMEX NEW YORK LTD p 102
18221 150th Ave, Springfield Gardens NY 11413
Tel (718) 553-8740 SIC 4513

■ **ABX AIR INC** p 13
145 Hunter Dr, Wilmington OH 45177
Tel (937) 382-5591
SIC 4513 5088 4581 8299

▲ **AIR TRANSPORT SERVICES GROUP INC** p 39
145 Hunter Dr, Wilmington OH 45177
Tel (937) 382-5591 SIC 4513

EVERGREEN HOLDINGS INC p 514
3850 Ne Three Mile Ln, Mcminnville OR 97128
Tel (503) 472-0011 SIC 4522 4513 4215

EVERGREEN INTERNATIONAL AVIATION INC p 514
3850 Ne Three Mile Ln, Mcminnville OR 97128
Tel (503) 472-0011 SIC 4522 4513 4215

AMERICAN EXPEDITING CO p 72
801 Primos Ave, Folcroft PA 19032
Tel (484) 540-8180 SIC 4215 4513

■ **FEDERAL EXPRESS CORP** p 534
3610 Hacks Cross Rd, Memphis TN 38125
Tel (901) 369-3600
SIC 4513 4512 4215 4213

▲ **FEDEX CORP** p 536
942 Shady Grove Rd S, Memphis TN 38120
Tel (901) 818-7500
SIC 4513 4512 4213 4215 7334

LONE STAR HOLDINGS LLC p 875
6500 River Place Blvd # 2, Austin TX 78730
Tel (512) 873-8067 SIC 4215 4513 4212

TF COURIER INC p 1445
5429 Lyndon B Johnson Fwy, Dallas TX 75240
Tel (214) 560-9000 SIC 4513 4215 8741

TF FINAL MILE LLC p 1445
5429 Lbj Fwy Ste 900, Dallas TX 75240
Tel (214) 560-9000 SIC 4215 4513

TFI HOLDINGS USA INC p 1445
5429 L B Johnson Fwy 10 Ste 1000, Dallas TX 75240
Tel (877) 396-2639 SIC 4215 8741 4513

■ **AMERICAN AIRLINES INC** p 67
4333 Amon Carter Blvd, Fort Worth TX 76155
Tel (817) 963-1234 SIC 4512 4513

SIC 4522 Air Transportation, Nonscheduled

HOTH INC p 710
4700 Old Intl Airport Rd, Anchorage AK 99502
Tel (907) 266-8300 SIC 4522 4512

CUTTER AVIATION p 403
2802 E Old Tower Rd, Phoenix AZ 85034
Tel (602) 273-1237
SIC 5599 5088 4522 5172 4581

MESA AIR GROUP INC p 951
410 N 44th St Ste 700, Phoenix AZ 85008
Tel (602) 685-4000 SIC 4512 4522

MESA AIRLINES INC p 951
410 N 44th St Ste 700, Phoenix AZ 85008
Tel (602) 685-4000 SIC 4512 4522 4581

■ **PHI AIR MEDICAL LLC** p 1142
2800 N 44th St Ste 800, Phoenix AZ 85008
Tel (602) 224-3500 SIC 4522

■ **MENLO WORLDWIDE FORWARDING INC** p 943
1 Lagoon Dr Ste 400, Redwood City CA 94065
Tel (650) 596-9600
SIC 4513 4215 4522 4731 6159 6351

▲ **AIR METHODS CORP** p 39
7301 S Peoria St, Englewood CO 80112
Tel (303) 749-1330 SIC 4522

BANYAN AIR SERVICES INC p 153
5360 Nw 20th Ter, Fort Lauderdale FL 33309
Tel (954) 491-3170
SIC 5172 4581 5088 4522

CENTURION AIR CARGO INC p 281
4500 Nw 36th St Bldg 916, Miami Springs FL 33166
Tel (305) 871-0130 SIC 4581 4522

▲ **UNITED PARCEL SERVICE INC** p 1510
55 Glenlake Pkwy, Atlanta GA 30328
Tel (404) 828-6000 SIC 4215 4513 4522

GLOBAL AVIATION HOLDINGS INC p 615
101 World Dr, Peachtree City GA 30269
Tel (770) 632-8000 SIC 4522

TIGERS (USA) GLOBAL LOGISTICS INC p 1453
25 Northwest Point Blvd # 1025, Elk Grove Village IL 60007
Tel (516) 825-4774
SIC 4731 4581 4522 4512

TRUCK CENTERS INC p 1485
2280 Formosa Rd, Troy IL 62294
Tel (618) 667-3454
SIC 5531 5511 7538 5012 4522 7699

CHAUTAUQUA AIRLINES INC p 292
8909 Purdue Rd Ste 300, Indianapolis IN 46268
Tel (317) 484-6000 SIC 4512 4522

COLLINS INDUSTRIES INC p 337
15 Compound Dr, Hutchinson KS 67502
Tel (620) 663-5551 SIC 4522

SHERWOOD CONSTRUCTION CO INC p 1316
3219 W May St, Wichita KS 67213
Tel (316) 943-0211 SIC 1794 4522

■ **SOUTHERN AIR HOLDINGS INC** p 1347
7310 Turfway Rd Ste 400, Florence KY 41042
Tel (859) 568-9200 SIC 4522 4581

■ **SOUTHERN AIR INC** p 1347
7310 Turfway Rd Ste 400, Florence KY 41042
Tel (859) 568-9200 SIC 4522

■ **WORLDWIDE AIR LOGISTICS GROUP INC** p 1626
7310 Turfway Rd Ste 490, Florence KY 41042
Tel (859) 568-9300 SIC 4522 4581

▲ **PHI INC** p 1142
2001 Se Evangeline Trwy, Lafayette LA 70508
Tel (337) 235-2452 SIC 4512 4522 4581

■ **BRISTOW US LLC** p 214
4605 Industrial Dr, New Iberia LA 70560
Tel (337) 365-6771 SIC 4522

■ **ACTIVE AERO GROUP INC** p 19
2068 E St, Belleville MI 48111
Tel (734) 547-7200 SIC 4522

■ **E C AVIATION SERVICES INC** p 466
600 N Centennial St, Zeeland MI 49464
Tel (616) 772-1800 SIC 4522

NORTHWEST AIRLINES INC p 1059
7500 Airline Dr, Minneapolis MN 55450
Tel (404) 715-2600 SIC 4512 4513 4522

KALISPELL REGIONAL HEALTHCARE SYSTEM p 801
310 Sunnyview Ln, Kalispell MT 59901
Tel (406) 752-8991
SIC 8051 8011 4522 7352

DUNCAN AVIATION INC p 461
3701 Aviation Rd, Lincoln NE 68524
Tel (402) 479-1616
SIC 7699 5088 4522 4512

▲ **ATLAS AIR WORLDWIDE HOLDINGS INC** p 127
2000 Westchester Ave, Purchase NY 10577
Tel (914) 701-8000 SIC 4522 4512 7359

AIRNET SYSTEMS INC p 40
7250 Star Check Dr, Columbus OH 43217
Tel (614) 409-4900 SIC 4522 4731

■ **NETJETS AVIATION INC** p 1027
4111 Bridgeway Ave, Columbus OH 43219
Tel (614) 239-5500 SIC 4522

■ **NETJETS INC** p 1027
4111 Bridgeway Ave, Columbus OH 43219
Tel (614) 239-5500 SIC 4522 5088 7359

■ **NETJETS SALES INC** p 1027
4111 Bridgeway Ave, Columbus OH 43219
Tel (614) 239-5500 SIC 5088 4522

OMNI AIR INTERNATIONAL LLC p 1084
3303 N Sheridan Rd Hngar19, Tulsa OK 74115
Tel (918) 836-5393 SIC 4522

COLUMBIA HELICOPTERS INC p 340
14452 Arndt Rd Ne, Aurora OR 97002
Tel (503) 678-7510 SIC 7699 2411 4522

SWANSON GROUP INC p 1411
2695 Glendale Valley Rd, Glendale OR 97442
Tel (541) 832-1121 SIC 2421 2436 4522

EVERGREEN HOLDINGS INC p 514
3850 Ne Three Mile Ln, Mcminnville OR 97128
Tel (503) 472-0011 SIC 4522 4513 4215

EVERGREEN INTERNATIONAL AVIATION INC p 514
3850 Ne Three Mile Ln, Mcminnville OR 97128
Tel (503) 472-0011 SIC 4522 4513 4215

PATTERSON-ERIE CORP p 1121
1250 Tower Ln Ste 1, Erie PA 16505
Tel (814) 455-8031 SIC 5812 6531 4522

STEVENS AVIATION INC p 1388
600 Delaware St, Greenville SC 29605
Tel (864) 678-6000
SIC 4522 4581 5088 5599

AEROSPACE PRODUCTS INTERNATIONAL INC p 31
2871 Business Park Dr, Memphis TN 38118
Tel (901) 365-3470 SIC 5088 4522

■ **TWA AIRLINES LLC** p 1494
4333 Amon Carter Blvd, Fort Worth TX 76155
Tel (817) 963-1234 SIC 4512 4522 4581

▲ **BRISTOW GROUP INC** p 214
2103 City West Blvd Fl 4, Houston TX 77042
Tel (713) 267-7600 SIC 4522

■ **CEVA FREIGHT LLC** p 284
15350 Vickery Dr, Houston TX 77032
Tel (281) 618-3100
SIC 4214 4225 4412 4512 4522 4731

PIEDMONT HAWTHORNE AVIATION LLC p 1147
1500 City W Blvd Ste 600, Houston TX 77042
Tel (713) 895-9243
SIC 5599 4581 4522 5172

■ **ATLANTIC AVIATION CORP** p 125
6652 Pinecrest Dr Ste 300, Plano TX 75024
Tel (972) 905-2500
SIC 4581 5088 5172 6331 6159 4522

VOLGA DNEPR - UNIQUE AIR CARGO INC p 1564
9400 Grogans Mill Rd, The Woodlands TX 77380
Tel (832) 585-8611 SIC 4522

EAGLE GROUP SYSTEMS INC p 468
230 Grant Rd, East Wenatchee WA 98802
Tel (509) 665-0319
SIC 4214 4119 4522 7373 7374 8741

■ **HORIZON AIR INDUSTRIES INC** p 706
19521 International Blvd, Seatac WA 98188
Tel (206) 241-6757 SIC 4512 4522

SIC 4581 Airports, Flying Fields & Terminal Svcs

GAT AIRLINE GROUND SUPPORT INC p 593
8400 Airport Blvd, Mobile AL 36608
Tel (251) 633-3888 SIC 4581

ST AEROSPACE MOBILE INC p 1364
2100 Aerospace Dr Brkley Brookley Complex, Mobile AL 36615
Tel (251) 438-8888 SIC 4581

ALASKA INTERNATIONAL AIRPORTS SYSTEM p 45
5000 W Intl Airport Rd, Anchorage AK 99502
Tel (907) 266-2404 SIC 4581

MARANA AEROSPACE SOLUTIONS INC p 904
24641 E Pinal Air Park Rd, Marana AZ 85653
Tel (520) 682-4181 SIC 4581

CUTTER AVIATION p 403
2802 E Old Tower Rd, Phoenix AZ 85034
Tel (602) 273-1237
SIC 5599 5088 4522 5172 4581

MESA AIRLINES INC p 951
410 N 44th St Ste 700, Phoenix AZ 85008
Tel (602) 685-4000 SIC 4512 4522 4581

TOTAL AIRPORT SERVICES INC p 1462
34406 N 27th Dr Ste 140, Phoenix AZ 85085
Tel (623) 215-9941 SIC 4581

AERCAP US GLOBAL AVIATION LLC p 30
10250 Constellation Blvd, Los Angeles CA 90067
Tel (310) 788-1999 SIC 3721 4581 6159

AIRPORT COMMISIONS p 40
San Francisco Intl Arprt, San Francisco CA 94128
Tel (650) 821-5000 SIC 4581

■ **URS HOLDINGS INC** p 1530
600 Montgomery St Fl 25, San Francisco CA 94111
Tel (415) 774-2700
SIC 8711 7389 6531 8249 4581

AEROGROUND INC p 30
270 Lawrence Ave, South San Francisco CA 94080
Tel (650) 266-6965 SIC 4581 4213

MERCURY AIR GROUP INC p 945
2780 Skypark Dr Ste 300, Torrance CA 90505
Tel (310) 602-3770 SIC 5172 7389 4581

DOSS AVIATION INC p 451
3670 Rebecca Ln Ste 100, Colorado Springs CO 80917
Tel (719) 570-9804 SIC 5172 4581

GREENWICH AEROGROUP INC p 638
475 Steamboat Rd Fl 2, Greenwich CT 06830
Tel (203) 618-4861
SIC 4581 5088 7699 5085

■ **SIKORSKY AIRCRAFT CORP** p 1322
6900 Main St, Stratford CT 06614
Tel (203) 386-4000 SIC 3721 4581 5599

■ **HELICOPTER SUPPORT INC** p 681
124 Quarry Rd, Trumbull CT 06611
Tel (203) 416-4000 SIC 5088 4581 3728

METROPOLITAN WASHINGTON AIRPORTS AUTHORITY p 957
1 Aviation Cir, Washington DC 20001
Tel (703) 417-8600 SIC 4581 4785

SUPPORT AVIATION LLC p 1408
208 W Highland St, Altamonte Springs FL 32714
Tel (407) 731-4118 SIC 4581

IAP WORLD SERVICES INC p 725
7315 N Atlantic Ave, Cape Canaveral FL 32920
Tel (321) 784-7100
SIC 4731 4581 8744 4911 1541 4813

IAP WORLDWIDE SERVICES INC p 725
7315 N Atlantic Ave, Cape Canaveral FL 32920
Tel (973) 633-5115
SIC 4731 4581 8744 4911

BANYAN AIR SERVICES INC p 153
5360 Nw 20th Ter, Fort Lauderdale FL 33309
Tel (954) 491-3170
SIC 5172 4581 5088 4522

FLIGHTSTAR AIRCRAFT SERVICES LLC p 557
6025 Flightline Dr, Jacksonville FL 32221
Tel (904) 741-0300 SIC 4581 3728

FLORIDA INSTITUTE OF TECHNOLOGY INC p 559
150 W University Blvd Ofc, Melbourne FL 32901
Tel (321) 674-8000 SIC 8221 4581 8299

SOUTHEAST AEROSPACE INC p 1345
1399 General Aviation Dr, Melbourne FL 32935
Tel (321) 255-9877
SIC 5088 3812 3728 3721 4581

AMERIJET HOLDINGS INC p 82
3401 Nw 72nd Ave Ste A, Miami FL 33122
Tel (800) 927-6059
SIC 4512 8741 4581 4213

SERVISAIR USA & CARRIBEAN p 1308
6065 Nw 18th St Bldg 716d, Miami FL 33126
Tel (305) 262-4059 *SIC* 4581

CENTURION AIR CARGO INC p 281
4500 Nw 36th St Bldg 916, Miami Springs FL 33166
Tel (305) 871-0130 *SIC* 4581 4522

AIRCRAFT SERVICE INTERNATIONAL INC p 40
201 S Orange Ave Ste 1100, Orlando FL 32801
Tel (407) 648-7373 *SIC* 4581 5172

GREATER ORLANDO AVIATION AUTHORITY p 635
1 Jeff Fuqua Blvd, Orlando FL 32827
Tel (407) 825-2001 *SIC* 4581

■ **CHROMALLOY GAS TURBINE LLC** p 304
3999 Rca Blvd, Palm Beach Gardens FL 33410
Tel (561) 935-3571
SIC 3724 7699 4581 3764 3769 3533

CARGO FORCE INC p 255
6705 Sw 57th Ave Ste 700, South Miami FL 33143
Tel (305) 740-3252 *SIC* 4581

PEMCO WORLD AIR SERVICES INC p 1128
4102 N West Shore Blvd, Tampa FL 33614
Tel (813) 322-9600 *SIC* 4581 3728

■ **AIR SERV CORP** p 39
3399 Peachtree Rd Ne, Atlanta GA 30326
Tel (404) 926-4200 *SIC* 4581 4111

AIR SERV SECURITY INC p 39
3399 Peachtree Rd Ne # 1800, Atlanta GA 30326
Tel (404) 926-4200 *SIC* 4581

WENCOR GROUP LLC p 1591
416 Dividend Dr, Peachtree City GA 30269
Tel (678) 490-0140 *SIC* 3728 4581

■ **GULFSTREAM AEROSPACE CORP** p 647
500 Gulfstream Rd, Savannah GA 31408
Tel (912) 965-3000 *SIC* 3721 4581

WESTERN AIRCRAFT INC p 1597
4300 S Kennedy St, Boise ID 83705
Tel (208) 338-1800
SIC 5088 4581 7359 5172

PROSPECT AIRPORT SERVICES INC p 1184
2130 S Wolf Rd Fl 2, Des Plaines IL 60018
Tel (847) 299-3636 *SIC* 4581 7349

TIGERS (USA) GLOBAL LOGISTICS INC p 1453
25 Northwest Point Blvd # 1025, Elk Grove Village IL 60007
Tel (516) 825-4774
SIC 4731 4581 4522 4512

ELLIOTT AVIATION INC p 488
6601 74th Ave, Milan IL 61264
Tel (309) 799-3183 *SIC* 4581 5599

▲ **AAR CORP** p 8
1100 N Wood Dale Rd, Wood Dale IL 60191
Tel (630) 227-2000
SIC 3724 4581 3537 5599 7359

ATA AIRLINES INC p 123
7337 W Washington St, Indianapolis IN 46231
Tel (317) 898-3110 *SIC* 4581

INDIANAPOLIS AIRPORT AUTHORITY p 739
7800 Col Weircook Dr # 100, Indianapolis IN 46241
Tel (317) 487-9594 *SIC* 4581

MIDWEST AIR TRAFFIC CONTROL SERVICE INC p 967
7285 W 132nd St Ste 340, Overland Park KS 66213
Tel (913) 782-7082 *SIC* 4581

AEROFLEX WICHITA INC p 30
10200 W York St, Wichita KS 67215
Tel (316) 522-4981 *SIC* 4581

IFR SYSTEMS INC p 730
10200 W York St, Wichita KS 67215
Tel (316) 522-4981 *SIC* 4581

■ **TEXTRON AVIATION INC** p 1445
1 Cessna Blvd, Wichita KS 67215
Tel (316) 517-6000 *SIC* 4581

■ **SOUTHERN AIR HOLDINGS INC** p 1347
7310 Turfway Rd Ste 400, Florence KY 41042
Tel (859) 568-9200 *SIC* 4522 4581

■ **WORLDWIDE AIR LOGISTICS GROUP INC** p 1626
7310 Turfway Rd Ste 490, Florence KY 41042
Tel (859) 568-9300 *SIC* 4522 4581

▲ **PHI INC** p 1142
2001 Se Evangeline Trwy, Lafayette LA 70508
Tel (337) 235-2452 *SIC* 4512 4522 4581

ST LANDRY PARISH AIRPORT AUTHORITY p 1369
299 Hangar Rd, Opelousas LA 70570
Tel (337) 407-1551 *SIC* 4581

L B & B ASSOCIATES INC p 833
9891 Broken Land Pkwy # 400, Columbia MD 21046
Tel (301) 621-3944
SIC 8744 7338 4225 8742 8748 4581

■ **AECOM GOVERNMENT SERVICES INC** p 28
20501 Seneca Meadows Pkwy, Germantown MD 20876
Tel (703) 921-1600
SIC 4959 4173 4581 7299

URS FEDERAL SUPPORT SERVICES INC p 1530
20501 Seneca Meadows Pkwy # 300, Germantown MD 20876
Tel (301) 944-3100 *SIC* 8249 4581

MASSACHUSETTS PORT AUTHORITY p 917
1 Harborside Dr Ste 200s, Boston MA 02128
Tel (617) 561-1600
SIC 4581 4491 6799 6512 4785

WAYNE COUNTY AIRPORT AUTHORITY p 1584
1 Detroit Metro Airport, Detroit MI 48242
Tel (734) 247-7364 *SIC* 4581

CENTURION p 281
12225 Stephens Rd, Warren MI 48089
Tel (586) 939-7000 *SIC* 4213 4212 4581

METROPOLITAN AIRPORTS COMMISSION p 955
6040 28th Ave S, Minneapolis MN 55450
Tel (612) 726-8100 *SIC* 4581

PETTERS AVIATION LLC p 1140
431 S 7th St Ste 2530, Minneapolis MN 55415
Tel (612) 238-7780 *SIC* 4581

■ **L-3 COMMUNICATIONS VERTEX AEROSPACE LLC** p 835
555 Industrial Dr S, Madison MS 39110
Tel (601) 856-2274 *SIC* 4581 5088

AIRPORT TERMINAL SERVICES FOREIGN HOLDINGS CORP p 40
111 West Port Plz Ste 400, Saint Louis MO 63146
Tel (314) 739-1900 *SIC* 4581

AIRPORT TERMINAL SERVICES INC p 40
111 West Port Plz Ste 400, Saint Louis MO 63146
Tel (314) 739-1900 *SIC* 4581

BI-STATE DEVELOPMENT AGENCY OF MISSOURI-ILLINOIS METROPOLITAN DISTRICT (INC) p 181
211 N Broadway Ste 700, Saint Louis MO 63102
Tel (314) 982-1400 *SIC* 4111 4581

INTEGRATED DEICING SERVICES LLC p 749
175 Ammon Dr, Manchester NH 03103
Tel (603) 647-1717 *SIC* 3728 4581

AIR SAFETY EQUIPMENT INC p 39
1601 State Route 27, Edison NJ 08817
Tel (732) 591-9412 *SIC* 4581

NIAGARA FRONTIER TRANSPORTATION AUTHORITY p 1042
181 Ellicott St Ste 1, Buffalo NY 14203
Tel (716) 855-7300 *SIC* 4111 4581

INTEGRATED AIRLINE SERVICES INC p 749
1639 W 23rd St Ste 240, Jamaica NY 11430
Tel (718) 880-3453 *SIC* 4581

TERMINAL ONE GROUP ASSOCIATION LP p 1439
Jfk International Airport, Jamaica NY 11430
Tel (718) 751-1700 *SIC* 4581

■ **ATLANTIC AVIATION FBO HOLDINGS LLC** p 126
600 5th Ave Fl 21, New York NY 10020
Tel (212) 548-6538 *SIC* 4581 4785 1731

▲ **MACQUARIE INFRASTRUCTURE CORP** p 893
125 W 55th St, New York NY 10019
Tel (212) 231-1000
SIC 5172 4581 4785 7521 4932

MATLINPATTERSON ATA HOLDINGS LLC p 920
520 Madison Ave Fl 35, New York NY 10022
Tel (212) 651-9500 *SIC* 4581

PORT AUTHORITY OF NEW YORK & NEW JERSEY p 1162
4 World Trade Ctr 150, New York NY 10007
Tel (212) 435-7000
SIC 4581 4785 6512 4491 4111

TRIANGLE SERVICES INC p 1478
10 5th St Ste 200, Valley Stream NY 11581
Tel (516) 561-1700
SIC 7349 4581 1799 7382

HAECO USA HOLDINGS INC p 652
623 Radar Rd, Greensboro NC 27410
Tel (336) 668-4410 *SIC* 4581

TAS HOLDING INC p 1425
623 Radar Rd, Greensboro NC 27410
Tel (336) 668-4410 *SIC* 4581 5088

TIMCO AVIATION SERVICES INC p 1454
623 Radar Rd, Greensboro NC 27410
Tel (336) 668-4410 *SIC* 4581 5088

TRIAD INTERNATIONAL MAINTENANCE CORP p 1478
623 Radar Rd, Greensboro NC 27410
Tel (336) 668-4410 *SIC* 4581

COLUMBUS REGIONAL AIRPORT AUTHORITY p 342
4600 Intl Gtwy Ste 2, Columbus OH 43219
Tel (614) 239-4015 *SIC* 4581

FLIGHT OPTIONS INC p 556
26180 Curtiss Wright Pkwy, Richmond Heights OH 44143
Tel (216) 261-3880 *SIC* 4581

EXEL INC p 518
570 Polaris Pkwy, Westerville OH 43082
Tel (614) 865-8500 *SIC* 4213 4225 4581

■ **ABX AIR INC** p 13
145 Hunter Dr, Wilmington OH 45177
Tel (937) 382-5591
SIC 4513 5088 4581 8299

PAPE GROUP INC p 1112
355 Goodpasture Island Rd # 300, Eugene OR 97401
Tel (541) 334-3400
SIC 5084 5082 7699 6141 5599 4581

EVERGREEN AVIATION GROUND LOGISTICS ENTERPRISE INC p 514
3850 Three Mile Ln, Mcminnville OR 97128
Tel (503) 472-9361 *SIC* 4581

ERICKSON INC p 507
5550 Sw Mcdam Ave Ste 200, Portland OR 97239
Tel (503) 505-5800
SIC 7363 4581 3721 7359 5599 3728

■ **LOCKHEED MARTIN AIRCRAFT CENTER** p 873
244 Terminal Rd, Greenville SC 29605
Tel (864) 422-6262 *SIC* 3721 4581

■ **LOCKHEED MARTIN LOGISTIC SERVICES INC** p 873
244 Terminal Rd, Greenville SC 29605
Tel (864) 236-3552 *SIC* 4581

STEVENS AVIATION INC p 1388
600 Delaware St, Greenville SC 29605
Tel (864) 678-6000
SIC 4522 4581 5088 5599

MEMPHIS-SHELBY COUNTY AIRPORT AUTHORITY p 942
2491 Winchester Rd # 113, Memphis TN 38116
Tel (901) 922-8000 *SIC* 4581

METROPOLITAN NASHVILLE AIRPORT AUTHORITY p 956
1 Terminal Dr Ste 501, Nashville TN 37214
Tel (615) 275-1600 *SIC* 4581

DALLAS/FORT WORTH INTERNATIONAL AIRPORT p 410
3200 E Airfield Dr, Dfw Airport TX 75261
Tel (972) 973-8888 *SIC* 4581

▲ **AMERICAN AIRLINES GROUP INC** p 67
4333 Amon Carter Blvd, Fort Worth TX 76155
Tel (817) 963-1234 *SIC* 4512 4581

PAE APPLIED TECHNOLOGIES LLC p 1107
6500 West Fwy Ste 600, Fort Worth TX 76116
Tel (817) 737-1500
SIC 8741 8711 8744 4581 7381

■ **TWA AIRLINES LLC** p 1494
4333 Amon Carter Blvd, Fort Worth TX 76155
Tel (817) 963-1234 *SIC* 4512 4522 4581

ETHOSENERGY GTS HOLDINGS (US) LLC p 511
2800 North Loop W # 1100, Houston TX 77092
Tel (281) 227-5600 *SIC* 1731 7699 4581

JOHN WOOD GROUP US HOLDINGS INC p 789
17325 Park Row Ste 500, Houston TX 77084
Tel (281) 828-3500 *SIC* 4581

LANDMARK FBO LLC p 843
1500 Citywest Blvd # 600, Houston TX 77042
Tel (713) 895-9243 *SIC* 4581

PIEDMONT HAWTHORNE AVIATION LLC p 1147
1500 City W Blvd Ste 600, Houston TX 77042
Tel (713) 895-9243
SIC 5599 4581 4522 5172

SERVISAIR LLC p 1308
151 Northpoint Dr, Houston TX 77060
Tel (281) 260-3900 *SIC* 4581

SWISSPORT USA INC p 1413
151 Northpoint Dr, Houston TX 77060
Tel (281) 443-7687 *SIC* 4581

UTC OVERSEAS INC p 1536
2 Northpoint Dr Ste 213, Houston TX 77060
Tel (713) 422-2850 *SIC* 4412 4581

HUNTLEIGH USA CORP p 720
545 E John Carpenter Fwy, Irving TX 75062
Tel (972) 719-9180 *SIC* 4581

PERIMETER INTERNATIONAL p 1136
2700 Story Rd W Ste 150, Irving TX 75038
Tel (877) 701-1919
SIC 7389 4412 4731 4581 4449

WORLDWIDE FLIGHT SERVICES INC p 1626
1925 W John Carpenter Fwy # 450, Irving TX 75063
Tel (972) 629-5001 *SIC* 4581 4789

■ **ATLANTIC AVIATION CORP** p 125
6652 Pinecrest Dr Ste 300, Plano TX 75024
Tel (972) 905-2500
SIC 4581 5088 5172 6331 6159 4522

■ **RAYTHEON E-SYSTEMS INC** p 1211
1727 Cityline Dr, Richardson TX 75082
Tel (972) 205-9374
SIC 3663 3812 7373 3575 4581 3721

■ **L-3 COMMUNICATIONS INTEGRATED SYSTEMS LP** p 835
1309 Ridge Rd Ste 401, Rockwall TX 75087
Tel (903) 455-3450 *SIC* 4581

DEE HOWARD CO p 421
9610 John Saunders Rd, San Antonio TX 78216
Tel (210) 828-1341 *SIC* 3721 3724 4581

TRUMAN ARNOLD COMPANIES p 1486
701 S Robison Rd, Texarkana TX 75501
Tel (903) 794-3835 *SIC* 5172 4581

PAE AVIATION AND TECHNICAL SERVICES LLC p 1107
1320 N Courthouse Rd # 800, Arlington VA 22201
Tel (856) 866-2200 *SIC* 4581 3728 8742

RELATIVITY CAPITAL LLC p 1221
1655 Fort Myer Dr Fl 7, Arlington VA 22209
Tel (703) 812-3020 *SIC* 6282 4581

SWISSPORT CARGO SERVICES LP p 1413
23723 Air Frt Ln Bldg 5, Dulles VA 20166
Tel (703) 742-4300 *SIC* 4581

SWISSPORT USA INC p 1413
45025 Aviation Dr Ste 350, Dulles VA 20166
Tel (703) 742-4300 *SIC* 4581

■ **NORTHROP GRUMMAN SYSTEMS CORP** p 1058
2980 Fairview Park Dr, Falls Church VA 22042
Tel (703) 280-2900
SIC 3721 3761 3728 3812 3825 4581

AKIMA MANAGEMENT SERVICES LLC p 42
13873 Park Center Rd 400n, Herndon VA 20171
Tel (571) 323-5200 *SIC* 4581

■ **NORTHROP GRUMMAN TECHNICAL SERVICES INC** p 1058
2340 Dulles Corner Blvd, Herndon VA 20171
Tel (703) 713-4096 *SIC* 4581 7699

■ **DYNCORP** p 465
1700 Old Meadow Rd, Mc Lean VA 22102
Tel (571) 722-0210
SIC 7373 7371 7374 7375 8744 4581

■ **TITAN II INC** p 1456
4101 Washington Ave, Newport News VA 23607
Tel (757) 380-2000
SIC 3728 3761 7373 3721 4581 3812

AVIATION TECHNICAL SERVICES INC p 138
3121 109th St Sw, Everett WA 98204
Tel (425) 347-3030 *SIC* 4581 8711

■ **PRATT & WHITNEY ENGINE SERVICES INC** p 1167
1525 Midway Park Rd, Bridgeport WV 26330
Tel (860) 565-4321 *SIC* 7699 3724 4581

SIC 4612 Crude Petroleum Pipelines

■ **TEXACO INC** p 1441
6001 Bollinger Canyon Rd, San Ramon CA 94583
Tel (925) 842-1000
SIC 5541 5511 1321 4612 4613 4412

▲ **TRANSMONTAIGNE PARTNERS LP** p 1472
1670 Broadway Ste 3100, Denver CO 80202
Tel (303) 626-8200 *SIC* 4612 5171

COLONIAL PIPELINE CO p 338
1185 Sanctuary Pkwy # 100, Alpharetta GA 30009
Tel (678) 762-2200
SIC 4613 4612 4226 1389 5171

CONTRACTING & MATERIAL CO p 364
9550 W 55th St Ste A, Countryside IL 60525
Tel (708) 588-6000
SIC 4922 1623 4612 1731

B P OIL PIPELINE CO p 142
28301 Ferry Rd, Warrenville IL 60555
Tel (630) 420-5111 *SIC* 4612

BP AMERICA INC p 205
4101 Winfield Rd Ste 200, Warrenville IL 60555
Tel (630) 420-5111
SIC 2911 5171 4612 4613 4424

BP PIPELINES (NORTH AMERICA) INC p 206
28100 Torch Pkwy Ste 600, Warrenville IL 60555
Tel (630) 836-5100 *SIC* 4612 4613

■ **CHS MCPHERSON REFINERY INC** p 304
2000 S Main St, Mcpherson KS 67460
Tel (620) 241-2340 *SIC* 2911 4612 4213

FLINT HILLS RESOURCES LP p 557
4111 E 37th St N, Wichita KS 67220
Tel (800) 292-3133
SIC 5172 4612 1382 2911

MINNESOTA PIPE LINE CO LLC p 974
4111 E 37th St N, Wichita KS 67220
Tel (316) 828-5500 *SIC* 4612

TOTAL AMERICAN SERVICES INC p 1462
100 Town Square Pl # 401, Jersey City NJ 07310
Tel (206) 626-3500
SIC 2911 4612 5541 2895

■ **PBF LOGISTICS LP** p 1123
1 Sylvan Way Ste 2, Parsippany NJ 07054
Tel (973) 455-7500 *SIC* 4612

■ **MARATHON PIPE LINE LLC** p 904
539 S Main St Ste 7614, Findlay OH 45840
Tel (419) 422-2121 *SIC* 4612 4613

▲ **MPLX LP** p 995
200 E Hardin St, Findlay OH 45840
Tel (419) 672-6500 *SIC* 4612 4613

▲ **BLUEKNIGHT ENERGY PARTNERS LP** p 193
201 Nw 10th St Ste 200, Oklahoma City OK 73103
Tel (405) 278-6400 *SIC* 4612 4226

■ **ENABLE MIDSTREAM PARTNERS LP** p 495
211 N Robinson Ave S410, Oklahoma City OK 73102
Tel (405) 525-7788 *SIC* 4922 4612 4619

ROSE ROCK MIDSTREAM LP p 1250
6120 S Yale Ave Ste 1500, Tulsa OK 74136
Tel (918) 524-7700 *SIC* 1311 4612

▲ **SEMGROUP CORP** p 1302
6120 S Yale Ave Ste 700, Tulsa OK 74136
Tel (918) 524-8100
SIC 1389 4612 5171 2951

▲ **SUNOCO LOGISTICS PARTNERS LP** p 1403
3807 West Chester Pike, Newtown Square PA 19073
Tel (866) 248-4344
SIC 4612 4613 5171 5172

■ **SUNOCO PARTNERS LLC** p 1403
3807 West Chester Pike, Newtown Square PA 19073
Tel (866) 248-4344 *SIC* 4612

ATLANTIC PETROLEUM CORP p 127
1801 Market St Ste 1500, Philadelphia PA 19103
Tel (215) 977-3000
SIC 5541 5172 2911 4612

UNITED REFINING INC p 1511
15 Bradley St, Warren PA 16365
Tel (814) 723-1500
SIC 2911 5541 5411 4612

■ **DELEK LOGISTICS PARTNERS LP** p 424
7102 Commerce Way, Brentwood TN 37027
Tel (615) 771-6701 *SIC* 4612 4613

■ **DELEK REFINING LIMITED PARTNERSHIP** p 424
7102 Commerce Way, Brentwood TN 37027
Tel (615) 771-6701 *SIC* 4612 2911

▲ **DELEK US HOLDINGS INC** p 424
7102 Commerce Way, Brentwood TN 37027
Tel (615) 771-6701
SIC 2911 4612 5541 5411

■ **LION OIL CO** p 869
7102 Commerce Way, Brentwood TN 37027
Tel (615) 771-6701 *SIC* 2911 4612 5172

VENABLES CONSTRUCTION INC p 1547
7410 Continental Pkwy, Amarillo TX 79119
Tel (806) 381-2121
SIC 1623 1794 1389 4922 4612 1799

■ **ALON USA LP** p 59
12700 Park Central Dr # 1600, Dallas TX 75251
Tel (972) 367-3600
SIC 2911 4612 5172 5541 2895

■ **HOLLY ENERGY PARTNERS LP** p 701
2828 N Harwood St # 1300, Dallas TX 75201
Tel (214) 871-3555 *SIC* 4612 4613 5171

■ **HOLLYFRONTIER REFINING & MARKETING LLC** p 701
2828 N Harwood St # 1300, Dallas TX 75201
Tel (214) 871-3555 *SIC* 2911 4612

■ **WESTERN REFINING LOGISTICS LP** p 1599
123 W Mills Ave Ste 200, El Paso TX 79901
Tel (915) 534-1400 *SIC* 4613 4612

■ **BLUE DOLPHIN ENERGY CO** p 192
801 Travis St Ste 2100, Houston TX 77002
Tel (713) 568-4725
SIC 1311 1382 4612 4922

BP CORP NORTH AMERICA INC p 205
501 Westlake Park Blvd, Houston TX 77079
Tel (281) 366-2000
SIC 2911 5541 5171 1311 4613 4612

▲ **BUCKEYE PARTNERS LP** p 223
1 Greenway Plz Ste 600, Houston TX 77046
Tel (832) 615-8600
SIC 4612 4789 4226 4213

■ **BURLINGTON RESOURCES INC** p 228
600 N Dairy Ashford Rd, Houston TX 77079
Tel (281) 293-1000
SIC 1311 5172 4922 4612

CITGO PETROLEUM CORP p 309
1293 Eldridge Pkwy, Houston TX 77077
Tel (832) 486-4000
SIC 2911 5171 4213 4612

■ **EL PASO CGP CO LLC** p 483
1001 Louisiana St, Houston TX 77002
Tel (713) 420-2600
SIC 2911 1311 4613 4612 5541 4922

ENBRIDGE (US) INC *p* 495
1100 Louisiana St # 3300, Houston TX 77002
Tel (713) 821-2000 *SIC* 4612

▲ ENBRIDGE ENERGY PARTNERS LP *p* 495
1100 La St Ste 3300, Houston TX 77002
Tel (713) 821-2000 *SIC* 4612 4922 4924

EQUILON ENTERPRISES LLC *p* 506
910 Louisiana St Ste 2, Houston TX 77002
Tel (713) 241-6161
SIC 2911 4612 2992 5172

■ EXXON PIPELINE HOLDINGS INC *p* 521
800 Bell St Rm 2441, Houston TX 77002
Tel (713) 656-3636 *SIC* 4612 4613

■ GENESIS CRUDE OIL LP *p* 602
919 Milam St Ste 2100, Houston TX 77002
Tel (713) 860-2500 *SIC* 4612

▲ GENESIS ENERGY LP *p* 602
919 Milam St Ste 2100, Houston TX 77002
Tel (713) 860-2500 *SIC* 4612 5171 4212

■ MARATHON OIL CO *p* 904
5555 San Felipe St # 2796, Houston TX 77056
Tel (713) 629-6600
SIC 2911 5171 5541 1311 4612 4613

■ PHILLIPS 66 PARTNERS LP *p* 1144
3010 Briarpark Dr, Houston TX 77042
Tel (855) 283-9237 *SIC* 4612 1311 5541

■ PLAINS ALL AMERICAN PIPELINE LP *p* 1153
333 Clay St Ste 1600, Houston TX 77002
Tel (713) 646-4100 *SIC* 4612 5172

▲ PLAINS GP HOLDINGS LP *p* 1153
333 Clay St Ste 1600, Houston TX 77002
Tel (713) 646-4100 *SIC* 4612 1321

SHELL MIDSTREAM PARTNERS LP *p* 1314
910 Louisiana St, Houston TX 77002
Tel (713) 241-6161 *SIC* 4612

SHELL OIL CO *p* 1314
910 Louisiana St Ste 1500, Houston TX 77002
Tel (713) 241-6161
SIC 5541 4612 1311 2821 2869 2911

SHELL PIPE LINE CORP *p* 1314
2 Shell Plz Ste 1160, Houston TX 77002
Tel (713) 241-6161 *SIC* 4612

▲ EXXON MOBIL CORP *p* 521
5959 Las Colinas Blvd, Irving TX 75039
Tel (972) 444-1000
SIC 2911 4612 5541 5171 4911

■ MOBIL CORP *p* 980
5959 Las Colinas Blvd, Irving TX 75039
Tel (972) 444-1000
SIC 2911 5171 4612 4613 1311

■ ENERGY TRANSFER CRUDE OIL CO LLC *p* 498
800 E Sonterra Blvd, San Antonio TX 78258
Tel (210) 403-7300 *SIC* 4612

▲ NUSTAR ENERGY LP *p* 1067
19003 W Ih 10, San Antonio TX 78257
Tel (210) 918-2000 *SIC* 4612 4613 4226

▲ NUSTAR GP HOLDINGS LLC *p* 1067
19003 W Ih 10, San Antonio TX 78257
Tel (210) 918-2000 *SIC* 4612 4613

▲ TESORO LOGISTICS LP *p* 1440
19100 Ridgewood Pkwy, San Antonio TX 78259
Tel (210) 626-6000 *SIC* 1311 4612

■ TPI PETROLEUM INC *p* 1467
6000 N Loop 1604 W, San Antonio TX 78249
Tel (210) 592-2000
SIC 2911 5541 4612 4212 4213

VALERO ENERGY PARTNERS LP *p* 1539
1 Valero Way, San Antonio TX 78249
Tel (210) 345-2000 *SIC* 4612 4613 4789

■ EXXONMOBIL PIPELINE CO *p* 521
22777 Sprngwoods Vlg Pkwy, Spring TX 77389
Tel (713) 656-3636 *SIC* 4612 4613 2911

■ CVR REFINING HOLDINGS LLC *p* 404
2277 Plaza Dr Ste 500, Sugar Land TX 77479
Tel (281) 207-3200 *SIC* 2911 4612

■ CVR REFINING LP *p* 404
2277 Plaza Dr Ste 500, Sugar Land TX 77479
Tel (281) 207-3200 *SIC* 2911 4612

SINCLAIR COMPANIES *p* 1326
550 E South Temple, Salt Lake City UT 84102
Tel (801) 363-5100
SIC 2911 4612 1382 5541 7011 0212

SIC 4613 Refined Petroleum Pipelines

■ TEXACO INC *p* 1441
6001 Bollinger Canyon Rd, San Ramon CA 94583
Tel (925) 842-1000
SIC 5541 5511 1321 4612 4613 4412

TAMPA PIPELINE CORP *p* 1423
5802 Hartford St, Tampa FL 33619
Tel (813) 623-2431 *SIC* 4613

COLONIAL PIPELINE CO *p* 338
1185 Sanctuary Pkwy # 100, Alpharetta GA 30009
Tel (678) 762-2200
SIC 4613 4612 4226 1389 5171

BP AMERICA INC *p* 205
4101 Winfield Rd Ste 200, Warrenville IL 60555
Tel (630) 420-5111
SIC 2911 5171 4612 4613 4424

BP PIPELINES (NORTH AMERICA) INC *p* 206
28100 Torch Pkwy Ste 600, Warrenville IL 60555
Tel (630) 836-5100 *SIC* 4612 4613

WOLVERINE PIPE LINE CO *p* 1621
8075 Creekside Dr Ste 210, Portage MI 49024
Tel (269) 323-2491 *SIC* 4613

CENEX INC *p* 275
5500 Cenex Dr, Inver Grove Heights MN 55077
Tel (800) 232-3639
SIC 1311 2911 4613 4922 4789 4213

▲ CHS INC *p* 304
5500 Cenex Dr, Inver Grove Heights MN 55077
Tel (651) 355-6000
SIC 5153 5191 2075 1311 2911 4613

ERGON INC *p* 507
2829 Lakeland Dr Ste 2000, Flowood MS 39232
Tel (601) 933-3000
SIC 2911 4213 4449 4613 5171 5172

■ PANENERGY CORP *p* 1111
526 S Church St, Charlotte NC 28202
Tel (704) 594-6200
SIC 4922 1321 2813 5172 4911 4613

■ MARATHON PIPE LINE LLC *p* 904
539 S Main St Ste 7614, Findlay OH 45840
Tel (419) 422-2121 *SIC* 4612 4613

▲ MPLX LP *p* 995
200 E Hardin St, Findlay OH 45840
Tel (419) 672-6500 *SIC* 4612 4613

■ DEVON OEI OPERATING INC *p* 434
20 N Broadway, Oklahoma City OK 73102
Tel (405) 235-3611
SIC 4922 4924 1311 4613

■ MAGELLAN MIDSTREAM HOLDINGS GP LLC *p* 895
1 One Williams Ctr Bsmt 2, Tulsa OK 74172
Tel (918) 574-7000 *SIC* 4613

▲ MAGELLAN MIDSTREAM PARTNERS LP *p* 895
1 Williams Ctr Bsmt 2, Tulsa OK 74172
Tel (918) 574-7000 *SIC* 5171 4613

■ MAGELLAN PIPELINE CO LP *p* 895
1 Williams Ctr, Tulsa OK 74172
Tel (918) 574-7000 *SIC* 4613

■ BUCKEYE PIPE LINE CO L P *p* 223
5002 Buckeye Rd, Emmaus PA 18049
Tel (484) 232-4000 *SIC* 4613

▲ SUNOCO LOGISTICS PARTNERS LP *p* 1403
3807 West Chester Pike, Newtown Square PA 19073
Tel (866) 248-4344
SIC 4612 4613 5171 5172

■ DELEK LOGISTICS PARTNERS LP *p* 424
7102 Commerce Way, Brentwood TN 37027
Tel (615) 771-6701 *SIC* 4612 4613

■ EXXONMOBIL OIL CORP *p* 521
2805 Sycamore St, Beaumont TX 77701
Tel (409) 757-3763
SIC 2911 5171 4613 1311

■ HOLLY ENERGY PARTNERS LP *p* 701
2828 N Harwood St # 1300, Dallas TX 75201
Tel (214) 871-3555 *SIC* 4612 4613 5171

▲ HOLLYFRONTIER CORP *p* 701
2828 N Harwood St # 1300, Dallas TX 75201
Tel (214) 871-3555 *SIC* 2911 4613

■ WESTERN REFINING LOGISTICS LP *p* 1599
123 W Mills Ave Ste 200, El Paso TX 79901
Tel (915) 534-1400 *SIC* 4613 4612

BP CORP NORTH AMERICA INC *p* 205
501 Westlake Park Blvd, Houston TX 77079
Tel (281) 366-2000
SIC 2911 5541 5171 1311 4613 4612

BP PRODUCTS NORTH AMERICA INC *p* 206
501 Westlake Park Blvd, Houston TX 77079
Tel (281) 366-2000 *SIC* 5541 5171 4613

■ EL PASO CGP CO LLC *p* 483
1001 Louisiana St, Houston TX 77002
Tel (713) 420-2600
SIC 2911 1311 4613 4612 5541 4922

■ EXXON PIPELINE HOLDINGS INC *p* 521
800 Bell St Rm 2441, Houston TX 77002
Tel (713) 656-3636 *SIC* 4612 4613

■ KINDER MORGAN ENERGY PARTNERS LP *p* 819
1001 La St Ste 1000, Houston TX 77002
Tel (713) 369-9000
SIC 4613 4925 4922 4226 4619 5171

■ MARATHON OIL CO *p* 904
5555 San Felipe St # 2796, Houston TX 77056
Tel (713) 629-6600
SIC 2911 5171 5541 1311 4612 4613

SHELL PETROLEUM INC *p* 1314
910 Louisiana St Ste 420, Houston TX 77002
Tel (713) 241-6161 *SIC* 2911 4613 5172

TE PRODUCTS PIPELINE CO LIMITED PARTNERSHIP *p* 1429
1100 La St Ste 1600, Houston TX 77002
Tel (713) 381-3636 *SIC* 4613 4922

■ MOBIL CORP *p* 980
5959 Las Colinas Blvd, Irving TX 75039
Tel (972) 444-1000
SIC 2911 5171 4612 4613 1311

■ LEGACYSTAR SERVICES LLC *p* 852
2435 N Central Expy # 700, Richardson TX 75080
Tel (972) 699-4062 *SIC* 4613 5172

■ NUSTAR PIPELINE PARTNERS LP *p* 1067
2435 N Central Expy Ste 7, Richardson TX 75080
Tel (972) 699-4062 *SIC* 4613

▲ NUSTAR ENERGY LP *p* 1067
19003 W Ih 10, San Antonio TX 78257
Tel (210) 918-2000 *SIC* 4612 4613 4226

▲ NUSTAR GP HOLDINGS LLC *p* 1067
19003 W Ih 10, San Antonio TX 78257
Tel (210) 918-2000 *SIC* 4612 4613

VALERO ENERGY PARTNERS LP *p* 1539
1 Valero Way, San Antonio TX 78249
Tel (210) 345-2000 *SIC* 4612 4613 4789

▲ EMERGE ENERGY SERVICES LP *p* 491
180 State St Ste 225, Southlake TX 76092
Tel (817) 865-5830 *SIC* 1311 1389 4613

■ EXXONMOBIL PIPELINE CO *p* 521
22777 Sprngwoods Vlg Pkwy, Spring TX 77389
Tel (713) 656-3636 *SIC* 4612 4613 2911

SIC 4619 Pipelines, NEC

■ ENABLE MIDSTREAM PARTNERS LP *p* 495
211 N Robinson Ave S410, Oklahoma City OK 73102
Tel (405) 525-7788 *SIC* 4922 4612 4619

■ ENABLE MISSISSIPPI RIVER TRANSMISSION LLC *p* 495
211 N Robinson Ave N950, Oklahoma City OK 73102
Tel (405) 557-5271 *SIC* 4619

■ KINDER MORGAN ENERGY PARTNERS LP *p* 819
1001 La St Ste 1000, Houston TX 77002
Tel (713) 369-9000
SIC 4613 4925 4922 4226 4619 5171

TEXAS UNITED CORP *p* 1444
4800 San Felipe St, Houston TX 77056
Tel (713) 877-1793
SIC 1479 2819 4619 2899 3299 7353

SIC 4724 Travel Agencies

INTERNATIONAL CRUISE & EXCURSION GALLERY INC *p* 755
15501 N Dial Blvd, Scottsdale AZ 85260
Tel (602) 395-1995 *SIC* 4724

IDEA TRAVEL CO *p* 729
13145 Byrd Ln Ste 101, Los Altos Hills CA 94022
Tel (650) 948-0207 *SIC* 4724

JTB AMERICAS LTD *p* 796
19700 Mariner Ave, Torrance CA 90503
Tel (310) 303-3750 *SIC* 4724

TRAV CORP *p* 1473
10249 Church Ranch Way # 200, Broomfield CO 80021
Tel (303) 426-7000 *SIC* 4724

DIRECT TRAVEL INC *p* 441
7430 E Caley Ave Ste 220, Centennial CO 80111
Tel (952) 746-3575 *SIC* 4724

■ TRAVELERS HOME AND MARINE INSURANCE CO *p* 1474
1 Tower Sq 2ms, Hartford CT 06183
Tel (860) 548-9948 *SIC* 4724

▲ PRICELINE GROUP INC *p* 1174
800 Connecticut Ave 3w01, Norwalk CT 06854
Tel (203) 299-8000 *SIC* 4724 7375

AAA CLUB ALLIANCE INC *p* 7
1 River Pl, Wilmington DE 19801
Tel (302) 299-4700
SIC 8699 6331 6351 6512 4724

TOURICO HOLIDAYS INC *p* 1464
220 E Central Pkwy # 4000, Altamonte Springs FL 32701
Tel (407) 667-8700 *SIC* 4724

TRAVEL HOLDINGS INC *p* 1473
220 E Central Pkwy # 4010, Altamonte Springs FL 32701
Tel (407) 215-7465 *SIC* 4724

CLUB MED SALES INC *p* 328
6505 Blue Lagoon Dr # 225, Miami FL 33126
Tel (305) 925-9000
SIC 4724 4725 7011 8741

■ INTERVAL ACQUISITION CORP *p* 759
6262 Sunset Dr Ste 400, South Miami FL 33143
Tel (954) 431-0060 *SIC* 4724

FLORIDA TOURISM INDUSTRY MARKETING CORP *p* 559
2450 W Exec Ctr Cir 200, Tallahassee FL 32301
Tel (850) 488-5607 *SIC* 4724 8743 8742

AAA AUTO CLUB SOUTH INC *p* 7
1515 N West Shore Blvd, Tampa FL 33607
Tel (813) 289-5000
SIC 4724 6331 8699 6311

BCD TRAVEL USA LLC *p* 164
6 Concourse Pkwy Ste 2400, Atlanta GA 30328
Tel (678) 441-5200 *SIC* 4724 7372

TRAVELPORT LIMITED *p* 1474
300 Galleria Pkwy Se, Atlanta GA 30339
Tel (770) 563-7400 *SIC* 4724

WORLD TRAVEL PARTNERS GROUP INC *p* 1625
6 Concourse Pkwy, Atlanta GA 30328
Tel (678) 441-5200 *SIC* 4724

DULUTH TRAVEL INC *p* 461
2860 Peachtree Industrial, Duluth GA 30097
Tel (770) 813-9895 *SIC* 4724

TRAVEL INC *p* 1473
4355 River Green Pkwy, Duluth GA 30096
Tel (770) 291-4100 *SIC* 4724

ROBERTS HAWAII INC *p* 1242
680 Iwilei Rd Ste 700, Honolulu HI 96817
Tel (808) 523-7750
SIC 4119 4724 7011 4489

■ ORBITZ INC *p* 1092
200 S Wacker Dr, Chicago IL 60606
Tel (312) 894-5000 *SIC* 4724

■ ORBITZ LLC *p* 1092
500 W Madison St Ste 1000, Chicago IL 60661
Tel (312) 894-5000 *SIC* 4724

■ ORBITZ WORLDWIDE INC *p* 1093
500 W Madison St Ste 1000, Chicago IL 60661
Tel (312) 894-5000 *SIC* 4724

SMITHBUCKLIN CORP *p* 1333
330 N Wabash Ave, Chicago IL 60611
Tel (312) 644-6610 *SIC* 8742 8743 4724

CORPORATE TRAVEL CONSULTANTS INC *p* 372
450 E 22nd St Ste 100, Lombard IL 60148
Tel (630) 691-9100 *SIC* 4724

ITA GROUP INC *p* 767
4600 Westown Pkwy Ste 100, West Des Moines IA 50266
Tel (515) 326-3400 *SIC* 8742 4724

■ TRIPADVISOR INC *p* 1482
400 1st Ave, Needham MA 02494
Tel (781) 800-5000 *SIC* 4724 7374

MORLEY COMPANIES INC *p* 989
1 Morley Plz, Saginaw MI 48603
Tel (989) 791-2550 *SIC* 8742 4724

B4 TRAVEL GROUP INC *p* 143
701 Carlson Pkwy, Minnetonka MN 55305
Tel (763) 212-5000 *SIC* 4724

CARLSON HOLDINGS INC *p* 257
701 Carlson Pkwy, Minnetonka MN 55305
Tel (763) 212-5000
SIC 7011 5812 6794 7389 4724

CARLSON WAGONLIT TRAVEL INC *p* 258
701 Carlson Pkwy, Minnetonka MN 55305
Tel (763) 212-1000 *SIC* 4724

TRAVEL LEADERS GROUP LLC *p* 1473
3033 Campus Dr Ste W320, Plymouth MN 55441
Tel (763) 744-3700 *SIC* 4724

MARITZ TRAVEL CO *p* 907
1395 N Highway Dr, Fenton MO 63026
Tel (636) 827-4000 *SIC* 4724

CNS CORP *p* 330
500 E 9th St, Kansas City MO 64106
Tel (816) 842-6300 *SIC* 6211 6311 4724

■ GREAT SOUTHERN BANK *p* 634
14309 State Highway 13, Reeds Spring MO 65737
Tel (417) 888-5880 *SIC* 6021 4724 6712

AUTOMOBILE CLUB OF MISSOURI *p* 134
12901 N 40 Dr, Saint Louis MO 63141
Tel (314) 523-7350 *SIC* 8699 4724

TRAVEL AND TRANSPORT INC *p* 1473
2120 S 72nd St Ste 120, Omaha NE 68124
Tel (402) 399-4500 *SIC* 4724

▲ ALLEGIANT TRAVEL CO *p* 53
1201 N Town Center Dr, Las Vegas NV 89144
Tel (702) 851-7300 *SIC* 4512 4724

FLIGHT CENTRE USA HOLDING CORP *p* 556
5 Paragon Dr Ste 200, Montvale NJ 07645
Tel (201) 312-6855 *SIC* 4724

TRAVELPORT INC *p* 1474
6 Campus Dr Ste 1, Parsippany NJ 07054
Tel (770) 563-7400 *SIC* 4724

NORTHSTAR TRAVEL MEDIA LLC *p* 1059
100 Lighting Way Ste 200, Secaucus NJ 07094
Tel (201) 902-2000 *SIC* 2721 4789 4724

YUSEN LOGISTICS (AMERICAS) INC *p* 1640
300 Lighting Way Ste 600, Secaucus NJ 07094
Tel (201) 553-3800 *SIC* 4724 4731

■ AMERICAN EXPRESS TRAVEL RELATED SERVICES CO INC *p* 72
200 Vesey St, New York NY 10285
Tel (212) 640-2000 *SIC* 4724

MILL-RUN TOURS INC *p* 969
424 Madison Ave Fl 12, New York NY 10017
Tel (212) 486-9840 *SIC* 4724 4725

TZELL TRAVEL LLC *p* 1497
119 W 40th St Fl 14, New York NY 10018
Tel (212) 944-2121 *SIC* 4724

RAPTIM INTERNATIONAL TRAVEL INC *p* 1209
6420 Inducon Dr W Ste A, Sanborn NY 14132
Tel (716) 754-2946 *SIC* 4724

CAROLINA MOTOR CLUB INC *p* 259
6600 Aaa Dr, Charlotte NC 28212
Tel (704) 377-3600 *SIC* 8699 4724

AAA ALLIED GROUP INC *p* 7
15 W Central Pkwy, Cincinnati OH 45202
Tel (513) 762-3100 *SIC* 4724 8699

LAUREL HOLDINGS INC *p* 847
111 Roosevelt Blvd, Johnstown PA 15906
Tel (814) 533-5777
SIC 4941 5063 3599 4724 7349

AAA NORTHEAST *p* 7
110 Royal Little Dr, Providence RI 02904
Tel (401) 868-2000 *SIC* 8699 6411 4724

MARY KAY HOLDING CORP *p* 914
16251 Dallas Pkwy, Addison TX 75001
Tel (972) 687-6300
SIC 5963 3961 3172 4724

CAMPBELL RESOURCES LTD *p* 245
14800 Landmark Blvd # 155, Dallas TX 75254
Tel (972) 716-2500 *SIC* 4724

■ SOUTHWEST A B Q RES CENTER *p* 1351
2702 Love Field Dr, Dallas TX 75235
Tel (214) 792-4000 *SIC* 4724

■ TRAVELOCITY.COM LP *p* 1474
5400 L B Johnson Fwy 50 Ste 500, Dallas TX 75240
Tel (682) 605-1000 *SIC* 4724

UNIVERSAL WEATHER AND AVIATION INC *p* 1518
1150 Gemini St, Houston TX 77058
Tel (713) 944-1622 *SIC* 4725 4724

USAA CAPITAL CORP *p* 1534
9800 Fredericksburg Rd, San Antonio TX 78288
Tel (210) 498-2211
SIC 6035 6798 6722 7299 4813 4724

▲ SABRE CORP *p* 1264
3150 Sabre Dr, Southlake TX 76092
Tel (682) 605-1000 *SIC* 4724 7375

■ SABRE HOLDINGS CORP *p* 1264
3150 Sabre Dr, Southlake TX 76092
Tel (682) 605-1000 *SIC* 4724

CASTLES OF WORLD INC *p* 264
11150 Cash Rd, Stafford TX 77477
Tel (281) 269-2600 *SIC* 4724

CB TRAVEL CORP *p* 268
5588 S Green St Ste 300, Salt Lake City UT 84123
Tel (801) 327-7700 *SIC* 4724

MORRIS MURDOCK LLC *p* 990
101 S 200 E Ste 100, Salt Lake City UT 84111
Tel (801) 483-6441 *SIC* 4724

OMEGA WORLD TRAVEL INC *p* 1084
3102 Omega Office Park # 1, Fairfax VA 22031
Tel (703) 359-0200 *SIC* 4724

AGA (VIRGINIA) INC *p* 34
9950 Mayland Dr, Richmond VA 23233
Tel (804) 285-3300 *SIC* 6411 4724

LANDOR INTERNATIONAL INC *p* 843
2120 Staples Mill Rd # 300, Richmond VA 23230
Tel (804) 346-8200 *SIC* 6552 8741 4724

CHRISTIAN BROADCASTING NETWORK INC *p* 302
977 Centerville Tpke, Virginia Beach VA 23463
Tel (757) 226-3030
SIC 8661 4833 4832 5999 4724

▲ EXPEDIA INC *p* 519
333 108th Ave Ne, Bellevue WA 98004
Tel (425) 679-7200 *SIC* 4724

MEETINGS & INCENTIVES WORLDWIDE INC *p* 939
10520 7 Mile Rd, Caledonia WI 53108
Tel (262) 835-6710 *SIC* 4724 8742 7389

SIC 4725 Tour Operators

PRINCESS CRUISE LINES LTD *p* 1176
24305 Town Center Dr, Santa Clarita CA 91355
Tel (661) 753-0000 *SIC* 4481 4725 7011

DNC PARKS & RESORTS AT YOSEMITE INC p 446
9001 Village Dr, Yosemite Ntpk CA 95389
Tel (209) 372-1001
SIC 7011 5399 5812 5947 5541 4725

GROUP VOYAGERS INC p 642
5301 S Federal Cir, Littleton CO 80123
Tel (303) 703-7000 SIC 4725

▲ CARNIVAL CORP p 259
3655 Nw 87th Ave, Doral FL 33178
Tel (305) 599-2600 SIC 4481 4725 7011

CLUB MED SALES INC p 328
6505 Blue Lagoon Dr # 225, Miami FL 33126
Tel (305) 925-9000
SIC 4724 4725 7011 8741

■ MLT VACATIONS LLC p 979
700 S Central Ave, Atlanta GA 30354
Tel (651) 289-8500 SIC 4725

GRAND CIRCLE LLC p 629
347 Congress St, Boston MA 02210
Tel (617) 350-7500 SIC 4725

OVERSEAS ADVENTURE TRAVEL p 1099
347 Congress St Ste 2, Boston MA 02210
Tel (800) 955-1925 SIC 4725

MARITZ HOLDINGS INC p 907
1375 N Highway Dr, Fenton MO 63099
Tel (636) 827-4000
SIC 4725 8748 8732 4899

MARITZ LLC p 907
1375 N Highway Dr, Fenton MO 63099
Tel (636) 827-4000
SIC 4725 8748 8732 4899

COACH USA INC p 331
160 S Route 17 N, Paramus NJ 07652
Tel (201) 225-7500 SIC 4725 4111 4121

MILL-RUN TOURS INC p 969
424 Madison Ave Fl 12, New York NY 10017
Tel (212) 486-9840 SIC 4724 4725

UNIVERSAL WEATHER AND AVIATION INC p 1518
1150 Gemini St, Houston TX 77058
Tel (713) 944-1622 SIC 4725 4724

■ HOLLAND AMERICA LINE INC p 700
300 Elliott Ave W Ste 100, Seattle WA 98119
Tel (206) 281-3535 SIC 4725

LAMERS BUS LINES INC p 841
2407 S Point Rd, Green Bay WI 54313
Tel (920) 496-3600
SIC 4151 4142 4119 4725 4141

MARK TRAVEL CORP p 907
8907 N Port Washington Rd, Milwaukee WI 53217
Tel (414) 228-7472 SIC 4725

SIC 4729 Passenger Transportation Arrangement, NEC

■ CELEBRITY CRUISES INC p 273
1050 Caribbean Way, Miami FL 33132
Tel (305) 262-6677 SIC 4729

■ NCL (BAHAMAS) LTD A BERMUDA CO p 1022
7665 Corporate Center Dr, Miami FL 33126
Tel (305) 436-4000 SIC 4729

■ UNITED AIRLINES INC p 1506
233 S Wacker Dr Ste 430, Chicago IL 60606
Tel (872) 825-4000 SIC 4512 4513 4729

INDEPENDENT TRANSPORTERS OF HANDICAPPED INC p 737
221 N Sunrise Service Rd, Manorville NY 11949
Tel (631) 878-9270 SIC 8361 4729

PIEDMONT EXPRESS INC p 1147
7343 W Friendly Ave, Greensboro NC 27410
Tel (336) 855-7300 SIC 4729 4731

G2 SECURE STAFF LLC p 588
400 Las Colinas Blvd E # 750, Irving TX 75039
Tel (972) 915-6979 SIC 6411 4789 4729

SIC 4731 Freight Forwarding & Arrangement

NORTON LILLY INTERNATIONAL INC p 1061
1 Saint Louis St Ste 5000, Mobile AL 36602
Tel (251) 431-6335 SIC 4731

CARLILE TRANSPORTATION SYSTEMS INC p 257
1800 E 1st Ave, Anchorage AK 99501
Tel (907) 276-7797 SIC 4212 4213 4731

APL LOGISTICS AMERICAS LTD p 97
16220 N Scottsdale Rd, Scottsdale AZ 85254
Tel (602) 586-4800 SIC 4731

APL LOGISTICS LTD p 97
16220 N Scottsdale Rd # 300, Scottsdale AZ 85254
Tel (602) 586-4800
SIC 4412 4731 4491 4011

GLOBALTRANZ ENTERPRISES INC p 617
7350 N Dobson Rd Ste 135, Scottsdale AZ 85256
Tel (480) 339-5600 SIC 4731

MACH 1 GLOBAL SERVICES INC p 892
1530 W Broadway Rd, Tempe AZ 85282
Tel (480) 921-3900 SIC 4731 4212

▲ ARCBEST CORP p 104
3801 Old Greenwood Rd, Fort Smith AR 72903
Tel (479) 785-6000 SIC 4213 4731

PROPAK LOGISTICS INC p 1183
1100 Garrison Ave, Fort Smith AR 72901
Tel (479) 478-7800 SIC 7699 4731

▲ JB HUNT TRANSPORT SERVICES INC p 779
615 Jb Hunt Corp Dr, Lowell AR 72745
Tel (479) 820-0000 SIC 4213 4731

■ BNSF LOGISTICS LLC p 194
2710 S 48th St, Springdale AR 72762
Tel (479) 927-5570 SIC 4731

▲ PAM TRANSPORTATION SERVICES INC p 1110
297 W Henri De Tonti Blvd, Tontitown AR 72770
Tel (479) 361-9111 SIC 4213 4731

JS INTERNATIONAL SHIPPING CORP p 795
1535 Rollins Rd Ste B, Burlingame CA 94010
Tel (650) 697-3963 SIC 4731

KW INTERNATIONAL INC p 832
18655 Bishop Ave, Carson CA 90746
Tel (310) 747-1380 SIC 4731 4226 8744

MAINFREIGHT INC p 898
1400 Glenn Curtiss St, Carson CA 90746
Tel (310) 900-1974 SIC 4731

TRAFFIC TECH INC p 1469
910 Hale Pl Ste 100, Chula Vista CA 91914
Tel (514) 343-0044 SIC 4731

PERFORMANCE TEAM FREIGHT SYS INC p 1135
2240 E Maple Ave, El Segundo CA 90245
Tel (562) 345-2200 SIC 4731 4225 4213

AGILITY HOLDINGS INC p 35
310 Commerce Ste 250, Irvine CA 92602
Tel (714) 617-6300 SIC 4731 4213 4214

AGILITY LOGISTICS CORP p 35
240 Commerce, Irvine CA 92602
Tel (714) 617-6300
SIC 4731 8742 7372 1381

ALLEN LUND CO INC p 53
4529 Angeles Crest Hwy, La Canada Flintridge CA 91011
Tel (818) 790-8412 SIC 4731

ALLEN LUND CO LLC p 53
4529 Angeles Crest Hwy # 300, La Canada Flintridge CA 91011
Tel (818) 790-1110 SIC 4731

NACA HOLDINGS INC p 1006
5000 Arprt Plz Dr Ste 200, Long Beach CA 90815
Tel (650) 872-0800 SIC 4731

VANGUARD LOGISTICS SERVICES (USA) INC p 1543
5000 Airport Plaza Dr, Long Beach CA 90815
Tel (310) 847-3000 SIC 4731

G3 ENTERPRISES INC p 588
502 E Whitmore Ave, Modesto CA 95358
Tel (209) 341-7515 SIC 4731

PACIFIC LOGISTICS CORP p 1105
7255 Rosemead Blvd, Pico Rivera CA 90660
Tel (562) 478-4700 SIC 4731

CONTINENTAL AGENCY INC p 362
1768 W 2nd St, Pomona CA 91766
Tel (909) 595-8884 SIC 4731

CJ KOREA EXPRESS USA CORP p 320
18805 S Laurel Park Rd, Rancho Dominguez CA 90220
Tel (714) 994-1200 SIC 4731 4783 4225

DHX-DEPENDABLE HAWAIIAN EXPRESS INC p 435
19201 S Susana Rd, Rancho Dominguez CA 90220
Tel (310) 537-2000 SIC 4731

■ MENLO WORLDWIDE FORWARDING INC p 943
1 Lagoon Dr Ste 400, Redwood City CA 94065
Tel (650) 596-9600
SIC 4513 4215 4522 4731 6159 6351

MATHESON TRUCKING INC p 920
9785 Goethe Rd, Sacramento CA 95827
Tel (916) 685-2330 SIC 4213 4731

■ FRITZ COMPANIES INC p 580
550-1 Eccles Ave, San Francisco CA 94101
Tel (650) 635-2693 SIC 4731

■ XPO LOGISTICS WORLDWIDE INC p 1633
560 Mission St Ste 2950, San Francisco CA 94105
Tel (415) 486-2660
SIC 4731 4225 4213 8741

FEDEX FREIGHT WEST INC p 536
6411 Guadalupe Mines Rd, San Jose CA 95120
Tel (775) 356-7600 SIC 4213 4731 4212

MERIT INTEGRATED LOGISTICS LLC p 949
29122 Rancho Viejo Rd # 211, San Juan Capistrano CA 92675
Tel (949) 481-0685 SIC 4731

PASHA GROUP p 1119
4040 Civic Center Dr # 350, San Rafael CA 94903
Tel (415) 927-6400 SIC 4731

■ CHEVRON GLOBAL ENERGY INC p 296
6001 Bollinger Canyon Rd, San Ramon CA 94583
Tel (925) 842-1000 SIC 2911 4731 5172

BINEX LINE CORP p 183
19515 S Vermont Ave, Torrance CA 90502
Tel (310) 416-8600 SIC 4731 4513

FNS INC p 562
1545 Francisco St, Torrance CA 90501
Tel (661) 615-2300 SIC 4731

HECNY TRANSPORTATION INC p 680
1416 Francisco St, Torrance CA 90501
Tel (310) 347-3400 SIC 4731

NISSIN INTERNATIONAL TRANSPORT USA INC p 1044
1540 W 190th St, Torrance CA 90501
Tel (310) 222-8500 SIC 4731

VANTEC HITACHI TRANSPORT SYSTEM (USA) INC p 1544
991 Francisco St, Torrance CA 90502
Tel (310) 525-2900 SIC 4731

VPS COMPANIES INC p 1566
310 Walker St, Watsonville CA 95076
Tel (831) 724-7551 SIC 5142 0723 4731

NETWORK GLOBAL LOGISTICS LLC p 1028
320 Interlocken Pkwy # 100, Broomfield CO 80021
Tel (866) 938-1870 SIC 4731

FAK INC p 526
10885 E 51st Ave, Denver CO 80239
Tel (303) 289-5433 SIC 4731

FREIGHT ALL KINDS INC p 577
10885 E 51st Ave, Denver CO 80239
Tel (800) 321-7182 SIC 4731 4213

ODYSSEY LOGISTICS & TECHNOLOGY CORP p 1075
39 Old Ridgebury Rd Ste 7, Danbury CT 06810
Tel (203) 448-3900 SIC 4731

BRYNWOOD PARTNERS II LIMITED PARTNERSHIP p 222
8 Sound Shore Dr Ste 265, Greenwich CT 06830
Tel (203) 622-1790 SIC 6282 4731

JACOBS PRIVATE EQUITY LLC p 775
350 Round Hill Rd, Greenwich CT 06831
Tel (203) 413-4000 SIC 4731 6282 6726

▲ XPO LOGISTICS INC p 1632
5 Greenwich Office Park, Greenwich CT 06831
Tel (844) 742-5976 SIC 4731

FRANCHISEE SHIPPING CENTER CO INC p 573
500 Bic Dr Bldg 3, Milford CT 06461
Tel (203) 301-0539 SIC 4731 5943

TRINITY LOGISTICS INC p 1481
50 Fallon Ave, Seaford DE 19973
Tel (302) 253-3900 SIC 4731

SECURITY STORAGE CO OF WASHINGTON p 1299
1701 Florida Ave Nw, Washington DC 20009
Tel (202) 797-5659
SIC 4213 4226 4214 4731

SUNTECK HOLDINGS LLC p 1405
6413 Congress Ave Ste 260, Boca Raton FL 33487
Tel (561) 988-9456 SIC 4731 6719

SUNTECK INC p 1405
6413 Congress Ave Ste 260, Boca Raton FL 33487
Tel (561) 988-9456 SIC 4731

SUNTECK TRANSPORT CO INC p 1405
6413 Congress Ave Ste 260, Boca Raton FL 33487
Tel (561) 988-9456 SIC 8741 4731

SUNTECK TRANSPORT GROUP INC p 1405
6413 Congress Ave Ste 260, Boca Raton FL 33487
Tel (561) 988-9456 SIC 4731

SOURCE INTERLINK COMPANIES INC p 1342
27200 Riverview Center Bl, Bonita Springs FL 34134
Tel (866) 276-5584 SIC 4731

IAP WORLD SERVICES INC p 725
7315 N Atlantic Ave, Cape Canaveral FL 32920
Tel (321) 784-7100
SIC 4731 4581 8744 4911 1541 4813

IAP WORLDWIDE SERVICES INC p 725
7315 N Atlantic Ave, Cape Canaveral FL 32920
Tel (973) 633-5115
SIC 4731 4581 8744 4911

AIR EXPRESS INTERNATIONAL USA INC p 38
1801 Nw 82nd Ave, Doral FL 33126
Tel (786) 264-3500 SIC 4731 4513

ANSA MCAL (US) INC p 93
11403 Nw 39th St, Doral FL 33178
Tel (305) 599-8766 SIC 7389 4731

ANSA MCAL TRADING INC p 93
11403 Nw 39th St, Doral FL 33178
Tel (305) 599-8766
SIC 8741 5084 5085 4731

HELLMANN WORLDWIDE LOGISTICS INC p 682
10450 Doral Blvd, Doral FL 33178
Tel (305) 406-4500 SIC 4731

CARROLL FULMER HOLDING CORP p 261
8340 American Way, Groveland FL 34736
Tel (352) 429-5000 SIC 4731

CARROLL FULMER LOGISTICS CORP p 261
8340 American Way, Groveland FL 34736
Tel (352) 429-5000 SIC 4731

■ LANDSTAR GLOBAL LOGISTICS INC p 843
13410 Sutton Park Dr S, Jacksonville FL 32224
Tel (904) 390-4751 SIC 4731

NETWORK FOB INC p 1028
6622 Sthpint Dr S Ste 210, Jacksonville FL 32216
Tel (651) 256-1000 SIC 4731

SUDDATH COMPANIES p 1396
815 S Main St Ste 400, Jacksonville FL 32207
Tel (904) 390-7100 SIC 4214 4731

SUDDATH VAN LINES INC p 1396
815 S Main St Ste 400, Jacksonville FL 32207
Tel (904) 390-7100 SIC 4213 4731 4214

JJJTB INC p 786
3200 Flightline Dr, Lakeland FL 33811
Tel (863) 607-5600 SIC 4731

SENATOR INTERNATIONAL FREIGHT FORWARDING LLC p 1303
10201 Nw 112th Ave Ste 10, Medley FL 33178
Tel (305) 593-5520 SIC 4731

SENATOR INTERNATIONAL HOLDING LLC p 1303
10201 Nw 112th Ave Ste 10, Medley FL 33178
Tel (305) 593-5520 SIC 4731

SCHENKER AMERICAS INC p 1286
1000 Nw 57th Ct Ste 700, Miami FL 33126
Tel (786) 388-4300 SIC 4731

NATIONAL AIR CARGO HOLDINGS INC p 1009
5955 T G Lee Blvd Ste 200, Orlando FL 32822
Tel (716) 631-0011 SIC 4731

ARMELLINI INDUSTRIES INC p 111
3446 Sw Armellini Ave, Palm City FL 34990
Tel (772) 287-0575 SIC 4213 5193 4731

DHL EXPRESS (USA) INC p 435
1210 S Pine Island Rd, Plantation FL 33324
Tel (954) 888-7000 SIC 4513 7389 4731

DPWN HOLDINGS (USA) INC p 454
1210 S Pine Island Rd, Plantation FL 33324
Tel (954) 888-7000 SIC 4513 4731

IQOR GLOBAL SERVICES LLC p 764
1 Progress Plz Ste 7, Saint Petersburg FL 33701
Tel (727) 369-0878 SIC 8748 4731

COMVEST INVESTMENT PARTNERS III LP p 353
525 Okeechobee Blvd # 1050, West Palm Beach FL 33401
Tel (561) 727-2000
SIC 4731 5912 5999 3652 8742 1731

INTEGRA LOGISTICS LLC p 748
4400 Alexander Dr 1w, Alpharetta GA 30022
Tel (678) 775-5140 SIC 4731

JAS AMERICA HOLDING INC p 778
5424 Glenridge Dr, Atlanta GA 30342
Tel (770) 688-1240 SIC 4731

JAS FORWARDING (USA) INC p 778
6165 Barfield Rd, Atlanta GA 30328
Tel (770) 688-1206 SIC 4731

■ LOGISTICARE SOLUTIONS LLC p 874
1275 Peachtree St Ne Fl 6, Atlanta GA 30309
Tel (404) 888-5800 SIC 4731

■ UPS LOGISTICS GROUP INC p 1529
55 Glenlake Pkwy, Atlanta GA 30328
Tel (678) 746-4100
SIC 7389 7513 4731 4513

BROWN INTEGRATED LOGISTICS INC p 219
6908 Chapman Rd, Lithonia GA 30058
Tel (770) 482-6521
SIC 4225 4213 4731 7359

■ XPO LAST MILE INC p 1632
1851 W Oak Pkwy Ste 100, Marietta GA 30062
Tel (866) 373-7874 SIC 4731

NOLAN TRANSPORTATION GROUP LLC p 1046
85 Mill St Ste 214, Roswell GA 30075
Tel (770) 509-9611 SIC 4731

AMERICAN TRANSPORT GROUP LLC p 80
1900 W Kinzie St, Chicago IL 60622
Tel (773) 235-9600 SIC 4731

BMM LOGISTICS INC p 194
209 W Jackson Blvd # 903, Chicago IL 60606
Tel (312) 730-7495 SIC 4731

■ COMMAND TRANSPORTATION LLC p 344
600 W Chicago Ave Ste 725, Chicago IL 60654
Tel (847) 213-2200 SIC 4731

■ COYOTE LOGISTICS LLC p 387
2545 W Diversey Ave Fl 3, Chicago IL 60647
Tel (877) 626-9683 SIC 4731

▲ ECHO GLOBAL LOGISTICS INC p 475
600 W Chicago Ave Ste 725, Chicago IL 60654
Tel (800) 354-7993 SIC 4731 4813

FLS TRANSPORTATION SERVICES INC p 561
180 N La Salle St # 2950, Chicago IL 60601
Tel (877) 744-7357 SIC 8742 4731

TRAFFIC TECH HOLDING CORP p 1469
180 N Michigan Ave # 700, Chicago IL 60601
Tel (514) 343-0044 SIC 4731

TRANSLOGIX LLC p 1472
2001 E 122nd St, Chicago IL 60633
Tel (773) 646-8300 SIC 4731

DSC LOGISTICS INC p 457
1750 S Wolf Rd, Des Plaines IL 60018
Tel (847) 390-6800
SIC 4225 4213 4212 4731

TIGERS (USA) GLOBAL LOGISTICS INC p 1453
25 Northwest Point Blvd # 1025, Elk Grove Village IL 60007
Tel (516) 825-4774
SIC 4731 4581 4522 4512

WEISS-ROHLIG USA LLC p 1588
1601 Estes Ave, Elk Grove Village IL 60007
Tel (224) 563-3200 SIC 4731

MEDSPEED LLC p 939
655 W Grand Ave Ste 320, Elmhurst IL 60126
Tel (630) 617-5050 SIC 4731

■ AMCOL INTERNATIONAL CORP p 65
2870 Forbs Ave, Hoffman Estates IL 60192
Tel (847) 851-1500
SIC 1459 5032 4213 4731

■ INNOVEL SOLUTIONS INC p 745
3333 Beverly Rd, Hoffman Estates IL 60179
Tel (847) 286-2500 SIC 4731 8741 8742

AIT WORLDWIDE LOGISTICS INC p 41
701 N Rohlwing Rd, Itasca IL 60143
Tel (630) 766-0711 SIC 4731

MID-AMERICA OVERSEAS INC p 963
650 E Devon Ave Ste 150, Itasca IL 60143
Tel (630) 285-9083 SIC 4731

NNR GLOBAL LOGISTICS USA INC p 1045
450 E Devon Ave Ste 260, Itasca IL 60143
Tel (630) 773-1490 SIC 4731

SEKO GLOBAL LOGISTICS NETWORK LLC p 1301
1100 Arlington Ste 600, Itasca IL 60143
Tel (630) 919-4800 SIC 4731

SEKO WORLDWIDE LLC p 1301
1100 N Arlingtn Hts 600, Itasca IL 60143
Tel (630) 919-4800 SIC 4731

MOL (AMERICA) INC p 982
700 E Bttrfeld Rd Ste 250, Lombard IL 60148
Tel (630) 424-3480 SIC 4731 7373 4412

STAR TRANSPORT INC p 1378
240 W Ashland St, Morton IL 61550
Tel (309) 266-7613 SIC 4213 4731

AFN LLC p 33
7230 N Caldwell Ave, Niles IL 60714
Tel (847) 498-8885 SIC 4731

CUSTOM COMPANIES INC p 403
317 W Lake St, Northlake IL 60164
Tel (708) 344-5555 SIC 4731 4214

▲ HUB GROUP INC p 715
2000 Clearwater Dr, Oak Brook IL 60523
Tel (630) 271-3600 SIC 4731

TRANSPORT SERVICE CO p 1472
2001 Spring Rd Ste 400, Oak Brook IL 60523
Tel (630) 472-5900 SIC 4213 4731

■ MATSON LOGISTICS INC p 920
1815 S Meyers Rd Ste 700, Oakbrook Terrace IL 60181
Tel (630) 203-3500 SIC 4731

SIRVA INC p 1327
1 Parkview Plz, Oakbrook Terrace IL 60181
Tel (630) 570-3047
SIC 4213 4214 4731 7513 6331

SIRVA WORLDWIDE INC p 1327
1 Parkview Plz Ste 300, Oakbrook Terrace IL 60181
Tel (630) 570-3047
SIC 4213 4214 4731 7513 6331

VONACHEN SERVICES INC p 1565
8900 N Pioneer Rd, Peoria IL 61615
Tel (309) 691-6202
SIC 7349 4731 8741 7361

EMERY AIR INC p 492
46 Airport Dr, Rockford IL 61109
Tel (815) 987-4100 SIC 4731

LESAINT LOGISTICS LLC p 857
868 W Crossroads Pkwy, Romeoville IL 60446
Tel (630) 243-5950 SIC 4731 4225 8742

RIM LOGISTICS LTD p 1235
200 N Gary Ave Ste B, Roselle IL 60172
Tel (630) 595-0610 SIC 4731

WLG INC p 1620
920 E Algonquin Rd # 120, Schaumburg IL 60173
Tel (773) 416-2803 SIC 4731

■ **CH ROBINSON FREIGHT SERVICES LTD** p 286
1501 N Mittel Blvd Ste A, Wood Dale IL 60191
Tel (630) 766-4445 *SIC* 4731 4225

RJW LOGISTICS INC p 1239
11240 Katherines Xing, Woodridge IL 60517
Tel (630) 424-2400 *SIC* 4731

CARTER LOGISTICS LLC p 262
4020 W 73rd St, Anderson IN 46011
Tel (765) 778-6960 *SIC* 4731

ADS LOGISTICS CO LLC p 24
116 E 1100 N, Chesterton IN 46304
Tel (219) 836-3900 *SIC* 4731

ATLAS WORLD GROUP INC p 128
1212 Saint George Rd, Evansville IN 47711
Tel (812) 424-2222 *SIC* 4213 4731

VAN ATLAS LINES INC p 1542
1212 Saint George Rd, Evansville IN 47711
Tel (812) 424-4326 *SIC* 4213 4731

BUCHANAN LOGISTICS INC p 222
4625 Industrial Rd, Fort Wayne IN 46825
Tel (260) 471-1877 *SIC* 4731

NORTH AMERICAN VAN LINES INC p 1050
5001 Us Highway 30 W, Fort Wayne IN 46818
Tel (260) 429-1682
SIC 4213 4731 4214 6331 7389 4212

BULKMATIC TRANSPORT CO INC p 225
2001 N Cline Ave, Griffith IN 46319
Tel (219) 972-7630 *SIC* 4213 4731 4212

LDI LOGISTICS INC p 849
54 Monument Cir Ste 800, Indianapolis IN 46204
Tel (317) 237-5400 *SIC* 4731

MAYS CHEMICAL CO INC p 924
5611 E 71st St, Indianapolis IN 46220
Tel (317) 842-8722 *SIC* 5169 4731

PROTRANS INTERNATIONAL INC p 1185
8311 N Perimeter Rd, Indianapolis IN 46241
Tel (317) 240-4100 *SIC* 4731

WHEATON VAN LINES INC p 1604
8010 Castleton Rd, Indianapolis IN 46250
Tel (317) 849-7900 *SIC* 4213 4731 4214

■ **CLP TOWNE INC** p 328
24805 Us Highway 20, South Bend IN 46628
Tel (574) 233-3183 *SIC* 4731

US 1 INDUSTRIES INC p 1530
336 W Us Highway 30 # 201, Valparaiso IN 46385
Tel (219) 476-1300 *SIC* 4213 4731

JACOBSON TRANSPORTATION CO INC p 775
1275 Nw 128th St, Clive IA 50325
Tel (515) 262-1236 *SIC* 4213 4731

ARLO TRANSPORTATION INC p 110
3811 Dixon St, Des Moines IA 50313
Tel (515) 265-6171 *SIC* 4731

MIQ HOLDINGS INC p 974
11501 Outlook St Ste 500, Overland Park KS 66211
Tel (913) 696-7363 *SIC* 4225 4731 8741

MIQ LOGISTICS LLC p 974
11501 Outlook St Ste 500, Overland Park KS 66211
Tel (913) 696-7100 *SIC* 4731 8741

SHAMROCK TRADING CORP p 1311
9300 Metcalf Ave, Overland Park KS 66212
Tel (913) 310-2200
SIC 4731 6153 8742 7323

A&R LOGISTICS INC p 7
600 N Hurstbourne Pkwy # 110, Louisville KY 40222
Tel (815) 941-5200 *SIC* 8742 4731

■ **UPS CUSTOMHOUSE BROKERAGE INC** p 1529
1930 Bishop Ln Ste 200, Louisville KY 40218
Tel (502) 485-2600 *SIC* 4731

DUPRE INVESTMENTS INC p 462
201 Energy Pkwy Ste 500, Lafayette LA 70508
Tel (337) 237-8471 *SIC* 4212 4213 4731

H & M BAY INC p 649
1800 Industrial Park Rd, Federalsburg MD 21632
Tel (410) 754-8001 *SIC* 4731

TRI-GAS & OIL CO INC p 1477
3941 Federalsburg Hwy, Federalsburg MD 21632
Tel (410) 754-2000 *SIC* 5172 5984 4731

CHOPTANK TRANSPORT INC p 302
3601 Choptank Rd, Preston MD 21655
Tel (410) 673-2240 *SIC* 4731

C H POWELL CO p 232
75 Shawmut Rd, Canton MA 02021
Tel (781) 302-7300 *SIC* 4731

WEST COAST DISTRIBUTING INC p 1594
350 Main St Fl 1, Malden MA 02148
Tel (781) 665-0300 *SIC* 4731 5148

SOLSTICE HOLDINGS INC p 1339
7575 Fulton St E, Ada MI 49355
Tel (616) 787-1000 *SIC* 4731

■ **XPO CNW INC** p 1632
2211 Old Earhart Rd, Ann Arbor MI 48105
Tel (253) 926-2251 *SIC* 4213 4731 3715

SYNCREON AMERICA INC p 1414
2851 High Meadow Cir, Auburn Hills MI 48326
Tel (248) 377-4700 *SIC* 4731

URS MIDWEST INC p 1530
10701 Middlebelt Rd, Romulus MI 48174
Tel (888) 278-2793 *SIC* 4731

THYSSENKRUPP INDUSTRIAL SERVICES NA INC p 1451
22355 W 11 Mile Rd, Southfield MI 48033
Tel (248) 233-5600 *SIC* 4225 4731

BAY & BAY TRANSPORTATION SERVICES INC p 160
2905 W Svc Rd Ste 2000, Eagan MN 55121
Tel (651) 480-7961 *SIC* 4731

■ **C H ROBINSON INTERNATIONAL INC** p 232
14701 Charlson Rd, Eden Prairie MN 55347
Tel (952) 683-2800 *SIC* 4731

■ **CH ROBINSON CO INC** p 286
14701 Charlson Rd, Eden Prairie MN 55347
Tel (952) 937-7896 *SIC* 4731

▲ **CH ROBINSON WORLDWIDE INC** p 286
14701 Charlson Rd, Eden Prairie MN 55347
Tel (952) 937-8500 *SIC* 4731

EBERSEN INC p 474
7401 Central Ave Ne Ste 2, Minneapolis MN 55432
Tel (763) 572-2661
SIC 4911 1521 6211 1382 4731 8711

STAN KOCH & SONS TRUCKING INC p 1375
4200 Dahlberg Dr Ste 100, Minneapolis MN 55422
Tel (763) 302-5400 *SIC* 4213 4731

CERNX MN LLC p 284
2355 Highway 36 W Ste 400, Roseville MN 55113
Tel (320) 372-7400
SIC 4212 7389 4731 4222

BERGER TRANSFER & STORAGE INC p 174
2950 Long Lake Rd, Saint Paul MN 55113
Tel (651) 639-2260 *SIC* 4731 4213 4214

HALL ENTERPRISES INC p 654
731 Bielenberg Dr Ste 108, Woodbury MN 55125
Tel (651) 552-4905 *SIC* 4731

MILLER TRANSPORTERS INC p 971
5500 Highway 80 W, Jackson MS 39209
Tel (601) 922-8331 *SIC* 4731

CPC LOGISTICS INC p 387
14528 South Outer 40 Rd # 210, Chesterfield MO 63017
Tel (314) 542-2266 *SIC* 4731

TRI-STATE MOTOR TRANSIT CO INC p 1478
8141 E 7th St, Joplin MO 64801
Tel (800) 234-8768 *SIC* 4213 4731

■ **FREIGHTQUOTE.COM INC** p 577
901 Carondelet Dr, Kansas City MO 64114
Tel (913) 642-4700 *SIC* 4731

WAGNER INDUSTRIES INC p 1571
1201 E 12th Ave, North Kansas City MO 64116
Tel (816) 421-3520 *SIC* 4225 4214 4731

ITS LOGISTICS LLC p 768
620 Spice Islands Dr, Reno NV 89501
Tel (775) 358-5300 *SIC* 4731 4225

SAVINO DEL BENE USA INC p 1284
34 Engelhard Ave, Avenel NJ 07001
Tel (347) 960-5568 *SIC* 3799 4731

TOLL GLOBAL FORWARDING (AMERICAS) INC p 1459
800 Federal Blvd Ste 3, Carteret NJ 07008
Tel (732) 750-9000 *SIC* 4789 4731

TOLL GLOBAL FORWARDING SCS (USA) INC p 1459
800 Federal Blvd Ste 2, Carteret NJ 07008
Tel (732) 750-9000 *SIC* 4731 8741

NFI INTERACTIVE LOGISTICS LLC p 1041
1515 Burnt Mill Rd, Cherry Hill NJ 08003
Tel (856) 857-1324 *SIC* 4731 8742

DSV AIR & SEA HOLDING INC p 458
100 Walnut Ave Ste 405, Clark NJ 07066
Tel (732) 850-8000 *SIC* 4731

UTI UNITED STATES INC p 1536
100 Walnut Ave Ste 405, Clark NJ 07066
Tel (732) 850-8000 *SIC* 4731

ALLIANCE SHIPPERS INC p 55
516 Sylvan Ave, Englewood Cliffs NJ 07632
Tel (201) 227-0400 *SIC* 4731

DAMCO USA INC p 410
180 Park Ave Ste 105, Florham Park NJ 07932
Tel (973) 514-5000 *SIC* 4412 4491 4731

MAERSK INC p 894
180 Park Ave Ste 105, Florham Park NJ 07932
Tel (973) 514-5000 *SIC* 4731 4491 4412

SHIPCO TRANSPORT INC p 1317
80 Washington St, Hoboken NJ 07030
Tel (973) 457-3300 *SIC* 8742 4731

SSNYC INC p 1364
80 Washington St, Hoboken NJ 07030
Tel (201) 216-1500 *SIC* 4731 6512

GEODIS WILSON USA INC p 605
485c Us Highway 1 S # 410, Iselin NJ 08830
Tel (732) 362-0600 *SIC* 4731 4412 4225

H & M INTERNATIONAL TRANSPORTATION INC p 649
485b Us Highway 1 S # 110, Iselin NJ 08830
Tel (732) 510-4640 *SIC* 4731 8741 4225

EVERGREEN SHIPPING AGENCY (AMERICA) CORP p 515
1 Evertrust Plz, Jersey City NJ 07302
Tel (201) 761-3000 *SIC* 4731

KUEHNE + NAGEL INC p 831
10 Exchange Pl Fl 19, Jersey City NJ 07302
Tel (201) 413-5500 *SIC* 4731

KUEHNE + NAGEL INVESTMENT INC p 831
10 Exchange Pl Fl 19, Jersey City NJ 07302
Tel (201) 413-5500 *SIC* 4731

PANALPINA INC p 1111
1776 On The Green 67, Morristown NJ 07960
Tel (973) 683-9000 *SIC* 4731

TOTE INC p 1463
14 Nassau St Ste 3, Princeton NJ 08542
Tel (609) 454-3651 *SIC* 4731

COSCO CONTAINER LINES AMERICAS INC p 373
100 Lighting Way Fl 3, Secaucus NJ 07094
Tel (201) 422-0500 *SIC* 4731

NYK GROUP AMERICAS INC p 1069
300 Lighting Way Ste 500, Secaucus NJ 07094
Tel (201) 330-3000
SIC 4412 4731 4011 4491 7519

NYK LINE (NORTH AMERICA) INC p 1069
300 Lighting Way 4th, Secaucus NJ 07094
Tel (201) 330-3000
SIC 4412 4731 4213 4011 7519 4491

YUSEN LOGISTICS (AMERICAS) INC p 1640
300 Lighting Way Ste 600, Secaucus NJ 07094
Tel (201) 553-3800 *SIC* 4724 4731

BETT-A-WAY TRAFFIC SYSTEMS INC p 178
110 Sylvania Pl, South Plainfield NJ 07080
Tel (908) 222-2500 *SIC* 4731

■ **FEDEX TRADE NETWORKS TRANSPORT & BROKERAGE INC** p 537
128 Dearborn St, Buffalo NY 14207
Tel (716) 879-1300 *SIC* 4731

EMO-TRANS INC p 493
135 Guy Lombardo Ave, Freeport NY 11520
Tel (516) 867-6800 *SIC* 4731

KARPELES FREIGHT SERVICES INC p 804
150 Albany Ave, Freeport NY 11520
Tel (516) 377-3000 *SIC* 4731

SCHENKER INC p 1286
150 Albany Ave, Freeport NY 11520
Tel (516) 377-3000 *SIC* 4731 4225

BOLLORE LOGISTICS USA INC p 198
15010 132nd Ave, Jamaica NY 11434
Tel (718) 276-3907 *SIC* 4731

KINTETSU WORLD EXPRESS (USA) INC p 821
1 Jericho Plz Ste 100, Jericho NY 11753
Tel (516) 933-7100 *SIC* 4731

NIPPON EXPRESS USA INC p 1044
2401 44th Rd Fl 14, Long Island City NY 11101
Tel (212) 758-6100 *SIC* 4731 4225

ASSOCIATED GLOBAL SYSTEMS INC p 120
3333 New Hyde Park Rd # 207, New Hyde Park NY 11042
Tel (516) 627-8910 *SIC* 4731

■ **BORDERFREE INC** p 201
292 Madison Ave, New York NY 10017
Tel (212) 299-3500 *SIC* 8742 4731 7312

CHOICE LOGISTICS INC p 302
1 Whitehall St Fl 12, New York NY 10004
Tel (917) 344-4000 *SIC* 4731

EXPRESS TRADE CAPITAL INC p 520
1410 Broadway Fl 26, New York NY 10018
Tel (212) 997-0155 *SIC* 6153 4731

FAIRFIELD-MAXWELL LTD p 525
60 E 42nd St Fl 55, New York NY 10165
Tel (212) 297-9030
SIC 8741 4731 5172 4412

MEDITERRANEAN SHIPPING CO (USA) INC p 938
420 5th Ave Fl 8, New York NY 10018
Tel (212) 764-8280 *SIC* 4731

MOHAWK CUSTOMS & SHIPPING CORP p 982
123 Air Cargo Rd, North Syracuse NY 13212
Tel (315) 455-3003 *SIC* 4731

ACTIVE MEDIA SERVICES INC p 20
1 Blue Hill Plz Ste 1705, Pearl River NY 10965
Tel (845) 735-1700 *SIC* 7319 4731 4789

DB US CORP p 418
120 White Plains Rd, Tarrytown NY 10591
Tel (914) 366-7200 *SIC* 4789 4731

DB US HOLDING CORP p 418
120 White Plains Rd, Tarrytown NY 10591
Tel (914) 366-7203 *SIC* 4731

SCHENKER (BAX) HOLDING CORP p 1286
120 White Plains Rd, Tarrytown NY 10591
Tel (914) 366-7200 *SIC* 4731

LIVINGSTON INTERNATIONAL INC p 871
670 Young St, Tonawanda NY 14150
Tel (716) 692-3100 *SIC* 4731

■ **SERVICE BY AIR INC** p 1307
222 Crossways Park Dr, Woodbury NY 11797
Tel (800) 243-5545 *SIC* 4731

■ **HORIZON LINES HOLDING CORP** p 707
2550 W Tyvola Rd Ste 530, Charlotte NC 28217
Tel (704) 973-7000 *SIC* 4731 6512

HORIZON LINES LLC p 707
2550 W Tyvola Rd Ste 530, Charlotte NC 28217
Tel (877) 678-7447
SIC 4424 4783 4731 4412

■ **MATSON ALASKA INC** p 920
2550 W Tyvola Rd, Charlotte NC 28217
Tel (704) 973-7000 *SIC* 4424 4731 4412

■ **RED CLASSIC TRANSIT LLC** p 1215
1800 Continental Blvd # 400, Charlotte NC 28273
Tel (980) 275-5721 *SIC* 4731

CARDINAL LOGISTICS HOLDINGS LLC p 253
5333 Davidson Hwy, Concord NC 28027
Tel (972) 228-7300 *SIC* 4213 4731

FREIGHT HANDLERS INC p 577
310 N Judd Pkwy Ne, Fuquay Varina NC 27526
Tel (919) 552-3157 *SIC* 4731 7363

EPES LOGISTICS SERVICES INC p 504
538 N Regional Rd, Greensboro NC 27409
Tel (336) 665-1553 *SIC* 4731

PIEDMONT EXPRESS INC p 1147
7343 W Friendly Ave, Greensboro NC 27410
Tel (336) 855-7300 *SIC* 4729 4731

■ **XPO LOGISITCS SUPPLY CHAIN HOLDING CO** p 1632
4035 Piedmont Pkwy, High Point NC 27265
Tel (336) 232-4100 *SIC* 4731

■ **XPO LOGISTICS SUPPLY CHAIN INC** p 1633
4035 Piedmont Pkwy, High Point NC 27265
Tel (336) 232-4100 *SIC* 4731

■ **XPO LOGISTICS WORLDWIDE GOVERNMENT SERVICES LLC** p 1633
4035 Piedmont Pkwy, High Point NC 27265
Tel (844) 742-5976
SIC 4731 4225 4213 8741

■ **XPO LOGISTICS WORLDWIDE LLC** p 1633
4035 Piedmont Pkwy, High Point NC 27265
Tel (415) 486-2660 *SIC* 4731 4512 4213

■ **XPO SUPPLY CHAIN INC** p 1633
4035 Piedmont Pkwy, High Point NC 27265
Tel (336) 232-4100 *SIC* 4731

▲ **OLD DOMINION FREIGHT LINE INC** p 1080
500 Old Dominion Way, Thomasville NC 27360
Tel (336) 889-5000 *SIC* 4213 4212 4731

MEGACORP LOGISTICS LLC p 939
7040 Wrightsville Ave, Wilmington NC 28403
Tel (910) 332-0820 *SIC* 4731

MBI ENERGY LOGISTICS LLC p 925
12980 35th St Sw, Belfield ND 58622
Tel (701) 575-8242 *SIC* 4731

KGBO HOLDINGS INC p 816
4289 Ivy Pointe Blvd, Cincinnati OH 45245
Tel (513) 831-2600 *SIC* 4731

TOTAL QUALITY LOGISTICS LLC p 1463
4289 Ivy Pointe Blvd, Cincinnati OH 45245
Tel (513) 831-2600 *SIC* 4731

WORLD SHIPPING INC p 1625
1340 Depot St Ste 200, Cleveland OH 44116
Tel (440) 356-7676 *SIC* 4213 4731

AIRNET SYSTEMS INC p 40
7250 Star Check Dr, Columbus OH 43217
Tel (614) 409-4900 *SIC* 4522 4731

WORKFLOWONE LLC p 1624
220 E Monument Ave, Dayton OH 45402
Tel (877) 735-4966
SIC 2754 2791 4225 4731 2752 2759

■ **PACER TRANSPORTATION SOLUTIONS INC** p 1103
5165 Emerald Pkwy, Dublin OH 43017
Tel (614) 923-1400 *SIC* 4731

■ **XPO INTERMODAL INC** p 1632
5165 Emerald Pkwy 300, Dublin OH 43017
Tel (614) 923-1400 *SIC* 4731

FARO SERVICES INC p 530
7070 Pontius Rd, Groveport OH 43125
Tel (614) 497-1700 *SIC* 4225 4731

■ **FEDEX SUPPLY CHAIN SERVICES INC** p 537
5455 Darrow Rd, Hudson OH 44236
Tel (800) 588-3020
SIC 8742 4213 8741 4731

TRIPLE T TRANSPORT INC p 1482
704 Radio Dr, Lewis Center OH 43035
Tel (740) 657-3244 *SIC* 4731

JARRETT LOGISTICS SYSTEMS INC p 778
1347 N Main St, Orrville OH 44667
Tel (330) 682-0099 *SIC* 8742 4731

NK PARTS INDUSTRIES INC p 1045
777 S Kuther Rd, Sidney OH 45365
Tel (937) 498-4651 *SIC* 5013 1796 4731

MILLWOOD INC p 971
3708 International Blvd, Vienna OH 44473
Tel (330) 393-4400 *SIC* 3565 4731

MMTF LOGISTICS LLC p 979
8080 Beckett Center Dr, West Chester OH 45069
Tel (513) 860-2871 *SIC* 4731

EXEL NORTH AMERICAN LOGISTICS INC p 518
570 Players Pkwy, Westerville OH 43081
Tel (800) 272-1052 *SIC* 4731

COMPREHENSIVE LOGISTICS CO INC p 352
4944 Belmont Ave Ste 202, Youngstown OH 44505
Tel (800) 734-0372 *SIC* 4225 4731

OKLAHOMA ROOF MASTERS INC p 1080
601 Evergreen Dr, Guthrie OK 73044
Tel (405) 814-6440
SIC 1761 1541 4731 4212 4213

■ **ATC DRIVETRAIN LLC** p 124
9901 W Reno Ave, Oklahoma City OK 73127
Tel (405) 350-3600 *SIC* 3714 4731

S B INC p 1262
32921 Diamond Hill Dr, Harrisburg OR 97446
Tel (541) 995-7751 *SIC* 4213 4731

INTRANSIT INC p 760
3525 Excel Dr, Medford OR 97504
Tel (541) 773-3993 *SIC* 4731

ENDEAVOUR CAPITAL FUND LIMITED PARTNERSHIP p 496
920 Sw 6th Ave Ste 1400, Portland OR 97204
Tel (503) 223-2721 *SIC* 4213 4731 6799

MARKET INDUSTRIES LTD p 908
110 N Marine Dr, Portland OR 97217
Tel (503) 283-2405 *SIC* 4731 4213

OIA GLOBAL LOGISTICS-SCM INC p 1078
2100 Sw Rver Pkwy Ste 800, Portland OR 97201
Tel (503) 736-5900 *SIC* 4731

OREGON INTERNATIONAL AIR FREIGHT CO INC p 1093
2100 Sw Rver Pkwy Ste 800, Portland OR 97201
Tel (503) 736-5900 *SIC* 4731

UTI (US) HOLDINGS INC p 1536
400 Sw 6th Ave Ste 906, Portland OR 97204
Tel (503) 953-1300 *SIC* 4731

KEYSTONE SHIPPING CO p 816
1 Bala Plz Ste 600, Bala Cynwyd PA 19004
Tel (610) 617-6800 *SIC* 4731 4412 4424

PITTSBURGH LOGISTICS SYSTEMS INC p 1152
3120 Unionville Rd Ste 110, Cranberry Township PA 16066
Tel (724) 814-5100 *SIC* 4731

LOGISTICS PLUS INC p 875
1406 Peach St Ste 3, Erie PA 16501
Tel (814) 461-7600 *SIC* 4731

TMS INTERNATIONAL CORP p 1457
12 Monongahela Ave, Glassport PA 15045
Tel (412) 678-6141
SIC 3312 4731 3399 7359 4213

TMS INTERNATIONAL HOLDING CORP p 1457
12 Monongahela Ave, Glassport PA 15045
Tel (412) 678-6141
SIC 3312 4731 3399 7359 4213

TMS INTERNATIONAL LLC p 1458
12 Monongahela Ave, Glassport PA 15045
Tel (412) 678-6141
SIC 3312 4731 3399 7359 4213

ESSEX BROKERAGE p 510
57 Center Church Rd, Grove City PA 16127
Tel (724) 748-3126 *SIC* 4731

PGT TRUCKING INC p 1141
1 Pgt Way, Monaca PA 15061
Tel (724) 728-3500 *SIC* 4213 4731

BDP INTERNATIONAL INC p 164
510 Walnut St Fl 14, Philadelphia PA 19106
Tel (215) 629-8900 *SIC* 4731

GEODIS USA INC p 605
5101 S Broad St, Philadelphia PA 19112
Tel (215) 238-8600 *SIC* 4731 8741

SCHENKER INTERNATIONAL INC p 1286
3501 Island Ave, Philadelphia PA 19153
Tel (724) 695-7886 *SIC* 4731

■ **GENCO DISTRIBUTION SYSTEM INC** p 598
100 Papercraft Park, Pittsburgh PA 15238
Tel (412) 820-3700 *SIC* 4225 4731

R & R EXPRESS INC p 1201
3 Crafton Sq, Pittsburgh PA 15205
Tel (412) 920-1336 *SIC* 4731

R & R EXPRESS LOGISTICS INC p 1201
3 Crafton Sq, Pittsburgh PA 15205
Tel (800) 223-8973 *SIC* 4731

■ TRANSTAR INC p 1473
1200 Penn Ave Ste 300, Pittsburgh PA 15222
Tel (412) 433-4644 SIC 4449 4731

INTERNATIONAL SHIPPING AGENCY INC p 756
500 Paseo Monaco Apt 55, Bayamon PR 00956
Tel (787) 778-2355 SIC 4491 4731

COLINX LLC p 336
1 Independence Pt Ste 210, Greenville SC 29615
Tel (864) 607-9431 SIC 4731

ALLIED TRANSPORTATION SERVICES INC p 57
1533 Nw 2nd St, Madison SD 57042
Tel (877) 241-6237 SIC 7363 4731

GEODIS LOGISTICS LLC p 605
7101 Executive Center Dr # 333, Brentwood TN 37027
Tel (615) 401-6400
SIC 4225 8742 4226 4731

LIPSEY LOGISTICS WORLDWIDE LLC p 870
5600 Brainerd Rd Ste E2, Chattanooga TN 37411
Tel (678) 336-1180 SIC 4731 5499

NEW MOUNTAIN LAKE HOLDINGS LLC p 1032
4080 Jenkins Rd, Chattanooga TN 37421
Tel (423) 510-3000 SIC 4213 4731

US XPRESS ENTERPRISES INC p 1533
4080 Jenkins Rd, Chattanooga TN 37421
Tel (423) 510-3000 SIC 4213 4731

▲ FORWARD AIR CORP p 570
430 Airport Rd, Greeneville TN 37745
Tel (423) 636-7000 SIC 4731

■ FORWARD AIR INC p 570
430 Airport Rd, Greeneville TN 37745
Tel (423) 639-7196 SIC 4731

DUNAVANT ENTERPRISES INC p 461
959 Ridg Loop Rd Ste 200, Memphis TN 38120
Tel (901) 369-1500
SIC 5159 4221 4731 0131

■ EFS TRANSPORTATION SERVICES INC p 481
2525 Horizon Lake Dr # 120, Memphis TN 38133
Tel (901) 371-8000 SIC 4731

■ FEDEX TRADE NETWORKS INC p 537
6075 Poplar Ave Ste 300, Memphis TN 38119
Tel (901) 684-4800 SIC 4731

■ FREDS STORES OF TENNESSEE INC p 576
4300 New Getwell Rd, Memphis TN 38118
Tel (901) 365-8880 SIC 5331 4731

MALLORY ALEXANDER INTERNATIONAL LOGISTICS LLC p 900
4294 Swinnea Rd, Memphis TN 38118
Tel (901) 367-9400 SIC 4731 4225 4789

RE TRANSPORTATION INC p 1212
855 Ridge Lake Blvd # 500, Memphis TN 38120
Tel (901) 271-8830 SIC 4731

TCW INC p 1428
22 Stanley St, Nashville TN 37210
Tel (615) 255-1122 SIC 4731 4225

NEWGISTICS INC p 1037
2700 Via Fortuna Ste 300, Austin TX 78746
Tel (512) 225-6000 SIC 4731

GREATWIDE DEDICATED TRANSPORT LLC p 636
12404 Park Central Dr # 300, Dallas TX 75251
Tel (972) 228-7344 SIC 4213 4731

GREATWIDE LOGISTICS SERVICES LLC p 636
12404 Park Central Dr # 300, Dallas TX 75251
Tel (972) 228-7389 SIC 4213 4731

TRANSPORTATION 100 LLC p 1472
12404 Park Central Dr 300s, Dallas TX 75251
Tel (972) 228-7300 SIC 4213 4731

■ BNSF RAILWAY CO p 194
2650 Lou Menk Dr, Fort Worth TX 76131
Tel (800) 795-2673 SIC 4731 4011

■ BURLINGTON NORTHERN SANTA FE LLC p 228
2650 Lou Menk Dr, Fort Worth TX 76131
Tel (800) 795-2673 SIC 4731 4011

MAALT LP p 891
4413 Carey St, Fort Worth TX 76119
Tel (817) 205-0460 SIC 4225 4731

CI (TRANSPLACE) HOLDINGS LLC p 305
3010 Gaylord Pkwy Ste 200, Frisco TX 75034
Tel (972) 731-4500 SIC 4731

TRANSPLACE TEXAS LP p 1472
3010 Gaylord Pkwy Ste 200, Frisco TX 75034
Tel (972) 731-4500 SIC 4731

AGILITY PROJECT LOGISTICS INC p 35
15600 Morales Rd, Houston TX 77032
Tel (504) 465-1000 SIC 4731 4225

BERTSCHI NORTH AMERICA INC p 176
16902 El Cmno Real 3b Ste 3, Houston TX 77058
Tel (281) 751-8800 SIC 4731

■ CEVA FREIGHT LLC p 284
15350 Vickery Dr, Houston TX 77032
Tel (281) 618-3100
SIC 4214 4225 4412 4512 4522 4731

■ CEVA FREIGHT MANAGEMENT INTERNATIONAL GROUP INC p 284
15350 Vickery Dr, Houston TX 77032
Tel (281) 618-3100 SIC 4731

■ CEVA LOGISTICS LLC p 284
15350 Vickery Dr, Houston TX 77032
Tel (281) 618-3100 SIC 4731

■ CEVA LOGISTICS US INC p 285
15350 Vickery Dr, Houston TX 77032
Tel (281) 618-3100 SIC 4731

■ CIRCLE INTERNATIONAL INC p 308
15350 Vickery Dr, Houston TX 77032
Tel (281) 618-3100 SIC 4731

CRANE WORLDWIDE LOGISTICS LLC p 389
1500 Rankin Rd, Houston TX 77073
Tel (281) 443-2777 SIC 4731

EXPEDITED LOGISTICS AND FREIGHT SERVICES LLC p 519
4740 Consulate Plaza Dr, Houston TX 77032
Tel (281) 442-3323 SIC 4731

GULF WINDS INTERNATIONAL INC p 647
411 Brisbane St, Houston TX 77061
Tel (713) 747-4909 SIC 4225 4731

STOLT-NIELSEN USA INC p 1391
15635 Jacintoport Blvd, Houston TX 77015
Tel (203) 299-3600 SIC 4731

TUBULAR RAIL INC p 1490
5000 Milwee St Apt 43, Houston TX 77092
Tel (713) 834-7905 SIC 4731

HYUNDAI MERCHANT MARINE (AMERICA) INC p 724
222 Las Colinas Blvd W, Irving TX 75039
Tel (972) 501-1100 SIC 4731

PERIMETER INTERNATIONAL p 1136
2700 Story Rd W Ste 150, Irving TX 75038
Tel (877) 701-1919
SIC 7389 4412 4731 4581 4449

FFE LOGISTICS INC p 539
3400 Stonewall St, Lancaster TX 75134
Tel (214) 630-8090 SIC 4731

FROZEN FOOD EXPRESS INDUSTRIES INC p 582
3400 Stonewall St, Lancaster TX 75134
Tel (800) 569-9200 SIC 4731 4213

TA SERVICES INC p 1420
241 Regency Pkwy, Mansfield TX 76063
Tel (800) 626-2185 SIC 4731 4213

SPIRIT TRUCK LINES INC p 1359
200 W Nolana, San Juan TX 78589
Tel (956) 781-7715 SIC 4731

OOCL (USA) INC p 1088
10913 S River Front Pkwy # 200, South Jordan UT 84095
Tel (801) 302-6625 SIC 4731

A N DERINGER INC p 6
64 N Main St, Saint Albans VT 05478
Tel (802) 524-8110 SIC 4731

BAX GLOBAL INC p 160
1305 Executive Blvd # 200, Chesapeake VA 23320
Tel (866) 744-7282 SIC 4731

■ NORTHROP GRUMMAN ENTERPRISE MANAGEMENT SERVICES CORP p 1058
2340 Dulles Corner Blvd, Herndon VA 20171
Tel (703) 713-4000
SIC 8741 8744 4731 8331 7349

CMA CGM (AMERICA) LLC p 328
5701 Lake Wright Dr, Norfolk VA 23502
Tel (757) 961-2100 SIC 4731

ZIM AMERICAN INTEGRATED SHIPPING SERVICES CO INC p 1643
5801 Lake Wright Dr, Norfolk VA 23502
Tel (757) 228-1300 SIC 4731

EXEL GLOBAL LOGISTICS INC p 518
22879 Glenn Dr Ste 100, Sterling VA 20164
Tel (703) 350-1298 SIC 4731 4225

▲ RADIANT LOGISTICS INC p 1204
405 114th Ave Se Fl 3, Bellevue WA 98004
Tel (425) 943-4599 SIC 4731

TRANS-SYSTEM INC p 1470
7405 S Hayford Rd, Cheney WA 99004
Tel (509) 623-4001 SIC 4213 4731

AFF INC p 32
7400 45th Street Ct E, Fife WA 98424
Tel (253) 926-5000 SIC 4731 4213 7389

AMERICAN FAST FREIGHT INC p 72
7400 45th Street Ct E, Fife WA 98424
Tel (253) 926-5000
SIC 4731 4213 7389 4214

▲ ALASKA AIR GROUP INC p 44
19300 International Blvd, Seatac WA 98188
Tel (206) 392-5040 SIC 4512 4731

LYNDEN AIR FREIGHT INC p 888
18000 Intl Blvd Ste 700, Seatac WA 98188
Tel (206) 777-5300 SIC 4731

LYNDEN INC p 888
18000 Intl Blvd Ste 800, Seatac WA 98188
Tel (206) 241-8778 SIC 4213 4731 4424

▲ EXPEDITORS INTERNATIONAL OF WASHINGTON INC p 519
1015 3rd Ave Fl 12, Seattle WA 98104
Tel (206) 674-3400 SIC 4731

SSA MARINE INC p 1363
1131 Sw Klickitat Way, Seattle WA 98134
Tel (206) 623-0304 SIC 4491 4731

STONEPATH GROUP INC p 1391
2200 Alaskan Way Ste 200, Seattle WA 98121
Tel (206) 336-5400 SIC 4731

■ ROADRUNNER TRANSPORTATION SERVICES INC p 1240
4900 S Pennsylvania Ave, Cudahy WI 53110
Tel (414) 615-1500 SIC 4731

▲ ROADRUNNER TRANSPORTATION SYSTEMS INC p 1240
4900 S Pennsylvania Ave, Cudahy WI 53110
Tel (414) 615-1500 SIC 4731

SCHNEIDER LOGISTICS INC p 1288
3101 Packerland Dr, Green Bay WI 54313
Tel (920) 592-0000
SIC 4731 4225 4789 4212

SCHNEIDER NATIONAL CARRIERS INC p 1288
3101 Packerland Dr, Green Bay WI 54313
Tel (920) 592-2000 SIC 4731

SIC 4741 Railroad Car Rental

▲ GATX CORP p 594
222 W Adams St, Chicago IL 60606
Tel (312) 621-6200 SIC 4741 7359 4491

■ MARMON HOLDINGS INC p 909
181 W Madison St Ste 2600, Chicago IL 60602
Tel (312) 372-9500
SIC 5051 3351 3743 4741 3423 3589

■ MARMON INDUSTRIAL LLC p 909
181 W Madison St Fl 26, Chicago IL 60602
Tel (312) 372-9500
SIC 3743 4741 3589 6159 3965 3492

TTX CO p 1490
101 N Wacker Dr, Chicago IL 60606
Tel (312) 853-3223 SIC 4741

■ UNION TANK CAR CO p 1505
175 W Jackson Blvd # 2100, Chicago IL 60604
Tel (312) 431-3111
SIC 3743 4741 4789 5051

CHICAGO FREIGHT CAR LEASING CO p 297
425 N Martingale Rd Fl 6, Schaumburg IL 60173
Tel (847) 318-8000 SIC 4741 3643

TRANSPORTATION TECHNOLOGIES INDUSTRIES INC p 1473
7140 Office Cir, Evansville IN 47715
Tel (812) 962-5000
SIC 2531 3714 3321 4741 3471

■ ALLIANT INDUSTRIES INC p 55
200 1st St Se, Cedar Rapids IA 52401
Tel (398) 786-4268
SIC 4011 4741 4911 4924

WATCO INC p 1581
315 W 3rd St, Pittsburg KS 66762
Tel (208) 734-4644 SIC 4013 4741 4789

ACF INDUSTRIES HOLDING CORP p 17
767 5th Ave, New York NY 10153
Tel (212) 702-4363
SIC 3743 4741 4789 6799

BUFFALO INVESTORS CORP p 224
1 Wall Street Ct Apt 980, New York NY 10005
Tel (212) 702-4363 SIC 3743 4741

HIGHCREST INVESTORS LLC p 691
Icahn Associates Corp 767, New York NY 10153
Tel (212) 702-4323
SIC 3743 4741 4789 4813

STARFIRE HOLDING CORP p 1379
445 Hamilton Ave Ste 1210, White Plains NY 10601
Tel (914) 614-7000 SIC 3743 4741 4789

■ DJJ HOLDING CORP p 445
300 Pike St, Cincinnati OH 45202
Tel (513) 621-8770 SIC 5093 5088 4741

▲ ANDERSONS INC p 90
480 W Dussel Dr, Maumee OH 43537
Tel (419) 893-5050
SIC 5153 0723 5191 2874 4789 4741

■ TRINITY INDUSTRIES LEASING CO p 1481
2525 N Stemmons Fwy, Dallas TX 75207
Tel (800) 227-8844 SIC 4741 4499

SIC 4783 Packing & Crating Svcs

PRIMETIME INTERNATIONAL INC p 1175
86705 Avenue 54 Ste A, Coachella CA 92236
Tel (760) 399-4166 SIC 5148 4783

CJ KOREA EXPRESS USA CORP p 320
18805 S Laurel Park Rd, Rancho Dominguez CA 90220
Tel (714) 994-1200 SIC 4731 4783 4225

MOONLIGHT PACKING CORP p 987
17719 E Huntsman Ave, Reedley CA 93654
Tel (559) 638-7799 SIC 5148 4783

MANN PACKING CO INC p 902
1333 Schilling Pl, Salinas CA 93901
Tel (831) 422-7405 SIC 0723 4783 0722

■ UPS STORE INC p 1529
6060 Cornerstone Ct W, San Diego CA 92121
Tel (858) 455-8800 SIC 7389 8742 4783

FLEXTRONICS LOGISTICS USA INC p 556
6201 America Center Dr, San Jose CA 95002
Tel (408) 576-7000 SIC 4783

ATLANTA COMMUNITY FOOD BANK INC p 125
732 Jseph E Lwery Blvd Nw, Atlanta GA 30318
Tel (404) 892-9822 SIC 8322 4783

PEACOCK FOODS LLC p 1125
1800 Averill Rd, Geneva IL 60134
Tel (630) 845-9400 SIC 4783 7389

EXPORT PACKAGING CO INC p 520
525 10th Ave E, Milan IL 61264
Tel (309) 756-4288 SIC 4783 2448 2441

FCA LLC p 532
7601 John Deere Pkwy, Moline IL 61265
Tel (309) 792-3444
SIC 4783 5031 5085 2448

KEM KREST LLC p 809
3221 Magnum Dr, Elkhart IN 46516
Tel (574) 389-2650
SIC 5169 5013 5085 4783 4225

GOODWILL INDUSTRIES OF CENTRAL INDIANA INC p 624
1635 W Michigan St, Indianapolis IN 46222
Tel (317) 564-4313
SIC 5932 4783 8331 4953

JACOBSON WAREHOUSE CO INC p 775
3811 Dixon St, Des Moines IA 50313
Tel (515) 265-6171
SIC 4226 4221 4225 8741 6552 4783

HOLLINGSWORTH LOGISTICS MANAGEMENT LLC p 701
14225 W Warren Ave, Dearborn MI 48126
Tel (313) 768-1400 SIC 4225 4783

HOWARD TERNES PACKAGING CO p 713
35275 Industrial Rd, Livonia MI 48150
Tel (734) 793-4130 SIC 4783 6512 6552

NFI INDUSTRIES INC p 1041
1515 Burnt Mill Rd, Cherry Hill NJ 08003
Tel (856) 691-7000
SIC 4213 4212 8741 4225 4214 4783

HORIZON LINES LLC p 707
2550 W Tyvola Rd Ste 530, Charlotte NC 28217
Tel (877) 678-7447
SIC 4424 4783 4731 4412

KENCO LOGISTIC SERVICES INC p 810
520 W 31st St, Chattanooga TN 37410
Tel (423) 756-5552 SIC 4225 4783

THIRD COAST PACKAGING INC p 1448
1871 Mykawa Rd, Pearland TX 77581
Tel (281) 412-0275 SIC 5172 4783 2899

BENTLEY WORLD-PACKAGING LTD p 173
4080 N Port Washington Rd, Milwaukee WI 53212
Tel (414) 967-8000 SIC 4783 5199

UNIFIED SOLUTIONS INC p 1503
9801 80th Ave, Pleasant Prairie WI 53158
Tel (262) 942-5200 SIC 4783

SIC 4785 Fixed Facilities, Inspection, Weighing Svcs Transptn

METROPOLITAN WASHINGTON AIRPORTS AUTHORITY p 957
1 Aviation Cir, Washington DC 20001
Tel (703) 417-8600 SIC 4581 4785

CENTRAL FLORIDA EXPRESSWAY AUTHORITY p 278
4974 Orl Tower Rd, Orlando FL 32807
Tel (407) 690-5000 SIC 4785

ITR CONCESSION CO HOLDINGS LLC p 768
8801 S Anthony Ave, Chicago IL 60617
Tel (312) 552-7100 SIC 4785 6719

KANSAS TURNPIKE AUTHORITY p 803
9401 E Kellogg Dr, Wichita KS 67207
Tel (316) 682-4537 SIC 4785

MAINE TURNPIKE AUTHORITY p 898
2360 Congress St Ste 1, Portland ME 04102
Tel (207) 842-4030 SIC 4785

MARYLAND TRASPORTATION AUTHORITY p 915
2400 Ste 115, Baltimore MD 21224
Tel (410) 537-5710 SIC 4785

MASSACHUSETTS PORT AUTHORITY p 917
1 Harborside Dr Ste 200s, Boston MA 02128
Tel (617) 561-1600
SIC 4581 4491 6799 6512 4785

MASSACHUSETTS TURNPIKE AUTHORITY p 917
10 Park Plz Ste 5170, Boston MA 02116
Tel (617) 248-2800 SIC 4785 9199

DELAWARE RIVER PORT AUTHORITY p 424
2 Riverside Dr Ste 603, Camden NJ 08103
Tel (856) 968-2000 SIC 4111 4785

SGS NORTH AMERICA INC p 1310
301 Route 17, Rutherford NJ 07070
Tel (201) 508-3000
SIC 8734 7389 8071 4499 4785

NEW JERSEY TURNPIKE AUTHORITY INC p 1032
581 Mack Cali Bldg Main, Woodbridge NJ 07095
Tel (732) 750-5300 SIC 4785

THRUWAY AUTHORITY OF NEW YORK STATE p 1451
200 Southern Blvd, Albany NY 12209
Tel (518) 436-2700 SIC 4785 4499

■ ATLANTIC AVIATION FBO HOLDINGS LLC p 126
600 5th Ave Fl 21, New York NY 10020
Tel (212) 548-6538 SIC 4581 4785 1731

▲ MACQUARIE INFRASTRUCTURE CORP p 893
125 W 55th St, New York NY 10019
Tel (212) 231-1000
SIC 5172 4581 4785 7521 4932

PORT AUTHORITY OF NEW YORK & NEW JERSEY p 1162
4 World Trade Ctr 150, New York NY 10007
Tel (212) 435-7000
SIC 4581 4785 6512 4491 4111

TRIBOROUGH BRIDGE & TUNNEL AUTHORITY p 1479
Robert Moses Bldg Randal, New York NY 10035
Tel (212) 360-3000 SIC 4785

OHIO TURNPIKE AND INFRASTRUCTURE COMMISSION p 1078
682 Prospect St, Berea OH 44017
Tel (440) 234-2081 SIC 4785

■ MAGNUM MANAGEMENT CORP p 897
1 Cedar Point Dr, Sandusky OH 44870
Tel (419) 627-2334 SIC 4785 6552 7996

OKLAHOMA TURNPIKE AUTHORITY p 1080
3500 N Martin Luther, Oklahoma City OK 73111
Tel (405) 425-3600 SIC 4785

ABS GROUP OF COMPANIES INC p 12
16855 Northchase Dr, Houston TX 77060
Tel (281) 673-2800 SIC 4785 8741

AMERICAN BUREAU OF SHIPPING INC p 69
16855 Northchase Dr, Houston TX 77060
Tel (281) 877-5800 SIC 4785

INTERTEK USA INC p 759
2 Riverway Ste 500, Houston TX 77056
Tel (713) 543-3600 SIC 4785 8734

SIC 4789 Transportation Svcs, NEC

■ PROGRESS RAIL SERVICES CORP p 1181
1600 Progress Dr, Albertville AL 35950
Tel (256) 593-1260 SIC 4789 7389

P&S TRANSPORTATION LLC p 1102
1810 Avenue C, Birmingham AL 35218
Tel (205) 788-4000 SIC 4213 4789

VIRGIN GALACTIC LLC p 1558
4022 E Conant St, Long Beach CA 90808
Tel (562) 384-4400 SIC 4789

SRA TRANSPORT INC p 1362
1041 N Willow Ave, Rialto CA 92376
Tel (909) 510-2481 SIC 4789

PACIFIC COAST CONTAINER INC p 1104
432 Estudillo Ave Ste 1, San Leandro CA 94577
Tel (510) 346-6100 SIC 4789 4225 4222

ARDENT MILLS LLC p 106
1875 Lawrence St Ste 1400, Denver CO 80202
Tel (800) 851-9618 SIC 2041 4789 8741

GATES CORP p 593
1551 Wewatta St, Denver CO 80202
Tel (303) 744-1911
SIC 3052 3089 3568 5084 4789

OMAHA HOLDINGS LLC p 1083
1551 Wewatta St, Denver CO 80202
Tel (303) 744-1911
SIC 3052 3089 3568 5084 4789

OMAHA INTERMEDIATE HOLDING LLC p 1083
1551 Wewatta St, Denver CO 80202
Tel (303) 744-1911
SIC 3052 3089 3568 5084 4789

TRANSMONTAIGNE PRODUCT SERVICES LLC p 1472
1670 Broadway Ste 3100, Denver CO 80202
Tel (303) 626-8200 SIC 4789

ABE ORLANDO BUSTAMANTE p 10
7859 Diagonal Hwy, Longmont CO 80503
Tel (303) 652-3394 SIC 5099 4789 4212

FORT LAUDERDALE TRANSPORTATION INC p 569
1330 Se 4th Ave Ste D, Fort Lauderdale FL 33316
Tel (954) 524-6500 SIC 7299 4789

■ HCA HEALTH SERVICES OF FLORIDA INC p 671
14000 Fivay Rd, Hudson FL 34667
Tel (727) 819-2929 SIC 4789

▲ LANDSTAR SYSTEM INC p 843
13410 Sutton Park Dr S, Jacksonville FL 32224
Tel (904) 398-9400 SIC 4789

LAN CARGO SA p 841
6500 Nw 22nd St, Miami FL 33122
Tel (786) 265-6000 SIC 4789

TROPICAL SHIPPING USA LLC p 1484
501 Avenue P, Riviera Beach FL 33404
Tel (561) 863-5737 SIC 4412 4789

AMERIFLEET TRANSPORTATION INC p 82
1111 Alderman Dr, Alpharetta GA 30005
Tel (770) 442-0222 SIC 4789

CAPSTONE LOGISTICS LLC p 251
6525 The Corners Pkwy, Norcross GA 30092
Tel (770) 414-1929 SIC 4789

BEST TRUCKING LOGISTICS INC p 177
126 Pine Meadow Dr, Pooler GA 31322
Tel (912) 349-6869 SIC 4789

CHICAGO TRANSIT AUTHORITY p 298
567 W Lake St Ste Cta, Chicago IL 60661
Tel (312) 664-7200 SIC 4111 4789

GENERAL ELECTRIC RAILCAR SERVICES CORP p 600
161 N Clark St Fl 7, Chicago IL 60601
Tel (312) 853-5000
SIC 7359 3743 4789 3462

TRANSCO INC p 1471
200 N La Salle St # 1550, Chicago IL 60601
Tel (312) 896-8527
SIC 4789 3743 3296 1742

■ UNION TANK CAR CO p 1505
175 W Jackson Blvd # 2100, Chicago IL 60604
Tel (312) 431-3111
SIC 3743 4741 4789 5051

ALDRIDGE ELECTRIC INC p 48
844 E Rockland Rd, Libertyville IL 60048
Tel (847) 680-5200 SIC 2899 4789 3643

ITS TECHNOLOGIES & LOGISTICS LLC p 768
8200 185th St Ste A, Tinley Park IL 60487
Tel (708) 225-2400 SIC 4789

ITS TECHNOLOGIES & LOGISTICS LLC p 768
8200 185th St Ste A, Tinley Park IL 60487
Tel (708) 225-2400 SIC 4789

ARNOLD LOGISTICS LLC p 112
3811 Dixon St, Des Moines IA 50313
Tel (515) 265-6171 SIC 4789

WATCO INC p 1581
315 W 3rd St, Pittsburg KS 66762
Tel (208) 734-4644 SIC 4013 4741 4789

ROAD & RAIL SERVICES INC p 1240
4233 Bardstown Rd Ste 200, Louisville KY 40218
Tel (502) 365-5361 SIC 4789 4013

RED RIVER MOTOR FREIGHT LLC p 1216
451050 Marlena St, Bossier City LA 71111
Tel (318) 884-9994 SIC 4789

■ PRODUCTION MANAGEMENT INDUSTRIES LLC p 1179
1204 Youngs Rd, Morgan City LA 70380
Tel (985) 631-3837 SIC 1389 8731 4789

■ LOCKHEED MARTIN SPACE OPERATIONS LLC p 873
700 N Frederick Ave, Gaithersburg MD 20879
Tel (301) 240-7000 SIC 4789

MTG ACQUISITIONS LLC p 998
69 Norman St, Everett MA 02149
Tel (800) 922-0343 SIC 4789

CENEX INC p 275
5500 Cenex Dr, Inver Grove Heights MN 55077
Tel (800) 232-3639
SIC 1311 2911 4613 4922 4789 4213

HDR INC p 673
8404 Indian Hills Dr, Omaha NE 68114
Tel (402) 399-1000
SIC 8712 8711 8742 8748 4789

TOLL GLOBAL FORWARDING (AMERICAS) INC p 1459
800 Federal Blvd Ste 3, Carteret NJ 07008
Tel (732) 750-9000 SIC 4789 4731

■ CEQUENT UK LTD p 283
123 Town Square Pl, Jersey City NJ 07310
Tel (734) 656-3078 SIC 4789 3714 5531

▲ RAND LOGISTICS INC p 1207
333 Washington St Ste 201, Jersey City NJ 07302
Tel (212) 863-9427 SIC 4789 4492

NORTHSTAR TRAVEL MEDIA LLC p 1059
100 Lighting Way Ste 200, Secaucus NJ 07094
Tel (201) 902-2000 SIC 2721 4789 4724

AMERICAN CARGO EXPRESS INC p 69
2345 Vauxhall Rd, Union NJ 07083
Tel (908) 351-3400 SIC 4789

ROMARK LOGISTICS LLC p 1249
822 South Ave W, Westfield NJ 07090
Tel (908) 789-2800 SIC 4225 4789 2631

RINCHEM CO INC p 1235
5131 Masthead St Ne, Albuquerque NM 87109
Tel (505) 998-4300 SIC 4789 4225

CARGO AIRPORT SERVICES USA LLC p 255
Cargo Bldg 261 N Boundary, Jamaica NY 11430
Tel (718) 244-0900 SIC 4789

ACF INDUSTRIES HOLDING CORP p 17
767 5th Ave, New York NY 10153
Tel (212) 702-4363
SIC 3743 4741 4789 6799

▲ FORTRESS TRANSPORTATION AND INFRASTRUCTURE INVESTORS LLC p 570
1345 Ave Of The Americas, New York NY 10105
Tel (212) 798-6100 SIC 4789

HIGHCREST INVESTORS LLC p 691
Icahn Associates Corp 767, New York NY 10153
Tel (212) 702-4323
SIC 3743 4741 4789 4813

ACTIVE MEDIA SERVICES INC p 20
1 Blue Hill Plz Ste 1705, Pearl River NY 10965
Tel (845) 735-1700 SIC 7319 4731 4789

GREENBRIAR EQUITY GROUP LLC p 637
555 Theodore Fremd Ave A201, Rye NY 10580
Tel (914) 925-9600 SIC 4789 6799

DB US CORP p 418
120 White Plains Rd, Tarrytown NY 10591
Tel (914) 366-7200 SIC 4789 4731

STARFIRE HOLDING CORP p 1379
445 Hamilton Ave Ste 1210, White Plains NY 10601
Tel (914) 614-7000 SIC 3743 4741 4789

PARSEC INC p 1117
1100 Gest St, Cincinnati OH 45203
Tel (513) 621-6111 SIC 4789

▲ ANDERSONS INC p 90
480 W Dussel Dr, Maumee OH 43537
Tel (419) 893-5050
SIC 5153 0723 5191 2874 4789 4741

▲ GREENBRIER COMPANIES INC p 637
1 Centerpointe Dr Ste 200, Lake Oswego OR 97035
Tel (503) 684-7000 SIC 3743 4789

DAIMLER TRUCKS NORTH AMERICA LLC p 408
4747 N Channel Ave, Portland OR 97217
Tel (503) 745-8011 SIC 3711 4789

JUBITZ CORP p 796
33 Ne Middlefield Rd, Portland OR 97211
Tel (503) 283-1111
SIC 5541 4789 5014 7011

▲ HARSCO CORP p 664
350 Poplar Church Rd, Camp Hill PA 17011
Tel (717) 763-7064
SIC 7359 7353 5082 3443 3585 4789

BERWIND CORP p 176
3000 Ctr Sq W 1500 Mkt St 1500 W, Philadelphia PA 19102
Tel (215) 563-2800
SIC 6519 5052 4789 3625 3669 2899

■ GENCO TRANSPORTATION MANAGEMENT LLC p 598
100 Papercraft Park, Pittsburgh PA 15238
Tel (412) 820-3700
SIC 4225 4111 5045 4789

LASKO GROUP INC p 846
820 Lincoln Ave, West Chester PA 19380
Tel (610) 692-7400 SIC 4789 3634

LASKO PRODUCTS INC p 846
820 Lincoln Ave, West Chester PA 19380
Tel (610) 692-7400 SIC 4789 3585 3564

GFR MEDIA LLC p 610
50 Carr 165 Ste 1, Guaynabo PR 00968
Tel (787) 641-8000 SIC 4789 2711 5963

MALLORY ALEXANDER INTERNATIONAL LOGISTICS LLC p 900
4294 Swinnea Rd, Memphis TN 38118
Tel (901) 367-9400 SIC 4731 4225 4789

DASEKE INC p 413
15455 Dallas Pkwy Ste 440, Addison TX 75001
Tel (972) 248-0412 SIC 4789

FIRST FINANCIAL RESOURCES INC p 547
611 Kimberly Dr, Denton TX 76208
Tel (940) 382-4599 SIC 4789 4953

HULCHER SERVICES INC p 718
611 Kimberly Dr, Denton TX 76208
Tel (940) 387-0099 SIC 4953 4789

BUCKEYE GP HOLDINGS LP p 223
1 Greenway Plz Ste 600, Houston TX 77046
Tel (832) 615-8600
SIC 4789 4213 4226 4212

▲ BUCKEYE PARTNERS LP p 223
1 Greenway Plz Ste 600, Houston TX 77046
Tel (832) 615-8600
SIC 4612 4789 4226 4213

LOOMIS ARMORED US LLC p 877
2500 Citywest Blvd # 2300, Houston TX 77042
Tel (713) 435-6700 SIC 7381 4789

TRANS-GLOBAL SOLUTIONS INC p 1470
11811 East Fwy Ste 630, Houston TX 77029
Tel (713) 453-0341 SIC 4491 4013 4789

TRICON INTERNATIONAL LTD p 1479
777 Post Oak Blvd Ste 550, Houston TX 77056
Tel (713) 963-0066 SIC 5169 7389 4789

TRIMAC TRANSPORTATION INC p 1480
15333 John F Kenn Blvd, Houston TX 77032
Tel (281) 985-0000 SIC 4789

VOPAK NORTH AMERICA INC p 1565
2000 West Loop S Ste 1550, Houston TX 77027
Tel (713) 561-7200
SIC 4491 4226 4953 4789

WARTSILA NORTH AMERICA INC p 1577
11710 N Gessner Rd Ste A, Houston TX 77064
Tel (281) 233-6200
SIC 1629 5084 1382 4789 3731

G2 SECURE STAFF LLC p 588
400 Las Colinas Blvd E # 750, Irving TX 75039
Tel (972) 915-6979 SIC 6411 4789 4729

NEOVIA LOGISTICS SERVICES LLC p 1026
6363 N State Highway 161 # 700, Irving TX 75038
Tel (469) 513-7000 SIC 4789 5082

WORLDWIDE FLIGHT SERVICES INC p 1626
1925 W John Carpenter Fwy # 450, Irving TX 75063
Tel (972) 629-5001 SIC 4581 4789

VALERO ENERGY PARTNERS LP p 1539
1 Valero Way, San Antonio TX 78249
Tel (210) 345-2000 SIC 4612 4613 4789

■ GE OIL & GAS LOGGING SERVICES INC p 596
13000 Executive Dr, Sugar Land TX 77478
Tel (281) 579-9879 SIC 1389 4789

BLUELINE RENTAL LLC p 193
8401 New Trils Dr Ste 150, The Woodlands TX 77381
Tel (832) 299-7515 SIC 7353 4789

ONRAMP TRANSPORTATION SERVICES LLC p 1088
5416 W Amelia Earhart Dr # 201, Salt Lake City UT 84116
Tel (801) 736-9420 SIC 4789

■ SIX3 ADVANCED SYSTEMS INC p 1328
45200 Business Ct Ste 100, Dulles VA 20166
Tel (703) 742-7660
SIC 3825 4899 8099 4789

TIGERS GLOBAL LOGISTICS INC p 1453
20024 85th Ave S, Kent WA 98031
Tel (253) 246-4184 SIC 4789

PARAMETRIX INC p 1114
1019 39th Ave Se Ste 100, Puyallup WA 98374
Tel (206) 394-3700
SIC 8748 8711 8742 1389 4789

PACIFIC RAIL SERVICES LLC p 1105
1131 Sw Klickitat Way, Seattle WA 98134
Tel (206) 382-4462 SIC 4789

SCHNEIDER LOGISTICS INC p 1288
3101 Packerland Dr, Green Bay WI 54313
Tel (920) 592-0000
SIC 4731 4225 4789 4212

SIC 4812 Radiotelephone Communications

▲ GENERAL COMMUNICATION INC p 599
2550 Denali St Ste 1000, Anchorage AK 99503
Tel (907) 868-5600 SIC 4813 4841 4812

E RITTER COMMUNICATIONS HOLDINGS INC p 467
2400 Ritter Dr, Jonesboro AR 72401
Tel (870) 336-3434 SIC 4813 4812 5045

■ ALLTEL COMMUNICATIONS LLC p 59
1 Allied Dr, Little Rock AR 72202
Tel (501) 905-8000 SIC 4812

■ ALLTEL COMMUNICATIONS OF VIRGINIA INC p 59
1 Allied Dr, Little Rock AR 72202
Tel (501) 905-8100 SIC 4812

■ ALLTEL CORP p 59
1001 Technology Dr, Little Rock AR 72223
Tel (866) 255-8357 SIC 4812 5999

■ WESTERN WIRELESS LLC p 1600
1 Allied Dr, Little Rock AR 72202
Tel (501) 905-8000 SIC 4812

4G WIRELESS INC p 3
8871 Research Dr, Irvine CA 92618
Tel (949) 748-6100 SIC 4812

PURPLE COMMUNICATIONS INC p 1193
595 Menlo Dr, Rocklin CA 95765
Tel (888) 600-4780 SIC 4812 7389

■ SUREWEST COMMUNICATIONS p 1408
211 Lincoln St, Roseville CA 95678
Tel (916) 786-6141 SIC 4813 4812

■ CRICKET COMMUNICATIONS LLC p 392
7337 Trade St, San Diego CA 92121
Tel (858) 882-6000 SIC 4812

■ LEAP WIRELESS INTERNATIONAL INC p 850
7337 Trade St, San Diego CA 92121
Tel (858) 882-6000 SIC 4812

STX WIRELESS OPERATIONS LLC p 1395
5887 Copley Dr, San Diego CA 92111
Tel (858) 882-6000 SIC 4812

▲ TWILIO INC p 1494
645 Harrison St Fl 3, San Francisco CA 94107
Tel (415) 390-2337 SIC 7372 4812

BLACKBERRY CORP p 187
3001 Bishop Dr, San Ramon CA 94583
Tel (972) 650-6126 SIC 5999 3661 4812

■ QWEST GOVERNMENT SERVICES INC p 1201
931 14th St Ste 1000b, Denver CO 80202
Tel (303) 992-1400 SIC 4813 4812

NE COLORADO CELLULAR INC p 1022
1224 W Platte Ave, Fort Morgan CO 80701
Tel (970) 467-3137 SIC 4812

■ TW TELECOM OF COLORADO LLC p 1494
10475 Park Meadows Dr, Littleton CO 80124
Tel (636) 625-7000 SIC 4812 4813

■ SOUTHERN NEW ENGLAND TELECOMMUNICATIONS CORP p 1349
2 Science Park, New Haven CT 06511
Tel (203) 771-5200
SIC 4813 4812 5065 6159 2741 4822

■ VERIZON DELAWARE LLC p 1550
901 N Tatnall St Fl 2, Wilmington DE 19801
Tel (302) 571-1571
SIC 4813 4812 7373 2741

■ MASTEC NETWORK SOLUTIONS LLC p 918
806 S Douglas Rd Fl 11, Coral Gables FL 33134
Tel (866) 545-1782 SIC 4812 7373

■ MASTEC NETWORK SOLUTIONS LLC p 918
806 S Douglas Rd Fl 11, Coral Gables FL 33134
Tel (866) 545-1782 SIC 4812 7373

REAGAN WIRELESS CORP p 1213
720 S Powerline Rd Ste D, Deerfield Beach FL 33442
Tel (954) 596-2355 SIC 5065 4812

VITEL MOBILE INC p 1563
8925 Nw 26th St, Doral FL 33172
Tel (305) 418-9790 SIC 4812

TRACFONE WIRELESS INC p 1468
9700 Nw 112th Ave, Medley FL 33178
Tel (305) 640-2000 SIC 4813 4812

IVOX SOLUTIONS LLC p 769
4485 Sw Port Way, Palm City FL 34990
Tel (772) 286-8183 SIC 5065 4812

BUCCANEER HOLDINGS LLC p 222
8125 Highwoods Palm Way, Tampa FL 33647
Tel (813) 637-5000 SIC 4813 4812

SYNIVERSE HOLDINGS INC p 1415
8125 Highwoods Palm Way, Tampa FL 33647
Tel (813) 637-5000 SIC 4812 3663

SYNIVERSE TECHNOLOGIES LLC p 1415
8125 Highwoods Palm Way, Tampa FL 33647
Tel (813) 637-5000 SIC 4812 3663

■ VERIZON WIRELESS OF EAST LP p 1551
1 Verizon Pl, Alpharetta GA 30004
Tel (678) 339-4000 SIC 4812

ALLCONNECT INC p 52
980 Hammond Dr Ste 1000, Atlanta GA 30328
Tel (404) 260-2200 SIC 4812

■ BELLSOUTH CORP p 171
675 W Peach St Ste 4300, Atlanta GA 30375
Tel (404) 420-6126
SIC 4813 4812 2741 5065

■ BELLSOUTH TELECOMMUNICATIONS INC p 171
675 W Peach St Ne St Ne, Atlanta GA 30375
Tel (912) 526-3440
SIC 4813 4812 2741 5065

■ SOUTHERN COMMUNICATIONS SERVICES INC p 1348
5555 Glenridge Connector, Atlanta GA 30342
Tel (678) 443-1500 SIC 4813 4812

■ AT&T MOBILITY LLC p 123
1025 Lenox Park Blvd Ne, Brookhaven GA 30319
Tel (425) 580-6014 SIC 4812 4813 5999

■ BELLSOUTH BUSINESS SYSTEMS INC p 171
2180 Lake Blvd Ne, Brookhaven GA 30319
Tel (404) 829-8000 SIC 4813 4812

■ WINDSTREAM GEORGIA LLC p 1615
906 Vista Dr, Dalton GA 30721
Tel (706) 279-7600 SIC 4813 4812

■ NEXTEL SOUTH CORP p 1040
6575 The Corners Pkwy, Norcross GA 30092
Tel (703) 592-7422 SIC 4812

STRATIX CORP p 1392
4920 Avalon Ridge Pkwy, Peachtree Corners GA 30071
Tel (770) 326-7580 SIC 4812

■ HAWAIIAN TELCOM COMMUNICATIONS INC p 669
1177 Bishop St, Honolulu HI 96813
Tel (808) 546-4511 SIC 4813 4812

▲ PC-TEL INC p 1123
471 Brighton Ct, Bloomingdale IL 60108
Tel (630) 372-6800 SIC 5731 4812 7372

■ AERIAL COMMUNICATIONS INC p 30
8410 W Bryn Mawr Ave, Chicago IL 60631
Tel (773) 399-4200 SIC 4812

■ AT&T TELEHOLDINGS INC p 123
30 S Wacker Dr Fl 34, Chicago IL 60606
Tel (800) 257-0902
SIC 4813 4812 2741 5065 6159 7382

■ FLORIDA RSA 8 INC p 559
8410 W Bryn Mawr Ave # 700, Chicago IL 60631
Tel (773) 399-8900 SIC 4812

■ GOGO LLC p 620
111 N Canal St Fl 15, Chicago IL 60606
Tel (630) 647-1400
SIC 3663 4812 4813 4899

MOTOROLA MOBILITY LLC p 993
222 Merchandise Mart Plz, Chicago IL 60654
Tel (800) 866-6765 SIC 3663 4812

▲ TELEPHONE AND DATA SYSTEMS INC p 1434
30 N La Salle St Ste 4000, Chicago IL 60602
Tel (312) 630-1900 SIC 4812 4813

■ UNITED STATES CELLULAR CORP p 1512
8410 W Bryn Mawr Ave # 700, Chicago IL 60631
Tel (773) 399-8900 SIC 4812 4813

NORTHWESTERN UNIVERSITY INFORMATION TECHNOLOGIES p 1061
1800 Sherman Ave Ste 7, Evanston IL 60201
Tel (847) 467-1766 SIC 4813 7374 4812

COBALT HOLDINGS INC p 332
101 Waukegan Rd Ste 990, Lake Bluff IL 60044
Tel (773) 230-3219 SIC 4812 4813

■ Q-COMM CORP p 1194
3701 Communications Way, Evansville IN 47715
Tel (812) 253-7000 SIC 4813 4812

■ TOUCHSTONE WIRELESS REPAIR AND LOGISTICS LP p 1464
501 Airtech Pkwy, Plainfield IN 46168
Tel (317) 707-2355 SIC 4812 5065

■ MCLEODUSA INC p 932
6400 C St Sw, Cedar Rapids IA 52404
Tel (319) 364-0000 SIC 4813 4812

■ MCLEODUSA HOLDINGS INC p 932
1770 Boyson Rd, Hiawatha IA 52233
Tel (319) 364-0000 SIC 4813 4812

■ NEXTEL OF CALIFORNIA INC p 1040
6200 Sprint Pkwy, Overland Park KS 66251
Tel (866) 505-2385 SIC 4812

■ NEXTEL PARTNERS OPERATING CORP p 1040
6200 Sprint Pkwy, Overland Park KS 66251
Tel (800) 829-0965 SIC 4812

■ SPRINT COMMUNICATIONS INC p 1361
6200 Sprint Pkwy, Overland Park KS 66251
Tel (855) 848-3280 SIC 4813 4812 5999

■ SPRINT CORP p 1361
6200 Sprint Pkwy, Overland Park KS 66251
Tel (855) 848-3280 SIC 4813 4812

WHEATLAND ELECTRIC COOPERATIVE INC p 1604
101 N Main St, Scott City KS 67871
Tel (620) 872-5885 SIC 4911 4812

■ EMBARQ MANAGEMENT CO p 490
5454 W 110th St, Shawnee Mission KS 66211
Tel (913) 323-4637 SIC 4813 4812

EAST KENTUCKY NETWORK LLC p 470
101 Technology Trl, Ivel KY 41642
Tel (606) 477-2355 SIC 4812 1731

CELLXION LLC p 274
5031 Hazel Jones Rd, Bossier City LA 71111
Tel (318) 213-2900
SIC 4812 1623 3448 3441

■ CENTEL CORP p 275
100 Centurylink Dr, Monroe LA 71203
Tel (318) 388-9000 SIC 4813 4812

▲ CENTURYLINK INC p 282
100 Centurylink Dr, Monroe LA 71203
Tel (318) 388-9000 SIC 4813 4812

■ CENTURYTEL HOLDINGS MISSOURI INC p 282
100 Centurylink Dr, Monroe LA 71203
Tel (318) 388-9000 SIC 4812

■ CENTURYTEL OF NORTHWEST INC p 283
100 Centurylink Dr, Monroe LA 71203
Tel (318) 388-9000 SIC 4813 4812

■ QWEST COMMUNICATIONS INTERNATIONAL INC p 1201
100 Centurylink Dr, Monroe LA 71203
Tel (318) 388-9000 SIC 4813 4822 4812

■ **AERONAUTICAL RADIO INC** p 30
2551 Riva Rd, Annapolis MD 21401
Tel (410) 266-4000 *SIC* 4812 4899

▲ **ATN INTERNATIONAL INC** p 128
500 Cummings Ctr Ste 2450, Beverly MA 01915
Tel (978) 619-1300 *SIC* 4813 4812 1711

■ **GALAXY INVESTMENT HOLDINGS INC** p 589
38 Glen Ave, Newton MA 02459
Tel (617) 928-9300 *SIC* 4813 4812

■ **RURAL CELLULAR CORP** p 1258
4133 Iowa St Ste 200, Alexandria MN 56308
Tel (320) 808-2111 *SIC* 4812 5999

■ **PEOPLENET COMMUNICATIONS CORP** p 1132
4400 Baker Rd, Minnetonka MN 55343
Tel (952) 908-6200 *SIC* 7373 3663 4812

CELLULAR SOUTH INC p 274
1018 Highland Pkwy # 330, Ridgeland MS 39157
Tel (855) 277-4732 *SIC* 4812

TELAPEX INC p 1433
1018 Highland Pkwy # 500, Ridgeland MS 39157
Tel (601) 355-1522 *SIC* 4812 4813

AEGIS CORP p 29
614 Dartmouth Terrace Ct, Ballwin MO 63011
Tel (636) 273-1011
SIC 3699 4812 3812 3444 2326

RUSSELL CELLULAR INC p 1259
5624 S Hwy Ff, Battlefield MO 65619
Tel (417) 886-7542 *SIC* 4812

BIRCH TELECOM INC p 185
2323 Grand Blvd Ste 925, Kansas City MO 64108
Tel (816) 300-3000 *SIC* 4813 7375 4812

■ **CELLCO PARTNERSHIP** p 273
1 Verizon Way, Basking Ridge NJ 07920
Tel (908) 306-7000 *SIC* 4812 5999 5065

■ **VERIZON WIRELESS INC** p 1551
1 Verizon Way, Basking Ridge NJ 07920
Tel (908) 559-2000 *SIC* 4812

VELOCITA WIRELESS LLC p 1547
70 Wood Ave S Ste 202, Iselin NJ 08830
Tel (848) 248-4722 *SIC* 4899 4812

■ **CENTENNIAL PUERTO RICO OPERATIONS CORP** p 275
3349 State Route 138 A, Wall Township NJ 07719
Tel (732) 556-2200 *SIC* 4812

■ **VIRGIN MOBILE USA INC** p 1558
10 Independence Blvd # 200, Warren NJ 07059
Tel (908) 607-4000 *SIC* 4812

■ **NEXTEL OF NEW YORK INC** p 1040
565 Taxter Rd Ste 450, Elmsford NY 10523
Tel (914) 421-2800 *SIC* 4812

■ **SYMBOL TECHNOLOGIES LLC** p 1414
1 Zebra Plz, Holtsville NY 11742
Tel (631) 737-6851 *SIC* 4812

■ **GTE CORP** p 644
140 West St, New York NY 10007
Tel (212) 395-1000
SIC 4813 4812 3661 3663 4899 2741

▲ **VERIZON COMMUNICATIONS INC** p 1550
1095 Ave Of The Americas, New York NY 10036
Tel (212) 395-1000 *SIC* 4813 4812 4841

VIRGIN MEDIA HOLDINGS INC p 1558
65 Bleecker St Fl 6, New York NY 10012
Tel (212) 966-2310 *SIC* 4812 4813 4841

SOHEL DISTRIBUTORS NY LLC p 1337
1091 Yonkers Ave, Yonkers NY 10704
Tel (914) 476-2073 *SIC* 4812

■ **SPECTRASITE COMMUNICATIONS LLC** p 1357
400 Regency Forest Dr # 300, Cary NC 27518
Tel (919) 468-0112
SIC 4812 8748 1623 3661 4813 4899

▲ **FAIRPOINT COMMUNICATIONS INC** p 525
521 E Morehead St Ste 500, Charlotte NC 28202
Tel (704) 344-8150 *SIC* 4813 4812 4899

■ **BUSINESS TELECOM LLC** p 229
4300 Six Forks Rd Ste 500, Raleigh NC 27609
Tel (919) 863-7000 *SIC* 4813 4812

REPUBLIC WIRELESS INC p 1226
900 Main Campus Dr, Raleigh NC 27606
Tel (877) 913-0894 *SIC* 4812

WIRELESS CENTER INC p 1618
1925 Saint Clair Ave Ne, Cleveland OH 44114
Tel (216) 503-3777 *SIC* 4812

■ **ALLTEL COMMUNICATIONS CORP** p 59
66 N 4th St, Newark OH 43055
Tel (740) 349-8551 *SIC* 4813 4812

■ **AMERICAN CELLULAR CORP** p 70
14201 Wireless Way, Oklahoma City OK 73134
Tel (405) 529-8500 *SIC* 4812

■ **DOBSON COMMUNICATIONS CORP** p 447
14201 Wireless Way, Oklahoma City OK 73134
Tel (405) 529-8500 *SIC* 4812

CONSUMER CELLULAR INC p 361
12447 Sw 69th Ave, Portland OR 97223
Tel (503) 675-8988 *SIC* 4812

■ **CROWN COMMUNICATION LLC** p 395
2000 Corporate Dr, Canonsburg PA 15317
Tel (724) 746-3600 *SIC* 4812

■ **BELL ATLANTIC GLOBAL WIRELESS INC** p 170
1717 Arch St Fl 33, Philadelphia PA 19103
Tel (215) 246-9494
SIC 4813 4812 5065 7379

■ **COMCAST TELEPHONY COMMUNICATIONS LLC** p 344
1701 Jfk Blvd, Philadelphia PA 19103
Tel (215) 665-1700 *SIC* 4812

MTPCS LLC p 998
1170 Devon Park Dr # 104, Wayne PA 19087
Tel (610) 688-1334 *SIC* 4812

■ **CELLULAR COMMUNICATIONS OF PUERTO RICO INC** p 274
103 Ave Ortegon, Guaynabo PR 00966
Tel (787) 397-1000 *SIC* 4812 5999

RICO CLARO PUERTO p 1233
1515 Frnklin D Rsvelt Ave, Guaynabo PR 00968
Tel (787) 766-2355 *SIC* 4812 8748

■ **AT&T MOBILITY PUERTO RICO INC** p 123
996 Calle San Roberto, Rio Piedras PR 00926
Tel (787) 717-9600 *SIC* 4813 4812

MIDCO COMMUNICATIONS INC p 964
3901 N Louise Ave, Sioux Falls SD 57107
Tel (605) 334-1200
SIC 8748 5961 7389 4812

■ **NEXTEL OF TEXAS INC** p 1040
8911 N Capital Of Texas, Austin TX 78759
Tel (512) 342-3800 *SIC* 4812

▲ **AT&T INC** p 123
208 S Akard St, Dallas TX 75202
Tel (210) 821-4105
SIC 4813 4812 3663 3661 2741

BEARCOM OPERATING LLC p 165
4009 Dist Dr Ste 200, Garland TX 75041
Tel (214) 765-7100 *SIC* 4812 5065

UNITED CELLULAR INC p 1507
1940 Enchanted Way, Grapevine TX 76051
Tel (940) 566-5735 *SIC* 4812

■ **CC HOLDINGS GS V LLC** p 269
1220 Augusta Dr Ste 500, Houston TX 77057
Tel (713) 570-3000 *SIC* 4812

■ **CC SCN FIBER LLC** p 269
1220 Augusta Dr Ste 600, Houston TX 77057
Tel (713) 570-3000 *SIC* 4899 7622 4812

CROWN CASTLE INTERNATIONAL CORP p 395
1220 Augusta Dr Ste 600, Houston TX 77057
Tel (713) 570-3000
SIC 4899 7622 4812 6798

▲ **CROWN CASTLE INTERNATIONAL CORP** p 395
1220 Augusta Dr Ste 600, Houston TX 77057
Tel (713) 570-3000
SIC 6798 4899 7622 4812

AMERICAN MESSAGING SERVICES LLC p 76
1720 Lakepointe Dr # 100, Lewisville TX 75057
Tel (888) 699-9014 *SIC* 4812

■ **SOUTHWESTERN BELL MOBILE SYSTEMS LLC** p 1353
5601 Legacy Dr, Plano TX 75024
Tel (972) 712-7305 *SIC* 4812

YOUGHIOGHENY COMMUNICATIONS-TEXAS LLC p 1637
2118 Fredericksburg Rd, San Antonio TX 78201
Tel (210) 777-7777 *SIC* 4812

PRIME COMMUNICATIONS LP p 1174
12550 Reed Rd Ste 100, Sugar Land TX 77478
Tel (281) 240-7800 *SIC* 4812

DIAMOND WIRELESS LLC p 437
10450 S State St, Sandy UT 84070
Tel (801) 501-7683 *SIC* 4812

DIAMOND WIRELESS-OREGON LLC p 437
7927 High Point Pkwy # 300, Sandy UT 84094
Tel (801) 733-6929 *SIC* 4812

■ **MCI COMMUNICATIONS CORP** p 929
22001 Loudoun County Pkwy, Ashburn VA 20147
Tel (703) 886-5600
SIC 4813 4812 4822 7372

■ **MCI INTERNATIONAL INC** p 929
22001 Loudoun County Pkwy, Ashburn VA 20147
Tel (703) 886-5600
SIC 4813 4812 4822 7372

▲ **SHENANDOAH TELECOMMUNICATIONS CO** p 1315
500 Shentel Way, Edinburg VA 22824
Tel (540) 984-4141 *SIC* 4813 4812 4841

LCC INTERNATIONAL INC p 849
2201 Coop Way Ste 600, Herndon VA 20171
Tel (703) 873-2065 *SIC* 4813 4812

SIMPLY WIRELESS INC p 1325
8484 Westpark Dr Ste 800, Mc Lean VA 22102
Tel (703) 343-2700 *SIC* 4812

■ **NEXTEL COMMUNICATIONS INC** p 1040
12502 Sunrise Valley Dr, Reston VA 20191
Tel (703) 433-4000 *SIC* 4812

■ **NEXTEL FINANCE CO** p 1040
2001 Edmund Halley Dr, Reston VA 20191
Tel (703) 433-4000 *SIC* 4812 6719

▲ **NII HOLDINGS INC** p 1043
1875 Explorer St Ste 800, Reston VA 20190
Tel (703) 390-5100 *SIC* 4812

CAVALIER TELEPHONE LLC p 267
2134 W Laburnum Ave, Richmond VA 23227
Tel (804) 422-4100 *SIC* 4813 4812

CAVALIER TELEPHONE MID-ATLANTIC LLC p 267
2134 W Laburnum Ave, Richmond VA 23227
Tel (804) 422-4100 *SIC* 4813 4812

■ **BELLSOUTH COMMUNICATION SYSTEMS LLC** p 171
1936 Blue Hills Dr Ne, Roanoke VA 24012
Tel (540) 983-6000 *SIC* 5065 4813 4812

■ **ARCH WIRELESS INC** p 104
6850 Versar Ctr Ste 420, Springfield VA 22151
Tel (703) 269-6850 *SIC* 5999 4812

▲ **SPOK HOLDINGS INC** p 1359
6850 Versar Ctr Ste 420, Springfield VA 22151
Tel (800) 611-8488 *SIC* 4812 4822 7372

■ **SPOK INC** p 1359
6850 Versar Ctr Ste 420, Springfield VA 22151
Tel (703) 269-6850 *SIC* 4812

■ **NTELOS HOLDINGS CORP** p 1065
1154 Shenandoah Vlg Dr, Waynesboro VA 22980
Tel (540) 946-3500 *SIC* 4813 4812

■ **SUNCOM WIRELESS HOLDINGS INC** p 1402
12920 Se 38th St, Bellevue WA 98006
Tel (425) 378-4000 *SIC* 4812

■ **T-MOBILE USA INC** p 1420
12920 Se 38th St, Bellevue WA 98006
Tel (425) 378-4000 *SIC* 4812 4899

■ **NEXTEL PARTNERS INC** p 1040
4500 Carillon Pt, Kirkland WA 98033
Tel (425) 576-3600 *SIC* 4812

■ **AT&T WIRELESS SERVICES OF CALIFORNIA LLC** p 123
7277 164th Ave Ne, Redmond WA 98052
Tel (425) 827-4500 *SIC* 4812 4833

C M T PARTNERS p 233
7277 164th Ave Ne Rtc1, Redmond WA 98052
Tel (425) 580-6000 *SIC* 4812

■ **NEW CINGULAR WIRELESS SERVICES INC** p 1029
7277 164th Ave Ne, Redmond WA 98052
Tel (425) 827-4500 *SIC* 4812

■ **NEXTEL WEST CORP** p 1040
10545 Willows Rd Ne # 100, Redmond WA 98052
Tel (253) 924-8545 *SIC* 4812

BROWN COUNTY MSA CELLULAR LIMITED PARTNERSHIP p 219
1580 Mid Valley Dr, De Pere WI 54115
Tel (920) 339-4004 *SIC* 4812 5999

NEW-CELL LLC p 1036
1580 Mid Valley Dr, De Pere WI 54115
Tel (920) 617-7800 *SIC* 4812

NORTHEAST COMMUNICATIONS OF WISCONSIN INC p 1054
450 Security Blvd, Green Bay WI 54313
Tel (920) 617-7000 *SIC* 4812 4813

UNION TELEPHONE CO p 1505
850 N Hwy 414, Mountain View WY 82939
Tel (307) 782-6131 *SIC* 4813 4812

SIC 4813 Telephone Communications, Except Radio

▲ **ADTRAN INC** p 24
901 Explorer Blvd Nw, Huntsville AL 35806
Tel (256) 963-8000 *SIC* 3661 3663 4813

■ **DELTACOM LLC** p 427
7037 Old Madison Pike Nw, Huntsville AL 35806
Tel (256) 382-2100 *SIC* 4813

ITC DELTACOM INC p 767
7037 Old Madison Pike Nw, Huntsville AL 35806
Tel (256) 382-5900 *SIC* 4813 4899

GLOBAL TEL LINK CORP p 617
2609 Cameron St, Mobile AL 36607
Tel (251) 479-4500 *SIC* 4813

■ **ALASCOM INC** p 44
505 E Bluff Dr, Anchorage AK 99501
Tel (907) 264-7000 *SIC* 4813 4833 4832

▲ **ALASKA COMMUNICATIONS SYSTEMS GROUP INC** p 44
600 Telephone Ave, Anchorage AK 99503
Tel (907) 297-3000 *SIC* 4813

▲ **GENERAL COMMUNICATION INC** p 599
2550 Denali St Ste 1000, Anchorage AK 99503
Tel (907) 868-5600 *SIC* 4813 4841 4812

MITEL (DELAWARE) INC p 977
1146 N Alma School Rd, Mesa AZ 85201
Tel (480) 449-8900
SIC 3661 5045 4813 5065 1731 7359

▲ **CABLE ONE INC** p 235
210 E Earll Dr Fl 6, Phoenix AZ 85012
Tel (602) 364-6000 *SIC* 4813 4841

▲ **GODADDY INC** p 619
14455 N Hayden Rd Ste 100, Scottsdale AZ 85260
Tel (480) 505-8800 *SIC* 7373 4813

E RITTER COMMUNICATIONS HOLDINGS INC p 467
2400 Ritter Dr, Jonesboro AR 72401
Tel (870) 336-3434 *SIC* 4813 4812 5045

■ **VALOR TELECOMMUNICATIONS ENTERPRISES LLC** p 1542
4001 N Rodney Parham Rd, Little Rock AR 72212
Tel (501) 748-7000 *SIC* 4813

■ **VALOR TELECOMMUNICATIONS LLC** p 1542
4001 N Rodney Parham Rd, Little Rock AR 72212
Tel (501) 748-7000 *SIC* 4813

■ **WINDSTREAM COMMUNICATIONS LLC** p 1615
4001 N Rodney Parham Rd, Little Rock AR 72212
Tel (800) 697-8153 *SIC* 4813

▲ **WINDSTREAM HOLDINGS INC** p 1615
4001 N Rodney Parham Rd # 101, Little Rock AR 72212
Tel (501) 748-7000 *SIC* 4813 5065

■ **WINDSTREAM IOWA COMMUNICATIONS LLC** p 1615
4001 N Rodney Parham Rd, Little Rock AR 72212
Tel (501) 748-7000 *SIC* 4813

■ **WINDSTREAM SERVICES LLC** p 1616
4001 N Rodney Parham Rd # 101, Little Rock AR 72212
Tel (501) 748-7000 *SIC* 4813 5065

E RITTER & CO p 466
10 Elm St, Marked Tree AR 72365
Tel (870) 358-7333
SIC 0131 0116 0724 4813 5211 5083

E RITTER AGRIBUSINESS HOLDINGS INC p 466
10 Elm St, Marked Tree AR 72365
Tel (870) 336-7310 *SIC* 0131 4813

LINKUS ENTERPRISES LLC p 869
18631 Lloyd Ln, Anderson CA 96007
Tel (530) 229-9197 *SIC* 1623 5731 4813

PROVIDEA CONFERENCING LLC p 1185
1297 Flynn Rd Ste 100, Camarillo CA 93012
Tel (805) 384-9995 *SIC* 4813

▲ **SALEM MEDIA GROUP INC** p 1272
4880 Santa Rosa Rd, Camarillo CA 93012
Tel (818) 956-0400 *SIC* 4832 2731 4813

COMPUTER CONSULTING OPERATIONS SPECIALISTS INC p 352
600 Corporate Pointe # 1010, Culver City CA 90230
Tel (310) 568-5000
SIC 4813 4899 5045 7378

INFONET SERVICES CORP p 741
2160 E Grand Ave, El Segundo CA 90245
Tel (310) 335-2859 *SIC* 4813 7373 7375

▲ **STAMPS.COM INC** p 1375
1990 E Grand Ave, El Segundo CA 90245
Tel (310) 482-5800 *SIC* 7331 5961 4813

■ **CITIZENS TELECOMMUNICATIONS CO OF CALIFORNIA INC** p 311
9260 E Stockton Blvd, Elk Grove CA 95624
Tel (916) 686-3000 *SIC* 4813

MAGPIE INTERNET COMMUNICATIONS CORP p 897
2762 Bayview Dr, Fremont CA 94538
Tel (510) 344-1200 *SIC* 4813 7379 7374

CURVATURE LLC p 402
6500 Hollister Ave # 210, Goleta CA 93117
Tel (805) 964-9975 *SIC* 4813

▲ **BOINGO WIRELESS INC** p 198
10960 Wilshire Blvd Fl 23, Los Angeles CA 90024
Tel (310) 586-5180 *SIC* 4813

CONNEXITY INC p 358
12200 W Olympic Blvd # 300, Los Angeles CA 90064
Tel (310) 571-1235 *SIC* 4813 7383

MPOWER COMMUNICATIONS CORP p 995
515 S Flower St, Los Angeles CA 90071
Tel (213) 213-3000 *SIC* 4813

TELEPACIFIC COMMUNICATIONS p 1434
515 S Flower St Fl 36, Los Angeles CA 90071
Tel (213) 213-3000 *SIC* 4813

US TELEPACIFIC CORP p 1533
515 S Flower St Fl 47, Los Angeles CA 90071
Tel (213) 213-3000 *SIC* 4813

US TELEPACIFIC HOLDINGS CORP p 1533
515 S Flower St Fl 47, Los Angeles CA 90071
Tel (213) 213-3000 *SIC* 4813

▲ **GLOBAL EAGLE ENTERTAINMENT INC** p 616
4553 Glencoe Ave Ste 200, Marina Del Rey CA 90292
Tel (310) 437-6000 *SIC* 4899 7371 4813

■ **GOOGLE INC** p 625
1600 Amphitheatre Pkwy, Mountain View CA 94043
Tel (650) 253-0000 *SIC* 4813 7375

■ **GOOGLE INTERNATIONAL LLC** p 625
1600 Amphitheatre Pkwy, Mountain View CA 94043
Tel (650) 253-0000 *SIC* 4813 7375

■ **PAYPAL GLOBAL HOLDINGS INC** p 1122
303 Bryant St, Mountain View CA 94041
Tel (408) 967-1000 *SIC* 7374 4813

SIERRA TEL COMMUNICATIONS GROUP p 1321
49150 Road 426, Oakhurst CA 93644
Tel (559) 683-4611 *SIC* 4813

OOMA INC p 1089
1880 Embarcadero Rd, Palo Alto CA 94303
Tel (650) 566-6600 *SIC* 4813

▲ **CALIX INC** p 242
1035 N Mcdowell Blvd, Petaluma CA 94954
Tel (707) 766-3000 *SIC* 3663 4899 4813

CAMEO GLOBAL INC p 245
4695 Chabot Dr Ste 101, Pleasanton CA 94588
Tel (925) 479-7800
SIC 7373 7371 7379 7363 4813 8742

■ **GTT COMMUNICATIONS (MP) INC** p 644
6800 Koll Center Pkwy # 200, Pleasanton CA 94566
Tel (925) 201-2500 *SIC* 4813 7375

MEGAPATH CLOUD CO LLC p 940
6800 Koll Center Pkwy, Pleasanton CA 94566
Tel (925) 201-2500 *SIC* 4813

MEGAPATH INC p 940
6800 Koll Center Pkwy # 200, Pleasanton CA 94566
Tel (877) 611-6342 *SIC* 4813

▲ **EQUINIX INC** p 506
1 Lagoon Dr Ste 400, Redwood City CA 94065
Tel (650) 598-6000 *SIC* 4813

EVERNOTE CORP p 515
305 Walnut St, Redwood City CA 94063
Tel (650) 216-7700 *SIC* 4813

■ **SUREWEST COMMUNICATIONS** p 1408
211 Lincoln St, Roseville CA 95678
Tel (916) 786-6141 *SIC* 4813 4812

GEARY LSF GROUP INC p 597
332 Pine St Fl 6, San Francisco CA 94104
Tel (877) 616-8226 *SIC* 4813

ON24 INC p 1086
201 3rd St Fl 3, San Francisco CA 94103
Tel (877) 202-9599 *SIC* 4813

■ **PACIFIC BELL TELEPHONE CO** p 1104
430 Bush St Fl 3, San Francisco CA 94108
Tel (415) 542-9000 *SIC* 4813 2741 4822

2WIRE INC p 2
1764 Automation Pkwy, San Jose CA 95131
Tel (678) 473-2907 *SIC* 4813

▲ **8X8 INC** p 4
2125 Onel Dr, San Jose CA 95131
Tel (408) 727-1885 *SIC* 4813 7372

▲ **BROCADE COMMUNICATIONS SYSTEMS INC** p 216
130 Holger Way, San Jose CA 95134
Tel (408) 333-8000 *SIC* 3577 4813

■ **CISCO WEBEX LLC** p 309
170 W Tasman Dr, San Jose CA 95134
Tel (408) 435-7000 *SIC* 7389 4813

MEGAPATH GROUP INC p 940
2510 Zanker Rd, San Jose CA 95131
Tel (408) 952-6400 *SIC* 4813

▲ **PAYPAL HOLDINGS INC** p 1123
2211 N 1st St, San Jose CA 95131
Tel (408) 967-1000 *SIC* 4813 7374

■ **PAYPAL INC** p 1123
2211 N 1st St, San Jose CA 95131
Tel (877) 981-2163 *SIC* 4813 7374

2100 FREEDOM INC p 1
625 N Grand Ave, Santa Ana CA 92701
Tel (714) 796-7000
SIC 2711 2721 7313 2741 5963 4813

FREEDOM COMMUNICATIONS HOLDINGS INC p 576
625 N Grand Ave, Santa Ana CA 92701
Tel (714) 796-7000
SIC 6719 2711 4813 2721

ASIAINFO-LINKAGE INC p 117
5201 Great America Pkwy # 356, Santa Clara CA 95054
Tel (408) 970-9788 *SIC* 4813

HULU LLC p 718
2500 Broadway Fl 2, Santa Monica CA 90404
Tel (310) 571-4700 *SIC* 4833 4813

■ **RUCKUS WIRELESS INC** p 1257
350 W Java Dr, Sunnyvale CA 94089
Tel (650) 265-4200 *SIC* 4813

■ **AB CELLULAR HOLDING LLC** p 9
1452 Edinger Ave, Tustin CA 92780
Tel (562) 468-6846 *SIC* 4813

■ **CONVERSANT LLC** p 365
30699 Russell Ranch Rd # 250, Westlake Village CA 91362
Tel (818) 575-4500 SIC 7375 4813

▲ **ZAYO GROUP HOLDINGS INC** p 1641
1805 29th St Unit 2050, Boulder CO 80301
Tel (303) 381-4683 SIC 4813 3661

■ **ZAYO GROUP LLC** p 1641
1805 29th St Unit 2050, Boulder CO 80301
Tel (303) 381-4683 SIC 4813 3661

▲ **LEVEL 3 COMMUNICATIONS INC** p 858
1025 Eldorado Blvd, Broomfield CO 80021
Tel (720) 888-1000 SIC 4813 7373 7374

■ **LEVEL 3 COMMUNICATIONS LLC** p 858
1025 Eldorado Blvd, Broomfield CO 80021
Tel (720) 888-2750 SIC 4813 7373

■ **LEVEL 3 FINANCING INC** p 858
1025 Eldorado Blvd, Broomfield CO 80021
Tel (720) 888-1000 SIC 4813

LENDERLIVE NETWORK INC p 855
710 S Ash St Ste 200, Denver CO 80246
Tel (303) 226-8000 SIC 4813 6163

LIBERTY GLOBAL INC p 861
1550 Wewatta St Ste 1000, Denver CO 80202
Tel (303) 220-6600 SIC 4841 4813

PETROLEUM PLACE INC p 1139
1670 Broadway Ste 2800, Denver CO 80202
Tel (303) 515-5400 SIC 4813 7371

■ **QWEST GOVERNMENT SERVICES INC** p 1201
931 14th St Ste 1000b, Denver CO 80202
Tel (303) 992-1400 SIC 4813 4812

■ **QWEST SERVICES CORP** p 1201
931 14th St Ste 1000b, Denver CO 80202
Tel (303) 992-1400 SIC 4813

HUGHES SATELLITE SYSTEMS CORP p 717
100 Inverness Ter E, Englewood CO 80112
Tel (303) 706-4000 SIC 4813

■ **LIBERTY INTERACTIVE LLC** p 862
12300 Liberty Blvd, Englewood CO 80112
Tel (720) 875-5400
SIC 5961 4841 7819 4813

▲ **STARZ** p 1379
8900 Liberty Cir, Englewood CO 80112
Tel (720) 852-7700 SIC 4841 4813

UNITEDGLOBALCOM INC p 1515
12300 Liberty Blvd, Englewood CO 80112
Tel (303) 220-6676 SIC 8999 4813

WIDEOPENWEST NETWORKS LLC p 1608
7887 E Belleview Ave, Englewood CO 80111
Tel (720) 479-3558 SIC 4813

VIRTELA TECHNOLOGY SERVICES INC p 1560
5680 Greenwood Plaza Blvd, Greenwood Village CO 80111
Tel (720) 475-4000 SIC 4813

CENTURYTEL INC p 282
519 Main St, La Jara CO 81140
Tel (719) 274-4437 SIC 4813

■ **SERVICEMAGIC INC** p 1307
14023 Denver West Pkwy # 2, Lakewood CO 80401
Tel (303) 963-7200 SIC 4813

■ **LEVEL 3 TELECOM HOLDINGS LLC** p 858
10475 Park Meadows Dr, Littleton CO 80124
Tel (303) 566-1000 SIC 4813

■ **LEVEL 3 TELECOM LLC** p 858
10475 Park Meadows Dr, Littleton CO 80124
Tel (303) 566-1000 SIC 4813

■ **TW TELECOM OF COLORADO LLC** p 1494
10475 Park Meadows Dr, Littleton CO 80124
Tel (636) 625-7000 SIC 4812 4813

CANBERRA INDUSTRIES INC p 246
800 Research Pkwy, Meriden CT 06450
Tel (203) 238-2351 SIC 3829 4813

■ **SOUTHERN NEW ENGLAND TELECOMMUNICATIONS CORP** p 1349
2 Science Park, New Haven CT 06511
Tel (203) 771-5200
SIC 4813 4812 5065 6159 2741 4822

■ **SOUTHERN NEW ENGLAND TELEPHONE CO INC** p 1349
310 Orange St, New Haven CT 06510
Tel (203) 771-5200 SIC 4813 4822

▲ **FRONTIER COMMUNICATIONS CORP** p 581
401 Merritt 7 Ste 1, Norwalk CT 06851
Tel (203) 614-5600 SIC 4813

■ **FRONTIER FLORIDA LLC** p 581
401 Merritt 7, Norwalk CT 06851
Tel (813) 483-2011
SIC 4813 6519 8721 5065 7629

CHARTER COMMUNICATIONS INC p 290
400 Atlantic St Fl 10, Stamford CT 06901
Tel (203) 905-7801 SIC 4841 4813

▲ **CHARTER COMMUNICATIONS INC** p 290
400 Atlantic St, Stamford CT 06901
Tel (203) 905-7801 SIC 4841 4813

■ **VERIZON DELAWARE LLC** p 1550
901 N Tatnall St Fl 2, Wilmington DE 19801
Tel (302) 571-1571
SIC 4813 4812 7373 2741

▲ **COGENT COMMUNICATIONS HOLDINGS INC** p 334
2450 N St Nw, Washington DC 20037
Tel (202) 295-4200 SIC 4813 7372

■ **COGENT COMMUNICATIONS INC** p 334
2450 N St Nw, Washington DC 20037
Tel (202) 295-4200 SIC 4813 7375

NETWORK FOR GOOD INC p 1028
1140 Conn Ave Nw Ste 700, Washington DC 20036
Tel (202) 627-1600 SIC 4813

■ **VERIZON WASHINGTON DC INC** p 1551
1300 I St Nw, Washington DC 20005
Tel (202) 392-9900 SIC 4813 8721

IAP WORLD SERVICES INC p 725
7315 N Atlantic Ave, Cape Canaveral FL 32920
Tel (321) 784-7100
SIC 4731 4581 8744 4911 1541 4813

FRIENDFINDER NETWORKS INC p 580
1615 S Congress Ave # 103, Delray Beach FL 33445
Tel (561) 912-7000 SIC 4813

GLOBENET CABOS SUBMARINOS AMERICA INC p 618
200 E Las Olas Blvd, Fort Lauderdale FL 33301
Tel (561) 314-0500 SIC 4813

RESULTS COMPANIES LLC p 1228
100 Ne 3rd Ave Ste 200, Fort Lauderdale FL 33301
Tel (954) 921-2400 SIC 4813

FORT PIERCE UTILITIES AUTHORITY p 569
206 S 6th St, Fort Pierce FL 34950
Tel (772) 466-1600
SIC 4931 4941 4924 4813

GRU p 642
301 Se 4th Ave, Gainesville FL 32601
Tel (352) 334-3434 SIC 4813

■ **COMCAST OF FLORIDA/GEORGIA/ILLINOIS/MICHIGAN LLC** p 343
4600 Touchton Rd E # 2200, Jacksonville FL 32246
Tel (904) 374-8000 SIC 4813 4841

TRACFONE WIRELESS INC p 1468
9700 Nw 112th Ave, Medley FL 33178
Tel (305) 640-2000 SIC 4813 4812

BUSINESS TELECOMMUNICATIONS SERVICES INC p 230
2620 Sw 27th Ave, Miami FL 33133
Tel (305) 358-5850 SIC 4813 5999 8748

ELANDIA INTERNATIONAL INC p 483
8333 Nw 53rd St Ste 400, Miami FL 33166
Tel (305) 415-8830
SIC 4813 4899 7371 5044

NEORIS USA INC p 1026
703 Waterford Way Ste 700, Miami FL 33126
Tel (305) 728-6000 SIC 4813

TELEFONICA USA p 1434
1111 Brickell Ave # 1000, Miami FL 33131
Tel (305) 925-5300 SIC 7375 7374 4813

TELEFONICA USA INC p 1434
1111 Brickell Ave # 1000, Miami FL 33131
Tel (305) 925-5298 SIC 5065 4813

■ **TERREMARK WORLDWIDE INC** p 1440
2 S Biscayne Blvd # 2800, Miami FL 33131
Tel (305) 961-3200 SIC 4813 8742

COLEMAN TECHNOLOGIES LLC p 336
5337 Millenia Lakes Blvd, Orlando FL 32839
Tel (407) 481-8600 SIC 4813

BUCCANEER HOLDINGS LLC p 222
8125 Highwoods Palm Way, Tampa FL 33647
Tel (813) 637-5000 SIC 4813 4812

■ **INTERMEDIA COMMUNICATIONS INC** p 753
3608 Queen Palm Dr, Tampa FL 33619
Tel (800) 940-0011 SIC 4813

MCS OF TAMPA INC p 932
8510 Sunstate St, Tampa FL 33634
Tel (813) 872-0217
SIC 1731 7373 4813 7378

■ **PRIMUS TELECOMMUNICATIONS INC** p 1176
3903 Northdale Blvd 220e, Tampa FL 33624
Tel (703) 902-2800 SIC 4813

CREATIVE CHOICE HOMES INC p 390
8895 N Military Trl 206e, West Palm Beach FL 33410
Tel (561) 627-7988 SIC 6552 4813

MEDIACOM SOUTHEAST LLC p 936
1104 N Westover Blvd, Albany GA 31707
Tel (229) 888-0242 SIC 4841 4813

EASYLINK SERVICES INTERNATIONAL CORP p 473
11720 Amberpark Dr # 200, Alpharetta GA 30009
Tel (678) 533-8000 SIC 4813

■ **BELLSOUTH CORP** p 171
675 W Peach St Ste 4300, Atlanta GA 30375
Tel (404) 420-6126
SIC 4813 4812 2741 5065

■ **BELLSOUTH TELECOMMUNICATIONS INC** p 171
675 W Peach St Ne St Ne, Atlanta GA 30375
Tel (912) 526-3440
SIC 4813 4812 2741 5065

BIRCH COMMUNICATIONS INC p 185
320 Interstate North Pkwy, Atlanta GA 30339
Tel (866) 424-5100 SIC 4813 5045

CBEYOND INC p 268
320 Interstate N Pkwy 500, Atlanta GA 30339
Tel (678) 424-2400
SIC 4813 7389 4899 1731

COX COMMUNICATIONS INC p 386
6205 B Pchtree Dunwody Ne, Atlanta GA 30328
Tel (404) 843-5000 SIC 4841 4813

COX ENTERPRISES INC p 386
6205 Pachtree Dunwoody Rd, Atlanta GA 30328
Tel (678) 645-0000
SIC 4841 4813 2711 4833 7389 4832

■ **CTC COMMUNICATIONS CORP** p 399
1170 Peachtree St Ne # 900, Atlanta GA 30309
Tel (404) 815-0770 SIC 4813

▲ **EARTHLINK HOLDINGS CORP** p 469
1170 Peachtree St Ne # 900, Atlanta GA 30309
Tel (404) 815-0770 SIC 4813

EARTHLINK INC p 469
1375 Peachtree St Ne A9, Atlanta GA 30309
Tel (404) 815-0770 SIC 4813

■ **EARTHLINK LLC** p 469
1170 Peachtree St Ne # 900, Atlanta GA 30309
Tel (877) 355-1501 SIC 4813

PIKSEL INC p 1148
2100 Powers Ferry Rd Se # 400, Atlanta GA 30339
Tel (646) 553-4845 SIC 4813

■ **SOUTHERN COMMUNICATIONS SERVICES INC** p 1348
5555 Glenridge Connector, Atlanta GA 30342
Tel (678) 443-1500 SIC 4813 4812

■ **TWCC HOLDING CORP** p 1494
300 Interstate N Pkwy Se, Atlanta GA 30339
Tel (770) 226-0000
SIC 4833 4813 7812 8999

■ **AT&T MOBILITY LLC** p 123
1025 Lenox Park Blvd Ne, Brookhaven GA 30319
Tel (425) 580-6014 SIC 4812 4813 5999

■ **BELLSOUTH BUSINESS SYSTEMS INC** p 171
2180 Lake Blvd Ne, Brookhaven GA 30319
Tel (404) 829-8000 SIC 4813 4812

COX BUSINESS SERVICES LLC p 386
1400 Lake Hearn Dr Ne, Brookhaven GA 30319
Tel (404) 843-5000 SIC 4813

COX HOLDINGS INC p 386
1400 Lake Hearn Dr Ne, Brookhaven GA 30319
Tel (404) 843-5000 SIC 4841 4813

COXCOM LLC p 386
1400 Lake Hearn Dr Ne, Brookhaven GA 30319
Tel (404) 843-5000 SIC 4841 4813

■ **VERIZON TELEMATICS INC** p 1550
2002 Summit Blvd Ste 1800, Brookhaven GA 30319
Tel (404) 573-5800 SIC 7379 4813

■ **WINDSTREAM GEORGIA LLC** p 1615
906 Vista Dr, Dalton GA 30721
Tel (706) 279-7600 SIC 4813 4812

WORLD TECHNOLOGY GROUP INC p 1625
8930 Muirfield Ct, Duluth GA 30097
Tel (404) 697-0985 SIC 4813

QUALITY TECHNOLOGY SERVICES LLC p 1197
300 Satellite Blvd Nw, Suwanee GA 30024
Tel (678) 546-0064
SIC 7373 4813 7378 7374

KNOLOGY INC p 825
1241 Og Skinner Dr, West Point GA 31833
Tel (334) 644-2611 SIC 4813 4841

■ **HAWAIIAN TELCOM COMMUNICATIONS INC** p 669
1177 Bishop St, Honolulu HI 96813
Tel (808) 546-4511 SIC 4813 4812

▲ **HAWAIIAN TELCOM HOLDCO INC** p 669
1177 Bishop St, Honolulu HI 96813
Tel (808) 546-4511 SIC 4813

■ **HAWAIIAN TELCOM INC** p 669
1177 Bishop St, Honolulu HI 96813
Tel (808) 643-3456 SIC 4813 5065 7629

■ **POTLATCH TELEPHONE CO** p 1164
702 E Main, Kendrick ID 83537
Tel (208) 289-5701 SIC 4813

▲ **WESTELL TECHNOLOGIES INC** p 1597
750 N Commons Dr, Aurora IL 60504
Tel (630) 898-2500 SIC 3661 4813 7389

ORIUS CORP p 1095
1000 Hart Rd Ste 140, Barrington IL 60010
Tel (847) 277-8444 SIC 4813

■ **AMERITECH PAYPHONE SERVICES OF MICHIGAN INC** p 84
225 W Randolph St, Chicago IL 60606
Tel (708) 458-8460 SIC 4813

■ **AT&T TELEHOLDINGS INC** p 123
30 S Wacker Dr Fl 34, Chicago IL 60606
Tel (800) 257-0902
SIC 4813 4812 2741 5065 6159 7382

▲ **ECHO GLOBAL LOGISTICS INC** p 475
600 W Chicago Ave Ste 725, Chicago IL 60654
Tel (800) 354-7993 SIC 4731 4813

■ **GOGO LLC** p 620
111 N Canal St Fl 15, Chicago IL 60606
Tel (630) 647-1400
SIC 3663 4812 4813 4899

HOSTWAY CORP p 710
100 N Riverside Plz # 800, Chicago IL 60606
Tel (312) 238-0125 SIC 4813

■ **ILLINOIS BELL TELEPHONE CO** p 732
225 W Randolph St Fl Ll, Chicago IL 60606
Tel (618) 344-9077 SIC 4813 8721 6512

▲ **INTELIQUENT INC** p 750
550 W Adams St Fl 9, Chicago IL 60661
Tel (312) 384-8000 SIC 4813

▲ **TELEPHONE AND DATA SYSTEMS INC** p 1434
30 N La Salle St Ste 4000, Chicago IL 60602
Tel (312) 630-1900 SIC 4812 4813

■ **TRIBUNE INTERACTIVE INC** p 1479
435 N Michigan Ave Fl 2, Chicago IL 60611
Tel (312) 222-3232 SIC 4813

■ **UNITED STATES CELLULAR CORP** p 1512
8410 W Bryn Mawr Ave # 700, Chicago IL 60631
Tel (773) 399-8900 SIC 4812 4813

NORTHWESTERN UNIVERSITY INFORMATION TECHNOLOGIES p 1061
1800 Sherman Ave Ste 7, Evanston IL 60201
Tel (847) 467-1766 SIC 4813 7374 4812

COBALT HOLDINGS INC p 332
101 Waukegan Rd Ste 990, Lake Bluff IL 60044
Tel (773) 230-3219 SIC 4812 4813

▲ **CONSOLIDATED COMMUNICATIONS HOLDINGS INC** p 359
121 S 17th St, Mattoon IL 61938
Tel (217) 235-3311 SIC 4813

■ **CONSOLIDATED COMMUNICATIONS INC** p 359
121 S 17th St, Mattoon IL 61938
Tel (217) 235-3311 SIC 4813

■ **CONSOLIDATED COMMUNICATIONS OF ILLINOIS CO** p 359
121 S 17th St, Mattoon IL 61938
Tel (217) 235-3311 SIC 4813

APPLICATIONS SOFTWARE TECHNOLOGY CORP p 99
1755 Park St Ste 100, Naperville IL 60563
Tel (630) 778-0707 SIC 4813

CORIANT INTERNATIONAL INC p 370
1415 W Diehl Rd, Naperville IL 60563
Tel (630) 798-8800 SIC 4813

■ **CAMDEN TELEPHONE CO INC** p 245
210 W Main St, Camden IN 46917
Tel (608) 831-1000 SIC 4813

TELAMON CORP p 1433
1000 E 116th St, Carmel IN 46032
Tel (317) 818-6888 SIC 4813 8711 3357

■ **Q-COMM CORP** p 1194
3701 Communications Way, Evansville IN 47715
Tel (812) 253-7000 SIC 4813 4812

■ **MERCHANTS AND FARMERS TELEPHONE CO** p 944
125 W Main St, Hillsboro IN 47949
Tel (765) 798-2145 SIC 4813

■ **AMERITECH** p 84
240 N Meridian St, Indianapolis IN 46204
Tel (317) 265-2266 SIC 4813 8721

■ **TIPTON TELEPHONE CO INC** p 1455
117 E Washington St, Tipton IN 46072
Tel (765) 675-4185 SIC 4813

■ **MCLEODUSA INC** p 932
6400 C St Sw, Cedar Rapids IA 52404
Tel (319) 364-0000 SIC 4813 4812

■ **MCLEODUSA HOLDINGS INC** p 932
1770 Boyson Rd, Hiawatha IA 52233
Tel (319) 364-0000 SIC 4813 4812

IOWA NETWORK SERVICES INC p 763
7760 Office Plaza Dr S, West Des Moines IA 50266
Tel (515) 830-0110 SIC 4813

▲ **EURONET WORLDWIDE INC** p 512
3500 College Blvd, Leawood KS 66211
Tel (913) 327-4200 SIC 6099 7372 4813

RURAL TELEPHONE SERVICE CO INC p 1258
145 N Main St, Lenora KS 67645
Tel (785) 567-4281 SIC 4813 5734 5045

■ **CLEARWIRE CORP** p 324
6200 Sprint Pkwy, Overland Park KS 66251
Tel (425) 216-7600 SIC 4813

■ **SPRINT COMMUNICATIONS CO LP** p 1361
6391 Sprint Pkwy, Overland Park KS 66251
Tel (800) 829-0965 SIC 4813

■ **SPRINT COMMUNICATIONS INC** p 1361
6200 Sprint Pkwy, Overland Park KS 66251
Tel (855) 848-3280 SIC 4813 4812 5999

■ **SPRINT CORP** p 1361
6200 Sprint Pkwy, Overland Park KS 66251
Tel (855) 848-3280 SIC 4813 4812

■ **SPRINT SPECTRUM LP** p 1361
6800 Sprint Pkwy, Overland Park KS 66251
Tel (703) 433-4000 SIC 4813

■ **EMBARQ MANAGEMENT CO** p 490
5454 W 110th St, Shawnee Mission KS 66211
Tel (913) 323-4637 SIC 4813 4812

■ **SPRINT SPECTRUM HOLDING CO LP** p 1361
6160 Sprint Pkwy, Shawnee Mission KS 66251
Tel (800) 829-0965 SIC 4813

■ **SPRINT INTERNATIONAL INC** p 1361
2330 Shawnee Mission Pkwy, Westwood KS 66205
Tel (913) 624-3000 SIC 4813

ELECTRIC & WATER PLANT BOARD OF CITY OF FRANKFORT KY p 484
317 W 2nd St, Frankfort KY 40601
Tel (502) 352-4372
SIC 4941 4911 7382 5063 4841 4813

■ **LESLIE COUNTY TELEPHONE CO** p 857
22076 Main St, Hyden KY 41749
Tel (606) 672-2303 SIC 4813

▲ **CAFEPRESS INC** p 237
11909 Shelbyville Rd, Louisville KY 40243
Tel (502) 995-2268 SIC 4813 5961

■ **SALEM TELEPHONE CO** p 1272
221 E Main St, Salem KY 42078
Tel (608) 831-1000 SIC 4813

▲ **GLOBALSTAR INC** p 617
300 Holiday Square Blvd # 300, Covington LA 70433
Tel (985) 335-1500 SIC 4813

■ **CAROLINA TELEPHONE AND TELEGRAPH CO LLC** p 259
100 Centurylink Dr, Monroe LA 71203
Tel (318) 388-9000 SIC 4813 8721 5065

■ **CENTEL CORP** p 275
100 Centurylink Dr, Monroe LA 71203
Tel (318) 388-9000 SIC 4813 4812

■ **CENTRAL TELEPHONE CO** p 280
100 Centurylink Dr, Monroe LA 71203
Tel (318) 361-5955 SIC 4813

▲ **CENTURYLINK INC** p 282
100 Centurylink Dr, Monroe LA 71203
Tel (318) 388-9000 SIC 4813 4812

■ **CENTURYTEL HOLDINGS INC** p 282
100 Centurylink Dr, Monroe LA 71203
Tel (318) 388-9000 SIC 4813

■ **CENTURYTEL OF NORTHWEST INC** p 283
100 Centurylink Dr, Monroe LA 71203
Tel (318) 388-9000 SIC 4813 4812

■ **CENTURYTEL.COM LLC** p 283
100 Centurylink Dr, Monroe LA 71203
Tel (318) 388-9500 SIC 4813

■ **EMBARQ CORP** p 490
100 Centurylink Dr, Monroe LA 71203
Tel (318) 388-9000 SIC 4813

■ **EMBARQ FLORIDA INC** p 490
100 Centurylink Dr, Monroe LA 71203
Tel (318) 388-9000 SIC 4813

■ **EMBARQ MID-ATLANTIC MANAGEMENT SERVICES INC** p 490
100 Centurylink Dr, Monroe LA 71203
Tel (318) 388-9000 SIC 4813

■ **QWEST COMMUNICATIONS INTERNATIONAL INC** p 1201
100 Centurylink Dr, Monroe LA 71203
Tel (318) 388-9000 SIC 4813 4822 4812

■ **QWEST CORP** p 1201
100 Centurylink Dr, Monroe LA 71203
Tel (318) 388-9000 SIC 4813

ASRC COMMUNICATIONS LTD p 119
7000 Muirkirk Meadows Dr, Beltsville MD 20705
Tel (301) 837-5500 SIC 4813

■ **LOCKHEED MARTIN GLOBAL TELECOMMUNICATIONS LLC** p 873
6560 Rock Spring Dr, Bethesda MD 20817
Tel (301) 571-7135 SIC 4813

■ **SYTEX GROUP INC** p 1419
700 N Frederick Ave, Gaithersburg MD 20879
Tel (301) 240-7000 SIC 4813

■ SYTEX INC p 1419
700 N Frederick Ave, Gaithersburg MD 20879
Tel (301) 240-7000 SIC 4813

■ HUGHES COMMUNICATIONS INC p 717
11717 Exploration Ln, Germantown MD 20876
Tel (301) 428-5500 SIC 4813 4899 3663

■ VERIZON MARYLAND LLC p 1550
1710 Undrpamd Way Ste 401, Hagerstown MD 21740
Tel (301) 790-7135 SIC 4813 8721

▲ ARGAN INC p 107
1 Church St Ste 201, Rockville MD 20850
Tel (301) 315-0027 SIC 4813 1623 8748

▲ RADIO ONE INC p 1204
1010 Wayne Ave Ste 1400, Silver Spring MD 20910
Tel (301) 429-3200 SIC 4832 4841 4813

■ NAVISITE LLC p 1020
400 Minuteman Rd, Andover MA 01810
Tel (978) 682-8300 SIC 4813

■ ALLIED WIRELESS COMMUNICATIONS CORP p 57
600 Cummings Ctr, Beverly MA 01915
Tel (978) 619-1300 SIC 4813

▲ ATN INTERNATIONAL INC p 128
500 Cummings Ctr Ste 2450, Beverly MA 01915
Tel (978) 619-1300 SIC 4813 4812 1711

▲ AMERICAN TOWER CORP p 80
116 Huntington Ave # 1100, Boston MA 02116
Tel (617) 375-7500 SIC 4813 3663

■ ATC TOWER SERVICES LLC p 124
116 Huntington Ave # 1100, Boston MA 02116
Tel (617) 375-7500 SIC 4813 3663

BIDMC TELECOMMUNICATIONS p 181
1 Jimmy Fund Way, Boston MA 02115
Tel (617) 278-6351 SIC 4813

▲ BRIGHTCOVE INC p 213
290 Congress St Fl 4, Boston MA 02210
Tel (888) 882-1880 SIC 4813 7372

■ COMMUNISPACE CORP p 347
290 Congress St Fl 7, Boston MA 02210
Tel (617) 316-4000 SIC 4813

■ VERIZON NEW ENGLAND INC p 1550
185 Franklin St 4th, Boston MA 02110
Tel (617) 743-9800 SIC 4813 8721

BT CONFERENCING INC p 222
30 Braintree Hill Park # 301, Braintree MA 02184
Tel (617) 801-6700 SIC 4813

ONE COMMUNICATIONS CORP p 1086
5 Wall St Fl 5, Burlington MA 01803
Tel (781) 362-5700 SIC 4813

IBASIS INC p 726
10 Maguire Rd Ste 300, Lexington MA 02421
Tel (781) 505-7500 SIC 4813

■ GALAXY INVESTMENT HOLDINGS INC p 589
38 Glen Ave, Newton MA 02459
Tel (617) 928-9300 SIC 4813 4812

ATLANTIC BROADBAND FINANCE LLC p 126
1 Pine Hill Dr Ste 205, Quincy MA 02169
Tel (617) 786-8800 SIC 4841 4813

GRANITE TELECOMMUNICATIONS LLC p 631
100 Newport Avenue Ext # 1, Quincy MA 02171
Tel (617) 933-5500 SIC 4813

▲ CARE.COM INC p 254
77 4th Ave Ste 5, Waltham MA 02451
Tel (781) 642-5900 SIC 4813

■ CONSTANT CONTACT INC p 360
1601 Trapelo Rd Ste 329, Waltham MA 02451
Tel (781) 472-8100 SIC 7373 4813 7331

■ ISLAND TELEPHONE CO p 766
37940 King Hwy, Beaver Island MI 49782
Tel (608) 831-1000 SIC 4813

■ MICHIGAN BELL TELEPHONE CO p 960
444 Michigan Ave, Detroit MI 48226
Tel (313) 223-9900 SIC 4813 8721

■ FRONTIER COMMUNICATIONS CORP p 581
14450 Burnhaven Dr, Burnsville MN 55306
Tel (952) 435-3133 SIC 4813

■ FRONTIER COMMUNICATIONS OF MINNESOTA INC p 581
1405 W 150th St, Burnsville MN 55306
Tel (952) 898-6422 SIC 4813

CONVERGEONE HOLDINGS CORP p 365
3344 Highway 149, Eagan MN 55121
Tel (651) 994-6800 SIC 4813 5999 1731

CONVERGEONE INC p 365
3344 Highway 149, Eagan MN 55121
Tel (651) 994-6800 SIC 4813 5999 1731

ENVENTIS CORP p 503
221 E Hickory St, Mankato MN 56001
Tel (507) 387-1151 SIC 4813

■ ENVENTIS TELECOM INC p 503
2950 Xenium Ln N Ste 138, Minneapolis MN 55441
Tel (763) 577-3900 SIC 4813

MIDCONTINENT COMMUNICATIONS p 964
3600 Minnesota Dr Ste 700, Minneapolis MN 55435
Tel (952) 844-2600 SIC 4841 4813

■ NEXTIRAONE LLC p 1040
5050 Lincoln Dr Ste 300, Minneapolis MN 55436
Tel (952) 352-4410
SIC 5065 7629 1731 5999 4813 4841

NORTH CENTRAL EQUITY LLC p 1051
60 S 6th St Ste 2535, Minneapolis MN 55402
Tel (612) 465-0260 SIC 6799 4813

DIGITAL RIVER INC p 439
10380 Bren Rd W, Minnetonka MN 55343
Tel (952) 253-1234 SIC 4813

■ MID-STATE TELEPHONE CO p 963
7902 Chapin Dr Ne, New London MN 56273
Tel (320) 354-7805 SIC 4813

ARVIG ENTERPRISES INC p 114
150 2nd St Sw Ste 100, Perham MN 56573
Tel (218) 346-4227 SIC 4813 4841

EAST OTTER TAIL TELEPHONE CO p 470
150 2nd Ave Sw, Perham MN 56573
Tel (218) 346-5500 SIC 4813

ONVOY LLC p 1088
10300 6th Ave N, Plymouth MN 55441
Tel (763) 230-2036 SIC 4813

MARCO TECHNOLOGIES LLC p 905
4510 Heatherwood Rd, Saint Cloud MN 56301
Tel (320) 259-3000
SIC 7371 4813 7313 7812

TELAPEX INC p 1433
1018 Highland Pkwy # 500, Ridgeland MS 39157
Tel (601) 355-1522 SIC 4812 4813

INTERFACE SECURITY SYSTEMS LLC p 752
3773 Corporate Centre Dr, Earth City MO 63045
Tel (314) 595-0100 SIC 4813

BIRCH TELECOM INC p 185
2323 Grand Blvd Ste 925, Kansas City MO 64108
Tel (816) 300-3000 SIC 4813 7375 4812

■ TW TELECOM MANAGEMENT CO LLC p 1494
2342 Technology Dr, O Fallon MO 63368
Tel (636) 625-7000 SIC 4813

■ CCO HOLDINGS LLC p 270
12405 Powerscourt Dr, Saint Louis MO 63131
Tel (314) 965-0555 SIC 4841 4813 7389

CEQUEL COMMUNICATIONS LLC p 283
520 Maryville Centre Dr # 300, Saint Louis MO 63141
Tel (314) 965-2020 SIC 4813 4841

CEQUEL CORP p 283
520 Maryville Centre Dr # 300, Saint Louis MO 63141
Tel (314) 315-9400 SIC 4841 4813

■ CHARTER COMMUNICATIONS HOLDINGS LLC p 290
12405 Powerscourt Dr, Saint Louis MO 63131
Tel (314) 543-2480 SIC 4841 4813

FIDELITY COMMUNICATIONS CO p 540
64 N Clark St, Sullivan MO 63080
Tel (800) 392-8070 SIC 4841 4813

■ SAVVIS COMMUNICATIONS CORP p 1284
1 Solutions Pkwy, Town And Country MO 63017
Tel (314) 628-7000 SIC 4813 7375

SAVVIS INC p 1284
1 Solutions Pkwy, Town And Country MO 63017
Tel (314) 628-7000
SIC 7373 7379 4813 7375

■ CENTURYTEL OF MISSOURI LLC p 283
1151 Century Tel Dr, Wentzville MO 63385
Tel (636) 332-3011 SIC 4813

■ CENTURYTEL OF IDAHO INC p 283
290 N Main St, Kalispell MT 59901
Tel (703) 363-8774 SIC 4813

BLACKFOOT TELEPHONE COOPERATIVE INC p 187
1221 N Russell St, Missoula MT 59808
Tel (406) 541-2121 SIC 4813

NEDELCO INC p 1023
1001 12th St, Aurora NE 68818
Tel (402) 694-5101 SIC 4813

■ ORIENTAL TRADING CO INC p 1094
5455 S 90th St, Omaha NE 68127
Tel (402) 596-1200 SIC 5199 4813

■ OTC WORLDWIDE HOLDINGS INC p 1097
4206 S 108th St, Omaha NE 68137
Tel (800) 348-6483 SIC 4813

▲ WEST CORP p 1594
11808 Miracle Hills Dr, Omaha NE 68154
Tel (402) 963-1200
SIC 7389 7372 4813 7374

■ WEST IP COMMUNICATIONS INC p 1594
11808 Miracle Hills Dr, Omaha NE 68154
Tel (402) 963-1200 SIC 4813

NOS COMMUNICATIONS INC p 1062
250 Pilot Rd Ste 300, Las Vegas NV 89119
Tel (702) 547-8000 SIC 8748 4813

■ ZAPPOS.COM INC p 1641
400 Stewart Ave Ste A, Las Vegas NV 89101
Tel (702) 943-7777
SIC 5661 4813 5632 5611

■ NEVADA BELL TELEPHONE CO p 1028
645 E Plumb Ln B128, Reno NV 89502
Tel (775) 333-3124 SIC 4813

■ UNION TELEPHONE CO p 1505
7 Central St, Farmington NH 03835
Tel (603) 859-3700 SIC 4813

■ GTE WIRELESS INC p 644
1 Verizon Way, Basking Ridge NJ 07920
Tel (908) 559-7000 SIC 4813

■ VERIZON CORPORATE SERVICES GROUP INC p 1550
295 N Maple Ave, Basking Ridge NJ 07920
Tel (908) 559-7000 SIC 4813

■ AT&T CORP p 123
1 At&T Way, Bedminster NJ 07921
Tel (800) 403-3302 SIC 4813 4822 7375

▲ SYNCHRONOSS TECHNOLOGIES INC p 1414
200 Crossing Blvd Fl 8, Bridgewater NJ 08807
Tel (866) 620-3940 SIC 7371 4813

■ TELEPORT COMMUNICATIONS GROUP INC (DEL CORP) p 1435
429 Ridge Rd, Dayton NJ 08810
Tel (732) 392-2000 SIC 4813

■ GLOBAL CROSSING NORTH AMERICA INC p 616
200 Park Ave Ste 300, Florham Park NJ 07932
Tel (973) 937-0100 SIC 4813

■ GLOBAL CROSSING NORTH AMERICAN HOLDINGS INC p 616
200 Park Ave Ste 300, Florham Park NJ 07932
Tel (973) 937-0100 SIC 4813

■ JET.COM INC p 784
221 River St Fl 8, Hoboken NJ 07030
Tel (844) 538-2255 SIC 4813

▲ VONAGE HOLDINGS CORP p 1565
23 Main St, Holmdel NJ 07733
Tel (732) 528-2600 SIC 4813

IPC SYSTEMS HOLDINGS CORP p 763
1500 Plaza Ten Fl 15, Jersey City NJ 07311
Tel (201) 253-2000 SIC 5045 4813

TATA COMMUNICATIONS (US) INC p 1426
90 Matawan Rd Ste 300, Matawan NJ 07747
Tel (732) 888-6700 SIC 4813

▲ IDT CORP p 729
550 Broad St, Newark NJ 07102
Tel (973) 438-1000 SIC 4813

■ IDT DOMESTIC TELECOM INC p 729
520 Broad St, Newark NJ 07102
Tel (973) 438-1000 SIC 4813

■ VERIZON NEW JERSEY INC p 1550
540 Broad St, Newark NJ 07102
Tel (973) 649-9900 SIC 4813 8721

RCN TELECOM SERVICES LLC p 1212
650 College Rd E Ste 3100, Princeton NJ 08540
Tel (609) 452-8197 SIC 4841 7375 4813

NORTH JERSEY MEDIA GROUP INC p 1052
1 Garret Mountain Plz # 201, Woodland Park NJ 07424
Tel (201) 646-4000 SIC 2711 4813

ENMR TELEPHONE COOPERATIVE p 500
7111 N Prince St, Clovis NM 88101
Tel (575) 389-5100 SIC 4813

CSC HOLDINGS LLC p 397
1111 Stewart Ave, Bethpage NY 11714
Tel (516) 803-2300 SIC 4841 4813

DOLLAR PHONE CORP p 448
34 Franklin Ave Ste 220, Brooklyn NY 11205
Tel (718) 889-1100 SIC 4813

GLOBAL SWITCHING INC p 617
34 Franklin Ave Ste 220, Brooklyn NY 11205
Tel (718) 889-1100 SIC 4813

■ DEPOSIT TELEPHONE CO INC p 431
87 Front St, Deposit NY 13754
Tel (607) 467-2111 SIC 4813

EDWARDS TELEPHONE CO INC p 480
159 Main St, Edwards NY 13635
Tel (315) 562-9913 SIC 1731 4813

■ PAETEC COMMUNICATIONS INC p 1107
600 Willowbrook Office Pa, Fairport NY 14450
Tel (585) 340-2500 SIC 4813 7375 7372

■ PAETEC HOLDING CORP p 1107
1 Paetec Plz, Fairport NY 14450
Tel (585) 340-2500 SIC 4813

■ CITIZENS TELECOMMUNICATIONS CO OF NEW YORK INC p 311
137 Harrison St, Gloversville NY 12078
Tel (518) 773-6466 SIC 4813

GLOBECOMM SYSTEMS INC p 618
45 Oser Ave, Hauppauge NY 11788
Tel (631) 231-9800 SIC 3663 4813

■ FRONTIER COMMUNICATIONS OF AUSABLE VALLEY INC p 581
310 Front St, Keeseville NY 12944
Tel (518) 834-7211 SIC 4813

BROADBAND TELECOM INC p 215
8002 Kew Gardens Rd # 1040, Kew Gardens NY 11415
Tel (718) 261-0148 SIC 4813

FRESH DIRECT HOLDINGS INC p 578
2330 Borden Ave, Long Island City NY 11101
Tel (718) 433-0982 SIC 5499 4813

MEDIACOM COMMUNICATIONS CORP p 936
1 Mediacom Way, Mediacom Park NY 10918
Tel (877) 847-6221 SIC 4841 4813

▲ NEWTEK BUSINESS SERVICES INC p 1039
1981 Marcus Ave Ste C130, New Hyde Park NY 11042
Tel (212) 356-9500 SIC 6153 7374 4813

APPNEXUS INC p 100
28 W 23rd St Fl 4, New York NY 10010
Tel (646) 825-6460 SIC 4813

BROADCAST MEDIA PARTNERS HOLDINGS INC p 215
605 3rd Ave Fl 12, New York NY 10158
Tel (212) 455-5200 SIC 4833 4813 7389

▲ DHI GROUP INC p 435
1040 Avenue Of The Amrcas, New York NY 10018
Tel (212) 725-6550 SIC 7361 4813 7375

■ FRONTIER CALIFORNIA INC p 581
140 West St, New York NY 10007
Tel (212) 395-1000
SIC 4813 6519 8721 5065 1731 7629

▲ FUSION TELECOMMUNICATIONS INTERNATIONAL INC p 585
420 Lexington Ave Rm 1718, New York NY 10170
Tel (212) 201-2400 SIC 7372 4813

■ GTE CORP p 644
140 West St, New York NY 10007
Tel (212) 395-1000
SIC 4813 4812 3661 3663 4899 2741

▲ HC2 HOLDINGS INC p 671
450 Park Ave Fl 30, New York NY 10022
Tel (212) 235-2690 SIC 4813 3325 8731

HIGHCREST INVESTORS LLC p 691
Icahn Associates Corp 767, New York NY 10153
Tel (212) 702-4323
SIC 3743 4741 4789 4813

■ INSIGHT COMMUNICATIONS CO INC p 746
810 7th Ave, New York NY 10019
Tel (917) 286-2300 SIC 4841 4813

KDDI AMERICA INC p 806
825 3rd Ave Fl 3, New York NY 10022
Tel (212) 295-1200
SIC 4813 7375 7374 8743

▲ LIVEPERSON INC p 871
475 10th Ave Fl 5, New York NY 10018
Tel (212) 609-4200 SIC 7371 4813

■ MARTHA STEWART LIVING OMNIMEDIA INC p 912
601 W 26th St Rm 900, New York NY 10001
Tel (212) 827-8000
SIC 2721 2731 4813 7812

METROMEDIA CO p 955
810 Seventh Ave Fl 29, New York NY 10019
Tel (212) 606-4437
SIC 5812 6794 4813 4911

NTT AMERICA INC p 1065
757 3rd Ave Ste 1400, New York NY 10017
Tel (212) 661-0810 SIC 4813

RADIANZ AMERICAS INC p 1204
620 8th Ave Fl 46, New York NY 10018
Tel (212) 205-1800 SIC 4813

ROCKEFELLER GROUP INTERNATIONAL INC p 1244
1221 Avenue Of The Americ, New York NY 10020
Tel (212) 282-2000 SIC 6512 6552 4813

TELECOM ITALIA SPARKLE OF NORTH AMERICA INC p 1434
622 3rd Ave Fl 38, New York NY 10017
Tel (212) 310-9000 SIC 4813

TRIDENT PRIVATE HOLDINGS I LLC p 1479
601 Lexington Ave 59thf, New York NY 10022
Tel (212) 231-0095 SIC 4813 7374

UNIVISION HOLDINGS INC p 1527
605 3rd Ave Fl 12, New York NY 10158
Tel (212) 455-5200 SIC 4833 4813 7389

USABLENET INC p 1534
142 W 57th St Fl 7, New York NY 10019
Tel (212) 965-5388 SIC 4813

▲ VERIZON COMMUNICATIONS INC p 1550
1095 Ave Of The Americas, New York NY 10036
Tel (212) 395-1000 SIC 4813 4812 4841

■ VERIZON NEW YORK INC p 1550
140 West St, New York NY 10007
Tel (212) 395-1000 SIC 4813 7359

VIRGIN MEDIA HOLDINGS INC p 1558
65 Bleecker St Fl 6, New York NY 10012
Tel (212) 966-2310 SIC 4812 4813 4841

▲ VOLT INFORMATION SCIENCES INC p 1564
1133 Avenue Of The Americ, New York NY 10036
Tel (212) 704-2400 SIC 7363 4813 4899

▲ WEBMD HEALTH CORP p 1586
395 Hudson St, New York NY 10014
Tel (212) 624-3700 SIC 7375 4813

■ YODLE WEB.COM INC p 1636
330 W 34th St Fl 18, New York NY 10001
Tel (877) 276-5104 SIC 4813

■ ACC CORP p 14
400 West Ave Ste 3, Rochester NY 14611
Tel (585) 987-3000 SIC 4813

■ GLOBAL CROSSING BANDWIDTH INC p 616
200 Meridian Centre Blvd # 130, Rochester NY 14618
Tel (212) 920-8201 SIC 4813 7373 7374

LICT CORP p 863
401 Theodore Fremd Ave, Rye NY 10580
Tel (914) 921-8821 SIC 4813 4841 4833

BROADVIEW NETWORKS HOLDINGS INC p 215
800 Westchester Ave Ste N, Rye Brook NY 10573
Tel (914) 922-7000 SIC 4813 4899

BROADVIEW NETWORKS INC p 215
800 Westchester Ave N501, Rye Brook NY 10573
Tel (914) 922-7000 SIC 4813

■ VERNON TELEPHONE CO INC p 1551
1 Curtis Rd, Vernon NY 13476
Tel (608) 831-1000 SIC 4813

■ ABOVENET INC p 12
360 Hamilton Ave, White Plains NY 10601
Tel (866) 859-6971 SIC 4813

FISK TELECOM LLC p 552
1091 Yonkers Ave, Yonkers NY 10704
Tel (914) 476-2073 SIC 4813

■ SPECTRASITE COMMUNICATIONS LLC p 1357
400 Regency Forest Dr # 300, Cary NC 27518
Tel (919) 468-0112
SIC 4812 8748 1623 3661 4813 4899

■ CHARLOTTE OBSERVER PUBLISHING CO p 290
550 S Caldwell St, Charlotte NC 28202
Tel (704) 358-5000 SIC 2711 4813

▲ FAIRPOINT COMMUNICATIONS INC p 525
521 E Morehead St Ste 500, Charlotte NC 28202
Tel (704) 344-8150 SIC 4813 4812 4899

PEAK 10 INC p 1125
8910 Lenox Pointe Dr G, Charlotte NC 28273
Tel (704) 264-1010 SIC 4813

■ US LEC COMMUNICATIONS LLC p 1532
6801 Morrison Blvd, Charlotte NC 28211
Tel (704) 319-1000 SIC 4813

NORTH STATE COMMUNICATIONS LLC p 1054
111 Hayden Pl, High Point NC 27260
Tel (336) 886-3600 SIC 4813

NORTH STATE TELECOMMUNICATIONS CORP p 1054
111 N Main St, High Point NC 27260
Tel (336) 472-6048 SIC 4813

NORTH STATE TELEPHONE CO p 1054
111 N Main St, High Point NC 27260
Tel (336) 886-3660 SIC 4813

LKN COMMUNICATIONS INC p 872
134 Medical Park Rd # 105, Mooresville NC 28117
Tel (704) 260-3323 SIC 4813

BANDWIDTH.COM INC p 150
900 Main Campus Dr # 400, Raleigh NC 27606
Tel (800) 808-5150 SIC 4813

■ BUSINESS TELECOM LLC p 229
4300 Six Forks Rd Ste 500, Raleigh NC 27609
Tel (919) 863-7000 SIC 4813 4812

WALKER AND ASSOCIATES INC p 1573
7129 Old Hwy 52, Welcome NC 27374
Tel (336) 731-6391
SIC 4813 5065 8731 8711 3572 3571

WALKER GROUP INC p 1573
7129 Old Hwy 52, Welcome NC 27374
Tel (336) 731-6391
SIC 4813 8748 5065 8711

HORIZON TELCOM INC p 707
68 E Main St, Chillicothe OH 45601
Tel (740) 772-8200 SIC 4813

▲ CINCINNATI BELL INC p 307
221 E 4th St Ste 700, Cincinnati OH 45202
Tel (513) 397-9900
SIC 4813 7373 7374 7379

■ CINCINNATI BELL TELEPHONE CO p 307
209 W 7th St Fl 1, Cincinnati OH 45202
Tel (513) 565-9402 SIC 4813

INFOTELECOM HOLDINGS LLC p 742
75 Erieview Plz Fl 4, Cleveland OH 44114
Tel (216) 373-4811 SIC 4813 7373

■ OHIO BELL TELEPHONE CO p 1077
45 Erieview Plz, Cleveland OH 44114
Tel (216) 822-3439 SIC 4813 8721

FIRST COMMUNICATIONS LLC p 546
3340 W Market St, Fairlawn OH 44333
Tel (330) 835-2323 SIC 4813

■ INTELLINEX LLC p 750
6000 Fredom Sq Dr Ste 100, Independence OH 44131
Tel (216) 685-6000 SIC 4813

■ ALLTEL COMMUNICATIONS CORP p 59
66 N 4th St, Newark OH 43055
Tel (740) 349-8551 SIC 4813 4812

■ MID-AMERICA TELEPHONE INC p 963
110 W 5th St, Stonewall OK 74871
Tel (608) 831-1000 SIC 4813

CHICKASAW HOLDING CO p 298
124 W Vinita Ave, Sulphur OK 73086
Tel (580) 622-2111 SIC 4813 7371 5065

■ WYANDOTTE TELEPHONE CO p 1629
5 N Main, Wyandotte OK 74370
Tel (918) 678-8992 SIC 4813

KEZI INC p 816
2975 Chad Dr, Eugene OR 97408
Tel (541) 485-5611 SIC 4833 6512 4813

LEHIGH VALLEY HEALTH SERVICES INC p 854
2166 S 12th St, Allentown PA 18103
Tel (610) 791-3682 SIC 4813 8741 8721

HOTWIRE COMMUNICATIONS LLC p 710
1 Belmont Ave Ste 1100, Bala Cynwyd PA 19004
Tel (800) 355-5668 SIC 4813

ACCT HOLDINGS LLC p 16
1235 Westlakes Dr Ste 160, Berwyn PA 19312
Tel (610) 695-0500 SIC 4813

ARMSTRONG GROUP OF COMPANIES INC p 111
1 Armstrong Pl, Butler PA 16001
Tel (724) 283-0925 SIC 4813

CCTM1 LLC p 270
2000 Corporate Dr, Canonsburg PA 15317
Tel (724) 416-2000 SIC 4813

■ CROWN CASTLE USA INC p 395
2000 Corporate Dr, Canonsburg PA 15317
Tel (724) 416-2000 SIC 4813

1&1 INTERNET INC p 1
701 Lee Rd Ste 300, Chesterbrook PA 19087
Tel (877) 461-2631 SIC 7374 4813 4822

■ COMMONWEALTH TELEPHONE CO LLC p 346
100 Cte Dr Ste 2, Dallas PA 18612
Tel (570) 631-4555 SIC 4813

■ COMMONWEALTH TELEPHONE ENTERPRISES INC p 346
100 Cte Dr Ste 2, Dallas PA 18612
Tel (570) 631-2700 SIC 4813

■ D&E COMMUNICATIONS INC p 407
124 E Main St Fl 6, Ephrata PA 17522
Tel (717) 733-4101 SIC 4813 4841

■ NORTH PITTSBURGH SYSTEMS INC p 1053
4008 Gibsonia Rd, Gibsonia PA 15044
Tel (724) 443-9600 SIC 4813 5065

PENCOR SERVICES INC p 1128
613 3rd Street Palmerton, Palmerton PA 18071
Tel (610) 826-2115
SIC 2711 7371 4813 4841

■ BELL ATLANTIC GLOBAL WIRELESS INC p 170
1717 Arch St Fl 33, Philadelphia PA 19103
Tel (215) 246-9494
SIC 4813 4812 5065 7379

▲ COMCAST CORP p 343
1701 Jfk Blvd, Philadelphia PA 19103
Tel (215) 286-1700
SIC 4841 4813 7812 7996

■ VERIZON PENNSYLVANIA INC p 1550
1717 Arch St Fl 15, Philadelphia PA 19103
Tel (215) 466-9900
SIC 4813 8721 1731 7629

■ AT&T MOBILITY PUERTO RICO INC p 123
996 Calle San Roberto, Rio Piedras PR 00926
Tel (787) 717-9600 SIC 4813 4812

TELECOMUNICACIONES DE PUERTO RICO INC p 1434
1515 Ave Fd Roosevelt 14 Flr 14, San Juan PR 00920
Tel (787) 782-8282 SIC 4813

SOUTH CAROLINA TELECOMMUNICATIONS GROUP HOLDING LLC p 1343
1500 Hampton St Ste 100, Columbia SC 29201
Tel (803) 726-7000 SIC 4813

HORRY TELEPHONE COOPERATIVE INC p 708
3480 Highway 701 N, Conway SC 29526
Tel (843) 365-2151 SIC 4813 4841 7382

■ GABRIEL COMMUNICATIONS FINANCE CO p 588
2 N Main St Ste 300, Greenville SC 29601
Tel (864) 672-5000 SIC 4813

■ NUVOX INC p 1068
2 N Main St, Greenville SC 29601
Tel (864) 672-5000 SIC 4813

■ WINDSTREAM NUVOX INC p 1615
2 N Main St, Greenville SC 29601
Tel (864) 672-5000 SIC 4813

HARGRAY COMMUNICATIONS GROUP INC p 661
856 William Hilton Pkwy, Hilton Head Island SC 29928
Tel (843) 785-2166 SIC 4813

FARMERS TELEPHONE COOPERATIVE INC p 530
1101 E Main St, Kingstree SC 29556
Tel (843) 382-2333 SIC 4813

■ NORWAY TELEPHONE CO INC p 1061
8432 Savannah Hwy, Norway SC 29113
Tel (608) 831-1000 SIC 4813

COMPORIUM INC p 351
330 E Black St, Rock Hill SC 29730
Tel (803) 326-6011 SIC 4813

■ WILLISTON TELEPHONE CO p 1612
4670 West St, Williston SC 29853
Tel (803) 266-7411 SIC 4813

AKA WIRELESS INC p 42
7505 S Louise Ave, Sioux Falls SD 57108
Tel (605) 275-3733 SIC 4813

GOLDEN WEST TELECOMMUNICATIONS COOPERATIVE INC p 622
415 Crown St, Wall SD 57790
Tel (605) 279-2161 SIC 4813

■ CITIZENS TELECOMMUNICATIONS CO OF TENNESSEE LLC p 311
250 S Franklin Ave, Cookeville TN 38501
Tel (931) 528-0501 SIC 4813

PUREWORKS INC p 1192
5000 Meridian Blvd # 600, Franklin TN 37067
Tel (615) 367-4404 SIC 4813

NATIONS BROADBAND INC p 1017
15455 Dallas Pkwy Ste 600, Addison TX 75001
Tel (972) 851-7851 SIC 4813

RIO HOLDINGS INC p 1235
600 Congress Ave Ste 200, Austin TX 78701
Tel (512) 917-1742 SIC 4813 4841

■ CONSOLIDATED COMMUNICATIONS SERVICES CO p 359
350 S Loop 336 W, Conroe TX 77304
Tel (936) 756-0611 SIC 4813

APEX CLEARING CORP p 96
350 N Paul St Ste 1300, Dallas TX 75201
Tel (214) 765-1100
SIC 6099 7389 4813 6289

▲ AT&T INC p 123
208 S Akard St, Dallas TX 75202
Tel (210) 821-4105
SIC 4813 4812 3663 3661 2741

■ AT&T SERVICES INC p 123
208 S Akard St Ste 110, Dallas TX 75202
Tel (210) 821-4105 SIC 4813

EVERCOM SYSTEMS INC p 513
14651 Dallas Pkwy Ste 600, Dallas TX 75254
Tel (972) 277-0300 SIC 4813

SECURUS HOLDINGS INC p 1299
14651 Dallas Pkwy Ste 600, Dallas TX 75254
Tel (972) 241-1535 SIC 4813

SECURUS TECHNOLOGIES INC p 1299
14651 Dallas Pkwy Ste 600, Dallas TX 75254
Tel (972) 241-1535 SIC 4813

SOFTLAYER TECHNOLOGIES INC p 1337
14001 Dallas Pkwy M100, Dallas TX 75240
Tel (214) 442-0600 SIC 7374 4813

TELVISTA INC p 1435
1605 Lyndon B Johnson Fwy, Dallas TX 75234
Tel (972) 919-7800 SIC 4813

TITAN GLOBAL HOLDINGS INC p 1456
17760 Preston Rd, Dallas TX 75252
Tel (214) 751-7777 SIC 5172 4813

TRUCONNECT COMMUNICATIONS INC p 1485
10440 N Cntl Expy Ste 700, Dallas TX 75231
Tel (877) 771-7736 SIC 4813

X5 OPCO LLC p 1630
2828 N Harwood St # 1700, Dallas TX 75201
Tel (214) 932-9293 SIC 4813

MULTIBAND CORP p 999
2801 Network Blvd Ste 300, Frisco TX 75034
Tel (763) 504-3000 SIC 4841 4813

■ VERIZON SELECT SERVICES INC p 1550
4255 Patriot Dr Ste 400, Grapevine TX 76051
Tel (972) 724-6000 SIC 4813

■ CAPROCK COMMUNICATIONS CORP p 251
4400 S Sam Houston Pkwy E, Houston TX 77048
Tel (281) 482-0289 SIC 4813

■ HARRIS CAPROCK COMMUNICATIONS INC p 663
4400 S Sam Houston Pkwy E, Houston TX 77048
Tel (888) 482-0289 SIC 4813

LOGIX COMMUNICATIONS LP p 875
2950 North Loop W Ste 140, Houston TX 77092
Tel (713) 862-2000 SIC 4813

▲ RIGNET INC p 1235
1880 S Dairy Ashford Rd # 300, Houston TX 77077
Tel (281) 674-0100 SIC 4899 4813

SUMMIT CONSOLIDATION GROUP INC p 1398
10497 Town Cntry Way 3, Houston TX 77024
Tel (713) 554-2244 SIC 7373 7371 4813

■ CONTEL FEDERAL SYSTEMS INC p 362
600 Hidden Rdg, Irving TX 75038
Tel (972) 718-5600 SIC 3661 4813

■ FRONTIER SOUTHWEST INC p 581
600 Hidden Rdg, Irving TX 75038
Tel (972) 718-5600 SIC 4813

■ GTE MIDWEST INC p 644
600 Hidden Rdg, Irving TX 75038
Tel (972) 718-1856 SIC 4813

MATRIX TELECOM LLC p 920
433 Las Colinas Blvd E # 500, Irving TX 75039
Tel (888) 411-0111 SIC 4813

NOKIA SOLUTIONS AND NETWORKS US LLC p 1046
6000 Connection Dr, Irving TX 75039
Tel (972) 374-3000 SIC 3663 5999 4813

PINNACLE ONE PARTNERS LP p 1150
300 Decker Dr, Irving TX 75062
Tel (214) 812-4600 SIC 4813

■ VERIZON NORTHWEST INC p 1550
600 Hidden Rdg, Irving TX 75038
Tel (972) 718-5600
SIC 4813 6519 8721 5065 7629

■ VERIZON SOUTH INC p 1550
600 Hidden Rdg, Irving TX 75038
Tel (972) 718-5600 SIC 4813 5065 8721

■ WINDSTREAM SOUTHWEST LONG DISTANCE LP p 1616
201 E John Carpenter Fwy, Irving TX 75062
Tel (972) 373-1000 SIC 4813

■ ALAMOSA HOLDINGS INC p 44
5225 S Loop 289 Ste 120, Lubbock TX 79424
Tel (806) 722-1111 SIC 4813

NTS COMMUNICATIONS INC p 1065
1220 Brdwy, Lubbock TX 79401
Tel (806) 791-0687 SIC 4813

NTS INC p 1065
1220 Broadway Ste 100, Lubbock TX 79401
Tel (806) 771-5212 SIC 4813

■ ARROW SYSTEMS INTEGRATION INC p 113
1820 Preston Park Blvd # 2800, Plano TX 75093
Tel (972) 462-5800 SIC 4813 1731 5999

FUTUREWEI TECHNOLOGIES INC p 586
5700 Tennyson Pkwy # 500, Plano TX 75024
Tel (972) 509-5599 SIC 4813

MASERGY COMMUNICATIONS INC p 915
2740 Dallas Pkwy Ste 260, Plano TX 75093
Tel (214) 442-5700 SIC 4813

MITEL MOBILITY INC p 977
1700 Intl Pkwy Ste 200, Richardson TX 75081
Tel (469) 916-4393 SIC 4813

■ AT&T MESSAGING LLC p 123
4801 Nw Loop 410 Ste 850, San Antonio TX 78229
Tel (210) 523-4300 SIC 4813

■ IHEARTMEDIA CAPITAL I LLC p 731
200 E Basse Rd, San Antonio TX 78209
Tel (210) 822-2828 SIC 4813 4899

■ IHEARTMEDIA CAPITAL II LLC p 731
200 E Basse Rd, San Antonio TX 78209
Tel (210) 822-2828 SIC 4899 4813

RACKSPACE HOSTING INC p 1203
1 Fanatical Pl, San Antonio TX 78218
Tel (210) 312-4000
SIC 7371 7374 7382 4813

RACKSPACE US INC p 1203
1 Fanatical Pl, San Antonio TX 78218
Tel (210) 312-4000 SIC 4813

USAA CAPITAL CORP p 1534
9800 Fredericksburg Rd, San Antonio TX 78288
Tel (210) 498-2211
SIC 6035 6798 6722 7299 4813 4724

TELENETWORK PARTNERS LTD p 1434
350 Barnes Dr, San Marcos TX 78666
Tel (512) 707-3100 SIC 4813

VERIO INC p 1549
1203 Research Way, Orem UT 84097
Tel (303) 645-1900 SIC 4813

BACKCOUNTRY.COM LLC p 143
1678 Redstone Center Dr # 210, Park City UT 84098
Tel (801) 746-7580 SIC 5091 4813

IBAHN CORP p 726
126 W 10000 S Ste 100, Sandy UT 84070
Tel (801) 952-2000 SIC 4813

INCONTACT INC p 735
75 W Towne Ridge Pkwy # 1, Sandy UT 84070
Tel (801) 320-3200 SIC 7372 4813

INNOVATIVE COMMUNICATIONS CORP p 744
4611 Tutu Park Mall # 200, St Thomas VI 00802
Tel (340) 777-7700 SIC 4813 4841

▲ ROSETTA STONE INC p 1251
1621 N Kent St Ste 1200, Arlington VA 22209
Tel (703) 387-5800 SIC 7372 4813 7371

■ SAVVIS FEDERAL SYSTEMS INC p 1284
4250 Fairfax Dr, Arlington VA 22203
Tel (703) 667-6000 SIC 4813 7379

■ MCI COMMUNICATIONS CORP p 929
22001 Loudoun County Pkwy, Ashburn VA 20147
Tel (703) 886-5600
SIC 4813 4812 4822 7372

■ MCI COMMUNICATIONS SERVICES INC p 929
22001 Loudoun County Pkwy, Ashburn VA 20147
Tel (703) 886-5600 SIC 4813

■ MCI INTERNATIONAL INC p 929
22001 Loudoun County Pkwy, Ashburn VA 20147
Tel (703) 886-5600
SIC 4813 4812 4822 7372

■ MCI INTERNATIONAL SERVICES INC p 929
22001 Loudoun County Pkwy, Ashburn VA 20147
Tel (703) 886-5600 SIC 4813

■ UUNET TECHNOLOGIES INC p 1537
22001 Loudoun County Pkwy, Ashburn VA 20147
Tel (703) 726-9240 SIC 4813

■ VERIZON BUSINESS GLOBAL LLC p 1550
22001 Loudoun County Pkwy, Ashburn VA 20147
Tel (703) 886-5600 SIC 4813 8721 4822

■ VERIZON BUSINESS NETWORK SERVICES INC p 1550
22001 Loudoun County Pkwy, Ashburn VA 20147
Tel (703) 729-5615 SIC 4813

VERIZON SELECT SERVICES INC p 1550
22001 Loudoun County Pkwy, Ashburn VA 20147
Tel (703) 886-7446 SIC 4813

■ VERIZON SERVICES CORP p 1550
22001 Loudoun County Pkwy, Ashburn VA 20147
Tel (703) 729-5931 SIC 4813

■ VERIZON VIRGINIA LLC p 1551
22001 Loudoun County Pkwy, Ashburn VA 20147
Tel (800) 837-4966 SIC 4813

ENGINEERING SOLUTIONS & PRODUCTS LLC p 499
14566 Lee Rd, Chantilly VA 20151
Tel (571) 375-1400
SIC 8711 7379 4813 8742 8748

■ HISTORIC AOL LLC p 696
22000 Aol Way, Dulles VA 20166
Tel (703) 265-1000 SIC 4813 7299

▲ SHENANDOAH TELECOMMUNICATIONS CO p 1315
500 Shentel Way, Edinburg VA 22824
Tel (540) 984-4141 SIC 4813 4812 4841

■ SIGNAL SOLUTIONS LLC p 1322
3211 Jermantown Rd # 700, Fairfax VA 22030
Tel (703) 205-0500
SIC 8711 7379 7374 4813 7373 8731

CHINA TELECOM (AMERICAS) CORP p 301
607 Herndon Pkwy Ste 201, Herndon VA 20170
Tel (703) 787-0088 SIC 4813

■ HOLDCO LLC p 700
13820 Sunrise Valley Dr, Herndon VA 20171
Tel (703) 345-2400 SIC 4813

LCC INTERNATIONAL INC p 849
2201 Coop Way Ste 600, Herndon VA 20171
Tel (703) 873-2065 SIC 4813 4812

LGS INNOVATIONS LLC p 860
13665 Dulles Technology D, Herndon VA 20171
Tel (866) 547-4243 SIC 4813

■ NETWORK SOLUTIONS LLC p 1028
13861 Sunrise Valley Dr # 300, Herndon VA 20171
Tel (703) 668-4600
SIC 7375 7389 4813 7374

ORANGE BUSINESS SERVICES HOLDINGS US INC p 1091
13775 Mclearen Rd, Herndon VA 20171
Tel (703) 471-2300 SIC 4813

ORANGE BUSINESS SERVICES US INC p 1091
13775 Mclearen Rd, Herndon VA 20171
Tel (866) 849-4185 SIC 4813 8748

PCCW GLOBAL INC p 1123
450 Springpark Pl Ste 100, Herndon VA 20170
Tel (703) 621-1600 SIC 4813

SIDERA NETWORKS INC p 1319
196 Van Buren St Ste 250, Herndon VA 20170
Tel (703) 434-8500 SIC 4841 4813 7375

TATA COMMUNICATIONS (AMERICA) INC p 1426
2355 Dulles Corner Blvd # 700, Herndon VA 20171
Tel (703) 657-8400 SIC 4813

XO COMMUNICATIONS LLC p 1632
13865 Sunrise Valley Dr # 400, Herndon VA 20171
Tel (703) 547-2000 SIC 4813

XO COMMUNICATIONS SERVICES LLC p 1632
13865 Sunrise Valley Dr, Herndon VA 20171
Tel (703) 547-2000 SIC 4813

XO HOLDINGS INC p 1632
13865 Sunrise Vley Dr 4 Ste 400, Herndon VA 20171
Tel (703) 547-2000 SIC 4813

■ GLOBAL TELECOM & TECHNOLOGY AMERICAS INC p 617
7900 Tysons One Pl, Mc Lean VA 22102
Tel (703) 442-5500 SIC 4813

▲ GTT COMMUNICATIONS INC p 644
7900 Tysons One Pl # 1450, Mc Lean VA 22102
Tel (703) 442-5500 SIC 4813

■ LOCKHEED MARTIN GLOBAL TELECOMMUNICATIONS INC p 873
1600 Tysons Blvd Ste 550, Mc Lean VA 22102
Tel (703) 556-9500 SIC 4813 1731

▲ TEGNA INC p 1432
7950 Jones Branch Dr, Mc Lean VA 22102
Tel (703) 854-7000
SIC 2711 4813 4841 4833

■ NEW CASTLE TELEPHONE CO p 1029
320 Salem Ave, New Castle VA 24127
Tel (608) 831-1000 SIC 4813

STG INC p 1389
11091 Sunset Hills Rd # 200, Reston VA 20190
Tel (703) 691-2480 SIC 4813

TALKAMERICA INC p 1422
12020 Sunrise Valley Dr # 250, Reston VA 20191
Tel (703) 391-7518 SIC 4813

TNS INC p 1458
10740 Parkridge Blvd # 100, Reston VA 20191
Tel (703) 453-8300 SIC 4813 7374

TRANSACTION NETWORK SERVICES INC p 1470
10740 Parkridge Blvd # 100, Reston VA 20191
Tel (703) 453-8300 SIC 4813 7389 7374

■ CAVALIER TELEPHONE CORP p 267
2134 W Laburnum Ave, Richmond VA 23227
Tel (804) 422-4000 SIC 4813

CAVALIER TELEPHONE LLC p 267
2134 W Laburnum Ave, Richmond VA 23227
Tel (804) 422-4100 SIC 4813 4812

CAVALIER TELEPHONE MID-ATLANTIC LLC p 267
2134 W Laburnum Ave, Richmond VA 23227
Tel (804) 422-4100 SIC 4813 4812

■ CAVTEL HOLDINGS LLC p 268
2134 W Laburnum Ave, Richmond VA 23227
Tel (804) 422-4107 SIC 4813

TALK AMERICA HOLDINGS INC p 1422
2134 W Laburnum Ave, Richmond VA 23227
Tel (804) 422-4100 SIC 4813

■ BELLSOUTH COMMUNICATION SYSTEMS LLC p 171
1936 Blue Hills Dr Ne, Roanoke VA 24012
Tel (540) 983-6000 SIC 5065 4813 4812

■ GENESYS CONFERENCING INC p 603
8020 Towers Crescent Dr, Vienna VA 22182
Tel (703) 749-2500 SIC 4813

▲ LUMOS NETWORKS CORP p 885
1 Lumos Plz, Waynesboro VA 22980
Tel (540) 946-2000 SIC 4813

■ NTELOS HOLDINGS CORP p 1065
1154 Shenandoah Vlg Dr, Waynesboro VA 22980
Tel (540) 946-3500 SIC 4813 4812

■ NTELOS NET LLC p 1065
1 Lumos Plz, Waynesboro VA 22980
Tel (540) 946-3500 SIC 4813

■ CLEAR WIRELESS LLC p 324
1475 120th Ave Ne, Bellevue WA 98005
Tel (425) 216-7974 SIC 4813

■ T-MOBILE US INC p 1420
12920 Se 38th St, Bellevue WA 98006
Tel (425) 378-4000 SIC 4813

■ FRONTIER COMMUNICATIONS WEST COAST INC p 581
1800 41st St, Everett WA 98203
Tel (425) 261-5321 SIC 4813

■ MICROSOFT NETWORK L L C p 962
1 Microsoft Way, Redmond WA 98052
Tel (425) 538-2948 SIC 4813

■ MCDANIEL TELEPHONE CO p 927
160 Stowell Rd, Salkum WA 98582
Tel (608) 831-1000 SIC 4813

ACCRETIVE TECHNOLOGY GROUP INC p 16
800 Stewart St, Seattle WA 98101
Tel (206) 443-6401 SIC 4813

AMAZON.COMINDC LLC p 65
440 Terry Ave N, Seattle WA 98109
Tel (206) 266-1000 SIC 4813 5999 7371

▲ **ZILLOW GROUP INC** p 1643
1301 2nd Ave Fl 31, Seattle WA 98101
Tel (206) 470-7000 SIC 7372 6531 4813

DOTSTER INC p 452
8100 Ne Parkway Dr # 300, Vancouver WA 98662
Tel (360) 883-5589 SIC 4813

ELECTRIC LIGHTWAVE COMMUNICATIONS INC p 484
18110 Se 34th St Bldg 1s, Vancouver WA 98683
Tel (360) 558-6900 SIC 7389 4813

ELECTRIC LIGHTWAVE HOLDINGS INC p 484
18110 Se 34th St, Vancouver WA 98683
Tel (360) 558-6900 SIC 4813

ELECTRIC LIGHTWAVE LLC p 484
18110 Se 34th St Bldg 1s, Vancouver WA 98683
Tel (360) 558-6900 SIC 4813

■ **FRONTIER WEST VIRGINIA INC** p 581
1500 Maccorkle Ave Se, Charleston WV 25396
Tel (304) 344-6409 SIC 4813 8721

■ **BLACK EARTH TELEPHONE CO LLC** p 186
1125 Mills St, Black Earth WI 53515
Tel (608) 767-2229 SIC 4813

■ **EASTCOAST TELECOM OF WISCONSIN LLC** p 471
1140 W Washington Ave, Cleveland WI 53015
Tel (920) 693-8121 SIC 4813

■ **DICKEYVILLE TELEPHONE LLC** p 438
200 W Main St, Dickeyville WI 53808
Tel (608) 831-1000 SIC 4813

■ **CDW TECHNOLOGIES LLC** p 271
5520 Research Park Dr, Fitchburg WI 53711
Tel (608) 288-3000 SIC 7373 4813

NORTHEAST COMMUNICATIONS OF WISCONSIN INC p 1054
450 Security Blvd, Green Bay WI 54313
Tel (920) 617-7000 SIC 4812 4813

■ **RIVERSIDE TELECOM LLC** p 1238
121 Depot St, Johnson Creek WI 53038
Tel (608) 831-1000 SIC 4813

■ **CENTRAL STATE TELEPHONE CO LLC** p 280
525 Junction Rd, Madison WI 53717
Tel (608) 831-1000 SIC 4813

HOLLIS TELEPHONE CO INC p 701
515 Junction Rd, Madison WI 53717
Tel (608) 831-1000 SIC 4813

■ **TDS LONG DISTANCE CORP** p 1429
525 Junction Rd Ste 6000, Madison WI 53717
Tel (608) 831-1000 SIC 4813

■ **TDS TELECOMMUNICATIONS CORP** p 1429
525 Junction Rd Ste 1000, Madison WI 53717
Tel (608) 664-4000 SIC 4813

TRI-COUNTY TELEPHONE CO INC p 1477
525 Junction Rd, Madison WI 53717
Tel (608) 661-3114 SIC 4813

JOURNAL COMMUNICATIONS INC p 794
333 W State St, Milwaukee WI 53203
Tel (414) 224-2000
SIC 4832 4833 2711 2759 4813

■ **WISCONSIN BELL INC** p 1618
722 N Broadway, Milwaukee WI 53202
Tel (414) 271-9619 SIC 4813 8721

■ **MOSINEE TELEPHONE CO LLC** p 992
410 4th St, Mosinee WI 54455
Tel (715) 693-2622 SIC 4813

FOSTER AND SMITH INC p 570
2253 Air Park Rd, Rhinelander WI 54501
Tel (715) 369-3305 SIC 4813 5961

■ **STOCKBRIDGE & SHERWOOD TELEPHONE CO LLC** p 1390
N287 Military Rd, Sherwood WI 54169
Tel (920) 989-1501 SIC 4813

SOUTHEAST TELEPHONE CO OF WISCONSIN LLC p 1346
311 Elizabeth St, Waterford WI 53185
Tel (608) 831-1000 SIC 4813

UNION TELEPHONE CO p 1505
850 N Hwy 414, Mountain View WY 82939
Tel (307) 782-6131 SIC 4813 4812

SIC 4822 Telegraph & Other Message Communications

■ **J2 CLOUD SERVICES INC** p 772
6922 Hollywood Blvd # 500, Los Angeles CA 90028
Tel (323) 860-9200 SIC 4822

▲ **J2 GLOBAL INC** p 772
6922 Hollywood Blvd # 500, Los Angeles CA 90028
Tel (323) 860-9200 SIC 4822

■ **PACIFIC BELL TELEPHONE CO** p 1104
430 Bush St Fl 3, San Francisco CA 94108
Tel (415) 542-9000 SIC 4813 2741 4822

■ **SOUTHERN NEW ENGLAND TELECOMMUNICATIONS CORP** p 1349
2 Science Park, New Haven CT 06511
Tel (203) 771-5200
SIC 4813 4812 5065 6159 2741 4822

■ **SOUTHERN NEW ENGLAND TELEPHONE CO INC** p 1349
310 Orange St, New Haven CT 06510
Tel (203) 771-5200 SIC 4813 4822

■ **QWEST COMMUNICATIONS INTERNATIONAL INC** p 1201
100 Centurylink Dr, Monroe LA 71203
Tel (318) 388-9000 SIC 4813 4822 4812

E MAIL SOLUTIONS INC p 466
12111 Emmet St, Omaha NE 68164
Tel (402) 496-2223 SIC 4822

■ **AT&T CORP** p 123
1 At&T Way, Bedminster NJ 07921
Tel (800) 403-3302 SIC 4813 4822 7375

ASSOCIATED PRESS p 121
450 W 33rd St Fl 16, New York NY 10001
Tel (212) 621-1500 SIC 7383 4822

EUREKA BROADBAND CORP p 512
39 Broad St Fl 19, New York NY 10004
Tel (212) 404-5000 SIC 4822

STRATACACHE INC p 1392
2 Emmet St Ste 200, Dayton OH 45405
Tel (937) 224-0485 SIC 5734 4822

1&1 INTERNET INC p 1
701 Lee Rd Ste 300, Chesterbrook PA 19087
Tel (877) 461-2631 SIC 7374 4813 4822

■ **MCI COMMUNICATIONS CORP** p 929
22001 Loudoun County Pkwy, Ashburn VA 20147
Tel (703) 886-5600
SIC 4813 4812 4822 7372

■ **MCI INTERNATIONAL INC** p 929
22001 Loudoun County Pkwy, Ashburn VA 20147
Tel (703) 886-5600
SIC 4813 4812 4822 7372

■ **VERIZON BUSINESS GLOBAL LLC** p 1550
22001 Loudoun County Pkwy, Ashburn VA 20147
Tel (703) 886-5600 SIC 4813 8721 4822

▲ **SPOK HOLDINGS INC** p 1359
6850 Versar Ctr Ste 420, Springfield VA 22151
Tel (800) 611-8488 SIC 4812 4822 7372

SIC 4832 Radio Broadcasting Stations

SUMMITMEDIA LLC p 1399
2700 Corporate Dr Ste 115, Birmingham AL 35242
Tel (205) 322-2987 SIC 4832

RAYCOM MEDIA INC p 1210
201 Monroe St Fl 20, Montgomery AL 36104
Tel (334) 206-1400 SIC 4833 4832

■ **ALASCOM INC** p 44
505 E Bluff Dr, Anchorage AK 99501
Tel (907) 264-7000 SIC 4813 4833 4832

COOK INLET REGION INC p 366
725 E Fireweed Ln Ste 800, Anchorage AK 99503
Tel (907) 274-8638
SIC 6552 1382 1389 6519 4832 4833

■ **ABC CABLE NETWORKS GROUP** p 10
500 S Buena Vista St, Burbank CA 91521
Tel (818) 460-7477 SIC 4832 4833

LBI MEDIA HOLDINGS INC p 849
1845 W Empire Ave, Burbank CA 91504
Tel (818) 563-5722 SIC 4832 4833

LIBERMAN BROADCASTING INC p 861
1845 W Empire Ave, Burbank CA 91504
Tel (818) 729-5300 SIC 4832

■ **NEW INSPIRATION BROADCASTING CO INC** p 1031
4880 Santa Rosa Rd, Camarillo CA 93012
Tel (805) 987-0400 SIC 4832 2731

▲ **SALEM MEDIA GROUP INC** p 1272
4880 Santa Rosa Rd, Camarillo CA 93012
Tel (818) 956-0400 SIC 4832 2731 4813

LOTUS COMMUNICATIONS CORP p 879
3301 Barham Blvd Ste 200, Los Angeles CA 90068
Tel (323) 512-2225 SIC 4832

▲ **PANDORA MEDIA INC** p 1111
2101 Webster St Ste 1650, Oakland CA 94612
Tel (510) 451-4100 SIC 4832

EDUCATIONAL MEDIA FOUNDATION p 479
5700 West Oaks Blvd, Rocklin CA 95765
Tel (916) 251-1600 SIC 4832

SAN BERNARDINO COMMUNITY COLLEGE DISTRICT p 1275
114 S Del Rosa Dr, San Bernardino CA 92408
Tel (909) 382-4000 SIC 8222 4832 4833

■ **CBS INTERACTIVE INC** p 269
235 2nd St, San Francisco CA 94105
Tel (415) 344-2000 SIC 7319 7375 4832

▲ **ENTRAVISION COMMUNICATIONS CORP** p 502
2425 Olympic Blvd Ste 600, Santa Monica CA 90404
Tel (310) 447-3870 SIC 4833 4832

TRITON MEDIA GROUP LLC p 1483
15303 Ventura Blvd # 1500, Sherman Oaks CA 91403
Tel (323) 290-6900 SIC 4832

TSA STORES INC p 1489
1050 W Hampden Ave, Englewood CO 80110
Tel (303) 200-5050 SIC 5941 4832

CHERRY CREEK RADIO LLC p 294
7400 E Orchard Rd # 2800, Greenwood Village CO 80111
Tel (303) 468-6500 SIC 4832

NEXTMEDIA OPERATING INC p 1041
6312 S Fiddlers Green Cir # 2, Greenwood Village CO 80111
Tel (303) 694-9118 SIC 4832

JONES INTERNATIONAL LTD p 792
300 E Mineral Ave Ste 5, Littleton CO 80122
Tel (303) 792-3111
SIC 4832 4841 7371 7372

■ **ESPN INC** p 509
Espn Plz, Bristol CT 06010
Tel (860) 766-2000 SIC 4841 4832

▲ **TOWNSQUARE MEDIA INC** p 1466
240 Greenwich Ave, Greenwich CT 06830
Tel (203) 861-0900 SIC 4832

UNITED STATES CONFERENCE OF CATHOLIC BISHOPS p 1512
3211 4th St Ne, Washington DC 20017
Tel (202) 541-3000 SIC 8661 4832 4833

PINELLAS COUNTY SCHOOL BOARD p 1149
301 4th St Sw, Largo FL 33770
Tel (727) 588-6000 SIC 8211 4832

▲ **SPANISH BROADCASTING SYSTEM INC** p 1354
7007 Nw 77th Ave, Miami FL 33166
Tel (305) 441-6901 SIC 4832 4833

▲ **BEASLEY BROADCAST GROUP INC** p 166
3033 Riviera Dr Ste 200, Naples FL 34103
Tel (239) 263-5000 SIC 4832

■ **GREATER MEDIA INC** p 635
3033 Riviera Dr Ste 200, Naples FL 34103
Tel (239) 263-5000 SIC 2711 8999 4832

W P C S FM p 1569
250 Brent Ln, Pensacola FL 32503
Tel (850) 478-8496 SIC 4832

DIGITY COMPANIES LLC p 439
701 Nrthpint Pkwy Ste 500, West Palm Beach FL 33407
Tel (561) 616-4600 SIC 4832

■ **CITADEL BROADCASTING CORP** p 309
3280 Peachtree Rd Ne # 2300, Atlanta GA 30305
Tel (404) 949-0700 SIC 4832

COX ENTERPRISES INC p 386
6205 Pachtree Dunwoody Rd, Atlanta GA 30328
Tel (678) 645-0000
SIC 4841 4813 2711 4833 7389 4832

COX MEDIA GROUP LLC p 386
6205 Pachtree Dunwoody Rd, Atlanta GA 30328
Tel (678) 645-0000
SIC 4833 4832 7922 7313

COX RADIO INC p 386
6205 Pachtree Dunwoody Rd, Atlanta GA 30328
Tel (678) 645-0000 SIC 4832

■ **CUMULUS BROADCASTING LLC** p 401
3280 Peachtree Rd Nw Ste, Atlanta GA 30305
Tel (404) 949-0700 SIC 4832

■ **CUMULUS MEDIA HOLDINGS INC** p 401
3280 Peachtree Rd Ne # 2300, Atlanta GA 30305
Tel (404) 949-0700 SIC 4832

▲ **CUMULUS MEDIA INC** p 401
3280 Peachtree Rd Ne Ne2300, Atlanta GA 30305
Tel (404) 949-0700 SIC 4832

WEATHER CHANNEL INC p 1585
300 Interstate North Pkwy, Atlanta GA 30339
Tel (770) 226-0000 SIC 4841 4832

SHIVERS TRADING & OPERATING CO p 1317
725 Broad St, Augusta GA 30901
Tel (706) 724-0851
SIC 2711 2721 2731 4832 7312 6512

MARATHON MEDIA GROUP LLC p 904
737 N Michigan Ave # 2060, Chicago IL 60611
Tel (312) 640-9700 SIC 4832

MOODY BIBLE INSTITUTE OF CHICAGO p 987
820 N La Salle Dr, Chicago IL 60610
Tel (312) 329-4000
SIC 8661 8299 8221 4832 2731

■ **TRIBUNE BROADCASTING CO LLC** p 1479
435 N Michigan Ave Fl 2, Chicago IL 60611
Tel (312) 222-3333 SIC 4833 4832

▲ **TRIBUNE MEDIA CO** p 1479
435 N Michigan Ave Fl 2, Chicago IL 60611
Tel (212) 210-2786
SIC 4833 4832 7922 7941

■ **WGN CONTINENTAL BROADCASTING CO** p 1604
2501 W Bradley Pl, Chicago IL 60618
Tel (773) 528-2311 SIC 4832 4833

▲ **EMMIS COMMUNICATIONS CORP** p 493
40 Monument Cir Ste 700, Indianapolis IN 46204
Tel (317) 266-0100 SIC 4832 2721

LESEA BROADCASTING CORP p 857
61300 Ironwood Rd, South Bend IN 46614
Tel (574) 291-8200 SIC 4833 4832

NRG MEDIA LLC p 1064
2875 Mount Vernon Rd Se, Cedar Rapids IA 52403
Tel (319) 862-0300 SIC 4832

WOODWARD COMMUNICATIONS INC p 1623
801 Bluff St, Dubuque IA 52001
Tel (563) 588-5611
SIC 2711 2741 4832 2752 7311

COMMUNICATIONS CORP OF AMERICA p 347
700 John St Ste 300, Lafayette LA 70501
Tel (337) 237-1142 SIC 4832 4833

CLARK ENTERPRISES INC p 322
7500 Old Georgetown Rd # 7, Bethesda MD 20814
Tel (301) 657-7100
SIC 6552 4832 7359 1521 1542 6726

■ **SINCLAIR TELEVISION GROUP INC** p 1326
10706 Beaver Dam Rd, Hunt Valley MD 21030
Tel (410) 568-1500 SIC 4832

▲ **RADIO ONE INC** p 1204
1010 Wayne Ave Ste 1400, Silver Spring MD 20910
Tel (301) 429-3200 SIC 4832 4841 4813

WGBH EDUCATIONAL FOUNDATION p 1604
1 Guest St, Boston MA 02135
Tel (617) 300-2000 SIC 7812 4833 4832

COUNTY BROADCASTING CO LLC p 375
30 How St, Haverhill MA 01830
Tel (603) 668-6400 SIC 4832

▲ **NATIONAL AMUSEMENTS INC** p 1009
846 University Ave, Norwood MA 02062
Tel (781) 461-1600
SIC 7832 7833 4832 4833 4841

▲ **SAGA COMMUNICATIONS INC** p 1267
73 Kercheval Ave, Grosse Pointe Farms MI 48236
Tel (313) 886-7070 SIC 4832 4833

■ **SAGA COMMUNICATIONS OF ILLINOIS LLC** p 1267
73 Kercheval Ave Ste 201, Grosse Pointe Farms MI 48236
Tel (313) 886-7070 SIC 4832

■ **SAGA COMMUNICATIONS OF NEW ENGLAND INC** p 1267
73 Kercheval Ave Ste 201, Grosse Pointe Farms MI 48236
Tel (313) 886-7070 SIC 4832

CENTRAL MICHIGAN UNIVERSITY p 279
1200 S Franklin St, Mount Pleasant MI 48859
Tel (989) 774-4000
SIC 8221 5942 4833 4832 5812

HUBBARD BROADCASTING INC p 716
3415 University Ave W, Saint Paul MN 55114
Tel (651) 642-4656 SIC 4833 7812 4832

MINNESOTA PUBLIC RADIO AMERICAN PUBLIC MEDIA p 974
480 Cedar St, Saint Paul MN 55101
Tel (651) 290-1446 SIC 4832

LEARFIELD COMMUNICATIONS INC p 850
505 Hobbs Rd, Jefferson City MO 65109
Tel (573) 893-7200 SIC 4832 4841

PULITZER INC p 1191
900 N Tucker Blvd, Saint Louis MO 63101
Tel (314) 340-8000 SIC 2711 4833 4832

MONTANA STATE UNIVERSITY-BILLINGS p 986
1500 University Dr, Billings MT 59101
Tel (406) 657-2011 SIC 4832 5942 8221

CITADEL BROADCASTING CO p 309
7201 W Lake Mead Blvd # 400, Las Vegas NV 89128
Tel (702) 804-5200 SIC 4832

NASSAU BROADCASTING PARTNERS LP p 1008
619 Alexander Rd Ste 300, Princeton NJ 08540
Tel (609) 452-9696 SIC 4832

ALLSUP ENTERPRISES INC p 58
2112 N Thornton St, Clovis NM 88101
Tel (575) 769-2311
SIC 5411 5541 4832 6519 5171

PAMAL BROADCASTING LTD p 1110
6 Johnson Rd, Latham NY 12110
Tel (518) 786-6600 SIC 4832

■ **ABC INC** p 10
77 W 66th St Rm 100, New York NY 10023
Tel (212) 456-7777
SIC 4833 4832 7812 6794 2711 2721

■ **CBS BROADCASTING INC** p 269
51 W 52nd St, New York NY 10019
Tel (212) 975-4321 SIC 4833 4832 7812

■ **CBS CORP** p 269
51 W 52nd St Bsmt 1, New York NY 10019
Tel (212) 975-4321
SIC 4833 4832 7312 2731

■ **CBS RADIO INC** p 269
1271 Ave OfThe Amer 44, New York NY 10020
Tel (212) 314-9200 SIC 4832 7312

HEARST CORP p 678
300 W 57th St Fl 42, New York NY 10019
Tel (212) 649-2000
SIC 2721 2731 2711 4832 4833 7383

▲ **MSG NETWORKS INC** p 997
11 Penn Plz, New York NY 10001
Tel (212) 465-6400
SIC 4841 7922 7941 4832

■ **MSGN HOLDINGS LP** p 997
4 Penn Plz, New York NY 10121
Tel (212) 465-6000 SIC 4832 7922

■ **NBC NEWS WORLDWIDE LLC** p 1021
30 Rockefeller Plz Fl 2, New York NY 10112
Tel (212) 664-4444
SIC 4832 4833 4841 6021 6531 7383

■ **NBC UNIVERSITY LLC** p 1021
30 Rockefeller Plz Fl 51, New York NY 10112
Tel (212) 664-4444
SIC 4832 4833 4841 6021 6531 7383

▲ **NEW YORK TIMES CO** p 1036
620 8th Ave, New York NY 10018
Tel (212) 556-1234
SIC 2711 4832 4833 7383 7375

■ **SIRIUS XM HOLDINGS INC** p 1327
1221 Avenue Of Americas Flr 36, New York NY 10020
Tel (212) 584-5100 SIC 4832

■ **SIRIUS XM RADIO INC** p 1327
1221 Avenue OfThe Americ, New York NY 10020
Tel (212) 584-5100 SIC 4832

■ **WESTWOOD ONE INC** p 1603
220 W 42nd St Fl 4, New York NY 10036
Tel (212) 967-2888 SIC 4832 7922

TRANS WORLD RADIO p 1470
300 Gregson Dr, Cary NC 27511
Tel (919) 460-3597 SIC 4832

BAHAKEL SPORTS INC p 145
1 Television Pl, Charlotte NC 28205
Tel (704) 372-4434 SIC 4833 4832

RAYCOM SPORTS NETWORK INC p 1210
1900 W Morehead St, Charlotte NC 28208
Tel (704) 378-4400
SIC 6311 6321 6324 6411 4832 4833

CAPITOL BROADCASTING CO INC p 250
2619 Western Blvd, Raleigh NC 27606
Tel (919) 890-6000
SIC 4833 4832 4841 8732

FORUM COMMUNICATIONS CO p 570
101 5th St N, Fargo ND 58102
Tel (701) 235-7311 SIC 2711 4833 4832

SANDUSKY NEWSPAPERS INC p 1278
314 W Market St, Sandusky OH 44870
Tel (419) 625-5500 SIC 4832 2711 2752

FEED CHILDREN INC p 537
333 N Meridian Ave, Oklahoma City OK 73107
Tel (800) 627-4556 SIC 8661 8699 4832

CONFEDERATED TRIBES OF WARM SPRINGS RESERVATION OF OREGON p 356
1233 Veterans St, Warm Springs OR 97761
Tel (541) 553-1161 SIC 7011 4832 0811

▲ **ENTERCOM COMMUNICATIONS CORP** p 501
401 E City Ave Ste 809, Bala Cynwyd PA 19004
Tel (610) 660-5610 SIC 4832

■ **ENTERCOM RADIO LLC** p 501
401 E City Ave Ste 409, Bala Cynwyd PA 19004
Tel (610) 660-5610 SIC 4832

SCRANTON TIMES L P p 1294
149 Penn Ave Ste 1, Scranton PA 18503
Tel (570) 348-9100 SIC 2711 4832

SUSQUEHANNA PFALTZGRAFF CO INC p 1409
140 E Market St, York PA 17401
Tel (717) 848-5500 SIC 4832 4841 6512

UNIVISION RADIO INC p 1527
2323 Bryan St Ste 1900, Dallas TX 75201
Tel (214) 758-2300 SIC 4832

■ **IHEARTCOMMUNICATIONS INC** p 731
200 E Basse Rd, San Antonio TX 78209
Tel (210) 822-2828 SIC 4832 4833 7312

▲ **IHEARTMEDIA INC** p 731
200 E Basse Rd Ste 100, San Antonio TX 78209
Tel (210) 822-2828 SIC 4832 7312

BONNEVILLE INTERNATIONAL CORP p 200
55 N 300 W, Salt Lake City UT 84101
Tel (801) 575-5555 SIC 4832

DESERET MANAGEMENT CORP p 432
55 N 300 W Ste 800, Salt Lake City UT 84101
Tel (801) 538-0651
SIC 4832 4833 5932 6512 6531 6411

GREATER WASHINGTON EDUCATIONAL TELECOMMUNICATIONS ASSOCIATION INC p 636
3939 Campbell Ave, Arlington VA 22206
Tel (703) 998-2600 *SIC* 4833 4832

MIDDLE EAST BROADCASTING NETWORKS INC p 964
7600 Boston Blvd, Springfield VA 22153
Tel (703) 852-9000 *SIC* 4841 4832

CHRISTIAN BROADCASTING NETWORK INC p 302
977 Centerville Tpke, Virginia Beach VA 23463
Tel (757) 226-3030
SIC 8661 4833 4832 5999 4724

■ ACKERLEY VENTURES INC p 17
1301 5th Ave Ste 3525, Seattle WA 98101
Tel (206) 624-2888
SIC 7941 4833 4832 7319 7312

■ FISHER COMMUNICATIONS INC p 552
140 4th Ave N Ste 500, Seattle WA 98109
Tel (206) 404-7000 *SIC* 4833 4832

BLISS COMMUNICATIONS INC p 189
1 S Parker Dr, Janesville WI 53545
Tel (608) 741-6650 *SIC* 2711 4832

WISCONSIN EDUCATIONAL COMMUNICATIONS BOARD p 1618
3319 W Beltline Hwy, Madison WI 53713
Tel (608) 264-9600 *SIC* 4833 4832

DESK BC MERGER LLC p 432
333 W State St, Milwaukee WI 53203
Tel (414) 224-2000 *SIC* 4832

JOURNAL COMMUNICATIONS INC p 794
333 W State St, Milwaukee WI 53203
Tel (414) 224-2000
SIC 4832 4833 2711 2759 4813

SIC 4833 Television Broadcasting Stations

COMMUNITY NEWSPAPER HOLDINGS INC p 349
445 Dexter Ave Ste 7000, Montgomery AL 36104
Tel (334) 293-5800 *SIC* 2711 4833

RAYCOM MEDIA INC p 1210
201 Monroe St Fl 20, Montgomery AL 36104
Tel (334) 206-1400 *SIC* 4833 4832

■ ALASCOM INC p 44
505 E Bluff Dr, Anchorage AK 99501
Tel (907) 264-7000 *SIC* 4813 4833 4832

COOK INLET REGION INC p 366
725 E Fireweed Ln Ste 800, Anchorage AK 99503
Tel (907) 274-8638
SIC 6552 1382 1389 6519 4832 4833

■ ABC CABLE NETWORKS GROUP p 10
500 S Buena Vista St, Burbank CA 91521
Tel (818) 460-7477 *SIC* 4832 4833

CW NETWORK LLC p 404
3300 W Olive Ave Fl 3, Burbank CA 91505
Tel (818) 977-2500 *SIC* 4833

LBI MEDIA HOLDINGS INC p 849
1845 W Empire Ave, Burbank CA 91504
Tel (818) 563-5722 *SIC* 4832 4833

▲ WALT DISNEY CO p 1574
500 S Buena Vista St, Burbank CA 91521
Tel (818) 560-1000
SIC 4833 4841 7011 7996 7812 2731

■ DETROIT TELEVISION STATION WKBD INC p 433
5555 Melrose Ave, Los Angeles CA 90038
Tel (323) 956-5000 *SIC* 4833

E ENTERTAINMENT TELEVISION INC p 466
5750 Wilshire Blvd # 500, Los Angeles CA 90036
Tel (323) 954-2400 *SIC* 4841 4833

■ FOX BROADCASTING CO p 572
10201 W Pico Blvd, Los Angeles CA 90064
Tel (310) 369-1000 *SIC* 4833

■ FOX INC p 572
2121 Ave Of The Ste 1100, Los Angeles CA 90067
Tel (310) 369-1000 *SIC* 4833 7812

■ FOX TELEVISION STATIONS LLC p 573
1999 S Bundy Dr, Los Angeles CA 90025
Tel (310) 584-2000 *SIC* 4833 7313

■ PARAMOUNT PICTURES CORP p 1114
5555 Melrose Ave, Los Angeles CA 90038
Tel (323) 956-5000
SIC 7812 5099 4833 7829

■ TWENTIETH CENTURY FOX HOME ENTERTAINMENT LLC p 1494
10201 W Pico Blvd, Los Angeles CA 90064
Tel (310) 369-1000 *SIC* 4833

SAN BERNARDINO COMMUNITY COLLEGE DISTRICT p 1275
114 S Del Rosa Dr, San Bernardino CA 92408
Tel (909) 382-4000 *SIC* 8222 4832 4833

ELLIS COMMUNICATIONS KDOC LLC p 488
625 N Grand Ave Fl 1, Santa Ana CA 92701
Tel (949) 442-9800 *SIC* 4833

▲ ENTRAVISION COMMUNICATIONS CORP p 502
2425 Olympic Blvd Ste 600, Santa Monica CA 90404
Tel (310) 447-3870 *SIC* 4833 4832

HULU LLC p 718
2500 Broadway Fl 2, Santa Monica CA 90404
Tel (310) 571-4700 *SIC* 4833 4813

TRINITY CHRISTIAN CENTER OF SANTA ANA INC p 1481
2442 Michelle Dr, Tustin CA 92780
Tel (714) 665-3619 *SIC* 4833 7922

OUTDOOR CHANNEL HOLDINGS INC p 1098
1000 Chopper Cir, Denver CO 80204
Tel (951) 699-6991 *SIC* 4841 4833

■ ESPN PRODUCTIONS INC p 510
545 Middle St, Bristol CT 06010
Tel (860) 766-2000 *SIC* 4833

UNITED STATES CONFERENCE OF CATHOLIC BISHOPS p 1512
3211 4th St Ne, Washington DC 20017
Tel (202) 541-3000 *SIC* 8661 4832 4833

UNIVISION PRODUCTIONS p 1527
9405 Nw 41st St, Doral FL 33178
Tel (305) 597-3097 *SIC* 4833

WATERMAN BROADCASTING CORP OF FLORIDA p 1582
3719 Central Ave, Fort Myers FL 33901
Tel (239) 939-2020 *SIC* 4833

■ TELEMUNDO COMMUNICATIONS GROUP INC p 1434
2290 W 8th Ave, Hialeah FL 33010
Tel (305) 884-8200 *SIC* 4833 7313

▲ SPANISH BROADCASTING SYSTEM INC p 1354
7007 Nw 77th Ave, Miami FL 33166
Tel (305) 441-6901 *SIC* 4832 4833

SUNBEAM TELEVISION CORP p 1401
1401 79th Street Cswy, North Bay Village FL 33141
Tel (305) 751-6692 *SIC* 4833 6512

■ USANI SUB LLC p 1534
1 Hsn Dr, Saint Petersburg FL 33729
Tel (727) 872-1000 *SIC* 4833 5961

■ WFTS p 1604
4045 N Himes Ave, Tampa FL 33607
Tel (813) 354-2800 *SIC* 4833

ION MEDIA NETWORKS INC p 762
601 Clearwater Park Rd, West Palm Beach FL 33401
Tel (561) 659-4122 *SIC* 4833

■ CABLE NEWS NETWORK INC p 235
1 Cnn Ctr Nw 12, Atlanta GA 30303
Tel (404) 878-2276 *SIC* 4833

■ CABLE NEWS NETWORK LP LLLP p 235
1 Cnn Ctr Nw, Atlanta GA 30303
Tel (404) 522-8873 *SIC* 4833

COX ENTERPRISES INC p 386
6205 Pachtree Dunwoody Rd, Atlanta GA 30328
Tel (678) 645-0000
SIC 4841 4813 2711 4833 7389 4832

COX MEDIA GROUP LLC p 386
6205 Pachtree Dunwoody Rd, Atlanta GA 30328
Tel (678) 645-0000
SIC 4833 4832 7922 7313

PUBLIC TELECOMMUNICATIONS COMMISSION GEORGIA p 1190
260 14th St Nw, Atlanta GA 30318
Tel (404) 685-4788 *SIC* 4833

■ TEN NETWORK HOLDING INC p 1436
1 Cnn Ctr Nw, Atlanta GA 30303
Tel (404) 827-1700 *SIC* 4833

■ TURNER BROADCASTING SYSTEM INC p 1492
1 Cnn Ctr Nw 14sw, Atlanta GA 30303
Tel (404) 575-7250
SIC 7822 4833 4841 7812

■ TWCC HOLDING CORP p 1494
300 Interstate N Pkwy Se, Atlanta GA 30339
Tel (770) 226-0000
SIC 4833 4813 7812 8999

■ GRAY TELEVISION GROUP INC p 632
4370 Peachtree Rd Ne # 500, Brookhaven GA 30319
Tel (404) 266-8333 *SIC* 4833

▲ GRAY TELEVISION INC p 632
4370 Peachtree Rd Ne # 500, Brookhaven GA 30319
Tel (404) 504-9828 *SIC* 4833

MORRIS MULTIMEDIA INC p 990
27 Abercorn St, Savannah GA 31401
Tel (912) 233-1281 *SIC* 4833 2752

■ TRIBUNE BROADCASTING CO LLC p 1479
435 N Michigan Ave Fl 2, Chicago IL 60611
Tel (312) 222-3333 *SIC* 4833 4832

▲ TRIBUNE MEDIA CO p 1479
435 N Michigan Ave Fl 2, Chicago IL 60611
Tel (212) 210-2786
SIC 4833 4832 7922 7941

■ WGN CONTINENTAL BROADCASTING CO p 1604
2501 W Bradley Pl, Chicago IL 60618
Tel (773) 528-2311 *SIC* 4832 4833

BARRINGTON BROADCASTING LLC p 157
500 W Higgins Rd Ste 880, Hoffman Estates IL 60195
Tel (847) 884-1877 *SIC* 4833

QUINCY MEDIA INC p 1200
130 S 5th St, Quincy IL 62301
Tel (217) 223-5100
SIC 2711 4833 2752 2741

■ SCHURZ COMMUNICATIONS INC p 1291
1301 E Douglas Rd, Mishawaka IN 46545
Tel (574) 247-7237 *SIC* 4833 2711

LESEA BROADCASTING CORP p 857
61300 Ironwood Rd, South Bend IN 46614
Tel (574) 291-8200 *SIC* 4833 4832

GAZETTE CO p 594
500 3rd Ave Se, Cedar Rapids IA 52401
Tel (319) 398-8211 *SIC* 2711 2752 4833

▲ MEREDITH CORP p 948
1716 Locust St, Des Moines IA 50309
Tel (515) 284-3000 *SIC* 2721 2731 4833

■ LOCALTV LLC p 873
300 Dave Cowans Dr, Newport KY 41071
Tel (859) 448-2700 *SIC* 4833

PAXTON MEDIA GROUP LLC p 1122
100 Television Ln, Paducah KY 42003
Tel (270) 575-8630 *SIC* 2711 4833

COMMUNICATIONS CORP OF AMERICA p 347
700 John St Ste 300, Lafayette LA 70501
Tel (337) 237-1142 *SIC* 4832 4833

DIVERSIFIED BUSINESS COMMUNICATIONS p 444
121 Free St, Portland ME 04101
Tel (207) 842-5400
SIC 4833 4841 2721 7389

▲ SINCLAIR BROADCAST GROUP INC p 1326
10706 Beaver Dam Rd, Hunt Valley MD 21030
Tel (410) 568-1500 *SIC* 4833

WGBH EDUCATIONAL FOUNDATION p 1604
1 Guest St, Boston MA 02135
Tel (617) 300-2000 *SIC* 7812 4833 4832

WHDH-TV INC p 1604
7 Bulfinch Pl, Boston MA 02114
Tel (617) 725-0777 *SIC* 4833

▲ NATIONAL AMUSEMENTS INC p 1009
846 University Ave, Norwood MA 02062
Tel (781) 461-1600
SIC 7832 7833 4832 4833 4841

▲ SAGA COMMUNICATIONS INC p 1267
73 Kercheval Ave, Grosse Pointe Farms MI 48236
Tel (313) 886-7070 *SIC* 4832 4833

CENTRAL MICHIGAN UNIVERSITY p 279
1200 S Franklin St, Mount Pleasant MI 48859
Tel (989) 774-4000
SIC 8221 5942 4833 4832 5812

HUBBARD BROADCASTING INC p 716
3415 University Ave W, Saint Paul MN 55114
Tel (651) 642-4656 *SIC* 4833 7812 4832

PULITZER INC p 1191
900 N Tucker Blvd, Saint Louis MO 63101
Tel (314) 340-8000 *SIC* 2711 4833 4832

INTERMOUNTAIN WEST COMMUNICATIONS CO p 754
701 S 9th St, Las Vegas NV 89101
Tel (702) 642-3333 *SIC* 4833

UNIVISION TELEVISION GROUP INC p 1528
500 Frank W Burr Blvd # 20, Teaneck NJ 07666
Tel (201) 287-4141 *SIC* 4833

■ 21ST CENTURY FOX AMERICA INC p 1
1211 Ave Of The Americas, New York NY 10036
Tel (212) 852-7000
SIC 2752 2721 4833 7812

■ ABC HOLDING CO INC p 10
77 W 66th St Rm 100, New York NY 10023
Tel (212) 456-7777 *SIC* 4833

■ ABC INC p 10
77 W 66th St Rm 100, New York NY 10023
Tel (212) 456-7777
SIC 4833 4832 7812 6794 2711 2721

■ AMERICAN BROADCASTING COMPANIES INC p 69
77 W 66th St Rm 100, New York NY 10023
Tel (212) 456-7777 *SIC* 4833

BBC WORLDWIDE AMERICAS INC p 163
1120 Ave Of The Amrcas, New York NY 10036
Tel (212) 705-9300 *SIC* 4833

■ BEE CEE INC p 168
30 Rockefeller Plz Fl 31, New York NY 10112
Tel (212) 664-4444 *SIC* 4833

BROADCAST MEDIA PARTNERS HOLDINGS INC p 215
605 3rd Ave Fl 12, New York NY 10158
Tel (212) 455-5200 *SIC* 4833 4813 7389

■ CBS BROADCASTING INC p 269
51 W 52nd St, New York NY 10019
Tel (212) 975-4321 *SIC* 4833 4832 7812

■ CBS CORP p 269
51 W 52nd St Bsmt 1, New York NY 10019
Tel (212) 975-4321
SIC 4833 4832 7312 2731

HEARST CORP p 678
300 W 57th St Fl 42, New York NY 10019
Tel (212) 649-2000
SIC 2721 2731 2711 4832 4833 7383

HEARST TELEVISION INC p 678
300 W 57th St, New York NY 10019
Tel (212) 887-6800 *SIC* 4833

MAJOR LEAGUE BASEBALL ENTERPRISES INC p 899
245 Park Ave, New York NY 10167
Tel (212) 931-7500 *SIC* 4833 8699

MAJOR LEAGUE BASEBALL PROPERTIES INC p 899
245 Park Ave Fl 34, New York NY 10167
Tel (212) 931-7800 *SIC* 6794 4833 8748

■ MTV NETWORKS INC p 998
1515 Broadway Fl 31, New York NY 10036
Tel (212) 258-8000 *SIC* 4833

■ NBC NEWS WORLDWIDE LLC p 1021
30 Rockefeller Plz Fl 2, New York NY 10112
Tel (212) 664-4444
SIC 4832 4833 4841 6021 6531 7383

■ NBC UNIVERSAL LLC p 1021
1221 Avenue Of The Americ, New York NY 10020
Tel (212) 664-4444 *SIC* 4833 8111

■ NBC UNIVERSITY LLC p 1021
30 Rockefeller Plz Fl 51, New York NY 10112
Tel (212) 664-4444
SIC 4832 4833 4841 6021 6531 7383

■ NBCUNIVERSAL MEDIA LLC p 1021
30 Rockefeller Plz Fl 2, New York NY 10112
Tel (212) 664-4444
SIC 4841 4833 7812 7996

▲ NEW YORK TIMES CO p 1036
620 8th Ave, New York NY 10018
Tel (212) 556-1234
SIC 2711 4832 4833 7383 7375

NEWBAY MEDIA LLC p 1037
28 E 28th St Fl 12, New York NY 10016
Tel (212) 378-0400 *SIC* 4833

PILOT GROUP LP p 1148
1270 Ave Of The Americas, New York NY 10020
Tel (212) 486-4446 *SIC* 4833

STERLING ENTERTAINMENT ENTERPRISES LLC p 1387
75 Rockefeller Plz Fl 29, New York NY 10019
Tel (212) 485-4400 *SIC* 4833

THIRTEEN PRODUCTIONS LLC p 1448
825 8th Ave Fl 14, New York NY 10019
Tel (212) 560-2000 *SIC* 4833

▲ TWENTY-FIRST CENTURY FOX INC p 1494
1211 Ave Of The Americas, New York NY 10036
Tel (212) 852-7000 *SIC* 4833 4841

UNIVISION COMMUNICATIONS INC p 1527
605 3rd Ave Fl 12, New York NY 10158
Tel (212) 455-5200 *SIC* 4833

UNIVISION HOLDINGS INC p 1527
605 3rd Ave Fl 12, New York NY 10158
Tel (212) 455-5200 *SIC* 4833 4813 7389

■ WESTINGHOUSE CBS HOLDING CO INC p 1601
51 W 52nd St Bsmt 1, New York NY 10019
Tel (212) 975-4321 *SIC* 4833

WNET p 1620
825 8th Ave Fl 14, New York NY 10019
Tel (212) 560-2000 *SIC* 4833

■ WPIX LLC p 1627
80 State St, New York NY 10017
Tel (212) 949-1100 *SIC* 4833

YOUNG BROADCASTING LLC p 1638
599 Lexington Ave, New York NY 10022
Tel (517) 372-8282 *SIC* 4833

LICT CORP p 863
401 Theodore Fremd Ave, Rye NY 10580
Tel (914) 921-8821 *SIC* 4813 4841 4833

BAHAKEL SPORTS INC p 145
1 Television Pl, Charlotte NC 28205
Tel (704) 372-4434 *SIC* 4833 4832

RAYCOM SPORTS NETWORK INC p 1210
1900 W Morehead St, Charlotte NC 28208
Tel (704) 378-4400
SIC 6311 6321 6324 6411 4832 4833

CAPITOL BROADCASTING CO INC p 250
2619 Western Blvd, Raleigh NC 27606
Tel (919) 890-6000
SIC 4833 4832 4841 8732

FORUM COMMUNICATIONS CO p 570
101 5th St N, Fargo ND 58102
Tel (701) 235-7311 *SIC* 2711 4833 4832

▲ E W SCRIPPS CO p 467
312 Walnut St Ste 2800, Cincinnati OH 45202
Tel (513) 977-3000
SIC 4841 2711 4833 7375

DISPATCH PRINTING CO p 443
62 E Broad St, Columbus OH 43215
Tel (614) 461-5000 *SIC* 4833

BLOCK COMMUNICATIONS INC p 189
405 Madison Ave Ste 2100, Toledo OH 43604
Tel (419) 724-6212 *SIC* 4841 4833 2711

MISSION BROADCASTING INC p 975
30400 Detroit Rd Ste 304, Westlake OH 44145
Tel (440) 526-2227 *SIC* 4833

WWST CORP LLC p 1629
186 S Hillcrest Dr, Wooster OH 44691
Tel (330) 264-5122 *SIC* 4833

KEZI INC p 816
2975 Chad Dr, Eugene OR 97408
Tel (541) 485-5611 *SIC* 4833 6512 4813

PEGASUS MEDIA & COMMUNICATIONS INC p 1127
225 E City Ave Ste 200, Bala Cynwyd PA 19004
Tel (610) 934-7000 *SIC* 4833 4841

PEGASUS TOWERS INC p 1127
225 E City Ave Ste 200, Bala Cynwyd PA 19004
Tel (610) 934-7000 *SIC* 4833

PEGASUS COMMUNICATIONS HOLDINGS INC p 1127
1055 Westlakes Dr Ste 300, Berwyn PA 19312
Tel (302) 651-8300 *SIC* 4833 4841

SISTEMA UNIVERSITARIO ANA G MENDEZ INC p 1327
Carr 176 Km 0 3 Cpey Lowr St Ca, San Juan PR 00928
Tel (787) 751-0178 *SIC* 8221 4833

LIN TV CORP p 866
1 W Exchange St Ste 305, Providence RI 02903
Tel (401) 454-2880 *SIC* 4833 7311

LIBERTY CORP p 861
135 S Main St Ste 1000, Greenville SC 29601
Tel (864) 609-8111 *SIC* 4833

■ WVLT-TV INC p 1628
6450 Papermill Dr, Knoxville TN 37919
Tel (865) 450-8888 *SIC* 4833

■ LIN TELEVISION CORP p 866
701 Brazos St Ste 800, Austin TX 78701
Tel (512) 774-6110 *SIC* 4833

WORD OF GOD FELLOWSHIP INC p 1624
3901 Highway 121, Bedford TX 76021
Tel (817) 571-1229 *SIC* 4833

GULF COAST BROADCASTING CO p 646
409 S Staples St, Corpus Christi TX 78401
Tel (361) 886-6100 *SIC* 4833 5812

HOAK MEDIA LLC p 698
3963 Maple Ave Ste 450, Dallas TX 75219
Tel (972) 960-4840 *SIC* 4833

■ KHOU-TV INC p 816
1945 Allen Pkwy, Houston TX 77019
Tel (713) 284-1011 *SIC* 4833

▲ NEXSTAR BROADCASTING GROUP INC p 1040
545 E John Carpenter Fwy # 700, Irving TX 75062
Tel (972) 373-8800 *SIC* 4833

■ IHEARTCOMMUNICATIONS INC p 731
200 E Basse Rd, San Antonio TX 78209
Tel (210) 822-2828 *SIC* 4832 4833 7312

DESERET MANAGEMENT CORP p 432
55 N 300 W Ste 800, Salt Lake City UT 84101
Tel (801) 538-0651
SIC 4832 4833 5932 6512 6531 6411

■ ALLBRITTON COMMUNICATIONS CO p 52
1000 Wilson Blvd Ste 2700, Arlington VA 22209
Tel (703) 647-8700 *SIC* 4833 7812

■ ALLBRITTON GROUP LLC p 52
1000 Wilson Blvd Ste 2700, Arlington VA 22209
Tel (703) 647-8700 *SIC* 4833

▲ GRAHAM HOLDINGS CO p 629
1300 17th St N Ste 1700, Arlington VA 22209
Tel (703) 345-6300
SIC 8299 4833 4841 2721

GREATER WASHINGTON EDUCATIONAL TELECOMMUNICATIONS ASSOCIATION INC p 636
3939 Campbell Ave, Arlington VA 22206
Tel (703) 998-2600 *SIC* 4833 4832

PUBLIC BROADCASTING SERVICE p 1189
2100 Crystal Dr Ste 100, Arlington VA 22202
Tel (703) 739-5000 *SIC* 4833

■ BELO CORP p 171
7950 Jones Branch Dr, Mc Lean VA 22102
Tel (703) 854-6000 *SIC* 4833

■ **GANNETT BROADCASTING INC** p 590
7950 Jones Branch Dr, Mc Lean VA 22102
Tel (703) 854-6000 SIC 4833

▲ **TEGNA INC** p 1432
7950 Jones Branch Dr, Mc Lean VA 22102
Tel (703) 854-7000
SIC 2711 4813 4841 4833

▲ **MEDIA GENERAL INC** p 936
333 E Franklin St, Richmond VA 23219
Tel (804) 887-5000 SIC 4833

■ **MEDIA GENERAL OPERATIONS INC** p 936
333 E Franklin St, Richmond VA 23219
Tel (804) 887-5000 SIC 2711 4833

■ **MGOC INC** p 958
333 E Franklin St, Richmond VA 23219
Tel (804) 887-5000 SIC 4833 4841

CHRISTIAN BROADCASTING NETWORK INC p 302
977 Centerville Tpke, Virginia Beach VA 23463
Tel (757) 226-3030
SIC 8661 4833 4832 5999 4724

■ **AT&T WIRELESS SERVICES OF CALIFORNIA LLC** p 123
7277 164th Ave Ne, Redmond WA 98052
Tel (425) 827-4500 SIC 4812 4833

■ **ACKERLEY VENTURES INC** p 17
1301 5th Ave Ste 3525, Seattle WA 98101
Tel (206) 624-2888
SIC 7941 4833 4832 7319 7312

■ **FISHER COMMUNICATIONS INC** p 552
140 4th Ave N Ste 500, Seattle WA 98109
Tel (206) 404-7000 SIC 4833 4832

COWLES PUBLISHING CO p 386
999 W Riverside Ave, Spokane WA 99201
Tel (509) 459-5000
SIC 2711 2611 2621 4833

TELEVISION WISCONSIN INC p 1435
7025 Raymond Rd, Madison WI 53719
Tel (608) 271-4321 SIC 4833

WISCONSIN EDUCATIONAL COMMUNICATIONS BOARD p 1618
3319 W Beltline Hwy, Madison WI 53713
Tel (608) 264-9600 SIC 4833 4832

JOURNAL BROADCAST GROUP INC p 794
720 E Capitol Dr, Milwaukee WI 53212
Tel (414) 799-9494 SIC 4833

JOURNAL COMMUNICATIONS INC p 794
333 W State St, Milwaukee WI 53203
Tel (414) 224-2000
SIC 4832 4833 2711 2759 4813

EVENING TELEGRAM CO p 513
1226 Ogden Ave, Superior WI 54880
Tel (715) 394-4411 SIC 4833

SIC 4841 Cable & Other Pay TV Svcs

UTILITIES BOARD OF CITY OF FOLEY p 1537
413 E Laurel Ave, Foley AL 36535
Tel (251) 943-5001 SIC 4911 1623 4841

▲ **GENERAL COMMUNICATION INC** p 599
2550 Denali St Ste 1000, Anchorage AK 99503
Tel (907) 868-5600 SIC 4813 4841 4812

▲ **CABLE ONE INC** p 235
210 E Earll Dr Fl 6, Phoenix AZ 85012
Tel (602) 364-6000 SIC 4813 4841

COX COMMUNICATIONS INC p 386
1550 W Deer Valley Rd, Phoenix AZ 85027
Tel (404) 269-6736 SIC 4841

YUMA CABLEVISION INC p 1640
1289 S 2nd Ave, Yuma AZ 85364
Tel (928) 329-9731 SIC 4841

CONWAY CORP p 365
1307 Prairie St, Conway AR 72034
Tel (501) 450-6000 SIC 4911 4941 4841

WEHCO MEDIA INC p 1587
115 E Capitol Ave, Little Rock AR 72201
Tel (501) 378-3529 SIC 2711 4841

ALAMEDA BUREAU OF ELECTRICITY IMPROVEMENT CORP p 44
2000 Grand St, Alameda CA 94501
Tel (510) 748-3901 SIC 4911 4899 4841

MONSTER INC p 985
455 Valley Dr, Brisbane CA 94005
Tel (415) 840-2000 SIC 5099 4841 3679

■ **ABC FAMILY WORLDWIDE INC** p 10
500 S Buena Vista St, Burbank CA 91521
Tel (818) 560-1000 SIC 7812 4841

▲ **WALT DISNEY CO** p 1574
500 S Buena Vista St, Burbank CA 91521
Tel (818) 560-1000
SIC 4833 4841 7011 7996 7812 2731

GLOBECAST AMERICA INC p 618
10525 Washington Blvd, Culver City CA 90232
Tel (212) 373-5140 SIC 4841

■ **DIRECTV ENTERPRISES LLC** p 442
2230 E Imperial Hwy, El Segundo CA 90245
Tel (310) 535-5000 SIC 4841

■ **DIRECTV GROUP HOLDINGS LLC** p 442
2260 E Imperial Hwy, El Segundo CA 90245
Tel (310) 964-5000 SIC 4841

■ **DIRECTV GROUP INC** p 442
2260 E Imperial Hwy, El Segundo CA 90245
Tel (310) 964-5000 SIC 4841

■ **DIRECTV HOLDINGS LLC** p 442
2230 E Imperial Hwy, El Segundo CA 90245
Tel (310) 964-5000 SIC 4841

■ **LIBERTY ENTERTAINMENT INC** p 861
2230 E Imperial Hwy, El Segundo CA 90245
Tel (310) 964-5000 SIC 4841

OC COMMUNICATIONS INC p 1072
2204 Kausen Dr Ste 100, Elk Grove CA 95758
Tel (916) 686-3700 SIC 4841

E ENTERTAINMENT TELEVISION INC p 466
5750 Wilshire Blvd # 500, Los Angeles CA 90036
Tel (323) 954-2400 SIC 4841 4833

■ **FOX CABLE NETWORK SERVICES LLC** p 572
10201 W Pico Blvd, Los Angeles CA 90064
Tel (310) 369-2362 SIC 4841

■ **FOX NETWORKS GROUP INC** p 572
10201 W Pico Blvd 101, Los Angeles CA 90064
Tel (310) 369-9369 SIC 4841

ROKU INC p 1247
150 Winchester Cir, Los Gatos CA 95032
Tel (408) 556-9040 SIC 4841

IRVINE CO LLC p 765
550 Newport Center Dr # 160, Newport Beach CA 92660
Tel (949) 720-2000
SIC 6552 6531 0174 0191 4841

ABS-CBN INTERNATIONAL p 12
150 Shoreline Dr, Redwood City CA 94065
Tel (800) 527-2820 SIC 4841 7822

■ **GAME SHOW NETWORK LLC** p 590
2150 Colorado Ave Ste 100, Santa Monica CA 90404
Tel (310) 255-6800 SIC 4841

VUBIQUITY HOLDINGS INC p 1567
15301 Ventura Blvd # 3000, Sherman Oaks CA 91403
Tel (818) 526-5000 SIC 4841

CROWN MEDIA HOLDINGS INC p 395
12700 Ventura Blvd # 100, Studio City CA 91604
Tel (888) 390-7474 SIC 4841

LIBERTY GLOBAL INC p 861
1550 Wewatta St Ste 1000, Denver CO 80202
Tel (303) 220-6600 SIC 4841 4813

OUTDOOR CHANNEL HOLDINGS INC p 1098
1000 Chopper Cir, Denver CO 80204
Tel (951) 699-6991 SIC 4841 4833

■ **DISH DBS CORP** p 442
9601 S Meridian Blvd, Englewood CO 80112
Tel (303) 723-1000 SIC 4841

▲ **DISH NETWORK CORP** p 442
9601 S Meridian Blvd, Englewood CO 80112
Tel (303) 723-1000 SIC 4841

■ **DISH NETWORK SERVICE LLC** p 442
9601 S Meridian Blvd, Englewood CO 80112
Tel (303) 723-1000 SIC 1799 4841

■ **DISH ORBITAL CORP** p 442
9601 S Meridian Blvd, Englewood CO 80112
Tel (303) 723-1000 SIC 3663 4841

■ **ECHOSPHERE LLC** p 475
9601 S Meridian Blvd, Englewood CO 80112
Tel (303) 723-1000 SIC 5065 4841

▲ **ECHOSTAR CORP** p 475
100 Inverness Ter E, Englewood CO 80112
Tel (303) 706-4000 SIC 3663 4841

■ **ECHOSTAR SATELLITE SERVICES LLC** p 475
100 Inverness Ter E, Englewood CO 80112
Tel (866) 359-8804 SIC 4841

LGI INTERNATIONAL INC p 860
12300 Liberty Blvd, Englewood CO 80112
Tel (720) 875-5800 SIC 4841

LIBERTY BROADBAND CORP p 861
12300 Liberty Blvd, Englewood CO 80112
Tel (720) 875-5700 SIC 4841 4899

▲ **LIBERTY INTERACTIVE CORP** p 862
12300 Liberty Blvd, Englewood CO 80112
Tel (720) 875-5300 SIC 4841 5961

■ **LIBERTY INTERACTIVE LLC** p 862
12300 Liberty Blvd, Englewood CO 80112
Tel (720) 875-5400
SIC 5961 4841 7819 4813

▲ **LIBERTY MEDIA CORP** p 862
12300 Liberty Blvd, Englewood CO 80112
Tel (720) 875-5400 SIC 4841

■ **LIBERTY QVC HOLDING LLC** p 862
12300 Liberty Blvd, Englewood CO 80112
Tel (484) 701-3777 SIC 4841 5961

■ **LIBERTY USA HOLDINGS LLC** p 863
12300 Liberty Blvd, Englewood CO 80112
Tel (720) 875-5300 SIC 4841

▲ **STARZ** p 1379
8900 Liberty Cir, Englewood CO 80112
Tel (720) 852-7700 SIC 4841 4813

WIDEOPENWEST FINANCE LLC p 1608
7887 E Belleview Ave, Englewood CO 80111
Tel (303) 663-0771 SIC 4841

JONES INTERNATIONAL LTD p 792
300 E Mineral Ave Ste 5, Littleton CO 80122
Tel (303) 792-3111
SIC 4832 4841 7371 7372

■ **ESPN INC** p 509
Espn Plz, Bristol CT 06010
Tel (860) 766-2000 SIC 4841 4832

CHARTER COMMUNICATIONS INC p 290
400 Atlantic St Fl 10, Stamford CT 06901
Tel (203) 905-7801 SIC 4841 4813

▲ **CHARTER COMMUNICATIONS INC** p 290
400 Atlantic St, Stamford CT 06901
Tel (203) 905-7801 SIC 4841 4813

ENCOMPASS DIGITAL MEDIA INC p 495
250 Harbor Dr, Stamford CT 06902
Tel (203) 965-6000 SIC 4841 8742

■ **SPECTRUM MANAGEMENT HOLDING CO LLC** p 1357
400 Atlantic St, Stamford CT 06901
Tel (203) 905-7801 SIC 4841

■ **TIME WARNER CABLE ENTERPRISES LLC** p 1454
400 Atlantic St Ste 6, Stamford CT 06901
Tel (877) 495-9201 SIC 7812 4841

■ **TIME WARNER ENTERTAINMENT-ADVANCE/NEWHOUSE PARTNERSHIP** p 1454
400 Atlantic St Ste 6, Stamford CT 06901
Tel (212) 364-8200 SIC 4841

■ **BLACK ENTERTAINMENT TELEVISION LLC** p 186
1235 W St Ne, Washington DC 20018
Tel (202) 526-4927 SIC 4841

■ **XM SATELLITE RADIO HOLDINGS INC** p 1632
1500 Eckington Pl Ne, Washington DC 20002
Tel (202) 380-4000 SIC 4841

▲ **HEMISPHERE MEDIA GROUP INC** p 682
4000 Ponce De Leon Blvd # 650, Coral Gables FL 33146
Tel (305) 421-6364 SIC 4841

OLE HBO PARTNERS p 1082
396 Alhambra Cir Ste 400, Coral Gables FL 33134
Tel (305) 648-8100 SIC 4841

■ **COMCAST OF FLORIDA/GEORGIA/ILLINOIS/MICHIGAN LLC** p 343
4600 Touchton Rd E # 2200, Jacksonville FL 32246
Tel (904) 374-8000 SIC 4813 4841

■ **EMERGING MARKETS COMMUNICATIONS LLC** p 492
3044 N Commerce Pkwy, Miramar FL 33025
Tel (954) 538-4000 SIC 4841

MEDIACOM SOUTHEAST LLC p 936
1104 N Westover Blvd, Albany GA 31707
Tel (229) 888-0242 SIC 4841 4813

COX COMMUNICATIONS ARIZONA LLC p 386
6305 Pchtree Dunwoody Rd, Atlanta GA 30328
Tel (404) 843-5000 SIC 4841

COX COMMUNICATIONS CALIFORNIA LLC p 386
6205 Pachtree Dunwoody Rd, Atlanta GA 30328
Tel (404) 843-5000 SIC 4841

COX COMMUNICATIONS INC p 386
6205 B Pchtree Dunwoody Ne, Atlanta GA 30328
Tel (404) 843-5000 SIC 4841 4813

COX COMMUNICATIONS LAS VEGAS INC p 386
6205 Pachtree Dunwoody Rd, Atlanta GA 30328
Tel (404) 269-7898 SIC 4841

COX ENTERPRISES INC p 386
6205 Pachtree Dunwoody Rd, Atlanta GA 30328
Tel (678) 645-0000
SIC 4841 4813 2711 4833 7389 4832

■ **TURNER BROADCASTING SYSTEM INC** p 1492
1 Cnn Ctr Nw 14sw, Atlanta GA 30303
Tel (404) 575-7250
SIC 7822 4833 4841 7812

WEATHER CHANNEL INC p 1585
300 Interstate North Pkwy, Atlanta GA 30339
Tel (770) 226-0000 SIC 4841 4832

COX ARIZONA TELCOM LLC p 386
1400 Lake Hearn Dr Ne, Brookhaven GA 30319
Tel (404) 843-5000 SIC 4841

COX HOLDINGS INC p 386
1400 Lake Hearn Dr Ne, Brookhaven GA 30319
Tel (404) 843-5000 SIC 4841 4813

COX MEDIA LLC p 386
1400 Lake Hearn Dr Ne, Brookhaven GA 30319
Tel (404) 843-5000 SIC 4841 7313

COX NEVADA TELCOM LLC p 386
1400 Lake Hearn Dr Ne, Brookhaven GA 30319
Tel (404) 269-7898 SIC 4841

COXCOM LLC p 386
1400 Lake Hearn Dr Ne, Brookhaven GA 30319
Tel (404) 843-5000 SIC 4841 4813

TANDBERG TELEVISION INC p 1424
4500 River Green Pkwy, Duluth GA 30096
Tel (678) 812-6300 SIC 4841

KNOLOGY BROADBAND INC p 825
1241 Og Skinner Dr, West Point GA 31833
Tel (706) 645-8553 SIC 4841

KNOLOGY INC p 825
1241 Og Skinner Dr, West Point GA 31833
Tel (334) 644-2611 SIC 4813 4841

■ **COMCAST OF ILLINOIS III INC** p 343
1585 S Waukegan Rd, Waukegan IL 60085
Tel (847) 856-5239 SIC 4841

ELECTRIC & WATER PLANT BOARD OF CITY OF FRANKFORT KY p 484
317 W 2nd St, Frankfort KY 40601
Tel (502) 352-4372
SIC 4941 4911 7382 5063 4841 4813

DIVERSIFIED BUSINESS COMMUNICATIONS p 444
121 Free St, Portland ME 04101
Tel (207) 842-5400
SIC 4833 4841 2721 7389

■ **COMCAST CABLEVISION** p 343
8031 Corporate Dr, Baltimore MD 21236
Tel (410) 931-4600 SIC 4841

■ **COMCAST OF MARYLAND LLC** p 343
9609 Annapolis Rd, Lanham MD 20706
Tel (301) 306-5774 SIC 4841

▲ **DISCOVERY COMMUNICATIONS INC** p 442
1 Discovery Pl, Silver Spring MD 20910
Tel (240) 662-2000 SIC 4841 7812 7922

■ **DISCOVERY COMMUNICATIONS LLC** p 442
1 Discovery Pl, Silver Spring MD 20910
Tel (240) 662-2000 SIC 4841

▲ **RADIO ONE INC** p 1204
1010 Wayne Ave Ste 1400, Silver Spring MD 20910
Tel (301) 429-3200 SIC 4832 4841 4813

▲ **NATIONAL AMUSEMENTS INC** p 1009
846 University Ave, Norwood MA 02062
Tel (781) 461-1600
SIC 7832 7833 4832 4833 4841

ATLANTIC BROADBAND FINANCE LLC p 126
1 Pine Hill Dr Ste 205, Quincy MA 02169
Tel (617) 786-8800 SIC 4841 4813

ATLANTIC BROADBAND MANAGEMENT LLC p 126
1 Pine Hill Dr Ste 205, Quincy MA 02169
Tel (617) 786-8800 SIC 4841

MIDCONTINENT COMMUNICATIONS p 964
3600 Minnesota Dr Ste 700, Minneapolis MN 55435
Tel (952) 844-2600 SIC 4841 4813

MIDCONTINENT MEDIA INC p 964
3600 Minnesota Dr Ste 700, Minneapolis MN 55435
Tel (952) 844-2600 SIC 4841

■ **NEXTIRAONE LLC** p 1040
5050 Lincoln Dr Ste 300, Minneapolis MN 55436
Tel (952) 352-4410
SIC 5065 7629 1731 5999 4813 4841

ARVIG ENTERPRISES INC p 114
150 2nd St Sw Ste 100, Perham MN 56573
Tel (218) 346-4227 SIC 4813 4841

ONMEDIA COMMUNICATIONS CO INC p 1088
115 N Industrial Park Rd, Excelsior Springs MO 64024
Tel (913) 491-4030 SIC 4841

LEARFIELD COMMUNICATIONS INC p 850
505 Hobbs Rd, Jefferson City MO 65109
Tel (573) 893-7200 SIC 4832 4841

■ **CC VIII HOLDINGS LLC** p 269
12405 Powerscourt Dr, Saint Louis MO 63131
Tel (314) 543-2411 SIC 4841

■ **CCH II LLC** p 270
12405 Powerscourt Dr, Saint Louis MO 63131
Tel (314) 965-0555 SIC 4841

■ **CCO HOLDINGS LLC** p 270
12405 Powerscourt Dr, Saint Louis MO 63131
Tel (314) 965-0555 SIC 4841 4813 7389

■ **CCO NR HOLDINGS LLC** p 270
12405 Powerscourt Dr, Saint Louis MO 63131
Tel (314) 965-0555 SIC 4841

CEQUEL COMMUNICATIONS HOLDINGS LLC p 283
520 Maryville Centre Dr, Saint Louis MO 63141
Tel (314) 965-0500 SIC 4841

CEQUEL COMMUNICATIONS LLC p 283
520 Maryville Centre Dr # 300, Saint Louis MO 63141
Tel (314) 965-2020 SIC 4813 4841

CEQUEL CORP p 283
520 Maryville Centre Dr # 300, Saint Louis MO 63141
Tel (314) 315-9400 SIC 4841 4813

■ **CHARTER COMMUNICATIONS ENTERTAINMENT II LLC** p 290
12405 Powerscourt Dr, Saint Louis MO 63131
Tel (314) 965-0555 SIC 4841

■ **CHARTER COMMUNICATIONS HOLDING CO LLC** p 290
12405 Powerscourt Dr, Saint Louis MO 63131
Tel (314) 965-0555 SIC 4841

■ **CHARTER COMMUNICATIONS HOLDINGS LLC** p 290
12405 Powerscourt Dr, Saint Louis MO 63131
Tel (314) 543-2480 SIC 4841 4813

■ **CHARTER COMMUNICATIONS OPERATING LLC** p 291
12405 Powerscourt Dr, Saint Louis MO 63131
Tel (314) 965-0555 SIC 4841

■ **FALCON CABLE COMMUNICATIONS LLC** p 526
12405 Powerscourt Dr, Saint Louis MO 63131
Tel (314) 965-0555 SIC 4841

FIDELITY COMMUNICATIONS CO p 540
64 N Clark St, Sullivan MO 63080
Tel (800) 392-8070 SIC 4841 4813

US CABLE OF COASTAL-TEXAS LP p 1531
28 W Grand Ave Ste 6, Montvale NJ 07645
Tel (201) 930-9000 SIC 4841

RCN TELECOM SERVICES LLC p 1212
650 College Rd E Ste 3100, Princeton NJ 08540
Tel (609) 452-8197 SIC 4841 7375 4813

■ **COMCAST CABLEVISION OF NEW JERSEY INC** p 343
800 Rahway Ave, Union NJ 07083
Tel (908) 206-8640 SIC 4841 1731 7375

■ **BRESNAN COMMUNICATIONS LLC** p 210
1111 Stewart Ave, Bethpage NY 11714
Tel (516) 803-2300 SIC 4841

CABLEVISION SYSTEMS CORP p 235
1111 Stewart Ave, Bethpage NY 11714
Tel (516) 803-2300 SIC 4841

CABLEVISION SYSTEMS LONG ISLAND CORP p 235
1111 Stewart Ave, Bethpage NY 11714
Tel (516) 803-2300 SIC 4841

CSC HOLDINGS LLC p 397
1111 Stewart Ave, Bethpage NY 11714
Tel (516) 803-2300 SIC 4841 4813

ADVANCE/NEWHOUSE COMMUNICATIONS PARTNERSHIP p 25
5823 Widewaters Pkwy, East Syracuse NY 13057
Tel (315) 438-4100 SIC 4841

CABLEVISION LIGHTPATH INC p 235
200 Jericho Quadrangle, Jericho NY 11753
Tel (516) 803-2300 SIC 4841

MEDIACOM BROADBAND LLC p 936
1 Mediacom Way, Mediacom Park NY 10918
Tel (845) 443-2600 SIC 4841

MEDIACOM COMMUNICATIONS CORP p 936
1 Mediacom Way, Mediacom Park NY 10918
Tel (877) 847-6221 SIC 4841 4813

MEDIACOM LLC p 936
1 Mediacom Way, Mediacom Park NY 10918
Tel (845) 443-2600 SIC 4841

11 PENN TV LLC p 1
11 Penn Plz Fl 2, New York NY 10001
Tel (212) 324-8506 SIC 4841

A&E TELEVISION NETWORKS LLC p 7
235 E 45th St Frnt C, New York NY 10017
Tel (212) 210-1400 SIC 4841

▲ **AMC NETWORKS INC** p 65
11 Penn Plz, New York NY 10001
Tel (212) 324-8500 SIC 4841

■ **COMEDY PARTNERS** p 344
345 Hudson St Fl 9, New York NY 10014
Tel (212) 767-8600 SIC 4841

■ **ESPN HOLDING CO INC** p 509
77 W 66th St, New York NY 10023
Tel (212) 916-9200 SIC 4841

■ **FOX ENTERTAINMENT GROUP INC** p 572
1211 Ave Of The Americas, New York NY 10036
Tel (212) 852-7000 SIC 7812 4841

HEARST HOLDINGS INC p 678
300 W 57th St, New York NY 10019
Tel (212) 649-2000 SIC 2721 4841

■ **HISTORIC TW INC** p 696
75 Rockefeller Plz, New York NY 10019
Tel (212) 484-8000
SIC 3652 6794 2741 7812 4841 2721

■ **HOME BOX OFFICE INC** p 703
1100 Avenue Of The Americ, New York NY 10036
Tel (212) 512-1000 SIC 4841 7812

■ **INSIGHT COMMUNICATIONS CO INC** p 746
810 7th Ave, New York NY 10019
Tel (917) 286-2300 SIC 4841 4813

INSIGHT COMMUNICATIONS OF KENTUCKY LP p 746
810 7th Ave Fl 28, New York NY 10019
Tel (917) 286-2300 SIC 4841

■ **INSIGHT MIDWEST LP** p 746
810 7th Ave Fl 28, New York NY 10019
Tel (917) 286-2300 SIC 4841

LIFETIME ENTERTAINMENT SERVICES LLC p 864
235 E 45th St, New York NY 10017
Tel (212) 424-7000 SIC 4841

MLB ADVANCED MEDIA LP p 979
75 9th Ave Fl 5, New York NY 10011
Tel (212) 485-3444 SIC 4841 7313 7929

▲ **MSG NETWORKS INC** p 997
11 Penn Plz, New York NY 10001
Tel (212) 465-6400
SIC 4841 7922 7941 4832

■ **NBC NEWS WORLDWIDE LLC** p 1021
30 Rockefeller Plz Fl 2, New York NY 10112
Tel (212) 664-4444
SIC 4832 4833 4841 6021 6531 7383

■ **NBC UNIVERSITY LLC** p 1021
30 Rockefeller Plz Fl 51, New York NY 10112
Tel (212) 664-4444
SIC 4832 4833 4841 6021 6531 7383

■ **NBCUNIVERSAL MEDIA LLC** p 1021
30 Rockefeller Plz Fl 2, New York NY 10112
Tel (212) 664-4444
SIC 4841 4833 7812 7996

STUDIO 3 PARTNERS LLC p 1394
1515 Broadway Rm 43, New York NY 10036
Tel (212) 846-4004 SIC 4841

■ **TELEVISION FOOD NETWORK GP** p 1435
75 9th Ave, New York NY 10011
Tel (212) 366-0509 SIC 4841

▲ **TIME WARNER INC** p 1454
1 Time Warner Ctr Bsmt B, New York NY 10019
Tel (212) 484-8000
SIC 4841 7812 2731 2721

▲ **TWENTY-FIRST CENTURY FOX INC** p 1494
1211 Ave Of The Americas, New York NY 10036
Tel (212) 852-7000 SIC 4833 4841

USA CABLE INC p 1534
30 Rockefeller Plz Conc28, New York NY 10112
Tel (212) 413-5000 SIC 4841

▲ **VERIZON COMMUNICATIONS INC** p 1550
1095 Ave Of The Americas, New York NY 10036
Tel (212) 395-1000 SIC 4813 4812 4841

▲ **VIACOM INC** p 1554
1515 Broadway, New York NY 10036
Tel (212) 258-6000 SIC 4841 7812

VIRGIN MEDIA HOLDINGS INC p 1558
65 Bleecker St Fl 6, New York NY 10012
Tel (212) 966-2310 SIC 4812 4813 4841

■ **WARNER COMMUNICATIONS INC** p 1576
1 Time Warner Ctr, New York NY 10019
Tel (212) 484-8000 SIC 7812 4841 7389

▲ **NEULION INC** p 1028
1600 Old Country Rd, Plainview NY 11803
Tel (516) 622-8300 SIC 4841 7372

LICT CORP p 863
401 Theodore Fremd Ave, Rye NY 10580
Tel (914) 921-8821 SIC 4813 4841 4833

CAPITOL BROADCASTING CO INC p 250
2619 Western Blvd, Raleigh NC 27606
Tel (919) 890-6000
SIC 4833 4832 4841 8732

DIRECT SAT TV LLC p 441
1930 N Poplar St Ste 21, Southern Pines NC 28387
Tel (910) 693-3000 SIC 4841

▲ **E W SCRIPPS CO** p 467
312 Walnut St Ste 2800, Cincinnati OH 45202
Tel (513) 977-3000
SIC 4841 2711 4833 7375

BUCKEYE CABLEVISION INC p 223
2700 Oregon Rd, Northwood OH 43619
Tel (419) 724-9802 SIC 4841

BLOCK COMMUNICATIONS INC p 189
405 Madison Ave Ste 2100, Toledo OH 43604
Tel (419) 724-6212 SIC 4841 4833 2711

SOUTHERN STAR INC p 1350
306 Kerr Ave, Poteau OK 74953
Tel (918) 647-8383 SIC 4841

PEGASUS MEDIA & COMMUNICATIONS INC p 1127
225 E City Ave Ste 200, Bala Cynwyd PA 19004
Tel (610) 934-7000 SIC 4833 4841

PEGASUS COMMUNICATIONS HOLDINGS INC p 1127
1055 Westlakes Dr Ste 300, Berwyn PA 19312
Tel (302) 651-8300 SIC 4833 4841

SERVICE ELECTRIC CABLE TV INC p 1307
2200 Avenue A Ste 101, Bethlehem PA 18017
Tel (610) 865-9100 SIC 4841 6719

ARMSTRONG UTILITIES INC p 111
1 Armstrong Pl, Butler PA 16001
Tel (724) 283-0925 SIC 4841

■ **D&E COMMUNICATIONS INC** p 407
124 E Main St Fl 6, Ephrata PA 17522
Tel (717) 733-4101 SIC 4813 4841

■ **COMCAST OF SOUTHEAST PENNSYLVANIA LLC** p 343
200 Cresson Blvd, Oaks PA 19456
Tel (610) 650-1000 SIC 4841

PENCOR SERVICES INC p 1128
613 3rd Street Palmerton, Palmerton PA 18071
Tel (610) 826-2115
SIC 2711 7371 4813 4841

■ **COMCAST CABLE COMMUNICATIONS LLC** p 343
1701 John Fk Blvd, Philadelphia PA 19103
Tel (215) 665-1700 SIC 4841

■ **COMCAST CABLE HOLDINGS LLC** p 343
1500 Market St Ste Lmw 3, Philadelphia PA 19102
Tel (215) 665-1700 SIC 4841 7922 5961

■ **COMCAST CABLEVISION OF MERCER COUNTY INC** p 343
1500 Market St, Philadelphia PA 19102
Tel (215) 665-1700 SIC 4841

▲ **COMCAST CORP** p 343
1701 Jfk Blvd, Philadelphia PA 19103
Tel (215) 286-1700
SIC 4841 4813 7812 7996

■ **COMCAST HOLDINGS CORP** p 343
1701 John F Kennedy Blvd C100, Philadelphia PA 19103
Tel (215) 665-1700 SIC 4841

TELE-MEDIA CORP p 1433
320 W College Ave, Pleasant Gap PA 16823
Tel (814) 359-3481 SIC 4841

PAGNOTTI ENTERPRISES INC p 1107
46 Public Sq Ste 600, Wilkes Barre PA 18701
Tel (570) 825-8700 SIC 6411 1231 4841

SUSQUEHANNA PFALTZGRAFF CO INC p 1409
140 E Market St, York PA 17401
Tel (717) 848-5500 SIC 4832 4841 6512

LIBERTY CABLEVISION OF PUERTO RICO LLC p 861
Urb Indl Tres Monjitas 1, San Juan PR 00918
Tel (787) 766-0909 SIC 4841

LIBERTY CABLEVISION OF PUERTO RICO LLC p 861
Urb Industrial Tres Monj, San Juan PR 00919
Tel (787) 657-3050 SIC 4841

AIKEN ELECTRIC COOPERATIVE INC p 38
2790 Wagener Rd, Aiken SC 29801
Tel (803) 649-6245 SIC 4911 4841

HORRY TELEPHONE COOPERATIVE INC p 708
3480 Highway 701 N, Conway SC 29526
Tel (843) 365-2151 SIC 4813 4841 7382

▲ **SCRIPPS NETWORKS INTERACTIVE INC** p 1294
9721 Sherrill Blvd, Knoxville TN 37932
Tel (865) 694-2700 SIC 4841

RIO HOLDINGS INC p 1235
600 Congress Ave Ste 200, Austin TX 78701
Tel (512) 917-1742 SIC 4813 4841

TIME WARNER ENTERTAINMENT ADVANCE NEWHOUSE PARTNERSHIP p 1454
7010 Airport Rd, El Paso TX 79906
Tel (512) 288-5440 SIC 4841

MULTIBAND CORP p 999
2801 Network Blvd Ste 300, Frisco TX 75034
Tel (763) 504-3000 SIC 4841 4813

■ **TIME WARNER CABLE SAN ANTONIO LP** p 1454
1900 Blue Crest Ln, San Antonio TX 78247
Tel (703) 713-9342 SIC 4841

GRANDE COMMUNICATIONS NETWORKS LLC p 630
401 Carlson Cir, San Marcos TX 78666
Tel (512) 878-4000 SIC 4841

COX SOUTHWEST HOLDINGS LP p 386
3015 S Southeast Loop 323, Tyler TX 75701
Tel (903) 595-3701 SIC 4841

UNIVERSAL CABLE HOLDINGS INC p 1516
6151 Paluxy Dr, Tyler TX 75703
Tel (330) 872-0462 SIC 4841

INNOVATIVE COMMUNICATIONS CORP p 744
4611 Tutu Park Mall # 200, St Thomas VI 00802
Tel (340) 777-7700 SIC 4813 4841

▲ **GRAHAM HOLDINGS CO** p 629
1300 17th St N Ste 1700, Arlington VA 22209
Tel (703) 345-6300
SIC 8299 4833 4841 2721

▲ **SHENANDOAH TELECOMMUNICATIONS CO** p 1315
500 Shentel Way, Edinburg VA 22824
Tel (540) 984-4141 SIC 4813 4812 4841

SIDERA NETWORKS INC p 1319
196 Van Buren St Ste 250, Herndon VA 20170
Tel (703) 434-8500 SIC 4841 4813 7375

INTELSAT CORP p 750
7900 Tysons One Pl, Mc Lean VA 22102
Tel (703) 559-6800 SIC 4841

▲ **TEGNA INC** p 1432
7950 Jones Branch Dr, Mc Lean VA 22102
Tel (703) 854-7000
SIC 2711 4813 4841 4833

■ **MGOC INC** p 958
333 E Franklin St, Richmond VA 23219
Tel (804) 887-5000 SIC 4833 4841

MIDDLE EAST BROADCASTING NETWORKS INC p 964
7600 Boston Blvd, Springfield VA 22153
Tel (703) 852-9000 SIC 4841 4832

WAVEDIVISION HOLDINGS LLC p 1584
401 Kirkland Prk Pl Ste 500, Kirkland WA 98033
Tel (425) 576-8200 SIC 4841

NORTHLAND TELECOMMUNICATIONS CORP p 1057
101 Stewart St Ste 700, Seattle WA 98101
Tel (206) 621-1351 SIC 4841 7371

CITY OF TACOMA DEPARTMENT OF PUBLIC UTILITIES p 319
3628 S 35th St, Tacoma WA 98409
Tel (253) 502-8900
SIC 4911 4941 4899 4013 4841

TULALIP TRIBES OF WASHINGTON p 1491
2832 116th St Ne, Tulalip WA 98271
Tel (360) 716-4000 SIC 4841

SIC 4899 Communication Svcs, NEC

ITC DELTACOM INC p 767
7037 Old Madison Pike Nw, Huntsville AL 35806
Tel (256) 382-5900 SIC 4813 4899

ALAMEDA BUREAU OF ELECTRICITY IMPROVEMENT CORP p 44
2000 Grand St, Alameda CA 94501
Tel (510) 748-3901 SIC 4911 4899 4841

▲ **RINGCENTRAL INC** p 1235
20 Davis Dr, Belmont CA 94002
Tel (650) 472-4100 SIC 7372 4899

COMPUTER CONSULTING OPERATIONS SPECIALISTS INC p 352
600 Corporate Pointe # 1010, Culver City CA 90230
Tel (310) 568-5000
SIC 4813 4899 5045 7378

OPLINK COMMUNICATIONS LLC p 1089
46335 Landing Pkwy, Fremont CA 94538
Tel (510) 933-7200 SIC 3661 4899

■ **TELETRAC INC** p 1435
7391 Lincoln Way, Garden Grove CA 92841
Tel (714) 897-0877 SIC 4899

▲ **GLOBAL EAGLE ENTERTAINMENT INC** p 616
4553 Glencoe Ave Ste 200, Marina Del Rey CA 90292
Tel (310) 437-6000 SIC 4899 7371 4813

SPACE SYSTEMS/LORAL LLC p 1354
3825 Fabian Way, Palo Alto CA 94303
Tel (650) 852-7320 SIC 4899 3663

▲ **CALIX INC** p 242
1035 N Mcdowell Blvd, Petaluma CA 94954
Tel (707) 766-3000 SIC 3663 4899 4813

DINCO INC p 440
27520 Hawthorne Blvd # 180, Rllng Hls Est CA 90274
Tel (424) 331-1200 SIC 4899

■ **QUALCOMM ATHEROS INC** p 1196
1700 Technology Dr, San Jose CA 95110
Tel (408) 773-5200 SIC 3674 4899

▲ **SILVER SPRING NETWORKSINC** p 1324
230 W Tasman Dr, San Jose CA 95134
Tel (669) 770-4000 SIC 4899 7372

MOBILEUM INC p 980
2880 Lakeside Dr Ste 135, Santa Clara CA 95054
Tel (408) 844-6600 SIC 4899 7373

DIMENSION DATA p 440
27202 Turnberry Ln # 100, Valencia CA 91355
Tel (661) 257-1500 SIC 4899

LIBERTY BROADBAND CORP p 861
12300 Liberty Blvd, Englewood CO 80112
Tel (720) 875-5700 SIC 4841 4899

■ **VIASAT COMMUNICATIONS INC** p 1554
349 Inverness Dr S, Englewood CO 80112
Tel (720) 493-6000 SIC 4899

ADELPHIA COMMUNICATIONS CORP p 22
5613 Dtc Pkwy Ste 850, Greenwood Village CO 80111
Tel (814) 274-6279 SIC 4899

▲ **DIGITALGLOBE INC** p 439
1300 W 120th Ave, Westminster CO 80234
Tel (303) 684-4000 SIC 4899

▲ **SBA COMMUNICATIONS CORP** p 1285
8051 Congress Ave Ste 100, Boca Raton FL 33487
Tel (561) 995-7670 SIC 4899

■ **SBA COMMUNICATIONS INC** p 1285
8051 Congress Ave Ste 100, Boca Raton FL 33487
Tel (561) 995-7670 SIC 4899

■ **SENIOR SBA FINANCE INC** p 1304
8051 Congress Ave Ste 100, Boca Raton FL 33487
Tel (561) 995-7670 SIC 4899 6519

■ **RJE TELECOM LLC** p 1239
4315 Metro Pkwy Ste 300, Fort Myers FL 33916
Tel (239) 454-1944 SIC 4899

TRUENET COMMUNICATIONS CORP p 1486
7666 Blanding Blvd, Jacksonville FL 32244
Tel (904) 777-9052 SIC 4899

ELANDIA INTERNATIONAL INC p 483
8333 Nw 53rd St Ste 400, Miami FL 33166
Tel (305) 415-8830
SIC 4813 4899 7371 5044

LIMECOM INC p 866
6303 Blue Lagoon Dr, Miami FL 33126
Tel (786) 408-6743 SIC 4899

■ **AT&T GLOBAL NETWORK SERVICES LLC** p 123
3405 W Dr Martin Lthr Kng, Tampa FL 33607
Tel (813) 878-3000 SIC 4899

■ **IMPSAT FIBER NETWORKS INC** p 735
2040 N Dixie Hwy, Wilton Manors FL 33305
Tel (954) 779-7171 SIC 4899

AMERICOLD LOGISTICS LLC p 82
10 Glenlake Pkwy Ste 324, Atlanta GA 30328
Tel (678) 441-1400
SIC 4222 4899 8742 7389

CBEYOND INC p 268
320 Interstate N Pkwy 500, Atlanta GA 30339
Tel (678) 424-2400
SIC 4813 7389 4899 1731

■ **EARTHLINK BUSINESS LLC** p 469
1170 Pchtree S Ne Ste 900, Atlanta GA 30309
Tel (404) 815-0770 SIC 4899

GEORGIA TECHNOLOGY AUTHORITY p 607
47 Trinity Ave Sw, Atlanta GA 30334
Tel (404) 463-2300 SIC 4899 9199

SITA INFORMATION NETWORKING COMPUTING USA INC p 1327
3100 Cumberland Blvd Se, Atlanta GA 30339
Tel (770) 850-4500 SIC 4899

■ **WESTOWER COMMUNICATIONS INC** p 1602
4401 Northside Pkwy Nw # 600, Atlanta GA 30327
Tel (360) 306-3300 SIC 4899

MYCOM NORTH AMERICA INC p 1004
1080 Holcomb Bridge Rd # 200210, Roswell GA 30076
Tel (770) 776-0000 SIC 4899

■ **COMMUNICATIONS SUPPLY CORP** p 347
200 E Lies Rd, Carol Stream IL 60188
Tel (630) 221-6400 SIC 4899

▲ **GOGO INC** p 620
111 N Canal St Ste 1500, Chicago IL 60606
Tel (312) 517-5000 SIC 4899

■ **GOGO LLC** p 620
111 N Canal St Fl 15, Chicago IL 60606
Tel (630) 647-1400
SIC 3663 4812 4813 4899

ASC COMMUNICATIONS INC p 115
315 Vernon Ave, Glencoe IL 60022
Tel (800) 417-2035 SIC 4899

■ **ANIXTER INC** p 92
2301 Patriot Blvd, Glenview IL 60026
Tel (224) 521-8000 SIC 5063 4899

■ **AERONAUTICAL RADIO INC** p 30
2551 Riva Rd, Annapolis MD 21401
Tel (410) 266-4000 SIC 4812 4899

■ **ARINC INC** p 108
2551 Riva Rd, Annapolis MD 21401
Tel (410) 266-4000 SIC 8711 4899

■ **RADIO HOLDINGS INC** p 1204
2551 Riva Rd, Annapolis MD 21401
Tel (410) 266-4000 SIC 8711 4899

■ **TELECOMMUNICATION SYSTEMS INC** p 1434
275 West St, Annapolis MD 21401
Tel (410) 263-7616 SIC 7373 4899

■ **KBRWYLE TECHNOLOGY SOLUTIONS LLC** p 806
7000 Columbia Gateway Dr # 100, Columbia MD 21046
Tel (410) 964-7000 SIC 4899 8711

■ **HUGHES COMMUNICATIONS INC** p 717
11717 Exploration Ln, Germantown MD 20876
Tel (301) 428-5500 SIC 4813 4899 3663

■ **HUGHES NETWORK SYSTEMS LLC** p 717
11717 Exploration Ln, Germantown MD 20876
Tel (301) 428-5500 SIC 4899

ABRY PARTNERS INC p 12
888 Boylston St Ste 1600, Boston MA 02199
Tel (617) 859-2959 SIC 4899 2741

LIGHTTOWER FIBER LLC p 865
80 Central St Ste 240, Boxborough MA 01719
Tel (978) 264-6000 SIC 4899

LTS BUYER LLC p 883
80 Central St, Boxborough MA 01719
Tel (978) 264-6001 SIC 4899

■ **ARBOR NETWORKS INC** p 103
76 Blanchard Rd Ste 1, Burlington MA 01803
Tel (781) 362-4300 SIC 4899

■ **AIRVANA LP** p 41
250 Apollo Dr, Chelmsford MA 01824
Tel (877) 855-4092 SIC 4899

MARITZ HOLDINGS INC p 907
1375 N Highway Dr, Fenton MO 63099
Tel (636) 827-4000
SIC 4725 8748 8732 4899

MARITZ LLC p 907
1375 N Highway Dr, Fenton MO 63099
Tel (636) 827-4000
SIC 4725 8748 8732 4899

TELECOMMUNICATIONS MANAGEMENT LLC p 1434
1 Montgomery Plz Fl 4, Sikeston MO 63801
Tel (573) 481-2420 SIC 4899

SWITCH LTD p 1413
7135 S Decatur Blvd, Las Vegas NV 89118
Tel (702) 444-4000 SIC 4899

VELOCITA WIRELESS LLC p 1547
70 Wood Ave S Ste 202, Iselin NJ 08830
Tel (848) 248-4722 SIC 4899 4812

ONE DIVERSIFIED LLC p 1086
37 Market St, Kenilworth NJ 07033
Tel (908) 245-4833
SIC 5099 7373 4899 8711

SES AMERICOM INC p 1308
4 Research Way, Princeton NJ 08540
Tel (609) 987-4000 SIC 4899

SES GLOBAL- AMERICAS INC p 1308
4 Research Way, Princeton NJ 08540
Tel (609) 987-4000 SIC 4899

▲ **ORBCOMM INC** p 1092
395 W Passaic St Ste 3, Rochelle Park NJ 07662
Tel (703) 433-6361 SIC 4899 8748

JNET COMMUNICATIONS LLC p 786
25 Independence Blvd # 103, Warren NJ 07059
Tel (203) 951-6400 SIC 4899 1731

BROKEN ARROW COMMUNICATIONS INC p 216
8316 Corona Loop Ne, Albuquerque NM 87113
Tel (505) 877-2100 SIC 4899 1623

AEGIS MEDIA AMERICAS INC p 29
150 E 42nd St, New York NY 10017
Tel (212) 591-9122 SIC 4899

■ **GTE CORP** p 644
140 West St, New York NY 10007
Tel (212) 395-1000
SIC 4813 4812 3661 3663 4899 2741

■ **INTRALINKS INC** p 760
150 E 42nd St Fl 8, New York NY 10017
Tel (212) 543-7700 SIC 4899 7375

▲ **LORAL SPACE & COMMUNICATIONS INC** p 878
565 5th Ave, New York NY 10017
Tel (212) 697-1105 SIC 3663 4899

■ **TELX LLC** p 1435
1 State St Fl 21, New York NY 10004
Tel (212) 480-9049 SIC 4899

▲ **VOLT INFORMATION SCIENCES INC** p 1564
1133 Avenue Of The Americ, New York NY 10036
Tel (212) 704-2400 SIC 7363 4813 4899

BROADVIEW NETWORKS HOLDINGS INC p 215
800 Westchester Ave Ste N, Rye Brook NY 10573
Tel (914) 922-7000 SIC 4813 4899

■ **SPECTRASITE COMMUNICATIONS LLC** p 1357
400 Regency Forest Dr # 300, Cary NC 27518
Tel (919) 468-0112
SIC 4812 8748 1623 3661 4813 4899

▲ **FAIRPOINT COMMUNICATIONS INC** p 525
521 E Morehead St Ste 500, Charlotte NC 28202
Tel (704) 344-8150 SIC 4813 4812 4899

■ **COMMSCOPE CONNECTIVITY LLC** p 346
1100 Commscope Pl Se, Hickory NC 28602
Tel (828) 324-2200 SIC 4899

▲ **COMMSCOPE HOLDING CO INC** p 346
1100 Commscope Pl Se, Hickory NC 28602
Tel (828) 324-2200 SIC 3663 4899

■ **VARISTAR CORP** p 1545
4334 18th Ave S Ste 200, Fargo ND 58103
Tel (701) 232-6414
SIC 6719 4899 1623 5047 1731 4213

PAMPLIN COMMUNICATIONS CORP p 1110
6605 Se Lake Rd, Portland OR 97222
Tel (503) 546-5100 SIC 4899

PR SITE DEVELOPMENT LLC p 1167
2000 Corporate Dr, Canonsburg PA 15317
Tel (724) 416-2000 SIC 4899

VITAC CORP p 1562
101 Hillpointe Dr Ste 200, Canonsburg PA 15317
Tel (724) 514-4000 SIC 4899 7819

GOODMAN NETWORKS INC p 624
2801 Network Blvd Ste 300, Frisco TX 75034
Tel (972) 406-9692 SIC 4899

IMAGINE COMMUNICATIONS CORP p 733
3001 Dallas Pkwy Ste 300, Frisco TX 75034
Tel (469) 803-4900 SIC 4899 3663

■ CC SCN FIBER LLC p 269
1220 Augusta Dr Ste 600, Houston TX 77057
Tel (713) 570-3000 SIC 4899 7622 4812

CROWN CASTLE INTERNATIONAL CORP p 395
1220 Augusta Dr Ste 600, Houston TX 77057
Tel (713) 570-3000
SIC 4899 7622 4812 6798

▲ CROWN CASTLE INTERNATIONAL CORP p 395
1220 Augusta Dr Ste 600, Houston TX 77057
Tel (713) 570-3000
SIC 6798 4899 7622 4812

▲ RIGNET INC p 1235
1880 S Dairy Ashford Rd # 300, Houston TX 77077
Tel (281) 674-0100 SIC 4899 4813

AIM MEDIA TEXAS OPERATING LLC p 38
1400 E Nolana Ave, Mcallen TX 78504
Tel (956) 683-4000 SIC 2711 4899

ERICSSON INC p 508
6300 Legacy Dr, Plano TX 75024
Tel (972) 583-0000 SIC 4899

■ IHEARTMEDIA CAPITAL I LLC p 731
200 E Basse Rd, San Antonio TX 78209
Tel (210) 822-2828 SIC 4813 4899

■ IHEARTMEDIA CAPITAL II LLC p 731
200 E Basse Rd, San Antonio TX 78209
Tel (210) 822-2828 SIC 4899 4813

▲ CACI INTERNATIONAL INC p 235
1100 N Glebe Rd Ste 200, Arlington VA 22201
Tel (703) 841-7800 SIC 7373 4899 7371

■ ORBITAL SCIENCES CORP p 1092
45101 Warp Dr, Dulles VA 20166
Tel (703) 406-5000 SIC 3812 4899 7372

■ SIX3 ADVANCED SYSTEMS INC p 1328
45200 Business Ct Ste 100, Dulles VA 20166
Tel (703) 742-7660
SIC 3825 4899 8099 4789

■ GEOEYE LLC p 606
2325 Dulles Corner Blvd # 1000, Herndon VA 20171
Tel (703) 480-7500 SIC 4899

VOLKSWAGEN GROUP OF AMERICA INC p 1564
2200 Ferdinand Porsche Dr, Herndon VA 20171
Tel (703) 364-7000
SIC 5511 5012 5013 6153 6141 4899

INTELSAT GLOBAL SERVICE LLC p 750
7900 Tysons One Pl, Mc Lean VA 22102
Tel (703) 559-7129 SIC 4899

INTELSAT HOLDING CORP p 750
7900 Tysons One Pl Fl 14, Mc Lean VA 22102
Tel (202) 703-5599 SIC 4899

INTELSAT USA SALES CORP p 750
7900 Tysons One Pl, Mc Lean VA 22102
Tel (703) 559-6800 SIC 4899

▲ IRIDIUM COMMUNICATIONS INC p 764
1750 Tysons Blvd Ste 1400, Mc Lean VA 22102
Tel (703) 287-7400 SIC 4899

RL2 INC p 1239
10802 Parkridge Blvd, Reston VA 20191
Tel (703) 390-1899 SIC 4899

▲ NEUSTAR INC p 1028
21575 Ridgetop Cir, Sterling VA 20166
Tel (571) 434-5400 SIC 7375 4899

■ NTELOS INC p 1065
1154 Shenandoah Vlg Dr, Waynesboro VA 22980
Tel (540) 946-3500 SIC 4899

■ T-MOBILE USA INC p 1420
12920 Se 38th St, Bellevue WA 98006
Tel (425) 378-4000 SIC 4812 4899

CITY OF TACOMA DEPARTMENT OF PUBLIC UTILITIES p 319
3628 S 35th St, Tacoma WA 98409
Tel (253) 502-8900
SIC 4911 4941 4899 4013 4841

SIC 4911 Electric Svcs

POWERSOUTH ENERGY COOPERATIVE p 1166
2027 E Three Notch St, Andalusia AL 36421
Tel (334) 427-3000 SIC 4911

■ ALABAMA POWER CO p 43
600 18th St N, Birmingham AL 35203
Tel (205) 257-1000 SIC 4911

HARBERT CORP p 659
2100 3rd Ave N Ste 600, Birmingham AL 35203
Tel (205) 987-5500 SIC 4911 6799

■ SOUTHERN ELECTRIC GENERATING CO p 1348
600 18th St N, Birmingham AL 35203
Tel (205) 257-1000 SIC 4911

CULLMAN ELECTRIC COOPERATIVE p 400
1749 Eva Rd Ne, Cullman AL 35055
Tel (256) 737-3200 SIC 4911

MUNICIPAL UTILITIES BOARD OF DECATUR MORGAN COUNTY ALABAMA p 1000
1002 Central Pkwy Sw, Decatur AL 35601
Tel (256) 552-1440 SIC 4911

UTILITIES BOARD OF CITY OF FOLEY p 1537
413 E Laurel Ave, Foley AL 36535
Tel (251) 943-5001 SIC 4911 1623 4841

CITY OF HUNTSVILLE ELECTRIC SYSTEMS p 315
112 Spragins St Nw, Huntsville AL 35801
Tel (256) 535-1200 SIC 4911

ALABAMA MUNICIPAL ELECTRIC AUTHORITY p 43
80 Technacenter Dr, Montgomery AL 36117
Tel (334) 262-1126 SIC 4911

CENTRAL ALABAMA ELECTRIC COOPERATIVE p 277
1802 Highway 31 N, Prattville AL 36067
Tel (334) 365-6762 SIC 4911

BALDWIN COUNTY ELECTRIC MEMBERSHIP CORP p 147
19600 State Highway 59, Summerdale AL 36580
Tel (251) 989-6247 SIC 4911

JOE WHEELER ELECTRIC MEMBERSHIP CORP p 787
25354 Al Highway 24, Trinity AL 35673
Tel (256) 552-2300 SIC 4911

CHUGACH ELECTRIC ASSOCIATION INC p 305
5601 Electron Dr, Anchorage AK 99518
Tel (907) 563-7494 SIC 4911

GOLDEN VALLEY ELECTRIC ASSOCIATION INC p 621
758 Illinois St, Fairbanks AK 99701
Tel (907) 452-1151 SIC 4911

MATANUSKA ELECTRIC ASSOCIATION INC p 919
163 E Industrial Way, Palmer AK 99645
Tel (907) 745-3231 SIC 4911

ARIZONA ELECTRIC POWER COOPERATIVE INC p 109
1000 S Highway 80, Benson AZ 85602
Tel (520) 586-3631 SIC 4911

MOHAVE ELECTRIC CO-OPERATIVE INC p 982
928 Hancock Rd, Bullhead City AZ 86442
Tel (928) 763-4115 SIC 4911 1731

NAVAJO TRIBAL UTILITY AUTHORITY p 1019
Hwy 12 N, Fort Defiance AZ 86504
Tel (928) 729-5721 SIC 4939 4924 4911

TRICO ELECTRIC COOPERATIVE INC p 1479
8600 W Tangerine Rd, Marana AZ 85658
Tel (520) 744-2944 SIC 4911

■ ARIZONA PUBLIC SERVICE CO p 109
400 N 5th St Fl 2, Phoenix AZ 85004
Tel (602) 250-1000 SIC 4911

▲ PINNACLE WEST CAPITAL CORP p 1150
400 N 5th St, Phoenix AZ 85004
Tel (602) 250-1000 SIC 4911 6552

SULPHUR SPRINGS VALLEY ELECTRIC COOPERATIVE INC CHARITABLE p 1397
311 E Wilcox Dr, Sierra Vista AZ 85635
Tel (520) 384-2221 SIC 4911 1731 1623

SALT RIVER PROJECT AGRICULTURAL IMPROVEMENT AND POWER DISTRICT p 1273
1521 N Project Dr, Tempe AZ 85281
Tel (602) 236-5900 SIC 4911

TUCSON ELECTRIC POWER CO INC p 1490
88 E Broadway Blvd, Tucson AZ 85701
Tel (520) 571-4000 SIC 4911

UNISOURCE ENERGY SERVICES INC p 1505
88 E Broadway Blvd, Tucson AZ 85701
Tel (520) 571-4000 SIC 4911 4923

UNS ELECTRIC INC p 1528
88 E Broadway Blvd 901, Tucson AZ 85701
Tel (928) 681-8966 SIC 4911

UNS ENERGY CORP p 1528
88 E Broadway Blvd, Tucson AZ 85701
Tel (520) 571-4000 SIC 4923 4911

CARROLL ELECTRIC COOPERATIVE CORP p 261
920 Highway 62 Spur, Berryville AR 72616
Tel (870) 423-2161 SIC 4911 5812

MISSISSIPPI COUNTY ELECTRIC COOPERATIVE INC p 975
510 N Broadway St, Blytheville AR 72315
Tel (870) 763-4563 SIC 4911

CONWAY CORP p 365
1307 Prairie St, Conway AR 72034
Tel (501) 450-6000 SIC 4911 4941 4841

OZARKS ELECTRIC COOPERATIVE CORP p 1101
3641 W Wedington Dr, Fayetteville AR 72704
Tel (479) 521-2900 SIC 4911

FIRST ELECTRIC CO-OPERATIVE CORP p 546
1000 S Jp Wright Loop Rd, Jacksonville AR 72076
Tel (501) 982-4545 SIC 4911

ARKANSAS ELECTRIC COOPERATIVE CORP p 109
1 Cooperative Way, Little Rock AR 72209
Tel (501) 570-2200 SIC 4911

■ ENTERGY ARKANSAS INC p 501
425 W Capitol Ave Fl 20, Little Rock AR 72201
Tel (501) 377-4000 SIC 4911

SOUTHWEST POWER POOL INC p 1352
201 Worthen Dr, Little Rock AR 72223
Tel (501) 614-3200 SIC 4911

■ KGEN HOT SPRING LLC p 816
696 Black Branch Rd, Malvern AR 72104
Tel (501) 609-4600 SIC 4911

ARKANSAS VALLEY ELECTRIC COOPERATIVE CORP p 110
1811 W Commercial St, Ozark AR 72949
Tel (479) 667-2176 SIC 4911

ALAMEDA BUREAU OF ELECTRICITY IMPROVEMENT CORP p 44
2000 Grand St, Alameda CA 94501
Tel (510) 748-3901 SIC 4911 4899 4841

■ SUNEDISON LLC p 1402
600 Clipper Dr, Belmont CA 94002
Tel (650) 453-5600 SIC 4911

HANERGY HOLDING AMERICA INC p 657
1350 Bayshore Hwy Ste 825, Burlingame CA 94010
Tel (650) 288-3722 SIC 4911 6719

COMBUSTION ASSOCIATES INC p 343
555 Monica Cir, Corona CA 92880
Tel (951) 272-6999 SIC 4911 3443

CALIFORNIA INDEPENDENT SYSTEM OPERATOR CORP p 240
250 Outcropping Way, Folsom CA 95630
Tel (916) 351-4400 SIC 4911

IMPERIAL IRRIGATION DISTRICT p 734
333 E Barioni Blvd, Imperial CA 92251
Tel (800) 303-7756 SIC 4911 4971 4931

LOS ANGELES DEPARTMENT OF WATER AND POWER p 878
111 N Hope St, Los Angeles CA 90012
Tel (213) 367-4211 SIC 4941 4911

MERCED IRRIGATION DISTRICT p 944
744 W 20th St, Merced CA 95340
Tel (209) 722-5761 SIC 4911 4971

MODESTO IRRIGATION DISTRICT (INC) p 981
1231 11th St, Modesto CA 95354
Tel (209) 526-7337 SIC 4911 4971

MSR PUBLIC POWER AGENCY p 997
1231 11th St, Modesto CA 95354
Tel (209) 526-7473 SIC 4911

OWL COMPANIES p 1100
4695 Macarthur Ct Ste 950, Newport Beach CA 92660
Tel (949) 797-2000 SIC 8331 6519 4911

CATALINA SOLAR LESSEE LLC p 264
11585 Willow Springs Rd, Rosamond CA 93560
Tel (888) 903-6926 SIC 4911

▲ EDISON INTERNATIONAL p 478
2244 Walnut Grove Ave, Rosemead CA 91770
Tel (626) 302-2222 SIC 4911

■ EDISON MISSION MIDWEST HOLDINGS CO p 478
2244 Walnut Grove Ave, Rosemead CA 91770
Tel (626) 302-2222 SIC 4911

■ SOUTHERN CALIFORNIA EDISON CO p 1347
2244 Walnut Grove Ave, Rosemead CA 91770
Tel (626) 302-1212 SIC 4911

NORTHERN CALIFORNIA POWER AGENCY p 1055
651 Commerce Dr, Roseville CA 95678
Tel (916) 781-3636 SIC 4911

SACRAMENTO MUNICIPAL UTILITY DISTRICT p 1265
6201 S St, Sacramento CA 95817
Tel (916) 452-3211 SIC 4911

CATALINA SOLAR 2 LLC p 264
15445 Innovation Dr, San Diego CA 92128
Tel (888) 903-6926 SIC 4911

EDF RENEWABLE ASSET HOLDINGS INC p 477
15445 Innovation Dr, San Diego CA 92128
Tel (888) 903-6926 SIC 4911

EDF RENEWABLE ENERGY INC p 477
15445 Innovation Dr, San Diego CA 92128
Tel (858) 521-3300 SIC 4911

■ ENOVA CORP p 500
101 Ash St, San Diego CA 92101
Tel (619) 239-7700 SIC 4911 4924

HIGH RIDGE WIND LLC p 691
15445 Innovation Dr, San Diego CA 92128
Tel (888) 903-6926 SIC 4911

JETMORE WIND LLC p 784
15445 Innovation Dr, San Diego CA 92128
Tel (888) 903-6926 SIC 4911

OASIS REPOWER LLC p 1072
15445 Innovation Dr, San Diego CA 92128
Tel (888) 903-6926 SIC 4911

ROOSEVELT WIND HOLDINGS LLC p 1249
15445 Innovation Dr, San Diego CA 92128
Tel (888) 903-6926 SIC 4911

■ SAN DIEGO GAS & ELECTRIC CO p 1276
8326 Century Park Ct, San Diego CA 92123
Tel (619) 696-2000 SIC 4931 4911 4924

▲ SEMPRA ENERGY p 1303
488 8th Ave, San Diego CA 92101
Tel (619) 696-2000
SIC 4932 4911 5172 4922

■ SEMPRA ENERGY GLOBAL ENTERPRISES p 1303
101 Ash St, San Diego CA 92101
Tel (619) 696-2000 SIC 4924 4911

■ SEMPRA ENERGY INTERNATIONAL p 1303
101 Ash St, San Diego CA 92101
Tel (619) 696-2000 SIC 4911

SLATE CREEK WIND PROJECT LLC p 1331
15445 Innovation Dr, San Diego CA 92128
Tel (888) 903-6926 SIC 4911

TYLER BLUFF WIND PROJECT LLC p 1496
15445 Innovation Dr, San Diego CA 92128
Tel (888) 903-6926 SIC 4911

WHEATLAND WIND PROJECT LLC p 1604
15445 Innovation Dr, San Diego CA 92128
Tel (888) 903-6926 SIC 4911

▲ AMERICAN STATES WATER CO p 80
630 E Foothill Blvd, San Dimas CA 91773
Tel (909) 394-3600 SIC 4941 4911

■ GOLDEN STATE WATER CO p 621
630 E Foothill Blvd, San Dimas CA 91773
Tel (909) 394-3600 SIC 4941 4911

■ PACIFIC GAS AND ELECTRIC CO p 1104
77 Beale St, San Francisco CA 94105
Tel (415) 973-7000 SIC 4911 4924

▲ PATTERN ENERGY GROUP INC p 1121
Bay 3 Pier 1, San Francisco CA 94111
Tel (415) 283-4000 SIC 4911

PATTERN ENERGY GROUP LP p 1121
Bay 3 Pier 1, San Francisco CA 94111
Tel (415) 283-4000 SIC 4911

TURLOCK IRRIGATION DISTRICT p 1492
333 E Canal Dr, Turlock CA 95380
Tel (209) 883-8222 SIC 4911 4971

UNITED POWER INC A COLORADO COOPERATIVE ASSOCIATION p 1511
500 Cooperative Way, Brighton CO 80603
Tel (303) 659-0551 SIC 4911

■ PUBLIC SERVICE CO OF COLORADO p 1189
1800 Larimer St Ste 1100, Denver CO 80202
Tel (303) 571-7511 SIC 4911 4922 4924

LA PLATA ELECTRIC ASSOCIATION INC p 835
45 Stewart St, Durango CO 81303
Tel (970) 247-5786 SIC 4911

▲ WESTMORELAND COAL CO p 1601
9540 Maroon Cir Unit 200, Englewood CO 80112
Tel (855) 922-6463 SIC 1221 4911

PLATTE RIVER POWER AUTHORITY (INC) p 1155
2000 E Horsetooth Rd, Fort Collins CO 80525
Tel (970) 229-5332 SIC 4911

HOLY CROSS ELECTRIC ASSOCIATION INC p 702
3799 Highway 82, Glenwood Springs CO 81601
Tel (970) 945-5491 SIC 4911

■ PEETZ TABLE WIND ENERGY LLC p 1127
9500 County Road 78, Peetz CO 80747
Tel (970) 334-2230 SIC 4911

■ BLACK HILLS/COLORADO ELECTRIC UTILITY CO LP p 187
105 S Victoria Ave, Pueblo CO 81003
Tel (719) 546-6589 SIC 4911

INTERMOUNTAIN RURAL ELECTRIC ASSOCIATION p 753
5496 N Us Highway 85, Sedalia CO 80135
Tel (303) 688-3100 SIC 4911

TRI-STATE GENERATION AND TRANSMISSION ASSOCIATION INC p 1477
1100 W 116th Ave, Westminster CO 80234
Tel (303) 452-6111 SIC 4911

■ CONNECTICUT LIGHT AND POWER CO p 357
107 Selden St, Berlin CT 06037
Tel (860) 665-5000 SIC 4911

■ NORTHEAST NUCLEAR ENERGY CO p 1055
107 Selden St, Berlin CT 06037
Tel (860) 665-5000 SIC 4911

■ NU ENTERPRISES INC p 1066
107 Selden St, Berlin CT 06037
Tel (860) 665-5000 SIC 4911

NOBLE ENVIRONMENTAL POWER LLC p 1046
6 Main St Ste 121, Centerbrook CT 06409
Tel (860) 581-5010 SIC 4911

FIRSTLIGHT POWER RESOURCES SERVICES LLC p 551
200 Glastonbury Blvd # 303, Glastonbury CT 06033
Tel (860) 430-2110 SIC 4911

■ EQUIPOWER RESOURCES CORP p 506
100 Constitution Plz # 10, Hartford CT 06103
Tel (203) 676-6700 SIC 4911

■ AVANGRID INC p 136
157 Church St, New Haven CT 06510
Tel (207) 688-6363 SIC 4911 4922 4924

■ UNITED ILLUMINATING CO p 1509
157 Church St Fl 16, New Haven CT 06510
Tel (203) 499-2000 SIC 4911

CONNECTICUT MUNICIPAL ELECTRIC ENERGY COOPERATIVE p 357
30 Stott Ave, Norwich CT 06360
Tel (860) 889-4088 SIC 4911

■ CONNECTICUT ENERGY CORP p 357
60 Marsh Hill Rd, Orange CT 06477
Tel (203) 382-8111 SIC 4911 4932

■ NORTHEAST GENERATION SERVICES CO p 1054
301 Hammer Mill Rd, Rocky Hill CT 06067
Tel (860) 810-1700 SIC 4911

ASTORIA GENERATING CO LP p 122
300 Atlantic St Ste 500, Stamford CT 06901
Tel (212) 792-0800 SIC 4911

DIRECT ENERGY INC p 441
263 Tresser Blvd Fl 8, Stamford CT 06901
Tel (800) 260-0300 SIC 4911 1311

US POWER GENERATING CO p 1533
300 Atlantic St Ste 500, Stamford CT 06901
Tel (212) 792-0800 SIC 4911

ALSTOM INC p 61
200 Great Pond Dr, Windsor CT 06095
Tel (866) 257-8664 SIC 4911 6719

ALGONQUIN POWER WINDSOR LOCKS LLC p 50
26 Canal Bank Rd, Windsor Locks CT 06096
Tel (860) 627-6616 SIC 4911

▲ CHESAPEAKE UTILITIES CORP p 295
909 Silver Lake Blvd, Dover DE 19904
Tel (302) 734-6799 SIC 4924 4911

DELAWARE ELECTRIC COOPERATIVE INC p 424
14198 Sussex Hwy, Greenwood DE 19950
Tel (302) 349-9090 SIC 4911

■ ATLANTIC CITY ELECTRIC CO p 126
500 N Wakefield Dr Fl 2, Newark DE 19702
Tel (202) 872-2000 SIC 4911

■ COGENTRIX DELAWARE HOLDINGS INC p 334
1105 N Market St Ste 1108, Wilmington DE 19801
Tel (847) 908-2800 SIC 4911

■ CONECTIV LLC p 355
800 N King St Ste 400, Wilmington DE 19801
Tel (202) 872-2680
SIC 4911 4924 1731 5172

■ POTOMAC ELECTRIC POWER CO p 1164
701 9th St Nw Ste 3, Washington DC 20001
Tel (202) 872-2000 SIC 4911

IAP WORLD SERVICES INC p 725
7315 N Atlantic Ave, Cape Canaveral FL 32920
Tel (321) 784-7100
SIC 4731 4581 8744 4911 1541 4813

IAP WORLDWIDE SERVICES INC p 725
7315 N Atlantic Ave, Cape Canaveral FL 32920
Tel (973) 633-5115
SIC 4731 4581 8744 4911

WITHLACOOCHEE RIVER ELECTRIC COOPERATIVE INC p 1619
14651 21st St, Dade City FL 33523
Tel (352) 567-5133 SIC 4911

CHOCTAWHATCHEE ELECTRIC COOPERATIVE INC p 302
1350 Baldwin Ave, Defuniak Springs FL 32435
Tel (850) 892-2111 SIC 4911

LEE COUNTY ELECTRIC COOPERATIVE INC p 851
4980 Bayline Dr, Fort Myers FL 33917
Tel (800) 599-2356 SIC 4911

GAINESVILLE REGIONAL UTILITIES (INC) p 589
301 Se 4th Ave, Gainesville FL 32601
Tel (352) 334-3400
SIC 4939 4941 4924 4911

INFINITE ENERGY HOLDINGS INC p 741
7001 Sw 24th Ave, Gainesville FL 32607
Tel (352) 240-4121 *SIC* 4911 4924

APR ENERGY LLC p 100
3600 Prt Jcksnvl Pkwy, Jacksonville FL 32226
Tel (904) 223-2278 *SIC* 4911

■ C AND C POWER LINE INC p 232
12035 Palm Lake Dr, Jacksonville FL 32218
Tel (904) 751-6020 *SIC* 4911 1731

JEA p 781
21 W Church St Fl 1, Jacksonville FL 32202
Tel (904) 665-6000 *SIC* 4911 1623

ST JOHNS RIVER POWER PARK p 1368
21 W Church St, Jacksonville FL 32202
Tel (904) 751-7700 *SIC* 4911

■ ENERGY DUANE ARNOLD LLC p 497
700 Universe Blvd, Juno Beach FL 33408
Tel (561) 691-7171 *SIC* 4911

ESI ENERGY LLC p 509
700 Universe Blvd, Juno Beach FL 33408
Tel (561) 691-7171 *SIC* 4911

■ FLORIDA POWER & LIGHT CO INC p 559
700 Universe Blvd, Juno Beach FL 33408
Tel (561) 694-4000 *SIC* 4911

■ GENESIS SOLAR LLC p 603
700 Universe Blvd, Juno Beach FL 33408
Tel (561) 691-3062 *SIC* 4911

▲ NEXTERA ENERGY INC p 1040
700 Universe Blvd, Juno Beach FL 33408
Tel (561) 694-4000 *SIC* 4911

■ NEXTERA ENERGY OPERATING SERVICES LLC p 1040
700 Universe Blvd, Juno Beach FL 33408
Tel (561) 691-7171 *SIC* 4911

▲ NEXTERA ENERGY PARTNERS LP p 1040
700 Universe Blvd, Juno Beach FL 33408
Tel (561) 694-4000 *SIC* 4911

■ NEXTERA ENERGY POWER MARKETING LLC p 1040
700 Universe Blvd, Juno Beach FL 33408
Tel (561) 691-7171 *SIC* 4911

■ NEXTERA ENERGY RESOURCES LLC p 1040
700 Universe Blvd, Juno Beach FL 33408
Tel (561) 691-7171 *SIC* 4911

NEXTERA ENERGY SERVICES HOLDINGS LLC p 1040
700 Universe Blvd, Juno Beach FL 33408
Tel (561) 691-7171 *SIC* 4911

NEXTERA ENERGY SERVICES LLC p 1040
700 Universe Blvd, Juno Beach FL 33408
Tel (561) 691-7171 *SIC* 4911

CLAY ELECTRIC COOPERATIVE INC p 323
225 W Walker Dr, Keystone Heights FL 32656
Tel (352) 473-8000 *SIC* 4911

KISSIMMEE UTILITY AUTHORITY (INC) p 822
1701 W Carroll St, Kissimmee FL 34741
Tel (407) 933-7777 *SIC* 4911

FLORIDA MUNICIPAL POWER AGENCY p 559
8553 Commodity Cir, Orlando FL 32819
Tel (407) 355-7767 *SIC* 4911

ORLANDO UTILITIES COMMISSION p 1095
100 W Anderson St, Orlando FL 32801
Tel (407) 246-2121
SIC 4941 4931 4939 4911

■ GULF POWER CO p 646
1 Energy Pl, Pensacola FL 32520
Tel (850) 444-6111 *SIC* 4911

■ DUKE ENERGY FLORIDA LLC p 460
299 1st Ave N, Saint Petersburg FL 33701
Tel (704) 382-3853 *SIC* 4911

PROGRESS ENERGY SERVICE CO LLC p 1181
299 1st Ave N, Saint Petersburg FL 33701
Tel (727) 820-5151 *SIC* 4911

SUMTER ELECTRIC COOPERATIVE INC p 1399
330 S Us 301, Sumterville FL 33585
Tel (352) 237-4107 *SIC* 4911

SEMINOLE ELECTRIC COOPERATIVE INC p 1302
16313 N Dale Mabry Hwy, Tampa FL 33618
Tel (813) 963-0994 *SIC* 4911

TAMPA ELECTRIC CO p 1423
702 N Franklin St, Tampa FL 33602
Tel (813) 228-1111 *SIC* 4911 4924

TECO ENERGY INC p 1432
702 N Franklin St, Tampa FL 33602
Tel (813) 228-1111
SIC 4911 4924 4424 1221 1222

FLORIDA KEYS ELECTRIC COOPERATIVE ASSOCIATION INC p 559
91630 Overseas Hwy, Tavernier FL 33070
Tel (305) 852-2431 *SIC* 4911 1731 1623

PEACE RIVER ELECTRIC COOPERATIVE INC p 1125
210 Metheny Rd, Wauchula FL 33873
Tel (800) 282-3824 *SIC* 4911

FLORIDA CRYSTALS CORP p 557
1 N Clematis St Ste 200, West Palm Beach FL 33401
Tel (561) 655-6303
SIC 2061 2062 2044 4911

■ FLORIDA PUBLIC UTILITIES CO p 559
331 W Central Ave Ste 200, Winter Haven FL 33880
Tel (352) 447-2790 *SIC* 4911 4922 5984

SATILLA RURAL ELECTRIC MEMBERSHIP CORP p 1283
928 Ga Highway 32 E, Alma GA 31510
Tel (912) 632-7222 *SIC* 4911

■ GE ENERGY MANAGEMENT SERVICES LLC p 596
4200 Wildwood Pkwy, Atlanta GA 30339
Tel (678) 844-6000 *SIC* 4911

■ GENON NORTH AMERICA LLC p 604
1155 Perimeter Ctr # 100, Atlanta GA 30338
Tel (678) 579-5000 *SIC* 4924 4911 6221

■ GEORGIA POWER CO p 607
241 Ralph Mcgill Blvd Ne, Atlanta GA 30308
Tel (404) 506-6526 *SIC* 4911

■ GRID SOLUTIONS (US) LLC p 640
4200 Wildwood Pkwy # 2018, Atlanta GA 30339
Tel (877) 605-6777 *SIC* 4911

▲ SOUTHERN CO p 1347
30 Ivan Allen Jr Blvd Nw, Atlanta GA 30308
Tel (404) 506-5000 *SIC* 4911

■ SOUTHERN POWER CO p 1350
30 Ivan Allen Jr Blvd Nw, Atlanta GA 30308
Tel (404) 506-5000 *SIC* 4911

CARROLL ELECTRIC MEMBERSHIP CORP p 261
155 N Highway 113, Carrollton GA 30117
Tel (770) 832-3552 *SIC* 4911

SNAPPING SHOALS ELECTRIC TRUST INC p 1335
14750 Brown Bridge Rd, Covington GA 30016
Tel (770) 786-3484 *SIC* 4911

SAWNEE ELECTRIC MEMBERSHIP CORP p 1284
543 Atlanta Rd, Cumming GA 30040
Tel (770) 887-2363 *SIC* 4911

NORTH GEORGIA ELECTRIC MEMBERSHIP FOUNDATION INC p 1052
1850 Cleveland Hwy, Dalton GA 30721
Tel (706) 259-9441 *SIC* 4911

GREYSTONE POWER CORP AN ELECTRIC MEMBERSHIP CORP p 640
4040 Bankhead Hwy 78, Douglasville GA 30134
Tel (770) 942-6576 *SIC* 4911

CENTRAL GEORGIA ELECTRIC MEMBERSHIP CORP p 278
923 S Mulberry St, Jackson GA 30233
Tel (770) 775-7857 *SIC* 4911 1711

JACKSON ELECTRIC MEMBERSHIP CORP p 773
850 Commerce Rd, Jefferson GA 30549
Tel (706) 367-5281 *SIC* 4911

DIVERSE POWER INC AN ELECTRIC MEMBERSHIP CORP p 443
1400 S Davis Rd, Lagrange GA 30241
Tel (706) 845-2000 *SIC* 4911

BOARD OF LIGHTS AND WATER p 195
675 N Marietta Pkwy Ne, Marietta GA 30060
Tel (770) 794-5150 *SIC* 4911 4941

COBB ELECTRIC MEMBERSHIP CORP p 332
1000 Emc Pkwy Ne, Marietta GA 30060
Tel (770) 429-2100 *SIC* 4911

WALTON ELECTRIC MEMBERSHIP CORP p 1575
842 Highway 78 Nw, Monroe GA 30655
Tel (770) 267-2505 *SIC* 4911

COLQUITT ELECTRIC MEMBERSHIP CORP p 339
15 Rowland Dr, Moultrie GA 31768
Tel (229) 985-3620 *SIC* 4911

FLINT ELECTRIC MEMBERSHIP CORP p 557
3 S Macon St, Reynolds GA 31076
Tel (478) 847-3415 *SIC* 4911

■ SAVANNAH ELECTRIC AND POWER CO p 1284
600 E Bay St, Savannah GA 31401
Tel (912) 644-7171 *SIC* 4911

GEORGIA ENERGY COOPERATIVE (AN ELECTRIC MEMBERSHIP CORP) p 607
2100 E Exch Pl Ste 300, Tucker GA 30084
Tel (770) 270-7500 *SIC* 4911

GEORGIA TRANSMISSION CORP p 607
2100 E Exchange Pl, Tucker GA 30084
Tel (770) 270-7400 *SIC* 4911

OGLETHORPE POWER CORP p 1077
2100 E Exch Pl Ste 203, Tucker GA 30084
Tel (770) 270-7600 *SIC* 4911

BLUE RIDGE MOUNTAIN ELECTRIC MEMBERSHIP CORP p 192
875 Main St, Young Harris GA 30582
Tel (706) 379-3121 *SIC* 4911

■ HAWAII ELECTRIC LIGHT CO INC p 669
54 Halekauila St, Hilo HI 96720
Tel (808) 935-1171 *SIC* 4911

■ HAWAIIAN ELECTRIC CO INC p 669
900 Richards St, Honolulu HI 96813
Tel (808) 543-7771 *SIC* 4911

▲ HAWAIIAN ELECTRIC INDUSTRIES INC p 669
1001 Bishop St Ste 2900, Honolulu HI 96813
Tel (808) 543-5662 *SIC* 4911 6035

■ MAUI ELECTRIC CO LIMITED p 921
210 W Kamehameha Ave, Kahului HI 96732
Tel (808) 871-8461 *SIC* 4911

■ COVANTA HONOLULU RESOURCE RECOVERY VENTURE p 384
91-174 Hanua St, Kapolei HI 96707
Tel (808) 682-2099 *SIC* 4911

KAUAI ISLAND UTILITY COOPERATIVE p 805
4463 Pahee St Ste 1, Lihue HI 96766
Tel (808) 246-4300 *SIC* 4911

▲ IDACORP INC p 728
1221 W Idaho St, Boise ID 83702
Tel (208) 388-2200 *SIC* 4911

■ IDAHO POWER CO p 728
1221 W Idaho St, Boise ID 83702
Tel (208) 388-2200 *SIC* 4911

■ DYNEGY MIDWEST GENERATION LLC p 465
10901 Baldwin Rd, Baldwin IL 62217
Tel (618) 785-2294 *SIC* 4911

CORN BELT ENERGY CORP p 370
1 Energy Way, Bloomington IL 61705
Tel (309) 661-1004 *SIC* 4911 4924

INDECK ENERGY SERVICES INC p 735
600 N Buffalo Grove Rd # 300, Buffalo Grove IL 60089
Tel (847) 520-3212 *SIC* 4911

SOUTHEASTERN ILLINOIS ELECTRIC COOPERATIVE INC p 1346
100 Cooperative Way, Carrier Mills IL 62917
Tel (618) 273-2611 *SIC* 4911

■ COMMONWEALTH EDISON CO p 346
440 S La Salle St, Chicago IL 60605
Tel (312) 394-4321 *SIC* 4911

EON CLIMATE & RENEWABLES NORTH AMERICA LLC p 504
353 N Clark St Fl 30, Chicago IL 60654
Tel (312) 245-3035 *SIC* 4911

▲ EXELON CORP p 518
10 S Dearborn St Fl 53, Chicago IL 60603
Tel (800) 483-3220 *SIC* 4911 4924

INTEGRYS ENERGY GROUP INC p 750
200 E Randolph St # 2200, Chicago IL 60601
Tel (312) 228-5400 *SIC* 4931 5172 4911

■ MIDWEST GENERATION EME LLC p 967
440 Suth La Salle St 3500, Chicago IL 60605
Tel (312) 583-6000 *SIC* 4911

■ PEOPLES ENERGY LLC p 1132
200 E Randolph St Fl 22, Chicago IL 60601
Tel (312) 240-4000 *SIC* 4924 4925 4911

■ AMEREN ILLINOIS CO p 66
6 Executive Dr, Collinsville IL 62234
Tel (618) 343-8150 *SIC* 4924 4911

SOUTHEASTERN ILLINOIS ELECTRIC COOPERATIVE p 1346
P.O. Box 251, Eldorado IL 62930
Tel (618) 273-2611 *SIC* 4911

NATIONAL MATERIAL LP p 1014
1965 Pratt Blvd, Elk Grove Village IL 60007
Tel (847) 806-7200
SIC 5051 3469 3354 5093 4911 4924

■ ELECTRIC ENERGY INC p 484
2100 Portland Rd, Joppa IL 62953
Tel (618) 543-7531 *SIC* 4911

■ KINCAID GENERATION LLC p 819
4 Miles W Of Kincaid, Kincaid IL 62540
Tel (217) 237-4311 *SIC* 4911

▲ PERNIX GROUP INC p 1136
151 E 22nd St Ste 101e, Lombard IL 60148
Tel (630) 620-4787 *SIC* 1542 4911

SOUTHERN ILLINOIS POWER CO-OPERATIVE p 1349
11543 Lake Of Egypt Rd, Marion IL 62959
Tel (618) 964-1448 *SIC* 4911

PRAIRIE STATE GENERATING CO LLC p 1167
3872 County Highway 12, Marissa IL 62257
Tel (618) 824-7600 *SIC* 4911

■ CILCORP INC p 307
300 Liberty St, Peoria IL 61602
Tel (309) 677-5271 *SIC* 4911 4924

■ MIDWEST GENERATION LLC p 967
529 E Romeo Rd, Romeoville IL 60446
Tel (609) 524-4526 *SIC* 4911

J-POWER USA DEVELOPMENT CO LTD p 772
1900 E Golf Rd Ste 1030, Schaumburg IL 60173
Tel (847) 908-2800 *SIC* 4911

ILLINOIS MUNICIPAL ELECTRIC AGENCY p 732
3400 Conifer Dr, Springfield IL 62711
Tel (217) 789-4632 *SIC* 4911

PRAIRIE POWER INC p 1167
3130 Pleasant Run, Springfield IL 62711
Tel (217) 245-6161 *SIC* 4911

HENDRICKS COUNTY RURAL ELECTRIC MEMBERSHIP CORP p 683
86 N County Road 500 E, Avon IN 46123
Tel (317) 745-5473 *SIC* 4911

HOOSIER ENERGY RURAL ELECTRIC COOPERATIVE INC p 706
2501 S Cooperative Way, Bloomington IN 47403
Tel (812) 876-2021 *SIC* 4911

ALLIANCE FOR COOPERATIVE ENERGY SERVICES POWER MARKETING LLC p 54
4140 W 99th St, Carmel IN 46032
Tel (317) 344-7000 *SIC* 4911

INDIANA MUNICIPAL POWER AGENCY p 738
11610 N College Ave, Carmel IN 46032
Tel (317) 573-9955 *SIC* 4911

MIDCONTINENT INDEPENDENT SYSTEM OPERATOR INC p 964
720 City Center Dr, Carmel IN 46032
Tel (317) 249-5400 *SIC* 4911

NORTHEASTERN REMC p 1055
4901 E Park Dr Fl 30, Columbia City IN 46725
Tel (260) 625-3700 *SIC* 4911

NORTHEASTERN RURAL ELECTRIC MEMBERSHIP CORP p 1055
4901 E Park 30 Dr, Columbia City IN 46725
Tel (260) 625-3700 *SIC* 4911

■ SOUTHERN INDIANA GAS & ELECTRIC CO p 1349
1 Vectren Sq, Evansville IN 47708
Tel (812) 424-6411 *SIC* 4911 4924 4932

▲ VECTREN CORP p 1546
1 Vectren Sq, Evansville IN 47708
Tel (812) 491-4000
SIC 4924 4911 1241 1623 6531

■ VECTREN UTILITY HOLDINGS INC p 1546
1 Vectren Sq, Evansville IN 47708
Tel (812) 491-4000 *SIC* 4932 4911 4924

■ INDIANAPOLIS POWER & LIGHT CO p 739
1 Monument Cir, Indianapolis IN 46204
Tel (317) 261-8261 *SIC* 4911

■ IPALCO ENTERPRISES INC p 763
1 Monument Cir, Indianapolis IN 46204
Tel (317) 261-8261 *SIC* 4911

WABASH VALLEY POWER ASSOCIATION INC p 1570
722 N High School Rd, Indianapolis IN 46214
Tel (317) 481-2800 *SIC* 4911

■ NORTHERN INDIANA PUBLIC SERVICE CO p 1056
801 E 86th Ave, Merrillville IN 46410
Tel (877) 647-5990 *SIC* 4924 4911

■ DUKE ENERGY INDIANA LLC p 460
1000 E Main St, Plainfield IN 46168
Tel (704) 382-3853 *SIC* 4911

■ ALLIANT INDUSTRIES INC p 55
200 1st St Se, Cedar Rapids IA 52401
Tel (398) 786-4268
SIC 4011 4741 4911 4924

CENTRAL IOWA POWER COOPERATIVE p 278
1400 Highway 13, Cedar Rapids IA 52403
Tel (319) 366-8011 *SIC* 4911

GREEN COMPANIES INC p 636
8710 Earhart Ln Sw, Cedar Rapids IA 52404
Tel (319) 841-4000
SIC 8711 8748 8713 4911 1623

■ INTERSTATE POWER AND LIGHT CO p 758
200 1st St Se, Cedar Rapids IA 52401
Tel (319) 398-4411 *SIC* 4911 4924 4961

■ BERKSHIRE HATHAWAY ENERGY CO p 175
666 Grand Ave Ste 500, Des Moines IA 50309
Tel (515) 242-4300 *SIC* 4911 4924 6531

■ MHC INC p 959
666 Grand Ave Ste 500, Des Moines IA 50309
Tel (515) 242-4300 *SIC* 4924 4911

■ MIDAMERICAN FUNDING LLC p 964
666 Grand Ave Ste 500, Des Moines IA 50309
Tel (515) 242-4300 *SIC* 4911 4924

■ PPW HOLDINGS LLC p 1166
666 Grand Ave Ste 500, Des Moines IA 50309
Tel (515) 242-4300 *SIC* 4911 4924 6531

CORN BELT POWER COOPERATIVE p 370
1300 13th St N, Humboldt IA 50548
Tel (515) 332-7700 *SIC* 4911

NORTHWEST IOWA POWER COOPERATIVE p 1060
31002 C38, Le Mars IA 51031
Tel (712) 546-4141 *SIC* 4911

MUSCATINE POWER & WATER (INC) p 1002
3205 Cedar St, Muscatine IA 52761
Tel (563) 263-2631 *SIC* 4911 4941

WOLF CREEK NUCLEAR OPERATING CORP p 1621
1550 Oxen Ln, Burlington KS 66839
Tel (620) 364-4141 *SIC* 4911

MIDWEST ENERGY INC p 967
1330 Canterbury Dr, Hays KS 67601
Tel (785) 625-3437 *SIC* 4911 8611

SUNFLOWER ELECTRIC HOLDINGS INC p 1402
301 W 13th St, Hays KS 67601
Tel (785) 628-2845 *SIC* 4911

SUNFLOWER ELECTRIC POWER CORP p 1402
301 W 13th St, Hays KS 67601
Tel (785) 628-2845 *SIC* 4911

WHEATLAND ELECTRIC COOPERATIVE INC p 1604
101 N Main St, Scott City KS 67871
Tel (620) 872-5885 *SIC* 4911 4812

KANSAS ELECTRIC POWER COOPERATIVE INC p 803
600 Sw Corporate Vw, Topeka KS 66615
Tel (785) 273-7010 *SIC* 4911

▲ WESTAR ENERGY INC p 1596
818 S Kansas Ave, Topeka KS 66612
Tel (785) 575-6300 *SIC* 4911

■ KANSAS GAS AND ELECTRIC CO p 803
120 E 1st St N, Wichita KS 67202
Tel (316) 721-1899 *SIC* 4911

SALT RIVER ELECTRIC COOPERATIVE CORP p 1273
111 W Brashear Ave, Bardstown KY 40004
Tel (502) 348-3931 *SIC* 4911

WARREN RURAL ELECTRIC COOPERATIVE CORP p 1577
951 Fairview Ave, Bowling Green KY 42101
Tel (270) 842-6541 *SIC* 4911

ELECTRIC & WATER PLANT BOARD OF CITY OF FRANKFORT KY p 484
317 W 2nd St, Frankfort KY 40601
Tel (502) 352-4372
SIC 4941 4911 7382 5063 4841 4813

BIG RIVERS ELECTRIC CORP p 182
201 3rd St, Henderson KY 42420
Tel (270) 827-2561 *SIC* 4911

KENERGY CORP p 810
6402 Old Corydon Rd, Henderson KY 42420
Tel (270) 926-4141 *SIC* 4911

■ WESTERN KENTUCKY ENERGY CORP p 1598
145 N Main St, Henderson KY 42420
Tel (270) 844-6000 *SIC* 4911

PENNYRILE RURAL ELECTRIC COOPERATIVE CORP p 1131
2000 Harrison St, Hopkinsville KY 42240
Tel (270) 886-2555 *SIC* 4911

■ KENTUCKY UTILITIES CO INC p 812
1 Quality St, Lexington KY 40507
Tel (502) 627-2000 *SIC* 4911

■ LG&E AND KU ENERGY LLC p 860
220 W Main St Ste 1400, Louisville KY 40202
Tel (502) 627-2000
SIC 4911 4931 4932 4924

■ LG&E AND KU SERVICES CO p 860
220 W Main St Ste 1400, Louisville KY 40202
Tel (502) 627-2000 *SIC* 4911

■ LOUISVILLE GAS AND ELECTRIC CO p 880
220 W Main St Ste 1400, Louisville KY 40202
Tel (502) 627-2000 *SIC* 4931 4911 4924

WHAYNE SUPPLY CO p 1604
10001 Linn Station Rd # 112, Louisville KY 40223
Tel (502) 774-4441 *SIC* 5082 4911

WEST KENTUCKY RURAL ELECTRIC COOP CORP p 1594
1218 W Broadway, Mayfield KY 42066
Tel (270) 247-1321 *SIC* 4911

JACKSON ENERGY COOPERATIVE CORP p 774
115 Jackson Energy Ln, Mc Kee KY 40447
Tel (606) 364-1000 *SIC* 4911

BLUE GRASS ENERGY COOPERATIVE CORP p 192
1201 Lexington Rd, Nicholasville KY 40356
Tel (859) 885-4191 *SIC* 4911

OWENSBORO MUNICIPAL UTILITIES p 1100
2070 Tamarack Rd, Owensboro KY 42301
Tel (270) 926-3200 *SIC* 4911

OWENSBORO MUNICIPAL UTILITIES ELECTRIC LIGHT & POWER SYSTEM p 1100
2070 Tamarack Rd, Owensboro KY 42301
Tel (270) 926-3200 *SIC* 4911 4941

OWEN ELECTRIC COOPERATIVE INC p 1099
8205 Highway 127 S, Owenton KY 40359
Tel (502) 484-3471 *SIC* 4911

BIG RIVERS ELECTRIC CORP p 182
9000 Hwy 2096, Robards KY 42452
Tel (270) 827-2561 *SIC* 4911

SOUTH KENTUCKY RURAL ELECTRIC CO-OPERATIVE CORP p 1344
925-929 N Main St, Somerset KY 42503
Tel (606) 678-4121 *SIC* 4911

EAST KENTUCKY POWER COOPERATIVE p 470
4775 Lexington Rd, Winchester KY 40391
Tel (859) 744-4812 *SIC* 4911

EAST KENTUCKY POWER COOPERATIVE INC p 470
4775 Lexington Rd, Winchester KY 40391
Tel (859) 744-4812 *SIC* 4911

ENTERGY TEXAS INC p 502
446 North Blvd, Baton Rouge LA 70802
Tel (800) 368-3749 *SIC* 4911

BEAUREGARD ELECTRIC COOPERATIVE INC p 166
1010 E 1st St, Deridder LA 70634
Tel (800) 367-0275 *SIC* 4911

DIXIE ELECTRIC MEMBERSHIP CORP p 444
16262 Wax Rd, Greenwell Springs LA 70739
Tel (225) 261-1221 *SIC* 4911

■ **EL INVESTMENT CO LLC** p 482
4809 Jefferson Hwy, Jefferson LA 70121
Tel (504) 576-4000 *SIC* 4911 4922

■ **ENTERGY GULF STATES LOUISIANA LLC** p 501
4809 Jefferson Hwy, Jefferson LA 70121
Tel (504) 576-4000 *SIC* 4911 4924

■ **ENTERGY LOUISIANA HOLDINGS INC** p 501
4809 Jefferson Hwy, Jefferson LA 70121
Tel (504) 840-2734 *SIC* 4911 4922

■ **ENTERGY LOUISIANA LLC** p 501
4809 Jefferson Hwy, Jefferson LA 70121
Tel (504) 576-4000 *SIC* 4911 4922

■ **ENTERGY UTILITY HOLDING CO LLC** p 502
4809 Jefferson Hwy, Jefferson LA 70121
Tel (504) 576-4000 *SIC* 4911 4922

SHORELINE ENERGY PARTNERS LP p 1318
400 E Kaliste Saloom Rd # 2600, Lafayette LA 70508
Tel (281) 872-0051 *SIC* 4911

SOUTHWEST LOUISIANA ELECTRIC MEMBERSHIP CORP p 1352
3420 Ne Evangeline Trwy, Lafayette LA 70507
Tel (337) 896-5384 *SIC* 4911

■ **ENTERGY NUCLEAR HOLDING CO** p 501
639 Loyola Ave, New Orleans LA 70113
Tel (504) 576-4000 *SIC* 4911

CLECO CORPORATE HOLDINGS LLC p 325
2030 Donahue Ferry Rd, Pineville LA 71360
Tel (318) 484-7400 *SIC* 4911

CLECO PARTNERS LP p 325
2030 Donahue Ferry Rd, Pineville LA 71360
Tel (318) 484-7400 *SIC* 4911

CLECO POWER LLC p 325
2030 Donahue Ferry Rd, Pineville LA 71360
Tel (318) 484-7400 *SIC* 4911

■ **CENTRAL MAINE POWER CO INC** p 279
83 Edison Dr, Augusta ME 04336
Tel (207) 623-3521 *SIC* 4911

■ **CMP GROUP INC** p 329
83 Edison Dr, Augusta ME 04336
Tel (207) 623-3521 *SIC* 4911

BHE HOLDINGS INC p 180
21 Telcom Dr, Bangor ME 04401
Tel (207) 947-2414 *SIC* 4911

EMERA MAINE p 491
21 Telcom Dr, Bangor ME 04401
Tel (207) 945-5621 *SIC* 4911

■ **CALVERT CLIFFS NUCLEAR POWER PLANT INC** p 243
750 E Pratt St, Baltimore MD 21202
Tel (410) 495-4600 *SIC* 4911

CONSTELLATION ENERGY GROUP INC p 361
100 Constellation Way, Baltimore MD 21202
Tel (410) 470-2800 *SIC* 4911 4924 1711

■ **CONSTELLATION ENERGY NUCLEAR GROUP LLC** p 361
100 Constellation Way 200c, Baltimore MD 21202
Tel (410) 783-2800 *SIC* 4911

■ **CONSTELLATION ENERGY RESOURCES LLC** p 361
750 E Pratt St, Baltimore MD 21202
Tel (410) 470-2800 *SIC* 4911 4924

■ **CONSTELLATION NEWENERGY INC** p 361
1310 Point St Fl 9, Baltimore MD 21231
Tel (410) 783-2800 *SIC* 4911 8748

■ **CONSTELLATION NUCLEAR SERVICES L L C** p 361
39 W Lexington St, Baltimore MD 21201
Tel (410) 234-7950 *SIC* 4911

■ **RAVEN POWER OPERATING LLC** p 1209
1000 Brandon Shores Rd, Baltimore MD 21226
Tel (410) 255-3072 *SIC* 4911

■ **TERRAFORM POWER INC** p 1439
7550 Wisconsin Ave Fl 9, Bethesda MD 20814
Tel (240) 762-7700 *SIC* 4911

WILDCAT POINT GENERATION FACILITY p 1609
179 Old Mill Rd, Conowingo MD 21918
Tel (724) 422-2169 *SIC* 4911

CHOPTANK ELECTRIC COOPERATIVE INC p 302
24820 Meeting House Rd, Denton MD 21629
Tel (410) 479-0420 *SIC* 4911 1731

MARYLAND SOUTHERN ELECTRIC COOPERATIVE INC p 915
15035 Burnt Store Rd, Hughesville MD 20637
Tel (301) 274-3111 *SIC* 4911

■ **POTOMAC EDISON CO** p 1164
10802 Bower Ave, Williamsport MD 21795
Tel (800) 686-0011 *SIC* 4911

ENEL GREEN POWER NORTH AMERICA INC p 497
1 Tech Dr Ste 220, Andover MA 01810
Tel (978) 681-1900 *SIC* 4911

■ **HARBOR ELECTRIC ENERGY CO** p 659
800 Boylston St, Boston MA 02199
Tel (617) 424-2000 *SIC* 4911

■ **NSTAR ELECTRIC & GAS CORP** p 1065
800 Boylston St Ste 1700, Boston MA 02199
Tel (617) 424-2000 *SIC* 4922 4911

■ **NSTAR ELECTRIC CO** p 1065
800 Boylston St Ste 1700, Boston MA 02199
Tel (617) 424-2000 *SIC* 4911 4924

■ **NSTAR LLC** p 1065
800 Boylston St Ste 1700, Boston MA 02199
Tel (617) 424-2000 *SIC* 4911 4924

▲ **ATLANTIC POWER CORP** p 127
3 Allied Dr Ste 220, Dedham MA 02026
Tel (617) 977-2400 *SIC* 4911 3621

▲ **EVERSOURCE ENERGY** p 515
300 Cadwell Dr, Springfield MA 01104
Tel (413) 785-5871 *SIC* 4911 4924

■ **WESTERN MASSACHUSETTS ELECTRIC CO** p 1599
300 Cadwell Dr, Springfield MA 01104
Tel (413) 785-5871 *SIC* 4911

TAUNTON MUNICIPAL LIGHTING PLANT p 1426
33 Weir St, Taunton MA 02780
Tel (508) 824-5844 *SIC* 4911

■ **GLOBAL OPERATING LLC** p 617
800 South St Ste 500, Waltham MA 02453
Tel (800) 542-0778 *SIC* 4924 4911

GLOBAL PETROLEUM CORP p 617
800 South St Ste 500, Waltham MA 02453
Tel (781) 894-6920 *SIC* 4924 5172 4911

MASSACHUSETTS ELECTRIC CO p 916
40 Sylvan Rd, Waltham MA 02451
Tel (781) 907-1000 *SIC* 4911

NATIONAL GRID USA p 1013
40 Sylvan Rd, Waltham MA 02451
Tel (781) 907-1000 *SIC* 4911

NATIONAL GRID USA SERVICE CO INC p 1013
40 Sylvan Rd, Waltham MA 02451
Tel (800) 260-0054 *SIC* 4911 1311

NEW ENGLAND ELECTRIC TRANSMISSION CORP p 1030
25 Research Dr, Westborough MA 01581
Tel (617) 322-3091 *SIC* 4911

NEW ENGLAND POWER CO p 1030
25 Research Dr, Westborough MA 01581
Tel (315) 460-3981 *SIC* 4911

■ **NORESCO INC** p 1048
1 Research Dr Ste 400c, Westborough MA 01581
Tel (508) 614-1000
SIC 8711 8741 8748 4911 4924

■ **NORESCO LLC** p 1048
1 Research Dr Ste 400c, Westborough MA 01581
Tel (508) 614-1000
SIC 8711 8741 8744 8748 4911 4924

SOUTHEASTERN MICHIGAN RURAL ELECTRIC COOPERATIVE p 1346
1610 E Maumee St, Adrian MI 49221
Tel (517) 263-1808 *SIC* 4911

■ **DTE ENERGY RESOURCES INC** p 458
414 S Main St Ste 600, Ann Arbor MI 48104
Tel (734) 302-4800 *SIC* 4911 1389

■ **DTE ENERGY SERVICES INC** p 458
414 S Main St Ste 600, Ann Arbor MI 48104
Tel (734) 302-4800 *SIC* 4911

■ **DTE ENERGY TRADING INC** p 458
414 S Main St Ste 200, Ann Arbor MI 48104
Tel (734) 887-2000 *SIC* 4911 4923

II STANLEY CO INC p 731
1500 Hill Brady Rd, Battle Creek MI 49037
Tel (269) 660-7777 *SIC* 5063 4911

GREAT LAKES ENERGY COOPERATIVE p 633
1323 Boyne Ave, Boyne City MI 49712
Tel (231) 582-6521 *SIC* 4911

WOLVERINE POWER SUPPLY COOPERATIVE INC p 1621
10125 W Watergate Rd, Cadillac MI 49601
Tel (231) 775-5700 *SIC* 4911

■ **ENTERGY NUCLEAR PALISADES LLC** p 501
27780 Blue Star Hwy, Covert MI 49043
Tel (269) 764-2000 *SIC* 4911

CLOVERLAND ELECTRIC COOPERATIVE INC p 328
2916 W M 28, Dafter MI 49724
Tel (906) 635-6800 *SIC* 4911

■ **DTE ELECTRIC CO** p 458
1 Energy Plz, Detroit MI 48226
Tel (313) 235-4000 *SIC* 4911

▲ **DTE ENERGY CO** p 458
1 Energy Plz, Detroit MI 48226
Tel (313) 235-4000 *SIC* 4911 4923 1311

▲ **CMS ENERGY CORP** p 329
1 Energy Plaza Dr, Jackson MI 49201
Tel (517) 788-0550
SIC 4931 4911 4924 4922

■ **CMS ENTERPRISES CO** p 329
1 Energy Plaza Dr, Jackson MI 49201
Tel (517) 788-0550 *SIC* 1382 4911

■ **CONSUMERS ENERGY CO** p 362
1 Energy Plaza Dr, Jackson MI 49201
Tel (517) 788-0550 *SIC* 4931 4911 4924

UPPER PENINSULA POWER CO INC p 1529
1002 Harbor Hills Dr, Marquette MI 49855
Tel (906) 232-1444 *SIC* 4911

INTERNATIONAL TRANSMISSION CO p 757
27175 Energy Way, Novi MI 48377
Tel (248) 374-7100 *SIC* 4911

ITC HOLDINGS CORP p 767
27175 Energy Way, Novi MI 48377
Tel (248) 946-3000 *SIC* 4911

WAPSIPINICON WIND PROJECT LLC p 1575
234 Industrial Park Dr, Dexter MN 55926
Tel (760) 329-1437 *SIC* 4911

▲ **OTTER TAIL CORP** p 1098
215 S Cascade St, Fergus Falls MN 56537
Tel (218) 739-8200
SIC 4911 3084 5047 2099 1731

■ **OTTER TAIL POWER CO** p 1098
215 S Cascade St, Fergus Falls MN 56537
Tel (218) 739-8200 *SIC* 4911

GREAT RIVER ENERGY p 634
12300 Elm Creek Blvd N, Maple Grove MN 55369
Tel (763) 445-5000 *SIC* 4911

EBERSEN INC p 474
7401 Central Ave Ne Ste 2, Minneapolis MN 55432
Tel (763) 572-2661
SIC 4911 1521 6211 1382 4731 8711

MINNESOTA MUNICIPAL POWER AGENCY p 973
220 S 6th St Ste 1300, Minneapolis MN 55402
Tel (612) 349-6868 *SIC* 4911

▲ **XCEL ENERGY INC** p 1631
414 Nicollet Mall, Minneapolis MN 55401
Tel (612) 330-5500 *SIC* 4911 4922

CONNEXUS ENERGY p 358
14601 Ramsey Blvd Nw, Ramsey MN 55303
Tel (763) 323-2600 *SIC* 4911

SOUTHERN MINNESOTA MUNICIPAL POWER AGENCY p 1349
500 1st Ave Sw, Rochester MN 55902
Tel (507) 285-0478 *SIC* 4911

WRIGHT-HENNEPIN COOPERATIVE ELECTRIC ASSOCIATION p 1627
6800 Electric Dr, Rockford MN 55373
Tel (763) 477-3000 *SIC* 4911

WRIGHT-HENNEPIN SECURITY CORP p 1627
6800 Electric Dr, Rockford MN 55373
Tel (763) 477-3664
SIC 1731 1711 7382 5063 4911

4- COUNTY ELECTRIC POWER ASSOCIATION p 3
5265 S Frontage Rd, Columbus MS 39701
Tel (662) 327-8900 *SIC* 4911

■ **MISSISSIPPI POWER CO** p 975
2992 W Beach Blvd, Gulfport MS 39501
Tel (228) 864-1211 *SIC* 4911

COOPERATIVE ENERGY A MISSISSIPPI ELECTRIC COOPERATIVE p 367
7037 U S Highway 49, Hattiesburg MS 39402
Tel (601) 579-0215 *SIC* 4911

■ **ENTERGY MISSISSIPPI INC** p 501
308 E Pearl St, Jackson MS 39201
Tel (601) 368-5000 *SIC* 4911

■ **ENTERGY NUCLEAR GENERATION CO** p 501
1340 Echelon Pkwy Ste 100, Jackson MS 39213
Tel (601) 368-5000 *SIC* 4911

■ **ENTERGY OPERATIONS INC** p 501
1340 Echelon Pkwy Ste 100, Jackson MS 39213
Tel (601) 366-2727 *SIC* 4911

■ **SYSTEM ENERGY RESOURCES INC** p 1418
1340 Echelon Pkwy Ste 100, Jackson MS 39213
Tel (601) 368-5000 *SIC* 4911

COAST ELECTRIC POWER ASSOCIATION p 331
18020 Highway 603, Kiln MS 39556
Tel (228) 363-7000 *SIC* 4911

SINGING RIVER ELECTRIC POWER ASSOCIATION p 1326
11187 Old 63 S, Lucedale MS 39452
Tel (601) 947-4211 *SIC* 4911

MAGNOLIA ELECTRIC POWER ASSOCIATION p 896
3012 Highway 98 E, Mccomb MS 39648
Tel (601) 876-5671 *SIC* 4911

EAST MISSISSIPPI ELECTRIC POWER ASSN INC p 470
2128 Highway 39 N, Meridian MS 39301
Tel (601) 581-8600 *SIC* 4911

NORTHCENTRAL MISSISSIPPI ELECTRIC POWER ASSOCIATION (INC) p 1054
4600 Northcentral Way, Olive Branch MS 38654
Tel (800) 325-8925 *SIC* 4911

SOUTHERN PINE ELECTRIC POWER ASSOCIATION p 1350
110 Risher St, Taylorsville MS 39168
Tel (601) 785-6511 *SIC* 4911

N W ELECTRIC POWER COOPERATIVE INC p 1005
1001 W Grand Ave, Cameron MO 64429
Tel (816) 632-2121 *SIC* 4911

MISSOURI JOINT MUNICIPAL ELECTRIC UTILITY COMMISSION p 976
1808 Interstate 70 Dr Sw, Columbia MO 65203
Tel (573) 445-3279 *SIC* 4911

CENTRAL ELECTRIC POWER COOPERATIVE INC p 278
2106 Jefferson St, Jefferson City MO 65109
Tel (573) 634-2454 *SIC* 4911

▲ **EMPIRE DISTRICT ELECTRIC CO** p 493
602 S Joplin Ave, Joplin MO 64801
Tel (417) 625-5100 *SIC* 4911 4941

▲ **GREAT PLAINS ENERGY INC** p 634
1200 Main St, Kansas City MO 64105
Tel (816) 556-2200 *SIC* 4911

■ **GREAT PLAINS ENERGY SERVICES INC** p 634
1201 Walnut St, Kansas City MO 64106
Tel (816) 556-2200 *SIC* 4911

■ **KANSAS CITY POWER & LIGHT CO** p 802
1200 Main St Ste 114, Kansas City MO 64105
Tel (816) 556-2200 *SIC* 4911

■ **KCP&L GREATER MISSOURI OPERATIONS CO** p 806
1200 Main St Fl 30, Kansas City MO 64105
Tel (816) 556-2200 *SIC* 4911

SHO-ME POWER ELECTRIC COOPERATIVE p 1317
301 W Jackson St, Marshfield MO 65706
Tel (417) 859-2615 *SIC* 4911

SUNEDISON INTERNATIONAL LLC p 1402
13736 Rverport Dr Ste 180, Maryland Heights MO 63043
Tel (443) 909-7200 *SIC* 4911

CITIZENS ELECTRIC CORP p 311
1500 Rand Ave, Perryville MO 63775
Tel (877) 876 3511 *SIC* 4911

▲ **AMEREN CORP** p 66
1901 Chouteau Ave, Saint Louis MO 63103
Tel (314) 621-3222 *SIC* 4911 4931 4923

■ **ILLINOIS POWER RESOURCES LLC** p 732
1901 Chouteau Ave, Saint Louis MO 63103
Tel (314) 554-4110 *SIC* 4911

■ **UNION ELECTRIC DEVELOPMENT CORP** p 1504
1901 Chouteau Ave, Saint Louis MO 63103
Tel (618) 234-3523 *SIC* 4911 4924

SIKESTON BOARD OF MUNICIPAL UTILITIES p 1322
107 E Malone Ave, Sikeston MO 63801
Tel (573) 471-5000 *SIC* 4911 1623

ASSOCIATED ELECTRIC COOPERATIVE INC p 120
2814 S Golden Ave, Springfield MO 65807
Tel (417) 881-1204 *SIC* 4911

CUIVRE RIVER ELECTRIC COOPERATIVE INC p 400
1112 E Cherry St, Troy MO 63379
Tel (636) 528-8261 *SIC* 4911

SOUTHERN MONTANA ELECTRIC GENERATION AND TRANSMISSION COOPERATIVE INC p 1349
7250 Entryway Dr, Billings MT 59101
Tel (406) 294-9527 *SIC* 4911

■ **TALEN MONTANA LLC** p 1422
303 N 28th St Ste 400, Billings MT 59101
Tel (406) 237-6900 *SIC* 4911

NORTHWESTERN ENERGY p 1060
11 E Park St, Butte MT 59701
Tel (406) 497-3000 *SIC* 4911

FLATHEAD ELECTRIC COOPERATIVE INC p 554
2510 Us Highway 2 E, Kalispell MT 59901
Tel (406) 751-4483 *SIC* 4911

UPPER MISSOURI G & T ELECTRIC CO-OPERATIVE INC p 1529
111 2nd Ave Sw, Sidney MT 59270
Tel (406) 433-4100 *SIC* 4911

LOUP RIVER PUBLIC POWER DISTRICT p 881
2404 15th St, Columbus NE 68601
Tel (402) 564-3171 *SIC* 4911

NEBRASKA ELECTRIC GENERATION & TRANSMISSION COOPERATIVE INC p 1023
2472 18th Ave, Columbus NE 68601
Tel (402) 564-8142 *SIC* 4911

NEBRASKA PUBLIC POWER DISTRICT p 1023
1414 15th St, Columbus NE 68601
Tel (402) 564-8561 *SIC* 4911

SOUTHERN POWER DISTRICT p 1350
101 16th Ave, Franklin NE 68939
Tel (308) 425-6217 *SIC* 4911

SOUTHERN NEBRASKA RURAL PUBLIC POWER DISTRICT p 1349
4550 W Husker Hwy, Grand Island NE 68803
Tel (402) 725-3370 *SIC* 4911

LINCOLN ELECTRIC SYSTEM p 867
1040 O St, Lincoln NE 68508
Tel (402) 475-4211 *SIC* 4911

MUNICIPAL ENERGY AGENCY OF NEBRASKA (INC) p 1000
8377 Glynoaks Dr, Lincoln NE 68516
Tel (402) 474-4759 *SIC* 4911

▲ **BERKSHIRE HATHAWAY INC** p 175
3555 Farnam St Ste 1440, Omaha NE 68131
Tel (402) 346-1400
SIC 6331 6321 4911 4924 6531 5963

OMAHA PUBLIC POWER DISTRICT p 1083
444 S 16th St, Omaha NE 68102
Tel (402) 636-2000 *SIC* 4911

TENASKA BROWNSVILLE PARTNERS LLC p 1437
14302 Fnb Pkwy, Omaha NE 68154
Tel (402) 691-9500 *SIC* 4911

TENASKA ENERGY INC p 1437
14302 Fnb Pkwy, Omaha NE 68154
Tel (402) 691-9500
SIC 4911 4924 4939 8742

TENASKA FRONTIER PARTNERS LTD p 1437
14302 Fnb Pkwy, Omaha NE 68154
Tel (402) 691-9500 *SIC* 4911

TENASKA INC p 1437
14302 Fnb Pkwy, Omaha NE 68154
Tel (402) 691-9500
SIC 4924 4911 4939 8742

TENASKA PENNSYLVANIA PARTNERS LLC p 1437
14302 Fnb Pkwy, Omaha NE 68154
Tel (402) 691-9581 *SIC* 4911

VIRGINIA TENASKA PARTNERS L P p 1560
14302 Fnb Pkwy, Omaha NE 68154
Tel (402) 691-9500 *SIC* 4911

■ **NEVADA POWER CO** p 1028
6226 W Sahara Ave, Las Vegas NV 89146
Tel (702) 402-5000 *SIC* 4911

■ **NV ENERGY INC** p 1068
6226 W Sahara Ave, Las Vegas NV 89146
Tel (702) 402-5000 *SIC* 4911 4924

VALLEY ELECTRIC ASSOCIATION INC p 1540
800 E Highway 372, Pahrump NV 89048
Tel (775) 727-5312 *SIC* 4911

▲ **ORMAT TECHNOLOGIES INC** p 1095
6225 Neil Rd, Reno NV 89511
Tel (775) 356-9029 *SIC* 4911 3511

■ **SIERRA PACIFIC POWER CO** p 1321
6100 Neil Rd Ste 100, Reno NV 89511
Tel (775) 834-4011
SIC 4911 4924 4941 4971

▲ **UNITIL CORP** p 1515
6 Liberty Ln W, Hampton NH 03842
Tel (603) 772-0775 *SIC* 4911 4924

■ **WHEELABRATOR ENVIRONMENTAL SYSTEMS INC** p 1604
4 Liberty Ln W, Hampton NH 03842
Tel (603) 929-3000 *SIC* 4953 4911

■ **PUBLIC SERVICE CO OF NEW HAMPSHIRE** p 1189
780 North Commercial St, Manchester NH 03101
Tel (603) 669-4000 *SIC* 4911

■ ESSENTIAL POWER NEWINGTON ENERGY LLC p 510
200 Shattuck Way, Newington NH 03801
Tel (603) 766-1880 *SIC* 4911

NEW HAMPSHIRE ELECTRIC COOPERATIVE INC p 1030
579 Tenney Mountain Hwy, Plymouth NH 03264
Tel (603) 536-8824 *SIC* 4911

■ NEXTERA ENERGY SEABROOK LLC p 1040
626 Lafayette Rd, Seabrook NH 03874
Tel (603) 474-3808 *SIC* 4911

■ NORTH ATLANTIC ENERGY CORP p 1050
626 Lafayette Rd, Seabrook NH 03874
Tel (603) 474-9521 *SIC* 4911

▲ SOUTH JERSEY INDUSTRIES INC p 1344
1 S Jersey Plz, Hammonton NJ 08037
Tel (609) 561-9000 *SIC* 4911 4922 4924

■ COVANTA ENERGY LLC p 384
445 South St Ste 400, Morristown NJ 07960
Tel (862) 345-5000 *SIC* 4953 4911

▲ COVANTA HOLDING CORP p 384
445 South St, Morristown NJ 07960
Tel (862) 345-5000 *SIC* 4953 4911

OLYMPUS HOLDINGS LLC p 1083
67 E Park Pl Ste 475, Morristown NJ 07960
Tel (973) 889-9100 *SIC* 4911

OLYMPUS POWER LLC p 1083
67 E Park Pl Ste 4, Morristown NJ 07960
Tel (973) 889-9100 *SIC* 4911

▲ GENIE ENERGY LTD p 603
550 Broad St, Newark NJ 07102
Tel (973) 438-3500 *SIC* 4911 4924 4931

■ PSEG FOSSIL LLC p 1188
80 Park Plz Ste 3, Newark NJ 07102
Tel (973) 430-7000 *SIC* 4911

■ PSEG POWER LLC p 1188
80 Park Plz T-9, Newark NJ 07102
Tel (973) 430-7000 *SIC* 4911

▲ PUBLIC SERVICE ENTERPRISE GROUP INC p 1190
80 Park Plz, Newark NJ 07102
Tel (973) 430-7000 *SIC* 4931 4911 4924

■ GENON AMERICAS GENERATION LLC p 604
211 Carnegie Ctr, Princeton NJ 08540
Tel (609) 524-4500 *SIC* 4911

■ GENON ENERGY INC p 604
804 Carnegie Ctr, Princeton NJ 08540
Tel (609) 524-4500 *SIC* 4911

■ GENON ENERGY SERVICES LLC p 604
211 Carnegie Ctr, Princeton NJ 08540
Tel (609) 524-4500 *SIC* 4911

■ GENON MID-ATLANTIC LLC p 604
211 Carnegie Ctr, Princeton NJ 08540
Tel (609) 524-4500 *SIC* 4911

■ LOUISIANA GENERATING LLC p 880
211 Carnegie Ctr, Princeton NJ 08540
Tel (609) 524-4500 *SIC* 4911

▲ NRG ENERGY INC p 1064
804 Carnegie Ctr, Princeton NJ 08540
Tel (609) 524-4500 *SIC* 4911

■ NRG NORTHEAST GENERATING LLC p 1064
211 Carnegie Ctr, Princeton NJ 08540
Tel (609) 524-4500 *SIC* 4911

■ NRG POWER MARKETING LLC p 1064
804 Carnegie Ctr, Princeton NJ 08540
Tel (609) 524-4500 *SIC* 4911 4924

■ NRG YIELD INC p 1064
804 Carnegie Ctr, Princeton NJ 08540
Tel (609) 524-4500 *SIC* 4911

■ OPTIM ENERGY TWIN OAKS LP p 1090
Alvarado Sq Ms-Z110, Albuquerque NM 87158
Tel (505) 241-2821 *SIC* 4911

▲ PNM RESOURCES INC p 1158
414 Silver Ave Sw Fl 4, Albuquerque NM 87102
Tel (505) 241-2700 *SIC* 4911 4922 4924

■ PUBLIC SERVICE CO OF NEW MEXICO p 1190
414 Silver Ave Sw Fl 4, Albuquerque NM 87102
Tel (505) 241-2700 *SIC* 4911

SOMERSET OPERATING CO LLC p 1339
7725 Lake Rd, Barker NY 14012
Tel (716) 795-9501 *SIC* 4911

NEW YORK STATE ELECTRIC & GAS CORP p 1036
18 Link Dr, Binghamton NY 13904
Tel (607) 762-7200 *SIC* 4911 4924 4923

AGERA ENERGY LLC p 34
555 Pleasantville Rd 107s, Briarcliff Manor NY 10510
Tel (844) 692-4372 *SIC* 4911

AGERA HOLDINGS LLC p 34
555 Pleasantville Rd 107s, Briarcliff Manor NY 10510
Tel (914) 236-1405 *SIC* 4911

NATIONAL GRID CORPORATE SERVICES LLC p 1013
175 E Old Country Rd, Hicksville NY 11801
Tel (718) 403-2000
SIC 4924 4911 1311 4922

■ CONSOLIDATED EDISON CO OF NEW YORK INC p 359
4 Irving Pl, New York NY 10003
Tel (212) 460-4600 *SIC* 4911 4924 4961

▲ HESS CORP p 688
1185 Ave Of The Americas, New York NY 10036
Tel (212) 997-8500
SIC 1311 2911 5171 5541 4911

MARUBENI POWER SERVICES INC p 913
375 Lexington Ave, New York NY 10017
Tel (212) 450-0640 *SIC* 1629 4911 8711

METROMEDIA CO p 955
810 Seventh Ave Fl 29, New York NY 10019
Tel (212) 606-4437
SIC 5812 6794 4813 4911

■ NRG TEXAS LLC p 1064
521 5th Ave Fl 30, New York NY 10175
Tel (713) 795-6000 *SIC* 4911

TERRA-GEN POWER LLC p 1439
1095 Avenue Of The Americ, New York NY 10036
Tel (646) 829-3900 *SIC* 4911

■ ORANGE AND ROCKLAND UTILITIES INC p 1091
1 Blue Hill Plz Ste 20, Pearl River NY 10965
Tel (845) 352-6000
SIC 4924 4911 1311 6552

■ ROCKLAND ELECTRIC CO p 1244
1 Blue Hill Plz Ste 20, Pearl River NY 10965
Tel (845) 352-6000 *SIC* 4911

CENTRAL HUDSON GAS & ELECTRIC CORP p 278
284 South Ave Dept 100, Poughkeepsie NY 12601
Tel (845) 452-2700 *SIC* 4911 4924 4932

CH ENERGY GROUP INC p 286
284 South Ave, Poughkeepsie NY 12601
Tel (845) 452-2000 *SIC* 4911 4924

NEW YORK INDEPENDENT SYSTEM OPERATOR INC p 1035
10 Krey Blvd, Rensselaer NY 12144
Tel (518) 356-6000 *SIC* 4911

■ ROCHESTER GAS AND ELECTRIC CORP p 1243
89 East Ave, Rochester NY 14649
Tel (800) 295-7323 *SIC* 4911 4924

NIAGARA MOHAWK HOLDINGS INC p 1042
300 Erie Blvd W, Syracuse NY 13202
Tel (315) 474-1511 *SIC* 4911 4924

NIAGARA MOHAWK POWER CORP p 1042
300 Erie Blvd W, Syracuse NY 13202
Tel (315) 474-1511 *SIC* 4911 4924

LONG ISLAND ELECTRIC UTILITY SERVCO LLC p 876
333 Earle Ovington Blvd, Uniondale NY 11553
Tel (516) 719-9810 *SIC* 4911

LONG ISLAND POWER AUTHORITY p 876
333 Earle Ovington Blvd # 403, Uniondale NY 11553
Tel (516) 222-7700 *SIC* 4911

■ CONSOLIDATED EDISON SOLUTIONS INC p 359
100 Summit Lake Dr # 410, Valhalla NY 10595
Tel (914) 286-7000 *SIC* 4924 4911 8748

FORTISTAR LLC p 569
1 N Lexington Ave Ste 620, White Plains NY 10601
Tel (914) 421-4900 *SIC* 4911

NEW YORK POWER AUTHORITY p 1035
123 Main St, White Plains NY 10601
Tel (914) 681-6200 *SIC* 4911

FOUR COUNTY ELECTRIC MEMBERSHIP CORP p 571
1822 Nc Highway 53 W, Burgaw NC 28425
Tel (910) 259-2361 *SIC* 4911

■ COGENTRIX ENERGY POWER MANAGEMENT LLC p 334
9405 Arrowpoint Blvd, Charlotte NC 28273
Tel (704) 525-3800 *SIC* 4911

■ DUKE ENERGY BUSINESS SERVICES LLC p 460
526 S Church St Ec-03t, Charlotte NC 28202
Tel (704) 594-6200 *SIC* 4911 4922

▲ DUKE ENERGY CORP p 460
550 S Tryon St, Charlotte NC 28202
Tel (704) 382-3853 *SIC* 4911 4924 4931

■ DUKE ENERGY CORPORATE SERVICES INC p 460
526 S Church St, Charlotte NC 28202
Tel (704) 594-6200 *SIC* 4911

■ DUKE ENERGY OHIO INC p 460
400 S Tryon, Charlotte NC 28285
Tel (704) 382-3853
SIC 4911 4922 4924 4931

■ DUKE ENERGY SERVICES INC p 460
526 S Church St, Charlotte NC 28202
Tel (704) 594-6200 *SIC* 4911

■ PANENERGY CORP p 1111
526 S Church St, Charlotte NC 28202
Tel (704) 594-6200
SIC 4922 1321 2813 5172 4911 4613

SOUTH RIVER ELECTRIC MEMBERSHIP CORP p 1345
17494 Us Highway 421 S, Dunn NC 28334
Tel (910) 892-8071 *SIC* 4911

PUBLIC WORKS COMMISSION OF CITY OF FAYETTEVILLE p 1190
955 Old Wilmington Rd, Fayetteville NC 28301
Tel (910) 223-4005 *SIC* 4911 4941

RUTHERFORD ELECTRIC MEMBERSHIP CORP p 1260
186 Hudlow Rd, Forest City NC 28043
Tel (704) 245-1621 *SIC* 4911

■ PROGRESS ENERGY SERVICE CO LLC p 1180
602 Raleigh Rd, Henderson NC 27536
Tel (919) 508-5400 *SIC* 4911

JONES-ONSLOW ELECTRIC MEMBERSHIP CORP p 793
259 Western Blvd, Jacksonville NC 28546
Tel (910) 353-1940 *SIC* 4911

BLUE RIDGE ELECTRIC MEMBERSHIP CORP p 192
1216 Blowing Rock Blvd, Lenoir NC 28645
Tel (828) 758-2383 *SIC* 4911

UNION ELECTRIC MEMBERSHIP CORP p 1504
1525 N Rocky River Rd, Monroe NC 28110
Tel (704) 220-1408 *SIC* 4911

■ DUKE ENERGY CAROLINAS LLC p 460
410 S Wilmington St, Raleigh NC 27601
Tel (704) 382-3853 *SIC* 4911

■ DUKE ENERGY PROGRESS LLC p 460
410 S Wilmington St, Raleigh NC 27601
Tel (704) 382-3853 *SIC* 4911

■ FLORIDA PROGRESS CORP p 559
410 S Wilmington St, Raleigh NC 27601
Tel (919) 546-6111
SIC 1221 4911 4011 4449

NORTH CAROLINA EASTERN MUNICIPAL POWER AGENCY p 1051
1427 Meadow Wood Blvd, Raleigh NC 27604
Tel (919) 760-6000 *SIC* 4911

NORTH CAROLINA ELECTRIC MEMBERSHIP CORP p 1051
3400 Sumner Blvd, Raleigh NC 27616
Tel (919) 872-0800 *SIC* 4911

■ PROGRESS ENERGY INC p 1180
410 S Wilmington St, Raleigh NC 27601
Tel (704) 382-3853 *SIC* 4911

LUMBEE RIVER ELECTRIC MEMBERSHIP CORP p 885
605 E 4th Ave, Red Springs NC 28377
Tel (910) 843-7932 *SIC* 4911

ENERGYUNITED ELECTRIC MEMBERSHIP CORP p 498
567 Mocksville Hwy, Statesville NC 28625
Tel (704) 873-5241 *SIC* 4911

BRUNSWICK ELECTRIC MEMBERSHIP CORP p 221
795 Ocean Hwy W, Supply NC 28462
Tel (910) 754-4391 *SIC* 4911

BASIN ELECTRIC POWER COOPERATIVE p 158
1717 E Interstate Ave, Bismarck ND 58503
Tel (701) 223-0441 *SIC* 4911 1311

■ CENTENNIAL ENERGY RESOURCES LLC p 275
1200 W Century Ave, Bismarck ND 58503
Tel (701) 530-1000 *SIC* 4911

■ MDU CONSTRUCTION SERVICES GROUP INC p 933
1150 W Century Ave, Bismarck ND 58503
Tel (701) 530-1000 *SIC* 4911

▲ MDU RESOURCES GROUP INC p 933
1200 W Century Ave, Bismarck ND 58503
Tel (701) 530-1000
SIC 4911 4924 4922 1221 1442 1311

CASS COUNTY ELECTRIC COOP INC p 263
3312 42nd St S Ste 200, Fargo ND 58104
Tel (701) 356-4400 *SIC* 4911

MINNKOTA POWER COOPERATIVE INC p 974
1822 Mill Rd, Grand Forks ND 58203
Tel (701) 795-4000 *SIC* 4911

NODAK ELECTRIC COOPERATIVE INC p 1046
4000 32nd Ave S, Grand Forks ND 58201
Tel (701) 746-4461 *SIC* 4911

CENTRAL POWER ELECTRIC COOPERATIVE INC p 280
525 20th Ave Sw, Minot ND 58701
Tel (701) 852-4407 *SIC* 4911

MCKENZIE ELECTRIC COOPERATIVE INC p 930
908 4th Ave Ne, Watford City ND 58854
Tel (701) 842-2311 *SIC* 4911

MOUNTRAIL-WILLIAMS ELECTRIC COOPERATIVE p 994
218 58th St W, Williston ND 58801
Tel (701) 577-3765 *SIC* 4911

■ CLEVELAND ELECTRIC ILLUMINATING CO p 325
76 S Main St, Akron OH 44308
Tel (800) 589-3101 *SIC* 4911

▲ FIRSTENERGY CORP p 550
76 S Main St Bsmt, Akron OH 44308
Tel (800) 736-3402 *SIC* 4911

■ FIRSTENERGY GENERATION LLC p 550
76 S Main St, Akron OH 44308
Tel (800) 633-4766 *SIC* 4911

■ FIRSTENERGY NUCLEAR OPERATING CO p 550
76 S Main St Bsmt, Akron OH 44308
Tel (800) 646-0400 *SIC* 4911

■ FIRSTENERGY SOLUTIONS CORP p 550
76 S Main St Bsmt, Akron OH 44308
Tel (800) 736-3402 *SIC* 4911

■ JERSEY CENTRAL POWER & LIGHT CO p 783
76 S Main St, Akron OH 44308
Tel (800) 736-3402 *SIC* 4911

■ METROPOLITAN EDISON CO p 955
76 S Main St, Akron OH 44308
Tel (800) 736-3402 *SIC* 4911

■ OHIO EDISON CO p 1077
76 S Main St Bsmt, Akron OH 44308
Tel (800) 736-3402 *SIC* 4911

■ PENNSYLVANIA ELECTRIC CO p 1130
76 S Main St Bsmt, Akron OH 44308
Tel (800) 545-7741 *SIC* 4911

■ PENNSYLVANIA POWER CO INC p 1130
76 S Main St Bsmt, Akron OH 44308
Tel (800) 720-3600 *SIC* 4911

■ TOLEDO EDISON CO p 1458
76 S Main St Bsmt, Akron OH 44308
Tel (800) 447-3333 *SIC* 4911

■ CINERGY CORP p 308
139 E 4th St, Cincinnati OH 45202
Tel (513) 421-9500 *SIC* 4911 4924

■ CINERGY POWER GENERATION SERVICES LLC p 308
139 E 4th St, Cincinnati OH 45202
Tel (513) 421-9500 *SIC* 4911

■ DUKE ENERGY BECKJORD LLC p 460
139 E 4th St, Cincinnati OH 45202
Tel (513) 287-2561 *SIC* 4911

■ DYNEGY COMMERCIAL ASSET MANAGEMENT LLC p 465
139 E 4th St, Cincinnati OH 45202
Tel (704) 382-5460 *SIC* 4924 4911

■ AEP GENERATING CO p 29
1 Riverside Plz Ste 1600, Columbus OH 43215
Tel (614) 223-1000 *SIC* 4911

■ AEP POWER MARKETING INC p 29
1 Riverside Plz Fl 1, Columbus OH 43215
Tel (614) 716-1000 *SIC* 4911

■ AEP TEXAS CENTRAL CO p 29
1 Riverside Plz, Columbus OH 43215
Tel (614) 716-1000 *SIC* 4911

▲ AMERICAN ELECTRIC POWER CO INC p 71
1 Riverside Plz Fl 1, Columbus OH 43215
Tel (614) 716-1000 *SIC* 4911

■ AMERICAN ELECTRIC POWER SERVICE CORP p 71
1 Riverside Plz Fl 1, Columbus OH 43215
Tel (614) 716-1000
SIC 4911 8711 8713 8721

AMERICAN MUNICIPAL POWER INC p 76
1111 Schrock Rd Ste 100, Columbus OH 43229
Tel (614) 540-1111 *SIC* 4911

■ APPALACHIAN POWER CO p 98
1 Riverside Plz, Columbus OH 43215
Tel (614) 716-1000 *SIC* 4911

BUCKEYE POWER INC p 223
6677 Busch Blvd, Columbus OH 43229
Tel (614) 781-0573 *SIC* 8611 4911

■ COLUMBUS SOUTHERN POWER CO p 342
1 Riverside Plz, Columbus OH 43215
Tel (614) 716-1000 *SIC* 4911

■ INDIANA MICHIGAN POWER CO p 738
1 Riverside Plz, Columbus OH 43215
Tel (614) 716-1000 *SIC* 4911

■ OHIO POWER CO p 1078
1 Riverside Plz, Columbus OH 43215
Tel (614) 716-1000 *SIC* 4911

■ PUBLIC SERVICE CO OF OKLAHOMA p 1190
1 Riverside Plz, Columbus OH 43215
Tel (614) 716-1000 *SIC* 4911

■ SOUTHWESTERN ELECTRIC POWER CO p 1353
1 Riverside Plz, Columbus OH 43215
Tel (614) 716-1000 *SIC* 4911

■ DAYTON POWER AND LIGHT CO p 418
1065 Woodman Dr, Dayton OH 45432
Tel (937) 224-6000 *SIC* 4911 4931

■ DPL INC p 454
1065 Woodman Dr, Dayton OH 45432
Tel (937) 331-4063 *SIC* 4911

SOUTH CENTRAL POWER CO INC p 1343
2780 Coonpath Rd Ne, Lancaster OH 43130
Tel (740) 653-4422 *SIC* 4911

▲ GAS NATURAL INC p 593
8470 Station St, Mentor OH 44060
Tel (440) 974-3770
SIC 4924 4911 5172 5984

INDIANA-KENTUCKY ELECTRIC CORP p 739
3932 Us Rte 23, Piketon OH 45661
Tel (740) 289-7200 *SIC* 4911

OHIO VALLEY ELECTRIC CORP p 1078
3932 Us Rte 23, Piketon OH 45661
Tel (740) 289-7200 *SIC* 4911

WESTERN FARMERS ELECTRIC COOPERATIVE p 1598
701 Ne 7th St, Anadarko OK 73005
Tel (405) 247-3351 *SIC* 4911

OKLAHOMA MUNICIPAL POWER AUTHORITY p 1079
2701 W I 35 Frontage Rd, Edmond OK 73013
Tel (405) 340-5047 *SIC* 4911

TRI-COUNTY ELECTRIC COOPERATIVE INC p 1477
995 Mile 46 Rd, Hooker OK 73945
Tel (580) 652-2418 *SIC* 4911

OKLAHOMA ELECTRIC CO-OPERATIVE INC p 1079
242 24th Ave Nw, Norman OK 73069
Tel (405) 321-2024 *SIC* 4911 2721

▲ OGE ENERGY CORP p 1076
321 N Harvey Ave, Oklahoma City OK 73102
Tel (405) 553-3000 *SIC* 4911 4922 4925

■ OKLAHOMA GAS AND ELECTRIC CO p 1079
321 N Harvey Ave, Oklahoma City OK 73102
Tel (405) 553-3000 *SIC* 4911

GRAND RIVER DAM AUTHORITY p 630
226 W Dwain Willis Ave, Vinita OK 74301
Tel (918) 256-5545 *SIC* 4911 1629

KAMO ELECTRIC COOPERATIVE INC p 802
500 S Kamo Dr, Vinita OK 74301
Tel (918) 256-5551 *SIC* 4911

UMATILLA ELECTRIC COOPERATIVE p 1501
750 W Elm Ave, Hermiston OR 97838
Tel (541) 567-6414 *SIC* 4911

OECO LLC p 1075
4607 Se International Way, Milwaukie OR 97222
Tel (503) 659-5999
SIC 3679 5065 4911 3621 3694

CENTRAL LINCOLN PEOPLES UTILITY DISTRICT JATC INC p 279
2129 N Coast Hwy, Newport OR 97365
Tel (541) 265-3211 *SIC* 4911

PACIFIC NORTHWEST GENERATING COOPERATIVE p 1105
711 Ne Halsey St, Portland OR 97232
Tel (503) 288-1234 *SIC* 4911

■ PACIFICORP p 1106
825 Ne Multnomah St # 300, Portland OR 97232
Tel (503) 813-5645 *SIC* 4911

▲ PORTLAND GENERAL ELECTRIC CO p 1163
121 Sw Salmon St, Portland OR 97204
Tel (503) 464-8000 *SIC* 4911 4922

COLLINS PINE CO p 337
29190 Sw Town Center Loop, Wilsonville OR 97070
Tel (503) 227-1219
SIC 2421 2426 5211 4911 4013

▲ PPL CORP p 1166
2 N 9th St, Allentown PA 18101
Tel (610) 774-5151 *SIC* 4911 4924

■ PPL ELECTRIC UTILITIES CORP p 1166
2 N 9th St, Allentown PA 18101
Tel (610) 774-5151 *SIC* 4911

■ PPL SERVICES CORP p 1166
2 N 9th St, Allentown PA 18101
Tel (610) 774-5151 *SIC* 6289 4911

STOCKTON COGEN (I) INC p 1390
7201 Hamilton Blvd, Allentown PA 18195
Tel (610) 481-4911 *SIC* 4911

▲ TALEN ENERGY CORP p 1422
835 Hamilton St Ste 150, Allentown PA 18101
Tel (888) 211-6011 *SIC* 4911

■ TALEN ENERGY MARKETING LLC p 1422
835 Hamilton St Ste 150, Allentown PA 18101
Tel (610) 774-5151 SIC 4911

■ TALEN ENERGY SERVICES GROUP LLC p 1422
2 N 9th St, Allentown PA 18101
Tel (610) 774-4005 SIC 4911

TALEN ENERGY SERVICES HOLDINGS LLC p 1422
835 Hamilton St, Allentown PA 18101
Tel (610) 774-5151 SIC 4911 1711 3625

■ TALEN ENERGY SUPPLY LLC p 1422
835 Hamilton St Ste 150, Allentown PA 18101
Tel (888) 211-6011 SIC 4911

■ TALEN GENERATION LLC p 1422
835 Hamilton St Ste 150, Allentown PA 18101
Tel (610) 774-6418 SIC 4911

■ ALLEGHENY ENERGY INC p 52
800 Cabin Hill Dr, Greensburg PA 15601
Tel (724) 837-3000 SIC 4911

■ ALLEGHENY ENERGY SERVICE CORP p 52
800 Cabin Hill Dr, Greensburg PA 15601
Tel (724) 837-3000 SIC 4911

■ ALLEGHENY ENERGY SUPPLY CO LLC p 52
800 Cabin Hill Dr, Greensburg PA 15601
Tel (724) 837-3000 SIC 4911

■ WEST PENN POWER CO p 1595
800 Cabin Hill Dr, Greensburg PA 15601
Tel (724) 837-3000 SIC 4911

ALLEGHENY ELECTRIC COOP INC p 52
212 Locust St Ste 500, Harrisburg PA 17101
Tel (717) 233-5704 SIC 4911 8741

■ AMERGEN ENERGY CO LLC p 66
200 Exelon Way, Kennett Square PA 19348
Tel (215) 841-4000 SIC 4911

■ EXELON GENERATION CO LLC p 519
300 Exelon Way, Kennett Square PA 19348
Tel (215) 841-4000 SIC 4911

PJM INTERCONNECTION LLC p 1153
2750 Monroe Blvd, Norristown PA 19403
Tel (610) 666-8980 SIC 4911

■ ENERGY PLUS HOLDINGS LLC p 498
3711 Market St Ste 1000, Philadelphia PA 19104
Tel (877) 320-0356 SIC 4911

■ PECO ENERGY CO p 1127
2301 Market St, Philadelphia PA 19103
Tel (215) 841-4000 SIC 4911 4924 4923

■ ALCOA WORLD ALUMINA LLC p 47
201 Isabella St, Pittsburgh PA 15212
Tel (412) 553-4545 SIC 1099 1081 4911

DIRECT ENERGY BUSINESS LLC p 441
1001 Liberty Ave Ste 1200, Pittsburgh PA 15222
Tel (800) 830-5923 SIC 4911

DUQUESNE LIGHT CO p 462
411 7th Ave 6-1, Pittsburgh PA 15219
Tel (412) 393-6000 SIC 4911

DUQUESNE LIGHT HOLDINGS INC p 462
411 7th Ave Ste 3, Pittsburgh PA 15219
Tel (412) 393-6000 SIC 4911

■ EQT PRODUCTION CO p 506
625 Liberty Ave Ste 1700, Pittsburgh PA 15222
Tel (412) 553-5700 SIC 4911

SUNBURY GENERATION LP p 1401
2384 N Old Trl, Selinsgrove PA 17870
Tel (570) 884-1200 SIC 4911

■ AES PUERTO RICO LP p 31
Carretera Ste 3 Km 142 0, Guayama PR 00784
Tel (787) 866-8117 SIC 4911

PUERTO RICO ELECTRIC POWER AUTHORITY p 1191
1110 Ave Ponce De Leon, San Juan PR 00907
Tel (787) 289-3434 SIC 4911

NARRAGANSETT ELECTRIC CO p 1007
280 Melrose St, Providence RI 02907
Tel (401) 784-7000 SIC 4911

AIKEN ELECTRIC COOPERATIVE INC p 38
2790 Wagener Rd, Aiken SC 29801
Tel (803) 649-6245 SIC 4911 4841

▲ SCANA CORP p 1286
100 Scana Pkwy, Cayce SC 29033
Tel (803) 217-9000
SIC 4931 4911 4924 4922

■ SOUTH CAROLINA ELECTRIC & GAS CO p 1343
100 Scana Pkwy, Cayce SC 29033
Tel (803) 217-9000
SIC 4931 4911 4922 4924

CENTRAL ELECTRIC POWER COOPERATIVE INC p 278
20 Cooperative Way, Columbia SC 29210
Tel (803) 779-4975 SIC 4911

DEE PEE ELECTRIC COOPERATIVE INC p 421
1355 E Mciver Rd, Darlington SC 29532
Tel (843) 665-4070 SIC 4911 8611

PIEDMONT MUNICIPAL POWER AGENCY p 1147
121 Village Dr, Greer SC 29651
Tel (864) 877-9632 SIC 4911

SANTEE ELECTRIC COOPERATIVE INC p 1281
424 Sumter Hwy, Kingstree SC 29556
Tel (843) 355-6187 SIC 4911

LAURENS ELECTRIC COOPERATIVE INC p 847
2254 Highway 14, Laurens SC 29360
Tel (864) 682-3141 SIC 4911

MID-CAROLINA ELECTRIC COOPERATIVE INC p 963
254 Longs Pond Rd, Lexington SC 29071
Tel (803) 749-6400 SIC 4911

BERKELEY ELECTRIC COOPERATIVE INC p 175
551 Rmbert C. Dnnis Blvd, Moncks Corner SC 29461
Tel (843) 761-8200 SIC 4911

SOUTH CAROLINA PUBLIC SERVICE AUTHORITY (INC) p 1343
1 Riverwood Dr, Moncks Corner SC 29461
Tel (843) 761-4121 SIC 4911

BLUE RIDGE ELECTRIC COOPERATIVE INC p 192
734 W Main St, Pickens SC 29671
Tel (800) 240-3400 SIC 4911

PALMETTO ELECTRIC COOPERATIVE INC p 1109
4063 Grays Hwy, Ridgeland SC 29936
Tel (843) 726-5551 SIC 8611 4911

MILLIKEN & CO p 971
920 Milliken Rd, Spartanburg SC 29303
Tel (864) 503-2020
SIC 2221 2211 2231 2273 2821 4911

■ NORTHWESTERN SERVICES LLC p 1061
600 Market St W, Huron SD 57350
Tel (605) 353-7478 SIC 4911 4924

EAST RIVER ELECTRIC POWER COOPERATIVE INC p 470
211 S Harth Ave, Madison SD 57042
Tel (605) 256-4536 SIC 4911 6163

▲ BLACK HILLS CORP p 187
625 9th St, Rapid City SD 57701
Tel (605) 721-1700 SIC 4911 4923 1241

■ BLACK HILLS NON-REGULATED HOLDINGS LLC p 187
625 9th St Ste 200, Rapid City SD 57701
Tel (605) 721-1700 SIC 4911 4923

■ BLACK HILLS POWER INC p 187
625 9th St, Rapid City SD 57701
Tel (605) 721-1700 SIC 4911

■ BLACK HILLS UTILITY HOLDINGS INC p 187
625 9th St Ste 200, Rapid City SD 57701
Tel (605) 721-1700 SIC 4911 4923

▲ NORTHWESTERN CORP p 1060
3010 W 69th St, Sioux Falls SD 57108
Tel (605) 978-2900 SIC 4911 4924

■ NORTHWESTERN ENERGY CORP p 1060
3010 W 69th St, Sioux Falls SD 57108
Tel (605) 978-2900 SIC 4911 4924

NIXON POWER SERVICES LLC p 1045
5038 Thoroughbred Ln, Brentwood TN 37027
Tel (615) 309-5823 SIC 5063 4911

SOUTHWEST TENNESSEE ELECTRIC MEMBERSHIP CORP p 1352
1009 E Main St, Brownsville TN 38012
Tel (731) 772-1322 SIC 4911

UPPER CUMBERLAND ELECTRIC MEMBERSHIP CORP p 1529
907 Main St N, Carthage TN 37030
Tel (615) 735-3208 SIC 4911

LEWIS MERIWETHER ELECTRIC COOPERATIVE p 858
1625 Highway 100, Centerville TN 37033
Tel (931) 729-3558 SIC 4911

ELECTRIC POWER BOARD OF CHATTANOOGA p 484
10 W Martin Luther King B, Chattanooga TN 37402
Tel (423) 756-2706 SIC 4911

CUMBERLAND ELECTRIC MEMBERSHIP CORP p 400
1940 Madison St, Clarksville TN 37043
Tel (931) 645-2481 SIC 4911

CLINTON UTILITIES BOARD p 327
1001 Chrles G Sivers Blvd, Clinton TN 37716
Tel (865) 457-9232 SIC 4911

VOLUNTEER ENERGY COOPERATIVE p 1565
18359 State Highway 58 N, Decatur TN 37322
Tel (423) 334-1020 SIC 4911

GREENEVILLE LIGHT & POWER SYSTEM (INC) p 638
110 N College St, Greeneville TN 37743
Tel (423) 636-6200 SIC 4911

JACKSON ENERGY AUTHORITY p 773
351 Dr Martin Luther, Jackson TN 38301
Tel (731) 422-7500
SIC 4925 4911 4941 4952

■ YOUNG TOUCHSTONE CO p 1639
200 Smith Ln, Jackson TN 38301
Tel (731) 424-5045 SIC 4911 3743

KNOXVILLE UTILITIES BOARD p 825
445 S Gay St, Knoxville TN 37902
Tel (865) 594-7324
SIC 4911 4924 4941 4952

■ TENNESSEE VALLEY AUTHORITY p 1438
400 W Summit Hill Dr, Knoxville TN 37902
Tel (865) 632-2101 SIC 4911 9631

TRI COUNTY ELECTRIC MEMBERSHIP CORP p 1476
405 College St, Lafayette TN 37083
Tel (615) 666-2111 SIC 4911

LENOIR CITY UTILITIES BOARD p 855
200 Depot St, Lenoir City TN 37771
Tel (865) 376-4421 SIC 4911

MIDDLE TENNESSEE ELECTRIC MEMBERSHIP CORP p 964
555 New Salem Hwy, Murfreesboro TN 37129
Tel (615) 890-9762 SIC 4911

ELECTRIC POWER BOARD OF METROPOLITAN GOVERNMENT OF NASHVILLE & DAVIDSON COUNTY p 484
1214 Church St, Nashville TN 37246
Tel (615) 747-3831 SIC 4911

APPALACHIAN ELECTRIC COOPERATIVE p 98
1109 Hill Dr, New Market TN 37820
Tel (423) 586-4755 SIC 4911

SEVIER COUNTY ELECTRIC SYSTEM INC p 1309
315 E Main St, Sevierville TN 37862
Tel (865) 453-2887 SIC 4911

DUCK RIVER ELECTRIC MEMBERSHIP CORP p 459
1411 Madison St, Shelbyville TN 37160
Tel (931) 684-4621 SIC 4911

SEQUACHEE VALLEY ELECTRIC CO-OPERATIVE INC p 1306
512 S Cedar Ave, South Pittsburg TN 37380
Tel (423) 837-8605 SIC 4911

GIBSON ELECTRIC MEMBERSHIP CORP p 611
1207 S College St, Trenton TN 38382
Tel (731) 855-4660 SIC 4911

GOLDEN SPREAD ELECTRIC COOPERATIVE INC p 621
905 S Fillmore St Ste 300, Amarillo TX 79101
Tel (806) 379-7766 SIC 4911

■ SOUTHWESTERN PUBLIC SERVICE CO p 1353
Tyler At Sixth, Amarillo TX 79101
Tel (303) 571-7511 SIC 4911

TEXAS MUNICIPAL POWER AGENCY p 1444
12824 Fm 244 Rd, Anderson TX 77830
Tel (936) 873-2013 SIC 4911

ELECTRIC RELIABILITY COUNCIL OF TEXAS INC p 484
7620 Metro Center Dr, Austin TX 78744
Tel (512) 225-7000 SIC 4911

■ GREEN MOUNTAIN ENERGY CO p 637
901 S Mo Pac Expy Ste 300, Austin TX 78746
Tel (512) 691-6100 SIC 4911

LOWER COLORADO RIVER AUTHORITY p 881
3700 Lake Austin Blvd, Austin TX 78703
Tel (512) 473-3200 SIC 4911 4941 1629

■ RAVEN POWER FINANCE LLC p 1209
2901 Via Fortuna Ste 600, Austin TX 78746
Tel (512) 314-8600 SIC 4911

■ RAVEN POWER GROUP LLC p 1209
2901 Via Fortuna Ste 600, Austin TX 78746
Tel (512) 314-8600 SIC 4911

■ SAPPHIRE POWER FINANCE LLC p 1282
2901 Via Fortuna Ste 600, Austin TX 78746
Tel (512) 314-8600 SIC 4911

■ SAPPHIRE POWER LLC p 1282
2901 Via Fortuna Ste 600, Austin TX 78746
Tel (512) 314-8600 SIC 4911

TRI-COUNTY ELECTRIC COOPERATIVE INC p 1477
600 Northwest Pkwy, Azle TX 76020
Tel (817) 444-3201 SIC 4911

BLUEBONNET ELECTRIC COOPERATIVE INC p 192
155 Electric Ave, Bastrop TX 78602
Tel (800) 842-7708 SIC 4911

■ ENTERGY TEXAS INC p 502
350 Pine St, Beaumont TX 77701
Tel (409) 981-2000 SIC 4911

BRYAN TEXAS UTILITIES p 221
205 E 28th St, Bryan TX 77803
Tel (979) 821-5700 SIC 4911

SAN MIGUEL ELECTRIC COOPERATIVE INC p 1277
6200 Fm 3387, Christine TX 78012
Tel (830) 784-3411 SIC 4911

UNITED ELECTRIC COOPERATIVE SERVICES INC p 1508
3309 N Main St, Cleburne TX 76033
Tel (817) 556-4000 SIC 4911

COSERV UTILITY HOLDINGS LP p 373
7701 S Stemmons Fwy, Corinth TX 76210
Tel (940) 321-4640 SIC 4911

DENTON COUNTY ELECTRIC COOPERATIVE INC p 429
7701 S Stemmons Fwy, Corinth TX 76210
Tel (940) 321-7800 SIC 4911

■ ATMOS PIPELINE AND STORAGE LLC p 128
5420 Lyndon B Johnson Fwy, Dallas TX 75240
Tel (972) 934-9227 SIC 4911 4922 4923

ENERGY FUTURE COMPETITIVE HOLDINGS CO LLC p 497
1601 Bryan St Ste 510, Dallas TX 75201
Tel (214) 812-4600 SIC 4911

ENERGY FUTURE HOLDINGS CORP p 497
1601 Bryan St Ste 510, Dallas TX 75201
Tel (214) 812-4600 SIC 4911

ENERGY FUTURE INTERMEDIATE HOLDING CO LLC p 497
1601 Bryan St Ste 510, Dallas TX 75201
Tel (214) 812-4600 SIC 4911

■ EXELON POWER CORP p 519
2233 Mountain Creek Pkwy A, Dallas TX 75211
Tel (214) 623-1051 SIC 4911

LEEWARD MEMBER LLC p 852
6688 N Central Expy # 500, Dallas TX 75206
Tel (214) 515-1100 SIC 4911

LUMINANT GENERATION CO LLC p 885
1601 Bryan St, Dallas TX 75201
Tel (214) 812-4600 SIC 4911 3621

ONCOR ELECTRIC DELIVERY CO LLC p 1086
1616 Woodall Rodgers Fwy, Dallas TX 75202
Tel (214) 486-2000 SIC 4911

ONCOR ELECTRIC DELIVERY HOLDINGS CO LLC p 1086
1616 Woodall Rodgers Fwy, Dallas TX 75202
Tel (214) 486-2000 SIC 4911

ONCOR ELECTRIC DELIVERY TRANSITION BOND CO LLC p 1086
1616 Woodall Rodgers Fwy, Dallas TX 75202
Tel (214) 486-2000 SIC 4911

PXU ELECTRIC DELIVERY p 1193
500 N Akard St Ste 14, Dallas TX 75201
Tel (214) 486-4760 SIC 4911

SHARYLAND UTILITIES LP p 1312
1807 Ross Ave Ste 460, Dallas TX 75201
Tel (214) 978-8958 SIC 4911

STREAM GAS & ELECTRIC LTD p 1393
1950 N Stemmons Fwy F, Dallas TX 75207
Tel (214) 800-4400 SIC 4911

TEXAS COMPETITIVE ELECTRIC HOLDINGS CO LLC p 1442
1601 Bryan St Ste 510, Dallas TX 75201
Tel (214) 812-4600 SIC 4911 4922

TXU ENERGY INDUSTRIES CO p 1495
1601 Bryan St Ste 34-068, Dallas TX 75201
Tel (214) 812-4600 SIC 4911

TXU ENERGY RETAIL CO LLC p 1495
1601 Bryan St, Dallas TX 75201
Tel (214) 812-4449 SIC 4911

TXU TRANSITION BOND CO L L C p 1495
1601 Bryan St, Dallas TX 75201
Tel (214) 814-4600 SIC 4911

TXU UNITED KINGDOM HOLDINGS CO p 1496
1601 Bryan St, Dallas TX 75201
Tel (214) 812-4600 SIC 4911

▲ EL PASO ELECTRIC CO p 483
Stanton Twr 100 N Stanton, El Paso TX 79901
Tel (915) 543-5711 SIC 4911

■ T N P ENTERPRISES INC p 1419
4100 Intl Plaza Ste 900, Fort Worth TX 76109
Tel (817) 731-0099 SIC 4911

TEXAS ENERGY FUTURE HOLDINGS LIMITED PARTNERSHIP p 1443
301 Commerce St Ste 3300, Fort Worth TX 76102
Tel (817) 871-4000 SIC 4911 6211

UPSHUR RURAL ELECTRIC COOPERATIVE CORP p 1529
1200 W Tyler St, Gilmer TX 75644
Tel (903) 843-2536 SIC 4911

GUADALUPE VALLEY ELECTRIC COOPERATIVE INC p 644
825 E Sarah Dewitt Dr, Gonzales TX 78629
Tel (830) 857-1200 SIC 4911

FARMERS ELECTRIC COOPERATIVE INC p 529
2000 I 30 E, Greenville TX 75402
Tel (903) 455-1715 SIC 4911

AEI SERVICES LLC p 29
2929 Allen Pkwy Ste 200, Houston TX 77019
Tel (713) 345-5200 SIC 4911

AGGREKO INTERNATIONAL PROJECTS p 35
2 Northpoint Dr Ste 810, Houston TX 77060
Tel (281) 848-1400 SIC 4911

▲ CALPINE CORP p 242
717 Texas St Ste 1000, Houston TX 77002
Tel (713) 830-2000 SIC 4911

■ CALPINE ENERGY SERVICES LP p 242
717 Texas St Ste 1000, Houston TX 77002
Tel (713) 830-2000 SIC 4911

■ CENTERPOINT ENERGY HOUSTON ELECTRIC LLC p 276
1111 Louisiana St, Houston TX 77002
Tel (713) 207-1111 SIC 4911

CHAMPION ENERGY HOLDINGS LLC p 287
1500 Rankin Rd Ste 200, Houston TX 77073
Tel (281) 653-5090 SIC 4911

■ CHAMPION ENERGY MARKETING LLC p 287
1500 Rankin Rd Ste 200, Houston TX 77073
Tel (281) 653-5090 SIC 4911

■ CHAMPION ENERGY SERVICES LLC p 287
1500 Rankin Rd Ste 200, Houston TX 77073
Tel (281) 653-5090 SIC 4911

DIRECT ENERGY LP p 441
12 Greenway Plz Ste 250, Houston TX 77046
Tel (713) 877-3500 SIC 4911

■ DYNEGY CONESVILLE LLC p 465
601 Travis St Ste 1400, Houston TX 77002
Tel (713) 507-6400 SIC 4911

■ DYNEGY HOLDINGS LLC p 465
601 Travis St Ste 1400, Houston TX 77002
Tel (713) 507-6400 SIC 4911 4923 5172

▲ DYNEGY INC p 465
601 Travis St Ste 1400, Houston TX 77002
Tel (713) 507-6400 SIC 4911

■ DYNEGY MARKETING & TRADE LLC p 465
601 Travis St Ste 1400, Houston TX 77002
Tel (713) 507-6400 SIC 4911 4924

■ DYNEGY MIAMI FORT LLC p 465
601 Travis St Ste 1400, Houston TX 77002
Tel (713) 507-6400 SIC 4911

■ DYNEGY MIDWEST GENERATION LLC p 465
601 Travis St Ste 1400, Houston TX 77002
Tel (713) 507-6400 SIC 4911

■ DYNEGY POWER CORP p 465
601 Travis St Ste 1400, Houston TX 77002
Tel (713) 507-6400 SIC 4911

■ DYNEGY RESOURCE I LLC p 465
601 Travis St Ste 1400, Houston TX 77002
Tel (713) 507-6400 SIC 4911 4924 4931

■ DYNEGY RESOURCES GENERATING HOLDCO LLC p 465
601 Travis St Ste 1400, Houston TX 77002
Tel (713) 507-6400 SIC 4911

■ DYNEGY ZIMMER LLC p 465
601 Travis St Ste 1400, Houston TX 77002
Tel (713) 507-6400 SIC 4911

EDP RENEWABLES NORTH AMERICA LLC p 478
808 Travis St Ste 700, Houston TX 77002
Tel (713) 265-0350 SIC 4911

ENGIE NORTH AMERICA INC p 498
1990 Post Oak Blvd # 1900, Houston TX 77056
Tel (713) 636-0000 SIC 4911

ENGIE RESOURCES LLC p 498
1990 Post Oak Blvd # 1900, Houston TX 77056
Tel (713) 636-0000 SIC 4911

ENRON CREDITORS RECOVERY CORP p 500
1221 Lamar St Ste 1325, Houston TX 77010
Tel (713) 853-6161
SIC 5172 4922 4911 1311 1321 2911

ENRON ENERGY SERVICES INC p 500
1400 Smith St Ste 501, Houston TX 77002
Tel (713) 853-6161 SIC 4924 4911

ENRON POWER CORP p 500
333 Clay St 400, Houston TX 77002
Tel (713) 853-6161 SIC 4911

ENTERGY-KOCH L P p 502
20 Greenway Plz Ste 950, Houston TX 77046
Tel (713) 544-6000 SIC 4923 4911

ENTRUST ENERGY INC p 503
1301 Mckinney St Ste 1200, Houston TX 77010
Tel (713) 338-2601 SIC 4911

GDF SUEZ ENERGY DEVELOPMENT NA INC p 595
1990 Post Oak Blvd # 1900, Houston TX 77056
Tel (713) 636-0000 SIC 4911

■ GENON ENERGY HOLDINGS INC p 604
1000 Main St, Houston TX 77002
Tel (832) 357-3000 SIC 4911

■ GENON POWER MIDWEST LP p 604
1000 Main St, Houston TX 77002
Tel (713) 497-3000 SIC 4911

■ GEXA ENERGY LP p 609
20455 State Highway 249 # 200, Houston TX 77070
Tel (713) 961-9399 SIC 4911

■ **ILLINOIS POWER GENERATING CO** p 732
601 Travis St Ste 1400, Houston TX 77002
Tel (713) 507-6400 *SIC* 4911

■ **IPH LLC** p 763
601 Travis St Ste 1400, Houston TX 77002
Tel (713) 507-6400 *SIC* 4911

LVDE CORP p 887
5100 San Felipe St 244e, Houston TX 77056
Tel (713) 840-1489 *SIC* 4911

NORTHERN STAR GENERATION LLC p 1056
2929 Allen Pkwy Ste 2200, Houston TX 77019
Tel (713) 580-6300 *SIC* 4911

NORTHERN STAR GENERATION SERVICES LLC p 1056
2929 Allen Pkwy Ste 2200, Houston TX 77019
Tel (713) 580-6300 *SIC* 4911

■ **NRG REMA LLC** p 1064
1000 Main St, Houston TX 77002
Tel (713) 497-3000 *SIC* 4911

■ **RELIANT ENERGY RETAIL HOLDINGS LLC** p 1222
1000 Main St, Houston TX 77002
Tel (713) 497-3000 *SIC* 4911

■ **RRI ENERGY BROADBAND INC** p 1255
1000 Main St, Houston TX 77002
Tel (713) 537-3000 *SIC* 4911

▲ **SPARK ENERGY INC** p 1354
12140 Wickchester Ln, Houston TX 77079
Tel (713) 600-2600 *SIC* 4931 4911

■ **SPARK ENERGY LLC** p 1354
12140 Wickchester Ln, Houston TX 77079
Tel (713) 977-5634 *SIC* 4911

■ **TEXAS GENCO HOLDINGS INC** p 1443
12301 Kurland Dr, Houston TX 77034
Tel (281) 897-2610 *SIC* 4911

TWIN EAGLE RESOURCE MANAGEMENT LLC p 1495
8847 W Sam Houston Pkwy N, Houston TX 77040
Tel (713) 341-7332 *SIC* 4911 4924 5983

▲ **EXXON MOBIL CORP** p 521
5959 Las Colinas Blvd, Irving TX 75039
Tel (972) 444-1000
SIC 2911 4612 5541 5171 4911

PEDERNALES ELECTRIC COOPERATIVE INC p 1127
201 S Avenue F, Johnson City TX 78636
Tel (830) 868-7155 *SIC* 4911

TRINITY VALLEY ELECTRIC COOPERATIVE INC p 1482
1800 E State Highway 243, Kaufman TX 75142
Tel (972) 932-2214 *SIC* 4911

■ **TEXAS-NEW MEXICO POWER CO** p 1445
577 N Garden Ridge Blvd, Lewisville TX 75067
Tel (972) 420-4189 *SIC* 4911

SAM HOUSTON ELECTRIC COOPERATIVE INC p 1274
1157 E Church St, Livingston TX 77351
Tel (936) 327-5711 *SIC* 4911

NORTHEAST TEXAS ELECTRIC COOPERATIVE INC p 1055
2221 H G Mosley Pkwy # 100, Longview TX 75604
Tel (903) 757-3282 *SIC* 4911

SOUTH PLAINS ELECTRIC COOPERATIVE INC p 1344
4727 S Loop 289 Ste 200, Lubbock TX 79424
Tel (806) 775-7732 *SIC* 4911

MAGIC VALLEY ELECTRIC COOPERATIVE INC p 895
1 3/4 Mi W Hwy 83, Mercedes TX 78570
Tel (866) 225-5683 *SIC* 4911

JIM F WEBB INC p 785
2401 E Interstate 20, Midland TX 79701
Tel (432) 684-4388 *SIC* 4911

TESSCO ENERGY SERVICES INC p 1440
1031 Andrews Hwy Ste 450, Midland TX 79701
Tel (432) 563-0071 *SIC* 4911

SAM RAYBURN G & T ELECTRIC COOPERATIVE INC p 1274
2905 Westward Dr, Nacogdoches TX 75964
Tel (936) 560-9532 *SIC* 4911

TEX-LA ELECTRIC COOPERATIVE OF TEXAS INC p 1441
2905 Westward Dr, Nacogdoches TX 75964
Tel (936) 560-9532 *SIC* 4911

NEW BRAUNFELS UTILITIES p 1029
263 Main Plz, New Braunfels TX 78130
Tel (830) 608-8867 *SIC* 4911 4941 4952

SOUTH TEXAS ELECTRIC COOPERATIVE INC p 1345
2849 Fm 447, Nursery TX 77976
Tel (361) 575-6491 *SIC* 4911

TECHWELL SURVEYS CORP p 1432
610 W 83rd St, Odessa TX 79764
Tel (432) 362-3711 *SIC* 4911 7389

RAYBURN COUNTRY ELECTRIC COOPERATIVE INC p 1210
980 Sids Rd, Rockwall TX 75032
Tel (972) 771-1336 *SIC* 4911

DEEP EAST TEXAS ELECTRIC p 421
880 State Highway 21 E, San Augustine TX 75972
Tel (936) 275-2314 *SIC* 4911

DEEP EAST TEXAS ELECTRIC COOPERATIVE INC p 421
U S Hwy 21 E, San Augustine TX 75972
Tel (936) 275-2314 *SIC* 4911

GUADALUPE-BLANCO RIVER AUTHORITY INDUSTRIAL DEVELOPMENT CORP p 644
933 E Court St, Seguin TX 78155
Tel (361) 575-6366 *SIC* 4911 4941 4952

■ **EGS HOLDINGS INC** p 481
2001 Timberloch Pl, Spring TX 77380
Tel (409) 981-2000 *SIC* 4911 4924

GRAYSON-COLLIN ELECTRIC CO-OP INC p 633
902 N Waco St, Van Alstyne TX 75495
Tel (903) 482-7100 *SIC* 4911

BRAZOS ELECTRIC POWER COOPERATIVE INC p 209
7616 Bagby Ave, Waco TX 76712
Tel (254) 750-6500 *SIC* 4911

STP NUCLEAR OPERATING CO p 1392
8 Miles W Wdsworth Fm 521, Wadsworth TX 77483
Tel (361) 972-3611 *SIC* 4911

INTERMOUNTAIN POWER SERVICE CORP p 753
850 W Brush Wellman Rd, Delta UT 84624
Tel (435) 864-4414 *SIC* 4911

UTAH ASSOCIATED MUNICIPAL POWER SYSTEMS p 1536
155 N 400 W, Salt Lake City UT 84103
Tel (801) 566-3938 *SIC* 4911

DESERET GENERATION AND TRANSMISSION CO-OPERATIVE p 432
10714 S Jordan Gtwy # 300, South Jordan UT 84095
Tel (435) 781-5737 *SIC* 4911

INTERMOUNTAIN POWER AGENCY p 753
10653 S River Front Pkwy # 120, South Jordan UT 84095
Tel (801) 938-1333 *SIC* 4911

GREEN MOUNTAIN POWER CORP p 637
163 Acorn Ln, Colchester VT 05446
Tel (888) 835-4672 *SIC* 4911 1623 1731

VERMONT ELECTRIC POWER CO INC p 1551
366 Pinnacle Ridge Rd, Rutland VT 05701
Tel (802) 773-9161 *SIC* 4911

NORTHERN NEW ENGLAND ENERGY CORP p 1056
85 Swift St, South Burlington VT 05403
Tel (802) 658-6555 *SIC* 4911

VIRGIN ISLANDS WATER & POWER AUTHORITY p 1558
9702 Estate Thomas, St Thomas VI 00802
Tel (340) 774-3552 *SIC* 4911

▲ **AES CORP** p 31
4300 Wilson Blvd Ste 1100, Arlington VA 22203
Tel (703) 522-1315 *SIC* 4911

■ **AES DPL HOLDINGS LLC** p 31
4300 Wilson Blvd, Arlington VA 22203
Tel (703) 522-1315 *SIC* 4911

CENTRAL VIRGINIA ELECTRIC COOPERATIVE INC p 281
800 Cooperative Way, Arrington VA 22922
Tel (434) 263-8336 *SIC* 4911

SOUTHSIDE ELECTRIC COOPERATIVE INC p 1351
2000 W Virginia Ave, Crewe VA 23930
Tel (800) 552-2118 *SIC* 4911

RAPPAHANNOCK ELECTRIC COOPERATIVE p 1209
247 Industrial Ct, Fredericksburg VA 22408
Tel (540) 898-8500 *SIC* 4911

OLD DOMINION ELECTRIC CO-OPERATIVE p 1080
4201 Dominion Blvd # 300, Glen Allen VA 23060
Tel (804) 747-0592 *SIC* 4911

BIRCHWOOD POWER PARTNERS LP p 185
10900 Birchwood Dr, King George VA 22485
Tel (540) 775-6303 *SIC* 4911

NORTHERN VIRGINIA ELECTRIC COOPERATIVE p 1057
10323 Lomond Dr, Manassas VA 20109
Tel (703) 335-0500
SIC 4911 8611 8741 4939

SHENANDOAH VALLEY ELECTRIC COOPERATIVE INC p 1315
147 Dinkel Ave, Mount Crawford VA 22841
Tel (540) 434-2200 *SIC* 4911

WHEELABRATOR PORTSMOUTH INC p 1604
3809 Elm Ave, Portsmouth VA 23704
Tel (757) 393-3100 *SIC* 4953 4911

■ **DOMINION CAPITAL INC** p 449
120 Tredegar St, Richmond VA 23219
Tel (804) 819-2000 *SIC* 4911

■ **DOMINION COVE POINT INC** p 449
120 Tredegar St, Richmond VA 23219
Tel (804) 819-2000 *SIC* 4911 4923 1311

■ **DOMINION ENERGY INC** p 449
120 Tredegar St, Richmond VA 23219
Tel (804) 819-2000 *SIC* 4911

■ **DOMINION MLP HOLDING CO LLC** p 449
120 Tredegar St, Richmond VA 23219
Tel (804) 819-2000 *SIC* 4911 4923 1311

▲ **DOMINION RESOURCES INC** p 449
120 Tredegar St, Richmond VA 23219
Tel (804) 819-2000 *SIC* 4911 4923 1311

■ **DOMINION RESOURCES SERVICES INC** p 449
120 Tredegar St, Richmond VA 23219
Tel (804) 775-2500 *SIC* 4911

■ **VIRGINIA ELECTRIC AND POWER CO** p 1559
120 Tredegar St, Richmond VA 23219
Tel (804) 819-2000 *SIC* 4911

■ **VIRGINIA POWER SERVICES ENERGY CORP INC** p 1559
120 Tredegar St, Richmond VA 23219
Tel (804) 819-2000 *SIC* 4911

PUBLIC UTILITY DISTRICT NO 1 OF GRAYS HARBOR COUNTY p 1190
2720 Sumner Ave, Aberdeen WA 98520
Tel (360) 532-4220 *SIC* 4911

PUGET EQUICO LLC p 1191
10885 Ne 4th St Ste 1200, Bellevue WA 98004
Tel (425) 454-6363 *SIC* 4911

PUGET HOLDING CO LLC p 1191
10885 Ne 4th St Ste 1200, Bellevue WA 98004
Tel (425) 454-6363 *SIC* 4911 4922 4924

PUGET SOUND ENERGY INC p 1191
10885 Ne 4th St Ste 1200, Bellevue WA 98004
Tel (425) 454-6363 *SIC* 4939 4911

TRANS ALTA p 1470
913 Big Hanaford Rd, Centralia WA 98531
Tel (360) 736-9901 *SIC* 4911

TRANSALTA CENTRALIA GENERATION LLC p 1470
913 Big Hanaford Rd, Centralia WA 98531
Tel (360) 330-8130 *SIC* 4911

PUBLIC UTILITY DISTRICT 2 GRANT COUNTY p 1190
30 C St Sw, Ephrata WA 98823
Tel (509) 754-0500 *SIC* 4911

PUBLIC UTILITY DISTRICT 1 OF SNOHOMISH COUNTY p 1190
2320 California St, Everett WA 98201
Tel (425) 257-9288 *SIC* 4911 4941

NAES CORP p 1006
1180 Nw Maple St Ste 200, Issaquah WA 98027
Tel (425) 961-4700 *SIC* 4911

PUBLIC UTILITY DISTRICT 1 OF BENTON COUNTY p 1190
2721 W 10th Ave, Kennewick WA 99336
Tel (509) 582-2175 *SIC* 4911

PUBLIC UTILITY DISTRICT NO 1 OF COWLITZ COUNTY p 1190
961 12th Ave, Longview WA 98632
Tel (360) 577-7507 *SIC* 4911

FRANKLIN PUD p 575
1411 W Clark St, Pasco WA 99301
Tel (509) 547-5591 *SIC* 4911

ENERGY NORTHWEST p 498
76 N Power Plant Loop, Richland WA 99354
Tel (509) 372-5000 *SIC* 4911 7699

CITY OF SEATTLE-CITY LIGHT DEPARTMENT p 318
700 5th Ave Ste 3200, Seattle WA 98104
Tel (206) 684-3200 *SIC* 4911

MASON COUNTY PUBLIC UTILITY DISTRICT NO 3 p 916
2621 E Johns Prairie Rd, Shelton WA 98584
Tel (360) 426-8255 *SIC* 4911

▲ **AVISTA CORP** p 138
1411 E Mission Ave, Spokane WA 99202
Tel (509) 489-0500 *SIC* 4911 4924 3499

CITY OF TACOMA DEPARTMENT OF PUBLIC UTILITIES p 319
3628 S 35th St, Tacoma WA 98409
Tel (253) 502-8900
SIC 4911 4941 4899 4013 4841

PUBLIC UTILITY DISTRICT 1 OF CLARK COUNTY p 1190
1200 Fort Vancouver Way, Vancouver WA 98663
Tel (360) 992-3000 *SIC* 4911

PUBLIC UTILITY DISTRICT NO 1 OF CHELAN COUNTY p 1190
327 N Wenatchee Ave, Wenatchee WA 98801
Tel (509) 663-8121 *SIC* 4911

■ **MONONGAHELA POWER CO** p 984
1310 Fairmont Ave, Fairmont WV 26554
Tel (800) 686-0022 *SIC* 4911

■ **CONSTELLATION ENERGY SERVICES INC** p 361
1716 Lawrence Dr, De Pere WI 54115
Tel (920) 617-6100 *SIC* 4911

DAIRYLAND POWER COOPERATIVE p 409
3200 East Ave S, La Crosse WI 54601
Tel (608) 788-4000 *SIC* 4911

▲ **ALLIANT ENERGY CORP** p 55
4902 N Biltmore Ln # 1000, Madison WI 53718
Tel (608) 458-3311 *SIC* 4911 4924

▲ **MGE ENERGY INC** p 958
133 S Blair St, Madison WI 53788
Tel (608) 252-7000 *SIC* 4939 4911 4924

■ **WE ENERGIES** p 1585
231 W Michigan St, Milwaukee WI 53203
Tel (414) 221-2345 *SIC* 4911 4924 4961

▲ **WEC ENERGY GROUP INC** p 1587
231 W Michigan St, Milwaukee WI 53203
Tel (414) 221-2345 *SIC* 4911 4924

WPPI ENERGY p 1627
1425 Corporate Center Dr, Sun Prairie WI 53590
Tel (608) 834-4500 *SIC* 4911

■ **NEXTERA ENERGY POINT BEACH LLC** p 1040
6610 Nuclear Rd, Two Rivers WI 54241
Tel (920) 755-7705 *SIC* 4911

JT PACKARD LLC p 796
275 Investment Ct, Verona WI 53593
Tel (800) 972-9778 *SIC* 4911

AMERICAN TRANSMISSION CO LLC p 80
W234n2000 Rdgview Pky Ct, Waukesha WI 53188
Tel (262) 506-6700 *SIC* 4911

HIGH PLAINS POWER INC p 690
1775 E Monroe, Riverton WY 82501
Tel (800) 826-3446 *SIC* 4911

POWDER RIVER ENERGY CORP p 1164
221 Main St, Sundance WY 82729
Tel (307) 283-3531 *SIC* 4911

SIC 4922 Natural Gas Transmission

▲ **ENERGEN CORP** p 497
605 Richard Arrington Jr, Birmingham AL 35203
Tel (205) 326-2700
SIC 1311 4924 4922 1321

■ **TENNESSEE GAS PIPELINE** p 1438
569 Brookwood Vlg Ste 749, Birmingham AL 35209
Tel (205) 325-3513 *SIC* 4922

■ **ENERGYSOUTH INC** p 498
2828 Dauphin St, Mobile AL 36606
Tel (251) 450-4774 *SIC* 4924 4922

NORSTAR PIPELINE CO INC p 1049
3000 Spenard Rd, Anchorage AK 99503
Tel (907) 277-5551 *SIC* 4922

■ **SOUTHERN CALIFORNIA GAS CO** p 1347
555 W 5th St Fl 31, Los Angeles CA 90013
Tel (213) 244-1200 *SIC* 4924 4922 4932

▲ **CLEAN ENERGY FUELS CORP** p 323
4675 Macarthur Ct Ste 800, Newport Beach CA 92660
Tel (949) 437-1000 *SIC* 4924 4922

▲ **SEMPRA ENERGY** p 1303
488 8th Ave, San Diego CA 92101
Tel (619) 696-2000
SIC 4932 4911 5172 4922

TPG PARTNERS III LP p 1467
345 California St # 3300, San Francisco CA 94104
Tel (415) 743-1500
SIC 1311 1389 4922 5082

ANTERO MIDSTREAM PARTNERS LP p 93
1615 Wynkoop St, Denver CO 80202
Tel (307) 357-7310 *SIC* 4922

▲ **DCP MIDSTREAM PARTNERS LP** p 418
370 17th St Ste 2500, Denver CO 80202
Tel (303) 595-3331 *SIC* 4922 4924

ENERGY CORP OF AMERICA p 497
4643 S Ulster St Ste 1100, Denver CO 80237
Tel (303) 694-2667
SIC 4924 4932 1382 4922 5172

■ **MARKWEST ENERGY PARTNERS LP** p 909
1515 Arapahoe St, Denver CO 80202
Tel (303) 925-9200 *SIC* 1321 4922 1389

■ **PUBLIC SERVICE CO OF COLORADO** p 1189
1800 Larimer St Ste 1100, Denver CO 80202
Tel (303) 571-7511 *SIC* 4911 4922 4924

■ **AVANGRID INC** p 136
157 Church St, New Haven CT 06510
Tel (207) 688-6363 *SIC* 4911 4922 4924

IROQUOIS GAS TRANSMISSION SYSTEM LP p 765
1 Corporate Dr Ste 600, Shelton CT 06484
Tel (203) 925-7200 *SIC* 4922

▲ **WGL HOLDINGS INC** p 1604
101 Constitution Ave Nw 200w, Washington DC 20001
Tel (703) 750-2000 *SIC* 4924 4923 4922

■ **FLORIDA PUBLIC UTILITIES CO** p 559
331 W Central Ave Ste 200, Winter Haven FL 33880
Tel (352) 447-2790 *SIC* 4911 4922 5984

■ **GPI HOLDINGS INC** p 627
1500 Riveredge Pkwy # 100, Atlanta GA 30328
Tel (770) 240-7200
SIC 2631 2653 2449 4922

■ **SOUTHERN CO GAS** p 1347
10 Peachtree Pl Ne, Atlanta GA 30309
Tel (404) 584-4000 *SIC* 4922 4924

MAIN STREET NATURAL GAS INC p 898
104 Townpark Dr Nw, Kennesaw GA 30144
Tel (770) 590-1000 *SIC* 4922

CONTRACTING & MATERIAL CO p 364
9550 W 55th St Ste A, Countryside IL 60525
Tel (708) 588-6000
SIC 4922 1623 4612 1731

■ **NORTHERN ILLINOIS GAS CO** p 1056
1844 W Ferry Rd, Naperville IL 60563
Tel (630) 983-8676 *SIC* 4924 4922

▲ **NISOURCE INC** p 1044
801 E 86th Ave, Merrillville IN 46410
Tel (877) 647-5990 *SIC* 4939 4922

TALLGRASS DEVELOPMENT LP p 1423
4200 W 115th St Ste 350, Leawood KS 66211
Tel (513) 941-0500 *SIC* 4922

TALLGRASS ENERGY GP LP p 1423
4200 W 115th St Ste 350, Leawood KS 66211
Tel (913) 928-6060 *SIC* 4922

▲ **TALLGRASS ENERGY PARTNERS LP** p 1423
4200 W 115th St Ste 350, Leawood KS 66211
Tel (913) 928-6060 *SIC* 4922 4923

TALLGRASS OPERATIONS LLC p 1423
4200 W 115th St Ste 350, Leawood KS 66211
Tel (913) 928-6060 *SIC* 4922

■ **BOARDWALK PIPELINES HOLDING CORP** p 196
610 W 2nd St, Owensboro KY 42301
Tel (270) 926-8686 *SIC* 4922 4923

■ **TEXAS GAS TRANSMISSION LLC** p 1443
610 W 2nd St, Owensboro KY 42301
Tel (270) 926-8686 *SIC* 4922

■ **KENTUCKY WEST VIRGINIA GAS CO** p 812
748 N Lake Dr, Prestonsburg KY 41653
Tel (606) 886-2311 *SIC* 1311 1389 4922

■ **EL INVESTMENT CO LLC** p 482
4809 Jefferson Hwy, Jefferson LA 70121
Tel (504) 576-4000 *SIC* 4911 4922

■ **ENTERGY LOUISIANA HOLDINGS INC** p 501
4809 Jefferson Hwy, Jefferson LA 70121
Tel (504) 840-2734 *SIC* 4911 4922

■ **ENTERGY LOUISIANA LLC** p 501
4809 Jefferson Hwy, Jefferson LA 70121
Tel (504) 576-4000 *SIC* 4911 4922

■ **ENTERGY UTILITY HOLDING CO LLC** p 502
4809 Jefferson Hwy, Jefferson LA 70121
Tel (504) 576-4000 *SIC* 4911 4922

■ **NSTAR ELECTRIC & GAS CORP** p 1065
800 Boylston St Ste 1700, Boston MA 02199
Tel (617) 424-2000 *SIC* 4922 4911

BOSTON GAS CO p 203
40 Sylvan Rd, Waltham MA 02451
Tel (781) 907-3646 *SIC* 4924 4922

■ **DTE GAS CO** p 458
1 Energy Plz Rm 1600, Detroit MI 48226
Tel (313) 235-4000 *SIC* 4924 4922

■ **MICHCON PIPELINE CO** p 960
500 Griswold St Fl 16th, Detroit MI 48226
Tel (313) 256-5505 *SIC* 4922

▲ **CMS ENERGY CORP** p 329
1 Energy Plaza Dr, Jackson MI 49201
Tel (517) 788-0550
SIC 4931 4911 4924 4922

CENEX INC p 275
5500 Cenex Dr, Inver Grove Heights MN 55077
Tel (800) 232-3639
SIC 1311 2911 4613 4922 4789 4213

▲ **XCEL ENERGY INC** p 1631
414 Nicollet Mall, Minneapolis MN 55401
Tel (612) 330-5500 *SIC* 4911 4922

■ **NORTHERN NATURAL GAS CO** p 1056
1111 S 103rd St, Omaha NE 68124
Tel (877) 654-0646
SIC 4226 4922 4923 4925

▲ SPRAGUE RESOURCES LP p 1360
185 International Dr, Portsmouth NH 03801
Tel (800) 225-1560 SIC 5172 4922

■ SOUTH JERSEY GAS CO p 1344
1 S Jersey Plz, Hammonton NJ 08037
Tel (609) 561-9000 SIC 4923 4924 4922

▲ SOUTH JERSEY INDUSTRIES INC p 1344
1 S Jersey Plz, Hammonton NJ 08037
Tel (609) 561-9000 SIC 4911 4922 4924

NEW MEXICO GAS CO p 1032
7120 Wyoming Blvd Ne # 20, Albuquerque NM 87109
Tel (505) 697-3803 SIC 4924 4922

▲ PNM RESOURCES INC p 1158
414 Silver Ave Sw Fl 4, Albuquerque NM 87102
Tel (505) 241-2700 SIC 4911 4922 4924

NATIONAL GRID CORPORATE SERVICES LLC p 1013
175 E Old Country Rd, Hicksville NY 11801
Tel (718) 403-2000
SIC 4924 4911 1311 4922

▲ LOEWS CORP p 874
667 Madison Ave Fl 7, New York NY 10065
Tel (212) 521-2000
SIC 6331 6311 1381 4922 7011

▲ NATIONAL FUEL GAS CO p 1012
6363 Main St, Williamsville NY 14221
Tel (716) 857-7000
SIC 4924 4922 1311 1382

■ DUKE ENERGY BUSINESS SERVICES LLC p 460
526 S Church St Ec-03t, Charlotte NC 28202
Tel (704) 594-6200 SIC 4911 4922

■ DUKE ENERGY OHIO INC p 460
400 S Tryon, Charlotte NC 28285
Tel (704) 382-3853
SIC 4911 4922 4924 4931

■ DUKE ENERGY REGISTRATION SERVICES INC p 460
526 S Church St, Charlotte NC 28202
Tel (704) 594-6200 SIC 4922

■ PANENERGY CORP p 1111
526 S Church St, Charlotte NC 28202
Tel (704) 594-6200
SIC 4922 1321 2813 5172 4911 4613

■ SPECTRA ENERGY CAPITAL LLC p 1356
526 S Church St, Charlotte NC 28202
Tel (704) 594-6200 SIC 4922

▲ MDU RESOURCES GROUP INC p 933
1200 W Century Ave, Bismarck ND 58503
Tel (701) 530-1000
SIC 4911 4924 4922 1221 1442 1311

■ WBI ENERGY TRANSMISSION INC p 1585
1250 W Century Ave, Bismarck ND 58503
Tel (701) 530-1601 SIC 4922 1311

■ WBI HOLDINGS INC p 1585
1250 W Century Ave, Bismarck ND 58503
Tel (701) 530-1600 SIC 4922 1311

■ COLUMBIA ENERGY GROUP p 340
200 Civic Center Dr, Columbus OH 43215
Tel (614) 460-4683 SIC 4922 1311 1731

■ COLUMBIA GAS TRANSMISSION LLC p 340
200 Cizzic Ctr Dr, Columbus OH 43216
Tel (614) 460-6000 SIC 4922

■ ACCESS PERMIAN MIDSTREAM LLC p 15
525 Central Park Dr # 1005, Oklahoma City OK 73105
Tel (877) 413-1023 SIC 4922

■ DEVON GAS SERVICES LP p 434
333 W Sheridan Ave, Oklahoma City OK 73102
Tel (405) 235-3611 SIC 4922

■ DEVON OEI OPERATING INC p 434
20 N Broadway, Oklahoma City OK 73102
Tel (405) 235-3611
SIC 4922 4924 1311 4613

■ ENABLE MIDSTREAM PARTNERS LP p 495
211 N Robinson Ave S410, Oklahoma City OK 73102
Tel (405) 525-7788 SIC 4922 4612 4619

■ ENABLE OKLAHOMA INTRASTATE TRANSMISSION LLC p 495
211 N Robinson Ave N950, Oklahoma City OK 73102
Tel (405) 525-7788
SIC 4922 1321 4923 2911

▲ OGE ENERGY CORP p 1076
321 N Harvey Ave, Oklahoma City OK 73102
Tel (405) 553-3000 SIC 4911 4922 4925

■ CAPROCK PIPELINE CO p 251
100 W 5th St Ste Ll, Tulsa OK 74103
Tel (918) 588-7900 SIC 4922

CONTINUUM MIDSTREAM LLC p 364
1323 E 71st St Ste 300, Tulsa OK 74136
Tel (918) 492-2840 SIC 4922

▲ ONEOK INC p 1087
100 W 5th St Ste Ll, Tulsa OK 74103
Tel (918) 588-7000
SIC 4922 4924 1311 1321 5172

▲ ONEOK PARTNERS LP p 1087
100 W 5th St Ste Ll, Tulsa OK 74103
Tel (918) 588-7000
SIC 4922 1321 1381 4925

■ TARGA PIPELINE MID-CONTINENT HOLDINGS LLC p 1425
110 W 7th St Ste 2300, Tulsa OK 74119
Tel (918) 574-3500 SIC 4922

▲ WILLIAMS COMPANIES INC p 1611
1 Williams Ctr, Tulsa OK 74172
Tel (918) 573-2000
SIC 4922 4924 1311 1321

■ WILLIAMS OLEFINS LLC p 1611
1 One Williams Ctr Bsmt 2, Tulsa OK 74172
Tel (918) 573-2000 SIC 4922

WILLIAMS PARTNERS LP p 1611
1 Williams Ctr Bsmt 2, Tulsa OK 74172
Tel (918) 573-2000 SIC 4922 1321 4925

▲ WILLIAMS PARTNERS LP p 1611
1 Williams Ctr, Tulsa OK 74172
Tel (918) 573-2000 SIC 1311 4922

▲ PORTLAND GENERAL ELECTRIC CO p 1163
121 Sw Salmon St, Portland OR 97204
Tel (503) 464-8000 SIC 4911 4922

CONE MIDSTREAM PARTNERS LP p 355
1000 Consol Energy Dr, Canonsburg PA 15317
Tel (724) 485-4000 SIC 4922

▲ RICE MIDSTREAM PARTNERS LP p 1232
400 Woodcliff Dr, Canonsburg PA 15317
Tel (724) 746-6720 SIC 4922

▲ ATLAS ENERGY GROUP LLC p 128
1000 Commerce Dr Ste 400, Pittsburgh PA 15275
Tel (412) 489-0006 SIC 1311 4922

CHEVRON AE RESOURCES LLC p 295
1000 Commerce Dr Fl 4, Pittsburgh PA 15275
Tel (800) 251-0171 SIC 4922 1311 4924

■ EQT GATHERING HOLDINGS LLC p 506
625 Liberty Ave Ste 1700, Pittsburgh PA 15222
Tel (412) 553-5700 SIC 4922

■ EQT GP HOLDINGS LP p 506
625 Liberty Ave Ste 1700, Pittsburgh PA 15222
Tel (412) 553-5700 SIC 4922

EQT MIDSTREAM PARTNERS LP p 506
625 Liberty Ave Ste 1700, Pittsburgh PA 15222
Tel (412) 553-5700 SIC 4922

■ EQUITRANS LP p 506
625 Liberty Ave Ste 1700, Pittsburgh PA 15222
Tel (412) 553-5700 SIC 4922

■ TARGA ENERGY LP p 1424
1000 Commerce Dr Ste 400, Pittsburgh PA 15275
Tel (412) 489-0006 SIC 1311 4922

■ TARGA PIPELINE PARTNERS LP p 1425
1000 Commerce Dr Ste 400, Pittsburgh PA 15275
Tel (877) 950-7473 SIC 4922

■ CCE HOLDINGS LLC p 270
1 Ugi Ctr Fl 2, Wilkes Barre PA 18711
Tel (713) 989-2000 SIC 4922

■ SOUTHERN UNION PANHANDLE LLC p 1350
1 Ugi Ctr Fl 2, Wilkes Barre PA 18711
Tel (570) 820-2400 SIC 4922

▲ SCANA CORP p 1286
100 Scana Pkwy, Cayce SC 29033
Tel (803) 217-9000
SIC 4931 4911 4924 4922

■ SOUTH CAROLINA ELECTRIC & GAS CO p 1343
100 Scana Pkwy, Cayce SC 29033
Tel (803) 217-9000
SIC 4931 4911 4922 4924

VENABLES CONSTRUCTION INC p 1547
7410 Continental Pkwy, Amarillo TX 79119
Tel (806) 381-2121
SIC 1623 1794 1389 4922 4612 1799

▲ ATMOS ENERGY CORP p 128
5430 Lbj Fwy Ste 1800, Dallas TX 75240
Tel (972) 934-9227 SIC 4924 4922 1629

■ ATMOS PIPELINE AND STORAGE LLC p 128
5420 Lyndon B Johnson Fwy, Dallas TX 75240
Tel (972) 934-9227 SIC 4911 4922 4923

▲ ENERGY TRANSFER EQUITY LP p 498
8111 Westchester Dr # 600, Dallas TX 75225
Tel (214) 981-0700 SIC 4922

ENERGY TRANSFER PARTNERS GP LP p 498
8111 Westchester Dr # 600, Dallas TX 75225
Tel (214) 981-0700 SIC 4922

▲ ENERGY TRANSFER PARTNERS LP p 498
8111 Westchester Dr # 600, Dallas TX 75225
Tel (214) 981-0700 SIC 4922 5984

▲ ENLINK MIDSTREAM PARTNERS LP p 500
2501 Cedar Springs Rd, Dallas TX 75201
Tel (214) 953-9500 SIC 4922 1321

■ LA GRANGE ACQUISITION LP p 835
8111 Westchester Dr, Dallas TX 75225
Tel (214) 981-0700 SIC 4922

■ PANHANDLE EASTERN PIPE LINE CO LP p 1111
8111 Westchester Dr # 600, Dallas TX 75225
Tel (214) 981-0700 SIC 4922

■ REGENCY ENERGY PARTNERS LP p 1218
8111 Westchester Dr # 600, Dallas TX 75225
Tel (214) 750-1771
SIC 1321 4925 5172 4922

▲ SOUTHCROSS ENERGY PARTNERS LP p 1345
1717 Main St Ste 5200, Dallas TX 75201
Tel (214) 979-3720 SIC 4922

TEXAS COMPETITIVE ELECTRIC HOLDINGS CO LLC p 1442
1601 Bryan St Ste 510, Dallas TX 75201
Tel (214) 812-4600 SIC 4911 4922

■ RINGWOOD GATHERING CO p 1235
810 Houston St Ste 2000, Fort Worth TX 76102
Tel (817) 870-2800 SIC 4922

SNYDER OIL CORP p 1336
777 Main St Ste 1400, Fort Worth TX 76102
Tel (817) 338-4043 SIC 1311 4922

▲ AMERICAN MIDSTREAM PARTNERS LP p 76
2103 Citywest Blvd # 800, Houston TX 77042
Tel (720) 457-6060 SIC 4922

■ AMERICAN NATURAL RESOURCES CO p 77
717 Texas St Ste 2400, Houston TX 77002
Tel (832) 320-5000 SIC 4922 1311 1222

■ ANADARKO HOLDING CO p 88
17001 Northchase Dr, Houston TX 77060
Tel (832) 636-7200
SIC 1311 1321 5172 4922

■ ANR PIPELINE CO p 92
700 Louisiana St Ste 700, Houston TX 77002
Tel (832) 320-2000 SIC 4922

■ ARCHROCK PARTNERS LP p 105
16666 Northchase Dr, Houston TX 77060
Tel (281) 836-8000 SIC 4922

BHP BILLITON PETROLEUM (ARKANSAS) INC p 180
1360 Post Blvd Ste 150, Houston TX 77056
Tel (713) 961-8500 SIC 4922 1311

BHP BILLITON PETROLEUM (NORTH AMERICA) INC p 180
1360 Post Oak Blvd # 150, Houston TX 77056
Tel (713) 961-8500 SIC 1311 4922

■ BLUE DOLPHIN ENERGY CO p 192
801 Travis St Ste 2100, Houston TX 77002
Tel (713) 568-4725
SIC 1311 1382 4612 4922

■ BOARDWALK PIPELINE PARTNERS LP p 196
9 Greenway Plz Ste 2800, Houston TX 77046
Tel (866) 913-2122 SIC 4922

■ BOARDWALK PIPELINES LP p 196
9 Greenway Plz Ste 2800, Houston TX 77046
Tel (713) 479-8000 SIC 4922 4923

■ BURLINGTON RESOURCES INC p 228
600 N Dairy Ashford Rd, Houston TX 77079
Tel (281) 293-1000
SIC 1311 5172 4922 4612

■ CENTERPOINT ENERGY RESOURCES CORP p 276
1111 Louisiana St, Houston TX 77002
Tel (713) 207-1111 SIC 4924 4922

▲ CHENIERE ENERGY INC p 294
700 Milam St Ste 1900, Houston TX 77002
Tel (713) 375-5000 SIC 1321 4925 4922

■ CHENIERE ENERGY INVESTMENTS LLC p 294
700 Louisiana St Ste 1900, Houston TX 77002
Tel (713) 375-5000 SIC 4922

■ CHENIERE ENERGY PARTNERS LP p 294
700 Milam St Ste 1900, Houston TX 77002
Tel (713) 375-5000 SIC 4924 4922

■ COLORADO INTERSTATE GAS CO LLC p 339
1001 La St Ste 1000, Houston TX 77002
Tel (713) 369-9000 SIC 4922

■ COLUMBIA GULF TRANSMISSION LLC p 340
5151 San Felipe St # 2500, Houston TX 77056
Tel (713) 386-3701 SIC 4922

■ COLUMBIA PIPELINE GROUP INC p 341
5151 San Felipe St, Houston TX 77056
Tel (713) 386-3701 SIC 4922

■ COLUMBIA PIPELINE PARTNERS LP p 341
5151 San Felipe St # 2500, Houston TX 77056
Tel (713) 386-3701 SIC 4922

■ COPANO ENERGY LLC p 368
1001 La St Ste 1000, Houston TX 77002
Tel (713) 621-9547 SIC 4922 4925

■ CRESTWOOD MIDSTREAM PARTNERS LP p 392
700 Louisiana St Ste 2550, Houston TX 77002
Tel (832) 519-2200 SIC 4922

CRESTWOOD MIDSTREAM PARTNERS LP p 392
700 Louisiana St Ste 2550, Houston TX 77002
Tel (832) 519-2200 SIC 4922

■ DUNCAN ENERGY PARTNERS LP p 461
1100 Louisiana St Fl 10, Houston TX 77002
Tel (713) 381-6500 SIC 4922

■ EL PASO CGP CO LLC p 483
1001 Louisiana St, Houston TX 77002
Tel (713) 420-2600
SIC 2911 1311 4613 4612 5541 4922

■ EL PASO LLC p 483
1001 Louisiana St, Houston TX 77002
Tel (713) 420-2600 SIC 4922 1311

EL PASO PIPELINE PARTNERS LP p 483
1001 La St Ste 1000, Houston TX 77002
Tel (713) 369-9000 SIC 4922

■ EL PASO TENNESSEE PIPELINE CO LLC p 483
1001 Louisiana St, Houston TX 77002
Tel (713) 420-2131 SIC 4922

■ ENABLE GAS TRANSMISSION LLC p 495
1111 Louisiana St, Houston TX 77002
Tel (713) 207-1111 SIC 4922

▲ ENBRIDGE ENERGY PARTNERS LP p 495
1100 La St Ste 3300, Houston TX 77002
Tel (713) 821-2000 SIC 4612 4922 4924

ENBRIDGE OFFSHORE (GAS TRANSMISSION) LLC p 495
1100 La St Ste 3300, Houston TX 77002
Tel (713) 821-2000 SIC 4922

ENRON CREDITORS RECOVERY CORP p 500
1221 Lamar St Ste 1325, Houston TX 77010
Tel (713) 853-6161
SIC 5172 4922 4911 1311 1321 2911

ENRON TRANSPORTATION SERVICES CO p 500
1400 Smith St, Houston TX 77002
Tel (713) 853-6161 SIC 4922

ENTERPRISE PRODUCTS HOLDINGS LLC p 502
1100 Louisiana St Fl 10, Houston TX 77002
Tel (713) 381-6500 SIC 4922 4925 4923

▲ ENTERPRISE PRODUCTS PARTNERS LP p 502
1100 Louisiana St Fl 10, Houston TX 77002
Tel (713) 381-6500 SIC 4922 4925 4923

EP ENERGY MANAGEMENT LLC p 504
1001 Louisiana St, Houston TX 77002
Tel (713) 997-1000 SIC 4922 1321

■ KINDER MORGAN ENERGY PARTNERS LP p 819
1001 La St Ste 1000, Houston TX 77002
Tel (713) 369-9000
SIC 4613 4925 4922 4226 4619 5171

▲ KINDER MORGAN INC p 819
1001 La St Ste 1000, Houston TX 77002
Tel (713) 369-9000 SIC 4922

■ KINDER MORGAN KANSAS INC p 819
1001 La St Ste 1000, Houston TX 77002
Tel (713) 369-9000 SIC 4922 4924

LNG FREEPORT DEVELOPMENT L P p 872
333 Clay St Ste 5050, Houston TX 77002
Tel (713) 980-2888 SIC 4922

MID-AMERICA PIPELINE CO LLC p 963
1100 La St Ste 1000, Houston TX 77002
Tel (713) 880-6500 SIC 4922

■ NATURAL GAS PIPELINE CO OF AMERICA LLC p 1018
1001 Louisiana St, Houston TX 77002
Tel (713) 369-9000 SIC 4922 1311 8741

NORTHERN BORDER PIPELINE CO p 1055
700 Louisiana St Ste 700, Houston TX 77002
Tel (832) 320-5000 SIC 4922

PIPELINE SUPPLY & SERVICE LLC p 1151
1010 Lamar St Ste 710, Houston TX 77002
Tel (713) 741-8127 SIC 4922 5085 1623

■ SABINE PASS LNG LP p 1264
700 Milam St Ste 1900, Houston TX 77002
Tel (713) 375-5000 SIC 4922

■ SABINE PASS LNG-LP LLC p 1264
700 Milam St Ste 800, Houston TX 77002
Tel (713) 375-5000 SIC 4922

SHELL EXPLORATION & PRODUCTION CO p 1314
200 N Dairy Ashford Rd, Houston TX 77079
Tel (832) 337-0369 SIC 4922

SHELL US GAS & POWER LLC p 1314
1301 Mckinney St Ste 700, Houston TX 77010
Tel (713) 658-0509 SIC 4922

▲ SPECTRA ENERGY CORP p 1356
5400 Westheimer Ct, Houston TX 77056
Tel (713) 627-5400 SIC 4922 4924

■ SPECTRA ENERGY PARTNERS LP p 1357
5400 Westheimer Ct, Houston TX 77056
Tel (713) 627-5400 SIC 4922 4924

■ SPECTRA ENERGY TRANSMISSION LLC p 1357
5400 Westheimer Ct, Houston TX 77056
Tel (713) 627-5400 SIC 4922 4924

▲ TARGA RESOURCES CORP p 1425
1000 La St Ste 4300, Houston TX 77002
Tel (713) 584-1000 SIC 4922 4924

■ TARGA RESOURCES PARTNERS LP p 1425
1000 Louisiana St # 4300, Houston TX 77002
Tel (713) 584-1000 SIC 4922 4924 5172

▲ TC PIPELINES LP p 1428
700 Louisiana St Ste 700, Houston TX 77002
Tel (877) 290-2772 SIC 4922

TE PRODUCTS PIPELINE CO LIMITED PARTNERSHIP p 1429
1100 La St Ste 1600, Houston TX 77002
Tel (713) 381-3636 SIC 4613 4922

■ TEXAS EASTERN TRANSMISSION LP p 1443
5400 Westheimer Ct, Houston TX 77056
Tel (713) 627-5400 SIC 4922

TRANSCONTINENTAL GAS PIPE LINE CO LLC p 1471
2800 Post Oak Blvd, Houston TX 77056
Tel (713) 215-2000 SIC 4922

■ TRANSWESTERN PIPELINE CO LLC p 1473
711 Louisiana St Ste 900, Houston TX 77002
Tel (281) 714-2000 SIC 4922

■ TRUNKLINE GAS CO LLC p 1487
5051 Westheimr Rd # 1428, Houston TX 77056
Tel (713) 989-2193 SIC 4922

■ UTILITY HOLDING LLC p 1537
1111 Louisiana St, Houston TX 77002
Tel (713) 207-1111 SIC 4924 4922

■ HOUSTON PIPE LINE CO LP p 712
800 E Sonterra Blvd, San Antonio TX 78258
Tel (713) 222-0414 SIC 4922

■ HPL HOUSTON PIPE LINE CO LLC p 714
800 E Sonterra Blvd, San Antonio TX 78258
Tel (713) 222-0414 SIC 4922

■ QEP MIDSTREAM PARTNERS LP p 1195
19100 Ridgewood Pkwy, San Antonio TX 78259
Tel (210) 626-6000 SIC 4922

■ TESORO LOGISTICS OPERATIONS LLC p 1440
19100 Ridgewood Pkwy, San Antonio TX 78259
Tel (210) 626-4280 SIC 4922

▲ SUMMIT MIDSTREAM PARTNERS LP p 1399
1790 Hughes, The Woodlands TX 77380
Tel (832) 413-4770 SIC 4922

■ WESTERN GAS PARTNERS LP p 1598
1201 Lake Robbins Dr, The Woodlands TX 77380
Tel (832) 636-6000 SIC 4923 4924 4922

■ KERN RIVER GAS SUPPLY CORP p 813
2755 E Cottonwood Pkwy # 300, Salt Lake City UT 84121
Tel (801) 937-6000 SIC 4922

■ QUESTAR CORP p 1199
333 S State St, Salt Lake City UT 84111
Tel (801) 324-5900 SIC 4922 1311 5172

■ QUESTAR PIPELINE LLC p 1199
333 S State St, Salt Lake City UT 84111
Tel (801) 324-5173 SIC 4922 4923

■ CONSOLIDATED NATURAL GAS CO p 360
120 Tredegar St, Richmond VA 23219
Tel (804) 819-2000 SIC 1311 4922 4924

■ DOMINION MIDSTREAM PARTNERS LP p 449
120 Tredegar St, Richmond VA 23219
Tel (804) 819-2000 SIC 4925 4922

■ DOMINION TRANSMISSION INC p 449
120 Tredegar St, Richmond VA 23219
Tel (804) 771-4795 SIC 4922 4923

PUGET HOLDING CO LLC p 1191
10885 Ne 4th St Ste 1200, Bellevue WA 98004
Tel (425) 454-6363 SIC 4911 4922 4924

EASTERN AMERICAN ENERGY CORP p 471
500 Corporate Lndg, Charleston WV 25311
Tel (304) 925-6100
SIC 1311 4922 5172 1321

SIC 4923 Natural Gas Transmission & Distribution

CENTURI CONSTRUCTION GROUP INC p 281
2355 W Utopia Rd, Phoenix AZ 85027
Tel (623) 582-1235 SIC 4923

UNISOURCE ENERGY SERVICES INC p 1505
88 E Broadway Blvd, Tucson AZ 85701
Tel (520) 571-4000 SIC 4911 4923

UNS ENERGY CORP p 1528
88 E Broadway Blvd, Tucson AZ 85701
Tel (520) 571-4000 SIC 4923 4911

A O G CORP p 6
115 N 12th St, Fort Smith AR 72901
Tel (479) 783-3181 SIC 4923 4924

ARKANSAS OKLAHOMA GAS CORP p 110
115 N 12th St, Fort Smith AR 72901
Tel (479) 784-2000 SIC 4923

▲ PG&E CORP p 1140
77 Beale St, San Francisco CA 94105
Tel (415) 973-1000 SIC 4931 4923

■ WESTERN GAS RESOURCES INC p 1598
1099 18th St, Denver CO 80202
Tel (303) 452-5603
SIC 4923 4925 1311 5172

CASTLETON COMMODITIES INTERNATIONAL LLC p 264
2200 Atlantic St Ste 800, Stamford CT 06902
Tel (203) 564-8100 *SIC* 4923

CASTLETON COMMODITIES TRADING GP LLC p 264
2200 Atlantic St Ste 800, Stamford CT 06902
Tel (203) 564-8100 *SIC* 4923

▲ WGL HOLDINGS INC p 1604
101 Constitution Ave Nw 200w, Washington DC 20001
Tel (703) 750-2000 *SIC* 4924 4923 4922

PEOPLES GAS p 1133
702 N Franklin St Ste 516, Tampa FL 33602
Tel (727) 824-0990 *SIC* 4923

PREMIER PERFORMANCE LLC p 1170
278 Dividend Dr, Rexburg ID 83440
Tel (208) 356-0106 *SIC* 4923

▲ TALLGRASS ENERGY PARTNERS LP p 1423
4200 W 115th St Ste 350, Leawood KS 66211
Tel (913) 928-6060 *SIC* 4922 4923

■ BOARDWALK PIPELINES HOLDING CORP p 196
610 W 2nd St, Owensboro KY 42301
Tel (270) 926-8686 *SIC* 4922 4923

SOUTHERN STAR CENTRAL CORP p 1350
4700 Highway 56, Owensboro KY 42301
Tel (270) 852-5000 *SIC* 4923

SOUTHERN STAR CENTRAL GAS PIPELINE INC p 1350
4700 Highway 56, Owensboro KY 42301
Tel (270) 852-5000 *SIC* 4923

■ BAY STATE GAS CO p 161
4 Technology Dr, Westborough MA 01581
Tel (508) 836-7000 *SIC* 4923

■ DTE ENERGY TRADING INC p 458
414 S Main St Ste 200, Ann Arbor MI 48104
Tel (734) 887-2000 *SIC* 4911 4923

▲ DTE ENERGY CO p 458
1 Energy Plz, Detroit MI 48226
Tel (313) 235-4000 *SIC* 4911 4923 1311

▲ AMEREN CORP p 66
1901 Chouteau Ave, Saint Louis MO 63103
Tel (314) 621-3222 *SIC* 4911 4931 4923

■ NORTHERN NATURAL GAS CO p 1056
1111 S 103rd St, Omaha NE 68124
Tel (877) 654-0646
SIC 4226 4922 4923 4925

▲ SOUTHWEST GAS CORP p 1352
5241 Spring Mountain Rd, Las Vegas NV 89150
Tel (702) 876-0711 *SIC* 4923 1623 1389

■ SOUTH JERSEY GAS CO p 1344
1 S Jersey Plz, Hammonton NJ 08037
Tel (609) 561-9000 *SIC* 4923 4924 4922

NEW YORK STATE ELECTRIC & GAS CORP p 1036
18 Link Dr, Binghamton NY 13904
Tel (607) 762-7200 *SIC* 4911 4924 4923

MSIP-SSCC HOLDINGS LLC p 997
1585 Broadway, New York NY 10036
Tel (270) 852-5000 *SIC* 4923

■ PIEDMONT NATURAL GAS CO INC p 1147
4720 Piedmont Row Dr # 100, Charlotte NC 28210
Tel (704) 364-3120 *SIC* 4924 4923 4925

■ EAST OHIO GAS CO p 470
19701 Libby Rd, Maple Heights OH 44137
Tel (800) 362-7557 *SIC* 4923

WARD PETROLEUM CORP p 1575
502 S Fillmore St, Enid OK 73703
Tel (580) 234-3229 *SIC* 4923

■ ENABLE OKLAHOMA INTRASTATE TRANSMISSION LLC p 495
211 N Robinson Ave N950, Oklahoma City OK 73102
Tel (405) 525-7788
SIC 4922 1321 4923 2911

MUSTANG FUEL CORP p 1002
9800 N Oklahoma Ave, Oklahoma City OK 73114
Tel (405) 884-2092 *SIC* 1311 4923

CONTINUUM ENERGY LLC p 364
1323 E 71st St Ste 300, Tulsa OK 74136
Tel (918) 492-2840 *SIC* 4923

CONTINUUM ENERGY SERVICES LLC p 364
1323 E 71st St Ste 300, Tulsa OK 74136
Tel (918) 492-2840 *SIC* 4923

■ SEMGAS LP p 1302
6120 S Yale Ave Ste 700, Tulsa OK 74136
Tel (918) 524-7100 *SIC* 4923

■ WILLIAMS ENERGY SERVICES LLC p 1611
1 One Williams Ctr Bsmt 2, Tulsa OK 74172
Tel (918) 573-2000 *SIC* 4923 5172

WILLIAMS PARTNERS OPERATING LLC p 1611
1 Williams Ctr, Tulsa OK 74172
Tel (918) 573-2000 *SIC* 4923

■ PECO ENERGY CO p 1127
2301 Market St, Philadelphia PA 19103
Tel (215) 841-4000 *SIC* 4911 4924 4923

PHILADEPHIA GAS WORKS p 1143
1800 N 9th St, Philadelphia PA 19122
Tel (215) 684-6710 *SIC* 4923

▲ EQT CORP p 506
625 Liberty Ave Ste 1700, Pittsburgh PA 15222
Tel (412) 553-5700
SIC 1311 4923 4924 4925

UTILICON SOLUTIONS LTD p 1537
708 Blair Mill Rd, Willow Grove PA 19090
Tel (215) 784-4200 *SIC* 4939 4923

▲ BLACK HILLS CORP p 187
625 9th St, Rapid City SD 57701
Tel (605) 721-1700 *SIC* 4911 4923 1241

■ BLACK HILLS NON-REGULATED HOLDINGS LLC p 187
625 9th St Ste 200, Rapid City SD 57701
Tel (605) 721-1700 *SIC* 4911 4923

■ BLACK HILLS UTILITY HOLDINGS INC p 187
625 9th St Ste 200, Rapid City SD 57701
Tel (605) 721-1700 *SIC* 4911 4923

■ ATMOS PIPELINE AND STORAGE LLC p 128
5420 Lyndon B Johnson Fwy, Dallas TX 75240
Tel (972) 934-9227 *SIC* 4911 4922 4923

■ ALGONQUIN GAS TRANSMISSION LLC p 50
5400 Westheimer Ct, Houston TX 77056
Tel (713) 627-5400 *SIC* 4923

■ BOARDWALK PIPELINES LP p 196
9 Greenway Plz Ste 2800, Houston TX 77046
Tel (713) 479-8000 *SIC* 4922 4923

CITRUS CORP p 311
1400 Smith St Ste 3902, Houston TX 77002
Tel (713) 853-6161 *SIC* 4923

DUKE ENERGY NATURAL GAS CORP p 460
5400 Westheimer Ct, Houston TX 77056
Tel (713) 627-5400 *SIC* 4923

■ DYNEGY HOLDINGS LLC p 465
601 Travis St Ste 1400, Houston TX 77002
Tel (713) 507-6400 *SIC* 4911 4923 5172

■ EAST TENNESSEE NATURAL GAS LLC p 471
5400 Westheimer Ct, Houston TX 77056
Tel (713) 627-5400 *SIC* 4923

■ ENBRIDGE MIDCOAST ENERGY INC p 495
1100 La St Ste 3300, Houston TX 77002
Tel (713) 650-8900 *SIC* 4923

ENTERGY-KOCH L P p 502
20 Greenway Plz Ste 950, Houston TX 77046
Tel (713) 544-6000 *SIC* 4923 4911

ENTERPRISE PRODUCTS HOLDINGS LLC p 502
1100 Louisiana St Fl 10, Houston TX 77002
Tel (713) 381-6500 *SIC* 4922 4925 4923

■ ENTERPRISE PRODUCTS OPERATING LLC p 502
1100 La St Ste 1000, Houston TX 77002
Tel (713) 381-6500 *SIC* 4923

▲ ENTERPRISE PRODUCTS PARTNERS LP p 502
1100 Louisiana St Fl 10, Houston TX 77002
Tel (713) 381-6500 *SIC* 4922 4925 4923

FLORIDA GAS TRANSMISSION CO LLC p 558
1300 Main St, Houston TX 77002
Tel (713) 989-7000 *SIC* 4923

■ GULF SOUTH PIPELINE CO LP p 647
9 Greenway Plz Ste 2800, Houston TX 77046
Tel (888) 315-5005 *SIC* 4923

■ MIDCOAST ENERGY PARTNERS LP p 964
1100 La St Ste 3300, Houston TX 77002
Tel (713) 821-2000 *SIC* 1311 4923

▲ PAR PACIFIC HOLDINGS INC p 1113
800 Gessner Rd Ste 875, Houston TX 77024
Tel (713) 969-3293 *SIC* 1311 2911 4923

SOUTHEAST SUPPLY HEADER LLC p 1346
5400 Westheimer Ct, Houston TX 77056
Tel (713) 627-5400 *SIC* 4923

TEXICAN NATURAL GAS CO p 1445
1 Allen Ctr 1 Allen Center, Houston TX 77002
Tel (713) 650-6579 *SIC* 4923

J L DAVIS CO p 771
211 N Colorado St, Midland TX 79701
Tel (432) 682-6311 *SIC* 5172 4923 1311

■ WESTERN GAS PARTNERS LP p 1598
1201 Lake Robbins Dr, The Woodlands TX 77380
Tel (832) 636-6000 *SIC* 4923 4924 4922

NORTHWEST PIPELINE LLC p 1060
295 S Chipeta Way Fl 4, Salt Lake City UT 84108
Tel (801) 583-8800 *SIC* 4923

■ QUESTAR GAS CO p 1199
333 S State St, Salt Lake City UT 84111
Tel (801) 324-5900 *SIC* 4924 4923

■ QUESTAR PIPELINE LLC p 1199
333 S State St, Salt Lake City UT 84111
Tel (801) 324-5173 *SIC* 4922 4923

SHERMAN V ALLEN INC p 1316
126 Post St, Rutland VT 05701
Tel (802) 775-7421
SIC 5172 5984 5411 4923

■ DOMINION COVE POINT INC p 449
120 Tredegar St, Richmond VA 23219
Tel (804) 819-2000 *SIC* 4911 4923 1311

■ DOMINION MLP HOLDING CO LLC p 449
120 Tredegar St, Richmond VA 23219
Tel (804) 819-2000 *SIC* 4911 4923 1311

▲ DOMINION RESOURCES INC p 449
120 Tredegar St, Richmond VA 23219
Tel (804) 819-2000 *SIC* 4911 4923 1311

■ DOMINION TRANSMISSION INC p 449
120 Tredegar St, Richmond VA 23219
Tel (804) 771-4795 *SIC* 4922 4923

■ PAPCO INC p 1112
4920 Southern Blvd, Virginia Beach VA 23462
Tel (757) 499-5977 *SIC* 4923

SIC 4924 Natural Gas Distribution

■ ALABAMA GAS CORP p 43
2101 6th Ave N Ste 240, Birmingham AL 35203
Tel (205) 326-8100 *SIC* 4924

▲ ENERGEN CORP p 497
605 Richard Arrington Jr, Birmingham AL 35203
Tel (205) 326-2700
SIC 1311 4924 4922 1321

■ ENERGYSOUTH INC p 498
2828 Dauphin St, Mobile AL 36606
Tel (251) 450-4774 *SIC* 4924 4922

■ MOBILE GAS SERVICE CORP p 980
2828 Dauphin St, Mobile AL 36606
Tel (251) 476-2720 *SIC* 4924 5722

NAVAJO TRIBAL UTILITY AUTHORITY p 1019
Hwy 12 N, Fort Defiance AZ 86504
Tel (928) 729-5721 *SIC* 4939 4924 4911

A O G CORP p 6
115 N 12th St, Fort Smith AR 72901
Tel (479) 783-3181 *SIC* 4923 4924

■ SOUTHERN CALIFORNIA GAS CO p 1347
555 W 5th St Fl 31, Los Angeles CA 90013
Tel (213) 244-1200 *SIC* 4924 4922 4932

■ SOUTHERN CALIFORNIA GAS TOWER INC p 1347
555 W 5th St Ste 1700, Los Angeles CA 90013
Tel (213) 244-1200 *SIC* 4924

■ CLEAN ENERGY p 323
4675 Macarthur Ct Ste 800, Newport Beach CA 92660
Tel (949) 437-1000 *SIC* 4924

▲ CLEAN ENERGY FUELS CORP p 323
4675 Macarthur Ct Ste 800, Newport Beach CA 92660
Tel (949) 437-1000 *SIC* 4924 4922

■ ENOVA CORP p 500
101 Ash St, San Diego CA 92101
Tel (619) 239-7700 *SIC* 4911 4924

■ PACIFIC ENTERPRISES p 1104
101 Ash St, San Diego CA 92101
Tel (619) 696-2020 *SIC* 4924

■ SAN DIEGO GAS & ELECTRIC CO p 1276
8326 Century Park Ct, San Diego CA 92123
Tel (619) 696-2000 *SIC* 4931 4911 4924

■ SEMPRA ENERGY GLOBAL ENTERPRISES p 1303
101 Ash St, San Diego CA 92101
Tel (619) 696-2000 *SIC* 4924 4911

■ PACIFIC GAS AND ELECTRIC CO p 1104
77 Beale St, San Francisco CA 94105
Tel (415) 973-7000 *SIC* 4911 4924

STEELRIVER INFRASTRUCTURE FUND NORTH AMERICA LP p 1384
1 Letterman Dr Ste 500, San Francisco CA 94129
Tel (415) 848-5448 *SIC* 4924

▲ DCP MIDSTREAM PARTNERS LP p 418
370 17th St Ste 2500, Denver CO 80202
Tel (303) 595-3331 *SIC* 4922 4924

ENERGY CORP OF AMERICA p 497
4643 S Ulster St Ste 1100, Denver CO 80237
Tel (303) 694-2667
SIC 4924 4932 1382 4922 5172

■ MARKWEST HYDROCARBON LLC p 909
1515 Arapahoe St, Denver CO 80202
Tel (303) 290-8700 *SIC* 1321 4924

■ PUBLIC SERVICE CO OF COLORADO p 1189
1800 Larimer St Ste 1100, Denver CO 80202
Tel (303) 571-7511 *SIC* 4911 4922 4924

■ SOURCEGAS LLC p 1342
1515 Wynkoop St Ste 500, Denver CO 80202
Tel (303) 243-3400 *SIC* 4924

■ BLACK HILLS GAS HOLDINGS LLC p 187
600 12th St Ste 300, Golden CO 80401
Tel (303) 243-3400 *SIC* 4924

■ YANKEE ENERGY SYSTEM INC p 1634
107 Selden St, Berlin CT 06037
Tel (860) 665-5000 *SIC* 4924

■ YANKEE GAS SERVICES CO p 1634
107 Selden St, Berlin CT 06037
Tel (860) 665-5000 *SIC* 4924

■ CONNECTICUT NATURAL GAS CORP p 357
77 Hartland St Ste 405, East Hartford CT 06108
Tel (860) 727-3000 *SIC* 4924

■ SOUTHERN CONNECTICUT GAS CO p 1348
77 Hartland St Ste 405, East Hartford CT 06108
Tel (800) 659-8299 *SIC* 4924

■ AVANGRID INC p 136
157 Church St, New Haven CT 06510
Tel (207) 688-6363 *SIC* 4911 4922 4924

STATOIL NATURAL GAS LLC p 1383
120 Long Ridge Rd, Stamford CT 06902
Tel (203) 978-6900 *SIC* 4924

▲ CHESAPEAKE UTILITIES CORP p 295
909 Silver Lake Blvd, Dover DE 19904
Tel (302) 734-6799 *SIC* 4924 4911

■ CONECTIV LLC p 355
800 N King St Ste 400, Wilmington DE 19801
Tel (202) 872-2680
SIC 4911 4924 1731 5172

■ WASHINGTON GAS LIGHT CO INC p 1578
101 Constitution Ave Nw 200w, Washington DC 20001
Tel (703) 750-4440 *SIC* 4924

▲ WGL HOLDINGS INC p 1604
101 Constitution Ave Nw 200w, Washington DC 20001
Tel (703) 750-2000 *SIC* 4924 4923 4922

FORT PIERCE UTILITIES AUTHORITY p 569
206 S 6th St, Fort Pierce FL 34950
Tel (772) 466-1600
SIC 4931 4941 4924 4813

GAINESVILLE REGIONAL UTILITIES (INC) p 589
301 Se 4th Ave, Gainesville FL 32601
Tel (352) 334-3400
SIC 4939 4941 4924 4911

INFINITE ENERGY HOLDINGS INC p 741
7001 Sw 24th Ave, Gainesville FL 32607
Tel (352) 240-4121 *SIC* 4911 4924

INFINITE ENERGY INC p 741
7001 Sw 24th Ave, Gainesville FL 32607
Tel (352) 331-1654 *SIC* 4924

TAMPA ELECTRIC CO p 1423
702 N Franklin St, Tampa FL 33602
Tel (813) 228-1111 *SIC* 4911 4924

TECO ENERGY INC p 1432
702 N Franklin St, Tampa FL 33602
Tel (813) 228-1111
SIC 4911 4924 4424 1221 1222

■ AGL RESOURCES SERVICE CO p 35
10 Peachtree Pl Ne # 1000, Atlanta GA 30309
Tel (404) 584-9470
SIC 8742 8721 8744 4924

■ ATLANTA GAS LIGHT CO p 125
10 Peachtree Pl Ne # 1000, Atlanta GA 30309
Tel (630) 388-2781 *SIC* 4924

CENTRAL VALLEY GAS STORAGE LLC p 280
10 Peachtree Pl Ne, Atlanta GA 30309
Tel (404) 584-3733 *SIC* 4924

■ GENON AMERICAS INC p 604
1155 Perimeter Ctr # 100, Atlanta GA 30338
Tel (678) 579-5000 *SIC* 4924

■ GENON NORTH AMERICA LLC p 604
1155 Perimeter Ctr # 100, Atlanta GA 30338
Tel (678) 579-5000 *SIC* 4924 4911 6221

■ SOUTHERN CO GAS p 1347
10 Peachtree Pl Ne, Atlanta GA 30309
Tel (404) 584-4000 *SIC* 4922 4924

PS ENERGY GROUP INC p 1187
4480 N Shallowford Rd # 100, Dunwoody GA 30338
Tel (770) 350-3000 *SIC* 8742 5172 4924

COLONIAL GROUP INC p 337
101 N Lathrop Ave, Savannah GA 31415
Tel (800) 944-3835
SIC 5171 5169 5172 4924 4492 4226

■ INTERMOUNTAIN GAS CO p 753
555 S Cole Rd, Boise ID 83709
Tel (208) 377-6000 *SIC* 4924

INTERMOUNTAIN INDUSTRIES INC p 753
555 S Cole Rd, Boise ID 83709
Tel (208) 377-6000 *SIC* 4924

CORN BELT ENERGY CORP p 370
1 Energy Way, Bloomington IL 61705
Tel (309) 661-1004 *SIC* 4911 4924

▲ EXELON CORP p 518
10 S Dearborn St Fl 53, Chicago IL 60603
Tel (800) 483-3220 *SIC* 4911 4924

■ NORTH SHORE GAS CO p 1053
200 E Randolph St # 2200, Chicago IL 60601
Tel (312) 240-4000 *SIC* 4924

■ PEOPLES ENERGY LLC p 1132
200 E Randolph St Fl 22, Chicago IL 60601
Tel (312) 240-4000 *SIC* 4924 4925 4911

■ AMEREN ILLINOIS CO p 66
6 Executive Dr, Collinsville IL 62234
Tel (618) 343-8150 *SIC* 4924 4911

NATIONAL MATERIAL LP p 1014
1965 Pratt Blvd, Elk Grove Village IL 60007
Tel (847) 806-7200
SIC 5051 3469 3354 5093 4911 4924

■ NICOR SERVICES p 1043
1751 W Diehl Rd Ste 200, Naperville IL 60563
Tel (630) 718-2707 *SIC* 4924

■ NORTHERN ILLINOIS GAS CO p 1056
1844 W Ferry Rd, Naperville IL 60563
Tel (630) 983-8676 *SIC* 4924 4922

■ OTTAWA ACQUISITION LLC p 1098
1844 W Ferry Rd, Naperville IL 60563
Tel (888) 642-6748 *SIC* 4924

■ CILCORP INC p 307
300 Liberty St, Peoria IL 61602
Tel (309) 677-5271 *SIC* 4911 4924

■ INDIANA GAS CO INC p 738
20 Nw 4th St, Evansville IN 47708
Tel (812) 491-4000 *SIC* 4924

■ SOUTHERN INDIANA GAS & ELECTRIC CO p 1349
1 Vectren Sq, Evansville IN 47708
Tel (812) 424-6411 *SIC* 4911 4924 4932

▲ VECTREN CORP p 1546
1 Vectren Sq, Evansville IN 47708
Tel (812) 491-4000
SIC 4924 4911 1241 1623 6531

■ VECTREN ENERGY SERVICES INC p 1546
1 Vectren Sq, Evansville IN 47708
Tel (812) 491-4000 *SIC* 4924

■ VECTREN UTILITY HOLDINGS INC p 1546
1 Vectren Sq, Evansville IN 47708
Tel (812) 491-4000 *SIC* 4932 4911 4924

CITIZENS ENERGY SERVICES CO LLC p 311
2020 N Meridian St, Indianapolis IN 46202
Tel (317) 927-6110 *SIC* 4924

■ NORTHERN INDIANA PUBLIC SERVICE CO p 1056
801 E 86th Ave, Merrillville IN 46410
Tel (877) 647-5990 *SIC* 4924 4911

■ ALLIANT INDUSTRIES INC p 55
200 1st St Se, Cedar Rapids IA 52401
Tel (398) 786-4268
SIC 4011 4741 4911 4924

■ INTERSTATE POWER AND LIGHT CO p 758
200 1st St Se, Cedar Rapids IA 52401
Tel (319) 398-4411 *SIC* 4911 4924 4961

■ BERKSHIRE HATHAWAY ENERGY CO p 175
666 Grand Ave Ste 500, Des Moines IA 50309
Tel (515) 242-4300 *SIC* 4911 4924 6531

■ MHC INC p 959
666 Grand Ave Ste 500, Des Moines IA 50309
Tel (515) 242-4300 *SIC* 4924 4911

■ MIDAMERICAN FUNDING LLC p 964
666 Grand Ave Ste 500, Des Moines IA 50309
Tel (515) 242-4300 *SIC* 4911 4924

■ PPW HOLDINGS LLC p 1166
666 Grand Ave Ste 500, Des Moines IA 50309
Tel (515) 242-4300 *SIC* 4911 4924 6531

■ BLACK HILLS/IOWA GAS UTILITY CO LLC p 187
1205 Sw 37th St, Grimes IA 50111
Tel (515) 224-1404 *SIC* 4924

■ CONSTELLATION NEWENERGY - GAS DIVISION LLC p 361
9960 Corporate Campus Dr, Louisville KY 40223
Tel (502) 426-4500 *SIC* 4924

■ LG&E AND KU ENERGY LLC p 860
220 W Main St Ste 1400, Louisville KY 40202
Tel (502) 627-2000
SIC 4911 4931 4932 4924

■ LOUISVILLE GAS AND ELECTRIC CO p 880
220 W Main St Ste 1400, Louisville KY 40202
Tel (502) 627-2000 *SIC* 4931 4911 4924

■ ENTERGY GULF STATES LOUISIANA LLC p 501
4809 Jefferson Hwy, Jefferson LA 70121
Tel (504) 576-4000 *SIC* 4911 4924

■ UIL HOLDINGS CORP p 1500
52 Farm View Dr, New Gloucester ME 04260
Tel (203) 499-2000 *SIC* 4931 4924

CONSTELLATION ENERGY GROUP INC p 361
100 Constellation Way, Baltimore MD 21202
Tel (410) 470-2800 *SIC* 4911 4924 1711

■ **CONSTELLATION ENERGY RESOURCES LLC** p 361
750 E Pratt St, Baltimore MD 21202
Tel (410) 470-2800 *SIC* 4911 4924

■ **NSTAR ELECTRIC CO** p 1065
800 Boylston St Ste 1700, Boston MA 02199
Tel (617) 424-2000 *SIC* 4911 4924

■ **NSTAR LLC** p 1065
800 Boylston St Ste 1700, Boston MA 02199
Tel (617) 424-2000 *SIC* 4911 4924

▲ **EVERSOURCE ENERGY** p 515
300 Cadwell Dr, Springfield MA 01104
Tel (413) 785-5871 *SIC* 4911 4924

BOSTON GAS CO p 203
40 Sylvan Rd, Waltham MA 02451
Tel (781) 907-3646 *SIC* 4924 4922

■ **GLOBAL ENERGY MARKETING LLC** p 616
800 South St Ste 500, Waltham MA 02453
Tel (781) 894-8800 *SIC* 5172 4924

■ **GLOBAL OPERATING LLC** p 617
800 South St Ste 500, Waltham MA 02453
Tel (800) 542-0778 *SIC* 4924 4911

GLOBAL PETROLEUM CORP p 617
800 South St Ste 500, Waltham MA 02453
Tel (781) 894-6920 *SIC* 4924 5172 4911

■ **NORESCO INC** p 1048
1 Research Dr Ste 400c, Westborough MA 01581
Tel (508) 614-1000
SIC 8711 8741 8748 4911 4924

■ **NORESCO LLC** p 1048
1 Research Dr Ste 400c, Westborough MA 01581
Tel (508) 614-1000
SIC 8711 8741 8744 8748 4911 4924

■ **DTE GAS CO** p 458
1 Energy Plz Rm 1600, Detroit MI 48226
Tel (313) 235-4000 *SIC* 4924 4922

▲ **CMS ENERGY CORP** p 329
1 Energy Plaza Dr, Jackson MI 49201
Tel (517) 788-0550
SIC 4931 4911 4924 4922

■ **CONSUMERS ENERGY CO** p 362
1 Energy Plaza Dr, Jackson MI 49201
Tel (517) 788-0550 *SIC* 4931 4911 4924

OPTION ENERGY LLC p 1090
5481 N Whitetail Ln, Ludington MI 49431
Tel (269) 329-4317
SIC 4924 1311 4931 1711

CONTINENTAL ENERGY SYSTEMS LLC p 363
1411 3rd St Ste A, Port Huron MI 48060
Tel (800) 624-2019 *SIC* 4924

SEMCO ENERGY INC p 1302
1411 3rd St Ste A, Port Huron MI 48060
Tel (810) 987-2200 *SIC* 4924

SEMCO HOLDING CORP p 1302
1411 3rd St Ste A, Port Huron MI 48060
Tel (810) 987-2200 *SIC* 4924

▲ **ALLETE INC** p 53
30 W Superior St, Duluth MN 55802
Tel (218) 279-5000
SIC 4931 4924 4941 1231 6552

■ **MINNESOTA ENERGY RESOURCES CORP** p 973
2665 145th St W, Rosemount MN 55068
Tel (651) 322-8900 *SIC* 4924

TATUM DEVELOPMENT CORP p 1426
11 Parkway Blvd, Hattiesburg MS 39401
Tel (601) 544-6043
SIC 5141 5084 4924 3443

■ **LACLEDE GAS CO** p 837
700 Market St, Saint Louis MO 63101
Tel (314) 342-0878 *SIC* 4924

▲ **SPIRE INC** p 1359
700 Market St, Saint Louis MO 63101
Tel (314) 342-0500 *SIC* 4924

■ **UNION ELECTRIC DEVELOPMENT CORP** p 1504
1901 Chouteau Ave, Saint Louis MO 63103
Tel (618) 234-3523 *SIC* 4911 4924

CITY UTILITIES OF SPRINGFIELD MO p 320
301 E Central St, Springfield MO 65802
Tel (417) 863-9000 *SIC* 4924 4941

■ **BLACK HILLS/NEBRASKA GAS UTILITY CO LLC** p 187
1600 Windhoek Dr, Lincoln NE 68512
Tel (402) 437-1705 *SIC* 4924

▲ **BERKSHIRE HATHAWAY INC** p 175
3555 Farnam St Ste 1440, Omaha NE 68131
Tel (402) 346-1400
SIC 6331 6321 4911 4924 6531 5963

TENASKA ENERGY INC p 1437
14302 Fnb Pkwy, Omaha NE 68154
Tel (402) 691-9500
SIC 4911 4924 4939 8742

TENASKA INC p 1437
14302 Fnb Pkwy, Omaha NE 68154
Tel (402) 691-9500
SIC 4924 4911 4939 8742

TENASKA MARKETING VENTURES p 1437
14302 Fnb Pkwy, Omaha NE 68154
Tel (402) 758-6100 *SIC* 4924

■ **NV ENERGY INC** p 1068
6226 W Sahara Ave, Las Vegas NV 89146
Tel (702) 402-5000 *SIC* 4911 4924

■ **SIERRA PACIFIC POWER CO** p 1321
6100 Neil Rd Ste 100, Reno NV 89511
Tel (775) 834-4011
SIC 4911 4924 4941 4971

▲ **UNITIL CORP** p 1515
6 Liberty Ln W, Hampton NH 03842
Tel (603) 772-0775 *SIC* 4911 4924

LIBERTY UTILITIES (ENERGYNORTH NATURAL GAS) CORP p 863
15 Buttrick Rd, Londonderry NH 03053
Tel (603) 328-2700 *SIC* 4924

■ **NORTH ATLANTIC ENERGY SERVICE CORP** p 1051
626 Lafayette Rd, Seabrook NH 03874
Tel (603) 474-9521 *SIC* 4924

■ **NJR ENERGY SERVICES CO** p 1045
1415 Wyckoff Rd, Belmar NJ 07719
Tel (732) 938-1273 *SIC* 4924

■ **SOUTH JERSEY GAS CO** p 1344
1 S Jersey Plz, Hammonton NJ 08037
Tel (609) 561-9000 *SIC* 4923 4924 4922

▲ **SOUTH JERSEY INDUSTRIES INC** p 1344
1 S Jersey Plz, Hammonton NJ 08037
Tel (609) 561-9000 *SIC* 4911 4922 4924

▲ **GENIE ENERGY LTD** p 603
550 Broad St, Newark NJ 07102
Tel (973) 438-3500 *SIC* 4911 4924 4931

▲ **PUBLIC SERVICE ENTERPRISE GROUP INC** p 1190
80 Park Plz, Newark NJ 07102
Tel (973) 430-7000 *SIC* 4931 4911 4924

■ **NRG POWER MARKETING LLC** p 1064
804 Carnegie Ctr, Princeton NJ 08540
Tel (609) 524-4500 *SIC* 4911 4924

■ **ELIZABETHTOWN GAS CO** p 487
1 Elizabethtown Plz, Union NJ 07083
Tel (908) 289-5000 *SIC* 4932 4924

■ **PIVOTAL UTILITY HOLDINGS INC** p 1152
1085 Morris Ave Ste 1, Union NJ 07083
Tel (908) 289-5000 *SIC* 4924

■ **NEW JERSEY NATURAL GAS CO** p 1031
1415 Wyckoff Rd, Wall Township NJ 07727
Tel (732) 938-1000 *SIC* 4924

▲ **NEW JERSEY RESOURCES CORP** p 1031
1415 Wyckoff Rd, Wall Township NJ 07727
Tel (732) 938-1480 *SIC* 4924

NEW MEXICO GAS CO p 1032
7120 Wyoming Blvd Ne # 20, Albuquerque NM 87109
Tel (505) 697-3803 *SIC* 4924 4922

NEW MEXICO GAS INTERMEDIATE INC p 1032
7201 Wyoming Blvd Ne, Albuquerque NM 87109
Tel (505) 697-3827 *SIC* 4924

▲ **PNM RESOURCES INC** p 1158
414 Silver Ave Sw Fl 4, Albuquerque NM 87102
Tel (505) 241-2700 *SIC* 4911 4922 4924

NEW YORK STATE ELECTRIC & GAS CORP p 1036
18 Link Dr, Binghamton NY 13904
Tel (607) 762-7200 *SIC* 4911 4924 4923

KEYSPAN CORP p 815
1 Metrotech Ctr Fl 1, Brooklyn NY 11201
Tel (718) 403-1000 *SIC* 4924

NATIONAL GRID SERVICES INC p 1013
1 Metrotech Ctr Fl 1, Brooklyn NY 11201
Tel (718) 403-2000 *SIC* 4924

KEYSPAN GAS EAST CORP p 815
175 Old Country Rd, Hicksville NY 11801
Tel (718) 403-1000 *SIC* 4924

NATIONAL GRID CORPORATE SERVICES LLC p 1013
175 E Old Country Rd, Hicksville NY 11801
Tel (718) 403-2000
SIC 4924 4911 1311 4922

NATIONAL GRID GENERATION LLC p 1013
175 E Old Country Rd, Hicksville NY 11801
Tel (631) 755-6650 *SIC* 4924

■ **CONSOLIDATED EDISON CO OF NEW YORK INC** p 359
4 Irving Pl, New York NY 10003
Tel (212) 460-4600 *SIC* 4911 4924 4961

■ **ORANGE AND ROCKLAND UTILITIES INC** p 1091
1 Blue Hill Plz Ste 20, Pearl River NY 10965
Tel (845) 352-6000
SIC 4924 4911 1311 6552

CENTRAL HUDSON GAS & ELECTRIC CORP p 278
284 South Ave Dept 100, Poughkeepsie NY 12601
Tel (845) 452-2700 *SIC* 4911 4924 4932

CH ENERGY GROUP INC p 286
284 South Ave, Poughkeepsie NY 12601
Tel (845) 452-2000 *SIC* 4911 4924

■ **ROCHESTER GAS AND ELECTRIC CORP** p 1243
89 East Ave, Rochester NY 14649
Tel (800) 295-7323 *SIC* 4911 4924

NIAGARA MOHAWK HOLDINGS INC p 1042
300 Erie Blvd W, Syracuse NY 13202
Tel (315) 474-1511 *SIC* 4911 4924

NIAGARA MOHAWK POWER CORP p 1042
300 Erie Blvd W, Syracuse NY 13202
Tel (315) 474-1511 *SIC* 4911 4924

NOCO INC p 1046
2440 Sheridan Dr Ste 202, Tonawanda NY 14150
Tel (716) 833-6626
SIC 2992 6719 5172 4924

■ **CES RETAIL ENERGY SUPPLY LLC** p 284
100 Summit Lake Dr # 410, Valhalla NY 10595
Tel (914) 286-7000 *SIC* 4924

■ **CONSOLIDATED EDISON SOLUTIONS INC** p 359
100 Summit Lake Dr # 410, Valhalla NY 10595
Tel (914) 286-7000 *SIC* 4924 4911 8748

▲ **NATIONAL FUEL GAS CO** p 1012
6363 Main St, Williamsville NY 14221
Tel (716) 857-7000
SIC 4924 4922 1311 1382

■ **NATIONAL FUEL GAS SUPPLY CORP** p 1012
6363 Main St, Williamsville NY 14221
Tel (716) 857-7000 *SIC* 4924

▲ **DUKE ENERGY CORP** p 460
550 S Tryon St, Charlotte NC 28202
Tel (704) 382-3853 *SIC* 4911 4924 4931

■ **DUKE ENERGY OHIO INC** p 460
400 S Tryon, Charlotte NC 28285
Tel (704) 382-3853
SIC 4911 4922 4924 4931

■ **PIEDMONT NATURAL GAS CO INC** p 1147
4720 Piedmont Row Dr # 100, Charlotte NC 28210
Tel (704) 364-3120 *SIC* 4924 4923 4925

■ **PUBLIC SERVICE CO OF NORTH CAROLINA INC** p 1190
800 Gaston 800 Gas, Gastonia NC 28056
Tel (704) 864-6731 *SIC* 4924

▲ **MDU RESOURCES GROUP INC** p 933
1200 W Century Ave, Bismarck ND 58503
Tel (701) 530-1000
SIC 4911 4924 4922 1221 1442 1311

■ **CINERGY CORP** p 308
139 E 4th St, Cincinnati OH 45202
Tel (513) 421-9500 *SIC* 4911 4924

■ **DYNEGY COMMERCIAL ASSET MANAGEMENT LLC** p 465
139 E 4th St, Cincinnati OH 45202
Tel (704) 382-5460 *SIC* 4924 4911

STAND ENERGY CORP p 1375
1077 Celestial St Ste 110, Cincinnati OH 45202
Tel (513) 621-1113 *SIC* 4924

■ **COLUMBIA GAS OF OHIO INC** p 340
290 W Nationwide Blvd # 114, Columbus OH 43215
Tel (614) 460-6000 *SIC* 4924

▲ **GAS NATURAL INC** p 593
8470 Station St, Mentor OH 44060
Tel (440) 974-3770
SIC 4924 4911 5172 5984

UNIMARK LLC p 1503
3540 S Boulevard Ste 205, Edmond OK 73013
Tel (405) 285-8670 *SIC* 4924

CLEARWATER ENTERPRISES LLC p 324
5637 N Classen Blvd, Oklahoma City OK 73118
Tel (405) 842-9200 *SIC* 4924

■ **DEVON OEI OPERATING INC** p 434
20 N Broadway, Oklahoma City OK 73102
Tel (405) 235-3611
SIC 4922 4924 1311 4613

▲ **ONE GAS INC** p 1086
15 E 5th St, Tulsa OK 74103
Tel (918) 947-7000 *SIC* 1311 4924

▲ **ONEOK INC** p 1087
100 W 5th St Ste Ll, Tulsa OK 74103
Tel (918) 588-7000
SIC 4922 4924 1311 1321 5172

▲ **WILLIAMS COMPANIES INC** p 1611
1 Williams Ctr, Tulsa OK 74172
Tel (918) 573-2000
SIC 4922 4924 1311 1321

▲ **NORTHWEST NATURAL GAS CO** p 1060
220 Nw 2nd Ave, Portland OR 97209
Tel (503) 226-4211 *SIC* 4924

▲ **PPL CORP** p 1166
2 N 9th St, Allentown PA 18101
Tel (610) 774-5151 *SIC* 4911 4924

■ **UGI CENTRAL PENN GAS INC** p 1499
2 N 9th St, Allentown PA 18101
Tel (610) 796-3499 *SIC* 4924

PEOPLES TWP LLC p 1133
205 N Main St, Butler PA 16001
Tel (724) 287-2751 *SIC* 4924

■ **COLUMBIA GAS OF PENNSYLVANIA INC** p 340
121 Champion Way Ste 100, Canonsburg PA 15317
Tel (724) 416-6300 *SIC* 4924

■ **PECO ENERGY CO** p 1127
2301 Market St, Philadelphia PA 19103
Tel (215) 841-4000 *SIC* 4911 4924 4923

CHEVRON AE RESOURCES LLC p 295
1000 Commerce Dr Fl 4, Pittsburgh PA 15275
Tel (800) 251-0171 *SIC* 4922 1311 4924

▲ **EQT CORP** p 506
625 Liberty Ave Ste 1700, Pittsburgh PA 15222
Tel (412) 553-5700
SIC 1311 4923 4924 4925

PEOPLES NATURAL GAS CO p 1133
225 N Shore Dr Fl 2, Pittsburgh PA 15212
Tel (412) 208-6810 *SIC* 4924

■ **UGI ENERGY SERVICES LLC** p 1499
1 Meridian Blvd Ste 2c01, Reading PA 19610
Tel (484) 663-5824 *SIC* 4924

▲ **SCANA CORP** p 1286
100 Scana Pkwy, Cayce SC 29033
Tel (803) 217-9000
SIC 4931 4911 4924 4922

■ **SOUTH CAROLINA ELECTRIC & GAS CO** p 1343
100 Scana Pkwy, Cayce SC 29033
Tel (803) 217-9000
SIC 4931 4911 4922 4924

■ **NORTHWESTERN SERVICES LLC** p 1061
600 Market St W, Huron SD 57350
Tel (605) 353-7478 *SIC* 4911 4924

▲ **NORTHWESTERN CORP** p 1060
3010 W 69th St, Sioux Falls SD 57108
Tel (605) 978-2900 *SIC* 4911 4924

■ **NORTHWESTERN ENERGY CORP** p 1060
3010 W 69th St, Sioux Falls SD 57108
Tel (605) 978-2900 *SIC* 4911 4924

TENNESSEE ENERGY ACQUISITION CORP p 1438
1808 Ashland City Rd A, Clarksville TN 37043
Tel (931) 920-3499 *SIC* 4924

KNOXVILLE UTILITIES BOARD p 825
445 S Gay St, Knoxville TN 37902
Tel (865) 594-7324
SIC 4911 4924 4941 4952

▲ **ATMOS ENERGY CORP** p 128
5430 Lbj Fwy Ste 1800, Dallas TX 75240
Tel (972) 934-9227 *SIC* 4924 4922 1629

EMPIRE PETROLEUM PARTNERS LLC p 493
8350 N Central Expy M2175, Dallas TX 75206
Tel (214) 750-9313 *SIC* 4924 5172

HYDROCARBON EXCHANGE CORP p 723
5910 N Cntrl Expy # 1380, Dallas TX 75206
Tel (214) 987-0257 *SIC* 4924

PARK COVEY GAS LLC p 1115
8401 N Central Expy # 700, Dallas TX 75225
Tel (214) 548-6000 *SIC* 4924

■ **APACHE GATHERING CO** p 96
2000 Post Oak Blvd # 100, Houston TX 77056
Tel (713) 296-6000 *SIC* 4924

BP ENERGY CO p 205
501 Westlake Park Blvd, Houston TX 77079
Tel (281) 679-9584 *SIC* 4924

CCJV p 270
5001 Rogerdale Rd, Houston TX 77072
Tel (713) 375-8051 *SIC* 4924

■ **CENTERPOINT ENERGY RESOURCES CORP** p 276
1111 Louisiana St, Houston TX 77002
Tel (713) 207-1111 *SIC* 4924 4922

■ **CENTERPOINT ENERGY SERVICES INC** p 276
1111 Louisiana St Ste 264, Houston TX 77002
Tel (713) 207-1111 *SIC* 4924

■ **CENTERPOINT ENERGY SERVICES RETAIL LLC** p 276
1111 La St Fl 20, Houston TX 77002
Tel (800) 752-8036 *SIC* 4924

■ **CENTERPOINT ENERGY TRANSITION BOND CO LLC** p 276
1111 La St Ste 4667, Houston TX 77002
Tel (713) 207-8272 *SIC* 4924

■ **CHENIERE ENERGY PARTNERS LP** p 294
700 Milam St Ste 1900, Houston TX 77002
Tel (713) 375-5000 *SIC* 4924 4922

COKINOS ENERGY CORP p 335
5718 Westheimer Rd # 900, Houston TX 77057
Tel (713) 974-0101 *SIC* 4924 1623

COKINOS NATURAL GAS CO INC p 335
5718 Westheimer Rd # 900, Houston TX 77057
Tel (713) 974-0101 *SIC* 4924 1623

■ **DYNEGY MARKETING & TRADE LLC** p 465
601 Travis St Ste 1400, Houston TX 77002
Tel (713) 507-6400 *SIC* 4911 4924

■ **DYNEGY RESOURCE I LLC** p 465
601 Travis St Ste 1400, Houston TX 77002
Tel (713) 507-6400 *SIC* 4911 4924 4931

▲ **ENBRIDGE ENERGY PARTNERS LP** p 495
1100 La St Ste 3300, Houston TX 77002
Tel (713) 821-2000 *SIC* 4612 4922 4924

ENRON ENERGY SERVICES INC p 500
1400 Smith St Ste 501, Houston TX 77002
Tel (713) 853-6161 *SIC* 4924 4911

JUST ENERGY (US) CORP p 797
5251 Westheimr Rd # 1000, Houston TX 77056
Tel (713) 850-6784 *SIC* 3621 4924

■ **KINDER MORGAN KANSAS INC** p 819
1001 La St Ste 1000, Houston TX 77002
Tel (713) 369-9000 *SIC* 4922 4924

■ **LAKESHORE ENERGY SERVICES LLC** p 840
1415 La St Ste 4200, Houston TX 77002
Tel (888) 200-3788 *SIC* 4924

■ **LONE STAR NGL PIPELINE LP** p 876
1300 Main St 10, Houston TX 77002
Tel (210) 403-7300 *SIC* 4924 1321

■ **OCCIDENTAL ENERGY MARKETING INC** p 1072
5 Greenway Plz Ste 110, Houston TX 77046
Tel (713) 215-7000 *SIC* 5172 1382 4924

■ **SABINE PASS LIQUEFACTION LLC** p 1264
700 Milam St Ste 1900, Houston TX 77002
Tel (713) 375-5000 *SIC* 4924

■ **SEQUENT ENERGY MANAGEMENT LP** p 1306
1200 Smith St, Houston TX 77002
Tel (832) 397-1700 *SIC* 4924

■ **SOUTHERN UNION CO** p 1350
1300 Main St, Houston TX 77002
Tel (713) 989-2000 *SIC* 4924

▲ **SPECTRA ENERGY CORP** p 1356
5400 Westheimer Ct, Houston TX 77056
Tel (713) 627-5400 *SIC* 4922 4924

■ **SPECTRA ENERGY PARTNERS LP** p 1357
5400 Westheimer Ct, Houston TX 77056
Tel (713) 627-5400 *SIC* 4922 4924

■ **SPECTRA ENERGY TRANSMISSION LLC** p 1357
5400 Westheimer Ct, Houston TX 77056
Tel (713) 627-5400 *SIC* 4922 4924

▲ **TARGA RESOURCES CORP** p 1425
1000 La St Ste 4300, Houston TX 77002
Tel (713) 584-1000 *SIC* 4922 4924

■ **TARGA RESOURCES PARTNERS LP** p 1425
1000 Louisiana St # 4300, Houston TX 77002
Tel (713) 584-1000 *SIC* 4922 4924 5172

TEXICAN INDUSTRIAL ENERGY MARKETING LLC p 1445
1 Allen Ctr Ste 1150, Houston TX 77002
Tel (713) 650-6579 *SIC* 4924

TWIN EAGLE RESOURCE MANAGEMENT LLC p 1495
8847 W Sam Houston Pkwy N, Houston TX 77040
Tel (713) 341-7332 *SIC* 4911 4924 5983

■ **UTILITY HOLDING LLC** p 1537
1111 Louisiana St, Houston TX 77002
Tel (713) 207-1111 *SIC* 4924 4922

MARTIN RESOURCE MANAGEMENT CORP p 913
4200 Stone Rd, Kilgore TX 75662
Tel (903) 983-6200
SIC 2911 4924 5984 5172

LEWIS RESOURCE MANAGEMENT LLC p 859
10101 Reunion Pl Ste 1000, San Antonio TX 78216
Tel (210) 384-3200 *SIC* 4924

■ **EGS HOLDINGS INC** p 481
2001 Timberloch Pl, Spring TX 77380
Tel (409) 981-2000 *SIC* 4911 4924

▲ **ANADARKO PETROLEUM CORP** p 88
1201 Lake Robbins Dr, The Woodlands TX 77380
Tel (832) 636-1000
SIC 1311 4924 5171 1382

■ **WESTERN GAS PARTNERS LP** p 1598
1201 Lake Robbins Dr, The Woodlands TX 77380
Tel (832) 636-6000 *SIC* 4923 4924 4922

■ **QUESTAR GAS CO** p 1199
333 S State St, Salt Lake City UT 84111
Tel (801) 324-5900 *SIC* 4924 4923

■ **COLUMBIA GAS OF VIRGINIA INC** p 340
1809 Coyote Dr, Chester VA 23836
Tel (800) 543-8911 *SIC* 4924

COYANOSA GAS SERVICES CORP p 387
10214 Walkerton Ln, Oakton VA 22124
Tel (703) 938-7984 SIC 4924

■ **CONSOLIDATED NATURAL GAS CO** p 360
120 Tredegar St, Richmond VA 23219
Tel (804) 819-2000 SIC 1311 4922 4924

■ **VIRGINIA NATURAL GAS INC** p 1559
544 S Independence Blvd, Virginia Beach VA 23452
Tel (757) 466-5400 SIC 4924

PUGET ENERGY INC p 1191
10885 Ne 4th St Ste 1200, Bellevue WA 98004
Tel (425) 454-6363 SIC 4931 4924

PUGET HOLDING CO LLC p 1191
10885 Ne 4th St Ste 1200, Bellevue WA 98004
Tel (425) 454-6363 SIC 4911 4922 4924

■ **CASCADE NATURAL GAS CORP** p 262
8113 W Grandridge Blvd, Kennewick WA 99336
Tel (509) 734-4500 SIC 4924

▲ **AVISTA CORP** p 138
1411 E Mission Ave, Spokane WA 99202
Tel (509) 489-0500 SIC 4911 4924 3499

MOUNTAINEER GAS CO p 994
501 56th St Se, Charleston WV 25304
Tel (888) 420-4427 SIC 4924

▲ **ALLIANT ENERGY CORP** p 55
4902 N Biltmore Ln # 1000, Madison WI 53718
Tel (608) 458-3311 SIC 4911 4924

▲ **MGE ENERGY INC** p 958
133 S Blair St, Madison WI 53788
Tel (608) 252-7000 SIC 4939 4911 4924

■ **WE ENERGIES** p 1585
231 W Michigan St, Milwaukee WI 53203
Tel (414) 221-2345 SIC 4911 4924 4961

▲ **WEC ENERGY GROUP INC** p 1587
231 W Michigan St, Milwaukee WI 53203
Tel (414) 221-2345 SIC 4911 4924

■ **WISCONSIN GAS LLC** p 1618
231 W Michigan St, Milwaukee WI 53203
Tel (414) 221-3236 SIC 4924

SIC 4925 Gas Production &/Or Distribution

WALTER ENERGY INC p 1574
3000 Riverchase Galleria # 1700, Hoover AL 35244
Tel (205) 745-2000 SIC 1241 4925

MIECO INC p 968
301 E Ocean Blvd Ste 1100, Long Beach CA 90802
Tel (562) 435-0085 SIC 5172 4925

DCP MIDSTREAM LP p 418
370 17th St Ste 2500, Denver CO 80202
Tel (303) 595-3331 SIC 4925

■ **WESTERN GAS RESOURCES INC** p 1598
1099 18th St, Denver CO 80202
Tel (303) 452-5603
SIC 4923 4925 1311 5172

■ **GAS CO LLC** p 593
745 Fort Street Mall # 1800, Honolulu HI 96813
Tel (808) 594-5530
SIC 4932 4925 5172 5984

■ **PEOPLES ENERGY LLC** p 1132
200 E Randolph St Fl 22, Chicago IL 60601
Tel (312) 240-4000 SIC 4924 4925 4911

■ **PEOPLES GAS LIGHT AND COKE CO** p 1133
200 E Randolph St # 2200, Chicago IL 60601
Tel (312) 744-7000 SIC 4925

VANTAGE SPECIALTIES INC p 1544
3938 Porett Dr, Gurnee IL 60031
Tel (847) 244-3410 SIC 4925 2869

CITIZENS ENERGY GROUP p 311
2020 N Meridian St, Indianapolis IN 46202
Tel (317) 924-3341 SIC 4925

LSCP LLLP p 883
4808 F Ave, Marcus IA 51035
Tel (712) 376-2800 SIC 4925 5191

■ **HEARTH & HOME TECHNOLOGIES LLC** p 678
7571 215th St W, Lakeville MN 55044
Tel (952) 985-6000 SIC 3429 4925

■ **NORTHERN NATURAL GAS CO** p 1056
1111 S 103rd St, Omaha NE 68124
Tel (877) 654-0646
SIC 4226 4922 4923 4925

MIRABITO HOLDINGS INC p 974
49 Court St Ste 1, Binghamton NY 13901
Tel (607) 561-2700
SIC 5172 4925 5541 5411 5983

PARACO GAS OF NEW YORK INC p 1113
800 Westchester Ave, Rye Brook NY 10573
Tel (914) 250-3740 SIC 4925

■ **NATIONAL FUEL GAS DISTRIBUTION CORP** p 1012
6363 Main St, Williamsville NY 14221
Tel (716) 857-7000 SIC 4925

■ **PIEDMONT NATURAL GAS CO INC** p 1147
4720 Piedmont Row Dr # 100, Charlotte NC 28210
Tel (704) 364-3120 SIC 4924 4923 4925

HERITAGE COOPERATIVE INC p 686
11177 Township Road 133, West Mansfield OH 43358
Tel (419) 294-2371
SIC 5153 5261 4925 4932

▲ **OGE ENERGY CORP** p 1076
321 N Harvey Ave, Oklahoma City OK 73102
Tel (405) 553-3000 SIC 4911 4922 4925

▲ **ONEOK PARTNERS LP** p 1087
100 W 5th St Ste Ll, Tulsa OK 74103
Tel (918) 588-7000
SIC 4922 1321 1381 4925

■ **WILLIAMS FIELD SERVICES GROUP LLC** p 1611
1 One Williams Ctr, Tulsa OK 74172
Tel (918) 573-2000 SIC 4925

WILLIAMS PARTNERS LP p 1611
1 Williams Ctr Bsmt 2, Tulsa OK 74172
Tel (918) 573-2000 SIC 4922 1321 4925

GT&S INC p 644
5275 Tilghman St, Allentown PA 18104
Tel (610) 398-2211
SIC 4925 5169 5084 5085 2813 5172

■ **PRAXAIR DISTRIBUTION MID-ATLANTIC LLC** p 1167
5275 Tilghman St, Allentown PA 18104
Tel (610) 398-2211 SIC 4925 3548

INTERSTATE GAS MARKETING INC p 758
2018 S 6th St, Indiana PA 15701
Tel (724) 465-7958 SIC 4925 5172

▲ **EQT CORP** p 506
625 Liberty Ave Ste 1700, Pittsburgh PA 15222
Tel (412) 553-5700
SIC 1311 4923 4924 4925

SSSI INC p 1364
2755a Park Ave, Washington PA 15301
Tel (724) 743-5815 SIC 1611 3312 4925

JACKSON ENERGY AUTHORITY p 773
351 Dr Martin Luther, Jackson TN 38301
Tel (731) 422-7500
SIC 4925 4911 4941 4952

■ **REGENCY ENERGY PARTNERS LP** p 1218
8111 Westchester Dr # 600, Dallas TX 75225
Tel (214) 750-1771
SIC 1321 4925 5172 4922

▲ **CHENIERE ENERGY INC** p 294
700 Milam St Ste 1900, Houston TX 77002
Tel (713) 375-5000 SIC 1321 4925 4922

■ **COPANO ENERGY LLC** p 368
1001 La St Ste 1000, Houston TX 77002
Tel (713) 621-9547 SIC 4922 4925

ENTERPRISE PRODUCTS CO p 502
1100 Louisiana St, Houston TX 77002
Tel (713) 880-6500 SIC 1321 4925

ENTERPRISE PRODUCTS HOLDINGS LLC p 502
1100 Louisiana St Fl 10, Houston TX 77002
Tel (713) 381-6500 SIC 4922 4925 4923

▲ **ENTERPRISE PRODUCTS PARTNERS LP** p 502
1100 Louisiana St Fl 10, Houston TX 77002
Tel (713) 381-6500 SIC 4922 4925 4923

■ **KINDER MORGAN ENERGY PARTNERS LP** p 819
1001 La St Ste 1000, Houston TX 77002
Tel (713) 369-9000
SIC 4613 4925 4922 4226 4619 5171

■ **TEPPCO PARTNERS LP** p 1439
1100 Louisiana St # 1600, Houston TX 77002
Tel (713) 381-3636 SIC 4925 5171

SEGUNDO NAVARRO DRILLING LTD p 1300
10101 Reunion Pl Ste 1000, San Antonio TX 78216
Tel (210) 384-3200 SIC 1382 4925

■ **DOMINION MIDSTREAM PARTNERS LP** p 449
120 Tredegar St, Richmond VA 23219
Tel (804) 819-2000 SIC 4925 4922

PETROENERGY LLC p 1139
920 10th Ave N, Onalaska WI 54650
Tel (608) 783-6411 SIC 5171 4925 5172

TEXPAR ENERGY LLC p 1445
920 10th Ave N, Onalaska WI 54650
Tel (800) 323-7350 SIC 5171 4925 5172

SIC 4931 Electric & Other Svcs Combined

CITY WATER & LIGHT PLANT OF CITY OF JONESBORO p 320
400 E Monroe Ave, Jonesboro AR 72401
Tel (870) 935-5581 SIC 4931

AMERICAN AIR LIQUIDE INC p 67
46409 Landing Pkwy, Fremont CA 94538
Tel (510) 624-4000
SIC 2813 5084 3533 4931

IMPERIAL IRRIGATION DISTRICT p 734
333 E Barioni Blvd, Imperial CA 92251
Tel (800) 303-7756 SIC 4911 4971 4931

■ **EDISON MISSION GROUP INC** p 478
2244 Walnut Grove Ave, Rosemead CA 91770
Tel (626) 302-2222
SIC 4931 6799 1629 1531

■ **CALPINE ENERGY SOLUTIONS LLC** p 242
401 W A St Ste 500, San Diego CA 92101
Tel (877) 273-6772 SIC 4931 4932

■ **SAN DIEGO GAS & ELECTRIC CO** p 1276
8326 Century Park Ct, San Diego CA 92123
Tel (619) 696-2000 SIC 4931 4911 4924

■ **SEMPRA GENERATION LLC** p 1303
101 Ash St, San Diego CA 92101
Tel (619) 696-2000 SIC 4931

UPWIND SOLUTIONS INC p 1530
4863 Shawline St Ste A, San Diego CA 92111
Tel (866) 927-3142 SIC 7374 4931 7373

▲ **PG&E CORP** p 1140
77 Beale St, San Francisco CA 94105
Tel (415) 973-1000 SIC 4931 4923

■ **EDISON MISSION ENERGY** p 478
3 Macarthur Pl Ste 100, Santa Ana CA 92707
Tel (714) 513-8000 SIC 4931

NORTH AMERICAN POWER AND GAS LLC p 1050
20 Glover Ave Ste 1, Norwalk CT 06850
Tel (203) 893-4196 SIC 4931

VERDE ENERGY USA HOLDINGS LLC p 1549
101 Merritt 7 Ste 2, Norwalk CT 06851
Tel (203) 663-5700 SIC 4931

VERDE ENERGY USA INC p 1549
101 Merritt 7 Ste 2, Norwalk CT 06851
Tel (203) 663-5700 SIC 4931

■ **PEPCO HOLDINGS LLC** p 1133
701 9th St Nw Ste 3, Washington DC 20001
Tel (202) 872-2000 SIC 4931

FORT PIERCE UTILITIES AUTHORITY p 569
206 S 6th St, Fort Pierce FL 34950
Tel (772) 466-1600
SIC 4931 4941 4924 4813

■ **US GAS & ELECTRIC INC** p 1532
3700 Lakeside Dr Fl 6, Miramar FL 33027
Tel (305) 947-7880 SIC 4931

ORLANDO UTILITIES COMMISSION p 1095
100 W Anderson St, Orlando FL 32801
Tel (407) 246-2121
SIC 4941 4931 4939 4911

TALQUIN ELECTRIC COOPERATIVE INC p 1423
1640 W Jefferson St, Quincy FL 32351
Tel (850) 627-7651 SIC 4931

■ **EXELON ENERGY DELIVERY CO LLC** p 519
10 S Dearborn St Fl 53, Chicago IL 60603
Tel (312) 394-7399 SIC 4931

INTEGRYS ENERGY GROUP INC p 750
200 E Randolph St # 2200, Chicago IL 60601
Tel (312) 228-5400 SIC 4931 5172 4911

■ **MIDAMERICAN ENERGY CO** p 964
666 Grand Ave Ste 500, Des Moines IA 50309
Tel (515) 242-4300 SIC 4931

KANSAS CITY BOARD OF PUBLIC UTILITIES p 802
540 Minnesota Ave, Kansas City KS 66101
Tel (913) 573-9000 SIC 4931 4941

■ **LG&E AND KU ENERGY LLC** p 860
220 W Main St Ste 1400, Louisville KY 40202
Tel (502) 627-2000
SIC 4911 4931 4932 4924

■ **LOUISVILLE GAS AND ELECTRIC CO** p 880
220 W Main St Ste 1400, Louisville KY 40202
Tel (502) 627-2000 SIC 4931 4911 4924

▲ **ENTERGY CORP** p 501
639 Loyola Ave Ste 300, New Orleans LA 70113
Tel (504) 576-4000 SIC 4931

■ **ENTERGY NEW ORLEANS INC** p 501
1600 Perdido St Bldg 505, New Orleans LA 70112
Tel (504) 670-3700 SIC 4931

■ **ENTERGY NEW ORLEANS TRANSMISSION OWNER** p 501
1600 Perdido St Bldg 505, New Orleans LA 70112
Tel (501) 228-2898 SIC 4931

■ **UIL HOLDINGS CORP** p 1500
52 Farm View Dr, New Gloucester ME 04260
Tel (203) 499-2000 SIC 4931 4924

■ **BALTIMORE GAS AND ELECTRIC CO** p 149
110 W Fayette St, Baltimore MD 21201
Tel (410) 234-5000 SIC 4931

■ **COVANTA HAVERHILL INC** p 384
100 Recovery Way, Haverhill MA 01835
Tel (978) 372-6288 SIC 4953 1629 4931

▲ **CMS ENERGY CORP** p 329
1 Energy Plaza Dr, Jackson MI 49201
Tel (517) 788-0550
SIC 4931 4911 4924 4922

■ **CONSUMERS ENERGY CO** p 362
1 Energy Plaza Dr, Jackson MI 49201
Tel (517) 788-0550 SIC 4931 4911 4924

OPTION ENERGY LLC p 1090
5481 N Whitetail Ln, Ludington MI 49431
Tel (269) 329-4317
SIC 4924 1311 4931 1711

▲ **ALLETE INC** p 53
30 W Superior St, Duluth MN 55802
Tel (218) 279-5000
SIC 4931 4924 4941 1231 6552

■ **NORTHERN STATES POWER CO** p 1057
414 Nicollet Mall, Minneapolis MN 55401
Tel (612) 330-5500 SIC 4931

■ **XCEL ENERGY SERVICES INC** p 1631
414 Nicollet Mall Fl 7, Minneapolis MN 55401
Tel (612) 330-5500 SIC 4931

■ **ENTERGY ENTERPRISES INC** p 501
905 Highway 80 E, Clinton MS 39056
Tel (601) 925-6504 SIC 4931

▲ **AMEREN CORP** p 66
1901 Chouteau Ave, Saint Louis MO 63103
Tel (314) 621-3222 SIC 4911 4931 4923

■ **UNION ELECTRIC CO** p 1504
1901 Chouteau Ave, Saint Louis MO 63103
Tel (314) 621-3222 SIC 4931

FOSTER WHEELER ZACK INC p 571
53 Frontage Rd, Hampton NJ 08827
Tel (908) 730-4000
SIC 8711 1629 3569 4931

■ **COVANTA ENERGY GROUP INC** p 384
445 South St, Morristown NJ 07960
Tel (862) 345-5000
SIC 1541 1629 4953 4931

▲ **GENIE ENERGY LTD** p 603
550 Broad St, Newark NJ 07102
Tel (973) 438-3500 SIC 4911 4924 4931

■ **PUBLIC SERVICE ELECTRIC AND GAS CO INC** p 1190
80 Park Plz Ste 3, Newark NJ 07102
Tel (973) 430-7000 SIC 4931

▲ **PUBLIC SERVICE ENTERPRISE GROUP INC** p 1190
80 Park Plz, Newark NJ 07102
Tel (973) 430-7000 SIC 4931 4911 4924

▲ **CONSOLIDATED EDISON INC** p 359
4 Irving Pl, New York NY 10003
Tel (212) 460-4600 SIC 4931

▲ **DUKE ENERGY CORP** p 460
550 S Tryon St, Charlotte NC 28202
Tel (704) 382-3853 SIC 4911 4924 4931

■ **DUKE ENERGY OHIO INC** p 460
400 S Tryon St, Charlotte NC 28285
Tel (704) 382-3853
SIC 4911 4922 4924 4931

PANTHER SUMMIT INDUSTRIES INC p 1111
4807 Beryl Rd, Raleigh NC 27606
Tel (919) 828-0641 SIC 5082 5084 4931

■ **POWERSECURE INTERNATIONAL INC** p 1166
1609 Heritage Commerce Ct, Wake Forest NC 27587
Tel (919) 556-3056 SIC 3629 4931

■ **NORTHSHORE MINING CO** p 1058
1100 Superior Ave E # 1500, Cleveland OH 44114
Tel (216) 694-5700 SIC 1011 4931

■ **DAYTON POWER AND LIGHT CO** p 418
1065 Woodman Dr, Dayton OH 45432
Tel (937) 224-6000 SIC 4911 4931

EUGENE WATER & ELECTRIC BOARD p 512
500 E 4th Ave, Eugene OR 97401
Tel (541) 685-7000 SIC 4931 9641

■ **AVANGRID RENEWABLES HOLDINGS INC** p 136
1125 Nw Couch St Ste 700, Portland OR 97209
Tel (503) 796-7000 SIC 4932 4931

■ **AVANGRID RENEWABLES LLC** p 136
1125 Nw Couch St Ste 700, Portland OR 97209
Tel (503) 796-7179 SIC 4932 4931

SPRINGFIELD UTILITY BOARD (INC) p 1361
250 A St, Springfield OR 97477
Tel (541) 746-8451 SIC 4931 4941

▲ **SCANA CORP** p 1286
100 Scana Pkwy, Cayce SC 29033
Tel (803) 217-9000
SIC 4931 4911 4924 4922

■ **SOUTH CAROLINA ELECTRIC & GAS CO** p 1343
100 Scana Pkwy, Cayce SC 29033
Tel (803) 217-9000
SIC 4931 4911 4922 4924

MORRISTOWN UTILITY COMMISSION p 990
441 W Main St, Morristown TN 37814
Tel (423) 317-8845 SIC 4931

PUBLIC UTILITIES BOARD p 1190
1425 Robinhood St, Brownsville TX 78521
Tel (956) 350-8819 SIC 4931

AMBIT ENERGY HOLDINGS LLC p 65
1801 N Lamar St Ste 200, Dallas TX 75202
Tel (214) 461-4736 SIC 4931

▲ **CENTERPOINT ENERGY INC** p 276
1111 Louisiana St Ste 264, Houston TX 77002
Tel (713) 207-1111 SIC 4931

DIRECT ENERGY SERVICES LLC p 441
12 Greenway Plz Ste 250, Houston TX 77046
Tel (713) 877-3500 SIC 4931

■ **DYNEGY RESOURCE I LLC** p 465
601 Travis St Ste 1400, Houston TX 77002
Tel (713) 507-6400 SIC 4911 4924 4931

▲ **SPARK ENERGY INC** p 1354
12140 Wickchester Ln, Houston TX 77079
Tel (713) 600-2600 SIC 4931 4911

CITY PUBLIC SERVICES OF SAN ANTONIO p 319
145 Navarro St, San Antonio TX 78205
Tel (210) 353-2222 SIC 4931 4932

BVU AUTHORITY p 230
15022 Lee Hwy, Bristol VA 24202
Tel (276) 821-6100 SIC 4931

■ **DOMINION NUCLEAR CONNECTICUT INC** p 449
120 Tredegar St, Richmond VA 23219
Tel (866) 366-4357 SIC 4931

■ **WGL ENERGY SERVICES INC** p 1604
8614 Westwood Center Dr # 1200, Vienna VA 22182
Tel (703) 333-3900 SIC 4931 1711

PUGET ENERGY INC p 1191
10885 Ne 4th St Ste 1200, Bellevue WA 98004
Tel (425) 454-6363 SIC 4931 4924

■ **NORTHERN STATES POWER CO** p 1057
1414 W Hamilton Ave, Eau Claire WI 54701
Tel (715) 839-2625 SIC 4931

■ **WISCONSIN PUBLIC SERVICE CORP** p 1619
700 N Adams St, Green Bay WI 54301
Tel (800) 450-7260 SIC 4931

■ **MADISON GAS AND ELECTRIC CO** p 894
133 S Blair St, Madison WI 53788
Tel (608) 252-7000 SIC 4931

■ **WISCONSIN POWER AND LIGHT CO** p 1619
4902 N Biltmore Ln # 1000, Madison WI 53718
Tel (608) 458-3311 SIC 4931

■ **INTEGRYS HOLDING INC** p 750
231 W Michigan St, Milwaukee WI 53201
Tel (414) 221-2345 SIC 4931

SIC 4932 Gas & Other Svcs Combined

■ **SOUTHERN CALIFORNIA GAS CO** p 1347
555 W 5th St Fl 31, Los Angeles CA 90013
Tel (213) 244-1200 SIC 4924 4922 4932

■ **CALPINE ENERGY SOLUTIONS LLC** p 242
401 W A St Ste 500, San Diego CA 92101
Tel (877) 273-6772 SIC 4931 4932

▲ **SEMPRA ENERGY** p 1303
488 8th Ave, San Diego CA 92101
Tel (619) 696-2000
SIC 4932 4911 5172 4922

ENERGY CORP OF AMERICA p 497
4643 S Ulster St Ste 1100, Denver CO 80237
Tel (303) 694-2667
SIC 4924 4932 1382 4922 5172

■ **CONNECTICUT ENERGY CORP** p 357
60 Marsh Hill Rd, Orange CT 06477
Tel (203) 382-8111 SIC 4911 4932

■ **GAS CO LLC** p 593
745 Fort Street Mall # 1800, Honolulu HI 96813
Tel (808) 594-5530
SIC 4932 4925 5172 5984

■ **SOUTHERN INDIANA GAS & ELECTRIC CO** p 1349
1 Vectren Sq, Evansville IN 47708
Tel (812) 424-6411 SIC 4911 4924 4932

■ **VECTREN UTILITY HOLDINGS INC** p 1546
1 Vectren Sq, Evansville IN 47708
Tel (812) 491-4000 SIC 4932 4911 4924

■ **LG&E AND KU ENERGY LLC** p 860
220 W Main St Ste 1400, Louisville KY 40202
Tel (502) 627-2000
SIC 4911 4931 4932 4924

■ **OTTER TAIL ENERGY SERVICES CO INC** p 1098
224 E Washington Ave, Fergus Falls MN 56537
Tel (218) 739-8888 SIC 4932

METROPOLITAN UTILITIES DISTRICT p 956
1723 Harney St, Omaha NE 68102
Tel (402) 554-6666 SIC 4932

■ **ELIZABETHTOWN GAS CO** p 487
1 Elizabethtown Plz, Union NJ 07083
Tel (908) 289-5000 SIC 4932 4924

▲ **MACQUARIE INFRASTRUCTURE CORP** p 893
125 W 55th St, New York NY 10019
Tel (212) 231-1000
SIC 5172 4581 4785 7521 4932

CENTRAL HUDSON GAS & ELECTRIC CORP p 278
284 South Ave Dept 100, Poughkeepsie NY 12601
Tel (845) 452-2700 SIC 4911 4924 4932

HERITAGE COOPERATIVE INC p 686
11177 Township Road 133, West Mansfield OH 43358
Tel (419) 294-2371
SIC 5153 5261 4925 4932

LAKEWOOD MIDSTREAM LLC p 840
6655 S Lewis Ave Ste 200, Tulsa OK 74136
Tel (918) 392-9356 SIC 4932

■ AVANGRID RENEWABLES HOLDINGS INC p 136
1125 Nw Couch St Ste 700, Portland OR 97209
Tel (503) 796-7000 SIC 4932 4931

■ AVANGRID RENEWABLES LLC p 136
1125 Nw Couch St Ste 700, Portland OR 97209
Tel (503) 796-7179 SIC 4932 4931

▲ UGI CORP p 1499
460 N Gulph Rd Ste 100, King Of Prussia PA 19406
Tel (610) 337-1000 SIC 4932

■ MASCOT PETROLEUM CO INC p 915
1801 Market St Fl 10, Philadelphia PA 19103
Tel (215) 977-3000 SIC 4932 5411

■ REGENCY GAS SERVICES LP p 1219
2001 Bryan St Ste 3700, Dallas TX 75201
Tel (214) 750-1771 SIC 4932

■ CALPINE MID-ATLANTIC ENERGY LLC p 242
717 Texas St Ste 1000, Houston TX 77002
Tel (713) 830-2000 SIC 4932

CITY PUBLIC SERVICES OF SAN ANTONIO p 319
145 Navarro St, San Antonio TX 78205
Tel (210) 353-2222 SIC 4931 4932

SIC 4939 Combination Utilities, NEC

LIBERTY UTILITIES CO p 863
12725 W Indian School Rd, Avondale AZ 85392
Tel (905) 465-4500 SIC 4939

NAVAJO TRIBAL UTILITY AUTHORITY p 1019
Hwy 12 N, Fort Defiance AZ 86504
Tel (928) 729-5721 SIC 4939 4924 4911

AGILE SOURCING PARTNERS INC p 35
2385 Railroad St, Corona CA 92880
Tel (951) 279-4154 SIC 4939

COLORADO SPRINGS UTILITIES p 339
121 S Tejon St Ste 200, Colorado Springs CO 80903
Tel (719) 448-4800 SIC 4939

NEXUS BIOENERGY INC p 1041
3026 Castle Peak Ave, Superior CO 80027
Tel (720) 318-2339 SIC 4939 7389 8731

■ DELMARVA POWER & LIGHT CO p 425
500 N Wakefield Dr Fl 2, Newark DE 19702
Tel (202) 872-2000 SIC 4939

GAINESVILLE REGIONAL UTILITIES (INC) p 589
301 Se 4th Ave, Gainesville FL 32601
Tel (352) 334-3400
SIC 4939 4941 4924 4911

ORLANDO UTILITIES COMMISSION p 1095
100 W Anderson St, Orlando FL 32801
Tel (407) 246-2121
SIC 4941 4931 4939 4911

WATER GAS & LIGHT COMMISSION p 1581
207 Pine Ave, Albany GA 31701
Tel (229) 883-8330 SIC 4939

▲ NISOURCE INC p 1044
801 E 86th Ave, Merrillville IN 46410
Tel (877) 647-5990 SIC 4939 4922

VEOLIA ENERGY NORTH AMERICA HOLDINGS INC p 1548
53 State St Ste 14, Boston MA 02109
Tel (617) 849-6612 SIC 4939 4961

TENASKA ENERGY INC p 1437
14302 Fnb Pkwy, Omaha NE 68154
Tel (402) 691-9500
SIC 4911 4924 4939 8742

TENASKA INC p 1437
14302 Fnb Pkwy, Omaha NE 68154
Tel (402) 691-9500
SIC 4924 4911 4939 8742

■ ORMAT NEVADA INC p 1095
6225 Neil Rd, Reno NV 89511
Tel (775) 356-9029 SIC 4939

▲ SUBURBAN PROPANE PARTNERS LP p 1396
240 Route 10 W, Whippany NJ 07981
Tel (973) 887-5300
SIC 5984 5172 4939 1711

■ UGI UTILITIES INC p 1499
2525 N 12th St Ste 360, Reading PA 19605
Tel (610) 796-3400 SIC 4939

UTILICON SOLUTIONS LTD p 1537
708 Blair Mill Rd, Willow Grove PA 19090
Tel (215) 784-4200 SIC 4939 4923

■ IPH II LLC p 763
601 Travis St Ste 1400, Houston TX 77002
Tel (713) 507-6400 SIC 4939

EAST TEXAS ELECTRIC COOPERATIVE INC p 471
2905 Westward Dr, Nacogdoches TX 75964
Tel (936) 560-9532 SIC 4939

NORTHERN VIRGINIA ELECTRIC COOPERATIVE p 1057
10323 Lomond Dr, Manassas VA 20109
Tel (703) 335-0500
SIC 4911 8611 8741 4939

PUGET SOUND ENERGY INC p 1191
10885 Ne 4th St Ste 1200, Bellevue WA 98004
Tel (425) 454-6363 SIC 4939 4911

■ AVISTA UTILITIES INC p 138
1411 E Mission Ave, Spokane WA 99202
Tel (509) 489-0500 SIC 4939

▲ MGE ENERGY INC p 958
133 S Blair St, Madison WI 53788
Tel (608) 252-7000 SIC 4939 4911 4924

SIC 4941 Water Sply

WATER WORKS BOARD OF CITY OF BIRMINGHAM p 1581
3600 1st Ave N, Birmingham AL 35222
Tel (205) 244-4000 SIC 4941

BOARD OF WATER AND SEWER COMMISSIONERS OF CITY OF MOBILE p 196
207 N Catherine St, Mobile AL 36604
Tel (251) 694-3100 SIC 4952 4941

ARIZONA WATER CO p 109
3805 N Black Canyon Hwy, Phoenix AZ 85015
Tel (480) 982-2201 SIC 4941

EPCOR WATER (USA) INC p 504
2355 W Pinnacle Peak Rd # 300, Phoenix AZ 85027
Tel (623) 445-2400 SIC 4941

CONWAY CORP p 365
1307 Prairie St, Conway AR 72034
Tel (501) 450-6000 SIC 4911 4941 4841

INLAND EMPIRE UTILITIES AGENCY A MUNICIPAL WATER DISTRICT (INC) p 743
6075 Kimball Ave, Chino CA 91708
Tel (909) 993-1600 SIC 4941

COACHELLA VALLEY WATER DISTRICT p 331
85995 Avenue 52, Coachella CA 92236
Tel (760) 398-2651
SIC 4941 4971 4952 7389

CONTRA COSTA WATER DISTRICT INC p 364
1331 Concord Ave, Concord CA 94520
Tel (925) 688-8000 SIC 4941

SOUTHWEST WATER CO p 1353
1325 N Grand Ave Ste 100, Covina CA 91724
Tel (626) 543-2500 SIC 4941 4952

LIBERTY UTILITIES (PARK WATER) CORP p 863
9750 Washburn Rd, Downey CA 90241
Tel (562) 923-0711 SIC 4941

SAN GABRIEL VALLEY WATER CO p 1277
11142 Garvey Ave, El Monte CA 91733
Tel (626) 448-6183 SIC 4941

ALAMEDA COUNTY WATER DISTRICT INC p 44
43885 S Grimmer Blvd, Fremont CA 94538
Tel (510) 668-4200 SIC 4941

IRVINE RANCH WATER DISTRICT INC p 765
15600 Sand Canyon Ave, Irvine CA 92618
Tel (949) 453-5300 SIC 4941 4952

LOS ANGELES DEPARTMENT OF WATER AND POWER p 878
111 N Hope St, Los Angeles CA 90012
Tel (213) 367-4211 SIC 4941 4911

METROPOLITAN WATER DISTRICT OF SOUTHERN CALIFORNIA p 957
700 N Alameda St, Los Angeles CA 90012
Tel (213) 217-6000 SIC 4941

EAST BAY MUNICIPAL UTILITY DISTRICT WATER SYSTEM p 469
375 11th St, Oakland CA 94607
Tel (866) 403-2683 SIC 4941

EASTERN MUNICIPAL WATER DISTRICT p 472
2270 Trumble Rd, Perris CA 92572
Tel (951) 928-3777 SIC 4941 4952

■ CALIFORNIA AMERICAN WATER CO p 239
655 W Broadway Ste 1410, San Diego CA 92101
Tel (619) 409-7703 SIC 4941

SAN DIEGO COUNTY WATER AUTHORITY p 1276
4677 Overland Ave, San Diego CA 92123
Tel (858) 522-6600 SIC 4941

▲ AMERICAN STATES WATER CO p 80
630 E Foothill Blvd, San Dimas CA 91773
Tel (909) 394-3600 SIC 4941 4911

■ GOLDEN STATE WATER CO p 621
630 E Foothill Blvd, San Dimas CA 91773
Tel (909) 394-3600 SIC 4941 4911

■ CALIFORNIA WATER SERVICE CO p 242
1720 N 1st St, San Jose CA 95112
Tel (408) 367-8200 SIC 4941

▲ CALIFORNIA WATER SERVICE GROUP p 242
1720 N 1st St, San Jose CA 95112
Tel (408) 367-8200 SIC 4941

■ SAN JOSE WATER CO p 1277
110 W Taylor St, San Jose CA 95110
Tel (408) 288-5314 SIC 4941

SANTA CLARA VALLEY WATER DISTRICT PUBLIC FACILITIES FINANCING CORP p 1280
5750 Almaden Expy, San Jose CA 95118
Tel (408) 265-2600 SIC 4941

▲ SJW CORP p 1328
110 W Taylor St, San Jose CA 95110
Tel (408) 279-7800 SIC 4941 6531

OTAY WATER DISTRICT (INC) p 1097
2554 Sweetwater Sprng Blvd, Spring Valley CA 91978
Tel (619) 670-2222 SIC 4941 1623

DENVER BOARD OF WATER COMMISSIONERS p 429
1600 W 12th Ave, Denver CO 80204
Tel (303) 893-2444 SIC 4941

OPERATIONS MANAGEMENT INTERNATIONAL INC p 1089
9193 S Jamaica St Ste 400, Englewood CO 80112
Tel (303) 740-0019 SIC 4952 4941

COUNTY OF JEFFERSON p 378
100 Jefferson County Pkwy, Golden CO 80419
Tel (303) 216-2987 SIC 4941

AQUARION WATER CO p 101
835 Main St, Bridgeport CT 06604
Tel (800) 732-9678 SIC 4941

▲ CONNECTICUT WATER SERVICE INC p 357
93 W Main St, Clinton CT 06413
Tel (860) 669-8636 SIC 4941 6531 1623

METROPOLITAN DISTRICT p 955
555 Main St, Hartford CT 06103
Tel (860) 247-6487 SIC 4941 4952

AQUARION WATER CO OF CONNECTICUT p 101
200 Monroe Tpke, Monroe CT 06468
Tel (203) 445-7310 SIC 4941

SOUTH CENTRAL CONNECTICUT REGIONAL WATER AUTHORITY p 1343
90 Sargent Dr, New Haven CT 06511
Tel (203) 562-4020 SIC 4941

SUEZ NORTH AMERICA INC p 1396
2000 First State Blvd, Wilmington DE 19804
Tel (302) 633-5670 SIC 4941 3569 3589

DC WATER AND SEWER AUTHORITY p 418
5000 Overlook Ave Sw, Washington DC 20032
Tel (202) 787-2000 SIC 4952 4941

■ AQUA UTILITIES FLORIDA INC p 101
1000 Colour Pl, Apopka FL 32703
Tel (386) 740-7174 SIC 4941 4952

TAMPA BAY WATER A REGIONAL WATER SUPPLY AUTHORITY p 1423
2575 Enterprise Rd, Clearwater FL 33763
Tel (727) 796-2355 SIC 4941

ST ENVIRONMENTAL SERVICES INC (I) p 1366
5726 Corporation Cir, Fort Myers FL 33905
Tel (239) 690-0175 SIC 4959 4941

FORT PIERCE UTILITIES AUTHORITY p 569
206 S 6th St, Fort Pierce FL 34950
Tel (772) 466-1600
SIC 4931 4941 4924 4813

GAINESVILLE REGIONAL UTILITIES (INC) p 589
301 Se 4th Ave, Gainesville FL 32601
Tel (352) 334-3400
SIC 4939 4941 4924 4911

US WATER SERVICES CORP p 1533
4939 Cross Bayou Blvd, New Port Richey FL 34652
Tel (727) 848-8292 SIC 4941

ORLANDO UTILITIES COMMISSION p 1095
100 W Anderson St, Orlando FL 32801
Tel (407) 246-2121
SIC 4941 4931 4939 4911

ELIZABETHTOWN WATER CO INC p 487
7303 Plantation Rd, Pensacola FL 32504
Tel (251) 656-9857 SIC 4941

EMERALD COAST UTILITIES AUTHORITY p 491
9255 Sturdevant St, Pensacola FL 32514
Tel (850) 476-5110 SIC 4959 4952 4941

SOUTH FLORIDA WATER MANAGEMENT DISTRICT LEASING CORP p 1344
3301 Gun Club Rd, West Palm Beach FL 33406
Tel (561) 686-8800 SIC 4941

CHEROKEE COUNTY WATER & SEWERAGE AUTHORITY p 294
391 W Main St, Canton GA 30114
Tel (770) 591-7156 SIC 4941 4952

MACON WATER AUTHORITY p 893
790 2nd St, Macon GA 31201
Tel (478) 464-5600 SIC 4941 4952

BOARD OF LIGHTS AND WATER p 195
675 N Marietta Pkwy Ne, Marietta GA 30060
Tel (770) 794-5150 SIC 4911 4941

CLAYTON COUNTY WATER AUTHORITY p 323
1600 Battle Creek Rd, Morrow GA 30260
Tel (770) 961-2130 SIC 4941 4952

SAVANNAH CITY WATER SUPPLY p 1284
6183 Hwy 21 N, Savannah GA 31407
Tel (912) 964-4473 SIC 4941

SEA ISLAND SERVICES INC p 1295
100 Hudson Pl, Sea Island GA 31561
Tel (912) 638-3611 SIC 4111 4941

BOARD OF WATER SUPPLY p 196
630 S Beretania St, Honolulu HI 96843
Tel (808) 748-5100 SIC 4941

C STEIN INC p 233
4719 S Market St, Boise ID 83705
Tel (208) 378-0550
SIC 5181 5182 5149 4941 5921

■ ILLINOIS-AMERICAN WATER CO p 733
300 N Water Works Dr, Belleville IL 62223
Tel (618) 236-1181 SIC 4941

UTILITIES INC p 1537
2335 Sanders Rd, Northbrook IL 60062
Tel (847) 498-6440 SIC 4941 4952

■ INDIANA-AMERICAN WATER CO INC p 739
555 E County Line Rd # 201, Greenwood IN 46143
Tel (800) 492-8373 SIC 4941

CITIZENS WATER p 311
2020 N Meridian St, Indianapolis IN 46202
Tel (317) 631-1431 SIC 4941

VEOLIA WATER AMERICAS LLC p 1548
101 W Washington St # 1400, Indianapolis IN 46204
Tel (317) 917-3700 SIC 4941 4952

VEOLIA WATER NORTH AMERICA OPERATING SERVICES LLC p 1548
101 W Washington St, Indianapolis IN 46204
Tel (317) 917-3700 SIC 4941

MUSCATINE POWER & WATER (INC) p 1002
3205 Cedar St, Muscatine IA 52761
Tel (563) 263-2631 SIC 4911 4941

KANSAS CITY BOARD OF PUBLIC UTILITIES p 802
540 Minnesota Ave, Kansas City KS 66101
Tel (913) 573-9000 SIC 4931 4941

WATER DISTRICT NO1 OF JOHNSON COUNTY KANSAS p 1581
10747 Renner Blvd, Lenexa KS 66219
Tel (913) 895-5500 SIC 4941

ELECTRIC & WATER PLANT BOARD OF CITY OF FRANKFORT KY p 484
317 W 2nd St, Frankfort KY 40601
Tel (502) 352-4372
SIC 4941 4911 7382 5063 4841 4813

LOUISVILLE WATER CO p 881
550 S 3rd St, Louisville KY 40202
Tel (502) 569-3600 SIC 4941

OWENSBORO MUNICIPAL UTILITIES ELECTRIC LIGHT & POWER SYSTEM p 1100
2070 Tamarack Rd, Owensboro KY 42301
Tel (270) 926-3200 SIC 4911 4941

PORTLAND WATER DISTRICT p 1163
225 Douglass St, Portland ME 04102
Tel (207) 761-8310 SIC 4941 4952 8741

WASHINGTON SUBURBAN SANITARY COMMISSION (INC) p 1579
14501 Sweitzer Ln, Laurel MD 20707
Tel (301) 206-8000 SIC 4941 4952

SPRINGFIELD WATER & SEWER COMMISSION p 1361
250 M St, Agawam MA 01001
Tel (413) 787-6060 SIC 4941

VEOLIA WATER NORTH AMERICA-CENTRAL LLC p 1549
53 State St Ste 14, Boston MA 02109
Tel (617) 849-6600 SIC 4952 4941

■ GE IONICS INC p 596
3 Burlington Woods Dr # 200, Burlington MA 01803
Tel (781) 359-7000
SIC 3589 2086 4941 3559 2899 3823

▲ ALLETE INC p 53
30 W Superior St, Duluth MN 55802
Tel (218) 279-5000
SIC 4931 4924 4941 1231 6552

ALLIANCE WATER RESOURCES INC p 55
206 S Keene St, Columbia MO 65201
Tel (573) 874-8080 SIC 4941 4952

▲ EMPIRE DISTRICT ELECTRIC CO p 493
602 S Joplin Ave, Joplin MO 64801
Tel (417) 625-5100 SIC 4911 4941

CITY UTILITIES OF SPRINGFIELD MO p 320
301 E Central St, Springfield MO 65802
Tel (417) 863-9000 SIC 4924 4941

LAS VEGAS VALLEY WATER DISTRICT p 845
1001 S Valley View Blvd, Las Vegas NV 89107
Tel (702) 870-2011 SIC 4941

SOUTHERN NEVADA WATER AUTHORITY p 1349
100 N City Pkwy Ste 700, Las Vegas NV 89106
Tel (702) 862-3400 SIC 4941

■ SIERRA PACIFIC POWER CO p 1321
6100 Neil Rd Ste 100, Reno NV 89511
Tel (775) 834-4011
SIC 4911 4924 4941 4971

■ NEW JERSEY AMERICAN WATER CO p 1031
131 Woodcrest Rd, Cherry Hill NJ 08003
Tel (856) 310-2206 SIC 4941

▲ MIDDLESEX WATER CO p 965
1500 Ronson Rd, Iselin NJ 08830
Tel (732) 634-1500 SIC 4941 1623

ETOWN CORP p 512
989 Lenox Dr Ste 224, Lawrenceville NJ 08648
Tel (609) 512-9400 SIC 4941

N A SUEZ p 1005
461 From Rd Ste F, Paramus NJ 07652
Tel (201) 767-9300 SIC 4941

SUEZ ENVIRONNEMENT p 1396
461 From Rd Ste 400, Paramus NJ 07652
Tel (201) 767-9300 SIC 4941

SUEZ WATER INC p 1396
461 From Rd Ste 400, Paramus NJ 07652
Tel (201) 767-9300 SIC 6719 4941 4952

SUEZ WATER NEW JERSEY INC p 1396
461 From Rd Ste 400, Paramus NJ 07652
Tel (201) 767-9300 SIC 4941

■ AMERICAN INTERNATIONAL WATER SERVICES CO p 75
1025 Laurel Oak Rd, Voorhees NJ 08043
Tel (856) 346-8200 SIC 4941

▲ AMERICAN WATER WORKS CO INC p 81
1025 Laurel Oak Rd, Voorhees NJ 08043
Tel (856) 346-8200 SIC 4941 1629 1623

NORTH JERSEY DISTRICT WATER SUPPLY COMMISSION p 1052
1 F A Orechio Dr, Wanaque NJ 07465
Tel (973) 831-6212 SIC 4971 4941

ALBUQUERQUE BERNALILLO COUNTY WATER UTILITY AUTHORITY p 47
1 Civic Plz Nw Fl 10, Albuquerque NM 87102
Tel (505) 768-2907 SIC 4941

ERIE COUNTY WATER AUTHORITY p 508
295 Main St Rm 350, Buffalo NY 14203
Tel (716) 849-8484 SIC 4941

EWT HOLDINGS III CORP p 516
666 5th Ave Fl 36, New York NY 10103
Tel (212) 644-5900
SIC 3589 3823 3826 4941 5051

SW MERGER ACQUISITION CORP p 1410
245 Park Ave, New York NY 10167
Tel (212) 648-2355 SIC 4941 4952

SUFFOLK COUNTY WATER AUTHORITY INC p 1396
4060 Sunrise Hwy, Oakdale NY 11769
Tel (631) 563-0255 SIC 4941

ORANGE WATER AND SEWER AUTHORITY p 1092
400 Jones Ferry Rd, Carrboro NC 27510
Tel (919) 960-6142 SIC 4941 4952

PUBLIC WORKS COMMISSION OF CITY OF FAYETTEVILLE p 1190
955 Old Wilmington Rd, Fayetteville NC 28301
Tel (910) 223-4005 SIC 4911 4941

CLEVELAND WATER DEPARTMENT p 326
5953 Deering Ave, Cleveland OH 44130
Tel (216) 664-3168 SIC 4941

SPRINGFIELD UTILITY BOARD (INC) p 1361
250 A St, Springfield OR 97477
Tel (541) 746-8451 SIC 4931 4941

▲ AQUA AMERICA INC p 101
762 W Lancaster Ave, Bryn Mawr PA 19010
Tel (610) 527-8000 SIC 4941 4952

■ AQUA PENNSYLVANIA INC p 101
762 W Lancaster Ave, Bryn Mawr PA 19010
Tel (610) 525-1400
SIC 4941 8741 4971 1623

CHESTER WATER AUTHORITY p 295
415 Welsh St, Chester PA 19013
Tel (610) 876-8181 SIC 4941

■ GE INFRASTRUCTURE SENSING p 596
4636 Somerton Rd, Feasterville Trevose PA 19053
Tel (617) 926-1749
SIC 3589 2086 4941 3559 2899 3823

■ PENNSYLVANIA - AMERICAN WATER CO p 1130
800 W Hershey Park Dr, Hershey PA 17033
Tel (717) 533-5000 SIC 4941

LAUREL HOLDINGS INC p 847
111 Roosevelt Blvd, Johnstown PA 15906
Tel (814) 533-5777
SIC 4941 5063 3599 4724 7349

PITTSBURGH WATER & SEWER AUTHORITY p 1152
1200 Penn Ave Ste 100, Pittsburgh PA 15222
Tel (412) 255-8935 SIC 4941 7389

EVOQUA WATER TECHNOLOGIES LLC p 516
181 Thorn Hill Rd, Warrendale PA 15086
Tel (724) 772-0044
SIC 3589 3569 3823 3826 4941

COMMISSIONERS OF PUBLIC WORKS p 345
103 Saint Philip St, Charleston SC 29403
Tel (843) 727-6800 SIC 4941

GRAND STRAND WATER & SEWER AUTHORITY p 630
166 Jackson Bluff Rd, Conway SC 29526
Tel (843) 443-8200 SIC 4941 4952

BERKELEY COUNTY WATER AND SANITATION AUTHORITY p 175
212 Oakley Plantation Dr, Moncks Corner SC 29461
Tel (843) 761-8817 SIC 4941 4953

SPARTANBURG WATER SYSTEM p 1355
200 Commerce St, Spartanburg SC 29306
Tel (864) 582-6375 SIC 4941 4952

JACKSON ENERGY AUTHORITY p 773
351 Dr Martin Luther, Jackson TN 38301
Tel (731) 422-7500
SIC 4925 4911 4941 4952

KNOXVILLE UTILITIES BOARD p 825
445 S Gay St, Knoxville TN 37902
Tel (865) 594-7324
SIC 4911 4924 4941 4952

LOWER COLORADO RIVER AUTHORITY p 881
3700 Lake Austin Blvd, Austin TX 78703
Tel (512) 473-3200 SIC 4911 4941 1629

EL PASO WATER UTILITIES PUBLIC SERVICE BOARD p 483
1154 Hawkins Blvd, El Paso TX 79925
Tel (915) 594-5500 SIC 4941 1623

FLUID DELIVERY SOLUTIONS LLC p 561
6795 Corp Pkwy Ste 200, Fort Worth TX 76126
Tel (817) 730-9761 SIC 4941

VEOLIA WATER NORTH AMERICA-NORTHEAST LLC p 1549
14950 Hathrow Forest Pkwy, Houston TX 77032
Tel (281) 449-1500 SIC 4952 4941

NEW BRAUNFELS UTILITIES p 1029
263 Main Plz, New Braunfels TX 78130
Tel (830) 608-8867 SIC 4911 4941 4952

BEXAR METROPOLITAN WATER DISTRICT PUBLIC FACILITY CORP p 179
2047 W Malone Ave, San Antonio TX 78225
Tel (210) 233-2335 SIC 4941

SAN ANTONIO WATER SYSTEM p 1275
2800 Us Highway 281 N, San Antonio TX 78212
Tel (210) 233-3814 SIC 4941

GUADALUPE-BLANCO RIVER AUTHORITY INDUSTRIAL DEVELOPMENT CORP p 644
933 E Court St, Seguin TX 78155
Tel (361) 575-6366 SIC 4911 4941 4952

NORTH TEXAS MUNICIPAL WATER DISTRICT p 1054
505 E Brown St, Wylie TX 75098
Tel (972) 442-5405 SIC 4953 4941

FAIRFAX COUNTY WATER AUTHORITY p 524
8570 Executive Park Ave, Fairfax VA 22031
Tel (703) 698-5600 SIC 4941

WESTERN VIRGINIA WATER AUTHORITY p 1600
601 S Jefferson St # 100, Roanoke VA 24011
Tel (540) 853-5700 SIC 4941

PRINCE WILLIAM COUNTY SERVICE AUTHORITY INC p 1176
4 County Complex Ct, Woodbridge VA 22192
Tel (703) 335-7900 SIC 4941 4952 4953

PUBLIC UTILITY DISTRICT 1 OF SNOHOMISH COUNTY p 1190
2320 California St, Everett WA 98201
Tel (425) 257-9288 SIC 4911 4941

CITY OF TACOMA DEPARTMENT OF PUBLIC UTILITIES p 319
3628 S 35th St, Tacoma WA 98409
Tel (253) 502-8900
SIC 4911 4941 4899 4013 4841

■ VIRGINIA WEST AMERICAN WATER CO p 1560
1600 Pennsylvania Ave, Charleston WV 25302
Tel (304) 353-6300 SIC 4941

VOGEL BROS BUILDING CO p 1564
2701 Packers Ave, Madison WI 53704
Tel (608) 241-5454 SIC 1542 1541 4941

SIC 4952 Sewerage Systems

BOARD OF WATER AND SEWER COMMISSIONERS OF CITY OF MOBILE p 196
207 N Catherine St, Mobile AL 36604
Tel (251) 694-3100 SIC 4952 4941

COACHELLA VALLEY WATER DISTRICT p 331
85995 Avenue 52, Coachella CA 92236
Tel (760) 398-2651
SIC 4941 4971 4952 7389

SOUTHWEST WATER CO p 1353
1325 N Grand Ave Ste 100, Covina CA 91724
Tel (626) 543-2500 SIC 4941 4952

IRVINE RANCH WATER DISTRICT INC p 765
15600 Sand Canyon Ave, Irvine CA 92618
Tel (949) 453-5300 SIC 4941 4952

CENTRAL CONTRA COSTA SANITARY DISTRICT FACILITIES FINANCING AUTHORITY p 278
5019 Imhoff Pl, Martinez CA 94553
Tel (925) 228-9500 SIC 4952 4959

EAST BAY MUNICIPAL UTILITY DISTRICT WASTEWATER SYSTEM p 469
375 111th St, Oakland CA 94607
Tel (866) 403-2683 SIC 4952 4953

EASTERN MUNICIPAL WATER DISTRICT p 472
2270 Trumble Rd, Perris CA 92572
Tel (951) 928-3777 SIC 4941 4952

METRO WASTEWATER RECLAMATION DISTRICT p 955
6450 York St, Denver CO 80229
Tel (303) 286-3000 SIC 4952

OPERATIONS MANAGEMENT INTERNATIONAL INC p 1089
9193 S Jamaica St Ste 400, Englewood CO 80112
Tel (303) 740-0019 SIC 4952 4941

METROPOLITAN DISTRICT p 955
555 Main St, Hartford CT 06103
Tel (860) 247-6487 SIC 4941 4952

DC WATER AND SEWER AUTHORITY p 418
5000 Overlook Ave Sw, Washington DC 20032
Tel (202) 787-2000 SIC 4952 4941

■ AQUA UTILITIES FLORIDA INC p 101
1000 Colour Pl, Apopka FL 32703
Tel (386) 740-7174 SIC 4941 4952

EMERALD COAST UTILITIES AUTHORITY p 491
9255 Sturdevant St, Pensacola FL 32514
Tel (850) 476-5110 SIC 4959 4952 4941

CHEROKEE COUNTY WATER & SEWERAGE AUTHORITY p 294
391 W Main St, Canton GA 30114
Tel (770) 591-7156 SIC 4941 4952

MACON WATER AUTHORITY p 893
790 2nd St, Macon GA 31201
Tel (478) 464-5600 SIC 4941 4952

CLAYTON COUNTY WATER AUTHORITY p 323
1600 Battle Creek Rd, Morrow GA 30260
Tel (770) 961-2130 SIC 4941 4952

UTILITIES INC p 1537
2335 Sanders Rd, Northbrook IL 60062
Tel (847) 498-6440 SIC 4941 4952

VEOLIA WATER AMERICAS LLC p 1548
101 W Washington St # 1400, Indianapolis IN 46204
Tel (317) 917-3700 SIC 4941 4952

LOUISVILLE & JEFFERSON COUNTY METROPOLITAN SEWER DISTRICT p 880
700 W Liberty St, Louisville KY 40203
Tel (502) 540-6000 SIC 4952

CAJUN CONSTRUCTORS LLC p 237
15635 Airline Hwy, Baton Rouge LA 70817
Tel (225) 753-5857
SIC 1623 4952 1541 1542

PORTLAND WATER DISTRICT p 1163
225 Douglass St, Portland ME 04102
Tel (207) 761-8310 SIC 4941 4952 8741

WASHINGTON SUBURBAN SANITARY COMMISSION (INC) p 1579
14501 Sweitzer Ln, Laurel MD 20707
Tel (301) 206-8000 SIC 4941 4952

VEOLIA WATER NORTH AMERICA-CENTRAL LLC p 1549
53 State St Ste 14, Boston MA 02109
Tel (617) 849-6600 SIC 4952 4941

ALLIANCE WATER RESOURCES INC p 55
206 S Keene St, Columbia MO 65201
Tel (573) 874-8080 SIC 4941 4952

METROPOLITAN ST LOUIS SEWER DISTRICT p 956
2350 Market St Ste 300, Saint Louis MO 63103
Tel (314) 768-6200 SIC 4952

ATLANTIC COUNTY UTILITIES AUTHORITY p 126
6700 Delilah Rd, Egg Harbor Township NJ 08234
Tel (609) 272-6950 SIC 4953 4952

PASSAIC VALLEY SEWERAGE COMMISSION p 1119
600 Wilson Ave, Newark NJ 07105
Tel (973) 344-1800 SIC 4952

SUEZ WATER INC p 1396
461 From Rd Ste 400, Paramus NJ 07652
Tel (201) 767-9300 SIC 6719 4941 4952

MIDDLESEX COUNTY UTILITIES AUTHORITY INC p 965
2571 Main St, Sayreville NJ 08872
Tel (732) 721-3800 SIC 4952

SW MERGER ACQUISITION CORP p 1410
245 Park Ave, New York NY 10167
Tel (212) 648-2355 SIC 4941 4952

ORANGE WATER AND SEWER AUTHORITY p 1092
400 Jones Ferry Rd, Carrboro NC 27510
Tel (919) 960-6142 SIC 4941 4952

CLEAN WATER SERVICES p 324
2550 Sw Hillsboro Hwy, Hillsboro OR 97123
Tel (503) 681-3600 SIC 4952

▲ AQUA AMERICA INC p 101
762 W Lancaster Ave, Bryn Mawr PA 19010
Tel (610) 527-8000 SIC 4941 4952

ALLEGHENY COUNTY SANITARY AUTHORITY p 52
3300 Preble Ave, Pittsburgh PA 15233
Tel (412) 732-8020 SIC 4952

■ WATER SOLUTIONS HOLDINGS LLC p 1581
310 Seven Fields Blvd, Seven Fields PA 16046
Tel (717) 508-0550 SIC 4952

GRAND STRAND WATER & SEWER AUTHORITY p 630
166 Jackson Bluff Rd, Conway SC 29526
Tel (843) 443-8200 SIC 4941 4952

RENEWABLE WATER RESOURCES p 1224
561 Mauldin Rd, Greenville SC 29607
Tel (864) 299-4000 SIC 4952

SPARTANBURG WATER SYSTEM p 1355
200 Commerce St, Spartanburg SC 29306
Tel (864) 582-6375 SIC 4941 4952

JACKSON ENERGY AUTHORITY p 773
351 Dr Martin Luther, Jackson TN 38301
Tel (731) 422-7500
SIC 4925 4911 4941 4952

KNOXVILLE UTILITIES BOARD p 825
445 S Gay St, Knoxville TN 37902
Tel (865) 594-7324
SIC 4911 4924 4941 4952

VEOLIA WATER NORTH AMERICA-NORTHEAST LLC p 1549
14950 Hathrow Forest Pkwy, Houston TX 77032
Tel (281) 449-1500 SIC 4952 4941

NEW BRAUNFELS UTILITIES p 1029
263 Main Plz, New Braunfels TX 78130
Tel (830) 608-8867 SIC 4911 4941 4952

GUADALUPE-BLANCO RIVER AUTHORITY INDUSTRIAL DEVELOPMENT CORP p 644
933 E Court St, Seguin TX 78155
Tel (361) 575-6366 SIC 4911 4941 4952

HAMPTON ROADS SANITATION DISTRICT (INC) p 656
1434 Air Rail Ave, Virginia Beach VA 23455
Tel (757) 460-2261 SIC 4952

PRINCE WILLIAM COUNTY SERVICE AUTHORITY INC p 1176
4 County Complex Ct, Woodbridge VA 22192
Tel (703) 335-7900 SIC 4941 4952 4953

SIC 4953 Refuse Systems

ROBBIE D WOOD INC p 1240
1051 Old Warrior River Rd, Dolomite AL 35061
Tel (205) 744-8440 SIC 4953

MARK DUNNING INDUSTRIES p 907
100 Race Track Rd, Dothan AL 36303
Tel (334) 983-1506 SIC 4953

■ CUROTTO-CAN LLC p 402
4301 Gault Ave N, Fort Payne AL 35967
Tel (256) 845-8359 SIC 4953

SOUTHWEST METAL INDUSTRIES LLC p 1352
4708 W Pasadena Ave, Glendale AZ 85301
Tel (623) 760-9014 SIC 5051 4953

■ ALLIED WASTE INDUSTRIES INC p 57
18500 N Allied Way # 100, Phoenix AZ 85054
Tel (480) 627-2700 SIC 4953

■ ALLIED WASTE NORTH AMERICA INC p 57
18500 N Allied Way # 100, Phoenix AZ 85054
Tel (480) 627-2700 SIC 4953

■ ALLIED WASTE SYSTEMS INC p 57
18500 N Allied Way # 100, Phoenix AZ 85054
Tel (480) 627-2700 SIC 4953

■ BFI WASTE SYSTEMS OF NORTH AMERICA INC p 179
2394 E Camelback Rd, Phoenix AZ 85016
Tel (480) 627-2700 SIC 4953

■ BROWNING-FERRIS INDUSTRIES INC p 220
18500 N Allied Way # 100, Phoenix AZ 85054
Tel (480) 627-2700 SIC 4953 4959 7359

▲ REPUBLIC SERVICES INC p 1225
18500 N Allied Way # 100, Phoenix AZ 85054
Tel (480) 627-2700 SIC 4953

■ REPUBLIC SERVICES OF FLORIDA LIMITED PARTNERSHIP p 1225
18500 N Allied Way, Phoenix AZ 85054
Tel (480) 627-2700 SIC 4953

■ ALLIED WASTE INDUSTRIES (ARIZONA) INC p 57
15880 N Greenway, Scottsdale AZ 85260
Tel (480) 627-2700 SIC 4953

■ ALLIED WASTE SERVICES OF MASSACHUSETTS LLC p 57
15880 N Hayden Rd, Scottsdale AZ 85260
Tel (480) 627-2700 SIC 4953

▲ NUVERRA ENVIRONMENTAL SOLUTIONS INC p 1068
14624 N Scottsdale Rd, Scottsdale AZ 85254
Tel (602) 903-7802 SIC 1389 4953

RINECO CHEMICAL INDUSTRIES INC p 1235
819 Vulcan Rd, Benton AR 72015
Tel (501) 778-9089 SIC 4953

■ TERRA RENEWAL SERVICES INC p 1439
201 S Denver Ave Ste B, Russellville AR 72801
Tel (479) 498-0500 SIC 4953 4212

MP ENVIRONMENTAL SERVICES INC p 995
3400 Manor St, Bakersfield CA 93308
Tel (800) 458-3036
SIC 4953 4213 8748 7699

ARAKELIAN ENTERPRISES INC p 102
14048 Valley Blvd, City Of Industry CA 91746
Tel (626) 336-3636 SIC 4953

TALCO PLASTICS INC p 1422
1000 W Rincon St, Corona CA 92880
Tel (951) 531-2000 SIC 4953 2821

BURRTEC WASTE GROUP INC p 229
9890 Cherry Ave, Fontana CA 92335
Tel (909) 429-4200 SIC 4953

BURRTEC WASTE INDUSTRIES INC p 229
9890 Cherry Ave, Fontana CA 92335
Tel (909) 429-4200 SIC 4953 4212

ORANGE COUNTY SANITATION DISTRICT FINANCING CORP p 1092
10844 Ellis Ave, Fountain Valley CA 92708
Tel (714) 962-2411 SIC 4953

ELECTRONIC RECYCLERS INTERNATIONAL INC p 485
7815 N Palm Ave Ste 140, Fresno CA 93711
Tel (800) 884-8466 SIC 4953

■ RAINBOW DISPOSAL CO INC p 1205
17121 Nichols Ln, Huntington Beach CA 92647
Tel (714) 847-3581 SIC 4953

ATHENS DISPOSAL CO INC p 124
14048 Valley Blvd, La Puente CA 91746
Tel (626) 336-3636 SIC 4953

■ AECOM TECHNICAL SERVICES INC p 28
300 S Grand Ave Ste 1100, Los Angeles CA 90071
Tel (213) 593-8000
SIC 4953 8748 8742 8711

■ EARTH TECHNOLOGY CORP USA p 469
1999 Avenue Of Stars Ste 2600, Los Angeles CA 90067
Tel (213) 593-8000
SIC 4953 8748 8742 8711

EAST BAY MUNICIPAL UTILITY DISTRICT WASTEWATER SYSTEM p 469
375 111th St, Oakland CA 94607
Tel (866) 403-2683 SIC 4952 4953

■ WASTE MANAGEMENT OF ALAMEDA COUNTY INC p 1580
172 98th Ave, Oakland CA 94603
Tel (510) 613-8710 SIC 4953

REPLANET LLC p 1224
800 N Haven Ave Ste 120, Ontario CA 91764
Tel (951) 520-1700 SIC 5084 4953

■ WASTE MANAGEMENT COLLECTION AND RECYCLING INC p 1580
2050 N Glassell St, Orange CA 92865
Tel (714) 282-0200 SIC 4953

SIMS GROUP USA CORP p 1325
600 S 4th St, Richmond CA 94804
Tel (510) 412-5300 SIC 5093 4953

MINGS RESOURCE CORP p 973
3316 47th Ave, Sacramento CA 95824
Tel (916) 421-5054 SIC 4953

SACRAMENTO AREA SEWER DISTRICT p 1264
10060 Goethe Rd, Sacramento CA 95827
Tel (916) 876-6000 SIC 4953

CALIFORNIA MARINE CLEANING INC p 240
2049 Main St, San Diego CA 92113
Tel (619) 231-8788 SIC 4953

■ MOLECULAR BIOPRODUCTS INC p 982
9389 Waples St, San Diego CA 92121
Tel (858) 453-7551 SIC 4953

RECOLOGY INC p 1214
50 California St Fl 24, San Francisco CA 94111
Tel (415) 875-1000 SIC 4953

GREENWASTE RECOVERY INC p 638
625 Charles St, San Jose CA 95112
Tel (408) 283-4800 SIC 4953

WASTE CONNECTIONS OF CALIFORNIA INC p 1580
1333 Oakland Rd, San Jose CA 95112
Tel (408) 282-4400 SIC 4953

EDCO WASTE & RECYCLING SERVICES INC p 477
224 S Las Posas Rd, San Marcos CA 92078
Tel (760) 744-2700 SIC 4953 4212

■ WASTE MANAGEMENT COLLECTION AND RECYCLING INC p 1580
1800 S Grand Ave, Santa Ana CA 92705
Tel (714) 637-3010 SIC 7353 4953

MARBORG INDUSTRIES p 904
728 E Yanonali St, Santa Barbara CA 93103
Tel (805) 963-1852
SIC 4953 7359 7699 4212

■ CONSOLIDATED DISPOSAL SERVICE LLC p 359
12949 Telegraph Rd, Santa Fe Springs CA 90670
Tel (562) 347-2100 SIC 4953

SCOPE INDUSTRIES p 1293
2811 Wilshire Blvd # 410, Santa Monica CA 90403
Tel (310) 458-1574 SIC 4953

ECHOPOWER CORP p 475
3720 Baseline Ave, Santa Ynez CA 93460
Tel (805) 729-4473 SIC 4953 5331

EDCO DISPOSAL CORP INC p 477
2755 California Ave, Signal Hill CA 90755
Tel (619) 287-7555 SIC 4953

WORLD OIL MARKETING CO p 1625
9302 Garfield Ave, South Gate CA 90280
Tel (562) 928-0100
SIC 2911 4953 2951 5541 4213 4212

CR&R INC p 388
11292 Western Ave, Stanton CA 90680
Tel (714) 826-9049 SIC 4953 4212 7359

■ BROWNING-FERRIS INDUSTRIES OF CALIFORNIA INC p 220
9200 Glenoaks Blvd, Sun Valley CA 91352
Tel (818) 790-5410 SIC 4953

■ WASTE MANAGEMENT OF CALIFORNIA INC p 1580
9081 Tujunga Ave, Sun Valley CA 91352
Tel (877) 836-6526 SIC 4953

SANITATION DISTRICTS OF LOS ANGELES COUNTY p 1279
1955 Workman Mill Rd, Whittier CA 90601
Tel (562) 908-4288 SIC 4953

POTENTIAL INDUSTRIES INC p 1164
922 E E St, Wilmington CA 90744
Tel (310) 807-4466 SIC 4953 5093

KAISER-HILL CO LLC p 801
11025 Dover St Unit 1000, Broomfield CO 80021
Tel (303) 966-7000 SIC 4953

US WASTE INDUSTRIES INC p 1533
7770 Palmer Park Blvd, Colorado Springs CO 80951
Tel (719) 535-9041 SIC 4953

ALPINE DISPOSAL INC p 60
7373 Washington St, Denver CO 80229
Tel (303) 289-8019 SIC 4953

■ AECOM ENERGY & CONSTRUCTION INC p 28
6200 S Quebec St, Greenwood Village CO 80111
Tel (303) 228-3000
SIC 1622 1629 1081 4953

■ WASTE MANAGEMENT OF COLORADO INC p 1580
5500 S Quebec St Ste 250, Greenwood Village CO 80111
Tel (303) 797-1600 SIC 4953

CANUSA HERSHMAN RECYCLING LLC p 248
45 Ne Industrial Rd # 105, Branford CT 06405
Tel (203) 488-0887 SIC 4953

WHEELABRATOR CONNECTICUT INC p 1604
6 Howard Ave, Bridgeport CT 06605
Tel (203) 579-2607 SIC 4953

TRADEBE TREATMENT AND RECYCLING NORTHEAST LLC p 1468
47 Gracey Ave, Meriden CT 06451
Tel (203) 238-8102 SIC 4953 1442 4212

CWPM LLC p 404
25 Norton Pl, Plainville CT 06062
Tel (860) 747-1335 SIC 4953

MANAFORT BROTHERS INC p 900
414 New Britain Ave, Plainville CT 06062
Tel (860) 229-4853
SIC 1794 1771 1622 1795 4953

■ OAKLEAF WASTE MANAGEMENT LLC p 1071
415 Day Hill Rd, Windsor CT 06095
Tel (860) 290-1250 SIC 8741 4953

DELAWARE SOLID WASTE AUTHORITY p 424
1128 S Bradford St, Dover DE 19904
Tel (302) 739-5361 SIC 4953

CLIFF BERRY INC p 326
851 Eller Dr, Fort Lauderdale FL 33316
Tel (954) 763-3390
SIC 4953 4959 4212 2992 4491

PROGRESSIVE WASTE SOLUTIONS OF FL INC p 1182
2860 W State Road 84, Fort Lauderdale FL 33312
Tel (954) 888-4300 *SIC* 4953

■ SOUTHLAND ENVIRONMENTAL SERVICES INC p 1351
8619 Western Way, Jacksonville FL 32256
Tel (904) 731-2456 *SIC* 4953

WASTE PRO OF FLORIDA INC p 1581
2101 W State Rd Ste 301, Longwood FL 32779
Tel (407) 774-0800 *SIC* 4953

WASTE PRO USA INC p 1581
2101 W State Road 434 # 305, Longwood FL 32779
Tel (407) 869-8800 *SIC* 4953

LGL RECYCLING LLC p 860
2401 Pga Blvd, Palm Beach Gardens FL 33410
Tel (561) 582-6688 *SIC* 4953

■ ADVANCED DISPOSAL SERVICES INC p 25
90 Fort Wade Rd Ste 200, Ponte Vedra FL 32081
Tel (904) 737-7900 *SIC* 4953

■ ADVANCED DISPOSAL SERVICES MIDWEST LLC p 25
90 Fort Wade Rd Ste 200, Ponte Vedra FL 32081
Tel (904) 737-7900 *SIC* 4953

■ ADVANCED DISPOSAL SERVICES SOLID WASTE MIDWEST LLC p 25
90 Fort Wade Rd Ste 200, Ponte Vedra FL 32081
Tel (904) 737-7900 *SIC* 7699 4953 4959

■ ADVANCED DISPOSAL SERVICES SOLID WASTE SOUTHEAST INC p 25
90 Fort Wade Rd Ste 200, Ponte Vedra FL 32081
Tel (904) 737-7900 *SIC* 4953

■ ADVANCED DISPOSAL SERVICES SOUTH LLC p 25
90 Fort Wade Rd Ste 200, Ponte Vedra FL 32081
Tel (904) 737-7900 *SIC* 4953 6719

▲ ADVANCED DISPOSAL WASTE HOLDINGS CORP p 25
90 Fort Wade Rd Ste 200, Ponte Vedra FL 32081
Tel (904) 737-7900 *SIC* 4953

■ MWSTAR WASTE HOLDINGS CORP p 1004
90 Fort Wade Rd Ste 200, Ponte Vedra FL 32081
Tel (904) 737-7900 *SIC* 1629 4953

BURKS COMPANIES p 227
191 Peachtree St Ne # 800, Atlanta GA 30303
Tel (404) 589-4600
SIC 1752 5085 7349 4953 8999

NEWELL RECYCLING OF ATLANTA LLC p 1037
1359 Central Ave, Atlanta GA 30344
Tel (404) 766-1621 *SIC* 4953

■ WASTE MANAGEMENT INC OF FLORIDA p 1580
2859 Paces Ferry Rd Se # 1600, Atlanta GA 30339
Tel (770) 805-4130 *SIC* 4953

BRAMBLES USA INC (DEL) p 207
180 Technology Pkwy # 600, Norcross GA 30092
Tel (770) 776-1900
SIC 4953 4212 7353 8741 7359

▲ US ECOLOGY INC p 1531
251 E Front St Ste 400, Boise ID 83702
Tel (208) 331-8400 *SIC* 4953

AMOCO OIL HOLDING CO p 86
200 E Randolph St, Chicago IL 60601
Tel (312) 856-4650 *SIC* 8699 4953

DANIELS SHARPSMART INC p 411
111 W Jackson Blvd # 720, Chicago IL 60604
Tel (312) 546-8900 *SIC* 4953 2834

■ NATIONAL WASTE SERVICE INC p 1017
2608 S Damen Ave, Chicago IL 60608
Tel (773) 579-3600 *SIC* 4953

VEOLIA ENVIRONMENTAL SERVICES NORTH AMERICA CORP p 1548
200 E Randolph St # 7900, Chicago IL 60601
Tel (312) 552-2800 *SIC* 4953

RESOURCE MANAGEMENT ENTERPRISES INC p 1227
9999 Anderson Ave, Chicago Ridge IL 60415
Tel (708) 425-8565 *SIC* 4953

■ FCC ENVIRONMENTAL LLC p 533
2175 Point Blvd Ste 375, Elgin IL 60123
Tel (281) 668-3300 *SIC* 4953

■ HERITAGE-CRYSTAL CLEAN LLC p 686
2175 Point Blvd Ste 375, Elgin IL 60123
Tel (847) 836-5670 *SIC* 4953

GROOT INDUSTRIES INC p 641
2500 Landmeier Rd, Elk Grove Village IL 60007
Tel (847) 734-6400 *SIC* 4953

▲ STERICYCLE INC p 1386
28161 N Keith Dr, Lake Forest IL 60045
Tel (847) 367-5910 *SIC* 4953

ONYX ENVIRONMENTAL SERVICES LLC p 1088
700 E Bttrfeld Rd Ste 201, Lombard IL 60148
Tel (630) 218-1500
SIC 8711 4953 2869 1799 1629

RECYCLE AMERICA ALLIANCE LLC p 1215
720 E Butterfield Rd Fl 2, Lombard IL 60148
Tel (630) 572-8800 *SIC* 4953

■ WASTE MANAGEMENT OF INDIANA LLC p 1580
720 E Butterfield Rd Fl 2, Lombard IL 60148
Tel (630) 572-8800 *SIC* 4953

LAKESHORE RECYCLING SYSTEMS LLC p 840
6132 Oakton St, Morton Grove IL 60053
Tel (773) 685-8811 *SIC* 4953

COULTER COMPANIES INC p 374
4700 N Sterling Ave Ste 2, Peoria IL 61615
Tel (309) 686-8033 *SIC* 4953 8711

PERORIA DISPOSAL CO p 1137
4700 N Sterling Ave Ste 2, Peoria IL 61615
Tel (309) 686-8033 *SIC* 4953

WATTS TRUCKING SERVICE INC p 1583
525 17th St, Rock Island IL 61201
Tel (309) 788-7700 *SIC* 4953

WILLIAM CHARLES LTD p 1610
1401 N 2nd St, Rockford IL 61107
Tel (815) 963-7400
SIC 1611 5211 1731 4953

■ ILLIANA DISPOSAL SERVICE INC p 732
865 Wheeler St, Crown Point IN 46307
Tel (219) 662-8600 *SIC* 4953

TRADEBE GP p 1468
4343 Kennedy Ave, East Chicago IN 46312
Tel (800) 388-7242 *SIC* 4953 7699 1389

TRADEBE TREATMENT AND RECYCLING LLC p 1468
4343 Kennedy Ave, East Chicago IN 46312
Tel (219) 397-3951 *SIC* 4953

GOODWILL INDUSTRIES OF CENTRAL INDIANA INC p 624
1635 W Michigan St, Indianapolis IN 46222
Tel (317) 564-4313
SIC 5932 4783 8331 4953

TRADEBE ENVIRONMENTAL SERVICES LLC p 1468
1433 E 83rd Ave Ste 200, Merrillville IN 46410
Tel (800) 388-7242 *SIC* 4953 7699 1389

■ DEFFENBAUGH INDUSTRIES INC p 422
2601 Midwest Dr, Kansas City KS 66111
Tel (913) 631-3300 *SIC* 4212 4953

STAINLESS STEEL ACQUISITION CO LLC p 1374
2615 E Highway 146, La Grange KY 40031
Tel (502) 805-1120 *SIC* 4953

CHARAH INC p 288
12601 Plantside Dr, Louisville KY 40299
Tel (502) 245-1353 *SIC* 1081 4953

■ WASTE MANAGEMENT OF KENTUCKY LLC p 1580
7501 Grade Ln, Louisville KY 40219
Tel (502) 969-2355 *SIC* 4953

SYNAGRO TECHNOLOGIES INC p 1414
435 Williams Ct Ste 100, Baltimore MD 21220
Tel (800) 370-0035 *SIC* 4953

■ WASTE MANAGEMENT OF MARYLAND INC p 1580
6994 Columbia Gateway Dr # 200, Columbia MD 21046
Tel (410) 796-7010 *SIC* 4953 4212

IESI MD CORP p 730
2911 52nd Ave Ste A, Hyattsville MD 20781
Tel (410) 768-1900 *SIC* 4953 4212

■ COVANTA HAVERHILL INC p 384
100 Recovery Way, Haverhill MA 01835
Tel (978) 372-6288 *SIC* 4953 1629 4931

■ CLEAN HARBORS ENVIRONMENTAL SERVICES INC p 324
42 Longwater Dr, Norwell MA 02061
Tel (781) 792-5000 *SIC* 4953

▲ CLEAN HARBORS INC p 324
42 Longwater Dr, Norwell MA 02061
Tel (781) 792-5000 *SIC* 4953

■ PCG PARENT CORP p 1124
4 Technology Dr, Peabody MA 01960
Tel (978) 538-8000
SIC 5045 5065 4953 5093 7378

■ PCG TRADING LLC p 1124
4 Technology Dr, Peabody MA 01960
Tel (978) 538-8000
SIC 5045 5065 4953 5093 7378

WESTON & SAMPSON INC p 1602
5 Centennial Dr Ste 1, Peabody MA 01960
Tel (978) 532-1900 *SIC* 8711 8748 4953

HARVEST POWER INC p 666
200 5th Ave Fl 4b, Waltham MA 02451
Tel (781) 314-9500 *SIC* 4953

EL HARVEY & SONS INC p 482
68 Hopkinton Rd, Westborough MA 01581
Tel (508) 836-3000 *SIC* 4953

UNITED SITE SERVICES INC p 1511
50 Washington St 1000, Westborough MA 01581
Tel (508) 594-2655 *SIC* 4953

■ NORTRU LLC p 1061
515 Lycaste St, Detroit MI 48214
Tel (313) 824-5840 *SIC* 4953 5169

PRESSURE VESSEL SERVICE INC p 1173
10900 Harper Ave, Detroit MI 48213
Tel (313) 921-1200
SIC 5169 2819 2899 4953 3535

GRANGER ASSOCIATES INC p 630
16980 Wood Rd, Lansing MI 48906
Tel (517) 372-2800 *SIC* 4953 1794 6552

■ WASTE MANAGEMENT OF MICHIGAN INC p 1580
48797 Alpha Dr Ste 100, Wixom MI 48393
Tel (586) 574-2760 *SIC* 4953

■ OTTER TAIL POWER CO p 1098
215 S Cascade St, Fergus Falls MN 56537
Tel (218) 739-8200 *SIC* 3699 4953 6531

▲ APPLIANCE RECYCLING CENTERS OF AMERICA INC p 99
175 Jackson Ave N Ste 102, Hopkins MN 55343
Tel (952) 930-9000 *SIC* 5722 4953

TRUCK BODIES & EQUIPMENT INTERNATIONAL INC p 1485
52182 Ember Rd, Lake Crystal MN 56055
Tel (507) 726-2728 *SIC* 3713 4953

VEIT & CO INC p 1547
14000 Veit Pl, Rogers MN 55374
Tel (763) 428-2242 *SIC* 1611 1795 4953

GOODWILL INDUSTRIES INC p 624
553 Fairview Ave N, Saint Paul MN 55104
Tel (651) 379-5800
SIC 4953 8331 8322 5932 4226

■ WASTE MANAGEMENT OF MISSISSIPPI INC p 1581
1450 Country Club Dr, Jackson MS 39209
Tel (601) 922-9647 *SIC* 4953

■ EBV EXPLOSIVES ENVIRONMENTAL CO p 474
4174 County Road 180, Carthage MO 64836
Tel (417) 624-0212 *SIC* 4953

■ CONTINENTAL CEMENT CO LLC p 363
16100 Swingley Ridge Rd, Chesterfield MO 63017
Tel (636) 532-7440 *SIC* 3241 4953

■ ALLIED WASTE SERVICES OF INDEPENDENCE p 57
1220 S Brookside Ave, Independence MO 64052
Tel (816) 254-1470 *SIC* 4953

HERZOG CONTRACTING CORP p 688
600 S Riverside Rd, Saint Joseph MO 64507
Tel (816) 233-9001 *SIC* 1629 1611 4953

QRS INC p 1195
345 Marshall Ave Ste 301, Saint Louis MO 63119
Tel (314) 963-8000 *SIC* 4953

SHAPIRO SALES CO p 1312
9666 Olive Blvd Ste 500, Saint Louis MO 63132
Tel (314) 381-9300 *SIC* 5093 4953

■ J & J SANITATION INC p 770
87181 494th Ave, Oneill NE 68763
Tel (402) 336-3011 *SIC* 4953

■ REPUBLIC SILVER STATE DISPOSAL INC p 1225
770 E Sahara Ave Ste 400, Las Vegas NV 89104
Tel (702) 735-5151 *SIC* 4953

RENO DISPOSAL CO p 1224
100 Vassar St, Reno NV 89502
Tel (775) 329-8822 *SIC* 4953

■ WASTE MANAGEMENT OF MASSACHUSETTS INC p 1580
4 Liberty Ln W, Hampton NH 03842
Tel (603) 929-3000 *SIC* 4953 8748

■ WHEELABRATOR ENVIRONMENTAL SYSTEMS INC p 1604
4 Liberty Ln W, Hampton NH 03842
Tel (603) 929-3000 *SIC* 4953 4911

WHEELABRATOR TECHNOLOGIES INC p 1604
100 Arboretum Dr Ste 310, Portsmouth NH 03801
Tel (603) 929-3156 *SIC* 4953

ATLANTIC COUNTY UTILITIES AUTHORITY p 126
6700 Delilah Rd, Egg Harbor Township NJ 08234
Tel (609) 272-6950 *SIC* 4953 4952

CLEAN VENTURE INC p 324
201 S 1st St, Elizabeth NJ 07206
Tel (908) 355-5800
SIC 4225 4212 4953 8748

IESI NY CORP p 730
99 Wood Ave S Ste 1001, Iselin NJ 08830
Tel (201) 443-3000 *SIC* 4953

JERSEY CITY INCINERATOR AUTHORITY p 783
501 State Rt 440, Jersey City NJ 07305
Tel (201) 432-4645 *SIC* 4953 0782 4212

■ COVANTA ARC LLC p 384
445 South St, Morristown NJ 07960
Tel (862) 345-5000 *SIC* 4953

■ COVANTA ENERGY GROUP INC p 384
445 South St, Morristown NJ 07960
Tel (862) 345-5000
SIC 1541 1629 4953 4931

■ COVANTA ENERGY LLC p 384
445 South St Ste 400, Morristown NJ 07960
Tel (862) 345-5000 *SIC* 4953 4911

▲ COVANTA HOLDING CORP p 384
445 South St, Morristown NJ 07960
Tel (862) 345-5000 *SIC* 4953 4911

■ COVANTA SYSTEMS INC p 384
445 South St, Morristown NJ 07960
Tel (862) 345-5000 *SIC* 4953

AERC.COM INC p 30
111 Howard Blvd Ste 108, Mount Arlington NJ 07856
Tel (973) 691-3200 *SIC* 4953

ENERGY CAPITAL PARTNERS II LLC p 497
51 John F Kennedy Pkwy # 200, Short Hills NJ 07078
Tel (973) 671-6100 *SIC* 6799 4953 8711

ACTION ENVIRONMENTAL GROUP INC p 19
300 Frank W Burr Blvd, Teaneck NJ 07666
Tel (212) 564-7600 *SIC* 4953

MIDJERSEY DISPOSAL INC p 965
1298 Industrial Way, Toms River NJ 08755
Tel (732) 341-6100 *SIC* 4212 4953

■ WASTE MANAGEMENT OF NEW YORK LLC p 1581
123 Varick Ave, Brooklyn NY 11237
Tel (718) 533-5100 *SIC* 4953

ONGWEOWEH CORP p 1088
767 Warren Rd, Ithaca NY 14850
Tel (607) 266-7070 *SIC* 8741 4953

TUNNEL HILL PARTNERS LP p 1491
390 N Broadway Ste 220, Jericho NY 11753
Tel (516) 806-6232 *SIC* 4953

GERSHOW RECYCLING CORP p 609
71 Peconic Ave, Medford NY 11763
Tel (631) 289-6188 *SIC* 4953

MODERN DISPOSAL SERVICES INC p 981
4746 Model City Rd, Model City NY 14107
Tel (716) 692-1272 *SIC* 4953

VEOLIA ES WASTE-TO-ENERGY INC p 1548
1 Penn Plz Ste 4401, New York NY 10119
Tel (212) 947-5824 *SIC* 4953

■ NORTHEAST RECYCLING CORP p 1055
1198 Prospect Ave, Westbury NY 11590
Tel (516) 937-0900 *SIC* 4953 4212

SHAMROCK ENVIRONMENTAL CORP p 1311
6106 Corporate Park Dr, Browns Summit NC 27214
Tel (336) 375-1989
SIC 4953 4212 8748 7699

RE COMMUNITY HOLDINGS II INC p 1212
809 W Hill St, Charlotte NC 28208
Tel (704) 697-2000 *SIC* 4953

RECOMMUNITY CORP p 1214
809 W Hill St Ste E, Charlotte NC 28208
Tel (860) 289-8480 *SIC* 4953

RECOMMUNITY RECYCLING p 1214
1007 Amble Dr, Charlotte NC 28206
Tel (704) 598-8595 *SIC* 4953

MARLIN HOLDCO LP p 909
3301 Benson Dr Ste 601, Raleigh NC 27609
Tel (919) 325-3000 *SIC* 4953

WASTE INDUSTRIES LLC p 1580
3301 Benson Dr Ste 601, Raleigh NC 27609
Tel (919) 325-3000 *SIC* 4953

WASTE INDUSTRIES USA INC p 1580
3301 Benson Dr Ste 601, Raleigh NC 27609
Tel (919) 325-3000 *SIC* 4953 3443

■ WASTE MANAGEMENT OF NORTH DAKOTA INC p 1581
7007 15th St Nw, Bismarck ND 58503
Tel (701) 223-2295 *SIC* 4953

RUMPKE CONSOLIDATED COMPANIES INC p 1258
10795 Hughes Rd, Cincinnati OH 45251
Tel (800) 582-3107 *SIC* 4953

RUMPKE OF INDIANA INC p 1258
3800 Struble Rd, Cincinnati OH 45251
Tel (513) 851-0122 *SIC* 4953

RUMPKE OF KENTUCKY INC p 1258
10795 Hughes Rd, Cincinnati OH 45251
Tel (513) 851-0122 *SIC* 4953

RUMPKE OF OHIO INC p 1258
3800 Struble Rd, Cincinnati OH 45251
Tel (513) 851-0122 *SIC* 4953 4212

RUMPKE TRANSPORTATION CO LLC p 1258
10795 Hughes Rd, Cincinnati OH 45251
Tel (513) 851-0122
SIC 3561 5084 7537 4953

RUMPKE WASTE INC p 1258
10795 Hughes Rd, Cincinnati OH 45251
Tel (513) 851-0122 *SIC* 4953

KIMBLE COMPANIES INC p 818
3596 State Route 39 Nw, Dover OH 44622
Tel (330) 343-5665 *SIC* 4953

■ CHEMICAL WASTE MANAGEMENT OF NORTHWEST INC p 293
17629 Cedar Springs Ln, Arlington OR 97812
Tel (541) 454-2030 *SIC* 4953

■ WASTE MANAGEMENT OF OREGON INC p 1581
5330 Ne Skyport Way, Portland OR 97218
Tel (503) 249-8078 *SIC* 4953

WESTMORELAND WASTE LLC p 1602
111 Conner Ln, Belle Vernon PA 15012
Tel (724) 929-7694 *SIC* 4953

■ BFI WASTE SERVICES OF PENNSYLVANIA LLC p 179
73 Noblestown Rd Ste A, Carnegie PA 15106
Tel (412) 429-2600 *SIC* 4953

A J CATAGNUS INC p 5
1299 W James St, Norristown PA 19401
Tel (610) 275-5328 *SIC* 4953

AMERICAN IRON OXIDE CO p 75
Fster Plz Ste 7 661 Adrsn, Pittsburgh PA 15220
Tel (412) 929-0177 *SIC* 4953 2816

LIBERTY TIRE RECYCLING LLC p 862
1251 Waterfront Pl # 400, Pittsburgh PA 15222
Tel (412) 562-1700 *SIC* 5093 4953 8744

RAND-WHITNEY RECYCLING LLC p 1207
546 Smith Rd, Port Matilda PA 16870
Tel (814) 692-8045 *SIC* 4953

■ EC WASTE LLC p 475
Int 923 Km 1/7 Rr 3, Humacao PR 00791
Tel (787) 852-4444 *SIC* 4953

■ SAVANNAH RIVER REMEDIATION LLC p 1284
Savannah River Site, Aiken SC 29808
Tel (803) 952-9630 *SIC* 4953

■ SAFETY-KLEEN (TULSA) INC p 1266
1301 Gervais St Ste 300, Columbia SC 29201
Tel (800) 669-5740 *SIC* 4953

■ WASTE CONNECTIONS US INC p 1580
1010 Rogers Bridge Rd, Duncan SC 29334
Tel (832) 801-1436 *SIC* 4953

CONTAINER CO OF CAROLINA p 362
3358 Highway 51, Fort Mill SC 29715
Tel (704) 377-0161 *SIC* 4953

■ FLUOR FEDERAL SOLUTIONS LLC p 561
100 Fluor Daniel Dr, Greenville SC 29607
Tel (864) 281-4400 *SIC* 4953

BERKELEY COUNTY WATER AND SANITATION AUTHORITY p 175
212 Oakley Plantation Dr, Moncks Corner SC 29461
Tel (843) 761-8817 *SIC* 4941 4953

■ OMNISOURCE SOUTHEAST LLC p 1085
2061 Nazareth Church Rd, Spartanburg SC 29301
Tel (864) 439-7039 *SIC* 4953

■ WASTE MANAGEMENT OF SOUTH CAROLINA INC p 1581
390 Innovation Way, Wellford SC 29385
Tel (864) 232-1537 *SIC* 4953 4212

■ WASTE MANAGEMENT INC OF TENNESSEE p 1580
1428 Antioch Pike, Antioch TN 37013
Tel (615) 831-9600 *SIC* 4953

SANTEK ENVIRONMENTAL INC p 1281
650 25th St Nw Ste 100, Cleveland TN 37311
Tel (423) 476-9160 *SIC* 4953

■ BROWNING-FERRIS INDUSTRIES OF TENNESSEE INC p 220
3840 Homewood Rd, Memphis TN 38118
Tel (901) 794-3800 *SIC* 4953

BALCONES RESOURCES INC p 147
9301 Johnny Morris Rd, Austin TX 78724
Tel (512) 472-3355 *SIC* 4953

MILLER ENVIRONMENTAL SERVICES LLC p 970
401 Navigation Blvd, Corpus Christi TX 78408
Tel (361) 289-9800 *SIC* 4953 7375

TEXAS DISPOSAL SYSTEMS INC p 1443
12200 Carl Rd, Creedmoor TX 78610
Tel (512) 421-1300 *SIC* 4953

TEXAS LANDFILL MANAGEMENT LLC p 1444
12200 Carl Rd, Creedmoor TX 78610
Tel (512) 421-1300 *SIC* 4953

QUEMETCO INC p 1198
2777 N Stemmons Fwy, Dallas TX 75207
Tel (317) 247-1303 *SIC* 3341 4953

■ **VALHI INC** p 1540
5430 Lbj Fwy Ste 1700, Dallas TX 75240
Tel (972) 233-1700
SIC 2816 2899 3429 4953

■ **WASTE CONTROL SPECIALISTS LLC** p 1580
5430 Lyndon B Johnson Fwy # 1700, Dallas TX 75240
Tel (888) 789-2783 SIC 4953

FIRST FINANCIAL RESOURCES INC p 547
611 Kimberly Dr, Denton TX 76208
Tel (940) 382-4599 SIC 4789 4953

HULCHER SERVICES INC p 718
611 Kimberly Dr, Denton TX 76208
Tel (940) 387-0099 SIC 4953 4789

PROGRESSIVE WASTE SOLUTIONS LTD p 1182
2301 Eagle Pkwy Ste 200, Fort Worth TX 76177
Tel (817) 632-4000 SIC 4953

WASTE SERVICES INC p 1581
2301 Eagle Pkwy Ste 200, Fort Worth TX 76177
Tel (817) 632-4000 SIC 4953

■ **CHAMBERS DEVELOPMENT CO INC** p 287
1001 Fannin St Ste 400, Houston TX 77002
Tel (713) 877-8793 SIC 4953

■ **CHEMICAL WASTE MANAGEMENT INC** p 293
1001 Fannin St Ste 4000, Houston TX 77002
Tel (713) 512-6200 SIC 4953 4959

COD INTERMEDIATE LLC p 333
1330 Post Oak Blvd, Houston TX 77056
Tel (713) 292-2400 SIC 4953

■ **GEORGIA WASTE SYSTEMS INC** p 608
1001 Fannin St Ste 4000, Houston TX 77002
Tel (713) 512-6200 SIC 4953

■ **GREENSTAR MID-AMERICA LLC** p 638
1001 Fannin St Ste 4000, Houston TX 77002
Tel (713) 512-6200 SIC 4953

■ **PSC ENVIRONMENTAL SERVICES LLC** p 1188
5151 San Felipe St # 1100, Houston TX 77056
Tel (713) 623-8777 SIC 4953 4959 5093

PSC HOLDINGS II LP p 1188
5151 San Felipe St # 1600, Houston TX 77056
Tel (713) 623-8777 SIC 4953 8748

PSC HOLDINGS INC p 1188
5151 San Felipe St # 1100, Houston TX 77056
Tel (713) 623-8777 SIC 4953 4959

PSC LLC p 1188
5151 San Felipe St Ste 11, Houston TX 77056
Tel (713) 623-8777 SIC 4953 4959

STRATEGIC MATERIALS INC p 1392
16365 Park Ten Pl Ste 200, Houston TX 77084
Tel (281) 647-2700 SIC 4953

VOPAK NORTH AMERICA INC p 1565
2000 West Loop S Ste 1550, Houston TX 77027
Tel (713) 561-7200
SIC 4491 4226 4953 4789

■ **WASTE AWAY GROUP INC** p 1580
1001 Fannin St Ste 4000, Houston TX 77002
Tel (713) 512-6200 SIC 4953

WASTE CORP OF AMERICA INC p 1580
1330 Post Oak Blvd Fl 30, Houston TX 77056
Tel (713) 572-3802 SIC 4953

■ **WASTE MANAGEMENT HOLDINGS INC** p 1580
1001 Fannin St Ste 4000, Houston TX 77002
Tel (713) 512-6200 SIC 4953

▲ **WASTE MANAGEMENT INC** p 1580
1001 Fannin St Ste 4000, Houston TX 77002
Tel (713) 512-6200 SIC 4953

■ **WASTE MANAGEMENT OF ILLINOIS INC** p 1580
1001 Fannin St Ste 4000, Houston TX 77002
Tel (713) 512-6200 SIC 4953

■ **WASTE MANAGEMENT OF OKLAHOMA INC** p 1581
1001 Fannin St Ste 3900, Houston TX 77002
Tel (713) 512-6200 SIC 4953

■ **WASTE MANAGEMENT OF TEXAS INC** p 1581
1001 Fannin St Ste 4000, Houston TX 77002
Tel (713) 512-6200 SIC 4953

WCA WASTE CORP p 1585
1330 Post Oak Blvd # 3000, Houston TX 77056
Tel (713) 292-2400 SIC 4953

■ **WESTERN WASTE OF TEXAS LLC** p 1600
1001 Fannin St Ste 4000, Houston TX 77002
Tel (713) 512-6200 SIC 4953

NEXCYCLE INC p 1039
5221 N O Connor Blvd # 850, Irving TX 75039
Tel (972) 506-7200 SIC 4953

■ **NEWPARK DRILLING FLUIDS LLC** p 1038
21920 Merchants Way, Katy TX 77449
Tel (281) 754-8600 SIC 5169 5172 4953

PROGRESSIVE WASTE SOLUTIONS LTD p 1182
2138 Country Ln, Mckinney TX 75069
Tel (469) 452-8000 SIC 4953

■ **SAFETY-KLEEN ENVIROSYSTEMS CO** p 1266
2600 N Central Expy # 400, Richardson TX 75080
Tel (800) 323-5040 SIC 4953

■ **SAFETY-KLEEN INC** p 1266
2600 N Central Expy # 400, Richardson TX 75080
Tel (800) 669-5740
SIC 4953 3559 4212 5172 5085 7389

SPRINT WASTE SERVICES LP p 1361
16011 W Bellfort St, Sugar Land TX 77498
Tel (281) 491-7775 SIC 5093 4953

▲ **QUEST RESOURCE HOLDING CORP** p 1199
3481 Plano Pkwy, The Colony TX 75056
Tel (972) 464-0004 SIC 4953

▲ **NEWPARK RESOURCES INC** p 1038
9320 Lkeside Blvd Ste 100, The Woodlands TX 77381
Tel (281) 362-6800
SIC 1389 4959 4953 2273

NORTH TEXAS MUNICIPAL WATER DISTRICT p 1054
505 E Brown St, Wylie TX 75098
Tel (972) 442-5405 SIC 4953 4941

ENERGYSOLUTIONS INC p 498
299 S Main St Ste 1700, Salt Lake City UT 84111
Tel (801) 649-2000 SIC 4953 8711

ENERGYSOLUTIONS LLC p 498
299 Suth Main St Ste 1700, Salt Lake City UT 84111
Tel (801) 649-2000 SIC 4953 8711

ENERGYSOLUTIONS SERVICES INC p 498
299 S Main St Ste 1700, Salt Lake City UT 84111
Tel (801) 649-2000 SIC 4953

■ **HEADWATERS RESOURCES INC** p 673
10701 S River Front Pkwy # 300, South Jordan UT 84095
Tel (801) 984-9400 SIC 5032 4953 8711

■ **CASELLA WASTE MANAGEMENT INC** p 263
25 Green Hill Ln, Rutland VT 05701
Tel (802) 775-0325 SIC 4953 4212

▲ **CASELLA WASTE SYSTEMS INC** p 263
25 Green Hill Ln, Rutland VT 05701
Tel (802) 775-0325 SIC 4953

GIANT CEMENT HOLDING INC p 610
1600 Duke St Ste 400, Alexandria VA 22314
Tel (571) 302-7150 SIC 3241 4953

BNG AMERICA LLC p 194
1235 S Clark St Ste 700a, Arlington VA 22202
Tel (703) 412-2500
SIC 8711 8741 4953 2819

FIRST PIEDMONT CORP p 549
108 S Main St, Chatham VA 24531
Tel (434) 432-0211 SIC 4953 5084

▲ **KAISER GROUP HOLDINGS INC** p 800
9300 Lee Hwy, Fairfax VA 22031
Tel (703) 934-3000 SIC 4953

AMERICAN DISPOSAL SERVICES INC p 71
10370 Central Park Dr, Manassas VA 20110
Tel (703) 789-7935 SIC 4953

ENVIROSOLUTIONS INC p 503
9650 Hawkins Dr, Manassas VA 20109
Tel (703) 633-3000 SIC 4953

CANON VIRGINIA INC p 247
12000 Canon Blvd, Newport News VA 23606
Tel (757) 881-6000
SIC 3861 3577 3555 4953

WHEELABRATOR PORTSMOUTH INC p 1604
3809 Elm Ave, Portsmouth VA 23704
Tel (757) 393-3100 SIC 4953 4911

BRENNER HOLDINGS INC p 210
2580 Broadway Ave Sw, Roanoke VA 24014
Tel (540) 981-1211
SIC 4953 5093 3341 3231

PRINCE WILLIAM COUNTY SERVICE AUTHORITY INC p 1176
4 County Complex Ct, Woodbridge VA 22192
Tel (703) 335-7900 SIC 4941 4952 4953

■ **WASTE MANAGEMENT OF WASHINGTON INC** p 1581
720 4th Ave Ste 400, Kirkland WA 98033
Tel (425) 823-6164 SIC 4953

■ **FLUOR HANFORD INC** p 561
3160 George Wash Way, Richland WA 99354
Tel (509) 372-2000 SIC 4953

CEDAR GROVE COMPOSTING INC p 272
7343 E Marginal Way S, Seattle WA 98108
Tel (206) 832-3000 SIC 4953

EMERALD SERVICES INC p 491
7343 E Marginal Way S, Seattle WA 98108
Tel (206) 430-7795
SIC 4953 7699 2911 8748 7359

■ **WASTE MANAGEMENT OF WISCONSIN INC** p 1581
N96 W 13600 Cnty Line Rd St N 96, Germantown WI 53022
Tel (262) 251-4000 SIC 4953 4212

VEOLIA ES SPECIAL SERVICES INC p 1548
W6490b Specialty Dr, Greenville WI 54942
Tel (800) 932-6216 SIC 4953

■ **VEOLIA ENVIRONMENTAL SERVICES NORTH AMERICA LLC** p 1548
125 S 84th St Ste 200, Milwaukee WI 53214
Tel (414) 479-7800 SIC 4953 4212

SIC 4959 Sanitary Svcs, NEC

CHUGACH ALASKA CORP p 304
3800 Cntrpint Dr Ste 1200, Anchorage AK 99503
Tel (907) 563-8866
SIC 8744 4959 7361 0851 7373

VECO CORP p 1546
949 E 36th Ave Ste 500, Anchorage AK 99508
Tel (907) 762-1500
SIC 1711 1389 1731 1381 4959

■ **BROWNING-FERRIS INDUSTRIES INC** p 220
18500 N Allied Way # 100, Phoenix AZ 85054
Tel (480) 627-2700 SIC 4953 4959 7359

AMPCO CONTRACTING INC p 86
1540 S Lewis St, Anaheim CA 92805
Tel (949) 955-2255 SIC 4959 1795 1794

CENTRAL CONTRA COSTA SANITARY DISTRICT FACILITIES FINANCING AUTHORITY p 278
5019 Imhoff Pl, Martinez CA 94553
Tel (925) 228-9500 SIC 4952 4959

■ **RICHMOND SANITARY SERVICE INC** p 1233
3260 Blume Dr Ste 100, Richmond CA 94806
Tel (510) 262-7100 SIC 4959

SACRAMENTO REGIONAL COUNTY SANITATION DISTRICT p 1265
10060 Goethe Rd, Sacramento CA 95827
Tel (916) 876-6000 SIC 4959

SULLIVAN INTERNATIONAL GROUP INC p 1397
2750 Womble Rd Ste 100, San Diego CA 92106
Tel (619) 260-1432 SIC 4959

ALL ENVIRONMENTAL INC p 51
2500 Camino Diablo, Walnut Creek CA 94597
Tel (925) 746-6000 SIC 4959

■ **CEHI ACQUISITION CORP** p 272
61 Wilton Rd Ste 2, Westport CT 06880
Tel (203) 221-1703 SIC 4959 6719

WITT OBRIENS LLC p 1619
1201 15th St Nw Ste 600, Washington DC 20005
Tel (202) 585-0780 SIC 4959 8748 8322

CLIFF BERRY INC p 326
851 Eller Dr, Fort Lauderdale FL 33316
Tel (954) 763-3390
SIC 4953 4959 4212 2992 4491

▲ **SEACOR HOLDINGS INC** p 1296
2200 Eller Dr, Fort Lauderdale FL 33316
Tel (954) 523-2200
SIC 4412 4424 4449 4959 8748

ST ENVIRONMENTAL SERVICES INC (I) p 1366
5726 Corporation Cir, Fort Myers FL 33905
Tel (239) 690-0175 SIC 4959 4941

PROGRESSIVE ENVIRONMENTAL SERVICES INC p 1181
1619 Moylan Rd, Panama City Beach FL 32407
Tel (850) 234-8428 SIC 4959

EMERALD COAST UTILITIES AUTHORITY p 491
9255 Sturdevant St, Pensacola FL 32514
Tel (850) 476-5110 SIC 4959 4952 4941

■ **ADVANCED DISPOSAL SERVICES SOLID WASTE MIDWEST LLC** p 25
90 Fort Wade Rd Ste 200, Ponte Vedra FL 32081
Tel (904) 737-7900 SIC 7699 4953 4959

HANDEX CONSULTING AND REMEDIATION LLC p 657
1350 Orange Ave Ste 101, Winter Park FL 32789
Tel (352) 735-1800 SIC 4959

■ **WASHINGTON CLOSURE CO LLC** p 1577
720 E Park Blvd Bsmt, Boise ID 83712
Tel (208) 386-5000
SIC 4959 1799 1795 4226

WASHINGTON GROUP INTERNATIONAL INC p 1578
720 E Park Blvd, Boise ID 83712
Tel (208) 386-5000
SIC 1611 1629 1221 1081 4959 1475

BRANDENBURG INDUSTRIAL SERVICE CO p 208
2625 S Loomis St, Chicago IL 60608
Tel (312) 326-5800 SIC 4959 1795 5093

CARYLON CORP p 262
2500 W Arthington St, Chicago IL 60612
Tel (312) 666-7700
SIC 7699 1629 7349 8748 4959

ACRES ENTERPRISES INC p 18
610 W Liberty St, Wauconda IL 60084
Tel (847) 526-4554 SIC 0782 0781 4959

OIL MOP LLC p 1079
131 Keating Dr, Belle Chasse LA 70037
Tel (504) 394-6110 SIC 4959

BERRY BROS GENERAL CONTRACTORS INC p 176
1414 River Rd, Berwick LA 70342
Tel (985) 384-8770 SIC 1629 4959

ECOSERV LLC p 476
207 Towncenter Pkwy Fl 2, Lafayette LA 70506
Tel (337) 984-4445 SIC 4959 7699

■ **AECOM GOVERNMENT SERVICES INC** p 28
20501 Seneca Meadows Pkwy, Germantown MD 20876
Tel (703) 921-1600
SIC 4959 4173 4581 7299

BRICKMAN GROUP HOLDINGS INC p 211
2275 Res Blvd Ste 700, Rockville MD 20850
Tel (301) 987-9200 SIC 0782 4959

ASPHALT SURFACE TECHNOLOGIES CORP p 118
8348 Ridgewood Rd, Saint Joseph MN 56374
Tel (320) 363-8500 SIC 1611 4959

MILLER ENVIRONMENTAL GROUP INC p 970
538 Edwards Ave, Calverton NY 11933
Tel (631) 369-4900 SIC 4959

NATIONAL RESPONSE CORP p 1015
3500 Sunrise Hwy, Great River NY 11739
Tel (631) 224-9141 SIC 4959 8999

SEVENSON ENVIRONMENTAL SERVICES INC p 1309
2749 Lockport Rd, Niagara Falls NY 14305
Tel (716) 284-0431 SIC 4959 1795

DEJANA INDUSTRIES INC p 422
30 Sagamore Hill Dr, Port Washington NY 11050
Tel (516) 944-3100 SIC 4959

A & A MAINTENANCE ENTERPRISE INC p 4
965 Midland Ave, Yonkers NY 10704
Tel (914) 969-0009
SIC 7349 1721 1542 4959 0782

HEPACO LLC p 685
2711 Burch Dr, Charlotte NC 28269
Tel (704) 598-9787 SIC 4959

CONTAMINANT CONTROL INC p 362
3434 Black And Decker Rd, Hope Mills NC 28348
Tel (910) 484-6841 SIC 4959

NORTHEAST OHIO REGIONAL SEWER DISTRICT p 1055
3900 Euclid Ave, Cleveland OH 44115
Tel (216) 881-6600 SIC 4959

C & K INDUSTRIAL SERVICES INC p 231
5617 E Schaaf Rd, Independence OH 44131
Tel (216) 642-0055 SIC 4959 7349

WASTREN ADVANTAGE INC p 1581
1571 Shyville Rd, Piketon OH 45661
Tel (970) 254-1277 SIC 4959 8744 8711

■ **CLEAN EARTH HOLDINGS INC** p 323
334 S Warminster Rd, Hatboro PA 19040
Tel (215) 734-1400 SIC 4959

■ **CLEAN EARTH INC** p 323
334 S Warminster Rd, Hatboro PA 19040
Tel (215) 734-1400 SIC 4959

■ **WASHINGTON SAVANNAH RIVER CO LLC** p 1579
Savannah River Site Rd 1, Aiken SC 29808
Tel (803) 725-6211 SIC 4959

JANUS GLOBAL OPERATIONS LLC p 778
2229 Old Highway 95, Lenoir City TN 37771
Tel (865) 988-6063
SIC 4959 7381 7373 7379 8742

ATKINS ENERGY GOVERNMENT GROUP INC p 125
545 Oak Ridge Tpke, Oak Ridge TN 37830
Tel (865) 481-6300 SIC 4959

GARNER ENVIRONMENTAL SERVICES INC p 592
1717 W 13th St, Deer Park TX 77536
Tel (281) 930-1200 SIC 4959

MO-VAC SERVICE CO p 980
3721 S Mccoll Rd, Edinburg TX 78539
Tel (956) 682-6381 SIC 1389 4959

■ **CHEMICAL WASTE MANAGEMENT INC** p 293
1001 Fannin St Ste 4000, Houston TX 77002
Tel (713) 512-6200 SIC 4953 4959

■ **PSC ENVIRONMENTAL SERVICES LLC** p 1188
5151 San Felipe St # 1100, Houston TX 77056
Tel (713) 623-8777 SIC 4953 4959 5093

PSC HOLDINGS INC p 1188
5151 San Felipe St # 1100, Houston TX 77056
Tel (713) 623-8777 SIC 4953 4959

PSC LLC p 1188
5151 San Felipe St Ste 11, Houston TX 77056
Tel (713) 623-8777 SIC 4953 4959

DARR EQUIPMENT LP p 412
350 Bank St, Southlake TX 76092
Tel (254) 420-2650
SIC 5084 7353 5013 4959

▲ **NEWPARK RESOURCES INC** p 1038
9320 Lkeside Blvd Ste 100, The Woodlands TX 77381
Tel (281) 362-6800
SIC 1389 4959 4953 2273

MARINE SPILL RESPONSE CORP p 906
220 Spring St Ste 500, Herndon VA 20170
Tel (703) 326-5600 SIC 4959

FOSS MARITIME CO p 570
1151 Fairview Ave N, Seattle WA 98109
Tel (206) 281-4001
SIC 4412 4424 4492 4491 3731 4959

GLOBAL DIVING & SALVAGE INC p 616
3840 W Marginal Way Sw, Seattle WA 98106
Tel (206) 623-0621 SIC 4959 1629 7389

SIC 4961 Steam & Air Conditioning Sply

■ **PEPCO ENERGY SERVICES INC** p 1133
701 9th St Nw Ste 2100, Washington DC 20001
Tel (703) 253-1800
SIC 1711 1731 1623 4961

WATERFURNACE RENEWABLE ENERGY INC p 1582
9000 Conservation Way, Fort Wayne IN 46809
Tel (260) 478-5667 SIC 4961

■ **INTERSTATE POWER AND LIGHT CO** p 758
200 1st St Se, Cedar Rapids IA 52401
Tel (319) 398-4411 SIC 4911 4924 4961

VEOLIA ENERGY NORTH AMERICA HOLDINGS INC p 1548
53 State St Ste 14, Boston MA 02109
Tel (617) 849-6612 SIC 4939 4961

■ **CONSOLIDATED EDISON CO OF NEW YORK INC** p 359
4 Irving Pl, New York NY 10003
Tel (212) 460-4600 SIC 4911 4924 4961

■ **WE ENERGIES** p 1585
231 W Michigan St, Milwaukee WI 53203
Tel (414) 221-2345 SIC 4911 4924 4961

SIC 4971 Irrigation Systems

■ **HORIZON DISTRIBUTORS INC** p 707
5214 S 30th St, Phoenix AZ 85040
Tel (480) 337-6700 SIC 4971 5083

COACHELLA VALLEY WATER DISTRICT p 331
85995 Avenue 52, Coachella CA 92236
Tel (760) 398-2651
SIC 4941 4971 4952 7389

IMPERIAL IRRIGATION DISTRICT p 734
333 E Barioni Blvd, Imperial CA 92251
Tel (800) 303-7756 SIC 4911 4971 4931

MERCED IRRIGATION DISTRICT p 944
744 W 20th St, Merced CA 95340
Tel (209) 722-5761 SIC 4911 4971

MODESTO IRRIGATION DISTRICT (INC) p 981
1231 11th St, Modesto CA 95354
Tel (209) 526-7337 SIC 4911 4971

TURLOCK IRRIGATION DISTRICT p 1492
333 E Canal Dr, Turlock CA 95380
Tel (209) 883-8222 SIC 4911 4971

WACHS VALVE AND HYDRANT SERVICES LLC p 1570
801 Asbury Dr, Buffalo Grove IL 60089
Tel (224) 357-2600 SIC 4971

PENTAIR INC p 1132
5500 Wayzata Blvd Ste 600, Minneapolis MN 55416
Tel (763) 545-1730
SIC 3491 3559 4971 3589

■ **SIERRA PACIFIC POWER CO** p 1321
6100 Neil Rd Ste 100, Reno NV 89511
Tel (775) 834-4011
SIC 4911 4924 4941 4971

NORTH JERSEY DISTRICT WATER SUPPLY COMMISSION p 1052
1 F A Orechio Dr, Wanaque NJ 07465
Tel (973) 831-6212 SIC 4971 4941

■ **AQUA PENNSYLVANIA INC** p 101
762 W Lancaster Ave, Bryn Mawr PA 19010
Tel (610) 525-1400
SIC 4941 8741 4971 1623

SIC 5012 Automobiles & Other Motor Vehicles Wholesale

NABI BUS LLC p 1006
106 National Dr, Anniston AL 36207
Tel (888) 452-7871 SIC 3713 5012

INNOVATIVE XCESSORIES & SERVICES LLC p 745
1862 Sparkman Dr Nw, Huntsville AL 35816
Tel (877) 330-1331 SIC 5012 3711

FOUR STAR FREIGHTLINER INC p 572
3140 Hayneville Rd, Montgomery AL 36108
Tel (334) 263-1085 SIC 5012 5531

■ **BROWN & BROWN CHEVROLET INC** p 219
145 E Main St, Mesa AZ 85201
Tel (480) 833-3456 SIC 5511 5521 5012

WHITEMAN FAMILY CORP p 1606
1725 S Country Club Dr, Mesa AZ 85210
Tel (480) 633-4413
SIC 5082 5083 7353 7699 7359 5012

VANTAGE MOBILITY INTERNATIONAL LLC p 1544
5202 S 28th Pl, Phoenix AZ 85040
Tel (602) 243-2700 SIC 5012 3559

FREIGHTLINER STERLING WESTERN STAR OF ARIZONA LTD p 577
9899 W Roosevelt St, Tolleson AZ 85353
Tel (623) 907-9900 SIC 5013 5012 7538

TRL INC p 1483
11700 Valentine Rd, North Little Rock AR 72117
Tel (501) 955-3200 SIC 5012

YAMAHA MOTOR CORP USA p 1634
6555 Katella Ave, Cypress CA 90630
Tel (714) 761-7300
SIC 5088 5013 5091 5012

INLAND KENWORTH (US) INC p 743
9730 Cherry Ave, Fontana CA 92335
Tel (909) 823-9955
SIC 5012 7538 5013 7513

UTILITY TRAILER SALES OF SOUTHERN CALIFORNIA LLC p 1537
15567 Valley Blvd, Fontana CA 92335
Tel (877) 275-4887
SIC 5012 5013 5531 5561

KAWASAKI MOTORS CORP USA p 805
26972 Burbank, Foothill Ranch CA 92610
Tel (949) 837-4683
SIC 5012 5013 5084 5091

MOBIS PARTS AMERICA LLC p 980
10550 Talbert Ave Fl 4, Fountain Valley CA 92708
Tel (786) 515-1101 SIC 5012

FRESNO TRUCK CENTER p 579
2727 E Central Ave, Fresno CA 93725
Tel (559) 486-4310
SIC 5511 5521 5531 5012 5013 6159

TOMS TRUCK CENTER INC p 1460
12221 Monarch St, Garden Grove CA 92841
Tel (714) 835-5070 SIC 5511 5012 7538

ATS NORTHEAST TOW INC p 129
2010 N Figueroa St, Los Angeles CA 90065
Tel (323) 342-0342 SIC 7549 5012

SSMB PACIFIC HOLDING CO INC p 1364
1755 Adams Ave, San Leandro CA 94577
Tel (510) 836-6100 SIC 5012 7699

▲ **TRUECAR INC** p 1486
120 Broadway Ste 200, Santa Monica CA 90401
Tel (800) 200-2000 SIC 5012 7299

ZERO MOTORCYCLES INC p 1642
380 El Pueblo Rd, Scotts Valley CA 95066
Tel (831) 438-3500 SIC 5012

AMERICAN HONDA MOTOR CO INC p 74
1919 Torrance Blvd, Torrance CA 90501
Tel (310) 783-2000 SIC 5012 3732

TOYOTA MOTOR SALES USA INC p 1467
19001 S Western Ave, Torrance CA 90501
Tel (310) 468-4000 SIC 6159 5012 3711

BONANDER PONTIAC INC p 199
231 S Center St, Turlock CA 95380
Tel (209) 632-8871 SIC 5511 7539 5012

■ **MCCANDLESS TRUCK CENTER LLC** p 926
16704 E 32nd Ave, Aurora CO 80011
Tel (331) 332-5000 SIC 5013 7538 5012

TRANS-WEST INC p 1470
20770 Interstate 76, Brighton CO 80603
Tel (303) 289-3161 SIC 5511 5012

SOUTHERN AUTO SALES INC p 1347
161 S Main St, East Windsor CT 06088
Tel (860) 292-7500 SIC 5012

JM FAMILY ENTERPRISES INC p 786
100 Jim Moran Blvd, Deerfield Beach FL 33442
Tel (954) 429-2000
SIC 5511 5012 5013 5531

SOUTHEAST TOYOTA DISTRIBUTORS LLC p 1346
100 Jim Moran Blvd, Deerfield Beach FL 33442
Tel (954) 429-2000 SIC 5012

FORD GREENWAY INC p 565
9001 E Colonial Dr, Orlando FL 32817
Tel (407) 275-3200 SIC 5511 5012

SANFORD AUTO DEALERS EXCHANGE INC p 1279
2851 Saint Johns Pkwy, Sanford FL 32771
Tel (407) 328-7300 SIC 5012

MANHEIM INVESTMENTS INC p 901
6205 Pachtree Dunwoody Rd, Atlanta GA 30328
Tel (866) 626-4346 SIC 5012

MANHEIM REMARKETING INC p 901
6325 Pchtree Dnwody Rd Ne, Atlanta GA 30328
Tel (678) 645-2067 SIC 5012

MERCEDES-BENZ USA LLC p 944
303 Perimeter Ctr N, Atlanta GA 30346
Tel (201) 573-0600
SIC 5012 5013 7538 5511

NEW MANHEIM AUTO AUCTIONS LIMITED (INC) p 1032
6205 Pachtree Dunwoody Rd, Atlanta GA 30328
Tel (678) 645-0000 SIC 5012

TOM GRADDY ENTERPRISES INC p 1459
3348 Peachtree Rd Ne, Atlanta GA 30326
Tel (404) 363-8390
SIC 5531 5511 7538 5012

TOTAL RESOURCE AUCTIONS INC p 1463
6205 Pachtree Dunwoody Rd, Atlanta GA 30328
Tel (678) 645-0000 SIC 5012

COX AUTOMOTIVE INC p 386
3003 Summit Blvd Fl 200, Brookhaven GA 30319
Tel (404) 843-5000 SIC 5012

INTERNATIONAL AUTO PROCESSING INC p 754
1 Joe Frank Harris Blvd, Brunswick GA 31523
Tel (912) 554-8432
SIC 5012 7542 7538 7532

GREAT DANE TRAILERS INC p 633
602 E Lathrop Ave, Savannah GA 31415
Tel (912) 644-2100 SIC 5013 5012

POWERTECH AMERICA INC p 1166
6801 Kia Pkwy, West Point GA 31833
Tel (706) 902-6800 SIC 5012 3714

MIDWEST TRANSIT EQUIPMENT INC p 968
146 W Issert Dr, Kankakee IL 60901
Tel (815) 933-2412 SIC 5012

CENTRAL ILLINOIS TRUCKS INC p 278
200 W Northtown Rd, Normal IL 61761
Tel (800) 322-5017 SIC 5013 7538 5012

TRUCK CENTERS INC p 1485
2280 Formosa Rd, Troy IL 62294
Tel (618) 667-3454
SIC 5531 5511 7538 5012 4522 7699

■ **AXLE HOLDINGS INC** p 140
2 Westbrook Corporate Ctr, Westchester IL 60154
Tel (708) 492-7000 SIC 5012

■ **INSURANCE AUTO AUCTIONS INC** p 747
2 Westbrook Corporate Ctr # 1000, Westchester IL 60154
Tel (708) 492-7000 SIC 5012

HENDRICKSON USA LLC p 683
800 S Frontage Rd, Woodridge IL 60517
Tel (630) 910-2844 SIC 5012

■ **ADESA CORP LLC** p 22
13085 Hamilton Crossing B, Carmel IN 46032
Tel (317) 249-4550 SIC 5012 6153

▲ **KAR AUCTION SERVICES INC** p 804
13085 Hmlton Crssing Blvd, Carmel IN 46032
Tel (800) 923-3725 SIC 5012 6153 5521

KAR HOLDINGS II LLC p 804
13085 Hamil Cross Blvd St Ste 500, Carmel IN 46032
Tel (317) 815-1100 SIC 5012 6153

■ **DMI HOLDING CORP** p 446
2164 Caragana Ct, Goshen IN 46526
Tel (574) 534-1224 SIC 3792 5012

AUCTION BROADCASTING CO LLC p 130
1919 S Post Rd, Indianapolis IN 46239
Tel (317) 862-7325 SIC 5012

PALMER TRUCKS INC p 1109
2929 S Holt Rd, Indianapolis IN 46241
Tel (317) 243-1668
SIC 5511 5531 7538 7513 5012

MEYER DISTRIBUTING INC p 957
560 E 25th St, Jasper IN 47546
Tel (812) 482-5102 SIC 5013 5012

▲ **WABASH NATIONAL CORP** p 1570
1000 Sagamore Pkwy S, Lafayette IN 47905
Tel (765) 771-5310 SIC 3715 3714 5012

■ **WABASH NATIONAL TRAILER CENTERS INC** p 1570
1000 Sagamore Pkwy S, Lafayette IN 47905
Tel (765) 771-5300 SIC 5012 7539 5013

THOMPSON TRUCK & TRAILER INC p 1449
2740 6th St Sw, Cedar Rapids IA 52404
Tel (319) 364-2491 SIC 5012

HAWK JIM GROUP INC p 669
3119 S 9th St, Council Bluffs IA 51501
Tel (712) 366-2241 SIC 5012 7539

JIM HAWK TRUCK TRAILER INC p 785
3119 S 9th St, Council Bluffs IA 51501
Tel (712) 366-2241 SIC 5012

MCCOY GROUP INC p 927
2099 Southpark Ct, Dubuque IA 52003
Tel (563) 556-3773 SIC 5012 7538 4213

TRUCK COUNTRY OF IOWA INC p 1485
2099 Southpark Ct Ste 2, Dubuque IA 52003
Tel (563) 556-3773 SIC 5012 5531 7538

MURPHY-HOFFMAN CO p 1001
11120 Tomahawk Creek Pkwy, Leawood KS 66211
Tel (816) 483-6444
SIC 5012 7513 7538 6159 5511

FORD OLATHE SALES INC p 566
1845 E Santa Fe St, Olathe KS 66062
Tel (913) 782-0881 SIC 5511 5561 5012

SAM SWOPE AUTO GROUP LLC p 1274
10 Swope Autocenter Dr, Louisville KY 40299
Tel (502) 499-5000 SIC 5511 5012 7532

WORLDWIDE EQUIPMENT INC p 1626
73 We Dr, Prestonsburg KY 41653
Tel (606) 874-2172
SIC 5012 5013 7538 7513

UNIVANCE INC p 1516
3400 Corporate Dr, Winchester KY 40391
Tel (859) 737-2306 SIC 3568 3714 5012

HUTCHINS MOTORS INC p 721
187 Riverside Dr, Augusta ME 04330
Tel (207) 622-3191 SIC 5511 5012

GALLERY AUTOMOTIVE GROUP LLC p 590
918 Providence Hwy, Norwood MA 02062
Tel (877) 201-8871 SIC 5511 5012 7538

OLD CARCO INTERNATIONAL CORP p 1080
1000 Chrysler Dr, Auburn Hills MI 48326
Tel (248) 576-5741 SIC 5012

DAIMLER PURCHASING COORDINATION CORP p 408
36455 Corporate Dr, Farmington Hills MI 48331
Tel (248) 991-6700 SIC 5012 5013

DELPHI AUTOMOTIVE LLP p 425
5725 Delphi Dr, Troy MI 48098
Tel (248) 813-2494 SIC 5065 5012

ABC BUS COMPANIES INC p 10
1506 30th St Nw, Faribault MN 55021
Tel (507) 334-1871 SIC 5012 4173 5599

ABC BUS INC p 10
1506 30th St Nw, Faribault MN 55021
Tel (507) 334-1871 SIC 5012 4173

POLAR CORP p 1159
1015 W St Germain St 42 Ste 420, Hopkins MN 55305
Tel (612) 430-6401 SIC 3443 5012 7699

W D LARSON COMPANIES LTD INC p 1568
10700 Lyndale Ave S Ste A, Minneapolis MN 55420
Tel (952) 888-4934
SIC 5012 5013 7538 6159

PSC CUSTOM LP p 1188
1015 W Saint Germain St # 420, Saint Cloud MN 56301
Tel (320) 746-2255 SIC 7539 5012

G S & L ENTERPRISES INC p 587
408 Highway 49 S, Jackson MS 39218
Tel (601) 939-1000 SIC 5012 5082

SOUTHERN STATES UTILITY TRAILER SALES INC p 1350
550 Highway 49 S, Jackson MS 39218
Tel (601) 939-9000 SIC 5012

ARROW TRUCK SALES INC p 113
3200 Manchester Trfy L-70, Kansas City MO 64129
Tel (816) 923-5000 SIC 5521 5012

MHC KENWORTH - KANSAS CITY p 959
1524 N Corrington Ave, Kansas City MO 64120
Tel (816) 483-7035 SIC 5012

OZARK KENWORTH INC p 1101
1524 N Corrington Ave, Kansas City MO 64120
Tel (816) 483-7035 SIC 5012

DAVE SINCLAIR FORD WEST p 415
7466 S Lindbergh Blvd, Saint Louis MO 63125
Tel (314) 892-2600
SIC 5511 7538 5521 5012

REDNECK INC p 1217
2100 N West Byp, Springfield MO 65803
Tel (417) 864-5210 SIC 5013 5561 5012

SRC AUTOMOTIVE INC p 1363
4431 W Calhoun St, Springfield MO 65802
Tel (417) 829-2400 SIC 5012

PETERBILT OF SPRINGFIELD INC p 1138
3026 N Mulroy Rd, Strafford MO 65757
Tel (417) 865-5355 SIC 5511 5012

WALTERS BAYER AUTOMOTIVE GROUP LLC p 1574
2030 E Flamingo Rd # 290, Las Vegas NV 89119
Tel (702) 450-8001 SIC 5012

MCDEVITT TRUCKS INC p 927
1 Mack Ave, Manchester NH 03103
Tel (800) 370-6225 SIC 5012 5013 7538

SUBARU OF AMERICA INC p 1395
2235 Rte 70 W, Cherry Hill NJ 08002
Tel (856) 488-8500
SIC 5012 5013 7515 8732

WARNOCK AUTOMOTIVE GROUP INC p 1576
175 State Route 10, East Hanover NJ 07936
Tel (973) 884-2100
SIC 5511 7515 5012 5013

FERRARI NORTH AMERICA INC p 538
250 Sylvan Ave, Englewood Cliffs NJ 07632
Tel (201) 816-2600 SIC 5511 5012

JAGUAR CARS INC p 776
555 Macarthur Blvd, Mahwah NJ 07430
Tel (201) 818-8500 SIC 5012 5013

WCAMPBELL SUPPLY CO LLC p 1585
1015 Cranbury S River Rd, Monroe Township NJ 08831
Tel (732) 287-8884 SIC 5012

TRAC INTERMODAL LLC p 1468
750 College Rd E, Princeton NJ 08540
Tel (609) 452-8900 SIC 7359 3715 5012

PRESTIGE OF BERGEN INC p 1173
50 Williams Dr, Ramsey NJ 07446
Tel (201) 825-2700 SIC 5511 5521 5012

BMW OF NORTH AMERICA LLC p 194
300 Chestnut Ridge Rd, Woodcliff Lake NJ 07677
Tel (201) 307-4000
SIC 5013 3751 5012 3711

■ **REMY USA INDUSTRIES LLC** p 1223
215 Candlewood Rd, Bay Shore NY 11706
Tel (631) 969-2222 SIC 5012

TRACEY ROAD EQUIPMENT INC p 1468
6803 Manlius Center Rd, East Syracuse NY 13057
Tel (315) 437-1471
SIC 5082 5012 7353 7699 5013

GAULT CHEVROLET CO INC p 594
2205 North St, Endicott NY 13760
Tel (607) 748-8244 SIC 5511 5012

REGIONAL INTERNATIONAL CORP p 1219
1007 Lehigh Station Rd, Henrietta NY 14467
Tel (585) 359-2011
SIC 5013 5012 7539 7538 5531

FIAT USA INC p 539
375 Park Ave Ste 2703, New York NY 10152
Tel (212) 355-2600
SIC 3714 8741 3535 5012 5013 5082

MARUBENI AMERICA CORP p 913
375 Lexington Ave, New York NY 10017
Tel (212) 450-0100
SIC 5131 5084 5012 5169 5172 5094

TOYOTA MOTOR NORTH AMERICA INC p 1467
601 Lexington Ave Fl 49, New York NY 10022
Tel (212) 751-3053 SIC 5511 5012 3711

ATLANTIC EXPRESS TRANSPORTATION GROUP INC p 126
7 North St, Staten Island NY 10302
Tel (718) 442-7000 SIC 4151 4141 5012

GREENSBORO AUTO AUCTION INC p 638
3907 W Wendover Ave, Greensboro NC 27407
Tel (336) 299-7777 SIC 5012

MACK TRUCKS INC p 892
7825 National Service Rd, Greensboro NC 27409
Tel (336) 291-9001
SIC 3711 3714 5012 6141 6153 7538

VNA HOLDING INC p 1563
7825 National Service Rd, Greensboro NC 27409
Tel (336) 393-4890
SIC 6159 3713 5012 5013

VOLVO GROUP NORTH AMERICA LLC p 1565
7900 National Service Rd, Greensboro NC 27409
Tel (336) 393-2000 SIC 3713 5012 5013

VOLVO TRUCKS NORTH AMERICA INC p 1565
7900 National Service Rd, Greensboro NC 27409
Tel (336) 393-2000 SIC 3713 5012 5013

FHA/RALEIGH INC p 539
9101 Glenwood Ave, Raleigh NC 27617
Tel (919) 787-0099 SIC 5511 5521 5012

HOL-DAV INC p 700
5839 Capital Blvd, Raleigh NC 27616
Tel (888) 240-7435 SIC 5511 5012

LEITH INC p 854
5607 Capital Blvd, Raleigh NC 27616
Tel (919) 876-5432
SIC 5511 7515 7513 5012

WW WALLWORK INC p 1629
900 35th St N, Fargo ND 58102
Tel (701) 282-6700 SIC 5511 5012 5013

MAC MANUFACTURING INC p 891
14599 Commerce St Ne, Alliance OH 44601
Tel (330) 823-9900 SIC 3715 5012

MAC TRAILER MANUFACTURING INC p 891
14599 Commerce St Ne, Alliance OH 44601
Tel (330) 823-9900
SIC 3715 5012 5013 5015 7539

VALLEY FORD TRUCK INC p 1540
5715 Canal Rd, Cleveland OH 44125
Tel (216) 524-2400
SIC 5013 5511 5521 5531 5012

VOSS AUTO NETWORK INC p 1566
766 Mmsburg Cnterville Rd, Dayton OH 45459
Tel (937) 428-2400
SIC 5511 7538 7515 7513 5521 5012

COLUMBUS FAIR AUTO AUCTION INC p 342
4700 Groveport Rd, Obetz OH 43207
Tel (614) 497-2000 SIC 5012 5521

COUGHLIN CHEVROLET INC p 374
9000 Broad St Sw, Pataskala OH 43062
Tel (740) 964-9191
SIC 5511 5012 7538 7532 5531

CROSS POINT NW LLC p 393
6803 Se Jhnson Creek Blvd, Portland OR 97206
Tel (503) 594-2800 SIC 5012

M H EBY INC p 889
1194 Main St, Blue Ball PA 17506
Tel (800) 292-4752 SIC 3713 5012

MANHEIM REMARKETING INC p 901
21095 Route 19, Cranberry Township PA 16066
Tel (724) 452-5555 SIC 5012

FRED BEANS FORD INC p 575
876 N Easton Rd, Doylestown PA 18902
Tel (888) 903-2085
SIC 5511 7513 5521 5012

WOLFINGTON BODY CO INC p 1621
N Off Pa Tpk Exit Rr 100, Exton PA 19341
Tel (610) 458-8501 SIC 3711 3713 5012

FORD MCCAFFERTY SALES INC p 565
1939 E Lincoln Hwy, Langhorne PA 19047
Tel (215) 945-8000
SIC 5511 5531 7538 7514 5521 5012

SFS INTEC INC p 1310
1045 Spring St, Wyomissing PA 19610
Tel (610) 376-5751 SIC 7699 5012 5085

K I INVESTMENTS INC p 799
Ave 65 De Infntria St1179, San Juan PR 00924
Tel (787) 622-0600 SIC 6519 5012 5511

NFA CORP p 1041
50 Martin St, Cumberland RI 02864
Tel (617) 232-6060 SIC 5012 2241

NORTH AMERICAN TRUCK & TRAILER INC p 1050
4500 N Cliff Ave, Sioux Falls SD 57104
Tel (605) 332-7112 SIC 5012 7538

NISSAN NORTH AMERICA INC p 1044
1 Nissan Way, Franklin TN 37067
Tel (615) 725-1000
SIC 5012 8711 8734 6141 8741 3711

DIRECT AUCTION SERVICES LLC p 441
101 Jessica Lauren Ct, Hendersonville TN 37075
Tel (878) 570-3493
SIC 5012 7539 7549 7542 7361

PETERBILT OF KNOXVILLE INC p 1138
5218 Rutledge Pike, Knoxville TN 37924
Tel (800) 552-7779 SIC 5012 7538

GOSSETT MOTOR CARS INC p 626
1901 Covington Pike, Memphis TN 38128
Tel (901) 363-6556 SIC 5511 5012

TRI-STATE TRUCK CENTER INC p 1478
494 E Eh Crump Blvd, Memphis TN 38126
Tel (901) 947-5000 SIC 5511 7513 5012

NEELY COBLE CO INC p 1024
319 Fesslers Ln, Nashville TN 37210
Tel (615) 244-8900 SIC 5012 5013

NISSAN TRADING CORP AMERICAS p 1044
1974 Midway Ln, Smyrna TN 37167
Tel (615) 220-7100
SIC 5013 5012 5051 5084

MACK CLEVELAND SALES INC p 892
1263 Us Highway 59 N, Cleveland TX 77327
Tel (281) 593-8888 SIC 5012

▲ **COPART INC** p 368
14185 Dallas Pkwy Ste 300, Dallas TX 75254
Tel (972) 391-5000 SIC 5012

TEXAS KENWORTH CO p 1444
4040 Irving Blvd, Dallas TX 75247
Tel (214) 920-7300
SIC 5012 5013 7513 7538

UTILITY TRAILER OF DALLAS INC p 1537
34241 Lyndon B Jhnson Fwy, Dallas TX 75241
Tel (972) 225-8845 SIC 5012 5015 5511

FRIEDKIN COMPANIES INC p 579
1345 Enclave Pkwy, Houston TX 77077
Tel (713) 580-3300 SIC 5012 6211

GULF STATES TOYOTA INC p 647
1375 Enclave Pkwy, Houston TX 77077
Tel (713) 580-3300 SIC 5012 5013

SELECTRANSPORTATION RESOURCES LLC p 1302
9550 North Loop E, Houston TX 77029
Tel (713) 672-4115
SIC 5012 5013 5511 7538

ROBERTS TRUCK CENTER HOLDING CO LLC p 1242
1825 Lakeway Dr Ste 700, Lewisville TX 75057
Tel (469) 645-7111 SIC 5012 7513 7538

BA & W ENTERPRISES INC p 143
13510 Toepperwein Rd, Live Oak TX 78233
Tel (361) 767-4100 *SIC* 5012

■ RUSH ADMINISTRATIVE SERVICES INC p 1258
555 S Interstate 35 # 500, New Braunfels TX 78130
Tel (830) 626-5286
SIC 5012 7538 5531 5014 7513

▲ RUSH ENTERPRISES INC p 1258
555 S Ih 35 Ste 500, New Braunfels TX 78130
Tel (830) 302-5200
SIC 5012 7538 5531 5014 7513

■ RUSH TRUCK CENTERS OF CALIFORNIA INC p 1259
555 S Interstate 35 # 500, New Braunfels TX 78130
Tel (830) 626-5200 *SIC* 5511 5012

■ RUSH TRUCK CENTERS OF ILLINOIS INC p 1259
555 S Interstate 35 # 500, New Braunfels TX 78130
Tel (830) 626-5200 *SIC* 5012

■ RUSH TRUCK CENTERS OF TEXAS INC p 1259
555 S Interstate 35 # 500, New Braunfels TX 78130
Tel (830) 626-5200 *SIC* 5012 5511

FRENCH-ELLISON TRUCK CENTER LLC p 578
4300 N Cage Blvd, Pharr TX 78577
Tel (956) 781-2401
SIC 5013 5531 5511 5012 7538

VIA MOTORS INC p 1554
165 Mountain Way Dr, Orem UT 84058
Tel (801) 764-9111 *SIC* 5012

ADESA UTAH LLC p 22
780 S 5600 W, Salt Lake City UT 84104
Tel (801) 322-1234 *SIC* 5012 5521 5084

ARNOLD MACHINERY CO p 112
2975 W 2100 S, Salt Lake City UT 84119
Tel (801) 972-4000
SIC 5082 5084 5012 5083

■ RUSH TRUCK CENTERS OF UTAH INC p 1259
964 S 3800 W, Salt Lake City UT 84104
Tel (801) 972-5320 *SIC* 5012 7538 5531

FREIGHTLINER OF UTAH A LIMITED LIABILITY CO p 577
2240 S 5370 W, West Valley City UT 84120
Tel (801) 978-8000
SIC 5012 5013 7539 7538 5511

KENWORTH SALES CO p 813
2125 S Constitution Blvd, West Valley City UT 84119
Tel (801) 487-4161
SIC 5012 5013 7538 3519

VOLKSWAGEN GROUP OF AMERICA CHATTANOOGA OPERATIONS LLC p 1564
2200 Ferdinand Porsche Dr, Herndon VA 20171
Tel (703) 364-7000 *SIC* 5012 5013

VOLKSWAGEN GROUP OF AMERICA INC p 1564
2200 Ferdinand Porsche Dr, Herndon VA 20171
Tel (703) 364-7000
SIC 5511 5012 5013 6153 6141 4899

EXCEL TRUCK GROUP p 516
267 Lee Hwy, Roanoke VA 24019
Tel (540) 777-7700
SIC 5511 5013 7538 5012

MARSHALLS HOLDING CO p 911
20220 International Blvd, Seatac WA 98198
Tel (206) 433-5911 *SIC* 5012 5013

GWP HOLDINGS LLC p 648
3801 Airport Way S, Seattle WA 98108
Tel (206) 624-7383
SIC 5511 7513 7538 5012

SEAGRAVE FIRE APPARATUS LLC p 1296
105 E 12th St, Clintonville WI 54929
Tel (715) 823-2141 *SIC* 5012 3713 8711

TRUCK COUNTRY OF WISCONSIN INC p 1485
4195 Anderson Rd, Deforest WI 53532
Tel (608) 249-1090 *SIC* 5012 7538

BROADWAY FORD-HYUNDAI INC p 216
1010 S Military Ave, Green Bay WI 54304
Tel (920) 499-3131
SIC 7515 5511 7513 5521 5012

JX ENTERPRISES INC p 798
1320 Walnut Ridge Dr, Hartland WI 53029
Tel (800) 810-3410
SIC 5012 5511 7538 6159 7513

CSM COMPANIES INC p 398
5100 Estpark Blvd Ste 210, Madison WI 53718
Tel (608) 241-5616 *SIC* 5012 5013

WILDE OF WEST ALLIS INC p 1609
3225 S 108th St, Milwaukee WI 53227
Tel (414) 329-6043
SIC 5511 5521 7538 7515 7513 5012

SIC 5013 Motor Vehicle Splys & New Parts Wholesale

TAMERON AUTOMOTIVE GROUP INC p 1423
1675 Montgomery Hwy, Birmingham AL 35216
Tel (205) 396-3108 *SIC* 5511 5013

COURTESY CHEVROLET p 383
1233 E Camelback Rd, Phoenix AZ 85014
Tel (602) 279-3232 *SIC* 5511 5013 7538

FREIGHTLINER STERLING WESTERN STAR OF ARIZONA LTD p 577
9899 W Roosevelt St, Tolleson AZ 85353
Tel (623) 907-9900 *SIC* 5013 5012 7538

CROW-BURLIGAME CO p 394
1901 E Roosevelt Rd, Little Rock AR 72206
Tel (501) 375-1215 *SIC* 5013

REPLACEMENT PARTS INC p 1224
1901 E Roosevelt Rd, Little Rock AR 72206
Tel (501) 375-1215 *SIC* 5013

ISUZU NORTH AMERICA CORP p 767
1400 S Douglass Rd # 100, Anaheim CA 92806
Tel (714) 935-9300
SIC 5511 5084 5013 5015

FLYERS ENERGY LLC p 562
2360 Lindbergh St, Auburn CA 95602
Tel (530) 885-0401 *SIC* 5411 5541 5013

FRANK EDWARDS CO INC p 574
1565 Adrian Rd, Burlingame CA 94010
Tel (650) 692-2347 *SIC* 5084 5013

■ INTERAMERICAN MOTOR CORP p 751
8901 Canoga Ave, Canoga Park CA 91304
Tel (818) 678-6571 *SIC* 5013 5599

CBOL CORP p 269
19850 Plummer St, Chatsworth CA 91311
Tel (818) 704-8200
SIC 5065 5072 5013 5088 5084 5162

AMERICAN EAGLE WHEEL CORP p 71
5780 Soestern Ct, Chino CA 91710
Tel (909) 590-8828 *SIC* 5013

MUTSUTECH LTD p 1003
3130 Bonita Rd Ste 107, Chula Vista CA 91910
Tel (619) 691-7056 *SIC* 5064 5013

KRACO ENTERPRISES LLC p 829
505 E Euclid Ave, Compton CA 90222
Tel (310) 639-0666 *SIC* 5531 3069 5013

TAP OPERATING CO LLC p 1424
400 W Artesia Blvd, Compton CA 90220
Tel (310) 900-5500 *SIC* 5013

TAP WORLDWIDE LLC p 1424
400 W Artesia Blvd, Compton CA 90220
Tel (310) 900-5500 *SIC* 5013

■ TRANSAMERICAN DISSOLUTION CO LLC p 1470
400 W Artesia Blvd, Compton CA 90220
Tel (310) 900-5500 *SIC* 5531 5013

MITSUBISHI MOTORS NORTH AMERICA INC p 978
6400 Katella Ave, Cypress CA 90630
Tel (714) 799-4730
SIC 5511 5013 6159 6512

YAMAHA MOTOR CORP USA p 1634
6555 Katella Ave, Cypress CA 90630
Tel (714) 761-7300
SIC 5088 5013 5091 5012

PBE WAREHOUSE INC p 1123
12171 Pangborn Ave, Downey CA 90241
Tel (562) 803-4691 *SIC* 5013

HARVEY & MADDING INC p 667
6300 Dublin Blvd, Dublin CA 94568
Tel (925) 828-8030
SIC 5511 7538 5015 5013

K MOTORS INC p 799
965 Arnele Ave, El Cajon CA 92020
Tel (619) 270-3000 *SIC* 5521 5013 5511

INLAND KENWORTH (US) INC p 743
9730 Cherry Ave, Fontana CA 92335
Tel (909) 823-9955
SIC 5012 7538 5013 7513

UTILITY TRAILER SALES OF SOUTHERN CALIFORNIA LLC p 1537
15567 Valley Blvd, Fontana CA 92335
Tel (877) 275-4887
SIC 5012 5013 5531 5561

KAWASAKI MOTORS CORP USA p 805
26972 Burbank, Foothill Ranch CA 92610
Tel (949) 837-4683
SIC 5012 5013 5084 5091

BRIX GROUP INC p 215
838 N Laverne Ave, Fresno CA 93727
Tel (559) 457-4700 *SIC* 5065 5013

FRESNO TRUCK CENTER p 579
2727 E Central Ave, Fresno CA 93725
Tel (559) 486-4310
SIC 5511 5521 5531 5012 5013 6159

BATTERY SYSTEMS INC p 160
12322 Monarch St, Garden Grove CA 92841
Tel (310) 667-9320 *SIC* 5013

TIRECO INC p 1455
500 W 190th St Ste 100, Gardena CA 90248
Tel (310) 767-7990 *SIC* 5014 5013 5051

MYGRANT GLASS CO INC p 1004
3271 Arden Rd, Hayward CA 94545
Tel (510) 785-4360 *SIC* 5013

KIA MOTORS AMERICA INC p 816
111 Peters Canyon Rd, Irvine CA 92606
Tel (949) 468-4800 *SIC* 5511 5013 8741

KATANA RACING INC p 804
14407 Alondra Blvd, La Mirada CA 90638
Tel (562) 977-8565 *SIC* 5013 5014

DENSO PRODUCTS AND SERVICES AMERICAS INC p 429
3900 Via Oro Ave, Long Beach CA 90810
Tel (310) 834-6352
SIC 5013 7361 5075 3714

CLUB ASSIST US LLC p 328
888 W 6th St Ste 300, Los Angeles CA 90017
Tel (213) 388-4333 *SIC* 5013

■ COAST DISTRIBUTION SYSTEM INC p 331
350 Woodview Ave Ste 100, Morgan Hill CA 95037
Tel (408) 782-6686 *SIC* 5013

■ WORLDPAC INC p 1626
37137 Hickory St, Newark CA 94560
Tel (510) 742-8900 *SIC* 5013 5531

MIKUNI AMERICAN CORP p 968
8910 Mikuni Ave, Northridge CA 91324
Tel (310) 676-0522 *SIC* 5013 5088

BI WAREHOUSING INC p 180
5404 Pacific St, Rocklin CA 95677
Tel (916) 624-0654 *SIC* 5531 5013 7539

METROPOLITAN AUTOMOTIVE WAREHOUSE p 955
535 Tennis Court Ln, San Bernardino CA 92408
Tel (909) 885-2886 *SIC* 5013

MERIDIAN RACK & PINION INC p 949
6740 Cobra Way Ste 200, San Diego CA 92121
Tel (858) 587-8777 *SIC* 5013 5961

GREEN HILLS SOFTWARE INC p 637
30 W Sola St, Santa Barbara CA 93101
Tel (805) 965-6044 *SIC* 5013

ALPS ELECTRIC (NORTH AMERICA) INC p 61
3151 Jay St Ste 101, Santa Clara CA 95054
Tel (408) 361-6400 *SIC* 5045 5065 5013

WARREN DISTRIBUTING INC p 1576
8737 Dice Rd, Santa Fe Springs CA 90670
Tel (562) 789-3360 *SIC* 5013

B&M RACING & PERFORMANCE PRODUCTS INC p 142
100 Stony Point Rd # 125, Santa Rosa CA 95401
Tel (707) 544-4761 *SIC* 5013

SSF IMPORTED AUTO PARTS LLC p 1363
466 Forbes Blvd, South San Francisco CA 94080
Tel (800) 203-9287 *SIC* 5013

HONDA TRADING AMERICA CORP p 705
19210 Van Ness Ave, Torrance CA 90501
Tel (310) 787-5000 *SIC* 5013

▲ MOTORCAR PARTS OF AMERICA INC p 993
2929 California St, Torrance CA 90503
Tel (310) 212-7910
SIC 3714 3694 3625 5013

■ MCCANDLESS TRUCK CENTER LLC p 926
16704 E 32nd Ave, Aurora CO 80011
Tel (331) 332-5000 *SIC* 5013 7538 5012

FMH MATERIAL HANDLING SOLUTIONS INC p 562
4105 Globeville Rd, Denver CO 80216
Tel (303) 292-5438 *SIC* 5084 7353 5013

CASTLE PARTNERS LLC p 264
6787 Millstone St, Highlands Ranch CO 80130
Tel (303) 884-1157 *SIC* 5172 5013

TOWN FAIR TIRE CENTERS INC p 1465
460 Coe Ave, East Haven CT 06512
Tel (203) 467-8600 *SIC* 5531 5014 5013

NGK NORTH AMERICA INC p 1041
1105 N Market St Ste 1300, Wilmington DE 19801
Tel (302) 654-1344
SIC 3714 5013 3264 5063

COMCAR INDUSTRIES INC p 343
502 E Bridgers Ave, Auburndale FL 33823
Tel (863) 967-1101
SIC 4213 5521 5013 4212

JM FAMILY ENTERPRISES INC p 786
100 Jim Moran Blvd, Deerfield Beach FL 33442
Tel (954) 429-2000
SIC 5511 5012 5013 5531

TPH ACQUISITION LLLP p 1467
10321 Fortune Pkwy, Jacksonville FL 32256
Tel (904) 731-3034 *SIC* 5013

INTEGRATED SUPPLY NETWORK LLC p 749
2727 Interstate Dr, Lakeland FL 33805
Tel (863) 603-0777 *SIC* 5013 5072

■ NESTOR SALES LLC p 1027
7337 Bryan Dairy Rd, Largo FL 33777
Tel (727) 544-6114 *SIC* 5013 5085

BENNETT AUTO SUPPLY INC p 173
3141 Sw 10th St, Pompano Beach FL 33069
Tel (954) 335-8700 *SIC* 5531 5013 3711

TRUCK COMPONENTS INC p 1485
8819 N Brooks St, Tampa FL 33604
Tel (813) 933-1166 *SIC* 5013

NATIONAL OAK DISTRIBUTORS INC p 1014
6529 Southern Blvd Ste 6, West Palm Beach FL 33413
Tel (561) 478-2711 *SIC* 5013 5198

CARROLLS LLC p 261
4281 Old Dixie Hwy, Atlanta GA 30354
Tel (404) 366-5476 *SIC* 5014 5013

▲ GENUINE PARTS CO p 605
2999 Wildwood Pkwy, Atlanta GA 30339
Tel (770) 953-1700
SIC 5013 5531 3714 5084 5085 5021

MERCEDES-BENZ USA LLC p 944
303 Perimeter Ctr N, Atlanta GA 30346
Tel (201) 573-0600
SIC 5012 5013 7538 5511

PORSCHE CARS NORTH AMERICA INC p 1161
1 Porsche Dr, Atlanta GA 30354
Tel (770) 290-3500 *SIC* 5511 5013

STAG-PARKWAY INC p 1374
6320 Boat Rock Blvd Sw, Atlanta GA 30336
Tel (404) 349-7800 *SIC* 5013

WHATLEY OIL AND AUTO PARTS CO p 1604
598 Blakely St, Cuthbert GA 39840
Tel (229) 732-2611 *SIC* 5171 5013 7389

■ ASBURY AUTOMOTIVE ATLANTA LLC p 115
3039 Premiere Pkwy # 900, Duluth GA 30097
Tel (404) 622-1921
SIC 5511 7515 5013 6159 5521

ROTARY CORP p 1252
801 W Barnard St, Glennville GA 30427
Tel (912) 654-3433 *SIC* 5083 3469 5013

UNI-SELECT USA INC p 1502
1155 Roberts Blvd Nw # 175, Kennesaw GA 30144
Tel (770) 701-5000 *SIC* 5013

MDSA LLC p 933
650 Engineering Dr, Norcross GA 30092
Tel (770) 448-3900 *SIC* 5013 6794

SINGLE SOURCE INC p 1326
601 W Crssvlle Rd Ste 100, Roswell GA 30075
Tel (770) 840-7877 *SIC* 5013 7532

GREAT DANE TRAILERS INC p 633
602 E Lathrop Ave, Savannah GA 31415
Tel (912) 644-2100 *SIC* 5013 5012

PAI INDUSTRIES INC p 1107
950 Northbrook Pkwy, Suwanee GA 30024
Tel (770) 822-1000 *SIC* 3714 5013

DAEHAN SOLUTION GEORGIA LLC p 408
791 S Progress Pkwy, West Point GA 31833
Tel (706) 902-5200 *SIC* 5013 8711 3714

POWERTECH AMERICA SALES LLC p 1166
6801 Kia Pkwy, West Point GA 31833
Tel (706) 902-6800 *SIC* 5013

SERVCO PACIFIC INC p 1307
2850 Pukoloa St Ste 300, Honolulu HI 96819
Tel (808) 564-1300 *SIC* 5013 5064 5511

FUTURE FOUNDATION INC p 585
380 E Parkcenter Blvd # 230, Boise ID 83706
Tel (208) 336-0150 *SIC* 3354 5013 6361

WESTERN POWER SPORTS INC p 1599
601 E Gowen Rd, Boise ID 83716
Tel (208) 376-8400 *SIC* 5013

ILLINOIS AUTO ELECTRIC CO p 732
700 Enterprise St, Aurora IL 60504
Tel (630) 862-3300
SIC 5084 5013 5083 5078 7699 3519

POWER STOP LLC p 1165
6112 W 73rd St Unit C, Bedford Park IL 60638
Tel (708) 575-9745 *SIC* 5013

MAC NEIL AUTOMOTIVE PRODUCTS LIMITED p 891
1 Macneil Ct, Bolingbrook IL 60440
Tel (630) 769-1500 *SIC* 5531 5013

ROBERT BOSCH LLC p 1241
2800 S 25th Ave, Broadview IL 60155
Tel (248) 876-1000
SIC 3714 3694 5013 5064 3565 3541

GOLD EAGLE CO p 620
4400 S Kildare Ave Front, Chicago IL 60632
Tel (773) 376-4400 *SIC* 5013

▲ LAWSON PRODUCTS INC p 848
8770 W Bryn Mawr Ave # 639, Chicago IL 60631
Tel (773) 304-5050
SIC 5072 5085 5084 5013

WANXIANG AMERICA CORP p 1575
88 Airport Rd, Elgin IL 60123
Tel (847) 622-8838 *SIC* 5013

S & S AUTOMOTIVE INC p 1261
740 N Larch Ave, Elmhurst IL 60126
Tel (630) 279-1613
SIC 5013 5999 5065 1731

AIRTEX PRODUCTS LP p 40
407 W Main St, Fairfield IL 62837
Tel (618) 842-2111 *SIC* 5013

R A ZWEIG INC p 1201
2500 Ravine Way, Glenview IL 60025
Tel (847) 832-9001 *SIC* 5013

UNITED COMPONENTS LLC p 1507
1900 W Field Ct, Lake Forest IL 60045
Tel (812) 867-4516 *SIC* 5013 3714

GRI ENGINEERING & DEVELOPMENT LLC p 640
6700 Wildlife Way, Long Grove IL 60047
Tel (847) 383-8478 *SIC* 5013

R & O SPECIALTIES INC p 1201
120 4th Ave E, Milan IL 61264
Tel (309) 736-8660 *SIC* 5085 5013 3479

CERTIFIED POWER INC p 284
970 Campus Dr, Mundelein IL 60060
Tel (847) 573-3800 *SIC* 3714 7539 5013

CENTRAL ILLINOIS TRUCKS INC p 278
200 W Northtown Rd, Normal IL 61761
Tel (800) 322-5017 *SIC* 5013 7538 5012

OLD WORLD INDUSTRIES LLC p 1081
4065 Commercial Ave, Northbrook IL 60062
Tel (847) 559-2000 *SIC* 5013 5169

BOSCH AUTOMOTIVE AFTER MARKET SERVICE SOLUTIONS p 202
1385 N Weber Rd, Romeoville IL 60446
Tel (815) 407-3903 *SIC* 5013

MCI SERVICE PARTS INC p 930
1700 E Golf Rd Fl 3, Schaumburg IL 60173
Tel (847) 285-2000 *SIC* 5013

PATRICK SCHAUMBURG AUTOMOBILES INC p 1120
526 Mall Dr, Schaumburg IL 60173
Tel (847) 605-4000
SIC 5511 7539 7538 7532 5531 5013

BEN TIRE DISTRIBUTORS LTD p 172
203 E Madison St, Toledo IL 62468
Tel (800) 252-8961
SIC 5014 5013 5531 7534

GKN NORTH AMERICA SERVICES INC p 613
2715 Davey Rd Ste 300, Woodridge IL 60517
Tel (630) 972-9300 *SIC* 3714 5013 7359

KEM KREST LLC p 809
3221 Magnum Dr, Elkhart IN 46516
Tel (574) 389-2650
SIC 5169 5013 5085 4783 4225

TREDIT TIRE & WHEEL CO INC p 1475
3305 Charlotte Ave, Elkhart IN 46517
Tel (574) 293-0581 *SIC* 5014 5013

BRAKE SUPPLY CO INC p 207
5501 Foundation Blvd, Evansville IN 47725
Tel (812) 467-1000
SIC 5082 5084 5088 5013 3532

CHIYODA USA CORP p 301
2200 E State Road 240, Greencastle IN 46135
Tel (765) 653-2993 *SIC* 5013

SPECTRA PREMIUM (USA) CORP p 1357
3052 N Distribution Way, Greenfield IN 46140
Tel (317) 891-1700 *SIC* 5013

■ BALKAMP INC p 148
2601 S Holt Rd, Indianapolis IN 46241
Tel (317) 244-7241 *SIC* 5013

BFS DIVERSIFIED PRODUCTS INC p 179
250 W 96th St Ste 150, Indianapolis IN 46260
Tel (317) 575-7000 *SIC* 5031 5013 5169

FINISHMASTER INC p 543
115 W Washington St Fl 7, Indianapolis IN 46204
Tel (317) 237-3678 *SIC* 5013

MACALLISTER MACHINERY CO INC p 891
7515 E 30th St, Indianapolis IN 46219
Tel (317) 545-2151 *SIC* 5082 7699 5013

JASPER ENGINE & TRANSMISSION EXCHANGE INC p 778
815 Wernsing Rd, Jasper IN 47546
Tel (812) 482-1041 *SIC* 5013

JASPER ENGINE & TRANSMISSION EXCHANGE INC p 778
815 Wernsing Rd, Jasper IN 47546
Tel (812) 482-1041 *SIC* 5013

JASPER ENGINE & TRANSMISSION EXCHANGE INC (KY) p 778
815 Wernsing Rd, Jasper IN 47546
Tel (812) 482-1041 *SIC* 5013 7537

MEYER DISTRIBUTING INC p 957
560 E 25th St, Jasper IN 47546
Tel (812) 482-5102 *SIC* 5013 5012

■ WABASH NATIONAL TRAILER CENTERS INC p 1570
1000 Sagamore Pkwy S, Lafayette IN 47905
Tel (765) 771-5300 *SIC* 5012 7539 5013

AURORA PARTS & ACCESSORIES LLC p 132
500 S Enterprise Blvd, Lebanon IN 46052
Tel (765) 483-5622 *SIC* 5013

■ JAYCO INC p 779
903 S Main St, Middlebury IN 46540
Tel (574) 825-5861 SIC 5013 3716 3792

■ REMY INC p 1223
600 Corporation Dr, Pendleton IN 46064
Tel (765) 778-6499
SIC 3714 3694 3625 3621 5013

AISIN HOLDINGS OF AMERICA INC p 41
1665 E 4th Street Rd, Seymour IN 47274
Tel (812) 524-8144 SIC 5013

THYSSENKRUPP PRESTA NORTH AMERICA LLC p 1452
1597 E Industrial Dr, Terre Haute IN 47802
Tel (812) 299-5000 SIC 5013

J&P CYCLES LLC p 772
13225 Circle Dr, Anamosa IA 52205
Tel (319) 462-4817 SIC 5571 5013

INLAND TRUCK PARTS CO INC p 744
4400 College Blvd Ste 145, Overland Park KS 66211
Tel (913) 345-9664 SIC 5013 7538

TOYOTA BOSHOKU AMERICA INC p 1466
1360 Dolwick Rd Ste 125, Erlanger KY 41018
Tel (859) 817-4000 SIC 3711 5013

ACK CONTROLS INC p 17
2600 Happy Valley Rd, Glasgow KY 42141
Tel (270) 678-6200 SIC 5013 3625 3357

BOGE RUBBER & PLASTICS USA LLC p 197
1102 Aviation Blvd, Hebron KY 41048
Tel (859) 689-5900 SIC 5013

MARTINREA HOPKINSVILLE LLC p 913
1500 Frank Yost Ln, Hopkinsville KY 42240
Tel (270) 475-2000 SIC 5013

WORLDWIDE EQUIPMENT INC p 1626
73 We Dr, Prestonsburg KY 41653
Tel (606) 874-2172
SIC 5012 5013 7538 7513

APOLLO OIL LLC p 97
1175 Early Dr, Winchester KY 40391
Tel (859) 744-5444 SIC 5172 5013

RED BALL OXYGEN CO INC p 1215
609 N Market St, Shreveport LA 71107
Tel (318) 425-6300
SIC 5084 5085 5169 5099 5531 5013

BETHESDA INVESTMENT HOLDING CO INC p 178
10400 Auto Park Ave, Bethesda MD 20817
Tel (301) 469-6600
SIC 5511 7539 5013 5531

DANIEL J QUIRK INC p 411
372 Quincy Ave, Braintree MA 02184
Tel (781) 843-4800
SIC 5511 5013 5531 7538 5521 7515

CONSUMER AUTO PARTS INC p 361
75 Fortune Blvd, Milford MA 01757
Tel (508) 634-0600 SIC 5531 5013

■ AUTOPART INTERNATIONAL INC p 135
192 Mansfield Ave, Norton MA 02766
Tel (781) 784-1111 SIC 5013 5531

OLYMPUS SCIENTIFIC SOLUTIONS AMERICAS CORP p 1083
48 Woerd Ave Ste 105, Waltham MA 02453
Tel (781) 419-3900 SIC 5013

ETX HOLDINGS INC p 512
2000 Michigan Ave, Alma MI 48801
Tel (989) 463-1151
SIC 3585 3621 3714 5013 3089

NSK AMERICAS INC p 1065
4200 Goss Rd, Ann Arbor MI 48105
Tel (734) 913-7500 SIC 3714 5013 5085

NSK CORP p 1065
4200 Goss Rd, Ann Arbor MI 48105
Tel (734) 913-7500
SIC 3714 5013 3594 3568 3562

ANDROID INDUSTRIES LLC p 91
2155 Executive Hills Dr, Auburn Hills MI 48326
Tel (248) 454-0500 SIC 5013

FAURECIA INTERIOR SYSTEMS INC p 531
2500 Executive Hills Dr, Auburn Hills MI 48326
Tel (248) 409-3500 SIC 5013 3999

GKN DRIVELINE NORTH AMERICA INC p 613
2200 N Opdyke Rd, Auburn Hills MI 48326
Tel (248) 296-7000 SIC 3714 5013

GKN NORTH AMERICA INC p 613
2200 N Opdyke Rd, Auburn Hills MI 48326
Tel (248) 296-7200 SIC 3714 5013 7359

SCHLEGEL CORP p 1287
2750 High Meadow Cir, Auburn Hills MI 48326
Tel (248) 340-4100 SIC 5013 7539

TI AUTOMOTIVE INC p 1452
1272 Doris Rd Ste 100, Auburn Hills MI 48326
Tel (248) 276-4721 SIC 5013 7538

SAIC USA INC p 1268
322 N Old Woodward Ave # 3, Birmingham MI 48009
Tel (248) 267-9117 SIC 5013

JOMAR INVESTMENTS INC p 792
400 Gordon Indus Ct Sw, Byron Center MI 49315
Tel (616) 878-3633 SIC 5013

YAZAKI INTERNATIONAL CORP p 1635
6801 N Haggerty Rd 4707e, Canton MI 48187
Tel (734) 983-1000 SIC 5013 3643

YAZAKI NORTH AMERICA INC p 1635
6801 N Haggerty Rd, Canton MI 48187
Tel (734) 983-1000 SIC 5013

BRIDGEWATER INTERIORS LLC p 212
4617 W Fort St, Detroit MI 48209
Tel (313) 842-3300 SIC 5013 2531

MAHLE AFTERMARKET INC p 897
23030 Mahle Dr, Farmington MI 48335
Tel (248) 347-9700 SIC 5013

DAIMLER PURCHASING COORDINATION CORP p 408
36455 Corporate Dr, Farmington Hills MI 48331
Tel (248) 991-6700 SIC 5012 5013

HINO MOTORS MANUFACTURING USA INC p 695
37777 Interchange Dr, Farmington Hills MI 48335
Tel (248) 442-9077 SIC 5013

HIRAIN TECHNOLOGIES USA INC p 695
37632 Hills Tech Dr, Farmington Hills MI 48331
Tel (248) 839-1309 SIC 5013 8711

■ FORD FLAT ROCK ASSEMBLY PLANT p 565
1 International Dr, Flat Rock MI 48134
Tel (734) 782-7800 SIC 5013 3711

VENTRA FOWLERVILLE LLC p 1548
8887 W Grand River Rd, Fowlerville MI 48836
Tel (517) 223-5900 SIC 5013

AWI HOLDINGS INC p 139
440 Kirtland St Sw, Grand Rapids MI 49507
Tel (616) 243-2125 SIC 5013 5531

J & H OIL CO p 769
2696 Chicago Dr Sw, Grand Rapids MI 49519
Tel (616) 534-2181 SIC 5172 5013

JASPER WELLER LLC p 778
1500 Gezon Pkwy Sw, Grand Rapids MI 49509
Tel (616) 724-2000 SIC 7538 5013

PRINCE MANUFACTURING CORP p 1176
36 W 8th St Ste 250, Holland MI 49423
Tel (616) 494-5374 SIC 1611 3613 5013

■ FLUID ROUTING SOLUTIONS INC p 561
30000 Stephenson Hwy, Madison Heights MI 48071
Tel (248) 228-8900 SIC 5013

QUALIS AUTOMOTIVE LLC p 1196
29380 John R Rd, Madison Heights MI 48071
Tel (248) 740-1668 SIC 5013 7539

GESTAMP MASON LLC p 609
200 E Kipp Rd, Mason MI 48854
Tel (517) 244-8800
SIC 3398 5013 3714 3711 3465

SAF-HOLLAND INC p 1265
1950 Industrial Blvd, Muskegon MI 49442
Tel (231) 773-3271 SIC 5013

AISIN WORLD CORP OF AMERICA p 41
15300 Centennial Dr, Northville MI 48168
Tel (734) 453-5551 SIC 5013

ZF NORTH AMERICA INC p 1642
15811 Centennial Dr, Northville MI 48168
Tel (734) 416-6200 SIC 3714 5013

PREH INC p 1170
28850 Cabot Dr Ste 1300, Novi MI 48377
Tel (248) 381-3800 SIC 5013

ASP MD HOLDINGS INC p 118
47659 Halyard Dr, Plymouth MI 48170
Tel (734) 207-6200 SIC 5013

BREMBO NORTH AMERICA INC p 209
47765 Halyard Dr, Plymouth MI 48170
Tel (734) 416-1275 SIC 3714 5013

HELLA CORPORATE CENTER USA INC p 681
43811 Plymouth Oaks Blvd, Plymouth MI 48170
Tel (586) 232-4788
SIC 3625 5013 5088 3822 3585 3429

JOHNSON ELECTRIC AUTOMOTIVE INC p 791
47660 Halyard Dr, Plymouth MI 48170
Tel (734) 392-1022 SIC 5013 8731 8742

JTEKT NORTH AMERICA INC p 796
47771 Halyard Dr, Plymouth MI 48170
Tel (734) 454-1500 SIC 5013

LINK GROUP INC p 869
43855 Plymouth Oaks Blvd, Plymouth MI 48170
Tel (734) 453-0800 SIC 5013

MOBIS NORTH AMERICA LLC p 980
46501 Commerce Dr, Plymouth MI 48170
Tel (248) 426-5577 SIC 5013 8731

FAURECIA INTERIOR SYSTEMS SALINE LLC p 531
7700 E Michigan Ave, Saline MI 48176
Tel (734) 429-0030 SIC 5013

ABC INOAC EXTERIOR SYSTEMS LLC p 10
24175 Northwestern Hwy, Southfield MI 48075
Tel (248) 619-6057 SIC 5013

BRANDMOTION LLC p 208
21518 Bridge St, Southfield MI 48033
Tel (734) 619-1250 SIC 5013

DENSO INTERNATIONAL AMERICA INC p 428
24777 Denso Dr, Southfield MI 48033
Tel (248) 350-7500 SIC 3714 5013

GU-YOUNG TECH CO LTD p 644
26555 Evergreen Rd, Southfield MI 48076
Tel (248) 701-6663 SIC 5013

INTERNATIONAL AUTOMOTIVE COMPONENTS GROUP NORTH AMERICA HOLDINGS INC p 754
28333 Telegraph Rd, Southfield MI 48034
Tel (248) 455-7000 SIC 5013

INTERNATIONAL AUTOMOTIVE COMPONENTS GROUP NORTH AMERICA INC p 754
28333 Telegraph Rd, Southfield MI 48034
Tel (248) 455-7000 SIC 3089 5013

■ ARVINMERITOR EXHAUST SYSTEMS INC p 114
2135 W Maple Rd, Troy MI 48084
Tel (248) 435-1000 SIC 5013

DRIVESOL WORLDWIDE HOLDING CORP p 456
1104 W Maple Rd, Troy MI 48084
Tel (248) 729-2222 SIC 5013

GESTAMP NORTH AMERICA INC p 609
2701 Troy Center Dr # 150, Troy MI 48084
Tel (248) 743-3400 SIC 5013

MAGNA POWERTRAIN OF AMERICA INC p 896
1870 Technology Dr, Troy MI 48083
Tel (248) 597-7811 SIC 5013

MAHLE BEHR MANUFACTURING MANAGEMENT INC p 897
2700 Daley Dr, Troy MI 48083
Tel (248) 735-3623 SIC 5013 3714

MERITOR WABCO VEHICLE CONTROL SYSTEMS p 949
2135 W Maple Rd, Troy MI 48084
Tel (248) 273-4698 SIC 5013

N S INTERNATIONAL LTD p 1005
600 Wilshire Dr, Troy MI 48084
Tel (248) 251-1600 SIC 5013

THYSSENKRUPP AUTOMOTIVE SALES & TECHNICAL CENTER INC p 1451
3155 W Big Beaver Rd # 260, Troy MI 48084
Tel (248) 530-2902 SIC 5013 3714

LANE AUTOMOTIVE INC p 843
8300 Lane Dr, Watervliet MI 49098
Tel (269) 463-4113 SIC 5013 5531

WELLER AUTO PARTS INC p 1589
2525 Chicago Dr Sw, Wyoming MI 49519
Tel (616) 538-5000 SIC 5013 5015 5531

BEST OIL CO p 177
30 N 8th St, Cloquet MN 55720
Tel (218) 879-0201
SIC 5171 5172 5013 5983 5541 5411

ELLIOTT AUTO SUPPLY CO INC p 488
1380 Corporate Center Cur, Eagan MN 55121
Tel (651) 454-4100 SIC 5013

L AND M SUPPLY INC p 833
1200 E Us Highway 169, Grand Rapids MN 55744
Tel (218) 326-9451 SIC 5251 5331 5013

MID-STATES DISTRIBUTING CO INC p 963
1370 Mendota Hts Rd, Mendota MN 55150
Tel (651) 280-4300
SIC 5072 5013 5191 5091 5092 5136

■ KEYSTONE AUTOMOTIVE INDUSTRIES MN INC p 815
3615 Marshall St Ne, Minneapolis MN 55418
Tel (612) 789-1919 SIC 5013 3312 3465

■ MINTER-WEISMAN CO p 974
1035 Nathan Ln N Ste A, Minneapolis MN 55441
Tel (763) 545-3706
SIC 5194 5149 5145 5013 5122

POHLAD COMPANIES p 1159
60 S 6th St Ste 3700, Minneapolis MN 55402
Tel (612) 661-3700
SIC 8742 7929 6531 5013 7549 7379

W D LARSON COMPANIES LTD INC p 1568
10700 Lyndale Ave S Ste A, Minneapolis MN 55420
Tel (952) 888-4934
SIC 5012 5013 7538 6159

AUTOMOTIVE PARTS HEADQUARTERS INC p 134
2959 Clearwater Rd, Saint Cloud MN 56301
Tel (320) 252-5411 SIC 5013

DUNLAP & KYLE CO INC p 461
280 Eureka St, Batesville MS 38606
Tel (662) 563-7601 SIC 5014 5531 5013

CENTRAL POWER SYSTEMS & SERVICES LLC p 280
9200 Liberty Dr, Pleasant Valley MO 64068
Tel (816) 781-8070 SIC 5013 7629

▲ OREILLY AUTOMOTIVE INC p 1094
233 S Patterson Ave, Springfield MO 65802
Tel (417) 862-6708 SIC 5531 5013

■ OREILLY AUTOMOTIVE STORES INC p 1094
233 S Patterson Ave, Springfield MO 65802
Tel (417) 862-6708 SIC 5013 5531

■ OZARK AUTOMOTIVE DISTRIBUTORS INC p 1101
233 S Patterson Ave, Springfield MO 65802
Tel (417) 862-6708 SIC 5013

REDNECK INC p 1217
2100 N West Byp, Springfield MO 65803
Tel (417) 864-5210 SIC 5013 5561 5012

AUTOMOTIVE SUPPLY ASSOCIATES INC p 134
129 Manchester St, Concord NH 03301
Tel (603) 225-4000
SIC 5013 7539 5531 5169 5015

MCDEVITT TRUCKS INC p 927
1 Mack Ave, Manchester NH 03103
Tel (800) 370-6225 SIC 5012 5013 7538

SUBARU OF AMERICA INC p 1395
2235 Rte 70 W, Cherry Hill NJ 08002
Tel (856) 488-8500
SIC 5012 5013 7515 8732

C R P INDUSTRIES INC p 233
35 Commerce Dr, Cranbury NJ 08512
Tel (609) 578-4100 SIC 5013 5085 5063

WARNOCK AUTOMOTIVE GROUP INC p 1576
175 State Route 10, East Hanover NJ 07936
Tel (973) 884-2100
SIC 5511 7515 5012 5013

INTER-CITY TIRE & AUTO CENTER INC p 751
777 Dowd Ave, Elizabeth NJ 07201
Tel (908) 354-5533 SIC 5531 5013 7538

JAGUAR CARS INC p 776
555 Macarthur Blvd, Mahwah NJ 07430
Tel (201) 818-8500 SIC 5012 5013

JOHNSON & TOWERS INC p 790
2021 Briggs Rd, Mount Laurel NJ 08054
Tel (856) 234-6990
SIC 5084 5013 7699 7538 5085

WURTH GROUP OF NORTH AMERICA INC p 1628
93 Grant St, Ramsey NJ 07446
Tel (201) 818-8877 SIC 5013 5099 5072

WURTH USA INC p 1628
93 Grant St, Ramsey NJ 07446
Tel (201) 825-2710 SIC 5013

VOLVO CARS OF NORTH AMERICA LLC p 1565
1 Volvo Dr, Rockleigh NJ 07647
Tel (201) 768-7300
SIC 5511 5013 6159 7515 3714

AUTOMANN INC p 134
850 Randolph Rd, Somerset NJ 08873
Tel (201) 529-4996 SIC 5013 3715

KSI TRADING CORP p 831
100a Wade Ave, South Plainfield NJ 07080
Tel (908) 754-7154 SIC 5013

HANWHA HOLDINGS (USA) INC p 659
300 Frank W Burr Blvd # 52, Teaneck NJ 07666
Tel (609) 655-2500 SIC 5169 5013 5084

BMW OF NORTH AMERICA LLC p 194
300 Chestnut Ridge Rd, Woodcliff Lake NJ 07677
Tel (201) 307-4000
SIC 5013 3751 5012 3711

MIDDLE ATLANTIC WAREHOUSE DISTRIBUTOR INC p 964
20 Hazelwood Dr Ste 100, Amherst NY 14228
Tel (716) 531-9200 SIC 5013

ALBERT KEMPERLE INC p 46
8400 New Horizons Blvd, Amityville NY 11701
Tel (631) 841-1241 SIC 5013

D & W DIESEL INC p 406
1503 Clark Street Rd, Auburn NY 13021
Tel (315) 253-5300 SIC 5013 5531

TRACEY ROAD EQUIPMENT INC p 1468
6803 Manlius Center Rd, East Syracuse NY 13057
Tel (315) 437-1471
SIC 5082 5012 7353 7699 5013

REGIONAL INTERNATIONAL CORP p 1219
1007 Lehigh Station Rd, Henrietta NY 14467
Tel (585) 359-2011
SIC 5013 5012 7539 7538 5531

ARCH-AUTO PARTS CORP p 104
17008 Jamaica Ave, Jamaica NY 11432
Tel (718) 657-9600 SIC 5013 5531

SOMERSET TIRE SERVICE INC p 1339
358 Saw Mill River Rd # 5, Millwood NY 10546
Tel (732) 356-8500
SIC 5531 5014 5013 7538

FIAT USA INC p 539
375 Park Ave Ste 2703, New York NY 10152
Tel (212) 355-2600
SIC 3714 8741 3535 5012 5013 5082

TOYOTA TSUSHO AMERICA INC p 1467
805 3rd Ave Fl 17, New York NY 10022
Tel (212) 355-3600
SIC 5051 5013 4225 6331 5153

SUPERIOR LUBRICANTS CO INC p 1406
32 Ward Rd, North Tonawanda NY 14120
Tel (716) 693-8412 SIC 5172 5013

HAHN AUTOMOTIVE WAREHOUSE INC p 653
415 W Main St, Rochester NY 14608
Tel (585) 235-1595 SIC 5013

PARTS AUTHORITY INC p 1118
495 Merrick Rd, Rockville Centre NY 11570
Tel (516) 678-3900 SIC 5013 5015 5531

KNORR BRAKE HOLDING CORP p 825
748 Starbuck Ave, Watertown NY 13601
Tel (315) 786-5356 SIC 3743 5013

CAROLINA TRACTOR & EQUIPMENT CO INC p 259
9000 Statesville Rd, Charlotte NC 28269
Tel (704) 596-6700
SIC 5082 5084 5013 7353 7359 7629

MANN+HUMMEL FILTRATION TECHNOLOGY GROUP INC p 902
1 Wix Way, Gastonia NC 28054
Tel (704) 869-3300 SIC 3714 5013

VNA HOLDING INC p 1563
7825 National Service Rd, Greensboro NC 27409
Tel (336) 393-4890
SIC 6159 3713 5012 5013

VOLVO GROUP NORTH AMERICA LLC p 1565
7900 National Service Rd, Greensboro NC 27409
Tel (336) 393-2000 SIC 3713 5012 5013

VOLVO TRUCKS NORTH AMERICA INC p 1565
7900 National Service Rd, Greensboro NC 27409
Tel (336) 393-2000 SIC 3713 5012 5013

■ KYOCERA INDUSTRIAL CERAMICS CORP p 833
100 Industrial Park Rd, Hendersonville NC 28792
Tel (828) 693-0241 SIC 5065 5013 5085

AMERICAN TIRE DISTRIBUTORS HOLDINGS INC p 80
12200 Herbert Wayne Ct # 150, Huntersville NC 28078
Tel (704) 992-2000 SIC 5014 5013

AMERICAN TIRE DISTRIBUTORS INC p 80
12200 Herbert Wayne Ct # 150, Huntersville NC 28078
Tel (704) 992-2000 SIC 5014 5013

■ GENERAL PARTS INC p 601
2635 E Millbrook Rd Ste C, Raleigh NC 27604
Tel (919) 573-3000 SIC 5013 5531

■ GENERAL PARTS INTERNATIONAL INC p 601
2635 E Millbrook Rd Ste B, Raleigh NC 27604
Tel (919) 573-3000 SIC 5013

NATIONAL COATINGS & SUPPLIES INC p 1010
4900 Falls Of Neuse Rd, Raleigh NC 27609
Tel (919) 573-2900 SIC 5013

■ REPUBLIC AUTOMOTIVE PARTS SALES INC p 1225
2635 E Millbrook Rd, Raleigh NC 27604
Tel (919) 573-3000 SIC 5013 5531

AUTO SUPPLY CO INC p 133
3740 N Patterson Ave, Winston Salem NC 27105
Tel (336) 661-6113 SIC 5013

WW WALLWORK INC p 1629
900 35th St N, Fargo ND 58102
Tel (701) 282-6700 SIC 5511 5012 5013

CHESTNUT HOLDINGS INC p 295
670 W Market St, Akron OH 44303
Tel (330) 849-6503
SIC 3053 5014 5013 3714

▲ GOODYEAR TIRE & RUBBER CO p 625
200 E Innovation Way, Akron OH 44316
Tel (330) 796-2121
SIC 3011 3052 7534 7538 7539 5013

▲ MYERS INDUSTRIES INC p 1004
1293 S Main St, Akron OH 44301
Tel (330) 253-5592
SIC 3089 3086 3069 3052 5013 5014

MAC TRAILER MANUFACTURING INC p 891
14599 Commerce St Ne, Alliance OH 44601
Tel (330) 823-9900
SIC 3715 5012 5013 5015 7539

TS TRIM INDUSTRIES INC p 1489
6380 Canal St, Canal Winchester OH 43110
Tel (614) 837-4114
SIC 5013 3465 3714 3083

K - O - I WAREHOUSE INC p 798
2701 Spring Grove Ave, Cincinnati OH 45225
Tel (513) 357-2400 SIC 5013

KOI ENTERPRISES INC p 826
2701 Spring Grove Ave, Cincinnati OH 45225
Tel (513) 357-2400 SIC 5013 5531

SMYTH AUTOMOTIVE INC p 1335
4275 Mt Carmel Tobasco Rd, Cincinnati OH 45244
Tel (513) 528-2800 SIC 5013 5531

INTERSTATE DIESEL SERVICE INC p 758
5300 Lakeside Ave E, Cleveland OH 44114
Tel (216) 881-0015 SIC 5013 3714

■ KAR PRODUCTS p 804
1301 E 9th St Ste 700, Cleveland OH 44114
Tel (216) 416-7200 SIC 5013 5084 5072

LINSALATA CORP p 869
5900 Landerbrook Dr # 280, Cleveland OH 44124
Tel (440) 684-1400 SIC 5013

■ NES INVESTMENT CO p 1026
6140 Parkland Blvd, Cleveland OH 44124
Tel (440) 461-6000
SIC 5065 5085 5169 5013

TRANSTAR INDUSTRIES INC p 1473
7350 Young Dr, Cleveland OH 44146
Tel (440) 232-5100 SIC 5013

VALLEY FORD TRUCK INC p 1540
5715 Canal Rd, Cleveland OH 44125
Tel (216) 524-2400
SIC 5013 5511 5521 5531 5012

AUTOMOTIVE DISTRIBUTORS CO INC p 134
2981 Morse Rd, Columbus OH 43231
Tel (614) 476-1315 SIC 5013

HY-TEK MATERIAL HANDLING INC p 722
2222 Rickenbacker Pkwy W, Columbus OH 43217
Tel (614) 497-2500
SIC 5084 5013 7538 7513 1796

AFTERMARKET PARTS CO LLC p 33
3229 Sawmill Pkwy, Delaware OH 43015
Tel (888) 333-6224 SIC 5013

BENDIX COMMERCIAL VEHICLE SYSTEMS LLC p 172
901 Cleveland St, Elyria OH 44035
Tel (440) 329-9000 SIC 5013 8711

G S WIRING SYSTEMS INC p 587
1801 Production Dr, Findlay OH 45840
Tel (419) 423-7111 SIC 3714 5013

ADVICS NORTH AMERICA INC p 28
1650 Kingsview Dr, Lebanon OH 45036
Tel (513) 696-5450
SIC 8731 8742 5013 5531

QUALITOR INC p 1196
1840 Mccullough St, Lima OH 45801
Tel (248) 204-8600 SIC 3714 5013

ARE INC p 106
400 Nave Rd Sw, Massillon OH 44646
Tel (330) 830-7800
SIC 3713 3714 3792 5013

BUYERS PRODUCTS CO p 230
9049 Tyler Blvd, Mentor OH 44060
Tel (440) 974-8888 SIC 5013 3714

KEIHIN THERMAL TECHNOLOGY OF AMERICA INC p 808
10500 Oday Harrison Rd, Mount Sterling OH 43143
Tel (740) 869-3000 SIC 5013 3714

GLOCKNER CHEVROLET CO p 618
4368 Us Route 23, Portsmouth OH 45662
Tel (740) 353-2161 SIC 5013 5172 5511

VENTRA SALEM LLC p 1548
800 Pennsylvania Ave, Salem OH 44460
Tel (330) 337-8002 SIC 5013

NK PARTS INDUSTRIES INC p 1045
777 S Kuther Rd, Sidney OH 45365
Tel (937) 498-4651 SIC 5013 1796 4731

PIONEER AUTOMOTIVE TECHNOLOGIES INC p 1150
100 S Pioneer Blvd, Springboro OH 45066
Tel (937) 746-2293 SIC 5013 3714 3651

■ MATCO TOOLS CORP p 919
4403 Allen Rd, Stow OH 44224
Tel (330) 929-4949
SIC 5251 5072 3469 3423 5013

OHASHI TECHNICA USA INC p 1077
111 Burrer Dr, Sunbury OH 43074
Tel (740) 965-5115 SIC 5013 5072 3452

FAURECIA EXHAUST SYSTEMS LLC p 531
543 Matzinger Rd, Toledo OH 43612
Tel (419) 727-5000 SIC 3714 5013

GTM SERVICE INC p 644
1366 Rockefeller Rd, Wickliffe OH 44092
Tel (440) 944-5099 SIC 5013

■ UNITED ENGINES LLC p 1508
5555 W Reno Ave, Oklahoma City OK 73127
Tel (800) 955-3321
SIC 5013 5084 7538 7537

■ UNITED HOLDINGS LLC p 1509
5 N Mccormick St Ste 200, Oklahoma City OK 73127
Tel (405) 947-3321
SIC 5084 5013 7538 7537 3441

▲ LITHIA MOTORS INC p 870
150 N Bartlett St, Medford OR 97501
Tel (541) 776-6401
SIC 5511 5531 5013 7539

PERFORMANCE WAREHOUSE CO p 1135
9440 N Whitaker Rd, Portland OR 97217
Tel (503) 417-5302 SIC 5013

■ NTP DISTRIBUTION INC p 1065
27150 Sw Kinsman Rd, Wilsonville OR 97070
Tel (503) 570-2154 SIC 5013

SERVICE CHAMP INC p 1307
180 New Britain Blvd, Chalfont PA 18914
Tel (215) 822-8500 SIC 5013

LA FRANCE CORP p 835
1 Lafrance Way, Concordville PA 19331
Tel (610) 361-4300
SIC 3089 3364 3993 5013 7389

■ KEYSTONE AUTOMOTIVE HOLDINGS INC p 815
44 Tunkhannock Ave, Exeter PA 18643
Tel (570) 655-4514 SIC 5013 5531

■ KEYSTONE AUTOMOTIVE OPERATIONS INC p 815
44 Tunkhannock Ave, Exeter PA 18643
Tel (570) 655-4514 SIC 5531 5013

■ KEYSTONE AUTOMOTIVE WAREHOUSE p 815
44 Tunkhannock Ave, Exeter PA 18643
Tel (570) 655-4514 SIC 5013

WETHERILL ASSOCIATES INC p 1603
411 Eagleview Blvd # 100, Exton PA 19341
Tel (484) 875-6600 SIC 5013

FIVE STAR INTERNATIONAL LLC p 553
1810 S 19th St, Harrisburg PA 17104
Tel (717) 986-1500 SIC 5511 7538 5013

EASTERN WAREHOUSE DISTRIBUTORS INC p 472
355 S Flowers Mill Rd, Langhorne PA 19047
Tel (215) 741-4228 SIC 5013

MORGAN TRUCK BODY LLC p 989
111 Morgan Way, Morgantown PA 19543
Tel (610) 286-5025
SIC 3713 7532 5013 5084

■ LIBERTY BELL EQUIPMENT CORP p 861
3201 S 76th St, Philadelphia PA 19153
Tel (215) 492-6700 SIC 5013

■ PITTSBURGH GLASS WORKS LLC p 1152
30 Isabella St Ste 500, Pittsburgh PA 15212
Tel (412) 995-6500 SIC 3211 5013

■ WHEELER BROS INC p 1605
384 Drum Ave, Somerset PA 15501
Tel (814) 443-2444 SIC 5013

BERGEYS INC p 174
462 Harleysville Pike, Souderton PA 18964
Tel (215) 721-3430
SIC 5511 5531 7538 5013 5014

BAIERL CHEVROLET INC p 145
10432 Perry Hwy, Wexford PA 15090
Tel (724) 935-3711 SIC 5511 5013

VOITH TURBO INC p 1564
25 Winship Rd, York PA 17406
Tel (717) 767-3200 SIC 5084 5013

FAURECIA INTERIOR SYSTEMS INC p 531
101 International Blvd, Fountain Inn SC 29644
Tel (864) 862-1900 SIC 5013

DACCO INC p 407
741 Dacco Dr, Cookeville TN 38506
Tel (931) 303-0112 SIC 3714 5013

CARLSTAR GROUP LLC p 258
725 Cool Springs Blvd, Franklin TN 37067
Tel (615) 503-0220
SIC 3714 5014 3499 5013 2296

■ HENNESSY INDUSTRIES INC p 683
1601 Jp Hennessy Dr, La Vergne TN 37086
Tel (615) 641-7533 SIC 3714 5013

TENNESSEE FARMERS COOPERATIVE INC p 1438
180 Old Nashville Hwy, La Vergne TN 37086
Tel (615) 793-8011
SIC 5191 5013 5014 5172 5122 2048

■ CUMMINS MID-SOUTH LLC p 401
3770 S Perkins Rd, Memphis TN 38118
Tel (901) 577-0600 SIC 5999 5013

VVP HOLDINGS LLC p 1567
965 Ridge Lake Blvd # 300, Memphis TN 38120
Tel (901) 767-7111
SIC 5039 5013 1793 3231 3444 5719

■ KEYSTONE AUTOMOTIVE INDUSTRIES INC p 815
655 Grassmere Park, Nashville TN 37211
Tel (615) 781-5200 SIC 5013 5531 3714

■ KEYSTONE AUTOMOTIVE INDUSTRIES TN INC p 815
655 Grassmere Park, Nashville TN 37211
Tel (615) 781-5200 SIC 5013

■ MID STATE AUTOMOTIVE DISTRIBUTORS INC p 963
485 Craighead St, Nashville TN 37204
Tel (615) 383-8566 SIC 5013 5531

NEELY COBLE CO INC p 1024
319 Fesslers Ln, Nashville TN 37210
Tel (615) 244-8900 SIC 5012 5013

NISSAN TRADING CORP AMERICAS p 1044
1974 Midway Ln, Smyrna TN 37167
Tel (615) 220-7100
SIC 5013 5012 5051 5084

CARLEX GLASS CO LLC p 257
77 Excellence Way, Vonore TN 37885
Tel (423) 884-1105 SIC 5013

TENNESSEE ZANINI INC p 1438
840 Industrial Dr, Winchester TN 37398
Tel (931) 967-8544 SIC 5013

ARNOLD OIL CO OF AUSTIN GP LLC p 112
5909 Burleson Rd, Austin TX 78744
Tel (512) 476-2401 SIC 5013 5172

QUALITY TRAILER PRODUCTS LP p 1197
604 W Main St, Azle TX 76020
Tel (817) 444-4518 SIC 3714 5013

PURVIS INDUSTRIES LTD p 1193
10500 N Stemmons Fwy, Dallas TX 75220
Tel (214) 358-5500 SIC 5013 5085 3822

TEXAS KENWORTH CO p 1444
4040 Irving Blvd, Dallas TX 75247
Tel (214) 920-7300
SIC 5012 5013 7513 7538

■ GENTHERM (TEXAS) INC p 605
2121b Frontera Rd, Del Rio TX 78840
Tel (830) 774-3094 SIC 5013

ED TUCKER DISTRIBUTOR INC p 477
4900 Alliance Gateway Fwy, Fort Worth TX 76177
Tel (817) 258-9000 SIC 5013

W M AUTOMOTIVE WAREHOUSE INC p 1568
208 Penland St, Fort Worth TX 76111
Tel (817) 834-5559 SIC 5013

■ PARTSCHANNEL INC p 1119
4003 Grand Lakes Way # 200, Grand Prairie TX 75050
Tel (214) 688-0018 SIC 5013

GULF STATES TOYOTA INC p 647
1375 Enclave Pkwy, Houston TX 77077
Tel (713) 580-3300 SIC 5012 5013

SELECTRANSPORTATION RESOURCES LLC p 1302
9550 North Loop E, Houston TX 77029
Tel (713) 672-4115
SIC 5012 5013 5511 7538

STEWART & STEVENSON CAPITAL CORP p 1388
601 W 38th St, Houston TX 77018
Tel (713) 868-7700
SIC 5084 5013 5078 5082 3711 3537

TASCO AUTO COLOR CORP p 1426
10323 Veterans Mem Dr, Houston TX 77038
Tel (281) 999-3761
SIC 5198 5013 5231 5531

VERSATECH AUTOMATION SERVICES LLC p 1551
11349 Fm 529 Rd, Houston TX 77041
Tel (713) 937-3100 SIC 5531 5013

FLEETPRIDE INC p 555
600 Las Colinas Blvd E # 400, Irving TX 75039
Tel (469) 249-7500 SIC 5531 5013

A2 HOLDINGS LTD p 7
15701 Nw Fwy, Jersey Village TX 77040
Tel (713) 983-1100 SIC 5013

ABC AUTO PARTS LTD p 10
920 W Marshall Ave, Longview TX 75604
Tel (903) 232-3010 SIC 5013 5531

BIG TEX TRAILER MANUFACTURING INC p 182
950 Interstate Hwy 30 E, Mount Pleasant TX 75455
Tel (903) 575-0300 SIC 3523 5013 5599

FRENCH-ELLISON TRUCK CENTER LLC p 578
4300 N Cage Blvd, Pharr TX 78577
Tel (956) 781-2401
SIC 5013 5531 5511 5012 7538

AVANZAR INTERIOR SYSTEMS LLC p 136
1 Lone Star Pass Bldg 41, San Antonio TX 78264
Tel (210) 271-2400 SIC 5013

DARR EQUIPMENT LP p 412
350 Bank St, Southlake TX 76092
Tel (254) 420-2650
SIC 5084 7353 5013 4959

DETROIT DIESEL REMANUFACTURING-WEST INC p 433
100 Lodestone Way, Tooele UT 84074
Tel (435) 843-6000 SIC 3519 3714 5013

FREIGHTLINER OF UTAH A LIMITED LIABILITY CO p 577
2240 S 5370 W, West Valley City UT 84120
Tel (801) 978-8000
SIC 5012 5013 7539 7538 5511

KENWORTH SALES CO p 813
2125 S Constitution Blvd, West Valley City UT 84119
Tel (801) 487-4161
SIC 5012 5013 7538 3519

BOND AUTO PARTS INC p 199
272 Morrison Rd, Barre VT 05641
Tel (802) 479-0571 SIC 5013 5531

SAFRAN USA INC p 1267
700 S Washington St # 320, Alexandria VA 22314
Tel (703) 351-9898
SIC 3643 3621 7699 3724 5013 5088

VOLKSWAGEN GROUP OF AMERICA CHATTANOOGA OPERATIONS LLC p 1564
2200 Ferdinand Porsche Dr, Herndon VA 20171
Tel (703) 364-7000 SIC 5012 5013

VOLKSWAGEN GROUP OF AMERICA INC p 1564
2200 Ferdinand Porsche Dr, Herndon VA 20171
Tel (703) 364-7000
SIC 5511 5012 5013 6153 6141 4899

GREATER RICHMOND BUSINESS INC p 636
1833 Commerce Rd, Richmond VA 23224
Tel (804) 232-3492
SIC 5511 5013 5531 7513

EXCEL TRUCK GROUP p 516
267 Lee Hwy, Roanoke VA 24019
Tel (540) 777-7700
SIC 5511 5013 7538 5012

PARTS DEPOT INC p 1118
401 Albemarle Ave Se, Roanoke VA 24013
Tel (540) 345-1001 SIC 5013 5531

FISHER AUTO PARTS INC p 552
512 Greenville Ave, Staunton VA 24401
Tel (540) 885-8901 SIC 5013 5531 4225

FUNKHOUSER AND CO H N p 585
2150 S Loudoun St, Winchester VA 22601
Tel (540) 662-9000 SIC 5461 5013

▲ PACCAR INC p 1103
777 106th Ave Ne, Bellevue WA 98004
Tel (425) 468-7400
SIC 3711 3714 3713 3537 5013 6153

MARSHALLS HOLDING CO p 911
20220 International Blvd, Seatac WA 98198
Tel (206) 433-5911 SIC 5012 5013

HARNISH GROUP INC p 662
17035 W Valley Hwy, Tukwila WA 98188
Tel (425) 251-9800 SIC 5082 5013 5083

N C MACHINERY CO p 1005
17025 W Valley Hwy, Tukwila WA 98188
Tel (425) 251-9800 SIC 5082 5013 5083

N C POWER SYSTEMS CO p 1005
17900 W Valley Hwy, Tukwila WA 98188
Tel (425) 251-5877 SIC 5013 5082 5083

APPALACHIAN TIRE PRODUCTS INC p 98
2907 4th Ave, Charleston WV 25387
Tel (304) 744-9473
SIC 5014 5531 5013 7534

NGK SPARK PLUGS (USA) INC p 1041
1 Ngk Dr, Sissonville WV 25320
Tel (304) 988-0060 SIC 5013 3694

US VENTURE INC p 1533
425 Better Way, Appleton WI 54915
Tel (920) 739-6101 SIC 5171 5014 5013

WENDORFF BROS CO INC p 1592
105 Steelcraft Dr, Hartford WI 53027
Tel (262) 673-6770
SIC 3469 3089 5013 3479

BLAIN SUPPLY INC p 188
3507 E Racine St, Janesville WI 53546
Tel (608) 754-2821
SIC 5083 5072 5039 5013 5023 5198

LEMANS CORP p 854
3501 Kennedy Rd, Janesville WI 53545
Tel (608) 758-1111 SIC 5013

■ IDSC HOLDINGS LLC p 729
2801 80th St, Kenosha WI 53143
Tel (262) 656-5200
SIC 3423 3559 7372 6794 5013 3546

CSM COMPANIES INC p 398
5100 Estpark Blvd Ste 210, Madison WI 53718
Tel (608) 241-5616 SIC 5012 5013

MONROE TRUCK EQUIPMENT INC p 985
1051 W 7th St, Monroe WI 53566
Tel (608) 328-8127 SIC 5013 3441 3599

PENDA CORP p 1128
2344 W Wisconsin St, Portage WI 53901
Tel (608) 742-5301
SIC 5013 3714 3792 3713 2273

SIC 5014 Tires & Tubes Wholesale

REDBURN TIRE CO p 1216
3801 W Clarendon Ave, Phoenix AZ 85019
Tel (602) 272-7601 SIC 5014 7534

TIRECO INC p 1455
500 W 190th St Ste 100, Gardena CA 90248
Tel (310) 767-7990 SIC 5014 5013 5051

KATANA RACING INC p 804
14407 Alondra Blvd, La Mirada CA 90638
Tel (562) 977-8565 SIC 5013 5014

CHINA MANUFACTURERS ALLIANCE LLC p 301
406 E Huntington Dr # 200, Monrovia CA 91016
Tel (626) 301-9575 SIC 5014

SUMITOMO RUBBER NORTH AMERICA INC p 1398
8656 Haven Ave, Rancho Cucamonga CA 91730
Tel (909) 466-1116 SIC 5014

YOKOHAMA TIRE CORP p 1637
1 Macarthur Pl Ste 800, Santa Ana CA 92707
Tel (714) 870-3800 SIC 5014 3011

LAKIN TIRE WEST INC p 840
15305 Spring Ave, Santa Fe Springs CA 90670
Tel (562) 802-2752 SIC 5014 5531

MC TIRES p 925
538 Olive Ave Ste 304, Vista CA 92083
Tel (760) 846-5613 SIC 5014 5531

A & E TIRE INC p 4
3855 E 52nd Ave, Denver CO 80216
Tel (303) 308-6900 SIC 5014 7534 5531

TOWN FAIR TIRE CENTERS INC p 1465
460 Coe Ave, East Haven CT 06512
Tel (203) 467-8600 SIC 5531 5014 5013

MORGAN TIRE & AUTO LLC p 989
2021 Sunnydale Blvd, Clearwater FL 33765
Tel (727) 441-3727 SIC 7539 5531 5014

TBC CORP p 1427
4300 Tbc Way, Palm Beach Gardens FL 33410
Tel (561) 227-0955 SIC 5014

CARROLLS LLC p 261
4281 Old Dixie Hwy, Atlanta GA 30354
Tel (404) 366-5476 SIC 5014 5013

KAUFFMAN TIRE INC p 805
2832 Anvil Block Rd, Ellenwood GA 30294
Tel (404) 762-4944 SIC 5014 5531

ATLANTA COMMERCIAL TIRE INC p 125
5067 Old Kennedy Rd, Forest Park GA 30297
Tel (404) 351-8016 SIC 5014 5531

COMMERCIAL TIRE INC p 345
2095 E Commercial St, Meridian ID 83642
Tel (208) 888-8800 SIC 5531 5014

BRIDGESTONE RETAIL OPERATIONS LLC p 211
333 E Lake St Ste 300, Bloomingdale IL 60108
Tel (630) 259-9000 SIC 5531 7534 5014

BEN TIRE DISTRIBUTORS LTD p 172
203 E Madison St, Toledo IL 62468
Tel (800) 252-8961
SIC 5014 5013 5531 7534

DEHCO INC p 422
3601 Charlotte Ave, Elkhart IN 46517
Tel (574) 294-2684
SIC 2891 5031 5074 5014 5084

TREDIT TIRE & WHEEL CO INC p 1475
3305 Charlotte Ave, Elkhart IN 46517
Tel (574) 293-0581 SIC 5014 5013

TRIPLE S TIRE CO INC p 1482
405 S 9th St, Elwood IN 46036
Tel (765) 552-5765 SIC 5014 5531

RABEN TIRE CO LLC p 1203
2100 N New York Ave, Evansville IN 47711
Tel (812) 465-5565 SIC 5531 5014

TIRE RACK INC p 1455
7101 Vorden Pkwy, South Bend IN 46628
Tel (888) 541-1777 SIC 5014 3714

BRIDGESTONE BANDAG LLC p 211
2000 Bandag Dr, Muscatine IA 52761
Tel (563) 262-2511
SIC 7534 3559 5014 3011 7549 6794

BECKER TIRE & TREADING INC p 167
904 Washington St, Great Bend KS 67530
Tel (620) 793-5414 SIC 5014 5531

C&M TIRE INC p 234
401 S 42nd St, Kansas City KS 66106
Tel (913) 321-3003
SIC 5531 7534 5014 3312

LALLY PIPE & TUBE CO p 841
8770 Railroad Dr, Taylor Mill KY 41015
Tel (606) 371-5600 SIC 5014

SULLIVAN TIRE CO INC p 1397
41 Accord Park Dr, Norwell MA 02061
Tel (781) 982-1550 SIC 5531 7538 5014

BELLE TIRE DISTRIBUTORS INC p 170
1000 Enterprise Dr, Allen Park MI 48101
Tel (888) 462-3553 SIC 5531 5014

DAVID AND LILY PENN INC p 415
10201 Wayzata Blvd, Minnetonka MN 55305
Tel (763) 746-0410 SIC 5014

DUNLAP & KYLE CO INC p 461
280 Eureka St, Batesville MS 38606
Tel (662) 563-7601 SIC 5014 5531 5013

SOUTHERN TIRE MART LLC p 1350
800 Us 98, Columbia MS 39429
Tel (601) 424-3200 SIC 7534 5014

PLAZA TIRE SERVICE INC p 1156
2075 Corporate Cir, Cape Girardeau MO 63703
Tel (573) 334-5036 SIC 5014 5531 7538

COMMUNITY WHOLESALE TIRE DIS INC p 350
9124 Pershall Rd, Hazelwood MO 63042
Tel (314) 241-3737 SIC 5014

FRIEND TIRE CO p 580
11 Indl Dr, Monett MO 65708
Tel (800) 950-8473 SIC 5014

TO HAAS TIRE CO INC p 1458
1415 W Commerce Way, Lincoln NE 68521
Tel (402) 434-3434 SIC 5014 5531 7539

ALLIED OIL & TIRE CO p 56
2209 S 24th St, Omaha NE 68108
Tel (402) 344-4343 SIC 5014 5172

RELIABLE TIRE DISTRIBUTORS INC p 1221
805 N Black Horse Pike, Blackwood NJ 08012
Tel (800) 342-3426 SIC 5014

ALBERT TIRE CO p 46
39 Phoenix Dr, West Deptford NJ 08086
Tel (856) 663-0574 SIC 5014

FORREST TIRE CO INC p 568
414 S Canal St, Carlsbad NM 88220
Tel (575) 887-3567 SIC 5531 5014

MAX FINKELSTEIN INC p 922
2840 31st St, Astoria NY 11102
Tel (718) 274-8900 SIC 5014 5531

KOST TIRE DISTRIBUTORS INC p 828
200 Holleder Pkwy, Binghamton NY 13904
Tel (607) 723-9471 SIC 5014 5531 7538

DUNN TIRE LLC p 461
475 Cayuga Rd Ste 500, Buffalo NY 14225
Tel (716) 683-3910 SIC 5531 5014

MAVIS TIRE SUPPLY LLC p 922
358 Saw Mill River Rd # 17, Millwood NY 10546
Tel (914) 984-2500 SIC 5014 5531

SOMERSET TIRE SERVICE INC p 1339
358 Saw Mill River Rd # 5, Millwood NY 10546
Tel (732) 356-8500
SIC 5531 5014 5013 7538

CAMSO USA INC p 246
306 Forsyth Hall Dr, Charlotte NC 28273
Tel (704) 374-9700 SIC 5531 5014

AMERICAN TIRE DISTRIBUTORS HOLDINGS INC p 80
12200 Herbert Wayne Ct # 150, Huntersville NC 28078
Tel (704) 992-2000 SIC 5014 5013

AMERICAN TIRE DISTRIBUTORS INC p 80
12200 Herbert Wayne Ct # 150, Huntersville NC 28078
Tel (704) 992-2000 SIC 5014 5013

TERRYS TIRE TOWN INC p 1440
12200 Herbert Wayne Ct, Huntersville NC 28078
Tel (330) 821-5022 SIC 5014 5531

S BLACK TIRE SERVICE INC p 1262
30 Bitmore Rd, Whiteville NC 28472
Tel (910) 642-4123 SIC 5531 5014

PARRISH TIRE CO p 1117
5130 Indiana Ave, Winston Salem NC 27106
Tel (336) 767-0202 SIC 5014 5531 7534

CHESTNUT HOLDINGS INC p 295
670 W Market St, Akron OH 44303
Tel (330) 849-6503
SIC 3053 5014 5013 3714

▲ MYERS INDUSTRIES INC p 1004
1293 S Main St, Akron OH 44301
Tel (330) 253-5592
SIC 3089 3086 3069 3052 5013 5014

DEALER TIRE LLC p 419
3711 Chester Ave, Cleveland OH 44114
Tel (216) 432-0088 SIC 5014

K & M TIRE INC p 798
965 Spencerville Rd, Delphos OH 45833
Tel (419) 695-1061 SIC 5014 7538 5531

TECHNICAL RUBBER CO INC p 1431
200 E Coshocton St, Johnstown OH 43031
Tel (740) 967-9015 SIC 3011 5014 2891

CAPITAL TIRE INC p 250
1001 Cherry St, Toledo OH 43608
Tel (419) 241-5111 SIC 5014

LES SCHWAB WAREHOUSE CENTER INC p 857
20900 Cooley Rd, Bend OR 97701
Tel (541) 447-4136 SIC 5014 7534 5531

JUBITZ CORP p 796
33 Ne Middlefield Rd, Portland OR 97211
Tel (503) 283-1111
SIC 5541 4789 5014 7011

TIRE FACTORY INC p 1455
6102 N Marine Dr, Portland OR 97203
Tel (503) 283-6494 SIC 5014

SUPERIOR TIRE SERVICE INC p 1407
4230 27th Ct Se, Salem OR 97302
Tel (503) 585-1955 SIC 5014 7534 3011

JACK WILLIAMS TIRE CO INC p 773
700 Rocky Glen Rd, Avoca PA 18641
Tel (570) 457-5000 SIC 5531 5014

VALLEY TIRE CO INC p 1541
15 Mckean Ave, Charleroi PA 15022
Tel (724) 489-4483
SIC 5531 7539 5014 7534

H & F GULF INC p 649
1834 Lincoln Hwy E, Lancaster PA 17602
Tel (717) 392-6793 SIC 5014 5531

BERGEYS INC p 174
462 Harleysville Pike, Souderton PA 18964
Tel (215) 721-3430
SIC 5511 5531 7538 5013 5014

MCCARTHY TIRE SERVICE CO INC p 926
340 Kidder St, Wilkes Barre PA 18702
Tel (570) 822-3151 SIC 5014 5531

TIRE CENTERS LLC p 1455
310 Inglesby Pkwy, Duncan SC 29334
Tel (864) 329-2700 SIC 5014 5531 7534

IH SERVICES INC p 730
127 Tanner Rd, Greenville SC 29607
Tel (864) 297-3748 SIC 7349 5014 7217

MICHELIN CORP p 960
1 Parkway S, Greenville SC 29615
Tel (864) 458-5000 SIC 5014

CARLSTAR GROUP LLC p 258
725 Cool Springs Blvd, Franklin TN 37067
Tel (615) 503-0220
SIC 3714 5014 3499 5013 2296

TENNESSEE FARMERS COOPERATIVE INC p 1438
180 Old Nashville Hwy, La Vergne TN 37086
Tel (615) 793-8011
SIC 5191 5013 5014 5172 5122 2048

CHINA SUTONG TIRE RESOURCES INC p 301
33402 Highway 290 A, Hockley TX 77447
Tel (713) 690-5500 SIC 5014

STROUHAL TIRE RECAPPING PLANT LTD p 1394
8206 Hwy 59, Hungerford TX 77448
Tel (979) 532-1579 SIC 5014

■ RUSH ADMINISTRATIVE SERVICES INC p 1258
555 S Interstate 35 # 500, New Braunfels TX 78130
Tel (830) 626-5286
SIC 5012 7538 5531 5014 7513

▲ RUSH ENTERPRISES INC p 1258
555 S Ih 35 Ste 500, New Braunfels TX 78130
Tel (830) 302-5200
SIC 5012 7538 5531 5014 7513

ALDEN PADFIELD INC p 47
203 N 5500 W, Hurricane UT 84737
Tel (435) 674-9883 SIC 5014 5531

PADFIELD INC p 1107
1335 W 2100 S, Salt Lake City UT 84119
Tel (801) 972-1944 SIC 5014 5531 3711

NOKIAN TYRES INC p 1046
1945 Main St, Colchester VT 05446
Tel (800) 852-5222 SIC 5014

MERCHANTS INC p 945
9073 Euclid Ave, Manassas VA 20110
Tel (703) 368-3171 SIC 5014 7539 5531

YOKOHAMA CORP OF NORTH AMERICA p 1637
1500 Indiana St, Salem VA 24153
Tel (540) 389-5426 SIC 3011 5014

APPALACHIAN TIRE PRODUCTS INC p 98
2907 4th Ave, Charleston WV 25387
Tel (304) 744-9473
SIC 5014 5531 5013 7534

US VENTURE INC p 1533
425 Better Way, Appleton WI 54915
Tel (920) 739-6101 SIC 5171 5014 5013

BAUER BUILT INC p 160
1111 W Prospect St, Durand WI 54736
Tel (715) 672-8300
SIC 5531 5014 7534 5171

POMPS TIRE SERVICE INC p 1161
1122 Cedar St, Green Bay WI 54301
Tel (920) 435-8301 SIC 5531 5014 7534

SCHIERL INC p 1287
2201 Madison St, Stevens Point WI 54481
Tel (715) 345-5060
SIC 5171 5014 5531 5983

SIC 5015 Motor Vehicle Parts, Used Wholesale

ISUZU NORTH AMERICA CORP p 767
1400 S Douglass Rd # 100, Anaheim CA 92806
Tel (714) 935-9300
SIC 5511 5084 5013 5015

HARVEY & MADDING INC p 667
6300 Dublin Blvd, Dublin CA 94568
Tel (925) 828-8030
SIC 5511 7538 5015 5013

▲ LKQ CORP p 872
500 W Madison St Ste 2800, Chicago IL 60661
Tel (312) 621-1950 SIC 5093 5015

LACY DISTRIBUTION INC p 837
54 Monument Cir Ste 800, Indianapolis IN 46204
Tel (317) 237-5400 SIC 5015

GEORGE J FALTER CO p 606
3501 Benson Ave, Baltimore MD 21227
Tel (410) 646-3641
SIC 5194 5145 5141 5015

SAVE MORE INC p 1284
9405 Livingston Rd, Fort Washington MD 20744
Tel (301) 372-1000 SIC 5531 5015

BROSE NORTH AMERICA INC p 218
3933 Automation Ave, Auburn Hills MI 48326
Tel (248) 339-4000 SIC 5015

JVIS MANUFACTURING LLC p 798
1285 N Crystal Ave, Benton Harbor MI 49022
Tel (269) 927-8200 SIC 5015

WELLER AUTO PARTS INC p 1589
2525 Chicago Dr Sw, Wyoming MI 49519
Tel (616) 538-5000 SIC 5013 5015 5531

AUTOMOTIVE SUPPLY ASSOCIATES INC p 134
129 Manchester St, Concord NH 03301
Tel (603) 225-4000
SIC 5013 7539 5531 5169 5015

POSCO DAEWOO AMERICA CORP p 1163
300 Frank W Burr Blvd, Teaneck NJ 07666
Tel (201) 591-8000
SIC 5131 5051 5169 5015

PARTS AUTHORITY INC p 1118
495 Merrick Rd, Rockville Centre NY 11570
Tel (516) 678-3900 SIC 5013 5015 5531

MAC TRAILER MANUFACTURING INC p 891
14599 Commerce St Ne, Alliance OH 44601
Tel (330) 823-9900
SIC 3715 5012 5013 5015 7539

▲ SCHNITZER STEEL INDUSTRIES INC p 1288
299 Sw Clay St Ste 350, Portland OR 97201
Tel (503) 224-9900
SIC 5093 3312 3449 3441 3433 5015

WESTPORT AXLE p 1602
650 Boulder Dr Ste 100a, Breinigsville PA 18031
Tel (610) 366-2900 SIC 5015

UTILITY TRAILER OF DALLAS INC p 1537
34241 Lyndon B Jhnson Fwy, Dallas TX 75241
Tel (972) 225-8845 SIC 5012 5015 5511

SIC 5021 Furniture Wholesale

ARCTIC OFFICE MACHINE INC p 106
100 W Fireweed Ln, Anchorage AK 99503
Tel (907) 276-2295
SIC 5112 5021 5044 7629

BENCHMASTER FURNITURE LLC p 172
1481 N Hundley St, Anaheim CA 92806
Tel (714) 414-0240 SIC 5021

STANDARD FIBER LLC p 1376
577 Airport Blvd Ste 200, Burlingame CA 94010
Tel (650) 872-6528 SIC 5021

COPPEL CORP p 368
503 Scaroni Ave, Calexico CA 92231
Tel (760) 357-3707 SIC 5021 5137 5136

NWT WORLD ARTS INC p 1068
36660 Bankside Dr Ste A, Cathedral City CA 92234
Tel (760) 321-8780 SIC 5021

LIVING SPACES FURNITURE LLC p 871
14501 Artesia Blvd, La Mirada CA 90638
Tel (714) 523-2000 SIC 5712 5021

INTEX RECREATION CORP p 759
4001 Via Oro Ave Ste 210, Long Beach CA 90810
Tel (310) 549-5400
SIC 5091 5092 5021 3081

NAJARIAN FURNITURE CO INC p 1006
265 N Euclid Ave, Pasadena CA 91101
Tel (626) 839-8700 SIC 5021 5023

AMINI INNOVATION CORP p 85
8725 Rex Rd, Pico Rivera CA 90660
Tel (562) 222-2500 SIC 5021

INSIDE SOURCE INC p 745
985 Industrial Rd Ste 101, San Carlos CA 94070
Tel (650) 508-9101 SIC 5021

GOFORTH & MARTI p 619
110 W A St Ste 140, San Diego CA 92101
Tel (951) 684-0870 SIC 5021

ONE WORKPLACE L FERRARI LLC p 1086
2500 De La Cruz Blvd, Santa Clara CA 95050
Tel (669) 800-2500 SIC 5021 8744

COA INC p 330
12928 Sandoval St, Santa Fe Springs CA 90670
Tel (562) 944-7899 SIC 5021

■ VIKING OFFICE PRODUCTS INC p 1557
3366 E Willow St, Signal Hill CA 90755
Tel (562) 490-1000
SIC 5112 5021 5045 5087 5043 5961

■ VIRCO INC p 1558
2027 Harpers Way, Torrance CA 90501
Tel (310) 533-0474 SIC 5021

WINNERS ONLY INC p 1616
1365 Park Center Dr, Vista CA 92081
Tel (760) 599-0300 SIC 5021

JUPITER I LLC p 797
9900 E 51st Ave, Denver CO 80238
Tel (303) 574-1115 SIC 5021

■ DGPM INVESTMENTS INC p 435
300 E River Dr, East Hartford CT 06108
Tel (860) 528-9981
SIC 5044 5021 5713 1752

DONGHIA INC p 450
500 Bic Dr Ste 20, Milford CT 06461
Tel (800) 366-4442
SIC 5198 5131 5021 2342

THULE INC p 1451
42 Silvermine Rd, Seymour CT 06483
Tel (203) 881-9600 SIC 3714 5021

■ DESIGN WITHIN REACH INC p 432
711 Canal St Ste 3, Stamford CT 06902
Tel (203) 614-0600 SIC 5021 5719

CORPORATE INTERIORS INC p 372
223 Lisa Dr, New Castle DE 19720
Tel (302) 322-1008 SIC 5021 2521

IKEA HOLDING US INC p 731
1105 N Market St Ste 1044, Wilmington DE 19801
Tel (302) 655-4126 SIC 5021 5712

■ OFFICEMAX INC p 1076
6600 N Military Trl, Boca Raton FL 33496
Tel (630) 438-7800 SIC 5943 5021

SUN WHOLESALE SUPPLY INC p 1401
6385 150th Ave N, Clearwater FL 33760
Tel (727) 524-3299
SIC 5169 5021 5023 5091

LIST INDUSTRIES INC p 870
401 Jim Moran Blvd, Deerfield Beach FL 33442
Tel (954) 429-9155 SIC 2541 5021 2542

RTG FURNITURE OF TEXAS LP p 1256
11540 E Us Highway 92, Seffner FL 33584
Tel (813) 628-9724 SIC 5712 5021

▲ GENUINE PARTS CO p 605
2999 Wildwood Pkwy, Atlanta GA 30339
Tel (770) 953-1700
SIC 5013 5531 3714 5084 5085 5021

▲ HAVERTY FURNITURE COMPANIES INC p 668
780 Johnson Ferry Rd, Atlanta GA 30342
Tel (404) 443-2900
SIC 5712 5722 5713 5021

NATIONAL FURNITURE LIQUIDATORS I LLC p 1012
2865 Log Cabin Dr Se, Atlanta GA 30339
Tel (404) 872-7280 SIC 5021 5712 5932

INNVISION HOSPITALITY INC p 745
504 Carver Rd, Griffin GA 30224
Tel (888) 875-6202 SIC 5131 5021 7389

■ S P RICHARDS CO p 1262
6300 Highlands Pkwy Se, Smyrna GA 30082
Tel (770) 434-4571 SIC 5112 5021

FORWARD SPACE LLC p 570
1142 N North Branch St, Chicago IL 60642
Tel (312) 942-1100 SIC 5021 7389

■ HOLLY HUNT ENTERPRISES INC p 701
801 W Adams St Ste 700, Chicago IL 60607
Tel (312) 329-5999 SIC 5021

▲ ESSENDANT INC p 510
1 Parkway North Blvd # 100, Deerfield IL 60015
Tel (847) 627-7000
SIC 5112 5111 5021 5044 5087 5045

HENRICKSEN & CO INC p 683
1101 W Thorndale Ave, Itasca IL 60143
Tel (630) 250-9090 SIC 5021 7389

I3 GROUP INC p 725
550 Bond St, Lincolnshire IL 60069
Tel (847) 325-1000 SIC 5021 1799

■ OFFICEMAX CONTRACT INC p 1076
263 Shuman Blvd, Naperville IL 60563
Tel (630) 438-7800
SIC 5021 5112 5044 5111 5943 5712

UNIVERSAL POOL CO INC p 1517
300 W Armory Dr, South Holland IL 60473
Tel (708) 339-6060 SIC 5021 5091

AMERICAN HOTEL REGISTER CO p 74
100 S Milwaukee Ave # 100, Vernon Hills IL 60061
Tel (847) 743-3000
SIC 5046 5023 5021 5113

DON EDWARD & CO p 449
9801 Adam Don Pkwy, Woodridge IL 60517
Tel (708) 442-9400
SIC 5021 5046 5087 5113 5169

BRISTOL LASALLE CORP p 214
601 County Road 17, Elkhart IN 46516
Tel (574) 295-4400
SIC 5023 5021 5051 5033 3645 3089

CENTRAL PRODUCTS LLC p 280
7750 Georgetown Rd, Indianapolis IN 46268
Tel (317) 634-2550 SIC 5046 5021

INDEPENDENT STATIONERS INC p 737
250 E 96th St Ste 510, Indianapolis IN 46240
Tel (317) 845-9155 SIC 5021 5112

DIRECTBUY INC p 441
8450 Broadway, Merrillville IN 46410
Tel (219) 736-1100
SIC 5021 5064 5023 5961 6794 7299

JORDAN MANUFACTURING CO INC p 793
1200 S 6th St, Monticello IN 47960
Tel (574) 583-6008 SIC 2392 5021

■ TEMPUR-PEDIC NORTH AMERICA LLC p 1436
1000 Tempur Way, Lexington KY 40511
Tel (888) 811-5053 SIC 5021

AMERICAN OFFICE EQUIPMENT CO INC p 77
309 N Calvert St, Baltimore MD 21202
Tel (410) 539-7529 SIC 5021

TRIMARK UNITED EAST INC p 1480
505 Collins St, Attleboro MA 02703
Tel (508) 399-6000
SIC 5046 5021 5113 5087

TRIMARK USA LLC p 1480
505 Collins St, Attleboro MA 02703
Tel (508) 399-2400 SIC 5021 5023

CREATIVE OFFICE INTERIORS INC p 390
1 Design Center Pl # 734, Boston MA 02210
Tel (617) 956-4100 SIC 5021

OFFICE RESOURCES INC p 1076
263 Summer St, Boston MA 02210
Tel (617) 423-9100 SIC 5021

■ RED THREAD SPACES LLC p 1216
101 Seaport Blvd Ste 600, Boston MA 02210
Tel (617) 439-4900
SIC 5999 5021 8712 5198

■ STAPLES INTERNATIONAL INC p 1378
500 Staples Dr, Framingham MA 01702
Tel (508) 253-5000
SIC 5943 5712 5044 5021 5112

FITZPATRICK COMPANIES INC p 553
705 Pleasant St, Lee MA 01238
Tel (413) 298-1610 SIC 5714 5021 5023

ALTICOR GLOBAL HOLDINGS INC p 62
7575 Fulton St E, Ada MI 49301
Tel (616) 787-1000
SIC 5169 5122 2833 5136 5137 5021

ALTICOR INC p 62
7575 Fulton St E, Ada MI 49355
Tel (616) 787-1000
SIC 5169 5122 2833 5136 5137 5021

INNOVATIVE OFFICE SOLUTIONS LLC p 745
151 Cliff Rd E Ste 40, Burnsville MN 55337
Tel (952) 808-9900 SIC 5112 5021

ATMOSPHERE COMMERCIAL INTERIORS LLC p 128
81 S 9th St Ste 350, Minneapolis MN 55402
Tel (612) 343-0868 SIC 5021 5023 7389

HALDEMAN-HOMME INC p 653
430 Industrial Blvd Ne, Minneapolis MN 55413
Tel (612) 331-4880 SIC 5021 5211 5084

U F I TRANSPORTATION LLC p 1497
60063 Puckett Dr, Amory MS 38821
Tel (662) 257-1811 SIC 5021

COLOR ART INTEGRATED INTERIORS LLC p 338
1325 N Warson Rd, Saint Louis MO 63132
Tel (314) 432-3000
SIC 5021 7641 5999 5712 5099 2521

INDOFF INC p 739
11816 Lackland Rd Ste 200, Saint Louis MO 63146
Tel (314) 997-1122 SIC 5021 5044 5084

■ INSTALLED BUILDING PRODUCTS LLC p 747
62 King St, Auburn NH 03032
Tel (603) 645-1604
SIC 1761 5021 5719 2515

DANCKER SELLEW & DOUGLAS INC p 411
291 Evans Way, Branchburg NJ 08876
Tel (908) 429-1200 SIC 5021 5063 5049

FOREMOST GROUPS INC p 566
906 Murray Rd Ste 2, East Hanover NJ 07936
Tel (973) 428-0400 SIC 5074 5021

GLOBAL INDUSTRIES INC p 616
17 W Stow Rd, Marlton NJ 08053
Tel (856) 596-3390 SIC 2522 5021

TEKNION LLC p 1433
350 Fellowship Rd Ste 100, Mount Laurel NJ 08054
Tel (856) 552-5750 SIC 5021

ARBEE ASSOCIATES p 102
1531 S Washington Ave # 3, Piscataway NJ 08854
Tel (908) 686-3900 SIC 5021

HITOUCH BUSINESS SERVICES LLC p 697
74 Kenny Pl, Saddle Brook NJ 07663
Tel (201) 636-9900 SIC 5112 5021 5149

EKORNES INC p 482
615 Pierce St, Somerset NJ 08873
Tel (732) 302-0097 SIC 5021

1 STOP ELECTRONICS CENTER INC p 1
1100 Coney Island Ave, Brooklyn NY 11230
Tel (718) 249-1211 SIC 5722 5021

BEECHWOOD MOUNTAIN LLC p 168
500 Broadway Ste A, Brooklyn NY 11211
Tel (718) 418-3205 SIC 5021

WEEKS-LERMAN GROUP LLC p 1587
5838 Page Pl, Maspeth NY 11378
Tel (718) 803-4700
SIC 5112 5021 2752 5044

ARTISTIC FRAME CORP p 114
979 3rd Ave Ste 1705, New York NY 10022
Tel (212) 289-2100 SIC 2426 5021

DELTA ENTERPRISE CORP p 427
114 W 26th St Fl 11, New York NY 10001
Tel (212) 736-7000 SIC 5021 5099

EMPIRE OFFICE INC p 493
105 Madison Ave Fl 15, New York NY 10016
Tel (212) 607-5500 SIC 5021

IDEA NUOVA INC p 729
302 5th Ave Fl 5, New York NY 10001
Tel (212) 643-0680 SIC 5021

MEADOWS OFFICE SUPPLY CO INC p 934
885 3rd Ave Fl 29, New York NY 10022
Tel (212) 741-0333 SIC 5021

MYSTIC APPAREL LLC p 1005
1333 Broadway Fl 6, New York NY 10018
Tel (212) 279-2466 SIC 5021 5137

STARK CARPET CORP p 1379
979 3rd Ave Fl 11, New York NY 10022
Tel (844) 407-8275 SIC 5099 5131 5021

JENNIFER CONVERTIBLES INC p 782
335 Crossways Park Dr, Woodbury NY 11797
Tel (516) 496-1900 SIC 5712 6794 5021

OFFICE ENVIRONMENTS INC p 1075
11407 Granite St Ste B, Charlotte NC 28273
Tel (704) 714-7200 SIC 5021 7641 7389

KOHLER INTERIORS FURNITURE CO p 826
1105 22nd St Se, Hickory NC 28602
Tel (828) 624-7000 SIC 2511 5021

NATUZZI AMERICAS INC p 1019
130 W Commerce Ave, High Point NC 27260
Tel (336) 887-8300 SIC 5021

VRUSH INDUSTRIES INC p 1566
118 N Wrenn St, High Point NC 27260
Tel (336) 886-7700
SIC 5045 5021 7379 3469 5712 7375

ALFRED WILLIAMS & CO p 50
410 S Salisbury St # 200, Raleigh NC 27601
Tel (919) 832-9570 SIC 5021

BEKAERT TEXTILES USA INC p 169
240 Business Park Dr, Winston Salem NC 27107
Tel (336) 747-4900 SIC 5021 2211

SAUDER WOODWORKING CO p 1283
502 Middle St, Archbold OH 43502
Tel (419) 446-3828 SIC 2519 5021

CONTINENTAL OFFICE FURNITURE CORP p 363
2601 Silver Dr, Columbus OH 43211
Tel (614) 262-5010 SIC 5021 1752

WASSERSTROM CO p 1580
477 S Front St, Columbus OH 43215
Tel (614) 737-8472
SIC 5087 3566 5021 5046 5112 5719

KELLEX CORP p 808
33390 Liberty Pkwy, North Ridgeville OH 44039
Tel (440) 327-4428 SIC 5021

ADMIRAL EXPRESS INC p 23
1823 N Yellowood Ave, Broken Arrow OK 74012
Tel (918) 249-4000 SIC 5112 5021 5943

K&D FUTURE INC p 799
908 W Street Rd, Warminster PA 18974
Tel (215) 674-3555 SIC 5021

A-Z OFFICE RESOURCE INC p 7
809 S Garden St, Columbia TN 38401
Tel (931) 388-1536
SIC 5112 5021 5044 5045 5087

G L SEAMAN & CO p 587
4201 International Pkwy, Carrollton TX 75007
Tel (214) 764-6400 SIC 5021

WINGATE PARTNERS LP p 1616
750 N Saint Paul St # 1200, Dallas TX 75201
Tel (214) 720-1313
SIC 2621 2672 3645 2519 5021 2521

STEVE SILVER CO p 1388
1000 Fm 548, Forney TX 75126
Tel (972) 564-2601 SIC 5021

MCCOY-ROCKFORD INC p 927
6869 Old Katy Rd, Houston TX 77024
Tel (713) 862-4600 SIC 5021 1799

FURNITURE MARKETING GROUP INC p 585
6100 W Plano Pkwy # 1400, Plano TX 75093
Tel (214) 556-4700 SIC 5021

SHELF RELIANCE LLC p 1314
691 S Auto Mall Dr, American Fork UT 84003
Tel (801) 756-9902 SIC 5021

CREATIVE OFFICE ENVIRONMENTS p 390
11798 N Lakeridge Pkwy, Ashland VA 23005
Tel (804) 329-0400 SIC 5021

▲ BASSETT FURNITURE INDUSTRIES INC p 159
3525 Fairystone Park Hwy, Bassett VA 24055
Tel (276) 629-6000
SIC 2511 2512 5021 5712

NEW ENERGY INC p 1029
2300 Prospect Dr, Christiansburg VA 24073
Tel (540) 382-7377 SIC 5021

MILLERS SUPPLIES AT WORK INC p 971
8600 Cinder Bed Rd, Lorton VA 22079
Tel (703) 644-2200 SIC 5112 5044 5021

■ HILTON SUPPLY MANAGEMENT LLC p 695
7930 Jones Branch Dr # 400, Mc Lean VA 22102
Tel (703) 883-1000 SIC 5046 5021

GRAND PIANO & FURNITURE CO p 630
4235 Electric Rd Ste 100, Roanoke VA 24018
Tel (540) 776-7000 SIC 5712 5021

WORKSPACE DEVELOPMENT LLC p 1624
5601 6th Ave S Ste 470, Seattle WA 98108
Tel (206) 768-8000 SIC 5021

SCHOOL SPECIALTY INC p 1290
W6316 Design Dr, Greenville WI 54942
Tel (920) 734-5712 SIC 5049 5021

▲ SCHOOL SPECIALTY INC p 1290
W6316 Design Dr, Greenville WI 54942
Tel (920) 734-5712 SIC 5049 5021 5961

DEMCO INC p 428
4810 Forest Run Rd, Madison WI 53704
Tel (800) 356-1200 SIC 5021 2521

NATIONAL BUSINESS FURNITURE LLC p 1010
770 S 70th St, Milwaukee WI 53214
Tel (414) 276-8511 SIC 5021

BUILDING SERVICE p 225
W222n630 Cheaney Rd, Waukesha WI 53186
Tel (414) 358-5080 SIC 5021 1542 5023

SIC 5023 Home Furnishings Wholesale

LONGUST DISTRIBUTING INC p 877
2432 W Birchwood Ave, Mesa AZ 85202
Tel (480) 820-6244 SIC 5023

JR MC DADE CO INC p 795
1102 N 21st Ave, Phoenix AZ 85009
Tel (602) 258-7134 SIC 5023 1752

BI-RITE RESTAURANT SUPPLY CO INC p 180
123 S Hill Dr, Brisbane CA 94005
Tel (415) 656-0187
SIC 5141 5147 5148 5023 5046 5963

BEN MYERSON CANDY CO INC p 172
6550 E Washington Blvd, Commerce CA 90040
Tel (800) 331-2829 SIC 5182 5023

GIBSON OVERSEAS INC p 611
2410 Yates Ave, Commerce CA 90040
Tel (323) 832-8900 SIC 5023

ANNAS LINENS INC p 92
3550 Hyland Ave, Costa Mesa CA 92626
Tel (714) 850-0504 SIC 5719 5714 5023

B R FUNSTEN & CO p 142
5200 Watt Ct Ste B, Fairfield CA 94534
Tel (209) 825-5375 SIC 5023

E & E CO LTD p 465
45875 Northport Loop E, Fremont CA 94538
Tel (510) 490-9788 SIC 5023

TRANS WESTERN POLYMERS INC p 1470
7539 Las Positas Rd, Livermore CA 94551
Tel (925) 449-7800 SIC 2673 5023 3089

MUTUAL TRADING CO INC p 1003
431 Crocker St, Los Angeles CA 90013
Tel (213) 626-9458 SIC 5149 5141 5023

TEST-RITE PRODUCTS CORP p 1441
1900 Burgundy Pl, Ontario CA 91761
Tel (909) 605-9899 SIC 5023

THOMPSON OLDE INC p 1449
3250 Camino Del Sol, Oxnard CA 93030
Tel (800) 827-1565 SIC 5023 2631 5149

NAJARIAN FURNITURE CO INC p 1006
265 N Euclid Ave, Pasadena CA 91101
Tel (626) 839-8700 SIC 5021 5023

BRADSHAW INTERNATIONAL INC p 207
9409 Buffalo Ave, Rancho Cucamonga CA 91730
Tel (909) 476-3884 SIC 5023

MARIAK INDUSTRIES INC p 906
575 W Manville St, Rancho Dominguez CA 90220
Tel (310) 661-4400 SIC 5023 2591

ANDREW LAUREN CO INC p 90
8909 Kenamar Dr Ste 101, San Diego CA 92121
Tel (858) 793-5319 SIC 5023

R W SMITH & CO p 1203
8555 Miralani Dr, San Diego CA 92126
Tel (858) 530-1800 SIC 5023

■ WILLIAMS-SONOMA STORES INC p 1612
3250 Van Ness Ave, San Francisco CA 94109
Tel (415) 421-7900 SIC 5023

GALLEHER CORP p 590
9303 Greenleaf Ave, Santa Fe Springs CA 90670
Tel (562) 944-8885 SIC 5023

TRI-WEST LTD p 1478
12005 Pike St, Santa Fe Springs CA 90670
Tel (562) 692-9166 SIC 5023

BONAKEMI USA INC p 199
2550 S Parker Rd Ste 600, Aurora CO 80014
Tel (303) 371-1411
SIC 5198 5169 5023 2851

VALIANT PRODUCTS CORP p 1540
2727 W 5th Ave, Denver CO 80204
Tel (303) 892-1234
SIC 5131 5023 7389 2511 2599 1752

VICTORINOX SWISS ARMY INC p 1555
7 Victoria Dr, Monroe CT 06468
Tel (203) 929-6391
SIC 5023 5099 5094 5072

FORBO AMERICA INC p 565
103 Foulk Rd Ste 123, Wilmington DE 19803
Tel (302) 691-6100 SIC 5023

FRANKE USA HOLDING INC p 574
1105 N Market St Ste 1300, Wilmington DE 19801
Tel (615) 462-4000 SIC 3589 5023 5084

SUN WHOLESALE SUPPLY INC p 1401
6385 150th Ave N, Clearwater FL 33760
Tel (727) 524-3299
SIC 5169 5021 5023 5091

■ HD BUILDER SOLUTIONS GROUP LLC p 672
2455 Paces Ferry Rd Se C9, Atlanta GA 30339
Tel (770) 443-8211 SIC 5023 1752 1799

■ HOME DEPOT USA INC p 703
2455 Paces Ferry Rd Se, Atlanta GA 30339
Tel (770) 433-8211 SIC 5023 5999

ELBERTA CRATE & BOX CO p 483
606 Dothan Rd, Bainbridge GA 39817
Tel (229) 243-1268 SIC 2449 5023 2448

■ SHAW INDUSTRIES GROUP INC p 1313
616 E Walnut Ave, Dalton GA 30721
Tel (800) 441-7429 SIC 5023

MARIETTA DRAPERY & WINDOW COVERINGS CO INC p 906
22 Trammell St Sw, Marietta GA 30064
Tel (770) 428-3335
SIC 5023 2391 2591 2392

REDI-FLOORS INC p 1217
1791 Williams Dr, Marietta GA 30066
Tel (770) 590-7334 SIC 5023 5032

SYNTEC INDUSTRIES LLC p 1416
438 Lavender Dr Nw, Rome GA 30165
Tel (706) 235-1158 SIC 2273 5023

SURYA CARPET INC p 1409
1 Surya Dr, White GA 30184
Tel (706) 625-4823 SIC 5023 2273

M BLOCK & SONS INC p 889
5020 W 73rd St, Bedford Park IL 60638
Tel (708) 728-8400 SIC 5064 5023

FOCUS PRODUCTS GROUP INTERNATIONAL LLC p 563
300 Knightsbridge Pkwy, Lincolnshire IL 60069
Tel (800) 238-2253 SIC 5023

1888 MILLS LLC p 1
1520 Kensington Rd # 115, Oak Brook IL 60523
Tel (630) 620-5222 SIC 5023 5131

AMERICAN HOTEL REGISTER CO p 74
100 S Milwaukee Ave # 100, Vernon Hills IL 60061
Tel (847) 743-3000
SIC 5046 5023 5021 5113

HORIZONS HOLDINGS LLC p 708
1705 S Waukegan Rd, Waukegan IL 60085
Tel (800) 858-2352 SIC 5023

WILTON BRANDS LLC p 1614
2240 75th St, Woodridge IL 60517
Tel (630) 963-7100
SIC 5023 2731 2721 7812 5199

WILTON HOLDINGS INC p 1614
2240 75th St, Woodridge IL 60517
Tel (630) 963-7100
SIC 5023 2731 2721 7812 5199

WILTON INDUSTRIES INC p 1614
2240 75th St, Woodridge IL 60517
Tel (630) 963-7100
SIC 5023 2731 2721 7812 5199

BRISTOL LASALLE CORP p 214
601 County Road 17, Elkhart IN 46516
Tel (574) 295-4400
SIC 5023 5021 5051 5033 3645 3089

ACORN DISTRIBUTORS INC p 18
5820 Fortune Cir W, Indianapolis IN 46241
Tel (317) 243-9234
SIC 5113 5087 5169 5046 5023

DIRECTBUY INC p 441
8450 Broadway, Merrillville IN 46410
Tel (219) 736-1100
SIC 5021 5064 5023 5961 6794 7299

MEL STEVENSON & ASSOCIATES INC p 940
2840 Roe Ln, Kansas City KS 66103
Tel (913) 262-0505 SIC 5033 5082 5023

GERSON CO p 609
1450 S Lone Elm Rd, Olathe KS 66061
Tel (913) 262-7400
SIC 5193 5199 5023 5094

NRF DISTRIBUTORS INC p 1064
485 Old Belgrade Rd, Augusta ME 04330
Tel (207) 622-4744 SIC 5023

JJ HAINES & CO LLC p 786
6950 Aviation Blvd, Glen Burnie MD 21061
Tel (410) 760-4040 SIC 5023

NEXT DAY BLINDS CORP p 1040
8251 Preston Ct Ste B, Jessup MD 20794
Tel (240) 568-8800
SIC 5023 2591 5719 1799

TRIMARK USA LLC p 1480
505 Collins St, Attleboro MA 02703
Tel (508) 399-2400 SIC 5021 5023

■ WAYFAIR LLC p 1584
4 Copley Pl Ste 700, Boston MA 02116
Tel (617) 532-6100 SIC 5963 5712 5023

DECOR HOLDINGS INC p 421
225 Foxboro Blvd, Foxboro MA 02035
Tel (508) 339-9151 SIC 5023

ROBERT ALLEN GROUP INC p 1241
2 Hampshire St Ste 300, Foxboro MA 02035
Tel (508) 339-9151 SIC 5023

FITZPATRICK COMPANIES INC p 553
705 Pleasant St, Lee MA 01238
Tel (413) 298-1610 SIC 5714 5021 5023

MILLBROOK DISTRIBUTION SERVICES INC p 970
88 Huntoon Memorial Hwy, Leicester MA 01524
Tel (508) 892-8171
SIC 5122 5023 5072 5112 5049 5199

BELKNAP WHITE GROUP INC p 169
111 Plymouth St, Mansfield MA 02048
Tel (508) 337-2700 SIC 5023

■ PARTYLITE INC p 1119
59 Armstrong Rd, Plymouth MA 02360
Tel (203) 661-1926
SIC 2023 3999 3641 5199 5023

KAMCO SUPPLY CORP OF BOSTON p 802
181 New Boston St, Woburn MA 01801
Tel (508) 587-1500
SIC 5032 5031 5039 5023 5033

HUMPHREY COMPANIES LLC p 718
2851 Prairie St Sw, Grandville MI 49418
Tel (616) 530-1717
SIC 3537 3714 3089 5023 5162

VIRGINIA TILE CO p 1560
28320 Plymouth Rd, Livonia MI 48150
Tel (248) 476-7850 SIC 5032 5023

ATMOSPHERE COMMERCIAL INTERIORS LLC p 128
81 S 9th St Ste 350, Minneapolis MN 55402
Tel (612) 343-0868 SIC 5021 5023 7389

TILE SHOP INC p 1453
14000 Carlson Pkwy, Plymouth MN 55441
Tel (763) 541-9720 SIC 5713 5023

BRADY INDUSTRIES INC p 207
7055 Lindell Rd, Las Vegas NV 89118
Tel (702) 876-3990
SIC 5169 5087 5999 5023 5064

DWL INTERNATIONAL TRADING INC p 463
65 Industrial Rd, Lodi NJ 07644
Tel (973) 916-9958 SIC 5023 5046

FRANCO MANUFACTURING CO INC p 574
555 Prospect St, Metuchen NJ 08840
Tel (732) 494-0503
SIC 2269 2392 2211 5023 5131

ARC INTERNATIONAL NORTH AMERICA INC p 103
601 S Wade Blvd, Millville NJ 08332
Tel (856) 825-5620 SIC 5023 2821

DURAND GLASS MANUFACTURING CO INC p 462
901 S Wade Blvd, Millville NJ 08332
Tel (856) 327-1850 SIC 3229 3269 5023

TMCI HOLDINGS INC p 1457
80 Avenue K, Newark NJ 07105
Tel (201) 553-1100
SIC 5122 5023 5072 5112 5049 5199

■ MIKASA INC p 968
1 Century Way, Secaucus NJ 07094
Tel (866) 645-2721 SIC 5023 5099 5719

WWRD US LLC p 1629
1330 Campus Pkwy, Wall Township NJ 07753
Tel (732) 938-5800 SIC 5023

TWOS CO INC p 1495
500 Saw Mill River Rd, Elmsford NY 10523
Tel (914) 664-2277 SIC 5199 5023 5094

▲ LIFETIME BRANDS INC p 864
1000 Stewart Ave, Garden City NY 11530
Tel (516) 683-6000 SIC 3421 5023 5719

ALLSTAR MARKETING GROUP LLC p 58
2 Skyline Dr, Hawthorne NY 10532
Tel (914) 347-7827 SIC 5023

■ JANOVIC-PLAZA INC p 777
3035 Thomson Ave, Long Island City NY 11101
Tel (718) 392-3999
SIC 5198 5231 5023 5719

ABC HOME FURNISHINGS INC p 10
888 Brdwy Fl 4, New York NY 10003
Tel (212) 473-3000 SIC 5712 5719 5023

▲ AVON PRODUCTS INC p 139
777 3rd Ave, New York NY 10017
Tel (212) 282-5000
SIC 2844 3961 5961 5023 5137

CHF INDUSTRIES INC p 296
1 Park Ave Fl 9, New York NY 10016
Tel (212) 951-7800 SIC 5023 2221

JAY FRANCO & SONS INC p 779
295 5th Ave Ste 312, New York NY 10016
Tel (212) 679-3022 SIC 5023 2211

JONATHAN ADLER ENTERPRISES LLC p 792
333 Hudson St Fl 7, New York NY 10013
Tel (212) 645-2802 SIC 5023

MADISON INDUSTRIES INC p 894
295 5th Ave Ste 512, New York NY 10016
Tel (212) 679-5110 SIC 2392 5023

MINDSINSYNC INC p 972
276 5th Ave Rm 505, New York NY 10001
Tel (212) 228-1828 SIC 5023

ONEIDA LTD p 1087
163 Kenwood Ave, Oneida NY 13421
Tel (315) 361-3000
SIC 5046 5719 5023 5094

ZWILLING JA HENCKELS LLC p 1645
270 Marble Ave, Pleasantville NY 10570
Tel (914) 749-3440 SIC 5023 5719

PRIDE PRODUCTS CORP p 1174
4333 Veterans Mem Hwy, Ronkonkoma NY 11779
Tel (631) 737-4444
SIC 5113 5122 5023 5072 5199

TRIBORO QUILT MANUFACTURING CORP p 1479
172 S Broadway Ste 100, White Plains NY 10605
Tel (914) 428-7551 SIC 5023 5999

CROSCILL HOME LLC p 393
1500 N Carolina St, Goldsboro NC 27530
Tel (919) 735-7111 SIC 5023 3431

■ L G SOURCING INC p 834
1605 Curtis Bridge Rd, North Wilkesboro NC 28659
Tel (866) 578-0563 SIC 5023 5031 2499

COLE PAPERS INC p 335
1300 38th St N, Fargo ND 58102
Tel (800) 800-8090
SIC 5113 5111 5169 5023 5112 5049

FAMOUS DISTRIBUTION INC p 527
2620 Ridgewood Rd Ste 200, Akron OH 44313
Tel (330) 762-9621
SIC 5074 5075 5085 5023

LUMINEX HOME DECOR & FRAGRANCE HOLDING CORP p 885
10521 Millington Ct, Blue Ash OH 45242
Tel (513) 563-1113 SIC 5023 2844

OHIO VALLEY FLOORING INC p 1078
5555 Murray Ave, Cincinnati OH 45227
Tel (513) 271-3434 SIC 5023

INTERDESIGN INC p 752
30725 Solon Indus Pkwy, Solon OH 44139
Tel (440) 248-0136 SIC 5023

BOSTWICK-BRAUN CO p 203
7349 Crossleigh Ct, Toledo OH 43617
Tel (419) 259-3600
SIC 5072 5084 5063 5083 5023

■ CINMAR LLC p 308
5566 W Chester Rd, West Chester OH 45069
Tel (513) 603-1000 SIC 5961 5023 5712

RODDA PAINT CO p 1246
6107 N Marine Dr Ste 3, Portland OR 97203
Tel (503) 521-4300
SIC 2851 5198 5023 5231 5719

SURE FIT INC p 1408
8000 Quarry Rd Ste C, Alburtis PA 18011
Tel (610) 264-7300 SIC 5023

DEGOL ORGANIZATION L P p 422
3229 Pleasant Valley Blvd, Altoona PA 16602
Tel (814) 941-7777
SIC 5031 5033 5211 5023 5713

FABTEX INC p 523
111 Woodbine Ln, Danville PA 17821
Tel (570) 275-7500
SIC 5072 2221 5023 2512 2392 2391

■ SYSCO PITTSBURGH LLC p 1417
1 Whitney Dr, Harmony PA 16037
Tel (724) 452-2100
SIC 5142 5149 5148 5023 5113 5046

TYCO ELECTRONICS BLANKET p 1496
100 Amp Dr, Harrisburg PA 17106
Tel (717) 810-2598 *SIC* 5023

FORBO FLOORING INC p 565
8 Maplewood Dr, Hazle Township PA 18202
Tel (570) 459-0771 *SIC* 5023

EVERFAST INC p 514
203 Gale Ln, Kennett Square PA 19348
Tel (610) 444-9700 *SIC* 5023

FITZ AND FLOYD ENTERPRISES LLC p 553
3 Friends Ln Ste 300, Newtown PA 18940
Tel (800) 527-9550
SIC 5023 5199 5947 5719

PHILADELPHIA BUNZL p 1142
10814 Northeast Ave, Philadelphia PA 19116
Tel (215) 969-0600
SIC 5087 5023 5113 7213

SWAROVSKI NORTH AMERICA LIMITED p 1411
1 Kenney Dr, Cranston RI 02920
Tel (401) 463-6400 *SIC* 3961 5023 3231

NATCO PRODUCTS CORP p 1009
155 Brookside Ave, West Warwick RI 02893
Tel (401) 828-0300 *SIC* 3996 2273 5023

LE CREUSET OF AMERICA INC p 849
114 Bob Gifford Blvd, Early Branch SC 29916
Tel (803) 943-4308 *SIC* 5023

SPRINGS GLOBAL US INC p 1361
205 N White St, Fort Mill SC 29715
Tel (803) 547-1500 *SIC* 2299 5023

GUARDIAN BUILDING PRODUCTS DISTRIBUTION INC p 645
979 Batesville Rd Ste A, Greer SC 29651
Tel (800) 569-4262
SIC 5031 5033 5051 5032 5039 5023

BUILDING PLASTICS INC p 225
3263 Sharpe Ave, Memphis TN 38111
Tel (901) 744-6200 *SIC* 5023

OLD TIME POTTERY LLC p 1081
480 River Rock Blvd, Murfreesboro TN 37128
Tel (615) 890-6060 *SIC* 5999 5023

CANDLE CORP OF AMERICA p 247
600 Sherwood Dr, Union City TN 38261
Tel (731) 885-7836 *SIC* 5023 5199

FOUR HANDS LLC p 571
2090 Woodward St, Austin TX 78744
Tel (512) 371-7575 *SIC* 5023 5712

NIELSEN & BAINBRIDGE LLC p 1043
12303 Tech Blvd Ste 950, Austin TX 78727
Tel (512) 506-8844 *SIC* 2499 5023

AMERICAN STEEL INC p 80
2500 Agnes St, Corpus Christi TX 78405
Tel (361) 883-1706
SIC 5023 5051 5084 5191

SWIFF-TRAIN CO LLC p 1412
2500 Agnes St, Corpus Christi TX 78405
Tel (361) 883-1706 *SIC* 5023

▲ JRJR33 INC p 795
2950 N Harwood St Fl 22, Dallas TX 75201
Tel (469) 913-4115
SIC 5499 5023 5122 2721 5251

FLOWORKS INTERNATIONAL LLC p 560
515 Post Oak Blvd Ste 800, Houston TX 77027
Tel (713) 839-1753 *SIC* 5051 5023

T & L DISTRIBUTING p 1419
7350 Langfield Rd, Houston TX 77092
Tel (713) 461-7802 *SIC* 5023

WISENBAKER BUILDER SERVICES INC p 1619
1703 Westfield Loop Rd, Houston TX 77073
Tel (281) 233-4000 *SIC* 5023 5084 5031

■ J C PENNEY EUROPE INC p 770
6501 Legacy Dr, Plano TX 75024
Tel (972) 431-1000 *SIC* 5137 5136 5023

■ J C PENNEY PURCHASING CORP p 770
6501 Legacy Dr, Plano TX 75024
Tel (972) 431-1000 *SIC* 5137 5136 5023

FLOORS INC p 557
200 Bank St, Southlake TX 76092
Tel (817) 421-8787 *SIC* 5023 5713

REDI-CARPET INC p 1217
10225 Mula Rd Ste 120, Stafford TX 77477
Tel (832) 310-2000 *SIC* 5023

ASSOCIATED FOOD STORES INC p 120
1850 W 2100 S, Salt Lake City UT 84119
Tel (801) 973-4400
SIC 5141 5147 5142 5148 5122 5023

CORNELL TRADING INC p 370
131 Battery St, Burlington VT 05401
Tel (802) 879-1271
SIC 5023 5137 5719 5621

UTTERMOST CO p 1537
3325 Grassy Hill Rd, Rocky Mount VA 24151
Tel (540) 483-5103 *SIC* 2392 5023

T & A SUPPLY CO INC p 1419
6821 S 216th St Bldg A, Kent WA 98032
Tel (206) 282-3770
SIC 1771 5023 1752 2431

WORLDWIDE DISTRIBUTORS p 1626
8211 S 194th St, Kent WA 98032
Tel (253) 872-8746
SIC 5091 5136 5137 5139 5199 5023

HARTUNG GLASS INDUSTRIES INC p 666
17830 W Valley Hwy, Tukwila WA 98188
Tel (425) 656-2626 *SIC* 5023

BLAIN SUPPLY INC p 188
3507 E Racine St, Janesville WI 53546
Tel (608) 754-2821
SIC 5083 5072 5039 5013 5023 5198

HY CITE ENTERPRISES LLC p 722
333 Holtzman Rd, Madison WI 53713
Tel (608) 273-3373 *SIC* 5023

BUILDING SERVICE p 225
W222n630 Cheaney Rd, Waukesha WI 53186
Tel (414) 358-5080 *SIC* 5021 1542 5023

SIC 5031 Lumber, Plywood & Millwork Wholesale

MARVINS LLC p 914
7480 Parkway Dr Ste 100, Leeds AL 35094
Tel (205) 702-7305
SIC 5211 5074 5031 5072

CONSTRUCTION MATERIALS INC p 361
4350 Northern Blvd, Montgomery AL 36110
Tel (334) 272-8200 *SIC* 5031 5051

CAPITAL LUMBER CO p 250
5110 N 40th St Ste 242, Phoenix AZ 85018
Tel (602) 381-0709 *SIC* 5031

WINROC CORP MIDWEST p 1617
4225 W Glenrosa Ave, Phoenix AZ 85019
Tel (602) 477-0341 *SIC* 5031

RUGBY USA INC p 1257
1440 S Priest Dr Ste 103, Tempe AZ 85281
Tel (480) 968-2208 *SIC* 5031

E C BARTON & CO p 466
2929 Browns Ln, Jonesboro AR 72401
Tel (870) 932-6673 *SIC* 5031 5211 5713

DYKE INDUSTRIES INC p 464
309 Center St, Little Rock AR 72201
Tel (501) 376-2921 *SIC* 5031

HIXSON LUMBER SALES INC p 697
310 S Tennessee St, Pine Bluff AR 71601
Tel (870) 535-1436 *SIC* 2421 5031

PAREX USA INC p 1114
4125 E La Palma Ave, Anaheim CA 92807
Tel (714) 778-2266 *SIC* 3299 5031

WALNUT INVESTMENT CORP p 1574
2940 E White Star Ave, Anaheim CA 92806
Tel (714) 238-9240 *SIC* 5031 5039 5072

■ METALS USA BUILDING PRODUCTS LP p 952
955 Columbia St, Brea CA 92821
Tel (713) 946-9000 *SIC* 3355 5031 1542

SWANER HARDWOOD CO INC p 1411
5 W Magnolia Blvd, Burbank CA 91502
Tel (818) 953-5350 *SIC* 2435 5031

LUMBER CITY CORP p 885
20525 Nordhoff St Ste 210, Chatsworth CA 91311
Tel (818) 407-3888 *SIC* 5211 5031

EL & ELWOOD PRODUCTS CORP p 482
6011 Schaefer Ave, Chino CA 91710
Tel (909) 591-0339 *SIC* 5031

COMMERCIAL LUMBER & PALLET CO INC p 345
135 Long Ln, City Of Industry CA 91746
Tel (626) 968-0631 *SIC* 2448 5031

FLEETWOOD ALUMINUM PRODUCTS INC p 555
1 Fleetwood Way, Corona CA 92879
Tel (800) 736-7363 *SIC* 5031 3442

PJS LUMBER INC p 1153
45055 Fremont Blvd, Fremont CA 94538
Tel (510) 743-5300 *SIC* 5031 5051

BUILDING MATERIAL DISTRIBUTORS INC p 225
225 Elm Ave, Galt CA 95632
Tel (209) 745-3001 *SIC* 5031

RELIABLE WHOLESALE LUMBER INC p 1221
7600 Redondo Cir, Huntington Beach CA 92648
Tel (714) 848-8222 *SIC* 5031 2421

H - INVESTMENT CO p 649
6999 Southfront Rd, Livermore CA 94551
Tel (925) 245-4300 *SIC* 5031

HOSKIN & MUIR INC p 708
6611 Preston Ave Ste C, Livermore CA 94551
Tel (925) 373-1135 *SIC* 5031

■ EDISON MATERIAL SUPPLY LLC p 478
125 Elm Ave, Long Beach CA 90802
Tel (562) 491-2341 *SIC* 5031

JONES WHOLESALE LUMBER CO INC p 793
10761 Alameda St, Lynwood CA 90262
Tel (323) 567-1301 *SIC* 5031

JAMES HARDIE BUILDING PRODUCTS INC p 776
26300 La Alameda Ste 400, Mission Viejo CA 92691
Tel (949) 348-1800 *SIC* 5031

PACIFIC STATES INDUSTRIES INC p 1106
10 Madrone Ave, Morgan Hill CA 95037
Tel (408) 779-7354 *SIC* 5031 2421 1751

HERITAGE INTERESTS LLC p 686
4300 Jetway Ct, North Highlands CA 95660
Tel (916) 481-5030 *SIC* 1751 5031 2431

PACIFIC COAST SUPPLY LLC p 1104
4290 Roseville Rd, North Highlands CA 95660
Tel (916) 971-2301 *SIC* 5031

GROVE LUMBER & BUILDING SUPPLIES INC p 642
1300 S Campus Ave, Ontario CA 91761
Tel (909) 947-0277 *SIC* 5031 5211

GOLDEN STATE LUMBER INC p 621
855 Lakeville St Ste 200, Petaluma CA 94952
Tel (707) 206-4100 *SIC* 5031 5211

JUDSON ENTERPRISES INC p 797
2440 Gold River Rd # 100, Rancho Cordova CA 95670
Tel (916) 631-9300 *SIC* 2431 5031

PACIFIC COAST BUILDING PRODUCTS INC p 1104
10600 White Rock Rd # 100, Rancho Cordova CA 95670
Tel (916) 631-6500
SIC 3275 3271 5031 1761 2952 2426

AMERICAN BUILDING SUPPLY INC p 69
8360 Elder Creek Rd, Sacramento CA 95828
Tel (916) 503-4100 *SIC* 5031 3231

ASSOCIATED MATERIALS GROUP INC p 120
1 Maritime Plz Fl 12, San Francisco CA 94111
Tel (415) 788-5111
SIC 3089 5033 5031 3442

ASSOCIATED MATERIALS INC p 121
1 Maritime Plz Fl 12, San Francisco CA 94111
Tel (415) 788-5111
SIC 3089 5033 5031 3442

KELLEHER CORP p 808
1543 5th Ave, San Rafael CA 94901
Tel (415) 454-8861 *SIC* 5031

MENDOCINO FOREST PRODUCTS CO LLC p 943
3700 Old Redwood Hwy # 200, Santa Rosa CA 95403
Tel (707) 620-2961 *SIC* 5031 2421

PIONEER SAND CO INC p 1151
5000 Northpark Dr, Colorado Springs CO 80918
Tel (719) 599-8100 *SIC* 5211 5031 1794

■ PROBUILD CO LLC p 1179
7595 E Technology Way # 500, Denver CO 80237
Tel (303) 262-8500 *SIC* 5211 5031

■ PROBUILD HOLDINGS LLC p 1179
7595 Tech Way Ste 500, Denver CO 80237
Tel (303) 262-8500 *SIC* 5031 5211

RINGS END INC p 1235
181 West Ave, Darien CT 06820
Tel (203) 655-2525 *SIC* 5031 5211

EAST HAVEN BUILDERS SUPPLY - US LBM LLC p 470
193 Silver Sands Rd, East Haven CT 06512
Tel (203) 469-2394 *SIC* 5031 5211

ATLAS HOLDINGS LLC p 128
100 Northfield St, Greenwich CT 06830
Tel (203) 622-9138
SIC 5031 2491 5039 5153

BRIDGEWELL RESOURCES HOLDINGS LLC p 212
1 Sound Shore Dr Ste 302, Greenwich CT 06830
Tel (203) 622-9138
SIC 5031 2491 5039 5153

BRYNWOOD PARTNERS V LIMITED PARTNERSHIP p 222
8 Sound Shore Dr Ste 265, Greenwich CT 06830
Tel (203) 622-1790
SIC 6282 1751 3442 5031 3354

▲ CRANE CO p 388
100 1st Stamford Pl # 300, Stamford CT 06902
Tel (203) 363-7300
SIC 3492 3494 3594 3589 3728 5031

■ BUILDERS FIRSTSOURCE - FLORIDA LLC p 225
6550 Roosevelt Blvd, Jacksonville FL 32244
Tel (904) 772-6100 *SIC* 5031

▲ RAYONIER INC p 1210
225 Water St Ste 1400, Jacksonville FL 32202
Tel (904) 357-9100
SIC 6798 5099 6552 5031

RO-MAC LUMBER & SUPPLY INC p 1240
700 E Main St, Leesburg FL 34748
Tel (352) 787-4545 *SIC* 5211 5031

A & M SUPPLY CORP p 4
6701 90th Ave N, Pinellas Park FL 33782
Tel (727) 541-6631 *SIC* 5031

ADVANTAGE TRIM & LUMBER CO INC p 26
7524 Commerce Pl, Sarasota FL 34243
Tel (941) 388-9299 *SIC* 5031 5211

CHADWELL SUPPLY INC p 286
4907 Joanne Kearney Blvd, Tampa FL 33619
Tel (888) 341-2423 *SIC* 5031 1752

■ BLUELINX CORP p 193
4300 Wildwood Pkwy, Atlanta GA 30339
Tel (770) 953-7000 *SIC* 5031

■ BLUELINX HOLDINGS INC p 193
4300 Wildwood Pkwy, Atlanta GA 30339
Tel (770) 953-7000 *SIC* 5031 5211

▲ BMC STOCK HOLDINGS INC p 193
980 Hammond Dr Ste 500, Atlanta GA 30328
Tel (678) 222-1219
SIC 5211 2431 5031 5713 5251

■ HD SUPPLY CONSTRUCTION SUPPLY GROUP INC p 673
3100 Cumberland Blvd Se, Atlanta GA 30339
Tel (770) 852-9000 *SIC* 5072 5039 5031

■ HD SUPPLY CONSTRUCTION SUPPLY LTD p 673
3100 Cumberland Blvd Se # 1700, Atlanta GA 30339
Tel (770) 852-9000 *SIC* 5031 5039 5072

■ HD SUPPLY INC p 673
3100 Cumberland Blvd Se # 1700, Atlanta GA 30339
Tel (770) 852-9000 *SIC* 5031 5033

MERCHANTS METALS LLC p 945
211 Perimeter Center Pkwy, Atlanta GA 30346
Tel (770) 741-0300 *SIC* 3496 3446 5031

OLDCASTLE BUILDING PRODUCTS INC p 1082
900 Ashwood Pkwy Ste 600, Atlanta GA 30338
Tel (770) 804-3363 *SIC* 5031

■ WHITE CAP CONSTRUCTION SUPPLY INC p 1606
3100 Cumberland Blvd Se # 1700, Atlanta GA 30339
Tel (404) 879-7740 *SIC* 5072 5039 5031

US LUMBER GROUP LLC p 1532
2160 Satellite Blvd # 450, Duluth GA 30097
Tel (678) 474-4577 *SIC* 5031

FOREST BEASLEY PRODUCTS INC p 566
712 Uvalda Hwy, Hazlehurst GA 31539
Tel (912) 375-5174 *SIC* 5031

VOGEL FOREST PRODUCTS LTD p 1564
138 Canal St Ste 408, Pooler GA 31322
Tel (912) 348-2233 *SIC* 5031

MANIS LUMBER CO p 901
15 Old Airport Rd Nw, Rome GA 30165
Tel (706) 232-2400 *SIC* 5031 5211

BRADLEY PLYWOOD CORP p 206
204 Old West Lathrop Ave, Savannah GA 31415
Tel (912) 447-7000 *SIC* 5031

▲ GMS INC p 619
100 Crescent Center Pkwy, Tucker GA 30084
Tel (800) 392-4619 *SIC* 3275 5031 5039

LANGDALE CO p 844
1202 Madison Hwy, Valdosta GA 31601
Tel (229) 242-7450
SIC 2421 2491 7011 7699 5031 5171

HONSADOR LUMBER LLC p 705
91-151 Malakole St, Kapolei HI 96707
Tel (808) 479-3071 *SIC* 5031 5211

BOISE CASCADE HOLDINGS LLC p 198
1111 W Jefferson St # 300, Boise ID 83702
Tel (208) 384-6161 *SIC* 5031 8744

BUILDING MATERIALS HOLDING CORP p 225
720 E Park Blvd Ste 115, Boise ID 83712
Tel (208) 331-4300 *SIC* 5211 5031

FOREST PRODUCTS HOLDINGS LLC p 567
1111 W Jefferson St # 300, Boise ID 83702
Tel (208) 384-6161 *SIC* 5031 8744

■ SELECTBUILD CONSTRUCTION INC p 1301
720 E Park Blvd Ste 115, Boise ID 83712
Tel (208) 331-4300
SIC 1521 1771 1751 2431 5031 5211

IDAHO PACIFIC LUMBER CO INC p 728
1770 S Spanish Sun Way, Meridian ID 83642
Tel (208) 375-8052 *SIC* 5031

PARKSITE INC p 1117
1563 Hubbard Ave, Batavia IL 60510
Tel (630) 761-9490 *SIC* 5031 5162

EDWARD HINES LUMBER CO p 480
1050 Corporate Grove Dr, Buffalo Grove IL 60089
Tel (847) 353-7700 *SIC* 5031 5211

LBM BORROWER LLC p 849
1000 Corporate Grove Dr, Buffalo Grove IL 60089
Tel (877) 787-5267 *SIC* 5031

US LBM HOLDINGS LLC p 1532
1000 Corporate Grove Dr, Buffalo Grove IL 60089
Tel (877) 787-5267 *SIC* 5072 5031 5198

▲ CONTINENTAL MATERIALS CORP p 363
440 S La Salle St # 3100, Chicago IL 60605
Tel (312) 541-7200 *SIC* 3585 3273 5031

■ GETZ BROS& CO INC p 609
225 W Washington St # 1900, Chicago IL 60606
Tel (312) 845-5686
SIC 5047 5031 5141 5065 5082

MADISON DEARBORN PARTNERS IV LP p 894
70 W Madison St Ste 3800, Chicago IL 60602
Tel (312) 895-1000 *SIC* 5031 8744

■ USG INTERIORS LLC p 1535
125 S Franklin St, Chicago IL 60606
Tel (800) 874-4968 *SIC* 5031

W R MEADOWS INC p 1569
300 Industrial Dr, Hampshire IL 60140
Tel (847) 214-2100 *SIC* 5031

MIDWEST AIR TECHNOLOGIES INC p 967
6700 Wildlife Way, Long Grove IL 60047
Tel (847) 821-9630
SIC 5072 5191 5063 5051 5031

FCA INC p 532
7601 John Deere Pkwy, Moline IL 61265
Tel (309) 792-3222 *SIC* 5085 5031

FCA LLC p 532
7601 John Deere Pkwy, Moline IL 61265
Tel (309) 792-3444
SIC 4783 5031 5085 2448

STERLING LUMBER CO p 1387
501 E 151st St, Phoenix IL 60426
Tel (708) 388-2223 *SIC* 5031 7389 2448

ROBERT WEED PLYWOOD CORP p 1241
705 Maple St, Bristol IN 46507
Tel (574) 848-7631 *SIC* 5031 2435 2431

SEEMAC INC p 1300
11350 N Meridian St # 450, Carmel IN 46032
Tel (317) 844-3995 *SIC* 5031

AS HOLDINGS INC p 115
5120 Beck Dr, Elkhart IN 46516
Tel (574) 295-8384
SIC 5033 5169 5031 5162

DEHCO INC p 422
3601 Charlotte Ave, Elkhart IN 46517
Tel (574) 294-2684
SIC 2891 5031 5074 5014 5084

▲ PATRICK INDUSTRIES INC p 1120
107 W Franklin St, Elkhart IN 46516
Tel (574) 294-7511
SIC 3275 2493 2435 5031 5033 2891

DO IT BEST CORP p 446
6502 Nelson Rd, Fort Wayne IN 46803
Tel (260) 748-5300 *SIC* 5072 5031 5063

BFS DIVERSIFIED PRODUCTS INC p 179
250 W 96th St Ste 150, Indianapolis IN 46260
Tel (317) 575-7000 *SIC* 5031 5013 5169

LEE SUPPLY CORP p 852
6610 Guion Rd, Indianapolis IN 46268
Tel (317) 290-2500
SIC 5074 5075 5064 5085 5031

KOUNTRY WOOD PRODUCTS LLC p 828
352 Shawnee St, Nappanee IN 46550
Tel (574) 773-5673 *SIC* 2434 5211 5031

FBI BUILDINGS INC p 532
3823 W 1800 S, Remington IN 47977
Tel (219) 261-2157 *SIC* 1542 5031 1541

NC INC p 1021
1023 Main St, Vincennes IN 47591
Tel (812) 886-4412 *SIC* 5031 5211

STATELINE COOPERATIVE p 1383
120 Walnut St, Burt IA 50522
Tel (515) 885-2642 *SIC* 5191 5172 5031

EMCO ENTERPRISES INC p 491
2121 E Walnut St, Des Moines IA 50317
Tel (515) 264-4283 *SIC* 5031

A Y MCDONALD INDUSTRIES INC p 7
4800 Chavenelle Rd, Dubuque IA 52002
Tel (800) 292-2737
SIC 3432 3561 3494 5074 5075 5031

CEDAR CREEK LLC p 272
5034 Grand Ridge Dr, West Des Moines IA 50265
Tel (405) 917-8300 *SIC* 2431 5031

AMERICAN DIRECT PROCUREMENT INC p 71
11000 Lakeview Ave, Lenexa KS 66219
Tel (913) 677-5588 *SIC* 5031

EE NEWCOMER ENTERPRISES INC p 480
1901 E 119th St, Olathe KS 66061
Tel (816) 221-0543 SIC 5031 5211 7699

FBM OHIO LLC p 532
2048 Rolling Hills Dr, Covington KY 41017
Tel (859) 431-0626 SIC 5031

FORTIS PLASTICS LLC p 569
390 Community Dr, Henderson KY 42420
Tel (270) 827-9801 SIC 5031

AL J SCHNEIDER CO p 43
325 W Main St Ste 1800, Louisville KY 40202
Tel (502) 584-5984 SIC 7011 5031

KENTUCKY-INDIANA LUMBER CO INC p 812
4010 Collins Ln, Louisville KY 40245
Tel (502) 637-1401 SIC 5031 2439 2431

DAIRYMANS SUPPLY CO INC p 409
3114 State Route 45 S, Mayfield KY 42066
Tel (270) 247-5641 SIC 5031

ALLIED BUILDING STORES INC p 56
850 Kansas Ln, Monroe LA 71203
Tel (318) 699-9100 SIC 5031

INTERIOR/EXTERIOR BUILDING SUPPLY LIMITED PARTNERSHIP p 753
727 S Cortez St, New Orleans LA 70119
Tel (504) 488-1998 SIC 5031

HAMMOND LUMBER CO p 656
2 Hammond Dr, Belgrade ME 04917
Tel (207) 495-3303 SIC 5211 2421 5031

HANCOCK LUMBER CO INC p 657
4 Edes Falls Rd, Casco ME 04015
Tel (207) 627-4201 SIC 5211 5031

CAPITAL FOREST PRODUCTS INC p 249
111 Gibraltar Ave, Annapolis MD 21401
Tel (410) 280-6102 SIC 5031

ATLANTIC FOREST PRODUCTS LLC p 126
240 W Dickman St, Baltimore MD 21230
Tel (410) 752-8092 SIC 5031

AWM LLC p 139
1800 Washington Blvd # 140, Baltimore MD 21230
Tel (916) 387-7317 SIC 5031

■ BUILDERS FIRSTSOURCE - ATLANTIC GROUP LLC p 225
5330 Spectrum Dr Ste L, Frederick MD 21703
Tel (301) 631-2282 SIC 5031 5211

ROBERT N KARPP CO INC p 1241
480 E 1st St, Boston MA 02127
Tel (617) 269-5880 SIC 5031 1799

SHEPLEY WOOD PRODUCTS INC p 1315
216 Thornton Dr, Hyannis MA 02601
Tel (508) 862-6200 SIC 5031

NORTH ATLANTIC CORP p 1050
1255 Grand Army Hwy, Somerset MA 02726
Tel (508) 324-7700 SIC 5031

■ BEACON SALES ACQUISITION INC p 165
50 Webster Ave, Somerville MA 02143
Tel (877) 645-7663 SIC 5033 5031

HARVEY INDUSTRIES INC p 667
1400 Main St Fl 3, Waltham MA 02451
Tel (781) 899-3500
SIC 5031 5033 3442 2431

BROCKWAY-SMITH CO p 216
35 Upton Dr Ste 100, Wilmington MA 01887
Tel (978) 475-7100 SIC 5031

ATLANTIC PLYWOOD CORP p 127
8 Roessler Rd, Woburn MA 01801
Tel (781) 933-1932 SIC 5031 5198

KAMCO SUPPLY CORP OF BOSTON p 802
181 New Boston St, Woburn MA 01801
Tel (508) 587-1500
SIC 5032 5031 5039 5023 5033

■ NORTH AMERICAN FOREST PRODUCTS LIQUIDATION INC p 1050
27263 May St, Edwardsburg MI 49112
Tel (269) 663-8500 SIC 2421 5031

FOREST BESSE PRODUCTS INC p 566
933 N 8th St, Gladstone MI 49837
Tel (906) 428-3113 SIC 5031 5099

LUMBERMENS INC p 885
4433 Stafford Ave Sw, Grand Rapids MI 49548
Tel (616) 261-3200 SIC 5033 5031 5198

CIRAULO BROTHERS BUILDING CO p 308
7670 19 Mile Rd, Sterling Heights MI 48314
Tel (586) 731-3670 SIC 5031 5211 1761

MILLIKEN MILLWORK INC p 971
6361 Sterling Dr N, Sterling Heights MI 48312
Tel (586) 264-0950 SIC 5031

EMPIRE CO LLC p 493
8181 Logistics Dr, Zeeland MI 49464
Tel (616) 772-7272 SIC 5031 2431

ANDERSEN DISTRIBUTION INC p 89
100 4th Ave N, Bayport MN 55003
Tel (651) 264-5150 SIC 5031

VIKING FOREST PRODUCTS LLC p 1557
7615 Smetana Ln Ste 140, Eden Prairie MN 55344
Tel (952) 941-6512 SIC 5031 5051

BEP/LYMAN LLC p 174
520 3rd St Ste 200, Excelsior MN 55331
Tel (952) 470-3600 SIC 5031 5211

MIDWEST HARDWOOD CORP p 967
9540 83rd Ave N, Maple Grove MN 55369
Tel (763) 425-8700 SIC 5031 2421

KLUMB LUMBER CO p 823
1080 River Oaks Dr Sa200, Flowood MS 39232
Tel (601) 932-6070 SIC 5031

BAILEY LUMBER & SUPPLY CO p 145
813 E Pass Rd, Gulfport MS 39507
Tel (228) 896-6071 SIC 5211 5031

NEWMAN LUMBER CO p 1038
11367 Reichold Rd, Gulfport MS 39503
Tel (228) 604-2178 SIC 5031

HOOD INDUSTRIES INC p 705
15 Professional Pkwy # 8, Hattiesburg MS 39402
Tel (601) 264-2962 SIC 2436 2421 5031

JT SHANNON LUMBER CO INC p 796
2200 Cole Rd, Horn Lake MS 38637
Tel (662) 393-3765 SIC 5031 3559 2421

CIMARRON LUMBER AND SUPPLY CO p 307
4000 Main St, Kansas City MO 64111
Tel (816) 756-3000 SIC 5031

PAXTON WOOD SOURCE INC p 1122
6311 Saint John Ave, Kansas City MO 64123
Tel (816) 483-7000
SIC 5031 2431 5211 5072

MID-AM BUILDING SUPPLY INC p 963
1615 Omar Bradley Rd, Moberly MO 65270
Tel (660) 263-2140 SIC 5031

CENTRAL STATES WHOLESALE & DISTRIBUTION INC p 280
33 Pcr 540, Perryville MO 63775
Tel (573) 547-4260 SIC 5031

▲ HUTTIG BUILDING PRODUCTS INC p 722
555 Maryville University, Saint Louis MO 63141
Tel (314) 216-2600 SIC 5031 5033

MILLMAN LUMBER CO p 971
9264 Manchester Rd, Saint Louis MO 63144
Tel (314) 961-6195 SIC 5031

BUILDERS SUPPLY CO INC p 225
5701 S 72nd St, Omaha NE 68127
Tel (402) 331-4500 SIC 5211 5031

MILLARD LUMBER INC p 970
12900 I St, Omaha NE 68137
Tel (402) 896-2800 SIC 5031 5211

COMPLETE MILLWORK SERVICES INC p 351
4909 Goni Rd Ste A, Carson City NV 89706
Tel (775) 246-0485 SIC 5031

RUGBY ACQUISITION p 1257
1 Pillsbury St Ste 302, Concord NH 03301
Tel (603) 369-4710 SIC 5031

RUGBY IPD CORP p 1257
1 Pillsbury St Ste 302, Concord NH 03301
Tel (603) 369-4710 SIC 5031

BRIDGEWATER WHOLESALERS INC p 212
210 Industrial Pkwy, Branchburg NJ 08876
Tel (908) 526-7555 SIC 2431 5031

PASSAIC METAL & BUILDING SUPPLIES CO p 1119
5 Central Ave Ste 1, Clifton NJ 07011
Tel (973) 546-9000
SIC 5033 5031 5051 5075 3444 3296

DIRECT CABINET SALES - US LBM LLC p 441
180 Herrod Blvd, Dayton NJ 08810
Tel (908) 587-9577 SIC 5031 5064

ALLIED BUILDING PRODUCTS CORP p 56
15 E Union Ave, East Rutherford NJ 07073
Tel (201) 507-8400 SIC 5031 5033

OLDCASTLE DISTRIBUTION INC p 1082
15 E Union Ave, East Rutherford NJ 07073
Tel (201) 507-8400 SIC 5031 5032

KUIKEN BROTHERS CO INC p 831
6-02 Fair Lawn Ave, Fair Lawn NJ 07410
Tel (201) 796-2082 SIC 5211 5031 3272

HANWA AMERICAN CORP p 659
Parker Plz 400 Kelby St F, Fort Lee NJ 07024
Tel (201) 363-4500
SIC 5051 5172 5031 5084 5146

UNIVERSAL SUPPLY CO LLC p 1517
582 S Egg Harbor Rd, Hammonton NJ 08037
Tel (609) 561-3000 SIC 5033 5031

DUBELL LUMBER CO p 459
148 Route 70, Medford NJ 08055
Tel (609) 654-4143 SIC 5031 5211

RAKS BUILDING SUPPLY INC p 1206
108 Carson Dr Se, Los Lunas NM 87031
Tel (505) 865-1100 SIC 5031 5211 5072

CERTIFIED LUMBER CORP p 284
Isack Rosenberg 470 Kent, Brooklyn NY 11211
Tel (718) 387-1233 SIC 5031 5211

EXTECH BUILDING MATERIALS INC p 521
87 Bowne St, Brooklyn NY 11231
Tel (718) 852-7090 SIC 5082 5033 5031

KAMCO SUPPLY CORP p 801
80 21st St, Brooklyn NY 11232
Tel (718) 840-1700 SIC 5031 5033

B & L WHOLESALE SUPPLY INC p 141
70 Hartford St, Buffalo NY 14206
Tel (716) 853-2600 SIC 5033 5031

RIVERHEAD BUILDING SUPPLY CORP p 1237
250 David Ct, Calverton NY 11933
Tel (631) 727-1400 SIC 5031 5211

MARJAM SUPPLY CO INC p 907
885 Conklin St, Farmingdale NY 11735
Tel (631) 249-4900 SIC 5211 5031

CRYSTAL WINDOW & DOOR SYSTEMS LTD p 397
3110 Whitestone Expy, Flushing NY 11354
Tel (718) 961-7300
SIC 5031 3442 3231 3211 2431 1751

KLEET LUMBER CO INC p 823
777 Park Ave, Huntington NY 11743
Tel (631) 427-7060 SIC 5031

EASTERN WHOLESALE FENCE CO INC p 473
274 Middle Island Rd, Medford NY 11763
Tel (631) 698-0900
SIC 5039 5031 5051 3496

LBM ADVANTAGE INC p 849
555 Hudson Valley Ave # 200, New Windsor NY 12553
Tel (845) 564-4900 SIC 5031

■ CERBERUS ABP INVESTOR LLC p 283
299 Park Ave, New York NY 10171
Tel (212) 891-2100 SIC 5031 5211

▲ CERBERUS CAPITAL MANAGEMENT LP p 283
875 3rd Ave, New York NY 10022
Tel (212) 891-2100
SIC 6722 6726 5031 5211

METROPOLITAN LUMBER p 956
617 11th Ave, New York NY 10036
Tel (212) 246-9090 SIC 5031 5211 5251

TOMEN AMERICA INC p 1459
805 3rd Ave Fl 16, New York NY 10022
Tel (212) 355-3600
SIC 5153 5169 5031 5131 2261

ERIE MATERIALS INC p 508
500 Factory Ave, Syracuse NY 13208
Tel (315) 455-7434 SIC 5033 5031

GREAT AMERICAN INDUSTRIES INC p 633
300 Plaza Dr, Vestal NY 13850
Tel (607) 729-9331
SIC 3086 5031 5074 3442 3069 5091

HENRIETTA BUILDING SUPPLIES INC p 683
1 Riverton Way, West Henrietta NY 14586
Tel (585) 334-2365 SIC 5031

S & K DISTRIBUTION LLC p 1261
535 Old Tarrytown Rd, White Plains NY 10603
Tel (914) 948-6363 SIC 5031 2952 5033

JELD-WEN INC p 782
440 S Church St Ste 400, Charlotte NC 28202
Tel (800) 535-3936 SIC 3442 5031 2421

WURTH WOOD GROUP INC p 1628
4250 Golf Acres Dr, Charlotte NC 28208
Tel (704) 394-9479 SIC 5211 5031

GUARANTEED SUPPLY CO p 644
1211 Rotherwood Rd, Greensboro NC 27406
Tel (336) 273-3491 SIC 5032 5031

▲ LOWES COMPANIES INC p 881
1000 Lowes Blvd, Mooresville NC 28117
Tel (704) 758-1000
SIC 5211 5031 5722 5064

GENE WHITLEY KELLY p 598
44439 Fish Camp Rd, New London NC 28127
Tel (704) 984-0811 SIC 5031

ECMD INC p 475
2 Grandview St, North Wilkesboro NC 28659
Tel (336) 667-5976 SIC 2431 5031

■ L G SOURCING INC p 834
1605 Curtis Bridge Rd, North Wilkesboro NC 28659
Tel (866) 578-0563 SIC 5023 5031 2499

BUILDING CENTER INC p 225
10201 Industrial Dr, Pineville NC 28134
Tel (704) 889-8182 SIC 5031 2431

■ BMC EAST LLC p 193
8020 Arco Corp Dr Ste 400, Raleigh NC 27617
Tel (919) 431-1000
SIC 5211 2431 5031 5713 5251

STOCK BUILDING SUPPLY HOLDINGS LLC p 1390
8020 Arco Corp Dr Ste 400, Raleigh NC 27617
Tel (919) 431-1000
SIC 5211 2431 5031 5713 5251

■ LOWES HOME CENTERS LLC p 881
1605 Curtis Bridge Rd, Wilkesboro NC 28697
Tel (336) 658-4000
SIC 5211 5031 5722 5064

AMARR CO p 64
165 Carriage Ct, Winston Salem NC 27105
Tel (336) 744-5100
SIC 2431 3442 5031 5211

FAMOUS ENTERPRISES INC p 527
2620 Ridgewood Rd Ste 200, Akron OH 44313
Tel (330) 762-9621
SIC 5075 5031 5074 7699

STARK TRUSS CO INC p 1379
109 Miles Ave Sw, Canton OH 44710
Tel (330) 478-2100 SIC 5031 2439

SIMS-LOHMAN INC p 1326
6325 Este Ave, Cincinnati OH 45232
Tel (513) 651-3510 SIC 5031 2435

GUNTON CORP p 648
26150 Richmond Rd, Cleveland OH 44146
Tel (216) 831-2420 SIC 5031

ASSOCIATED MATERIALS HOLDINGS LLC p 120
3773 State Rd, Cuyahoga Falls OH 44223
Tel (330) 929-1811
SIC 3089 5033 5031 5063 3442

ASSOCIATED MATERIALS LLC p 121
3773 State Rd, Cuyahoga Falls OH 44223
Tel (330) 929-1811
SIC 3089 5033 5031 3442

NORANDEX BUILDING MATERIALS DISTRIBUTION INC p 1047
300 Executive Park Ste 100, Hudson OH 44236
Tel (330) 656-8924 SIC 5033 5031

CARTER-JONES COMPANIES INC p 262
601 Tallmadge Rd, Kent OH 44240
Tel (330) 673-6100 SIC 5211 5031 6552

CARTER-JONES LUMBER CO p 262
601 Tallmadge Rd, Kent OH 44240
Tel (330) 673-6100 SIC 5211 5031

TRI-STATE FOREST PRODUCTS INC p 1477
2105 Sheridan Ave, Springfield OH 45505
Tel (937) 323-6325 SIC 5031

PROVIA DOOR INC p 1185
2150 State Route 39, Sugarcreek OH 44681
Tel (330) 852-4711 SIC 3442 5031

CEDAR CREEK HOLDINGS INC p 272
450 N Macarthur Blvd, Oklahoma City OK 73127
Tel (405) 917-8300 SIC 5031 5082

CEDAR CREEK LLC p 272
450 N Macarthur Blvd, Oklahoma City OK 73127
Tel (405) 917-8300 SIC 5031

NORTHWEST BUILDING SUPPLY INC p 1059
5535 Nw 5th St, Oklahoma City OK 73127
Tel (405) 946-0500 SIC 5033 5031 5211

MILL CREEK LUMBER & SUPPLY CO INC p 969
6974 E 38th St, Tulsa OK 74145
Tel (405) 671-3540
SIC 3442 1771 5031 5211

AMERICAN INTERNATIONAL FOREST PRODUCTS LLC p 75
5560 Sw 107th Ave, Beaverton OR 97005
Tel (503) 641-1611 SIC 5031

INTERNATIONAL BUILDING MATERIALS LLC p 754
14421 Se 98th Ct, Clackamas OR 97015
Tel (503) 650-9663 SIC 5031

SHAMROCK BUILDING MATERIALS INC p 1311
4725 Village Plaza Loop # 201, Eugene OR 97401
Tel (877) 426-2341 SIC 5031 5051

PARR LUMBER CO p 1117
5630 Nw Century Blvd, Hillsboro OR 97124
Tel (503) 614-2500
SIC 5031 5211 5072 5251

LUMBER PRODUCTS AN OREGON CORP p 885
5200 Meadows Rd Ste 150, Lake Oswego OR 97035
Tel (503) 692-3322 SIC 5031

■ BENSON INDUSTRIES INC p 173
1650 Nw Naito Pkwy # 250, Portland OR 97209
Tel (503) 226-7611
SIC 5031 1793 3231 3211

FCTG HOLDINGS INC p 533
10250 Sw Greenburg Rd # 200, Portland OR 97223
Tel (503) 246-8500 SIC 5031

FOREST CITY TRADING GROUP LLC p 566
10250 Sw Greenburg Rd # 200, Portland OR 97223
Tel (503) 246-8500 SIC 5031

HAMPTON INVESTMENT CO p 656
9600 Sw Barnes Rd Ste 200, Portland OR 97225
Tel (503) 297-7691 SIC 5031 2435 2426

HAMPTON LUMBER SALES CO p 656
9600 Sw Barnes Rd Ste 200, Portland OR 97225
Tel (503) 297-7691 SIC 5031 2421 7389

HAMPTON RESOURCES INC p 656
9600 Sw Barnes Rd Ste 200, Portland OR 97225
Tel (503) 297-7691 SIC 5031 2421 0811

SHELTER PRODUCTS INC p 1315
1490 Se Gideon St Ste 100, Portland OR 97202
Tel (503) 872-3600 SIC 5031

TUMAC LUMBER CO INC p 1491
805 Sw Broadway Ste 1500, Portland OR 97205
Tel (503) 721-7696 SIC 5031 5159

ROSEBURG FOREST PRODUCTS CO p 1250
3660 Gateway St Ste A, Springfield OR 97477
Tel (541) 679-3311
SIC 2436 2421 2493 5031 5211 0811

TIMBER PRODUCTS CO LIMITED PARTNERSHIP p 1454
305 S 4th St, Springfield OR 97477
Tel (541) 747-4577
SIC 2436 2435 5031 2493

BRIDGEWELL RESOURCES LLC p 212
10200 Sw Greenburg Rd # 500, Tigard OR 97223
Tel (503) 872-3566
SIC 5031 5039 5153 5159

OREGON PACIFIC BUILDING PRODUCTS (CALIF) INC p 1093
30170 Sw Ore Pac Ave, Wilsonville OR 97070
Tel (503) 685-5499 SIC 5031

OREPAC HOLDING CO p 1094
30170 Sw Orepac Ave, Wilsonville OR 97070
Tel (503) 682-5050 SIC 5031

UFP WOODBURN LLC p 1499
2895 Progress Way, Woodburn OR 97071
Tel (503) 226-6240 SIC 5031

DEGOL ORGANIZATION L P p 422
3229 Pleasant Valley Blvd, Altoona PA 16602
Tel (814) 941-7777
SIC 5031 5033 5211 5023 5713

SEVEN D WHOLESALE OF PA LP p 1309
3229 Pleasant Valley Blvd, Altoona PA 16602
Tel (814) 941-7777 SIC 5031

LUMBERMEN ASSOCIATES INC p 885
2101 Hunter Rd, Bristol PA 19007
Tel (215) 785-4600 SIC 5031

■ CARLISLE CONSTRUCTION MATERIALS LLC p 257
1285 Ritner Hwy, Carlisle PA 17013
Tel (717) 245-7000
SIC 2952 3069 5031 2899 2891

KAMCO BUILDING SUPPLY CORP OF PENNSYLVANIA p 801
1100 Township Line Rd, Chester PA 19013
Tel (610) 364-1356 SIC 5031

TREVDAN INC p 1476
1031 Pottstown Pike, Chester Springs PA 19425
Tel (610) 458-9860 SIC 5031

84 LUMBER CO p 4
1019 Route 519, Eighty Four PA 15330
Tel (724) 228-8820
SIC 2431 2439 5031 5211

IRWIN BUILDERS SUPPLY CORP p 765
10249 Garnet Ln, Irwin PA 15642
Tel (724) 863-5200 SIC 5031 5211

SHUSTERS BUILDERS SUPPLIES INC p 1319
2920 Clay Pike, Irwin PA 15642
Tel (724) 446-7000 SIC 5031 5211

INTERNATIONAL TIMBER AND VENEER LLC p 757
75 Mcquiston Dr, Jackson Center PA 16133
Tel (724) 662-0880 SIC 2435 5031

WOLSELEY INVESTMENTS INC p 1621
1904 Ligonier St, Latrobe PA 15650
Tel (757) 874-7795
SIC 5074 5085 5075 5064 5211 5031

BERKS PRODUCTS CORP p 175
167 Berks Products Dr, Leesport PA 19533
Tel (610) 374-5131
SIC 5031 3273 5983 5172 2439 1711

FOREST SNAVELY PRODUCTS INC p 567
600 Delwar Rd, Pittsburgh PA 15236
Tel (412) 885-4005 SIC 5031

LUMBERMENS MERCHANDISING CORP p 885
137 W Wayne Ave, Wayne PA 19087
Tel (610) 293-3678 SIC 5031 5072

DIAMOND HILL PLYWOOD CO INC p 436
600 E Broad St, Darlington SC 29532
Tel (843) 393-4036 SIC 5031

GUARDIAN BUILDING PRODUCTS DISTRIBUTION INC p 645
979 Batesville Rd Ste A, Greer SC 29651
Tel (800) 569-4262
SIC 5031 5033 5051 5032 5039 5023

CANFOR SOUTHERN PINE LLC p 247
3700 Claypond Rd, Myrtle Beach SC 29579
Tel (843) 236-8402 SIC 5031

LARSON MANUFACTURING CO INC p 845
2333 Eastbrook Dr, Brookings SD 57006
Tel (605) 692-6115 SIC 5031

WESTERN REFLECTIONS LLC p 1599
261 Commerce Way, Gallatin TN 37066
Tel (615) 451-9700 SIC 5031

GENERAL SHALE BRICK INC p 602
3015 Bristol Hwy, Johnson City TN 37601
Tel (423) 282-4661 SIC 5211 5031

HOUSE-HASSON HARDWARE CO p 711
3125 Water Plant Rd, Knoxville TN 37914
Tel (800) 333-0520 SIC 5072 5031

TINDELLS INC p 1455
7751 Norris Fwy, Knoxville TN 37938
Tel (865) 922-7751 SIC 5031 5211 2439

■ BUILDERS FIRSTSOURCE-TEXAS GROUP LP p 225
3403 E Abram St, Arlington TX 76010
Tel (214) 880-3500 SIC 5031 5033 2439

■ AMERICAN GYPSUM CO LLC p 73
3811 Turtle Creek Blvd # 1200, Dallas TX 75219
Tel (214) 530-5500 SIC 3275 5031

MASTER-HALCO INC p 918
3010 Lbj Fwy Ste 800, Dallas TX 75234
Tel (972) 714-7300
SIC 3315 5039 3496 3446 5031 1799

DW DISTRIBUTION INC p 463
1200 E Centre Park Blvd, Desoto TX 75115
Tel (214) 381-2200 SIC 5033 5031 5072

DEFORD LUMBER CO LTD p 422
1018 N Duncanville Rd, Duncanville TX 75116
Tel (972) 298-7121 SIC 5031 5211

GENERAL ALUMINUM CO OF TEXAS LP p 599
1900 Lakeside Pkwy, Flower Mound TX 75028
Tel (972) 242-5271 SIC 3442 5031

CONNER INDUSTRIES INC p 358
3800 Sandshell Dr Ste 235, Fort Worth TX 76137
Tel (817) 847-0361 SIC 5211 5031

TEXAS PLYWOOD AND LUMBER CO INC p 1444
1001 E Avenue K, Grand Prairie TX 75050
Tel (972) 262-1331 SIC 5031 2431

UFP GRANDVIEW LLC p 1499
1000 S 3rd St, Grandview TX 76050
Tel (817) 866-3306 SIC 5031 2439

■ BISON BUILDING MATERIALS OF TEXAS INC p 185
1445 W Sam Houston Pkwy N, Houston TX 77043
Tel (713) 467-6700 SIC 5031

HANDY HARDWARE WHOLESALE INC p 657
8300 Tewantin Dr, Houston TX 77061
Tel (713) 644-1495
SIC 5072 5074 5063 5031 5198

ISC ACQUISITION CORP p 766
7645 Railhead Ln, Houston TX 77086
Tel (281) 590-6000 SIC 5032 5031

RMC USA INC p 1239
920 Memorial City Way, Houston TX 77024
Tel (713) 650-6200
SIC 3273 3272 3271 5031

TRUSSWAY MANUFACTURING INC p 1487
9411 Alcorn St, Houston TX 77093
Tel (719) 322-9662 SIC 2439 5031

WISENBAKER BUILDER SERVICES INC p 1619
1703 Westfield Loop Rd, Houston TX 77073
Tel (281) 233-4000 SIC 5023 5084 5031

MJB WOOD GROUP INC p 978
2201 W Royal Ln Ste 250, Irving TX 75063
Tel (972) 401-0005 SIC 5031

PRIMESOURCE BUILDING PRODUCTS INC p 1175
1321 Greenway Dr, Irving TX 75038
Tel (972) 999-8500 SIC 5033 5031

■ US HOME SYSTEMS INC p 1532
2951 Kinwest Pkwy, Irving TX 75063
Tel (214) 488-6300 SIC 3429 5031 1751

FOXWORTH GALBRAITH LUMBER CO p 573
4965 Preston Park Blvd # 400, Plano TX 75093
Tel (972) 665-2400
SIC 5211 5031 2439 2431

GROTHUES BROTHERS HOLDINGS LTD p 641
2651 Sw Military Dr, San Antonio TX 78224
Tel (830) 569-1131 SIC 5031 5211 6719

FOREST TOMBALL PRODUCTS INC p 567
16801 Fm 2920 Rd, Tomball TX 77377
Tel (281) 357-8196 SIC 5083 5211 5031

WESTLINK TRADING LLC p 1601
17926 Highway 3, Webster TX 77598
Tel (832) 295-9778
SIC 5032 5099 5074 5051 5031

SUNROC BUILDING MATERIALS INC p 1404
520 S 800 W, Lindon UT 84042
Tel (801) 802-6952 SIC 5031

JM THOMAS FOREST PRODUCTS CO p 786
2525 N Hwy 89 91, Ogden UT 84404
Tel (801) 782-8090 SIC 5031

CLYDE COMPANIES INC p 328
730 N 1500 W, Orem UT 84057
Tel (801) 802-6900 SIC 1611 5031 6411

NATIONAL WOOD PRODUCTS INC p 1017
2705 S 600 W, Salt Lake City UT 84115
Tel (801) 977-1171 SIC 5031

SUNROC CORP p 1404
3657 S River Rd, St George UT 84790
Tel (435) 634-2200
SIC 5031 3273 5032 3271 1442

■ STOCK BUILDING SUPPLY WEST LLC p 1390
1133 W 9000 S, West Jordan UT 84088
Tel (801) 561-9000 SIC 5031 5211 2439

LAMINATE CO p 841
6612 James Madison Hwy, Haymarket VA 20169
Tel (703) 753-0699 SIC 5031 2431

▲ BEACON ROOFING SUPPLY INC p 165
505 Huntmar Park Dr # 300, Herndon VA 20170
Tel (571) 323-3939 SIC 5033 5031

LANSING BUILDING PRODUCTS INC p 844
8501 Sanford Dr, Richmond VA 23228
Tel (804) 266-8893 SIC 5033 5031 5032

■ LUMBER LIQUIDATORS INC p 885
3000 John Deere Rd, Toano VA 23168
Tel (757) 259-4280 SIC 5031 5211

INTERFOR US INC p 752
2211 Rimland Dr Ste 220, Bellingham WA 98226
Tel (360) 788-2299 SIC 0811 2421 5031

■ WEYERHAEUSER INTERNATIONAL INC p 1603
33663 Weyerhaeuser Way S, Federal Way WA 98001
Tel (253) 924-2345 SIC 5031

■ LANOGA CORP p 844
17946 Ne 65th St, Redmond WA 98052
Tel (425) 883-4125 SIC 5211 5031

MCLENDON HARDWARE INC p 931
440 Rainier Ave S, Renton WA 98057
Tel (425) 264-1541 SIC 5031 5251

■ PLUM CREEK MANUFACTURING LP p 1156
999 3rd Ave Ste 4300, Seattle WA 98104
Tel (206) 467-3600
SIC 2421 2436 2493 5031

■ PLUM CREEK TIMBERLANDS LP p 1156
601 Union St Ste 3100, Seattle WA 98101
Tel (206) 467-3600
SIC 2421 2436 2493 5031

SILVARIS CORP p 1323
505 5th Ave S Ste 610, Seattle WA 98104
Tel (888) 856-6677 SIC 5031

METRIE INC p 954
2200 140th Ave E Ste 600, Sumner WA 98390
Tel (253) 470-5050 SIC 5031

NORTHWEST HARDWOODS INC p 1059
820 A St Ste 500, Tacoma WA 98402
Tel (253) 568-6800 SIC 2426 5031

MATHEUS LUMBER CO INC p 920
15800 Woodinville Redmond, Woodinville WA 98072
Tel (206) 284-7500 SIC 5031

AMERICAN BUILDERS & CONTRACTORS SUPPLY CO INC p 69
1 Abc Pkwy, Beloit WI 53511
Tel (608) 362-7777 SIC 5033 5031

MIDWEST MANUFACTURING INC p 967
5311 Kane Rd, Eau Claire WI 54703
Tel (715) 876-5555 SIC 5033 5031 3965

AMERHART LIMITED p 66
2455 Century Rd, Green Bay WI 54303
Tel (920) 494-4744 SIC 5031

AWS/GB CORP p 139
2929 Walker Dr, Green Bay WI 54311
Tel (920) 406-4000
SIC 5031 2431 3442 5033 1542 1541

BAY INDUSTRIES INC p 161
2929 Walker Dr, Green Bay WI 54311
Tel (920) 406-4000 SIC 5031 5033

LA FORCE INC p 835
1060 W Mason St, Green Bay WI 54303
Tel (920) 497-7100 SIC 5072 5031 3442

BADGER CORRUGATING CO p 143
1801 West Ave S, La Crosse WI 54601
Tel (608) 788-0100 SIC 5031

PRINCE CORP p 1176
8351 County Road H, Marshfield WI 54449
Tel (800) 777-2486
SIC 5031 5191 2048 5083 5072

LAKE STATES LUMBER INC p 839
312 S Chester St, Sparta WI 54656
Tel (608) 269-6714 SIC 5031

■ UFP WARRENS LLC p 1499
County Rd 0 610 Rr St, Warrens WI 54666
Tel (608) 378-4904 SIC 5031

KOLBE & KOLBE MILLWORK CO INC p 826
1323 S 11th Ave, Wausau WI 54401
Tel (715) 842-5666 SIC 5031 2431

SIC 5032 Brick, Stone & Related Construction Mtrls Wholesale

WELLBORN CABINET INC p 1589
38669 Highway 77, Ashland AL 36251
Tel (256) 354-7151 SIC 2434 2511 5032

AGGREGATES USA LLC p 35
3300 Cahaba Rd Ste 302, Birmingham AL 35223
Tel (205) 777-6340 SIC 5032

PREFERRED MATERIALS INC p 1169
500 Rvrhills Bus Park, Birmingham AL 35242
Tel (205) 995-5900
SIC 1611 1771 3531 5032

CEMEX CORP p 274
4646 E Van Buren St # 250, Phoenix AZ 85008
Tel (602) 416-2600 SIC 5032 3273

MEADOW VALLEY CORP p 934
3333 E Camelback Rd # 240, Phoenix AZ 85018
Tel (602) 437-5400 SIC 1611 5032

MEADOW VALLEY HOLDINGS LLC p 934
4602 E Thomas Rd, Phoenix AZ 85018
Tel (602) 437-5400 SIC 1611 5032

SALT RIVER SAND & ROCK p 1273
8800 E Chaparral Rd # 155, Scottsdale AZ 85250
Tel (480) 850-5757 SIC 5032 1442

ARIZONA TILE LLC p 109
8829 S Priest Dr, Tempe AZ 85284
Tel (480) 991-3066 SIC 5032

PINE BLUFF SAND AND GRAVEL CO p 1148
1501 Heartwood St, White Hall AR 71602
Tel (870) 534-7120
SIC 2951 3273 1442 5032 1629

WESTSIDE BUILDING MATERIAL CORP p 1603
1111 E Howell Ave, Anaheim CA 92805
Tel (714) 385-1644 SIC 5032

LEHIGH SOUTHWEST CEMENT CO p 854
2300 Clayton Rd Ste 300, Concord CA 94520
Tel (972) 653-5500
SIC 3241 2891 5032 5211

ALL AMERICAN ASPHALT p 51
400 E 6th St, Corona CA 92879
Tel (951) 736-7600 SIC 1611 5032

ROBERTSONS READY MIX LTD A CALIFORNIA LIMITED PARTNERSHIP p 1242
200 S Main St Ste 200, Corona CA 92882
Tel (951) 493-6500
SIC 3273 3531 5032 2951 1442

■ PACIFIC GYPSUM SUPPLY INC p 1104
1165 N Johnson Ave, El Cajon CA 92020
Tel (619) 447-2413 SIC 5032 5211

SUPERIOR READY MIX CONCRETE LP p 1407
1508 Mission Rd, Escondido CA 92029
Tel (760) 745-0556 SIC 3273 1611 5032

PARAGON INDUSTRIES INC p 1113
4285 N Golden State Blvd, Fresno CA 93722
Tel (559) 275-5000 SIC 5211 5032

CALPORTLAND CO p 243
2025 E Financial Way, Glendora CA 91741
Tel (626) 852-6200 SIC 3241 3273 5032

EMSER INTERNATIONAL LLC p 495
8431 Santa Monica Blvd, Los Angeles CA 90069
Tel (323) 650-2000 SIC 5032

EMSER TILE LLC p 495
8431 Santa Monica Blvd, Los Angeles CA 90069
Tel (323) 650-2000 SIC 5032 5211

SYAR INDUSTRIES INC p 1413
2301 Napa Vallejo Hwy, Napa CA 94558
Tel (707) 252-8711
SIC 5032 2951 0762 7992 5932

M S INTERNATIONAL INC p 890
2095 N Batavia St, Orange CA 92865
Tel (714) 685-7500 SIC 5032

A TEICHERT & SON INC p 6
3500 American River Dr, Sacramento CA 95864
Tel (916) 484-3011
SIC 5032 3273 1611 1442 1521

TEICHERT INC p 1433
3500 American River Dr, Sacramento CA 95864
Tel (916) 484-3011
SIC 3273 5032 1611 1442 1521 5039

GRANITE ROCK CO p 631
350 Technology Dr, Watsonville CA 95076
Tel (831) 768-2000
SIC 1442 3273 5032 2951 1611 3271

CLARK - PACIFIC CORP p 322
1980 S River Rd, West Sacramento CA 95691
Tel (916) 371-0305 SIC 3272 5032

BARTON LEASING INC p 158
14800 E Moncrieff Pl, Aurora CO 80011
Tel (303) 576-2200 SIC 5032

ROCKY MOUNTAIN MATERIALS AND ASPHALT INC p 1245
1910 Rand Ave, Colorado Springs CO 80905
Tel (719) 473-3100
SIC 1611 1771 1794 5032

BRANNAN SAND AND GRAVEL CO LLC p 208
2500 Brannan Way, Denver CO 80229
Tel (303) 534-1231 SIC 1611 5032

OLDCASTLE SW GROUP INC p 1082
2273 River Rd, Grand Junction CO 81505
Tel (970) 243-4900 SIC 1611 3273 5032

LAFARGE WEST INC p 837
10170 Church Ranch Way # 200, Westminster CO 80021
Tel (303) 657-4355 SIC 5032 1611 3273

LANE CONSTRUCTION CORP p 843
90 Fieldstone Ct, Cheshire CT 06410
Tel (203) 235-3351
SIC 1622 1611 1629 3272 5032

LANE INDUSTRIES INC p 843
90 Fieldstone Ct, Cheshire CT 06410
Tel (203) 235-3351
SIC 1629 1611 5032 3272 1622

SUPERIOR PRODUCTS DISTRIBUTORS INC p 1407
1403 Meriden Waterbury Rd, Milldale CT 06467
Tel (860) 621-3621
SIC 5074 5032 5082 7353

TILCON CONNECTICUT INC p 1453
642 Black Rock Ave, New Britain CT 06052
Tel (860) 224-6010
SIC 5032 1611 3273 2951

TILCON INC p 1453
301 Hartford Ave, Newington CT 06111
Tel (860) 223-3651
SIC 1611 5032 3273 2951

O & G INDUSTRIES INC p 1070
112 Wall St, Torrington CT 06790
Tel (860) 489-9261
SIC 1542 1541 1611 1623 5032 2951

A H HARRIS & SONS INC p 5
433 S Main St Ste 202, West Hartford CT 06110
Tel (860) 216-9500 SIC 5032

DEVCON INTERNATIONAL CORP p 433
595 S Federal Hwy Ste 500, Boca Raton FL 33432
Tel (954) 926-5200
SIC 3699 3273 3281 3271 2951 5032

CONRAD YELVINGTON DISTRIBUTORS INC p 358
2328 Bellevue Ave, Daytona Beach FL 32114
Tel (386) 257-5504 SIC 5032 5261

CCP MANAGEMENT INC p 270
3401 Phillips Hwy, Jacksonville FL 32207
Tel (904) 398-7177 SIC 5032 5169

STUART BUILDING PRODUCTS LLC p 1394
1341 Nw 15th St, Pompano Beach FL 33069
Tel (954) 971-7264 SIC 5032

ARGOS USA LLC p 107
3015 Windward Plz Ste 300, Alpharetta GA 30005
Tel (678) 368-4300 SIC 3272 5032

APAC HOLDINGS INC p 95
900 Ashwood Pkwy Ste 700, Atlanta GA 30338
Tel (770) 392-5300 SIC 1611 3531 5032

OLDCASTLE MATERIALS INC p 1082
900 Ashwood Pkwy Ste 700, Atlanta GA 30338
Tel (770) 522-5600
SIC 3272 1622 1611 2951 5032

THOMAS CONCRETE INDUSTRIES INC p 1448
2500 Cumberland Pkwy Se # 200, Atlanta GA 30339
Tel (770) 431-3300 SIC 3273 5032

REDI-FLOORS INC p 1217
1791 Williams Dr, Marietta GA 30066
Tel (770) 590-7334 SIC 5023 5032

BORAL INDUSTRIES INC p 201
200 Mansell Ct E Ste 310, Roswell GA 30076
Tel (770) 645-4500
SIC 3251 3272 3275 5032 3271 2899

■ SITEONE LANDSCAPE SUPPLY HOLDING LLC p 1328
300 Colonial Center Pkwy, Roswell GA 30076
Tel (770) 255-2100
SIC 5083 5191 5193 5032 5063

▲ SITEONE LANDSCAPE SUPPLY INC p 1328
300 Colonial Center Pkwy, Roswell GA 30076
Tel (770) 255-2100
SIC 5083 5191 5193 5032 5063

■ GYPSUM MANAGEMENT AND SUPPLY INC p 649
100 Crescent Center Pkwy # 800, Tucker GA 30084
Tel (770) 939-1711 SIC 5032 8742

L & W SUPPLY CORP p 833
550 W Adams St, Chicago IL 60661
Tel (312) 606-4000 SIC 5032

■ AMCOL INTERNATIONAL CORP p 65
2870 Forbs Ave, Hoffman Estates IL 60192
Tel (847) 851-1500
SIC 1459 5032 4213 4731

OZINGA BROS INC p 1102
19001 Old Lagrange Rd # 30, Mokena IL 60448
Tel (708) 326-4200 SIC 3273 5032

SOUTHFIELD CORP p 1351
8995 W 95th St, Palos Hills IL 60465
Tel (708) 344-1000
SIC 3273 1442 3241 4212 4213 5032

GYPSUM SUPPLY CO p 649
1125 Harrison Ave, Rockford IL 61104
Tel (815) 397-5718 SIC 5032

IRVING MATERIALS INC p 765
8032 N State Road 9, Greenfield IN 46140
Tel (317) 326-3101
SIC 3273 3271 5032 2951

MARCO GROUP INTERNATIONAL INC p 905
3425 E Locust St, Davenport IA 52803
Tel (563) 324-2519 SIC 5084 5032

KCG INC p 806
15720 W 108th St Ste 100, Lenexa KS 66219
Tel (913) 438-4142 SIC 5032 2992

LOUISVILLE TILE DISTRIBUTORS INC p 881
4520 Bishop Ln, Louisville KY 40218
Tel (502) 452-2037 SIC 5032 5211 1743

PORT AGGREGATES INC p 1161
314 N Main St, Jennings LA 70546
Tel (337) 656-3224 SIC 5032 3273

CHANEY ENTERPRISES LIMITED PARTNERSHIP p 288
2410 Evergreen Rd Ste 201, Gambrills MD 21054
Tel (410) 451-0197
SIC 3273 1442 5032 3429

DANIEL G SCHUSTER LLC p 411
3717 Crondall Ln Ste B, Owings Mills MD 21117
Tel (410) 363-9620 SIC 5032 1771

EAST COAST TILE IMPORTS INC p 470
8 Stony Brook St Ste 1, Ludlow MA 01056
Tel (518) 344-7000 SIC 5032 8741

ALL STATES ASPHALT INC p 51
325 Amherst Rd, Sunderland MA 01375
Tel (413) 665-7021 SIC 5032

KAMCO SUPPLY CORP OF BOSTON p 802
181 New Boston St, Woburn MA 01801
Tel (508) 587-1500
SIC 5032 5031 5039 5023 5033

■ GYPSUM SUPPLY CO p 649
859 74th St Sw, Byron Center MI 49315
Tel (616) 583-9300 SIC 5032

EDW C LEVY CO p 479
9300 Dix, Dearborn MI 48120
Tel (313) 429-2200 SIC 3295 5032 2951

CONSUMERS CONCRETE CORP p 362
3508 S Sprinkle Rd, Kalamazoo MI 49001
Tel (269) 342-0136 SIC 3273 3271 5032

VIRGINIA TILE CO p 1560
28320 Plymouth Rd, Livonia MI 48150
Tel (248) 476-7850 SIC 5032 5023

CEMSTONE PRODUCTS CO p 274
2025 Centr Poin Blvd Ste 300, Mendota Heights MN 55120
Tel (651) 688-9292 SIC 3273 5032 1442

TWIN CITY CONCRETE PRODUCTS CO INC p 1495
2025 Centre Pointe Blvd # 300, Mendota Heights MN 55120
Tel (651) 688-9116
SIC 5032 3273 3255 1442

H ENTERPRISES INTERNATIONAL INC p 650
120 S 6th St Ste 2300, Minneapolis MN 55402
Tel (612) 343-8293 SIC 5032 8611 5211

APAC-MISSISSIPPI INC p 95
101 Riverview Dr, Richland MS 39218
Tel (601) 376-4000
SIC 1611 1771 3531 5032 2951

NU WAY CONCRETE FORMS INC p 1066
4190 Hoffmeister Ave, Saint Louis MO 63125
Tel (573) 893-8786
SIC 5032 5051 5072 7359

ELIASON & KNUTH COMPANIES INC p 487
13324 Chandler Rd, Omaha NE 68138
Tel (402) 896-1614 SIC 1742 5032

LYMAN-RICHEY CORP p 887
4315 Cuming St, Omaha NE 68131
Tel (402) 556-3600
SIC 3273 1442 3271 5211 5032

MITSUBISHI CEMENT CORP p 977
151 Cassia Way, Henderson NV 89014
Tel (702) 932-3900 SIC 3297 5032

AGGREGATE INDUSTRIES-SWR INC p 35
3101 E Craig Rd, North Las Vegas NV 89030
Tel (702) 281-9696 SIC 1611 5032

GLASS MTN PUMICE INC p 614
3400 Kauai Ct Ste 206, Reno NV 89509
Tel (775) 826-3399 SIC 5032

WALLBOARD SUPPLY CO - US LBM LLC p 1573
527 Mammoth Rd, Londonderry NH 03053
Tel (603) 434-4597 SIC 5032

OLDCASTLE DISTRIBUTION INC p 1082
15 E Union Ave, East Rutherford NJ 07073
Tel (201) 507-8400 SIC 5031 5032

RALPH CLAYTON & SONS LLC p 1206
1355 Campus Pkwy, Wall Township NJ 07753
Tel (732) 363-1995 SIC 5032

▲ MINERALS TECHNOLOGIES INC p 973
622 3rd Ave Fl 38, New York NY 10017
Tel (212) 878-1800
SIC 3295 2819 3274 1411 3281 5032

■ SPECIALTY MINERALS INC p 1356
622 3rd Ave Fl 38, New York NY 10017
Tel (212) 878-1800
SIC 2819 5032 1422 5169 2899

STONE SOURCE LLC p 1391
215 Park Ave S Fl 7, New York NY 10003
Tel (212) 979-6400 SIC 5032

APAC-ATLANTIC INC p 95
300 S Benbow Rd, Greensboro NC 27401
Tel (336) 412-6800
SIC 1611 1771 3531 5032

GUARANTEED SUPPLY CO p 644
1211 Rotherwood Rd, Greensboro NC 27406
Tel (336) 273-3491 SIC 5032 5031

HANSON AGGREGATES EAST LLC p 658
3131 Rdu Center Dr, Morrisville NC 27560
Tel (919) 380-2500 SIC 3531 5032

PINE HALL BRICK CO INC p 1149
2701 Shorefair Dr, Winston Salem NC 27105
Tel (336) 721-7500 SIC 3251 5032

STRATA CORP p 1392
1600 N 48th St, Grand Forks ND 58203
Tel (701) 775-4205
SIC 1611 3273 1442 5032

KENMORE CONSTRUCTION CO INC p 810
700 Home Ave, Akron OH 44310
Tel (330) 762-8936 SIC 1611 5032

NEXGEN ENTERPRISES INC p 1040
3274 Spring Grove Ave, Cincinnati OH 45225
Tel (513) 618-0300 SIC 5032

HWZ DISTRIBUTION GROUP LLC p 722
40 W Crescentville Rd, West Chester OH 45246
Tel (513) 618-0300 SIC 5032

MODERN BUILDERS SUPPLY INC p 981
302 Mcclurg Rd, Youngstown OH 44512
Tel (330) 729-2690
SIC 5032 3089 3446 3442

HASKELL LEMON CONSTRUCTION CO p 667
3800 Sw 10th St, Oklahoma City OK 73108
Tel (405) 947-6069
SIC 5032 1611 3272 2951

EVANS & ASSOCIATES ENTERPRISES INC p 513
3320 N 14th St, Ponca City OK 74601
Tel (580) 765-6693
SIC 5032 2951 1442 1611 3273 1311

CIESCO INC p 306
109 Miller Ln, Harrisburg PA 17110
Tel (717) 232-5825
SIC 5032 5033 5169 5039

PENNSY SUPPLY INC p 1130
1001 Paxton St, Harrisburg PA 17104
Tel (717) 233-4511
SIC 1422 2951 3273 4212 5032

STABLER COMPANIES INC p 1374
635 Lucknow Rd, Harrisburg PA 17110
Tel (717) 236-9307
SIC 5032 3089 7359 3531 1611 3648

NTP MARBLE INC p 1065
201 W Church Rd Ste 300, King Of Prussia PA 19406
Tel (610) 994-2222 SIC 5032

NOVINGER GROUP INC p 1063
1441 Stoneridge Dr, Middletown PA 17057
Tel (717) 930-0300
SIC 1742 1799 5032 5033 5039

ESSROC CORP p 511
3251 Bath Pike, Nazareth PA 18064
Tel (610) 837-6725 SIC 3241 5032 3273

RESCO PRODUCTS INC p 1226
1 Robinson Plz Ste 300, Pittsburgh PA 15205
Tel (412) 494-4491
SIC 3297 3255 1455 1499 5032

EASTERN INDUSTRIES INC p 472
3724 Crescent Ct W 200, Whitehall PA 18052
Tel (610) 866-0932 SIC 5032 3273 1611

ALLAN MYERS INC p 51
1805 Berks Rd, Worcester PA 19490
Tel (610) 222-8800
SIC 1629 1794 1611 1622 3281 5032

GUARDIAN BUILDING PRODUCTS DISTRIBUTION INC p 645
979 Batesville Rd Ste A, Greer SC 29651
Tel (800) 569-4262
SIC 5031 5033 5051 5032 5039 5023

APAC-ATLANTIC INC p 95
4817 Rutledge Pike, Knoxville TN 37914
Tel (865) 983-3100
SIC 5032 3531 3273 2951 1611

LOJAC ENTERPRISES INC p 875
1401 Toshiba Dr, Lebanon TN 37087
Tel (615) 449-1401 SIC 1611 1794 5032

MAYMEAD INC p 923
1995 Roan Creek Rd, Mountain City TN 37683
Tel (423) 727-2000
SIC 1611 2951 5032 5191

ALLEY-CASSETTY COMPANIES INC p 53
2 Oldham St, Nashville TN 37213
Tel (615) 244-7077 SIC 5032 5052

AUSTIN MATERIALS LLC p 133
9020 N Cpitl Of Texas Hwy, Austin TX 78759
Tel (512) 251-3713 SIC 1611 5032

CRISP INDUSTRIES INC p 392
323 Energy Way, Bridgeport TX 76426
Tel (940) 683-4070 SIC 5032

■ AMERICAN TILE AND STONE INC p 80
2244 Luna Rd Ste 160, Carrollton TX 75006
Tel (972) 243-2377 SIC 5032

BARNSCO INC p 156
2609 Willowbrook Rd, Dallas TX 75220
Tel (214) 352-9091 SIC 5032

CUSTOM CRETE INC p 403
2624 Joe Field Rd, Dallas TX 75229
Tel (972) 243-4466 SIC 5032 3273

■ DAL-TILE DISTRIBUTION INC p 409
7834 C F Hawn Fwy, Dallas TX 75217
Tel (214) 398-1411 SIC 5032

GEORGECO INC p 606
2609 Willowbrook Rd, Dallas TX 75220
Tel (214) 352-9091 SIC 5032

CEMEX EL PASO INC p 274
1 Mckelligon Canyon Rd, El Paso TX 79930
Tel (915) 565-4681
SIC 3273 2951 5032 1442

■ ACME BRICK CO p 17
3024 Acme Brick Plz, Fort Worth TX 76109
Tel (817) 332-4101 SIC 3251 5032 5211

■ JUSTIN INDUSTRIES INC p 798
3024 Acme Brick Plz, Fort Worth TX 76109
Tel (817) 332-4101
SIC 3251 3271 5211 5032

INTERCERAMIC INC p 751
2333 S Jupiter Rd, Garland TX 75041
Tel (214) 503-4967 SIC 3253 5032

CEMEX INC p 274
929 Gessner Rd Ste 1900, Houston TX 77024
Tel (713) 650-6200
SIC 3273 3271 3272 5032

CENTURY ASPHALT LTD p 282
5303 Navigation Blvd, Houston TX 77011
Tel (713) 292-2868 SIC 5032

CHERRY CRUSHED CONCRETE INC p 294
6131 Selinsky Rd, Houston TX 77048
Tel (713) 987-0000 SIC 5032

■ D & I SILICA LLC p 406
3 Riverway Ste 1350, Houston TX 77056
Tel (713) 980-6200 SIC 5032

ISC ACQUISITION CORP p 766
7645 Railhead Ln, Houston TX 77086
Tel (281) 590-6000 SIC 5032 5031

HANSON AGGREGATES LLC p 658
8505 Freeport Pkwy Ste 500, Irving TX 75063
Tel (469) 417-1200 SIC 3273 2951 5032

LEHIGH CEMENT CO LLC p 853
300 E John Carpenter Fwy, Irving TX 75062
Tel (877) 534-4442 SIC 3241 3273 5032

MARTIN PRODUCT SALES LLC p 913
4200 Stone Rd, Kilgore TX 75662
Tel (903) 983-6200 SIC 5052 5032 5172

C & C NORTH AMERICA INC p 231
2245 Texas Dr Ste 600, Sugar Land TX 77479
Tel (281) 207-4461 SIC 5032

WESTLINK TRADING LLC p 1601
17926 Highway 3, Webster TX 77598
Tel (832) 295-9778
SIC 5032 5099 5074 5051 5031

GENEVA ROCK PRODUCTS INC p 603
302 W 5400 S Ste 201, Murray UT 84107
Tel (801) 765-7800 SIC 5032

STAKER & PARSON COMPANIES p 1374
2350 S 1900 W Ste 100, Ogden UT 84401
Tel (801) 298-7500
SIC 1611 5032 3273 4212 2951 1771

■ HEADWATERS RESOURCES INC p 673
10701 S River Front Pkwy # 300, South Jordan UT 84095
Tel (801) 984-9400 SIC 5032 4953 8711

SUNROC CORP p 1404
3657 S River Rd, St George UT 84790
Tel (435) 634-2200
SIC 5031 3273 5032 3271 1442

GRANISER LLC p 631
5650 General Wash Dr, Alexandria VA 22312
Tel (703) 256-5650 SIC 5032

CAPITOL BUILDING SUPPLY INC p 251
8429 Euclid Ave, Manassas Park VA 20111
Tel (703) 631-6772
SIC 5032 5039 5033 5051

ASHGROVE HOLDINGS LLC p 117
12001 Sunrise Valley Dr, Reston VA 20191
Tel (703) 821-1175 SIC 5032

REINFORCED EARTH CO p 1221
12001 Sunrise Valley Dr # 400, Reston VA 20191
Tel (703) 821-1175 SIC 5032

LANSING BUILDING PRODUCTS INC p 844
8501 Sanford Dr, Richmond VA 23228
Tel (804) 266-8893 SIC 5033 5031 5032

ASSOCIATED ASPHALT INC p 119
130 Church Ave Sw, Roanoke VA 24011
Tel (540) 345-8867 SIC 5032

LAKESIDE INDUSTRIES INC p 840
6505 226th Pl Se Ste 200, Issaquah WA 98027
Tel (425) 313-2600 SIC 1611 2951 5032

■ GTS DRYWALL SUPPLY CO p 644
10819 120th Ave Ne, Kirkland WA 98033
Tel (425) 828-0608 SIC 5032

MILES SAND & GRAVEL CO p 969
400 Valley Ave Ne, Puyallup WA 98372
Tel (253) 833-3705 SIC 3273 5032

EDEN STONE CO INC p 477
W4520 Lime Rd, Eden WI 53019
Tel (920) 477-2521 SIC 1411 5032

SIC 5033 Roofing, Siding & Insulation Mtrls Wholesale

SHOOK & FLETCHER INSULATION CO INC p 1317
4625 Valleydale Rd, Birmingham AL 35242
Tel (205) 991-7606 SIC 5033 1799 5085

ROOFING WHOLESALE CO INC p 1249
1918 W Grant St, Phoenix AZ 85009
Tel (602) 258-3794 SIC 5033

ASSOCIATED MATERIALS GROUP INC p 120
1 Maritime Plz Fl 12, San Francisco CA 94111
Tel (415) 788-5111
SIC 3089 5033 5031 3442

ASSOCIATED MATERIALS INC p 121
1 Maritime Plz Fl 12, San Francisco CA 94111
Tel (415) 788-5111
SIC 3089 5033 5031 3442

▲ TOPBUILD CORP p 1460
260 Jimmy Ann Dr, Daytona Beach FL 32114
Tel (386) 304-2200
SIC 1742 1761 1751 5033

SUNNILAND CORP p 1403
1735 State Road 419, Longwood FL 32750
Tel (407) 322-2421 SIC 5033 5191

GULFSIDE SUPPLY INC p 647
2900 E 7th Ave Ste 200, Tampa FL 33605
Tel (813) 636-9808 SIC 5033

COMMERCIAL ROOFING SPECIALTIES INC p 345
2703 Peachtree Sq, Atlanta GA 30360
Tel (770) 458-0539 SIC 5033

■ HD SUPPLY INC p 673
3100 Cumberland Blvd Se # 1700, Atlanta GA 30339
Tel (770) 852-9000 SIC 5031 5033

HEELY-BROWN CO p 680
1280 Chattahoochee Ave Nw, Atlanta GA 30318
Tel (404) 352-0022 SIC 5033

CHICAGO METALLIC CO LLC p 297
4849 S Austin Ave, Chicago IL 60638
Tel (708) 563-4600 SIC 3446 5033

CHICAGO METALLIC CORP p 297
4849 S Austin Ave, Chicago IL 60638
Tel (708) 563-4600 SIC 3446 5033

USG INTERNATIONAL LTD p 1535
125 S Franklin St Ste 4, Chicago IL 60606
Tel (312) 606-4000 SIC 5033

RICHARDS BUILDING SUPPLY CO p 1232
12070 W 159th St, Homer Glen IL 60491
Tel (773) 586-7777 SIC 5033 5211

AS HOLDINGS INC p 115
5120 Beck Dr, Elkhart IN 46516
Tel (574) 295-8384
SIC 5033 5169 5031 5162

BRISTOL LASALLE CORP p 214
601 County Road 17, Elkhart IN 46516
Tel (574) 295-4400
SIC 5023 5021 5051 5033 3645 3089

▲ PATRICK INDUSTRIES INC p 1120
107 W Franklin St, Elkhart IN 46516
Tel (574) 294-7511
SIC 3275 2493 2435 5031 5033 2891

FIRESTONE BUILDING PRODUCTS CO LLC p 544
250 W 96th St Ste 150, Indianapolis IN 46260
Tel (317) 575-7000 SIC 5033

MEL STEVENSON & ASSOCIATES INC p 940
2840 Roe Ln, Kansas City KS 66103
Tel (913) 262-0505 SIC 5033 5082 5023

■ K & R HOLDINGS INC p 798
400 Warren Ave, Portland ME 04103
Tel (207) 797-7950 SIC 5033 3089

GENERAL INSULATION CO p 601
278 Mystic Ave Ste 209, Medford MA 02155
Tel (781) 391-2070 SIC 5033 7389

■ BEACON SALES ACQUISITION INC p 165
50 Webster Ave, Somerville MA 02143
Tel (877) 645-7663 SIC 5033 5031

HARVEY INDUSTRIES INC p 667
1400 Main St Fl 3, Waltham MA 02451
Tel (781) 899-3500
SIC 5031 5033 3442 2431

KAMCO SUPPLY CORP OF BOSTON p 802
181 New Boston St, Woburn MA 01801
Tel (508) 587-1500
SIC 5032 5031 5039 5023 5033

LUMBERMENS INC p 885
4433 Stafford Ave Sw, Grand Rapids MI 49548
Tel (616) 261-3200 SIC 5033 5031 5198

LOUIS T OLLESHEIMER & SON INC p 880
605 E 12 Mile Rd, Madison Heights MI 48071
Tel (248) 544-3900 SIC 5033 5082

WIMSATT BUILDING MATERIALS CORP p 1614
36340 Van Born Rd, Wayne MI 48184
Tel (734) 722-3460 SIC 5033 8742

INSULATION DISTRIBUTORS INC p 747
8303 Audubon Rd, Chanhassen MN 55317
Tel (952) 279-6400 SIC 5033

JAMAR CO p 776
4701 Mike Colalillo Dr, Duluth MN 55807
Tel (218) 628-1027
SIC 1711 1761 1742 5033 7699 3444

A P I INC p 6
1100 Old Highway 8 Nw, Saint Paul MN 55112
Tel (651) 636-4320 SIC 1742 5033

MAC ARTHUR CO p 891
2400 Wycliff St, Saint Paul MN 55114
Tel (651) 646-2773 SIC 5033 3448

▲ HUTTIG BUILDING PRODUCTS INC p 722
555 Maryville University, Saint Louis MO 63141
Tel (314) 216-2600 SIC 5031 5033

MISSOURI PETROLEUM PRODUCTS CO LLC p 976
1620 Woodson Rd, Saint Louis MO 63114
Tel (314) 219-7305 SIC 5033 1611 2951

BRADCO SUPPLY CORP p 206
34 Engelhard Ave, Avenel NJ 07001
Tel (732) 382-3400 SIC 5033 5211

PASSAIC METAL & BUILDING SUPPLIES CO p 1119
5 Central Ave Ste 1, Clifton NJ 07011
Tel (973) 546-9000
SIC 5033 5031 5051 5075 3444 3296

ALLIED BUILDING PRODUCTS CORP p 56
15 E Union Ave, East Rutherford NJ 07073
Tel (201) 507-8400 SIC 5031 5033

UNIVERSAL SUPPLY CO LLC p 1517
582 S Egg Harbor Rd, Hammonton NJ 08037
Tel (609) 561-3000 SIC 5033 5031

ENGLERT INC p 499
1200 Amboy Ave, Perth Amboy NJ 08861
Tel (800) 364-5378 SIC 3444 5033

S & J SHEET METAL SUPPLY INC p 1261
608 E 133rd St, Bronx NY 10454
Tel (718) 993-0460 SIC 5033 3444

EXTECH BUILDING MATERIALS INC p 521
87 Bowne St, Brooklyn NY 11231
Tel (718) 852-7090 SIC 5082 5033 5031

KAMCO SUPPLY CORP p 801
80 21st St, Brooklyn NY 11232
Tel (718) 840-1700 SIC 5031 5033

B & L WHOLESALE SUPPLY INC p 141
70 Hartford St, Buffalo NY 14206
Tel (716) 853-2600 SIC 5033 5031

ERIE MATERIALS INC p 508
500 Factory Ave, Syracuse NY 13208
Tel (315) 455-7434 SIC 5033 5031

S & K DISTRIBUTION LLC p 1261
535 Old Tarrytown Rd, White Plains NY 10603
Tel (914) 948-6363 SIC 5031 2952 5033

MUELLER ROOFING DISTRIBUTORS INC p 998
327 E Wyoming Ave, Cincinnati OH 45215
Tel (513) 679-8540 SIC 5033 5099

■ ALPINE INSULATION I LLC p 60
495 S High St Ste 50, Columbus OH 43215
Tel (614) 221-3399 SIC 5033 5211

▲ INSTALLED BUILDING PRODUCTS INC p 746
495 S High St Ste 50, Columbus OH 43215
Tel (614) 221-3399 SIC 1522 5033 5211

PALMER-DONAVIN MANUFACTURING CO p 1109
3210 Centerpoint Dr, Columbus OH 43212
Tel (614) 486-0975 SIC 5033

ASSOCIATED MATERIALS HOLDINGS LLC p 120
3773 State Rd, Cuyahoga Falls OH 44223
Tel (330) 929-1811
SIC 3089 5033 5031 5063 3442

ASSOCIATED MATERIALS LLC p 121
3773 State Rd, Cuyahoga Falls OH 44223
Tel (330) 929-1811
SIC 3089 5033 5031 3442

NORANDEX BUILDING MATERIALS DISTRIBUTION INC p 1047
300 Executive Park Ste 100, Hudson OH 44236
Tel (330) 656-8924 SIC 5033 5031

WILLOUGHBY SUPPLY CO p 1613
7433 Clover Ave, Mentor OH 44060
Tel (440) 942-7939 SIC 5033

SOPREMA INC p 1341
310 Quadral Dr, Wadsworth OH 44281
Tel (330) 334-0066 SIC 5033

NORTHWEST BUILDING SUPPLY INC p 1059
5535 Nw 5th St, Oklahoma City OK 73127
Tel (405) 946-0500 SIC 5033 5031 5211

DEGOL ORGANIZATION L P p 422
3229 Pleasant Valley Blvd, Altoona PA 16602
Tel (814) 941-7777
SIC 5031 5033 5211 5023 5713

CIESCO INC p 306
109 Miller Ln, Harrisburg PA 17110
Tel (717) 232-5825
SIC 5032 5033 5169 5039

SUPERIOR PLUS CONSTRUCTION PRODUCTS CORP p 1406
1650 Manheim Pike Ste 202, Lancaster PA 17601
Tel (717) 569-3900 SIC 5039 5033

NOVINGER GROUP INC p 1063
1441 Stoneridge Dr, Middletown PA 17057
Tel (717) 930-0300
SIC 1742 1799 5032 5033 5039

GUARDIAN BUILDING PRODUCTS DISTRIBUTION INC p 645
979 Batesville Rd Ste A, Greer SC 29651
Tel (800) 569-4262
SIC 5031 5033 5051 5032 5039 5023

■ BUILDERS FIRSTSOURCE-TEXAS GROUP LP p 225
3403 E Abram St, Arlington TX 76010
Tel (214) 880-3500 SIC 5031 5033 2439

ELKCORP p 488
14911 Quorum Dr Ste 600, Dallas TX 75254
Tel (972) 851-0500
SIC 2952 5033 2426 2431 3471

■ ROOFING SUPPLY GROUP LLC p 1249
3890 W Northwest Hwy # 400, Dallas TX 75220
Tel (214) 956-5100 SIC 5033

■ ROOFING SUPPLY GROUP-TUSCALOOSA LLC p 1249
3890 W Northwest Hwy # 400, Dallas TX 75220
Tel (214) 956-5100 SIC 5033

DW DISTRIBUTION INC p 463
1200 E Centre Park Blvd, Desoto TX 75115
Tel (214) 381-2200 SIC 5033 5031 5072

DISTRIBUTION INTERNATIONAL INC p 443
9000 Railwood Dr, Houston TX 77078
Tel (713) 428-3740 SIC 5033 5099

ENDURO COMPOSITES INC p 497
16602 Central Green Blvd, Houston TX 77032
Tel (713) 358-4000 SIC 5033

PRIMESOURCE BUILDING PRODUCTS INC p 1175
1321 Greenway Dr, Irving TX 75038
Tel (972) 999-8500 SIC 5033 5031

MOBLEY INDUSTRIAL SERVICES INC p 980
1220 Miller Cut Off Rd, La Porte TX 77571
Tel (281) 470-9120 SIC 1721 1799 5033

SRS DISTRIBUTION INC p 1363
5900 S Lake Forest Dr # 400, Mckinney TX 75070
Tel (214) 491-4149 SIC 5033

ROOFERS SUPPLY INC p 1249
3359 S 500 W, Salt Lake City UT 84115
Tel (801) 266-1311 SIC 5033

■ SERVICE PARTNERS LLC p 1307
1029 Technology Park Dr, Glen Allen VA 23059
Tel (804) 515-7400 SIC 5033

▲ BEACON ROOFING SUPPLY INC p 165
505 Huntmar Park Dr # 300, Herndon VA 20170
Tel (571) 323-3939 SIC 5033 5031

CAPITOL BUILDING SUPPLY INC p 251
8429 Euclid Ave, Manassas Park VA 20111
Tel (703) 631-6772
SIC 5032 5039 5033 5051

LANSING BUILDING PRODUCTS INC p 844
8501 Sanford Dr, Richmond VA 23228
Tel (804) 266-8893 SIC 5033 5031 5032

WACO INC p 1570
5450 Lewis Rd, Sandston VA 23150
Tel (804) 222-8440
SIC 1711 1799 3448 5033

RHEM LLC p 1231
700 Powell Ave Sw, Renton WA 98057
Tel (425) 228-4111 SIC 5033 3086 1742

AMERICAN BUILDERS & CONTRACTORS SUPPLY CO INC p 69
1 Abc Pkwy, Beloit WI 53511
Tel (608) 362-7777 SIC 5033 5031

MIDWEST MANUFACTURING INC p 967
5311 Kane Rd, Eau Claire WI 54703
Tel (715) 876-5555 SIC 5033 5031 3965

AWS/GB CORP p 139
2929 Walker Dr, Green Bay WI 54311
Tel (920) 406-4000
SIC 5031 2431 3442 5033 1542 1541

BAY INDUSTRIES INC p 161
2929 Walker Dr, Green Bay WI 54311
Tel (920) 406-4000 SIC 5031 5033

WAUSAU SUPPLY CO p 1583
7102 Commerce Dr, Schofield WI 54476
Tel (715) 359-2524 SIC 5033

SIC 5039 Construction Materials, NEC Wholesale

WALNUT INVESTMENT CORP p 1574
2940 E White Star Ave, Anaheim CA 92806
Tel (714) 238-9240 SIC 5031 5039 5072

NATIONAL BUSINESS GROUP INC p 1010
15319 Chatsworth St, Mission Hills CA 91345
Tel (818) 221-6000
SIC 7353 5039 7359 3496 7519

TEICHERT INC p 1433
3500 American River Dr, Sacramento CA 95864
Tel (916) 484-3011
SIC 3273 5032 1611 1442 1521 5039

LANDSCAPE DEVELOPMENT INC p 843
28447 Witherspoon Pkwy, Valencia CA 91355
Tel (661) 295-1970 SIC 0782 5039

CR LAURENCE CO INC p 388
2503 E Vernon Ave, Vernon CA 90058
Tel (323) 588-1281 SIC 3714 5072 5039

TEPA LLC p 1439
5045 List Dr, Colorado Springs CO 80919
Tel (719) 596-8114 SIC 5039

ATLAS HOLDINGS LLC p 128
100 Northfield St, Greenwich CT 06830
Tel (203) 622-9138
SIC 5031 2491 5039 5153

BRIDGEWELL RESOURCES HOLDINGS LLC p 212
1 Sound Shore Dr Ste 302, Greenwich CT 06830
Tel (203) 622-9138
SIC 5031 2491 5039 5153

DAVE CARTER & ASSOCIATES INC p 415
3530 Sw 7th St, Ocala FL 34474
Tel (352) 732-3317 SIC 5063 5039

FLORIDA A&G CO INC p 557
10200 Nw 67th St, Tamarac FL 33321
Tel (800) 432-8132 SIC 3442 5039

■ HD SUPPLY CONSTRUCTION SUPPLY GROUP INC p 673
3100 Cumberland Blvd Se, Atlanta GA 30339
Tel (770) 852-9000 SIC 5072 5039 5031

■ HD SUPPLY CONSTRUCTION SUPPLY LTD p 673
3100 Cumberland Blvd Se # 1700, Atlanta GA 30339
Tel (770) 852-9000 SIC 5031 5039 5072

■ WHITE CAP CONSTRUCTION SUPPLY INC p 1606
3100 Cumberland Blvd Se # 1700, Atlanta GA 30339
Tel (404) 879-7740 SIC 5072 5039 5031

▲ GMS INC p 619
100 Crescent Center Pkwy, Tucker GA 30084
Tel (800) 392-4619 SIC 3275 5031 5039

■ GSI GROUP LLC p 643
1004 E Illinois St, Assumption IL 62510
Tel (217) 226-4421 SIC 5039

GOLD STAR FS INC p 620
101 N East St, Cambridge IL 61238
Tel (309) 937-3369
SIC 5171 5153 5039 5191

MANKO WINDOW SYSTEMS INC p 902
800 Hayes Dr, Manhattan KS 66502
Tel (785) 776-9643 SIC 3442 1799 5039

WILLIAMS SCOTSMAN INC p 1611
901 S Bond St Ste 600, Baltimore MD 21231
Tel (410) 931-6000
SIC 1531 1541 5039 7359

KAMCO SUPPLY CORP OF BOSTON p 802
181 New Boston St, Woburn MA 01801
Tel (508) 587-1500
SIC 5032 5031 5039 5023 5033

■ HARMON INC p 662
7900 Xerxes Ave S # 1800, Bloomington MN 55431
Tel (952) 944-5700 SIC 5039

EASTERN WHOLESALE FENCE CO INC p 473
274 Middle Island Rd, Medford NY 11763
Tel (631) 698-0900
SIC 5039 5031 5051 3496

CEDAR CREEK CORP p 272
450 N Macarthur Blvd, Oklahoma City OK 73127
Tel (405) 917-8300 SIC 5039

BRIDGEWELL RESOURCES LLC p 212
10200 Sw Greenburg Rd # 500, Tigard OR 97223
Tel (503) 872-3566
SIC 5031 5039 5153 5159

CONSOLIDATED GLASS HOLDINGS INC p 359
500 Grant Ave Ste 201, East Butler PA 16029
Tel (866) 412-6977
SIC 5039 3211 6719 1793

CIESCO INC p 306
109 Miller Ln, Harrisburg PA 17110
Tel (717) 232-5825
SIC 5032 5033 5169 5039

SUPERIOR PLUS CONSTRUCTION PRODUCTS CORP p 1406
1650 Manheim Pike Ste 202, Lancaster PA 17601
Tel (717) 569-3900 SIC 5039 5033

NOVINGER GROUP INC p 1063
1441 Stoneridge Dr, Middletown PA 17057
Tel (717) 930-0300
SIC 1742 1799 5032 5033 5039

VELUX AMERICA LLC p 1547
450 Old Brickyard Rd, Greenwood SC 29649
Tel (864) 941-4700 SIC 5039

GUARDIAN BUILDING PRODUCTS DISTRIBUTION INC p 645
979 Batesville Rd Ste A, Greer SC 29651
Tel (800) 569-4262
SIC 5031 5033 5051 5032 5039 5023

VVP HOLDINGS LLC p 1567
965 Ridge Lake Blvd # 300, Memphis TN 38120
Tel (901) 767-7111
SIC 5039 5013 1793 3231 3444 5719

MUELLER SUPPLY CO INC p 998
1913 Hutchins Ave, Ballinger TX 76821
Tel (325) 365-3555 SIC 3448 3496 5039

JAMIESON MANUFACTURING CO p 777
4221 Platinum Way, Dallas TX 75237
Tel (214) 339-8384 SIC 5039 2499

KING SUPPLY CO LLC p 820
9611 E R L Thornton Fwy, Dallas TX 75228
Tel (214) 388-9834 SIC 5039 5051

MASTER-HALCO INC p 918
3010 Lbj Fwy Ste 800, Dallas TX 75234
Tel (972) 714-7300
SIC 3315 5039 3496 3446 5031 1799

GICON PUMPS & EQUIPMENT INC p 611
1001 Texas Ave, Lubbock TX 79401
Tel (806) 401-8287 SIC 5084 5074 5039

DOE FL SMIDTH p 447
7158 Fl Smidth Dr, Midvale UT 84047
Tel (801) 526-2500 SIC 5039

MORRELL INTERNATIONAL INC p 990
14901 S Heritagecrest Way, Riverton UT 84065
Tel (801) 495-3111 SIC 4213 4226 5039

CAPITOL BUILDING SUPPLY INC p 251
8429 Euclid Ave, Manassas Park VA 20111
Tel (703) 631-6772
SIC 5032 5039 5033 5051

PENROD CO p 1131
272 Bendix Rd Ste 550, Virginia Beach VA 23452
Tel (757) 498-0186 SIC 3429 5039 2821

SIMEX INC p 1324
181 Pleasant Indus Ctr, Saint Marys WV 26170
Tel (304) 665-1104 SIC 5039 2431

BLAIN SUPPLY INC p 188
3507 E Racine St, Janesville WI 53546
Tel (608) 754-2821
SIC 5083 5072 5039 5013 5023 5198

FARM & FLEET OF MADISON INC p 528
3507 E Racine St, Janesville WI 53546
Tel (608) 754-2821
SIC 5199 5531 5251 5261 5039

SIC 5043 Photographic Eqpt & Splys Wholesale

NORITSU AMERICA CORP p 1048
6900 Noritsu Ave, Buena Park CA 90620
Tel (714) 521-9040 SIC 5043

CHRISTIE DIGITAL SYSTEMS USA INC p 303
10550 Camden Dr, Cypress CA 90630
Tel (714) 527-7056 SIC 5043

JK IMAGING LTD p 786
17239 S Main St, Gardena CA 90248
Tel (310) 755-6848 SIC 5043

■ KYOCERA INTERNATIONAL INC p 833
8611 Balboa Ave, San Diego CA 92123
Tel (858) 576-2600 SIC 5043

■ VIKING OFFICE PRODUCTS INC p 1557
3366 E Willow St, Signal Hill CA 90755
Tel (562) 490-1000
SIC 5112 5021 5045 5087 5043 5961

FUJIFILM MEDICAL SYSTEMS USA INC p 583
419 West Ave, Stamford CT 06902
Tel (203) 324-2000 SIC 5047 5043 3861

VA CELL INC p 1538
8400 Nw 33rd St Ste 103, Doral FL 33122
Tel (305) 592-1367 SIC 5065 5043

LEXJET LLC p 860
1605 Main St Ste 400, Sarasota FL 34236
Tel (941) 330-1210
SIC 5045 5112 5111 2672 5043

AUDIO VISUAL INNOVATIONS INC p 130
6301 Benjamin Rd Ste 101, Tampa FL 33634
Tel (813) 884-7168
SIC 3669 5064 3861 3663 3651 5043

AVI-SPL EMPLOYEE EMERGENCY RELIEF FUND INC p 137
6301 Benjamin Rd Ste 101, Tampa FL 33634
Tel (813) 884-7168
SIC 3669 3861 3663 3651 5043 5064

HEARTLAND IMAGING COMPANIES INC p 679
1211 W Cambridge Cir Dr, Kansas City KS 66103
Tel (913) 621-1211 SIC 5043

DISTRICT PHOTO INC p 443
10501 Rhode Island Ave, Beltsville MD 20705
Tel (301) 595-5300 SIC 7384 5043 5946

TIERNEY BROTHERS INC p 1453
1771 Energy Park Dr, Saint Paul MN 55108
Tel (612) 331-5500 SIC 5049 5043 3651

LEICA CAMERA INC p 854
1 Pearl Ct Unit A, Allendale NJ 07401
Tel (201) 995-0051 SIC 5043

SAKAR INTERNATIONAL INC p 1271
195 Carter Dr, Edison NJ 08817
Tel (732) 248-1306 SIC 5043

KONICA MINOLTA HOLDINGS USA INC p 827
100 Williams Dr, Ramsey NJ 07446
Tel (201) 825-4000
SIC 5043 5065 5044 5047

SAMSUNG OPTO-ELECTRONICS AMERICA INC p 1275
100 Challenger Rd Ste 700, Ridgefield Park NJ 07660
Tel (201) 325-2612 SIC 5043 7699 3861

VALOR GROUP LLC p 1542
245 Belmont Dr, Somerset NJ 08873
Tel (732) 357-2426 SIC 5043

RICOH AMERICAS HOLDINGS INC p 1233
5 Dedrick Pl, West Caldwell NJ 07006
Tel (973) 882-2000 SIC 5044 5065 5043

CANON USA INC p 247
1 Canon Park, Melville NY 11747
Tel (516) 328-5000
SIC 5044 5065 5045 3861 3577 5043

NIKON AMERICAS INC p 1043
1300 Walt Whitman Rd Fl 2, Melville NY 11747
Tel (631) 547-4200 SIC 5043 5084

NIKON INC p 1043
1300 Walt Whitman Rd Fl 2, Melville NY 11747
Tel (631) 547-4200 SIC 5043 5049

FUJIFILM HOLDINGS AMERICA CORP p 583
200 Summit Lake Dr Fl 2, Valhalla NY 10595
Tel (914) 789-8100 SIC 5043 5065

FUJIFILM NORTH AMERICA CORP p 583
200 Summit Lake Dr Fl 2, Valhalla NY 10595
Tel (914) 789-8100
SIC 7384 5043 5065 3695 2673 3861

COMP-VIEW INC p 350
10035 Sw Arctic Dr, Beaverton OR 97005
Tel (503) 641-8439 SIC 5043

OLYMPUS AMERICA INC p 1083
3500 Corporate Pkwy, Center Valley PA 18034
Tel (484) 896-5000
SIC 5047 5043 5064 3827 3695 3572

OLYMPUS CORP OF AMERICAS p 1083
3500 Corp Pkwy, Center Valley PA 18034
Tel (484) 896-5000
SIC 5047 5043 5064 3827 3695 3572

RICOH AMERICAS CORP p 1233
70 Valley Stream Pkwy, Malvern PA 19355
Tel (610) 296-8000
SIC 5044 5065 5045 5043 3861 3661

THIELSCH ENGINEERING INC p 1448
195 Frances Ave, Cranston RI 02910
Tel (401) 785-0241
SIC 5084 5043 5172 5085

FUJIFILM ELECTRONIC MATERIALS USA INC p 583
80 Circuit Dr, North Kingstown RI 02852
Tel (401) 522-9499 SIC 5043 5065

WYNIT DISTRIBUTION LLC p 1630
2 W Washington St Ste 500, Greenville SC 29601
Tel (864) 605-9920
SIC 5045 5043 5046 5199 7372

SIC 5044 Office Eqpt Wholesale

CAPITOL BUSINESS EQUIPMENT INC p 251
645 S Mcdonough St, Montgomery AL 36104
Tel (334) 265-8903
SIC 5045 5044 7699 5065

ARCTIC OFFICE MACHINE INC p 106
100 W Fireweed Ln, Anchorage AK 99503
Tel (907) 276-2295
SIC 5112 5021 5044 7629

SWEDA CO LLC p 1411
17411 E Valley Blvd, City Of Industry CA 91744
Tel (626) 357-9999 SIC 5094 5044

MITSUBISHI KAGAKU IMAGING CORP p 978
655 N Central Ave # 1550, Glendale CA 91203
Tel (818) 837-8100 SIC 5044 3699

HAWAII BUSINESS EQUIPMENT INC p 668
2 Musick, Irvine CA 92618
Tel (949) 462-6000 SIC 5999 7629 5044

TOPAC USA INC p 1460
9740 Irvine Blvd, Irvine CA 92618
Tel (949) 462-6000 SIC 5044

TOSHIBA AMERICA BUSINESS SOLUTIONS INC p 1462
9740 Irvine Blvd, Irvine CA 92618
Tel (949) 462-6000 SIC 5044

TOSHIBA BUSINESS SOLUTIONS (USA) INC p 1462
9740 Irvine Blvd, Irvine CA 92618
Tel (949) 462-6000 SIC 7629 5044 5999

■ MR COPY INC p 996
5657 Copley Dr, San Diego CA 92111
Tel (858) 573-6300 SIC 5044

ALL COPY PRODUCTS INC p 51
4141 Colorado Blvd, Denver CO 80216
Tel (303) 373-1105 SIC 5044 5112 7371

■ DGPM INVESTMENTS INC p 435
300 E River Dr, East Hartford CT 06108
Tel (860) 528-9981
SIC 5044 5021 5713 1752

OCE-USA HOLDING INC p 1072
100 Oakview Dr, Trumbull CT 06611
Tel (773) 714-8500 SIC 3861 5044

▲ OFFICE DEPOT INC p 1075
6600 N Military Trl, Boca Raton FL 33496
Tel (561) 438-4800
SIC 5943 5044 5734 5045

ELANDIA INTERNATIONAL INC p 483
8333 Nw 53rd St Ste 400, Miami FL 33166
Tel (305) 415-8830
SIC 4813 4899 7371 5044

DEX IMAGING INC p 434
5109 W Lemon St, Tampa FL 33609
Tel (813) 288-8080 SIC 5044

■ GLOBAL IMAGING SYSTEMS INC p 616
3903 Northdale Blvd 200w, Tampa FL 33624
Tel (813) 960-5508 SIC 5044 5045 7629

APTOS INC p 101
945 E Paces Ferry Rd Ne, Atlanta GA 30326
Tel (866) 493-7037
SIC 5044 5045 7378 7699

MILNER INC p 972
5125 Peachtree Indus Blvd, Norcross GA 30092
Tel (770) 458-0999
SIC 7372 5999 7389 5065 5049 5044

LANIER WORLDWIDE INC p 844
4667 N Royal Atlanta Dr, Tucker GA 30084
Tel (770) 493-2100
SIC 5044 5999 7359 7629

■ CHICAGO OFFICE TECHNOLOGY GROUP INC p 297
3 Territorial Ct, Bolingbrook IL 60440
Tel (630) 378-9339 SIC 5044 5112

▲ ESSENDANT INC p 510
1 Parkway North Blvd # 100, Deerfield IL 60015
Tel (847) 627-7000
SIC 5112 5111 5021 5044 5087 5045

OMRON MANAGEMENT CENTER OF AMERICA INC p 1085
2895 Greenspoint Pkwy # 100, Hoffman Estates IL 60169
Tel (224) 520-7650
SIC 5044 5046 5065 5047 5045 8732

GENERAL BINDING CORP p 599
4 Corporate Dr, Lake Zurich IL 60047
Tel (847) 541-9500
SIC 5044 2782 3559 3589 7629 3579

GLORY GLOBAL SOLUTIONS INC p 618
3333 Warrenville Rd # 310, Lisle IL 60532
Tel (920) 262-3300 SIC 5087 5046 5044

■ OFFICEMAX CONTRACT INC p 1076
263 Shuman Blvd, Naperville IL 60563
Tel (630) 438-7800
SIC 5021 5112 5044 5111 5943 5712

CDS OFFICE SYSTEMS INC p 271
612 S Dirksen Pkwy, Springfield IL 62703
Tel (800) 367-1508
SIC 5044 5999 7629 7378 3861 3577

PROVEN BUSINESS SYSTEMS LLC p 1185
18450 Crossing Dr Ste D, Tinley Park IL 60487
Tel (708) 614-1770 SIC 5044 5999

FKI SECURITY GROUP LLC p 554
101 Security Pkwy, New Albany IN 47150
Tel (812) 948-8400
SIC 2522 5044 3499 3429

ADAMS REMCO INC p 21
2612 Foundation Dr, South Bend IN 46628
Tel (574) 288-2113 SIC 5044 7629 8243

■ R K DIXON CO p 1202
5700 Utica Ridge Rd, Davenport IA 52807
Tel (563) 344-9100 SIC 5044 7629 7359

ADVANCE BUSINESS SYSTEMS & SUPPLY CO p 24
10755 York Rd, Cockeysville MD 21030
Tel (410) 252-4800 SIC 5044

■ STAPLES INTERNATIONAL INC p 1378
500 Staples Dr, Framingham MA 01702
Tel (508) 253-5000
SIC 5943 5712 5044 5021 5112

LOWRY HOLDING CO INC p 882
9420 Maltby Rd, Brighton MI 48116
Tel (810) 229-7200
SIC 5045 2672 8742 7373 5044 5734

■ MICHIGAN OFFICE SOLUTIONS INC p 961
2859 Walkent Dr Nw, Grand Rapids MI 49544
Tel (616) 459-1161 SIC 5044 5045 7629

BORROUGHS CORP p 201
3002 N Burdick St, Kalamazoo MI 49004
Tel (800) 748-0227 SIC 5044

METRO SALES INC p 955
1640 E 78th St, Minneapolis MN 55423
Tel (612) 861-4000
SIC 5044 5112 5065 7359

INDOFF INC p 739
11816 Lackland Rd Ste 200, Saint Louis MO 63146
Tel (314) 997-1122 SIC 5021 5044 5084

SUMNER GROUP INC p 1399
6717 Waldemar Ave, Saint Louis MO 63139
Tel (314) 633-8000 SIC 5044 7699 5112

DATA SYSTEMS INC p 414
6515 S 118th St Ste 100, Omaha NE 68137
Tel (402) 597-6477 SIC 5044

■ CONWAY TECHNOLOGY GROUP LLC p 365
10 Capitol St, Nashua NH 03063
Tel (603) 889-1665
SIC 5044 5065 7699 7359

BROTHER INTERNATIONAL CORP p 219
200 Crossing Blvd, Bridgewater NJ 08807
Tel (908) 704-1700
SIC 5044 3579 3559 5084 5064 5065

CASIO AMERICA INC p 263
570 Mount Pleasant Ave, Dover NJ 07801
Tel (973) 361-5400
SIC 5044 5045 5094 5099

CASIO HOLDINGS INC p 263
570 Mount Pleasant Ave, Dover NJ 07801
Tel (973) 361-5400 SIC 5044

■ KYOCERA DOCUMENT SOLUTIONS AMERICA INC p 833
225 Sand Rd, Fairfield NJ 07004
Tel (973) 808-8444 SIC 5044 5084 5065

SHARP ELECTRONICS CORP p 1312
1 Sharp Plz Ste 1, Mahwah NJ 07495
Tel (201) 529-8200
SIC 5044 5064 3651 3631 3861 3674

PANASONIC CORP OF NORTH AMERICA p 1111
2 Riverfront Plz Ste 200, Newark NJ 07102
Tel (201) 348-7000
SIC 5064 5045 5065 5044 5084 5063

KONICA MINOLTA BUSINESS SOLUTIONS USA INC p 827
100 Williams Dr, Ramsey NJ 07446
Tel (201) 825-4000 SIC 5044 5045

KONICA MINOLTA HOLDINGS USA INC p 827
100 Williams Dr, Ramsey NJ 07446
Tel (201) 825-4000
SIC 5043 5065 5044 5047

RICOH AMERICAS HOLDINGS INC p 1233
5 Dedrick Pl, West Caldwell NJ 07006
Tel (973) 882-2000 SIC 5044 5065 5043

Section III Businesses by Industry Classification

■ CARR BUSINESS SYSTEMS INC p 260
500 Commack Rd Unit 110, Commack NY 11725
Tel (631) 249-9880 SIC 5044 7699

WEEKS-LERMAN GROUP LLC p 1587
5838 Page Pl, Maspeth NY 11378
Tel (718) 803-4700
SIC 5112 5021 2752 5044

CANON USA INC p 247
1 Canon Park, Melville NY 11747
Tel (516) 328-5000
SIC 5044 5065 5045 3861 3577 5043

AMERICAN PRODUCT DISTRIBUTORS INC p 78
8350 Arrowridge Blvd, Charlotte NC 28273
Tel (704) 522-9411
SIC 5111 5112 5047 5044 5085 5087

CAROLINA WHOLESALE GROUP INC p 259
425 E Arrowhead Dr, Charlotte NC 28213
Tel (704) 598-8101 SIC 5044

PACIFIC OFFICE AUTOMATION INC p 1105
14747 Nw Greenbrier Pkwy, Beaverton OR 97006
Tel (503) 641-2000 SIC 5044

D & H DISTRIBUTING CO p 406
2525 N 7th St, Harrisburg PA 17110
Tel (717) 236-8001
SIC 5045 5065 5064 5063 5044

DATABANK IMX LLC p 414
620 Freedom Business Ctr, King Of Prussia PA 19406
Tel (610) 233-0251 SIC 7374 5044

RICOH AMERICAS CORP p 1233
70 Valley Stream Pkwy, Malvern PA 19355
Tel (610) 296-8000
SIC 5044 5065 5045 5043 3861 3661

RICOH USA INC p 1233
70 Valley Stream Pkwy, Malvern PA 19355
Tel (610) 296-8000
SIC 5044 5065 7359 5112 7334 6159

A-Z OFFICE RESOURCE INC p 7
809 S Garden St, Columbia TN 38401
Tel (931) 388-1536
SIC 5112 5021 5044 5045 5087

■ CONCORD EFS INC p 354
7000 Goodlett Farms Pkwy # 300, Cordova TN 38016
Tel (901) 371-8000
SIC 6099 7389 6091 5044

ROBERT J YOUNG CO INC p 1241
809 Division St, Nashville TN 37203
Tel (615) 255-8551 SIC 5044

LES OLSON CO p 857
3244 S 300 W, Salt Lake City UT 84115
Tel (435) 586-2345 SIC 5044

SYMQUEST GROUP INC p 1414
30 Community Dr Ste 5, South Burlington VT 05403
Tel (802) 658-9890 SIC 5044 8243

GIESECKE & DEVRIENT AMERICA INC p 611
45925 Horseshoe Dr # 100, Dulles VA 20166
Tel (703) 480-2000 SIC 2672 5044

MILLERS SUPPLIES AT WORK INC p 971
8600 Cinder Bed Rd, Lorton VA 22079
Tel (703) 644-2200 SIC 5112 5044 5021

AUDIO FIDELITY COMMUNICATIONS CORP p 130
12820 West Creek Pkwy, Richmond VA 23238
Tel (804) 273-9100 SIC 5044 5065

ALVAREZ LLC p 63
8251 Greensboro Dr # 230, Tysons Corner VA 22102
Tel (301) 830-4020
SIC 8742 8741 7379 5044

■ ELECTRONIC SYSTEMS INC p 486
369 Edwin Dr, Virginia Beach VA 23462
Tel (757) 497-8000 SIC 5044

DOUGLAS STEWART CO INC p 452
2402 Advance Rd, Madison WI 53718
Tel (608) 221-1155 SIC 5045 5044 5049

PNA HOLDINGS LLC p 1158
3150 Pleasant View Rd, Madison WI 53713
Tel (608) 203-1500
SIC 5044 5045 5112 7699

SIC 5045 Computers & Peripheral Eqpt & Software Wholesale

COMMAND ALKON INC p 344
1800 Intl Pk Dr Ste 400, Birmingham AL 35243
Tel (205) 879-3282 SIC 7371 5045

CAPITOL BUSINESS EQUIPMENT INC p 251
645 S Mcdonough St, Montgomery AL 36104
Tel (334) 265-8903
SIC 5045 5044 7699 5065

MITEL (DELAWARE) INC p 977
1146 N Alma School Rd, Mesa AZ 85201
Tel (480) 449-8900
SIC 3661 5045 4813 5065 1731 7359

▲ AVNET INC p 138
2211 S 47th St, Phoenix AZ 85034
Tel (480) 643-2000 SIC 5065 5045 7379

■ INSIGHT DIRECT USA INC p 746
201 N Central Ave, Phoenix AZ 85004
Tel (480) 333-3000 SIC 5045 3571

▲ INSIGHT ENTERPRISES INC p 746
201 N Central Ave, Phoenix AZ 85004
Tel (480) 333-3000 SIC 5045 7379 5065

GLOBAL AGGREGATE LLC p 615
8901 E Mountain View Rd, Scottsdale AZ 85258
Tel (480) 414-9400 SIC 6798 7389 5045

ARTESYN EMBEDDED TECHNOLOGIES INC p 114
2900 S Diablo Way Ste 190, Tempe AZ 85282
Tel (800) 759-1107
SIC 3679 3577 3571 7629 5045

E RITTER COMMUNICATIONS HOLDINGS INC p 467
2400 Ritter Dr, Jonesboro AR 72401
Tel (870) 336-3434 SIC 4813 4812 5045

TP-LINK USA CORP p 1467
145 S State College Blvd # 400, Brea CA 92821
Tel (626) 333-0234 SIC 5045

DATA EXCHANGE CORP p 413
3600 Via Pescador, Camarillo CA 93012
Tel (805) 388-1711 SIC 5045 7378

GROUPWARE TECHNOLOGY INC p 642
541 Division St, Campbell CA 95008
Tel (408) 540-0090 SIC 7373 5045

GOLDEN STAR TECHNOLOGY INC p 621
12881 166th St Ste 100, Cerritos CA 90703
Tel (562) 345-8700 SIC 5734 7378 5045

SEGA HOLDINGS USA INC p 1300
9737 Lurline Ave, Chatsworth CA 91311
Tel (415) 701-6000 SIC 3999 5045

AMERICAN FUTURE TECHNOLOGY CORP p 73
529 Baldwin Park Blvd, City Of Industry CA 91746
Tel (888) 462-3899 SIC 5045

CYBERPOWER INC p 405
730 Baldwin Park Blvd, City Of Industry CA 91746
Tel (626) 813-7730 SIC 5045

MAGNELL ASSOCIATE INC p 896
17560 Rowland St, City Of Industry CA 91748
Tel (562) 695-8823 SIC 5045

MAX GROUP CORP p 922
17011 Green Dr, City Of Industry CA 91745
Tel (626) 935-0050 SIC 5045

MTC DIRECT INC p 997
17837 Rowland St, City Of Industry CA 91748
Tel (626) 839-6800 SIC 5045

INSIGHT INVESTMENTS CORP p 746
611 Anton Blvd Ste 700, Costa Mesa CA 92626
Tel (714) 939-2300 SIC 7377 5045

INSIGHT INVESTMENTS LLC p 746
611 Anton Blvd Ste 700, Costa Mesa CA 92626
Tel (714) 939-2300 SIC 7377 5045

SYSPRO IMPACT SOFTWARE INC p 1418
959 S Coast Dr Ste 100, Costa Mesa CA 92626
Tel (714) 437-1000 SIC 5045 7372 7371

COMPUTER CONSULTING OPERATIONS SPECIALISTS INC p 352
600 Corporate Pointe # 1010, Culver City CA 90230
Tel (310) 568-5000
SIC 4813 4899 5045 7378

MITSUBISHI ELECTRIC US HOLDINGS INC p 977
5900 Katella Ave Ste A, Cypress CA 90630
Tel (714) 220-2500
SIC 5065 5045 3651 3663

MITSUBISHI ELECTRIC US INC p 977
5900 Katella Ave Ste A, Cypress CA 90630
Tel (714) 220-2500
SIC 5065 5045 1796 3534

▲ PCM INC p 1124
1940 E Mariposa Ave, El Segundo CA 90245
Tel (310) 354-5600
SIC 5734 5961 5731 5045

SQUARE ENIX OF AMERICA HOLDINGS INC p 1362
999 N Sepulveda Blvd Fl 3, El Segundo CA 90245
Tel (310) 846-0400 SIC 5045

D-LINK SYSTEMS INC p 407
17595 Mount Herrmann St, Fountain Valley CA 92708
Tel (714) 885-6000 SIC 5045 3577

ACCESS INTERNATIONAL CO p 15
45630 Northport Loop E, Fremont CA 94538
Tel (510) 226-1000 SIC 5045

AMAX ENGINEERING CORP p 64
1565 Reliance Way, Fremont CA 94539
Tel (510) 651-8886 SIC 5045

ASI COMPUTER TECHNOLOGIES INC p 117
48289 Fremont Blvd, Fremont CA 94538
Tel (510) 226-8000 SIC 5045 3577

ASUS COMPUTER INTERNATIONAL INC p 123
800 Corp Way, Fremont CA 94539
Tel (510) 739-3777 SIC 5045 3577

DELTA PRODUCTS CORP p 427
46101 Fremont Blvd, Fremont CA 94538
Tel (510) 668-5100
SIC 5065 5045 8741 5063 3577

PENGUIN COMPUTING INC p 1128
45800 Northport Loop W, Fremont CA 94538
Tel (415) 954-2800 SIC 5045 7379

PHIHONG USA CORP p 1142
47800 Fremont Blvd, Fremont CA 94538
Tel (510) 445-0100 SIC 5045 3572

QUANTA COMPUTER USA INC p 1198
45630 Northport Loop E, Fremont CA 94538
Tel (510) 226-1371 SIC 5045

QUANTA SERVICE INCORPORATION p 1198
45630 Northport Loop E, Fremont CA 94538
Tel (510) 226-1000 SIC 5045

ARBITECH LLC p 102
15330 Barranca Pkwy, Irvine CA 92618
Tel (949) 376-6650 SIC 5045

■ INGRAM MICRO INC p 743
3351 Michelson Dr Ste 100, Irvine CA 92612
Tel (714) 566-1000 SIC 5045

ROLAND DGA CORP p 1247
15363 Barranca Pkwy, Irvine CA 92618
Tel (949) 727-2100 SIC 5045 8741

THOMAS GALLAWAY CORP p 1448
100 Spectrum Center Dr # 700, Irvine CA 92618
Tel (949) 716-9500 SIC 7371 5045

WONDERWARE CORP p 1622
26561 Rancho Pkwy S, Lake Forest CA 92630
Tel (949) 727-3200 SIC 5045

LD PRODUCTS INC p 849
3700 Cover St, Long Beach CA 90808
Tel (562) 986-6940 SIC 5045 2621

US EPSON INC p 1531
3840 Kilroy Airport Way, Long Beach CA 90806
Tel (562) 290-5678 SIC 5045 3577

ROLAND CORP US p 1247
5100 S Eastern Ave, Los Angeles CA 90040
Tel (323) 890-3700 SIC 5099 5045 3931

ADVANTECH CORP p 27
380 Fairview Way, Milpitas CA 95035
Tel (408) 519-3800 SIC 5045 7379

CREATIVE HOLDINGS INC p 390
1901 Mccarthy Blvd, Milpitas CA 95035
Tel (408) 428-6600
SIC 5045 3577 3931 3674 8711 3651

CREATIVE LABS INC p 390
1901 Mccarthy Blvd, Milpitas CA 95035
Tel (408) 428-6600 SIC 5045 5734 3577

SIGMANET INC p 1321
4290 E Brickell St, Ontario CA 91761
Tel (909) 230-7500 SIC 5045 7373

BUSINESS OBJECTS INC p 229
3410 Hillview Ave, Palo Alto CA 94304
Tel (650) 849-4000 SIC 5045

INTEGRATED ARCHIVE SYSTEMS INC p 749
1121 San Antonio Rd D100, Palo Alto CA 94303
Tel (650) 390-9995 SIC 8742 5045

IDEALAB HOLDINGS LLC p 729
130 W Union St, Pasadena CA 91103
Tel (626) 585-6900 SIC 6799 5045 5734

BELKIN INTERNATIONAL INC p 169
12045 Waterfront Dr, Playa Vista CA 90094
Tel (310) 751-5100 SIC 5065 5045

ENVIRONMENTAL SYSTEMS RESEARCH INSTITUTE INC p 503
380 New York St, Redlands CA 92373
Tel (909) 793-2853 SIC 5045

I2C INC p 725
1300 Island Dr Ste 105, Redwood City CA 94065
Tel (650) 480-5222 SIC 5045

HITACHI SOLUTIONS AMERICA LTD p 697
851 Traeger Ave Ste 200, San Bruno CA 94066
Tel (650) 615-7600 SIC 5045 7372 7373

ABF DATA SYSTEMS INC p 11
9020 Kenamar Dr Ste 201, San Diego CA 92121
Tel (858) 547-8300 SIC 5045 7377

BLUE TECH INC p 192
4025 Hancock St Ste 100, San Diego CA 92110
Tel (619) 497-6060 SIC 5045

BROADWAY TYPEWRITER CO INC p 216
1055 6th Ave Ste 101, San Diego CA 92101
Tel (619) 645-0253 SIC 5045 7378

NTH GENERATION COMPUTING INC p 1065
17055 Camino San Bernardo, San Diego CA 92127
Tel (858) 451-2383 SIC 5045

PC SPECIALISTS INC p 1123
10240 Flanders Ct, San Diego CA 92121
Tel (858) 566-1900 SIC 5045 5734 7371

INSIDEVIEW TECHNOLOGIES INC p 745
444 De Haro St Ste 210, San Francisco CA 94107
Tel (415) 728-9309 SIC 5045

■ OLD REPUBLIC TITLE HOLDING CO INC p 1081
275 Battery St Ste 1500, San Francisco CA 94111
Tel (415) 421-3500 SIC 6361 6531 5045

RIVERBED TECHNOLOGY INC p 1237
680 Folsom St Ste 500, San Francisco CA 94107
Tel (415) 247-8800 SIC 3577 5045

SEGA OF AMERICA INC p 1300
350 Rhode Island St # 400, San Francisco CA 94103
Tel (415) 701-6000 SIC 5045 5092

MA LABORATORIES INC p 891
2075 N Capitol Ave, San Jose CA 95132
Tel (408) 941-0808 SIC 5045

SAMSUNG SEMICONDUCTOR INC p 1275
3655 N 1st St, San Jose CA 95134
Tel (408) 544-4000 SIC 5065 5045

SK HYNIX AMERICA INC p 1328
3101 N 1st St, San Jose CA 95134
Tel (408) 232-8000 SIC 5065 5045

SUPER TALENT TECHNOLOGY CORP p 1406
2077 N Capitol Ave, San Jose CA 95132
Tel (408) 957-8133 SIC 5045

GENERAL PROCUREMENT INC p 601
800 E Dyer Rd, Santa Ana CA 92705
Tel (949) 679-7960 SIC 5045

NHR NEWCO HOLDINGS LLC p 1042
6500 Hollister Ave # 210, Santa Barbara CA 93117
Tel (800) 230-6638 SIC 5045 5065 7379

ALPS ELECTRIC (NORTH AMERICA) INC p 61
3151 Jay St Ste 101, Santa Clara CA 95054
Tel (408) 361-6400 SIC 5045 5065 5013

CMT HOLDINGS INC p 329
590 Laurelwood Rd, Santa Clara CA 95054
Tel (408) 734-3339 SIC 5045

HITACHI DATA SYSTEMS CORP p 696
2845 Lafayette St, Santa Clara CA 95050
Tel (408) 970-1000
SIC 5045 7378 7379 5734 4225 3571

RENESAS ELECTRONICS AMERICA INC p 1223
2801 Scott Blvd, Santa Clara CA 95050
Tel (408) 588-6000
SIC 5065 8731 5731 5045 8711

■ WYSE TECHNOLOGY LLC p 1630
5455 Great America Pkwy, Santa Clara CA 95054
Tel (800) 438-9973 SIC 5045

SWANN COMMUNICATIONS USA INC p 1411
12636 Clark St, Santa Fe Springs CA 90670
Tel (562) 777-2551 SIC 5045 7382

■ VIKING OFFICE PRODUCTS INC p 1557
3366 E Willow St, Signal Hill CA 90755
Tel (562) 490-1000
SIC 5112 5021 5045 5087 5043 5961

FUJITSU COMPUTER PRODUCTS OF AMERICA INC p 584
1250 E Arques Ave, Sunnyvale CA 94085
Tel (408) 746-6000 SIC 5045

ELECTRO RENT CORP p 485
6060 Sepulveda Blvd # 300, Van Nuys CA 91411
Tel (818) 786-2525
SIC 7359 7377 5065 5045

CHG-MERIDIAN US HOLDING INC p 296
21800 Oxnard St Ste 400, Woodland Hills CA 91367
Tel (818) 702-1800
SIC 7377 6159 5045 7378

COUNTERTRADE PRODUCTS INC p 375
7585 W 66th Ave, Arvada CO 80003
Tel (303) 424-7015 SIC 5045

■ MCDATA CORP p 927
4 Brocade Pkwy, Broomfield CO 80021
Tel (720) 558-8000
SIC 3679 5045 3825 3577

▲ ARROW ELECTRONICS INC p 113
9201 E Dry Creek Rd, Centennial CO 80112
Tel (303) 824-4000 SIC 5065 5045

OPTIV INC p 1090
1125 17th St Ste 1700, Denver CO 80202
Tel (303) 298-0600
SIC 5045 5065 6719 7381

OPTIV SECURITY INC p 1090
1125 17th St Ste 1700, Denver CO 80202
Tel (888) 732-9406
SIC 5045 7379 7382 5065

■ ARROW ENTERPRISE COMPUTING SOLUTIONS INC p 113
7459 S Lima St Bldg 2, Englewood CO 80112
Tel (303) 824-7650 SIC 5045

■ STARTEK USA INC p 1379
8200 E Maplewood Ave # 100, Greenwood Village CO 80111
Tel (303) 262-4150 SIC 7372 7379 5045

CARDNO USA INC p 253
10004 Park Meadows Dr # 300, Lone Tree CO 80124
Tel (720) 257-5800 SIC 8711 5045 8748

KELSER CORP p 809
111 Roberts St Ste D, East Hartford CT 06108
Tel (860) 610-2200 SIC 5045

RADIO FREQUENCY SYSTEMS INC p 1204
200 Pond View Dr, Meriden CT 06450
Tel (203) 630-3311
SIC 3663 3661 5045 5065

FLO-TECH LLC p 557
699 Middle St, Middletown CT 06457
Tel (860) 613-3333 SIC 5045 3577

SURESOURCE LLC p 1408
20 Constitution Blvd S, Shelton CT 06484
Tel (203) 922-7500 SIC 5045

METRO BUSINESS SYSTEMS INC p 954
11 Largo Dr S, Stamford CT 06907
Tel (203) 967-3435 SIC 5045

MTM TECHNOLOGIES INC p 998
4 High Ridge Park Ste 102, Stamford CT 06905
Tel (203) 588-1981 SIC 5045 7379

■ 4 SURE.COM INC p 3
55 Corporate Dr Ste 5, Trumbull CT 06611
Tel (203) 615-7000 SIC 5045 5734

AUGUST TECHNIC CORP CO p 131
8 The Grn Ste 4934, Dover DE 19901
Tel (302) 223-5215 SIC 5065 5045 7389

CANON FINANCIAL SERVICES INC p 247
5600 Broken Sound Blvd Nw, Boca Raton FL 33487
Tel (561) 997-3100 SIC 5045

CHAMPION SOLUTIONS GROUP INC p 287
791 Park Of Commerce Blvd, Boca Raton FL 33487
Tel (800) 771-7000 SIC 5045 5734

■ MOREDIRECT INC p 988
1001 Yamato Rd Ste 200, Boca Raton FL 33431
Tel (561) 237-3300 SIC 5045 7373 7376

▲ OFFICE DEPOT INC p 1075
6600 N Military Trl, Boca Raton FL 33496
Tel (561) 438-4800
SIC 5943 5044 5734 5045

▲ TECH DATA CORP p 1430
5350 Tech Data Dr, Clearwater FL 33760
Tel (727) 539-7429 SIC 5045

■ TECH DATA PRODUCT MANAGEMENT INC p 1430
5350 Tech Data Dr, Clearwater FL 33760
Tel (727) 539-7429 SIC 5045

ALLPLUS COMPUTER SYSTEMS CORP p 58
3075 Nw 107th Ave, Doral FL 33172
Tel (305) 436-3993 SIC 5065 5045

■ INTCOMEX INC p 748
3505 Nw 107th Ave Ste 1, Doral FL 33178
Tel (305) 477-6230 SIC 7371 5045

■ SOFTWARE BROKERS OF AMERICA INC p 1337
3505 Nw 107th Ave Ste 1, Doral FL 33178
Tel (305) 477-5993 SIC 5045

TWC WISE COMPUTER INC p 1494
3515 Nw 114th Ave, Doral FL 33178
Tel (305) 594-5725 SIC 5045

TECHNISOURCE INC p 1431
2050 Spectrum Blvd, Fort Lauderdale FL 33309
Tel (954) 308-7600 SIC 7363 5045 7361

■ SUNGARD PUBLIC SECTOR INC p 1402
1000 Business Center Dr, Lake Mary FL 32746
Tel (407) 304-3235 SIC 5045

TRADING CORP p 1469
5516 Scott View Ln, Lakeland FL 33813
Tel (754) 900-7666 SIC 5045 5961

■ TECH DATA LATIN AMERICA INC p 1430
2200 Nw 112th Ave, Miami FL 33172
Tel (305) 593-5000 SIC 5045

▲ ACI WORLDWIDE INC p 17
3520 Kraft Rd Ste 300, Naples FL 34105
Tel (239) 403-4600 SIC 7372 5045

ARMA GLOBAL CORP p 110
2701 N Rocky Point Dr # 1150, Rocky Point FL 33607
Tel (866) 554-9333 SIC 5045 8748 8742

LEXJET LLC p 860
1605 Main St Ste 400, Sarasota FL 34236
Tel (941) 330-1210
SIC 5045 5112 5111 2672 5043

■ GLOBAL IMAGING SYSTEMS INC p 616
3903 Northdale Blvd 200w, Tampa FL 33624
Tel (813) 960-5508 SIC 5044 5045 7629

APTEAN INC p 101
4325 Alexander Dr Ste 100, Alpharetta GA 30022
Tel (770) 351-9600 SIC 5045

CDC SOFTWARE INC p 270
4325 Alexander Dr, Alpharetta GA 30022
Tel (770) 351-9600 SIC 5045

PROMETHEAN INC p 1183
1165 Sanctuary Pkwy # 400, Alpharetta GA 30009
Tel (678) 762-1500 SIC 5049 5045

APTOS INC p 101
945 E Paces Ferry Rd Ne, Atlanta GA 30326
Tel (866) 493-7037
SIC 5044 5045 7378 7699

ATLANTA NETWORK TECHNOLOGIES INC p 125
710 Morgan Falls Rd, Atlanta GA 30350
Tel (877) 293-9797 *SIC* 5045 5065

BIRCH COMMUNICATIONS INC p 185
320 Interstate North Pkwy, Atlanta GA 30339
Tel (866) 424-5100 *SIC* 4813 5045

▲ MANHATTAN ASSOCIATES INC p 901
2300 Windy Ridge Pkwy Se 1000n, Atlanta GA 30339
Tel (770) 955-7070 *SIC* 7373 7372 5045

▲ SED INTERNATIONAL HOLDINGS INC p 1299
2150 Cedars Rd Ste 200, Lawrenceville GA 30043
Tel (678) 878-2600 *SIC* 5045 5065

■ SED INTERNATIONAL INC p 1299
2150 Cedars Rd Ste 200, Lawrenceville GA 30043
Tel (844) 501-5858 *SIC* 5045

ACS ACQUISITION CORP p 18
6575 The Corners Pkwy, Norcross GA 30092
Tel (678) 268-1300 *SIC* 5045 7374

PROSYS INC p 1185
6575 The Corners Pkwy # 300, Norcross GA 30092
Tel (678) 268-1300 *SIC* 5045 7374

PROSYS INFORMATION SYSTEMS INC p 1185
6575 The Corners Pkwy # 300, Norcross GA 30092
Tel (678) 268-1300 *SIC* 5045 7373

CENTRICSIT LLC p 281
3140 Northwoods Pkwy, Peachtree Corners GA 30071
Tel (678) 495-4732 *SIC* 5045

B2B COMPUTER PRODUCTS LLC p 143
313 S Rohlwing Rd, Addison IL 60101
Tel (630) 627-1400 *SIC* 5045

■ INSIGHT PUBLIC SECTOR INC p 746
2250 W Pinehurst Blvd # 200, Addison IL 60101
Tel (630) 924-6801 *SIC* 5045

■ INSIGHT NORTH AMERICA INC p 746
444 Scott Dr, Bloomingdale IL 60108
Tel (630) 924-6700 *SIC* 5045

ARLINGTON COMPUTER PRODUCTS INC p 110
851 Commerce Ct, Buffalo Grove IL 60089
Tel (847) 541-2475 *SIC* 5045

■ ASAP SOFTWARE EXPRESS INC p 115
850 Asbury Dr, Buffalo Grove IL 60089
Tel (847) 465-3700 *SIC* 5045

MNJ TECHNOLOGIES DIRECT INC p 980
1025 Busch Pkwy, Buffalo Grove IL 60089
Tel (847) 634-0700 *SIC* 5734 5045 7373

SOFTCHOICE CORP p 1337
314 W Superior St Ste 400, Chicago IL 60654
Tel (416) 588-9002 *SIC* 5045

▲ ESSENDANT INC p 510
1 Parkway North Blvd # 100, Deerfield IL 60015
Tel (847) 627-7000
SIC 5112 5111 5021 5044 5087 5045

MEREX TECHNOLOGY LEASING CORP p 948
570 Lake Cook Rd Ste 300, Deerfield IL 60015
Tel (847) 940-1200 *SIC* 6159 5045

MERIDIAN IT INC p 949
9 Parkway N Ste 500, Deerfield IL 60015
Tel (847) 964-2664 *SIC* 5045

ENRIQUE MENDOZA p 500
2350 Nantucket Ln, Elgin IL 60123
Tel (630) 364-1808 *SIC* 7379 5045

OMRON MANAGEMENT CENTER OF AMERICA INC p 1085
2895 Greenspoint Pkwy # 100, Hoffman Estates IL 60169
Tel (224) 520-7650
SIC 5044 5046 5065 5047 5045 8732

▲ CDW CORP p 271
75 Tri State Intl, Lincolnshire IL 60069
Tel (847) 465-6000
SIC 5963 5045 5734 5961

■ CDW LLC p 271
75 Tri State Intl, Lincolnshire IL 60069
Tel (847) 465-6000 *SIC* 5045

▲ ZEBRA TECHNOLOGIES CORP p 1641
3 Overlook Pt, Lincolnshire IL 60069
Tel (847) 634-6700
SIC 3577 2672 2679 5045

■ CAT LOGISTICS INC p 264
500 N Morton Ave, Morton IL 61550
Tel (309) 675-1000 *SIC* 4225 5045 4213

FORSYTHE TECHNOLOGY INC p 568
7770 Frontage Rd, Skokie IL 60077
Tel (847) 213-7000 *SIC* 7377 5045 7373

FORSYTHE/MCARTHUR ASSOCIATES INC p 568
7770 Frontage Rd, Skokie IL 60077
Tel (847) 213-7000 *SIC* 7377 7373 5045

LEVI RAY & SHOUP INC p 858
2401 W Monroe St, Springfield IL 62704
Tel (217) 793-3800 *SIC* 7371 5045 7379

CDW HOLDINGS LLC p 271
3 First National Pl, Vernon Hills IL 60061
Tel (847) 465-6000
SIC 5963 5045 5734 5961

APTEAN HOLDINGS INC p 101
450 E 96th St Ste 300, Indianapolis IN 46240
Tel (317) 249-1700 *SIC* 7371 5045

INKCYCLE INC p 743
11100 W 82nd St, Lenexa KS 66214
Tel (913) 894-8387
SIC 3955 7699 7378 5045 8249 5734

RURAL TELEPHONE SERVICE CO INC p 1258
145 N Main St, Lenora KS 67645
Tel (785) 567-4281 *SIC* 4813 5734 5045

ALEXANDER OPEN SYSTEMS INC p 49
12980 Foster St Ste 300, Overland Park KS 66213
Tel (913) 307-2300
SIC 5045 7373 8748 7376 3577 1731

POMEROY IT SOLUTIONS INC p 1160
1020 Petersburg Rd, Hebron KY 41048
Tel (859) 586-0600 *SIC* 7373 5045 7378

SOFTWARE INFORMATION SYSTEMS LLC p 1337
165 Barr St, Lexington KY 40507
Tel (859) 977-4747 *SIC* 5045 7379

PEAK-RYZEX INC p 1126
10330 Old Columbia Rd # 102, Columbia MD 21046
Tel (410) 312-6000 *SIC* 7378 5045 7372

FORCE 3 LLC p 565
2151 Priest Bridge Dr # 7, Crofton MD 21114
Tel (301) 261-0204 *SIC* 7373 5045 3571

CYBERCORE TECHNOLOGIES LLC p 404
6605 Business Pkwy, Elkridge MD 21075
Tel (410) 561-7177 *SIC* 5045

NEW WAVE TECHNOLOGIES INC p 1033
4635 Wedgewood Blvd # 107, Frederick MD 21703
Tel (301) 624-5300 *SIC* 5045

RAND WORLDWIDE SUBSIDIARY INC p 1207
11201 Dlfeld Blvd Ste 112, Owings Mills MD 21117
Tel (877) 726-3243
SIC 7379 7373 5045 5734

PHILIPS HOLDING USA INC p 1143
3000 Minuteman Rd Ste 109, Andover MA 01810
Tel (978) 687-1501
SIC 5064 3674 5045 5047 3641

CONTINENTAL RESOURCES INC p 363
175 Middlesex Tpke Ste 1, Bedford MA 01730
Tel (781) 275-0850
SIC 5045 5065 7377 7359 7378 7629

ENTEGEE INC p 501
70 Blanchard Rd Ste 102, Burlington MA 01803
Tel (781) 221-5800 *SIC* 7363 5045

BULL HN INFORMATION SYSTEMS INC p 225
285 Billerica Rd Ste 200, Chelmsford MA 01824
Tel (978) 294-6000 *SIC* 5045 7373

ELIZA CORP p 487
75 Sylvan St Ste B205, Danvers MA 01923
Tel (978) 921-2700 *SIC* 5045

■ NEW ENGLAND BUSINESS SERVICE INC p 1030
500 Main St, Groton MA 01471
Tel (978) 448-6111
SIC 2759 2771 5045 2653 3089 3069

IPSWITCH INC p 764
83 Hartwell Ave, Lexington MA 02421
Tel (781) 676-5700 *SIC* 5045

■ PCG PARENT CORP p 1124
4 Technology Dr, Peabody MA 01960
Tel (978) 538-8000
SIC 5045 5065 4953 5093 7378

■ PCG TRADING LLC p 1124
4 Technology Dr, Peabody MA 01960
Tel (978) 538-8000
SIC 5045 5065 4953 5093 7378

IKASYSTEMS CORP p 731
134 Turnpike Rd Ste 200, Southborough MA 01772
Tel (508) 251-3182 *SIC* 5045

WHALLEY COMPUTER ASSOCIATES INC p 1604
1 Whalley Way, Southwick MA 01077
Tel (413) 569-4200 *SIC* 5045 7378

CAMBRIDGE COMPUTER SERVICES INC p 244
271 Waverley Oaks Rd # 301, Waltham MA 02452
Tel (781) 250-3000
SIC 5045 7373 7371 7379

DYNATRACE LLC p 464
404 Wyman St Ste 500, Waltham MA 02451
Tel (781) 530-1000 *SIC* 7372 5045

■ MODUSLINK CORP p 981
1601 Trapelo Rd Ste 170, Waltham MA 02451
Tel (781) 663-5000 *SIC* 7379 7389 5045

SOURCE CODE CORP p 1342
159 Overland Rd Ste 3, Waltham MA 02451
Tel (781) 255-2022 *SIC* 5045

TELERIK INC p 1435
201 Jones Rd Ste 200, Waltham MA 02451
Tel (888) 365-2779 *SIC* 5045

EXAGRID SYSTEMS INC p 516
2000 W Park Dr Ste 110, Westborough MA 01581
Tel (508) 898-2872 *SIC* 5045

LOWRY HOLDING CO INC p 882
9420 Maltby Rd, Brighton MI 48116
Tel (810) 229-7200
SIC 5045 2672 8742 7373 5044 5734

DATA STRATEGY LLC p 413
4020 E Beltline Ave Ne # 201, Grand Rapids MI 49525
Tel (616) 281-5566 *SIC* 5045

■ MICHIGAN OFFICE SOLUTIONS INC p 961
2859 Walkent Dr Nw, Grand Rapids MI 49544
Tel (616) 459-1161 *SIC* 5044 5045 7629

DATA SALES CO INC p 413
3450 W Burnsville Pkwy, Burnsville MN 55337
Tel (952) 890-8838 *SIC* 5045 7377

DIRECT SOURCE INC p 441
8176 Mallory Ct, Chanhassen MN 55317
Tel (952) 934-8000 *SIC* 5046 5045

▲ DATALINK CORP p 414
10050 Crosstown Cir # 500, Eden Prairie MN 55344
Tel (952) 944-3462 *SIC* 5045 7371 7373

EXPRESSPOINT TECHNOLOGY SERVICES INC p 521
10900 Wayzata Blvd # 800, Hopkins MN 55305
Tel (763) 543-6000
SIC 5045 7379 7699 8741 7389 7378

CALABRIO INC p 238
400 1st Ave N Ste 300, Minneapolis MN 55401
Tel (763) 592-4600 *SIC* 5045 7371

■ HEALTHLAND INC p 677
1600 Utica Ave S Ste 300, Minneapolis MN 55416
Tel (612) 787-3120 *SIC* 7373 5045

POWER/MATION DIVISION INC p 1165
1310 Energy Ln, Saint Paul MN 55108
Tel (651) 605-3300
SIC 5085 5065 5084 5045 8742 7549

VSS LLC p 1567
382 Galleria Pkwy Ste 400, Madison MS 39110
Tel (601) 853-8550 *SIC* 5045 7373

GKR SYSTEMS INC p 613
860 Centre St, Ridgeland MS 39157
Tel (601) 956-5440 *SIC* 5045 7373

ACLARA METERS LLC p 17
945 Hornet Dr, Hazelwood MO 63042
Tel (800) 297-2728 *SIC* 5045

WORLD WIDE TECHNOLOGY INC p 1625
60 Weldon Pkwy, Maryland Heights MO 63043
Tel (314) 569-7000 *SIC* 5045 5065 8741

CSI LEASING INC p 398
9990 Old Olive Street Rd # 101, Saint Louis MO 63141
Tel (314) 997-4934 *SIC* 7377 5045

WORLD WIDE TECHNOLOGY HOLDING CO INC p 1625
60 Weldon Pkwy, Saint Louis MO 63101
Tel (314) 919-1400 *SIC* 5045 5065 8748

■ ACI WORLDWIDE CORP p 17
6060 Coventry Dr, Elkhorn NE 68022
Tel (402) 390-7600 *SIC* 7372 5045

■ INFORMATION TECHNOLOGY INC p 742
1345 Old Cheney Rd, Lincoln NE 68512
Tel (402) 423-2682
SIC 5045 7373 7374 7371

QCH INC p 1194
241 Ridge St Fl 4, Reno NV 89501
Tel (510) 226-1000 *SIC* 5045

■ PC CONNECTION SALES CORP p 1123
730 Milford Rd, Merrimack NH 03054
Tel (603) 423-2000 *SIC* 5961 5045

■ ENTERASYS NETWORKS INC p 501
9 Northstern Blvd Ste 300, Salem NH 03079
Tel (603) 952-5000
SIC 3577 7373 3357 5045

WORLDCOM EXCHANGE INC p 1625
43 Northwestern Dr, Salem NH 03079
Tel (603) 893-0900 *SIC* 7373 5045 7379

ARCHBROOK LAGUNA LLC p 104
350 Starke Rd Ste 400, Carlstadt NJ 07072
Tel (201) 372-0304 *SIC* 5045 5065

CASIO AMERICA INC p 263
570 Mount Pleasant Ave, Dover NJ 07801
Tel (973) 361-5400
SIC 5044 5045 5094 5099

■ ORACLE FINANCIAL SERVICES SOFTWARE INC p 1091
399 Thornall St Ste 6, Edison NJ 08837
Tel (732) 623-0399 *SIC* 5045

IPC SYSTEMS HOLDINGS CORP p 763
1500 Plaza Ten Fl 15, Jersey City NJ 07311
Tel (201) 253-2000 *SIC* 5045 4813

GOTHAM TECHNOLOGY GROUP LLC p 626
1 Paragon Dr Ste 200, Montvale NJ 07645
Tel (201) 802-9600 *SIC* 5045 7361 5932

OKI DATA AMERICAS INC p 1079
2000 Bishops Gate Blvd, Mount Laurel NJ 08054
Tel (856) 235-2600 *SIC* 5045

PANASONIC CORP OF NORTH AMERICA p 1111
2 Riverfront Plz Ste 200, Newark NJ 07102
Tel (201) 348-7000
SIC 5064 5045 5065 5044 5084 5063

KONICA MINOLTA BUSINESS SOLUTIONS USA INC p 827
100 Williams Dr, Ramsey NJ 07446
Tel (201) 825-4000 *SIC* 5044 5045

SAMSUNG ELECTRONICS AMERICA INC p 1275
85 Challenger Rd, Ridgefield Park NJ 07660
Tel (201) 229-4000 *SIC* 5064 5065 5045

▲ WAYSIDE TECHNOLOGY GROUP INC p 1584
1157 Shrewsbury Ave, Shrewsbury NJ 07702
Tel (732) 389-8950 *SIC* 5045 7373 7379

STAR MICRONICS AMERICA INC p 1378
65 Clyde Rd Ste G, Somerset NJ 08873
Tel (732) 623-5500 *SIC* 5065 5045

HIGH POINT SOLUTIONS INC p 691
5 Gail Ct, Sparta NJ 07871
Tel (973) 940-0040 *SIC* 5045 7373

MEADOWGATE TECHNOLOGIES LLC p 934
171 Jersey St Ste 1, Trenton NJ 08611
Tel (609) 393-3618 *SIC* 5045 8711

DUMAC BUSINESS SYSTEMS INC p 461
19 Corporate Cir Ste 1, East Syracuse NY 13057
Tel (315) 463-1010 *SIC* 5045 7699 3578

■ CBORD GROUP INC p 269
950 Danby Rd Ste 100c, Ithaca NY 14850
Tel (607) 257-2410 *SIC* 7372 5045

CANON USA INC p 247
1 Canon Park, Melville NY 11747
Tel (516) 328-5000
SIC 5044 5065 5045 3861 3577 5043

DATA VISION COMPUTER VIDEO INC p 414
50 W 23rd St, New York NY 10010
Tel (212) 689-1111 *SIC* 5045 5961

ETRALI NORTH AMERICA LLC p 512
1500 Broadway Ste 708, New York NY 10036
Tel (212) 418-9328 *SIC* 5045 7378 1731

LOGICALIS INC p 874
1 Penn Plz Ste 5130, New York NY 10119
Tel (212) 596-7160 *SIC* 5045

LOGICALIS US HOLDINGS INC p 874
1 Penn Plz, New York NY 10119
Tel (212) 596-7160 *SIC* 5045

TOSHIBA AMERICA INFORMATION SYSTEMS INC p 1462
1251 Ave Of The Ste 4110, New York NY 10020
Tel (949) 583-3000
SIC 3571 3577 3572 3661 5045

VNU MARKETING INFORMATION INC p 1564
770 Broadway Fl 15, New York NY 10003
Tel (646) 654-5011
SIC 8732 6282 7374 5045

ISLAND COMPUTER PRODUCTS INC p 766
20 Clifton Ave, Staten Island NY 10305
Tel (718) 556-6700
SIC 5045 7373 7379 7378

■ SENECA DATA DISTRIBUTORS INC p 1303
6040 Tarbell Rd Ste 103, Syracuse NY 13206
Tel (315) 433-1160 *SIC* 5045

HITACHI AMERICA LTD p 696
50 Prospect Ave, Tarrytown NY 10591
Tel (914) 332-5800
SIC 5084 5065 3577 5063 5045 3651

WESTCON GROUP INC p 1597
520 White Plains Rd # 200, Tarrytown NY 10591
Tel (914) 829-7000 *SIC* 5045

WESTCON GROUP NORTH AMERICA INC p 1597
520 White Plains Rd # 200, Tarrytown NY 10591
Tel (914) 829-7000 *SIC* 5045

ERGONOMIC GROUP INC p 507
609 Cantiague Rock Rd # 3, Westbury NY 11590
Tel (516) 746-7777
SIC 5045 7373 7374 7376 7379

BAKER & TAYLOR FULFILLMENT INC p 145
2550 W Tyvola Rd Ste 300, Charlotte NC 28217
Tel (704) 998-3154
SIC 5192 5045 7822 5065

BAKER & TAYLOR HOLDINGS LLC p 145
2550 W Tyvola Rd Ste 300, Charlotte NC 28217
Tel (704) 998-3100
SIC 5192 7822 5065 5045

BAKER & TAYLOR LLC p 145
2550 W Tyvola Rd Ste 300, Charlotte NC 28217
Tel (704) 998-3100
SIC 5192 7822 5065 5045 5099

BTAC ACQUISITION LLC p 222
2550 W Tyvola Rd Ste 300, Charlotte NC 28217
Tel (704) 998-3100
SIC 5192 7822 5065 5045

BTAC HOLDING CORP p 222
2550 W Tyvola Rd Ste 300, Charlotte NC 28217
Tel (704) 998-3100
SIC 5192 7822 5065 5045

VRUSH INDUSTRIES INC p 1566
118 N Wrenn St, High Point NC 27260
Tel (336) 886-7700
SIC 5045 5021 7379 3469 5712 7375

▲ AGILYSYS INC p 35
425 Walnut St Ste 1800, Cincinnati OH 45202
Tel (770) 810-7800 *SIC* 5045

MCPC INC p 932
1801 Superior Ave E # 300, Cleveland OH 44114
Tel (440) 238-0102 *SIC* 5045

CRANEL INC p 389
8999 Gemini Pkwy Ste A, Columbus OH 43240
Tel (614) 431-8000 *SIC* 5045

MICRO ELECTRONICS INC p 961
4119 Leap Rd, Hilliard OH 43026
Tel (614) 850-3000 *SIC* 5045 5734

VIRTUAL TECHNOLOGIES GROUP p 1560
3820 S Dixie Hwy, Lima OH 45806
Tel (419) 991-4694 *SIC* 5045

GBS CORP p 595
7233 Freedom Ave Nw, North Canton OH 44720
Tel (330) 494-5330
SIC 5045 5112 2675 2672 2761 2759

PROVANTAGE LLC p 1185
7576 Freedom Ave Nw, North Canton OH 44720
Tel (330) 494-3781
SIC 5961 5719 5734 5045

WOODARD TECHNOLOGY & INVESTMENTS LLC p 1622
10205 E 61st St Ste D, Tulsa OK 74133
Tel (918) 270-7000 *SIC* 5045

STRUCTURED COMMUNICATION SYSTEMS INC p 1394
12901 Se 97th Ave Ste 400, Clackamas OR 97015
Tel (503) 513-9979 *SIC* 7373 5045

CRJKK INC p 393
450 Acorn Ln, Downingtown PA 19335
Tel (610) 518-4000 *SIC* 5045

SICOM SYSTEMS INC p 1319
4434 Progress Meadow Dr, Doylestown PA 18902
Tel (215) 489-2500 *SIC* 5045 3578 7379

D & H DISTRIBUTING CO p 406
2525 N 7th St, Harrisburg PA 17110
Tel (717) 236-8001
SIC 5045 5065 5064 5063 5044

PERLITE INSTITUTE INC p 1136
2207 Forest Hills Dr, Harrisburg PA 17112
Tel (717) 238-9723 *SIC* 5045

GE RICHARDS GRAPHIC SUPPLIES CO INC p 596
928 Links Ave, Landisville PA 17538
Tel (717) 892-4620 *SIC* 5084 5045

▲ BLACK BOX CORP p 186
1000 Park Dr, Lawrence PA 15055
Tel (724) 746-5500
SIC 3577 3679 3661 5045 5065 5063

■ BLACK BOX CORP OF PENNSYLVANIA p 186
1000 Park Dr, Lawrence PA 15055
Tel (724) 746-5500
SIC 5045 5063 5065 3577 3679 3661

COMMUNICATION CABLE CO p 346
140 Quaker Ln, Malvern PA 19355
Tel (610) 644-5155 *SIC* 5045 7379

RICOH AMERICAS CORP p 1233
70 Valley Stream Pkwy, Malvern PA 19355
Tel (610) 296-8000
SIC 5044 5065 5045 5043 3861 3661

■ GENCO TRANSPORTATION MANAGEMENT LLC p 598
100 Papercraft Park, Pittsburgh PA 15238
Tel (412) 820-3700
SIC 4225 4111 5045 4789

■ I GENCO INC p 725
100 Papercraft Park, Pittsburgh PA 15238
Tel (800) 677-3110 *SIC* 4225 4111 5045

■ FIS EPROCESS INTELLIGENCE LLC p 551
680 E Swedesford Rd, Wayne PA 19087
Tel (888) 601-2361 *SIC* 7374 5045

■ COMPAQ COMPUTER CARIBBEAN INC p 350
1 Calle Sonata 3, Guaynabo PR 00969
Tel (787) 781-0505 *SIC* 5045 7378

▲ SCANSOURCE INC p 1286
6 Logue Ct Ste G, Greenville SC 29615
Tel (864) 288-2432 *SIC* 5045

WYNIT DISTRIBUTION LLC p 1630
2 W Washington St Ste 500, Greenville SC 29601
Tel (864) 605-9920
SIC 5045 5043 5046 5199 7372

LPS INTEGRATION INC p 882
5300 Virginia Way Ste 100, Brentwood TN 37027
Tel (866) 706-7904 *SIC* 5045 7379

A-Z OFFICE RESOURCE INC p 7
809 S Garden St, Columbia TN 38401
Tel (931) 388-1536
SIC 5112 5021 5044 5045 5087

ESSEX TECHNOLOGY GROUP INC p 510
455 Industrial Blvd Ste C, La Vergne TN 37086
Tel (615) 620-5444 *SIC* 5045 8732 5261

INGRAM ENTERTAINMENT HOLDINGS INC p 743
2 Ingram Blvd, La Vergne TN 37089
Tel (615) 287-4000 *SIC* 5065 5045

QCH NASHVILLE LLC p 1194
1621 Heil Quaker Blvd, La Vergne TN 37086
Tel (615) 501-7500 *SIC* 5045 3577

SUPPLIES DISTRIBUTORS INC p 1407
505 Millenium Dr, Allen TX 75013
Tel (972) 881-2900 *SIC* 5045 5112

GEMALTO INC p 598
9442 Capital Of, Austin TX 78759
Tel (215) 340-2000 *SIC* 5045

GTS TECHNOLOGY SOLUTIONS INC p 644
9211 Wterford Centre Blvd, Austin TX 78758
Tel (512) 452-0651 *SIC* 5045 5112

SHI/GOVERNMENT SOLUTIONS INC p 1316
1301 St Mo Pac Expy Ste, Austin TX 78746
Tel (512) 634-8100 *SIC* 5045 7372

M&A TECHNOLOGY INC p 890
2045 Chenault Dr, Carrollton TX 75006
Tel (972) 490-5803 *SIC* 5045 7373

COMPAREX USA INC p 350
600 N Pearl St Ste 1960, Dallas TX 75201
Tel (972) 734-5223 *SIC* 5045 7371

COMPUCOM SYSTEMS HOLDING LLC p 352
7171 Forest Ln, Dallas TX 75230
Tel (972) 856-3600
SIC 7373 5045 7378 8748

■ **COMPUSA INC** p 352
14951 Dallas Pkwy, Dallas TX 75254
Tel (972) 982-4000 *SIC* 5734 5045 5961

DATASPAN INC p 414
1245 Viceroy Dr, Dallas TX 75247
Tel (800) 660-3586 *SIC* 5045 7375

■ **SAFEGUARD BUSINESS SYSTEMS INC** p 1266
8585 N Stemmons Fwy, Dallas TX 75247
Tel (214) 640-3916
SIC 7374 2759 5112 5045

NEXIUS SOLUTIONS INC p 1040
2595 Dallas Pkwy Ste 300, Frisco TX 75034
Tel (703) 650-7777 *SIC* 5045

PCPC DIRECT LTD p 1124
10690 Shadow Wood Dr # 132, Houston TX 77043
Tel (713) 984-8808 *SIC* 5045 7378 7379

PCPC INC p 1124
10690 Shadow Wood Dr # 132, Houston TX 77043
Tel (713) 984-8808 *SIC* 5045 7378 7379

UNIVERSAL COMPUTER SYSTEMS INC p 1516
6700 Hollister St, Houston TX 77040
Tel (713) 718-1800 *SIC* 5045

NEC CORP OF AMERICA p 1023
3929 W John Carpenter Fwy, Irving TX 75063
Tel (214) 262-6000 *SIC* 5045 5065

PRESIDIO NETWORKED SOLUTIONS GROUP LLC p 1172
1955 Lakeway Dr Ste 220, Lewisville TX 75057
Tel (469) 549-3800 *SIC* 5045 7372 7373

COMPUCOM SYSTEMS INC p 352
8383 Dominion Pkwy, Plano TX 75024
Tel (972) 856-3600
SIC 7373 5045 7378 8748

■ **SOFTWARE SPECTRUM INC** p 1337
3480 Lotus Dr, Plano TX 75075
Tel (469) 443-3900 *SIC* 5045 7373

SPEED COMMERCE INC p 1358
1303 E Arapaho Rd Ste 200, Richardson TX 75081
Tel (866) 377-3331 *SIC* 5045 5099

■ **DELL MARKETING LP** p 425
1 Dell Way, Round Rock TX 78682
Tel (512) 338-4400 *SIC* 5045

■ **DELL USA CORP** p 425
1 Dell Way, Round Rock TX 78682
Tel (512) 338-4400 *SIC* 8741 5045

SIRIUS COMPUTER SOLUTIONS INC p 1327
10100 Reunion Pl Ste 500, San Antonio TX 78216
Tel (210) 369-8000 *SIC* 7373 5045

ABOUT TIME TECHNOLOGIES LLC p 12
58 N 1100 W Apt 2, Payson UT 84651
Tel (801) 465-8181 *SIC* 5045 7372 7375

COMPUTER SECURITY SOLUTIONS LLC p 353
11 Canal Center Plz Fl 2, Alexandria VA 22314
Tel (703) 956-5700 *SIC* 5045

INTELLIGENT DECISIONS INC p 750
21445 Beaumeade Cir, Ashburn VA 20147
Tel (703) 554-1600 *SIC* 3571 5045

FOUR POINTS TECHNOLOGY LLC p 571
14900 Confrnce Ctr Dr # 100, Chantilly VA 20151
Tel (703) 657-6102 *SIC* 5045

UNICOM GOVERNMENT INC p 1502
15010 Conference Center D, Chantilly VA 20151
Tel (703) 502-2000 *SIC* 5045

DIGITEK IMAGING PRODUCTS INC p 439
44258 Mercure Cir, Dulles VA 20166
Tel (703) 421-0300 *SIC* 5045

GIESECKE & DEVRIENT MOBILE SECURITY AMERICA INC p 611
45925 Horseshoe Dr, Dulles VA 20166
Tel (703) 480-2100
SIC 7382 3089 5045 7374

AFFIGENT LLC p 32
13873 Park Center Rd # 127, Herndon VA 20171
Tel (866) 977-8524 *SIC* 5045

■ **EPLUS GROUP INC** p 505
13595 Dulles Tech Dr, Herndon VA 20171
Tel (703) 984-8400 *SIC* 7377 5734 5045

▲ **EPLUS INC** p 505
13595 Dulles Tech Dr, Herndon VA 20171
Tel (703) 984-8400
SIC 5045 7377 7379 7372

■ **EPLUS TECHNOLOGY INC** p 505
13595 Dulles Tech Dr, Herndon VA 20171
Tel (703) 984-8400 *SIC* 5045 5734

VION CORP p 1558
196 Van Buren St Ste 300, Herndon VA 20170
Tel (571) 353-6000 *SIC* 5045

PANAMERICA COMPUTERS INC p 1111
1386 Big Oak Rd, Luray VA 22835
Tel (540) 635-4402 *SIC* 5045

ADVANCED COMPUTER CONCEPTS INC p 25
7927 Jones Branch Dr 600n, Mc Lean VA 22102
Tel (703) 276-7800 *SIC* 5045

■ **EC AMERICA INC** p 474
8444 Westpark Dr Ste 200, Mc Lean VA 22102
Tel (703) 752-0610 *SIC* 5045

■ **IMMIXTECHNOLOGY INC** p 734
8444 Westpark Dr Ste 200, Mc Lean VA 22102
Tel (703) 752-0610 *SIC* 5045

SMS DATA PRODUCTS GROUP INC p 1334
1751 Pinnacle Dr Ste 1200, Mc Lean VA 22102
Tel (703) 288-8100 *SIC* 5045 7373

TVAR SOLUTIONS LLC p 1494
1320 Old Chain Bridge Rd # 445, Mc Lean VA 22101
Tel (703) 635-3900 *SIC* 5045 7379 3571

LANDMARK MEDIA ENTERPRISES LLC p 843
150 Granby St, Norfolk VA 23510
Tel (757) 351-7000
SIC 2711 5045 2721 6531

CARAHSOFT TECHNOLOGY CORP p 252
1860 Michael Faraday Dr # 100, Reston VA 20190
Tel (703) 871-8500 *SIC* 5045

CLEARPATH SOLUTIONS GROUP LLC p 324
12100 Sunset Hills Rd # 610, Reston VA 20190
Tel (703) 673-9370 *SIC* 5045

MA FEDERAL INC p 891
12030 Sunrise Valley Dr # 300, Reston VA 20191
Tel (703) 356-1160 *SIC* 5045

THUNDERCAT TECHNOLOGY LLC p 1451
1925 Isaac Newton Sq E # 180, Reston VA 20190
Tel (703) 674-0216 *SIC* 5045

MYTHICS INC p 1005
1439 N Great Neck Rd, Virginia Beach VA 23454
Tel (757) 965-6756 *SIC* 5045

SLAIT PARTNERS INC p 1331
100 Landmark Sq, Virginia Beach VA 23452
Tel (757) 313-6500
SIC 5045 3571 8748 7373

3MD INC p 3
17735 Ne 65th St Ste 130, Redmond WA 98052
Tel (425) 467-8000 *SIC* 5045 8742

REDAPT INC p 1216
12226 134th Ct Ne Bldg D, Redmond WA 98052
Tel (425) 882-0400 *SIC* 5045

REDAPT SYSTEMS INC p 1216
12226 134th Ct Ne Bldg D, Redmond WA 98052
Tel (206) 210-5440 *SIC* 5045

DAPTIV SOLUTIONS LLC p 412
1111 3rd Ave Ste 700, Seattle WA 98101
Tel (206) 341-9117 *SIC* 5045

DOUGLAS STEWART CO INC p 452
2402 Advance Rd, Madison WI 53718
Tel (608) 221-1155 *SIC* 5045 5044 5049

PNA HOLDINGS LLC p 1158
3150 Pleasant View Rd, Madison WI 53713
Tel (608) 203-1500
SIC 5044 5045 5112 7699

EXTREME ENGINEERING SOLUTIONS INC p 521
3225 Deming Way Ste 120, Middleton WI 53562
Tel (608) 833-1155 *SIC* 5045

F DOHMEN CO p 522
190 N Milwaukee St, Milwaukee WI 53202
Tel (414) 299-4913 *SIC* 5122 5045 7374

DEDICATED COMPUTING LLC p 421
N26w23880 Commerce Cir B, Waukesha WI 53188
Tel (262) 951-7200 *SIC* 3571 3577 5045

SOFTWARE ONE INC p 1337
20875 Crssroads Cir Ste 1, Waukesha WI 53186
Tel (262) 317-5555 *SIC* 5045

E O JOHNSON CO INC p 466
8400 Stewart Ave, Wausau WI 54401
Tel (715) 842-9999 *SIC* 5112 7699 5045

SIC 5046 Commercial Eqpt, NEC Wholesale

LEGACY EQUIPMENT INC p 852
12526 Celeste Rd, Chunchula AL 36521
Tel (251) 679-1965 *SIC* 5046

WOOD-FRUITTICHER GROCERY CO INC p 1622
2900 Alton Rd, Irondale AL 35210
Tel (205) 836-9663
SIC 5142 5141 5147 5087 5046

BEST WESTERN INTERNATIONAL INC p 177
6201 N 24th Pkwy, Phoenix AZ 85016
Tel (602) 957-4200
SIC 7389 7311 5046 8743

BI-RITE RESTAURANT SUPPLY CO INC p 180
123 S Hill Dr, Brisbane CA 94005
Tel (415) 656-0187
SIC 5141 5147 5148 5023 5046 5963

HARMAN MANAGEMENT CORP p 662
199 1st St Ste 212, Los Altos CA 94022
Tel (650) 941-5681 *SIC* 8741 5812 5046

HANNAM CHAIN USA INC p 658
2740 W Olympic Blvd, Los Angeles CA 90006
Tel (213) 382-2922 *SIC* 5046 5411

P & R PAPER SUPPLY CO INC p 1102
1898 E Colton Ave, Redlands CA 92374
Tel (909) 389-1811
SIC 5113 5169 5149 5072 5046

SUNKIST GROWERS INC p 1402
27770 N Entertainment Dr # 120, Valencia CA 91355
Tel (818) 986-4800
SIC 5148 2033 2037 2899 6794 5046

■ **GOLDBERG AND SOLOVY FOODS INC** p 620
5925 Alcoa Ave, Vernon CA 90058
Tel (323) 581-6161
SIC 5141 5149 5046 5169

TUNDRA RESTAURANT SUPPLY INC p 1491
3825 Walnut St Unit E, Boulder CO 80301
Tel (303) 440-4142 *SIC* 5046 5074

NATIONAL ENTERTAINMENT NETWORK LLC p 1011
325 Interlocken Pkwy B, Broomfield CO 80021
Tel (303) 444-2559 *SIC* 5046 5962

UNITED FOOD SERVICE INC p 1508
5199 Ivy St, Commerce City CO 80022
Tel (303) 289-3595
SIC 5141 5142 5147 5148 5046

FOODSERVICEWAREHOUSE.COM LLC p 564
84 Inverness Cir E, Englewood CO 80112
Tel (303) 801-0629 *SIC* 5046

EASTERN BAG AND PAPER CO INC p 471
200 Research Dr, Milford CT 06460
Tel (203) 878-1814 *SIC* 5113 5087 5046

TOMRA OF NORTH AMERICA (INC) p 1460
1 Corporate Dr Ste 710, Shelton CT 06484
Tel (203) 447-8800 *SIC* 5046

AZELIS AMERICAS INC p 140
262 Harbor Dr, Stamford CT 06902
Tel (203) 274-8691 *SIC* 5085 5046 5169

GREENFIELD WORLD TRADE INC p 638
3355 Entp Ave Ste 160, Fort Lauderdale FL 33331
Tel (954) 202-7419 *SIC* 5046

■ **LAND N SEA DISTRIBUTING INC** p 842
3131 N Andrews Avenue Ext, Pompano Beach FL 33064
Tel (954) 792-9971
SIC 5088 5091 5046 5531

ATLANTA ORIENTAL FOOD WHOLESALE CO p 125
5600 Buford Hwy Ne, Atlanta GA 30340
Tel (770) 455-0770
SIC 5146 5421 5046 5719

■ **SYSCO SPOKANE INC** p 1418
300 N Baugh Way, Post Falls ID 83854
Tel (208) 777-9511 *SIC* 5046 5141

PT HOLDINGS LLC p 1189
1150 N Swift Rd Ste A, Addison IL 60101
Tel (800) 438-8898
SIC 5084 5046 7699 6719

TRIMARK MARLINN INC p 1480
6100 W 73rd St Ste 1, Chicago IL 60638
Tel (708) 496-1700 *SIC* 5046

OMRON MANAGEMENT CENTER OF AMERICA INC p 1085
2895 Greenspoint Pkwy # 100, Hoffman Estates IL 60169
Tel (224) 520-7650
SIC 5044 5046 5065 5047 5045 8732

GLORY GLOBAL SOLUTIONS INC p 618
3333 Warrenville Rd # 310, Lisle IL 60532
Tel (920) 262-3300 *SIC* 5087 5046 5044

DIVERSIFIED FOODSERVICE SUPPLY INC p 444
607 Dempster St, Mount Prospect IL 60056
Tel (847) 966-9700 *SIC* 5046 7699

N KOHL GROCER CO p 1005
130 Jersey St, Quincy IL 62301
Tel (217) 222-5000 *SIC* 5141 5113 5046

SOUTHERN IMPERIAL INC p 1349
1400 Eddy Ave, Rockford IL 61103
Tel (815) 877-7041 *SIC* 5046 2542

A H MANAGEMENT GROUP INC p 5
1151 Rohlwing Rd, Rolling Meadows IL 60008
Tel (847) 342-8065
SIC 5962 7993 5963 7389 5046

AMERICAN HOTEL REGISTER CO p 74
100 S Milwaukee Ave # 100, Vernon Hills IL 60061
Tel (847) 743-3000
SIC 5046 5023 5021 5113

DON EDWARD & CO p 449
9801 Adam Don Pkwy, Woodridge IL 60517
Tel (708) 442-9400
SIC 5021 5046 5087 5113 5169

ACORN DISTRIBUTORS INC p 18
5820 Fortune Cir W, Indianapolis IN 46241
Tel (317) 243-9234
SIC 5113 5087 5169 5046 5023

CENTRAL PRODUCTS LLC p 280
7750 Georgetown Rd, Indianapolis IN 46268
Tel (317) 634-2550 *SIC* 5046 5021

■ **SYSCO INDIANAPOLIS LLC** p 1417
4000 W 62nd St, Indianapolis IN 46268
Tel (317) 291-2020 *SIC* 5149 5046 5411

MARTIN BROTHERS DISTRIBUTING CO INC p 912
6623 Chancellor Dr, Cedar Falls IA 50613
Tel (319) 266-1775
SIC 5141 5169 5046 5087

B & J FOOD SERVICE EQUIPMENT INC p 141
236 N 7th St, Kansas City KS 66101
Tel (913) 621-6165 *SIC* 5046

MAREL INC p 905
8145 Flint St, Lenexa KS 66214
Tel (913) 888-9110 *SIC* 5046

REGAL DISTRIBUTING CO p 1218
17201 W 113th St, Lenexa KS 66219
Tel (913) 894-8787 *SIC* 5112 5113 5046

KANEQUIP INC p 802
1152 Pony Express Hwy, Marysville KS 66508
Tel (785) 562-2377 *SIC* 5046 5083

UNITED RADIO INC p 1511
3345 Point Pleasant Rd, Hebron KY 41048
Tel (859) 371-4423 *SIC* 5046

N GLANTZ & SON LLC p 1005
2501 Constant Comment Pl, Louisville KY 40299
Tel (502) 426-4473 *SIC* 5046

RESTAURANT SUPPLY CHAIN SOLUTIONS LLC p 1228
950 Breckenridge Ln # 300, Louisville KY 40207
Tel (502) 896-5900
SIC 5812 5046 5141 5149

■ **FRYMASTER LLC** p 582
8700 Line Ave, Shreveport LA 71106
Tel (318) 865-1711 *SIC* 3589 5046

CUMMINS-WAGNER CO INC p 401
10901 Pump House Rd, Annapolis Junction MD 20701
Tel (410) 792-4230 *SIC* 5046

ADAMS-BURCH LLC p 21
1901 Stanford Ct, Landover MD 20785
Tel (301) 276-2000 *SIC* 5046 5113 5087

TRIMARK UNITED EAST INC p 1480
505 Collins St, Attleboro MA 02703
Tel (508) 399-6000
SIC 5046 5021 5113 5087

SEABOARD FLOUR LLC p 1295
1320 Centre St Ste 200, Newton MA 02459
Tel (617) 928-6040 *SIC* 5046

PERKINS PAPER INC p 1136
630 John Hancock Rd, Taunton MA 02780
Tel (508) 824-2800
SIC 5113 5149 5087 5046

■ **DOMINOS PIZZA LLC** p 449
30 Frank Lloyd Wright Dr, Ann Arbor MI 48105
Tel (734) 930-3030
SIC 5812 6794 5046 5149 8741 2045

LITTLE CAESAR ENTERPRISES INC p 870
2211 Woodward Ave, Detroit MI 48201
Tel (313) 983-6000
SIC 5812 6794 5141 5046 8741

DAWN EQUIPMENT CO INC p 416
2021 Micor Dr, Jackson MI 49203
Tel (517) 789-4500 *SIC* 5046 3556

DAWN FOOD PRODUCTS INC p 416
3333 Sargent Rd, Jackson MI 49201
Tel (517) 789-4400 *SIC* 2045 5046 3556

DAWN FOODS INC p 416
3333 Sargent Rd, Jackson MI 49201
Tel (517) 789-4400
SIC 2053 2045 3556 5046 6719

STAFFORD-SMITH INC p 1374
3414 S Burdick St, Kalamazoo MI 49001
Tel (269) 343-1240 *SIC* 5046 5078

BAKERY CRAFTS LLC p 147
3500 Thurston Ave 100, Anoka MN 55303
Tel (513) 942-0862 *SIC* 5046 5149 2064

DIRECT SOURCE INC p 441
8176 Mallory Ct, Chanhassen MN 55317
Tel (952) 934-8000 *SIC* 5046 5045

■ **GCS SYSTEMS INC** p 595
370 Wabasha St N, Saint Paul MN 55102
Tel (651) 293-2134 *SIC* 5046 7699

FANCOR INC p 527
821 Locust St, Kansas City MO 64106
Tel (816) 471-0231 *SIC* 3596 7699 5046

CASH-WA DISTRIBUTING CO OF KEARNEY INC p 263
401 W 4th St, Kearney NE 68845
Tel (308) 237-3151 *SIC* 5149 5046 5194

HOCKENBERGS EQUIPMENT AND SUPPLY CO INC p 699
7002 F St, Omaha NE 68117
Tel (402) 339-8900 *SIC* 5046

LOZIER STORE FIXTURES LLC p 882
6336 John J Pershing Dr, Omaha NE 68110
Tel (402) 457-8000 *SIC* 5046

JIM L SHETAKIS DISTRIBUTING CO p 785
3840 Civic Center Dr A, North Las Vegas NV 89030
Tel (702) 940-3663 *SIC* 5141 5046

H BETTI INDUSTRIES INC p 649
303 Paterson Plank Rd, Carlstadt NJ 07072
Tel (201) 438-1300 *SIC* 5046 5091 7699

DWL INTERNATIONAL TRADING INC p 463
65 Industrial Rd, Lodi NJ 07644
Tel (973) 916-9958 *SIC* 5023 5046

TUBE LIGHT CO INC p 1490
300 E Park St, Moonachie NJ 07074
Tel (201) 641-6660 *SIC* 5046 5085

GLANTZ HOLDINGS INC p 614
16 Court St Ste 3000, Brooklyn NY 11241
Tel (502) 271-5560 *SIC* 5046

JETRO CASH AND CARRY ENTERPRISES LLC p 784
1524 132nd St, College Point NY 11356
Tel (718) 939-6400
SIC 5142 5046 5181 5147 5411

RD FOOD SERVICES LLC p 1212
1524 132nd St, College Point NY 11356
Tel (718) 961-4356
SIC 5141 5148 5142 5113 5046 5087

NESPRESSO USA INC p 1026
2401 44th Rd Fl 12, Long Island City NY 11101
Tel (800) 562-1465 *SIC* 5149 5046 5499

ONEIDA LTD p 1087
163 Kenwood Ave, Oneida NY 13421
Tel (315) 361-3000
SIC 5046 5719 5023 5094

▲ **SYSTEMAX INC** p 1418
11 Harbor Park Dr, Port Washington NY 11050
Tel (516) 608-7000 *SIC* 5961 5046

POP DISPLAYS USA LLC p 1161
555 Tuckahoe Rd, Yonkers NY 10710
Tel (914) 771-4200 *SIC* 5046

SCHAEFER SYSTEMS INTERNATIONAL INC p 1286
10021 Westlake Dr, Charlotte NC 28273
Tel (704) 944-4500
SIC 3089 5046 5084 5099 7372

S S KEMP & CO p 1262
4567 Willow Pkwy, Cleveland OH 44125
Tel (216) 271-7062 *SIC* 5046

N WASSERSTROM & SONS INC p 1005
2300 Lockbourne Rd, Columbus OH 43207
Tel (614) 737-8543 *SIC* 3556 5046 3444

WASSERSTROM CO p 1580
477 S Front St, Columbus OH 43215
Tel (614) 737-8472
SIC 5087 3566 5021 5046 5112 5719

HUBERT CO LLC p 716
9555 Dry Fork Rd, Harrison OH 45030
Tel (513) 367-8600 SIC 5046

■ ITW FOOD EQUIPMENT GROUP LLC p 769
701 S Ridge Ave, Troy OH 45374
Tel (937) 332-3000 SIC 5046 3556

S&R COMPRESSION LLC p 1263
4234 S Jackson Ave, Tulsa OK 74107
Tel (918) 447-1947 SIC 5046

■ SYSCO PORTLAND INC p 1418
26250 Sw Parkway Ctr Dr, Wilsonville OR 97070
Tel (503) 682-8700 SIC 5141 5046

HOSSS STEAK & SEA HOUSE INC p 710
170 Patchway Rd, Duncansville PA 16635
Tel (814) 695-7600 SIC 5812 5146 5046

SINGER EQUIPMENT CO INC p 1326
150 S Twin Valley Rd, Elverson PA 19520
Tel (610) 387-6400 SIC 5046

■ SYSCO PITTSBURGH LLC p 1417
1 Whitney Dr, Harmony PA 16037
Tel (724) 452-2100
SIC 5142 5149 5148 5023 5113 5046

CLARK ASSOCIATES INC p 322
2205 Old Phladelphia Pike, Lancaster PA 17602
Tel (717) 392-7550 SIC 5046 7623

■ SYSCO COLUMBIA LLC p 1417
131 Sysco Ct, Columbia SC 29209
Tel (803) 239-4000
SIC 5141 5046 5142 5147 5148

WYNIT DISTRIBUTION LLC p 1630
2 W Washington St Ste 500, Greenville SC 29601
Tel (864) 605-9920
SIC 5045 5043 5046 5199 7372

LILLY CO p 866
3613 Knight Arnold Rd, Memphis TN 38118
Tel (901) 363-6000
SIC 5084 7699 7359 5046

FRANKE SSG INC p 574
800 Aviation Pkwy, Smyrna TN 37167
Tel (615) 462-4000 SIC 5046

NJ MALIN & ASSOCIATES LLC p 1045
15870 Midway Rd, Addison TX 75001
Tel (972) 458-2680 SIC 5046 5084

ACCENT FOOD SERVICES LLC p 14
16209 Central Commerce Dr, Austin TX 73301
Tel (512) 251-9500 SIC 5046

■ COOKTEK INDUCTION SYSTEM LLC p 366
2801 Trade Ctr, Carrollton TX 75007
Tel (312) 563-9600 SIC 5046

STRATEGIC EQUIPMENT AND SUPPLY CORP p 1392
1461 S Belt Line Rd # 100, Coppell TX 75019
Tel (469) 240-7200 SIC 5046

STRATEGIC EQUIPMENT LLC p 1392
1461 S Belt Line Rd # 100, Coppell TX 75019
Tel (469) 240-7200 SIC 5046

EL CHICO RESTAURANTS INC p 482
12200 N Stemmons Fwy, Dallas TX 75234
Tel (972) 241-5500 SIC 5812 6794 5046

■ HOUSTON SYSCO INC p 712
10710 Grens Crossing Blvd, Houston TX 77038
Tel (713) 672-8080
SIC 5149 5142 5046 5141 2099

MEXICAN RESTAURANTS INC p 957
12000 Aerospace Ave # 400, Houston TX 77034
Tel (832) 300-5858 SIC 5812 6794 5046

WILLISTON HOLDINGS INC p 1612
12000 Aerospace Ave # 400, Houston TX 77034
Tel (832) 300-5858 SIC 5812 6794 5046

ACE MART RESTAURANT SUPPLY CO p 16
2653 Austin Hwy, San Antonio TX 78218
Tel (210) 323-4400 SIC 5169 5046

JOHNSON BROS BAKERY SUPPLY INC p 790
10731 N Ih 35, San Antonio TX 78233
Tel (210) 590-2575 SIC 5149 5046

LIBERTO SPECIALTY CO INC p 861
830 S Presa St, San Antonio TX 78210
Tel (210) 222-1415 SIC 5046 5145

TRAMONTINA USA INC p 1469
12955 W Airport Blvd, Sugar Land TX 77478
Tel (281) 340-8400 SIC 5046 5072 5085

BENCHMARK HOSPITALITY INC p 172
4 Waterway Square Pl # 300, The Woodlands TX 77380
Tel (281) 367-5757 SIC 8741 5046

NICHOLAS & CO INC p 1042
5520 W Harold Gatty Dr, Salt Lake City UT 84116
Tel (801) 531-1100 SIC 5046 5141 5142

KEURIG GREEN MOUNTAIN INC p 814
33 Coffee Ln, Waterbury VT 05676
Tel (802) 244-5621 SIC 5046

■ VIRGINIA FOODSERVICE GROUP LLC p 1559
7420 Ranco Rd, Henrico VA 23228
Tel (804) 237-1001 SIC 5141 5046

■ HILTON SUPPLY MANAGEMENT LLC p 695
7930 Jones Branch Dr # 400, Mc Lean VA 22102
Tel (703) 883-1000 SIC 5046 5021

BARGREEN-ELLINGSON INC p 155
6626 Tacoma Mall Blvd B, Tacoma WA 98409
Tel (253) 475-9201 SIC 5046 2541

■ SYSCO BARABOO LLC p 1416
910 South Blvd, Baraboo WI 53913
Tel (800) 733-8217
SIC 5141 5142 5046 5148

VALLEY BAKERS COOPERATIVE ASSOCIATION p 1540
W6470 Quality Dr, Greenville WI 54942
Tel (920) 560-3200 SIC 5149 5046

GUSTAVE A LARSON CO p 648
W233n2869 Roundy Cir W, Pewaukee WI 53072
Tel (262) 542-0200
SIC 5075 5078 5084 5046

BOELTER COMPANIES INC p 197
N22 W23685 Rdgview Pkwy W, Waukesha WI 53188
Tel (262) 523-6200
SIC 5113 5046 7389 5087

SIC 5047 Medical, Dental & Hospital Eqpt & Splys Wholesale

INFIRMARY HEALTH SYSTEM INC p 741
5 Mobile Infirmary Cir, Mobile AL 36607
Tel (251) 435-3030
SIC 8062 6512 1542 7322 5047 7389

SAAD ENTERPRISES INC p 1263
1515 S University Blvd, Mobile AL 36609
Tel (251) 343-9600
SIC 8082 5047 7352 5912 5621 8741

OPTION 1 NUTRITION SOLUTIONS LLC p 1090
2460 E Germann Rd Ste 18, Chandler AZ 85286
Tel (480) 883-1188 SIC 5047

SMARTHEALTH INC p 1332
3400 E Mcdowell Rd, Phoenix AZ 85008
Tel (602) 225-9090 SIC 5047

■ STRYKER SUSTAINABILITY SOLUTIONS INC p 1394
1810 W Drake Dr Ste 101, Tempe AZ 85283
Tel (888) 888-3433
SIC 5084 5047 7699 3842 3841

K & K VETERINARY SUPPLY INC p 798
675 Laura Ln, Tontitown AR 72770
Tel (479) 361-1516 SIC 5199 5047 5072

DR FRESH LLC p 454
6645 Caballero Blvd, Buena Park CA 90620
Tel (714) 690-1573 SIC 5047 3843

■ ALPHATEC SPINE INC p 60
5818 El Camino Real, Carlsbad CA 92008
Tel (760) 494-6610 SIC 3842 8711 5047

JOERNS LLC p 787
19748 Dearborn St, Chatsworth CA 91311
Tel (800) 966-6662 SIC 5047

■ THERAPAK LLC p 1447
651 Wharton Dr, Claremont CA 91711
Tel (909) 267-2000 SIC 5047

DIASORIN MOLECULAR LLC p 437
11331 Valley View St, Cypress CA 90630
Tel (562) 240-6500 SIC 2835 5047

KARL STORZ ENDOSCOPY-AMERICA INC p 804
2151 E Grand Ave, El Segundo CA 90245
Tel (424) 218-8100 SIC 3841 5047

NITINOL DEVICES AND COMPONENTS INC p 1045
47533 Westinghouse Dr, Fremont CA 94539
Tel (510) 683-2000 SIC 3841 5047

VICTOR INSTRUMENTS INC p 1555
50 Bunsen, Irvine CA 92618
Tel (949) 855-0337 SIC 5122 5047

APRIA HEALTHCARE LLC p 100
26220 Enterprise Ct, Lake Forest CA 92630
Tel (949) 616-2606 SIC 5047 7352 5999

SHIMADZU PRECISION INSTRUMENTS INC p 1316
3645 N Lakewood Blvd, Long Beach CA 90808
Tel (562) 420-6226 SIC 5088 5047 5084

GRIFOLS USA LLC p 640
2410 Lillyvale Ave, Los Angeles CA 90032
Tel (800) 421-0008 SIC 5047

▲ VCA INC p 1545
12401 W Olympic Blvd, Los Angeles CA 90064
Tel (310) 571-6500 SIC 0742 5999 5047

VETERINARY SERVICE INC p 1553
4100 Bangs Ave, Modesto CA 95356
Tel (209) 545-5100 SIC 5047 5199 5083

KAISER HOSPITAL ASSET MANAGEMENT INC p 800
1 Kaiser Plz 19l, Oakland CA 94612
Tel (510) 271-5910 SIC 5047

■ CAREFUSION SOLUTIONS LLC p 255
3750 Torrey View Ct, San Diego CA 92130
Tel (858) 617-2100 SIC 5047

MERRY X-RAY CHEMICAL CORP p 950
4444 Viewridge Ave A, San Diego CA 92123
Tel (858) 565-4472 SIC 5047

MERRY X-RAY CORP p 950
4444 Viewridge Ave, San Diego CA 92123
Tel (858) 565-4472 SIC 5047

▲ MCKESSON CORP p 930
1 Post St Fl 18, San Francisco CA 94104
Tel (415) 983-8300
SIC 5122 5047 5199 7372

LUMENIS INC p 885
2033 Gateway Pl Ste 200, San Jose CA 95110
Tel (408) 764-3000 SIC 5047

■ NDS SURGICAL IMAGING LLC p 1022
5750 Hellyer Ave, San Jose CA 95138
Tel (408) 776-0085 SIC 5047

TWIN MED LLC p 1495
11333 Greenstone Ave, Santa Fe Springs CA 90670
Tel (323) 582-9900 SIC 5047

FFF ENTERPRISES INC p 539
41093 County Center Dr, Temecula CA 92591
Tel (951) 296-2500 SIC 5122 5047

PROFESSIONAL HOSPITAL SUPPLY INC p 1180
42500 Winchester Rd, Temecula CA 92590
Tel (951) 699-5000 SIC 5047

TOSHIBA AMERICA MEDICAL SYSTEMS INC p 1462
2441 Michelle Dr, Tustin CA 92780
Tel (714) 730-5000 SIC 5047

■ PRECISION DYNAMICS CORP p 1168
27770 N Entrmt Dr Ste 200, Valencia CA 91355
Tel (818) 897-1111
SIC 2672 2754 5047 3069

QIAGEN INC p 1195
27220 Turnberry Ln # 200, Valencia CA 91355
Tel (661) 702-3598
SIC 3826 5047 8731 2835

ANDWIN CORP p 91
6636 Variel Ave, Woodland Hills CA 91303
Tel (818) 999-2828
SIC 5113 3842 5199 5087 5047 2835

VCP MOBILITY INC p 1545
6899 Winchester Cir # 200, Boulder CO 80301
Tel (303) 218-4500
SIC 3842 2599 2515 5047 3841

COCHLEAR AMERICAS CORP p 333
13059 E Peakview Ave, Centennial CO 80111
Tel (303) 790-9010 SIC 5047

UNITED STATES WELDING INC p 1514
600 S Santa Fe Dr, Denver CO 80223
Tel (303) 777-2475
SIC 5169 5084 5085 5047 7359

■ ANIMAL HEALTH INTERNATIONAL INC p 91
822 7th St Ste 740, Greeley CO 80631
Tel (970) 353-2600
SIC 5122 5047 5999 5191 5083 5154

TERUMO BCT INC p 1440
10811 W Collins Ave, Lakewood CO 80215
Tel (303) 232-6800
SIC 8733 3842 3845 5047 7352 7699

■ MOORE MEDICAL LLC p 987
1690 New Britain Ave A, Farmington CT 06032
Tel (860) 826-3600 SIC 5047 5122

AERO-MED LTD p 30
85 Commerce St, Glastonbury CT 06033
Tel (860) 659-0602 SIC 5047

ASSISTIVE TECHNOLOGY GROUP INC p 119
1111 Cromwell Ave Ste 601, Rocky Hill CT 06067
Tel (860) 257-3443 SIC 5047

ATG HOLDINGS INC p 124
1111 Cromwell Ave Ste 601, Rocky Hill CT 06067
Tel (860) 257-3443 SIC 5047

FUJIFILM MEDICAL SYSTEMS USA INC p 583
419 West Ave, Stamford CT 06902
Tel (203) 324-2000 SIC 5047 5043 3861

■ COOPERSURGICAL INC p 367
95 Corporate Dr, Trumbull CT 06611
Tel (203) 601-5200
SIC 5047 3842 3841 3845

■ ANDERSON GROUP INC p 90
3411 Silverside Rd # 103, Wilmington DE 19810
Tel (302) 478-6160
SIC 5047 5063 5099 7699 3443

SMITH & NEPHEW HOLDINGS INC p 1333
1201 N Orange St Ste 788, Wilmington DE 19801
Tel (302) 884-6720 SIC 5047 3841

MED-CARE DIABETIC & MEDICAL SUPPLIES INC p 935
901 Yamato Rd Ste 101, Boca Raton FL 33431
Tel (800) 407-0109 SIC 5047

NIPRO MEDICAL CORP p 1044
3150 Nw 107th Ave, Doral FL 33172
Tel (305) 599-7174 SIC 5047

LEESAR INC p 852
2727 Winkler Ave, Fort Myers FL 33901
Tel (239) 939-8800 SIC 5047

■ GULF SOUTH MEDICAL SUPPLY INC p 647
4345 Sthpint Blvd Ste 100, Jacksonville FL 32216
Tel (904) 332-3000 SIC 5047

■ PSS WORLD MEDICAL INC p 1188
4345 Southpoint Blvd # 110, Jacksonville FL 32216
Tel (904) 332-3000 SIC 5122 5047

WORLD MEDICAL GOVERNMENT SOLUTIONS LLC p 1625
4345 Southpoint Blvd, Jacksonville FL 32216
Tel (904) 332-3000 SIC 5047

ACCESS MEDIQUIP LLC p 15
255 Primera Blvd Ste 230, Lake Mary FL 32746
Tel (713) 985-4850 SIC 5047

■ PRIORITY HEALTHCARE DISTRIBUTION INC p 1177
255 Technology Park, Lake Mary FL 32746
Tel (407) 833-7000 SIC 5122 5047

SANARE LLC p 1277
3620 Enterprise Way, Miramar FL 33025
Tel (305) 438-9696 SIC 5047

UNIVITA OF FLORIDA INC p 1528
15800 Sw 25th St, Miramar FL 33027
Tel (305) 826-0244 SIC 5047 7352

UNITED STATES PHARMACEUTICAL GROUP LLC p 1514
13621 Nw 12th St Ste 100, Sunrise FL 33323
Tel (954) 903-5000 SIC 5047

SYNERGY HEALTH NORTH AMERICA INC p 1415
401 E Jackson St Ste 3100, Tampa FL 33602
Tel (813) 891-9550 SIC 5047 7213

ENDOCHOICE INC p 496
11405 Old Roswell Rd, Alpharetta GA 30009
Tel (888) 682-3636 SIC 5047

ELEKTA HOLDINGS US INC p 486
400 Perimeter Center Ter, Atlanta GA 30346
Tel (770) 300-9725 SIC 5047 3841

MOLNLYCKE HEALTH CARE US LLC p 983
5550 Peachtree Pkwy # 500, Norcross GA 30092
Tel (678) 250-7900 SIC 5047

PETER BRASSELER HOLDINGS LLC p 1138
1 Brasseler Blvd, Savannah GA 31419
Tel (912) 925-8525 SIC 5047 3841 3843

MED-ACOUSTICS INC p 935
1685 E Park Place Blvd, Stone Mountain GA 30087
Tel (770) 498-8075 SIC 5047 1742

■ MWI ANIMAL HEALTH p 1004
3041 W Pasadena Dr, Boise ID 83705
Tel (208) 955-8930 SIC 5047 5149

■ MWI VETERINARY SUPPLY CO p 1004
3041 W Pasadena Dr, Boise ID 83705
Tel (208) 955-8930
SIC 5047 2834 2835 2836

ARJOHUNTLEIGH INC p 109
2349 W Lake St Ste 250, Addison IL 60101
Tel (630) 785-4490 SIC 5047

DRYER CANCER CENTER p 457
1221 N Highland Ave, Aurora IL 60506
Tel (630) 264-8656 SIC 5047 8011

SCRIP HOLDING CORP p 1294
360 Veterans Pkwy Ste 115, Bolingbrook IL 60440
Tel (630) 771-7400 SIC 5047

■ SAGE PRODUCTS LLC p 1267
3909 3 Oaks Rd, Cary IL 60013
Tel (815) 455-4700 SIC 3842 5047

■ GETZ BROS& CO INC p 609
225 W Washington St # 1900, Chicago IL 60606
Tel (312) 845-5686
SIC 5047 5031 5141 5065 5082

UNLIMITED ADVACARE INC p 1528
2939 N Pulaski Rd, Chicago IL 60641
Tel (773) 725-8858 SIC 5047

■ BAXTER HEALTHCARE CORP p 160
1 Baxter Pkwy, Deerfield IL 60015
Tel (224) 948-2000
SIC 3841 2835 2389 3842 5047

■ COVENTRY HEALTH CARE WORKERS COMPENSATION INC p 385
3200 Highland Ave, Downers Grove IL 60515
Tel (630) 737-7900 SIC 5047

MR CHIPS INC p 996
1380 Gateway Dr Ste 7, Elgin IL 60124
Tel (847) 468-9000 SIC 5092 5047

▲ LANDAUER INC p 842
2 Science Rd, Glenwood IL 60425
Tel (708) 755-7000 SIC 8734 5047 3829

OMRON MANAGEMENT CENTER OF AMERICA INC p 1085
2895 Greenspoint Pkwy # 100, Hoffman Estates IL 60169
Tel (224) 520-7650
SIC 5044 5046 5065 5047 5045 8732

RIVERSIDE HEALTH SYSTEM p 1238
350 N Wall St, Kankakee IL 60901
Tel (815) 933-1671
SIC 8082 8062 5912 5047

▲ AKORN INC p 42
1925 W Field Ct Ste 300, Lake Forest IL 60045
Tel (847) 279-6100 SIC 2834 5047

FENWAL HOLDINGS INC p 537
3 Corporate Dr Ste 300, Lake Zurich IL 60047
Tel (847) 550-2300 SIC 3069 5047

FENWAL INC p 537
3 Corporate Dr Ste 300, Lake Zurich IL 60047
Tel (847) 550-2300 SIC 5047 3069

SYSMEX AMERICA INC p 1418
577 Aptakisic Rd, Lincolnshire IL 60069
Tel (847) 996-4500 SIC 5047 3841

MEDELA INC p 935
1101 Corporate Dr, Mchenry IL 60050
Tel (800) 435-8316 SIC 5047 3596

MEDLINE INDUSTRIES INC p 938
3 Lakes Dr, Northfield IL 60093
Tel (847) 949-5500 SIC 3841 5047 5999

LIFEWATCH CORP p 865
10255 W Higgins Rd # 100, Rosemont IL 60018
Tel (847) 720-2100 SIC 8099 5047 3845

LIFEWATCH SERVICES INC p 865
10255 W Higgins Rd # 100, Rosemont IL 60018
Tel (847) 720-2100
SIC 5047 8099 3845 8071

RICHARD WOLF MEDICAL INSTRUMENTS CORP p 1232
353 Corporate Woods Pkwy, Vernon Hills IL 60061
Tel (847) 913-1113 SIC 5047 3841

■ CARDINAL HEALTH 200 LLC p 253
3651 Birchwood Dr, Waukegan IL 60085
Tel (847) 578-9500 SIC 5047

BRAINLAB INC p 207
5 Westbrook Corp Ctr, Westchester IL 60154
Tel (800) 784-7700 SIC 5047 3841

ST VINCENT ANDERSON REGIONAL HOSPITAL INC p 1373
2015 Jackson St, Anderson IN 46016
Tel (765) 649-2511 SIC 8062 5047

WILLIAMS BROS HEALTH CARE PHARMACY INC p 1611
10 Williams Brothers Dr, Washington IN 47501
Tel (812) 254-2497
SIC 5047 7352 5999 5169 3999

INTEGRATED DNA TECHNOLOGIES INC p 749
1710 Commercial Park, Coralville IA 52241
Tel (319) 626-8400 SIC 8733 5047

VGM GROUP INC p 1553
1111 W San Marnan Dr, Waterloo IA 50701
Tel (319) 235-7100 SIC 8748 5047

BRIGGS MEDICAL SERVICE CO p 212
7300 Westown Pkwy Ste 100, West Des Moines IA 50266
Tel (515) 327-6400 SIC 5047

NEWMAN MEMORIAL HOSPITAL FOUNDATION p 1038
1201 W 12th Ave, Emporia KS 66801
Tel (620) 343-6800 SIC 8062 5047 8011

LABORATORY SUPPLY CO p 836
1951 Bishop Ln Ste 300, Louisville KY 40218
Tel (800) 888-5227 SIC 5047

RECOVERCARE LLC p 1215
1920 Stanley Gault Pkwy # 100, Louisville KY 40223
Tel (502) 489-9449 SIC 5047 8099

■ RAPIDES HEALTHCARE SYSTEM LLC p 1208
211 4th St, Alexandria LA 71301
Tel (318) 473-3150 SIC 8062 5047

AFFILIATED HEALTHCARE SYSTEMS p 32
931 Union St, Bangor ME 04401
Tel (207) 973-6720
SIC 5047 8071 8741 7322 6512

▲ IDEXX LABORATORIES INC p 729
1 Idexx Dr, Westbrook ME 04092
Tel (207) 556-0300 SIC 3826 2834 5047

CHINDEX INTERNATIONAL INC p 301
4340 East West Hwy # 1100, Bethesda MD 20814
Tel (301) 215-7777 SIC 5047 8062

AMBU INC p 65
6230 Old Dobbin Ln # 250, Columbia MD 21045
Tel (410) 768-6464 SIC 5047

SHIMADZU AMERICA INC p 1316
7102 Riverwood Dr, Columbia MD 21046
Tel (410) 381-1227 SIC 5049 5047 5088

ROBERTS OXYGEN CO INC p 1242
15830 Redland Rd, Rockville MD 20855
Tel (301) 315-9090 SIC 5085 5169 5047

PHILIPS ELECTRONICS NORTH AMERICA CORP p 1143
3000 Minuteman Rd Ms1203, Andover MA 01810
Tel (978) 687-1501
SIC 5064 3651 3674 3641 3645 5047

PHILIPS HOLDING USA INC p 1143
3000 Minuteman Rd Ste 109, Andover MA 01810
Tel (978) 687-1501
SIC 5064 3674 5045 5047 3641

STRAUMANN USA LLC p 1393
60 Minuteman Rd, Andover MA 01810
Tel (978) 747-2500 *SIC* 5047

■ PATTERSON VETERINARY SUPPLY INC p 1121
137 Barnum Rd, Devens MA 01434
Tel (978) 353-6000 *SIC* 5047

KAZ INC p 805
400 Donald Lynch Blvd # 300, Marlborough MA 01752
Tel (508) 490-7000 *SIC* 8082 2834 5047

CARL ZEISS MICROSCOPY LLC p 256
1 Corporate Pl Ste 3, Peabody MA 01960
Tel (978) 826-1500 *SIC* 5047 3826

GYRUS ACMI LLC p 649
136 Turnpike Rd Ste 300, Southborough MA 01772
Tel (508) 804-2600 *SIC* 3841 5047

MEDICAL SPECIALTIES DISTRIBUTORS LLC p 937
800 Technology Center Dr # 3, Stoughton MA 02072
Tel (781) 344-6000 *SIC* 5047 7352

FRESENIUS MEDICAL CARE CARDIOVASCULAR RESOURCES INC p 578
920 Winter St Ste A, Waltham MA 02451
Tel (781) 402-9000 *SIC* 8092 5047 8071

OLYMPUS SCIENTIFIC SOLUTIONS TECHNOLOGIES INC p 1083
48 Woerd Ave, Waltham MA 02453
Tel (781) 419-3900 *SIC* 5047

■ ASPEN SURGICAL PRODUCTS INC p 118
6945 Southbelt Dr Se, Caledonia MI 49316
Tel (616) 698-7100 *SIC* 5047

IRB MEDICAL EQUIPMENT LLC p 764
1000 Health Park Blvd B, Grand Blanc MI 48439
Tel (810) 953-0760 *SIC* 5047 7389

GENERIC DRUG HOLDINGS INC p 602
31778 Enterprise Dr, Livonia MI 48150
Tel (734) 743-6000 *SIC* 8734 5122 5047

■ HARVARD DRUG GROUP L L C p 666
17177 N Laurel Park Dr # 233, Livonia MI 48152
Tel (734) 525-8700 *SIC* 5122 5047 8734

LAKE COURT MEDICAL SUPPLIES INC p 839
27733 Groesbeck Hwy, Roseville MI 48066
Tel (800) 860-3130 *SIC* 5047

J&B MEDICAL SUPPLY CO INC p 772
50496 Pontiac Trl Ste 500, Wixom MI 48393
Tel (800) 737-0045 *SIC* 5047

▲ OTTER TAIL CORP p 1098
215 S Cascade St, Fergus Falls MN 56537
Tel (218) 739-8200
SIC 4911 3084 5047 2099 1731

MIDWEST VETERINARY SUPPLY INC p 968
21467 Holyoke Ave, Lakeville MN 55044
Tel (952) 894-4350 *SIC* 5122 5047

COLOPLAST CORP p 338
1601 W River Rd, Minneapolis MN 55411
Tel (612) 337-7800 *SIC* 3842 2844 5047

■ MCKESSON MEDICAL-SURGICAL MEDIMART INC p 930
8121 10th Ave N, Minneapolis MN 55427
Tel (763) 595-6000 *SIC* 5047 5999

MEDTRONIC USA INC p 939
710 Medtronic Pkwy, Minneapolis MN 55432
Tel (763) 514-4000 *SIC* 3841 5047

MEDTRONIC WORLD TRADE CORP p 939
710 Medtronic Pkwy, Minneapolis MN 55432
Tel (763) 574-4000 *SIC* 5047

■ STERILMED INC p 1386
5010 Cheshire Pkwy N # 2, Plymouth MN 55446
Tel (888) 541-0078 *SIC* 5047

■ GUIDANT SALES LLC p 645
4100 Hamline Ave N, Saint Paul MN 55112
Tel (800) 949-9459
SIC 3841 3845 5047 8733

▲ PATTERSON COMPANIES INC p 1121
1031 Mendota Heights Rd, Saint Paul MN 55120
Tel (651) 686-1600
SIC 5047 5112 7372 7699 2834

■ PATTERSON DENTAL SUPPLY INC p 1121
1031 Mendota Heights Rd, Saint Paul MN 55120
Tel (651) 686-1600 *SIC* 5047

■ ST JUDE MEDICAL SC INC p 1369
1 Lillehei Plz, Saint Paul MN 55117
Tel (651) 483-2000 *SIC* 5047

DIASORIN INC p 437
1951 Northwestern Ave S, Stillwater MN 55082
Tel (651) 439-9710 *SIC* 2835 5047

FIRST CHOICE MEDICAL SUPPLY LLC p 545
127 Interstate Dr, Richland MS 39218
Tel (800) 809-4556 *SIC* 5047

MIDWEST MEDICAL SUPPLY CO LLC p 967
13400 Lakefront Dr, Earth City MO 63045
Tel (314) 291-2900 *SIC* 5047

UNITED SEATING & MOBILITY LLC p 1511
975 Hornet Dr, Hazelwood MO 63042
Tel (314) 731-7867 *SIC* 5047

VEDCO INC p 1546
5503 Corporate Dr, Saint Joseph MO 64507
Tel (816) 238-8840 *SIC* 5047

MEDICAL WEST RESPIRATORY SVCS LLC p 937
9301 Dielman Indus Dr, Saint Louis MO 63132
Tel (314) 993-8100 *SIC* 5047 8082

LAMBERT VET SUPPLY LLC p 841
714 5th St, Fairbury NE 68352
Tel (402) 729-3044 *SIC* 5047

CASSLING DIAGNOSTIC IMAGING INC p 264
13808 F St, Omaha NE 68137
Tel (402) 334-5000 *SIC* 5047 7699

SHARED SERVICE SYSTEMS INC p 1312
1725 S 20th St, Omaha NE 68108
Tel (402) 536-5300
SIC 5047 5142 7211 5149 5113 7218

MYCONE DENTAL SUPPLY CO INC p 1004
480 S Democrat Rd, Gibbstown NJ 08027
Tel (856) 663-4700 *SIC* 5047 3843 2844

■ HOWMEDICA OSTEONICS CORP p 713
325 Corporate Dr, Mahwah NJ 07430
Tel (201) 831-5000 *SIC* 3842 5047

PENTAX OF AMERICA INC p 1132
3 Paragon Dr, Montvale NJ 07645
Tel (201) 391-4229 *SIC* 5047

■ BIOSCRIP INFUSION SERVICES LLC p 184
102 The American Rd, Morris Plains NJ 07950
Tel (973) 597-0444 *SIC* 5047

■ ASCENSIA DIABETES CARE US INC p 116
5 Woodhollow Rd, Parsippany NJ 07054
Tel (973) 560-6500 *SIC* 5047 2835 3841

■ EBI LLC p 474
399 Jefferson Rd, Parsippany NJ 07054
Tel (973) 299-9300 *SIC* 5047

DATWYLER PHARMA PACKAGING USA REALTY INC p 414
9012 Pennsauken Hwy, Pennsauken NJ 08110
Tel (856) 663-2202 *SIC* 5047 3841

KONICA MINOLTA HOLDINGS USA INC p 827
100 Williams Dr, Ramsey NJ 07446
Tel (201) 825-4000
SIC 5043 5065 5044 5047

COMMUNITY SURGICAL SUPPLY OF TOMS RIVER INC p 350
1390 Rte 37 W, Toms River NJ 08755
Tel (732) 349-2990 *SIC* 5047 7352 5912

KONICA MINOLTA HEALTHCARE AMERICAS INC p 827
411 Newark Pompton Tpke, Wayne NJ 07470
Tel (973) 633-1500 *SIC* 5047 3861 3845

MAQUET CARDIOVASCULAR US SALES LLC p 904
45 Barbour Pond Dr, Wayne NJ 07470
Tel (201) 995-8700 *SIC* 5047

MAQUET INC p 904
45 Barbour Pond Dr, Wayne NJ 07470
Tel (973) 709-7000 *SIC* 5047

AMBERCARE CORP p 65
420 N Main St, Belen NM 87002
Tel (505) 861-0060
SIC 8082 8361 5047 7352

IVOCLAR VIVADENT INC p 769
175 Pineview Dr, Amherst NY 14228
Tel (716) 691-0010 *SIC* 5047 8021

BELLCO DRUG CORP p 170
5500 New Horizons Blvd, Amityville NY 11701
Tel (631) 789-6900 *SIC* 5122 5047

ACCUMED TECHNOLOGIES INC p 16
160 Bud Mil Dr Ste 1, Buffalo NY 14206
Tel (716) 853-1800 *SIC* 5047

BUFFALO HOSPITAL SUPPLY CO INC p 224
4039 Genesee St Ste 100, Buffalo NY 14225
Tel (716) 626-9400 *SIC* 5047

DIVAL SAFETY EQUIPMENT INC p 443
1721 Niagara St, Buffalo NY 14207
Tel (716) 874-9060
SIC 5099 8748 8734 5047 5136 5661

CREATIVE ORTHOTICS & PROSTHETICS INC p 390
1300 College Ave Ste 1, Elmira NY 14901
Tel (607) 734-7215 *SIC* 3842 5999 5047

TRINITY BIOTECH INC p 1481
2823 Girts Rd, Jamestown NY 14701
Tel (800) 325-3424 *SIC* 5047

DARBY DENTAL SUPPLY LLC p 412
300 Jericho Quadrangle Ll, Jericho NY 11753
Tel (516) 688-6252 *SIC* 5047

▲ HENRY SCHEIN INC p 684
135 Duryea Rd, Melville NY 11747
Tel (631) 843-5500 *SIC* 5047 5122 7372

NAGASE AMERICA CORP p 1006
546 5th Ave Fl 16, New York NY 10036
Tel (212) 703-1340
SIC 5169 5162 5122 5065 5047

UHS HOLDCO INC p 1500
383 Madison Ave Fl 40, New York NY 10179
Tel (212) 272-2000 *SIC* 7352 5047

SOURCE-RAY INC p 1342
50 Fleetwood Ct, Ronkonkoma NY 11779
Tel (631) 244-8200 *SIC* 5047

SIEMENS HEALTHCARE DIAGNOSTICS INC p 1320
511 Benedict Ave, Tarrytown NY 10591
Tel (914) 631-8000 *SIC* 5047

LAERDAL MEDICAL CORP p 837
167 Myers Corners Rd, Wappingers Falls NY 12590
Tel (845) 297-7770 *SIC* 5047 3845 3841

SAMARITAN MEDICAL CENTER p 1274
830 Washington St, Watertown NY 13601
Tel (315) 785-4000 *SIC* 8062 5047

BYRAM HEALTHCARE CENTERS INC p 231
120 Bloomingdale Rd # 301, White Plains NY 10605
Tel (914) 286-2000 *SIC* 5999 5047

AMERICAN PRODUCT DISTRIBUTORS INC p 78
8350 Arrowridge Blvd, Charlotte NC 28273
Tel (704) 522-9411
SIC 5111 5112 5047 5044 5085 5087

JOERNS HEALTHCARE LLC p 787
2430 Whit Park Dr Ste 100, Charlotte NC 28273
Tel (704) 499-6000 *SIC* 5047

■ KAVO DENTAL TECHNOLOGIES LLC p 805
11729 Fruehauf Dr, Charlotte NC 28273
Tel (888) 275-5286 *SIC* 5047

QUAD-C JH HOLDINGS INC p 1195
2430 Whitehall Park Dr, Charlotte NC 28273
Tel (800) 826-0270 *SIC* 5047

HILLCO LTD p 693
1435 Hwy 258 N, Kinston NC 28504
Tel (252) 523-9094
SIC 8051 8059 5047 5122

GREINER BIO-ONE NORTH AMERICA INC p 639
4238 Capital Dr, Monroe NC 28110
Tel (704) 261-7883 *SIC* 5047

TECAN US GROUP INC p 1430
9401 Globe Center Dr # 140, Morrisville NC 27560
Tel (919) 361-5200 *SIC* 5047 3841

TRIAD GROUP INC p 1478
623 W Main St, Yadkinville NC 27055
Tel (336) 679-8852 *SIC* 8051 5047 7374

■ VARISTAR CORP p 1545
4334 18th Ave S Ste 200, Fargo ND 58103
Tel (701) 232-6414
SIC 6719 4899 1623 5047 1731 4213

PARTSSOURCE INC p 1119
777 Lena Dr, Aurora OH 44202
Tel (330) 562-9900 *SIC* 5047

BIOTECH MEDICAL INC p 184
7800 Whipple Ave Nw, Canton OH 44767
Tel (330) 494-5504 *SIC* 5047

■ BIORX LLC p 184
7167 E Kemper Rd, Cincinnati OH 45249
Tel (866) 442-4679
SIC 5122 8748 2834 5047 8051

■ MEDPACE INC p 938
5375 Medpace Way, Cincinnati OH 45227
Tel (513) 579-9911 *SIC* 8731 5122 5047

■ NEIGHBORCARE INC p 1024
201 E 4th St Ste 900, Cincinnati OH 45202
Tel (513) 719-2600
SIC 5122 5912 5047 7389

■ OMNICARE INC p 1085
900 Omnicare Ctr, Cincinnati OH 45202
Tel (513) 719-2600
SIC 5122 5047 8082 8741

PHILIPS MEDICAL SYSTEMS (CLEVELAND) INC p 1143
595 Miner Rd, Cleveland OH 44143
Tel (440) 247-2652
SIC 3844 5047 5137 3842 3821 3699

BOUND TREE MEDICAL LLC p 204
5000 Tuttle Crossing Blvd, Dublin OH 43016
Tel (614) 760-5000 *SIC* 5047

■ BUTLER ANIMAL HEALTH HOLDING CO LLC p 230
400 Metro Pl N Ste 100, Dublin OH 43017
Tel (614) 761-9095 *SIC* 5122 5149 5047

■ BUTLER ANIMAL HEALTH SUPPLY LLC p 230
400 Metro Pl N Ste 100, Dublin OH 43017
Tel (855) 724-3461 *SIC* 5122 5149 5047

■ CARDINAL HEALTH 100 INC p 253
7000 Cardinal Pl, Dublin OH 43017
Tel (614) 757-5000 *SIC* 5122 5047

■ CARDINAL HEALTH 301 LLC p 253
7000 Cardinal Pl, Dublin OH 43017
Tel (614) 757-5000 *SIC* 5047

▲ CARDINAL HEALTH INC p 253
7000 Cardinal Pl, Dublin OH 43017
Tel (614) 757-5000
SIC 5122 5047 8741 3842

SARNOVA INC p 1282
5000 Tuttle Crossing Blvd, Dublin OH 43016
Tel (614) 760-5000 *SIC* 5999 5047

TOSOH AMERICA INC p 1462
3600 Gantz Rd, Grove City OH 43123
Tel (614) 539-8622
SIC 5169 3564 5047 5052

WBC GROUP LLC p 1585
6333 Hudson Crossing Pkwy, Hudson OH 44236
Tel (800) 472-4221 *SIC* 5122 5047 3843

SOURCEONE HEALTHCARE TECHNOLOGIES INC p 1342
8020 Tyler Blvd, Mentor OH 44060
Tel (440) 701-1200 *SIC* 5047

COMPASS HEALTH BRANDS CORP p 351
6753 Engle Rd Ste A, Middleburg Heights OH 44130
Tel (800) 947-1728 *SIC* 5047

CONCORDANCE HEALTHCARE SOLUTIONS LLC p 355
85 Shaffer Park Dr, Tiffin OH 44883
Tel (419) 455-2153 *SIC* 5047

SENECA MEDICAL LLC p 1303
85 Shaffer Park Dr, Tiffin OH 44883
Tel (419) 447-0236 *SIC* 5047

■ ASSURAMED INC p 121
1810 Summit Commerce Park, Twinsburg OH 44087
Tel (330) 963-6998 *SIC* 5047

HITACHI MEDICAL SYSTEMS AMERICA INC p 697
1959 Summit Commerce Park, Twinsburg OH 44087
Tel (330) 425-1313 *SIC* 5047

■ RGH ENTERPRISES INC p 1231
1810 Summit Commerce Park, Twinsburg OH 44087
Tel (330) 963-6998 *SIC* 5999 5047 8011

FERNO-WASHINGTON INC p 538
70 Weil Way, Wilmington OH 45177
Tel (877) 733-0911 *SIC* 5047

BIOTRONIK INC p 184
6024 Jean Rd Ste C8, Lake Oswego OR 97035
Tel (503) 635-3594 *SIC* 5047

A-DEC DENTAL UK LTD p 7
2601 Crestview Dr, Newberg OR 97132
Tel (503) 538-9471 *SIC* 5047

A CARING DOCTOR (TEXAS) PC p 5
8000 Ne Tillamook St, Portland OR 97213
Tel (503) 922-5000 *SIC* 0742 5047

A CARING DOCTOR MINNESOTA PA p 5
8000 Ne Tillamook St, Portland OR 97213
Tel (503) 922-5000 *SIC* 0742 5047

MEDICAL MANAGEMENT INTERNATIONAL INC p 937
8000 Ne Tillamook St, Portland OR 97213
Tel (503) 922-5000 *SIC* 0742 5047

OLYMPUS AMERICA INC p 1083
3500 Corporate Pkwy, Center Valley PA 18034
Tel (484) 896-5000
SIC 5047 5043 5064 3827 3695 3572

OLYMPUS CORP OF AMERICAS p 1083
3500 Corp Pkwy, Center Valley PA 18034
Tel (484) 896-5000
SIC 5047 5043 5064 3827 3695 3572

▲ AMERISOURCEBERGEN CORP p 83
1300 Morris Dr Ste 100, Chesterbrook PA 19087
Tel (610) 727-7000 *SIC* 5122 5047

■ AMERISOURCEBERGEN SERVICES CORP p 83
1300 Morris Dr Ste 100, Chesterbrook PA 19087
Tel (610) 727-7000
SIC 5122 5047 5199 8721

DENTAL IMAGING TECHNOLOGIES CORP p 429
2800 Crystal Dr, Hatfield PA 19440
Tel (215) 997-5666 *SIC* 3843 5047

VYGON CORP p 1567
2750 Morris Rd Ste 200, Lansdale PA 19446
Tel (215) 390-2002 *SIC* 5047

FUJIREBIO DIAGNOSTICS INC p 583
201 Great Valley Pkwy, Malvern PA 19355
Tel (610) 240-3800 *SIC* 5047 8011

SIEMENS MEDICAL SOLUTIONS USA INC p 1320
40 Liberty Blvd, Malvern PA 19355
Tel (610) 219-6300
SIC 5047 3845 3842 3843

WOODEN HEART INC p 1623
64 Amanda Blvd, New Bloomfield PA 17068
Tel (717) 834-7144 *SIC* 5047

QMES LLC p 1195
122 Mill Rd Ste A130, Phoenixville PA 19460
Tel (610) 630-6357 *SIC* 5047 6719

BENCO DENTAL SUPPLY CO p 172
295 Centerpoint Blvd, Pittston PA 18640
Tel (570) 602-7781 *SIC* 5047

VARIETAL DISTRIBUTION HOLDINGS LLC p 1544
100 Matsonford Rd, Radnor PA 19087
Tel (610) 386-1700 *SIC* 5047

▲ VWR CORP p 1567
100 Matsonford Rd 1-200, Radnor PA 19087
Tel (610) 386-1700
SIC 2869 2819 3821 5047

■ CARDINAL HEALTH PR 120 INC p 253
10 Carr 165 Km24, Guaynabo PR 00968
Tel (787) 625-4100 *SIC* 5122 5047

DDH INC p 419
211 Circuit Dr, North Kingstown RI 02852
Tel (401) 667-0800 *SIC* 5047

SYMMETRY SURGICAL INC p 1414
3034 Owen Dr, Antioch TN 37013
Tel (615) 883-9090 *SIC* 5047

MICROPORT ORTHOPEDICS INC p 962
5677 Airline Rd, Arlington TN 38002
Tel (866) 872-0211 *SIC* 5047

ALADDIN TEMP-RITE LLC p 43
250 E Main St, Hendersonville TN 37075
Tel (615) 537-3600 *SIC* 5047

■ CARDINAL HEALTH 108 LLC p 253
305 Tech Park Dr Ste 113, La Vergne TN 37086
Tel (615) 287-5200 *SIC* 5122 5047

PERMOBIL INC p 1136
300 Duke Dr, Lebanon TN 37090
Tel (615) 547-1889 *SIC* 5047

BAPTIST MEMORIAL HEALTH CARE CORP p 154
350 N Humphreys Blvd, Memphis TN 38120
Tel (901) 227-2727
SIC 8062 8011 8741 5047

SMITH & NEPHEW INC p 1333
1450 E Brooks Rd, Memphis TN 38116
Tel (901) 396-2121 *SIC* 3842 5047

ASHLEY MEDICAL SUPPLY INC p 117
1911 Church St, Nashville TN 37203
Tel (615) 329-3150 *SIC* 5047

DIALYSIS CLINIC INC p 436
1633 Church St Ste 500, Nashville TN 37203
Tel (615) 327-3061 *SIC* 8092 5047 8071

■ FIBERWEB INC p 539
9335 Harris Corners Pkwy, Old Hickory TN 37138
Tel (704) 697-5100 *SIC* 2281 5047 5137

■ ENCORE MEDICAL LP p 496
9800 Metric Blvd, Austin TX 78758
Tel (512) 832-9500 *SIC* 3842 5047

HANGER INC p 657
10910 Domain Dr Ste 300, Austin TX 78758
Tel (512) 777-3800 *SIC* 8093 5047 3842

OTTO BOCK HEALTHCARE LP p 1098
11501 Alterra Pkwy # 600, Austin TX 78758
Tel (800) 328-4058 *SIC* 5047

BROADLANE GROUP INC p 215
13727 Noel Rd Ste 1400, Dallas TX 75240
Tel (972) 813-7500 *SIC* 5047

DISTRIBUTION INTERNATIONAL SOUTHWEST INC p 443
9000 Railwood Dr, Houston TX 77078
Tel (713) 428-3900 *SIC* 5087 5047

KURARAY HOLDINGS USA INC p 832
2625 Bay Area Blvd, Houston TX 77058
Tel (713) 495-7311 *SIC* 5047 5049 2821

PROFESSIONAL COMPOUNDING CENTERS OF AMERICA INC p 1180
9901 S Wilcrest Dr, Houston TX 77099
Tel (281) 933-6948 *SIC* 5047 5122

VALLEN SAFETY SUPPLY CO p 1540
521 N Sam Houston Pkwy E # 300, Houston TX 77060
Tel (281) 500-5000
SIC 5099 5084 5047 5063

HEALTH CARE UNLIMITED INC p 674
1100 E Laurel Ave, Mcallen TX 78501
Tel (956) 994-9911 *SIC* 5047 8082

KCI USA INC p 806
12930 W Interstate 10, San Antonio TX 78249
Tel (800) 275-4524 *SIC* 7352 3842 5047

GOLDEN MAX LLC p 621
12701 Directors Dr, Stafford TX 77477
Tel (832) 886-5300 *SIC* 5047

ZEVACOR PHARMA INC p 1642
21000 Atl Blvd Ste 730, Dulles VA 20166
Tel (703) 547-8161 *SIC* 5122 5047

■ MCKESSON MEDICAL-SURGICAL HOLDINGS INC p 930
9954 Mayland Dr Ste 4000, Henrico VA 23233
Tel (804) 264-7500 *SIC* 5047

■ OWENS & MINOR DISTRIBUTION INC p 1100
9120 Lockwood Blvd, Mechanicsville VA 23116
Tel (804) 723-7000 *SIC* 5047

▲ OWENS & MINOR INC p 1100
9120 Lockwood Blvd, Mechanicsville VA 23116
Tel (804) 723-7000 *SIC* 5047

■ OWENS & MINOR MEDICAL INC p 1100
9120 Lockwood Blvd, Mechanicsville VA 23116
Tel (804) 723-7000 *SIC* 5047

GOVERNMENT SCIENTIFIC SOURCE INC p 627
12351 Sunrise Valley Dr, Reston VA 20191
Tel (703) 734-1805 *SIC* 5049 5047

■ MCKESSON MEDICAL-SURGICAL INC p 930
9954 Mayland Dr Ste 4000, Richmond VA 23233
Tel (804) 264-7500 *SIC* 5047

■ AVID MEDICAL INC p 138
9000 Westmont Dr, Toano VA 23168
Tel (757) 566-3510 *SIC* 5047

VALLEY HEALTH SYSTEM p 1540
1840 Amherst St, Winchester VA 22601
Tel (540) 536-8000
SIC 8062 8051 5047 8699

BURKHART DENTAL SUPPLY CO p 227
2502 S 78th St, Tacoma WA 98409
Tel (253) 474-7761 *SIC* 5047

WISCONSIN VISION ASSOCIATES INC p 1619
139 W Chestnut St, Burlington WI 53105
Tel (262) 763-0100 *SIC* 5048 5122 5047

MGS MFG GROUP INC p 958
W188n11707 Maple Rd, Germantown WI 53022
Tel (262) 255-5790 *SIC* 3089 5047 2821

DIRECT SUPPLY INC p 441
6767 N Industrial Rd, Milwaukee WI 53223
Tel (414) 358-2805 *SIC* 5047

MERCO GROUP INC p 945
7711 N 81st St, Milwaukee WI 53223
Tel (414) 365-2600 *SIC* 5199 5047

TIDI PRODUCTS LLC p 1452
570 Enterprise Dr, Neenah WI 54956
Tel (920) 751-4300 *SIC* 3843 3841 5047

SIC 5048 Ophthalmic Goods Wholesale

NEW OPTICS USA INC p 1032
510 W Main St, El Centro CA 92243
Tel (760) 547-7136 *SIC* 5048

NEW OPTICS USA INC p 1032
653 W Main St Ste 1, El Centro CA 92243
Tel (760) 996-9067 *SIC* 5048

VISION SERVICE PLAN p 1561
3333 Quality Dr, Rancho Cordova CA 95670
Tel (916) 851-5000 *SIC* 6324 5048

ABB/CON-CISE OPTICAL GROUP LLC p 9
12301 Nw 39th St, Coral Springs FL 33065
Tel (800) 852-8089 *SIC* 5048 3851 8741

ARANON CORP p 102
285 W 74th Pl, Hialeah FL 33014
Tel (305) 557-9004 *SIC* 5048

WALMAN OPTICAL CO p 1573
801 12th Ave N Ste 1, Minneapolis MN 55411
Tel (612) 520-6000 *SIC* 5048 3851

MARCOLIN USA EYEWEAR CORP p 905
3140 Rte 22, Branchburg NJ 08876
Tel (800) 345-8482 *SIC* 5099 5048

MARCOLIN USA INC p 905
3140 Us Highway 22, Branchburg NJ 08876
Tel (480) 951-7174 *SIC* 5048

NASSAU LENS CO INC p 1009
160 Legrand Ave, Northvale NJ 07647
Tel (201) 767-8033 *SIC* 5048

SAFILO AMERICA INC p 1267
801 Jefferson Rd, Parsippany NJ 07054
Tel (973) 952-2800 *SIC* 5048 5099 5091

SAFILO USA INC p 1267
801 Jefferson Rd, Parsippany NJ 07054
Tel (973) 952-2800 *SIC* 5048

MARCHON EYEWEAR INC p 905
201 Old Country Rd Fl 3, Melville NY 11747
Tel (631) 756-8530 *SIC* 5048

LUXOTTICA US HOLDINGS CORP p 887
12 Harbor Park Dr, Port Washington NY 11050
Tel (516) 484-3800
SIC 5048 5099 5995 5999

SWAROVSKI US HOLDING LIMITED p 1411
1 Kenney Dr, Cranston RI 02920
Tel (401) 463-6400
SIC 3961 3231 5048 5099

ESSILOR LABORATORIES OF AMERICA INC p 510
13515 N Stemmons Fwy, Dallas TX 75234
Tel (972) 241-4141 *SIC* 3851 5048

ESSILOR OF AMERICA INC p 510
13555 N Stemmons Fwy, Dallas TX 75234
Tel (214) 496-4000 *SIC* 3851 5048

WISCONSIN VISION ASSOCIATES INC p 1619
139 W Chestnut St, Burlington WI 53105
Tel (262) 763-0100 *SIC* 5048 5122 5047

SIC 5049 Professional Eqpt & Splys, NEC Wholesale

S & S WORLDWIDE INC p 1261
75 Mill St, Colchester CT 06415
Tel (860) 537-3451 *SIC* 5199 5049 3944

BIO MEDIC CORP p 183
742 Sussex Ave, Seaford DE 19973
Tel (302) 628-4300
SIC 5049 3821 3496 3914 3661

■ METAVANTE HOLDINGS LLC p 953
601 Riverside Ave, Jacksonville FL 32204
Tel (904) 438-6000 *SIC* 3578 5049 7374

PROMETHEAN INC p 1183
1165 Sanctuary Pkwy # 400, Alpharetta GA 30009
Tel (678) 762-1500 *SIC* 5049 5045

MILNER INC p 972
5125 Peachtree Indus Blvd, Norcross GA 30092
Tel (770) 458-0999
SIC 7372 5999 7389 5065 5049 5044

FLINN SCIENTIFIC INC p 557
770 N Raddant Rd, Batavia IL 60510
Tel (800) 452-1261 *SIC* 3821 5049

CPI BUYER LLC p 387
300 N La Salle Dr # 5600, Chicago IL 60654
Tel (312) 382-2200 *SIC* 5049

GTCR LLC p 644
300 N La Salle Dr # 5600, Chicago IL 60654
Tel (312) 382-2200 *SIC* 5049

HARRY J KLOEPPEL & ASSOCIATES INC p 664
246 E Janata Blvd Ste 300, Lombard IL 60148
Tel (630) 206-5810 *SIC* 5049

OPTICSPLANET INC p 1090
3150 Commercial Ave, Northbrook IL 60062
Tel (847) 513-6190 *SIC* 5995 5049

COLE-PARMER INSTRUMENT CO LLC p 336
625 Bunker Ct, Vernon Hills IL 60061
Tel (847) 549-7600 *SIC* 5049

HAND2MIND INC p 657
500 Greenview Ct, Vernon Hills IL 60061
Tel (847) 816-5060 *SIC* 5049 5169

TECHNIKS LLC p 1431
9930 E 56th St, Indianapolis IN 46236
Tel (317) 803-8000 *SIC* 5084 5049

TEMPLETON COAL CO INC p 1436
701 Wabash Ave Ste 501, Terre Haute IN 47807
Tel (812) 232-7037
SIC 5074 3567 3961 5049 3089

■ BUSHNELL HOLDINGS INC p 229
9200 Cody St, Overland Park KS 66214
Tel (913) 752-3400 *SIC* 3851 5049 5091

SHIMADZU AMERICA INC p 1316
7102 Riverwood Dr, Columbia MD 21046
Tel (410) 381-1227 *SIC* 5049 5047 5088

■ INDIGO AMERICA INC p 739
165 Dascomb Rd 1, Andover MA 01810
Tel (978) 474-2000 *SIC* 5049

■ BRUKER DALTONICS INC p 221
40 Manning Rd, Billerica MA 01821
Tel (978) 667-9580 *SIC* 3826 5049

MILLBROOK DISTRIBUTION SERVICES INC p 970
88 Huntoon Memorial Hwy, Leicester MA 01524
Tel (508) 892-8171
SIC 5122 5023 5072 5112 5049 5199

CASCADE SCHOOL SUPPLIES INC p 262
1 Brown St, North Adams MA 01247
Tel (413) 663-3716 *SIC* 5049

JEOL USA INC p 783
11 Dearborn Rd, Peabody MA 01960
Tel (978) 535-5900 *SIC* 5049

SABIC INNOVATIVE PLASTICS US LLC p 1264
1 Plastics Ave, Pittsfield MA 01201
Tel (413) 448-7110 *SIC* 5049

■ FISHER SCIENTIFIC INTERNATIONAL LLC p 552
81 Wyman St, Waltham MA 02451
Tel (781) 622-1000
SIC 2869 3821 5169 5049

ETAS INC p 511
3021 Miller Rd, Ann Arbor MI 48103
Tel (734) 997-9393 *SIC* 5049

ARCH GLOBAL PRECISION LLC p 104
12955 Inkster Rd, Livonia MI 48150
Tel (734) 266-6900 *SIC* 5049 3399

BURROUGHS INC p 228
41100 Plymouth Rd, Plymouth MI 48170
Tel (734) 737-4000 *SIC* 5049

BURROUGHS PAYMENT SYSTEMS INC p 228
41100 Plymouth Rd, Plymouth MI 48170
Tel (734) 737-4000 *SIC* 5049

TIERNEY BROTHERS INC p 1453
1771 Energy Park Dr, Saint Paul MN 55108
Tel (612) 331-5500 *SIC* 5049 5043 3651

U S TOY CO INC p 1497
13201 Arrington Rd, Grandview MO 64030
Tel (816) 761-5900 *SIC* 5049 5092 5945

DANCKER SELLEW & DOUGLAS INC p 411
291 Evans Way, Branchburg NJ 08876
Tel (908) 429-1200 *SIC* 5021 5063 5049

TMCI HOLDINGS INC p 1457
80 Avenue K, Newark NJ 07105
Tel (201) 553-1100
SIC 5122 5023 5072 5112 5049 5199

TOPCON MEDICAL SYSTEMS INC p 1461
111 Bauer Dr, Oakland NJ 07436
Tel (201) 599-5100
SIC 3841 3826 3827 3829 3851 5049

ROSE BRAND WIPERS INC p 1250
4 Emerson Ln, Secaucus NJ 07094
Tel (201) 809-1730 *SIC* 5049 2399

ARTHUR H THOMAS CO p 114
1654 High Hill Rd, Swedesboro NJ 08085
Tel (856) 467-2000 *SIC* 3821 5049

RIO GRANDE INC p 1235
7500 Bluewater Rd Nw, Albuquerque NM 87121
Tel (505) 839-3550 *SIC* 5094 5049 3915

NIKON INC p 1043
1300 Walt Whitman Rd Fl 2, Melville NY 11747
Tel (631) 547-4200 *SIC* 5043 5049

▲ TRANSCAT INC p 1471
35 Vantage Point Dr, Rochester NY 14624
Tel (585) 352-7777 *SIC* 5049 7699

CARL ZEISS INC p 256
1 Zeiss Dr, Thornwood NY 10594
Tel (914) 747-1800
SIC 3827 5049 3829 5084 3826

CARL ZEISS MICROSCOPY LLC p 256
1 Zeiss Dr, Thornwood NY 10594
Tel (914) 747-1800 *SIC* 5049

CAROLINA BIOLOGICAL SUPPLY CO p 259
2700 York Rd, Burlington NC 27215
Tel (336) 584-0381
SIC 5049 2836 3829 3826 3821

ARCATECH SYSTEMS LLC p 104
1151 Holmes Rd, Mebane NC 27302
Tel (919) 442-5200 *SIC* 5049

COLE PAPERS INC p 335
1300 38th St N, Fargo ND 58102
Tel (800) 800-8090
SIC 5113 5111 5169 5023 5112 5049

■ METTLER-TOLEDO LLC p 957
1900 Polaris Pkwy Fl 6, Columbus OH 43240
Tel (614) 438-4511
SIC 3596 5049 7699 3821 3823 3826

■ FISHER SCIENTIFIC CO LLC p 552
300 Industry Dr, Pittsburgh PA 15275
Tel (412) 490-8300
SIC 5049 5169 3821 3826 2869 2819

■ VWR FUNDING INC p 1567
100 Matsonford Rd, Radnor PA 19087
Tel (610) 386-1700 *SIC* 5049 5169

■ VWR INTERNATIONAL LLC p 1567
100 Matsonford Rd Bldg 1, Radnor PA 19087
Tel (610) 386-1700 *SIC* 5169 5049

PACE RESOURCES INC p 1103
140 E Market St Fl 2, York PA 17401
Tel (717) 852-1300
SIC 2752 5049 7334 2789

▲ CARDTRONICS INC p 253
3250 Briarpark Dr Ste 400, Houston TX 77042
Tel (832) 308-4000 *SIC* 7389 5049

EDUCATIONAL PRODUCTS INC p 479
4100 N Sam Houston Pkwy W P, Houston TX 77086
Tel (800) 365-5345 *SIC* 5112 5049

KURARAY HOLDINGS USA INC p 832
2625 Bay Area Blvd, Houston TX 77058
Tel (713) 495-7311 *SIC* 5047 5049 2821

FLSMIDTH USA INC p 561
7158 S Flsmidth Dr, Midvale UT 84047
Tel (801) 871-7000 *SIC* 5049

GOVERNMENT SCIENTIFIC SOURCE INC p 627
12351 Sunrise Valley Dr, Reston VA 20191
Tel (703) 734-1805 *SIC* 5049 5047

SATISLOH NORTH AMERICA INC p 1283
N106w13131 Bradley Way # 200, Germantown WI 53022
Tel (262) 255-6001 *SIC* 5049 5072

SCHOOL SPECIALTY INC p 1290
W6316 Design Dr, Greenville WI 54942
Tel (920) 734-5712 *SIC* 5049 5021

▲ SCHOOL SPECIALTY INC p 1290
W6316 Design Dr, Greenville WI 54942
Tel (920) 734-5712 *SIC* 5049 5021 5961

DOUGLAS STEWART CO INC p 452
2402 Advance Rd, Madison WI 53718
Tel (608) 221-1155 *SIC* 5045 5044 5049

SHELTERED WINGS INC p 1315
2120 W Greenview Dr Ste 4, Middleton WI 53562
Tel (608) 664-9856 *SIC* 5049

SIC 5051 Metals Service Centers

B A E SYSTEM p 141
2101 W 10th St, Anniston AL 36201
Tel (256) 235-9671 *SIC* 5051

ONEAL INDUSTRIES INC p 1087
2311 Highland Ave S # 200, Birmingham AL 35205
Tel (205) 721-2880 *SIC* 5051

ONEAL STEEL INC p 1087
744 41st St N, Birmingham AL 35222
Tel (205) 599-8000 *SIC* 5051

POLYMET ALLOYS INC p 1160
1701 Providence Park # 100, Birmingham AL 35242
Tel (205) 981-2200 *SIC* 5051

■ METALS USA PLATES AND SHAPES SOUTHEAST INC p 953
1251 Woodland Ave, Mobile AL 36610
Tel (251) 456-4531 *SIC* 5051

CONSTRUCTION MATERIALS INC p 361
4350 Northern Blvd, Montgomery AL 36110
Tel (334) 272-8200 *SIC* 5031 5051

FASTENING SOLUTIONS INC p 531
3075 Selma Hwy, Montgomery AL 36108
Tel (334) 284-8300 *SIC* 5085 5072 5051

SABEL STEEL SERVICE INC p 1263
749 N Court St, Montgomery AL 36104
Tel (334) 265-6771 *SIC* 5088 5051

JEFFERSON IRON AND METAL BROKERAGE INC p 782
3940 Montclair Rd Ste 300, Mountain Brk AL 35213
Tel (205) 803-5200 *SIC* 5051

SAGINAW PIPE CO INC p 1268
1980 Hwy 31 S, Saginaw AL 35137
Tel (205) 664-3670 *SIC* 5051

SOUTHWEST METAL INDUSTRIES LLC p 1352
4708 W Pasadena Ave, Glendale AZ 85301
Tel (623) 760-9014 *SIC* 5051 4953

RUSSELLVILLE STEEL CO INC p 1259
280 Steel City Ln, Russellville AR 72802
Tel (479) 968-2211 *SIC* 5051

WEST MEMPHIS STEEL & PIPE INC p 1595
1101 Thompson Ave, West Memphis AR 72301
Tel (870) 735-8244 *SIC* 5051

JIMS SUPPLY CO INC p 786
3530 Buck Owens Blvd, Bakersfield CA 93308
Tel (661) 324-6514 *SIC* 5051

CUSTOM ALLOY SALES INC p 403
13191 Crssrds Pkwy N 37, City Of Industry CA 91746
Tel (626) 369-3641 *SIC* 3341 5051

PJS LUMBER INC p 1153
45055 Fremont Blvd, Fremont CA 94538
Tel (510) 743-5300 *SIC* 5031 5051

ACME METALS & STEEL SUPPLY INC p 18
14930 S San Pedro St, Gardena CA 90248
Tel (310) 329-2263 *SIC* 5051

■ SOS METALS INC p 1341
201 E Gardena Blvd, Gardena CA 90248
Tel (310) 217-8848 *SIC* 5093 5051

TIRECO INC p 1455
500 W 190th St Ste 100, Gardena CA 90248
Tel (310) 767-7990 *SIC* 5014 5013 5051

GEORG FISCHER LLC p 606
9271 Jeronimo Rd, Irvine CA 92618
Tel (714) 731-8800 *SIC* 5051 5085

ARCHITECTURAL GLASS & ALUMINUM CO INC p 105
6400 Brisa St, Livermore CA 94550
Tel (925) 583-2460
SIC 5051 1793 1791 3442

SHOJI JFE TRADE AMERICA INC p 1317
301 E Ocean Blvd Ste 1750, Long Beach CA 90802
Tel (562) 637-3500 *SIC* 5051

TA CHEN INTERNATIONAL INC p 1420
5855 Obispo Ave, Long Beach CA 90805
Tel (562) 808-8000 *SIC* 3452 5051

▲ RELIANCE STEEL & ALUMINUM CO p 1222
350 S Grand Ave Ste 5100, Los Angeles CA 90071
Tel (213) 687-7700 *SIC* 5051

■ EARLE M JORGENSEN CO p 468
10650 Alameda St, Lynwood CA 90262
Tel (323) 567-1122 *SIC* 5051

■ BLUE CHIP STAMPS p 191
301 E Colo Blvd Ste 300, Pasadena CA 91101
Tel (626) 585-6700 *SIC* 5051

AOC TECHNOLOGIES INC p 94
5960 Inglewood Dr, Pleasanton CA 94588
Tel (925) 875-0808 *SIC* 5051 3357

■ CREST STEEL CORP p 392
6580 General Rd, Riverside CA 92509
Tel (310) 830-2651 *SIC* 5051

ARMCO METALS HOLDINGS INC p 111
1730 S Amphlett Blvd # 230, San Mateo CA 94402
Tel (650) 212-7630 *SIC* 5051

COAST ALUMINUM AND ARCHITECTURAL INC p 331
10628 Fulton Wells Ave, Santa Fe Springs CA 90670
Tel (562) 946-6061 *SIC* 5051

KELLY PIPE CO LLC p 809
11680 Bloomfield Ave, Santa Fe Springs CA 90670
Tel (562) 868-0456 *SIC* 5051

SHAPCO INC p 1311
1666 20th St Ste 100, Santa Monica CA 90404
Tel (310) 264-1666 *SIC* 5051 3317 6799

BAKERSFIELD PIPE AND SUPPLY INC p 146
3301 Zachary Ave, Shafter CA 93263
Tel (661) 589-9141 *SIC* 5051 5085

JDRUSH CO INC p 781
5900 E Lerdo Hwy, Shafter CA 93263
Tel (661) 392-1900 *SIC* 5051

■ PDM STEEL SERVICE CENTERS INC p 1124
3535 E Myrtle St, Stockton CA 95205
Tel (209) 943-0555 *SIC* 5051

NORMAN INDUSTRIAL MATERIALS INC p 1049
8300 San Fernando Rd, Sun Valley CA 91352
Tel (818) 729-3333 *SIC* 5051 3441 3449

KUBOTA USA INC p 831
3401 Del Amo Blvd, Torrance CA 90503
Tel (310) 370-3370
SIC 5083 3577 5051 3531 3571

CONSOLIDATED FABRICATORS CORP p 359
14620 Arminta St, Van Nuys CA 91402
Tel (818) 901-1005 *SIC* 3443 5051 3444

■ AMERICAN METALS CORP p 76
1499 Parkway Blvd, West Sacramento CA 95691
Tel (916) 371-7700 *SIC* 5051

BROWN STRAUSS INC p 220
2495 Uravan St, Aurora CO 80011
Tel (303) 371-2200 *SIC* 5051

BSI HOLDINGS INC p 222
2495 Uravan St, Aurora CO 80011
Tel (303) 371-2200
SIC 6719 3589 5093 3715 3823 5051

ONEAL FLAT ROLLED METALS LLC p 1087
1229 Fulton St, Brighton CO 80601
Tel (303) 654-0300 *SIC* 5051

■ BUSHWICK METALS LLC p 229
560 N Washington Ave # 2, Bridgeport CT 06604
Tel (888) 399-4070 *SIC* 5051

ULBRICH STAINLESS STEELS & SPECIAL METALS INC p 1500
153 Washington Ave, North Haven CT 06473
Tel (203) 239-4481
SIC 3316 3356 5051 3341 3312

CELLMARK USA LLC p 274
2 Corporate Dr 5, Shelton CT 06484
Tel (203) 541-9000 *SIC* 5169 5051 5084

■ YARDE METALS INC p 1635
45 Newell St, Southington CT 06489
Tel (860) 406-6061 *SIC* 5051 3499

GERALD METALS LLC p 608
680 Washington Blvd Fl 9, Stamford CT 06901
Tel (203) 609-8300 *SIC* 5051

ASBURY CARBONS INC p 115
103 Foulk Rd Ste 202, Wilmington DE 19803
Tel (302) 652-0266
SIC 1499 3295 1241 5051 3952 3069

CORPAC STEEL PRODUCTS CORP p 372
20803 Biscayne Blvd # 502, Aventura FL 33180
Tel (305) 933-8599 *SIC* 5051

ALRO METALS SERVICE CENTER CORP p 61
6200 Pk Of Commerce Blvd, Boca Raton FL 33487
Tel (561) 997-6766 *SIC* 5051 5085

■ FLAG INTERMEDIATE HOLDINGS CORP p 554
2400 E Coml Blvd Ste 905, Fort Lauderdale FL 33308
Tel (954) 202-4000 *SIC* 5051 3354 3315

■ METALS USA HOLDINGS CORP p 952
2400 E Coml Blvd Ste 905, Fort Lauderdale FL 33308
Tel (954) 202-4000 *SIC* 5051 3272 3354

W & O SUPPLY INC p 1568
2677 Port Industrial Dr, Jacksonville FL 32226
Tel (904) 354-3800 *SIC* 5085 5051

STEEL FABRICATORS LLC p 1384
721 Ne 44th St, Oakland Park FL 33334
Tel (954) 772-0440 *SIC* 5051

AA METALS INC p 7
11616 Landstar Blvd, Orlando FL 32824
Tel (407) 377-0246 *SIC* 5051

■ HD SUPPLY WATERWORKS GROUP INC p 673
501 W Church St Ste 100, Orlando FL 32805
Tel (407) 841-4755
SIC 5051 5074 5084 5099

MCNICHOLS CO p 932
2502 N Rocky Point Dr # 750, Rocky Point FL 33607
Tel (877) 884-4653 *SIC* 5051

AGROYCE METAL MARKETING LLC p 36
1381 Sawgrs Corp Pkwy, Sunrise FL 33323
Tel (954) 561-3607 SIC 5051

■ HD SUPPLY HOLDINGS LLC p 673
3100 Cumberland Blvd Se # 1700, Atlanta GA 30339
Tel (770) 852-9000
SIC 5051 5074 5084 5099

SPECTRA METAL SALES INC p 1357
6104 Boat Rock Blvd Sw, Atlanta GA 30336
Tel (404) 344-4305
SIC 5051 3354 3355 3479 3444 2952

PACESETTER STEEL SERVICE INC p 1103
1045 Big Shanty Rd Nw, Kennesaw GA 30144
Tel (770) 919-8000 SIC 5051

FIRST AMERICAN RESOURCES CO LLC p 544
2030 Rverview Indus Dr Se, Mableton GA 30126
Tel (404) 505-3499 SIC 5051 3479

FURUKAWA ELECTRIC TECHNOLOGIES INC p 585
2000 Northeast Expy, Norcross GA 30071
Tel (770) 798-2082 SIC 5051

■ PHOENIX CORP p 1144
4685 Buford Hwy, Peachtree Corners GA 30071
Tel (770) 447-4211 SIC 5051

KLOCKNER NAMASCO HOLDING CORP p 823
500 Colonial Center Pkwy # 500, Roswell GA 30076
Tel (678) 259-8800 SIC 5051

KLOCKNER USA HOLDING INC p 823
500 Colonial Center Pkwy # 500, Roswell GA 30076
Tel (678) 259-8800 SIC 6799 5051

KLOECKNER METALS CORP p 823
500 Colonial Center Pkwy # 500, Roswell GA 30076
Tel (678) 259-8800 SIC 5051

■ CHATHAM STEEL CORP p 291
501 W Boundary St, Savannah GA 31401
Tel (912) 233-4182 SIC 5051 3317

STAINLESS SALES CORP p 1374
2301 W Windsor Ct Unit B, Addison IL 60101
Tel (773) 247-9060 SIC 5051

ULBRICH OF ILLINOIS INC p 1500
12340 S Laramie Ave, Alsip IL 60803
Tel (708) 489-9500 SIC 5051

DYWIDAG SYSTEMS INTERNATIONAL USA INC p 465
320 Marmon Dr, Bolingbrook IL 60440
Tel (630) 739-1100 SIC 5051

SCHMOLZ + BICKENBACH USA INC p 1287
365 Village Dr, Carol Stream IL 60188
Tel (630) 682-3900 SIC 5051

SPECIALTY ROLLED METALS LLC p 1356
423 Saint Paul Blvd, Carol Stream IL 60188
Tel (630) 871-5765 SIC 5051

VESUVIUS CRUCIBLE CO p 1552
1404 Newton Dr, Champaign IL 61822
Tel (217) 351-5000 SIC 3297 5051

ARCELOR USA HOLDING INC p 104
1 S Dearborn St Ste 1800, Chicago IL 60603
Tel (312) 899-3400 SIC 5051

▲ CENTRAL STEEL AND WIRE CO p 280
3000 W 51st St, Chicago IL 60632
Tel (773) 471-3800 SIC 5051

COLUMBIA PIPE & SUPPLY CO p 341
1120 W Pershing Rd, Chicago IL 60609
Tel (773) 927-6600 SIC 5051 5085 5074

■ FERALLOY CORP p 537
8755 W Higgins Rd Ste 970, Chicago IL 60631
Tel (503) 286-8869
SIC 5051 3471 3444 3312

■ JOSEPH T RYERSON & SON INC p 794
227 W Monroe St Fl 27, Chicago IL 60606
Tel (312) 292-5000 SIC 5051 5162

LAPHAM-HICKEY STEEL CORP p 845
5500 W 73rd St, Chicago IL 60638
Tel (708) 496-6111
SIC 5051 3398 3355 3317 3316

MADISON INDUSTRIES HOLDINGS LLC p 894
500 W Madison St Ste 3890, Chicago IL 60661
Tel (312) 277-0156
SIC 6719 5051 3443 3316

■ MARMON HOLDINGS INC p 909
181 W Madison St Ste 2600, Chicago IL 60602
Tel (312) 372-9500
SIC 5051 3351 3743 4741 3423 3589

▲ RYERSON HOLDING CORP p 1260
227 W Monroe St Fl 27, Chicago IL 60606
Tel (312) 292-5000 SIC 5051

RYERSON INC p 1261
227 W Monroe St Ste 2700, Chicago IL 60606
Tel (312) 292-5000 SIC 5051

■ RYERSON PROCUREMENT CORP p 1261
227 W Monroe St Fl 27, Chicago IL 60606
Tel (312) 292-5000 SIC 5051

TEMPEL STEEL CO p 1436
5500 N Wolcott Ave, Chicago IL 60640
Tel (773) 250-8000
SIC 3469 3313 3316 3398 5051

■ UNION TANK CAR CO p 1505
175 W Jackson Blvd # 2100, Chicago IL 60604
Tel (312) 431-3111
SIC 3743 4741 4789 5051

ESMARK STEEL GROUP LLC p 509
2500 Euclid Ave, Chicago Heights IL 60411
Tel (708) 756-0400 SIC 5051

JDM STEEL SERVICE INC p 781
330 E Joe Orr Rd Unit 3, Chicago Heights IL 60411
Tel (708) 757-2092 SIC 5051 4225

■ SUGAR STEEL CORP p 1397
2521 State St Ste 1, Chicago Heights IL 60411
Tel (708) 757-9500 SIC 5051

COREY STEEL CO p 370
2800 S 61st Ct, Cicero IL 60804
Tel (800) 323-2750 SIC 3316 5051

OUTOKUMPU STAINLESS INC p 1099
2275 Half Day Rd Ste 300, Deerfield IL 60015
Tel (847) 317-1400 SIC 5051

BOHLER-UDDEHOLM CORP p 198
2505 Millennium Dr, Elgin IL 60124
Tel (877) 992-8764 SIC 5051

MATERIAL SCIENCES CORP p 919
2250 Pratt Blvd, Elk Grove Village IL 60007
Tel (888) 603-1553 SIC 3312 5051

NATIONAL MATERIAL LP p 1014
1965 Pratt Blvd, Elk Grove Village IL 60007
Tel (847) 806-7200
SIC 5051 3469 3354 5093 4911 4924

NATIONAL MATERIAL TRADING LLC p 1014
1965 Pratt Blvd, Elk Grove Village IL 60007
Tel (847) 806-0990 SIC 5051

ROUND GROUND METALS INC p 1252
4825 Turnberry Dr, Hanover Park IL 60133
Tel (630) 539-5300 SIC 5051 7389

MIDWEST AIR TECHNOLOGIES INC p 967
6700 Wildlife Way, Long Grove IL 60047
Tel (847) 821-9630
SIC 5072 5191 5063 5051 5031

CUSTOM STEEL PROCESSING INC p 403
1001 College St, Madison IL 62060
Tel (618) 876-7276 SIC 5051

KREHER STEEL CO LLC p 829
1550 N 25th Ave, Melrose Park IL 60160
Tel (708) 345-8180 SIC 5051

■ METALS USA SPECIALTY METALS NORTHCENTRAL INC p 953
3000 Shermer Rd, Northbrook IL 60062
Tel (847) 291-2400 SIC 5051

▲ A M CASTLE & CO p 6
1420 Kensington Rd # 220, Oak Brook IL 60523
Tel (847) 455-7111 SIC 5051 5162

■ LIEBOVICH BROS INC p 863
2116 Preston St, Rockford IL 61102
Tel (815) 987-3200 SIC 5051

■ LIEBOVICH STEEL & ALUMINUM CO p 863
2116 Preston St, Rockford IL 61102
Tel (815) 987-3200 SIC 5051

■ CHICAGO TUBE AND IRON CO p 298
1 Chicago Tube Dr, Romeoville IL 60446
Tel (815) 834-2500 SIC 5051 3441

COILPLUS INC p 335
6250 N River Rd Ste 6050, Rosemont IL 60018
Tel (847) 384-3000 SIC 5051

METAL ONE HOLDINGS AMERICA INC p 952
6250 N River Rd Ste 6055, Rosemont IL 60018
Tel (847) 318-0019 SIC 5085 5051

■ CERRO FLOW PRODUCTS LLC p 284
3000 Mississippi Ave, Sauget IL 62206
Tel (618) 337-6000
SIC 3351 3331 3498 3585 5051

NATIONAL TUBE SUPPLY CO p 1016
925 Central Ave, University Park IL 60484
Tel (708) 534-2700 SIC 5051

TRU-SPEC METALS INC p 1485
3075 N Oak Grove Ave, Waukegan IL 60087
Tel (847) 360-8400 SIC 5051

FAGOR ARRASATE USA INC p 524
636 Executive Dr, Willowbrook IL 60527
Tel (630) 920-0422 SIC 5051 5064

S&S STEEL SERVICES INC p 1263
444 E 29th St, Anderson IN 46016
Tel (765) 622-4545 SIC 5051 3316

BRISTOL LASALLE CORP p 214
601 County Road 17, Elkhart IN 46516
Tel (574) 295-4400
SIC 5023 5021 5051 5033 3645 3089

OSCAR WINSKI CO INC p 1096
2407 N 9th Street Rd, Lafayette IN 47904
Tel (765) 742-1102 SIC 5051 5093

VOESTALPINE ROTEC INC p 1564
3709 Us Highway 52 S, Lafayette IN 47905
Tel (765) 471-2808 SIC 5051

STEEL WAREHOUSE CO LLC p 1384
2722 Tucker Dr, South Bend IN 46619
Tel (574) 236-5100 SIC 5051

■ OLYMPIC STEEL IOWA INC p 1083
6425 State St, Bettendorf IA 52722
Tel (563) 332-7785 SIC 5051 3444

OWEN INDUSTRIES INC p 1099
501 Avenue H, Carter Lake IA 51510
Tel (800) 831-9252 SIC 5051 3441

PMX INDUSTRIES INC p 1158
5300 Willow Creek Dr Sw, Cedar Rapids IA 52404
Tel (319) 368-7700
SIC 3366 5051 3444 3364 3351 3331

SIOUX CITY FOUNDRY CO p 1326
801 Division St, Sioux City IA 51105
Tel (712) 252-4181
SIC 5051 3443 3321 3316 3444 3441

STEEL AND PIPE SUPPLY CO INC p 1384
555 Poyntz Ave Ste 122, Manhattan KS 66502
Tel (800) 521-2345 SIC 5051

CORKEN STEEL PRODUCTS CO p 370
7920 Kentucky Dr, Florence KY 41042
Tel (859) 291-4664
SIC 5075 3444 5051 8742 6411

■ WESTPORT AXLE CORP p 1602
12740 Westport Rd Ste H, Louisville KY 40245
Tel (502) 425-2103 SIC 5051 3483 3714

MODERN WELDING CO INC p 981
2880 New Hartford Rd, Owensboro KY 42303
Tel (270) 685-4400
SIC 3443 5051 3441 5085

STEPHENS PIPE & STEEL LLC p 1386
2224 E Highway 619, Russell Springs KY 42642
Tel (270) 866-3331 SIC 5051 3315

L B INDUSTRIES INC p 833
8770 Railroad Dr, Taylor Mill KY 41015
Tel (859) 431-8300 SIC 5051

PALISADES HOLDINGS INC p 1108
2266 Groom Rd, Baker LA 70714
Tel (225) 236-1440 SIC 5051

EDGEN GROUP INC p 477
18444 Highland Rd, Baton Rouge LA 70809
Tel (225) 756-9868 SIC 5051

MURRAY EDGEN CORP p 1001
18444 Highland Rd, Baton Rouge LA 70809
Tel (225) 756-9868 SIC 5051

MURRAY EDGEN II L P p 1001
18444 Highland Rd, Baton Rouge LA 70809
Tel (225) 756-9868 SIC 5051

SENTRY SUPPLY INC p 1305
318 S Cities Service Hwy, Sulphur LA 70663
Tel (337) 625-2300 SIC 5085 5051

D-S PIPE & STEEL SUPPLY LLC p 407
1301 Wicomico St Ste 3, Baltimore MD 21230
Tel (410) 837-1717 SIC 5085 5051

LYON CONKLIN & CO INC p 888
4501 Hollins Ferry Rd # 140, Baltimore MD 21227
Tel (410) 540-4880 SIC 5075 5051

CRISTAL METALS INC p 393
20 Wight Ave Ste 100, Hunt Valley MD 21030
Tel (410) 229-4400 SIC 5051

CANAM STEEL CORP p 246
4010 Clay St, Point Of Rocks MD 21777
Tel (301) 874-5141 SIC 3441 5051

AMERICAN STEEL AND ALUMINUM CORP p 80
27 Elm St, Auburn MA 01501
Tel (508) 832-9681 SIC 5051

THOMPSON STEEL CO INC p 1449
120 Royall St Ste 2, Canton MA 02021
Tel (781) 828-8800 SIC 5051 3316

PIERCE ALUMINUM CO INC p 1147
34 Forge Pkwy, Franklin MA 02038
Tel (508) 541-7007 SIC 5051

MICROGROUP INC p 962
7 Industrial Park Rd, Medway MA 02053
Tel (508) 533-4925
SIC 5051 3312 3498 3494 3492 3317

ADMIRAL METALS SERVICENTER CO INC p 23
11 Forbes Rd, Woburn MA 01801
Tel (781) 933-8300 SIC 5051

BMH CORP p 194
11 Forbes Rd, Woburn MA 01801
Tel (781) 933-8300 SIC 5051

BENTELER NORTH AMERICA CORP p 173
2650 N Opdyke Rd Ste B, Auburn Hills MI 48326
Tel (248) 377-9999 SIC 5051

JO GALLOUP CO p 786
130 Helmer Rd N, Battle Creek MI 49037
Tel (269) 965-2303 SIC 5051 5085 5162

KENWAL STEEL CORP p 813
8223 W Warren Ave, Dearborn MI 48126
Tel (313) 739-1000 SIC 5051

■ OLYMPIC STEEL LAFAYETTE INC p 1083
3600 Military St, Detroit MI 48210
Tel (313) 894-4552 SIC 5051

NK STEEL LLC p 1045
31731 Northwstrn Hwy 15 Ste 157 W, Farmington Hills MI 48334
Tel (248) 865-9000 SIC 5051

MAGIC STEEL CORP p 895
4242 Clay Ave Sw Ste 2, Grand Rapids MI 49548
Tel (616) 532-4071 SIC 5051

MAGIC STEEL SALES LLC p 895
4242 Clay Ave Sw Ste 2, Grand Rapids MI 49548
Tel (616) 532-4071 SIC 5051

SCHUPAN & SONS INC p 1291
2619 Miller Rd, Kalamazoo MI 49001
Tel (269) 382-0000 SIC 5093 5051 3341

CONTRACTORS STEEL CO p 364
36555 Amrhein Rd, Livonia MI 48150
Tel (734) 464-4000 SIC 5051

NATIONAL GALVANIZING LP p 1012
1500 Telb St, Monroe MI 48162
Tel (734) 243-1882
SIC 3312 3316 3471 3341 5051

HARBOR GROUP INC p 659
1115 E Broadway Ave, Norton Shores MI 49444
Tel (231) 739-7152 SIC 5051

HARBOR STEEL AND SUPPLY CORP p 660
1115 E Broadway Ave, Norton Shores MI 49444
Tel (231) 739-7152 SIC 5051

LEE STEEL CORP p 851
45525 Grand River Ave, Novi MI 48374
Tel (855) 533-7833 SIC 5051

NEW JERNBERG SALES INC p 1031
39475 W 13 Mile Rd # 105, Novi MI 48377
Tel (248) 479-2699 SIC 5051

EATON STEEL CORP p 473
10221 Capital St, Oak Park MI 48237
Tel (248) 398-3434 SIC 5051 3312

THYSSENKRUPP MATERIALS NA INC p 1451
22355 W 11 Mile Rd, Southfield MI 48033
Tel (248) 233-5600
SIC 5051 5162 3444 8741

BETA STEEL LLC p 177
6300 Hughes Dr, Sterling Heights MI 48312
Tel (586) 698-9200 SIC 5051

COMMERCIAL GROUP INC p 345
12801 Universal Dr, Taylor MI 48180
Tel (313) 931-6100
SIC 5085 5051 3496 3537 3534

ROLLED ALLOYS INC p 1247
125 W Sterns Rd, Temperance MI 48182
Tel (800) 521-0332
SIC 5051 3369 3341 3317 2899 2851

PEERLESS STEEL CO p 1127
2450 Austin Dr, Troy MI 48083
Tel (248) 528-3200 SIC 5051

MNP CORP p 980
44225 Utica Rd, Utica MI 48317
Tel (586) 254-1320
SIC 3452 5051 5072 3714

■ HOWMET HOLDINGS CORP p 713
1 Misco Dr, Whitehall MI 49461
Tel (231) 894-5686
SIC 3324 3542 5051 3479

BEHLER-YOUNG CO p 168
4900 Clyde Park Ave Sw, Wyoming MI 49509
Tel (616) 531-3400 SIC 5075 5051 5074

MCNEILUS STEEL INC p 932
702 2nd Ave Se, Dodge Center MN 55927
Tel (507) 374-6336 SIC 5051

VIKING FOREST PRODUCTS LLC p 1557
7615 Smetana Ln Ste 140, Eden Prairie MN 55344
Tel (952) 941-6512 SIC 5031 5051

■ INTEGRIS METALS CORP p 749
455 85th Ave Nw, Minneapolis MN 55433
Tel (763) 717-9000 SIC 5051

RATNER STEEL SUPPLY CO p 1209
2500 County Road B W 1a, Saint Paul MN 55113
Tel (219) 787-6700 SIC 5051 7389

WEST CENTRAL STEEL INC p 1594
110 19th St Nw, Willmar MN 56201
Tel (320) 235-4070 SIC 5051

TAYLOR HOLDINGS INC p 1427
650 N Church Ave, Louisville MS 39339
Tel (662) 773-3421 SIC 5051

■ MITEK USA INC p 977
16023 Swingley Ridge Rd, Chesterfield MO 63017
Tel (314) 434-1200
SIC 3443 3429 3542 8711 5051 5085

STAHL SPECIALTY CO p 1374
111 E Pacific St, Kingsville MO 64061
Tel (816) 597-3322
SIC 5051 3544 3365 3567 3369

NU WAY CONCRETE FORMS INC p 1066
4190 Hoffmeister Ave, Saint Louis MO 63125
Tel (573) 893-8786
SIC 5032 5051 5072 7359

TRIDENT STEEL CORP p 1480
12825 Flushing Meadows Dr # 110, Saint Louis MO 63131
Tel (314) 822-0500 SIC 5051

TSI HOLDING CO p 1489
999 Exectve Pkwy Dr # 202, Saint Louis MO 63141
Tel (314) 628-6000 SIC 5094 5051

■ TUBULAR STEEL INC p 1490
1031 Executive Parkway Dr, Saint Louis MO 63141
Tel (314) 851-9200 SIC 5051

2 M CO INC p 1
5249 Holiday Ave, Billings MT 59101
Tel (406) 245-1490
SIC 5084 5083 5074 5051

PACIFIC HIDE & FUR DEPOT p 1104
5 River Dr S, Great Falls MT 59405
Tel (406) 771-7222 SIC 5051 5093

ALL METALS INDUSTRIES INC p 51
4 Higgins Dr, Belmont NH 03220
Tel (603) 267-7023 SIC 5051

ADELPHIA METALS I LIMITED LIABILITY CO p 22
1930 Marlton Pike E M66, Cherry Hill NJ 08003
Tel (856) 988-8889 SIC 5051

PASSAIC METAL & BUILDING SUPPLIES CO p 1119
5 Central Ave Ste 1, Clifton NJ 07011
Tel (973) 546-9000
SIC 5033 5031 5051 5075 3444 3296

▲ EMPIRE RESOURCES INC p 493
2115 Linwood Ave Ste 200, Fort Lee NJ 07024
Tel (201) 944-2200 SIC 5051

HANWA AMERICAN CORP p 659
Parker Plz 400 Kelby St F, Fort Lee NJ 07024
Tel (201) 363-4500
SIC 5051 5172 5031 5084 5146

MB INDUSTRIES INC p 925
560 Salem Ave, Newfield NJ 08344
Tel (609) 970-1503 SIC 5051

■ SKYLINE STEEL LLC p 1330
8 Woodhollow Rd Ste 102, Parsippany NJ 07054
Tel (973) 428-6100 SIC 3317 5051

QUALITY COMPUTER ACCESSORIES INC p 1196
70 Ethel Rd W Ste 1, Piscataway NJ 08854
Tel (732) 572-2719
SIC 5063 5051 3315 3644

TITANIUM INDUSTRIES INC p 1456
18 Green Pond Rd Ste 1, Rockaway NJ 07866
Tel (973) 983-1185 SIC 5051 3542 3462

POSCO DAEWOO AMERICA CORP p 1163
300 Frank W Burr Blvd, Teaneck NJ 07666
Tel (201) 591-8000
SIC 5131 5051 5169 5015

INTER-WIRE PRODUCTS INC p 751
355 Main St Ste 2, Armonk NY 10504
Tel (914) 273-6633 SIC 5051

SEFAR INC p 1300
111 Calumet St, Depew NY 14043
Tel (716) 683-4050
SIC 5131 5051 5084 3496 2297 2221

LAURAND ASSOCIATES INC p 847
11 Grace Ave Ste 405, Great Neck NY 11021
Tel (516) 829-8821 SIC 5051

RUSAL AMERICA CORP p 1258
500 Mmaroneck Ave Ste 102, Harrison NY 10528
Tel (914) 670-5771 SIC 5051

SAMUEL SON & CO INC p 1275
4334 Walden Ave, Lancaster NY 14086
Tel (716) 681-4200 SIC 5085 5051

EASTERN WHOLESALE FENCE CO INC p 473
274 Middle Island Rd, Medford NY 11763
Tel (631) 698-0900
SIC 5039 5031 5051 3496

ALBANY STEEL INC p 45
566 Broadway Ste 2, Menands NY 12204
Tel (518) 436-4851 SIC 5051 3441

VASS PIPE & STEEL CO INC p 1545
158 3rd St Ste 2, Mineola NY 11501
Tel (516) 741-8398 SIC 5051 3317

ALBEA COSMETICS AMERICA INC p 46
595 Madison Ave Fl 10, New York NY 10022
Tel (212) 371-5100
SIC 3089 3911 5162 5051

BLUE TEE CORP p 192
387 Park Ave S Fl 5, New York NY 10016
Tel (212) 598-0880
SIC 3533 3589 5093 3715 3823 5051

EWT HOLDINGS III CORP p 516
666 5th Ave Fl 36, New York NY 10103
Tel (212) 644-5900
SIC 3589 3823 3826 4941 5051

ITOCHU INTERNATIONAL INC p 768
1251 Avenue Of The Americ, New York NY 10020
Tel (212) 818-8000
SIC 5131 5084 5065 5051 5153 5141

KANEMATSU USA INC p 802
500 5th Ave Fl 29, New York NY 10110
Tel (212) 704-9400
SIC 5084 5051 5065 5153

MARUBENI-ITOCHU STEEL AMERICA INC p 913
150 E 42nd St Fl 7, New York NY 10017
Tel (212) 660-6000 SIC 5051

MITSUBISHI CORP (AMERICAS) p 977
655 3rd Ave, New York NY 10017
Tel (212) 605-2000
SIC 5051 5172 5141 5153 5169 5084

MITSUBISHI INTERNATIONAL CORP p 978
655 3rd Ave Ste 800, New York NY 10017
Tel (212) 605-2000
SIC 5051 5172 5141 5153 5169 5084

MITSUI & CO (USA) INC p 978
200 Park Ave Fl 35, New York NY 10166
Tel (212) 878-4000
SIC 5051 5094 5084 5153 5172 5169

NIPPON STEEL & SUMITOMO METAL USA INC p 1044
1251 Ave Of The Ave Fl 23, New York NY 10020
Tel (212) 486-7150 SIC 5051 5084

SOJITZ CORP OF AMERICA p 1337
1120 Ave Of The, New York NY 10036
Tel (212) 704-6500
SIC 5065 5084 5169 5051 5099 5052

STEMCOR USA INC p 1385
2 Park Ave Rm 1600, New York NY 10016
Tel (212) 563-0262 SIC 5051 8711

SUMITOMO CORP OF AMERICAS p 1398
300 Madison Ave, New York NY 10017
Tel (212) 207-0700
SIC 5051 5172 5084 5063 5141

TOYOTA TSUSHO AMERICA INC p 1467
805 3rd Ave Fl 17, New York NY 10022
Tel (212) 355-3600
SIC 5051 5013 4225 6331 5153

UTTAM GALVA NORTH AMERICA INC p 1537
1500 Broadway Fl 16, New York NY 10036
Tel (917) 722-8177 SIC 5051

BEN WEITSMAN AND SON INC p 172
15 W Main St, Owego NY 13827
Tel (607) 687-2780 SIC 5051 5093 3341

WEITSMAN SHREDDING p 1588
15 W Main St, Owego NY 13827
Tel (607) 687-2780 SIC 5051 5093 5099

APOLLO MANAGEMENT V LP p 97
1 Manhattanville Rd # 201, Purchase NY 10577
Tel (914) 467-6510 SIC 5051 3272 3354

HITACHI METALS AMERICA LTD p 697
2 Manhattanville Rd # 301, Purchase NY 10577
Tel (914) 694-9200
SIC 3264 3577 3365 5051 3321 3559

EASTERN METAL SUPPLY OF NORTH CAROLINA INC p 472
2925 Stewart Creek Blvd, Charlotte NC 28216
Tel (704) 391-2266 SIC 5051

DILLON SUPPLY CO p 440
440 Civic Blvd, Raleigh NC 27610
Tel (919) 838-4200
SIC 5084 5085 5051 5074 5072

UMICORE USA INC p 1501
3600 Glenwood Ave Ste 250, Raleigh NC 27612
Tel (919) 874-7171
SIC 5052 5051 5093 5169 3339

DUBOSE STEEL INC OF NORTH CAROLINA p 459
767 Dr Mlk Jr Blvd, Roseboro NC 28382
Tel (910) 525-4161 SIC 5051

KIRTLAND CAPITAL PARTNERS LP p 822
3201 Entp Pkwy Ste 200, Beachwood OH 44122
Tel (216) 593-0100
SIC 5051 3312 3498 3494 3492 3317

HICKMAN WILLIAMS & CO p 690
250 E 5th St Ste 300, Cincinnati OH 45202
Tel (513) 621-1946
SIC 5051 5052 5169 5085 5084

RIVERFRONT STEEL INC p 1237
10310 S Medallion Dr, Cincinnati OH 45241
Tel (513) 769-9999 SIC 5051

COLUMBIA NATIONAL GROUP INC p 341
6600 Grant Ave, Cleveland OH 44105
Tel (216) 883-4972 SIC 5051 5093 1542

KEN-MAC METALS INC p 810
17901 Englewood Dr, Cleveland OH 44130
Tel (440) 891-1480 SIC 5051

MAJESTIC STEEL USA INC p 899
31099 Chagrin Blvd # 150, Cleveland OH 44124
Tel (440) 786-2666 SIC 5051

MAZZELLA HOLDING CO INC p 924
21000 Aerospace Pkwy, Cleveland OH 44142
Tel (513) 772-4466
SIC 5051 5085 5088 5072

▲ **OLYMPIC STEEL INC** p 1083
22901 Millcreek Blvd # 650, Cleveland OH 44122
Tel (216) 292-3800 SIC 5051

PRINCE & IZANT CO p 1176
12999 Plaza Dr, Cleveland OH 44130
Tel (216) 362-7000
SIC 5051 3398 3351 3341 3339 2899

MATANDY STEEL & METAL PRODUCTS LLC p 919
1200 Central Ave, Hamilton OH 45011
Tel (513) 887-5274
SIC 5051 3312 3444 3399

CLINTON ALUMINUM ACQUISITION LLC p 327
6270 Van Buren Rd, New Franklin OH 44216
Tel (330) 882-6743 SIC 5051

■ **HOWMET CORP** p 713
1616 Harvard Ave, Newburgh Heights OH 44105
Tel (800) 242-9898
SIC 3324 3542 5051 3479

■ **TIMKEN CORP** p 1455
4500 Mount Pleasant St Nw, North Canton OH 44720
Tel (330) 471-3378 SIC 5085 5051

MIAMI VALLEY STEEL SERVICE INC p 959
201 Fox Dr, Piqua OH 45356
Tel (937) 773-7127 SIC 5051

■ **LATROBE SPECIALTY METALS DISTRIBUTION INC** p 846
1551 Vienna Pkwy, Vienna OH 44473
Tel (330) 609-5137 SIC 5051 3312

MISA METALS INC p 974
9050 Centre Pointe Dr, West Chester OH 45069
Tel (212) 660-6000 SIC 5051

ALUMINUM LINE PRODUCTS CO p 63
24460 Sperry Cir, Westlake OH 44145
Tel (440) 835-8880 SIC 5051 3365 3999

■ **METALS USA PLATES AND SHAPES SOUTHCENTRAL INC** p 953
101 E Illinois Ave, Enid OK 73701
Tel (580) 233-0411 SIC 5051

YAFFE COMPANIES INC p 1633
1200 S G St, Muskogee OK 74403
Tel (918) 687-7543 SIC 5093 5051

▲ **WEBCO INDUSTRIES INC** p 1586
9101 W 21st St, Sand Springs OK 74063
Tel (918) 245-2211 SIC 3312 5051

INDUSTRIAL PIPING SPECIALISTS INC p 740
606 N 145th East Ave, Tulsa OK 74116
Tel (918) 437-9100 SIC 5051 5085

FARWEST STEEL CORP p 530
2000 Henderson Ave, Eugene OR 97403
Tel (541) 686-2000 SIC 5051

SHAMROCK BUILDING MATERIALS INC p 1311
4725 Village Plaza Loop # 201, Eugene OR 97401
Tel (877) 426-2341 SIC 5031 5051

OREGON METAL SLITTERS INC p 1093
7227 N Leadbetter Rd, Portland OR 97203
Tel (503) 286-0300 SIC 5051 7389

SERVICE STEEL INC p 1307
5555 N Channel Ave Bldg 2, Portland OR 97217
Tel (503) 224-9500 SIC 5051 3711

CRONIMET CORP p 393
1 Pilarsky Way, Aliquippa PA 15001
Tel (724) 375-5004 SIC 5093 5051 3312

■ **CHAPEL STEEL CORP** p 288
590 N Bethlehem Pike, Ambler PA 19002
Tel (215) 793-0899 SIC 5051

HADCO METAL TRADING CO LLC p 652
555 State Rd, Bensalem PA 19020
Tel (215) 695-2705 SIC 5051

■ **MARMON DISTRIBUTION SERVICES INC** p 909
225 E Cunningham St, Butler PA 16001
Tel (724) 283-3000 SIC 5051 4213

■ **MARMON/KEYSTONE LLC** p 909
225 E Cunningham St, Butler PA 16001
Tel (724) 283-3000 SIC 5051 4213

SUPERIOR GROUP INC p 1406
100 Front St Ste 525, Conshohocken PA 19428
Tel (610) 397-2040
SIC 5051 3357 3317 3491 3469 7389

HIGH INDUSTRIES INC p 690
1853 William Penn Way, Lancaster PA 17601
Tel (717) 293-4444
SIC 1791 3272 5051 3441

■ **INFRA-METALS CO** p 742
580 Middletown Blvd D100, Langhorne PA 19047
Tel (215) 741-1000 SIC 5051

■ **METALS USA PLATES AND SHAPES NORTHEAST LP** p 953
50 Cabot Blvd E, Langhorne PA 19047
Tel (267) 580-2100 SIC 5051

ARMSTRONG WORTHINGTON VENTURE p 112
101 Lindenwood Dr Ste 350, Malvern PA 19355
Tel (610) 722-1200 SIC 3446 5051

LANE STEEL CO INC p 844
4 River Rd Ste 2, Mc Kees Rocks PA 15136
Tel (412) 331-1400 SIC 5051

ELG HANIEL METALS CORP p 486
369 River Rd, Mckeesport PA 15132
Tel (412) 672-9200 SIC 5093 5051

TIOGA PIPE INC p 1455
2450 Wheatsheaf Ln, Philadelphia PA 19137
Tel (215) 831-0700 SIC 5051

METAL TRADERS INC p 952
3480 Grand Ave, Pittsburgh PA 15225
Tel (412) 331-7772 SIC 5051

■ **UNITED STATES STEEL INTERNATIONAL INC** p 1514
600 Grant St Ste 468, Pittsburgh PA 15219
Tel (412) 433-1121 SIC 5051

PENN STAINLESS PRODUCTS INC p 1129
190 Kelly Rd, Quakertown PA 18951
Tel (215) 536-3053 SIC 5051 3443 3471

CAMBRIDGE-LEE HOLDINGS INC p 244
86 Tube Dr, Reading PA 19605
Tel (610) 926-4141 SIC 5051 3351 5084

WHEATLAND TUBE CO p 1604
700 S Dock St, Sharon PA 16146
Tel (724) 342-6851 SIC 5051

PENNEX ALUMINUM CO LLC p 1130
50 Community St, Wellsville PA 17365
Tel (717) 432-9647 SIC 5051

STEEL AND PIPES INC p 1384
Road 1rio, Caguas PR 00725
Tel (787) 747-9415
SIC 5051 3446 3317 5085

■ **A J OSTER LLC** p 5
457 Warwick Industrial Dr, Warwick RI 02886
Tel (401) 736-2600 SIC 5051

EASTERN INDUSTRIAL SUPPLIES INC p 472
11 Caledon Ct Ste A, Greenville SC 29615
Tel (864) 451-5285 SIC 5085 5051

GOWER CORP p 627
355 Woodruff Rd Ste 101, Greenville SC 29607
Tel (864) 458-3114 SIC 3535 5051 7373

GUARDIAN BUILDING PRODUCTS DISTRIBUTION INC p 645
979 Batesville Rd Ste A, Greer SC 29651
Tel (800) 569-4262
SIC 5031 5033 5051 5032 5039 5023

■ **AMI METALS INC** p 85
1738 Gen George Patton Dr, Brentwood TN 37027
Tel (615) 370-4917 SIC 5051

■ **SISKIN STEEL & SUPPLY CO INC** p 1327
1901 Riverfront Pkwy, Chattanooga TN 37408
Tel (423) 756-3671 SIC 3312 5051

RUSSEL JMS METALS CORP p 1259
25 College Park Cv, Jackson TN 38301
Tel (731) 984-8121 SIC 5051

STEELSUMMIT HOLDINGS INC p 1385
1718 Jp Hennessy Dr, La Vergne TN 37086
Tel (615) 641-8600 SIC 5051

NISSAN TRADING CORP AMERICAS p 1044
1974 Midway Ln, Smyrna TN 37167
Tel (615) 220-7100
SIC 5013 5012 5051 5084

BD VINTON LLC p 164
I-10 Vinton Rd, Canutillo TX 79835
Tel (915) 886-2000
SIC 5051 3312 3449 3316

TUBULAR MACHINED PRODUCTS p 1490
90 Campbell Acres Rd, Cleveland TX 77328
Tel (713) 504-8932 SIC 5051 3492 7389

AMERICAN STEEL INC p 80
2500 Agnes St, Corpus Christi TX 78405
Tel (361) 883-1706
SIC 5023 5051 5084 5191

KING SUPPLY CO LLC p 820
9611 E R L Thornton Fwy, Dallas TX 75228
Tel (214) 388-9834 SIC 5039 5051

US STEEL TUBULAR PRODUCTS INC p 1533
15660 Dallas Pkwy Ste 500, Dallas TX 75248
Tel (972) 386-3981 SIC 5051

AMSCO STEEL CO LLC p 87
3430 Mccart Ave, Fort Worth TX 76110
Tel (817) 926-3355 SIC 5051

WILLBANKS METALS INC p 1610
1155 Ne 28th St, Fort Worth TX 76106
Tel (817) 625-6161 SIC 5051 3449

CORYELL STEEL INC p 373
2005 N Main St 136, Gatesville TX 76528
Tel (254) 223-3987 SIC 5051

ACT PIPE & SUPPLY INC p 19
6950 W Sam Houston Pkwy N, Houston TX 77041
Tel (713) 937-0600 SIC 5051 5085

BENTELER STEEL & TUBE p 173
3050 Post Oak Blvd # 1130, Houston TX 77056
Tel (713) 629-9111 SIC 5051

CHAMPIONS CINCO PIPE & SUPPLY LLC p 287
4 Greenspoint Mall # 16945, Houston TX 77060
Tel (713) 468-6555 SIC 5051

CHICKASAW DISTRIBUTORS INC p 298
800 Bering Dr Ste 330, Houston TX 77057
Tel (713) 974-2905 SIC 5051

CPW AMERICA CO p 388
750 Town And Country Blvd # 920, Houston TX 77024
Tel (281) 752-7300 SIC 5051

■ **DELTA STEEL INC** p 427
7355 Roundhouse Ln, Houston TX 77078
Tel (713) 635-1200 SIC 5051

FLOWORKS INTERNATIONAL LLC p 560
515 Post Oak Blvd Ste 800, Houston TX 77027
Tel (713) 839-1753 SIC 5051 5023

GLOBAL STAINLESS SUPPLY INC p 617
8900 Railwood Dr Unit A, Houston TX 77078
Tel (713) 980-0733 SIC 5051

HOWCO METALS MANAGEMENT LLC p 713
9611 Telge Rd, Houston TX 77095
Tel (281) 649-8800 SIC 5051 3999 8741

INTSEL STEEL DISTRIBUTORS LLC p 760
11310 W Little York Rd, Houston TX 77041
Tel (713) 937-9500 SIC 5051 3312 3444

J D FIELDS & CO INC p 770
55 Waugh Dr Ste 1250, Houston TX 77007
Tel (281) 558-7199 SIC 5051 7359 3443

J D RUSH CORP p 770
2 Northpoint Dr Ste 150, Houston TX 77060
Tel (281) 558-8004 SIC 3498 5051

JEFFERSON ENERGY I LP p 781
3104 Edloe St Ste 205, Houston TX 77027
Tel (713) 552-0002 SIC 1389 5051

■ **MRC GLOBAL (US) INC** p 996
1301 Mckinney St Ste 2300, Houston TX 77010
Tel (877) 294-7574 SIC 5051 5085

▲ **MRC GLOBAL INC** p 996
1301 Mckinney St Ste 2300, Houston TX 77010
Tel (877) 294-7574 SIC 5051 5085

NEW PROCESS STEEL HOLDING CO INC p 1033
5800 Westview Dr, Houston TX 77055
Tel (713) 686-9631 SIC 5051

NEW PROCESS STEEL LP p 1033
1322 N Post Oak Rd, Houston TX 77055
Tel (713) 686-9631 SIC 5051 3469

NORTH SHORE SUPPLY CO INC p 1053
1566 Miles St, Houston TX 77015
Tel (713) 453-3533 SIC 5051 5085 3441

PROLER SOUTHWEST INC p 1182
90 Hirsch Rd, Houston TX 77020
Tel (713) 671-2900 SIC 5051

SERVICE STEEL WAREHOUSE CO LP p 1307
8415 Clinton Dr, Houston TX 77029
Tel (713) 675-2631 SIC 5051

■ **SFI-GRAY STEEL LLC** p 1310
3511 W 12th St, Houston TX 77008
Tel (713) 864-6450 SIC 3325 5051

SOUTHWEST STAINLESS LP p 1352
515 Post Oak Blvd Ste 800, Houston TX 77027
Tel (713) 943-3544 SIC 3498 5051 5085

STEMCOR SPECIAL STEELS LLC p 1385
5847 San Felipe St # 2400, Houston TX 77057
Tel (281) 252-3625 SIC 5051

TEJAS TUBULAR PRODUCTS INC p 1433
8526 Green River Dr, Houston TX 77028
Tel (281) 822-3400 SIC 5051

TEXAS PIPE AND SUPPLY CO LTD p 1444
2330 Holmes Rd, Houston TX 77051
Tel (713) 799-9235 SIC 5051

■ **TEXAS STEEL PROCESSING INC** p 1444
5480 Windfern Rd, Houston TX 77041
Tel (281) 822-3200 SIC 5051

TRIPLE-S STEEL HOLDINGS INC p 1482
6000 Jensen Dr, Houston TX 77026
Tel (713) 697-7105 SIC 5051 6719

TRIPLE-S STEEL SUPPLY LLC p 1482
6000 Jensen Dr, Houston TX 77026
Tel (713) 354-4100 SIC 5051

▲ **COMMERCIAL METALS CO** p 345
6565 N Mcarthr Blvd # 800, Irving TX 75039
Tel (214) 689-4300
SIC 3312 3441 5051 5093

SCOT INDUSTRIES INC p 1293
3756 Fm 250 N, Lone Star TX 75668
Tel (903) 639-2551
SIC 7389 5051 3498 3471

REGAL METALS INTERNATIONAL INC p 1218
207 Sentry Dr, Mansfield TX 76063
Tel (817) 477-2568 SIC 5051

CITY PIPE AND SUPPLY CORP p 319
2101 W 2nd St, Odessa TX 79763
Tel (432) 332-1541 SIC 5051 5085

CUSTOM COMPUTER CABLES OF AMERICA INC p 403
2901 Summit Ave Ste 400, Plano TX 75074
Tel (972) 638-9309 SIC 5051 3357

■ **RICHARDSON TRIDENT CO LLC** p 1233
405 N Plano Rd, Richardson TX 75081
Tel (972) 231-5176
SIC 5051 5085 5063 5065 3316

ATLAS TUBULAR LLC p 128
1710 S Highway 77, Robstown TX 78380
Tel (361) 387-7505 SIC 5051 3498

■ **CONTINENTAL ALLOYS & SERVICES INC** p 362
18334 Stuebner Airline Rd, Spring TX 77379
Tel (281) 376-9600 SIC 5051

DELTA CENTRIFUGAL CORP p 426
3402 Center St, Temple TX 76504
Tel (254) 773-9055 SIC 5051 3325 3369

ENERGY ALLOYS LLC p 497
3 Waterway Square Pl # 600, The Woodlands TX 77380
Tel (832) 601-5800 SIC 5051

ACCENT PACKAGING INC p 14
10131 Fm 2920 Rd, Tomball TX 77375
Tel (281) 251-3700 SIC 5051 5084 5085

WESTLINK TRADING LLC p 1601
17926 Highway 3, Webster TX 77598
Tel (832) 295-9778
SIC 5032 5099 5074 5051 5031

GREAT WESTERN SUPPLY INC p 635
2626 Industrial Dr, Ogden UT 84401
Tel (801) 621-5412
SIC 5074 5051 5999 1711

HANDY CO N B p 657
65 10th St, Lynchburg VA 24504
Tel (434) 847-4495 SIC 5051 5074 5075

CAPITOL BUILDING SUPPLY INC p 251
8429 Euclid Ave, Manassas Park VA 20111
Tel (703) 631-6772
SIC 5032 5039 5033 5051

BMG METALS INC p 194
950 Masonic Ln, Richmond VA 23223
Tel (804) 226-1024 SIC 5051

ALASKAN COPPER COMPANIES INC p 45
27402 72nd Ave S, Kent WA 98032
Tel (206) 623-5800 SIC 5051 3498 3443

ALCO INVESTMENT CO p 47
27402 72nd Ave S, Kent WA 98032
Tel (206) 623-5800 SIC 5051 3498 3443

ISSC INC p 767
3660 E Marginal Way S, Seattle WA 98134
Tel (206) 343-0700 SIC 5051

■ **HASKINS STEEL CO INC** p 667
3613 E Main Ave, Spokane WA 99202
Tel (509) 252-9724 SIC 5051

CORE METALS GROUP LLC p 369
324 1/2 Penco Rd, Weirton WV 26062
Tel (304) 914-4360 SIC 5051

■ **RATHGIBSON HOLDING CO LLC** p 1209
2505 Foster Ave, Janesville WI 53545
Tel (608) 754-2222 SIC 3317 5051

RUSSEL METALS WILLIAMS BAHCALL INC p 1259
999 W Armour Ave, Milwaukee WI 53221
Tel (414) 481-7100 SIC 5051

STEEL WAREHOUSE OF WISCONSIN INC p 1384
535 W Forest Hill Ave, Oak Creek WI 53154
Tel (414) 764-4800 SIC 5051

MATENAER CORP p 919
810 Schoenhaar Dr, West Bend WI 53090
Tel (262) 338-0700 SIC 5051 3452

SIC 5052 Coal & Other Minerals & Ores Wholesale

DRUMMOND CO INC p 457
1000 Urban Center Dr # 300, Vestavia AL 35242
Tel (205) 945-6500
SIC 1221 1222 3312 5052 5085 5172

R T VANDERBILT CO INC p 1203
30 Winfield St, Norwalk CT 06855
Tel (203) 853-1400
SIC 5169 2869 2819 5052 1499 1459

H J BAKER & BRO INC p 650
2 Corporate Dr Ste 545, Shelton CT 06484
Tel (203) 682-9200 SIC 2048 5191 5052

NOBLE AMERICAS CORP p 1046
107 Elm St Fl 1, Stamford CT 06902
Tel (203) 324-8555 SIC 5052 1311

OXBOW CARBON & MINERALS HOLDINGS INC p 1100
1601 Forum Pl Ste 1400, West Palm Beach FL 33401
Tel (561) 907-5400 SIC 5052 1222

OXBOW CARBON LLC p 1100
1601 Forum Pl Ste 1400, West Palm Beach FL 33401
Tel (561) 907-5400 SIC 1241 2999 5052

OXBOW ENERGY SOLUTIONS LLC p 1100
1601 Forum Pl Ste 1400, West Palm Beach FL 33401
Tel (561) 907-4300 SIC 5052

S&B INDUSTRIAL MINERALS NORTH AMERICA INC p 1263
100 Mansell Ct E Ste 200, Roswell GA 30076
Tel (610) 647-1123 SIC 5052

AMERICAN COAL CO p 70
9085 Highway 34 N, Galatia IL 62935
Tel (618) 268-6311 SIC 1222 5052

■ DTE COAL SERVICES INC p 458
414 S Main St Ste 600, Ann Arbor MI 48104
Tel (734) 913-2080 SIC 5052 4212

PEABODY COALSALES LLC p 1125
701 Market St Fl 9, Saint Louis MO 63101
Tel (314) 342-3400 SIC 5052

PEABODY HOLDING CO LLC p 1125
701 Market St Ste 700, Saint Louis MO 63101
Tel (314) 342-3400
SIC 1221 1222 5052 2873 6719

■ SPRAGUE OPERATING RESOURCES LLC p 1360
185 International Dr, Portsmouth NH 03801
Tel (603) 431-1000 SIC 5172 5052 5171

SOJITZ CORP OF AMERICA p 1337
1120 Ave Of The, New York NY 10036
Tel (212) 704-6500
SIC 5065 5084 5169 5051 5099 5052

NYCO MINERALS INC p 1069
803 Mountain View Dr, Willsboro NY 12996
Tel (518) 963-4262
SIC 1499 5052 3295 3291

UMICORE USA INC p 1501
3600 Glenwood Ave Ste 250, Raleigh NC 27612
Tel (919) 874-7171
SIC 5052 5051 5093 5169 3339

HICKMAN WILLIAMS & CO p 690
250 E 5th St Ste 300, Cincinnati OH 45202
Tel (513) 621-1946
SIC 5051 5052 5169 5085 5084

TOSOH AMERICA INC p 1462
3600 Gantz Rd, Grove City OH 43123
Tel (614) 539-8622
SIC 5169 3564 5047 5052

■ CONSOL ENERGY SALES CO p 359
1000 Consol Energy Dr, Canonsburg PA 15317
Tel (724) 485-4000 SIC 5052

DRA TAGGART LLC p 455
4000 Town Center Way # 200, Canonsburg PA 15317
Tel (724) 754-9800 SIC 5052

ROBINDALE ENERGY SERVICES INC p 1242
1 Lloyd Ave Fl 2, Latrobe PA 15650
Tel (814) 446-6700 SIC 5052

■ SUNOCO INC p 1403
3801 West Chester Pike, Newtown Square PA 19073
Tel (215) 977-3000
SIC 5541 2911 2869 2865 5171 5052

BERWIND CORP p 176
3000 Ctr Sq W 1500 Mkt St 1500 W, Philadelphia PA 19102
Tel (215) 563-2800
SIC 6519 5052 4789 3625 3669 2899

CONVERSE AND CO INC p 365
314 S Pine St Ste 200, Spartanburg SC 29302
Tel (864) 542-2301 SIC 5052

ALLEY-CASSETTY COMPANIES INC p 53
2 Oldham St, Nashville TN 37213
Tel (615) 244-7077 SIC 5032 5052

MARTIN PRODUCT SALES LLC p 913
4200 Stone Rd, Kilgore TX 75662
Tel (903) 983-6200 SIC 5052 5032 5172

CONTURA COAL SALES LLC p 364
1 Alpha Pl, Bristol VA 24209
Tel (276) 619-4451 SIC 5052

L&L ENERGY INC p 834
130 Andover Park E # 200, Tukwila WA 98188
Tel (206) 264-8065 SIC 1241 1221 5052

SIC 5063 Electrl Apparatus, Eqpt, Wiring Splys Wholesale

MAYER ELECTRIC SUPPLY CO INC p 923
3405 4th Ave S, Birmingham AL 35222
Tel (205) 583-3500 SIC 5063 5719

ANDES INDUSTRIES INC p 90
2260 W Broadway Rd # 101, Mesa AZ 85202
Tel (480) 813-0925 SIC 5063 3663 3643

LOFTIN EQUIPMENT CO p 874
2111 E Highland Ave # 255, Phoenix AZ 85016
Tel (800) 437-4376 SIC 5063 5084 5999

LEONI WIRING SYSTEMS INC p 856
3100 N Campbell Ave # 101, Tucson AZ 85719
Tel (520) 741-0895 SIC 3643 8741 5063

ARKANSAS ELECTRIC COOPERATIVES INC p 109
1 Cooperative Way, Little Rock AR 72209
Tel (501) 570-2361
SIC 5063 1623 1629 7629

PRIORITY WIRE & CABLE INC p 1178
1800 E Roosevelt Rd, Little Rock AR 72206
Tel (501) 372-5444 SIC 5063

■ THORCO INDUSTRIES LLC p 1450
1401 Highway 49b, Paragould AR 72450
Tel (417) 682-3375 SIC 5063

CHEYENNE INDUSTRIES LLC p 296
5512 W Walsh Ln Ste 201, Rogers AR 72758
Tel (501) 812-6590 SIC 5063

MULTIQUIP INC p 1000
18910 Wilmington Ave, Carson CA 90746
Tel (310) 537-3700 SIC 5063 5082 3645

FLAME ENTERPRISES INC p 554
21500 Gledhill St, Chatsworth CA 91311
Tel (301) 668-0636 SIC 5065 5063

NMB (USA) INC p 1045
9730 Independence Ave, Chatsworth CA 91311
Tel (818) 709-1770
SIC 3562 5063 5084 3728 5065

REGENCY ENTERPRISES INC p 1218
9261 Jordan Ave, Chatsworth CA 91311
Tel (818) 901-0255 SIC 5063

AMERICAN ELECTRIC SUPPLY INC p 71
361 S Maple St, Corona CA 92880
Tel (951) 734-7910 SIC 5063

MINKA LIGHTING INC p 973
1151 Bradford Cir, Corona CA 92882
Tel (951) 735-9220 SIC 5063

USHIO AMERICA INC p 1535
5440 Cerritos Ave, Cypress CA 90630
Tel (714) 236-8600 SIC 5063

DELTA PRODUCTS CORP p 427
46101 Fremont Blvd, Fremont CA 94538
Tel (510) 668-5100
SIC 5065 5045 8741 5063 3577

ELECTRIC MOTOR SHOP p 484
253 Fulton St, Fresno CA 93721
Tel (559) 233-1153
SIC 5063 1731 7694 7922

ALAMEDA ELECTRIC SUPPLY p 44
3875 Bay Center Pl, Hayward CA 94545
Tel (510) 786-1400 SIC 5063

■ CUMMINS PACIFIC LLC p 401
1939 Deere Ave, Irvine CA 92606
Tel (949) 253-6000 SIC 3519 5063 7538

ONESOURCE DISTRIBUTORS LLC p 1088
3951 Oceanic Dr, Oceanside CA 92056
Tel (760) 966-4500 SIC 5063 3699

BAY ALARM CO p 160
60 Berry Dr, Pacheco CA 94553
Tel (925) 935-1100 SIC 1731 7382 5063

LGE ELECTRICAL SALES INC p 860
650 University Ave # 218, Sacramento CA 95825
Tel (916) 563-2737 SIC 5063

BUCKLES-SMITH ELECTRIC CO p 223
801 Savaker Ave, San Jose CA 95126
Tel (408) 280-7777 SIC 5084 5063

CHESTER C LEHMANN CO INC p 295
1135 Auzerais Ave, San Jose CA 95126
Tel (408) 293-5818 SIC 5063

EDGES ELECTRICAL GROUP LLC p 477
1135 Auzerais Ave, San Jose CA 95126
Tel (408) 293-5818 SIC 5063

HITACHI CHEMICAL CO AMERICA LTD p 696
2150 N 1st St Ste 350, San Jose CA 95131
Tel (408) 873-2200 SIC 5063 5065

INDEPENDENT ELECTRIC SUPPLY INC p 736
2001 Marina Blvd, San Leandro CA 94577
Tel (520) 908-7900 SIC 5063

■ AEE SOLAR INC p 29
775 Fiero Ln Ste 200, San Luis Obispo CA 93401
Tel (800) 777-6609 SIC 5063 3645

MAIN ELECTRIC SUPPLY CO p 897
3600 W Segerstrom Ave, Santa Ana CA 92704
Tel (949) 833-3052 SIC 5063

▲ REAL INDUSTRY INC p 1213
15301 Ventura Blvd # 400, Sherman Oaks CA 91403
Tel (805) 435-1255 SIC 5063 6162

WALTERS WHOLESALE ELECTRIC CO p 1574
2825 Temple Ave, Signal Hill CA 90755
Tel (562) 988-3100 SIC 5063 3699 1731

FUJIKURA AMERICA INC p 583
920 Stewart Dr Ste 150, Sunnyvale CA 94085
Tel (408) 748-6991 SIC 5063

PANAVISION INC p 1111
6101 Variel Ave, Woodland Hills CA 91367
Tel (818) 316-1000
SIC 7359 3861 3648 5063

WESTERN UNITED ELECTRIC SUPPLY CORP p 1600
100 Bromley Business Pkwy, Brighton CO 80603
Tel (303) 659-2356 SIC 5063

QED INC p 1194
1661 W 3rd Ave, Denver CO 80223
Tel (303) 825-5011 SIC 5063

■ TIMKEN MOTOR & CRANE SERVICES LLC p 1455
4850 Moline St, Denver CO 80239
Tel (303) 623-8658
SIC 5063 1731 7694 3613 3536

CAPITOL LIGHT & SUPPLY CO p 251
270 Locust St, Hartford CT 06114
Tel (860) 549-1230 SIC 5063

US ELECTRICAL SERVICES INC p 1531
701 Middle St, Middletown CT 06457
Tel (860) 522-3232 SIC 5063

ASEA BROWN BOVERI INC p 116
501 Merritt 7, Norwalk CT 06851
Tel (203) 750-2200
SIC 3612 3613 5063 3511 3625 8711

GENERAL SUPPLY & SERVICES INC p 602
1000 Bridgeport Ave 5-1, Shelton CT 06484
Tel (203) 925-2400 SIC 5063 8742

UNITED ELECTRIC SUPPLY CO INC p 1508
10 Bellecor Dr, New Castle DE 19720
Tel (800) 322-3374 SIC 5063

■ ANDERSON GROUP INC p 90
3411 Silverside Rd # 103, Wilmington DE 19810
Tel (302) 478-6160
SIC 5047 5063 5099 7699 3443

NGK NORTH AMERICA INC p 1041
1105 N Market St Ste 1300, Wilmington DE 19801
Tel (302) 654-1344
SIC 3714 5013 3264 5063

SONEPAR USA HOLDINGS INC p 1339
1011 Centre Rd Ste 327, Wilmington DE 19805
Tel (302) 573-3807 SIC 5063

DYNAFIRE INC p 464
109 Concord Dr Ste B, Casselberry FL 32707
Tel (407) 740-0232 SIC 5063

PANTROPIC POWER INC p 1112
8205 Nw 58th St, Doral FL 33166
Tel (305) 477-3329
SIC 5084 5085 5063 7353

HUGHES SUPPLY INC p 717
2920 Ford St, Fort Myers FL 33916
Tel (239) 334-2205
SIC 5063 5074 5075 5085 1711

■ INTERLINE BRANDS INC p 753
801 W Bay St, Jacksonville FL 32204
Tel (904) 421-1400 SIC 5074 5063 5072

■ INTERLINE BRANDS INC p 753
701 San Marco Blvd, Jacksonville FL 32207
Tel (904) 421-1400 SIC 5074 5063 5072

■ SAFT AMERICA INC p 1267
13575 Waterworks St, Jacksonville FL 32221
Tel (904) 861-1501 SIC 3691 5063

WORLD ELECTRIC SUPPLY INC p 1625
569 Stuart Ln, Jacksonville FL 32254
Tel (904) 378-4000 SIC 5063

DAVE CARTER & ASSOCIATES INC p 415
3530 Sw 7th St, Ocala FL 34474
Tel (352) 732-3317 SIC 5063 5039

ANIXTER POWER SOLUTIONS LLC p 92
501 W Church St Ste 100, Orlando FL 32805
Tel (407) 841-4755 SIC 5063

■ HD SUPPLY POWER SOLUTIONS GROUP INC p 673
501 W Church St Ste 100, Orlando FL 32805
Tel (407) 841-4755 SIC 5063

TAMPA ARMATURE WORKS INC p 1423
6312 S 78th St, Riverview FL 33578
Tel (813) 621-5661 SIC 5063 3613 3621

■ CARLISLE INTERCONNECT TECHNOLOGIES INC p 257
100 Tensolite Dr, Saint Augustine FL 32092
Tel (904) 829-5600
SIC 3679 3399 3678 3357 3643 5063

ELECTRIC SUPPLY OF TAMPA INC p 485
4407 N Manhattan Ave, Tampa FL 33614
Tel (813) 872-1894 SIC 5063

PENINSULAR ELECTRIC DISTRIBUTORS INC p 1129
1301 Okeechobee Rd, West Palm Beach FL 33401
Tel (561) 832-1626 SIC 5063

■ ACCU-TECH CORP p 16
11350 Old Roswell Rd # 100, Alpharetta GA 30009
Tel (770) 740-2240 SIC 5065 5063

AUBREY SILVEY ENTERPRISES INC p 130
371 Hamp Jones Rd, Carrollton GA 30117
Tel (770) 834-0738
SIC 1629 1541 3643 7389 3699 5063

GRESCO UTILITY SUPPLY INC p 639
1135 Rumble Rd, Forsyth GA 31029
Tel (478) 315-0800 SIC 5063

MCNAUGHTON-MCKAY SOUTHEAST INC p 932
6685 Best Friend Rd, Norcross GA 30071
Tel (770) 825-8600 SIC 5063

■ SITEONE LANDSCAPE SUPPLY HOLDING LLC p 1328
300 Colonial Center Pkwy, Roswell GA 30076
Tel (770) 255-2100
SIC 5083 5191 5193 5032 5063

▲ SITEONE LANDSCAPE SUPPLY INC p 1328
300 Colonial Center Pkwy, Roswell GA 30076
Tel (770) 255-2100
SIC 5083 5191 5193 5032 5063

■ SITEONE LANDSCAPE SUPPLY LLC p 1328
300 Colonial Center Pkwy # 600, Roswell GA 30076
Tel (770) 255-2100 SIC 5063 5193 5083

FIRST CALL JEWEL INC p 545
1410 Hollipark Dr, Idaho Falls ID 83401
Tel (208) 522-7777
SIC 1731 1711 5078 5063

RAYCAP INC p 1210
806 S Clearwater Loop, Post Falls ID 83854
Tel (208) 457-0895 SIC 3643 5063

SUNRISE ELECTRIC SUPPLY INC p 1404
130 S Addison Rd, Addison IL 60101
Tel (630) 543-1111 SIC 5063 5211

SIEMENS INDUSTRY INC p 1320
1000 Deerfield Pkwy, Buffalo Grove IL 60089
Tel (847) 215-1000
SIC 3822 5063 3669 1731 7382 3625

ADVANCE ELECTRICAL SUPPLY CO LLC p 24
263 N Oakley Blvd, Chicago IL 60612
Tel (312) 421-2300 SIC 5063

■ NEWARK ELECTRONICS CORP p 1037
300 S Riverside Plz, Chicago IL 60606
Tel (773) 784-5100 SIC 5065 5063 5961

RATHJE ENTERPRISES INC p 1209
1845 N 22nd St, Decatur IL 62526
Tel (217) 423-2593 SIC 1731 7694 5063

CRESCENT ELECTRIC SUPPLY CO p 391
7750 Timmerman Dr, East Dubuque IL 61025
Tel (815) 747-3145 SIC 5063

STEINER ELECTRIC CO p 1385
1250 Touhy Ave, Elk Grove Village IL 60007
Tel (847) 228-0400 SIC 5065 5063

■ ANIXTER INC p 92
2301 Patriot Blvd, Glenview IL 60026
Tel (224) 521-8000 SIC 5063 4899

▲ ANIXTER INTERNATIONAL INC p 92
2301 Patriot Blvd, Glenview IL 60026
Tel (224) 521-8000 SIC 5063 5085

OPTIMAS OE SOLUTIONS HOLDING LLC p 1090
2651 Compass Rd, Glenview IL 60026
Tel (224) 521-8000 SIC 5063

OPTIMAS OE SOLUTIONS INTERMED LLC p 1090
2651 Compass Rd, Glenview IL 60026
Tel (224) 521-8000 SIC 5063

EQUIPMENT DEPOT OF ILLINOIS INC p 506
751 Expressway Dr, Itasca IL 60143
Tel (847) 836-5005
SIC 5084 5087 5063 7699

■ DAYTON ELECTRIC MFG CO p 417
100 Grainger Pkwy, Lake Forest IL 60045
Tel (847) 535-1000 SIC 5063 5084 5072

▲ WW GRAINGER INC p 1628
100 Grainger Pkwy, Lake Forest IL 60045
Tel (847) 535-1000
SIC 5063 5084 5075 5085 5072

LSIS USA INC p 883
2000 Millbrook Dr, Lincolnshire IL 60069
Tel (847) 941-8240 SIC 5063

MIDWEST AIR TECHNOLOGIES INC p 967
6700 Wildlife Way, Long Grove IL 60047
Tel (847) 821-9630
SIC 5072 5191 5063 5051 5031

REVERE ELECTRIC SUPPLY CO p 1229
8807 187th St, Mokena IL 60448
Tel (312) 738-3636 SIC 5063

■ MONONA HOLDINGS LLC p 984
1952 Mc Dowell Rd Ste 207, Naperville IL 60563
Tel (630) 946-0630 SIC 3694 5063

BODINE ELECTRIC CO p 197
201 Northfield Rd, Northfield IL 60093
Tel (773) 478-3515 SIC 5063 3625 3621

ACE HARDWARE CORP p 16
2200 Kensington Ct, Oak Brook IL 60523
Tel (630) 990-6600
SIC 5251 5198 5063 5074 5083

TECH LIGHTING LLC p 1431
7400 Linder Ave, Skokie IL 60077
Tel (847) 410-4400 SIC 5063

SPRINGFIELD ELECTRIC SUPPLY CO p 1360
700 N 9th St, Springfield IL 62702
Tel (217) 788-2100 SIC 5063 5719

PANDUIT CORP p 1111
18900 Panduit Dr, Tinley Park IL 60487
Tel (708) 532-1800 SIC 3699 3644 5063

YASKAWA AMERICA INC p 1635
2121 Norman Dr, Waukegan IL 60085
Tel (847) 887-7000
SIC 3621 7694 5063 3566 3823 3625

US TSUBAKI POWER TRANSMISSION LLC p 1533
301 E Marquardt Dr, Wheeling IL 60090
Tel (847) 459-9500
SIC 3568 5085 5063 3714 3462 3325

CNA INTERNATIONAL INC p 330
940 N Central Ave, Wood Dale IL 60191
Tel (630) 238-9800 SIC 5063 5064

ELECTRONIC TECHNOLOGIES CORP USA p 486
11819 N Pennsylvania St, Carmel IN 46032
Tel (317) 810-3177 SIC 5065 5063 7382

FLANDERS ELECTRIC MOTOR SERVICE INC p 554
8101 Baumgart Rd, Evansville IN 47725
Tel (812) 867-7421 SIC 7694 5063

DO IT BEST CORP p 446
6502 Nelson Rd, Fort Wayne IN 46803
Tel (260) 748-5300 SIC 5072 5031 5063

CENTRAL SUPPLY CO INC p 280
8900 E 30th St, Indianapolis IN 46219
Tel (317) 898-2411
SIC 5074 5063 5085 5719

■ CUMMINS CROSSPOINT LLC p 401
2601 Fortune Cir E 300c, Indianapolis IN 46241
Tel (317) 243-7979
SIC 5084 7538 5063 3519

KOORSEN FIRE & SECURITY INC p 827
2719 N Arlington Ave, Indianapolis IN 46218
Tel (317) 542-1800
SIC 5099 7389 5199 5063 1731

KIRBY RISK CORP p 821
1815 Sagamore Pkwy N, Lafayette IN 47904
Tel (765) 448-4567
SIC 5063 7694 3599 3679 3629

KW SERVICES LLC p 832
3801 Voorde Dr Ste B, South Bend IN 46628
Tel (574) 232-2051 SIC 6719 1799 5063

WABASH ELECTRIC SUPPLY INC p 1570
1400 S Wabash St, Wabash IN 46992
Tel (260) 563-2240 SIC 5063

VAN METER INC p 1543
850 32nd Ave Sw, Cedar Rapids IA 52404
Tel (319) 366-5301 SIC 5063

ECHO GROUP INC p 475
1851 Madison Ave Ste 710, Council Bluffs IA 51503
Tel (712) 322-4120 SIC 5063

DSI DISTRIBUTING INC p 457
3601 109th St, Urbandale IA 50322
Tel (515) 276-9181 SIC 5063 5731

ELECTRICAL ENGINEERING AND EQUIPMENT CO p 485
953 73rd St, Windsor Heights IA 50324
Tel (515) 273-0100 SIC 5063 8711

STANION WHOLESALE ELECTRIC CO INC p 1377
812 S Main St, Pratt KS 67124
Tel (620) 672-5678 SIC 5063

SUMITOMO ELECTRIC WIRING SYSTEMS INC p 1398
1018 Ashley St, Bowling Green KY 42103
Tel (270) 782-7397 SIC 3714 5063 3694

ELECTRIC & WATER PLANT BOARD OF CITY OF FRANKFORT KY p 484
317 W 2nd St, Frankfort KY 40601
Tel (502) 352-4372
SIC 4941 4911 7382 5063 4841 4813

KENTUCKY ASSOCIATION OF ELECTRIC COOPERATIVES INC p 812
4515 Bishop Ln, Louisville KY 40218
Tel (502) 451-2430
SIC 3612 2721 7629 5063

REV-A-SHELF CO LLC p 1229
12400 Earl Jones Way, Louisville KY 40299
Tel (502) 499-5835 SIC 3823 5063

UNITED UTILITY SUPPLY COOPERATIVE INC p 1515
4515 Bishop Ln, Louisville KY 40218
Tel (502) 459-4011 SIC 5063

NU-LITE ELECTRICAL WHOLESALERS LLC p 1066
850 Edwards Ave, Harahan LA 70123
Tel (504) 733-3300 SIC 5063

LINEAR CONTROLS INC p 869
107 1/2 Commission Blvd, Lafayette LA 70508
Tel (337) 839-9702 SIC 5063

CREST INDUSTRIES p 392
4725 Highway 28 E, Pineville LA 71360
Tel (318) 767-5530
SIC 3699 3612 3441 5063 2439

CREST OPERATIONS LLC p 392
4725 Highway 28 E, Pineville LA 71360
Tel (318) 448-0274
SIC 3441 2439 3699 5063 3612

■ IBERDROLA USA MANAGEMENT CORP p 726
52 Farm View Dr, New Gloucester ME 04260
Tel (207) 688-6300 *SIC* 5063

SHEPHERD ELECTRIC CO INC p 1315
7401 Pulaski Hwy, Baltimore MD 21237
Tel (410) 866-6000 *SIC* 5063

ELECTRICAL WHOLESALERS METRO DC INC p 485
6500a Sheriff Rd, Landover MD 20785
Tel (301) 333-5990 *SIC* 5063

CENTRAL WHOLESALERS INC p 281
13401 Konterra Dr, Laurel MD 20707
Tel (800) 935-2947
SIC 5074 5063 5087 5072 5211 1799

FIDELITY ENGINEERING CORP p 540
25 Loveton Cir, Sparks MD 21152
Tel (410) 771-9400
SIC 1711 5063 1799 8711

BRANCH GROUP INC p 207
1049 Prince Georges Blvd, Upper Marlboro MD 20774
Tel (301) 249-5005 *SIC* 5063 5211

CAPITAL LIGHTING & SUPPLY LLC p 249
8511 Pepco Pl, Upper Marlboro MD 20772
Tel (301) 909-6500 *SIC* 5063

SCHNEIDER ELECTRIC USA INC p 1288
800 Federal St, Andover MA 01810
Tel (978) 975-9600
SIC 3613 3643 3612 3823 3625 5063

SONEPAR DISTRIBUTION NEW ENGLAND INC p 1339
560 Oak St, Brockton MA 02301
Tel (508) 998-8900 *SIC* 5063

■ NEEDHAM ELECTRIC SUPPLY CORP p 1024
5 Shawmut Rd, Canton MA 02021
Tel (781) 828-9494 *SIC* 5063 3648

YALE ELECTRICAL SUPPLY CO p 1634
55 Shawmut Rd, Canton MA 02021
Tel (781) 737-2500 *SIC* 5063

ADVANCED CABLE TIES INC p 25
245 Suffolk Ln, Gardner MA 01440
Tel (978) 630-3900 *SIC* 5063

GRANITE CITY ELECTRIC SUPPLY CO INC p 631
19 Quincy Ave, Quincy MA 02169
Tel (617) 472-6500 *SIC* 5063 5719

INDEPENDENT ELECTRIC SUPPLY CORP p 736
41 Innerbelt Rd, Somerville MA 02143
Tel (617) 625-5155 *SIC* 5063

CONCORD ELECTRIC SUPPLY LIMITED p 354
2701 Boston Rd Ste 100, Wilbraham MA 01095
Tel (413) 599-1750 *SIC* 5063

HEILIND ELECTRONICS INC p 681
58 Jonspin Rd, Wilmington MA 01887
Tel (978) 658-7000 *SIC* 5065 3679 5063

LEDVANCE LLC p 851
200 Ballardvale St, Wilmington MA 01887
Tel (978) 570-3000 *SIC* 5063

STANDARD ELECTRIC SUPPLY CO INC p 1376
14 Jewel Dr, Wilmington MA 01887
Tel (978) 658-5050 *SIC* 5063

II STANLEY CO INC p 731
1500 Hill Brady Rd, Battle Creek MI 49037
Tel (269) 660-7777 *SIC* 5063 4911

ELECTRO-MATIC VENTURES INC p 485
23409 Industrial Park Ct, Farmington Hills MI 48335
Tel (248) 478-1182 *SIC* 5063 3674

CHAMPION INC p 287
180 Traders Mine Rd, Iron Mountain MI 49801
Tel (906) 779-2300
SIC 8741 1542 5063 5082 3273 3272

A123 SYSTEMS LLC p 7
39000 7 Mile Rd, Livonia MI 48152
Tel (734) 772-0300 *SIC* 5063 3691

MCNAUGHTON-MCKAY ELECTRIC CO p 932
1357 E Lincoln Ave, Madison Heights MI 48071
Tel (248) 399-7500 *SIC* 5065 5063

JOHNSON ELECTRIC NORTH AMERICA INC p 791
47660 Halyard Dr, Plymouth MI 48170
Tel (734) 392-5300
SIC 5063 3625 3674 8711

ABC APPLIANCE INC p 10
1 W Silverdome Indus Park, Pontiac MI 48342
Tel (248) 335-4222
SIC 5722 5731 5999 5065 5064 5063

KENDALL ELECTRIC INC p 810
5101 S Sprinkle Rd, Portage MI 49002
Tel (800) 632-5422 *SIC* 5063 7629 5084

POWER LINE SUPPLY CO p 1165
420 S Roth St Ste A, Reed City MI 49677
Tel (231) 832-2297 *SIC* 5063

UTILITY SUPPLY AND CONSTRUCTION CO p 1537
420 S Roth St Ste A, Reed City MI 49677
Tel (231) 832-2297
SIC 2411 2491 2631 5063

STANDARD ELECTRIC CO p 1376
2650 Trautner Dr, Saginaw MI 48604
Tel (989) 497-2100 *SIC* 5063

QUAD ELECTRONICS INC p 1195
379 Executive Dr, Troy MI 48083
Tel (800) 969-9220 *SIC* 5063

MADISON ELECTRIC CO p 894
31855 Van Dyke Ave, Warren MI 48093
Tel (586) 825-0200 *SIC* 5063 3679

ARROW MOTOR & PUMP INC p 113
629 Cent St, Wyandotte MI 48192
Tel (734) 285-7860
SIC 7694 5063 7699 5084

BERGQUIST CO p 174
18930 W 78th St, Chanhassen MN 55317
Tel (952) 835-2322
SIC 5731 5063 3645 3646 2822

WERNER ELECTRIC VENTURES LLC p 1592
7450 95th St S, Cottage Grove MN 55016
Tel (651) 458-3701 *SIC* 5063 5084 5085

VIKING ELECTRIC SUPPLY INC p 1557
451 Industrial Blvd Ne # 2, Minneapolis MN 55413
Tel (612) 627-1234 *SIC* 5063

J H LARSON ELECTRICAL CO p 771
10200 51st Ave N Ste B, Plymouth MN 55442
Tel (763) 545-1717 *SIC* 5063 5074 5075

WRIGHT-HENNEPIN SECURITY CORP p 1627
6800 Electric Dr, Rockford MN 55373
Tel (763) 477-3664
SIC 1731 1711 7382 5063 4911

MIDWEST SIGN & SCREEN PRINTING SUPPLY CO INC p 968
45 Maryland Ave E, Saint Paul MN 55117
Tel (651) 489-9999 *SIC* 5084 5063

■ CUMMINS NPOWER LLC p 401
1600 Buerkle Rd, White Bear Lake MN 55110
Tel (800) 642-0085
SIC 5084 5063 7538 3519

▲ FASTENAL CO p 531
2001 Theurer Blvd, Winona MN 55987
Tel (507) 454-5374
SIC 5085 5072 5063 5169 5198

PUCKETT MACHINERY CO p 1190
100 Caterpillar Dr, Flowood MS 39232
Tel (601) 969-6000
SIC 5082 5084 5063 7699

STUART C IRBY CO p 1394
815 Irby Dr, Jackson MS 39201
Tel (601) 960-7346 *SIC* 5063

SOUTHERN ELECTRIC SUPPLY CO INC p 1348
301 46th Ct, Meridian MS 39305
Tel (601) 693-4141 *SIC* 5063

CAPE ELECTRICAL SUPPLY LLC p 248
489 Kell Farm Dr, Cape Girardeau MO 63701
Tel (573) 431-1838 *SIC* 3699 5063

BUTLER SUPPLY INC p 230
965 Horan Dr, Fenton MO 63026
Tel (636) 349-9000 *SIC* 5063

WESTERN EXTRALITE CO p 1598
1470 Liberty St, Kansas City MO 64102
Tel (816) 421-8404 *SIC* 5063

FROST ELECTRIC SUPPLY CO p 581
2429 Schuetz Rd, Maryland Heights MO 63043
Tel (314) 567-4004 *SIC* 5063

■ ENERGIZER BRANDS LLC p 497
533 Maryville Univ Dr, Saint Louis MO 63141
Tel (314) 985-2000 *SIC* 5063

FRENCH-GERLEMAN ELECTRIC CO p 578
2023 Westport Center Dr, Saint Louis MO 63146
Tel (314) 569-3122 *SIC* 5063

GRAYBAR ELECTRIC CO INC p 632
34 N Meramec Ave, Saint Louis MO 63105
Tel (314) 573-9200 *SIC* 5063 5065

ST LOUIS ELECTRIC SUPPLY INC p 1369
6801 Hoffman Ave, Saint Louis MO 63139
Tel (314) 645-9000 *SIC* 5063 5719

TECH L ENTERPRISES INC p 1431
7701 Forsyth Blvd Ste 600, Saint Louis MO 63105
Tel (314) 727-5550 *SIC* 5063

VILLA LIGHTING SUPPLY INC p 1557
2929 Chouteau Ave, Saint Louis MO 63103
Tel (314) 531-2600 *SIC* 5063

KRIZ-DAVIS CO p 830
2400 W 3rd St, Grand Island NE 68803
Tel (308) 382-2230 *SIC* 5063

DUTTON-LAINSON CO p 463
451 W 2nd St, Hastings NE 68901
Tel (402) 463-6702
SIC 3531 5999 5063 5074

CASHMAN EQUIPMENT CO p 263
3300 Saint Rose Pkwy, Henderson NV 89052
Tel (702) 649-8777
SIC 5084 5063 7353 7699

PHILCOR TV & ELECTRONIC LEASING INC p 1143
4200 Spring Mountain Rd, Las Vegas NV 89102
Tel (702) 367-0400 *SIC* 5063 5065

■ BURNDY AMERICAS INC p 228
47 E Industrial Pk Dr, Manchester NH 03109
Tel (603) 647-5000 *SIC* 3643 5063

■ BURNDY LLC p 228
47 E Industrial Park Dr, Manchester NH 03109
Tel (603) 626-3730 *SIC* 3643 5063

ROCKINGHAM ELECTRICAL SUPPLY CO INC p 1244
437 Shattuck Way, Portsmouth NH 03801
Tel (603) 436-7731 *SIC* 5063

DANCKER SELLEW & DOUGLAS INC p 411
291 Evans Way, Branchburg NJ 08876
Tel (908) 429-1200 *SIC* 5021 5063 5049

ANTRONIX INC p 94
440 Forsgate Dr, Cranbury NJ 08512
Tel (609) 860-0160 *SIC* 3663 5063

C R P INDUSTRIES INC p 233
35 Commerce Dr, Cranbury NJ 08512
Tel (609) 578-4100 *SIC* 5013 5085 5063

BILLOWS ELECTRIC SUPPLY CO INC p 182
1813 Underwood Blvd, Delran NJ 08075
Tel (215) 332-9700
SIC 5063 3679 3621 3643 3644

TYCO ELECTRONICS SUBSEA COMMUNICATIONS LLC p 1496
250 Industrial Way W, Eatontown NJ 07724
Tel (732) 578-7000
SIC 3661 5063 7373 1731 8999

ALPHA WIRE CORP p 60
711 Lidgerwood Ave, Elizabeth NJ 07202
Tel (908) 259-2613 *SIC* 5063 3082 3357

■ ASCO VALVE INC p 116
50-60 Hanover Rd, Florham Park NJ 07932
Tel (973) 966-2437
SIC 3443 3491 3492 3625 5063

LAPP USA LLC p 845
29 Hanover Rd, Florham Park NJ 07932
Tel (973) 660-9700 *SIC* 5063 3678

WIND TURBINE AND ENERGY CABLES CORP p 1615
1 Bridge Plz N Ste 260, Fort Lee NJ 07024
Tel (201) 242-9906 *SIC* 5063

EMERGING POWER INC p 492
200 Holt St, Hackensack NJ 07601
Tel (201) 441-3590 *SIC* 5063

TURTLE & HUGHES INC p 1493
1900 Lower Rd, Linden NJ 07036
Tel (732) 574-3600 *SIC* 5063 5085

PANASONIC CORP OF NORTH AMERICA p 1111
2 Riverfront Plz Ste 200, Newark NJ 07102
Tel (201) 348-7000
SIC 5064 5045 5065 5044 5084 5063

QUALITY COMPUTER ACCESSORIES INC p 1196
70 Ethel Rd W Ste 1, Piscataway NJ 08854
Tel (732) 572-2719
SIC 5063 5051 3315 3644

GAFFNEY-KROESE ELECTRICAL SUPPLY CORP p 589
50 Randolph Rd, Somerset NJ 08873
Tel (732) 885-9000 *SIC* 5063 5084 5085

SWIFT ELECTRICAL SUPPLY CO p 1412
100 Hollister Rd Unit C1, Teterboro NJ 07608
Tel (201) 462-0900 *SIC* 5063

PAIGE ELECTRIC CO LP p 1108
1160 Springfield Rd, Union NJ 07083
Tel (908) 687-7810 *SIC* 5063 3699

SWATCH GROUP U S INC p 1411
1200 Harbor Blvd Fl 7, Weehawken NJ 07086
Tel (201) 271-1400
SIC 5063 3625 5094 3873

PARIS CORP OF NEW JERSEY p 1115
800 Highland Dr, Westampton NJ 08060
Tel (609) 265-9200 *SIC* 5112 2752 5063

SUMMIT ELECTRIC SUPPLY CO INC p 1398
2900 Stanford Dr Ne, Albuquerque NM 87107
Tel (505) 346-2900 *SIC* 5063

QUALITY HOME BRANDS HOLDINGS LLC p 1197
125 Rose Feiss Blvd, Bronx NY 10454
Tel (718) 292-2024 *SIC* 3645 5063

TIME WARNER INC p 1454
6005 Fair Lakes Rd, East Syracuse NY 13057
Tel (315) 234-1000 *SIC* 5063

HARDWARE SPECIALTY CO INC p 661
4875 36th St, Long Island City NY 11101
Tel (718) 361-9320 *SIC* 5063 5085

■ ADI CORPORATE p 22
263 Old Country Rd, Melville NY 11747
Tel (800) 233-6261 *SIC* 5063 5085

▲ MSC INDUSTRIAL DIRECT CO INC p 996
75 Maxess Rd, Melville NY 11747
Tel (516) 812-2000
SIC 5084 5085 5063 5072

DITTMAN AND GREER INC p 443
270 Park Ave, New Hyde Park NY 11040
Tel (860) 347-4655 *SIC* 5063

■ LSI LIGHTRON INC p 883
500 Hudson Valley Ave, New Windsor NY 12553
Tel (845) 562-5500 *SIC* 3646 5063

SUMITOMO CORP OF AMERICAS p 1398
300 Madison Ave, New York NY 10017
Tel (212) 207-0700
SIC 5051 5172 5084 5063 5141

ZGS INC p 1643
456 W 55th St, New York NY 10019
Tel (212) 586-1620 *SIC* 5063

LIGHTING HOLDINGS INTERNATIONAL LLC p 865
4 Manhattanville Rd, Purchase NY 10577
Tel (845) 306-1850
SIC 3641 5719 5063 4225 3643 3229

HORIZON SOLUTIONS LLC p 707
175 Josons Dr, Rochester NY 14623
Tel (585) 274-8235 *SIC* 5063 5085

■ KIT ZELLER INC p 822
1000 University Ave # 800, Rochester NY 14607
Tel (585) 254-8840 *SIC* 5063

■ GE POWER & WATER p 596
1 River Rd Bldg 5-419, Schenectady NY 12345
Tel (518) 385-2211 *SIC* 7382 5063

CITY ELECTRIC CO INC p 312
501 W Genesee St, Syracuse NY 13204
Tel (315) 474-7841 *SIC* 5063 5085

HITACHI AMERICA LTD p 696
50 Prospect Ave, Tarrytown NY 10591
Tel (914) 332-5800
SIC 5084 5065 3577 5063 5045 3651

HH BENFIELD ELECTRIC SUPPLY CO INC p 689
25 Lafayette Ave, White Plains NY 10603
Tel (914) 948-6660 *SIC* 5063

ACE WIRE & CABLE CO INC p 16
7201 51st Ave, Woodside NY 11377
Tel (718) 458-9200 *SIC* 5063

HUNT ELECTRIC SUPPLY CO p 719
1213 Maple Ave, Burlington NC 27215
Tel (336) 229-5351 *SIC* 5063 5211

ABB INC p 9
12040 Regency Pkwy # 200, Cary NC 27518
Tel (919) 856-2360
SIC 8711 3612 3511 5063 3613 3625

■ GE LIGHTING SYSTEMS LLC p 596
3010 Spartanburg Hwy, East Flat Rock NC 28726
Tel (828) 693-2000 *SIC* 5063

GENEVA HOLDINGS INC p 603
8015 Piedmont Triad Pkwy, Greensboro NC 27409
Tel (336) 275-9936 *SIC* 5084 5063

ELECTRICAL EQUIPMENT CO INC p 485
1440 Diggs Dr, Raleigh NC 27603
Tel (919) 828-5411 *SIC* 5063 7699

LONGLEY SUPPLY CO p 877
2018 Oleander Dr, Wilmington NC 28403
Tel (910) 762-7793 *SIC* 5074 5063 5075

BORDER STATES ELECTRIC SUPPLY OF MINNESOTA INC p 201
105 25th St N, Fargo ND 58102
Tel (701) 258-6060 *SIC* 5063

BORDER STATES ELECTRIC SUPPLY OF TEXAS INC p 201
105 25th St N, Fargo ND 58102
Tel (701) 293-5834 *SIC* 5063

BORDER STATES INDUSTRIES INC p 201
105 25th St N, Fargo ND 58102
Tel (701) 293-5834 *SIC* 5063

DAKOTA SUPPLY GROUP INC p 409
2601 3rd Ave N, Fargo ND 58102
Tel (701) 237-9440 *SIC* 5063

ACME ELECTRIC MOTOR INC p 17
1705 13th Ave N, Grand Forks ND 58203
Tel (701) 746-2823
SIC 5084 5063 5082 5072 5251 5211

TECHNICAL CONSUMER PRODUCTS INC p 1431
325 Campus Dr, Aurora OH 44202
Tel (800) 324-1496 *SIC* 5063

BELTING CO OF CINCINNATI p 171
5500 Ridge Ave, Cincinnati OH 45213
Tel (513) 621-9050 *SIC* 5085 5063

RICHARDS ELECTRIC SUPPLY CO INC p 1232
4620 Reading Rd, Cincinnati OH 45229
Tel (513) 242-8800 *SIC* 5063

■ APPLIED INDUSTRIAL TECHNOLOGIES - CA LLC p 99
1 Applied Plz, Cleveland OH 44115
Tel (216) 426-4000 *SIC* 5063

H LEFF ELECTRIC CO p 650
4700 Spring Rd, Cleveland OH 44131
Tel (216) 325-0941 *SIC* 5063

LOEB ELECTRIC CO p 874
1800 E 5th Ave Ste A, Columbus OH 43219
Tel (614) 294-6351 *SIC* 5063

MCNAUGHTON-MCKAY ELECTRIC CO OF OHIO INC p 932
2255 Citygate Dr, Columbus OH 43219
Tel (614) 476-2800 *SIC* 5063

ASSOCIATED MATERIALS HOLDINGS LLC p 120
3773 State Rd, Cuyahoga Falls OH 44223
Tel (330) 929-1811
SIC 3089 5033 5031 5063 3442

JOHN A BECKER CO p 787
1341 E 4th St, Dayton OH 45402
Tel (937) 226-1341 *SIC* 5063

MULTILINK INC p 999
580 Ternes Ln, Elyria OH 44035
Tel (440) 366-6966 *SIC* 5063 3829

■ AMETEK TECHNICAL & INDUSTRIAL PRODUCTS INC p 84
100 E Erie St Ste 130, Kent OH 44240
Tel (330) 677-3754 *SIC* 3621 5063 3566

WOLFF BROS SUPPLY INC p 1621
6078 Wolff Rd, Medina OH 44256
Tel (330) 725-3451 *SIC* 5063 5074 5075

NOLAND CO p 1046
3110 Kettering Blvd, Moraine OH 45439
Tel (937) 396-7980
SIC 5074 5075 5063 5085

DICKMAN SUPPLY INC p 438
1991 St Marys Ave, Sidney OH 45365
Tel (937) 492-6166 *SIC* 5063 5084

BOSTWICK-BRAUN CO p 203
7349 Crossleigh Ct, Toledo OH 43617
Tel (419) 259-3600
SIC 5072 5084 5063 5083 5023

BROKEN ARROW ELECTRIC SUPPLY INC p 216
2350 W Vancouver St, Broken Arrow OK 74012
Tel (918) 258-3581 *SIC* 5063

■ REMY POWER PRODUCTS LLC p 1223
3400 S Kelly Ave, Edmond OK 73013
Tel (405) 475-9800 *SIC* 5063

HUNZICKER BROTHERS INC p 721
501 N Virginia Ave, Oklahoma City OK 73106
Tel (405) 239-7771 *SIC* 5063

LOCKE SUPPLY CO p 873
1300 Se 82nd St, Oklahoma City OK 73149
Tel (405) 635-3230
SIC 5063 5074 5075 1711

PLATT ELECTRIC SUPPLY INC p 1155
10605 Sw Allen Blvd, Beaverton OR 97005
Tel (503) 641-6121 *SIC* 5063

DOLAN NORTHWEST LLC p 447
1919 Nw 19th Ave, Portland OR 97209
Tel (503) 221-1919 *SIC* 5063 5719

EC CO p 474
2121 Nw Thurman St, Portland OR 97210
Tel (503) 224-3511
SIC 1731 7694 5063 5084

JOHNSTONE SUPPLY INC p 791
11632 Ne Ainsworth Cir, Portland OR 97220
Tel (503) 256-3663
SIC 5075 5085 5063 5064

HITE CO p 697
3101 Beale Ave, Altoona PA 16601
Tel (814) 944-6121 *SIC* 5063

GEO W KISTLER INC p 605
2210 City Line Rd, Bethlehem PA 18017
Tel (610) 266-7100
SIC 5063 7382 5087 7389

■ CUMMINS POWER SYSTEMS LLC p 401
2727 Ford Rd, Bristol PA 19007
Tel (215) 785-6005
SIC 5084 5063 7538 7629 3519

RAM INDUSTRIAL SERVICES LLC p 1206
2850 Appleton St Ste D, Camp Hill PA 17011
Tel (717) 737-7810 *SIC* 5063 7629

PENNSYLVANIA TRANSFORMER TECHNOLOGY INC p 1130
30 Curry Ave Ste 2, Canonsburg PA 15317
Tel (724) 873-2100 *SIC* 3612 5063 3677

ALLIED WIRE & CABLE INC p 57
101 Kestrel Dr, Collegeville PA 19426
Tel (484) 928-6700 *SIC* 5063

RUMSEY ELECTRIC CO p 1258
15 Colwell Ln, Conshohocken PA 19428
Tel (610) 832-9000 *SIC* 5063

SCOTT ELECTRIC CO p 1293
1000 S Main St, Greensburg PA 15601
Tel (800) 442-8045 *SIC* 5063

D & H DISTRIBUTING CO p 406
2525 N 7th St, Harrisburg PA 17110
Tel (717) 236-8001
SIC 5045 5065 5064 5063 5044

SCHAEDLER/YESCO DISTRIBUTION INC p 1286
3982 Paxton St, Harrisburg PA 17111
Tel (717) 843-9991 *SIC* 5063

LAUREL HOLDINGS INC p 847
111 Roosevelt Blvd, Johnstown PA 15906
Tel (814) 533-5777
SIC 4941 5063 3599 4724 7349

▲ BLACK BOX CORP p 186
1000 Park Dr, Lawrence PA 15055
Tel (724) 746-5500
SIC 3577 3679 3661 5045 5065 5063

■ BLACK BOX CORP OF PENNSYLVANIA p 186
1000 Park Dr, Lawrence PA 15055
Tel (724) 746-5500
SIC 5045 5063 5065 3577 3679 3661

GDT PROPERTIES INC p 595
312 N 8th St, Lebanon PA 17046
Tel (717) 273-4514 *SIC* 5063

EAST PENN MANUFACTURING CO p 470
102 Deka Rd, Lyon Station PA 19536
Tel (610) 682-6361
SIC 3694 3691 5063 4225

PHOENIX CONTACT SERVICES INC p 1144
586 Fulling Mill Rd, Middletown PA 17057
Tel (717) 944-1300 *SIC* 5063 3678 3643

SECURITY AND DATA TECHNOLOGIES INC p 1299
101 Pheasant Run, Newtown PA 18940
Tel (215) 579-7000 *SIC* 5063

ALMO CORP p 59
2709 Commerce Way, Philadelphia PA 19154
Tel (215) 698-4000 *SIC* 5064 5063

SONEPAR MANAGEMENT US INC p 1339
510 Walnut St Ste 400, Philadelphia PA 19106
Tel (215) 399-5900 *SIC* 5063

WESTINGHOUSE LIGHTING CORP p 1601
12401 Mcnulty Rd Ofc, Philadelphia PA 19154
Tel (215) 671-2000 *SIC* 5063 3641 3645

■ EMERSON PROCESS MANAGEMENT POWER & WATER SOLUTIONS INC p 492
200 Beta Dr, Pittsburgh PA 15238
Tel (412) 963-4000 *SIC* 3823 5063

■ WESCO DISTRIBUTION INC p 1593
225 W Station Square Dr # 700, Pittsburgh PA 15219
Tel (412) 454-2200
SIC 5063 5085 5065 7389

▲ WESCO INTERNATIONAL INC p 1593
225 W Station Square Dr # 700, Pittsburgh PA 15219
Tel (412) 454-2200
SIC 5063 5084 5065 7389

■ ENERSYS DELAWARE INC p 498
2366 Bernville Rd, Reading PA 19605
Tel (214) 324-8990 *SIC* 3691 5063

FROMM ELECTRIC SUPPLY CORP OF READING PENNA p 580
2101 Centre Ave Ste 4, Reading PA 19605
Tel (610) 374-4441 *SIC* 5063

OMNI CABLE CORP p 1084
2 Hagerty Blvd, West Chester PA 19382
Tel (610) 701-0100 *SIC* 5063

HAGEMEYER PPS LTD p 652
1460 Tobias Gadson Blvd, Charleston SC 29407
Tel (843) 745-2400 *SIC* 5063

COOPERATIVE ELECTRIC ENERGY UTILITY SUPPLY INC p 367
101 Enterprise Pkwy, West Columbia SC 29170
Tel (800) 922-3590 *SIC* 5063

SHEALY ELECTRICAL WHOLESALERS INC p 1313
120 Saxe Gotha Rd, West Columbia SC 29172
Tel (803) 252-5668 *SIC* 5063

D M G INC p 407
809 W Russell St, Sioux Falls SD 57104
Tel (605) 336-3693
SIC 5063 7694 3599 1731

NIXON POWER SERVICES LLC p 1045
5038 Thoroughbred Ln, Brentwood TN 37027
Tel (615) 309-5823 *SIC* 5063 4911

WIREMASTERS INC p 1618
1788 N Pointe Rd, Columbia TN 38401
Tel (615) 791-0281 *SIC* 5063

HEAVY MACHINES INC p 680
3926 E Raines Rd, Memphis TN 38118
Tel (901) 260-2200
SIC 5082 7699 7353 3531 5063

POWER & TELEPHONE SUPPLY CO p 1165
2673 Yale Ave, Memphis TN 38112
Tel (901) 324-6116 *SIC* 5063 5999

■ HAWKER POWERSOURCE INC p 669
9404 Ooltewah Indus Blvd, Ooltewah TN 37363
Tel (423) 238-5700 *SIC* 5063

■ A E PETSCHE CO INC p 5
1501 Nolan Ryan Expy, Arlington TX 76011
Tel (817) 461-9473 *SIC* 5063

SCIS AIR SECURITY CORP p 1292
1521 N Cooper St Ste 300, Arlington TX 76011
Tel (817) 792-4500 *SIC* 5063 7382

FACILITY SOLUTIONS GROUP INC p 523
4401 West Gate Blvd # 310, Austin TX 78745
Tel (512) 440-7985 *SIC* 5063 1731

■ HILL COUNTRY ELECTRIC SUPPLY LP p 693
4801 Freidrich Ln Ste 200, Austin TX 78744
Tel (512) 428-9300 *SIC* 5063

COBURN SUPPLY CO INC p 333
390 Park St Ste 100, Beaumont TX 77701
Tel (409) 838-6363
SIC 5063 5064 5072 5074 5075 5078

INNOVATIVE IDM LLC p 745
1625 Wallace Dr Ste 110, Carrollton TX 75006
Tel (214) 574-9500 *SIC* 5063 7622 3699

CRAFTMADE INTERNATIONAL INC p 388
650 S Royal Ln Ste 100, Coppell TX 75019
Tel (972) 393-3800 *SIC* 5064 5063

UNIVERSAL POWER GROUP INC p 1517
488 S Royal Ln, Coppell TX 75019
Tel (469) 892-1122 *SIC* 5065 5063

CITY ELECTRIC SUPPLY CO p 312
400 S Record St Ste 100, Dallas TX 75202
Tel (214) 123-1234 *SIC* 5063

PARRISH-HARE ELECTRICAL SUPPLY LP p 1117
1211 Regal Row, Dallas TX 75247
Tel (214) 905-1001 *SIC* 5063

POWERCARE AND SERVICE SOLUTIONS INC p 1166
12770 Merit Dr Ste 400, Dallas TX 75251
Tel (972) 991-1444 *SIC* 5063

REXEL HOLDINGS USA CORP p 1230
14951 Dallas Pkwy, Dallas TX 75254
Tel (972) 387-3600 *SIC* 5063

REXEL INC p 1230
14951 Dallas Pkwy # 1000, Dallas TX 75254
Tel (972) 387-3600 *SIC* 5063

REXEL INC p 1230
14951 Dallas Pkwy # 1000, Dallas TX 75254
Tel (972) 387-3600 *SIC* 5063

D REYNOLDS CO LLC p 407
2680 Sylvania Cross Dr, Fort Worth TX 76137
Tel (214) 630-9000 *SIC* 5063

UNIDEN HOLDING INC p 1503
4700 Amon Carter Blvd, Fort Worth TX 76155
Tel (817) 858-3300 *SIC* 5063 5065

CONDUMEX INC p 355
900 Avenue S, Grand Prairie TX 75050
Tel (800) 925-9473 *SIC* 7389 5063

LITEX INDUSTRIES LIMITED p 870
3401 Trinity Blvd, Grand Prairie TX 75050
Tel (972) 871-4350 *SIC* 5064 5063

1155 DISTRIBUTOR PARTNERS LLC p 1
4200 N Sam Houston Pkwy W, Houston TX 77086
Tel (832) 855-3400 *SIC* 5063

AMERIMEX MOTOR & CONTROLS LLC p 82
610 N Milby St, Houston TX 77003
Tel (713) 225-4300 *SIC* 5063 3625 7694

CRAWFORD ELECTRIC SUPPLY CO HOUSTON LTD p 389
7390 Northcourt Rd, Houston TX 77040
Tel (281) 501-4440 *SIC* 5063

CRAWFORD ELECTRIC SUPPLY CO INC p 389
7390 Northcourt Rd, Houston TX 77040
Tel (713) 476-0788 *SIC* 5063

▲ DXP ENTERPRISES INC p 464
7272 Pinemont Dr, Houston TX 77040
Tel (713) 996-4700 *SIC* 5084 5063

HANDY HARDWARE WHOLESALE INC p 657
8300 Tewantin Dr, Houston TX 77061
Tel (713) 644-1495
SIC 5072 5074 5063 5031 5198

HIS CO INC p 696
6650 Concord Park Dr, Houston TX 77040
Tel (713) 934-1600 *SIC* 5065 5063

▲ HOUSTON WIRE & CABLE CO INC p 712
10201 North Loop E, Houston TX 77029
Tel (713) 609-2100 *SIC* 5063

■ HWC WIRE & CABLE CO p 722
10201 North Loop E, Houston TX 77029
Tel (713) 609-2160 *SIC* 5063

TELCO INTERCONTINENTAL CORP p 1433
9812 Whithorn Dr, Houston TX 77095
Tel (281) 500-8270 *SIC* 5063 5065 3575

TOSHIBA INTERNATIONAL CORP p 1462
13131 W Little York Rd, Houston TX 77041
Tel (713) 466-0277
SIC 3621 5084 5063 3613 3594 3572

VALLEN SAFETY SUPPLY CO p 1540
521 N Sam Houston Pkwy E # 300, Houston TX 77060
Tel (281) 500-5000
SIC 5099 5084 5047 5063

CONSOLIDATED ELECTRICAL DISTRIBUTORS INC p 359
1920 Westridge Dr Ste 107, Irving TX 75038
Tel (972) 582-5300 *SIC* 5063 5211

ELECTRICAL DISTRIBUTORS LLC p 485
2301 Century Cir, Irving TX 75062
Tel (469) 533-6250 *SIC* 5063 5999

SHERMCO INDUSTRIES INC p 1316
2425 E Pioneer Dr, Irving TX 75061
Tel (972) 793-5523 *SIC* 8711 7694 5063

BUTTERY CO LLP p 230
201 W Main St, Llano TX 78643
Tel (325) 247-4141
SIC 5072 5074 5063 5091 5211 5251

ELLIOTT ELECTRIC SUPPLY INC p 488
2526 N Stallings Dr, Nacogdoches TX 75964
Tel (936) 569-1184 *SIC* 5063 5084

■ RICHARDSON TRIDENT CO LLC p 1233
405 N Plano Rd, Richardson TX 75081
Tel (972) 231-5176
SIC 5051 5085 5063 5065 3316

WHOLESALE ELECTRIC SUPPLY CO INC p 1607
1400 Waterall St, Texarkana TX 75501
Tel (903) 794-3404 *SIC* 5063

MID-COAST ELECTRIC SUPPLY INC p 963
1801 Stolz St, Victoria TX 77901
Tel (361) 575-6311 *SIC* 5063

DEALERS ELECTRICAL SUPPLY CO p 420
2320 Columbus Ave, Waco TX 76701
Tel (254) 756-7251 *SIC* 5063 5719

BAYCO PRODUCTS INC p 161
640 Sanden Blvd, Wylie TX 75098
Tel (214) 342-0288 *SIC* 5063

INTERMOUNTAIN ELECTRONICS INC OF PRICE UTAH p 753
1511 S Highway 6, Price UT 84501
Tel (435) 637-7160 *SIC* 3699 5063

CODALE ELECTRIC SUPPLY INC p 333
5225 W 2400 S England Ct, Salt Lake City UT 84120
Tel (801) 975-7300 *SIC* 5063

KIMBALL ELECTRONICS INC p 818
2233 S 300 E, Salt Lake City UT 84115
Tel (801) 466-0569 *SIC* 5065 5063

SMITH POWER PRODUCTS INC p 1333
3065 W California Ave, Salt Lake City UT 84104
Tel (801) 262-2631
SIC 5084 7538 3714 5063

M CASPERSON ENTERPRISE LLC p 889
220 S 100 E, St George UT 84770
Tel (800) 275-8802 *SIC* 5063 1731

DOMINION ELECTRIC SUPPLY CO INC p 449
5053 Lee Hwy, Arlington VA 22207
Tel (703) 532-0741 *SIC* 5063 5719

ELECTRO-MECHANICAL CORP p 485
329 Williams St, Bristol VA 24201
Tel (276) 669-9428
SIC 3612 5063 3829 3822 3613 3354

JO-KELL INC p 787
1716 Lambert Ct, Chesapeake VA 23320
Tel (757) 523-2900 *SIC* 5063 8711

SUMITOMO MACHINERY CORP OF AMERICA p 1398
4200 Holland Blvd, Chesapeake VA 23323
Tel (757) 485-3355 *SIC* 5063 3568

VOLVO PENTA OF AMERICAS LLC p 1565
1300 Volvo Penta Dr, Chesapeake VA 23320
Tel (757) 436-2800
SIC 5088 3519 5091 5063

WOMACK ELECTRIC & SUPPLY CO INC p 1621
518 Newton St, Danville VA 24541
Tel (434) 793-5134 *SIC* 5063

ECK ENTERPRISES INC p 475
1405 W Main St, Richmond VA 23220
Tel (804) 359-5781 *SIC* 5063 6512

ECK SUPPLY CO p 475
1405 W Main St, Richmond VA 23220
Tel (804) 359-5781 *SIC* 5063

FIRE & LIFE SAFETY AMERICA INC p 543
3017 Vernon Rd, Richmond VA 23228
Tel (804) 222-1381 *SIC* 5063

■ FLUKE INTERNATIONAL CORP p 561
6920 Seaway Blvd, Everett WA 98203
Tel (425) 347-6100 *SIC* 5063

CARLISLE INC p 257
7911 S 188th St Ste 100, Kent WA 98032
Tel (425) 251-0700 *SIC* 3643 5065 5063

CARLYLE HOLDINGS INC p 258
7911 S 188th St Ste 100, Kent WA 98032
Tel (425) 251-0700 *SIC* 3643 5065 5063

■ ALLIED TRADE GROUP LLC p 57
11410 Ne 122nd Way Ste 20, Kirkland WA 98034
Tel (425) 814-2515 *SIC* 5063

NORTH COAST ELECTRIC CO p 1052
2450 8th Ave S Ste 200, Seattle WA 98134
Tel (206) 442-9898 *SIC* 5063

STUSSER ELECTRIC CO p 1395
660 S Andover St, Seattle WA 98108
Tel (206) 623-1501 *SIC* 5063

STONEWAY ELECTRIC SUPPLY CO p 1391
402 N Perry St, Spokane WA 99202
Tel (509) 535-2933 *SIC* 5063

STONEWAY ELECTRIC SUPPLY CO OF SPOKANE (INC) p 1391
1212 E Front Ave, Spokane WA 99202
Tel (509) 535-2933 *SIC* 5063

PACIFIC POWER GROUP LLC p 1105
805 Broadway St Ste 700, Vancouver WA 98660
Tel (360) 887-7400
SIC 5088 3621 5063 3519 5084

STATE ELECTRIC SUPPLY CO p 1380
2010 2nd Ave, Huntington WV 25703
Tel (304) 523-7491 *SIC* 5063 3357

STATE ELECTRIC SUPPLY CO p 1380
2010 2nd Ave, Huntington WV 25703
Tel (304) 523-7491 *SIC* 5063 3357

WERNER ELECTRIC SUPPLY CO p 1592
4800 W Prospect Ave, Appleton WI 54914
Tel (920) 337-6700 *SIC* 5063

WAGO CORP p 1571
N120 W 19129 Freistadt Rd N 120 W, Germantown WI 53022
Tel (262) 255-6333 *SIC* 5063 3643 3678

ELECTRONIC THEATRE CONTROLS INC p 486
3031 Pleasant View Rd, Middleton WI 53562
Tel (608) 831-4116 *SIC* 5063

RURAL ELECTRIC SUPPLY COOPERATIVE p 1258
2250 Pinehurst Dr, Middleton WI 53562
Tel (608) 831-2600 *SIC* 5063

TRAFFIC AND PARKING CONTROL CO INC p 1469
5100 W Brown Deer Rd, Milwaukee WI 53223
Tel (262) 814-7000 *SIC* 5063 3444 3646

IEWC CORP p 730
5001 S Towne Dr, New Berlin WI 53151
Tel (262) 782-2255 *SIC* 5063

L & S ELECTRIC INC p 833
5101 Mesker St, Schofield WI 54476
Tel (715) 359-3155
SIC 7694 5063 8711 3613

SIC 5064 Electrical Appliances, TV & Radios Wholesale

LG ELECTRONICS ALABAMA INC p 860
201 James Record Rd Sw, Huntsville AL 35824
Tel (256) 772-0623
SIC 3651 3695 5064 5085 5065 4225

TROXELL COMMUNICATIONS INC p 1485
4675 E Cotton Center Blvd # 155, Phoenix AZ 85040
Tel (602) 437-7240 *SIC* 5064

TXL HOLDING CORP p 1495
4675 E Cotton Center Blvd, Phoenix AZ 85040
Tel (602) 437-7240 *SIC* 5064

SPENCERS AIR CONDITIONING & APPLIANCE INC p 1358
525 W 21st St, Tempe AZ 85282
Tel (480) 505-2355 *SIC* 5064

RUSSELL SIGLER INC p 1259
9702 W Tonto St, Tolleson AZ 85353
Tel (623) 388-5100 *SIC* 5064

MUTSUTECH LTD p 1003
3130 Bonita Rd Ste 107, Chula Vista CA 91910
Tel (619) 691-7056 *SIC* 5064 5013

HKF INC p 697
5983 Smithway St, Commerce CA 90040
Tel (323) 225-1318
SIC 5075 3873 5064 3567 3643

FISHER & PAYKEL APPLIANCES USA HOLDINGS INC p 552
695 Town Center Dr # 180, Costa Mesa CA 92626
Tel (888) 936-7872 *SIC* 5064

CLARION CORP OF AMERICA p 321
6200 Gateway Dr, Cypress CA 90630
Tel (310) 327-9100 *SIC* 5064

TOSHIBA AMERICA ELECTRONIC COMPONENTS INC p 1462
9740 Irvine Blvd Ste D700, Irvine CA 92618
Tel (949) 462-7700
SIC 3651 3631 3674 3679 5065 5064

PAULSTV LLC p 1122
900 Glenneyre St, Laguna Beach CA 92651
Tel (949) 596-8800 *SIC* 5064

JVCKENWOOD USA CORP p 798
2201 E Dominguez St, Long Beach CA 90810
Tel (310) 639-9000 *SIC* 5064

PIONEER ELECTRONICS (USA) INC p 1150
1925 E Dominguez St, Long Beach CA 90810
Tel (310) 952-2000 *SIC* 5064

PIONEER NORTH AMERICA INC p 1151
2265 E 220th St, Long Beach CA 90810
Tel (213) 746-6337 *SIC* 5064 3651

R & B WHOLESALE DISTRIBUTORS INC p 1201
2350 S Milliken Ave, Ontario CA 91761
Tel (909) 230-5400 *SIC* 5064

SONY ELECTRONICS INC p 1341
16535 Via Esprillo Bldg 1, San Diego CA 92127
Tel (858) 942-2400
SIC 3651 5064 3695 3671 3572 3674

ALPINE ELECTRONICS OF AMERICA INC p 60
19145 Gramercy Pl, Torrance CA 90501
Tel (310) 326-8000 *SIC* 5064 3651 3679

E & S INTERNATIONAL ENTERPRISES INC p 465
7801 Hayvenhurst Ave, Van Nuys CA 91406
Tel (818) 702-2207 *SIC* 5064

HB COMMUNICATIONS INC p 671
60 Dodge Ave, North Haven CT 06473
Tel (203) 747-7174 *SIC* 5064 5065 5731

GROUPE SEB HOLDINGS INC p 642
1105 N Market St Ste 1142, Wilmington DE 19801
Tel (973) 736-0300 *SIC* 5064

REGAL WORLDWIDE TRADING LLC p 1218
9500 Nw 108th Ave, Medley FL 33178
Tel (305) 714-7425 *SIC* 5064

AUDIO VISUAL INNOVATIONS INC p 130
6301 Benjamin Rd Ste 101, Tampa FL 33634
Tel (813) 884-7168
SIC 3669 5064 3861 3663 3651 5043

AVI-SPL EMPLOYEE EMERGENCY RELIEF FUND INC p 137
6301 Benjamin Rd Ste 101, Tampa FL 33634
Tel (813) 884-7168
SIC 3669 3861 3663 3651 5043 5064

AVI-SPL HOLDINGS INC p 137
6301 Benjamin Rd Ste 101, Tampa FL 33634
Tel (866) 708-5034
SIC 3669 3861 3663 3651 1731 5064

SERVCO PACIFIC INC p 1307
2850 Pukoloa St Ste 300, Honolulu HI 96819
Tel (808) 564-1300 *SIC* 5013 5064 5511

WEBCO HAWAII INC p 1586
2840 Mokumoa St, Honolulu HI 96819
Tel (808) 839-4551
SIC 5122 5199 5141 5064

MIZAR HOLDING CO INC p 978
3702 Prairie Lake Ct, Aurora IL 60504
Tel (630) 978-2500 *SIC* 5064

M BLOCK & SONS INC p 889
5020 W 73rd St, Bedford Park IL 60638
Tel (708) 728-8400 *SIC* 5064 5023

ROBERT BOSCH LLC p 1241
2800 S 25th Ave, Broadview IL 60155
Tel (248) 876-1000
SIC 3714 3694 5013 5064 3565 3541

FAGOR ARRASATE USA INC p 524
636 Executive Dr, Willowbrook IL 60527
Tel (630) 920-0422 *SIC* 5051 5064

CNA INTERNATIONAL INC p 330
940 N Central Ave, Wood Dale IL 60191
Tel (630) 238-9800 *SIC* 5063 5064

LEE SUPPLY CORP p 852
6610 Guion Rd, Indianapolis IN 46268
Tel (317) 290-2500
SIC 5074 5075 5064 5085 5031

DIRECTBUY INC p 441
8450 Broadway, Merrillville IN 46410
Tel (219) 736-1100
SIC 5021 5064 5023 5961 6794 7299

MODERN DISTRIBUTORS INC p 981
817 W Columbia St, Somerset KY 42501
Tel (606) 679-1178
SIC 5194 5962 5145 5064

AGGREKO LLC p 35
4610 W Admiral Doyle Dr, New Iberia LA 70560
Tel (337) 367-7884 *SIC* 5064 3822

STONEWALL KITCHEN LLC p 1391
2 Stonewall Ln, York ME 03909
Tel (207) 351-2713
SIC 2033 2035 2032 5149 5064

PHILIPS ELECTRONICS NORTH AMERICA CORP p 1143
3000 Minuteman Rd Ms1203, Andover MA 01810
Tel (978) 687-1501
SIC 5064 3651 3674 3641 3645 5047

PHILIPS HOLDING USA INC p 1143
3000 Minuteman Rd Ste 109, Andover MA 01810
Tel (978) 687-1501
SIC 5064 3674 5045 5047 3641

ABC APPLIANCE INC p 10
1 W Silverdome Indus Park, Pontiac MI 48342
Tel (248) 335-4222
SIC 5722 5731 5999 5065 5064 5063

CAPITOL SALES CO INC p 251
1245 Trapp Rd Ste 130, Eagan MN 55121
Tel (651) 688-6830 *SIC* 5064 5065 8742

■ **VIKING RANGE LLC** p 1557
111 W Front St, Greenwood MS 38930
Tel (662) 455-1200 *SIC* 3631 5064

MAR-CONE APPLIANCE PARTS CO p 904
1 Cityplace Dr Ste 400, Saint Louis MO 63141
Tel (877) 993-9196 *SIC* 5064

BRADY INDUSTRIES INC p 207
7055 Lindell Rd, Las Vegas NV 89118
Tel (702) 876-3990
SIC 5169 5087 5999 5023 5064

BROTHER INTERNATIONAL CORP p 219
200 Crossing Blvd, Bridgewater NJ 08807
Tel (908) 704-1700
SIC 5044 3579 3559 5084 5064 5065

DIRECT CABINET SALES - US LBM LLC p 441
180 Herrod Blvd, Dayton NJ 08810
Tel (908) 587-9577 *SIC* 5031 5064

LG ELECTRONICS USA INC p 860
1000 Sylvan Ave, Englewood Cliffs NJ 07632
Tel (201) 816-2000 *SIC* 5064 3651

SHARP ELECTRONICS CORP p 1312
1 Sharp Plz Ste 1, Mahwah NJ 07495
Tel (201) 529-8200
SIC 5044 5064 3651 3631 3861 3674

APPLIANCE DEALERS COOPERATIVE INC p 99
2 Matrix Dr, Monroe Township NJ 08831
Tel (609) 235-1000 *SIC* 5064

PANASONIC CORP OF NORTH AMERICA p 1111
2 Riverfront Plz Ste 200, Newark NJ 07102
Tel (201) 348-7000
SIC 5064 5045 5065 5044 5084 5063

MIELE INC p 968
9 Independence Way, Princeton NJ 08540
Tel (609) 419-9898 *SIC* 5064

SAMSUNG ELECTRONICS AMERICA INC p 1275
85 Challenger Rd, Ridgefield Park NJ 07660
Tel (201) 229-4000 *SIC* 5064 5065 5045

HAIER AMERICA CO LLC p 653
1800 Valley Rd, Wayne NJ 07470
Tel (973) 617-1800 *SIC* 5064

HAIER AMERICA TRADING LLC p 653
1800 Valley Rd, Wayne NJ 07470
Tel (973) 617-1800 *SIC* 5064

JAZZY ELECTRONICS CORP p 779
1600 63rd St, Brooklyn NY 11204
Tel (718) 236-8000 *SIC* 6512 5064 3651

MARTIN ATTEA p 912
1509 Clinton St, Buffalo NY 14206
Tel (716) 822-0378 *SIC* 5064 5722

P C RICHARD & SON LONG ISLAND CORP p 1102
150 Price Pkwy, Farmingdale NY 11735
Tel (631) 843-4300 *SIC* 5722 5731 5064

PC RICHARD & SON INC p 1123
150 Price Pkwy, Farmingdale NY 11735
Tel (631) 843-4300
SIC 5722 5064 7629 7623

INTERCOUNTY APPLIANCE CORP p 752
10 National Blvd, Medford NY 11763
Tel (631) 543-6900 *SIC* 5064

FACTORYOUTLETSTORE LLC p 524
1407 Broadway Rm 700, New York NY 10018
Tel (646) 367-6141 *SIC* 5722 5064

SINGER WORLDWIDE LLC p 1326
295 Madison Ave Fl 6, New York NY 10017
Tel (615) 213-0880 *SIC* 5064

SONY MUSIC ENTERTAINMENT INC p 1341
25 Madison Ave Fl 19, New York NY 10010
Tel (212) 833-8500 *SIC* 3652 5064

TOSHIBA AMERICA INC p 1462
1251 Ave Of Ameri Ste 4100, New York NY 10020
Tel (212) 596-0600
SIC 3651 3631 5064 5075 3571 3661

COINMACH CORP p 335
303 Sunnyside Blvd # 70, Plainview NY 11803
Tel (516) 349-8555
SIC 7215 7359 5087 5064 7211 8741

AZ METRO DISTRIBUTORS LLC p 140
60 Crossways Park Dr W # 400, Woodbury NY 11797
Tel (516) 812-0300 *SIC* 5064

ELECTROLUX HOME CARE PRODUCTS INC p 485
10200 David Taylor Dr, Charlotte NC 28262
Tel (980) 236-2000 *SIC* 5064

ELECTROLUX HOME PRODUCTS INC p 485
10200 David Taylor Dr, Charlotte NC 28262
Tel (980) 236-2000 *SIC* 5064

▲ **LOWES COMPANIES INC** p 881
1000 Lowes Blvd, Mooresville NC 28117
Tel (704) 758-1000
SIC 5211 5031 5722 5064

■ **LOWES HOME CENTERS LLC** p 881
1605 Curtis Bridge Rd, Wilkesboro NC 28697
Tel (336) 658-4000
SIC 5211 5031 5722 5064

■ **KITCHENAID INC** p 822
101 E Maple St, Canton OH 44720
Tel (330) 499-9200 *SIC* 5064

ROYAL APPLIANCE MFG CO p 1254
7005 Cochran Rd, Cleveland OH 44139
Tel (440) 996-2000 *SIC* 5064

DANBY PRODUCTS INC p 411
1800 Production Dr, Findlay OH 45840
Tel (519) 837-0920 *SIC* 5064

HOOVER INC p 706
7005 Cochran Rd, Solon OH 44139
Tel (330) 499-9200 *SIC* 5064

TRUMBULL INDUSTRIES INC p 1487
400 Dietz Rd Ne, Warren OH 44483
Tel (330) 393-6624 *SIC* 5074 5085 5064

VSM SEWING INC p 1566
31000 Viking Pkwy, Westlake OH 44145
Tel (440) 808-6550 *SIC* 5064

V AND V APPLIANCE PARTS INC p 1538
27 W Myrtle Ave, Youngstown OH 44507
Tel (330) 743-5144 *SIC* 5064

JASCO PRODUCTS CO LLC p 778
10 E Memorial Rd Bldg B, Oklahoma City OK 73114
Tel (405) 752-0710 *SIC* 5065 5064

METRO BUILDERS SUPPLY INC p 954
5313 S Mingo Rd, Tulsa OK 74146
Tel (918) 622-7692 *SIC* 5064

VTECH COMMUNICATIONS INC p 1567
9590 Sw Gemini Dr Ste 120, Beaverton OR 97008
Tel (503) 596-1200 *SIC* 5065 5064

JOHNSTONE SUPPLY INC p 791
11632 Ne Ainsworth Cir, Portland OR 97220
Tel (503) 256-3663
SIC 5075 5085 5063 5064

OLYMPUS AMERICA INC p 1083
3500 Corporate Pkwy, Center Valley PA 18034
Tel (484) 896-5000
SIC 5047 5043 5064 3827 3695 3572

OLYMPUS CORP OF AMERICAS p 1083
3500 Corp Pkwy, Center Valley PA 18034
Tel (484) 896-5000
SIC 5047 5043 5064 3827 3695 3572

HAAN CORP p 651
225 Wilmington W Chester, Chadds Ford PA 19317
Tel (717) 209-7000 *SIC* 5064

D & H DISTRIBUTING CO p 406
2525 N 7th St, Harrisburg PA 17110
Tel (717) 236-8001
SIC 5045 5065 5064 5063 5044

WOLSELEY INVESTMENTS INC p 1621
1904 Ligonier St, Latrobe PA 15650
Tel (757) 874-7795
SIC 5074 5085 5075 5064 5211 5031

DAS COMPANIES INC p 413
724 Lawn Rd, Palmyra PA 17078
Tel (717) 964-3642 *SIC* 5064

ALMO CORP p 59
2709 Commerce Way, Philadelphia PA 19154
Tel (215) 698-4000 *SIC* 5064 5063

CE CARIBE LLC p 271
Carretera 14 Km 25 3 St Carrete, Coamo PR 00769
Tel (787) 825-6000 *SIC* 3639 5064

CREGGER CO INC p 391
637 N 12th St, West Columbia SC 29169
Tel (803) 217-0710 *SIC* 5074 5064

STELLAR MANAGEMENT GROUP INC p 1385
412 Georgia Ave Ste 300, Chattanooga TN 37403
Tel (423) 265-7090 *SIC* 5064

ORECK CORP p 1093
1400 Salem Rd, Cookeville TN 38506
Tel (800) 219-2044
SIC 3589 3564 5064 5087

■ **APCOM INC** p 96
125 Se Parkway, Franklin TN 37064
Tel (615) 794-5574 *SIC* 3491 5064

SINGER SEWING CO p 1326
1224 Heil Quaker Blvd, La Vergne TN 37086
Tel (615) 213-0880 *SIC* 5064

HUNTER FAN CO p 719
7130 Goodlett Farms Pkwy Ste 400, Memphis TN 38103
Tel (901) 743-1360 *SIC* 5064 3634 3645

ELECTRONIC EXPRESS INC p 485
418 Harding Industrial Dr, Nashville TN 37211
Tel (615) 259-2031 *SIC* 5064

COBURN SUPPLY CO INC p 333
390 Park St Ste 100, Beaumont TX 77701
Tel (409) 838-6363
SIC 5063 5064 5072 5074 5075 5078

CRAFTMADE INTERNATIONAL INC p 388
650 S Royal Ln Ste 100, Coppell TX 75019
Tel (972) 393-3800 *SIC* 5064 5063

APPLIANCE PARTS DEPOT LP p 99
4754 Almond Ave, Dallas TX 75247
Tel (214) 631-6331 *SIC* 5064 5722

LITEX INDUSTRIES LIMITED p 870
3401 Trinity Blvd, Grand Prairie TX 75050
Tel (972) 871-4350 *SIC* 5064 5063

WAVE ELECTRONICS INC p 1583
8648 Glenmont Dr Ste 130, Houston TX 77036
Tel (713) 849-2710 *SIC* 5064

FERGUSON ENTERPRISES INC p 538
12500 Jefferson Ave, Newport News VA 23602
Tel (757) 874-7795
SIC 5074 5085 5075 5064

ENGLEWOOD MARKETING GROUP INC p 499
1471 Partnership Rd, Green Bay WI 54304
Tel (920) 337-9800 *SIC* 5064

SIC 5065 Electronic Parts & Eqpt Wholesale

LG ELECTRONICS ALABAMA INC p 860
201 James Record Rd Sw, Huntsville AL 35824
Tel (256) 772-0623
SIC 3651 3695 5064 5085 5065 4225

CAPITOL BUSINESS EQUIPMENT INC p 251
645 S Mcdonough St, Montgomery AL 36104
Tel (334) 265-8903
SIC 5045 5044 7699 5065

ASML US INC p 118
2650 W Geronimo Pl, Chandler AZ 85224
Tel (480) 696-2888 *SIC* 5065 7629

INTER-TEL TECHNOLOGIES INC p 751
1146 N Alma School Rd, Mesa AZ 85201
Tel (480) 858-9600
SIC 5999 1731 5065 3661 3577

MITEL (DELAWARE) INC p 977
1146 N Alma School Rd, Mesa AZ 85201
Tel (480) 449-8900
SIC 3661 5045 4813 5065 1731 7359

MITEL TECHNOLOGIES INC p 977
1146 N Alma School Rd, Mesa AZ 85201
Tel (480) 449-8900 *SIC* 5065

■ **AVNET ELECTRONICS MARKETING** p 138
2211 S 47th St, Phoenix AZ 85034
Tel (480) 643-2000 *SIC* 5065

▲ **AVNET INC** p 138
2211 S 47th St, Phoenix AZ 85034
Tel (480) 643-2000 *SIC* 5065 5045 7379

▲ **INSIGHT ENTERPRISES INC** p 746
201 N Central Ave, Phoenix AZ 85004
Tel (480) 333-3000 *SIC* 5045 7379 5065

■ **DBL DISTRIBUTING LLC** p 418
15880 N Greenwy Hdn Loop # 150, Scottsdale AZ 85260
Tel (480) 419-3559 *SIC* 5065

■ **HYPERCOM CORP** p 724
8888 E Raintree Dr # 300, Scottsdale AZ 85260
Tel (480) 642-5000
SIC 3578 7372 7299 5065

■ **CARLTON-BATES CO** p 258
3600 W 69th St, Little Rock AR 72209
Tel (501) 562-9100 *SIC* 5065

▲ **WINDSTREAM HOLDINGS INC** p 1615
4001 N Rodney Parham Rd # 101, Little Rock AR 72212
Tel (501) 748-7000 *SIC* 4813 5065

■ **WINDSTREAM SERVICES LLC** p 1616
4001 N Rodney Parham Rd # 101, Little Rock AR 72212
Tel (501) 748-7000 *SIC* 4813 5065

■ **BISCO INDUSTRIES INC** p 185
1500 N Lakeview Ave, Anaheim CA 92807
Tel (714) 876-2400 *SIC* 5065

▲ **EACO CORP** p 467
1500 N Lakeview Ave, Anaheim CA 92807
Tel (714) 876-2490 *SIC* 5065

NORTH AMERICAN VIDEO CORP p 1050
1041 N Pacificenter Dr, Anaheim CA 92806
Tel (714) 779-7499 *SIC* 5065 3812

SUPERIOR COMMUNICATIONS INC p 1406
5027 Irwindale Ave # 900, Baldwin Park CA 91706
Tel (626) 388-2573 *SIC* 5065

NIKON PRECISION INC p 1043
1399 Shoreway Rd, Belmont CA 94002
Tel (650) 508-4674 *SIC* 5084 5065

YAMAHA CORP OF AMERICA INC p 1634
6600 Orangethorpe Ave, Buena Park CA 90620
Tel (714) 522-9011
SIC 5099 5065 5091 3931

WDPT FILM DISTRIBUTION LLC p 1585
500 S Buena Vista St, Burbank CA 91521
Tel (818) 560-1000 *SIC* 5065

CBOL CORP p 269
19850 Plummer St, Chatsworth CA 91311
Tel (818) 704-8200
SIC 5065 5072 5013 5088 5084 5162

FLAME ENTERPRISES INC p 554
21500 Gledhill St, Chatsworth CA 91311
Tel (301) 668-0636 *SIC* 5065 5063

NMB (USA) INC p 1045
9730 Independence Ave, Chatsworth CA 91311
Tel (818) 709-1770
SIC 3562 5063 5084 3728 5065

CELLUPHONE INC p 274
6119 E Washington Blvd, Commerce CA 90040
Tel (323) 727-9131 *SIC* 5065 5999

MITSUBISHI ELECTRIC US HOLDINGS INC p 977
5900 Katella Ave Ste A, Cypress CA 90630
Tel (714) 220-2500
SIC 5065 5045 3651 3663

MITSUBISHI ELECTRIC US INC p 977
5900 Katella Ave Ste A, Cypress CA 90630
Tel (714) 220-2500
SIC 5065 5045 1796 3534

DELTA AMERICA LTD p 426
46101 Fremont Blvd, Fremont CA 94538
Tel (510) 668-5100 *SIC* 5065 3679 8731

DELTA PRODUCTS CORP p 427
46101 Fremont Blvd, Fremont CA 94538
Tel (510) 668-5100
SIC 5065 5045 8741 5063 3577

DET LOGISTICS USA CORP p 433
46101 Fremont Blvd, Fremont CA 94538
Tel (510) 668-5100 *SIC* 5065

NITTO AMERICAS INC p 1045
48500 Fremont Blvd, Fremont CA 94538
Tel (510) 445-5400
SIC 2672 3589 5162 5065

BRIX GROUP INC p 215
838 N Laverne Ave, Fresno CA 93727
Tel (559) 457-4700 *SIC* 5065 5013

ALTURA COMMUNICATION SOLUTIONS LLC p 63
1335 S Acacia Ave, Fullerton CA 92831
Tel (714) 948-8400 *SIC* 5065

BITECHNOLOGIES CORP p 180
4200 Bonita Pl, Fullerton CA 92835
Tel (714) 447-2300 *SIC* 3679 5065 8711

■ **THALES-RAYTHEON SYSTEMS CO LLC** p 1446
1801 Hughes Dr, Fullerton CA 92833
Tel (714) 446-3118 *SIC* 5065

■ **FLIR COMMERCIAL SYSTEMS INC** p 557
6769 Hollister Ave # 100, Goleta CA 93117
Tel (805) 690-6685 *SIC* 5065 3699

INTEGRATED PROCUREMENT TECHNOLOGIES INC p 749
7230 Hollister Ave, Goleta CA 93117
Tel (805) 682-0842 *SIC* 5088 5065

METRIC EQUIPMENT SALES INC p 954
25841 Industrial Blvd # 200, Hayward CA 94545
Tel (510) 264-0887
SIC 5065 5084 7359 3825

JAE ELECTRONICS INC p 775
142 Technology Dr Ste 100, Irvine CA 92618
Tel (949) 753-2600
SIC 5065 5088 3679 3829 3678

LINKSYS LLC p 869
131 Theory, Irvine CA 92617
Tel (949) 270-8500 *SIC* 5065

TCT MOBILE (US) INC p 1428
25 Edelman Ste 200, Irvine CA 92618
Tel (949) 892-2990 *SIC* 5999 5065

TOSHIBA AMERICA ELECTRONIC COMPONENTS INC p 1462
9740 Irvine Blvd Ste D700, Irvine CA 92618
Tel (949) 462-7700
SIC 3651 3631 3674 3679 5065 5064

INSULECTRO p 747
20362 Windrow Dr Ste 100, Lake Forest CA 92630
Tel (949) 587-3200 *SIC* 5065

ANRITSU CO p 92
490 Jarvis Dr, Morgan Hill CA 95037
Tel (408) 201-1551 *SIC* 5065 3825 3663

ANRITSU US HOLDING INC p 93
490 Jarvis Dr, Morgan Hill CA 95037
Tel (408) 778-2000 *SIC* 3825 3663 5065

■ **JOSLYN SUNBANK CO LLC** p 794
1740 Commerce Way, Paso Robles CA 93446
Tel (805) 238-2840 *SIC* 3678 3643 5065

CYAN INC p 404
1383 N Mcdowell Blvd # 300, Petaluma CA 94954
Tel (707) 735-2300 *SIC* 5065

BELKIN INTERNATIONAL INC p 169
12045 Waterfront Dr, Playa Vista CA 90094
Tel (310) 751-5100 *SIC* 5065 5045

NUCOURSE DISTRIBUTION INC p 1067
22342 Avenida Empresa # 200, Rcho Sta Marg CA 92688
Tel (866) 655-4366 *SIC* 5065

SMA SOLAR TECHNOLOGY AMERICA LLC p 1331
6020 West Oaks Blvd, Rocklin CA 95765
Tel (916) 625-0870 *SIC* 5065

INTERLEMO USA INC p 753
635 Park Ct, Rohnert Park CA 94928
Tel (707) 578-8811 *SIC* 5065

LEMO USA INC p 855
635 Park Ct, Rohnert Park CA 94928
Tel (707) 206-3700 *SIC* 5065 3678

SOLIGENT DISTRIBUTION LLC p 1338
1500 Valley House Dr # 210, Rohnert Park CA 94928
Tel (707) 992-3100 *SIC* 5065

PENINSULA COMPONENTS INC p 1129
1300 Industrial Rd Ste 21, San Carlos CA 94070
Tel (650) 593-3288 *SIC* 5085 5065

ADVANCED MP TECHNOLOGY INC p 26
1010 Calle Sombra, San Clemente CA 92673
Tel (949) 492-6589 *SIC* 5065

CRYDOM INC p 396
2320 Paseo Delas Amer 2 Ste 201, San Diego CA 92154
Tel (619) 210-1600
SIC 3625 5065 3674 3643

LG ELECTRONICS MOBILECOMM USA INC p 860
10225 Willow Creek Rd, San Diego CA 92131
Tel (858) 635-5300 *SIC* 5065 3663

ALIPHCOM p 50
99 Rhode Island St Fl 3, San Francisco CA 94103
Tel (415) 230-7600 *SIC* 5065 5999

CYPRESS SEMICONDUCTOR INTERNATIONAL INC p 405
4001 N 1st St, San Jose CA 95134
Tel (408) 943-2600 *SIC* 5065

FUJITSU COMPONENTS AMERICA INC p 584
2290 N 1st St Ste 212, San Jose CA 95131
Tel (408) 745-4900 *SIC* 5065

HITACHI CHEMICAL CO AMERICA LTD p 696
2150 N 1st St Ste 350, San Jose CA 95131
Tel (408) 873-2200 *SIC* 5063 5065

KOKUSAI SEMICONDUCTOR EQUIPMENT CORP p 826
2460 N 1st St Ste 290, San Jose CA 95131
Tel (408) 456-2750 *SIC* 5065 7629

SAMSUNG SEMICONDUCTOR INC p 1275
3655 N 1st St, San Jose CA 95134
Tel (408) 544-4000 *SIC* 5065 5045

SK HYNIX AMERICA INC p 1328
3101 N 1st St, San Jose CA 95134
Tel (408) 232-8000 *SIC* 5065 5045

ACE WIRELESS & TRADING INC p 17
3031 Orange Ave Ste B, Santa Ana CA 92707
Tel (949) 748-5700 *SIC* 5065

NHR NEWCO HOLDINGS LLC p 1042
6500 Hollister Ave # 210, Santa Barbara CA 93117
Tel (800) 230-6638 *SIC* 5045 5065 7379

ALPS ELECTRIC (NORTH AMERICA) INC p 61
3151 Jay St Ste 101, Santa Clara CA 95054
Tel (408) 361-6400 *SIC* 5045 5065 5013

GLOBALFOUNDRIES US INC p 617
2600 Great America Way, Santa Clara CA 95054
Tel (408) 462-3900 *SIC* 3559 3825 5065

RENESAS ELECTRONICS AMERICA INC p 1223
2801 Scott Blvd, Santa Clara CA 95050
Tel (408) 588-6000
SIC 5065 8731 5731 5045 8711

TALLEY INC p 1423
12976 Sandoval St, Santa Fe Springs CA 90670
Tel (562) 906-8000 *SIC* 5065

MASTER INTERNATIONAL CORP p 918
1301 Olympic Blvd, Santa Monica CA 90404
Tel (310) 452-1229 *SIC* 5065

AVAD LLC p 135
5805 Sepulvda Blvd # 750, Sherman Oaks CA 91411
Tel (818) 742-4800 *SIC* 5065 7359

■ **ARCONIC GLOBAL FASTENERS & RINGS INC** p 106
3990a Heritage Oak Ct, Simi Valley CA 93063
Tel (310) 530-2220 *SIC* 5085 5072 5065

NOKIA INC p 1046
200 S Mathilda Ave, Sunnyvale CA 94086
Tel (408) 530-7600
SIC 3663 5065 3661 3577

I C CLASS COMPONENTS CORP p 724
23605 Telo Ave, Torrance CA 90505
Tel (310) 539-5500 *SIC* 5065

STELLAR MICROELECTRONICS INC p 1385
28454 Livingston Ave, Valencia CA 91355
Tel (661) 775-3500 *SIC* 5065

ELECTRO RENT CORP p 485
6060 Sepulveda Blvd # 300, Van Nuys CA 91411
Tel (818) 786-2525
SIC 7359 7377 5065 5045

YIFANG USA INC p 1636
136 N Grand Ave Ste 148, West Covina CA 91791
Tel (909) 593-1562 *SIC* 5065

▲ARROW ELECTRONICS INC p 113
9201 E Dry Creek Rd, Centennial CO 80112
Tel (303) 824-4000 SIC 5065 5045

OPTIV INC p 1090
1125 17th St Ste 1700, Denver CO 80202
Tel (303) 298-0600
SIC 5045 5065 6719 7381

OPTIV SECURITY INC p 1090
1125 17th St Ste 1700, Denver CO 80202
Tel (888) 732-9406
SIC 5045 7379 7382 5065

■ ECHOSPHERE LLC p 475
9601 S Meridian Blvd, Englewood CO 80112
Tel (303) 723-1000 SIC 5065 4841

RADIO FREQUENCY SYSTEMS INC p 1204
200 Pond View Dr, Meriden CT 06450
Tel (203) 630-3311
SIC 3663 3661 5045 5065

ASSA ABLOY INC p 119
110 Sargent Dr, New Haven CT 06511
Tel (203) 624-5225
SIC 5065 5072 3699 3429

■ SOUTHERN NEW ENGLAND TELECOMMUNICATIONS CORP p 1349
2 Science Park, New Haven CT 06511
Tel (203) 771-5200
SIC 4813 4812 5065 6159 2741 4822

HB COMMUNICATIONS INC p 671
60 Dodge Ave, North Haven CT 06473
Tel (203) 747-7174 SIC 5064 5065 5731

■ FRONTIER FLORIDA LLC p 581
401 Merritt 7, Norwalk CT 06851
Tel (813) 483-2011
SIC 4813 6519 8721 5065 7629

AUGUST TECHNIC CORP CO p 131
8 The Grn Ste 4934, Dover DE 19901
Tel (302) 223-5215 SIC 5065 5045 7389

PACE AMERICAS LLC p 1103
3701 Fau Blvd Ste 200, Boca Raton FL 33431
Tel (561) 995-6000 SIC 7371 5065

SENSORMATIC INTERNATIONAL INC p 1305
6600 Congress Ave, Boca Raton FL 33487
Tel (561) 912-6000 SIC 5065

ABSTRACT ELECTRONICS INC p 13
11526 53rd St N, Clearwater FL 33760
Tel (727) 540-0236 SIC 5065

REAGAN WIRELESS CORP p 1213
720 S Powerline Rd Ste D, Deerfield Beach FL 33442
Tel (954) 596-2355 SIC 5065 4812

ACCESS TELECOM GROUP INC p 15
1882 Nw 97th Ave, Doral FL 33172
Tel (305) 468-1955 SIC 5065 5999

ALLPLUS COMPUTER SYSTEMS CORP p 58
3075 Nw 107th Ave, Doral FL 33172
Tel (305) 436-3993 SIC 5065 5045

INNOCO TECHNOLOGY GROUP INC p 744
1608 Nw 84th Ave, Doral FL 33126
Tel (305) 477-8117 SIC 5065

NASA ELECTRONICS CORP p 1007
2330 Nw 102nd Pl, Doral FL 33172
Tel (305) 716-7706 SIC 5065

TM WIRELESS COMMUNICATION SERVICES INC p 1457
10205 Nw 19th St Ste 101, Doral FL 33172
Tel (305) 421-9938 SIC 5065

UNIFIED COMMUNICATIONS INTERNATIONAL LLC p 1503
1921 Nw 82nd Ave, Doral FL 33126
Tel (305) 677-7888 SIC 5065

VA CELL INC p 1538
8400 Nw 33rd St Ste 103, Doral FL 33122
Tel (305) 592-1367 SIC 5065 5043

■ UTC FIRE & SECURITY AMERICAS CORP INC p 1536
8985 Town Center Pkwy, Lakewood Ranch FL 34202
Tel (941) 739-4200 SIC 3669 5065

ABBOUD TRADING CORP p 10
10910 Nw 92nd Ter, Medley FL 33178
Tel (786) 235-7007 SIC 5065

■ BRIGHTSTAR CORP p 213
9725 Nw 117th Ave Ste 105, Medley FL 33178
Tel (305) 421-6000 SIC 5065

INTRADECO INC p 759
9500 Nw 108th Ave, Medley FL 33178
Tel (305) 264-6022 SIC 5136 5199 5065

ALL AMERICAN SEMICONDUCTOR LLC p 51
3100 Nw 36th St, Miami FL 33142
Tel (305) 626-4183 SIC 5065

CLC ENTERPRISES INC p 323
11231 Nw 20th St Unit 133, Miami FL 33172
Tel (305) 640-1803 SIC 5065

TELEFONICA USA INC p 1434
1111 Brickell Ave # 1000, Miami FL 33131
Tel (305) 925-5298 SIC 5065 4813

JL AUDIO INC p 786
10369 N Commerce Pkwy, Miramar FL 33025
Tel (954) 443-1100 SIC 5065 2519

VOLOGY INC p 1564
4027 Tampa Rd Ste 3900, Oldsmar FL 34677
Tel (813) 852-6400 SIC 5065

QUALITY ONE WIRELESS LLC p 1197
1500 Tradeport Dr Ste B, Orlando FL 32824
Tel (407) 857-3737 SIC 5065

IVOX SOLUTIONS LLC p 769
4485 Sw Port Way, Palm City FL 34990
Tel (772) 286-8183 SIC 5065 4812

RENCO ELECTRONICS INC p 1223
595 International Pl, Rockledge FL 32955
Tel (321) 637-1000 SIC 5065 3677

AMERICA II ELECTRONICS INC p 67
2600 118th Ave N, Saint Petersburg FL 33716
Tel (727) 573-0900 SIC 5065

DEDC INC p 421
8603 E Adamo Dr, Tampa FL 33619
Tel (813) 626-5195 SIC 5065

VARSATEL CORP p 1545
2813 Executive Park Dr # 112, Weston FL 33331
Tel (954) 667-6550 SIC 5065

■ACCU-TECH CORP p 16
11350 Old Roswell Rd # 100, Alpharetta GA 30009
Tel (770) 740-2240 SIC 5065 5063

GLOBAL CELLULAR INC p 616
6485 Shiloh Rd Ste B100, Alpharetta GA 30005
Tel (678) 513-4020 SIC 5065

■WINDSTREAM SUPPLY LLC p 1616
13560 Morris Rd Ste 4350, Alpharetta GA 30004
Tel (678) 381-0984 SIC 5065

ATLANTA NETWORK TECHNOLOGIES INC p 125
710 Morgan Falls Rd, Atlanta GA 30350
Tel (877) 293-9797 SIC 5045 5065

■ BELLSOUTH CORP p 171
675 W Peach St Ste 4300, Atlanta GA 30375
Tel (404) 420-6126
SIC 4813 4812 2741 5065

■ BELLSOUTH TELECOMMUNICATIONS INC p 171
675 W Peach St Ne St Ne, Atlanta GA 30375
Tel (912) 526-3440
SIC 4813 4812 2741 5065

■ EIS INC p 482
2018 Powers Ferry Rd Se # 500, Atlanta GA 30339
Tel (678) 255-3600 SIC 5065

■ GE ENERGY PARTS INC p 596
4200 Wildwood Pkwy, Atlanta GA 30339
Tel (678) 844-6000 SIC 5065 3612

■ NISCAYAH INC p 1044
2400 Commerce Ave Ste 500, Duluth GA 30096
Tel (678) 474-1720 SIC 5065

▲ SED INTERNATIONAL HOLDINGS INC p 1299
2150 Cedars Rd Ste 200, Lawrenceville GA 30043
Tel (678) 878-2600 SIC 5045 5065

EGO NORTH AMERICA INC p 481
83 Hillwood Cir, Newnan GA 30263
Tel (770) 251-3980 SIC 3634 5065

MILNER INC p 972
5125 Peachtree Indus Blvd, Norcross GA 30092
Tel (770) 458-0999
SIC 7372 5999 7389 5065 5049 5044

MCSI INC p 933
2975 Northwoods Pkwy, Peachtree Corners GA 30071
Tel (770) 441-5263 SIC 1731 5065 7359

MURATA ELECTRONICS NORTH AMERICA INC p 1001
2200 Lake Park Dr Se, Smyrna GA 30080
Tel (770) 436-1300 SIC 5065 3675 3679

■ HAWAIIAN TELCOM INC p 669
1177 Bishop St, Honolulu HI 96813
Tel (808) 643-3456 SIC 4813 5065 7629

■ MICRON SEMICONDUCTOR PRODUCTS INC p 962
8000 S Federal Way, Boise ID 83716
Tel (208) 368-4000 SIC 5065

■AT&T TELEHOLDINGS INC p 123
30 S Wacker Dr Fl 34, Chicago IL 60606
Tel (800) 257-0902
SIC 4813 4812 2741 5065 6159 7382

BARCODES LLC p 155
200 W Monroe St Ste 1050, Chicago IL 60606
Tel (312) 588-5960 SIC 5065

■ GETZ BROS& CO INC p 609
225 W Washington St # 1900, Chicago IL 60606
Tel (312) 845-5686
SIC 5047 5031 5141 5065 5082

■ NEWARK CORP p 1037
300 S Riverside Plz # 2200, Chicago IL 60606
Tel (773) 784-5100 SIC 5065

■ NEWARK ELECTRONICS CORP p 1037
300 S Riverside Plz, Chicago IL 60606
Tel (773) 784-5100 SIC 5065 5063 5961

PFINGSTEN PARTNERS LLC p 1140
300 N Lasalle St 5400, Chicago IL 60654
Tel (312) 222-8707
SIC 5065 6211 3679 3578

STEINER ELECTRIC CO p 1385
1250 Touhy Ave, Elk Grove Village IL 60007
Tel (847) 228-0400 SIC 5065 5063

DISCOUNT MEDIA PRODUCTS LLC p 442
845 N Church Ct, Elmhurst IL 60126
Tel (630) 834-3113 SIC 5065 5999

S & S AUTOMOTIVE INC p 1261
740 N Larch Ave, Elmhurst IL 60126
Tel (630) 279-1613
SIC 5013 5999 5065 1731

OMRON ELECTRONICS LLC p 1085
2895 Greenspt Pkwy 200, Hoffman Estates IL 60169
Tel (847) 843-7900 SIC 5065 3699

OMRON MANAGEMENT CENTER OF AMERICA INC p 1085
2895 Greenspoint Pkwy # 100, Hoffman Estates IL 60169
Tel (224) 520-7650
SIC 5044 5046 5065 5047 5045 8732

▲ RICHARDSON ELECTRONICS LTD p 1232
40w267 Keslinger Rd, Lafox IL 60147
Tel (630) 208-2316 SIC 5065 7373 3671

■ BRIGHTSTAR US INC p 213
850 Technology Way, Libertyville IL 60048
Tel (847) 573-2600 SIC 5065

CORIANT NORTH AMERICA LLC p 370
1415 W Diehl Rd, Naperville IL 60563
Tel (630) 798-4238 SIC 5065

WALDOM ELECTRONICS CORP p 1572
1801 Morgan St, Rockford IL 61102
Tel (815) 968-9661 SIC 5065

OMRON AUTOMOTIVE ELECTRONICS INC p 1085
3709 Ohio Ave, Saint Charles IL 60174
Tel (630) 443-6800
SIC 5065 3625 3714 8742

HITACHI HIGH TECHNOLOGIES AMERICA INC p 696
10 N Martingale Rd # 500, Schaumburg IL 60173
Tel (847) 273-4141 SIC 5065

■ MOTOROLA SOLUTIONS SALES AND SERVICES p 993
1303 E Algonquin Rd, Schaumburg IL 60196
Tel (847) 576-1000 SIC 5065

RITTAL CORP p 1237
425 N Martingale Rd # 400, Schaumburg IL 60173
Tel (847) 240-4600 SIC 3469 5065

■ CDW GOVERNMENT LLC p 271
230 N Milwaukee Ave, Vernon Hills IL 60061
Tel (847) 465-6000 SIC 5961 5065 5734

OHMITE HOLDING LLC p 1078
27501 Bella Vista Pkwy, Warrenville IL 60555
Tel (847) 258-0300 SIC 3625 5065

JST CORP p 796
1957 S Lakeside Dr, Waukegan IL 60085
Tel (847) 473-1957 SIC 5065

■TOUCHSENSOR TECHNOLOGIES LLC p 1463
203 N Gables Blvd, Wheaton IL 60187
Tel (630) 221-9000 SIC 5065 3674

XFMRS INC p 1631
7570 E Landersdale Rd, Camby IN 46113
Tel (317) 834-1066 SIC 3677 5065 3612

CELLULAR CONNECTION LLC p 274
525 Congressional Blvd, Carmel IN 46032
Tel (765) 651-2001
SIC 5065 1731 5999 5731

ELECTRONIC TECHNOLOGIES CORP USA p 486
11819 N Pennsylvania St, Carmel IN 46032
Tel (317) 810-3177 SIC 5065 5063 7382

■ BRIGHTPOINT INC p 213
501 Airtech Pkwy, Plainfield IN 46168
Tel (317) 707-2355 SIC 5065

■ BRIGHTPOINT NORTH AMERICA LLC p 213
501 Airtech Pkwy, Plainfield IN 46168
Tel (317) 707-2355 SIC 5065

■ BRIGHTPOINT NORTH AMERICA LP p 213
501 Airtech Pkwy, Plainfield IN 46168
Tel (317) 707-2355 SIC 5065

■TOUCHSTONE WIRELESS REPAIR AND LOGISTICS LP p 1464
501 Airtech Pkwy, Plainfield IN 46168
Tel (317) 707-2355 SIC 4812 5065

■ ROCKWELL COLLINS SALES & SERVICES INC p 1245
400 Collins Rd Ne, Cedar Rapids IA 52498
Tel (319) 295-8899 SIC 5065

SKC COMMUNICATION PRODUCTS LLC p 1329
8320 Hedge Lane Ter, Shawnee Mission KS 66227
Tel (913) 422-4222 SIC 5065 5999

■ CAROLINA TELEPHONE AND TELEGRAPH CO LLC p 259
100 Centurylink Dr, Monroe LA 71203
Tel (318) 388-9000 SIC 4813 8721 5065

■ ACTERNA LLC p 19
20250 Century Blvd # 100, Germantown MD 20874
Tel (301) 353-1550
SIC 3669 7379 3825 5065 3679 8734

■TESSCO INC p 1440
11126 Mccormick Rd, Hunt Valley MD 21031
Tel (410) 229-1000 SIC 5065

▲TESSCO TECHNOLOGIES INC p 1440
11126 Mccormick Rd, Hunt Valley MD 21031
Tel (410) 229-1000 SIC 5065

CONTINENTAL RESOURCES INC p 363
175 Middlesex Tpke Ste 1, Bedford MA 01730
Tel (781) 275-0850
SIC 5045 5065 7377 7359 7378 7629

ORBOTECH INC p 1093
44 Manning Rd, Billerica MA 01821
Tel (978) 667-6037 SIC 5065 3823 3674

FAI ELECTRONICS CORP p 524
41 Main St, Bolton MA 01740
Tel (978) 779-3111 SIC 5065

FUTURE ELECTRONICS CORP p 585
41 Main St, Bolton MA 01740
Tel (800) 444-0050 SIC 5065

■ VARIAN SEMICONDUCTOR EQUIPMENT ASSOCIATES INC p 1544
35 Dory Rd, Gloucester MA 01930
Tel (978) 282-2000 SIC 5065 3674

■ SAGER ELECTRICAL SUPPLY CO INC p 1268
19 Leona Dr, Middleboro MA 02346
Tel (508) 923-6600 SIC 5065

EQUITY INTERNATIONAL INC p 507
54 Concord St, North Reading MA 01864
Tel (978) 664-2712 SIC 5065

■ PCG PARENT CORP p 1124
4 Technology Dr, Peabody MA 01960
Tel (978) 538-8000
SIC 5045 5065 4953 5093 7378

■ PCG TRADING LLC p 1124
4 Technology Dr, Peabody MA 01960
Tel (978) 538-8000
SIC 5045 5065 4953 5093 7378

D B ROBERTS INC p 406
30 Upton Dr Ste 3, Wilmington MA 01887
Tel (978) 988-5777 SIC 5065

HEILIND ELECTRONICS INC p 681
58 Jonspin Rd, Wilmington MA 01887
Tel (978) 658-7000 SIC 5065 3679 5063

MORRELL INC p 990
3333 Bald Mountain Rd, Auburn Hills MI 48326
Tel (248) 373-1600
SIC 5084 5065 3621 3643 3559 3357

NEXLINK COMMUNICATIONS LLC p 1040
3355 Bald Mountain Rd # 10, Auburn Hills MI 48326
Tel (248) 409-2511 SIC 5065

CCI SYSTEMS INC p 270
105 Kent St, Iron Mountain MI 49801
Tel (906) 774-6621 SIC 5065

GALCO INDUSTRIAL ELECTRONICS INC p 589
26010 Pinehurst Dr, Madison Heights MI 48071
Tel (248) 542-9090 SIC 5065

MCNAUGHTON-MCKAY ELECTRIC CO p 932
1357 E Lincoln Ave, Madison Heights MI 48071
Tel (248) 399-7500 SIC 5065 5063

ABC APPLIANCE INC p 10
1 W Silverdome Indus Park, Pontiac MI 48342
Tel (248) 335-4222
SIC 5722 5731 5999 5065 5064 5063

DELPHI AUTOMOTIVE LLP p 425
5725 Delphi Dr, Troy MI 48098
Tel (248) 813-2494 SIC 5065 5012

NESS ELECTRONICS INC p 1026
1800 E 121st St, Burnsville MN 55337
Tel (651) 251-5700 SIC 5065

CAPITOL SALES CO INC p 251
1245 Trapp Rd Ste 130, Eagan MN 55121
Tel (651) 688-6830 SIC 5064 5065 8742

AVI SYSTEMS INC p 137
9675 W 76th St Ste 200, Eden Prairie MN 55344
Tel (952) 949-3700
SIC 5065 7622 8748 1799

KGP TELECOMMUNICATIONS INC p 816
3305 Highway 60 W, Faribault MN 55021
Tel (507) 334-2268 SIC 5065

■ 3M INTERAMERICA INC p 2
2501 Old Hudson Rd, Maplewood MN 55144
Tel (651) 733-1110
SIC 5113 5085 5065 5084 5122 8741

METRO SALES INC p 955
1640 E 78th St, Minneapolis MN 55423
Tel (612) 861-4000
SIC 5044 5112 5065 7359

■ NEXTIRAONE LLC p 1040
5050 Lincoln Dr Ste 300, Minneapolis MN 55436
Tel (952) 352-4410
SIC 5065 7629 1731 5999 4813 4841

■ NORSTAN COMMUNICATIONS INC p 1049
5050 Lincoln Dr Ste 300, Minneapolis MN 55436
Tel (952) 935-9002 SIC 5065 1731 7629

ATRENNE INTEGRATED SOLUTIONS INC p 129
9210 Science Center Dr, New Hope MN 55428
Tel (763) 533-3533 SIC 8711 5065

■ BUY BEST PURCHASING LLC p 230
7601 Penn Ave S, Richfield MN 55423
Tel (612) 291-1000 SIC 5065

POWER/MATION DIVISION INC p 1165
1310 Energy Ln, Saint Paul MN 55108
Tel (651) 605-3300
SIC 5085 5065 5084 5045 8742 7549

DIGI-KEY CORP p 439
701 Brooks Ave S, Thief River Falls MN 56701
Tel (800) 344-4539 SIC 5065

TELCOBUY.COM LLC p 1433
60 Weldon Pkwy, Maryland Heights MO 63043
Tel (314) 569-7000 SIC 5065

WORLD WIDE TECHNOLOGY INC p 1625
60 Weldon Pkwy, Maryland Heights MO 63043
Tel (314) 569-7000 SIC 5045 5065 8741

GRAYBAR ELECTRIC CO INC p 632
34 N Meramec Ave, Saint Louis MO 63105
Tel (314) 573-9200 SIC 5063 5065

WORLD WIDE TECHNOLOGY HOLDING CO INC p 1625
60 Weldon Pkwy, Saint Louis MO 63101
Tel (314) 919-1400 SIC 5045 5065 8748

PHILCOR TV & ELECTRONIC LEASING INC p 1143
4200 Spring Mountain Rd, Las Vegas NV 89102
Tel (702) 367-0400 SIC 5063 5065

■ CONWAY TECHNOLOGY GROUP LLC p 365
10 Capitol St, Nashua NH 03063
Tel (603) 889-1665
SIC 5044 5065 7699 7359

■ CELLCO PARTNERSHIP p 273
1 Verizon Way, Basking Ridge NJ 07920
Tel (908) 306-7000 SIC 4812 5999 5065

■AT&T COMMUNICATIONS AMERICAS INC p 123
900 Us Highway 202 206, Bedminster NJ 07921
Tel (404) 861-9188 SIC 5065

BROTHER INTERNATIONAL CORP p 219
200 Crossing Blvd, Bridgewater NJ 08807
Tel (908) 704-1700
SIC 5044 3579 3559 5084 5064 5065

ARCHBROOK LAGUNA LLC p 104
350 Starke Rd Ste 400, Carlstadt NJ 07072
Tel (201) 372-0304 SIC 5045 5065

EMPIRE TECHNOLOGIES LLC p 494
246 Industrial Way W # 1, Eatontown NJ 07724
Tel (732) 625-3200 SIC 5065 1731 5999

C & A MARKETING INC p 231
114 Tived Ln E, Edison NJ 08837
Tel (201) 881-1900
SIC 5065 8742 7384 5946 7359 7221

DGL GROUP LTD p 435
195 Raritan Center Pkwy, Edison NJ 08837
Tel (718) 499-1000 SIC 5731 5065

RADVISION INC p 1205
17-17 State Rt 208 # 300, Fair Lawn NJ 07410
Tel (201) 689-6300 SIC 5065

ACUATIVE CORP p 20
30 Two Bridges Rd Ste 240, Fairfield NJ 07004
Tel (862) 926-5600 SIC 7373 5065 1731

DIALECTIC DISTRIBUTION LLC p 436
1275 Bloomfield Ave # 66, Fairfield NJ 07004
Tel (973) 870-0250 SIC 5065

■ KYOCERA DOCUMENT SOLUTIONS AMERICA INC p 833
225 Sand Rd, Fairfield NJ 07004
Tel (973) 808-8444 SIC 5044 5084 5065

TELQUEST INTERNATIONAL CORP p 1435
26 Commerce Rd Ste B, Fairfield NJ 07004
Tel (973) 808-4588 SIC 5065

PCS WIRELESS LLC p 1124
11 Vreeland Rd, Florham Park NJ 07932
Tel (973) 805-7400 SIC 5065 5999

EPCOS INC p 504
485b Route 1 S Ste 200, Iselin NJ 08830
Tel (732) 906-4300
SIC 3679 3546 5065 3671

NEKTOVA GROUP LIMITED LIABILITY CO p 1025
534 Whitesville Rd, Jackson NJ 08527
Tel (732) 835-2303 SIC 5065

D & M HOLDINGS US INC p 406
100 Corporate Dr, Mahwah NJ 07430
Tel (201) 762-6500 *SIC* 5065 3651

LUCENT TECHNOLOGIES INTERNATIONAL INC p 884
600 Mountain Ave 700, New Providence NJ 07974
Tel (908) 582-8500 *SIC* 5065

PANASONIC CORP OF NORTH AMERICA p 1111
2 Riverfront Plz Ste 200, Newark NJ 07102
Tel (201) 348-7000
SIC 5064 5045 5065 5044 5084 5063

G P JOHNSTON INC p 587
322 Belleville Tpke, North Arlington NJ 07031
Tel (201) 991-7400 *SIC* 5065

KONICA MINOLTA HOLDINGS USA INC p 827
100 Williams Dr, Ramsey NJ 07446
Tel (201) 825-4000
SIC 5043 5065 5044 5047

SAMSUNG ELECTRONICS AMERICA INC p 1275
85 Challenger Rd, Ridgefield Park NJ 07660
Tel (201) 229-4000 *SIC* 5064 5065 5045

STAR MICRONICS AMERICA INC p 1378
65 Clyde Rd Ste G, Somerset NJ 08873
Tel (732) 623-5500 *SIC* 5065 5045

RICOH AMERICAS HOLDINGS INC p 1233
5 Dedrick Pl, West Caldwell NJ 07006
Tel (973) 882-2000 *SIC* 5044 5065 5043

RICOH CORP p 1233
5 Dedrick Pl, West Caldwell NJ 07006
Tel (973) 882-2000 *SIC* 5065

RADWELL INTERNATIONAL INC p 1205
1 Millenium Dr, Willingboro NJ 08046
Tel (609) 288-9393 *SIC* 5065 7629

STAMPEDE PRESENTATION PRODUCTS INC p 1375
55 Woodridge Dr, Amherst NY 14228
Tel (716) 635-9474 *SIC* 5065

ISHAN INTERNATIONAL INC p 766
500 Smith St, Farmingdale NY 11735
Tel (631) 618-3000 *SIC* 5065

NATIONAL ELECTRONICS INC p 1011
500 Smith St, Farmingdale NY 11735
Tel (631) 683-8000 *SIC* 5065

RELIANCE COMMUNICATIONS LLC p 1221
555 Wireless Blvd, Hauppauge NY 11788
Tel (631) 952-4800 *SIC* 5065 5999

■ **VOXX ELECTRONICS CORP** p 1566
150 Marcus Blvd, Hauppauge NY 11788
Tel (631) 231-7750 *SIC* 5065 5731

CANON USA INC p 247
1 Canon Park, Melville NY 11747
Tel (516) 328-5000
SIC 5044 5065 5045 3861 3577 5043

■ **NU HORIZONS ELECTRONICS CORP** p 1066
70 Maxess Rd, Melville NY 11747
Tel (631) 396-5000 *SIC* 5065

■ **FRONTIER CALIFORNIA INC** p 581
140 West St, New York NY 10007
Tel (212) 395-1000
SIC 4813 6519 8721 5065 1731 7629

ITOCHU INTERNATIONAL INC p 768
1251 Avenue Of The Americ, New York NY 10020
Tel (212) 818-8000
SIC 5131 5084 5065 5051 5153 5141

KANEMATSU USA INC p 802
500 5th Ave Fl 29, New York NY 10110
Tel (212) 704-9400
SIC 5084 5051 5065 5153

NAGASE AMERICA CORP p 1006
546 5th Ave Fl 16, New York NY 10036
Tel (212) 703-1340
SIC 5169 5162 5122 5065 5047

SOJITZ CORP OF AMERICA p 1337
1120 Ave Of The, New York NY 10036
Tel (212) 704-6500
SIC 5065 5084 5169 5051 5099 5052

CONTEC LLC p 362
1011 State St, Schenectady NY 12307
Tel (518) 382-8150 *SIC* 5065 7629

WORLDWIDE DIGITAL CO LLC p 1626
1023 State St, Schenectady NY 12307
Tel (518) 382-8000 *SIC* 5065

■ **AMPHENOL AEROSPACE FRANCE INC** p 86
191 Delaware Ave, Sidney NY 13838
Tel (800) 678-0141 *SIC* 5065

HITACHI AMERICA LTD p 696
50 Prospect Ave, Tarrytown NY 10591
Tel (914) 332-5800
SIC 5084 5065 3577 5063 5045 3651

FUJIFILM HOLDINGS AMERICA CORP p 583
200 Summit Lake Dr Fl 2, Valhalla NY 10595
Tel (914) 789-8100 *SIC* 5043 5065

FUJIFILM NORTH AMERICA CORP p 583
200 Summit Lake Dr Fl 2, Valhalla NY 10595
Tel (914) 789-8100
SIC 7384 5043 5065 3695 2673 3861

NORTHERN VIDEO SYSTEMS INC p 1057
135 Cronyways Park Dr Ste 101, Woodbury NY 11797
Tel (516) 941-2800 *SIC* 5065

TRI-ED DISTRIBUTION INC p 1477
135 Crossways Park Dr # 101, Woodbury NY 11797
Tel (516) 941-2800 *SIC* 5065

TRI-NORTHERN SECURITY DISTRIBUTION INC p 1477
135 Crossways Park Dr # 101, Woodbury NY 11797
Tel (516) 941-2800 *SIC* 5065

BAKER & TAYLOR FULFILLMENT INC p 145
2550 W Tyvola Rd Ste 300, Charlotte NC 28217
Tel (704) 998-3154
SIC 5192 5045 7822 5065

BAKER & TAYLOR HOLDINGS LLC p 145
2550 W Tyvola Rd Ste 300, Charlotte NC 28217
Tel (704) 998-3100
SIC 5192 7822 5065 5045

BAKER & TAYLOR LLC p 145
2550 W Tyvola Rd Ste 300, Charlotte NC 28217
Tel (704) 998-3100
SIC 5192 7822 5065 5045 5099

BTAC ACQUISITION LLC p 222
2550 W Tyvola Rd Ste 300, Charlotte NC 28217
Tel (704) 998-3100
SIC 5192 7822 5065 5045

BTAC HOLDING CORP p 222
2550 W Tyvola Rd Ste 300, Charlotte NC 28217
Tel (704) 998-3100
SIC 5192 7822 5065 5045

HUBER + SUHNER INC p 716
8530 Steele Creek Place D, Charlotte NC 28273
Tel (704) 790-7300
SIC 3679 3678 3357 5065

MURATA MACHINERY USA HOLDINGS INC p 1001
2120 Queen City Dr, Charlotte NC 28208
Tel (704) 394-8331 *SIC* 3542 3552 5065

■ **KYOCERA INDUSTRIAL CERAMICS CORP** p 833
100 Industrial Park Rd, Hendersonville NC 28792
Tel (828) 693-0241 *SIC* 5065 5013 5085

WALKER AND ASSOCIATES INC p 1573
7129 Old Hwy 52, Welcome NC 27374
Tel (336) 731-6391
SIC 4813 5065 8731 8711 3572 3571

WALKER GROUP INC p 1573
7129 Old Hwy 52, Welcome NC 27374
Tel (336) 731-6391
SIC 4813 8748 5065 8711

AIRBORN ELECTRONICS INC p 39
2230 Picton Pkwy, Akron OH 44312
Tel (330) 245-2630 *SIC* 5065

FAMOUS INDUSTRIES INC p 527
2620 Ridgewood Rd Ste 200, Akron OH 44313
Tel (330) 535-1811 *SIC* 5074 3444 5065

MORGENTHALER MANAGEMENT PARTNERS VI LLC p 989
50 Public Sq Ste 2700, Cleveland OH 44113
Tel (216) 416-7500
SIC 1731 5065 7622 7373 5999

■ **NES INVESTMENT CO** p 1026
6140 Parkland Blvd, Cleveland OH 44124
Tel (440) 461-6000
SIC 5065 5085 5169 5013

■ **ELEMENT14 US HOLDINGS INC** p 486
4180 Highlander Pkwy, Richfield OH 44286
Tel (330) 523-4280 *SIC* 5065 3429

■ **PREMIER FARNELL HOLDING INC** p 1170
4180 Highlander Pkwy, Richfield OH 44286
Tel (330) 523-4273 *SIC* 5065 3429

AUDIO-TECHNICA US INC p 131
1221 Commerce Dr, Stow OH 44224
Tel (330) 686-2600 *SIC* 5065 5731

PEPPERL + FUCHS INC p 1134
1600 Enterprise Pkwy, Twinsburg OH 44087
Tel (330) 425-3555
SIC 5065 3625 3822 3674

PETRA INDUSTRIES LLC p 1139
2101 S Kelly Ave, Edmond OK 73013
Tel (405) 216-2100 *SIC* 5065

JASCO PRODUCTS CO LLC p 778
10 E Memorial Rd Bldg B, Oklahoma City OK 73114
Tel (405) 752-0710 *SIC* 5065 5064

CHICKASAW HOLDING CO p 298
124 W Vinita Ave, Sulphur OK 73086
Tel (580) 622-2111 *SIC* 4813 7371 5065

VTECH COMMUNICATIONS INC p 1567
9590 Sw Gemini Dr Ste 120, Beaverton OR 97008
Tel (503) 596-1200 *SIC* 5065 5064

OECO HOLDINGS LLC p 1075
4607 Se International Way, Milwaukie OR 97222
Tel (503) 659-5999 *SIC* 3679 5065

OECO LLC p 1075
4607 Se International Way, Milwaukie OR 97222
Tel (503) 659-5999
SIC 3679 5065 4911 3621 3694

CONNECT AMERICA.COM LLC p 356
1 Belmont Ave Fl 9, Bala Cynwyd PA 19004
Tel (610) 356-3307 *SIC* 5065 5999

ALLIANCE PLASTICS INC p 55
3123 Station Rd, Erie PA 16510
Tel (814) 899-7671 *SIC* 5162 5065

■ **NORTH PITTSBURGH SYSTEMS INC** p 1053
4008 Gibsonia Rd, Gibsonia PA 15044
Tel (724) 443-9600 *SIC* 4813 5065

D & H DISTRIBUTING CO p 406
2525 N 7th St, Harrisburg PA 17110
Tel (717) 236-8001
SIC 5045 5065 5064 5063 5044

COLONIAL ELECTRIC SUPPLY CO p 337
201 W Church Rd Ste 100, King Of Prussia PA 19406
Tel (610) 312-8100 *SIC* 5065

▲ **BLACK BOX CORP** p 186
1000 Park Dr, Lawrence PA 15055
Tel (724) 746-5500
SIC 3577 3679 3661 5045 5065 5063

■ **BLACK BOX CORP OF PENNSYLVANIA** p 186
1000 Park Dr, Lawrence PA 15055
Tel (724) 746-5500
SIC 5045 5063 5065 3577 3679 3661

RICOH AMERICAS CORP p 1233
70 Valley Stream Pkwy, Malvern PA 19355
Tel (610) 296-8000
SIC 5044 5065 5045 5043 3861 3661

RICOH USA INC p 1233
70 Valley Stream Pkwy, Malvern PA 19355
Tel (610) 296-8000
SIC 5044 5065 7359 5112 7334 6159

■ **BELL ATLANTIC GLOBAL WIRELESS INC** p 170
1717 Arch St Fl 33, Philadelphia PA 19103
Tel (215) 246-9494
SIC 4813 4812 5065 7379

INTERTECH CI p 759
1501 Preble Ave, Pittsburgh PA 15233
Tel (412) 246-1200 *SIC* 5065

■ **WESCO DISTRIBUTION INC** p 1593
225 W Station Square Dr # 700, Pittsburgh PA 15219
Tel (412) 454-2200
SIC 5063 5085 5065 7389

▲ **WESCO INTERNATIONAL INC** p 1593
225 W Station Square Dr # 700, Pittsburgh PA 15219
Tel (412) 454-2200
SIC 5063 5084 5065 7389

COMMUNICATIONS TEST DESIGN INC p 347
1373 Enterprise Dr, West Chester PA 19380
Tel (610) 436-5203
SIC 7629 7378 5065 5999

FUJIFILM ELECTRONIC MATERIALS USA INC p 583
80 Circuit Dr, North Kingstown RI 02852
Tel (401) 522-9499 *SIC* 5043 5065

ATRION INC p 129
125 Metro Center Blvd, Warwick RI 02886
Tel (401) 736-6400 *SIC* 7373 5065

■ **AVX CORP** p 139
1 Avx Blvd, Fountain Inn SC 29644
Tel (864) 967-2150 *SIC* 3675 5065 3678

EARTHBEND LLC p 469
2300 E 54th St N Ste 3, Sioux Falls SD 57104
Tel (605) 789-5700 *SIC* 5065

▲ **RAVEN INDUSTRIES INC** p 1209
205 E 6th St, Sioux Falls SD 57104
Tel (605) 336-2750
SIC 5065 3523 3081 3823 3083

INGRAM ENTERTAINMENT HOLDINGS INC p 743
2 Ingram Blvd, La Vergne TN 37089
Tel (615) 287-4000 *SIC* 5065 5045

INGRAM ENTERTAINMENT INC p 743
2 Ingram Blvd, La Vergne TN 37089
Tel (615) 287-4000 *SIC* 5065 5092 5099

VELOCITY ELECTRONICS LP p 1547
2208 Energy Dr, Austin TX 78758
Tel (512) 973-9500 *SIC* 5065

UNIVERSAL POWER GROUP INC p 1517
488 S Royal Ln, Coppell TX 75019
Tel (469) 892-1122 *SIC* 5065 5063

GENERAL DATATECH LP p 600
999 Metro Media Pl, Dallas TX 75247
Tel (214) 857-6100 *SIC* 5065

SOURCE INC p 1342
4550 Spring Valley Rd # 200, Dallas TX 75244
Tel (972) 371-2600 *SIC* 5065 7629

■ **POLLOK INC** p 1160
6 Butterfield Trail Blvd, El Paso TX 79906
Tel (915) 592-5700
SIC 5065 3823 3714 3545

ALLIED ELECTRONICS INC p 56
7151 Jack Newell Blvd S, Fort Worth TX 76118
Tel (817) 595-3500 *SIC* 5065 7389 3999

■ **NUCLEAR LOGISTICS INC** p 1066
7410 Pebble Dr, Fort Worth TX 76118
Tel (817) 284-0077 *SIC* 5065 8711

■ **TTI INC** p 1489
2441 Northeast Pkwy, Fort Worth TX 76106
Tel (817) 740-9000 *SIC* 5065

UNIDEN HOLDING INC p 1503
4700 Amon Carter Blvd, Fort Worth TX 76155
Tel (817) 858-3300 *SIC* 5063 5065

BEARCOM GROUP INC p 165
4009 Dist Dr Ste 200, Garland TX 75041
Tel (214) 340-8876 *SIC* 5999 5065

BEARCOM OPERATING LLC p 165
4009 Dist Dr Ste 200, Garland TX 75041
Tel (214) 765-7100 *SIC* 4812 5065

C&J SPEC-RENT SERVICES INC p 234
3990 Rogerdale Rd, Houston TX 77042
Tel (713) 260-9900 *SIC* 5065

HIS CO INC p 696
6650 Concord Park Dr, Houston TX 77040
Tel (713) 934-1600 *SIC* 5065 5063

N F SMITH & ASSOCIATES LP p 1005
5306 Hollister St, Houston TX 77040
Tel (713) 430-3000 *SIC* 5065

NATIONAL PROCESSING CO p 1015
20405 State Highway 249 # 700, Houston TX 77070
Tel (281) 376-3399 *SIC* 5065

TELCO INTERCONTINENTAL CORP p 1433
9812 Whithorn Dr, Houston TX 77095
Tel (281) 500-8270 *SIC* 5063 5065 3575

WHOLESALE ELECTRIC SUPPLY CO OF HOUSTON INC p 1607
4040 Gulf Fwy, Houston TX 77004
Tel (713) 748-6100 *SIC* 5065

NEC CORP OF AMERICA p 1023
3929 W John Carpenter Fwy, Irving TX 75063
Tel (214) 262-6000 *SIC* 5045 5065

■ **VERIZON NORTHWEST INC** p 1550
600 Hidden Rdg, Irving TX 75038
Tel (972) 718-5600
SIC 4813 6519 8721 5065 7629

■ **VERIZON SOUTH INC** p 1550
600 Hidden Rdg, Irving TX 75038
Tel (972) 718-5600 *SIC* 4813 5065 8721

PRIME CONTROLS LP p 1175
1725 Lakepointe Dr, Lewisville TX 75057
Tel (972) 221-4849 *SIC* 5065 1731

■ **MOUSER ELECTRONICS INC** p 995
1000 N Main St, Mansfield TX 76063
Tel (817) 804-3800 *SIC* 5065

MACH SPEED HOLDINGS LLC p 892
7200 Bishop Rd Ste 280, Plano TX 75024
Tel (214) 978-3800 *SIC* 5091 5065 3679

■ **RICHARDSON TRIDENT CO LLC** p 1233
405 N Plano Rd, Richardson TX 75081
Tel (972) 231-5176
SIC 5051 5085 5063 5065 3316

SAMSUNG TELECOMMUNICATIONS AMERICA LLC p 1275
1301 E Lookout Dr, Richardson TX 75082
Tel (972) 761-7000 *SIC* 5065

■ **SOUTHWESTERN BELL TELECOMMUNICATIONS INC** p 1353
1651 N Collins Blvd, Richardson TX 75080
Tel (972) 705-7658 *SIC* 5065 5999

ZTE (USA) INC p 1644
2425 N Central Expy # 600, Richardson TX 75080
Tel (972) 671-8885 *SIC* 5065 5999

APX GROUP HOLDINGS INC p 101
4931 N 300 W, Provo UT 84604
Tel (801) 377-9111
SIC 7382 5065 3822 1711

APX GROUP INC p 101
4931 N 300 W, Provo UT 84604
Tel (801) 377-9111
SIC 8711 3822 1711 5065

APX PARENT HOLDCO INC p 101
4931 N 300 W, Provo UT 84604
Tel (801) 377-9111
SIC 6719 3822 1711 8711 5065 5074

KIMBALL ELECTRONICS INC p 818
2233 S 300 E, Salt Lake City UT 84115
Tel (801) 466-0569 *SIC* 5065 5063

THALES USA INC p 1446
2733 Crystal Dr, Arlington VA 22202
Tel (703) 413-6029
SIC 5065 3699 3679 3841 8711 7371

■ **NEXTIRAONE FEDERAL LLC** p 1040
510 Spring St Ste 200, Herndon VA 20170
Tel (703) 885-7900 *SIC* 5065

■ **SCITOR HOLDINGS INC** p 1292
12010 Sunset Hills Rd # 800, Reston VA 20190
Tel (703) 481-5892 *SIC* 7382 5065 7373

AUDIO FIDELITY COMMUNICATIONS CORP p 130
12820 West Creek Pkwy, Richmond VA 23238
Tel (804) 273-9100 *SIC* 5044 5065

■ **BELLSOUTH COMMUNICATION SYSTEMS LLC** p 171
1936 Blue Hills Dr Ne, Roanoke VA 24012
Tel (540) 983-6000 *SIC* 5065 4813 4812

CORNET TECHNOLOGY INC p 371
6800 Versar Ctr, Springfield VA 22151
Tel (703) 658-3400 *SIC* 5065 3669 3577

VIRGINIA INTEGRATED COMMUNICATION INC p 1559
5361 Cleveland St, Virginia Beach VA 23462
Tel (757) 490-7777 *SIC* 5065

■ **FLUKE CORP** p 561
6920 Seaway Blvd, Everett WA 98203
Tel (425) 446-5400 *SIC* 3823 5065 7629

CARLISLE INC p 257
7911 S 188th St Ste 100, Kent WA 98032
Tel (425) 251-0700 *SIC* 3643 5065 5063

CARLYLE HOLDINGS INC p 258
7911 S 188th St Ste 100, Kent WA 98032
Tel (425) 251-0700 *SIC* 3643 5065 5063

SCAFCO CORP p 1285
2800 E Main Ave, Spokane WA 99202
Tel (509) 343-9000
SIC 3523 5065 6531 3444

SHIN-ETSU HANDOTAI AMERICA INC p 1316
4111 Ne 112th Ave, Vancouver WA 98682
Tel (360) 883-7000 *SIC* 3674 5065

HEARTLAND LABEL PRINTERS LLC p 679
1700 Stephen St, Little Chute WI 54140
Tel (920) 788-7720 *SIC* 5065 2672

■ **DERCO AEROSPACE INC** p 431
8000 W Tower Ave, Milwaukee WI 53223
Tel (414) 355-3066 *SIC* 5065 5088

SIC 5072 Hardware Wholesale

LONG-LEWIS INC p 877
2551 Highway 150, Hoover AL 35244
Tel (205) 989-3673 *SIC* 5511 5072

MARVINS LLC p 914
7480 Parkway Dr Ste 100, Leeds AL 35094
Tel (205) 702-7305
SIC 5211 5074 5031 5072

FASTENING SOLUTIONS INC p 531
3075 Selma Hwy, Montgomery AL 36108
Tel (334) 284-8300 *SIC* 5085 5072 5051

SOUTHERN FASTENING SYSTEMS LLC p 1348
635 Fairgrounds Rd, Muscle Shoals AL 35661
Tel (256) 381-3628
SIC 5084 5085 5251 5072

ALASKA INDUSTRIAL HARDWARE INC p 45
2192 Viking Dr, Anchorage AK 99501
Tel (907) 279-6691 *SIC* 5072 5251

COPPER STATE BOLT & NUT CO INC p 368
3602 N 35th Ave, Phoenix AZ 85017
Tel (602) 272-2384 *SIC* 5072 3452

K & K VETERINARY SUPPLY INC p 798
675 Laura Ln, Tontitown AR 72770
Tel (479) 361-1516 *SIC* 5199 5047 5072

HD SUPPLY DISTRIBUTION SERVICES LLC p 673
26940 Aliso Viejo Pkwy, Aliso Viejo CA 92656
Tel (949) 643-4700 *SIC* 5072

WALNUT INVESTMENT CORP p 1574
2940 E White Star Ave, Anaheim CA 92806
Tel (714) 238-9240 *SIC* 5031 5039 5072

KING HOLDING CORP p 820
360 N Crescent Dr, Beverly Hills CA 90210
Tel (586) 254-3900
SIC 3452 3465 3469 3089 5072

LOUIS WURTH AND CO p 880
895 Columbia St, Brea CA 92821
Tel (714) 529-1771 *SIC* 5072 5198

CORDOVA BOLT INC p 369
5601 Dolly Ave, Buena Park CA 90621
Tel (714) 739-7500 *SIC* 5072

CBOL CORP p 269
19850 Plummer St, Chatsworth CA 91311
Tel (818) 704-8200
SIC 5065 5072 5013 5088 5084 5162

S & STOOL & SUPPLY INC p 1261
2700 Maxwell Way, Fairfield CA 94534
Tel (925) 335-4000
SIC 5085 7699 5072 7359

HAMPTON PRODUCTS INTERNATIONAL CORP p 656
50 Icon, Foothill Ranch CA 92610
Tel (949) 472-4256 *SIC* 5072

MAKITA USA INC p 899
14930 Northam St, La Mirada CA 90638
Tel (714) 522-8088 *SIC* 5072

TOMARCO CONTRACTOR SPECIALTIES INC p 1459
14848 Northam St, La Mirada CA 90638
Tel (714) 523-1771 *SIC* 5072

BRIGHTON-BEST INTERNATIONAL INC p 213
5855 Obispo Ave, Long Beach CA 90805
Tel (562) 808-8000 *SIC* 5072

ALS TESTING SERVICES GROUP INC p 61
818 W 7th St Ste 930, Los Angeles CA 90017
Tel (213) 627-8252 *SIC* 5141 5072 5084

JAMES HARDIE TRANSITION CO INC p 776
26300 La Alameda Ste 400, Mission Viejo CA 92691
Tel (949) 348-1800
SIC 3275 3523 3494 5072

■ **CPO COMMERCE LLC** p 387
120 W Bellevue Dr Ste 300, Pasadena CA 91105
Tel (626) 585-3600 *SIC* 5072

P & R PAPER SUPPLY CO INC p 1102
1898 E Colton Ave, Redlands CA 92374
Tel (909) 389-1811
SIC 5113 5169 5149 5072 5046

PRIME-LINE PRODUCTS CO p 1175
26950 San Bernardino Ave, Redlands CA 92374
Tel (909) 887-8118 *SIC* 5072

■ **ARCONIC GLOBAL FASTENERS & RINGS INC** p 106
3990a Heritage Oak Ct, Simi Valley CA 93063
Tel (310) 530-2220 *SIC* 5085 5072 5065

ADEPT FASTENERS INC p 22
28709 Industry Dr, Valencia CA 91355
Tel (661) 257-6600 *SIC* 5072

▲ **WESCO AIRCRAFT HOLDINGS INC** p 1593
24911 Avenue Stanford, Valencia CA 91355
Tel (661) 775-7200 *SIC* 8741 5072

CR LAURENCE CO INC p 388
2503 E Vernon Ave, Vernon CA 90058
Tel (323) 588-1281 *SIC* 3714 5072 5039

E B BRADLEY CO p 466
5602 Bickett St, Vernon CA 90058
Tel (323) 585-9917 *SIC* 5072 2452

NEFCO CORP p 1024
411 Burnham St, East Hartford CT 06108
Tel (860) 290-9044 *SIC* 5085 5072

VICTORINOX SWISS ARMY INC p 1555
7 Victoria Dr, Monroe CT 06468
Tel (203) 929-6391
SIC 5023 5099 5094 5072

ASSA ABLOY INC p 119
110 Sargent Dr, New Haven CT 06511
Tel (203) 624-5225
SIC 5065 5072 3699 3429

▲ **QEP CO INC** p 1194
1001 Brkn Snd Pkwy Nw A, Boca Raton FL 33487
Tel (561) 994-5550 *SIC* 5072 5085 2891

■ **INTERLINE BRANDS INC** p 753
801 W Bay St, Jacksonville FL 32204
Tel (904) 421-1400 *SIC* 5074 5063 5072

■ **INTERLINE BRANDS INC** p 753
701 San Marco Blvd, Jacksonville FL 32207
Tel (904) 421-1400 *SIC* 5074 5063 5072

INTEGRATED SUPPLY NETWORK LLC p 749
2727 Interstate Dr, Lakeland FL 33805
Tel (863) 603-0777 *SIC* 5013 5072

DOLMAR GMBH (INC) p 448
1005 Alderman Dr Ste 106, Alpharetta GA 30005
Tel (770) 569-4945 *SIC* 5072

PRO MARKETING INC p 1178
1350 Bluegrass Lakes Pkwy, Alpharetta GA 30004
Tel (770) 521-1421 *SIC* 5072 5085

■ **HD SUPPLY CONSTRUCTION SUPPLY GROUP INC** p 673
3100 Cumberland Blvd Se, Atlanta GA 30339
Tel (770) 852-9000 *SIC* 5072 5039 5031

■ **HD SUPPLY CONSTRUCTION SUPPLY LTD** p 673
3100 Cumberland Blvd Se # 1700, Atlanta GA 30339
Tel (770) 852-9000 *SIC* 5031 5039 5072

▲ **HD SUPPLY HOLDINGS INC** p 673
3100 Cumberland Blvd Se # 1480, Atlanta GA 30339
Tel (770) 852-9000 *SIC* 5087 5072 5085

■ **HDS HOLDING CORP** p 673
3100 Cumberland Blvd Se, Atlanta GA 30339
Tel (770) 852-9000 *SIC* 5087 5072 5085

■ **WHITE CAP CONSTRUCTION SUPPLY INC** p 1606
3100 Cumberland Blvd Se # 1700, Atlanta GA 30339
Tel (404) 879-7740 *SIC* 5072 5039 5031

US LBM HOLDINGS LLC p 1532
1000 Corporate Grove Dr, Buffalo Grove IL 60089
Tel (877) 787-5267 *SIC* 5072 5031 5198

▲ **LAWSON PRODUCTS INC** p 848
8770 W Bryn Mawr Ave # 639, Chicago IL 60631
Tel (773) 304-5050
SIC 5072 5085 5084 5013

■ **MARMON GROUP LLC** p 909
181 W Madison St Ste 2600, Chicago IL 60602
Tel (312) 372-9500 *SIC* 3452 5072

TRUE VALUE CO p 1486
8600 W Bryn Mawr Ave 100s, Chicago IL 60631
Tel (773) 695-5000 *SIC* 5072 2851 3991

■ **DAYTON ELECTRIC MFG CO** p 417
100 Grainger Pkwy, Lake Forest IL 60045
Tel (847) 535-1000 *SIC* 5063 5084 5072

■ **GRAINGER INTERNATIONAL INC** p 629
100 Grainger Pkwy, Lake Forest IL 60045
Tel (847) 535-1000
SIC 5074 5084 5085 5072

▲ **WW GRAINGER INC** p 1628
100 Grainger Pkwy, Lake Forest IL 60045
Tel (847) 535-1000
SIC 5063 5084 5075 5085 5072

MIDWEST AIR TECHNOLOGIES INC p 967
6700 Wildlife Way, Long Grove IL 60047
Tel (847) 821-9630
SIC 5072 5191 5063 5051 5031

GRABBER HOLDINGS LLC p 628
1 Dot Way, Mount Sterling IL 62353
Tel (217) 773-4411 *SIC* 5072 5211 6719

HAGERTY BROTHERS CO p 652
1506 W Detweiller Dr, Peoria IL 61615
Tel (309) 589-0200 *SIC* 5072

SUPPLYCORE INC p 1407
303 N Main St Ste 800, Rockford IL 61101
Tel (815) 997-1624 *SIC* 5072 5085

WURTH BAER SUPPLY CO p 1628
909 Forest Edge Dr, Vernon Hills IL 60061
Tel (847) 913-2237 *SIC* 5072

■ **AWW 10 INC** p 139
1441 N Wood Dale Rd, Wood Dale IL 60191
Tel (630) 595-0000 *SIC* 3452 5072

DO IT BEST CORP p 446
6502 Nelson Rd, Fort Wayne IN 46803
Tel (260) 748-5300 *SIC* 5072 5031 5063

WURTH/SERVICE SUPPLY INC p 1628
4935 W 86th St, Indianapolis IN 46268
Tel (317) 704-1000 *SIC* 5072

BLISH-MIZE CO p 189
223 S 5th St, Atchison KS 66002
Tel (913) 367-1250 *SIC* 5072

HARDWARE RESOURCES INC p 661
4319 Marlena St, Bossier City LA 71111
Tel (318) 742-0660 *SIC* 5072 2499

EMERY-WATERHOUSE CO p 492
7 Rand Rd, Portland ME 04102
Tel (207) 775-2371 *SIC* 5072

COMMERCE LLC p 345
7603 Energy Pkwy, Baltimore MD 21226
Tel (410) 255-3500 *SIC* 5191 5072 5199

CENTRAL WHOLESALERS INC p 281
13401 Konterra Dr, Laurel MD 20707
Tel (800) 935-2947
SIC 5074 5063 5087 5072 5211 1799

P4 CORP p 1103
16001 Trade Zone Ave, Upper Marlboro MD 20774
Tel (301) 218-7039 *SIC* 5087 5072

MILLBROOK DISTRIBUTION SERVICES INC p 970
88 Huntoon Memorial Hwy, Leicester MA 01524
Tel (508) 892-8171
SIC 5122 5023 5072 5112 5049 5199

ND INDUSTRIES INC p 1022
1000 N Crooks Rd, Clawson MI 48017
Tel (248) 288-0000
SIC 3452 2851 5072 2891 3479

ROGER ZATKOFF CO p 1246
23230 Industrial Park Dr, Farmington Hills MI 48335
Tel (248) 478-2400 *SIC* 5085 5072 3053

FASTENERS INC p 531
640 44th St Sw Ste 1, Grand Rapids MI 49548
Tel (616) 241-3448 *SIC* 5072

ALL STATE FASTENER CORP p 51
15460 E 12 Mile Rd, Roseville MI 48066
Tel (586) 773-5400 *SIC* 5072

ACUMENT GLOBAL TECHNOLOGIES INC p 20
6125 18 Mile Rd, Sterling Heights MI 48314
Tel (586) 254-3900 *SIC* 3965 5072

MNP CORP p 980
44225 Utica Rd, Utica MI 48317
Tel (586) 254-1320
SIC 3452 5051 5072 3714

WURTH ADAMS NUT & BOLT CO p 1628
9485 Winnetka Ave N, Brooklyn Park MN 55445
Tel (763) 424-3374 *SIC* 5072

MID-STATES DISTRIBUTING CO INC p 963
1370 Mendota Hts Rd, Mendota MN 55150
Tel (651) 280-4300
SIC 5072 5013 5191 5091 5092 5136

▲ **FASTENAL CO** p 531
2001 Theurer Blvd, Winona MN 55987
Tel (507) 454-5374
SIC 5085 5072 5063 5169 5198

PAXTON WOOD SOURCE INC p 1122
6311 Saint John Ave, Kansas City MO 64123
Tel (816) 483-7000
SIC 5031 2431 5211 5072

DYNAMIC FASTENER SERVICE INC p 464
9911 E 53rd St, Raytown MO 64133
Tel (816) 358-9898 *SIC* 5072

NU WAY CONCRETE FORMS INC p 1066
4190 Hoffmeister Ave, Saint Louis MO 63125
Tel (573) 893-8786
SIC 5032 5051 5072 7359

HBC HOLDINGS LLC p 671
324a Half Acre Rd, Cranbury NJ 08512
Tel (609) 860-9990 *SIC* 5072 5087 5074

WORLD AND MAIN (CRANBURY) LLC p 1624
324a Half Acre Rd, Cranbury NJ 08512
Tel (609) 860-9990 *SIC* 5072 5087 5074

TMCI HOLDINGS INC p 1457
80 Avenue K, Newark NJ 07105
Tel (201) 553-1100
SIC 5122 5023 5072 5112 5049 5199

WURTH GROUP OF NORTH AMERICA INC p 1628
93 Grant St, Ramsey NJ 07446
Tel (201) 818-8877 *SIC* 5013 5099 5072

STAR STAINLESS SCREW CO p 1378
30 W End Rd, Totowa NJ 07512
Tel (973) 256-2300 *SIC* 5072

RAKS BUILDING SUPPLY INC p 1206
108 Carson Dr Se, Los Lunas NM 87031
Tel (505) 865-1100 *SIC* 5031 5211 5072

▲ **MSC INDUSTRIAL DIRECT CO INC** p 996
75 Maxess Rd, Melville NY 11747
Tel (516) 812-2000
SIC 5084 5085 5063 5072

GREAT NECK SAW MANUFACTURERS INC p 634
165 E 2nd St, Mineola NY 11501
Tel (800) 457-0600 *SIC* 5072

HMAN INTERMEDIATE HOLDINGS CORP p 697
245 Park Ave Fl 16, New York NY 10167
Tel (513) 851-4900 *SIC* 6719 5072 7699

MCGARD LLC p 929
3875 California Rd, Orchard Park NY 14127
Tel (716) 662-8980 *SIC* 5072

PAINT APPLICATOR CORP OF AMERICA p 1108
7 Harbor Park Dr, Port Washington NY 11050
Tel (516) 284-3000 *SIC* 5072 5198

PRIDE PRODUCTS CORP p 1174
4333 Veterans Mem Hwy, Ronkonkoma NY 11779
Tel (631) 737-4444
SIC 5113 5122 5023 5072 5199

HAFELE AMERICA CO p 652
3901 Cheyenne Dr, Archdale NC 27263
Tel (336) 434-2322 *SIC* 5072

POSITEC TOOL CORP p 1163
10130 Perimeter Pkwy # 300, Charlotte NC 28216
Tel (704) 599-3711 *SIC* 5072 6719

POSITEC USA INC p 1163
10130 Perimeter Pkwy # 300, Charlotte NC 28216
Tel (704) 599-3711 *SIC* 5072

HICKORY SPRINGS MANUFACTURING CO p 690
235 2nd Ave Nw, Hickory NC 28601
Tel (828) 328-2201
SIC 3069 3495 2514 5072 2399

MONROE HARDWARE CO INC p 985
101 N Sutherland Ave, Monroe NC 28110
Tel (704) 289-3121 *SIC* 5072 5083

DILLON SUPPLY CO p 440
440 Civic Blvd, Raleigh NC 27610
Tel (919) 838-4200
SIC 5084 5085 5051 5074 5072

■ **LIBERTY HARDWARE MFG CORP** p 861
140 Business Park Dr, Winston Salem NC 27107
Tel (336) 769-4077 *SIC* 5072

ACME ELECTRIC MOTOR INC p 17
1705 13th Ave N, Grand Forks ND 58203
Tel (701) 746-2823
SIC 5084 5063 5082 5072 5251 5211

HILLMAN COMPANIES INC p 693
10590 Hamilton Ave, Cincinnati OH 45231
Tel (513) 851-4900 *SIC* 5072 7699

HILLMAN GROUP INC p 693
10590 Hamilton Ave, Cincinnati OH 45231
Tel (513) 851-4900 *SIC* 5072

HMAN GROUP HOLDINGS INC p 697
10590 Hamilton Ave, Cincinnati OH 45231
Tel (513) 851-4900 *SIC* 6719 5072 7699

HMAN INTERMEDIATE II HOLDINGS CORP p 697
10590 Hamilton Ave, Cincinnati OH 45231
Tel (513) 851-4900 *SIC* 5072 7699

■ **KAR PRODUCTS** p 804
1301 E 9th St Ste 700, Cleveland OH 44114
Tel (216) 416-7200 *SIC* 5013 5084 5072

MAZZELLA HOLDING CO INC p 924
21000 Aerospace Pkwy, Cleveland OH 44142
Tel (513) 772-4466
SIC 5051 5085 5088 5072

STATE INDUSTRIAL PRODUCTS CORP p 1381
5915 Landerbrook Dr # 300, Cleveland OH 44124
Tel (877) 747-6986
SIC 2841 5072 2842 2992 2952 2899

WAXMAN INDUSTRIES INC p 1584
24460 Aurora Rd, Cleveland OH 44146
Tel (440) 439-1830
SIC 5072 5074 3494 3491 3432

F & M MAFCO INC p 522
9149 Dry Fork Rd, Harrison OH 45030
Tel (513) 367-2151
SIC 5085 5072 7353 5082

TTI FLOOR CARE NORTH AMERICA INC p 1489
7005 Cochran Rd, Solon OH 44139
Tel (440) 996-2000 *SIC* 5072 3825

■ **MATCO TOOLS CORP** p 919
4403 Allen Rd, Stow OH 44224
Tel (330) 929-4949
SIC 5251 5072 3489 3423 5013

OHASHI TECHNICA USA INC p 1077
111 Burrer Dr, Sunbury OH 43074
Tel (740) 965-5115 *SIC* 5013 5072 3452

BOSTWICK-BRAUN CO p 203
7349 Crossleigh Ct, Toledo OH 43617
Tel (419) 259-3600
SIC 5072 5084 5063 5083 5023

FACIL NORTH AMERICA INC p 523
2242 Pinnacle Pkwy # 100, Twinsburg OH 44087
Tel (330) 487-2500 *SIC* 5072 3452 5085

SILICONE SPECIALTIES INC p 1323
430 S Rockford Ave, Tulsa OK 74120
Tel (918) 587-5567 *SIC* 5072

PARR LUMBER CO p 1117
5630 Nw Century Blvd, Hillsboro OR 97124
Tel (503) 614-2500
SIC 5031 5211 5072 5251

ACME CONSTRUCTION SUPPLY CO INC p 17
330 Se Salmon St, Portland OR 97214
Tel (503) 239-5230 *SIC* 5072

■ **ONITY INC** p 1088
4001 Fairview Indus Dr Se, Salem OR 97302
Tel (503) 581-9101 *SIC* 5072

FABTEX INC p 523
111 Woodbine Ln, Danville PA 17821
Tel (570) 275-7500
SIC 5072 2221 5023 2512 2392 2391

BOLTTECH MANNINGS INC p 199
501 Mosside Blvd, North Versailles PA 15137
Tel (724) 872-4873
SIC 3546 5072 3599 7359 3545 3423

C H BRIGGS CO p 232
2047 Kutztown Rd, Reading PA 19605
Tel (800) 355-1000 *SIC* 5072

LUMBERMENS MERCHANDISING CORP p 885
137 W Wayne Ave, Wayne PA 19087
Tel (610) 293-3678 *SIC* 5031 5072

BRADLEY CALDWELL INC p 206
200 Kiwanis Blvd, West Hazleton PA 18202
Tel (570) 455-7511 *SIC* 5191 5199 5072

SCHULL CONSTRUCTION CO p 1290
405 1st Ave Ne, Watertown SD 57201
Tel (605) 886-3495 *SIC* 5072

HOUSE-HASSON HARDWARE CO p 711
3125 Water Plant Rd, Knoxville TN 37914
Tel (800) 333-0520 *SIC* 5072 5031

ORGILL INC p 1094
3742 Tyndale Dr, Memphis TN 38125
Tel (901) 754-8850 *SIC* 5072

WALLACE HARDWARE CO INC p 1573
5050 S Davy Crockett Pkwy, Morristown TN 37813
Tel (423) 586-5650
SIC 5072 5074 5085 5083 5211

COBURN SUPPLY CO INC p 333
390 Park St Ste 100, Beaumont TX 77701
Tel (409) 838-6363
SIC 5063 5064 5072 5074 5075 5078

DW DISTRIBUTION INC p 463
1200 E Centre Park Blvd, Desoto TX 75115
Tel (214) 381-2200 *SIC* 5033 5031 5072

HANDY HARDWARE WHOLESALE INC p 657
8300 Tewantin Dr, Houston TX 77061
Tel (713) 644-1495
SIC 5072 5074 5063 5031 5198

HOLLOWAY-HOUSTON INC p 701
5833 Armour Dr, Houston TX 77020
Tel (713) 674-5631 *SIC* 5072

BUTTERY CO LLP p 230
201 W Main St, Llano TX 78643
Tel (325) 247-4141
SIC 5072 5074 5063 5091 5211 5251

HILTI INC p 694
7250 Dallas Pkwy Ste 1000, Plano TX 75024
Tel (800) 879-8000 *SIC* 5072

WINZER CORP p 1617
4060 E Plano Pkwy, Plano TX 75074
Tel (800) 527-4126
SIC 5072 3452 5251 5169

MAINTENANCE SUPPLY HEADQUARTERS LP p 898
12315 Parc Crest Dr # 100, Stafford TX 77477
Tel (281) 530-6300 *SIC* 5072

TRAMONTINA USA INC p 1469
12955 W Airport Blvd, Sugar Land TX 77478
Tel (281) 340-8400 *SIC* 5046 5072 5085

GRABBER CONSTRUCTION PRODUCTS INC p 628
5255 W 11000 N Ste 100, Highland UT 84003
Tel (801) 492-3880 *SIC* 5072 5211

JENSEN-BYRD CO LLC p 783
314 W Riverside Ave, Spokane WA 99201
Tel (509) 624-1321 *SIC* 5072

ENDRIES INTERNATIONAL INC p 496
714 W Ryan St, Brillion WI 54110
Tel (920) 756-2174 *SIC* 5085 5072

SATISLOH NORTH AMERICA INC p 1283
N106w13131 Bradley Way # 200, Germantown WI 53022
Tel (262) 255-6001 *SIC* 5049 5072

LA FORCE INC p 835
1060 W Mason St, Green Bay WI 54303
Tel (920) 497-7100 *SIC* 5072 5031 3442

BLAIN SUPPLY INC p 188
3507 E Racine St, Janesville WI 53546
Tel (608) 754-2821
SIC 5083 5072 5039 5013 5023 5198

PRINCE CORP p 1176
8351 County Road H, Marshfield WI 54449
Tel (800) 777-2486
SIC 5031 5191 2048 5083 5072

RENAISSANCE LEARNING INC p 1223
2911 Peach St, Wisconsin Rapids WI 54494
Tel (715) 424-4242 *SIC* 7372 5072

SIC 5074 Plumbing & Heating Splys Wholesale

MARVINS LLC p 914
7480 Parkway Dr Ste 100, Leeds AL 35094
Tel (205) 702-7305
SIC 5211 5074 5031 5072

JONES STEPHENS CORP p 792
3249 Moody Pkwy, Moody AL 35004
Tel (205) 640-7200 *SIC* 5074

EWING IRRIGATION PRODUCTS INC p 516
3441 E Harbour Dr, Phoenix AZ 85034
Tel (602) 437-9530 *SIC* 5085 5087 5074

RYAN HERCO PRODUCTS CORP p 1260
3010 N San Fernando Blvd, Burbank CA 91504
Tel (818) 841-1141 *SIC* 5074 5162

BUILD.COM INC p 224
402 Otterson Dr Ste 100, Chico CA 95928
Tel (800) 375-3403 *SIC* 5074 5999

HARRINGTON INDUSTRIAL PLASTICS LLC p 663
14480 Yorba Ave, Chino CA 91710
Tel (909) 597-8641 *SIC* 5074

WESTERN WATER WORKS SUPPLY CO p 1600
5831 Pine Ave, Chino Hills CA 91709
Tel (909) 597-7000 *SIC* 5074

GEORGE FISCHER INC p 606
3401 Aero Jet Ave, El Monte CA 91731
Tel (626) 571-2770
SIC 3599 5074 3829 3559

SLAKEY BROTHERS INC p 1331
2215 Kausen Dr Ste 1, Elk Grove CA 95758
Tel (916) 478-2000 *SIC* 5075 5074 5078

GCO INC p 595
27750 Industrial Blvd, Hayward CA 94545
Tel (510) 786-3333 *SIC* 5074 5087

R F MACDONALD CO p 1202
25920 Eden Landing Rd, Hayward CA 94545
Tel (510) 784-0110 *SIC* 5084 7699 5074

CIVICSOLAR INC p 320
426 17th St Ste 600, Oakland CA 94612
Tel (800) 409-2257 *SIC* 5074 5211

FERGUSON FIRE & FABRICATION INC p 538
2750 S Towne Ave, Pomona CA 91766
Tel (909) 517-3085 *SIC* 5074 5099

PACE SUPPLY CORP p 1103
6000 State Farm Dr # 200, Rohnert Park CA 94928
Tel (707) 303-0320 *SIC* 5074
SOLIGENT HOLDINGS INC p 1338
1500 Valley House Dr, Rohnert Park CA 94928
Tel (707) 992-3100 *SIC* 5074 7359 1711
■ **SUNRUN SOUTH LLC** p 1404
595 Market St Fl 29, San Francisco CA 94105
Tel (415) 580-6900 *SIC* 5074
ZHONGLI NEW ENERGY USA CO LLC p 1643
25 Metro Dr Ste 228, San Jose CA 95110
Tel (408) 638-7627 *SIC* 5074
HIRSCH PIPE & SUPPLY CO INC p 696
15025 Oxnard St Ste 100, Van Nuys CA 91411
Tel (818) 756-0900 *SIC* 5074
TUNDRA RESTAURANT SUPPLY INC p 1491
3825 Walnut St Unit E, Boulder CO 80301
Tel (303) 440-4142 *SIC* 5046 5074
RAMPART PLUMBING AND HEATING SUPPLY INC p 1207
1801 N Union Blvd, Colorado Springs CO 80909
Tel (719) 471-7200 *SIC* 5074
MOTION AND FLOW CONTROL PRODUCTS INC p 992
7941 Shaffer Pkwy, Littleton CO 80127
Tel (303) 762-8012 *SIC* 5085 5074
GEORGE T SANDERS CO p 606
10201 W 49th Ave, Wheat Ridge CO 80033
Tel (303) 423-9660 *SIC* 5074
WW LIQUIDATION INC p 1629
60 Backus Ave, Danbury CT 06810
Tel (203) 546-6000 *SIC* 5074 5999 5211
BLAKE GROUP HOLDINGS INC p 188
4 New Park Rd, East Windsor CT 06088
Tel (860) 243-1491
SIC 5074 5084 7699 8741
BELL PUMP SERVICE CO p 170
29 Lafayette St, Hartford CT 06106
Tel (860) 525-6678 *SIC* 5075 5078 5074
PLIMPTON & HILLS CORP p 1156
2 Brainard Rd, Hartford CT 06114
Tel (860) 522-4233 *SIC* 5074 5085
SUPERIOR PRODUCTS DISTRIBUTORS INC p 1407
1403 Meriden Waterbury Rd, Milldale CT 06467
Tel (860) 621-3621
SIC 5074 5032 5082 7353
KEENEY MANUFACTURING CO p 807
1170 Main St, Newington CT 06111
Tel (603) 239-6371 *SIC* 3432 5074
PENTAIR AQUATIC ECO-SYSTEMS INC p 1131
2395 Apopka Blvd, Apopka FL 32703
Tel (407) 886-7575 *SIC* 5074 5999
MORGAN BROSUPPLY INC p 988
7559 W Gulf To Lake Hwy, Crystal River FL 34429
Tel (386) 255-2200 *SIC* 5074
HUGHES SUPPLY INC p 717
2920 Ford St, Fort Myers FL 33916
Tel (239) 334-2205
SIC 5063 5074 5075 5085 1711
■ **INTERLINE BRANDS INC** p 753
801 W Bay St, Jacksonville FL 32204
Tel (904) 421-1400 *SIC* 5074 5063 5072
■ **INTERLINE BRANDS INC** p 753
701 San Marco Blvd, Jacksonville FL 32207
Tel (904) 421-1400 *SIC* 5074 5063 5072
■ **HD SUPPLY WATERWORKS GROUP INC** p 673
501 W Church St Ste 100, Orlando FL 32805
Tel (407) 841-4755
SIC 5051 5074 5084 5099
■ **HANSGROHE INC** p 658
1490 Bluegrass Lakes Pkwy, Alpharetta GA 30004
Tel (770) 360-9880 *SIC* 3432 5074 3431
■ **HD SUPPLY HOLDINGS LLC** p 673
3100 Cumberland Blvd Se # 1700, Atlanta GA 30339
Tel (770) 852-9000
SIC 5051 5074 5084 5099
■ **HD SUPPLY WATERWORKS LTD** p 673
3100 Cumberland Blvd Se, Atlanta GA 30339
Tel (770) 852-9000 *SIC* 5074
■ **YOUR OTHER WAREHOUSE LLC** p 1639
2455 Paces Ferry Rd Se B8, Atlanta GA 30339
Tel (770) 433-8211 *SIC* 5074 5075
PLUMBING DISTRIBUTORS INC p 1156
1025 Old Norcross Rd, Lawrenceville GA 30046
Tel (770) 963-9231 *SIC* 5074
COLUMBIA PIPE & SUPPLY CO p 341
1120 W Pershing Rd, Chicago IL 60609
Tel (773) 927-6600 *SIC* 5051 5085 5074
■ **GRAINGER INTERNATIONAL INC** p 629
100 Grainger Pkwy, Lake Forest IL 60045
Tel (847) 535-1000
SIC 5074 5084 5085 5072
CRAWFORD SUPPLY GROUP INC p 389
8150 Lehigh Ave Ste A, Morton Grove IL 60053
Tel (847) 967-0550 *SIC* 5074
ACE HARDWARE CORP p 16
2200 Kensington Ct, Oak Brook IL 60523
Tel (630) 990-6600
SIC 5251 5198 5063 5074 5083
CONNOR CO p 358
2800 Ne Adams St, Peoria IL 61603
Tel (309) 693-7229 *SIC* 5074 5075
INDECK POWER EQUIPMENT CO p 736
1111 Willis Ave, Wheeling IL 60090
Tel (847) 541-8300 *SIC* 5084 5074 7359
DEHCO INC p 422
3601 Charlotte Ave, Elkhart IN 46517
Tel (574) 294-2684
SIC 2891 5031 5074 5014 5084
CENTRAL SUPPLY CO INC p 280
8900 E 30th St, Indianapolis IN 46219
Tel (317) 898-2411
SIC 5074 5063 5085 5719
LEE SUPPLY CORP p 852
6610 Guion Rd, Indianapolis IN 46268
Tel (317) 290-2500
SIC 5074 5075 5064 5085 5031

TEMPLETON COAL CO INC p 1436
701 Wabash Ave Ste 501, Terre Haute IN 47807
Tel (812) 232-7037
SIC 5074 3567 3961 5049 3089
JMF CO p 786
2735 62nd Street Ct, Bettendorf IA 52722
Tel (563) 332-9200 *SIC* 5074
SCHIMBERG CO p 1287
1106 Shaver Rd Ne, Cedar Rapids IA 52402
Tel (319) 365-9421 *SIC* 5074 3498
PLUMB SUPPLY CO LLC p 1156
1622 Ne 51st Ave, Des Moines IA 50313
Tel (515) 262-9511 *SIC* 5074 5075
A Y MCDONALD INDUSTRIES INC p 7
4800 Chavenelle Rd, Dubuque IA 52002
Tel (800) 292-2737
SIC 3432 3561 3494 5074 5075 5031
SMITH AND LOVELESS INC p 1333
14040 Santa Fe Trail Dr, Shawnee Mission KS 66215
Tel (913) 888-5201 *SIC* 3589 5074
VIEGA LLC p 1556
100 N Broadway Ave # 600, Wichita KS 67202
Tel (316) 425-7400 *SIC* 5074
AQUIONICS INC p 102
1455 Jamike Ave Ste 100, Erlanger KY 41018
Tel (859) 341-0710 *SIC* 5074
HARSHAW SERVICE INC p 664
12700 Plantside Dr, Louisville KY 40299
Tel (502) 499-7000 *SIC* 5075 1711 5074
PLUMBERS SUPPLY CO p 1156
1000 E Main St, Louisville KY 40206
Tel (502) 582-2261 *SIC* 5074 5085
LCR-M LIMITED PARTNERSHIP p 849
6232 Siegen Ln, Baton Rouge LA 70809
Tel (225) 292-9910 *SIC* 5074
EVERETT J PRESCOTT INC p 514
32 Prescott St Libby Hill, Gardiner ME 04345
Tel (207) 582-2006 *SIC* 5074
NORTHEASTERN SUPPLY INC p 1055
8323 Pulaski Hwy, Baltimore MD 21237
Tel (410) 574-0010 *SIC* 5074
CENTRAL WHOLESALERS INC p 281
13401 Konterra Dr, Laurel MD 20707
Tel (800) 935-2947
SIC 5074 5063 5087 5072 5211 1799
THOS SOMERVILLE CO p 1450
16155 Trade Zone Ave, Upper Marlboro MD 20774
Tel (301) 390-9575 *SIC* 5074 5075
SUPPLY NEW ENGLAND INC p 1407
123 East St, Attleboro MA 02703
Tel (508) 222-5555 *SIC* 5074
F W WEBB CO p 522
160 Middlesex Tpke, Bedford MA 01730
Tel (781) 272-6600 *SIC* 5074 5085 5075
PORTLAND GROUP INC p 1163
74 Salem Rd, Billerica MA 01821
Tel (978) 262-1444 *SIC* 5074
INDEPENDENT PIPE & SUPPLY BUSINESS TRUST p 736
6 Whitman Rd, Canton MA 02021
Tel (781) 828-8500 *SIC* 5074
UNITED PIPE & STEEL CORP p 1510
83 Turnpike Rd, Ipswich MA 01938
Tel (978) 356-9300 *SIC* 5074
PLUMBERS SUPPLY CO p 1156
429 Church St, New Bedford MA 02745
Tel (508) 985-4966 *SIC* 5074 5084 5082
EMERSON-SWAN INC p 492
300 Pond St Ste 1, Randolph MA 02368
Tel (781) 986-2000 *SIC* 5084 5074
ETNA DISTRIBUTORS LLC p 511
529 32nd St Se, Grand Rapids MI 49548
Tel (616) 245-4373 *SIC* 5074
BEHLER-YOUNG CO p 168
4900 Clyde Park Ave Sw, Wyoming MI 49509
Tel (616) 531-3400 *SIC* 5075 5051 5074
GOODIN CO p 624
2700 N 2nd St, Minneapolis MN 55411
Tel (612) 588-7811 *SIC* 5074 5075
SPS COMPANIES INC p 1362
6363 Highway 7, Minneapolis MN 55416
Tel (952) 929-1377 *SIC* 5074 5075 3498
J H LARSON ELECTRICAL CO p 771
10200 51st Ave N Ste B, Plymouth MN 55442
Tel (763) 545-1717 *SIC* 5063 5074 5075
▲ **HAWKINS INC** p 670
2381 Rosegate, Roseville MN 55113
Tel (612) 331-6910 *SIC* 5169 5074 2899
■ **ECOWATER SYSTEMS LLC** p 476
1890 Woodlane Dr, Saint Paul MN 55125
Tel (651) 731-7401 *SIC* 5074 3589
SOUTHERN PIPE & SUPPLY CO INC p 1350
4330 Highway 39 N, Meridian MS 39301
Tel (601) 693-2911 *SIC* 5074 1711 1623
2 M CO INC p 1
5249 Holiday Ave, Billings MT 59101
Tel (406) 245-1490
SIC 5084 5083 5074 5051
DUTTON-LAINSON CO p 463
451 W 2nd St, Hastings NE 68901
Tel (402) 463-6702
SIC 3531 5999 5063 5074
WESTERN NEVADA SUPPLY CO p 1599
950 S Rock Blvd, Sparks NV 89431
Tel (775) 359-5800 *SIC* 5074 5083
GRANITE GROUP WHOLESALERS LLC p 631
6 Storrs St, Concord NH 03301
Tel (603) 545-3345 *SIC* 5074 5075
GRANITE GROUP WHOLESALERS LLC p 631
6 Storrs St, Concord NH 03301
Tel (603) 224-1901 *SIC* 5075 5074
PIPELINE SUPPLY INC p 1151
100 Middlesex Ave Ste 1, Carteret NJ 07008
Tel (908) 436-1100 *SIC* 5074
HBC HOLDINGS LLC p 671
324a Half Acre Rd, Cranbury NJ 08512
Tel (609) 860-9990 *SIC* 5072 5087 5074

WORLD AND MAIN (CRANBURY) LLC p 1624
324a Half Acre Rd, Cranbury NJ 08512
Tel (609) 860-9990 *SIC* 5072 5087 5074
SIGMA CORP p 1321
700 Goldman Dr, Cream Ridge NJ 08514
Tel (609) 758-0800 *SIC* 5074 5199
FOREMOST GROUPS INC p 566
906 Murray Rd Ste 2, East Hanover NJ 07936
Tel (973) 428-0400 *SIC* 5074 5021
INDUSTRIAL CONTROLS DISTRIBUTORS LLC p 739
17 Christopher Way, Eatontown NJ 07724
Tel (732) 918-9000 *SIC* 5075 5074
GENERAL PLUMBING SUPPLY INC p 601
980 New Durham Rd, Edison NJ 08817
Tel (732) 248-1000 *SIC* 5075 5074
▲ **CCOM GROUP INC** p 270
275 Wagaraw Rd, Hawthorne NJ 07506
Tel (973) 427-8224 *SIC* 5074 5075
AARON AND CO INC p 8
30 Turner Pl, Piscataway NJ 08854
Tel (732) 752-8200 *SIC* 5074 5075
PETRA SYSTEMS INC p 1139
1 Cragwood Rd Ste 303, South Plainfield NJ 07080
Tel (908) 462-5200 *SIC* 5074 3671
BLACKMAN PLUMBING SUPPLY CO INC p 188
900 Sylvan Ave, Bayport NY 11705
Tel (631) 823-4300 *SIC* 5074 5075
A F SUPPLY CORP p 5
942 Lafayette Ave, Brooklyn NY 11221
Tel (212) 243-5400 *SIC* 5074
BRUCE SUPPLY CORP p 220
8805 18th Ave, Brooklyn NY 11214
Tel (718) 259-4900 *SIC* 5074
CENTRAL PURCHASING CORP p 280
205 Old Route 9, Fishkill NY 12524
Tel (845) 896-6291 *SIC* 5074 5075
OKIN-WALLACK CORP p 1079
65 S Columbus Ave, Freeport NY 11520
Tel (516) 379-0449 *SIC* 5074
DAVIS & WARSHOW INC p 416
5722 49th St, Maspeth NY 11378
Tel (718) 937-9500 *SIC* 5074
GAMECHANGE SOLAR LLC p 590
152 W 57th St Fl 17, New York NY 10019
Tel (212) 359-0200 *SIC* 5074
CAMBRIDGE PETROLEUM HOLDING INC p 244
31 S Plank Rd Unit 105, Newburgh NY 12550
Tel (516) 542-4900
SIC 5983 5541 5984 5172 5074
IRR SUPPLY CENTERS INC p 765
908 Niagara Falls Blvd # 125, North Tonawanda NY 14120
Tel (716) 692-1600 *SIC* 5074
WALLACE EANNACE ASSOCIATES INC p 1573
50 Newtown Rd, Plainview NY 11803
Tel (516) 454-9300 *SIC* 5074
V P SUPPLY CORP p 1538
3445 Winton Pl Ste 101, Rochester NY 14623
Tel (585) 272-0110 *SIC* 5074
SECURITY PLUMBING & HEATING SUPPLY CO p 1299
196 Maple Ave, Selkirk NY 12158
Tel (518) 767-2226 *SIC* 5074
BEST PLUMBING SUPPLY INC p 177
49 Route 138, Somers NY 10589
Tel (914) 232-2020 *SIC* 5074 5999
GREAT AMERICAN INDUSTRIES INC p 633
300 Plaza Dr, Vestal NY 13850
Tel (607) 729-9331
SIC 3086 5031 5074 3442 3069 5091
DILLON SUPPLY CO p 440
440 Civic Blvd, Raleigh NC 27610
Tel (919) 838-4200
SIC 5084 5085 5051 5074 5072
LONGLEY SUPPLY CO p 877
2018 Oleander Dr, Wilmington NC 28403
Tel (910) 762-7793 *SIC* 5074 5063 5075
FAMOUS DISTRIBUTION INC p 527
2620 Ridgewood Rd Ste 200, Akron OH 44313
Tel (330) 762-9621
SIC 5074 5075 5085 5023
FAMOUS ENTERPRISES INC p 527
2620 Ridgewood Rd Ste 200, Akron OH 44313
Tel (330) 762-9621
SIC 5075 5031 5074 7699
FAMOUS INDUSTRIES INC p 527
2620 Ridgewood Rd Ste 200, Akron OH 44313
Tel (330) 535-1811 *SIC* 5074 3444 5065
OATEY SUPPLY CHAIN SERVICES INC p 1072
20600 Emerald Pkwy, Cleveland OH 44135
Tel (216) 267-7100 *SIC* 5074
WAXMAN INDUSTRIES INC p 1584
24460 Aurora Rd, Cleveland OH 44146
Tel (440) 439-1830
SIC 5072 5074 3494 3491 3432
WOLFF BROS SUPPLY INC p 1621
6078 Wolff Rd, Medina OH 44256
Tel (330) 725-3451 *SIC* 5063 5074 5075
NOLAND CO p 1046
3110 Kettering Blvd, Moraine OH 45439
Tel (937) 396-7980
SIC 5074 5075 5063 5085
WINSUPPLY INC p 1617
3110 Kettering Blvd, Moraine OH 45439
Tel (937) 294-5331 *SIC* 1542 5074 5085
KINETICO INC p 820
10845 Kinsman Rd, Newbury OH 44065
Tel (440) 564-9111 *SIC* 3589 5074
MANSFIELD PLUMBING PRODUCTS LLC p 903
150 E 1st St, Perrysville OH 44864
Tel (419) 938-5211
SIC 3261 3463 3088 3431 3432 5074
TRUMBULL INDUSTRIES INC p 1487
400 Dietz Rd Ne, Warren OH 44483
Tel (330) 393-6624 *SIC* 5074 5085 5064

LOCKE SUPPLY CO p 873
1300 Se 82nd St, Oklahoma City OK 73149
Tel (405) 635-3230
SIC 5063 5074 5075 1711
CONSOLIDATED SUPPLY CO p 360
7337 Sw Kable Ln, Tigard OR 97224
Tel (503) 620-7050 *SIC* 5074 5085
HAJOCA CORP p 653
127 Coulter Ave, Ardmore PA 19003
Tel (610) 649-1430 *SIC* 5074
DEACON INDUSTRIAL SUPPLY CO INC p 419
1510 Gehman Rd, Harleysville PA 19438
Tel (215) 256-1715 *SIC* 5074 5085
WOLSELEY INVESTMENTS INC p 1621
1904 Ligonier St, Latrobe PA 15650
Tel (757) 874-7795
SIC 5074 5085 5075 5064 5211 5031
L/B WATER SERVICE INC p 835
540 S High St, Selinsgrove PA 17870
Tel (570) 374-2355 *SIC* 5074
GATEWAY SUPPLY CO INC p 594
1312 Hamrick St, Columbia SC 29201
Tel (803) 771-7160 *SIC* 5075 5074
WOLVERINE BRASS INC p 1621
2951 E Highway 501, Conway SC 29526
Tel (843) 347-3121 *SIC* 5074 3432 3431
C C DICKSON CO p 232
456 Lakeshore Pkwy, Rock Hill SC 29730
Tel (803) 980-8000 *SIC* 5075 5078 5074
CREGGER CO INC p 391
637 N 12th St, West Columbia SC 29169
Tel (803) 217-0710 *SIC* 5074 5064
■ **LOCHINVAR LLC** p 873
300 Maddox Simpson Pkwy, Lebanon TN 37090
Tel (615) 889-8900 *SIC* 3639 3443 5074
WALLACE HARDWARE CO INC p 1573
5050 S Davy Crockett Pkwy, Morristown TN 37813
Tel (423) 586-5650
SIC 5072 5074 5085 5083 5211
KENNY PIPE & SUPPLY INC p 811
811 Cowan St, Nashville TN 37207
Tel (615) 242-5909 *SIC* 5074
FRANKE KITCHEN SYSTEMS LLC p 574
800 Aviation Pkwy, Smyrna TN 37167
Tel (800) 637-6485 *SIC* 3431 5074
RENTECH BOILER SYSTEMS INC p 1224
5025 E Business 20, Abilene TX 79601
Tel (325) 672-3400 *SIC* 5074
COBURN SUPPLY CO INC p 333
390 Park St Ste 100, Beaumont TX 77701
Tel (409) 838-6363
SIC 5063 5064 5072 5074 5075 5078
HUGH M CUNNINGHAM INC p 717
2029 Westgate Dr Ste 120, Carrollton TX 75006
Tel (972) 888-3833
SIC 5074 5085 5083 5199
CLEAVER-BROOKS SALES AND SERVICE INC p 325
1956 Singleton Blvd, Dallas TX 75212
Tel (214) 637-0020 *SIC* 5074 7699 1711
NATIONAL WHOLESALE SUPPLY INC p 1017
1972 Cal Crossing Rd, Dallas TX 75220
Tel (972) 331-7770 *SIC* 5074
MORRISON SUPPLY CO p 990
311 E Vickery Blvd, Fort Worth TX 76104
Tel (817) 336-0451 *SIC* 5074
MORSCO INC p 990
100 E 15th St Ste 200, Fort Worth TX 76102
Tel (877) 709-2227 *SIC* 5074 1711
PREFERRED PUMP & EQUIPMENT LP p 1169
2201 Scott Ave Ste 100, Fort Worth TX 76103
Tel (817) 536-9800
SIC 5084 5083 5074 3533 5082
SUPPLY SOURCE DYNAMICS INC p 1407
311 E Vickery Blvd, Fort Worth TX 76104
Tel (817) 336-0451 *SIC* 5074
HANDY HARDWARE WHOLESALE INC p 657
8300 Tewantin Dr, Houston TX 77061
Tel (713) 644-1495
SIC 5072 5074 5063 5031 5198
BUTTERY CO LLP p 230
201 W Main St, Llano TX 78643
Tel (325) 247-4141
SIC 5072 5074 5063 5091 5211 5251
GICON PUMPS & EQUIPMENT INC p 611
1001 Texas Ave, Lubbock TX 79401
Tel (806) 401-8287 *SIC* 5084 5074 5039
SERVICE EXPERTS LLC p 1307
3820 American Dr Ste 200, Plano TX 75075
Tel (972) 231-5468
SIC 1711 5074 5075 8742
SERVICE EXPERTS HEATING & AIR CONDITIONING LLC p 1307
2140 Lake Park Blvd, Richardson TX 75080
Tel (972) 535-3800
SIC 1711 5074 5075 8742
HATFIELD AND CO INC p 668
2475 Discovery Blvd, Rockwall TX 75032
Tel (972) 288-7625 *SIC* 5084 3677 5074
WESTLINK TRADING LLC p 1601
17926 Highway 3, Webster TX 77598
Tel (832) 295-9778
SIC 5032 5099 5074 5051 5031
313 ACQUISITION LLC p 2
3301 N Thanksgiving Way, Lehi UT 84043
Tel (877) 404-4129 *SIC* 5074
▲ **VIVINT SOLAR INC** p 1563
1850 W Ashton Blvd, Lehi UT 84043
Tel (877) 404-4129 *SIC* 5074
GREAT WESTERN SUPPLY INC p 635
2626 Industrial Dr, Ogden UT 84401
Tel (801) 621-5412
SIC 5074 5051 5999 1711
APX PARENT HOLDCO INC p 101
4931 N 300 W, Provo UT 84604
Tel (801) 377-9111
SIC 6719 3822 1711 8711 5065 5074

STANDARD PLUMBING SUPPLY CO INC p 1376
9150 S 300W Bldg 5, Sandy UT 84070
Tel (801) 255-7145 SIC 5074

MICHAEL & SON SERVICES INC p 959
5740 General Wash Dr, Alexandria VA 22312
Tel (703) 658-3998 SIC 1521 1731 5074

HANDY CO N B p 657
65 10th St, Lynchburg VA 24504
Tel (434) 847-4495 SIC 5051 5074 5075

FERGUSON ENTERPRISES INC p 538
12500 Jefferson Ave, Newport News VA 23602
Tel (757) 874-7795
SIC 5074 5085 5075 5064

GENSCO INC p 604
4402 20th St E, Fife WA 98424
Tel (253) 620-8203 SIC 5074 3444

PUGET SOUND PIPE AND SUPPLY CO p 1191
7816 S 202nd St, Kent WA 98032
Tel (206) 682-9350 SIC 5074 5085

WASHINGTON ENERGY SERVICES CO p 1578
3909 196th St Sw, Lynnwood WA 98036
Tel (800) 398-4663 SIC 5074 1711 8711

KELLER SUPPLY CO p 808
3209 17th Ave W, Seattle WA 98119
Tel (206) 285-3300 SIC 5074

CRANE ENGINEERING SALES INC p 389
707 Ford St, Kimberly WI 54136
Tel (920) 733-4425 SIC 5084 5085 5074

UNITED P&H SUPPLY CO p 1510
9947 W Carmen Ave, Milwaukee WI 53225
Tel (414) 393-6600
SIC 5085 5074 3312 3463

FIRST SUPPLY LLC p 549
6800 Gisholt Dr, Monona WI 53713
Tel (608) 222-7799
SIC 5074 5078 5075 5712 5713

REINDERS INC p 1221
W227n6225 Sussex Rd, Sussex WI 53089
Tel (262) 786-3300
SIC 5191 5169 5074 5999 5083

SIC 5075 Heating & Air Conditioning Eqpt & Splys Wholesale

WITTICHEN SUPPLY CO p 1619
2912 3rd Ave N, Birmingham AL 35203
Tel (205) 251-8500 SIC 5078 5075

JAVINE VENTURES INC p 779
2851 W Kathleen Rd, Phoenix AZ 85053
Tel (602) 944-3330 SIC 5075 1731

GEARY PACIFIC CORP p 597
1360 N Hancock St, Anaheim CA 92807
Tel (714) 279-2950 SIC 5075

AIRTREATMENT CORP p 39
640 N Puente St, Brea CA 92821
Tel (909) 869-7975 SIC 5075

NORMAN S WRIGHT MECHANICAL EQUIPMENT CORP p 1049
99 S Hill Dr Ste A, Brisbane CA 94005
Tel (415) 467-7600 SIC 5075

GREE USA INC p 636
20035 E Walnut Dr N, City Of Industry CA 91789
Tel (909) 718-0478 SIC 5075

US AIRCONDITIONING DISTRIBUTORS INC p 1530
16900 Chestnut St, City Of Industry CA 91748
Tel (626) 854-4500 SIC 5075 1711

HKF INC p 697
5983 Smithway St, Commerce CA 90040
Tel (323) 225-1318
SIC 5075 3873 5064 3567 3643

SLAKEY BROTHERS INC p 1331
2215 Kausen Dr Ste 1, Elk Grove CA 95758
Tel (916) 478-2000 SIC 5075 5074 5078

MATERIAL SUPPLY INC p 919
11700 Industry Ave, Fontana CA 92337
Tel (951) 727-2200
SIC 3444 5075 7623 1711

REFRIGERATION SUPPLIES DISTRIBUTOR p 1218
26021 Atlantic Ocean Dr, Lake Forest CA 92630
Tel (949) 380-7878 SIC 5078 5075

DENSO PRODUCTS AND SERVICES AMERICAS INC p 429
3900 Via Oro Ave, Long Beach CA 90810
Tel (310) 834-6352
SIC 5013 7361 5075 3714

DMG CORP p 446
1110 W Taft Ave Ste A, Orange CA 92865
Tel (562) 692-1277 SIC 5075 5078

ALLIED REFRIGERATION INC p 56
2300 E 28th St, Signal Hill CA 90755
Tel (562) 595-5301 SIC 5075 5078

■ ADA-ES INC p 21
9135 Ridgeline Blvd # 200, Highlands Ranch CO 80129
Tel (303) 734-1727 SIC 5075

LONG BUILDING TECHNOLOGIES INC p 876
5001 S Zuni St, Littleton CO 80120
Tel (303) 975-2100 SIC 5075 1711

BELL PUMP SERVICE CO p 170
29 Lafayette St, Hartford CT 06106
Tel (860) 525-6678 SIC 5075 5078 5074

■ GEMAIRE DISTRIBUTORS LLC p 598
2151 W Hillsboro Blvd # 400, Deerfield Beach FL 33442
Tel (954) 246-2665 SIC 5075

HUGHES SUPPLY INC p 717
2920 Ford St, Fort Myers FL 33916
Tel (239) 334-2205
SIC 5063 5074 5075 5085 1711

■ BAKER DISTRIBUTING CO LLC p 146
14610 Breakers Dr Ste 100, Jacksonville FL 32258
Tel (904) 407-4500 SIC 5075 5078

WARE GROUP INC p 1575
11710 Central Pkwy, Jacksonville FL 32224
Tel (904) 641-2282 SIC 5075

WARE GROUP LLC p 1575
11710 Central Pkwy, Jacksonville FL 32224
Tel (904) 641-2282 SIC 5075

REFRICENTER OF MIAMI INC p 1218
7101 Nw 43rd St, Miami FL 33166
Tel (305) 477-8880 SIC 5075 5078

TROPIC SUPPLY INC p 1484
151 Ne 179th St, Miami FL 33162
Tel (305) 652-7717 SIC 5078 5075

▲ WATSCO INC p 1583
2665 S Byshr Dr Ste 901, Miami FL 33133
Tel (305) 714-4100 SIC 5075

GOODMAN DISTRIBUTION INC p 624
1426 Ne 8th Ave, Ocala FL 34470
Tel (352) 620-2727 SIC 5075

■ YOUR OTHER WAREHOUSE LLC p 1639
2455 Paces Ferry Rd Se B8, Atlanta GA 30339
Tel (770) 433-8211 SIC 5074 5075

MINGLEDORFFS INC p 973
6675 Jones Mill Ct, Norcross GA 30092
Tel (770) 446-6311 SIC 5075

TOYOTA INDUSTRIES COMPRESSOR PARTS AMERICA CO p 1466
500 Valentine Indus Pkwy, Pendergrass GA 30567
Tel (706) 693-7200 SIC 5075

NEUCO INC p 1028
5101 Thatcher Rd, Downers Grove IL 60515
Tel (630) 960-3800 SIC 5075

MCMASTER-CARR SUPPLY CO p 932
600 N County Line Rd, Elmhurst IL 60126
Tel (630) 834-9600 SIC 5085 5075

▲ WW GRAINGER INC p 1628
100 Grainger Pkwy, Lake Forest IL 60045
Tel (847) 535-1000
SIC 5063 5084 5075 5085 5072

LEXINGTON CORPORATE ENTERPRISES INC p 859
17725 Volbrecht Rd, Lansing IL 60438
Tel (708) 418-0700 SIC 5075 1711

TEMPERATURE EQUIPMENT CORP p 1436
17725 Volbrecht Rd Ste 1, Lansing IL 60438
Tel (708) 418-0900 SIC 5075

CONNOR CO p 358
2800 Ne Adams St, Peoria IL 61603
Tel (309) 693-7229 SIC 5074 5075

KOCH AIR LLC p 825
1900 W Lloyd Expy, Evansville IN 47712
Tel (812) 962-5200 SIC 5075

KOCH ENTERPRISES INC p 825
14 S 11th Ave, Evansville IN 47712
Tel (812) 465-9800
SIC 3363 5075 3559 5084 2891 3069

KOCH HVAC DISTRIBUTION INC p 825
1900 W Lloyd Expy, Evansville IN 47712
Tel (812) 962-5200 SIC 5075

MOBILE CLIMATE CONTROL CORP p 980
17103 State Road 4, Goshen IN 46528
Tel (574) 534-1516 SIC 5075 3714

LEE SUPPLY CORP p 852
6610 Guion Rd, Indianapolis IN 46268
Tel (317) 290-2500
SIC 5074 5075 5064 5085 5031

G W BERKHEIMER CO INC p 587
6000 Southport Rd, Portage IN 46368
Tel (219) 764-5200 SIC 5075 5078

PLUMB SUPPLY CO LLC p 1156
1622 Ne 51st Ave, Des Moines IA 50313
Tel (515) 262-9511 SIC 5074 5075

A Y MCDONALD INDUSTRIES INC p 7
4800 Chavenelle Rd, Dubuque IA 52002
Tel (800) 292-2737
SIC 3432 3561 3494 5074 5075 5031

AIRTEX MANUFACTURING LLLP p 40
32050 W 83rd St, De Soto KS 66018
Tel (913) 583-3181
SIC 3585 5075 3564 3433

OCONNOR CO INC p 1074
16910 W 116th St, Lenexa KS 66219
Tel (913) 894-8788 SIC 5075

CORKEN STEEL PRODUCTS CO p 370
7920 Kentucky Dr, Florence KY 41042
Tel (859) 291-4664
SIC 5075 3444 5051 8742 6411

AAF-MCQUAY GROUP INC p 8
9920 Corporate Campus Dr # 2200, Louisville KY 40223
Tel (502) 637-0111
SIC 5075 3585 3564 7623

HARSHAW SERVICE INC p 664
12700 Plantside Dr, Louisville KY 40299
Tel (502) 499-7000 SIC 5075 1711 5074

SOLAR SUPPLY INC p 1338
1212 12th St, Lake Charles LA 70601
Tel (337) 310-1000 SIC 5075 5078

LYON CONKLIN & CO INC p 888
4501 Hollins Ferry Rd # 140, Baltimore MD 21227
Tel (410) 540-4880 SIC 5075 5051

BOLAND TRANE SERVICES INC p 198
30 W Watkins Mill Rd # 300, Gaithersburg MD 20878
Tel (240) 306-3000 SIC 5075

R E MICHEL CO LLC p 1202
1 Re Michel Dr, Glen Burnie MD 21060
Tel (410) 760-4000 SIC 5075 5078

AIRECO SUPPLY INC p 40
8860 Gorman Rd, Laurel MD 20723
Tel (301) 953-8800 SIC 5075 5078

THOS SOMERVILLE CO p 1450
16155 Trade Zone Ave, Upper Marlboro MD 20774
Tel (301) 390-9575 SIC 5074 5075

F W WEBB CO p 522
160 Middlesex Tpke, Bedford MA 01730
Tel (781) 272-6600 SIC 5074 5085 5075

WILLIAMS DISTRIBUTING CO p 1611
658 Richmond St Nw, Grand Rapids MI 49504
Tel (616) 771-0505 SIC 5075

BEHLER-YOUNG CO p 168
4900 Clyde Park Ave Sw, Wyoming MI 49509
Tel (616) 531-3400 SIC 5075 5051 5074

DAIKIN APPLIED AMERICAS INC p 408
13600 Industrial Pk Blvd, Minneapolis MN 55441
Tel (763) 553-5330 SIC 5075 3585

GOODIN CO p 624
2700 N 2nd St, Minneapolis MN 55411
Tel (612) 588-7811 SIC 5074 5075

SPS COMPANIES INC p 1362
6363 Highway 7, Minneapolis MN 55416
Tel (952) 929-1377 SIC 5074 5075 3498

J H LARSON ELECTRICAL CO p 771
10200 51st Ave N Ste B, Plymouth MN 55442
Tel (763) 545-1717 SIC 5063 5074 5075

NOOTER/ERIKSEN INC p 1047
1509 Ocello Dr, Fenton MO 63026
Tel (636) 651-1000 SIC 5075

CRESCENT PARTS & EQUIPMENT CO INC p 391
5121 Manchester Ave, Saint Louis MO 63110
Tel (314) 647-5511 SIC 5075

GRANITE GROUP WHOLESALERS LLC p 631
6 Storrs St, Concord NH 03301
Tel (603) 224-1901 SIC 5075 5074

GRANITE GROUP WHOLESALERS LLC p 631
6 Storrs St, Concord NH 03301
Tel (603) 545-3345 SIC 5074 5075

BOSCH THERMOTECHNOLOGY CORP p 202
50 Wentworth Ave, Londonderry NH 03053
Tel (603) 552-1100 SIC 5075

PASSAIC METAL & BUILDING SUPPLIES CO p 1119
5 Central Ave Ste 1, Clifton NJ 07011
Tel (973) 546-9000
SIC 5033 5031 5051 5075 3444 3296

INDUSTRIAL CONTROLS DISTRIBUTORS LLC p 739
17 Christopher Way, Eatontown NJ 07724
Tel (732) 918-9000 SIC 5075 5074

GENERAL PLUMBING SUPPLY INC p 601
980 New Durham Rd, Edison NJ 08817
Tel (732) 248-1000 SIC 5075 5074

▲ CCOM GROUP INC p 270
275 Wagaraw Rd, Hawthorne NJ 07506
Tel (973) 427-8224 SIC 5074 5075

AARON AND CO INC p 8
30 Turner Pl, Piscataway NJ 08854
Tel (732) 752-8200 SIC 5074 5075

BLACKMAN PLUMBING SUPPLY CO INC p 188
900 Sylvan Ave, Bayport NY 11705
Tel (631) 823-4300 SIC 5074 5075

MEIER SUPPLY CO INC p 940
275 Broome Corporate Pkwy, Conklin NY 13748
Tel (607) 797-7700 SIC 5075 5078

CENTRAL PURCHASING CORP p 280
205 Old Route 9, Fishkill NY 12524
Tel (845) 896-6291 SIC 5074 5075

TOSHIBA AMERICA INC p 1462
1251 Ave Of Ameri Ste 4100, New York NY 10020
Tel (212) 596-0600
SIC 3651 3631 5064 5075 3571 3661

■ CARRIER ENTERPRISE LLC p 261
4300 Golf Acres Dr, Charlotte NC 28208
Tel (704) 394-7311 SIC 5075

■ EAST COAST METAL DISTRIBUTORS LLC p 470
1313 S Briggs Ave, Durham NC 27703
Tel (919) 598-5030 SIC 5075

BRADY SALES AND SERVICE INC p 207
1915 N Church St, Greensboro NC 27405
Tel (336) 378-0670 SIC 5075

BRADY TRANE SERVICE INC p 207
1915 N Church St, Greensboro NC 27405
Tel (919) 781-0458 SIC 5075 1711 7623

HOFFMAN & HOFFMAN INC p 699
3816 Patterson St, Greensboro NC 27407
Tel (336) 292-8777 SIC 5075

JAMES M PLEASANTS CO INC p 776
603 Diamond Hill Ct, Greensboro NC 27406
Tel (336) 275-3152
SIC 5075 3585 3561 3494

LONGLEY SUPPLY CO p 877
2018 Oleander Dr, Wilmington NC 28403
Tel (910) 762-7793 SIC 5074 5063 5075

FAMOUS DISTRIBUTION INC p 527
2620 Ridgewood Rd Ste 200, Akron OH 44313
Tel (330) 762-9621
SIC 5074 5075 5085 5023

FAMOUS ENTERPRISES INC p 527
2620 Ridgewood Rd Ste 200, Akron OH 44313
Tel (330) 762-9621
SIC 5075 5031 5074 7699

HABEGGER CORP p 651
4995 Winton Rd, Cincinnati OH 45232
Tel (513) 853-6644 SIC 5075

STYLE CREST ENTERPRISES INC p 1395
2450 Enterprise St, Fremont OH 43420
Tel (419) 355-8586 SIC 3089 5075

STYLE CREST INC p 1395
2450 Enterprise St, Fremont OH 43420
Tel (419) 332-7369 SIC 3089 5075

WOLFF BROS SUPPLY INC p 1621
6078 Wolff Rd, Medina OH 44256
Tel (330) 725-3451 SIC 5063 5074 5075

NOLAND CO p 1046
3110 Kettering Blvd, Moraine OH 45439
Tel (937) 396-7980
SIC 5074 5075 5063 5085

GARDINER SERVICE CO p 592
31200 Bainbridge Rd Ste 1, Solon OH 44139
Tel (440) 349-5588 SIC 5075 1711 7623

NORMAN YORK INTERNATIONAL p 1049
5005 York Dr, Norman OK 73069
Tel (405) 364-4040 SIC 5075

LOCKE SUPPLY CO p 873
1300 Se 82nd St, Oklahoma City OK 73149
Tel (405) 635-3230
SIC 5063 5074 5075 1711

JOHNSTONE SUPPLY INC p 791
11632 Ne Ainsworth Cir, Portland OR 97220
Tel (503) 256-3663
SIC 5075 5085 5063 5064

AIREFCO INC p 40
18755 Sw Teton Ave, Tualatin OR 97062
Tel (503) 692-3210 SIC 5075

NATIONAL REFRIGERATION & AIR CONDITIONING PRODUCTS INC p 1015
539 Dunksferry Rd, Bensalem PA 19020
Tel (215) 244-1400 SIC 3585 5075

PEIRCE-PHELPS INC p 1128
516 Township Line Rd, Blue Bell PA 19422
Tel (215) 879-7000 SIC 5075

WOLSELEY INVESTMENTS INC p 1621
1904 Ligonier St, Latrobe PA 15650
Tel (757) 874-7795
SIC 5074 5085 5075 5064 5211 5031

HVAC DISTRIBUTORS INC p 722
2 Old Market St, Mount Joy PA 17552
Tel (717) 653-6674 SIC 5075

CLIMATIC CORP p 326
1074 Pinnacle Point Dr, Columbia SC 29223
Tel (803) 765-2595 SIC 5075

GATEWAY SUPPLY CO INC p 594
1312 Hamrick St, Columbia SC 29201
Tel (803) 771-7160 SIC 5075 5074

C C DICKSON CO p 232
456 Lakeshore Pkwy, Rock Hill SC 29730
Tel (803) 980-8000 SIC 5075 5078 5074

■ ALLIED AIR ENTERPRISES LLC p 56
215 Metropolitan Dr, West Columbia SC 29170
Tel (803) 738-4000 SIC 3585 3433 5075

OCONNOR CO p 1074
4909 N Lewis Ave, Sioux Falls SD 57104
Tel (605) 336-0333 SIC 5075

KELE INC p 808
3300 Brother Blvd, Memphis TN 38133
Tel (901) 382-6084 SIC 5075 3822 3829

BLEVINS INC p 189
421 Hart Ln, Nashville TN 37216
Tel (615) 226-6453 SIC 5075

COBURN SUPPLY CO INC p 333
390 Park St Ste 100, Beaumont TX 77701
Tel (409) 838-6363
SIC 5063 5064 5072 5074 5075 5078

■ OHMSTEDE LTD p 1078
895 N Main St, Beaumont TX 77701
Tel (409) 833-6375 SIC 5075 3443

GUNDER & ASSOCIATES INC p 647
1215 W Crosby Rd Ste 206, Carrollton TX 75006
Tel (972) 620-2801 SIC 5075

STANDARD SUPPLY AND DISTRIBUTING CO INC p 1376
1431 Regal Row, Dallas TX 75247
Tel (214) 630-7800 SIC 5075

TIMBERLAKE & DICKSON INC p 1454
3520 W Miller Rd Ste 110, Garland TX 75041
Tel (214) 349-2320 SIC 5075

HEAT TRANSFER SOLUTIONS INC p 679
3350 Yale St, Houston TX 77018
Tel (832) 328-1010 SIC 5075

HTI LTD p 715
10555 Westpark Dr, Houston TX 77042
Tel (713) 266-3900 SIC 5075

JACKSON SUPPLY CO p 774
6655 Roxburgh Dr Ste 100, Houston TX 77041
Tel (713) 849-5865 SIC 5075

JOHNSON SUPPLY AND EQUIPMENT CORP p 791
10151 Stella Link Rd, Houston TX 77025
Tel (713) 830-2300 SIC 5075

AUTO AIR EXPORT INC p 133
1401 Valley View Ln # 100, Irving TX 75061
Tel (972) 812-7000 SIC 5075 3585 5531

TEXAS AIR SYSTEMS INC p 1442
6029 Campus Circle Dr W # 100, Irving TX 75063
Tel (972) 570-4700 SIC 5075 1711

ROBERT MADDEN INDUSTRIES LTD p 1241
6021 43rd St, Lubbock TX 79407
Tel (806) 797-4251 SIC 5075

SERVICE EXPERTS LLC p 1307
3820 American Dr Ste 200, Plano TX 75075
Tel (972) 231-5468
SIC 1711 5074 5075 8742

■ LENNOX INDUSTRIES INC p 855
2100 Lake Park Blvd, Richardson TX 75080
Tel (972) 497-5000 SIC 5075

SERVICE EXPERTS HEATING & AIR CONDITIONING LLC p 1307
2140 Lake Park Blvd, Richardson TX 75080
Tel (972) 535-3800
SIC 1711 5074 5075 8742

INSCO DISTRIBUTING INC p 745
12501 Network Blvd, San Antonio TX 78249
Tel (210) 690-8400 SIC 5078 5075

HANDY CO N B p 657
65 10th St, Lynchburg VA 24504
Tel (434) 847-4495 SIC 5051 5074 5075

FERGUSON ENTERPRISES INC p 538
12500 Jefferson Ave, Newport News VA 23602
Tel (757) 874-7795
SIC 5074 5085 5075 5064

RESEARCH PRODUCTS CORP p 1226
1015 E Washington Ave, Madison WI 53703
Tel (608) 257-8801 SIC 5075 3564 3569

FIRST SUPPLY LLC p 549
6800 Gisholt Dr, Monona WI 53713
Tel (608) 222-7799
SIC 5074 5078 5075 5712 5713

GUSTAVE A LARSON CO p 648
W233n2869 Roundy Cir W, Pewaukee WI 53072
Tel (262) 542-0200
SIC 5075 5078 5084 5046

SIC 5078 Refrigeration Eqpt & Splys Wholesale

WITTICHEN SUPPLY CO p 1619
2912 3rd Ave N, Birmingham AL 35203
Tel (205) 251-8500 SIC 5078 5075

KITCHELL CORP p 822
1707 E Highland Ave # 100, Phoenix AZ 85016
Tel (602) 264-4411
SIC 1542 1541 1521 8711 5078 6552

SLAKEY BROTHERS INC p 1331
2215 Kausen Dr Ste 1, Elk Grove CA 95758
Tel (916) 478-2000 SIC 5075 5074 5078

REFRIGERATION SUPPLIES DISTRIBUTOR p 1218
26021 Atlantic Ocean Dr, Lake Forest CA 92630
Tel (949) 380-7878 SIC 5078 5075

DMG CORP p 446
1110 W Taft Ave Ste A, Orange CA 92865
Tel (562) 692-1277 SIC 5075 5078

ALLIED REFRIGERATION INC p 56
2300 E 28th St, Signal Hill CA 90755
Tel (562) 595-5301 SIC 5075 5078

BELL PUMP SERVICE CO p 170
29 Lafayette St, Hartford CT 06106
Tel (860) 525-6678 SIC 5075 5078 5074

■ **BAKER DISTRIBUTING CO LLC** p 146
14610 Breakers Dr Ste 100, Jacksonville FL 32258
Tel (904) 407-4500 SIC 5075 5078

REFRICENTER OF MIAMI INC p 1218
7101 Nw 43rd St, Miami FL 33166
Tel (305) 477-8880 SIC 5075 5078

TROPIC SUPPLY INC p 1484
151 Ne 179th St, Miami FL 33162
Tel (305) 652-7717 SIC 5078 5075

HOSHIZAKI AMERICA INC p 708
618 Highway 74 S, Peachtree City GA 30269
Tel (770) 487-2331 SIC 3585 5078

FIRST CALL JEWEL INC p 545
1410 Hollipark Dr, Idaho Falls ID 83401
Tel (208) 522-7777
SIC 1731 1711 5078 5063

ILLINOIS AUTO ELECTRIC CO p 732
700 Enterprise St, Aurora IL 60504
Tel (630) 862-3300
SIC 5084 5013 5083 5078 7699 3519

WAGNER-MEINERT LLC p 1571
7617 Freedom Way, Fort Wayne IN 46818
Tel (260) 489-7555 SIC 5078 1711 1799

G W BERKHEIMER CO INC p 587
6000 Southport Rd, Portage IN 46368
Tel (219) 764-5200 SIC 5075 5078

CENTRAL STATES THERMO KING INC p 280
7200 W 132nd St Ste 270, Overland Park KS 66213
Tel (888) 566-5743 SIC 5078 7623 5084

SOLAR SUPPLY INC p 1338
1212 12th St, Lake Charles LA 70601
Tel (337) 310-1000 SIC 5075 5078

R E MICHEL CO LLC p 1202
1 Re Michel Dr, Glen Burnie MD 21060
Tel (410) 760-4000 SIC 5075 5078

AIRECO SUPPLY INC p 40
8860 Gorman Rd, Laurel MD 20723
Tel (301) 953-8800 SIC 5075 5078

STAFFORD-SMITH INC p 1374
3414 S Burdick St, Kalamazoo MI 49001
Tel (269) 343-1240 SIC 5046 5078

■ **3 WIRE GROUP INC** p 2
101 Broadway St W Ste 300, Osseo MN 55369
Tel (763) 488-3000 SIC 5078

MEIER SUPPLY CO INC p 940
275 Broome Corporate Pkwy, Conklin NY 13748
Tel (607) 797-7700 SIC 5075 5078

ABCO REFRIGERATION SUPPLY CORP p 10
4970 31st St, Long Island City NY 11101
Tel (718) 937-9000 SIC 5078

BEVERAGE-AIR CORP p 178
3779 Champion Blvd, Winston Salem NC 27105
Tel (336) 245-6400 SIC 5078

QUENCH USA INC p 1198
780 5th Ave Ste 200, King Of Prussia PA 19406
Tel (888) 554-2782 SIC 5078

C C DICKSON CO p 232
456 Lakeshore Pkwy, Rock Hill SC 29730
Tel (803) 980-8000 SIC 5075 5078 5074

COBURN SUPPLY CO INC p 333
390 Park St Ste 100, Beaumont TX 77701
Tel (409) 838-6363
SIC 5063 5064 5072 5074 5075 5078

STEWART & STEVENSON CAPITAL CORP p 1388
601 W 38th St, Houston TX 77018
Tel (713) 868-7700
SIC 5084 5013 5078 5082 3711 3537

INSCO DISTRIBUTING INC p 745
12501 Network Blvd, San Antonio TX 78249
Tel (210) 690-8400 SIC 5078 5075

SOUTHWEST TEXAS EQUIPMENT DISTRIBUTORS INC p 1352
1126 S Saint Marys St, San Antonio TX 78210
Tel (210) 354-0691 SIC 5078

■ **VILTER MANUFACTURING LLC** p 1557
5555 S Packard Ave, Cudahy WI 53110
Tel (414) 744-0111 SIC 5078

FIRST SUPPLY LLC p 549
6800 Gisholt Dr, Monona WI 53713
Tel (608) 222-7799
SIC 5074 5078 5075 5712 5713

GUSTAVE A LARSON CO p 648
W233n2869 Roundy Cir W, Pewaukee WI 53072
Tel (262) 542-0200
SIC 5075 5078 5084 5046

SIC 5082 Construction & Mining Mach & Eqpt Wholesale

C & C HOLDING INC p 231
2238 Pinson Valley Pkwy, Birmingham AL 35217
Tel (205) 841-6666 SIC 5082 1629 5084

COWIN EQUIPMENT CO INC p 385
2238 Pinson Valley Pkwy, Birmingham AL 35217
Tel (205) 841-6666 SIC 5082

THOMPSON TRACTOR CO INC p 1449
2258 Pinson Valley Pkwy, Birmingham AL 35217
Tel (334) 215-5000 SIC 5082 5084 5085

TRACTOR & EQUIPMENT CO INC p 1468
5336 Airport Hwy, Birmingham AL 35212
Tel (205) 591-2131 SIC 5082

EMPIRE SOUTHWEST LLC p 493
1725 S Country Club Dr, Mesa AZ 85210
Tel (480) 633-4000 SIC 5082 7353 7699

WHITEMAN FAMILY CORP p 1606
1725 S Country Club Dr, Mesa AZ 85210
Tel (480) 633-4413
SIC 5082 5083 7353 7699 7359 5012

ROAD MACHINERY LLC p 1240
4710 E Elwood St Ste 6, Phoenix AZ 85040
Tel (602) 256-5128
SIC 5082 7359 7699 7353 7629

HUGG AND HALL EQUIPMENT CO p 717
7201 Scott Hamilton Dr, Little Rock AR 72209
Tel (501) 562-1262
SIC 5084 5082 7353 7699 5083 3531

JA RIGGS TRACTOR CO p 773
9125 Interstate 30, Little Rock AR 72209
Tel (501) 570-3100 SIC 5082 5511

GREENWAY EQUIPMENT INC p 638
412 S Van Buren, Weiner AR 72479
Tel (870) 684-7740 SIC 5999 5082

PACIFIC PROCESS SYSTEMS INC p 1105
7401 Rosedale Hwy, Bakersfield CA 93308
Tel (661) 321-9681 SIC 1389 7353 5082

MULTIQUIP INC p 1000
18910 Wilmington Ave, Carson CA 90746
Tel (310) 537-3700 SIC 5063 5082 3645

M BRADY & ASSOCIATES p 889
9753 Independence Ave, Chatsworth CA 91311
Tel (818) 700-8813 SIC 5082

QUINN CO p 1200
10006 Rose Hills Rd, City Of Industry CA 90601
Tel (562) 463-4000
SIC 5082 5083 5084 7353

QUINN GROUP INC p 1200
10006 Rose Hills Rd, City Of Industry CA 90601
Tel (562) 463-4000
SIC 5084 5082 7353 7359

QUINN SHEPHERD MACHINERY p 1200
10006 Rose Hills Rd, City Of Industry CA 90601
Tel (562) 463-6000 SIC 5082 5084

VALLEY POWER SYSTEMS INC p 1541
425 S Hacienda Blvd, City Of Industry CA 91745
Tel (626) 333-1243 SIC 3519 5082

HOC HOLDINGS INC p 699
7310 Pacific Ave, Pleasant Grove CA 95668
Tel (916) 921-8950
SIC 5082 5084 5083 7359

HOLT OF CALIFORNIA p 702
7310 Pacific Ave, Pleasant Grove CA 95668
Tel (916) 991-8200
SIC 5082 5084 5083 7359

JOHNSON MACHINERY CO p 791
800 E La Cadena Dr, Riverside CA 92507
Tel (951) 686-4560 SIC 5082

HAWTHORNE MACHINERY CO p 670
16945 Camino San Bernardo, San Diego CA 92127
Tel (858) 674-7000
SIC 7353 7699 5082 7359

TPG PARTNERS III LP p 1467
345 California St # 3300, San Francisco CA 94104
Tel (415) 743-1500
SIC 1311 1389 4922 5082

PETERSON HOLDING CO p 1138
955 Marina Blvd, San Leandro CA 94577
Tel (510) 357-6200 SIC 5082

PETERSON TRACTOR CO p 1138
955 Marina Blvd, San Leandro CA 94577
Tel (530) 343-1911 SIC 5082 5084 5083

■ **WHITE CAP CONSTRUCTION SUPPLY** p 1606
1815 Ritchey St, Santa Ana CA 92705
Tel (949) 794-5300 SIC 5082

WAGNER EQUIPMENT CO p 1571
18000 Smith Rd, Aurora CO 80011
Tel (303) 739-3000 SIC 5082 7699 7353

HONNEN EQUIPMENT CO p 705
5055 E 72nd Ave, Commerce City CO 80022
Tel (303) 287-7506 SIC 5082 5084

RIO TINTO AMERICA INC p 1236
8051 E Maplewood Ave # 100, Greenwood Village CO 80111
Tel (303) 713-5000 SIC 3412 5082 1044

CTAP LLC p 399
2585 Trailridge Dr E # 200, Lafayette CO 80026
Tel (303) 661-9475 SIC 5082

SUPERIOR PRODUCTS DISTRIBUTORS INC p 1407
1403 Meriden Waterbury Rd, Milldale CT 06467
Tel (860) 621-3621
SIC 5074 5032 5082 7353

KELLY TRACTOR CO p 809
8255 Nw 58th St, Doral FL 33166
Tel (305) 592-5360
SIC 5082 5083 7359 7353 5084 7699

VERMEER SOUTHEAST SALES & SERVICE INC p 1551
4559 Old Winter Garden Rd, Orlando FL 32811
Tel (407) 295-2020 SIC 5082

LINDER INDUSTRIAL MACHINERY CO p 868
1601 S Frontage Rd # 100, Plant City FL 33563
Tel (813) 754-2727 SIC 5082 7353

LINDER INDUSTRIAL MACHINERY CO p 868
1601 S Frontage Rd # 100, Plant City FL 33563
Tel (813) 754-2727 SIC 5082

RING POWER CORP p 1235
500 World Commerce Pkwy, Saint Augustine FL 32092
Tel (904) 201-7400 SIC 5082 5084 7353

RPC INC p 1255
500 World Commerce Pkwy, Saint Augustine FL 32092
Tel (904) 448-1055 SIC 5082

■ **NORTRAX INC** p 1061
4042 Park Oaks Blvd # 200, Tampa FL 33610
Tel (813) 635-2300 SIC 5082

YANCEY BROS CO p 1634
330 Lee Industrial Blvd # 1, Austell GA 30168
Tel (770) 941-2424
SIC 5082 5084 7699 7353

AG-PRO LLC p 34
19595 Us Hwy 84, Boston GA 31626
Tel (229) 498-8833 SIC 3523 5082

TAKEUCHI MFG (US) LTD p 1422
519 Bonnie Valentine Way, Pendergrass GA 30567
Tel (706) 693-3600 SIC 5082

JCB INC p 780
2000 Bamford Blvd, Pooler GA 31322
Tel (912) 447-2000
SIC 5082 5084 3531 3537

CAPITOL MATERIALS OF SAVANNAH INC p 251
305 Telfair Rd, Savannah GA 31415
Tel (912) 232-0952 SIC 5082

SANDVIK MINING AND CONSTRUCTION USA LLC p 1279
300 Technology Ct Se, Smyrna GA 30082
Tel (404) 589-3800 SIC 5082

DOOSAN INFRACORE AMERICA CORP p 451
2905 Shawnee Industrial W, Suwanee GA 30024
Tel (770) 831-2200 SIC 5084 5082

TERTELING HOLDING CO INC p 1440
3858 N Garden Center Way, Boise ID 83703
Tel (208) 342-0018 SIC 5082

WESTERN STATES EQUIPMENT CO p 1600
500 E Overland Rd, Meridian ID 83642
Tel (208) 888-2287 SIC 5082 7699 5084

ESSEX RENTAL CORP p 510
1110 W Lake Cook Rd # 220, Buffalo Grove IL 60089
Tel (847) 215-6500 SIC 7353 5082

BIRKEYS FARM STORE INC p 185
2102 W Park Ct, Champaign IL 61821
Tel (217) 693-7200 SIC 5083 5082 5511

■ **GETZ BROS& CO INC** p 609
225 W Washington St # 1900, Chicago IL 60606
Tel (312) 845-5686
SIC 5047 5031 5141 5065 5082

NES RENTALS HOLDINGS INC p 1026
8420 W Bryn Mawr Ave # 310, Chicago IL 60631
Tel (773) 695-3999 SIC 7359 7699 5082

ARENDS HOGAN WALKER LLC p 106
27688 E 3200 North Rd, Dwight IL 60420
Tel (217) 388-7717 SIC 5999 5082

PATTEN INDUSTRIES INC p 1121
635 W Lake St, Elmhurst IL 60126
Tel (630) 279-4400 SIC 5084 5082 7353

■ **JOHN DEERE CONSTRUCTION & FORESTRY CO** p 788
1 John Deere Pl, Moline IL 61265
Tel (309) 765-8000 SIC 5084 5082

■ **JOHN DEERE SHARED SERVICES INC** p 788
1515 5th Ave Ste 200, Moline IL 61265
Tel (309) 765-0260 SIC 5082

WEST SIDE TRACTOR SALES CO p 1595
1400 W Ogden Ave, Naperville IL 60563
Tel (630) 355-7150 SIC 5082

■ **CATERPILLAR S A R L LLC** p 265
100 Ne Adams St, Peoria IL 61629
Tel (309) 675-1000 SIC 5082

KOMATSU AMERICA CORP p 827
1701 Golf Rd Ste 1-100, Rolling Meadows IL 60008
Tel (847) 437-5800 SIC 5082 3532 3531

ROLAND MACHINERY CO p 1247
816 N Dirksen Pkwy, Springfield IL 62702
Tel (217) 789-7711 SIC 7353 5082

UNITED CONTRACTORS MIDWEST INC p 1507
3151 Robbins Rd Ste A, Springfield IL 62704
Tel (217) 546-6192 SIC 8742 1622 5082

BRAKE SUPPLY CO INC p 207
5501 Foundation Blvd, Evansville IN 47725
Tel (812) 467-1000
SIC 5082 5084 5088 5013 3532

MACALLISTER MACHINERY CO INC p 891
7515 E 30th St, Indianapolis IN 46219
Tel (317) 545-2151 SIC 5082 7699 5013

LOGAN CONTRACTORS SUPPLY INC p 874
4101 106th St, Urbandale IA 50322
Tel (515) 253-9048 SIC 5082

G W VAN KEPPEL CO p 587
1801 N 9th St, Kansas City KS 66101
Tel (913) 281-4800
SIC 5082 7699 5084 7359

MEL STEVENSON & ASSOCIATES INC p 940
2840 Roe Ln, Kansas City KS 66103
Tel (913) 262-0505 SIC 5033 5082 5023

ROAD BUILDERS MACHINERY & SUPPLY CO INC p 1240
1001 S 7th St, Kansas City KS 66105
Tel (913) 371-3822 SIC 5082 7353 7699

HUSQVARNA CONSTRUCTION PRODUCTS NORTH AMERICA INC p 721
17400 W 119th St, Olathe KS 66061
Tel (913) 928-1000
SIC 3541 3291 5085 5082 3425 2951

MURPHY TRACTOR & EQUIPMENT CO INC p 1001
5375 N Deere Rd, Park City KS 67219
Tel (855) 246-9124 SIC 5082

WALL-TIES & FORMS INC p 1573
4000 Bonner Industrial Dr, Shawnee KS 66226
Tel (913) 441-0073 SIC 5082 3444 3443

BERRY COMPANIES INC p 176
3223 N Hydraulic St, Wichita KS 67219
Tel (316) 838-3321
SIC 5082 7353 7699 5084

FOLEY EQUIPMENT CO p 563
1550 S West St, Wichita KS 67213
Tel (316) 943-4211 SIC 5084 5082 5083

FOLEY INDUSTRIES INC p 563
1550 S West St, Wichita KS 67213
Tel (316) 943-4211
SIC 5082 5084 7353 6512

MURFIN DRILLING CO INC p 1001
250 N Water St Ste 300, Wichita KS 67202
Tel (316) 267-3241
SIC 1381 1382 5082 6512 6514

ORICA GROUND SUPPORT INC p 1094
150 Summer Ct, Georgetown KY 40324
Tel (502) 863-6800
SIC 5082 3564 2439 7699

BOYD CO LLC p 205
1400 Cecil Ave, Louisville KY 40211
Tel (502) 774-4441 SIC 5082

BRAMCO INC p 207
1801 Watterson Trl, Louisville KY 40299
Tel (502) 493-4300 SIC 5082 7353

HOLT EQUIPMENT CO LLC p 702
4508 River Rd, Louisville KY 40222
Tel (502) 899-7513 SIC 5082

RUDD EQUIPMENT CO INC p 1257
4344 Poplar Level Rd, Louisville KY 40213
Tel (502) 456-4050 SIC 5082 7353

WHAYNE SUPPLY CO p 1604
10001 Linn Station Rd # 112, Louisville KY 40223
Tel (502) 774-4441 SIC 5082 4911

▲ **H&E EQUIPMENT SERVICES INC** p 651
7500 Pecue Ln, Baton Rouge LA 70809
Tel (225) 298-5200 SIC 7359 5082

SCOTT EQUIPMENT CO LLC p 1293
1000 M L King Jr Dr J, Monroe LA 71203
Tel (318) 387-4160 SIC 7353 5082

LOUISIANA MACHINERY CO LLC p 880
3799 W Airline Hwy, Reserve LA 70084
Tel (985) 536-1121 SIC 5082 7699 7353

TRACO PRODUCTION SERVICES INC p 1468
425 Griffin Rd, Youngsville LA 70592
Tel (337) 857-6000 SIC 5082 1389

ALBAN TRACTOR CO INC p 45
8531 Pulaski Hwy, Baltimore MD 21237
Tel (410) 686-7777 SIC 5082 5084 7699

M-L HOLDINGS CO p 890
4601 Washington Blvd, Baltimore MD 21227
Tel (410) 242-6500 SIC 5082 6719

MCKINNEY DRILLING CO LLC p 930
7550 Teague Rd Ste 300, Hanover MD 21076
Tel (410) 874-1235 SIC 1794 5082

SOUTHWORTH-MILTON INC p 1353
100 Quarry Dr, Milford MA 01757
Tel (508) 634-3400 SIC 5082 7353

PLUMBERS SUPPLY CO p 1156
429 Church St, New Bedford MA 02745
Tel (508) 985-4966 SIC 5074 5084 5082

AIS CONSTRUCTION EQUIPMENT SERVICE CORP p 41
600 44th St Sw, Grand Rapids MI 49548
Tel (616) 538-2400 SIC 5082

CHAMPION INC p 287
180 Traders Mine Rd, Iron Mountain MI 49801
Tel (906) 779-2300
SIC 8741 1542 5063 5082 3273 3272

LOUIS T OLLESHEIMER & SON INC p 880
605 E 12 Mile Rd, Madison Heights MI 48071
Tel (248) 544-3900 SIC 5033 5082

MILAN SUPPLY CO p 968
7125 E Pickard Rd, Mount Pleasant MI 48858
Tel (989) 773-9938 SIC 5082

HINES CORP p 695
1218 E Pontaluna Rd Ste B, Norton Shores MI 49456
Tel (231) 799-6240
SIC 3443 3823 3589 3531 3535 5082

MACALLISTER MACHINERY CO INC p 891
24800 Novi Rd, Novi MI 48375
Tel (248) 349-4800 SIC 5082

BANDIT INDUSTRIES INC p 150
6750 W Millbrook Rd, Remus MI 49340
Tel (989) 561-2270 SIC 3531 5082

ZIEGLER INC p 1643
901 W 94th St, Minneapolis MN 55420
Tel (952) 888-4121 SIC 5082 5084

ROAD MACHINERY & SUPPLIES CO p 1240
5633 Highway 13 W, Savage MN 55378
Tel (952) 895-9595 SIC 5082

PUCKETT MACHINERY CO p 1190
100 Caterpillar Dr, Flowood MS 39232
Tel (601) 969-6000
SIC 5082 5084 5063 7699

G S & L ENTERPRISES INC p 587
408 Highway 49 S, Jackson MS 39218
Tel (601) 939-1000 SIC 5012 5082

STRIBLING EQUIPMENT LLC p 1393
408 Highway 49 S, Richland MS 39218
Tel (601) 939-1000 SIC 5082 7353

ERB EQUIPMENT CO INC p 507
200 Erb Industrial Dr, Fenton MO 63026
Tel (636) 349-0200 SIC 5082 7353 5084

JOHN FABICK TRACTOR CO p 788
1 Fabick Dr, Fenton MO 63026
Tel (636) 343-5900 SIC 5082 7699

COGENT INC p 334
318 Brdwy St, Kansas City MO 64105
Tel (816) 221-0650 SIC 5084 5082 7359

VERNON L GOEDECKE CO INC p 1551
812 E Taylor Ave, Saint Louis MO 63147
Tel (314) 652-1810 SIC 5082 5085

MODERN MACHINERY CO INC p 981
101 International Dr, Missoula MT 59808
Tel (406) 523-1100 SIC 5082

WASHINGTON CORPS p 1577
101 International Dr, Missoula MT 59808
Tel (406) 523-1300
SIC 5082 7353 4213 8741

NMC GROUP INC p 1045
11002 Sapp Brothers Dr, Omaha NE 68138
Tel (402) 891-8600 SIC 5082 5084

CONNELL CO p 357
200 Connell Dr Ste 4100, Berkeley Heights NJ 07922
Tel (908) 673-3700
SIC 6552 6512 7359 5082

FOLEY INC p 563
855 Centennial Ave, Piscataway NJ 08854
Tel (732) 885-5555 SIC 5082 7699 7353

BINDER MACHINERY CO INC p 183
2820 Hamilton Blvd, South Plainfield NJ 07080
Tel (908) 561-9000
SIC 5082 5084 7353 7699

EXTECH BUILDING MATERIALS INC p 521
87 Bowne St, Brooklyn NY 11231
Tel (718) 852-7090 *SIC* 5082 5033 5031

HANES SUPPLY INC p 657
55 James E Casey Dr, Buffalo NY 14206
Tel (716) 826-2636
SIC 5085 5082 3496 1799

TRACEY ROAD EQUIPMENT INC p 1468
6803 Manlius Center Rd, East Syracuse NY 13057
Tel (315) 437-1471
SIC 5082 5012 7353 7699 5013

MONROE TRACTOR & IMPLEMENT CO INC p 985
1001 Lehigh Station Rd, Henrietta NY 14467
Tel (585) 334-3867 *SIC* 5082 5083 7353

DIAMOND CASTLE HOLDINGS LLC p 436
280 Pk Ave Fl 25 E Tower, New York NY 10017
Tel (212) 300-1900 *SIC* 7353 7699 5082

FIAT USA INC p 539
375 Park Ave Ste 2703, New York NY 10152
Tel (212) 355-2600
SIC 3714 8741 3535 5012 5013 5082

MARUBENI AUTO & CONSTRUCTION MACHINERY (AMERICA) INC p 913
450 Lexington Ave, New York NY 10017
Tel (212) 450-0447 *SIC* 5082 7353 7699

SAFWAY HOLDINGS LLC p 1267
280 Park Ave Fl 38, New York NY 10017
Tel (212) 351-7900 *SIC* 7359 5082 1799

H O PENN MACHINERY CO INC p 650
122 Noxon Rd, Poughkeepsie NY 12603
Tel (845) 452-1200 *SIC* 5082 5084

ADMAR SUPPLY CO INC p 23
1950 Brghtn Hnrietta Town, Rochester NY 14623
Tel (585) 272-9390 *SIC* 5082

ASC CONSTRUCTION EQUIPMENT USA INC p 115
9115 Harris Corners Pkwy # 450, Charlotte NC 28269
Tel (704) 494-8100 *SIC* 5082

ASHTEAD US HOLDINGS INC p 117
401 S Tryon St, Charlotte NC 28202
Tel (803) 578-5811 *SIC* 7353 7359 5082

CAROLINA TRACTOR & EQUIPMENT CO INC p 259
9000 Statesville Rd, Charlotte NC 28269
Tel (704) 596-6700
SIC 5082 5084 5013 7353 7359 7629

CENTRAL CAROLINA FARM & MOWER INC p 277
801 E Wendover Ave, Greensboro NC 27405
Tel (336) 574-4400 *SIC* 5261 5082

GREGORY POOLE EQUIPMENT CO p 639
4807 Beryl Rd, Raleigh NC 27606
Tel (919) 828-0641 *SIC* 5082

PANTHER SUMMIT INDUSTRIES INC p 1111
4807 Beryl Rd, Raleigh NC 27606
Tel (919) 828-0641 *SIC* 5082 5084 4931

RDO CONSTRUCTION EQUIPMENT CO p 1212
2000 Industrial Dr, Bismarck ND 58501
Tel (701) 223-5798 *SIC* 5082 5084 7353

BUTLER MACHINERY CO p 230
3401 33rd St S, Fargo ND 58104
Tel (701) 298-1700 *SIC* 5082 7353 7699

RDO EQUIPMENT CO p 1212
700 7th St S, Fargo ND 58103
Tel (701) 239-8700
SIC 5083 5082 5084 7699 7359 7353

RDO HOLDINGS CO p 1212
700 7th St S, Fargo ND 58103
Tel (701) 239-8700 *SIC* 5083 5082

ACME ELECTRIC MOTOR INC p 17
1705 13th Ave N, Grand Forks ND 58203
Tel (701) 746-2823
SIC 5084 5063 5082 5072 5251 5211

▲TITAN MACHINERY INC p 1456
644 E Beaton Dr, West Fargo ND 58078
Tel (701) 356-0130 *SIC* 5251 5082

OHIO MACHINERY CO p 1077
3993 E Royalton Rd, Broadview Heights OH 44147
Tel (440) 526-6200
SIC 7513 6159 7699 5082 7353

COLUMBUS EQUIPMENT CO p 342
2323 Performance Way, Columbus OH 43207
Tel (614) 437-0352 *SIC* 5082 7353

F & M MAFCO INC p 522
9149 Dry Fork Rd, Harrison OH 45030
Tel (513) 367-2151
SIC 5085 5072 7353 5082

CEDAR CREEK HOLDINGS INC p 272
450 N Macarthur Blvd, Oklahoma City OK 73127
Tel (405) 917-8300 *SIC* 5031 5082

KIRBY - SMITH MACHINERY INC p 821
6715 W Reno Ave, Oklahoma City OK 73127
Tel (888) 861-0219 *SIC* 7353 5082 7692

PANHANDLE OILFIELD SERVICE COMPANIES INC p 1111
14000 Quail Springs Pkwy # 300, Oklahoma City OK 73134
Tel (405) 608-5330
SIC 1389 7389 3498 4212 5082 1794

WARREN POWER & MACHINERY LP p 1577
4501 W Reno Ave, Oklahoma City OK 73127
Tel (405) 947-6771 *SIC* 5082

SAMSON INVESTMENT CO p 1274
2 W 2nd St Ste 1500, Tulsa OK 74103
Tel (918) 583-1791 *SIC* 1311 7353 5082

PAPE GROUP INC p 1112
355 Goodpasture Island Rd # 300, Eugene OR 97401
Tel (541) 334-3400
SIC 5084 5082 7699 6141 5599 4581

PAPE MACHINERY INC p 1112
355 Goodpasture Island Rd, Eugene OR 97401
Tel (541) 683-5073 *SIC* 5082

GILES & RANSOME INC p 612
2975 Galloway Rd, Bensalem PA 19020
Tel (215) 639-4300 *SIC* 5082 5084 7353

ANDERSON EQUIPMENT CO p 90
1000 Washington Pike, Bridgeville PA 15017
Tel (412) 343-2300
SIC 5082 7699 7353 5531

▲HARSCO CORP p 664
350 Poplar Church Rd, Camp Hill PA 17011
Tel (717) 763-7064
SIC 7359 7353 5082 3443 3585 4789

LEE SUPPLY CO INC p 851
305 1st St, Charleroi PA 15022
Tel (724) 483-3543 *SIC* 5082 5084

TRI-BORO CONSTRUCTION SUPPLIES INC p 1477
465 E Locust St, Dallastown PA 17313
Tel (717) 246-3095 *SIC* 5082 3496 5251

MESSICK FARM EQUIPMENT INC p 951
187 Merts Dr, Elizabethtown PA 17022
Tel (800) 222-3373 *SIC* 5083 5082

CLEVELAND BROTHERS HOLDINGS INC p 325
5300 Paxton St, Harrisburg PA 17111
Tel (717) 564-2121
SIC 7353 5082 5084 7629

BECKWITH MACHINERY CO INC p 167
4565 William Penn Hwy, Murrysville PA 15668
Tel (724) 327-1300
SIC 5082 5084 7629 7353

CLEVELAND BROTHERS EQUIPMENT CO INC p 325
4565 William Penn Hwy, Murrysville PA 15668
Tel (724) 325-9421 *SIC* 5082

DIAMOND TOOL & FASTENERS INC p 437
2800 Grays Ferry Ave, Philadelphia PA 19146
Tel (215) 952-1919 *SIC* 5082

VOLVO CONSTRUCTION EQUIPMENT NORTH AMERICA LLC p 1565
312 Volvo Way, Shippensburg PA 17257
Tel (717) 532-9181 *SIC* 5082

BEST LINE LEASING INC p 177
140 Hawbaker Indus Dr, State College PA 16803
Tel (814) 237-9050 *SIC* 5082

FAIRMONT SUPPLY CO p 525
437 Jefferson Ave, Washington PA 15301
Tel (724) 223-2200 *SIC* 5085 5082

ASHTEAD HOLDINGS LLC p 117
2341 Deerfield Dr, Fort Mill SC 29715
Tel (803) 578-5811 *SIC* 7353 7359 5082

■AMERICAN EQUIPMENT CO INC p 71
2106 Anderson Rd, Greenville SC 29611
Tel (864) 295-7800
SIC 7699 7359 5082 7353

BLANCHARD MACHINERY CO p 188
3151 Charleston Hwy, West Columbia SC 29172
Tel (803) 791-7100 *SIC* 5082 7353

WIRTGEN AMERICA INC p 1618
6030 Dana Way, Antioch TN 37013
Tel (615) 501-0600 *SIC* 5082

UNITED CENTRAL INDUSTRIAL SUPPLY CO LLC p 1507
1241 Vlntr Pkwy Ste 1000, Bristol TN 37620
Tel (423) 573-7300 *SIC* 5082

UNITED DISTRIBUTORS GROUP INC p 1507
1241 Vlntr Pkwy Ste 1000, Bristol TN 37620
Tel (423) 573-7300 *SIC* 5082

POWER EQUIPMENT CO p 1165
3300 Alcoa Hwy, Knoxville TN 37920
Tel (865) 577-5563 *SIC* 5082 3531 7353

THOMPSON MACHINERY COMMERCE CORP p 1449
1245 Bridgestone Pkwy, La Vergne TN 37086
Tel (615) 256-2424 *SIC* 5082 7353

HEAVY MACHINES INC p 680
3926 E Raines Rd, Memphis TN 38118
Tel (901) 260-2200
SIC 5082 7699 7353 3531 5063

FESCO LTD p 539
1000 Fesco Dr, Alice TX 78332
Tel (361) 664-3479 *SIC* 8711 5082

COUFAL-PRATER EQUIPMENT LLC p 374
3110 W Highway 21, Bryan TX 77803
Tel (979) 822-7684 *SIC* 5999 7699 5082

ED BELL INVESTMENTS INC p 476
10605 Harry Hines Blvd, Dallas TX 75220
Tel (214) 358-3414 *SIC* 1611 5082 4424

FTS INTERNATIONAL MANUFACTURING LLC p 583
777 Main St Ste 2900, Fort Worth TX 76102
Tel (817) 850-8004 *SIC* 5082 7353 5211

HOWARD SUPPLY CO LLC p 713
4100 Intl Plz Ste 850, Fort Worth TX 76109
Tel (817) 529-9950 *SIC* 5084 5082

PREFERRED PUMP & EQUIPMENT LP p 1169
2201 Scott Ave Ste 100, Fort Worth TX 76103
Tel (817) 536-9800
SIC 5084 5083 5074 3533 5082

A & B VALVE AND PIPING SYSTEMS LLC p 4
3845 Cypress Creek Pkwy # 451, Houston TX 77068
Tel (281) 444-6996 *SIC* 5082

AZKU INC p 140
1616 S Voss Rd Ste 550, Houston TX 77057
Tel (713) 782-1080 *SIC* 5082 8711

EAGLE PIPE LLC p 468
9525 Katy Fwy Ste 306, Houston TX 77024
Tel (713) 464-7473 *SIC* 3533 5082

HEALTH CARE TEMPORARIES INC p 674
8926 Sherbourne St Ste D, Houston TX 77016
Tel (713) 631-7106
SIC 8082 1542 1522 1081 5082

LOGAN OIL TOOLS INC p 874
11006 Lucerne St, Houston TX 77016
Tel (281) 219-6613 *SIC* 5082

MUSTANG MACHINERY CO LTD p 1002
12800 Northwest Fwy, Houston TX 77040
Tel (713) 861-1440 *SIC* 5082 5084

■NATIONAL OILWELL VARCO LP p 1014
1530 W Sam Houston Pkwy N, Houston TX 77043
Tel (713) 960-5100 *SIC* 3533 5082 5084

■OIL STATES ENERGY SERVICES LLC p 1079
333 Clay St Ste 2100, Houston TX 77002
Tel (713) 425-2400 *SIC* 3533 5082

PEARCE INDUSTRIES INC p 1126
12320 Main St, Houston TX 77035
Tel (713) 723-1050 *SIC* 5084 3533 5082

PON NORTH AMERICA INC p 1161
840 Gessner Rd Ste 950, Houston TX 77024
Tel (713) 365-2547 *SIC* 5942 5082

STEWART & STEVENSON CAPITAL CORP p 1388
601 W 38th St, Houston TX 77018
Tel (713) 868-7700
SIC 5084 5013 5078 5082 3711 3537

STEWART & STEVENSON LLC p 1389
1000 La St Ste 5900, Houston TX 77002
Tel (713) 751-2600
SIC 5084 5082 3533 7353

STEWART & STEVENSON POWER PRODUCTS LLC p 1389
1000 La St Ste 5900, Houston TX 77002
Tel (713) 751-2600
SIC 1389 5084 5082 3533 7353

■TESCO CORP (US) p 1440
11330 Clay Rd Ste 350, Houston TX 77041
Tel (713) 359-7000
SIC 7353 5082 1389 1381

VALLOUREC & MANNESMANN HOLDINGS INC p 1541
4424 W Sam Houston Pkwy N # 150, Houston TX 77041
Tel (713) 479-3200 *SIC* 5082

VALLOUREC USA CORP p 1541
4424 W Sm Hstn Pkwy N 1, Houston TX 77041
Tel (713) 479-3277 *SIC* 5082

WAUKESHA-PEARCE INDUSTRIES INC p 1583
12320 Main St, Houston TX 77035
Tel (713) 723-1050 *SIC* 5084 5082 3621

NEOVIA LOGISTICS SERVICES LLC p 1026
6363 N State Highway 161 # 700, Irving TX 75038
Tel (469) 513-7000 *SIC* 4789 5082

VERMEER EQUIPMENT OF TEXAS INC p 1551
3025 State Highway 161, Irving TX 75062
Tel (972) 255-3500 *SIC* 5082 7699 7353

ASSOCIATED SUPPLY CO INC p 121
2102 E Slaton Rd, Lubbock TX 79404
Tel (806) 745-2000 *SIC* 5084 5082 7353

LINCOLN MANUFACTURING INC p 867
31209 Fm 2978 Rd, Magnolia TX 77354
Tel (281) 252-9494 *SIC* 3533 5082

PRODUCTION SPECIALTY SERVICES LLC p 1180
511 W Missouri Ave, Midland TX 79701
Tel (432) 620-0059 *SIC* 5082 7699

WARREN EQUIPMENT CO p 1577
10325 Younger Rd, Midland TX 79706
Tel (432) 571-8462
SIC 5082 5084 7699 3563 7359

WARREN POWER & MACHINERY INC p 1577
10325 Younger Rd, Midland TX 79706
Tel (432) 563-1170 *SIC* 5082

■PECOFACET (US) INC p 1127
118 Washington Ave, Mineral Wells TX 76067
Tel (940) 325-2575 *SIC* 3823 5082

B S W INC p 142
111 Naida St, Pampa TX 79065
Tel (806) 669-1103 *SIC* 5082 5084

HOLT TEXAS LTD p 702
5665 Se Loop 410, San Antonio TX 78222
Tel (210) 648-1111
SIC 3531 5082 7353 7699

PINNACLE COMPANIES INC p 1149
903 Interstate Hwy 30 E, Sulphur Springs TX 75482
Tel (903) 885-6772 *SIC* 5082

ARNOLD MACHINERY CO p 112
2975 W 2100 S, Salt Lake City UT 84119
Tel (801) 972-4000
SIC 5082 5084 5012 5083

WHEELER MACHINERY CO p 1605
4901 W 2100 S, Salt Lake City UT 84120
Tel (801) 974-0511
SIC 5082 5084 7359 7353

JAMES RIVER EQUIPMENT INC p 777
11047 Leadbetter Rd, Ashland VA 23005
Tel (804) 748-9324 *SIC* 5084 5082

JAMES RIVER EQUIPMENT VIRGINIA LLC p 777
11047 Leadbetter Rd, Ashland VA 23005
Tel (804) 798-6001 *SIC* 5082

DAVIS MINING & MANUFACTURING INC p 416
613 Front St E, Coeburn VA 24230
Tel (276) 395-3354
SIC 2892 5082 2426 1221 1222

LIEBHERR MINING & CONSTRUCTION EQUIPMENT INC p 863
4100 Chestnut Ave, Newport News VA 23607
Tel (757) 245-5251 *SIC* 5082 5084 3532

CARTER MACHINERY CO INC p 262
1330 Lynchburg Tpke, Salem VA 24153
Tel (540) 387-1111 *SIC* 5082 3531

HARNISH GROUP INC p 662
17035 W Valley Hwy, Tukwila WA 98188
Tel (425) 251-9800 *SIC* 5082 5013 5083

N C MACHINERY CO p 1005
17025 W Valley Hwy, Tukwila WA 98188
Tel (425) 251-9800 *SIC* 5082 5013 5083

N C POWER SYSTEMS CO p 1005
17900 W Valley Hwy, Tukwila WA 98188
Tel (425) 251-5877 *SIC* 5013 5082 5083

SAFEWORKS LLC p 1267
365 Upland Dr, Tukwila WA 98188
Tel (206) 575-6445
SIC 3536 3531 3446 5082

TRACTOR & EQUIPMENT CO p 1468
17035 W Valley Hwy, Tukwila WA 98188
Tel (425) 251-9800 *SIC* 5082

JEAN NELL ENTERPRISES INC p 781
1 Nell Jean Sq 19, Beckley WV 25801
Tel (304) 253-0200 *SIC* 5941 5082 5091

RISH EQUIPMENT CO p 1236
6384 Airport Rd, Bluefield WV 24701
Tel (304) 327-5124 *SIC* 5082 7699

J H FLETCHER & CO p 771
402 High St, Huntington WV 25705
Tel (304) 525-7811
SIC 5082 3532 3743 3546 3541

SAFWAY SERVICES LLC p 1267
N19w24200 Riverwood Dr # 200, Waukesha WI 53188
Tel (262) 523-6500 *SIC* 5082

WYOMING MACHINERY CO p 1630
5300 W Old Yllowstone Hwy, Casper WY 82604
Tel (307) 686-1500 *SIC* 5082

SIC 5083 Farm & Garden Mach & Eqpt Wholesale

AGRI-AFC LLC p 36
121 Somerville Rd Ne, Decatur AL 35601
Tel (256) 560-2848
SIC 5159 5153 5083 5191

SUNSOUTH LLC p 1404
4100 Hartford Hwy, Dothan AL 36305
Tel (334) 678-7861 *SIC* 5083

WHITEMAN FAMILY CORP p 1606
1725 S Country Club Dr, Mesa AZ 85210
Tel (480) 633-4413
SIC 5082 5083 7353 7699 7359 5012

■HORIZON DISTRIBUTORS INC p 707
5214 S 30th St, Phoenix AZ 85040
Tel (480) 337-6700 *SIC* 4971 5083

HUGG AND HALL EQUIPMENT CO p 717
7201 Scott Hamilton Dr, Little Rock AR 72209
Tel (501) 562-1262
SIC 5084 5082 7353 7699 5083 3531

E RITTER & CO p 466
10 Elm St, Marked Tree AR 72365
Tel (870) 358-7333
SIC 0131 0116 0724 4813 5211 5083

BOND MANUFACTURING CO INC p 200
1700 W 4th St, Antioch CA 94509
Tel (925) 252-1135 *SIC* 5083 3272

QUINN CO p 1200
10006 Rose Hills Rd, City Of Industry CA 90601
Tel (562) 463-4000
SIC 5082 5083 5084 7353

PIONEER FARM EQUIPMENT CO p 1150
2589 N A Fresno Drste 109, Fresno CA 93727
Tel (559) 253-0526 *SIC* 5083

JAMES MORIEL p 776
25701 Taladro Cir Ste B, Mission Viejo CA 92691
Tel (949) 240-3340 *SIC* 5083

VETERINARY SERVICE INC p 1553
4100 Bangs Ave, Modesto CA 95356
Tel (209) 545-5100 *SIC* 5047 5199 5083

HOC HOLDINGS INC p 699
7310 Pacific Ave, Pleasant Grove CA 95668
Tel (916) 921-8950
SIC 5082 5084 5083 7359

HOLT OF CALIFORNIA p 702
7310 Pacific Ave, Pleasant Grove CA 95668
Tel (916) 991-8200
SIC 5082 5084 5083 7359

PETERSON TRACTOR CO p 1138
955 Marina Blvd, San Leandro CA 94577
Tel (530) 343-1911 *SIC* 5082 5084 5083

SPEARS MANUFACTURING CO p 1355
15853 Olden St, Sylmar CA 91342
Tel (818) 364-7306 *SIC* 3494 5083

KUBOTA TRACTOR CORP p 831
3401 Del Amo Blvd, Torrance CA 90503
Tel (310) 370-3370 *SIC* 5083 3531 3799

KUBOTA USA INC p 831
3401 Del Amo Blvd, Torrance CA 90503
Tel (310) 370-3370
SIC 5083 3577 5051 3531 3571

GARTON TRACTOR INC p 592
2400 N Golden State Blvd, Turlock CA 95382
Tel (209) 632-3931 *SIC* 5999 5083

TURLOCK DAIRY & REFRIGERATION INC p 1492
1819 S Walnut Rd, Turlock CA 95380
Tel (209) 667-6455 *SIC* 5083 7699 1542

■ANIMAL HEALTH INTERNATIONAL INC p 91
822 7th St Ste 740, Greeley CO 80631
Tel (970) 353-2600
SIC 5122 5047 5999 5191 5083 5154

ENGINEERING SERVICES & PRODUCTS CO p 499
1395 John Fitch Blvd, South Windsor CT 06074
Tel (860) 528-1119 *SIC* 3523 5083 3081

KELLY TRACTOR CO p 809
8255 Nw 58th St, Doral FL 33166
Tel (305) 592-5360
SIC 5082 5083 7359 7353 5084 7699

WINCORP INTERNATIONAL INC p 1615
10025 Nw 116th Way Ste 14, Medley FL 33178
Tel (305) 887-1294
SIC 5191 5083 5199 7338 5144

YANMAR AMERICA CORP p 1635
101 International Pkwy, Adairsville GA 30103
Tel (770) 877-9894
SIC 5084 7699 5083 3519

ROTARY CORP p 1252
801 W Barnard St, Glennville GA 30427
Tel (912) 654-3433 *SIC* 5083 3469 5013

■SITEONE LANDSCAPE SUPPLY HOLDING LLC p 1328
300 Colonial Center Pkwy, Roswell GA 30076
Tel (770) 255-2100
SIC 5083 5191 5193 5032 5063

▲SITEONE LANDSCAPE SUPPLY INC p 1328
300 Colonial Center Pkwy, Roswell GA 30076
Tel (770) 255-2100
SIC 5083 5191 5193 5032 5063

■SITEONE LANDSCAPE SUPPLY LLC p 1328
300 Colonial Center Pkwy # 600, Roswell GA 30076
Tel (770) 255-2100 *SIC* 5063 5193 5083

MCLEAN IMPLEMENT INC p 931
793 Illinois Route 130, Albion IL 62806
Tel (618) 445-3676 *SIC* 5083

BEARD IMPLEMENT CO (INC) p 165
216 W Frederick St, Arenzville IL 62611
Tel (217) 997-5514 SIC 5083 7699

SLOAN IMPLEMENT CO INC p 1331
120 N Business 51, Assumption IL 62510
Tel (217) 226-4411 SIC 5083

ILLINOIS AUTO ELECTRIC CO p 732
700 Enterprise St, Aurora IL 60504
Tel (630) 862-3300
SIC 5084 5013 5083 5078 7699 3519

BIRKEYS FARM STORE INC p 185
2102 W Park Ct, Champaign IL 61821
Tel (217) 693-7200 SIC 5083 5082 5511

MARTIN SULLIVAN INC p 913
250 E Main St Ste 402, Galesburg IL 61401
Tel (309) 343-1423 SIC 5083 5261

GEA FARM TECHNOLOGIES INC p 597
1880 Country Farm Dr, Naperville IL 60563
Tel (630) 548-8200
SIC 5083 3523 2841 2842

ACE HARDWARE CORP p 16
2200 Kensington Ct, Oak Brook IL 60523
Tel (630) 990-6600
SIC 5251 5198 5063 5074 5083

AGRI-FAB INC p 36
809 S Hamilton St, Sullivan IL 61951
Tel (217) 728-8388 SIC 3469 3429 5083

WM NOBBE AND CO INC p 1620
6469 State Route 3, Waterloo IL 62298
Tel (618) 939-6717 SIC 5083

VETTER EQUIPMENT CO p 1553
610 14th Ave S, Denison IA 51442
Tel (712) 263-6440 SIC 5083

KBC GROUP INC p 806
3400 109th St, Des Moines IA 50322
Tel (515) 270-2417 SIC 1542 5083

FARMCHEM CORP p 529
616 Madison, Floyd IA 50435
Tel (800) 247-1854 SIC 5083

CARRICO IMPLEMENT CO INC p 260
3160 Us 24 Hwy, Beloit KS 67420
Tel (785) 738-5744 SIC 5083

AMERICAN IMPLEMENT INC p 74
2611 W Jones Ave, Garden City KS 67846
Tel (620) 275-4114 SIC 5083

STRAUB INTERNATIONAL INC p 1393
214 Sw 40 Ave, Great Bend KS 67530
Tel (620) 792-5256 SIC 5083 5531

KANEQUIP INC p 802
1152 Pony Express Hwy, Marysville KS 66508
Tel (785) 562-2377 SIC 5046 5083

KANEQUIP INC p 802
18035 E Us Highway 24, Wamego KS 66547
Tel (785) 456-2041 SIC 5999 5083

FOLEY EQUIPMENT CO p 563
1550 S West St, Wichita KS 67213
Tel (316) 943-4211 SIC 5084 5082 5083

ISCO INDUSTRIES INC p 766
100 Witherspoon St, Louisville KY 40202
Tel (502) 318-6626 SIC 5085 5083

TECHTRONIC INDUSTRIES NORTH AMERICA INC p 1432
303 Intrntl Cir Ste 490, Hunt Valley MD 21030
Tel (443) 391-1541 SIC 5083 5251

IMA DAIRY & FOOD USA INC p 733
7 New Lancaster Rd, Leominster MA 01453
Tel (732) 343-7600 SIC 5083

■ AVERY WEIGH-TRONIX LLC p 137
1000 Armstrong Dr, Fairmont MN 56031
Tel (507) 238-4461 SIC 3596 5083

AGRILIANCE LLC p 36
5500 Cenex Dr, Inver Grove Heights MN 55077
Tel (651) 481-2031 SIC 5083

CHURCHILL COMPANIES p 305
333 S 7th St Ste 3100, Minneapolis MN 55402
Tel (612) 673-6700 SIC 3211 3824 5083

■ TORO LLC p 1462
8111 Lyndale Ave S, Minneapolis MN 55420
Tel (952) 887-8041 SIC 3524 5083

UNITED FARMERS COOPERATIVE p 1508
705 E 4th St, Winthrop MN 55396
Tel (507) 237-2281
SIC 5153 5191 5983 5083

MISSISSIPPI AG CO p 975
441 Haley Barbour Pkwy, Yazoo City MS 39194
Tel (662) 746-6208 SIC 5083

BLOUNT INTERNATIONAL INC p 190
10331 Nw Transcon Dr, Kansas City MO 64153
Tel (816) 231-5007 SIC 5083 3524 3469

DAIRY FARMERS OF AMERICA INC p 408
10220 N Ambassador Dr, Kansas City MO 64153
Tel (816) 801-6455
SIC 2026 2023 2021 2022 5083 2024

DELAVAL INC p 423
11100 N Congress Ave, Kansas City MO 64153
Tel (816) 891-7700
SIC 5083 3523 2842 0241

BAKER IMPLEMENT CO p 146
915 Homecrest St, Kennett MO 63857
Tel (573) 888-4646 SIC 5083 7699

CRADER EQUIPMENT CO p 388
808 Highway 34 W, Marble Hill MO 63764
Tel (573) 238-2675 SIC 5083 5084

KAISER MIDWEST INC p 800
808 Highway 34 W, Marble Hill MO 63764
Tel (573) 238-2675 SIC 5083 5084

2 M CO INC p 1
5249 Holiday Ave, Billings MT 59101
Tel (406) 245-1490
SIC 5084 5083 5074 5051

GLOBAL INDUSTRIES INC p 617
1804 E 4th St, Grand Island NE 68801
Tel (800) 247-6621
SIC 7992 3589 3444 5084 5083 3535

DULTMEIER SALES LIMITED LIABILITY CO p 460
13808 Industrial Rd, Omaha NE 68137
Tel (402) 333-1444 SIC 5083 5084

WESTERN NEVADA SUPPLY CO p 1599
950 S Rock Blvd, Sparks NV 89431
Tel (775) 359-5800 SIC 5074 5083

GEA WESTFALIA SEPARATOR INC p 597
100 Fairway Ct, Northvale NJ 07647
Tel (201) 767-3900 SIC 5083 5084 3523

MONROE TRACTOR & IMPLEMENT CO INC p 985
1001 Lehigh Station Rd, Henrietta NY 14467
Tel (585) 334-3867 SIC 5082 5083 7353

DIXIE SERVANTAGE SALES INC p 445
5920 Summit Ave, Browns Summit NC 27214
Tel (336) 375-7500 SIC 5083

■ ATI PRODUCTS INC p 124
5100 W WT Harris Blvd H, Charlotte NC 28269
Tel (800) 438-0660 SIC 5083 5084 5085

SMITH TURF & IRRIGATION LLC p 1333
4355 Golf Acres Dr, Charlotte NC 28208
Tel (704) 393-8873 SIC 5083

MONROE HARDWARE CO INC p 985
101 N Sutherland Ave, Monroe NC 28110
Tel (704) 289-3121 SIC 5072 5083

RDO AGRICULTURE EQUIPMENT CO p 1212
700 7th St S, Fargo ND 58103
Tel (701) 239-8730 SIC 5083

RDO EQUIPMENT CO p 1212
700 7th St S, Fargo ND 58103
Tel (701) 239-8700
SIC 5083 5082 5084 7699 7359 7353

RDO HOLDINGS CO p 1212
700 7th St S, Fargo ND 58103
Tel (701) 239-8700 SIC 5083 5082

GATEWAY BUILDING SYSTEMS INC p 593
2138 Main Ave W, West Fargo ND 58078
Tel (701) 293-7202 SIC 1542 5083

■ LESCO INC p 857
1385 E 36th St, Cleveland OH 44114
Tel (216) 706-9250 SIC 5191 5083 5261

JD EQUIPMENT INC p 780
3979 Parkway Ln, Hilliard OH 43026
Tel (614) 527-8800 SIC 5999 5083

BOSTWICK-BRAUN CO p 203
7349 Crossleigh Ct, Toledo OH 43617
Tel (419) 259-3600
SIC 5072 5084 5063 5083 5023

LIVINGSTON MACHINERY CO p 871
5201 S Highway 81, Chickasha OK 73018
Tel (405) 224-5056
SIC 5083 5999 7699 5261

MESSICK FARM EQUIPMENT INC p 951
187 Merts Dr, Elizabethtown PA 17022
Tel (800) 222-3373 SIC 5083 5082

HOOBER INC p 705
3452 Old Philadelphia Pike, Intercourse PA 17534
Tel (717) 768-8231 SIC 5999 7699 5083

VALCO COMPANIES INC p 1539
2710 Division Hwy, New Holland PA 17557
Tel (717) 354-4586 SIC 5083

HOMELITE CONSUMER PRODUCTS INC p 703
1428 Pearman Dairy Rd, Anderson SC 29625
Tel (864) 226-6511 SIC 5083

WALLACE HARDWARE CO INC p 1573
5050 S Davy Crockett Pkwy, Morristown TN 37813
Tel (423) 586-5650
SIC 5072 5074 5085 5083 5211

HUGH M CUNNINGHAM INC p 717
2029 Westgate Dr Ste 120, Carrollton TX 75006
Tel (972) 888-3833
SIC 5074 5085 5083 5199

UNITED AGRICULTURAL COOPERATIVE INC p 1506
911 S Wharton St, El Campo TX 77437
Tel (979) 543-6284
SIC 5251 0724 5083 4221 5153

PREFERRED PUMP & EQUIPMENT LP p 1169
2201 Scott Ave Ste 100, Fort Worth TX 76103
Tel (817) 536-9800
SIC 5084 5083 5074 3533 5082

EQUIPMENT DEPOT LTD p 506
840 Gessner Rd Ste 950, Houston TX 77024
Tel (713) 365-2547
SIC 5083 5084 7359 7699 7353

KING RANCH INC p 820
3 Riverway Ste 1600, Houston TX 77056
Tel (832) 681-5700
SIC 0212 2711 5083 5948

MAHINDRA USA INC p 897
9020 Jackrabbit Rd # 600, Houston TX 77095
Tel (281) 449-7771 SIC 5083

RAY LEE EQUIPMENT CO LTD p 1209
910 N Date St, Plainview TX 79072
Tel (806) 293-2538 SIC 5083 7699

FOREST TOMBALL PRODUCTS INC p 567
16801 Fm 2920 Rd, Tomball TX 77377
Tel (281) 357-8196 SIC 5083 5211 5031

ARNOLD MACHINERY CO p 112
2975 W 2100 S, Salt Lake City UT 84119
Tel (801) 972-4000
SIC 5082 5084 5012 5083

H D FOWLER CO INC p 649
13440 Se 30th St, Bellevue WA 98005
Tel (425) 746-8400
SIC 5084 5083 5085 3321

DAIRY EXPORT CO INC p 408
635 Elliott Ave W, Seattle WA 98119
Tel (206) 284-7220 SIC 5191 5083 2033

WASHINGTON TRACTOR INC p 1579
2700 136th Avenue Ct E, Sumner WA 98390
Tel (253) 863-4436
SIC 3523 5083 5261 7699 7353

HARNISH GROUP INC p 662
17035 W Valley Hwy, Tukwila WA 98188
Tel (425) 251-9800 SIC 5082 5013 5083

N C MACHINERY CO p 1005
17025 W Valley Hwy, Tukwila WA 98188
Tel (425) 251-9800 SIC 5082 5013 5083

N C POWER SYSTEMS CO p 1005
17900 W Valley Hwy, Tukwila WA 98188
Tel (425) 251-5877 SIC 5013 5082 5083

BLAIN SUPPLY INC p 188
3507 E Racine St, Janesville WI 53546
Tel (608) 754-2821
SIC 5083 5072 5039 5013 5023 5198

PRINCE CORP p 1176
8351 County Road H, Marshfield WI 54449
Tel (800) 777-2486
SIC 5031 5191 2048 5083 5072

RIESTERER & SCHNELL INC p 1234
N2909 State Highway 32, Pulaski WI 54162
Tel (920) 775-4146 SIC 5083 5261

REINDERS INC p 1221
W227n6225 Sussex Rd, Sussex WI 53089
Tel (262) 786-3300
SIC 5191 5169 5074 5999 5083

SIC 5084 Industrial Mach & Eqpt Wholesale

C & C HOLDING INC p 231
2238 Pinson Valley Pkwy, Birmingham AL 35217
Tel (205) 841-6666 SIC 5082 1629 5084

THOMPSON TRACTOR CO INC p 1449
2258 Pinson Valley Pkwy, Birmingham AL 35217
Tel (334) 215-5000 SIC 5082 5084 5085

HILLER COMPANIES INC p 693
3751 Joy Springs Dr, Mobile AL 36693
Tel (251) 661-1275 SIC 1731 5084 5088

SOUTHERN FASTENING SYSTEMS LLC p 1348
635 Fairgrounds Rd, Muscle Shoals AL 35661
Tel (256) 381-3628
SIC 5084 5085 5251 5072

HEAT TRANSFER PRODUCTS GROUP LLC p 679
201 Thomas French Dr, Scottsboro AL 35769
Tel (256) 259-7400 SIC 5084

■ AMERICAN TRAFFIC SOLUTIONS INC p 80
1150 N Alma School Rd, Mesa AZ 85201
Tel (480) 443-7000 SIC 7374 1731 5084

CERTEX USA INC p 284
1721 W Culver St, Phoenix AZ 85007
Tel (602) 271-9048 SIC 5084

LOFTIN EQUIPMENT CO p 874
2111 E Highland Ave # 255, Phoenix AZ 85016
Tel (800) 437-4376 SIC 5063 5084 5999

NAUMANN/HOBBS MATERIAL HANDLING CORP II INC p 1019
4335 E Wood St, Phoenix AZ 85040
Tel (602) 437-1331 SIC 5084

■ STRYKER SUSTAINABILITY SOLUTIONS INC p 1394
1810 W Drake Dr Ste 101, Tempe AZ 85283
Tel (888) 888-3433
SIC 5084 5047 7699 3842 3841

NABHOLZ INC p 1006
612 Garland St, Conway AR 72032
Tel (501) 505-5800 SIC 5084 7359

MOUNTAIN VALLEY SPRING CO LLC p 994
283 Mountain Vly Wtr Pl, Hot Springs Village AR 71909
Tel (501) 623-6671 SIC 5084

HUGG AND HALL EQUIPMENT CO p 717
7201 Scott Hamilton Dr, Little Rock AR 72209
Tel (501) 562-1262
SIC 5084 5082 7353 7699 5083 3531

ISUZU NORTH AMERICA CORP p 767
1400 S Douglass Rd # 100, Anaheim CA 92806
Tel (714) 935-9300
SIC 5511 5084 5013 5015

NIKON PRECISION INC p 1043
1399 Shoreway Rd, Belmont CA 94002
Tel (650) 508-4674 SIC 5084 5065

AMADA AMERICA INC p 64
7025 Firestone Blvd, Buena Park CA 90621
Tel (714) 739-2111 SIC 5084 6159

HASKEL INTERNATIONAL LLC p 667
100 E Graham Pl, Burbank CA 91502
Tel (818) 843-4000
SIC 3561 3594 5084 5085 3699

FRANK EDWARDS CO INC p 574
1565 Adrian Rd, Burlingame CA 94010
Tel (650) 692-2347 SIC 5084 5013

CBOL CORP p 269
19850 Plummer St, Chatsworth CA 91311
Tel (818) 704-8200
SIC 5065 5072 5013 5088 5084 5162

NMB (USA) INC p 1045
9730 Independence Ave, Chatsworth CA 91311
Tel (818) 709-1770
SIC 3562 5063 5084 3728 5065

QUINN CO p 1200
10006 Rose Hills Rd, City Of Industry CA 90601
Tel (562) 463-4000
SIC 5082 5083 5084 7353

QUINN GROUP INC p 1200
10006 Rose Hills Rd, City Of Industry CA 90601
Tel (562) 463-4000
SIC 5084 5082 7353 7359

QUINN SHEPHERD MACHINERY p 1200
10006 Rose Hills Rd, City Of Industry CA 90601
Tel (562) 463-6000 SIC 5082 5084

YALE/CHASE EQUIPMENT AND SERVICES INC p 1634
2615 Pellissier Pl, City Of Industry CA 90601
Tel (562) 463-8000 SIC 5084 7699 7359

■ MT SUPPLY INC p 997
3505 Cadillac Ave Ste K2, Costa Mesa CA 92626
Tel (714) 434-4748 SIC 5085 5084

KAWASAKI MOTORS CORP USA p 805
26972 Burbank, Foothill Ranch CA 92610
Tel (949) 837-4683
SIC 5012 5013 5084 5091

AMERICAN AIR LIQUIDE INC p 67
46409 Landing Pkwy, Fremont CA 94538
Tel (510) 624-4000
SIC 2813 5084 3533 4931

METRIC EQUIPMENT SALES INC p 954
25841 Industrial Blvd # 200, Hayward CA 94545
Tel (510) 264-0887
SIC 5065 5084 7359 3825

R F MACDONALD CO p 1202
25920 Eden Landing Rd, Hayward CA 94545
Tel (510) 784-0110 SIC 5084 7699 5074

RJMS CORP p 1239
31010 San Antonio St, Hayward CA 94544
Tel (510) 675-0500 SIC 5084 5085 7699

WESTERN HYDRO CORP p 1598
3449 Enterprise Ave, Hayward CA 94545
Tel (559) 275-3305 SIC 5084

STATCO ENGINEERING & FABRICATORS INC p 1380
7595 Reynolds Cir, Huntington Beach CA 92647
Tel (714) 375-6300 SIC 5084 3556

▲ MCGRATH RENTCORP p 929
5700 Las Positas Rd, Livermore CA 94551
Tel (925) 606-9200 SIC 7359 5084

SHIMADZU PRECISION INSTRUMENTS INC p 1316
3645 N Lakewood Blvd, Long Beach CA 90808
Tel (562) 420-6226 SIC 5088 5047 5084

ALS TESTING SERVICES GROUP INC p 61
818 W 7th St Ste 930, Los Angeles CA 90017
Tel (213) 627-8252 SIC 5141 5072 5084

▲ WILLIS LEASE FINANCE CORP p 1612
773 San Marin Dr Ste 2215, Novato CA 94945
Tel (415) 408-4700 SIC 6159 5084

REPLANET LLC p 1224
800 N Haven Ave Ste 120, Ontario CA 91764
Tel (951) 520-1700 SIC 5084 4953

TORIN INC p 1461
4355 E Brickell St, Ontario CA 91761
Tel (909) 390-8588 SIC 5084

HOC HOLDINGS INC p 699
7310 Pacific Ave, Pleasant Grove CA 95668
Tel (916) 921-8950
SIC 5082 5084 5083 7359

HOLT OF CALIFORNIA p 702
7310 Pacific Ave, Pleasant Grove CA 95668
Tel (916) 991-8200
SIC 5082 5084 5083 7359

■ SYSCO SAN DIEGO INC p 1418
12180 Kirkham Rd, Poway CA 92064
Tel (858) 513-7300
SIC 5141 5142 5147 5148 5084

NEWAY PACKAGING CORP p 1037
1973 E Via Arado, Rancho Dominguez CA 90220
Tel (602) 454-9000 SIC 5113 5084

WESTAIR GASES & EQUIPMENT INC p 1596
2506 Market St, San Diego CA 92102
Tel (866) 937-8247 SIC 5084

BUCKLES-SMITH ELECTRIC CO p 223
801 Savaker Ave, San Jose CA 95126
Tel (408) 280-7777 SIC 5084 5063

■ CSE HOLDINGS INC p 397
650 Brennan St, San Jose CA 95131
Tel (408) 436-1907
SIC 5087 5084 7699 5113 5199 5112

PETERSON POWER SYSTEMS INC p 1138
2828 Teagarden St, San Leandro CA 94577
Tel (510) 618-2921 SIC 5084 7353

PETERSON TRACTOR CO p 1138
955 Marina Blvd, San Leandro CA 94577
Tel (530) 343-1911 SIC 5082 5084 5083

WH ACQUISITIONS INC p 1604
800 Concar Dr Ste 100, San Mateo CA 94402
Tel (650) 358-5000 SIC 5084 6719

CHAMPION POWER EQUIPMENT INC p 287
12039 Smith Ave, Santa Fe Springs CA 90670
Tel (877) 338-0999 SIC 5084

ELLISON MACHINERY CO p 489
9912 Pioneer Blvd, Santa Fe Springs CA 90670
Tel (562) 949-8311 SIC 5084

ELLISON TECHNOLOGIES INC p 489
9912 Pioneer Blvd, Santa Fe Springs CA 90670
Tel (562) 949-8311 SIC 5084

MAXON LIFT CORP p 922
11921 Slauson Ave, Santa Fe Springs CA 90670
Tel (562) 464-0099 SIC 5084 3537 3534

RAYMOND HANDLING SOLUTIONS INC p 1210
9939 Norwalk Blvd, Santa Fe Springs CA 90670
Tel (562) 944-8067 SIC 5084 7699 7359

MCCAIN INC p 926
2365 Oak Ridge Way, Vista CA 92081
Tel (760) 727-8100 SIC 5084 3444 3669

■ SYSCO LOS ANGELES INC p 1417
20701 Currier Rd, Walnut CA 91789
Tel (909) 595-9595 SIC 5141 5084

■ MICRO MOTION INC p 961
7070 Winchester Cir, Boulder CO 80301
Tel (303) 530-8400 SIC 3824 5084

■ CUMMINS ROCKY MOUNTAIN LLC p 401
390 Interlocken Cres # 200, Broomfield CO 80021
Tel (800) 927-7201 SIC 5084 3519

4 RIVERS EQUIPMENT LLC p 3
1100 E Cheyenne Rd, Colorado Springs CO 80905
Tel (800) 364-3029 SIC 5084

BAE SYSTEMS POWER INC p 144
5840 Dahlia St, Commerce City CO 80022
Tel (303) 287-7441
SIC 5084 3531 3999 3569

HONNEN EQUIPMENT CO p 705
5055 E 72nd Ave, Commerce City CO 80022
Tel (303) 287-7506 SIC 5082 5084

DENCO SALES CO p 428
55 S Yuma St, Denver CO 80223
Tel (303) 733-0607 SIC 5199 5084

FMH MATERIAL HANDLING SOLUTIONS INC p 562
4105 Globeville Rd, Denver CO 80216
Tel (303) 292-5438 SIC 5084 7353 5013

GATES CORP p 593
1551 Wewatta St, Denver CO 80202
Tel (303) 744-1911
SIC 3052 3089 3568 5084 4789

GENERAL AIR SERVICE & SUPPLY CO p 599
1105 Zuni St, Denver CO 80204
Tel (303) 892-7003
SIC 5169 5085 5084 5149

KARCHER NORTH AMERICA INC p 804
4555 Airport Way Fl 4, Denver CO 80239
Tel (303) 762-1800 SIC 3635 5084

OMAHA HOLDINGS LLC p 1083
1551 Wewatta St, Denver CO 80202
Tel (303) 744-1911
SIC 3052 3089 3568 5084 4789

OMAHA INTERMEDIATE HOLDING LLC p 1083
1551 Wewatta St, Denver CO 80202
Tel (303) 744-1911
SIC 3052 3089 3568 5084 4789

UNITED STATES WELDING INC p 1514
600 S Santa Fe Dr, Denver CO 80223
Tel (303) 777-2475
SIC 5169 5084 5085 5047 7359

FORNEY INDUSTRIES INC p 568
2057 Vermont Dr, Fort Collins CO 80525
Tel (800) 521-6038 SIC 5084

■ **PCS FERGUSON INC** p 1124
3771 Eureka Way, Frederick CO 80516
Tel (720) 407-3550 SIC 3533 5084

■ **PRAXAIR DISTRIBUTION INC** p 1167
39 Old Ridgebury Rd, Danbury CT 06810
Tel (203) 837-2000 SIC 2813 5084 5999

■ **PRAXAIR TECHNOLOGY INC** p 1168
39 Old Ridgebury Rd, Danbury CT 06810
Tel (203) 837-2000
SIC 5172 5084 5169 5085

BLAKE GROUP HOLDINGS INC p 188
4 New Park Rd, East Windsor CT 06088
Tel (860) 243-1491
SIC 5074 5084 7699 8741

EBM INDUSTRIES MANAGEMENT GROUP INC p 474
100 Hyde Rd, Farmington CT 06032
Tel (860) 674-1515 SIC 5084

EBM-PAPST INC p 474
100 Hyde Rd, Farmington CT 06032
Tel (860) 674-1515 SIC 5084 3564

FRC FOUNDERS CORP p 575
1 Lafayette Pl Ste 3, Greenwich CT 06830
Tel (203) 661-6601
SIC 8741 1311 1389 8731 5084

■ **GEMS SENSORS INC** p 598
1 Cowles Rd, Plainville CT 06062
Tel (860) 747-3000
SIC 3824 5084 3812 3625 3613

CELLMARK USA LLC p 274
2 Corporate Dr 5, Shelton CT 06484
Tel (203) 541-9000 SIC 5169 5051 5084

■ **ITT WATER & WASTEWATER USA INC** p 768
1 Greenwich Pl Ste 2, Shelton CT 06484
Tel (203) 712-8999 SIC 5084

■ **UNITED RENTALS (NORTH AMERICA) INC** p 1511
100 Frist Stamford 700, Stamford CT 06902
Tel (203) 622-3131 SIC 7353 7359 5084

GARDNER DENVER NASH LLC p 592
2 Trefoil Dr, Trumbull CT 06611
Tel (203) 459-3923
SIC 5084 3563 8711 3561

MORRIS GROUP INC p 990
910 Day Hill Rd, Windsor CT 06095
Tel (860) 687-3300 SIC 5084

BARLOWORLD USA INC p 155
1105 N Market St Ste 1300, Wilmington DE 19801
Tel (302) 427-2765 SIC 5084 7699 7359

■ **DELAWARE CAPITAL FORMATION INC** p 423
501 Silverside Rd Ste 5, Wilmington DE 19809
Tel (302) 793-4921
SIC 5084 3463 3542 3823

■ **DELAWARE CAPITAL HOLDINGS INC** p 423
501 Silverside Rd Ste 5, Wilmington DE 19809
Tel (302) 793-4921 SIC 5084 3533 7699

FRANKE USA HOLDING INC p 574
1105 N Market St Ste 1300, Wilmington DE 19801
Tel (615) 462-4000 SIC 3589 5023 5084

AMERICAN SHRINKWRAP CO p 79
1901 Mason Ave, Daytona Beach FL 32117
Tel (800) 229-2904 SIC 5084

ANSA MCAL TRADING INC p 93
11403 Nw 39th St, Doral FL 33178
Tel (305) 599-8766
SIC 8741 5084 5085 4731

KELLY TRACTOR CO p 809
8255 Nw 58th St, Doral FL 33166
Tel (305) 592-5360
SIC 5082 5083 7359 7353 5084 7699

PANTROPIC POWER INC p 1112
8205 Nw 58th St, Doral FL 33166
Tel (305) 477-3329
SIC 5084 5085 5063 7353

STEWART & STEVENSON FDDA LLC p 1389
5040 University Blvd W, Jacksonville FL 32216
Tel (904) 737-7330 SIC 5084 7699

MITSUBISHI HITACHI POWER SYSTEMS AMERICAS INC p 977
400 Colonial Center Pkwy # 400, Lake Mary FL 32746
Tel (407) 688-6100 SIC 5084 1796

HIG CAPITAL PARTNERS III LP p 690
1450 Brickell Ave # 3100, Miami FL 33131
Tel (305) 379-2322
SIC 6211 5084 7352 7699 8748 3842

M-SKO IAS HOLDINGS INC p 890
1395 Brickell Ave Ste 800, Miami FL 33131
Tel (786) 871-2904 SIC 5084

■ **HD SUPPLY WATERWORKS GROUP INC** p 673
501 W Church St Ste 100, Orlando FL 32805
Tel (407) 841-4755
SIC 5051 5074 5084 5099

RING POWER CORP p 1235
500 World Commerce Pkwy, Saint Augustine FL 32092
Tel (904) 201-7400 SIC 5082 5084 7353

FLORIDA IRRIGATION SUPPLY INC p 559
300 Central Park Dr, Sanford FL 32771
Tel (407) 425-6669 SIC 5084

AERO HARDWARE & SUPPLY INC p 30
300 International Pkwy, Sunrise FL 33325
Tel (954) 845-1040 SIC 5084 5085

ADAMS AIR & HYDRAULICS INC p 21
7209 E Adamo Dr, Tampa FL 33619
Tel (813) 626-4128 SIC 5084

FLORIDA LIFT SYSTEMS LLC p 559
115 S 78th St, Tampa FL 33619
Tel (904) 764-7662 SIC 5084 7359 7699

YANMAR AMERICA CORP p 1635
101 International Pkwy, Adairsville GA 30103
Tel (770) 877-9894
SIC 5084 7699 5083 3519

FLINT EQUIPMENT HOLDINGS INC p 557
1206 Blaylock St, Albany GA 31705
Tel (229) 888-1212 SIC 5084

▲ **GENUINE PARTS CO** p 605
2999 Wildwood Pkwy, Atlanta GA 30339
Tel (770) 953-1700
SIC 5013 5531 3714 5084 5085 5021

■ **HD SUPPLY HOLDINGS LLC** p 673
3100 Cumberland Blvd Se # 1700, Atlanta GA 30339
Tel (770) 852-9000
SIC 5051 5074 5084 5099

LOR INC p 878
2170 Piedmont Rd Ne, Atlanta GA 30324
Tel (404) 486-5600 SIC 6799 5084 3443

YANCEY BROS CO p 1634
330 Lee Industrial Blvd # 1, Austell GA 30168
Tel (770) 941-2424
SIC 5082 5084 7699 7353

HITACHI KOKI USA LTD p 696
1111 Broadway Ave, Braselton GA 30517
Tel (770) 925-1774 SIC 5084

AUTOMATIONDIRECT.COM INC p 134
3505 Hutchinson Rd, Cumming GA 30040
Tel (770) 889-2858 SIC 5084

METSO AUTOMATION p 957
2425 Commerce Ave Ste 100, Duluth GA 30096
Tel (770) 476-3641 SIC 5084

VALMET INC p 1541
2425 Commerce Ave Ste 100, Duluth GA 30096
Tel (770) 263-7863 SIC 3554 5084

HEIDELBERG AMERICAS INC p 680
1000 Gutenberg Dr Nw, Kennesaw GA 30144
Tel (770) 419-6500 SIC 5084

HEIDELBERG USA INC p 680
1000 Gutenberg Dr Nw, Kennesaw GA 30144
Tel (770) 419-6500 SIC 5084 3555

OCAMPOS INC p 1072
480 Tam Oshanter Dr Se, Marietta GA 30067
Tel (770) 509-2595 SIC 5084

ACE INDUSTRIES INC p 16
6295 Mcdonough Dr, Norcross GA 30093
Tel (770) 441-0898 SIC 5084

DEUTZ CORP p 433
3883 Steve Reynolds Blvd, Norcross GA 30093
Tel (770) 564-7100 SIC 5084

SIDEL INC p 1319
5600 Sun Ct, Norcross GA 30092
Tel (678) 221-3000 SIC 5084

JCB INC p 780
2000 Bamford Blvd, Pooler GA 31322
Tel (912) 447-2000
SIC 5082 5084 3531 3537

JCB MANUFACTURING INC p 780
2000 Bamford Blvd, Pooler GA 31322
Tel (912) 447-2000 SIC 5084

CONTROL SOUTHERN INC p 364
3850 Lakefield Dr, Suwanee GA 30024
Tel (770) 495-3100 SIC 5084

DOOSAN INDUSTRIAL VEHICLE AMERICA CORP p 451
2905 Shawnee Indus Way, Suwanee GA 30024
Tel (770) 831-2200 SIC 5084

DOOSAN INFRACORE AMERICA CORP p 451
2905 Shawnee Industrial W, Suwanee GA 30024
Tel (770) 831-2200 SIC 5084 5082

HAWTHORNE PACIFIC CORP p 670
94-025 Farrington Hwy, Waipahu HI 96797
Tel (808) 676-0227 SIC 5084 7353

NORCO INC p 1047
1125 W Amity Rd, Boise ID 83705
Tel (208) 336-1643
SIC 5084 5169 7352 5999 3548 2813

WESTERN STATES EQUIPMENT CO p 1600
500 E Overland Rd, Meridian ID 83642
Tel (208) 888-2287 SIC 5082 7699 5084

ASSOCIATED MATERIAL HANDLING INDUSTRIES INC p 120
133 N Swift Rd, Addison IL 60101
Tel (630) 588-8800 SIC 5084 7699 7353

PARTS TOWN LLC p 1118
1150 N Swift Rd Ste A, Addison IL 60101
Tel (708) 865-7278 SIC 5084

PT HOLDINGS LLC p 1189
1150 N Swift Rd Ste A, Addison IL 60101
Tel (800) 438-8898
SIC 5084 5046 7699 6719

STS OPERATING INC p 1394
2301 W Windsor Ct, Addison IL 60101
Tel (630) 317-2700 SIC 5084

GREAT LAKES SYNERGY CORP p 634
85 W Algonquin Rd Ste 600, Arlington Heights IL 60005
Tel (847) 437-0200 SIC 5084 4226 4213

HANCHETT PAPER CO p 656
4000 Ferry Rd, Aurora IL 60502
Tel (630) 978-1000 SIC 5084 5199

ILLINOIS AUTO ELECTRIC CO p 732
700 Enterprise St, Aurora IL 60504
Tel (630) 862-3300
SIC 5084 5013 5083 5078 7699 3519

MITUTOYO AMERICA CORP p 978
965 Corporate Blvd, Aurora IL 60502
Tel (630) 820-9666 SIC 5084 7373

HEADCO INDUSTRIES INC p 673
2601 Parkes Dr, Broadview IL 60155
Tel (708) 681-4400 SIC 5085 3599 5084

CHS CAPITAL LLC p 304
300 N La Salle Dr # 4925, Chicago IL 60654
Tel (312) 876-1840 SIC 5084

▲ **LAWSON PRODUCTS INC** p 848
8770 W Bryn Mawr Ave # 639, Chicago IL 60631
Tel (773) 304-5050
SIC 5072 5085 5084 5013

MH EQUIPMENT CO p 958
2001 Hartman, Chillicothe IL 61523
Tel (309) 579-8020 SIC 5084

MH LOGISTICS CORP p 958
2001 Hartman, Chillicothe IL 61523
Tel (309) 579-8030 SIC 5084

MAZAK OPTONICS CORP p 924
2725 Galvin Ct, Elgin IL 60124
Tel (847) 252-4500 SIC 5084

LIFT SOURCE INC p 865
1815 Landmeier Rd, Elk Grove Village IL 60007
Tel (847) 678-3450 SIC 5999 5084

WYNRIGHT CORP p 1630
2500 Elmhurst Rd, Elk Grove Village IL 60007
Tel (847) 595-9400 SIC 5084 3535 8711

PATTEN INDUSTRIES INC p 1121
635 W Lake St, Elmhurst IL 60126
Tel (630) 279-4400 SIC 5084 5082 7353

LANCO INTERNATIONAL INC p 842
3111 167th St, Hazel Crest IL 60429
Tel (708) 596-5200
SIC 3531 8711 5084 3536 7353 3537

STAR SU CO LLC p 1378
5200 Prairie Stone Pkwy, Hoffman Estates IL 60192
Tel (847) 649-1450 SIC 5084

EQUIPMENT DEPOT OF ILLINOIS INC p 506
751 Expressway Dr, Itasca IL 60143
Tel (847) 836-5005
SIC 5084 5087 5063 7699

■ **DAYTON ELECTRIC MFG CO** p 417
100 Grainger Pkwy, Lake Forest IL 60045
Tel (847) 535-1000 SIC 5063 5084 5072

■ **GRAINGER INTERNATIONAL INC** p 629
100 Grainger Pkwy, Lake Forest IL 60045
Tel (847) 535-1000
SIC 5074 5084 5085 5072

▲ **WW GRAINGER INC** p 1628
100 Grainger Pkwy, Lake Forest IL 60045
Tel (847) 535-1000
SIC 5063 5084 5075 5085 5072

GF MACHINING SOLUTIONS LLC p 609
560 Bond St, Lincolnshire IL 60069
Tel (847) 913-5300 SIC 5084

UNICARRIERS AMERICAS CORP p 1502
240 N Prospect St, Marengo IL 60152
Tel (800) 871-5438 SIC 3537 3519 5084

INTERLAKE MECALUX INC p 753
1600 N 25th Ave, Melrose Park IL 60160
Tel (708) 344-9999 SIC 5084 2542

BI-STATE PACKAGING INC p 181
4905 77th Ave E, Milan IL 61264
Tel (309) 736-8500 SIC 5199 5084

■ **JOHN DEERE CONSTRUCTION & FORESTRY CO** p 788
1 John Deere Pl, Moline IL 61265
Tel (309) 765-8000 SIC 5084 5082

SUMITOMO ELECTRIC CARBIDE INC p 1398
1001 E Business Center Dr, Mount Prospect IL 60056
Tel (847) 635-0044 SIC 5084

PLANT EQUIPMENT CO p 1154
2515 5th Ave, Rock Island IL 61201
Tel (309) 786-3369 SIC 5084

KOMATSU AMERICA INDUSTRIES LLC p 827
1701 Golf Rd Ste 1-100, Rolling Meadows IL 60008
Tel (847) 437-5800 SIC 5084

M & R PRINTING EQUIPMENT INC p 889
440 Medinah Rd, Roselle IL 60172
Tel (800) 736-6431 SIC 3555 3552 5084

MISUMI USA INC p 976
1717 N Penny Ln Ste 200, Schaumburg IL 60173
Tel (800) 681-7475 SIC 5084

BARREL ACCESSORIES AND SUPPLY CO INC p 156
2595 Palmer Ave, University Park IL 60484
Tel (708) 534-0900 SIC 5085 5084

DOALL CO p 446
1480 S Wolf Rd, Wheeling IL 60090
Tel (847) 495-6800 SIC 5085 5084

INDECK POWER EQUIPMENT CO p 736
1111 Willis Ave, Wheeling IL 60090
Tel (847) 541-8300 SIC 5084 5074 7359

■ **POWER SOLUTIONS INC** p 1165
201 Mittel Dr, Wood Dale IL 60191
Tel (630) 350-9400 SIC 5084

▲ **POWER SOLUTIONS INTERNATIONAL INC** p 1165
201 Mittel Dr, Wood Dale IL 60191
Tel (630) 350-9400 SIC 5084

GOSS INTERNATIONAL CORP p 626
9018 Heritage Pkwy # 1200, Woodridge IL 60517
Tel (630) 796-7560 SIC 3555 5084

■ **CATALENT PHARMA SOLUTIONS LLC** p 264
2210 Lake Shore Dr, Woodstock IL 60098
Tel (815) 338-9500 SIC 5084

TOYOTA INDUSTRIES NORTH AMERICA INC p 1466
3030 Barker Dr, Columbus IN 47201
Tel (812) 341-3810 SIC 3585 5084

TOYOTA MATERIAL HANDLING USA INC p 1466
5559 Inwood Dr, Columbus IN 47201
Tel (800) 381-5879 SIC 5084

DEHCO INC p 422
3601 Charlotte Ave, Elkhart IN 46517
Tel (574) 294-2684
SIC 2891 5031 5074 5014 5084

BRAKE SUPPLY CO INC p 207
5501 Foundation Blvd, Evansville IN 47725
Tel (812) 467-1000
SIC 5082 5084 5088 5013 3532

KOCH ENTERPRISES INC p 825
14 S 11th Ave, Evansville IN 47712
Tel (812) 465-9800
SIC 3363 5075 3559 5084 2891 3069

FLODRAULIC GROUP INC p 557
3539 N 700 W, Greenfield IN 46140
Tel (317) 890-3700 SIC 5084

NAHI LLC p 1006
3539 N 700 W, Greenfield IN 46140
Tel (317) 890-3700 SIC 5084

ITR NORTH AMERICA LLC p 768
6301 Northwind Pkwy, Hobart IN 46342
Tel (219) 947-8230 SIC 5084

■ **CUMMINS CROSSPOINT LLC** p 401
2601 Fortune Cir E 300c, Indianapolis IN 46241
Tel (317) 243-7979
SIC 5084 7538 5063 3519

■ **CUMMINS CROSSPOINT LLC** p 401
2601 Fortune Cir E Ste 30, Indianapolis IN 46241
Tel (317) 243-7979 SIC 5084 7538 3519

TECHNIKS LLC p 1431
9930 E 56th St, Indianapolis IN 46236
Tel (317) 803-8000 SIC 5084 5049

ARIENS SPECIALTY BRANDS LLC p 108
1919 Hospitality Dr, Jasper IN 47546
Tel (800) 457-7444 SIC 5084

NOVAE CORP p 1062
1 Novae Pkwy, Markle IN 46770
Tel (260) 758-9800 SIC 5084 3524

MARCO GROUP INTERNATIONAL INC p 905
3425 E Locust St, Davenport IA 52803
Tel (563) 324-2519 SIC 5084 5032

S J SMITH CO INC p 1262
3707 W River Dr, Davenport IA 52802
Tel (563) 324-5237 SIC 5169 5084 5999

CPM HOLDINGS INC p 387
2975 Airline Cir, Waterloo IA 50703
Tel (336) 248-5181 SIC 5084

G W VAN KEPPEL CO p 587
1801 N 9th St, Kansas City KS 66101
Tel (913) 281-4800
SIC 5082 7699 5084 7359

CARAVAN INGREDIENTS INC p 252
7905 Quivira Rd, Lenexa KS 66215
Tel (913) 890-5500
SIC 2099 2821 5084 2087

GRUNDFOS PUMPS CORP p 642
17100 W 118th Ter, Olathe KS 66061
Tel (913) 227-3400 SIC 5084

TVH PARTS CO p 1494
16355 S Lone Elm Rd, Olathe KS 66062
Tel (913) 829-1000 SIC 5084

CENTRAL STATES THERMO KING INC p 280
7200 W 132nd St Ste 270, Overland Park KS 66213
Tel (888) 566-5743 SIC 5078 7623 5084

FERRELLGAS INC p 538
7500 College Blvd # 1000, Overland Park KS 66210
Tel (913) 661-1500 SIC 5084 5172

▲ **FERRELLGAS PARTNERS LP** p 538
7500 College Blvd # 1000, Overland Park KS 66210
Tel (913) 661-1500 SIC 5084 5172

HANTOVER INC p 659
5200 W 110th St Ste 200, Overland Park KS 66211
Tel (913) 214-4800 SIC 5099 5084

TANK CONNECTION LLC p 1424
3609 N 16th St, Parsons KS 67357
Tel (620) 423-0251 SIC 5084 3443

I2 ASIA LLC p 725
21983 W 83rd St, Shawnee KS 66227
Tel (913) 422-1600 SIC 5084

IBT INC p 726
9400 W 55th St, Shawnee Mission KS 66203
Tel (913) 677-3151 SIC 5085 5084

BERRY COMPANIES INC p 176
3223 N Hydraulic St, Wichita KS 67219
Tel (316) 838-3321
SIC 5082 7353 7699 5084

FLINT HILLS RESOURCES LLC p 557
4111 E 37th St N, Wichita KS 67220
Tel (316) 828-5500 SIC 5169 5084

FOLEY EQUIPMENT CO p 563
1550 S West St, Wichita KS 67213
Tel (316) 943-4211 SIC 5084 5082 5083

FOLEY INDUSTRIES INC p 563
1550 S West St, Wichita KS 67213
Tel (316) 943-4211
SIC 5082 5084 7353 6512

KRAUSS-MAFFEI CORP p 829
7095 Industrial Rd, Florence KY 41042
Tel (859) 283-0200 SIC 5084 3559

MAZAK CORP p 924
8025 Production Dr, Florence KY 41042
Tel (859) 342-1700 SIC 3541 5084

BROWN FOODSERVICE INC p 219
500 E Clayton Ln, Louisa KY 41230
Tel (606) 638-1139
SIC 5142 5141 5084 5087

CALDWELL TANKS INC p 238
4000 Tower Rd, Louisville KY 40219
Tel (502) 964-3361 SIC 3443 5084 3441

CARDINAL CARRYOR INC p 252
1055 Grade Ln, Louisville KY 40213
Tel (502) 363-6641
SIC 5084 7699 7359 5085 3535

MATERIAL HANDLING SYSTEMS INC p 919
3955 E Blue Lick Rd, Louisville KY 40229
Tel (502) 636-0690 SIC 5084

ORR CORP p 1095
11601 Interchange Dr, Louisville KY 40229
Tel (502) 774-5791 SIC 5084

JOHN H CARTER CO INC p 788
17630 Perkins Rd Ste West, Baton Rouge LA 70810
Tel (225) 751-3788 SIC 5084

MOODY-PRICE LLC p 987
18320 Petroleum Dr, Baton Rouge LA 70809
Tel (225) 751-7001 SIC 5084

SETPOINT INTEGRATED SOLUTIONS INC p 1309
19011 Highland Rd, Baton Rouge LA 70809
Tel (225) 753-3290 SIC 5085 5084

CHARTER SUPPLY CO p 291
8100 Ambssdor Cffery Pkwy, Broussard LA 70518
Tel (337) 837-2724 SIC 5084

WHITCO SUPPLY LLC p 1605
200 N Morgan Ave, Broussard LA 70518
Tel (337) 837-2440 SIC 5084

BABEN MANAGEMENT LLC p 143
3400 Industrial Park, Houma LA 70363
Tel (985) 879-2487 SIC 5084 3599

RED BALL OXYGEN CO INC p 1215
609 N Market St, Shreveport LA 71107
Tel (318) 425-6300
SIC 5084 5085 5169 5099 5531 5013

MAINE OXY-ACETYLENE SUPPLY CO p 898
22 Albiston Way, Auburn ME 04210
Tel (207) 784-5788 SIC 5169 5084

ALBAN TRACTOR CO INC p 45
8531 Pulaski Hwy, Baltimore MD 21237
Tel (410) 686-7777 SIC 5082 5084 7699

BHS CORRUGATED - NORTH AMERICA INC p 180
9103 Yellow Brick Rd N, Baltimore MD 21237
Tel (410) 574-1550 SIC 5084 7699 3316

PHILLIPS CORP p 1144
7390 Coca Cola Dr Ste 200, Hanover MD 21076
Tel (800) 878-4747 SIC 5084 7373 3542

SAFEWARE INC p 1266
4403 Forbes Blvd, Lanham MD 20706
Tel (301) 683-1234 SIC 5084

■ **GE INFRASTRUCTURE SENSING INC** p 596
1100 Technology Park Dr # 100, Billerica MA 01821
Tel (978) 437-1000
SIC 3823 5084 3699 3674 3663 3625

SEURAT HOLDINGS INC p 1309
5 Fortune Dr, Billerica MA 01821
Tel (877) 489-9449 SIC 3544 5084

METSO USA INC p 957
133 Federal St Ste 302, Boston MA 02110
Tel (617) 369-7850 SIC 3554 5084

HAYES PUMP INC p 670
66 Old Powder Mill Rd I, Concord MA 01742
Tel (978) 369-8800 SIC 5084 3561

ABEL WOMACK INC p 11
1 International Way, Lawrence MA 01843
Tel (978) 989-9400 SIC 5084 7699

HTP INC p 715
272 Duchaine Blvd, New Bedford MA 02745
Tel (508) 763-8071 SIC 5084 3443

PLUMBERS SUPPLY CO p 1156
429 Church St, New Bedford MA 02745
Tel (508) 985-4966 SIC 5074 5084 5082

THG CORP p 1447
70 Bearfoot Rd, Northborough MA 01532
Tel (508) 393-7660
SIC 5085 5084 3569 3728 3625 3494

EMERSON-SWAN INC p 492
300 Pond St Ste 1, Randolph MA 02368
Tel (781) 986-2000 SIC 5084 5074

METHODS MACHINE TOOLS INC p 954
65 Union Ave, Sudbury MA 01776
Tel (978) 443-5388 SIC 5084

NEW ENGLAND ICE CREAM CORP p 1030
555 Constitution Dr, Taunton MA 02780
Tel (508) 824-0500 SIC 5084

OLYMPUS SCIENTIFIC SOLUTIONS AMERICAS INC p 1083
48 Woerd Ave, Waltham MA 02453
Tel (781) 419-3900 SIC 5084

NORTHLAND INDUSTRIAL TRUCK CO INC p 1057
6 Jonspin Rd, Wilmington MA 01887
Tel (978) 658-5900 SIC 5084 7699 7359

PACIFIC PACKAGING PRODUCTS INC p 1105
24 Industrial Way, Wilmington MA 01887
Tel (978) 657-9100
SIC 5113 5199 5084 5162 2671 2653

KRAFT POWER CORP p 829
199 Wildwood Ave, Woburn MA 01801
Tel (781) 938-9100 SIC 5084 7699

ABB FLEXIBLE AUTOMATION INC p 9
1250 Brown Rd, Auburn Hills MI 48326
Tel (248) 391-9000 SIC 5084

MORRELL INC p 990
3333 Bald Mountain Rd, Auburn Hills MI 48326
Tel (248) 373-1600
SIC 5084 5065 3621 3643 3559 3357

BELCO INDUSTRIES INC p 169
9138 W Belding Rd, Belding MI 48809
Tel (616) 794-0410
SIC 3567 5084 3541 3535 3444

H H BARNUM CO p 650
7915 Lochlin Dr, Brighton MI 48116
Tel (800) 695-3055 SIC 5084

SCHULER INC p 1290
7145 Commerce Blvd, Canton MI 48187
Tel (734) 207-7200 SIC 5084 3444 3599

SHIVELY BROTHERS INC p 1317
2919 S Grand Traverse St, Flint MI 48507
Tel (810) 232-7401 SIC 5084 5085

MORRISON INDUSTRIES INC p 990
1825 Monroe Ave Nw, Grand Rapids MI 49505
Tel (616) 447-3838 SIC 5084 7699 7359

OLIVER PRODUCTS CO p 1082
445 6th St Nw, Grand Rapids MI 49504
Tel (616) 456-7711 SIC 5084 5199 3053

STILES MACHINERY INC p 1389
3965 44th St Se, Grand Rapids MI 49512
Tel (616) 698-7500 SIC 5084

■ **AUTOCAM CORP** p 134
4180 40th St Se, Kentwood MI 49512
Tel (616) 698-0707
SIC 3714 3572 3841 5084

ALTA EQUIPMENT CO INC p 61
13211 Merriman Rd, Livonia MI 48150
Tel (248) 449-6700 SIC 3537 5084

■ **CUMMINS BRIDGEWAY LLC** p 401
21810 Clessie Ct, New Hudson MI 48165
Tel (248) 573-1600 SIC 5084 7538 3519

K & S PROPERTY INC p 798
21810 Clessie Ct, New Hudson MI 48165
Tel (248) 573-1600 SIC 5084 3519

KENDALL ELECTRIC INC p 810
5101 S Sprinkle Rd, Portage MI 49002
Tel (800) 632-5422 SIC 5063 7629 5084

PARI ROBOTICS INC p 1114
2930 Technology Dr, Rochester Hills MI 48309
Tel (248) 377-4447 SIC 5084

IWKA HOLDING CORP p 769
6600 Center Dr, Sterling Heights MI 48312
Tel (586) 795-2000
SIC 3549 5084 7371 8711

HOUGEN MANUFACTURING INC p 711
3001 Hougen Dr, Swartz Creek MI 48473
Tel (810) 635-7111
SIC 5084 3545 3546 3541

SECO TOOLS LLC p 1298
2805 Bellingham Dr, Troy MI 48083
Tel (248) 528-5200 SIC 5084 3545

PRODUCTION TOOL SUPPLY CO LLC p 1180
8655 E 8 Mile Rd, Warren MI 48089
Tel (586) 755-2200 SIC 5085 5084

ARROW MOTOR & PUMP INC p 113
629 Cent St, Wyandotte MI 48192
Tel (734) 285-7860
SIC 7694 5063 7699 5084

NOTT CO p 1062
4480 Round Lake Rd W, Arden Hills MN 55112
Tel (651) 415-3400
SIC 5084 5085 3492 3053

ISTATE TRUCK INC p 767
2601 American Blvd E, Bloomington MN 55425
Tel (952) 854-2044 SIC 5084

FORCE AMERICA INC p 565
501 Cliff Rd E Ste 100, Burnsville MN 55337
Tel (952) 707-1300 SIC 5084 3568

■ **ROSEMOUNT INC** p 1251
8200 Market Blvd, Chanhassen MN 55317
Tel (952) 906-8888
SIC 3823 3824 3545 5084 3829

WERNER ELECTRIC VENTURES LLC p 1592
7450 95th St S, Cottage Grove MN 55016
Tel (651) 458-3701 SIC 5063 5084 5085

BRAAS CO p 206
7970 Wallace Rd, Eden Prairie MN 55344
Tel (952) 937-8902 SIC 5084

GRAIN MILLERS INC p 629
10400 Viking Dr Ste 301, Eden Prairie MN 55344
Tel (952) 829-8821 SIC 2041 5084

JACOBS INDUSTRIES INC p 775
8096 Excelsior Blvd, Hopkins MN 55343
Tel (612) 339-9500
SIC 2841 2087 2099 2844 5084 6794

■ **3M INTERAMERICA INC** p 2
2501 Old Hudson Rd, Maplewood MN 55144
Tel (651) 733-1110
SIC 5113 5085 5065 5084 5122 8741

DESIGN READY CONTROLS INC p 432
9325 Winnetka Ave N, Minneapolis MN 55445
Tel (763) 565-3000 SIC 5084 3613 3561

EATON CORP p 473
505 Hghway 169 N Ste 1200, Minneapolis MN 55441
Tel (763) 595-7777 SIC 5084

GDG HOLDINGS INC p 595
2901 E 78th St, Minneapolis MN 55425
Tel (952) 854-2044 SIC 5084

HALDEMAN-HOMME INC p 653
430 Industrial Blvd Ne, Minneapolis MN 55413
Tel (612) 331-4880 SIC 5021 5211 5084

INTERSTATE POWER SYSTEMS INC p 758
2901 E 78th St, Minneapolis MN 55425
Tel (952) 854-2044 SIC 5084

PRODUCTIVITY INC p 1180
15150 25th Ave N, Minneapolis MN 55447
Tel (763) 476-8600 SIC 5085 5084

TWIN CITY FAN COMPANIES LTD p 1495
5959 Trenton Ln N, Minneapolis MN 55442
Tel (763) 551-7500 SIC 3564 5084

ZIEGLER INC p 1643
901 W 94th St, Minneapolis MN 55420
Tel (952) 888-4121 SIC 5082 5084

■ **D B INDUSTRIES INC** p 406
3833 Sala Way, Red Wing MN 55066
Tel (651) 388-8282 SIC 5099 5084 7352

MIDWEST SIGN & SCREEN PRINTING SUPPLY CO INC p 968
45 Maryland Ave E, Saint Paul MN 55117
Tel (651) 489-9999 SIC 5084 5063

POWER/MATION DIVISION INC p 1165
1310 Energy Ln, Saint Paul MN 55108
Tel (651) 605-3300
SIC 5085 5065 5084 5045 8742 7549

SMYTH COMPANIES LLC p 1335
1085 Snelling Ave N, Saint Paul MN 55108
Tel (651) 646-4544
SIC 2679 2752 3993 7389 5084 7699

■ **CUMMINS NPOWER LLC** p 401
1600 Buerkle Rd, White Bear Lake MN 55110
Tel (800) 642-0085
SIC 5084 5063 7538 3519

PUCKETT MACHINERY CO p 1190
100 Caterpillar Dr, Flowood MS 39232
Tel (601) 969-6000
SIC 5082 5084 5063 7699

TATUM DEVELOPMENT CORP p 1426
11 Parkway Blvd, Hattiesburg MS 39401
Tel (601) 544-6043
SIC 5141 5084 4924 3443

MEDART INC p 935
124 Manufacturers Dr, Arnold MO 63010
Tel (636) 282-2300 SIC 5084 5088

CROWN PACKAGING CORP p 395
17854 Chstrfld Aprt Rd, Chesterfield MO 63005
Tel (636) 681-8000
SIC 5113 5169 5131 5084

EXPERITEC INC p 520
504 Trade Center Blvd, Chesterfield MO 63005
Tel (636) 681-1500 SIC 5085 5084

ERB EQUIPMENT CO INC p 507
200 Erb Industrial Dr, Fenton MO 63026
Tel (636) 349-0200 SIC 5082 7353 5084

COGENT INC p 334
318 Brdwy St, Kansas City MO 64105
Tel (816) 221-0650 SIC 5084 5082 7359

SCHENCK PROCESS LLC p 1286
7901 Nw 107th Ter, Kansas City MO 64153
Tel (816) 891-9300 SIC 5084

VC999 PACKAGING SYSTEMS INC p 1545
419 E 11th Ave, Kansas City MO 64116
Tel (816) 472-8999 SIC 5084 3565

CRADER EQUIPMENT CO p 388
808 Highway 34 W, Marble Hill MO 63764
Tel (573) 238-2675 SIC 5083 5084

KAISER MIDWEST INC p 800
808 Highway 34 W, Marble Hill MO 63764
Tel (573) 238-2675 SIC 5083 5084

HYDROMAT INC p 723
11600 Adie Rd, Maryland Heights MO 63043
Tel (314) 432-0070 SIC 5084

APEX OIL CO INC p 96
8235 Forsyth Blvd Ste 400, Saint Louis MO 63105
Tel (314) 889-9600 SIC 4412 5084

HOUSE OF TOOLS AND ENGINEERING INC p 711
2021 Congressional Dr, Saint Louis MO 63146
Tel (314) 731-4444 SIC 5084

INDOFF INC p 739
11816 Lackland Rd Ste 200, Saint Louis MO 63146
Tel (314) 997-1122 SIC 5021 5044 5084

SBI INC p 1285
8500 Valcour Ave, Saint Louis MO 63123
Tel (314) 615-2000
SIC 5199 5122 7334 5084

WESTERN DIESEL SERVICES INC p 1598
1100 Research Blvd, Saint Louis MO 63132
Tel (314) 868-8620 SIC 5084 7538

WIESE HOLDING CO p 1608
1445 Woodson Rd, Saint Louis MO 63132
Tel (314) 997-4444 SIC 5084 7359

WIESE MATERIAL HANDLING INC p 1608
1435 Woodson Rd, Saint Louis MO 63132
Tel (314) 997-4210 SIC 5084

2 M CO INC p 1
5249 Holiday Ave, Billings MT 59101
Tel (406) 245-1490
SIC 5084 5083 5074 5051

BOSSELMAN INC p 202
3123 W Stolley Park Rd, Grand Island NE 68801
Tel (308) 381-2800
SIC 5541 5411 5812 7011 5172 5084

GLOBAL INDUSTRIES INC p 617
1804 E 4th St, Grand Island NE 68801
Tel (800) 247-6621
SIC 7992 3589 3444 5084 5083 3535

■ **CUMMINS CENTRAL POWER LLC** p 401
10088 S 136th St, Omaha NE 68138
Tel (402) 551-7678
SIC 5084 7538 5999 3519

DULTMEIER SALES LIMITED LIABILITY CO p 460
13808 Industrial Rd, Omaha NE 68137
Tel (402) 333-1444 SIC 5083 5084

NMC GROUP INC p 1045
11002 Sapp Brothers Dr, Omaha NE 68138
Tel (402) 891-8600 SIC 5082 5084

CASHMAN EQUIPMENT CO p 263
3300 Saint Rose Pkwy, Henderson NV 89052
Tel (702) 649-8777
SIC 5084 5063 7353 7699

CALTROL INC p 243
1385 Pama Ln Ste 111, Las Vegas NV 89119
Tel (702) 966-1800 SIC 5084

MATHESON TRI-GAS INC p 919
150 Allen Rd Ste 302, Basking Ridge NJ 07920
Tel (908) 991-9200 SIC 2813 5084

■ **XYLEM DEWATERING SOLUTIONS INC** p 1633
84 Floodgate Rd, Bridgeport NJ 08014
Tel (410) 243-4900 SIC 7353 3561 5084

BROTHER INTERNATIONAL CORP p 219
200 Crossing Blvd, Bridgewater NJ 08807
Tel (908) 704-1700
SIC 5044 3579 3559 5084 5064 5065

LINDE GAS USA LLC p 868
200 Somset Cor B Ste 7000, Bridgewater NJ 08807
Tel (908) 464-8100 SIC 2813 5084

KEYENCE CORP OF AMERICA p 815
669 River Dr Ste 403, Elmwood Park NJ 07407
Tel (201) 930-0100 SIC 3825 5084 3674

JASON INDUSTRIAL INC p 778
340 Kaplan Dr, Fairfield NJ 07004
Tel (973) 227-4904 SIC 5084 3052

■ **KYOCERA DOCUMENT SOLUTIONS AMERICA INC** p 833
225 Sand Rd, Fairfield NJ 07004
Tel (973) 808-8444 SIC 5044 5084 5065

HANWA AMERICAN CORP p 659
Parker Plz 400 Kelby St F, Fort Lee NJ 07024
Tel (201) 363-4500
SIC 5051 5172 5031 5084 5146

ATLANTIC DETROIT DIESEL ALLISON LLC p 126
180 Route 17 South, Lodi NJ 07644
Tel (201) 489-5800 SIC 5084 7538 7389

ARGO TURBOSERVE CORP p 107
160 Chubb Ave Ste 102, Lyndhurst NJ 07071
Tel (201) 804-6200 SIC 5084

EASTERN LIFT TRUCK CO INC p 472
549 E Linwood Ave, Maple Shade NJ 08052
Tel (856) 779-8880 SIC 5084 7699 7359

JOHNSON & TOWERS INC p 790
2021 Briggs Rd, Mount Laurel NJ 08054
Tel (856) 234-6990
SIC 5084 5013 7699 7538 5085

PANASONIC CORP OF NORTH AMERICA p 1111
2 Riverfront Plz Ste 200, Newark NJ 07102
Tel (201) 348-7000
SIC 5064 5045 5065 5044 5084 5063

GEA MECHANICAL EQUIPMENT US INC p 597
100 Fairway Ct, Northvale NJ 07647
Tel (201) 767-3900 SIC 5084 7699

GEA WESTFALIA SEPARATOR INC p 597
100 Fairway Ct, Northvale NJ 07647
Tel (201) 767-3900 SIC 5083 5084 3523

ARAMSCO INC p 102
1480 Grandview Ave, Paulsboro NJ 08066
Tel (856) 686-7700
SIC 5085 5084 5136 5139

GLATT AIR TECHNIQUES INC p 614
20 Spear Rd, Ramsey NJ 07446
Tel (201) 825-6308 SIC 5084

BOBST NORTH AMERICA INC p 196
146 Harrison Ave, Roseland NJ 07068
Tel (973) 226-8000 SIC 5084

GAFFNEY-KROESE ELECTRICAL SUPPLY CORP p 589
50 Randolph Rd, Somerset NJ 08873
Tel (732) 885-9000 SIC 5063 5084 5085

HAMON CORP p 656
58 E Main St, Somerville NJ 08876
Tel (908) 333-2000
SIC 1629 3564 3499 5084

BINDER MACHINERY CO INC p 183
2820 Hamilton Blvd, South Plainfield NJ 07080
Tel (908) 561-9000
SIC 5082 5084 7353 7699

HANWHA HOLDINGS (USA) INC p 659
300 Frank W Burr Blvd # 52, Teaneck NJ 07666
Tel (609) 655-2500 SIC 5169 5013 5084

ARAMSCO HOLDINGS INC p 102
1480 Grand View Ave, Thorofare NJ 08086
Tel (856) 686-7700
SIC 5085 5136 5084 5139

HMP SERVICES HOLDING INC p 698
721 Union Blvd, Totowa NJ 07512
Tel (973) 812-0400 SIC 5084 5199

PROCESS EQUIPMENT & SERVICE CO INC p 1179
5680 Us 64, Farmington NM 87401
Tel (505) 327-2222
SIC 3443 5084 7699 3533

JOHNSTON PAPER CO INC p 791
2 Eagle Dr, Auburn NY 13021
Tel (315) 253-8435 SIC 5113 5084

MAKERBOT INDUSTRIES LLC p 899
1 Metrotech Ctr Fl 21, Brooklyn NY 11201
Tel (347) 334-6800 SIC 3621 3625 5084

API HEAT TRANSFER INC p 96
2777 Walden Ave Ste 1, Buffalo NY 14225
Tel (716) 684-6700 SIC 5084

SEFAR INC p 1300
111 Calumet St, Depew NY 14043
Tel (716) 683-4050
SIC 5131 5051 5084 3496 2297 2221

MULLER MARTINI CORP p 999
456 Wheeler Rd, Hauppauge NY 11788
Tel (631) 582-4343 SIC 5084 7699

▲ **MSC INDUSTRIAL DIRECT CO INC** p 996
75 Maxess Rd, Melville NY 11747
Tel (516) 812-2000
SIC 5084 5085 5063 5072

NIKON AMERICAS INC p 1043
1300 Walt Whitman Rd Fl 2, Melville NY 11747
Tel (631) 547-4200 SIC 5043 5084

■ **SID TOOL CO INC** p 1319
75 Maxess Rd, Melville NY 11747
Tel (516) 812-2000 SIC 5085 5084

IHI INC p 731
150 E 52nd St Fl 24, New York NY 10022
Tel (212) 599-8100
SIC 5099 8732 8711 5084

ITOCHU INTERNATIONAL INC p 768
1251 Avenue Of The Americ, New York NY 10020
Tel (212) 818-8000
SIC 5131 5084 5065 5051 5153 5141

KANEMATSU USA INC p 802
500 5th Ave Fl 29, New York NY 10110
Tel (212) 704-9400
SIC 5084 5051 5065 5153

KPS CAPITAL PARTNERS LP p 829
485 Lexington Ave Fl 31, New York NY 10017
Tel (212) 338-5100
SIC 3541 6722 3545 5084

MARUBENI AMERICA CORP p 913
375 Lexington Ave, New York NY 10017
Tel (212) 450-0100
SIC 5131 5084 5012 5169 5172 5094

MITSUBISHI CORP (AMERICAS) p 977
655 3rd Ave, New York NY 10017
Tel (212) 605-2000
SIC 5051 5172 5141 5153 5169 5084

MITSUBISHI INTERNATIONAL CORP p 978
655 3rd Ave Ste 800, New York NY 10017
Tel (212) 605-2000
SIC 5051 5172 5141 5153 5169 5084

MITSUI & CO (USA) INC p 978
200 Park Ave Fl 35, New York NY 10166
Tel (212) 878-4000
SIC 5051 5094 5084 5153 5172 5169

NIPPON STEEL & SUMITOMO METAL USA INC p 1044
1251 Ave Of The Ave Fl 23, New York NY 10020
Tel (212) 486-7150 SIC 5051 5084

SOJITZ CORP OF AMERICA p 1337
1120 Ave Of The, New York NY 10036
Tel (212) 704-6500
SIC 5065 5084 5169 5051 5099 5052

SUMITOMO CORP OF AMERICAS p 1398
300 Madison Ave, New York NY 10017
Tel (212) 207-0700
SIC 5051 5172 5084 5063 5141

HUNTER DOUGLAS INC p 719
1 Blue Hill Plz Ste 1569, Pearl River NY 10965
Tel (845) 664-7000 SIC 2591 3444 5084

H O PENN MACHINERY CO INC p 650
122 Noxon Rd, Poughkeepsie NY 12603
Tel (845) 452-1200 SIC 5082 5084

■ GOULDS PUMPS INC p 627
240 Fall St, Seneca Falls NY 13148
Tel (315) 568-2811 SIC 3561 5084

■ ITT GOULDS PUMPS INC p 768
240 Fall St, Seneca Falls NY 13148
Tel (914) 641-2129 SIC 3561 5084

HITACHI AMERICA LTD p 696
50 Prospect Ave, Tarrytown NY 10591
Tel (914) 332-5800
SIC 5084 5065 3577 5063 5045 3651

CARL ZEISS INC p 256
1 Zeiss Dr, Thornwood NY 10594
Tel (914) 747-1800
SIC 3827 5049 3829 5084 3826

OERLIKON METCO (US) INC p 1075
1101 Prospect Ave, Westbury NY 11590
Tel (516) 334-1300 SIC 3399 5084 3479

IDG USA LLC p 729
2100 The Oaks Pkwy, Belmont NC 28012
Tel (704) 398-5600 SIC 5085 5084

INDUSTRIAL DISTRIBUTION GROUP INC p 740
2100 The Oaks Pkwy, Belmont NC 28012
Tel (704) 398-5600 SIC 5084 7699

■ ATI PRODUCTS INC p 124
5100 W WT Harris Blvd H, Charlotte NC 28269
Tel (800) 438-0660 SIC 5083 5084 5085

BARLOWORLD HANDLING LLC p 155
7621 Little Ave Ste 201, Charlotte NC 28226
Tel (704) 588-1300 SIC 5084

CAROLINA HANDLING LLC p 259
3101 Piper Ln, Charlotte NC 28208
Tel (704) 357-6273 SIC 5084

CAROLINA TRACTOR & EQUIPMENT CO INC p 259
9000 Statesville Rd, Charlotte NC 28269
Tel (704) 596-6700
SIC 5082 5084 5013 7353 7359 7629

LIFTONE LLC p 865
440 E Westinghouse Blvd, Charlotte NC 28273
Tel (704) 588-1300 SIC 5084

MURATA MACHINERY USA INC p 1001
2120 Queen City Dr, Charlotte NC 28208
Tel (704) 875-9280 SIC 5084 5085 3542

SCHAEFER SYSTEMS INTERNATIONAL INC p 1286
10021 Westlake Dr, Charlotte NC 28273
Tel (704) 944-4500
SIC 3089 5046 5084 5099 7372

SOUTHEAST INDUSTRIAL EQUIPMENT INC p 1346
12200 Steele Creek Rd, Charlotte NC 28273
Tel (704) 363-6432 SIC 7353 7359 5084

SOUTHERN PUMP & TANK CO LLC p 1350
4800 N Graham St, Charlotte NC 28269
Tel (704) 596-4373 SIC 5084 1799

STORK UNITED CORP p 1392
3201 Rotary Dr, Charlotte NC 28269
Tel (704) 598-7171 SIC 5084 3552 3556

ARC3 GASES INC p 103
1636 Us Highway 301 S, Dunn NC 28334
Tel (910) 892-4016
SIC 2813 5084 5169 7359 7692

MACHINE & WELDING SUPPLY CO p 892
1660 Us Highway 301 S, Dunn NC 28334
Tel (910) 892-4016 SIC 5084 5169

CROSS TECHNOLOGIES INC p 394
4400 Piedmont Pkwy, Greensboro NC 27410
Tel (336) 856-6000 SIC 5084 3492

GENEVA HOLDINGS INC p 603
8015 Piedmont Triad Pkwy, Greensboro NC 27409
Tel (336) 275-9936 SIC 5084 5063

TENCARVA MACHINERY CO LLC p 1437
1115 Pleasant Ridge Rd, Greensboro NC 27409
Tel (336) 665-1435 SIC 5084

DILLON SUPPLY CO p 440
440 Civic Blvd, Raleigh NC 27610
Tel (919) 838-4200
SIC 5084 5085 5051 5074 5072

JF ACQUISITION LLC p 785
1330 Saint Marys St # 210, Raleigh NC 27605
Tel (757) 857-5700 SIC 5084 1799 7299

PANTHER SUMMIT INDUSTRIES INC p 1111
4807 Beryl Rd, Raleigh NC 27606
Tel (919) 828-0641 SIC 5082 5084 4931

RDO CONSTRUCTION EQUIPMENT CO p 1212
2000 Industrial Dr, Bismarck ND 58501
Tel (701) 223-5798 SIC 5082 5084 7353

FISHER SAND & GRAVEL CO p 552
3020 Energy Dr, Dickinson ND 58601
Tel (701) 456-9184 SIC 1442 3532 5084

RDO EQUIPMENT CO p 1212
700 7th St S, Fargo ND 58103
Tel (701) 239-8700
SIC 5083 5082 5084 7699 7359 7353

ACME ELECTRIC MOTOR INC p 17
1705 13th Ave N, Grand Forks ND 58203
Tel (701) 746-2823
SIC 5084 5063 5082 5072 5251 5211

FREEMAN MANUFACTURING & SUPPLY CO p 577
1101 Moore Rd, Avon OH 44011
Tel (440) 934-1902
SIC 5084 3087 3543 2821

EQUIPMENT DEPOT OHIO INC p 506
4331 Rossplain Dr, Blue Ash OH 45236
Tel (513) 891-0600 SIC 5084

ARGO-HYTOS INC p 107
1835 N Research Dr, Bowling Green OH 43402
Tel (419) 353-6070 SIC 5084

TOWLIFT INC p 1464
1395 Valley Belt Rd, Brooklyn Heights OH 44131
Tel (216) 749-6800 SIC 5084 7699 7359

▲ CINTAS CORP p 308
6800 Cintas Blvd, Cincinnati OH 45262
Tel (513) 459-1200
SIC 7218 2337 2326 5084

CLARKE POWER SERVICES INC p 322
3133 E Kemper Rd, Cincinnati OH 45241
Tel (513) 771-2200 SIC 5084

HICKMAN WILLIAMS & CO p 690
250 E 5th St Ste 300, Cincinnati OH 45202
Tel (513) 621-1946
SIC 5051 5052 5169 5085 5084

RUMPKE TRANSPORTATION CO LLC p 1258
10795 Hughes Rd, Cincinnati OH 45251
Tel (513) 851-0122
SIC 3561 5084 7537 4953

ENPROTECH CORP p 500
4259 E 49th St, Cleveland OH 44125
Tel (216) 206-0080 SIC 5084

■ KAR PRODUCTS p 804
1301 E 9th St Ste 700, Cleveland OH 44114
Tel (216) 416-7200 SIC 5013 5084 5072

PARK CORP p 1115
6200 Riverside Dr, Cleveland OH 44135
Tel (216) 267-4870
SIC 3547 1711 3443 5084 6512 7999

STEIN INC p 1385
1929 E Royalton Rd Ste C, Cleveland OH 44147
Tel (440) 526-9301 SIC 3399 3312 5084

FCX PERFORMANCE INC p 533
3000 E 14th Ave, Columbus OH 43219
Tel (614) 324-6050 SIC 5084 5085 3494

GARDNER INC p 592
3641 Interchange Rd, Columbus OH 43204
Tel (614) 351-1325 SIC 5084 6512

HY-TEK MATERIAL HANDLING INC p 722
2222 Rickenbacker Pkwy W, Columbus OH 43217
Tel (614) 497-2500
SIC 5084 5013 7538 7513 1796

OHIO TRANSMISSION CORP p 1078
1900 Jetway Blvd, Columbus OH 43219
Tel (614) 342-6247 SIC 5084 5085

POWER DISTRIBUTORS LLC p 1165
3700 Paragon Dr, Columbus OH 43228
Tel (614) 876-3533 SIC 5084

PROSPECT MOLD & DIE CO p 1184
1100 Main St, Cuyahoga Falls OH 44221
Tel (330) 929-3311 SIC 5084 3544

GOSIGER INC p 626
108 Mcdonough St, Dayton OH 45402
Tel (937) 228-5174 SIC 5084

■ SAFETY SOLUTIONS INC p 1266
6161 Shamrock Ct, Dublin OH 43016
Tel (614) 799-9900 SIC 5084 5136 5139

ATS SYSTEMS OREGON INC p 129
425 Enterprise Dr, Lewis Center OH 43035
Tel (541) 738-0932 SIC 3569 5084

■ CINTAS CORP NO 2 p 308
6800 Cintas Blvd, Mason OH 45040
Tel (513) 459-1200 SIC 5084

■ INTELLIGRATED SYSTEMS INC p 750
7901 Innovation Way, Mason OH 45040
Tel (866) 936-7300 SIC 3535 5084 7371

■ INTELLIGRATED SYSTEMS LLC p 750
7901 Innovation Way, Mason OH 45040
Tel (513) 701-7300 SIC 3535 5084 7371

■ INTELLIGRATED SYSTEMS OF OHIO LLC p 750
7901 Innovation Way, Mason OH 45040
Tel (513) 701-7300 SIC 3535 5084 3537

■ ESKO-GRAPHICS INC p 509
8535 Gander Creek Dr, Miamisburg OH 45342
Tel (937) 454-1721 SIC 5084 7372

ROLLS-ROYCE ENERGY SYSTEMS INC p 1247
105 N Sandusky St, Mount Vernon OH 43050
Tel (740) 393-8888 SIC 3511 5084 8711

CROWN EQUIPMENT CORP p 395
44 S Washington St, New Bremen OH 45869
Tel (419) 629-2311 SIC 5084

DAIFUKU AMERICA CORP p 408
6700 Tussing Rd, Reynoldsburg OH 43068
Tel (614) 863-1888 SIC 5084

DICKMAN SUPPLY INC p 438
1991 St Marys Ave, Sidney OH 45365
Tel (937) 492-6166 SIC 5063 5084

MMH AMERICAS INC p 979
4401 Gateway Blvd, Springfield OH 45502
Tel (414) 764-6200 SIC 3536 5084 6719

MMH HOLDINGS INC p 979
4401 Gateway Blvd, Springfield OH 45502
Tel (937) 525-5533 SIC 3536 5084

BOSTWICK-BRAUN CO p 203
7349 Crossleigh Ct, Toledo OH 43617
Tel (419) 259-3600
SIC 5072 5084 5063 5083 5023

■ IMPACT PRODUCTS LLC p 734
2840 Centennial Rd, Toledo OH 43617
Tel (419) 841-2891
SIC 5084 5087 2392 3089

KEN MILLER SUPPLY INC p 810
1537 Blachleyville Rd, Wooster OH 44691
Tel (330) 264-9146 SIC 5084

PENNSYLVANIA TOOL SALES & SERVICE INC p 1130
625 Bev Rd, Youngstown OH 44512
Tel (330) 758-0845 SIC 7699 5085 5084

A G EQUIPMENT CO p 5
3401 W Albany St, Broken Arrow OK 74012
Tel (918) 250-7386 SIC 3563 5084

BLACKHAWK INDUSTRIAL DISTRIBUTION INC p 187
1501 Sw Expressway Dr, Broken Arrow OK 74012
Tel (918) 663-3252 SIC 5085 3561 5084

■ TULSA WINCH INC p 1491
11135 S James Ave, Jenks OK 74037
Tel (918) 298-8300 SIC 5084 3566 3531

GREAT PLAINS OILFIELD RENTAL LLC p 634
777 Nw 63rd St, Oklahoma City OK 73116
Tel (405) 608-7777 SIC 5084

MERIDIAN DRILLING CO LLC p 948
11500 S Meridian Ave, Oklahoma City OK 73173
Tel (405) 691-1202 SIC 1381 1799 5084

■ UE MANUFACTURING LLC p 1499
10000 Nw 2nd St, Oklahoma City OK 73127
Tel (405) 947-3321 SIC 5084

■ UNITED ENGINES LLC p 1508
5555 W Reno Ave, Oklahoma City OK 73127
Tel (800) 955-3321
SIC 5013 5084 7538 7537

■ UNITED HOLDINGS LLC p 1509
5 N Mccormick St Ste 200, Oklahoma City OK 73127
Tel (405) 947-3321
SIC 5084 5013 7538 7537 3441

BERENDSEN FLUID POWER INC p 174
401 S Boston Ave Ste 1200, Tulsa OK 74103
Tel (918) 592-3781 SIC 5084

MIDCON INVESTORS INC p 964
401 S Boston Ave Ste 3600, Tulsa OK 74103
Tel (918) 587-7325 SIC 5084

■ ORS NASCO INC p 1096
907 S Detroit Ave Ste 500, Tulsa OK 74120
Tel (918) 781-5300 SIC 5085 5084

PAPE GROUP INC p 1112
355 Goodpasture Island Rd # 300, Eugene OR 97401
Tel (541) 334-3400
SIC 5084 5082 7699 6141 5599 4581

PAPE MATERIAL HANDLING INC p 1112
355 Goodpasture Island Rd, Eugene OR 97401
Tel (541) 683-5073 SIC 5084

EC CO p 474
2121 Nw Thurman St, Portland OR 97210
Tel (503) 224-3511
SIC 1731 7694 5063 5084

NMHG HOLDING CO p 1045
650 Ne Holladay St # 1600, Portland OR 97232
Tel (503) 721-6000 SIC 3537 5084

VESTAS-AMERICAN WIND TECHNOLOGY INC p 1552
1417 Sw Naito Pkwy # 100, Portland OR 97201
Tel (503) 327-2000 SIC 3523 3511 5084

GT&S INC p 644
5275 Tilghman St, Allentown PA 18104
Tel (610) 398-2211
SIC 4925 5169 5084 5085 2813 5172

AIRLINE HYDRAULICS CORP p 40
3557 Progress Dr, Bensalem PA 19020
Tel (610) 758-9400 SIC 5085 5084

GILES & RANSOME INC p 612
2975 Galloway Rd, Bensalem PA 19020
Tel (215) 639-4300 SIC 5082 5084 7353

FLSMIDTH INC p 561
2040 Avenue C, Bethlehem PA 18017
Tel (610) 264-6011 SIC 5084

■ CUMMINS POWER SYSTEMS LLC p 401
2727 Ford Rd, Bristol PA 19007
Tel (215) 785-6005
SIC 5084 5063 7538 7629 3519

MODERN GROUP LTD p 981
2501 Durham Rd, Bristol PA 19007
Tel (215) 943-9100 SIC 5084 7353 7699

MODERN HANDLING EQUIPMENT CO p 981
2501 Durham Rd Ste G, Bristol PA 19007
Tel (215) 943-9100 SIC 5084 7353

PRIMETALS TECHNOLOGIES USA HOLDINGS INC p 1175
501 Technology Dr, Canonsburg PA 15317
Tel (724) 514-8500 SIC 5084 6719

LEE SUPPLY CO INC p 851
305 1st St, Charleroi PA 15022
Tel (724) 483-3543 SIC 5082 5084

CAPP INC p 251
201 Marple Ave, Clifton Heights PA 19018
Tel (610) 394-1100 SIC 5084 3699

VICTREX USA INC p 1556
300 Conshohocken State Rd # 120, Conshohocken PA 19428
Tel (484) 342-6001 SIC 5084

OERLIKON USA HOLDING INC p 1075
5700 Mellon Rd, Export PA 15632
Tel (303) 273-9700
SIC 3563 3823 3699 3479 3599 5084

CLEVELAND BROTHERS HOLDINGS INC p 325
5300 Paxton St, Harrisburg PA 17111
Tel (717) 564-2121
SIC 7353 5082 5084 7629

GE RICHARDS GRAPHIC SUPPLIES CO INC p 596
928 Links Ave, Landisville PA 17538
Tel (717) 892-4620 SIC 5084 5045

AIRGAS SAFETY INC p 40
2501 Green Ln, Levittown PA 19057
Tel (215) 826-9000
SIC 5084 5085 3561 3841

MORGAN TRUCK BODY LLC p 989
111 Morgan Way, Morgantown PA 19543
Tel (610) 286-5025
SIC 3713 7532 5013 5084

LIFT INC p 865
3745 Hempland Rd, Mountville PA 17554
Tel (717) 295-1800 SIC 5084 7353

BECKWITH MACHINERY CO INC p 167
4565 William Penn Hwy, Murrysville PA 15668
Tel (724) 327-1300
SIC 5082 5084 7629 7353

▲ WESCO INTERNATIONAL INC p 1593
225 W Station Square Dr # 700, Pittsburgh PA 15219
Tel (412) 454-2200
SIC 5063 5084 5065 7389

AIRGAS INC p 40
259 N Radnor Chester Rd # 100, Radnor PA 19087
Tel (610) 687-5253
SIC 5169 5084 5085 2813 2819

AIRGAS USA LLC p 40
259 N Radnor Chester Rd # 100, Radnor PA 19087
Tel (610) 687-5253
SIC 5169 5084 5085 2813 2819

CAMBRIDGE-LEE HOLDINGS INC p 244
86 Tube Dr, Reading PA 19605
Tel (610) 926-4141 SIC 5051 3351 5084

FRES-CO SYSTEMS USA INC p 578
3005 State Rd, Telford PA 18969
Tel (215) 721-4600 SIC 5084 3565 2891

■ GE BETZ INC p 595
4636 Somerton Rd, Trevose PA 19053
Tel (215) 355-3300
SIC 2899 3826 5084 3823

BRIDON-AMERICAN CORP p 212
C280 New Commerce Blvd, Wilkes Barre PA 18706
Tel (570) 822-3349 SIC 3533 3532 5084

ENGEL MACHINERY INC p 498
3740 Board Rd, York PA 17406
Tel (717) 764-6818 SIC 5084 7699

VOITH TURBO INC p 1564
25 Winship Rd, York PA 17406
Tel (717) 767-3200 SIC 5084 5013

THIELSCH ENGINEERING INC p 1448
195 Frances Ave, Cranston RI 02910
Tel (401) 785-0241
SIC 5084 5043 5172 5085

MAHR FEDERAL INC p 897
1144 Eddy St, Providence RI 02905
Tel (401) 784-3100 SIC 5084

ENGINEERED SYSTEMS INC p 499
1121 Duncan Reidville Rd, Duncan SC 29334
Tel (864) 879-7438 SIC 5084

■ TRACTOR SUPPLY CO OF TEXAS LP p 1468
5401 Virginia Way, Brentwood TN 37027
Tel (877) 718-6750 SIC 5084 5999

ASSOCIATED PACKAGING INC p 121
435 Calvert Dr, Gallatin TN 37066
Tel (615) 452-2131 SIC 5199 5084

H T HACKNEY CO p 650
502 S Gay St Ste 300, Knoxville TN 37902
Tel (865) 546-1291
SIC 5141 5172 2434 5084

HOLSTON GASES INC p 702
545 W Baxter Ave, Knoxville TN 37921
Tel (865) 573-1917 SIC 5169 5084 2813

LILLY CO p 866
3613 Knight Arnold Rd, Memphis TN 38118
Tel (901) 363-6000
SIC 5084 7699 7359 5046

NEXAIR LLC p 1039
1385 Corporate Ave, Memphis TN 38132
Tel (901) 396-5050
SIC 5169 5084 7699 7359

BAILEY CO INC p 145
501 Cowan St, Nashville TN 37207
Tel (615) 242-0351 SIC 5084

FRANKE FOODSERVICE SUPPLY INC p 574
800 Aviation Pkwy, Smyrna TN 37167
Tel (615) 459-3486 SIC 5084

NISSAN TRADING CORP AMERICAS p 1044
1974 Midway Ln, Smyrna TN 37167
Tel (615) 220-7100
SIC 5013 5012 5051 5084

FLETCHLINE INC p 555
5480 Lakeview Rd, Springfield TN 37172
Tel (615) 382-0764 SIC 5084 1796

UNARCO MATERIAL HANDLING INC p 1502
701 16th Ave E, Springfield TN 37172
Tel (615) 384-3531 SIC 5084 2542

PETROSMITH EQUIPMENT LP p 1139
7435 Us Highway 277 S, Abilene TX 79606
Tel (325) 691-1085 SIC 5084 7353

NJ MALIN & ASSOCIATES LLC p 1045
15870 Midway Rd, Addison TX 75001
Tel (972) 458-2680 SIC 5046 5084

■ CUMMINS SOUTHERN PLAINS LLC p 401
600 N Watson Rd, Arlington TX 76011
Tel (817) 640-6801 SIC 5084 3519

■ ISCAR METALS INC p 766
300 Westway Pl, Arlington TX 76018
Tel (817) 258-3200 SIC 5084

JET SPECIALTY INC p 783
211 Market Ave, Boerne TX 78006
Tel (830) 331-9457 SIC 5084 5085

AIRGAS - SOUTHWEST INC p 40
4817 Agnes St, Corpus Christi TX 78405
Tel (361) 882-1141 SIC 5169 5084

AMERICAN STEEL INC p 80
2500 Agnes St, Corpus Christi TX 78405
Tel (361) 883-1706
SIC 5023 5051 5084 5191

BRIGGS EQUIPMENT INC p 212
10540 N Stemmons Fwy, Dallas TX 75220
Tel (214) 630-0808 SIC 5084

GAS EQUIPMENT CO INC p 593
11616 Harry Hines Blvd, Dallas TX 75229
Tel (972) 241-2333 SIC 5084 5085 3321

GRAPHIC SOLUTIONS GROUP INC p 632
4601 Spring Valley Rd, Dallas TX 75244
Tel (214) 748-3271 SIC 5084

SAMMONS ENTERPRISES INC p 1274
5949 Sherry Ln Ste 1900, Dallas TX 75225
Tel (214) 210-5000 SIC 5084 6311

24 HR SAFETY LLC p 2
4912 Railroad St, Deer Park TX 77536
Tel (337) 316-0541 SIC 5084

TETRA PAK INC p 1441
3300 Airport Rd, Denton TX 76207
Tel (940) 565-8800 SIC 2671 3565 5084

HYLA INC p 724
Prk W 1 & 2 1507 Lbj Fwy, Farmers Branch TX 75234
Tel (972) 573-0300 SIC 5084

HOWARD SUPPLY CO LLC p 713
4100 Intl Plz Ste 850, Fort Worth TX 76109
Tel (817) 529-9950 SIC 5084 5082

HYDRADYNE LLC p 723
15050 Faa Blvd, Fort Worth TX 76155
Tel (817) 391-1547 *SIC* 5084

PREFERRED PUMP & EQUIPMENT LP p 1169
2201 Scott Ave Ste 100, Fort Worth TX 76103
Tel (817) 536-9800
SIC 5084 5083 5074 3533 5082

■ ULTERRA DRILLING TECHNOLOGIES LP p 1500
420 Throckmorton St # 1110, Fort Worth TX 76102
Tel (817) 293-7555 *SIC* 5084 3533

BELL SUPPLY CO LLC p 170
114 E Foreline St, Gainesville TX 76240
Tel (940) 612-0612 *SIC* 5084

SES HOLDINGS LLC p 1308
114 E Foreline St, Gainesville TX 76240
Tel (940) 668-0251 *SIC* 6719 5084

SYNERGY ENERGY HOLDINGS LLC p 1415
114 E Foreline St, Gainesville TX 76240
Tel (940) 612-0417 *SIC* 5084

MASTER PUMPS & EQUIPMENT CORP p 918
805 Port America Pl # 100, Grapevine TX 76051
Tel (817) 251-6745 *SIC* 5084 7699

AIR LIQUIDE AMERICA LP p 39
9811 Katy Fwy Ste 100, Houston TX 77024
Tel (713) 624-8000
SIC 5084 3533 2813 3569

AXIP ENERGY SERVICES LP p 140
1301 Mckinney St Ste 900, Houston TX 77010
Tel (832) 294-6500 *SIC* 5084 7699

BAE SYSTEMS RESOLUTION INC p 144
1000 La St Ste 4950, Houston TX 77002
Tel (713) 868-7700
SIC 3713 5084 3711 7699 3351 3829

■ BEST EQUIPMENT SERVICE & SALES CO LLC p 177
8885 Monroe Rd, Houston TX 77061
Tel (713) 956-2002 *SIC* 5084

CAMERON TECHNOLOGIES INC p 245
4646 W Sam Houston Pkwy N, Houston TX 77041
Tel (713) 513-3300 *SIC* 5084 3533

CARRUTH-DOGGETT INC p 261
7110 North Fwy, Houston TX 77076
Tel (713) 675-7000 *SIC* 5084 7359 7699

■ DNOW LP p 446
7402 N Eldridge Pkwy, Houston TX 77041
Tel (281) 823-4700 *SIC* 5084 7353 3533

▲ DXP ENTERPRISES INC p 464
7272 Pinemont Dr, Houston TX 77040
Tel (713) 996-4700 *SIC* 5084 5063

EMPLOYEE OWNED HOLDINGS INC p 494
5500 N Sam Houston Pkwy W # 100, Houston TX 77086
Tel (281) 569-7000 *SIC* 5084

EQUIPMENT DEPOT LTD p 506
840 Gessner Rd Ste 950, Houston TX 77024
Tel (713) 365-2547
SIC 5083 5084 7359 7699 7353

■ EXTERRAN INC p 521
16666 Northchase Dr, Houston TX 77060
Tel (281) 836-7000 *SIC* 7353 5084

■ EXTERRAN TRINIDAD LLC p 521
12001 N Huston Rosslyn Rd, Houston TX 77086
Tel (281) 921-9337 *SIC* 7353 5084 1389

■ FET HOLDINGS LLC p 539
920 Memorial City Way, Houston TX 77024
Tel (281) 949-2500 *SIC* 5084

■ GE ENERGY MANUFACTURING INC p 596
1333 West Loop S Ste 700, Houston TX 77027
Tel (713) 803-0900 *SIC* 3621 3568 5084

GROVES INDUSTRIAL SUPPLY CORP p 642
7301 Pinemont Dr, Houston TX 77040
Tel (713) 675-4747 *SIC* 5085 5084 5198

HYDRAQUIP INC p 723
16330 Central Green Blvd # 200, Houston TX 77032
Tel (713) 680-1951 *SIC* 5084

INNOVATIVE ENERGY SERVICES INC p 744
16600 Park Row, Houston TX 77084
Tel (281) 392-5199 *SIC* 5084

MITSUBISHI CATERPILLAR FORKLIFT AMERICA INC p 977
2121 W Sam Houston Pkwy N, Houston TX 77043
Tel (713) 365-1000 *SIC* 3537 5084

MITSUBISHI HEAVY INDUSTRIES AMERICA INC p 977
20 Greenway Plz Ste 830, Houston TX 77046
Tel (346) 308-8800 *SIC* 5084

MUSTANG MACHINERY CO LTD p 1002
12800 Northwest Fwy, Houston TX 77040
Tel (713) 861-1440 *SIC* 5082 5084

▲ NATIONAL OILWELL VARCO INC p 1014
7909 Parkwood Circle Dr, Houston TX 77036
Tel (713) 346-7500 *SIC* 3533 3594 5084

■ NATIONAL OILWELL VARCO LP p 1014
1530 W Sam Houston Pkwy N, Houston TX 77043
Tel (713) 960-5100 *SIC* 3533 5082 5084

NCS MULTISTAGE LLC p 1022
19450 State Highway 249 # 200, Houston TX 77070
Tel (281) 453-2222 *SIC* 5084

▲ NOW INC p 1064
7402 N Eldridge Pkwy, Houston TX 77041
Tel (281) 823-4700 *SIC* 5084

PEARCE INDUSTRIES INC p 1126
12320 Main St, Houston TX 77035
Tel (713) 723-1050 *SIC* 5084 3533 5082

PON MATERIAL HANDLING NA INC p 1161
840 Gessner Rd Ste 950, Houston TX 77024
Tel (713) 365-2547 *SIC* 5084

PVI HOLDINGS INC p 1193
840 Gessner Rd Ste 950, Houston TX 77024
Tel (713) 365-6805 *SIC* 5085 5084 7699

RAWSON LP p 1209
2010 Mcallister Rd, Houston TX 77092
Tel (713) 684-1400 *SIC* 5085 5084

STEWART & STEVENSON CAPITAL CORP p 1388
601 W 38th St, Houston TX 77018
Tel (713) 868-7700
SIC 5084 5013 5078 5082 3711 3537

STEWART & STEVENSON LLC p 1389
1000 La St Ste 5900, Houston TX 77002
Tel (713) 751-2600
SIC 5084 5082 3533 7353

STEWART & STEVENSON POWER PRODUCTS LLC p 1389
1000 La St Ste 5900, Houston TX 77002
Tel (713) 751-2600
SIC 1389 5084 5082 3533 7353

SUN COAST RESOURCES INC p 1400
6405 Cavalcade St Bldg 1, Houston TX 77026
Tel (713) 844-9600
SIC 5172 2992 5084 1389

TOSHIBA INTERNATIONAL CORP p 1462
13131 W Little York Rd, Houston TX 77041
Tel (713) 466-0277
SIC 3621 5084 5063 3613 3594 3572

TOTAL SAFETY US INC p 1463
11111 Wilcrest Green Dr # 375, Houston TX 77042
Tel (713) 353-7100 *SIC* 8748 5084 7699

VALLEN SAFETY SUPPLY CO p 1540
521 N Sam Houston Pkwy E # 300, Houston TX 77060
Tel (281) 500-5000
SIC 5099 5084 5047 5063

WARTSILA HOLDING INC p 1577
11710 N Gessner Rd Ste A, Houston TX 77064
Tel (281) 233-6200 *SIC* 5084 1629

WARTSILA NORTH AMERICA INC p 1577
11710 N Gessner Rd Ste A, Houston TX 77064
Tel (281) 233-6200
SIC 1629 5084 1382 4789 3731

WAUKESHA-PEARCE INDUSTRIES INC p 1583
12320 Main St, Houston TX 77035
Tel (713) 723-1050 *SIC* 5084 5082 3621

WEATHERFORD ARTIFICIAL LIFT SYSTEMS LLC p 1586
2000 Saint James Pl, Houston TX 77056
Tel (713) 836-4000 *SIC* 3561 5084

WISENBAKER BUILDER SERVICES INC p 1619
1703 Westfield Loop Rd, Houston TX 77073
Tel (281) 233-4000 *SIC* 5023 5084 5031

EPRODUCTION SOLUTIONS LLC p 505
22001 Northpark Dr, Kingwood TX 77339
Tel (281) 348-1000 *SIC* 3491 5084 1389

VINSON PROCESS CONTROLS CO LP p 1558
2747 Highpoint Oaks Dr, Lewisville TX 75067
Tel (972) 459-8200 *SIC* 5084 3533 3498

ASSOCIATED SUPPLY CO INC p 121
2102 E Slaton Rd, Lubbock TX 79404
Tel (806) 745-2000 *SIC* 5084 5082 7353

GICON PUMPS & EQUIPMENT INC p 611
1001 Texas Ave, Lubbock TX 79401
Tel (806) 401-8287 *SIC* 5084 5074 5039

ABATIX CORP p 9
2400 Skyline Dr Ste 400, Mesquite TX 75149
Tel (214) 381-1146 *SIC* 5084 5085

WARREN EQUIPMENT CO p 1577
10325 Younger Rd, Midland TX 79706
Tel (432) 571-8462
SIC 5082 5084 7699 3563 7359

ALPHA MATERIALS HANDLING INC p 60
313 N 9th St, Midlothian TX 76065
Tel (972) 775-2555 *SIC* 5084

ELLIOTT ELECTRIC SUPPLY INC p 488
2526 N Stallings Dr, Nacogdoches TX 75964
Tel (936) 569-1184 *SIC* 5063 5084

■ ODESSA PUMPS AND EQUIPMENT INC p 1074
8161 Dorado Dr, Odessa TX 79765
Tel (432) 333-2817 *SIC* 5084

B S W INC p 142
111 Naida St, Pampa TX 79065
Tel (806) 669-1103 *SIC* 5082 5084

INDUSTRIAL AIRTOOL p 739
1305 W Jackson Ave, Pasadena TX 77506
Tel (713) 477-3144 *SIC* 5084

VENTECH ENGINEERS INTERNATIONAL CORP p 1548
1149 Ellsworth Dr Ofc, Pasadena TX 77506
Tel (713) 477-0201
SIC 1629 8711 3559 5084

VENTECH INC p 1548
1149 Ellsworth Dr Ofc, Pasadena TX 77506
Tel (713) 477-0201
SIC 8711 3491 5084 6512

■ B27 LLC p 143
1417 Gables Ct Ste 201, Plano TX 75075
Tel (972) 244-4350 *SIC* 8741 5084

HILTI OF AMERICA INC p 694
7250 Dallas Pkwy Ste 1000, Plano TX 75024
Tel (800) 879-8000 *SIC* 5084 3546 3825

HATFIELD AND CO INC p 668
2475 Discovery Blvd, Rockwall TX 75032
Tel (972) 288-7625 *SIC* 5084 3677 5074

MINER CORP p 973
11827 Tech Com Rd Ste 115, San Antonio TX 78233
Tel (210) 655-8600 *SIC* 5084

DARR EQUIPMENT LP p 412
350 Bank St, Southlake TX 76092
Tel (254) 420-2650
SIC 5084 7353 5013 4959

▲ INTEGRATED DRILLING EQUIPMENT HOLDINGS CORP p 749
25311 I 45 N Bldg 6, Spring TX 77380
Tel (281) 465-9393 *SIC* 3533 7539 5084

GLEN GEO ENTERPRISES INC p 614
13395 Murphy Rd, Stafford TX 77477
Tel (281) 242-6945 *SIC* 1799 5198 5084

PUFFER-SWEIVEN HOLDINGS INC p 1191
4230 Greenbriar Dr, Stafford TX 77477
Tel (281) 240-2000 *SIC* 5084

▲ LAYNE CHRISTENSEN CO p 848
1800 Hughes Landing Blvd, The Woodlands TX 77380
Tel (281) 475-2600
SIC 1781 1623 5084 1481 8748

ACCENT PACKAGING INC p 14
10131 Fm 2920 Rd, Tomball TX 77375
Tel (281) 251-3700 *SIC* 5051 5084 5085

ALIMAK HEK INC p 50
12552 Galveston Rd Ste A 160, Webster TX 77598
Tel (713) 640-8500
SIC 5084 7699 3535 3534

■ ROBBINS & MYERS INC p 1241
10586 N Highway 75, Willis TX 77378
Tel (936) 890-1064
SIC 3533 3443 3823 5084

PETERSEN INC p 1138
1527 N 2000 W, Ogden UT 84404
Tel (801) 731-1366
SIC 5084 3441 7692 3444

ADESA UTAH LLC p 22
780 S 5600 W, Salt Lake City UT 84104
Tel (801) 322-1234 *SIC* 5012 5521 5084

ARNOLD MACHINERY CO p 112
2975 W 2100 S, Salt Lake City UT 84119
Tel (801) 972-4000
SIC 5082 5084 5012 5083

BOART LONGYEAR MANUFACTURING AND DISTRIBUTION INC p 196
2640 W 1700 S, Salt Lake City UT 84104
Tel (801) 972-6430 *SIC* 1381 5084 3533

INDUSTRIAL SUPPLY CO INC p 740
1635 S 300 W, Salt Lake City UT 84115
Tel (801) 484-8644 *SIC* 5084 5085

SMITH POWER PRODUCTS INC p 1333
3065 W California Ave, Salt Lake City UT 84104
Tel (801) 262-2631
SIC 5084 7538 3714 5063

WHEELER MACHINERY CO p 1605
4901 W 2100 S, Salt Lake City UT 84120
Tel (801) 974-0511
SIC 5082 5084 7359 7353

HUSKY INJECTION MOLDING SYSTEMS INC p 721
288 North Rd, Milton VT 05468
Tel (905) 951-5000 *SIC* 5084 7699

JAMES RIVER EQUIPMENT INC p 777
11047 Leadbetter Rd, Ashland VA 23005
Tel (804) 748-9324 *SIC* 5084 5082

FIRST PIEDMONT CORP p 549
108 S Main St, Chatham VA 24531
Tel (434) 432-0211 *SIC* 4953 5084

FINCANTIERI MARINE SYSTEMS NORTH AMERICA INC p 543
800 Principal Ct Ste C, Chesapeake VA 23320
Tel (757) 548-6000 *SIC* 7699 5084

KAESER COMPRESSORS INC p 800
511 Sigma Dr, Fredericksburg VA 22408
Tel (540) 898-5500 *SIC* 5084

LIEBHERR MINING & CONSTRUCTION EQUIPMENT INC p 863
4100 Chestnut Ave, Newport News VA 23607
Tel (757) 245-5251 *SIC* 5082 5084 3532

WESTERN BRANCH DIESEL INC p 1597
3504 Shipwright St, Portsmouth VA 23703
Tel (757) 673-7000 *SIC* 5084 7699

MARYLAND AND VIRGINIA MILK PRODUCERS COOPERATIVE ASSOCIATION INC p 914
1985 Isaac Newton Sq W # 200, Reston VA 20190
Tel (703) 742-6800 *SIC* 5143 2026 5084

ARCET EQUIPMENT CO p 104
1700 Chamberlayne Ave, Richmond VA 23222
Tel (804) 644-4521 *SIC* 5085 5084 5169

KSB AMERICA CORP p 831
4415 Sarellen Rd, Richmond VA 23231
Tel (804) 222-1818
SIC 3561 3494 3625 5084

BUSCH CONSOLIDATED INC p 229
516 Viking Dr, Virginia Beach VA 23452
Tel (757) 463-7800 *SIC* 5084 3563

H D FOWLER CO INC p 649
13440 Se 30th St, Bellevue WA 98005
Tel (425) 746-8400
SIC 5084 5083 5085 3321

WEST COAST PAPER CO p 1594
6703 S 234th St Ste 120, Kent WA 98032
Tel (253) 850-1900
SIC 5085 5169 5084 2677

WESTERN INTEGRATED TECHNOLOGIES INC p 1598
13406 Se 32nd St, Kent WA 98032
Tel (800) 456-6248 *SIC* 5084

NORTH PACIFIC PAPER CO LLC p 1053
3001 Indl Way, Longview WA 98632
Tel (360) 636-6400 *SIC* 2621 5084 3554

NORTH WEST HANDLING SYSTEMS INC p 1054
1100 Sw 7th St, Renton WA 98057
Tel (425) 255-0500 *SIC* 5084 7699

PACIFIC POWER GROUP LLC p 1105
805 Broadway St Ste 700, Vancouver WA 98660
Tel (360) 887-7400
SIC 5088 3621 5063 3519 5084

USNR LLC p 1535
1981 Schurman Way, Woodland WA 98674
Tel (360) 225-8267
SIC 3585 3553 3625 1221 5084

SWANSON INDUSTRIES INC p 1411
2608 Smithtown Rd, Morgantown WV 26508
Tel (304) 292-0021
SIC 3593 3471 7629 5084

HAMMOND POWER SOLUTIONS INC p 656
1100 Lake St, Baraboo WI 53913
Tel (608) 356-3921 *SIC* 5084

■ FISERV SOLUTIONS LLC p 551
255 Fiserv Dr, Brookfield WI 53045
Tel (262) 879-5000 *SIC* 7374 2754 5084

WISCONSIN LIFT TRUCK CORP p 1619
3125 Intertech Dr, Brookfield WI 53045
Tel (262) 790-6230 *SIC* 5084 5085 7699

ALLIED DIESEL INC p 56
13015 W Custer Ave, Butler WI 53007
Tel (262) 781-7100 *SIC* 5084 5531 7699

STA-RITE INDUSTRIES LLC p 1374
293 S Wright St, Delavan WI 53115
Tel (888) 782-7483 *SIC* 3561 5084 5251

FABIO PERINI NORTH AMERICA INC p 523
3060 S Ridge Rd, Green Bay WI 54304
Tel (920) 336-5000 *SIC* 5084

PRICE ENGINEERING CO INC p 1174
1175 Cottonwood Ave, Hartland WI 53029
Tel (262) 369-2147 *SIC* 5084

CRANE ENGINEERING SALES INC p 389
707 Ford St, Kimberly WI 54136
Tel (920) 733-4425 *SIC* 5084 5085 5074

NELSON-JAMESON INC p 1025
2400 E 5th St, Marshfield WI 54449
Tel (715) 387-1151 *SIC* 5084

ENGMAN-TAYLOR CO INC p 499
W142n9351 Fountain Blvd, Menomonee Falls WI 53051
Tel (262) 255-9300 *SIC* 5084 5085

■ C&H DISTRIBUTORS LLC p 234
11200 W Parkland Ave, Milwaukee WI 53224
Tel (800) 607-8520 *SIC* 5084

RITE-HITE CO LLC p 1236
8900 N Arbon Dr, Milwaukee WI 53223
Tel (414) 355-2600 *SIC* 5084 3842 3448

RITE-HITE HOLDING CORP p 1237
8900 N Arbon Dr, Milwaukee WI 53223
Tel (414) 355-2600 *SIC* 5084 3449 3537

TAKKT AMERICA HOLDING INC p 1422
770 S 70th St, Milwaukee WI 53214
Tel (414) 443-1700 *SIC* 5084

GS GLOBAL RESOURCES INC p 643
926 Perkins Dr, Mukwonago WI 53149
Tel (262) 786-0100 *SIC* 5084

WEBEX INC p 1586
1035 Breezewood Ln, Neenah WI 54956
Tel (920) 729-6666 *SIC* 5084

GUSTAVE A LARSON CO p 648
W233n2869 Roundy Cir W, Pewaukee WI 53072
Tel (262) 542-0200
SIC 5075 5078 5084 5046

POCLAIN HYDRAULICS INC p 1158
1300 Grandview Pkwy, Sturtevant WI 53177
Tel (262) 321-0676 *SIC* 5084

SIC 5085 Industrial Splys Wholesale

BIRMINGHAM FASTENER & SUPPLY INC p 185
931 Avenue W, Birmingham AL 35214
Tel (205) 595-3511 *SIC* 5085 3452

■ MOTION INDUSTRIES INC p 992
1605 Alton Rd, Birmingham AL 35210
Tel (205) 956-1122 *SIC* 5085

RAM TOOL & SUPPLY CO INC p 1206
3620 8th Ave S Ste 200, Birmingham AL 35222
Tel (205) 714-3300 *SIC* 5085

SHOOK & FLETCHER INSULATION CO INC p 1317
4625 Valleydale Rd, Birmingham AL 35242
Tel (205) 991-7606 *SIC* 5033 1799 5085

THOMPSON TRACTOR CO INC p 1449
2258 Pinson Valley Pkwy, Birmingham AL 35217
Tel (334) 215-5000 *SIC* 5082 5084 5085

HWASEUNG AUTOMOTIVE AMERICA HOLDINGS INC p 722
100 Sonata Dr, Enterprise AL 36330
Tel (334) 348-9516 *SIC* 3069 5085

MARTIN INC p 912
125 N Court St, Florence AL 35630
Tel (256) 383-3131 *SIC* 5085

LG ELECTRONICS ALABAMA INC p 860
201 James Record Rd Sw, Huntsville AL 35824
Tel (256) 772-0623
SIC 3651 3695 5064 5085 5065 4225

TURNER SUPPLY CO p 1493
250 N Royal St, Mobile AL 36602
Tel (205) 252-6000 *SIC* 5085 5251

FASTENING SOLUTIONS INC p 531
3075 Selma Hwy, Montgomery AL 36108
Tel (334) 284-8300 *SIC* 5085 5072 5051

SOUTHERN FASTENING SYSTEMS LLC p 1348
635 Fairgrounds Rd, Muscle Shoals AL 35661
Tel (256) 381-3628
SIC 5084 5085 5251 5072

WHITESELL CORP p 1606
2703 Avalon Ave, Muscle Shoals AL 35661
Tel (256) 248-8500
SIC 3965 5085 3444 3452 3451

DRUMMOND CO INC p 457
1000 Urban Center Dr # 300, Vestavia AL 35242
Tel (205) 945-6500
SIC 1221 1222 3312 5052 5085 5172

EWING IRRIGATION PRODUCTS INC p 516
3441 E Harbour Dr, Phoenix AZ 85034
Tel (602) 437-9530 *SIC* 5085 5087 5074

CYTEC ENGINEERED MATERIALS INC p 406
2085 E Tech Cir Ste 300, Tempe AZ 85284
Tel (480) 730-2000 *SIC* 3769 5085 2821

POMWONDERFUL LLC p 1161
4805 Centennial Ste 100, Bakersfield CA 93301
Tel (310) 966-5800 *SIC* 5149 5148 5085

HASKEL INTERNATIONAL LLC p 667
100 E Graham Pl, Burbank CA 91502
Tel (818) 843-4000
SIC 3561 3594 5084 5085 3699

CENTRAL PURCHASING LLC p 280
3491 Mission Oaks Blvd, Camarillo CA 93012
Tel (805) 388-1000 *SIC* 5085 5961 5251

PRH PRO INC p 1173
13089 Peyton Dr Ste C362, Chino Hills CA 91709
Tel (714) 510-7226 *SIC* 5085

SMITH COOPER INTERNATIONAL INC p 1333
2867 Vail Ave, Commerce CA 90040
Tel (323) 890-4455 *SIC* 5085 3494

■ MT SUPPLY INC p 997
3505 Cadillac Ave Ste K2, Costa Mesa CA 92626
Tel (714) 434-4748 *SIC* 5085 5084

RENO JONES INC p 1224
2373 N Watney Way, Fairfield CA 94533
Tel (707) 422-4300 *SIC* 5199 5085 3221

S & S TOOL & SUPPLY INC p 1261
2700 Maxwell Way, Fairfield CA 94534
Tel (925) 335-4000
SIC 5085 7699 5072 7359

CALPINE CONTAINERS INC p 242
6425 N Palm Ave Ste 104, Fresno CA 93704
Tel (559) 519-7199
SIC 5113 5085 2441 2448

RJMS CORP p 1239
31010 San Antonio St, Hayward CA 94544
Tel (510) 675-0500 *SIC* 5084 5085 7699

GEORG FISCHER LLC p 606
9271 Jeronimo Rd, Irvine CA 92618
Tel (714) 731-8800 *SIC* 5051 5085

POM WONDERFUL HOLDINGS LLC p 1160
11444 W Olympic Blvd # 210, Los Angeles CA 90064
Tel (310) 966-5800 *SIC* 5149 5148 5085

▲ GENERAL FINANCE CORP p 600
39 E Union St Ste 206, Pasadena CA 91103
Tel (626) 584-9722 *SIC* 7359 5085

PENINSULA COMPONENTS INC p 1129
1300 Industrial Rd Ste 21, San Carlos CA 94070
Tel (650) 593-3288 *SIC* 5085 5065

CONTROLLED MOTION SOLUTIONS INC p 364
911 N Poinsettia St, Santa Ana CA 92701
Tel (661) 324-2260 *SIC* 5085

BAKERSFIELD PIPE AND SUPPLY INC p 146
3301 Zachary Ave, Shafter CA 93263
Tel (661) 589-9141 *SIC* 5051 5085

■ ARCONIC GLOBAL FASTENERS & RINGS INC p 106
3990a Heritage Oak Ct, Simi Valley CA 93063
Tel (310) 530-2220 *SIC* 5085 5072 5065

STEVEN ENGINEERING INC p 1388
230 Ryan Way, South San Francisco CA 94080
Tel (650) 588-9200 *SIC* 5085

RS HUGHES CO INC p 1255
1162 Sonora Ct, Sunnyvale CA 94086
Tel (408) 739-3211 *SIC* 5085

CITY OF COLORADO SPRINGS p 314
107 N Nevada Ave Ste 300, Colorado Springs CO 80903
Tel (719) 385-2489 *SIC* 5085

BRON TAPES INC p 217
875 W Ellsworth Ave, Denver CO 80223
Tel (303) 534-2002 *SIC* 5085

GENERAL AIR SERVICE & SUPPLY CO p 599
1105 Zuni St, Denver CO 80204
Tel (303) 892-7003
SIC 5169 5085 5084 5149

UNITED STATES WELDING INC p 1514
600 S Santa Fe Dr, Denver CO 80223
Tel (303) 777-2475
SIC 5169 5084 5085 5047 7359

MOTION & FLOW CONTROL PRODUCTS INC p 992
7941 Shaffer Pkwy, Littleton CO 80127
Tel (303) 666-2183 *SIC* 5085

MOTION AND FLOW CONTROL PRODUCTS INC p 992
7941 Shaffer Pkwy, Littleton CO 80127
Tel (303) 762-8012 *SIC* 5085 5074

▲ KAMAN CORP p 801
1332 Blue Hills Ave, Bloomfield CT 06002
Tel (860) 243-7100 *SIC* 5085 3721 3728

■ KAMAN INDUSTRIAL TECHNOLOGIES CORP p 801
1 Vision Way, Bloomfield CT 06002
Tel (860) 687-5000 *SIC* 3491 5085

■ PRAXAIR TECHNOLOGY INC p 1168
39 Old Ridgebury Rd, Danbury CT 06810
Tel (203) 837-2000
SIC 5172 5084 5169 5085

NEFCO CORP p 1024
411 Burnham St, East Hartford CT 06108
Tel (860) 290-9044 *SIC* 5085 5072

GREENWICH AEROGROUP INC p 638
475 Steamboat Rd Fl 2, Greenwich CT 06830
Tel (203) 618-4861
SIC 4581 5088 7699 5085

PLIMPTON & HILLS CORP p 1156
2 Brainard Rd, Hartford CT 06114
Tel (860) 522-4233 *SIC* 5074 5085

AZELIS AMERICAS INC p 140
262 Harbor Dr, Stamford CT 06902
Tel (203) 274-8691 *SIC* 5085 5046 5169

ALRO METALS SERVICE CENTER CORP p 61
6200 Pk Of Commerce Blvd, Boca Raton FL 33487
Tel (561) 997-6766 *SIC* 5051 5085

▲ QEP CO INC p 1194
1001 Brkn Snd Pkwy Nw A, Boca Raton FL 33487
Tel (561) 994-5550 *SIC* 5072 5085 2891

ANSA MCAL TRADING INC p 93
11403 Nw 39th St, Doral FL 33178
Tel (305) 599-8766
SIC 8741 5084 5085 4731

PANTROPIC POWER INC p 1112
8205 Nw 58th St, Doral FL 33166
Tel (305) 477-3329
SIC 5084 5085 5063 7353

HUGHES SUPPLY INC p 717
2920 Ford St, Fort Myers FL 33916
Tel (239) 334-2205
SIC 5063 5074 5075 5085 1711

W & O SUPPLY INC p 1568
2677 Port Industrial Dr, Jacksonville FL 32226
Tel (904) 354-3800 *SIC* 5085 5051

■ NESTOR SALES LLC p 1027
7337 Bryan Dairy Rd, Largo FL 33777
Tel (727) 544-6114 *SIC* 5013 5085

ALL AMERICAN CONTAINERS INC p 51
9330 Nw 110th Ave, Medley FL 33178
Tel (305) 887-0797 *SIC* 5085 5099

BRIDGESTONE HOSEPOWER LLC p 211
50 Industrial Loop N, Orange Park FL 32073
Tel (904) 264-1267 *SIC* 5085 3542

AERO HARDWARE & SUPPLY INC p 30
300 International Pkwy, Sunrise FL 33325
Tel (954) 845-1040 *SIC* 5084 5085

INDUSTRIAL CONTAINER SERVICES - FL LLC p 739
2400 Maitland Ctr, Zellwood FL 32798
Tel (407) 930-4182 *SIC* 5085

HAGEMEYER NORTH AMERICA HOLDINGS INC p 652
11680 Great Oaks Way, Alpharetta GA 30022
Tel (843) 745-2400 *SIC* 5085

PRO MARKETING INC p 1178
1350 Bluegrass Lakes Pkwy, Alpharetta GA 30004
Tel (770) 521-1421 *SIC* 5072 5085

BURKS COMPANIES p 227
191 Peachtree St Ne # 800, Atlanta GA 30303
Tel (404) 589-4600
SIC 1752 5085 7349 4953 8999

▲ GENUINE PARTS CO p 605
2999 Wildwood Pkwy, Atlanta GA 30339
Tel (770) 953-1700
SIC 5013 5531 3714 5084 5085 5021

▲ HD SUPPLY HOLDINGS INC p 673
3100 Cumberland Blvd Se # 1480, Atlanta GA 30339
Tel (770) 852-9000 *SIC* 5087 5072 5085

■ HDS HOLDING CORP p 673
3100 Cumberland Blvd Se, Atlanta GA 30339
Tel (770) 852-9000 *SIC* 5087 5072 5085

THERMAL CERAMICS INC p 1447
2102 Old Savannah Rd, Augusta GA 30906
Tel (706) 796-4200
SIC 3299 3255 5085 3296 3264 3053

BEARINGS & DRIVES INC p 166
607 Lower Poplar St, Macon GA 31201
Tel (478) 746-7623 *SIC* 5085

NAKANISHI MANUFACTURING CORP p 1006
1225 Voyles Rd, Winterville GA 30683
Tel (706) 353-0006 *SIC* 5085 3562

HEADCO INDUSTRIES INC p 673
2601 Parkes Dr, Broadview IL 60155
Tel (708) 681-4400 *SIC* 5085 3599 5084

VESUVIUS U S A CORP p 1552
1404 Newton Dr, Champaign IL 61822
Tel (217) 402-9204 *SIC* 3297 5085

BERLIN PACKAGING LLC p 175
525 W Monroe St Ste 1400, Chicago IL 60661
Tel (312) 876-9292 *SIC* 5085

CHS PRIVATE EQUITY V LP p 304
300 N La Salle Dr # 4925, Chicago IL 60654
Tel (312) 876-1840 *SIC* 5085

COLUMBIA PIPE & SUPPLY CO p 341
1120 W Pershing Rd, Chicago IL 60609
Tel (773) 927-6600 *SIC* 5051 5085 5074

▲ LAWSON PRODUCTS INC p 848
8770 W Bryn Mawr Ave # 639, Chicago IL 60631
Tel (773) 304-5050
SIC 5072 5085 5084 5013

■ RR DONNELLEY PRINTING CO LP p 1255
111 S Wacker Dr Ste 3500, Chicago IL 60606
Tel (312) 326-8000 *SIC* 2754 2752 5085

MCMASTER-CARR SUPPLY CO p 932
600 N County Line Rd, Elmhurst IL 60126
Tel (630) 834-9600 *SIC* 5085 5075

▲ ANIXTER INTERNATIONAL INC p 92
2301 Patriot Blvd, Glenview IL 60026
Tel (224) 521-8000 *SIC* 5063 5085

■ AFC CABLE SYSTEMS INC p 32
16100 Lathrop Ave, Harvey IL 60426
Tel (508) 998-1131
SIC 3429 3444 3599 5085

■ GRAINGER INTERNATIONAL INC p 629
100 Grainger Pkwy, Lake Forest IL 60045
Tel (847) 535-1000
SIC 5074 5084 5085 5072

▲ WW GRAINGER INC p 1628
100 Grainger Pkwy, Lake Forest IL 60045
Tel (847) 535-1000
SIC 5063 5084 5075 5085 5072

GROUP O INC p 642
4905 77th Ave E, Milan IL 61264
Tel (309) 736-8100
SIC 8742 7389 4226 5085

R & O SPECIALTIES INC p 1201
120 4th Ave E, Milan IL 61264
Tel (309) 736-8660 *SIC* 5085 5013 3479

FCA INC p 532
7601 John Deere Pkwy, Moline IL 61265
Tel (309) 792-3222 *SIC* 5085 5031

FCA LLC p 532
7601 John Deere Pkwy, Moline IL 61265
Tel (309) 792-3444
SIC 4783 5031 5085 2448

NTN BEARING CORP OF AMERICA p 1065
1600 Bishop Ct, Mount Prospect IL 60056
Tel (847) 298-7500 *SIC* 5085

NTN USA CORP p 1065
1600 Bishop Ct, Mount Prospect IL 60056
Tel (847) 298-4652 *SIC* 5085 3562 3568

SUPPLYCORE INC p 1407
303 N Main St Ste 800, Rockford IL 61101
Tel (815) 997-1624 *SIC* 5072 5085

METAL ONE HOLDINGS AMERICA INC p 952
6250 N River Rd Ste 6055, Rosemont IL 60018
Tel (847) 318-0019 *SIC* 5085 5051

MW INDUSTRIES INC p 1004
9501 Tech Blvd Ste 401, Rosemont IL 60018
Tel (847) 349-5760 *SIC* 6719 5085

KURIYAMA OF AMERICA INC p 832
360 E State Pkwy, Schaumburg IL 60173
Tel (847) 755-0360 *SIC* 5085 3052

BARREL ACCESSORIES AND SUPPLY CO INC p 156
2595 Palmer Ave, University Park IL 60484
Tel (708) 534-0900 *SIC* 5085 5084

DOALL CO p 446
1480 S Wolf Rd, Wheeling IL 60090
Tel (847) 495-6800 *SIC* 5085 5084

DOALL INDUSTRIAL SUPPLY CORP p 446
1480 S Wolf Rd, Wheeling IL 60090
Tel (800) 923-6255 *SIC* 5085

US TSUBAKI HOLDINGS INC p 1533
301 E Marquardt Dr, Wheeling IL 60090
Tel (847) 459-9500 *SIC* 5085 3568

US TSUBAKI POWER TRANSMISSION LLC p 1533
301 E Marquardt Dr, Wheeling IL 60090
Tel (847) 459-9500
SIC 3568 5085 5063 3714 3462 3325

SAMUEL STRAPPING SYSTEMS INC p 1275
1401 Davey Rd Ste 300, Woodridge IL 60517
Tel (630) 783-8900 *SIC* 3499 5085

KEM KREST LLC p 809
3221 Magnum Dr, Elkhart IN 46516
Tel (574) 389-2650
SIC 5169 5013 5085 4783 4225

TRI-STATE REFRACTORIES CORP p 1478
1127 E Virginia St, Evansville IN 47711
Tel (812) 425-3466 *SIC* 1741 5085

CENTRAL SUPPLY CO INC p 280
8900 E 30th St, Indianapolis IN 46219
Tel (317) 898-2411
SIC 5074 5063 5085 5719

HARRIS & FORD LLC p 663
9307 E 56th St, Indianapolis IN 46216
Tel (317) 591-0000 *SIC* 5169 5085

LEE SUPPLY CORP p 852
6610 Guion Rd, Indianapolis IN 46268
Tel (317) 290-2500
SIC 5074 5075 5064 5085 5031

FAIRFIELD MANUFACTURING CO INC p 525
2400 Sagamore Pkwy S, Lafayette IN 47905
Tel (765) 772-4000 *SIC* 3462 3714 5085

ILPEA INDUSTRIES INC p 733
745 S Gardner St, Scottsburg IN 47170
Tel (812) 752-2526 *SIC* 5085

STANZ CHEESE CO INC p 1377
1840 Commerce Dr, South Bend IN 46628
Tel (574) 232-6666
SIC 5142 5141 5148 5113 5087 5085

MULZER CRUSHED STONE INC p 1000
534 Mozart St, Tell City IN 47586
Tel (812) 547-7921
SIC 1422 3273 5191 5085

BOSSARD NORTH AMERICA INC p 202
6521 Production Dr, Cedar Falls IA 50613
Tel (319) 268-3700 *SIC* 5085

APACHE HOSE & BELTING CO INC p 96
4805 Bowling St Sw, Cedar Rapids IA 52404
Tel (319) 365-0471 *SIC* 3496 3052 5085

HUSQVARNA CONSTRUCTION PRODUCTS NORTH AMERICA INC p 721
17400 W 119th St, Olathe KS 66061
Tel (913) 928-1000
SIC 3541 3291 5085 5082 3425 2951

CHARLES WALKER NORTH AMERICA p 289
9400 W 55th St, Shawnee Mission KS 66203
Tel (913) 236-9233 *SIC* 5085

IBT INC p 726
9400 W 55th St, Shawnee Mission KS 66203
Tel (913) 677-3151 *SIC* 5085 5084

G T SALES & MANUFACTURING INC p 587
2202 S West St, Wichita KS 67213
Tel (316) 943-2171 *SIC* 5085 3053 3052

CARDINAL CARRYOR INC p 252
1055 Grade Ln, Louisville KY 40213
Tel (502) 363-6641
SIC 5084 7699 7359 5085 3535

ISCO INDUSTRIES INC p 766
100 Witherspoon St, Louisville KY 40202
Tel (502) 318-6626 *SIC* 5085 5083

PLUMBERS SUPPLY CO p 1156
1000 E Main St, Louisville KY 40206
Tel (502) 582-2261 *SIC* 5074 5085

PREMIER PACKAGING LLC p 1170
3900 Produce Rd, Louisville KY 40218
Tel (502) 935-8786 *SIC* 5085 5113 3086

MODERN WELDING CO INC p 981
2880 New Hartford Rd, Owensboro KY 42303
Tel (270) 685-4400
SIC 3443 5051 3441 5085

HENRY A PETTER SUPPLY CO LLC p 684
5110 Charter Oak Dr, Paducah KY 42001
Tel (270) 575-6922 *SIC* 5085

SETPOINT INTEGRATED SOLUTIONS INC p 1309
19011 Highland Rd, Baton Rouge LA 70809
Tel (225) 753-3290 *SIC* 5085 5084

TOTAL SERVICE SUPPLY LP p 1463
513 Vortex Dr, New Iberia LA 70560
Tel (337) 365-5954 *SIC* 5085

RED BALL OXYGEN CO INC p 1215
609 N Market St, Shreveport LA 71107
Tel (318) 425-6300
SIC 5084 5085 5169 5099 5531 5013

SENTRY SUPPLY INC p 1305
318 S Cities Service Hwy, Sulphur LA 70663
Tel (337) 625-2300 *SIC* 5085 5051

D-S PIPE & STEEL SUPPLY LLC p 407
1301 Wicomico St Ste 3, Baltimore MD 21230
Tel (410) 837-1717 *SIC* 5085 5051

DIXON VALVE & COUPLING CO p 445
800 High St, Chestertown MD 21620
Tel (410) 778-2000 *SIC* 3492 5085

DVCC INC p 463
800 High St, Chestertown MD 21620
Tel (410) 778-2000
SIC 3492 5085 3535 3321 3364

ROBERTS OXYGEN CO INC p 1242
15830 Redland Rd, Rockville MD 20855
Tel (301) 315-9090 *SIC* 5085 5169 5047

F W WEBB CO p 522
160 Middlesex Tpke, Bedford MA 01730
Tel (781) 272-6600 *SIC* 5074 5085 5075

▲ ALTRA INDUSTRIAL MOTION CORP p 62
300 Granite St Ste 201, Braintree MA 02184
Tel (781) 917-0600
SIC 3568 5085 3542 3625

RAY MURRAY INC p 1210
50 Limestone, Lee MA 01238
Tel (413) 243-7700 *SIC* 5085 5091

NEW ENGLAND CONTROLS INC p 1030
9 Oxford Rd, Mansfield MA 02048
Tel (508) 339-5522 *SIC* 5085

THG CORP p 1447
70 Bearfoot Rd, Northborough MA 01532
Tel (508) 393-7660
SIC 5085 5084 3569 3728 3625 3494

SAINT-GOBAIN SEMICONDUCTOR COMPONENTS p 1271
1 New Bond St, Worcester MA 01606
Tel (508) 795-5400 *SIC* 5085

EAST WEST INDUSTRIAL ENGINEERING CO p 471
1099 Highland Dr Ste D, Ann Arbor MI 48108
Tel (734) 971-6265 *SIC* 5085 5172

NSK AMERICAS INC p 1065
4200 Goss Rd, Ann Arbor MI 48105
Tel (734) 913-7500 *SIC* 3714 5013 5085

JO GALLOUP CO p 786
130 Helmer Rd N, Battle Creek MI 49037
Tel (269) 965-2303 *SIC* 5051 5085 5162

ROGER ZATKOFF CO p 1246
23230 Industrial Park Dr, Farmington Hills MI 48335
Tel (248) 478-2400 *SIC* 5085 5072 3053

SHIVELY BROTHERS INC p 1317
2919 S Grand Traverse St, Flint MI 48507
Tel (810) 232-7401 *SIC* 5084 5085

ALRO STEEL CORP p 61
3100 E High St, Jackson MI 49203
Tel (517) 787-5500 *SIC* 5085 5162

A RAYMOND CORPORATE NORTH AMERICA INC p 6
2350 Austin Ave Ste 200, Rochester Hills MI 48309
Tel (248) 853-2500 *SIC* 5085 3469 6719

A RAYMOND TINNERMAN AUTOMOTIVE INC p 6
3091 Research Dr, Rochester Hills MI 48309
Tel (248) 260-2121 *SIC* 5085 3469

MAHAR TOOL SUPPLY CO INC p 897
112 Williams St, Saginaw MI 48602
Tel (989) 799-5530 *SIC* 5085

PRODUCTION SERVICES MANAGEMENT INC p 1180
1255 Beach Ct, Saline MI 48176
Tel (734) 677-0454 *SIC* 5085

■ E & R INDUSTRIAL SALES INC p 465
40800 Enterprise Dr, Sterling Heights MI 48314
Tel (586) 795-2400 *SIC* 5085

FONTANA AMERICA INC p 563
6125 18 Mile Rd, Sterling Heights MI 48314
Tel (586) 997-5600 *SIC* 5085

MACOMB GROUP INC p 893
6600 15 Mile Rd, Sterling Heights MI 48312
Tel (586) 274-4100 *SIC* 5085

COMMERCIAL GROUP INC p 345
12801 Universal Dr, Taylor MI 48180
Tel (313) 931-6100
SIC 5085 5051 3496 3537 3534

INTEVA PRODUCTS LLC p 759
1401 Crooks Rd, Troy MI 48084
Tel (248) 655-8886 *SIC* 3714 5085

PRODUCTION TOOL SUPPLY CO LLC p 1180
8655 E 8 Mile Rd, Warren MI 48089
Tel (586) 755-2200 *SIC* 5085 5084

PURITY CYLINDER GASES INC p 1192
2580 28th St Sw, Wyoming MI 49519
Tel (616) 532-2375
SIC 5085 7359 5999 7699

NOTT CO p 1062
4480 Round Lake Rd W, Arden Hills MN 55112
Tel (651) 415-3400
SIC 5084 5085 3492 3053

■ CANNON EQUIPMENT LLC p 247
324 Washington St W, Cannon Falls MN 55009
Tel (507) 263-6426 *SIC* 5085

WERNER ELECTRIC VENTURES LLC p 1592
7450 95th St S, Cottage Grove MN 55016
Tel (651) 458-3701 *SIC* 5063 5084 5085

APPLIED POWER PRODUCTS INC p 100
1240 Trapp Rd, Eagan MN 55121
Tel (651) 452-2250 *SIC* 5085

■ 3M INTERAMERICA INC p 2
2501 Old Hudson Rd, Maplewood MN 55144
Tel (651) 733-1110
SIC 5113 5085 5065 5084 5122 8741

INTERSTATE COMPANIES INC p 758
2501 American Blvd E, Minneapolis MN 55425
Tel (952) 854-2044 *SIC* 7538 8711 5085

PRODUCTIVITY INC p 1180
15150 25th Ave N, Minneapolis MN 55447
Tel (763) 476-8600 *SIC* 5085 5084

POWER/MATION DIVISION INC p 1165
1310 Energy Ln, Saint Paul MN 55108
Tel (651) 605-3300
SIC 5085 5065 5084 5045 8742 7549

▲ FASTENAL CO p 531
2001 Theurer Blvd, Winona MN 55987
Tel (507) 454-5374
SIC 5085 5072 5063 5169 5198

EXPERITEC INC p 520
504 Trade Center Blvd, Chesterfield MO 63005
Tel (636) 681-1500 *SIC* 5085 5084

■ MITEK USA INC p 977
16023 Swingley Ridge Rd, Chesterfield MO 63017
Tel (314) 434-1200
SIC 3443 3429 3542 8711 5051 5085

MSS LIQUIDATION CORP p 997
1716 Guinotte Ave, Kansas City MO 64120
Tel (816) 842-4290 *SIC* 5085 3545

BUNZL USA INC p 226
1 Cityplace Dr Ste 200, Saint Louis MO 63141
Tel (314) 997-5959 *SIC* 5113 5162 5085

C L SMITH CO INC p 232
1311 S 39th St, Saint Louis MO 63110
Tel (314) 771-1202 *SIC* 5085

TRICORBRAUN INC p 1479
6 Cityplace Dr Ste 100, Saint Louis MO 63141
Tel (314) 569-3633 SIC 5085

VERNON L GOEDECKE CO INC p 1551
812 E Taylor Ave, Saint Louis MO 63147
Tel (314) 652-1810 SIC 5082 5085

CARLSON SYSTEMS HOLDINGS INC p 258
10840 Harney St, Omaha NE 68154
Tel (402) 593-5300 SIC 5085 5199

C R P INDUSTRIES INC p 233
35 Commerce Dr, Cranbury NJ 08512
Tel (609) 578-4100 SIC 5013 5085 5063

CORBAN ENERGY GROUP CORP p 368
418 Falmouth Ave, Elmwood Park NJ 07407
Tel (201) 509-8555 SIC 1623 3443 5085

WORMSER CORP p 1626
150 Coolidge Ave, Englewood NJ 07631
Tel (800) 666-9676 SIC 5085 5199

TURTLE & HUGHES INC p 1493
1900 Lower Rd, Linden NJ 07036
Tel (732) 574-3600 SIC 5063 5085

TUBE LIGHT CO INC p 1490
300 E Park St, Moonachie NJ 07074
Tel (201) 641-6660 SIC 5046 5085

JOHNSON & TOWERS INC p 790
2021 Briggs Rd, Mount Laurel NJ 08054
Tel (856) 234-6990
SIC 5084 5013 7699 7538 5085

KENNEDY CULVERT & SUPPLY CO p 811
125 6th Ave Ste 100, Mount Laurel NJ 08054
Tel (856) 813-5000 SIC 5085

■ WELCO-CGI GAS TECHNOLOGIES LLC p 1588
425 Avenue P, Newark NJ 07105
Tel (973) 589-8795
SIC 5085 5169 5999 5984

ARAMSCO INC p 102
1480 Grandview Ave, Paulsboro NJ 08066
Tel (856) 686-7700
SIC 5085 5084 5136 5139

GAFFNEY-KROESE ELECTRICAL SUPPLY CORP p 589
50 Randolph Rd, Somerset NJ 08873
Tel (732) 885-9000 SIC 5063 5084 5085

ARAMSCO HOLDINGS INC p 102
1480 Grand View Ave, Thorofare NJ 08086
Tel (856) 686-7700
SIC 5085 5136 5084 5139

SARTORIUS STEDIM NORTH AMERICA INC p 1282
5 Orville Dr Ste 200, Bohemia NY 11716
Tel (631) 254-4249 SIC 5085

HANES SUPPLY INC p 657
55 James E Casey Dr, Buffalo NY 14206
Tel (716) 826-2636
SIC 5085 5082 3496 1799

BARTON MINES CO LLC p 158
6 Warren St, Glens Falls NY 12801
Tel (518) 798-5462 SIC 1499 3291 5085

FESTO CORP p 539
395 Moreland Rd, Hauppauge NY 11788
Tel (800) 993-3786
SIC 5085 3593 3566 3492

SAMUEL SON & CO INC p 1275
4334 Walden Ave, Lancaster NY 14086
Tel (716) 681-4200 SIC 5085 5051

SEALING DEVICES INC p 1296
4400 Walden Ave, Lancaster NY 14086
Tel (716) 684-7600 SIC 5085 3069 3053

PROTECTIVE INDUSTRIAL PRODUCTS INC p 1185
968 Albany Shaker Rd, Latham NY 12110
Tel (518) 861-0133 SIC 5085

JGB ENTERPRISES INC p 785
115 Metropolitan Dr, Liverpool NY 13088
Tel (315) 451-2770 SIC 3052 5085 3429

HARDWARE SPECIALTY CO INC p 661
4875 36th St, Long Island City NY 11101
Tel (718) 361-9320 SIC 5063 5085

■ ADI CORPORATE p 22
263 Old Country Rd, Melville NY 11747
Tel (800) 233-6261 SIC 5063 5085

▲ MSC INDUSTRIAL DIRECT CO INC p 996
75 Maxess Rd, Melville NY 11747
Tel (516) 812-2000
SIC 5084 5085 5063 5072

■ SID TOOL CO INC p 1319
75 Maxess Rd, Melville NY 11747
Tel (516) 812-2000 SIC 5085 5084

JAMAICA BEARINGS CO INC p 776
1700 Jericho Tpke Ste 1, New Hyde Park NY 11040
Tel (516) 326-1350 SIC 5085 5088

■ GLOBAL EQUIPMENT CO INC p 616
11 Harbor Park Dr, Port Washington NY 11050
Tel (516) 608-7000 SIC 5085

■ WESCO INTEGRATED SUPPLY INC p 1593
36 Harbor Park Dr, Port Washington NY 11050
Tel (516) 484-6070 SIC 5085

TAL INTERNATIONAL GROUP INC p 1422
100 Manhattanville Rd # 13, Purchase NY 10577
Tel (914) 251-9000 SIC 7359 5085 4412

HORIZON SOLUTIONS LLC p 707
175 Josons Dr, Rochester NY 14623
Tel (585) 274-8235 SIC 5063 5085

PRECISION VALVE CORP p 1169
800 Westchester Ave, Rye Brook NY 10573
Tel (914) 969-6500 SIC 3499 0273 5085

CITY ELECTRIC CO INC p 312
501 W Genesee St, Syracuse NY 13204
Tel (315) 474-7841 SIC 5063 5085

IDG USA LLC p 729
2100 The Oaks Pkwy, Belmont NC 28012
Tel (704) 398-5600 SIC 5085 5084

AMERICAN PRODUCT DISTRIBUTORS INC p 78
8350 Arrowridge Blvd, Charlotte NC 28273
Tel (704) 522-9411
SIC 5111 5112 5047 5044 5085 5087

AREVA INC p 107
7207 Ibm Dr, Charlotte NC 28262
Tel (704) 805-2000
SIC 3823 3829 8711 5085 3561 2819

■ ATI PRODUCTS INC p 124
5100 W W T Harris Blvd H, Charlotte NC 28269
Tel (800) 438-0660 SIC 5083 5084 5085

E MASON ROBERT & ASSOCIATES INC p 466
1726 N Graham St, Charlotte NC 28206
Tel (704) 375-4465 SIC 5085 7699

ENVIRONMENTAL FILTRATION TECHNOLOGIES LLC p 503
4404a Chesapeake Dr, Charlotte NC 28216
Tel (704) 399-7441
SIC 3569 5085 3564 3444 3469 3561

MURATA MACHINERY USA INC p 1001
2120 Queen City Dr, Charlotte NC 28208
Tel (704) 875-9280 SIC 5084 5085 3542

FORTILINE INC p 569
7025 Northwinds Dr Nw, Concord NC 28027
Tel (704) 788-9800 SIC 5085

FORTILINE LLC p 569
7025 Northwinds Dr Nw, Concord NC 28027
Tel (704) 788-9800 SIC 3317 5085

UCHIYAMA MANUFACTURING AMERICA LLC p 1499
494 Arrington Bridge Rd, Goldsboro NC 27530
Tel (919) 731-2364 SIC 5085 3714 3053

■ KYOCERA INDUSTRIAL CERAMICS CORP p 833
100 Industrial Park Rd, Hendersonville NC 28792
Tel (828) 693-0241 SIC 5065 5013 5085

SNYDER PAPER CORP p 1336
250 26th Street Dr Se, Hickory NC 28602
Tel (828) 328-2501 SIC 5199 5085

DILLON SUPPLY CO p 440
440 Civic Blvd, Raleigh NC 27610
Tel (919) 838-4200
SIC 5084 5085 5051 5074 5072

CHALLENGER INDUSTRIES INC p 287
2005 N Kavaney Dr Ste A, Bismarck ND 58501
Tel (701) 255-1665 SIC 5085

FAMOUS DISTRIBUTION INC p 527
2620 Ridgewood Rd Ste 200, Akron OH 44313
Tel (330) 762-9621
SIC 5074 5075 5085 5023

BELTING CO OF CINCINNATI p 171
5500 Ridge Ave, Cincinnati OH 45213
Tel (513) 621-9050 SIC 5085 5063

HICKMAN WILLIAMS & CO p 690
250 E 5th St Ste 300, Cincinnati OH 45202
Tel (513) 621-1946
SIC 5051 5052 5169 5085 5084

▲ APPLIED INDUSTRIAL TECHNOLOGIES INC p 99
1 Applied Plz, Cleveland OH 44115
Tel (216) 426-4000 SIC 5085 5169 7699

BEARING DISTRIBUTORS INC p 165
8000 Hub Pkwy, Cleveland OH 44125
Tel (216) 642-9100 SIC 5085

MAZZELLA HOLDING CO INC p 924
21000 Aerospace Pkwy, Cleveland OH 44142
Tel (513) 772-4466
SIC 5051 5085 5088 5072

■ NES INVESTMENT CO p 1026
6140 Parkland Blvd, Cleveland OH 44124
Tel (440) 461-6000
SIC 5065 5085 5169 5013

■ SUPPLY TECHNOLOGIES LLC p 1407
6065 Parkland Blvd Ste 1, Cleveland OH 44124
Tel (440) 947-2100 SIC 5085 3452 3469

FCX PERFORMANCE INC p 533
3000 E 14th Ave, Columbus OH 43219
Tel (614) 324-6050 SIC 5084 5085 3494

OHIO TRANSMISSION CORP p 1078
1900 Jetway Blvd, Columbus OH 43219
Tel (614) 342-6247 SIC 5084 5085

F & M MAFCO INC p 522
9149 Dry Fork Rd, Harrison OH 45030
Tel (513) 367-2151
SIC 5085 5072 7353 5082

NOLAND CO p 1046
3110 Kettering Blvd, Moraine OH 45439
Tel (937) 396-7980
SIC 5074 5075 5063 5085

WINSUPPLY INC p 1617
3110 Kettering Blvd, Moraine OH 45439
Tel (937) 294-5331 SIC 1542 5074 5085

■ TIMKEN CORP p 1455
4500 Mount Pleasant St Nw, North Canton OH 44720
Tel (330) 471-3378 SIC 5085 5051

■ APPLIED MAINTENANCE SUPPLIES & SOLUTIONS LLC p 99
12420 Plaza Dr, Parma OH 44130
Tel (216) 433-7700 SIC 5085

FACIL NORTH AMERICA INC p 523
2242 Pinnacle Pkwy # 100, Twinsburg OH 44087
Tel (330) 487-2500 SIC 5072 3452 5085

CORNWELL QUALITY TOOLS CO p 371
667 Seville Rd, Wadsworth OH 44281
Tel (330) 336-3506 SIC 5085 3423 6794

TRUMBULL INDUSTRIES INC p 1487
400 Dietz Rd Ne, Warren OH 44483
Tel (330) 393-6624 SIC 5074 5085 5064

JTEKT NORTH AMERICA CORP p 796
29570 Clemens Rd, Westlake OH 44145
Tel (440) 835-1000 SIC 5085 3562

FORGE INDUSTRIES INC p 567
4450 Market St, Youngstown OH 44512
Tel (330) 782-8301
SIC 5085 3566 3599 3531 6411 7699

PENNSYLVANIA TOOL SALES & SERVICE INC p 1130
625 Bev Rd, Youngstown OH 44512
Tel (330) 758-0845 SIC 7699 5085 5084

BLACKHAWK INDUSTRIAL DISTRIBUTION INC p 187
1501 Sw Expressway Dr, Broken Arrow OK 74012
Tel (918) 663-3252 SIC 5085 3561 5084

CHEROKEE NATION BUSINESSES LLC p 294
777 W Cherokee St Bldg 2, Catoosa OK 74015
Tel (918) 384-7474 SIC 3728 5085 5088

BALON CORP p 149
3245 S Hattie Ave, Oklahoma City OK 73129
Tel (405) 677-3321 SIC 3491 3494 5085

MID-WEST HOSE & SPECIALTY INC p 964
3312 S I 35 Service Rd, Oklahoma City OK 73129
Tel (405) 670-6718 SIC 5085

INDUSTRIAL PIPING SPECIALISTS INC p 740
606 N 145th East Ave, Tulsa OK 74116
Tel (918) 437-9100 SIC 5051 5085

■ ORS NASCO INC p 1096
907 S Detroit Ave Ste 500, Tulsa OK 74120
Tel (918) 781-5300 SIC 5085 5084

WALVOIL FLUID POWER CORP p 1575
4111 N Garnett Rd, Tulsa OK 74116
Tel (918) 858-7100 SIC 5085

INDUSTRIAL FINISHES & SYSTEMS INC p 740
3455 W 1st Ave, Eugene OR 97402
Tel (541) 485-1503 SIC 5085 5198

WILLAMETTE VALLEY CO p 1609
1075 Arrowsmith St, Eugene OR 97402
Tel (541) 484-9621
SIC 5085 2851 2891 5169

JOHNSTONE SUPPLY INC p 791
11632 Ne Ainsworth Cir, Portland OR 97220
Tel (503) 256-3663
SIC 5075 5085 5063 5064

CONSOLIDATED SUPPLY CO p 360
7337 Sw Kable Ln, Tigard OR 97224
Tel (503) 620-7050 SIC 5074 5085

GT&S INC p 644
5275 Tilghman St, Allentown PA 18104
Tel (610) 398-2211
SIC 4925 5169 5084 5085 2813 5172

AIRLINE HYDRAULICS CORP p 40
3557 Progress Dr, Bensalem PA 19020
Tel (610) 758-9400 SIC 5085 5084

VICTAULIC CO p 1555
4901 Kesslersville Rd, Easton PA 18040
Tel (610) 559-3300
SIC 3321 3491 3494 5085

DEACON INDUSTRIAL SUPPLY CO INC p 419
1510 Gehman Rd, Harleysville PA 19438
Tel (215) 256-1715 SIC 5074 5085

SUPPLYFORCE.COM LLC p 1408
700 American Ave Ste 300, King Of Prussia PA 19406
Tel (866) 776-8289 SIC 5085

TYCO FIRE PRODUCTS LP p 1496
1400 Pennbrook Pkwy, Lansdale PA 19446
Tel (215) 362-0700
SIC 3569 3494 3321 5085

WOLSELEY INVESTMENTS INC p 1621
1904 Ligonier St, Latrobe PA 15650
Tel (757) 874-7795
SIC 5074 5085 5075 5064 5211 5031

AIRGAS SAFETY INC p 40
2501 Green Ln, Levittown PA 19057
Tel (215) 826-9000
SIC 5084 5085 3561 3841

LEWIS-GOETZ AND CO INC p 859
650 Washington Rd Ste 500, Pittsburgh PA 15228
Tel (800) 937-9070 SIC 5085

■ WESCO DISTRIBUTION INC p 1593
225 W Station Square Dr # 700, Pittsburgh PA 15219
Tel (412) 454-2200
SIC 5063 5085 5065 7389

AIRGAS INC p 40
259 N Radnor Chester Rd # 100, Radnor PA 19087
Tel (610) 687-5253
SIC 5169 5084 5085 2813 2819

AIRGAS USA LLC p 40
259 N Radnor Chester Rd # 100, Radnor PA 19087
Tel (610) 687-5253
SIC 5169 5084 5085 2813 2819

SYNOVOS INC p 1415
100 Matsonford Rd Ste 400, Radnor PA 19087
Tel (610) 293-5940 SIC 5085 8741

STAUFFER MANUFACTURING CO p 1383
361 E 6th St, Red Hill PA 18076
Tel (215) 679-4446 SIC 5085 5199

FAIRMONT SUPPLY CO p 525
437 Jefferson Ave, Washington PA 15301
Tel (724) 223-2200 SIC 5085 5082

COLOURS INC p 339
233 S Washington St, Wilkes Barre PA 18701
Tel (570) 655-9510 SIC 5198 5085 5088

■ TECHNI-TOOL INC p 1431
1547 N Trooper Rd, Worcester PA 19490
Tel (610) 941-2400 SIC 5085

SFS INTEC INC p 1310
1045 Spring St, Wyomissing PA 19610
Tel (610) 376-5751 SIC 7699 5012 5085

STEEL AND PIPES INC p 1384
Road 1rio, Caguas PR 00725
Tel (787) 747-9415
SIC 5051 3446 3317 5085

THIELSCH ENGINEERING INC p 1448
195 Frances Ave, Cranston RI 02910
Tel (401) 785-0241
SIC 5084 5043 5172 5085

VALLEN DISTRIBUTION INC p 1540
1460 Tobias Gadson Blvd, Charleston SC 29407
Tel (843) 745-2400 SIC 5085

WDS INC p 1585
1632 Village Harbor Dr, Clover SC 29710
Tel (803) 619-0301 SIC 5085 1541 8742

FASTCO THREADED PRODUCTS INC p 531
539 Clemson Rd, Columbia SC 29229
Tel (803) 788-1000 SIC 5085

EASTERN INDUSTRIAL SUPPLIES INC p 472
11 Caledon Ct Ste A, Greenville SC 29615
Tel (864) 451-5285 SIC 5085 5051

NAVISTAR INC p 1020
Caller Service 59010, Knoxville TN 37950
Tel (865) 558-1904 SIC 5085

RADIANS INC p 1204
5305 Distriplex Farms Dr, Memphis TN 38141
Tel (901) 388-7776 SIC 5085

WALLACE HARDWARE CO INC p 1573
5050 S Davy Crockett Pkwy, Morristown TN 37813
Tel (423) 586-5650
SIC 5072 5074 5085 5083 5211

SETECH INC p 1308
410 New Salem Hwy Ste 106, Murfreesboro TN 37129
Tel (615) 890-1758 SIC 8742 8748 5085

BRIDGESTONE INDUSTRIAL PRODUCTS AMERICA INC p 211
402 Bna Dr Ste 212, Nashville TN 37217
Tel (615) 365-0600 SIC 5085 8711

■ MILLER SPRINGS MATERIALS LLC p 971
6218 State Highway 317, Belton TX 76513
Tel (254) 780-9959 SIC 5085 5999

JET SPECIALTY INC p 783
211 Market Ave, Boerne TX 78006
Tel (830) 331-9457 SIC 5084 5085

HUGH M CUNNINGHAM INC p 717
2029 Westgate Dr Ste 120, Carrollton TX 75006
Tel (972) 888-3833
SIC 5074 5085 5083 5199

GAS EQUIPMENT CO INC p 593
11616 Harry Hines Blvd, Dallas TX 75229
Tel (972) 241-2333 SIC 5084 5085 3321

PURVIS INDUSTRIES LTD p 1193
10500 N Stemmons Fwy, Dallas TX 75220
Tel (214) 358-5500 SIC 5013 5085 3822

PIONEER FASTENERS & TOOL INC p 1150
202 S Ector Dr, Euless TX 76040
Tel (817) 545-0121 SIC 5085

ACT PIPE & SUPPLY INC p 19
6950 W Sam Houston Pkwy N, Houston TX 77041
Tel (713) 937-0600 SIC 5051 5085

ACTION GYPSUM SUPPLY LP p 19
9635 W Little York Rd, Houston TX 77040
Tel (713) 896-4002 SIC 5085

ALLIED FITTING LP p 56
7200 Mykawa Rd, Houston TX 77033
Tel (800) 969-5565 SIC 5085

BLP SETTLEMENT CO p 190
125 Mccarty St, Houston TX 77029
Tel (713) 674-2266 SIC 5085 3496

C&C INDUSTRIES INC p 233
10350 Clay Rd Ste 250, Houston TX 77041
Tel (713) 466-1644 SIC 3999 5085

FORGINGS FLANGES & FITTINGS LLC p 567
8900 Railwood Dr Unit B, Houston TX 77078
Tel (713) 695-5400 SIC 5085

GROVES INDUSTRIAL SUPPLY CORP p 642
7301 Pinemont Dr, Houston TX 77040
Tel (713) 675-4747 SIC 5085 5084 5198

■ LAMONS GASKET CO p 841
7300 Airport Blvd, Houston TX 77061
Tel (713) 547-9527 SIC 3053 5085

LOCKWOOD INTERNATIONAL INC p 873
10203 Wallisville Rd, Houston TX 77013
Tel (866) 898-2583 SIC 5085

■ MRC GLOBAL (US) INC p 996
1301 Mckinney St Ste 2300, Houston TX 77010
Tel (877) 294-7574 SIC 5051 5085

▲ MRC GLOBAL INC p 996
1301 Mckinney St Ste 2300, Houston TX 77010
Tel (877) 294-7574 SIC 5051 5085

NORTH SHORE SUPPLY CO INC p 1053
1566 Miles St, Houston TX 77015
Tel (713) 453-3533 SIC 5051 5085 3441

PIPELINE SUPPLY & SERVICE LLC p 1151
1010 Lamar St Ste 710, Houston TX 77002
Tel (713) 741-8127 SIC 4922 5085 1623

■ PRECISION INDUSTRIES INC p 1168
7272 Pinemont Dr, Houston TX 77040
Tel (713) 996-4700 SIC 5211 5085

PVI HOLDINGS INC p 1193
840 Gessner Rd Ste 950, Houston TX 77024
Tel (713) 365-6805 SIC 5085 5084 7699

RAWSON LP p 1209
2010 Mcallister Rd, Houston TX 77092
Tel (713) 684-1400 SIC 5085 5084

SBP HOLDING LP p 1285
125 Mccarty St, Houston TX 77029
Tel (713) 953-1113 SIC 5085 3496

SOUTHWEST STAINLESS LP p 1352
515 Post Oak Blvd Ste 800, Houston TX 77027
Tel (713) 943-3544 SIC 3498 5051 5085

US METALS INC p 1532
19102 Gundle Rd, Houston TX 77073
Tel (281) 443-7473 SIC 5085

PARTSMASTER INC p 1119
1400 E Northgate Dr, Irving TX 75062
Tel (972) 438-0711 SIC 5085

ABATIX CORP p 9
2400 Skyline Dr Ste 400, Mesquite TX 75149
Tel (214) 381-1146 SIC 5084 5085

CITY PIPE AND SUPPLY CORP p 319
2101 W 2nd St, Odessa TX 79763
Tel (432) 332-1541 SIC 5051 5085

SUNBELT SUPPLY CO INC p 1401
3750 Hwy 225, Pasadena TX 77503
Tel (713) 672-2222 SIC 5085

■ RICHARDSON TRIDENT CO LLC p 1233
405 N Plano Rd, Richardson TX 75081
Tel (972) 231-5176
SIC 5051 5085 5063 5065 3316

■ SAFETY-KLEEN INC p 1266
2600 N Central Expy # 400, Richardson TX 75080
Tel (800) 669-5740
SIC 4953 3559 4212 5172 5085 7389

■ **SAFETY-KLEEN SYSTEMS INC** p 1266
2600 N Central Expy # 400, Richardson TX 75080
Tel (972) 265-2000
SIC 3559 7359 5172 4212 7389 5085

BANA INC p 149
624 E Mcleroy Blvd, Saginaw TX 76179
Tel (817) 232-3750 SIC 5085 2441 2448

HOWARD MIDSTREAM ENERGY PARTNERS LLC p 713
17806 W Ih 10 Ste 210, San Antonio TX 78257
Tel (210) 298-2222 SIC 5085

EADS DISTRIBUTION LLC p 467
13843 N Promenade Blvd, Stafford TX 77477
Tel (281) 243-2900 SIC 5085

KITZ CORP OF AMERICA p 822
10750 Corporate Dr, Stafford TX 77477
Tel (281) 491-7333 SIC 5085

TRAMONTINA USA INC p 1469
12955 W Airport Blvd, Sugar Land TX 77478
Tel (281) 340-8400 SIC 5046 5072 5085

ACCENT PACKAGING INC p 14
10131 Fm 2920 Rd, Tomball TX 77375
Tel (281) 251-3700 SIC 5051 5084 5085

INDUSTRIAL SUPPLY CO INC p 740
1635 S 300 W, Salt Lake City UT 84115
Tel (801) 484-8644 SIC 5084 5085

HAMPTON RUBBER CO p 656
1669 W Pembroke Ave, Hampton VA 23661
Tel (757) 722-9818 SIC 5085

FERGUSON ENTERPRISES INC p 538
12500 Jefferson Ave, Newport News VA 23602
Tel (757) 874-7795
SIC 5074 5085 5075 5064

ALFA LAVAL US HOLDING INC p 49
5400 Intl Trade Dr, Richmond VA 23231
Tel (804) 222-5300 SIC 3569 5085

ARCET EQUIPMENT CO p 104
1700 Chamberlayne Ave, Richmond VA 23222
Tel (804) 644-4521 SIC 5085 5084 5169

FRISCHKORN INC p 580
1801 Roseneath Rd, Richmond VA 23230
Tel (804) 353-0181 SIC 5085

SALEM TOOLS INC p 1272
1602 Midland Rd, Salem VA 24153
Tel (540) 389-0726 SIC 5085

H D FOWLER CO INC p 649
13440 Se 30th St, Bellevue WA 98005
Tel (425) 746-8400
SIC 5084 5083 5085 3321

PUGET SOUND PIPE AND SUPPLY CO p 1191
7816 S 202nd St, Kent WA 98032
Tel (206) 682-9350 SIC 5074 5085

WEST COAST PAPER CO p 1594
6703 S 234th St Ste 120, Kent WA 98032
Tel (253) 850-1900
SIC 5085 5169 5084 2677

RALEIGH MINE AND INDUSTRIAL SUPPLY INC p 1206
1500 Mill Creek Rd, Mount Hope WV 25880
Tel (304) 877-5503
SIC 5085 1629 3532 3441

ENDRIES INTERNATIONAL INC p 496
714 W Ryan St, Brillion WI 54110
Tel (920) 756-2174 SIC 5085 5072

WISCONSIN LIFT TRUCK CORP p 1619
3125 Intertech Dr, Brookfield WI 53045
Tel (262) 790-6230 SIC 5084 5085 7699

ELLSWORTH CORP p 489
W129n10825 Washington Dr, Germantown WI 53022
Tel (262) 253-8600 SIC 5169 5085

CRANE ENGINEERING SALES INC p 389
707 Ford St, Kimberly WI 54136
Tel (920) 733-4425 SIC 5084 5085 5074

ENGMAN-TAYLOR CO INC p 499
W142n9351 Fountain Blvd, Menomonee Falls WI 53051
Tel (262) 255-9300 SIC 5084 5085

BOSTIK FINDLEY F S C INC p 202
11320 W Wtertown Plank Rd, Milwaukee WI 53226
Tel (414) 774-2250 SIC 5085

■ **FALK SERVICE CORP** p 526
3001 W Canal St, Milwaukee WI 53208
Tel (414) 342-3131 SIC 5085

INTERNATIONAL COMMERCE & MARKETING CORP p 755
500 W Oklahoma Ave, Milwaukee WI 53207
Tel (414) 290-1500 SIC 5085 5961

UNITED P&H SUPPLY CO p 1510
9947 W Carmen Ave, Milwaukee WI 53225
Tel (414) 393-6600
SIC 5085 5074 3312 3463

PALMER JOHNSON ENTERPRISES INC p 1109
128 Kentucky St, Sturgeon Bay WI 54235
Tel (920) 746-6342 SIC 5085 4493 3732

SIC 5087 Service Establishment Eqpt & Splys Wholesale

BTC WHOLESALE DISTRIBUTORS INC p 222
100 Airview Ln, Alabaster AL 35007
Tel (205) 324-2581
SIC 5194 5145 5087 5149 5122

WOOD-FRUITTICHER GROCERY CO INC p 1622
2900 Alton Rd, Irondale AL 35210
Tel (205) 836-9663
SIC 5142 5141 5147 5087 5046

ARIZONA PARTSMASTER INC p 109
7125 W Sherman St, Phoenix AZ 85043
Tel (602) 233-3580 SIC 5087

EWING IRRIGATION PRODUCTS INC p 516
3441 E Harbour Dr, Phoenix AZ 85034
Tel (602) 437-9530 SIC 5085 5087 5074

DOLCE SALON & SPA LLC p 448
7898 E Acoma Dr Ste 108, Scottsdale AZ 85260
Tel (602) 515-0420 SIC 5087

ARROW USA p 113
1105 Highland Ct, Beaumont CA 92223
Tel (951) 845-6144 SIC 5087

WEST COAST BEAUTY SUPPLY CO p 1594
5001 Industrial Way, Benicia CA 94510
Tel (707) 748-4800 SIC 5087 3069

CHIRO INC p 301
2260 S Vista Ave, Bloomington CA 92316
Tel (909) 879-1160 SIC 5087 7349 5169

■ **CORE-MARK INTERRELATED COMPANIES INC** p 369
311 Reed Cir, Corona CA 92879
Tel (951) 272-4790 SIC 5199 5122 5087

GCO INC p 595
27750 Industrial Blvd, Hayward CA 94545
Tel (510) 786-3333 SIC 5074 5087

QUALITY CUSTOM DISTRIBUTION SERVICES INC p 1197
18301 Von Karman Ave, Irvine CA 92612
Tel (949) 252-2000 SIC 5087 7319

OAK PAPER PRODUCTS CO INC p 1070
3686 E Olympic Blvd, Los Angeles CA 90023
Tel (323) 268-0507
SIC 5113 5199 5087 2653

■ **O P I PRODUCTS INC** p 1070
13034 Saticoy St, North Hollywood CA 91605
Tel (818) 759-8688 SIC 5087 2844

■ **CLOROX SALES CO** p 327
1221 Broadway Ste 13, Oakland CA 94612
Tel (510) 271-7000 SIC 5087

OAKLAND PAPER & SUPPLY INC p 1071
3200 Regatta Blvd Ste F, Richmond CA 94804
Tel (510) 307-4242 SIC 5113 5087

WAXIES ENTERPRISES INC p 1584
9353 Waxie Way, San Diego CA 92123
Tel (858) 292-8111 SIC 5087

■ **CSE HOLDINGS INC** p 397
650 Brennan St, San Jose CA 95131
Tel (408) 436-1907
SIC 5087 5084 7699 5113 5199 5112

PACIFIC GROSERVICE INC p 1104
567 Cinnabar St, San Jose CA 95110
Tel (408) 727-4826
SIC 5194 5145 5141 5113 5087

HUNTER INDUSTRIES INC p 719
1940 Diamond St, San Marcos CA 92078
Tel (800) 383-4747 SIC 5087 3084

■ **VIKING OFFICE PRODUCTS INC** p 1557
3366 E Willow St, Signal Hill CA 90755
Tel (562) 490-1000
SIC 5112 5021 5045 5087 5043 5961

ANDWIN CORP p 91
6636 Variel Ave, Woodland Hills CA 91303
Tel (818) 999-2828
SIC 5113 3842 5199 5087 5047 2835

TUNDRA SPECIALTIES INC p 1491
2845 29th St Unit E, Boulder CO 80301
Tel (888) 388-6372 SIC 5087

■ **RED ROBIN INTERNATIONAL INC** p 1216
6312 S Fiddlers Green Cir 200n, Greenwood Village CO 80111
Tel (303) 846-6000
SIC 5812 6794 5813 5087

EASTERN BAG AND PAPER CO INC p 471
200 Research Dr, Milford CT 06460
Tel (203) 878-1814 SIC 5113 5087 5046

MUNICIPAL EMERGENCY SERVICES INC p 1000
7 Poverty Rd Ste 85h, Southbury CT 06488
Tel (203) 364-0620 SIC 5087

SIMPLEXGRINNELL LP p 1325
4700 Exchange Ct, Boca Raton FL 33431
Tel (561) 988-7200
SIC 5087 1711 3669 7382

MANAGEMENT CONSULTING INC p 900
2503 Se 17th Ave, Cape Coral FL 33910
Tel (239) 458-3611 SIC 5531 5087

GOODWILL INDUSTRIES OF SOUTHWEST FLORIDA INC p 625
5100 Tice St, Fort Myers FL 33905
Tel (239) 995-2106 SIC 5932 5087

MARGARITAVILLE ENTERPRISES LLC p 906
6900 Turkey Lake Rd # 200, Orlando FL 32819
Tel (407) 224-3213 SIC 5087

JENSEN USA INC p 783
99 Aberdeen Loop, Panama City FL 32405
Tel (850) 271-8464 SIC 5087

WARE OIL & SUPPLY CO INC p 1575
2715 S Byron Butler Pkwy, Perry FL 32348
Tel (850) 838-1852 SIC 5172 5087 5411

CHENEY BROS INC p 294
1 Cheney Way, Riviera Beach FL 33404
Tel (561) 845-4700
SIC 5141 5087 5113 5169 5149

SONNYS ENTERPRISES INC p 1340
5605 Hiatus Rd, Tamarac FL 33321
Tel (954) 720-4100 SIC 5087 3589

HD SUPPLY FACILITIES MAINTENANCE GROUP INC p 673
3100 Cumberland Blvd Se, Atlanta GA 30339
Tel (770) 852-9000 SIC 5087

■ **HD SUPPLY FACILITIES MAINTENANCE LTD** p 673
3100 Cumberland Blvd Se # 1700, Atlanta GA 30339
Tel (770) 852-9000 SIC 5087

▲ **HD SUPPLY HOLDINGS INC** p 673
3100 Cumberland Blvd Se # 1480, Atlanta GA 30339
Tel (770) 852-9000 SIC 5087 5072 5085

■ **HDS HOLDING CORP** p 673
3100 Cumberland Blvd Se, Atlanta GA 30339
Tel (770) 852-9000 SIC 5087 5072 5085

JINNY BEAUTY SUPPLY CO INC p 786
3587 Oakcliff Rd, Atlanta GA 30340
Tel (770) 734-9222 SIC 5087

▲ **VERITIV CORP** p 1550
1000 Abernathy Rd # 1700, Atlanta GA 30328
Tel (770) 391-8200 SIC 5111 5112 5087

BAILY INTERNATIONAL OF ATLANTA INC p 145
3312-B N Berkeley Lk Rd, Duluth GA 30096
Tel (770) 452-8212 SIC 5087

BADGER FARMS INC p 143
652 N Western Ave, Chicago IL 60612
Tel (773) 278-9100
SIC 5143 5149 5147 5144 5142 5087

▲ **ESSENDANT INC** p 510
1 Parkway North Blvd # 100, Deerfield IL 60015
Tel (847) 627-7000
SIC 5112 5111 5021 5044 5087 5045

■ **LAGASSE INC** p 838
1 Parkway North Blvd # 100, Deerfield IL 60015
Tel (847) 627-7000 SIC 5087 5141

EQUIPMENT DEPOT OF ILLINOIS INC p 506
751 Expressway Dr, Itasca IL 60143
Tel (847) 836-5005
SIC 5084 5087 5063 7699

W S DARLEY & CO p 1569
325 Spring Lake Dr, Itasca IL 60143
Tel (630) 735-3500
SIC 3561 5087 5099 3569 3812

GLORY GLOBAL SOLUTIONS INC p 618
3333 Warrenville Rd # 310, Lisle IL 60532
Tel (920) 262-3300 SIC 5087 5046 5044

JON-DON INC p 792
400 Medinah Rd, Roselle IL 60172
Tel (630) 872-5401 SIC 5087

MARTIN-BROWER CO L L C p 913
6250 N River Rd Ste 9000, Rosemont IL 60018
Tel (847) 227-6500
SIC 5142 5113 5149 5087

DON EDWARD & CO p 449
9801 Adam Don Pkwy, Woodridge IL 60517
Tel (708) 442-9400
SIC 5021 5046 5087 5113 5169

HERITAGE FOOD SERVICE GROUP INC p 686
5130 Executive Blvd, Fort Wayne IN 46808
Tel (260) 482-1444 SIC 5087

ACORN DISTRIBUTORS INC p 18
5820 Fortune Cir W, Indianapolis IN 46241
Tel (317) 243-9234
SIC 5113 5087 5169 5046 5023

H P PRODUCTS CORP p 650
4220 Saguaro Trl, Indianapolis IN 46268
Tel (317) 298-9957 SIC 5087

STANZ CHEESE CO INC p 1377
1840 Commerce Dr, South Bend IN 46628
Tel (574) 232-6666
SIC 5142 5141 5148 5113 5087 5085

MARTIN BROTHERS DISTRIBUTING CO INC p 912
6623 Chancellor Dr, Cedar Falls IA 50613
Tel (319) 266-1775
SIC 5141 5169 5046 5087

CITY WIDE HOLDING CO INC p 320
15447 W 100th Ter, Lenexa KS 66219
Tel (913) 888-5700
SIC 1542 1522 5087 7349

SCRIPTPRO USA INC p 1295
5828 Reeds Rd, Shawnee Mission KS 66202
Tel (913) 384-1008 SIC 5087

BROWN FOODSERVICE INC p 219
500 E Clayton Ln, Louisa KY 41230
Tel (606) 638-1139
SIC 5142 5141 5084 5087

■ **PJ FOOD SERVICE INC** p 1153
2002 Papa Johns Blvd, Louisville KY 40299
Tel (502) 261-7272 SIC 5149 5087 2045

DOERLE FOOD SERVICES LLC p 447
113 Kol Dr, Broussard LA 70518
Tel (337) 252-8551
SIC 5142 5141 5087 5148

NEILL CORP p 1024
303 S Pine St, Hammond LA 70403
Tel (985) 345-1085 SIC 5087 5999

FERRARA FIREFIGHTING EQUIPMENT INC p 538
27855 James Chapel Rd N, Holden LA 70744
Tel (225) 567-7100 SIC 5087

■ **STEWART ENTERPRISES INC** p 1389
1333 S Clearview Pkwy, New Orleans LA 70121
Tel (504) 729-1400 SIC 7261 5087

UNITED SOURCE ONE INC p 1511
4610 Mercedes Dr Ste 110, Belcamp MD 21017
Tel (410) 278-0800 SIC 5147 5087

■ **SYSCO BALTIMORE LLC** p 1416
8000 Dorsey Run Rd, Jessup MD 20794
Tel (410) 799-7000 SIC 5142 5149 5087

ADAMS-BURCH LLC p 21
1901 Stanford Ct, Landover MD 20785
Tel (301) 276-2000 SIC 5046 5113 5087

S FREEDMAN & SONS INC p 1262
3322 Pennsy Dr, Landover MD 20785
Tel (301) 322-6400 SIC 5113 5087

CENTRAL WHOLESALERS INC p 281
13401 Konterra Dr, Laurel MD 20707
Tel (800) 935-2947
SIC 5074 5063 5087 5072 5211 1799

HOLT PAPER AND CHEMICAL CO INC p 702
31375 John Deere Dr, Salisbury MD 21804
Tel (410) 742-7577
SIC 5142 5087 5113 5147

ACME PAPER & SUPPLY CO INC p 18
8229 Sandy Ct, Savage MD 20763
Tel (410) 792-2333 SIC 5113 5087

P4 CORP p 1103
16001 Trade Zone Ave, Upper Marlboro MD 20774
Tel (301) 218-7039 SIC 5087 5072

TRIMARK UNITED EAST INC p 1480
505 Collins St, Attleboro MA 02703
Tel (508) 399-6000
SIC 5046 5021 5113 5087

PERKINS PAPER INC p 1136
630 John Hancock Rd, Taunton MA 02780
Tel (508) 824-2800
SIC 5113 5149 5087 5046

■ **SYSCO DETROIT LLC** p 1417
41600 Van Born Rd, Canton MI 48188
Tel (734) 397-7990 SIC 5087

■ **SYSCO GRAND RAPIDS LLC** p 1417
3700 Sysco Ct Se, Grand Rapids MI 49512
Tel (616) 956-0700 SIC 5141 5087

SUPPLY NETWORK INC p 1407
210 N Industrial Park Rd, Hastings MI 49058
Tel (269) 945-9501 SIC 5087

TNG WORLDWIDE INC p 1458
29683 Wk Smith Dr Stet, New Hudson MI 48165
Tel (248) 347-7700 SIC 5099 5087

NICHOLS PAPER & SUPPLY CO p 1042
1391 Judson Rd, Norton Shores MI 49456
Tel (231) 799-2120 SIC 5113 5087

NILFISK INC p 1043
9435 Winnetka Ave N, Brooklyn Park MN 55445
Tel (800) 334-1083 SIC 3589 5087

■ **US FOODS CULINARY EQUIPMENT & SUPPLIES LLC** p 1531
5353 Nathan Ln N, Plymouth MN 55442
Tel (763) 268-1200 SIC 5087

JACKSON PAPER CO p 774
4400 Mangum Dr, Flowood MS 39232
Tel (800) 844-5449 SIC 5111 5113 5087

UNIGROUP INC p 1503
1 Premier Dr, Fenton MO 63026
Tel (636) 305-5000 SIC 4213 7513 5087

MENU MAKER FOODS INC p 943
913 Big Horn Dr, Jefferson City MO 65109
Tel (573) 893-3000
SIC 5141 5087 2011 5149

HILLYARD INC p 694
302 N 4th St, Saint Joseph MO 64501
Tel (816) 233-1321 SIC 5169 5087

■ **CRANE MERCHANDISING SYSTEMS INC** p 389
2043 Wdlnd Pkwy Ste 102, Saint Louis MO 63146
Tel (314) 298-3500 SIC 3589 5087

■ **LINCOLN SYSCO INC** p 868
900 King Bird Rd, Lincoln NE 68521
Tel (402) 423-1031
SIC 5148 5142 5143 5141 5087 5113

BRADY INDUSTRIES INC p 207
7055 Lindell Rd, Las Vegas NV 89118
Tel (702) 876-3990
SIC 5169 5087 5999 5023 5064

HBC HOLDINGS LLC p 671
324a Half Acre Rd, Cranbury NJ 08512
Tel (609) 860-9990 SIC 5072 5087 5074

WORLD AND MAIN (CRANBURY) LLC p 1624
324a Half Acre Rd, Cranbury NJ 08512
Tel (609) 860-9990 SIC 5072 5087 5074

IMPERIAL BAG & PAPER CO LLC p 734
255 Us Highway 1 And 9, Jersey City NJ 07306
Tel (201) 437-7440 SIC 5087

■ **SYSCO METRO NEW YORK LLC** p 1417
20 Theodore Conrad Dr, Jersey City NJ 07305
Tel (201) 451-0997
SIC 5141 5144 5142 5147 5087

AMANO USA HOLDINGS INC p 64
140 Harrison Ave, Roseland NJ 07068
Tel (973) 403-1900
SIC 3589 2842 3579 3559 5169 5087

TINGUE BROWN & CO p 1455
535 N Midland Ave, Saddle Brook NJ 07663
Tel (201) 796-4490 SIC 5087 3089 2394

HILL & MARKES INC p 693
1997 State Highway 5s, Amsterdam NY 12010
Tel (518) 842-2410 SIC 5087 5113

PAPER ENTERPRISES INC p 1112
770 E 132nd St, Bronx NY 10454
Tel (718) 402-1200 SIC 5113 5087

RD FOOD SERVICES LLC p 1212
1524 132nd St, College Point NY 11356
Tel (718) 961-4356
SIC 5141 5148 5142 5113 5046 5087

MAINES PAPER & FOOD SERVICE INC p 898
101 Broome Corporate Pkwy, Conklin NY 13748
Tel (607) 779-1200
SIC 5142 5113 5141 5087 5147 5146

METROPLEX HOLDINGS INC p 955
15 Commerce Dr S, Harriman NY 10926
Tel (845) 781-5000 SIC 6512 5149 5087

BURMAX CO INC p 228
28 Barretts Ave, Holtsville NY 11742
Tel (631) 447-8700 SIC 5087 7231

MARK GOLDEN MAINTENANCE LTD INC p 907
420 Doughty Blvd Ste 4, Inwood NY 11096
Tel (516) 239-3400 SIC 7349 5087

WILLOW RUN FOODS INC p 1613
1006 Us Route 11, Kirkwood NY 13795
Tel (607) 338-5221
SIC 5142 5149 5147 5113 5148 5087

SALONCENTRIC INC p 1273
575 5th Ave, New York NY 10017
Tel (800) 282-2843 SIC 5087

COINMACH CORP p 335
303 Sunnyside Blvd # 70, Plainview NY 11803
Tel (516) 349-8555
SIC 7215 7359 5087 5064 7211 8741

COINMACH SERVICE CORP p 335
303 Sunnyside Blvd # 70, Plainview NY 11803
Tel (516) 349-8555 SIC 3633 5087

CSC SERVICEWORKS HOLDINGS INC p 397
303 Sunnyside Blvd # 70, Plainview NY 11803
Tel (516) 349-8555 SIC 3633 5087

CSC SERVICEWORKS INC p 397
303 Sunnyside Blvd # 70, Plainview NY 11803
Tel (516) 349-8555 SIC 3633 5087

SPIN HOLDCO INC p 1358
303 Sunnyside Blvd # 70, Plainview NY 11803
Tel (516) 349-8555 SIC 3633 5087

MODEL MODEL HAIR FASHION INC p 981
83 Harbor Rd, Port Washington NY 11050
Tel (516) 944-7777 SIC 5087

TWEEZERMAN INTERNATIONAL LLC p 1494
2 Tri Harbor Ct, Port Washington NY 11050
Tel (516) 676-7772 SIC 5087

■ **PRESTIGE BRANDS INC** p 1173
660 White Plains Rd, Tarrytown NY 10591
Tel (914) 524-6810 SIC 5149 5087

MORRISETTE PAPER CO INC p 990
5925 Summit Ave, Browns Summit NC 27214
Tel (336) 375-1515 SIC 5113 5111 5087

AMERICAN PRODUCT DISTRIBUTORS INC p 78
8350 Arrowridge Blvd, Charlotte NC 28273
Tel (704) 522-9411
SIC 5111 5112 5047 5044 5085 5087

■ BURTS BEES INC p 229
210 W Pettigrew St, Durham NC 27701
Tel (919) 998-5200 *SIC* 2844 5122 5087

WASSERSTROM CO p 1580
477 S Front St, Columbus OH 43215
Tel (614) 737-8472
SIC 5087 3566 5021 5046 5112 5719

I SUPPLY CO p 725
1255 Spangler Rd, Fairborn OH 45324
Tel (937) 878-5240 *SIC* 5087 5113

■ IMPACT PRODUCTS LLC p 734
2840 Centennial Rd, Toledo OH 43617
Tel (419) 841-2891
SIC 5084 5087 2392 3089

WALTER E NELSON CO p 1574
5937 N Cutter Cir, Portland OR 97217
Tel (503) 285-3037 *SIC* 5169 5087

GEO W KISTLER INC p 605
2210 City Line Rd, Bethlehem PA 18017
Tel (610) 266-7100
SIC 5063 7382 5087 7399

PENN JERSEY PAPER CO p 1129
9355 Blue Grass Rd, Philadelphia PA 19114
Tel (215) 671-9800 *SIC* 5113 5087

PHILADELPHIA BUNZL p 1142
10814 Northeast Ave, Philadelphia PA 19116
Tel (215) 969-0600
SIC 5087 5023 5113 7213

ST MORITZ BUILDING SERVICES INC p 1372
4616 Clairton Blvd, Pittsburgh PA 15236
Tel (412) 885-2100 *SIC* 7349 5087

BUDGET MAINTENANCE CONCRETE SERVICES INC p 224
135 Walnut St, Pottstown PA 19464
Tel (610) 323-7702 *SIC* 5087 7349

KEYSTONE FOODS LLC p 815
905 Airport Rd Ste 400, West Chester PA 19380
Tel (610) 667-6700 *SIC* 2013 2015 5087

MATOSANTOS COMMERCIAL CORP p 920
Parque Industrial Ca, Vega Baja PR 00693
Tel (787) 793-6900 *SIC* 5141 5113 5087

HAMRICKS INC p 656
742 Peachoid Rd, Gaffney SC 29341
Tel (864) 489-6095
SIC 5651 2337 2331 2335 2339 5087

A-Z OFFICE RESOURCE INC p 7
809 S Garden St, Columbia TN 38401
Tel (931) 388-1536
SIC 5112 5021 5044 5045 5087

ORECK CORP p 1093
1400 Salem Rd, Cookeville TN 38506
Tel (800) 219-2044
SIC 3589 3564 5064 5087

SERVPRO INDUSTRIES INC p 1308
801 Industrial Blvd, Gallatin TN 37066
Tel (615) 451-0200 *SIC* 5087

SERVPRO INTELLECTUAL PROPERTY INC p 1308
801 Industrial Blvd, Gallatin TN 37066
Tel (615) 451-0200 *SIC* 7349 8741 5087

KELSAN INC p 809
5109 N National Dr, Knoxville TN 37914
Tel (865) 525-7132 *SIC* 5087 5169 7699

AMERICAN PAPER & TWINE CO p 77
7400 Cockrill Bend Blvd, Nashville TN 37209
Tel (615) 350-9000 *SIC* 5113 5087 5112

SWS RE-DISTRIBUTION CO INC p 1413
1440 Lemay Dr Ste 104, Carrollton TX 75007
Tel (214) 483-1076 *SIC* 5087

SHRED-IT DALLAS INC p 1319
825 W Sandy Lake Rd # 100, Coppell TX 75019
Tel (972) 556-0197 *SIC* 7389 5093 5087

■ BEAUTY SYSTEMS GROUP LLC p 166
3001 Colorado Blvd, Denton TX 76210
Tel (940) 297-2000 *SIC* 5999 5122 5087

▲ SALLY BEAUTY HOLDINGS INC p 1273
3001 Colorado Blvd, Denton TX 76210
Tel (940) 898-7500 *SIC* 5999 5087

■ SALLY BEAUTY SUPPLY LLC p 1273
3001 Colorado Blvd, Denton TX 76210
Tel (940) 898-7500 *SIC* 5999 5122 5087

■ SALLY HOLDINGS LLC p 1273
3001 Colorado Blvd, Denton TX 76210
Tel (940) 898-7500 *SIC* 5087

POLLOCK INVESTMENTS INC p 1160
1 Pollock Pl, Grand Prairie TX 75050
Tel (972) 263-8448 *SIC* 5113 5087

DISTRIBUTION INTERNATIONAL SOUTHWEST INC p 443
9000 Railwood Dr, Houston TX 77078
Tel (713) 428-3900 *SIC* 5087 5047

RUG DOCTOR LLC p 1257
4701 Old Shepard Pl, Plano TX 75093
Tel (972) 673-1400 *SIC* 2842 3589 5087

MATERA PAPER CO INC p 919
835 N Ww White Rd, San Antonio TX 78219
Tel (210) 892-5101 *SIC* 5087

GULF COAST PAPER CO INC p 646
3705 Houston Hwy, Victoria TX 77901
Tel (361) 852-5252 *SIC* 5113 5087

SCHENCK FOODS CO INC p 1286
3578 Valley Pike, Winchester VA 22602
Tel (540) 869-1870
SIC 5141 5142 5087 5147 5148

BOELTER COMPANIES INC p 197
N22 W23685 Rdgview Pkwy W, Waukesha WI 53188
Tel (262) 523-6200
SIC 5113 5046 7389 5087

SIC 5088 Transportation Eqpt & Splys, Except Motor Vehicles Wholesale

HILLER COMPANIES INC p 693
3751 Joy Springs Dr, Mobile AL 36693
Tel (251) 661-1275 *SIC* 1731 5084 5088

TECHNIFY MOTOR (USA) INC p 1431
2039 S Broad St, Mobile AL 36615
Tel (251) 438-3411 *SIC* 5088

SABEL STEEL SERVICE INC p 1263
749 N Court St, Montgomery AL 36104
Tel (334) 265-6771 *SIC* 5088 5051

CUTTER AVIATION p 403
2802 E Old Tower Rd, Phoenix AZ 85034
Tel (602) 273-1237
SIC 5599 5088 4522 5172 4581

KIRKHILL AIRCRAFT PARTS CO p 821
3120 Enterprise St, Brea CA 92821
Tel (714) 223-5400 *SIC* 5088 3728

ALIGN AEROSPACE LLC p 50
21123 Nordhoff St, Chatsworth CA 91311
Tel (818) 727-7800 *SIC* 5088

CBOL CORP p 269
19850 Plummer St, Chatsworth CA 91311
Tel (818) 704-8200
SIC 5065 5072 5013 5088 5084 5162

ONTIC ENGINEERING AND MANUFACTURING INC p 1088
20400 Plummer St, Chatsworth CA 91311
Tel (818) 678-6555 *SIC* 5088 3728 3812

UNICAL AVIATION INC p 1502
680 S Lemon Ave, City Of Industry CA 91789
Tel (626) 813-1901 *SIC* 5088

IRWIN INTERNATIONAL INC p 765
225 Airport Cir, Corona CA 92880
Tel (951) 372-9555 *SIC* 5599 5088

YAMAHA MOTOR CORP USA p 1634
6555 Katella Ave, Cypress CA 90630
Tel (714) 761-7300
SIC 5088 5013 5091 5012

INTEGRATED PROCUREMENT TECHNOLOGIES INC p 749
7230 Hollister Ave, Goleta CA 93117
Tel (805) 682-0842 *SIC* 5088 5065

JAE ELECTRONICS INC p 775
142 Technology Dr Ste 100, Irvine CA 92618
Tel (949) 753-2600
SIC 5065 5088 3679 3829 3678

AERO PRECISION INDUSTRIES LLC p 30
201 Lindbergh Ave, Livermore CA 94551
Tel (925) 579-5327 *SIC* 5088

SHIMADZU PRECISION INSTRUMENTS INC p 1316
3645 N Lakewood Blvd, Long Beach CA 90808
Tel (562) 420-6226 *SIC* 5088 5047 5084

MIKUNI AMERICAN CORP p 968
8910 Mikuni Ave, Northridge CA 91324
Tel (310) 676-0522 *SIC* 5013 5088

■ WESCO AIRCRAFT HARDWARE CORP p 1593
24911 Avenue Stanford, Valencia CA 91355
Tel (661) 775-7200 *SIC* 5088

▲ WEST MARINE INC p 1595
500 Westridge Dr, Watsonville CA 95076
Tel (831) 728-2700
SIC 5551 5961 5088 5611 5661 5621

GREENWICH AEROGROUP INC p 638
475 Steamboat Rd Fl 2, Greenwich CT 06830
Tel (203) 618-4861
SIC 4581 5088 7699 5085

■ SIKORSKY SUPPORT SERVICES INC p 1322
6900 Main St, Stratford CT 06614
Tel (203) 386-4000 *SIC* 5088

■ HELICOPTER SUPPORT INC p 681
124 Quarry Rd, Trumbull CT 06611
Tel (203) 416-4000 *SIC* 5088 4581 3728

TLD AMERICA CORP p 1457
812 Bloomfield Ave, Windsor CT 06095
Tel (860) 602-3400 *SIC* 5088 3728 7629

AERSALE HOLDINGS INC p 31
121 Alhambra Plz Ste 1700, Coral Gables FL 33134
Tel (305) 764-3200 *SIC* 5088 7359

AERSALE INC p 31
121 Alhambra Plz Ste 1700, Coral Gables FL 33134
Tel (305) 764-3200 *SIC* 5088

■ M & M AEROSPACE HARDWARE INC p 888
10000 Nw 15th Ter, Doral FL 33172
Tel (305) 925-2600 *SIC* 5088

BANYAN AIR SERVICES INC p 153
5360 Nw 20th Ter, Fort Lauderdale FL 33309
Tel (954) 491-3170
SIC 5172 4581 5088 4522

EMBRAER AIRCRAFT CUSTOMER SERVICES INC p 490
276 Sw 34th St, Fort Lauderdale FL 33315
Tel (954) 359-3700 *SIC* 5088

GA TELESIS LLC p 588
1850 Nw 49th St, Fort Lauderdale FL 33309
Tel (954) 676-3111 *SIC* 5088 3724

NATIONAL MARINE SUPPLIERS INC p 1014
2800 Sw 2nd Ave, Fort Lauderdale FL 33315
Tel (954) 462-3131 *SIC* 5088

SOUTHEAST AEROSPACE INC p 1345
1399 General Aviation Dr, Melbourne FL 32935
Tel (321) 255-9877
SIC 5088 3812 3728 3721 4581

KELLSTROM AEROSPACE LLC p 809
14400 Nw 77th Ct Ste 306, Miami Lakes FL 33016
Tel (847) 233-5800 *SIC* 5088

■ LAND N SEA DISTRIBUTING INC p 842
3131 N Andrews Avenue Ext, Pompano Beach FL 33064
Tel (954) 792-9971
SIC 5088 5091 5046 5531

■ DAL GLOBAL SERVICES LLC p 409
980 Virginia Ave 4th, Atlanta GA 30354
Tel (404) 715-4300
SIC 7361 8331 7382 5088

SATAIR USA INC p 1283
3993 Tradeport Blvd, Atlanta GA 30354
Tel (404) 675-6333 *SIC* 5088

AIRGAS CARBONIC INC p 40
2530 Sever Rd Ste 300, Lawrenceville GA 30043
Tel (770) 717-2210 *SIC* 2813 7359 5088

PRECISION COMPONENTS INTERNATIONAL INC p 1168
8801 Macon Rd, Midland GA 31820
Tel (706) 568-5900 *SIC* 3728 5088 3724

■ GULFSTREAM DELAWARE CORP p 647
500 Gulfstream Rd, Savannah GA 31408
Tel (912) 965-3000 *SIC* 3721 5088

WESTERN AIRCRAFT INC p 1597
4300 S Kennedy St, Boise ID 83705
Tel (208) 338-1800
SIC 5088 4581 7359 5172

■ MARINE ACQUISITION CORP p 906
1 Sierra Pl, Litchfield IL 62056
Tel (217) 324-9400 *SIC* 5088

SIERRA INTERNATIONAL INC p 1320
1 Sierra Pl, Litchfield IL 62056
Tel (217) 324-9400 *SIC* 5088 3519

NATIONAL RAILWAY EQUIPMENT CO p 1015
1100 Shawnee St, Mount Vernon IL 62864
Tel (618) 242-6590 *SIC* 5088 3743

KELLSTROM COMMERCIAL AEROSPACE INC p 809
450 Medinah Rd, Roselle IL 60172
Tel (630) 351-8813 *SIC* 5088

■ AAR INTERNATIONAL INC p 8
1100 N Wood Dale Rd, Wood Dale IL 60191
Tel (630) 227-2000 *SIC* 5088

■ AAR SUPPLY CHAIN INC p 8
1100 N Wood Dale Rd, Wood Dale IL 60191
Tel (630) 227-2000 *SIC* 5088 3728

NATIONAL SALVAGE & SERVICE CORP p 1016
6755 S Old State Road 37, Bloomington IN 47401
Tel (812) 339-8437
SIC 5088 1629 1795 5099 5093

BRAKE SUPPLY CO INC p 207
5501 Foundation Blvd, Evansville IN 47725
Tel (812) 467-1000
SIC 5082 5084 5088 5013 3532

DONOVAN MARINE INC p 451
6316 Humphreys St, Harahan LA 70123
Tel (504) 729-2520 *SIC* 5088

ASRC AEROSPACE CORP p 119
7000 Muirkirk Meadows Dr # 100, Beltsville MD 20705
Tel (301) 837-5500
SIC 3812 7371 7373 5088

SHIMADZU AMERICA INC p 1316
7102 Riverwood Dr, Columbia MD 21046
Tel (410) 381-1227 *SIC* 5049 5047 5088

■ TEXTRON SYSTEMS CORP p 1445
201 Lowell St, Wilmington MA 01887
Tel (978) 657-5111 *SIC* 3483 5088

■ PRATT & WHITNEY COMPONENT SOLUTIONS INC p 1167
4905 Stariha Dr, Norton Shores MI 49441
Tel (231) 798-8464 *SIC* 5088

HELLA CORPORATE CENTER USA INC p 681
43811 Plymouth Oaks Blvd, Plymouth MI 48170
Tel (586) 232-4788
SIC 3625 5013 5088 3822 3585 3429

■ GENERAL DYNAMICS LAND SYSTEMS INC p 600
38500 Mound Rd, Sterling Heights MI 48310
Tel (586) 825-4000 *SIC* 5088 8711

■ GOODRICH CORP p 624
14300 Judicial Rd, Burnsville MN 55306
Tel (952) 892-4000 *SIC* 5088

■ L-3 COMMUNICATIONS VERTEX AEROSPACE LLC p 835
555 Industrial Dr S, Madison MS 39110
Tel (601) 856-2274 *SIC* 4581 5088

MEDART INC p 935
124 Manufacturers Dr, Arnold MO 63010
Tel (636) 282-2300 *SIC* 5084 5088

■ HERNDON AEROSPACE & DEFENSE LLC p 687
3801 Lloyd King Dr, O Fallon MO 63368
Tel (314) 739-7400 *SIC* 5088

■ HERNDON PRODUCTS LLC p 687
3801 Lloyd King Dr, O Fallon MO 63368
Tel (314) 739-7400 *SIC* 5088

DUNCAN AVIATION INC p 461
3701 Aviation Rd, Lincoln NE 68524
Tel (402) 479-1616
SIC 7699 5088 4522 4512

ATLANTIC TRACK & TURNOUT CO p 127
400 Broadacres Dr Ste 415, Bloomfield NJ 07003
Tel (973) 748-5885 *SIC* 5088

CARL F EWIG INC p 256
529 Dowd Ave, Elizabeth NJ 07201
Tel (908) 248-9001 *SIC* 5088

DASSAULT FALCON JET CORP p 413
200 Riser Rd, Little Ferry NJ 07643
Tel (201) 440-6700 *SIC* 5088 3721

ADVANCED ACOUSTIC CONCEPTS LLC p 25
425 Oser Ave Unit 1, Hauppauge NY 11788
Tel (631) 273-5700 *SIC* 5088

SAGE PARTS PLUS INC p 1267
30 Hub Dr Ste 1, Melville NY 11747
Tel (631) 501-1300 *SIC* 5088 3812 3537

JAMAICA BEARINGS CO INC p 776
1700 Jericho Tpke Ste 1, New Hyde Park NY 11040
Tel (516) 326-1350 *SIC* 5085 5088

TRI VANTAGE LLC p 1477
1831 N Park Ave, Burlington NC 27217
Tel (800) 786-1876
SIC 5199 5088 5099 5091 2394

MAGELLAN AIRCRAFT SERVICES LLLP p 895
2345 Township Rd Ste B, Charlotte NC 28273
Tel (704) 504-9204 *SIC* 5088

MAGELLAN AVIATION GROUP LLLP p 895
2345 Township Rd Ste B, Charlotte NC 28273
Tel (704) 504-9204 *SIC* 5088

TAS HOLDING INC p 1425
623 Radar Rd, Greensboro NC 27410
Tel (336) 668-4410 *SIC* 4581 5088

TIMCO AVIATION SERVICES INC p 1454
623 Radar Rd, Greensboro NC 27410
Tel (336) 668-4410 *SIC* 4581 5088

■ DJJ HOLDING CORP p 445
300 Pike St, Cincinnati OH 45202
Tel (513) 621-8770 *SIC* 5093 5088 4741

MAZZELLA HOLDING CO INC p 924
21000 Aerospace Pkwy, Cleveland OH 44142
Tel (513) 772-4466
SIC 5051 5085 5088 5072

▲ TRANSDIGM GROUP INC p 1471
1301 E 9th St Ste 3000, Cleveland OH 44114
Tel (216) 706-2960 *SIC* 3728 5088

■ TRANSDIGM INC p 1471
4223 Monticello Blvd, Cleveland OH 44121
Tel (216) 706-2939
SIC 5088 3563 3625 3492 3691 3491

■ NETJETS INC p 1027
4111 Bridgeway Ave, Columbus OH 43219
Tel (614) 239-5500 *SIC* 4522 5088 7359

■ NETJETS SALES INC p 1027
4111 Bridgeway Ave, Columbus OH 43219
Tel (614) 239-5500 *SIC* 5088 4522

CEDAR ELECTRONICS HOLDINGS CORP p 272
5440 W Chester Rd, West Chester OH 45069
Tel (513) 870-8500 *SIC* 3812 5088

■ ABX AIR INC p 13
145 Hunter Dr, Wilmington OH 45177
Tel (937) 382-5591
SIC 4513 5088 4581 8299

CHEROKEE NATION BUSINESSES LLC p 294
777 W Cherokee St Bldg 2, Catoosa OK 74015
Tel (918) 384-7474 *SIC* 3728 5085 5088

ALSTOM SIGNALING OPERATION LLC p 61
2901 E Lake Rd Bldg 122, Erie PA 16531
Tel (800) 825-3178
SIC 3669 5088 3672 3663

PHILADELPHIA AGUSTAWESTLAND CORP p 1142
3050 Red Lion Rd, Philadelphia PA 19114
Tel (215) 281-1400 *SIC* 3721 5088

COLOURS INC p 339
233 S Washington St, Wilkes Barre PA 18701
Tel (570) 655-9510 *SIC* 5198 5085 5088

STEVENS AVIATION INC p 1388
600 Delaware St, Greenville SC 29605
Tel (864) 678-6000
SIC 4522 4581 5088 5599

FLEXIAL CORP p 556
1483 Gould Dr, Cookeville TN 38506
Tel (931) 432-1853 *SIC* 5088

AEROSPACE PRODUCTS INTERNATIONAL INC p 31
2871 Business Park Dr, Memphis TN 38118
Tel (901) 365-3470 *SIC* 5088 4522

■ AVIALL INC p 137
2750 Rgent Blvd Dfw Arprt Dfw Airport, Dallas TX 75261
Tel (972) 586-1000 *SIC* 5088

■ VICTOR EQUIPMENT CO p 1555
2800 Airport Rd, Denton TX 76207
Tel (940) 566-2000 *SIC* 5088 3541 3548

■ AVIALL SERVICES INC p 137
2750 Regent Blvd, Dfw Airport TX 75261
Tel (972) 586-1000 *SIC* 5088 7699

■ BELL HELICOPTER TEXTRON INC p 170
3255 Bell Helicopter Blvd, Fort Worth TX 76118
Tel (817) 280-2011 *SIC* 3728 5088 3721

PATTONAIR USA INC p 1121
1900 Robotics Pl, Fort Worth TX 76118
Tel (817) 284-4449 *SIC* 5088

ZODIAC SEATS US LLC p 1644
2000 Zodiac Dr, Gainesville TX 76240
Tel (940) 668-8541 *SIC* 5088 3728

AIRBUS HELICOPTERS INC p 40
2701 N Forum Dr, Grand Prairie TX 75052
Tel (972) 641-0000 *SIC* 5088 7699 3721

UNITOR HOLDING INC p 1515
9400 New Century Dr, Pasadena TX 77507
Tel (281) 867-2000 *SIC* 5088

WILHELMSEN SHIPS SERVICE INC p 1609
9400 New Century Dr, Pasadena TX 77507
Tel (281) 867-2000 *SIC* 5551 5088 7699

■ ATLANTIC AVIATION CORP p 125
6652 Pinecrest Dr Ste 300, Plano TX 75024
Tel (972) 905-2500
SIC 4581 5088 5172 6331 6159 4522

BOMBARDIER AEROSPACE CORP p 199
3400 Waterview Pkwy # 400, Richardson TX 75080
Tel (972) 960-3810 *SIC* 5088 3721

A & K RAILROAD MATERIALS INC p 4
1505 S Redwood Rd, Salt Lake City UT 84104
Tel (801) 974-5484 *SIC* 5088

SAFRAN USA INC p 1267
700 S Washington St # 320, Alexandria VA 22314
Tel (703) 351-9898
SIC 3643 3621 7699 3724 5013 5088

SAAB NORTH AMERICA INC p 1263
20700 Loudoun County Pkwy # 152, Ashburn VA 20147
Tel (703) 406-7277 *SIC* 5088 3699 7371

DYNAMIC AVIATION GROUP INC p 464
1402 Airport Rd, Bridgewater VA 22812
Tel (540) 828-6070 *SIC* 5088

■ NORTHROP GRUMMAN MARITIME SYSTEMS p 1058
1070 Seminole Trl, Charlottesville VA 22901
Tel (434) 974-2000 *SIC* 5088

VOLVO PENTA OF AMERICAS LLC p 1565
1300 Volvo Penta Dr, Chesapeake VA 23320
Tel (757) 436-2800
SIC 5088 3519 5091 5063

IAT INTERNATIONAL INC p 726
555 E Main St Ste 1101, Norfolk VA 23510
Tel (757) 622-7239 *SIC* 5088

ROLLS-ROYCE NORTH AMERICA (USA) HOLDINGS CO p 1247
1875 Explorer St Ste 200, Reston VA 20190
Tel (703) 834-1700
SIC 5088 8741 6159 3724

ROLLS-ROYCE NORTH AMERICA HOLDINGS INC p 1248
1875 Explorer St Ste 200, Reston VA 20190
Tel (703) 834-1700 SIC 5088 8741 7699

ROLLS-ROYCE NORTH AMERICA INC p 1248
1875 Explorer St Ste 200, Reston VA 20190
Tel (703) 834-1700 SIC 5088 8741 1731

HEATH TECNA INC p 679
3225 Woburn St, Bellingham WA 98226
Tel (360) 738-2005 SIC 3728 5088

PACIFIC POWER GROUP LLC p 1105
805 Broadway St Ste 700, Vancouver WA 98660
Tel (360) 887-7400
SIC 5088 3621 5063 3519 5084

■ DERCO AEROSPACE INC p 431
8000 W Tower Ave, Milwaukee WI 53223
Tel (414) 355-3066 SIC 5065 5088

SIC 5091 Sporting & Recreational Goods & Splys Wholesale

DEVTEK INC p 434
220 Cedar St Nw, Hartselle AL 35640
Tel (256) 751-9441 SIC 5091

LESLIES POOLMART INC p 857
2005 E Indian School Rd, Phoenix AZ 85016
Tel (602) 366-3999 SIC 5091

SHASTA INDUSTRIES INC p 1312
6031 N 16th St, Phoenix AZ 85016
Tel (602) 532-3750
SIC 1799 1771 5169 7389 3088 5091

DAVIDSONS INC p 416
6100 Wilkinson Dr, Prescott AZ 86301
Tel (928) 776-8055 SIC 5091

■ SUPERIOR POOL PRODUCTS LLC p 1407
4900 E Landon Dr, Anaheim CA 92807
Tel (714) 693-8035 SIC 5091

YAMAHA CORP OF AMERICA INC p 1634
6600 Orangethorpe Ave, Buena Park CA 90620
Tel (714) 522-9011
SIC 5099 5065 5091 3931

■ CALLAWAY GOLF BALL OPERATIONS INC p 242
2180 Rutherford Rd, Carlsbad CA 92008
Tel (760) 931-1771 SIC 5091

TIANJIN POOL & SPA CORP p 1452
2701-2711 Garfield Ave, Commerce CA 90040
Tel (626) 571-1885 SIC 5169 5091

YAMAHA MOTOR CORP USA p 1634
6555 Katella Ave, Cypress CA 90630
Tel (714) 761-7300
SIC 5088 5013 5091 5012

KAWASAKI MOTORS CORP USA p 805
26972 Burbank, Foothill Ranch CA 92610
Tel (949) 837-4683
SIC 5012 5013 5084 5091

POOL WATER PRODUCTS p 1161
17872 Mitchell N Ste 250, Irvine CA 92614
Tel (949) 756-1666 SIC 5091 2899 2812

SHIMANO AMERICAN CORP p 1316
1 Holland, Irvine CA 92618
Tel (949) 951-5003 SIC 5091

INTEX RECREATION CORP p 759
4001 Via Oro Ave Ste 210, Long Beach CA 90810
Tel (310) 549-5400
SIC 5091 5092 5021 3081

SPECIALIZED BICYCLE COMPONENTS INC p 1356
15130 Concord Cir, Morgan Hill CA 95037
Tel (408) 779-6229 SIC 5091

POOL & ELECTRICAL PRODUCTS INC p 1161
1250 E Francis St, Ontario CA 91761
Tel (909) 673-1160 SIC 5091

EASTON HOCKEY INC p 473
7855 Haskell Ave Ste 200, Van Nuys CA 91406
Tel (818) 782-6445 SIC 5091

RBG HOLDINGS CORP p 1211
7855 Haskell Ave Ste 350, Van Nuys CA 91406
Tel (818) 782-6445 SIC 3949 5091 3751

HEAD USA INC p 673
3125 Sterling Cir Ste 101, Boulder CO 80301
Tel (800) 874-3235 SIC 5091

HTM USA HOLDINGS INC p 715
3125 Sterling Cir Ste 101, Boulder CO 80301
Tel (800) 874-3235 SIC 5091 5139 3949

OURAY SPORTSWEAR LLC p 1098
1201 W Mansfield Ave, Englewood CO 80110
Tel (303) 798-4035 SIC 5091

FIT FOR LIFE LLC p 552
833 W S Boulder Rd Bldg G, Louisville CO 80027
Tel (303) 222-3600 SIC 5091 5941

BIC CORP p 181
1 Bic Way Ste 1, Shelton CT 06484
Tel (203) 783-2000
SIC 3951 2899 3999 3421 5091 3952

MP DIRECT INC p 995
4800 126th Ave N, Clearwater FL 33762
Tel (727) 572-8443 SIC 5094 5944 5091

PORPOISE POOL & PATIO INC p 1161
14480 62nd St N, Clearwater FL 33760
Tel (727) 531-8913
SIC 6794 5999 5712 5091

SUN WHOLESALE SUPPLY INC p 1401
6385 150th Ave N, Clearwater FL 33760
Tel (727) 524-3299
SIC 5169 5021 5023 5091

HORNERXPRESS INC p 708
5755 Powerline Rd, Fort Lauderdale FL 33309
Tel (954) 772-6966 SIC 5091 3949 3561

HORNERXPRESS-SOUTH FLORIDA INC p 708
5755 Powerline Rd, Fort Lauderdale FL 33309
Tel (800) 432-6966 SIC 5091

J & B IMPORTERS INC p 769
11925 Sw 128th St, Miami FL 33186
Tel (305) 238-1866 SIC 5091

■ LAND N SEA DISTRIBUTING INC p 842
3131 N Andrews Avenue Ext, Pompano Beach FL 33064
Tel (954) 792-9971
SIC 5088 5091 5046 5531

SEABRING MARINE INDUSTRIES INC p 1296
1579 Sw 18th St, Williston FL 32696
Tel (352) 529-9161 SIC 5091 3732

BRIDGESTONE GOLF INC p 211
15320 Indsrial Pk Blvd Ne, Covington GA 30014
Tel (770) 787-7400 SIC 5091 3949

CAROLINA SKIFF LLC p 259
3231 Fulford Rd, Waycross GA 31503
Tel (912) 287-0547 SIC 5091 3732

WILSON SPORTING GOODS CO p 1614
8750 W Bryn Mawr Ave Fl 2, Chicago IL 60631
Tel (773) 714-6400 SIC 5091 3949

▲ BRUNSWICK CORP p 221
1 N Field Ct, Lake Forest IL 60045
Tel (847) 735-4700
SIC 3519 3732 3949 7933 5091

MAURICE SPORTING GOODS INC p 921
1910 Techny Rd, Northbrook IL 60062
Tel (847) 715-1500 SIC 5091

RIDDELL INC p 1234
9801 W Higgins Rd Ste 800, Rosemont IL 60018
Tel (847) 292-1472 SIC 5091 3949

UNIVERSAL POOL CO INC p 1517
300 W Armory Dr, South Holland IL 60473
Tel (708) 339-6060 SIC 5021 5091

■ FORT WAYNE POOLS p 569
6930 Gettysburg Pike, Fort Wayne IN 46804
Tel (260) 459-4100 SIC 5091 3949

BROWNELLS INC p 220
200 S Front St, Montezuma IA 50171
Tel (641) 623-5401 SIC 5091 5941

■ BUSHNELL HOLDINGS INC p 229
9200 Cody St, Overland Park KS 66214
Tel (913) 752-3400 SIC 3851 5049 5091

■ RUSSELL BRANDS LLC p 1259
1 Fruit Of The Loom Dr, Bowling Green KY 42103
Tel (270) 781-6400
SIC 2253 2211 2329 2339 3949 5091

LIPSEYS LLC p 870
7277 Exchequer Dr, Baton Rouge LA 70809
Tel (225) 755-1333 SIC 5091

▲ POOL CORP p 1161
109 Northpark Blvd # 400, Covington LA 70433
Tel (985) 892-5521 SIC 5091

■ SCP DISTRIBUTORS LLC p 1294
109 Northpark Blvd, Covington LA 70433
Tel (985) 892-5521 SIC 5091

SPORTS SOUTH LLC p 1360
1039 Kay Ln, Shreveport LA 71115
Tel (318) 797-4848 SIC 5091

BERETTA USA CORP p 174
17601 Beretta Dr, Accokeek MD 20607
Tel (301) 283-2191 SIC 5091 3484

■ Z MARINE NORTH AMERICA LLC p 1640
540 Thompson Creek Rd, Stevensville MD 21666
Tel (843) 376-3470 SIC 5091

BAY STATE POOL SUPPLIES INC p 161
691 Concord Ave, Cambridge MA 02138
Tel (617) 547-9145 SIC 5169 5091

RAY MURRAY INC p 1210
50 Limestone, Lee MA 01238
Tel (413) 243-7700 SIC 5085 5091

■ SMITH & WESSON CORP p 1333
2100 Roosevelt Ave, Springfield MA 01104
Tel (413) 781-8300
SIC 3484 3429 3999 5091

FAMILY FARM & HOME INC p 526
900 3rd St Ste 302, Muskegon MI 49440
Tel (231) 722-8335
SIC 5999 5261 5149 5611 5211 5091

QUALITY BICYCLE PRODUCTS INC p 1196
6400 W 105th St, Bloomington MN 55438
Tel (952) 941-9391 SIC 5091

MID-STATES DISTRIBUTING CO INC p 963
1370 Mendota Hts Rd, Mendota MN 55150
Tel (651) 280-4300
SIC 5072 5013 5191 5091 5092 5136

HARVEST SPORTING GROUP INC p 667
2219 Hitzert Ct, Fenton MO 63026
Tel (314) 378-8905 SIC 5091

SPORTSMANS SUPPLY INC p 1360
2219 Hitzert Ct, Fenton MO 63026
Tel (636) 600-9301 SIC 5091

■ RAWLINGS SPORTING GOODS CO INC p 1209
510 Maryville University, Saint Louis MO 63141
Tel (866) 678-4327 SIC 3949 5091

SPORTS INC p 1360
333 2nd Ave N, Lewistown MT 59457
Tel (406) 538-3496 SIC 5091

H BETTI INDUSTRIES INC p 649
303 Paterson Plank Rd, Carlstadt NJ 07072
Tel (201) 438-1300 SIC 5046 5091 7699

SAFILO AMERICA INC p 1267
801 Jefferson Rd, Parsippany NJ 07054
Tel (973) 952-2800 SIC 5048 5099 5091

BEL-AQUA POOL SUPPLY INC p 169
20 Commerce Dr, New Rochelle NY 10801
Tel (914) 235-2200 SIC 5091

MORRIS ROTHENBERG & SON INC p 990
3015 Veterans Mem Hwy, Ronkonkoma NY 11779
Tel (631) 585-9446
SIC 5199 5091 5139 5136

GREAT AMERICAN INDUSTRIES INC p 633
300 Plaza Dr, Vestal NY 13850
Tel (607) 729-9331
SIC 3086 5031 5074 3442 3069 5091

TRI VANTAGE LLC p 1477
1831 N Park Ave, Burlington NC 27217
Tel (800) 786-1876
SIC 5199 5088 5099 5091 2394

ADVANCED SPORTS ENTERPRISES INC p 26
1 Performance Way, Chapel Hill NC 27517
Tel (919) 933-9113 SIC 5091

POOL BUILDERS SUPPLY OF CAROLINAS INC p 1161
1124 Central Ave, Charlotte NC 28204
Tel (704) 375-7573 SIC 5091 5999

BIG ROCK SPORTS LLC p 182
158 Little Nine Rd, Morehead City NC 28557
Tel (252) 808-3500 SIC 5091

HENRYS TACKLE LLC p 684
158 Little Nine Rd, Morehead City NC 28557
Tel (252) 726-6186 SIC 5091

BALL BOUNCE AND SPORT INC p 148
1 Hedstrom Dr, Ashland OH 44805
Tel (419) 759-3838 SIC 5092 5091 3089

ACUSPORT CORP p 20
1 Hunter Pl, Bellefontaine OH 43311
Tel (937) 593-7010 SIC 5091

■ GOLF GALAXY GOLFWORKS INC p 622
4820 Jacksontown Rd, Newark OH 43056
Tel (740) 328-4193
SIC 5091 2731 3949 5941

LMN DEVELOPMENT LLC p 872
7000 Kalahari Dr, Sandusky OH 44870
Tel (419) 433-7200 SIC 7011 7996 5091

CENTURY LLC p 282
1000 Century Blvd, Oklahoma City OK 73110
Tel (405) 732-2226 SIC 5091 3949

RADIAL INC p 1204
935 1st Ave, King Of Prussia PA 19406
Tel (610) 491-7000
SIC 3149 5139 5091 5136 5137 7375

SCHUYLKILL VALLEY SPORTS INC p 1291
118 Industrial Dr Ste 1, Pottstown PA 19464
Tel (610) 495-8813 SIC 5091 5941

WEXCO INC p 1603
3490 Board Rd, York PA 17406
Tel (717) 764-8585
SIC 3089 3949 3999 5091 3081

ELLETT BROTHERS LLC p 488
267 Columbia Ave, Chapin SC 29036
Tel (803) 345-3751
SIC 5091 3949 2499 2541

UNITED SPORTING COMPANIES INC p 1512
267 Columbia Ave, Chapin SC 29036
Tel (803) 345-3751 SIC 5091

■ KNIGHTS APPAREL INC p 824
5475 N Blackstock Rd, Spartanburg SC 29303
Tel (864) 587-9690 SIC 5091 5699

TRUE TEMPER SPORTS INC p 1486
8275 Tournament Dr # 200, Memphis TN 38125
Tel (901) 746-2000 SIC 5091 3949

VARSITY BRANDS LLC p 1545
6745 Lenox Center Ct # 300, Memphis TN 38115
Tel (901) 387-4306 SIC 5091

EVERGREEN ALLIANCE GOLF LIMITED LP p 514
4851 Lydon B Johnson Ste 600, Dallas TX 75244
Tel (214) 722-6000 SIC 7992 5091

BSN SPORTS LLC p 222
1901 Diplomat Dr, Farmers Branch TX 75234
Tel (972) 484-9484 SIC 5091

VARSITY BRANDS HOLDING CO INC p 1545
1901 Diplomat Dr, Farmers Branch TX 75234
Tel (972) 406-7162 SIC 5091 7299 6719

BELL SPORTS CORP p 170
6333 N State Highway 161 # 300, Irving TX 75038
Tel (469) 417-6600 SIC 3949 3751 5091

BOY SCOUTS OF AMERICA p 205
1325 W Walnut Hill Ln, Irving TX 75038
Tel (972) 580-2000
SIC 8641 5136 5091 2721

BUTTERY CO LLP p 230
201 W Main St, Llano TX 78643
Tel (325) 247-4141
SIC 5072 5074 5063 5091 5211 5251

MACH SPEED HOLDINGS LLC p 892
7200 Bishop Rd Ste 280, Plano TX 75024
Tel (214) 978-3800 SIC 5091 5065 3679

TEAM EXPRESS DISTRIBUTING LLC p 1429
5750 Northwest Pkwy # 100, San Antonio TX 78249
Tel (210) 525-9161 SIC 5941 5091

BACKCOUNTRY.COM LLC p 143
1678 Redstone Center Dr # 210, Park City UT 84098
Tel (801) 746-7580 SIC 5091 4813

JAS D EASTON INC p 778
5215 W Wiley Post Way # 130, Salt Lake City UT 84116
Tel (801) 526-6211 SIC 3949 5091 6552

VOLVO PENTA OF AMERICAS LLC p 1565
1300 Volvo Penta Dr, Chesapeake VA 23320
Tel (757) 436-2800
SIC 5088 3519 5091 5063

ATLANTIC DIVING SUPPLY INC p 126
621 Lynnhven Pkwy Ste 400, Virginia Beach VA 23452
Tel (757) 481-7758 SIC 5091

WORLDWIDE DISTRIBUTORS p 1626
8211 S 194th St, Kent WA 98032
Tel (253) 872-8746
SIC 5091 5136 5137 5139 5199 5023

TRIDENT SEAFOODS CORP p 1479
5303 Shilshole Ave Nw, Seattle WA 98107
Tel (206) 783-3818
SIC 2092 5146 5091 0912

CORE HEALTH & FITNESS LLC p 369
4400 Ne 77th Ave Ste 300, Vancouver WA 98662
Tel (360) 326-4090 SIC 5091

CORE INDUSTRIES LLC p 369
4400 Ne 77th Ave Ste 300, Vancouver WA 98662
Tel (360) 326-4090 SIC 5091

JEAN NELL ENTERPRISES INC p 781
1 Nell Jean Sq 19, Beckley WV 25801
Tel (304) 253-0200 SIC 5941 5082 5091

JOHNSON HEALTH TECH NORTH AMERICA INC p 791
1600 Landmark Dr, Cottage Grove WI 53527
Tel (608) 839-1240 SIC 5091 5941

PACIFIC CYCLE INC p 1104
4902 Hammersley Rd, Madison WI 53711
Tel (608) 268-2468 SIC 5091 5941

SIC 5092 Toys & Hobby Goods & Splys Wholesale

AMERICAN PROMOTIONAL EVENTS INC p 78
4511 Helton Dr, Florence AL 35630
Tel (256) 284-1003 SIC 5092 5999

JOE TORNANTE-MDP HOLDING LLC p 787
233 S Beverly Dr, Beverly Hills CA 90212
Tel (310) 228-6800
SIC 5145 5092 5112 2064

PERFORMANCE DESIGNED PRODUCTS LLC p 1135
2300 W Empire Ave # 600, Burbank CA 91504
Tel (323) 234-9911 SIC 5092

■ MATTEL TOY CO p 920
333 Continental Blvd, El Segundo CA 90245
Tel (310) 252-2357 SIC 5092

SONY INTERACTIVE ENTERTAINMENT AMERICA LLC p 1341
2207 Bridgepointe Pkwy, Foster City CA 94404
Tel (650) 655-8000 SIC 5092

SEGA OF AMERICA INC p 1300
6400 Oak Cyn Ste 100, Irvine CA 92618
Tel (415) 806-0169 SIC 3999 5092

SOLUTIONS 2 GO LLC p 1339
111 Theory Ste 250, Irvine CA 92617
Tel (949) 825-7700 SIC 5092

VICTORY INTERNATIONAL GROUP LLC p 1556
9800 Irvine Center Dr, Irvine CA 92618
Tel (949) 407-5888 SIC 5092

INTEX RECREATION CORP p 759
4001 Via Oro Ave Ste 210, Long Beach CA 90810
Tel (310) 549-5400
SIC 5091 5092 5021 3081

SEGA OF AMERICA INC p 1300
350 Rhode Island St # 400, San Francisco CA 94103
Tel (415) 701-6000 SIC 5045 5092

BANDAI NAMCO ENTERTAINMENT AMERICA INC p 150
2051 Mission College Blvd, Santa Clara CA 95054
Tel (408) 235-2000 SIC 5092

MGA ENTERTAINMENT INC p 958
16300 Roscoe Blvd Ste 150, Van Nuys CA 91406
Tel (818) 894-2525 SIC 5092

LEGO SYSTEMS INC p 853
555 Taylor Rd, Enfield CT 06082
Tel (860) 749-2291 SIC 3944 5092

MELISSA & DOUG INC p 940
141 Danbury Rd, Wilton CT 06897
Tel (203) 762-4500 SIC 5092

MELISSA & DOUG LLC p 940
141 Danbury Rd, Wilton CT 06897
Tel (203) 762-4500 SIC 5092

AVALANCHE STRATEGIES LLC p 135
144 Dixon St, Selbyville DE 19975
Tel (302) 436-7060 SIC 5092 5945

SANDY PAGES p 1279
1794 S Kihei Rd Ste 4, Kihei HI 96753
Tel (808) 205-0321 SIC 5192 5092

HOBBICO INC p 698
1608 Interstate Dr, Champaign IL 61822
Tel (217) 398-3630 SIC 5092 5961

HORIZON HOBBY LLC p 707
4105 Fieldstone Rd, Champaign IL 61822
Tel (217) 352-1913 SIC 5092

MR CHIPS INC p 996
1380 Gateway Dr Ste 7, Elgin IL 60124
Tel (847) 468-9000 SIC 5092 5047

TOMY HOLDINGS INC p 1460
2015 Spring Rd Ste 400, Oak Brook IL 60523
Tel (630) 573-7200 SIC 5092 5945

TY INC p 1496
280 Chestnut Ave, Westmont IL 60559
Tel (630) 920-1515 SIC 5092

TOMY CORP p 1460
2021 9th St Se, Dyersville IA 52040
Tel (563) 875-2000 SIC 5092

TOMY INTERNATIONAL INC p 1460
2021 9th St Se, Dyersville IA 52040
Tel (563) 875-2000 SIC 5092

VARIETY DISTRIBUTORS INC p 1544
609 7th St, Harlan IA 51537
Tel (712) 755-2184
SIC 5131 5092 5122 5112 5145 5199

■ UNITED STATES PLAYING CARD CO p 1514
300 Gap Way, Erlanger KY 41018
Tel (859) 815-7300 SIC 2752 5092

NOTIONS MARKETING CORP p 1062
1500 Buchanan Ave Sw, Grand Rapids MI 49507
Tel (616) 243-8424 SIC 5131 5199 5092

MID-STATES DISTRIBUTING CO INC p 963
1370 Mendota Hts Rd, Mendota MN 55150
Tel (651) 280-4300
SIC 5072 5013 5191 5091 5092 5136

COKEM INTERNATIONAL LTD p 335
3880 4th Ave E, Shakopee MN 55379
Tel (952) 358-6000 SIC 5092

SHELTON WHOLESALE INC p 1315
24073 24th St, Eagleville MO 64442
Tel (660) 867-3354 SIC 5092

U STOY CO INC p 1497
13201 Arrington Rd, Grandview MO 64030
Tel (816) 761-5900 SIC 5049 5092 5945

PROGRESSIVE BALLOONS INC p 1181
3100 Industrial Park Pl W, Saint Peters MO 63376
Tel (636) 240-0444 SIC 5092

KONAMI GAMING INC p 827
585 Konami Cir, Las Vegas NV 89119
Tel (702) 616-1400 SIC 5092 3999

DAN-DEE INTERNATIONAL LIMITED p 410
106 Harbor Dr, Jersey City NJ 07305
Tel (201) 332-7600 SIC 5092

NICOLE CRAFTS LLC p 1043
14 Sbar Blvd, Moorestown NJ 08057
Tel (856) 234-8220 SIC 5092

SBARS INC p 1285
14 Sbar Blvd, Moorestown NJ 08057
Tel (856) 234-8220 SIC 5092

HORIZON GROUP USA INC p 707
45 Technology Dr, Warren NJ 07059
Tel (908) 810-1111 SIC 5092
■ FISHER-PRICE INC p 552
636 Girard Ave, East Aurora NY 14052
Tel (716) 687-3000 SIC 5092 5945 3944
MECCA ELECTRONICS INDUSTRIES INC p 934
1016 44th Dr, Long Island City NY 11101
Tel (718) 361-9001 SIC 5092
■ MULTI PACKAGING SOLUTIONS INC p 999
150 E 52nd St Ste 2800, New York NY 10022
Tel (646) 885-0005
SIC 2759 2731 2761 3089 5092 2671
TOPPS CO INC p 1461
1 Whitehall St Fl 4, New York NY 10004
Tel (212) 376-0300
SIC 5145 5092 5112 2064
BALL BOUNCE AND SPORT INC p 148
1 Hedstrom Dr, Ashland OH 44805
Tel (419) 759-3838 SIC 5092 5091 3089
■ CLOSEOUT DISTRIBUTION INC p 327
300 Phillipi Rd, Columbus OH 43228
Tel (614) 278-6800 SIC 5092
■ CSC DISTRIBUTION INC p 397
300 Phillipi Rd, Columbus OH 43228
Tel (614) 278-6800 SIC 5092
CHECKER NOTIONS CO INC p 292
400 W Dussel Dr Ste B, Maumee OH 43537
Tel (419) 893-3636 SIC 5131 5092
■ LAMRITE WEST INC p 841
14225 Pearl Rd, Strongsville OH 44136
Tel (440) 238-7318 SIC 5999 5199 5092
BJ ALAN CO p 185
555 Mrtin Lther King Blvd, Youngstown OH 44502
Tel (330) 746-1064 SIC 5092
SKH MANAGEMENT CO p 1329
813 Lititz Pike, Lititz PA 17543
Tel (717) 627-0090
SIC 5141 5092 5261 5411
FAMOSA NORTH AMERICA INC p 527
1357 Ashford Ave Se, San Juan PR 00907
Tel (206) 316-8315 SIC 5092
INGRAM ENTERTAINMENT INC p 743
2 Ingram Blvd, La Vergne TN 37089
Tel (615) 287-4000 SIC 5065 5092 5099
ABOUT TIME LTD p 12
7220 Bob Bullock Loop, Laredo TX 78041
Tel (956) 723-1198 SIC 5092 5945
PROVO CRAFT & NOVELTY INC p 1187
10855 S Rvr Frnt Pkwy # 400, South Jordan UT 84095
Tel (800) 937-7686
SIC 5092 5199 5945 5947
NINTENDO OF AMERICA INC p 1044
4600 150th Ave Ne, Redmond WA 98052
Tel (425) 882-2040 SIC 5092

SIC 5093 Scrap & Waste Materials Wholesale

■ THERMO FLUIDS INC p 1447
8925 E Pima Center Pkwy # 105, Scottsdale AZ 85258
Tel (480) 270-5702 SIC 5093
■ PICK-YOUR-PART AUTO WRECKING p 1146
1235 S Beach Blvd, Anaheim CA 92804
Tel (714) 385-1200 SIC 5531 5093
CEDARWOOD-YOUNG CO p 272
14620 Joanbridge St, Baldwin Park CA 91706
Tel (626) 962-4047 SIC 5093
AMERICA CHUNG NAM (GROUP) HOLDINGS LLC p 67
1163 Fairway Dr, City Of Industry CA 91789
Tel (909) 839-8383 SIC 5093
AMERICA CHUNG NAM LLC p 67
1163 Fairway Dr Fl 3, City Of Industry CA 91789
Tel (909) 839-8383 SIC 5093
JAPAN PULP & PAPER (USA) CORP p 778
5928 S Malt Ave, Commerce CA 90040
Tel (323) 889-7750 SIC 5113 5093 5099
CYCLE LINK (USA) INC p 405
1330 Valley Vista Dr, Diamond Bar CA 91765
Tel (909) 861-5888 SIC 5093
ADVANCED STEEL RECOVERY LLC p 26
14451 Whittram Ave, Fontana CA 92335
Tel (909) 355-2372 SIC 5093
■ SOS METALS INC p 1341
201 E Gardena Blvd, Gardena CA 90248
Tel (310) 217-8848 SIC 5093 5051
PAVEMENT RECYCLING SYSTEMS INC p 1122
10240 San Sevaine Way, Jurupa Valley CA 91752
Tel (951) 682-1091 SIC 5093 1611
NEWPORT CH INTERNATIONAL LLC p 1038
1100 W Town And Country R, Orange CA 92868
Tel (714) 572-8881 SIC 5093
SA RECYCLING LLC p 1263
2411 N Glassell St, Orange CA 92865
Tel (714) 632-2000 SIC 5093
■ PICK AND PULL AUTO DISMANTLING INC p 1146
10850 Gold Center Dr # 325, Rancho Cordova CA 95670
Tel (916) 689-2000 SIC 5093
B & B PLASTICS RECYCLERS INC p 141
3040 N Locust Ave, Rialto CA 92377
Tel (909) 829-3606 SIC 5093 2673
SIMS GROUP USA CORP p 1325
600 S 4th St, Richmond CA 94804
Tel (510) 412-5300 SIC 5093 4953
CELLMARK INC p 273
22 Pelican Way, San Rafael CA 94901
Tel (415) 927-1700 SIC 5099 5093 5111
ECS REFINING LLC p 476
705 Reed St, Santa Clara CA 95050
Tel (408) 988-4386 SIC 5093
SOLARIS PAPER INC p 1338
13415 Carmenita Rd, Santa Fe Springs CA 90670
Tel (562) 376-9717 SIC 5093

POTENTIAL INDUSTRIES INC p 1164
922 E E St, Wilmington CA 90744
Tel (310) 807-4466 SIC 4953 5093
BSI HOLDINGS INC p 222
2495 Uravan St, Aurora CO 80011
Tel (303) 371-2200
SIC 6719 3589 5093 3715 3823 5051
PRIME MATERIALS RECOVERY INC p 1175
99 E River Dr, East Hartford CT 06108
Tel (860) 622-7626 SIC 5093
■ TRADEMARK METALS RECYCLING LLC p 1468
The Lincoln Center 5401 W, Tampa FL 33609
Tel (813) 226-0088 SIC 5093 1081
■ SCHNITZER SOUTHEAST LLC p 1288
906 Adamson St Sw, Atlanta GA 30315
Tel (404) 332-1750 SIC 5093
SCRAP METAL SERVICES LLC p 1294
13830 S Brainard Ave, Burnham IL 60633
Tel (708) 730-1400 SIC 5093
BRANDENBURG INDUSTRIAL SERVICE CO p 208
2625 S Loomis St, Chicago IL 60608
Tel (312) 326-5800 SIC 4959 1795 5093
CONTINENTAL PAPER GRADING CO p 363
1623 S Lumber St, Chicago IL 60616
Tel (312) 226-2010 SIC 5093
▲ LKQ CORP p 872
500 W Madison St Ste 2800, Chicago IL 60661
Tel (312) 621-1950 SIC 5093 5015
METAL MANAGEMENT INC p 952
2500 S Paulina St, Chicago IL 60608
Tel (312) 645-0700 SIC 5093 1795
METAL MANAGEMENT MIDWEST INC p 952
2500 S Paulina St, Chicago IL 60608
Tel (773) 254-1200 SIC 5093
UNITED SCRAP METAL INC p 1511
1545 S Cicero Ave, Cicero IL 60804
Tel (708) 780-6800 SIC 5093
MERVIS INDUSTRIES INC p 951
3295 E Main St Ste C, Danville IL 61834
Tel (217) 442-5300 SIC 5093
NATIONAL MATERIAL LP p 1014
1965 Pratt Blvd, Elk Grove Village IL 60007
Tel (847) 806-7200
SIC 5051 3469 3354 5093 4911 4924
TOTALL METAL RECYCLING INC p 1463
2700 Missouri Ave, Granite City IL 62040
Tel (618) 877-0585 SIC 5093
PURE METAL RECYCLING LLC p 1192
100 Tri State Intl # 215, Lincolnshire IL 60069
Tel (773) 523-4500 SIC 5093
CIMCO RESOURCES INC p 307
1616 Windsor Rd, Loves Park IL 61111
Tel (815) 986-7211 SIC 5093 7389
JOSEPH BEHR & SONS INC p 793
1100 Seminary St, Rockford IL 61104
Tel (815) 987-2755 SIC 5093
NATIONAL SALVAGE & SERVICE CORP p 1016
6755 S Old State Road 37, Bloomington IN 47401
Tel (812) 339-8437
SIC 5088 1629 1795 5099 5093
■ OMNISOURCE CORP p 1085
7575 W Jefferson Blvd, Fort Wayne IN 46804
Tel (260) 422-5541 SIC 5093 3462 3399
HERITAGE ENVIRONMENTAL SERVICES INC p 686
7901 W Morris St, Indianapolis IN 46231
Tel (317) 243-0811
SIC 5093 4213 8731 7389 1799 8711
HERITAGE ENVIRONMENTAL SERVICES LLC p 686
7901 W Morris St, Indianapolis IN 46231
Tel (317) 243-0811
SIC 5093 4213 8731 7389 1799 8711
OSCAR WINSKI CO INC p 1096
2407 N 9th Street Rd, Lafayette IN 47904
Tel (765) 742-1102 SIC 5051 5093
INTRA AMERICAN METALS INC p 759
14297 Bergen Blvd Ste 200, Noblesville IN 46060
Tel (317) 219-4444 SIC 5093
METALX LLC p 953
295 S Commerce Dr, Waterloo IN 46793
Tel (260) 232-3000 SIC 5093
SHINE BROS CORP p 1317
225 10th Ave Se, Spencer IA 51301
Tel (712) 262-5579 SIC 5093 3341
SOLOMON TRANSFORMERS LLC p 1338
103 W Main St, Solomon KS 67480
Tel (785) 655-2191 SIC 3612 5093
HOUCHENS FOOD GROUP INC p 710
700 Church St, Bowling Green KY 42101
Tel (270) 843-3252 SIC 5411 5541 5093
■ RIVER METALS RECYCLING LLC p 1237
334 Beechwood Rd Ste 401, Fort Mitchell KY 41017
Tel (859) 292-8400 SIC 5093 3341
STAINLESS STEEL MIDWEST LLC p 1374
2615 E Highway 146, La Grange KY 40031
Tel (502) 805-1120 SIC 5093
SOUTHERN RECYCLING LLC p 1350
902 Julia St, New Orleans LA 70113
Tel (504) 636-7200 SIC 5093
■ PCG PARENT CORP p 1124
4 Technology Dr, Peabody MA 01960
Tel (978) 538-8000
SIC 5045 5065 4953 5093 7378
■ PCG TRADING LLC p 1124
4 Technology Dr, Peabody MA 01960
Tel (978) 538-8000
SIC 5045 5065 4953 5093 7378
FERROUS PROCESSING AND TRADING CO p 538
3400 E Lafayette St, Detroit MI 48207
Tel (313) 582-2910 SIC 5093
LOUIS PADNOS IRON AND METAL CO p 879
185 W 8th St, Holland MI 49423
Tel (616) 396-6521 SIC 5093 4491 3599
SCHUPAN & SONS INC p 1291
2619 Miller Rd, Kalamazoo MI 49001
Tel (269) 382-0000 SIC 5093 5051 3341

FRITZ ENTERPRISES INC p 580
1650 W Jefferson Ave, Trenton MI 48183
Tel (734) 692-4231 SIC 5093
HURON VALLEY STEEL CORP p 721
1650 W Jefferson Ave, Trenton MI 48183
Tel (734) 479-3500 SIC 5093 3341 3559
MIDWEST SCRAP MANAGEMENT INC p 967
4501 Packers Ave, Saint Joseph MO 64504
Tel (816) 214-9204 SIC 5093
ALTER TRADING CORP p 62
700 Office Pkwy, Saint Louis MO 63141
Tel (314) 872-2400 SIC 5093
GROSSMAN IRON AND STEEL CO p 641
5 N Market St, Saint Louis MO 63102
Tel (314) 231-9423 SIC 5093
METAL EXCHANGE CORP p 952
111 West Port Plz Ste 350, Saint Louis MO 63146
Tel (314) 542-7250 SIC 3334 5093
SHAPIRO SALES CO p 1312
9666 Olive Blvd Ste 500, Saint Louis MO 63132
Tel (314) 381-9300 SIC 5093 4953
PACIFIC HIDE & FUR DEPOT p 1104
5 River Dr S, Great Falls MT 59405
Tel (406) 771-7222 SIC 5051 5093
GDB INTERNATIONAL INC p 595
1 Home News Row, New Brunswick NJ 08901
Tel (732) 246-3001
SIC 2851 5162 5111 5093
K-C INTERNATIONAL LLC p 799
1800 Rte 34 Ste 401, Wall Township NJ 07719
Tel (732) 202-9500 SIC 5093
GP HARMON RECYCLING LLC p 627
2 Jericho Plz Ste 200, Jericho NY 11753
Tel (516) 997-3400 SIC 5093
BLUE TEE CORP p 192
387 Park Ave S Fl 5, New York NY 10016
Tel (212) 598-0880
SIC 3533 3589 5093 3715 3823 5051
■ ICAHN ENTERPRISES HOLDINGS LP p 726
767 5th Ave Fl 17, New York NY 10153
Tel (212) 702-4300
SIC 6512 5719 6211 5093
▲ ICAHN ENTERPRISES LP p 726
767 5th Ave Ste 4700, New York NY 10153
Tel (212) 702-4300
SIC 6722 3714 7999 3743 5093 6531
SIMS GROUP USA HOLDINGS CORP p 1326
16 W 22nd St Fl 10, New York NY 10010
Tel (212) 604-0710 SIC 5093
BEN WEITSMAN AND SON INC p 172
15 W Main St, Owego NY 13827
Tel (607) 687-2780 SIC 5051 5093 3341
WEITSMAN SHREDDING p 1588
15 W Main St, Owego NY 13827
Tel (607) 687-2780 SIC 5051 5093 5099
▲ NUCOR CORP p 1066
1915 Rexford Rd Ste 400, Charlotte NC 28211
Tel (704) 366-7000
SIC 3312 3441 3448 3452 5093
D H GRIFFIN WRECKING CO INC p 407
4716 Hilltop Rd, Greensboro NC 27407
Tel (336) 855-7030 SIC 1795 5093
UMICORE USA INC p 1501
3600 Glenwood Ave Ste 250, Raleigh NC 27612
Tel (919) 874-7171
SIC 5052 5051 5093 5169 3339
■ DAVID J JOSEPH CO p 415
300 Pike St Fl 3, Cincinnati OH 45202
Tel (513) 621-8770 SIC 5093
■ DJJ HOLDING CORP p 445
300 Pike St, Cincinnati OH 45202
Tel (513) 621-8770 SIC 5093 5088 4741
COLUMBIA NATIONAL GROUP INC p 341
6600 Grant Ave, Cleveland OH 44105
Tel (216) 883-4972 SIC 5051 5093 1542
■ CONTAINER LIFE CYCLE MANAGEMENT LLC p 362
425 Winter Rd, Delaware OH 43015
Tel (740) 549-6087 SIC 5093
■ GREIF USA LLC p 639
366 Greif Pkwy, Delaware OH 43015
Tel (740) 549-6000 SIC 5093
COHEN BROTHERS INC p 335
1723 Woodlawn Ave, Middletown OH 45044
Tel (513) 422-3696
SIC 5093 3441 3341 3312
YAFFE COMPANIES INC p 1633
1200 S G St, Muskogee OK 74403
Tel (918) 687-7543 SIC 5093 5051
METRO METALS NORTHWEST INC p 955
5611 Ne Columbia Blvd, Portland OR 97218
Tel (503) 287-8861 SIC 5093
▲ SCHNITZER STEEL INDUSTRIES INC p 1288
299 Sw Clay St Ste 350, Portland OR 97201
Tel (503) 224-9900
SIC 5093 3312 3449 3441 3433 5015
CRONIMET CORP p 393
1 Pilarsky Way, Aliquippa PA 15001
Tel (724) 375-5004 SIC 5093 5051 3312
ELG HANIEL METALS CORP p 486
369 River Rd, Mckeesport PA 15132
Tel (412) 672-9200 SIC 5093 5051
ELG METALS INC p 486
369 River Rd, Mckeesport PA 15132
Tel (412) 672-9200 SIC 5093 3341
AXIOM METALS INC p 140
401 Penn Ave, Pittsburgh PA 15221
Tel (412) 243-8000 SIC 5093
LENMORE INC p 855
401 Penn Ave, Pittsburgh PA 15221
Tel (412) 243-8000 SIC 5093
LIBERTY TIRE RECYCLING LLC p 862
1251 Waterfront Pl # 400, Pittsburgh PA 15222
Tel (412) 562-1700 SIC 5093 4953 8744
FORTUNE METAL INC OF RHODE ISLAND p 570
2 Crow Point Rd, Lincoln RI 02865
Tel (661) 387-1100 SIC 5093

■ SONOCO RECYCLING LLC p 1340
1 N 2nd St, Hartsville SC 29550
Tel (843) 383-0273 SIC 5093
SEFA GROUP INC p 1300
217 Cedar Rd, Lexington SC 29073
Tel (803) 520-9000 SIC 5093
CAROLINAS RECYCLING GROUP LLC p 259
2061 Nazareth Church Rd, Spartanburg SC 29301
Tel (864) 439-7039 SIC 5093
MARTEX FIBER SOUTHERN CORP p 912
3200b Southport Rd, Spartanburg SC 29302
Tel (864) 583-6412 SIC 5093
ESCO MARINE INC p 509
16200 Jose Garza Rd, Brownsville TX 78521
Tel (956) 554-5300 SIC 4499 5093 7389
SHRED-IT DALLAS INC p 1319
825 W Sandy Lake Rd # 100, Coppell TX 75019
Tel (972) 556-0197 SIC 7389 5093 5087
EMR GOLD RECYCLING LLC p 495
4305 S Lamar St, Dallas TX 75215
Tel (214) 421-0247 SIC 5093 6719
GOLD METAL RECYCLERS LTD p 620
4305 S Lamar St, Dallas TX 75215
Tel (214) 421-0247 SIC 5093
LOPEZ SCRAP METAL INC p 878
351 N Nevarez Rd, El Paso TX 79927
Tel (915) 859-0770 SIC 5093 3341
MID-WEST TEXTILE CO p 964
1600 E San Antonio Ave, El Paso TX 79901
Tel (915) 351-0231 SIC 5093 5137 5136
GAMTEX INDUSTRIES LP p 590
2600 Shamrock Ave, Fort Worth TX 76107
Tel (800) 749-0423 SIC 5093
ALLIED ALLOYS LP p 56
6002 Donoho St, Houston TX 77033
Tel (713) 643-6966 SIC 5093
DERICHEBOURG RECYCLING USA INC p 431
7501 Wallisville Rd, Houston TX 77020
Tel (713) 675-2281 SIC 5093
■ PSC ENVIRONMENTAL SERVICES LLC p 1188
5151 San Felipe St # 1100, Houston TX 77056
Tel (713) 623-8777 SIC 4953 4959 5093
■ WM RECYCLE AMERICA LLC p 1620
1001 Fannin St Ste 4000, Houston TX 77002
Tel (713) 512-6200 SIC 5093
▲ COMMERCIAL METALS CO p 345
6565 N Mcarthr Blvd # 800, Irving TX 75039
Tel (214) 689-4300
SIC 3312 3441 5051 5093
SPRINT WASTE SERVICES LP p 1361
16011 W Bellfort St, Sugar Land TX 77498
Tel (281) 491-7775 SIC 5093 4953
ROCKY MOUNTAIN RECYCLING LLC p 1245
2950 W 900 S, Salt Lake City UT 84104
Tel (801) 975-1820 SIC 5093
BRENNER HOLDINGS INC p 210
2580 Broadway Ave Sw, Roanoke VA 24014
Tel (540) 981-1211
SIC 4953 5093 3341 3231
GLANT PACIFIC INC p 614
2230 4th Ave S, Seattle WA 98134
Tel (206) 628-6222
SIC 5949 5093 5094 5945
SDR PLASTICS INC p 1295
1 Plastics Ave, Ravenswood WV 26164
Tel (304) 273-5326 SIC 5093
SADOFF & RUDOY INDUSTRIES LLP p 1265
240 W Arndt St 272, Fond Du Lac WI 54935
Tel (920) 921-2070 SIC 5093
ALTER METAL RECYCLING p 62
4400 Sycamore Ave, Madison WI 53714
Tel (608) 241-7191 SIC 5093

SIC 5094 Jewelry, Watches, Precious Stones Wholesale

SWEDA CO LLC p 1411
17411 E Valley Blvd, City Of Industry CA 91744
Tel (626) 357-9999 SIC 5094 5044
HUB DISTRIBUTING INC p 715
1260 Corona Pointe Ct, Corona CA 92879
Tel (951) 340-3149
SIC 5611 5621 5632 5137 5136 5094
▲ SPECTRUM GROUP INTERNATIONAL INC p 1357
1063 Mcgaw Ave Ste 250, Irvine CA 92614
Tel (949) 748-4800 SIC 7389 5094 5944
■ SPECTRUM NUMISMATICS INTERNATIONAL INC p 1357
1063 Mcgaw Ave Ste 250, Irvine CA 92614
Tel (949) 955-1250 SIC 5094
▲ PRECIOUS A-MARK METALS INC p 1168
429 Santa Monica Blvd # 230, Santa Monica CA 90401
Tel (310) 587-1477 SIC 5094
UNIQUE PREMIUM METALS INC p 1505
3250 Ocean Park Blvd # 350, Santa Monica CA 90405
Tel (213) 622-9995 SIC 5094
CITIZEN WATCH CO OF AMERICA INC p 310
1000 W 190th St, Torrance CA 90502
Tel (310) 532-8463 SIC 5094 3829
WESTERN STONE & METAL CORP p 1600
8085 S Chester St Ste 300, Centennial CO 80112
Tel (303) 792-3500 SIC 5944 5094
VICTORINOX SWISS ARMY INC p 1555
7 Victoria Dr, Monroe CT 06468
Tel (203) 929-6391
SIC 5023 5099 5094 5072
MICHAELS ENTERPRISES INC p 960
150 Mattatuck Heights Rd # 3, Waterbury CT 06705
Tel (203) 597-4942 SIC 5094
MP DIRECT INC p 995
4800 126th Ave N, Clearwater FL 33762
Tel (727) 572-8443 SIC 5094 5944 5091
INTERNATIONAL BULLION AND METAL BROKERS (USA) INC p 754
14051 Nw 14th St Ste 3, Sunrise FL 33323
Tel (954) 660-6900 SIC 5094

MAUI DIVERS OF HAWAII LIMITED p 921
1520 Liona St, Honolulu HI 96814
Tel (808) 946-7979 SIC 3911 5944 5094

■ SILVERTOWNE LP p 1324
120 E Union City Pike, Winchester IN 47394
Tel (765) 584-7481 SIC 5999 5094

GERSON CO p 609
1450 S Lone Elm Rd, Olathe KS 66061
Tel (913) 262-7400
SIC 5193 5199 5023 5094

STULLER INC p 1394
302 Rue Louis Xiv, Lafayette LA 70508
Tel (337) 262-7700 SIC 5094 3911

PANDORA JEWELRY LLC p 1111
250 W Pratt St, Baltimore MD 21201
Tel (410) 309-0200 SIC 5094

■ LEACH GARNER - A BERKSHIRE HATHAWAY CO p 850
49 Pearl St, Attleboro MA 02703
Tel (508) 222-7400 SIC 5094

DDJ CAPITAL MANAGEMENT LLC p 419
130 Turner St Ste 600, Waltham MA 02453
Tel (781) 283-8500 SIC 6282 5094 5812

▲ AMERICAN BILTRITE INC p 69
57 River St Ste 302, Wellesley MA 02481
Tel (781) 237-6655
SIC 3069 2672 2241 3961 5094

TSI HOLDING CO p 1489
999 Exectve Pkwy Dr # 202, Saint Louis MO 63141
Tel (314) 628-6000 SIC 5094 5051

CASIO AMERICA INC p 263
570 Mount Pleasant Ave, Dover NJ 07801
Tel (973) 361-5400
SIC 5044 5045 5094 5099

BASF CATALYSTS LLC p 158
25 Middlesex Tpke, Iselin NJ 08830
Tel (732) 205-5000
SIC 2819 2816 5094 3339

SEIKO CORP OF AMERICA p 1301
1111 Macarthur Blvd # 101, Mahwah NJ 07430
Tel (201) 529-3316 SIC 5094

■ LCI HOLDINGS INC p 849
5901 W Side Ave, North Bergen NJ 07047
Tel (201) 295-6300
SIC 5651 5136 5137 5094 5122 5944

SWATCH GROUP U S INC p 1411
1200 Harbor Blvd Fl 7, Weehawken NJ 07086
Tel (201) 271-1400
SIC 5063 3625 5094 3873

RIO GRANDE INC p 1235
7500 Bluewater Rd Nw, Albuquerque NM 87121
Tel (505) 839-3550 SIC 5094 5049 3915

TWOS CO INC p 1495
500 Saw Mill River Rd, Elmsford NY 10523
Tel (914) 664-2277 SIC 5199 5023 5094

E GLUCK CORP p 466
6015 Little Neck Pkwy, Little Neck NY 11362
Tel (718) 784-0700 SIC 3873 5094

ANAYA GEMS INC p 88
3100 47th Ave Unit 5, Long Island City NY 11101
Tel (718) 391-7400 SIC 5094 3911

MICHAEL C FINA CO INC p 960
3301 Hunters Point Ave, Long Island City NY 11101
Tel (212) 557-2500 SIC 5094 5947

MZ BERGER & CO INC p 1005
2976 Northern Blvd Fl 4, Long Island City NY 11101
Tel (718) 472-7500 SIC 5094 3873

ALMOD DIAMONDS LTD p 59
592 5th Ave Fl 9, New York NY 10036
Tel (212) 764-6900 SIC 5094

AWC LIQUIDATING CO p 139
1407 Brdwy Ste 400, New York NY 10018
Tel (212) 221-1177
SIC 5112 5199 3873 5094

BULOVA CORP p 225
350 5th Ave Fl 29, New York NY 10118
Tel (212) 497-1875 SIC 5094

DHARM INTERNATIONAL LLC p 435
15 W 47th St Ste 506, New York NY 10036
Tel (212) 398-7777 SIC 5094

DIAMLINK INC p 436
25 W 45th St Ste 1406, New York NY 10036
Tel (212) 704-0777 SIC 5094

HERAEUS METALS NEW YORK LLC p 685
540 Madison Ave, New York NY 10022
Tel (212) 752-2181 SIC 5094

HK DESIGNS INC p 697
535 5th Ave Fl 18, New York NY 10017
Tel (212) 201-0755 SIC 5094

LOUIS GLICK DIAMOND CORP p 879
810 7th Ave Fl 28, New York NY 10019
Tel (212) 259-0300 SIC 5094 3911

LUCENT JEWELERS INC p 884
1200 Ave Of Americas, New York NY 10036
Tel (212) 869-2820 SIC 5094

MARUBENI AMERICA CORP p 913
375 Lexington Ave, New York NY 10017
Tel (212) 450-0100
SIC 5131 5084 5012 5169 5172 5094

MITSUI & CO (USA) INC p 978
200 Park Ave Fl 35, New York NY 10166
Tel (212) 878-4000
SIC 5051 5094 5084 5153 5172 5169

RENAISSANCE JEWELRY NEW YORK INC p 1223
3 E 54th St Ste 603, New York NY 10022
Tel (212) 986-7287 SIC 5094

■ RICHLINE GROUP INC p 1233
1385 Broadway Fl 12, New York NY 10018
Tel (212) 886-6000 SIC 5094 3911

ROLEX INDUSTRIES INC p 1247
665 5th Ave Fl 6, New York NY 10022
Tel (212) 758-7700 SIC 5094 7631 6512

SAUMIL DIAM LLC p 1283
15 W 47th St Ste 1707, New York NY 10036
Tel (212) 575-3655 SIC 5094

▲ TIFFANY & CO p 1453
200 5th Ave Bsmt 2, New York NY 10010
Tel (212) 755-8000
SIC 5944 5094 5719 5943 5999 5961

ONEIDA LTD p 1087
163 Kenwood Ave, Oneida NY 13421
Tel (315) 361-3000
SIC 5046 5719 5023 5094

FIRE MOUNTAIN GEMS & BEADS INC p 543
1 Fire Mountain Way, Grants Pass OR 97526
Tel (541) 956-7700 SIC 5094

KOMODIDAD DISTRIBUTORS INC p 827
156 Km 58 8, Caguas PR 00727
Tel (787) 746-3188 SIC 5137 5136 5094

AMERICAS COLLECTIBLES NETWORK INC p 81
9600 Parkside Dr, Knoxville TN 37922
Tel (865) 692-6000 SIC 5094

AMERICAN ACHIEVEMENT GROUP HOLDING CORP p 67
7211 Circle S Rd, Austin TX 78745
Tel (512) 444-0571 SIC 5094

■ DGSE CORP p 435
15850 Dallas Pkwy, Dallas TX 75248
Tel (972) 484-3662 SIC 5094

HERITAGE CAPITAL CORP p 686
3500 Maple Ave Ste 1700, Dallas TX 75219
Tel (214) 528-3500 SIC 5094

JM BULLION INC p 786
12655 N Cntl Expy Ste 800, Dallas TX 75243
Tel (800) 276-6508 SIC 5094

PAJ INC p 1108
18325 Waterview Pkwy Frnt, Dallas TX 75252
Tel (214) 575-6080 SIC 5094

PREMIER DESIGNS INC p 1170
1551 Corporate Dr Ste 150, Irving TX 75038
Tel (972) 550-0955 SIC 5094

▲ FOSSIL GROUP INC p 570
901 S Central Expy, Richardson TX 75080
Tel (972) 234-2525
SIC 3873 5944 5094 5651 5632

■ FOSSIL PARTNERS LP p 570
901 S Central Expy, Richardson TX 75080
Tel (972) 234-2525
SIC 5137 2389 2339 5094

O C TANNER RECOGNITION CO p 1070
1930 S State St, Salt Lake City UT 84115
Tel (801) 486-2430 SIC 5094

GLANT PACIFIC INC p 614
2230 4th Ave S, Seattle WA 98134
Tel (206) 628-6222
SIC 5949 5093 5094 5945

SIC 5099 Durable Goods: NEC Wholesale

ALABAMA RIVER WOODLANDS INC p 43
2373 Lena Landegger Hwy, Perdue Hill AL 36470
Tel (251) 575-2039 SIC 5099

SEALASKA CORP p 1296
1 Sealaska Plz Ste 400, Juneau AK 99801
Tel (907) 586-1512
SIC 5099 8744 7371 8748 1542

MONSTER INC p 985
455 Valley Dr, Brisbane CA 94005
Tel (415) 840-2000 SIC 5099 4841 3679

YAMAHA CORP OF AMERICA INC p 1634
6600 Orangethorpe Ave, Buena Park CA 90620
Tel (714) 522-9011
SIC 5099 5065 5091 3931

JAPAN PULP & PAPER (USA) CORP p 778
5928 S Malt Ave, Commerce CA 90040
Tel (323) 889-7750 SIC 5113 5093 5099

SUN COAST MERCHANDISE CORP p 1400
6315 Bandini Blvd, Commerce CA 90040
Tel (323) 720-9700 SIC 5099

GUTHY-RENKER LLC p 648
100 N Sepulveda Blvd # 1600, El Segundo CA 90245
Tel (760) 773-9022
SIC 5099 7812 5999 7389

WELK GROUP INC p 1589
8860 Lawrence Welk Dr, Escondido CA 92026
Tel (760) 749-3000 SIC 7011 5099

C D LISTENING BAR INC p 232
17822 Gillette Ave Ste A, Irvine CA 92614
Tel (949) 225-1170 SIC 5099

■ PARAMOUNT PICTURES CORP p 1114
5555 Melrose Ave, Los Angeles CA 90038
Tel (323) 956-5000
SIC 7812 5099 4833 7829

ROLAND CORP US p 1247
5100 S Eastern Ave, Los Angeles CA 90040
Tel (323) 890-3700 SIC 5099 5045 3931

OLIVET INTERNATIONAL INC p 1082
11015 Hopkins St, Mira Loma CA 91752
Tel (951) 681-8888 SIC 5099

DAMAO LUGGAGE INTERNATIONAL INC p 410
1909 S Vineyard Ave, Ontario CA 91761
Tel (909) 923-6531 SIC 5099 3161

FERGUSON FIRE & FABRICATION INC p 538
2750 S Towne Ave, Pomona CA 91766
Tel (909) 517-3085 SIC 5074 5099

MONOPRICE INC p 985
11701 6th St, Rancho Cucamonga CA 91730
Tel (909) 989-6887 SIC 5099

SMARTDRIVE SYSTEMS INC p 1332
9450 Carroll Park Dr, San Diego CA 92121
Tel (866) 933-9930 SIC 5099

CELLMARK INC p 273
22 Pelican Way, San Rafael CA 94901
Tel (415) 927-1700 SIC 5099 5093 5111

CELLMARK PULP & PAPER INC p 273
22 Pelican Way, San Rafael CA 94901
Tel (415) 927-1700 SIC 5099 5111

DURAFLAME INC p 462
2894 Monte Diablo Ave, Stockton CA 95203
Tel (209) 461-6600 SIC 5099

ABE ORLANDO BUSTAMANTE p 10
7859 Diagonal Hwy, Longmont CO 80503
Tel (303) 652-3394 SIC 5099 4789 4212

ROKR DISTRIBUTION US INC p 1247
310 W Newberry Rd, Bloomfield CT 06002
Tel (860) 509-8888 SIC 5099 3931

VICTORINOX SWISS ARMY INC p 1555
7 Victoria Dr, Monroe CT 06468
Tel (203) 929-6391
SIC 5023 5099 5094 5072

CELLMARK PAPER INC p 273
80 Washington St, Norwalk CT 06854
Tel (203) 363-7800 SIC 5099 5111

■ ANDERSON GROUP INC p 90
3411 Silverside Rd # 103, Wilmington DE 19810
Tel (302) 478-6160
SIC 5047 5063 5099 7699 3443

■ HONEYWELL SAFETY PRODUCTS USA INC p 705
2711 Centerville Rd, Wilmington DE 19808
Tel (302) 636-5401 SIC 5099

EKMAN & CO INC p 482
8750 Nw 36th St Ste 400, Doral FL 33178
Tel (305) 579-1200 SIC 5099

EKMAN HOLDING INC p 482
8750 Nw 36th St Ste 400, Doral FL 33178
Tel (305) 579-1200 SIC 5099

▲ RAYONIER INC p 1210
225 Water St Ste 1400, Jacksonville FL 32202
Tel (904) 357-9100
SIC 6798 5099 6552 5031

AUDIO AMERICA INC p 130
15132 Park Of Commerce Bl, Jupiter FL 33478
Tel (561) 863-7704 SIC 5099

ALL AMERICAN CONTAINERS INC p 51
9330 Nw 110th Ave, Medley FL 33178
Tel (305) 887-0797 SIC 5085 5099

CIAT p 305
7343 Nw 79th Ter, Medley FL 33166
Tel (305) 863-9126 SIC 5099

■ HD SUPPLY WATERWORKS GROUP INC p 673
501 W Church St Ste 100, Orlando FL 32805
Tel (407) 841-4755
SIC 5051 5074 5084 5099

RSR GROUP INC p 1256
4405 Metric Dr, Winter Park FL 32792
Tel (407) 677-6114 SIC 5099

CMPC USA INC p 329
1040 Crown Pointe Pkwy # 800, Atlanta GA 30338
Tel (770) 551-2640 SIC 5099

■ HD SUPPLY HOLDINGS LLC p 673
3100 Cumberland Blvd Se # 1700, Atlanta GA 30339
Tel (770) 852-9000
SIC 5051 5074 5084 5099

MNS LTD p 980
766 Pohukaina St, Honolulu HI 96813
Tel (808) 591-1063 SIC 5099

■ BOISE CASCADE WOOD PRODUCTS LLC p 198
1111 W Jefferson St # 300, Boise ID 83728
Tel (208) 384-6161 SIC 5099

RILEY CREEK LUMBER CO p 1235
30 Riley Creek Rd, Laclede ID 83841
Tel (208) 255-3200 SIC 5099

ATK SPORTING GROUP p 125
2299 Snake River Ave, Lewiston ID 83501
Tel (208) 746-2351 SIC 5099

BATHXCESSORIES INC p 159
1481 N Larrabee St, Chicago IL 60610
Tel (312) 951-2885 SIC 5099

W S DARLEY & CO p 1569
325 Spring Lake Dr, Itasca IL 60143
Tel (630) 735-3500
SIC 3561 5087 5099 3569 3812

MAUI JIM USA INC p 921
1 Aloha Ln, Peoria IL 61615
Tel (309) 589-6158 SIC 5099 3851

NATIONAL SALVAGE & SERVICE CORP p 1016
6755 S Old State Road 37, Bloomington IN 47401
Tel (812) 339-8437
SIC 5088 1629 1795 5099 5093

ASA ELECTRONICS LLC p 115
2602 Marina Dr, Elkhart IN 46514
Tel (574) 264-3135 SIC 5099

KOORSEN FIRE & SECURITY INC p 827
2719 N Arlington Ave, Indianapolis IN 46218
Tel (317) 542-1800
SIC 5099 7389 5199 5063 1731

■ VERA BRADLEY DESIGNS INC p 1549
12420 Stonebridge Rd, Roanoke IN 46783
Tel (260) 482-4673 SIC 5099

PER MAR SECURITY AND RESEARCH CORP p 1134
1910 E Kimberly Rd, Davenport IA 52807
Tel (563) 359-3200
SIC 8732 7381 5099 7389 7382

HANTOVER INC p 659
5200 W 110th St Ste 200, Overland Park KS 66211
Tel (913) 214-4800 SIC 5099 5084

ORR SAFETY CORP p 1095
11601 Interchange Dr, Louisville KY 40229
Tel (502) 774-5791 SIC 5099

RED BALL OXYGEN CO INC p 1215
609 N Market St, Shreveport LA 71107
Tel (318) 425-6300
SIC 5084 5085 5169 5099 5531 5013

BLAUER MANUFACTURING CO INC p 189
20 Aberdeen St, Boston MA 02215
Tel (617) 536-6606 SIC 5099 3842 2337

AMWAY INTERNATIONAL INC p 87
7575 Fulton St E, Ada MI 49355
Tel (616) 787-1000
SIC 5169 5122 5099 5199 2099 2032

FOREST BESSE PRODUCTS INC p 566
933 N 8th St, Gladstone MI 49837
Tel (906) 428-3113 SIC 5031 5099

TNG WORLDWIDE INC p 1458
29683 Wk Smith Dr Stet, New Hudson MI 48165
Tel (248) 347-7700 SIC 5099 5087

BELL LUMBER & POLE CO p 170
778 1st St Nw, New Brighton MN 55112
Tel (651) 633-4334 SIC 5099 2411

■ D B INDUSTRIES INC p 406
3833 Sala Way, Red Wing MN 55066
Tel (651) 388-8282 SIC 5099 5084 7352

TENACIOUS HOLDINGS INC p 1437
1021 Bandana Blvd E # 220, Saint Paul MN 55108
Tel (651) 642-9889 SIC 5099

YAK MAT LLC p 1634
2438 Highway 98 E, Columbia MS 39429
Tel (601) 876-2427 SIC 5211 5099

COLOR ART INTEGRATED INTERIORS LLC p 338
1325 N Warson Rd, Saint Louis MO 63132
Tel (314) 432-3000
SIC 5021 7641 5999 5712 5099 2521

ARISTOCRAT TECHNOLOGIES INC p 108
7230 Amigo St, Las Vegas NV 89119
Tel (702) 270-1000 SIC 5099

INTERNATIONAL GAME TECHNOLOGY p 755
9295 Prototype Dr, Reno NV 89521
Tel (775) 448-7777 SIC 3999 5099

MARCOLIN USA EYEWEAR CORP p 905
3140 Rte 22, Branchburg NJ 08876
Tel (800) 345-8482 SIC 5099 5048

ESCADA US SUBCO LLC p 509
26 Main St, Chatham NJ 07928
Tel (212) 852-5300
SIC 5137 5621 5632 5099

CASIO AMERICA INC p 263
570 Mount Pleasant Ave, Dover NJ 07801
Tel (973) 361-5400
SIC 5044 5045 5094 5099

LG CHEM AMERICA INC p 860
910 Sylvan Ave, Englewood Cliffs NJ 07632
Tel (201) 816-2000 SIC 5099 5169 5199

NATIONAL MUSIC RACK INC p 1014
440a Boulevard Apt 1, Hasbrouck Heights NJ 07604
Tel (201) 641-8188 SIC 5099

ONE DIVERSIFIED LLC p 1086
37 Market St, Kenilworth NJ 07033
Tel (908) 245-4833
SIC 5099 7373 4899 8711

SAFILO AMERICA INC p 1267
801 Jefferson Rd, Parsippany NJ 07054
Tel (973) 952-2800 SIC 5048 5099 5091

AUDIO AND VIDEO LABS INC p 130
7905 N Crescent Blvd, Pennsauken NJ 08110
Tel (856) 663-9030
SIC 3652 5099 7389 3651

WURTH GROUP OF NORTH AMERICA INC p 1628
93 Grant St, Ramsey NJ 07446
Tel (201) 818-8877 SIC 5013 5099 5072

■ MIKASA INC p 968
1 Century Way, Secaucus NJ 07094
Tel (866) 645-2721 SIC 5023 5099 5719

ICON EYEWEAR INC p 727
5 Empire Blvd, South Hackensack NJ 07606
Tel (201) 330-9333 SIC 5099

DIVAL SAFETY EQUIPMENT INC p 443
1721 Niagara St, Buffalo NY 14207
Tel (716) 874-9060
SIC 5099 8748 8734 5047 5136 5661

SCHOTT NORTH AMERICA INC p 1290
555 Taxter Rd Ste 470, Elmsford NY 10523
Tel (914) 831-2200 SIC 5099

NORTHERN SAFETY CO INC p 1056
232 Industrial Park Dr, Frankfort NY 13340
Tel (315) 793-4900 SIC 5099

■ VOXX ACCESSORIES CORP p 1566
3502 Wodview Trce Ste 220, Hauppauge NY 11788
Tel (631) 231-7750 SIC 5099

SAM ASH MUSIC CORP p 1273
278 Duffy Ave Unit A, Hicksville NY 11801
Tel (516) 932-6400 SIC 5099 5736

KORG USA INC p 828
316 S Service Rd, Melville NY 11747
Tel (631) 390-6500 SIC 5099

COACH STORES INC p 331
516 W 34th St Bsmt 5, New York NY 10001
Tel (212) 643-9727
SIC 3171 3161 3172 2387 5137 5099

DELTA ENTERPRISE CORP p 427
114 W 26th St Fl 11, New York NY 10001
Tel (212) 736-7000 SIC 5021 5099

IHI INC p 731
150 E 52nd St Fl 24, New York NY 10022
Tel (212) 599-8100
SIC 5099 8732 8711 5084

IRVING PLACE CAPITAL LLC p 765
745 5th Ave Fl 7, New York NY 10151
Tel (212) 551-4500 SIC 5999 5099

SOJITZ CORP OF AMERICA p 1337
1120 Ave Of The, New York NY 10036
Tel (212) 704-6500
SIC 5065 5084 5169 5051 5099 5052

SONY MUSIC HOLDINGS INC p 1341
550 Madison Ave Fl 16, New York NY 10022
Tel (212) 833-8000 SIC 3652 5099 2741

STARK CARPET CORP p 1379
979 3rd Ave Fl 11, New York NY 10022
Tel (844) 407-8275 SIC 5099 5131 5021

WEITSMAN SHREDDING p 1588
15 W Main St, Owego NY 13827
Tel (607) 687-2780 SIC 5051 5093 5099

LUXOTTICA US HOLDINGS CORP p 887
12 Harbor Park Dr, Port Washington NY 11050
Tel (516) 484-3800
SIC 5048 5099 5995 5999

CENTRAL NATIONAL GOTTESMAN INC p 279
3 Manhattanville Rd # 301, Purchase NY 10577
Tel (914) 696-9000 SIC 5111 5099

TRI VANTAGE LLC p 1477
1831 N Park Ave, Burlington NC 27217
Tel (800) 786-1876
SIC 5199 5088 5099 5091 2394

BAKER & TAYLOR LLC p 145
2550 W Tyvola Rd Ste 300, Charlotte NC 28217
Tel (704) 998-3100
SIC 5192 7822 5065 5045 5099

CDA INC p 270
8500 S Tryon St, Charlotte NC 28273
Tel (704) 504-1877 *SIC* 5099 3652

SCHAEFER SYSTEMS INTERNATIONAL INC p 1286
10021 Westlake Dr, Charlotte NC 28273
Tel (704) 944-4500
SIC 3089 5046 5084 5099 7372

■ **REMINGTON OUTDOOR CO INC** p 1222
870 Remington Dr, Madison NC 27025
Tel (336) 548-8700 *SIC* 5099 3949

MUELLER ROOFING DISTRIBUTORS INC p 998
327 E Wyoming Ave, Cincinnati OH 45215
Tel (513) 679-8540 *SIC* 5033 5099

WCM HOLDINGS INC p 1585
1150 Canal Rd, Cincinnati OH 45241
Tel (513) 705-2100 *SIC* 5099 2381 3842

MIDWEST TAPE LLC p 968
1417 Timber Wolf Dr, Holland OH 43528
Tel (419) 868-9370
SIC 7822 5099 8741 7389 5961 7374

TS TECH AMERICAS INC p 1489
8458 E Broad St, Reynoldsburg OH 43068
Tel (614) 575-4100 *SIC* 5099

CHESTER WEST HOLDINGS INC p 295
11500 Canal Rd, Sharonville OH 45241
Tel (800) 647-1900
SIC 3842 5136 5099 5137 2381

PIPELINE PACKAGING CORP p 1151
30310 Emerald Valley Pkwy, Solon OH 44139
Tel (440) 349-3200 *SIC* 5099

NORTH AMERICAN TIE & TIMBER LLC p 1050
6406 N Santa Fe Ave Ste B, Oklahoma City OK 73116
Tel (405) 848-1800 *SIC* 5099

VANPORT MANUFACTURING INC p 1544
28590 Se Wally Rd, Boring OR 97009
Tel (503) 663-4447 *SIC* 2421 5099

WESTERN PNEUMATICS INC p 1599
110 N Seneca Rd, Eugene OR 97402
Tel (541) 461-2600 *SIC* 3535 3553 5099

■ **HCSG SUPPLY INC** p 672
45 Runway Dr Ste H, Levittown PA 19057
Tel (215) 269-0988 *SIC* 5099

▲ **FAB UNIVERSAL CORP** p 523
5001 Baum Blvd Ste 770, Pittsburgh PA 15213
Tel (412) 621-0902
SIC 7371 7372 5735 5942 5994 5099

■ **GLATFELTER PULP WOOD CO INC** p 614
228 S Main St, Spring Grove PA 17362
Tel (717) 225-4711 *SIC* 5099 2411 2621

FIBRO SOURCE USA INC p 540
985 Old Eagle School Rd # 514, Wayne PA 19087
Tel (610) 293-3200
SIC 5099 5113 5141 5112

SWAROVSKI US HOLDING LIMITED p 1411
1 Kenney Dr, Cranston RI 02920
Tel (401) 463-6400
SIC 3961 3231 5048 5099

FGX INTERNATIONAL HOLDINGS LIMITED p 539
500 Washington Hwy, Smithfield RI 02917
Tel (401) 231-3800 *SIC* 5099 3851

FGX INTERNATIONAL INC p 539
500 George Washington Hwy, Smithfield RI 02917
Tel (401) 231-3800 *SIC* 5099 3851

ANDERSON MEDIA CORP p 90
265 Brookview Town Ste, Knoxville TN 37919
Tel (865) 474-8500 *SIC* 5099 5192

INGRAM ENTERTAINMENT INC p 743
2 Ingram Blvd, La Vergne TN 37089
Tel (615) 287-4000 *SIC* 5065 5092 5099

■ **VF IMAGEWEAR INC** p 1553
545 Marriott Dr Ste 200, Nashville TN 37214
Tel (615) 565-5000
SIC 2326 5099 2339 2311

ANCONNECT LLC p 89
421 Se 34th Ave, Amarillo TX 79103
Tel (806) 376-6251 *SIC* 5099 5192

PRODUCT CENTRE - SW INC p 1179
730 S Jupiter Rd Ste B, Garland TX 75042
Tel (972) 487-0580 *SIC* 5099

DISTRIBUTION INTERNATIONAL INC p 443
9000 Railwood Dr, Houston TX 77078
Tel (713) 428-3740 *SIC* 5033 5099

VALLEN SAFETY SUPPLY CO p 1540
521 N Sam Houston Pkwy E # 300, Houston TX 77060
Tel (281) 500-5000
SIC 5099 5084 5047 5063

MICHAELS HOLDINGS LLC p 960
8000 Bent Branch Dr, Irving TX 75063
Tel (972) 409-1300
SIC 5945 5999 5949 5947 5199 5099

■ **MICHAELS STORES INC** p 960
8000 Bent Branch Dr, Irving TX 75063
Tel (972) 409-1300
SIC 5945 5999 5949 5947 5199 5099

MED ASSETS INC p 935
5543 Legacy Dr, Plano TX 75024
Tel (800) 390-7459 *SIC* 5099

SPEED COMMERCE INC p 1358
1303 E Arapaho Rd Ste 200, Richardson TX 75081
Tel (866) 377-3331 *SIC* 5045 5099

WESTLINK TRADING LLC p 1601
17926 Highway 3, Webster TX 77598
Tel (832) 295-9778
SIC 5032 5099 5074 5051 5031

SOURCE HOME ENTERTAINMENT LLC p 1342
8251 Greensboro Dr # 400, Mc Lean VA 22102
Tel (239) 949-4450
SIC 5192 5099 8742 2541

SUMITOMO FORESTRY AMERICA INC p 1398
1110 112th Ave Ne Ste 202, Bellevue WA 98004
Tel (425) 454-2355 *SIC* 8741 5099

BEVERLY RICARDO HILLS INC p 179
6329 S 226th St Unit 101, Kent WA 98032
Tel (425) 207-1900 *SIC* 5099

MALLORY CO p 900
1040 Industrial Way, Longview WA 98632
Tel (360) 636-5750 *SIC* 5099

MALLORY SAFETY AND SUPPLY LLC p 900
1040 Industrial Way, Longview WA 98632
Tel (360) 636-5750 *SIC* 5099 8331

DW SAWMILL LLC p 463
N8972 County Road Jj, Westfield WI 53964
Tel (608) 296-1863 *SIC* 5099 2491 5211

SIC 5111 Printing & Writing Paper Wholesale

CELLMARK INC p 273
22 Pelican Way, San Rafael CA 94901
Tel (415) 927-1700 *SIC* 5099 5093 5111

CELLMARK PULP & PAPER INC p 273
22 Pelican Way, San Rafael CA 94901
Tel (415) 927-1700 *SIC* 5099 5111

BLOWER-DEMPSAY CORP p 190
4042 W Garry Ave, Santa Ana CA 92704
Tel (714) 481-3800 *SIC* 5111

SPICERS PAPER INC p 1358
12310 Slauson Ave, Santa Fe Springs CA 90670
Tel (562) 698-1199 *SIC* 5111

KELLY PAPER CO p 809
288 Brea Canyon Rd, Walnut CA 91789
Tel (909) 859-8200 *SIC* 5111 5943

WESTERN PAPER DISTRIBUTORS INC p 1599
11551 E 45th Ave Unit A, Denver CO 80239
Tel (303) 371-8710 *SIC* 5113 5111 5169

CELLMARK PAPER INC p 273
80 Washington St, Norwalk CT 06854
Tel (203) 363-7800 *SIC* 5099 5111

SUZANO PULP AND PAPER AMERICA INC p 1410
800 Corporate Dr Ste 320, Fort Lauderdale FL 33334
Tel (954) 772-7716 *SIC* 5111

MAC PAPERS INC p 891
3300 Phillips Hwy, Jacksonville FL 32207
Tel (904) 396-5312 *SIC* 5112 5111

LEXJET LLC p 860
1605 Main St Ste 400, Sarasota FL 34236
Tel (941) 330-1210
SIC 5045 5112 5111 2672 5043

GNN INVESTOR LLC p 619
133 Peachtree St Ne, Atlanta GA 30303
Tel (404) 652-4000
SIC 2621 2611 2631 2653 5111 2677

▲ **VERITIV CORP** p 1550
1000 Abernathy Rd # 1700, Atlanta GA 30328
Tel (770) 391-8200 *SIC* 5111 5112 5087

■ **VERITIV OPERATING CO** p 1550
1000 Abernathy Rd, Atlanta GA 30328
Tel (770) 391-8200 *SIC* 5113 5112 5111

ICONEX LLC p 728
3097 Satellite Blvd, Duluth GA 30096
Tel (917) 282-0861 *SIC* 5111 2621

MOORIM USA INC p 988
3700 Crestwood Pkwy Nw, Duluth GA 30096
Tel (303) 770-8809 *SIC* 5111

VICTOR ENVELOPE CO p 1555
301 Arthur Ct, Bensenville IL 60106
Tel (630) 616-2750 *SIC* 5111 5112

▲ **ESSENDANT INC** p 510
1 Parkway North Blvd # 100, Deerfield IL 60015
Tel (847) 627-7000
SIC 5112 5111 5021 5044 5087 5045

■ **OFFICEMAX CONTRACT INC** p 1076
263 Shuman Blvd, Naperville IL 60563
Tel (630) 438-7800
SIC 5021 5112 5044 5111 5943 5712

LEWIS PAPER INTERNATIONAL INC p 859
1400 S Wolf Rd Ste 100, Wheeling IL 60090
Tel (847) 520-3386 *SIC* 5111

MIDLAND PAPER CO p 966
101 E Palatine Rd, Wheeling IL 60090
Tel (847) 777-2700 *SIC* 5111

FRANK AMBROSE INC p 574
550 Hulet Dr Ste 103, Bloomfield Hills MI 48302
Tel (248) 655-2300 *SIC* 5111

HENRYS FOODS INC p 684
234 Mckay Ave N, Alexandria MN 56308
Tel (320) 763-3194
SIC 5194 5145 5111 5113 5141

JACKSON PAPER CO p 774
4400 Mangum Dr, Flowood MS 39232
Tel (800) 844-5449 *SIC* 5111 5113 5087

SHAUGHNESSY-KNIEP-HAWE-PAPER CO p 1312
2355 Ball Dr, Saint Louis MO 63146
Tel (314) 810-8100 *SIC* 5111

■ **CENTRAL LEWMAR LLC** p 279
261 River Rd, Clifton NJ 07014
Tel (973) 405-2300 *SIC* 5111 5199

PAPER MART INC p 1112
151 Ridgedale Ave, East Hanover NJ 07936
Tel (973) 884-2505 *SIC* 5111

GDB INTERNATIONAL INC p 595
1 Home News Row, New Brunswick NJ 08901
Tel (732) 246-3001
SIC 2851 5162 5111 5093

CLIFFORD PAPER INC p 326
600 E Crescent Ave # 301, Upper Saddle River NJ 07458
Tel (201) 934-5115 *SIC* 5111

GRAPHIC PAPER INC p 632
31 Windsor Pl, Central Islip NY 11722
Tel (631) 761-9700 *SIC* 5111

CASE PAPER CO INC p 263
500 Mamaroneck Ave Fl 2, Harrison NY 10528
Tel (914) 899-3500 *SIC* 5111

DNP CORP USA p 446
335 Madison Ave Fl 3, New York NY 10017
Tel (212) 503-1060 *SIC* 5111

GOULD PAPER CORP p 626
99 Park Ave Fl 10, New York NY 10016
Tel (212) 301-0000 *SIC* 5111 2759

GOULD PAPER CORP p 626
99 Park Ave Fl 10, New York NY 10016
Tel (212) 301-0000 *SIC* 5113 5111 3523

HEINZEL IMPORT & EXPORT INC p 681
220 E 42nd St Rm 3010, New York NY 10017
Tel (212) 953-3200 *SIC* 5111

SABIN ROBBINS CONVERTING CO LLC p 1264
455 E 86th St Apt 5e, New York NY 10028
Tel (513) 874-5270 *SIC* 5111

CENTRAL NATIONAL GOTTESMAN INC p 279
3 Manhattanville Rd # 301, Purchase NY 10577
Tel (914) 696-9000 *SIC* 5111 5099

MORRISETTE PAPER CO INC p 990
5925 Summit Ave, Browns Summit NC 27214
Tel (336) 375-1515 *SIC* 5113 5111 5087

AMERICAN PRODUCT DISTRIBUTORS INC p 78
8350 Arrowridge Blvd, Charlotte NC 28273
Tel (704) 522-9411
SIC 5111 5112 5047 5044 5085 5087

MCGRANN PAPER CORP p 929
3800 Arco Corprt Dr # 350, Charlotte NC 28273
Tel (800) 240-9455 *SIC* 5111 2752

COLE PAPERS INC p 335
1300 38th St N, Fargo ND 58102
Tel (800) 800-8090
SIC 5113 5111 5169 5023 5112 5049

MILLCRAFT GROUP LLC p 970
6800 Grant Ave, Cleveland OH 44105
Tel (216) 441-5500 *SIC* 5111 5113 2679

MILLCRAFT PAPER CO p 970
6800 Grant Ave, Cleveland OH 44105
Tel (216) 441-5505 *SIC* 5111 5113

ROSEMARK PAPER INC p 1250
1845 Progress Ave, Columbus OH 43207
Tel (614) 443-0303 *SIC* 5111 5199

STERLING PAPER CO p 1387
1845 Progress Ave, Columbus OH 43207
Tel (614) 443-0303 *SIC* 5111 5199

■ **GRAPHIC COMMUNICATIONS HOLDINGS INC** p 631
5700 Darrow Rd Ste 110, Hudson OH 44236
Tel (330) 650-5522 *SIC* 5111 7389

PAPER PRODUCTS MARKETING (USA) INC p 1112
4380 Sw Mcdam Ave Ste 370, Portland OR 97239
Tel (503) 227-6615 *SIC* 5111 5113

E AARON ENTERPRISES INC p 466
161 Wshington St Fl 11, Conshohocken PA 19428
Tel (610) 940-0800 *SIC* 5111

KAPPA MEDIA GROUP INC p 803
40 Skippack Pike, Fort Washington PA 19034
Tel (215) 643-5800 *SIC* 2721 2741 5111

LEEDSWORLD INC p 852
400 Hunt Valley Rd, New Kensington PA 15068
Tel (724) 334-9000
SIC 5199 5111 5112 3172 3161 2394

POLYCONCEPT NORTH AMERICA INC p 1160
400 Hunt Valley Rd, New Kensington PA 15068
Tel (724) 334-9000
SIC 5199 5111 5112 3172 3161 2394

DOMTAR INDUSTRIES LLC p 449
100 Kingsley Park Dr, Fort Mill SC 29715
Tel (803) 802-7500 *SIC* 2621 5111

ABITIBI CONSOLIDATED SALES CORP p 11
55 E Camperdown Way, Greenville SC 29601
Tel (864) 656-3975 *SIC* 5111 5113

CHRIS CAM CORP p 302
808 W Cherokee St, Sioux Falls SD 57104
Tel (605) 336-1190 *SIC* 5113 5169 5111

ATHENS PAPER CO INC p 124
1898 Elm Tree Dr, Nashville TN 37210
Tel (615) 889-7900 *SIC* 5111

CLAMPITT PAPER CO OF DALLAS GP LLC p 321
9207 Ambassador Row, Dallas TX 75247
Tel (214) 638-3300 *SIC* 5111

OLMSTED-KIRK PAPER CO p 1083
1601 Valley View Ln # 101, Dallas TX 75234
Tel (214) 637-2220 *SIC* 5111

CATALYST PAPER (USA) INC p 264
2200 6th Ave Ste 800, Seattle WA 98121
Tel (206) 838-2070 *SIC* 5111

SIC 5112 Stationery & Office Splys Wholesale

ARCTIC OFFICE MACHINE INC p 106
100 W Fireweed Ln, Anchorage AK 99503
Tel (907) 276-2295
SIC 5112 5021 5044 7629

JOE TORNANTE-MDP HOLDING LLC p 787
233 S Beverly Dr, Beverly Hills CA 90212
Tel (310) 228-6800
SIC 5145 5092 5112 2064

MERCHSOURCE LLC p 945
15 Cushing, Irvine CA 92618
Tel (949) 900-0900 *SIC* 5112

GIVE SOMETHING BACK INC p 613
7730 Pardee Ln Ste A, Oakland CA 94621
Tel (800) 261-2619 *SIC* 5112

MINTED LLC p 974
747 Front St Ste 200, San Francisco CA 94111
Tel (415) 399-1100 *SIC* 5112

■ **CSE HOLDINGS INC** p 397
650 Brennan St, San Jose CA 95131
Tel (408) 436-1907
SIC 5087 5084 7699 5113 5199 5112

■ **VIKING OFFICE PRODUCTS INC** p 1557
3366 E Willow St, Signal Hill CA 90755
Tel (562) 490-1000
SIC 5112 5021 5045 5087 5043 5961

ALL COPY PRODUCTS INC p 51
4141 Colorado Blvd, Denver CO 80216
Tel (303) 373-1105 *SIC* 5044 5112 7371

XSE GROUP INC p 1633
35 Phil Mack Dr, Middletown CT 06457
Tel (888) 272-8340 *SIC* 5112

■ **OFFICE CLUB INC** p 1075
2200 Germantown Rd, Delray Beach FL 33445
Tel (561) 438-4800 *SIC* 5943 5112

MAC PAPERS INC p 891
3300 Phillips Hwy, Jacksonville FL 32207
Tel (904) 396-5312 *SIC* 5112 5111

PILOT CORP OF AMERICA p 1148
3855 Regent Blvd, Jacksonville FL 32224
Tel (904) 645-9999 *SIC* 5112 3951

PEARL PAINT CO INC p 1126
1033 E Oakland Park Blvd, Oakland Park FL 33334
Tel (954) 564-5700
SIC 5999 5199 7699 5112 5947 7311

LEXJET LLC p 860
1605 Main St Ste 400, Sarasota FL 34236
Tel (941) 330-1210
SIC 5045 5112 5111 2672 5043

▲ **VERITIV CORP** p 1550
1000 Abernathy Rd # 1700, Atlanta GA 30328
Tel (770) 391-8200 *SIC* 5111 5112 5087

■ **VERITIV OPERATING CO** p 1550
1000 Abernathy Rd, Atlanta GA 30328
Tel (770) 391-8200 *SIC* 5113 5112 5111

■ **S P RICHARDS CO** p 1262
6300 Highlands Pkwy Se, Smyrna GA 30082
Tel (770) 434-4571 *SIC* 5112 5021

ARTCO (US) INC p 114
1 Stationery Pl, Rexburg ID 83441
Tel (208) 359-1000 *SIC* 5112 2759

VICTOR ENVELOPE CO p 1555
301 Arthur Ct, Bensenville IL 60106
Tel (630) 616-2750 *SIC* 5111 5112

■ **CHICAGO OFFICE TECHNOLOGY GROUP INC** p 297
3 Territorial Ct, Bolingbrook IL 60440
Tel (630) 378-9339 *SIC* 5044 5112

■ **ESSENDANT CO** p 510
1 Parkway North Blvd # 100, Deerfield IL 60015
Tel (847) 627-7000 *SIC* 5112

▲ **ESSENDANT INC** p 510
1 Parkway North Blvd # 100, Deerfield IL 60015
Tel (847) 627-7000
SIC 5112 5111 5021 5044 5087 5045

WAREHOUSE DIRECT INC p 1575
2001 S Mount Prospect Rd, Des Plaines IL 60018
Tel (847) 952-1925 *SIC* 5112

■ **OFFICEMAX CONTRACT INC** p 1076
263 Shuman Blvd, Naperville IL 60563
Tel (630) 438-7800
SIC 5021 5112 5044 5111 5943 5712

ARLINGTON INDUSTRIES INC p 110
1616 S Lakeside Dr, Waukegan IL 60085
Tel (847) 689-2754 *SIC* 5112

TOYO INK INTERNATIONAL CORP p 1466
1225 N Michael Dr, Wood Dale IL 60191
Tel (866) 969-8696 *SIC* 2893 5112

INDEPENDENT STATIONERS INC p 737
250 E 96th St Ste 510, Indianapolis IN 46240
Tel (317) 845-9155 *SIC* 5021 5112

ALLIED GROUP INC p 56
1100 Locust St, Des Moines IA 50391
Tel (515) 280-4211 *SIC* 6331 6211 5112

VARIETY DISTRIBUTORS INC p 1544
609 7th St, Harlan IA 51537
Tel (712) 755-2184
SIC 5131 5092 5122 5112 5145 5199

REGAL DISTRIBUTING CO p 1218
17201 W 113th St, Lenexa KS 66219
Tel (913) 894-8787 *SIC* 5112 5113 5046

■ **STAPLES INTERNATIONAL INC** p 1378
500 Staples Dr, Framingham MA 01702
Tel (508) 253-5000
SIC 5943 5712 5044 5021 5112

MILLBROOK DISTRIBUTION SERVICES INC p 970
88 Huntoon Memorial Hwy, Leicester MA 01524
Tel (508) 892-8171
SIC 5122 5023 5072 5112 5049 5199

INTEGRITY BUSINESS SOLUTIONS LLC p 750
4740 Talon Ct Se Ste 8, Grand Rapids MI 49512
Tel (616) 656-6010 *SIC* 5112

DIVERSIFIED DISTRIBUTION SYSTEMS LLC p 444
7351 Boone Ave N, Brooklyn Park MN 55428
Tel (612) 813-5200 *SIC* 5112

INNOVATIVE OFFICE SOLUTIONS LLC p 745
151 Cliff Rd E Ste 40, Burnsville MN 55337
Tel (952) 808-9900 *SIC* 5112 5021

KATUN CORP p 804
10951 Bush Lake Rd # 100, Minneapolis MN 55438
Tel (952) 941-9505 *SIC* 5112

METRO SALES INC p 955
1640 E 78th St, Minneapolis MN 55423
Tel (612) 861-4000
SIC 5044 5112 5065 7359

LIBERTY DIVERSIFIED INTERNATIONAL INC p 861
5600 Highway 169 N, New Hope MN 55428
Tel (763) 536-6600
SIC 2653 2631 5112 2542 3089 5961

■ **IMATION ENTERPRISES CORP** p 733
1099 Helmo Ave N Ste 250, Saint Paul MN 55128
Tel (651) 704-4000 *SIC* 3695 3845 5112

▲ **PATTERSON COMPANIES INC** p 1121
1031 Mendota Heights Rd, Saint Paul MN 55120
Tel (651) 686-1600
SIC 5047 5112 7372 7699 2834

DISTRIBUTION MANAGEMENT INC p 443
5 Research Park Dr, Saint Charles MO 63304
Tel (636) 300-4000 *SIC* 5112

SUPPLIES NETWORK INC p 1407
5 Research Park Dr, Saint Charles MO 63304
Tel (636) 300-4001 *SIC* 5112

SUMNER GROUP INC p 1399
6717 Waldemar Ave, Saint Louis MO 63139
Tel (314) 633-8000 *SIC* 5044 7699 5112

TMCI HOLDINGS INC p 1457
80 Avenue K, Newark NJ 07105
Tel (201) 553-1100
SIC 5122 5023 5072 5112 5049 5199

HITOUCH BUSINESS SERVICES LLC p 697
74 Kenny Pl, Saddle Brook NJ 07663
Tel (201) 636-9900 *SIC* 5112 5021 5149

VILLAGE OFFICE SUPPLY INC p 1557
600 Apgar Dr, Somerset NJ 08873
Tel (908) 526-0600 *SIC* 5112

SPIRAL BINDING CO INC p 1359
1 Maltese Dr, Totowa NJ 07512
Tel (973) 256-0666
SIC 2789 3083 5112 2891

PARIS CORP OF NEW JERSEY p 1115
800 Highland Dr, Westampton NJ 08060
Tel (609) 265-9200 *SIC* 5112 2752 5063

■ **COMMERCIAL ENVELOPE MANUFACTURING CO INC** p 345
900 Grand Blvd, Deer Park NY 11729
Tel (631) 242-2500 *SIC* 2677 5112

WEEKS-LERMAN GROUP LLC p 1587
5838 Page Pl, Maspeth NY 11378
Tel (718) 803-4700
SIC 5112 5021 2752 5044

AWC LIQUIDATING CO p 139
1407 Brdwy Ste 400, New York NY 10018
Tel (212) 221-1177
SIC 5112 5199 3873 5094

CENTRE PARTNERS MANAGEMENT LLC p 281
825 3rd Ave Fl 40, New York NY 10022
Tel (212) 332-5800 *SIC* 6726 5112

FASHION ACCESSORY BAZAAR LLC p 531
15 W 34th St Fl 2, New York NY 10001
Tel (212) 947-9001 *SIC* 5199 5112

PREMIER & COMPANIES INC p 1170
460 W 34th St Fl 5, New York NY 10001
Tel (212) 947-1365 *SIC* 5112

TOPPS CO INC p 1461
1 Whitehall St Fl 4, New York NY 10004
Tel (212) 376-0300
SIC 5145 5092 5112 2064

AMERICAN PRODUCT DISTRIBUTORS INC p 78
8350 Arrowridge Blvd, Charlotte NC 28273
Tel (704) 522-9411
SIC 5111 5112 5047 5044 5085 5087

COLE PAPERS INC p 335
1300 38th St N, Fargo ND 58102
Tel (800) 800-8090
SIC 5113 5111 5169 5023 5112 5049

WASSERSTROM CO p 1580
477 S Front St, Columbus OH 43215
Tel (614) 737-8472
SIC 5087 3566 5021 5046 5112 5719

GBS CORP p 595
7233 Freedom Ave Nw, North Canton OH 44720
Tel (330) 494-5330
SIC 5045 5112 2675 2672 2761 2759

SHAMROCK COMPANIES INC p 1311
24090 Detroit Rd, Westlake OH 44145
Tel (440) 899-9510
SIC 5112 5199 7336 7389 2754 2395

ADMIRAL EXPRESS INC p 23
1823 N Yellowood Ave, Broken Arrow OK 74012
Tel (918) 249-4000 *SIC* 5112 5021 5943

OFFICE BASICS INC p 1075
22 Creek Cir, Boothwyn PA 19061
Tel (610) 471-1000 *SIC* 5112

RICOH USA INC p 1233
70 Valley Stream Pkwy, Malvern PA 19355
Tel (610) 296-8000
SIC 5044 5065 7359 5112 7334 6159

LEEDSWORLD INC p 852
400 Hunt Valley Rd, New Kensington PA 15068
Tel (724) 334-9000
SIC 5199 5111 5112 3172 3161 2394

POLYCONCEPT NORTH AMERICA INC p 1160
400 Hunt Valley Rd, New Kensington PA 15068
Tel (724) 334-9000
SIC 5199 5111 5112 3172 3161 2394

FIBRO SOURCE USA INC p 540
985 Old Eagle School Rd # 514, Wayne PA 19087
Tel (610) 293-3200
SIC 5099 5113 5141 5112

GUY BROWN MANAGEMENT LLC p 648
320 Seven Springs Way # 450, Brentwood TN 37027
Tel (615) 777-1500 *SIC* 5112

A-Z OFFICE RESOURCE INC p 7
809 S Garden St, Columbia TN 38401
Tel (931) 388-1536
SIC 5112 5021 5044 5045 5087

AMERICAN PAPER & TWINE CO p 77
7400 Cockrill Bend Blvd, Nashville TN 37209
Tel (615) 350-9000 *SIC* 5113 5087 5112

MYOFFICEPRODUCTS INC p 1004
22 Century Blvd Ste 420, Nashville TN 37214
Tel (615) 507-3515 *SIC* 5112 5943

SUPPLIES DISTRIBUTORS INC p 1407
505 Millenium Dr, Allen TX 75013
Tel (972) 881-2900 *SIC* 5045 5112

GTS TECHNOLOGY SOLUTIONS INC p 644
9211 Wterford Centre Blvd, Austin TX 78758
Tel (512) 452-0651 *SIC* 5045 5112

■ **ACS IMAGE SOLUTIONS INC** p 19
3988 N Central Expy, Dallas TX 75204
Tel (214) 818-3000
SIC 7389 5112 7374 7375

HFS HOLDING CORP p 689
8900 Ambassador Row, Dallas TX 75247
Tel (214) 634-8600 *SIC* 2679 5112 2675

■ **SAFEGUARD BUSINESS SYSTEMS INC** p 1266
8585 N Stemmons Fwy, Dallas TX 75247
Tel (214) 640-3916
SIC 7374 2759 5112 5045

EDUCATIONAL PRODUCTS INC p 479
4100 N Sam Houston Pkwy W P, Houston TX 77086
Tel (800) 365-5345 *SIC* 5112 5049

COMPUDATA PRODUCTS INC p 352
1301 Ridgeview Ste 100, Lewisville TX 75057
Tel (972) 280-0922 *SIC* 5112

MILLERS SUPPLIES AT WORK INC p 971
8600 Cinder Bed Rd, Lorton VA 22079
Tel (703) 644-2200 *SIC* 5112 5044 5021

CSC/TECHNOLOGY MGMT GRP p 397
P.O. Box 1728, Sterling VA 20167
Tel (703) 876-3636 *SIC* 5112

TUFCO LP p 1491
3161 S Ridge Rd, Green Bay WI 54304
Tel (920) 336-0054 *SIC* 5122 5112 2676

PNA HOLDINGS LLC p 1158
3150 Pleasant View Rd, Madison WI 53713
Tel (608) 203-1500
SIC 5044 5045 5112 7699

E O JOHNSON CO INC p 466
8400 Stewart Ave, Wausau WI 54401
Tel (715) 842-9999 *SIC* 5112 7699 5045

SIC 5113 Indl & Personal Svc Paper Wholesale

ANDALUSIA DISTRIBUTING CO INC p 89
117 Allen Ave, Andalusia AL 36420
Tel (334) 222-3671
SIC 5172 5113 5194 5149

JOE PIPER INC p 787
123 Industrial Dr, Birmingham AL 35211
Tel (205) 290-2211 *SIC* 5113

SYSTEMS SERVICES OF AMERICA INC p 1419
1640 S 39th Ave, Phoenix AZ 85009
Tel (480) 927-4700
SIC 5147 5113 5142 5149 5143

AMCOR PACKAGING (USA) INC p 65
6600 Valley View St, Buena Park CA 90620
Tel (714) 562-6000 *SIC* 2653 5113

OASIS BRANDS INC p 1071
6700 Artesia Blvd, Buena Park CA 90620
Tel (540) 658-2830 *SIC* 5113

ORORA PACKAGING SOLUTIONS p 1095
6600 Valley View St, Buena Park CA 90620
Tel (714) 562-6000 *SIC* 5113 2653

AMERICAN PAPER & PLASTICS INC p 77
550 S 7th Ave, City Of Industry CA 91746
Tel (626) 444-0000 *SIC* 5113

ELKAY PLASTICS CO INC p 487
6000 Sheila St, Commerce CA 90040
Tel (323) 722-7073 *SIC* 5113

ERNEST PACKAGING SOLUTIONS INC p 508
5777 Smithway St, Commerce CA 90040
Tel (800) 233-7788 *SIC* 5113 5199 7389

JAPAN PULP & PAPER (USA) CORP p 778
5928 S Malt Ave, Commerce CA 90040
Tel (323) 889-7750 *SIC* 5113 5093 5099

SCHURMAN FINE PAPERS p 1291
500 Chadbourne Rd, Fairfield CA 94534
Tel (707) 425-8006
SIC 5113 2679 2771 5947

CALPINE CONTAINERS INC p 242
6425 N Palm Ave Ste 104, Fresno CA 93704
Tel (559) 519-7199
SIC 5113 5085 2441 2448

PACKAGING INNOVATORS CORP p 1106
6650 National Dr, Livermore CA 94550
Tel (925) 371-2000 *SIC* 5113 2653 3993

OAK PAPER PRODUCTS CO INC p 1070
3686 E Olympic Blvd, Los Angeles CA 90023
Tel (323) 268-0507
SIC 5113 5199 5087 2653

MAXCO SUPPLY INC p 922
605 S Zediker Ave, Parlier CA 93648
Tel (559) 646-8449 *SIC* 5113 2436 3554

NEWAY PACKAGING CORP p 1037
1973 E Via Arado, Rancho Dominguez CA 90220
Tel (602) 454-9000 *SIC* 5113 5084

P & R PAPER SUPPLY CO INC p 1102
1898 E Colton Ave, Redlands CA 92374
Tel (909) 389-1811
SIC 5113 5169 5149 5072 5046

OAKLAND PAPER & SUPPLY INC p 1071
3200 Regatta Blvd Ste F, Richmond CA 94804
Tel (510) 307-4242 *SIC* 5113 5087

CALVEY INC p 243
7728 Wilbur Way, Sacramento CA 95828
Tel (916) 681-4800 *SIC* 5113

MPCI HOLDINGS INC p 995
7850 Waterville Rd, San Diego CA 92154
Tel (619) 294-2222
SIC 5147 5143 5148 5113

■ **CSE HOLDINGS INC** p 397
650 Brennan St, San Jose CA 95131
Tel (408) 436-1907
SIC 5087 5084 7699 5113 5199 5112

PACIFIC GROSERVICE INC p 1104
567 Cinnabar St, San Jose CA 95110
Tel (408) 727-4826
SIC 5194 5145 5141 5113 5087

PIONEER PACKING INC p 1151
2430 S Grand Ave, Santa Ana CA 92705
Tel (714) 540-9751 *SIC* 5113 2653

FRUIT GROWERS SUPPLY CO INC p 582
27770 N Entrmt Dr Fl 3, Valencia CA 91355
Tel (818) 986-6480
SIC 2653 0811 5191 2448 5113

ANDWIN CORP p 91
6636 Variel Ave, Woodland Hills CA 91303
Tel (818) 999-2828
SIC 5113 3842 5199 5087 5047 2835

WESTERN PAPER DISTRIBUTORS INC p 1599
11551 E 45th Ave Unit A, Denver CO 80239
Tel (303) 371-8710 *SIC* 5113 5111 5169

EASTERN BAG AND PAPER CO INC p 471
200 Research Dr, Milford CT 06460
Tel (203) 878-1814 *SIC* 5113 5087 5046

THURSTON FOODS INC p 1451
30 Thurston Dr, Wallingford CT 06492
Tel (203) 265-1525
SIC 5141 5147 5142 5113

CITY LINE DISTRIBUTORS INC p 312
20 Industry Dr, West Haven CT 06516
Tel (203) 931-3707
SIC 5141 5142 5147 5113

WORLD INDUSTRIAL RESOURCES CORP p 1625
13100 56th Ct Ste 710, Clearwater FL 33760
Tel (727) 572-9991
SIC 3999 2542 5113 2671

TRIVIDIA HEALTH INC p 1483
2400 Nw 55th Ct, Fort Lauderdale FL 33309
Tel (800) 342-7226 *SIC* 5113

SOFIDEL AMERICA CORP p 1337
1006 Marley Dr, Haines City FL 33844
Tel (863) 547-3920 *SIC* 5113

DADE PAPER & BAG CO p 408
9601 Nw 112th Ave, Medley FL 33178
Tel (305) 805-2600 *SIC* 5113

■ **SYSCO SOUTH FLORIDA INC** p 1418
12500 Nw 112th Ave, Medley FL 33178
Tel (305) 651-5421
SIC 5149 5147 5142 5113 5143 5144

CHENEY BROS INC p 294
1 Cheney Way, Riviera Beach FL 33404
Tel (561) 845-4700
SIC 5141 5087 5113 5169 5149

CONSOLIDATED CONTAINER HOLDINGS LLC p 359
3101 Towercreek Pkwy Se P, Atlanta GA 30339
Tel (678) 742-4600 *SIC* 2671 7389 5113

CONSOLIDATED CONTAINER INTERMEDIARY LLC p 359
3101 Towercreek Pkwy Se, Atlanta GA 30339
Tel (678) 742-4600 *SIC* 5113 2671

PIEDMONT NATIONAL CORP p 1147
1561 Southland Cir Nw, Atlanta GA 30318
Tel (404) 351-6130 *SIC* 5199 5113

■ **VERITIV OPERATING CO** p 1550
1000 Abernathy Rd, Atlanta GA 30328
Tel (770) 391-8200 *SIC* 5113 5112 5111

■ **WESTROCK CP LLC** p 1602
504 Thrasher St, Norcross GA 30071
Tel (770) 448-2193 *SIC* 5113

■ **CORE-MARK DISTRIBUTORS INC** p 369
4820 N Church Ln, Smyrna GA 30080
Tel (404) 792-2000
SIC 5194 5141 5145 5113

HAVI GROUP LIMITED PARTNERSHIP p 668
3500 Lacey Rd Ste 600, Downers Grove IL 60515
Tel (630) 353-4200 *SIC* 5113 5142 5199

NORTH AMERICAN CORP OF ILLINOIS p 1050
2101 Claire Ct, Glenview IL 60025
Tel (847) 832-4000 *SIC* 5113 5169

PACTIV LLC p 1107
1900 W Field Ct, Lake Forest IL 60045
Tel (847) 482-2000 *SIC* 5113 3089 2673

MICHAEL LEWIS CO p 960
8900 W 50th St, Mc Cook IL 60525
Tel (708) 688-2200
SIC 5113 5141 5142 2782 2759 2621

N KOHL GROCER CO p 1005
130 Jersey St, Quincy IL 62301
Tel (217) 222-5000 *SIC* 5141 5113 5046

MARTIN-BROWER CO L L C p 913
6250 N River Rd Ste 9000, Rosemont IL 60018
Tel (847) 227-6500
SIC 5142 5113 5149 5087

NETWORK ASSOCIATES INC p 1028
1100 E Wdfield Rd Ste 200, Schaumburg IL 60173
Tel (847) 803-4888 *SIC* 8742 5113

NETWORK SERVICES CO p 1028
1100 E Wdfield Rd Ste 200, Schaumburg IL 60173
Tel (847) 803-4888 *SIC* 5113

AMERICAN HOTEL REGISTER CO p 74
100 S Milwaukee Ave # 100, Vernon Hills IL 60061
Tel (847) 743-3000
SIC 5046 5023 5021 5113

CHAMPION CONTAINER CORP p 287
1455 N Michael Dr, Wood Dale IL 60191
Tel (630) 279-4600 *SIC* 5113

SIMU LTD p 1326
201 Mittel Dr, Wood Dale IL 60191
Tel (630) 350-1060
SIC 5113 5141 5142 2782 2759 2621

DON EDWARD & CO p 449
9801 Adam Don Pkwy, Woodridge IL 60517
Tel (708) 442-9400
SIC 5021 5046 5087 5113 5169

ACORN DISTRIBUTORS INC p 18
5820 Fortune Cir W, Indianapolis IN 46241
Tel (317) 243-9234
SIC 5113 5087 5169 5046 5023

STANZ CHEESE CO INC p 1377
1840 Commerce Dr, South Bend IN 46628
Tel (574) 232-6666
SIC 5142 5141 5148 5113 5087 5085

■ **SYSCO IOWA INC** p 1417
1 Sysco Dr, Ankeny IA 50021
Tel (515) 289-5300
SIC 5149 5147 5142 5144 5113 5143

EARP MEAT CO p 469
2730 S 98th St, Edwardsville KS 66111
Tel (913) 287-3311 *SIC* 5142 5141 5113

REGAL DISTRIBUTING CO p 1218
17201 W 113th St, Lenexa KS 66219
Tel (913) 894-8787 *SIC* 5112 5113 5046

ALL STAR DAIRY ASSOCIATION INC p 51
1050 Monarch St Ste 101, Lexington KY 40513
Tel (859) 255-3644
SIC 5149 5169 5113 5199

PREMIER PACKAGING LLC p 1170
3900 Produce Rd, Louisville KY 40218
Tel (502) 935-8786 *SIC* 5085 5113 3086

DENNIS BEVERAGE CO p 428
101 Mecaw Rd, Bangor ME 04401
Tel (207) 947-0321 *SIC* 5141 5113

FOODPRO CORP p 564
321 E 5th St, Frederick MD 21701
Tel (301) 663-3171
SIC 5142 5149 5148 5147 5143 5113

ADAMS-BURCH LLC p 21
1901 Stanford Ct, Landover MD 20785
Tel (301) 276-2000 *SIC* 5046 5113 5087

S FREEDMAN & SONS INC p 1262
3322 Pennsy Dr, Landover MD 20785
Tel (301) 322-6400 *SIC* 5113 5087

CENTURY DISTRIBUTORS INC p 282
15710 Crabbs Branch Way, Rockville MD 20855
Tel (301) 212-9100
SIC 5194 5145 5149 5113

HOLT PAPER AND CHEMICAL CO INC p 702
31375 John Deere Dr, Salisbury MD 21804
Tel (410) 742-7577
SIC 5142 5087 5113 5147

ACME PAPER & SUPPLY CO INC p 18
8229 Sandy Ct, Savage MD 20763
Tel (410) 792-2333 *SIC* 5113 5087

TRIMARK UNITED EAST INC p 1480
505 Collins St, Attleboro MA 02703
Tel (508) 399-6000
SIC 5046 5021 5113 5087

PERKINS PAPER INC p 1136
630 John Hancock Rd, Taunton MA 02780
Tel (508) 824-2800
SIC 5113 5149 5087 5046

PACIFIC PACKAGING PRODUCTS INC p 1105
24 Industrial Way, Wilmington MA 01887
Tel (978) 657-9100
SIC 5113 5199 5084 5162 2671 2653

GRAD INC p 628
4001 3 Mile Rd Nw, Grand Rapids MI 49534
Tel (616) 676-5969
SIC 5141 5194 5145 5122 5113 5411

NICHOLS PAPER & SUPPLY CO p 1042
1391 Judson Rd, Norton Shores MI 49456
Tel (231) 799-2120 *SIC* 5113 5087

HENRYS FOODS INC p 684
234 Mckay Ave N, Alexandria MN 56308
Tel (320) 763-3194
SIC 5194 5145 5111 5113 5141

■ **3M INTERAMERICA INC** p 2
2501 Old Hudson Rd, Maplewood MN 55144
Tel (651) 733-1110
SIC 5113 5085 5065 5084 5122 8741

JACKSON PAPER CO p 774
4400 Mangum Dr, Flowood MS 39232
Tel (800) 844-5449 *SIC* 5111 5113 5087

CROWN PACKAGING CORP p 395
17854 Chstrfld Aprt Rd, Chesterfield MO 63005
Tel (636) 681-8000
SIC 5113 5169 5131 5084

BUNZL DISTRIBUTION CALIFORNIA LLC p 226
1 Cityplace Dr Ste 200, Saint Louis MO 63141
Tel (888) 997-5959 *SIC* 5113

BUNZL USA HOLDINGS LLC p 226
1 Cityplace Dr Ste 200, Saint Louis MO 63141
Tel (314) 997-5959 *SIC* 5162 5113

BUNZL USA INC p 226
1 Cityplace Dr Ste 200, Saint Louis MO 63141
Tel (314) 997-5959 *SIC* 5113 5162 5085

MID-CONTINENT PAPER AND DISTRIBUTING CO INC p 963
11809 Borman Dr, Saint Louis MO 63146
Tel (314) 989-0894 *SIC* 5113

■ **MIDDENDORF MEAT CO LLC** p 964
3737 N Broadway, Saint Louis MO 63147
Tel (314) 241-4800
SIC 5147 5141 5148 5146 5113 2011

PACKAGING CONCEPTS INC p 1106
9832 Evergreen Indus Dr, Saint Louis MO 63123
Tel (314) 329-9700 *SIC* 5113 2674 2671

■ **LINCOLN SYSCO INC** p 868
900 King Bird Rd, Lincoln NE 68521
Tel (402) 423-1031
SIC 5148 5142 5143 5141 5087 5113

▲ **AMCON DISTRIBUTING CO INC** p 65
7405 Irvington Rd, Omaha NE 68122
Tel (402) 331-3727
SIC 5194 5141 5145 5113 5122

SHARED SERVICE SYSTEMS INC p 1312
1725 S 20th St, Omaha NE 68108
Tel (402) 536-5300
SIC 5047 5142 7211 5149 5113 7218

■ **E & H DISTRIBUTING LLC** p 465
1685 W Cheyenne Ave, North Las Vegas NV 89032
Tel (702) 636-3663
SIC 5141 5113 5142 5149

JPC ENTERPRISES INC p 795
47 Brunswick Ave, Edison NJ 08817
Tel (732) 750-1900 *SIC* 5113

HANSOL AMERICA INC p 658
400 Kelby St Ste 6, Fort Lee NJ 07024
Tel (201) 461-6661 *SIC* 5113

BUNZL NEW JERSEY INC p 226
27 Distribution Way, Monmouth Junction NJ 08852
Tel (732) 821-7000 *SIC* 5113 5169

PRO TAPES & SPECIALTIES INC p 1178
621 Us Highway 1 Unit A, North Brunswick NJ 08902
Tel (732) 346-0900 *SIC* 5113 2675

HILL & MARKES INC p 693
1997 State Highway 5s, Amsterdam NY 12010
Tel (518) 842-2410 *SIC* 5087 5113

JOHNSTON PAPER CO INC p 791
2 Eagle Dr, Auburn NY 13021
Tel (315) 253-8435 *SIC* 5113 5084

PAPER ENTERPRISES INC p 1112
770 E 132nd St, Bronx NY 10454
Tel (718) 402-1200 *SIC* 5113 5087

RD FOOD SERVICES LLC p 1212
1524 132nd St, College Point NY 11356
Tel (718) 961-4356
SIC 5141 5148 5142 5113 5046 5087

MAINES PAPER & FOOD SERVICE INC p 898
101 Broome Corporate Pkwy, Conklin NY 13748
Tel (607) 779-1200
SIC 5142 5113 5141 5087 5147 5146

■ **AMSCAN INC** p 87
80 Grasslands Rd Ste 3, Elmsford NY 10523
Tel (914) 345-2020
SIC 2656 3089 5113 2676

GENPAK LLC p 604
68 Warren St, Glens Falls NY 12801
Tel (518) 798-9511 SIC 5113

WILLOW RUN FOODS INC p 1613
1006 Us Route 11, Kirkwood NY 13795
Tel (607) 338-5221
SIC 5142 5149 5147 5113 5148 5087

GOULD PAPER CORP p 626
99 Park Ave Fl 10, New York NY 10016
Tel (212) 301-0000 SIC 5113 5111 3523

STRAUSS PAPER CO INC p 1393
10 Slater St, Port Chester NY 10573
Tel (914) 937-0004 SIC 5113

PRIDE PRODUCTS CORP p 1174
4333 Veterans Mem Hwy, Ronkonkoma NY 11779
Tel (631) 737-4444
SIC 5113 5122 5023 5072 5199

PERK-UP INC p 1136
399 Knollwood Rd Ste 309, White Plains NY 10603
Tel (914) 580-3200
SIC 5113 5149 2673 3411 2674 2035

MORRISETTE PAPER CO INC p 990
5925 Summit Ave, Browns Summit NC 27214
Tel (336) 375-1515 SIC 5113 5111 5087

■ MEADOWBROOK MEAT CO INC p 934
2641 Meadowbrook Rd, Rocky Mount NC 27801
Tel (252) 985-7200
SIC 5147 5113 5149 5142

ATLANTIC CORP OF WILMINGTON INC p 126
806 N 23rd St, Wilmington NC 28405
Tel (910) 343-0624 SIC 5113 2621 2679

COLE PAPERS INC p 335
1300 38th St N, Fargo ND 58102
Tel (800) 800-8090
SIC 5113 5111 5169 5023 5112 5049

RIVER VALLEY PAPER CO p 1237
120 E Mill St Ste 337, Akron OH 44308
Tel (330) 535-1001 SIC 5113

AVALON FOODSERVICE INC p 135
1 Avalon Dr, Canal Fulton OH 44614
Tel (330) 854-4551
SIC 5142 5149 5169 5113 8322 5812

■ PROCTER & GAMBLE DISTRIBUTING LLC p 1179
1 Procter And Gamble Plz, Cincinnati OH 45202
Tel (513) 983-1100
SIC 5169 5122 5149 5113 5137

■ SYSCO CINCINNATI LLC p 1416
10510 Evendale Dr, Cincinnati OH 45241
Tel (513) 563-6300
SIC 5144 5149 5143 5113

JOSHEN PAPER & PACKAGING CO p 794
5800 Grant Ave, Cleveland OH 44105
Tel (216) 441-5600 SIC 5113 5169

MILLCRAFT GROUP LLC p 970
6800 Grant Ave, Cleveland OH 44105
Tel (216) 441-5500 SIC 5111 5113 2679

MILLCRAFT PAPER CO p 970
6800 Grant Ave, Cleveland OH 44105
Tel (216) 441-5505 SIC 5111 5113

■ MAST LOGISTICS SERVICES INC p 917
2 Limited Pkwy, Columbus OH 43230
Tel (614) 415-7500 SIC 5113

I SUPPLY CO p 725
1255 Spangler Rd, Fairborn OH 45324
Tel (937) 878-5240 SIC 5087 5113

G R B INC p 587
6392 Gano Rd, West Chester OH 45069
Tel (800) 628-9195 SIC 5113

STEPHENSON WHOLESALE CO INC p 1386
230 S 22nd Ave, Durant OK 74701
Tel (580) 920-0125
SIC 5194 5145 5143 5142 5141 5113

PAPER PRODUCTS MARKETING (USA) INC p 1112
4380 Sw Mcdam Ave Ste 370, Portland OR 97239
Tel (503) 227-6615 SIC 5111 5113

HUFF PAPER CO p 717
10 Crk Pky Namns Crk Ctr Namns Crk Cntr, Boothwyn PA 19061
Tel (610) 497-5100 SIC 5113

MCANENY BROTHERS INC p 926
470 Industrial Park Rd, Ebensburg PA 15931
Tel (814) 472-9800
SIC 5141 5147 5148 5194 5113 5142

■ PCA CORRUGATED AND DISPLAY LLC p 1123
148 Penn St, Hanover PA 17331
Tel (717) 632-4727 SIC 2653 5113

■ SYSCO PITTSBURGH LLC p 1417
1 Whitney Dr, Harmony PA 16037
Tel (724) 452-2100
SIC 5142 5149 5148 5023 5113 5046

SUPPLYONE HOLDINGS CO INC p 1408
11 Campus Blvd, Newtown Square PA 19073
Tel (484) 582-5005 SIC 2653 5113

SUPPLYONE INC p 1408
11 Campus Blvd Ste 150, Newtown Square PA 19073
Tel (484) 582-1004 SIC 5113

PENN JERSEY PAPER CO p 1129
9355 Blue Grass Rd, Philadelphia PA 19114
Tel (215) 671-9800 SIC 5113 5087

PHILADELPHIA BUNZL p 1142
10814 Northeast Ave, Philadelphia PA 19116
Tel (215) 969-0600
SIC 5087 5023 5113 7213

FIBRO SOURCE USA INC p 540
985 Old Eagle School Rd # 514, Wayne PA 19087
Tel (610) 293-3200
SIC 5099 5113 5141 5112

MATOSANTOS COMMERCIAL CORP p 920
Parque Industrial Ca, Vega Baja PR 00693
Tel (787) 793-6900 SIC 5141 5113 5087

ABITIBI CONSOLIDATED SALES CORP p 11
55 E Camperdown Way, Greenville SC 29601
Tel (864) 656-3975 SIC 5111 5113

SOUTHEASTERN PAPER GROUP INC p 1346
50 Old Blackstock Rd, Spartanburg SC 29301
Tel (800) 858-7230 SIC 5113

CHRIS CAM CORP p 302
808 W Cherokee St, Sioux Falls SD 57104
Tel (605) 336-1190 SIC 5113 5169 5111

AMERICAN PAPER & TWINE CO p 77
7400 Cockrill Bend Blvd, Nashville TN 37209
Tel (615) 350-9000 SIC 5113 5087 5112

■ MCLANE FOODSERVICE INC p 931
2085 Midway Rd, Carrollton TX 75006
Tel (972) 364-2000
SIC 8742 5141 5311 5113

NORTH FOOD GROUP INC p 1052
1245 W Royal Ln, Dallas TX 75261
Tel (972) 445-3322
SIC 5146 5147 5149 5113

POLLOCK INVESTMENTS INC p 1160
1 Pollock Pl, Grand Prairie TX 75050
Tel (972) 263-8448 SIC 5113 5087

HOOVER MATERIALS HANDLING GROUP INC p 706
2135 Highway 6 S, Houston TX 77077
Tel (800) 844-8683 SIC 5113 3089

■ VICTORY PACKAGING LP p 1556
3555 Timmons Ln Ste 1440, Houston TX 77027
Tel (888) 261-1268 SIC 5113 5199

■ MCLANE HIGH PLAINS INC p 931
1717 E Loop 289, Lubbock TX 79403
Tel (806) 766-2900 SIC 5141 5142 5113

SMURFIT KAPPA BATES LLC p 1335
6433 Davis Blvd, North Richland Hills TX 76182
Tel (817) 498-3200 SIC 2653 5113

■ MCLANE CO INC p 930
4747 Mclane Pkwy, Temple TX 76504
Tel (254) 771-7500
SIC 5141 5149 5311 5113

GULF COAST PAPER CO INC p 646
3705 Houston Hwy, Victoria TX 77901
Tel (361) 852-5252 SIC 5113 5087

■ SYSCO VIRGINIA LLC p 1418
5081 S Valley Pike, Rockingham VA 22801
Tel (540) 434-0761
SIC 5149 5142 5113 5148 5147 5143

BOX MAKER INC p 205
6412 S 190th St, Kent WA 98032
Tel (425) 251-0655
SIC 5113 2653 2672 3086 5199 2631

MICHELSEN PACKAGING CO OF CALIFORNIA p 960
202 N 2nd Ave, Yakima WA 98902
Tel (509) 248-6270 SIC 5113 2653

VOLM COMPANIES INC p 1564
1804 Edison St, Antigo WI 54409
Tel (715) 627-4826 SIC 5113 5199 3565

GREEN BAY CONVERTING INC p 636
600 Packerland Dr, Green Bay WI 54303
Tel (920) 498-5100 SIC 5113

CHAMBERS & OWEN INC p 287
1733 Morse St, Janesville WI 53545
Tel (608) 752-7865
SIC 5194 5145 5113 5141

ASSOCIATED SALES & BAG CO p 121
400 W Boden St, Milwaukee WI 53207
Tel (414) 769-1000 SIC 5113

■ DUNSIRN INDUSTRIES INC p 461
2415 Industrial Dr, Neenah WI 54956
Tel (920) 725-3814
SIC 2671 5113 3081 2672 2621

ULINE INC p 1500
12575 Uline Dr, Pleasant Prairie WI 53158
Tel (262) 612-4200 SIC 5113

BOELTER COMPANIES INC p 197
N22W23685 Rdgview Pkwy W, Waukesha WI 53188
Tel (262) 523-6200
SIC 5113 5046 7389 5087

HOLIDAY WHOLESALE INC p 700
225 Pioneer Dr, Wisconsin Dells WI 53965
Tel (608) 253-0404
SIC 5194 5145 5113 5199

SIC 5122 Drugs, Drug Proprietaries & Sundries Wholesale

BTC WHOLESALE DISTRIBUTORS INC p 222
100 Airview Ln, Alabaster AL 35007
Tel (205) 324-2581
SIC 5194 5145 5087 5149 5122

CITY WHOLESALE GROCERY CO INC p 320
300 Industrial Dr, Birmingham AL 35211
Tel (205) 795-4533
SIC 5194 5141 5145 5122

BRENN DISTRIBUTION INC p 210
130 Vintage Dr Ne, Huntsville AL 35811
Tel (256) 859-4011 SIC 5122

HPC LLC p 714
63 S Royal St Ste 800, Mobile AL 36602
Tel (251) 441-1990 SIC 5122

AMERICAN ASSOCIATED PHARMACIES INC p 68
201 Lnnie E Crawford Blvd, Scottsboro AL 35769
Tel (256) 574-6819 SIC 5122

ASSOCIATED PHARMACIES INC p 121
211 Lonnie Crawford Blvd, Scottsboro AL 35769
Tel (256) 574-6819 SIC 5122

FOREVER LIVING PRODUCTS US INC p 567
7501 E Mccormick Pkwy # 105, Scottsdale AZ 85258
Tel (480) 998-8888 SIC 5122

▲ MAGELLAN HEALTH INC p 895
4800 N Scottsdale Rd, Scottsdale AZ 85251
Tel (602) 572-6050 SIC 8063 8011 5122

■ MCKESSON SPECIALTY ARIZONA INC p 930
4343 N Scottsdale Rd # 370, Scottsdale AZ 85251
Tel (480) 663-4000 SIC 5122

VEMMA NUTRITION CO p 1547
1621 W Rio Salado Pkwy # 101, Tempe AZ 85281
Tel (480) 927-8999 SIC 5122 5149

■ STEPHEN L LAFRANCE PHARMACY INC p 1386
3017 N Midland Dr, Pine Bluff AR 71603
Tel (870) 535-5171 SIC 5122 5912

HARPS FOOD STORES INC p 663
918 S Gutensohn Rd, Springdale AR 72762
Tel (479) 751-7601 SIC 5411 5122

METAGENICS INC p 952
25 Enterprise Ste 200, Aliso Viejo CA 92656
Tel (949) 366-0818 SIC 5122

DAKO NORTH AMERICA INC p 409
6392 Via Real, Carpinteria CA 93013
Tel (805) 566-6655 SIC 5122 3841

■ LEINER HEALTH PRODUCTS INC p 854
901 E 233rd St, Carson CA 90745
Tel (631) 200-2000 SIC 2834 5122

NATROL LLC p 1018
21411 Prairie St, Chatsworth CA 91311
Tel (818) 739-6000 SIC 5122 2099

AMERICAN INTERNATIONAL INDUSTRIES p 75
2220 Gaspar Ave, Commerce CA 90040
Tel (323) 728-2999 SIC 5122 2844

■ CORE-MARK INTERRELATED COMPANIES INC p 369
311 Reed Cir, Corona CA 92879
Tel (951) 272-4790 SIC 5199 5122 5087

■ SKILLED HEALTHCARE LLC p 1330
27442 Portola Pkwy # 200, Foothill Ranch CA 92610
Tel (949) 282-5800 SIC 8051 6513 5122

GNLD INTERNATIONAL LLC p 619
3500 Gateway Blvd, Fremont CA 94538
Tel (510) 651-0405 SIC 5122

ALLERGAN SALES LLC p 53
2525 Dupont Dr 14th, Irvine CA 92612
Tel (714) 246-4500 SIC 5122

PACIFIC PHARMA INC p 1105
18600 Von Karman Ave, Irvine CA 92612
Tel (714) 246-4600 SIC 5122

VICTOR INSTRUMENTS INC p 1555
50 Bunsen, Irvine CA 92618
Tel (949) 855-0337 SIC 5122 5047

GRIFOLS SHARED SERVICES NORTH AMERICA INC p 640
2410 Lillyvale Ave, Los Angeles CA 90032
Tel (323) 225-2221 SIC 5122 2834

HATCHBEAUTY PRODUCTS LLC p 668
10951 W Pico Blvd Ste 300, Los Angeles CA 90064
Tel (310) 396-7070 SIC 5122

HERBALIFE INTERNATIONAL OF AMERICA INC p 685
800 W Olympic Blvd # 406, Los Angeles CA 90015
Tel (310) 410-9600 SIC 5122

JARROW FORMULAS INC p 778
1824 S Robertson Blvd, Los Angeles CA 90035
Tel (310) 204-6936 SIC 5122

FAIRN & SWANSON INC p 525
400 Lancaster St, Oakland CA 94601
Tel (510) 533-8260 SIC 5122 5182

BEAUTY 21 COSMETICS INC p 166
2021 S Archibald Ave, Ontario CA 91761
Tel (909) 945-2220 SIC 5122 2844

BERGEN BRUNSWIG DRUG CO p 174
4000 W Metropolitan Dr # 200, Orange CA 92868
Tel (714) 385-4000 SIC 5122

SHAKLEE US INC p 1311
4747 Willow Rd, Pleasanton CA 94588
Tel (925) 924-2000 SIC 5122

NUVI GLOBAL CORP p 1068
8423 Rochester Ave # 101, Rancho Cucamonga CA 91730
Tel (844) 740-6938 SIC 5122

▲ NATURAL HEALTH TRENDS CORP p 1018
609 Deep Valley Dr # 390, Rllng Hls Est CA 90274
Tel (310) 541-0888 SIC 5122 5961

■ AGOURON PHARMACEUTICALS INC p 35
10777 Science Center Dr, San Diego CA 92121
Tel (858) 622-3000 SIC 2834 5122 8731

KINSALE HOLDINGS INC p 821
475 Sansome St Ste 700, San Francisco CA 94111
Tel (415) 400-2600 SIC 5122

▲ MCKESSON CORP p 930
1 Post St Fl 18, San Francisco CA 94104
Tel (415) 983-8300
SIC 5122 5047 5199 7372

OTSUKA AMERICA INC p 1097
1 Embarcadero Ctr # 2020, San Francisco CA 94111
Tel (415) 986-5300
SIC 3829 3499 5122 2833 2084 2086

JOHN PAUL MITCHELL SYSTEMS p 789
20705 Centre Pointe Pkwy, Santa Clarita CA 91350
Tel (661) 298-0400 SIC 5122

▲ CORE-MARK HOLDING CO INC p 369
395 Oyster Point Blvd # 415, South San Francisco CA 94080
Tel (650) 589-9445
SIC 5141 5194 5145 5122 5199 5149

VALLEY WHOLESALE DRUG CO LLC p 1541
1401 W Fremont St, Stockton CA 95203
Tel (209) 466-0131 SIC 5122

FFF ENTERPRISES INC p 539
41093 County Center Dr, Temecula CA 92591
Tel (951) 296-2500 SIC 5122 5047

QIAGEN NORTH AMERICAN HOLDINGS INC p 1195
27220 Turnberry Ln # 200, Valencia CA 91355
Tel (661) 702-3000 SIC 5122

PLANT SCIENCES INC p 1154
342 Green Valley Rd, Watsonville CA 95076
Tel (831) 728-3323 SIC 5122 8748 8731

WELLDYNERX INC p 1589
7472 S Tucson Way Ste 100, Centennial CO 80112
Tel (888) 479-2000 SIC 5122 5912

■ BEAUTYGE BRANDS USA INC p 166
1515 Wazee St Ste 200, Denver CO 80202
Tel (800) 598-2739 SIC 5122 2844

■ ANIMAL HEALTH INTERNATIONAL INC p 91
822 7th St Ste 740, Greeley CO 80631
Tel (970) 353-2600
SIC 5122 5047 5999 5191 5083 5154

▲ HESKA CORP p 688
3760 Rocky Mountain Ave, Loveland CO 80538
Tel (970) 493-7272 SIC 2834 5122

■ MOORE MEDICAL LLC p 987
1690 New Britain Ave A, Farmington CT 06032
Tel (860) 826-3600 SIC 5047 5122

EURPAC SERVICE INC p 513
101 Merritt 7 Corp Park 7 Corporate, Norwalk CT 06851
Tel (203) 847-0800 SIC 5141 5122

PHARMACEUTICAL RESEARCH ASSOCIATES INC p 1141
1 Stamford Forum, Stamford CT 06901
Tel (203) 588-8000 SIC 2834 5122

PRA HOLDINGS INC p 1167
1 Stamford Forum, Stamford CT 06901
Tel (203) 853-0123 SIC 2834 5122 8742

PURDUE PHARMA LP p 1192
201 Tresser Blvd Fl 1, Stamford CT 06901
Tel (203) 588-8000 SIC 2834 5122

BEIERSDORF NORTH AMERICA INC p 169
45 Danbury Rd, Wilton CT 06897
Tel (203) 563-5800
SIC 2844 5122 3842 2841 2672

CRABTREE & EVELYN LTD p 388
102 Peake Brook Rd, Woodstock CT 06281
Tel (800) 272-2873 SIC 5122 5149 2844

ASTRAZENECA PHARMACEUTICALS LP p 122
1800 Concord Pike, Wilmington DE 19803
Tel (302) 886-3000 SIC 2834 5122

BMP SUNSTONE CORP p 194
3711 Kennett Pike Ste 200, Wilmington DE 19807
Tel (610) 940-1675 SIC 5122

SPI PHARMA INC p 1358
503 Carr Rd Ste 210, Wilmington DE 19809
Tel (302) 576-8500 SIC 5122

BIO-ENGINEERED SUPPLEMENTS & NUTRITION INC p 183
5901 Broken Sound Pkwy Nw, Boca Raton FL 33487
Tel (561) 994-8335 SIC 5122 5499

CSL PLASMA INC p 398
900 Broken Sound Pkwy # 4, Boca Raton FL 33487
Tel (561) 981-3700 SIC 5122

PURITY WHOLESALE GROCERS INC p 1192
5300 Broken Sound Blvd Nw # 110, Boca Raton FL 33487
Tel (561) 997-8302 SIC 5141 5122 5199

ION LABS INC p 762
5355 115th Ave N, Clearwater FL 33760
Tel (727) 527-1072 SIC 5122 2834

ANDRX CORP p 91
4955 Orange Dr, Davie FL 33314
Tel (954) 585-1400 SIC 2834 5122

GREAT AMERICAN BEAUTY INC p 633
124 N Swinton Ave, Delray Beach FL 33444
Tel (561) 496-2730 SIC 5122 2844

■ PERFUMANIA INC p 1135
5900 N Andrews Ave # 500, Fort Lauderdale FL 33309
Tel (866) 600-3600 SIC 5122 5999

■ PSS WORLD MEDICAL INC p 1188
4345 Southpoint Blvd # 110, Jacksonville FL 32216
Tel (904) 332-3000 SIC 5122 5047

■ PRIORITY HEALTHCARE DISTRIBUTION INC p 1177
255 Technology Park, Lake Mary FL 32746
Tel (407) 833-7000 SIC 5122 5047

PARBEL OF FLORIDA INC p 1114
6100 Blue Lagoon Dr # 200, Miami FL 33126
Tel (305) 262-7500 SIC 5122

■ CURASCRIPT INC p 401
6272 Lee Vista Blvd, Orlando FL 32822
Tel (407) 852-4903 SIC 5122

KSF ACQUISITION CORP p 831
11780 Us Highway 1 400n, Palm Beach Gardens FL 33408
Tel (561) 231-6548 SIC 5122

▲ PETMED EXPRESS INC p 1139
1441 Sw 29th Ave, Pompano Beach FL 33069
Tel (954) 979-5995 SIC 5999 5122

WELLSPRING PHARMACEUTICAL CORP p 1591
5911 N Honore Ave Ste 211, Sarasota FL 34243
Tel (941) 312-4727 SIC 5122 2834

MOTCO INC p 992
7900 Sw 57th Ave Ste 10, South Miami FL 33143
Tel (305) 662-8814 SIC 5182 5122 5199

NATURES PRODUCTS INC p 1019
1301 Sawgrs Corp Pkwy, Sunrise FL 33323
Tel (954) 233-3300 SIC 5122 5499

■ PHARMERICA LONG-TERM CARE LLC p 1141
3625 Queen Palm Dr, Tampa FL 33619
Tel (877) 975-2273
SIC 5912 5961 8082 5122

ANDA INC p 89
2915 Weston Rd, Weston FL 33331
Tel (954) 217-4500 SIC 5122

ARBOR PHARMACEUTICALS LLC p 103
6 Cncurse Pkwy Ste 1800, Atlanta GA 30328
Tel (678) 334-2420 SIC 5122

MERIAL INC p 948
3239 Satellite Blvd, Duluth GA 30096
Tel (678) 638-3000 SIC 5122

MERIAL SELECT INC p 948
1168 Airport Pkwy, Gainesville GA 30501
Tel (770) 536-8787 SIC 5122 2836

CURANT HEALTH GEORGIA LLC p 401
200 Technology Ct Se B, Smyrna GA 30082
Tel (770) 437-8040 SIC 5122

UCB INC p 1498
1950 Lake Park Dr Se, Smyrna GA 30080
Tel (770) 970-7500 SIC 5122 8731 8732

WEBCO HAWAII INC p 1586
2840 Mokumoa St, Honolulu HI 96819
Tel (808) 839-4551
SIC 5122 5199 5141 5064

MELALEUCA INC p 940
4609 W 65th S, Idaho Falls ID 83402
Tel (208) 522-0700
SIC 2833 5122 2844 2841 2834

■ **GE HEALTHCARE HOLDINGS INC** p 596
3350 N Ridge Ave, Arlington Heights IL 60004
Tel (847) 398-8400
SIC 2835 2833 5169 5122

OPTION CARE ENTERPRISES INC p 1090
3000 Lakeside Dr Ste 300n, Bannockburn IL 60015
Tel (847) 964-4950
SIC 8082 5122 6794 5912 8049

WALGREENS INFUSION SERVICES INC p 1573
3000 Lakeside Dr Ste 300n, Bannockburn IL 60015
Tel (312) 940-2500
SIC 8082 8011 8059 5999 5122

LUNDBECK LLC p 886
6 Parkway N Ste 400, Deerfield IL 60015
Tel (847) 282-1000 *SIC* 2834 5122

GLANBIA PERFORMANCE NUTRITION INC p 614
3500 Lacey Rd, Downers Grove IL 60515
Tel (630) 236-0097 *SIC* 2833 5149 5122

CENTRAL GROCERS INC p 278
2600 Haven Ave, Joliet IL 60433
Tel (815) 553-8800
SIC 5141 5147 5142 5148 5143 5122

RENAISSANCE ACQUISITION HOLDINGS LLC p 1223
272 E Deerpath Ste 206, Lake Forest IL 60045
Tel (847) 283-7772 *SIC* 5122

TAP PHARMACEUTICAL PRODUCTS INC p 1424
675 N Field Dr, Lake Forest IL 60045
Tel (847) 582-2000 *SIC* 5122

MECHANICAL SERVANTS LLC p 934
2755 Thomas St, Melrose Park IL 60160
Tel (708) 486-1500 *SIC* 5122

EBY-BROWN CO LLC p 474
1415 W Diehl Rd Ste 300, Naperville IL 60563
Tel (630) 778-2800
SIC 5194 5145 5141 5122 5149

ASTELLAS PHARMA US INC p 122
1 Astellas Way, Northbrook IL 60062
Tel (800) 888-7704 *SIC* 5122

SAGENT PHARMACEUTICALS INC p 1268
1901 N Roselle Rd Ste 700, Schaumburg IL 60195
Tel (847) 908-1600 *SIC* 2834 5122

H D SMITH LLC p 650
3063 Fiat Ave, Springfield IL 62703
Tel (866) 232-1222 *SIC* 5122 8082

SHAMBAUGH & SON LP p 1311
7614 Opportunity Dr, Fort Wayne IN 46825
Tel (260) 487-7814 *SIC* 8711 3556 5122

ALCHEMY AROMATICS LLC p 47
621 Park East Blvd, New Albany IN 47150
Tel (812) 755-6660 *SIC* 5169 5122

MERCY MEDICAL CENTER-CLINTON INC p 948
1410 N 4th St, Clinton IA 52732
Tel (563) 244-5555 *SIC* 8062 8051 5122

VARIETY DISTRIBUTORS INC p 1544
609 7th St, Harlan IA 51537
Tel (712) 755-2184
SIC 5131 5092 5122 5112 5145 5199

FRONTIER COOPERATIVE p 581
3021 78th St, Norway IA 52318
Tel (319) 227-7996 *SIC* 5122 2099 5149

UNIVERSITY OF KENTUCKY p 1522
203 Brcknrdg Hl 168 Fnkhs, Lexington KY 40506
Tel (859) 257-9185 *SIC* 5122

LAUREL GROCERY CO LLC p 847
129 Barbourville Rd, London KY 40744
Tel (606) 878-6601
SIC 5141 5147 5122 5143

PCA-CORRECTIONS LLC p 1123
2701 Chestnut Station Ct, Louisville KY 40299
Tel (502) 526-0375 *SIC* 5122

▲ **PHARMERICA CORP** p 1141
1901 Campus Pl, Louisville KY 40299
Tel (502) 627-7000 *SIC* 5912 5122

MORRIS & DICKSON CO LLC p 990
410 Kay Ln, Shreveport LA 71115
Tel (318) 797-7900 *SIC* 5122

LOUISIANA WHOLESALE DRUG CO INC p 880
2085 I 49 S Service Rd, Sunset LA 70584
Tel (337) 662-1040 *SIC* 5122 5912

ASSOCIATED GROCERS OF MAINE INC p 120
190 Water St, Gardiner ME 04345
Tel (207) 596-0636
SIC 5141 5147 5148 5122

PROGRESSIVE DISTRIBUTORS INC p 1181
145 Pleasant Hill Rd, Scarborough ME 04074
Tel (207) 883-2911 *SIC* 5122 5149 5199

HEALTHSOURCE DISTRIBUTORS LLC p 677
7200 Rutherford Rd # 150, Baltimore MD 21244
Tel (410) 653-1113 *SIC* 5122

LUPIN PHARMACEUTICALS INC p 886
111 S Calvert St Fl 21, Baltimore MD 21202
Tel (410) 576-2000 *SIC* 5122

REMEDI SENIORCARE OF MARYLAND LLC p 1222
9006 Yellow Brick Rd, Baltimore MD 21237
Tel (443) 927-8400 *SIC* 5122

SIGMA-TAU PHARMACEUTICALS INC p 1321
9841 Wash Blvd Ste 500, Gaithersburg MD 20878
Tel (301) 948-1041 *SIC* 5122

CORRECT RX PHARMACY SERVICES INC p 372
1352 Charwood Rd Ste C, Hanover MD 21076
Tel (800) 636-0501 *SIC* 5122

PHARMACEUTICS INTERNATIONAL INC p 1141
10819 Gilroy Rd Ste 100, Hunt Valley MD 21031
Tel (410) 584-0001 *SIC* 2834 5122

C-CARE LLC p 234
979 Corporate Blvd, Linthicum Heights MD 21090
Tel (410) 850-0035 *SIC* 5122

IMPERIAL DISTRIBUTORS INC p 734
33 Sword St, Auburn MA 01501
Tel (508) 756-5156 *SIC* 5122

INVENTIV HEALTH CLINICAL SRE LLC p 761
1 Van De Graaff Dr, Burlington MA 01803
Tel (800) 416-0555 *SIC* 5122

GENZYME CORP p 605
500 Kendall St, Cambridge MA 02142
Tel (617) 252-7500
SIC 2835 2834 8071 3842 2836 5122

MILLBROOK DISTRIBUTION SERVICES INC p 970
88 Huntoon Memorial Hwy, Leicester MA 01524
Tel (508) 892-8171
SIC 5122 5023 5072 5112 5049 5199

SHIRE US INC p 1317
300 Shire Way, Lexington MA 02421
Tel (781) 482-9222 *SIC* 5122

COVIDIEN LP p 385
15 Hampshire St, Mansfield MA 02048
Tel (508) 261-8000
SIC 3842 3841 3845 5122

■ **GE HEALTHCARE BIO-SCIENCES CORP** p 596
100 Results Way, Marlborough MA 01752
Tel (800) 526-3593 *SIC* 5122

■ **GE HEALTHCARE INC** p 596
100 Results Way, Marlborough MA 01752
Tel (800) 292-8514 *SIC* 5122 2833

■ **MEDI-PHYSICS INC** p 935
100 Results Way, Marlborough MA 01752
Tel (800) 526-3593 *SIC* 5122

GARBER BROS INC p 591
Kay Way Rr 139, Stoughton MA 02072
Tel (781) 341-0800
SIC 5194 5145 5141 5122

ACCESS BUSINESS GROUP LLC p 14
7575 Fulton St E, Ada MI 49355
Tel (616) 787-6000
SIC 5169 2842 5122 2833 5136 5137

ALTICOR GLOBAL HOLDINGS INC p 62
7575 Fulton St E, Ada MI 49301
Tel (616) 787-1000
SIC 5169 5122 2833 5136 5137 5021

ALTICOR INC p 62
7575 Fulton St E, Ada MI 49355
Tel (616) 787-1000
SIC 5169 5122 2833 5136 5137 5021

AMWAY INTERNATIONAL INC p 87
7575 Fulton St E, Ada MI 49355
Tel (616) 787-1000
SIC 5169 5122 5099 5199 2099 2032

GRAD INC p 628
4001 3 Mile Rd Nw, Grand Rapids MI 49534
Tel (616) 676-5969
SIC 5141 5194 5145 5122 5113 5411

GENERIC DRUG HOLDINGS INC p 602
31778 Enterprise Dr, Livonia MI 48150
Tel (734) 743-6000 *SIC* 8734 5122 5047

■ **HARVARD DRUG GROUP L L C** p 666
17177 N Laurel Park Dr # 233, Livonia MI 48152
Tel (734) 525-8700 *SIC* 5122 5047 8734

■ **MCKESSON PHARMACY SYSTEMS LLC** p 930
30881 Schoolcraft Rd, Livonia MI 48150
Tel (734) 421-0260 *SIC* 7372 5122

FRANK W KERR CO p 574
43155 W 9 Mile Rd Ste 1, Novi MI 48375
Tel (248) 349-5000 *SIC* 5122

APOTHECARY PRODUCTS LLC p 97
11750 12th Ave S, Burnsville MN 55337
Tel (800) 328-2742 *SIC* 2834 5122 3069

MIDWEST VETERINARY SUPPLY INC p 968
21467 Holyoke Ave, Lakeville MN 55044
Tel (952) 894-4350 *SIC* 5122 5047

DISTRIBUTION ALTERNATIVES INC p 443
435 Park Ct, Lino Lakes MN 55014
Tel (651) 636-9167 *SIC* 5122 5912

■ **3M INTERAMERICA INC** p 2
2501 Old Hudson Rd, Maplewood MN 55144
Tel (651) 733-1110
SIC 5113 5065 5065 5084 5122 8741

FAIRVIEW PHARMACY SERVICES LLC p 525
711 Kasota Ave Se, Minneapolis MN 55414
Tel (612) 672-5200 *SIC* 5912 5122

■ **MINTER-WEISMAN CO** p 974
1035 Nathan Ln N Ste A, Minneapolis MN 55441
Tel (763) 545-3706
SIC 5194 5149 5145 5013 5122

DURVET INC p 463
100 Se Magellan Dr, Blue Springs MO 64014
Tel (816) 229-9101 *SIC* 5122

MIKE STUART ENTERPRISES INC p 968
18565 Business 13, Branson West MO 65737
Tel (417) 272-8064 *SIC* 5122

■ **D & K HEALTHCARE RESOURCES LLC** p 406
8235 Forsyth Blvd, Saint Louis MO 63105
Tel (888) 727-3485 *SIC* 5122

SBI INC p 1285
8500 Valcour Ave, Saint Louis MO 63123
Tel (314) 615-2000
SIC 5199 5122 7334 5084

PTI UNION LLC p 1189
1310 Stylemaster Dr, Union MO 63084
Tel (636) 583-8664 *SIC* 5122

▲ **AMCON DISTRIBUTING CO INC** p 65
7405 Irvington Rd, Omaha NE 68122
Tel (402) 331-3727
SIC 5194 5141 5145 5113 5122

MARIANNA INDUSTRIES INC p 906
11222 I St Ste A, Omaha NE 68137
Tel (402) 593-0211 *SIC* 5122 2844 7231

C&S WHOLESALE GROCERS INC p 234
7 Corporate Dr, Keene NH 03431
Tel (603) 354-7000
SIC 5141 5147 5143 5142 5122 5145

SALONCENTRIC INC p 1273
50 Connell Dr, Berkeley Heights NJ 07922
Tel (212) 984-4000 *SIC* 5122

SANOFI-AVENTIS US LLC p 1280
55 Corporate Dr, Bridgewater NJ 08807
Tel (908) 981-5000 *SIC* 5122 2834

TRISH MCEVOY LTD p 1482
430 Commerce Blvd, Carlstadt NJ 07072
Tel (201) 559-9234 *SIC* 5122

WHITE ROSE INC p 1606
380 Middlesex Ave, Carteret NJ 07008
Tel (732) 541-5555
SIC 5141 5143 5142 5122 7311 8721

AUROBINDO PHARMA USA INC p 131
6 Wheeling Rd, Dayton NJ 08810
Tel (732) 839-9400 *SIC* 5122

SHISEIDO AMERICA INC p 1317
366 Prncton Hightstown Rd, East Windsor NJ 08520
Tel (609) 371-5800 *SIC* 5122 2844

NANDANSONS INTERNATIONAL INC p 1007
55 Mayfield Ave, Edison NJ 08837
Tel (908) 561-2400 *SIC* 5122

CEI HOLDINGS INC p 273
2182 State Route 35, Holmdel NJ 07733
Tel (732) 888-7788
SIC 2844 7389 4225 5122

▲ **MERCK & CO INC** p 945
2000 Galloping Hill Rd, Kenilworth NJ 07033
Tel (908) 740-4000
SIC 2834 2836 2844 5122

GLENMARK PHARMACEUTICALS INC USA p 615
750 Corporate Dr, Mahwah NJ 07430
Tel (201) 684-8000 *SIC* 5122

■ **SYSCO GUEST SUPPLY LLC** p 1417
4301 Us Highway 1 Ste 300, Monmouth Junction NJ 08852
Tel (609) 514-9696
SIC 5122 2844 5131 5139 7011 8741

CLONDALKIN PHARMA & HEALTHCARE LLC p 327
1224 N Church St, Moorestown NJ 08057
Tel (856) 439-1700 *SIC* 5122 8361

TMCI HOLDINGS INC p 1457
80 Avenue K, Newark NJ 07105
Tel (201) 553-1100
SIC 5122 5023 5072 5112 5049 5199

■ **LCI HOLDINGS INC** p 849
5901 W Side Ave, North Bergen NJ 07047
Tel (201) 295-6300
SIC 5651 5136 5137 5094 5122 5944

BIOLIFE PLASMA SERVICES LP p 184
203 N Center Dr, North Brunswick NJ 08902
Tel (732) 422-4200 *SIC* 5122

ACTAVIS LLC p 19
400 Interpace Pkwy, Parsippany NJ 07054
Tel (862) 261-7000 *SIC* 2834 5122

DAIICHI SANKYO INC p 408
2 Hilton Ct Ste 1, Parsippany NJ 07054
Tel (973) 359-2600 *SIC* 5122 8731

FERRING PHARMACEUTICALS INC p 538
100 Interpace Pkwy, Parsippany NJ 07054
Tel (973) 796-1600 *SIC* 2834 5122

▲ **ZOETIS INC** p 1644
10 Sylvan Way Ste 105, Parsippany NJ 07054
Tel (973) 822-7000 *SIC* 2834 5122

■ **GREENSTONE LLC** p 638
100 Rte 206 N, Peapack NJ 07977
Tel (800) 447-3360 *SIC* 5122

HELM AMERICA CORP p 682
1110 Centennial Ave Ste 2, Piscataway NJ 08854
Tel (732) 981-1160
SIC 5169 5122 5191 4231 4226

NOVO-NORDISK OF NORTH AMERICA INC p 1063
800 Scudders Mill Rd, Plainsboro NJ 08536
Tel (609) 987-5800
SIC 8741 8733 5122 2833 2834

DR REDDYS LABORATORIES INC p 455
107 College Rd E Ste 100, Princeton NJ 08540
Tel (908) 203-4900 *SIC* 5122 3089

NEOSTRATA CO INC p 1026
307 College Rd E, Princeton NJ 08540
Tel (609) 520-0715 *SIC* 5122

RANBAXY PHARMACEUTICALS INC p 1207
600 College Rd E Ste 2100, Princeton NJ 08540
Tel (609) 720-9200 *SIC* 2834 5122

SANDOZ INC p 1278
100 College Rd W, Princeton NJ 08540
Tel (609) 627-8500 *SIC* 2834 5122

TRISTRATA INC p 1483
307 College Rd E, Princeton NJ 08540
Tel (609) 520-0715 *SIC* 5122

SPECIALTY RX INC p 1356
2 Bergen Tpke, Ridgefield Park NJ 07660
Tel (908) 241-6337 *SIC* 5122

PHARMSCRIPT LLC p 1141
150 Pierce St, Somerset NJ 08873
Tel (908) 389-1818 *SIC* 5122

PARTNERS PHARMACY LLC p 1118
50 Lawrence Rd, Springfield NJ 07081
Tel (908) 931-9111 *SIC* 5122

GLAXOSMITHKLINE CONSUMER HEALTHCARE LP p 614
184 Libery Corner Rd, Warren NJ 07059
Tel (251) 591-4188 *SIC* 5122

VITAQUEST INTERNATIONAL LLC p 1563
8 Henderson Dr, West Caldwell NJ 07006
Tel (973) 575-9200
SIC 2834 5149 5122 8742

■ **MERCK SHARP & DOHME (IA) LLC** p 945
1 Merck Dr, Whitehouse Station NJ 08889
Tel (908) 423-1000 *SIC* 5122

■ **ALO ACQUISITION LLC** p 59
26 Corporate Cir, Albany NY 12203
Tel (518) 464-0279 *SIC* 2833 5122 8733

BELLCO DRUG CORP p 170
5500 New Horizons Blvd, Amityville NY 11701
Tel (631) 789-6900 *SIC* 5122 5047

▲ **PERFUMANIA HOLDINGS INC** p 1135
35 Sawgrass Dr Ste 2, Bellport NY 11713
Tel (631) 866-4100 *SIC* 5122 5999

PROS CHOICE BEAUTY CARE INC p 1184
35 Sawgrass Dr Ste 4, Bellport NY 11713
Tel (631) 803-3200 *SIC* 5122

QUALITY KING DISTRIBUTORS INC p 1197
35 Sawgrass Dr Ste 3, Bellport NY 11713
Tel (631) 439-2000 *SIC* 5122

■ **QUALITY KING FRAGRANCE INC** p 1197
35 Sawgrass Dr Ste 1, Bellport NY 11713
Tel (631) 866-4100 *SIC* 5122

■ **REXALL SUNDOWN INC** p 1230
110 Orville Dr, Bohemia NY 11716
Tel (631) 567-9500 *SIC* 5961 5122 2833

AMNEAL PHARMACEUTICALS OF NEW YORK LLC p 86
50 Horseblock Rd, Brookhaven NY 11719
Tel (631) 952-0214 *SIC* 2834 5122

L & R DISTRIBUTORS INC p 833
9301 Avenue D, Brooklyn NY 11236
Tel (718) 272-2100 *SIC* 5122 5131

TRIPIFOODS INC p 1482
1427 William St, Buffalo NY 14206
Tel (716) 853-7400
SIC 5141 5194 5145 5143 5142 5122

INVAGEN PHARMACEUTICALS INC p 760
7 Oser Ave Ste 4, Hauppauge NY 11788
Tel (631) 231-3233 *SIC* 2834 5122

TARO PHARMACEUTICALS USA INC p 1425
3 Skyline Dr Ste 120, Hawthorne NY 10532
Tel (914) 345-9000 *SIC* 5122

AMERICAN SALES CO LLC p 79
4201 Walden Ave, Lancaster NY 14086
Tel (716) 686-7000 *SIC* 5199 5122

MANA PRODUCTS INC p 900
3202 Queens Blvd Fl 6, Long Island City NY 11101
Tel (718) 361-2550 *SIC* 2844 5122

▲ **HENRY SCHEIN INC** p 684
135 Duryea Rd, Melville NY 11747
Tel (631) 843-5500 *SIC* 5047 5122 7372

■ **ARAMIS INC** p 102
767 5th Ave, New York NY 10153
Tel (212) 572-4200 *SIC* 5122 2844

CHANEL INC p 288
9 W 57th St Fl 44, New York NY 10019
Tel (212) 688-5055
SIC 5632 2844 5122 5944 5961 5999

CLARINS USA INC p 321
1 Park Ave Fl 19, New York NY 10016
Tel (212) 223-2956 *SIC* 5122

FOREST LABORATORIES LLC p 566
909 3rd Ave Fl 23, New York NY 10022
Tel (212) 421-7850 *SIC* 2834 5122

GIORGIO ARMANI CORP p 612
450 W 15th St 3, New York NY 10011
Tel (212) 209-3500
SIC 5136 5137 5122 5611 5621 5632

ICC CHEMICAL CORP p 727
460 Park Ave Fl 7, New York NY 10022
Tel (212) 521-1700 *SIC* 5169 5122 5182

INTERNATIONAL COSMETICS & PERFUMES p 755
30 W 21st St Fl 7, New York NY 10010
Tel (212) 643-0011 *SIC* 5122

LOCCITANE INC p 873
1430 Broadway Fl 2, New York NY 10018
Tel (212) 333-4880 *SIC* 5122 5999 5961

LOREAL USA INC p 878
10 Hudson Yards Fl 30, New York NY 10001
Tel (212) 818-1500 *SIC* 5122 2844

MOET HENNESSY USA INC p 982
85 10th Ave Fl 2, New York NY 10011
Tel (212) 888-7575
SIC 0172 2844 6153 5182 5122

NAGASE AMERICA CORP p 1006
546 5th Ave Fl 16, New York NY 10036
Tel (212) 703-1340
SIC 5169 5162 5122 5065 5047

NARS COSMETICS INC p 1007
900 3rd Ave Fl 6, New York NY 10022
Tel (212) 941-0890 *SIC* 5122

■ **NEW AVON LLC** p 1029
777 3rd Ave Fl 8, New York NY 10017
Tel (212) 282-8500 *SIC* 2844 5122 5999

■ **ORAL COLGATE PHARMACEUTICALS INC** p 1091
300 Park Ave Fl 3, New York NY 10022
Tel (212) 310-2000 *SIC* 5122 2834

■ **ORIGINS NATURAL RESOURCES INC** p 1094
767 5th Ave Fl 38, New York NY 10153
Tel (212) 572-4200 *SIC* 5122

REV HOLDINGS INC p 1229
466 Lexington Ave Fl 21, New York NY 10017
Tel (212) 527-4000
SIC 2844 3421 5122 5199 5999

REVLON HOLDINGS INC p 1229
237 Park Ave, New York NY 10017
Tel (212) 527-4000
SIC 2844 3421 5122 5199 5999

■ **REVLON REAL ESTATE CORP** p 1229
466 Lexington Ave Fl 13, New York NY 10017
Tel (212) 527-4000
SIC 5122 2844 3421 5199 5999

RGI GROUP INC p 1231
625 Madison Ave Frnt 4, New York NY 10022
Tel (212) 527-4000
SIC 2844 3421 5122 5199 5999

SHISEIDO AMERICAS CORP p 1317
900 3rd Ave Fl 15, New York NY 10022
Tel (212) 805-2300 *SIC* 2844 5122

TAKEDA AMERICA HOLDINGS INC p 1422
767 3rd Ave, New York NY 10017
Tel (212) 421-6954 *SIC* 5122 5169 2819

▲ **ACETO CORP** p 17
4 Tri Harbor Ct, Port Washington NY 11050
Tel (516) 627-6000 *SIC* 5122 5169

ROCHESTER DRUG CO-OPERATIVE INC p 1243
50 Jetview Dr, Rochester NY 14624
Tel (585) 271-7220 *SIC* 5122

■ **ALPHABET HOLDING CO INC** p 60
2100 Smithtown Ave, Ronkonkoma NY 11779
Tel (631) 200-2000
SIC 2833 5122 5499 5961

■ **NBTY INC** p 1021
2100 Smithtown Ave, Ronkonkoma NY 11779
Tel (631) 200-2000
SIC 2833 5122 5499 5961

PERFUME CENTER OF AMERICA INC p 1135
2020 Ocean Ave, Ronkonkoma NY 11779
Tel (516) 348-1127 *SIC* 5122

PERFUME WORLDWIDE INC p 1135
2020 Ocean Ave Unit A, Ronkonkoma NY 11779
Tel (516) 575-2499 *SIC* 5122 5999

PRIDE PRODUCTS CORP p 1174
4333 Veterans Mem Hwy, Ronkonkoma NY 11779
Tel (631) 737-4444
SIC 5113 5122 5023 5072 5199

■ **KINRAY INC** p 821
15235 10th Ave, Whitestone NY 11357
Tel (718) 767-1234 *SIC* 5122

TOPS MARKETS LLC p 1461
6363 Main St, Williamsville NY 14221
Tel (716) 635-5000
SIC 5411 5141 5147 5148 5122 5912

EUROPA SPORTS PRODUCTS INC p 513
11401 Granite St Ste H, Charlotte NC 28273
Tel (704) 405-2022 *SIC* 5122 5149 5941

JOHNS LONE STAR DISTRIBUTION GP LLC p 790
11401 Granite St, Charlotte NC 28273
Tel (214) 340-0718 *SIC* 5122 5149

ACCORD HEALTHCARE INC p 15
1009 Slater Rd Ste 210b, Durham NC 27703
Tel (919) 941-7878 *SIC* 5122

■ **BURTS BEES INC** p 229
210 W Pettigrew St, Durham NC 27701
Tel (919) 998-5200 *SIC* 2844 5122 5087

NORTH CAROLINA MUTUAL WHOLESALE DRUG CO p 1051
816 Ellis Rd, Durham NC 27703
Tel (919) 596-2151 *SIC* 5122

STIEFEL LABORATORIES INC p 1389
20 Tw Alexander Dr, Durham NC 27709
Tel (888) 784-3335 *SIC* 5122 2834

BOB BARKER CO INC p 196
134 N Main St, Fuquay Varina NC 27526
Tel (800) 235-8586
SIC 5131 5122 2392 5136 3441

■ **MAYNE PHARMA INC** p 923
1240 Sugg Pkwy, Greenville NC 27834
Tel (252) 752-3800 *SIC* 5122 2834

MERCHANTS DISTRIBUTORS LLC p 944
5005 Alex Lee Blvd, Hickory NC 28601
Tel (828) 725-4424
SIC 5141 5142 5147 5148 5194 5122

HILLCO LTD p 693
1435 Hwy 258 N, Kinston NC 28504
Tel (252) 523-9094
SIC 8051 8059 5047 5122

DHHS-BROUGHTON HOSPITAL p 435
1000 S Sterling St, Morganton NC 28655
Tel (828) 433-2516 *SIC* 5122

■ **PHILOSOPHY INC** p 1144
1400 Broadway Rd, Sanford NC 27332
Tel (602) 794-8500 *SIC* 5122 2844

PHYSICIANS WEIGHT LOSS CENTERS OF AMERICA INC p 1146
395 Springside Dr, Akron OH 44333
Tel (330) 666-7952 *SIC* 5141 5122 6794

■ **BIORX LLC** p 184
7167 E Kemper Rd, Cincinnati OH 45249
Tel (866) 442-4679
SIC 5122 8748 2834 5047 8051

■ **MEDPACE INC** p 938
5375 Medpace Way, Cincinnati OH 45227
Tel (513) 579-9911 *SIC* 8731 5122 5047

■ **NEIGHBORCARE INC** p 1024
201 E 4th St Ste 900, Cincinnati OH 45202
Tel (513) 719-2600
SIC 5122 5912 5047 7389

■ **NEIGHBORCARE SERVICES CORP** p 1024
201 E 4th St Ste 900, Cincinnati OH 45202
Tel (513) 719-2600 *SIC* 5122

■ **OMNICARE INC** p 1085
900 Omnicare Ctr, Cincinnati OH 45202
Tel (513) 719-2600
SIC 5122 5047 8082 8741

■ **PROCTER & GAMBLE DISTRIBUTING LLC** p 1179
1 Procter And Gamble Plz, Cincinnati OH 45202
Tel (513) 983-1100
SIC 5169 5122 5149 5113 5137

NCS HEALTHCARE INC p 1022
3201 Entp Pkwy Ste 220, Cleveland OH 44122
Tel (216) 514-3350
SIC 5122 8093 8049 8082 8742 5912

■ **BUTLER ANIMAL HEALTH HOLDING CO LLC** p 230
400 Metro Pl N Ste 100, Dublin OH 43017
Tel (614) 761-9095 *SIC* 5122 5149 5047

■ **BUTLER ANIMAL HEALTH SUPPLY LLC** p 230
400 Metro Pl N Ste 100, Dublin OH 43017
Tel (855) 724-3461 *SIC* 5122 5149 5047

■ **CARDINAL HEALTH 100 INC** p 253
7000 Cardinal Pl, Dublin OH 43017
Tel (614) 757-5000 *SIC* 5122 5047

▲ **CARDINAL HEALTH INC** p 253
7000 Cardinal Pl, Dublin OH 43017
Tel (614) 757-5000
SIC 5122 5047 8741 3842

WBC GROUP LLC p 1585
6333 Hudson Crossing Pkwy, Hudson OH 44236
Tel (800) 472-4221 *SIC* 5122 5047 3843

MASTERS PHARMACEUTICAL INC p 918
3600 Pharma Way, Lebanon OH 45036
Tel (513) 354-2690 *SIC* 5122

PRASCO LLC p 1167
6125 Commerce Ct, Mason OH 45040
Tel (513) 204-1100 *SIC* 5122

SKILLED CARE PHARMACY INC p 1329
6175 Hi Tek Ct, Mason OH 45040
Tel (513) 459-7626 *SIC* 5122

DISCOUNT DRUG MART INC p 442
211 Commerce Dr, Medina OH 44256
Tel (330) 725-2340
SIC 5912 5331 5411 5451 5122 8082

PRESCRIPTION SUPPLY INC p 1171
2233 Tracy Rd, Northwood OH 43619
Tel (419) 661-6600 *SIC* 5122

BROTHERS TRADING CO INC p 219
400 Victory Ln, Springboro OH 45066
Tel (937) 746-1010 *SIC* 5141 5122 5149

MIAMI-LUKEN INC p 959
265 S Pioneer Blvd, Springboro OH 45066
Tel (937) 743-7775 *SIC* 5122

REMEDI SENIORCARE OF OHIO LLC p 1222
962 S Dorset Rd, Troy OH 45373
Tel (800) 232-4239 *SIC* 5122

PHARMA CORR LLC p 1141
6705 Camille Ave, Oklahoma City OK 73149
Tel (405) 670-1400 *SIC* 5122

WESTERN FAMILY HOLDING CO p 1598
6700 Sw Sandburg St, Tigard OR 97223
Tel (503) 639-6300
SIC 5141 5142 5199 5122 5149

■ **FISHER CLINICAL SERVICES INC** p 552
7554 Schantz Rd, Allentown PA 18106
Tel (610) 391-0800 *SIC* 5122

▲ **AMERISOURCEBERGEN CORP** p 83
1300 Morris Dr Ste 100, Chesterbrook PA 19087
Tel (610) 727-7000 *SIC* 5122 5047

■ **AMERISOURCEBERGEN DRUG CORP** p 83
1300 Morris Dr Ste 100, Chesterbrook PA 19087
Tel (610) 727-7000 *SIC* 5122

■ **AMERISOURCEBERGEN SERVICES CORP** p 83
1300 Morris Dr Ste 100, Chesterbrook PA 19087
Tel (610) 727-7000
SIC 5122 5047 5199 8721

■ **WYETH PHARMACEUTICALS INC** p 1629
500 Arcola Rd, Collegeville PA 19426
Tel (484) 865-5000 *SIC* 5122 8731

VALUE DRUG CO p 1542
195 Theater Dr, Duncansville PA 16635
Tel (814) 944-9316 *SIC* 5122

LARON PHARMA INC p 845
500 Office Center Dr # 400, Fort Washington PA 19034
Tel (267) 575-1470 *SIC* 2834 5122

CORIXA CORP p 370
325 N Bridge St, Marietta PA 17547
Tel (717) 426-6557 *SIC* 5122

COOPER-BOOTH WHOLESALE CO LP p 367
200 Lincoln West Dr, Mountville PA 17554
Tel (717) 285-8000
SIC 5194 5145 5122 5141

TEVA PHARMACEUTICALS USA INC p 1441
1090 Horsham Rd, North Wales PA 19454
Tel (215) 591-3000 *SIC* 2834 2833 5122

BIOLIFE PLASMA SERVICES LP p 184
1435 Lake Cook Rd, Philadelphia PA 19182
Tel (847) 940-5559 *SIC* 5122 8099

GLAXOSMITHKLINE LLC p 614
5 Crescent Dr, Philadelphia PA 19112
Tel (215) 751-4000 *SIC* 2834 5122

V L H INC p 1538
600 Boyce Rd, Pittsburgh PA 15205
Tel (800) 245-4440 *SIC* 2833 5122 2834

■ **CHEROKEE PHARMACEUTICALS LLC** p 294
100 Ave C, Riverside PA 17868
Tel (570) 271-4195 *SIC* 5122

ASSOCIATED WHOLESALERS INC p 121
336 E Penn Ave, Robesonia PA 19551
Tel (610) 693-3161
SIC 5141 5147 5122 5142 5148 5411

LIBERTY USA INC p 863
920 Irwin Run Rd, West Mifflin PA 15122
Tel (412) 461-2700
SIC 5194 5145 5122 5141

CLINIGEN CTS INC p 326
790 Township Line Rd # 120, Yardley PA 19067
Tel (215) 558-7001 *SIC* 5122

LUIS GARRATON INC p 884
Luchetti Ind Park Rd 28 C, Bayamon PR 00961
Tel (787) 788-6100 *SIC* 5122 5141

PUERTO RICO SUPPLIES GROUP INC p 1191
Parkeast, Bayamon PR 00961
Tel (787) 780-4043
SIC 5194 5149 5122 5143 5148

DROGUERIA BETANCES LLC p 456
Luis Munoz Marin Ave Esq, Caguas PR 00725
Tel (787) 653-1200 *SIC* 5122

NEOLPHARMA INC p 1026
99 Calle Jardines, Caguas PR 00725
Tel (787) 286-4000 *SIC* 5122

■ **WYETH PHARMACEUTICALS CO INC** p 1629
1 Carr 3, Guayama PR 00784
Tel (787) 864-4010 *SIC* 5122

■ **CARDINAL HEALTH PR 120 INC** p 253
10 Carr 165 Km24, Guaynabo PR 00968
Tel (787) 625-4100 *SIC* 5122 5047

CESAR CASTILLO INC p 284
Km 21 1 Pr 1 Rr 1, Guaynabo PR 00971
Tel (787) 999-1616 *SIC* 5122 6552

■ **COLGATE PALMOLIVE CO DISTRIBUTORS** p 336
1 St Lot 8colgate, Guaynabo PR 00968
Tel (787) 273-5000 *SIC* 5122

■ **JOHNSON & JOHNSON INTERNATIONAL** p 790
475 Calle C Ste 200, Guaynabo PR 00969
Tel (787) 272-1905 *SIC* 5122

▲ **UNITED NATURAL FOODS INC** p 1510
313 Iron Horse Way, Providence RI 02908
Tel (401) 528-8634 *SIC* 5149 5122 5142

■ **CVS PHARMACY INC** p 404
1 Cvs Dr, Woonsocket RI 02895
Tel (401) 765-1500 *SIC* 5912 5122

■ **CVS VA DISTRIBUTION INC** p 404
1 Cvs Dr, Woonsocket RI 02895
Tel (401) 765-1500 *SIC* 5122

MVP GROUP INTERNATIONAL INC p 1003
1031 Legrand Blvd, Charleston SC 29492
Tel (843) 216-8380 *SIC* 3999 5122

J M SMITH CORP p 771
101 W Saint John St # 305, Spartanburg SC 29306
Tel (864) 542-9419 *SIC* 5122 7374

CONSUMERS SUPPLY DISTRIBUTING LLC p 362
718 N Derby Ln, North Sioux City SD 57049
Tel (712) 255-6927 *SIC* 5122

TOP RX LLC p 1460
2950 Brother Blvd Ste 102, Bartlett TN 38133
Tel (800) 542-8677 *SIC* 5122

■ **CARDINAL HEALTH 108 LLC** p 253
305 Tech Park Dr Ste 113, La Vergne TN 37086
Tel (615) 287-5200 *SIC* 5122 5047

TENNESSEE FARMERS COOPERATIVE INC p 1438
180 Old Nashville Hwy, La Vergne TN 37086
Tel (615) 793-8011
SIC 5191 5013 5014 5172 5122 2048

DDN/OBERGFEL LLC p 419
4580 S Mendenhall Rd, Memphis TN 38141
Tel (901) 795-7117 *SIC* 5122

TEAM TECHNOLOGIES INC p 1430
5949 Commerce Blvd, Morristown TN 37814
Tel (423) 587-2199
SIC 2844 5122 5719 3991

FHG CORP p 539
4637 Port Royal Rd, Spring Hill TN 37174
Tel (931) 499-7070 *SIC* 7389 5122

PRICE & CO p 1174
3530 W Cardinal Dr, Beaumont TX 77705
Tel (409) 842-0677
SIC 5194 5145 5122 5141

WOODBOLT DISTRIBUTION LLC p 1622
3891 S Traditions Dr, Bryan TX 77807
Tel (800) 870-2070 *SIC* 5122

BAYLOR HEALTH ENTERPRISES LP p 162
411 N Washington Ave # 7200, Dallas TX 75246
Tel (214) 820-2492 *SIC* 5122 7011 7991

▲ **JRJR33 INC** p 795
2950 N Harwood St Fl 22, Dallas TX 75201
Tel (469) 913-4115
SIC 5499 5023 5122 2721 5251

■ **BEAUTY SYSTEMS GROUP LLC** p 166
3001 Colorado Blvd, Denton TX 76210
Tel (940) 297-2000 *SIC* 5999 5122 5087

■ **SALLY BEAUTY SUPPLY LLC** p 1273
3001 Colorado Blvd, Denton TX 76210
Tel (940) 898-7500 *SIC* 5999 5122 5087

FRUIT OF EARTH INC p 582
3101 High Rver Rd Ste 175, Fort Worth TX 76155
Tel (817) 510-1600 *SIC* 5122 2844

VIRBAC CORP p 1558
3200 Meacham Blvd, Fort Worth TX 76137
Tel (800) 338-3659 *SIC* 2834 5122

■ **AMERISOURCEBERGEN SPECIALTY GROUP INC** p 83
3101 Gaylord Pkwy, Frisco TX 75034
Tel (866) 408-3761 *SIC* 5122

■ **ASD SPECIALTY HEALTHCARE INC** p 116
3101 Gaylord Pkwy Fl 3, Frisco TX 75034
Tel (469) 365-8000 *SIC* 5122

GENESIS PURE INC p 603
7164 Tech Dr Ste 100, Frisco TX 75033
Tel (469) 213-2900 *SIC* 5122

2ML REAL ESTATE INTERESTS INC p 2
952 Echo Ln Ste 314, Houston TX 77024
Tel (713) 747-5000 *SIC* 5141 5142 5122

MIDWAY IMPORTING INC p 967
1807 Brittmoore Rd, Houston TX 77043
Tel (713) 802-9363 *SIC* 5122

PROFESSIONAL COMPOUNDING CENTERS OF AMERICA INC p 1180
9901 S Wilcrest Dr, Houston TX 77099
Tel (281) 933-6948 *SIC* 5047 5122

VERIFINC CORP p 1549
12000 Westheimer Rd # 380, Houston TX 77077
Tel (832) 858-5548 *SIC* 7371 5734 5122

SSB HOLDINGS INC p 1363
4300 Fm 2225, Quitman TX 75783
Tel (903) 878-7513 *SIC* 5122

SPFM LP p 1358
4310 West Ave, San Antonio TX 78213
Tel (210) 805-8931
SIC 5122 5149 2834 2833 2841 2844

■ **C D HARTNETT CO** p 232
302 N Main St, Weatherford TX 76086
Tel (817) 594-3813 *SIC* 5141 5122

XANGO LLC p 1630
2889 W Ashton Blvd Ste 1, Lehi UT 84043
Tel (801) 753-3000 *SIC* 5122

■ **MAKERS OF KAL INC** p 899
1500 Kearns Blvd, Park City UT 84060
Tel (435) 655-6000 *SIC* 5122

▲ **NU SKIN ENTERPRISES INC** p 1066
75 W Center St, Provo UT 84601
Tel (801) 345-1000 *SIC* 2844 5122

■ **NU SKIN ENTERPRISES UNITED STATES INC** p 1066
75 W Center St, Provo UT 84601
Tel (801) 377-6056 *SIC* 5122

ASSOCIATED FOOD STORES INC p 120
1850 W 2100 S, Salt Lake City UT 84119
Tel (801) 973-4400
SIC 5141 5147 5142 5148 5122 5023

CAPITAL CANDY CO INC p 249
32 Burnham St, Barre VT 05641
Tel (802) 476-6689
SIC 5145 5194 5122 5141 5149

BURLINGTON DRUG CO INC p 228
91 Catamount Dr, Milton VT 05468
Tel (802) 893-5105 *SIC* 5122

ZEVACOR PHARMA INC p 1642
21000 Atl Blvd Ste 730, Dulles VA 20166
Tel (703) 547-8161 *SIC* 5122 5047

INDIVIOR INC p 739
10710 Midilothian Turnpik Ste 430, Richmond VA 23235
Tel (804) 379-1090 *SIC* 5122

CONCORDIA HEALTHCARE USA INC p 355
4950 Brambleton Ave Ste F, Roanoke VA 24018
Tel (434) 980-8146 *SIC* 5122

HARBOR WHOLESALE GROCERY INC p 660
3901 Hogum Bay Rd Ne, Lacey WA 98516
Tel (360) 754-4484
SIC 5141 5194 5142 5122

ASSOCIATED GROCERS INC p 120
3301 S Norfolk St, Seattle WA 98118
Tel (206) 762-2100
SIC 5141 5147 5143 5122 5148 5142

PACIFIC NUTRITIONAL INC p 1105
6317 Ne 131st Ave Buildb, Vancouver WA 98682
Tel (360) 253-3197 *SIC* 5122 2099

WISCONSIN VISION ASSOCIATES INC p 1619
139 W Chestnut St, Burlington WI 53105
Tel (262) 763-0100 *SIC* 5048 5122 5047

TUFCO LP p 1491
3161 S Ridge Rd, Green Bay WI 54304
Tel (920) 336-0054 *SIC* 5122 5112 2676

F DOHMEN CO p 522
190 N Milwaukee St, Milwaukee WI 53202
Tel (414) 299-4913 *SIC* 5122 5045 7374

INDEPENDENT PHARMACY COOPERATIVE p 736
1550 Columbus St, Sun Prairie WI 53590
Tel (608) 825-9556 *SIC* 5122 7299

SIC 5131 Piece Goods, Notions & Dry Goods Wholesale

MOMENTUM TEXTILES LLC p 983
17811 Fitch, Irvine CA 92614
Tel (949) 833-8886 *SIC* 5131 2221

PINDLER & PINDLER INC p 1148
11910 Poindexter Ave, Moorpark CA 93021
Tel (805) 531-9090 *SIC* 5131

CHARMING TRIM & PACKAGING INC p 290
28 Brookside Ct, Novato CA 94947
Tel (415) 302-7021 *SIC* 5131 3111

TEIJIN PHARMA USA LLC p 1433
773 San Marin Dr Ste 2230, Novato CA 94945
Tel (415) 893-1518 *SIC* 5131

VALIANT PRODUCTS CORP p 1540
2727 W 5th Ave, Denver CO 80204
Tel (303) 892-1234
SIC 5131 5023 7389 2511 2599 1752

DONGHIA INC p 450
500 Bic Dr Ste 20, Milford CT 06461
Tel (800) 366-4442
SIC 5198 5131 5021 2342

WINE LABELS LLC p 1616
100 Westport Ave, Norwalk CT 06851
Tel (203) 847-7213 *SIC* 5131

W L GORE & ASSOCIATES INC p 1568
555 Paper Mill Rd, Newark DE 19711
Tel (302) 738-4880
SIC 3357 2821 5131 3841 2819 3069

CAROLE FABRICS CORP p 259
633 Nw Frontage Rd, Augusta GA 30907
Tel (706) 863-4742
SIC 2221 2591 5131 5949 2392 2391

TEIJIN ARAMID USA INC p 1433
801 Blacklawn Rd Sw Ste F, Conyers GA 30012
Tel (770) 929-0781 *SIC* 5131

BROWN INDUSTRIES INC p 219
205 W Industrial Blvd, Dalton GA 30720
Tel (706) 277-1977
SIC 2759 5131 2273 3552 3315 2671

INNVISION HOSPITALITY INC p 745
504 Carver Rd, Griffin GA 30224
Tel (888) 875-6202 *SIC* 5131 5021 7389

KEYSTON BROS (INC) p 815
1000 Holcomb Wds Pkwy # 111, Roswell GA 30076
Tel (770) 587-2555 *SIC* 5199 5131 5191

KUDZU FABRICS INC p 831
2154 River Cliff Dr, Roswell GA 30076
Tel (770) 641-0379 *SIC* 5199 5131 5191

1888 MILLS LLC p 1
1520 Kensington Rd # 115, Oak Brook IL 60523
Tel (630) 620-5222 *SIC* 5023 5131

VARIETY DISTRIBUTORS INC p 1544
609 7th St, Harlan IA 51537
Tel (712) 755-2184
SIC 5131 5092 5122 5112 5145 5199

■ **FILA USA INC** p 542
930 Ridgebrook Rd Ste 200, Sparks MD 21152
Tel (410) 773-3000
SIC 5139 5131 5137 5611 5621 5632

MICROFIBRES INC p 962
124 Washington St Ste 101, Foxboro MA 02035
Tel (401) 725-4883
SIC 2221 2295 5131 2262

NOTIONS MARKETING CORP p 1062
1500 Buchanan Ave Sw, Grand Rapids MI 49507
Tel (616) 243-8424 *SIC* 5131 5199 5092

CROWN PACKAGING CORP p 395
17854 Chstrfld Aprt Rd, Chesterfield MO 63005
Tel (636) 681-8000
SIC 5113 5169 5131 5084

BUNZL DISTRIBUTION USA LLC p 226
1 Cityplace Dr Ste 200, Saint Louis MO 63141
Tel (314) 997-5959 *SIC* 5131

BUNZL INTERNATIONAL SERVICES INC p 226
1 Cityplace Dr Ste 200, Saint Louis MO 63141
Tel (314) 997-5959 *SIC* 5131

FRANCO MANUFACTURING CO INC p 574
555 Prospect St, Metuchen NJ 08840
Tel (732) 494-0503
SIC 2269 2392 2211 5023 5131

■ **SYSCO GUEST SUPPLY LLC** p 1417
4301 Us Highway 1 Ste 300, Monmouth Junction NJ 08852
Tel (609) 514-9696
SIC 5122 2844 5131 5139 7011 8741

TEXTILES FROM EUROPE INC p 1445
5901 W Side Ave Fl 6, North Bergen NJ 07047
Tel (212) 213-1828 *SIC* 5131

DAZIAN LLC p 418
18 Central Blvd, South Hackensack NJ 07606
Tel (877) 232-9426 *SIC* 5131

POSCO DAEWOO AMERICA CORP p 1163
300 Frank W Burr Blvd, Teaneck NJ 07666
Tel (201) 591-8000
SIC 5131 5051 5169 5015

KRAVET INC p 829
225 Cent Ave S, Bethpage NY 11714
Tel (516) 293-2000 *SIC* 5131 5198 2392

L & R DISTRIBUTORS INC p 833
9301 Avenue D, Brooklyn NY 11236
Tel (718) 272-2100 *SIC* 5122 5131

SEFAR INC p 1300
111 Calumet St, Depew NY 14043
Tel (716) 683-4050
SIC 5131 5051 5084 3496 2297 2221

BROOKWOOD COMPANIES INC p 218
485 Madison Ave Frnt 5, New York NY 10022
Tel (212) 551-0100 *SIC* 5131

■ **DESIGNTEX GROUP INC** p 432
200 Varick St Fl 8, New York NY 10014
Tel (212) 886-8100 *SIC* 5131

F SCHUMACHER & CO p 522
875 Ave Of The Amrcs 14, New York NY 10001
Tel (212) 213-7900 *SIC* 5131 2299

ITOCHU INTERNATIONAL INC p 768
1251 Avenue Of The Americ, New York NY 10020
Tel (212) 818-8000
SIC 5131 5084 5065 5051 5153 5141

MARUBENI AMERICA CORP p 913
375 Lexington Ave, New York NY 10017
Tel (212) 450-0100
SIC 5131 5084 5012 5169 5172 5094

P KAUFMANN INC p 1102
3 Park Ave, New York NY 10016
Tel (212) 292-2200
SIC 5131 5714 5712 2262

STARK CARPET CORP p 1379
979 3rd Ave Fl 11, New York NY 10022
Tel (844) 407-8275 *SIC* 5099 5131 5021

TEIJIN HOLDINGS USA INC p 1433
600 Lexington Ave Fl 27, New York NY 10022
Tel (212) 308-8744 *SIC* 5131

TOMEN AMERICA INC p 1459
805 3rd Ave Fl 16, New York NY 10022
Tel (212) 355-3600
SIC 5153 5169 5031 5131 2261

WELSPUN USA INC p 1591
295 Textile Bldg 5th Ave, New York NY 10016
Tel (212) 620-2000 *SIC* 5131

ARC-COM FABRICS INC p 103
33 Ramland Rd S, Orangeburg NY 10962
Tel (845) 365-1100 *SIC* 5131

■ **MAHARAM FABRIC CORP** p 897
74 Horseblock Rd, Yaphank NY 11980
Tel (631) 582-3434 *SIC* 5131 7389

BOB BARKER CO INC p 196
134 N Main St, Fuquay Varina NC 27526
Tel (800) 235-8586
SIC 5131 5122 2392 5136 3441

SOUTHCO DISTRIBUTING CO p 1345
2201 S John St, Goldsboro NC 27530
Tel (919) 735-8012 *SIC* 5194 5141 5131

COVILLE INC p 385
8065 N Point Blvd Ste O, Winston Salem NC 27106
Tel (336) 759-0115 *SIC* 5131

CHECKER NOTIONS CO INC p 292
400 W Dussel Dr Ste B, Maumee OH 43537
Tel (419) 893-3636 *SIC* 5131 5092

LOUIS DREYFUS CO COTTON LLC p 879
7255 Goodlett Farms Pkwy, Cordova TN 38016
Tel (901) 383-5000 *SIC* 5159 5131

FRANK KASMIR ASSOCIATES INC p 574
3191 Commonwealth Dr, Dallas TX 75247
Tel (214) 631-8040 *SIC* 5131

VOITH HOLDING INC p 1564
2200 N Roemer Rd, Appleton WI 54911
Tel (920) 731-7724
SIC 5131 3554 2221 6719

SIC 5136 Men's & Boys' Clothing & Furnishings Wholesale

ANTIGUA GROUP INC p 94
16651 N 84th Ave, Peoria AZ 85382
Tel (623) 523-6000
SIC 5137 5136 2395 2339 3993

ASTRACO LLC p 122
1411 E Hidalgo Ave, Phoenix AZ 85040
Tel (602) 931-2981 *SIC* 5136 5699

OUTDOOR CAP CO INC p 1098
1200 Melissa Dr, Bentonville AR 72712
Tel (479) 273-3732 *SIC* 5136

COPPEL CORP p 368
503 Scaroni Ave, Calexico CA 92231
Tel (760) 357-3707 *SIC* 5021 5137 5136

■ **PRANA LIVING LLC** p 1167
3209 Lionshead Ave, Carlsbad CA 92010
Tel (866) 915-6457 *SIC* 5136 5137

GONZALES ENTERPRISES INC p 623
495 Ryan Ave, Chico CA 95973
Tel (530) 343-8725 *SIC* 5136

COLOR IMAGE APPAREL INC p 338
6670 Flotilla St, Commerce CA 90040
Tel (855) 793-3100 *SIC* 5137 5136

HUB DISTRIBUTING INC p 715
1260 Corona Pointe Ct, Corona CA 92879
Tel (951) 340-3149
SIC 5611 5621 5632 5137 5136 5094

VOLCOM LLC p 1564
1740 Monrovia Ave, Costa Mesa CA 92627
Tel (949) 646-2175
SIC 7389 2253 7822 5136 5137

HYBRID PROMOTIONS LLC p 723
10711 Walker St, Cypress CA 90630
Tel (714) 952-3866 *SIC* 5136 5137 5611

JAMES PERSE ENTERPRISES INC p 776
7373 Flores St, Downey CA 90242
Tel (323) 588-2226 *SIC* 5136 5137

■ **QUIKSILVER INC** p 1200
5600 Argosy Ave Ste 100, Huntington Beach CA 92649
Tel (714) 889-2200
SIC 2329 2339 3949 5136 5137

ASICS AMERICA CORP p 117
80 Technology Dr, Irvine CA 92618
Tel (949) 453-8888
SIC 5139 5136 5137 2369 2339 2321

FOX HEAD INC p 572
16752 Armstrong Ave, Irvine CA 92606
Tel (408) 776-8633 *SIC* 5136 5137 5961

LIFTED RESEARCH GROUP INC p 865
7 Holland, Irvine CA 92618
Tel (949) 581-1144 *SIC* 5136

UNION SUPPLY GROUP INC p 1505
2301 E Pacifica Pl, Rancho Dominguez CA 90220
Tel (310) 603-8899 *SIC* 5141 5139 5136

▲ **WALKING CO HOLDINGS INC** p 1573
25 W Anapamu St, Santa Barbara CA 93101
Tel (805) 963-8727
SIC 5651 5961 5136 5137 5699

DORFMAN-PACIFIC CO p 451
2615 Boeing Way, Stockton CA 95206
Tel (209) 982-1400 *SIC* 5136 5137

ARIAT INTERNATIONAL INC p 108
3242 Whipple Rd, Union City CA 94587
Tel (510) 477-7000
SIC 3199 5139 5137 5136

APPAREL CONCEPTS INTERNATIONAL INC p 98
4804 Laurel Canyon Blvd # 59, Valley Village CA 91607
Tel (626) 233-9198 *SIC* 5136

RCRV INC p 1212
4715 S Alameda St, Vernon CA 90058
Tel (323) 235-8070 *SIC* 2673 5137 5136

SOEX WEST USA LLC p 1337
3294 E 26th St, Vernon CA 90058
Tel (323) 264-8300 *SIC* 5136

VINEYARD VINES LLC p 1558
181 Harbor Dr Fl 1, Stamford CT 06902
Tel (203) 661-1803
SIC 5136 5137 5699 5611 5621

INTRADECO INC p 759
9500 Nw 108th Ave, Medley FL 33178
Tel (305) 264-6022 *SIC* 5136 5199 5065

ISACO INTERNATIONAL CORP p 766
5980 Miami Lakes Dr E, Miami Lakes FL 33014
Tel (305) 594-4455 *SIC* 5136

S&S ACTIVEWEAR LLC p 1263
581 Territorial Dr, Bolingbrook IL 60440
Tel (630) 679-9940 *SIC* 5136

RANDA ACCESSORIES LEATHER GOODS LLC p 1207
5600 N River Rd Ste 500, Rosemont IL 60018
Tel (847) 292-8300 *SIC* 5136 5948 3172

ITS GREEK TO ME INC p 768
520 Mccall Rd Ste A, Manhattan KS 66502
Tel (785) 537-8822
SIC 5136 5699 5137 5947 2759

PUMA NORTH AMERICA INC p 1192
10 Lyberty Way, Westford MA 01886
Tel (978) 698-1000
SIC 5136 5139 8741 5137

ACCESS BUSINESS GROUP LLC p 14
7575 Fulton St E, Ada MI 49355
Tel (616) 787-6000
SIC 5169 2842 5122 2833 5136 5137

ALTICOR GLOBAL HOLDINGS INC p 62
7575 Fulton St E, Ada MI 49301
Tel (616) 787-1000
SIC 5169 5122 2833 5136 5137 5021

ALTICOR INC p 62
7575 Fulton St E, Ada MI 49355
Tel (616) 787-1000
SIC 5169 5122 2833 5136 5137 5021

MID-STATES DISTRIBUTING CO INC p 963
1370 Mendota Hts Rd, Mendota MN 55150
Tel (651) 280-4300
SIC 5072 5013 5191 5091 5092 5136

KELLWOOD CO LLC p 809
600 Kellwood Pkwy Ste 200, Chesterfield MO 63017
Tel (314) 576-3100 *SIC* 5136 5137

NASSIRI INC p 1009
2035 Helm Dr, Las Vegas NV 89119
Tel (702) 837-7332 *SIC* 5136 5137

ERMENEGILDO ZEGNA CORP p 508
100 W Forest Ave Ste A, Englewood NJ 07631
Tel (201) 816-0921 *SIC* 5136 5611

WICKED FASHIONS INC p 1608
222 Bridge Plz S, Fort Lee NJ 07024
Tel (201) 242-5909 *SIC* 5137 5136

STEVE SELVIN ASSOCIATES INC p 1388
207 Union St, Hackensack NJ 07601
Tel (201) 488-3332 *SIC* 5136 5137

■ **VF SPORTSWEAR INC** p 1553
545 Wshngton Blvd Fl 8, Jersey City NJ 07310
Tel (212) 541-5757
SIC 2329 2384 5136 5137 5611 6794

MARCRAFT CLOTHES INC p 905
301 Island Rd, Mahwah NJ 07430
Tel (201) 828-2085 *SIC* 5136

■ **LCI HOLDINGS INC** p 849
5901 W Side Ave, North Bergen NJ 07047
Tel (201) 295-6300
SIC 5651 5136 5137 5094 5122 5944

ARAMSCO INC p 102
1480 Grandview Ave, Paulsboro NJ 08066
Tel (856) 686-7700
SIC 5085 5084 5136 5139

FERRAGAMO U S A INC p 538
700 Castle Rd, Secaucus NJ 07094
Tel (201) 553-6100
SIC 5139 5136 5137 5621 5632

ARAMSCO HOLDINGS INC p 102
1480 Grand View Ave, Thorofare NJ 08086
Tel (856) 686-7700
SIC 5085 5136 5084 5139

DIVAL SAFETY EQUIPMENT INC p 443
1721 Niagara St, Buffalo NY 14207
Tel (716) 874-9060
SIC 5099 8748 8734 5047 5136 5661

AMEREX GROUP INC p 66
512 Fashion Ave Fl 9, New York NY 10018
Tel (212) 221-3151 *SIC* 5137 5136

BILLION TOWER INTL LLC p 182
989 6th Ave Fl 8, New York NY 10018
Tel (212) 220-0608 *SIC* 2326 5136

BRAVADO INTERNATIONAL GROUP MERCHANDISING SERVICES INC p 209
1755 Broadway Fl 2, New York NY 10019
Tel (212) 445-3400
SIC 5136 5137 5611 5621

■ **CALVIN KLEIN INC** p 243
205 W 39th St Lbby 2, New York NY 10018
Tel (212) 719-2600
SIC 5661 5137 5136 5611 5621 6794

DIESEL USA INC p 438
220 W 19th St Fl 5, New York NY 10011
Tel (212) 755-9200
SIC 5137 5136 5621 5632 5611

ELIAS BEN INDUSTRIES CORP p 487
550 Fashion Ave Fl 12, New York NY 10018
Tel (212) 354-8300 *SIC* 5137 5136

FOWNES BROTHERS & CO INC p 572
16 E 34th St Fl 5, New York NY 10016
Tel (212) 683-0150
SIC 3151 2381 5136 5137 3949

FREE COUNTRY LTD p 576
1071 6th Ave Fl 9, New York NY 10018
Tel (212) 719-4596 *SIC* 5136 5137

▲ **G-III APPAREL GROUP LTD** p 588
512 7th Ave Fl 35, New York NY 10018
Tel (212) 403-0500
SIC 2337 2339 2311 2329 2386 5136

GBG USA INC p 594
350 5th Ave Lbby 9, New York NY 10118
Tel (646) 839-7083 *SIC* 5139 5137 5136

GCE INTERNATIONAL INC p 595
1385 Broadway Fl 21, New York NY 10018
Tel (212) 704-4800
SIC 2253 2389 2331 5137 5136

GIORGIO ARMANI CORP p 612
450 W 15th St 3, New York NY 10011
Tel (212) 209-3500
SIC 5136 5137 5122 5611 5621 5632

GLOBAL BRANDS HOLDING GROUP LLC p 615
350 5th Ave, New York NY 10118
Tel (646) 839-7000 *SIC* 5136 5137 5139

HIS INTERNATIONAL GROUP LLC p 696
34 W 33rd St Fl 2, New York NY 10001
Tel (212) 967-3990 *SIC* 5136

HUGO BOSS USA INC p 717
55 Water St Fl 48, New York NY 10041
Tel (212) 940-0600
SIC 2311 2325 2337 5136 5611 6794

■ **JA HOLDING INC** p 773
650 5th Ave Fl 20, New York NY 10019
Tel (212) 586-9140 *SIC* 5136

JACHS NY LLC p 773
359 Broadway Fl 3, New York NY 10013
Tel (212) 334-4380 *SIC* 5136

JACKTHREADS INC p 774
568 Broadway Rm 607, New York NY 10012
Tel (646) 786-1980 *SIC* 5136

JOHN VARVATOS ENTERPRISES INC p 789
26 W 17th St Fl 12, New York NY 10011
Tel (212) 812-8000 *SIC* 5136

JORDACHE LIMITED p 793
1400 Broadway Rm 1404b, New York NY 10018
Tel (212) 944-1330 *SIC* 5137 5136 6153

▲ **KATE SPADE & CO** p 804
2 Park Ave Fl 8, New York NY 10016
Tel (212) 354-4900
SIC 2331 5651 5136 5137 5961

LF MENS GROUP LLC p 860
1359 Broadway Fl 21, New York NY 10018
Tel (646) 839-7000 *SIC* 5136

PRADA USA CORP p 1167
609 W 51st St, New York NY 10019
Tel (212) 307-9300
SIC 5136 5137 5139 5661 5632 8741

R SISKIND & CO INC p 1202
1385 Broadway Fl 24, New York NY 10018
Tel (212) 840-0880 *SIC* 5137 5136

REUNITED LLC p 1229
1385 Broadway Fl 22, New York NY 10018
Tel (646) 439-7576 *SIC* 5137 5136

■ **ROBERT GRAHAM DESIGNS LLC** p 1241
264 W 40th St Fl 10, New York NY 10018
Tel (212) 869-8001 *SIC* 5137 5136

■ **TOMMY HILFIGER USA INC** p 1459
601 W 26th St Rm 500, New York NY 10001
Tel (212) 840-8888
SIC 5611 5632 5641 5136 5137 5139

■ **VINCE LLC** p 1557
500 5th Ave Ste 20, New York NY 10110
Tel (212) 515-2600 *SIC* 5137 5136

MORRIS ROTHENBERG & SON INC p 990
3015 Veterans Mem Hwy, Ronkonkoma NY 11779
Tel (631) 585-9446
SIC 5199 5091 5139 5136

TUXEDO JUNCTION INC p 1493
120 Earhart Dr, Williamsville NY 14221
Tel (716) 633-2400 *SIC* 5136 5699 7299

GILDAN ACTIVEWEAR (EDEN) INC p 612
602 E Meadow Rd, Eden NC 27288
Tel (336) 623-9555 *SIC* 5136 5311

BOB BARKER CO INC p 196
134 N Main St, Fuquay Varina NC 27526
Tel (800) 235-8586
SIC 5131 5122 2392 5136 3441

GOLD TOE MORETZ HOLDINGS CORP p 620
2121 Heilig Rd, Salisbury NC 28146
Tel (828) 464-0751 *SIC* 5136 5137 5699

ROYCE TOO LLC p 1254
3330 Healy Dr Ste 200, Winston Salem NC 27103
Tel (212) 356-1627 *SIC* 5137 5136

PROFILL HOLDINGS LLC p 1180
255 W Crescentville Rd, Cincinnati OH 45246
Tel (513) 742-4000
SIC 5199 5136 5137 6798

STANDARD TEXTILE CO INC p 1376
1 Knollcrest Dr, Cincinnati OH 45237
Tel (513) 761-9255
SIC 2389 2326 2337 2211 2391 5136

■ **MAST INDUSTRIES INC** p 917
2 Limited Pkwy, Columbus OH 43230
Tel (614) 415-7000 *SIC* 5137 5136

MGF SOURCING US LLC p 958
4200 Regent St Ste 205, Columbus OH 43219
Tel (614) 904-3269 *SIC* 5137 5136

■ **SAFETY SOLUTIONS INC** p 1266
6161 Shamrock Ct, Dublin OH 43016
Tel (614) 799-9900 *SIC* 5084 5136 5139

HERITAGE SPORTSWEAR INC p 686
102 Reliance Dr, Hebron OH 43025
Tel (740) 928-7771 *SIC* 5136 5137

■ **CINTAS CORP NO 1** p 308
6800 Cintas Blvd, Mason OH 45040
Tel (513) 459-1200
SIC 7213 5136 5137 7549

■ **ABERCROMBIE & FITCH TRADING CO** p 11
6301 Fitch Path, New Albany OH 43054
Tel (614) 283-6500
SIC 5136 5137 5641 5621 5611

CHESTER WEST HOLDINGS INC p 295
11500 Canal Rd, Sharonville OH 45241
Tel (800) 647-1900
SIC 3842 5136 5099 5137 2381

▲ **NIKE INC** p 1043
1 Sw Bowerman Dr, Beaverton OR 97005
Tel (503) 671-6453
SIC 3021 2329 2339 5139 5661 5136

■ **NIKE INTERNATIONAL LTD** p 1043
1 Sw Bowerman Dr, Beaverton OR 97005
Tel (503) 671-6750 *SIC* 5139 5136 5137

ADIDAS AMERICA INC p 22
5055 N Greeley Ave, Portland OR 97217
Tel (971) 234-2300
SIC 5139 5136 5137 3021 2339

■ **COLUMBIA SPORTSWEAR USA CORP** p 341
14375 Nw Science Park Dr, Portland OR 97229
Tel (503) 985-4000
SIC 5137 5136 2329 2339 3021 2353

BOLLMAN HAT CO p 198
110 E Main St, Adamstown PA 19501
Tel (717) 484-4361 *SIC* 2353 5136

ALPHA SHIRT CO p 60
6 Neshaminy Interplex Dr # 6, Feasterville Trevose PA 19053
Tel (215) 291-0300 *SIC* 5136 5137

RADIAL INC p 1204
935 1st Ave, King Of Prussia PA 19406
Tel (610) 491-7000
SIC 3149 5139 5091 5136 5137 7375

■ **SUGARTOWN WORLDWIDE LLC** p 1397
800 3rd Ave, King Of Prussia PA 19406
Tel (610) 878-5550
SIC 2339 2361 5136 5611

▲ **ARAMARK CORP** p 102
1101 Market St Ste 45, Philadelphia PA 19107
Tel (215) 238-3000 *SIC* 5812 7218 5136

■ **ARAMARK INTERMEDIATE HOLDCO CORP** p 102
1101 Market St Ste 45, Philadelphia PA 19107
Tel (215) 238-3000 *SIC* 5812 7218 5136

■ **ARAMARK SERVICES INC** p 102
1101 Market St Ste 45, Philadelphia PA 19107
Tel (215) 238-3000 *SIC* 5812 7218 5136

BODEK AND RHODES INC p 197
2951 Grant Ave, Philadelphia PA 19114
Tel (215) 673-6767 *SIC* 5136 5137

BRODER BROS CO p 216
6 Neshaminy Interplex Dr, Trevose PA 19053
Tel (215) 291-0300 *SIC* 5136 5137

KOMODIDAD DISTRIBUTORS INC p 827
156 Km 58 8, Caguas PR 00727
Tel (787) 746-3188 *SIC* 5137 5136 5094

BASIC SPORTS APPAREL INC p 158
301 Williams St, El Paso TX 79901
Tel (915) 532-0561 *SIC* 5136

MID-WEST TEXTILE CO p 964
1600 E San Antonio Ave, El Paso TX 79901
Tel (915) 351-0231 *SIC* 5093 5137 5136

■ **JA APPAREL CORP** p 772
6380 Rogerdale Rd, Houston TX 77072
Tel (877) 986-9669 *SIC* 5136

WAYNE D ENTERPRISES INC p 1584
14300 Hollister St, Houston TX 77066
Tel (713) 856-0300 *SIC* 5136 5199

BOY SCOUTS OF AMERICA p 205
1325 W Walnut Hill Ln, Irving TX 75038
Tel (972) 580-2000
SIC 8641 5136 5091 2721

■ **J C PENNEY EUROPE INC** p 770
6501 Legacy Dr, Plano TX 75024
Tel (972) 431-1000 *SIC* 5137 5136 5023

■ **J C PENNEY PURCHASING CORP** p 770
6501 Legacy Dr, Plano TX 75024
Tel (972) 431-1000 *SIC* 5137 5136 5023

ATLANTIC COAST COTTON INC p 126
14251 John Marshall Hwy, Gainesville VA 20155
Tel (703) 753-7000 *SIC* 5136 5137

VIRGINIA TS INC p 1560
2001 Anchor Ave, Petersburg VA 23803
Tel (804) 862-2600 *SIC* 5136 5137

SANMAR CORP p 1279
22833 Se Black Nugget Rd, Issaquah WA 98029
Tel (206) 727-3200 *SIC* 5136 5137

WORLDWIDE DISTRIBUTORS p 1626
8211 S 194th St, Kent WA 98032
Tel (253) 872-8746
SIC 5091 5136 5137 5139 5199 5023

GREENSOURCE BRAND APPAREL INC p 638
1020 Sw 34th St, Renton WA 98057
Tel (425) 656-9123 *SIC* 5136 5137

SEATTLE PACIFIC INDUSTRIES INC p 1297
1633 Westlake Ave N # 300, Seattle WA 98109
Tel (253) 872-8822 *SIC* 5136 5137

■ TOMMY BAHAMA GROUP INC p 1459
400 Fairview Ave N # 488, Seattle WA 98109
Tel (206) 622-8688
SIC 7389 5651 5136 5137

■ VIEWPOINT INTERNATIONAL INC p 1556
428 Westlake Ave N # 388, Seattle WA 98109
Tel (206) 622-8688 *SIC* 5136 5137

BENSUSSEN DEUTSCH & ASSOCIATES LLC p 173
15525 Woodinville Rdmnd, Woodinville WA 98072
Tel (425) 492-6111 *SIC* 5199 5136 5137

RIVERS END HOLDINGS LLC p 1237
301 N Broom St Fl 2, Madison WI 53703
Tel (952) 912-2500 *SIC* 5137 5136

SIC 5137 Women's, Children's & Infants Clothing Wholesale

ANTIGUA GROUP INC p 94
16651 N 84th Ave, Peoria AZ 85382
Tel (623) 523-6000
SIC 5137 5136 2395 2339 3993

COPPEL CORP p 368
503 Scaroni Ave, Calexico CA 92231
Tel (760) 357-3707 *SIC* 5021 5137 5136

■ PRANA LIVING LLC p 1167
3209 Lionshead Ave, Carlsbad CA 92010
Tel (866) 915-6457 *SIC* 5136 5137

COLOR IMAGE APPAREL INC p 338
6670 Flotilla St, Commerce CA 90040
Tel (855) 793-3100 *SIC* 5137 5136

HUB DISTRIBUTING INC p 715
1260 Corona Pointe Ct, Corona CA 92879
Tel (951) 340-3149
SIC 5611 5621 5632 5137 5136 5094

■ HURLEY INTERNATIONAL LLC p 721
1945 Placentia Ave, Costa Mesa CA 92627
Tel (949) 548-9375 *SIC* 2329 5137

VOLCOM LLC p 1564
1740 Monrovia Ave, Costa Mesa CA 92627
Tel (949) 646-2175
SIC 7389 2253 7822 5136 5137

TOPSON DOWNS OF CALIFORNIA INC p 1461
3840 Watseka Ave, Culver City CA 90232
Tel (310) 558-0300 *SIC* 5137

HYBRID PROMOTIONS LLC p 723
10711 Walker St, Cypress CA 90630
Tel (714) 952-3866 *SIC* 5136 5137 5611

JAMES PERSE ENTERPRISES INC p 776
7373 Flores St, Downey CA 90242
Tel (323) 588-2226 *SIC* 5136 5137

■ QUIKSILVER INC p 1200
5600 Argosy Ave Ste 100, Huntington Beach CA 92649
Tel (714) 889-2200
SIC 2329 2339 3949 5136 5137

ASICS AMERICA CORP p 117
80 Technology Dr, Irvine CA 92618
Tel (949) 453-8888
SIC 5139 5136 5137 2369 2339 2321

FOX HEAD INC p 572
16752 Armstrong Ave, Irvine CA 92606
Tel (408) 776-8633 *SIC* 5136 5137 5961

SIGNAL PRODUCTS INC p 1322
320 W 31st St, Los Angeles CA 90007
Tel (213) 748-0990 *SIC* 5137

GURU DENIM INC p 648
1888 Rosecrans Ave # 1000, Manhattan Beach CA 90266
Tel (323) 266-3072 *SIC* 5137 5611

▲ WALKING CO HOLDINGS INC p 1573
25 W Anapamu St, Santa Barbara CA 93101
Tel (805) 963-8727
SIC 5651 5961 5136 5137 5699

MIAS FASHION MANUFACTURING CO INC p 959
12623 Cisneros Ln, Santa Fe Springs CA 90670
Tel (562) 906-1060 *SIC* 5137

DORFMAN-PACIFIC CO p 451
2615 Boeing Way, Stockton CA 95206
Tel (209) 982-1400 *SIC* 5136 5137

ARIAT INTERNATIONAL INC p 108
3242 Whipple Rd, Union City CA 94587
Tel (510) 477-7000
SIC 3199 5139 5137 5136

JERRY LEIGH OF CALIFORNIA INC p 783
7860 Nelson Rd, Van Nuys CA 91402
Tel (818) 909-6200 *SIC* 5137

BCBG MAX AZRIA GROUP LLC p 163
2761 Fruitland Ave, Vernon CA 90058
Tel (323) 589-2224 *SIC* 5137 5621 2335

DUTCH LLC p 463
5301 S Santa Fe Ave, Vernon CA 90058
Tel (323) 277-3900 *SIC* 5137

RCRV INC p 1212
4715 S Alameda St, Vernon CA 90058
Tel (323) 235-8070 *SIC* 2673 5137 5136

SWEET PEOPLE APPAREL INC p 1411
4715 S Alameda St, Vernon CA 90058
Tel (323) 235-7300 *SIC* 5137

VINEYARD VINES LLC p 1558
181 Harbor Dr Fl 1, Stamford CT 06902
Tel (203) 661-1803
SIC 5136 5137 5699 5611 5621

TYNDALE ENTERPRISES INVESTMENT CORP p 1496
22341 Sw 66th Ave # 1205, Boca Raton FL 33428
Tel (561) 239-5273 *SIC* 5137

■ WILLIAM CARTER CO p 1610
3438 Peachtree Rd Ne, Atlanta GA 30326
Tel (678) 791-1000 *SIC* 5641 5137

ITS GREEK TO ME INC p 768
520 Mccall Rd Ste A, Manhattan KS 66502
Tel (785) 537-8822
SIC 5136 5699 5137 5947 2759

■ FILA USA INC p 542
930 Ridgebrook Rd Ste 200, Sparks MD 21152
Tel (410) 773-3000
SIC 5139 5131 5137 5611 5621 5632

TALBOTS INC p 1422
1 Talbots Dr Ste 1, Hingham MA 02043
Tel (781) 749-7600
SIC 5621 5137 5632 5641

CAUSE FOR CHANGE LLC p 267
370 Hudson Rd, Sudbury MA 01776
Tel (617) 571-6990 *SIC* 5137

PUMA NORTH AMERICA INC p 1192
10 Lyberty Way, Westford MA 01886
Tel (978) 698-1000
SIC 5136 5139 8741 5137

ACCESS BUSINESS GROUP LLC p 14
7575 Fulton St E, Ada MI 49355
Tel (616) 787-6000
SIC 5169 2842 5122 2833 5136 5137

ALTICOR GLOBAL HOLDINGS INC p 62
7575 Fulton St E, Ada MI 49301
Tel (616) 787-1000
SIC 5169 5122 2833 5136 5137 5021

ALTICOR INC p 62
7575 Fulton St E, Ada MI 49355
Tel (616) 787-1000
SIC 5169 5122 2833 5136 5137 5021

KELLWOOD CO LLC p 809
600 Kellwood Pkwy Ste 200, Chesterfield MO 63017
Tel (314) 576-3100 *SIC* 5136 5137

NASSIRI INC p 1009
2035 Helm Dr, Las Vegas NV 89119
Tel (702) 837-7332 *SIC* 5136 5137

HADDAD APPAREL GROUP LTD p 652
90 E 5th St Ste 1, Bayonne NJ 07002
Tel (201) 356-2000 *SIC* 5137

ESCADA US SUBCO LLC p 509
26 Main St, Chatham NJ 07928
Tel (212) 852-5300
SIC 5137 5621 5632 5099

UBI LIQUIDATING CORP p 1498
300 Nixon Ln, Edison NJ 08837
Tel (201) 319-9093
SIC 5621 5641 5651 5137 5632

WICKED FASHIONS INC p 1608
222 Bridge Plz S, Fort Lee NJ 07024
Tel (201) 242-5909 *SIC* 5137 5136

STEVE SELVIN ASSOCIATES INC p 1388
207 Union St, Hackensack NJ 07601
Tel (201) 488-3332 *SIC* 5136 5137

CHARLES KOMAR & SONS INC p 289
16 E 34th St Fl 10, Jersey City NJ 07308
Tel (212) 725-1500 *SIC* 2341 2384 5137

■ QUIDSI INC p 1199
10 Exchange Pl Fl 25, Jersey City NJ 07302
Tel (973) 509-5444 *SIC* 5137

■ VF SPORTSWEAR INC p 1553
545 Wshngton Blvd Fl 8, Jersey City NJ 07310
Tel (212) 541-5757
SIC 2329 2384 5136 5137 5611 6794

■ LCI HOLDINGS INC p 849
5901 W Side Ave, North Bergen NJ 07047
Tel (201) 295-6300
SIC 5651 5136 5137 5094 5122 5944

FERRAGAMO U S A INC p 538
700 Castle Rd, Secaucus NJ 07094
Tel (201) 553-6100
SIC 5139 5136 5137 5621 5632

TRI-COASTAL DESIGN GROUP INC p 1477
40 Harry Shupe Blvd, Wharton NJ 07885
Tel (973) 560-0300 *SIC* 5137 5199

ADRIANNA PAPELL LLC p 24
500 7th Ave Fl 10a, New York NY 10018
Tel (212) 695-5244 *SIC* 5137

AGE GROUP LTD p 34
2 Park Ave Fl 18, New York NY 10016
Tel (212) 213-9500 *SIC* 5137

AMEREX GROUP INC p 66
512 Fashion Ave Fl 9, New York NY 10018
Tel (212) 221-3151 *SIC* 5137 5136

AMERICAN MARKETING ENTERPRISES INC p 75
Empir State Bldg 350fif, New York NY 10018
Tel (646) 839-7000 *SIC* 5137

ANVIL HOLDINGS INC p 94
228 E 45th St Fl 4, New York NY 10017
Tel (843) 774-8211 *SIC* 5137

▲ AVON PRODUCTS INC p 139
777 3rd Ave, New York NY 10017
Tel (212) 282-5000
SIC 2844 3961 5961 5023 5137

BRAVADO INTERNATIONAL GROUP MERCHANDISING SERVICES INC p 209
1755 Broadway Fl 2, New York NY 10019
Tel (212) 445-3400
SIC 5136 5137 5611 5621

■ CALVIN KLEIN INC p 243
205 W 39th St Lbby 2, New York NY 10018
Tel (212) 719-2600
SIC 5651 5137 5136 5611 5621 6794

CAYRE GROUP LTD p 268
1407 Broadway Fl 41, New York NY 10018
Tel (212) 789-7000 *SIC* 5137

CELEBRITY INTERNATIONAL INC p 273
10 W 33rd St Rm 910, New York NY 10001
Tel (212) 279-1616 *SIC* 5137

COACH STORES INC p 331
516 W 34th St Bsmt 5, New York NY 10001
Tel (212) 643-9727
SIC 3171 3161 3172 2387 5137 5099

CONNAUGHT GROUP LTD p 356
423 W 55th St Fl 3, New York NY 10019
Tel (212) 315-4486 *SIC* 5137

DIESEL USA INC p 438
220 W 19th St Fl 5, New York NY 10011
Tel (212) 755-9200
SIC 5137 5136 5621 5632 5611

E S SUTTON INC p 467
1400 Broadway Fl 26, New York NY 10018
Tel (212) 944-9494 *SIC* 5137

E-LO SPORTSWEAR LLC p 467
500 Fashion Ave, New York NY 10018
Tel (862) 902-5225 *SIC* 5137 5621

ELIAS BEN INDUSTRIES CORP p 487
550 Fashion Ave Fl 12, New York NY 10018
Tel (212) 354-8300 *SIC* 5137 5136

FASHION AVENUE KNITS INC p 531
525 Fashion Ave Fl 4, New York NY 10018
Tel (718) 456-9000 *SIC* 5137

FOWNES BROTHERS & CO INC p 572
16 E 34th St Fl 5, New York NY 10016
Tel (212) 683-0150
SIC 3151 2381 5136 5137 3949

FREE COUNTRY LTD p 576
1071 6th Ave Fl 9, New York NY 10018
Tel (212) 719-4596 *SIC* 5136 5137

GBG ACCESSORIES GROUP LLC p 594
350 5th Ave Lbby 9, New York NY 10118
Tel (646) 839-7000 *SIC* 5137

GBG USA INC p 594
350 5th Ave Lbby 9, New York NY 10118
Tel (646) 839-7083 *SIC* 5139 5137 5136

GCE INTERNATIONAL INC p 595
1385 Broadway Fl 21, New York NY 10018
Tel (212) 704-4800
SIC 2253 2389 2331 5137 5136

GIORGIO ARMANI CORP p 612
450 W 15th St 3, New York NY 10011
Tel (212) 209-3500
SIC 5136 5137 5122 5611 5621 5632

GIRL SCOUTS OF UNITED STATES OF AMERICA p 613
420 5th Ave Fl 13, New York NY 10018
Tel (212) 852-8000
SIC 8641 5137 6794 2721

GLOBAL BRANDS HOLDING GROUP LLC p 615
350 5th Ave, New York NY 10118
Tel (646) 839-7000 *SIC* 5136 5137 5139

GMA ACCESSORIES INC p 618
1 E 33rd St Fl 9, New York NY 10016
Tel (212) 684-3344 *SIC* 5137 5139

GUCCI AMERICA INC p 645
195 Broadway Fl 12, New York NY 10007
Tel (212) 750-5220
SIC 5632 5948 5661 5611 5621 5137

HANKY PANKY LTD p 658
373 Park Ave S Fl 12, New York NY 10016
Tel (212) 725-4996 *SIC* 5137

HIS INTERNATIONAL CORP p 696
34 W 33rd St Fl 2, New York NY 10001
Tel (212) 594-4250 *SIC* 5137

JACQUES MORET INC p 775
1411 Broadway Fl 8, New York NY 10018
Tel (212) 354-2400 *SIC* 2339 5137

JONES GROUP INC p 792
1411 Broadway Fl 15, New York NY 10018
Tel (212) 642-3860
SIC 5632 5137 5139 5661 5641

JONES HOLDINGS LLC p 792
1411 Brdwy, New York NY 10018
Tel (215) 785-4000 *SIC* 5137

JORDACHE LIMITED p 793
1400 Broadway Rm 1404b, New York NY 10018
Tel (212) 944-1330 *SIC* 5137 5136 6153

▲ KATE SPADE & CO p 804
2 Park Ave Fl 8, New York NY 10016
Tel (212) 354-4900
SIC 2331 5651 5136 5137 5961

■ KATE SPADE LLC p 804
2 Park Ave Fl 8, New York NY 10016
Tel (201) 295-6000 *SIC* 5137 5632

LAFAYETTE 148 INC p 837
148 Lafayette St Fl 2, New York NY 10013
Tel (646) 708-7010 *SIC* 5137

LOUISE PARIS LTD p 880
1407 Broadway Rm 1405, New York NY 10018
Tel (212) 354-5411 *SIC* 5137

MAMIYE BROTHERS INC p 900
1385 Brdwy Fl 18, New York NY 10018
Tel (212) 279-4150 *SIC* 5137

MICHAEL KORS (USA) INC p 960
11 W 42nd St Fl 20, New York NY 10036
Tel (212) 201-8100 *SIC* 5137 5651 5621

MYSTIC APPAREL LLC p 1005
1333 Broadway Fl 6, New York NY 10018
Tel (212) 279-2466 *SIC* 5021 5137

NURTURE INC p 1067
40 Fulton St Fl 17, New York NY 10038
Tel (212) 374-2779 *SIC* 5137

OSCAR DE LA RENTA LLC p 1096
11 W 42nd St Fl 24, New York NY 10036
Tel (212) 282-0500 *SIC* 5137

PAPER CUT CLOTHING LLC p 1112
499 7th Ave Frnt 2, New York NY 10018
Tel (917) 475-9356 *SIC* 5137

PARIGI GROUP LTD p 1114
20 W 33rd St Fl 12, New York NY 10001
Tel (212) 736-0688 *SIC* 5137

PRADA USA CORP p 1167
609 W 51st St, New York NY 10019
Tel (212) 307-9300
SIC 5136 5137 5139 5661 5632 8741

R SISKIND & CO INC p 1202
1385 Broadway Fl 24, New York NY 10018
Tel (212) 840-0880 *SIC* 5137 5136

REUNITED LLC p 1229
1385 Broadway Fl 22, New York NY 10018
Tel (646) 439-7576 *SIC* 5137 5136

■ ROBERT GRAHAM DESIGNS LLC p 1241
264 W 40th St Fl 10, New York NY 10018
Tel (212) 869-8001 *SIC* 5137 5136

■ TOMMY HILFIGER USA INC p 1459
601 W 26th St Rm 500, New York NY 10001
Tel (212) 840-8888
SIC 5611 5632 5641 5136 5137 5139

■ VINCE LLC p 1557
500 5th Ave Ste 20, New York NY 10110
Tel (212) 515-2600 *SIC* 5137 5136

▲ CATO CORP p 267
8100 Denmark Rd, Charlotte NC 28273
Tel (704) 554-8510
SIC 5621 5632 5137 5699 5311 5641

GOLD TOE MORETZ HOLDINGS CORP p 620
2121 Heilig Rd, Salisbury NC 28146
Tel (828) 464-0751 *SIC* 5136 5137 5699

■ MAIDENFORM LLC p 897
1000 E Hanes Mill Rd, Winston Salem NC 27105
Tel (336) 519-8080 *SIC* 5137

ROYCE TOO LLC p 1254
3330 Healy Dr Ste 200, Winston Salem NC 27103
Tel (212) 356-1627 *SIC* 5137 5136

ATRIUM BUYING CORP p 129
1010 Jackson Hole Dr # 100, Blacklick OH 43004
Tel (740) 966-8200 *SIC* 5137

■ PROCTER & GAMBLE DISTRIBUTING LLC p 1179
1 Procter And Gamble Plz, Cincinnati OH 45202
Tel (513) 983-1100
SIC 5169 5122 5149 5113 5137

PROFILL HOLDINGS LLC p 1180
255 W Crescentville Rd, Cincinnati OH 45246
Tel (513) 742-4000
SIC 5199 5136 5137 6798

PHILIPS MEDICAL SYSTEMS (CLEVELAND) INC p 1143
595 Miner Rd, Cleveland OH 44143
Tel (440) 247-2652
SIC 3844 5047 5137 3842 3821 3699

■ MAST INDUSTRIES INC p 917
2 Limited Pkwy, Columbus OH 43230
Tel (614) 415-7000 *SIC* 5137 5136

MGF SOURCING US LLC p 958
4200 Regent St Ste 205, Columbus OH 43219
Tel (614) 904-3269 *SIC* 5137 5136

HERITAGE SPORTSWEAR INC p 686
102 Reliance Dr, Hebron OH 43025
Tel (740) 928-7771 *SIC* 5136 5137

■ CINTAS CORP NO 1 p 308
6800 Cintas Blvd, Mason OH 45040
Tel (513) 459-1200
SIC 7213 5136 5137 7549

■ ABERCROMBIE & FITCH TRADING CO p 11
6301 Fitch Path, New Albany OH 43054
Tel (614) 283-6500
SIC 5136 5137 5641 5621 5611

■ TWEEN BRANDS SERVICE CO p 1494
8323 Walton Pkwy, New Albany OH 43054
Tel (614) 775-3500 *SIC* 5137

CHESTERWEST HOLDINGS INC p 295
11500 Canal Rd, Sharonville OH 45241
Tel (800) 647-1900
SIC 3842 5136 5099 5137 2381

■ NIKE INTERNATIONAL LTD p 1043
1 Sw Bowerman Dr, Beaverton OR 97005
Tel (503) 671-6750 *SIC* 5139 5136 5137

ADIDAS AMERICA INC p 22
5055 N Greeley Ave, Portland OR 97217
Tel (971) 234-2300
SIC 5139 5136 5137 3021 2339

■ COLUMBIA SPORTSWEAR USA CORP p 341
14375 Nw Science Park Dr, Portland OR 97229
Tel (503) 985-4000
SIC 5137 5136 2329 2339 3021 2353

ALPHA SHIRT CO p 60
6 Neshaminy Interplex Dr # 6, Feasterville Trevose PA 19053
Tel (215) 291-0300 *SIC* 5136 5137

RADIAL INC p 1204
935 1st Ave, King Of Prussia PA 19406
Tel (610) 491-7000
SIC 3149 5139 5091 5136 5137 7375

BODEK AND RHODES INC p 197
2951 Grant Ave, Philadelphia PA 19114
Tel (215) 673-6767 *SIC* 5136 5137

▲ URBAN OUTFITTERS INC p 1530
5000 S Broad St, Philadelphia PA 19112
Tel (215) 454-5500
SIC 5621 5611 5632 5661 5719 5137

BRODER BROS CO p 216
6 Neshaminy Interplex Dr, Trevose PA 19053
Tel (215) 291-0300 *SIC* 5136 5137

KOMODIDAD DISTRIBUTORS INC p 827
156 Km 58 8, Caguas PR 00727
Tel (787) 746-3188 *SIC* 5137 5136 5094

■ SEAMLESS TEXTILES LLC p 1297
Km 86 3 Rr 3, Humacao PR 00791
Tel (787) 850-3440 *SIC* 5137

SHELBY GROUP INTERNATIONAL INC p 1314
1255 W Schilling Blvd, Collierville TN 38017
Tel (901) 795-5810
SIC 3842 2381 3851 5137

■ FIBERWEB INC p 539
9335 Harris Corners Pkwy, Old Hickory TN 37138
Tel (704) 697-5100 *SIC* 2281 5047 5137

MID-WEST TEXTILE CO p 964
1600 E San Antonio Ave, El Paso TX 79901
Tel (915) 351-0231 *SIC* 5093 5137 5136

▲ SYSCO CORP p 1417
1390 Enclave Pkwy, Houston TX 77077
Tel (281) 584-1390
SIC 5149 5142 5143 5144 5148 5137

■ J C PENNEY EUROPE INC p 770
6501 Legacy Dr, Plano TX 75024
Tel (972) 431-1000 *SIC* 5137 5136 5023

■ J C PENNEY PURCHASING CORP p 770
6501 Legacy Dr, Plano TX 75024
Tel (972) 431-1000 *SIC* 5137 5136 5023

■ **FOSSIL PARTNERS LP** p 570
901 S Central Expy, Richardson TX 75080
Tel (972) 234-2525
SIC 5137 2389 2339 5094

CORNELL TRADING INC p 370
131 Battery St, Burlington VT 05401
Tel (802) 879-1271
SIC 5023 5137 5719 5621

ATLANTIC COAST COTTON INC p 126
14251 John Marshall Hwy, Gainesville VA 20155
Tel (703) 753-7000 SIC 5136 5137

VIRGINIA TS INC p 1560
2001 Anchor Ave, Petersburg VA 23803
Tel (804) 862-2600 SIC 5136 5137

SANMAR CORP p 1279
22833 Se Black Nugget Rd, Issaquah WA 98029
Tel (206) 727-3200 SIC 5136 5137

WORLDWIDE DISTRIBUTORS p 1626
8211 S 194th St, Kent WA 98032
Tel (253) 872-8746
SIC 5091 5136 5137 5139 5199 5023

GREENSOURCE BRAND APPAREL INC p 638
1020 Sw 34th St, Renton WA 98057
Tel (425) 656-9123 SIC 5136 5137

SEATTLE PACIFIC INDUSTRIES INC p 1297
1633 Westlake Ave N # 300, Seattle WA 98109
Tel (253) 872-8822 SIC 5136 5137

■ **TOMMY BAHAMA GROUP INC** p 1459
400 Fairview Ave N # 488, Seattle WA 98109
Tel (206) 622-8688
SIC 7389 5651 5136 5137

■ **VIEWPOINT INTERNATIONAL INC** p 1556
428 Westlake Ave N # 388, Seattle WA 98109
Tel (206) 622-8688 SIC 5136 5137

HELLY HANSEN (US) INC p 682
14218 Stewart Rd Ste 100a, Sumner WA 98390
Tel (800) 435-5901
SIC 5137 5699 2339 2329

LULULEMON USA INC p 885
2201 140th Ave E, Sumner WA 98390
Tel (604) 732-6124 SIC 5137 5331

BENSUSSEN DEUTSCH & ASSOCIATES LLC p 173
15525 Woodinville Rdmnd, Woodinville WA 98072
Tel (425) 492-6111 SIC 5199 5136 5137

RIVERS END HOLDINGS LLC p 1237
301 N Broom St Fl 2, Madison WI 53703
Tel (952) 912-2500 SIC 5137 5136

SIC 5139 Footwear Wholesale

STRATEGIC PARTNERS INC p 1392
9800 De Soto Ave, Chatsworth CA 91311
Tel (818) 671-2100
SIC 3143 3144 5139 2339 2389 2329

ROMEO & JULIETTE INC p 1249
7524 Old Auburn Rd, Citrus Heights CA 95610
Tel (916) 726-4413 SIC 5139

511 INC p 3
1360 Reynolds Ave Ste 101, Irvine CA 92614
Tel (949) 800-1511
SIC 5699 2231 5139 2393

ASICS AMERICA CORP p 117
80 Technology Dr, Irvine CA 92618
Tel (949) 453-8888
SIC 5139 5136 5137 2369 2339 2321

UNION SUPPLY GROUP INC p 1505
2301 E Pacifica Pl, Rancho Dominguez CA 90220
Tel (310) 603-8899 SIC 5141 5139 5136

ARIAT INTERNATIONAL INC p 108
3242 Whipple Rd, Union City CA 94587
Tel (510) 477-7000
SIC 3199 5139 5137 5136

HTM USA HOLDINGS INC p 715
3125 Sterling Cir Ste 101, Boulder CO 80301
Tel (800) 874-3235 SIC 5091 5139 3949

▲ **CROCS INC** p 393
7477 Dry Creek Pkwy, Niwot CO 80503
Tel (303) 848-7000
SIC 3021 5139 3069 5661 2389

CAMUTO GROUP LLC p 246
411 W Putnam Ave Ste 210, Greenwich CT 06830
Tel (203) 413-7100 SIC 5139

JAG FOOTWEAR ACCESSORIES AND RETAIL CORP p 776
411 W Putnam Ave Fl 3, Greenwich CT 06830
Tel (239) 301-3001 SIC 5139

VCS GROUP LLC p 1545
411 W Putnam Ave Ste 210, Greenwich CT 06830
Tel (203) 413-6500 SIC 5139

SHOES FOR CREWS LLC p 1317
250 S Australian Ave # 1700, West Palm Beach FL 33401
Tel (561) 683-5090 SIC 5139

BENCHMARK BRANDS INC p 172
1375 Peachtree St Ne Fl 6, Atlanta GA 30309
Tel (770) 242-1254 SIC 5139

■ **FILA USA INC** p 542
930 Ridgebrook Rd Ste 200, Sparks MD 21152
Tel (410) 773-3000
SIC 5139 5131 5137 5611 5621 5632

■ **CONVERSE INC** p 365
1 Love Joy Wharf, Boston MA 02114
Tel (978) 983-3300 SIC 5139 5661

NEW BALANCE INC p 1029
100 Guest St, Brighton MA 02135
Tel (617) 783-4000 SIC 5139

C & J CLARK AMERICA INC p 231
60 Tower Rd, Waltham MA 02451
Tel (617) 964-1222 SIC 3143 5139 5661

CLARKS AMERICAS INC p 322
60 Tower Rd, Waltham MA 02451
Tel (617) 796-5000 SIC 5661 5139

■ **KEDS LLC** p 807
500 Totten Pond Rd Ste 1, Waltham MA 02451
Tel (617) 824-6000 SIC 5139 5661

■ **STRIDE RITE CHILDRENS GROUP LLC** p 1393
500 Totten Pond Rd Ste 1, Waltham MA 02451
Tel (617) 824-6000 SIC 5139 5661

■ **STRIDE RITE CORP** p 1393
500 Totten Pond Rd Ste 1, Waltham MA 02451
Tel (617) 824-6000 SIC 5139 5661 3149

PUMA NORTH AMERICA INC p 1192
10 Lyberty Way, Westford MA 01886
Tel (978) 698-1000
SIC 5136 5139 8741 5137

▲ **CALERES INC** p 238
8300 Maryland Ave, Saint Louis MO 63105
Tel (314) 854-4000 SIC 5661 5139

ECCO USA INC p 475
16 Delta Dr, Londonderry NH 03053
Tel (603) 537-7300 SIC 5139 5661

AEROGROUP INTERNATIONAL INC p 30
201 Meadow Rd, Edison NJ 08817
Tel (732) 985-6900 SIC 5139 5661

■ **SYSCO GUEST SUPPLY LLC** p 1417
4301 Us Highway 1 Ste 300, Monmouth Junction NJ 08852
Tel (609) 514-9696
SIC 5122 2844 5131 5139 7011 8741

ARAMSCO INC p 102
1480 Grandview Ave, Paulsboro NJ 08066
Tel (856) 686-7700
SIC 5085 5084 5136 5139

FERRAGAMO U S A INC p 538
700 Castle Rd, Secaucus NJ 07094
Tel (201) 553-6100
SIC 5139 5136 5137 5621 5632

ARAMSCO HOLDINGS INC p 102
1480 Grand View Ave, Thorofare NJ 08086
Tel (856) 686-7700
SIC 5085 5136 5084 5139

INFINITY CLASSICS INTERNATIONAL INC p 741
1368 38th St, Brooklyn NY 11218
Tel (718) 851-2577 SIC 5139

GBG USA INC p 594
350 5th Ave Lbby 9, New York NY 10118
Tel (646) 839-7083 SIC 5139 5137 5136

GLOBAL BRANDS HOLDING GROUP LLC p 615
350 5th Ave, New York NY 10118
Tel (646) 839-7000 SIC 5136 5137 5139

GMA ACCESSORIES INC p 618
1 E 33rd St Fl 9, New York NY 10016
Tel (212) 684-3344 SIC 5137 5139

JIMLAR CORP p 785
350 5th Ave Lbby 8, New York NY 10118
Tel (212) 475-0787 SIC 5139

JONES GROUP INC p 792
1411 Broadway Fl 15, New York NY 10018
Tel (212) 642-3860
SIC 5632 5137 5139 5661 5641

NINE WEST FOOTWEAR CORP p 1044
1411 Broadway Fl 20, New York NY 10018
Tel (800) 999-1877
SIC 3144 3171 5661 5632 5139

PRADA USA CORP p 1167
609 W 51st St, New York NY 10019
Tel (212) 307-9300
SIC 5136 5137 5139 5661 5632 8741

■ **TOMMY HILFIGER USA INC** p 1459
601 W 26th St Rm 500, New York NY 10001
Tel (212) 840-8888
SIC 5611 5632 5641 5136 5137 5139

WIESNER PRODUCTS INC p 1608
1333 Brdwy Fl 6, New York NY 10018
Tel (212) 279-2466 SIC 5139 2252

MORRIS ROTHENBERG & SON INC p 990
3015 Veterans Mem Hwy, Ronkonkoma NY 11779
Tel (631) 585-9446
SIC 5199 5091 5139 5136

IMPLUS FOOTCARE LLC p 735
2001 Tw Alexander Dr, Durham NC 27709
Tel (919) 544-7900 SIC 5139

JAY GROUP LTD p 779
1450 Atlantic Ave, Rocky Mount NC 27801
Tel (252) 442-2139 SIC 5139

■ **SAFETY SOLUTIONS INC** p 1266
6161 Shamrock Ct, Dublin OH 43016
Tel (614) 799-9900 SIC 5084 5136 5139

■ **LEHIGH OUTFITTERS LLC** p 853
39 E Canal St, Nelsonville OH 45764
Tel (740) 753-1951 SIC 5661 5139

▲ **NIKE INC** p 1043
1 Sw Bowerman Dr, Beaverton OR 97005
Tel (503) 671-6453
SIC 3021 2329 2339 5139 5661 5136

■ **NIKE INTERNATIONAL LTD** p 1043
1 Sw Bowerman Dr, Beaverton OR 97005
Tel (503) 671-6750 SIC 5139 5136 5137

ADIDAS AMERICA INC p 22
5055 N Greeley Ave, Portland OR 97217
Tel (971) 234-2300
SIC 5139 5136 5137 3021 2339

KEEN INC p 807
515 Nw 13th Ave, Portland OR 97209
Tel (503) 402-1520 SIC 5139 5661

RADIAL INC p 1204
935 1st Ave, King Of Prussia PA 19406
Tel (610) 491-7000
SIC 3149 5139 5091 5136 5137 7375

IRON AGE HOLDINGS CORP p 764
3 Robinson Plz Ste 300, Pittsburgh PA 15205
Tel (412) 788-0888
SIC 5139 5661 3143 3144

DANSKO HOLDINGS INC p 412
33 Federal Rd, West Grove PA 19390
Tel (610) 869-8335 SIC 5139

▲ **GENESCO INC** p 602
1415 Murfreesboro Pike, Nashville TN 37217
Tel (615) 367-7000 SIC 5661 5139 5961

SAN ANTONIO SHOE INC p 1275
1717 Sas Dr, San Antonio TX 78224
Tel (877) 727-7463
SIC 3131 5661 5139 5632 3144

WORLDWIDE DISTRIBUTORS p 1626
8211 S 194th St, Kent WA 98032
Tel (253) 872-8746
SIC 5091 5136 5137 5139 5199 5023

■ **BROOKS SPORTS INC** p 218
3400 Stone Way N Ste 500, Seattle WA 98103
Tel (425) 488-3131 SIC 5139

▲ **WEYCO GROUP INC** p 1603
333 W Estabrook Blvd # 1, Glendale WI 53212
Tel (414) 908-1600 SIC 5139 5661

SIC 5141 Groceries, General Line Wholesale

ASSOCIATED GROCERS OF SOUTH INC p 120
3600 Vanderbilt Rd, Birmingham AL 35217
Tel (205) 841-6781 SIC 5141 5411

CITY WHOLESALE GROCERY CO INC p 320
300 Industrial Dr, Birmingham AL 35211
Tel (205) 795-4533
SIC 5194 5141 5145 5122

WOOD-FRUITTICHER GROCERY CO INC p 1622
2900 Alton Rd, Irondale AL 35210
Tel (205) 836-9663
SIC 5142 5141 5147 5087 5046

W L PETREY WHOLESALE CO INC p 1568
10345 Petrey Hwy, Luverne AL 36049
Tel (334) 230-5674 SIC 5141 5194

W L HALSEY GROCERY CO INC p 1568
401 Lanier Rd, Madison AL 35758
Tel (256) 772-9691 SIC 5141

RED DIAMOND INC p 1215
400 Park Ave, Moody AL 35004
Tel (205) 577-4000 SIC 5141 2095 2099

SOUTHEASTERN FOOD MERCHANDISERS INC p 1346
201 Parker Dr, Pelham AL 35124
Tel (205) 664-3322 SIC 5141

SAFEWAY SELECT GIFT SOURCE INC p 1267
6401 A St, Anchorage AK 99518
Tel (907) 561-1944 SIC 5411 5141 5921

■ **MCLANE/SUNWEST INC** p 931
14149 W Mcdowell Rd, Goodyear AZ 85395
Tel (623) 935-7500 SIC 5141

■ **ADVANTAGE LOGISTICS SOUTHWEST INC** p 26
5305 W Buckeye Rd, Phoenix AZ 85043
Tel (602) 477-3100 SIC 5141

FACTOR SALES INC p 523
676 N Archibald St, San Luis AZ 85349
Tel (928) 627-8033 SIC 5411 5651 5141

FOOD SERVICES OF AMERICA INC p 564
16100 N 71st St Ste 400, Scottsdale AZ 85254
Tel (480) 927-4000
SIC 5148 5142 5146 5141

SERVICES GROUP OF AMERICA INC p 1308
16100 N 71st St Ste 500, Scottsdale AZ 85254
Tel (480) 927-4000
SIC 5141 5148 6331 6552

PREMIER CONCEPTS SC p 1170
2701 Se J St, Bentonville AR 72712
Tel (479) 271-6000 SIC 5141

■ **FORREST CITY GROCERY CO** p 568
3400 Commerce Rd, Forrest City AR 72335
Tel (870) 633-2044 SIC 5141 5993

■ **PFG BROADLINE HOLDINGS LLC** p 1140
4901 Asher Ave, Little Rock AR 72204
Tel (501) 568-3141
SIC 5149 5148 5147 5141

ADVANTAGE-CROWN SALES & MARKETING LLC p 27
1400 S Douglass Rd # 200, Anaheim CA 92806
Tel (714) 780-3000 SIC 5141

PERRIN BERNARD SUPOWITZ INC p 1137
5496 Lindbergh Ln, Bell CA 90201
Tel (323) 981-2800 SIC 5141

BI-RITE RESTAURANT SUPPLY CO INC p 180
123 S Hill Dr, Brisbane CA 94005
Tel (415) 656-0187
SIC 5141 5147 5148 5023 5046 5963

HOUWELING NURSERIES OXNARD INC p 712
645 Laguna Rd, Camarillo CA 93012
Tel (805) 488-8832 SIC 5141

JACMAR COMPANIES p 775
300 Baldwin Park Blvd, City Of Industry CA 91746
Tel (800) 834-8806 SIC 5141 5812 6552

MARQUEZ BROTHERS ENTERPRISES INC p 910
15480 Valley Blvd, City Of Industry CA 91746
Tel (626) 330-3310 SIC 5141

MERCADO LATINO INC p 943
245 Baldwin Park Blvd, City Of Industry CA 91746
Tel (626) 333-6862 SIC 5141 5148

■ **AMERIFOODS TRADING CO LLC** p 82
600 Citadel Dr, Commerce CA 90040
Tel (323) 869-7500 SIC 5141

GROCERS SPECIALTY CO p 641
5200 Sheila St, Commerce CA 90040
Tel (323) 264-5200 SIC 5141

■ **SMART & FINAL INC** p 1332
600 Citadel Dr, Commerce CA 90040
Tel (323) 869-7500 SIC 5141 5411

UNIFIED GROCERS INC p 1503
5200 Sheila St, Commerce CA 90040
Tel (323) 264-5200 SIC 5141 6331

GOURMET FOODS INC p 627
2910 E Harcourt St, Compton CA 90221
Tel (310) 632-3300 SIC 5141 5812 2099

RIO VISTA VENTURES LLC p 1236
15651 Old Milky Way, Escondido CA 92027
Tel (760) 480-8502 SIC 5141

■ **SYSCO SAN FRANCISCO INC** p 1418
5900 Stewart Ave, Fremont CA 94538
Tel (510) 226-3000 SIC 5141 5147 5142

SALADINOS INC p 1271
3325 W Figarden Dr, Fresno CA 93711
Tel (559) 271-3700 SIC 5141 2099

PULMUONE FOODS USA INC p 1191
2315 Moore Ave, Fullerton CA 92833
Tel (714) 578-2800 SIC 5149 5141 2075

PULMUONE USA INC p 1191
2315 Moore Ave, Fullerton CA 92833
Tel (714) 578-2800 SIC 5149 5141 2075

VIELE & SONS INC p 1556
1820 E Valencia Dr, Fullerton CA 92831
Tel (714) 446-1686 SIC 5141

ADVANTAGE SALES & MARKETING INC p 26
18100 Von Karman Ave # 900, Irvine CA 92612
Tel (949) 797-2900 SIC 5141

ADVANTAGE SALES & MARKETING LLC p 26
18100 Von Karman Ave # 900, Irvine CA 92612
Tel (949) 797-2900 SIC 5141 8732

ALS TESTING SERVICES GROUP INC p 61
818 W 7th St Ste 930, Los Angeles CA 90017
Tel (213) 627-8252 SIC 5141 5072 5084

CANTON FOOD CO INC p 247
750 S Alameda St, Los Angeles CA 90021
Tel (213) 688-7707
SIC 5141 5146 5411 5421 5149 4222

MUTUAL TRADING CO INC p 1003
431 Crocker St, Los Angeles CA 90013
Tel (213) 626-9458 SIC 5149 5141 5023

SMART & FINAL HOLDINGS LLC p 1332
10205 Constellation Blvd, Los Angeles CA 90067
Tel (310) 843-1900 SIC 5141 5411

TAPIA ENTERPRISES INC p 1424
6067 District Blvd, Maywood CA 90270
Tel (323) 560-7415 SIC 5141

■ **MCLANE/PACIFIC INC** p 931
3876 E Childs Ave, Merced CA 95341
Tel (209) 725-2500 SIC 5141

SAVE MART SUPERMARKETS p 1284
1800 Standiford Ave, Modesto CA 95350
Tel (209) 577-1600
SIC 5411 5141 4213 4212

OTIS MCALLISTER INC p 1097
300 Frank H Ogawa Plz # 400, Oakland CA 94612
Tel (415) 421-6010 SIC 5149 5141

SHOEI FOODS USA INC p 1317
1900 Feather River Blvd, Olivehurst CA 95961
Tel (530) 742-7866 SIC 5141

CONCORD FOODS INC p 354
4601 E Guasti Rd, Ontario CA 91761
Tel (909) 975-2000 SIC 5141

DPI SPECIALTY FOODS WEST INC p 454
601 S Rockefeller Ave, Ontario CA 91761
Tel (909) 975-1019 SIC 5141

MEGAMEX FOODS LLC p 940
333 S Anita Dr Ste 1000, Orange CA 92868
Tel (714) 385-4500 SIC 5141

■ **VENTURA SYSCO INC** p 1548
3100 Sturgis Rd, Oxnard CA 93030
Tel (805) 205-7000 SIC 5141

■ **SYSCO SACRAMENTO INC** p 1418
7062 Pacific Ave, Pleasant Grove CA 95668
Tel (916) 275-2714 SIC 5141 5142

NORTHERN CALIFORNIA TPG INC p 1055
6673 Owens Dr, Pleasanton CA 94588
Tel (925) 556-0512 SIC 5141

■ **SYSCO SAN DIEGO INC** p 1418
12180 Kirkham Rd, Poway CA 92064
Tel (858) 513-7300
SIC 5141 5142 5147 5148 5084

NONGSHIM AMERICA INC p 1047
12155 6th St, Rancho Cucamonga CA 91730
Tel (909) 481-3698 SIC 5141 2098

UNION SUPPLY GROUP INC p 1505
2301 E Pacifica Pl, Rancho Dominguez CA 90220
Tel (310) 603-8899 SIC 5141 5139 5136

BICARA LTD p 181
1611 S Catalina Ave, Redondo Beach CA 90277
Tel (310) 316-6222 SIC 5147 5146 5141

■ **UNITED NATURAL FOODS WEST INC** p 1510
1101 Sunset Blvd, Rocklin CA 95765
Tel (401) 528-8634 SIC 5149 5141

LEE BROS FOODSERVICES INC p 851
660 E Gish Rd, San Jose CA 95112
Tel (408) 275-0700 SIC 5141 5142

PACIFIC GROSERVICE INC p 1104
567 Cinnabar St, San Jose CA 95110
Tel (408) 727-4826
SIC 5194 5145 5141 5113 5087

PITCO FOODS p 1152
567 Cinnabar St, San Jose CA 95110
Tel (916) 372-7772 SIC 5141

JORDANOS INC p 793
550 S Patterson Ave, Santa Barbara CA 93111
Tel (805) 964-0611
SIC 5181 5182 5149 5141 5142 5148

▲ **CORE-MARK HOLDING CO INC** p 369
395 Oyster Point Blvd # 415, South San Francisco CA 94080
Tel (650) 589-9445
SIC 5141 5194 5145 5122 5199 5149

■ **CORE-MARK INTERNATIONAL INC** p 369
395 Oyster Point Blvd # 415, South San Francisco CA 94080
Tel (650) 589-9445 SIC 5141 5194

■ **CORE-MARK MIDCONTINENT INC** p 369
395 Oyster Point Blvd # 415, South San Francisco CA 94080
Tel (650) 589-9445 SIC 5194 5141

COASTAL PACIFIC FOOD DISTRIBUTORS INC p 332
1015 Performance Dr, Stockton CA 95206
Tel (909) 983-2066
SIC 5141 4225 7519 4222

SOUTHWEST TRADERS INC p 1352
27565 Diaz Rd, Temecula CA 92590
Tel (951) 699-7800 SIC 5141

ANSAR GALLERY p 93
2505 El Camino Rd, Tustin CA 92782
Tel (949) 220-0000 SIC 5141

■ **GOLDBERG AND SOLOVY FOODS INC** p 620
5925 Alcoa Ave, Vernon CA 90058
Tel (323) 581-6161
SIC 5141 5149 5046 5169

■ **SYSCO LOS ANGELES INC** p 1417
20701 Currier Rd, Walnut CA 91789
Tel (909) 595-9595 SIC 5141 5084

NASSER CO INC p 1009
22720 Savi Ranch Pkwy, Yorba Linda CA 92887
Tel (714) 279-2100 SIC 5141

ACOSTA SALES & MARKETING CORP p 18
3045 S Parker Rd Ste 255, Aurora CO 80014
Tel (303) 752-0030 SIC 5141

UNITED FOOD SERVICE INC p 1508
5199 Ivy St, Commerce City CO 80022
Tel (303) 289-3595
SIC 5141 5142 5147 5148 5046

ROCKY QCD MOUNTAIN LLC p 1245
4770 E 51st Ave, Denver CO 80216
Tel (303) 399-6066 SIC 5141

DPI SPECIALTY FOODS ROCKY MOUNTAIN INC p 454
8125 E 88th Ave, Henderson CO 80640
Tel (303) 301-1226 SIC 5141

■ MCLANE/WESTERN INC p 931
2100 E Ken Pratt Blvd, Longmont CO 80504
Tel (303) 682-7500 SIC 5141

ANDREWS PRODUCE INC p 90
717 E Industrial Blvd, Pueblo West CO 81007
Tel (719) 543-3846 SIC 5141 5148

BOZZUTOS INC p 205
275 Schoolhouse Rd, Cheshire CT 06410
Tel (203) 272-3511 SIC 5141 5411

ROWE BROTHERS p 1253
367 Alumni Rd, Newington CT 06111
Tel (203) 265-5533 SIC 5141

EURPAC SERVICE INC p 513
101 Merritt 7 Corp Park 7 Corporate, Norwalk CT 06851
Tel (203) 847-0800 SIC 5141 5122

▲ CHEFS WAREHOUSE INC p 292
100 E Ridge Rd, Ridgefield CT 06877
Tel (203) 894-1345 SIC 5141

HARTFORD PROVISION CO p 665
625 Nutmeg Rd N, South Windsor CT 06074
Tel (860) 583-3908 SIC 5141

VISTAR/VSA OF HARTFORD INC p 1562
175 Sullivan Ave, South Windsor CT 06074
Tel (860) 688-7702 SIC 5141 5812 8322

THURSTON FOODS INC p 1451
30 Thurston Dr, Wallingford CT 06492
Tel (203) 265-1525
SIC 5141 5147 5142 5113

CITY LINE DISTRIBUTORS INC p 312
20 Industry Dr, West Haven CT 06516
Tel (203) 931-3707
SIC 5141 5142 5147 5113

ULTRA TRADING INTERNATIONAL LTD p 1501
2875 Ne 191st St Ste 201, Aventura FL 33180
Tel (305) 466-4443 SIC 5141

PURITY WHOLESALE GROCERS INC p 1192
5300 Broken Sound Blvd Nw # 110, Boca Raton FL 33487
Tel (561) 997-8302 SIC 5141 5122 5199

ACOSTA INC p 18
6600 Corporate Ctr Pkwy, Jacksonville FL 32216
Tel (904) 332-7986 SIC 5141

ACOSTA SALES CO INC p 18
6600 Corporate Ctr Pkwy, Jacksonville FL 32216
Tel (904) 281-9800 SIC 5149 5141

ADVANTAGE SALES LLC p 26
7411 Fullerton St Ste 101, Jacksonville FL 32256
Tel (904) 292-9009 SIC 5141

BEAVER STREET FISHERIES INC p 166
1741 W St Beaver, Jacksonville FL 32209
Tel (904) 354-5661 SIC 5142 5141

CUSTOMIZED DISTRIBUTION LLC p 403
5545 Shawland Rd, Jacksonville FL 32254
Tel (904) 783-0848 SIC 5141 7319

KELLEY-CLARKE LLC p 808
6600 Corporate Ctr Pkwy, Jacksonville FL 32216
Tel (904) 281-9800 SIC 5141

DIANA FOODS INC p 437
13300 Nw 25th St, Miami FL 33182
Tel (305) 593-8317 SIC 5141 5149

TRUJILLO & SONS INC p 1486
3325 Nw 62nd St, Miami FL 33147
Tel (305) 633-6482 SIC 5141

■ SYSCO WEST COAST FLORIDA INC p 1418
3000 69th St E, Palmetto FL 34221
Tel (941) 721-1450 SIC 5149 5141

CHENEY BROS INC p 294
1 Cheney Way, Riviera Beach FL 33404
Tel (561) 845-4700
SIC 5141 5087 5113 5169 5149

JMJ CONSULTING GROUP INC p 786
1197 Perregrine Cir E, Saint Johns FL 32259
Tel (904) 538-0944 SIC 5141

ADVANTAGE SALES & MARKETING p 26
3922 Coconut Palm Dr # 300, Tampa FL 33619
Tel (813) 281-8080 SIC 5141

ADVANTAGE WAYPOINT LLC p 27
13521 Prestige Pl, Tampa FL 33635
Tel (813) 358-5900 SIC 5141

COLONIAL GROCERS INC p 337
4001 E Lake Ave, Tampa FL 33610
Tel (813) 621-8880 SIC 0132 5141

WILLIAM P HEARNE PRODUCE LLC p 1610
707 W Lake Dr, Wimauma FL 33598
Tel (813) 633-8910 SIC 5141

■ MCLANE/SOUTHEAST p 931
300 Highway 29 N, Athens GA 30601
Tel (706) 549-4520 SIC 5141

DIAZ WHOLESALE & MFG CO INC p 437
5501 Fulton Indus Blvd Sw, Atlanta GA 30336
Tel (404) 346-9312 SIC 5141

INTERRA GROUP INC p 757
400 Interstate N Pkwy Ste, Atlanta GA 30339
Tel (770) 612-8101 SIC 5141 6719

SOUTO FOODS LLC p 1353
3077 Mccall Dr Ste 5, Atlanta GA 30340
Tel (404) 317-0674 SIC 5141

UNIPRO FOODSERVICE INC p 1505
2500 Cumbrld Pkwy Se 60 Ste 600, Atlanta GA 30339
Tel (770) 952-0871
SIC 5147 5141 5146 5142

IRA HIGDON GROCERY CO p 764
150 Iga Way, Cairo GA 39828
Tel (229) 377-1272
SIC 5141 5147 5142 5143 2111 5194

■ SYSCO ATLANTA LLC p 1416
2225 Riverdale Rd, College Park GA 30337
Tel (404) 765-9900 SIC 5141

WILLIAMS INSTITUTIONAL FOODS INC p 1611
1325 Bowens Mill Rd Sw, Douglas GA 31533
Tel (912) 384-5270 SIC 5141

PILGRIMS PRIDE CORP p 1148
1965 Evergreen Blvd # 100, Duluth GA 30096
Tel (770) 232-4200 SIC 2015 5144 5141

SUTHERLANDS FOODSERVICE INC p 1410
16 Forest Pkwy Bldg K, Forest Park GA 30297
Tel (404) 366-8550
SIC 5144 5148 5147 5143 5141

PERFORMANCE FOOD GROUP OF GEORGIA LLC p 1135
3501 Old Oakwood Rd, Oakwood GA 30566
Tel (770) 532-7779 SIC 5141

SIGNATURE FOOD MARKETING LLC p 1322
5786 Us Highway 129 N, Pendergrass GA 30567
Tel (706) 693-0095 SIC 5141

■ CORE-MARK DISTRIBUTORS INC p 369
4820 N Church Ln, Smyrna GA 30080
Tel (404) 792-2000
SIC 5194 5141 5145 5113

HAWAII FOODSERVICE ALLIANCE LLC p 669
2720 Waiwai Loop, Honolulu HI 96819
Tel (808) 839-2004 SIC 5141 5812

WEBCO HAWAII INC p 1586
2840 Mokumoa St, Honolulu HI 96819
Tel (808) 839-4551
SIC 5122 5199 5141 5064

Y HATA & CO LIMITED p 1633
285 Sand Island Access Rd, Honolulu HI 96819
Tel (808) 447-4100 SIC 5142 5141

HAWAIIAN HOUSEWARES LTD p 669
96-1282 Waihona St, Pearl City HI 96782
Tel (808) 453-8000
SIC 5199 5194 5141 5145

ABS FINANCE CO INC p 12
250 E Parkcenter Blvd, Boise ID 83706
Tel (208) 395-6200 SIC 5141

■ SYSCO SPOKANE INC p 1418
300 N Baugh Way, Post Falls ID 83854
Tel (208) 777-9511 SIC 5046 5141

■ EUROPEAN IMPORTS INC p 513
600 E Brook Dr, Arlington Heights IL 60005
Tel (800) 323-3464 SIC 5141 5149 5147

HAAG FOOD SERVICE INC p 651
300 N Haag St, Breese IL 62230
Tel (618) 526-7120 SIC 5142 5144 5141

PRINOVA US LLC p 1177
285 Fullerton Ave, Carol Stream IL 60188
Tel (630) 868-0300 SIC 5141

BATTAGLIA DISTRIBUTING CORP INC p 159
2500 S Ashland Ave, Chicago IL 60608
Tel (312) 738-1111 SIC 5141

DEARBORN WHOLESALE GROCERS LP p 420
2455 S Damen Ave Ste 100, Chicago IL 60608
Tel (773) 254-4300 SIC 5141

■ GETZ BROS& CO INC p 609
225 W Washington St # 1900, Chicago IL 60606
Tel (312) 845-5686
SIC 5047 5031 5141 5065 5082

■ MCLANE/MIDWEST INC p 931
3400 E Main St, Danville IL 61834
Tel (217) 477-7500 SIC 5141

SINGLE SOURCE INC p 1326
8160 Cass Ave, Darien IL 60561
Tel (630) 324-5982 SIC 5141

■ LAGASSE INC p 838
1 Parkway North Blvd # 100, Deerfield IL 60015
Tel (847) 627-7000 SIC 5087 5141

TOPCO ASSOCIATES LLC p 1461
150 Northwest Point Blvd # 6, Elk Grove Village IL 60007
Tel (847) 676-3030 SIC 5141

TOPCO HOLDINGS INC (COOPERATIVE) p 1461
150 Northwest Point Blvd, Elk Grove Village IL 60007
Tel (847) 676-3030 SIC 5141 8699

KRONOS FOODS CORP p 830
1 Kronos, Glendale Heights IL 60139
Tel (773) 847-2250
SIC 2013 2051 5141 5963

WM H LEAHY ASSOCIATES INC p 1620
2350 Ravine Way Ste 200, Glenview IL 60025
Tel (847) 904-5250 SIC 5141 5142

ARRO CORP p 113
7440 Santa Fe Dr, Hodgkins IL 60525
Tel (708) 352-8200 SIC 5141

CENTRAL GROCERS INC p 278
2600 Haven Ave, Joliet IL 60433
Tel (815) 553-8800
SIC 5141 5147 5142 5148 5143 5122

HPR PARTNERS LLC p 714
801 Warrenville Rd # 550, Lisle IL 60532
Tel (630) 737-0788 SIC 5141

MICHAEL LEWIS CO p 960
8900 W 50th St, Mc Cook IL 60525
Tel (708) 688-2200
SIC 5113 5141 5142 2782 2759 2621

DOT FOODS INC p 451
1 Dot Way, Mount Sterling IL 62353
Tel (217) 773-4411 SIC 5141 5142

EBY-BROWN CO LLC p 474
1415 W Diehl Rd Ste 300, Naperville IL 60563
Tel (630) 778-2800
SIC 5194 5145 5141 5122 5149

N KOHL GROCER CO p 1005
130 Jersey St, Quincy IL 62301
Tel (217) 222-5000 SIC 5141 5113 5046

WALTER LAGESTEE INC p 1574
16145 State St, South Holland IL 60473
Tel (708) 596-3166 SIC 5411 5141

SIMU LTD p 1326
201 Mittel Dr, Wood Dale IL 60191
Tel (630) 350-1060
SIC 5113 5141 5142 2782 2759 2621

WINKLER INC p 1616
535 E Medcalf St, Dale IN 47523
Tel (812) 937-4421 SIC 5141 5411

TROYER FOODS INC p 1485
17141 State Road 4, Goshen IN 46528
Tel (574) 533-0302
SIC 5147 5144 5141 5146

STANZ CHEESE CO INC p 1377
1840 Commerce Dr, South Bend IN 46628
Tel (574) 232-6666
SIC 5142 5141 5148 5113 5087 5085

■ CASEYS MARKETING CO p 263
1 Se Convenience Blvd, Ankeny IA 50021
Tel (515) 965-6100
SIC 5411 5172 5141 5812

MARTIN BROTHERS DISTRIBUTING CO INC p 912
6623 Chancellor Dr, Cedar Falls IA 50613
Tel (319) 266-1775
SIC 5141 5169 5046 5087

F&A FOOD SALES INC p 522
2221 Lincoln St, Concordia KS 66901
Tel (785) 243-2301 SIC 5141

EARP MEAT CO p 469
2730 S 98th St, Edwardsville KS 66111
Tel (913) 287-3311 SIC 5142 5141 5113

ASSOCIATED WHOLESALE GROCERS INC p 121
5000 Kansas Ave, Kansas City KS 66106
Tel (913) 288-1000
SIC 5141 5143 5142 5147 5146 5148

■ SYSCO KANSAS CITY INC p 1417
1915 E Kansas City Rd, Olathe KS 66061
Tel (913) 829-5555 SIC 5149 5141

KMS INC p 824
811 E Waterman St Ste 1, Wichita KS 67202
Tel (316) 264-8833 SIC 5199 5141

LAUREL GROCERY CO LLC p 847
129 Barbourville Rd, London KY 40744
Tel (606) 878-6601
SIC 5141 5147 5122 5143

BROWN FOODSERVICE INC p 219
500 E Clayton Ln, Louisa KY 41230
Tel (606) 638-1139
SIC 5142 5141 5084 5087

RESTAURANT SUPPLY CHAIN SOLUTIONS LLC p 1228
950 Breckenridge Ln # 300, Louisville KY 40207
Tel (502) 896-5900
SIC 5812 5046 5141 5149

■ SYSCO LOUISVILLE INC p 1417
7705 National Tpke, Louisville KY 40214
Tel (502) 367-6131 SIC 5141

ASSOCIATED GROCERS INC p 120
8600 Anselmo Ln, Baton Rouge LA 70810
Tel (225) 444-1000 SIC 5141

HARRISON CO LLC p 664
4801 Viking Dr, Bossier City LA 71111
Tel (318) 747-0700 SIC 5194 5145 5141

DOERLE FOOD SERVICES LLC p 447
113 Kol Dr, Broussard LA 70518
Tel (337) 252-8551
SIC 5142 5141 5087 5148

IMPERIAL TRADING CO LLC p 734
701 Edwards Ave, Harahan LA 70123
Tel (504) 733-1400 SIC 5194 5141 5145

■ CARO FOODS INC p 259
2324 Bayou Blue Rd, Houma LA 70364
Tel (985) 872-1483 SIC 5141

CONSOLIDATED COMPANIES INC p 359
918 Edwards Ave, New Orleans LA 70123
Tel (318) 869-3061 SIC 5141

DENNIS BEVERAGE CO p 428
101 Mecaw Rd, Bangor ME 04401
Tel (207) 947-0321 SIC 5141 5113

ASSOCIATED GROCERS OF MAINE INC p 120
190 Water St, Gardiner ME 04345
Tel (207) 596-0636
SIC 5141 5147 5148 5122

■ SYSCO NORTHERN NEW ENGLAND INC p 1417
55 Thomas Dr, Westbrook ME 04092
Tel (207) 871-0700
SIC 5141 5147 5148 5142

B GREEN & CO INC p 142
1300 S Monroe St Ste 1, Baltimore MD 21230
Tel (410) 783-7777 SIC 5141

GEORGE J FALTER CO p 606
3501 Benson Ave, Baltimore MD 21227
Tel (410) 646-3641
SIC 5194 5145 5141 5015

SAVAL FOODS CORP p 1284
6740 Dorsey Rd, Elkridge MD 21075
Tel (410) 379-5100 SIC 5141 2013

RHEE BROS INC p 1231
7461 Coca Cola Dr, Hanover MD 21076
Tel (410) 381-9000 SIC 5141

■ SYSCO EASTERN MARYLAND LLC p 1417
33239 Costen Rd, Pocomoke City MD 21851
Tel (410) 677-5555 SIC 5141

JOHNSON OHARE CO INC p 791
1 Progress Rd, Billerica MA 01821
Tel (978) 663-9000 SIC 5141

COSTA FRUIT & PRODUCE CO p 374
18 Bunker Hill Indus Park, Boston MA 02129
Tel (617) 241-8007
SIC 5148 5143 5142 5141

CONSUMER PRODUCT DISTRIBUTORS INC p 361
705 Meadow St, Chicopee MA 01013
Tel (413) 592-4141
SIC 5194 5141 7389 5145

GARBER BROS INC p 591
Kay Way Rr 139, Stoughton MA 02072
Tel (781) 341-0800
SIC 5194 5145 5141 5122

TRIBE MEDITERRANEAN FOODS INC p 1479
100 Myles Standish Blvd # 1, Taunton MA 02780
Tel (774) 961-0000 SIC 5141

GROVE SERVICES INC p 642
100 William St Ste 210, Wellesley MA 02481
Tel (781) 772-1187 SIC 5141

▲ SPARTANNASH CO p 1355
850 76th St Sw, Byron Center MI 49315
Tel (616) 878-2000 SIC 5141 5411 5912

ALLIANCE FOODS INC p 54
605 W Chicago Rd, Coldwater MI 49036
Tel (517) 278-2395 SIC 5411 5141

CARAMAGNO FOODS CO p 252
14255 Dequindre St, Detroit MI 48212
Tel (313) 869-8200 SIC 5141 5142

LITTLE CAESAR ENTERPRISES INC p 870
2211 Woodward Ave, Detroit MI 48201
Tel (313) 983-6000
SIC 5812 6794 5141 5046 8741

GRAD INC p 628
4001 3 Mile Rd Nw, Grand Rapids MI 49534
Tel (616) 676-5969
SIC 5141 5194 5145 5122 5113 5411

LIMSON TRADING INC p 866
1300 Gezon Pkwy Sw, Grand Rapids MI 49509
Tel (616) 530-3110 SIC 5141

MEIJER DISTRIBUTION INC p 940
2929 Walker Ave Nw, Grand Rapids MI 49544
Tel (616) 453-6711 SIC 5141

■ SYSCO GRAND RAPIDS LLC p 1417
3700 Sysco Ct Se, Grand Rapids MI 49512
Tel (616) 956-0700 SIC 5141 5087

CAPITAL SALES CO p 250
1471 E 9 Mile Rd, Hazel Park MI 48030
Tel (248) 542-4400 SIC 5141 7311

DETROIT CITY DAIRY p 433
21405 Trolley Indus Dr, Taylor MI 48180
Tel (313) 295-6300
SIC 5143 5141 5147 5149

HOLLYWOOD HOLDING CO LLC p 701
2670 W Maple Rd, Troy MI 48084
Tel (248) 643-0309 SIC 5921 5141 5411

COUNTRYSIDE FOODS LLC p 375
26661 Bunert Rd, Warren MI 48089
Tel (586) 447-3500 SIC 5141 2099

MARKET DAY LLC p 908
1300 Gezon Pkwy Sw, Wyoming MI 49509
Tel (630) 285-1470 SIC 5141

HENRYS FOODS INC p 684
234 Mckay Ave N, Alexandria MN 56308
Tel (320) 763-3194
SIC 5194 5145 5111 5113 5141

▲ SUPERVALU INC p 1407
11840 Valley View Rd, Eden Prairie MN 55344
Tel (952) 828-4000 SIC 5411 5141

BELLISIO FOODS FOODSERVICE p 171
1201 Hennepin Ave, Minneapolis MN 55403
Tel (952) 469-2000 SIC 5141

■ NASH-FINCH CO p 1008
7600 France Ave S Ste 200, Minneapolis MN 55435
Tel (952) 832-0534
SIC 5141 5148 5142 5147 5411

■ MCLANE MINNESOTA INC p 931
1111 5th St W, Northfield MN 55057
Tel (507) 664-3000 SIC 5141

■ APPERTS INC p 98
900 Highway 10 S, Saint Cloud MN 56304
Tel (320) 251-3200
SIC 5142 5141 5411 5421 2013

■ SYSCO WESTERN MINNESOTA INC p 1418
900 Highway 10 S, Saint Cloud MN 56304
Tel (320) 251-3200
SIC 5141 5142 5143 5144 5145 5146

■ SYSCO MINNESOTA INC p 1417
2400 County Road J, Saint Paul MN 55112
Tel (763) 785-9000 SIC 5141 5812 5813

■ MCLANE/SOUTHERN INC p 931
2104 Mfrs Blvd Ne, Brookhaven MS 39601
Tel (601) 833-6761 SIC 5141

MERCHANTS CO p 944
1100 Edwards St, Hattiesburg MS 39401
Tel (601) 353-2461 SIC 5141

TATUM DEVELOPMENT CORP p 1426
11 Parkway Blvd, Hattiesburg MS 39401
Tel (601) 544-6043
SIC 5141 5084 4924 3443

■ MORAN FOODS LLC p 988
100 Corporate Office Dr, Earth City MO 63045
Tel (314) 592-9100 SIC 5141 5411

MENU MAKER FOODS INC p 943
913 Big Horn Dr, Jefferson City MO 65109
Tel (573) 893-3000
SIC 5141 5087 2011 5149

■ SYSCO ST LOUIS LLC p 1418
3850 Mueller Rd, Saint Charles MO 63301
Tel (636) 940-9230
SIC 5141 5149 5146 5143 5142

■ MIDDENDORF MEAT CO LLC p 964
3737 N Broadway, Saint Louis MO 63147
Tel (314) 241-4800
SIC 5147 5141 5148 5146 5113 2011

SPRINGFIELD GROCER CO p 1361
2415 W Battlefield St, Springfield MO 65807
Tel (417) 883-4230 SIC 5142 5141 5149

■ SYSCO MONTANA INC p 1417
1509 Monad Rd, Billings MT 59101
Tel (406) 247-1100 SIC 5149 5142 5141

TOBA INC p 1458
2621 W Us Highway 30, Grand Island NE 68803
Tel (308) 389-5987
SIC 5148 5194 5145 5141

■ LINCOLN SYSCO INC p 868
900 King Bird Rd, Lincoln NE 68521
Tel (402) 423-1031
SIC 5148 5142 5143 5141 5087 5113

AFFILIATED FOODS MIDWEST COOPERATIVE INC p 32
1301 W Omaha Ave, Norfolk NE 68701
Tel (402) 371-0555 SIC 5141 5142

▲ AMCON DISTRIBUTING CO INC p 65
7405 Irvington Rd, Omaha NE 68122
Tel (402) 331-3727
SIC 5194 5141 5145 5113 5122

MIDJIT MARKET INC p 965
1580 S Jones Blvd, Las Vegas NV 89146
Tel (702) 216-2154 SIC 5541 5141

■ E & H DISTRIBUTING LLC p 465
1685 W Cheyenne Ave, North Las Vegas NV 89032
Tel (702) 636-3663
SIC 5113 5141 5142 5149

JIM L SHETAKIS DISTRIBUTING CO p 785
3840 Civic Center Dr A, North Las Vegas NV 89030
Tel (702) 940-3663 SIC 5141 5046

C&S WHOLESALE GROCERS INC p 234
7 Corporate Dr, Keene NH 03431
Tel (603) 354-7000
SIC 5141 5147 5143 5142 5122 5145

ASSOCIATED GROCERS OF NEW ENGLAND INC p 120
11 Cooperative Way, Pembroke NH 03275
Tel (603) 223-6710 SIC 5141

KENOVER MARKETING CORP p 812
72 Hook Rd, Bayonne NJ 07002
Tel (718) 369-4600 SIC 5141

GENERAL TRADING CO INC p 602
455 16th St, Carlstadt NJ 07072
Tel (201) 935-7717 SIC 5141

WHITE ROSE INC p 1606
380 Middlesex Ave, Carteret NJ 07008
Tel (732) 541-5555
SIC 5141 5143 5142 5122 7311 8721

METROPOLITAN FOODS INC p 955
174 Delawanna Ave, Clifton NJ 07014
Tel (973) 672-9400
SIC 5142 5149 2099 5141

AFI FOOD SERVICE DISTRIBUTORS INC p 33
1 Ikea Dr, Elizabeth NJ 07201
Tel (908) 629-1800 SIC 5141

REMA FOODS INC p 1222
140 Sylvan Ave Ste 200, Englewood Cliffs NJ 07632
Tel (201) 947-1000 SIC 5142 5149 5141

LOSURDO FOODS INC p 879
20 Owens Rd, Hackensack NJ 07601
Tel (201) 343-6680
SIC 5141 2022 2033 2045

■ SYSCO METRO NEW YORK LLC p 1417
20 Theodore Conrad Dr, Jersey City NJ 07305
Tel (201) 451-0997
SIC 5141 5144 5142 5147 5087

WAKEFERN FOOD CORP p 1572
5000 Riverside Dr, Keasbey NJ 08832
Tel (908) 527-3300
SIC 5141 5149 5411 4213 2026

MAXIMUM QUALITY FOODS INC p 922
3351 Tremley Point Rd # 2, Linden NJ 07036
Tel (908) 474-0003 SIC 5141

S BERTRAM INC p 1262
3401 Tremley Point Rd, Linden NJ 07036
Tel (908) 862-8200 SIC 5143 5141

GRAND SUPERCENTER INC p 630
300 Chubb Ave, Lyndhurst NJ 07071
Tel (201) 507-9900 SIC 5141

■ MCLANE NEW JERSEY p 931
742 Courses Landing Rd, Penns Grove NJ 08069
Tel (856) 351-6200 SIC 5141 5149

J AMBROGI FOOD DISTRIBUTION INC p 770
1400 Metropolitan Ave, Thorofare NJ 08086
Tel (856) 845-0377 SIC 5141

RLB FOOD DISTRIBUTORS LP p 1239
2 Dedrick Pl Cn2285, West Caldwell NJ 07006
Tel (973) 575-9526 SIC 5148 5141

CENTO FINE FOODS INC p 277
100 Cento Blvd, West Deptford NJ 08086
Tel (856) 853-7800 SIC 5141

REDDY RAW INC p 1216
1 Ethel Blvd Ste 1, Wood Ridge NJ 07075
Tel (201) 804-7633 SIC 5142 5141

■ SYSCO NEW MEXICO LLC p 1417
601 Comanche Rd Ne, Albuquerque NM 87107
Tel (505) 761-1200 SIC 5141

■ MCLANE/EASTERN INC p 931
2828 Mclane Rd, Baldwinsville NY 13027
Tel (315) 638-7500 SIC 5141

CONSTANCE FOOD GROUP INC p 360
545 Johnson Ave Ste 10, Bohemia NY 11716
Tel (631) 582-1144 SIC 5149 5141

ACE ENDICO CORP p 16
80 International Blvd, Brewster NY 10509
Tel (914) 347-3131 SIC 5141 5142 5148

BALDOR SPECIALTY FOODS INC p 147
155 Food Center Dr Ste 1, Bronx NY 10474
Tel (718) 860-9100 SIC 5141

■ DAIRYLAND USA CORP p 409
1250 Waters Pl Ste 704, Bronx NY 10461
Tel (718) 842-8700 SIC 5141

WEST SIDE FOODS INC p 1595
355 Food Center Dr A23, Bronx NY 10474
Tel (718) 842-8500 SIC 5141

BOGOPA ENTERPRISES INC p 197
650 Fountain Ave, Brooklyn NY 11208
Tel (718) 346-6500 SIC 5141

H SCHRIER & CO INC p 650
4901 Glenwood Rd, Brooklyn NY 11234
Tel (718) 258-7500 SIC 5141

NEW YUNG WAH TRADING LLC p 1036
311 Richardson St, Brooklyn NY 11222
Tel (718) 388-3322 SIC 5141

TRIPIFOODS INC p 1482
1427 William St, Buffalo NY 14206
Tel (716) 853-7400
SIC 5141 5194 5145 5143 5142 5122

JETRO HOLDINGS LLC p 784
1506 132nd St, College Point NY 11356
Tel (718) 762-8700 SIC 5149 5141 5812

JRD HOLDINGS INC p 795
1524 132nd St, College Point NY 11356
Tel (718) 762-8700
SIC 5141 5142 5147 5181 5194

RD FOOD SERVICES LLC p 1212
1524 132nd St, College Point NY 11356
Tel (718) 961-4356
SIC 5141 5148 5142 5113 5046 5087

RESTAURANT DEPOT LLC p 1228
1524 132nd St, College Point NY 11356
Tel (718) 762-8700
SIC 5147 5141 5142 5181 5194

MAINES PAPER & FOOD SERVICE INC p 898
101 Broome Corporate Pkwy, Conklin NY 13748
Tel (607) 779-1200
SIC 5142 5113 5141 5087 5147 5146

MAPLEVALE FARMS INC p 904
2063 Allen Street Ext, Falconer NY 14733
Tel (716) 355-4114 SIC 5141

DI CARLO DISTRIBUTORS INC p 436
1630 N Ocean Ave, Holtsville NY 11742
Tel (800) 342-2756 SIC 5142 5141 5143

LANDMARK FOOD CORP p 843
865 Waverly Ave, Holtsville NY 11742
Tel (631) 654-4500
SIC 5142 5141 5148 5147

GINSBERGS INSTITUTIONAL FOODS INC p 612
29 Ginsburg Ln, Hudson NY 12534
Tel (518) 828-4004
SIC 5148 5147 5142 5141 5143

BARTLETT DAIRY INC p 157
9004 161st St Ste 609, Jamaica NY 11432
Tel (718) 658-2299 SIC 5143 5141

LGS SPECIALTY SALES LTD p 860
1 Radisson Plz Fl 10, New Rochelle NY 10801
Tel (718) 542-2200 SIC 5141 5148

ITOCHU INTERNATIONAL INC p 768
1251 Avenue Of The Americ, New York NY 10020
Tel (212) 818-8000
SIC 5131 5084 5065 5051 5153 5141

KIND LLC p 819
1372 Broadway Frnt 3, New York NY 10018
Tel (855) 884-5463 SIC 5141

MITSUBISHI CORP (AMERICAS) p 977
655 3rd Ave, New York NY 10017
Tel (212) 605-2000
SIC 5051 5172 5141 5153 5169 5084

MITSUBISHI INTERNATIONAL CORP p 978
655 3rd Ave Ste 800, New York NY 10017
Tel (212) 605-2000
SIC 5051 5172 5141 5153 5169 5084

SUMITOMO CORP OF AMERICAS p 1398
300 Madison Ave, New York NY 10017
Tel (212) 207-0700
SIC 5051 5172 5084 5063 5141

AIR STREAM CORP p 39
3400 Lawson Blvd, Oceanside NY 11572
Tel (516) 763-1600 SIC 5141 5148

KEY FOOD STORES CO-OPERATIVE INC p 814
1200 South Ave, Staten Island NY 10314
Tel (718) 370-4200 SIC 5141

RLE CORP p 1239
1301 Broad St, Utica NY 13501
Tel (315) 724-4189 SIC 5141

■ SYSCO SYRACUSE LLC p 1418
2508 Warners Rd, Warners NY 13164
Tel (315) 672-7000 SIC 5141

RENZI BROS INC p 1224
901 Rail Dr, Watertown NY 13601
Tel (315) 755-5610 SIC 5141

KRASDALE FOODS INC p 829
65 W Red Oak Ln Ste 2, White Plains NY 10604
Tel (914) 694-6400 SIC 5141

TOPS MARKETS LLC p 1461
6363 Main St, Williamsville NY 14221
Tel (716) 635-5000
SIC 5411 5141 5147 5148 5122 5912

■ MCLANE/CAROLINA INC p 931
7253 Nc 48, Battleboro NC 27809
Tel (252) 972-2500 SIC 5141 5142 5149

WINN-DIXIE CHARLOTTE INC p 1616
2401 Nevada Blvd, Charlotte NC 28273
Tel (704) 587-4000
SIC 5411 8741 5141 4226 4222

PDNC LLC p 1125
402 Commerce Ct, Goldsboro NC 27534
Tel (919) 778-3000
SIC 5142 5141 5147 5148 5431

SOUTHCO DISTRIBUTING CO p 1345
2201 S John St, Goldsboro NC 27530
Tel (919) 735-8012 SIC 5194 5141 5131

ALEX LEE INC p 48
120 4th St Sw, Hickory NC 28602
Tel (828) 725-4424
SIC 5141 5142 5147 5148 5194 5411

■ INSTITUTION FOOD HOUSE INC p 747
543 12th Street Dr Nw, Hickory NC 28601
Tel (800) 800-0434 SIC 5141 5142

MERCHANTS DISTRIBUTORS LLC p 944
5005 Alex Lee Blvd, Hickory NC 28601
Tel (828) 725-4424
SIC 5141 5142 5147 5148 5194 5122

SELLETHICS MARKETING GROUP INC p 1302
941 Matthews Mint Hill Rd, Matthews NC 28105
Tel (704) 847-4450 SIC 5141

KINEXO p 820
800 Tiffany Blvd Ste 300, Rocky Mount NC 27804
Tel (252) 407-2000 SIC 5141

E G FORREST CO p 466
1023 N Chestnut St, Winston Salem NC 27101
Tel (336) 723-9151 SIC 5142 5141

▲ PRIMO WATER CORP p 1176
101 N Cherry St Ste 501, Winston Salem NC 27101
Tel (336) 331-4000 SIC 5149 3585 5141

BLACK GOLD POTATO SALES INC p 186
4320 18th Ave S, Grand Forks ND 58201
Tel (701) 248-3788 SIC 5141

PHYSICIANS WEIGHT LOSS CENTERS OF AMERICA INC p 1146
395 Springside Dr, Akron OH 44333
Tel (330) 666-7952 SIC 5141 5122 6794

EMPIRE MARKETING STRATEGIES INC p 493
11243 Cornell Park Dr, Blue Ash OH 45242
Tel (513) 793-6241 SIC 5141

■ KPS LLC p 829
1014 Vine St, Cincinnati OH 45202
Tel (513) 762-4000 SIC 5141

LAROSAS INC p 845
2334 Boudinot Ave, Cincinnati OH 45238
Tel (513) 347-5660
SIC 5812 6794 5141 5921

NOVELART MANUFACTURING CO p 1063
2121 Section Rd, Cincinnati OH 45237
Tel (513) 351-7700 SIC 5141 5145 5194

■ SYSCO CENTRAL OHIO INC p 1416
2400 Harrison Rd, Columbus OH 43204
Tel (614) 272-0658 SIC 5141 5142

BLUE LINE DISTRIBUTION p 192
2250 Spiegel Dr Ste P, Groveport OH 43125
Tel (614) 497-9610 SIC 5141

MAMA ROSAS LLC p 900
1910 Fair Rd, Sidney OH 45365
Tel (937) 498-4511 SIC 5141 5142

BROTHERS TRADING CO INC p 219
400 Victory Ln, Springboro OH 45066
Tel (937) 746-1010 SIC 5141 5122 5149

ANDERSON AND DUBOSE INC p 89
5300 Tod Ave Sw, Warren OH 44481
Tel (440) 248-8800 SIC 5142 5141

MATTINGLY FOODS INC p 921
302 State St, Zanesville OH 43701
Tel (740) 454-0136 SIC 5149 5142 5141

STEPHENSON WHOLESALE CO INC p 1386
230 S 22nd Ave, Durant OK 74701
Tel (580) 920-0125
SIC 5194 5145 5143 5142 5141 5113

QUIKTRIP CORP p 1200
4705 S 129th East Ave, Tulsa OK 74134
Tel (918) 615-7700
SIC 5411 5541 5172 2099 5141 6512

RESERS FINE FOODS INC p 1226
15570 Sw Jenkins Rd, Beaverton OR 97006
Tel (503) 643-6431 SIC 2099 5141

MAJOR EAGLE INC p 899
2350 W Broadway, Eugene OR 97402
Tel (541) 345-8421
SIC 5181 5141 5194 5142

MCDONALD WHOLESALE CO p 927
2350 W Broadway, Eugene OR 97402
Tel (541) 345-8421 SIC 5141

NESS HOLDING CO p 1026
4550 Kruse Way Ste 350, Lake Oswego OR 97035
Tel (503) 240-0400 SIC 5141

AAS HOLDING CO p 8
2401 Ne Argyle St, Portland OR 97211
Tel (503) 284-3314 SIC 5147 5142 5141

BOYD COFFEE CO p 205
19730 Ne Sandy Blvd, Portland OR 97230
Tel (503) 666-4545
SIC 2095 5499 5141 3634 2099

KERR PACIFIC CORP p 813
1211 Sw 6th Ave, Portland OR 97204
Tel (503) 221-1301 SIC 5141 2041

WESTERN FAMILY FOODS INC p 1598
6700 Sw Sandburg St, Portland OR 97223
Tel (503) 639-6300 SIC 5141 5142

WESTERN FAMILY HOLDING CO p 1598
6700 Sw Sandburg St, Tigard OR 97223
Tel (503) 639-6300
SIC 5141 5142 5199 5122 5149

■ SYSCO PORTLAND INC p 1418
26250 Sw Parkway Ctr Dr, Wilsonville OR 97070
Tel (503) 682-8700 SIC 5141 5046

IMLERS POULTRY LP p 734
1887 Route 764, Duncansville PA 16635
Tel (814) 943-5563
SIC 5144 5147 5141 5142

MCANENY BROTHERS INC p 926
470 Industrial Park Rd, Ebensburg PA 15931
Tel (814) 472-9800
SIC 5141 5147 5148 5194 5113 5142

CA CURTZE CO p 234
1717 E 12th St, Erie PA 16511
Tel (814) 452-2281 SIC 5141 5147 5142

FEESERS INC p 537
5561 Grayson Rd, Harrisburg PA 17111
Tel (717) 248-9658 SIC 5141

BENJAMIN FOODS LLC p 173
1001 S York Rd, Hatboro PA 19040
Tel (215) 437-5000 SIC 5141 8741

SKH MANAGEMENT CO p 1329
813 Lititz Pike, Lititz PA 17543
Tel (717) 627-0090
SIC 5141 5092 5261 5411

MOZA LLC p 995
101 Church St Ofc 5, Moscow PA 18444
Tel (570) 848-7926 SIC 5141 7389

COOPER-BOOTH WHOLESALE CO LP p 367
200 Lincoln West Dr, Mountville PA 17554
Tel (717) 285-8000
SIC 5194 5145 5122 5141

DUTCH VALLEY FOOD DISTRIBUTORS INC p 463
7615 Lancaster Ave, Myerstown PA 17067
Tel (717) 933-4191 SIC 5141

HONOR HOLDINGS INC p 705
1801 N 5th St, Philadelphia PA 19122
Tel (215) 236-1700 SIC 5141 5142

GIANT EAGLE INC p 610
101 Kappa Dr, Pittsburgh PA 15238
Tel (800) 362-8899
SIC 5411 5141 5147 5148 5143 6794

ASSOCIATED WHOLESALERS INC p 121
336 E Penn Ave, Robesonia PA 19551
Tel (610) 693-3161
SIC 5141 5147 5122 5142 5148 5411

PARAGON WHOLESALE FOODS CORP p 1113
173 Thorn Hill Rd, Warrendale PA 15086
Tel (412) 621-2626 SIC 5148 5141

FIBRO SOURCE USA INC p 540
985 Old Eagle School Rd # 514, Wayne PA 19087
Tel (610) 293-3200
SIC 5099 5113 5141 5112

LIBERTY USA INC p 863
920 Irwin Run Rd, West Mifflin PA 15122
Tel (412) 461-2700
SIC 5194 5145 5122 5141

ETTLINE FOODS CORP p 512
525 N State St, York PA 17403
Tel (717) 848-1564 SIC 5141

B FERNANDEZ & HNOS INC p 142
Carr 5 305 Urb Rr St Ca, Bayamon PR 00961
Tel (787) 288-7272 SIC 5181 5141 5182

LUIS GARRATON INC p 884
Luchetti Ind Park Rd 28 C, Bayamon PR 00961
Tel (787) 788-6100 SIC 5122 5141

V SUAREZ & CO INC p 1538
Industrial Luchetti # 300, Bayamon PR 00961
Tel (787) 792-1212 SIC 5181 5141 5182

BALLESTER HERMANOS INC p 148
Carr 869 Parq, Catano PR 00962
Tel (787) 788-4110 SIC 5141 5182

JF MONTALVO CASH AND CARRY INC p 785
Amelia Ind Park 46, Guaynabo PR 00968
Tel (787) 781-2962 SIC 5141

MENDEZ & CO INC p 943
Km 2/4 Mrtnez Nadal Rr 20, Guaynabo PR 00969
Tel (787) 793-8888 SIC 5182 5141

DESTILERIA SERRALLES INC p 432
Calle Central 1, Mercedita PR 00715
Tel (787) 840-1000 SIC 2085 2084 5141

■ MONDELEZ PUERTO RICO LLC p 984
9615 Ave Los Romeros # 801, San Juan PR 00926
Tel (787) 522-9810 SIC 5141

MATOSANTOS COMMERCIAL CORP p 920
Parque Industrial Ca, Vega Baja PR 00693
Tel (787) 793-6900 SIC 5141 5113 5087

PIGGLY WIGGLY CAROLINA CO INC p 1147
176 Croghan Spur Ste 400, Charleston SC 29407
Tel (843) 554-9880
SIC 7311 5411 5148 5141 2752 1542

■ SYSCO COLUMBIA LLC p 1417
131 Sysco Ct, Columbia SC 29209
Tel (803) 239-4000
SIC 5141 5046 5142 5147 5148

TIMBERLAKE & HITE CO INC p 1454
209 Flintlake Rd, Columbia SC 29223
Tel (803) 276-0510 SIC 5141

VENDORS SUPPLY INC p 1547
201 Saluda River Rd, Columbia SC 29210
Tel (803) 772-6390 SIC 5141

C&S WHOLESALE SERVICES INC p 234
208 Bi Lo Blvd, Greenville SC 29607
Tel (864) 234-1999 SIC 5141

W LEE FLOWERS AND CO INC p 1568
127 E W Lee Flowers Rd, Scranton SC 29591
Tel (843) 389-2731 SIC 5141 5147 5194

BARGAIN BARN INC p 155
2924 Lee Hwy, Athens TN 37303
Tel (423) 746-0746 SIC 5411 5141

INSTITUTIONAL WHOLESALE CO INC p 747
535 Dry Valley Rd, Cookeville TN 38506
Tel (931) 537-4000 SIC 5141 5142

H T HACKNEY CO p 650
502 S Gay St Ste 300, Knoxville TN 37902
Tel (865) 546-1291
SIC 5141 5172 2434 5084

■ KENNETH O LESTER CO INC p 811
245 N Castle Heights Ave, Lebanon TN 37087
Tel (615) 444-9901 SIC 5141 5142 5148

AFFILIATED FOODS INC p 32
1401 W Farmers Ave, Amarillo TX 79118
Tel (806) 345-7773
SIC 5141 2026 2051 5149 6153

SELL-THRU SERVICES INC p 1302
4807 Spicewd Spgs Rd # 3120, Austin TX 78759
Tel (512) 346-5075 SIC 5141 8742

PRICE & CO p 1174
3530 W Cardinal Dr, Beaumont TX 77705
Tel (409) 842-0677
SIC 5194 5145 5122 5141

BRENHAM WHOLESALE GROCERY CO INC p 210
602 W First St, Brenham TX 77833
Tel (979) 836-7925
SIC 5194 5147 5142 5141 5148

■ MCLANE FOODSERVICE INC p 931
2085 Midway Rd, Carrollton TX 75006
Tel (972) 364-2000
SIC 8742 5141 5311 5113

LARROC INC p 845
6420 Boeing Dr, El Paso TX 79925
Tel (915) 772-3733 SIC 5141 5149

BASSHAM WHOLESALE EGG CO INC p 159
5409 Hemphill St, Fort Worth TX 76115
Tel (817) 921-1600
SIC 5144 5143 5141 5147

BEN E KEITH CO p 172
601 E 7th St, Fort Worth TX 76102
Tel (817) 877-5700 SIC 5181 5141

MARKETING MANAGEMENT INC p 908
4717 Fletcher Ave, Fort Worth TX 76107
Tel (817) 731-4176 SIC 5141

2ML REAL ESTATE INTERESTS INC p 2
952 Echo Ln Ste 314, Houston TX 77024
Tel (713) 747-5000 SIC 5141 5142 5122

CYCLONE ENTERPRISES INC p 405
146 Knobcrest Dr, Houston TX 77060
Tel (281) 872-0087 SIC 5141

GLAZIER FOODS CO p 614
11303 Antoine Dr, Houston TX 77066
Tel (713) 869-6411 SIC 5142 5141

■ HOUSTON SYSCO INC p 712
10710 Grens Crossing Blvd, Houston TX 77038
Tel (713) 672-8080
SIC 5149 5142 5046 5141 2099

JAKES INC p 776
13400 Hollister Dr, Houston TX 77086
Tel (713) 868-1301 SIC 5144 5142 5141

PREFERRED FOODS MARTIN L P p 1169
2011 Silver St, Houston TX 77007
Tel (713) 869-6191
SIC 5142 2015 2011 5141 5144

RIVIANA FOODS INC p 1239
2777 Allen Pkwy Fl 15, Houston TX 77019
Tel (713) 529-3251
SIC 2044 2052 2033 5141

■ SYSCO HOLDINGS LLC p 1417
1390 Enclave Pkwy, Houston TX 77077
Tel (281) 584-1728
SIC 5141 5142 5143 5144 5145 5146

■ SYSCO USA I INC p 1418
1390 Enclave Pkwy, Houston TX 77077
Tel (281) 584-1390
SIC 5141 5142 5143 5144 5145 5146

■ SYSCO USA II LLC p 1418
1390 Enclave Pkwy, Houston TX 77077
Tel (281) 584-1390
SIC 5141 5143 5144 5145 5146

■ SYSCO NORTH TEXAS p 1417
800 Trinity Dr, Lewisville TX 75056
Tel (469) 384-6000 SIC 5141

■ MCLANE HIGH PLAINS INC p 931
1717 E Loop 289, Lubbock TX 79403
Tel (806) 766-2900 SIC 5141 5142 5113

WUESTS INC p 1628
9318 Fm 725, Mc Queeney TX 78123
Tel (830) 379-3442 SIC 5141 5411 0173

■ SYSCO CENTRAL TEXAS INC p 1416
1260 Schwab Rd, New Braunfels TX 78132
Tel (830) 730-1000 SIC 5141

CROSSMARK INC p 394
5100 Legacy Dr, Plano TX 75024
Tel (469) 814-1000 SIC 5141 5912 7299

LABATT INSTITUTIONAL SUPPLY CO INC p 836
4500 Industry Park Dr, San Antonio TX 78218
Tel (210) 661-4216 SIC 5141

■ KROGER TEXAS LP p 830
19245 David Memorial Dr, Shenandoah TX 77385
Tel (713) 507-4800 SIC 5141 5411

WHOLESOME SWEETENERS INC p 1607
14141 Southwest Fwy # 160, Sugar Land TX 77478
Tel (281) 275-3199 SIC 5141

GSC ENTERPRISES INC p 643
130 Hillcrest Dr, Sulphur Springs TX 75482
Tel (903) 885-7621 SIC 5141 6099

■ MCLANE CO INC p 930
4747 Mclane Pkwy, Temple TX 76504
Tel (254) 771-7500
SIC 5141 5149 5311 5113

■ MCLANE/SOUTHERN CALIFORNIA INC p 931
4472 Georgia Blvd, Temple TX 76504
Tel (909) 887-7500 SIC 5141

■ MCLANE/SUNEAST INC p 931
4747 Mclane Pkwy, Temple TX 76504
Tel (254) 771-7500 SIC 5141

■ C D HARTNETT CO p 232
302 N Main St, Weatherford TX 76086
Tel (817) 594-3813 SIC 5141 5122

ASSOCIATED FOOD STORES INC p 120
1850 W 2100 S, Salt Lake City UT 84119
Tel (801) 973-4400
SIC 5141 5147 5142 5148 5122 5023

NICHOLAS & CO INC p 1042
5520 W Harold Gatty Dr, Salt Lake City UT 84116
Tel (801) 531-1100 SIC 5046 5141 5142

CAPITAL CANDY CO INC p 249
32 Burnham St, Barre VT 05641
Tel (802) 476-6689
SIC 5145 5194 5122 5141 5149

K-VA-T FOOD STORES INC p 799
1 Food City Cir E, Abingdon VA 24210
Tel (800) 826-8451 SIC 5411 5141 6512

MID-MOUNTAIN FOODS INC p 963
26331 Hillman Hwy, Abingdon VA 24210
Tel (276) 623-5000 SIC 5141

J L CULPEPPER & CO INC p 771
201 Haley Rd, Ashland VA 23005
Tel (804) 752-6576 SIC 5141

MERCHANTS GROCERY CO INC p 944
800 Maddox Dr, Culpeper VA 22701
Tel (540) 825-0786 SIC 5194 5141 5145

■ MCLANE/MID-ATLANTIC INC p 931
56 Mclane Dr, Fredericksburg VA 22406
Tel (540) 374-2000 SIC 5141

■ VIRGINIA FOODSERVICE GROUP LLC p 1559
7420 Ranco Rd, Henrico VA 23228
Tel (804) 237-1001 SIC 5141 5046

■ RICHFOOD INC p 1233
8258 Richfood Rd, Mechanicsville VA 23116
Tel (804) 746-6000
SIC 5141 5147 5142 5148 5143 2026

■ AFFLINK HOLDING CORP p 32
12500 West Creek Pkwy, Richmond VA 23238
Tel (804) 484-6217 SIC 5141

▲ PERFORMANCE FOOD GROUP CO p 1135
12500 West Creek Pkwy, Richmond VA 23238
Tel (804) 484-7700 SIC 5141

PFG HOLDINGS LLC p 1140
12500 West Creek Pkwy, Richmond VA 23238
Tel (804) 484-7700
SIC 5141 5144 5147 5146 5142 5148

■ PFGC INC p 1140
12500 West Creek Pkwy, Richmond VA 23238
Tel (804) 484-7700 SIC 5141 5142

■ SYSCO HAMPTON ROADS INC p 1417
7000 Harbour View Blvd, Suffolk VA 23435
Tel (757) 399-2451 SIC 5141 5147 5148

SCHENCK FOODS CO INC p 1286
3578 Valley Pike, Winchester VA 22602
Tel (540) 869-1870
SIC 5141 5142 5087 5147 5148

FLOYD PETERSON CO p 561
1102 D St Ne, Auburn WA 98002
Tel (253) 735-0313 SIC 5141 5149 5143

COSTCO WHOLESALE CANADA LTD p 374
999 Lake Dr Ste 200, Issaquah WA 98027
Tel (425) 313-8100 SIC 5141

■ SYSCO SEATTLE INC p 1418
22820 54th Ave S, Kent WA 98032
Tel (206) 622-2261 SIC 5142 5141

HARBOR WHOLESALE GROCERY INC p 660
3901 Hogum Bay Rd Ne, Lacey WA 98516
Tel (360) 754-4484
SIC 5141 5194 5142 5122

ASSOCIATED GROCERS INC p 120
3301 S Norfolk St, Seattle WA 98118
Tel (206) 762-2100
SIC 5141 5147 5143 5122 5148 5142

DAVID OPPENHEIMER & CO I LLC p 415
180 Nickerson St Ste 211, Seattle WA 98109
Tel (206) 284-1705 SIC 5141

UWAJIMAYA INC p 1538
4601 6th Ave S, Seattle WA 98108
Tel (206) 624-6248 SIC 5141 5411

URM STORES INC p 1530
7511 N Freya St, Spokane WA 99217
Tel (509) 467-2620 SIC 5141 5147

NORTHERN SALES CO INC p 1056
15022 Puyallup St E # 101, Sumner WA 98390
Tel (253) 299-0500
SIC 5145 5149 5194 5141

FORTHS FOODS INC p 569
3090 Woodville Dr, Huntington WV 25701
Tel (304) 525-3293 SIC 5141 5411

■ SYSCO BARABOO LLC p 1416
910 South Blvd, Baraboo WI 53913
Tel (800) 733-8217
SIC 5141 5142 5046 5148

INDIANHEAD FOODSERVICE DISTRIBUTOR INC p 739
313 N Hastings Pl, Eau Claire WI 54703
Tel (715) 834-2777
SIC 5142 5141 5147 5143

CERTCO INC p 284
5321 Verona Rd, Fitchburg WI 53711
Tel (608) 271-4500 SIC 5141

CHAMBERS & OWEN INC p 287
1733 Morse St, Janesville WI 53545
Tel (608) 752-7865
SIC 5194 5145 5113 5141

■ ROUNDYS SUPERMARKETS INC p 1253
875 E Wscnsin Ave Ste 100, Milwaukee WI 53202
Tel (414) 231-5000 SIC 5411 5141

PIGGLY WIGGLY MIDWEST LLC p 1147
2215 Union Ave, Sheboygan WI 53081
Tel (920) 457-4433 SIC 5141 5411

■ WAUKESHA WHOLESALE FOODS INC p 1583
900 Gale St, Waukesha WI 53186
Tel (262) 542-8841 SIC 5141

SIC 5142 Packaged Frozen Foods Wholesale

■ SYSCO CENTRAL ALABAMA INC p 1416
1000 Sysco Dr, Calera AL 35040
Tel (205) 668-0001
SIC 5149 5147 5142 5144 5143

WOOD-FRUITTICHER GROCERY CO INC p 1622
2900 Alton Rd, Irondale AL 35210
Tel (205) 836-9663
SIC 5142 5141 5147 5087 5046

SHAMROCK FOODS CO p 1311
3900 E Camelback Rd # 300, Phoenix AZ 85018
Tel (602) 477-2500
SIC 5146 5149 5147 5148 5142 2026

SYSTEMS SERVICES OF AMERICA INC p 1419
1640 S 39th Ave, Phoenix AZ 85009
Tel (480) 927-4700
SIC 5147 5113 5142 5149 5143

FOOD SERVICES OF AMERICA INC p 564
16100 N 71st St Ste 400, Scottsdale AZ 85254
Tel (480) 927-4000
SIC 5148 5142 5146 5141

TWIN RIVERS GROUP INC p 1495
1 E Colt Square Dr, Fayetteville AR 72703
Tel (479) 444-8898 SIC 5142

CCF BRANDS LLC p 270
5211 W Village Pkwy # 101, Rogers AR 72758
Tel (479) 464-0544 SIC 5144 5142

VEG LIQUIDATION INC p 1546
305 E Main St, Siloam Springs AR 72761
Tel (479) 524-6431 SIC 2033 5142

TANKERSLEY FOOD SERVICE LLC p 1424
3203 Industrial Park Rd # 303, Van Buren AR 72956
Tel (479) 471-6800 SIC 5142

WEI-CHUAN USA INC p 1587
6655 Garfield Ave, Bell Gardens CA 90201
Tel (323) 587-2101 SIC 5142 2038

BONERTS INC p 200
273 S Canon Dr, Beverly Hills CA 90212
Tel (714) 540-3535 SIC 5142

■ FRESHPOINT OF SOUTHERN CALIFORNIA INC p 579
155 N Orange Ave, City Of Industry CA 91744
Tel (626) 855-1400 SIC 5148 5142

INTERSTATE MEAT & PROVISION p 758
6114 Scott Way, Commerce CA 90040
Tel (323) 838-9400 SIC 5142 5147

ZHONGLU AMERICA CORP p 1643
6055 E Wash Blvd Ste 412, Commerce CA 90040
Tel (323) 869-9999 SIC 5142

■ SYSCO SAN FRANCISCO INC p 1418
5900 Stewart Ave, Fremont CA 94538
Tel (510) 226-3000 SIC 5141 5147 5142

PRODUCERS DAIRY FOODS INC p 1179
250 E Belmont Ave, Fresno CA 93701
Tel (559) 264-6583 SIC 5142 5143

GOLDEN STATE FOODS CORP p 621
18301 Von Karman Ave # 1100, Irvine CA 92612
Tel (949) 252-2000
SIC 5147 2087 5142 5148 5149

■ SYSCO NEWPORT MEAT CO p 1417
16691 Hale Ave, Irvine CA 92606
Tel (949) 399-4200 SIC 5147 5142

SJ DISTRIBUTORS INC p 1328
625 Vista Way, Milpitas CA 95035
Tel (888) 988-2328 SIC 5142 5148 5149

LUSAMERICA FOODS INC p 886
16480 Railroad Ave, Morgan Hill CA 95037
Tel (408) 294-6622 SIC 5146 5142

GOLD STAR FOODS INC p 620
3781 E Airport Dr, Ontario CA 91761
Tel (909) 843-9600 SIC 5142

SPECIALTY BRANDS INC p 1356
4200 Concours Ste 100, Ontario CA 91764
Tel (909) 477-4851 SIC 2038 5142

FOODCOMM INTERNATIONAL p 564
4260 El Camino Real, Palo Alto CA 94306
Tel (650) 813-1300 SIC 5147 5142

■ SYSCO SACRAMENTO INC p 1418
7062 Pacific Ave, Pleasant Grove CA 95668
Tel (916) 275-2714 SIC 5141 5142

■ SYSCO SAN DIEGO INC p 1418
12180 Kirkham Rd, Poway CA 92064
Tel (858) 513-7300
SIC 5141 5142 5147 5148 5084

SANTA MONICA SEAFOOD CO p 1281
18531 S Broadwick St, Rancho Dominguez CA 90220
Tel (310) 886-7900 SIC 5421 5146 5142

TRANSHUMANCE HOLDING CO INC p 1471
2530 River Plaza Dr # 200, Sacramento CA 95833
Tel (530) 758-3091 SIC 5421 5142

LEE BROS FOODSERVICES INC p 851
660 E Gish Rd, San Jose CA 95112
Tel (408) 275-0700 SIC 5141 5142

JORDANOS INC p 793
550 S Patterson Ave, Santa Barbara CA 93111
Tel (805) 964-0611
SIC 5181 5182 5149 5141 5142 5148

▲ CALAVO GROWERS INC p 238
1141 Cummings Rd Ste A, Santa Paula CA 93060
Tel (805) 525-1245 SIC 5148 5142 5149

SUPER STORE INDUSTRIES p 1406
2800 W March Ln Ste 210, Stockton CA 95219
Tel (209) 473-8100
SIC 2026 2024 5149 5142

GOLDEN WEST TRADING INC p 622
4401 S Downey Rd, Vernon CA 90058
Tel (323) 581-3663 SIC 5147 5142

WEST PICO FOODS INC p 1595
5201 S Downey Rd, Vernon CA 90058
Tel (323) 586-9050 SIC 5142 5144

SUPERIOR FOODS INC p 1406
275 Westgate Dr, Watsonville CA 95076
Tel (831) 728-3691 SIC 5142

VPS COMPANIES INC p 1566
310 Walker St, Watsonville CA 95076
Tel (831) 724-7551 SIC 5142 0723 4731

UNITED FOOD SERVICE INC p 1508
5199 Ivy St, Commerce City CO 80022
Tel (303) 289-3595
SIC 5141 5142 5147 5148 5046

DUQUESNE ENERGY SERVCES LLC p 462
4949 S Syracuse St # 550, Denver CO 80237
Tel (832) 278-5980 SIC 2911 5142

■ SYSCO CONNECTICUT LLC p 1417
100 Inwood Rd, Rocky Hill CT 06067
Tel (860) 571-5600 SIC 5149 5142

THURSTON FOODS INC p 1451
30 Thurston Dr, Wallingford CT 06492
Tel (203) 265-1525
SIC 5141 5147 5142 5113

CITY LINE DISTRIBUTORS INC p 312
20 Industry Dr, West Haven CT 06516
Tel (203) 931-3707
SIC 5141 5142 5147 5113

BURRIS LOGISTICS p 228
501 Se 5th St, Milford DE 19963
Tel (302) 839-4531 SIC 5142 4222 4213

COLORADO BOXED BEEF CO p 338
302 Progress Rd, Auburndale FL 33823
Tel (863) 967-0636 SIC 5142 5147

PESCANOVA INC p 1137
1430 S Dixie Hwy Ste 303, Coral Gables FL 33146
Tel (305) 663-4380 SIC 5142

QUIRCH FOODS CO p 1200
2701 S Le Jeune Rd, Coral Gables FL 33134
Tel (305) 691-3535
SIC 5147 5142 5144 5146

BEAVER STREET FISHERIES INC p 166
1741 W St Beaver, Jacksonville FL 32209
Tel (904) 354-5661 SIC 5142 5141

■ SYSCO SOUTH FLORIDA INC p 1418
12500 Nw 112th Ave, Medley FL 33178
Tel (305) 651-5421
SIC 5149 5147 5142 5113 5143 5144

BLUMAR USA LLC p 193
6303 Blue Lagoon Dr 385, Miami FL 33126
Tel (305) 261-2417 SIC 5146 5142

SOUTHEAST FROZEN FOODS CO LP p 1345
3261 Executive Way, Miramar FL 33025
Tel (954) 882-1044 SIC 5142 4222 5411

ROYAL FOOD SERVICE CO INC p 1254
3720 Zip Indus Blvd Se, Atlanta GA 30354
Tel (404) 366-4299 SIC 5148 5142

UNIPRO FOODSERVICE INC p 1505
2500 Cumbrld Pkwy Se 60 Ste 600, Atlanta GA 30339
Tel (770) 952-0871
SIC 5147 5141 5146 5142

IRA HIGDON GROCERY CO p 764
150 Iga Way, Cairo GA 39828
Tel (229) 377-1272
SIC 5141 5147 5142 5143 2111 5194

■ BUCKHEAD BEEF CO INC p 223
4500 Wickersham Dr, College Park GA 30337
Tel (404) 355-4400 SIC 5142 5146 5421

FOC ACQUISITION LLC p 562
146 Forest Pkwy Ste B, Forest Park GA 30297
Tel (404) 361-2201
SIC 5142 5421 5144 2092

CMU & ASSOCIATES INC p 329
55 Holomua St, Hilo HI 96720
Tel (808) 961-0877 SIC 5146 5148 5142

SUISAN CO p 1397
333 Kilauea Ave Ste 202, Hilo HI 96720
Tel (808) 935-8511 SIC 5142 5146

Y HATA & CO LIMITED p 1633
285 Sand Island Access Rd, Honolulu HI 96819
Tel (808) 447-4100 SIC 5142 5141

OCHOA AG UNLIMITED FOODS INC p 1073
910 W Main St Ste 248, Boise ID 83702
Tel (208) 343-6882 SIC 5142

DICKINSON FROZEN FOODS INC p 438
1205 E Iron Eagle Dr B, Eagle ID 83616
Tel (208) 938-7540 SIC 5142

HAAG FOOD SERVICE INC p 651
300 N Haag St, Breese IL 62230
Tel (618) 526-7120 SIC 5142 5144 5141

BADGER FARMS INC p 143
652 N Western Ave, Chicago IL 60612
Tel (773) 278-9100
SIC 5143 5149 5147 5144 5142 5087

■ BRUSS CO p 221
3548 N Kostner Ave, Chicago IL 60641
Tel (773) 282-2900
SIC 5147 5142 2013 2011

LINCOLN PROVISION INC p 868
824 W 38th Pl, Chicago IL 60609
Tel (773) 254-2400 SIC 5142 5147

MID-WEST INSTITUTIONAL FOOD DISTRIBUTORS INC p 964
3100 W 36th St, Chicago IL 60632
Tel (773) 927-8870
SIC 5142 5143 5144 5147 5148

NATIONWIDE FOODS INC p 1017
700 E 107th St, Chicago IL 60628
Tel (773) 787-4900 SIC 2013 5142 5147

■ SYSCO CHICAGO INC p 1416
250 Wieboldt Dr, Des Plaines IL 60016
Tel (847) 699-5400 SIC 5149 5142

HAVI GROUP LIMITED PARTNERSHIP p 668
3500 Lacey Rd Ste 600, Downers Grove IL 60515
Tel (630) 353-4200 SIC 5113 5142 5199

KUNA MEAT CO INC p 832
704 Kuna Industrial Ct, Dupo IL 62239
Tel (618) 286-4000
SIC 5144 5142 5147 5169 5149 5148

WM H LEAHY ASSOCIATES INC p 1620
2350 Ravine Way Ste 200, Glenview IL 60025
Tel (847) 904-5250 SIC 5141 5142

WATERSHED FOODS LLC p 1582
202 N Ford St, Gridley IL 61744
Tel (309) 747-3000 SIC 5142

CENTRAL GROCERS INC p 278
2600 Haven Ave, Joliet IL 60433
Tel (815) 553-8800
SIC 5141 5147 5142 5148 5143 5122

LANTMANNEN UNIBAKE USA INC p 844
5007 Lincoln Ave Ste 300, Lisle IL 60532
Tel (630) 963-4781 SIC 5142

MICHAEL LEWIS CO p 960
8900 W 50th St, Mc Cook IL 60525
Tel (708) 688-2200
SIC 5113 5141 5142 2782 2759 2621

■ FOX RIVER FOODS INC p 572
5030 Baseline Rd, Montgomery IL 60538
Tel (630) 896-1991
SIC 5142 5149 5148 5147

DOT FOODS INC p 451
1 Dot Way, Mount Sterling IL 62353
Tel (217) 773-4411 SIC 5141 5142

NATIONWIDE OF CHICAGO-FOOD BROKERS INC p 1018
915 Harger Rd Ste 110, Oak Brook IL 60523
Tel (630) 286-1500 SIC 5142

JASONS FOODS p 778
208 E Helen Rd, Palatine IL 60067
Tel (847) 358-9901 SIC 5144 5147 5142

KOCH MEAT CO INC p 825
1300 Higgins Rd Ste 100, Park Ridge IL 60068
Tel (847) 384-8018 SIC 5142 5144

MARTIN-BROWER CO L L C p 913
6250 N River Rd Ste 9000, Rosemont IL 60018
Tel (847) 227-6500
SIC 5142 5113 5149 5087

REYES HOLDINGS LLC p 1230
6250 N River Rd Ste 9000, Rosemont IL 60018
Tel (847) 227-6500 SIC 5181 5142

▲ US FOODS HOLDING CORP p 1531
9399 W Higgins Rd Ste 500, Rosemont IL 60018
Tel (847) 720-8000
SIC 5149 5147 5142 5144 5146 5143

■ US FOODS INC p 1531
9399 W Higgins Rd Ste 500, Rosemont IL 60018
Tel (847) 720-8000
SIC 5149 5147 5142 5144 5146 5143

SIMU LTD p 1326
201 Mittel Dr, Wood Dale IL 60191
Tel (630) 350-1060
SIC 5113 5141 5142 2782 2759 2621

STANZ CHEESE CO INC p 1377
1840 Commerce Dr, South Bend IN 46628
Tel (574) 232-6666
SIC 5142 5141 5148 5113 5087 5085

■ SYSCO IOWA INC p 1417
1 Sysco Dr, Ankeny IA 50021
Tel (515) 289-5300
SIC 5149 5147 5142 5144 5113 5143

EARP MEAT CO p 469
2730 S 98th St, Edwardsville KS 66111
Tel (913) 287-3311 *SIC* 5142 5141 5113

ASSOCIATED WHOLESALE GROCERS INC p 121
5000 Kansas Ave, Kansas City KS 66106
Tel (913) 288-1000
SIC 5141 5143 5142 5147 5146 5148

MARCUS FOOD CO p 905
240 N Rock Rd Ste 246, Wichita KS 67206
Tel (316) 686-7649 *SIC* 5144 5142

BROWN FOODSERVICE INC p 219
500 E Clayton Ln, Louisa KY 41230
Tel (606) 638-1139
SIC 5142 5141 5084 5087

DOERLE FOOD SERVICES LLC p 447
113 Kol Dr, Broussard LA 70518
Tel (337) 252-8551
SIC 5142 5141 5087 5148

RIVERSIDE FOOD DISTRIBUTORS LLC p 1238
7251 River Rd, Marrero LA 70072
Tel (504) 328-7383 *SIC* 5142

■ **SYSCO NORTHERN NEW ENGLAND INC** p 1417
55 Thomas Dr, Westbrook ME 04092
Tel (207) 871-0700
SIC 5141 5147 5148 5142

FOODPRO CORP p 564
321 E 5th St, Frederick MD 21701
Tel (301) 663-3171
SIC 5142 5149 5148 5147 5143 5113

GILBERT FOODS LLC p 612
7251 Standard Dr, Hanover MD 21076
Tel (410) 712-6000
SIC 5148 5147 5146 5142

■ **SYSCO BALTIMORE LLC** p 1416
8000 Dorsey Run Rd, Jessup MD 20794
Tel (410) 799-7000 *SIC* 5142 5149 5087

HOLT PAPER AND CHEMICAL CO INC p 702
31375 John Deere Dr, Salisbury MD 21804
Tel (410) 742-7577
SIC 5142 5087 5113 5147

COSTA FRUIT & PRODUCE CO p 374
18 Bunker Hill Indus Park, Boston MA 02129
Tel (617) 241-8007
SIC 5148 5143 5142 5141

MARKETFARE FOODS LLC p 908
222 Rosewood Dr Fl 2, Danvers MA 01923
Tel (978) 716-2530 *SIC* 5142

ISLAND OASIS FROZEN COCKTAIL CO INC p 766
141 Norfolk St, Walpole MA 02081
Tel (508) 660-1177 *SIC* 5142

CARAMAGNO FOODS CO p 252
14255 Dequindre St, Detroit MI 48212
Tel (313) 869-8200 *SIC* 5141 5142

SHERWOOD FOOD DISTRIBUTORS LLC p 1316
12499 Evergreen Ave, Detroit MI 48228
Tel (313) 659-7300
SIC 5147 5144 5146 5142 5143

WOLVERINE PACKING CO p 1621
2535 Rivard St, Detroit MI 48207
Tel (313) 259-7500 *SIC* 5147 2011 5142

ORLEANS INTERNATIONAL INC p 1095
30600 Northwestern Hwy # 300, Farmington Hills MI 48334
Tel (248) 855-5556 *SIC* 5142

NATIONAL FOOD GROUP INC p 1012
46820 Magellan Dr Ste A, Novi MI 48377
Tel (734) 453-4544 *SIC* 5142

GORDON FOOD SERVICE INC p 626
1300 Gezon Pkwy Sw, Wyoming MI 49509
Tel (888) 437-3663
SIC 5149 5142 5147 5146 5144 5143

SCHWANS CONSUMER BRANDS INC p 1291
8500 Normandale Lake Blvd, Bloomington MN 55437
Tel (952) 346-0100 *SIC* 5142

E A SWEEN CO p 466
16101 W 78th St, Eden Prairie MN 55344
Tel (952) 937-9440 *SIC* 2099 5142

■ **NASH-FINCH CO** p 1008
7600 France Ave S Ste 200, Minneapolis MN 55435
Tel (952) 832-0534
SIC 5141 5148 5142 5147 5411

■ **APPERTS INC** p 98
900 Highway 10 S, Saint Cloud MN 56304
Tel (320) 251-3200
SIC 5142 5141 5411 5421 2013

■ **SYSCO WESTERN MINNESOTA INC** p 1418
900 Highway 10 S, Saint Cloud MN 56304
Tel (320) 251-3200
SIC 5141 5142 5143 5144 5145 5146

J & B WHOLESALE DISTRIBUTING INC p 769
13200 43rd St Ne, Saint Michael MN 55376
Tel (763) 497-3913
SIC 5147 5144 5142 5143 5148

■ **SYSCO JACKSON LLC** p 1417
4400 Milwaukee St, Jackson MS 39209
Tel (601) 354-1701 *SIC* 5142

■ **SYSCO ST LOUIS LLC** p 1418
3850 Mueller Rd, Saint Charles MO 63301
Tel (636) 940-9230
SIC 5141 5149 5146 5143 5142

SPRINGFIELD GROCER CO p 1361
2415 W Battlefield St, Springfield MO 65807
Tel (417) 883-4230 *SIC* 5142 5141 5149

■ **SYSCO MONTANA INC** p 1417
1509 Monad Rd, Billings MT 59101
Tel (406) 247-1100 *SIC* 5149 5142 5141

■ **LINCOLN SYSCO INC** p 868
900 King Bird Rd, Lincoln NE 68521
Tel (402) 423-1031
SIC 5148 5142 5143 5141 5087 5113

AFFILIATED FOODS MIDWEST COOPERATIVE INC p 32
1301 W Omaha Ave, Norfolk NE 68701
Tel (402) 371-0555 *SIC* 5141 5142

OMAHA STEAKS INTERNATIONAL INC p 1083
11030 O St, Omaha NE 68137
Tel (402) 597-3000 *SIC* 5142 8741

SHARED SERVICE SYSTEMS INC p 1312
1725 S 20th St, Omaha NE 68108
Tel (402) 536-5300
SIC 5047 5142 7211 5149 5113 7218

■ **E & H DISTRIBUTING LLC** p 465
1685 W Cheyenne Ave, North Las Vegas NV 89032
Tel (702) 636-3663
SIC 5113 5141 5142 5149

C&S WHOLESALE GROCERS INC p 234
7 Corporate Dr, Keene NH 03431
Tel (603) 354-7000
SIC 5141 5147 5143 5142 5122 5145

WHITE ROSE INC p 1606
380 Middlesex Ave, Carteret NJ 07008
Tel (732) 541-5555
SIC 5141 5143 5142 5122 7311 8721

METROPOLITAN FOODS INC p 955
174 Delawanna Ave, Clifton NJ 07014
Tel (973) 672-9400
SIC 5142 5149 2099 5141

ATALANTA CORP p 123
1 Atlanta Plz Ste 3, Elizabeth NJ 07206
Tel (908) 351-8000 *SIC* 5143 5149 5142

REMA FOODS INC p 1222
140 Sylvan Ave Ste 200, Englewood Cliffs NJ 07632
Tel (201) 947-1000 *SIC* 5142 5149 5141

AJINOMOTO NORTH AMERICA INC p 41
400 Kelby St, Fort Lee NJ 07024
Tel (201) 292-3200
SIC 5142 5169 2869 2899

GOYA FOODS INC p 627
350 County Rd, Jersey City NJ 07307
Tel (201) 348-4900 *SIC* 5142

■ **SYSCO METRO NEW YORK LLC** p 1417
20 Theodore Conrad Dr, Jersey City NJ 07305
Tel (201) 451-0997
SIC 5141 5144 5142 5147 5087

DESSERT SERVICE INC p 432
630 Belleville Tpke, Kearny NJ 07032
Tel (201) 246-7292 *SIC* 5142

MITSUI FOODS INC p 978
35 Maple St, Norwood NJ 07648
Tel (201) 750-0500 *SIC* 5142 5149 5499

REDDY RAW INC p 1216
1 Ethel Blvd Ste 1, Wood Ridge NJ 07075
Tel (201) 804-7633 *SIC* 5142 5141

ACE ENDICO CORP p 16
80 International Blvd, Brewster NY 10509
Tel (914) 347-3131 *SIC* 5141 5142 5148

TRIPIFOODS INC p 1482
1427 William St, Buffalo NY 14206
Tel (716) 853-7400
SIC 5141 5194 5145 5143 5142 5122

JETRO CASH AND CARRY ENTERPRISES LLC p 784
1524 132nd St, College Point NY 11356
Tel (718) 939-6400
SIC 5142 5046 5181 5147 5411

JRD HOLDINGS INC p 795
1524 132nd St, College Point NY 11356
Tel (718) 762-8700
SIC 5141 5142 5147 5181 5194

RD FOOD SERVICES LLC p 1212
1524 132nd St, College Point NY 11356
Tel (718) 961-4356
SIC 5141 5148 5142 5113 5046 5087

RESTAURANT DEPOT LLC p 1228
1524 132nd St, College Point NY 11356
Tel (718) 762-8700
SIC 5147 5141 5142 5181 5194

MAINES PAPER & FOOD SERVICE INC p 898
101 Broome Corporate Pkwy, Conklin NY 13748
Tel (607) 779-1200
SIC 5142 5113 5141 5087 5147 5146

INTER-COUNTY BAKERS INC p 751
1095 Long Island Ave A, Deer Park NY 11729
Tel (631) 957-1350 *SIC* 5142

DI CARLO DISTRIBUTORS INC p 436
1630 N Ocean Ave, Holtsville NY 11742
Tel (800) 342-2756 *SIC* 5142 5141 5143

J KINGS FOOD SERVICE PROFESSIONALS INC p 771
700 Furrows Rd, Holtsville NY 11742
Tel (631) 289-8401
SIC 5149 5143 5144 5142 5148

LANDMARK FOOD CORP p 843
865 Waverly Ave, Holtsville NY 11742
Tel (631) 654-4500
SIC 5142 5141 5148 5147

GINSBERGS INSTITUTIONAL FOODS INC p 612
29 Ginsburg Ln, Hudson NY 12534
Tel (518) 828-4004
SIC 5148 5147 5142 5141 5143

WILLOW RUN FOODS INC p 1613
1006 Us Route 11, Kirkwood NY 13795
Tel (607) 338-5221
SIC 5142 5149 5147 5113 5148 5087

PALMER FISH CO INC p 1109
900 Jefferson Rd Ste 1000, Rochester NY 14623
Tel (585) 424-3210
SIC 5146 5147 5142 2013

RIVER VALLEY FOODS INC p 1237
5881 Court Street Rd # 2, Syracuse NY 13206
Tel (315) 437-4636 *SIC* 5142

■ **MCLANE/CAROLINA INC** p 931
7253 Nc 48, Battleboro NC 27809
Tel (252) 972-2500 *SIC* 5141 5142 5149

PDNC LLC p 1125
402 Commerce Ct, Goldsboro NC 27534
Tel (919) 778-3000
SIC 5142 5141 5147 5148 5431

SOUTHERN FOODS INC p 1348
3500 Old Battlegrd Rd A, Greensboro NC 27410
Tel (336) 545-3800
SIC 5147 5143 5146 5148 5142

ALEX LEE INC p 48
120 4th St Sw, Hickory NC 28602
Tel (828) 725-4424
SIC 5141 5142 5147 5148 5194 5411

■ **INSTITUTION FOOD HOUSE INC** p 747
543 12th Street Dr Nw, Hickory NC 28601
Tel (800) 800-0434 *SIC* 5141 5142

MERCHANTS DISTRIBUTORS LLC p 944
5005 Alex Lee Blvd, Hickory NC 28601
Tel (828) 725-4424
SIC 5141 5142 5147 5148 5194 5122

■ **MEADOWBROOK MEAT CO INC** p 934
2641 Meadowbrook Rd, Rocky Mount NC 27801
Tel (252) 985-7200
SIC 5147 5113 5149 5142

E G FORREST CO p 466
1023 N Chestnut St, Winston Salem NC 27101
Tel (336) 723-9151 *SIC* 5142 5141

CAVENDISH FARMS INC p 267
5855 3rd St Se, Jamestown ND 58401
Tel (701) 252-5222 *SIC* 5142 2099

AVALON FOODSERVICE INC p 135
1 Avalon Dr, Canal Fulton OH 44614
Tel (330) 854-4551
SIC 5142 5149 5169 5113 8322 5812

HILLCREST EGG & CHEESE CO p 693
2735 E 40th St, Cleveland OH 44115
Tel (216) 361-4625
SIC 5143 5142 5147 5144 5149 5148

NORTHERN FROZEN FOODS INC p 1056
21500 Alexander Rd, Cleveland OH 44146
Tel (440) 439-0600 *SIC* 5142 5149 5147

■ **SYSCO CENTRAL OHIO INC** p 1416
2400 Harrison Rd, Columbus OH 43204
Tel (614) 272-0658 *SIC* 5141 5142

WHITE CASTLE SYSTEM INC p 1606
555 W Goodale St, Columbus OH 43215
Tel (614) 228-5781
SIC 5812 5142 2051 2013

MAMA ROSAS LLC p 900
1910 Fair Rd, Sidney OH 45365
Tel (937) 498-4511 *SIC* 5141 5142

ANDERSON AND DUBOSE INC p 89
5300 Tod Ave Sw, Warren OH 44481
Tel (440) 248-8800 *SIC* 5142 5141

MATTINGLY FOODS INC p 921
302 State St, Zanesville OH 43701
Tel (740) 454-0136 *SIC* 5149 5142 5141

STEPHENSON WHOLESALE CO INC p 1386
230 S 22nd Ave, Durant OK 74701
Tel (580) 920-0125
SIC 5194 5145 5143 5142 5141 5113

BAMA FROZEN DOUGH LLC p 149
2435 N Lewis Ave, Tulsa OK 74110
Tel (918) 732-2600 *SIC* 5142

PACIFIC SEA FOOD CO INC p 1106
16797 Se 130th Ave, Clackamas OR 97015
Tel (503) 905-4500 *SIC* 5146 5142

MAJOR EAGLE INC p 899
2350 W Broadway, Eugene OR 97402
Tel (541) 345-8421
SIC 5181 5141 5194 5142

ALPINE FOOD DISTRIBUTING INC p 60
2400 Se Mailwell Dr, Milwaukie OR 97222
Tel (503) 905-5201 *SIC* 5142 5149

AAS HOLDING CO p 8
2401 Ne Argyle St, Portland OR 97211
Tel (503) 284-3314 *SIC* 5147 5142 5141

AJINOMOTO NORTH AMERICA HOLDINGS INC p 41
7124 N Marine Dr, Portland OR 97203
Tel (503) 505-5783
SIC 5142 6719 2038 2037

WESTERN BOXED MEATS DISTRIBUTORS p 1597
2401 Ne Argyle St, Portland OR 97211
Tel (503) 284-3314 *SIC* 5147 5142

WESTERN FAMILY FOODS INC p 1598
6700 Sw Sandburg St, Portland OR 97223
Tel (503) 639-6300 *SIC* 5141 5142

WESTERN FAMILY HOLDING CO p 1598
6700 Sw Sandburg St, Tigard OR 97223
Tel (503) 639-6300
SIC 5141 5142 5199 5122 5149

IMLERS POULTRY LP p 734
1887 Route 764, Duncansville PA 16635
Tel (814) 943-5563
SIC 5144 5147 5141 5142

MCANENY BROTHERS INC p 926
470 Industrial Park Rd, Ebensburg PA 15931
Tel (814) 472-9800
SIC 5141 5147 5148 5194 5113 5142

CA CURTZE CO p 234
1717 E 12th St, Erie PA 16511
Tel (814) 452-2281 *SIC* 5141 5147 5142

■ **SYSCO PITTSBURGH LLC** p 1417
1 Whitney Dr, Harmony PA 16037
Tel (724) 452-2100
SIC 5142 5149 5148 5023 5113 5046

CEDAR FARMS CO INC p 272
2100 Hornig Rd, Philadelphia PA 19116
Tel (215) 934-7100
SIC 5142 5144 5143 5149

HONOR HOLDINGS INC p 705
1801 N 5th St, Philadelphia PA 19122
Tel (215) 236-1700 *SIC* 5141 5142

QUAKER VALLEY FOODS INC p 1196
2701 Red Lion Rd, Philadelphia PA 19114
Tel (215) 992-0900 *SIC* 5142

LENTZ MILLING CO p 856
2045 N 11th St, Reading PA 19604
Tel (610) 921-0666 *SIC* 5149 5142

ASSOCIATED WHOLESALERS INC p 121
336 E Penn Ave, Robesonia PA 19551
Tel (610) 693-3161
SIC 5141 5147 5122 5142 5148 5411

POCONO PRODUCE CO INC p 1158
Chipperfield Dr Rr 191, Stroudsburg PA 18360
Tel (570) 421-1533 *SIC* 5149 5142 5148

JOSE SANTIAGO INC p 793
5 Calle Marginal # 5, Bayamon PR 00959
Tel (787) 288-8835 *SIC* 5142 5149

NORTHWESTERN SELECTA INC p 1061
796 Calle C M Julia Indst, San Juan PR 00920
Tel (787) 781-1950 *SIC* 5147 5146 5142

TRAFON GROUP INC p 1469
Mercado Cntl 1229 Crr 28 St Mercado Centr, San Juan PR 00920
Tel (787) 783-0011 *SIC* 5142

ALL AMERICAN FOODS INC p 51
1 All American Way, North Kingstown RI 02852
Tel (401) 294-5455 *SIC* 5147 5146 5142

▲ **UNITED NATURAL FOODS INC** p 1510
313 Iron Horse Way, Providence RI 02908
Tel (401) 528-8634 *SIC* 5149 5122 5142

■ **SYSCO COLUMBIA LLC** p 1417
131 Sysco Ct, Columbia SC 29209
Tel (803) 239-4000
SIC 5141 5046 5142 5147 5148

INSTITUTIONAL WHOLESALE CO INC p 747
535 Dry Valley Rd, Cookeville TN 38506
Tel (931) 537-4000 *SIC* 5141 5142

■ **KENNETH O LESTER CO INC** p 811
245 N Castle Heights Ave, Lebanon TN 37087
Tel (615) 444-9901 *SIC* 5141 5142 5148

MONOGRAM FOOD SOLUTIONS LLC p 984
530 Oak Court Dr Ste 400, Memphis TN 38117
Tel (901) 685-7167 *SIC* 5142 2013 5147

■ **SYSCO NASHVILLE LLC** p 1417
1 Hermitage Plz, Nashville TN 37209
Tel (615) 350-7100 *SIC* 5142 5149

BRENHAM WHOLESALE GROCERY CO INC p 210
602 W First St, Brenham TX 77833
Tel (979) 836-7925
SIC 5194 5147 5142 5141 5148

■ **FRESHPOINT DALLAS INC** p 579
4721 Simonton Rd, Dallas TX 75244
Tel (972) 385-5800 *SIC* 5148 5142

LOCAL & WESTERN OF TEXAS INC p 872
5445 La Sierra Dr Ste 100, Dallas TX 75231
Tel (214) 750-6633 *SIC* 5142

2ML REAL ESTATE INTERESTS INC p 2
952 Echo Ln Ste 314, Houston TX 77024
Tel (713) 747-5000 *SIC* 5141 5142 5122

CHUNGS PRODUCTS LP p 305
3907 Dennis St, Houston TX 77004
Tel (713) 741-2118 *SIC* 5142 2038

GLAZIER FOODS CO p 614
11303 Antoine Dr, Houston TX 77066
Tel (713) 869-6411 *SIC* 5142 5141

■ **HOUSTON SYSCO INC** p 712
10710 Grens Crossing Blvd, Houston TX 77038
Tel (713) 672-8080
SIC 5149 5142 5046 5141 2099

JAKES INC p 776
13400 Hollister Dr, Houston TX 77086
Tel (713) 868-1301 *SIC* 5144 5142 5141

PREFERRED FOODS MARTIN L P p 1169
2011 Silver St, Houston TX 77007
Tel (713) 869-6191
SIC 5142 2015 2011 5141 5144

▲ **SYSCO CORP** p 1417
1390 Enclave Pkwy, Houston TX 77077
Tel (281) 584-1390
SIC 5149 5142 5143 5144 5148 5137

■ **SYSCO HOLDINGS LLC** p 1417
1390 Enclave Pkwy, Houston TX 77077
Tel (281) 584-1728
SIC 5141 5142 5143 5144 5145 5146

■ **SYSCO USA I INC** p 1418
1390 Enclave Pkwy, Houston TX 77077
Tel (281) 584-1390
SIC 5141 5142 5143 5144 5145 5146

■ **MCLANE HIGH PLAINS INC** p 931
1717 E Loop 289, Lubbock TX 79403
Tel (806) 766-2900 *SIC* 5141 5142 5113

MAGIC VALLEY FRESH FROZEN LLC p 895
3701 W Military Hwy, Mcallen TX 78503
Tel (956) 994-8947 *SIC* 5142

HASSLOCHER ENTERPRISES INC p 667
8520 Crownhill Blvd, San Antonio TX 78209
Tel (210) 828-1493 *SIC* 5812 5142 6552

ASSOCIATED FOOD STORES INC p 120
1850 W 2100 S, Salt Lake City UT 84119
Tel (801) 973-4400
SIC 5141 5147 5142 5148 5122 5023

NICHOLAS & CO INC p 1042
5520 W Harold Gatty Dr, Salt Lake City UT 84116
Tel (801) 531-1100 *SIC* 5046 5141 5142

■ **RICHFOOD INC** p 1233
8258 Richfood Rd, Mechanicsville VA 23116
Tel (804) 746-6000
SIC 5141 5147 5142 5148 5143 2026

PFG HOLDINGS LLC p 1140
12500 West Creek Pkwy, Richmond VA 23238
Tel (804) 484-7700
SIC 5141 5144 5147 5146 5142 5148

■ **PFGC INC** p 1140
12500 West Creek Pkwy, Richmond VA 23238
Tel (804) 484-7700 *SIC* 5141 5142

■ **SYSCO VIRGINIA LLC** p 1418
5081 S Valley Pike, Rockingham VA 22801
Tel (540) 434-0761
SIC 5149 5142 5113 5148 5147 5143

VIE DE FRANCE YAMAZAKI INC p 1556
2070 Chain Bridge Rd # 500, Vienna VA 22182
Tel (703) 442-9205 *SIC* 5142 5461

SCHENCK FOODS CO INC p 1286
3578 Valley Pike, Winchester VA 22602
Tel (540) 869-1870
SIC 5141 5142 5087 5147 5148

■ **SYSCO SEATTLE INC** p 1418
22820 54th Ave S, Kent WA 98032
Tel (206) 622-2261 *SIC* 5142 5141

HARBOR WHOLESALE GROCERY INC p 660
3901 Hogum Bay Rd Ne, Lacey WA 98516
Tel (360) 754-4484
SIC 5141 5194 5142 5122

ASSOCIATED GROCERS INC p 120
3301 S Norfolk St, Seattle WA 98118
Tel (206) 762-2100
SIC 5141 5147 5143 5122 5148 5142

SUGAR MOUNTAIN CAPITAL LLC p 1397
801 Blanchard St Ste 300, Seattle WA 98121
Tel (206) 322-1644 *SIC* 5142

COLUMBIA FRUIT LLC p 340
2530 Dike Rd, Woodland WA 98674
Tel (360) 225-9575 *SIC* 5142 5411

SLEDD CO CHAS M p 1331
100 E Cove Ave, Wheeling WV 26003
Tel (800) 333-0374 *SIC* 5194 5142 5149

■ **SYSCO BARABOO LLC** p 1416
910 South Blvd, Baraboo WI 53913
Tel (800) 733-8217
SIC 5141 5142 5046 5148

INDIANHEAD FOODSERVICE DISTRIBUTOR INC p 739
313 N Hastings Pl, Eau Claire WI 54703
Tel (715) 834-2777
SIC 5142 5141 5147 5143

SIC 5143 Dairy Prdts, Except Dried Or Canned Wholesale

■ **SYSCO CENTRAL ALABAMA INC** p 1416
1000 Sysco Dr, Calera AL 35040
Tel (205) 668-0001
SIC 5149 5147 5142 5144 5143

BORDEN DAIRY CO OF ALABAMA LLC p 201
509 S Craft Hwy, Mobile AL 36617
Tel (251) 456-3381 *SIC* 5143

SYSTEMS SERVICES OF AMERICA INC p 1419
1640 S 39th Ave, Phoenix AZ 85009
Tel (480) 927-4700
SIC 5147 5113 5142 5149 5143

NESTLE ICE CREAM CO p 1027
7301 District Blvd, Bakersfield CA 93313
Tel (661) 398-3500 *SIC* 5143 5451

LOS ALTOS FOOD PRODUCTS INC p 878
450 Baldwin Park Blvd, City Of Industry CA 91746
Tel (626) 330-6555 *SIC* 5143

ROCKVIEW DAIRIES INC p 1245
7011 Stewart And Gray Rd, Downey CA 90241
Tel (562) 927-5511 *SIC* 5149 5143 2026

CHALLENGE DAIRY PRODUCTS INC p 286
6701 Donlon Way, Dublin CA 94568
Tel (925) 828-6160 *SIC* 5143 5149

DAIRYAMERICA INC p 409
7815 N Palm Ave Ste 250, Fresno CA 93711
Tel (559) 251-0992 *SIC* 5143

PRODUCERS DAIRY FOODS INC p 1179
250 E Belmont Ave, Fresno CA 93701
Tel (559) 264-6583 *SIC* 5142 5143

LUBERSKI INC p 883
310 N Harbor Blvd Ste 205, Fullerton CA 92832
Tel (714) 680-3447 *SIC* 5144 5143

■ **BERKELEY FARMS LLC** p 175
25500 Clawiter Rd, Hayward CA 94545
Tel (510) 265-8600 *SIC* 5143 2026 0241

COLUMBUS FOODS LLC p 342
30977 San Antonio St, Hayward CA 94544
Tel (510) 921-3400 *SIC* 2011 5143 5147

PACIFIC CHEESE CO INC p 1104
21090 Cabot Blvd, Hayward CA 94545
Tel (510) 784-8800 *SIC* 5143

CACIQUE DISTRIBUTORS US p 236
14923 Proctor Ave, La Puente CA 91746
Tel (626) 961-3399 *SIC* 5143

FOSTER DAIRY PRODUCTS DISTRIBUTING p 570
529 Kansas Ave, Modesto CA 95351
Tel (209) 576-3400 *SIC* 5143 2026

DREYERS GRAND ICE CREAM HOLDINGS INC p 456
5929 College Ave, Oakland CA 94618
Tel (510) 652-8187 *SIC* 5143 5451 2024

EDYS GRAND ICE CREAM p 480
5929 College Ave, Oakland CA 94618
Tel (510) 652-8187 *SIC* 2024 5143

DPI SPECIALTY FOODS INC p 454
601 S Rockefeller Ave, Ontario CA 91761
Tel (909) 390-0892 *SIC* 5149 5143

IDB HOLDINGS INC p 728
601 S Rockefeller Ave, Ontario CA 91761
Tel (909) 390-5624 *SIC* 5143 2022

BON SUISSE INC p 199
11860 Cmnty Rd Ste 100, Poway CA 92064
Tel (858) 486-0005 *SIC* 5143

MPCI HOLDINGS INC p 995
7850 Waterville Rd, San Diego CA 92154
Tel (619) 294-2222
SIC 5147 5143 5148 5113

SSI-TURLOCK DAIRY DIVISION p 1364
2600 Spengler Way, Turlock CA 95380
Tel (209) 668-2100
SIC 5143 2024 5144 2022

■ **TONYS FINE FOODS** p 1460
3575 Reed Ave, West Sacramento CA 95605
Tel (916) 374-4000 *SIC* 5147 5143 5149

SOUTHEAST MILK INC p 1346
1950 Se County Hwy 484, Belleview FL 34420
Tel (352) 245-2437 *SIC* 5143 2048

MONTEBIANCO USA LLC p 986
2315 Nw 107th Ave Ste 75, Doral FL 33172
Tel (305) 597-8248 *SIC* 5143

■ **SYSCO SOUTH FLORIDA INC** p 1418
12500 Nw 112th Ave, Medley FL 33178
Tel (305) 651-5421
SIC 5149 5147 5142 5113 5143 5144

■ **DEAN DAIRY HOLDINGS LLC** p 420
6851 Ne 2nd Ave, Miami FL 33138
Tel (305) 795-7700 *SIC* 5143

INTERFOOD INC p 752
777 Brickell Ave Ste 702, Miami FL 33131
Tel (786) 953-8320 *SIC* 5143

SUNSHINE STATE DAIRY FARMS LLC p 1404
3304 Sydney Rd, Plant City FL 33566
Tel (813) 754-1847 *SIC* 5143 2048

■ **FRESHPOINT SOUTH FLORIDA INC** p 579
2300 Nw 19th St, Pompano Beach FL 33069
Tel (954) 917-7272 *SIC* 5148 5143

BORDEN DAIRY CO OF FLORIDA LLC p 201
308 Avenue G Sw, Winter Haven FL 33880
Tel (863) 297-7300
SIC 5143 2026 2024 2022 2021

FOCUS BRANDS INC p 562
5620 Glenridge Dr, Atlanta GA 30342
Tel (404) 255-3250 *SIC* 5461 5143 6794

RUSSELL MCCALLS INC p 1259
255 Ted Turner Dr Sw, Atlanta GA 30303
Tel (404) 954-7600 *SIC* 5149 5143 5147

IRA HIGDON GROCERY CO p 764
150 Iga Way, Cairo GA 39828
Tel (229) 377-1272
SIC 5141 5147 5142 5143 2111 5194

SUTHERLANDS FOODSERVICE INC p 1410
16 Forest Pkwy Bldg K, Forest Park GA 30297
Tel (404) 366-8550
SIC 5144 5148 5147 5143 5141

CHEESE MERCHANTS OF AMERICA LLC p 292
1301 Schiferl Rd, Bartlett IL 60103
Tel (630) 221-0580 *SIC* 5143 2022

P F D SUPPLY CORP p 1102
1100 Broadway, Carlinville IL 62626
Tel (217) 854-2547 *SIC* 5143

BADGER FARMS INC p 143
652 N Western Ave, Chicago IL 60612
Tel (773) 278-9100
SIC 5143 5149 5147 5144 5142 5087

DUTCH FARMS INC p 463
700 E 107th St, Chicago IL 60628
Tel (773) 660-0900 *SIC* 5143

MID-WEST INSTITUTIONAL FOOD DISTRIBUTORS INC p 964
3100 W 36th St, Chicago IL 60632
Tel (773) 927-8870
SIC 5142 5143 5144 5147 5148

CENTRAL GROCERS INC p 278
2600 Haven Ave, Joliet IL 60433
Tel (815) 553-8800
SIC 5141 5147 5142 5148 5143 5122

CHICAGO DAIRY CORP p 297
27820 Irma Lee Cir # 200, Lake Forest IL 60045
Tel (847) 680-0300 *SIC* 5143

WISCON CORP p 1618
2050 N 15th Ave, Melrose Park IL 60160
Tel (708) 450-0074 *SIC* 5143 2022

MID-WEST DAIRYMENS CO p 964
4313 W State St, Rockford IL 61102
Tel (815) 968-0504 *SIC* 5143

▲ **US FOODS HOLDING CORP** p 1531
9399 W Higgins Rd Ste 500, Rosemont IL 60018
Tel (847) 720-8000
SIC 5149 5147 5142 5144 5146 5143

■ **US FOODS INC** p 1531
9399 W Higgins Rd Ste 500, Rosemont IL 60018
Tel (847) 720-8000
SIC 5149 5147 5142 5144 5146 5143

JEL SERT CO p 782
Conde St Rr 59, West Chicago IL 60185
Tel (630) 231-7590
SIC 2087 2024 2099 5499 5143

■ **SYSCO IOWA INC** p 1417
1 Sysco Dr, Ankeny IA 50021
Tel (515) 289-5300
SIC 5149 5147 5142 5144 5113 5143

SWISS VALLEY FARMS COOPERATIVE p 1413
247 Research Pkwy, Davenport IA 52806
Tel (563) 468-6600
SIC 5143 2022 5191 2023

LOMAR DISTRIBUTING INC p 875
2500 Dixon St, Des Moines IA 50316
Tel (515) 244-3105 *SIC* 5143 5149

ASSOCIATED WHOLESALE GROCERS INC p 121
5000 Kansas Ave, Kansas City KS 66106
Tel (913) 288-1000
SIC 5141 5143 5142 5147 5146 5148

BORDEN DAIRY CO OF KENTUCKY LLC p 201
221 W Highway 80, London KY 40741
Tel (606) 878-7301 *SIC* 5143

LAUREL GROCERY CO LLC p 847
129 Barbourville Rd, London KY 40744
Tel (606) 878-6601
SIC 5141 5147 5122 5143

SURE WINNER FOODS INC p 1408
2 Lehner Rd, Saco ME 04072
Tel (207) 282-1258 *SIC* 5143 4226 2024

FOODPRO CORP p 564
321 E 5th St, Frederick MD 21701
Tel (301) 663-3171
SIC 5142 5149 5148 5147 5143 5113

MMSP INC p 979
1920 Stanford Ct, Landover MD 20785
Tel (301) 773-2175
SIC 5143 5144 5146 5147

COSTA FRUIT & PRODUCE CO p 374
18 Bunker Hill Indus Park, Boston MA 02129
Tel (617) 241-8007
SIC 5148 5143 5142 5141

FREEZE OPERATIONS HOLDING CORP p 577
1855 Boston Rd, Wilbraham MA 01095
Tel (413) 543-2445 *SIC* 5812 2024 5143

SHERWOOD FOOD DISTRIBUTORS LLC p 1316
12499 Evergreen Ave, Detroit MI 48228
Tel (313) 659-7300
SIC 5147 5144 5146 5142 5143

MELODY FOODS INC p 941
30777 Northwestern Hwy # 300, Farmington Hills MI 48334
Tel (248) 851-6990
SIC 5143 2026 5149 5145

■ **MICHIGAN DAIRY LLC** p 960
29601 Industrial Rd, Livonia MI 48150
Tel (734) 367-5390 *SIC* 5143

MICHIGAN MILK PRODUCERS ASSOCIATION p 961
41310 Bridge St, Novi MI 48375
Tel (248) 474-6672
SIC 5143 2023 2021 8611 2026

DETROIT CITY DAIRY p 433
21405 Trolley Indus Dr, Taylor MI 48180
Tel (313) 295-6300
SIC 5143 5141 5147 5149

GORDON FOOD SERVICE INC p 626
1300 Gezon Pkwy Sw, Wyoming MI 49509
Tel (888) 437-3663
SIC 5149 5142 5147 5146 5144 5143

POLKA DOT DAIRY INC p 1160
110 17th St E, Hastings MN 55033
Tel (651) 438-2793 *SIC* 5143

■ **CRYSTAL FARMS REFRIGERATED DISTRIBUTION CO** p 396
301 Carlson Pkwy Ste 400, Minnetonka MN 55305
Tel (800) 672-8260 *SIC* 5143 5144

■ **MICHAEL FOODS GROUP INC** p 960
301 Carlson Pkwy Ste 400, Minnetonka MN 55305
Tel (952) 258-4000
SIC 0252 2015 5144 5143 5148 6719

■ **MICHAEL FOODS INC** p 960
301 Carlson Pkwy Ste 400, Minnetonka MN 55305
Tel (507) 237-4600
SIC 0252 2015 5144 5143 5148 5499

■ **MICHAEL FOODS OF DELAWARE INC** p 960
301 Carlson Pkwy Ste 400, Minnetonka MN 55305
Tel (952) 258-4000
SIC 0252 2015 5144 5143 5148 2024

ASSOCIATED MILK PRODUCERS INC p 121
315 N Brdwy St, New Ulm MN 56073
Tel (507) 354-8295
SIC 2023 2022 2021 2024 2026 5143

■ **SYSCO WESTERN MINNESOTA INC** p 1418
900 Highway 10 S, Saint Cloud MN 56304
Tel (320) 251-3200
SIC 5141 5142 5143 5144 5145 5146

J & B WHOLESALE DISTRIBUTING INC p 769
13200 43rd St Ne, Saint Michael MN 55376
Tel (763) 497-3913
SIC 5147 5144 5142 5143 5148

BIX PRODUCE CO LLC p 185
1415 L Orient St, Saint Paul MN 55117
Tel (651) 487-8000 *SIC* 5148 5143

■ **SYSCO ST LOUIS LLC** p 1418
3850 Mueller Rd, Saint Charles MO 63301
Tel (636) 940-9230
SIC 5141 5149 5146 5143 5142

HILAND DAIRY FOODS CO LLC p 692
1133 E Kearney St, Springfield MO 65803
Tel (417) 862-9311
SIC 2026 2024 2037 5143

■ **LINCOLN SYSCO INC** p 868
900 King Bird Rd, Lincoln NE 68521
Tel (402) 423-1031
SIC 5148 5142 5143 5141 5087 5113

■ **MODEL DAIRY LLC** p 981
500 Gould St, Reno NV 89502
Tel (775) 788-7900 *SIC* 2026 5143

C&S WHOLESALE GROCERS INC p 234
7 Corporate Dr, Keene NH 03431
Tel (603) 354-7000
SIC 5141 5147 5143 5142 5122 5145

ARLA FOODS INC p 110
106 Allen Rd Ste 401, Basking Ridge NJ 07920
Tel (908) 604-6551 *SIC* 5143

MILK INDUSTRY MANAGEMENT CORP p 969
4 Manhattan Dr, Burlington NJ 08016
Tel (609) 747-9542 *SIC* 5143

PORKY PRODUCTS INC p 1161
400 Port Carteret Dr, Carteret NJ 07008
Tel (732) 541-0200
SIC 5147 5146 5144 5143

WHITE ROSE INC p 1606
380 Middlesex Ave, Carteret NJ 07008
Tel (732) 541-5555
SIC 5141 5143 5142 5122 7311 8721

ATALANTA CORP p 123
1 Atlanta Plz Ste 3, Elizabeth NJ 07206
Tel (908) 351-8000 *SIC* 5143 5149 5142

SCHRATTER FOODS INC p 1290
333 Fairfield Rd Ste 2, Fairfield NJ 07004
Tel (973) 461-2400 *SIC* 5143 5149

CREAM-O-LAND DAIRIES LLC p 390
529 Cedar Ln, Florence NJ 08518
Tel (609) 499-3601 *SIC* 5143

CREAM-O-LAND DAIRY INC p 390
529 Cedar Ln, Florence NJ 08518
Tel (609) 499-3601 *SIC* 5143 5149

S BERTRAM INC p 1262
3401 Tremley Point Rd, Linden NJ 07036
Tel (908) 862-8200 *SIC* 5143 5141

CLOFINE DAIRY PRODUCTS INC p 327
1407 New Rd, Linwood NJ 08221
Tel (609) 653-1000 *SIC* 5143 5149

SIMCO LOGISTICS INC p 1324
101 Commerce Dr, Moorestown NJ 08057
Tel (856) 813-2300 *SIC* 5143

TROPICAL CHEESE INDUSTRIES INC p 1484
452 Fayette St, Perth Amboy NJ 08861
Tel (732) 442-4898 *SIC* 2022 5143

FARMLAND DAIRIES LLC p 530
520 Main Ave, Wallington NJ 07057
Tel (973) 777-2500 *SIC* 5143 2026 2023

SOUTHWEST CHEESE CO LLC p 1351
1141 Cr N Ste 4, Clovis NM 88101
Tel (575) 742-9200 *SIC* 5143 2022

VISTA FOOD EXCHANGE INC p 1562
355 Food Center Dr B101, Bronx NY 10474
Tel (718) 542-4401
SIC 5144 5147 5146 5148 5143

TRIPIFOODS INC p 1482
1427 William St, Buffalo NY 14206
Tel (716) 853-7400
SIC 5141 5194 5145 5143 5142 5122

YANCEYS FANCY INC p 1634
857 Main Rd, Corfu NY 14036
Tel (585) 599-4448 *SIC* 5143

DI CARLO DISTRIBUTORS INC p 436
1630 N Ocean Ave, Holtsville NY 11742
Tel (800) 342-2756 *SIC* 5142 5141 5143

J KINGS FOOD SERVICE PROFESSIONALS INC p 771
700 Furrows Rd, Holtsville NY 11742
Tel (631) 289-8401
SIC 5149 5143 5144 5142 5148

GINSBERGS INSTITUTIONAL FOODS INC p 612
29 Ginsburg Ln, Hudson NY 12534
Tel (518) 828-4004
SIC 5148 5147 5142 5141 5143

BARTLETT DAIRY INC p 157
9004 161st St Ste 609, Jamaica NY 11432
Tel (718) 658-2299 *SIC* 5143 5141

DERLE FARMS INC p 431
15602 Liberty Ave, Jamaica NY 11433
Tel (718) 257-2040 *SIC* 5143

FAGE USA HOLDINGS p 524
1 Opportunity Dr, Johnstown NY 12095
Tel (518) 762-5912 *SIC* 2026 5143

J & J FARMS CREAMERY INC p 769
5748 49th St Ste 1, Maspeth NY 11378
Tel (718) 821-1200 *SIC* 5143 5149

LACTALIS DELI INC p 837
77 Water St Fl Mezz, New York NY 10005
Tel (212) 758-6666 *SIC* 5143 2022

CACTUS HOLDINGS INC p 236
4705 Metropolitan Ave, Ridgewood NY 11385
Tel (718) 417-3770
SIC 5411 5147 5144 5146 5148 5143

SOUTHERN FOODS INC p 1348
3500 Old Battlegrd Rd A, Greensboro NC 27410
Tel (336) 545-3800
SIC 5147 5143 5146 5148 5142

■ **SYSCO CINCINNATI LLC** p 1416
10510 Evendale Dr, Cincinnati OH 45241
Tel (513) 563-6300
SIC 5144 5149 5143 5113

UNITED DAIRY FARMERS INC p 1507
3955 Montgomery Rd, Cincinnati OH 45212
Tel (513) 396-8700
SIC 5411 5143 2026 2024 5541 5451

HILLCREST EGG & CHEESE CO p 693
2735 E 40th St, Cleveland OH 44115
Tel (216) 361-4625
SIC 5143 5142 5147 5144 5149 5148

GREAT LAKES CHEESE CO INC p 633
17825 Great Lakes Pkwy, Hiram OH 44234
Tel (440) 834-2500 *SIC* 5143 2022

COBLENTZ DISTRIBUTING INC p 333
3850 State Route 39, Millersburg OH 44654
Tel (800) 543-6848 *SIC* 5143 5451

■ **INTERNATIONAL MULTIFOODS CORP** p 756
1 Strawberry Ln, Orrville OH 44667
Tel (330) 682-3000
SIC 5145 5149 5143 2048 2041

STEPHENSON WHOLESALE CO INC p 1386
230 S 22nd Ave, Durant OK 74701
Tel (580) 920-0125
SIC 5194 5145 5143 5142 5141 5113

ALOUETTE CHEESE USA LLC p 60
400 S Custer Ave, New Holland PA 17557
Tel (717) 355-8500 *SIC* 5143 2022

CEDAR FARMS CO INC p 272
2100 Hornig Rd, Philadelphia PA 19116
Tel (215) 934-7100
SIC 5142 5144 5143 5149

GIANT EAGLE INC p 610
101 Kappa Dr, Pittsburgh PA 15238
Tel (800) 362-8899
SIC 5411 5141 5147 5148 5143 6794

PUERTO RICO SUPPLIES GROUP INC p 1191
Parkeast, Bayamon PR 00961
Tel (787) 780-4043
SIC 5194 5149 5122 5143 5148

■ **LAND-O-SUN DAIRIES LLC** p 842
2900 Bristol Hwy, Johnson City TN 37601
Tel (423) 283-5700 *SIC* 2026 2024 5143

BLUE BELL CREAMERIES LP p 190
1101 S Blue Bell Rd, Brenham TX 77833
Tel (979) 836-7977 *SIC* 2024 5143

▲ **DEAN FOODS CO** p 420
2711 N Haskell Ave, Dallas TX 75204
Tel (214) 303-3400 *SIC* 2026 2033 5143

■ **DEAN HOLDING CO** p 420
2711 N Haskell Ave, Dallas TX 75204
Tel (214) 303-3400 *SIC* 2023 5143 5451

LALA BRANDED PRODUCTS LLC p 840
8750 N Central Expy # 400, Dallas TX 75231
Tel (214) 459-1100 *SIC* 5143

NATIONAL DAIRY LLC p 1011
8750 N Central Expy # 400, Dallas TX 75231
Tel (469) 587-0190 *SIC* 5143

BASSHAM WHOLESALE EGG CO INC p 159
5409 Hemphill St, Fort Worth TX 76115
Tel (817) 921-1600
SIC 5144 5143 5141 5147

▲ **SYSCO CORP** p 1417
1390 Enclave Pkwy, Houston TX 77077
Tel (281) 584-1390
SIC 5149 5142 5143 5144 5148 5137

■ **SYSCO HOLDINGS LLC** p 1417
1390 Enclave Pkwy, Houston TX 77077
Tel (281) 584-1728
SIC 5141 5142 5143 5144 5145 5146

■ **SYSCO USA I INC** p 1418
1390 Enclave Pkwy, Houston TX 77077
Tel (281) 584-1390
SIC 5141 5142 5143 5144 5145 5146

■ **SYSCO USA II LLC** p 1418
1390 Enclave Pkwy, Houston TX 77077
Tel (281) 584-1390
SIC 5141 5143 5144 5145 5146

LONE STAR MILK PRODUCERS INC p 876
2716 Commerce St, Wichita Falls TX 76301
Tel (817) 781-1194 SIC 5143

CABOT CREAMERY COOPERATIVE INC p 235
193 Home Farm Way, Waitsfield VT 05673
Tel (978) 552-5500 SIC 2022 5143 5451

■ **RICHFOOD INC** p 1233
8258 Richfood Rd, Mechanicsville VA 23116
Tel (804) 746-6000
SIC 5141 5147 5142 5148 5143 2026

MARYLAND AND VIRGINIA MILK PRODUCERS COOPERATIVE ASSOCIATION INC p 914
1985 Isaac Newton Sq W # 200, Reston VA 20190
Tel (703) 742-6800 SIC 5143 2026 5084

■ **SYSCO VIRGINIA LLC** p 1418
5081 S Valley Pike, Rockingham VA 22801
Tel (540) 434-0761
SIC 5149 5142 5113 5148 5147 5143

FLOYD PETERSON CO p 561
1102 D St Ne, Auburn WA 98002
Tel (253) 735-0313 SIC 5141 5149 5143

■ **HAIN REFRIGERATED FOODS INC** p 653
21707 66th Ave W, Mountlake Terrace WA 98043
Tel (425) 485-2476 SIC 2024 5143

DAIRY FRESH FARMS INC p 409
9636 Blomberg St Sw, Olympia WA 98512
Tel (360) 357-9411 SIC 5143

ASSOCIATED GROCERS INC p 120
3301 S Norfolk St, Seattle WA 98118
Tel (206) 762-2100
SIC 5141 5147 5143 5122 5148 5142

DARIGOLD INC p 412
1130 Rainier Ave S, Seattle WA 98144
Tel (206) 284-7220
SIC 2023 2026 2022 5143

INDEPENDENT PROCUREMENT ALLIANCE PROGRAM LLC p 737
1650 Tri Park Way Ste B, Appleton WI 54914
Tel (920) 832-1100 SIC 5143

DAIRYFOOD USA INC p 409
2819 County Road F, Blue Mounds WI 53517
Tel (608) 437-5598 SIC 5143 2022 2023

INDIANHEAD FOODSERVICE DISTRIBUTOR INC p 739
313 N Hastings Pl, Eau Claire WI 54703
Tel (715) 834-2777
SIC 5142 5141 5147 5143

SCHREIBER INTERNATIONAL INC p 1290
425 Pine St, Green Bay WI 54301
Tel (920) 437-7601 SIC 5143

GRASSLAND DAIRY PRODUCTS INC p 632
N8790 Fairground Ave, Greenwood WI 54437
Tel (715) 267-6182 SIC 2021 5143

COOPERATIVE REGIONS OF ORGANIC PRODUCER POOLS p 367
1 Organic Way, La Farge WI 54639
Tel (608) 625-2602 SIC 5148 5143

FARMFIRST DAIRY COOPERATIVE p 530
4001 Nakoosa Trl Ste 100, Madison WI 53714
Tel (608) 244-3373 SIC 5143 8611

MARATHON CHEESE CORP p 904
304 East St, Marathon WI 54448
Tel (715) 443-2211 SIC 2022 5143

COLONY BRANDS INC p 338
1112 7th Ave, Monroe WI 53566
Tel (608) 328-8400 SIC 5961 5143 2051

WISCONSIN CHEESE GROUP LLC p 1618
105 3rd St, Monroe WI 53566
Tel (608) 325-8342 SIC 5143 2022

MASTERS GALLERY FOODS INC p 918
328 Count Hwy Pp Pp, Plymouth WI 53073
Tel (920) 893-8431 SIC 5143

SIC 5144 Poultry & Poultry Prdts Wholesale

■ **SYSCO CENTRAL ALABAMA INC** p 1416
1000 Sysco Dr, Calera AL 35040
Tel (205) 668-0001
SIC 5149 5147 5142 5144 5143

MARSHALL DURBIN FOOD CORP p 911
2830 Commerce Blvd, Irondale AL 35210
Tel (205) 841-7315
SIC 0252 0254 2048 0251 2015 5144

CCF BRANDS LLC p 270
5211 W Village Pkwy # 101, Rogers AR 72758
Tel (479) 464-0544 SIC 5144 5142

OZARK MOUNTAIN POULTRY INC p 1101
750 W E St, Rogers AR 72756
Tel (479) 633-8700 SIC 2015 5144

C B NICHOLS EGG RANCH p 232
331 W Citrus St, Colton CA 92324
Tel (626) 452-9110 SIC 5144 5499

LUBERSKI INC p 883
310 N Harbor Blvd Ste 205, Fullerton CA 92832
Tel (714) 680-3447 SIC 5144 5143

LUBERSKI INC p 883
310 N Harbor Blvd Ste 205, Fullerton CA 92832
Tel (714) 680-3447 SIC 5144

R W ZANT CO p 1203
1470 E 4th St, Los Angeles CA 90033
Tel (323) 980-5457
SIC 5147 5146 5144 4222

DAY-LEE FOODS INC p 417
10350 Hritg Pk Dr Ste 111, Santa Fe Springs CA 90670
Tel (562) 903-3020 SIC 5147 5144 5146

SSI-TURLOCK DAIRY DIVISION p 1364
2600 Spengler Way, Turlock CA 95380
Tel (209) 668-2100
SIC 5143 2024 5144 2022

WEST PICO FOODS INC p 1595
5201 S Downey Rd, Vernon CA 90058
Tel (323) 586-9050 SIC 5142 5144

MOARK LLC p 980
28 Under The Mountain Rd, North Franklin CT 06254
Tel (951) 332-3300
SIC 5144 2048 0252 2015

QUIRCH FOODS CO p 1200
2701 S Le Jeune Rd, Coral Gables FL 33134
Tel (305) 691-3535
SIC 5147 5142 5144 5146

FOODONICS INTERNATIONAL INC p 564
5139 Edgewood Ct, Jacksonville FL 32254
Tel (904) 783-0950 SIC 5144

■ **SYSCO JACKSONVILLE INC** p 1417
1501 Lewis Industrial Dr, Jacksonville FL 32254
Tel (904) 781-5070
SIC 5149 5147 5144 5963

NORTH SOUTH FOODS GROUP INC p 1054
3373 Sterling Ridge Ct, Longwood FL 32779
Tel (407) 805-9075 SIC 5144 5147 5146

■ **SYSCO SOUTH FLORIDA INC** p 1418
12500 Nw 112th Ave, Medley FL 33178
Tel (305) 651-5421
SIC 5149 5147 5142 5113 5143 5144

WINCORP INTERNATIONAL INC p 1615
10025 Nw 116th Way Ste 14, Medley FL 33178
Tel (305) 887-1294
SIC 5191 5083 5199 7338 5144

■ **SYSCO INTERNATIONAL FOOD GROUP INC** p 1417
2401 Police Center Dr, Plant City FL 33566
Tel (813) 707-6161 SIC 5144 5149

AJC INTERNATIONAL INC p 41
1000 Abernathy Rd Ste 600, Atlanta GA 30328
Tel (404) 252-6750
SIC 5144 5147 5148 5146

GERBER AGRI INTERNATIONAL LLC p 608
1000 Parkwood Cir Se # 335, Atlanta GA 30339
Tel (770) 952-4187 SIC 5144 5147

TOSCA SERVICES LLC p 1462
303 Peachtree Center Ave, Atlanta GA 30303
Tel (920) 569-5335 SIC 7359 5144

GOLD CREEK FOODS LLC p 620
686 Highway 9 N, Dawsonville GA 30534
Tel (706) 216-8640 SIC 5144

PILGRIMS PRIDE CORP p 1148
1965 Evergreen Blvd # 100, Duluth GA 30096
Tel (770) 232-4200 SIC 2015 5144 5141

FOC ACQUISITION LLC p 562
146 Forest Pkwy Ste B, Forest Park GA 30297
Tel (404) 361-2201
SIC 5142 5421 5144 2092

SUTHERLANDS FOODSERVICE INC p 1410
16 Forest Pkwy Bldg K, Forest Park GA 30297
Tel (404) 366-8550
SIC 5144 5148 5147 5143 5141

VICTORY FOODS LLC p 1555
1100 Airport Pkwy, Gainesville GA 30501
Tel (678) 343-2070 SIC 5144

INLAND FRESH SEAFOOD CORP OF AMERICA INC p 743
1651 Montreal Cir, Tucker GA 30084
Tel (404) 350-5850 SIC 5146 5144 5147

HAAG FOOD SERVICE INC p 651
300 N Haag St, Breese IL 62230
Tel (618) 526-7120 SIC 5142 5144 5141

BADGER FARMS INC p 143
652 N Western Ave, Chicago IL 60612
Tel (773) 278-9100
SIC 5143 5149 5147 5144 5142 5087

JCG INDUSTRIES INC p 780
4404 W Berteau Ave, Chicago IL 60641
Tel (847) 384-5940 SIC 5144

MID-WEST INSTITUTIONAL FOOD DISTRIBUTORS INC p 964
3100 W 36th St, Chicago IL 60632
Tel (773) 927-8870
SIC 5142 5143 5144 5147 5148

KUNA MEAT CO INC p 832
704 Kuna Industrial Ct, Dupo IL 62239
Tel (618) 286-4000
SIC 5144 5142 5147 5169 5149 5148

NATIONAL PASTEURIZED EGGS INC p 1015
2963 Bernice Rd Ste 1, Lansing IL 60438
Tel (708) 418-8500 SIC 5144

JASONS FOODS p 778
208 E Helen Rd, Palatine IL 60067
Tel (847) 358-9901 SIC 5144 5147 5142

KOCH MEAT CO INC p 825
1300 Higgins Rd Ste 100, Park Ridge IL 60068
Tel (847) 384-8018 SIC 5142 5144

▲ **US FOODS HOLDING CORP** p 1531
9399 W Higgins Rd Ste 500, Rosemont IL 60018
Tel (847) 720-8000
SIC 5149 5147 5142 5144 5146 5143

■ **US FOODS INC** p 1531
9399 W Higgins Rd Ste 500, Rosemont IL 60018
Tel (847) 720-8000
SIC 5149 5147 5142 5144 5146 5143

ED MINIAT LLC p 476
16250 Vincennes Ave, South Holland IL 60473
Tel (708) 589-2400 SIC 5147 5144

MINIAT COMPANIES INC p 973
16250 Vincennes Ave, South Holland IL 60473
Tel (708) 589-2400 SIC 5147 5144

MINIAT HOLDINGS LLC p 973
16250 Vincennes Ave, South Holland IL 60473
Tel (708) 589-2400 SIC 5147 5144

WABASH VALLEY PRODUCE INC p 1570
4886 E 450n, Dubois IN 47527
Tel (812) 678-3131 SIC 5144 5191

TF INTER-HOLDINGS INC p 1445
17141 State Road 4, Goshen IN 46528
Tel (574) 533-0302 SIC 5147 4213 5144

TROYER FOODS INC p 1485
17141 State Road 4, Goshen IN 46528
Tel (574) 533-0302
SIC 5147 5144 5141 5146

MCFARLING FOODS INC p 928
333 W 14th St, Indianapolis IN 46202
Tel (317) 687-6827
SIC 5147 5149 5144 5146

CRYSTAL VALLEY FARMS LLC p 397
9622 W 350 N, Orland IN 46776
Tel (260) 829-6550 SIC 5144

PERISHABLE DISTRIBUTORS OF IOWA LTD p 1136
2741 Se Pdi Pl, Ankeny IA 50021
Tel (515) 965-6300 SIC 5146 5144 5147

■ **SYSCO IOWA INC** p 1417
1 Sysco Dr, Ankeny IA 50021
Tel (515) 289-5300
SIC 5149 5147 5142 5144 5113 5143

MARCUS FOOD CO p 905
240 N Rock Rd Ste 246, Wichita KS 67206
Tel (316) 686-7649 SIC 5144 5142

EQUITY GROUP - KENTUCKY DIVISION LLC p 507
2294 Ky Highway 90 W, Albany KY 42602
Tel (606) 387-2300 SIC 2048 5144

HOLLY POULTRY INC p 701
2221 Berlin St, Baltimore MD 21230
Tel (410) 727-6210 SIC 5144 5147

■ **AM BRIGGS INC** p 63
1920 Stanford Ct, Landover MD 20785
Tel (301) 773-2175 SIC 5147 5144 5146

MMSP INC p 979
1920 Stanford Ct, Landover MD 20785
Tel (301) 773-2175
SIC 5143 5144 5146 5147

GROVE SERVICES (UKRAINE) LLC p 642
100 William St Ste 210, Wellesley MA 02481
Tel (617) 558-1991 SIC 5144

SHERWOOD FOOD DISTRIBUTORS LLC p 1316
12499 Evergreen Ave, Detroit MI 48228
Tel (313) 659-7300
SIC 5147 5144 5146 5142 5143

GORDON FOOD SERVICE INC p 626
1300 Gezon Pkwy Sw, Wyoming MI 49509
Tel (888) 437-3663
SIC 5149 5142 5147 5146 5144 5143

LAMEX FOODS INC p 841
8500 Normandale Ste 1150, Bloomington MN 55437
Tel (952) 844-0585 SIC 5144 5147

■ **CRYSTAL FARMS REFRIGERATED DISTRIBUTION CO** p 396
301 Carlson Pkwy Ste 400, Minnetonka MN 55305
Tel (800) 672-8260 SIC 5143 5144

■ **MICHAEL FOODS GROUP INC** p 960
301 Carlson Pkwy Ste 400, Minnetonka MN 55305
Tel (952) 258-4000
SIC 0252 2015 5144 5143 5148 6719

■ **MICHAEL FOODS INC** p 960
301 Carlson Pkwy Ste 400, Minnetonka MN 55305
Tel (507) 237-4600
SIC 0252 2015 5144 5143 5148 5499

■ **MICHAEL FOODS OF DELAWARE INC** p 960
301 Carlson Pkwy Ste 400, Minnetonka MN 55305
Tel (952) 258-4000
SIC 0252 2015 5144 5143 5148 2024

■ **SYSCO WESTERN MINNESOTA INC** p 1418
900 Highway 10 S, Saint Cloud MN 56304
Tel (320) 251-3200
SIC 5141 5142 5143 5144 5145 5146

J & B WHOLESALE DISTRIBUTING INC p 769
13200 43rd St Ne, Saint Michael MN 55376
Tel (763) 497-3913
SIC 5147 5144 5142 5143 5148

KOCH FOODS INC p 825
1300 W Higgins Rd, Flowood MS 39232
Tel (601) 732-8911 SIC 5144

POULTRY PRODUCTS CO INC p 1164
11 Bemis Rd, Hooksett NH 03106
Tel (603) 668-7414 SIC 5144

PORKY PRODUCTS INC p 1161
400 Port Carteret Dr, Carteret NJ 07008
Tel (732) 541-0200
SIC 5147 5146 5144 5143

■ **SYSCO METRO NEW YORK LLC** p 1417
20 Theodore Conrad Dr, Jersey City NJ 07305
Tel (201) 451-0997
SIC 5141 5144 5142 5147 5087

FANCY FOODS INC p 527
Hunts Pt Cooperative Mkt, Bronx NY 10474
Tel (718) 617-3000 SIC 5144 5147

VISTA FOOD EXCHANGE INC p 1562
355 Food Center Dr B101, Bronx NY 10474
Tel (718) 542-4401
SIC 5144 5147 5146 5148 5143

J KINGS FOOD SERVICE PROFESSIONALS INC p 771
700 Furrows Rd, Holtsville NY 11742
Tel (631) 289-8401
SIC 5149 5143 5144 5142 5148

PM BEEF HOLDINGS LLC p 1157
810 7th Ave Fl 29, New York NY 10019
Tel (507) 831-2761 SIC 5144 5147 2011

CACTUS HOLDINGS INC p 236
4705 Metropolitan Ave, Ridgewood NY 11385
Tel (718) 417-3770
SIC 5411 5147 5144 5146 5148 5143

PRESTIGE FARMS INC p 1173
7120 Orr Rd, Charlotte NC 28213
Tel (704) 596-2824 SIC 5144

■ **SYSCO CINCINNATI LLC** p 1416
10510 Evendale Dr, Cincinnati OH 45241
Tel (513) 563-6300
SIC 5144 5149 5143 5113

HILLCREST EGG & CHEESE CO p 693
2735 E 40th St, Cleveland OH 44115
Tel (216) 361-4625
SIC 5143 5142 5147 5144 5149 5148

OHIO FRESH EGGS LLC p 1077
11212 Croton Rd, Croton OH 43013
Tel (740) 893-7200 SIC 5144 2015

WILLAMETTE EGG FARMS LLC p 1609
31348 S Highway 170, Canby OR 97013
Tel (503) 651-0000 SIC 5144

IMLERS POULTRY LP p 734
1887 Route 764, Duncansville PA 16635
Tel (814) 943-5563
SIC 5144 5147 5141 5142

R W SAUDER INC p 1203
570 Furnace Hills Pike, Lititz PA 17543
Tel (717) 626-2074 SIC 5144

CEDAR FARMS CO INC p 272
2100 Hornig Rd, Philadelphia PA 19116
Tel (215) 934-7100
SIC 5142 5144 5143 5149

WENGER FEEDS LLC p 1592
101 W Harrisburg Ave, Rheems PA 17570
Tel (717) 367-1195 SIC 2048 5144 0252

PRESTAGE FARMS OF SOUTH CAROLINA LIMITED LIABILITY CO p 1173
1889 Highway 1 N, Cassatt SC 29032
Tel (803) 432-6396 SIC 5144 0253

SONSTEGARD FOODS CO p 1340
5005 S Bur Oak Pl, Sioux Falls SD 57108
Tel (605) 338-4642 SIC 5144

MAXIM FARM EGG CO INC p 922
580 Maxim Dr, Boling TX 77420
Tel (979) 657-2891 SIC 5144

BASSHAM WHOLESALE EGG CO INC p 159
5409 Hemphill St, Fort Worth TX 76115
Tel (817) 921-1600
SIC 5144 5143 5141 5147

JAKES INC p 776
13400 Hollister Dr, Houston TX 77086
Tel (713) 868-1301 SIC 5144 5142 5141

PREFERRED FOODS MARTIN L P p 1169
2011 Silver St, Houston TX 77007
Tel (713) 869-6191
SIC 5142 2015 2011 5141 5144

▲ **SYSCO CORP** p 1417
1390 Enclave Pkwy, Houston TX 77077
Tel (281) 584-1390
SIC 5149 5142 5143 5144 5148 5137

■ **SYSCO HOLDINGS LLC** p 1417
1390 Enclave Pkwy, Houston TX 77077
Tel (281) 584-1728
SIC 5141 5142 5143 5144 5145 5146

■ **SYSCO USA I INC** p 1418
1390 Enclave Pkwy, Houston TX 77077
Tel (281) 584-1390
SIC 5141 5142 5143 5144 5145 5146

■ **SYSCO USA II LLC** p 1418
1390 Enclave Pkwy, Houston TX 77077
Tel (281) 584-1390
SIC 5141 5143 5144 5145 5146

IRVING BRAKEBUSH INC p 765
2230 E Union Bower Rd, Irving TX 75061
Tel (972) 554-0590 SIC 5144

PFG HOLDINGS LLC p 1140
12500 West Creek Pkwy, Richmond VA 23238
Tel (804) 484-7700
SIC 5141 5144 5147 5146 5142 5148

DAYBREAK FOODS INC p 417
533 E Tyranena Park Rd, Lake Mills WI 53551
Tel (920) 648-8341 SIC 5144

SIC 5145 Confectionery Wholesale

BTC WHOLESALE DISTRIBUTORS INC p 222
100 Airview Ln, Alabaster AL 35007
Tel (205) 324-2581
SIC 5194 5145 5087 5149 5122

CITY WHOLESALE GROCERY CO INC p 320
300 Industrial Dr, Birmingham AL 35211
Tel (205) 795-4533
SIC 5194 5141 5145 5122

MORRIS NATIONAL INC p 990
760 N Mckeever Ave, Azusa CA 91702
Tel (626) 385-2000 SIC 5145 5149

JOE TORNANTE-MDP HOLDING LLC p 787
233 S Beverly Dr, Beverly Hills CA 90212
Tel (310) 228-6800
SIC 5145 5092 5112 2064

LIQUID INVESTMENTS INC p 870
3840 Via De La Valle # 300, Del Mar CA 92014
Tel (858) 509-8510 SIC 5181 5145 5182

TORN & GLASSER INC p 1461
1622 E Olympic Blvd, Los Angeles CA 90021
Tel (213) 593-1332
SIC 5149 5153 5145 5191

MTC DISTRIBUTING p 997
4900 Stoddard Rd, Modesto CA 95356
Tel (209) 523-6449 SIC 5194 5145 5149

■ **ICEE CO** p 727
1205 S Dupont Ave, Ontario CA 91761
Tel (800) 426-4233
SIC 2038 5145 3559 2087

PACIFIC GROSERVICE INC p 1104
567 Cinnabar St, San Jose CA 95110
Tel (408) 727-4826
SIC 5194 5145 5141 5113 5087

▲ **CORE-MARK HOLDING CO INC** p 369
395 Oyster Point Blvd # 415, South San Francisco CA 94080
Tel (650) 589-9445
SIC 5141 5194 5145 5122 5199 5149

NASSAU-SOSNICK DISTRIBUTION CO LLC p 1009
258 Littlefield Ave, South San Francisco CA 94080
Tel (650) 952-2226 SIC 5149 5145 5182

PEZ CANDY INC p 1140
35 Prindle Hill Rd, Orange CT 06477
Tel (203) 795-0531 SIC 5145

■ **CORE-MARK DISTRIBUTORS INC** p 369
4820 N Church Ln, Smyrna GA 30080
Tel (404) 792-2000
SIC 5194 5141 5145 5113

HAWAIIAN HOUSEWARES LTD p 669
96-1282 Waihona St, Pearl City HI 96782
Tel (808) 453-8000
SIC 5199 5194 5141 5145

RUCKERS WHOLESALE & SERVICE CO p 1257
777 E State St, Bridgeport IL 62417
Tel (618) 945-2411 SIC 5145

EBY-BROWN CO LLC p 474
1415 W Diehl Rd Ste 300, Naperville IL 60563
Tel (630) 778-2800
SIC 5194 5145 5141 5122 5149

WEAVER POPCORN CO INC p 1586
4485 S Perry Worth Rd, Whitestown IN 46075
Tel (765) 934-2101 SIC 5145 4213

FARNER-BOCKEN CO p 530
1751 E Us Highway 30, Carroll IA 51401
Tel (712) 792-7454 SIC 5145 5194

VARIETY DISTRIBUTORS INC p 1544
609 7th St, Harlan IA 51537
Tel (712) 755-2184
SIC 5131 5092 5122 5112 5145 5199

PERFETTI VAN MELLE USA INC p 1135
3645 Turfway Rd, Erlanger KY 41018
Tel (859) 283-1234 SIC 5145 2064

ROSS ACQUISITION CO p 1251
3380 Langley Dr, Hebron KY 41048
Tel (859) 538-8000 SIC 5145 6211

MODERN DISTRIBUTORS INC p 981
817 W Columbia St, Somerset KY 42501
Tel (606) 679-1178
SIC 5194 5962 5145 5064

HARRISON CO LLC p 664
4801 Viking Dr, Bossier City LA 71111
Tel (318) 747-0700 SIC 5194 5145 5141

IMPERIAL TRADING CO LLC p 734
701 Edwards Ave, Harahan LA 70123
Tel (504) 733-1400 SIC 5194 5141 5145

LYONS SPECIALTY CO LLC p 888
2800 La Highway 1 N, Port Allen LA 70767
Tel (225) 356-1319 SIC 5194 5145 5149

PINE STATE TRADING CO p 1149
47 Market St, Gardiner ME 04345
Tel (207) 622-2345 SIC 5181 5194 5145

GEORGE J FALTER CO p 606
3501 Benson Ave, Baltimore MD 21227
Tel (410) 646-3641
SIC 5194 5145 5141 5015

BLACKSTREET CAPITAL MANAGEMENT LLC p 188
5425 Wisconsin Ave # 701, Chevy Chase MD 20815
Tel (240) 223-1330
SIC 6726 5149 5145 5961

CENTURY DISTRIBUTORS INC p 282
15710 Crabbs Branch Way, Rockville MD 20855
Tel (301) 212-9100
SIC 5194 5145 5149 5113

BOSTON CULINARY GROUP INC p 202
55 Cambridge Pkwy Ste 200, Cambridge MA 02142
Tel (617) 225-0005 SIC 5812 5145

CONSUMER PRODUCT DISTRIBUTORS INC p 361
705 Meadow St, Chicopee MA 01013
Tel (413) 592-4141
SIC 5194 5141 7389 5145

GARBER BROS INC p 591
Kay Way Rr 139, Stoughton MA 02072
Tel (781) 341-0800
SIC 5194 5145 5141 5122

ADMIRAL PETROLEUM CO p 23
785 W Randall St, Coopersville MI 49404
Tel (616) 837-6218
SIC 5541 5411 5194 5145

MARTIN AND SNYDER PRODUCT SALES CO p 912
8880 Hubbell St, Detroit MI 48228
Tel (313) 272-4900 SIC 5194 5145

MELODY FOODS INC p 941
30777 Northwestern Hwy # 300, Farmington Hills MI 48334
Tel (248) 851-6990
SIC 5143 2026 5149 5145

GRAD INC p 628
4001 3 Mile Rd Nw, Grand Rapids MI 49534
Tel (616) 676-5969
SIC 5141 5194 5145 5122 5113 5411

KAR NUT PRODUCTS CO p 804
1200 E 14 Mile Rd Ste A, Madison Heights MI 48071
Tel (248) 588-1903 SIC 5145 2068

WESCO INC p 1593
1460 Whitehall Rd, Muskegon MI 49445
Tel (231) 719-4300
SIC 5411 5541 5145 5149

LIPARI FOODS OPERATING CO LLC p 870
26661 Bunert Rd, Warren MI 48089
Tel (586) 447-3500 SIC 5146 5145 5149

HENRYS FOODS INC p 684
234 Mckay Ave N, Alexandria MN 56308
Tel (320) 763-3194
SIC 5194 5145 5111 5113 5141

■ **MINTER-WEISMAN CO** p 974
1035 Nathan Ln N Ste A, Minneapolis MN 55441
Tel (763) 545-3706
SIC 5194 5149 5145 5013 5122

FARLEYS & SATHERS CANDY CO INC p 528
1 Sather Plz, Round Lake MN 56167
Tel (507) 945-8181 SIC 5145

■ **SYSCO WESTERN MINNESOTA INC** p 1418
900 Highway 10 S, Saint Cloud MN 56304
Tel (320) 251-3200
SIC 5141 5142 5143 5144 5145 5146

HOLLOWAY DISTRIBUTING INC p 701
210 E Owen Ave, Puxico MO 63960
Tel (573) 222-6255 SIC 5145 5194 5149

TOBA INC p 1458
2621 W Us Highway 30, Grand Island NE 68803
Tel (308) 389-5987
SIC 5148 5194 5145 5141

▲ **AMCON DISTRIBUTING CO INC** p 65
7405 Irvington Rd, Omaha NE 68122
Tel (402) 331-3727
SIC 5194 5141 5145 5113 5122

GREAT STATE BEVERAGES INC p 634
1000 Quality Dr, Hooksett NH 03106
Tel (603) 644-2337 SIC 5181 5149 5145

C&S WHOLESALE GROCERS INC p 234
7 Corporate Dr, Keene NH 03431
Tel (603) 354-7000
SIC 5141 5147 5143 5142 5122 5145

PROMOTION IN MOTION INC p 1183
25 Commerce Dr, Allendale NJ 07401
Tel (201) 962-8530
SIC 2064 5441 5145 2066

CONSOLIDATED SERVICE DISTRIBUTORS INC p 360
905 Murray Rd, East Hanover NJ 07936
Tel (908) 687-5800 SIC 5145 5194

THAYER DISTRIBUTION p 1446
333 Swedesboro Ave, Gibbstown NJ 08027
Tel (800) 999-4271 SIC 5145

PLAINFIELD TOBACCO AND CANDY CO INC p 1153
25 Van Dyke Ave, New Brunswick NJ 08901
Tel (732) 296-8900 SIC 5194 5145

FERRERO U S A INC p 538
600 Cottontail Ln, Somerset NJ 08873
Tel (732) 764-9300 SIC 5145 2064

■ **VISTAR MIDATLANTIC** p 1562
1109 Commerce Blvd 100, Swedesboro NJ 08085
Tel (856) 294-0500 SIC 5145

SULTANA DISTRIBUTION SERVICES INC p 1397
600 Food Center Dr, Bronx NY 10474
Tel (718) 842-4674 SIC 5145 5149

CHOCOLAT FREY USA LTD p 301
3500 Genesee St, Buffalo NY 14225
Tel (716) 340-0880 SIC 5145

TRIPIFOODS INC p 1482
1427 William St, Buffalo NY 14206
Tel (716) 853-7400
SIC 5141 5194 5145 5143 5142 5122

HAROLD LEVINSON ASSOCIATES INC p 662
21 Banfi Plz N, Farmingdale NY 11735
Tel (631) 962-2400 SIC 5194 5145

NASSAU CANDY DISTRIBUTORS INC p 1008
530 W John St, Hicksville NY 11801
Tel (516) 433-7100 SIC 5145

CONTINENTAL CONCESSION SUPPLIES INC p 363
575 Jericho Tpke Ste 300, Jericho NY 11753
Tel (516) 739-8777 SIC 5145

TOPPS CO INC p 1461
1 Whitehall St Fl 4, New York NY 10004
Tel (212) 376-0300
SIC 5145 5092 5112 2064

▲ **SNYDERS-LANCE INC** p 1336
13515 Balntyn Corp Pl, Charlotte NC 28277
Tel (704) 554-1421
SIC 2052 2064 2068 2096 5145

TROPICAL NUT & FRUIT CO p 1484
1100 Continental Blvd, Charlotte NC 28273
Tel (704) 588-0400
SIC 5149 5145 2099 2068

MEHERRIN AGRICULTURAL & CHEMICAL CO p 940
413 Main St, Severn NC 27877
Tel (252) 585-1744 SIC 5159 5191 5145

RED RIVER COMMODITIES INC p 1216
501 42nd St N, Fargo ND 58102
Tel (701) 282-2600 SIC 5153 5145 5149

GOLD MEDAL PRODUCTS CO p 620
10700 Medallion Dr, Cincinnati OH 45241
Tel (513) 769-7676
SIC 3556 3589 5145 3581

NOVELART MANUFACTURING CO p 1063
2121 Section Rd, Cincinnati OH 45237
Tel (513) 351-7700 SIC 5141 5145 5194

SHEARERS FOODS LLC p 1313
100 Lincoln Way E, Massillon OH 44646
Tel (330) 834-4030 SIC 2096 5145

■ **INTERNATIONAL MULTIFOODS CORP** p 756
1 Strawberry Ln, Orrville OH 44667
Tel (330) 682-3000
SIC 5145 5149 5143 2048 2041

STEPHENSON WHOLESALE CO INC p 1386
230 S 22nd Ave, Durant OK 74701
Tel (580) 920-0125
SIC 5194 5145 5143 5142 5141 5113

CALBEE NORTH AMERICA LLC p 238
72600 Lewis & Clark Dr, Boardman OR 97818
Tel (541) 481-6550 SIC 5145

■ **S-L DISTRIBUTION CO INC** p 1263
1250 York St, Hanover PA 17331
Tel (717) 632-4477 SIC 5145

COOPER-BOOTH WHOLESALE CO LP p 367
200 Lincoln West Dr, Mountville PA 17554
Tel (717) 285-8000
SIC 5194 5145 5122 5141

LIBERTY USA INC p 863
920 Irwin Run Rd, West Mifflin PA 15122
Tel (412) 461-2700
SIC 5194 5145 5122 5141

■ **MCCARTY-HULL CIGAR CO INC** p 926
4714 Ne 24th Ave, Amarillo TX 79107
Tel (806) 383-1313 SIC 5194 5145

PRICE & CO p 1174
3530 W Cardinal Dr, Beaumont TX 77705
Tel (409) 842-0677
SIC 5194 5145 5122 5141

TEXAS STAR NUT AND FOOD CO INC p 1444
206 Market Ave, Boerne TX 78006
Tel (830) 249-8300 SIC 5145 2068

TRUCO ENTERPRISES LP p 1485
2727 Realty Dr Ste 134, Carrollton TX 75006
Tel (972) 869-4600 SIC 5145

BARCEL USA LLC p 154
301 S Nrthpint Dr Ste 100, Coppell TX 75019
Tel (972) 607-4500 SIC 5145

MOUNT FRANKLIN FOODS LLC p 993
1800 Northwestern Dr, El Paso TX 79912
Tel (915) 877-4079 SIC 5145 2068 2064

■ **SYSCO HOLDINGS LLC** p 1417
1390 Enclave Pkwy, Houston TX 77077
Tel (281) 584-1728
SIC 5141 5142 5143 5144 5145 5146

■ **SYSCO USA I INC** p 1418
1390 Enclave Pkwy, Houston TX 77077
Tel (281) 584-1390
SIC 5141 5142 5143 5144 5145 5146

■ **SYSCO USA II LLC** p 1418
1390 Enclave Pkwy, Houston TX 77077
Tel (281) 584-1390
SIC 5141 5143 5144 5145 5146

LIBERTO SPECIALTY CO INC p 861
830 S Presa St, San Antonio TX 78210
Tel (210) 222-1415 SIC 5046 5145

CAPITAL CANDY CO INC p 249
32 Burnham St, Barre VT 05641
Tel (802) 476-6689
SIC 5145 5194 5122 5141 5149

MERCHANTS GROCERY CO INC p 944
800 Maddox Dr, Culpeper VA 22701
Tel (540) 825-0786 SIC 5194 5141 5145

OLD DOMINION TOBACCO CO INC p 1080
5400 Virginia Beach Blvd, Virginia Beach VA 23462
Tel (757) 497-1001 SIC 5194 5145

NORTHERN SALES CO INC p 1056
15022 Puyallup St E # 101, Sumner WA 98390
Tel (253) 299-0500
SIC 5145 5149 5194 5141

EILLIENS CANDIES INC p 481
1301 Waube Ln, Green Bay WI 54304
Tel (920) 336-7549 SIC 5145

CHAMBERS & OWEN INC p 287
1733 Morse St, Janesville WI 53545
Tel (608) 752-7865
SIC 5194 5145 5113 5141

HOLIDAY WHOLESALE INC p 700
225 Pioneer Dr, Wisconsin Dells WI 53965
Tel (608) 253-0404
SIC 5194 5145 5113 5199

SIC 5146 Fish & Seafood Wholesale

COPPER RIVER SEAFOODS INC p 368
1118 E 5th Ave, Anchorage AK 99501
Tel (907) 424-3721 SIC 2091 5146

SILVER BAY SEAFOODS LLC p 1323
208 Lake St Ste 2e, Sitka AK 99835
Tel (907) 966-3110 SIC 5146

SHAMROCK FOODS CO p 1311
3900 E Camelback Rd # 300, Phoenix AZ 85018
Tel (602) 477-2500
SIC 5146 5149 5147 5148 5142 2026

FOOD SERVICES OF AMERICA INC p 564
16100 N 71st St Ste 400, Scottsdale AZ 85254
Tel (480) 927-4000
SIC 5148 5142 5146 5141

SOUTHWIND FOODS LLC p 1353
20644 S Fordyce Ave, Carson CA 90810
Tel (323) 262-8222 SIC 5146 5147

TRI-UNION FROZEN PRODUCTS INC p 1478
222 N Sepulveda Blvd # 155, El Segundo CA 90245
Tel (516) 740-4100 SIC 5146

MSEAFOOD CORP p 997
17934 Point Sur St, Fountain Valley CA 92708
Tel (714) 842-7900 SIC 5146

CANTON FOOD CO INC p 247
750 S Alameda St, Los Angeles CA 90021
Tel (213) 688-7707
SIC 5141 5146 5411 5421 5149 4222

PROSPECT ENTERPRISES INC p 1184
625 Kohler St, Los Angeles CA 90021
Tel (213) 599-5700 SIC 5146 2092

R W ZANT CO p 1203
1470 E 4th St, Los Angeles CA 90033
Tel (323) 980-5457
SIC 5147 5146 5144 4222

LUSAMERICA FOODS INC p 886
16480 Railroad Ave, Morgan Hill CA 95037
Tel (408) 294-6622 SIC 5146 5142

SANTA MONICA SEAFOOD CO p 1281
18531 S Broadwick St, Rancho Dominguez CA 90220
Tel (310) 886-7900 SIC 5421 5146 5142

BICARA LTD p 181
1611 S Catalina Ave, Redondo Beach CA 90277
Tel (310) 316-6222 SIC 5147 5146 5141

PACIFIC SHELLFISH INC p 1106
5040 Cass St, San Diego CA 92109
Tel (858) 272-9940 SIC 5146 5421 5812

TRI-UNION SEAFOODS LLC p 1478
9330 Scranton Rd Ste 500, San Diego CA 92121
Tel (858) 558-9662 SIC 5146 2091

▲ **UMAMI SUSTAINABLE SEAFOOD INC** p 1501
1230 Columbia St Ste 440, San Diego CA 92101
Tel (619) 544-9177 SIC 5146 0912

DAY-LEE FOODS INC p 417
10350 Hritg Pk Dr Ste 111, Santa Fe Springs CA 90670
Tel (562) 903-3020 SIC 5147 5144 5146

MERCURY OVERSEAS INC p 945
830 Mission St, South Pasadena CA 91030
Tel (626) 799-9141 SIC 5147 5146

S C S INC p 1262
2910 Faber St, Union City CA 94587
Tel (510) 477-0008 SIC 5146 5147

H & N FOODS INTERNATIONAL INC p 649
5580 S Alameda St, Vernon CA 90058
Tel (323) 586-9300 SIC 5146

H & N GROUP INC p 649
5580 S Alameda St, Vernon CA 90058
Tel (323) 586-9388 SIC 5146

PACIFIC AMERICAN FISH CO INC p 1104
5525 S Santa Fe Ave, Vernon CA 90058
Tel (323) 319-1551 SIC 5146 2091

RED CHAMBER CO p 1215
1912 E Vernon Ave, Vernon CA 90058
Tel (323) 234-9000 SIC 5146 4222

PROTEIN PROVIDERS INC p 1185
1770 Promontory Cir, Greeley CO 80634
Tel (970) 506-7678 SIC 5147 5146

PROPEMAR INC p 1183
19101 Mystic Pointe Dr # 1709, Aventura FL 33180
Tel (954) 775-7002 SIC 5146

QUIRCH FOODS CO p 1200
2701 S Le Jeune Rd, Coral Gables FL 33134
Tel (305) 691-3535
SIC 5147 5142 5144 5146

MARINE HARVEST USA LLC p 906
8550 Nw 17th St Ste 105, Doral FL 33126
Tel (305) 591-8550 SIC 5146

C & W FISH CO INC p 232
7508 Se Autumn Ln, Hobe Sound FL 33455
Tel (772) 283-1184 SIC 5199 5146

NORTH SOUTH FOODS GROUP INC p 1054
3373 Sterling Ridge Ct, Longwood FL 32779
Tel (407) 805-9075 SIC 5144 5147 5146

BLUMAR USA LLC p 193
6303 Blue Lagoon Dr 385, Miami FL 33126
Tel (305) 261-2417 SIC 5146 5142

CAMANCHACA INC p 243
7200 Nw 19th St Ste 410, Miami FL 33126
Tel (305) 406-9560 SIC 5146

MULTIEXPORT FOODS INC p 999
703 Nw 62nd Ave Ste 510, Miami FL 33126
Tel (305) 364-0009 SIC 5146

PATAGONIA SEAFARMS INC p 1120
7205 Corp Cntr Dr Ste 402, Miami FL 33126
Tel (786) 693-8711 SIC 5146

REGAL SPRINGS TRADING CO p 1218
2801 Sw 149th Ave Ste 270, Miramar FL 33027
Tel (954) 283-9035 SIC 5146

BAR HARBOR LOBSTER CO INC p 154
2000 Premier Row, Orlando FL 32809
Tel (407) 851-4001 SIC 5146 5812

AJC INTERNATIONAL INC p 41
1000 Abernathy Rd Ste 600, Atlanta GA 30328
Tel (404) 252-6750
SIC 5144 5147 5148 5146

ATLANTA ORIENTAL FOOD WHOLESALE CO p 125
5600 Buford Hwy Ne, Atlanta GA 30340
Tel (770) 455-0770
SIC 5146 5421 5046 5719

UNIPRO FOODSERVICE INC p 1505
2500 Cumbrld Pkwy Se 60 Ste 600, Atlanta GA 30339
Tel (770) 952-0871
SIC 5147 5141 5146 5142

■ **BUCKHEAD BEEF CO INC** p 223
4500 Wickersham Dr, College Park GA 30337
Tel (404) 355-4400 SIC 5142 5146 5421

INLAND FRESH SEAFOOD CORP OF AMERICA INC p 743
1651 Montreal Cir, Tucker GA 30084
Tel (404) 350-5850 SIC 5146 5144 5147

CMU & ASSOCIATES INC p 329
55 Holomua St, Hilo HI 96720
Tel (808) 961-0877 SIC 5146 5148 5142

SUISAN CO p 1397
333 Kilauea Ave Ste 202, Hilo HI 96720
Tel (808) 935-8511 SIC 5142 5146

CENSEA INC p 275
650 Dundee Rd Ste 180, Northbrook IL 60062
Tel (224) 723-5800 SIC 5146

CENTRAL SEAWAY CO INC p 280
650 Dundee Rd Ste 180, Northbrook IL 60062
Tel (224) 723-5800 SIC 5146

▲ **US FOODS HOLDING CORP** p 1531
9399 W Higgins Rd Ste 500, Rosemont IL 60018
Tel (847) 720-8000
SIC 5149 5147 5142 5144 5146 5143

■ **US FOODS INC** p 1531
9399 W Higgins Rd Ste 500, Rosemont IL 60018
Tel (847) 720-8000
SIC 5149 5147 5142 5144 5146 5143

SUPREME LOBSTER AND SEAFOOD CO p 1408
220 E North Ave, Villa Park IL 60181
Tel (630) 834-3474 SIC 5146

TROYER FOODS INC p 1485
17141 State Road 4, Goshen IN 46528
Tel (574) 533-0302
SIC 5147 5144 5141 5146

MCFARLING FOODS INC p 928
333 W 14th St, Indianapolis IN 46202
Tel (317) 687-6827
SIC 5147 5149 5144 5146

PERISHABLE DISTRIBUTORS OF IOWA LTD p 1136
2741 Se Pdi Pl, Ankeny IA 50021
Tel (515) 965-6300 SIC 5146 5144 5147

ASSOCIATED WHOLESALE GROCERS INC p 121
5000 Kansas Ave, Kansas City KS 66106
Tel (913) 288-1000
SIC 5141 5143 5142 5147 5146 5148

CARI INVESTMENT CO LLC p 256
222 N Vermont St, Covington LA 70433
Tel (985) 635-6009
SIC 6211 4424 3731 5146

GILBERT FOODS LLC p 612
7251 Standard Dr, Hanover MD 21076
Tel (410) 712-6000
SIC 5148 5147 5146 5142

■ **AM BRIGGS INC** p 63
1920 Stanford Ct, Landover MD 20785
Tel (301) 773-2175 SIC 5147 5144 5146

MMSP INC p 979
1920 Stanford Ct, Landover MD 20785
Tel (301) 773-2175
SIC 5143 5144 5146 5147

GORTON SLADE & CO INC p 626
225 Southampton St, Boston MA 02118
Tel (617) 442-5800 SIC 5146

LEGAL SEA FOODS LLC p 853
1 Seafood Way, Boston MA 02210
Tel (617) 530-9000 SIC 5812 5146 5961

SG SEAFOOD HOLDINGS INC p 1310
225 Southampton St, Boston MA 02118
Tel (617) 442-5800 SIC 5146

STAVIS SEAFOODS INC p 1383
212 Northern Ave Ste 305, Boston MA 02210
Tel (617) 482-6349 SIC 5146

NATIONAL FISH AND SEAFOOD INC p 1012
11 15 Parker St, Gloucester MA 01930
Tel (978) 282-7880 SIC 5146 2092

AMERICAN HOLDCO LLC p 74
448 Boston St, Topsfield MA 01983
Tel (978) 561-3800 SIC 5146 4213

EAST COAST SEAFOOD INC p 470
448 Boston St, Topsfield MA 01983
Tel (978) 561-3800 SIC 5146

SHERWOOD FOOD DISTRIBUTORS LLC p 1316
12499 Evergreen Ave, Detroit MI 48228
Tel (313) 659-7300
SIC 5147 5144 5146 5142 5143

LIPARI FOODS OPERATING CO LLC p 870
26661 Bunert Rd, Warren MI 48089
Tel (586) 447-3500 SIC 5146 5145 5149

GORDON FOOD SERVICE INC p 626
1300 Gezon Pkwy Sw, Wyoming MI 49509
Tel (888) 437-3663
SIC 5149 5142 5147 5146 5144 5143

MOREYS SEAFOOD INTERNATIONAL LLC p 988
742 Decatur Ave N, Minneapolis MN 55427
Tel (763) 541-0129 SIC 5146 2091

■ **SYSCO WESTERN MINNESOTA INC** p 1418
900 Highway 10 S, Saint Cloud MN 56304
Tel (320) 251-3200
SIC 5141 5142 5143 5144 5145 5146

■ **SYSCO ST LOUIS LLC** p 1418
3850 Mueller Rd, Saint Charles MO 63301
Tel (636) 940-9230
SIC 5141 5149 5146 5143 5142

■ **MIDDENDORF MEAT CO LLC** p 964
3737 N Broadway, Saint Louis MO 63147
Tel (314) 241-4800
SIC 5147 5141 5148 5146 5113 2011

ATLANTIC CAPES FISHERIES INC p 126
985 Ocean Dr, Cape May NJ 08204
Tel (609) 884-3000 SIC 5146

PORKY PRODUCTS INC p 1161
400 Port Carteret Dr, Carteret NJ 07008
Tel (732) 541-0200
SIC 5147 5146 5144 5143

TRUE WORLD FOODS NEW YORK LLC p 1486
32-34 Papetti Plz, Elizabeth NJ 07206
Tel (908) 351-9090 SIC 5146

HANWA AMERICAN CORP p 659
Parker Plz 400 Kelby St F, Fort Lee NJ 07024
Tel (201) 363-4500
SIC 5051 5172 5031 5084 5146

TRUE WORLD HOLDINGS LLC p 1486
24 Link Dr, Rockleigh NJ 07647
Tel (201) 750-0024 SIC 5146

VISTA FOOD EXCHANGE INC p 1562
355 Food Center Dr B101, Bronx NY 10474
Tel (718) 542-4401
SIC 5144 5147 5146 5148 5143

MAINES PAPER & FOOD SERVICE INC p 898
101 Broome Corporate Pkwy, Conklin NY 13748
Tel (607) 779-1200
SIC 5142 5113 5141 5087 5147 5146

GREENWICH VILLAGE FISH CO INC p 639
2135 Broadway, New York NY 10023
Tel (631) 324-9190 SIC 5146

MARK FOODS INC p 907
20 W 22nd St Ste 901, New York NY 10010
Tel (212) 255-6048 SIC 5146

CACTUS HOLDINGS INC p 236
4705 Metropolitan Ave, Ridgewood NY 11385
Tel (718) 417-3770
SIC 5411 5147 5144 5146 5148 5143

PALMER FISH CO INC p 1109
900 Jefferson Rd Ste 1000, Rochester NY 14623
Tel (585) 424-3210
SIC 5146 5147 5142 2013

G & C FOOD DISTRIBUTORS & BROKERS INC p 586
3407 Walters Rd, Syracuse NY 13209
Tel (315) 422-3191 SIC 5147 5146 4222

LWIN FAMILY CO p 887
11949 Steele Creek Rd, Charlotte NC 28273
Tel (704) 926-2200 SIC 5146

MEAT AND SEAFOOD SOLUTIONS LLC p 934
3500 Old Battleground Rd, Greensboro NC 27410
Tel (336) 545-3827 SIC 5146 5147

SOUTHERN FOODS INC p 1348
3500 Old Battlegrd Rd A, Greensboro NC 27410
Tel (336) 545-3800
SIC 5147 5143 5146 5148 5142

DULCICH INC p 460
16797 Se 130th Ave, Clackamas OR 97015
Tel (503) 226-2200 SIC 5146 2092

PACIFIC SEA FOOD CO INC p 1106
16797 Se 130th Ave, Clackamas OR 97015
Tel (503) 905-4500 SIC 5146 5142

HOSSS STEAK & SEA HOUSE INC p 710
170 Patchway Rd, Duncansville PA 16635
Tel (814) 695-7600 SIC 5812 5146 5046

FISHIN CO p 552
3714 Main St, Munhall PA 15120
Tel (412) 464-9000 SIC 5146

SAMUELS AND SON SEAFOOD CO INC p 1275
3400 S Lawrence St, Philadelphia PA 19148
Tel (215) 336-7810 SIC 5146

NORTHWESTERN SELECTA INC p 1061
796 Calle C M Julia Indst, San Juan PR 00920
Tel (787) 781-1950 SIC 5147 5146 5142

ALL AMERICAN FOODS INC p 51
1 All American Way, North Kingstown RI 02852
Tel (401) 294-5455 SIC 5147 5146 5142

NORTH FOOD GROUP INC p 1052
1245 W Royal Ln, Dallas TX 75261
Tel (972) 445-3322
SIC 5146 5147 5149 5113

■ **SYSCO HOLDINGS LLC** p 1417
1390 Enclave Pkwy, Houston TX 77077
Tel (281) 584-1728
SIC 5141 5142 5143 5144 5145 5146

■ **SYSCO USA I INC** p 1418
1390 Enclave Pkwy, Houston TX 77077
Tel (281) 584-1390
SIC 5141 5142 5143 5144 5145 5146

■ **SYSCO USA II LLC** p 1418
1390 Enclave Pkwy, Houston TX 77077
Tel (281) 584-1390
SIC 5141 5143 5144 5145 5146

FRESH ACQUISITIONS LLC p 578
1001 E 33rd St, Lubbock TX 79404
Tel (806) 723-5600 SIC 5149 5146

■ **SYSCO WEST TEXAS INC** p 1418
714 2nd Pl, Lubbock TX 79401
Tel (806) 747-2678 SIC 5146 5147

SAGERS SEAFOOD PLUS INC p 1268
4802 Bridal Wreath Dr, Richmond TX 77406
Tel (281) 342-8833 SIC 5146

PFG HOLDINGS LLC p 1140
12500 West Creek Pkwy, Richmond VA 23238
Tel (804) 484-7700
SIC 5141 5144 5147 5146 5142 5148

DIRECT SOURCE SEAFOOD LLC p 441
840 140th Ave Ne, Bellevue WA 98005
Tel (908) 240-9374 SIC 5146

CHANG INTERNATIONAL INC p 288
1611 Market St, Kirkland WA 98033
Tel (206) 283-9098 SIC 5146

NIPPON SUISAN (USA) INC p 1044
15400 Ne 90th St 100, Redmond WA 98052
Tel (425) 869-1703 SIC 5146

AMERICAN SEAFOODS GROUP LLC p 79
2025 1st Ave Ste 900, Seattle WA 98121
Tel (206) 374-1515 SIC 5421 5146

AMERICAN SEAFOODS LP p 79
2025 1st Ave Ste 900, Seattle WA 98121
Tel (206) 374-1515 SIC 5421 5146

AQUA STAR (USA) CORP p 101
2025 1st Ave Ste 200, Seattle WA 98121
Tel (206) 448-5400 SIC 5146

ASG CONSOLIDATED LLC p 116
2025 1st Ave Ste 900, Seattle WA 98121
Tel (206) 374-1515 SIC 5421 5146

E & E FOODS INC p 465
801 S Fidalgo St Ste 100, Seattle WA 98108
Tel (206) 768-8979 SIC 5146 2092

ODYSSEY ENTERPRISES INC p 1075
2729 6th Ave S, Seattle WA 98134
Tel (206) 285-7445 SIC 5146

TRIDENT SEAFOODS CORP p 1479
5303 Shilshole Ave Nw, Seattle WA 98107
Tel (206) 783-3818
SIC 2092 5146 5091 0912

SQUAXIN ISLAND TRIBE OF SQUAXIN ISLAND RESERVATION p 1362
10 Se Squaxin Ln, Shelton WA 98584
Tel (360) 426-9781
SIC 5411 5146 7011 0132

SIC 5147 Meats & Meat Prdts Wholesale

■ **SYSCO CENTRAL ALABAMA INC** p 1416
1000 Sysco Dr, Calera AL 35040
Tel (205) 668-0001
SIC 5149 5147 5142 5144 5143

WOOD-FRUITTICHER GROCERY CO INC p 1622
2900 Alton Rd, Irondale AL 35210
Tel (205) 836-9663
SIC 5142 5141 5147 5087 5046

BASHAS INC p 158
22402 S Basha Rd, Chandler AZ 85248
Tel (480) 883-6131
SIC 5411 5149 5148 5147 6512

SHAMROCK FOODS CO p 1311
3900 E Camelback Rd # 300, Phoenix AZ 85018
Tel (602) 477-2500
SIC 5146 5149 5147 5148 5142 2026

SYSTEMS SERVICES OF AMERICA INC p 1419
1640 S 39th Ave, Phoenix AZ 85009
Tel (480) 927-4700
SIC 5147 5113 5142 5149 5143

■ **PFG BROADLINE HOLDINGS LLC** p 1140
4901 Asher Ave, Little Rock AR 72204
Tel (501) 568-3141
SIC 5149 5148 5147 5141

WEST COAST PRIME MEATS LLC p 1594
344 Cliffwood Park St, Brea CA 92821
Tel (714) 255-8560 SIC 5147

BI-RITE RESTAURANT SUPPLY CO INC p 180
123 S Hill Dr, Brisbane CA 94005
Tel (415) 656-0187
SIC 5141 5147 5148 5023 5046 5963

TREX CORP INC p 1476
851 Burlway Rd Ste 400, Burlingame CA 94010
Tel (650) 342-7333 SIC 5147

SOUTHWIND FOODS LLC p 1353
20644 S Fordyce Ave, Carson CA 90810
Tel (323) 262-8222 SIC 5146 5147

AMERICAN BEEF PACKERS INC p 68
13677 Yorba Ave, Chino CA 91710
Tel (909) 628-4888 SIC 0751 2011 5147

INTERSTATE MEAT & PROVISION p 758
6114 Scott Way, Commerce CA 90040
Tel (323) 838-9400 SIC 5142 5147

■ **SYSCO SAN FRANCISCO INC** p 1418
5900 Stewart Ave, Fremont CA 94538
Tel (510) 226-3000 SIC 5141 5147 5142

COLUMBUS FOODS LLC p 342
30977 San Antonio St, Hayward CA 94544
Tel (510) 921-3400 SIC 2011 5143 5147

GOLDEN STATE FOODS CORP p 621
18301 Von Karman Ave # 1100, Irvine CA 92612
Tel (949) 252-2000
SIC 5147 2087 5142 5148 5149

■ **SYSCO NEWPORT MEAT CO** p 1417
16691 Hale Ave, Irvine CA 92606
Tel (949) 399-4200 SIC 5147 5142

ICREST INTERNATIONAL LLC p 728
725 S Figueroa St # 3050, Los Angeles CA 90017
Tel (213) 488-8303 SIC 5148 5147

R W ZANT CO p 1203
1470 E 4th St, Los Angeles CA 90033
Tel (323) 980-5457
SIC 5147 5146 5144 4222

HARVEST MEAT CO INC p 666
1022 Bay Marina Dr # 106, National City CA 91950
Tel (619) 477-0185 SIC 5147

SAND DOLLAR HOLDINGS INC p 1278
1022 Bay Marina Dr # 106, National City CA 91950
Tel (619) 477-0185 SIC 5147

FOODCOMM INTERNATIONAL p 564
4260 El Camino Real, Palo Alto CA 94306
Tel (650) 813-1300 SIC 5147 5142

■ **SYSCO SAN DIEGO INC** p 1418
12180 Kirkham Rd, Poway CA 92064
Tel (858) 513-7300
SIC 5141 5142 5147 5148 5084

BICARA LTD p 181
1611 S Catalina Ave, Redondo Beach CA 90277
Tel (310) 316-6222 SIC 5147 5146 5141

RICHMOND WHOLESALE MEAT CO p 1233
2920 Regatta Blvd, Richmond CA 94804
Tel (510) 233-5111 SIC 5147

JENSEN MEAT CO INC p 782
2550 Britannia Blvd # 101, San Diego CA 92154
Tel (619) 754-6450 SIC 5147

MPCI HOLDINGS INC p 995
7850 Waterville Rd, San Diego CA 92154
Tel (619) 294-2222
SIC 5147 5143 5148 5113

■ **AIDELLS SAUSAGE CO INC** p 37
2411 Baumann Ave, San Lorenzo CA 94580
Tel (510) 614-5450 SIC 2013 5147

DAY-LEE FOODS INC p 417
10350 Hritg Pk Dr Ste 111, Santa Fe Springs CA 90670
Tel (562) 903-3020 SIC 5147 5144 5146

MERCURY OVERSEAS INC p 945
830 Mission St, South Pasadena CA 91030
Tel (626) 799-9141 SIC 5147 5146

S C S INC p 1262
2910 Faber St, Union City CA 94587
Tel (510) 477-0008 SIC 5146 5147

GOLDEN WEST TRADING INC p 622
4401 S Downey Rd, Vernon CA 90058
Tel (323) 581-3663 SIC 5147 5142

KING MEAT SERVICE INC p 820
4215 Exchange Ave, Vernon CA 90058
Tel (323) 835-8989 SIC 5147

LAWRENCE WHOLESALE LLC p 848
4353 Exchange Ave, Vernon CA 90058
Tel (323) 235-7525 SIC 5147

RANCHO FOODS INC p 1207
2528 E 37th St, Vernon CA 90058
Tel (323) 585-0503 SIC 5147 2013

RANDALL FOODS INC p 1207
2905 E 50th St, Vernon CA 90058
Tel (323) 261-6565 SIC 5147 7299

■ **TONYS FINE FOODS** p 1460
3575 Reed Ave, West Sacramento CA 95605
Tel (916) 374-4000 SIC 5147 5143 5149

UNITED FOOD SERVICE INC p 1508
5199 Ivy St, Commerce City CO 80022
Tel (303) 289-3595
SIC 5141 5142 5147 5148 5046

COLORADO FOOD PRODUCTS INC p 339
3600 S Yosemite St # 800, Denver CO 80237
Tel (303) 409-8400 SIC 5147

COLEMAN NATURAL FOODS LLC p 336
1767 Denver West Blvd # 200, Golden CO 80401
Tel (303) 468-2500 SIC 2011 5147 0251

JBS USA HOLDINGS LLC p 780
1770 Promontory Cir, Greeley CO 80634
Tel (970) 506-8000 SIC 2011 5147

K2D INC p 799
2035 2nd Ave, Greeley CO 80631
Tel (970) 313-4400 SIC 5147

PROTEIN PROVIDERS INC p 1185
1770 Promontory Cir, Greeley CO 80634
Tel (970) 506-7678 SIC 5147 5146

S&C RESALE CO p 1263
1770 Promontory Cir, Greeley CO 80634
Tel (970) 506-8000 SIC 5147 5421

THURSTON FOODS INC p 1451
30 Thurston Dr, Wallingford CT 06492
Tel (203) 265-1525
SIC 5141 5147 5142 5113

CITY LINE DISTRIBUTORS INC p 312
20 Industry Dr, West Haven CT 06516
Tel (203) 931-3707
SIC 5141 5142 5147 5113

COLORADO BOXED BEEF CO p 338
302 Progress Rd, Auburndale FL 33823
Tel (863) 967-0636 SIC 5142 5147

QUIRCH FOODS CO p 1200
2701 S Le Jeune Rd, Coral Gables FL 33134
Tel (305) 691-3535
SIC 5147 5142 5144 5146

■ **SYSCO JACKSONVILLE INC** p 1417
1501 Lewis Industrial Dr, Jacksonville FL 32254
Tel (904) 781-5070
SIC 5149 5147 5144 5963

NORTH SOUTH FOODS GROUP INC p 1054
3373 Sterling Ridge Ct, Longwood FL 32779
Tel (407) 805-9075 SIC 5144 5147 5146

■ **SYSCO SOUTH FLORIDA INC** p 1418
12500 Nw 112th Ave, Medley FL 33178
Tel (305) 651-5421
SIC 5149 5147 5142 5113 5143 5144

NATIONAL DELI LLC p 1011
7250 Nw 35th Ter Tce, Miami FL 33122
Tel (305) 592-0300 SIC 5147

BOARS HEAD PROVISIONS CO INC p 196
1819 Main St Ste 800, Sarasota FL 34236
Tel (941) 955-0994 SIC 5147

FRANK BRUNCKHORST CO LLC p 574
1819 Main St Ste 800, Sarasota FL 34236
Tel (941) 955-0994 SIC 5147

SANWA GROWERS INC p 1281
2801 E Hillsborough Ave, Tampa FL 33610
Tel (813) 642-5159 SIC 5147 5148

AJC INTERNATIONAL INC p 41
1000 Abernathy Rd Ste 600, Atlanta GA 30328
Tel (404) 252-6750
SIC 5144 5147 5148 5146

GERBER AGRI INTERNATIONAL LLC p 608
1000 Parkwood Cir Se # 335, Atlanta GA 30339
Tel (770) 952-4187 SIC 5144 5147

HALPERNS STEAK AND SEAFOOD CO LLC p 655
4685 Welcome All Rd Sw, Atlanta GA 30349
Tel (404) 767-9229 SIC 5147

RUSSELL MCCALLS INC p 1259
255 Ted Turner Dr Sw, Atlanta GA 30303
Tel (404) 954-7600 SIC 5149 5143 5147

UNIPRO FOODSERVICE INC p 1505
2500 Cumbrld Pkwy Se 60 Ste 600, Atlanta GA 30339
Tel (770) 952-0871
SIC 5147 5141 5146 5142

IRA HIGDON GROCERY CO p 764
150 Iga Way, Cairo GA 39828
Tel (229) 377-1272
SIC 5141 5147 5142 5143 2111 5194

SUTHERLANDS FOODSERVICE INC p 1410
16 Forest Pkwy Bldg K, Forest Park GA 30297
Tel (404) 366-8550
SIC 5144 5148 5147 5143 5141

ROGER WOOD FOODS INC p 1246
7 Alfred St, Savannah GA 31408
Tel (912) 652-9600 SIC 2013 5147

INLAND FRESH SEAFOOD CORP OF AMERICA INC p 743
1651 Montreal Cir, Tucker GA 30084
Tel (404) 350-5850 SIC 5146 5144 5147

INTERMOUNTAIN NATURAL LLC p 753
1740 S Yellowstone Hwy, Idaho Falls ID 83402
Tel (208) 227-9000 SIC 5147 2013

■ **EUROPEAN IMPORTS INC** p 513
600 E Brook Dr, Arlington Heights IL 60005
Tel (800) 323-3464 SIC 5141 5149 5147

TRIM-RITE FOOD CORP INC p 1480
801 Commerce Pkwy, Carpentersville IL 60110
Tel (847) 649-3400 SIC 5147

BADGER FARMS INC p 143
652 N Western Ave, Chicago IL 60612
Tel (773) 278-9100
SIC 5143 5149 5147 5144 5142 5087

■ **BRUSS CO** p 221
3548 N Kostner Ave, Chicago IL 60641
Tel (773) 282-2900
SIC 5147 5142 2013 2011

LINCOLN PROVISION INC p 868
824 W 38th Pl, Chicago IL 60609
Tel (773) 254-2400 SIC 5142 5147

MID-WEST INSTITUTIONAL FOOD DISTRIBUTORS INC p 964
3100 W 36th St, Chicago IL 60632
Tel (773) 927-8870
SIC 5142 5143 5144 5147 5148

NATIONWIDE FOODS INC p 1017
700 E 107th St, Chicago IL 60628
Tel (773) 787-4900 SIC 2013 5142 5147

T & J FOODS LLC p 1419
233 S Wacker Dr Ste 8325, Chicago IL 60606
Tel (312) 357-5137 SIC 5147

VIENNA BEEF LTD p 1556
2501 N Damen Ave, Chicago IL 60647
Tel (773) 278-7800
SIC 2013 2035 2053 5411 5149 5147

PLUMROSE USA INC p 1157
1901 Butterfield Rd # 305, Downers Grove IL 60515
Tel (732) 257-6600
SIC 2011 5147 2013 5149

KUNA MEAT CO INC p 832
704 Kuna Industrial Ct, Dupo IL 62239
Tel (618) 286-4000
SIC 5144 5142 5147 5169 5149 5148

CENTRAL GROCERS INC p 278
2600 Haven Ave, Joliet IL 60433
Tel (815) 553-8800
SIC 5141 5147 5142 5148 5143 5122

■ **FOX RIVER FOODS INC** p 572
5030 Baseline Rd, Montgomery IL 60538
Tel (630) 896-1991
SIC 5142 5149 5148 5147

RUPRECHT CO p 1258
1301 Allanson Rd, Mundelein IL 60060
Tel (312) 829-4100 SIC 5147

TRI-MEATS INC p 1477
17 W 662 Butterfi, Oakbrook Terrace IL 60181
Tel (630) 705-2800 SIC 5147

JASONS FOODS p 778
208 E Helen Rd, Palatine IL 60067
Tel (847) 358-9901 SIC 5144 5147 5142

▲ **US FOODS HOLDING CORP** p 1531
9399 W Higgins Rd Ste 500, Rosemont IL 60018
Tel (847) 720-8000
SIC 5149 5147 5142 5144 5146 5143

■ **US FOODS INC** p 1531
9399 W Higgins Rd Ste 500, Rosemont IL 60018
Tel (847) 720-8000
SIC 5149 5147 5142 5144 5146 5143

BRANDING IRON HOLDINGS INC p 208
1682 Sauget Business Blvd, Sauget IL 62206
Tel (618) 337-8400 SIC 2013 5147

ED MINIAT LLC p 476
16250 Vincennes Ave, South Holland IL 60473
Tel (708) 589-2400 SIC 5147 5144

MINIAT COMPANIES INC p 973
16250 Vincennes Ave, South Holland IL 60473
Tel (708) 589-2400 SIC 5147 5144

MINIAT HOLDINGS LLC p 973
16250 Vincennes Ave, South Holland IL 60473
Tel (708) 589-2400 *SIC* 5147 5144

H C SCHAU & SON INC p 649
10350 Argonne Dr Ste 400, Woodridge IL 60517
Tel (630) 783-1000 *SIC* 5147 2099

TF INTER-HOLDINGS INC p 1445
17141 State Road 4, Goshen IN 46528
Tel (574) 533-0302 *SIC* 5147 4213 5144

TROYER FOODS INC p 1485
17141 State Road 4, Goshen IN 46528
Tel (574) 533-0302
SIC 5147 5144 5141 5146

MCFARLING FOODS INC p 928
333 W 14th St, Indianapolis IN 46202
Tel (317) 687-6827
SIC 5147 5149 5144 5146

PERISHABLE DISTRIBUTORS OF IOWA LTD p 1136
2741 Se Pdi Pl, Ankeny IA 50021
Tel (515) 965-6300 *SIC* 5146 5144 5147

■ **SYSCO IOWA INC** p 1417
1 Sysco Dr, Ankeny IA 50021
Tel (515) 289-5300
SIC 5149 5147 5142 5144 5113 5143

NATIONAL PORK BOARD p 1015
1776 Nw 114th St, Des Moines IA 50325
Tel (515) 223-2600 *SIC* 5147

TUR-PAK FOODS INC p 1492
6201 Macarthur St, Sioux City IA 51111
Tel (712) 258-9354 *SIC* 5147

ASSOCIATED WHOLESALE GROCERS INC p 121
5000 Kansas Ave, Kansas City KS 66106
Tel (913) 288-1000
SIC 5141 5143 5142 5147 5146 5148

■ **SEABOARD FOODS LLC** p 1295
9000 W 67th St Ste 200, Shawnee Mission KS 66202
Tel (913) 261-2600 *SIC* 0213 5147 2011

CARGILL MEAT SOLUTIONS CORP p 255
151 N Main St Ste 900, Wichita KS 67202
Tel (316) 291-2500 *SIC* 2011 5147 4213

LAUREL GROCERY CO LLC p 847
129 Barbourville Rd, London KY 40744
Tel (606) 878-6601
SIC 5141 5147 5122 5143

ASSOCIATED GROCERS OF MAINE INC p 120
190 Water St, Gardiner ME 04345
Tel (207) 596-0636
SIC 5141 5147 5148 5122

■ **SYSCO NORTHERN NEW ENGLAND INC** p 1417
55 Thomas Dr, Westbrook ME 04092
Tel (207) 871-0700
SIC 5141 5147 5148 5142

HOLLY POULTRY INC p 701
2221 Berlin St, Baltimore MD 21230
Tel (410) 727-6210 *SIC* 5144 5147

UNITED SOURCE ONE INC p 1511
4610 Mercedes Dr Ste 110, Belcamp MD 21017
Tel (410) 278-0800 *SIC* 5147 5087

FOODPRO CORP p 564
321 E 5th St, Frederick MD 21701
Tel (301) 663-3171
SIC 5142 5149 5148 5147 5143 5113

GILBERT FOODS LLC p 612
7251 Standard Dr, Hanover MD 21076
Tel (410) 712-6000
SIC 5148 5147 5146 5142

■ **AM BRIGGS INC** p 63
1920 Stanford Ct, Landover MD 20785
Tel (301) 773-2175 *SIC* 5147 5144 5146

MMSP INC p 979
1920 Stanford Ct, Landover MD 20785
Tel (301) 773-2175
SIC 5143 5144 5146 5147

HOLT PAPER AND CHEMICAL CO INC p 702
31375 John Deere Dr, Salisbury MD 21804
Tel (410) 742-7577
SIC 5142 5087 5113 5147

SHERWOOD FOOD DISTRIBUTORS LLC p 1316
12499 Evergreen Ave, Detroit MI 48228
Tel (313) 659-7300
SIC 5147 5144 5146 5142 5143

WOLVERINE PACKING CO p 1621
2535 Rivard St, Detroit MI 48207
Tel (313) 259-7500 *SIC* 5147 2011 5142

DETROIT CITY DAIRY p 433
21405 Trolley Indus Dr, Taylor MI 48180
Tel (313) 295-6300
SIC 5143 5141 5147 5149

GORDON FOOD SERVICE INC p 626
1300 Gezon Pkwy Sw, Wyoming MI 49509
Tel (888) 437-3663
SIC 5149 5142 5147 5146 5144 5143

■ **HORMEL FOODS CORPORATE SERVICES LLC** p 708
1 Hormel Pl, Austin MN 55912
Tel (507) 437-5611 *SIC* 5147

LAMEX FOODS INC p 841
8500 Normandale Ste 1150, Bloomington MN 55437
Tel (952) 844-0585 *SIC* 5144 5147

■ **NASH-FINCH CO** p 1008
7600 France Ave S Ste 200, Minneapolis MN 55435
Tel (952) 832-0534
SIC 5141 5148 5142 5147 5411

J & B WHOLESALE DISTRIBUTING INC p 769
13200 43rd St Ne, Saint Michael MN 55376
Tel (763) 497-3913
SIC 5147 5144 5142 5143 5148

R & D MARKETING LLC p 1201
4110 Westside Dr, Tupelo MS 38801
Tel (662) 620-2828 *SIC* 5147

BURGERS OZARK COUNTRY CURED HAMS INC p 227
32819 Highway 87, California MO 65018
Tel (573) 796-3134
SIC 5147 5812 2015 2013

■ **MIDDENDORF MEAT CO LLC** p 964
3737 N Broadway, Saint Louis MO 63147
Tel (314) 241-4800
SIC 5147 5141 5148 5146 5113 2011

GREATER OMAHA PACKING CO INC p 635
3001 L St, Omaha NE 68107
Tel (402) 731-1700 *SIC* 2011 5147

ARMAND AGRA INC p 110
1330 Capital Blvd, Reno NV 89502
Tel (775) 322-4073 *SIC* 0291 5147

POULTRY PRODUCTS CO OF NEW ENGLAND INC p 1164
11 Bemis Rd, Hooksett NH 03106
Tel (603) 263-1600 *SIC* 5147 5149

C&S WHOLESALE GROCERS INC p 234
7 Corporate Dr, Keene NH 03431
Tel (603) 354-7000
SIC 5141 5147 5143 5142 5122 5145

CATELLI BROS INC p 265
50 Ferry Ave, Camden NJ 08103
Tel (856) 869-9293 *SIC* 5147

PORKY PRODUCTS INC p 1161
400 Port Carteret Dr, Carteret NJ 07008
Tel (732) 541-0200
SIC 5147 5146 5144 5143

■ **SYSCO METRO NEW YORK LLC** p 1417
20 Theodore Conrad Dr, Jersey City NJ 07305
Tel (201) 451-0997
SIC 5141 5144 5142 5147 5087

PAT LAFRIEDA MEAT PURVEYORS INC p 1120
3701 Tonnelle Ave, North Bergen NJ 07047
Tel (201) 537-8210 *SIC* 5147

GLOBAL TRADING ENTERPRISES LLC p 617
504 Sharptown Rd, Swedesboro NJ 08085
Tel (856) 223-9966 *SIC* 5147

RASTELLI BROTHERS INC p 1209
300 Heron Dr, Swedesboro NJ 08085
Tel (856) 803-1100 *SIC* 5147 5421 2011

DARTAGNAN INC p 413
600 Green Ln, Union NJ 07083
Tel (973) 344-0565
SIC 5147 5148 5149 2011

FANCY FOODS INC p 527
Hunts Pt Cooperative Mkt, Bronx NY 10474
Tel (718) 617-3000 *SIC* 5144 5147

NEBRASKALAND INC p 1023
355 Food Center Dr Ste G4, Bronx NY 10474
Tel (718) 842-0700 *SIC* 5147

VISTA FOOD EXCHANGE INC p 1562
355 Food Center Dr B101, Bronx NY 10474
Tel (718) 542-4401
SIC 5144 5147 5146 5148 5143

JETRO CASH AND CARRY ENTERPRISES LLC p 784
1524 132nd St, College Point NY 11356
Tel (718) 939-6400
SIC 5142 5046 5181 5147 5411

JRD HOLDINGS INC p 795
1524 132nd St, College Point NY 11356
Tel (718) 762-8700
SIC 5141 5142 5147 5181 5194

RESTAURANT DEPOT LLC p 1228
1524 132nd St, College Point NY 11356
Tel (718) 762-8700
SIC 5147 5141 5142 5181 5194

MAINES PAPER & FOOD SERVICE INC p 898
101 Broome Corporate Pkwy, Conklin NY 13748
Tel (607) 779-1200
SIC 5142 5113 5141 5087 5147 5146

CRESCENT PACKING CORP p 391
1970 New Hwy, Farmingdale NY 11735
Tel (631) 253-0700 *SIC* 5147

AVA PORK PRODUCTS INC p 135
383 W John St Unit A, Hicksville NY 11801
Tel (516) 750-1500 *SIC* 5147

LANDMARK FOOD CORP p 843
865 Waverly Ave, Holtsville NY 11742
Tel (631) 654-4500
SIC 5142 5141 5148 5147

GINSBERGS INSTITUTIONAL FOODS INC p 612
29 Ginsburg Ln, Hudson NY 12534
Tel (518) 828-4004
SIC 5148 5147 5142 5141 5143

WILLOW RUN FOODS INC p 1613
1006 Us Route 11, Kirkwood NY 13795
Tel (607) 338-5221
SIC 5142 5149 5147 5113 5148 5087

PM BEEF HOLDINGS LLC p 1157
810 7th Ave Fl 29, New York NY 10019
Tel (507) 831-2761 *SIC* 5144 5147 2011

CACTUS HOLDINGS INC p 236
4705 Metropolitan Ave, Ridgewood NY 11385
Tel (718) 417-3770
SIC 5411 5147 5144 5146 5148 5143

PALMER FISH CO INC p 1109
900 Jefferson Rd Ste 1000, Rochester NY 14623
Tel (585) 424-3210
SIC 5146 5147 5142 2013

G & C FOOD DISTRIBUTORS & BROKERS INC p 586
3407 Walters Rd, Syracuse NY 13209
Tel (315) 422-3191 *SIC* 5147 5146 4222

TOPS MARKETS LLC p 1461
6363 Main St, Williamsville NY 14221
Tel (716) 635-5000
SIC 5411 5141 5147 5148 5122 5912

STAR FOOD PRODUCTS INC p 1378
2050 Willow Spring Ln A, Burlington NC 27215
Tel (336) 227-4079 *SIC* 5147 2099

PDNC LLC p 1125
402 Commerce Ct, Goldsboro NC 27534
Tel (919) 778-3000
SIC 5142 5141 5147 5148 5431

MEAT AND SEAFOOD SOLUTIONS LLC p 934
3500 Old Battleground Rd, Greensboro NC 27410
Tel (336) 545-3827 *SIC* 5146 5147

SOUTHERN FOODS INC p 1348
3500 Old Battlegrd Rd A, Greensboro NC 27410
Tel (336) 545-3800
SIC 5147 5143 5146 5148 5142

ALEX LEE INC p 48
120 4th St Sw, Hickory NC 28602
Tel (828) 725-4424
SIC 5141 5142 5147 5148 5194 5411

MERCHANTS DISTRIBUTORS LLC p 944
5005 Alex Lee Blvd, Hickory NC 28601
Tel (828) 725-4424
SIC 5141 5142 5147 5148 5194 5122

■ **MEADOWBROOK MEAT CO INC** p 934
2641 Meadowbrook Rd, Rocky Mount NC 27801
Tel (252) 985-7200
SIC 5147 5113 5149 5142

CLOVERDALE FOODS CO p 328
3015 34th St Nw, Mandan ND 58554
Tel (701) 663-9511 *SIC* 2013 5147

HILLCREST EGG & CHEESE CO p 693
2735 E 40th St, Cleveland OH 44115
Tel (216) 361-4625
SIC 5143 5142 5147 5144 5149 5148

NORTHERN FROZEN FOODS INC p 1056
21500 Alexander Rd, Cleveland OH 44146
Tel (440) 439-0600 *SIC* 5142 5149 5147

FRESH MARK INC p 578
1888 Southway St Se, Massillon OH 44646
Tel (330) 834-3669 *SIC* 2013 5147 2011

TILLAMOOK COUNTRY SMOKER INC p 1453
8250 Warren Ave, Bay City OR 97107
Tel (503) 377-2222 *SIC* 5147

AAS HOLDING CO p 8
2401 Ne Argyle St, Portland OR 97211
Tel (503) 284-3314 *SIC* 5147 5142 5141

WESTERN BOXED MEATS DISTRIBUTORS p 1597
2401 Ne Argyle St, Portland OR 97211
Tel (503) 284-3314 *SIC* 5147 5142

IMLERS POULTRY LP p 734
1887 Route 764, Duncansville PA 16635
Tel (814) 943-5563
SIC 5144 5147 5141 5142

MCANENY BROTHERS INC p 926
470 Industrial Park Rd, Ebensburg PA 15931
Tel (814) 472-9800
SIC 5141 5147 5148 5194 5113 5142

CA CURTZE CO p 234
1717 E 12th St, Erie PA 16511
Tel (814) 452-2281 *SIC* 5141 5147 5142

GIANT EAGLE INC p 610
101 Kappa Dr, Pittsburgh PA 15238
Tel (800) 362-8899
SIC 5411 5141 5147 5148 5143 6794

ASSOCIATED WHOLESALERS INC p 121
336 E Penn Ave, Robesonia PA 19551
Tel (610) 693-3161
SIC 5141 5147 5122 5142 5148 5411

GODSHALLS QUALITY MEATS INC p 619
675 Mill Rd, Telford PA 18969
Tel (215) 256-8867 *SIC* 5147 5421

M T G LLC p 890
Carre 175km 27 2 Hc 34 Bo, Caguas PR 00725
Tel (787) 783-1988 *SIC* 5147

NORTHWESTERN SELECTA INC p 1061
796 Calle C M Julia Indst, San Juan PR 00920
Tel (787) 781-1950 *SIC* 5147 5146 5142

EAST COAST DISTRIBUTORS INC p 470
1705 Broad St, Cranston RI 02905
Tel (401) 780-8800 *SIC* 5147

ALL AMERICAN FOODS INC p 51
1 All American Way, North Kingstown RI 02852
Tel (401) 294-5455 *SIC* 5147 5146 5142

■ **SYSCO COLUMBIA LLC** p 1417
131 Sysco Ct, Columbia SC 29209
Tel (803) 239-4000
SIC 5141 5046 5142 5147 5148

W LEE FLOWERS AND CO INC p 1568
127 E W Lee Flowers Rd, Scranton SC 29591
Tel (843) 389-2731 *SIC* 5141 5147 5194

EMPIRE PACKING CO LP p 493
1837 Harbor Ave, Memphis TN 38113
Tel (901) 948-4788 *SIC* 5147 2011

MONOGRAM FOOD SOLUTIONS LLC p 984
530 Oak Court Dr Ste 400, Memphis TN 38117
Tel (901) 685-7167 *SIC* 5142 2013 5147

BRENHAM WHOLESALE GROCERY CO INC p 210
602 W First St, Brenham TX 77833
Tel (979) 836-7925
SIC 5194 5147 5142 5141 5148

NORTHERN BEEF INDUSTRIES INC p 1055
719 S Shoreline Blvd # 204, Corpus Christi TX 78401
Tel (361) 654-6180 *SIC* 5147

■ **FREEDMAN MEATS INC** p 576
2901 S Polk St, Dallas TX 75224
Tel (713) 229-8000 *SIC* 5147

NORTH FOOD GROUP INC p 1052
1245 W Royal Ln, Dallas TX 75261
Tel (972) 445-3322
SIC 5146 5147 5149 5113

AA TRADING LLC p 7
1702 S State Highway 336 B, Edinburg TX 78539
Tel (956) 618-3006 *SIC* 5147

LA BODEGA MEAT INC p 835
14330 Gillis Rd, Farmers Branch TX 75244
Tel (972) 926-6129 *SIC* 5147

BASSHAM WHOLESALE EGG CO INC p 159
5409 Hemphill St, Fort Worth TX 76115
Tel (817) 921-1600
SIC 5144 5143 5141 5147

AMIGOS MEAT DISTRIBUTORS LP p 85
611 Crosstimbers St, Houston TX 77022
Tel (713) 928-3111 *SIC* 5147

SIGMA ALIMENTOS INTERNATIONAL INC p 1321
1009 Black Diamond Cir, Laredo TX 78045
Tel (956) 417-2693 *SIC* 5147

■ **SYSCO WEST TEXAS INC** p 1418
714 2nd Pl, Lubbock TX 79401
Tel (806) 747-2678 *SIC* 5146 5147

LEONARD FAMILY CORP p 856
647 Steves Ave, San Antonio TX 78210
Tel (210) 532-3241 *SIC* 5147

JOHN SOULES FOODS INC p 789
10150 Fm 14, Tyler TX 75706
Tel (903) 592-9800 *SIC* 2013 2015 5147

J & B SAUSAGE CO INC p 769
100 Main, Waelder TX 78959
Tel (830) 788-7661 *SIC* 2011 5147 2013

PRIME INTERNATIONAL LLC p 1175
1047 S 100 W Ste 240, Logan UT 84321
Tel (435) 753-6533 *SIC* 5147

ASSOCIATED FOOD STORES INC p 120
1850 W 2100 S, Salt Lake City UT 84119
Tel (801) 973-4400
SIC 5141 5147 5142 5148 5122 5023

MONOGRAM SNACKS MARTINSVILLE LLC p 984
200 Knauss Dr, Martinsville VA 24112
Tel (901) 685-7167 *SIC* 5147

■ **RICHFOOD INC** p 1233
8258 Richfood Rd, Mechanicsville VA 23116
Tel (804) 746-6000
SIC 5141 5147 5142 5148 5143 2026

PFG HOLDINGS LLC p 1140
12500 West Creek Pkwy, Richmond VA 23238
Tel (804) 484-7700
SIC 5141 5144 5147 5146 5142 5148

■ **SYSCO VIRGINIA LLC** p 1418
5081 S Valley Pike, Rockingham VA 22801
Tel (540) 434-0761
SIC 5149 5142 5113 5148 5147 5143

SMITHFIELD FARMLAND SALES CORP p 1333
111 Commerce St, Smithfield VA 23430
Tel (757) 357-3131 *SIC* 5147 8743 5963

■ **SYSCO HAMPTON ROADS INC** p 1417
7000 Harbour View Blvd, Suffolk VA 23435
Tel (757) 399-2451 *SIC* 5141 5147 5148

SCHENCK FOODS CO INC p 1286
3578 Valley Pike, Winchester VA 22602
Tel (540) 869-1870
SIC 5141 5142 5087 5147 5148

ASSOCIATED GROCERS INC p 120
3301 S Norfolk St, Seattle WA 98118
Tel (206) 762-2100
SIC 5141 5147 5143 5122 5148 5142

URM STORES INC p 1530
7511 N Freya St, Spokane WA 99217
Tel (509) 467-2620 *SIC* 5141 5147

AB FOODS LLC p 9
201 Elmwood Rd, Toppenish WA 98948
Tel (509) 865-2121 *SIC* 5147

INDIANHEAD FOODSERVICE DISTRIBUTOR INC p 739
313 N Hastings Pl, Eau Claire WI 54703
Tel (715) 834-2777
SIC 5142 5141 5147 5143

U W PROVISION CO INC p 1497
2315 Pleasant View Rd, Middleton WI 53562
Tel (608) 836-7421 *SIC* 5147

SIC 5148 Fresh Fruits & Vegetables Wholesale

BASHAS INC p 158
22402 S Basha Rd, Chandler AZ 85248
Tel (480) 883-6131
SIC 5411 5149 5148 5147 6512

DIVINE FLAVOR LLC p 444
766 N Target Range Rd, Nogales AZ 85621
Tel (520) 281-8328 *SIC* 5148

KODIAK FRESH PRODUCE LLC p 826
1033 E Maricopa Fwy, Phoenix AZ 85034
Tel (602) 253-2236 *SIC* 5148

SHAMROCK FOODS CO p 1311
3900 E Camelback Rd # 300, Phoenix AZ 85018
Tel (602) 477-2500
SIC 5146 5149 5147 5148 5142 2026

FOOD SERVICES OF AMERICA INC p 564
16100 N 71st St Ste 400, Scottsdale AZ 85254
Tel (480) 927-4000
SIC 5148 5142 5146 5141

SERVICES GROUP OF AMERICA INC p 1308
16100 N 71st St Ste 500, Scottsdale AZ 85254
Tel (480) 927-4000
SIC 5141 5148 6331 6552

PAPA JOHNS SALADS & PRODUCE INC p 1112
859 S 86th Ave, Tolleson AZ 85353
Tel (480) 894-6885 *SIC* 5148

■ **PFG BROADLINE HOLDINGS LLC** p 1140
4901 Asher Ave, Little Rock AR 72204
Tel (501) 568-3141
SIC 5149 5148 5147 5141

POMWONDERFUL LLC p 1161
4805 Centennial Ste 100, Bakersfield CA 93301
Tel (310) 966-5800 *SIC* 5149 5148 5085

GREENTHUMB PRODUCE p 637
2648 W Ramsey St, Banning CA 92220
Tel (951) 849-4711 *SIC* 5148

BI-RITE RESTAURANT SUPPLY CO INC p 180
123 S Hill Dr, Brisbane CA 94005
Tel (415) 656-0187
SIC 5141 5147 5148 5023 5046 5963

OAKVILLE PRODUCE PARTNERS LLC p 1071
453 Valley Dr, Brisbane CA 94005
Tel (415) 647-2991 *SIC* 5148 5451

LEGACY FARMS LLC p 852
6625 Caballero Blvd, Buena Park CA 90620
Tel (714) 736-1800 *SIC* 5148

■ **FRESHPOINT OF SOUTHERN CALIFORNIA INC** p 579
155 N Orange Ave, City Of Industry CA 91744
Tel (626) 855-1400 *SIC* 5148 5142

HARMONI INTERNATIONAL SPICE INC CALIFORNIA p 662
881 S Azusa Ave, City Of Industry CA 91748
Tel (626) 330-1550 *SIC* 5148 5149

MERCADO LATINO INC p 943
245 Baldwin Park Blvd, City Of Industry CA 91746
Tel (626) 333-6862 SIC 5141 5148

PRIMETIME INTERNATIONAL INC p 1175
86705 Avenue 54 Ste A, Coachella CA 92236
Tel (760) 399-4166 SIC 5148 4783

4 EARTH FARMS INC p 3
5555 E Olympic Blvd, Commerce CA 90022
Tel (323) 201-5800 SIC 5148

VEG-FRESH FARMS LLC p 1546
1400 W Rincon St, Corona CA 92880
Tel (800) 422-5535 SIC 5148

FRUIT PATCH SALES LLC p 582
38773 Road 48, Dinuba CA 93618
Tel (559) 591-1170 SIC 5148

CHARLIES ENTERPRISES p 290
1888 S East Ave, Fresno CA 93721
Tel (559) 445-8600 SIC 5148

FRESH PACIFIC FRUIT AND VEGETABLE INC p 579
7650 N Palm Ave Ste 103, Fresno CA 93711
Tel (559) 432-3500 SIC 5148

PACIFIC TRELLIS FRUIT LLC p 1106
5108 E Clinton Way # 108, Fresno CA 93727
Tel (559) 255-5437 SIC 5148

GOLDEN STATE FOODS CORP p 621
18301 Von Karman Ave # 1100, Irvine CA 92612
Tel (949) 252-2000
SIC 5147 2087 5142 5148 5149

READY PAC FOODS INC p 1213
4401 Foxdale St, Irwindale CA 91706
Tel (626) 856-8686 SIC 2099 5148

READY PAC PRODUCE INC p 1213
4401 Foxdale St, Irwindale CA 91706
Tel (800) 800-4088 SIC 2099 5148

WESTLAKE DISTRIBUTORS INC p 1601
5301 Rivergrade Rd # 200, Irwindale CA 91706
Tel (213) 624-8676 SIC 5148

KINGSBURG APPLE PACKERS INC p 821
10363 Davis Ave, Kingsburg CA 93631
Tel (559) 897-5132 SIC 5148

FRESH CONNECTION p 578
3722 Mt Diablo Blvd, Lafayette CA 94549
Tel (925) 299-9939 SIC 5148

PRODUCE EXCHANGE INC p 1179
7407 Southfront Rd, Livermore CA 94551
Tel (925) 454-8700 SIC 5148

REYNOLDS PACKING CO p 1231
33 E Tokay St, Lodi CA 95240
Tel (209) 369-2725 SIC 0723 5148 2449

BERRY ECLIPSE FARMS LLC p 176
11812 San Vicente Blvd # 250, Los Angeles CA 90049
Tel (310) 207-7879 SIC 0171 5148

DAVALAN SALES INC p 414
1601 E Olympic Blvd # 325, Los Angeles CA 90021
Tel (213) 623-2500 SIC 5148

GREEN FARMS INC p 637
1661 Mcgarry St, Los Angeles CA 90021
Tel (213) 747-4411 SIC 5148

ICREST INTERNATIONAL LLC p 728
725 S Figueroa St # 3050, Los Angeles CA 90017
Tel (213) 488-8303 SIC 5148 5147

POM WONDERFUL HOLDINGS LLC p 1160
11444 W Olympic Blvd # 210, Los Angeles CA 90064
Tel (310) 966-5800 SIC 5149 5148 5085

VAL-PRO INC p 1539
1601 E Olympic Blvd # 300, Los Angeles CA 90021
Tel (213) 627-8736 SIC 5148

▲ LANDEC CORP p 842
3603 Haven Ave, Menlo Park CA 94025
Tel (650) 306-1650 SIC 2033 5148 5999

SJ DISTRIBUTORS INC p 1328
625 Vista Way, Milpitas CA 95035
Tel (888) 988-2328 SIC 5142 5148 5149

MURANAKA FARM p 1001
11018 E Los Angeles Ave, Moorpark CA 93021
Tel (805) 529-6692 SIC 5148

WEST CENTRAL PRODUCE INC p 1594
12840 Leyva St, Norwalk CA 90650
Tel (213) 629-3600 SIC 5148

MISSION PRODUCE INC p 975
2500 E Vineyard Ave # 300, Oxnard CA 93036
Tel (805) 981-3650 SIC 5148

SUN PACIFIC MARKETING COOPERATIVE INC p 1400
1095 E Green St, Pasadena CA 91106
Tel (213) 612-9957 SIC 5148

SUNRISE GROWERS INC p 1404
701 W Kimberly Ave # 210, Placentia CA 92870
Tel (714) 630-2170 SIC 5148 2037

■ SYSCO SAN DIEGO INC p 1418
12180 Kirkham Rd, Poway CA 92064
Tel (858) 513-7300
SIC 5141 5142 5147 5148 5084

■ EVOLUTION FRESH INC p 515
11655 Jersey Blvd, Rancho Cucamonga CA 91730
Tel (909) 478-0895 SIC 5148

BERRY FRESH LLC p 176
19640 S Rancho Way, Rancho Dominguez CA 90220
Tel (310) 637-2401 SIC 5148

MOONLIGHT PACKING CORP p 987
17719 E Huntsman Ave, Reedley CA 93654
Tel (559) 638-7799 SIC 5148 4783

GENERAL PRODUCE CO A CALIFORNIA LIMITED PARTNERSHIP p 602
1330 N B St, Sacramento CA 95811
Tel (916) 441-6431 SIC 5148

RIVER RANCH FRESH FOODS LLC p 1237
911 Blanco Cir Ste B, Salinas CA 93901
Tel (831) 758-1390 SIC 5148

COAST CITRUS DISTRIBUTORS p 331
7597 Bristow Ct, San Diego CA 92154
Tel (619) 661-7950 SIC 5148

MPCI HOLDINGS INC p 995
7850 Waterville Rd, San Diego CA 92154
Tel (619) 294-2222
SIC 5147 5143 5148 5113

JORDANOS INC p 793
550 S Patterson Ave, Santa Barbara CA 93111
Tel (805) 964-0611
SIC 5181 5182 5149 5141 5142 5148

DIMETRI GARDIKAS PRODUCE CO INC p 440
14811 Marquardt Ave, Santa Fe Springs CA 90670
Tel (562) 404-4779 SIC 5148

LA SPECIALTY PRODUCE CO p 836
13527 Orden Dr, Santa Fe Springs CA 90670
Tel (562) 741-2200 SIC 5148

▲ CALAVO GROWERS INC p 238
1141 Cummings Rd Ste A, Santa Paula CA 93060
Tel (805) 525-1245 SIC 5148 5142 5149

DYNASTY FARMS INC p 464
11900 Big Tujunga Cyn Rd, Tujunga CA 91042
Tel (831) 755-1398 SIC 5148

MARIANI PACKING CO INC p 906
500 Crocker Dr, Vacaville CA 95688
Tel (707) 452-2800 SIC 0723 2034 5148

SUNKIST GROWERS INC p 1402
27770 N Entertainment Dr # 120, Valencia CA 91355
Tel (818) 986-4800
SIC 5148 2033 2037 2899 6794 5046

DRISCOLL STRAWBERRY ASSOCIATES INC p 456
345 Westridge Dr, Watsonville CA 95076
Tel (831) 424-0506 SIC 5148 5431

DFC HOLDINGS LLC p 435
1 Dole Dr, Westlake Village CA 91362
Tel (818) 879-6600
SIC 0174 0175 0161 5148 2033

DHM HOLDING CO INC p 435
1 Dole Dr, Westlake Village CA 91362
Tel (818) 879-6600
SIC 0179 0174 0175 0161 5148 2033

DOLE FOOD CO INC p 448
1 Dole Dr, Westlake Village CA 91362
Tel (818) 874-4000
SIC 0179 0174 0175 0161 5148 2033

DOLE FRESH FRUIT CO p 448
1 Dole Dr, Westlake Village CA 91362
Tel (818) 874-4000 SIC 5148

DOLE HOLDING CO LLC p 448
1 Dole Dr, Westlake Village CA 91362
Tel (818) 879-6600
SIC 0179 0174 0175 0161 5148 2033

LIBERTY PACKING CO LLC p 862
724 Main St, Woodland CA 95695
Tel (209) 826-7100 SIC 5148

UNITED FOOD SERVICE INC p 1508
5199 Ivy St, Commerce City CO 80022
Tel (303) 289-3595
SIC 5141 5142 5147 5148 5046

FRESHPACK PRODUCE INC p 579
5151 Bannock St Ste 12, Denver CO 80216
Tel (303) 412-6232 SIC 5148

GROWERS SALES AND MARKETING LLC p 642
15 Washington St Ste 207, Monte Vista CO 81144
Tel (719) 852-2600 SIC 5148

ANDREWS PRODUCE INC p 90
717 E Industrial Blvd, Pueblo West CO 81007
Tel (719) 543-3846 SIC 5141 5148

COAST-TO-COAST PRODUCE CO LLC p 331
125 Commerce Ct Ste 2, Cheshire CT 06410
Tel (203) 271-2006 SIC 5148

BOUNTY FRESH LLC p 204
806 S Douglas Rd Ste 580, Coral Gables FL 33134
Tel (305) 592-6969 SIC 5148

DEL MONTE FRESH PRODUCE CO p 423
241 Sevilla Ave Ste 200, Coral Gables FL 33134
Tel (305) 520-8400 SIC 5148

DEL MONTE FRESH PRODUCE NA INC p 423
241 Sevilla Ave Ste 200, Coral Gables FL 33134
Tel (305) 520-8400 SIC 5148

TURBANA CORP p 1492
999 Ponce De Leon Blvd # 900, Coral Gables FL 33134
Tel (305) 445-1542 SIC 5148

PERO FAMILY FARMS FOOD CO LLC p 1137
14095 Us Highway 441, Delray Beach FL 33446
Tel (561) 498-4533 SIC 5148

PERO FAMILY FARMS LLC p 1137
14095 Us Highway 441, Delray Beach FL 33446
Tel (561) 498-4533 SIC 5148

HORTIFRUT IMPORTS INC p 708
9450 Corkscrew Palms Cir, Estero FL 33928
Tel (239) 552-4453 SIC 5148

CHIQUITA BRANDS LLC p 301
2051 Se 35th St, Fort Lauderdale FL 33316
Tel (954) 453-1201
SIC 0175 0174 0179 0161 5148 7389

LIPMAN-TEXAS LLC p 870
315 New Market Rd E, Immokalee FL 34142
Tel (239) 657-4421 SIC 5148

SIX LS PACKING CO INC p 1328
315 New Market Rd E, Immokalee FL 34142
Tel (239) 657-3117 SIC 5148

J & J PRODUCE INC p 770
4003 Seminole Pratt, Loxahatchee FL 33470
Tel (561) 422-9777 SIC 5148 0161

FLORIDA VEG INVESTMENTS LLC p 559
7350 Nw 30th Ave, Miami FL 33147
Tel (305) 836-3152 SIC 5148

GARGIULO INC p 592
15000 Old Hwy 41 N, Naples FL 34110
Tel (239) 597-3131 SIC 5148

■ FRESHPOINT CENTRAL FLORIDA INC p 579
8801 Exchange Dr, Orlando FL 32809
Tel (407) 383-8427 SIC 5148 5431

A DUDA & SONS INC p 5
1200 Duda Trl, Oviedo FL 32765
Tel (407) 365-2111
SIC 0161 5148 2033 0133 6552 0174

DUDA FARM FRESH FOODS INC p 459
1200 Duda Trl, Oviedo FL 32765
Tel (407) 365-2111 SIC 5148 0161 0174

MARIO CAMACHO FOODS LLC p 907
2502 Walden Woods Dr, Plant City FL 33566
Tel (813) 305-4534 SIC 5148

WISHNATZKI INC p 1619
100 Stearns St, Plant City FL 33563
Tel (813) 752-5111 SIC 5148

AYCO FARMS INC p 140
1501 Nw 12th Ave, Pompano Beach FL 33069
Tel (954) 788-6800 SIC 5148 0161

■ FRESHPOINT SOUTH FLORIDA INC p 579
2300 Nw 19th St, Pompano Beach FL 33069
Tel (954) 917-7272 SIC 5148 5143

SUN COMMODITIES INC p 1400
2230 Sw 2nd St, Pompano Beach FL 33069
Tel (954) 972-8383 SIC 5148

PRODUCE EXCHANGE CO INC p 1179
2801 E Hillsborough Ave, Tampa FL 33610
Tel (813) 237-3374 SIC 5148

SANWA GROWERS INC p 1281
2801 E Hillsborough Ave, Tampa FL 33610
Tel (813) 642-5159 SIC 5147 5148

SOUTHERN FULFILLMENT SERVICES LLC p 1348
1650 90th Ave, Vero Beach FL 32966
Tel (772) 226-3500 SIC 5148 5149

AJC INTERNATIONAL INC p 41
1000 Abernathy Rd Ste 600, Atlanta GA 30328
Tel (404) 252-6750
SIC 5144 5147 5148 5146

ROYAL FOOD SERVICE CO INC p 1254
3720 Zip Indus Blvd Se, Atlanta GA 30354
Tel (404) 366-4299 SIC 5148 5142

■ FRESHPOINT INC p 579
16 Forest Pkwy Bldg H, Forest Park GA 30297
Tel (404) 362-6100 SIC 5148

GPI LIQUIDATION INC p 627
16 Forest Pkwy Bldg M, Forest Park GA 30297
Tel (404) 361-0215 SIC 5148

SUTHERLANDS FOODSERVICE INC p 1410
16 Forest Pkwy Bldg K, Forest Park GA 30297
Tel (404) 366-8550
SIC 5144 5148 5147 5143 5141

CMU & ASSOCIATES INC p 329
55 Holomua St, Hilo HI 96720
Tel (808) 961-0877 SIC 5146 5148 5142

IDAHO POTATO PACKERS CORP p 728
40 N 400 W, Blackfoot ID 83221
Tel (208) 785-3030 SIC 5148

BLAINE LARSEN FARMS INC p 188
2650 N 2375 E, Hamer ID 83425
Tel (208) 662-5501
SIC 5148 2099 0111 0139

EAGLE EYE PRODUCE INC p 468
4050 E Lincoln Rd, Idaho Falls ID 83401
Tel (208) 522-2343 SIC 5148

POTANDON PRODUCE LLC p 1164
1210 Pier View Dr, Idaho Falls ID 83402
Tel (208) 419-4200 SIC 5148 0161 0722

WADA FARMS MARKETING GROUP LLC p 1571
2155 Providence Way, Idaho Falls ID 83404
Tel (208) 542-2898 SIC 5148

GET FRESH PRODUCE INC p 609
1441 Brewster Creek Blvd, Bartlett IL 60103
Tel (630) 837-9700 SIC 5148

PRODUCE ALLIANCE LLC p 1179
100 Lexington Dr Ste 201, Buffalo Grove IL 60089
Tel (847) 808-3030 SIC 5148

RUBY ROBINSON CO INC p 1257
100 Lexington Dr Ste 201, Buffalo Grove IL 60089
Tel (847) 808-3030 SIC 5148

CAPUTOS NEW FARM PRODUCE INC p 252
520 E North Ave, Carol Stream IL 60188
Tel (630) 620-4444
SIC 5431 5411 5148 5149

ANTHONY MARANO CO p 94
3000 S Ashland Ave # 100, Chicago IL 60608
Tel (773) 321-7500 SIC 5148

MID-WEST INSTITUTIONAL FOOD DISTRIBUTORS INC p 964
3100 W 36th St, Chicago IL 60632
Tel (773) 927-8870
SIC 5142 5143 5144 5147 5148

PETES FRESH MARKET 4700 CORP p 1138
4333 S Pulaski Rd, Chicago IL 60632
Tel (773) 927-4300 SIC 5148 5431

TESTA PRODUCE INC p 1441
4555 S Racine Ave, Chicago IL 60609
Tel (312) 226-3237 SIC 5148 5812

KUNA MEAT CO INC p 832
704 Kuna Industrial Ct, Dupo IL 62239
Tel (618) 286-4000
SIC 5144 5142 5147 5169 5149 5148

CENTRAL GROCERS INC p 278
2600 Haven Ave, Joliet IL 60433
Tel (815) 553-8800
SIC 5141 5147 5142 5148 5143 5122

■ FOX RIVER FOODS INC p 572
5030 Baseline Rd, Montgomery IL 60538
Tel (630) 896-1991
SIC 5142 5149 5148 5147

SUN BELLE INC p 1400
3810 Rose St, Schiller Park IL 60176
Tel (708) 343-4545 SIC 5148

TOM LANGE CO INC p 1459
755 Apple Orchard Rd, Springfield IL 62703
Tel (217) 786-3300 SIC 5148

CAITO FOODS SERVICE INC p 237
3120 N Post Rd, Indianapolis IN 46226
Tel (800) 652-8165 SIC 5148

IF&P FOODS INC p 730
4501 Massachusetts Ave, Indianapolis IN 46218
Tel (317) 546-2425 SIC 5148

PIAZZA PRODUCE INC p 1146
5941 W 82nd St, Indianapolis IN 46278
Tel (317) 872-0101 SIC 5148

PIAZZA PRODUCE LLC p 1146
5941 W 82nd St, Indianapolis IN 46278
Tel (317) 872-0101 SIC 5148

STANZ CHEESE CO INC p 1377
1840 Commerce Dr, South Bend IN 46628
Tel (574) 232-6666
SIC 5142 5141 5148 5113 5087 5085

LOFFREDO GARDENS INC p 874
4001 Sw 63rd St, Des Moines IA 50321
Tel (816) 421-7480 SIC 5148

ASSOCIATED WHOLESALE GROCERS INC p 121
5000 Kansas Ave, Kansas City KS 66106
Tel (913) 288-1000
SIC 5141 5143 5142 5147 5146 5148

LIBERTY FRUIT CO INC p 861
1247 Argentine Blvd, Kansas City KS 66105
Tel (913) 238-4606 SIC 5148

CLUB CHEF LLC p 328
3776 Lake Park Dr Unit 1, Covington KY 41017
Tel (859) 578-3100 SIC 5148

CASTELLINI CO LLC p 264
2 Plum St, Highland Heights KY 41076
Tel (800) 233-8560 SIC 5148 4212 4213

CASTELLINI HOLDING CO LLC p 264
2 Plum St, Highland Heights KY 41076
Tel (859) 442-4673 SIC 5148

CROSSET CO LLC p 394
10295 Toebben Dr, Independence KY 41051
Tel (859) 283-5830 SIC 5148

HORTON FRUIT CO INC p 708
4701 Jennings Ln, Louisville KY 40218
Tel (502) 969-1371 SIC 5148

DOERLE FOOD SERVICES LLC p 447
113 Kol Dr, Broussard LA 70518
Tel (337) 252-8551
SIC 5142 5141 5087 5148

ASSOCIATED GROCERS OF MAINE INC p 120
190 Water St, Gardiner ME 04345
Tel (207) 596-0636
SIC 5141 5147 5148 5122

■ SYSCO NORTHERN NEW ENGLAND INC p 1417
55 Thomas Dr, Westbrook ME 04092
Tel (207) 871-0700
SIC 5141 5147 5148 5142

FOODPRO CORP p 564
321 E 5th St, Frederick MD 21701
Tel (301) 663-3171
SIC 5142 5149 5148 5147 5143 5113

GILBERT FOODS LLC p 612
7251 Standard Dr, Hanover MD 21076
Tel (410) 712-6000
SIC 5148 5147 5146 5142

CLASS PRODUCE GROUP LLC p 323
8477 Dorsey Run Rd, Jessup MD 20794
Tel (410) 799-5700 SIC 5148

LANCASTER FOODS LLC p 841
7700 Conowingo Ave, Jessup MD 20794
Tel (410) 799-0010 SIC 5148

P J K FOOD SERVICE CORP p 1102
3310 75th Ave, Landover MD 20785
Tel (301) 772-3333 SIC 5148

COASTAL SUNBELT INC p 332
9001 Whiskey Bottom Rd, Laurel MD 20723
Tel (410) 799-8000
SIC 5148 4214 0723 2099

COSTA FRUIT & PRODUCE CO p 374
18 Bunker Hill Indus Park, Boston MA 02129
Tel (617) 241-8007
SIC 5148 5143 5142 5141

DIMARE BROTHERS INC p 440
84 New England Prod Ctr, Chelsea MA 02150
Tel (617) 889-3800 SIC 5148

WEST COAST DISTRIBUTING INC p 1594
350 Main St Fl 1, Malden MA 02148
Tel (781) 665-0300 SIC 4731 5148

FRIENDLY FRUIT INC p 580
2301 Purchase St Unit 1, New Bedford MA 02746
Tel (508) 999-6408 SIC 5148 5149

LAGRASSO BROS INC p 838
5001 Bellevue St, Detroit MI 48211
Tel (313) 579-1455 SIC 5148

RIGGIO DISTRIBUTION CO p 1234
7939 Lafayette Blvd, Detroit MI 48209
Tel (313) 841-7911 SIC 5148

NORTH BAY PRODUCE INC p 1051
1771 N Us Highway 31 S, Traverse City MI 49685
Tel (231) 946-1941 SIC 5148

■ NASH-FINCH CO p 1008
7600 France Ave S Ste 200, Minneapolis MN 55435
Tel (952) 832-0534
SIC 5141 5148 5142 5147 5411

WHOLESALE PRODUCE SUPPLY LLC p 1607
752 Kasota Cir Se, Minneapolis MN 55414
Tel (612) 378-2025 SIC 5148

■ MICHAEL FOODS GROUP INC p 960
301 Carlson Pkwy Ste 400, Minnetonka MN 55305
Tel (952) 258-4000
SIC 0252 2015 5144 5143 5148 6719

■ MICHAEL FOODS INC p 960
301 Carlson Pkwy Ste 400, Minnetonka MN 55305
Tel (507) 237-4600
SIC 0252 2015 5144 5143 5148 5499

■ MICHAEL FOODS OF DELAWARE INC p 960
301 Carlson Pkwy Ste 400, Minnetonka MN 55305
Tel (952) 258-4000
SIC 0252 2015 5144 5143 5148 2024

J & B WHOLESALE DISTRIBUTING INC p 769
13200 43rd St Ne, Saint Michael MN 55376
Tel (763) 497-3913
SIC 5147 5144 5142 5143 5148

BIX PRODUCE CO LLC p 185
1415 L Orient St, Saint Paul MN 55117
Tel (651) 487-8000 SIC 5148 5143

DAVIS RUSS WHOLESALE INC p 416
266 4th St Ne, Wadena MN 56482
Tel (218) 631-3078 SIC 5148

C & C PRODUCE INC p 231
1100 Atlantic Ave, North Kansas City MO 64116
Tel (816) 241-4425 SIC 5148

PROFFER WHOLESALE PRODUCE INC p 1180
920 5th St, Park Hills MO 63601
Tel (573) 431-0625 SIC 5148 4213

■ **MIDDENDORF MEAT CO LLC** p 964
3737 N Broadway, Saint Louis MO 63147
Tel (314) 241-4800
SIC 5147 5141 5148 5146 5113 2011

UNITED INDUSTRIES INC p 1509
55 Produce Row, Saint Louis MO 63102
Tel (314) 621-9440 SIC 5148

TOBA INC p 1458
2621 W Us Highway 30, Grand Island NE 68803
Tel (308) 389-5987
SIC 5148 5194 5145 5141

■ **LINCOLN SYSCO INC** p 868
900 King Bird Rd, Lincoln NE 68521
Tel (402) 423-1031
SIC 5148 5142 5143 5141 5087 5113

GLOBAL PACIFIC PRODUCE INC p 617
11500 S Eastern Ave # 160, Henderson NV 89052
Tel (702) 898-8051 SIC 5148

GET FRESH SALES INC p 609
6745 Escondido St, Las Vegas NV 89119
Tel (702) 897-8522 SIC 5148

FRANK M GARGIULO & SON INC p 574
535 Sweetland Ave Ste 1, Hillside NJ 07205
Tel (908) 233-8222 SIC 5148

■ **ALBERTS ORGANICS INC** p 46
1155 Commerce Blvd, Logan Township NJ 08085
Tel (800) 899-5944 SIC 5149 5148

WUHL SHAFMAN & LIEBERMAN INC p 1628
52 Cornelia St Ste 62, Newark NJ 07105
Tel (973) 589-3513 SIC 5148

DARTAGNAN INC p 413
600 Green Ln, Union NJ 07083
Tel (973) 344-0565
SIC 5147 5148 5149 2011

DANDREA PRODUCE INC p 411
3665 N Mill Rd, Vineland NJ 08360
Tel (856) 205-1830 SIC 5148

RLB FOOD DISTRIBUTORS LP p 1239
2 Dedrick Pl Cn2285, West Caldwell NJ 07006
Tel (973) 575-9526 SIC 5148 5141

ACE ENDICO CORP p 16
80 International Blvd, Brewster NY 10509
Tel (914) 347-3131 SIC 5141 5142 5148

DARRIGO BROS CO OF NEW YORK INC p 412
315 Nyc Terminal Mkt, Bronx NY 10474
Tel (718) 991-5900 SIC 5148

E ARMATA INC p 466
114 Nyc Term Mkt, Bronx NY 10474
Tel (718) 991-5600 SIC 5148

NATHEL & NATHEL INC p 1009
357 Nyc Term Mkt C, Bronx NY 10474
Tel (718) 991-6050 SIC 5148

S KATZMAN PRODUCE INC p 1262
Row A 153 157 Hnts Pt Mkt, Bronx NY 10474
Tel (718) 991-4700 SIC 5148

VISTA FOOD EXCHANGE INC p 1562
355 Food Center Dr B101, Bronx NY 10474
Tel (718) 542-4401
SIC 5144 5147 5146 5148 5143

RD FOOD SERVICES LLC p 1212
1524 132nd St, College Point NY 11356
Tel (718) 961-4356
SIC 5141 5148 5142 5113 5046 5087

WILLIAM H KOPKE JR INC p 1610
1000 Nthrn Blvd Ste 200, Great Neck NY 11021
Tel (516) 328-6800 SIC 5148

J KINGS FOOD SERVICE PROFESSIONALS INC p 771
700 Furrows Rd, Holtsville NY 11742
Tel (631) 289-8401
SIC 5149 5143 5144 5142 5148

LANDMARK FOOD CORP p 843
865 Waverly Ave, Holtsville NY 11742
Tel (631) 654-4500
SIC 5142 5141 5148 5147

GINSBERGS INSTITUTIONAL FOODS INC p 612
29 Ginsburg Ln, Hudson NY 12534
Tel (518) 828-4004
SIC 5148 5147 5142 5141 5143

WILLOW RUN FOODS INC p 1613
1006 Us Route 11, Kirkwood NY 13795
Tel (607) 338-5221
SIC 5142 5149 5147 5113 5148 5087

LGS SPECIALTY SALES LTD p 860
1 Radisson Plz Fl 10, New Rochelle NY 10801
Tel (718) 542-2200 SIC 5141 5148

AIR STREAM CORP p 39
3400 Lawson Blvd, Oceanside NY 11572
Tel (516) 763-1600 SIC 5141 5148

CACTUS HOLDINGS INC p 236
4705 Metropolitan Ave, Ridgewood NY 11385
Tel (718) 417-3770
SIC 5411 5147 5144 5146 5148 5143

TOPS MARKETS LLC p 1461
6363 Main St, Williamsville NY 14221
Tel (716) 635-5000
SIC 5411 5141 5147 5148 5122 5912

JAC VANDENBERG INC p 773
100 Corporate Dr Ste 155, Yonkers NY 10701
Tel (914) 964-5900 SIC 5148

WAYNE BAILEY INC p 1584
490 Old Hwy 74, Chadbourn NC 28431
Tel (910) 654-5163 SIC 5148 0139

PDNC LLC p 1125
402 Commerce Ct, Goldsboro NC 27534
Tel (919) 778-3000
SIC 5142 5141 5147 5148 5431

SOUTHERN FOODS INC p 1348
3500 Old Battlegrd Rd A, Greensboro NC 27410
Tel (336) 545-3800
SIC 5147 5143 5146 5148 5142

ALEX LEE INC p 48
120 4th St Sw, Hickory NC 28602
Tel (828) 725-4424
SIC 5141 5142 5147 5148 5194 5411

MERCHANTS DISTRIBUTORS LLC p 944
5005 Alex Lee Blvd, Hickory NC 28601
Tel (828) 725-4424
SIC 5141 5142 5147 5148 5194 5122

FLAVOR 1ST GROWERS & PACKERS LLC p 555
331 Banner Farm Rd, Mills River NC 28759
Tel (828) 890-3630 SIC 5148

FRESHOUSE II LLC p 579
311 Long Meadow Dr, Salisbury NC 28147
Tel (704) 630-6950 SIC 5148

W R VERNON PRODUCE CO p 1569
1035 N Cherry St, Winston Salem NC 27101
Tel (336) 725-9741 SIC 5148

HILLCREST EGG & CHEESE CO p 693
2735 E 40th St, Cleveland OH 44115
Tel (216) 361-4625
SIC 5143 5142 5147 5144 5149 5148

SIRNA & SONS INC p 1327
7176 State Route 88, Ravenna OH 44266
Tel (330) 298-2222 SIC 5148

FRESHWAY FOODS INC p 579
601 Stolle Ave, Sidney OH 45365
Tel (937) 498-4664 SIC 5148 2099

ORGANICALLY GROWN CO p 1094
1800 Prairie Rd Ste B, Eugene OR 97402
Tel (541) 689-5320 SIC 5148

DUCK DELIVERY PRODUCE INC p 459
8448 Ne 33rd Dr Ste 120, Portland OR 97211
Tel (503) 288-9380 SIC 5148 4212

SPADA PROPERTIES INC p 1354
8448 Ne 33rd Dr Ste 100, Portland OR 97211
Tel (503) 288-8300 SIC 5148

UNITED SALAD CO p 1511
8448 Ne 33rd Dr Ste 100, Portland OR 97211
Tel (503) 288-8300 SIC 5148 0175 2033

PRIMO NO 1 IN PRODUCE INC p 1176
2100 Hoover Ave, Allentown PA 18109
Tel (610) 264-5000 SIC 5148

BASCIANI FOODS INC p 158
8876 Gap Newport Pike, Avondale PA 19311
Tel (610) 268-3610 SIC 5148

MCANENY BROTHERS INC p 926
470 Industrial Park Rd, Ebensburg PA 15931
Tel (814) 472-9800
SIC 5141 5147 5148 5194 5113 5142

FOUR SEASONS PRODUCE INC p 572
400 Wabash Rd, Ephrata PA 17522
Tel (717) 721-2800 SIC 5148

■ **SYSCO PITTSBURGH LLC** p 1417
1 Whitney Dr, Harmony PA 16037
Tel (724) 452-2100
SIC 5142 5149 5148 5023 5113 5046

SOUTH MILL MUSHROOM SALES INC p 1344
649 W South St, Kennett Square PA 19348
Tel (610) 444-4800 SIC 5148

PROCACCI BROS SALES CORP p 1179
3333 S Front St, Philadelphia PA 19148
Tel (215) 463-8000 SIC 5148

GIANT EAGLE INC p 610
101 Kappa Dr, Pittsburgh PA 15238
Tel (800) 362-8899
SIC 5411 5141 5147 5148 5143 6794

DIGIORGIO MUSHROOM CORP p 439
1161 Park Rd, Reading PA 19605
Tel (610) 926-2139
SIC 2033 5148 2037 6512

GIORGIO FOODS INC p 613
1161 Park Rd, Reading PA 19605
Tel (610) 926-2139
SIC 2033 2037 5148 2038

ASSOCIATED WHOLESALERS INC p 121
336 E Penn Ave, Robesonia PA 19551
Tel (610) 693-3161
SIC 5141 5147 5122 5142 5148 5411

POCONO PRODUCE CO INC p 1158
Chipperfield Dr Rr 191, Stroudsburg PA 18360
Tel (570) 421-1533 SIC 5149 5142 5148

PARAGON WHOLESALE FOODS CORP p 1113
173 Thorn Hill Rd, Warrendale PA 15086
Tel (412) 621-2626 SIC 5148 5141

PUERTO RICO SUPPLIES GROUP INC p 1191
Parkeast, Bayamon PR 00961
Tel (787) 780-4043
SIC 5194 5149 5122 5143 5148

CARIBBEAN PRODUCE EXCHANGE LLC p 256
2 Carr 869, Catano PR 00962
Tel (787) 793-0750 SIC 5148

PIGGLY WIGGLY CAROLINA CO INC p 1147
176 Croghan Spur Ste 400, Charleston SC 29407
Tel (843) 554-9880
SIC 7311 5411 5148 5141 2752 1542

■ **SYSCO COLUMBIA LLC** p 1417
131 Sysco Ct, Columbia SC 29209
Tel (803) 239-4000
SIC 5141 5046 5142 5147 5148

WALTER P RAWL & SONS INC p 1574
824 Fairview Rd, Pelion SC 29123
Tel (803) 894-1900 SIC 0161 0723 5148

■ **KENNETH O LESTER CO INC** p 811
245 N Castle Heights Ave, Lebanon TN 37087
Tel (615) 444-9901 SIC 5141 5142 5148

BRENHAM WHOLESALE GROCERY CO INC p 210
602 W First St, Brenham TX 77833
Tel (979) 836-7925
SIC 5194 5147 5142 5141 5148

■ **FRESHPOINT DALLAS INC** p 579
4721 Simonton Rd, Dallas TX 75244
Tel (972) 385-5800 SIC 5148 5142

HARDIES FRUIT AND VEGETABLE CO LP p 660
1005 N Cockrell Hill Rd, Dallas TX 75211
Tel (214) 426-5666 SIC 5148

NOGALES PRODUCE INC p 1046
8220 Forney Rd, Dallas TX 75227
Tel (214) 275-3500 SIC 5148

J & D PRODUCE INC p 769
7310 N Expressway 281, Edinburg TX 78542
Tel (956) 380-0353 SIC 5148

DIMARE FRESH INC p 440
4629 Diplomacy Rd, Fort Worth TX 76155
Tel (817) 385-3000 SIC 5148

BROTHERS PRODUCE INC p 219
3173 Produce Row, Houston TX 77023
Tel (713) 924-4196 SIC 5148

■ **FRESHPOINT INC** p 579
1390 Enclave Pkwy, Houston TX 77077
Tel (281) 899-4242 SIC 5148

SCHOENMANN PRODUCE CO INC p 1288
6950 Neuhaus St, Houston TX 77061
Tel (713) 923-2728 SIC 5148

SYNDEX CORP p 1415
6950 Neuhaus St, Houston TX 77061
Tel (713) 923-1057 SIC 5148

▲ **SYSCO CORP** p 1417
1390 Enclave Pkwy, Houston TX 77077
Tel (281) 584-1390
SIC 5149 5142 5143 5144 5148 5137

DE BRUYN PRODUCE CO p 419
26 Fm 491, La Villa TX 78562
Tel (956) 262-6286 SIC 5148

LA VALENCIANA AVOCADOS CORP p 836
214 N 16th St Ste 127, Mcallen TX 78501
Tel (956) 994-0561 SIC 5148 0179

LIMEX SICAR LTD CO p 866
701 Trinity St, Mission TX 78572
Tel (956) 581-6080 SIC 5148

VILLITA AVOCADOS INC p 1557
9800 Keystone, Pharr TX 78577
Tel (956) 843-1118 SIC 5148

RIO FRESH INC p 1235
6504 S Stewart Rd, San Juan TX 78589
Tel (956) 787-0023 SIC 5148

ASSOCIATED FOOD STORES INC p 120
1850 W 2100 S, Salt Lake City UT 84119
Tel (801) 973-4400
SIC 5141 5147 5142 5148 5122 5023

GUEST SERVICES INC p 645
3055 Prosperity Ave, Fairfax VA 22031
Tel (703) 849-9300 SIC 5148 8741

■ **RICHFOOD INC** p 1233
8258 Richfood Rd, Mechanicsville VA 23116
Tel (804) 746-6000
SIC 5141 5147 5142 5148 5143 2026

PFG HOLDINGS LLC p 1140
12500 West Creek Pkwy, Richmond VA 23238
Tel (804) 484-7700
SIC 5141 5144 5147 5146 5142 5148

■ **SYSCO VIRGINIA LLC** p 1418
5081 S Valley Pike, Rockingham VA 22801
Tel (540) 434-0761
SIC 5149 5142 5113 5148 5147 5143

■ **SYSCO HAMPTON ROADS INC** p 1417
7000 Harbour View Blvd, Suffolk VA 23435
Tel (757) 399-2451 SIC 5141 5147 5148

SCHENCK FOODS CO INC p 1286
3578 Valley Pike, Winchester VA 22602
Tel (540) 869-1870
SIC 5141 5142 5087 5147 5148

VANGUARD INTERNATIONAL INC p 1543
22605 Se 56th St Ste 200, Issaquah WA 98029
Tel (425) 557-8250 SIC 5148

BASIN GOLD COOPERATIVE p 159
5802 N Industrial Way C, Pasco WA 99301
Tel (509) 545-4161 SIC 5148

ASSOCIATED GROCERS INC p 120
3301 S Norfolk St, Seattle WA 98118
Tel (206) 762-2100
SIC 5141 5147 5143 5122 5148 5142

TRIPLE "B" CORP p 1482
4103 2nd Ave S, Seattle WA 98134
Tel (206) 625-1412 SIC 5148

SPOKANE PRODUCE INC p 1359
1905 S Geiger Blvd, Spokane WA 99224
Tel (509) 455-8970 SIC 5148

ONEONTA TRADING CORP p 1088
1 Oneonta Dr, Wenatchee WA 98801
Tel (509) 663-2631 SIC 5148

HOLTZINGER FRUIT CO INC p 702
1312 N 6th Ave, Yakima WA 98902
Tel (509) 457-5115 SIC 5148 4222

WASHINGTON FRUIT & PRODUCE CO p 1578
1111 River Rd, Yakima WA 98902
Tel (509) 457-6177 SIC 5148 0723

■ **SYSCO BARABOO LLC** p 1416
910 South Blvd, Baraboo WI 53913
Tel (800) 733-8217
SIC 5141 5142 5046 5148

COOPERATIVE REGIONS OF ORGANIC PRODUCER POOLS p 367
1 Organic Way, La Farge WI 54639
Tel (608) 625-2602 SIC 5148 5143

SIC 5149 Groceries & Related Prdts, NEC Wholesale

BTC WHOLESALE DISTRIBUTORS INC p 222
100 Airview Ln, Alabaster AL 35007
Tel (205) 324-2581
SIC 5194 5145 5087 5149 5122

ANDALUSIA DISTRIBUTING CO INC p 89
117 Allen Ave, Andalusia AL 36420
Tel (334) 222-3671
SIC 5172 5113 5194 5149

BUFFALO ROCK CO p 224
111 Oxmoor Rd, Birmingham AL 35209
Tel (205) 942-3435 SIC 2086 5962 5149

ROYAL CUP INC p 1254
160 Cleage Dr, Birmingham AL 35217
Tel (205) 849-5836 SIC 2095 5149

■ **SYSCO CENTRAL ALABAMA INC** p 1416
1000 Sysco Dr, Calera AL 35040
Tel (205) 668-0001
SIC 5149 5147 5142 5144 5143

BIG SPRINGS INC p 182
2700 Meridian St N, Huntsville AL 35811
Tel (256) 532-4545 SIC 5149

SUNSHINE MILLS INC p 1404
500 6th St Sw, Red Bay AL 35582
Tel (256) 356-9541 SIC 2047 2048 5149

BASHAS INC p 158
22402 S Basha Rd, Chandler AZ 85248
Tel (480) 883-6131
SIC 5411 5149 5148 5147 6512

MACAYO RESTAURANTS LLC p 892
1480 E Bethany Home Rd # 130, Phoenix AZ 85014
Tel (602) 264-1831 SIC 5813 5812 5149

SHAMROCK FOODS CO p 1311
3900 E Camelback Rd # 300, Phoenix AZ 85018
Tel (602) 477-2500
SIC 5146 5149 5147 5148 5142 2026

SYSTEMS SERVICES OF AMERICA INC p 1419
1640 S 39th Ave, Phoenix AZ 85009
Tel (480) 927-4700
SIC 5147 5113 5142 5149 5143

CHAI BAGEL CORP p 286
14431 N 73rd St, Scottsdale AZ 85260
Tel (480) 860-0475
SIC 5149 5461 5812 2052 2051

PLEXUS HOLDINGS INC p 1156
9145 E Pima Center Pkwy, Scottsdale AZ 85258
Tel (480) 998-3490 SIC 5149

WILDFLOWER BREAD CO p 1609
7755 E Gray Rd, Scottsdale AZ 85260
Tel (480) 951-9453 SIC 5149

VEMMA NUTRITION CO p 1547
1621 W Rio Salado Pkwy # 101, Tempe AZ 85281
Tel (480) 927-8999 SIC 5122 5149

GOLDEN EAGLE DISTRIBUTORS INC p 620
705 E Ajo Way, Tucson AZ 85713
Tel (520) 884-5999 SIC 5181 5149

SOUTHERN BAKERIES LLC p 1347
2700 E 3rd St, Hope AR 71801
Tel (870) 777-9031 SIC 5149

MOUNTAIN VALLEY SPRING CO LLC p 994
283 Mountain Vly Wtr Pl, Hot Springs AR 71909
Tel (501) 624-7329 SIC 5149 5499

■ **PFG BROADLINE HOLDINGS LLC** p 1140
4901 Asher Ave, Little Rock AR 72204
Tel (501) 568-3141
SIC 5149 5148 5147 5141

HARRIS FREEMAN & CO INC p 663
3110 E Miraloma Ave, Anaheim CA 92806
Tel (714) 765-1190 SIC 5149 2099

MORRIS NATIONAL INC p 990
760 N Mckeever Ave, Azusa CA 91702
Tel (626) 385-2000 SIC 5145 5149

POMWONDERFUL LLC p 1161
4805 Centennial Ste 100, Bakersfield CA 93301
Tel (310) 966-5800 SIC 5149 5148 5085

NATURES BEST DISTRIBUTION LLC p 1019
6 Pointe Dr Ste 300, Brea CA 92821
Tel (714) 255-4600 SIC 5149

WILSEY FOODS INC p 1613
40 Pointe Dr, Brea CA 92821
Tel (714) 257-3700 SIC 2079 5149

TAWA SERVICES INC p 1426
6281 Regio Ave Fl 2, Buena Park CA 90620
Tel (714) 521-8899 SIC 5149 5411

JENNY CRAIG INC p 782
5770 Fleet St, Carlsbad CA 92008
Tel (760) 696-4000
SIC 7299 6794 5149 5499

BAKKAVOR FOODS USA INC p 147
18201 Central Ave, Carson CA 90746
Tel (310) 533-0190 SIC 2051 5149

CULINARY HISPANIC FOODS INC p 400
805 Bow St, Chula Vista CA 91914
Tel (619) 955-6101 SIC 5149

HARALAMBOS BEVERAGE CO p 659
2300 Pellissier Pl, City Of Industry CA 90601
Tel (562) 347-4300 SIC 5181 5149

HARMONI INTERNATIONAL SPICE INC CALIFORNIA p 662
881 S Azusa Ave, City Of Industry CA 91748
Tel (626) 330-1550 SIC 5148 5149

JFC INTERNATIONAL INC p 785
7101 E Slauson Ave, Commerce CA 90040
Tel (323) 721-6100 SIC 5149

OAKHURST INDUSTRIES INC p 1071
2050 S Tubeway Ave, Commerce CA 90040
Tel (323) 724-3000 SIC 2051 5149

■ **MONSTER ENERGY CO** p 985
1 Monster Way, Corona CA 92879
Tel (951) 739-6200 SIC 5149

IL FORNAIO (AMERICA) CORP p 731
770 Tamalpais Dr Ste 400, Corte Madera CA 94925
Tel (415) 945-0500
SIC 5812 5813 5149 5461 2051

ROCKVIEW DAIRIES INC p 1245
7011 Stewart And Gray Rd, Downey CA 90241
Tel (562) 927-5511 SIC 5149 5143 2026

CHALLENGE DAIRY PRODUCTS INC p 286
6701 Donlon Way, Dublin CA 94568
Tel (925) 828-6160 SIC 5143 5149

CLIF BAR & CO p 326
1451 66th St, Emeryville CA 94608
Tel (510) 596-6300 SIC 2052 5149

PEETS COFFEE & TEA LLC p 1127
1400 Park Ave, Emeryville CA 94608
Tel (510) 594-2100 SIC 2095 5149

■ **WHOLE FOODS MARKET CALIFORNIA INC** p 1607
5980 Horton St Ste 200, Emeryville CA 94608
Tel (510) 428-7400 SIC 5411 5149

MANA DEVELOPMENT LLC p 900
2339 11th St, Encinitas CA 92024
Tel (760) 944-1070 SIC 5149

PULMUONE FOODS USA INC p 1191
2315 Moore Ave, Fullerton CA 92833
Tel (714) 578-2800 SIC 5149 5141 2075

PULMUONE USA INC p 1191
2315 Moore Ave, Fullerton CA 92833
Tel (714) 578-2800 SIC 5149 5141 2075

GOLDEN STATE FOODS CORP p 621
18301 Von Karman Ave # 1100, Irvine CA 92612
Tel (949) 252-2000
SIC 5147 2087 5142 5148 5149

SOUTH COAST BAKING LLC p 1343
1722 Kettering, Irvine CA 92614
Tel (949) 851-9654 SIC 2052 5149

SUN-MAID GROWERS OF CALIFORNIA p 1401
13525 S Bethel Ave, Kingsburg CA 93631
Tel (559) 897-6235 SIC 5149

CALIFORNIA BEES INC p 239
14381 Industry Cir, La Mirada CA 90638
Tel (714) 228-1999 SIC 5149

■ **COTTAGE BAKERY INC** p 374
1831 S Stockton St, Lodi CA 95240
Tel (209) 334-3616 SIC 5149 2051 2053

APP WHOLESALE LLC p 97
3686 E Olympic Blvd, Los Angeles CA 90023
Tel (323) 980-8315 SIC 5149

CANTON FOOD CO INC p 247
750 S Alameda St, Los Angeles CA 90021
Tel (213) 688-7707
SIC 5141 5146 5411 5421 5149 4222

MUTUAL TRADING CO INC p 1003
431 Crocker St, Los Angeles CA 90013
Tel (213) 626-9458 SIC 5149 5141 5023

POM WONDERFUL HOLDINGS LLC p 1160
11444 W Olympic Blvd # 210, Los Angeles CA 90064
Tel (310) 966-5800 SIC 5149 5148 5085

TORN & GLASSER INC p 1461
1622 E Olympic Blvd, Los Angeles CA 90021
Tel (213) 593-1332
SIC 5149 5153 5145 5191

SJ DISTRIBUTORS INC p 1328
625 Vista Way, Milpitas CA 95035
Tel (888) 988-2328 SIC 5142 5148 5149

MTC DISTRIBUTING p 997
4900 Stoddard Rd, Modesto CA 95356
Tel (209) 523-6449 SIC 5194 5145 5149

OTIS MCALLISTER INC p 1097
300 Frank H Ogawa Plz # 400, Oakland CA 94612
Tel (415) 421-6010 SIC 5149 5141

DPI SPECIALTY FOODS INC p 454
601 S Rockefeller Ave, Ontario CA 91761
Tel (909) 390-0892 SIC 5149 5143

THOMPSON OLDE INC p 1449
3250 Camino Del Sol, Oxnard CA 93030
Tel (800) 827-1565 SIC 5023 2631 5149

BAKEMARK USA LLC p 145
7351 Crider Ave, Pico Rivera CA 90660
Tel (562) 949-1054
SIC 2045 5149 3556 2099

P & R PAPER SUPPLY CO INC p 1102
1898 E Colton Ave, Redlands CA 92374
Tel (909) 389-1811
SIC 5113 5169 5149 5072 5046

T F LOUDERBACK INC p 1419
700 National Ct, Richmond CA 94804
Tel (510) 965-6120
SIC 5181 5149 2037 2033

■ **UNITED NATURAL FOODS WEST INC** p 1510
1101 Sunset Blvd, Rocklin CA 95765
Tel (401) 528-8634 SIC 5149 5141

FALCON TRADING CO p 526
423 Salinas Rd, Royal Oaks CA 95076
Tel (831) 786-7000 SIC 5149

MARKSTEIN BEVERAGE CO OF SACRAMENTO p 909
60 Main Ave, Sacramento CA 95838
Tel (916) 920-3911 SIC 5181 5149

LENORE JOHN & CO p 856
1250 Delevan Dr, San Diego CA 92102
Tel (619) 232-6136 SIC 5149 5182 5181

SUJA LIFE LLC p 1397
8380 Camino Santa Fe, San Diego CA 92121
Tel (855) 879-7852 SIC 5149

TOMATOES EXTRAORDINAIRE INC p 1459
1929 Hancock St Ste 150, San Diego CA 92110
Tel (619) 295-3172 SIC 5149

KIKKOMAN SALES USA INC p 817
50 California St Ste 3600, San Francisco CA 94111
Tel (415) 956-7750 SIC 5149 2035

GHIRARDELLI CHOCOLATE CO p 610
1111 139th Ave, San Leandro CA 94578
Tel (510) 483-6970
SIC 5441 2066 5812 5149

GOGLANIAN BAKERIES INC p 620
3401 W Segerstrom Ave, Santa Ana CA 92704
Tel (714) 549-1524 SIC 5149

JORDANOS INC p 793
550 S Patterson Ave, Santa Barbara CA 93111
Tel (805) 964-0611
SIC 5181 5182 5149 5141 5142 5148

WISMETTAC ASIAN FOODS INC p 1619
13409 Orden Dr, Santa Fe Springs CA 90670
Tel (562) 802-1900 SIC 5149

RED BULL DISTRIBUTION CO INC p 1215
1740 Stewart St, Santa Monica CA 90404
Tel (916) 515-3501 SIC 5149

▲ **CALAVO GROWERS INC** p 238
1141 Cummings Rd Ste A, Santa Paula CA 93060
Tel (805) 525-1245 SIC 5148 5142 5149

LA TORTILLA FACTORY INC p 836
3300 Westwind Blvd, Santa Rosa CA 95403
Tel (707) 586-4000 SIC 5149 2051

▲ **CORE-MARK HOLDING CO INC** p 369
395 Oyster Point Blvd # 415, South San Francisco CA 94080
Tel (650) 589-9445
SIC 5141 5194 5145 5122 5199 5149

MATAGRANO INC p 919
440 Forbes Blvd, South San Francisco CA 94080
Tel (650) 829-4829 SIC 5181 5149

NASSAU-SOSNICK DISTRIBUTION CO LLC p 1009
258 Littlefield Ave, South San Francisco CA 94080
Tel (650) 952-2226 SIC 5149 5145 5182

SUPER STORE INDUSTRIES p 1406
2800 W March Ln Ste 210, Stockton CA 95219
Tel (209) 473-8100
SIC 2026 2024 5149 5142

■ **GOLDBERG AND SOLOVY FOODS INC** p 620
5925 Alcoa Ave, Vernon CA 90058
Tel (323) 581-6161
SIC 5141 5149 5046 5169

■ **J & J SNACK FOODS CORP OF CALIFORNIA** p 770
5353 S Downey Rd, Vernon CA 90058
Tel (323) 581-0171 SIC 2052 5149

DEL MONTE FOODS INC p 423
3003 Oak Rd Ste 600, Walnut Creek CA 94597
Tel (925) 949-2772 SIC 2033 5149

DBI BEVERAGE SACRAMENTO p 418
3500 Carlin Dr, West Sacramento CA 95691
Tel (916) 373-5700 SIC 5182 5149

PHILLIPS PET FOOD AND SUPPLIES p 1144
3885 Seaport Blvd Ste 10, West Sacramento CA 95691
Tel (916) 373-7300 SIC 5149

■ **TONYS FINE FOODS** p 1460
3575 Reed Ave, West Sacramento CA 95605
Tel (916) 374-4000 SIC 5147 5143 5149

■ **BOULDER BRANDS USA INC** p 204
1600 Pearl St Ste 300, Boulder CO 80302
Tel (201) 568-9300 SIC 5149

GENERAL AIR SERVICE & SUPPLY CO p 599
1105 Zuni St, Denver CO 80204
Tel (303) 892-7003
SIC 5169 5085 5084 5149

TRINIDAD/BENHAM CORP p 1481
3650 S Yosemite St # 300, Denver CO 80237
Tel (303) 220-1400
SIC 5149 5153 2034 2099

TRINIDAD/BENHAM HOLDING CO p 1481
3650 S Yosemite St # 300, Denver CO 80237
Tel (303) 220-1400 SIC 5153 5149

CONNECTICUT PIE INC p 357
35 Pearl St, Enfield CT 06082
Tel (860) 741-3781 SIC 5149 5461

NORTH CASTLE PARTNERS LLC p 1051
183 E Putnam Ave, Greenwich CT 06830
Tel (203) 485-0216
SIC 7299 6794 5149 5499

SUNLAND TRADING INC p 1403
21 Locust Ave Ste 1a, New Canaan CT 06840
Tel (203) 966-4166 SIC 5149

■ **SYSCO CONNECTICUT LLC** p 1417
100 Inwood Rd, Rocky Hill CT 06067
Tel (860) 571-5600 SIC 5149 5142

COFCO AMERICAS RESOURCES CORP p 334
4 Stamford Plz, Stamford CT 06902
Tel (203) 658-2820
SIC 6221 5153 5149 2099

HARVEST HILL BEVERAGE CO p 666
1 High Ridge Park Fl 2, Stamford CT 06905
Tel (203) 914-1620 SIC 5149

NESTLE WATERS NORTH AMERICA HOLDINGS INC p 1027
900 Long Ridge Rd Bldg 2, Stamford CT 06902
Tel (203) 531-4100 SIC 5149

NESTLE WATERS NORTH AMERICA INC p 1027
900 Long Ridge Rd Bldg 2, Stamford CT 06902
Tel (203) 531-4100 SIC 5149

■ **BLUE BUFFALO CO LTD** p 190
11 River Rd Ste 103, Wilton CT 06897
Tel (203) 762-9751 SIC 2047 5149

CRABTREE & EVELYN LTD p 388
102 Peake Brook Rd, Woodstock CT 06281
Tel (800) 272-2873 SIC 5122 5149 2844

SUCRO CAN SOURCING LLC p 1396
2990 Ponce De Leon Blvd # 401, Coral Gables FL 33134
Tel (305) 901-5222 SIC 5159 5149

ACOSTA SALES CO INC p 18
6600 Corporate Ctr Pkwy, Jacksonville FL 32216
Tel (904) 281-9800 SIC 5149 5141

■ **SYSCO JACKSONVILLE INC** p 1417
1501 Lewis Industrial Dr, Jacksonville FL 32254
Tel (904) 781-5070
SIC 5149 5147 5144 5963

■ **SOUTHERN BAKERIES INC** p 1347
3355 W Memorial Blvd, Lakeland FL 33815
Tel (863) 682-1155 SIC 2051 5149

DP DISTRIBUTION LLC p 454
9601 Nw 112th Ave, Medley FL 33178
Tel (305) 777-6108 SIC 5149 5963

■ **SYSCO SOUTH FLORIDA INC** p 1418
12500 Nw 112th Ave, Medley FL 33178
Tel (305) 651-5421
SIC 5149 5147 5142 5113 5143 5144

DIANA FOODS INC p 437
13300 Nw 25th St, Miami FL 33182
Tel (305) 593-8317 SIC 5141 5149

■ **SYSCO CENTRAL FLORIDA INC** p 1416
200 W Story Rd, Ocoee FL 34761
Tel (407) 877-8500 SIC 5149

■ **SYSCO WEST COAST FLORIDA INC** p 1418
3000 69th St E, Palmetto FL 34221
Tel (941) 721-1450 SIC 5149 5141

■ **SYSCO INTERNATIONAL FOOD GROUP INC** p 1417
2401 Police Center Dr, Plant City FL 33566
Tel (813) 707-6161 SIC 5144 5149

CHENEY BROS INC p 294
1 Cheney Way, Riviera Beach FL 33404
Tel (561) 845-4700
SIC 5141 5087 5113 5169 5149

■ **SYSCO SOUTHEAST FLORIDA LLC** p 1418
1999 Dr M Lthr Kng Jr Bld Martin, Riviera Beach FL 33404
Tel (561) 842-1999 SIC 5149

JOHNSON BROTHERS OF FLORIDA INC p 790
4520 S Church Ave, Tampa FL 33611
Tel (813) 832-4477 SIC 5182 5149

VITALITY FOODSERVICE INC p 1562
400 N Tampa St Ste 1700, Tampa FL 33602
Tel (813) 301-4600 SIC 5149 3586

SOUTHERN FULFILLMENT SERVICES LLC p 1348
1650 90th Ave, Vero Beach FL 32966
Tel (772) 226-3500 SIC 5148 5149

■ **COCA-COLA EXPORT CORP** p 333
1 Coca Cola Plz Nw, Atlanta GA 30313
Tel (404) 676-2121 SIC 5149

DS SERVICES HOLDINGS INC p 457
5660 New Northside Dr # 500, Atlanta GA 30328
Tel (770) 933-1400 SIC 5499 5149

LAVOI CORP p 847
1749 Tullie Cir Ne, Atlanta GA 30329
Tel (404) 325-1016
SIC 2045 2053 2051 5149

RUSSELL MCCALLS INC p 1259
255 Ted Turner Dr Sw, Atlanta GA 30303
Tel (404) 954-7600 SIC 5149 5143 5147

SOUTHEASTERN MILLS INC p 1346
333 Old Lindale Rd Se, Rome GA 30161
Tel (706) 291-6528
SIC 2099 2041 5149 2045

PARADISE BEVERAGES INC p 1113
94-1450 Moaniani St, Waipahu HI 96797
Tel (808) 678-4000 SIC 5181 5182 5149

C STEIN INC p 233
4719 S Market St, Boise ID 83705
Tel (208) 378-0550
SIC 5181 5182 5149 4941 5921

■ **MWI ANIMAL HEALTH** p 1004
3041 W Pasadena Dr, Boise ID 83705
Tel (208) 955-8930 SIC 5047 5149

RITE STUFF FOODS INC p 1236
2155 S Lincoln Ave, Jerome ID 83338
Tel (208) 324-8410 SIC 5149

■ **EUROPEAN IMPORTS INC** p 513
600 E Brook Dr, Arlington Heights IL 60005
Tel (800) 323-3464 SIC 5141 5149 5147

GRECO & SONS INC p 636
1550 Hecht Dr, Bartlett IL 60103
Tel (630) 668-1000 SIC 5149

CHICAGO PASTRY INC p 297
6501 Roosevelt Rd, Berwyn IL 60402
Tel (708) 788-5320 SIC 5149 5461

CAPUTOS NEW FARM PRODUCE INC p 252
520 E North Ave, Carol Stream IL 60188
Tel (630) 620-4444
SIC 5431 5411 5148 5149

BADGER FARMS INC p 143
652 N Western Ave, Chicago IL 60612
Tel (773) 278-9100
SIC 5143 5149 5147 5144 5142 5087

BEST FOOD SERVICES INC p 177
7131 W 61st St, Chicago IL 60638
Tel (773) 966-1123 SIC 5149

FAIRLIFE LLC p 525
1001 W Adams St, Chicago IL 60607
Tel (312) 624-9444 SIC 5149

FLYING FOOD FARE INC p 562
212 N Sangamon St Ste 1a, Chicago IL 60607
Tel (312) 243-2122 SIC 5812 5149 5947

■ **GATORADE CO** p 594
555 W Monroe St Fl 1, Chicago IL 60661
Tel (312) 821-1000 SIC 2086 5149

HINCKLEY & SCHMITT INC p 695
6055 S Harlem Ave, Chicago IL 60638
Tel (773) 586-8600 SIC 2086 5149 7359

K+S SALT LLC p 799
123 N Wacker Dr Fl 6, Chicago IL 60606
Tel (844) 789-3991 SIC 2899 5149 5169

VIENNA BEEF LTD p 1556
2501 N Damen Ave, Chicago IL 60647
Tel (773) 278-7800
SIC 2013 2035 2053 5411 5149 5147

■ **SYSCO CHICAGO INC** p 1416
250 Wieboldt Dr, Des Plaines IL 60016
Tel (847) 699-5400 SIC 5149 5142

TOTAL SWEETENERS INC p 1463
1700 E Higgins Rd Ste 300, Des Plaines IL 60018
Tel (847) 299-1999 SIC 5149

GLANBIA PERFORMANCE NUTRITION INC p 614
3500 Lacey Rd, Downers Grove IL 60515
Tel (630) 236-0097 SIC 2833 5149 5122

PLUMROSE USA INC p 1157
1901 Butterfield Rd # 305, Downers Grove IL 60515
Tel (732) 257-6600
SIC 2011 5147 2013 5149

KUNA MEAT CO INC p 832
704 Kuna Industrial Ct, Dupo IL 62239
Tel (618) 286-4000
SIC 5144 5142 5147 5169 5149 5148

OLYMPIA FOOD INDUSTRIES INC p 1083
9501 Nevada Ave, Franklin Park IL 60131
Tel (847) 349-9358 SIC 5149

■ **H J M P CORP** p 650
1930 George St Ste 2, Melrose Park IL 60160
Tel (708) 345-5370
SIC 2033 5149 0174 2037

■ **FOX RIVER FOODS INC** p 572
5030 Baseline Rd, Montgomery IL 60538
Tel (630) 896-1991
SIC 5142 5149 5148 5147

EBY-BROWN CO LLC p 474
1415 W Diehl Rd Ste 300, Naperville IL 60563
Tel (630) 778-2800
SIC 5194 5145 5141 5122 5149

KEHE DISTRIBUTORS HOLDINGS LLC p 807
1245 E Diehl Rd Ste 200, Naperville IL 60563
Tel (630) 343-0000 SIC 5149

KEHE DISTRIBUTORS LLC p 807
1245 E Diehl Rd Ste 200, Naperville IL 60563
Tel (630) 343-0000 SIC 5149

HIGHLAND BAKING CO INC p 691
2301 Shermer Rd, Northbrook IL 60062
Tel (847) 677-2789 SIC 5149 2051

RAHAL FOODS INC p 1205
915 Harger Rd Ste 110, Oak Brook IL 60523
Tel (630) 286-1500 SIC 5149 5431

PERFORMANCE FOOD SERVICE TPC p 1135
8001 51st St W, Rock Island IL 61201
Tel (309) 787-1234 SIC 5149

MARTIN-BROWER CO L L C p 913
6250 N River Rd Ste 9000, Rosemont IL 60018
Tel (847) 227-6500
SIC 5142 5113 5149 5087

REINHART FOODSERVICE LOUISIANA LLC p 1221
6250 N River Rd, Rosemont IL 60018
Tel (847) 227-6500 SIC 5149

▲ **US FOODS HOLDING CORP** p 1531
9399 W Higgins Rd Ste 500, Rosemont IL 60018
Tel (847) 720-8000
SIC 5149 5147 5142 5144 5146 5143

■ **US FOODS INC** p 1531
9399 W Higgins Rd Ste 500, Rosemont IL 60018
Tel (847) 720-8000
SIC 5149 5147 5142 5144 5146 5143

■ **PEPSI-COLA GENERAL BOTTLERS INC** p 1134
1475 E Wdfeld Rd Ste 1300, Schaumburg IL 60173
Tel (847) 598-3000 SIC 2086 5149

SUN BELLE INC p 1400
3810 Rose St, Schiller Park IL 60176
Tel (708) 343-4545 SIC 5149

WOODLAND FOODS LTD p 1623
3751 Sunset Ave, Waukegan IL 60087
Tel (847) 625-8600 SIC 5149

HARLAN BAKERIES LLC p 661
7597 E Us Highway 36, Avon IN 46123
Tel (317) 272-3600 SIC 5149 2051 2045

HARLAN BAKERIES-AVON LLC p 661
7597 E Us Highway 36, Avon IN 46123
Tel (317) 272-3600 SIC 5149 2051 2045

LEWIS BROTHERS BAKERIES INC p 858
500 N Fulton Ave, Evansville IN 47710
Tel (812) 425-4642 SIC 2051 5149

CADILLAC COFFEE CO p 236
7221 Innovation Blvd, Fort Wayne IN 46818
Tel (248) 545-2266 SIC 5149 7389

INDIANA SUGARS INC p 738
911 Virginia St, Gary IN 46402
Tel (219) 886-9151 SIC 5149

MCFARLING FOODS INC p 928
333 W 14th St, Indianapolis IN 46202
Tel (317) 687-6827
SIC 5147 5149 5144 5146

■ **SYSCO INDIANAPOLIS LLC** p 1417
4000 W 62nd St, Indianapolis IN 46268
Tel (317) 291-2020 SIC 5149 5046 5411

SOUTH BEND CHOCOLATE CO INC p 1343
3300 W Sample St Ste 110, South Bend IN 46619
Tel (574) 233-2577
SIC 5149 2066 5441 5812

■ **SYSCO IOWA INC** p 1417
1 Sysco Dr, Ankeny IA 50021
Tel (515) 289-5300
SIC 5149 5147 5142 5144 5113 5143

■ **VISTA BAKERY INC** p 1562
3000 Mount Pleasant St, Burlington IA 52601
Tel (704) 554-1421 SIC 5149

LOMAR DISTRIBUTING INC p 875
2500 Dixon St, Des Moines IA 50316
Tel (515) 244-3105 SIC 5143 5149

FRONTIER COOPERATIVE p 581
3021 78th St, Norway IA 52318
Tel (319) 227-7996 SIC 5122 2099 5149

■ **SYSCO KANSAS CITY INC** p 1417
1915 E Kansas City Rd, Olathe KS 66061
Tel (913) 829-5555 SIC 5149 5141

■ **HILLS PET NUTRITION INC** p 694
400 Sw 8th Ave Ste 101, Topeka KS 66603
Tel (785) 354-8523 SIC 5149 2048 2047

ALL STAR DAIRY ASSOCIATION INC p 51
1050 Monarch St Ste 101, Lexington KY 40513
Tel (859) 255-3644
SIC 5149 5169 5113 5199

■ **PJ FOOD SERVICE INC** p 1153
2002 Papa Johns Blvd, Louisville KY 40299
Tel (502) 261-7272 SIC 5149 5087 2045

RESTAURANT SUPPLY CHAIN SOLUTIONS LLC p 1228
950 Breckenridge Ln # 300, Louisville KY 40207
Tel (502) 896-5900
SIC 5812 5046 5141 5149

CLARK DISTRIBUTING CO INC p 322
300 Oakland Flatrock Rd, Oakland KY 42159
Tel (270) 563-4735 SIC 5149 5181

CCC HOLDING LLC p 269
3332 Partridge Ln Bldg A, Baton Rouge LA 70809
Tel (225) 368-3900 SIC 2095 5149 5812

LYONS SPECIALTY CO LLC p 888
2800 La Highway 1 N, Port Allen LA 70767
Tel (225) 356-1319 SIC 5194 5145 5149

PROGRESSIVE DISTRIBUTORS INC p 1181
145 Pleasant Hill Rd, Scarborough ME 04074
Tel (207) 883-2911 SIC 5122 5149 5199

STONEWALL KITCHEN LLC p 1391
2 Stonewall Ln, York ME 03909
Tel (207) 351-2713
SIC 2033 2035 2032 5149 5064

NORTHEAST FOODS INC p 1054
601 S Caroline St, Baltimore MD 21231
Tel (410) 276-7254 SIC 2051 5149

BLACKSTREET CAPITAL MANAGEMENT LLC p 188
5425 Wisconsin Ave # 701, Chevy Chase MD 20815
Tel (240) 223-1330
SIC 6726 5149 5145 5961

FOODPRO CORP p 564
321 E 5th St, Frederick MD 21701
Tel (301) 663-3171
SIC 5142 5149 5148 5147 5143 5113

CANADA DRY POTOMAC CORP p 246
3600 Pennsy Dr, Hyattsville MD 20785
Tel (301) 773-5500 SIC 5149

■ **SYSCO BALTIMORE LLC** p 1416
8000 Dorsey Run Rd, Jessup MD 20794
Tel (410) 799-7000 SIC 5142 5149 5087

CENTURY DISTRIBUTORS INC p 282
15710 Crabbs Branch Way, Rockville MD 20855
Tel (301) 212-9100
SIC 5194 5145 5149 5113

DPI SPECIALTY FOODS MID ATLANTIC INC p 454
1000 Prince Georges Blvd, Upper Marlboro MD 20774
Tel (301) 430-2200 *SIC* 5149

OCEAN SPRAY INTERNATIONAL SALES INC p 1073
1 Ocean Spray Dr, Lakeville MA 02347
Tel (508) 946-1000 *SIC* 5149

FRIENDLY FRUIT INC p 580
2301 Purchase St Unit 1, New Bedford MA 02746
Tel (508) 999-6408 *SIC* 5148 5149

■ SYSCO BOSTON LLC p 1416
99 Spring St, Plympton MA 02367
Tel (781) 422-2300 *SIC* 5149

PERKINS PAPER INC p 1136
630 John Hancock Rd, Taunton MA 02780
Tel (508) 824-2800
SIC 5113 5149 5087 5046

ROHTSTEIN CORP p 1247
70 Olympia Ave, Woburn MA 01801
Tel (781) 935-8300
SIC 5149 2099 2087 2062 2041 2033

VITASOY USA INC p 1563
57 Russell St, Woburn MA 01801
Tel (781) 430-8988 *SIC* 5149 2099

POLAR CORP p 1159
1001 Southbridge St, Worcester MA 01610
Tel (508) 753-6383 *SIC* 2086 5149

▲ DOMINOS PIZZA INC p 449
30 Frank Lloyd Wright Dr, Ann Arbor MI 48105
Tel (734) 930-3030 *SIC* 5812 5149 6794

■ DOMINOS PIZZA LLC p 449
30 Frank Lloyd Wright Dr, Ann Arbor MI 48105
Tel (734) 930-3030
SIC 5812 6794 5046 5149 8741 2045

■ KELLOGG SALES CO p 809
1 Kellogg Sq, Battle Creek MI 49017
Tel (269) 961-2000 *SIC* 5149

INNOVATION VENTURES LLC p 744
38955 Hills Tech Dr Ste 1, Farmington Hills MI 48331
Tel (248) 960-1700 *SIC* 5149

MELODY FOODS INC p 941
30777 Northwestern Hwy # 300, Farmington Hills MI 48334
Tel (248) 851-6990
SIC 5143 2026 5149 5145

ROTHBURY FARMS INC p 1252
3061 Shaffer Ave Se, Grand Rapids MI 49512
Tel (616) 574-5757 *SIC* 5149 2051 2043

TWINLAB HOLDINGS INC p 1495
3133 Orchard Vista Dr Se, Grand Rapids MI 49546
Tel (616) 464-5000
SIC 2833 2834 5149 2721

CKL CORP p 320
3825 Emerald Dr, Kalamazoo MI 49001
Tel (269) 382-4200 *SIC* 5181 5182 5149

FAMILY FARM & HOME INC p 526
900 3rd St Ste 302, Muskegon MI 49440
Tel (231) 722-8335
SIC 5999 5261 5149 5611 5211 5091

WESCO INC p 1593
1460 Whitehall Rd, Muskegon MI 49445
Tel (231) 719-4300
SIC 5411 5541 5145 5149

ABSOPURE WATER CO LLC p 13
8845 General Dr, Plymouth MI 48170
Tel (313) 898-1200 *SIC* 5499 5149

DETROIT CITY DAIRY p 433
21405 Trolley Indus Dr, Taylor MI 48180
Tel (313) 295-6300
SIC 5143 5141 5147 5149

LIPARI FOODS OPERATING CO LLC p 870
26661 Bunert Rd, Warren MI 48089
Tel (586) 447-3500 *SIC* 5146 5145 5149

GORDON FOOD SERVICE INC p 626
1300 Gezon Pkwy Sw, Wyoming MI 49509
Tel (888) 437-3663
SIC 5149 5142 5147 5146 5144 5143

BAKERY CRAFTS LLC p 147
3500 Thurston Ave 100, Anoka MN 55303
Tel (513) 942-0862 *SIC* 5046 5149 2064

MILK SPECIALTIES CO p 969
7500 Flying Cloud Dr # 500, Eden Prairie MN 55344
Tel (952) 942-7310 *SIC* 2026 2834 5149

SUNOPTA FOODS INC p 1403
7301 Ohms Ln Ste 600, Edina MN 55439
Tel (952) 820-2518 *SIC* 5149

ROSENS DIVERSIFIED INC p 1251
1120 Lake Ave, Fairmont MN 56031
Tel (507) 238-4201
SIC 2011 8748 5149 2879

RESTAURANT TECHNOLOGIES INC p 1228
2250 Pilot Knob Rd # 100, Mendota Heights MN 55120
Tel (651) 796-1600 *SIC* 5149 3631

■ MINTER-WEISMAN CO p 974
1035 Nathan Ln N Ste A, Minneapolis MN 55441
Tel (763) 545-3706
SIC 5194 5149 5145 5013 5122

UNITED SUGARS CORP p 1514
8000 W 78th St Ste 300, Minneapolis MN 55439
Tel (952) 896-0131 *SIC* 5149

PAN-O-GOLD BAKING CO p 1110
444 E Saint Germain St, Saint Cloud MN 56304
Tel (320) 251-9361 *SIC* 5149 2051

BEST BRANDS CORP p 177
111 Cheshire Ln Ste 100, Saint Paul MN 55121
Tel (952) 404-7500
SIC 5149 2045 2053 2052 2051

JOHNSON BROTHERS LIQUOR CO p 790
1999 Shepard Rd, Saint Paul MN 55116
Tel (651) 649-5800 *SIC* 5182 5149

■ SYSCO ASIAN FOODS INC p 1416
1300 L Orient St, Saint Paul MN 55117
Tel (651) 558-2400 *SIC* 5149

BREWERS SUPPLY GROUP INC p 210
800 1st Ave W, Shakopee MN 55379
Tel (952) 224-1380 *SIC* 5149

BROWN BOTTLING GROUP INC p 219
591 Highland Colony Pkwy, Ridgeland MS 39157
Tel (601) 607-3011 *SIC* 5149

C C CLARK INC p 232
501 Academy Rd, Starkville MS 39759
Tel (662) 323-4317 *SIC* 5149 2086

MENU MAKER FOODS INC p 943
913 Big Horn Dr, Jefferson City MO 65109
Tel (573) 893-3000
SIC 5141 5087 2011 5149

JASPER PRODUCTS LLC p 778
3877 E 27th St, Joplin MO 64804
Tel (417) 206-3333 *SIC* 5149

D & D DISTRIBUTORS LLLP p 406
2340 Millpark Dr, Maryland Heights MO 63043
Tel (314) 429-9100 *SIC* 5182 5149

3D CORPORATE SOLUTIONS LLC p 2
601 13th St, Monett MO 65708
Tel (417) 236-9602 *SIC* 5199 5149 2048

HOLLOWAY DISTRIBUTING INC p 701
210 E Owen Ave, Puxico MO 63960
Tel (573) 222-6255 *SIC* 5145 5194 5149

■ SYSCO ST LOUIS LLC p 1418
3850 Mueller Rd, Saint Charles MO 63301
Tel (636) 940-9230
SIC 5141 5149 5146 5143 5142

NAG LLC p 1006
1260 Andes Blvd, Saint Louis MO 63132
Tel (314) 214-2700 *SIC* 5149

TROVERCO INC p 1485
727 N 1st St, Saint Louis MO 63102
Tel (800) 468-3354 *SIC* 2099 5149

OZARKS COCA-COLA/DR PEPPER BOTTLING CO p 1101
1777 N Packer Rd, Springfield MO 65803
Tel (417) 865-9900 *SIC* 2086 5149

SPRINGFIELD GROCER CO p 1361
2415 W Battlefield St, Springfield MO 65807
Tel (417) 883-4230 *SIC* 5142 5141 5149

■ SYSCO MONTANA INC p 1417
1509 Monad Rd, Billings MT 59101
Tel (406) 247-1100 *SIC* 5149 5142 5141

NUTRAMED INC p 1068
1001 S 3rd St W, Missoula MT 59801
Tel (406) 273-5493 *SIC* 5149

WHEAT MONTANA FARMS INC p 1604
10778 Us Highway 287, Three Forks MT 59752
Tel (406) 285-3614 *SIC* 5149 0111

CASH-WA DISTRIBUTING CO OF KEARNEY INC p 263
401 W 4th St, Kearney NE 68845
Tel (308) 237-3151 *SIC* 5149 5046 5194

■ CONAGRA GROCERY PRODUCTS CO LLC p 354
11 Conagra Dr, Omaha NE 68102
Tel (630) 857-1000
SIC 2033 2079 2099 2032 2066 5149

SHARED SERVICE SYSTEMS INC p 1312
1725 S 20th St, Omaha NE 68108
Tel (402) 536-5300
SIC 5047 5142 7211 5149 5113 7218

■ E & H DISTRIBUTING LLC p 465
1685 W Cheyenne Ave, North Las Vegas NV 89032
Tel (702) 636-3663
SIC 5113 5141 5142 5149

GREAT STATE BEVERAGES INC p 634
1000 Quality Dr, Hooksett NH 03106
Tel (603) 644-2337 *SIC* 5181 5149 5145

POULTRY PRODUCTS CO OF NEW ENGLAND INC p 1164
11 Bemis Rd, Hooksett NH 03106
Tel (603) 263-1600 *SIC* 5147 5149

LINDT & SPRUNGLI (USA) INC p 868
1 Fine Chocolate Pl, Stratham NH 03885
Tel (603) 778-8100 *SIC* 2066 5149 5441

GEL SPICE CO INC p 598
48 Hook Rd, Bayonne NJ 07002
Tel (201) 339-0700 *SIC* 2099 5149

WORLD FINER FOODS LLC p 1625
1455 Broad St Ste 4, Bloomfield NJ 07003
Tel (973) 338-0300 *SIC* 5149

METROPOLITAN FOODS INC p 955
174 Delawanna Ave, Clifton NJ 07014
Tel (973) 672-9400
SIC 5142 5149 2099 5141

DI GIORGIO CORP p 436
160 Fieldcrest Ave Ste A, Edison NJ 08837
Tel (718) 470-1744 *SIC* 5149

ATALANTA CORP p 123
1 Atlanta Plz Ste 3, Elizabeth NJ 07206
Tel (908) 351-8000 *SIC* 5143 5149 5142

SUPREME OIL CO INC p 1408
66 Grand Ave Ste 201, Englewood NJ 07631
Tel (201) 408-0800 *SIC* 5149 2079

REMA FOODS INC p 1222
140 Sylvan Ave Ste 200, Englewood Cliffs NJ 07632
Tel (201) 947-1000 *SIC* 5142 5149 5141

SCHRATTER FOODS INC p 1290
333 Fairfield Rd Ste 2, Fairfield NJ 07004
Tel (973) 461-2400 *SIC* 5143 5149

CREAM-O-LAND DAIRY INC p 390
529 Cedar Ln, Florence NJ 08518
Tel (609) 499-3601 *SIC* 5143 5149

INTERNATIONAL VITAMIN CORP p 757
500 Halls Mill Rd, Freehold NJ 07728
Tel (951) 361-1120 *SIC* 2834 5149 8099

ZUEGG USA CORP p 1644
50 Harrison St Ste 214b, Hoboken NJ 07030
Tel (201) 222-0291 *SIC* 5149

DOMINO FOODS INC p 449
99 Wood Ave S Ste 901, Iselin NJ 08830
Tel (732) 590-1173 *SIC* 5149

WELL LUCK CO INC p 1589
104 Harbor Dr Ste 1, Jersey City NJ 07305
Tel (201) 434-1177 *SIC* 5149

WAKEFERN FOOD CORP p 1572
5000 Riverside Dr, Keasbey NJ 08832
Tel (908) 527-3300
SIC 5141 5149 5411 4213 2026

CLOFINE DAIRY PRODUCTS INC p 327
1407 New Rd, Linwood NJ 08221
Tel (609) 653-1000 *SIC* 5143 5149

■ ALBERTS ORGANICS INC p 46
1155 Commerce Blvd, Logan Township NJ 08085
Tel (800) 899-5944 *SIC* 5149 5148

■ HADDON HOUSE FOOD PRODUCTS INC p 652
250 Old Marlton Pike, Medford NJ 08055
Tel (609) 654-7901 *SIC* 5149

EIGHT OCLOCK COFFEE CO p 481
155 Chestnut Ridge Rd # 2, Montvale NJ 07645
Tel (201) 571-9214 *SIC* 5149 2095

MITSUI FOODS INC p 978
35 Maple St, Norwood NJ 07648
Tel (201) 750-0500 *SIC* 5142 5149 5499

DSM FOOD SPECIALTIES USA INC p 458
45 Waterview Blvd, Parsippany NJ 07054
Tel (973) 257-1063 *SIC* 5149

■ MCLANE NEW JERSEY p 931
742 Courses Landing Rd, Penns Grove NJ 08069
Tel (856) 351-6200 *SIC* 5141 5149

FOULKROD ASSOCIATES p 571
8275 N Crescent Blvd, Pennsauken NJ 08110
Tel (856) 662-6767 *SIC* 3411 5149

FERRARO FOODS INC p 538
287 S Randolphville Rd, Piscataway NJ 08854
Tel (732) 424-3400 *SIC* 5149 5812

HITOUCH BUSINESS SERVICES LLC p 697
74 Kenny Pl, Saddle Brook NJ 07663
Tel (201) 636-9900 *SIC* 5112 5021 5149

DORAS NATURALS INC p 451
21 Empire Blvd, South Hackensack NJ 07606
Tel (201) 229-0500 *SIC* 5149

WELLSHIRE FARMS INC p 1591
509 Woodstown Rd, Swedesboro NJ 08085
Tel (877) 467-2331 *SIC* 5149

DARTAGNAN INC p 413
600 Green Ln, Union NJ 07083
Tel (973) 344-0565
SIC 5147 5148 5149 2011

VITAQUEST INTERNATIONAL LLC p 1563
8 Henderson Dr, West Caldwell NJ 07006
Tel (973) 575-9200
SIC 2834 5149 5122 8742

MALOOF DISTRIBUTING LLC p 900
701 Comanche Rd Ne, Albuquerque NM 87107
Tel (505) 345-1218 *SIC* 5181 5149

PREMIER DISTRIBUTING CO p 1170
4321 Yale Blvd Ne, Albuquerque NM 87107
Tel (575) 524-1661 *SIC* 5181 5149

1550 BAYSHORE CORP p 1
1550 5th Ave, Bay Shore NY 11706
Tel (631) 206-7100 *SIC* 5149

CONSTANCE FOOD GROUP INC p 360
545 Johnson Ave Ste 10, Bohemia NY 11716
Tel (631) 582-1144 *SIC* 5149 5141

SULTANA DISTRIBUTION SERVICES INC p 1397
600 Food Center Dr, Bronx NY 10474
Tel (718) 842-4674 *SIC* 5145 5149

BOGOPA SERVICE CORP p 197
650 Fountain Ave, Brooklyn NY 11208
Tel (718) 257-7801 *SIC* 5411 4225 5149

CANADA DRY BOTTLING CO OF NEW YORK LP p 246
11202 15th Ave, College Point NY 11356
Tel (718) 358-2000 *SIC* 5149

JETRO HOLDINGS LLC p 784
1506 132nd St, College Point NY 11356
Tel (718) 762-8700 *SIC* 5149 5141 5812

■ CENTRAL COCA-COLA BOTTLING CO INC p 277
555 Taxter Rd Ste 550, Elmsford NY 10523
Tel (914) 789-1100 *SIC* 5149 2086 8741

■ MOTTS LLP p 993
55 Hunter Ln, Elmsford NY 10523
Tel (972) 673-8088 *SIC* 2033 5149 2087

HOUSE OF SPICES (INDIA) INC p 711
12740 Willets Point Blvd, Flushing NY 11368
Tel (718) 507-4900
SIC 5149 2099 5153 2033 2024

FIRST QUALITY ENTERPRISES INC p 549
80 Cuttermill Rd Ste 500, Great Neck NY 11021
Tel (516) 829-3030 *SIC* 5149

■ SYSCO ALBANY LLC p 1416
1 Liebich Ln, Halfmoon NY 12065
Tel (518) 877-3200 *SIC* 5149 5963

METROPLEX HOLDINGS INC p 955
15 Commerce Dr S, Harriman NY 10926
Tel (845) 781-5000 *SIC* 6512 5149 5087

J KINGS FOOD SERVICE PROFESSIONALS INC p 771
700 Furrows Rd, Holtsville NY 11742
Tel (631) 289-8401
SIC 5149 5143 5144 5142 5148

WILLOW RUN FOODS INC p 1613
1006 Us Route 11, Kirkwood NY 13795
Tel (607) 338-5221
SIC 5142 5149 5147 5113 5148 5087

NESPRESSO USA INC p 1026
2401 44th Rd Fl 12, Long Island City NY 11101
Tel (800) 562-1465 *SIC* 5149 5046 5499

BIG GEYSER INC p 181
5765 48th St, Maspeth NY 11378
Tel (718) 821-2200 *SIC* 5149

J & J FARMS CREAMERY INC p 769
5748 49th St Ste 1, Maspeth NY 11378
Tel (718) 821-1200 *SIC* 5143 5149

AMERICAN ROLAND FOOD CORP p 78
71 W 23rd St Ste 1500, New York NY 10010
Tel (800) 221-4030 *SIC* 5149

ED & F MAN HOLDINGS INC p 476
33 Whitehall St Broad, New York NY 10004
Tel (212) 618-2802 *SIC* 5149

GODIVA CHOCOLATIER INC p 619
333 W 34th St Fl 6, New York NY 10001
Tel (212) 984-5900
SIC 2066 5149 5441 2064

LAVAZZA PREMIUM COFFEES CORP p 847
120 Wall St Fl 27, New York NY 10005
Tel (212) 725-8800 *SIC* 5149

M & F WORLDWIDE CORP p 888
35 E 62nd St, New York NY 10065
Tel (212) 572-8600 *SIC* 5149 8741 2782

ROLAND FOODS LLC p 1247
71 W 23rd St, New York NY 10010
Tel (212) 741-8290 *SIC* 5149

■ SPF HOLDINGS II LLC p 1358
9 W 57th St Ste 4200, New York NY 10019
Tel (212) 750-8300
SIC 2033 5149 6719 2099

SUNTORY INTERNATIONAL CORP p 1405
600 3rd Ave Fl 21, New York NY 10016
Tel (212) 891-6600
SIC 5149 2084 2086 5499 5812

NERIS BAKERY PRODUCTS INC p 1026
31 Pearl St 37, Port Chester NY 10573
Tel (914) 937-3235 *SIC* 5149 5461 2051

WRIGHT WISNER DISTRIBUTING CORP p 1627
3165 Brghtn Hnrietta Twn, Rochester NY 14623
Tel (585) 427-2880 *SIC* 5181 5149

SOVENA USA INC p 1353
1 Olive Grove St, Rome NY 13441
Tel (315) 797-7070 *SIC* 5149

▲ COFFEE HOLDING CO INC p 334
3475 Victory Blvd Ste 4, Staten Island NY 10314
Tel (718) 832-0800 *SIC* 2095 5149 5499

■ PRESTIGE BRANDS INC p 1173
660 White Plains Rd, Tarrytown NY 10591
Tel (914) 524-6810 *SIC* 5149 5087

DANONE NORTH AMERICA LLC p 412
100 Hillside Ave, White Plains NY 10603
Tel (212) 441-1000 *SIC* 5149

PERK-UP INC p 1136
399 Knollwood Rd Ste 309, White Plains NY 10603
Tel (914) 580-3200
SIC 5113 5149 2673 3411 2674 2035

ARIZONA BEVERAGES USA LLC p 108
60 Crossways Park Dr W, Woodbury NY 11797
Tel (516) 812-0300 *SIC* 5149

PORT ROYAL SALES LTD p 1162
95 Froehlich Farm Blvd # 200, Woodbury NY 11797
Tel (516) 921-8383 *SIC* 5149

PUGH OIL CO INC p 1191
701 Mcdowell Rd, Asheboro NC 27205
Tel (336) 629-2061
SIC 5172 5983 5541 5411 5149

■ MCLANE/CAROLINA INC p 931
7253 Nc 48, Battleboro NC 27809
Tel (252) 972-2500 *SIC* 5141 5142 5149

EUROPA SPORTS PRODUCTS INC p 513
11401 Granite St Ste H, Charlotte NC 28273
Tel (704) 405-2022 *SIC* 5122 5149 5941

JOHNS LONE STAR DISTRIBUTION GP LLC p 790
11401 Granite St, Charlotte NC 28273
Tel (214) 340-0718 *SIC* 5122 5149

TROPICAL NUT & FRUIT CO p 1484
1100 Continental Blvd, Charlotte NC 28273
Tel (704) 588-0400
SIC 5149 5145 2099 2068

S & D COFFEE INC p 1261
300 Concord Pkwy S, Concord NC 28027
Tel (704) 782-3121 *SIC* 2095 5149 2086

S&D COFFEE HOLDING CO p 1263
300 Concord Pkwy S, Concord NC 28027
Tel (704) 782-3121
SIC 6719 2095 5149 2086

PEPSI-COLA BOTTLING CO OF HICKORY NC INC p 1134
2401 14th Avenue Cir Nw, Hickory NC 28601
Tel (828) 322-8090 *SIC* 5149 2086

BJT INC p 186
2233 Capital Blvd, Raleigh NC 27604
Tel (919) 828-3842 *SIC* 5182 5149 5181

LONG BEVERAGE INC p 876
10500 World Trade Blvd, Raleigh NC 27617
Tel (919) 481-2738 *SIC* 5181 5149

PEPSI BOTTLING VENTURES LLC p 1134
4141 Parklake Ave Ste 600, Raleigh NC 27612
Tel (919) 865-2300 *SIC* 5149 2086

■ MEADOWBROOK MEAT CO INC p 934
2641 Meadowbrook Rd, Rocky Mount NC 27801
Tel (252) 985-7200
SIC 5147 5113 5149 5142

KRISPY KREME DOUGHNUTS INC p 830
370 Knollwood St Ste 500, Winston Salem NC 27103
Tel (336) 726-8876 *SIC* 5461 5149 2051

▲ PRIMO WATER CORP p 1176
101 N Cherry St Ste 501, Winston Salem NC 27101
Tel (336) 331-4000 *SIC* 5149 3585 5141

RED RIVER COMMODITIES INC p 1216
501 42nd St N, Fargo ND 58102
Tel (701) 282-2600 *SIC* 5153 5145 5149

■ SPECIALTY COMMODITIES INC p 1356
1530 47th St N, Fargo ND 58102
Tel (701) 282-8222 *SIC* 5149 5153

■ AKRON COCA-COLA BOTTLING CO p 42
1560 Triplett Blvd, Akron OH 44306
Tel (330) 784-2653 *SIC* 5149

AVALON FOODSERVICE INC p 135
1 Avalon Dr, Canal Fulton OH 44614
Tel (330) 854-4551
SIC 5142 5149 5169 5113 8322 5812

■ PROCTER & GAMBLE DISTRIBUTING LLC p 1179
1 Procter And Gamble Plz, Cincinnati OH 45202
Tel (513) 983-1100
SIC 5169 5122 5149 5113 5137

■ SYSCO CINCINNATI LLC p 1416
10510 Evendale Dr, Cincinnati OH 45241
Tel (513) 563-6300
SIC 5144 5149 5143 5113

■ CLEVELAND SYSCO INC p 326
4747 Grayton Rd, Cleveland OH 44135
Tel (216) 201-3000 *SIC* 5149

HILLCREST EGG & CHEESE CO p 693
2735 E 40th St, Cleveland OH 44115
Tel (216) 361-4625
SIC 5143 5142 5147 5144 5149 5148

NORTHERN FROZEN FOODS INC p 1056
21500 Alexander Rd, Cleveland OH 44146
Tel (440) 439-0600 *SIC* 5142 5149 5147

LIQUI-BOX CORP p 870
480 Schrock Rd Ste G, Columbus OH 43229
Tel (804) 325-1400
SIC 2673 3585 3089 3081 5149

■ BUTLER ANIMAL HEALTH HOLDING CO LLC p 230
400 Metro Pl N Ste 100, Dublin OH 43017
Tel (614) 761-9095 *SIC* 5122 5149 5047

■ BUTLER ANIMAL HEALTH SUPPLY LLC p 230
400 Metro Pl N Ste 100, Dublin OH 43017
Tel (855) 724-3461 *SIC* 5122 5149 5047

■ SYGMA NETWORK INC p 1413
5550 Blazer Pkwy Ste 300, Dublin OH 43017
Tel (614) 734-2500 *SIC* 5149

SKYLINE CHILI INC p 1330
4180 Thunderbird Ln, Fairfield OH 45014
Tel (513) 874-1188
SIC 5812 2038 6794 5149 2032

OHIO PIZZA PRODUCTS INC p 1078
201 Lawton Ave, Monroe OH 45050
Tel (937) 294-6969 *SIC* 5149

■ INTERNATIONAL MULTIFOODS CORP p 756
1 Strawberry Ln, Orrville OH 44667
Tel (330) 682-3000
SIC 5145 5149 5143 2048 2041

SUPERIOR BEVERAGE GROUP LTD p 1406
31031 Diamond Pkwy, Solon OH 44139
Tel (440) 703-4580 *SIC* 5149 5499

BROTHERS TRADING CO INC p 219
400 Victory Ln, Springboro OH 45066
Tel (937) 746-1010 *SIC* 5141 5122 5149

SKIDMORE SALES & DISTRIBUTING CO INC p 1329
9889 Cincinnati Dayton Rd, West Chester OH 45069
Tel (513) 755-4200 *SIC* 5149 5169

MATTINGLY FOODS INC p 921
302 State St, Zanesville OH 43701
Tel (740) 454-0136 *SIC* 5149 5142 5141

AZURE FARMS INC p 141
79709 Dufur Valley Rd, Dufur OR 97021
Tel (971) 200-8350 *SIC* 5149 0723 2099

ALPINE FOOD DISTRIBUTING INC p 60
2400 Se Mailwell Dr, Milwaukie OR 97222
Tel (503) 905-5201 *SIC* 5142 5149

CDC OREGON INC p 270
3601 Nw Yeon Ave, Portland OR 97210
Tel (503) 289-9600 *SIC* 5182 5181 5149

■ COFFEE BEAN INTERNATIONAL INC p 334
9120 Ne Alderwood Rd, Portland OR 97220
Tel (503) 227-4490 *SIC* 5149

YOSHIDAS INC p 1637
8440 Ne Alderwood Rd A, Portland OR 97220
Tel (503) 731-3702 *SIC* 5149 8741

WESTERN FAMILY HOLDING CO p 1598
6700 Sw Sandburg St, Tigard OR 97223
Tel (503) 639-6300
SIC 5141 5142 5199 5122 5149

VIGON INTERNATIONAL INC p 1556
127 Airport Rd, East Stroudsburg PA 18301
Tel (570) 476-4172 *SIC* 2869 5149 2077

■ SYSCO PITTSBURGH LLC p 1417
1 Whitney Dr, Harmony PA 16037
Tel (724) 452-2100
SIC 5142 5149 5148 5023 5113 5046

M SIMON ZOOK CO p 890
4960 Horseshoe Pike, Honey Brook PA 19344
Tel (800) 327-4406 *SIC* 5149 2048 4013

ARNOLD FOODS CO INC p 112
255 Business Center Dr # 200, Horsham PA 19044
Tel (215) 672-8010 *SIC* 2051 5149

GEORGE DELALLO CO INC p 606
6390 Route 30, Jeannette PA 15644
Tel (724) 925-2222 *SIC* 5149

DUTCH GOLD HONEY INC p 463
2220 Dutch Gold Dr, Lancaster PA 17601
Tel (717) 393-1716 *SIC* 2099 5149

CEDAR FARMS CO INC p 272
2100 Hornig Rd, Philadelphia PA 19116
Tel (215) 934-7100
SIC 5142 5144 5143 5149

■ SYSCO PHILADELPHIA LLC p 1417
600 Packer Ave, Philadelphia PA 19148
Tel (215) 218-1348 *SIC* 5149

ABARTA INC p 9
200 Alpha Dr, Pittsburgh PA 15238
Tel (412) 963-6226
SIC 2086 2711 2721 5149 1382 5812

LENTZ MILLING CO p 856
2045 N 11th St, Reading PA 19604
Tel (610) 921-0666 *SIC* 5149 5142

ROARING SPRING BLANK BOOK CO p 1240
740 Spang St, Roaring Spring PA 16673
Tel (814) 224-2306
SIC 2678 5149 2653 7389

POCONO PRODUCE CO INC p 1158
Chipperfield Dr Rr 191, Stroudsburg PA 18360
Tel (570) 421-1533 *SIC* 5149 5142 5148

JOSE SANTIAGO INC p 793
5 Calle Marginal # 5, Bayamon PR 00959
Tel (787) 288-8835 *SIC* 5142 5149

PUERTO RICO SUPPLIES GROUP INC p 1191
Parkeast, Bayamon PR 00961
Tel (787) 780-4043
SIC 5194 5149 5122 5143 5148

V SUAREZ & CO INC p 1538
Industrial Luchetti 300 C, Bayamon PR 00961
Tel (787) 792-1212 *SIC* 5182 5149

RALPHS FOOD WAREHOUSE INC p 1206
Carr 183 Industrial Park, Las Piedras PR 00771
Tel (787) 733-0959 *SIC* 5411 5149

▲ UNITED NATURAL FOODS INC p 1510
313 Iron Horse Way, Providence RI 02908
Tel (401) 528-8634 *SIC* 5149 5122 5142

ORION FOOD SYSTEMS LLC p 1094
2930 W Maple St, Sioux Falls SD 57107
Tel (605) 336-6961
SIC 5149 2033 2026 2041

JUICE PLUS CO LLC p 797
140 Crescent Dr, Collierville TN 38017
Tel (901) 850-3000 *SIC* 5149

CHARLES C PARKS CO INC p 289
500 N Belvedere Dr, Gallatin TN 37066
Tel (615) 452-2406 *SIC* 5149

DBI BEVERAGE INC p 418
2 Ingram Blvd, La Vergne TN 37089
Tel (615) 793-2337 *SIC* 5149

BDT BEVERAGE LLC p 164
2712 Westwood Dr, Nashville TN 37204
Tel (615) 742-3771 *SIC* 5149

■ SYSCO NASHVILLE LLC p 1417
1 Hermitage Plz, Nashville TN 37209
Tel (615) 350-7100 *SIC* 5142 5149

TBHC DELIVERS LLC p 1427
2967 Sidco Dr, Nashville TN 37204
Tel (800) 235-3798 *SIC* 5149

AFFILIATED FOODS INC p 32
1401 W Farmers Ave, Amarillo TX 79118
Tel (806) 345-7773
SIC 5141 2026 2051 5149 6153

ECOM ATLANTIC INC p 476
13760 Noel Rd Ste 500, Dallas TX 75240
Tel (214) 520-1717 *SIC* 5159 5149

KSF HOLDINGS LLP p 831
2100 Mckinney Ave # 1600, Dallas TX 75201
Tel (214) 740-7300 *SIC* 5149

NORTH FOOD GROUP INC p 1052
1245 W Royal Ln, Dallas TX 75261
Tel (972) 445-3322
SIC 5146 5147 5149 5113

TAYLOR FARMS TEXAS INC p 1427
1001 N Cockrell Hill Rd, Dallas TX 75211
Tel (214) 421-1947 *SIC* 5149

SERENGETI TRADING CO LP p 1306
19100 Hamilton Pool Rd, Dripping Springs TX 78620
Tel (512) 358-9593 *SIC* 5149

JARRITOS INC p 778
500 W Overland Ave # 300, El Paso TX 79901
Tel (915) 594-1618 *SIC* 5149

LARROC INC p 845
6420 Boeing Dr, El Paso TX 79925
Tel (915) 772-3733 *SIC* 5141 5149

TIPP DISTRIBUTORS INC p 1455
500 W Overland Ave # 300, El Paso TX 79901
Tel (915) 594-1618 *SIC* 5149

▲ FARMER BROS CO p 529
13601 North Fwy Ste 200, Fort Worth TX 76177
Tel (682) 549-6600 *SIC* 2095 5149

MOTHER PARKERS TEA & COFFEE USA LTD p 992
7800 Will Rogers Blvd, Fort Worth TX 76140
Tel (817) 551-5500 *SIC* 5149 2095 2099

■ HOUSTON SYSCO INC p 712
10710 Grens Crossing Blvd, Houston TX 77038
Tel (713) 672-8080
SIC 5149 5142 5046 5141 2099

INDUS ENTERPRISES INC p 739
7051 Southwest Fwy, Houston TX 77074
Tel (713) 784-4335 *SIC* 5149 5194 5912

▲ SYSCO CORP p 1417
1390 Enclave Pkwy, Houston TX 77077
Tel (281) 584-1390
SIC 5149 5142 5143 5144 5148 5137

FRESH ACQUISITIONS LLC p 578
1001 E 33rd St, Lubbock TX 79404
Tel (806) 723-5600 *SIC* 5149 5146

NORTH DALLAS HONEY CO LP p 1052
2910 Nature Nate Farms, Mckinney TX 75071
Tel (214) 642-9367 *SIC* 5149

HILL COUNTRY BAKERY LLC p 693
122 Stribling, San Antonio TX 78204
Tel (210) 475-9981 *SIC* 5149 5461

JOHNSON BROS BAKERY SUPPLY INC p 790
10731 N Ih 35, San Antonio TX 78233
Tel (210) 590-2575 *SIC* 5149 5046

SPFM LP p 1358
4310 West Ave, San Antonio TX 78213
Tel (210) 805-8931
SIC 5122 5149 2834 2833 2841 2844

VILORE FOODS CO INC p 1557
3838 Medical Dr Ste 207, San Antonio TX 78229
Tel (210) 509-9496 *SIC* 5149 5169

IMPERIAL SUGAR CO p 734
3 Sugar Creek Center Blvd # 500, Sugar Land TX 77478
Tel (281) 491-9181 *SIC* 2062 5149

■ MCLANE CO INC p 930
4747 Mclane Pkwy, Temple TX 76504
Tel (254) 771-7500
SIC 5141 5149 5311 5113

MORINDA HOLDINGS INC p 989
737 E 1180 S, American Fork UT 84003
Tel (801) 234-1000 *SIC* 5149 8099 3999

ZIJA INTERNATIONAL INC p 1643
3300 N Ashton Blvd # 100, Lehi UT 84043
Tel (801) 494-2300 *SIC* 5149

■ LOFTHOUSE BAKERY PRODUCTS INC p 874
215 N 700 W Ste A10, Ogden UT 84404
Tel (801) 776-3500 *SIC* 5149

UNICITY INTERNATIONAL INC p 1502
1201 N 800 E, Orem UT 84097
Tel (801) 226-2600 *SIC* 5149

CAPITAL CANDY CO INC p 249
32 Burnham St, Barre VT 05641
Tel (802) 476-6689
SIC 5145 5194 5122 5141 5149

KING ARTHUR FLOUR CO INC p 820
135 Us Route 5 S, Norwich VT 05055
Tel (802) 649-3881
SIC 5149 5961 5461 8299

KING ARTHUR FLOUR CO INC p 820
62 Fogg Farm Rd, White River Junction VT 05001
Tel (802) 649-3881 *SIC* 5149

NORTHERN STAR VENTURES LLC p 1057
10440 Leadbetter Rd, Ashland VA 23005
Tel (804) 368-0747 *SIC* 5149 5461

PBM HOLDINGS INC p 1123
652 Peter Jefferson Pkwy # 300, Charlottesville VA 22911
Tel (540) 832-3282 *SIC* 5149

■ PERFORMANCE FOOD GROUP INC p 1135
12500 West Creek Pkwy, Richmond VA 23238
Tel (804) 484-7700 *SIC* 5149

■ SYSCO VIRGINIA LLC p 1418
5081 S Valley Pike, Rockingham VA 22801
Tel (540) 434-0761
SIC 5149 5142 5113 5148 5147 5143

FLOYD PETERSON CO p 561
1102 D St Ne, Auburn WA 98002
Tel (253) 735-0313 *SIC* 5141 5149 5143

COCA-COLA BOTTLING OF HAWAII LLC p 333
11400 Se 8th St Ste 300, Bellevue WA 98004
Tel (800) 767-6366 *SIC* 5149

ODOM CORP p 1074
11400 Se 8th St Ste 300, Bellevue WA 98004
Tel (425) 456-3535 *SIC* 5149

JAVA TRADING CO LLC p 779
801 Houser Way N, Renton WA 98057
Tel (425) 917-2920 *SIC* 5149 2095

▲ STARBUCKS CORP p 1378
2401 Utah Ave S, Seattle WA 98134
Tel (206) 447-1575
SIC 5812 5499 5461 5149

TC GLOBAL INC p 1428
2003 Western Ave Ste 660, Seattle WA 98121
Tel (206) 233-2070 *SIC* 2095 5149

NORTHERN SALES CO INC p 1056
15022 Puyallup St E # 101, Sumner WA 98390
Tel (253) 299-0500
SIC 5145 5149 5194 5141

INNOVASIAN CUISINE ENTERPRISES INC p 744
18251 Cascade Ave S, Tukwila WA 98188
Tel (425) 251-3706 *SIC* 5149

UNDERWOOD FRUIT AND WAREHOUSE CO LLC p 1502
401 N 1st Ave, Yakima WA 98902
Tel (509) 457-6177 *SIC* 5149 2033

SLEDD CO CHAS M p 1331
100 E Cove Ave, Wheeling WV 26003
Tel (800) 333-0374 *SIC* 5194 5142 5149

VALLEY BAKERS COOPERATIVE ASSOCIATION p 1540
W6470 Quality Dr, Greenville WI 54942
Tel (920) 560-3200 *SIC* 5149 5046

TRILLIANT FOOD AND NUTRITION LLC p 1480
1101 Moasis Dr, Little Chute WI 54140
Tel (920) 788-1252 *SIC* 5149 2099 2095

■ STURM FOODS INC p 1395
215 Center St, Manawa WI 54949
Tel (920) 596-2511 *SIC* 5149

LESAFFRE YEAST CORP p 857
7475 W Main St, Milwaukee WI 53214
Tel (414) 615-3300 *SIC* 5149

PALERMO VILLA INC p 1108
3301 W Canal St, Milwaukee WI 53208
Tel (414) 342-8898 *SIC* 5149

GOOD FOODS GROUP LLC p 623
10100 88th Ave, Pleasant Prairie WI 53158
Tel (262) 465-6900 *SIC* 2038 5149

ADMIRAL BEVERAGE CORP p 23
821 Pulliam Ave, Worland WY 82401
Tel (801) 782-5072 *SIC* 5149 2086

SIC 5153 Grain & Field Beans Wholesale

AGRI-AFC LLC p 36
121 Somerville Rd Ne, Decatur AL 35601
Tel (256) 560-2848
SIC 5159 5153 5083 5191

ALABAMA FARMERS COOPERATIVE INC p 43
121 Somerville Rd Ne, Decatur AL 35601
Tel (256) 353-6843 *SIC* 5191 5153 5159

E RITTER SEED CO p 467
300 Adamson St, Marked Tree AR 72365
Tel (870) 358-2130 *SIC* 5153 5191

BRUCE OAKLEY INC p 220
3700 Lincoln Ave, North Little Rock AR 72114
Tel (501) 945-0875
SIC 4449 5153 5261 5191 4213

BAYOU GRAIN & CHEMICAL CORP p 162
P.O. Box 67, Parkdale AR 71661
Tel (870) 473-2281 *SIC* 4221 2873 5153

PRODUCERS RICE MILL INC p 1179
518 E Harrison St, Stuttgart AR 72160
Tel (870) 673-4444 *SIC* 2044 5153 2099

RICELAND FOODS INC p 1232
2120 S Park Ave, Stuttgart AR 72160
Tel (870) 673-5500
SIC 2044 2079 5153 2075

C&F FOODS INC p 234
15620 E Valley Blvd, City Of Industry CA 91744
Tel (626) 723-1000 *SIC* 5153

PENNY NEWMAN GRAIN CO p 1131
2691 S Cedar Ave, Fresno CA 93725
Tel (559) 499-0691 *SIC* 5153

TORN & GLASSER INC p 1461
1822 E Olympic Blvd, Los Angeles CA 90021
Tel (213) 593-1332
SIC 5149 5153 5145 5191

TRC GROUP INC p 1475
3721 Douglas Blvd Ste 375, Roseville CA 95661
Tel (916) 784-7745 *SIC* 5153

TRINIDAD/BENHAM CORP p 1481
3650 S Yosemite St # 300, Denver CO 80237
Tel (303) 220-1400
SIC 5149 5153 2034 2099

TRINIDAD/BENHAM HOLDING CO p 1481
3650 S Yosemite St # 300, Denver CO 80237
Tel (303) 220-1400 *SIC* 5153 5149

STRATTON EQUITY COOPERATIVE CO p 1393
98 Colorado Ave, Stratton CO 80836
Tel (719) 348-5326
SIC 5153 5191 5171 5541

ATLAS HOLDINGS LLC p 128
100 Northfield St, Greenwich CT 06830
Tel (203) 622-9138
SIC 5031 2491 5039 5153

BRIDGEWELL RESOURCES HOLDINGS LLC p 212
1 Sound Shore Dr Ste 302, Greenwich CT 06830
Tel (203) 622-9138
SIC 5031 2491 5039 5153

COFCO AMERICAS RESOURCES CORP p 334
4 Stamford Plz, Stamford CT 06902
Tel (203) 658-2820
SIC 6221 5153 5149 2099

LOUIS DREYFUS CO NA LLC p 879
40 Danbury Rd, Wilton CT 06897
Tel (203) 761-2000 *SIC* 5153

LOUIS DREYFUS HOLDING CO INC p 879
10 Westport Rd Ste 200, Wilton CT 06897
Tel (203) 761-2000
SIC 6221 5153 6512 6531 1311

NIDERA US LLC p 1043
195 Danbury Rd Ste 240, Wilton CT 06897
Tel (203) 834-5700 *SIC* 5153

CENTRAL STATES ENTERPRISES LLC p 280
1275 Lake Heathrow Ln # 101, Heathrow FL 32746
Tel (407) 333-3503 *SIC* 5153 0213 0723

REGAN INTERNATIONAL INC p 1218
2141 Whittier Pl Nw, Atlanta GA 30318
Tel (603) 624-9615 *SIC* 5153

PACIFIC NORTHWEST FARMERS COOPERATIVE INC p 1105
117 W Chestnut, Genesee ID 83832
Tel (208) 285-1141 *SIC* 5153 2099

GOLD STAR FS INC p 620
101 N East St, Cambridge IL 61238
Tel (309) 937-3369
SIC 5171 5153 5039 5191

M & M SERVICE CO INC p 888
130 N Chiles St, Carlinville IL 62626
Tel (217) 854-4516 *SIC* 5153 5191 5171

PREMIER COOPERATIVE INC p 1170
2104 W Park Ct, Champaign IL 61821
Tel (217) 355-1983 *SIC* 5153 5191

▲ ARCHER-DANIELS-MIDLAND CO p 105
77 W Wacker Dr Ste 4600, Chicago IL 60601
Tel (312) 634-8100
SIC 2046 2041 2075 2074 5153 2083

CHICAGO & ILLINOIS RIVER MARKETING LLC p 297
141 W Jackson Blvd Ste 2800, Chicago IL 60604
Tel (312) 341-3174 *SIC* 5153

■ ADM GRAIN RIVER SYSTEM INC p 23
4666 E Faries Pkwy, Decatur IL 62526
Tel (312) 634-8100 *SIC* 5153

AKRON SERVICES INC p 42
17705 N Elevator Rd, Edelstein IL 61526
Tel (309) 243-7533 *SIC* 5153 5191

CGB DIVERSIFIED SERVICES INC p 285
1608b W Lafayette Ave, Jacksonville IL 62650
Tel (217) 245-4599 *SIC* 5153

JERSEY COUNTY GRAIN CO p 783
426 E Exchange St, Jerseyville IL 62052
Tel (618) 498-2183 *SIC* 5153 5191

WEST CENTRAL FS INC p 1594
1202 W Piper St, Macomb IL 61455
Tel (309) 833-2168 *SIC* 5153

NORTHERN PARTNERS COOPERATIVE p 1056
1000 6th Ave, Mendota IL 61342
Tel (815) 539-6772 *SIC* 5153

TOP FLIGHT GRAIN MONTICELLO CO p 1460
420 W Marion St, Monticello IL 61856
Tel (217) 762-2163 *SIC* 5153 5191 4221

COLUSA ELEVATOR CO p 343
13 Broadway, Nauvoo IL 62354
Tel (217) 453-2216 *SIC* 5153

TOP AG COOPERATIVE INC p 1460
702 S Elevator St, Okawville IL 62271
Tel (618) 243-5293 *SIC* 5153 5191

BUREAU SERVICE CO p 226
22069 Us Highway 34, Princeton IL 61356
Tel (815) 875-2800
SIC 5191 5172 5153 5411 7542

MAPLEHURST FARMS INC p 904
936 S Moore Rd, Rochelle IL 61068
Tel (815) 562-8723 *SIC* 5153 2879 4212

EASTLAND FEED AND GRAIN INC p 473
210 N Stanton St, Shannon IL 61078
Tel (815) 864-2723 *SIC* 5191 5153

FARMERS ELEVATOR CO OF LOWDER p 529
10955 North St, Waverly IL 62692
Tel (217) 435-9023 *SIC* 5153

CONSOLIDATED GRAIN & BARGE CO p 359
Washington & Water St, Wayne City IL 62895
Tel (618) 895-2181
SIC 4221 5153 4449 4491

CO-ALLIANCE LLP p 330
5250 E Us Hwy 3, Avon IN 46123
Tel (317) 745-4491
SIC 5191 5171 5153 2875

PREMIER AG CO-OP INC p 1170
785 S Marr Rd, Columbus IN 47201
Tel (812) 379-9501
SIC 5153 5191 5172 5411 2429

POSEY COUNTY FARM BUREAU COOPERATIVE ASSOCIATION INC p 1163
817 W 4th St, Mount Vernon IN 47620
Tel (812) 838-4468 *SIC* 5191 5172 5153

HARVEST LAND CO-OP INC p 666
1435 Nw 5th St, Richmond IN 47374
Tel (765) 962-1527 SIC 5191 5153

JBS UNITED INC p 780
4310 W State Road 38, Sheridan IN 46069
Tel (317) 758-4495 SIC 2048 5153 0213

AG PLUS INC p 33
401 N Main St, South Whitley IN 46787
Tel (260) 723-5141 SIC 5191 2041 5153

CERES SOLUTIONS p 283
2600 S 13th St, Terre Haute IN 47802
Tel (812) 235-8123 SIC 5153 5172 5191

NORTH CENTRAL COOPERATIVE INC p 1051
2025 S Wabash St, Wabash IN 46992
Tel (800) 992-3495 SIC 5172 5153 5191

FRICK SERVICES INC p 579
3154 Depot St, Wawaka IN 46794
Tel (260) 761-3311
SIC 5191 5153 5261 4221 2048 4213

AG PARTNERS LLC p 33
30 Main St, Albert City IA 50510
Tel (712) 843-2291 SIC 5153 5191 2048

LANDUS COOPERATIVE p 843
2321 N Loop Dr Ste 220, Ames IA 50010
Tel (515) 817-2100 SIC 5153

AGRI INDUSTRIES INC p 36
700 Se Dalbey Dr, Ankeny IA 50021
Tel (515) 964-2200 SIC 5153 7359

FARMERS COOPERATIVE ELEVATOR CO p 529
12543 190th St, Arcadia IA 51430
Tel (712) 689-2296 SIC 5191 5153

FIRST COOPERATIVE ASSOCIATION p 546
960 Riverview Dr, Cherokee IA 51012
Tel (712) 225-5400 SIC 5191 5153

NORTH CENTRAL COOPERATIVE p 1051
221 4th Ave Nw, Clarion IA 50525
Tel (515) 532-2881 SIC 5153 5191 5172

MID IOWA COOPERATIVE p 963
201 S Main St, Conrad IA 50621
Tel (641) 366-2740 SIC 5153 5191 2048

NEW CO-OPERATIVE INC p 1029
2626 1st Ave S, Fort Dodge IA 50501
Tel (515) 955-2040 SIC 5153 5191

NEW CO-OPERATIVE INC p 1029
2626 1st Ave S, Fort Dodge IA 50501
Tel (515) 955-2040 SIC 5153

FARM SERVICE COOPERATIVE p 529
2308 Pine St, Harlan IA 51537
Tel (712) 755-2207 SIC 5153

CHEM GRO OF HOUGHTON INC p 293
504 Main St, Houghton IA 52631
Tel (319) 469-2611 SIC 5153 5191

EAST CENTRAL IOWA COOP p 470
602 Washington St, Hudson IA 50643
Tel (319) 988-3257 SIC 5153 5191

■ **OPTIMUM QUALITY GRAINS LLC** p 1090
7100 Nw 62nd Ave, Johnston IA 50131
Tel (515) 270-3200 SIC 5153

VIAFIELD p 1554
533 Bradford St, Marble Rock IA 50653
Tel (641) 315-2515 SIC 5153

LINN CO-OPERATIVE OIL CO p 869
325 35th St, Marion IA 52302
Tel (319) 377-4881 SIC 5153 5171 5191

FIVE STAR COOPERATIVE p 553
1949 N Linn Ave, New Hampton IA 50659
Tel (641) 394-3052 SIC 5153 5191

TRIOAK FOODS INC p 1482
103 W Railroad St, Oakville IA 52646
Tel (319) 766-2230 SIC 0213 5153

FARMERS UNION COOPERATIVE p 530
1913 County Road B32, Ossian IA 52161
Tel (563) 532-9381 SIC 5153 5261 5983

PRO COOPERATIVE p 1178
17 3rd Ave Ne, Pocahontas IA 50574
Tel (712) 335-3060 SIC 5153 5191 5172

WEST CENTRAL COOPERATIVE p 1594
406 1st St, Ralston IA 51459
Tel (712) 667-3200
SIC 5153 2075 2048 5191

UNITED FARMERS MERCANTILE COOPERATIVE p 1508
203 W Oak St, Red Oak IA 51566
Tel (712) 623-5453
SIC 5153 5191 5541 5211 2048

COOPERATIVE FARMERS ELEVATOR p 367
1219 Main St, Rock Valley IA 51247
Tel (712) 476-5321 SIC 5153 5191

KEY COOPERATIVE p 814
13585 620th Ave, Roland IA 50236
Tel (515) 388-4341
SIC 5153 5541 2048 5191

FARMERS COOPERATIVE SOCIETY p 529
317 3rd St Nw, Sioux Center IA 51250
Tel (712) 722-2671 SIC 5153 5191 5211

SIOUXLAND FARMERS COOPERATIVE p 1326
317 3rd St Nw, Sioux Center IA 51250
Tel (712) 722-2671 SIC 5153 5191

RIVER VALLEY COOPERATIVE p 1237
102 S Main St, Walcott IA 52773
Tel (563) 284-6223 SIC 5153 5191

MAXYIELD COOPERATIVE p 923
313 3rd Ave Nw, West Bend IA 50597
Tel (515) 887-7211
SIC 5153 5191 2999 0723

HEARTLAND CO-OP p 679
2829 Westown Pkwy Ste 350, West Des Moines IA 50266
Tel (515) 225-1334 SIC 5153 0762 2048

GARDEN CITY CO-OP INC p 591
106 N 6th St, Garden City KS 67846
Tel (620) 275-6161 SIC 5153 5191 5172

WINDRIVER GRAIN LLC p 1615
2810 E Us Highway 50, Garden City KS 67846
Tel (620) 275-2101 SIC 5153

GREAT BEND COOPERATIVE ASSOCIATION p 633
606 Main St, Great Bend KS 67530
Tel (620) 793-3531
SIC 5153 5191 5171 4221

MIDLAND MARKETING CO-OP INC p 966
219 E 9th St, Hays KS 67601
Tel (785) 625-5138
SIC 5153 5191 5541 5171 4221

KANZA COOPERATIVE ASSOCIATION p 803
102 N Main St, Iuka KS 67066
Tel (620) 546-2231
SIC 5153 5191 5541 4221

JOHNSON COOPERATIVE GRAIN CO INC p 791
304 E Highland Ave, Johnson KS 67855
Tel (620) 492-6210 SIC 5153 5191 5172

MID-KANSAS COOPERATIVE ASSOCIATION p 963
307 W Cole St, Moundridge KS 67107
Tel (620) 345-6328 SIC 5153 5191

TEAM MARKETING ALLIANCE LLC p 1430
307 W Cole St, Moundridge KS 67107
Tel (620) 345-3560 SIC 5153

FRONTIER AG INC p 580
415 W 2nd St, Oakley KS 67748
Tel (785) 462-2063 SIC 5153 5191

MIDWAY CO-OP ASSOCIATION p 967
210 W Harrison St, Osborne KS 67473
Tel (785) 346-5451 SIC 5153 5171

OTTAWA COOPERATIVE ASSOCIATION INC p 1098
302 N Main St, Ottawa KS 66067
Tel (785) 242-5170 SIC 5191 5171 5153

AGREX INC p 36
10975 Grandview Dr # 200, Overland Park KS 66210
Tel (913) 851-6300 SIC 5153

LANSING TRADE GROUP LLC p 844
10975 Benson Dr Ste 400, Overland Park KS 66210
Tel (913) 748-3000 SIC 5153 6221

BEACHNER GRAIN INC p 164
2600 Flynn Dr, Parsons KS 67357
Tel (620) 449-8500 SIC 5153

SCOTT COOPERATIVE ASSOCIATION INC p 1293
410 E 1st St, Scott City KS 67871
Tel (620) 872-5823
SIC 5153 5541 5191 4221

NEMAHA COUNTY COOPERATIVE ASSOCIATION p 1025
223 E Main St, Seneca KS 66538
Tel (785) 336-6153 SIC 5153 5191 5541

CONSOLIDATED GRAIN & BARGE INC p 360
1001 Highway 190 E Svc Rd, Covington LA 70433
Tel (985) 867-3500 SIC 5153

ZEN-NOH GRAIN CORP p 1642
1127 Hwy 190 E Service Rd, Covington LA 70433
Tel (985) 867-3500 SIC 5153

CALEDONIA FARMERS ELEVATOR CO INC p 238
146 E Main St Se, Caledonia MI 49316
Tel (616) 891-4150
SIC 5153 5169 5251 5261

STAR OF WEST MILLING CO p 1378
121 E Tuscola St, Frankenmuth MI 48734
Tel (330) 673-2941 SIC 2041 5153 5191

COOPERATIVE ELEVATOR CO p 367
7211 E Michigan Ave, Pigeon MI 48755
Tel (989) 453-4500
SIC 5172 5191 5541 5261 5153

CITIZENS LLC p 311
870 S Main St, Vermontville MI 49096
Tel (517) 726-0514
SIC 5191 5153 5999 2041

MINNESOTA SOYBEAN PROCESSORS p 974
121 Zeh Ave, Brewster MN 56119
Tel (507) 842-6677 SIC 5153 2075

NEW VISION CO-OP p 1033
38438 210th St, Brewster MN 56119
Tel (507) 842-2001 SIC 5153

CENTRA SOTA COOPERATIVE p 277
805 Highway 55 E, Buffalo MN 55313
Tel (763) 682-2557
SIC 5191 2875 5171 5153

AG PARTNERS COOP p 33
1st And Bdwy Way, Goodhue MN 55027
Tel (651) 345-3328 SIC 5153 5191

WESTERN CONSOLIDATED COOPERATIVE p 1597
520 County Road 9, Holloway MN 56249
Tel (320) 394-2171 SIC 5153 4221 2875

▲ **CHS INC** p 304
5500 Cenex Dr, Inver Grove Heights MN 55077
Tel (651) 355-6000
SIC 5153 5191 2075 1311 2911 4613

■ **TEMCO LLC** p 1436
5500 Cnex Dr Mail Stn 370 Mail Station, Inver Grove Heights MN 55077
Tel (651) 355-6471 SIC 5153

MEADOWLAND FARMERS COOP p 934
25861 Us Highway 14, Lamberton MN 56152
Tel (507) 752-7335 SIC 5153 5191 0723

AGMOTION INC p 35
730 2nd Ave S Ste 700, Minneapolis MN 55402
Tel (612) 486-3800 SIC 5153

RIVERLAND AG CORP p 1237
1660 Highway 100 S # 350, Minneapolis MN 55416
Tel (952) 746-6800 SIC 5153 4221

■ **MG WALDBAUM CO** p 958
301 Carlson Pkwy Ste 400, Minnetonka MN 55305
Tel (952) 258-4000 SIC 2015 5153 5191

HARVEST LAND COOPERATIVE p 666
711 Front St W, Morgan MN 56266
Tel (507) 249-3196 SIC 5153 5191 0253

CANNON VALLEY COOPERATIVE p 247
1500 Highway 3 S, Northfield MN 55057
Tel (507) 645-9556
SIC 5541 5171 1711 5191 5153 5211

PRINSBURG FARMERS CO-OP p 1177
404 Railroad Ave, Prinsburg MN 56281
Tel (320) 978-8100 SIC 5153 5191 0253

CO-OP COUNTRY FARMERS ELEVATOR p 330
340 Dupont Ave Ne, Renville MN 56284
Tel (320) 329-8377 SIC 5153 5191

AGSPRING IDAHO LLC p 36
600 Highway 169 S Ste 720, Saint Louis Park MN 55426
Tel (952) 956-6720 SIC 5153

WATONWAN FARM SERVICE INC p 1583
233 W Ciro St, Truman MN 56088
Tel (507) 776-1244 SIC 5153 5191 5172

CARGILL INC p 255
15407 Mcginty Rd W, Wayzata MN 55391
Tel (952) 742-7575
SIC 5153 2075 2046 2048 2011 2015

COOP WHEATON-DUMONT ELEVATOR INC p 366
6587 Us Highway 75, Wheaton MN 56296
Tel (320) 563-8152 SIC 5153 5191

UNITED FARMERS COOPERATIVE p 1508
705 E 4th St, Winthrop MN 55396
Tel (507) 237-2281
SIC 5153 5191 5983 5083

FARMERS GRAIN TERMINAL INC p 529
1977 Harbor Front Rd, Greenville MS 38701
Tel (662) 332-0987 SIC 5153

AGRI SERVICES OF BRUNSWICK LLC p 36
Hwy 24 W, Brunswick MO 65236
Tel (660) 549-3351 SIC 5153 5191

MFA INC p 957
201 Ray Young Dr, Columbia MO 65201
Tel (573) 874-5111
SIC 2875 2048 5191 5153

BARTLETT AGRI ENTERPRISES INC p 157
4900 Main St Ste 1200, Kansas City MO 64112
Tel (816) 753-6300 SIC 5153 5154 2041

WEST PLAINS LLC p 1595
11500 N Ambassador Dr # 250, Kansas City MO 64153
Tel (816) 270-4000 SIC 5153 4221

RAY CARROLL COUNTY GRAIN GROWERS INC p 1209
807 W Main St, Richmond MO 64085
Tel (816) 776-2291 SIC 5171 5191 5153

BUNGE NORTH AMERICA INC p 226
11720 Borman Dr, Saint Louis MO 63146
Tel (314) 292-2000 SIC 5153

BUSCH AGRICULTURAL RESOURCES LLC p 229
3636 S Geyer Rd Fl 2, Saint Louis MO 63127
Tel (314) 577-2000
SIC 2044 2083 0181 5153

ITALGRANI USA INC p 767
7900 Van Buren St, Saint Louis MO 63111
Tel (314) 638-1447 SIC 2041 5153

MOUNTAIN VIEW CO-OP p 994
2200 Old Havre Hwy, Black Eagle MT 59414
Tel (406) 453-5900
SIC 5541 5153 2875 5191

TROTTER INC p 1484
300 Railway, Arcadia NE 68815
Tel (308) 789-6200 SIC 5191 5153 5172

AURORA COOPERATIVE ELEVATOR CO p 132
2225 Q St, Aurora NE 68818
Tel (402) 694-2106 SIC 5153 5191

BATTLE CREEK FARMERS COOPERATIVE NON-STOCK p 160
83755 Highway 121, Battle Creek NE 68715
Tel (402) 675-2375
SIC 5153 5191 5172 5541 5411

SOUTHEAST NEBRASKA COOPERATIVE CO p 1346
403 S 3rd St, Beatrice NE 68310
Tel (402) 228-3458 SIC 5191 5153 2048

FRONTIER COOPERATIVE CO p 581
211 S Lincoln St, Brainard NE 68626
Tel (402) 545-2811 SIC 5153 5191

J E MEURET GRAIN CO INC p 771
101 N Franklin St, Brunswick NE 68720
Tel (402) 842-2515 SIC 5153

COOP HUSKER p 366
2468 33rd Ave, Columbus NE 68601
Tel (402) 564-2704 SIC 5153 5191

FARMERS COOPERATIVE p 529
208 W Depot St, Dorchester NE 68343
Tel (402) 946-4631 SIC 5153 5191 5172

AG VALLEY COOPERATIVE NON-STOCK p 34
72133 State Hwy 136, Edison NE 68936
Tel (308) 927-3681 SIC 5153 5191

MIDWEST FARMERS COOPERATIVE p 967
304 S 3rd St, Elmwood NE 68349
Tel (402) 994-2585 SIC 5153 5191 5541

ALL POINTS COOPERATIVE p 51
120 8th St, Gothenburg NE 69138
Tel (308) 537-7141 SIC 5153 5191 5541

COOPERATIVE PRODUCERS INC p 367
265 N Showboat Blvd, Hastings NE 68901
Tel (402) 463-5148 SIC 2048 5153

FRENCHMAN VALLEY FARMERS COOPERATIVE INC p 578
202 Broadway, Imperial NE 69033
Tel (308) 882-3220 SIC 5153 5191 5541

AG PROCESSING INC A COOPERATIVE p 33
12700 W Dodge Rd, Omaha NE 68154
Tel (402) 496-7809
SIC 5153 2075 2048 5999 0254

AGP GRAIN LTD p 35
12700 W Dodge Rd, Omaha NE 68154
Tel (402) 496-7809 SIC 5153

GAVILON AGRICULTURE HOLDINGS CO p 594
1331 Capitol Ave, Omaha NE 68102
Tel (402) 889-4000 SIC 5153 5191

GAVILON AGRICULTURE INVESTMENT INC p 594
1331 Capitol Ave, Omaha NE 68102
Tel (402) 889-4000 SIC 5153 5191

GAVILON GRAIN LLC p 594
1331 Capitol Ave, Omaha NE 68102
Tel (402) 889-4000
SIC 6221 5153 4221 4226

GAVILON GROUP LLC p 594
1331 Capitol Ave, Omaha NE 68102
Tel (402) 889-4000 SIC 5153 5191

■ **NGL CRUDE LOGISTICS LLC** p 1041
1299 Farnam St Ste 120, Omaha NE 68102
Tel (402) 889-4000 SIC 6221 5153

SCOULAR CO p 1294
2027 Dodge St Ste 200, Omaha NE 68102
Tel (402) 342-3500 SIC 5153

KELLEY BEAN CO INC p 808
2407 Circle Dr, Scottsbluff NE 69361
Tel (308) 635-6438 SIC 5153 2034

COFCO (USA) INC p 334
910 Sylvan Ave Fl 1, Englewood Cliffs NJ 07632
Tel (201) 568-6788 SIC 5153

HOUSE OF SPICES (INDIA) INC p 711
12740 Willets Point Blvd, Flushing NY 11368
Tel (718) 507-4900
SIC 5149 2099 5153 2033 2024

ITOCHU INTERNATIONAL INC p 768
1251 Avenue Of The Americ, New York NY 10020
Tel (212) 818-8000
SIC 5131 5084 5065 5051 5153 5141

KANEMATSU USA INC p 802
500 5th Ave Fl 29, New York NY 10110
Tel (212) 704-9400
SIC 5084 5051 5065 5153

MITSUBISHI CORP (AMERICAS) p 977
655 3rd Ave, New York NY 10017
Tel (212) 605-2000
SIC 5051 5172 5141 5153 5169 5084

MITSUBISHI INTERNATIONAL CORP p 978
655 3rd Ave Ste 800, New York NY 10017
Tel (212) 605-2000
SIC 5051 5172 5141 5153 5169 5084

MITSUI & CO (USA) INC p 978
200 Park Ave Fl 35, New York NY 10166
Tel (212) 878-4000
SIC 5051 5094 5084 5153 5172 5169

TOMEN AMERICA INC p 1459
805 3rd Ave Fl 16, New York NY 10022
Tel (212) 355-3600
SIC 5153 5169 5031 5131 2261

TOYOTA TSUSHO AMERICA INC p 1467
805 3rd Ave Fl 17, New York NY 10022
Tel (212) 355-3600
SIC 5051 5013 4225 6331 5153

BUNGE GLOBAL MARKETS INC p 225
50 Main St, White Plains NY 10606
Tel (914) 684-3300 SIC 5153 5159

LACKAWANNA PRODUCTS CORP p 837
8545 Main St Ste 1, Williamsville NY 14221
Tel (716) 633-1940 SIC 5191 5153

ARTHUR COMPANIES INC p 114
429 Main St, Arthur ND 58006
Tel (701) 967-8312 SIC 5153

MAPLE RIVER GRAIN & AGRONOMY LLC p 904
1630 1st Ave S, Casselton ND 58012
Tel (701) 347-4465 SIC 5153 5191

PLAINS GRAIN & AGRONOMY LLC p 1153
109 3rd Ave, Enderlin ND 58027
Tel (701) 437-2565 SIC 5153 5191 5171

RED RIVER COMMODITIES INC p 1216
501 42nd St N, Fargo ND 58102
Tel (701) 282-2600 SIC 5153 5145 5149

■ **SPECIALTY COMMODITIES INC** p 1356
1530 47th St N, Fargo ND 58102
Tel (701) 282-8222 SIC 5149 5153

FULLERTON FARMERS ELEVATOR p 584
202 Minneapolis Ave, Fullerton ND 58441
Tel (701) 375-7881 SIC 5153 5191

CHS INC p 304
3645 98th Ave Sw, Taylor ND 58656
Tel (701) 483-6781 SIC 5153 5191

AGLAND CO-OP INC p 35
364 Lisbon St, Canfield OH 44406
Tel (330) 533-5551 SIC 5153

MERCER LANDMARK INC p 944
426 W Market St, Celina OH 45822
Tel (419) 628-3093 SIC 5153 5999

EDON FARMERS COOPERATIVE ASSOCIATION p 478
205 S Michigan St, Edon OH 43518
Tel (419) 272-2121 SIC 5153 5191

LEGACY FARMERS COOPERATIVE p 852
6566 County Road 236, Findlay OH 45840
Tel (419) 423-2611
SIC 5153 5191 5984 2875 2048 2041

CENTRAL OHIO FARMERS CO-OP INC p 279
730 Bellefontaine Ave, Marion OH 43302
Tel (740) 383-2158 SIC 5153 5261

▲ **ANDERSONS INC** p 90
480 W Dussel Dr, Maumee OH 43537
Tel (419) 893-5050
SIC 5153 0723 5191 2874 4789 4741

COOPER HATCHERY INC p 366
22348 Road 140, Oakwood OH 45873
Tel (419) 594-3325
SIC 0254 0253 2015 5153 2048

TRUPOINTE COOPERATIVE INC p 1487
215 Looney Rd, Piqua OH 45356
Tel (937) 575-6780 SIC 5153 5191

HERITAGE COOPERATIVE INC p 686
11177 Township Road 133, West Mansfield OH 43358
Tel (419) 294-2371
SIC 5153 5261 4925 4932

LUCKEY FARMERS INC p 884
1200 W Main St, Woodville OH 43469
Tel (419) 849-2711 SIC 5153

JOHNSTON ENTERPRISES INC p 791
411 W Chestnut Ave, Enid OK 73701
Tel (580) 233-5800 SIC 5153 5191

W B JOHNSTON GRAIN CO p 1568
411 W Chestnut Ave, Enid OK 73701
Tel (580) 233-5800
SIC 5153 5191 4491 4213 0111 0211

WHEELER BROTHERS GRAIN CO LLC p 1605
501 Russworm Dr, Watonga OK 73772
Tel (580) 623-7223 SIC 5153

COLUMBIA GRAIN INC p 340
1300 Sw 5th Ave Ste 2929, Portland OR 97201
Tel (503) 224-8624 SIC 5153

BRIDGEWELL RESOURCES LLC p 212
10200 Sw Greenburg Rd # 500, Tigard OR 97223
Tel (503) 872-3566
SIC 5031 5039 5153 5159

SOUTH DAKOTA WHEAT GROWERS ASSOCIATION p 1344
908 Lamont St S, Aberdeen SD 57401
Tel (605) 225-5500 SIC 5153

FULL CIRCLE AG p 584
520 Vander Horck Ave, Britton SD 57430
Tel (605) 448-2231 SIC 5191 5153 5541

AGFIRST FARMERS COOPERATIVE p 34
204 1st St S, Brookings SD 57006
Tel (605) 692-6216 SIC 5191 5153

NORTH CENTRAL FARMERS ELEVATOR p 1052
12 5th Ave, Ipswich SD 57451
Tel (605) 426-6021
SIC 5153 5191 5171 5541

LAKE PRESTON COOPERATIVE ASSOCIATION p 839
106 2nd St Nw, Lake Preston SD 57249
Tel (605) 847-4414 SIC 5153 5191 5172

FREMAR LLC p 577
44608 273rd St, Marion SD 57043
Tel (605) 648-3941 SIC 5153 2873

WATERTOWN COOPERATIVE ELEVATOR ASSOCIATION p 1582
811 Burlington Northern D, Watertown SD 57201
Tel (605) 886-8333 SIC 5153 5191 4221

COUNTRY PRIDE COOPERATIVE INC p 375
648 W 2nd St, Winner SD 57580
Tel (605) 842-2711
SIC 5153 5172 5191 5411 5211

ATTEBURY GRAIN LLC p 129
3905 Bell St Ste A, Amarillo TX 79109
Tel (806) 335-1639 SIC 5153

DALHART CONSUMERS FUEL ASSOCIATION INC p 409
919 Liberal St, Dalhart TX 79022
Tel (806) 249-4660
SIC 5153 5172 5191 5541

UNITED AGRICULTURAL COOPERATIVE INC p 1506
911 S Wharton St, El Campo TX 77437
Tel (979) 543-6284
SIC 5251 0724 5083 4221 5153

GULF PACIFIC INC p 646
12010 Taylor Rd, Houston TX 77041
Tel (713) 464-0606 SIC 5153 0723

PERRYTON EQUITY EXCHANGE p 1137
4219 S Main St, Perryton TX 79070
Tel (806) 435-4016 SIC 5153 5191 5541

HONEYVILLE INC p 705
1080 N Main St Ste 101, Brigham City UT 84302
Tel (435) 494-4193 SIC 5153

EGT LLC p 481
150 E Mill Rd, Longview WA 98632
Tel (503) 827-4066 SIC 5153

RITZVILLE WAREHOUSE CO p 1237
201 E 1st Ave, Ritzville WA 99169
Tel (509) 659-0130 SIC 5153 4221

UNITED COOPERATIVE p 1507
N7160 Raceway Rd, Beaver Dam WI 53916
Tel (920) 887-1756
SIC 5191 5171 5541 5153 5812

DELONG CO INC p 425
513 Front St, Clinton WI 53525
Tel (800) 356-0784 SIC 5153

DIDION MILLING INC p 438
520 Hartwig Blvd Ste C, Johnson Creek WI 53038
Tel (920) 348-5868 SIC 5153 2041

VP HOLDINGS CORP p 1566
2514 Fish Hatchery Rd, Madison WI 53713
Tel (608) 256-1988 SIC 2048 5191 5153

CP FEEDS LLC p 387
16322 W Washington St, Valders WI 54245
Tel (920) 775-9600 SIC 5153 5191

SIC 5154 Livestock Wholesale

■ **ANIMAL HEALTH INTERNATIONAL INC** p 91
822 7th St Ste 740, Greeley CO 80631
Tel (970) 353-2600
SIC 5122 5047 5999 5191 5083 5154

SWIFT PORK CO p 1412
1770 Promontory Cir, Greeley CO 80634
Tel (970) 506-8000 SIC 5154

GEORGIA FARM BUREAU FEDERATION INC p 607
1620 Bass Rd, Macon GA 31210
Tel (478) 474-8411
SIC 6111 5154 8699 5191

ADM ALLIANCE NUTRITION INC p 23
1000 N 30th St, Quincy IL 62301
Tel (217) 231-2674 SIC 2048 5154

IOWA FARM BUREAU FEDERATION p 762
5400 University Ave, West Des Moines IA 50266
Tel (515) 225-5400
SIC 8699 5154 6311 6321 6411

FARMERS RANCHERS LIVSTOCK COMMUNITY INC p 530
1500 W Old Highway 40, Salina KS 67401
Tel (785) 825-0211 SIC 5154

KEENELAND ASSOCIATION INC p 807
4201 Versailles Rd, Lexington KY 40510
Tel (859) 288-4236 SIC 5154 7948 0751

BARTLETT AGRI ENTERPRISES INC p 157
4900 Main St Ste 1200, Kansas City MO 64112
Tel (816) 753-6300 SIC 5153 5154 2041

ACOMA BUSINESS ENTERPRISES p 18
I 40 Exit 102, Pueblo Of Acoma NM 87034
Tel (888) 759-2489 SIC 6719 5154

UNITED PRODUCERS INC p 1511
8351 N High St Ste 250, Columbus OH 43235
Tel (614) 433-2150 SIC 5154

STOCKMENS LIVESTOCK MARKET INC p 1390
1200 E Highway 50, Yankton SD 57078
Tel (402) 640-8420 SIC 5154

SIC 5159 Farm-Prdt Raw Mtrls, NEC Wholesale

AGRI-AFC LLC p 36
121 Somerville Rd Ne, Decatur AL 35601
Tel (256) 560-2848
SIC 5159 5153 5083 5191

ALABAMA FARMERS COOPERATIVE INC p 43
121 Somerville Rd Ne, Decatur AL 35601
Tel (256) 353-6843 SIC 5191 5153 5159

CALCOT LTD p 238
1900 E Brundage Ln, Bakersfield CA 93307
Tel (661) 327-5961 SIC 5159

IMPERIAL WESTERN PRODUCTS INC p 734
86600 Avenue 54, Coachella CA 92236
Tel (760) 398-0815 SIC 5159 2841 2869

HARLAND M BRAUN & CO INC p 661
4010 Whiteside St, Los Angeles CA 90063
Tel (323) 263-9275 SIC 5159 5199

SELECT HARVEST USA LLC p 1301
14827 W Harding Rd, Turlock CA 95380
Tel (209) 668-2471 SIC 5159 0173

■ **HARKEMA SERVICES INC** p 661
305 Albany Tpke, Canton CT 06019
Tel (860) 693-8378 SIC 5159

JOHN I HAAS INC p 789
5185 Mcarthur Blvd Nw # 300, Washington DC 20016
Tel (202) 777-4800 SIC 0139 5159

SUCRO CAN SOURCING LLC p 1396
2990 Ponce De Leon Blvd # 401, Coral Gables FL 33134
Tel (305) 901-5222 SIC 5159 5149

GOLDEN PEANUT & TREE NUTS p 621
275 Industrial Blvd, Camilla GA 31730
Tel (229) 336-7282 SIC 5159 2068

BLACK HORSE CARRIERS INC p 187
150 Village Ct, Carol Stream IL 60188
Tel (630) 690-8900 SIC 4212 5159

AJINOMOTO HEARTLAND INC p 41
8430 W Bryn Mawr Ave, Chicago IL 60631
Tel (773) 380-7000 SIC 5159

MAPLE LEAF INC p 903
101 E Church St, Leesburg IN 46538
Tel (574) 453-4455 SIC 0259 2015 5159

TASMAN INDUSTRIES INC p 1426
930 Geiger St, Louisville KY 40206
Tel (502) 785-7477 SIC 3111 5159

PERDUE AGRIBUSINESS LLC p 1134
6906 Zion Church Rd, Salisbury MD 21804
Tel (410) 543-3000 SIC 5159 3556

SUNOPTA INGREDIENTS INC p 1403
7301 Ohms Ln Ste 600, Edina MN 55439
Tel (831) 685-6506 SIC 5159

STAPLE COTTON CO-OPERATIVE ASSOCIATION p 1377
214 W Market St, Greenwood MS 38930
Tel (662) 453-6231 SIC 5159 4221 6159

■ **ZOETIS P&U LLC** p 1644
100 Campus Dr, Florham Park NJ 07932
Tel (973) 822-7000 SIC 5159 0742 8734

CENIBRA INC p 275
335 Madison Ave Fl 23, New York NY 10017
Tel (212) 818-8242 SIC 2611 5159

BUNGE GLOBAL MARKETS INC p 225
50 Main St, White Plains NY 10606
Tel (914) 684-3300 SIC 5153 5159

JIMBOS JUMBOS INC p 785
185 Peanut Dr, Edenton NC 27932
Tel (252) 482-2193 SIC 5159

▲ **ALLIANCE ONE INTERNATIONAL INC** p 54
8001 Aerial Center Pkwy # 100, Morrisville NC 27560
Tel (919) 379-4300 SIC 5159

MEHERRIN AGRICULTURAL & CHEMICAL CO p 940
413 Main St, Severn NC 27877
Tel (252) 585-1744 SIC 5159 5191 5145

TUMAC LUMBER CO INC p 1491
805 Sw Broadway Ste 1500, Portland OR 97205
Tel (503) 721-7696 SIC 5031 5159

BRIDGEWELL RESOURCES LLC p 212
10200 Sw Greenburg Rd # 500, Tigard OR 97223
Tel (503) 872-3566
SIC 5031 5039 5153 5159

LOUIS DREYFUS CO COTTON LLC p 879
7255 Goodlett Farms Pkwy, Cordova TN 38016
Tel (901) 383-5000 SIC 5159 5131

DUNAVANT ENTERPRISES INC p 461
959 Ridg Loop Rd Ste 200, Memphis TN 38120
Tel (901) 369-1500
SIC 5159 4221 4731 0131

ECOM ATLANTIC INC p 476
13760 Noel Rd Ste 500, Dallas TX 75240
Tel (214) 520-1717 SIC 5159 5149

ECOM USA INC p 476
13760 Noel Rd Ste 500, Dallas TX 75240
Tel (214) 520-1717 SIC 5159

PLAINS COTTON COOPERATIVE ASSOCIATION p 1153
3301 E 50th St, Lubbock TX 79404
Tel (806) 763-8011 SIC 5159 4221

■ **ALTRIA GROUP DISTRIBUTION CO** p 63
6601 W Broad St, Richmond VA 23230
Tel (804) 274-2000 SIC 5159

▲ **UNIVERSAL CORP** p 1516
9201 Forest Hill Ave, Richmond VA 23235
Tel (804) 359-9311 SIC 5159 2141

COOPERATIVE RESOURCES INTERNATIONAL INC p 367
117 E Green Bay St, Shawano WI 54166
Tel (715) 526-2141
SIC 0751 5159 0762 8731

GENEX COOPERATIVE INC p 603
100 Mbc Dr, Shawano WI 54166
Tel (715) 526-2141 SIC 0751 5159

SIC 5162 Plastics Materials & Basic Shapes Wholesale

HILLMAN GROUP INC p 694
8990 S Kyrene Rd, Tempe AZ 85284
Tel (800) 800-4900 SIC 3429 5162 3599

RYAN HERCO PRODUCTS CORP p 1260
3010 N San Fernando Blvd, Burbank CA 91504
Tel (818) 841-1141 SIC 5074 5162

CBOL CORP p 269
19850 Plummer St, Chatsworth CA 91311
Tel (818) 704-8200
SIC 5065 5072 5013 5088 5084 5162

NITTO AMERICAS INC p 1045
48500 Fremont Blvd, Fremont CA 94538
Tel (510) 445-5400
SIC 2672 3589 5162 5065

PROFESSIONAL PLASTICS INC p 1180
1810 E Valencia Dr, Fullerton CA 92831
Tel (714) 446-6500 SIC 5162

DONGALEN ENTERPRISES INC p 450
330 Commerce Cir, Sacramento CA 95815
Tel (916) 422-3110 SIC 5162

NISHIBA INDUSTRIES CORP p 1044
2360 Marconi Ct, San Diego CA 92154
Tel (619) 661-8866 SIC 3089 3544 5162

OSTERMAN & CO INC p 1097
726 S Main St, Cheshire CT 06410
Tel (203) 272-2233 SIC 5162

NEVAMAR CO LLC p 1029
20 Progress Dr, Shelton CT 06484
Tel (203) 925-1556 SIC 3089 5162

MUEHLSTEIN INTERNATIONAL LTD p 998
10 Westport Rd Ste 200, Wilton CT 06897
Tel (203) 855-6000 SIC 5169 5162

JOSE MASSUH REVOCABLE TRUST p 793
825 Brickell Bay Dr, Miami FL 33131
Tel (305) 358-1900 SIC 5162

PACIFIC LTD CORP p 1105
825 Brickell Bay Dr, Miami FL 33131
Tel (305) 358-1900 SIC 5162

ENTEC POLYMERS LLC p 501
1900 Summit Tower Blvd # 900, Orlando FL 32810
Tel (407) 875-9595 SIC 5162 1459

RAVAGO AMERICAS LLC p 1209
1900 Summit Tower Blvd, Orlando FL 32810
Tel (407) 875-9595 SIC 5162

RAVAGO HOLDINGS AMERICA INC p 1209
1900 Summit Tower Blvd, Orlando FL 32810
Tel (407) 875-9595 SIC 5162

CYTEC SURFACE SPECIALTIES INC p 406
1950 Lake Park Dr Se, Smyrna GA 30080
Tel (770) 434-6188
SIC 3086 5169 5191 5162 3081 2823

UCB CHEMICALS CORP p 1498
2000 Lake Park Dr Se, Smyrna GA 30080
Tel (770) 434-6188 SIC 5169 5191 5162

COPE PLASTICS INC p 368
4441 Indl Dr, Alton IL 62002
Tel (618) 466-0221 SIC 5162 3599

COMPOSITES ONE LLC p 351
85 W Algonquin Rd Ste 600, Arlington Heights IL 60005
Tel (847) 437-0200 SIC 5162

PARKSITE INC p 1117
1563 Hubbard Ave, Batavia IL 60510
Tel (630) 761-9490 SIC 5031 5162

■ **JOSEPH T RYERSON & SON INC** p 794
227 W Monroe St Fl 27, Chicago IL 60606
Tel (312) 292-5000 SIC 5051 5162

TRANSCENDIA INC p 1471
9201 Belmont Ave, Franklin Park IL 60131
Tel (847) 678-1800 SIC 3081 5162

ALP LIGHTING & CEILING PRODUCTS INC p 60
6333 W Gross Point Rd, Niles IL 60714
Tel (773) 774-9550
SIC 3089 3354 5162 3496 3442 3229

M HOLLAND CO p 889
400 Skokie Blvd Ste 600, Northbrook IL 60062
Tel (847) 272-7370 SIC 5162

▲ **A M CASTLE & CO** p 6
1420 Kensington Rd # 220, Oak Brook IL 60523
Tel (847) 455-7111 SIC 5051 5162

■ **AMERI KART CORP** p 67
17196 State Road 120, Bristol IN 46507
Tel (574) 848-7462
SIC 3089 3537 2821 5162

AS HOLDINGS INC p 115
5120 Beck Dr, Elkhart IN 46516
Tel (574) 295-8384
SIC 5033 5169 5031 5162

■ **LUCENT POLYMERS INC** p 884
1700 Lynch Rd, Evansville IN 47711
Tel (812) 421-2216 SIC 5162

■ **MATRIXX GROUP INC** p 920
15000 Highway 41 N, Evansville IN 47725
Tel (812) 421-3600 SIC 5162

SUPERIOR OIL CO INC p 1406
1402 N Capitol Ave # 100, Indianapolis IN 46202
Tel (317) 781-4400 SIC 5169 5162

INTERCONTINENTAL EXPORT IMPORT INC p 752
8815 Centre Park Dr # 400, Columbia MD 21045
Tel (410) 674-5600 SIC 5162

WEB INDUSTRIES INC p 1586
377 Simarano Dr Ste 220, Marlborough MA 01752
Tel (508) 898-2988
SIC 2671 5162 3089 2269 3441

PACIFIC PACKAGING PRODUCTS INC p 1105
24 Industrial Way, Wilmington MA 01887
Tel (978) 657-9100
SIC 5113 5199 5084 5162 2671 2653

JO GALLOUP CO p 786
130 Helmer Rd N, Battle Creek MI 49037
Tel (269) 965-2303 SIC 5051 5085 5162

HUMPHREY COMPANIES LLC p 718
2851 Prairie St Sw, Grandville MI 49418
Tel (616) 530-1717
SIC 3537 3714 3089 5023 5162

ALRO STEEL CORP p 61
3100 E High St, Jackson MI 49203
Tel (517) 787-5500 SIC 5085 5162

TOTAL PLASTICS RESOURCES LLC p 1463
2810 N Burdick St Ste A, Kalamazoo MI 49004
Tel (269) 344-0009 SIC 3083 5162

THYSSENKRUPP MATERIALS NA INC p 1451
22355 W 11 Mile Rd, Southfield MI 48033
Tel (248) 233-5600
SIC 5051 5162 3444 8741

FLEX-N-GATE LLC p 555
5663 E 9 Mile Rd, Warren MI 48091
Tel (800) 398-1496 SIC 5162

STONE PLASTICS AND MANUFACTURING INC p 1391
8245 Riley St Ste 100, Zeeland MI 49464
Tel (616) 748-9740 SIC 5162 3089

NORTH AMERICAN COMPOSITES CO p 1049
300 Apollo Dr, Circle Pines MN 55014
Tel (651) 766-6892 SIC 5162

REGAL SUPPLY CO p 1218
111 E 10th Ave, Kansas City MO 64116
Tel (816) 421-6290 SIC 5162

BUNZL USA HOLDINGS LLC p 226
1 Cityplace Dr Ste 200, Saint Louis MO 63141
Tel (314) 997-5959 SIC 5162 5113

BUNZL USA INC p 226
1 Cityplace Dr Ste 200, Saint Louis MO 63141
Tel (314) 997-5959 SIC 5113 5162 5085

ALLENTOWN INC p 53
165 Route 526, Allentown NJ 08501
Tel (609) 259-7951 SIC 3444 3496 5162

AMERICAN PRIDE PAPER & PLASTIC LLC p 78
601 Prospect St, Lakewood NJ 08701
Tel (732) 367-4444 SIC 5162

GDB INTERNATIONAL INC p 595
1 Home News Row, New Brunswick NJ 08901
Tel (732) 246-3001
SIC 2851 5162 5111 5093

CHEMICAL RESOURCES INC p 293
103 Carnegie Ctr Ste 100, Princeton NJ 08540
Tel (609) 520-0000 SIC 5162 5169 2865

CV HOLDINGS LLC p 404
1030 Riverfront Ctr, Amsterdam NY 12010
Tel (518) 627-0051 SIC 5162 3089

BAMBERGER POLYMERS CORP p 149
2 Jericho Plz Ste 109, Jericho NY 11753
Tel (516) 622-3600 SIC 5162

BAMBERGER POLYMERS INC p 149
2 Jericho Plz Ste 109, Jericho NY 11753
Tel (516) 622-3600 SIC 5162

ALBEA COSMETICS AMERICA INC p 46
595 Madison Ave Fl 10, New York NY 10022
Tel (212) 371-5100
SIC 3089 3911 5162 5051

ICC CHEMICAL CORP p 727
460 Park Ave Fl 7, New York NY 10022
Tel (212) 521-1700 SIC 5169 5122 5162

NAGASE AMERICA CORP p 1006
546 5th Ave Fl 16, New York NY 10036
Tel (212) 703-1340
SIC 5169 5162 5122 5065 5047

CURBELL INC p 402
7 Cobham Dr, Orchard Park NY 14127
Tel (716) 667-3377 SIC 5162 3669 3842

CURBELL PLASTICS INC p 402
7 Cobham Dr, Orchard Park NY 14127
Tel (716) 667-3377 SIC 5162

AMPAC PAPER LLC p 86
30 Coldenham Rd, Walden NY 12586
Tel (845) 778-5511 SIC 2674 2621 5162

MITSUI PLASTICS INC p 978
11 Martine Ave Ste 1175, White Plains NY 10606
Tel (914) 287-6800 SIC 5162

WILBERT INC p 1608
2001 Oaks Pkwy, Belmont NC 28012
Tel (704) 247-3850 SIC 5162 3272

PIEDMONT PLASTICS INC p 1147
5010 W Wt Harris Blvd, Charlotte NC 28269
Tel (704) 597-8200 SIC 3081 3082 5162

REICHHOLD HOLDINGS US INC p 1220
1035 Swabia Ct, Durham NC 27703
Tel (919) 990-7500
SIC 2821 2822 2891 3089 5169 5162

▲ **POLYONE CORP** p 1160
33587 Walker Rd, Avon Lake OH 44012
Tel (440) 930-1000
SIC 2821 3087 5162 3081

■ **CITADEL INTERMEDIATE HOLDINGS LLC** p 309
3637 Ridgewood Rd, Fairlawn OH 44333
Tel (330) 666-3751 SIC 5162

MULTI-PLASTICS INC p 999
7770 N Central Dr, Lewis Center OH 43035
Tel (740) 548-4894 SIC 5162

ALLIANCE PLASTICS INC p 55
3123 Station Rd, Erie PA 16510
Tel (814) 899-7671 SIC 5162 5065

PALRAM AMERICAS INC p 1110
9735 Commerce Cir, Kutztown PA 19530
Tel (610) 285-9918 SIC 5162

GRAHAM PACKAGING CO INC p 629
700 Indian Springs Dr # 100, Lancaster PA 17601
Tel (717) 849-8500 SIC 5199 3089 5162

■ **CITADEL PLASTICS HOLDINGS INC** p 309
150 N Radnor Chester Rd, Wayne PA 19087
Tel (484) 844-0231 SIC 5162

KYOWA AMERICA CORP p 833
1039 Fred White Blvd, Portland TN 37148
Tel (615) 323-2194 SIC 5162

INTERNATIONAL ASSEMBLY INC p 754
750 E Los Ebanos Blvd A, Brownsville TX 78520
Tel (956) 499-7933 SIC 5162

ASIA CHEMICAL CORP INC p 117
11950 Airline Dr Ste 300, Houston TX 77037
Tel (281) 445-1793 *SIC* 5162

ULTRAPAK LTD p 1501
9690 W Wingfoot Rd, Houston TX 77041
Tel (713) 329-9183 *SIC* 5162

LAIRD PLASTICS INC p 838
5800 Campus Circle Dr E, Irving TX 75063
Tel (469) 299-7000 *SIC* 5162 3089

PORT PLASTICS INC p 1162
5800 Campus Circle Dr E 150a, Irving TX 75063
Tel (469) 299-7000 *SIC* 5162

BRAWLER INDUSTRIES LLC p 209
11701 County Rd W 125 125 W, Midland TX 79711
Tel (432) 563-4005 *SIC* 5162

■ NEXEO SOLUTIONS HOLDINGS LLC p 1039
3 Waterway Square Pl # 1000, The Woodlands TX 77380
Tel (281) 297-0700 *SIC* 5169 5162

■ NEXEO SOLUTIONS LLC p 1040
3 Waterway Square Pl # 1000, The Woodlands TX 77380
Tel (281) 297-0700 *SIC* 5169 5162 2821

INTERMOUNTAIN PLASTIC DISTRIBUTION INC p 753
2300 S Decker Lake Blvd B, Salt Lake City UT 84119
Tel (801) 201-1212 *SIC* 5162

STAR PLASTICS INC p 1378
326 Jack Burlingame Dr, Millwood WV 25262
Tel (304) 273-0352 *SIC* 5162 2821

CPT INC p 388
3706 Enterprise Dr, Janesville WI 53546
Tel (608) 314-2020 *SIC* 3089 5162

SIC 5169 Chemicals & Allied Prdts, NEC Wholesale

NELSON BROTHERS INC p 1025
820 Shades Creek Pkwy # 2000, Birmingham AL 35209
Tel (205) 414-2900 *SIC* 2892 5169

EVONIK CORP p 515
4201 Degussa Rd, Theodore AL 36582
Tel (251) 443-4000 *SIC* 5169

INDUSTRIAL CHEMICALS INC p 739
2042 Montreat Dr Ste A, Vestavia AL 35216
Tel (205) 823-7330 *SIC* 5169

BRENNTAG PACIFIC INC p 210
4199 Lathrop St, Fairbanks AK 99701
Tel (907) 452-1555 *SIC* 5169

SHASTA INDUSTRIES INC p 1312
6031 N 16th St, Phoenix AZ 85016
Tel (602) 532-3750
SIC 1799 1771 5169 7389 3088 5091

APACHE NITROGEN PRODUCTS INC p 96
1436 S Apache Powder Rd, Saint David AZ 85630
Tel (520) 720-2217
SIC 2873 5169 2875 2819

HART CHEMICALS INC p 664
2424 4th St, Berkeley CA 94710
Tel (510) 549-3535 *SIC* 5191 5169

CHIRO INC p 301
2260 S Vista Ave, Bloomington CA 92316
Tel (909) 879-1160 *SIC* 5087 7349 5169

TRI-ISO TRYLINE LLC p 1477
2187 Newcastle Ave # 101, Cardiff By The Sea CA 92007
Tel (909) 626-4855 *SIC* 5169

GLANBIA NUTRITIONALS (NA) INC p 614
2840 Loker Ave E Ste 100, Carlsbad CA 92010
Tel (760) 438-0089 *SIC* 5169 2833 8099

TIANJIN POOL & SPA CORP p 1452
2701-2711 Garfield Ave, Commerce CA 90040
Tel (626) 571-1885 *SIC* 5169 5091

SASOL WAX NORTH AMERICA CORP p 1283
3563 Inv Blvd Ste 2, Hayward CA 94545
Tel (510) 783-9295 *SIC* 5172 5169

ET HORN CO p 467
16050 Canary Ave, La Mirada CA 90638
Tel (714) 523-8050 *SIC* 5169

HILL BROTHERS CHEMICAL CO p 693
1675 N Main St, Orange CA 92867
Tel (714) 998-8800 *SIC* 5169 2819

MOC PRODUCTS CO INC p 980
12306 Montague St, Pacoima CA 91331
Tel (818) 794-3500 *SIC* 5169 7549

P & R PAPER SUPPLY CO INC p 1102
1898 E Colton Ave, Redlands CA 92374
Tel (909) 389-1811
SIC 5113 5169 5149 5072 5046

CLIPPER OIL p 327
2040 Harbor Island Dr # 203, San Diego CA 92101
Tel (619) 692-9701 *SIC* 5172 2873 5169

WILBUR-ELLIS HOLDINGS II INC p 1608
345 California St Fl 27, San Francisco CA 94104
Tel (415) 772-4000 *SIC* 5999 5191 5169

REACH AMERICA ESG LTD p 1213
2033 Gateway Pl Ste 500, San Jose CA 95110
Tel (408) 573-6170 *SIC* 5169

JACOB STERN & SONS INC p 775
1464 E Valley Rd, Santa Barbara CA 93108
Tel (805) 565-4532 *SIC* 5169 5191 5199

BRENNTAG PACIFIC INC p 210
10747 Patterson Pl, Santa Fe Springs CA 90670
Tel (562) 903-9626 *SIC* 5169

CALAMCO p 238
1776 W March Ln Ste 420, Stockton CA 95207
Tel (209) 982-1000 *SIC* 5169

■ GOLDBERG AND SOLOVY FOODS INC p 620
5925 Alcoa Ave, Vernon CA 90058
Tel (323) 581-6161
SIC 5141 5149 5046 5169

BONAKEMI USA INC p 199
2550 S Parker Rd Ste 600, Aurora CO 80014
Tel (303) 371-1411
SIC 5198 5169 5023 2851

GENERAL AIR SERVICE & SUPPLY CO p 599
1105 Zuni St, Denver CO 80204
Tel (303) 892-7003
SIC 5169 5085 5084 5149

SMALLEY & CO p 1332
861 S Jason St, Denver CO 80223
Tel (303) 777-3435 *SIC* 5169

UNITED STATES WELDING INC p 1514
600 S Santa Fe Dr, Denver CO 80223
Tel (303) 777-2475
SIC 5169 5084 5085 5047 7359

WESTERN PAPER DISTRIBUTORS INC p 1599
11551 E 45th Ave Unit A, Denver CO 80239
Tel (303) 371-8710 *SIC* 5113 5111 5169

ALCOHOL MONITORING SYSTEMS INC p 47
1241 W Mineral Ave # 200, Littleton CO 80120
Tel (303) 785-7813 *SIC* 5169 3825

REPUBLIC NATIONAL DISTRIBUTING CO LLC p 1225
8000 Southpark Ter, Littleton CO 80120
Tel (303) 734-2400 *SIC* 5169

ORICA US SERVICES INC p 1094
33101 E Quincy Ave, Watkins CO 80137
Tel (303) 268-5000 *SIC* 2892 5169

ORICA USA INC p 1094
33101 E Quincy Ave, Watkins CO 80137
Tel (720) 870-1809 *SIC* 2892 5169

■ PRAXAIR TECHNOLOGY INC p 1168
39 Old Ridgebury Rd, Danbury CT 06810
Tel (203) 837-2000
SIC 5172 5084 5169 5085

CHARKIT CHEMICAL CORP p 289
32 Haviland St Unit 1, Norwalk CT 06854
Tel (203) 299-3220 *SIC* 5169

RT VANDERBILT CO INC p 1203
30 Winfield St, Norwalk CT 06855
Tel (203) 853-1400
SIC 5169 2869 2819 5052 1499 1459

RT VANDERBILT HOLDING CO INC p 1256
30 Winfield St, Norwalk CT 06855
Tel (203) 295-2141
SIC 5169 2869 2819 1499 1459

VANDERBILT CHEMICALS LLC p 1543
30 Winfield St, Norwalk CT 06855
Tel (203) 853-1400 *SIC* 2819 2869 5169

CELLMARK USA LLC p 274
2 Corporate Dr 5, Shelton CT 06484
Tel (203) 541-9000 *SIC* 5169 5051 5084

GALATA CHEMICALS HOLDING CO LLC p 589
464 Heritage Rd Ste 1, Southbury CT 06488
Tel (203) 236-9000 *SIC* 5169 6719

GALATA CHEMICALS LLC p 589
464 Heritage Rd Ste A1, Southbury CT 06488
Tel (203) 236-9000 *SIC* 5169 3999

AZELIS AMERICAS INC p 140
262 Harbor Dr, Stamford CT 06902
Tel (203) 274-8691 *SIC* 5085 5046 5169

MUEHLSTEIN INTERNATIONAL LTD p 998
10 Westport Rd Ste 200, Wilton CT 06897
Tel (203) 855-6000 *SIC* 5169 5162

HAIFA NORTH AMERICA INC p 653
307 Cranes Roost Blvd, Altamonte Springs FL 32701
Tel (407) 862-6400 *SIC* 5191 5169

J TECH SALES LLC p 772
6531 Park Of Cmrc Blvd Ste 170, Boca Raton FL 33487
Tel (561) 995-0070 *SIC* 5169

SUN WHOLESALE SUPPLY INC p 1401
6385 150th Ave N, Clearwater FL 33760
Tel (727) 524-3299
SIC 5169 5021 5023 5091

ALLIED UNIVERSAL CORP p 57
3901 Nw 115th Ave, Doral FL 33178
Tel (305) 888-2623 *SIC* 5169

MONTACHEM INTERNATIONAL INC p 986
200 S Andrews Ave Ste 702, Fort Lauderdale FL 33301
Tel (954) 385-9908 *SIC* 5169

ALLCHEM INDUSTRIES HOLDING CORP p 52
6010 Nw 1st Pl, Gainesville FL 32607
Tel (352) 378-9696 *SIC* 5169

CCP MANAGEMENT INC p 270
3401 Phillips Hwy, Jacksonville FL 32207
Tel (904) 398-7177 *SIC* 5032 5169

JBT FOODTECH CITRUS SYSTEMS p 780
400 Fairway Ave, Lakeland FL 33801
Tel (863) 683-5411 *SIC* 5169

AMZ HOLDING CORP p 88
4800 State Road 60 E, Mulberry FL 33860
Tel (863) 578-1206 *SIC* 5169

CHENEY BROS INC p 294
1 Cheney Way, Riviera Beach FL 33404
Tel (561) 845-4700
SIC 5141 5087 5113 5169 5149

JCI JONES CHEMICALS INC p 780
1765 Ringling Blvd, Sarasota FL 34236
Tel (941) 330-1537 *SIC* 5169 2842

■ NUCO2 INC p 1066
2800 Se Market Pl, Stuart FL 34997
Tel (772) 221-1754 *SIC* 5169

YARA NORTH AMERICA INC p 1635
100 N Tampa St Ste 3200, Tampa FL 33602
Tel (813) 222-5700 *SIC* 5191 5169

AGC AMERICA INC p 34
11175 Cicero Dr Ste 400, Alpharetta GA 30022
Tel (404) 446-4200
SIC 6719 3211 2869 5169 3229

ACUITY SPECIALTY PRODUCTS INC p 20
1310 Sboard Indus Blvd Nw, Atlanta GA 30318
Tel (404) 352-1680
SIC 2841 2879 2842 5169

■ EAGLE SPINCO INC p 468
115 Perimeter Center Pl, Atlanta GA 30346
Tel (770) 395-4500 *SIC* 2812 5169

GP CHEMICALS EQUITY LLC p 627
55 Park Pl Ne, Atlanta GA 30303
Tel (404) 652-4000 *SIC* 5169

WHITAKER OIL CO p 1605
1557 Marietta Rd Nw, Atlanta GA 30318
Tel (404) 355-8220 *SIC* 5169

DSM FINANCE USA INC p 458
1408 Columbia Nitrogen Dr, Augusta GA 30901
Tel (706) 849-6515
SIC 2891 2816 3089 3083 5169

TEXTILE RUBBER AND CHEMICAL CO INC p 1445
1300-1350 Tiarco Dr Sw, Dalton GA 30721
Tel (706) 277-1300 *SIC* 5169 2821

■ BIOLAB WATER ADDITIVES p 184
N Brown Rd, Lawrenceville GA 30045
Tel (678) 502-4699 *SIC* 5169

LINTECH INTERNATIONAL LLC p 869
7705 Ne Industrial Blvd, Macon GA 31216
Tel (877) 546-8324 *SIC* 5169

COLONIAL GROUP INC p 337
101 N Lathrop Ave, Savannah GA 31415
Tel (800) 944-3835
SIC 5171 5169 5172 4924 4492 4226

COMPASS CHEMICAL INTERNATIONAL LLC p 351
5544 Oakdale Rd Se, Smyrna GA 30082
Tel (404) 696-6711 *SIC* 5169 3589

CYTEC SURFACE SPECIALTIES INC p 406
1950 Lake Park Dr Se, Smyrna GA 30080
Tel (770) 434-6188
SIC 3086 5169 5191 5162 3081 2823

UCB CHEMICALS CORP p 1498
2000 Lake Park Dr Se, Smyrna GA 30080
Tel (770) 434-6188 *SIC* 5169 5191 5162

PHOENIX V LLC p 1145
311 Pacific St, Honolulu HI 96817
Tel (808) 532-7400 *SIC* 5169 8748

NORCO INC p 1047
1125 W Amity Rd, Boise ID 83705
Tel (208) 336-1643
SIC 5084 5169 7352 5999 3548 2813

LAND VIEW INC p 842
20504 4th St, Rupert ID 83350
Tel (208) 531-4100
SIC 2879 2873 2874 5999 5261 5169

■ GE HEALTHCARE HOLDINGS INC p 596
3350 N Ridge Ave, Arlington Heights IL 60004
Tel (847) 398-8400
SIC 2835 2833 5169 5122

GLS COMPOSITES DISTIBUTION CORP p 618
85 W Algonquin Rd Ste 600, Arlington Heights IL 60005
Tel (800) 621-8003 *SIC* 5169

DIVERSIFIED CPC INTERNATIONAL INC p 444
24338 W Durkee Rd, Channahon IL 60410
Tel (815) 423-5991 *SIC* 2813 5169

K+S SALT LLC p 799
123 N Wacker Dr Fl 6, Chicago IL 60606
Tel (844) 789-3991 *SIC* 2899 5149 5169

VANTAGE OLEOCHEMICALS INC p 1544
4650 S Racine Ave, Chicago IL 60609
Tel (773) 376-9000 *SIC* 2869 2841 5169

ADM COCOA INC p 23
4666 E Faries Pkwy, Decatur IL 62526
Tel (217) 424-5200 *SIC* 5169

▲ UNIVAR INC p 1516
3075 Highland Pkwy # 200, Downers Grove IL 60515
Tel (331) 777-6000 *SIC* 5169 5191 8741

KUNA MEAT CO INC p 832
704 Kuna Industrial Ct, Dupo IL 62239
Tel (618) 286-4000
SIC 5144 5142 5147 5169 5149 5148

NORTH AMERICAN CORP OF ILLINOIS p 1050
2101 Claire Ct, Glenview IL 60025
Tel (847) 832-4000 *SIC* 5113 5169

ROWELL CHEMICAL CORP p 1253
15 Salt Creek Ln Ste 205, Hinsdale IL 60521
Tel (630) 920-8833 *SIC* 5169

OLD WORLD INDUSTRIES LLC p 1081
4065 Commercial Ave, Northbrook IL 60062
Tel (847) 559-2000 *SIC* 5013 5169

RILCO INC p 1235
1320 1st St, Rock Island IL 61201
Tel (309) 788-5631 *SIC* 5172 5169

HAND2MIND INC p 657
500 Greenview Ct, Vernon Hills IL 60061
Tel (847) 816-5060 *SIC* 5049 5169

DON EDWARD & CO p 449
9801 Adam Don Pkwy, Woodridge IL 60517
Tel (708) 442-9400
SIC 5021 5046 5087 5113 5169

AS HOLDINGS INC p 115
5120 Beck Dr, Elkhart IN 46516
Tel (574) 295-8384
SIC 5033 5169 5031 5162

KEM KREST LLC p 809
3221 Magnum Dr, Elkhart IN 46516
Tel (574) 389-2650
SIC 5169 5013 5085 4783 4225

ACORN DISTRIBUTORS INC p 18
5820 Fortune Cir W, Indianapolis IN 46241
Tel (317) 243-9234
SIC 5113 5087 5169 5046 5023

BFS DIVERSIFIED PRODUCTS INC p 179
250 W 96th St Ste 150, Indianapolis IN 46260
Tel (317) 575-7000 *SIC* 5031 5013 5169

HARRIS & FORD LLC p 663
9307 E 56th St, Indianapolis IN 46216
Tel (317) 591-0000 *SIC* 5169 5085

MAYS CHEMICAL CO INC p 924
5611 E 71st St, Indianapolis IN 46220
Tel (317) 842-8722 *SIC* 5169 4731

SUPERIOR OIL CO INC p 1406
1402 N Capitol Ave # 100, Indianapolis IN 46202
Tel (317) 781-4400 *SIC* 5169 5162

ALCHEMY AROMATICS LLC p 47
621 Park East Blvd, New Albany IN 47150
Tel (812) 755-6660 *SIC* 5169 5122

WILLIAMS BROS HEALTH CARE PHARMACY INC p 1611
10 Williams Brothers Dr, Washington IN 47501
Tel (812) 254-2497
SIC 5047 7352 5999 5169 3999

MARTIN BROTHERS DISTRIBUTING CO INC p 912
6623 Chancellor Dr, Cedar Falls IA 50613
Tel (319) 266-1775
SIC 5141 5169 5046 5087

S J SMITH CO INC p 1262
3707 W River Dr, Davenport IA 52802
Tel (563) 324-5237 *SIC* 5169 5084 5999

BARTON SOLVENTS INC p 158
1920 Ne 46th Ave, Des Moines IA 50313
Tel (515) 265-7998 *SIC* 5169

CHANNEL PRIME ALLIANCE LLC p 288
1803 Hull Ave, Des Moines IA 50313
Tel (515) 264-4110 *SIC* 5169

GELITA NORTH AMERICA INC p 598
2445 Port Neal Rd, Sergeant Bluff IA 51054
Tel (712) 943-5516 *SIC* 5169 2099

HARCROS CHEMICALS INC p 660
5200 Speaker Rd, Kansas City KS 66106
Tel (913) 321-3131 *SIC* 5169 2869

CLEAN HARBORS WICHITA LLC p 324
2824 N Ohio St, Wichita KS 67219
Tel (316) 832-0151 *SIC* 2992 5169 5172

ETHANOL PRODUCTS LLC p 511
3939 N Webb Rd, Wichita KS 67226
Tel (316) 303-1380 *SIC* 5172 5169

FLINT HILLS RESOURCES LLC p 557
4111 E 37th St N, Wichita KS 67220
Tel (316) 828-5500 *SIC* 5169 5084

KOCH FERTILIZER LLC p 825
4111 E 37th St N, Wichita KS 67220
Tel (316) 828-5010 *SIC* 2873 5169 2813

KOCH INDUSTRIES INC p 825
4111 E 37th St N, Wichita KS 67220
Tel (316) 828-5500 *SIC* 5172 2911 5169

▲ ASHLAND GLOBAL HOLDINGS INC p 117
50 E Rivercenter Blvd, Covington KY 41011
Tel (859) 815-3333 *SIC* 5169

■ ASHLAND LLC p 117
50 E Rivercenter Blvd # 1600, Covington KY 41011
Tel (859) 815-3333
SIC 2899 2851 2821 2911 5169 7549

BRENNTAG MID-SOUTH INC p 210
1405 State Route 136 W, Henderson KY 42420
Tel (270) 827-3545 *SIC* 5169

ALL STAR DAIRY ASSOCIATION INC p 51
1050 Monarch St Ste 101, Lexington KY 40513
Tel (859) 255-3644
SIC 5149 5169 5113 5199

COASTAL CHEMICAL CO LLC p 331
3520 Veterans Memorial Dr, Abbeville LA 70510
Tel (337) 898-0001 *SIC* 5172 5169

FRANCIS DRILLING FLUIDS LTD p 573
240 Jasmine Rd, Crowley LA 70526
Tel (337) 783-8685 *SIC* 5169 1389 7353

X-CHEM INC p 1630
6141 River Rd, Harahan LA 70123
Tel (504) 733-5806 *SIC* 5169

CAL-CHLOR CORP p 237
627 Jefferson St, Lafayette LA 70501
Tel (337) 264-1449 *SIC* 5169

RED BALL OXYGEN CO INC p 1215
609 N Market St, Shreveport LA 71107
Tel (318) 425-6300
SIC 5084 5085 5169 5099 5531 5013

MAINE OXY-ACETYLENE SUPPLY CO p 898
22 Albiston Way, Auburn ME 04210
Tel (207) 784-5788 *SIC* 5169 5084

ROBERTS OXYGEN CO INC p 1242
15830 Redland Rd, Rockville MD 20855
Tel (301) 315-9090 *SIC* 5085 5169 5047

■ CABOT INTERNATIONAL CAPITAL CORP p 235
2 Seaport Ln Ste 1300, Boston MA 02210
Tel (617) 345-0100 *SIC* 5169

BAY STATE POOL SUPPLIES INC p 161
691 Concord Ave, Cambridge MA 02138
Tel (617) 547-9145 *SIC* 5169 5091

A W CHESTERTON CO p 7
860 Salem St, Groveland MA 01834
Tel (781) 438-7000
SIC 3053 2851 2992 2891 5169

MONSON COMPANIES INC p 985
154 Pioneer Dr, Leominster MA 01453
Tel (978) 840-7007
SIC 5169 5172 2899 2842

■ FISHER THERMO SCIENTIFIC CHEMICALS INC p 552
2 Radcliff Rd, Tewksbury MA 01876
Tel (978) 521-6300 *SIC* 5169

■ FISHER SCIENTIFIC INTERNATIONAL LLC p 552
81 Wyman St, Waltham MA 02451
Tel (781) 622-1000
SIC 2869 3821 5169 5049

ACCESS BUSINESS GROUP LLC p 14
7575 Fulton St E, Ada MI 49355
Tel (616) 787-6000
SIC 5169 2842 5122 2833 5136 5137

ALTICOR GLOBAL HOLDINGS INC p 62
7575 Fulton St E, Ada MI 49301
Tel (616) 787-1000
SIC 5169 5122 2833 5136 5137 5021

ALTICOR INC p 62
7575 Fulton St E, Ada MI 49355
Tel (616) 787-1000
SIC 5169 5122 2833 5136 5137 5021

AMWAY INTERNATIONAL INC p 87
7575 Fulton St E, Ada MI 49355
Tel (616) 787-1000
SIC 5169 5122 5099 5199 2099 2032

WACKER CHEMICAL CORP p 1570
3301 Sutton Rd, Adrian MI 49221
Tel (517) 264-8500 *SIC* 2869 5169

RECTICEL NORTH AMERICA INC p 1215
1653 Atlantic Blvd, Auburn Hills MI 48326
Tel (248) 393-2100 *SIC* 5169

CALEDONIA FARMERS ELEVATOR CO INC p 238
146 E Main St Se, Caledonia MI 49316
Tel (616) 891-4150
SIC 5153 5169 5251 5261

■ **NORTRU LLC** p 1061
515 Lycaste St, Detroit MI 48214
Tel (313) 824-5840 *SIC* 4953 5169

PRESSURE VESSEL SERVICE INC p 1173
10900 Harper Ave, Detroit MI 48213
Tel (313) 921-1200
SIC 5169 2819 2899 4953 3535

PVS CHEMICAL SOLUTIONS INC p 1193
10900 Harper Ave, Detroit MI 48213
Tel (313) 921-1200 *SIC* 5169

PVS-NOLWOOD CHEMICALS INC p 1193
10900 Harper Ave, Detroit MI 48213
Tel (313) 921-1200 *SIC* 5169

GRANITE HOLDINGS INC p 631
2580 28th St Sw, Grand Rapids MI 49519
Tel (616) 532-2375 *SIC* 5169

HAVILAND ENTERPRISES INC p 668
421 Ann St Nw, Grand Rapids MI 49504
Tel (616) 361-6691 *SIC* 5169

HAVILAND PRODUCTS CO p 668
421 Ann St Nw, Grand Rapids MI 49504
Tel (616) 361-6691 *SIC* 5169 2819

WEBB CHEMICAL SERVICE CORP p 1586
2708 Jarman St, Muskegon MI 49444
Tel (231) 733-2181 *SIC* 5169

LUBRICATION TECHNOLOGIES INC p 884
900 Mendelssohn Ave N, Minneapolis MN 55427
Tel (763) 545-0707 *SIC* 5172 5169

▲ **HAWKINS INC** p 670
2381 Rosegate, Roseville MN 55113
Tel (612) 331-6910 *SIC* 5169 5074 2899

UNIVERSAL COOPERATIVES INC p 1516
1300 Corporate Ctr Curv, Saint Paul MN 55121
Tel (651) 239-1000 *SIC* 2879 5169 2298

▲ **FASTENAL CO** p 531
2001 Theurer Blvd, Winona MN 55987
Tel (507) 454-5374
SIC 5085 5072 5063 5169 5198

CROWN PACKAGING CORP p 395
17854 Chstrfld Aprt Rd, Chesterfield MO 63005
Tel (636) 681-8000
SIC 5113 5169 5131 5084

DASH MULTI-CORP INC p 413
2500 Adie Rd, Maryland Heights MO 63043
Tel (314) 432-3200
SIC 2821 3069 6512 5169 7359

PLAZE INC p 1156
105 Bolte Ln, Saint Clair MO 63077
Tel (630) 543-7800 *SIC* 5169 2819

HILLYARD INC p 694
302 N 4th St, Saint Joseph MO 64501
Tel (816) 233-1321 *SIC* 5169 5087

ARCHWAY SALES LLC p 105
4155 Manchester Ave, Saint Louis MO 63110
Tel (314) 533-4662 *SIC* 5169

SIGMA - ALDRICH CO LLC p 1321
3050 Spruce St, Saint Louis MO 63103
Tel (314) 771-5765 *SIC* 2899 5169

SIGMA-ALDRICH CORP p 1321
3050 Spruce St, Saint Louis MO 63103
Tel (314) 771-5765 *SIC* 2899 5169 8099

ARM STRONG GROUP LLC p 110
3960 Howard Hughes Pkwy, Las Vegas NV 89169
Tel (702) 948-8960 *SIC* 5169

BRADY INDUSTRIES INC p 207
7055 Lindell Rd, Las Vegas NV 89118
Tel (702) 876-3990
SIC 5169 5087 5999 5023 5064

AUTOMOTIVE SUPPLY ASSOCIATES INC p 134
129 Manchester St, Concord NH 03301
Tel (603) 225-4000
SIC 5013 7539 5531 5169 5015

PRIDE SOLVENTS & CHEMICAL CO OF NEW JERSEY INC p 1174
211 Randolph Ave, Avenel NJ 07001
Tel (732) 499-0123 *SIC* 5169

BERJE INC p 174
700 Blair Rd, Carteret NJ 07008
Tel (973) 748-8980 *SIC* 5169 2869

LG CHEM AMERICA INC p 860
910 Sylvan Ave, Englewood Cliffs NJ 07632
Tel (201) 816-2000 *SIC* 5099 5169 5199

AJINOMOTO NORTH AMERICA INC p 41
400 Kelby St, Fort Lee NJ 07024
Tel (201) 292-3200
SIC 5142 5169 2869 2899

INFINEUM USA LP p 740
1900 E Linden Ave, Linden NJ 07036
Tel (908) 474-0100 *SIC* 5169

BUNZL NEW JERSEY INC p 226
27 Distribution Way, Monmouth Junction NJ 08852
Tel (732) 821-7000 *SIC* 5113 5169

GANTRADE CORP p 591
210 Summit Ave Ste B5, Montvale NJ 07645
Tel (201) 573-1955 *SIC* 5169

■ **HONEYWELL SPECIALTY WAX & ADDITIVES INC** p 705
101 Columbia Rd, Morristown NJ 07960
Tel (973) 455-2000 *SIC* 2999 5169

MITSUBISHI INTERNATIONAL POLYMERTRADE CORP p 978
2 Penn Plz E Fl 11, Newark NJ 07105
Tel (732) 357-2000 *SIC* 5169

TROY CHEMICAL CORP INC p 1485
1 Avenue L, Newark NJ 07105
Tel (973) 443-4200 *SIC* 5169

■ **WELCO-CGI GAS TECHNOLOGIES LLC** p 1588
425 Avenue P, Newark NJ 07105
Tel (973) 589-8795
SIC 5085 5169 5999 5984

PHOENIX AROMAS HOLDINGS LLC p 1144
355 Chestnut St, Norwood NJ 07648
Tel (201) 784-6100 *SIC* 5169

CALLAHAN CHEMICAL CO p 242
S Broad St & Filmore Ave, Palmyra NJ 08065
Tel (856) 786-7900 *SIC* 5169

CHEMTRADE SOLUTIONS LLC p 293
90 E Halsey Rd, Parsippany NJ 07054
Tel (973) 515-0900 *SIC* 5169 2819

DSM HOLDING CO USA INC p 458
45 Waterview Blvd, Parsippany NJ 07054
Tel (973) 257-1063
SIC 2891 2816 3089 3083 5169

HELM AMERICA CORP p 682
1110 Centennial Ave Ste 2, Piscataway NJ 08854
Tel (732) 981-1160
SIC 5169 5122 5191 4231 4226

HELM US CORP p 682
1110 Centennial Ave Ste 2, Piscataway NJ 08854
Tel (732) 981-1116 *SIC* 5169

CHEMICAL RESOURCES INC p 293
103 Carnegie Ctr Ste 100, Princeton NJ 08540
Tel (609) 520-0000 *SIC* 5162 5169 2865

■ **ROCKWOOD SPECIALTIES CONSOLIDATED INC** p 1245
100 Overlook Ctr Ste 101, Princeton NJ 08540
Tel (609) 514-0300 *SIC* 5169

■ **ROCKWOOD SPECIALTIES GROUP INC** p 1245
100 Overlook Ctr Ste 101, Princeton NJ 08540
Tel (609) 514-0300 *SIC* 5169 2899

SAMSUNG C&T AMERICA INC p 1275
105 Challenger Rd Fl 3, Ridgefield Park NJ 07660
Tel (201) 229-4000 *SIC* 5169 6799 8742

AMANO USA HOLDINGS INC p 64
140 Harrison Ave, Roseland NJ 07068
Tel (973) 403-1900
SIC 3589 2842 3579 3559 5169 5087

BRENNTAG SPECIALTIES INC p 210
1000 Coolidge St, South Plainfield NJ 07080
Tel (800) 732-0562 *SIC* 5169 2816 2899

HANWHA HOLDINGS (USA) INC p 659
300 Frank W Burr Blvd # 52, Teaneck NJ 07666
Tel (609) 655-2500 *SIC* 5169 5013 5084

■ **PHIBRO ANIMAL HEALTH CORP** p 1142
300 Frank W Burr Blvd, Teaneck NJ 07666
Tel (201) 329-7300
SIC 2819 5169 2899 2834

POSCO DAEWOO AMERICA CORP p 1163
300 Frank W Burr Blvd, Teaneck NJ 07666
Tel (201) 591-8000
SIC 5131 5051 5169 5015

DREW MARINE GROUP INC p 455
100 S Jefferson Rd # 204, Whippany NJ 07981
Tel (973) 526-5700 *SIC* 8999 5169

DREW MARINE PARTNERS LP p 455
100 S Jefferson Rd # 102, Whippany NJ 07981
Tel (973) 526-5700 *SIC* 5169

DREW MARINE USA INC p 455
100 S Jefferson Rd # 204, Whippany NJ 07981
Tel (973) 526-5700 *SIC* 5169

EISAI CORP OF NORTH AMERICA p 482
100 Tice Blvd, Woodcliff Lake NJ 07677
Tel (201) 692-1100 *SIC* 5169 8731

MPS ENTERPRISES INC p 995
1224 W Broadway Pl, Hobbs NM 88240
Tel (432) 563-3332 *SIC* 5169

NOVA MUD INC p 1062
5800 Nova, Hobbs NM 88240
Tel (575) 393-8786 *SIC* 5169

DASTECH INTERNATIONAL INC p 413
10 Cuttermill Rd Ste 400, Great Neck NY 11021
Tel (516) 466-7676 *SIC* 5169

ICC CHEMICAL CORP p 727
460 Park Ave Fl 7, New York NY 10022
Tel (212) 521-1700 *SIC* 5169 5122 5162

MARUBENI AMERICA CORP p 913
375 Lexington Ave, New York NY 10017
Tel (212) 450-0100
SIC 5131 5084 5012 5169 5172 5094

MITSUBISHI CORP (AMERICAS) p 977
655 3rd Ave, New York NY 10017
Tel (212) 605-2000
SIC 5051 5172 5141 5153 5169 5084

MITSUBISHI GAS CHEMICAL AMERICA INC p 977
655 3rd Ave Fl 24, New York NY 10017
Tel (212) 687-9030 *SIC* 5169 8742

MITSUBISHI INTERNATIONAL CORP p 978
655 3rd Ave Ste 800, New York NY 10017
Tel (212) 605-2000
SIC 5051 5172 5141 5153 5169 5084

MITSUBISHI RAYON AMERICA INC p 978
655 3rd Ave Fl 15, New York NY 10017
Tel (212) 223-3043 *SIC* 5169

MITSUI & CO (USA) INC p 978
200 Park Ave Fl 35, New York NY 10166
Tel (212) 878-4000
SIC 5051 5094 5084 5153 5172 5169

NAGASE AMERICA CORP p 1006
546 5th Ave Fl 16, New York NY 10036
Tel (212) 703-1340
SIC 5169 5162 5122 5065 5047

SOJITZ CORP OF AMERICA p 1337
1120 Ave Of The, New York NY 10036
Tel (212) 704-6500
SIC 5065 5084 5169 5051 5099 5052

■ **SPECIALTY MINERALS INC** p 1356
622 3rd Ave Fl 38, New York NY 10017
Tel (212) 878-1800
SIC 2819 5032 1422 5169 2899

TAKEDA AMERICA HOLDINGS INC p 1422
767 3rd Ave, New York NY 10017
Tel (212) 421-6954 *SIC* 5122 5169 2819

TOMEN AMERICA INC p 1459
805 3rd Ave Fl 16, New York NY 10022
Tel (212) 355-3600
SIC 5153 5169 5031 5131 2261

TRAMMO INC p 1469
1 Rockefeller Plz Fl 9, New York NY 10020
Tel (212) 223-3200 *SIC* 5191 5172 5169

TRIPLE A SUPPLIES INC p 1482
50 Jeanne Dr, Newburgh NY 12550
Tel (845) 566-4200 *SIC* 5169

▲ **ACETO CORP** p 17
4 Tri Harbor Ct, Port Washington NY 11050
Tel (516) 627-6000 *SIC* 5122 5169

■ **AMRI RENSSELAER INC** p 86
33 Riverside Ave, Rensselaer NY 12144
Tel (518) 433-7700 *SIC* 5169

AMERICAN ROCK SALT CO LLC p 78
3846 Retsof Rd, Retsof NY 14539
Tel (585) 991-6878 *SIC* 1479 5169

MITSUI CHEMICALS AMERICA INC p 978
800 Westchester Ave N607, Rye Brook NY 10573
Tel (914) 253-0777
SIC 2821 2865 3082 8731 5169 6159

ISOCHEM NORTH AMERICA INC p 767
6800 Jericho Tpke 120w, Syosset NY 11791
Tel (516) 393-5915 *SIC* 5169

ITOCHU CHEMICALS AMERICA INC p 768
360 Hamilton Ave Fl 6, White Plains NY 10601
Tel (914) 333-7800 *SIC* 5169

MARUBENI SPECIALTY CHEMICALS INC p 913
10 Bank St Ste 740, White Plains NY 10606
Tel (914) 428-8900 *SIC* 5169

PHT INTERNATIONAL INC p 1145
8133 Ardrey Kell Rd # 204, Charlotte NC 28277
Tel (704) 246-3480 *SIC* 5169

SWISHER HYGIENE INC p 1412
4725 Piedmont Row Dr # 400, Charlotte NC 28210
Tel (704) 364-7707 *SIC* 5169

ARC3 GASES INC p 103
1636 Us Highway 301 S, Dunn NC 28334
Tel (910) 892-4016
SIC 2813 5084 5169 7359 7692

MACHINE & WELDING SUPPLY CO p 892
1660 Us Highway 301 S, Dunn NC 28334
Tel (910) 892-4016 *SIC* 5084 5169

REICHHOLD HOLDINGS US INC p 1220
1035 Swabia Ct, Durham NC 27703
Tel (919) 990-7500
SIC 2821 2822 2891 3089 5169 5162

KAO SPECIALTIES AMERICAS LLC p 803
243 Woodbine St, High Point NC 27260
Tel (336) 878-4230 *SIC* 5169

UMICORE USA INC p 1501
3600 Glenwood Ave Ste 250, Raleigh NC 27612
Tel (919) 874-7171
SIC 5052 5051 5093 5169 3339

DAKOTA GASIFICATION CO INC p 409
1717 E Interstate Ave, Bismarck ND 58503
Tel (701) 223-0441 *SIC* 2873 5169 1311

COLE PAPERS INC p 335
1300 38th St N, Fargo ND 58102
Tel (800) 800-8090
SIC 5113 5111 5169 5023 5112 5049

AKROCHEM CORP p 42
3770 Embassy Pkwy, Akron OH 44333
Tel (330) 535-2100 *SIC* 5169

HARWICK STANDARD DISTRIBUTION CORP p 667
60 S Seiberling St, Akron OH 44305
Tel (330) 798-9300 *SIC* 5169

MAROON GROUP LLC p 910
1390 Jaycox Rd, Avon OH 44011
Tel (440) 937-1000 *SIC* 5169

AVALON FOODSERVICE INC p 135
1 Avalon Dr, Canal Fulton OH 44614
Tel (330) 854-4551
SIC 5142 5149 5169 5113 8322 5812

■ **CIMCOOL INDUSTRIAL PRODUCTS LLC** p 307
3000 Disney St, Cincinnati OH 45209
Tel (888) 246-2665 *SIC* 5169

HICKMAN WILLIAMS & CO p 690
250 E 5th St Ste 300, Cincinnati OH 45202
Tel (513) 621-1946
SIC 5051 5052 5169 5085 5084

■ **PROCTER & GAMBLE DISTRIBUTING LLC** p 1179
1 Procter And Gamble Plz, Cincinnati OH 45202
Tel (513) 983-1100
SIC 5169 5122 5149 5113 5137

AIRGAS MERCHANT GASES LLC p 40
6055 Rckside Woods Blvd N, Cleveland OH 44131
Tel (800) 242-0105 *SIC* 5169

■ **APPLIED INDUSTRIAL TECHNOLOGIES - DIXIE INC** p 99
1 Applied Plz, Cleveland OH 44115
Tel (216) 426-4000 *SIC* 5172 5169

▲ **APPLIED INDUSTRIAL TECHNOLOGIES INC** p 99
1 Applied Plz, Cleveland OH 44115
Tel (216) 426-4000 *SIC* 5085 5169 7699

CHEMICAL SOLVENTS INC p 293
3751 Jennings Rd, Cleveland OH 44109
Tel (216) 741-9310
SIC 5169 7349 3471 2992

JOSHEN PAPER & PACKAGING CO p 794
5800 Grant Ave, Cleveland OH 44105
Tel (216) 441-5600 *SIC* 5113 5169

■ **NES INVESTMENT CO** p 1026
6140 Parkland Blvd, Cleveland OH 44124
Tel (440) 461-6000
SIC 5065 5085 5169 5013

CHEMGROUP INC p 293
2600 Thunderhawk Ct, Dayton OH 45414
Tel (937) 898-5566 *SIC* 5169

MITSUBISHI INTERNATIONAL FOOD INGREDIENTS INC p 978
5080 Tuttle Crossing Blvd, Dublin OH 43016
Tel (614) 652-1111 *SIC* 5169

TOSOH AMERICA INC p 1462
3600 Gantz Rd, Grove City OH 43123
Tel (614) 539-8622
SIC 5169 3564 5047 5052

POLYMER ADDITIVES HOLDINGS INC p 1160
7500 E Pleasant Valley Rd, Independence OH 44131
Tel (216) 875-7200 *SIC* 5169 2899

POLYMER ADDITIVES INC p 1160
7500 E Pleasant Valley Rd, Independence OH 44131
Tel (216) 875-7200 *SIC* 5169 2899

IMCD US LLC p 733
14725 Detroit Ave Ste 300, Lakewood OH 44107
Tel (216) 228-8900 *SIC* 5169

WASHING SYSTEMS LLC p 1577
167 Commerce Dr, Loveland OH 45140
Tel (800) 272-1974 *SIC* 5169 2841

PALMER HOLLAND INC p 1109
25000 Country Club Blvd # 444, North Olmsted OH 44070
Tel (440) 686-2300 *SIC* 5169

SKIDMORE SALES & DISTRIBUTING CO INC p 1329
9889 Cincinnati Dayton Rd, West Chester OH 45069
Tel (513) 755-4200 *SIC* 5149 5169

SEA-LAND CHEMICAL CO p 1295
821 Westpoint Pkwy, Westlake OH 44145
Tel (440) 871-7887 *SIC* 5169

■ **ANCHOR DRILLING FLUIDS USA INC** p 89
2431 E 61st St Ste 710, Tulsa OK 74136
Tel (918) 583-7701 *SIC* 5169

WILLAMETTE VALLEY CO p 1609
1075 Arrowsmith St, Eugene OR 97402
Tel (541) 484-9621
SIC 5085 2851 2891 5169

WALTER E NELSON CO p 1574
5937 N Cutter Cir, Portland OR 97217
Tel (503) 285-3037 *SIC* 5169 5087

GT&S INC p 644
5275 Tilghman St, Allentown PA 18104
Tel (610) 398-2211
SIC 4925 5169 5084 5085 2813 5172

■ **TAMINCO US LLC** p 1423
7540 Windsor Dr Ste 411, Allentown PA 18195
Tel (610) 366-6730 *SIC* 2869 5169

GEORGE S COYNE CHEMICAL CO INC p 606
3015 State Rd, Croydon PA 19021
Tel (215) 785-4500 *SIC* 5169

CIESCO INC p 306
109 Miller Ln, Harrisburg PA 17110
Tel (717) 232-5825
SIC 5032 5033 5169 5039

INTERSTATE CHEMICAL CO INC p 758
2797 Freedland Rd, Hermitage PA 16148
Tel (724) 981-3771 *SIC* 5169 2819

WANHUA CHEMICAL (AMERICA) CO LTD p 1575
3803 West Chester Pike, Newtown Square PA 19073
Tel (613) 796-1606 *SIC* 5169

NATIONAL REFRIGERANTS INC p 1015
11401 Roosevelt Blvd, Philadelphia PA 19154
Tel (215) 698-6620 *SIC* 5169

■ **PEROXYCHEM LLC** p 1137
1 Commerce Sq, Philadelphia PA 19103
Tel (267) 422-2400 *SIC* 5169 2819

■ **FISHER SCIENTIFIC CO LLC** p 552
300 Industry Dr, Pittsburgh PA 15275
Tel (412) 490-8300
SIC 5049 5169 3821 3826 2869 2819

BUCKMANS INC p 223
105 Airport Rd, Pottstown PA 19464
Tel (610) 495-7495 *SIC* 5169 5941

AIRGAS INC p 40
259 N Radnor Chester Rd # 100, Radnor PA 19087
Tel (610) 687-5253
SIC 5169 5084 5085 2813 2819

AIRGAS USA LLC p 40
259 N Radnor Chester Rd # 100, Radnor PA 19087
Tel (610) 687-5253
SIC 5169 5084 5085 2813 2819

■ **VWR FUNDING INC** p 1567
100 Matsonford Rd, Radnor PA 19087
Tel (610) 386-1700 *SIC* 5049 5169

■ **VWR INTERNATIONAL LLC** p 1567
100 Matsonford Rd Bldg 1, Radnor PA 19087
Tel (610) 386-1700 *SIC* 5169 5049

BRENNTAG NORTH AMERICA INC p 210
5083 Pottsville Pike, Reading PA 19605
Tel (610) 926-6100 *SIC* 5169

BRENNTAG NORTHEAST INC p 210
81 W Huller Ln, Reading PA 19605
Tel (610) 926-4151 *SIC* 5169

INTERNATIONAL WAXES INC p 757
45 Route 446, Smethport PA 16749
Tel (814) 887-5501 *SIC* 5169

TANNER INDUSTRIES INC p 1424
735 Davisville Rd Ste 3, Southampton PA 18966
Tel (215) 322-1238 *SIC* 5169

INTERNATIONAL GROUP INC p 755
1007 E Spring St, Titusville PA 16354
Tel (814) 827-4900 *SIC* 5169 2911

AUDIA GROUP LLC p 130
450 Racetrack Rd, Washington PA 15301
Tel (724) 228-1260 *SIC* 5169

B FERNANDEZ & HNOS INC p 142
Urb Luchetti Calle B, Bayamon PR 00960
Tel (787) 288-7272 *SIC* 5169

NATIONAL BUILDING MAINTENANCE CORP p 1010
855 Ave Hostos, Ponce PR 00716
Tel (787) 290-7020 *SIC* 7349 5169

CHRIS CAM CORP p 302
808 W Cherokee St, Sioux Falls SD 57104
Tel (605) 336-1190 *SIC* 5113 5169 5111

KORDSA INC p 828
4501 N Access Rd, Chattanooga TN 37415
Tel (423) 643-8300 *SIC* 5169

■ **EASTMAN CHEMICAL LTD CORP** p 473
200 S Wilcox Dr, Kingsport TN 37660
Tel (423) 229-2000 *SIC* 5169 8742

HOLSTON GASES INC p 702
545 W Baxter Ave, Knoxville TN 37921
Tel (865) 573-1917 *SIC* 5169 5084 2813

KELSAN INC p 809
5109 N National Dr, Knoxville TN 37914
Tel (865) 525-7132 *SIC* 5087 5169 7699

IDEAL CHEMICAL AND SUPPLY CO p 729
4025 Air Park St, Memphis TN 38118
Tel (901) 363-7720 SIC 5169 7389

NEXAIR LLC p 1039
1385 Corporate Ave, Memphis TN 38132
Tel (901) 396-5050
SIC 5169 5084 7699 7359

WESTERN INTERNATIONAL GAS & CYLINDERS INC p 1598
7173 Highway 159 E, Bellville TX 77418
Tel (979) 865-5991 SIC 5169 2813

AIRGAS - SOUTHWEST INC p 40
4817 Agnes St, Corpus Christi TX 78405
Tel (361) 882-1141 SIC 5169 5084

■ **KMG-BERNUTH INC** p 824
300 Throckmorton St, Fort Worth TX 76102
Tel (817) 761-6100 SIC 5169 2869

BENCHMARK PERFORMANCE GROUP INC p 172
2801 Post Oak Blvd, Houston TX 77056
Tel (713) 986-2500 SIC 5169

BRENNTAG LATIN AMERICA INC p 210
5300 Memorial Dr Ste 1100, Houston TX 77007
Tel (713) 880-5400 SIC 5169

DX HOLDING CO INC p 464
300 Jackson Hill St, Houston TX 77007
Tel (713) 863-1947 SIC 2869 2819 5169

KNIGHT-CHEMSTAR INC p 824
9204 Emmott Rd, Houston TX 77040
Tel (713) 466-8751 SIC 5169 5172

■ **KRONOS (US) INC** p 830
14950 Heathrow Ste 230, Houston TX 77032
Tel (281) 423-3300 SIC 5169

SABIC AMERICAS INC p 1264
2500 Citywest Blvd, Houston TX 77042
Tel (713) 532-4999 SIC 5172 5169

SASOL CHEMICALS (USA) LLC p 1283
12120 Wickchester Ln, Houston TX 77079
Tel (281) 588-3000 SIC 2869 5169

SK LUBRICANTS AMERICAS INC p 1329
11700 Katy Fwy Ste 900, Houston TX 77079
Tel (713) 341-5828 SIC 5169

SWEPI LP p 1412
200 N Dairy Ashford Rd, Houston TX 77079
Tel (713) 241-6161 SIC 1311 1382 5169

TRIBUTE ENERGY INC p 1479
2100 West Loop S Ste 1220, Houston TX 77027
Tel (281) 768-5300 SIC 5169 3295 2821

TRICON INTERNATIONAL LTD p 1479
777 Post Oak Blvd Ste 550, Houston TX 77056
Tel (713) 963-0066 SIC 5169 7389 4789

VINMAR INTERNATIONAL HOLDINGS LTD p 1558
16800 Imperial Valley Dr, Houston TX 77060
Tel (281) 618-1300 SIC 5169

VINMAR INTERNATIONAL LTD p 1558
16800 Imperial Valley Dr, Houston TX 77060
Tel (281) 618-1300 SIC 5169

■ **CELANESE AMERICAS LLC** p 273
222 Colinas Blvd W 900n, Irving TX 75039
Tel (972) 443-4000
SIC 2821 2819 2824 5169

■ **CNA HOLDINGS LLC** p 330
222 Las Colinas Blvd W, Irving TX 75039
Tel (972) 443-4000
SIC 2823 2821 2819 5169 8731

■ **NEWPARK DRILLING FLUIDS LLC** p 1038
21920 Merchants Way, Katy TX 77449
Tel (281) 754-8600 SIC 5169 5172 4953

BRENNTAG SOUTHWEST INC p 210
610 Fisher Rd, Longview TX 75604
Tel (903) 241-7117 SIC 5169

BENCHMARK ENERGY PRODUCTS LP p 172
4113 W Industrial Ave, Midland TX 79703
Tel (432) 697-8171 SIC 5169

IMPACT CHEMICAL TECHNOLOGIES INC p 734
10501 E Hwy 80, Midland TX 79706
Tel (432) 458-3500 SIC 5169

RELIANT HOLDINGS LTD p 1222
10817 W County Road 60, Midland TX 79707
Tel (432) 617-4200 SIC 5169

METHANEX METHANOL CO LLC p 953
5850 Granite Pkwy Ste 400, Plano TX 75024
Tel (972) 702-0909 SIC 5169

WINZER CORP p 1617
4060 E Plano Pkwy, Plano TX 75074
Tel (800) 527-4126
SIC 5072 3452 5251 5169

ACE MART RESTAURANT SUPPLY CO p 16
2653 Austin Hwy, San Antonio TX 78218
Tel (210) 323-4400 SIC 5169 5046

BORAL MATERIAL TECHNOLOGIES LLC p 201
45 Ne Loop 410 Ste 700, San Antonio TX 78216
Tel (210) 349-4069 SIC 5169

VILORE FOODS CO INC p 1557
3838 Medical Dr Ste 207, San Antonio TX 78229
Tel (210) 509-9496 SIC 5149 5169

SEALTECH INC p 1296
28420 Hardy Toll Rd # 220, Spring TX 77373
Tel (281) 475-4770 SIC 5169

MEGLOBAL AMERICAS INC p 940
2150 Town Square Pl # 750, Sugar Land TX 77479
Tel (844) 634-5622 SIC 5169

CHEVRON PHILLIPS CHEMICAL CO LP p 296
10001 Six Pines Dr, The Woodlands TX 77380
Tel (832) 813-4100
SIC 5169 3292 3089 3084 3432 2911

■ **HUNTSMAN INTERNATIONAL TRADING CORP** p 720
10003 Woodloch Forest Dr # 260, The Woodlands TX 77380
Tel (281) 719-6000 SIC 5169

■ **INDEPENDENCE OILFIELD CHEMICALS LLC** p 736
1450 Lake Robbins Dr # 400, The Woodlands TX 77380
Tel (713) 936-4340 SIC 2899 5169

■ **NEXEO SOLUTIONS HOLDINGS LLC** p 1039
3 Waterway Square Pl # 1000, The Woodlands TX 77380
Tel (281) 297-0700 SIC 5169 5162

■ **NEXEO SOLUTIONS LLC** p 1040
3 Waterway Square Pl # 1000, The Woodlands TX 77380
Tel (281) 297-0700 SIC 5169 5162 2821

OXBOW SULPHUR INC p 1100
1450 Lake Robbins Dr # 500, The Woodlands TX 77380
Tel (281) 907-9500 SIC 5191 5169

SHRIEVE CHEMICAL CO p 1319
1755 Woodstead Ct, The Woodlands TX 77380
Tel (281) 367-4226 SIC 5169

WESTERN EXPLOSIVES SYSTEMS CO p 1598
3135 S Richmond St, Salt Lake City UT 84106
Tel (801) 484-6557
SIC 5169 1629 1241 1081 1481 2892

ARCET EQUIPMENT CO p 104
1700 Chamberlayne Ave, Richmond VA 23222
Tel (804) 644-4521 SIC 5085 5084 5169

■ **ETHYL CORP** p 511
330 S 4th St, Richmond VA 23219
Tel (804) 788-5000
SIC 2869 5169 2899 2841 2865

■ **CHEMPOINT.COM INC** p 293
411 108th Ave Ne Ste 1050, Bellevue WA 98004
Tel (425) 378-8600 SIC 5169

WEST COAST PAPER CO p 1594
6703 S 234th St Ste 120, Kent WA 98032
Tel (253) 850-1900
SIC 5085 5169 5084 2677

■ **UNIVAR USA INC** p 1516
17411 Ne Union Hill Rd, Redmond WA 98052
Tel (331) 777-6000 SIC 5169 5191 8741

BIG RIVER RESOURCES BOYCEVILLE LLC p 181
N10185 370th St, Boyceville WI 54725
Tel (715) 643-2602 SIC 5169

HYDRITE CHEMICAL CO p 723
300 N Patrick Blvd Fl 2, Brookfield WI 53045
Tel (262) 792-1450
SIC 5169 2819 2841 2869

ELLSWORTH CORP p 489
W129n10825 Washington Dr, Germantown WI 53022
Tel (262) 253-8600 SIC 5169 5085

BRENNTAG GREAT LAKES LLC p 210
4420 N Hrley Davidson Ave, Milwaukee WI 53225
Tel (262) 252-3550 SIC 5169

EMCO CHEMICAL DISTRIBUTORS INC p 491
8601 95th St, Pleasant Prairie WI 53158
Tel (262) 427-0400 SIC 5169 7389 2819

REINDERS INC p 1221
W227n6225 Sussex Rd, Sussex WI 53089
Tel (262) 786-3300
SIC 5191 5169 5074 5999 5083

SIC 5171 Petroleum Bulk Stations & Terminals

HOME OIL CO INC p 703
5744 E Us Highway 84, Cowarts AL 36321
Tel (334) 793-1544
SIC 5171 5411 5541 5172

COUGAR OIL INC p 374
1411 Water Ave, Selma AL 36703
Tel (334) 875-2023 SIC 5171 5983 5172

MCPHERSON COMPANIES INC p 932
5051 Cardinal St, Trussville AL 35173
Tel (205) 661-2799 SIC 5171 5411 5541

CPD ALASKA LLC p 387
201 Arctic Slope Ave, Anchorage AK 99518
Tel (907) 777-5505 SIC 5171

CROWLEY PETROLEUM DIST INC p 395
201 Arctic Slope Ave, Anchorage AK 99518
Tel (907) 822-3375 SIC 5171

■ **WESTERN REFINING SOUTHWEST INC** p 1599
1250 W Washington St # 101, Tempe AZ 85281
Tel (602) 286-1400
SIC 2911 5171 5411 5541

■ **WESTERN REFINING TERMINALS LLC** p 1599
1250 W Washington St # 101, Tempe AZ 85281
Tel (602) 286-1401 SIC 5171

■ **WESTERN REFINING WHOLESALE INC** p 1599
1250 W Washington St # 101, Tempe AZ 85281
Tel (602) 286-1401 SIC 5171 2911 2992

SNAKEBITE LEASING INC p 1335
821 S Pacific Ave, Yuma AZ 85365
Tel (928) 276-3328 SIC 5171

MAGNESS OIL CO p 896
167 Tucker Cemetery Rd, Gassville AR 72635
Tel (870) 425-4353 SIC 5171 5541 5411

R E GOODSPEED AND SONS DISTRIBUTING INC p 1202
11211 G Ave, Hesperia CA 92345
Tel (760) 949-3356 SIC 5171

KAMPS PROPANE INC p 802
1262 Dupont Ct, Manteca CA 95336
Tel (209) 858-6000 SIC 5171

SOUTHERN COUNTIES OIL CO p 1348
1800 W Katella Ave # 400, Orange CA 92867
Tel (714) 744-7140 SIC 5171 5541 5172

R M PARKS INC p 1202
1061 N Main St, Porterville CA 93257
Tel (559) 784-2384 SIC 5171

■ **CHEVRON USA INC** p 296
6001 Bollinger Canyon Rd D1248, San Ramon CA 94583
Tel (925) 842-1000
SIC 5541 5511 2911 5171

JACO HILL CO p 775
4960 Adobe Rd, Twentynine Palms CA 92277
Tel (760) 361-1407 SIC 5171

RAMOS OIL CO INC p 1207
1515 S River Rd, West Sacramento CA 95691
Tel (916) 371-2570 SIC 5171 5172

▲ **TRANSMONTAIGNE PARTNERS LP** p 1472
1670 Broadway Ste 3100, Denver CO 80202
Tel (303) 626-8200 SIC 4612 5171

GRAY OIL CO INC p 632
804 Denver Ave, Fort Lupton CO 80621
Tel (303) 857-2288 SIC 5171 5541 5411

STRATTON EQUITY COOPERATIVE CO p 1393
98 Colorado Ave, Stratton CO 80836
Tel (719) 348-5326
SIC 5153 5191 5171 5541

HARPEL OIL CO p 662
4204 E 105th Ave, Thornton CO 80233
Tel (303) 294-0767 SIC 5171 5983 5172

LEXA INTERNATIONAL CORP p 859
1 Landmark Sq Ste 407, Stamford CT 06901
Tel (203) 326-5200 SIC 5171 3822

CROWLEY HOLDINGS INC p 394
9487 Regency Square Blvd # 101, Jacksonville FL 32225
Tel (904) 727-2200
SIC 4412 4424 5171 5172 5541 4492

CROWLEY MARITIME CORP p 395
9487 Regency Square Blvd, Jacksonville FL 32225
Tel (904) 727-2200
SIC 4412 4424 5171 5172 5541 4492

LV HIERS INC p 887
253 Florida Ave, Macclenny FL 32063
Tel (904) 259-2314 SIC 5171

URBIETA OIL INC p 1530
9701 Nw 89th Ave, Medley FL 33178
Tel (305) 884-0008 SIC 5171 5172

RADIANT GROUP LLC p 1204
1320 E 9th Ave Ste 211, Tampa FL 33605
Tel (813) 247-4731 SIC 5171 5411

GEORGE E WARREN CORP p 606
3001 Ocean Dr Ste 203, Vero Beach FL 32963
Tel (772) 778-7100 SIC 5171

BRAD LANIER OIL CO INC p 206
611 W Roosevelt Ave, Albany GA 31701
Tel (229) 436-0131 SIC 5171 5541 5411

COLONIAL PIPELINE CO p 338
1185 Sanctuary Pkwy # 100, Alpharetta GA 30009
Tel (678) 762-2200
SIC 4613 4612 4226 1389 5171

SOUTHWEST GEORGIA OIL CO INC p 1352
1711 E Shotwell St, Bainbridge GA 39819
Tel (229) 246-1553
SIC 5171 5541 5411 5921

WHATLEY OIL AND AUTO PARTS CO p 1604
598 Blakely St, Cuthbert GA 39840
Tel (229) 732-2611 SIC 5171 5013 7389

COLONIAL GROUP INC p 337
101 N Lathrop Ave, Savannah GA 31415
Tel (800) 944-3835
SIC 5171 5169 5172 4924 4492 4226

COLONIAL OIL INDUSTRIES INC p 337
101 N Lathrop Ave, Savannah GA 31415
Tel (904) 396-1388 SIC 5171 5541

LANGDALE CO p 844
1202 Madison Hwy, Valdosta GA 31601
Tel (229) 242-7450
SIC 2421 2491 7011 7699 5031 5171

LEWIS AND RAULERSON INC p 858
1759 State St, Waycross GA 31501
Tel (912) 283-5951 SIC 5171

HAWAII ENERGY RESOURCES INC p 669
733 Bishop St Fl 28, Honolulu HI 96813
Tel (808) 547-3111 SIC 5172 2911 5171

BINGHAM COOPERATIVE INC p 183
477 W Highway 26, Blackfoot ID 83221
Tel (208) 785-3440 SIC 5191 5171 5541

CONRAD & BISCHOFF INC p 358
2251 N Holmes Ave, Idaho Falls ID 83401
Tel (208) 522-8174 SIC 5171 5411 5541

VALLEY CO-OPS INC p 1540
1833 S Lincoln Ave, Jerome ID 83338
Tel (208) 324-8000 SIC 5171 5191 5251

VALLEY WIDE COOPERATIVE INC p 1541
2114 N 20th St, Nampa ID 83687
Tel (208) 436-0141
SIC 5191 5251 5541 5171

MEIER OIL SERVICE INC p 940
405 N Second St, Ashkum IL 60911
Tel (815) 698-2343 SIC 5171 5172

GOLD STAR FS INC p 620
101 N East St, Cambridge IL 61238
Tel (309) 937-3369
SIC 5171 5153 5039 5191

M & M SERVICE CO INC p 888
130 N Chiles St, Carlinville IL 62626
Tel (217) 854-4516 SIC 5153 5191 5171

MORGAN DISTRIBUTING INC p 988
3425 N 22nd St, Decatur IL 62526
Tel (217) 877-3570 SIC 5171

SUNRISE AG SERVICE CO p 1403
104 S 1st St, Easton IL 62633
Tel (309) 562-7296 SIC 5191 5171 5541

SOUTH CENTRAL FS INC p 1343
405 S Banker St, Effingham IL 62401
Tel (217) 342-9231 SIC 5171 5191 2875

PDV MIDWEST REFINING LLC p 1125
135th St New Ave, Lemont IL 60439
Tel (630) 257-7761
SIC 2992 2911 5171 4213

KELLEY WILLIAMSON CO p 808
1132 Harrison Ave, Rockford IL 61104
Tel (815) 397-9410 SIC 5541 5411 5171

BP AMERICA INC p 205
4101 Winfield Rd Ste 200, Warrenville IL 60555
Tel (630) 420-5111
SIC 2911 5171 4612 4613 4424

CONSERV FS INC p 358
1110 Mcconnell Rd, Woodstock IL 60098
Tel (815) 334-5950 SIC 5171 5191

RICKER OIL CO INC p 1233
30 W 11th St, Anderson IN 46016
Tel (765) 643-3016 SIC 5171

CO-ALLIANCE LLP p 330
5250 E Us Hwy 3, Avon IN 46123
Tel (317) 745-4491
SIC 5191 5171 5153 2875

GLADIEUX TRADING AND MARKETING CO LP p 614
4133 New Haven Ave, Fort Wayne IN 46803
Tel (260) 423-4477 SIC 5171

GASAMERICA SERVICES INC p 593
2700 W Main St, Greenfield IN 46140
Tel (317) 468-2515 SIC 5541 5171

CRYSTAL FLASH PETROLEUM LLC p 396
5221 Ivy Tech Dr, Indianapolis IN 46268
Tel (317) 879-2849 SIC 5541 5411 5171

WHITE RIVER COOPERATIVE INC p 1606
416 Church St, Loogootee IN 47553
Tel (812) 295-4835 SIC 5191 5171

QUALITY OIL INC p 1197
55 N 400 E, Valparaiso IN 46383
Tel (219) 462-2951 SIC 5171 5172

MULGREW OIL CO p 999
10314 Silverwood Dr, Dubuque IA 52003
Tel (563) 583-7386 SIC 5171 5172 5541

LINN CO-OPERATIVE OIL CO p 869
325 35th St, Marion IA 52302
Tel (319) 377-4881 SIC 5153 5171 5191

GREAT BEND COOPERATIVE ASSOCIATION p 633
606 Main St, Great Bend KS 67530
Tel (620) 793-3531
SIC 5153 5191 5171 4221

MIDLAND MARKETING CO-OP INC p 966
219 E 9th St, Hays KS 67601
Tel (785) 625-5138
SIC 5153 5191 5541 5171 4221

LEISZLER OIL CO INC p 854
8228 Southport Dr, Manhattan KS 66502
Tel (785) 632-5648 SIC 5171 5411 5541

MIDWAY CO-OP ASSOCIATION p 967
210 W Harrison St, Osborne KS 67473
Tel (785) 346-5451 SIC 5153 5171

OTTAWA COOPERATIVE ASSOCIATION INC p 1098
302 N Main St, Ottawa KS 66067
Tel (785) 242-5170 SIC 5191 5171 5153

HAMPEL OIL DISTRIBUTORS INC p 656
3727 S West St, Wichita KS 67217
Tel (316) 529-1162 SIC 5171

UNIVERSAL COMPANIES INC p 1516
2824 N Ohio St, Wichita KS 67219
Tel (316) 832-0151
SIC 5171 5541 6512 8741 6099 2992

NEWCOMB OIL CO LLC p 1037
901 Withrow Ct, Bardstown KY 40004
Tel (502) 348-3961 SIC 5411 5171

KENTUCKY OIL AND REFINING CO p 812
156 Ky Oil Vlg, Betsy Layne KY 41605
Tel (606) 478-2303 SIC 5171 5541

KEYSTOPS LLC p 816
376 Reasonover Ave, Franklin KY 42134
Tel (270) 586-8283 SIC 5541 5171

MAX ARNOLD & SONS LLC p 922
702 N Main St, Hopkinsville KY 42240
Tel (270) 885-8488
SIC 5171 5541 5411 5812

KENTUCKY LAKE OIL CO INC p 812
620 S 4th St, Murray KY 42071
Tel (270) 753-1323
SIC 5541 5571 5171 5411

VALOR LLC p 1542
1200 Alsop Ln, Owensboro KY 42303
Tel (270) 683-2461 SIC 5171 5172

SOUTHERN PETROLEUM INC p 1350
600 Monticello St, Somerset KY 42501
Tel (606) 678-5127 SIC 5171

CHILDERS OIL CO p 298
51 Highway 2034, Whitesburg KY 41858
Tel (606) 633-2525 SIC 5171

RETIF OIL & FUEL L L C p 1228
1840 Jutland Dr, Harvey LA 70058
Tel (504) 349-9000 SIC 5171

CENTRAL OIL & SUPPLY CORP p 279
2300 Booth St, Monroe LA 71201
Tel (318) 388-2602 SIC 5171 5541

LOTT OIL CO INC p 879
1855 South Dr, Natchitoches LA 71457
Tel (318) 356-5858 SIC 5171

CANAL BARGE CO INC p 246
835 Union St Ste 300, New Orleans LA 70112
Tel (504) 581-2424 SIC 4449 4424 5171

CROWN CENTRAL PETROLEUM CORP p 395
1 N Charles St Ste 2100, Baltimore MD 21201
Tel (410) 539-7400 SIC 2911 5171 6794

ROSEMORE HOLDINGS INC p 1251
1 N Charles St Ste 2200, Baltimore MD 21201
Tel (410) 347-7090
SIC 2911 5171 5541 5411

■ **GLOBAL COMPANIES LLC** p 616
800 South St Ste 500, Waltham MA 02453
Tel (800) 542-0778 SIC 5172 5171

▲ **GLOBAL PARTNERS LP** p 617
800 South St Ste 500, Waltham MA 02453
Tel (781) 894-8800 SIC 5172 5171

GULF OIL LIMITED PARTNERSHIP p 646
80 William St Ste 400, Wellesley Hills MA 02481
Tel (339) 933-7200 SIC 5171 5172

BLARNEY CASTLE OIL CO p 189
12218 West St, Bear Lake MI 49614
Tel (231) 864-3111 SIC 5541 5411 5171

JOHNSON OIL CO OF GAYLORD p 791
507 S Otsego Ave, Gaylord MI 49735
Tel (989) 732-6014 SIC 5171 5541 5983

WALTERS-DIMMICK PETROLEUM INC p 1574
1620 S Kalamazoo Ave, Marshall MI 49068
Tel (269) 781-4654
SIC 5541 5411 6512 5172 5171 5983

ATLAS OIL CO p 128
24501 Ecorse Rd, Taylor MI 48180
Tel (313) 292-5500 SIC 5172 5171

CENTRA SOTA COOPERATIVE p 277
805 Highway 55 E, Buffalo MN 55313
Tel (763) 682-2557
SIC 5191 2875 5171 5153

BEST OIL CO p 177
30 N 8th St, Cloquet MN 55720
Tel (218) 879-0201
SIC 5171 5172 5013 5983 5541 5411

RIVER COUNTRY COOPERATIVE p 1237
9072 Cahill Ave, Inver Grove Heights MN 55076
Tel (651) 451-1151 *SIC* 5171 5172 5191

CANNON VALLEY COOPERATIVE p 247
1500 Highway 3 S, Northfield MN 55057
Tel (507) 645-9556
SIC 5541 5171 1711 5191 5153 5211

CENTRAL VALLEY COOPERATIVE p 280
900 30th Pl Nw, Owatonna MN 55060
Tel (507) 451-1230 *SIC* 5191 5171 5541

GREEN-WAY COOPERATIVE SERVICE CO p 637
3520 E River Rd Ne, Rochester MN 55906
Tel (507) 289-4086 *SIC* 5541 5171 5191

NU WAY COOPERATIVE (INC) p 1066
440 Highway 4 S, Trimont MN 56176
Tel (507) 639-2311
SIC 5191 5171 5541 2875

GRAVES OIL CO p 632
226 Pearson St, Batesville MS 38606
Tel (662) 563-4604 *SIC* 5171 5541 5411

SAYLE OIL CO INC p 1285
410 W Main St, Charleston MS 38921
Tel (800) 844-8120 *SIC* 5541 5171 5411

ERGON INC p 507
2829 Lakeland Dr Ste 2000, Flowood MS 39232
Tel (601) 933-3000
SIC 2911 4213 4449 4613 5171 5172

GRESHAM PETROLEUM CO p 639
415 Pershing Ave, Indianola MS 38751
Tel (662) 887-2160 *SIC* 5171 5984

SCOTT PETROLEUM CORP p 1293
102 Main St, Itta Bena MS 38941
Tel (662) 254-9024 *SIC* 5171 5984 5411

LAMPTON-LOVE INC p 841
2829 Lakeland Dr Ste 1505, Jackson MS 39232
Tel (601) 933-3400 *SIC* 5171

AYERS OIL CO p 140
401 N 4th St, Canton MO 63435
Tel (573) 288-4464
SIC 5171 5411 5541 5172

WALLIS OIL CO p 1573
106 E Washington St, Cuba MO 65453
Tel (573) 885-2277 *SIC* 5541 5171

ABEL OIL CO p 11
10406 Highway 79, Louisiana MO 63353
Tel (573) 754-5595 *SIC* 5171 5411

J D STREETT & CO INC p 771
144 Weldon Pkwy, Maryland Heights MO 63043
Tel (314) 432-6600
SIC 5171 5541 7389 5172

RAY CARROLL COUNTY GRAIN GROWERS INC p 1209
807 W Main St, Richmond MO 64085
Tel (816) 776-2291 *SIC* 5171 5191 5153

▲WORLD POINT TERMINALS LP p 1625
8235 Forsyth Blvd Ste 400, Saint Louis MO 63105
Tel (314) 889-9660 *SIC* 5171

ROCKY MOUNTAIN SUPPLY INC p 1245
350 Jackrabbit Ln Stop 1, Belgrade MT 59714
Tel (406) 388-4008
SIC 5171 5191 5541 5411

REBEL OIL CO INC p 1214
2200 Highland Dr, Las Vegas NV 89102
Tel (702) 382-5866 *SIC* 5171 5411

IRVING OIL TERMINALS INC p 765
190 Commerce Way, Portsmouth NH 03801
Tel (603) 559-8736 *SIC* 5171

■ SPRAGUE OPERATING RESOURCES LLC p 1360
185 International Dr, Portsmouth NH 03801
Tel (603) 431-1000 *SIC* 5172 5052 5171

RIGGINS INC p 1234
3938 S Main Rd, Vineland NJ 08360
Tel (856) 825-7600 *SIC* 5171

DESERT FUELS INC p 432
4421 Irving Blvd Nw Ste A, Albuquerque NM 87114
Tel (505) 750-3835 *SIC* 5172 5171

ALLSUP ENTERPRISES INC p 58
2112 N Thornton St, Clovis NM 88101
Tel (575) 769-2311
SIC 5411 5541 4832 6519 5171

BAYSIDE FUEL OIL CORP p 162
1776 Shore Pkwy, Brooklyn NY 11214
Tel (718) 622-2900 *SIC* 5171

BAYSIDE FUEL OIL DEPOT CORP p 162
1776 Shore Pkwy, Brooklyn NY 11214
Tel (718) 372-9800 *SIC* 5171

TOWNSEND OIL CORP p 1466
64 Main St, Le Roy NY 14482
Tel (585) 768-8188 *SIC* 5171 5983

AXEL JOHNSON INC p 140
155 Spring St Fl 6, New York NY 10012
Tel (646) 291-2445 *SIC* 5171

▲ HESS CORP p 688
1185 Ave Of The Americas, New York NY 10036
Tel (212) 997-8500
SIC 1311 2911 5171 5541 4911

SUPERIOR PLUS ENERGY SERVICES INC p 1407
1870 Winton Rd S Ste 200, Rochester NY 14618
Tel (585) 328-3930 *SIC* 5171 5983

NOCO NATURAL GAS LLC p 1046
2440 Sheridan Dr, Tonawanda NY 14150
Tel (716) 614-1152 *SIC* 5171

JERNIGAN OIL CO INC p 783
415 Main St E, Ahoskie NC 27910
Tel (252) 332-2131 *SIC* 5411 5171

PETROLIANCE LLC p 1139
1009 Schieffelin Rd, Apex NC 27502
Tel (919) 387-9810 *SIC* 5171

CARY OIL CO INC p 262
110 Mackenan Dr Ste 300, Cary NC 27511
Tel (919) 462-1100 *SIC* 5172 5171

SAMPSON-BLADEN OIL CO INC p 1274
510 Commerce St, Clinton NC 28328
Tel (910) 592-4177 *SIC* 5171 5411 5983

WARREN OIL CO INC p 1577
2340 Us Highway 301 N, Dunn NC 28334
Tel (910) 892-6456
SIC 5172 5171 3826 2911

CAMPBELL RENTALS LLC p 245
418 Peanut Plant Rd, Elizabethtown NC 28337
Tel (910) 862-7657 *SIC* 5171 5411 5541

MALLARD OIL CO p 899
1502 Dr Martin Luther, Kinston NC 28501
Tel (252) 527-0364 *SIC* 5171 5983 5984

EDEN OIL CO INC p 477
2507 Richardson Dr, Reidsville NC 27320
Tel (336) 349-8228 *SIC* 5171 5983

PLAINS GRAIN & AGRONOMY LLC p 1153
109 3rd Ave, Enderlin ND 58027
Tel (701) 437-2565 *SIC* 5153 5191 5171

FARMERS UNION OIL OF SOUTHERN VALLEY p 530
100 S Front St, Fairmount ND 58030
Tel (701) 474-5440
SIC 5171 5191 5541 5251

NORTHDALE OIL INC p 1054
448 Main Ave, Neche ND 58265
Tel (218) 773-4345 *SIC* 5171

RELADYNE I LLC p 1221
9395 Kenwood Rd Ste 104, Blue Ash OH 45242
Tel (513) 489-6000 *SIC* 5171 5172

GREAT LAKES PETROLEUM CO p 633
4500 Renaissance Pkwy, Cleveland OH 44128
Tel (216) 478-0501 *SIC* 5171

BECK SUPPLIERS INC p 167
1000 N Front St, Fremont OH 43420
Tel (419) 332-5527
SIC 5171 5541 5411 5984 1542

DISTRICT PETROLEUM PRODUCTS INC p 443
1814 River Rd, Huron OH 44839
Tel (419) 433-8373 *SIC* 5541 5171 5172

CAMPBELL OIL CO p 245
7977 Hills & Dales Rd Ne, Massillon OH 44646
Tel (330) 833-8555 *SIC* 5171

NEY OIL CO INC p 1041
145 S Water St, Ney OH 43549
Tel (419) 658-2324 *SIC* 5171

ELMER SMITH OIL CO p 489
Hwy 183 S, Clinton OK 73601
Tel (580) 323-2929 *SIC* 5171 5411

HUTCHINSON OIL CO INC p 722
515 S Main St, Elk City OK 73644
Tel (580) 225-0301 *SIC* 5171 5541

CAREY JOHNSON OIL CO INC p 255
701 Sw F Ave, Lawton OK 73501
Tel (580) 595-8300 *SIC* 5171

B & M OIL CO INC p 141
5731 S 49th West Ave, Tulsa OK 74107
Tel (918) 445-0725 *SIC* 5171

▲ MAGELLAN MIDSTREAM PARTNERS LP p 895
1 Williams Ctr Bsmt 2, Tulsa OK 74172
Tel (918) 574-7000 *SIC* 5171 4613

■ MAGELLAN TERMINALS HOLDINGS LP p 895
1 One Williams Ctr Bsmt 2, Tulsa OK 74172
Tel (918) 574-7000 *SIC* 5171

PDV HOLDING INC p 1125
6100 S Yale Ave, Tulsa OK 74136
Tel (918) 495-4000
SIC 2911 2992 5171 4213

▲ SEMGROUP CORP p 1302
6120 S Yale Ave Ste 700, Tulsa OK 74136
Tel (918) 524-8100
SIC 1389 4612 5171 2951

MARTIN OIL CO p 913
528 N 1st St, Bellwood PA 16617
Tel (814) 742-8438
SIC 5983 5171 5541 5411

AMERICAN REFINING GROUP INC p 78
77 N Kendall Ave, Bradford PA 16701
Tel (814) 368-1200 *SIC* 5171 2911

■ SUNOCO INC p 1403
3801 West Chester Pike, Newtown Square PA 19073
Tel (215) 977-3000
SIC 5541 2911 2869 2865 5171 5052

▲ SUNOCO LOGISTICS PARTNERS LP p 1403
3807 West Chester Pike, Newtown Square PA 19073
Tel (866) 248-4344
SIC 4612 4613 5171 5172

■ ATLANTIC REFINING & MARKETING CORP p 127
1801 Market St, Philadelphia PA 19103
Tel (215) 977-3000
SIC 2911 5171 5541 5411

NITTANY OIL CO INC p 1045
1540 Martin St, State College PA 16803
Tel (814) 237-4859 *SIC* 5171 1711

RICO SOL PUERTO LIMITED p 1233
450 Ave De La Const 18c, San Juan PR 00901
Tel (787) 721-0150 *SIC* 5171

BRABHAM OIL CO INC p 206
525 Midway St, Bamberg SC 29003
Tel (803) 245-2471
SIC 5171 5541 5411 5921

WINNSBORO PETROLEUM CO INC p 1617
401 S Congress St, Winnsboro SC 29180
Tel (803) 635-4668 *SIC* 5171 5411

EASTERN FARMERS COOPERATIVE p 472
26033 482nd Ave, Brandon SD 57005
Tel (605) 582-2415 *SIC* 5191 5171 5541

NORTH CENTRAL FARMERS ELEVATOR p 1052
12 5th Ave, Ipswich SD 57451
Tel (605) 426-6021
SIC 5153 5191 5171 5541

ROBERTS-GIBSON INC p 1242
115 Highway 51 Byp, Dyersburg TN 38024
Tel (731) 285-4941 *SIC* 5171 5541

HIGHLAND CORP p 691
108 Mill Ave, Hohenwald TN 38462
Tel (800) 924-8514 *SIC* 5171 5411

ROGERS PETROLEUM INC p 1246
1634 W 1st North St, Morristown TN 37814
Tel (423) 581-7460 *SIC* 5171

BEST-WADE PETROLEUM INC p 177
201 Dodge Dr, Ripley TN 38063
Tel (731) 635-9661 *SIC* 5171 5541 5411

HOLLINGSWORTH OIL CO INC p 701
1503 Memorial Blvd Ste B, Springfield TN 37172
Tel (615) 242-8466 *SIC* 5171

■ EXXONMOBIL OIL CORP p 521
2805 Sycamore St, Beaumont TX 77701
Tel (409) 757-3763
SIC 2911 5171 4613 1311

TAYLOR-SMART LLC p 1427
2207 N Center St, Bonham TX 75418
Tel (903) 583-7481 *SIC* 5171

COLORADO COUNTY OIL CO INC p 338
1348 Business 71, Columbus TX 78934
Tel (979) 732-6870 *SIC* 5171

▲ ALON USA ENERGY INC p 59
12700 Park Central Dr # 1600, Dallas TX 75251
Tel (972) 367-3600 *SIC* 2911 5171 5411

■ HOLLY ENERGY PARTNERS LP p 701
2828 N Harwood St # 1300, Dallas TX 75201
Tel (214) 871-3555 *SIC* 4612 4613 5171

MAXUM ENTERPRISES LLC p 923
201 N Rupert St Ste 101, Fort Worth TX 76107
Tel (817) 877-8300 *SIC* 5171 5172

SIMONS PETROLEUM p 1325
201 N Rupert St Ste 101, Fort Worth TX 76107
Tel (405) 551-2403
SIC 5172 5171 5541 5411

SIMONS PETROLEUM INC p 1325
201 N Rupert St Ste 101, Fort Worth TX 76107
Tel (405) 848-3500 *SIC* 5171 5172

BP CORP NORTH AMERICA INC p 205
501 Westlake Park Blvd, Houston TX 77079
Tel (281) 366-2000
SIC 2911 5541 5171 1311 4613 4612

BP PRODUCTS NORTH AMERICA INC p 206
501 Westlake Park Blvd, Houston TX 77079
Tel (281) 366-2000 *SIC* 5541 5171 4613

CITGO HOLDING INC p 309
1293 Eldridge Pkwy, Houston TX 77077
Tel (281) 531-0004
SIC 2911 2992 5171 4213

CITGO PETROLEUM CORP p 309
1293 Eldridge Pkwy, Houston TX 77077
Tel (832) 486-4000
SIC 2911 5171 4213 4612

■ CONOCOPHILLIPS HOLDING CO p 358
600 N Dairy Ashford Rd, Houston TX 77079
Tel (281) 293-1000 *SIC* 2911 5171 5541

▲ GENESIS ENERGY LP p 602
919 Milam St Ste 2100, Houston TX 77002
Tel (713) 860-2500 *SIC* 4612 5171 4212

J AND L HOLDING CO INC p 770
12235 Robin Blvd, Houston TX 77045
Tel (713) 434-7600 *SIC* 5171

■ KINDER MORGAN ENERGY PARTNERS LP p 819
1001 La St Ste 1000, Houston TX 77002
Tel (713) 369-9000
SIC 4613 4925 4922 4226 4619 5171

■ MARATHON OIL CO p 904
5555 San Felipe St # 2796, Houston TX 77056
Tel (713) 629-6600
SIC 2911 5171 5541 1311 4612 4613

▲ MARATHON OIL CORP p 904
5555 San Felipe St # 2796, Houston TX 77056
Tel (713) 629-6600
SIC 1311 2911 5171 5541

MARTIN ENERGY SERVICES LLC p 912
3 Riverway Ste 400, Houston TX 77056
Tel (713) 350-6800
SIC 5171 4492 5172 5551

OROURKE DISTRIBUTING CO INC p 1095
223 Mccarty St, Houston TX 77029
Tel (713) 672-4500 *SIC* 5171 5172

■ PHILLIPS PETROLEUM CO p 1144
600 N Dairy Ashford Rd, Houston TX 77079
Tel (281) 293-1000
SIC 1382 2911 5171 5541

■ TEPPCO PARTNERS LP p 1439
1100 Louisiana St # 1600, Houston TX 77002
Tel (713) 381-3636 *SIC* 4925 5171

▲ EXXON MOBIL CORP p 521
5959 Las Colinas Blvd, Irving TX 75039
Tel (972) 444-1000
SIC 2911 4612 5541 5171 4911

■ MOBIL CORP p 980
5959 Las Colinas Blvd, Irving TX 75039
Tel (972) 444-1000
SIC 2911 5171 4612 4613 1311

▲ MARTIN MIDSTREAM PARTNERS LP p 913
4200 Stone Rd, Kilgore TX 75662
Tel (903) 983-6200
SIC 5171 4226 1321 4424 2819 2875

ARGUINDEGUI OIL CO II LTD p 108
6551 Star Ct, Laredo TX 78041
Tel (956) 722-5251 *SIC* 5171

MIDTEX OIL LP p 966
3455 Ih 35 S, New Braunfels TX 78132
Tel (830) 625-4214 *SIC* 5541 5171

■ DIAMOND SHAMROCK REFINING AND MARKETING CO p 437
6000 N Loop 1604 W, San Antonio TX 78249
Tel (210) 345-2000 *SIC* 5541 5171 2911

■ VALERO MARKETING AND SUPPLY CO p 1539
1 Valero Way, San Antonio TX 78249
Tel (210) 345-2000 *SIC* 5171

HOUSTON LBC L P p 712
11666 Port Rd, Seabrook TX 77586
Tel (281) 474-4433 *SIC* 5171

ALEXANDER OIL CO p 49
2993 N Hwy 123 Byp, Seguin TX 78155
Tel (830) 379-1736 *SIC* 5171

INSIGHT EQUITY A P X L P p 746
1400 Civic Pl Ste 250, Southlake TX 76092
Tel (817) 488-7775
SIC 6722 3441 3443 3556 3714 5171

INSIGHT EQUITY LP p 746
1400 Civic Pl Ste 250, Southlake TX 76092
Tel (817) 488-7775
SIC 6722 3441 3443 3556 3714 5171

FIKES WHOLESALE INC p 542
6261 Central Pointe Pkwy, Temple TX 76504
Tel (254) 791-0009 *SIC* 5411 5171

▲ ANADARKO PETROLEUM CORP p 88
1201 Lake Robbins Dr, The Woodlands TX 77380
Tel (832) 636-1000
SIC 1311 4924 5171 1382

NEW DISTRIBUTING CO INC p 1029
4102 Us Highway 59 N, Victoria TX 77905
Tel (361) 575-1981 *SIC* 5171

THOMAS PETROLEUM LLC p 1449
9701 Us Highway 59 N, Victoria TX 77905
Tel (361) 582-5100 *SIC* 5171 4225

DATS TRUCKING INC p 414
321 N Old Highway 91, Hurricane UT 84737
Tel (435) 673-1886 *SIC* 4212 4213 5171

CARDWELL DISTRIBUTING INC p 253
8137 S State St Bldg 1, Midvale UT 84047
Tel (801) 561-4251
SIC 5171 7549 5172 5983

PARKER HOLDING CO INC p 1116
1428 W Danville St, South Hill VA 23970
Tel (434) 447-3146 *SIC* 5171 5541 5983

PARKER OIL CO INC p 1116
1428 W Danville St, South Hill VA 23970
Tel (434) 447-3146 *SIC* 5171 5541 5983

POWELL - CHRISTENSEN INC p 1164
501 E Wine Country Rd, Grandview WA 98930
Tel (509) 882-2115 *SIC* 5171 4212

R H SMITH DISTRIBUTING CO INC p 1202
315 E Wine Country Rd, Grandview WA 98930
Tel (509) 882-3377
SIC 5171 5541 5411 5172

CONNELL OIL INC p 358
1015 N Oregon Ave, Pasco WA 99301
Tel (509) 547-3326 *SIC* 5171

DELTA WESTERN INC p 427
1177 Fairview Ave N, Seattle WA 98109
Tel (907) 276-2688 *SIC* 5171 5251 5411

PETROLEUM PRODUCTS LLC p 1139
500 River East Dr Ste 1, Belle WV 25015
Tel (304) 204-1720 *SIC* 5171

TRI-STATE PETROLEUM CORP p 1478
2627 Vance Ave, Wheeling WV 26003
Tel (304) 277-3232 *SIC* 5171

ALLIED COOPERATIVE p 56
540 S Main St, Adams WI 53910
Tel (608) 339-3394 *SIC* 5191 5171 5251

US VENTURE INC p 1533
425 Better Way, Appleton WI 54915
Tel (920) 739-6101 *SIC* 5171 5014 5013

UNITED COOPERATIVE p 1507
N7160 Raceway Rd, Beaver Dam WI 53916
Tel (920) 887-1756
SIC 5191 5171 5541 5153 5812

LANDMARK SERVICES COOPERATIVE p 843
1401 Landmark Dr, Cottage Grove WI 53527
Tel (608) 819-3115
SIC 4221 5171 5191 1711

BAUER BUILT INC p 160
1111 W Prospect St, Durand WI 54736
Tel (715) 672-8300
SIC 5531 5014 7534 5171

CROSSROADS AG LLC p 394
N6055 State Road 40, Elk Mound WI 54739
Tel (715) 879-5454 *SIC* 5191 5171

PREMIER COOPERATIVE p 1170
501 W Main St, Mount Horeb WI 53572
Tel (608) 251-0199
SIC 5211 5171 5191 5541

MATHY CONSTRUCTION CO p 920
920 10th Ave N, Onalaska WI 54650
Tel (608) 783-6411
SIC 1611 1771 1442 5171

PETROENERGY LLC p 1139
920 10th Ave N, Onalaska WI 54650
Tel (608) 783-6411 *SIC* 5171 4925 5172

TEXPAR ENERGY LLC p 1445
920 10th Ave N, Onalaska WI 54650
Tel (800) 323-7350 *SIC* 5171 4925 5172

QUALITY STATE OIL CO INC p 1197
2201 Calumet Dr, Sheboygan WI 53083
Tel (920) 459-5640 *SIC* 5171 5541 5411

H WOLF EDWARD AND SONS INC p 651
414 Kettle Moraine Dr S, Slinger WI 53086
Tel (262) 644-5030 *SIC* 5983 5171

SCHIERL INC p 1287
2201 Madison St, Stevens Point WI 54481
Tel (715) 345-5060
SIC 5171 5014 5531 5983

HOPSON OIL CO INC p 706
1225 Whiterock Ave, Waukesha WI 53186
Tel (262) 542-5343 *SIC* 5171 5983 1711

SIC 5172 Petroleum & Petroleum Prdts Wholesale

ANDALUSIA DISTRIBUTING CO INC p 89
117 Allen Ave, Andalusia AL 36420
Tel (334) 222-3671
SIC 5172 5113 5194 5149

HOME OIL CO INC p 703
5744 E Us Highway 84, Cowarts AL 36321
Tel (334) 793-1544
SIC 5171 5411 5541 5172

CHATTAHOOCHEE OIL CO INC p 292
1405 Lee Road 270, Cusseta AL 36852
Tel (706) 566-6561 *SIC* 5172

WILLIAMSON OIL CO INC p 1612
1603 Godfrey Ave Se, Fort Payne AL 35967
Tel (256) 845-9466 *SIC* 5541 5411 5172

SPENCER COMPANIES INC p 1358
120 Woodson St Nw, Huntsville AL 35801
Tel (256) 533-1150 *SIC* 5541 5172

COUGAR OIL INC p 374
1411 Water Ave, Selma AL 36703
Tel (334) 875-2023 SIC 5171 5983 5172

R K ALLEN OIL CO INC p 1202
36002 Al Highway 21, Talladega AL 35160
Tel (256) 315-9825 SIC 5172

DRUMMOND CO INC p 457
1000 Urban Center Dr # 300, Vestavia AL 35242
Tel (205) 945-6500
SIC 1221 1222 3312 5052 5085 5172

NORTH STAR UTILITIES GROUP INC p 1054
420 L St Ste 101, Anchorage AK 99501
Tel (206) 792-0077 SIC 5172

CANYON STATE OIL CO INC p 248
2640 N 31st Ave, Phoenix AZ 85009
Tel (602) 269-7981 SIC 5172 5531

CUTTER AVIATION p 403
2802 E Old Tower Rd, Phoenix AZ 85034
Tel (602) 273-1237
SIC 5599 5088 4522 5172 4581

■ **GIANT INDUSTRIES INC** p 611
1250 W Washington St # 101, Tempe AZ 85281
Tel (915) 534-1400 SIC 2911 5541 5172

FARMERS SUPPLY ASSOCIATION p 530
16240 Highway 14 E, Harrisburg AR 72432
Tel (870) 578-2468
SIC 5191 5172 5261 5541 5999

MID SOUTH SALES INC p 963
243 County Road 414, Jonesboro AR 72404
Tel (870) 933-6457 SIC 5172

MIDCON FUEL SERVICES LLC p 964
8401 Lindsey Rd, Little Rock AR 72206
Tel (501) 708-2000 SIC 5172

COULSON OIL CO INC p 374
1434 Pike Ave 38, North Little Rock AR 72114
Tel (501) 376-4222
SIC 5172 5541 5411 6512

WHOLESALE FUELS INC p 1607
2200 E Brundage Ln, Bakersfield CA 93307
Tel (661) 327-4900 SIC 5172

GENERAL PETROLEUM CORP p 601
19501 S Santa Fe Ave, Compton CA 90221
Tel (562) 983-7300 SIC 5172

PECOS INC p 1127
19501 S Santa Fe Ave, Compton CA 90221
Tel (310) 356-2300 SIC 5172

UNITED EL SEGUNDO INC p 1508
17311 S Main St, Gardena CA 90248
Tel (310) 323-3992 SIC 5172 6531

BUFORD OIL CO INC p 224
9925 8 3/4 Ave, Hanford CA 93230
Tel (559) 582-9028 SIC 5172

SASOL WAX NORTH AMERICA CORP p 1283
3563 Inv Blvd Ste 2, Hayward CA 94545
Tel (510) 783-9295 SIC 5172 5169

PETRO-DIAMOND INC p 1139
1100 Main St Fl 2, Irvine CA 92614
Tel (949) 553-0112 SIC 5172

M O DION & SONS INC p 889
1543 W 16th St, Long Beach CA 90813
Tel (714) 540-5535 SIC 5172

MIECO INC p 968
301 E Ocean Blvd Ste 1100, Long Beach CA 90802
Tel (562) 435-0085 SIC 5172 4925

GOLDEN GATE PETROLEUM CO p 621
1340 Arnold Dr Ste 231, Martinez CA 94553
Tel (925) 335-3700 SIC 5172

JS WEST & COMPANIES p 795
501 9th St, Modesto CA 95354
Tel (209) 577-3221
SIC 5172 5211 5251 0723 5499

STAN BOYETT & SON INC p 1375
601 Mchenry Ave, Modesto CA 95350
Tel (209) 577-6000 SIC 5172 5541

NOVA GROUP INC p 1062
185 Devlin Rd, Napa CA 94558
Tel (707) 265-1100
SIC 1629 1623 1622 5172

SOUTHERN COUNTIES OIL CO p 1348
1800 W Katella Ave # 400, Orange CA 92867
Tel (714) 744-7140 SIC 5171 5541 5172

APOLLO IDEMITSU CORP p 97
1831 16th St, Sacramento CA 95811
Tel (916) 443-0890 SIC 5172 2911

RIVER CITY PETROLEUM INC p 1237
3775 N Freeway Blvd # 101, Sacramento CA 95834
Tel (916) 371-4960 SIC 5172

STURDY OIL CO p 1395
1511 Abbott St, Salinas CA 93901
Tel (831) 422-8801 SIC 5172 5541

CLIPPER OIL p 327
2040 Harbor Island Dr # 203, San Diego CA 92101
Tel (619) 692-9701 SIC 5172 2873 5169

▲ **SEMPRA ENERGY** p 1303
488 8th Ave, San Diego CA 92101
Tel (619) 696-2000
SIC 4932 4911 5172 4922

■ **CHEVRON GLOBAL ENERGY INC** p 296
6001 Bollinger Canyon Rd, San Ramon CA 94583
Tel (925) 842-1000 SIC 2911 4731 5172

IPC (USA) INC p 763
4 Hutton Cntre Dr Ste 700, Santa Ana CA 92707
Tel (949) 648-5600 SIC 5172

ROBINSON OIL SUPPLY & TRANSPORT INC p 1242
955 Martin Ave, Santa Clara CA 95050
Tel (408) 327-4300 SIC 5172

VALLEY PACIFIC PETROLEUM SERVICES INC p 1541
152 Frank West Cir # 100, Stockton CA 95206
Tel (209) 948-9412 SIC 5172 5541

VAN DE POL ENTERPRISES INC p 1542
4895 S Airport Way, Stockton CA 95206
Tel (209) 465-3421 SIC 5172

MERCURY AIR GROUP INC p 945
2780 Skypark Dr Ste 300, Torrance CA 90505
Tel (310) 602-3770 SIC 5172 7389 4581

TOWER ENERGY GROUP p 1464
1983 W 190th St Ste 100, Torrance CA 90504
Tel (310) 538-8000 SIC 5172

RINEHART OIL INC p 1235
2401 N State St, Ukiah CA 95482
Tel (707) 462-8811 SIC 5172 5541

RAMOS OIL CO INC p 1207
1515 S River Rd, West Sacramento CA 95691
Tel (916) 371-2570 SIC 5171 5172

DOSS AVIATION INC p 451
3670 Rebecca Ln Ste 100, Colorado Springs CO 80917
Tel (719) 570-9804 SIC 5172 4581

OFFEN PETROLEUM INC p 1075
5100 E 78th Ave, Commerce City CO 80022
Tel (303) 297-3835 SIC 5172 5541

DCP MIDSTREAM LLC p 418
370 17th St Ste 2500, Denver CO 80202
Tel (303) 633-2900 SIC 5172

ENERGY CORP OF AMERICA p 497
4643 S Ulster St Ste 1100, Denver CO 80237
Tel (303) 694-2667
SIC 4924 4932 1382 4922 5172

ENSERCO ENERGY LLC p 500
1900 16th St Ste 450, Denver CO 80202
Tel (303) 568-3242 SIC 5172

■ **HIGH SIERRA ENERGY LP** p 691
3773 Cherry Creek N Dr St, Denver CO 80209
Tel (303) 815-1010 SIC 5172

■ **QEP ENERGY CO** p 1195
1050 17th St Ste 800, Denver CO 80265
Tel (303) 672-6900
SIC 1311 1382 1389 5172

ROCKY TEP MOUNTAIN LLC p 1245
1001 17th St Ste 1200, Denver CO 80202
Tel (303) 572-3900 SIC 5172

SIEGEL OIL CO p 1320
1380 Zuni St, Denver CO 80204
Tel (303) 893-5273 SIC 5172 8734

TRANSMONTAIGNE LLC p 1472
1670 Broadway Ste 3100, Denver CO 80202
Tel (303) 626-8200 SIC 5172

■ **WESTERN GAS RESOURCES INC** p 1598
1099 18th St, Denver CO 80202
Tel (303) 452-5603
SIC 4923 4925 1311 5172

AGFINITY INC p 34
260 Factory Rd, Eaton CO 80615
Tel (970) 454-4000
SIC 5172 2048 7549 5191

MONUMENT OIL CO p 987
560 Colorado Ave, Grand Junction CO 81501
Tel (970) 245-3440 SIC 5172

CASTLE PARTNERS LLC p 264
6787 Millstone St, Highlands Ranch CO 80130
Tel (303) 884-1157 SIC 5172 5013

MIDWEST UNITED ENERGY LLC p 968
12687 W Cedar Dr Ste 200, Lakewood CO 80228
Tel (303) 989-7165 SIC 5172

HARPEL OIL CO p 662
4204 E 105th Ave, Thornton CO 80233
Tel (303) 294-0767 SIC 5171 5983 5172

KOLMAR AMERICAS INC p 827
10 Middle St Ph, Bridgeport CT 06604
Tel (203) 873-2078 SIC 5172

■ **PRAXAIR TECHNOLOGY INC** p 1168
39 Old Ridgebury Rd, Danbury CT 06810
Tel (203) 837-2000
SIC 5172 5084 5169 5085

BOOTH WALTZ ENTERPRISES INC p 200
42 Rumsey Rd, East Hartford CT 06108
Tel (860) 289-7800 SIC 5172

WATERFRONT ENTERPRISES INC p 1582
400 Waterfront St, New Haven CT 06512
Tel (203) 467-1997 SIC 5172

APACHE OIL CO INC p 96
261 Ledyard St, New London CT 06320
Tel (860) 437-6200 SIC 5172 5541

■ **PETROLEUM HEAT AND POWER CO INC** p 1139
9 W Broad St Ste 3, Stamford CT 06902
Tel (800) 645-4328 SIC 5983 5172 5722

▲ **STAR GAS PARTNERS LP** p 1378
9 W Broad St Ste 3, Stamford CT 06902
Tel (203) 328-7310 SIC 1711 5172

STATOIL MARKETING & TRADING (US) INC p 1383
120 Long Ridge Rd 3eo1, Stamford CT 06902
Tel (203) 978-6900 SIC 5172

STATOIL US HOLDINGS INC p 1383
120 Long Ridge Rd, Stamford CT 06902
Tel (203) 978-6900 SIC 5172 1382

MERCURY FUEL SERVICE INC p 945
43 Lafayette St, Waterbury CT 06708
Tel (203) 756-7284
SIC 5172 5541 5411 5983 1711 2911

■ **CONECTIV LLC** p 355
800 N King St Ste 400, Wilmington DE 19801
Tel (202) 872-2680
SIC 4911 4924 1731 5172

SOUTHEAST PETRO DISTRIBUTORS INC p 1346
402 High Point Dr Ste A, Cocoa FL 32926
Tel (321) 631-0245 SIC 5172

▲ **WORLD FUEL SERVICES CORP** p 1625
9800 Nw 41st St Ste 400, Doral FL 33178
Tel (305) 428-8000 SIC 5172 3519 5541

■ **WORLD FUEL SERVICES INC** p 1625
9800 Nw 41st St Ste 400, Doral FL 33178
Tel (305) 428-8000 SIC 5172

BANYAN AIR SERVICES INC p 153
5360 Nw 20th Ter, Fort Lauderdale FL 33309
Tel (954) 491-3170
SIC 5172 4581 5088 4522

PORT CONSOLIDATED INC p 1162
3141 Se 14th Ave, Fort Lauderdale FL 33316
Tel (954) 522-1182 SIC 5172

SMF ENERGY CORP p 1332
200 W Cypress Creek Rd # 400, Fort Lauderdale FL 33309
Tel (954) 308-4200 SIC 5172

PALMDALE OIL CO INC p 1109
911 N 2nd St, Fort Pierce FL 34950
Tel (772) 461-2300 SIC 5172

MACMILLAN OIL CO OF FLORIDA INC p 892
2955 E 11th Ave, Hialeah FL 33013
Tel (305) 691-7814 SIC 5172

CROWLEY HOLDINGS INC p 394
9487 Regency Square Blvd # 101, Jacksonville FL 32225
Tel (904) 727-2200
SIC 4412 4424 5171 5172 5541 4492

CROWLEY MARITIME CORP p 395
9487 Regency Square Blvd, Jacksonville FL 32225
Tel (904) 727-2200
SIC 4412 4424 5171 5172 5541 4492

FIRST COAST ENERGY LLP p 545
7014 A C Skinner Pkwy # 290, Jacksonville FL 32256
Tel (904) 596-3200 SIC 5541 5411 5172

BUNKERS INTERNATIONAL CORP p 226
1071 S Sun Dr Ste 3, Lake Mary FL 32746
Tel (407) 328-7757 SIC 7389 5172

FLEETWING CORP p 555
742 S Combee Rd, Lakeland FL 33801
Tel (863) 665-7557 SIC 5172 5411

TROPIC OIL CO p 1484
9970 Nw 89th Ct, Medley FL 33178
Tel (305) 888-4611 SIC 5172

URBIETA OIL INC p 1530
9701 Nw 89th Ave, Medley FL 33178
Tel (305) 884-0008 SIC 5171 5172

AIRCRAFT SERVICE INTERNATIONAL INC p 40
201 S Orange Ave Ste 1100, Orlando FL 32801
Tel (407) 648-7373 SIC 4581 5172

WARE OIL & SUPPLY CO INC p 1575
2715 S Byron Butler Pkwy, Perry FL 32348
Tel (850) 838-1852 SIC 5172 5087 5411

ALLIED AVIATION LLC p 56
4120 Higel Ave, Sarasota FL 34242
Tel (212) 868-5593 SIC 5172

RACETRAC PETROLEUM INC p 1203
3225 Cumberland Blvd Se # 100, Atlanta GA 30339
Tel (770) 850-3491 SIC 5541 5411 5172

■ **UPS FUEL SERVICES INC** p 1529
55 Glenlake Pkwy, Atlanta GA 30328
Tel (678) 339-3250 SIC 5172

PS ENERGY GROUP INC p 1187
4480 N Shallowford Rd # 100, Dunwoody GA 30338
Tel (770) 350-3000 SIC 8742 5172 4924

MANSFIELD ENERGY CORP p 903
1025 Airport Pkwy, Gainesville GA 30501
Tel (678) 450-2000 SIC 5172 4212 1796

MANSFIELD OIL CO OF GAINESVILLE INC p 903
1025 Airport Pkwy, Gainesville GA 30501
Tel (678) 450-2000 SIC 5172

MUNICIPAL GAS AUTHORITY OF GEORGIA p 1000
104 Townpark Dr Nw, Kennesaw GA 30144
Tel (770) 590-1000 SIC 5172

WALTHALL OIL CO p 1575
2510 Allen Rd, Macon GA 31216
Tel (478) 781-1234 SIC 5172 5541 5411

SOMMERS CO p 1339
1000 Sommers Blvd, Richmond Hill GA 31324
Tel (800) 654-6466 SIC 5172 5541 7033

CHEMOIL CORP p 293
101 N Lathrop Ave, Savannah GA 31415
Tel (912) 236-1331 SIC 5172

COLONIAL GROUP INC p 337
101 N Lathrop Ave, Savannah GA 31415
Tel (800) 944-3835
SIC 5171 5169 5172 4924 4492 4226

JONES CO p 792
215 Pendleton St Ste A, Waycross GA 31501
Tel (912) 285-4011 SIC 5541 5411 5172

■ **ALOHA PETROLEUM LTD** p 59
1132 Bishop St Ste 1700, Honolulu HI 96813
Tel (808) 833-3249 SIC 5172 5541 5411

■ **GAS CO LLC** p 593
745 Fort Street Mall # 1800, Honolulu HI 96813
Tel (808) 594-5530
SIC 4932 4925 5172 5984

HAWAII ENERGY RESOURCES INC p 669
733 Bishop St Fl 28, Honolulu HI 96813
Tel (808) 547-3111 SIC 5172 2911 5171

■ **KOKO OHA INVESTMENTS INC** p 826
1100 Alakea St Fl 8, Honolulu HI 96813
Tel (808) 535-5999 SIC 5172 6719

■ **MID PAC PETROLEUM LLC** p 963
1132 Bishop St Ste 2500, Honolulu HI 96813
Tel (808) 535-5999 SIC 5984 5172

WESTERN AIRCRAFT INC p 1597
4300 S Kennedy St, Boise ID 83705
Tel (208) 338-1800
SIC 5088 4581 7359 5172

MEIER OIL SERVICE INC p 940
405 N Second St, Ashkum IL 60911
Tel (815) 698-2343 SIC 5171 5172

DICKERSON PETROLEUM INC p 438
920 N Illinois St, Belleville IL 62220
Tel (618) 233-0786 SIC 5172

TRI STAR MARKETING INC p 1477
2211 W Bradley Ave, Champaign IL 61821
Tel (217) 367-8386 SIC 5541 5411 5172

INTEGRYS ENERGY GROUP INC p 750
200 E Randolph St # 2200, Chicago IL 60601
Tel (312) 228-5400 SIC 4931 5172 4911

HWRT OIL CO LLC p 722
1 Piasa Ln, Hartford IL 62048
Tel (618) 254-2855 SIC 5172

FUCHS CORP p 583
17050 Lathrop Ave, Harvey IL 60426
Tel (800) 323-7755 SIC 2992 5172 2899

OSCO INC p 1096
13351 Main St, Lemont IL 60439
Tel (630) 257-8000 SIC 5172

HFI ENTERPRISES INC p 689
2s181 County Line Rd, Maple Park IL 60151
Tel (630) 557-2406 SIC 5172 5191

BUREAU SERVICE CO p 226
22069 Us Highway 34, Princeton IL 61356
Tel (815) 875-2800
SIC 5191 5172 5153 5411 7542

TEXOR PETROLEUM CO INC p 1445
3340 Harlem Ave, Riverside IL 60546
Tel (708) 447-1999 SIC 5172 5541

RILCO INC p 1235
1320 1st St, Rock Island IL 61201
Tel (309) 788-5631 SIC 5172 5169

JX NIPPON OIL & ENERGY USA INC p 798
20 N Martingale Rd # 300, Schaumburg IL 60173
Tel (847) 413-2188 SIC 5172

GRAHAM ENTERPRISE INC p 629
750 Bunker Ct Ste 100, Vernon Hills IL 60061
Tel (847) 837-0777 SIC 5172 5411

BP OIL SUPPLY CO p 205
28100 Torch Pkwy, Warrenville IL 60555
Tel (630) 836-5000 SIC 5172

MERS LLC p 951
200 S Amoco Cutoff, Wood River IL 62095
Tel (618) 254-4500 SIC 5172

PREMIER AG CO-OP INC p 1170
785 S Marr Rd, Columbus IN 47201
Tel (812) 379-9501
SIC 5153 5191 5172 5411 2429

PETROLEUM TRADERS CORP p 1139
7120 Pointe Inverness Way, Fort Wayne IN 46804
Tel (260) 432-6622 SIC 5172

AL WARREN OIL CO INC p 43
1646 Summer St, Hammond IN 46320
Tel (773) 735-6900 SIC 5172 5541

COUNTRYMARK COOPERATIVE HOLDING CORP p 375
225 S East St Ste 144, Indianapolis IN 46202
Tel (800) 808-3170
SIC 5172 2911 1382 1311 6719

JACKSON OIL & SOLVENTS INC p 774
1970 Kentucky Ave, Indianapolis IN 46221
Tel (317) 481-2244
SIC 5172 5541 5983 5531

PINNACLE OIL HOLDINGS LLC p 1150
5009 W 81st St, Indianapolis IN 46268
Tel (317) 875-9465 SIC 2992 5172 8742

POSEY COUNTY FARM BUREAU COOPERATIVE ASSOCIATION INC p 1163
817 W 4th St, Mount Vernon IN 47620
Tel (812) 838-4468 SIC 5191 5172 5153

JAY PETROLEUM INC p 779
533 S 200 W, Portland IN 47371
Tel (260) 726-9374 SIC 5411 5172

CERES SOLUTIONS p 283
2600 S 13th St, Terre Haute IN 47802
Tel (812) 235-8123 SIC 5153 5172 5191

QUALITY OIL INC p 1197
55 N 400 E, Valparaiso IN 46383
Tel (219) 462-2951 SIC 5171 5172

NORTH CENTRAL COOPERATIVE INC p 1051
2025 S Wabash St, Wabash IN 46992
Tel (800) 992-3495 SIC 5172 5153 5191

■ **CASEYS MARKETING CO** p 263
1 Se Convenience Blvd, Ankeny IA 50021
Tel (515) 965-6100
SIC 5411 5172 5141 5812

REIF OIL CO p 1221
801 N 3rd St, Burlington IA 52601
Tel (319) 758-1240 SIC 5172 5411

STATELINE COOPERATIVE p 1383
120 Walnut St, Burt IA 50522
Tel (515) 885-2642 SIC 5191 5172 5031

NORTH CENTRAL COOPERATIVE p 1051
221 4th Ave Nw, Clarion IA 50525
Tel (515) 532-2881 SIC 5153 5191 5172

MULGREW OIL CO p 999
10314 Silverwood Dr, Dubuque IA 52003
Tel (563) 583-7386 SIC 5171 5172 5541

PRO COOPERATIVE p 1178
17 3rd Ave Ne, Pocahontas IA 50574
Tel (712) 335-3060 SIC 5153 5191 5172

GARDEN CITY CO-OP INC p 591
106 N 6th St, Garden City KS 67846
Tel (620) 275-6161 SIC 5153 5191 5172

JOHNSON COOPERATIVE GRAIN CO INC p 791
304 E Highland Ave, Johnson KS 67855
Tel (620) 492-6210 SIC 5153 5191 5172

STAR FUEL CENTERS INC p 1378
11161 Overbrook Rd, Leawood KS 66211
Tel (913) 652-9400
SIC 5172 7542 5541 5411

FERRELLGAS INC p 538
7500 College Blvd # 1000, Overland Park KS 66210
Tel (913) 661-1500 SIC 5084 5172

▲ **FERRELLGAS PARTNERS LP** p 538
7500 College Blvd # 1000, Overland Park KS 66210
Tel (913) 661-1500 SIC 5084 5172

CLEAN HARBORS WICHITA LLC p 324
2824 N Ohio St, Wichita KS 67219
Tel (316) 832-0151 SIC 2992 5169 5172

ETHANOL PRODUCTS LLC p 511
3939 N Webb Rd, Wichita KS 67226
Tel (316) 303-1380 SIC 5172 5169

FLINT HILLS RESOURCES LP p 557
4111 E 37th St N, Wichita KS 67220
Tel (800) 292-3133
SIC 5172 4612 1382 2911

INLAND CRUDE PURCHASING LLC p 743
727 N Waco Ave Ste 400, Wichita KS 67203
Tel (316) 263-3201 SIC 5172

KOCH INDUSTRIES INC p 825
4111 E 37th St N, Wichita KS 67220
Tel (316) 828-5500 SIC 5172 2911 5169

■ **VALVOLINE INTERNATIONAL INC** p 1542
3499 Blazer Pkwy, Lexington KY 40509
Tel (800) 832-6825 SIC 7549 5172

ICAP ENERGY LLC p 726
9931 Corporate Campus Dr, Louisville KY 40223
Tel (502) 327-1400 SIC 5172

VALOR LLC p 1542
1200 Alsop Ln, Owensboro KY 42303
Tel (270) 683-2461 SIC 5171 5172

HOMETOWN CONVENIENCE LLC p 704
51 Highway 2034, Whitesburg KY 41858
Tel (606) 633-2525 SIC 5172

APOLLO OIL LLC p 97
1175 Early Dr, Winchester KY 40391
Tel (859) 744-5444 SIC 5172 5013

COASTAL CHEMICAL CO LLC p 331
3520 Veterans Memorial Dr, Abbeville LA 70510
Tel (337) 898-0001 SIC 5172 5169

JOHN W STONE OIL DISTRIBUTOR LLC p 789
87 1st St, Gretna LA 70053
Tel (504) 366-3401 SIC 5172

■ TALENS MARINE & FUEL LLC p 1422
1707 Evangeline Hwy, Jennings LA 70546
Tel (800) 256-3835 SIC 5172 7389

EVANS OIL CO LLC p 513
8450 Millhaven Rd, Monroe LA 71203
Tel (318) 345-1502 SIC 5172

SMITTYS SUPPLY INC p 1334
63399 Highway 51, Roseland LA 70456
Tel (985) 748-9687 SIC 5172 5531

GAUBERT OIL CO INC p 594
1201 Saint Patrick St, Thibodaux LA 70301
Tel (800) 256-1250 SIC 5172 5411

DEAD RIVER CO p 419
80 Exchange St Ste 3, Bangor ME 04401
Tel (207) 947-8641
SIC 6512 5172 5983 5541 5411

R H FOSTER ENERGY LLC p 1202
110 Mecaw Rd, Hampden ME 04444
Tel (207) 947-3835
SIC 5172 5541 5411 5983

CARROLL INDEPENDENT FUEL LLC p 261
2700 Loch Raven Rd, Baltimore MD 21218
Tel (410) 235-1066 SIC 5172 5983

TRI-GAS & OIL CO INC p 1477
3941 Federalsburg Hwy, Federalsburg MD 21632
Tel (410) 754-2000 SIC 5172 5984 4731

C & T A CO INC p 231
11535 Hopewell Rd, Hagerstown MD 21740
Tel (800) 458-3835
SIC 5541 5172 7359 7699

SMO INC p 1334
6355 Crain Hwy, La Plata MD 20646
Tel (301) 932-3600 SIC 5172

WILLS GROUP INC p 1613
6355 Crain Hwy, La Plata MD 20646
Tel (301) 932-3600
SIC 5541 5983 5172 5411

CATO INC p 267
1004 Parsons Rd, Salisbury MD 21801
Tel (410) 546-1215 SIC 5172

DENNIS K BURKE INC p 428
284 Eastern Ave, Chelsea MA 02150
Tel (617) 884-7800 SIC 5172 5541

CUMBERLAND FARMS INC p 400
100 Crossing Blvd, Framingham MA 01702
Tel (508) 270-1400
SIC 5411 5541 5172 2086 2051 2026

DENNISON LUBRICANTS INC p 428
102 Charles Eldridge Rd, Lakeville MA 02347
Tel (508) 946-0500 SIC 5172

MONSON COMPANIES INC p 985
154 Pioneer Dr, Leominster MA 01453
Tel (978) 840-7007
SIC 5169 5172 2899 2842

NEW ENGLAND PETROLEUM LIMITED PARTNERSHIP p 1030
6 Kimball Ln Ste 400, Lynnfield MA 01940
Tel (617) 660-7400 SIC 5172

VOLTA OIL CO INC p 1565
1 Roberts Rd Ste 2, Plymouth MA 02360
Tel (508) 747-3778 SIC 5172 1799

FLYNN PETROLEUM LLC p 562
307 Hartford Tpke, Shrewsbury MA 01545
Tel (508) 756-7693 SIC 5172

■ GLOBAL COMPANIES LLC p 616
800 South St Ste 500, Waltham MA 02453
Tel (800) 542-0778 SIC 5172 5171

■ GLOBAL ENERGY MARKETING LLC p 616
800 South St Ste 500, Waltham MA 02453
Tel (781) 894-8800 SIC 5172 4924

▲ GLOBAL PARTNERS LP p 617
800 South St Ste 500, Waltham MA 02453
Tel (781) 894-8800 SIC 5172 5171

GLOBAL PETROLEUM CORP p 617
800 South St Ste 500, Waltham MA 02453
Tel (781) 894-6920 SIC 4924 5172 4911

GULF OIL LIMITED PARTNERSHIP p 646
80 William St Ste 400, Wellesley Hills MA 02481
Tel (339) 933-7200 SIC 5171 5172

NOONAN BROTHERS PETROLEUM PRODUCTS INC p 1047
415 West St, West Bridgewater MA 02379
Tel (508) 588-8026 SIC 5172

GREAT LAKES PETROLEUM CORP p 634
6525 N Jerome Rd, Alma MI 48801
Tel (989) 463-4654 SIC 5172

AVFUEL CORP p 137
47 W Ellsworth Rd, Ann Arbor MI 48108
Tel (734) 663-6466 SIC 5172

EAST WEST INDUSTRIAL ENGINEERING CO p 471
1099 Highland Dr Ste D, Ann Arbor MI 48108
Tel (734) 971-6265 SIC 5085 5172

GAS CITY LTD p 593
401 S Old Woodward Ave # 340, Birmingham MI 48009
Tel (815) 469-9000 SIC 5541 5411 5172

CRYSTAL FLASH LIMITED PARTNERSHIP OF MICHIGAN p 396
1754 Alpine Ave Nw, Grand Rapids MI 49504
Tel (616) 363-4851 SIC 5172 5984

J & H OIL CO p 769
2696 Chicago Dr Sw, Grand Rapids MI 49519
Tel (616) 534-2181 SIC 5172 5013

VAN MANEN PETROLEUM INC p 1542
O-305 Lake Michigan Dr Nw, Grand Rapids MI 49534
Tel (616) 453-6344 SIC 5172

BRENNER OIL CO p 210
12948 Quincy St, Holland MI 49424
Tel (616) 399-9742 SIC 5172 4212

WALTERS-DIMMICK PETROLEUM INC p 1574
1620 S Kalamazoo Ave, Marshall MI 49068
Tel (269) 781-4654
SIC 5541 5411 6512 5172 5171 5983

B&R OIL CO INC p 142
2147 S 3rd St, Niles MI 49120
Tel (269) 687-9642 SIC 5172

COOPERATIVE ELEVATOR CO p 367
7211 E Michigan Ave, Pigeon MI 48755
Tel (989) 453-4500
SIC 5172 5191 5541 5261 5153

METALWORKING LUBRICANTS CO p 953
25 W Silverdome Indus Par, Pontiac MI 48342
Tel (248) 332-3500
SIC 5172 2869 2843 2992

RKA PETROLEUM COMPANIES INC p 1239
28340 Wick Rd, Romulus MI 48174
Tel (734) 946-2199 SIC 5172

PRI MAR PETROLEUM INC p 1173
1207 Broad St, Saint Joseph MI 49085
Tel (269) 983-7314 SIC 5411 5172

VESCO OIL CORP p 1552
16055 W 12 Mile Rd, Southfield MI 48076
Tel (800) 527-5358 SIC 5172

FORWARD CORP p 570
219 N Front St, Standish MI 48658
Tel (989) 846-4501
SIC 5411 5541 5172 5812

ATLAS OIL CO p 128
24501 Ecorse Rd, Taylor MI 48180
Tel (313) 292-5500 SIC 5172 5171

HOLIDAY COMPANIES p 700
4567 American Blvd W, Bloomington MN 55437
Tel (952) 830-8700 SIC 5541 5411 5172

ALPHA OIL & GAS SERVICES INC p 60
453 Tower St Nw, Clearbrook MN 56634
Tel (218) 776-2278 SIC 5172 1623 1522

BEST OIL CO p 177
30 N 8th St, Cloquet MN 55720
Tel (218) 879-0201
SIC 5171 5172 5013 5983 5541 5411

RIVER COUNTRY COOPERATIVE p 1237
9072 Cahill Ave, Inver Grove Heights MN 55076
Tel (651) 451-1151 SIC 5171 5172 5191

LUBRICATION TECHNOLOGIES INC p 884
900 Mendelssohn Ave N, Minneapolis MN 55427
Tel (763) 545-0707 SIC 5172 5169

NORTHERN RESOURCES COOPERATIVE p 1056
1504 Center St W, Roseau MN 56751
Tel (218) 463-1805
SIC 5191 5172 5251 5541

WATONWAN FARM SERVICE INC p 1583
233 W Ciro St, Truman MN 56088
Tel (507) 776-1244 SIC 5153 5191 5172

ALLIANCE ENERGY SERVICES LLC p 54
1405 Highway 12 E, Willmar MN 56201
Tel (320) 875-2641 SIC 5172

LITCO PETROLEUM INC p 870
323 Highway 72 W, Corinth MS 38834
Tel (662) 287-1471 SIC 5541 5172 5411

ERGON ASPHALT & EMULSIONS INC p 507
2829 Lakeland Dr Ste 2000, Flowood MS 39232
Tel (601) 933-3000 SIC 5172 2951

ERGON INC p 507
2829 Lakeland Dr Ste 2000, Flowood MS 39232
Tel (601) 933-3000
SIC 2911 4213 4449 4613 5171 5172

BUFFALO SERVICES INC p 224
747 S Broadway St, Mccomb MS 39648
Tel (601) 684-7702
SIC 5172 5411 6519 4212

ELTM LP p 489
1374 Highway 11, Petal MS 39465
Tel (601) 583-9991 SIC 5172

PINE BELT OIL CO INC p 1148
343 Highway 589, Purvis MS 39475
Tel (601) 794-5900 SIC 5172

CLARK OIL CO INC p 322
720 Station St, Waynesboro MS 39367
Tel (601) 735-4847 SIC 5541 5172

TRI-LAKES PETROLEUM CO LLC p 1477
943 E State Highway 76, Branson MO 65616
Tel (417) 334-3940 SIC 5172

AYERS OIL CO p 140
401 N 4th St, Canton MO 63435
Tel (573) 288-4464
SIC 5171 5411 5541 5172

CRESTWOOD EQUITY PARTNERS LP p 392
2 Brush Creek Blvd Ste 20, Kansas City MO 64112
Tel (816) 842-8181 SIC 5172

INERGY HOLDINGS LP p 740
2 Brush Creek Blvd # 200, Kansas City MO 64112
Tel (816) 842-8181 SIC 5172 6719

■ INERGY PROPANE LLC p 740
2 Brush Creek Blvd # 200, Kansas City MO 64112
Tel (816) 842-8181 SIC 5984 5172

J D STREETT & CO INC p 771
144 Weldon Pkwy, Maryland Heights MO 63043
Tel (314) 432-6600
SIC 5171 5541 7389 5172

AROGAS INC p 112
1821 Sherman Dr Ste 200, Saint Charles MO 63303
Tel (636) 947-0255 SIC 5172

G P & W INC p 587
600 Mason Ridge Center Dr # 2, Saint Louis MO 63141
Tel (314) 682-3500 SIC 5172

SMI-FUEL LLC p 1333
11420 Lackland Rd, Saint Louis MO 63146
Tel (314) 994-9900 SIC 5172

■ HERITAGE OPERATING LP p 686
754 River Rock Dr, Helena MT 59602
Tel (406) 442-9759 SIC 5984 5172

CITYSERVICEVALCON LLC p 320
640 W Montana St, Kalispell MT 59901
Tel (406) 755-4321 SIC 5172 5983

WESTERN COOPERATIVE CO INC p 1598
724 W 3rd St, Alliance NE 69301
Tel (308) 762-3291 SIC 5172 5541 5191

TROTTER INC p 1484
300 Railway, Arcadia NE 68815
Tel (308) 789-6200 SIC 5191 5153 5172

BATTLE CREEK FARMERS COOPERATIVE NON-STOCK p 160
83755 Highway 121, Battle Creek NE 68715
Tel (402) 675-2375
SIC 5153 5191 5172 5541 5411

NEBRASKA-IOWA SUPPLY CO INC p 1023
1160 Lincoln St, Blair NE 68008
Tel (402) 426-2171 SIC 5172

FARMERS COOPERATIVE p 529
208 W Depot St, Dorchester NE 68343
Tel (402) 946-4631 SIC 5153 5191 5172

BOSSELMAN ENERGY INC p 202
3123 W Stolley Park Rd B, Grand Island NE 68801
Tel (308) 381-6900 SIC 5172

BOSSELMAN INC p 202
3123 W Stolley Park Rd, Grand Island NE 68801
Tel (308) 381-2800
SIC 5541 5411 5812 7011 5172 5084

ALLIED OIL & TIRE CO p 56
2209 S 24th St, Omaha NE 68108
Tel (402) 344-4343 SIC 5014 5172

RITE WAY INVESTMENTS INC p 1236
8400 I St, Omaha NE 68127
Tel (402) 331-6400 SIC 5172 5541 5411

HO-CHUNK INC p 698
1 Mission Dr, Winnebago NE 68071
Tel (402) 878-4135 SIC 5172

HIGHLANDS FUEL DELIVERY LLC p 691
190 Commerce Way, Portsmouth NH 03801
Tel (603) 559-8700 SIC 5172 5541 1389

■ SPRAGUE OPERATING RESOURCES LLC p 1360
185 International Dr, Portsmouth NH 03801
Tel (603) 431-1000 SIC 5172 5052 5171

▲ SPRAGUE RESOURCES LP p 1360
185 International Dr, Portsmouth NH 03801
Tel (800) 225-1560 SIC 5172 4922

HANWA AMERICAN CORP p 659
Parker Plz 400 Kelby St F, Fort Lee NJ 07024
Tel (201) 363-4500
SIC 5051 5172 5031 5084 5146

P & J FUEL INC p 1102
2456 Saint Georges Ave, Rahway NJ 07065
Tel (732) 382-5100 SIC 5172

WOROCO MANAGEMENT LLC p 1626
40 Woodbridge Ave Ste 3, Sewaren NJ 07077
Tel (732) 855-7720 SIC 5172

▲ SUBURBAN PROPANE PARTNERS LP p 1396
240 Route 10 W, Whippany NJ 07981
Tel (973) 887-5300
SIC 5984 5172 4939 1711

DESERT FUELS INC p 432
4421 Irving Blvd Nw Ste A, Albuquerque NM 87114
Tel (505) 750-3835 SIC 5172 5171

MIRABITO HOLDINGS INC p 974
49 Court St Ste 1, Binghamton NY 13901
Tel (607) 561-2700
SIC 5172 4925 5541 5411 5983

SCHMITT SALES INC p 1287
2101 Saint Ritas Ln, Buffalo NY 14221
Tel (716) 639-1500 SIC 5172 5541

REID PETROLEUM CORP p 1221
100 W Genesee St, Lockport NY 14094
Tel (716) 434-2885 SIC 5541 5172

NIC HOLDING CORP p 1042
225 Brd Hllow Rd Ste 212w, Melville NY 11747
Tel (631) 753-4200 SIC 5172

ALLIED AVIATION SERVICES INC p 56
462 7th Ave Fl 17, New York NY 10018
Tel (212) 868-3870 SIC 5172

FAIRFIELD-MAXWELL LTD p 525
60 E 42nd St Fl 55, New York NY 10165
Tel (212) 297-9030
SIC 8741 4731 5172 4412

HARTREE PARTNERS LP p 666
1185 Avenue Of The Americ, New York NY 10036
Tel (212) 536-8915 SIC 6221 5172

▲ MACQUARIE INFRASTRUCTURE CORP p 893
125 W 55th St, New York NY 10019
Tel (212) 231-1000
SIC 5172 4581 4785 7521 4932

MARUBENI AMERICA CORP p 913
375 Lexington Ave, New York NY 10017
Tel (212) 450-0100
SIC 5131 5084 5012 5169 5172 5094

MITSUBISHI CORP (AMERICAS) p 977
655 3rd Ave, New York NY 10017
Tel (212) 605-2000
SIC 5051 5172 5141 5153 5169 5084

MITSUBISHI INTERNATIONAL CORP p 978
655 3rd Ave Ste 800, New York NY 10017
Tel (212) 605-2000
SIC 5051 5172 5141 5153 5169 5084

MITSUI & CO (USA) INC p 978
200 Park Ave Fl 35, New York NY 10166
Tel (212) 878-4000
SIC 5051 5094 5084 5153 5172 5169

■ STARSUPPLY PETROLEUM LLC p 1379
55 Water St, New York NY 10041
Tel (212) 968-2920 SIC 5172

SUMITOMO CORP OF AMERICAS p 1398
300 Madison Ave, New York NY 10017
Tel (212) 207-0700
SIC 5051 5172 5084 5063 5141

TRAMMO INC p 1469
1 Rockefeller Plz Fl 9, New York NY 10020
Tel (212) 223-3200 SIC 5191 5172 5169

UNIPEC AMERICA INC p 1505
410 Park Ave Ste 610, New York NY 10022
Tel (212) 759-5085 SIC 5172

CAMBRIDGE PETROLEUM HOLDING INC p 244
31 S Plank Rd Unit 105, Newburgh NY 12550
Tel (516) 542-4900
SIC 5983 5541 5984 5172 5074

■ WAREX TERMINALS CORP p 1575
1 S Water St, Newburgh NY 12550
Tel (845) 561-4000 SIC 5172

SUPERIOR LUBRICANTS CO INC p 1406
32 Ward Rd, North Tonawanda NY 14120
Tel (716) 693-8412 SIC 5172 5013

BLUEOX CORP p 193
38 N Canal St, Oxford NY 13830
Tel (607) 843-2583 SIC 5172 5411 5541

PETRO VM INC p 1139
2188 Kirby Ln, Syosset NY 11791
Tel (516) 921-7190 SIC 5172

PETR-ALL PETROLEUM CONSULTING CORP p 1139
7401 Round Pond Rd, Syracuse NY 13212
Tel (315) 446-0125 SIC 5172 5411

NOCO INC p 1046
2440 Sheridan Dr Ste 202, Tonawanda NY 14150
Tel (716) 833-6626
SIC 2992 6719 5172 4924

M SPIEGEL & SONS OIL CORP p 890
10 E Village Rd, Tuxedo Park NY 10987
Tel (845) 351-4700 SIC 5172 5983

PUGH OIL CO INC p 1191
701 Mcdowell Rd, Asheboro NC 27205
Tel (336) 629-2061
SIC 5172 5983 5541 5411 5149

CARY OIL CO INC p 262
110 Mackenan Dr Ste 300, Cary NC 27511
Tel (919) 462-1100 SIC 5172 5171

■ PANENERGY CORP p 1111
526 S Church St, Charlotte NC 28202
Tel (704) 594-6200
SIC 4922 1321 2813 5172 4911 4613

WARREN OIL CO INC p 1577
2340 Us Highway 301 N, Dunn NC 28334
Tel (910) 892-6456
SIC 5172 5171 3826 2911

UNITED OIL OF CAROLINAS INC p 1510
1627 Spencer Mountain Rd, Gastonia NC 28054
Tel (704) 824-3561 SIC 5172

BUMGARNER OIL CO INC p 225
2004 Highland Ave Ne, Hickory NC 28601
Tel (828) 322-4377 SIC 5172 5983

MISSOURI VALLEY PETROLEUM INC p 976
1722 Mandan Ave, Mandan ND 58554
Tel (701) 663-5091 SIC 5172 3443

FARSTAD OIL INC p 530
100 27th St Ne, Minot ND 58703
Tel (701) 852-1194 SIC 5172

FARMERS UNION OIL CO OF STANLEY p 530
8149 Highway 2, Stanley ND 58784
Tel (701) 628-2322
SIC 5172 5251 5541 5411

HORIZON RESOURCES p 707
317 2nd St W, Williston ND 58801
Tel (701) 572-2171
SIC 5172 5541 5411 5191

HOLLAND OIL CO p 700
1485 Marion Ave, Akron OH 44313
Tel (330) 835-1815 SIC 5541 5172 5411

RELADYNE I LLC p 1221
9395 Kenwood Rd Ste 104, Blue Ash OH 45242
Tel (513) 489-6000 SIC 5171 5172

TRUE NORTH ENERGY LLC p 1486
10346 Brecksville Rd, Brecksville OH 44141
Tel (877) 245-9336 SIC 5541 5172

HARTLEY CO p 666
319 Wheeling Ave, Cambridge OH 43725
Tel (740) 432-2328 SIC 5541 5172

■ APPLIED INDUSTRIAL TECHNOLOGIES - DIXIE INC p 99
1 Applied Plz, Cleveland OH 44115
Tel (216) 426-4000 SIC 5172 5169

DUNCAN OIL CO p 461
849 Factory Rd, Dayton OH 45434
Tel (937) 426-5945
SIC 5172 5411 5983 1542

■ MARATHON PETROLEUM CO LP p 904
539 S Main St, Findlay OH 45840
Tel (419) 422-2121 SIC 5172 2951 2865

▲ MARATHON PETROLEUM CORP p 904
539 S Main St, Findlay OH 45840
Tel (419) 422-2121 SIC 2911 5172

DISTRICT PETROLEUM PRODUCTS INC p 443
1814 River Rd, Huron OH 44839
Tel (419) 433-8373 SIC 5541 5171 5172

BAZELL OIL CO INC p 163
14371 State Route 328, Logan OH 43138
Tel (740) 385-5420 SIC 5172 5983

▲ GAS NATURAL INC p 593
8470 Station St, Mentor OH 44060
Tel (440) 974-3770
SIC 4924 4911 5172 5984

HIGHTOWERS PETROLEUM CO INC p 692
3577 Commerce Dr, Middletown OH 45005
Tel (513) 423-4272 SIC 5172

COLES ENERGY INC p 336
3619 St Rt 113 E, Milan OH 44846
Tel (419) 499-1120 SIC 5172 5411 5541

LYKINS COMPANIES INC p 887
5163 Wlfpn Plsnt Hl Rd, Milford OH 45150
Tel (513) 831-8820 SIC 5172 4213 5411

LYKINS OIL CO p 887
5163 Wlfpn Plsnt Hl Rd, Milford OH 45150
Tel (513) 831-8820 SIC 5172 5983

GLOCKNER CHEVROLET CO p 618
4368 Us Route 23, Portsmouth OH 45662
Tel (740) 353-2161 SIC 5013 5172 5511

JACK A ALLEN INC p 773
2105 Old State Route 7, Steubenville OH 43952
Tel (740) 282-4531
SIC 5172 5983 5541 5411

NZR RETAIL OF TOLEDO INC p 1070
4820 Monroe St, Toledo OH 43623
Tel (419) 724-0005 *SIC* 5172

EARHART PETROLEUM INC p 468
1494 Lytle Rd, Troy OH 45373
Tel (937) 335-2928 *SIC* 5172 5541 5983

LYDEN OIL CO p 887
30692 Tracy Rd, Walbridge OH 43465
Tel (419) 666-1948 *SIC* 5172

PORTS PETROLEUM CO INC p 1163
1337 Blachleyville Rd, Wooster OH 44691
Tel (330) 264-1885 *SIC* 5172 5983 5541

SANTMYER OIL CO INC p 1281
3000 Old Airport Rd, Wooster OH 44691
Tel (330) 262-6501
SIC 5172 5983 4212 5531

SHEPHERD OIL CO LLC p 1315
1831 S Main St, Blackwell OK 74631
Tel (580) 363-4280 *SIC* 5411 5172

■ **DEVON ENERGY PRODUCTION CO LP** p 434
333 W Sheridan Ave, Oklahoma City OK 73102
Tel (405) 235-3611 *SIC* 1311 5172

MUSKET CORP p 1002
10601 N Pennsylvania Ave, Oklahoma City OK 73120
Tel (713) 332-5726 *SIC* 5172

ASPHALT AND FUEL SUPPLY LLC p 118
4200 E Skelly Dr Ste 600, Tulsa OK 74135
Tel (918) 488-1339 *SIC* 5172

MURPHY ENERGY CORP p 1001
2250 E 73rd St Ste 600, Tulsa OK 74136
Tel (918) 743-7979 *SIC* 5172

▲ **NGL ENERGY PARTNERS LP** p 1041
6120 S Yale Ave Ste 805, Tulsa OK 74136
Tel (918) 481-1119 *SIC* 5172 5984

■ **NGL SUPPLY LLC** p 1041
6120 S Yale Ave Ste 805, Tulsa OK 74136
Tel (918) 481-1119 *SIC* 5172

▲ **ONEOK INC** p 1087
100 W 5th St Ste LI, Tulsa OK 74103
Tel (918) 588-7000
SIC 4922 4924 1311 1321 5172

PACER ENERGY MARKETING LLC p 1103
823 S Detroit Ave Ste 300, Tulsa OK 74120
Tel (918) 398-2713 *SIC* 5172

QUIKTRIP CORP p 1200
4705 S 129th East Ave, Tulsa OK 74134
Tel (918) 615-7700
SIC 5411 5541 5172 2099 5141 6512

■ **WILLIAMS ENERGY SERVICES LLC** p 1611
1 One Williams Ctr Bsmt 2, Tulsa OK 74172
Tel (918) 573-2000 *SIC* 4923 5172

ED STAUB & SONS PETROLEUM INC p 476
1301 Esplanade Ave, Klamath Falls OR 97601
Tel (541) 887-8900 *SIC* 5172 5541 5411

CARSON OIL CO INC p 261
3125 Nw 35th Ave, Portland OR 97210
Tel (503) 829-5441 *SIC* 5172

MCCALL OIL AND CHEMICAL CORP p 926
5480 Nw Front Ave, Portland OR 97210
Tel (503) 221-6400 *SIC* 5172

EPIC AVIATION LLC p 505
3841 Fairview Indust 15, Salem OR 97302
Tel (503) 362-3633 *SIC* 5172

▲ **CROSSAMERICA PARTNERS LP** p 394
515 Hamilton St Ste 200, Allentown PA 18101
Tel (610) 625-8000 *SIC* 5172

GT&S INC p 644
5275 Tilghman St, Allentown PA 18104
Tel (610) 398-2211
SIC 4925 5169 5084 5085 2813 5172

GUTTMAN ENERGY INC p 648
200 Speers Rd, Belle Vernon PA 15012
Tel (724) 489-5199 *SIC* 8731 5172

ZIPCORP INC p 1643
33 Barbour St, Bradford PA 16701
Tel (814) 368-2700 *SIC* 3999 5172

ZIPPO MANUFACTURING CO INC p 1643
33 Barbour St, Bradford PA 16701
Tel (814) 368-2700
SIC 3914 3993 5172 3999 3421 3172

PETROCHOICE HOLDINGS INC p 1139
1300 Virginia Dr Ste 405, Fort Washington PA 19034
Tel (267) 705-2015 *SIC* 5172

INTERSTATE GAS MARKETING INC p 758
2018 S 6th St, Indiana PA 15701
Tel (724) 465-7958 *SIC* 4925 5172

PPC LUBRICANTS INC p 1166
305 Micro Dr, Jonestown PA 17038
Tel (717) 865-9993 *SIC* 5172

■ **AMERIGAS INC** p 82
460 N Gulph Rd Ste 100, King Of Prussia PA 19406
Tel (610) 337-7000
SIC 5984 5172 5722 2911 2813

▲ **AMERIGAS PARTNERS LP** p 82
460 N Gulph Rd Ste 100, King Of Prussia PA 19406
Tel (610) 337-7000 *SIC* 5984 5172

■ **TITAN PROPANE LLC** p 1456
460 N Gulph Rd Ste 100, King Of Prussia PA 19406
Tel (610) 337-7000 *SIC* 5984 5172

AMERIGREEN ENERGY INC p 82
1650 Manheim Pike Ste 201, Lancaster PA 17601
Tel (717) 945-1392 *SIC* 5172

BERKS PRODUCTS CORP p 175
167 Berks Products Dr, Leesport PA 19533
Tel (610) 374-5131
SIC 5031 3273 5983 5172 2439 1711

RENKERT OIL LLC p 1224
3817 Main St, Morgantown PA 19543
Tel (610) 286-8010 *SIC* 5172

INFINITY OILFIELD SERVICES LLC p 741
1 Eye Center Dr, Muncy PA 17756
Tel (570) 567-7027 *SIC* 5172

▲ **SUNOCO LOGISTICS PARTNERS LP** p 1403
3807 West Chester Pike, Newtown Square PA 19073
Tel (866) 248-4344
SIC 4612 4613 5171 5172

ATLANTIC PETROLEUM CORP p 127
1801 Market St Ste 1500, Philadelphia PA 19103
Tel (215) 977-3000
SIC 5541 5172 2911 4612

UNI-MARTS LLC p 1502
1155 Benner Pike 100, State College PA 16801
Tel (814) 234-6000
SIC 5411 5541 5993 6794 5172

PETROCHOICE LLC p 1139
18385 Route 287, Tioga PA 16946
Tel (570) 835-5858 *SIC* 5172

WILLIAMS OIL CO INC p 1611
44 Reuter Blvd, Towanda PA 18848
Tel (570) 265-6673 *SIC* 5172 5983

■ **UGI ENTERPRISES INC** p 1499
460 N Gulph Rd, Valley Forge PA 19482
Tel (610) 337-1000 *SIC* 5172

AMERICAN PETROLEUM CO INC p 77
Km 0 Hm 2 Cam Rr 865, Toa Baja PR 00949
Tel (787) 794-1985 *SIC* 5172

BEST PETROLEUM CORP p 177
Km 20 Hm 5 Rr 2, Toa Baja PR 00951
Tel (787) 251-6218 *SIC* 5172

THIELSCH ENGINEERING INC p 1448
195 Frances Ave, Cranston RI 02910
Tel (401) 785-0241
SIC 5084 5043 5172 5085

■ **WARREN EQUITIES INC** p 1577
27 Warren Way, Providence RI 02905
Tel (401) 781-9900 *SIC* 5172 5541 5411

DILMAR OIL CO INC p 440
1951 W Darlington St, Florence SC 29501
Tel (843) 662-4179 *SIC* 5172 2819

WEST OIL INC p 1595
312 Lakeview Blvd, Hartsville SC 29550
Tel (843) 332-2201 *SIC* 5172 5541 5411

BRANDI BOB STATIONS INC p 208
279 Cedarcrest Dr, Lexington SC 29072
Tel (803) 957-3096 *SIC* 5411 5172

DEARYBURY OIL & GAS INC p 420
2560 Southport Rd, Spartanburg SC 29302
Tel (864) 585-6226 *SIC* 5172 5983 4212

R L JORDAN OIL CO OF NORTH CAROLINA INC p 1202
1451 Fernwood Glendale Rd, Spartanburg SC 29307
Tel (864) 585-2784
SIC 5411 5172 5541 5812

HARMS OIL CO p 662
337 22nd Ave S, Brookings SD 57006
Tel (605) 696-5000 *SIC* 5172

LAKE PRESTON COOPERATIVE ASSOCIATION p 839
106 2nd St Nw, Lake Preston SD 57249
Tel (605) 847-4414 *SIC* 5153 5191 5172

BIG D OIL CO p 181
3685 Sturgis Rd, Rapid City SD 57702
Tel (605) 342-6777 *SIC* 5541 5172 8741

MG OIL CO p 958
1180 Creek Dr, Rapid City SD 57703
Tel (605) 342-0527 *SIC* 5172 5541 5411

COUNTRY PRIDE COOPERATIVE INC p 375
648 W 2nd St, Winner SD 57580
Tel (605) 842-2711
SIC 5153 5172 5191 5411 5211

■ **LION OIL CO** p 869
7102 Commerce Way, Brentwood TN 37027
Tel (615) 771-6701 *SIC* 2911 4612 5172

JAT OIL INC p 779
600 W Main St, Chattanooga TN 37402
Tel (423) 629-6611 *SIC* 5172

WESTPORT PETROLEUM INC p 1602
810 Crescent Centre Dr # 530, Franklin TN 37067
Tel (615) 771-6800 *SIC* 5172

GREENEVILLE OIL & PETROLEUM INC p 638
860 W Andrew Johnson Hwy, Greeneville TN 37745
Tel (423) 638-3145 *SIC* 5172 5411 5541

H T HACKNEY CO p 650
502 S Gay St Ste 300, Knoxville TN 37902
Tel (865) 546-1291
SIC 5141 5172 2434 5084

MAXUM PETROLEUM INC p 923
5508 Lonas Dr, Knoxville TN 37909
Tel (865) 588-7488 *SIC* 5172

TENNESSEE FARMERS COOPERATIVE INC p 1438
180 Old Nashville Hwy, La Vergne TN 37086
Tel (615) 793-8011
SIC 5191 5013 5014 5172 5122 2048

EDWARDS OIL CO OF LAWRENCEBURG INC p 480
105 Helton Dr, Lawrenceburg TN 38464
Tel (931) 762-5531 *SIC* 5172

PARMAN ENERGY CORP p 1117
7101 Cockrill Bend Blvd, Nashville TN 37209
Tel (615) 350-7447 *SIC* 5172

TRI STAR ENERGY LLC p 1477
1740 Ed Temple Blvd, Nashville TN 37208
Tel (615) 313-3600 *SIC* 5331 5172

WESTERN MARKETING INC p 1599
20 Exit 278, Abilene TX 79601
Tel (800) 588-4662 *SIC* 5172

ARNOLD OIL CO OF AUSTIN GP LLC p 112
5909 Burleson Rd, Austin TX 78744
Tel (512) 476-2401 *SIC* 5013 5172

TEXAS ENTERPRISES INC p 1443
5005 E 7th St, Austin TX 78702
Tel (512) 385-2167 *SIC* 5172

TRI-CON INC p 1477
7076 W Port Arthur Rd, Beaumont TX 77705
Tel (409) 835-2237 *SIC* 5541 5172 5411

■ **SUSSER HOLDINGS CORP** p 1409
4525 Ayers St, Corpus Christi TX 78415
Tel (361) 884-2463 *SIC* 5411 5541 5172

DALHART CONSUMERS FUEL ASSOCIATION INC p 409
919 Liberal St, Dalhart TX 79022
Tel (806) 249-4660
SIC 5153 5172 5191 5541

■ **ALON USA LP** p 59
12700 Park Central Dr # 1600, Dallas TX 75251
Tel (972) 367-3600
SIC 2911 4612 5172 5541 2895

EMPIRE PETROLEUM PARTNERS LLC p 493
8350 N Central Expy M2175, Dallas TX 75206
Tel (214) 750-9313 *SIC* 4924 5172

■ **ENLINK MIDSTREAM GP LLC** p 500
2501 Cedar Springs Rd, Dallas TX 75201
Tel (214) 953-9500 *SIC* 5172

NGL CROSSTEX MARKETING L P p 1041
2501 Cedar Springs Rd, Dallas TX 75201
Tel (214) 754-4752 *SIC* 5172

■ **REGENCY ENERGY PARTNERS LP** p 1218
8111 Westchester Dr # 600, Dallas TX 75225
Tel (214) 750-1771
SIC 1321 4925 5172 4922

▲ **SUNOCO LP** p 1403
8020 Park Ln Ste 200, Dallas TX 75231
Tel (214) 981-0700 *SIC* 5172 6519 5541

TITAN GLOBAL HOLDINGS INC p 1456
17760 Preston Rd, Dallas TX 75252
Tel (214) 751-7777 *SIC* 5172 4813

MAXUM ENTERPRISES LLC p 923
201 N Rupert St Ste 101, Fort Worth TX 76107
Tel (817) 877-8300 *SIC* 5171 5172

PILOT THOMAS LOGISTICS LLC p 1148
201 N Rupert St Ste 101, Fort Worth TX 76107
Tel (435) 789-1832 *SIC* 5172

SIMONS PETROLEUM p 1325
201 N Rupert St Ste 101, Fort Worth TX 76107
Tel (405) 551-2403
SIC 5172 5171 5541 5411

SIMONS PETROLEUM INC p 1325
201 N Rupert St Ste 101, Fort Worth TX 76107
Tel (405) 848-3500 *SIC* 5171 5172

■ **INDEPENDENT PROPANE CO LLC** p 737
2591 Dallas Pkwy Ste 105, Frisco TX 75034
Tel (972) 731-5454 *SIC* 5984 5172

J CINCO INC p 770
1113 E Sarah Dewitt Dr, Gonzales TX 78629
Tel (830) 672-9574 *SIC* 5172 5541

CLASSIC STAR GROUP LP p 323
6324 Eden Dr, Haltom City TX 76117
Tel (817) 834-2868 *SIC* 5172

▲ **ADAMS RESOURCES & ENERGY INC** p 21
17 S Briar Hollow Ln, Houston TX 77027
Tel (713) 881-3600
SIC 5172 4212 1382 1311

ADDAX PETROLEUM US SERVICES CORP p 21
1301 Mckinney St Ste 2050, Houston TX 77010
Tel (713) 341-3150 *SIC* 5172

■ **ANADARKO HOLDING CO** p 88
17001 Northchase Dr, Houston TX 77060
Tel (832) 636-7200
SIC 1311 1321 5172 4922

ASTRA OIL CO LLC p 122
5847 San Felipe St # 2850, Houston TX 77057
Tel (713) 357-0640 *SIC* 5172

■ **ATLANTIC TRADING & MARKETING INC** p 127
5847 San Felipe St # 2100, Houston TX 77057
Tel (713) 243-2200 *SIC* 5172

BIOURJA TRADING LLC p 185
1080 Eldridge Pkwy # 1175, Houston TX 77077
Tel (832) 775-9000 *SIC* 5172

BOMIN BUNKER OIL CORP p 199
333 Clay St Ste 2400, Houston TX 77002
Tel (713) 952-5151 *SIC* 5172

BUFFALO MARINE SERVICE INC p 224
8201 E Erath St, Houston TX 77012
Tel (713) 923-2106 *SIC* 5172

■ **BURLINGTON RESOURCES INC** p 228
600 N Dairy Ashford Rd, Houston TX 77079
Tel (281) 293-1000
SIC 1311 5172 4922 4612

CHEMIUM INTERNATIONAL CORP p 293
1455 West Loop S Ste 550, Houston TX 77027
Tel (713) 622-7766 *SIC* 5172

■ **CHEVRON MARINE PRODUCTS LLC** p 296
1500 Louisiana St, Houston TX 77002
Tel (832) 854-2767 *SIC* 5172 2992 2869

CITATION CRUDE MARKETING INC p 309
14077 Cutten Rd, Houston TX 77069
Tel (281) 891-1000 *SIC* 5172

▲ **CRESTWOOD EQUITY PARTNERS LP** p 392
700 Louisiana St Ste 2550, Houston TX 77002
Tel (832) 519-2200 *SIC* 5984 5172

DAN-BUNKERING (AMERICA) INC p 410
840 Gessner Rd Ste 210, Houston TX 77024
Tel (281) 833-5801 *SIC* 5172

■ **DYNEGY HOLDINGS LLC** p 465
601 Travis St Ste 1400, Houston TX 77002
Tel (713) 507-6400 *SIC* 4911 4923 5172

ENI TRADING & SHIPPING INC p 499
1200 Smith St Ste 1707, Houston TX 77002
Tel (713) 393-6340 *SIC* 5172

ENJET LLC p 499
5373 W Alabama St Ste 502, Houston TX 77056
Tel (713) 552-1559 *SIC* 5172

ENRON CREDITORS RECOVERY CORP p 500
1221 Lamar St Ste 1325, Houston TX 77010
Tel (713) 853-6161
SIC 5172 4922 4911 1311 1321 2911

■ **ENTERPRISE CRUDE OIL LLC** p 502
1100 Louisiana St, Houston TX 77002
Tel (713) 381-6500 *SIC* 5172

EQUILON ENTERPRISES LLC p 506
910 Louisiana St Ste 2, Houston TX 77002
Tel (713) 241-6161
SIC 2911 4612 2992 5172

FRONTIER PETROLEUM RESOURCES INC p 581
6200 Savoy Dr Ste 650, Houston TX 77036
Tel (832) 242-1510 *SIC* 2911 5172

■ **GULFMARK ENERGY INC** p 647
17 S Briar Hollow Ln # 100, Houston TX 77027
Tel (210) 524-9725 *SIC* 5172

JAM DISTRIBUTING CO p 776
7010 Mykawa Rd, Houston TX 77033
Tel (713) 844-7788 *SIC* 5172

■ **KINDER MORGAN PRODUCTION CO LP** p 819
1001 La St Ste 1000, Houston TX 77002
Tel (800) 525-3752 *SIC* 5172

■ **KIRBY OFFSHORE MARINE LLC** p 821
55 Waugh Dr Ste 1000, Houston TX 77007
Tel (713) 435-1000 *SIC* 5172 4212 4213

KNIGHT-CHEMSTAR INC p 824
9204 Emmott Rd, Houston TX 77040
Tel (713) 466-8751 *SIC* 5169 5172

MARTIN ENERGY SERVICES LLC p 912
3 Riverway Ste 400, Houston TX 77056
Tel (713) 350-6800
SIC 5171 4492 5172 5551

■ **MIDCOAST OPERATING LP** p 964
1100 La St Ste 3300, Houston TX 77002
Tel (713) 821-2000 *SIC* 5172 1389

■ **OCCIDENTAL ENERGY MARKETING INC** p 1072
5 Greenway Plz Ste 110, Houston TX 77046
Tel (713) 215-7000 *SIC* 5172 1382 4924

OROURKE DISTRIBUTING CO INC p 1095
223 Mccarty St, Houston TX 77029
Tel (713) 672-4500 *SIC* 5171 5172

PENNZOIL-QUAKER STATE NOMINEE CO p 1131
700 Milam St Ste 400, Houston TX 77002
Tel (713) 546-4000 *SIC* 5172

PENTHOL LLC p 1132
333 Clay St Ste 3300, Houston TX 77002
Tel (832) 548-5832 *SIC* 5172

PETROBRAS AMERICA INC p 1139
10350 Richmond Ave, Houston TX 77042
Tel (713) 808-2000 *SIC* 5172 1382 2911

PIEDMONT HAWTHORNE AVIATION LLC p 1147
1500 City W Blvd Ste 600, Houston TX 77042
Tel (713) 895-9243
SIC 5599 4581 4522 5172

■ **PLAINS ALL AMERICAN PIPELINE LP** p 1153
333 Clay St Ste 1600, Houston TX 77002
Tel (713) 646-4100 *SIC* 4612 5172

■ **PLAINS MARKETING LP** p 1153
333 Clay St Ste 1600, Houston TX 77002
Tel (713) 646-4100 *SIC* 5172 4213

RIO ENERGY INTERNATIONAL INC p 1235
5718 Westheimer Rd # 1806, Houston TX 77057
Tel (713) 977-5718 *SIC* 5172

SABIC AMERICAS INC p 1264
2500 Citywest Blvd, Houston TX 77042
Tel (713) 532-4999 *SIC* 5172 5169

SHELL OFFSHORE INC p 1314
200 N Dairy Ashford Rd, Houston TX 77079
Tel (281) 544-4800 *SIC* 5172

SHELL PETROLEUM INC p 1314
910 Louisiana St Ste 420, Houston TX 77002
Tel (713) 241-6161 *SIC* 2911 4613 5172

SHELL TRADING NORTH AMERICA CO p 1314
1000 Main St, Houston TX 77002
Tel (713) 241-6161 *SIC* 5172

SOUTHERN PETROLEUM LABORATORIES INC p 1350
8850 Interchange Dr, Houston TX 77054
Tel (713) 660-0901 *SIC* 5172 8999 8734

SUN COAST RESOURCES INC p 1400
6405 Cavalcade St Bldg 1, Houston TX 77026
Tel (713) 844-9600
SIC 5172 2992 5084 1389

■ **SUSSER PETROLEUM CORP** p 1409
555 E Airtex Dr, Houston TX 77073
Tel (832) 234-3746 *SIC* 5172 7389

■ **SUSSER PETROLEUM OPERATING CO LLC** p 1409
555 E Airtex Dr, Houston TX 77073
Tel (832) 234-3600 *SIC* 5172

■ **SUSSER PETROLEUM PROPERTY CO LLC** p 1409
555 E Airtex Dr, Houston TX 77073
Tel (832) 234-3600 *SIC* 5172 6519

■ **TARGA RESOURCES PARTNERS LP** p 1425
1000 Louisiana St # 4300, Houston TX 77002
Tel (713) 584-1000 *SIC* 4922 4924 5172

TERRA ENERGY PARTNERS LLC p 1439
4828 Loop Central Dr # 900, Houston TX 77081
Tel (281) 936-0355 *SIC* 5172

TEXAS AROMATICS LP p 1442
3555 Timmons Ln Ste 700, Houston TX 77027
Tel (713) 520-2900 *SIC* 5172

TEXON DISTRIBUTING LP p 1445
11757 Katy Fwy Ste 1400, Houston TX 77079
Tel (281) 531-8400 *SIC* 5172

■ **NEWPARK DRILLING FLUIDS LLC** p 1038
21920 Merchants Way, Katy TX 77449
Tel (281) 754-8600 *SIC* 5169 5172 4953

■ **MARTIN OPERATING PARTNERSHIP LP** p 913
4200 Stone Rd, Kilgore TX 75662
Tel (903) 983-6200 *SIC* 5172

MARTIN PRODUCT SALES LLC p 913
4200 Stone Rd, Kilgore TX 75662
Tel (903) 983-6200 *SIC* 5052 5032 5172

MARTIN RESOURCE MANAGEMENT CORP p 913
4200 Stone Rd, Kilgore TX 75662
Tel (903) 983-6200
SIC 2911 4924 5984 5172

PRO PETROLEUM INC p 1178
4710 4th St, Lubbock TX 79416
Tel (806) 795-8785 *SIC* 5172

GIBSON ENERGY MARKETING LLC p 611
3819 Towne Crossing Blvd, Mesquite TX 75150
Tel (214) 461-5600 *SIC* 5172 5984

J L DAVIS CO p 771
211 N Colorado St, Midland TX 79701
Tel (432) 682-6311 *SIC* 5172 4923 1311

LPC CRUDE OIL INC p 882
408 W Wall St Ste B, Midland TX 79701
Tel (432) 682-8555 SIC 5172
OXITENO USA LLC p 1101
9801 Bay Area Blvd, Pasadena TX 77507
Tel (281) 909-7600 SIC 5172
THIRD COAST PACKAGING INC p 1448
1871 Mykawa Rd, Pearland TX 77581
Tel (281) 412-0275 SIC 5172 4783 2899
GARRISON FRED OIL CO p 592
1107 Walter Griffin St, Plainview TX 79072
Tel (806) 296-6353 SIC 5172 5541
■ **ATLANTIC AVIATION CORP** p 125
6652 Pinecrest Dr Ste 300, Plano TX 75024
Tel (972) 905-2500
SIC 4581 5088 5172 6331 6159 4522
MUREX LLC p 1001
7160 Dallas Pkwy Ste 300, Plano TX 75024
Tel (972) 702-0018 SIC 5172
■ **LEGACYSTAR SERVICES LLC** p 852
2435 N Central Expy # 700, Richardson TX 75080
Tel (972) 699-4062 SIC 4613 5172
■ **SAFETY-KLEEN INC** p 1266
2600 N Central Expy # 400, Richardson TX 75080
Tel (800) 669-5740
SIC 4953 3559 4212 5172 5085 7389
■ **SAFETY-KLEEN SYSTEMS INC** p 1266
2600 N Central Expy # 400, Richardson TX 75080
Tel (972) 265-2000
SIC 3559 7359 5172 4212 7389 5085
HEBCO PETROLEUM DISTRIBUTORS INC p 680
646 S Main Ave, San Antonio TX 78204
Tel (210) 938-8419 SIC 5172
■ **NUSTAR SUPPLY & TRADING LLC** p 1067
19003 W Interstate 10, San Antonio TX 78257
Tel (210) 918-2000 SIC 5172
■ **ULTRAMAR INC** p 1501
1 Valero Way, San Antonio TX 78249
Tel (210) 345-2000 SIC 2911 5172 5541
VALERO SERVICES INC p 1539
1 Valero Way, San Antonio TX 78249
Tel (210) 345-2000 SIC 2911 5172 5411
VICNRG LLC p 1555
930 S Kimball Ave Ste 100, Southlake TX 76092
Tel (817) 562-4888 SIC 5172
TRUMAN ARNOLD COMPANIES p 1486
701 S Robison Rd, Texarkana TX 75501
Tel (903) 794-3835 SIC 5172 4581
PETROLEUM WHOLESALE LP p 1139
8550 Technology Forest Pl, The Woodlands TX 77381
Tel (281) 681-7500 SIC 5172 5541
■ **COLT INTERNATIONAL LLC** p 339
300 Flint Ridge Rd, Webster TX 77598
Tel (281) 280-2100 SIC 6411 5172
CARDWELL DISTRIBUTING INC p 253
8137 S State St Bldg 1, Midvale UT 84047
Tel (801) 561-4251
SIC 5171 7549 5172 5983
BIG WEST OIL LLC p 182
333 W Center St, North Salt Lake UT 84054
Tel (801) 624-1000 SIC 2911 5172
PINNACLE ENERGY MARKETING LLC p 1149
90 S 400 W Ste 320, Salt Lake City UT 84101
Tel (435) 940-9001 SIC 5172
■ **QUESTAR CORP** p 1199
333 S State St, Salt Lake City UT 84111
Tel (801) 324-5900 SIC 4922 1311 5172
SINCLAIR OIL CORP p 1326
550 E South Temple, Salt Lake City UT 84102
Tel (801) 524-2700 SIC 2911 5172
SINCLAIR SERVICES CO p 1326
550 E South Temple, Salt Lake City UT 84102
Tel (801) 363-5100 SIC 5172
TURNER GAS CO INC p 1492
2825 W 500 S, Salt Lake City UT 84104
Tel (801) 973-6886 SIC 5172 4213
SHERMAN V ALLEN INC p 1316
126 Post St, Rutland VT 05701
Tel (802) 775-7421
SIC 5172 5984 5411 4923
R L VALLEE INC p 1202
282 S Main St, Saint Albans VT 05478
Tel (802) 524-8710 SIC 5172 5541
CHAMPLAIN OIL CO INC p 287
45 San Remo Dr, South Burlington VT 05403
Tel (802) 864-5380 SIC 5172 5984
DAVENPORT ENERGY INC p 415
108 Main St, Chatham VA 24531
Tel (434) 432-0251 SIC 5172 5983 5984
SWISSPORT FUELING INC p 1413
45025 Aviation Dr Ste 350, Dulles VA 20166
Tel (703) 742-4338 SIC 5172
CLINE ENERGY INC p 326
1890 S Main St, Harrisonburg VA 22801
Tel (540) 434-7344 SIC 5172 5541 1521
HOLTZMAN OIL CORP p 702
5534 Main St, Mount Jackson VA 22842
Tel (540) 477-3131 SIC 5172
I S O INDUSTRIES INC p 725
5353 E Princess Anne Rd F, Norfolk VA 23502
Tel (757) 855-0900 SIC 5172
MILLER OIL CO INC p 970
1000 E City Hall Ave, Norfolk VA 23504
Tel (757) 623-6600
SIC 5411 5172 5983 7549
GPM INVESTMENTS LLC p 627
8565 Magellan Pkwy # 400, Richmond VA 23227
Tel (804) 266-1363 SIC 5541 5411 5172
SOUTHERN STATES COOPERATIVE INC p 1350
6606 W Broad St Ste B, Richmond VA 23230
Tel (804) 281-1000
SIC 2048 0181 2873 2874 5191 5172
WOODFIN HEATING INC p 1623
1823 N Hamilton St, Richmond VA 23230
Tel (804) 730-4500
SIC 5172 5983 1711 7382

SKAGIT FARMERS SUPPLY p 1329
1833 Park Ln, Burlington WA 98233
Tel (360) 757-6053
SIC 5191 5172 5983 5451 5331 5261
R H SMITH DISTRIBUTING CO INC p 1202
315 E Wine Country Rd, Grandview WA 98930
Tel (509) 882-3377
SIC 5171 5541 5411 5172
SUN PACIFIC ENERGY INC p 1400
501 W Canal Dr, Kennewick WA 99336
Tel (509) 586-1135 SIC 5172 5541 5411
PETROCARD INC p 1139
730 Central Ave S, Kent WA 98032
Tel (253) 852-7801 SIC 5172
WHITTEN GROUP INTERNATIONAL CORP p 1607
2622 Lilac St, Longview WA 98632
Tel (360) 560-3319 SIC 5172 3559
WILSON OIL INC p 1614
95 Panel Way, Longview WA 98632
Tel (360) 575-9222 SIC 5541 5983 5172
US OIL TRADING LLC p 1532
3001 Marshall Ave, Tacoma WA 98421
Tel (253) 383-1651 SIC 5172
GLENN DISTRIBUTOR INC p 615
1301 N Wenatchee Ave, Wenatchee WA 98801
Tel (509) 663-7173 SIC 5172 5541 7359
EASTERN AMERICAN ENERGY CORP p 471
500 Corporate Lndg, Charleston WV 25311
Tel (304) 925-6100
SIC 1311 4922 5172 1321
R M ROACH & SONS INC p 1202
333 E John St, Martinsburg WV 25401
Tel (304) 263-3329 SIC 5541 5172
BRUCETON FARM SERVICE INC p 220
1768 Mileground Rd, Morgantown WV 26505
Tel (304) 291-6980
SIC 5411 5172 5999 5983 5812 2048
LARSEN COOPERATIVE CO p 845
8290 County Hwy T, Larsen WI 54947
Tel (920) 982-1111 SIC 5191 5172 5541
JACOBUS ENERGY INC p 775
11815 W Bradley Rd, Milwaukee WI 53224
Tel (414) 577-0217 SIC 5983 5172
PETROENERGY LLC p 1139
920 10th Ave N, Onalaska WI 54650
Tel (608) 783-6411 SIC 5171 4925 5172
TEXPAR ENERGY LLC p 1445
920 10th Ave N, Onalaska WI 54650
Tel (800) 323-7350 SIC 5171 4925 5172
CKT SERVICES INC p 320
412 N Main St Ste 100, Buffalo WY 82834
Tel (713) 581-0819 SIC 5172 7699

SIC 5181 Beer & Ale Wholesale

SUPREME BEVERAGE CO INC p 1408
3217 Messer Airport Hwy, Birmingham AL 35222
Tel (205) 251-8010 SIC 5181
ALLSTATE BEVERAGE CO INC p 58
130 6th St, Montgomery AL 36104
Tel (334) 265-0507 SIC 5181
ALLIANCE BEVERAGE DISTRIBUTING CO LLC p 54
1115 N 47th Ave, Phoenix AZ 85043
Tel (602) 760-5500 SIC 5182 5181
SOUTHERN GLAZERS WINE AND SPIRITS OF ARIZONA LLC p 1348
2375 S 45th Ave, Phoenix AZ 85043
Tel (602) 533-8000 SIC 5181 5182
GOLDEN EAGLE DISTRIBUTORS INC p 620
705 E Ajo Way, Tucson AZ 85713
Tel (520) 884-5999 SIC 5181 5149
STRAUB DISTRIBUTING CO LTD p 1393
4633 E La Palma Ave, Anaheim CA 92807
Tel (714) 779-4000 SIC 5181
CLASSIC DISTRIBUTING AND BEVERAGE GROUP INC p 323
120 Puente Ave, City Of Industry CA 91746
Tel (626) 330-8231 SIC 5181
HARALAMBOS BEVERAGE CO p 659
2300 Pellissier Pl, City Of Industry CA 90601
Tel (562) 347-4300 SIC 5181 5149
LIQUID INVESTMENTS INC p 870
3840 Via De La Valle # 300, Del Mar CA 92014
Tel (858) 509-8510 SIC 5181 5145 5182
DONAGHY SALES INC p 450
2363 S Cedar Ave, Fresno CA 93725
Tel (559) 486-0901 SIC 5181
FRESNO BEVERAGE CO INC p 579
4010 E Hardy Ave, Fresno CA 93725
Tel (559) 650-1500 SIC 5181
HARBOR DISTRIBUTING LLC p 659
5901 Bolsa Ave, Huntington Beach CA 92647
Tel (714) 933-2400 SIC 5181
TOPA EQUITIES LTD p 1460
1800 Ave Of The Ste 1400, Los Angeles CA 90067
Tel (310) 203-9199 SIC 6163 5181 7538
T F LOUDERBACK INC p 1419
700 National Ct, Richmond CA 94804
Tel (510) 965-6120
SIC 5181 5149 2037 2033
MARKSTEIN BEVERAGE CO OF SACRAMENTO p 909
60 Main Ave, Sacramento CA 95838
Tel (916) 920-3911 SIC 5181 5149
LENORE JOHN & CO p 856
1250 Delevan Dr, San Diego CA 92102
Tel (619) 232-6136 SIC 5149 5182 5181
JORDANOS INC p 793
550 S Patterson Ave, Santa Barbara CA 93111
Tel (805) 964-0611
SIC 5181 5182 5149 5141 5142 5148
TRIANGLE DISTRIBUTING CO p 1478
12065 Pike St, Santa Fe Springs CA 90670
Tel (562) 699-3424 SIC 5181
MATAGRANO INC p 919
440 Forbes Blvd, South San Francisco CA 94080
Tel (650) 829-4829 SIC 5181 5149

ALLIED BEVERAGES INC p 56
13235 Golden State Rd, Sylmar CA 91342
Tel (818) 493-6400 SIC 5181
NOR-CAL BEVERAGE CO INC p 1047
2150 Stone Blvd, West Sacramento CA 95691
Tel (916) 372-0600 SIC 5181 2086
■ **COORS DISTRIBUTING CO** p 368
5400 Pecos St, Denver CO 80221
Tel (303) 433-6541 SIC 5181 4212
WESTERN DISTRIBUTING CO p 1598
4955 Bannock St, Denver CO 80216
Tel (303) 388-5755 SIC 5181 5182
ALLAN S GOODMAN INC p 52
180 Goodwin St, East Hartford CT 06108
Tel (860) 289-2731 SIC 5181 5182
HARTFORD DISTRIBUTORS INC p 665
131 Chapel Rd, Manchester CT 06042
Tel (860) 643-2337 SIC 5181
BARTON BRESCOME INC p 158
69 Defco Park Rd, North Haven CT 06473
Tel (203) 239-4901 SIC 5182 5181
DICHELLO DISTRIBUTORS INC p 437
55 Marsh Hill Rd, Orange CT 06477
Tel (203) 891-2100 SIC 5182 5181
STAR DISTRIBUTORS INC p 1378
460 Frontage Rd, West Haven CT 06516
Tel (203) 932-3636 SIC 5181
RMET HOLDINGS INC p 1239
133 Sevilla Ave, Coral Gables FL 33134
Tel (305) 567-3582 SIC 5181 5182
GOLD COAST BEVERAGE LLC p 620
10055 Nw 12th St, Doral FL 33172
Tel (305) 591-9800 SIC 5181
CHAMPION BRANDS INC p 287
5571 Fl Min Blvd S, Jacksonville FL 32257
Tel (660) 885-8151 SIC 5181
JJ TAYLOR COMPANIES INC p 786
655 N Highway A1a, Jupiter FL 33477
Tel (813) 247-4000 SIC 5181
GOLD COAST EAGLE DISTRIBUTING LIMITED LIABILITY LIMITED PARTNERSHIP p 620
7051 Wireless Ct, Lakewood Ranch FL 34240
Tel (941) 355-7685 SIC 5181
SOUTHERN GLAZERS WINE AND SPIRITS LLC p 1348
1600 Nw 163rd St, Miami FL 33169
Tel (305) 625-4171 SIC 5182 5181
PREMIER BEVERAGE CO LLC p 1170
9801 Premier Pkwy, Miramar FL 33025
Tel (954) 436-9200 SIC 5181 5182
CITY BEVERAGES LLC p 312
10928 Florida Crown Dr, Orlando FL 32824
Tel (407) 851-7100 SIC 5181
GREAT BAY DISTRIBUTORS INC p 633
2750 Eagle Ave N, Saint Petersburg FL 33716
Tel (727) 584-8626 SIC 5181
PEPIN DISTRIBUTING CO p 1133
4121 N 50th St, Tampa FL 33610
Tel (813) 626-6176 SIC 5181
BROWN DISTRIBUTING CO INC p 219
1300 Allendale Rd, West Palm Beach FL 33405
Tel (561) 655-3791 SIC 5181
ATLANTA BEVERAGE CO p 125
5000 Fulton Indus Blvd Sw, Atlanta GA 30336
Tel (404) 699-6700 SIC 5181
GENERAL WHOLESALE CO p 602
1271 Tacoma Dr Nw, Atlanta GA 30318
Tel (404) 352-1041 SIC 5182 5181
NATIONAL DISTRIBUTING CO INC p 1011
1 National Dr Sw, Atlanta GA 30336
Tel (404) 696-1681 SIC 5182 5181
GEORGIA CROWN DISTRIBUTING CO p 607
100 Georgia Crown Dr, Mcdonough GA 30253
Tel (770) 302-3000 SIC 5182 5181
EAGLE ROCK DISTRIBUTING CO LLC p 468
6205 Best Friend Rd, Norcross GA 30071
Tel (770) 498-5500 SIC 5181 5182
UNISTAN INC p 1505
5500 United Dr Se, Smyrna GA 30082
Tel (678) 305-2080 SIC 5182 5181
PARADISE BEVERAGES INC p 1113
94-1450 Moaniani St, Waipahu HI 96797
Tel (808) 678-4000 SIC 5181 5182 5149
C STEIN INC p 233
4719 S Market St, Boise ID 83705
Tel (208) 378-0550
SIC 5181 5182 5149 4941 5921
■ **CROWN IMPORTS LLC** p 395
1 S Dearborn St Ste 1700, Chicago IL 60603
Tel (312) 873-9600 SIC 5181
WIRTZ BEVERAGE GROUP LLC p 1618
680 N Lake Shore Dr # 1900, Chicago IL 60611
Tel (312) 943-7000 SIC 5181 5182
WIRTZ CORP p 1618
680 N Lake Shore Dr # 1900, Chicago IL 60611
Tel (312) 943-7000
SIC 5181 5182 6513 6512 7011 6411
REYES HOLDINGS LLC p 1230
6250 N River Rd Ste 9000, Rosemont IL 60018
Tel (847) 227-6500 SIC 5181 5142
MONARCH BEVERAGE CO INC p 983
9347 Pendleton Pike, Indianapolis IN 46236
Tel (317) 612-1310 SIC 5181 5182
LDF SALES & DISTRIBUTING INC p 849
10610 E 26th Cir N, Wichita KS 67226
Tel (316) 636-5575 SIC 5181
CLARK DISTRIBUTING CO INC p 322
300 Oakland Flatrock Rd, Oakland KY 42159
Tel (270) 563-4735 SIC 5149 5181
MOCKLER BEVERAGE CO p 980
11811 Reiger Rd, Baton Rouge LA 70809
Tel (225) 408-4283 SIC 5181 5921
SOUTHERN EAGLE SALES & SERVICE LP p 1348
5300 Blair St, Metairie LA 70003
Tel (504) 733-8656 SIC 5181

SOUTHERN EAGLE SALES MANAGEMENT LLC p 1348
5300 Blair St, Metairie LA 70003
Tel (504) 733-8656 SIC 5181
CRESCENT CROWN DISTRIBUTING LLC p 391
5900 Almonaster Ave, New Orleans LA 70126
Tel (504) 240-5900 SIC 5181
PINE STATE TRADING CO p 1149
47 Market St, Gardiner ME 04345
Tel (207) 622-2345 SIC 5181 5194 5145
FREDERICK P WINNER LTD p 576
7001 Quad Ave, Baltimore MD 21237
Tel (410) 646-5500 SIC 5181 5182
MITCHELL BEVERAGE OF MARYLAND LLC p 977
7001 Quad Ave, Baltimore MD 21237
Tel (410) 646-5500 SIC 5181 5182
KRONHEIM CO INC p 830
8201 Stayton Dr, Jessup MD 20794
Tel (410) 724-3300 SIC 5182 5181
UNITED GROUP OPERATING COMPANIES LLC p 1508
175 Campanelli Dr, Braintree MA 02184
Tel (781) 348-8000 SIC 5181 5182
L KNIFE & SON INC p 834
35 Elder Ave, Kingston MA 02364
Tel (781) 585-2364 SIC 5181 5182
HORIZON BEVERAGE CO INC p 707
45 Commerce Way, Norton MA 02766
Tel (508) 587-1110 SIC 5181 5182
BURKE DISTRIBUTING CORP p 227
89 Teed Dr, Randolph MA 02368
Tel (781) 767-6056 SIC 5181
UNITED LIQUORS LLC p 1510
500 John Hancock Rd, Taunton MA 02780
Tel (781) 348-8000 SIC 5182 5181
FABIANO BROS INC p 523
1885 Bevanda Ct, Bay City MI 48706
Tel (989) 509-0200 SIC 5181 5182
ALLIANCE BEVERAGE DISTRIBUTING LLC p 54
4490 60th St Se, Grand Rapids MI 49512
Tel (616) 241-5022 SIC 5181
WOLPIN CO p 1621
1600 Modern St, Highland Park MI 48203
Tel (586) 757-4900 SIC 5181
CKL CORP p 320
3825 Emerald Dr, Kalamazoo MI 49001
Tel (269) 382-4200 SIC 5181 5182 5149
POWERS DISTRIBUTING CO INC p 1166
3700 Giddings Rd, Orion MI 48359
Tel (248) 393-3700 SIC 5181
MITCHELL DISTRIBUTING CO INC p 977
100 James E Chaney Dr, Meridian MS 39307
Tel (601) 482-6161 SIC 5181
SLBS MANAGEMENT INC p 1331
3201 Rider Trl S, Earth City MO 63045
Tel (314) 874-0400 SIC 5181
ANHEUSER-BUSCH INTERNATIONAL INC p 91
1 Busch Pl, Saint Louis MO 63118
Tel (314) 577-2000 SIC 5181
ANHEUSER-BUSCH LLC p 91
1 Busch Pl, Saint Louis MO 63118
Tel (314) 632-6777 SIC 5181 2082
LOHR DISTRIBUTING CO INC p 875
1100 S 9th St, Saint Louis MO 63104
Tel (314) 436-8299 SIC 5181
MAJOR BRANDS INC p 899
6701 Southwest Ave, Saint Louis MO 63143
Tel (314) 645-1843 SIC 5182 5181
BONANZA BEVERAGE CO p 199
6333 Ensworth St, Las Vegas NV 89119
Tel (702) 361-4166 SIC 5181
NEVADA BEVERAGE CO p 1028
3940 W Tropicana Ave, Las Vegas NV 89103
Tel (702) 739-9998 SIC 5181
GREAT STATE BEVERAGES INC p 634
1000 Quality Dr, Hooksett NH 03106
Tel (603) 644-2337 SIC 5181 5149 5145
HIGH GRADE BEVERAGE p 690
891 Georges Rd, Monmouth Junction NJ 08852
Tel (732) 821-7600 SIC 5181
ROUST CORP p 1253
3000 Atrium Way Ste 265, Mount Laurel NJ 08054
Tel (856) 273-6980 SIC 5181 2085 5182
PEERLESS BEVERAGE CO p 1127
1000 Floral Ave, Union NJ 07083
Tel (908) 351-0101 SIC 5181
MALOOF DISTRIBUTING LLC p 900
701 Comanche Rd Ne, Albuquerque NM 87107
Tel (505) 345-1218 SIC 5181 5149
PREMIER DISTRIBUTING CO p 1170
4321 Yale Blvd Ne, Albuquerque NM 87107
Tel (575) 524-1661 SIC 5181 5149
OAK BEVERAGES INC p 1070
1 Flower Ln, Blauvelt NY 10913
Tel (718) 652-8555 SIC 5181
MANHATTAN BEER DISTRIBUTORS LLC p 901
955 E 149th St, Bronx NY 10455
Tel (718) 292-9300 SIC 5181
PHOENIX BEVERAGES INC p 1144
2 Atlantic Ave Pier 7, Brooklyn NY 11201
Tel (718) 609-7200 SIC 5181
UB DISTRIBUTORS LLC p 1498
1213 Grand St, Brooklyn NY 11211
Tel (718) 497-2407 SIC 5181
JETRO CASH AND CARRY ENTERPRISES LLC p 784
1524 132nd St, College Point NY 11356
Tel (718) 939-6400
SIC 5142 5046 5181 5147 5411
JRD HOLDINGS INC p 795
1524 132nd St, College Point NY 11356
Tel (718) 762-8700
SIC 5141 5142 5147 5181 5194
RESTAURANT DEPOT LLC p 1228
1524 132nd St, College Point NY 11356
Tel (718) 762-8700
SIC 5147 5141 5142 5181 5194

CLARE ROSE INC p 321
100 Rose Executive Blvd, East Yaphank NY 11967
Tel (631) 475-2337 SIC 5181

WRIGHT WISNER DISTRIBUTING CORP p 1627
3165 Brghtn Hnrietta Twn, Rochester NY 14623
Tel (585) 427-2880 SIC 5181 5149

▲ CONSTELLATION BRANDS INC p 360
207 High Point Dr # 100, Victor NY 14564
Tel (585) 678-7100
SIC 2084 5182 5181 2082 2085 2087

HEINEKEN USA INC p 681
360 Hamilton Ave Ste 1103, White Plains NY 10601
Tel (914) 681-4100 SIC 5181

■ EMPIRE DISTRIBUTORS OF NORTH CAROLINA INC p 493
13833 Carowinds Blvd, Charlotte NC 28273
Tel (704) 588-9463 SIC 5182 5181

CAFFEY DISTRIBUTING CO INC p 237
8749 W Market St, Greensboro NC 27409
Tel (336) 668-0877 SIC 5181

R H BARRINGER DISTRIBUTING CO INC p 1202
1620 Fairfax Rd, Greensboro NC 27407
Tel (336) 854-0555 SIC 5181

UNITED BEVERAGES OF NORTH CAROLINA LLC p 1506
105 9th St Nw, Hickory NC 28601
Tel (828) 322-1933 SIC 5181

BJT INC p 186
2233 Capital Blvd, Raleigh NC 27604
Tel (919) 828-3842 SIC 5182 5149 5181

LONG BEVERAGE INC p 876
10500 World Trade Blvd, Raleigh NC 27617
Tel (919) 481-2738 SIC 5181 5149

COASTAL BEVERAGE CO INC p 331
301 Harley Dr, Wilmington NC 28405
Tel (910) 799-3011 SIC 5181

HOUSE OF LA ROSE CLEVELAND INC p 711
6745 Southpointe Pkwy, Brecksville OH 44141
Tel (440) 746-7500 SIC 5181

COLUMBUS DISTRIBUTING CO p 342
4949 Freeway Dr E, Columbus OH 43229
Tel (614) 846-1000 SIC 5181

DAYTON HEIDELBERG DISTRIBUTING CO p 417
3601 Dryden Rd, Moraine OH 45439
Tel (937) 222-8692 SIC 5181

CAPITAL DISTRIBUTING LLC p 249
421 N Portland Ave, Oklahoma City OK 73107
Tel (405) 521-1511 SIC 5181

MAJOR EAGLE INC p 899
2350 W Broadway, Eugene OR 97402
Tel (541) 345-8421
SIC 5181 5141 5194 5142

CDC OREGON INC p 270
3601 Nw Yeon Ave, Portland OR 97210
Tel (503) 289-9600 SIC 5182 5181 5149

ANTONIO ORIGLIO INC p 94
3000 Meetinghouse Rd, Philadelphia PA 19154
Tel (215) 698-9500 SIC 5181

FRANK B FUHRER HOLDINGS INC p 574
3100 E Carson St, Pittsburgh PA 15203
Tel (412) 488-8844 SIC 5181

B FERNANDEZ & HNOS INC p 142
Carr 5 305 Urb Rr St Ca, Bayamon PR 00961
Tel (787) 288-7272 SIC 5181 5141 5182

C C 1 BEER DISTRIBUTORS INC p 232
107 Carr 174, Bayamon PR 00959
Tel (787) 288-6400 SIC 5181

V SUAREZ & CO INC p 1538
Industrial Luchetti # 300, Bayamon PR 00961
Tel (787) 792-1212 SIC 5181 5141 5182

YAHNIS CO p 1633
1440 N Schlitz Dr, Florence SC 29501
Tel (843) 662-6627 SIC 5181

■ PEPSI BEVERAGES CO p 1134
110 S Byhalia Rd, Collierville TN 38017
Tel (901) 853-5736 SIC 2086 5181

CHEROKEE DISTRIBUTING CO INC p 294
200 Miller Main Cir, Knoxville TN 37919
Tel (865) 588-7641 SIC 5181

DET DISTRIBUTING CO p 433
301 Great Circle Rd, Nashville TN 37228
Tel (615) 244-4113 SIC 5181

BROWN DISTRIBUTING CO LTD p 219
8711 Johnny Morris Rd, Austin TX 78724
Tel (512) 478-9353 SIC 5181

COORS OF AUSTIN LP p 368
10300 Metropolitan Dr, Austin TX 78758
Tel (512) 837-6550 SIC 5181

ANDREWS DISTRIBUTING CO OF NORTH TEXAS LLC p 90
2730 Irving Blvd, Dallas TX 75207
Tel (214) 525-9400 SIC 5181

BEN E KEITH CO p 172
601 E 7th St, Fort Worth TX 76102
Tel (817) 877-5700 SIC 5181 5141

COORS DISTRIBUTING CO OF FORT WORTH p 368
2550 Mcmillian Pkwy, Fort Worth TX 76137
Tel (817) 838-1600 SIC 5181

FAUST DC LTD p 531
10040 East Fwy, Houston TX 77029
Tel (713) 673-5111 SIC 5181

SILVER EAGLE DISTRIBUTORS LIMITED PARTNERSHIP p 1323
7777 Washington Ave, Houston TX 77007
Tel (713) 869-4361 SIC 5181

SILVER EAGLE DISTRIBUTORS LLC p 1323
7777 Washington Ave, Houston TX 77007
Tel (713) 869-4361 SIC 5181

L & F DISTRIBUTORS LLC p 833
3900 N Mccoll Rd, Mcallen TX 78501
Tel (956) 687-7751 SIC 5181

STANDARD SALES CO LP p 1376
4800 E 42nd St Ste 400, Odessa TX 79762
Tel (432) 367-7662 SIC 5181

GAMBRINUS CO p 590
14800 San Pedro Ave # 310, San Antonio TX 78232
Tel (210) 483-5100 SIC 5181 2082

GLI INC p 615
803 S Medina St, San Antonio TX 78207
Tel (210) 226-4376 SIC 5181

DEL PAPA DISTRIBUTING CO LP p 423
120 Gulf Fwy, Texas City TX 77591
Tel (409) 842-5215 SIC 5181

GENERAL DISTRIBUTING CO p 600
5350 W Amelia Earhart Dr, Salt Lake City UT 84116
Tel (801) 531-7895 SIC 5181

BLUE RIDGE BEVERAGE CO INC p 192
4446 Barley Dr, Salem VA 24153
Tel (540) 380-2000 SIC 5181 5182

STEIN DISTRIBUTING INC p 1385
5408 Ne 88th St Ste B101, Vancouver WA 98665
Tel (360) 693-8251 SIC 5181 5182

HOPUNION LLC p 706
203 Division St, Yakima WA 98902
Tel (509) 453-4792 SIC 5181

GENERAL BEVERAGE SALES CO-MILWAUKEE p 599
6169 Mckee Rd, Fitchburg WI 53719
Tel (608) 271-1237 SIC 5182 5181

FRANK LIQUOR CO INC p 574
2115 Pleasant View Rd, Middleton WI 53562
Tel (608) 836-6000 SIC 5182 5181

BEECHWOOD DISTRIBUTORS INC p 168
5350 S Emmer Dr, New Berlin WI 53151
Tel (262) 717-2831 SIC 5181

BEER CAPITOL DISTRIBUTING INC p 168
W222n5700 Miller Way, Sussex WI 53089
Tel (262) 932-2337 SIC 5181

SIC 5182 Wine & Distilled Alcoholic Beverages Wholesale

ALLIANCE BEVERAGE DISTRIBUTING CO LLC p 54
1115 N 47th Ave, Phoenix AZ 85043
Tel (602) 760-5500 SIC 5182 5181

SOUTHERN GLAZERS WINE AND SPIRITS OF ARIZONA LLC p 1348
2375 S 45th Ave, Phoenix AZ 85043
Tel (602) 533-8000 SIC 5181 5182

YOUNGS MARKET CO OF ARIZONA LLC p 1639
402 S 54th Pl, Phoenix AZ 85034
Tel (602) 233-1900 SIC 5182

BRONCO WINE CO p 217
6342 Bystrum Rd, Ceres CA 95307
Tel (209) 538-3131 SIC 5182 2084

BEN MYERSON CANDY CO INC p 172
6550 E Washington Blvd, Commerce CA 90040
Tel (800) 331-2829 SIC 5182 5023

LIQUID INVESTMENTS INC p 870
3840 Via De La Valle # 300, Del Mar CA 92014
Tel (858) 509-8510 SIC 5181 5145 5182

FRANK-LIN DISTILLERS PRODUCTS LTD p 574
2455 Huntington Dr, Fairfield CA 94533
Tel (408) 259-8900 SIC 5182 2085

VINO FARMS LLC p 1558
1377 E Lodi Ave, Lodi CA 95240
Tel (209) 334-6975 SIC 5182

FAIRN & SWANSON INC p 525
400 Lancaster St, Oakland CA 94601
Tel (510) 533-8260 SIC 5122 5182

LENORE JOHN & CO p 856
1250 Delevan Dr, San Diego CA 92102
Tel (619) 232-6136 SIC 5149 5182 5181

JORDANOS INC p 793
550 S Patterson Ave, Santa Barbara CA 93111
Tel (805) 964-0611
SIC 5181 5182 5149 5141 5142 5148

NASSAU-SOSNICK DISTRIBUTION CO LLC p 1009
258 Littlefield Ave, South San Francisco CA 94080
Tel (650) 952-2226 SIC 5149 5145 5182

YOUNGS HOLDINGS INC p 1639
14402 Franklin Ave, Tustin CA 92780
Tel (714) 368-4615 SIC 5182

YOUNGS INTERCO INC p 1639
14402 Franklin Ave, Tustin CA 92780
Tel (714) 368-4615 SIC 5182

YOUNGS MARKET CO LLC p 1639
14402 Franklin Ave, Tustin CA 92780
Tel (714) 368-4615 SIC 5182

DBI BEVERAGE SACRAMENTO p 418
3500 Carlin Dr, West Sacramento CA 95691
Tel (916) 373-5700 SIC 5182 5149

BEVERAGE DISTRIBUTORS CO LLC p 178
14200 E Moncrieff Pl, Aurora CO 80011
Tel (303) 371-3421 SIC 5182

WESTERN DISTRIBUTING CO p 1598
4955 Bannock St, Denver CO 80216
Tel (303) 388-5755 SIC 5181 5182

ALLAN S GOODMAN INC p 52
180 Goodwin St, East Hartford CT 06108
Tel (860) 289-2731 SIC 5181 5182

BARTON BRESCOME INC p 158
69 Defco Park Rd, North Haven CT 06473
Tel (203) 239-4901 SIC 5182 5181

DICHELLO DISTRIBUTORS INC p 437
55 Marsh Hill Rd, Orange CT 06477
Tel (203) 891-2100 SIC 5182 5181

WJ DEUTSCH & SONS LTD p 1619
201 Tresser Blvd Ste 324, Stamford CT 06901
Tel (914) 305-5765 SIC 5182

CONNECTICUT DISTRIBUTORS INC p 357
333 Lordship Blvd, Stratford CT 06615
Tel (203) 377-1440 SIC 5182

HARTLEY & PARKER LIMITED INC p 666
100 Browning St, Stratford CT 06615
Tel (203) 375-5671 SIC 5182

BACARDI USA INC p 143
2701 S Le Jeune Rd, Coral Gables FL 33134
Tel (305) 573-8600 SIC 5182

RMET HOLDINGS INC p 1239
133 Sevilla Ave, Coral Gables FL 33134
Tel (305) 567-3582 SIC 5181 5182

PERNOD RICARD AMERICAS TRAVEL RETAIL INC p 1136
200 E Las Olas Blvd, Fort Lauderdale FL 33301
Tel (954) 940-9000 SIC 5182

SEMINOLE TRIBE OF FLORIDA INC p 1302
6300 Stirling Rd, Hollywood FL 33024
Tel (954) 966-6300
SIC 7999 5194 2011 5182 2911

DFA HOLDINGS INC p 435
6100 Hllywood Blvd Fl 7, Miami FL 33180
Tel (954) 986-7700 SIC 5182 5399

EAGLE BRANDS WEDCO LIMITED PARTNERSHIP p 467
3201 Nw 72nd Ave, Miami FL 33122
Tel (305) 599-2337 SIC 5182

SGWSNHC LLC p 1310
1600 Nw 163rd St, Miami FL 33169
Tel (305) 625-4171 SIC 5182

SOUTHERN GLAZERS WINE AND SPIRITS LLC p 1348
1600 Nw 163rd St, Miami FL 33169
Tel (305) 625-4171 SIC 5182 5181

PREMIER BEVERAGE CO LLC p 1170
9801 Premier Pkwy, Miramar FL 33025
Tel (954) 436-9200 SIC 5181 5182

SHAW-ROSS INTERNATIONAL IMPORTERS INC p 1313
2900 Sw 149th Ave Ste 200, Miramar FL 33027
Tel (954) 430-5020 SIC 5182

SHAW-ROSS INTERNATIONAL IMPORTERS LLC p 1313
2900 Sw 149th Ave Ste 200, Miramar FL 33027
Tel (954) 430-5020 SIC 5182

MOTCO INC p 992
7900 Sw 57th Ave Ste 10, South Miami FL 33143
Tel (305) 662-8814 SIC 5182 5122 5199

JOHNSON BROTHERS OF FLORIDA INC p 790
4520 S Church Ave, Tampa FL 33611
Tel (813) 832-4477 SIC 5182 5149

■ EMPIRE DISTRIBUTORS INC p 493
3755 Atlanta Indus Pkwy, Atlanta GA 30331
Tel (404) 572-4100 SIC 5182

GENERAL WHOLESALE CO p 602
1271 Tacoma Dr Nw, Atlanta GA 30318
Tel (404) 352-1041 SIC 5182 5181

NATIONAL DISTRIBUTING CO INC p 1011
1 National Dr Sw, Atlanta GA 30336
Tel (404) 696-1681 SIC 5182 5181

GEORGIA CROWN DISTRIBUTING CO p 607
100 Georgia Crown Dr, Mcdonough GA 30253
Tel (770) 302-3000 SIC 5182 5181

EAGLE ROCK DISTRIBUTING CO LLC p 468
6205 Best Friend Rd, Norcross GA 30071
Tel (770) 498-5500 SIC 5181 5182

UNISTAN INC p 1505
5500 United Dr Se, Smyrna GA 30082
Tel (678) 305-2080 SIC 5182 5181

UNITED DISTRIBUTORS INC p 1507
5500 United Dr Se, Smyrna GA 30082
Tel (678) 305-2000 SIC 5182

PARADISE BEVERAGES INC p 1113
94-1450 Moaniani St, Waipahu HI 96797
Tel (808) 678-4000 SIC 5181 5182 5149

C STEIN INC p 233
4719 S Market St, Boise ID 83705
Tel (208) 378-0550
SIC 5181 5182 5149 4941 5921

SOUTHERN GLAZERS WINE AND SPIRITS OF ILLINOIS LLC p 1348
300 E Crossroads Pkwy, Bolingbrook IL 60440
Tel (630) 685-3000 SIC 5182

CONSOLIDATED ENTERPRISES INC p 359
680 N Lake Shore Dr Fl 19, Chicago IL 60611
Tel (312) 943-7000 SIC 5182

WIRTZ BEVERAGE GROUP LLC p 1618
680 N Lake Shore Dr # 1900, Chicago IL 60611
Tel (312) 943-7000 SIC 5181 5182

WIRTZ CORP p 1618
680 N Lake Shore Dr # 1900, Chicago IL 60611
Tel (312) 943-7000
SIC 5181 5182 6513 6512 7011 6411

BREAKTHRU BEVERAGE ILLINOIS LLC p 209
3333 S Laramie Ave, Cicero IL 60804
Tel (708) 298-3333 SIC 5182

COOPERS HAWK INTERMEDIATE HOLDING LLC p 367
5325 9th Ave, Countryside IL 60525
Tel (708) 839-2920
SIC 8741 2084 5182 5812

TERLATO WINE GROUP LTD p 1439
900 Armour Dr, Lake Bluff IL 60044
Tel (847) 604-8900 SIC 5182 2084 8743

GLAZERS DISTRIBUTORS OF INDIANA LLC p 614
5337 W 78th St, Indianapolis IN 46268
Tel (317) 876-1188 SIC 5182

MONARCH BEVERAGE CO INC p 983
9347 Pendleton Pike, Indianapolis IN 46236
Tel (317) 612-1310 SIC 5181 5182

NATIONAL WINE & SPIRITS INC p 1017
733 S West St, Indianapolis IN 46225
Tel (317) 636-6092 SIC 5182

SAZERAC CO INC p 1285
3850 N Causeway Blvd # 1695, Metairie LA 70002
Tel (504) 831-9450 SIC 5182 2085

REPUBLIC NATIONAL DISTRIBUTING CO LLC p 1225
809 Jefferson Hwy, New Orleans LA 70121
Tel (404) 696-9440 SIC 5182

FREDERICK P WINNER LTD p 576
7001 Quad Ave, Baltimore MD 21237
Tel (410) 646-5500 SIC 5181 5182

MITCHELL BEVERAGE OF MARYLAND LLC p 977
7001 Quad Ave, Baltimore MD 21237
Tel (410) 646-5500 SIC 5181 5182

RELIABLE CHURCHILL LLLP p 1221
1413 Tangier Dr, Baltimore MD 21220
Tel (410) 439-5000 SIC 5182

KRONHEIM CO INC p 830
8201 Stayton Dr, Jessup MD 20794
Tel (410) 724-3300 SIC 5182 5181

UNITED GROUP OPERATING COMPANIES LLC p 1508
175 Campanelli Dr, Braintree MA 02184
Tel (781) 348-8000 SIC 5181 5182

L KNIFE & SON INC p 834
35 Elder Ave, Kingston MA 02364
Tel (781) 585-2364 SIC 5181 5182

HORIZON BEVERAGE CO INC p 707
45 Commerce Way, Norton MA 02766
Tel (508) 587-1110 SIC 5181 5182

M S WALKER INC p 890
20 3rd Ave, Somerville MA 02143
Tel (617) 776-6700 SIC 5182

MARTIGNETTI CORP p 912
500 John Hancock Rd, Taunton MA 02780
Tel (781) 278-2000 SIC 5182 5921

MARTIGNETTI GROCERY CO INC p 912
500 John Hancock Rd, Taunton MA 02780
Tel (781) 278-2000 SIC 5182

UNITED LIQUORS LLC p 1510
500 John Hancock Rd, Taunton MA 02780
Tel (781) 348-8000 SIC 5182 5181

FABIANO BROS INC p 523
1885 Bevanda Ct, Bay City MI 48706
Tel (989) 509-0200 SIC 5181 5182

NWS MICHIGAN INC p 1068
17550 Allen Rd, Brownstown MI 48193
Tel (734) 324-3000 SIC 5182

GREAT LAKES WINE & SPIRITS LLC p 634
373 Victor St, Highland Park MI 48203
Tel (313) 278-5400 SIC 5182 2084

CKL CORP p 320
3825 Emerald Dr, Kalamazoo MI 49001
Tel (269) 382-4200 SIC 5181 5182 5149

JOHNSON BROTHERS LIQUOR CO p 790
1999 Shepard Rd, Saint Paul MN 55116
Tel (651) 649-5800 SIC 5182 5149

D & D DISTRIBUTORS LLLP p 406
2340 Millpark Dr, Maryland Heights MO 63043
Tel (314) 429-9100 SIC 5182 5149

MAJOR BRANDS INC p 899
6701 Southwest Ave, Saint Louis MO 63143
Tel (314) 645-1843 SIC 5182 5181

FEDWAY ASSOCIATES INC p 537
505 Martinsville Rd Fl 1, Basking Ridge NJ 07920
Tel (973) 624-6444 SIC 5182

ALLIED BEVERAGE GROUP LLC p 56
600 Washington Ave, Carlstadt NJ 07072
Tel (201) 842-6200 SIC 5182

B D AMERICAN CO p 141
25 De Boer Dr, Glen Rock NJ 07452
Tel (201) 689-1200 SIC 5182

PROXIMO SPIRITS INC p 1187
333 Washington St Ste 401, Jersey City NJ 07302
Tel (201) 204-1720 SIC 5182

WINEBOW INC p 1616
75 Chestnut Ridge Rd # 1, Montvale NJ 07645
Tel (201) 445-0620 SIC 5182

ROUST CORP p 1253
3000 Atrium Way Ste 265, Mount Laurel NJ 08054
Tel (856) 273-6980 SIC 5181 2085 5182

R & R MARKETING LLC p 1201
10 Patton Dr, West Caldwell NJ 07006
Tel (973) 228-5100 SIC 5182

CHARMER INDUSTRIES INC p 290
1950 48th St, Astoria NY 11105
Tel (718) 726-2500 SIC 5182

EMPIRE MERCHANTS LLC p 493
16 Bridgewater St, Brooklyn NY 11222
Tel (718) 383-5500 SIC 5182

PEERLESS IMPORTERS INC p 1127
16 Bridgewater St, Brooklyn NY 11222
Tel (718) 383-5500 SIC 5182

EMPIRE MERCHANTS NORTH LLC p 493
16 Houghtaling Rd, Coxsackie NY 12051
Tel (518) 731-5200 SIC 5182

BREAKTHRU BEVERAGE GROUP LLC p 209
60 E 42nd St Ste 1915, New York NY 10165
Tel (212) 699-7000 SIC 5182

MOET HENNESSY USA INC p 982
85 10th Ave Fl 2, New York NY 10011
Tel (212) 888-7575
SIC 0172 2844 6153 5182 5122

QUAKER EQUITIES LTD p 1196
257 Park Ave S Fl 7, New York NY 10010
Tel (212) 473-1510 SIC 5182

REMY COINTREAU USA INC p 1222
1290 Ave Of The Americas, New York NY 10104
Tel (646) 277-2307 SIC 5182

SUNBELT BEVERAGE CO LLC p 1401
60 E 42nd St Ste 1915, New York NY 10165
Tel (212) 699-7000 SIC 5182

SWSNY INC p 1413
345 Underhill Blvd, Syosset NY 11791
Tel (516) 921-9005 SIC 5182

▲ CONSTELLATION BRANDS INC p 360
207 High Point Dr # 100, Victor NY 14564
Tel (585) 678-7100
SIC 2084 5182 5181 2082 2085 2087

■ EMPIRE DISTRIBUTORS OF NORTH CAROLINA INC p 493
13833 Carowinds Blvd, Charlotte NC 28273
Tel (704) 588-9463 SIC 5182 5181

BJT INC p 186
2233 Capital Blvd, Raleigh NC 27604
Tel (919) 828-3842 SIC 5182 5149 5181

CDC OREGON INC p 270
3601 Nw Yeon Ave, Portland OR 97210
Tel (503) 289-9600 SIC 5182 5181 5149

COHO DISTRIBUTING LLC p 335
6840 N Cutter Cir, Portland OR 97217
Tel (503) 289-9600 SIC 5182

B FERNANDEZ & HNOS INC p 142
Carr 5 305 Urb Rr St Ca, Bayamon PR 00961
Tel (787) 288-7272 SIC 5181 5141 5182

V SUAREZ & CO INC p 1538
Industrial Luchetti 300 C, Bayamon PR 00961
Tel (787) 792-1212 SIC 5182 5149

V SUAREZ & CO INC p 1538
Industrial Luchetti # 300, Bayamon PR 00961
Tel (787) 792-1212 SIC 5181 5141 5182

BALLESTER HERMANOS INC p 148
Carr 869 Parq, Catano PR 00962
Tel (787) 788-4110 SIC 5141 5182

MENDEZ & CO INC p 943
Km 2/4 Mrtnez Nadal Rr 20, Guaynabo PR 00969
Tel (787) 793-8888 SIC 5182 5141

PLAZA PROVISION CO (PUERTO RICO) p 1156
Carretera 165 Esq, Guaynabo PR 00965
Tel (787) 781-2070 SIC 5182 4222 2841

BEN ARNOLD-SUNBELT BEVERAGE CO OF SOUTH CAROLINA L P p 172
101 Beverage Blvd, Ridgeway SC 29130
Tel (803) 337-3500 SIC 5182

AJAX TURNER CO INC p 41
4010 Centre Pointe Dr, La Vergne TN 37086
Tel (615) 244-2424 SIC 5182

LIPMAN BROTHERS LLC p 870
411 Great Circle Rd, Nashville TN 37228
Tel (615) 244-2230 SIC 5182

SOUTHERN GLAZERS WINE AND SPIRITS OF CANADA LLC p 1348
14911 Quorum Dr Ste 150, Dallas TX 75254
Tel (972) 392-8200 SIC 5182

SOUTHERN GLAZERS WINE AND SPIRITS OF TEXAS LLC p 1348
14911 Quorum Dr Ste 150, Dallas TX 75254
Tel (972) 392-8200 SIC 2082 5182 5199

REPUBLIC NATIONAL DISTRIBUTING CO LLC p 1225
8045 Northcourt Rd, Houston TX 77040
Tel (813) 885-3200 SIC 5182

RNDC TEXAS LLC p 1240
6511 Tri County Pkwy, Schertz TX 78154
Tel (210) 224-7531 SIC 5182

COUNTRY VINTNER INC p 375
12305 N Lakeridge Pkwy, Ashland VA 23005
Tel (804) 752-3670 SIC 5182

WINEBOW GROUP LLC p 1616
4800 Cox Rd Ste 300, Glen Allen VA 23060
Tel (804) 752-3670 SIC 5182

BLUE RIDGE BEVERAGE CO INC p 192
4446 Barley Dr, Salem VA 24153
Tel (540) 380-2000 SIC 5181 5182

ASSOCIATED DISTRIBUTORS LLC p 120
5800 Technology Blvd, Sandston VA 23150
Tel (757) 424-6300 SIC 5182

SOUTHERN WINE & SPIRITS-PACIFIC NORTHWEST HOLDINGS LLC p 1351
10500 Ne 8th St Ste 2000, Bellevue WA 98004
Tel (425) 456-3535 SIC 5182

COLUMBIA DISTRIBUTING OF SEATTLE LLC p 340
20301 59th Pl S, Kent WA 98032
Tel (425) 251-9300 SIC 5182

K AND L DISTRIBUTORS INC p 798
3215 Lind Ave Sw, Renton WA 98057
Tel (206) 454-8800 SIC 5182

PRECEPT BRANDS LLC p 1168
1910 Frview Ave E Ste 400, Seattle WA 98102
Tel (206) 267-5252 SIC 5182

STEIN DISTRIBUTING INC p 1385
5408 Ne 88th St Ste B101, Vancouver WA 98665
Tel (360) 693-8251 SIC 5181 5182

WATERBROOK WINERY INC p 1581
10518 W Highway 12, Walla Walla WA 99362
Tel (509) 522-1262 SIC 5182

GENERAL BEVERAGE SALES CO-MILWAUKEE p 599
6169 Mckee Rd, Fitchburg WI 53719
Tel (608) 271-1237 SIC 5182 5181

BADGER LIQUOR CO INC p 143
850 Morris St, Fond Du Lac WI 54935
Tel (920) 923-8160 SIC 5182

FRANK LIQUOR CO INC p 574
2115 Pleasant View Rd, Middleton WI 53562
Tel (608) 836-6000 SIC 5182 5181

SIC 5191 Farm Splys Wholesale

AGRI-AFC LLC p 36
121 Somerville Rd Ne, Decatur AL 35601
Tel (256) 560-2848
SIC 5159 5153 5083 5191

ALABAMA FARMERS COOPERATIVE INC p 43
121 Somerville Rd Ne, Decatur AL 35601
Tel (256) 353-6843 SIC 5191 5153 5159

FARMERS SUPPLY ASSOCIATION p 530
16240 Highway 14 E, Harrisburg AR 72432
Tel (870) 578-2468
SIC 5191 5172 5261 5541 5999

E RITTER SEED CO p 467
300 Adamson St, Marked Tree AR 72365
Tel (870) 358-2130 SIC 5153 5191

BRUCE OAKLEY INC p 220
3700 Lincoln Ave, North Little Rock AR 72114
Tel (501) 945-0875
SIC 4449 5153 5261 5191 4213

OAKLEY INTERNATIONAL LLC p 1071
3700 Lincoln Ave, North Little Rock AR 72114
Tel (501) 945-0875 SIC 5191

FARMERS COOPERATIVE p 529
2105 Industrial Park Rd, Van Buren AR 72956
Tel (479) 474-8051 SIC 5191

HART CHEMICALS INC p 664
2424 4th St, Berkeley CA 94710
Tel (510) 549-3535 SIC 5191 5169

BUTTONWILLOW WAREHOUSE CO INC p 230
125 Front St, Buttonwillow CA 93206
Tel (661) 764-5234 SIC 5191

TECH AGRICULTURAL INC p 1430
125 Front St, Buttonwillow CA 93206
Tel (661) 323-1001 SIC 5191

BRITZ FERTILIZERS INC p 214
3265 W Figarden Dr, Fresno CA 93711
Tel (559) 448-8000 SIC 5191

INTEGRATED AGRIBUSINESS PROFESSIONALS COOPERATIVE INC p 749
7108 N Fresno St Ste 150, Fresno CA 93720
Tel (559) 440-1980 SIC 5191

WESTERN MILLING LLC p 1599
31120 West St, Goshen CA 93227
Tel (559) 302-1000 SIC 5191

KEITHLY-WILLIAMS SEEDS INC p 808
420 Palm Ave, Holtville CA 92250
Tel (760) 356-5533 SIC 5191 0721 0181

L A HEARNE CO p 833
512 Metz Rd, King City CA 93930
Tel (831) 385-5441
SIC 5191 0723 5699 4214 2048 5261

MID VALLEY AGRICULTURAL SERVICES INC p 963
16401 E Highway 26, Linden CA 95236
Tel (209) 931-7600 SIC 5191

FOSTER POULTRY FARMS p 570
1000 Davis St, Livingston CA 95334
Tel (209) 394-6914
SIC 0254 2015 5812 0173 5191 4212

TORN & GLASSER INC p 1461
1622 E Olympic Blvd, Los Angeles CA 90021
Tel (213) 593-1332
SIC 5149 5153 5145 5191

STANISLAUS FARM SUPPLY CO p 1377
624 E Service Rd, Modesto CA 95358
Tel (860) 678-5160 SIC 5191

SAKATA SEED AMERICA INC p 1271
18095 Serene Dr, Morgan Hill CA 95037
Tel (408) 778-7758 SIC 5191 0182

A L GILBERT CO p 6
304 N Yosemite Ave, Oakdale CA 95361
Tel (209) 847-1721 SIC 5191

■ SEMINIS VEGETABLE SEEDS INC p 1302
2700 Camino Del Sol, Oxnard CA 93030
Tel (855) 733-3834 SIC 5191 0723

BUTTE COUNTY RICE GROWERS ASSOCIATION INC p 230
1193 Richvale Hwy, Richvale CA 95974
Tel (530) 345-7103 SIC 5191 0723 5261

L & L NURSERY SUPPLY INC p 833
2552 Shenandoah Way, San Bernardino CA 92407
Tel (909) 591-0461
SIC 5191 2875 2449 5193

WILBUR-ELLIS CO LLC p 1608
345 California St Fl 27, San Francisco CA 94104
Tel (415) 772-4000 SIC 5191 0711

WILBUR-ELLIS HOLDINGS II INC p 1608
345 California St Fl 27, San Francisco CA 94104
Tel (415) 772-4000 SIC 5999 5191 5169

JACOB STERN & SONS INC p 775
1464 E Valley Rd, Santa Barbara CA 93108
Tel (805) 565-4532 SIC 5169 5191 5199

■ EXCEL GARDEN PRODUCTS p 516
10708 Norwalk Blvd, Santa Fe Springs CA 90670
Tel (562) 567-2000 SIC 5191

SELEY & CO p 1302
1515 Hope St, South Pasadena CA 91030
Tel (626) 799-1196 SIC 5191

J D HEISKELL HOLDINGS LLC p 770
1939 Hillman St, Tulare CA 93274
Tel (559) 685-6100 SIC 5191 5999

ASSOCIATED FEED & SUPPLY CO p 120
5213 W Main St, Turlock CA 95380
Tel (209) 667-2708 SIC 5191

FRUIT GROWERS SUPPLY CO INC p 582
27770 N Entrmt Dr Fl 3, Valencia CA 91355
Tel (818) 986-6480
SIC 2653 0811 5191 2448 5113

▲ CENTRAL GARDEN & PET CO p 278
1340 Treat Blvd Ste 600, Walnut Creek CA 94597
Tel (925) 948-4000 SIC 5199 5191

AL DAHRA ACX GLOBAL INC p 43
920 E Pacific Coast Hwy, Wilmington CA 90744
Tel (209) 465-3718 SIC 5191

LYMAN GROUP INC p 887
201 East St, Woodland CA 95776
Tel (530) 662-5442 SIC 5191

TREMONT GROUP INC p 1476
201 East St, Woodland CA 95776
Tel (530) 662-5442 SIC 5191

AGFINITY INC p 34
260 Factory Rd, Eaton CO 80615
Tel (970) 454-4000
SIC 5172 2048 7549 5191

DASCO INC p 413
9785 Maroon Cir Ste 110, Englewood CO 80112
Tel (303) 350-5050 SIC 5191

AGU US HOLDINGS INC p 36
7251 W 4th St, Greeley CO 80634
Tel (970) 356-4400 SIC 2879 5191

■ ANIMAL HEALTH INTERNATIONAL INC p 91
822 7th St Ste 740, Greeley CO 80631
Tel (970) 353-2600
SIC 5122 5047 5999 5191 5083 5154

GRAINLAND COOPERATIVE p 629
421 S Colorado Ave, Haxtun CO 80731
Tel (970) 774-6166
SIC 5191 4221 5531 5541

CROP PRODUCTION SERVICES INC p 393
3005 Rocky Mountain Ave, Loveland CO 80538
Tel (970) 685-3300 SIC 5191

STRATTON EQUITY COOPERATIVE CO p 1393
98 Colorado Ave, Stratton CO 80836
Tel (719) 348-5326
SIC 5153 5191 5171 5541

■ SHEMIN NURSERIES INC p 1315
42 Old Ridgebury Rd Ste 3, Danbury CT 06810
Tel (203) 207-5000 SIC 5191 5193

H J BAKER & BRO INC p 650
2 Corporate Dr Ste 545, Shelton CT 06484
Tel (203) 682-9200 SIC 2048 5191 5052

SYNGENTA CORP p 1415
3411 Silverside Rd # 100, Wilmington DE 19810
Tel (302) 425-2000 SIC 2879 5191 8741

HAIFA NORTH AMERICA INC p 653
307 Cranes Roost Blvd, Altamonte Springs FL 32701
Tel (407) 862-6400 SIC 5191 5169

HARRELLS INC p 663
720 Kraft Rd, Lakeland FL 33815
Tel (863) 687-2774 SIC 2875 5191

HARRELLS LLC p 663
5105 New Tampa Hwy, Lakeland FL 33815
Tel (863) 687-2774 SIC 2875 5191

SUNNILAND CORP p 1403
1735 State Road 419, Longwood FL 32750
Tel (407) 322-2421 SIC 5033 5191

WINCORP INTERNATIONAL INC p 1615
10025 Nw 116th Way Ste 14, Medley FL 33178
Tel (305) 887-1294
SIC 5191 5083 5199 7338 5144

ADAPCO INC p 21
550 Aero Ln, Sanford FL 32771
Tel (407) 330-4800 SIC 5191

HELM FERTILIZER CORP (FLORIDA) p 682
401 E Jackson St Ste 1400, Tampa FL 33602
Tel (813) 621-8846 SIC 5191 6221

YARA NORTH AMERICA INC p 1635
100 N Tampa St Ste 3200, Tampa FL 33602
Tel (813) 222-5700 SIC 5191 5169

CHEM-NUT INC p 293
800 Business Park Dr, Leesburg GA 31763
Tel (229) 883-7050 SIC 5191 8611

GEORGIA FARM BUREAU FEDERATION INC p 607
1620 Bass Rd, Macon GA 31210
Tel (478) 474-8411
SIC 6111 5154 8699 5191

TRIANGLE CHEMICAL CO p 1478
206 Lower Elm St, Macon GA 31206
Tel (478) 743-1548 SIC 5191

■ PENNINGTON SEED INC p 1130
1280 Atlanta Hwy, Madison GA 30650
Tel (706) 342-1234
SIC 5261 2873 5191 6799 0723

KEYSTON BROS (INC) p 815
1000 Holcomb Wds Pkwy # 111, Roswell GA 30076
Tel (770) 587-2555 SIC 5199 5131 5191

KUDZU FABRICS INC p 831
2154 River Cliff Dr, Roswell GA 30076
Tel (770) 641-0379 SIC 5199 5131 5191

■ SITEONE LANDSCAPE SUPPLY HOLDING LLC p 1328
300 Colonial Center Pkwy, Roswell GA 30076
Tel (770) 255-2100
SIC 5083 5191 5193 5032 5063

▲ SITEONE LANDSCAPE SUPPLY INC p 1328
300 Colonial Center Pkwy, Roswell GA 30076
Tel (770) 255-2100
SIC 5083 5191 5193 5032 5063

CYTEC SURFACE SPECIALTIES INC p 406
1950 Lake Park Dr Se, Smyrna GA 30080
Tel (770) 434-6188
SIC 3086 5169 5191 5162 3081 2823

UCB CHEMICALS CORP p 1498
2000 Lake Park Dr Se, Smyrna GA 30080
Tel (770) 434-6188 SIC 5169 5191 5162

BINGHAM COOPERATIVE INC p 183
477 W Highway 26, Blackfoot ID 83221
Tel (208) 785-3440 SIC 5191 5171 5541

D&B SUPPLY CO p 407
3303 E Linden St, Caldwell ID 83605
Tel (208) 459-7446
SIC 5191 5699 5251 5261 5999 5531

STANDLEE HAY TRUCKING CO INC p 1376
990 S 1690 E, Eden ID 83325
Tel (208) 825-5117 SIC 5191

C-A-L STORES COMPANIES INC p 234
665 E Anderson St, Idaho Falls ID 83401
Tel (208) 523-3359 SIC 5191

VALLEY CO-OPS INC p 1540
1833 S Lincoln Ave, Jerome ID 83338
Tel (208) 324-8000 SIC 5171 5191 5251

VALLEY WIDE COOPERATIVE INC p 1541
2114 N 20th St, Nampa ID 83687
Tel (208) 436-0141
SIC 5191 5251 5541 5171

GROWMARK INC p 642
1701 Towanda Ave, Bloomington IL 61701
Tel (309) 557-6000 SIC 5191

GOLD STAR FS INC p 620
101 N East St, Cambridge IL 61238
Tel (309) 937-3369
SIC 5171 5153 5039 5191

M & M SERVICE CO INC p 888
130 N Chiles St, Carlinville IL 62626
Tel (217) 854-4516 SIC 5153 5191 5171

PREMIER COOPERATIVE INC p 1170
2104 W Park Ct, Champaign IL 61821
Tel (217) 355-1983 SIC 5153 5191

ADM EDIBLE BEAN SPECIALTIES INC p 23
4666 E Faries Pkwy, Decatur IL 62526
Tel (217) 424-5200 SIC 5191

▲ UNIVAR INC p 1516
3075 Highland Pkwy # 200, Downers Grove IL 60515
Tel (331) 777-6000 SIC 5169 5191 8741

SUNRISE AG SERVICE CO p 1403
104 S 1st St, Easton IL 62633
Tel (309) 562-7296 SIC 5191 5171 5541

AKRON SERVICES INC p 42
17705 N Elevator Rd, Edelstein IL 61526
Tel (309) 243-7533 SIC 5153 5191

SOUTH CENTRAL FS INC p 1343
405 S Banker St, Effingham IL 62401
Tel (217) 342-9231 SIC 5171 5191 2875

FURST-MCNESS CO p 585
120 E Clark St, Freeport IL 61032
Tel (800) 435-5100 SIC 2048 5191

BURPEE HOLDING CO INC p 228
800 Roosevelt Rd Ste 216, Glen Ellyn IL 60137
Tel (215) 674-4900 SIC 0181 5191

JERSEY COUNTY GRAIN CO p 783
426 E Exchange St, Jerseyville IL 62052
Tel (618) 498-2183 SIC 5153 5191

MIDWEST AIR TECHNOLOGIES INC p 967
6700 Wildlife Way, Long Grove IL 60047
Tel (847) 821-9630
SIC 5072 5191 5063 5051 5031

HFI ENTERPRISES INC p 689
2s181 County Line Rd, Maple Park IL 60151
Tel (630) 557-2406 SIC 5172 5191

TOP FLIGHT GRAIN MONTICELLO CO p 1460
420 W Marion St, Monticello IL 61856
Tel (217) 762-2163 SIC 5153 5191 4221

PCS SALES (USA) INC p 1124
1101 Skokie Blvd Ste 400, Northbrook IL 60062
Tel (847) 849-4200 SIC 5191

TOP AG COOPERATIVE INC p 1460
702 S Elevator St, Okawville IL 62271
Tel (618) 243-5293 SIC 5153 5191

V-G SUPPLY CO p 1538
1400 Renaissance Dr # 309, Park Ridge IL 60068
Tel (708) 891-1500 SIC 5191 5193

BUREAU SERVICE CO p 226
22069 Us Highway 34, Princeton IL 61356
Tel (815) 875-2800
SIC 5191 5172 5153 5411 7542

AQUASCAPE DESIGNS INC p 101
901 Aqualand Way, Saint Charles IL 60174
Tel (630) 659-2000
SIC 5191 1629 0782 0781

EASTLAND FEED AND GRAIN INC p 473
210 N Stanton St, Shannon IL 61078
Tel (815) 864-2723 SIC 5191 5153

BRANDT CONSOLIDATED INC p 208
2935 S Koke Mill Rd, Springfield IL 62711
Tel (217) 547-5800 SIC 2875 5191

CONSERV FS INC p 358
1110 Mcconnell Rd, Woodstock IL 60098
Tel (815) 334-5950 SIC 5171 5191

CO-ALLIANCE LLP p 330
5250 E Us Hwy 3, Avon IN 46123
Tel (317) 745-4491
SIC 5191 5171 5153 2875

PREMIER AG CO-OP INC p 1170
785 S Marr Rd, Columbus IN 47201
Tel (812) 379-9501
SIC 5153 5191 5172 5411 2429

CERES SOLUTIONS LLP p 283
2112 Indianapolis Rd, Crawfordsville IN 47933
Tel (765) 362-6108 SIC 5191

WABASH VALLEY PRODUCE INC p 1570
4886 E 450n, Dubois IN 47527
Tel (812) 678-3131 SIC 5144 5191

■ AGRIGENETICS INC p 36
9330 Zionsville Rd, Indianapolis IN 46268
Tel (317) 337-3000 SIC 5191

■ DOW AGROSCIENCES LLC p 453
9330 Zionsville Rd, Indianapolis IN 46268
Tel (317) 337-3000
SIC 2879 5191 0721 8731

■ MYCOGEN CORP p 1004
9330 Zionsville Rd, Indianapolis IN 46268
Tel (317) 337-3000
SIC 5191 2879 0721 8731

■ MYCOGEN PLANT SCIENCE INC p 1004
9330 Zionsville Rd, Indianapolis IN 46268
Tel (317) 337-3000 SIC 5191

WHITE RIVER COOPERATIVE INC p 1606
416 Church St, Loogootee IN 47553
Tel (812) 295-4835 SIC 5191 5171

POSEY COUNTY FARM BUREAU COOPERATIVE ASSOCIATION INC p 1163
817 W 4th St, Mount Vernon IN 47620
Tel (812) 838-4468 SIC 5191 5172 5153

POSEY COUNTY LLC p 1163
817 W 4th St, Mount Vernon IN 47620
Tel (812) 838-4468 SIC 5191

HARVEST LAND CO-OP INC p 666
1435 Nw 5th St, Richmond IN 47374
Tel (765) 962-1527 SIC 5191 5153

AG PLUS INC p 33
401 N Main St, South Whitley IN 46787
Tel (260) 723-5141 SIC 5191 2041 5153

MULZER CRUSHED STONE INC p 1000
534 Mozart St, Tell City IN 47586
Tel (812) 547-7921
SIC 1422 3273 5191 5085

CERES SOLUTIONS p 283
2600 S 13th St, Terre Haute IN 47802
Tel (812) 235-8123 SIC 5153 5172 5191

NORTH CENTRAL COOPERATIVE INC p 1051
2025 S Wabash St, Wabash IN 46992
Tel (800) 992-3495 SIC 5172 5153 5191

FRICK SERVICES INC p 579
3154 Depot St, Wawaka IN 46794
Tel (260) 761-3311
SIC 5191 5153 5261 4221 2048 4213

AGRELIANT GENETICS LLC p 35
1122 E 169th St, Westfield IN 46074
Tel (317) 896-5552 SIC 5191

AG PARTNERS LLC p 33
30 Main St, Albert City IA 50510
Tel (712) 843-2291 SIC 5153 5191 2048

ALIGNED AG DISTRIBUTORS LLC p 50
224b S Bell Ave, Ames IA 50010
Tel (641) 858-2341 SIC 5191

FARMERS COOPERATIVE ELEVATOR CO p 529
12543 190th St, Arcadia IA 51430
Tel (712) 689-2296 SIC 5191 5153

STATELINE COOPERATIVE p 1383
120 Walnut St, Burt IA 50522
Tel (515) 885-2642 SIC 5191 5172 5031

FIRST COOPERATIVE ASSOCIATION p 546
960 Riverview Dr, Cherokee IA 51012
Tel (712) 225-5400 *SIC* 5191 5153

NORTH CENTRAL COOPERATIVE p 1051
221 4th Ave Nw, Clarion IA 50525
Tel (515) 532-2881 *SIC* 5153 5191 5172

MID IOWA COOPERATIVE p 963
201 S Main St, Conrad IA 50621
Tel (641) 366-2740 *SIC* 5153 5191 2048

SWISS VALLEY FARMS COOPERATIVE p 1413
247 Research Pkwy, Davenport IA 52806
Tel (563) 468-6600
SIC 5143 2022 5191 2023

UNITED SERVICES ASSOCIATION INC p 1511
11280 Aurora Ave, Des Moines IA 50322
Tel (515) 276-6763 *SIC* 5191

UNITED SUPPLIERS INC p 1514
224 S Bell Ave, Eldora IA 50627
Tel (515) 509-2400 *SIC* 5191

NEW CO-OPERATIVE INC p 1029
2626 1st Ave S, Fort Dodge IA 50501
Tel (515) 955-2040 *SIC* 5153 5191

FARMERS WIN COOPERATIVE p 530
110 N Jefferson Ave, Fredericksburg IA 50630
Tel (563) 237-5324 *SIC* 5191

ELDON C STUTSMAN INC p 484
121 Lassie, Hills IA 52235
Tel (319) 679-2281 *SIC* 5191 3523

CHEM GRO OF HOUGHTON INC p 293
504 Main St, Houghton IA 52631
Tel (319) 469-2611 *SIC* 5153 5191

EAST CENTRAL IOWA COOP p 470
602 Washington St, Hudson IA 50643
Tel (319) 988-3257 *SIC* 5153 5191

■ **PIONEER HI-BRED INTERNATIONAL INC** p 1150
7100 Nw 62nd Ave, Johnston IA 50131
Tel (515) 535-3200 *SIC* 5191

■ **PIONEER OVERSEAS CORP** p 1151
7100 Nw 62nd Ave, Johnston IA 50131
Tel (515) 535-3200 *SIC* 5191

LSCP LLLP p 883
4808 F Ave, Marcus IA 51035
Tel (712) 376-2800 *SIC* 4925 5191

LINN CO-OPERATIVE OIL CO p 869
325 35th St, Marion IA 52302
Tel (319) 377-4881 *SIC* 5153 5171 5191

FIVE STAR COOPERATIVE p 553
1949 N Linn Ave, New Hampton IA 50659
Tel (641) 394-3052 *SIC* 5153 5191

PRO COOPERATIVE p 1178
17 3rd Ave Ne, Pocahontas IA 50574
Tel (712) 335-3060 *SIC* 5153 5191 5172

WEST CENTRAL COOPERATIVE p 1594
406 1st St, Ralston IA 51459
Tel (712) 667-3200
SIC 5153 2075 2048 5191

UNITED FARMERS MERCANTILE COOPERATIVE p 1508
203 W Oak St, Red Oak IA 51566
Tel (712) 623-5453
SIC 5153 5191 5541 5211 2048

COOPERATIVE FARMERS ELEVATOR p 367
1219 Main St, Rock Valley IA 51247
Tel (712) 476-5321 *SIC* 5153 5191

KEY COOPERATIVE p 814
13585 620th Ave, Roland IA 50236
Tel (515) 388-4341
SIC 5153 5541 2048 5191

FARMERS COOPERATIVE SOCIETY p 529
317 3rd St Nw, Sioux Center IA 51250
Tel (712) 722-2671 *SIC* 5153 5191 5211

SIOUXLAND FARMERS COOPERATIVE p 1326
317 3rd St Nw, Sioux Center IA 51250
Tel (712) 722-2671 *SIC* 5153 5191

CSD INC p 397
5101 Harbor Dr, Sioux City IA 51111
Tel (712) 255-6927 *SIC* 5191

IOWA LIMESTONE CO p 763
3301 106th Cir, Urbandale IA 50322
Tel (515) 243-3160 *SIC* 1422 5191

RIVER VALLEY COOPERATIVE p 1237
102 S Main St, Walcott IA 52773
Tel (563) 284-6223 *SIC* 5153 5191

VAN DIEST SUPPLY CO p 1542
1434 220th St, Webster City IA 50595
Tel (515) 832-2366 *SIC* 5191 2875 2879

MAXYIELD COOPERATIVE p 923
313 3rd Ave Nw, West Bend IA 50597
Tel (515) 887-7211
SIC 5153 5191 2999 0723

GARDEN CITY CO-OP INC p 591
106 N 6th St, Garden City KS 67846
Tel (620) 275-6161 *SIC* 5153 5191 5172

GREAT BEND COOPERATIVE ASSOCIATION p 633
606 Main St, Great Bend KS 67530
Tel (620) 793-3531
SIC 5153 5191 5171 4221

MIDLAND MARKETING CO-OP INC p 966
219 E 9th St, Hays KS 67601
Tel (785) 625-5138
SIC 5153 5191 5541 5171 4221

KANZA COOPERATIVE ASSOCIATION p 803
102 N Main St, Iuka KS 67066
Tel (620) 546-2231
SIC 5153 5191 5541 4221

JOHNSON COOPERATIVE GRAIN CO INC p 791
304 E Highland Ave, Johnson KS 67855
Tel (620) 492-6210 *SIC* 5153 5191 5172

MID-KANSAS COOPERATIVE ASSOCIATION p 963
307 W Cole St, Moundridge KS 67107
Tel (620) 345-6328 *SIC* 5153 5191

FRONTIER AG INC p 580
415 W 2nd St, Oakley KS 67748
Tel (785) 462-2063 *SIC* 5153 5191

OTTAWA COOPERATIVE ASSOCIATION INC p 1098
302 N Main St, Ottawa KS 66067
Tel (785) 242-5170 *SIC* 5191 5171 5153

MID-WEST FERTILIZER INC p 964
1105 Baptiste Dr, Paola KS 66071
Tel (913) 294-5555 *SIC* 5191

SCOTT COOPERATIVE ASSOCIATION INC p 1293
410 E 1st St, Scott City KS 67871
Tel (620) 872-5823
SIC 5153 5541 5191 4221

NEMAHA COUNTY COOPERATIVE ASSOCIATION p 1025
223 E Main St, Seneca KS 66538
Tel (785) 336-6153 *SIC* 5153 5191 5541

KOCH AG & ENERGY SOLUTIONS LLC p 825
4111 E 37th St N, Wichita KS 67220
Tel (316) 828-8310 *SIC* 5191

CAUDILL SEED AND WAREHOUSE CO INC p 267
1402 W Main St, Louisville KY 40203
Tel (502) 583-4402 *SIC* 5191 5261

CGB ENTERPRISES INC p 285
1127 Hwy 190 E Service Rd, Covington LA 70433
Tel (985) 867-3500 *SIC* 4221 5191 4491

ABELL CORP p 11
2500 Sterlington Rd, Monroe LA 71203
Tel (318) 343-7565 *SIC* 5191 3089

RED RIVER SPECIALTIES INC p 1216
1324 N Hearne Ave Ste 120, Shreveport LA 71107
Tel (318) 425-5944 *SIC* 5191

COMMERCE LLC p 345
7603 Energy Pkwy, Baltimore MD 21226
Tel (410) 255-3500 *SIC* 5191 5072 5199

CERTIS USA LLC p 284
9145 Guilford Rd Ste 175, Columbia MD 21046
Tel (301) 604-7340 *SIC* 5191 2879

CONRAD FAFARD INC p 358
770 Silver St, Agawam MA 01001
Tel (413) 786-4343 *SIC* 5191 2875

GRIFFIN GREENHOUSE SUPPLIES INC p 640
1619 Main St, Tewksbury MA 01876
Tel (978) 851-4346 *SIC* 5191

STAR OF WEST MILLING CO p 1378
121 E Tuscola St, Frankenmuth MI 48734
Tel (330) 673-2941 *SIC* 2041 5153 5191

RESIDEX LLC p 1226
46495 Humboldt Dr, Novi MI 48377
Tel (855) 737-4339
SIC 5191 7342 0781 0782

COOPERATIVE ELEVATOR CO p 367
7211 E Michigan Ave, Pigeon MI 48755
Tel (989) 453-4500
SIC 5172 5191 5541 5261 5153

CITIZENS LLC p 311
870 S Main St, Vermontville MI 49096
Tel (517) 726-0514
SIC 5191 5153 5999 2041

CENTRA SOTA COOPERATIVE p 277
805 Highway 55 E, Buffalo MN 55313
Tel (763) 682-2557
SIC 5191 2875 5171 5153

ROSENS INC p 1251
1120 Lake Ave, Fairmont MN 56031
Tel (507) 238-4201 *SIC* 5191

AG PARTNERS COOP p 33
1st And Bdwy Way, Goodhue MN 55027
Tel (651) 345-3328 *SIC* 5153 5191

SYNGENTA SEEDS INC p 1415
11055 Wayzata Blvd, Hopkins MN 55305
Tel (612) 656-8600
SIC 2074 2075 2076 5191

▲ **CHS INC** p 304
5500 Cenex Dr, Inver Grove Heights MN 55077
Tel (651) 355-6000
SIC 5153 5191 2075 1311 2911 4613

RIVER COUNTRY COOPERATIVE p 1237
9072 Cahill Ave, Inver Grove Heights MN 55076
Tel (651) 451-1151 *SIC* 5171 5172 5191

MEADOWLAND FARMERS COOP p 934
25861 Us Highway 14, Lamberton MN 56152
Tel (507) 752-7335 *SIC* 5153 5191 0723

MID-STATES DISTRIBUTING CO INC p 963
1370 Mendota Hts Rd, Mendota MN 55150
Tel (651) 280-4300
SIC 5072 5013 5191 5091 5092 5136

COMMODITY SPECIALISTS CO p 345
920 2nd Ave S Ste 850, Minneapolis MN 55402
Tel (612) 330-9889 *SIC* 5191

US COMMODITIES LLC p 1531
730 2nd Ave S Ste 700, Minneapolis MN 55402
Tel (612) 486-3800 *SIC* 5191 6221

■ **MG WALDBAUM CO** p 958
301 Carlson Pkwy Ste 400, Minnetonka MN 55305
Tel (952) 258-4000 *SIC* 2015 5153 5191

HARVEST LAND COOPERATIVE p 666
711 Front St W, Morgan MN 56266
Tel (507) 249-3196 *SIC* 5153 5191 0253

CANNON VALLEY COOPERATIVE p 247
1500 Highway 3 S, Northfield MN 55057
Tel (507) 645-9556
SIC 5541 5171 1711 5191 5153 5211

CENTRAL VALLEY COOPERATIVE p 280
900 30th Pl Nw, Owatonna MN 55060
Tel (507) 451-1230 *SIC* 5191 5171 5541

PRINSBURG FARMERS CO-OP p 1177
404 Railroad Ave, Prinsburg MN 56281
Tel (320) 978-8100 *SIC* 5153 5191 0253

CO-OP COUNTRY FARMERS ELEVATOR p 330
340 Dupont Ave Ne, Renville MN 56284
Tel (320) 329-8377 *SIC* 5153 5191

GREEN-WAY COOPERATIVE SERVICE CO p 637
3520 E River Rd Ne, Rochester MN 55906
Tel (507) 289-4086 *SIC* 5541 5171 5191

NORTHERN RESOURCES COOPERATIVE p 1056
1504 Center St W, Roseau MN 56751
Tel (218) 463-1805
SIC 5191 5172 5251 5541

WINFIELD SOLUTIONS LLC p 1616
1080 County Road F W, Saint Paul MN 55126
Tel (651) 481-2222 *SIC* 5191

PURINA ANIMAL NUTRITION LLC p 1192
1080 County Road F W, Shoreview MN 55126
Tel (651) 375-5500 *SIC* 5191

NU WAY COOPERATIVE (INC) p 1066
440 Highway 4 S, Trimont MN 56176
Tel (507) 639-2311
SIC 5191 5171 5541 2875

WATONWAN FARM SERVICE INC p 1583
233 W Ciro St, Truman MN 56088
Tel (507) 776-1244 *SIC* 5153 5191 5172

COOP WHEATON-DUMONT ELEVATOR INC p 366
6587 Us Highway 75, Wheaton MN 56296
Tel (320) 563-8152 *SIC* 5153 5191

WEST CENTRAL DISTRIBUTION LLC p 1594
2700 Trott Ave Sw, Willmar MN 56201
Tel (320) 235-8518 *SIC* 5191

UNITED FARMERS COOPERATIVE p 1508
705 E 4th St, Winthrop MN 55396
Tel (507) 237-2281
SIC 5153 5191 5983 5083

AGRI SERVICES OF BRUNSWICK LLC p 36
Hwy 24 W, Brunswick MO 65236
Tel (660) 549-3351 *SIC* 5153 5191

MFA INC p 957
201 Ray Young Dr, Columbia MO 65201
Tel (573) 874-5111
SIC 2875 2048 5191 5153

RAY CARROLL COUNTY GRAIN GROWERS INC p 1209
807 W Main St, Richmond MO 64085
Tel (816) 776-2291 *SIC* 5171 5191 5153

BOEHRINGER INGELHEIM VETMEDICA INC p 197
2621 N Belt Hwy, Saint Joseph MO 64506
Tel (800) 325-9167 *SIC* 2836 2834 5191

ROCKY MOUNTAIN SUPPLY INC p 1245
350 Jackrabbit Ln Stop 1, Belgrade MT 59714
Tel (406) 388-4008
SIC 5171 5191 5541 5411

MOUNTAIN VIEW CO-OP p 994
2200 Old Havre Hwy, Black Eagle MT 59414
Tel (406) 453-5900
SIC 5541 5153 2875 5191

RANCH AND HOME SUPPLY LLC p 1207
2311 N 7th Ave, Bozeman MT 59715
Tel (406) 586-8466
SIC 5699 5191 5531 5251

TOWN AND COUNTRY SUPPLY ASSOCIATION p 1464
18 8th Ave, Laurel MT 59044
Tel (406) 628-6314
SIC 5984 5191 5411 5999

WESTERN COOPERATIVE CO INC p 1598
724 W 3rd St, Alliance NE 69301
Tel (308) 762-3291 *SIC* 5172 5541 5191

TROTTER INC p 1484
300 Railway, Arcadia NE 68815
Tel (308) 789-6200 *SIC* 5191 5153 5172

AURORA COOPERATIVE ELEVATOR CO p 132
2225 O St, Aurora NE 68818
Tel (402) 694-2106 *SIC* 5153 5191

BATTLE CREEK FARMERS COOPERATIVE NON-STOCK p 160
83755 Highway 121, Battle Creek NE 68715
Tel (402) 675-2375
SIC 5153 5191 5172 5541 5411

SOUTHEAST NEBRASKA COOPERATIVE CO p 1346
403 S 3rd St, Beatrice NE 68310
Tel (402) 228-3458 *SIC* 5191 5153 2048

FRONTIER COOPERATIVE CO p 581
211 S Lincoln St, Brainard NE 68626
Tel (402) 545-2811 *SIC* 5153 5191

COOP HUSKER p 366
2468 33rd Ave, Columbus NE 68601
Tel (402) 564-2704 *SIC* 5153 5191

FARMERS COOPERATIVE p 529
208 W Depot St, Dorchester NE 68343
Tel (402) 946-4631 *SIC* 5153 5191 5172

AG VALLEY COOPERATIVE NON-STOCK p 34
72133 State Hwy 136, Edison NE 68936
Tel (308) 927-3681 *SIC* 5153 5191

GREENWOOD FARMERS COOPERATIVE p 639
304 S 3rd St, Elmwood NE 68349
Tel (402) 994-2585 *SIC* 5191

MIDWEST FARMERS COOPERATIVE p 967
304 S 3rd St, Elmwood NE 68349
Tel (402) 994-2585 *SIC* 5153 5191 5541

ALL POINTS COOPERATIVE p 51
120 8th St, Gothenburg NE 69138
Tel (308) 537-7141 *SIC* 5153 5191 5541

FRENCHMAN VALLEY FARMERS COOPERATIVE INC p 578
202 Broadway, Imperial NE 69033
Tel (308) 882-3220 *SIC* 5153 5191 5541

GAVILON AGRICULTURE HOLDINGS CO p 594
1331 Capitol Ave, Omaha NE 68102
Tel (402) 889-4000 *SIC* 5153 5191

GAVILON AGRICULTURE INVESTMENT INC p 594
1331 Capitol Ave, Omaha NE 68102
Tel (402) 889-4000 *SIC* 5153 5191

GAVILON GROUP LLC p 594
1331 Capitol Ave, Omaha NE 68102
Tel (402) 889-4000 *SIC* 5153 5191

CENTRAL VALLEY AG COOPERATIVE NONSTOCK p 280
415 E Highway 20, Oneill NE 68763
Tel (402) 336-1263 *SIC* 5191

ARETT SALES CORP p 107
9285 Commerce Hwy, Pennsauken NJ 08110
Tel (856) 751-1224 *SIC* 5191

HELM AMERICA CORP p 682
1110 Centennial Ave Ste 2, Piscataway NJ 08854
Tel (732) 981-1160
SIC 5169 5122 5191 4231 4226

STEEL PARTNERS II LP p 1384
590 Madison Ave Rm 3202, New York NY 10022
Tel (212) 758-3232 *SIC* 5191 2874

TRAMMO INC p 1469
1 Rockefeller Plz Fl 9, New York NY 10020
Tel (212) 223-3200 *SIC* 5191 5172 5169

LACKAWANNA PRODUCTS CORP p 837
8545 Main St Ste 1, Williamsville NY 14221
Tel (716) 633-1940 *SIC* 5191 5153

BAYER CROPSCIENCE LP p 161
2 Tw Alexander Dr, Durham NC 27709
Tel (919) 549-2000 *SIC* 2879 5191

COASTAL AGROBUSINESS INC p 331
3702 Evans St, Greenville NC 27834
Tel (252) 756-1126 *SIC* 5191 3523

AG PROVISION LLC p 33
277 Faison W Mcgowan Rd, Kenansville NC 28349
Tel (910) 296-0302 *SIC* 5191

HARVEY FERTILIZER AND GAS CO p 667
303 Bohannon Rd, Kinston NC 28501
Tel (252) 526-4150 *SIC* 5191 2873 2875

MEHERRIN AGRICULTURAL & CHEMICAL CO p 940
413 Main St, Severn NC 27877
Tel (252) 585-1744 *SIC* 5159 5191 5145

PARKWAY AG CENTER INC p 1117
2801 Industrial Pkwy, Tarboro NC 27886
Tel (252) 823-5778 *SIC* 5191

MAPLE RIVER GRAIN & AGRONOMY LLC p 904
1630 1st Ave S, Casselton ND 58012
Tel (701) 347-4465 *SIC* 5153 5191

PLAINS GRAIN & AGRONOMY LLC p 1153
109 3rd Ave, Enderlin ND 58027
Tel (701) 437-2565 *SIC* 5153 5191 5171

FARMERS UNION OIL OF SOUTHERN VALLEY p 530
100 S Front St, Fairmount ND 58030
Tel (701) 474-5440
SIC 5171 5191 5541 5251

FULLERTON FARMERS ELEVATOR p 584
202 Minneapolis Ave, Fullerton ND 58441
Tel (701) 375-7881 *SIC* 5153 5191

UNITED PRAIRIE COOPERATIVE p 1511
307 Main St, New Town ND 58763
Tel (701) 627-3636 *SIC* 5191

CHS INC p 304
3645 98th Ave Sw, Taylor ND 58656
Tel (701) 483-6781 *SIC* 5153 5191

HORIZON RESOURCES p 707
317 2nd St W, Williston ND 58801
Tel (701) 572-2171
SIC 5172 5541 5411 5191

PROVIMI NORTH AMERICA INC p 1186
10 Collective Way, Brookville OH 45309
Tel (937) 770-2400 *SIC* 2048 5191

BFG SUPPLY CO LLC p 179
14500 Kinsman Rd, Burton OH 44021
Tel (440) 834-1883 *SIC* 5191 5261

■ **LESCO INC** p 857
1385 E 36th St, Cleveland OH 44114
Tel (216) 706-9250 *SIC* 5191 5083 5261

PRIMERATURF INC p 1175
2065 Lamberton Rd, Cleveland Heights OH 44118
Tel (216) 397-9716 *SIC* 5191

EDON FARMERS COOPERATIVE ASSOCIATION p 478
205 S Michigan St, Edon OH 43518
Tel (419) 272-2121 *SIC* 5153 5191

LEGACY FARMERS COOPERATIVE p 852
6566 County Road 236, Findlay OH 45840
Tel (419) 423-2611
SIC 5153 5191 5984 2875 2048 2041

▲ **ANDERSONS INC** p 90
480 W Dussel Dr, Maumee OH 43537
Tel (419) 893-5050
SIC 5153 0723 5191 2874 4789 4741

WESTERN RESERVE FARM COOPERATIVE INC p 1600
16003 E High St, Middlefield OH 44062
Tel (440) 632-0271 *SIC* 5191 5983 5211

TRUPOINTE COOPERATIVE INC p 1487
215 Looney Rd, Piqua OH 45356
Tel (937) 575-6780 *SIC* 5153 5191

JOHNSTON ENTERPRISES INC p 791
411 W Chestnut Ave, Enid OK 73701
Tel (580) 233-5800 *SIC* 5153 5191

W B JOHNSTON GRAIN CO p 1568
411 W Chestnut Ave, Enid OK 73701
Tel (580) 233-5800
SIC 5153 5191 4491 4213 0111 0211

INTERNATIONAL CHEMICAL CO p 754
1887 E 71st St, Tulsa OK 74136
Tel (918) 496-7711 *SIC* 5191

LAUGHLIN-CARTRELL INC p 847
12850 Ne Hendricks Rd, Carlton OR 97111
Tel (503) 852-7151 *SIC* 5191

DLF PICKSEED USA INC p 445
175 W H St, Halsey OR 97348
Tel (541) 369-2251 *SIC* 5191

SMITH SEED SERVICES LLC p 1333
26890 Powerline Rd, Halsey OR 97348
Tel (541) 369-2831 *SIC* 5191

TRI-STATE GARDEN SUPPLY INC p 1477
And Sandy Pt Rd Rr 38, Eau Claire PA 16030
Tel (724) 867-1711 *SIC* 5191

UNITED PHOSPHORUS INC p 1510
630 Freedom Business Ctr, King Of Prussia PA 19406
Tel (610) 491-2800 *SIC* 5191

LEBANON SEABOARD CORP p 850
1600 E Cumberland St, Lebanon PA 17042
Tel (717) 273-1685 *SIC* 5191 2875 2048

AGRICULTURAL COMMODITIES INC p 36
2224 Oxford Rd, New Oxford PA 17350
Tel (717) 624-8249
SIC 5191 2048 2041 0723 2875

F M BROWNS SONS INC p 522
205 Woodrow Ave, Reading PA 19608
Tel (800) 334-8816
SIC 5191 2041 0723 2048

JC EHRLICH CHEMICAL CO p 780
1125 Berkshire Blvd # 150, Reading PA 19610
Tel (610) 372-9700 SIC 5191

MOYER & SON INC p 995
113 E Reliance Rd, Souderton PA 18964
Tel (215) 799-2000
SIC 5191 5983 2875 0782 1711

BRADLEY CALDWELL INC p 206
200 Kiwanis Blvd, West Hazleton PA 18202
Tel (570) 455-7511 SIC 5191 5199 5072

RENTOKIL NORTH AMERICA INC p 1224
1125 Berkshire Blvd # 150, Wyomissing PA 19610
Tel (610) 372-9700 SIC 7342 0781 5191

CAROLINA EASTERN INC p 259
1820 Savannah Hwy Ste G1, Charleston SC 29407
Tel (843) 571-0411 SIC 5261 5191

AMICK FARMS LLC p 85
3682 Highway 23, Monetta SC 29105
Tel (803) 532-1400 SIC 5191

EASTERN FARMERS COOPERATIVE p 472
26033 482nd Ave, Brandon SD 57005
Tel (605) 582-2415 SIC 5191 5171 5541

FULL CIRCLE AG p 584
520 Vander Horck Ave, Britton SD 57430
Tel (605) 448-2231 SIC 5191 5153 5541

AGFIRST FARMERS COOPERATIVE p 34
204 1st St S, Brookings SD 57006
Tel (605) 692-6216 SIC 5191 5153

NORTH CENTRAL FARMERS ELEVATOR p 1052
12 5th Ave, Ipswich SD 57451
Tel (605) 426-6021
SIC 5153 5191 5171 5541

LAKE PRESTON COOPERATIVE ASSOCIATION p 839
106 2nd St Nw, Lake Preston SD 57249
Tel (605) 847-4414 SIC 5153 5191 5172

WATERTOWN COOPERATIVE ELEVATOR ASSOCIATION p 1582
811 Burlington Northern D, Watertown SD 57201
Tel (605) 886-8333 SIC 5153 5191 4221

COUNTRY PRIDE COOPERATIVE INC p 375
648 W 2nd St, Winner SD 57580
Tel (605) 842-2711
SIC 5153 5172 5191 5411 5211

HELENA CHEMICAL CO p 681
255 Schilling Blvd # 200, Collierville TN 38017
Tel (901) 761-0050 SIC 5191 2819

TENNESSEE FARMERS COOPERATIVE INC p 1438
180 Old Nashville Hwy, La Vergne TN 37086
Tel (615) 793-8011
SIC 5191 5013 5014 5172 5122 2048

GREENPOINT AG p 638
3350 Players Club Pkwy, Memphis TN 38125
Tel (901) 758-1341 SIC 5191

MAYMEAD INC p 923
1995 Roan Creek Rd, Mountain City TN 37683
Tel (423) 727-2000
SIC 1611 2951 5032 5191

AMERICAN STEEL INC p 80
2500 Agnes St, Corpus Christi TX 78405
Tel (361) 883-1706
SIC 5023 5051 5084 5191

DALHART CONSUMERS FUEL ASSOCIATION INC p 409
919 Liberal St, Dalhart TX 79022
Tel (806) 249-4660
SIC 5153 5172 5191 5541

STOLLER INTERNATIONAL INC p 1390
9090 Katy Fwy Ste 400, Houston TX 77024
Tel (713) 461-1493 SIC 5191 2879

STOLLER USA INC p 1390
9090 Katy Fwy Ste 400, Houston TX 77024
Tel (713) 461-1493 SIC 5191 8731

BWI COMPANIES INC p 231
1355 N Kings Hwy, Nash TX 75569
Tel (903) 838-8561 SIC 5191

PERRYTON EQUITY EXCHANGE p 1137
4219 S Main St, Perryton TX 79070
Tel (806) 435-4016 SIC 5153 5191 5541

CAPSTONE COMMODITIES LLC p 251
1311 Chisholm Trl, Round Rock TX 78681
Tel (512) 671-6626 SIC 5191 5999

OXBOW SULPHUR INC p 1100
1450 Lake Robbins Dr # 500, The Woodlands TX 77380
Tel (281) 907-9500 SIC 5191 5169

INTERMOUNTAIN FARMERS ASSOCIATION p 753
1147 W 2100 S, South Salt Lake UT 84119
Tel (801) 972-2122 SIC 5999 5191

SOUTHERN STATES COOPERATIVE INC p 1350
6606 W Broad St Ste B, Richmond VA 23230
Tel (804) 281-1000
SIC 2048 0181 2873 2874 5191 5172

SOUTHERN STATES HOLDINGS INC p 1350
6606 W Broad St Ste B, Richmond VA 23230
Tel (804) 281-1206 SIC 5191 5261 0724

SKAGIT FARMERS SUPPLY p 1329
1833 Park Ln, Burlington WA 98233
Tel (360) 757-6053
SIC 5191 5172 5983 5451 5331 5261

MCGREGOR CO p 929
401 Colfax Airport Rd, Colfax WA 99111
Tel (509) 397-4355 SIC 5191 3523 2874

ANDERSON HAY & GRAIN CO INC p 90
910 Anderson Rd, Ellensburg WA 98926
Tel (509) 925-9818 SIC 5191

TWO RIVERS TERMINAL LLC p 1495
3300c N Glade Rd, Pasco WA 99301
Tel (509) 547-7776 SIC 5191 5999

■ **UNIVAR USA INC** p 1516
17411 Ne Union Hill Rd, Redmond WA 98052
Tel (331) 777-6000 SIC 5169 5191 8741

DAIRY EXPORT CO INC p 408
635 Elliott Ave W, Seattle WA 98119
Tel (206) 284-7220 SIC 5191 5083 2033

G S LONG CO INC p 587
2517 Old Town Rd, Union Gap WA 98903
Tel (509) 575-8382 SIC 5191

SUNLIGHT SUPPLY INC p 1403
5408 Ne 88th St Ste A101, Vancouver WA 98665
Tel (360) 883-8846 SIC 3524 5191

ALLIED COOPERATIVE p 56
540 S Main St, Adams WI 53910
Tel (608) 339-3394 SIC 5191 5171 5251

FLEET WHOLESALE SUPPLY CO LLC p 555
3035 W Wisconsin Ave, Appleton WI 54914
Tel (920) 734-8231
SIC 5191 5331 5531 5211 5541

UNITED COOPERATIVE p 1507
N7160 Raceway Rd, Beaver Dam WI 53916
Tel (920) 887-1756
SIC 5191 5171 5541 5153 5812

LANDMARK SERVICES COOPERATIVE p 843
1401 Landmark Dr, Cottage Grove WI 53527
Tel (608) 819-3115
SIC 4221 5171 5191 1711

QUALITY LIQUID FEEDS INC p 1197
3586 State Road 23, Dodgeville WI 53533
Tel (608) 935-2345 SIC 5191

CROSSROADS AG LLC p 394
N6055 State Road 40, Elk Mound WI 54739
Tel (715) 879-5454 SIC 5191 5171

FARM & FLEET OF RICE LAKE INC p 528
3507 E Racine St, Janesville WI 53546
Tel (608) 754-2821 SIC 5191 5251 5531

LARSEN COOPERATIVE CO p 845
8290 County Hwy T, Larsen WI 54947
Tel (920) 982-1111 SIC 5191 5172 5541

VP HOLDINGS CORP p 1566
2514 Fish Hatchery Rd, Madison WI 53713
Tel (608) 256-1988 SIC 2048 5191 5153

PRINCE CORP p 1176
8351 County Road H, Marshfield WI 54449
Tel (800) 777-2486
SIC 5031 5191 2048 5083 5072

PROVISION PARTNERS COOPERATIVE p 1187
2327 W Veterans Pkwy, Marshfield WI 54449
Tel (715) 687-4443 SIC 5191 5984 5541

PREMIER COOPERATIVE p 1170
501 W Main St, Mount Horeb WI 53572
Tel (608) 251-0199
SIC 5211 5171 5191 5541

REINDERS INC p 1221
W227n6225 Sussex Rd, Sussex WI 53089
Tel (262) 786-3300
SIC 5191 5169 5074 5999 5083

CP FEEDS LLC p 387
16322 W Washington St, Valders WI 54245
Tel (920) 775-9600 SIC 5153 5191

SIC 5192 Books, Periodicals & Newspapers Wholesale

TEN ENTHUSIAST NETWORK LLC p 1436
831 S Douglas St Ste 100, El Segundo CA 90245
Tel (310) 531-9900 SIC 5192

■ **SCHOLASTIC LIBRARY PUBLISHING INC** p 1288
90 Sherman Tpke, Danbury CT 06816
Tel (203) 797-3500
SIC 2731 5963 5192 2721 5961 7371

AARP p 8
601 E St Nw, Washington DC 20049
Tel (202) 434-2277 SIC 5192 8399

SOURCE INTERLINK DISTRIBUTION LLC p 1342
27500 Riverview Center Bl, Bonita Springs FL 34134
Tel (239) 949-4450 SIC 5192

■ **SCHOLASTIC BOOK FAIRS INC** p 1288
1080 Greenwood Blvd, Lake Mary FL 32746
Tel (407) 829-7300 SIC 5192 5199 5942

TNG GP p 1458
1955 Lake Park Dr Se # 400, Smyrna GA 30080
Tel (770) 863-9000 SIC 5192

SANDY PAGES p 1279
1794 S Kihei Rd Ste 4, Kihei HI 96753
Tel (808) 205-0321 SIC 5192 5092

CHICAGO REVIEW PRESS INC p 297
814 N Franklin St Ste 100, Chicago IL 60610
Tel (312) 337-0747 SIC 5192 2731

FOLLETT SCHOOL SOLUTIONS INC p 563
1340 Ridgeview Dr, Mchenry IL 60050
Tel (815) 759-1700 SIC 5192

CHAS LEVY CIRCULATING CO p 291
1930 George St Ste 4, Melrose Park IL 60160
Tel (708) 356-3600 SIC 4213 4214 5192

READERLINK DISTRIBUTION SERVICES LLC p 1213
1420 Kensington Rd # 300, Oak Brook IL 60523
Tel (708) 356-3717 SIC 5192

READERLINK LLC p 1213
1420 Kensington Rd # 300, Oak Brook IL 60523
Tel (708) 356-3600 SIC 5192

HERTZBERG-NEW METHOD INC p 688
617 E Vandalia Rd, South Jacksonville IL 62650
Tel (217) 243-5451 SIC 5192

FOLLETT CORP p 563
3 Westbrook Ctr Ste 200, Westchester IL 60154
Tel (708) 884-0000 SIC 5942 5192

FOLLETT SCHOOL SOLUTIONS INC p 563
1433 Internationale Pkwy, Woodridge IL 60517
Tel (630) 972-5600 SIC 5192

DIAMOND COMIC DISTRIBUTORS INC p 436
10150 York Rd Ste 300, Cockeysville MD 21030
Tel (443) 318-8001 SIC 5192

NATIONAL BOOK NETWORK INC p 1010
4501 Forbes Blvd Ste 200, Lanham MD 20706
Tel (301) 459-8020 SIC 5192

ROWMAN & LITTLEFIELD PUBLISHING GROUP INC p 1253
4501 Forbes Blvd Ste 200, Lanham MD 20706
Tel (301) 459-3366 SIC 2731 5192

HUDSON-RPM DISTRIBUTORS LLC p 717
150 Blackstone River Rd # 6, Worcester MA 01607
Tel (617) 328-9500 SIC 5192

PARTNERS BOOK DISTRIBUTING INC p 1118
2325 Jarco Dr, Holt MI 48842
Tel (517) 694-3205 SIC 5192

MACKIN BOOK CO p 892
3505 County Road 42 W, Burnsville MN 55306
Tel (952) 895-9540 SIC 5192

MBS TEXTBOOK EXCHANGE INC p 925
2711 W Ash St, Columbia MO 65203
Tel (573) 445-2243 SIC 5192

GL GROUP INC p 613
5111 Southwest Ave, Saint Louis MO 63110
Tel (314) 647-0600 SIC 5192 2789

NORTHWEST NEWS CO INC p 1060
1701 Rankin St, Missoula MT 59808
Tel (406) 721-7801 SIC 5192

NBC ACQUISITION CORP p 1021
4700 S 19th St, Lincoln NE 68512
Tel (402) 421-7300 SIC 5192 5942

NBC HOLDINGS CORP p 1021
4700 S 19th St, Lincoln NE 68512
Tel (402) 421-7300 SIC 5192 6719

NEBRASKA BOOK CO INC p 1023
4700 S 19th St, Lincoln NE 68512
Tel (402) 421-7300 SIC 5942 5192 5961

NEBRASKA BOOK HOLDINGS INC p 1023
4700 S 19th St, Lincoln NE 68512
Tel (402) 421-0500
SIC 6719 5942 5192 5961

NEBRASKA BOOK INTERMEDIATE HOLDINGS INC p 1023
4701 S 19th St, Lincoln NE 68512
Tel (402) 421-7300
SIC 6719 5942 5192 5961

BOOKAZINE CO INC p 200
75 Hook Rd, Bayonne NJ 07002
Tel (201) 339-7777 SIC 5192 2741

CBA INDUSTRIES INC p 268
669 River Dr Ste 101, Elmwood Park NJ 07407
Tel (201) 587-1717 SIC 5192

CURTIS CIRCULATION CO p 402
730 River Rd Ste 2, New Milford NJ 07646
Tel (201) 634-7400 SIC 5192

HUDSON NEWS DISTRIBUTORS LLC p 717
701 Jefferson Rd, Parsippany NJ 07054
Tel (201) 867-3600 SIC 5192

HARLEQUIN DISTRIBUTION CENTER p 661
3010 Walden Ave, Depew NY 14043
Tel (716) 684-1800 SIC 5192

■ **HARLEQUIN SALES CORP** p 661
3010 Walden Ave, Depew NY 14043
Tel (716) 684-1800 SIC 5192

AMBASSADOR BOOK SERVICE INC p 65
445 Broadhollow Rd, Melville NY 11747
Tel (631) 770-1010 SIC 5192

■ **BARNES & NOBLE PURCHASING INC** p 156
122 5th Ave Fl 2, New York NY 10011
Tel (212) 633-4068 SIC 5192

HACHETTE BOOK GROUP INC p 652
1290 Ave Of The Americas, New York NY 10104
Tel (800) 759-0190 SIC 2731 5192

HACHETTE DISTRIBUTION INC p 652
60 E 42nd St Ste 1940, New York NY 10165
Tel (212) 477-7373 SIC 5192 5994 5947

KABLE MEDIA SERVICES INC p 800
14 Wall St Ste 4c, New York NY 10005
Tel (212) 705-4600 SIC 5192 7389

MACMILLAN PUBLISHERS INC p 892
175 5th Ave Ste 400, New York NY 10010
Tel (646) 307-5151 SIC 2731 5192

MACMILLAN PUBLISHING GROUP LLC p 893
175 5th Ave, New York NY 10010
Tel (212) 674-5151 SIC 2731 5192

■ **STERLING PUBLISHING CO INC** p 1387
1166 Avenue Of The Flr 17, New York NY 10036
Tel (212) 532-7160 SIC 5192 2731

W W NORTON & CO INC p 1569
500 5th Ave Fl 6, New York NY 10110
Tel (212) 354-5500 SIC 2731 5192

BAKER & TAYLOR FULFILLMENT INC p 145
2550 W Tyvola Rd Ste 300, Charlotte NC 28217
Tel (704) 998-3154
SIC 5192 5045 7822 5065

BAKER & TAYLOR HOLDINGS LLC p 145
2550 W Tyvola Rd Ste 300, Charlotte NC 28217
Tel (704) 998-3100
SIC 5192 7822 5065 5045

BAKER & TAYLOR LLC p 145
2550 W Tyvola Rd Ste 300, Charlotte NC 28217
Tel (704) 998-3100
SIC 5192 7822 5065 5045 5099

BTAC ACQUISITION LLC p 222
2550 W Tyvola Rd Ste 300, Charlotte NC 28217
Tel (704) 998-3100
SIC 5192 7822 5065 5045

BTAC HOLDING CORP p 222
2550 W Tyvola Rd Ste 300, Charlotte NC 28217
Tel (704) 998-3100
SIC 5192 7822 5065 5045

ED MAP INC p 476
296 S Harper St Ste 1, Nelsonville OH 45764
Tel (740) 753-3439 SIC 5192

HARRISBURG NEWS CO p 664
980 Briarsdale Rd, Harrisburg PA 17109
Tel (717) 561-8377 SIC 5192

RITTENHOUSE BOOK DISTRIBUTORS INC p 1237
511 Feheley Dr, King Of Prussia PA 19406
Tel (800) 345-6425 SIC 5192

BRODART CO p 216
500 Arch St, Williamsport PA 17701
Tel (570) 326-2461
SIC 5192 5942 2752 2782 2789 2531

GREAT ATLANTIC NEWS LLC p 633
1962 Highway 160 W # 102, Fort Mill SC 29708
Tel (803) 802-8630 SIC 5192

DAKOTA NEWS INC p 409
221 S Petro Ave, Sioux Falls SD 57107
Tel (605) 336-3000 SIC 5192

SEND LIGHT DISTRIBUTION LLC p 1303
212 Industrial Dr, Bristol TN 37620
Tel (423) 547-5100 SIC 5192

PERSEUS DISTRIBUTION INC p 1137
210 American Dr, Jackson TN 38301
Tel (731) 988-4440 SIC 5192

AMERICAN BOOK CO p 69
10267 Kingston Pike, Knoxville TN 37922
Tel (865) 966-7454 SIC 5192 2731

ANDERSON MEDIA CORP p 90
265 Brookview Town Ste, Knoxville TN 37919
Tel (865) 474-8500 SIC 5099 5192

ANDERSON NEWS LLC p 90
265 Brookview Town Ste, Knoxville TN 37919
Tel (865) 584-9765 SIC 5192

CONTENT INGRAM GROUP INC p 362
1 Ingram Blvd, La Vergne TN 37086
Tel (615) 793-5000 SIC 5192

INGRAM BOOK GROUP INC p 743
1 Ingram Blvd, La Vergne TN 37086
Tel (615) 213-5000 SIC 5192

INGRAM INDUSTRIES INC p 743
4400 Harding Pike Ste 310, Nashville TN 37205
Tel (615) 298-8200 SIC 5192 4449

SOUTHWESTERN/GREAT AMERICAN INC p 1353
2451 Atrium Way, Nashville TN 37214
Tel (615) 391-2717 SIC 5192

UNITED METHODIST PUBLISHING HOUSE p 1510
2222 Rosa L Parks Blvd, Nashville TN 37228
Tel (615) 749-6000
SIC 2731 5192 5942 2741 2721

ANCONNECT LLC p 89
421 Se 34th Ave, Amarillo TX 79103
Tel (806) 376-6251 SIC 5099 5192

HALF PRICE BOOKS RECORDS MAGAZINES INC p 654
5803 E Northwest Hwy, Dallas TX 75231
Tel (214) 379-8000 SIC 5942 5192

NEWS GROUP INC p 1039
5130 Comm Pkwy, San Antonio TX 78218
Tel (210) 226-9333 SIC 5192 5994

PMG INTERNATIONAL LTD p 1157
1011 N Frio St, San Antonio TX 78207
Tel (210) 226-6820 SIC 5192

DESERET BOOK CO p 432
57 W South Temple, Salt Lake City UT 84101
Tel (801) 517-3294 SIC 5192 5942 2731

SOURCE HOME ENTERTAINMENT LLC p 1342
8251 Greensboro Dr # 400, Mc Lean VA 22102
Tel (239) 949-4450
SIC 5192 5099 8742 2541

GREAT PACIFIC NEWS CO INC p 634
3995 70th Ave E Ste B, Fife WA 98424
Tel (425) 226-3250 SIC 5192

SIC 5193 Flowers, Nursery Stock & Florists' Splys Wholesale

CCC ASSOCIATES CO p 269
3601 Wetumpka Hwy, Montgomery AL 36110
Tel (334) 272-2140 SIC 5193 5992

MOON VALLEY NURSERY INC p 987
18047 N Tatum Blvd, Phoenix AZ 85032
Tel (602) 493-0403 SIC 5193 5261

MONROVIA NURSERY CO p 985
817 E Monrovia Pl, Azusa CA 91702
Tel (626) 334-9321 SIC 0181 5193 5261

MELLANO & CO p 940
766 Wall St, Los Angeles CA 90014
Tel (213) 622-0796 SIC 5193

VILLAGE NURSERIES WHOLESALE LLC p 1557
1589 N Main St, Orange CA 92867
Tel (714) 279-3100 SIC 5193

L & L NURSERY SUPPLY INC p 833
2552 Shenandoah Way, San Bernardino CA 92407
Tel (909) 591-0461
SIC 5191 2875 2449 5193

NORMANS NURSERY INC p 1049
8665 Duarte Rd, San Gabriel CA 91775
Tel (626) 285-9795 SIC 5193 0181

ALTMAN SPECIALTY PLANTS INC p 62
3742 Blue Bird Canyon Rd, Vista CA 92084
Tel (760) 744-8191 SIC 5193 3999

GREENLEAF WHOLESALE FLORIST INC p 638
540 E Bridge St Ste A, Brighton CO 80601
Tel (303) 659-8000 SIC 5193

DENVER WHOLESALE FLORISTS CO p 429
4800 Dahlia St Ste A, Denver CO 80216
Tel (303) 399-0970 SIC 5193

■ **SHEMIN NURSERIES INC** p 1315
42 Old Ridgebury Rd Ste 3, Danbury CT 06810
Tel (203) 207-5000 SIC 5191 5193

ROBERT W BAKER NURSERY INC p 1241
1700 Mountain Rd, West Suffield CT 06093
Tel (860) 668-7371 SIC 5193 5261

J T WALKER INDUSTRIES INC p 772
861 N Hercules Ave, Clearwater FL 33765
Tel (727) 461-0501
SIC 3442 3089 3585 5193

USA BOUQUET LLC p 1533
1500 Nw 95th Ave, Doral FL 33172
Tel (786) 437-6500 SIC 5193

ELITE FLOWER SERVICES INC p 487
3200 Nw 67th Ave Bldg 2s, Miami FL 33122
Tel (305) 436-7400 SIC 5193

FALCON FARMS INC p 526
2330 Nw 82nd Ave, Miami FL 33122
Tel (305) 477-8088 SIC 5992 5193

PASSION GROWERS LLC p 1120
7499 Nw 31st St, Miami FL 33122
Tel (305) 935-6657 SIC 5193

ARMELLINI INDUSTRIES INC p 111
3446 Sw Armellini Ave, Palm City FL 34990
Tel (772) 287-0575 SIC 4213 5193 4731

DELRAY PLANTS CO p 425
956 Old State Road 8, Venus FL 33960
Tel (800) 854-5393 SIC 5193

■ SITEONE LANDSCAPE SUPPLY HOLDING LLC p 1328
300 Colonial Center Pkwy, Roswell GA 30076
Tel (770) 255-2100
SIC 5083 5191 5193 5032 5063

▲ SITEONE LANDSCAPE SUPPLY INC p 1328
300 Colonial Center Pkwy, Roswell GA 30076
Tel (770) 255-2100
SIC 5083 5191 5193 5032 5063

■ SITEONE LANDSCAPE SUPPLY LLC p 1328
300 Colonial Center Pkwy # 600, Roswell GA 30076
Tel (770) 255-2100 SIC 5063 5193 5083

VANS INC p 1544
3730 W 131st St, Alsip IL 60803
Tel (708) 371-8000 SIC 5193

KENNICOTT BROS CO p 811
1638 W Hubbard St, Chicago IL 60622
Tel (312) 492-8200 SIC 5193

■ FLORISTS TRANSWORLD DELIVERY INC p 560
3113 Woodcreek Dr, Downers Grove IL 60515
Tel (630) 719-7800 SIC 5193 7389 2771

■ FTD GROUP INC p 582
3113 Woodcreek Dr, Downers Grove IL 60515
Tel (630) 719-7800 SIC 5193 7389

■ FTD INC p 582
3113 Woodcreek Dr, Downers Grove IL 60515
Tel (630) 719-7800 SIC 5193 7389

V-G SUPPLY CO p 1538
1400 Renaissance Dr # 309, Park Ridge IL 60068
Tel (708) 891-1500 SIC 5191 5193

BILL DORAN CO p 182
707 W Jefferson St, Rockford IL 61101
Tel (815) 965-8791 SIC 5193

GERSON CO p 609
1450 S Lone Elm Rd, Olathe KS 66061
Tel (913) 262-7400
SIC 5193 5199 5023 5094

TREES N TRENDS INC p 1475
3229 Benton Rd, Paducah KY 42003
Tel (270) 443-5100
SIC 5999 3999 5947 5193

NEAL MAST AND SON INC p 1023
1780 4 Mile Rd Nw, Grand Rapids MI 49544
Tel (616) 784-3323 SIC 5193

GERTEN GREENHOUSES & GARDEN CENTER INC p 609
5500 Blaine Ave, Inver Grove Heights MN 55076
Tel (651) 450-1501 SIC 5261 5193

BACHMANS INC p 143
6010 Lyndale Ave S, Minneapolis MN 55419
Tel (612) 861-7600
SIC 5992 5261 0181 5193 7359

BAILEY NURSERIES INC p 145
1325 Bailey Rd, Newport MN 55055
Tel (651) 459-9744 SIC 5193

TETERS FLORAL PRODUCTS INC p 1441
1425 S Lillian Ave, Bolivar MO 65613
Tel (800) 333-7178 SIC 5193

SUNSHINE BOUQUET CO p 1404
3 Chris Ct Ste A, Dayton NJ 08810
Tel (732) 274-2900 SIC 5193 3999

DELAWARE VALLEY FLORAL GROUP INC p 424
520 Mantua Blvd, Sewell NJ 08080
Tel (800) 676-1212 SIC 5193 4213 4214

DELAWARE VALLEY WHOLESALE FLORIST INC p 424
520 Mantua Blvd, Sewell NJ 08080
Tel (856) 468-7000 SIC 5193

KURT WEISS GREENHOUSES INC p 832
95 Main St, Center Moriches NY 11934
Tel (631) 878-2500 SIC 0181 5193

S BAUCOM NURSERY CO p 1262
10020 John Russell Rd, Charlotte NC 28213
Tel (704) 596-3220 SIC 0181 5193

VAN WINGERDEN INTERNATIONAL INC p 1543
4112 Haywood Rd, Mills River NC 28759
Tel (828) 696-4500 SIC 5193

■ DARICE INC p 412
13000 Darice Pkwy 82, Strongsville OH 44149
Tel (440) 238-9150 SIC 5945 5193 5999

SEVILLE FARMS INC p 1309
8805 Levy County Line Rd, Mansfield TX 76063
Tel (817) 473-2249 SIC 5193

CONTINENTAL WHOLESALE FLORISTS INC p 364
1777 Ne Loop 410, San Antonio TX 78217
Tel (210) 654-6543 SIC 5193

TETCO INC p 1441
1100 Ne Loop 410 Ste 900, San Antonio TX 78209
Tel (210) 821-5900
SIC 4213 5411 1611 5193

EVERGREEN ENTERPRISES INC p 514
5915 Midlothian Tpke, Richmond VA 23225
Tel (804) 231-1800
SIC 3253 2399 5193 5999

SIC 5194 Tobacco & Tobacco Prdts Wholesale

BTC WHOLESALE DISTRIBUTORS INC p 222
100 Airview Ln, Alabaster AL 35007
Tel (205) 324-2581
SIC 5194 5145 5087 5149 5122

ANDALUSIA DISTRIBUTING CO INC p 89
117 Allen Ave, Andalusia AL 36420
Tel (334) 222-3671
SIC 5172 5113 5194 5149

CITY WHOLESALE GROCERY CO INC p 320
300 Industrial Dr, Birmingham AL 35211
Tel (205) 795-4533
SIC 5194 5141 5145 5122

W L PETREY WHOLESALE CO INC p 1568
10345 Petrey Hwy, Luverne AL 36049
Tel (334) 230-5674 SIC 5141 5194

MTC DISTRIBUTING p 997
4900 Stoddard Rd, Modesto CA 95356
Tel (209) 523-6449 SIC 5194 5145 5149

PACIFIC GROSERVICE INC p 1104
567 Cinnabar St, San Jose CA 95110
Tel (408) 727-4826
SIC 5194 5145 5141 5113 5087

▲ CORE-MARK HOLDING CO INC p 369
395 Oyster Point Blvd # 415, South San Francisco CA 94080
Tel (650) 589-9445
SIC 5141 5194 5145 5122 5199 5149

■ CORE-MARK INTERNATIONAL INC p 369
395 Oyster Point Blvd # 415, South San Francisco CA 94080
Tel (650) 589-9445 SIC 5141 5194

■ CORE-MARK MIDCONTINENT INC p 369
395 Oyster Point Blvd # 415, South San Francisco CA 94080
Tel (650) 589-9445 SIC 5194 5141

HAY ISLAND HOLDING CORP p 670
20 Thorndal Cir, Darien CT 06820
Tel (203) 656-8000 SIC 5194 2131

SWISHER INTERNATIONAL GROUP INC p 1412
20 Thorndal Cir, Darien CT 06820
Tel (203) 656-8000 SIC 5194

SWISHER INTERNATIONAL INC p 1412
20 Thorndal Cir, Darien CT 06820
Tel (203) 656-8000 SIC 5194

COMMONWEALTH - ALTADIS INC p 345
5900 N Andrews Ave # 1100, Fort Lauderdale FL 33309
Tel (954) 772-9000 SIC 5194

SEMINOLE TRIBE OF FLORIDA INC p 1302
6300 Stirling Rd, Hollywood FL 33024
Tel (954) 966-6300
SIC 7999 5194 2011 5182 2911

GOOD TIMES USA LLC p 624
8408 Temple Terrace Hwy, Tampa FL 33637
Tel (813) 621-8702 SIC 5194

IRA HIGDON GROCERY CO p 764
150 Iga Way, Cairo GA 39828
Tel (229) 377-1272
SIC 5141 5147 5142 5143 2111 5194

■ CORE-MARK DISTRIBUTORS INC p 369
4820 N Church Ln, Smyrna GA 30080
Tel (404) 792-2000
SIC 5194 5141 5145 5113

HAWAIIAN HOUSEWARES LTD p 669
96-1282 Waihona St, Pearl City HI 96782
Tel (808) 453-8000
SIC 5199 5194 5141 5145

EBY-BROWN CO LLC p 474
1415 W Diehl Rd Ste 300, Naperville IL 60563
Tel (630) 778-2800
SIC 5194 5145 5141 5122 5149

FARNER-BOCKEN CO p 530
1751 E Us Highway 30, Carroll IA 51401
Tel (712) 792-7454 SIC 5145 5194

MODERN DISTRIBUTORS INC p 981
817 W Columbia St, Somerset KY 42501
Tel (606) 679-1178
SIC 5194 5962 5145 5064

HARRISON CO LLC p 664
4801 Viking Dr, Bossier City LA 71111
Tel (318) 747-0700 SIC 5194 5145 5141

IMPERIAL TRADING CO LLC p 734
701 Edwards Ave, Harahan LA 70123
Tel (504) 733-1400 SIC 5194 5141 5145

LYONS SPECIALTY CO LLC p 888
2800 La Highway 1 N, Port Allen LA 70767
Tel (225) 356-1319 SIC 5194 5145 5149

PINE STATE TRADING CO p 1149
47 Market St, Gardiner ME 04345
Tel (207) 622-2345 SIC 5181 5194 5145

GEORGE J FALTER CO p 606
3501 Benson Ave, Baltimore MD 21227
Tel (410) 646-3641
SIC 5194 5145 5141 5015

CENTURY DISTRIBUTORS INC p 282
15710 Crabbs Branch Way, Rockville MD 20855
Tel (301) 212-9100
SIC 5194 5145 5149 5113

CONSUMER PRODUCT DISTRIBUTORS INC p 361
705 Meadow St, Chicopee MA 01013
Tel (413) 592-4141
SIC 5194 5141 7389 5145

GARBER BROS INC p 591
Kay Way Rr 139, Stoughton MA 02072
Tel (781) 341-0800
SIC 5194 5145 5141 5122

ADMIRAL PETROLEUM CO p 23
785 W Randall St, Coopersville MI 49404
Tel (616) 837-6218
SIC 5541 5411 5194 5145

MARTIN AND SNYDER PRODUCT SALES CO p 912
8880 Hubbell St, Detroit MI 48228
Tel (313) 272-4900 SIC 5194 5145

GRAD INC p 628
4001 3 Mile Rd Nw, Grand Rapids MI 49534
Tel (616) 676-5969
SIC 5141 5194 5145 5122 5113 5411

HENRYS FOODS INC p 684
234 Mckay Ave N, Alexandria MN 56308
Tel (320) 763-3194
SIC 5194 5145 5111 5113 5141

■ MINTER-WEISMAN CO p 974
1035 Nathan Ln N Ste A, Minneapolis MN 55441
Tel (763) 545-3706
SIC 5194 5149 5145 5013 5122

HOLLOWAY DISTRIBUTING INC p 701
210 E Owen Ave, Puxico MO 63960
Tel (573) 222-6255 SIC 5145 5194 5149

TOBA INC p 1458
2621 W Us Highway 30, Grand Island NE 68803
Tel (308) 389-5987
SIC 5148 5194 5145 5141

CASH-WA DISTRIBUTING CO OF KEARNEY INC p 263
401 W 4th St, Kearney NE 68845
Tel (308) 237-3151 SIC 5149 5046 5194

▲ AMCON DISTRIBUTING CO INC p 65
7405 Irvington Rd, Omaha NE 68122
Tel (402) 331-3727
SIC 5194 5141 5145 5113 5122

CONSOLIDATED SERVICE DISTRIBUTORS INC p 360
905 Murray Rd, East Hanover NJ 07936
Tel (908) 687-5800 SIC 5145 5194

PLAINFIELD TOBACCO AND CANDY CO INC p 1153
25 Van Dyke Ave, New Brunswick NJ 08901
Tel (732) 296-8900 SIC 5194 5145

800-JR CIGAR INC p 4
301 State Route 10, Whippany NJ 07981
Tel (973) 884-9555 SIC 5194 5993 5961

TRIPIFOODS INC p 1482
1427 William St, Buffalo NY 14206
Tel (716) 853-7400
SIC 5141 5194 5145 5143 5142 5122

JRD HOLDINGS INC p 795
1524 132nd St, College Point NY 11356
Tel (718) 762-8700
SIC 5141 5142 5147 5181 5194

RESTAURANT DEPOT LLC p 1228
1524 132nd St, College Point NY 11356
Tel (718) 762-8700
SIC 5147 5141 5142 5181 5194

HAROLD LEVINSON ASSOCIATES INC p 662
21 Banfi Plz N, Farmingdale NY 11735
Tel (631) 962-2400 SIC 5194 5145

SOUTHCO DISTRIBUTING CO p 1345
2201 S John St, Goldsboro NC 27530
Tel (919) 735-8012 SIC 5194 5141 5131

ALEX LEE INC p 48
120 4th St Sw, Hickory NC 28602
Tel (828) 725-4424
SIC 5141 5142 5147 5148 5194 5411

MERCHANTS DISTRIBUTORS LLC p 944
5005 Alex Lee Blvd, Hickory NC 28601
Tel (828) 725-4424
SIC 5141 5142 5147 5148 5194 5122

NOVELART MANUFACTURING CO p 1063
2121 Section Rd, Cincinnati OH 45237
Tel (513) 351-7700 SIC 5141 5145 5194

CORE-MARK OHIO p 369
30300 Emerald Valley Pkwy, Solon OH 44139
Tel (650) 589-9445 SIC 5194

STEPHENSON WHOLESALE CO INC p 1386
230 S 22nd Ave, Durant OK 74701
Tel (580) 920-0125
SIC 5194 5145 5143 5142 5141 5113

MAJOR EAGLE INC p 899
2350 W Broadway, Eugene OR 97402
Tel (541) 345-8421
SIC 5181 5141 5194 5142

MCANENY BROTHERS INC p 926
470 Industrial Park Rd, Ebensburg PA 15931
Tel (814) 472-9800
SIC 5141 5147 5148 5194 5113 5142

COOPER-BOOTH WHOLESALE CO LP p 367
200 Lincoln West Dr, Mountville PA 17554
Tel (717) 285-8000
SIC 5194 5145 5122 5141

LIBERTY USA INC p 863
920 Irwin Run Rd, West Mifflin PA 15122
Tel (412) 461-2700
SIC 5194 5145 5122 5141

PUERTO RICO SUPPLIES GROUP INC p 1191
Parkeast, Bayamon PR 00961
Tel (787) 780-4043
SIC 5194 5149 5122 5143 5148

W LEE FLOWERS AND CO INC p 1568
127 E W Lee Flowers Rd, Scranton SC 29591
Tel (843) 389-2731 SIC 5141 5147 5194

■ MCCARTY-HULL CIGAR CO INC p 926
4714 Ne 24th Ave, Amarillo TX 79107
Tel (806) 383-1313 SIC 5194 5145

PRICE & CO p 1174
3530 W Cardinal Dr, Beaumont TX 77705
Tel (409) 842-0677
SIC 5194 5145 5122 5141

BRENHAM WHOLESALE GROCERY CO INC p 210
602 W First St, Brenham TX 77833
Tel (979) 836-7925
SIC 5194 5147 5142 5141 5148

INDUS ENTERPRISES INC p 739
7051 Southwest Fwy, Houston TX 77074
Tel (713) 784-4335 SIC 5149 5194 5912

CAPITAL CANDY CO INC p 249
32 Burnham St, Barre VT 05641
Tel (802) 476-6689
SIC 5145 5194 5122 5141 5149

MERCHANTS GROCERY CO INC p 944
800 Maddox Dr, Culpeper VA 22701
Tel (540) 825-0786 SIC 5194 5141 5145

■ PHILIP MORRIS USA INC p 1143
6601 W Brd St, Richmond VA 23230
Tel (804) 274-2000 SIC 2111 2141 5194

■ UNIVERSAL CORP p 1516
9201 Forest Hl Ave Stony, Richmond VA 23235
Tel (804) 359-9311 SIC 5194

OLD DOMINION TOBACCO CO INC p 1080
5400 Virginia Beach Blvd, Virginia Beach VA 23462
Tel (757) 497-1001 SIC 5194 5145

HARBOR WHOLESALE GROCERY INC p 660
3901 Hogum Bay Rd Ne, Lacey WA 98516
Tel (360) 754-4484
SIC 5141 5194 5142 5122

NORTHERN SALES CO INC p 1056
15022 Puyallup St E # 101, Sumner WA 98390
Tel (253) 299-0500
SIC 5145 5149 5194 5141

SLEDD CO CHAS M p 1331
100 E Cove Ave, Wheeling WV 26003
Tel (800) 333-0374 SIC 5194 5142 5149

CHAMBERS & OWEN INC p 287
1733 Morse St, Janesville WI 53545
Tel (608) 752-7865
SIC 5194 5145 5113 5141

HOLIDAY WHOLESALE INC p 700
225 Pioneer Dr, Wisconsin Dells WI 53965
Tel (608) 253-0404
SIC 5194 5145 5113 5199

SIC 5198 Paints, Varnishes & Splys Wholesale

MOBILE PAINT MANUFACTURING CO OF DELAWARE INC p 980
4775 Hamilton Blvd, Theodore AL 36582
Tel (251) 443-6110 SIC 2851 5198 5231

LOUIS WURTH AND CO p 880
895 Columbia St, Brea CA 92821
Tel (714) 529-1771 SIC 5072 5198

TCP GLOBAL CORP p 1428
6695 Rasha St, San Diego CA 92121
Tel (858) 909-2110 SIC 5198 5231

BONAKEMI USA INC p 199
2550 S Parker Rd Ste 600, Aurora CO 80014
Tel (303) 371-1411
SIC 5198 5169 5023 2851

GUIRYS INC p 646
620 Canosa Ct, Denver CO 80204
Tel (720) 360-4840 SIC 5198 5231 5999

DONGHIA INC p 450
500 Bic Dr Ste 20, Milford CT 06461
Tel (800) 366-4442
SIC 5198 5131 5021 2342

NATIONAL OAK DISTRIBUTORS INC p 1014
6529 Southern Blvd Ste 6, West Palm Beach FL 33413
Tel (561) 478-2711 SIC 5013 5198

TRONOX LLC p 1484
1 Kerr Mcgee Rd, Savannah GA 31404
Tel (912) 652-1000 SIC 2816 2819 5198

US LBM HOLDINGS LLC p 1532
1000 Corporate Grove Dr, Buffalo Grove IL 60089
Tel (877) 787-5267 SIC 5072 5031 5198

EPKO INDUSTRIES INC p 505
400 High Grove Blvd, Glendale Heights IL 60139
Tel (847) 437-4000 SIC 5198

ACE HARDWARE CORP p 16
2200 Kensington Ct, Oak Brook IL 60523
Tel (630) 990-6600
SIC 5251 5198 5063 5074 5083

VOGEL PAINT & WAX CO INC p 1564
1110 Albany Pl Se, Orange City IA 51041
Tel (712) 737-4993 SIC 2851 5198

■ RED THREAD SPACES LLC p 1216
101 Seaport Blvd Ste 600, Boston MA 02210
Tel (617) 439-4900
SIC 5999 5021 8712 5198

BREWSTER WALLPAPER CORP p 210
67 Pacella Park Dr, Randolph MA 02368
Tel (781) 963-4800 SIC 5198

ATLANTIC PLYWOOD CORP p 127
8 Roessler Rd, Woburn MA 01801
Tel (781) 933-1932 SIC 5031 5198

LUMBERMENS INC p 885
4433 Stafford Ave Sw, Grand Rapids MI 49548
Tel (616) 261-3200 SIC 5033 5031 5198

VENTRA IONIA MAIN LLC p 1548
14 Beardsley St, Ionia MI 48846
Tel (616) 597-3220 SIC 3469 3089 5198

PAINTERS SUPPLY AND EQUIPMENT CO p 1108
25195 Brest, Taylor MI 48180
Tel (734) 946-8119 SIC 5198 5231

HIRSHFIELDS INC p 696
725 2nd Ave N Ste 1, Minneapolis MN 55405
Tel (612) 377-3910 SIC 5198 5231 2851

▲ FASTENAL CO p 531
2001 Theurer Blvd, Winona MN 55987
Tel (507) 454-5374
SIC 5085 5072 5063 5169 5198

RICCIARDI BROS INC p 1232
1915 Springfield Ave, Maplewood NJ 07040
Tel (973) 762-3830 SIC 5198 5231

KRAVET INC p 829
225 Cent Ave S, Bethpage NY 11714
Tel (516) 293-2000 SIC 5131 5198 2392

ABOFFS INC p 12
33 Gerard St Ste 204, Huntington NY 11743
Tel (631) 427-2008 SIC 5198 5231

■ JANOVIC-PLAZA INC p 777
3035 Thomson Ave, Long Island City NY 11101
Tel (718) 392-3999
SIC 5198 5231 5023 5719

PAINT APPLICATOR CORP OF AMERICA p 1108
7 Harbor Park Dr, Port Washington NY 11050
Tel (516) 284-3000 SIC 5072 5198

LINZER PRODUCTS CORP p 869
248 Wyandanch Ave, West Babylon NY 11704
Tel (631) 253-3333 SIC 5198 3991

■ COMEX NORTH AMERICA INC p 344
101 W Prospect Ave # 1020, Cleveland OH 44115
Tel (303) 307-2100
SIC 2851 8742 5198 5231

JMAC INC p 786
200 W Nationwide Blvd # 1, Columbus OH 43215
Tel (614) 436-2418
SIC 3325 5198 7999 5511 8741

AKZO NOBEL COATINGS INC p 42
8220 Mohawk Dr, Strongsville OH 44136
Tel (440) 297-5100 SIC 2851 5198 2821

TRONOX US HOLDINGS INC p 1484
3301 Nw 150th St, Oklahoma City OK 73134
Tel (405) 775-5000 SIC 2816 2819 5198

SPECTRUM PAINT CO INC p 1357
15247 E Skelly Dr, Tulsa OK 74116
Tel (918) 836-9911 SIC 5198 5231

INDUSTRIAL FINISHES & SYSTEMS INC p 740
3455 W 1st Ave, Eugene OR 97402
Tel (541) 485-1503 *SIC* 5085 5198

RODDA PAINT CO p 1246
6107 N Marine Dr Ste 3, Portland OR 97203
Tel (503) 521-4300
SIC 2851 5198 5023 5231 5719

COLOURS INC p 339
233 S Washington St, Wilkes Barre PA 18701
Tel (570) 655-9510 *SIC* 5198 5085 5088

MERIT DISTRIBUTION GROUP LLC p 949
1310 Union St, Spartanburg SC 29302
Tel (864) 583-3011 *SIC* 5198

GROVES INDUSTRIAL SUPPLY CORP p 642
7301 Pinemont Dr, Houston TX 77040
Tel (713) 675-4747 *SIC* 5085 5084 5198

HANDY HARDWARE WHOLESALE INC p 657
8300 Tewantin Dr, Houston TX 77061
Tel (713) 644-1495
SIC 5072 5074 5063 5031 5198

TASCO AUTO COLOR CORP p 1426
10323 Veterans Mem Dr, Houston TX 77038
Tel (281) 999-3761
SIC 5198 5013 5231 5531

ENGLISH COLOR & SUPPLY INC p 499
806 N Grove Rd, Richardson TX 75081
Tel (972) 235-3108 *SIC* 5198 5231

GLEN GEO ENTERPRISES INC p 614
13395 Murphy Rd, Stafford TX 77477
Tel (281) 242-6945 *SIC* 1799 5198 5084

PAINT SUNDRIES SOLUTIONS INC p 1108
930 7th Ave, Kirkland WA 98033
Tel (425) 827-9200 *SIC* 5198

BLAIN SUPPLY INC p 188
3507 E Racine St, Janesville WI 53546
Tel (608) 754-2821
SIC 5083 5072 5039 5013 5023 5198

SIC 5199 Nondurable Goods, NEC Wholesale

COOPER MARINE & TIMBERLANDS CORP p 367
118 N Royal St, Mobile AL 36602
Tel (251) 434-5000 *SIC* 5199 2421

MEMORY CO LLC p 942
25 Downing Dr, Phenix City AL 36869
Tel (334) 448-0708 *SIC* 5199

K & K VETERINARY SUPPLY INC p 798
675 Laura Ln, Tontitown AR 72770
Tel (479) 361-1516 *SIC* 5199 5047 5072

TARGUS INTERNATIONAL LLC p 1425
1211 N Miller St, Anaheim CA 92806
Tel (714) 765-5555 *SIC* 5199

QUETICO LLC p 1199
5521 Schaefer Ave, Chino CA 91710
Tel (909) 628-6200 *SIC* 5199 7389

99 CENTS ONLY STORES LLC p 4
4000 Union Pacific Ave, Commerce CA 90023
Tel (323) 980-8145 *SIC* 5411 5331 5199

ERNEST PACKAGING SOLUTIONS INC p 508
5777 Smithway St, Commerce CA 90040
Tel (800) 233-7788 *SIC* 5113 5199 7389

NUMBER HOLDINGS INC p 1067
4000 Union Pacific Ave, Commerce CA 90023
Tel (323) 980-8145 *SIC* 5331 5199

■ **CORE-MARK INTERRELATED COMPANIES INC** p 369
311 Reed Cir, Corona CA 92879
Tel (951) 272-4790 *SIC* 5199 5122 5087

PET PARTNERS INC p 1137
450 N Sheridan St, Corona CA 92880
Tel (951) 279-9888 *SIC* 5199

ART SUPPLY ENTERPRISES INC p 113
1375 Ocean Ave, Emeryville CA 94608
Tel (510) 768-6633 *SIC* 5199

RENO JONES INC p 1224
2373 N Watney Way, Fairfield CA 94533
Tel (707) 422-4300 *SIC* 5199 5085 3221

NIKKEN INTERNATIONAL INC p 1043
2 Corporate Park Ste 100, Irvine CA 92606
Tel (949) 789-2000 *SIC* 5199

REDBARN PET PRODUCTS INC p 1216
3229 E Spring St Ste 310, Long Beach CA 90806
Tel (562) 495-7315 *SIC* 5199 2047

GREAT WALL TEXTILE INC p 634
2150 E 10th St, Los Angeles CA 90021
Tel (626) 688-0271 *SIC* 5199

HARLAND M BRAUN & CO INC p 661
4010 Whiteside St, Los Angeles CA 90063
Tel (323) 263-9275 *SIC* 5159 5199

JACK NADEL INC p 773
8701 Bellanca Ave, Los Angeles CA 90045
Tel (310) 815-2600 *SIC* 8742 5199

OAK PAPER PRODUCTS CO INC p 1070
3686 E Olympic Blvd, Los Angeles CA 90023
Tel (323) 268-0507
SIC 5113 5199 5087 2653

VETERINARY SERVICE INC p 1553
4100 Bangs Ave, Modesto CA 95356
Tel (209) 545-5100 *SIC* 5047 5199 5083

WONDERTREATS INC p 1622
2200 Lapham Dr, Modesto CA 95354
Tel (209) 521-8881 *SIC* 5199 5947

KATZKIN LEATHER INC p 805
6868 W Acco St, Montebello CA 90640
Tel (323) 725-1243 *SIC* 5199 2531

WORLDWISE INC p 1626
6 Hamilton Landing # 150, Novato CA 94949
Tel (415) 721-7400 *SIC* 5199

ATA RETAIL SERVICES LLC p 123
7133 Koll Center Pkwy # 100, Pleasanton CA 94566
Tel (925) 621-4700 *SIC* 5199

VEGETABLE GROWERS SUPPLY CO p 1546
1360 Merrill St, Salinas CA 93901
Tel (831) 759-4600 *SIC* 5199 2449

■ **WAL-MART.COM USA LLC** p 1572
850 Cherry Ave, San Bruno CA 94066
Tel (650) 837-5000 *SIC* 5961 5199

IMAGE ONE MARKETING GROUP INC p 733
11956 Bernardo Plaza Dr # 525, San Diego CA 92128
Tel (858) 673-8299 *SIC* 7311 5199

PETCO ANIMAL SUPPLIES INC p 1137
10850 Via Frontera, San Diego CA 92127
Tel (858) 453-7845 *SIC* 0752 5199 5999

PETCO ANIMAL SUPPLIES STORES INC p 1137
9125 Rehco Rd, San Diego CA 92121
Tel (858) 453-7845 *SIC* 5999 0752 5199

AHI INVESTMENT INC p 36
675 Glenoaks Blvd, San Fernando CA 91340
Tel (818) 979-0030 *SIC* 5199 3991

DELANCEY STREET FOUNDATION p 423
600 The Embarcadero, San Francisco CA 94107
Tel (415) 957-9800
SIC 8361 5199 8322 4212 5812

▲ **MCKESSON CORP** p 930
1 Post St Fl 18, San Francisco CA 94104
Tel (415) 983-8300
SIC 5122 5047 5199 7372

■ **CSE HOLDINGS INC** p 397
650 Brennan St, San Jose CA 95131
Tel (408) 436-1907
SIC 5087 5084 7699 5113 5199 5112

JACOB STERN & SONS INC p 775
1464 E Valley Rd, Santa Barbara CA 93108
Tel (805) 565-4532 *SIC* 5169 5191 5199

SMART LIVING CO p 1332
4100 Guardian St, Simi Valley CA 93063
Tel (805) 578-5500 *SIC* 5199

▲ **CORE-MARK HOLDING CO INC** p 369
395 Oyster Point Blvd # 415, South San Francisco CA 94080
Tel (650) 589-9445
SIC 5141 5194 5145 5122 5199 5149

LOGOMARK INC p 875
1201 Bell Ave, Tustin CA 92780
Tel (714) 675-6100 *SIC* 5199

SHIMS BARGAIN INC p 1316
2600 S Soto St, Vernon CA 90058
Tel (323) 881-0099 *SIC* 5199

▲ **CENTRAL GARDEN & PET CO** p 278
1340 Treat Blvd Ste 600, Walnut Creek CA 94597
Tel (925) 948-4000 *SIC* 5199 5191

ANDWIN CORP p 91
6636 Variel Ave, Woodland Hills CA 91303
Tel (818) 999-2828
SIC 5113 3842 5199 5087 5047 2835

DENCO SALES CO p 428
55 S Yuma St, Denver CO 80223
Tel (303) 733-0607 *SIC* 5199 5084

CHUCK LATHAM ASSOCIATES INC p 304
18403 Longs Way Unit 102, Parker CO 80134
Tel (303) 699-2905 *SIC* 5199

S & S WORLDWIDE INC p 1261
75 Mill St, Colchester CT 06415
Tel (860) 537-3451 *SIC* 5199 5049 3944

PURITY WHOLESALE GROCERS INC p 1192
5300 Broken Sound Blvd Nw # 110, Boca Raton FL 33487
Tel (561) 997-8302 *SIC* 5141 5122 5199

C & W FISH CO INC p 232
7508 Se Autumn Ln, Hobe Sound FL 33455
Tel (772) 283-1184 *SIC* 5199 5146

■ **STEIN MART BUYING CORP** p 1385
1200 Riverplace Blvd # 1000, Jacksonville FL 32207
Tel (904) 346-1500 *SIC* 5199

■ **SCHOLASTIC BOOK FAIRS INC** p 1288
1080 Greenwood Blvd, Lake Mary FL 32746
Tel (407) 829-7300 *SIC* 5192 5199 5942

INTRADECO INC p 759
9500 Nw 108th Ave, Medley FL 33178
Tel (305) 264-6022 *SIC* 5136 5199 5065

WINCORP INTERNATIONAL INC p 1615
10025 Nw 116th Way Ste 14, Medley FL 33178
Tel (305) 887-1294
SIC 5191 5083 5199 7338 5144

PEREZ TRADING CO INC p 1135
3490 Nw 125th St, Miami FL 33167
Tel (305) 769-0761 *SIC* 5199

PEARL PAINT CO INC p 1126
1033 E Oakland Park Blvd, Oakland Park FL 33334
Tel (954) 564-5700
SIC 5999 5199 7699 5112 5947 7311

BUFKOR INC p 224
1801 Stonebrook Ln, Safety Harbor FL 34695
Tel (727) 572-9991 *SIC* 5199 2084

PARADIES GIFTS INC p 1113
2305 W Airport Blvd, Sanford FL 32771
Tel (407) 290-5288 *SIC* 5199

MOTCO INC p 992
7900 Sw 57th Ave Ste 10, South Miami FL 33143
Tel (305) 662-8814 *SIC* 5182 5122 5199

ALLIANCE ENTERTAINMENT HOLDING CORP p 54
1401 Nw 136th Ave Ste 100, Sunrise FL 33323
Tel (954) 255-4000 *SIC* 5199 6719

ALLIANCE ENTERTAINMENT LLC p 54
1401 Nw 136th Ave Ste 100, Sunrise FL 33323
Tel (954) 255-4403 *SIC* 5199 3651

PET SUPERMARKET INC p 1137
1100 International Pkwy # 200, Sunrise FL 33323
Tel (866) 434-1990 *SIC* 5999 3999 5199

MERCHANDISING SOLUTIONS GROUP INC p 944
260 Peachtree St Nw, Atlanta GA 30303
Tel (800) 417-1320 *SIC* 5199 1542

PIEDMONT NATIONAL CORP p 1147
1561 Southland Cir Nw, Atlanta GA 30318
Tel (404) 351-6130 *SIC* 5199 5113

SPG HOLDINGS LLC p 1358
133 Peachtree St Se, Atlanta GA 30303
Tel (404) 652-4000 *SIC* 2621 5199

MORRIS COMMUNICATIONS CO LLC p 990
725 Broad St, Augusta GA 30901
Tel (706) 724-0851
SIC 2711 5199 2721 2731

AQUAFIL USA INC p 101
1 Aquafil Dr, Cartersville GA 30120
Tel (678) 605-8100 *SIC* 5199

KEYSTON BROS (INC) p 815
1000 Holcomb Wds Pkwy # 111, Roswell GA 30076
Tel (770) 587-2555 *SIC* 5199 5131 5191

KUDZU FABRICS INC p 831
2154 River Cliff Dr, Roswell GA 30076
Tel (770) 641-0379 *SIC* 5199 5131 5191

FRESH BEGINNINGS INC p 578
4001 Coleman Rd N, Valdosta GA 31602
Tel (229) 242-0237 *SIC* 5199 2052 2064

WEBCO HAWAII INC p 1586
2840 Mokumoa St, Honolulu HI 96819
Tel (808) 839-4551
SIC 5122 5199 5141 5064

HAWAIIAN HOUSEWARES LTD p 669
96-1282 Waihona St, Pearl City HI 96782
Tel (808) 453-8000
SIC 5199 5194 5141 5145

HANCHETT PAPER CO p 656
4000 Ferry Rd, Aurora IL 60502
Tel (630) 978-1000 *SIC* 5084 5199

VELTEX CORP p 1547
123 W Madison St Ste 1500, Chicago IL 60602
Tel (312) 235-4014 *SIC* 2211 5199

PREGIS HOLDING I CORP p 1170
1650 Lake Cook Rd Ste 400, Deerfield IL 60015
Tel (847) 597-2200 *SIC* 2671 5199 7336

HAVI GROUP LIMITED PARTNERSHIP p 668
3500 Lacey Rd Ste 600, Downers Grove IL 60515
Tel (630) 353-4200 *SIC* 5113 5142 5199

■ **SILGAN WHITE CAP LLC** p 1323
1140 31st St, Downers Grove IL 60515
Tel (630) 515-8383 *SIC* 5199

WPS LEGACY INC p 1627
6450 Muirfield Dr, Hanover Park IL 60133
Tel (800) 232-4155 *SIC* 5199

BI-STATE PACKAGING INC p 181
4905 77th Ave E, Milan IL 61264
Tel (309) 736-8500 *SIC* 5199 5084

LYNCO DISTRIBUTION INC p 887
1410 11th St W, Milan IL 61264
Tel (309) 787-2300 *SIC* 5199

SCHWARZ PAPER CO LLC p 1291
8338 Austin Ave, Morton Grove IL 60053
Tel (847) 966-2550 *SIC* 2621 5199 4225

BRADFORD EXCHANGE LTD p 206
9333 N Milwaukee Ave, Niles IL 60714
Tel (847) 966-2770 *SIC* 5961 5199

RICO INDUSTRIES INC p 1233
7000 N Austin Ave, Niles IL 60714
Tel (312) 427-0313
SIC 5199 3172 2396 3993

CANDLELIGHT INVESTMENT HOLDINGS INC p 247
1980 Industrial Dr, Sterling IL 61081
Tel (815) 632-6800 *SIC* 5199

HALO BRANDED SOLUTIONS INC p 655
1980 Industrial Dr, Sterling IL 61081
Tel (815) 632-6988 *SIC* 5199

HALO HOLDING CORP p 655
1980 Industrial Dr, Sterling IL 61081
Tel (815) 632-6800 *SIC* 5199

■ **ASPEN MARKETING SERVICES LLC** p 118
1240 W North Ave, West Chicago IL 60185
Tel (630) 293-9600 *SIC* 8743 8748 5199

E K SUCCESS LTD p 466
2240 75th St, Woodridge IL 60517
Tel (630) 963-7100 *SIC* 5199 2679

WILTON BRANDS LLC p 1614
2240 75th St, Woodridge IL 60517
Tel (630) 963-7100
SIC 5023 2731 2721 7812 5199

WILTON HOLDINGS INC p 1614
2240 75th St, Woodridge IL 60517
Tel (630) 963-7100
SIC 5023 2731 2721 7812 5199

WILTON INDUSTRIES INC p 1614
2240 75th St, Woodridge IL 60517
Tel (630) 963-7100
SIC 5023 2731 2721 7812 5199

KOORSEN FIRE & SECURITY INC p 827
2719 N Arlington Ave, Indianapolis IN 46218
Tel (317) 542-1800
SIC 5099 7389 5199 5063 1731

STUMP PRINTING CO INC p 1395
101 Carroll Rd, South Whitley IN 46787
Tel (260) 723-5171
SIC 5199 2679 5961 2759

VARIETY DISTRIBUTORS INC p 1544
609 7th St, Harlan IA 51537
Tel (712) 755-2184
SIC 5131 5092 5122 5112 5145 5199

VALU MERCHANDISERS CO p 1542
5000 Kansas Ave, Kansas City KS 66106
Tel (913) 319-8500 *SIC* 5199

DD TRADERS INC p 419
5000 W 134th St, Leawood KS 66209
Tel (913) 402-6800 *SIC* 5199

POWER SALES AND ADVERTISING p 1165
9909 Lakeview Ave, Lenexa KS 66219
Tel (913) 324-4900 *SIC* 5199

GERSON CO p 609
1450 S Lone Elm Rd, Olathe KS 66061
Tel (913) 262-7400
SIC 5193 5199 5023 5094

KMS INC p 824
811 E Waterman St Ste 1, Wichita KS 67202
Tel (316) 264-8833 *SIC* 5199 5141

FLEX AMERICA INC p 555
1221 N Black Branch Rd, Elizabethtown KY 42701
Tel (270) 982-3456 *SIC* 5199

ALL STAR DAIRY ASSOCIATION INC p 51
1050 Monarch St Ste 101, Lexington KY 40513
Tel (859) 255-3644
SIC 5149 5169 5113 5199

GEIGER BROS p 597
70 Mount Hope Ave, Lewiston ME 04240
Tel (207) 755-2000
SIC 5199 3993 2752 2782 2789

PROGRESSIVE DISTRIBUTORS INC p 1181
145 Pleasant Hill Rd, Scarborough ME 04074
Tel (207) 883-2911 *SIC* 5122 5149 5199

COMMERCE LLC p 345
7603 Energy Pkwy, Baltimore MD 21226
Tel (410) 255-3500 *SIC* 5191 5072 5199

PETEDGE INC p 1138
100 Cummings Ctr Ste 307b, Beverly MA 01915
Tel (978) 998-8100 *SIC* 5199

PETEDGE MASSACHUSETTS BUSINESS TRUST p 1138
100 Cummings Ctr Ste 307b, Beverly MA 01915
Tel (978) 998-8100 *SIC* 5199

SPORTS IMAGES INC p 1360
1000 Franklin Village Dr # 104, Franklin MA 02038
Tel (508) 530-3225 *SIC* 5199

MILLBROOK DISTRIBUTION SERVICES INC p 970
88 Huntoon Memorial Hwy, Leicester MA 01524
Tel (508) 892-8171
SIC 5122 5023 5072 5112 5049 5199

SAMSONITE LLC p 1274
575 West St Ste 110, Mansfield MA 02048
Tel (508) 851-1400 *SIC* 5948 5199

■ **PARTYLITE WORLDWIDE LLC** p 1119
600 Cordwainer Dr Ste 202, Norwell MA 02061
Tel (508) 830-3100 *SIC* 5199

■ **PARTYLITE INC** p 1119
59 Armstrong Rd, Plymouth MA 02360
Tel (203) 661-1926
SIC 2023 3999 3641 5199 5023

PROLAMINA CORP p 1182
132 N Elm St, Westfield MA 01085
Tel (413) 562-2315 *SIC* 2671 5199

PACIFIC PACKAGING PRODUCTS INC p 1105
24 Industrial Way, Wilmington MA 01887
Tel (978) 657-9100
SIC 5113 5199 5084 5162 2671 2653

AMWAY INTERNATIONAL INC p 87
7575 Fulton St E, Ada MI 49355
Tel (616) 787-1000
SIC 5169 5122 5099 5199 2099 2032

CHASE CASH & CARRY INC p 291
6661 Chase Rd, Dearborn MI 48126
Tel (313) 582-1200 *SIC* 5199

OAKWOOD METAL FABRICATING CO p 1071
1100 Oakwood Blvd, Dearborn MI 48124
Tel (313) 561-7740 *SIC* 5199 3714 3469

NOTIONS MARKETING CORP p 1062
1500 Buchanan Ave Sw, Grand Rapids MI 49507
Tel (616) 243-8424 *SIC* 5131 5199 5092

OLIVER PRODUCTS CO p 1082
445 6th St Nw, Grand Rapids MI 49504
Tel (616) 456-7711 *SIC* 5084 5199 3053

GRAND RAPIDS FOAM TECHNOLOGIES INC p 630
2788 Remico St Sw, Wyoming MI 49519
Tel (616) 726-1677 *SIC* 5199

MILLER MANUFACTURING CO p 970
2910 Waters Rd Ste 150, Eagan MN 55121
Tel (651) 982-5100 *SIC* 1542 5199

POLAROID CONSUMER ELECTRONICS INTERNATIONAL LLC p 1159
4400 Baker Rd Ste 900, Minnetonka MN 55343
Tel (952) 936-5000 *SIC* 5199

MIDWEST QUALITY GLOVES INC p 967
835 Industrial Rd, Chillicothe MO 64601
Tel (660) 646-2165 *SIC* 5199 3151

3D CORPORATE SOLUTIONS LLC p 2
601 13th St, Monett MO 65708
Tel (417) 236-9602 *SIC* 5199 5149 2048

BUNZL DISTRIBUTION MIDCENTRAL INC p 226
11434 Moog Dr, Saint Louis MO 63146
Tel (314) 569-2800 *SIC* 5199

GLASS GALLERY LTD p 614
10300 Lake Bluff Dr, Saint Louis MO 63123
Tel (314) 416-4200 *SIC* 5947 5199

■ **POLYONE DESIGNED STRUCTURES AND SOLUTIONS LLC** p 1160
11650 Lkeside Crossing Ct, Saint Louis MO 63105
Tel (888) 721-4242 *SIC* 5199

SBI INC p 1285
8500 Valcour Ave, Saint Louis MO 63123
Tel (314) 615-2000
SIC 5199 5122 7334 5084

CARLSON SYSTEMS HOLDINGS INC p 258
10840 Harney St, Omaha NE 68154
Tel (402) 593-5300 *SIC* 5085 5199

■ **ORIENTAL TRADING CO INC** p 1094
5455 S 90th St, Omaha NE 68127
Tel (402) 596-1200 *SIC* 5199 4813

SERGEANTS PET CARE PRODUCTS INC p 1306
10077 S 134th St, Omaha NE 68138
Tel (402) 938-7000 *SIC* 2834 5199 2048

■ **CENTRAL LEWMAR LLC** p 279
261 River Rd, Clifton NJ 07014
Tel (973) 405-2300 *SIC* 5111 5199

SIGMA CORP p 1321
700 Goldman Dr, Cream Ridge NJ 08514
Tel (609) 758-0800 *SIC* 5074 5199

WORMSER CORP p 1626
150 Coolidge Ave, Englewood NJ 07631
Tel (800) 666-9676 *SIC* 5085 5199

LG CHEM AMERICA INC p 860
910 Sylvan Ave, Englewood Cliffs NJ 07632
Tel (201) 816-2000 *SIC* 5099 5169 5199

NATIONAL ENTERTAINMENT COLLECTIBLES ASSOCIATION INC p 1011
603 Sweetland Ave, Hillside NJ 07205
Tel (908) 686-3300 *SIC* 5199

MYRON CORP p 1005
205 Maywood Ave, Maywood NJ 07607
Tel (201) 843-6464 *SIC* 5199

CSS INC p 398
35 Love Ln, Netcong NJ 07857
Tel (973) 364-1118 SIC 5199

TMCI HOLDINGS INC p 1457
80 Avenue K, Newark NJ 07105
Tel (201) 553-1100
SIC 5122 5023 5072 5112 5049 5199

WESTPORT CORP p 1602
331 Changebridge Rd Ste 3, Pine Brook NJ 07058
Tel (973) 575-0110 SIC 5948 5199

HARTZ MOUNTAIN CORP p 666
400 Plaza Dr Ste 400, Secaucus NJ 07094
Tel (201) 271-4800 SIC 5199 3999

TUMI INC p 1491
1001 Durham Ave Ste 1b, South Plainfield NJ 07080
Tel (908) 756-4400 SIC 5199 5948 3161

HMP SERVICES HOLDING INC p 698
721 Union Blvd, Totowa NJ 07512
Tel (973) 812-0400 SIC 5084 5199

TRI-COASTAL DESIGN GROUP INC p 1477
40 Harry Shupe Blvd, Wharton NJ 07885
Tel (973) 560-0300 SIC 5137 5199

DK MAGAZINES CORP p 445
24 Meadow St, Brooklyn NY 11206
Tel (718) 417-3573 SIC 5199

▲ PARTY CITY HOLDCO INC p 1119
80 Grasslands Rd, Elmsford NY 10523
Tel (914) 345-2020
SIC 5947 5963 5199 6794

TWOS CO INC p 1495
500 Saw Mill River Rd, Elmsford NY 10523
Tel (914) 664-2277 SIC 5199 5023 5094

DURALEE FABRICS LTD p 462
49 Wireless Blvd Ste 150, Hauppauge NY 11788
Tel (631) 273-8800 SIC 5199

AMERICAN SALES CO LLC p 79
4201 Walden Ave, Lancaster NY 14086
Tel (716) 686-7000 SIC 5199 5122

PEARL ARTIST & CRAFT SUPPLY CORP p 1126
185 Merrick Rd, Lynbrook NY 11563
Tel (954) 564-5700 SIC 5999 5199

ACCESSORY CORP p 15
575 8th Ave Fl 16, New York NY 10018
Tel (212) 391-8607 SIC 3089 5199

AI FRIEDMAN LP p 37
44 W 18th St Fl 4, New York NY 10011
Tel (212) 243-9000 SIC 5199 5945

APAX PARTNERS OF NEW YORK p 96
601 Lexington Ave Fl 53, New York NY 10022
Tel (212) 419-2447
SIC 6282 5399 5199 5812 5813

AWC LIQUIDATING CO p 139
1407 Brdwy Ste 400, New York NY 10018
Tel (212) 221-1177
SIC 5112 5199 3873 5094

DSJS INC p 458
16 W 36th St Rm 901, New York NY 10018
Tel (212) 564-9326 SIC 5199

FASHION ACCESSORY BAZAAR LLC p 531
15 W 34th St Fl 2, New York NY 10001
Tel (212) 947-9001 SIC 5199 5112

■ G-III LEATHER FASHIONS INC p 588
512 Fashion Ave Fl 35, New York NY 10018
Tel (212) 403-0500 SIC 5199

■ HESS TRADING CORP p 688
1185 Ave Of The Americas, New York NY 10036
Tel (212) 997-8500 SIC 5199

ITOCHU PROMINENT USA LLC p 768
1411 Broadway Fl 7, New York NY 10018
Tel (212) 827-5707 SIC 5199

LVMH MOET HENNESSY LOUIS VUITTON INC p 887
19 E 57th St, New York NY 10022
Tel (212) 931-2700 SIC 5948 5199

REV HOLDINGS INC p 1229
466 Lexington Ave Fl 21, New York NY 10017
Tel (212) 527-4000
SIC 2844 3421 5122 5199 5999

REVLON HOLDINGS INC p 1229
237 Park Ave, New York NY 10017
Tel (212) 527-4000
SIC 2844 3421 5122 5199 5999

■ REVLON REAL ESTATE CORP p 1229
466 Lexington Ave Fl 13, New York NY 10017
Tel (212) 527-4000
SIC 5122 2844 3421 5199 5999

RGI GROUP INC p 1231
625 Madison Ave Frnt 4, New York NY 10022
Tel (212) 527-4000
SIC 2844 3421 5122 5199 5999

INTRAPAC (PLATTSBURGH) INC p 760
4 Plant St, Plattsburgh NY 12901
Tel (518) 561-2030 SIC 5199 3565

ADAMS FAIRACRE FARMS INC p 21
765 Dutchess Tpke, Poughkeepsie NY 12603
Tel (845) 454-4330 SIC 5411 5261 5199

MORRIS ROTHENBERG & SON INC p 990
3015 Veterans Mem Hwy, Ronkonkoma NY 11779
Tel (631) 585-9446
SIC 5199 5091 5139 5136

PRIDE PRODUCTS CORP p 1174
4333 Veterans Mem Hwy, Ronkonkoma NY 11779
Tel (631) 737-4444
SIC 5113 5122 5023 5072 5199

ALNOR OIL CO INC p 59
70 E Sunrise Hwy Ste 418, Valley Stream NY 11581
Tel (516) 561-6146 SIC 5199

WILSON FARMS INC p 1613
1780 Wehrle Dr Ste 110, Williamsville NY 14221
Tel (716) 204-4300 SIC 5199

TECHNIMARK LLC p 1431
180 Commerce Pl, Asheboro NC 27203
Tel (336) 498-4171 SIC 3089 5199

TRI VANTAGE LLC p 1477
1831 N Park Ave, Burlington NC 27217
Tel (800) 786-1876
SIC 5199 5088 5099 5091 2394

HYOSUNG USA INC p 724
15801 Brixham Hill Ave # 575, Charlotte NC 28277
Tel (704) 790-6136 SIC 2221 2296 5199

LOW & BONAR INC p 881
1301 Sand Hill Rd, Enka NC 28728
Tel (828) 665-5000
SIC 5199 3296 2899 2297 2221

MARKET AMERICA INC p 908
1302 Pleasant Ridge Rd, Greensboro NC 27409
Tel (336) 605-0040 SIC 5199

MARKET AMERICA WORLDWIDE INC p 908
1302 Pleasant Ridge Rd, Greensboro NC 27409
Tel (336) 605-0040 SIC 5199

SNYDER PAPER CORP p 1336
250 26th Street Dr Se, Hickory NC 28602
Tel (828) 328-2501 SIC 5199 5085

J T DAVENPORT & SONS INC p 772
1144 Broadway Rd, Sanford NC 27332
Tel (919) 774-9444 SIC 5199

THARPE CO INC p 1446
149 Crawford Rd, Statesville NC 28625
Tel (704) 872-5231 SIC 5199

PROFILL HOLDINGS LLC p 1180
255 W Crescentville Rd, Cincinnati OH 45246
Tel (513) 742-4000
SIC 5199 5136 5137 6798

ROSEMARK PAPER INC p 1250
1845 Progress Ave, Columbus OH 43207
Tel (614) 443-0303 SIC 5111 5199

STERLING PAPER CO p 1387
1845 Progress Ave, Columbus OH 43207
Tel (614) 443-0303 SIC 5111 5199

FLOWER FACTORY INC p 560
5655 Whipple Ave Nw, North Canton OH 44720
Tel (330) 494-7978 SIC 5199

■ WHITE BARN CANDLE CO p 1606
7 Limited Pkwy E, Reynoldsburg OH 43068
Tel (614) 856-6000 SIC 5199

■ LAMRITE WEST INC p 841
14225 Pearl Rd, Strongsville OH 44136
Tel (440) 238-7318 SIC 5999 5199 5092

H B CHEMICAL CORP p 649
1665 Enterprise Pkwy, Twinsburg OH 44087
Tel (330) 920-8023 SIC 5199

STOROPACK INC p 1392
4758 Devitt Dr, West Chester OH 45246
Tel (513) 874-0314 SIC 5199 3086 2671

SHAMROCK COMPANIES INC p 1311
24090 Detroit Rd, Westlake OH 44145
Tel (440) 899-9510
SIC 5112 5199 7336 7389 2754 2395

FABRICUT INC p 523
9303 E 46th St, Tulsa OK 74145
Tel (918) 622-7700 SIC 5199

WESTERN FAMILY HOLDING CO p 1598
6700 Sw Sandburg St, Tigard OR 97223
Tel (503) 639-6300
SIC 5141 5142 5199 5122 5149

■ AMERISOURCEBERGEN SERVICES CORP p 83
1300 Morris Dr Ste 100, Chesterbrook PA 19087
Tel (610) 727-7000
SIC 5122 5047 5199 8721

PHILLIPS FEED SERVICE INC p 1144
3747 Hecktown Rd, Easton PA 18045
Tel (610) 250-2099 SIC 5199

LAMI PRODUCTS INC p 841
860 Welsh Rd, Huntingdon Valley PA 19006
Tel (215) 947-5333 SIC 5199

GRAHAM PACKAGING CO INC p 629
700 Indian Springs Dr # 100, Lancaster PA 17601
Tel (717) 849-8500 SIC 5199 3089 5162

JAY GROUP INC p 779
700 Indian Springs Dr, Lancaster PA 17601
Tel (717) 285-6200
SIC 5961 7389 7331 7319 5199

LEEDSWORLD INC p 852
400 Hunt Valley Rd, New Kensington PA 15068
Tel (724) 334-9000
SIC 5199 5111 5112 3172 3161 2394

POLYCONCEPT NORTH AMERICA INC p 1160
400 Hunt Valley Rd, New Kensington PA 15068
Tel (724) 334-9000
SIC 5199 5111 5112 3172 3161 2394

FITZ AND FLOYD ENTERPRISES LLC p 553
3 Friends Ln Ste 300, Newtown PA 18940
Tel (800) 527-9550
SIC 5023 5199 5947 5719

STAUFFER MANUFACTURING CO p 1383
361 E 6th St, Red Hill PA 18076
Tel (215) 679-4446 SIC 5085 5199

BRADLEY CALDWELL INC p 206
200 Kiwanis Blvd, West Hazleton PA 18202
Tel (570) 455-7511 SIC 5191 5199 5072

OCEAN STATE JOBBERS INC p 1073
375 Commerce Park Rd, North Kingstown RI 02852
Tel (401) 295-2672 SIC 5331 5199

PET FOOD EXPERTS INC p 1137
175 Main St, Pawtucket RI 02860
Tel (401) 721-5593 SIC 5199 2047

WYNIT DISTRIBUTION LLC p 1630
2 W Washington St Ste 500, Greenville SC 29601
Tel (864) 605-9920
SIC 5045 5043 5046 5199 7372

KRUGER LTD p 830
1513 Absco Dr, Longs SC 29568
Tel (843) 399-2165 SIC 5199

WILLIAM BARNET & SON LLC p 1610
1300 Hayne St, Spartanburg SC 29301
Tel (864) 327-4620
SIC 5199 2823 2221 2824

ASSOCIATED PACKAGING INC p 121
435 Calvert Dr, Gallatin TN 37066
Tel (615) 452-2131 SIC 5199 5084

▲ FREDS INC p 576
4300 New Getwell Rd, Memphis TN 38118
Tel (901) 365-8880
SIC 5331 5912 5199 6794

CANDLE CORP OF AMERICA p 247
600 Sherwood Dr, Union City TN 38261
Tel (731) 885-7836 SIC 5023 5199

CLASSIC SOFT TRIM INC p 323
4516 Seton Center Pkwy # 135, Austin TX 78759
Tel (512) 873-7770 SIC 5199

HUGH M CUNNINGHAM INC p 717
2029 Westgate Dr Ste 120, Carrollton TX 75006
Tel (972) 888-3833
SIC 5074 5085 5083 5199

REDDY ICE GROUP INC p 1216
5720 Lbj Fwy Ste 200, Dallas TX 75240
Tel (877) 295-0024 SIC 5199 2097

SELECT PRODUCT GROUP LP p 1301
8214 Westchester Dr # 800, Dallas TX 75225
Tel (214) 363-7427 SIC 5199

SOUTHERN GLAZERS WINE AND SPIRITS OF TEXAS LLC p 1348
14911 Quorum Dr Ste 150, Dallas TX 75254
Tel (972) 392-8200 SIC 2082 5182 5199

▲ TANDY LEATHER FACTORY INC p 1424
1900 Se Loop 820, Fort Worth TX 76140
Tel (817) 872-3200 SIC 5948 5199 3111

PC INTERNATIONAL SALES INC p 1123
730 S Jupiter Rd Ste B, Garland TX 75042
Tel (972) 487-0580 SIC 5199

PROFESSIONAL PACKAGING SYSTEMS LLC p 1180
2010 S Great Sw Pkwy, Grand Prairie TX 75051
Tel (972) 988-0777 SIC 5199

HDC DISTRIBUTING LTD p 673
7100 High Life Dr, Houston TX 77066
Tel (281) 880-2730 SIC 5199

▲ OMEGA PROTEIN CORP p 1084
2105 Citywest Blvd # 500, Houston TX 77042
Tel (713) 623-0060 SIC 2077 5199

■ VICTORY PACKAGING LP p 1556
3555 Timmons Ln Ste 1440, Houston TX 77027
Tel (888) 261-1268 SIC 5113 5199

WAYNE D ENTERPRISES INC p 1584
14300 Hollister St, Houston TX 77066
Tel (713) 856-0300 SIC 5136 5199

ANIMAL SUPPLY CO LLC p 91
600 Las Colinas Blvd E, Irving TX 75039
Tel (972) 616-9600 SIC 5199

BIO WORLD MERCHANDISING INC p 183
2111 W Walnut Hill Ln, Irving TX 75038
Tel (888) 831-2138
SIC 2353 3161 2253 5199 3021

MICHAELS HOLDINGS LLC p 960
8000 Bent Branch Dr, Irving TX 75063
Tel (972) 409-1300
SIC 5945 5999 5949 5947 5199 5099

■ MICHAELS STORES INC p 960
8000 Bent Branch Dr, Irving TX 75063
Tel (972) 409-1300
SIC 5945 5999 5949 5947 5199 5099

MARIBEL RESENDIZ p 906
711 Mispola Dr, Laredo TX 78046
Tel (956) 236-2907 SIC 5199

GVH DISTRIBUTION LTD p 648
2601 Se Loop 289 Lubbock, Lubbock TX 79404
Tel (806) 687-5264 SIC 5199

HERCULES FILMS LLC p 685
12600 Cardinal Mdw, Sugar Land TX 77478
Tel (972) 284-0796 SIC 3081 5199

PROVO CRAFT & NOVELTY INC p 1187
10855 S Rvr Frnt Pkwy # 400, South Jordan UT 84095
Tel (800) 937-7686
SIC 5092 5199 5945 5947

■ GREENBRIER INTERNATIONAL INC p 637
500 Volvo Pkwy, Chesapeake VA 23320
Tel (757) 321-5900 SIC 5199 7389

SMITH MOUNTAIN INDUSTRIES OF VIRGINIA INC p 1333
1000 Dillard Dr, Forest VA 24551
Tel (800) 827-2231 SIC 5199 5947

GENERAL CIGAR CO INC p 599
10900 Nuckols Rd Ste 100, Glen Allen VA 23060
Tel (860) 602-3500 SIC 2121 5199 0132

RCMA AMERICAS INC p 1212
150 Boush St Ste 1000, Norfolk VA 23510
Tel (757) 627-4000 SIC 5199 6221

SWEDISH MATCH NORTH AMERICA LLC p 1411
1021 E Cary St Ste 1600, Richmond VA 23219
Tel (804) 787-5100 SIC 2131 5199

NILIT AMERICA INC p 1043
420 Industrial Park Rd, Ridgeway VA 24148
Tel (276) 638-2434 SIC 5199 2299 5531

PROLOGIX DISTRIBUTION SERVICES (WEST) LLC p 1183
3995 70th Ave E Ste B, Fife WA 98424
Tel (253) 952-7150 SIC 5199

BOX MAKER INC p 205
6412 S 190th St, Kent WA 98032
Tel (425) 251-0655
SIC 5113 2653 2672 3086 5199 2631

WORLDWIDE DISTRIBUTORS p 1626
8211 S 194th St, Kent WA 98032
Tel (253) 872-8746
SIC 5091 5136 5137 5139 5199 5023

PAC WORLDWIDE CORP p 1103
15435 Ne 92nd St, Redmond WA 98052
Tel (425) 202-4015 SIC 5199

PAC WORLDWIDE HOLDING CO p 1103
15435 Ne 92nd St, Redmond WA 98052
Tel (800) 535-0039 SIC 5199

BENSUSSEN DEUTSCH & ASSOCIATES LLC p 173
15525 Woodinville Rdmnd, Woodinville WA 98072
Tel (425) 492-6111 SIC 5199 5136 5137

VOLM COMPANIES INC p 1564
1804 Edison St, Antigo WI 54409
Tel (715) 627-4826 SIC 5113 5199 3565

GREAT NORTHERN CORP p 634
395 Stroebe Rd, Appleton WI 54914
Tel (920) 739-3671 SIC 2653 5199 2671

CHOICE PRODUCTS USA LLC p 302
3421 Truax Ct, Eau Claire WI 54703
Tel (715) 833-8761 SIC 5199 7389 2041

SANIMAX CORP p 1279
2099 Badgerland Dr, Green Bay WI 54303
Tel (920) 494-5233 SIC 5199 2077

SANIMAX USA LLC p 1279
2099 Badgerland Dr, Green Bay WI 54303
Tel (920) 494-5233 SIC 5199 2077

FARM & FLEET OF MADISON INC p 528
3507 E Racine St, Janesville WI 53546
Tel (608) 754-2821
SIC 5199 5531 5251 5261 5039

BENTLEY WORLD-PACKAGING LTD p 173
4080 N Port Washington Rd, Milwaukee WI 53212
Tel (414) 967-8000 SIC 4783 5199

GENERAL PET SUPPLY INC p 601
7711 N 81st St, Milwaukee WI 53223
Tel (414) 365-3400 SIC 5199

MERCO GROUP INC p 945
7711 N 81st St, Milwaukee WI 53223
Tel (414) 365-2600 SIC 5199 5047

PAX HOLDINGS LLC p 1122
758 N Broadway Ste 910, Milwaukee WI 53202
Tel (414) 803-9983
SIC 5199 2759 2672 2671 2657 2752

AIA CORP p 37
800 W Winneconne Ave, Neenah WI 54956
Tel (920) 886-3700 SIC 5199

4IMPRINT INC p 3
101 Commerce St, Oshkosh WI 54901
Tel (920) 236-7272 SIC 5199

HOLIDAY WHOLESALE INC p 700
225 Pioneer Dr, Wisconsin Dells WI 53965
Tel (608) 253-0404
SIC 5194 5145 5113 5199

SIC 5211 Lumber & Other Bldg Mtrl Dealers

RUSSELL LANDS INC p 1259
2544 Willow Point Rd, Alexander City AL 35010
Tel (256) 329-0835
SIC 5211 6514 4493 7997 7011

READY MIX USA LLC p 1213
2657 Ruffner Rd, Birmingham AL 35210
Tel (205) 967-5211 SIC 5211 3241

MARVINS LLC p 914
7480 Parkway Dr Ste 100, Leeds AL 35094
Tel (205) 702-7305
SIC 5211 5074 5031 5072

■ SPENARD BUILDERS SUPPLY LLC p 1358
300 E 54th Ave Ste 201, Anchorage AK 99518
Tel (907) 261-9126 SIC 5211

■ PALM HARBOR HOMES INC p 1109
1001 N Central Ave # 800, Phoenix AZ 85004
Tel (602) 256-6263 SIC 2452 5211 6141

DEPCOM POWER INC p 430
9200 E Pima Center Pkwy # 180, Scottsdale AZ 85258
Tel (480) 270-6910 SIC 1623 5211

E C BARTON & CO p 466
2929 Browns Ln, Jonesboro AR 72401
Tel (870) 932-6673 SIC 5031 5211 5713

E RITTER & CO p 466
10 Elm St, Marked Tree AR 72365
Tel (870) 358-7333
SIC 0131 0116 0724 4813 5211 5083

GANAHL LUMBER CO p 590
1220 E Ball Rd, Anaheim CA 92805
Tel (714) 772-5444 SIC 5211

LUMBER CITY CORP p 885
20525 Nordhoff St Ste 210, Chatsworth CA 91311
Tel (818) 407-3888 SIC 5211 5031

CONCEPT GREEN ENERGY SOLUTIONS INC p 354
13824 Yorba Ave, Chino CA 91710
Tel (855) 459-6535 SIC 7389 5211

CLOSET WORLD INC p 327
3860 Capitol Ave, City Of Industry CA 90601
Tel (562) 699-9945 SIC 1751 5211

LEHIGH SOUTHWEST CEMENT CO p 854
2300 Clayton Rd Ste 300, Concord CA 94520
Tel (972) 653-5500
SIC 3241 2891 5032 5211

■ PACIFIC GYPSUM SUPPLY INC p 1104
1165 N Johnson Ave, El Cajon CA 92020
Tel (619) 447-2413 SIC 5032 5211

DRYCO CONSTRUCTION INC p 457
42745 Boscell Rd, Fremont CA 94538
Tel (510) 438-6500 SIC 1611 1721 5211

PARAGON INDUSTRIES INC p 1113
4285 N Golden State Blvd, Fresno CA 93722
Tel (559) 275-5000 SIC 5211 5032

EMSER TILE LLC p 495
8431 Santa Monica Blvd, Los Angeles CA 90069
Tel (323) 650-2000 SIC 5032 5211

JS WEST & COMPANIES p 795
501 9th St, Modesto CA 95354
Tel (209) 577-3221
SIC 5172 5211 5251 0723 5499

A & A STEPPING STONE MFG INC p 4
10291 Ophir Rd, Newcastle CA 95658
Tel (530) 885-7481 SIC 5211 3272

LOMBARDY HOLDINGS INC p 875
3166 Hrseless Carriage Rd, Norco CA 92860
Tel (951) 808-4550 SIC 1623 5211

CIVICSOLAR INC p 320
426 17th St Ste 600, Oakland CA 94612
Tel (800) 409-2257 SIC 5074 5211

GROVE LUMBER & BUILDING SUPPLIES INC p 642
1300 S Campus Ave, Ontario CA 91761
Tel (909) 947-0277 SIC 5031 5211

GOLDEN STATE LUMBER INC p 621
855 Lakeville St Ste 200, Petaluma CA 94952
Tel (707) 206-4100 SIC 5031 5211

■ HD SUPPLY REPAIR & REMODEL LLC p 673
1695 Eureka Rd, Roseville CA 95661
Tel (916) 751-2300 SIC 5211

FRIEDMANS HOME IMPROVEMENT p 579
4055 Santa Rosa Ave, Santa Rosa CA 95407
Tel (707) 584-7811 *SIC* 5251 5211 5261

PIONEER SAND CO INC p 1151
5000 Northpark Dr, Colorado Springs CO 80918
Tel (719) 599-8100 *SIC* 5211 5031 1794

■ PROBUILD CO LLC p 1179
7595 E Technology Way # 500, Denver CO 80237
Tel (303) 262-8500 *SIC* 5211 5031

■ PROBUILD HOLDINGS LLC p 1179
7595 Tech Way Ste 500, Denver CO 80237
Tel (303) 262-8500 *SIC* 5031 5211

ALPINE LUMBER CO p 60
10170 Church Ranch Way # 300, Westminster CO 80021
Tel (303) 451-8001 *SIC* 5211

WW LIQUIDATION INC p 1629
60 Backus Ave, Danbury CT 06810
Tel (203) 546-6000 *SIC* 5074 5999 5211

RINGS END INC p 1235
181 West Ave, Darien CT 06820
Tel (203) 655-2525 *SIC* 5031 5211

EAST HAVEN BUILDERS SUPPLY - US LBM LLC p 470
193 Silver Sands Rd, East Haven CT 06512
Tel (203) 469-2394 *SIC* 5031 5211

RAYMOND BUILDING SUPPLY p 1210
7751 Bayshore Rd, Fort Myers FL 33917
Tel (941) 429-1212
SIC 5211 2439 2431 3442 2434 3634

RO-MAC LUMBER & SUPPLY INC p 1240
700 E Main St, Leesburg FL 34748
Tel (352) 787-4545 *SIC* 5211 5031

ADVANTAGE TRIM & LUMBER CO INC p 26
7524 Commerce Pl, Sarasota FL 34243
Tel (941) 388-9299 *SIC* 5031 5211

■ BLUELINX HOLDINGS INC p 193
4300 Wildwood Pkwy, Atlanta GA 30339
Tel (770) 953-7000 *SIC* 5031 5211

▲ BMC STOCK HOLDINGS INC p 193
980 Hammond Dr Ste 500, Atlanta GA 30328
Tel (678) 222-1219
SIC 5211 2431 5031 5713 5251

▲ HOME DEPOT INC p 703
2455 Paces Ferry Rd Se, Atlanta GA 30339
Tel (770) 433-8211
SIC 5261 5211 5231 5251 1751 1752

■ HOME DEPOT INTERNATIONAL INC p 703
2455 Paces Ferry Rd Se, Atlanta GA 30339
Tel (770) 384-3869 *SIC* 5211

MANIS LUMBER CO p 901
15 Old Airport Rd Nw, Rome GA 30165
Tel (706) 232-2400 *SIC* 5031 5211

BORAL BRICKS INC p 201
200 Mansell Ct E Ste 310, Roswell GA 30076
Tel (770) 645-4500 *SIC* 3251 5211 3271

BATSON-COOK CO p 159
817 4th Ave, West Point GA 31833
Tel (706) 643-2500 *SIC* 1542 5211 1541

MAGBEE BROS LUMBER AND SUPPLY CO INC p 895
1065 Bankhead Hwy, Winder GA 30680
Tel (678) 425-2600
SIC 2431 5211 3531 2439

CITY MILL CO LIMITED p 312
660 N Nimitz Hwy, Honolulu HI 96817
Tel (808) 533-3811 *SIC* 5211

HONSADOR LUMBER LLC p 705
91-151 Malakole St, Kapolei HI 96707
Tel (808) 479-3071 *SIC* 5031 5211

BUILDING MATERIALS HOLDING CORP p 225
720 E Park Blvd Ste 115, Boise ID 83712
Tel (208) 331-4300 *SIC* 5211 5031

■ SELECTBUILD CONSTRUCTION INC p 1301
720 E Park Blvd Ste 115, Boise ID 83712
Tel (208) 331-4300
SIC 1521 1771 1751 2431 5031 5211

IDAHO FOREST GROUP LLC p 728
687 W Cnfield Ave Ste 100, Coeur D Alene ID 83815
Tel (208) 255-3200 *SIC* 5211

SUNRISE ELECTRIC SUPPLY INC p 1404
130 S Addison Rd, Addison IL 60101
Tel (630) 543-1111 *SIC* 5063 5211

EDWARD HINES LUMBER CO p 480
1050 Corporate Grove Dr, Buffalo Grove IL 60089
Tel (847) 353-7700 *SIC* 5031 5211

LOGAN SQUARE ALUMINUM SUPPLY INC p 874
2500 N Pulaski Rd, Chicago IL 60639
Tel (773) 235-2500 *SIC* 5211 3089

R P LUMBER CO INC p 1202
514 E Vandalia St, Edwardsville IL 62025
Tel (618) 656-1514 *SIC* 5211 5251

RICHARDS BUILDING SUPPLY CO p 1232
12070 W 159th St, Homer Glen IL 60491
Tel (773) 586-7777 *SIC* 5033 5211

GRABBER HOLDINGS LLC p 628
1 Dot Way, Mount Sterling IL 62353
Tel (217) 773-4411 *SIC* 5072 5211 6719

WILLIAM CHARLES LTD p 1610
1401 N 2nd St, Rockford IL 61107
Tel (815) 963-7400
SIC 1611 5211 1731 4953

RTC INDUSTRIES INC p 1256
2800 Golf Rd, Rolling Meadows IL 60008
Tel (847) 640-2400 *SIC* 2599 5211

KOUNTRY WOOD PRODUCTS LLC p 828
352 Shawnee St, Nappanee IN 46550
Tel (574) 773-5673 *SIC* 2434 5211 5031

NC INC p 1021
1023 Main St, Vincennes IN 47591
Tel (812) 886-4412 *SIC* 5031 5211

UNITED FARMERS MERCANTILE COOPERATIVE p 1508
203 W Oak St, Red Oak IA 51566
Tel (712) 623-5453
SIC 5153 5191 5541 5211 2048

FARMERS COOPERATIVE SOCIETY p 529
317 3rd St Nw, Sioux Center IA 51250
Tel (712) 722-2671 *SIC* 5153 5191 5211

■ OMEGA CABINETS LTD p 1084
1205 Peters Dr, Waterloo IA 50703
Tel (319) 235-5700 *SIC* 2434 5211

D H PACE CO INC p 407
1901 E 119th St, Olathe KS 66061
Tel (816) 221-0543 *SIC* 5211 7699

EE NEWCOMER ENTERPRISES INC p 480
1901 E 119th St, Olathe KS 66061
Tel (816) 221-0543 *SIC* 5031 5211 7699

STAR LUMBER & SUPPLY CO INC p 1378
325 S West St, Wichita KS 67213
Tel (316) 942-2221 *SIC* 5211 5713

LOUISVILLE TILE DISTRIBUTORS INC p 881
4520 Bishop Ln, Louisville KY 40218
Tel (502) 452-2037 *SIC* 5032 5211 1743

STINE LLC p 1390
2950 Ruth St, Sulphur LA 70665
Tel (337) 527-0121 *SIC* 5211

HAMMOND LUMBER CO p 656
2 Hammond Dr, Belgrade ME 04917
Tel (207) 495-3303 *SIC* 5211 2421 5031

HANCOCK LUMBER CO INC p 657
4 Edes Falls Rd, Casco ME 04015
Tel (207) 627-4201 *SIC* 5211 5031

■ BUILDERS FIRSTSOURCE - ATLANTIC GROUP LLC p 225
5330 Spectrum Dr Ste L, Frederick MD 21703
Tel (301) 631-2282 *SIC* 5031 5211

ROMMEL HOLDINGS INC p 1249
103 E Main St, Fruitland MD 21826
Tel (410) 749-3600 *SIC* 5211 8741

CENTRAL WHOLESALERS INC p 281
13401 Konterra Dr, Laurel MD 20707
Tel (800) 935-2947
SIC 5074 5063 5087 5072 5211 1799

BRANCH GROUP INC p 207
1049 Prince Georges Blvd, Upper Marlboro MD 20774
Tel (301) 249-5005 *SIC* 5063 5211

NATIONAL LUMBER CO p 1014
245 Oakland St, Mansfield MA 02048
Tel (508) 337-8020 *SIC* 5211 2431

W E AUBUCHON CO INC p 1568
95 Aubuchon Dr, Westminster MA 01473
Tel (978) 874-0521
SIC 5251 5211 5231 5719

AGGREGATE INDUSTRIES p 34
6211 N Ann Arbor Rd, Dundee MI 48131
Tel (734) 529-5876
SIC 3273 2951 1442 1411 1771 5211

FAMILY FARM & HOME INC p 526
900 3rd St Ste 302, Muskegon MI 49440
Tel (231) 722-8335
SIC 5999 5261 5149 5611 5211 5091

CIRAULO BROTHERS BUILDING CO p 308
7670 19 Mile Rd, Sterling Heights MI 48314
Tel (586) 731-3670 *SIC* 5031 5211 1761

BEP/LYMAN LLC p 174
520 3rd St Ste 200, Excelsior MN 55331
Tel (952) 470-3600 *SIC* 5031 5211

CHS COOPERATIVES p 304
5500 Cenex Dr Ste 1, Inver Grove Heights MN 55077
Tel (651) 355-6000 *SIC* 5211

CAMBRIA CO LLC p 244
31496 Cambria Ave, Le Sueur MN 56058
Tel (507) 665-5003 *SIC* 5211 3429

H ENTERPRISES INTERNATIONAL INC p 650
120 S 6th St Ste 2300, Minneapolis MN 55402
Tel (612) 343-8293 *SIC* 5032 8611 5211

HALDEMAN-HOMME INC p 653
430 Industrial Blvd Ne, Minneapolis MN 55413
Tel (612) 331-4880 *SIC* 5021 5211 5084

CANNON VALLEY COOPERATIVE p 247
1500 Highway 3 S, Northfield MN 55057
Tel (507) 645-9556
SIC 5541 5171 1711 5191 5153 5211

▲ TILE SHOP HOLDINGS INC p 1453
14000 Carlson Pkwy, Plymouth MN 55441
Tel (763) 852-2988 *SIC* 5211 5961 2891

SIMONSON PROPERTIES CO p 1325
2455 12th St Se, Saint Cloud MN 56304
Tel (320) 252-9385 *SIC* 5211

LAMPERT YARDS INC p 841
1850 Como Ave, Saint Paul MN 55108
Tel (651) 695-3600
SIC 5211 1521 2439 2426

YAK MAT LLC p 1634
2438 Highway 98 E, Columbia MS 39429
Tel (601) 876-2427 *SIC* 5211 5099

BAILEY LUMBER & SUPPLY CO p 145
813 E Pass Rd, Gulfport MS 39507
Tel (228) 896-6071 *SIC* 5211 5031

W G YATES & SONS CONSTRUCTION CO p 1568
1 Gully Ave, Philadelphia MS 39350
Tel (904) 714-1376
SIC 1542 1541 2339 1611 5211 1731

YATES COMPANIES INC p 1635
1 Gully Ave, Philadelphia MS 39350
Tel (601) 656-5411
SIC 1542 1541 1611 5211 1731

PAXTON WOOD SOURCE INC p 1122
6311 Saint John Ave, Kansas City MO 64123
Tel (816) 483-7000
SIC 5031 2431 5211 5072

MEEK LUMBER YARD INC p 939
1311 E Woodhurst Dr, Springfield MO 65804
Tel (417) 521-2801 *SIC* 5211

SWANK ENTERPRISES p 1411
615 Pondera Ave, Valier MT 59486
Tel (406) 279-3241 *SIC* 1542 5211

MEAD HOLDING CO INC p 933
2218 11th St, Columbus NE 68601
Tel (402) 564-5225 *SIC* 6719 5211

BUILDERS SUPPLY CO INC p 225
5701 S 72nd St, Omaha NE 68127
Tel (402) 331-4500 *SIC* 5211 5031

LYMAN-RICHEY CORP p 887
4315 Cuming St, Omaha NE 68131
Tel (402) 556-3600
SIC 3273 1442 3271 5211 5032

MILLARD LUMBER INC p 970
12900 I St, Omaha NE 68137
Tel (402) 896-2800 *SIC* 5031 5211

BRADCO SUPPLY CORP p 206
34 Engelhard Ave, Avenel NJ 07001
Tel (732) 382-3400 *SIC* 5033 5211

KUIKEN BROTHERS CO INC p 831
6-02 Fair Lawn Ave, Fair Lawn NJ 07410
Tel (201) 796-2082 *SIC* 5211 5031 3272

DUBELL LUMBER CO p 459
148 Route 70, Medford NJ 08055
Tel (609) 654-4143 *SIC* 5031 5211

ENERGY CAPITAL PARTNERS III LLC p 497
51 John F Kennedy Pkwy, Short Hills NJ 07078
Tel (973) 671-6100 *SIC* 5211

RAKS BUILDING SUPPLY INC p 1206
108 Carson Dr Se, Los Lunas NM 87031
Tel (505) 865-1100 *SIC* 5031 5211 5072

CURTIS LUMBER CO INC p 402
885 State Route 67, Ballston Spa NY 12020
Tel (518) 885-5311 *SIC* 5211

CERTIFIED LUMBER CORP p 284
Isack Rosenberg 470 Kent, Brooklyn NY 11211
Tel (718) 387-1233 *SIC* 5031 5211

VALU HOME CENTERS INC p 1542
45 S Rossler Ave, Buffalo NY 14206
Tel (716) 824-4150 *SIC* 5211

RIVERHEAD BUILDING SUPPLY CORP p 1237
250 David Ct, Calverton NY 11933
Tel (631) 727-1400 *SIC* 5031 5211

MARJAM SUPPLY CO INC p 907
885 Conklin St, Farmingdale NY 11735
Tel (631) 249-4900 *SIC* 5211 5031

FORT MILLER SERVICE CORP p 569
688 Wilbur Ave, Greenwich NY 12834
Tel (518) 695-5000
SIC 3272 3271 5211 1799

BAILLIE LUMBER CO LP p 145
4002 Legion Dr, Hamburg NY 14075
Tel (800) 950-2850 *SIC* 5211

■ CERBERUS ABP INVESTOR LLC p 283
299 Park Ave, New York NY 10171
Tel (212) 891-2100 *SIC* 5031 5211

▲ CERBERUS CAPITAL MANAGEMENT LP p 283
875 3rd Ave, New York NY 10022
Tel (212) 891-2100
SIC 6722 6726 5031 5211

METROPOLITAN LUMBER p 956
617 11th Ave, New York NY 10036
Tel (212) 246-9090 *SIC* 5031 5211 5251

HUNT ELECTRIC SUPPLY CO p 719
1213 Maple Ave, Burlington NC 27215
Tel (336) 229-5351 *SIC* 5063 5211

TOSHIBA AMERICA NUCLEAR ENERGY CORP p 1462
3545 Whitehall Park Dr # 500, Charlotte NC 28273
Tel (704) 548-7777 *SIC* 3443 5211

WURTH WOOD GROUP INC p 1628
4250 Golf Acres Dr, Charlotte NC 28208
Tel (704) 394-9479 *SIC* 5211 5031

▲ LOWES COMPANIES INC p 881
1000 Lowes Blvd, Mooresville NC 28117
Tel (704) 758-1000
SIC 5211 5031 5722 5064

■ BMC EAST LLC p 193
8020 Arco Corp Dr Ste 400, Raleigh NC 27617
Tel (919) 431-1000
SIC 5211 2431 5031 5713 5251

STOCK BUILDING SUPPLY HOLDINGS LLC p 1390
8020 Arco Corp Dr Ste 400, Raleigh NC 27617
Tel (919) 431-1000
SIC 5211 2431 5031 5713 5251

■ LOWES HOME CENTERS LLC p 881
1605 Curtis Bridge Rd, Wilkesboro NC 28697
Tel (336) 658-4000
SIC 5211 5031 5722 5064

AMARR CO p 64
165 Carriage Ct, Winston Salem NC 27105
Tel (336) 744-5100
SIC 2431 3442 5031 5211

ACME ELECTRIC MOTOR INC p 17
1705 13th Ave N, Grand Forks ND 58203
Tel (701) 746-2823
SIC 5084 5063 5082 5072 5251 5211

■ ALPINE INSULATION I LLC p 60
495 S High St Ste 50, Columbus OH 43215
Tel (614) 221-3399 *SIC* 5033 5211

■ FORTUNE BRANDS WINDOWS INC p 570
3948 Townsfair Way # 200, Columbus OH 43219
Tel (614) 532-3500 *SIC* 1751 5211

▲ INSTALLED BUILDING PRODUCTS INC p 746
495 S High St Ste 50, Columbus OH 43215
Tel (614) 221-3399 *SIC* 1522 5033 5211

■ INSTALLED BUILDING PRODUCTS LLC p 746
495 S High St Ste 50, Columbus OH 43215
Tel (614) 221-3399 *SIC* 1742 5211 1761

CARTER LUMBER INC p 262
601 Tallmadge Rd, Kent OH 44240
Tel (330) 673-6100 *SIC* 5211

CARTER-JONES COMPANIES INC p 262
601 Tallmadge Rd, Kent OH 44240
Tel (330) 673-6100 *SIC* 5211 5031 6552

CARTER-JONES LUMBER CO p 262
601 Tallmadge Rd, Kent OH 44240
Tel (330) 673-6100 *SIC* 5211 5031

HC COMPANIES INC p 671
15150 Madison Rd, Middlefield OH 44062
Tel (440) 632-3333 *SIC* 5211

WESTERN RESERVE FARM COOPERATIVE INC p 1600
16003 E High St, Middlefield OH 44062
Tel (440) 632-0271 *SIC* 5191 5983 5211

■ GREAT LAKES WINDOW INC p 634
30499 Tracy Rd, Walbridge OH 43465
Tel (419) 666-5555 *SIC* 3089 5211

NORTHWEST BUILDING SUPPLY INC p 1059
5535 Nw 5th St, Oklahoma City OK 73127
Tel (405) 946-0500 *SIC* 5033 5031 5211

MILL CREEK LUMBER & SUPPLY CO INC p 969
6974 E 38th St, Tulsa OK 74145
Tel (405) 671-3540
SIC 3442 1771 5031 5211

JERRYS BUILDING MATERIALS INC p 783
2600 Highway 99 N, Eugene OR 97402
Tel (541) 689-1911 *SIC* 5211

PARR LUMBER CO p 1117
5630 Nw Century Blvd, Hillsboro OR 97124
Tel (503) 614-2500
SIC 5031 5211 5072 5251

■ FRED MEYER INC p 576
3800 Se 22nd Ave, Portland OR 97202
Tel (503) 232-8844
SIC 5411 5311 5912 5211 5731 5944

■ FRED MEYER STORES INC p 576
3800 Se 22nd Ave, Portland OR 97202
Tel (503) 232-8844
SIC 5211 5411 5912 5731 5944

ROSEBURG FOREST PRODUCTS CO p 1250
3660 Gateway St Ste A, Springfield OR 97477
Tel (541) 679-3311
SIC 2436 2421 2493 5031 5211 0811

COLLINS PINE CO p 337
29190 Sw Town Center Loop, Wilsonville OR 97070
Tel (503) 227-1219
SIC 2421 2426 5211 4911 4013

DEGOL ORGANIZATION L P p 422
3229 Pleasant Valley Blvd, Altoona PA 16602
Tel (814) 941-7777
SIC 5031 5033 5211 5023 5713

LEZZER HOLDINGS INC p 860
311 Schofield St, Curwensville PA 16833
Tel (814) 236-0220 *SIC* 5211

LEZZER LUMBER INC p 860
311 Schofield St, Curwensville PA 16833
Tel (814) 236-0220 *SIC* 5211

MARTIN LIMESTONE INC p 912
3580 Division Hwy, East Earl PA 17519
Tel (717) 335-4500
SIC 3273 3271 1611 1422 8741 5211

84 LUMBER CO p 4
1019 Route 519, Eighty Four PA 15330
Tel (724) 228-8820
SIC 2431 2439 5031 5211

IRWIN BUILDERS SUPPLY CORP p 765
10249 Garnet Ln, Irwin PA 15642
Tel (724) 863-5200 *SIC* 5031 5211

SHUSTERS BUILDERS SUPPLIES INC p 1319
2920 Clay Pike, Irwin PA 15642
Tel (724) 446-7000 *SIC* 5031 5211

WOLSELEY INVESTMENTS INC p 1621
1904 Ligonier St, Latrobe PA 15650
Tel (757) 874-7795
SIC 5074 5085 5075 5064 5211 5031

TRANSPORT INTERNATIONAL POOL INC p 1472
530 E Swedesford Rd, Wayne PA 19087
Tel (484) 254-0100
SIC 7519 7513 5511 5211

COOLEY GROUP HOLDINGS INC p 366
50 Esten Ave, Pawtucket RI 02860
Tel (401) 724-0510 *SIC* 5211 3069

■ BUILDERS FIRSTSOURCE- SOUTHEAST GROUP LLC p 225
2451 E Highway 501, Conway SC 29526
Tel (843) 347-4224 *SIC* 5211 2431

■ NUGEN ENERGY LLC p 1067
27283 447th Ave, Marion SD 57043
Tel (605) 648-2100 *SIC* 0139 1731 5211

KNECHT LLC p 824
320 West Blvd, Rapid City SD 57701
Tel (605) 342-4840 *SIC* 5211 5251

COUNTRY PRIDE COOPERATIVE INC p 375
648 W 2nd St, Winner SD 57580
Tel (605) 842-2711
SIC 5153 5172 5191 5411 5211

GENERAL SHALE BRICK INC p 602
3015 Bristol Hwy, Johnson City TN 37601
Tel (423) 282-4661 *SIC* 5211 5031

TINDELLS INC p 1455
7751 Norris Fwy, Knoxville TN 37938
Tel (865) 922-7751 *SIC* 5031 5211 2439

CENTRAL NETWORK RETAIL GROUP LLC p 279
3753 Tyndale Dr Ste 102, Memphis TN 38125
Tel (901) 205-9075 *SIC* 5211

WALLACE HARDWARE CO INC p 1573
5050 S Davy Crockett Pkwy, Morristown TN 37813
Tel (423) 586-5650
SIC 5072 5074 5085 5083 5211

▲ BUILDERS FIRSTSOURCE INC p 225
2001 Bryan St Ste 1600, Dallas TX 75201
Tel (214) 880-3500 *SIC* 2431 2421 5211

ROOFING SUPPLY GROUP HOLDINGS INC p 1249
3890 W Northwest Hwy # 400, Dallas TX 75220
Tel (214) 956-5100 *SIC* 5211

STERLING GROUP PARTNERS II LP p 1387
3890 W Northwest Hwy # 400, Dallas TX 75220
Tel (214) 956-5100 *SIC* 5211

DEFORD LUMBER CO LTD p 422
1018 N Duncanville Rd, Duncanville TX 75116
Tel (972) 298-7121 *SIC* 5031 5211

■ ACME BRICK CO p 17
3024 Acme Brick Plz, Fort Worth TX 76109
Tel (817) 332-4101 *SIC* 3251 5032 5211

CONNER INDUSTRIES INC p 358
3800 Sandshell Dr Ste 235, Fort Worth TX 76137
Tel (817) 847-0361 *SIC* 5211 5031

FTS INTERNATIONAL MANUFACTURING LLC p 583
777 Main St Ste 2900, Fort Worth TX 76102
Tel (817) 850-8004 *SIC* 5082 7353 5211

■ JUSTIN INDUSTRIES INC p 798
3024 Acme Brick Plz, Fort Worth TX 76109
Tel (817) 332-4101
SIC 3251 3271 5211 5032

NINE ENERGY SERVICE INC p 1044
16945 Northchase Dr, Houston TX 77060
Tel (281) 730-5100 SIC 5211 1382

■ PRECISION INDUSTRIES INC p 1168
7272 Pinemont Dr, Houston TX 77040
Tel (713) 996-4700 SIC 5211 5085

■ T-3 ENERGY SERVICES INC p 1420
140 Cypress Station Dr # 225, Houston TX 77090
Tel (713) 944-5950 SIC 5211 3491 7699

CONSOLIDATED ELECTRICAL DISTRIBUTORS INC p 359
1920 Westridge Dr Ste 107, Irving TX 75038
Tel (972) 582-5300 SIC 5063 5211

BUTTERY CO LLP p 230
201 W Main St, Llano TX 78643
Tel (325) 247-4141
SIC 5072 5074 5063 5091 5211 5251

REPUBLIC NATIONAL INDUSTRIES OF TEXAS LP p 1225
1400 Warren Dr, Marshall TX 75672
Tel (903) 935-3680 SIC 2434 5211 2541

FOXWORTH GALBRAITH LUMBER CO p 573
4965 Preston Park Blvd # 400, Plano TX 75093
Tel (972) 665-2400
SIC 5211 5031 2439 2431

GROTHUES BROTHERS HOLDINGS LTD p 641
2651 Sw Military Dr, San Antonio TX 78224
Tel (830) 569-1131 SIC 5031 5211 6719

MG BUILDING MATERIALS LTD p 958
2651 Sw Military Dr, San Antonio TX 78224
Tel (210) 924-8604 SIC 2421 4212 5211

MCCOY CORP p 927
1350 N Ih 35, San Marcos TX 78666
Tel (512) 353-5400 SIC 5211 5251 5231

FOREST TOMBALL PRODUCTS INC p 567
16801 Fm 2920 Rd, Tomball TX 77377
Tel (281) 357-8196 SIC 5083 5211 5031

GRABBER CONSTRUCTION PRODUCTS INC p 628
5255 W 11000 N Ste 100, Highland UT 84003
Tel (801) 492-3880 SIC 5072 5211

BURTON LUMBER & HARDWARE CO p 229
1170 S 4400 W, Salt Lake City UT 84104
Tel (801) 952-3700 SIC 5211 5251

■ STOCK BUILDING SUPPLY WEST LLC p 1390
1133 W 9000 S, West Jordan UT 84088
Tel (801) 561-9000 SIC 5031 5211 2439

LUCK STONE CORP p 884
515 Stone Mill Dr, Manakin Sabot VA 23103
Tel (804) 784-3383
SIC 1423 2899 3281 5211 8741

▲ LUMBER LIQUIDATORS HOLDINGS INC p 885
3000 John Deere Rd, Toano VA 23168
Tel (757) 259-4280 SIC 5211

■ LUMBER LIQUIDATORS INC p 885
3000 John Deere Rd, Toano VA 23168
Tel (757) 259-4280 SIC 5031 5211

■ LANOGA CORP p 844
17946 Ne 65th St, Redmond WA 98052
Tel (425) 883-4125 SIC 5211 5031

LAIRD NORTON CO LLC p 838
801 2nd Ave Ste 1700, Seattle WA 98104
Tel (206) 464-5245 SIC 5211

WINDOW PRODUCTS INC p 1615
10507 E Montgomery Dr, Spokane Valley WA 99206
Tel (800) 442-8544 SIC 3442 5211

FLEET WHOLESALE SUPPLY CO LLC p 555
3035 W Wisconsin Ave, Appleton WI 54914
Tel (920) 734-8231
SIC 5191 5331 5531 5211 5541

DETERVILLE LUMBER & SUPPLY LLC p 433
3749 S County Road T, Denmark WI 54208
Tel (920) 863-2191 SIC 5211

MENARD INC p 943
5101 Menard Dr, Eau Claire WI 54703
Tel (715) 876-5911 SIC 2431 5211

COUNTY MATERIALS CORP p 375
205 North St, Marathon WI 54448
Tel (715) 443-2434
SIC 3271 5211 3273 3272 1442

ARBON EQUIPMENT CORP p 103
8900 N Arbon Dr, Milwaukee WI 53223
Tel (414) 355-2600 SIC 5211

PREMIER COOPERATIVE p 1170
501 W Main St, Mount Horeb WI 53572
Tel (608) 251-0199
SIC 5211 5171 5191 5541

DESIGN HOMES INC p 432
600 N Marquette Rd, Prairie Du Chien WI 53821
Tel (608) 326-8406 SIC 2452 3663 5211

RICHARDSON INDUSTRIES INC p 1232
635 Old County Road Pp, Sheboygan Falls WI 53085
Tel (920) 467-2950
SIC 2511 2439 5211 2491 2434 2426

DW SAWMILL LLC p 463
N8972 County Road Jj, Westfield WI 53964
Tel (608) 296-1863 SIC 5099 2491 5211

SIC 5231 Paint, Glass, Wallpaper Stores

MOBILE PAINT MANUFACTURING CO OF DELAWARE INC p 980
4775 Hamilton Blvd, Theodore AL 36582
Tel (251) 443-6110 SIC 2851 5198 5231

VISTA PAINT CORP p 1562
2020 E Orangethorpe Ave, Fullerton CA 92831
Tel (714) 680-3800 SIC 5231 2851

GUILDERY INC p 646
170 State St Ste A, Los Altos CA 94022
Tel (650) 257-0157 SIC 5231

TCP GLOBAL CORP p 1428
6695 Rasha St, San Diego CA 92121
Tel (858) 909-2110 SIC 5198 5231

WOODBRIDGE GLASS INC p 1622
14321 Myford Rd, Tustin CA 92780
Tel (714) 838-4444 SIC 1793 5231

DUNN-EDWARDS CORP p 461
4885 E 52nd Pl, Vernon CA 90058
Tel (323) 771-3330 SIC 2851 5231

GUIRYS INC p 646
620 Canosa Ct, Denver CO 80204
Tel (720) 360-4840 SIC 5198 5231 5999

■ ETHAN ALLEN RETAIL INC p 511
Ethan Allen Dr, Danbury CT 06811
Tel (203) 743-8000
SIC 5712 5719 5713 5231 2273

ROBB & STUCKY LIMITED LLLP p 1240
14550 Plantation Rd, Fort Myers FL 33912
Tel (239) 437-7997
SIC 5712 5713 5714 5231

▲ HOME DEPOT INC p 703
2455 Paces Ferry Rd Se, Atlanta GA 30339
Tel (770) 433-8211
SIC 5261 5211 5231 5251 1751 1752

DIAMOND-VOGEL PAINT CO p 437
1110 Albany Pl Se, Orange City IA 51041
Tel (712) 737-8880 SIC 2851 5231

W E AUBUCHON CO INC p 1568
95 Aubuchon Dr, Westminster MA 01473
Tel (978) 874-0521
SIC 5251 5211 5231 5719

PAINTERS SUPPLY AND EQUIPMENT CO p 1108
25195 Brest, Taylor MI 48180
Tel (734) 946-8119 SIC 5198 5231

HIRSHFIELDS INC p 696
725 2nd Ave N Ste 1, Minneapolis MN 55405
Tel (612) 377-3910 SIC 5198 5231 2851

RICCIARDI BROS INC p 1232
1915 Springfield Ave, Maplewood NJ 07040
Tel (973) 762-3830 SIC 5198 5231

■ BENJAMIN MOORE & CO p 173
101 Paragon Dr, Montvale NJ 07645
Tel (201) 573-9600 SIC 2851 5231

ABOFFS INC p 12
33 Gerard St Ste 204, Huntington NY 11743
Tel (631) 427-2008 SIC 5198 5231

■ JANOVIC-PLAZA INC p 777
3035 Thomson Ave, Long Island City NY 11101
Tel (718) 392-3999
SIC 5198 5231 5023 5719

■ COMEX NORTH AMERICA INC p 344
101 W Prospect Ave # 1020, Cleveland OH 44115
Tel (303) 307-2100
SIC 2851 8742 5198 5231

■ SHERWIN-WILLIAMS AUTOMOTIVE FINISHES CORP p 1316
4440 Warrensville Ctr Rd, Cleveland OH 44128
Tel (216) 332-8330 SIC 5231 2851

▲ SHERWIN-WILLIAMS CO p 1316
101 W Prospect Ave # 1020, Cleveland OH 44115
Tel (216) 566-2000 SIC 5231 2851

SAFELITE FULFILLMENT INC p 1266
7400 Safelite Way, Columbus OH 43235
Tel (614) 210-9747 SIC 5231

SPECTRUM PAINT CO INC p 1357
15247 E Skelly Dr, Tulsa OK 74116
Tel (918) 836-9911 SIC 5198 5231

MILLER PAINT CO INC p 971
12812 Ne Whitaker Way, Portland OR 97230
Tel (503) 255-0190 SIC 2851 5231

RODDA PAINT CO p 1246
6107 N Marine Dr Ste 3, Portland OR 97203
Tel (503) 521-4300
SIC 2851 5198 5023 5231 5719

OLDCASTLE BUILDINGENVELOPE INC p 1082
5005 Lndn B Jnsn Fwy 10 Ste 1050, Dallas TX 75244
Tel (214) 273-3400 SIC 3231 5231

TASCO AUTO COLOR CORP p 1426
10323 Veterans Mem Dr, Houston TX 77038
Tel (281) 999-3761
SIC 5198 5013 5231 5531

ENGLISH COLOR & SUPPLY INC p 499
806 N Grove Rd, Richardson TX 75081
Tel (972) 235-3108 SIC 5198 5231

MCCOY CORP p 927
1350 N Ih 35, San Marcos TX 78666
Tel (512) 353-5400 SIC 5211 5251 5231

SIC 5251 Hardware Stores

TURNER SUPPLY CO p 1493
250 N Royal St, Mobile AL 36602
Tel (205) 252-6000 SIC 5085 5251

SOUTHERN FASTENING SYSTEMS LLC p 1348
635 Fairgrounds Rd, Muscle Shoals AL 35661
Tel (256) 381-3628
SIC 5084 5085 5251 5072

ALASKA INDUSTRIAL HARDWARE INC p 45
2192 Viking Dr, Anchorage AK 99501
Tel (907) 279-6691 SIC 5072 5251

AK-CHIN INDIAN COMMUNITY DEVELOPMENT CORP p 41
42507 W Peters & Nall Rd, Maricopa AZ 85138
Tel (520) 568-1000
SIC 0131 0139 5251 7993

COOPER COMMUNITIES INC p 366
903 N 47th St, Rogers AR 72756
Tel (479) 246-6500 SIC 5251

HARBOR FREIGHT TOOLS USA INC p 659
26541 Agoura Rd, Calabasas CA 91302
Tel (818) 836-5000 SIC 5251

CENTRAL PURCHASING LLC p 280
3491 Mission Oaks Blvd, Camarillo CA 93012
Tel (805) 388-1000 SIC 5085 5961 5251

JS WEST & COMPANIES p 795
501 9th St, Modesto CA 95354
Tel (209) 577-3221
SIC 5172 5211 5251 0723 5499

■ ORCHARD SUPPLY CO LLC p 1093
6450 Via Del Oro, San Jose CA 95119
Tel (408) 281-3500 SIC 5251 5261

OSH 1 LIQUIDATING CORP p 1096
6450 Via Del Oro, San Jose CA 95119
Tel (408) 281-3500 SIC 5251

FRIEDMANS HOME IMPROVEMENT p 579
4055 Santa Rosa Ave, Santa Rosa CA 95407
Tel (707) 584-7811 SIC 5251 5211 5261

▲ BMC STOCK HOLDINGS INC p 193
980 Hammond Dr Ste 500, Atlanta GA 30328
Tel (678) 222-1219
SIC 5211 2431 5031 5713 5251

▲ HOME DEPOT INC p 703
2455 Paces Ferry Rd Se, Atlanta GA 30339
Tel (770) 433-8211
SIC 5261 5211 5231 5251 1751 1752

D&B SUPPLY CO p 407
3303 E Linden St, Caldwell ID 83605
Tel (208) 459-7446
SIC 5191 5699 5251 5261 5999 5531

VALLEY CO-OPS INC p 1540
1833 S Lincoln Ave, Jerome ID 83338
Tel (208) 324-8000 SIC 5171 5191 5251

VALLEY WIDE COOPERATIVE INC p 1541
2114 N 20th St, Nampa ID 83687
Tel (208) 436-0141
SIC 5191 5251 5541 5171

R P LUMBER CO INC p 1202
514 E Vandalia St, Edwardsville IL 62025
Tel (618) 656-1514 SIC 5211 5251

EFFINGHAM EQUITY p 480
201 W Roadway Ave, Effingham IL 62401
Tel (217) 342-4101 SIC 5999 5251

▲ SEARS HOMETOWN AND OUTLET STORES INC p 1297
5500 Trillium Blvd # 501, Hoffman Estates IL 60192
Tel (847) 286-2500 SIC 5251 5261 5722

ACE HARDWARE CORP p 16
2200 Kensington Ct, Oak Brook IL 60523
Tel (630) 990-6600
SIC 5251 5198 5063 5074 5083

WATSEKA RURAL KING SUPPLY INC p 1583
200 N Ernest Grove Pkwy, Watseka IL 60970
Tel (815) 432-3440
SIC 5999 5651 5251 5311

WESTLAKE HARDWARE INC p 1601
14000 Marshall Dr, Lenexa KS 66215
Tel (913) 888-8438 SIC 5251

ZOELLER CO p 1644
3649 Cane Run Rd, Louisville KY 40211
Tel (502) 778-2731
SIC 3561 5251 3432 3491

TECHTRONIC INDUSTRIES NORTH AMERICA INC p 1432
303 Intrntl Cir Ste 490, Hunt Valley MD 21030
Tel (443) 391-1541 SIC 5083 5251

ROCKYS HARDWARE INC p 1245
40 Island Pond Rd, Springfield MA 01118
Tel (413) 781-1650 SIC 5251

W E AUBUCHON CO INC p 1568
95 Aubuchon Dr, Westminster MA 01473
Tel (978) 874-0521
SIC 5251 5211 5231 5719

CALEDONIA FARMERS ELEVATOR CO INC p 238
146 E Main St Se, Caledonia MI 49316
Tel (616) 891-4150
SIC 5153 5169 5251 5261

ACO INC p 18
27555 Farmington Rd # 100, Farmington Hills MI 48334
Tel (248) 471-0100 SIC 5251

NORTHERN TOOL & EQUIPMENT CO INC p 1057
2800 Southcross Dr W, Burnsville MN 55306
Tel (952) 894-9510 SIC 5961 5251

JERRYS ENTERPRISES INC p 783
5125 Vernon Ave S, Edina MN 55436
Tel (952) 922-8335 SIC 5411 5812 5251

MET-CON CONSTRUCTION INC p 952
15760 Acorn Trl, Faribault MN 55021
Tel (507) 332-2266 SIC 1541 1542 5251

L AND M SUPPLY INC p 833
1200 E Us Highway 169, Grand Rapids MN 55744
Tel (218) 326-9451 SIC 5251 5331 5013

ROCKLER COMPANIES INC p 1245
4365 Willow Dr, Medina MN 55340
Tel (763) 478-8201 SIC 5251 5961 2721

UNITED HARDWARE DISTRIBUTING CO p 1509
5005 Nathan Ln N, Plymouth MN 55442
Tel (763) 559-1800 SIC 5251

NORTHERN RESOURCES COOPERATIVE p 1056
1504 Center St W, Roseau MN 56751
Tel (218) 463-1805
SIC 5191 5172 5251 5541

CENTRAL MISSOURI AGRISERVICE LLC p 279
211 N Lyon Ave, Marshall MO 65340
Tel (660) 886-7880 SIC 2875 2048 5251

ORSCHELN FARM AND HOME LLC p 1096
1800 Overcenter Dr, Moberly MO 65270
Tel (800) 577-2580
SIC 5251 5999 5945 5731

BUCHHEIT ENTERPRISES INC p 222
33 Pcr 540, Perryville MO 63775
Tel (573) 547-1010
SIC 4213 4212 5251 4225

RANCH AND HOME SUPPLY LLC p 1207
2311 N 7th Ave, Bozeman MT 59715
Tel (406) 586-8466
SIC 5699 5191 5531 5251

METROPOLITAN LUMBER p 956
617 11th Ave, New York NY 10036
Tel (212) 246-9090 SIC 5031 5211 5251

■ BMC EAST LLC p 193
8020 Arco Corp Dr Ste 400, Raleigh NC 27617
Tel (919) 431-1000
SIC 5211 2431 5031 5713 5251

STOCK BUILDING SUPPLY HOLDINGS LLC p 1390
8020 Arco Corp Dr Ste 400, Raleigh NC 27617
Tel (919) 431-1000
SIC 5211 2431 5031 5713 5251

TRI-ENERGY COOPERATIVE p 1477
219 N 20th St, Bismarck ND 58501
Tel (701) 223-8707 SIC 5812 5541 5251

FARMERS UNION OIL OF SOUTHERN VALLEY p 530
100 S Front St, Fairmount ND 58030
Tel (701) 474-5440
SIC 5171 5191 5541 5251

SCHEELS ALL SPORTS INC p 1286
4550 15th Ave S, Fargo ND 58103
Tel (701) 364-0572
SIC 5661 5941 5699 5251 5261

ACME ELECTRIC MOTOR INC p 17
1705 13th Ave N, Grand Forks ND 58203
Tel (701) 746-2823
SIC 5084 5063 5082 5072 5251 5211

FARMERS UNION OIL CO OF STANLEY p 530
8149 Highway 2, Stanley ND 58784
Tel (701) 628-2322
SIC 5172 5251 5541 5411

▲ TITAN MACHINERY INC p 1456
644 E Beaton Dr, West Fargo ND 58078
Tel (701) 356-0130 SIC 5251 5082

■ MATCO TOOLS CORP p 919
4403 Allen Rd, Stow OH 44224
Tel (330) 929-4949
SIC 5251 5072 3469 3423 5013

ATWOOD DISTRIBUTING LP p 130
500 S Garland Rd, Enid OK 73703
Tel (580) 233-3702
SIC 5261 5251 5531 5311

PARR LUMBER CO p 1117
5630 Nw Century Blvd, Hillsboro OR 97124
Tel (503) 614-2500
SIC 5031 5211 5072 5251

YOUR BUILDING CENTERS INC p 1639
2607 Beale Ave, Altoona PA 16601
Tel (814) 944-5098 SIC 5251

TRI-BORO CONSTRUCTION SUPPLIES INC p 1477
465 E Locust St, Dallastown PA 17313
Tel (717) 246-3095 SIC 5082 3496 5251

ONE WORLD TECHNOLOGIES INC p 1086
1428 Pearman Dairy Rd, Anderson SC 29625
Tel (864) 226-6511 SIC 5251

BLATCHFORDS INC p 189
207 S Chicago St, Hot Springs SD 57747
Tel (605) 745-5173
SIC 5251 5712 5531 5947 5722

KNECHT LLC p 824
320 West Blvd, Rapid City SD 57701
Tel (605) 342-4840 SIC 5211 5251

NEWKIRK HOLDING CO INC p 1037
320 West Blvd, Rapid City SD 57701
Tel (605) 342-4840 SIC 5251

▲ TRACTOR SUPPLY CO p 1468
5401 Virginia Way, Brentwood TN 37027
Tel (615) 440-4000
SIC 5999 5261 5251 5531 5699

■ WINCOR NIXDORF INC p 1615
12345 N Lamar Blvd # 200, Austin TX 78753
Tel (512) 676-5000 SIC 7379 5734 5251

ALLEYTON RESOURCE CO LLC p 53
755 Fm 762, Columbus TX 78934
Tel (281) 238-1010 SIC 5251

▲ JRJR33 INC p 795
2950 N Harwood St Fl 22, Dallas TX 75201
Tel (469) 913-4115
SIC 5499 5023 5122 2721 5251

UNITED AGRICULTURAL COOPERATIVE INC p 1506
911 S Wharton St, El Campo TX 77437
Tel (979) 543-6284
SIC 5251 0724 5083 4221 5153

BUTTERY CO LLP p 230
201 W Main St, Llano TX 78643
Tel (325) 247-4141
SIC 5072 5074 5063 5091 5211 5251

WINZER CORP p 1617
4060 E Plano Pkwy, Plano TX 75074
Tel (800) 527-4126
SIC 5072 3452 5251 5169

MCCOY CORP p 927
1350 N Ih 35, San Marcos TX 78666
Tel (512) 353-5400 SIC 5211 5251 5231

BURTON LUMBER & HARDWARE CO p 229
1170 S 4400 W, Salt Lake City UT 84104
Tel (801) 952-3700 SIC 5211 5251

ROCKINGHAM CO-OPERATIVE FARM BUREAU INC p 1244
1040 S High St, Harrisonburg VA 22801
Tel (540) 434-3856 SIC 5999 5251

PLOW & HEARTH LLC p 1156
7021 Wolftown Hood Rd, Madison VA 22727
Tel (540) 948-2272 SIC 5961 5251

TVI INC p 1494
11400 Se 6th St Ste 220, Bellevue WA 98004
Tel (425) 462-1515
SIC 5932 5251 5311 5331

GRIZZLY INDUSTRIAL INC p 641
1821 Valencia St, Bellingham WA 98229
Tel (360) 676-6090 SIC 5251

MCLENDON HARDWARE INC p 931
440 Rainier Ave S, Renton WA 98057
Tel (425) 264-1541 SIC 5031 5251

DELTA WESTERN INC p 427
1177 Fairview Ave N, Seattle WA 98109
Tel (907) 276-2688 SIC 5171 5251 5411

WOODCRAFT SUPPLY LLC p 1622
1177 Rosemar Rd, Parkersburg WV 26105
Tel (304) 422-5412 SIC 5961 5251

ALLIED COOPERATIVE p 56
540 S Main St, Adams WI 53910
Tel (608) 339-3394 SIC 5191 5171 5251

STA-RITE INDUSTRIES LLC p 1374
293 S Wright St, Delavan WI 53115
Tel (888) 782-7483 SIC 3561 5084 5251

FARM & FLEET OF MADISON INC p 528
3507 E Racine St, Janesville WI 53546
Tel (608) 754-2821
SIC 5199 5531 5251 5261 5039

FARM & FLEET OF RICE LAKE INC p 528
3507 E Racine St, Janesville WI 53546
Tel (608) 754-2821 SIC 5191 5251 5531

■ **SNAP-ON-TOOLS CORP** p 1335
2801 80th St, Kenosha WI 53143
Tel (262) 656-5200 SIC 5251

SIC 5261 Retail Nurseries, Lawn & Garden Sply Stores

MOON VALLEY NURSERY INC p 987
18047 N Tatum Blvd, Phoenix AZ 85032
Tel (602) 493-0403 SIC 5193 5261

FARMERS SUPPLY ASSOCIATION p 530
16240 Highway 14 E, Harrisburg AR 72432
Tel (870) 578-2468
SIC 5191 5172 5261 5541 5999

BRUCE OAKLEY INC p 220
3700 Lincoln Ave, North Little Rock AR 72114
Tel (501) 945-0875
SIC 4449 5153 5261 5191 4213

MONROVIA NURSERY CO p 985
817 E Monrovia Pl, Azusa CA 91702
Tel (626) 334-9321 SIC 0181 5193 5261

ARMSTRONG GARDEN CENTERS INC p 111
2200 E Route 66 Ste 200, Glendora CA 91740
Tel (626) 914-1091 SIC 5261 0782

HINES HORTICULTURE INC p 695
12621 Jeffrey Rd, Irvine CA 92620
Tel (949) 559-4444 SIC 0181 5261

L A HEARNE CO p 833
512 Metz Rd, King City CA 93930
Tel (831) 385-5441
SIC 5191 0723 5699 4214 2048 5261

BUTTE COUNTY RICE GROWERS ASSOCIATION INC p 230
1193 Richvale Hwy, Richvale CA 95974
Tel (530) 345-7103 SIC 5191 0723 5261

▲ **WILLIAMS-SONOMA INC** p 1612
3250 Van Ness Ave, San Francisco CA 94109
Tel (415) 421-7900
SIC 5719 5722 5261 5961

■ **ORCHARD SUPPLY CO LLC** p 1093
6450 Via Del Oro, San Jose CA 95119
Tel (408) 281-3500 SIC 5251 5261

FRIEDMANS HOME IMPROVEMENT p 579
4055 Santa Rosa Ave, Santa Rosa CA 95407
Tel (707) 584-7811 SIC 5251 5211 5261

BOETHING TREELAND FARMS INC p 197
23475 Long Valley Rd, Woodland Hills CA 91367
Tel (818) 883-1222 SIC 0811 5261

ROBERT W BAKER NURSERY INC p 1241
1700 Mountain Rd, West Suffield CT 06093
Tel (860) 668-7371 SIC 5193 5261

CONRAD YELVINGTON DISTRIBUTORS INC p 358
2328 Bellevue Ave, Daytona Beach FL 32114
Tel (386) 257-5504 SIC 5032 5261

▲ **HOME DEPOT INC** p 703
2455 Paces Ferry Rd Se, Atlanta GA 30339
Tel (770) 433-8211
SIC 5261 5211 5231 5251 1751 1752

ROARK CAPITAL GROUP INC p 1240
1180 Peachtree St Ne # 2500, Atlanta GA 30309
Tel (404) 591-5200
SIC 6726 3993 7331 6794 5261

PIKE NURSERY HOLDING LLC p 1148
3555 Koger Blvd Ste 360, Duluth GA 30096
Tel (770) 921-1022 SIC 5261

■ **PENNINGTON SEED INC** p 1130
1280 Atlanta Hwy, Madison GA 30650
Tel (706) 342-1234
SIC 5261 2873 5191 6799 0723

D&B SUPPLY CO p 407
3303 E Linden St, Caldwell ID 83605
Tel (208) 459-7446
SIC 5191 5699 5251 5261 5999 5531

LAND VIEW INC p 842
20504 4th St, Rupert ID 83350
Tel (208) 531-4100
SIC 2879 2873 2874 5999 5261 5169

MARTIN SULLIVAN INC p 913
250 E Main St Ste 402, Galesburg IL 61401
Tel (309) 343-1423 SIC 5083 5261

▲ **SEARS HOMETOWN AND OUTLET STORES INC** p 1297
5500 Trillium Blvd # 501, Hoffman Estates IL 60192
Tel (847) 286-2500 SIC 5251 5261 5722

WHITE RIVER LLC p 1606
610 Church St, Loogootee IN 47553
Tel (812) 295-4835 SIC 5261 5984

FRICK SERVICES INC p 579
3154 Depot St, Wawaka IN 46794
Tel (260) 761-3311
SIC 5191 5153 5261 4221 2048 4213

THEISENS INC p 1446
6201 Chavenelle Rd, Dubuque IA 52002
Tel (563) 556-4738
SIC 5531 5999 5699 5261

FARMERS UNION COOPERATIVE p 530
1913 County Road B32, Ossian IA 52161
Tel (563) 532-9381 SIC 5153 5261 5983

AGRI TRAILS COOP INC p 36
508 N Main St, Hope KS 67451
Tel (785) 366-7213 SIC 5999 5261

CAUDILL SEED AND WAREHOUSE CO INC p 267
1402 W Main St, Louisville KY 40203
Tel (502) 583-4402 SIC 5191 5261

CALEDONIA FARMERS ELEVATOR CO INC p 238
146 E Main St Se, Caledonia MI 49316
Tel (616) 891-4150
SIC 5153 5169 5251 5261

FAMILY FARM & HOME INC p 526
900 3rd St Ste 302, Muskegon MI 49440
Tel (231) 722-8335
SIC 5999 5261 5149 5611 5211 5091

COOPERATIVE ELEVATOR CO p 367
7211 E Michigan Ave, Pigeon MI 48755
Tel (989) 453-4500
SIC 5172 5191 5541 5261 5153

GERTEN GREENHOUSES & GARDEN CENTER INC p 609
5500 Blaine Ave, Inver Grove Heights MN 55076
Tel (651) 450-1501 SIC 5261 5193

BACHMANS INC p 143
6010 Lyndale Ave S, Minneapolis MN 55419
Tel (612) 861-7600
SIC 5992 5261 0181 5193 7359

FOODARAMA SUPERMARKETS INC p 564
922 State Route 33 Bldg 1, Freehold NJ 07728
Tel (732) 462-3120 SIC 5411 5261 5921

SAKER HOLDINGS CORP p 1271
922 State Route 33 Bldg 1, Freehold NJ 07728
Tel (732) 462-4700 SIC 5411 5261 5921

ZAHM & MATSON INC p 1641
1756 Lindquist Dr, Falconer NY 14733
Tel (716) 665-3110 SIC 5261 5999

SEEDWAY LLC p 1300
1734 Railroad Pl, Hall NY 14463
Tel (585) 526-6391 SIC 5261

ADAMS FAIRACRE FARMS INC p 21
765 Dutchess Tpke, Poughkeepsie NY 12603
Tel (845) 454-4330 SIC 5411 5261 5199

CENTRAL CAROLINA FARM & MOWER INC p 277
801 E Wendover Ave, Greensboro NC 27405
Tel (336) 574-4400 SIC 5261 5082

SCHEELS ALL SPORTS INC p 1286
4550 15th Ave S, Fargo ND 58103
Tel (701) 364-0572
SIC 5661 5941 5699 5251 5261

TOWN AND COUNTRY CO-OP INC p 1464
813 Clark Ave, Ashland OH 44805
Tel (419) 281-2153 SIC 5541 5261 5999

BFG SUPPLY CO LLC p 179
14500 Kinsman Rd, Burton OH 44021
Tel (440) 834-1883 SIC 5191 5261

■ **LESCO INC** p 857
1385 E 36th St, Cleveland OH 44114
Tel (216) 706-9250 SIC 5191 5083 5261

CENTRAL OHIO FARMERS CO-OP INC p 279
730 Bellefontaine Ave, Marion OH 43302
Tel (740) 383-2158 SIC 5153 5261

HERITAGE COOPERATIVE INC p 686
11177 Township Road 133, West Mansfield OH 43358
Tel (419) 294-2371
SIC 5153 5261 4925 4932

LIVINGSTON MACHINERY CO p 871
5201 S Highway 81, Chickasha OK 73018
Tel (405) 224-5056
SIC 5083 5999 7699 5261

ATWOOD DISTRIBUTING LP p 130
500 S Garland Rd, Enid OK 73703
Tel (580) 233-3702
SIC 5261 5251 5531 5311

LANPHERE ENTERPRISES INC p 844
12505 Sw Brdwy St, Beaverton OR 97005
Tel (503) 643-5577 SIC 5571 5511 5261

SKH MANAGEMENT CO p 1329
813 Lititz Pike, Lititz PA 17543
Tel (717) 627-0090
SIC 5141 5092 5261 5411

CAROLINA EASTERN INC p 259
1820 Savannah Hwy Ste G1, Charleston SC 29407
Tel (843) 571-0411 SIC 5261 5191

▲ **TRACTOR SUPPLY CO** p 1468
5401 Virginia Way, Brentwood TN 37027
Tel (615) 440-4000
SIC 5999 5261 5251 5531 5699

ESSEX TECHNOLOGY GROUP INC p 510
455 Industrial Blvd Ste C, La Vergne TN 37086
Tel (615) 620-5444 SIC 5045 8732 5261

▲ **CALLOWAYS NURSERY INC** p 242
4200 Airport Fwy Ste 200, Fort Worth TX 76117
Tel (817) 222-1122 SIC 5261

▲ **CONNS INC** p 358
4055 Technology Frst, The Woodlands TX 77381
Tel (936) 230-5899
SIC 5722 5731 5261 5712

SOUTHERN STATES HOLDINGS INC p 1350
6606 W Broad St Ste B, Richmond VA 23230
Tel (804) 281-1206 SIC 5191 5261 0724

SKAGIT FARMERS SUPPLY p 1329
1833 Park Ln, Burlington WA 98233
Tel (360) 757-6053
SIC 5191 5172 5983 5451 5331 5261

WASHINGTON TRACTOR INC p 1579
2700 136th Avenue Ct E, Sumner WA 98390
Tel (253) 863-4436
SIC 3523 5083 5261 7699 7353

FARM & FLEET OF MADISON INC p 528
3507 E Racine St, Janesville WI 53546
Tel (608) 754-2821
SIC 5199 5531 5251 5261 5039

STEIN GARDEN CENTERS INC p 1385
5400 S 27th St, Milwaukee WI 53221
Tel (414) 761-5400 SIC 5261 5992

RIESTERER & SCHNELL INC p 1234
N2909 State Highway 32, Pulaski WI 54162
Tel (920) 775-4146 SIC 5083 5261

SIC 5271 Mobile Home Dealers

■ **SOUTHERN ENERGY HOMES INC** p 1348
144 Corporate Way, Addison AL 35540
Tel (256) 747-8589 SIC 2451 5271

▲ **CAVCO INDUSTRIES INC** p 267
1001 N Central Ave # 800, Phoenix AZ 85004
Tel (602) 256-6263 SIC 2451 5271

■ **FLEETWOOD HOMES INC** p 555
1001 N Central Ave # 800, Phoenix AZ 85004
Tel (602) 256-6263 SIC 2451 5271

HORTON INDUSTRIES INC p 708
101 Industrial Blvd, Eatonton GA 31024
Tel (706) 485-8506 SIC 2451 5271

CEI LIQUIDATION ESTATES p 273
755 W Big Beaver Rd, Troy MI 48084
Tel (248) 614-8200 SIC 2451 5271

■ **CLAYTON HOMES INC** p 323
5000 Clayton Rd, Maryville TN 37804
Tel (865) 380-3000
SIC 2451 5271 6141 6351 6331

■ **CMH HOMES INC** p 329
5000 Clayton Rd, Maryville TN 37804
Tel (865) 380-3000 SIC 5271

■ **FLEETWOOD RETAIL CORP** p 555
2150 W 18th St Ste 300, Houston TX 77008
Tel (713) 965-0520 SIC 5271

AMERICAN HOMESTAR CORP p 74
2450 S Shore Blvd Ste 300, League City TX 77573
Tel (281) 334-9700
SIC 2451 4213 5271 6351 6515

SIC 5311 Department Stores

■ **FRED MEYER OF ALASKA INC** p 576
1000 E Nthrn Lights Blvd, Anchorage AK 99508
Tel (907) 264-9600 SIC 5311

▲ **WAL-MART STORES INC** p 1572
702 Sw 8th St, Bentonville AR 72716
Tel (479) 273-4000
SIC 5311 5331 5411 5399

▲ **DILLARDS INC** p 439
1600 Cantrell Rd, Little Rock AR 72201
Tel (501) 376-5200
SIC 5311 5611 5621 5641 5712

J & M SALES INC p 770
15001 S Figueroa St, Gardena CA 90248
Tel (310) 324-9962
SIC 5651 6531 5311 5611 5621

ADIR INTERNATIONAL LLC p 22
1605 W Olympic Blvd # 405, Los Angeles CA 90015
Tel (213) 639-2100 SIC 5311

SUN CAPITAL PARTNERS INC p 1400
5200 Town Center Cir # 600, Boca Raton FL 33486
Tel (561) 962-3400
SIC 6799 2672 2671 5812 5411 5311

BEALLS DEPARTMENT STORES INC p 165
1806 38th Ave E, Bradenton FL 34208
Tel (941) 747-2355 SIC 5311 5651 5947

BEALLS INC p 165
1806 13th Ave E, Bradenton FL 34208
Tel (941) 747-2355
SIC 5311 5719 5651 5947

▲ **STEIN MART INC** p 1385
1200 Riverplace Blvd # 1000, Jacksonville FL 32207
Tel (904) 346-1500 SIC 5311 5651

■ **KMART CORP** p 824
3333 Beverly Rd, Hoffman Estates IL 60179
Tel (847) 286-2500 SIC 5311 5912 5399

■ **KMART HOLDING CORP** p 824
3333 Beverly Rd, Hoffman Estates IL 60179
Tel (847) 286-2500 SIC 5311

▲ **SEARS HOLDINGS CORP** p 1297
3333 Beverly Rd, Hoffman Estates IL 60179
Tel (847) 286-2500
SIC 5311 5411 5531 5961

■ **SEARS ROEBUCK AND CO** p 1297
3333 Beverly Rd, Hoffman Estates IL 60179
Tel (847) 286-2500 SIC 5311

WATSEKA RURAL KING SUPPLY INC p 1583
200 N Ernest Grove Pkwy, Watseka IL 60970
Tel (815) 432-3440
SIC 5999 5651 5251 5311

VON MAUR INC p 1565
6565 N Brady St, Davenport IA 52806
Tel (563) 388-2200 SIC 5311

BOMGAARS SUPPLY INC p 199
1805 Zenith Dr, Sioux City IA 51103
Tel (712) 226-5000 SIC 5311 5999 5651

MARDENS INC p 905
184 College Ave, Waterville ME 04901
Tel (207) 873-6111 SIC 5311

■ **MARMAXX OPERATING CORP** p 909
770 Cochituate Rd, Framingham MA 01701
Tel (508) 390-1000 SIC 5311 5651

▲ **TJX COMPANIES INC** p 1457
770 Cochituate Rd Ste 1, Framingham MA 01701
Tel (508) 390-1000 SIC 5311 5651 5719

BUILDING 19 INC p 225
319 Lincoln St, Hingham MA 02043
Tel (781) 749-6900 SIC 5311

MEIJER COMPANIES LTD p 940
2929 Walker Ave Nw, Grand Rapids MI 49544
Tel (616) 453-6711 SIC 5311 5411 5912

MEIJER INC p 940
2929 Walker Ave Nw, Grand Rapids MI 49544
Tel (616) 453-6711 SIC 5411 5311

LYNDALE TERMINAL CO p 887
4567 American Blvd W, Minneapolis MN 55437
Tel (952) 830-8700 SIC 5311 5411 5541

▲ **TARGET CORP** p 1425
1000 Nicollet Mall, Minneapolis MN 55403
Tel (612) 304-6073 SIC 5311 5411

■ **TARGET STORES INC** p 1425
1000 Nicollet Mall, Minneapolis MN 55403
Tel (612) 304-6073 SIC 5411 5311 5461

■ **DEALS-NOTHING OVER A DOLLAR LLC** p 420
12100 St Charles Rock Rd, Bridgeton MO 63044
Tel (314) 291-5081 SIC 5311

GORDMANS INC p 625
1926 S 67th St, Omaha NE 68106
Tel (402) 691-4000 SIC 5311

■ **BURLINGTON COAT FACTORY HOLDINGS LLC** p 227
1830 N Route 130, Burlington NJ 08016
Tel (609) 387-7800 SIC 5311

■ **BURLINGTON COAT FACTORY INVESTMENTS HOLDINGS INC** p 227
1830 N Route 130, Burlington NJ 08016
Tel (609) 387-7800 SIC 5311

■ **BURLINGTON COAT FACTORY WAREHOUSE CORP** p 227
1830 N Route 130 # 2006, Burlington NJ 08016
Tel (609) 387-7800 SIC 5311

▲ **BURLINGTON STORES INC** p 228
2006 Route 130, Burlington NJ 08016
Tel (609) 387-7800 SIC 5311 5961

SPIRIT HALLOWEEN SUPER STORES LLC p 1359
6826 Black Horse Pike, Egg Harbor Township NJ 08234
Tel (609) 645-5691 SIC 5311

BARD COLLEGE PUBLICATIONS p 155
Annandale Rd, Annandale On Hudson NY 12504
Tel (845) 758-7417 SIC 8999 2759 5311

BLUE GOLD EQUITIES LLC p 192
6818 Main St, Flushing NY 11367
Tel (718) 268-6469 SIC 5411 5311

BEAR PARENT INC p 165
9 W 57th St Ste 3100, New York NY 10019
Tel (212) 796-8500 SIC 5311

■ **BLOOMINGDALES INC** p 190
1000 3rd Ave, New York NY 10022
Tel (212) 705-2000 SIC 5311 2389

CENTURY 21 DEPARTMENT STORES LLC p 281
22 Cortland St, New York NY 10007
Tel (212) 227-9092 SIC 5311

■ **MACYS MERCHANDISING CORP** p 893
151 W 34th St, New York NY 10001
Tel (212) 695-4400 SIC 5311

SAKS & CO p 1271
611 5th Ave, New York NY 10022
Tel (212) 753-4000 SIC 5621 5311 5651

SAKS FIFTH AVENUE LLC p 1271
12 E 49th St Fl 2, New York NY 10017
Tel (212) 940-5013 SIC 5311

SAKS INC p 1271
12 E 49th St Fl 2, New York NY 10017
Tel (212) 940-5305
SIC 5311 5611 5621 5641

SW GROUP LLC p 1410
9 E 40th St Fl Mezz, New York NY 10016
Tel (646) 688-2608 SIC 5311

SW RETAIL GROUP LLC p 1411
9 E 40th St Fl Mezz, New York NY 10016
Tel (646) 688-2608 SIC 5311

HUDSONS BAY TRADING CO LP p 717
3 Manhattanville Rd, Purchase NY 10577
Tel (914) 694-4444 SIC 5311

MORALE WELFARE RECREATION ACTIVITY p 988
1401 West Rd, Camp Lejeune NC 28547
Tel (910) 451-2861
SIC 5311 5812 8322 7999 9711

BELK INC p 169
2801 W Tyvola Rd, Charlotte NC 28217
Tel (704) 357-1000 SIC 5311

▲ **CATO CORP** p 267
8100 Denmark Rd, Charlotte NC 28273
Tel (704) 554-8510
SIC 5621 5632 5137 5699 5311 5641

GILDAN ACTIVEWEAR (EDEN) INC p 612
602 E Meadow Rd, Eden NC 27288
Tel (336) 623-9555 SIC 5136 5311

■ **MACYS CORPORATE SERVICES INC** p 893
7 W 7th St Ste 1100, Cincinnati OH 45202
Tel (513) 579-7000 SIC 5311

■ **MACYS FLORIDA STORES LLC** p 893
7 W 7th St Fl 17, Cincinnati OH 45202
Tel (513) 579-7000 SIC 5311

▲ **MACYS INC** p 893
7 W 7th St, Cincinnati OH 45202
Tel (513) 579-7000 SIC 5311

■ **MACYS RETAIL HOLDINGS INC** p 893
7 W 7th St Ste 1100, Cincinnati OH 45202
Tel (513) 579-7000 SIC 5311

■ **MACYS WEST STORES INC** p 893
7 W 7th St Fl 17, Cincinnati OH 45202
Tel (513) 579-7000 SIC 5311

■ **MACYS.COM INC** p 893
7 W 7th St, Cincinnati OH 45202
Tel (513) 579-7000 SIC 5961 5311

SCHOTTENSTEIN STORES CORP p 1290
4300 E 5th Ave, Columbus OH 43219
Tel (614) 221-9200
SIC 5311 5712 5912 5999

■ **ELDER-BEERMAN STORES CORP** p 484
3155 Elbee Rd Ste 201, Moraine OH 45439
Tel (937) 296-2700 SIC 5311 5661 7389

ATWOOD DISTRIBUTING LP p 130
500 S Garland Rd, Enid OK 73703
Tel (580) 233-3702
SIC 5261 5251 5531 5311

■ **FRED MEYER INC** p 576
3800 Se 22nd Ave, Portland OR 97202
Tel (503) 232-8844
SIC 5411 5311 5912 5211 5731 5944

▲ **OLLIES BARGAIN OUTLET HOLDINGS INC** p 1082
6295 Allentown Blvd Ste 1, Harrisburg PA 17112
Tel (717) 657-2300 SIC 5399 5311

BOSCOVS DEPARTMENT STORE LLC p 202
4500 Perkiomen Ave, Reading PA 19606
Tel (610) 779-2000 SIC 8741 5311

BOSCOVS INC p 202
4500 Perkiomen Ave, Reading PA 19606
Tel (610) 779-2000 SIC 8741 5311

▲ **BON-TON STORES INC** p 199
2801 E Market St Ofc C, York PA 17402
Tel (717) 757-7660 SIC 5311

PR RETAIL STORES INC p 1167
Edif Kodak Ave Campo, San Juan PR 00924
Tel (787) 641-8200
SIC 5311 5712 5722 5331

■ **SEARS ROEBUCK DE PUERTO RICO INC** p 1297
383 Ave Fd Roosevelt # 105, San Juan PR 00918
Tel (787) 773-7000 SIC 5311

■ **MCLANE FOODSERVICE INC** p 931
2085 Midway Rd, Carrollton TX 75006
Tel (972) 364-2000
SIC 8742 5141 5311 5113

ALCO STORES INC p 47
751 Freeport Pkwy, Coppell TX 75019
Tel (469) 322-2900 *SIC* 5311 5331

MARIPOSA INTERMEDIATE HOLDINGS LLC p 907
1618 Main St, Dallas TX 75201
Tel (214) 743-7600 *SIC* 5311

NEIMAN MARCUS GROUP INC p 1025
1618 Main St, Dallas TX 75201
Tel (214) 743-7600 *SIC* 5311 5961

NEIMAN MARCUS GROUP LLC p 1025
1618 Main St, Dallas TX 75201
Tel (214) 741-6911 *SIC* 5311

NEIMAN MARCUS GROUP LTD LLC p 1025
1618 Main St, Dallas TX 75201
Tel (214) 743-7600 *SIC* 5311 5961

■ **TUESDAY MORNING INC** p 1490
6250 Lbj Fwy, Dallas TX 75240
Tel (972) 387-3562 *SIC* 5311 2392 5719

DUNLAP CO p 461
200 Bailey Ave Ste 100, Fort Worth TX 76107
Tel (817) 336-4985 *SIC* 5311

▲ **J C PENNEY CO INC** p 770
6501 Legacy Dr, Plano TX 75024
Tel (972) 431-1000 *SIC* 5311 5961

■ **J C PENNEY MEXICO INC** p 770
6501 Legacy Dr, Plano TX 75024
Tel (972) 431-1000 *SIC* 5311

■ **JC PENNEY CORP INC** p 780
6501 Legacy Dr, Plano TX 75024
Tel (972) 431-1000 *SIC* 5311 5961

■ **JCP PUBLICATIONS CORP** p 780
6501 Legacy Dr, Plano TX 75024
Tel (972) 431-1000 *SIC* 5311

■ **MCLANE CO INC** p 930
4747 Mclane Pkwy, Temple TX 76504
Tel (254) 771-7500
SIC 5141 5149 5311 5113

■ **COAST GUARD EXCHANGE SYSTEM** p 331
510 Independence Pkwy # 500, Chesapeake VA 23320
Tel (757) 420-2480 *SIC* 5399 5311

SAVERS INC p 1284
11400 Se 6th St Ste 220, Bellevue WA 98004
Tel (425) 462-1515 *SIC* 5932 5311 5331

TVI INC p 1494
11400 Se 6th St Ste 220, Bellevue WA 98004
Tel (425) 462-1515
SIC 5932 5251 5311 5331

SHOPKO HOLDING CO INC p 1318
700 Pilgrim Way, Green Bay WI 54304
Tel (920) 429-2211 *SIC* 5311

SHOPKO STORES OPERATING CO LLC p 1318
700 Pilgrim Way, Green Bay WI 54304
Tel (920) 429-2211 *SIC* 5311 5912 8042

▲ **KOHLS CORP** p 826
N56w17000 Ridgewood Dr, Menomonee Falls WI 53051
Tel (262) 703-7000 *SIC* 5311 5961

■ **KOHLS DEPARTMENT STORES INC** p 826
N56w17000 Ridgewood Dr, Menomonee Falls WI 53051
Tel (262) 703-7000 *SIC* 5311

SIC 5331 Variety Stores

ALABAMA THRIFT STORES INC p 43
1125 Huffman Rd, Birmingham AL 35215
Tel (205) 856-1234 *SIC* 5331 5932

ATS OPERATING LLC p 129
1900 Crestwood Blvd, Irondale AL 35210
Tel (205) 215-9829 *SIC* 5932 5331

▲ **WAL-MART STORES INC** p 1572
702 Sw 8th St, Bentonville AR 72716
Tel (479) 273-4000
SIC 5311 5331 5411 5399

■ **DISNEY ENTERPRISES INC** p 443
500 S Buena Vista St, Burbank CA 91521
Tel (818) 560-1000
SIC 7812 6794 5331 7996 7941

99 CENTS ONLY STORES LLC p 4
4000 Union Pacific Ave, Commerce CA 90023
Tel (323) 980-8145 *SIC* 5411 5331 5199

NUMBER HOLDINGS INC p 1067
4000 Union Pacific Ave, Commerce CA 90023
Tel (323) 980-8145 *SIC* 5331 5199

GOODWILL INDUSTRIES OF SOUTHERN CALIFORNIA p 625
342 N San Fernando Rd, Los Angeles CA 90031
Tel (323) 223-1211 *SIC* 5331 8331

BUCK HOLDING LP p 223
2800 Sand Hill Rd Ste 200, Menlo Park CA 94025
Tel (615) 855-5161 *SIC* 5331

CPL HOLDINGS LLC p 387
12181 Bluff Creek Dr # 250, Playa Vista CA 90094
Tel (310) 348-6800 *SIC* 5331 6719 5961

▲ **PRICESMART INC** p 1174
9740 Scranton Rd Ste 125, San Diego CA 92121
Tel (858) 404-8800 *SIC* 5331

ECHOPOWER CORP p 475
3720 Baseline Ave, Santa Ynez CA 93460
Tel (805) 729-4473 *SIC* 4953 5331

MICCOSUKEE TRIBE OF INDIANS OF FLORIDA p 959
Sw 8th St & Us Hwy 41, Miami FL 33194
Tel (305) 223-8380
SIC 5812 5331 8412 5947 4489

▲ **HSN INC** p 715
1 Hsn Dr, Saint Petersburg FL 33729
Tel (727) 872-1000 *SIC* 5961 5331 5712

DON QUIJOTE (USA) CO LTD p 450
801 Kaheka St, Honolulu HI 96814
Tel (808) 973-4800
SIC 5411 5331 6512 5912

NEW ALBERTSONS INC p 1029
150 E Pierce Rd Ste 200, Itasca IL 60143
Tel (630) 948-6000 *SIC* 5411 5912 5331

L AND M SUPPLY INC p 833
1200 E Us Highway 169, Grand Rapids MN 55744
Tel (218) 326-9451 *SIC* 5251 5331 5013

CHANNEL CONTROL MERCHANTS LLC p 288
6892 U S Highway 49, Hattiesburg MS 39402
Tel (601) 268-7555 *SIC* 5331

PAMIDA BRANDS HOLDING LLC p 1110
8800 F St, Omaha NE 68127
Tel (402) 493-4765 *SIC* 5331 5912

SHOPKO p 1318
8800 F St, Omaha NE 68127
Tel (402) 339-2400 *SIC* 5331 5912

BROOKSTONE CO INC p 218
1 Innovation Way, Merrimack NH 03054
Tel (866) 576-7337
SIC 5947 5399 5331 5961

■ **CHRISTMAS TREE SHOPS INC** p 303
650 Liberty Ave, Union NJ 07083
Tel (908) 688-0888 *SIC* 5331

VARIETY STORES INC p 1544
218 S Garnett St, Henderson NC 27536
Tel (252) 430-2600 *SIC* 5331

VARIETY WHOLESALERS INC p 1545
218 S Garnett St, Henderson NC 27536
Tel (252) 430-2600 *SIC* 5331

■ **FAMILY DOLLAR SERVICES INC** p 526
10401 Monroe Rd, Matthews NC 28105
Tel (704) 847-6961 *SIC* 5331

■ **FAMILY DOLLAR STORES INC** p 526
10401 Monroe Rd, Matthews NC 28105
Tel (704) 847-6961 *SIC* 5331

■ **FAMILY DOLLAR STORES OF LOUISIANA INC** p 526
10401 Monroe Rd, Matthews NC 28105
Tel (704) 847-6961 *SIC* 5331

■ **FAMILY DOLLAR STORES OF MISSOURI INC** p 526
10401 Monroe Rd, Matthews NC 28105
Tel (704) 847-6961 *SIC* 5331

■ **FAMILY DOLLAR STORES OF VIRGINIA INC** p 526
10401 Old Monroe St, Matthews NC 28105
Tel (704) 847-6961 *SIC* 5331

MARC GLASSMAN INC p 904
5841 W 130th St, Cleveland OH 44130
Tel (216) 265-7700 *SIC* 5331

▲ **BIG LOTS INC** p 181
300 Phillipi Rd, Columbus OH 43228
Tel (614) 278-6800 *SIC* 5331

■ **BIG LOTS STORES INC** p 181
300 Phillipi Rd, Columbus OH 43228
Tel (614) 278-6800 *SIC* 5331

DISCOUNT DRUG MART INC p 442
211 Commerce Dr, Medina OH 44256
Tel (330) 725-2340
SIC 5912 5331 5411 5451 5122 8082

▲ **FIVE BELOW INC** p 553
1818 Market St Ste 2000, Philadelphia PA 19103
Tel (215) 546-7909 *SIC* 5331 5945

■ **WAL-MART PUERTO RICO INC** p 1572
Carr 1 Km 28 7 Bo St Ca, Caguas PR 00725
Tel (787) 653-7777 *SIC* 5331 5411 5399

PR RETAIL STORES INC p 1167
Edif Kodak Ave Campo, San Juan PR 00924
Tel (787) 641-8200
SIC 5311 5712 5722 5331

OCEAN STATE JOBBERS INC p 1073
375 Commerce Park Rd, North Kingstown RI 02852
Tel (401) 295-2672 *SIC* 5331 5199

■ **DOLGENCORP LLC** p 448
100 Mission Ridg, Goodlettsville TN 37072
Tel (615) 855-4000 *SIC* 5331

■ **DOLGENCORP OF TEXAS INC** p 448
100 Mission Ridg, Goodlettsville TN 37072
Tel (615) 855-4000 *SIC* 5331

▲ **DOLLAR GENERAL CORP** p 448
100 Mission Ridg, Goodlettsville TN 37072
Tel (615) 855-4000 *SIC* 5331

▲ **FREDS INC** p 576
4300 New Getwell Rd, Memphis TN 38118
Tel (901) 365-8880
SIC 5331 5912 5199 6794

■ **FREDS STORES OF TENNESSEE INC** p 576
4300 New Getwell Rd, Memphis TN 38118
Tel (901) 365-8880 *SIC* 5331 4731

TRI STAR ENERGY LLC p 1477
1740 Ed Temple Blvd, Nashville TN 37208
Tel (615) 313-3600 *SIC* 5331 5172

ALCO STORES INC p 47
751 Freeport Pkwy, Coppell TX 75019
Tel (469) 322-2900 *SIC* 5311 5331

■ **GREENBACKS INC** p 637
2369 W Orton Cir, Salt Lake City UT 84119
Tel (801) 977-7777 *SIC* 5331

▲ **DOLLAR TREE INC** p 448
500 Volvo Pkwy, Chesapeake VA 23320
Tel (757) 321-5000 *SIC* 5331

■ **DOLLAR TREE STORES INC** p 448
500 Volvo Pkwy, Chesapeake VA 23320
Tel (757) 321-5000 *SIC* 5331

SAVERS INC p 1284
11400 Se 6th St Ste 220, Bellevue WA 98004
Tel (425) 462-1515 *SIC* 5932 5311 5331

TVI INC p 1494
11400 Se 6th St Ste 220, Bellevue WA 98004
Tel (425) 462-1515
SIC 5932 5251 5311 5331

SKAGIT FARMERS SUPPLY p 1329
1833 Park Ln, Burlington WA 98233
Tel (360) 757-6053
SIC 5191 5172 5983 5451 5331 5261

LULULEMON USA INC p 885
2201 140th Ave E, Sumner WA 98390
Tel (604) 732-6124 *SIC* 5137 5331

FLEET WHOLESALE SUPPLY CO LLC p 555
3035 W Wisconsin Ave, Appleton WI 54914
Tel (920) 734-8231
SIC 5191 5331 5531 5211 5541

FARM & FLEET OF JANESVILLE INC p 528
2421 Old Humes Rd Hwy 14, Janesville WI 53545
Tel (608) 752-6377 *SIC* 5331

SIC 5399 General Merchandise Stores, Misc

ALASKA COMMERCIAL CO p 44
550 W 64th Ave Ste 200, Anchorage AK 99518
Tel (907) 273-4600 *SIC* 5399

■ **SAMS WEST INC** p 1274
2101 Se Simple Savings Dr, Bentonville AR 72712
Tel (479) 273-4000 *SIC* 5399

▲ **WAL-MART STORES INC** p 1572
702 Sw 8th St, Bentonville AR 72716
Tel (479) 273-4000
SIC 5311 5331 5411 5399

COLDWATER CREEK OUTLET STORES INC p 335
17000 Ventura Blvd # 300, Encino CA 91316
Tel (208) 265-3468 *SIC* 5399

DNC PARKS & RESORTS AT YOSEMITE INC p 446
9001 Village Dr, Yosemite Ntpk CA 95389
Tel (209) 372-1001
SIC 7011 5399 5812 5947 5541 4725

STARBOARD CRUISE SERVICES INC p 1378
8400 Nw 36th St Ste 600, Doral FL 33166
Tel (786) 845-7300 *SIC* 5399

AREAS USA INC p 106
5301 Blue Lagoon Dr # 690, Miami FL 33126
Tel (305) 264-1709 *SIC* 5399 5812

DFA HOLDINGS INC p 435
6100 Hllywood Blvd Fl 7, Miami FL 33180
Tel (954) 986-7700 *SIC* 5182 5399

■ **KMART CORP** p 824
3333 Beverly Rd, Hoffman Estates IL 60179
Tel (847) 286-2500 *SIC* 5311 5912 5399

MATTOON RURAL KING SUPPLY INC p 921
4216 Dewitt Ave, Mattoon IL 61938
Tel (217) 254-6678 *SIC* 5399

IOWA 80 GROUP INC p 762
515 Sterling Dr, Walcott IA 52773
Tel (563) 468-5500
SIC 5541 5399 7542 5812

IOWA 80 TRUCKSTOP INC p 762
755 W Iowa 80 Rd I-80, Walcott IA 52773
Tel (563) 284-6961
SIC 5541 5399 7542 5812

GALLS LLC p 590
1340 Russell Cave Rd, Lexington KY 40505
Tel (859) 266-7227 *SIC* 5961 5399 2395

BEACON HOLDING INC p 164
25 Research Dr, Westborough MA 01581
Tel (774) 512-7400 *SIC* 5399 5541

BJS WHOLESALE CLUB INC p 186
25 Research Dr, Westborough MA 01581
Tel (774) 512-7400 *SIC* 5399

PREMIER IMAGE CORP p 1170
635 Trade Center Dr, Las Vegas NV 89119
Tel (702) 263-3500 *SIC* 5399

BROOKSTONE CO INC p 218
1 Innovation Way, Merrimack NH 03054
Tel (866) 576-7337
SIC 5947 5399 5331 5961

AUTHENTIC LIFESTYLE PRODUCTS LLC p 133
485 S Broadway Ste 11, Hicksville NY 11801
Tel (212) 354-2170 *SIC* 5399

AMAZING SAVINGS HOLDING LLC p 64
20 Industry Dr, Mountainville NY 10953
Tel (845) 534-1000 *SIC* 5399

APAX PARTNERS OF NEW YORK p 96
601 Lexington Ave Fl 53, New York NY 10022
Tel (212) 419-2447
SIC 6282 5399 5199 5812 5813

■ **MACYS MERCHANDISING GROUP INC** p 893
11 Penn Plz Fl 10, New York NY 10001
Tel (646) 429-6000 *SIC* 5699 5399

SB CAPITAL ACQUISITIONS LLC p 1285
4010 E 5th Ave, Columbus OH 43219
Tel (614) 443-4080 *SIC* 5399

BI-MART ACQUISITION CORP p 180
220 Seneca Rd, Eugene OR 97402
Tel (541) 344-0681 *SIC* 5912 5399

BI-MART CORP p 180
220 S Seneca Rd, Eugene OR 97402
Tel (541) 344-0681 *SIC* 5399

▲ **OLLIES BARGAIN OUTLET HOLDINGS INC** p 1082
6295 Allentown Blvd Ste 1, Harrisburg PA 17112
Tel (717) 657-2300 *SIC* 5399 5311

■ **WAL-MART PUERTO RICO INC** p 1572
Carr 1 Km 28 7 Bo St Ca, Caguas PR 00725
Tel (787) 653-7777 *SIC* 5331 5411 5399

■ **ARMY & AIR FORCE EXCHANGE SERVICE** p 112
3911 S Walton Walker Blvd, Dallas TX 75236
Tel (214) 312-2011 *SIC* 5399 9711

WERE READY TO ASSEMBLE INC p 1592
2201 W Royal Ln Ste 230, Irving TX 75063
Tel (972) 373-9484 *SIC* 7389 5399

VERMONT COUNTRY STORE INC p 1551
5650 Main St, Manchester Center VT 05255
Tel (802) 362-4667 *SIC* 5961 5399 5812

■ **COAST GUARD EXCHANGE SYSTEM** p 331
510 Independence Pkwy # 500, Chesapeake VA 23320
Tel (757) 420-2480 *SIC* 5399 5311

■ **NAVY EXCHANGE SERVICE COMMAND** p 1020
3280 Virginia Beach Blvd, Virginia Beach VA 23452
Tel (757) 631-3696 *SIC* 5399 9711

▲ **COSTCO WHOLESALE CORP** p 374
999 Lake Dr Ste 200, Issaquah WA 98027
Tel (425) 313-8100 *SIC* 5399

■ **PRICE CO** p 1174
999 Lake Dr Ste 200, Issaquah WA 98027
Tel (425) 313-8100 *SIC* 5399

SIC 5411 Grocery Stores

MITCHELL GROCERY CORP p 977
550 Railroad Ave, Albertville AL 35950
Tel (256) 878-4211 *SIC* 5411

ASSOCIATED GROCERS OF SOUTH INC p 120
3600 Vanderbilt Rd, Birmingham AL 35217
Tel (205) 841-6781 *SIC* 5141 5411

BFW LIQUIDATION LLC p 179
1800 Intl Pk Dr Ste 500, Birmingham AL 35243
Tel (205) 853-2663 *SIC* 5411 5912 5921

HOME OIL CO INC p 703
5744 E Us Highway 84, Cowarts AL 36321
Tel (334) 793-1544
SIC 5171 5411 5541 5172

GEMSTONE FOODS p 598
412 8th Ave Ne, Decatur AL 35601
Tel (256) 686-3601 *SIC* 5411 2499

WILLIAMSON OIL CO INC p 1612
1603 Godfrey Ave Se, Fort Payne AL 35967
Tel (256) 845-9466 *SIC* 5541 5411 5172

GREER AUTRY & SONS INC p 639
2850 W Main St, Mobile AL 36612
Tel (251) 342-7964 *SIC* 5411

MCPHERSON COMPANIES INC p 932
5051 Cardinal St, Trussville AL 35173
Tel (205) 661-2799 *SIC* 5171 5411 5541

SAFEWAY SELECT GIFT SOURCE INC p 1267
6401 A St, Anchorage AK 99518
Tel (907) 561-1944 *SIC* 5411 5141 5921

BASHAS INC p 158
22402 S Basha Rd, Chandler AZ 85248
Tel (480) 883-6131
SIC 5411 5149 5148 5147 6512

CARIOCA CO p 256
2601 W Dunlap Ave Ste 10, Phoenix AZ 85021
Tel (602) 395-2600 *SIC* 5541 5411

▲ **SPROUTS FARMERS MARKET INC** p 1361
5455 E High St Ste 111, Phoenix AZ 85054
Tel (480) 814-8016 *SIC* 5411

FACTOR SALES INC p 523
676 N Archibald St, San Luis AZ 85349
Tel (928) 627-8033 *SIC* 5411 5651 5141

CIRCLE K STORES INC p 308
1130 W Warner Rd, Tempe AZ 85284
Tel (602) 728-8000 *SIC* 5411 5541

■ **WESTERN REFINING SOUTHWEST INC** p 1599
1250 W Washington St # 101, Tempe AZ 85281
Tel (602) 286-1400
SIC 2911 5171 5411 5541

■ **FRYS FOOD STORES OF ARIZONA INC** p 582
500 S 99th Ave, Tolleson AZ 85353
Tel (623) 936-2100 *SIC* 5411

▲ **WAL-MART STORES INC** p 1572
702 Sw 8th St, Bentonville AR 72716
Tel (479) 273-4000
SIC 5311 5331 5411 5399

WALMART FOUNDATION p 1573
702 Sw 8th Stre Dept 8687, Bentonville AR 72716
Tel (479) 204-2044 *SIC* 5411

DIAMOND HOSPITALITY ENTERPRISES p 436
5 Mystic Isle Rd, Edgemont AR 72044
Tel (501) 723-5150 *SIC* 5812 5541 5411

MAGNESS OIL CO p 896
167 Tucker Cemetery Rd, Gassville AR 72635
Tel (870) 425-4353 *SIC* 5171 5541 5411

CRACKER BOX LLC p 388
110 Cracker Box Ln, Hot Springs AR 71913
Tel (501) 455-4909 *SIC* 5411

COULSON OIL CO INC p 374
1434 Pike Ave 38, North Little Rock AR 72114
Tel (501) 376-4222
SIC 5172 5541 5411 6512

HARPS FOOD STORES INC p 663
918 S Gutensohn Rd, Springdale AR 72762
Tel (479) 751-7601 *SIC* 5411 5122

FLASH MARKET INC p 554
105 W Harrison Ave, West Memphis AR 72301
Tel (870) 732-2242 *SIC* 5541 5411

NORTHGATE GONZALEZ INC p 1057
1201 N Magnolia Ave, Anaheim CA 92801
Tel (714) 778-3784 *SIC* 5411

NORTHGATE GONZALEZ LLC p 1057
1201 N Magnolia Ave, Anaheim CA 92801
Tel (714) 778-3784 *SIC* 5411

FLYERS ENERGY LLC p 562
2360 Lindbergh St, Auburn CA 95602
Tel (530) 885-0401 *SIC* 5411 5541 5013

TAWA SERVICES INC p 1426
6281 Regio Ave Fl 2, Buena Park CA 90620
Tel (714) 521-8899 *SIC* 5149 5411

TAWA SUPERMARKET INC p 1426
6281 Regio Ave, Buena Park CA 90620
Tel (714) 521-8899 *SIC* 5411

BRISTOL FARMS p 214
915 E 230th St, Carson CA 90745
Tel (310) 233-4700 *SIC* 5411

KOSHAN INC p 828
23501 Avalon Blvd, Carson CA 90745
Tel (310) 830-8241 *SIC* 5411

99 CENTS ONLY STORES LLC p 4
4000 Union Pacific Ave, Commerce CA 90023
Tel (323) 980-8145 *SIC* 5411 5331 5199

■ **SMART & FINAL INC** p 1332
600 Citadel Dr, Commerce CA 90040
Tel (323) 869-7500 *SIC* 5141 5411

▲ **SMART & FINAL STORES INC** p 1332
600 Citadel Dr, Commerce CA 90040
Tel (323) 869-7500 *SIC* 5411

■ **SMART & FINAL STORES LLC** p 1332
600 Citadel Dr, Commerce CA 90040
Tel (323) 869-7500 *SIC* 5411

SUPER A FOODS INC p 1405
7200 Dominion Cir, Commerce CA 90040
Tel (323) 869-0600 *SIC* 5411

■ **FOOD 4 LESS HOLDINGS INC** p 563
1100 W Artesia Blvd, Compton CA 90220
Tel (310) 884-9000 *SIC* 5411

■ **RALPHS GROCERY CO** p 1206
1100 W Artesia Blvd, Compton CA 90220
Tel (310) 884-9000 *SIC* 5411

APPA SEAFOOD INC p 97
135 Klug Cir, Corona CA 92880
Tel (951) 278-2772 *SIC* 5411

NORTH STATE GROCERY INC p 1054
20803 Front St, Cottonwood CA 96022
Tel (530) 347-4621 SIC 5411

GROCERY OUTLET INC p 641
5650 Hollis St Ste 100, Emeryville CA 94608
Tel (510) 845-1999 SIC 5411

■ WHOLE FOODS MARKET CALIFORNIA INC p 1607
5980 Horton St Ste 200, Emeryville CA 94608
Tel (510) 428-7400 SIC 5411 5149

WHOLE FOODS MARKET SOPAC p 1607
207 N Goode Ave, Glendale CA 91203
Tel (818) 501-8484 SIC 5411

R-RANCH MARKET INC p 1203
13985 Live Oak Ave, Irwindale CA 91706
Tel (626) 814-2900 SIC 5411

BERBERIAN ENTERPRISES INC p 174
5315 Santa Monica Blvd, Los Angeles CA 90029
Tel (323) 460-4646 SIC 5411

CANTON FOOD CO INC p 247
750 S Alameda St, Los Angeles CA 90021
Tel (213) 688-7707
SIC 5141 5146 5411 5421 5149 4222

HANNAM CHAIN USA INC p 658
2740 W Olympic Blvd, Los Angeles CA 90006
Tel (213) 382-2922 SIC 5046 5411

SMART & FINAL HOLDINGS LLC p 1332
10205 Constellation Blvd, Los Angeles CA 90067
Tel (310) 843-1900 SIC 5141 5411

ALBECO INC p 46
150 Shoreline Hwy Ste 5, Mill Valley CA 94941
Tel (415) 289-5720 SIC 5411

SAVE MART SUPERMARKETS p 1284
1800 Standiford Ave, Modesto CA 95350
Tel (209) 577-1600
SIC 5411 5141 4213 4212

TRADER JOES CO p 1469
800 S Shamrock Ave, Monrovia CA 91016
Tel (626) 599-3700 SIC 5411 5921

PROS MARKET INC p 1184
1700 S De Soto Pl Ste A, Ontario CA 91761
Tel (909) 930-9552 SIC 5411

VALLARTA SUPERMARKETS INC p 1540
10147 San Fernando Rd, Pacoima CA 91331
Tel (818) 485-0596 SIC 5411

BODEGA LATINA CORP p 197
14601b Lakewood Blvd, Paramount CA 90723
Tel (562) 616-8800 SIC 5411

PACIFIC CONVENIENCE & FUELS LLC p 1104
7180 Koll Center Pkwy, Pleasanton CA 94566
Tel (925) 884-0800 SIC 5411 5541

SAFEWAY CANADA HOLDINGS INC p 1267
5918 Stoneridge Mall Rd, Pleasanton CA 94588
Tel (925) 467-3000 SIC 5411

SAFEWAY DENVER INC p 1267
5918 Stoneridge Mall Rd, Pleasanton CA 94588
Tel (925) 467-3000 SIC 5411

SAFEWAY INC p 1267
5918 Stoneridge Mall Rd, Pleasanton CA 94588
Tel (925) 467-3000 SIC 5411 5912

SAFEWAY STORES 46 INC p 1267
5918 Stoneridge Mall Rd, Pleasanton CA 94588
Tel (925) 467-3000 SIC 5411

VONS COMPANIES INC p 1565
5918 Stoneridge Mall Rd, Pleasanton CA 94588
Tel (626) 821-7000 SIC 5411 2026 2024

LA CADENA INVESTMENTS INC p 835
3750 University Ave # 610, Riverside CA 92501
Tel (909) 733-5000 SIC 5411

STATER BROS HOLDINGS INC p 1383
301 S Tippecanoe Ave, San Bernardino CA 92408
Tel (909) 733-5000 SIC 5411

STATER BROS MARKETS INC p 1383
301 S Tippecanoe Ave, San Bernardino CA 92408
Tel (909) 733-5000 SIC 5411

TRESIERRAS BROTHERS CORP p 1476
618 San Fernando Rd, San Fernando CA 91340
Tel (818) 365-8859 SIC 5411 5461

ARLINGTON ENTERPRISES LP p 110
1200 Irving St Ste 2, San Francisco CA 94122
Tel (415) 753-0403 SIC 5411

MI PUEBLO LLC p 959
1775 Story Rd Ste 120, San Jose CA 95122
Tel (408) 928-1171 SIC 5411

■ CHEVRON STATIONS INC p 296
6001 Bollinger Canyon Rd, San Ramon CA 94583
Tel (925) 842-1000 SIC 5541 5411

EAGLE CANYON CAPITAL LLC p 467
3130 Crow Canyon Pl # 240, San Ramon CA 94583
Tel (925) 884-0800 SIC 5411 5499 2092

ROBINSON OIL CORP p 1242
955 Martin Ave, Santa Clara CA 95050
Tel (408) 327-4300 SIC 5541 5411

ARDEN GROUP INC p 106
13833 Freeway Dr, Santa Fe Springs CA 90670
Tel (310) 638-2842 SIC 5411

ARDEN-MAYFAIR INC p 106
13833 Freeway Dr, Santa Fe Springs CA 90670
Tel (310) 638-2842 SIC 5411

EITAPATIO MARKETS INC p 481
13635 Freeway Dr, Santa Fe Springs CA 90670
Tel (562) 293-4200 SIC 5411

GELSONS MARKETS p 598
13833 Freeway Dr, Santa Fe Springs CA 90670
Tel (310) 638-2842 SIC 5411

SUPER CENTER CONCEPTS INC p 1405
15510 Carmenita Rd, Santa Fe Springs CA 90670
Tel (562) 345-9000 SIC 5411

DRAEGERS SUPER MARKETS p 455
291 Utah Ave, South San Francisco CA 94080
Tel (650) 244-6500 SIC 5411

■ PAQ INC p 1112
8014 Lower Sacramento Rd I, Stockton CA 95210
Tel (209) 957-4917 SIC 5411

VALLARTA FOOD ENTERPRISES INC p 1540
12881 Bradley Ave, Sylmar CA 91342
Tel (818) 898-0088 SIC 5411

FRESH & EASY NEIGHBORHOOD MARKET INC p 578
20101 Hamilton Ave # 350, Torrance CA 90502
Tel (310) 341-1200 SIC 5411

MITSUWA CORP p 978
21515 S Western Ave, Torrance CA 90501
Tel (310) 782-6800 SIC 5411

CAR ENTERPRISES INC p 252
1040 N Benson Ave, Upland CA 91786
Tel (909) 932-9242 SIC 5541 5411

UKAS BIG SAVER FOODS INC p 1500
4260 Charter St, Vernon CA 90058
Tel (323) 582-7222 SIC 5411

NOB HILL GENERAL STORE INC p 1046
500 W Capitol Ave, West Sacramento CA 95605
Tel (916) 373-3333 SIC 5411 5961

RALEYS p 1206
500 W Capitol Ave, West Sacramento CA 95605
Tel (916) 373-3333 SIC 5411 5912

NUGGET MARKET INC p 1067
168 Court St, Woodland CA 95695
Tel (530) 669-3300 SIC 5411

WALDOS HOLDINGS LLC p 1572
831 Pearl St, Boulder CO 80302
Tel (303) 381-2640 SIC 5411

PRIMA MARKETING LLC p 1174
21 Inverness Way E, Englewood CO 80112
Tel (303) 436-9510 SIC 5411 5541

GRAY OIL CO INC p 632
804 Denver Ave, Fort Lupton CO 80621
Tel (303) 857-2288 SIC 5171 5541 5411

▲ NATURAL GROCERS BY VITAMIN COTTAGE INC p 1018
12612 W Alameda Pkwy, Lakewood CO 80228
Tel (303) 986-4600 SIC 5411 5499

■ MINI MART INC p 973
442 Keeler Pkwy, Pueblo CO 81001
Tel (719) 948-3071 SIC 5411

BOZZUTOS INC p 205
275 Schoolhouse Rd, Cheshire CT 06410
Tel (203) 272-3511 SIC 5141 5411

ALDIN ASSOCIATES LIMITED PARTNERSHIP p 48
77 Sterling Rd, East Hartford CT 06108
Tel (860) 282-0651 SIC 5541 5411

■ DRAKE PETROLEUM CO INC p 455
221 Quinebaug Rd, North Grosvenordale CT 06255
Tel (860) 935-5200 SIC 5541 5411

A GRADE MARKET INC p 5
360 Connecticut Ave, Norwalk CT 06854
Tel (203) 838-0504 SIC 5411

STEW LEONARDS HOLDINGS LLC p 1388
100 Westport Ave, Norwalk CT 06851
Tel (203) 847-9088 SIC 5411

MERCURY FUEL SERVICE INC p 945
43 Lafayette St, Waterbury CT 06708
Tel (203) 756-7284
SIC 5172 5541 5411 5983 1711 2911

DELAWARE SUPERMARKETS INC p 424
501 S Walnut St, Wilmington DE 19801
Tel (302) 652-3412 SIC 5411

SUN CAPITAL PARTNERS INC p 1400
5200 Town Center Cir # 600, Boca Raton FL 33486
Tel (561) 962-3400
SIC 6799 2672 2671 5812 5411 5311

ALL AMERICAN OIL INC OF BREVARD p 51
402 High Point Dr Ste 102, Cocoa FL 32926
Tel (321) 690-0807 SIC 5541 5411

M & R UNITED INC p 889
402 High Point Dr Ste 101, Cocoa FL 32926
Tel (321) 631-0245 SIC 5812 5411

3801 FLAGLE SUPERMARKET LLC p 2
3801 W Flagler St, Coral Gables FL 33134
Tel (305) 846-9796 SIC 5411 5912

■ JUNIOR FOOD STORES OF WEST FLORIDA INC p 797
619 8th Ave, Crestview FL 32536
Tel (850) 587-5023 SIC 5541 5411

LAND OSUN MANAGEMENT CORP p 842
3715 Nw 97th Blvd Ste A, Gainesville FL 32606
Tel (352) 333-3011 SIC 5541 5411

SEDANOS MANAGEMENT INC p 1300
3140 W 76th St, Hialeah FL 33018
Tel (305) 824-1034 SIC 5411 5912

BI-LO HOLDING FINANCE LLC p 180
5050 Edgewood Ct, Jacksonville FL 32254
Tel (904) 783-5000 SIC 5411

BI-LO HOLDING LLC p 180
5050 Edgewood Ct, Jacksonville FL 32254
Tel (904) 783-5000 SIC 5411

BI-LO HOLDINGS FOUNDATION INC p 180
5050 Edgewood Ct, Jacksonville FL 32254
Tel (904) 783-5000 SIC 5411

BI-LO LLC p 180
8928 Prominence Pkwy # 200, Jacksonville FL 32256
Tel (904) 783-5000 SIC 5411

FIRST COAST ENERGY LLP p 545
7014 A C Skinner Pkwy # 290, Jacksonville FL 32256
Tel (904) 596-3200 SIC 5541 5411 5172

GATE PETROLEUM CO p 593
9540 San Jose Blvd, Jacksonville FL 32257
Tel (904) 730-3470
SIC 5541 3272 5411 7997

LSF5 BI-LO HOLDINGS LLC p 883
5050 Edgewood Ct, Jacksonville FL 32254
Tel (904) 783-5000 SIC 5411

MORRIS HOLDINGS INC p 990
1650 County Road 210 W, Jacksonville FL 32259
Tel (904) 829-3946 SIC 5541 5812 5411

RALEIGH WINN-DIXIE INC p 1206
5050 Edgewood Ct, Jacksonville FL 32254
Tel (904) 783-5000 SIC 5411

SOUTHEASTERN GROCERS LLC p 1346
8928 Prominence Pkwy # 200, Jacksonville FL 32256
Tel (904) 783-5000 SIC 5411

WINN-DIXIE STORES INC p 1616
8928 Prominence Pkwy # 200, Jacksonville FL 32256
Tel (904) 783-5000 SIC 5411 5541 5912

WINN-DIXIE STORES OF JACKSONVILLE (INC) p 1616
5050 Edgewood Ct, Jacksonville FL 32254
Tel (904) 783-5000 SIC 5411

SCAFFS INC p 1285
134 Se Colburn Ave, Lake City FL 32025
Tel (386) 752-7344 SIC 5411

FLEETWING CORP p 555
742 S Combee Rd, Lakeland FL 33801
Tel (863) 665-7557 SIC 5172 5411

PUBLIX SUPER MARKETS INC p 1190
3300 Publix Corp Pkwy, Lakeland FL 33811
Tel (863) 688-1188 SIC 5411

FARM STORES CORP p 529
2937 Sw 27th Ave Ste 203, Miami FL 33133
Tel (800) 726-3276 SIC 5411

SOUTHEAST FROZEN FOODS CO LP p 1345
3261 Executive Way, Miramar FL 33025
Tel (954) 882-1044 SIC 5142 4222 5411

WARE OIL & SUPPLY CO INC p 1575
2715 S Byron Butler Pkwy, Perry FL 32348
Tel (850) 838-1852 SIC 5172 5087 5411

■ WHOLE FOODS MARKET GROUP INC p 1607
7720 Peters Rd, Plantation FL 33324
Tel (954) 236-0600 SIC 5411

RADIANT GROUP LLC p 1204
1320 E 9th Ave Ste 211, Tampa FL 33605
Tel (813) 247-4731 SIC 5171 5411

BRAD LANIER OIL CO INC p 206
611 W Roosevelt Ave, Albany GA 31701
Tel (229) 436-0131 SIC 5171 5541 5411

BIGMOUTHBEN CONVENIENCE STORE LLC p 182
370 Auburn Ave Ne Ste A, Atlanta GA 30312
Tel (404) 331-3973 SIC 5411 5947

RACETRAC PETROLEUM INC p 1203
3225 Cumberland Blvd Se # 100, Atlanta GA 30339
Tel (770) 850-3491 SIC 5541 5411 5172

SOUTHWEST GEORGIA OIL CO INC p 1352
1711 E Shotwell St, Bainbridge GA 39819
Tel (229) 246-1553
SIC 5171 5541 5411 5921

WALTHALL OIL CO p 1575
2510 Allen Rd, Macon GA 31216
Tel (478) 781-1234 SIC 5172 5541 5411

JH HARVEY CO LLC p 785
107 S Davis St, Nashville GA 31639
Tel (704) 633-8250 SIC 5411

JET FOOD STORES OF GEORGIA INC p 783
1106 S Harris St, Sandersville GA 31082
Tel (478) 552-2588 SIC 5411

ALL AMERICAN QUALITY FOODS INC p 51
125 Eagles Landing Pkwy, Stockbridge GA 30281
Tel (770) 474-5904 SIC 5411

GOLDEN PANTRY FOOD STORES INC p 621
1150 Wall St, Watkinsville GA 30677
Tel (800) 533-3816 SIC 5411 5541

■ FLASH FOODS LLC p 554
215 Pendleton St, Waycross GA 31501
Tel (912) 285-4011 SIC 5541 5411

JONES CO p 792
215 Pendleton St Ste A, Waycross GA 31501
Tel (912) 285-4011 SIC 5541 5411 5172

PUNA PLANTATION HAWAII LIMITED p 1192
50 E Puainako St, Hilo HI 96720
Tel (808) 959-9111 SIC 5411

■ ALOHA PETROLEUM LTD p 59
1132 Bishop St Ste 1700, Honolulu HI 96813
Tel (808) 833-3249 SIC 5172 5541 5411

DON QUIJOTE (USA) CO LTD p 450
801 Kaheka St, Honolulu HI 96814
Tel (808) 973-4800
SIC 5411 5331 6512 5912

FOOD PANTRY LTD p 564
3536 Harding Ave Ste 500, Honolulu HI 96816
Tel (808) 732-5515 SIC 5411 5947

FOODLAND SUPER MARKET LIMITED p 564
3536 Harding Ave Fl 1, Honolulu HI 96816
Tel (808) 732-0791 SIC 5411

QSI INC p 1195
3375 Koapaka St Ste D108, Honolulu HI 96819
Tel (808) 831-0811 SIC 5411

SEVEN-ELEVEN HAWAII INC p 1309
1755 Nuuanu Ave Fl 2, Honolulu HI 96817
Tel (808) 526-1711 SIC 5411

TERUYA BROS LIMITED p 1440
1276 Young St Ste B, Honolulu HI 96814
Tel (808) 591-8946 SIC 5411

AB ACQUISITION LLC p 9
250 E Parkcenter Blvd, Boise ID 83706
Tel (208) 395-6200 SIC 5411

ALBERTSONS HOLDINGS LLC p 46
250 E Parkcenter Blvd, Boise ID 83706
Tel (208) 395-6200 SIC 5411

JOAH INC p 787
250 E Parkcenter Blvd, Boise ID 83706
Tel (208) 395-6200 SIC 5411

NEW ALBERTSONS INC p 1029
250 E Parkcenter Blvd, Boise ID 83706
Tel (208) 395-6200 SIC 5411

WINCO FOODS LLC p 1615
650 N Armstrong Pl, Boise ID 83704
Tel (208) 377-0110 SIC 5411

WINCO HOLDINGS INC p 1615
650 N Armstrong Pl, Boise ID 83704
Tel (208) 377-0110 SIC 5411

MANITO SUPER 1 FOODS INC p 902
240 W Hayden Ave, Hayden Lake ID 83835
Tel (208) 772-5722 SIC 5411

CONRAD & BISCHOFF INC p 358
2251 N Holmes Ave, Idaho Falls ID 83401
Tel (208) 522-8174 SIC 5171 5411 5541

JACKSONS FOOD STORES INC p 774
3450 E Commercial Ct, Meridian ID 83642
Tel (208) 888-6061 SIC 5541 5411

RIDLEYS FOOD CORP p 1234
621 Washington St S, Twin Falls ID 83301
Tel (208) 324-4633 SIC 5411 2099

ALDI INC p 47
1200 N Kirk Rd, Batavia IL 60510
Tel (630) 879-8100 SIC 5411

DICKERSON STATIONS INC p 438
920 N Illinois St, Belleville IL 62220
Tel (618) 233-0786 SIC 5541 5411

MARTIN & BAYLEY INC p 912
1311a W Main St, Carmi IL 62821
Tel (618) 382-2334 SIC 5411

CAPUTOS NEW FARM PRODUCE INC p 252
520 E North Ave, Carol Stream IL 60188
Tel (630) 620-4444
SIC 5431 5411 5148 5149

TRI STAR MARKETING INC p 1477
2211 W Bradley Ave, Champaign IL 61821
Tel (217) 367-8386 SIC 5541 5411 5172

FAIRPLAY INC p 525
4640 S Halsted St, Chicago IL 60609
Tel (773) 247-3077 SIC 5411

KIRBY FOODS INC p 821
8745 W Higgins Rd, Chicago IL 60631
Tel (217) 352-2600 SIC 5411

TREASURE ISLAND FOODS INC p 1475
3460 N Broadway St, Chicago IL 60657
Tel (773) 327-3880 SIC 5411 5921

VIENNA BEEF LTD p 1556
2501 N Damen Ave, Chicago IL 60647
Tel (773) 278-7800
SIC 2013 2035 2053 5411 5149 5147

SUNSET FOOD MART INC p 1404
777 Central Ave Ste 2, Highland Park IL 60035
Tel (847) 234-8380 SIC 5411 5921

▲ SEARS HOLDINGS CORP p 1297
3333 Beverly Rd, Hoffman Estates IL 60179
Tel (847) 286-2500
SIC 5311 5411 5531 5961

DOMINICKS FINER FOODS LLC p 449
150 E Pierce Rd Ste 400, Itasca IL 60143
Tel (630) 990-2880 SIC 5411

JEWEL OSCO INC p 784
150 E Pierce Rd Ste 200, Itasca IL 60143
Tel (630) 551-2672 SIC 5411 2834

NEW ALBERTSONS INC p 1029
150 E Pierce Rd Ste 200, Itasca IL 60143
Tel (630) 948-6000 SIC 5411 5912 5331

SUPERMERCADO LA HACIENDA INC p 1407
224 S Larkin Ave, Joliet IL 60436
Tel (815) 724-0200 SIC 5411

MCCAIN USA INC p 926
2275 Cabot Dr, Lisle IL 60532
Tel (800) 938-7799 SIC 2037 2038 5411

DOMINICKS FINER FOODS INC p 449
711 Jorie Blvd Ms-4000, Oak Brook IL 60523
Tel (630) 891-5000 SIC 5411

BERKOT LTD p 175
11333 W 159th St, Orland Park IL 60467
Tel (708) 590-4088 SIC 5411

BUREAU SERVICE CO p 226
22069 Us Highway 34, Princeton IL 61356
Tel (815) 875-2800
SIC 5191 5172 5153 5411 7542

NIEMANN FOODS FOUNDATION p 1043
923 N 12th St, Quincy IL 62301
Tel (217) 221-5600 SIC 5411 5541

KELLEY WILLIAMSON CO p 808
1132 Harrison Ave, Rockford IL 61104
Tel (815) 397-9410 SIC 5541 5411 5171

REOPCO INC p 1224
4930 E State St Ste 1, Rockford IL 61108
Tel (815) 387-1700 SIC 5411 5541

J B SULLIVAN INC p 770
425 1st St Ste 1, Savanna IL 61074
Tel (815) 273-4511 SIC 5411

PEAPOD LLC p 1126
9933 Woods Dr, Skokie IL 60077
Tel (847) 583-9400 SIC 5411

WALTER LAGESTEE INC p 1574
16145 State St, South Holland IL 60473
Tel (708) 596-3166 SIC 5411 5141

GRAHAM ENTERPRISE INC p 629
750 Bunker Ct Ste 100, Vernon Hills IL 60061
Tel (847) 837-0777 SIC 5172 5411

COUCHE-TARD US INC p 374
4080 W Jnathan Moore Pike, Columbus IN 47201
Tel (812) 379-9227 SIC 5411

MACS CONVENIENCE STORES LLC p 893
4080 W Jnathan Moore Pike, Columbus IN 47201
Tel (812) 379-9227 SIC 5411

PREMIER AG CO-OP INC p 1170
785 S Marr Rd, Columbus IN 47201
Tel (812) 379-9501
SIC 5153 5191 5172 5411 2429

WINKLER INC p 1616
535 E Medcalf St, Dale IN 47523
Tel (812) 937-4421 SIC 5141 5411

LASSUS BROS OIL INC p 846
1800 Magnavox Way, Fort Wayne IN 46804
Tel (260) 436-1415 SIC 5541 5411

STRACK AND VAN TIL SUPER MARKET INC p 1392
9632 Cline Ave, Highland IN 46322
Tel (219) 924-6932 SIC 5411 8741 4226

CRYSTAL FLASH PETROLEUM LLC p 396
5221 Ivy Tech Dr, Indianapolis IN 46268
Tel (317) 879-2849 SIC 5541 5411 5171

MARSH SUPERMARKETS CO LLC p 911
9800 Crosspoint Blvd, Indianapolis IN 46256
Tel (317) 594-2406 SIC 5411

MARSH SUPERMARKETS HOLDING LLC p 911
9800 Crosspoint Blvd, Indianapolis IN 46256
Tel (317) 594-2100 SIC 5411

■ SYSCO INDIANAPOLIS LLC p 1417
4000 W 62nd St, Indianapolis IN 46268
Tel (317) 291-2020 SIC 5149 5046 5411

BUEHLER FOODS INC p 224
1100 W 12th Ave, Jasper IN 47546
Tel (812) 482-1366 *SIC* 5411

JAY PETROLEUM INC p 779
533 S 200 W, Portland IN 47371
Tel (260) 726-9374 *SIC* 5411 5172

JOHN C GROUB CO INC p 787
900 A Ave E, Seymour IN 47274
Tel (812) 522-1998 *SIC* 5411

KOCOLENE MARKETING LLC p 826
2060 1st Ave, Seymour IN 47274
Tel (812) 522-2224 *SIC* 5541 5411

SWIFTY OIL LLC p 1412
1515 W Tipton St, Seymour IN 47274
Tel (812) 522-1640 *SIC* 5541 5411

MARTINS SUPER MARKETS INC p 913
760 Cotter St, South Bend IN 46613
Tel (574) 234-5848 *SIC* 5411

FAMILY EXPRESS CORP p 526
213 S State Road 49, Valparaiso IN 46383
Tel (219) 531-6490 *SIC* 5541 5411

▲ CASEYS GENERAL STORES INC p 263
1 Se Convenience Blvd, Ankeny IA 50021
Tel (515) 965-6100 *SIC* 5411 5541

■ CASEYS MARKETING CO p 263
1 Se Convenience Blvd, Ankeny IA 50021
Tel (515) 965-6100
SIC 5411 5172 5141 5812

■ CASEYS RETAIL CO p 263
1 Se Convenience Blvd, Ankeny IA 50021
Tel (515) 965-6100 *SIC* 5411

FAREWAY STORES INC p 528
715 8th St, Boone IA 50036
Tel (515) 432-2623 *SIC* 5411

REIF OIL CO p 1221
801 N 3rd St, Burlington IA 52601
Tel (319) 758-1240 *SIC* 5172 5411

GIT-N-GO CONVENIENCE STORES INC p 613
2716 Indianola Ave, Des Moines IA 50315
Tel (515) 288-8565 *SIC* 5411 5541 6722

HY-VEE INC p 723
5820 Westown Pkwy, West Des Moines IA 50266
Tel (515) 267-2800 *SIC* 5411 5912 5921

KRAUSE HOLDINGS INC p 829
6400 Westown Pkwy, West Des Moines IA 50266
Tel (515) 226-0128 *SIC* 5411

KUM & GO LC p 832
6400 Westown Pkwy, West Des Moines IA 50266
Tel (515) 226-0128 *SIC* 5411

■ DILLON COMPANIES INC p 439
2700 E 4th Ave, Hutchinson KS 67501
Tel (620) 665-5511 *SIC* 5411

■ KWIK SHOP INC p 832
734 E 4th Ave, Hutchinson KS 67501
Tel (620) 669-8504 *SIC* 5411

STAR FUEL CENTERS INC p 1378
11161 Overbrook Rd, Leawood KS 66211
Tel (913) 652-9400
SIC 5172 7542 5541 5411

LEISZLER OIL CO INC p 854
8228 Southport Dr, Manhattan KS 66502
Tel (785) 632-5648 *SIC* 5171 5411 5541

NEWCOMB OIL CO LLC p 1037
901 Withrow Ct, Bardstown KY 40004
Tel (502) 348-3961 *SIC* 5411 5171

HOUCHENS FOOD GROUP INC p 710
700 Church St, Bowling Green KY 42101
Tel (270) 843-3252 *SIC* 5411 5541 5093

MAX ARNOLD & SONS LLC p 922
702 N Main St, Hopkinsville KY 42240
Tel (270) 885-8488
SIC 5171 5541 5411 5812

THORNTONS INC p 1450
10101 Linn Station Rd # 200, Louisville KY 40223
Tel (502) 425-8022 *SIC* 5461 5411

KENTUCKY LAKE OIL CO INC p 812
620 S 4th St, Murray KY 42071
Tel (270) 753-1323
SIC 5541 5571 5171 5411

SHOP RITE INC p 1318
115 E 1st St, Crowley LA 70526
Tel (337) 785-2924 *SIC* 5411

SOUTHEAST FOODS INC p 1345
1001 N 11th St, Monroe LA 71201
Tel (318) 388-1884 *SIC* 5411

GAUBERT OIL CO INC p 594
1201 Saint Patrick St, Thibodaux LA 70301
Tel (800) 256-1250 *SIC* 5172 5411

ROUSES ENTERPRISES LLC p 1253
1301 Saint Mary St, Thibodaux LA 70301
Tel (985) 447-5998 *SIC* 5411

DEAD RIVER CO p 419
80 Exchange St Ste 3, Bangor ME 04401
Tel (207) 947-8641
SIC 6512 5172 5983 5541 5411

OCEAN INVESTMENTS CORP p 1073
700 Maine Ave, Bangor ME 04401
Tel (207) 942-7000 *SIC* 5541 5411

R H FOSTER ENERGY LLC p 1202
110 Mecaw Rd, Hampden ME 04444
Tel (207) 947-3835
SIC 5172 5541 5411 5983

FABIAN OIL INC p 523
15 Oak St, Oakland ME 04963
Tel (207) 465-7958
SIC 5541 5983 5984 5411

HANNAFORD BROS CO LLC p 658
145 Pleasant Hill Rd, Scarborough ME 04074
Tel (207) 883-2911 *SIC* 5411 5912

HANNAFORD BROTHERS CO p 658
145 Pleasant Hill Rd, Scarborough ME 04074
Tel (207) 883-2911 *SIC* 5411 6519

MARTINS FOODS OF S BURLINGTON INC p 913
145 Pleasant Hill Rd, Scarborough ME 04074
Tel (207) 883-2911 *SIC* 5411

CN BROWN CO p 329
1 C N Brown Way, South Paris ME 04281
Tel (207) 743-9212 *SIC* 5411 5541 5983

FAST FARE INC p 531
1 N Charles St, Baltimore MD 21201
Tel (410) 539-7400 *SIC* 5411 5541

MARS SUPER MARKETS INC p 910
9627 Philadelphia Rd # 100, Baltimore MD 21237
Tel (410) 590-0500 *SIC* 5411

NEW RIDGE ASSOCIATES INC p 1033
2700 Loch Raven Rd, Baltimore MD 21218
Tel (410) 859-3636 *SIC* 5411

ROSEMORE HOLDINGS INC p 1251
1 N Charles St Ste 2200, Baltimore MD 21201
Tel (410) 347-7090
SIC 2911 5171 5541 5411

TWO FARMS INC p 1495
3611 Roland Ave, Baltimore MD 21211
Tel (410) 889-0200 *SIC* 5411

GIANT FOOD LLC p 610
8301 Profess Pl Ste 115, Hyattsville MD 20785
Tel (301) 341-4100 *SIC* 5411 6512 5912

DASH IN FOOD STORES INC p 413
6355 Crain Hwy, La Plata MD 20646
Tel (301) 932-3600 *SIC* 5541 5411 6794

WILLS GROUP INC p 1613
6355 Crain Hwy, La Plata MD 20646
Tel (301) 932-3600
SIC 5541 5983 5172 5411

■ FOODARAMA INC (DE) p 564
4600 Forbes Blvd Ste 1, Lanham MD 20706
Tel (301) 306-8600 *SIC* 5411

■ SHOPPERS FOOD WAREHOUSE CORP p 1318
4600 Forbes Blvd, Lanham MD 20706
Tel (301) 306-8600 *SIC* 5411

MENDELSON HOLDING CO LTD INC p 943
8300 Pennsylvania Ave, Upper Marlboro MD 20772
Tel (301) 420-6400 *SIC* 5411

CUMBERLAND FARMS INC p 400
100 Crossing Blvd, Framingham MA 01702
Tel (508) 270-1400
SIC 5411 5541 5172 2086 2051 2026

AHOLD USA INC p 37
1385 Hancock St, Quincy MA 02169
Tel (717) 249-4000 *SIC* 5411

STOP & SHOP SUPERMARKET CO p 1391
1385 Hancock St, Quincy MA 02169
Tel (717) 960-1700 *SIC* 5411

STOP & SHOP SUPERMARKET CO LLC p 1391
1385 Hancock St, Quincy MA 02169
Tel (800) 767-7772 *SIC* 5411

TEDESCHI FOOD SHOPS INC p 1432
14 Howard St, Rockland MA 02370
Tel (781) 878-8210 *SIC* 5411

TFS NEWCO LLC p 1445
14 Howard St, Rockland MA 02370
Tel (781) 878-8210 *SIC* 5411

BIG Y FOODS INC p 182
2145 Roosevelt Ave, Springfield MA 01104
Tel (413) 784-0600 *SIC* 5411

DEMOULAS SUPER MARKETS INC p 428
875 East St, Tewksbury MA 01876
Tel (978) 640-8100 *SIC* 5411

MARKET BASKET PRODUCE INC p 908
875 East St, Tewksbury MA 01876
Tel (978) 851-8000 *SIC* 5411

■ ALLIANCE ENERGY LLC p 54
800 South St Ste 500, Waltham MA 02453
Tel (781) 674-7780 *SIC* 5411 5541

ROCHE BROS SUPERMARKETS INC p 1242
70 Hastings St Ste 1, Wellesley MA 02481
Tel (781) 235-9400 *SIC* 5411

SHAWS HOLDINGS INC p 1313
750 W Center St, West Bridgewater MA 02379
Tel (508) 313-4000 *SIC* 5411

SHAWS SUPERMARKETS INC p 1313
750 W Center St, West Bridgewater MA 02379
Tel (508) 313-4000 *SIC* 5411

BUSCHS INC p 229
2240 S Main St, Ann Arbor MI 48103
Tel (734) 998-2666 *SIC* 5411

BLARNEY CASTLE OIL CO p 189
12218 West St, Bear Lake MI 49614
Tel (231) 864-3111 *SIC* 5541 5411 5171

GAS CITY LTD p 593
401 S Old Woodward Ave # 340, Birmingham MI 48009
Tel (815) 469-9000 *SIC* 5541 5411 5172

▲ SPARTANNASH CO p 1355
850 76th St Sw, Byron Center MI 49315
Tel (616) 878-2000 *SIC* 5141 5411 5912

ALLIANCE FOODS INC p 54
605 W Chicago Rd, Coldwater MI 49036
Tel (517) 278-2395 *SIC* 5411 5141

ADMIRAL PETROLEUM CO p 23
785 W Randall St, Coopersville MI 49404
Tel (616) 837-6218
SIC 5541 5411 5194 5145

GRAD INC p 628
4001 3 Mile Rd Nw, Grand Rapids MI 49534
Tel (616) 676-5969
SIC 5141 5194 5145 5122 5113 5411

LRR FOOD INC p 882
850 76th St Sw, Grand Rapids MI 49518
Tel (810) 629-1383 *SIC* 5411 5921

MEIJER COMPANIES LTD p 940
2929 Walker Ave Nw, Grand Rapids MI 49544
Tel (616) 453-6711 *SIC* 5311 5411 5912

MEIJER INC p 940
2929 Walker Ave Nw, Grand Rapids MI 49544
Tel (616) 453-6711 *SIC* 5411 5311

■ SPARTAN STORES FUEL LLC p 1355
850 76th St Sw, Grand Rapids MI 49518
Tel (616) 878-2000 *SIC* 5541 5411

FAMILY FARE INC p 526
3030 Corporate Grove Dr, Hudsonville MI 49426
Tel (616) 896-5910 *SIC* 5411

KRIST OIL CO p 830
303 Selden Rd, Iron River MI 49935
Tel (906) 265-6144 *SIC* 5541 5411

POLLYS FOOD SERVICE INC p 1160
1821 Spring Arbor Rd, Jackson MI 49203
Tel (517) 787-5228 *SIC* 5411 5921

QUALITY DAIRY CO p 1197
111 W Mount Hope Ave 3a, Lansing MI 48910
Tel (517) 319-4100 *SIC* 5451 5411

WALTERS-DIMMICK PETROLEUM INC p 1574
1620 S Kalamazoo Ave, Marshall MI 49068
Tel (269) 781-4654
SIC 5541 5411 6512 5172 5171 5983

WESCO INC p 1593
1460 Whitehall Rd, Muskegon MI 49445
Tel (231) 719-4300
SIC 5411 5541 5145 5149

HARDINGS MARKET-WEST INC p 661
211 E Bannister St Ste E, Plainwell MI 49080
Tel (269) 427-8003 *SIC* 5411

PRI MAR PETROLEUM INC p 1173
1207 Broad St, Saint Joseph MI 49085
Tel (269) 983-7314 *SIC* 5411 5172

FORWARD CORP p 570
219 N Front St, Standish MI 48658
Tel (989) 846-4501
SIC 5411 5541 5172 5812

HOLLYWOOD HOLDING CO LLC p 701
2670 W Maple Rd, Troy MI 48084
Tel (248) 643-0309 *SIC* 5921 5141 5411

JOHANNESONS INC p 787
2301 Johanneson Dr Nw, Bemidji MN 56601
Tel (218) 751-9644 *SIC* 5411

HOLIDAY COMPANIES p 700
4567 American Blvd W, Bloomington MN 55437
Tel (952) 830-8700 *SIC* 5541 5411 5172

HOLIDAY STATIONSTORES INC p 700
4567 American Blvd W, Bloomington MN 55437
Tel (952) 830-8700 *SIC* 5541 5411

BEST OIL CO p 177
30 N 8th St, Cloquet MN 55720
Tel (218) 879-0201
SIC 5171 5172 5013 5983 5541 5411

■ SUPERMARKET OPERATORS OF AMERICA INC p 1407
11840 Valley View Rd, Eden Prairie MN 55344
Tel (952) 828-4000 *SIC* 5411 4225

■ SUPERVALU HOLDINGS INC p 1407
11840 Valley View Rd, Eden Prairie MN 55344
Tel (952) 828-4000 *SIC* 5411

▲ SUPERVALU INC p 1407
11840 Valley View Rd, Eden Prairie MN 55344
Tel (952) 828-4000 *SIC* 5411 5141

JERRYS ENTERPRISES INC p 783
5125 Vernon Ave S, Edina MN 55436
Tel (952) 922-8335 *SIC* 5411 5812 5251

MINERS INC p 973
5065 Miller Trunk Hwy, Hermantown MN 55811
Tel (218) 729-5882 *SIC* 5411

SCHWANS HOME SERVICE INC p 1291
115 W College Dr, Marshall MN 56258
Tel (507) 532-3274 *SIC* 5411

LUND FOOD HOLDINGS INC p 885
4100 W 50th St Ste 100, Minneapolis MN 55424
Tel (952) 927-3663 *SIC* 5411

LUNDS INC p 886
4100 W 50th St Ste 100, Minneapolis MN 55424
Tel (952) 927-3663 *SIC* 5411

LYNDALE TERMINAL CO p 887
4567 American Blvd W, Minneapolis MN 55437
Tel (952) 830-8700 *SIC* 5311 5411 5541

■ NASH-FINCH CO p 1008
7600 France Ave S Ste 200, Minneapolis MN 55435
Tel (952) 832-0534
SIC 5141 5148 5142 5147 5411

▲ TARGET CORP p 1425
1000 Nicollet Mall, Minneapolis MN 55403
Tel (612) 304-6073 *SIC* 5311 5411

■ TARGET STORES INC p 1425
1000 Nicollet Mall, Minneapolis MN 55403
Tel (612) 304-6073 *SIC* 5411 5311 5461

■ APPERTS INC p 98
900 Highway 10 S, Saint Cloud MN 56304
Tel (320) 251-3200
SIC 5142 5141 5411 5421 2013

COBORNS INC p 333
1921 Coborn Blvd, Saint Cloud MN 56301
Tel (320) 252-4222 *SIC* 5411 5541 5921

■ FLAGSTONE FOODS INC p 554
380 Sint Pter St Ste 1000, Saint Paul MN 55102
Tel (651) 348-4100 *SIC* 5411 2068

■ CUB FOODS INC p 399
421 3rd St S, Stillwater MN 55082
Tel (651) 439-7200 *SIC* 5411

KNOWLANS SUPER MARKETS INC p 825
111 County Road F E, Vadnais Heights MN 55127
Tel (651) 483-9242 *SIC* 5411

STAPLES OIL CO INC p 1378
1680 N Redding Ave, Windom MN 56101
Tel (507) 831-4450 *SIC* 5411

KOWALSKI COMPANIES INC p 828
8505 Valley Creek Rd, Woodbury MN 55125
Tel (651) 578-8800 *SIC* 5411

GRAVES OIL CO p 632
226 Pearson St, Batesville MS 38606
Tel (662) 563-4604 *SIC* 5171 5541 5411

SAYLE OIL CO INC p 1285
410 W Main St, Charleston MS 38921
Tel (800) 844-8120 *SIC* 5541 5171 5411

LITCO PETROLEUM INC p 870
323 Highway 72 W, Corinth MS 38834
Tel (662) 287-1471 *SIC* 5541 5172 5411

SCOTT PETROLEUM CORP p 1293
102 Main St, Itta Bena MS 38941
Tel (662) 254-9024 *SIC* 5171 5984 5411

BUFFALO SERVICES INC p 224
747 S Broadway St, Mccomb MS 39648
Tel (601) 684-7702
SIC 5172 5411 6519 4212

AYERS OIL CO p 140
401 N 4th St, Canton MO 63435
Tel (573) 288-4464
SIC 5171 5411 5541 5172

DIERBERGS INC p 438
16690 Swingley Ridge Rd # 300, Chesterfield MO 63017
Tel (636) 532-8884 *SIC* 5411 5992

DIERBERGS MARKETS INC p 438
16690 Swingley Ridge Rd # 300, Chesterfield MO 63017
Tel (636) 532-8884 *SIC* 5411

DIERBERGS OFALLON LLC p 438
16690 Swingley Ridge Rd, Chesterfield MO 63017
Tel (636) 532-8884 *SIC* 5411

■ MORAN FOODS LLC p 988
100 Corporate Office Dr, Earth City MO 63045
Tel (314) 592-9100 *SIC* 5141 5411

■ SAVE-A-LOT FOOD STORES LTD p 1284
100 Corporate Office Dr, Earth City MO 63045
Tel (314) 592-9261 *SIC* 5411

WESTERN OIL INC p 1599
3553 Rider Trl S, Earth City MO 63045
Tel (314) 738-9900
SIC 5541 5411 7542 4225

TOWN AND COUNTRY GROCERS OF FREDERICKTOWN MISSOURI INC p 1464
208 Lincoln Dr, Fredericktown MO 63645
Tel (573) 783-6477 *SIC* 5411

MCKEEVER ENTERPRISES INC p 930
4216 S Hocker Dr, Independence MO 64055
Tel (816) 478-3095 *SIC* 5411

COSENTINO ENTERPRISES INC p 373
8700 E 63rd St, Kansas City MO 64133
Tel (913) 749-1500 *SIC* 5411

COSENTINO GROUP II INC p 373
8700 E 63rd St, Kansas City MO 64133
Tel (816) 358-2270 *SIC* 5411

ABEL OIL CO p 11
10406 Highway 79, Louisiana MO 63353
Tel (573) 754-5595 *SIC* 5171 5411

ROSWIL INC p 1252
1878 S State Highway 125, Rogersville MO 65742
Tel (417) 667-7530 *SIC* 5411

SCHNUCK MARKETS INC p 1288
11420 Lackland Rd, Saint Louis MO 63146
Tel (314) 994-9900
SIC 5411 5912 5812 7841

■ SHOP N SAVE WAREHOUSE FOODS INC p 1318
10461 Manchester Rd, Saint Louis MO 63122
Tel (314) 984-0322 *SIC* 5411

TOWN AND COUNTRY SUPER MARKET INC p 1464
1104 E Highway 32, Salem MO 65560
Tel (573) 729-2325 *SIC* 5411

FOOD GIANT SUPERMARKETS INC p 564
120 Industrial Dr, Sikeston MO 63801
Tel (573) 471-3500 *SIC* 5411

G W FOODS INC p 587
2041 Railroad Ave, Willow Springs MO 65793
Tel (417) 469-4000 *SIC* 5411

ROCKY MOUNTAIN SUPPLY INC p 1245
350 Jackrabbit Ln Stop 1, Belgrade MT 59714
Tel (406) 388-4008
SIC 5171 5191 5541 5411

TOWN PUMP INC p 1465
600 S Main St, Butte MT 59701
Tel (406) 497-6700
SIC 5541 5411 7993 6512 5812

TOWN AND COUNTRY SUPPLY ASSOCIATION p 1464
18 8th Ave, Laurel MT 59044
Tel (406) 628-6314
SIC 5984 5191 5411 5999

BATTLE CREEK FARMERS COOPERATIVE NON-STOCK p 160
83755 Highway 121, Battle Creek NE 68715
Tel (402) 675-2375
SIC 5153 5191 5172 5541 5411

BOSSELMAN INC p 202
3123 W Stolley Park Rd, Grand Island NE 68801
Tel (308) 381-2800
SIC 5541 5411 5812 7011 5172 5084

NEBRASKALAND TIRE INC p 1023
Hwy 283 & Hwy I 80, Lexington NE 68850
Tel (308) 324-2338 *SIC* 5531 5541 5411

B & R STORES INC p 141
4554 W St, Lincoln NE 68503
Tel (402) 423-9602 *SIC* 5411

GROWTH MANAGEMENT CORP p 642
3201 Pioneers Blvd # 112, Lincoln NE 68502
Tel (402) 488-8500 *SIC* 5812 5411

BAKERS SUPERMARKETS INC p 146
4509 S 143rd St Ste 4, Omaha NE 68137
Tel (402) 397-4321 *SIC* 5411

NO FRILLS SUPERMARKETS INC OF OMAHA p 1046
11163 Mill Valley Rd, Omaha NE 68154
Tel (402) 399-9244 *SIC* 5411

RITE WAY INVESTMENTS INC p 1236
8400 I St, Omaha NE 68127
Tel (402) 331-6400 *SIC* 5172 5541 5411

WINCO FOODS p 1614
80 N Stephanie St, Henderson NV 89074
Tel (702) 558-5366 *SIC* 5411

REBEL OIL CO INC p 1214
2200 Highland Dr, Las Vegas NV 89102
Tel (702) 382-5866 *SIC* 5171 5411

SCOLARIS WAREHOUSE MARKETS INC p 1292
950 Holman Way, Sparks NV 89431
Tel (775) 355-8568 *SIC* 5411

SOUTHERN FAMILY MARKETS LLC p 1348
7 Corporate Dr, Keene NH 03431
Tel (973) 605-6381 *SIC* 5411

BERAT CORP p 174
1230 Blckwood Clmenton Rd, Clementon NJ 08021
Tel (856) 627-6501 *SIC* 5411

SAFEWAY CONTRACTING INC p 1267
107 Trumbull St, Elizabeth NJ 07206
Tel (212) 627-8050 *SIC* 5411

FOODARAMA SUPERMARKETS INC p 564
922 State Route 33 Bldg 1, Freehold NJ 07728
Tel (732) 462-3120 *SIC* 5411 5261 5921

SAKER HOLDINGS CORP p 1271
922 State Route 33 Bldg 1, Freehold NJ 07728
Tel (732) 462-4700 *SIC* 5411 5261 5921

SAKER SHOPRITES INC p 1271
922 Hwy 33 Bldg 1, Freehold NJ 07728
Tel (732) 462-4700 *SIC* 5411

SHOP-RITE SUPERMARKETS INC p 1318
5000 Riverside Dr, Keasbey NJ 08832
Tel (908) 527-3300 *SIC* 5411

WAKEFERN FOOD CORP p 1572
5000 Riverside Dr, Keasbey NJ 08832
Tel (908) 527-3300
SIC 5141 5149 5411 4213 2026

RONETCO SUPERMARKETS INC p 1249
1070 Us Highway 46 Ste 1, Ledgewood NJ 07852
Tel (973) 927-8300 *SIC* 5411 5921

INSERRA SUPERMARKETS INC p 745
20 Ridge Rd Ste 1, Mahwah NJ 07430
Tel (201) 529-5900 *SIC* 5411 5735

SINGER SUPERMARKETS INC p 1326
20 Ridge Rd, Mahwah NJ 07430
Tel (201) 529-5900 *SIC* 5411 5912

FOOD CIRCUS SUPER MARKETS INC p 564
853 State Route 35, Middletown NJ 07748
Tel (732) 671-2220 *SIC* 5411

GREAT ATLANTIC & PACIFIC TEA CO INC p 633
2 Paragon Dr, Montvale NJ 07645
Tel (201) 573-9700 *SIC* 5411

PATHMARK STORES INC p 1120
2 Paragon Dr, Montvale NJ 07645
Tel (866) 443-7374 *SIC* 5411

WALDBAUM INC p 1572
2 Paragon Dr, Montvale NJ 07645
Tel (201) 571-4132 *SIC* 5411

RAB FOOD GROUP p 1203
80 Avenue K, Newark NJ 07105
Tel (201) 553-1100 *SIC* 5411

KINGS SUPER MARKETS INC p 820
700 Lanidex Plz Ste 2, Parsippany NJ 07054
Tel (973) 463-6300 *SIC* 5411

NORKUS ENTERPRISES INC p 1048
505 Richmond Ave, Point Pleasant Beach NJ 08742
Tel (732) 899-8485 *SIC* 5411

GLASS GARDENS INC p 614
220 W Passaic St, Rochelle Park NJ 07662
Tel (201) 843-1424 *SIC* 5411 5921

▲VILLAGE SUPER MARKET INC p 1557
733 Mountain Ave, Springfield NJ 07081
Tel (973) 467-2200 *SIC* 5411

PERLMART INC p 1136
954 Route 166 Ste 1, Toms River NJ 08753
Tel (732) 341-0700 *SIC* 5411 5912

BROWNS SUPER STORES INC p 220
700 Delsea Dr, Westville NJ 08093
Tel (856) 933-7000 *SIC* 5411

QUICK CHEK CORP p 1199
3 Old Highway 28, Whitehouse Station NJ 08889
Tel (908) 534-2200 *SIC* 5411

LAGUNA DEVELOPMENT CORP p 838
14500 Central Ave Sw I40, Albuquerque NM 87121
Tel (505) 352-7877 *SIC* 7011 5411

ALLSUP ENTERPRISES INC p 58
2112 N Thornton St, Clovis NM 88101
Tel (575) 769-2311
SIC 5411 5541 4832 6519 5171

ALLSUPS CONVENIENCE STORES INC p 58
2112 N Thornton St, Clovis NM 88101
Tel (575) 769-2311 *SIC* 5411 5541

STEWARTS SHOPS CORP p 1389
2907 State Route 9, Ballston Spa NY 12020
Tel (518) 581-1201 *SIC* 5411

BEST YET MARKET INC p 177
1 Lexington Ave, Bethpage NY 11714
Tel (516) 570-5300 *SIC* 5411

KING KULLEN GROCERY CO INC p 820
185 Central Ave, Bethpage NY 11714
Tel (516) 733-7100 *SIC* 5411

MIRABITO HOLDINGS INC p 974
49 Court St Ste 1, Binghamton NY 13901
Tel (607) 561-2700
SIC 5172 4925 5541 5411 5983

BOGOPA SERVICE CORP p 197
650 Fountain Ave, Brooklyn NY 11208
Tel (718) 257-7801 *SIC* 5411 4225 5149

SUPERMARKET MANAGEMENT INC p 1407
460 Niagara St Ste 1, Buffalo NY 14201
Tel (716) 853-5787 *SIC* 5411

NICE N EASY GROCERY SHOPPES INC p 1042
7840 Oxbow Rd, Canastota NY 13032
Tel (315) 397-2802 *SIC* 5411 5541

JETRO CASH AND CARRY ENTERPRISES LLC p 784
1524 132nd St, College Point NY 11356
Tel (718) 939-6400
SIC 5142 5046 5181 5147 5411

BLUE GOLD EQUITIES LLC p 192
6818 Main St, Flushing NY 11367
Tel (718) 268-6469 *SIC* 5411 5311

DANS SUPREME SUPER MARKETS INC p 412
474 Fulton Ave Fl 3, Hempstead NY 11550
Tel (516) 483-2400 *SIC* 5411

DAGOSTINO SUPERMARKETS INC p 408
1385 Boston Post Rd Ste 1, Larchmont NY 10538
Tel (914) 833-4000 *SIC* 5411

GU MARKETS LLC p 644
4350 Middle Settlement Rd, New Hartford NY 13413
Tel (315) 793-9226 *SIC* 5411

2328 ON TWELFTH LLC p 2
2328 12th Ave, New York NY 10027
Tel (212) 234-3883 *SIC* 5411

AG SUPERMARKET HOLDINGS LLC p 34
245 Park Ave, New York NY 10167
Tel (212) 692-2000 *SIC* 5411

BTF/CFI INC p 222
144 W 38th St, New York NY 10018
Tel (212) 993-0300
SIC 6794 7991 5621 5411

FAIRWAY GROUP HOLDINGS CORP p 525
2284 12th Ave, New York NY 10027
Tel (646) 616-8000 *SIC* 5411

GRISTEDES FOODS INC p 641
800 3rd Ave Fl 5, New York NY 10022
Tel (212) 956-5770 *SIC* 5411

NAMDAR INC p 1007
800 3rd Ave Fl 5, New York NY 10022
Tel (212) 956-5770 *SIC* 5411

RED APPLE GROUP INC p 1215
800 3rd Ave Fl 5, New York NY 10022
Tel (212) 956-5803 *SIC* 5461 5541 5411

SHOPWELL INC p 1318
42 W 39th St Fl 18, New York NY 10018
Tel (212) 915-2202 *SIC* 5411

BLUEOX CORP p 193
38 N Canal St, Oxford NY 13830
Tel (607) 843-2583 *SIC* 5172 5411 5541

ADAMS FAIRACRE FARMS INC p 21
765 Dutchess Tpke, Poughkeepsie NY 12603
Tel (845) 454-4330 *SIC* 5411 5261 5199

CACTUS HOLDINGS INC p 236
4705 Metropolitan Ave, Ridgewood NY 11385
Tel (718) 417-3770
SIC 5411 5147 5144 5146 5148 5143

WESTERN BEEF RETAIL INC p 1597
4705 Metropolitan Ave, Ridgewood NY 11385
Tel (718) 417-3770 *SIC* 5411

WEGMANS FOOD MARKETS INC p 1587
1500 Brooks Ave, Rochester NY 14624
Tel (585) 328-2550 *SIC* 5411

GOLUB CORP p 622
461 Nott St, Schenectady NY 12308
Tel (518) 355-5000 *SIC* 5411

PRICE CHOPPER OPERATING CO INC p 1174
501 Duanesburg Rd, Schenectady NY 12306
Tel (518) 379-1600 *SIC* 5411

PRICE CHOPPER OPERATING CO OF CONNECTICUT INC p 1174
501 Duanesburg Rd, Schenectady NY 12306
Tel (518) 861-5099 *SIC* 5411

PRICE CHOPPER OPERATING CO OF VERMONT INC p 1174
501 Duanesburg Rd, Schenectady NY 12306
Tel (518) 355-5000 *SIC* 5411

PETR-ALL PETROLEUM CONSULTING CORP p 1139
7401 Round Pond Rd, Syracuse NY 13212
Tel (315) 446-0125 *SIC* 5172 5411

WAYNES FOOD MARKET INC p 1584
235 E Division St, Watertown NY 13601
Tel (315) 493-2854 *SIC* 5411

TOPS HOLDING II CORP p 1461
6363 Main St, Williamsville NY 14221
Tel (716) 635-5000 *SIC* 5411

TOPS HOLDING LLC p 1461
6363 Main St, Williamsville NY 14221
Tel (716) 635-5000 *SIC* 5411

TOPS MARKETS LLC p 1461
6363 Main St, Williamsville NY 14221
Tel (716) 635-5000
SIC 5411 5141 5147 5148 5122 5912

TOPS PT LLC p 1461
6363 Main St, Williamsville NY 14221
Tel (716) 635-5000 *SIC* 5411

JERNIGAN OIL CO INC p 783
415 Main St E, Ahoskie NC 27910
Tel (252) 332-2131 *SIC* 5411 5171

PUGH OIL CO INC p 1191
701 Mcdowell Rd, Asheboro NC 27205
Tel (336) 629-2061
SIC 5172 5983 5541 5411 5149

▲INGLES MARKETS INC p 743
2913 Us Highway 70, Black Mountain NC 28711
Tel (828) 669-2941
SIC 5411 5912 5541 2026 6512

COC PROPERTIES INC p 333
110 Mackenan Dr Ste 300, Cary NC 27511
Tel (919) 462-1100 *SIC* 6512 5541 5411

PANTRY INC p 1112
305 Gregson Dr, Cary NC 27511
Tel (919) 774-6700 *SIC* 5541 5411

■RUDDICK OPERATING CO LLC p 1257
301 S Tryon St Ste 1800, Charlotte NC 28282
Tel (704) 372-5404 *SIC* 5411 2284

WINN-DIXIE CHARLOTTE INC p 1616
2401 Nevada Blvd, Charlotte NC 28273
Tel (704) 587-4000
SIC 5411 8741 5141 4226 4222

SAMPSON-BLADEN OIL CO INC p 1274
510 Commerce St, Clinton NC 28328
Tel (910) 592-4177 *SIC* 5171 5411 5983

UNITED ENERGY INC p 1508
932 N Hwy 421, Clinton NC 28328
Tel (919) 785-1904 *SIC* 5541 5411

FUEL USA LLC p 583
1 Stoneglen Ct, Durham NC 27712
Tel (434) 525-1615 *SIC* 5411

CAMPBELL RENTALS LLC p 245
418 Peanut Plant Rd, Elizabethtown NC 28337
Tel (910) 862-7657 *SIC* 5171 5411 5541

LIL THRIFT FOOD MARTS INC p 866
1007 Arsenal Ave, Fayetteville NC 28305
Tel (910) 433-4490 *SIC* 5541 5411

FRESH MARKET INC p 579
628 Green Valley Rd # 500, Greensboro NC 27408
Tel (336) 272-1338 *SIC* 5411

POMEGRANATE HOLDINGS INC p 1160
628 Green Valley Rd # 500, Greensboro NC 27408
Tel (336) 272-1338 *SIC* 5411

ALEX LEE INC p 48
120 4th St Sw, Hickory NC 28602
Tel (828) 725-4424
SIC 5141 5142 5147 5148 5194 5411

■HARRIS TEETER LLC p 664
701 Crestdale Rd, Matthews NC 28105
Tel (704) 844-3100 *SIC* 5411

■HARRIS TEETER SUPERMARKETS INC p 664
701 Crestdale Rd, Matthews NC 28105
Tel (704) 844-3100 *SIC* 5411

NEIGHBORS STORES INC p 1024
1314 Old Highway 601, Mount Airy NC 27030
Tel (336) 789-5561 *SIC* 5541 5411

DELHAIZE AMERICA LLC p 424
2110 Executive Dr, Salisbury NC 28147
Tel (704) 633-8250 *SIC* 5411

FOOD LION LLC p 564
2110 Executive Dr, Salisbury NC 28147
Tel (704) 633-8250 *SIC* 5411

CENAMA INC p 274
1410 Commwl Dr Ste 202, Wilmington NC 28403
Tel (910) 395-5300 *SIC* 5411

LOWES FOODS LLC p 881
1381 Old Mill Cir Ste 200, Winston Salem NC 27103
Tel (336) 659-2429 *SIC* 5411

LEEVERS FOODS PARTNERSHIP LLP p 852
501 4th St Se, Devils Lake ND 58301
Tel (701) 662-8646 *SIC* 5411

S-N-GO STORES INC p 1263
2701 University Dr S, Fargo ND 58103
Tel (701) 235-7531 *SIC* 5541 5411

SPF ENERGY INC p 1358
100 27th St Ne, Minot ND 58703
Tel (701) 852-1194 *SIC* 5541 5411

SUPERPUMPER INC p 1407
100 27th St Ne, Minot ND 58703
Tel (701) 852-0061 *SIC* 5541 5411

FARMERS UNION OIL CO OF STANLEY p 530
8149 Highway 2, Stanley ND 58784
Tel (701) 628-2322
SIC 5172 5251 5541 5411

SERVICE OIL INC p 1307
1718 Main Ave E, West Fargo ND 58078
Tel (701) 277-1050 *SIC* 5541 5411

HORIZON RESOURCES p 707
317 2nd St W, Williston ND 58801
Tel (701) 572-2171
SIC 5172 5541 5411 5191

FRED W ALBRECHT GROCERY CO p 576
2700 Gilchrist Rd Ste A, Akron OH 44305
Tel (330) 733-2861 *SIC* 5411

HOLLAND OIL CO p 700
1485 Marion Ave, Akron OH 44313
Tel (330) 835-1815 *SIC* 5541 5172 5411

DAVES SUPERMARKET INC p 415
5300 Richmond Rd, Bedford OH 44146
Tel (216) 361-5130 *SIC* 5411

FISHER FOODS MARKETING INC p 552
4855 Frank Ave Nw, Canton OH 44720
Tel (330) 433-1180 *SIC* 5411 8741

▲KROGER CO p 830
1014 Vine St Ste 1000, Cincinnati OH 45202
Tel (513) 762-4000
SIC 5411 5912 5541 5944

■KROGER LIMITED PARTNERSHIP I p 830
1014 Vine St Ste 1000, Cincinnati OH 45202
Tel (513) 762-4000 *SIC* 5411

UNITED DAIRY FARMERS INC p 1507
3955 Montgomery Rd, Cincinnati OH 45212
Tel (513) 396-8700
SIC 5411 5143 2026 2024 5541 5451

■VIGOR ACQUISITION CORP p 1556
1014 Vine St, Cincinnati OH 45202
Tel (513) 762-4000 *SIC* 5411

DUNCAN OIL CO p 461
849 Factory Rd, Dayton OH 45434
Tel (937) 426-5945
SIC 5172 5411 5983 1542

CHIEF SUPER MARKET INC p 298
705 Deatrick St, Defiance OH 43512
Tel (419) 782-0950 *SIC* 5411

■KROGER CO p 830
2000 Nutter Farms Ln, Delaware OH 43015
Tel (740) 657-2124 *SIC* 5411

■SPEEDWAY LLC p 1358
500 Speedway Dr, Enon OH 45323
Tel (937) 864-3000 *SIC* 5411 5541 2869

NEEDLER ENTERPRISES INC p 1024
317 W Main Cross St, Findlay OH 45840
Tel (419) 422-8090 *SIC* 5411

BECK SUPPLIERS INC p 167
1000 N Front St, Fremont OH 43420
Tel (419) 332-5527
SIC 5171 5541 5411 5984 1542

PAR MAR OIL CO p 1113
114 Westview Ave Unit A, Marietta OH 45750
Tel (740) 373-7406 *SIC* 5411

DISCOUNT DRUG MART INC p 442
211 Commerce Dr, Medina OH 44256
Tel (330) 725-2340
SIC 5912 5331 5411 5451 5122 8082

COLES ENERGY INC p 336
3619 St Rt 113 E, Milan OH 44846
Tel (419) 499-1120 *SIC* 5172 5411 5541

LYKINS COMPANIES INC p 887
5163 Wlfpn Plsnt Hl Rd, Milford OH 45150
Tel (513) 831-8820 *SIC* 5172 4213 5411

DOROTHY LANE MARKET INC p 451
2710 Far Hills Ave, Oakwood OH 45419
Tel (937) 299-3561 *SIC* 5411

RIESBECK FOOD MARKETS INC p 1234
48661 National Rd W, Saint Clairsville OH 43950
Tel (740) 695-7050 *SIC* 5411

NESTLE PREPARED FOODS CO p 1027
5750 Harper Rd, Solon OH 44139
Tel (440) 248-3600 *SIC* 2038 5411 2037

JACK A ALLEN INC p 773
2105 Old State Route 7, Steubenville OH 43952
Tel (740) 282-4531
SIC 5172 5983 5541 5411

HEINENS INC p 681
4540 Richmond Rd, Warrensville Heights OH 44128
Tel (216) 475-2300 *SIC* 5411

■TA OPERATING LLC p 1420
24601 Center Ridge Rd # 200, Westlake OH 44145
Tel (440) 808-9100
SIC 5541 7538 5812 5411 6794

■TRAVELCENTERS OF AMERICA INC p 1474
24601 Center Ridge Rd # 200, Westlake OH 44145
Tel (440) 808-9100
SIC 5541 7538 5812 5411

BUEHLER FOOD MARKETS INC p 224
1401 Old Mansfield Rd, Wooster OH 44691
Tel (330) 264-4355 *SIC* 5411

E&H FAMILY GROUP INC p 467
1401 Old Mansfield Rd, Wooster OH 44691
Tel (330) 264-4355 *SIC* 5411

SHEPHERD OIL CO LLC p 1315
1831 S Main St, Blackwell OK 74631
Tel (580) 363-4280 *SIC* 5411 5172

G L N INC p 587
207 S Broadway St, Checotah OK 74426
Tel (918) 473-2369 *SIC* 5411

DOMINO FOOD AND FUEL INC p 449
Hwy 183 S, Clinton OK 73601
Tel (580) 323-0341 *SIC* 5411

ELMER SMITH OIL CO p 489
Hwy 183 S, Clinton OK 73601
Tel (580) 323-2929 *SIC* 5171 5411

CREST DISCOUNT FOODS INC p 392
2200 W 15th And Santa Fe, Edmond OK 73013
Tel (405) 733-2330 *SIC* 5411

7-ELEVEN LLC p 3
2021 S Macarthur Blvd, Oklahoma City OK 73128
Tel (405) 682-5711 *SIC* 5411 5541

BRAUMS INC p 208
3000 Ne 63rd St, Oklahoma City OK 73121
Tel (405) 478-1656 *SIC* 5411 5812

HAC INC p 652
390 Ne 36th St, Oklahoma City OK 73105
Tel (405) 290-3000 *SIC* 5411

LOVES TRAVEL STOPS & COUNTRY STORES INC p 881
10601 N Pennsylvania Ave, Oklahoma City OK 73120
Tel (405) 302-6500 *SIC* 5541 5411 5947

CITIZEN POTAWATOMI NATION p 310
1601 Gordon Cooper Dr, Shawnee OK 74801
Tel (405) 275-3121
SIC 7992 5411 7011 8412

REASORS LLC p 1214
200 W Choctaw St, Tahlequah OK 74464
Tel (918) 456-1472 *SIC* 5411

QUIKTRIP CORP p 1200
4705 S 129th East Ave, Tulsa OK 74134
Tel (918) 615-7700
SIC 5411 5541 5172 2099 5141 6512

WAREHOUSE MARKET INC p 1575
6207 S Peoria Ave Ste A, Tulsa OK 74136
Tel (918) 749-4732 *SIC* 5411

PLAID PANTRIES INC p 1153
10025 Sw Allen Blvd, Beaverton OR 97005
Tel (503) 646-4246 *SIC* 5411

MARKET OF CHOICE INC p 908
2580 Willakenzie Rd, Eugene OR 97401
Tel (541) 345-3349 *SIC* 5411

ED STAUB & SONS PETROLEUM INC p 476
1301 Esplanade Ave, Klamath Falls OR 97601
Tel (541) 887-8900 *SIC* 5172 5541 5411

C & K MARKET INC p 231
850 Ohare Pkwy Ste 100, Medford OR 97504
Tel (541) 469-3113 *SIC* 5411

THUNDERBIRD SHERMS MARKET INC p 1451
730 S Grape St, Medford OR 97501
Tel (541) 857-0850 *SIC* 5411

■FRED MEYER INC p 576
3800 Se 22nd Ave, Portland OR 97202
Tel (503) 232-8844
SIC 5411 5311 5912 5211 5731 5944

■FRED MEYER STORES INC p 576
3800 Se 22nd Ave, Portland OR 97202
Tel (503) 232-8844
SIC 5211 5411 5912 5731 5944

NEW SEASONS MARKET LLC p 1033
1300 Se Stark St Ste 401, Portland OR 97214
Tel (503) 292-1987 *SIC* 5411

ROTH IGA FOODLINER INC p 1252
4895 Indian School Rd Ne, Salem OR 97305
Tel (503) 393-7684 *SIC* 5411

■PETROLEUM MARKETERS INC p 1139
645 Hamilton St Ste 500, Allentown PA 18101
Tel (540) 772-4900 *SIC* 5983 5411

SHEETZ INC p 1313
5700 6th Ave, Altoona PA 16602
Tel (814) 946-3611 *SIC* 5411

MARTIN OIL CO p 913
528 N 1st St, Bellwood PA 16617
Tel (814) 742-8438
SIC 5983 5171 5541 5411

GIANT FOOD STORES LLC p 610
1149 Harrisburg Pike, Carlisle PA 17013
Tel (717) 249-4000 *SIC* 5411

SHEETZ DISTRIBUTION SERVICES LLC p 1313
242 Sheetz Way, Claysburg PA 16625
Tel (814) 239-1600 *SIC* 5411

COUNTRY FAIR INC p 375
2251 E 30th St, Erie PA 16510
Tel (814) 898-1111 *SIC* 5411 5541

CMI HOLDING CORP p 329
1555 Bustard Rd, Kulpsville PA 19443
Tel (215) 361-9000 *SIC* 5411 6512

SKH MANAGEMENT CO p 1329
813 Lititz Pike, Lititz PA 17543
Tel (717) 627-0090
SIC 5141 5092 5261 5411

ACME MARKETS INC p 18
75 Valley Stream Pkwy # 100, Malvern PA 19355
Tel (610) 889-4000 *SIC* 5411

KARNS PRIME AND FANCY FOOD LTD p 804
675 Silver Spring Rd, Mechanicsburg PA 17050
Tel (717) 766-6477 *SIC* 5411

WAWA INC p 1584
260 W Baltimore Pike, Media PA 19063
Tel (610) 358-8000 *SIC* 5411 2026

■ SUNOCO INC (R&M) p 1403
3801 West Chester Pike, Newtown Square PA 19073
Tel (215) 977-3000
SIC 5541 2869 2911 5411

GENUARDIS FAMILY MARKETS LP p 605
301 E Germantown Pike, Norristown PA 19401
Tel (610) 277-6000 *SIC* 5912 5411

BOYERS FOOD MARKETS INC p 205
301 S Warren St, Orwigsburg PA 17961
Tel (570) 366-1477 *SIC* 5411

■ ATLANTIC REFINING & MARKETING CORP p 127
1801 Market St, Philadelphia PA 19103
Tel (215) 977-3000
SIC 2911 5171 5541 5411

■ MASCOT PETROLEUM CO INC p 915
1801 Market St Fl 10, Philadelphia PA 19103
Tel (215) 977-3000 *SIC* 4932 5411

GIANT EAGLE INC p 610
101 Kappa Dr, Pittsburgh PA 15238
Tel (800) 362-8899
SIC 5411 5141 5147 5148 5143 6794

REDNERS MARKETS INC p 1217
3 Quarry Rd, Reading PA 19605
Tel (610) 926-3700 *SIC* 5411 5541 5912

ASSOCIATED WHOLESALERS INC p 121
336 E Penn Ave, Robesonia PA 19551
Tel (610) 693-3161
SIC 5141 5147 5122 5142 5148 5411

GERRITYS SUPER MARKET INC p 609
950 N South Rd Ste 5, Scranton PA 18504
Tel (570) 342-4144 *SIC* 5411

UNI-MARTS LLC p 1502
1155 Benner Pike 100, State College PA 16801
Tel (814) 234-6000
SIC 5411 5541 5993 6794 5172

▲ WEIS MARKETS INC p 1588
1000 S 2nd St, Sunbury PA 17801
Tel (570) 286-4571 *SIC* 5411

UNITED REFINING CO p 1511
15 Bradley St, Warren PA 16365
Tel (814) 723-1500 *SIC* 2911 5541 5411

UNITED REFINING CO OF PENNSYLVANIA p 1511
15 Bradley St, Warren PA 16365
Tel (814) 723-1500 *SIC* 5541 5411

UNITED REFINING INC p 1511
15 Bradley St, Warren PA 16365
Tel (814) 723-1500
SIC 2911 5541 5411 4612

ATLANTIS PETROLEUM LLC p 127
998 Old Eagle School Rd # 1205, Wayne PA 19087
Tel (610) 265-8081 *SIC* 5411 5541

C H R CORP p 232
2295 N Susquehanna Trl C, York PA 17404
Tel (717) 848-9827 *SIC* 5411

NK LIQUIDATION INC p 1045
600 Arsenal Rd, York PA 17402
Tel (717) 854-1505 *SIC* 5411

■ WAL-MART PUERTO RICO INC p 1572
Carr 1 Km 28 7 Bo St Ca, Caguas PR 00725
Tel (787) 653-7777 *SIC* 5331 5411 5399

PUEBLO INC p 1190
Calle Diana Ste 14, Guaynabo PR 00968
Tel (787) 757-3131 *SIC* 5411

RALPHS FOOD WAREHOUSE INC p 1206
Carr 183 Industrial Park, Las Piedras PR 00771
Tel (787) 733-0959 *SIC* 5411 5149

MR SPECIAL SUPERMARKETS INC p 996
620 Ave Sta Tresa Journet, Mayaguez PR 00682
Tel (787) 834-2695 *SIC* 5411

■ WARREN EQUITIES INC p 1577
27 Warren Way, Providence RI 02905
Tel (401) 781-9900 *SIC* 5172 5541 5411

BRABHAM OIL CO INC p 206
525 Midway St, Bamberg SC 29003
Tel (803) 245-2471
SIC 5171 5541 5411 5921

PIGGLY WIGGLY CAROLINA CO INC p 1147
176 Croghan Spur Ste 400, Charleston SC 29407
Tel (843) 554-9880
SIC 7311 5411 5148 5141 2752 1542

OPAL HOLDINGS LLC p 1089
208 Bi Lo Blvd, Greenville SC 29607
Tel (864) 213-2500 *SIC* 5411 5541 5912

SPINX CO INC p 1358
1414 E Washington St N, Greenville SC 29607
Tel (864) 233-5421 *SIC* 5541 5411 5812

WEST OIL INC p 1595
312 Lakeview Blvd, Hartsville SC 29550
Tel (843) 332-2201 *SIC* 5172 5541 5411

BRANDI BOB STATIONS INC p 208
279 Cedarcrest Dr, Lexington SC 29072
Tel (803) 957-3096 *SIC* 5411 5172

R L JORDAN OIL CO OF NORTH CAROLINA INC p 1202
1451 Fernwood Glendale Rd, Spartanburg SC 29307
Tel (864) 585-2784
SIC 5411 5172 5541 5812

PIGGLY WIGGLY CENTRAL INC p 1147
415 N Salem Ave, Sumter SC 29150
Tel (803) 775-3020 *SIC* 5411

WINNSBORO PETROLEUM CO INC p 1617
401 S Congress St, Winnsboro SC 29180
Tel (803) 635-4668 *SIC* 5171 5411

MG OIL CO p 958
1180 Creek Dr, Rapid City SD 57703
Tel (605) 342-0527 *SIC* 5172 5541 5411

MOYLE PETROLEUM CO p 995
2504 W Main St, Rapid City SD 57702
Tel (605) 343-1966 *SIC* 5541 5411

COUNTRY PRIDE COOPERATIVE INC p 375
648 W 2nd St, Winner SD 57580
Tel (605) 842-2711
SIC 5153 5172 5191 5411 5211

BARGAIN BARN INC p 155
2924 Lee Hwy, Athens TN 37303
Tel (423) 746-0746 *SIC* 5411 5141

▲ DELEK US HOLDINGS INC p 424
7102 Commerce Way, Brentwood TN 37027
Tel (615) 771-6701
SIC 2911 4612 5541 5411

MAPCO EXPRESS INC p 903
7102 Commerce Way, Brentwood TN 37027
Tel (615) 771-6701 *SIC* 5541 5411

GREENEVILLE OIL & PETROLEUM INC p 638
860 W Andrew Johnson Hwy, Greeneville TN 37745
Tel (423) 638-3145 *SIC* 5172 5411 5541

HIGHLAND CORP p 691
108 Mill Ave, Hohenwald TN 38462
Tel (800) 924-8514 *SIC* 5171 5411

MOUNTAIN EMPIRE OIL CO p 994
282 Christian Church Rd, Johnson City TN 37615
Tel (423) 928-7241 *SIC* 5541 5411

CFJ PROPERTIES LLC p 285
5508 Lonas Dr, Knoxville TN 37909
Tel (801) 624-1000 *SIC* 5541 5812 5411

PILOT CORP p 1148
5508 Lonas Dr, Knoxville TN 37909
Tel (865) 588-7488 *SIC* 5411 5541

PILOT TRAVEL CENTERS LLC p 1148
5508 Lonas Dr, Knoxville TN 37909
Tel (865) 588-7488 *SIC* 5411 5541

SOUTH TENNESSEE OIL CO INC p 1345
105 Helton Dr, Lawrenceburg TN 38464
Tel (931) 762-9600 *SIC* 5541 5411

ADAMS & SULLIVAN LLC p 21
1188 N Market St, Paris TN 38242
Tel (731) 642-2752 *SIC* 5411

BEST-WADE PETROLEUM INC p 177
201 Dodge Dr, Ripley TN 38063
Tel (731) 635-9661 *SIC* 5171 5541 5411

COX OIL CO INC p 386
623 Perkins St, Union City TN 38261
Tel (731) 885-6444 *SIC* 5541 5411

TOOT N TOTUM FOOD STORES LLC p 1460
1201 S Taylor St, Amarillo TX 79101
Tel (806) 373-4351 *SIC* 5411 5541

TOOT N TOTUM FOOD STORES LP p 1460
1201 S Taylor St, Amarillo TX 79101
Tel (806) 373-4351 *SIC* 5541 5411

K & N MANAGEMENT INC p 798
11570 Research Blvd, Austin TX 78759
Tel (512) 418-0444 *SIC* 5411 5812

▲ WHOLE FOODS MARKET INC p 1607
550 Bowie St, Austin TX 78703
Tel (512) 477-4455 *SIC* 5411

TRI-CON INC p 1477
7076 W Port Arthur Rd, Beaumont TX 77705
Tel (409) 835-2237 *SIC* 5541 5172 5411

WHARTON COUNTY FOODS LLC p 1604
4429 Fm 442 Rd, Boling TX 77420
Tel (979) 657-2891 *SIC* 5411

KWIK CHEK FOOD STORES INC p 832
2207 N Center St, Bonham TX 75418
Tel (903) 583-7484 *SIC* 5541 5411

AVT GROCERY INC p 139
777 Freeport Pkwy, Coppell TX 75019
Tel (972) 241-2184 *SIC* 5411 5912

■ STRIPES LLC p 1394
4525 Ayers St, Corpus Christi TX 78415
Tel (361) 225-0129 *SIC* 5411

■ SUSSER HOLDINGS CORP p 1409
4525 Ayers St, Corpus Christi TX 78415
Tel (361) 884-2463 *SIC* 5411 5541 5172

■ SUSSER HOLDINGS LLC p 1409
4433 Baldwin Blvd, Corpus Christi TX 78408
Tel (361) 693-3698 *SIC* 5411

▲ ALON USA ENERGY INC p 59
12700 Park Central Dr # 1600, Dallas TX 75251
Tel (972) 367-3600 *SIC* 2911 5171 5411

■ WHOLE FOODS MARKET ROCKY MOUNTAIN/SOUTHWEST LP p 1607
11770 Preston Rd Ste 119, Dallas TX 75230
Tel (214) 361-8887 *SIC* 5411

BIG 8 FOODS LTD p 181
1480 George Dieter Dr, El Paso TX 79936
Tel (915) 857-6080 *SIC* 5411

ACQUISITION VEHICLE TEXAS II LLC p 18
301 Commerce St Ste 3232, Fort Worth TX 76102
Tel (972) 915-2895 *SIC* 5411 5912

SIMONS PETROLEUM p 1325
201 N Rupert St Ste 101, Fort Worth TX 76107
Tel (405) 551-2403
SIC 5172 5171 5541 5411

MEXICO FOODS LLC p 957
2600 Mccree Rd Ste 101, Garland TX 75041
Tel (972) 526-7200 *SIC* 5411

COXS FOODARAMA INC p 387
10810 S Post Oak Rd, Houston TX 77035
Tel (713) 723-8683 *SIC* 5411

FIESTA MART INC p 541
5235 Katy Fwy, Houston TX 77007
Tel (713) 869-5060 *SIC* 5411

GERLAND CORP p 608
3131 Pawnee St, Houston TX 77054
Tel (713) 746-3600 *SIC* 5411

■ KAYO OIL CO p 805
600 N Dairy Ashford Rd, Houston TX 77079
Tel (281) 293-1000 *SIC* 5541 5411

LANDMARK INDUSTRIES HOLDINGS LTD p 843
11111 S Wilcrest Dr, Houston TX 77099
Tel (713) 789-0310 *SIC* 5411 5541

LEWIS FOOD TOWN INC p 858
3131 Pawnee St, Houston TX 77054
Tel (713) 746-3600 *SIC* 5411

RANDALLS FOOD MARKETS INC p 1207
3663 Briarpark Dr, Houston TX 77042
Tel (713) 268-3500 *SIC* 5411 5912

RICE EPICUREAN MARKETS INC p 1232
5333 Gulfton St, Houston TX 77081
Tel (713) 662-7700 *SIC* 5411 5812

SELLERS BROS INC p 1302
4580 S Wayside Dr, Houston TX 77087
Tel (713) 640-1611 *SIC* 5411

SUPERBAG USA CORP p 1406
9291 Baythorne Dr, Houston TX 77041
Tel (713) 462-1173 *SIC* 2673 5411

TOM THUMB FOOD & DRUGS INC p 1459
3663 Briarpark Dr, Houston TX 77042
Tel (713) 268-3500
SIC 5411 5912 5499 6512 6552

7-ELEVEN INC p 3
3200 Hackberry Rd, Irving TX 75063
Tel (972) 828-0711 *SIC* 5411 6794

PAY AND SAVE INC p 1122
1804 Hall Ave, Littlefield TX 79339
Tel (806) 385-3366 *SIC* 5411

UNITED SUPERMARKETS LLC p 1514
7830 Orlando Ave, Lubbock TX 79423
Tel (806) 791-0220 *SIC* 5411

BROOKSHIRE BROTHERS LTD p 218
1201 Ellen Trout Dr, Lufkin TX 75904
Tel (936) 634-8155 *SIC* 5411

WUESTS INC p 1628
9318 Fm 725, Mc Queeney TX 78123
Tel (830) 379-3442 *SIC* 5141 5411 0173

WEST TEXAS GAS INC p 1595
211 N Colorado St, Midland TX 79701
Tel (432) 682-4349 *SIC* 5411

MARKET BASKET STORES INC p 908
2420 Nederland Ave, Nederland TX 77627
Tel (409) 727-3104 *SIC* 5411

RETAIL INVESTORS OF TEXAS LTD p 1228
2420 Nederland Ave, Nederland TX 77627
Tel (409) 727-3104 *SIC* 5411

■ SOUTHWEST CONVENIENCE STORES LLC p 1351
4001 Penbrook St Ste 400, Odessa TX 79762
Tel (432) 580-8850 *SIC* 5411

■ TCFS HOLDINGS INC p 1428
3515 S Bryant Blvd, San Angelo TX 76903
Tel (325) 655-0676 *SIC* 5411

■ TOWN & COUNTRY FOOD STORES INC p 1464
3515 S Bryant Blvd, San Angelo TX 76903
Tel (325) 655-0676 *SIC* 5411

BEXAR COUNTY MARKETS INC p 179
340 Enrque M Barrera Pkwy, San Antonio TX 78237
Tel (210) 227-8755 *SIC* 5411

▲ CST BRANDS INC p 398
19500 Bulverde Rd Ste 100, San Antonio TX 78259
Tel (210) 692-5000 *SIC* 5983 5411

H E BUTT GROCERY CO p 650
646 S Flores St, San Antonio TX 78204
Tel (210) 938-8000 *SIC* 5411

HEB GROCERY CO LP p 680
646 S Flores St, San Antonio TX 78204
Tel (210) 938-8000 *SIC* 5411

MASS MARKETING INC p 916
401 Isom Rd Ste 210, San Antonio TX 78216
Tel (210) 314-7005 *SIC* 5411

■ NATIONAL CONVENIENCE STORES INC p 1011
6000 N Loop 1604 W, San Antonio TX 78249
Tel (830) 995-4303 *SIC* 5411 5812

TETCO INC p 1441
1100 Ne Loop 410 Ste 900, San Antonio TX 78209
Tel (210) 821-5900
SIC 4213 5411 1611 5193

VALERO SERVICES INC p 1539
1 Valero Way, San Antonio TX 78249
Tel (210) 345-2000 *SIC* 2911 5172 5411

■ KROGER TEXAS LP p 830
19245 David Memorial Dr, Shenandoah TX 77385
Tel (713) 507-4800 *SIC* 5141 5411

DOUGLASS DISTRIBUTING RETAIL CO INC p 452
325 E Forest Ave, Sherman TX 75090
Tel (903) 893-1181 *SIC* 5411 5541

MAL ENTERPRISES INC p 899
300 Hailey St, Sweetwater TX 79556
Tel (325) 236-6351 *SIC* 5411

FIKES WHOLESALE INC p 542
6261 Central Pointe Pkwy, Temple TX 76504
Tel (254) 791-0009 *SIC* 5411 5171

E-Z MART STORES INC p 467
602 Falvey Ave, Texarkana TX 75501
Tel (903) 832-6502 *SIC* 5541 5411

BROOKSHIRE GROCERY CO INC p 218
1600 W Southwest Loop 323, Tyler TX 75701
Tel (903) 534-3000 *SIC* 5411 5983

CL THOMAS INC p 320
9701 Us Highway 59 N, Victoria TX 77905
Tel (361) 573-7662 *SIC* 5411 5541

SPEEDY STOP FOOD STORES LLC p 1358
8701 N Navarro St, Victoria TX 77904
Tel (361) 573-7662 *SIC* 5812 5541 5411

FJ MANAGEMENT INC p 553
185 S State St Ste 201, Salt Lake City UT 84111
Tel (801) 624-1000
SIC 5541 2911 5411 1382 6022

HARMON CITY INC p 662
3540 S 4000 W, Salt Lake City UT 84120
Tel (801) 969-8261 *SIC* 5411

MAVERIK INC p 921
185 S State St Ste 800, Salt Lake City UT 84111
Tel (801) 936-9155 *SIC* 5541 5411

SHERMAN V ALLEN INC p 1316
126 Post St, Rutland VT 05701
Tel (802) 775-7421
SIC 5172 5984 5411 4923

K-VA-T FOOD STORES INC p 799
1 Food City Cir E, Abingdon VA 24210
Tel (800) 826-8451 *SIC* 5411 5141 6512

HIGHWAY SERVICE VENTURES INC p 692
100 Arbor Oak Dr Ste 305, Ashland VA 23005
Tel (804) 752-4966 *SIC* 5541 5411 5812

■ FF ACQUISITION LLC p 539
4860 Cox Rd, Glen Allen VA 23060
Tel (757) 306-7006 *SIC* 5411

MILLER OIL CO INC p 970
1000 E City Hall Ave, Norfolk VA 23504
Tel (757) 623-6600
SIC 5411 5172 5983 7549

UPPYS CONVENIENCE STORES INC p 1529
1011 Boulder Springs Dr, North Chesterfield VA 23225
Tel (804) 706-4702 *SIC* 5411 5541

GPM INVESTMENTS LLC p 627
8565 Magellan Pkwy # 400, Richmond VA 23227
Tel (804) 266-1363 *SIC* 5541 5411 5172

UKROPS SUPER MARKETS INC p 1500
2001 Maywill St Ste 100, Richmond VA 23230
Tel (804) 304-3000 *SIC* 5411

■ STOP IN FOOD STORES INC p 1391
3000 Ogden Rd, Roanoke VA 24018
Tel (540) 772-4900 *SIC* 5411

■ QUALITY FOOD CENTERS INC p 1197
10116 Ne 8th St, Bellevue WA 98004
Tel (425) 455-0870 *SIC* 5411

HAGGEN INC p 653
2211 Rimland Dr Ste 300, Bellingham WA 98226
Tel (360) 733-8720 *SIC* 5411 5912

MARKETS LLC p 908
4350 Cordata Pkwy, Bellingham WA 98226
Tel (360) 714-9797 *SIC* 5411

TOWN & COUNTRY MARKETS INC p 1464
130 5th Ave S Ste 126, Edmonds WA 98020
Tel (360) 598-7300 *SIC* 5411

R H SMITH DISTRIBUTING CO INC p 1202
315 E Wine Country Rd, Grandview WA 98930
Tel (509) 882-3377
SIC 5171 5541 5411 5172

SUN PACIFIC ENERGY INC p 1400
501 W Canal Dr, Kennewick WA 99336
Tel (509) 586-1135 *SIC* 5172 5541 5411

DELTA WESTERN INC p 427
1177 Fairview Ave N, Seattle WA 98109
Tel (907) 276-2688 *SIC* 5171 5251 5411

METROPOLITAN MARKET LLC p 956
4025 Delridge Way Sw # 100, Seattle WA 98106
Tel (206) 284-2530 *SIC* 5411

PUGET CONSUMERS CO-OP p 1191
4201 Roosevelt Way Ne, Seattle WA 98105
Tel (206) 547-1222 *SIC* 5411

UWAJIMAYA INC p 1538
4601 6th Ave S, Seattle WA 98108
Tel (206) 624-6248 *SIC* 5141 5411

SQUAXIN ISLAND TRIBE OF SQUAXIN ISLAND RESERVATION p 1362
10 Se Squaxin Ln, Shelton WA 98584
Tel (360) 426-9781
SIC 5411 5146 7011 0132

ROSAUERS SUPERMARKETS INC p 1250
1815 W Garland Ave, Spokane WA 99205
Tel (509) 326-8900 *SIC* 5411

ALSAKER CORP p 61
6409 E Sharp Ave, Spokane Valley WA 99212
Tel (509) 242-6327 *SIC* 5541 5411

TIDYMANS LLC p 1452
10020 E Knox Ave Ste 500, Spokane Valley WA 99206
Tel (509) 928-7480 *SIC* 5411

TIDYMANS MANAGEMENT SERVICES INC p 1452
10020 E Knox Ave Ste 500, Spokane Valley WA 99206
Tel (509) 928-7480 *SIC* 5411

COLUMBIA FRUIT LLC p 340
2530 Dike Rd, Woodland WA 98674
Tel (360) 225-9575 *SIC* 5142 5411

LITTLE GENERAL STORE INC p 871
4036 Robert C. Byrd Dr, Beckley WV 25801
Tel (304) 253-9592 *SIC* 5411

GO-MART INC p 619
915 Riverside Dr, Gassaway WV 26624
Tel (304) 364-8000 *SIC* 5411 5541

FORTHS FOODS INC p 569
3090 Woodville Dr, Huntington WV 25701
Tel (304) 525-3293 *SIC* 5141 5411

BRUCETON FARM SERVICE INC p 220
1768 Mileground Rd, Morgantown WV 26505
Tel (304) 291-6980
SIC 5411 5172 5999 5983 5812 2048

CONSUMERS COOPERATIVE ASSOCIATION OF EAU CLAIRE p 362
1201 S Hastings Way, Eau Claire WI 54701
Tel (715) 836-8700 *SIC* 5411 5541

DITTO II LLC p 443
1201 S Hastings Way, Eau Claire WI 54701
Tel (715) 836-8710 *SIC* 5541 5411

■ ERICKSON OIL PRODUCTS INC p 507
1231 Industrial St, Hudson WI 54016
Tel (715) 386-8241 *SIC* 5541 5411

S/S/G CORP p 1263
512 2nd St Ste 12, Hudson WI 54016
Tel (715) 386-8281 *SIC* 5541 5411

WOODMANS FOOD MARKET INC p 1623
2631 Liberty Ln, Janesville WI 53545
Tel (608) 754-8382 *SIC* 5411

LAC DU FLAMBEAU BAND OF LAKE SUPERIOR CHIPPEWA INDIANS (INC) p 836
418 Little Pines Rd, Lac Du Flambeau WI 54538
Tel (715) 588-3303
SIC 8011 7999 5411 5541 8031

■ ROUNDYS INC p 1253
875 E Wisconsin Ave, Milwaukee WI 53202
Tel (414) 231-5000 *SIC* 5411

■ ROUNDYS SUPERMARKETS INC p 1253
875 E Wscnsin Ave Ste 100, Milwaukee WI 53202
Tel (414) 231-5000 *SIC* 5411 5141

MDSFEST INC p 933
237 2nnd Ave S, Onalaska WI 54650
Tel (608) 779-2720 *SIC* 5411

SKOGENS FOODLINER INC p 1330
3800 Emerald Dr E, Onalaska WI 54650
Tel (608) 783-5500 *SIC* 5411 5461 5421

PIGGLY WIGGLY MIDWEST LLC p 1147
2215 Union Ave, Sheboygan WI 53081
Tel (920) 457-4433 *SIC* 5141 5411

QUALITY STATE OIL CO INC p 1197
2201 Calumet Dr, Sheboygan WI 53083
Tel (920) 459-5640 *SIC* 5171 5541 5411

■ STEVENS POINT DISTRIBUTION CENTER LLC p 1388
2828 Wayne St, Stevens Point WI 54481
Tel (952) 828-4000 *SIC* 5411

SIC 5421 Meat & Fish Markets

CANTON FOOD CO INC p 247
750 S Alameda St, Los Angeles CA 90021
Tel (213) 688-7707
SIC 5141 5146 5411 5421 5149 4222

SANTA MONICA SEAFOOD CO p 1281
18531 S Broadwick St, Rancho Dominguez CA 90220
Tel (310) 886-7900 *SIC* 5421 5146 5142

TRANSHUMANCE HOLDING CO INC p 1471
2530 River Plaza Dr # 200, Sacramento CA 95833
Tel (530) 758-3091 *SIC* 5421 5142

PACIFIC SHELLFISH INC p 1106
5040 Cass St, San Diego CA 92109
Tel (858) 272-9940 *SIC* 5146 5421 5812

S&C RESALE CO p 1263
1770 Promontory Cir, Greeley CO 80634
Tel (970) 506-8000 *SIC* 5147 5421

HONEY BAKED HAM CO LLC p 705
3875 Mansell Rd Ste 100, Alpharetta GA 30022
Tel (678) 966-3100 *SIC* 5421

ATLANTA ORIENTAL FOOD WHOLESALE CO p 125
5600 Buford Hwy Ne, Atlanta GA 30340
Tel (770) 455-0770
SIC 5146 5421 5046 5719

■ BUCKHEAD BEEF CO INC p 223
4500 Wickersham Dr, College Park GA 30337
Tel (404) 355-4400 *SIC* 5142 5146 5421

DEKALB FARMERS MARKET INC p 423
3000 E Ponce De Leon Ave, Decatur GA 30030
Tel (404) 377-6400
SIC 5431 5421 5461 5451 5921 5812

FOC ACQUISITION LLC p 562
146 Forest Pkwy Ste B, Forest Park GA 30297
Tel (404) 361-2201
SIC 5142 5421 5144 2092

MURRYS OF MARYLAND INC p 1002
7852 Walker Dr Ste 420, Greenbelt MD 20770
Tel (888) 668-7797 *SIC* 5421

■ APPERTS INC p 98
900 Highway 10 S, Saint Cloud MN 56304
Tel (320) 251-3200
SIC 5142 5141 5411 5421 2013

RASTELLI BROTHERS INC p 1209
300 Heron Dr, Swedesboro NJ 08085
Tel (856) 803-1100 *SIC* 5147 5421 2011

COLORADO PRIME OF PENNSYLVANIA INC p 339
1 Michael Ave, Farmingdale NY 11735
Tel (631) 694-1111 *SIC* 5421 5722

GODSHALLS QUALITY MEATS INC p 619
675 Mill Rd, Telford PA 18969
Tel (215) 256-8867 *SIC* 5147 5421

AMERICAN SEAFOODS GROUP LLC p 79
2025 1st Ave Ste 900, Seattle WA 98121
Tel (206) 374-1515 *SIC* 5421 5146

AMERICAN SEAFOODS LP p 79
2025 1st Ave Ste 900, Seattle WA 98121
Tel (206) 374-1515 *SIC* 5421 5146

ASG CONSOLIDATED LLC p 116
2025 1st Ave Ste 900, Seattle WA 98121
Tel (206) 374-1515 *SIC* 5421 5146

SKOGENS FOODLINER INC p 1330
3800 Emerald Dr E, Onalaska WI 54650
Tel (608) 783-5500 *SIC* 5411 5461 5421

SIC 5431 Fruit & Vegetable Markets

DRISCOLL STRAWBERRY ASSOCIATES INC p 456
345 Westridge Dr, Watsonville CA 95076
Tel (831) 424-0506 *SIC* 5148 5431

LFC ENTERPRISES INC p 860
315 New Market Rd E, Immokalee FL 34142
Tel (239) 657-3117 *SIC* 5431

■ FRESHPOINT CENTRAL FLORIDA INC p 579
8801 Exchange Dr, Orlando FL 32809
Tel (407) 383-8427 *SIC* 5148 5431

DEKALB FARMERS MARKET INC p 423
3000 E Ponce De Leon Ave, Decatur GA 30030
Tel (404) 377-6400
SIC 5431 5421 5461 5451 5921 5812

CAPUTOS NEW FARM PRODUCE INC p 252
520 E North Ave, Carol Stream IL 60188
Tel (630) 620-4444
SIC 5431 5411 5148 5149

PETES FRESH MARKET 4700 CORP p 1138
4333 S Pulaski Rd, Chicago IL 60632
Tel (773) 927-4300 *SIC* 5148 5431

RAHAL FOODS INC p 1205
915 Harger Rd Ste 110, Oak Brook IL 60523
Tel (630) 286-1500 *SIC* 5149 5431

TAYLOR FARMS MARYLAND INC p 1427
9055 Junction Dr, Annapolis Junction MD 20701
Tel (301) 617-2942 *SIC* 5431 0723

PDNC LLC p 1125
402 Commerce Ct, Goldsboro NC 27534
Tel (919) 778-3000
SIC 5142 5141 5147 5148 5431

VALLEY ROZ ORCHARDS INC p 1541
10 E Mead Ave, Yakima WA 98903
Tel (509) 457-4153 *SIC* 0175 5431

SIC 5441 Candy, Nut & Confectionery Stores

SPRINKLES CUPCAKES INC p 1361
9635 Santa Monica Blvd, Beverly Hills CA 90210
Tel (310) 274-8765 *SIC* 5441

SWEET CANDY LLC p 1411
929 W Barkley Ave, Orange CA 92868
Tel (877) 817-9338 *SIC* 5441

GHIRARDELLI CHOCOLATE CO p 610
1111 139th Ave, San Leandro CA 94578
Tel (510) 483-6970
SIC 5441 2066 5812 5149

■ SEES CANDIES INC p 1300
210 El Camino Real, South San Francisco CA 94080
Tel (650) 761-2490 *SIC* 2064 5441

■ SEES CANDY SHOPS INC p 1300
210 El Camino Real, South San Francisco CA 94080
Tel (650) 761-2490 *SIC* 2064 5441

■ FANNIE MAY CONFECTIONS BRANDS INC p 527
2457 W North Ave, Melrose Park IL 60160
Tel (773) 693-9100 *SIC* 2064 5441

SOUTH BEND CHOCOLATE CO INC p 1343
3300 W Sample St Ste 110, South Bend IN 46619
Tel (574) 233-2577
SIC 5149 2066 5441 5812

RUSSELL STOVER CHOCOLATES LLC p 1259
4900 Oak St, Kansas City MO 64112
Tel (816) 842-9240 *SIC* 2064 5441

LINDT & SPRUNGLI (USA) INC p 868
1 Fine Chocolate Pl, Stratham NH 03885
Tel (603) 778-8100 *SIC* 2066 5149 5441

PROMOTION IN MOTION INC p 1183
25 Commerce Dr, Allendale NJ 07401
Tel (201) 962-8530
SIC 2064 5441 5145 2066

GODIVA CHOCOLATIER INC p 619
333 W 34th St Fl 6, New York NY 10001
Tel (212) 984-5900
SIC 2066 5149 5441 2064

AUXILIARY SERVICES STATE UNIVERSITY COLLEGE AT OSWEGO INC p 135
7060 Route 104, Oswego NY 13126
Tel (315) 312-2106
SIC 5812 5942 5962 5441

■ CONSOLIDATED THEATRES INC p 360
5970 Fairview Rd Ste 600, Charlotte NC 28210
Tel (704) 554-1695 *SIC* 7832 5441

■ FANNIE MAY CONFECTIONS BRANDS INC p 527
5353 Lauby Rd, North Canton OH 44720
Tel (330) 494-0833 *SIC* 5441 2066

SAINT ANNS HOSPITAL AUXILIARY p 1268
500 S Cleveland Ave, Westerville OH 43081
Tel (614) 769-4459
SIC 5947 5621 5611 5992 5441

SIC 5451 Dairy Products Stores

NESTLE ICE CREAM CO p 1027
7301 District Blvd, Bakersfield CA 93313
Tel (661) 398-3500 *SIC* 5143 5451

OAKVILLE PRODUCE PARTNERS LLC p 1071
453 Valley Dr, Brisbane CA 94005
Tel (415) 647-2991 *SIC* 5148 5451

DREYERS GRAND ICE CREAM HOLDINGS INC p 456
5929 College Ave, Oakland CA 94618
Tel (510) 652-8187 *SIC* 5143 5451 2024

AMERICAN DAIRY INC p 71
2275 Huntington Dr 278, San Marino CA 91108
Tel (626) 757-8885 *SIC* 5451

DEKALB FARMERS MARKET INC p 423
3000 E Ponce De Leon Ave, Decatur GA 30030
Tel (404) 377-6400
SIC 5431 5421 5461 5451 5921 5812

OBERWEIS DAIRY INC p 1072
951 Ice Cream Dr, North Aurora IL 60542
Tel (630) 801-6100 *SIC* 5963 5451

QUALITY DAIRY CO p 1197
111 W Mount Hope Ave 3a, Lansing MI 48910
Tel (517) 319-4100 *SIC* 5451 5411

BONGARDS CREAMERIES p 200
13200 County Road 51, Norwood MN 55368
Tel (952) 466-5521
SIC 2023 2022 5451 2021

UNITED DAIRY FARMERS INC p 1507
3955 Montgomery Rd, Cincinnati OH 45212
Tel (513) 396-8700
SIC 5411 5143 2026 2024 5541 5451

DISCOUNT DRUG MART INC p 442
211 Commerce Dr, Medina OH 44256
Tel (330) 725-2340
SIC 5912 5331 5411 5451 5122 8082

COBLENTZ DISTRIBUTING INC p 333
3850 State Route 39, Millersburg OH 44654
Tel (800) 543-6848 *SIC* 5143 5451

W H BRAUM INC p 1568
3000 Ne 63rd St, Oklahoma City OK 73121
Tel (405) 478-1656 *SIC* 5451 5812

■ DEAN HOLDING CO p 420
2711 N Haskell Ave, Dallas TX 75204
Tel (214) 303-3400 *SIC* 2023 5143 5451

CABOT CREAMERY COOPERATIVE INC p 235
193 Home Farm Way, Waitsfield VT 05673
Tel (978) 552-5500 *SIC* 2022 5143 5451

EMERALD DAIRY INC p 491
11990 Market St Unit 205, Reston VA 20190
Tel (703) 867-9247 *SIC* 5451

SKAGIT FARMERS SUPPLY p 1329
1833 Park Ln, Burlington WA 98233
Tel (360) 757-6053
SIC 5191 5172 5983 5451 5331 5261

GEHL FOODS LLC p 597
N116w15970 Main St, Germantown WI 53022
Tel (262) 251-8570 *SIC* 2022 5451

SIC 5461 Retail Bakeries

CHAI BAGEL CORP p 286
14431 N 73rd St, Scottsdale AZ 85260
Tel (480) 860-0475
SIC 5149 5461 5812 2052 2051

IL FORNAIO (AMERICA) CORP p 731
770 Tamalpais Dr Ste 400, Corte Madera CA 94925
Tel (415) 945-0500
SIC 5812 5813 5149 5461 2051

TRESIERRAS BROTHERS CORP p 1476
618 San Fernando Rd, San Fernando CA 91340
Tel (818) 365-8859 *SIC* 5411 5461

ANDRE-BOUDIN BAKERIES INC p 90
50 Francisco St Ste 200, San Francisco CA 94133
Tel (415) 882-1849
SIC 2051 5812 5961 5461

BOUDIN HOLDINGS INC p 204
221 Main St Ste 1230, San Francisco CA 94105
Tel (415) 287-1709 *SIC* 5461

NEW FRENCH BAKERY INC p 1030
2325 Pine St, San Francisco CA 94115
Tel (415) 440-0356 *SIC* 5461

MRS FIELDS COMPANIES INC p 996
8001 Arista Pl Unit 600, Broomfield CO 80021
Tel (720) 599-3374 *SIC* 6794 5461

MRS FIELDS HOLDING CO INC p 996
8001 Arista Pl Unit 600, Broomfield CO 80021
Tel (720) 599-3350 *SIC* 5461 6794

CONNECTICUT PIE INC p 357
35 Pearl St, Enfield CT 06082
Tel (860) 741-3781 *SIC* 5149 5461

CAPRICORN INVESTORS II LP p 251
30 E Elm St, Greenwich CT 06830
Tel (203) 861-6600 *SIC* 2676 5461 6794

■ FLOWERS BAKING CO OF MIAMI LLC p 560
17800 Nw Miami Ct, Miami FL 33169
Tel (305) 652-3416 *SIC* 2051 5461

FOCUS BRANDS INC p 562
5620 Glenridge Dr, Atlanta GA 30342
Tel (404) 255-3250 *SIC* 5461 5143 6794

GFG MANAGEMENT LLC p 610
5555 Glenridge Connector # 850, Atlanta GA 30342
Tel (770) 514-4871 *SIC* 5461

GLOBAL FRANCHISE GROUP LLC p 616
5555 Glenridge Connector # 850, Atlanta GA 30342
Tel (770) 514-4500 *SIC* 5461 6794

DEKALB FARMERS MARKET INC p 423
3000 E Ponce De Leon Ave, Decatur GA 30030
Tel (404) 377-6400
SIC 5431 5421 5461 5451 5921 5812

NATIONAL DCP LLC p 1011
3805 Crestwood Pkwy Nw, Duluth GA 30096
Tel (770) 369-8600 *SIC* 5461

GREAT AMERICAN COOKIE CO INC p 633
4685 Frederick Dr Sw, Norcross GA 30093
Tel (877) 639-2361 *SIC* 5461

■ DERST BAKING CO LLC p 431
1311 W 52nd St, Savannah GA 31405
Tel (912) 233-2235 *SIC* 2051 5461

CHICAGO PASTRY INC p 297
6501 Roosevelt Rd, Berwyn IL 60402
Tel (708) 788-5320 *SIC* 5149 5461

THORNTONS INC p 1450
10101 Linn Station Rd # 200, Louisville KY 40223
Tel (502) 425-8022 *SIC* 5461 5411

■ LEPAGE BAKERIES INC p 856
11 Adamian Dr, Auburn ME 04210
Tel (207) 783-9161 *SIC* 2051 5461

ABP CORP p 12
19 Fid Kennedy Ave, Boston MA 02210
Tel (617) 423-0629 *SIC* 5461 5812 2051

▲ DUNKIN BRANDS GROUP INC p 461
130 Royall St, Canton MA 02021
Tel (781) 737-3000
SIC 5461 5499 6794 5812

■ DUNKIN BRANDS INC p 461
130 Royall St, Canton MA 02021
Tel (781) 737-5200 *SIC* 5461 5812

DONUT MANAGEMENT INC p 451
3 Pluff Ave, Haverhill MA 01835
Tel (978) 664-2854 *SIC* 5461

PR RESTAURANTS LLC p 1167
2150 Washington St # 125, Newton MA 02462
Tel (617) 581-6160 *SIC* 5461 5812

CAP GROUP INC p 248
77 Washington St, Weymouth MA 02188
Tel (781) 335-9650 *SIC* 5461

■ TARGET STORES INC p 1425
1000 Nicollet Mall, Minneapolis MN 55403
Tel (612) 304-6073 *SIC* 5411 5311 5461

▲ HOSTESS BRANDS INC p 710
1 E Armour Blvd, Kansas City MO 64111
Tel (816) 701-4600 *SIC* 2051 5461

■ HOSTESS HOLDINGS LP p 710
1 E Armour Blvd, Kansas City MO 64111
Tel (816) 701-4600 *SIC* 5461

OLD HB INC p 1081
3101 Mercier St Ste 422, Kansas City MO 64111
Tel (816) 502-4000 *SIC* 2051 5461

BREADS OF WORLD LLC p 209
2127 Innerbelt Business C, Saint Louis MO 63114
Tel (314) 965-3304 *SIC* 5812 5461

▲ PANERA BREAD CO p 1111
3630 S Geyer Rd Ste 100, Saint Louis MO 63127
Tel (314) 984-1000 *SIC* 5812 5461 6794

TRADITIONAL BAKERY INC p 1469
2040 W Vista St, Springfield MO 65807
Tel (417) 889-8282 *SIC* 5461 5812

BELLA FOUR BAKERY INC p 170
1150 Trademark Dr Ste 101, Reno NV 89521
Tel (775) 883-2253 *SIC* 2064 5461

WENNER BREAD PRODUCTS INC p 1592
33 Rajon Rd, Bayport NY 11705
Tel (800) 869-6262 *SIC* 2051 2053 5461

DELAWARE NORTH COMPANIES INC p 424
250 Delaware Ave, Buffalo NY 14202
Tel (716) 858-5000
SIC 5461 7011 7993 7999

DELTA-SONIC CARWASH SYSTEMS INC p 427
570 Delaware Ave, Buffalo NY 14202
Tel (716) 874-5668 *SIC* 5461 7542

FLOUR CITY BAGELS INC p 560
585 Moseley Rd Ste 3, Fairport NY 14450
Tel (585) 223-0450 *SIC* 5461 2051

RED APPLE GROUP INC p 1215
800 3rd Ave Fl 5, New York NY 10022
Tel (212) 956-5803 *SIC* 5461 5541 5411

NERIS BAKERY PRODUCTS INC p 1026
31 Pearl St 37, Port Chester NY 10573
Tel (914) 937-3235 *SIC* 5149 5461 2051

COTTON PARENT INC p 374
370 Knollwood St, Winston Salem NC 27103
Tel (336) 726-8876 *SIC* 5461

KRISPY KREME DOUGHNUT CORP p 830
259 S Stratford Rd, Winston Salem NC 27103
Tel (336) 724-2484 *SIC* 5461 2051

KRISPY KREME DOUGHNUTS INC p 830
370 Knollwood St Ste 500, Winston Salem NC 27103
Tel (336) 726-8876 *SIC* 5461 5149 2051

WILCOHESS LLC p 1608
5446 University Pkwy, Winston Salem NC 27105
Tel (336) 767-6280 *SIC* 5461 5812 5541

UNITED STATES BAKERY p 1512
315 Ne 10th Ave, Portland OR 97232
Tel (503) 232-2191 *SIC* 2051 5461

METZ CULINARY MANAGEMENT INC p 957
2 Woodland Dr, Dallas PA 18612
Tel (570) 675-8100 *SIC* 5461

STROEHMANN BAKERIES LC p 1394
255 Business Center Dr # 200, Horsham PA 19044
Tel (215) 672-8010 *SIC* 2051 5461

AUNTIE ANNES INC p 131
48-50 W Chestnut St # 200, Lancaster PA 17603
Tel (717) 435-1435 *SIC* 6794 2051 5461

MAPLE DONUTS INC p 903
3455 E Market St, York PA 17402
Tel (717) 757-7826 *SIC* 2051 5461

BRUEGGERS ENTERPRISES INC p 220
12201 Merit Dr Ste 900, Dallas TX 75251
Tel (802) 660-4020 *SIC* 5461

HILL COUNTRY BAKERY LLC p 693
122 Stribling, San Antonio TX 78204
Tel (210) 475-9981 *SIC* 5149 5461

KING ARTHUR FLOUR CO INC p 820
135 Us Route 5 S, Norwich VT 05055
Tel (802) 649-3881
SIC 5149 5961 5461 8299

NORTHERN STAR VENTURES LLC p 1057
10440 Leadbetter Rd, Ashland VA 23005
Tel (804) 368-0747 *SIC* 5149 5461

VIE DE FRANCE YAMAZAKI INC p 1556
2070 Chain Bridge Rd # 500, Vienna VA 22182
Tel (703) 442-9205 *SIC* 5142 5461

FUNKHOUSER AND CO H N p 585
2150 S Loudoun St, Winchester VA 22601
Tel (540) 662-9000 *SIC* 5461 5013

R U CORP p 1203
411 1st Ave S Ste 200n, Seattle WA 98104
Tel (206) 634-0550 *SIC* 5812 5813 5461

▲ STARBUCKS CORP p 1378
2401 Utah Ave S, Seattle WA 98134
Tel (206) 447-1575
SIC 5812 5499 5461 5149

KWIK TRIP INC p 832
1626 Oak St, La Crosse WI 54603
Tel (608) 781-8988
SIC 5921 5993 5541 5983 5461

SKOGENS FOODLINER INC p 1330
3800 Emerald Dr E, Onalaska WI 54650
Tel (608) 783-5500 *SIC* 5411 5461 5421

SIC 5499 Food Stores, Misc

MOUNTAIN VALLEY SPRING CO LLC p 994
283 Mountain Vly Wtr Pl, Hot Springs AR 71909
Tel (501) 624-7329 *SIC* 5149 5499

■ COST PLUS INC p 373
1201 Marina Village Pkwy # 100, Alameda CA 94501
Tel (510) 893-7300
SIC 5712 5713 5719 5947 5499 5921

JENNY CRAIG INC p 782
5770 Fleet St, Carlsbad CA 92008
Tel (760) 696-4000
SIC 7299 6794 5149 5499

▲ YOUNGEVITY INTERNATIONAL INC p 1639
2400 Boswell Rd, Chula Vista CA 91914
Tel (619) 934-3980 *SIC* 5499 5999

C B NICHOLS EGG RANCH p 232
331 W Citrus St, Colton CA 92324
Tel (626) 452-9110 *SIC* 5144 5499

BEVERAGES & MORE INC p 178
1401 Willow Pass Rd # 900, Concord CA 94520
Tel (925) 609-6000 *SIC* 5921 5499 5993

BEVMO HOLDINGS LLC p 179
1470 Civic Ct Ste 1600, Concord CA 94520
Tel (925) 609-6000 *SIC* 5921 5499 5993

NELLSON NUTRACEUTICAL LLC p 1025
5801 Ayala Ave, Irwindale CA 91706
Tel (626) 812-6522 *SIC* 5499

INTERNATIONAL COFFEE & TEA LLC p 754
5700 Wilshire Blvd # 120, Los Angeles CA 90036
Tel (310) 237-2326 *SIC* 5812 5499 6794

JS WEST & COMPANIES p 795
501 9th St, Modesto CA 95354
Tel (209) 577-3221
SIC 5172 5211 5251 0723 5499

SHAKLEE CORP p 1310
4747 Willow Rd, Pleasanton CA 94588
Tel (925) 924-2000 *SIC* 5499

EAGLE CANYON CAPITAL LLC p 467
3130 Crow Canyon Pl # 240, San Ramon CA 94583
Tel (925) 884-0800 *SIC* 5411 5499 2092

HERBALIFE INTERNATIONAL INC p 685
990 W 190th St, Torrance CA 90502
Tel (310) 410-9600 *SIC* 5499

ALFALFAS MARKET INC p 49
1651 Broadway, Boulder CO 80302
Tel (303) 449-5343 SIC 5499

▲NATURAL GROCERS BY VITAMIN COTTAGE INC p 1018
12612 W Alameda Pkwy, Lakewood CO 80228
Tel (303) 986-4600 SIC 5411 5499

■VITAMIN COTTAGE NATURAL FOOD MARKETS INC p 1562
12612 W Alameda Pkwy, Lakewood CO 80228
Tel (303) 986-4600 SIC 5499

NORTH CASTLE PARTNERS LLC p 1051
183 E Putnam Ave, Greenwich CT 06830
Tel (203) 485-0216
SIC 7299 6794 5149 5499

BIO-ENGINEERED SUPPLEMENTS & NUTRITION INC p 183
5901 Broken Sound Pkwy Nw, Boca Raton FL 33487
Tel (561) 994-8335 SIC 5122 5499

BARNIES COFFEE & TEA CO INC p 156
29 S Orange Ave, Orlando FL 32801
Tel (407) 854-6600 SIC 5499 5812

NATURES PRODUCTS INC p 1019
1301 Sawgrs Corp Pkwy, Sunrise FL 33323
Tel (954) 233-3300 SIC 5122 5499

DS SERVICES HOLDINGS INC p 457
5660 New Northside Dr # 500, Atlanta GA 30328
Tel (770) 933-1400 SIC 5499 5149

■TEAVANA CORP p 1430
3630 Peachtree Rd Ne # 1480, Atlanta GA 30326
Tel (404) 495-0760 SIC 5499

■TEAVANA HOLDINGS INC p 1430
3393 Peachtree Rd Ne # 317, Atlanta GA 30326
Tel (404) 995-8200 SIC 5499

ALBERTSONS COMPANIES INC p 46
250 E Parkcenter Blvd, Boise ID 83706
Tel (208) 395-6200 SIC 5912 5499

ALBERTSONS COMPANIES LLC p 46
250 E Parkcenter Blvd, Boise ID 83706
Tel (208) 395-6200 SIC 5912 5499

ALBERTSONS LLC p 46
250 E Parkcenter Blvd, Boise ID 83706
Tel (208) 395-6200 SIC 5499 5912

■VITALIZE LLC p 1562
5777 N Meeker Ave Ste 500, Boise ID 83713
Tel (208) 377-3326 SIC 5499

JEL SERT CO p 782
Conde St Rr 59, West Chicago IL 60185
Tel (630) 231-7590
SIC 2087 2024 2099 5499 5143

WBG-PSS HOLDINGS LLC p 1585
3231 Se 6th Ave, Topeka KS 66607
Tel (785) 233-5171 SIC 5499

▲DUNKIN BRANDS GROUP INC p 461
130 Royall St, Canton MA 02021
Tel (781) 737-3000
SIC 5461 5499 6794 5812

ABSOPURE WATER CO LLC p 13
8845 General Dr, Plymouth MI 48170
Tel (313) 898-1200 SIC 5499 5149

CARIBOU COFFEE CO INC p 256
3900 Lake Breeze Ave, Minneapolis MN 55429
Tel (763) 592-2200 SIC 5812 5499 6794

■MICHAEL FOODS INC p 960
301 Carlson Pkwy Ste 400, Minnetonka MN 55305
Tel (507) 237-4600
SIC 0252 2015 5144 5143 5148 5499

VS PARENT INC p 1566
2101 91st St, North Bergen NJ 07047
Tel (201) 868-5959 SIC 5961 5499

MITSUI FOODS INC p 978
35 Maple St, Norwood NJ 07648
Tel (201) 750-0500 SIC 5142 5149 5499

FABER COE & GREGG INC p 523
550 Madowlands Pkwy Ste 2, Secaucus NJ 07094
Tel (201) 330-1515 SIC 5994 5499 5813

▲VITAMIN SHOPPE INC p 1562
300 Harmon Meadow Blvd # 2, Secaucus NJ 07094
Tel (201) 868-5959 SIC 5961 5499

VWRE HOLDINGS INC p 1567
105 Orville Dr, Bohemia NY 11716
Tel (631) 567-9500 SIC 6719 5499

VITAMIN WORLD INC p 1562
4320 Veterans Mem Hwy, Holbrook NY 11741
Tel (631) 567-9500 SIC 5499

HUNTINGTON HOSPITAL AUXILIARY p 720
270 Park Ave, Huntington NY 11743
Tel (631) 351-2257 SIC 5947 5499 8322

NATURAL MARKETS FOOD GROUP p 1018
1 Bridge St Ste 2, Irvington NY 10533
Tel (914) 472-7900 SIC 5499

FRESH DIRECT HOLDINGS INC p 578
2330 Borden Ave, Long Island City NY 11101
Tel (718) 433-0982 SIC 5499 4813

NESPRESSO USA INC p 1026
2401 44th Rd Fl 12, Long Island City NY 11101
Tel (800) 562-1465 SIC 5149 5046 5499

ALL MARKET INC p 51
250 Park Ave S Fl 7, New York NY 10003
Tel (212) 206-0763 SIC 5499

DEAN & DE LUCA BRANDS INC p 420
560 Broadway Frnt 2, New York NY 10012
Tel (212) 226-6800 SIC 5499 5812 2099

DEAN & DELUCA INC p 420
560 Broadway Frnt 2, New York NY 10012
Tel (212) 226-6800
SIC 5499 5812 5961 2099

SUNTORY INTERNATIONAL CORP p 1405
600 3rd Ave Fl 21, New York NY 10016
Tel (212) 891-6600
SIC 5149 2084 2086 5499 5812

■ALPHABET HOLDING CO INC p 60
2100 Smithtown Ave, Ronkonkoma NY 11779
Tel (631) 200-2000
SIC 2833 5122 5499 5961

■NBTY INC p 1021
2100 Smithtown Ave, Ronkonkoma NY 11779
Tel (631) 200-2000
SIC 2833 5122 5499 5961

▲COFFEE HOLDING CO INC p 334
3475 Victory Blvd Ste 4, Staten Island NY 10314
Tel (718) 832-0800 SIC 2095 5149 5499

FIRST SOURCE LLC p 549
100 Pirson Pkwy, Tonawanda NY 14150
Tel (716) 877-0800 SIC 5499 2064

DERROUGH AND TALLEY INC p 431
145 Cane Cr Ind P Rd 15, Fletcher NC 28732
Tel (828) 281-4800 SIC 5499

EARTH FARE INC p 469
220 Continuum Dr, Fletcher NC 28732
Tel (828) 281-4800 SIC 5499

SWANSON HEALTH PRODUCTS INC p 1411
4075 40th Ave S, Fargo ND 58104
Tel (701) 356-2700 SIC 5499 2834

TRILLIUM FARM HOLDINGS LLC p 1480
10513 Croton Rd, Johnstown OH 43031
Tel (740) 893-7200 SIC 5499

SUPERIOR BEVERAGE GROUP LTD p 1406
31031 Diamond Pkwy, Solon OH 44139
Tel (440) 703-4580 SIC 5149 5499

BOYD COFFEE CO p 205
19730 Ne Sandy Blvd, Portland OR 97230
Tel (503) 666-4545
SIC 2095 5499 5141 3634 2099

■GENERAL NUTRITION CENTERS INC p 601
300 6th Ave, Pittsburgh PA 15222
Tel (412) 288-4600 SIC 5499 2023

■GENERAL NUTRITION COMPANIES INC p 601
300 6th Ave, Pittsburgh PA 15222
Tel (412) 288-4600 SIC 5499

■GENERAL NUTRITION CORP p 601
300 6th Ave, Pittsburgh PA 15222
Tel (412) 288-4600
SIC 5499 5999 5941 5699 6794

▲GNC HOLDINGS INC p 619
300 6th Ave Fl 2, Pittsburgh PA 15222
Tel (412) 288-4600 SIC 5499

■GNC INC p 619
300 6th Ave Fl 2, Pittsburgh PA 15222
Tel (412) 288-4600 SIC 5499

LIPSEY LOGISTICS WORLDWIDE LLC p 870
5600 Brainerd Rd Ste E2, Chattanooga TN 37411
Tel (678) 336-1180 SIC 4731 5499

▲JRJR33 INC p 795
2950 N Harwood St Fl 22, Dallas TX 75201
Tel (469) 913-4115
SIC 5499 5023 5122 2721 5251

■WALCO INTERNATIONAL INC p 1572
9500 Ray White Rd Ste 200, Fort Worth TX 76244
Tel (817) 859-3000 SIC 5499

TOM THUMB FOOD & DRUGS INC p 1459
3663 Briarpark Dr, Houston TX 77042
Tel (713) 268-3500
SIC 5411 5912 5499 6512 6552

■SMITHS FOOD & DRUG CENTERS INC p 1334
1550 S Redwood Rd, Salt Lake City UT 84104
Tel (801) 974-1400 SIC 5912 5499

▲STARBUCKS CORP p 1378
2401 Utah Ave S, Seattle WA 98134
Tel (206) 447-1575
SIC 5812 5499 5461 5149

SIC 5511 Motor Vehicle Dealers (New & Used)

SOUTHLAND INTERNATIONAL TRUCKS INC p 1351
200 Oxmoor Blvd, Birmingham AL 35209
Tel (205) 942-6226
SIC 5511 5531 7538 7513

TAMERON AUTOMOTIVE GROUP INC p 1423
1675 Montgomery Hwy, Birmingham AL 35216
Tel (205) 396-3108 SIC 5511 5013

LONG-LEWIS INC p 877
2551 Highway 150, Hoover AL 35244
Tel (205) 989-3673 SIC 5511 5072

R M L HUNTSVILLE CHEVROLET LLC p 1202
4930 University Dr Nw, Huntsville AL 35816
Tel (256) 830-1600 SIC 5511

HONDA MANUFACTURING OF ALABAMA LLC p 704
1800 Honda Dr, Lincoln AL 35096
Tel (205) 355-5000 SIC 5511

BLOUNT-STRANGE FORD LINCOLN MERCURY INC p 190
4000 Eastern Blvd, Montgomery AL 36116
Tel (334) 613-5000 SIC 5511

HYUNDAI MOTOR MANUFACTURING ALABAMA LLC p 724
700 Hyundai Blvd, Montgomery AL 36105
Tel (334) 387-8000 SIC 5511

REINHARDT MOTORS INC p 1221
720 Eastern Blvd, Montgomery AL 36117
Tel (334) 272-7147 SIC 5511 7532

CHANDLER EARNHARDTS MAZDA p 288
7300 W Orchid Ln, Chandler AZ 85226
Tel (480) 893-0000 SIC 5511

DON FORD SANDERSON INC p 450
6400 N 51st Ave, Glendale AZ 85301
Tel (623) 842-8600 SIC 5511

BERGE FORD INC p 174
460 E Auto Center Dr, Mesa AZ 85204
Tel (480) 497-7600 SIC 5511

■BROWN & BROWN CHEVROLET INC p 219
145 E Main St, Mesa AZ 85201
Tel (480) 833-3456 SIC 5511 5521 5012

AUTOMOTIVE INVESTMENT GROUP INC p 134
1300 E Camelback Rd, Phoenix AZ 85014
Tel (602) 264-2332 SIC 5511

COURTESY CHEVROLET p 383
1233 E Camelback Rd, Phoenix AZ 85014
Tel (602) 279-3232 SIC 5511 5013 7538

MIDWAY CHEVROLET CO p 966
2323 W Bell Rd, Phoenix AZ 85023
Tel (602) 866-0102 SIC 5511

■PAG WEST LLC p 1107
7015 E Chauncey Ln, Phoenix AZ 85054
Tel (480) 538-6677 SIC 5511

TIMS BUICK HYUNDAI SUBARU & GMC INC p 1455
1006 Comm Dr, Prescott AZ 86305
Tel (877) 838-6541 SIC 5511

VT MOTORS INC p 1567
8585 E Frank Lloyd Wright, Scottsdale AZ 85260
Tel (480) 991-8300 SIC 5511

EARNHARDT FORD SALES CO INC p 469
7300 W Orchid Ln, Tempe AZ 85284
Tel (480) 893-0000
SIC 5511 5531 7538 5561

BEAUDRY MOTOR CO p 166
4600 E 22nd St, Tucson AZ 85711
Tel (520) 750-1264 SIC 5511 5561

JIM CLICK INC p 785
780 W Competition Rd, Tucson AZ 85705
Tel (520) 884-4100 SIC 5511

BILL ALEXANDER FORD LINCOLN MERCURY INC p 182
801 E 32nd St, Yuma AZ 85365
Tel (928) 344-2200 SIC 5511

■ASBURY AUTOMOTIVE ARKANSAS DEALERSHIP HOLDINGS LLC p 115
4400 Landers Rd, Little Rock AR 72201
Tel (501) 945-1200 SIC 5511

JA RIGGS TRACTOR CO p 773
9125 Interstate 30, Little Rock AR 72209
Tel (501) 570-3100 SIC 5082 5511

CONMAC INVESTMENTS INC p 356
2301 Mclain St, Newport AR 72112
Tel (870) 523-6576 SIC 5511

RUSSELL CHEVROLET CO p 1259
6100 Landers Rd, North Little Rock AR 72117
Tel (501) 835-8996 SIC 5511

CRAIN AUTOMOTIVE HOLDINGS LLC p 388
5890 Warden Rd, Sherwood AR 72120
Tel (501) 542-5000 SIC 5511

HARDIN AUTOMOTIVE p 660
1381 S Auto Center Dr, Anaheim CA 92806
Tel (714) 533-6200 SIC 5511

ISUZU NORTH AMERICA CORP p 767
1400 S Douglass Rd # 100, Anaheim CA 92806
Tel (714) 935-9300
SIC 5511 5084 5013 5015

FORD HABERFELDE p 565
2001 Oak St, Bakersfield CA 93301
Tel (661) 328-3600 SIC 5511

NORTH BAKERSFIELD TOYOTA SCION p 1051
19651 Industry Parkway Dr, Bakersfield CA 93308
Tel (661) 615-1100 SIC 5511

THREE-WAY CHEVROLET CO p 1450
4501 Wible Rd, Bakersfield CA 93313
Tel (661) 847-6400
SIC 5511 5531 7515 7538 7532

HOEHN MOTORS INC p 699
5475 Car Country Dr, Carlsbad CA 92008
Tel (760) 438-4454 SIC 5511

NORM REEVES INC p 1048
18500 Studebaker Rd, Cerritos CA 90703
Tel (562) 402-3844 SIC 5511 5521

MITSUBISHI MOTORS NORTH AMERICA INC p 978
6400 Katella Ave, Cypress CA 90630
Tel (714) 799-4730
SIC 5511 5013 6159 6512

HARVEY & MADDING INC p 667
6300 Dublin Blvd, Dublin CA 94568
Tel (925) 828-8030
SIC 5511 7538 5015 5013

K MOTORS INC p 799
965 Arnele Ave, El Cajon CA 92020
Tel (619) 270-3000 SIC 5521 5013 5511

PENSKE MOTOR GROUP LLC p 1131
3534 Peck Rd, El Monte CA 91731
Tel (626) 580-6000 SIC 5511

ELK GROVE AUTO GROUP INC p 487
8575 Laguna Grove Dr, Elk Grove CA 95757
Tel (916) 405-2600 SIC 5511

GARRICK MOTORS INC p 592
231 E Lincoln Ave, Escondido CA 92026
Tel (760) 746-0601 SIC 5511

ROTOLO CHEVROLET INC p 1252
16666 S Highland Ave, Fontana CA 92336
Tel (866) 756-9776 SIC 5511 5521 7538

HYUNDAI MOTOR AMERICA p 724
10550 Talbert Ave, Fountain Valley CA 92708
Tel (714) 965-3000 SIC 5511 6141 6153

FRESNO TRUCK CENTER p 579
2727 E Central Ave, Fresno CA 93725
Tel (559) 486-4310
SIC 5511 5521 5531 5012 5013 6159

MICHAEL CADILLAC INC p 960
50 W Bullard Ave, Fresno CA 93704
Tel (559) 431-6000 SIC 5511

PAPE TRUCKS INC p 1112
2892 E Jensen Ave, Fresno CA 93706
Tel (559) 268-4344 SIC 5511

TOMS TRUCK CENTER INC p 1460
12221 Monarch St, Garden Grove CA 92841
Tel (714) 835-5070 SIC 5511 5012 7538

KIA MOTORS AMERICA INC p 816
111 Peters Canyon Rd, Irvine CA 92606
Tel (949) 468-4800 SIC 5511 5013 8741

MAZDA MOTOR OF AMERICA INC p 924
7755 Irvine Center Dr, Irvine CA 92618
Tel (949) 727-1990 SIC 5511 5531

TUTTLE-CLICK INC p 1493
41 Auto Center Dr, Irvine CA 92618
Tel (949) 472-7400 SIC 5511

H W HUNTER INC p 651
1130 Auto Mall Dr, Lancaster CA 93534
Tel (661) 948-8411 SIC 5511 7538

JOHN L SULLIVAN INVESTMENTS INC p 789
6200 Northfront Rd, Livermore CA 94551
Tel (916) 969-5911 SIC 5511 7538

ALANT CORP p 44
1850 Outer Traffic Cir, Long Beach CA 90815
Tel (562) 494-1911 SIC 5511

HARBOR CHEVROLET CORP p 659
3770 Cherry Ave, Long Beach CA 90807
Tel (562) 426-3341 SIC 5511

FOX HILLS AUTO INC p 572
5880 W Centinela Ave, Los Angeles CA 90045
Tel (310) 649-3673
SIC 5511 7538 5531 5521

MIDWAY RENT A CAR INC p 967
4751 Wilshire Blvd # 120, Los Angeles CA 90010
Tel (323) 692-4000
SIC 5511 7515 5521 4119 7513

SAGE HOLDING CO p 1267
3550 Cahuenga Blvd W, Los Angeles CA 90068
Tel (310) 271-3476 SIC 5511

CENTRAL VALLEY AUTOMOTIVE INC p 280
4460 Mchenry Ave, Modesto CA 95356
Tel (209) 526-3300 SIC 5511

NEW AGE INVESTMENTS INC p 1029
9440 Autoplex St, Montclair CA 91763
Tel (909) 625-8990 SIC 5511

FORNACA INC p 568
2400 National City Blvd, National City CA 91950
Tel (619) 474-5573 SIC 5511 7532 5531

FLETCHER JONES MOTOR CARS INC p 555
3300 Jamboree Rd, Newport Beach CA 92660
Tel (949) 718-3000 SIC 5511

GALPIN MOTORS INC p 590
15505 Roscoe Blvd, North Hills CA 91343
Tel (818) 787-3800
SIC 5511 5521 7538 7515 7514 5531

GOLDEN GATE FREIGHTLINER INC p 621
8200 Baldwin St, Oakland CA 94621
Tel (559) 486-4310 SIC 5511 5531 7538

SAVAGE BMW INC p 1283
1301 Auto Center Dr, Ontario CA 91761
Tel (909) 390-7888 SIC 5511

ENTERPRISE RENT-A-CAR CO OF LOS ANGELES LLC p 502
333 City Blvd W Ste 1000, Orange CA 92868
Tel (657) 221-4400
SIC 7515 7513 5511 7514

IDEALAB p 729
130 W Union St, Pasadena CA 91103
Tel (626) 356-3654 SIC 5511 6726

DAVID A CAMPBELL CORP p 415
3060 Adams St, Riverside CA 92504
Tel (951) 785-4444 SIC 5511 7538

ENTERPRISE RENT-A-CAR CO OF SACRAMENTO LLC p 502
150 N Sunrise Ave, Roseville CA 95661
Tel (916) 787-4500 SIC 7515 7514 5511

BOB FRINK MANAGEMENT INC p 196
5112 Madison Ave Ste 201, Sacramento CA 95841
Tel (916) 338-7333 SIC 8741 5511

RPM LUXURY AUTO SALES INC p 1255
5112 Madison Ave Ste 201, Sacramento CA 95841
Tel (916) 485-3987 SIC 5511

BOB BAKER ENTERPRISES INC p 196
591 Camino De La Reina # 1100, San Diego CA 92108
Tel (619) 683-5591 SIC 5511

NISSAN MOSSY INC p 1044
4625 Brinell St, San Diego CA 92111
Tel (619) 474-7011 SIC 5511

EUROMOTORS INC p 512
500 8th St, San Francisco CA 94103
Tel (415) 673-1700 SIC 5511

GERMAN MOTORS CORP p 608
1140 Harrison St, San Francisco CA 94103
Tel (415) 590-3773 SIC 5511 7532

CORBRO LLC p 368
4490 Stevens Creek Blvd, San Jose CA 95129
Tel (408) 260-9300 SIC 5511

■CHEVRON USA INC p 296
6001 Bollinger Canyon Rd D1248, San Ramon CA 94583
Tel (925) 842-1000
SIC 5541 5511 2911 5171

■TEXACO INC p 1441
6001 Bollinger Canyon Rd, San Ramon CA 94583
Tel (925) 842-1000
SIC 5541 5511 1321 4612 4613 4412

WESTRUX INTERNATIONAL INC p 1603
15555 Valley View Ave, Santa Fe Springs CA 90670
Tel (562) 404-1020
SIC 5511 5531 7513 7538

VOLKSWAGEN SANTA MONICA INC p 1564
2440 Santa Monica Blvd, Santa Monica CA 90404
Tel (310) 829-1888 SIC 5511 7532 7538

■MILLER AUTOMOTIVE GROUP INC p 970
5425 Van Nuys Blvd, Sherman Oaks CA 91401
Tel (818) 787-8400 SIC 5511 7538 5521

HONDA R&D AMERICAS INC p 705
1900 Harpers Way, Torrance CA 90501
Tel (310) 781-5500 SIC 5511

TOYOTA FINANCIAL SERVICES INTERNATIONAL CORP p 1466
19001 S Western Ave, Torrance CA 90501
Tel (310) 618-4000 SIC 5511

BONANDER PONTIAC INC p 199
231 S Center St, Turlock CA 95380
Tel (209) 632-8871 SIC 5511 7539 5012

COUNTY FORD NORTH INC p 375
450 W Vista Way, Vista CA 92083
Tel (760) 945-9900
SIC 5511 5521 7538 7515 5531

STEAD MOTORS INC p 1384
1800 N Main St, Walnut Creek CA 94596
Tel (925) 937-5060 SIC 5511

VISTA FORD INC p 1562
21501 Ventura Blvd, Woodland Hills CA 91364
Tel (818) 884-7600 SIC 5511

TRANS-WEST INC p 1470
20770 Interstate 76, Brighton CO 80603
Tel (303) 289-3161 SIC 5511 5012

PHIL LONG DEALERSHIPS INC p 1142
1114 Motor City Dr, Colorado Springs CO 80905
Tel (719) 575-7555 SIC 5511 7514 7515

PHIL LONG FORD LLC p 1142
1212 Motor City Dr, Colorado Springs CO 80905
Tel (719) 575-7100
SIC 5511 7515 7538 5531

STEVINSON AUTOMOTIVE INC p 1388
1726 Cole Blvd Ste 300, Golden CO 80401
Tel (303) 232-2006 SIC 5511

MCDONALD AUTOMOTIVE GROUP LLC p 927
6060 S Broadway, Littleton CO 80121
Tel (866) 775-9743 SIC 5511

MEDVED CHEVROLET INC p 939
11001 W I 70 Frontage Rd, Wheat Ridge CO 80033
Tel (303) 421-0100 SIC 5511

JETOBRA INC p 784
700 Connecticut Blvd, East Hartford CT 06108
Tel (877) 274-8207 SIC 5511

GRIFFIN MANAGEMENT CO INC p 640
19 Railroad Ave, Greenwich CT 06830
Tel (203) 869-6700 SIC 5511

HOMETOWN AUTO RETAILERS INC p 704
1230 Main St, Watertown CT 06795
Tel (203) 756-8908 SIC 5511

IG BURTON & CO INC p 730
793 Bay Rd, Milford DE 19963
Tel (302) 422-3041 SIC 5511 7538

RCP III LLC p 1212
303 E Cleveland Ave, Newark DE 19711
Tel (302) 368-6300 SIC 5511

WILLIAM H PORTER INC p 1610
414 E Cleveland Ave, Newark DE 19711
Tel (302) 453-6800 SIC 5511

LOKEY AUTOMOTIVE GROUP INC p 875
27850 Us Highway 19 N, Clearwater FL 33761
Tel (888) 275-8388 SIC 5511 7532

LOKEY MOTOR GROUP INC p 875
19820 Us Highway 19 N, Clearwater FL 33764
Tel (727) 530-1661 SIC 5511

BILL USSERY MOTORS BODY SHOP INC p 182
300 Almeria Ave, Coral Gables FL 33134
Tel (305) 445-8593 SIC 5511 7538

COLLECTION INC p 336
200 Bird Rd, Coral Gables FL 33146
Tel (305) 444-5555 SIC 5511

TERRY TAYLOR FORD CO p 1440
1420 N Tomoka Farms Rd, Daytona Beach FL 32124
Tel (386) 274-6700 SIC 5511 7532

JM FAMILY ENTERPRISES INC p 786
100 Jim Moran Blvd, Deerfield Beach FL 33442
Tel (954) 429-2000
SIC 5511 5012 5013 5531

MORSE OPERATIONS INC p 991
2850 S Federal Hwy, Delray Beach FL 33483
Tel (561) 276-5000 SIC 5511

■ASE MOTORS HOLDING CORP p 116
200 Sw 1st Ave, Fort Lauderdale FL 33301
Tel (954) 769-7000 SIC 5511

■AUTO CO XXVIII INC p 133
200 Sw 1st Ave, Fort Lauderdale FL 33301
Tel (954) 769-7000 SIC 5511

■AUTONATION ENTERPRISES INC p 135
200 Sw 1st Ave Ste 1700, Fort Lauderdale FL 33301
Tel (954) 769-7000 SIC 5511

▲AUTONATION INC p 135
200 Sw 1st Ave Ste 1700, Fort Lauderdale FL 33301
Tel (954) 769-6000 SIC 5511 5521

■AUTONATION MOTORS HOLDING CORP p 135
200 Sw 1st Ave, Fort Lauderdale FL 33301
Tel (954) 769-7000 SIC 5511

■ FIRST TEAM AUTOMOTIVE CORP p 549
200 Sw 1st Ave, Fort Lauderdale FL 33301
Tel (954) 769-7000 SIC 5511

HOLMAN AUTOMOTIVE INC p 701
12 E Sunrise Blvd, Fort Lauderdale FL 33304
Tel (954) 779-2000 SIC 5511 5531

■ REPUBLIC RESOURCES CO p 1225
200 Sw 1st Ave, Fort Lauderdale FL 33301
Tel (954) 769-7000 SIC 5511

OBRIEN AUTOMOTIVE OF FLORIDA LLC p 1072
2850 Colonial Blvd, Fort Myers FL 33966
Tel (239) 277-1222 SIC 5511

SAM GALLOWAY FORD INC p 1274
1800 Boy Scout Dr, Fort Myers FL 33907
Tel (239) 936-3673 SIC 5511

TRIANGLE AUTO CENTER INC p 1478
1841 N State Road 7, Hollywood FL 33021
Tel (855) 398-2449 SIC 5511 7532

CRYSTAL MOTOR CAR CO INC p 397
1035 S Suncoast Blvd, Homosassa FL 34448
Tel (352) 795-1515 SIC 5511

BRUMOS MOTOR CARS INC p 221
10231 Atlantic Blvd, Jacksonville FL 32225
Tel (904) 724-1080 SIC 5511

BUSH INDUSTRIES CORP p 229
9850 Atlantic Blvd, Jacksonville FL 32225
Tel (904) 725-0911 SIC 5511

■ COGGIN AUTOMOTIVE CORP p 334
7245 Blanding Blvd, Jacksonville FL 32244
Tel (904) 779-8030 SIC 5511

DUVAL MOTOR CO INC p 463
1616 Cassat Ave, Jacksonville FL 32210
Tel (904) 387-6541 SIC 5521 5511

NEXTRAN CORP p 1041
1986 W Beaver St, Jacksonville FL 32209
Tel (904) 354-3721 SIC 5511 5531 7538

SCOTT-MCRAE AUTOMOTIVE GROUP INC p 1294
701 Riverside Park Pl # 120, Jacksonville FL 32204
Tel (904) 354-4000 SIC 5511 7515 6159

TOM BUSH VOLKSWAGEN INC p 1459
9850 Atlantic Blvd, Jacksonville FL 32225
Tel (904) 725-0911 SIC 5511

TOM NEHL TRUCK CO p 1459
417 Edgewood Ave S, Jacksonville FL 32254
Tel (904) 389-3653 SIC 5511 5531 7538

MUTZ MOTORS LTD PARTNERSHIP p 1003
1430 W Memorial Blvd, Lakeland FL 33815
Tel (863) 682-1100
SIC 5511 7538 7532 7515 5531 5521

LONGWOOD LINCOLN-MERCURY INC p 877
3505 N Us Highway 17 92, Longwood FL 32750
Tel (407) 322-4884 SIC 5511

KELLY MANAGEMENT CORP p 809
2415 S Babcock St Ste C, Melbourne FL 32901
Tel (321) 768-2424 SIC 5511

KENDALL IMPORTS LLC p 810
10943 S Dixie Hwy, Miami FL 33156
Tel (305) 666-1784 SIC 5511 5521

LEHMAN DEALERSHIP ENTERPRISES INC p 854
21400 Nw 2nd Ave, Miami FL 33169
Tel (305) 653-7111 SIC 5511

SEIDLE ENTERPRISES INC p 1301
2900 Nw 36th St, Miami FL 33142
Tel (305) 635-8000 SIC 5511 7538 7532

SOUTH MOTOR CO OF DADE COUNTY p 1344
16165 S Dixie Hwy, Miami FL 33157
Tel (888) 418-3508 SIC 5511 5521

WARREN HENRY AUTOMOBILES INC p 1577
20800 Nw 2nd Ave, Miami FL 33169
Tel (305) 690-6010 SIC 5511 5531 7538

PLANET AUTOMOTIVE GROUP INC p 1154
6200 Nw 167th St B, Miami Lakes FL 33014
Tel (305) 728-5000 SIC 5511

HYUNDAI OF NEW PORT RICHEY LLC p 724
3936 Us Highway 19, New Port Richey FL 34652
Tel (727) 569-0999 SIC 5511 7549

DELUCA INC p 427
1719 Sw College Rd, Ocala FL 34471
Tel (352) 732-0770 SIC 5511

DJ PROPERTY INVESTMENTS INC p 445
1602 Sw College Rd, Ocala FL 34471
Tel (352) 620-2264 SIC 5511

ACTION NISSAN INC p 19
12785 S Ornge Blossom Trl, Orlando FL 32837
Tel (407) 926-7050 SIC 5511

FORD GREENWAY INC p 565
9001 E Colonial Dr, Orlando FL 32817
Tel (407) 275-3200 SIC 5511 5012

■AN MOTORS OF PEMBROKE LLC p 88
8600 Pines Blvd, Pembroke Pines FL 33024
Tel (954) 433-3377 SIC 5511

B C S S LTD p 141
1801 W Atlantic Blvd, Pompano Beach FL 33069
Tel (954) 971-3000 SIC 5511

CROWN AUTO DEALERSHIPS INC p 395
6001 34th St N, Saint Petersburg FL 33714
Tel (727) 525-4990 SIC 5511

BILL CURRIE FORD INC p 182
5815 N Dale Mabry Hwy, Tampa FL 33614
Tel (813) 872-5555 SIC 5511 7538

FERMAN MOTOR CAR CO INC p 538
1306 W Kennedy Blvd, Tampa FL 33606
Tel (813) 251-2765 SIC 5511

FERMAN CHEVROLET OF TARPON SPRINGS p 538
43520 Us Highway 19 N, Tarpon Springs FL 34689
Tel (727) 942-4800
SIC 5511 7538 7515 7513 5521

BAYVIEW CADILLAC NEW CARS & SERVICE LLC p 162
1240 N Federal Hwy, West Palm Beach FL 33403
Tel (954) 537-6200 SIC 5511

BRAMAN MOTOR CARS p 207
2901 Okeechobee Blvd, West Palm Beach FL 33409
Tel (561) 615-4800 SIC 5511

MYERS AUTO GROUP LLC p 1004
915 S Dixie Hwy, West Palm Beach FL 33401
Tel (561) 659-6206 SIC 5511

ROGER DEAN ENTERPRISES INC p 1246
2235 Okeechobee Blvd, West Palm Beach FL 33409
Tel (561) 683-8100
SIC 5511 5521 7538 7532 7515

DINGMAN GROUP INC p 440
1051 W Webster Ave, Winter Park FL 32789
Tel (407) 644-6043 SIC 5511 5531 7539

DAYS CHEVROLET INC p 417
3693 Cobb Pkwy Nw, Acworth GA 30101
Tel (770) 974-4242 SIC 5511

ELLIS ATLANTA JIM INC p 488
5901 Peachtree Indus Blvd, Atlanta GA 30341
Tel (770) 454-8200 SIC 5511 5521

HENNESSY CADILLAC INC p 683
3040 Piedmont Rd Ne, Atlanta GA 30305
Tel (404) 261-5700 SIC 5511

MERCEDES-BENZ USA LLC p 944
303 Perimeter Ctr N, Atlanta GA 30346
Tel (201) 573-0600
SIC 5012 5013 7538 5511

PORSCHE CARS NORTH AMERICA INC p 1161
1 Porsche Dr, Atlanta GA 30354
Tel (770) 290-3500 SIC 5511 5013

TOM GRADDY ENTERPRISES INC p 1459
3348 Peachtree Rd Ne, Atlanta GA 30326
Tel (404) 363-8390
SIC 5531 5511 7538 5012

■ GA H IMPORTS LLC p 588
3000 N Lake Pkwy Ste 400, Columbus GA 31909
Tel (706) 522-2090 SIC 5511

■ASBURY AUTOMOTIVE ATLANTA LLC p 115
3039 Premiere Pkwy # 900, Duluth GA 30097
Tel (404) 622-1921
SIC 5511 7515 5013 6159 5521

▲ASBURY AUTOMOTIVE GROUP INC p 115
2905 Premiere Pkwy, Duluth GA 30097
Tel (770) 418-8200 SIC 5511

MARTIN CAR FINANCING INC p 912
3150 Mlton Mrtn Tyota Way, Gainesville GA 30507
Tel (770) 532-4355 SIC 5511

HAYES CHRYSLER-DODGE-JEEP INC p 670
719 Duluth Hwy, Lawrenceville GA 30046
Tel (770) 963-5261 SIC 5511

ALLAN VIGIL FORD LINCOLN INC p 52
6790 Mount Zion Blvd, Morrow GA 30260
Tel (678) 364-3675 SIC 5511

■ NISSAN CONYERS INC p 1044
1420 Iris Dr, Morrow GA 30260
Tel (770) 922-7600 SIC 5511

KIA MOTORS MANUFACTURING GEORGIA INC p 816
7777 Kia Pkwy, West Point GA 31833
Tel (706) 902-7777 SIC 5511

CUTTER MANAGEMENT CO p 403
1100 Alakea St Steth2, Honolulu HI 96814
Tel (808) 529-2000 SIC 5511 7515

JARDINE HAWAII MOTOR HOLDINGS LTD p 778
818 Kapiolani Blvd, Honolulu HI 96813
Tel (808) 592-5600 SIC 5511

SERVCO PACIFIC INC p 1307
2850 Pukoloa St Ste 300, Honolulu HI 96819
Tel (808) 564-1300 SIC 5013 5064 5511

DNIS DLN ATOPRK&TRCK CNTR p 446
2573 S Orchard St, Boise ID 83705
Tel (208) 336-6000 SIC 5511

MOTOR WERKS PARTNERS LP p 993
1475 S Barrington Rd, Barrington IL 60010
Tel (847) 842-1352 SIC 5511 7515

BIRKEYS FARM STORE INC p 185
2102 W Park Ct, Champaign IL 61821
Tel (217) 693-7200 SIC 5083 5082 5511

FLEXPOINT PARTNERS LLC p 556
676 N Michigan Ave # 3300, Chicago IL 60611
Tel (312) 327-4520 SIC 5511

MID-CITY TRUCK DRIVING ACADEMY INC p 963
6740 W Belmont Ave, Chicago IL 60634
Tel (773) 725-3000 SIC 8299 5511

DOWNERS GROVE IMPORTS LTD p 453
2020 Ogden Ave, Downers Grove IL 60515
Tel (630) 964-9500 SIC 5511

ELM HURST AUTO GROUP p 489
466 W Lake St, Elmhurst IL 60126
Tel (630) 833-7945 SIC 5511

ADELPHI ENTERPRISES LIMITED PARTNERSHIP p 22
2000 Waukegan Rd, Glenview IL 60025
Tel (847) 698-3700 SIC 5511

LOREN BUICK & PONTIAC INC p 878
1610 Waukegan Rd, Glenview IL 60025
Tel (847) 729-8900 SIC 5511 5521

ROSEN MOTOR SALES INC p 1251
7000 Grand Ave, Gurnee IL 60031
Tel (847) 856-8439 SIC 5511

CIT INC p 309
103 S Larkin Ave, Joliet IL 60436
Tel (815) 741-7500 SIC 5511

KARL KNAUZ MOTORS INC p 804
775 Rockland Rd, Lake Bluff IL 60044
Tel (847) 615-3670 SIC 5511

GROSSINGER AUTOPLEX INC p 641
6900 N Mccormick Blvd # 1, Lincolnwood IL 60712
Tel (847) 674-9000 SIC 5511

LOEBER MOTORS INC p 874
4255 W Touhy Ave, Lincolnwood IL 60712
Tel (847) 675-1000 SIC 5511

SUTTON FORD INC p 1410
21315 Central Ave, Matteson IL 60443
Tel (708) 720-8000 SIC 5511

BILL JACOBS MOTORSPORT HOLDINGS INC p 182
1564 W Ogden Ave, Naperville IL 60540
Tel (630) 357-1200 SIC 5511 5521

ARLINGTON AUTOMOTIVE GROUP INC p 110
2095 N Rand Rd, Palatine IL 60074
Tel (847) 394-5100
SIC 7538 5521 5511 5531 7532

PATRICK SCHAUMBURG AUTOMOBILES INC p 1120
526 Mall Dr, Schaumburg IL 60173
Tel (847) 605-4000
SIC 5511 7539 7538 7532 5531 5013

ROBERT V ROHRMAN INC p 1241
750 E Golf Rd, Schaumburg IL 60173
Tel (847) 884-6632 SIC 5511 6159

TRUCK CENTERS INC p 1485
2280 Formosa Rd, Troy IL 62294
Tel (618) 667-3454
SIC 5531 5511 7538 5012 4522 7699

D-PATRICK INC p 407
200 N Green River Rd, Evansville IN 47715
Tel (812) 473-6500 SIC 5511

ODANIEL AUTOMOTIVE INC p 1074
5611 Illinois Rd, Fort Wayne IN 46804
Tel (260) 435-5300 SIC 5511

■ DUTCHMEN MANUFACTURING INC p 463
2164 Caragana Ct, Goshen IN 46526
Tel (574) 537-0600 SIC 5511

PALMER TRUCKS INC p 1109
2929 S Holt Rd, Indianapolis IN 46241
Tel (317) 243-1668
SIC 5511 5531 7538 7513 5012

TRUCK COUNTRY OF INDIANA INC p 1485
1851 W Thompson Rd, Indianapolis IN 46217
Tel (317) 788-1533
SIC 5511 5531 7538 7539

HARRISON TRUCK CENTERS INC p 664
3601 Adventureland Dr, Altoona IA 50009
Tel (515) 967-3500 SIC 5511 7538

MCGRATH AUTOMOTIVE GROUP INC p 929
4610 Center Point Rd Ne, Cedar Rapids IA 52402
Tel (319) 688-2937 SIC 5511

QUAD CITY AUTOMOTIVE GROUP LLC p 1195
3700 N Harrison St, Davenport IA 52806
Tel (563) 386-1511 SIC 5511 5521

SIOUX CITY TRUCK SALES INC p 1326
2601 Voyager Ave, Sioux City IA 51111
Tel (712) 234-2728 SIC 5511

CONKLIN CARS SALINA LLC p 356
1400 E 11th Ave, Hutchinson KS 67501
Tel (785) 825-8271 SIC 5511

CONKLIN FANGMAN INVESTMENT CO INC p 356
1400 E 11th Ave, Hutchinson KS 67501
Tel (620) 662-4467
SIC 7515 5511 7538 5521

COLORADO KENWORTH INC p 339
11120 Tomahawk Creek Pkwy, Leawood KS 66211
Tel (720) 941-0833 SIC 5511

MURPHY-HOFFMAN CO p 1001
11120 Tomahawk Creek Pkwy, Leawood KS 66211
Tel (816) 483-6444
SIC 5012 7513 7538 6159 5511

FORD OLATHE SALES INC p 566
1845 E Santa Fe St, Olathe KS 66062
Tel (913) 782-0881 SIC 5511 5561 5012

KUNI ENTERPRISES LLC p 832
8035 Lenexa Dr, Overland Park KS 66214
Tel (360) 553-7350 SIC 5511

RUSTY ECK FORD INC p 1260
7310 E Kellogg Dr, Wichita KS 67207
Tel (316) 685-9211 SIC 5511

TOYOTA BOSHOKU KENTUCKY LLC p 1466
1051 Withrow Ct, Bardstown KY 40004
Tel (502) 349-6000 SIC 5511

MARTIN MANAGEMENT GROUP INC p 912
1048 Ashley St Ste 401, Bowling Green KY 42103
Tel (270) 783-8080 SIC 5511

TOYOTA MOTOR MANUFACTURING KENTUCKY INC p 1466
1001 Cherry Blossom Way, Georgetown KY 40324
Tel (502) 868-2000 SIC 5511

SAM SWOPE AUTO GROUP LLC p 1274
10 Swope Autocenter Dr, Louisville KY 40299
Tel (502) 499-5000 SIC 5511 5012 7532

WORLDWIDE EQUIPMENT ENTERPRISES INC p 1626
107 We Dr, Prestonsburg KY 41653
Tel (606) 874-2772 SIC 5511

ALL STAR AUTOMOTIVE GROUP p 51
13000 Florida Blvd, Baton Rouge LA 70815
Tel (225) 298-3210 SIC 5511

GERRY LANE ENTERPRISES INC p 609
6505 Florida Blvd, Baton Rouge LA 70806
Tel (225) 926-4600 SIC 5511

RAY BRANDT NISSAN INC p 1209
4000 Lapalco Blvd, Harvey LA 70058
Tel (504) 367-1666 SIC 5511 5521

BENSCO INC p 173
5800 Airline Dr, Metairie LA 70003
Tel (210) 349-6200 SIC 5511

ROUNDTREE AUTOMOTIVE GROUP LLC p 1253
7607 Fern Ave Ste 401, Shreveport LA 71105
Tel (318) 798-6500 SIC 5511

ROUNDTREE OF SHREVEPORT LLC p 1253
910 Pierremont Rd Ste 312, Shreveport LA 71106
Tel (318) 798-6500 SIC 5511

HUTCHINS MOTORS INC p 721
187 Riverside Dr, Augusta ME 04330
Tel (207) 622-3191 SIC 5511 5012

DARLINGS p 412
96 Parkway S Unit 1, Brewer ME 04412
Tel (207) 992-1720 SIC 5511 6411

RUSSEL MOTOR CARS INC p 1259
6700 Baltimore Nat Pike, Baltimore MD 21228
Tel (410) 788-8400
SIC 5511 7538 7532 5521

BETHESDA INVESTMENT HOLDING CO INC p 178
10400 Auto Park Ave, Bethesda MD 20817
Tel (301) 469-6600
SIC 5511 7539 5013 5531

EURO MOTORCARS INC p 512
7020 Arlington Rd, Bethesda MD 20814
Tel (888) 250-2987 SIC 5511

FITZGERALD AUTO MALL INC p 553
114 Baughmans Ln, Frederick MD 21702
Tel (301) 696-9200 SIC 5511

LEN STOLER INC p 855
11275 Reisterstown Rd, Owings Mills MD 21117
Tel (410) 581-7000 SIC 5511

R & H MOTOR CARS LTD p 1201
9727 Reisterstown Rd, Owings Mills MD 21117
Tel (410) 363-7793 SIC 5511 7538 5531

FITZGERALD AUTOMALL p 553
11411 Rockville Pike, Rockville MD 20852
Tel (301) 881-4000 SIC 5511

POHANKA OF SALISBURY INC p 1159
2015 N Salisbury Blvd, Salisbury MD 21801
Tel (410) 749-2301
SIC 5511 7513 7514 7538 7515

MARIAM INC p 906
12210 Cherry Hill Rd, Silver Spring MD 20904
Tel (888) 841-9679 SIC 5511

DAR CARS DODGE INC p 412
5060 Auth Way, Suitland MD 20746
Tel (301) 423-5111 SIC 5511

INTERNATIONAL MOTOR CARS INC p 756
5000 Auth Way, Suitland MD 20746
Tel (301) 423-8400 SIC 5511 7538 5521

ATLANTIC AUTOMOTIVE CORP p 125
1 Olympic Pl Ste 1210, Towson MD 21204
Tel (410) 602-6177 SIC 5511 7538 7515

DANIEL J QUIRK INC p 411
372 Quincy Ave, Braintree MA 02184
Tel (781) 843-4800
SIC 5511 5013 5531 7538 5521 7515

INTERNATIONAL CARS LTD INC p 754
382 Newbury St, Danvers MA 01923
Tel (800) 514-1627 SIC 5511 5521

FOREIGN MOTORS WEST INC p 566
253 N Main St, Natick MA 01760
Tel (508) 655-5350 SIC 5511 7538

GALLERY AUTOMOTIVE GROUP LLC p 590
918 Providence Hwy, Norwood MA 02062
Tel (877) 201-8871 SIC 5511 5012 7538

HERB CHAMBERS I-93 INC p 685
259 Mcgrath Hwy, Somerville MA 02143
Tel (617) 666-4100 SIC 5511

BALISE MOTOR SALES CO p 148
400 Riverdale St, West Springfield MA 01089
Tel (413) 733-8604 SIC 5511

FRED LAVERY CO p 576
34602 Woodward Ave, Birmingham MI 48009
Tel (248) 645-5930 SIC 5511

US AUTO GROUP LIMITED p 1531
34602 Woodward Ave, Birmingham MI 48009
Tel (248) 645-5930 SIC 5511

▲ PENSKE AUTOMOTIVE GROUP INC p 1131
2555 S Telegraph Rd, Bloomfield Hills MI 48302
Tel (248) 648-2500 SIC 5511
PENSKE CORP p 1131
2555 S Telegraph Rd, Bloomfield Hills MI 48302
Tel (248) 648-2000 SIC 5511 7538 7948
M & K TRUCK AND TRAILER INC p 888
8800 Byron Commerce Dr Sw, Byron Center MI 49315
Tel (616) 583-2100 SIC 5511 4212
TD AUTO FINANCE LLC p 1428
27777 Inkster Rd, Farmington Hills MI 48334
Tel (248) 427-6800 SIC 6153 5511
SERRA AUTOMOTIVE INC p 1306
3118 E Hill Rd, Grand Blanc MI 48439
Tel (810) 695-1451 SIC 5511 8742
GARBER MANAGEMENT GROUP INC p 591
999 S Washington Ave # 1, Saginaw MI 48601
Tel (989) 790-9090 SIC 5511
MEADE GROUP INC p 933
6951 19 Mile Rd, Sterling Heights MI 48314
Tel (586) 803-6250 SIC 5511
SUBURBAN MOTORS CO INC p 1396
1810 Maplelawn Dr, Troy MI 48084
Tel (248) 643-0070 SIC 5511
GOLDEN VALLEY TCA A LLC p 621
9393 Wayzata Blvd, Minneapolis MN 55426
Tel (763) 744-9393 SIC 5511
LUTHER HOLDING CO p 886
3701 Alabama Ave S, Minneapolis MN 55416
Tel (763) 593-5755
SIC 5511 7515 7513 6512 6552 5611
REID ENTERPRISES INC p 1220
8000 Penn Ave S, Minneapolis MN 55431
Tel (952) 238-4300 SIC 5511
NUSS TRUCK GROUP INC p 1067
6500 Highway 63 S, Rochester MN 55904
Tel (507) 288-9488 SIC 5511 5531
GILLELAND CHEVROLET CADILLAC INC p 612
3019 W Division St, Saint Cloud MN 56301
Tel (320) 281-4290 SIC 5511 5531 7538
GATR OF SAUK RAPIDS INC p 594
218 Stearns Dr, Sauk Rapids MN 56379
Tel (320) 251-7356 SIC 5511
WATSON QUALITY FORD INC p 1583
6130 I 55 N, Jackson MS 39211
Tel (601) 956-7000 SIC 5511
JOE MACHENS FORD INC p 787
1911 W Worley St, Columbia MO 65203
Tel (573) 445-4411 SIC 5511
BEHLMANN AUTOMOTIVE HOLDING CO INC p 168
820 Jmes S Mcdonnell Blvd, Hazelwood MO 63042
Tel (314) 895-1600 SIC 5511
KCR INTERNATIONAL TRUCKS INC p 806
7700 Ne 38th St, Kansas City MO 64161
Tel (816) 455-1833
SIC 5511 5531 7538 7513
MIDWAY FORD TRUCK CENTER INC p 967
7601 Ne 38th St, Kansas City MO 64161
Tel (816) 455-3000 SIC 5511 7538
BLACKWELL BALDWIN CHEVROLET GEO OLDSMOBILE CADILLAC INC p 188
621 S Westwood Blvd, Poplar Bluff MO 63901
Tel (573) 785-0893 SIC 5511
DAVE SINCLAIR FORD WEST p 415
7466 S Lindbergh Blvd, Saint Louis MO 63125
Tel (314) 892-2600
SIC 5511 7538 5521 5012
LOU FUSZ AUTOMOTIVE NETWORK INC p 879
925 N Lindbergh Blvd, Saint Louis MO 63141
Tel (314) 997-3400 SIC 5511 5531 5521
LOU FUSZ MOTOR CO p 879
10329 Old Olive Street Rd, Saint Louis MO 63141
Tel (314) 994-1500 SIC 5511 7514
PETERBILT OF SPRINGFIELD INC p 1138
3026 N Mulroy Rd, Strafford MO 65757
Tel (417) 865-5355 SIC 5511 5012
FORD ATCHLEY INC p 565
3633 N 72nd St, Omaha NE 68134
Tel (402) 571-8801 SIC 5511
OMAHA TRUCK CENTER INC p 1083
10550 I St, Omaha NE 68127
Tel (402) 592-2440 SIC 5511
FINDLAY AUTOMOTIVE INC p 543
310 N Gibson Rd, Henderson NV 89014
Tel (702) 558-8888 SIC 5511
FLETCHER JONES LAS VEGAS INC p 555
7300 W Sahara Ave, Las Vegas NV 89117
Tel (702) 739-9800 SIC 5511
TEAM FORD LLC p 1430
5445 Drexel Rd, Las Vegas NV 89130
Tel (702) 395-5100 SIC 5511
TOWBIN AUTOMOTIVE ENTERPRISES INC p 1464
5550 W Sahara Ave, Las Vegas NV 89146
Tel (702) 253-7000 SIC 5511 7514
PORTSMOUTH CHEVROLET INC p 1163
549 Us Highway 1 Byp, Portsmouth NH 03801
Tel (603) 436-5010 SIC 5511
■ CLASSIC AUTO GROUP INC p 323
Black Horse Pike Rr 555, Blackwood NJ 08012
Tel (856) 629-1900 SIC 5511
RYAN AUTOMOTIVE LLC p 1260
1120 Us Highway 22 Bldg 2, Bridgewater NJ 08807
Tel (732) 650-1550 SIC 5511
FOULKE MANAGEMENT CORP p 571
1708 Marlton Pike W, Cherry Hill NJ 08002
Tel (856) 665-9000 SIC 5511
WARNOCK AUTOMOTIVE GROUP INC p 1576
175 State Route 10, East Hanover NJ 07936
Tel (973) 884-2100
SIC 5511 7515 5012 5013
FERRARI NORTH AMERICA INC p 538
250 Sylvan Ave, Englewood Cliffs NJ 07632
Tel (201) 816-2600 SIC 5511 5012
JACK DANIELS MOTORS INC p 773
16-01 Mcbride Ave, Fair Lawn NJ 07410
Tel (201) 796-8500 SIC 5511

PINE BELT ENTERPRISES INC p 1148
1088 Route 88, Lakewood NJ 08701
Tel (732) 363-2900 SIC 5511 7537 5531
HOLMAN AUTOMOTIVE GROUP INC p 701
244 E Kings Hwy, Maple Shade NJ 08052
Tel (856) 663-5200 SIC 5511
HOLMAN ENTERPRISES INC p 701
244 E Kings Hwy, Maple Shade NJ 08052
Tel (856) 662-1042 SIC 5511
PRESTIGE OF BERGEN INC p 1173
50 Williams Dr, Ramsey NJ 07446
Tel (201) 825-2700 SIC 5511 5521 5012
VOLVO CARS OF NORTH AMERICA LLC p 1565
1 Volvo Dr, Rockleigh NJ 07647
Tel (201) 768-7300
SIC 5511 5013 6159 7515 3714
■ DCH AUTO GROUP (USA) INC p 418
955 Route 9 N, South Amboy NJ 08879
Tel (732) 727-9168
SIC 5511 7515 6512 6514
JMK AUTO SALES INC p 786
391-399 Rt 22 E, Springfield NJ 07081
Tel (973) 379-7744 SIC 7538 5511
TIMCO INC p 1454
2285 Us Highway 22 W, Union NJ 07083
Tel (908) 964-1600 SIC 5511
HALE TRAILER BRAKE & WHEEL INC p 653
Cooper Rd Rr 73, Voorhees NJ 08043
Tel (800) 232-6535 SIC 5511 7539 5531
ELRAC LLC p 489
1550 Route 23, Wayne NJ 07470
Tel (973) 709-2499
SIC 7514 7515 5511 5521
BMW (US) HOLDING CORP p 194
300 Chestnut Ridge Rd, Woodcliff Lake NJ 07677
Tel (201) 307-4000 SIC 5511
MELLOY BROTHERS ENTERPRISES INC p 941
7707 Lomas Blvd Ne, Albuquerque NM 87110
Tel (505) 265-8721 SIC 5511
FUCCILLO AUTOMOTIVE GROUP INC p 583
10524 Us Route 11, Adams NY 13605
Tel (315) 232-4117 SIC 5511
NORTHTOWN AUTOMOTIVE COMPANIES INC p 1059
1135 Millersport Hwy, Amherst NY 14226
Tel (716) 836-4600 SIC 5511
BOTNICK/5 VENTURES INC p 203
159 Front St 163, Binghamton NY 13905
Tel (607) 723-8971 SIC 5511 7218
GAULT CHEVROLET CO INC p 594
2205 North St, Endicott NY 13760
Tel (607) 748-8244 SIC 5511 5012
GABRIELLI TRUCK SALES LTD p 588
15320 S Conduit Ave, Jamaica NY 11434
Tel (718) 977-7348 SIC 5511 5531 7538
ED SHULTS CHEVROLET INC p 476
300 Fluvanna Ave, Jamestown NY 14701
Tel (716) 484-7151 SIC 5511
MAJOR AUTOMOTIVE COMPANIES INC p 899
4340 Northern Blvd, Long Island City NY 11101
Tel (718) 625-6753 SIC 5511
MAJOR WORLD CHEVROLET LLC p 899
4340 Northern Blvd, Long Island City NY 11101
Tel (718) 937-3700
SIC 5511 7515 7538 5521
PREMIER COLLECTION p 1170
299 Kisco Ave, Mount Kisco NY 10549
Tel (877) 360-9162 SIC 5511
GARAGE MANAGEMENT CO LLC p 591
770 Lexington Ave Rm 1102, New York NY 10065
Tel (212) 888-7400 SIC 5511
MERCEDES-BENZ MANHATTAN INC p 944
770 11th Ave, New York NY 10019
Tel (212) 629-1600 SIC 5511
TOYOTA MOTOR NORTH AMERICA INC p 1467
601 Lexington Ave Fl 49, New York NY 10022
Tel (212) 751-3053 SIC 5511 5012 3711
NYLSI INC p 1069
3984 Sunrise Hwy, Oakdale NY 11769
Tel (631) 589-9000 SIC 5511
DORSCHEL REALTY CORP p 451
3817 W Henrietta Rd, Rochester NY 14623
Tel (585) 475-1700 SIC 5511 7538 7549
FUCCILLO HYUNDAI OF GREECE INC p 583
3975 W Ridge Rd, Rochester NY 14626
Tel (585) 720-9000 SIC 5511 5531
VISION BUICK GMC LLC p 1561
800 Panorama Trl S, Rochester NY 14625
Tel (585) 586-6940 SIC 5511
NISSAN SMITHTOWN INC p 1044
535 Middle Country Rd, Saint James NY 11780
Tel (631) 361-9696 SIC 5511
NEW COUNTRY MOTOR CAR GROUP INC p 1029
358 Broadway Ste 403, Saratoga Springs NY 12866
Tel (518) 583-4896 SIC 8741 5511
JAMES FORD OF WILLIAMSON LLC p 776
3923 Route 104, Williamson NY 14589
Tel (800) 246-2000 SIC 5511
OVERSEAS MILITARY SALES CORP - OMSC LTD p 1099
175 Crossways Park Dr W, Woodbury NY 11797
Tel (516) 921-2800 SIC 5511
BURLINGTON MOTORS INC p 228
660 Huffman Mill Rd, Burlington NC 27215
Tel (336) 584-1701 SIC 5511
HENDRICK AUTOMOTIVE GROUP p 683
6000 Monroe Rd Ste 100, Charlotte NC 28212
Tel (704) 568-5550 SIC 5511
▲ SONIC AUTOMOTIVE INC p 1340
4401 Colwick Rd, Charlotte NC 28211
Tel (704) 566-2400 SIC 5511 7538
■ TOWN & COUNTRY FORD INC p 1464
5401 E Independence Blvd, Charlotte NC 28212
Tel (704) 536-5600
SIC 5511 7538 7532 5521
YOUNGS TRUCK CENTER INC p 1639
3880 Jeff Adams Dr, Charlotte NC 28206
Tel (704) 597-0551 SIC 5511 7513 7532

TT OF LAKE NORMAN LLC p 1489
20700 Torrence Chapel Rd, Cornelius NC 28031
Tel (704) 896-3800 SIC 5511
■ ASBURY AUTOMOTIVE NORTH CAROLINA LLC p 115
3633c W Wendover Ave, Greensboro NC 27407
Tel (336) 851-3500 SIC 5511
AL SMITH CO INC p 43
2511 Wake Forest Rd, Raleigh NC 27609
Tel (919) 839-7481 SIC 5511 5521
CAPITAL FORD INC p 249
4900 Capital Blvd, Raleigh NC 27616
Tel (919) 790-4600 SIC 5511
FHA/RALEIGH INC p 539
9101 Glenwood Ave, Raleigh NC 27617
Tel (919) 787-0099 SIC 5511 5521 5012
HOL-DAV INC p 700
5839 Capital Blvd, Raleigh NC 27616
Tel (888) 240-7435 SIC 5511 5012
LEITH INC p 854
5607 Capital Blvd, Raleigh NC 27616
Tel (919) 876-5432
SIC 5511 7515 7513 5012
WW WALLWORK INC p 1629
900 35th St N, Fargo ND 58102
Tel (701) 282-6700 SIC 5511 5012 5013
RYDELL CO p 1260
2700 S Washington St, Grand Forks ND 58201
Tel (701) 780-1380 SIC 5511
WESTLIE MOTOR CO p 1601
500 S Broadway, Minot ND 58701
Tel (701) 852-1354 SIC 7513 5511
VAN DEVERE INC p 1542
300 W Market St, Akron OH 44303
Tel (330) 253-6137 SIC 5511 7515
KINGS FORD INC p 820
9555 Kings Auto Mall Rd, Cincinnati OH 45249
Tel (513) 683-0220 SIC 5511
VALLEY FORD TRUCK INC p 1540
5715 Canal Rd, Cleveland OH 44125
Tel (216) 524-2400
SIC 5013 5511 5521 5531 5012
GEO BYERS SONS HOLDING INC p 605
427 S Hamilton Rd, Columbus OH 43213
Tel (614) 228-5111 SIC 5511
GERMAIN TOYOTA p 608
4250 Morse Xing, Columbus OH 43219
Tel (239) 592-5550 SIC 5511
JMAC INC p 786
200 W Nationwide Blvd # 1, Columbus OH 43215
Tel (614) 436-2418
SIC 3325 5198 7999 5511 8741
VOSS AUTO NETWORK INC p 1566
766 Mmsburg Cnterville Rd, Dayton OH 45459
Tel (937) 428-2400
SIC 5511 7538 7515 7513 5521 5012
HILL INTERNATIONAL TRUCKS NA LLC p 693
47866 Y And O Rd, East Liverpool OH 43920
Tel (330) 386-6440 SIC 5511 5531 7538
FORD MONTROSE INC p 565
3960 Medina Rd, Fairlawn OH 44333
Tel (330) 666-0711
SIC 5511 5521 7515 7513 7538 7532
RICART PROPERTIES INC p 1232
4255 S Hamilton Rd, Groveport OH 43125
Tel (614) 836-6680 SIC 5511
FORD LEBANON INC p 565
770 Columbus Ave, Lebanon OH 45036
Tel (513) 932-1010 SIC 5511 5521 7538
COUGHLIN CHEVROLET INC p 374
9000 Broad St Sw, Pataskala OH 43062
Tel (740) 964-9191
SIC 5511 5012 7538 7532 5531
GLOCKNER CHEVROLET CO p 618
4368 Us Route 23, Portsmouth OH 45662
Tel (740) 353-2161 SIC 5013 5172 5511
WMK LLC p 1620
4199 Kinross Lakes Pkwy # 300, Richfield OH 44286
Tel (234) 312-2000 SIC 5511 7532
MD AUTO GROUP LLC p 933
5013 Detroit Rd, Sheffield Village OH 44054
Tel (440) 934-6001 SIC 5511
YARK AUTOMOTIVE GROUP INC p 1635
6019 W Central Ave, Toledo OH 43615
Tel (419) 841-7771 SIC 5511 7515
Q N P CORP p 1194
979 High St, Worthington OH 43085
Tel (614) 846-0371 SIC 5511
BOB MOORE AUTO GROUP LLC p 196
101 N Robinson Ave # 820, Oklahoma City OK 73102
Tel (405) 605-2350 SIC 5511
BOB MOORE CADILLAC INC p 196
13020 Broadway Ext, Oklahoma City OK 73114
Tel (888) 876-9554 SIC 5511
CARR CHEVROLET INC p 260
15005 Sw Tualatin Vly, Beaverton OR 97003
Tel (503) 644-2161 SIC 5511
LANPHERE ENTERPRISES INC p 844
12505 Sw Brdwy St, Beaverton OR 97005
Tel (503) 643-5577 SIC 5571 5511 5261
KENDALL AUTOMOTIVE GROUP INC p 810
1400 Executive Pkwy # 400, Eugene OR 97401
Tel (541) 335-4000 SIC 5511
MACKENZIE MOTOR CO p 892
4151 Se Tualatin Vly Hwy, Hillsboro OR 97123
Tel (503) 693-1133 SIC 5511 5521
GUARANTY RV INC p 644
20 Highway 99 S, Junction City OR 97448
Tel (541) 998-2333 SIC 5561 5511
▲ LITHIA MOTORS INC p 870
150 N Bartlett St, Medford OR 97501
Tel (541) 776-6401
SIC 5511 5531 5013 7539
DON RASMUSSEN CO p 450
720 Ne Grand Ave, Portland OR 97232
Tel (503) 230-7700 SIC 5511

RON TONKIN CHEVROLET CO p 1249
122 Ne 122nd Ave, Portland OR 97230
Tel (503) 255-4100 SIC 5511
RON TONKIN IMPORTS INC p 1249
9655 Sw Canyon Rd, Portland OR 97225
Tel (503) 292-0662 SIC 5511
TEC EQUIPMENT INC p 1430
750 Ne Columbia Blvd, Portland OR 97211
Tel (503) 285-7667 SIC 5511 7538 7549
HUNTER TRUCK SALES & SERVICE INC p 719
480 Pittsburgh Rd, Butler PA 16002
Tel (724) 586-5770 SIC 5511 5531 7538
FRED BEANS FORD INC p 575
876 N Easton Rd, Doylestown PA 18902
Tel (888) 903-2085
SIC 5511 7513 5521 5012
BROWN-DAUB INC p 220
3903 Hecktown Rd, Easton PA 18045
Tel (610) 253-3521 SIC 5511
KENNEDY AUTOMOTIVE GROUP INC p 811
620 Bustleton Pike, Feasterville Trevose PA 19053
Tel (215) 357-6600 SIC 5511
RGS INC p 1231
527 N Easton Rd, Glenside PA 19038
Tel (215) 885-5400 SIC 5511
FIVE STAR INTERNATIONAL LLC p 553
1810 S 19th St, Harrisburg PA 17104
Tel (717) 986-1500 SIC 5511 7538 5013
TRANSTECK INC p 1473
4303 Lewis Rd, Harrisburg PA 17111
Tel (717) 564-6151 SIC 5511
FORD MCCAFFERTY SALES INC p 565
1939 E Lincoln Hwy, Langhorne PA 19047
Tel (215) 945-8000
SIC 5511 5531 7538 7514 5521 5012
REEDMAN CHEVROLET INC p 1217
Rr 1, Langhorne PA 19047
Tel (215) 757-4961
SIC 5511 5531 7538 5521
COCHRAN OLDSMOBILE INC p 333
4520 William Penn Hwy, Monroeville PA 15146
Tel (412) 373-3333 SIC 5511
BEANS-CLASS FORD MERCURY INC p 165
508 W Main St, New Holland PA 17557
Tel (717) 354-4901 SIC 5511
BERGEYS INC p 174
462 Harleysville Pike, Souderton PA 18964
Tel (215) 721-3430
SIC 5511 5531 7538 5013 5014
TRANSPORT INTERNATIONAL POOL INC p 1472
530 E Swedesford Rd, Wayne PA 19087
Tel (484) 254-0100 SIC 5511 7519
TRANSPORT INTERNATIONAL POOL INC p 1472
530 E Swedesford Rd, Wayne PA 19087
Tel (484) 254-0100
SIC 7519 7513 5511 5211
BAIERL CHEVROLET INC p 145
10432 Perry Hwy, Wexford PA 15090
Tel (724) 935-3711 SIC 5511 5013
BELLA INTERNATIONAL CORP p 170
Ave Kennedy Sector Bechar, San Juan PR 00921
Tel (787) 620-7010 SIC 5511
K I INVESTMENTS INC p 799
Ave 65 De Infntria St1179, San Juan PR 00924
Tel (787) 622-0600 SIC 6519 5012 5511
CAROLINA INTERNATIONAL TRUCKS INC p 259
1619 Bluff Rd, Columbia SC 29201
Tel (803) 799-4923 SIC 5511
DICK SMITH AUTOMOTIVE GROUP INC p 438
9940 Two Notch Rd, Columbia SC 29223
Tel (800) 944-8570 SIC 5511 7515
DYER INC p 464
240 Killian Commons Pkwy, Columbia SC 29203
Tel (803) 691-5602 SIC 5511 7532
HYATT AUTOMOTIVE LLC p 723
1887 Highway 501, Myrtle Beach SC 29577
Tel (843) 626-3657 SIC 5511
T & W OF KNOXVILLE INC p 1419
10315 Parkside Dr, Knoxville TN 37922
Tel (865) 218-3300 SIC 5511 7538 5531
TED RUSSELL FORD INC p 1432
8551 Kingston Pike, Knoxville TN 37919
Tel (865) 693-7611 SIC 5511 5521 5531
NASHVILLE AUTOMOTIVE LLC p 1008
2340 Gallatin Pike N, Madison TN 37115
Tel (615) 851-8000 SIC 5511
CHUCK HUTTON CHEVROLET CO p 304
2471 Mount Moriah Rd, Memphis TN 38115
Tel (901) 365-9700 SIC 5511
COUNTY OF SHELBY p 382
160 N Main St Fl 4, Memphis TN 38103
Tel (901) 222-2050 SIC 5511
GOSSETT MOTOR CARS INC p 626
1901 Covington Pike, Memphis TN 38128
Tel (901) 363-6556 SIC 5511 5012
TAG TRUCK ENTERPRISES LLC p 1421
1650 E Brooks Rd, Memphis TN 38116
Tel (901) 345-5633 SIC 5511
TRI-STATE TRUCK CENTER INC p 1478
494 E Eh Crump Blvd, Memphis TN 38126
Tel (901) 947-5000 SIC 5511 7513 5012
BEAMAN MOTOR CO p 165
1525 Broadway, Nashville TN 37203
Tel (615) 251-8430 SIC 5511 7538
■ RUSH TRUCK LEASING INC p 1259
900 Expo Dr, Smyrna TN 37167
Tel (615) 220-7600 SIC 5511
BRUCKNER TRUCK SALES INC p 220
9471 E Interstate 40, Amarillo TX 79118
Tel (806) 376-6273 SIC 5511
DON DAVIS AUTO GROUP INC p 449
1901 N Collins St, Arlington TX 76011
Tel (817) 461-1000 SIC 5511
MORITZ PARTNERS LP p 989
2111 N Collins St Ste 323, Arlington TX 76011
Tel (817) 461-9222 SIC 5511
COVERT BUICK INC p 385
11750 Research Blvd Ste D, Austin TX 78759
Tel (512) 583-3000 SIC 5511 7532

LEIF JOHNSON FORD INC p 854
501 E Koenig Ln, Austin TX 78751
Tel (512) 454-3711 SIC 5521 5511

SOUTHEAST TEXAS CLASSIC AUTOMOTIVE INC p 1346
1000 Interstate 10 N, Beaumont TX 77702
Tel (409) 898-8001 SIC 5511 7515

NISSAN GRUBBS MID-CITIES LTD p 1044
310 Airport Fwy, Bedford TX 76022
Tel (817) 268-1000 SIC 5511

SAM PACKS FIVE STAR FORD LTD p 1274
1635 S Interstate 35e, Carrollton TX 75006
Tel (972) 447-0606 SIC 5511

TONY GULLO MOTORS I LP p 1460
500 Interstate 45 S, Conroe TX 77304
Tel (936) 539-9191 SIC 7549 5511 5531

PARK PLACE MOTORCARS LTD p 1115
6113 Lemmon Ave, Dallas TX 75209
Tel (214) 526-8701 SIC 5511

SEWELL CORP p 1309
6421 Lemmon Ave, Dallas TX 75209
Tel (214) 352-8100 SIC 5511

SEWELL VILLAGE CADILLAC CO INC p 1309
7310 Lemmon Ave, Dallas TX 75209
Tel (214) 350-2000 SIC 5511

SOUTHWEST INTERNATIONAL TRUCKS INC p 1352
3722 Irving Blvd, Dallas TX 75247
Tel (214) 689-1400 SIC 5511 5531

UTILITY TRAILER OF DALLAS INC p 1537
34241 Lyndon B Jhnson Fwy, Dallas TX 75241
Tel (972) 225-8845 SIC 5012 5015 5511

JAMES WOOD MOTORS INC p 777
2111 S Highway 287, Decatur TX 76234
Tel (940) 627-2177 SIC 5511

FORD CASA INC p 565
5815 Montana Ave, El Paso TX 79925
Tel (915) 779-2272 SIC 5511

RUDOLPH CHEVROLET LLC p 1257
5625 S Desert Blvd, El Paso TX 79932
Tel (915) 544-4321 SIC 5511

TRINITY BAY CITY HOLDINGS LLC p 1481
712 Waltham Ct, El Paso TX 79922
Tel (915) 877-1700 SIC 5511

AUTOBAHN INC p 133
3000 White Settlement Rd, Fort Worth TX 76107
Tel (817) 336-0885 SIC 5511

CLASSIC CHEVROLET LTD p 323
1101 W State Highway 114, Grapevine TX 76051
Tel (817) 421-1200 SIC 5511

LONESTAR FREIGHTLINER GROUP LLC p 876
2051 Hughes Rd, Grapevine TX 76051
Tel (817) 428-9736 SIC 5511 7538

BECK & MASTEN PONTIAC-GMC INC p 167
11300 Fm 1960 Rd W, Houston TX 77065
Tel (281) 469-5222 SIC 5511

CHASTANG ENTERPRISES INC p 291
6200 North Loop E, Houston TX 77026
Tel (713) 678-5000 SIC 5511

DEMONTROND BUICK CO p 428
14101 North Fwy, Houston TX 77090
Tel (281) 872-7200 SIC 5511

DON MCGILL TOYOTA INC p 450
11800 Katy Fwy I10, Houston TX 77079
Tel (281) 496-2000 SIC 5511 5521

FORD MAC HAIK LTD p 565
10333 Katy Fwy, Houston TX 77024
Tel (713) 932-5000 SIC 5511

GILLMAN INTERESTS INC p 612
10595 W Sam Huston Pkwy S, Houston TX 77099
Tel (713) 776-7000 SIC 5511

▲ GROUP 1 AUTOMOTIVE INC p 641
800 Gessner Rd Ste 500, Houston TX 77024
Tel (713) 647-5700
SIC 5511 6141 7538 7532 5531

INTERNATIONAL TRUCKS OF HOUSTON LLC p 757
8900 North Loop E, Houston TX 77029
Tel (713) 674-3444 SIC 5511 5531

MAC HAIK ENTERPRISES p 891
11757 Katy Fwy Ste 1500, Houston TX 77079
Tel (281) 496-7788 SIC 5511

■ MIKE HALL CHEVROLET INC p 968
8100 Highway 6 S, Houston TX 77083
Tel (281) 561-9900 SIC 5511

MOSSY HOLDING CO INC p 992
12150 Old Katy Rd, Houston TX 77079
Tel (281) 558-9970 SIC 5511 6159 7532

RUSSELL & SMITH FORD INC p 1259
3440 South Loop W, Houston TX 77025
Tel (713) 663-4111 SIC 5511

SELECTRANSPORTATION RESOURCES LLC p 1302
9550 North Loop E, Houston TX 77029
Tel (713) 672-4115
SIC 5012 5013 5511 7538

■ SONIC AUTOMOTIVE OF TEXAS LP p 1340
8477 North Fwy, Houston TX 77037
Tel (281) 931-3300 SIC 5511 7538

■ TEXACO EXPLORATION AND PRODUCTION INC p 1441
1500 Louisiana St, Houston TX 77002
Tel (800) 962-1223 SIC 5541 5511 1321

TOMMIE VAUGHN MOTORS INC p 1459
1201 N Shepherd Dr, Houston TX 77008
Tel (713) 869-4661 SIC 5511

NISSAN ROBBINS INC p 1044
18711 Highway 59 N, Humble TX 77338
Tel (281) 446-3181 SIC 5511

■ ASBURY AUTOMOTIVE SOUTHERN CALIFORNIA LLC p 115
3700 W Airport Fwy, Irving TX 75062
Tel (972) 790-6000 SIC 5511

■ BERKSHIRE HATHAWAY AUTOMOTIVE INC p 175
8333 Royal Ridge Pkwy # 100, Irving TX 75063
Tel (972) 536-2900 SIC 7549 5511

IRVING MCDAVID HONDA LP p 765
3700 W Airport Fwy, Irving TX 75062
Tel (972) 790-2000 SIC 5511

■ MCDAVID IRVING-HON LP p 927
3700 W Airport Fwy, Irving TX 75062
Tel (972) 790-6100 SIC 5511

BENSON - SABIN INC p 173
2112 Gulf Fwy S, League City TX 77573
Tel (281) 338-9700 SIC 5511 7538

JORDAN FORD LTD p 793
13010 N Interstate 35, Live Oak TX 78233
Tel (210) 653-3673 SIC 5511

JIM BURNS AUTOMOTIVE GROUP INC p 785
8230 Urbana Ave, Lubbock TX 79424
Tel (806) 747-3211 SIC 5511

MCKINNEY DODGE INC p 930
321 N Central Expy # 240, Mckinney TX 75070
Tel (972) 569-9650 SIC 5511

SUPERIOR TRAILER SALES CO p 1407
501 Us Highway 80 E, Mesquite TX 75182
Tel (972) 226-3893 SIC 5511

KAHLIG ENTERPRISES INC p 800
351 S Interstate 35, New Braunfels TX 78130
Tel (830) 606-8011 SIC 5511

■ RUSH TRUCK CENTERS OF CALIFORNIA INC p 1259
555 S Interstate 35 # 500, New Braunfels TX 78130
Tel (830) 626-5200 SIC 5511 5012

■ RUSH TRUCK CENTERS OF TEXAS INC p 1259
555 S Interstate 35 # 500, New Braunfels TX 78130
Tel (830) 626-5200 SIC 5012 5511

RUSH SALES CO p 1258
2700 E I 20 Service Rd, Odessa TX 79766
Tel (432) 337-2397 SIC 3533 5511

SEWELL FAMILY OF COMPANIES INC p 1309
2425 E 8th St, Odessa TX 79761
Tel (432) 498-0421 SIC 5511

FRENCH-ELLISON TRUCK CENTER LLC p 578
4300 N Cage Blvd, Pharr TX 78577
Tel (956) 781-2401
SIC 5013 5531 5511 5012 7538

CREST CADILLAC INC p 392
2701 Northcrest Dr, Plano TX 75075
Tel (972) 423-7700 SIC 5511

ANCIRA ENTERPRISES INC p 89
10855 W Interstate 10, San Antonio TX 78230
Tel (210) 681-4900 SIC 5511

CURTIS C GUNN INC p 402
227 Broadway St, San Antonio TX 78205
Tel (210) 472-2501 SIC 5511 6531

KAHLIG MOTOR CO p 800
611 Lockhill Selma Rd, San Antonio TX 78216
Tel (210) 308-8900 SIC 5511 7515

PARK NORTH LINCOLN-MERCURY INC p 1115
9207 San Pedro Ave, San Antonio TX 78216
Tel (210) 341-8841 SIC 5511

RED MCCOMBS HYUNDAI LTD p 1215
4800 Nw Loop 410, San Antonio TX 78229
Tel (210) 684-7440 SIC 5511 5521

TOYOTA MOTOR MANUFACTURING TEXAS INC p 1467
1 Lone Star Pass, San Antonio TX 78264
Tel (210) 263-4000 SIC 5511

WORLD CLASS AUTOMOTIVE GROUP LP p 1625
20403 Interstate 45, Spring TX 77388
Tel (281) 719-3700 SIC 5511

RANDALL NOE CHRYSLER DODGE LLP p 1207
1608 W Moore Ave, Terrell TX 75160
Tel (972) 524-3775 SIC 5511

RANDALL NOE FORD-MERCURY INC p 1207
1608 W Moore Ave, Terrell TX 75160
Tel (972) 524-3775 SIC 5511 5521

PARKWAY CHEVROLET INC p 1117
25500 State Highway 249, Tomball TX 77375
Tel (281) 351-8211 SIC 5511 7549 5531

BIG 3 HOLDING CO INC p 181
1625 N Valley Mills Dr, Waco TX 76710
Tel (254) 772-8850 SIC 5511 5571

PATTERSON AUTO CENTER INC p 1121
315 Central Fwy E, Wichita Falls TX 76301
Tel (940) 766-0293 SIC 5511

M & M AUTOMOTIVE INC p 888
11453 S Lone Peak Pkwy, Draper UT 84020
Tel (801) 553-5800 SIC 5511

YOUNG AUTOMOTIVE GROUP INC p 1638
645 N Main St, Layton UT 84041
Tel (801) 544-1234 SIC 5511

GARFF ENTERPRISES INC p 592
405 S Main St Ste 1200, Salt Lake City UT 84111
Tel (801) 257-3400 SIC 5511 6512

UTILITY TRAILER SALES OF UTAH INC p 1537
4970 W 2100 S, Salt Lake City UT 84120
Tel (801) 973-4040 SIC 5511 5531 7539

FREIGHTLINER OF UTAH A LIMITED LIABILITY CO p 577
2240 S 5370 W, West Valley City UT 84120
Tel (801) 978-8000
SIC 5012 5013 7539 7538 5511

HANDY PONTIAC CADILLAC BUICK G M C INC p 657
405 Swanton Rd, Saint Albans VT 05478
Tel (802) 524-6531 SIC 5511

AMERICAN SERVICE CENTER ASSOCIATES OF ALEXANDRIA LLC p 79
200 S Pickett St, Alexandria VA 22304
Tel (703) 284-2490 SIC 5511 7538

LINDSAY MOTOR CAR CO p 868
1525 Kenwood Ave, Alexandria VA 22302
Tel (703) 998-6600 SIC 5511

BRITT FORD SALES INC TED p 214
4175 Auto Park Cir, Chantilly VA 20151
Tel (703) 673-2300 SIC 5511

PETERSBURG MOTOR CO INC p 1138
100 Myers Dr, Charlottesville VA 22901
Tel (434) 951-1000 SIC 5511 7515

SHELOR CHEVROLET CORP p 1314
2265 Roanoke St, Christiansburg VA 24073
Tel (540) 382-2981 SIC 5511

BRITT TRANSPORTATION ENTERPRISES INC TED p 214
11165 Fairfax Blvd, Fairfax VA 22030
Tel (703) 591-8484 SIC 5511

BROWN AUTOMOTIVE GROUP LTD p 219
12500 Fair Lakes Cir # 375, Fairfax VA 22033
Tel (703) 352-5555 SIC 5511

BEYER MOTORS INC DON p 179
118 Gordon Rd, Falls Church VA 22046
Tel (703) 237-5000 SIC 5511

TRUCK ENTERPRISES INC p 1485
3440 S Main St, Harrisonburg VA 22801
Tel (540) 564-6900
SIC 5511 5531 7538 7539

VOLKSWAGEN GROUP OF AMERICA INC p 1564
2200 Ferdinand Porsche Dr, Herndon VA 20171
Tel (703) 364-7000
SIC 5511 5012 5013 6153 6141 4899

GENEVA ENTERPRISES INC p 603
1902 Association Dr, Reston VA 20191
Tel (703) 553-4300 SIC 5511

▲ CARMAX INC p 258
12800 Tuckahoe Creek Pkwy, Richmond VA 23238
Tel (804) 747-0422 SIC 5521 5511 6141

GREATER RICHMOND BUSINESS INC p 636
1833 Commerce Rd, Richmond VA 23224
Tel (804) 232-3492
SIC 5511 5013 5531 7513

PEARSON COMPANIES INC p 1126
9530 Midlothian Pike, Richmond VA 23225
Tel (804) 745-0300 SIC 5511

EXCEL TRUCK GROUP p 516
267 Lee Hwy, Roanoke VA 24019
Tel (540) 777-7700
SIC 5511 5013 7538 5012

CHECKERED FLAG MOTOR CAR CO INC p 292
5225 Virginia Beach Blvd, Virginia Beach VA 23462
Tel (757) 490-1111 SIC 5511 7532

HALL AUTOMOTIVE LLC p 654
441 Viking Dr, Virginia Beach VA 23452
Tel (757) 431-9944 SIC 5511

MCCURLEY INTEGRITY DEALERSHIPS LLC p 927
1325 N Autoplex Way, Pasco WA 99301
Tel (509) 547-5555 SIC 5511

GWP HOLDINGS LLC p 648
3801 Airport Way S, Seattle WA 98108
Tel (206) 624-7383
SIC 5511 7513 7538 5012

■ APPLEWAY CHEVROLET INC p 99
8600 E Sprague Ave, Spokane WA 99212
Tel (509) 924-1150 SIC 5511

HANNAH MOTOR CO p 658
3400 Ne Auto Mall Dr, Vancouver WA 98662
Tel (360) 944-3424 SIC 5511

JRS HOLDING INC p 795
20445 W Capitol Dr, Brookfield WI 53045
Tel (262) 781-2626 SIC 5511

MIKE SHANNON AUTOMOTIVE INC p 968
321 N Rolling Meadows Dr, Fond Du Lac WI 54937
Tel (920) 921-8898 SIC 5511

BROADWAY AUTOMOTIVE - GREEN BAY INC p 216
2700 S Ashland Ave, Green Bay WI 54304
Tel (920) 498-6666 SIC 5511

BROADWAY ENTERPRISES INC p 216
1106 S Military Ave, Green Bay WI 54304
Tel (920) 429-6249 SIC 5511 7514

BROADWAY FORD-HYUNDAI INC p 216
1010 S Military Ave, Green Bay WI 54304
Tel (920) 499-3131
SIC 7515 5511 7513 5521 5012

HOLZ MOTORS INC p 702
5961 S 108th Pl, Hales Corners WI 53130
Tel (414) 425-2400 SIC 5511

JX ENTERPRISES INC p 798
1320 Walnut Ridge Dr, Hartland WI 53029
Tel (800) 810-3410
SIC 5012 5511 7538 6159 7513

FORD KAYSER INC p 565
2303 W Beltline Hwy, Madison WI 53713
Tel (608) 271-6000
SIC 5511 7538 7532 7515 5521

ZIMBRICK INC p 1643
1601 W Beltline Hwy, Madison WI 53713
Tel (608) 277-2277 SIC 5511 7538 5521

V & H INC p 1538
1505 S Central Ave, Marshfield WI 54449
Tel (715) 387-2545 SIC 5511 7513

DARROW RUSS GROUP INC p 412
W133n8569 Executive Pkwy, Menomonee Falls WI 53051
Tel (262) 250-9600 SIC 5511 7538

FOUR KEYS LLC p 571
5505 S 27th St, Milwaukee WI 53221
Tel (414) 282-9300 SIC 5511

KRIETE TRUCK CENTER MILWAUKEE INC p 830
4444 W Blue Mound Rd, Milwaukee WI 53208
Tel (414) 258-8484 SIC 5511

LAKESIDE INTERNATIONAL LLC p 840
11000 W Silver Spring Dr, Milwaukee WI 53225
Tel (414) 353-4800
SIC 5511 5531 7538 7532 6159 7513

WILDE OF WEST ALLIS INC p 1609
3225 S 108th St, Milwaukee WI 53227
Tel (414) 329-6043
SIC 5511 5521 7538 7515 7513 5012

BERGSTROM CHEVROLET-BUICK-CADILLAC INC p 174
150 N Green Bay Rd, Neenah WI 54956
Tel (866) 575-8036 SIC 5511

BERGSTROM CORP p 174
1 Neenah Ctr Ste 700, Neenah WI 54956
Tel (920) 725-4444 SIC 5511

WILDE AUTOS INC p 1609
1710a State Road 164 S, Waukesha WI 53186
Tel (262) 970-5900 SIC 5511

SIC 5521 Motor Vehicle Dealers (Used Only)

■ BROWN & BROWN CHEVROLET INC p 219
145 E Main St, Mesa AZ 85201
Tel (480) 833-3456 SIC 5511 5521 5012

DRIVETIME AUTOMOTIVE GROUP INC p 456
1720 W Rio Salado Pkwy, Tempe AZ 85281
Tel (602) 852-6600 SIC 5521

▲ AMERICAS CAR-MART INC p 81
802 Se Plaza Ave Ste 200, Bentonville AR 72712
Tel (479) 464-9944 SIC 5521 6141

NORM REEVES INC p 1048
18500 Studebaker Rd, Cerritos CA 90703
Tel (562) 402-3844 SIC 5511 5521

K MOTORS INC p 799
965 Arnele Ave, El Cajon CA 92020
Tel (619) 270-3000 SIC 5521 5013 5511

ROTOLO CHEVROLET INC p 1252
16666 S Highland Ave, Fontana CA 92336
Tel (866) 756-9776 SIC 5511 5521 7538

FRESNO TRUCK CENTER p 579
2727 E Central Ave, Fresno CA 93725
Tel (559) 486-4310
SIC 5511 5521 5531 5012 5013 6159

FOX HILLS AUTO INC p 572
5880 W Centinela Ave, Los Angeles CA 90045
Tel (310) 649-3673
SIC 5511 7538 5531 5521

MIDWAY RENT A CAR INC p 967
4751 Wilshire Blvd # 120, Los Angeles CA 90010
Tel (323) 692-4000
SIC 5511 7515 5521 4119 7513

GALPIN MOTORS INC p 590
15505 Roscoe Blvd, North Hills CA 91343
Tel (818) 787-3800
SIC 5511 5521 7538 7515 7514 5531

CROWS LLC p 396
1141 S 1st St, San Jose CA 95110
Tel (408) 230-4049 SIC 5521

■ MILLER AUTOMOTIVE GROUP INC p 970
5425 Van Nuys Blvd, Sherman Oaks CA 91401
Tel (818) 787-8400 SIC 5511 7538 5521

COUNTY FORD NORTH INC p 375
450 W Vista Way, Vista CA 92083
Tel (760) 945-9900
SIC 5511 5521 7538 7515 5531

COMCAR INDUSTRIES INC p 343
502 E Bridgers Ave, Auburndale FL 33823
Tel (863) 967-1101
SIC 4213 5521 5013 4212

■ HERTZ CORP p 687
8501 Williams Rd, Estero FL 33928
Tel (239) 301-7000
SIC 7514 7515 7513 7359 5521 6794

▲ AUTONATION INC p 135
200 Sw 1st Ave Ste 1700, Fort Lauderdale FL 33301
Tel (954) 769-6000 SIC 5511 5521

DUVAL MOTOR CO INC p 463
1616 Cassat Ave, Jacksonville FL 32210
Tel (904) 387-6541 SIC 5521 5511

MUTZ MOTORS LTD PARTNERSHIP p 1003
1430 W Memorial Blvd, Lakeland FL 33815
Tel (863) 682-1100
SIC 5511 7538 7532 7515 5531 5521

KENDALL IMPORTS LLC p 810
10943 S Dixie Hwy, Miami FL 33156
Tel (305) 666-1784 SIC 5511 5521

SOUTH MOTOR CO OF DADE COUNTY p 1344
16165 S Dixie Hwy, Miami FL 33157
Tel (888) 418-3508 SIC 5511 5521

FERMAN CHEVROLET OF TARPON SPRINGS p 538
43520 Us Highway 19 N, Tarpon Springs FL 34689
Tel (727) 942-4800
SIC 5511 7538 7515 7513 5521

■ SMART CHOICE AUTOMOTIVE GROUP INC p 1332
5130 S Washington Ave, Titusville FL 32780
Tel (321) 269-9680 SIC 5521 3714 6141

ROGER DEAN ENTERPRISES INC p 1246
2235 Okeechobee Blvd, West Palm Beach FL 33409
Tel (561) 683-8100
SIC 5511 5521 7538 7532 7515

ELLIS ATLANTA JIM INC p 488
5901 Peachtree Indus Blvd, Atlanta GA 30341
Tel (770) 454-8200 SIC 5511 5521

ENTERPRISE LEASING CO OF GEORGIA LLC p 502
5909 Peachtree Ind, Atlanta GA 30341
Tel (770) 821-0399 SIC 7514 7515 5521

AUTOTRADER.COM INC p 135
3003 Summit Blvd Fl 200, Brookhaven GA 30319
Tel (404) 568-8000 SIC 5521

■ ASBURY AUTOMOTIVE ATLANTA LLC p 115
3039 Premiere Pkwy # 900, Duluth GA 30097
Tel (404) 622-1921
SIC 5511 7515 5013 6159 5521

LOREN BUICK & PONTIAC INC p 878
1610 Waukegan Rd, Glenview IL 60025
Tel (847) 729-8900 SIC 5511 5521

BILL JACOBS MOTORSPORT HOLDINGS INC p 182
1564 W Ogden Ave, Naperville IL 60540
Tel (630) 357-1200 SIC 5511 5521

ARLINGTON AUTOMOTIVE GROUP INC p 110
2095 N Rand Rd, Palatine IL 60074
Tel (847) 394-5100
SIC 7538 5521 5511 5531 7532

BYRIDER SALES OF INDIANA S LLC p 231
12802 Hmlton Crssing Blvd, Carmel IN 46032
Tel (317) 249-3000 SIC 5521

JD BYRIDER SYSTEMS LLC p 780
12802 Hmlton Crssing Blvd, Carmel IN 46032
Tel (317) 249-3000
SIC 6794 5734 7538 7515 5521

▲ KAR AUCTION SERVICES INC p 804
13085 Hmlton Crssing Blvd, Carmel IN 46032
Tel (800) 923-3725 SIC 5012 6153 5521

QUAD CITY AUTOMOTIVE GROUP LLC p 1195
3700 N Harrison St, Davenport IA 52806
Tel (563) 386-1511 SIC 5511 5521

CONKLIN FANGMAN INVESTMENT CO INC p 356
1400 E 11th Ave, Hutchinson KS 67501
Tel (620) 662-4467
SIC 7515 5511 7538 5521

RAY BRANDT NISSAN INC p 1209
4000 Lapalco Blvd, Harvey LA 70058
Tel (504) 367-1666 SIC 5511 5521

RUSSEL MOTOR CARS INC p 1259
6700 Baltimore Nat Pike, Baltimore MD 21228
Tel (410) 788-8400
SIC 5511 7538 7532 5521

INTERNATIONAL MOTOR CARS INC p 756
5000 Auth Way, Suitland MD 20746
Tel (301) 423-8400 SIC 5511 7538 5521

DANIEL J QUIRK INC p 411
372 Quincy Ave, Braintree MA 02184
Tel (781) 843-4800
SIC 5511 5013 5531 7538 5521 7515

INTERNATIONAL CARS LTD INC p 754
382 Newbury St, Danvers MA 01923
Tel (800) 514-1627 SIC 5511 5521

ARROW TRUCK SALES INC p 113
3200 Manchester Trfy I-70, Kansas City MO 64129
Tel (816) 923-5000 SIC 5521 5012

DAVE SINCLAIR FORD WEST p 415
7466 S Lindbergh Blvd, Saint Louis MO 63125
Tel (314) 892-2600
SIC 5511 7538 5521 5012

LOU FUSZ AUTOMOTIVE NETWORK INC p 879
925 N Lindbergh Blvd, Saint Louis MO 63141
Tel (314) 997-3400 SIC 5511 5531 5521

MALCO ENTERPRISES OF NEVADA INC p 899
7120 Haven St, Las Vegas NV 89119
Tel (702) 736-1212 SIC 5521 7514 7513

MERCHANTS AUTOMOTIVE GROUP INC p 944
1278 Hooksett Rd, Hooksett NH 03106
Tel (603) 669-4100 SIC 5521 7515

■ **HERTZ INVESTORS INC** p 687
225 Brae Blvd, Park Ridge NJ 07656
Tel (201) 307-2000
SIC 7514 7515 7513 7359 5521 6794

PRESTIGE OF BERGEN INC p 1173
50 Williams Dr, Ramsey NJ 07446
Tel (201) 825-2700 SIC 5511 5521 5012

ELRAC LLC p 489
1550 Route 23, Wayne NJ 07470
Tel (973) 709-2499
SIC 7514 7515 5511 5521

MAJOR WORLD CHEVROLET LLC p 899
4340 Northern Blvd, Long Island City NY 11101
Tel (718) 937-3700
SIC 5511 7515 7538 5521

■ **TOWN & COUNTRY FORD INC** p 1464
5401 E Independence Blvd, Charlotte NC 28212
Tel (704) 536-5600
SIC 5511 7538 7532 5521

AL SMITH CO INC p 43
2511 Wake Forest Rd, Raleigh NC 27609
Tel (919) 839-7481 SIC 5511 5521

FHA/RALEIGH INC p 539
9101 Glenwood Ave, Raleigh NC 27617
Tel (919) 787-0099 SIC 5511 5521 5012

VALLEY FORD TRUCK INC p 1540
5715 Canal Rd, Cleveland OH 44125
Tel (216) 524-2400
SIC 5013 5511 5521 5531 5012

■ **CORE AUTOMOTIVE TECHNOLOGIES LLC** p 369
800 Manor Park Dr, Columbus OH 43228
Tel (614) 870-5000 SIC 3714 5521

VOSS AUTO NETWORK INC p 1566
766 Mmsburg Cnterville Rd, Dayton OH 45459
Tel (937) 428-2400
SIC 5511 7538 7515 7513 5521 5012

FORD MONTROSE INC p 565
3960 Medina Rd, Fairlawn OH 44333
Tel (330) 666-0711
SIC 5511 5521 7515 7513 7538 7532

FORD LEBANON INC p 565
770 Columbus Ave, Lebanon OH 45036
Tel (513) 932-1010 SIC 5511 5521 7538

COLUMBUS FAIR AUTO AUCTION INC p 342
4700 Groveport Rd, Obetz OH 43207
Tel (614) 497-2000 SIC 5012 5521

MACKENZIE MOTOR CO p 892
4151 Se Tualatin Vly Hwy, Hillsboro OR 97123
Tel (503) 693-1133 SIC 5511 5521

FRED BEANS FORD INC p 575
876 N Easton Rd, Doylestown PA 18902
Tel (888) 903-2085
SIC 5511 7513 5521 5012

FORD MCCAFFERTY SALES INC p 565
1939 E Lincoln Hwy, Langhorne PA 19047
Tel (215) 945-8000
SIC 5511 5531 7538 7514 5521 5012

REEDMAN CHEVROLET INC p 1217
Rr 1, Langhorne PA 19047
Tel (215) 757-4961
SIC 5511 5531 7538 5521

K INVESTMENTS LIMITED PARTNERSHIP p 799
1500 Sycamore Rd Ste 10, Montoursville PA 17754
Tel (570) 327-0111 SIC 7011 5521 5712

TED RUSSELL FORD INC p 1432
8551 Kingston Pike, Knoxville TN 37919
Tel (865) 693-7611 SIC 5511 5521 5531

■ **PAACO AUTOMOTIVE GROUP LP** p 1103
3200 E Randol Mill Rd, Arlington TX 76011
Tel (817) 635-2000 SIC 5521

LEIF JOHNSON FORD INC p 854
501 E Koenig Ln, Austin TX 78751
Tel (512) 454-3711 SIC 5521 5511

DON MCGILL TOYOTA INC p 450
11800 Katy Fwy I10, Houston TX 77079
Tel (281) 496-2000 SIC 5511 5521

RED MCCOMBS HYUNDAI LTD p 1215
4800 Nw Loop 410, San Antonio TX 78229
Tel (210) 684-7440 SIC 5511 5521

RANDALL NOE FORD-MERCURY INC p 1207
1608 W Moore Ave, Terrell TX 75160
Tel (972) 524-3775 SIC 5511 5521

ADESA UTAH LLC p 22
780 S 5600 W, Salt Lake City UT 84104
Tel (801) 322-1234 SIC 5012 5521 5084

▲ **CARMAX INC** p 258
12800 Tuckahoe Creek Pkwy, Richmond VA 23238
Tel (804) 747-0422 SIC 5521 5511 6141

SABMD LLC p 1264
22705 Commerce Center Ct, Sterling VA 20166
Tel (703) 790-1000 SIC 5521

BROADWAY FORD-HYUNDAI INC p 216
1010 S Military Ave, Green Bay WI 54304
Tel (920) 499-3131
SIC 7515 5511 7513 5521 5012

FORD KAYSER INC p 565
2303 W Beltline Hwy, Madison WI 53713
Tel (608) 271-6000
SIC 5511 7538 7532 7515 5521

ZIMBRICK INC p 1643
1601 W Beltline Hwy, Madison WI 53713
Tel (608) 277-2277 SIC 5511 7538 5521

WILDE OF WEST ALLIS INC p 1609
3225 S 108th St, Milwaukee WI 53227
Tel (414) 329-6043
SIC 5511 5521 7538 7515 7513 5012

SIC 5531 Automotive & Home Supply Stores

SOUTHLAND INTERNATIONAL TRUCKS INC p 1351
200 Oxmoor Blvd, Birmingham AL 35209
Tel (205) 942-6226
SIC 5511 5531 7538 7513

MCGRIFF INDUSTRIES INC p 929
86 Walnut St Ne, Cullman AL 35055
Tel (256) 739-0780 SIC 5531 7534

HWASHIN AMERICA CORP p 722
661 Montgomery Hwy, Greenville AL 36037
Tel (334) 382-1100 SIC 5531

FOUR STAR FREIGHTLINER INC p 572
3140 Hayneville Rd, Montgomery AL 36108
Tel (334) 263-1085 SIC 5012 5531

CANYON STATE OIL CO INC p 248
2640 N 31st Ave, Phoenix AZ 85009
Tel (602) 269-7981 SIC 5172 5531

■ **CSK AUTO CORP** p 398
645 E Mazouri Ave Ste 400, Phoenix AZ 85012
Tel (602) 265-9200 SIC 5531

CSK AUTO INC p 398
645 E Missouri Ave # 400, Phoenix AZ 85012
Tel (602) 265-9200 SIC 5531

■ **U-HAUL INTERNATIONAL INC** p 1498
2727 N Central Ave, Phoenix AZ 85004
Tel (602) 263-6011
SIC 7513 7519 7359 5531 4226 8741

DISCOUNT TIRE CO INC p 442
20225 N Scottsdale Rd, Scottsdale AZ 85255
Tel (480) 606-6000 SIC 5531

DISCOUNT TIRE CO OF NEW MEXICO INC p 442
20225 N Scottsdale Rd, Scottsdale AZ 85255
Tel (480) 606-6000 SIC 5531

DISCOUNT TIRE CO OF TEXAS INC p 442
20225 N Scottsdale Rd, Scottsdale AZ 85255
Tel (817) 460-0162 SIC 5531

REINALT-THOMAS CORP p 1221
20225 N Scottsdale Rd, Scottsdale AZ 85255
Tel (480) 606-6000 SIC 5531

SOUTHERN CALIFORNIA DISCOUNT TIRE CO INC p 1347
5310 E Shea Blvd, Scottsdale AZ 85254
Tel (480) 606-6000 SIC 5531

EARNHARDT FORD SALES CO INC p 469
7300 W Orchid Ln, Tempe AZ 85284
Tel (480) 893-0000
SIC 5511 5531 7538 5561

▲ **MURPHY USA INC** p 1001
200 E Peach St, El Dorado AR 71730
Tel (870) 875-7600 SIC 5531 5541

■ **PICK-YOUR-PART AUTO WRECKING** p 1146
1235 S Beach Blvd, Anaheim CA 92804
Tel (714) 385-1200 SIC 5531 5093

THREE-WAY CHEVROLET CO p 1450
4501 Wible Rd, Bakersfield CA 93313
Tel (661) 847-6400
SIC 5511 5531 7515 7538 7532

PARKHOUSE TIRE SERVICE INC p 1116
5960 Shull St, Bell Gardens CA 90201
Tel (562) 928-0421 SIC 5531

GRIFFIN MOTORWERKE INC p 640
1146 6th St, Berkeley CA 94710
Tel (510) 524-7447 SIC 7538 5531

ECOLOGY AUTO PARTS INC p 476
14150 Vine Pl, Cerritos CA 90703
Tel (562) 404-2277 SIC 5531

KRACO ENTERPRISES LLC p 829
505 E Euclid Ave, Compton CA 90222
Tel (310) 639-0666 SIC 5531 3069 5013

■ **TRANSAMERICAN DISSOLUTION CO LLC** p 1470
400 W Artesia Blvd, Compton CA 90220
Tel (310) 900-5500 SIC 5531 5013

UTILITY TRAILER SALES OF SOUTHERN CALIFORNIA LLC p 1537
15567 Valley Blvd, Fontana CA 92335
Tel (877) 275-4887
SIC 5012 5013 5531 5561

FRESNO TRUCK CENTER p 579
2727 E Central Ave, Fresno CA 93725
Tel (559) 486-4310
SIC 5511 5521 5531 5012 5013 6159

MAZDA MOTOR OF AMERICA INC p 924
7755 Irvine Center Dr, Irvine CA 92618
Tel (949) 727-1990 SIC 5511 5531

ATV INC p 129
14407 Alondra Blvd, La Mirada CA 90638
Tel (562) 977-8565 SIC 5531 7538

FOX HILLS AUTO INC p 572
5880 W Centinela Ave, Los Angeles CA 90045
Tel (310) 649-3673
SIC 5511 7538 5531 5521

RENT A WHEEL p 1224
11726 San Vicente Blvd # 400, Los Angeles CA 90049
Tel (818) 786-7906 SIC 5531

RENT-A-TIRE LP p 1224
11726 San Vicente Blvd # 400, Los Angeles CA 90049
Tel (818) 786-7906 SIC 5531 3312

FORNACA INC p 568
2400 National City Blvd, National City CA 91950
Tel (619) 474-5573 SIC 5511 7532 5531

■ **WORLDPAC INC** p 1626
37137 Hickory St, Newark CA 94560
Tel (510) 742-8900 SIC 5013 5531

GALPIN MOTORS INC p 590
15505 Roscoe Blvd, North Hills CA 91343
Tel (818) 787-3800
SIC 5511 5521 7538 7515 7514 5531

GOLDEN GATE FREIGHTLINER INC p 621
8200 Baldwin St, Oakland CA 94621
Tel (559) 486-4310 SIC 5511 5531 7538

BI WAREHOUSING INC p 180
5404 Pacific St, Rocklin CA 95677
Tel (916) 624-0654 SIC 5531 5013 7539

LAKIN TIRE WEST INC p 840
15305 Spring Ave, Santa Fe Springs CA 90670
Tel (562) 802-2752 SIC 5014 5531

WESTRUX INTERNATIONAL INC p 1603
15555 Valley View Ave, Santa Fe Springs CA 90670
Tel (562) 404-1020
SIC 5511 5531 7513 7538

TBC SHARED SERVICES INC p 1427
742 S Main St, Sebastopol CA 95472
Tel (707) 829-9864 SIC 5531 7534

COUNTY FORD NORTH INC p 375
450 W Vista Way, Vista CA 92083
Tel (760) 945-9900
SIC 5511 5521 7538 7515 5531

MC TIRES p 925
538 Olive Ave Ste 304, Vista CA 92083
Tel (760) 846-5613 SIC 5014 5531

PHIL LONG FORD LLC p 1142
1212 Motor City Dr, Colorado Springs CO 80905
Tel (719) 575-7100
SIC 5511 7515 7538 5531

A & E TIRE INC p 4
3855 E 52nd Ave, Denver CO 80216
Tel (303) 308-6900 SIC 5014 7534 5531

PEERLESS TYRE CO p 1127
5000 Kingston St, Denver CO 80239
Tel (303) 371-4300 SIC 5541 5531

GRAINLAND COOPERATIVE p 629
421 S Colorado Ave, Haxtun CO 80731
Tel (970) 774-6166
SIC 5191 4221 5531 5541

TOWN FAIR TIRE CENTERS INC p 1465
460 Coe Ave, East Haven CT 06512
Tel (203) 467-8600 SIC 5531 5014 5013

MANAGEMENT CONSULTING INC p 900
2503 Se 17th Ave, Cape Coral FL 33910
Tel (239) 458-3611 SIC 5531 5087

MORGAN TIRE & AUTO LLC p 989
2021 Sunnydale Blvd, Clearwater FL 33765
Tel (727) 441-3727 SIC 7539 5531 5014

JM FAMILY ENTERPRISES INC p 786
100 Jim Moran Blvd, Deerfield Beach FL 33442
Tel (954) 429-2000
SIC 5511 5012 5013 5531

EARL W COLVARD INC p 468
816 S Woodland Blvd, Deland FL 32720
Tel (386) 734-6447 SIC 5531 7534

HOLMAN AUTOMOTIVE INC p 701
12 E Sunrise Blvd, Fort Lauderdale FL 33304
Tel (954) 779-2000 SIC 5511 5531

NEXTRAN CORP p 1041
1986 W Beaver St, Jacksonville FL 32209
Tel (904) 354-3721 SIC 5511 5531 7538

TOM NEHL TRUCK CO p 1459
417 Edgewood Ave S, Jacksonville FL 32254
Tel (904) 389-3653 SIC 5511 5531 7538

■ **DISCOUNT AUTO PARTS LLC** p 442
4900 Frontage Rd S, Lakeland FL 33815
Tel (863) 248-2056 SIC 5531

MCGEE TIRE STORES INC p 929
3939 Us Highway 98 S # 101, Lakeland FL 33812
Tel (863) 667-3347 SIC 5531 7538

MUTZ MOTORS LTD PARTNERSHIP p 1003
1430 W Memorial Blvd, Lakeland FL 33815
Tel (863) 682-1100
SIC 5511 7538 7532 7515 5531 5521

WARREN HENRY AUTOMOBILES INC p 1577
20800 Nw 2nd Ave, Miami FL 33169
Tel (305) 690-6010 SIC 5511 5531 7538

CHRISTENSEN ENTERPRISES INC p 302
333 Thorpe Rd, Orlando FL 32824
Tel (407) 830-6401 SIC 5531 7538 7532

TBC RETAIL GROUP INC p 1427
4280 Prof Ctr Dr Ste 400, Palm Beach Gardens FL 33410
Tel (561) 383-3000 SIC 7538 5531 7534

BENNETT AUTO SUPPLY INC p 173
3141 Sw 10th St, Pompano Beach FL 33069
Tel (954) 335-8700 SIC 5531 5013 3711

■ **LAND N SEA DISTRIBUTING INC** p 842
3131 N Andrews Avenue Ext, Pompano Beach FL 33064
Tel (954) 792-9971
SIC 5088 5091 5046 5531

DINGMAN GROUP INC p 440
1051 W Webster Ave, Winter Park FL 32789
Tel (407) 644-6043 SIC 5511 5531 7539

▲ **GENUINE PARTS CO** p 605
2999 Wildwood Pkwy, Atlanta GA 30339
Tel (770) 953-1700
SIC 5013 5531 3714 5084 5085 5021

TOM GRADDY ENTERPRISES INC p 1459
3348 Peachtree Rd Ne, Atlanta GA 30326
Tel (404) 363-8390
SIC 5531 5511 7538 5012

PANASONIC ENERGY CORP OF AMERICA p 1111
1 Panasonic Dr, Columbus GA 31907
Tel (706) 561-7730 SIC 3691 5531

BROOKS AUTO PARTS INC p 218
402 Peterson Ave S, Douglas GA 31533
Tel (912) 384-7818 SIC 5531

KAUFFMAN TIRE INC p 805
2832 Anvil Block Rd, Ellenwood GA 30294
Tel (404) 762-4944 SIC 5014 5531

ATLANTA COMMERCIAL TIRE INC p 125
5067 Old Kennedy Rd, Forest Park GA 30297
Tel (404) 351-8016 SIC 5014 5531

D&B SUPPLY CO p 407
3303 E Linden St, Caldwell ID 83605
Tel (208) 459-7446
SIC 5191 5699 5251 5261 5999 5531

COMMERCIAL TIRE INC p 345
2095 E Commercial St, Meridian ID 83642
Tel (208) 888-8800 SIC 5531 5014

BRIDGESTONE RETAIL OPERATIONS LLC p 211
333 E Lake St Ste 300, Bloomingdale IL 60108
Tel (630) 259-9000 SIC 5531 7534 5014

MAC NEIL AUTOMOTIVE PRODUCTS LIMITED p 891
1 Macneil Ct, Bolingbrook IL 60440
Tel (630) 769-1500 SIC 5531 5013

▲ **SEARS HOLDINGS CORP** p 1297
3333 Beverly Rd, Hoffman Estates IL 60179
Tel (847) 286-2500
SIC 5311 5411 5531 5961

ARLINGTON AUTOMOTIVE GROUP INC p 110
2095 N Rand Rd, Palatine IL 60074
Tel (847) 394-5100
SIC 7538 5521 5511 5531 7532

PATRICK SCHAUMBURG AUTOMOBILES INC p 1120
526 Mall Dr, Schaumburg IL 60173
Tel (847) 605-4000
SIC 5511 7539 7538 7532 5531 5013

BEN TIRE DISTRIBUTORS LTD p 172
203 E Madison St, Toledo IL 62468
Tel (800) 252-8961
SIC 5014 5013 5531 7534

TRUCK CENTERS INC p 1485
2280 Formosa Rd, Troy IL 62294
Tel (618) 667-3454
SIC 5531 5511 7538 5012 4522 7699

TRIPLE S TIRE CO INC p 1482
405 S 9th St, Elwood IN 46036
Tel (765) 552-5765 SIC 5014 5531

RABEN TIRE CO LLC p 1203
2100 N New York Ave, Evansville IN 47711
Tel (812) 465-5565 SIC 5531 5014

FIRESTONE INDUSTRIAL PRODUCTS CO LLC p 544
250 W 96th St Ste 150, Indianapolis IN 46260
Tel (317) 818-8600
SIC 5531 3469 3714 3495

JACKSON OIL & SOLVENTS INC p 774
1970 Kentucky Ave, Indianapolis IN 46221
Tel (317) 481-2244
SIC 5172 5541 5983 5531

PALMER TRUCKS INC p 1109
2929 S Holt Rd, Indianapolis IN 46241
Tel (317) 243-1668
SIC 5511 5531 7538 7513 5012

TRUCK COUNTRY OF INDIANA INC p 1485
1851 W Thompson Rd, Indianapolis IN 46217
Tel (317) 788-1533
SIC 5511 5531 7538 7539

THEISENS INC p 1446
6201 Chavenelle Rd, Dubuque IA 52002
Tel (563) 556-4738
SIC 5531 5999 5699 5261

TRUCK COUNTRY OF IOWA INC p 1485
2099 Southpark Ct Ste 2, Dubuque IA 52003
Tel (563) 556-3773 SIC 5012 5531 7538

BECKER TIRE & TREADING INC p 167
904 Washington St, Great Bend KS 67530
Tel (620) 793-5414 SIC 5014 5531

STRAUB INTERNATIONAL INC p 1393
214 Sw 40 Ave, Great Bend KS 67530
Tel (620) 792-5256 SIC 5083 5531

C&M TIRE INC p 234
401 S 42nd St, Kansas City KS 66106
Tel (913) 321-3003
SIC 5531 7534 5014 3312

S & S FIRESTONE INC p 1261
1475 Jingle Bell Ln, Lexington KY 40509
Tel (859) 281-8500 SIC 5531

SMITTYS SUPPLY INC p 1334
63399 Highway 51, Roseland LA 70456
Tel (985) 748-9687 SIC 5172 5531

RED BALL OXYGEN CO INC p 1215
609 N Market St, Shreveport LA 71107
Tel (318) 425-6300
SIC 5084 5085 5169 5099 5531 5013

V I P INC p 1538
12 Lexington St, Lewiston ME 04240
Tel (207) 784-5423 SIC 5531

BETHESDA INVESTMENT HOLDING CO INC p 178
10400 Auto Park Ave, Bethesda MD 20817
Tel (301) 469-6600
SIC 5511 7539 5013 5531

SAVE MORE INC p 1284
9405 Livingston Rd, Fort Washington MD 20744
Tel (301) 372-1000 SIC 5531 5015

R & H MOTOR CARS LTD p 1201
9727 Reisterstown Rd, Owings Mills MD 21117
Tel (410) 363-7793 SIC 5511 7538 5531

DANIEL J QUIRK INC p 411
372 Quincy Ave, Braintree MA 02184
Tel (781) 843-4800
SIC 5511 5013 5531 7538 5521 7515

CONSUMER AUTO PARTS INC p 361
75 Fortune Blvd, Milford MA 01757
Tel (508) 634-0600 SIC 5531 5013

■ AUTOPART INTERNATIONAL INC p 135
192 Mansfield Ave, Norton MA 02766
Tel (781) 784-1111 SIC 5013 5531

SULLIVAN INVESTMENT CO INC p 1397
41 Accord Park Dr, Norwell MA 02061
Tel (781) 982-1550 SIC 5531 7534

SULLIVAN TIRE CO INC p 1397
41 Accord Park Dr, Norwell MA 02061
Tel (781) 982-1550 SIC 5531 7538 5014

BELLE TIRE DISTRIBUTORS INC p 170
1000 Enterprise Dr, Allen Park MI 48101
Tel (888) 462-3553 SIC 5531 5014

DENSO MANUFACTURING MICHIGAN INC p 429
1 Denso Rd, Battle Creek MI 49037
Tel (269) 965-3322 SIC 5531

■ MURRAYS DISCOUNT AUTO STORES INC p 1002
8080 Haggerty Rd, Belleville MI 48111
Tel (734) 957-8080 SIC 5531

AWI HOLDINGS INC p 139
440 Kirtland St Sw, Grand Rapids MI 49507
Tel (616) 243-2125 SIC 5013 5531

FICOSA NORTH AMERICA CORP p 540
30870 Stephenson Hwy, Madison Heights MI 48071
Tel (248) 307-2230 SIC 5531

AFX INDUSTRIES LLC p 33
1411 3rd St Ste G, Port Huron MI 48060
Tel (810) 966-4650 SIC 3111 5531

▲ HORIZON GLOBAL CORP p 707
2600 W Big Beaver Rd # 555, Troy MI 48084
Tel (248) 593-8820 SIC 3714 3711 5531

LANE AUTOMOTIVE INC p 843
8300 Lane Dr, Watervliet MI 49098
Tel (269) 463-4113 SIC 5013 5531

WELLER AUTO PARTS INC p 1589
2525 Chicago Dr Sw, Wyoming MI 49519
Tel (616) 538-5000 SIC 5013 5015 5531

NUSS TRUCK GROUP INC p 1067
6500 Highway 63 S, Rochester MN 55904
Tel (507) 288-9488 SIC 5511 5531

GILLELAND CHEVROLET CADILLAC INC p 612
3019 W Division St, Saint Cloud MN 56301
Tel (320) 281-4290 SIC 5511 5531 7538

DUNLAP & KYLE CO INC p 461
280 Eureka St, Batesville MS 38606
Tel (662) 563-7601 SIC 5014 5531 5013

PLAZA TIRE SERVICE INC p 1156
2075 Corporate Cir, Cape Girardeau MO 63703
Tel (573) 334-5036 SIC 5014 5531 7538

DOBBS TIRE & AUTO CENTERS INC p 447
1983 Brennan Plz, High Ridge MO 63049
Tel (636) 677-2101 SIC 5531

KCR INTERNATIONAL TRUCKS INC p 806
7700 Ne 38th St, Kansas City MO 64161
Tel (816) 455-1833
SIC 5511 5531 7538 7513

TG MISSOURI CORP p 1446
2200 Plattin Rd, Perryville MO 63775
Tel (573) 547-1041 SIC 5531

LOU FUSZ AUTOMOTIVE NETWORK INC p 879
925 N Lindbergh Blvd, Saint Louis MO 63141
Tel (314) 997-3400 SIC 5511 5531 5521

■ OREILLY AUTO ENTERPRISES LLC p 1094
233 S Patterson Ave, Springfield MO 65802
Tel (417) 862-6708 SIC 5531

▲ OREILLY AUTOMOTIVE INC p 1094
233 S Patterson Ave, Springfield MO 65802
Tel (417) 862-6708 SIC 5531 5013

■ OREILLY AUTOMOTIVE STORES INC p 1094
233 S Patterson Ave, Springfield MO 65802
Tel (417) 862-6708 SIC 5013 5531

TIRE GUYS INC p 1455
1401 Industrial Ave, Billings MT 59101
Tel (406) 245-4006 SIC 5531

RANCH AND HOME SUPPLY LLC p 1207
2311 N 7th Ave, Bozeman MT 59715
Tel (406) 586-8466
SIC 5699 5191 5531 5251

NEBRASKALAND TIRE INC p 1023
Hwy 283 & Hwy I 80, Lexington NE 68850
Tel (308) 324-2338 SIC 5531 5541 5411

TO HAAS TIRE CO INC p 1458
1415 W Commerce Way, Lincoln NE 68521
Tel (402) 434-3434 SIC 5014 5531 7539

AUTOMOTIVE SUPPLY ASSOCIATES INC p 134
129 Manchester St, Concord NH 03301
Tel (603) 225-4000
SIC 5013 7539 5531 5169 5015

WINDWARD PETROLEUM INC p 1616
1064 Goffs Falls Rd, Manchester NH 03103
Tel (603) 222-2900 SIC 5531

INTER-CITY TIRE & AUTO CENTER INC p 751
777 Dowd Ave, Elizabeth NJ 07201
Tel (908) 354-5533 SIC 5531 5013 7538

■ CEQUENT UK LTD p 283
123 Town Square Pl, Jersey City NJ 07310
Tel (734) 656-3078 SIC 4789 3714 5531

PINE BELT ENTERPRISES INC p 1148
1088 Route 88, Lakewood NJ 08701
Tel (732) 363-2900 SIC 5511 7537 5531

R & S PARTS AND SERVICE INC p 1201
7 Brick Plant Rd Ste C, South River NJ 08882
Tel (732) 525-5938 SIC 5531

HALE TRAILER BRAKE & WHEEL INC p 653
Cooper Rd Rr 73, Voorhees NJ 08043
Tel (800) 232-6535 SIC 5511 7539 5531

WWL VEHICLE SERVICES AMERICAS INC p 1629
188 Broadway Ste 1, Woodcliff Lake NJ 07677
Tel (201) 505-5100 SIC 4225 5531 7549

FORREST TIRE CO INC p 568
414 S Canal St, Carlsbad NM 88220
Tel (575) 887-3567 SIC 5531 5014

MAX FINKELSTEIN INC p 922
2840 31st St, Astoria NY 11102
Tel (718) 274-8900 SIC 5014 5531

D & W DIESEL INC p 406
1503 Clark Street Rd, Auburn NY 13021
Tel (315) 253-5300 SIC 5013 5531

KOST TIRE DISTRIBUTORS INC p 828
200 Holleder Pkwy, Binghamton NY 13904
Tel (607) 723-9471 SIC 5014 5531 7538

DUNN TIRE LLC p 461
475 Cayuga Rd Ste 500, Buffalo NY 14225
Tel (716) 683-3910 SIC 5531 5014

VAN BORTEL FORD INC p 1542
71 Marsh Rd, East Rochester NY 14445
Tel (585) 586-4415 SIC 5531 7539

REGIONAL INTERNATIONAL CORP p 1219
1007 Lehigh Station Rd, Henrietta NY 14467
Tel (585) 359-2011
SIC 5013 5012 7539 7538 5531

ARCH-AUTO PARTS CORP p 104
17008 Jamaica Ave, Jamaica NY 11432
Tel (718) 657-9600 SIC 5013 5531

GABRIELLI TRUCK SALES LTD p 588
15320 S Conduit Ave, Jamaica NY 11434
Tel (718) 977-7348 SIC 5511 5531 7538

MAVIS TIRE SUPPLY LLC p 922
358 Saw Mill River Rd # 17, Millwood NY 10546
Tel (914) 984-2500 SIC 5014 5531

SOMERSET TIRE SERVICE INC p 1339
358 Saw Mill River Rd # 5, Millwood NY 10546
Tel (732) 356-8500
SIC 5531 5014 5013 7538

FUCCILLO HYUNDAI OF GREECE INC p 583
3975 W Ridge Rd, Rochester NY 14626
Tel (585) 720-9000 SIC 5511 5531

PARTS AUTHORITY INC p 1118
495 Merrick Rd, Rockville Centre NY 11570
Tel (516) 678-3900 SIC 5013 5015 5531

SUMITOMO RUBBER USA LLC p 1398
80 State St, Tonawanda NY 14150
Tel (716) 879-8200 SIC 5531

CAMSO USA INC p 246
306 Forsyth Hall Dr, Charlotte NC 28273
Tel (704) 374-9700 SIC 5531 5014

SNIDER TIRE INC p 1335
200 E Meadowview Rd, Greensboro NC 27406
Tel (336) 691-5480 SIC 5531 7534

TERRYS TIRE TOWN INC p 1440
12200 Herbert Wayne Ct, Huntersville NC 28078
Tel (330) 821-5022 SIC 5014 5531

FIRESTONE FIBERS & TEXTILES CO LLC p 544
100 Firestone Ln, Kings Mountain NC 28086
Tel (704) 734-2110 SIC 5531

■ GENERAL PARTS INC p 601
2635 E Millbrook Rd Ste C, Raleigh NC 27604
Tel (919) 573-3000 SIC 5013 5531

■ REPUBLIC AUTOMOTIVE PARTS SALES INC p 1225
2635 E Millbrook Rd, Raleigh NC 27604
Tel (919) 573-3000 SIC 5013 5531

S BLACK TIRE SERVICE INC p 1262
30 Bitmore Rd, Whiteville NC 28472
Tel (910) 642-4123 SIC 5531 5014

BARNES MOTOR & PARTS CO INC p 156
2728 Forest Hills Rd Sw, Wilson NC 27893
Tel (252) 243-2161 SIC 5531

PARRISH TIRE CO p 1117
5130 Indiana Ave, Winston Salem NC 27106
Tel (336) 767-0202 SIC 5014 5531 7534

■ MYERS TIRE SUPPLY DISTRIBUTION INC p 1004
1293 S Main St, Akron OH 44301
Tel (330) 253-5592 SIC 5531

KOI ENTERPRISES INC p 826
2701 Spring Grove Ave, Cincinnati OH 45225
Tel (513) 357-2400 SIC 5013 5531

SMYTH AUTOMOTIVE INC p 1335
4275 Mt Carmel Tobasco Rd, Cincinnati OH 45244
Tel (513) 528-2800 SIC 5013 5531

VALLEY FORD TRUCK INC p 1540
5715 Canal Rd, Cleveland OH 44125
Tel (216) 524-2400
SIC 5013 5511 5521 5531 5012

K & M TIRE INC p 798
965 Spencerville Rd, Delphos OH 45833
Tel (419) 695-1061 SIC 5014 7538 5531

HILL INTERNATIONAL TRUCKS NA LLC p 693
47866 Y And O Rd, East Liverpool OH 43920
Tel (330) 386-6440 SIC 5511 5531 7538

ADVICS NORTH AMERICA INC p 28
1650 Kingsview Dr, Lebanon OH 45036
Tel (513) 696-5450
SIC 8731 8742 5013 5531

COUGHLIN CHEVROLET INC p 374
9000 Broad St Sw, Pataskala OH 43062
Tel (740) 964-9191
SIC 5511 5012 7538 7532 5531

■ CEQUENT CONSUMER PRODUCTS INC p 283
29000 Aurora Rd Ste 2, Solon OH 44139
Tel (440) 498-0001 SIC 5531 3714

SANTMYER OIL CO INC p 1281
3000 Old Airport Rd, Wooster OH 44691
Tel (330) 262-6501
SIC 5172 5983 4212 5531

ATWOOD DISTRIBUTING LP p 130
500 S Garland Rd, Enid OK 73703
Tel (580) 233-3702
SIC 5261 5251 5531 5311

T & W TIRE LLC p 1419
25 N Council Rd, Oklahoma City OK 73127
Tel (405) 787-6711 SIC 5531

CCC PARTS CO p 270
420 S 145th East Ave, Tulsa OK 74108
Tel (918) 838-9797 SIC 5531

CCI CORP p 270
420 S 145th East Ave, Tulsa OK 74108
Tel (918) 743-6005 SIC 5531

NATIONAL TRUCK PARTS OF MIDWEST INC p 1016
1901 N Sheridan Rd, Tulsa OK 74115
Tel (918) 836-0151 SIC 5531

LES SCHWAB TIRE CENTERS OF PORTLAND INC p 857
20900 Cooley Rd, Bend OR 97701
Tel (541) 447-4136 SIC 5531

LES SCHWAB TIRE CENTERS OF WASHINGTON INC p 857
20900 Cooley Rd, Bend OR 97701
Tel (541) 447-4136 SIC 5531

LES SCHWAB WAREHOUSE CENTER INC p 857
20900 Cooley Rd, Bend OR 97701
Tel (541) 447-4136 SIC 5014 7534 5531

▲ LITHIA MOTORS INC p 870
150 N Bartlett St, Medford OR 97501
Tel (541) 776-6401
SIC 5511 5531 5013 7539

LES SCHWAB TIRE CENTERS OF IDAHO INC p 857
646 Nw Madras Hwy, Prineville OR 97754
Tel (541) 447-4136 SIC 5531

G I JOES INC p 587
9805 Sw Boeckman Rd, Wilsonville OR 97070
Tel (503) 682-2242
SIC 5941 5699 5531 5999

JACK WILLIAMS TIRE CO INC p 773
700 Rocky Glen Rd, Avoca PA 18641
Tel (570) 457-5000 SIC 5531 5014

SERVICE TIRE TRUCK CENTER INC p 1307
2255 Avenue A, Bethlehem PA 18017
Tel (610) 691-8473 SIC 7534 5531

READING EQUIPMENT & DISTRIBUTION LLC p 1213
1363 Bowmansville Rd, Bowmansville PA 17507
Tel (717) 445-6746 SIC 5531 7532

ANDERSON EQUIPMENT CO p 90
1000 Washington Pike, Bridgeville PA 15017
Tel (412) 343-2300
SIC 5082 7699 7353 5531

HUNTER TRUCK SALES & SERVICE INC p 719
480 Pittsburgh Rd, Butler PA 16002
Tel (724) 586-5770 SIC 5511 5531 7538

VALLEY TIRE CO INC p 1541
15 Mckean Ave, Charleroi PA 15022
Tel (724) 489-4483
SIC 5531 7539 5014 7534

■ KEYSTONE AUTOMOTIVE HOLDINGS INC p 815
44 Tunkhannock Ave, Exeter PA 18643
Tel (570) 655-4514 SIC 5013 5531

■ KEYSTONE AUTOMOTIVE OPERATIONS INC p 815
44 Tunkhannock Ave, Exeter PA 18643
Tel (570) 655-4514 SIC 5531 5013

H & F GULF INC p 649
1834 Lincoln Hwy E, Lancaster PA 17602
Tel (717) 392-6793 SIC 5014 5531

FORD MCCAFFERTY SALES INC p 565
1939 E Lincoln Hwy, Langhorne PA 19047
Tel (215) 945-8000
SIC 5511 5531 7538 7514 5521 5012

REEDMAN CHEVROLET INC p 1217
Rr 1, Langhorne PA 19047
Tel (215) 757-4961
SIC 5511 5531 7538 5521

TURN 5 INC p 1492
7 Lee Blvd, Malvern PA 19355
Tel (610) 251-2397 SIC 5531

■ PEP BOYS - MANNY MOE & JACK p 1133
3111 W Allegheny Ave, Philadelphia PA 19132
Tel (215) 430-9000 SIC 5531 7539 7533

■ PEP BOYS - MANNY MOE & JACK OF DELAWARE INC p 1133
3111 W Allegheny Ave, Philadelphia PA 19132
Tel (215) 229-7555 SIC 5531

■ PEP BOYS MANNY MOE & JACK OF CALIFORNIA p 1133
3111 W Allegheny Ave, Philadelphia PA 19132
Tel (215) 430-9095 SIC 5531 7533 7539

■ PEP BOYS-MANNY MOE & JACK OF PUERTO RICO INC p 1133
3111 W Allegheny Ave, Philadelphia PA 19132
Tel (215) 229-9000 SIC 5531

RETIREES OF GOODYEAR TIRE AND RUBBER CO HEALTH CARE TRUST p 1229
60 Blvd Of The Allies, Pittsburgh PA 15222
Tel (866) 694-6477 SIC 5531

TRG WIND DOWN LLC p 1476
201 Hancock Blvd, Reading PA 19611
Tel (610) 775-3301
SIC 3713 3792 3469 5531 7532

BERGEYS INC p 174
462 Harleysville Pike, Souderton PA 18964
Tel (215) 721-3430
SIC 5511 5531 7538 5013 5014

MCCARTHY TIRE SERVICE CO INC p 926
340 Kidder St, Wilkes Barre PA 18702
Tel (570) 822-3151 SIC 5014 5531

BENNYS INC p 173
340 Waterman Ave, Smithfield RI 02917
Tel (401) 231-0965 SIC 5531

TIRE CENTERS LLC p 1455
310 Inglesby Pkwy, Duncan SC 29334
Tel (864) 329-2700 SIC 5014 5531 7534

BLATCHFORDS INC p 189
207 S Chicago St, Hot Springs SD 57747
Tel (605) 745-5173
SIC 5251 5712 5531 5947 5722

▲ TRACTOR SUPPLY CO p 1468
5401 Virginia Way, Brentwood TN 37027
Tel (615) 440-4000
SIC 5999 5261 5251 5531 5699

T & W OF KNOXVILLE INC p 1419
10315 Parkside Dr, Knoxville TN 37922
Tel (865) 218-3300 SIC 5511 7538 5531

TED RUSSELL FORD INC p 1432
8551 Kingston Pike, Knoxville TN 37919
Tel (865) 693-7611 SIC 5511 5521 5531

▲ AUTOZONE INC p 135
123 S Front St, Memphis TN 38103
Tel (901) 495-6500 SIC 5531 5734

TRUCKPRO HOLDING CORP p 1485
1610 Century Center Pkwy, Memphis TN 38134
Tel (901) 252-4200 SIC 5531 7539

TRUCKPRO LLC p 1485
1610 Century Center Pkwy, Memphis TN 38134
Tel (901) 252-4200 SIC 5531 7539

BRIDGESTONE AMERICAS TIRE OPERATIONS LLC p 211
535 Marriott Dr, Nashville TN 37214
Tel (615) 937-1000 SIC 3011 5531

■ KEYSTONE AUTOMOTIVE INDUSTRIES INC p 815
655 Grassmere Park, Nashville TN 37211
Tel (615) 781-5200 SIC 5013 5531 3714

■ MID STATE AUTOMOTIVE DISTRIBUTORS INC p 963
485 Craighead St, Nashville TN 37204
Tel (615) 383-8566 SIC 5013 5531

FIRESTONE HOLDINGS LLC p 544
6501 W William Cannon Dr, Austin TX 78735
Tel (512) 895-2000 SIC 5531

HILITE INTERNATIONAL INC p 693
1671 S Broadway St, Carrollton TX 75006
Tel (972) 242-2116 SIC 5531

TONY GULLO MOTORS I LP p 1460
500 Interstate 45 S, Conroe TX 77304
Tel (936) 539-9191 SIC 7549 5511 5531

INTERSTATE BATTERIES INC p 758
12770 Merit Dr Ste 400, Dallas TX 75251
Tel (972) 991-1444 SIC 5531 3694

INTERSTATE BATTERY SYSTEM INTERNATIONAL INC p 758
12770 Merit Dr Ste 1000, Dallas TX 75251
Tel (972) 991-1444 SIC 5531

SOUTHWEST INTERNATIONAL TRUCKS INC p 1352
3722 Irving Blvd, Dallas TX 75247
Tel (214) 689-1400 SIC 5511 5531

LTG LONESTAR TRUCK GROUP EAST LLC p 883
2051 Hughes Rd, Grapevine TX 76051
Tel (817) 428-9736 SIC 5531

▲ GROUP 1 AUTOMOTIVE INC p 641
800 Gessner Rd Ste 500, Houston TX 77024
Tel (713) 647-5700
SIC 5511 6141 7538 7532 5531

INTERNATIONAL TRUCKS OF HOUSTON LLC p 757
8900 North Loop E, Houston TX 77029
Tel (713) 674-3444 SIC 5511 5531

TASCO AUTO COLOR CORP p 1426
10323 Veterans Mem Dr, Houston TX 77038
Tel (281) 999-3761
SIC 5198 5013 5231 5531

VERSATECH AUTOMATION SERVICES LLC p 1551
11349 Fm 529 Rd, Houston TX 77041
Tel (713) 937-3100 SIC 5531 5013

AUTO AIR EXPORT INC p 133
1401 Valley View Ln # 100, Irving TX 75061
Tel (972) 812-7000 SIC 5075 3585 5531

FLEETPRIDE INC p 555
600 Las Colinas Blvd E # 400, Irving TX 75039
Tel (469) 249-7500 SIC 5531 5013

ABC AUTO PARTS LTD p 10
920 W Marshall Ave, Longview TX 75604
Tel (903) 232-3010 SIC 5013 5531

■ RUSH ADMINISTRATIVE SERVICES INC p 1258
555 S Interstate 35 # 500, New Braunfels TX 78130
Tel (830) 626-5286
SIC 5012 7538 5531 5014 7513

▲ RUSH ENTERPRISES INC p 1258
555 S Ih 35 Ste 500, New Braunfels TX 78130
Tel (830) 302-5200
SIC 5012 7538 5531 5014 7513

FRENCH-ELLISON TRUCK CENTER LLC p 578
4300 N Cage Blvd, Pharr TX 78577
Tel (956) 781-2401
SIC 5013 5531 5511 5012 7538

■ RENT-A-CENTER FRANCHISING INTERNATIONAL INC p 1224
5501 Headquarters Dr, Plano TX 75024
Tel (972) 403-4900 SIC 5722 5531

PARKWAY CHEVROLET INC p 1117
25500 State Highway 249, Tomball TX 77375
Tel (281) 351-8211 SIC 5511 7549 5531

ALDEN PADFIELD INC p 47
203 N 5500 W, Hurricane UT 84737
Tel (435) 674-9883 SIC 5014 5531

PADFIELD INC p 1107
1335 W 2100 S, Salt Lake City UT 84119
Tel (801) 972-1944 SIC 5014 5531 3711

■ RUSH TRUCK CENTERS OF UTAH INC p 1259
964 S 3800 W, Salt Lake City UT 84104
Tel (801) 972-5320 SIC 5012 7538 5531

UTILITY TRAILER SALES OF UTAH INC p 1537
4970 W 2100 S, Salt Lake City UT 84120
Tel (801) 973-4040 SIC 5511 5531 7539

BOND AUTO PARTS INC p 199
272 Morrison Rd, Barre VT 05641
Tel (802) 479-0571 SIC 5013 5531

TRUCK ENTERPRISES INC p 1485
3440 S Main St, Harrisonburg VA 22801
Tel (540) 564-6900
SIC 5511 5531 7538 7539

MERCHANTS INC p 945
9073 Euclid Ave, Manassas VA 20110
Tel (703) 368-3171 SIC 5014 7539 5531

GREATER RICHMOND BUSINESS INC p 636
1833 Commerce Rd, Richmond VA 23224
Tel (804) 232-3492
SIC 5511 5013 5531 7513

NILIT AMERICA INC p 1043
420 Industrial Park Rd, Ridgeway VA 24148
Tel (276) 638-2434 *SIC* 5199 2299 5531

▲ ADVANCE AUTO PARTS INC p 24
5008 Airport Rd Nw, Roanoke VA 24012
Tel (877) 238-2623 *SIC* 5531

■ ADVANCE STORES CO INC p 25
5008 Airport Rd Nw, Roanoke VA 24012
Tel (540) 362-4911 *SIC* 5531

PARTS DEPOT INC p 1118
401 Albemarle Ave Se, Roanoke VA 24013
Tel (540) 345-1001 *SIC* 5013 5531

FISHER AUTO PARTS INC p 552
512 Greenville Ave, Staunton VA 24401
Tel (540) 885-8901 *SIC* 5013 5531 4225

APPALACHIAN TIRE PRODUCTS INC p 98
2907 4th Ave, Charleston WV 25387
Tel (304) 744-9473
SIC 5014 5531 5013 7534

FLEET WHOLESALE SUPPLY CO LLC p 555
3035 W Wisconsin Ave, Appleton WI 54914
Tel (920) 734-8231
SIC 5191 5331 5531 5211 5541

ALLIED DIESEL INC p 56
13015 W Custer Ave, Butler WI 53007
Tel (262) 781-7100 *SIC* 5084 5531 7699

BAUER BUILT INC p 160
1111 W Prospect St, Durand WI 54736
Tel (715) 672-8300
SIC 5531 5014 7534 5171

POMPS TIRE SERVICE INC p 1161
1122 Cedar St, Green Bay WI 54301
Tel (920) 435-8301 *SIC* 5531 5014 7534

FARM & FLEET OF MADISON INC p 528
3507 E Racine St, Janesville WI 53546
Tel (608) 754-2821
SIC 5199 5531 5251 5261 5039

FARM & FLEET OF RICE LAKE INC p 528
3507 E Racine St, Janesville WI 53546
Tel (608) 754-2821 *SIC* 5191 5251 5531

LAKESIDE INTERNATIONAL LLC p 840
11000 W Silver Spring Dr, Milwaukee WI 53225
Tel (414) 353-4800
SIC 5511 5531 7538 7532 6159 7513

SCHIERL INC p 1287
2201 Madison St, Stevens Point WI 54481
Tel (715) 345-5060
SIC 5171 5014 5531 5983

SIC 5541 Gasoline Service Stations

HOME OIL CO INC p 703
5744 E Us Highway 84, Cowarts AL 36321
Tel (334) 793-1544
SIC 5171 5411 5541 5172

WILLIAMSON OIL CO INC p 1612
1603 Godfrey Ave Se, Fort Payne AL 35967
Tel (256) 845-9466 *SIC* 5541 5411 5172

JET PEP INC p 783
9481 Highway 278 W, Holly Pond AL 35083
Tel (256) 796-2237 *SIC* 5541

SPENCER COMPANIES INC p 1358
120 Woodson St Nw, Huntsville AL 35801
Tel (256) 533-1150 *SIC* 5541 5172

MCPHERSON COMPANIES INC p 932
5051 Cardinal St, Trussville AL 35173
Tel (205) 661-2799 *SIC* 5171 5411 5541

CARIOCA CO p 256
2601 W Dunlap Ave Ste 10, Phoenix AZ 85021
Tel (602) 395-2600 *SIC* 5541 5411

CIRCLE K STORES INC p 308
1130 W Warner Rd, Tempe AZ 85284
Tel (602) 728-8000 *SIC* 5411 5541

■ GIANT INDUSTRIES INC p 611
1250 W Washington St # 101, Tempe AZ 85281
Tel (915) 534-1400 *SIC* 2911 5541 5172

■ WESTERN REFINING SOUTHWEST INC p 1599
1250 W Washington St # 101, Tempe AZ 85281
Tel (602) 286-1400
SIC 2911 5171 5411 5541

DIAMOND HOSPITALITY ENTERPRISES p 436
5 Mystic Isle Rd, Edgemont AR 72044
Tel (501) 723-5150 *SIC* 5812 5541 5411

▲ MURPHY USA INC p 1001
200 E Peach St, El Dorado AR 71730
Tel (870) 875-7600 *SIC* 5531 5541

MAGNESS OIL CO p 896
167 Tucker Cemetery Rd, Gassville AR 72635
Tel (870) 425-4353 *SIC* 5171 5541 5411

FARMERS SUPPLY ASSOCIATION p 530
16240 Highway 14 E, Harrisburg AR 72432
Tel (870) 578-2468
SIC 5191 5172 5261 5541 5999

PETROMARK INC p 1139
308 W Industrial Park Rd, Harrison AR 72601
Tel (870) 741-3560 *SIC* 5541

COULSON OIL CO INC p 374
1434 Pike Ave 38, North Little Rock AR 72114
Tel (501) 376-4222
SIC 5172 5541 5411 6512

FLASH MARKET INC p 554
105 W Harrison Ave, West Memphis AR 72301
Tel (870) 732-2242 *SIC* 5541 5411

FLYERS ENERGY LLC p 562
2360 Lindbergh St, Auburn CA 95602
Tel (530) 885-0401 *SIC* 5411 5541 5013

JACO OIL CO p 775
3101 State Rd, Bakersfield CA 93308
Tel (661) 393-7000 *SIC* 5541

JAMIESON-HILL A GENERAL PARTNERSHIP p 777
3101 State Rd, Bakersfield CA 93308
Tel (661) 393-7000 *SIC* 5541 6798

HARRIS FARMS INC p 663
29475 Fresno Coalinga Rd, Coalinga CA 93210
Tel (559) 884-2435
SIC 0191 0211 2011 7011 5812 5541

VINTNERS DISTRIBUTORS INC p 1558
41805 Albrae St, Fremont CA 94538
Tel (510) 657-9150 *SIC* 5541

APRO LLC p 100
17311 S Main St, Gardena CA 90248
Tel (310) 323-3992 *SIC* 5541

RAPID GAS INC p 1208
17311 S Main St, Gardena CA 90248
Tel (310) 323-3992 *SIC* 5541

G & M OIL CO INC p 586
16868 A Ln, Huntington Beach CA 92647
Tel (714) 375-4700 *SIC* 5541

ATLANTIC RICHFIELD CO INC p 127
4 Centerpointe Dr Ste 200, La Palma CA 90623
Tel (800) 333-3991 *SIC* 5541 1321 2911

STAN BOYETT & SON INC p 1375
601 Mchenry Ave, Modesto CA 95350
Tel (209) 577-6000 *SIC* 5172 5541

MOLLER INVESTMENT GROUP INC p 983
6591 Collins Dr Ste E11, Moorpark CA 93021
Tel (805) 299-8200 *SIC* 5541

CHEVRON FEDERAL CREDIT UNION p 296
500 12th St Ste 200, Oakland CA 94607
Tel (888) 884-4630 *SIC* 5541

SOUTHERN COUNTIES OIL CO p 1348
1800 W Katella Ave # 400, Orange CA 92867
Tel (714) 744-7140 *SIC* 5171 5541 5172

PACIFIC CONVENIENCE & FUELS LLC p 1104
7180 Koll Center Pkwy, Pleasanton CA 94566
Tel (925) 884-0800 *SIC* 5411 5541

TOMS SIERRA CO INC p 1460
1020 Winding Creek Rd, Roseville CA 95678
Tel (916) 218-1600 *SIC* 5541

STURDY OIL CO p 1395
1511 Abbott St, Salinas CA 93901
Tel (831) 422-8801 *SIC* 5172 5541

CANADIAN AMERICAN OIL CO INC p 246
444 Divisadero St 100, San Francisco CA 94117
Tel (415) 621-8676 *SIC* 5541 6512 6552

▲ CHEVRON CORP p 295
6001 Bollinger Canyon Rd, San Ramon CA 94583
Tel (925) 842-1000
SIC 2911 1311 1382 1321 5541

■ CHEVRON STATIONS INC p 296
6001 Bollinger Canyon Rd, San Ramon CA 94583
Tel (925) 842-1000 *SIC* 5541 5411

■ CHEVRON USA INC p 296
6001 Bollinger Canyon Rd D1248, San Ramon CA 94583
Tel (925) 842-1000
SIC 5541 5511 2911 5171

■ TEXACO INC p 1441
6001 Bollinger Canyon Rd, San Ramon CA 94583
Tel (925) 842-1000
SIC 5541 5511 1321 4612 4613 4412

ROBINSON OIL CORP p 1242
955 Martin Ave, Santa Clara CA 95050
Tel (408) 327-4300 *SIC* 5541 5411

WORLD OIL MARKETING CO p 1625
9302 Garfield Ave, South Gate CA 90280
Tel (562) 928-0100
SIC 2911 4953 2951 5541 4213 4212

VALLEY PACIFIC PETROLEUM SERVICES INC p 1541
152 Frank West Cir # 100, Stockton CA 95206
Tel (209) 948-9412 *SIC* 5172 5541

RINEHART OIL INC p 1235
2401 N State St, Ukiah CA 95482
Tel (707) 462-8811 *SIC* 5172 5541

CAR ENTERPRISES INC p 252
1040 N Benson Ave, Upland CA 91786
Tel (909) 932-9242 *SIC* 5541 5411

DNC PARKS & RESORTS AT YOSEMITE INC p 446
9001 Village Dr, Yosemite Ntpk CA 95389
Tel (209) 372-1001
SIC 7011 5399 5812 5947 5541 4725

WESTERN CONVENIENCE STORES INC p 1597
9849 E Easter Ave, Centennial CO 80112
Tel (303) 706-0340 *SIC* 5541

OFFEN PETROLEUM INC p 1075
5100 E 78th Ave, Commerce City CO 80022
Tel (303) 297-3835 *SIC* 5172 5541

PEERLESS TYRE CO p 1127
5000 Kingston St, Denver CO 80239
Tel (303) 371-4300 *SIC* 5541 5531

REGIS 66 INC p 1220
4890 Lowell Blvd, Denver CO 80221
Tel (303) 455-6636 *SIC* 5541

PRIMA MARKETING LLC p 1174
21 Inverness Way E, Englewood CO 80112
Tel (303) 436-9510 *SIC* 5411 5541

GRAY OIL CO INC p 632
804 Denver Ave, Fort Lupton CO 80621
Tel (303) 857-2288 *SIC* 5171 5541 5411

GRAINLAND COOPERATIVE p 629
421 S Colorado Ave, Haxtun CO 80731
Tel (970) 774-6166
SIC 5191 4221 5531 5541

K & G PETROLEUM LLC p 798
10459 Park Meadows Dr # 101, Lone Tree CO 80124
Tel (303) 792-9467 *SIC* 5541

STRATTON EQUITY COOPERATIVE CO p 1393
98 Colorado Ave, Stratton CO 80836
Tel (719) 348-5326
SIC 5153 5191 5171 5541

ALDIN ASSOCIATES LIMITED PARTNERSHIP p 48
77 Sterling Rd, East Hartford CT 06108
Tel (860) 282-0651 *SIC* 5541 5411

APACHE OIL CO INC p 96
261 Ledyard St, New London CT 06320
Tel (860) 437-6200 *SIC* 5172 5541

■ DRAKE PETROLEUM CO INC p 455
221 Quinebaug Rd, North Grosvenordale CT 06255
Tel (860) 935-5200 *SIC* 5541 5411

MERCURY FUEL SERVICE INC p 945
43 Lafayette St, Waterbury CT 06708
Tel (203) 756-7284
SIC 5172 5541 5411 5983 1711 2911

UNITED ACQUISITION CORP p 1506
802 N West St, Wilmington DE 19801
Tel (302) 651-9856 *SIC* 2911 5541 2951

ALL AMERICAN OIL INC OF BREVARD p 51
402 High Point Dr Ste 102, Cocoa FL 32926
Tel (321) 690-0807 *SIC* 5541 5411

■ JUNIOR FOOD STORES OF WEST FLORIDA INC p 797
619 8th Ave, Crestview FL 32536
Tel (850) 587-5023 *SIC* 5541 5411

▲ WORLD FUEL SERVICES CORP p 1625
9800 Nw 41st St Ste 400, Doral FL 33178
Tel (305) 428-8000 *SIC* 5172 3519 5541

LAND OSUN MANAGEMENT CORP p 842
3715 Nw 97th Blvd Ste A, Gainesville FL 32606
Tel (352) 333-3011 *SIC* 5541 5411

CROWLEY HOLDINGS INC p 394
9487 Regency Square Blvd # 101, Jacksonville FL 32225
Tel (904) 727-2200
SIC 4412 4424 5171 5172 5541 4492

CROWLEY MARITIME CORP p 395
9487 Regency Square Blvd, Jacksonville FL 32225
Tel (904) 727-2200
SIC 4412 4424 5171 5172 5541 4492

FIRST COAST ENERGY LLP p 545
7014 A C Skinner Pkwy # 290, Jacksonville FL 32256
Tel (904) 596-3200 *SIC* 5541 5411 5172

GATE PETROLEUM CO p 593
9540 San Jose Blvd, Jacksonville FL 32257
Tel (904) 730-3470
SIC 5541 3272 5411 7997

MORRIS HOLDINGS INC p 990
1650 County Road 210 W, Jacksonville FL 32259
Tel (904) 829-3946 *SIC* 5541 5812 5411

WINN-DIXIE STORES INC p 1616
8928 Prominence Pkwy # 200, Jacksonville FL 32256
Tel (904) 783-5000 *SIC* 5411 5541 5912

SIGNATURE FLIGHT SUPPORT CORP p 1322
201 S Orange Ave Ste 1100, Orlando FL 32801
Tel (407) 648-7200 *SIC* 5541

BRAD LANIER OIL CO INC p 206
611 W Roosevelt Ave, Albany GA 31701
Tel (229) 436-0131 *SIC* 5171 5541 5411

RACETRAC PETROLEUM INC p 1203
3225 Cumberland Blvd Se # 100, Atlanta GA 30339
Tel (770) 850-3491 *SIC* 5541 5411 5172

SOUTHWEST GEORGIA OIL CO INC p 1352
1711 E Shotwell St, Bainbridge GA 39819
Tel (229) 246-1553
SIC 5171 5541 5411 5921

MCDONALD OIL CO INC p 927
1700 Lukken Indus Dr W, Lagrange GA 30240
Tel (706) 884-6191 *SIC* 5541 5921 6519

WALTHALL OIL CO p 1575
2510 Allen Rd, Macon GA 31216
Tel (478) 781-1234 *SIC* 5172 5541 5411

SOMMERS CO p 1339
1000 Sommers Blvd, Richmond Hill GA 31324
Tel (800) 654-6466 *SIC* 5172 5541 7033

COLONIAL OIL INDUSTRIES INC p 337
101 N Lathrop Ave, Savannah GA 31415
Tel (912) 396-1388 *SIC* 5171 5541

GOLDEN PANTRY FOOD STORES INC p 621
1150 Wall St, Watkinsville GA 30677
Tel (800) 533-3816 *SIC* 5411 5541

■ FLASH FOODS LLC p 554
215 Pendleton St, Waycross GA 31501
Tel (912) 285-4011 *SIC* 5541 5411

JONES CO p 792
215 Pendleton St Ste A, Waycross GA 31501
Tel (912) 285-4011 *SIC* 5541 5411 5172

■ ALOHA PETROLEUM LTD p 59
1132 Bishop St Ste 1700, Honolulu HI 96813
Tel (808) 833-3249 *SIC* 5172 5541 5411

BINGHAM COOPERATIVE INC p 183
477 W Highway 26, Blackfoot ID 83221
Tel (208) 785-3440 *SIC* 5191 5171 5541

STINKER STORES INC p 1390
3184 W Elder St, Boise ID 83705
Tel (208) 375-0942 *SIC* 5541

CONRAD & BISCHOFF INC p 358
2251 N Holmes Ave, Idaho Falls ID 83401
Tel (208) 522-8174 *SIC* 5171 5411 5541

JACKSONS FOOD STORES INC p 774
3450 E Commercial Ct, Meridian ID 83642
Tel (208) 888-6061 *SIC* 5541 5411

VALLEY WIDE COOPERATIVE INC p 1541
2114 N 20th St, Nampa ID 83687
Tel (208) 436-0141
SIC 5191 5251 5541 5171

DICKERSON STATIONS INC p 438
920 N Illinois St, Belleville IL 62220
Tel (618) 233-0786 *SIC* 5541 5411

FKG OIL CO p 554
721 W Main St, Belleville IL 62220
Tel (618) 233-6754 *SIC* 5541

A MICHAEL OWENS INC p 6
814 W Chestnut St, Bloomington IL 61701
Tel (309) 828-7750 *SIC* 5541 4213

FREEDOM OIL CO p 576
814 W Chestnut St, Bloomington IL 61701
Tel (309) 828-7750 *SIC* 5541

TRI STAR MARKETING INC p 1477
2211 W Bradley Ave, Champaign IL 61821
Tel (217) 367-8386 *SIC* 5541 5411 5172

PILOT TRAVEL CENTERS LLC p 1148
1340 Piggott Ave, East Saint Louis IL 62201
Tel (618) 875-5800 *SIC* 5541

SUNRISE AG SERVICE CO p 1403
104 S 1st St, Easton IL 62633
Tel (309) 562-7296 *SIC* 5191 5171 5541

CLARK BRANDS LLC p 322
4200 Commerce Ct Ste 350, Lisle IL 60532
Tel (630) 355-8918
SIC 6794 7389 5541 5812

NIEMANN FOODS FOUNDATION p 1043
923 N 12th St, Quincy IL 62301
Tel (217) 221-5600 *SIC* 5411 5541

TEXOR PETROLEUM CO INC p 1445
3340 Harlem Ave, Riverside IL 60546
Tel (708) 447-1999 *SIC* 5172 5541

KELLEY WILLIAMSON CO p 808
1132 Harrison Ave, Rockford IL 61104
Tel (815) 397-9410 *SIC* 5541 5411 5171

REOPCO INC p 1224
4930 E State St Ste 1, Rockford IL 61108
Tel (815) 387-1700 *SIC* 5411 5541

LASSUS BROS OIL INC p 846
1800 Magnavox Way, Fort Wayne IN 46804
Tel (260) 436-1415 *SIC* 5541 5411

GASAMERICA SERVICES INC p 593
2700 W Main St, Greenfield IN 46140
Tel (317) 468-2515 *SIC* 5541 5171

AL WARREN OIL CO INC p 43
1646 Summer St, Hammond IN 46320
Tel (773) 735-6900 *SIC* 5172 5541

CRYSTAL FLASH PETROLEUM LLC p 396
5221 Ivy Tech Dr, Indianapolis IN 46268
Tel (317) 879-2849 *SIC* 5541 5411 5171

JACKSON OIL & SOLVENTS INC p 774
1970 Kentucky Ave, Indianapolis IN 46221
Tel (317) 481-2244
SIC 5172 5541 5983 5531

KOCOLENE MARKETING LLC p 826
2060 1st Ave, Seymour IN 47274
Tel (812) 522-2224 *SIC* 5541 5411

SWIFTY OIL LLC p 1412
1515 W Tipton St, Seymour IN 47274
Tel (812) 522-1640 *SIC* 5541 5411

FAMILY EXPRESS CORP p 526
213 S State Road 49, Valparaiso IN 46383
Tel (219) 531-6490 *SIC* 5541 5411

▲ CASEYS GENERAL STORES INC p 263
1 Se Convenience Blvd, Ankeny IA 50021
Tel (515) 965-6100 *SIC* 5411 5541

GIT-N-GO CONVENIENCE STORES INC p 613
2716 Indianola Ave, Des Moines IA 50315
Tel (515) 288-8565 *SIC* 5411 5541 6722

MULGREW OIL CO p 999
10314 Silverwood Dr, Dubuque IA 52003
Tel (563) 583-7386 *SIC* 5171 5172 5541

UNITED FARMERS MERCANTILE COOPERATIVE p 1508
203 W Oak St, Red Oak IA 51566
Tel (712) 623-5453
SIC 5153 5191 5541 5211 2048

KEY COOPERATIVE p 814
13585 620th Ave, Roland IA 50236
Tel (515) 388-4341
SIC 5153 5541 2048 5191

IOWA 80 GROUP INC p 762
515 Sterling Dr, Walcott IA 52773
Tel (563) 468-5500
SIC 5541 5399 7542 5812

IOWA 80 TRUCKSTOP INC p 762
755 W Iowa 80 Rd I-80, Walcott IA 52773
Tel (563) 284-6961
SIC 5541 5399 7542 5812

MIDLAND MARKETING CO-OP INC p 966
219 E 9th St, Hays KS 67601
Tel (785) 625-5138
SIC 5153 5191 5541 5171 4221

KANZA COOPERATIVE ASSOCIATION p 803
102 N Main St, Iuka KS 67066
Tel (620) 546-2231
SIC 5153 5191 5541 4221

STAR FUEL CENTERS INC p 1378
11161 Overbrook Rd, Leawood KS 66211
Tel (913) 652-9400
SIC 5172 7542 5541 5411

LEISZLER OIL CO INC p 854
8228 Southport Dr, Manhattan KS 66502
Tel (785) 632-5648 *SIC* 5171 5411 5541

SCOTT COOPERATIVE ASSOCIATION INC p 1293
410 E 1st St, Scott City KS 67871
Tel (620) 872-5823
SIC 5153 5541 5191 4221

NEMAHA COUNTY COOPERATIVE ASSOCIATION p 1025
223 E Main St, Seneca KS 66538
Tel (785) 336-6153 *SIC* 5153 5191 5541

UNIVERSAL COMPANIES INC p 1516
2824 N Ohio St, Wichita KS 67219
Tel (316) 832-0151
SIC 5171 5541 6512 8741 6099 2992

KENTUCKY OIL AND REFINING CO p 812
156 Ky Oil Vlg, Betsy Layne KY 41605
Tel (606) 478-2303 *SIC* 5171 5541

HOUCHENS FOOD GROUP INC p 710
700 Church St, Bowling Green KY 42101
Tel (270) 843-3252 *SIC* 5411 5541 5093

KEYSTOPS LLC p 816
376 Reasonover Ave, Franklin KY 42134
Tel (270) 586-8283 *SIC* 5541 5171

MAX ARNOLD & SONS LLC p 922
702 N Main St, Hopkinsville KY 42240
Tel (270) 885-8488
SIC 5171 5541 5411 5812

KENTUCKY LAKE OIL CO INC p 812
620 S 4th St, Murray KY 42071
Tel (270) 753-1323
SIC 5541 5571 5171 5411

JAMES MARINE INC p 776
4500 Clarks River Rd, Paducah KY 42003
Tel (270) 898-7392
SIC 3731 4492 5541 3732

CENTRAL OIL & SUPPLY CORP p 279
2300 Booth St, Monroe LA 71201
Tel (318) 388-2602 SIC 5171 5541

DEAD RIVER CO p 419
80 Exchange St Ste 3, Bangor ME 04401
Tel (207) 947-8641
SIC 6512 5172 5983 5541 5411

OCEAN INVESTMENTS CORP p 1073
700 Maine Ave, Bangor ME 04401
Tel (207) 942-7000 SIC 5541 5411

R H FOSTER ENERGY LLC p 1202
110 Mecaw Rd, Hampden ME 04444
Tel (207) 947-3835
SIC 5172 5541 5411 5983

FABIAN OIL INC p 523
15 Oak St, Oakland ME 04963
Tel (207) 465-7958
SIC 5541 5983 5984 5411

CN BROWN CO p 329
1 C N Brown Way, South Paris ME 04281
Tel (207) 743-9212 SIC 5411 5541 5983

FAST FARE INC p 531
1 N Charles St, Baltimore MD 21201
Tel (410) 539-7400 SIC 5411 5541

ROSEMORE HOLDINGS INC p 1251
1 N Charles St Ste 2200, Baltimore MD 21201
Tel (410) 347-7090
SIC 2911 5171 5541 5411

ROSEMORE INC p 1251
1 N Charles St Ste 2200, Baltimore MD 21201
Tel (410) 347-7080 SIC 5541

C & T A CO INC p 231
11535 Hopewell Rd, Hagerstown MD 21740
Tel (800) 458-3835
SIC 5541 5172 7359 7699

DASH IN FOOD STORES INC p 413
6355 Crain Hwy, La Plata MD 20646
Tel (301) 932-3600 SIC 5541 5411 6794

WILLS GROUP INC p 1613
6355 Crain Hwy, La Plata MD 20646
Tel (301) 932-3600
SIC 5541 5983 5172 5411

SUPER PETROLEUM INC p 1405
25 Braintree Hill Park # 409, Braintree MA 02184
Tel (781) 356-1960 SIC 5541

DENNIS K BURKE INC p 428
284 Eastern Ave, Chelsea MA 02150
Tel (617) 884-7800 SIC 5172 5541

VERC ENTERPRISES INC p 1549
5 Chestnut St, Duxbury MA 02332
Tel (781) 934-7300 SIC 5541 7542

CUMBERLAND FARMS INC p 400
100 Crossing Blvd, Framingham MA 01702
Tel (508) 270-1400
SIC 5411 5541 5172 2086 2051 2026

WASH DEPOT AUTO CENTERS LP p 1577
435 Eastern Ave, Malden MA 02148
Tel (781) 324-2000 SIC 7542 5541 5947

WASH DEPOT HOLDINGS INC p 1577
14 Summer St Ste 302, Malden MA 02148
Tel (781) 324-2000 SIC 7542 5541

■ **ALLIANCE ENERGY LLC** p 54
800 South St Ste 500, Waltham MA 02453
Tel (781) 674-7780 SIC 5411 5541

BEACON HOLDING INC p 164
25 Research Dr, Westborough MA 01581
Tel (774) 512-7400 SIC 5399 5541

DAVIS OIL CO p 416
1265 Columbia Ave E, Battle Creek MI 49014
Tel (269) 965-2201 SIC 5541

BLARNEY CASTLE OIL CO p 189
12218 West St, Bear Lake MI 49614
Tel (231) 864-3111 SIC 5541 5411 5171

GAS CITY LTD p 593
401 S Old Woodward Ave # 340, Birmingham MI 48009
Tel (815) 469-9000 SIC 5541 5411 5172

ADMIRAL PETROLEUM CO p 23
785 W Randall St, Coopersville MI 49404
Tel (616) 837-6218
SIC 5541 5411 5194 5145

JOHNSON OIL CO OF GAYLORD p 791
507 S Otsego Ave, Gaylord MI 49735
Tel (989) 732-6014 SIC 5171 5541 5983

■ **SPARTAN STORES FUEL LLC** p 1355
850 76th St Sw, Grand Rapids MI 49518
Tel (616) 878-2000 SIC 5541 5411

KRIST OIL CO p 830
303 Selden Rd, Iron River MI 49935
Tel (906) 265-6144 SIC 5541 5411

WALTERS-DIMMICK PETROLEUM INC p 1574
1620 S Kalamazoo Ave, Marshall MI 49068
Tel (269) 781-4654
SIC 5541 5411 6512 5172 5171 5983

WESCO INC p 1593
1460 Whitehall Rd, Muskegon MI 49445
Tel (231) 719-4300
SIC 5411 5541 5145 5149

COOPERATIVE ELEVATOR CO p 367
7211 E Michigan Ave, Pigeon MI 48755
Tel (989) 453-4500
SIC 5172 5191 5541 5261 5153

BARRICK ENTERPRISES INC p 157
4338 Delemere Blvd, Royal Oak MI 48073
Tel (248) 549-3737 SIC 5541

FORWARD CORP p 570
219 N Front St, Standish MI 48658
Tel (989) 846-4501
SIC 5411 5541 5172 5812

HOLIDAY COMPANIES p 700
4567 American Blvd W, Bloomington MN 55437
Tel (952) 830-8700 SIC 5541 5411 5172

HOLIDAY STATIONSTORES INC p 700
4567 American Blvd W, Bloomington MN 55437
Tel (952) 830-8700 SIC 5541 5411

BEST OIL CO p 177
30 N 8th St, Cloquet MN 55720
Tel (218) 879-0201
SIC 5171 5172 5013 5983 5541 5411

LYNDALE TERMINAL CO p 887
4567 American Blvd W, Minneapolis MN 55437
Tel (952) 830-8700 SIC 5311 5411 5541

ROBERT A WILLIAMS ENTERPRISES p 1241
3701 Central Ave Ne, Minneapolis MN 55421
Tel (763) 788-1113 SIC 5541 6519

CANNON VALLEY COOPERATIVE p 247
1500 Highway 3 S, Northfield MN 55057
Tel (507) 645-9556
SIC 5541 5171 1711 5191 5153 5211

CENTRAL VALLEY COOPERATIVE p 280
900 30th Pl Nw, Owatonna MN 55060
Tel (507) 451-1230 SIC 5191 5171 5541

GREEN-WAY COOPERATIVE SERVICE CO p 637
3520 E River Rd Ne, Rochester MN 55906
Tel (507) 289-4086 SIC 5541 5171 5191

NORTHERN RESOURCES COOPERATIVE p 1056
1504 Center St W, Roseau MN 56751
Tel (218) 463-1805
SIC 5191 5172 5251 5541

COBORNS INC p 333
1921 Coborn Blvd, Saint Cloud MN 56301
Tel (320) 252-4222 SIC 5411 5541 5921

NU WAY COOPERATIVE (INC) p 1066
440 Highway 4 S, Trimont MN 56176
Tel (507) 639-2311
SIC 5191 5171 5541 2875

GRAVES OIL CO p 632
226 Pearson St, Batesville MS 38606
Tel (662) 563-4604 SIC 5171 5541 5411

SAYLE OIL CO INC p 1285
410 W Main St, Charleston MS 38921
Tel (800) 844-8120 SIC 5541 5171 5411

LITCO PETROLEUM INC p 870
323 Highway 72 W, Corinth MS 38834
Tel (662) 287-1471 SIC 5541 5172 5411

CLARK OIL CO INC p 322
720 Station St, Waynesboro MS 39367
Tel (601) 735-4847 SIC 5541 5172

AYERS OIL CO p 140
401 N 4th St, Canton MO 63435
Tel (573) 288-4464
SIC 5171 5411 5541 5172

WATERWAY GAS & WASH CO p 1582
727 Goddard Ave, Chesterfield MO 63005
Tel (636) 537-1111 SIC 5541 7542

MFA OIL CO p 957
1 Ray Young Dr, Columbia MO 65201
Tel (573) 442-0171 SIC 7549 5541

WALLIS OIL CO p 1573
106 E Washington St, Cuba MO 65453
Tel (573) 885-2277 SIC 5541 5171

WESTERN OIL INC p 1599
3553 Rider Trl S, Earth City MO 63045
Tel (314) 738-9900
SIC 5541 5411 7542 4225

U-GAS INC p 1497
895 Bolger Ct, Fenton MO 63026
Tel (636) 343-9770 SIC 5541

J D STREETT & CO INC p 771
144 Weldon Pkwy, Maryland Heights MO 63043
Tel (314) 432-6600
SIC 5171 5541 7389 5172

MIDWEST PETROLEUM CO p 967
6760 Southwest Ave, Saint Louis MO 63143
Tel (314) 647-5550 SIC 5541

ROCKY MOUNTAIN SUPPLY INC p 1245
350 Jackrabbit Ln Stop 1, Belgrade MT 59714
Tel (406) 388-4008
SIC 5171 5191 5541 5411

MOUNTAIN VIEW CO-OP p 994
2200 Old Havre Hwy, Black Eagle MT 59414
Tel (406) 453-5900
SIC 5541 5153 2875 5191

TOWN PUMP INC p 1465
600 S Main St, Butte MT 59701
Tel (406) 497-6700
SIC 5541 5411 7993 6512 5812

WESTERN COOPERATIVE CO INC p 1598
724 W 3rd St, Alliance NE 69301
Tel (308) 762-3291 SIC 5172 5541 5191

BATTLE CREEK FARMERS COOPERATIVE NON-STOCK p 160
83755 Highway 121, Battle Creek NE 68715
Tel (402) 675-2375
SIC 5153 5191 5172 5541 5411

MIDWEST FARMERS COOPERATIVE p 967
304 S 3rd St, Elmwood NE 68349
Tel (402) 994-2585 SIC 5153 5191 5541

ALL POINTS COOPERATIVE p 51
120 8th St, Gothenburg NE 69138
Tel (308) 537-7141 SIC 5153 5191 5541

BOSSELMAN INC p 202
3123 W Stolley Park Rd, Grand Island NE 68801
Tel (308) 381-2800
SIC 5541 5411 5812 7011 5172 5084

FRENCHMAN VALLEY FARMERS COOPERATIVE INC p 578
202 Broadway, Imperial NE 69033
Tel (308) 882-3220 SIC 5153 5191 5541

NEBRASKALAND TIRE INC p 1023
Hwy 283 & Hwy I 80, Lexington NE 68850
Tel (308) 324-2338 SIC 5531 5541 5411

BUCKS INC p 223
5001 Dodge St, Omaha NE 68132
Tel (402) 558-9860 SIC 5541

RITE WAY INVESTMENTS INC p 1236
8400 I St, Omaha NE 68127
Tel (402) 331-6400 SIC 5172 5541 5411

SAPP BROS TRAVEL CENTERS INC p 1281
9915 S 148th St, Omaha NE 68138
Tel (402) 895-2202 SIC 5541

PANHANDLE COOPERATIVE ASSOCIATION p 1111
401 S Beltline Hwy W, Scottsbluff NE 69361
Tel (308) 632-5301 SIC 5541 0721

MIDJIT MARKET INC p 965
1580 S Jones Blvd, Las Vegas NV 89146
Tel (702) 216-2154 SIC 5541 5141

TERRIBLE HERBST INC p 1440
5195 Las Vegas Blvd S, Las Vegas NV 89119
Tel (702) 597-6296 SIC 5541

HIGHLANDS FUEL DELIVERY LLC p 691
190 Commerce Way, Portsmouth NH 03801
Tel (603) 559-8700 SIC 5172 5541 1389

TOTAL AMERICAN SERVICES INC p 1462
100 Town Square Pl # 401, Jersey City NJ 07310
Tel (206) 626-3500
SIC 2911 4612 5541 2895

ALLSUP ENTERPRISES INC p 58
2112 N Thornton St, Clovis NM 88101
Tel (575) 769-2311
SIC 5411 5541 4832 6519 5171

ALLSUPS CONVENIENCE STORES INC p 58
2112 N Thornton St, Clovis NM 88101
Tel (575) 769-2311 SIC 5411 5541

MIRABITO HOLDINGS INC p 974
49 Court St Ste 1, Binghamton NY 13901
Tel (607) 561-2700
SIC 5172 4925 5541 5411 5983

SCHMITT SALES INC p 1287
2101 Saint Ritas Ln, Buffalo NY 14221
Tel (716) 639-1500 SIC 5172 5541

NICE N EASY GROCERY SHOPPES INC p 1042
7840 Oxbow Rd, Canastota NY 13032
Tel (315) 397-2802 SIC 5411 5541

REID COMPANIES INC p 1220
100 W Genesee St, Lockport NY 14094
Tel (716) 434-2885 SIC 5541

REID PETROLEUM CORP p 1221
100 W Genesee St, Lockport NY 14094
Tel (716) 434-2885 SIC 5541 5172

▲ **HESS CORP** p 688
1185 Ave Of The Americas, New York NY 10036
Tel (212) 997-8500
SIC 1311 2911 5171 5541 4911

RED APPLE GROUP INC p 1215
800 3rd Ave Fl 5, New York NY 10022
Tel (212) 956-5803 SIC 5461 5541 5411

CAMBRIDGE PETROLEUM HOLDING INC p 244
31 S Plank Rd Unit 105, Newburgh NY 12550
Tel (516) 542-4900
SIC 5983 5541 5984 5172 5074

BLUEOX CORP p 193
38 N Canal St, Oxford NY 13830
Tel (607) 843-2583 SIC 5172 5411 5541

PUGH OIL CO INC p 1191
701 Mcdowell Rd, Asheboro NC 27205
Tel (336) 629-2061
SIC 5172 5983 5541 5411 5149

▲ **INGLES MARKETS INC** p 743
2913 Us Highway 70, Black Mountain NC 28711
Tel (828) 669-2941
SIC 5411 5912 5541 2026 6512

COC PROPERTIES INC p 333
110 Mackenan Dr Ste 300, Cary NC 27511
Tel (919) 462-1100 SIC 6512 5541 5411

PANTRY INC p 1112
305 Gregson Dr, Cary NC 27511
Tel (919) 774-6700 SIC 5541 5411

UNITED ENERGY INC p 1508
932 N Hwy 421, Clinton NC 28328
Tel (919) 785-1904 SIC 5541 5411

CAMPBELL RENTALS LLC p 245
418 Peanut Plant Rd, Elizabethtown NC 28337
Tel (910) 862-7657 SIC 5171 5411 5541

LIL THRIFT FOOD MARTS INC p 866
1007 Arsenal Ave, Fayetteville NC 28305
Tel (910) 433-4490 SIC 5541 5411

NEIGHBORS STORES INC p 1024
1314 Old Highway 601, Mount Airy NC 27030
Tel (336) 789-5561 SIC 5541 5411

QUALITY OIL CO LLC p 1197
1540 Silas Creek Pkwy, Winston Salem NC 27127
Tel (336) 722-3441 SIC 5983 5541 7011

WILCOHESS LLC p 1608
5446 University Pkwy, Winston Salem NC 27105
Tel (336) 767-6280 SIC 5461 5812 5541

TRI-ENERGY COOPERATIVE p 1477
219 N 20th St, Bismarck ND 58501
Tel (701) 223-8707 SIC 5812 5541 5251

FARMERS UNION OIL OF SOUTHERN VALLEY p 530
100 S Front St, Fairmount ND 58030
Tel (701) 474-5440
SIC 5171 5191 5541 5261

S-N-GO STORES INC p 1263
2701 University Dr S, Fargo ND 58103
Tel (701) 235-7531 SIC 5541 5411

SPF ENERGY INC p 1358
100 27th St Ne, Minot ND 58703
Tel (701) 852-1194 SIC 5541 5411

SUPERPUMPER INC p 1407
100 27th St Ne, Minot ND 58703
Tel (701) 852-0061 SIC 5541 5411

FARMERS UNION OIL CO OF STANLEY p 530
8149 Highway 2, Stanley ND 58784
Tel (701) 628-2322
SIC 5172 5251 5541 5411

SERVICE OIL INC p 1307
1718 Main Ave E, West Fargo ND 58078
Tel (701) 277-1050 SIC 5541 5411

HORIZON RESOURCES p 707
317 2nd St W, Williston ND 58801
Tel (701) 572-2171
SIC 5172 5541 5411 5191

HOLLAND OIL CO p 700
1485 Marion Ave, Akron OH 44313
Tel (330) 835-1815 SIC 5541 5172 5411

TOWN AND COUNTRY CO-OP INC p 1464
813 Clark Ave, Ashland OH 44805
Tel (419) 281-2153 SIC 5541 5261 5999

TRUE NORTH ENERGY LLC p 1486
10346 Brecksville Rd, Brecksville OH 44141
Tel (877) 245-9336 SIC 5541 5172

HARTLEY CO p 666
319 Wheeling Ave, Cambridge OH 43725
Tel (740) 432-2328 SIC 5541 5172

▲ **KROGER CO** p 830
1014 Vine St Ste 1000, Cincinnati OH 45202
Tel (513) 762-4000
SIC 5411 5912 5541 5944

UNITED DAIRY FARMERS INC p 1507
3955 Montgomery Rd, Cincinnati OH 45212
Tel (513) 396-8700
SIC 5411 5143 2026 2024 5541 5451

■ **T A HOLDINGS CORP** p 1419
24601 Center Ridge Rd # 200, Cleveland OH 44145
Tel (440) 808-9100 SIC 5541

■ **SPEEDWAY LLC** p 1358
500 Speedway Dr, Enon OH 45323
Tel (937) 864-3000 SIC 5411 5541 2869

BECK SUPPLIERS INC p 167
1000 N Front St, Fremont OH 43420
Tel (419) 332-5527
SIC 5171 5541 5411 5984 1542

ENGLEFIELD INC p 499
447 James Pkwy, Heath OH 43056
Tel (740) 928-8215 SIC 5541

DISTRICT PETROLEUM PRODUCTS INC p 443
1814 River Rd, Huron OH 44839
Tel (419) 433-8373 SIC 5541 5171 5172

COLES ENERGY INC p 336
3619 St Rt 113 E, Milan OH 44846
Tel (419) 499-1120 SIC 5172 5411 5541

JACK A ALLEN INC p 773
2105 Old State Route 7, Steubenville OH 43952
Tel (740) 282-4531
SIC 5172 5983 5541 5411

EARHART PETROLEUM INC p 468
1494 Lytle Rd, Troy OH 45373
Tel (937) 335-2928 SIC 5172 5541 5983

■ **TA OPERATING LLC** p 1420
24601 Center Ridge Rd # 200, Westlake OH 44145
Tel (440) 808-9100
SIC 5541 7538 5812 5411 6794

■ **TRAVELCENTERS OF AMERICA INC** p 1474
24601 Center Ridge Rd # 200, Westlake OH 44145
Tel (440) 808-9100
SIC 5541 7538 5812 5411

▲ **TRAVELCENTERS OF AMERICA LLC** p 1474
24601 Center Ridge Rd # 200, Westlake OH 44145
Tel (440) 808-9100 SIC 5541 5812 7538

PORTS PETROLEUM CO INC p 1163
1337 Blachleyville Rd, Wooster OH 44691
Tel (330) 264-1885 SIC 5172 5983 5541

CHEROKEE NATION ENTERTAINMENT LLC p 294
777 W Cherokee St, Catoosa OK 74015
Tel (918) 458-1696
SIC 7999 7011 7948 5541 5993

HUTCHINSON OIL CO INC p 722
515 S Main St, Elk City OK 73644
Tel (580) 225-0301 SIC 5171 5541

7-ELEVEN LLC p 3
2021 S Macarthur Blvd, Oklahoma City OK 73128
Tel (405) 682-5711 SIC 5411 5541

LOVES TRAVEL STOPS & COUNTRY STORES INC p 881
10601 N Pennsylvania Ave, Oklahoma City OK 73120
Tel (405) 302-6500 SIC 5541 5411 5947

QUIKTRIP CORP p 1200
4705 S 129th East Ave, Tulsa OK 74134
Tel (918) 615-7700
SIC 5411 5541 5172 2099 5141 6512

LEATHERS ENTERPRISES INC p 850
255 Depot St, Fairview OR 97024
Tel (503) 661-1244 SIC 5541 6519

ED STAUB & SONS PETROLEUM INC p 476
1301 Esplanade Ave, Klamath Falls OR 97601
Tel (541) 887-8900 SIC 5172 5541 5411

WILCO FARMERS p 1608
200 Industrial Way Ne, Mount Angel OR 97362
Tel (503) 845-6122 SIC 5541

JUBITZ CORP p 796
33 Ne Middlefield Rd, Portland OR 97211
Tel (503) 283-1111
SIC 5541 4789 5014 7011

MARTIN OIL CO p 913
528 N 1st St, Bellwood PA 16617
Tel (814) 742-8438
SIC 5983 5171 5541 5411

COUNTRY FAIR INC p 375
2251 E 30th St, Erie PA 16510
Tel (814) 898-1111 SIC 5411 5541

WORLEY & OBETZ INC p 1626
85 White Oak Rd, Manheim PA 17545
Tel (717) 665-6891 SIC 5983 5541

■ **SUNOCO INC** p 1403
3801 West Chester Pike, Newtown Square PA 19073
Tel (215) 977-3000
SIC 5541 2911 2869 2865 5171 5052

■ **SUNOCO INC (R&M)** p 1403
3801 West Chester Pike, Newtown Square PA 19073
Tel (215) 977-3000
SIC 5541 2869 2911 5411

ATLANTIC PETROLEUM CORP p 127
1801 Market St Ste 1500, Philadelphia PA 19103
Tel (215) 977-3000
SIC 5541 5172 2911 4612

■ **ATLANTIC REFINING & MARKETING CORP** p 127
1801 Market St, Philadelphia PA 19103
Tel (215) 977-3000
SIC 2911 5171 5541 5411

HANUMAN BUSINESS INC p 659
5026 Wynnefield Ave, Philadelphia PA 19131
Tel (609) 929-5146 SIC 5541 7538

REDNERS MARKETS INC p 1217
3 Quarry Rd, Reading PA 19605
Tel (610) 926-3700 SIC 5411 5541 5912

UNI-MARTS LLC p 1502
1155 Benner Pike 100, State College PA 16801
Tel (814) 234-6000
SIC 5411 5541 5993 6794 5172

UNITED REFINING CO p 1511
15 Bradley St, Warren PA 16365
Tel (814) 723-1500 SIC 2911 5541 5411

UNITED REFINING CO OF PENNSYLVANIA p 1511
15 Bradley St, Warren PA 16365
Tel (814) 723-1500 SIC 5541 5411

UNITED REFINING INC p 1511
15 Bradley St, Warren PA 16365
Tel (814) 723-1500
SIC 2911 5541 5411 4612

ATLANTIS PETROLEUM LLC p 127
998 Old Eagle School Rd # 1205, Wayne PA 19087
Tel (610) 265-8081 SIC 5411 5541

■ **WARREN EQUITIES INC** p 1577
27 Warren Way, Providence RI 02905
Tel (401) 781-9900 SIC 5172 5541 5411

BRABHAM OIL CO INC p 206
525 Midway St, Bamberg SC 29003
Tel (803) 245-2471
SIC 5171 5541 5411 5921

OPAL HOLDINGS LLC p 1089
208 Bi Lo Blvd, Greenville SC 29607
Tel (864) 213-2500 SIC 5411 5541 5912

SPINX CO INC p 1358
1414 E Washington St N, Greenville SC 29607
Tel (864) 233-5421 SIC 5541 5411 5812

WEST OIL INC p 1595
312 Lakeview Blvd, Hartsville SC 29550
Tel (843) 332-2201 SIC 5172 5541 5411

R L JORDAN OIL CO OF NORTH CAROLINA INC p 1202
1451 Fernwood Glendale Rd, Spartanburg SC 29307
Tel (864) 585-2784
SIC 5411 5172 5541 5812

EASTERN FARMERS COOPERATIVE p 472
26033 482nd Ave, Brandon SD 57005
Tel (605) 582-2415 SIC 5191 5171 5541

FULL CIRCLE AG p 584
520 Vander Horck Ave, Britton SD 57430
Tel (605) 448-2231 SIC 5191 5153 5541

NORTH CENTRAL FARMERS ELEVATOR p 1052
12 5th Ave, Ipswich SD 57451
Tel (605) 426-6021
SIC 5153 5191 5171 5541

BIG D OIL CO p 181
3685 Sturgis Rd, Rapid City SD 57702
Tel (605) 342-6777 SIC 5541 5172 8741

MG OIL CO p 958
1180 Creek Dr, Rapid City SD 57703
Tel (605) 342-0527 SIC 5172 5541 5411

MOYLE PETROLEUM CO p 995
2504 W Main St, Rapid City SD 57702
Tel (605) 343-1966 SIC 5541 5411

▲ **DELEK US HOLDINGS INC** p 424
7102 Commerce Way, Brentwood TN 37027
Tel (615) 771-6701
SIC 2911 4612 5541 5411

MAPCO EXPRESS INC p 903
7102 Commerce Way, Brentwood TN 37027
Tel (615) 771-6701 SIC 5541 5411

ROBERTS-GIBSON INC p 1242
115 Highway 51 Byp, Dyersburg TN 38024
Tel (731) 285-4941 SIC 5171 5541

GREENEVILLE OIL & PETROLEUM INC p 638
860 W Andrew Johnson Hwy, Greeneville TN 37745
Tel (423) 638-3145 SIC 5172 5411 5541

MOUNTAIN EMPIRE OIL CO p 994
282 Christian Church Rd, Johnson City TN 37615
Tel (423) 928-7241 SIC 5541 5411

CFJ PROPERTIES LLC p 285
5508 Lonas Dr, Knoxville TN 37909
Tel (801) 624-1000 SIC 5541 5812 5411

PILOT CORP p 1148
5508 Lonas Dr, Knoxville TN 37909
Tel (865) 588-7488 SIC 5411 5541

PILOT TRAVEL CENTERS LLC p 1148
5508 Lonas Dr, Knoxville TN 37909
Tel (865) 588-7488 SIC 5411 5541

SOUTH TENNESSEE OIL CO INC p 1345
105 Helton Dr, Lawrenceburg TN 38464
Tel (931) 762-9600 SIC 5541 5411

BEST-WADE PETROLEUM INC p 177
201 Dodge Dr, Ripley TN 38063
Tel (731) 635-9661 SIC 5171 5541 5411

COX OIL CO INC p 386
623 Perkins St, Union City TN 38261
Tel (731) 885-6444 SIC 5541 5411

TOOT N TOTUM FOOD STORES LLC p 1460
1201 S Taylor St, Amarillo TX 79101
Tel (806) 373-4351 SIC 5411 5541

TOOT N TOTUM FOOD STORES LP p 1460
1201 S Taylor St, Amarillo TX 79101
Tel (806) 373-4351 SIC 5541 5411

TRI-CON INC p 1477
7076 W Port Arthur Rd, Beaumont TX 77705
Tel (409) 835-2237 SIC 5541 5172 5411

■ **CHEVRON PIPE LINE CO** p 296
4800 Fournace Pl, Bellaire TX 77401
Tel (877) 596-2800 SIC 5541

KWIK CHEK FOOD STORES INC p 832
2207 N Center St, Bonham TX 75418
Tel (903) 583-7484 SIC 5541 5411

■ **SUSSER HOLDINGS CORP** p 1409
4525 Ayers St, Corpus Christi TX 78415
Tel (361) 884-2463 SIC 5411 5541 5172

DALHART CONSUMERS FUEL ASSOCIATION INC p 409
919 Liberal St, Dalhart TX 79022
Tel (806) 249-4660
SIC 5153 5172 5191 5541

■ **ALON USA LP** p 59
12700 Park Central Dr # 1600, Dallas TX 75251
Tel (972) 367-3600
SIC 2911 4612 5172 5541 2895

▲ **SUNOCO LP** p 1403
8020 Park Ln Ste 200, Dallas TX 75231
Tel (214) 981-0700 SIC 5172 6519 5541

SIMONS PETROLEUM p 1325
201 N Rupert St Ste 101, Fort Worth TX 76107
Tel (405) 551-2403
SIC 5172 5171 5541 5411

J CINCO INC p 770
1113 E Sarah Dewitt Dr, Gonzales TX 78629
Tel (830) 672-9574 SIC 5172 5541

ALTA MESA RESOURCES LP p 61
15021 Katy Fwy Ste 400, Houston TX 77094
Tel (281) 530-0991 SIC 5541

BP CORP NORTH AMERICA INC p 205
501 Westlake Park Blvd, Houston TX 77079
Tel (281) 366-2000
SIC 2911 5541 5171 1311 4613 4612

BP PRODUCTS NORTH AMERICA INC p 206
501 Westlake Park Blvd, Houston TX 77079
Tel (281) 366-2000 SIC 5541 5171 4613

■ **CONOCOPHILLIPS HOLDING CO** p 358
600 N Dairy Ashford Rd, Houston TX 77079
Tel (281) 293-1000 SIC 2911 5171 5541

■ **EL PASO CGP CO LLC** p 483
1001 Louisiana St, Houston TX 77002
Tel (713) 420-2600
SIC 2911 1311 4613 4612 5541 4922

■ **KAYO OIL CO** p 805
600 N Dairy Ashford Rd, Houston TX 77079
Tel (281) 293-1000 SIC 5541 5411

LANDMARK INDUSTRIES HOLDINGS LTD p 843
11111 S Wilcrest Dr, Houston TX 77099
Tel (713) 789-0310 SIC 5411 5541

■ **MARATHON OIL CO** p 904
5555 San Felipe St # 2796, Houston TX 77056
Tel (713) 629-6600
SIC 2911 5171 5541 1311 4612 4613

▲ **MARATHON OIL CORP** p 904
5555 San Felipe St # 2796, Houston TX 77056
Tel (713) 629-6600
SIC 1311 2911 5171 5541

MOTIVA ENTERPRISES LLC p 992
500 Dallas St, Houston TX 77002
Tel (713) 241-6161 SIC 2911 5541

■ **PAR HAWAII REFINING LLC** p 1113
800 Gessner Rd Ste 875, Houston TX 77024
Tel (281) 899-4800 SIC 5541 2911

■ **PHILLIPS 66 PARTNERS LP** p 1144
3010 Briarpark Dr, Houston TX 77042
Tel (855) 283-9237 SIC 4612 1311 5541

■ **PHILLIPS PETROLEUM CO** p 1144
600 N Dairy Ashford Rd, Houston TX 77079
Tel (281) 293-1000
SIC 1382 2911 5171 5541

SHELL OIL CO p 1314
910 Louisiana St Ste 1500, Houston TX 77002
Tel (713) 241-6161
SIC 5541 4612 1311 2821 2869 2911

■ **TEXACO EXPLORATION AND PRODUCTION INC** p 1441
1500 Louisiana St, Houston TX 77002
Tel (800) 962-1223 SIC 5541 5511 1321

▲ **EXXON MOBIL CORP** p 521
5959 Las Colinas Blvd, Irving TX 75039
Tel (972) 444-1000
SIC 2911 4612 5541 5171 4911

MIDTEX OIL LP p 966
3455 Ih 35 S, New Braunfels TX 78132
Tel (830) 625-4214 SIC 5541 5171

PERRYTON EQUITY EXCHANGE p 1137
4219 S Main St, Perryton TX 79070
Tel (806) 435-4016 SIC 5153 5191 5541

GARRISON FRED OIL CO p 592
1107 Walter Griffin St, Plainview TX 79072
Tel (806) 296-6353 SIC 5172 5541

■ **DIAMOND SHAMROCK REFINING AND MARKETING CO** p 437
6000 N Loop 1604 W, San Antonio TX 78249
Tel (210) 345-2000 SIC 5541 5171 2911

■ **TESORO REFINING & MARKETING CO LLC** p 1440
19100 Ridgewood Pkwy, San Antonio TX 78259
Tel (210) 828-8484 SIC 2911 5541

■ **TPI PETROLEUM INC** p 1467
6000 N Loop 1604 W, San Antonio TX 78249
Tel (210) 592-2000
SIC 2911 5541 4612 4212 4213

■ **ULTRAMAR INC** p 1501
1 Valero Way, San Antonio TX 78249
Tel (210) 345-2000 SIC 2911 5172 5541

WARREN FUEL CO p 1577
1405 United Dr, San Marcos TX 78666
Tel (512) 395-8557 SIC 5541

DOUGLASS DISTRIBUTING RETAIL CO INC p 452
325 E Forest Ave, Sherman TX 75090
Tel (903) 893-1181 SIC 5411 5541

■ **MOBIL EXPLORATION & PRODUCING US INC** p 980
22777 Sprngwoods Vlg Pkwy, Spring TX 77389
Tel (281) 288-4545 SIC 5541

E-Z MART STORES INC p 467
602 Falvey Ave, Texarkana TX 75501
Tel (903) 832-6502 SIC 5541 5411

PETROLEUM WHOLESALE LP p 1139
8550 Technology Forest Pl, The Woodlands TX 77381
Tel (281) 681-7500 SIC 5172 5541

CL THOMAS INC p 320
9701 Us Highway 59 N, Victoria TX 77905
Tel (361) 573-7662 SIC 5411 5541

SPEEDY STOP FOOD STORES LLC p 1358
8701 N Navarro St, Victoria TX 77904
Tel (361) 573-7662 SIC 5812 5541 5411

AFJ LLC p 33
1104 Country Hills Dr, Ogden UT 84403
Tel (801) 624-1000 SIC 5541 5963

FJ MANAGEMENT INC p 553
185 S State St Ste 201, Salt Lake City UT 84111
Tel (801) 624-1000
SIC 5541 2911 5411 1382 6022

MAVERIK INC p 921
185 S State St Ste 800, Salt Lake City UT 84111
Tel (801) 936-9155 SIC 5541 5411

SINCLAIR COMPANIES p 1326
550 E South Temple, Salt Lake City UT 84102
Tel (801) 363-5100
SIC 2911 4612 1382 5541 7011 0212

R L VALLEE INC p 1202
282 S Main St, Saint Albans VT 05478
Tel (802) 524-8710 SIC 5172 5541

HIGHWAY SERVICE VENTURES INC p 692
100 Arbor Oak Dr Ste 305, Ashland VA 23005
Tel (804) 752-4966 SIC 5541 5411 5812

WORKMAN OIL CO p 1624
14670 Forest Rd, Forest VA 24551
Tel (434) 525-1615 SIC 5541

CLINE ENERGY INC p 326
1890 S Main St, Harrisonburg VA 22801
Tel (540) 434-7344 SIC 5172 5541 1521

UPPYS CONVENIENCE STORES INC p 1529
1011 Boulder Springs Dr, North Chesterfield VA 23225
Tel (804) 706-4702 SIC 5411 5541

GPM INVESTMENTS LLC p 627
8565 Magellan Pkwy # 400, Richmond VA 23227
Tel (804) 266-1363 SIC 5541 5411 5172

PARKER HOLDING CO INC p 1116
1428 W Danville St, South Hill VA 23970
Tel (434) 447-3146 SIC 5171 5541 5983

PARKER OIL CO INC p 1116
1428 W Danville St, South Hill VA 23970
Tel (434) 447-3146 SIC 5171 5541 5983

E & C ENTERPRISES INC p 465
2359 Research Ct, Woodbridge VA 22192
Tel (703) 494-5800 SIC 5541

BP WEST COAST PRODUCTS LLC p 206
4519 Grandview Rd, Blaine WA 98230
Tel (310) 549-6204 SIC 5541

R H SMITH DISTRIBUTING CO INC p 1202
315 E Wine Country Rd, Grandview WA 98930
Tel (509) 882-3377
SIC 5171 5541 5411 5172

SUN PACIFIC ENERGY INC p 1400
501 W Canal Dr, Kennewick WA 99336
Tel (509) 586-1135 SIC 5172 5541 5411

WILSON OIL INC p 1614
95 Panel Way, Longview WA 98632
Tel (360) 575-9222 SIC 5541 5983 5172

ALSAKER CORP p 61
6409 E Sharp Ave, Spokane Valley WA 99212
Tel (509) 242-6327 SIC 5541 5411

GLENN DISTRIBUTOR INC p 615
1301 N Wenatchee Ave, Wenatchee WA 98801
Tel (509) 663-7173 SIC 5172 5541 7359

GO-MART INC p 619
915 Riverside Dr, Gassaway WV 26624
Tel (304) 364-8000 SIC 5411 5541

R M ROACH & SONS INC p 1202
333 E John St, Martinsburg WV 25401
Tel (304) 263-3329 SIC 5541 5172

FLEET WHOLESALE SUPPLY CO LLC p 555
3035 W Wisconsin Ave, Appleton WI 54914
Tel (920) 734-8231
SIC 5191 5331 5531 5211 5541

UNITED COOPERATIVE p 1507
N7160 Raceway Rd, Beaver Dam WI 53916
Tel (920) 887-1756
SIC 5191 5171 5541 5153 5812

CONSUMERS COOPERATIVE ASSOCIATION OF EAU CLAIRE p 362
1201 S Hastings Way, Eau Claire WI 54701
Tel (715) 836-8700 SIC 5411 5541

DITTO II LLC p 443
1201 S Hastings Way, Eau Claire WI 54701
Tel (715) 836-8710 SIC 5541 5411

■ **ERICKSON OIL PRODUCTS INC** p 507
1231 Industrial St, Hudson WI 54016
Tel (715) 386-8241 SIC 5541 5411

S/S/G CORP p 1263
512 2nd St Ste 12, Hudson WI 54016
Tel (715) 386-8281 SIC 5541 5411

KWIK TRIP INC p 832
1626 Oak St, La Crosse WI 54603
Tel (608) 781-8988
SIC 5921 5993 5541 5983 5461

LAC DU FLAMBEAU BAND OF LAKE SUPERIOR CHIPPEWA INDIANS (INC) p 836
418 Little Pines Rd, Lac Du Flambeau WI 54538
Tel (715) 588-3303
SIC 8011 7999 5411 5541 8031

LARSEN COOPERATIVE CO p 845
8290 County Hwy T, Larsen WI 54947
Tel (920) 982-1111 SIC 5191 5172 5541

PROVISION PARTNERS COOPERATIVE p 1187
2327 W Veterans Pkwy, Marshfield WI 54449
Tel (715) 687-4443 SIC 5191 5984 5541

T A SOLBERG CO INC p 1419
420 Oneida St, Minocqua WI 54548
Tel (715) 356-7711 SIC 5541

PREMIER COOPERATIVE p 1170
501 W Main St, Mount Horeb WI 53572
Tel (608) 251-0199
SIC 5211 5171 5191 5541

CONDON OIL CO p 355
126 E Jackson St, Ripon WI 54971
Tel (920) 748-3186 SIC 5541

QUALITY STATE OIL CO INC p 1197
2201 Calumet Dr, Sheboygan WI 53083
Tel (920) 459-5640 SIC 5171 5541 5411

SIC 5551 Boat Dealers

T - H MARINE SUPPLIES INC p 1419
200 Finney Dr Sw, Huntsville AL 35824
Tel (256) 772-0164 SIC 5551 3999 3429

▲ **WEST MARINE INC** p 1595
500 Westridge Dr, Watsonville CA 95076
Tel (831) 728-2700
SIC 5551 5961 5088 5611 5661 5621

■ **WEST MARINE PRODUCTS INC** p 1595
500 Westridge Dr, Watsonville CA 95076
Tel (831) 728-2700 SIC 5551 5561

GALATI YACHT SALES LLC p 589
902 Bay Blvd, Anna Maria FL 34216
Tel (941) 778-0755 SIC 5551 4493

▲ **MARINEMAX INC** p 906
2600 Mccormick Dr Ste 200, Clearwater FL 33759
Tel (727) 531-1700 SIC 5551

SMOKER CRAFT INC p 1334
68143 Clunette St, New Paris IN 46553
Tel (574) 831-2103 SIC 3732 5551 3731

BASS PRO LLC p 159
2500 E Kearney St, Springfield MO 65898
Tel (417) 873-5000
SIC 5961 5941 5551 5661

ALPIN HAUS SKI SHOP INC p 60
4850 State Highway 30, Amsterdam NY 12010
Tel (518) 843-4400 SIC 5561 5551 5941

■ **MARINE ACQUISITION (US) INC** p 906
640 N Lewis Rd, Limerick PA 19468
Tel (610) 495-7011 SIC 3531 5551

MARTIN ENERGY SERVICES LLC p 912
3 Riverway Ste 400, Houston TX 77056
Tel (713) 350-6800
SIC 5171 4492 5172 5551

WILHELMSEN SHIPS SERVICE INC p 1609
9400 New Century Dr, Pasadena TX 77507
Tel (281) 867-2000 SIC 5551 5088 7699

SIC 5561 Recreational Vehicle Dealers

EARNHARDT FORD SALES CO INC p 469
7300 W Orchid Ln, Tempe AZ 85284
Tel (480) 893-0000
SIC 5511 5531 7538 5561

BEAUDRY MOTOR CO p 166
4600 E 22nd St, Tucson AZ 85711
Tel (520) 750-1264 SIC 5511 5561

FLEETWOOD ENTERPRISES INC p 555
1351 Pomona Rd Ste 230, Corona CA 92882
Tel (951) 354-3000 SIC 3799 2451 5561

UTILITY TRAILER SALES OF SOUTHERN CALIFORNIA LLC p 1537
15567 Valley Blvd, Fontana CA 92335
Tel (877) 275-4887
SIC 5012 5013 5531 5561

GIANT INLAND EMPIRE RV CENTER INC p 611
9150 Benson Ave, Montclair CA 91763
Tel (909) 981-0444 SIC 5561 7538

LA MESA R V CENTER INC p 835
7430 Copley Park Pl, San Diego CA 92111
Tel (858) 874-8001 SIC 5561 7538

■ **WEST MARINE PRODUCTS INC** p 1595
500 Westridge Dr, Watsonville CA 95076
Tel (831) 728-2700 SIC 5551 5561

LDRV HOLDINGS CORP p 849
6130 Lazy Days Blvd, Seffner FL 33584
Tel (813) 246-4333 SIC 5561

FREEDOMROADS LLC p 576
250 Parkway Dr Ste 270, Lincolnshire IL 60069
Tel (866) 838-5304 SIC 5561

GOOD SAM ENTERPRISES LLC p 623
250 Parkway Dr Ste 270, Lincolnshire IL 60069
Tel (847) 229-6720 SIC 5561 7997 2721

DOMETIC CORP p 449
2320 Industrial Pkwy, Elkhart IN 46516
Tel (574) 294-2511 SIC 5561

■ **FOREST RIVER INC** p 567
900 County Road 1 N, Elkhart IN 46514
Tel (574) 389-4600 SIC 5561 3715

FORD OLATHE SALES INC p 566
1845 E Santa Fe St, Olathe KS 66062
Tel (913) 782-0881 SIC 5511 5561 5012

CAMPING WORLD INC p 246
650 Three Springs Rd, Bowling Green KY 42104
Tel (270) 781-2718 SIC 5561 5961

GENERAL RV CENTER INC p 602
25000 Assembly Park Dr, Wixom MI 48393
Tel (248) 349-0900 SIC 5561

REDNECK INC p 1217
2100 N West Byp, Springfield MO 65803
Tel (417) 864-5210 SIC 5013 5561 5012

AMERICAN RV CENTERS LLC p 78
14303 Central Ave Nw, Albuquerque NM 87121
Tel (505) 293-1983 SIC 5561

ALPIN HAUS SKI SHOP INC p 60
4850 State Highway 30, Amsterdam NY 12010
Tel (518) 843-4400 SIC 5561 5551 5941

GUARANTY RV INC p 644
20 Highway 99 S, Junction City OR 97448
Tel (541) 998-2333 SIC 5561 5511

GHM CORP p 610
12700 Hillcrest Rd # 291, Dallas TX 75230
Tel (972) 840-1200
SIC 3448 1799 5999 5561

R V MCCLAINS INC p 1203
5601 S I 35 E, Denton TX 76210
Tel (940) 498-4398 SIC 5561 7538

POULSBO RV INC p 1164
19705 Viking Ave Nw, Poulsbo WA 98370
Tel (360) 697-4445 SIC 5561

NORDIC GROUP OF COMPANIES LTD p 1048
715 Lynn Ave Ste 100, Baraboo WI 53913
Tel (608) 356-7303 SIC 8742 8111 5561

SIC 5571 Motorcycle Dealers

CYCLE GEAR INC p 405
4705 Industrial Way, Benicia CA 94510
Tel (707) 747-5053 SIC 5571

HD AMERICAN ROAD LLC p 672
3770 37th St, Orlando FL 32805
Tel (407) 423-0346 SIC 5571

J&P CYCLES LLC p 772
13225 Circle Dr, Anamosa IA 52205
Tel (319) 462-4817 SIC 5571 5013

KENTUCKY LAKE OIL CO INC p 812
620 S 4th St, Murray KY 42071
Tel (270) 753-1323
SIC 5541 5571 5171 5411

KAWASAKI MOTORS MANUFACTURING CORP USA p 805
6600 Nw 27th St, Lincoln NE 68524
Tel (402) 476-6600 *SIC* 3751 5571

LANPHERE ENTERPRISES INC p 844
12505 Sw Brdwy St, Beaverton OR 97005
Tel (503) 643-5577 *SIC* 5571 5511 5261

MOTOSPORT INC p 993
15353 Sw Sequoia Pkwy # 140, Portland OR 97224
Tel (503) 783-5600 *SIC* 5571

AMERICAS POWERSPORTS INC p 81
825 Market St Bldg M, Allen TX 75013
Tel (214) 383-4835 *SIC* 5571 7941

HARRISON WORLDWIDE ENTERPRISES INC p 664
1650 Independence Dr, New Braunfels TX 78132
Tel (830) 609-9200 *SIC* 5571

BIG 3 HOLDING CO INC p 181
1625 N Valley Mills Dr, Waco TX 76710
Tel (254) 772-8850 *SIC* 5511 5571

SIC 5599 Automotive Dealers, NEC

CUTTER AVIATION p 403
2802 E Old Tower Rd, Phoenix AZ 85034
Tel (602) 273-1237
SIC 5599 5088 4522 5172 4581

■ INTERAMERICAN MOTOR CORP p 751
8901 Canoga Ave, Canoga Park CA 91304
Tel (818) 678-6571 *SIC* 5013 5599

IRWIN INTERNATIONAL INC p 765
225 Airport Cir, Corona CA 92880
Tel (951) 372-9555 *SIC* 5599 5088

INTERNATIONAL LEASE FINANCE CORP p 755
10250 Constellation Blvd, Los Angeles CA 90067
Tel (310) 788-1999 *SIC* 7359 8741 5599

■ SIKORSKY AIRCRAFT CORP p 1322
6900 Main St, Stratford CT 06614
Tel (203) 386-4000 *SIC* 3721 4581 5599

TRAILER COUNTRY INC p 1469
5326 Land O Lakes Blvd, Land O Lakes FL 34639
Tel (813) 929-0700 *SIC* 5599

ELLIOTT AVIATION INC p 488
6601 74th Ave, Milan IL 61264
Tel (309) 799-3183 *SIC* 4581 5599

▲ AAR CORP p 8
1100 N Wood Dale Rd, Wood Dale IL 60191
Tel (630) 227-2000
SIC 3724 4581 3537 5599 7359

ABC BUS COMPANIES INC p 10
1506 30th St Nw, Faribault MN 55021
Tel (507) 334-1871 *SIC* 5012 4173 5599

PAPE GROUP INC p 1112
355 Goodpasture Island Rd # 300, Eugene OR 97401
Tel (541) 334-3400
SIC 5084 5082 7699 6141 5599 4581

ERICKSON INC p 507
5550 Sw Mcdam Ave Ste 200, Portland OR 97239
Tel (503) 505-5800
SIC 7363 4581 3721 7359 5599 3728

STEVENS AVIATION INC p 1388
600 Delaware St, Greenville SC 29605
Tel (864) 678-6000
SIC 4522 4581 5088 5599

PIEDMONT HAWTHORNE AVIATION LLC p 1147
1500 City W Blvd Ste 600, Houston TX 77042
Tel (713) 895-9243
SIC 5599 4581 4522 5172

BIG TEX TRAILER MANUFACTURING INC p 182
950 Interstate Hwy 30 E, Mount Pleasant TX 75455
Tel (903) 575-0300 *SIC* 3523 5013 5599

■ ATLANTIC AVIATION HOLDING CORP p 126
6652 Pinecrest Dr Ste 300, Plano TX 75024
Tel (972) 905-2500 *SIC* 5599

SIC 5611 Men's & Boys' Clothing & Access Stores

▲ DILLARDS INC p 439
1600 Cantrell Rd, Little Rock AR 72201
Tel (501) 376-5200
SIC 5311 5611 5621 5641 5712

PACIFIC SUNWEAR OF CALIFORNIA LLC p 1106
3450 E Miraloma Ave, Anaheim CA 92806
Tel (714) 414-4000 *SIC* 5611 5621 5699

PACIFIC SUNWEAR STORES CORP p 1106
3450 E Miraloma Ave, Anaheim CA 92806
Tel (714) 414-4000
SIC 5611 5699 5661 5621 5999

HUB DISTRIBUTING INC p 715
1260 Corona Pointe Ct, Corona CA 92879
Tel (951) 340-3149
SIC 5611 5621 5632 5137 5136 5094

HYBRID PROMOTIONS LLC p 723
10711 Walker St, Cypress CA 90630
Tel (714) 952-3866 *SIC* 5136 5137 5611

▲ ROSS STORES INC p 1252
5130 Hacienda Dr, Dublin CA 94568
Tel (925) 965-4400
SIC 5651 5661 5944 5632 5611 5999

J & M SALES INC p 770
15001 S Figueroa St, Gardena CA 90248
Tel (310) 324-9962
SIC 5651 6531 5311 5611 5621

■ SHEPLERS INC p 1315
15345 Barranca Pkwy, Irvine CA 92618
Tel (316) 946-3835
SIC 5699 5661 5961 5651 5632 5611

▲ GUESS INC p 645
1444 S Alameda St, Los Angeles CA 90021
Tel (213) 765-3100
SIC 2325 2339 5611 5621 5641

GURU DENIM INC p 648
1888 Rosecrans Ave # 1000, Manhattan Beach CA 90266
Tel (323) 266-3072 *SIC* 5137 5611

▲ GAP INC p 591
2 Folsom St, San Francisco CA 94105
Tel (415) 427-0100
SIC 5651 5641 5632 5621 5611

▲ WEST MARINE INC p 1595
500 Westridge Dr, Watsonville CA 95076
Tel (831) 728-2700
SIC 5551 5961 5088 5611 5661 5621

AMHERST NY BOBS INC p 85
160 Corporate Ct, Meriden CT 06450
Tel (203) 235-5775
SIC 5651 5611 5699 5621 5641 5661

BI RETAIL INC p 180
160 Corporate Ct, Meriden CT 06450
Tel (203) 235-5775
SIC 5651 5611 5699 5621 5641 5661

EASTERN OUTFITTERS LLC p 472
160 Corporate Ct, Meriden CT 06450
Tel (203) 235-5775 *SIC* 5611 6719

H C BOBS INC p 649
160 Corporate Ct, Meriden CT 06450
Tel (203) 235-5775
SIC 5651 5611 5699 5621 5641 5661

VINEYARD VINES LLC p 1558
181 Harbor Dr Fl 1, Stamford CT 06902
Tel (203) 661-1803
SIC 5136 5137 5699 5611 5621

BEALLS OUTLET STORES INC p 165
1806 38th Ave E, Bradenton FL 34208
Tel (941) 747-2355
SIC 5611 5621 5661 5719

▲ PERRY ELLIS INTERNATIONAL INC p 1137
3000 Nw 107th Ave, Doral FL 33172
Tel (305) 592-2830
SIC 2321 2325 2339 2337 5611 5621

PARADIES SHOPS LLC p 1113
2849 Paces Ferry Rd Se, Atlanta GA 30339
Tel (404) 344-7905
SIC 5947 5994 5621 5611 5912 5941

■ AFTER HOURS FORMALWEAR INC p 33
4444 Shackleford Rd # 100, Norcross GA 30093
Tel (770) 448-8381 *SIC* 5611

▲ CITITRENDS INC p 310
104 Coleman Blvd, Savannah GA 31408
Tel (912) 236-1561
SIC 5611 5621 5641 5632

W DIAMOND GROUP CORP p 1568
1680 E Touhy Ave, Des Plaines IL 60018
Tel (646) 647-2791 *SIC* 2326 5611

EBHI HOLDINGS INC p 474
1000 Field Dr Ste 240, Lake Forest IL 60045
Tel (312) 251-3430
SIC 5611 5699 5941 5719 5947 5961

L L BEAN INC p 834
15 Casco St, Freeport ME 04033
Tel (207) 552-2000
SIC 5961 5621 5611 5941 5661 5948

■ JOS A BANK CLOTHIERS INC p 793
500 Hanover Pike, Hampstead MD 21074
Tel (410) 239-2700 *SIC* 5611 5961

DTLR INC p 458
1300 Mercedes Dr, Hanover MD 21076
Tel (410) 850-5900 *SIC* 5611 5661

■ FILA USA INC p 542
930 Ridgebrook Rd Ste 200, Sparks MD 21152
Tel (410) 773-3000
SIC 5139 5131 5137 5611 5621 5632

ORCHARD BRANDS CORP p 1093
138 Conant St Ste 3, Beverly MA 01915
Tel (978) 998-3800 *SIC* 5621 5611 5719

FAMILY FARM & HOME INC p 526
900 3rd St Ste 302, Muskegon MI 49440
Tel (231) 722-8335
SIC 5999 5261 5149 5611 5211 5091

LUTHER HOLDING CO p 886
3701 Alabama Ave S, Minneapolis MN 55416
Tel (763) 593-5755
SIC 5511 7515 7513 6512 6552 5611

▲ BUCKLE INC p 223
2407 W 24th St, Kearney NE 68845
Tel (308) 236-8491
SIC 5661 5632 5621 5611

■ CAESARS WORLD INC p 237
3570 Las Vegas Blvd S, Las Vegas NV 89109
Tel (702) 731-7110
SIC 7011 7999 5812 6552 5611 5621

MARSHALL RETAIL GROUP LLC p 911
3755 W Sunset Rd Ste A, Las Vegas NV 89118
Tel (702) 385-5233
SIC 5661 5621 5641 5611

■ ZAPPOS.COM INC p 1641
400 Stewart Ave Ste A, Las Vegas NV 89101
Tel (702) 943-7777
SIC 5661 4813 5632 5611

ERMENEGILDO ZEGNA CORP p 508
100 W Forest Ave Ste A, Englewood NJ 07631
Tel (201) 816-0921 *SIC* 5136 5611

ALDO US INC p 48
180 Passaic Ave, Fairfield NJ 07004
Tel (888) 818-2536 *SIC* 5611

■ VF SPORTSWEAR INC p 1553
545 Wshngton Blvd Fl 8, Jersey City NJ 07310
Tel (212) 541-5757
SIC 2329 2384 5136 5137 5611 6794

AERO OPCO LLC p 30
125 Chubb Ave Fl 5, Lyndhurst NJ 07071
Tel (201) 508-4500 *SIC* 5621 5611

HABAND CO LLC p 651
1 International Blvd # 800, Mahwah NJ 07495
Tel (570) 383-3226 *SIC* 5961 5611

ELIE TAHARI LTD p 487
16 Bleeker St, Millburn NJ 07041
Tel (973) 671-6300
SIC 2331 2339 2335 2337 5621 5611

▲ AEROPOSTALE INC p 30
100 W 33rd St Ste 1100, New York NY 10001
Tel (646) 485-5410 *SIC* 5621 5611

BARNEYS INC p 156
575 5th Ave Fl 11, New York NY 10017
Tel (212) 450-8700
SIC 5611 5621 5632 5932 5947 6794

BERGDORF GOODMAN INC p 174
754 5th Ave, New York NY 10019
Tel (800) 558-1855 *SIC* 5621 5632 5611

BRAVADO INTERNATIONAL GROUP MERCHANDISING SERVICES INC p 209
1755 Broadway Fl 2, New York NY 10019
Tel (212) 445-3400
SIC 5136 5137 5611 5621

BROOKS BROTHERS INC p 218
346 Madison Ave, New York NY 10017
Tel (212) 682-8800 *SIC* 5611 5621 5651

■ CALVIN KLEIN INC p 243
205 W 39th St Lbby 2, New York NY 10018
Tel (212) 719-2600
SIC 5651 5137 5136 5611 5621 6794

■ CALVIN KLEIN JEANSWEAR CO p 243
205 W 39th St Lbby 2, New York NY 10018
Tel (212) 292-9290 *SIC* 5611 5621

CHELSEY DIRECT LLC p 293
110 E 59th St, New York NY 10022
Tel (201) 863-7300 *SIC* 5961 5947 5611

CHINOS HOLDINGS INC p 301
770 Broadway, New York NY 10003
Tel (212) 209-2500
SIC 5961 5621 5611 5632 6794

CHINOS INTERMEDIATE HOLDINGS B INC p 301
770 Broadway, New York NY 10003
Tel (212) 209-2500
SIC 5961 5621 5611 5632 6794

DELIAS INC p 424
50 W 23rd St, New York NY 10010
Tel (212) 590-6200 *SIC* 5632 5611

DIESEL USA INC p 438
220 W 19th St Fl 5, New York NY 10011
Tel (212) 755-9200
SIC 5137 5136 5621 5632 5611

DR JAYS INC p 454
15 W 37th St Fl 11, New York NY 10018
Tel (212) 239-3355 *SIC* 5611 5661

FULLBEAUTY BRANDS INC p 584
1 New York Plz Fl 13, New York NY 10004
Tel (212) 613-9500 *SIC* 5961 7389 5611

GILT GROUPE HOLDINGS INC p 612
2 Park Ave Fl 4, New York NY 10016
Tel (877) 445-8692 *SIC* 5611

GIORGIO ARMANI CORP p 612
450 W 15th St 3, New York NY 10011
Tel (212) 209-3500
SIC 5136 5137 5122 5611 5621 5632

GRACE HOLMES INC p 628
770 Broadway Fl 11, New York NY 10003
Tel (212) 209-2500 *SIC* 5611 5621

GUCCI AMERICA INC p 645
195 Broadway Fl 12, New York NY 10007
Tel (212) 750-5220
SIC 5632 5948 5661 5611 5621 5137

HENRY MODELL & CO INC p 684
498 7th Ave Fl 20, New York NY 10018
Tel (212) 822-1000
SIC 5941 5661 5611 5621 5641 5961

HUGO BOSS USA INC p 717
55 Water St Fl 48, New York NY 10041
Tel (212) 940-0600
SIC 2311 2325 2337 5136 5611 6794

J CREW INC p 770
770 Broadway Fl 14, New York NY 10003
Tel (212) 209-8010 *SIC* 5961 5621 5611

J CREW OPERATING CORP p 770
770 Brdwy Fl 11 & 12, New York NY 10003
Tel (212) 209-2500
SIC 5961 5621 5611 5661 5632 6794

JCREW GROUP INC p 780
770 Broadway Fl 11, New York NY 10003
Tel (212) 209-2500
SIC 5961 5621 5611 5632

KCP HOLDCO INC p 806
603 W 50th St, New York NY 10019
Tel (212) 265-1500
SIC 3143 3171 5661 5632 5611

KENNETH COLE PRODUCTIONS INC p 811
603 W 50th St, New York NY 10019
Tel (212) 265-1500
SIC 3143 3144 3171 5661 5632 5611

LF SOURCING SPORTSWEAR LLC p 860
1359 Broadway Fl 18, New York NY 10018
Tel (646) 943-8505 *SIC* 5611

LORD & TAYLOR LLC p 878
424 5th Ave, New York NY 10018
Tel (212) 391-3344
SIC 5621 5611 5632 5999

■ NAUTICA RETAIL USA INC p 1019
40 W 57th St Fl 3, New York NY 10019
Tel (212) 541-5990 *SIC* 5611

▲ PVH CORP p 1193
200 Madison Ave Bsmt 1, New York NY 10016
Tel (212) 381-3500
SIC 2321 2331 2253 3143 5621 5611

■ RG PARENT LLC p 1231
264 W 40th St Fl 10, New York NY 10018
Tel (212) 869-8001 *SIC* 5611

SAKS INC p 1271
12 E 49th St Fl 2, New York NY 10017
Tel (212) 940-5305
SIC 5311 5611 5621 5641

■ TOMMY HILFIGER USA INC p 1459
601 W 26th St Rm 500, New York NY 10001
Tel (212) 840-8888
SIC 5611 5632 5641 5136 5137 5139

▲ VINCE HOLDING CORP p 1557
500 5th Ave Ste 20, New York NY 10110
Tel (212) 515-2600 *SIC* 5632 5611 5621

▲ EXPRESS INC p 520
1 Express Dr, Columbus OH 43230
Tel (614) 474-4001 *SIC* 5621 5632 5611

■ EXPRESS LLC p 520
1 Express Dr, Columbus OH 43230
Tel (614) 474-4001 *SIC* 5621 5611

■ EXPRESS TOPCO LLC p 520
1 Express Dr, Columbus OH 43230
Tel (614) 474-4001 *SIC* 5621 5611

■ A&F TRADEMARK INC p 7
6301 Fitch Path, New Albany OH 43054
Tel (614) 283-6500 *SIC* 5611

▲ ABERCROMBIE & FITCH CO p 11
6301 Fitch Path, New Albany OH 43054
Tel (614) 283-6500
SIC 5611 5621 5641 5632 5651 5961

■ ABERCROMBIE & FITCH HOLDING CORP p 11
6301 Fitch Path, New Albany OH 43054
Tel (614) 283-6500 *SIC* 5611

■ ABERCROMBIE & FITCH MANAGEMENT CO p 11
6301 Fitch Path, New Albany OH 43054
Tel (614) 283-6500 *SIC* 5611

■ ABERCROMBIE & FITCH STORES INC p 11
6301 Fitch Path, New Albany OH 43054
Tel (614) 283-6500 *SIC* 5611

■ ABERCROMBIE & FITCH TRADING CO p 11
6301 Fitch Path, New Albany OH 43054
Tel (614) 283-6500
SIC 5136 5137 5641 5621 5611

■ JMH TRADEMARK INC p 786
6301 Fitch Path, New Albany OH 43054
Tel (614) 283-6500 *SIC* 5611

■ EXPRESS HOLDING LLC p 520
11431 W Airport Svc Rd, Swanton OH 43558
Tel (614) 474-4001 *SIC* 5621 5611

SAINT ANNS HOSPITAL AUXILIARY p 1268
500 S Cleveland Ave, Westerville OH 43081
Tel (614) 769-4459
SIC 5947 5621 5611 5992 5441

■ SUGARTOWN WORLDWIDE LLC p 1397
800 3rd Ave, King Of Prussia PA 19406
Tel (610) 878-5550
SIC 2339 2361 5136 5611

▲ URBAN OUTFITTERS INC p 1530
5000 S Broad St, Philadelphia PA 19112
Tel (215) 454-5500
SIC 5621 5611 5632 5661 5719 5137

▲ AMERICAN EAGLE OUTFITTERS INC p 71
77 Hot Metal St, Pittsburgh PA 15203
Tel (412) 432-3300
SIC 5621 5611 5661 5632

■ VF INDUSTRIAL PARK INC p 1553
801 Hill Ave Ofc, Reading PA 19610
Tel (610) 378-0408 *SIC* 5611

RUE21 INC p 1257
800 Commonwealth Dr, Warrendale PA 15086
Tel (724) 776-9780 *SIC* 5611 5621

TOM JAMES CO p 1459
263 Seaboard Ln, Franklin TN 37067
Tel (615) 771-6633
SIC 2311 2325 2323 2321 5611

TEXAS CLOTHING HOLDING CORP p 1442
11511 Luna Rd, Dallas TX 75234
Tel (214) 956-4494
SIC 2325 2311 2321 5611

HAGGAR CLOTHING CO p 653
1507 Lbj Fwy Ste 100, Farmers Branch TX 75234
Tel (214) 352-8481
SIC 2325 2311 2321 5611 5651

HAGGAR CORP p 653
1507 Lyndon B Johnson Fwy, Farmers Branch TX 75234
Tel (214) 352-8481
SIC 2325 2311 2321 5611 6794

■ K&G MENS CO INC p 799
6380 Rogerdale Rd, Houston TX 77072
Tel (281) 776-7000 *SIC* 5611 5621

■ MENS WEARHOUSE INC p 943
6380 Rogerdale Rd, Houston TX 77072
Tel (281) 776-7000
SIC 5611 5621 5632 5661 5699

▲ TAILORED BRANDS INC p 1421
6380 Rogerdale Rd, Houston TX 77072
Tel (281) 776-7000
SIC 5611 5621 5632 5661 5699

UNITED FASHIONS OF TEXAS LLC p 1508
4629 Macro, San Antonio TX 78218
Tel (210) 662-7140 *SIC* 5611 5621 5651

DOWNEAST OUTFITTERS INC p 453
375 W Hope Ave, Salt Lake City UT 84115
Tel (801) 467-7520
SIC 5611 5621 5963 2512

S & K FAMOUS BRANDS INC p 1261
20 N 8th St, Richmond VA 23219
Tel (804) 827-1000 *SIC* 5611 5661

AMARGOSA INC p 64
10401 Ne 8th St Ste 500, Bellevue WA 98004
Tel (425) 755-6100
SIC 5611 5699 5941 5719 5947 5961

EDDIE BAUER LLC p 477
10401 Ne 8th St Ste 500, Bellevue WA 98004
Tel (425) 755-6100 *SIC* 5611 5961 5621

EVEREST HOLDINGS LLC p 514
10401 Ne 8th St Ste 500, Bellevue WA 98004
Tel (425) 755-6544 *SIC* 5699 5611 5961

▲ NORDSTROM INC p 1048
1617 6th Ave, Seattle WA 98101
Tel (206) 628-2111
SIC 5651 5661 5632 5611 5641 5961

AMCP RETAIL ACQUISITION CORP p 66
55 Scott Ave, Morgantown WV 26508
Tel (304) 292-6965 *SIC* 5611 5621

AMCP RETAIL HOLDINGS CORP p 66
55 Scott Ave, Morgantown WV 26508
Tel (304) 292-6965 *SIC* 5621 5611

▲ DULUTH HOLDINGS INC p 460
170 Countryside Dr, Belleville WI 53508
Tel (608) 424-1544 *SIC* 5961 5611 5621

▲ LANDS END INC p 843
1 Lands End Ln, Dodgeville WI 53595
Tel (608) 935-9341 *SIC* 5961 5611 5621

JOCKEY INTERNATIONAL DOMESTIC INC p 787
2300 60th St, Kenosha WI 53140
Tel (262) 658-8111 *SIC* 5651 5611

JOCKEY INTERNATIONAL GLOBAL INC p 787
2300 60th St, Kenosha WI 53140
Tel (262) 658-8111 SIC 2211 5611

SIC 5621 Women's Clothing Stores

FACTORY CONNECTION LLC p 523
2300 Highway 79 S, Guntersville AL 35976
Tel (256) 264-9400 SIC 5621

SIMPLY FASHION STORES LTD p 1325
2500 Crestwood Blvd # 100, Irondale AL 35210
Tel (205) 951-1700 SIC 5621

SAAD ENTERPRISES INC p 1263
1515 S University Blvd, Mobile AL 36609
Tel (251) 343-9600
SIC 8082 5047 7352 5912 5621 8741

BUFFALO EXCHANGE LTD p 224
203 E Helen St, Tucson AZ 85705
Tel (520) 622-2711 SIC 5621

▲ DILLARDS INC p 439
1600 Cantrell Rd, Little Rock AR 72201
Tel (501) 376-5200
SIC 5311 5611 5621 5641 5712

PACIFIC SUNWEAR OF CALIFORNIA LLC p 1106
3450 E Miraloma Ave, Anaheim CA 92806
Tel (714) 414-4000 SIC 5611 5621 5699

PACIFIC SUNWEAR STORES CORP p 1106
3450 E Miraloma Ave, Anaheim CA 92806
Tel (714) 414-4000
SIC 5611 5699 5661 5621 5999

STYLES FOR LESS INC p 1395
1205 N Miller St Ste 120, Anaheim CA 92806
Tel (714) 400-2525 SIC 5621

MERCHANT OF TENNIS INC p 944
8737 Wilshire Blvd, Beverly Hills CA 90211
Tel (310) 228-4000
SIC 5941 5621 5661 5961 5999

TORRID LLC p 1462
18305 San Jose Ave, City Of Industry CA 91748
Tel (626) 839-4681 SIC 5621

CORNERSTONE APPAREL INC p 371
5807 Smithway St, Commerce CA 90040
Tel (323) 724-3600 SIC 5621

HUB DISTRIBUTING INC p 715
1260 Corona Pointe Ct, Corona CA 92879
Tel (951) 340-3149
SIC 5611 5621 5632 5137 5136 5094

COLDWATER CREEK INC p 335
17000 Ventura Blvd # 300, Encino CA 91316
Tel (208) 263-2266 SIC 5621 5961

SEAL123 INC p 1296
26972 Burbank, Foothill Ranch CA 92610
Tel (949) 699-3900 SIC 5621 5632 5961

J & M SALES INC p 770
15001 S Figueroa St, Gardena CA 90248
Tel (310) 324-9962
SIC 5651 6531 5311 5611 5621

DRAPERS & DAMONS LLC p 455
9 Pasteur Ste 200, Irvine CA 92618
Tel (949) 784-3000 SIC 5961 5621 5632

WET SEAL LLC p 1603
7555 Irvine Center Dr, Irvine CA 92618
Tel (949) 699-3900 SIC 5621 5632 5961

FOH GROUP INC p 563
6255 W Sunset Blvd # 2212, Los Angeles CA 90028
Tel (323) 466-5151
SIC 2341 2342 2339 5621 5632

FOREVER 21 INC p 567
3880 N Mission Rd, Los Angeles CA 90031
Tel (213) 741-5100 SIC 5632 5661 5621

▲ GUESS INC p 645
1444 S Alameda St, Los Angeles CA 90021
Tel (213) 765-3100
SIC 2325 2339 5611 5621 5641

LOVE CULTURE INC p 881
2423 E 23rd St, Los Angeles CA 90058
Tel (614) 625-4781 SIC 5621

CHARLOTTE RUSSE HOLDING INC p 290
5910 Pcf Ctr Blvd Ste 120, San Diego CA 92121
Tel (858) 587-1500 SIC 5621

CHARLOTTE RUSSE INC p 290
5910 Pcf Ctr Blvd Ste 120, San Diego CA 92121
Tel (858) 587-1500 SIC 5621

▲ GAP INC p 591
2 Folsom St, San Francisco CA 94105
Tel (415) 427-0100
SIC 5651 5641 5632 5621 5611

GOLDEN GATE PRIVATE EQUITY INC p 621
1 Embarcadero Ctr Fl 39, San Francisco CA 94111
Tel (415) 983-2706 SIC 8741 5621

WINDSOR FASHIONS INC p 1615
9603 John St, Santa Fe Springs CA 90670
Tel (323) 282-9000 SIC 5621 5632

C P SHADES INC p 233
403 Coloma St, Sausalito CA 94965
Tel (415) 331-4581 SIC 2339 5621

BCBG MAX AZRIA GROUP LLC p 163
2761 Fruitland Ave, Vernon CA 90058
Tel (323) 589-2224 SIC 5137 5621 2335

MAX RAVE LLC p 922
2761 Fruitland Ave, Vernon CA 90058
Tel (201) 861-1416 SIC 5621

▲ WEST MARINE INC p 1595
500 Westridge Dr, Watsonville CA 95076
Tel (831) 728-2700
SIC 5551 5961 5088 5611 5661 5621

AMHERST NY BOBS INC p 85
160 Corporate Ct, Meriden CT 06450
Tel (203) 235-5775
SIC 5651 5611 5699 5621 5641 5661

BI RETAIL INC p 180
160 Corporate Ct, Meriden CT 06450
Tel (203) 235-5775
SIC 5651 5611 5699 5621 5641 5661

H C BOBS INC p 649
160 Corporate Ct, Meriden CT 06450
Tel (203) 235-5775
SIC 5651 5611 5699 5621 5641 5661

VINEYARD VINES LLC p 1558
181 Harbor Dr Fl 1, Stamford CT 06902
Tel (203) 661-1803
SIC 5136 5137 5699 5611 5621

BEALLS OUTLET STORES INC p 165
1806 38th Ave E, Bradenton FL 34208
Tel (941) 747-2355
SIC 5611 5621 5661 5719

▲ PERRY ELLIS INTERNATIONAL INC p 1137
3000 Nw 107th Ave, Doral FL 33172
Tel (305) 592-2830
SIC 2321 2325 2339 2337 5611 5621

▲ CHICOS FAS INC p 298
11215 Metro Pkwy, Fort Myers FL 33966
Tel (239) 277-6200 SIC 5621

■ CHICOS PRODUCTION SERVICES INC p 298
11215 Metro Pkwy, Fort Myers FL 33966
Tel (239) 277-6200 SIC 5621

BODY CENTRAL CORP p 197
6225 Powers Ave, Jacksonville FL 32217
Tel (904) 737-0811 SIC 5621 5961

PARADIES SHOPS LLC p 1113
2849 Paces Ferry Rd Se, Atlanta GA 30339
Tel (404) 344-7905
SIC 5947 5994 5621 5611 5912 5941

▲ CITI TRENDS INC p 310
104 Coleman Blvd, Savannah GA 31408
Tel (912) 236-1561
SIC 5611 5621 5641 5632

R & R GOLDMAN & ASSOCIATES INC p 1201
4300 N Knox Ave, Chicago IL 60641
Tel (773) 777-4494 SIC 5621

BROMENN SERVICE AUXILIARY GIFT SHOP p 217
Franklin Ave Virginia St, Normal IL 61761
Tel (309) 454-1400 SIC 5947 5641 5621

L L BEAN INC p 834
15 Casco St, Freeport ME 04033
Tel (207) 552-2000
SIC 5961 5621 5611 5941 5661 5948

■ FILA USA INC p 542
930 Ridgebrook Rd Ste 200, Sparks MD 21152
Tel (410) 773-3000
SIC 5139 5131 5137 5611 5621 5632

ORCHARD BRANDS CORP p 1093
138 Conant St Ste 3, Beverly MA 01915
Tel (978) 998-3800 SIC 5621 5611 5719

CHARLOTTE RUSSE ENTERPRISE INC p 290
75 State St, Boston MA 02109
Tel (617) 951-9400 SIC 5621

TALBOTS INC p 1422
1 Talbots Dr Ste 1, Hingham MA 02043
Tel (781) 749-7600
SIC 5621 5137 5632 5641

J JILL GROUP INC p 771
4 Batterymarch Park, Quincy MA 02169
Tel (617) 376-4300
SIC 5961 5621 5661 5632

JILL ACQUISITION LLC p 785
4 Batterymarch Park, Quincy MA 02169
Tel (617) 376-4300 SIC 5961 5621

■ MAURICES INC p 921
425 W Superior St, Duluth MN 55802
Tel (218) 727-8431 SIC 5621

▲ CHRISTOPHER & BANKS CORP p 303
2400 Xenium Ln N, Plymouth MN 55441
Tel (763) 551-5000 SIC 5621 5632 5961

■ CHRISTOPHER & BANKS INC p 303
2400 Xenium Ln N, Plymouth MN 55441
Tel (763) 551-5000 SIC 5621

▲ BUCKLE INC p 223
2407 W 24th St, Kearney NE 68845
Tel (308) 236-8491
SIC 5661 5632 5621 5611

■ CAESARS WORLD INC p 237
3570 Las Vegas Blvd S, Las Vegas NV 89109
Tel (702) 731-7110
SIC 7011 7999 5812 6552 5611 5621

MARSHALL RETAIL GROUP LLC p 911
3755 W Sunset Rd Ste A, Las Vegas NV 89118
Tel (702) 385-5233
SIC 5661 5621 5641 5611

ESCADA US SUBCO LLC p 509
26 Main St, Chatham NJ 07928
Tel (212) 852-5300
SIC 5137 5621 5632 5099

UBI LIQUIDATING CORP p 1498
300 Nixon Ln, Edison NJ 08837
Tel (201) 319-9093
SIC 5621 5641 5651 5137 5632

■ MAIDENFORM BRANDS INC p 897
485 Us Highway 1 S, Iselin NJ 08830
Tel (888) 573-0299 SIC 2341 2342 5621

KOMAR INTIMATES LLC p 827
90 Hudson St, Jersey City NJ 07302
Tel (212) 725-1500 SIC 5621

AERO OPCO LLC p 30
125 Chubb Ave Fl 5, Lyndhurst NJ 07071
Tel (201) 508-4500 SIC 5621 5611

▲ ASCENA RETAIL GROUP INC p 115
933 Macarthur Blvd, Mahwah NJ 07430
Tel (551) 777-6700 SIC 5621 5632

■ DRESS BARN INC p 455
933 Macarthur Blvd, Mahwah NJ 07430
Tel (800) 373-7722 SIC 5621 5632

ELIE TAHARI LTD p 487
16 Bleeker St, Millburn NJ 07041
Tel (973) 671-6300
SIC 2331 2339 2335 2337 5621 5611

▲ DESTINATION MATERNITY CORP p 432
232 Strawbridge Dr # 100, Moorestown NJ 08057
Tel (856) 291-9700 SIC 5621

618 MAIN CLOTHING CORP p 3
5601 W Side Ave Ste 2, North Bergen NJ 07047
Tel (201) 319-1400 SIC 5621

A & M (2015) LLC p 4
5901 W Side Ave Ste 500, North Bergen NJ 07047
Tel (201) 868-6220 SIC 5621

AVENUE STORES LLC p 137
365 W Passaic St Ste 230, Rochelle Park NJ 07662
Tel (201) 845-0880 SIC 5621

UNITED RETAIL GROUP INC p 1511
365 W Passaic St Ste 205, Rochelle Park NJ 07662
Tel (201) 845-0880 SIC 5621

UNITED RETAIL GROUP INC p 1511
365 W Passaic St Ste 12, Rochelle Park NJ 07662
Tel (201) 845-0880 SIC 5621

FERRAGAMO U S A INC p 538
700 Castle Rd, Secaucus NJ 07094
Tel (201) 553-6100
SIC 5139 5136 5137 5621 5632

A & E STORES INC p 4
1000 Huyler St, Teterboro NJ 07608
Tel (201) 393-0600
SIC 5621 8721 4226 7389

LOEHMANNS HOLDINGS INC p 874
2500 Halsey St Frnt 1, Bronx NY 10461
Tel (718) 409-2000 SIC 5621 5661 3171

LOEHMANNS INC p 874
2500 Halsey St, Bronx NY 10461
Tel (718) 409-2000 SIC 5621

AIJJ ENTERPRISES INC p 38
1000 Pennsylvania Ave, Brooklyn NY 11207
Tel (718) 485-3000 SIC 5621

NEW 5-7-9 AND BEYOND INC p 1029
1000 Pennsylvania Ave, Brooklyn NY 11207
Tel (718) 485-3000 SIC 5621

RAINBOW USA INC p 1205
1000 Pennsylvania Ave, Brooklyn NY 11207
Tel (718) 485-3000 SIC 5621

AEON USA INC p 29
1 Penn Plz Fl 36, New York NY 10119
Tel (212) 946-8780
SIC 5621 5961 2211 2391

▲ AEROPOSTALE INC p 30
100 W 33rd St Ste 1100, New York NY 10001
Tel (646) 485-5410 SIC 5621 5611

■ ANN INC p 92
7 Times Sq Bsmt Sb4, New York NY 10036
Tel (212) 541-3300 SIC 5621 5632 5661

■ ANNTAYLOR INC p 92
7 Times Sq, New York NY 10036
Tel (212) 541-3300 SIC 5621 5632 5661

■ ANNTAYLOR RETAIL INC p 92
7 Times Sq, New York NY 10036
Tel (212) 541-3300 SIC 5621 5632 5661

BARNEYS INC p 156
575 5th Ave Fl 11, New York NY 10017
Tel (212) 450-8700
SIC 5611 5621 5632 5932 5947 6794

BERGDORF GOODMAN INC p 174
754 5th Ave, New York NY 10019
Tel (800) 558-1855 SIC 5621 5632 5611

BRAVADO INTERNATIONAL GROUP MERCHANDISING SERVICES INC p 209
1755 Broadway Fl 2, New York NY 10019
Tel (212) 445-3400
SIC 5136 5137 5611 5621

BROOKS BROTHERS INC p 218
346 Madison Ave, New York NY 10017
Tel (212) 682-8800 SIC 5611 5621 5651

BTF/CFI INC p 222
144 W 38th St, New York NY 10018
Tel (212) 993-0300
SIC 6794 7991 5621 5411

CACHE INC p 235
256 W 38th St Fl 3, New York NY 10018
Tel (212) 575-3200 SIC 5632 5621 5961

CACHE OF VIRGINIA INC p 235
256 W 38th St Fl 3, New York NY 10018
Tel (212) 840-4226 SIC 5632 5621

■ CALVIN KLEIN INC p 243
205 W 39th St Lbby 2, New York NY 10018
Tel (212) 719-2600
SIC 5651 5137 5136 5611 5621 6794

■ CALVIN KLEIN JEANSWEAR CO p 243
205 W 39th St Lbby 2, New York NY 10018
Tel (212) 292-9290 SIC 5611 5621

CHINOS HOLDINGS INC p 301
770 Broadway, New York NY 10003
Tel (212) 209-2500
SIC 5961 5621 5611 5632 6794

CHINOS INTERMEDIATE HOLDINGS B INC p 301
770 Broadway, New York NY 10003
Tel (212) 209-2500
SIC 5961 5621 5611 5632 6794

DIESEL USA INC p 438
220 W 19th St Fl 5, New York NY 10011
Tel (212) 755-9200
SIC 5137 5136 5621 5632 5611

E-LO SPORTSWEAR LLC p 467
500 Fashion Ave, New York NY 10018
Tel (862) 902-5225 SIC 5137 5621

GIORGIO ARMANI CORP p 612
450 W 15th St 3, New York NY 10011
Tel (212) 209-3500
SIC 5136 5137 5122 5611 5621 5632

GRACE HOLMES INC p 628
770 Broadway Fl 11, New York NY 10003
Tel (212) 209-2500 SIC 5611 5621

GUCCI AMERICA INC p 645
195 Broadway Fl 12, New York NY 10007
Tel (212) 750-5220
SIC 5632 5948 5661 5611 5621 5137

HENRY MODELL & CO INC p 684
498 7th Ave Fl 20, New York NY 10018
Tel (212) 822-1000
SIC 5941 5661 5611 5621 5641 5961

J CREW INC p 770
770 Broadway Fl 14, New York NY 10003
Tel (212) 209-8010 SIC 5961 5621 5611

J CREW OPERATING CORP p 770
770 Brdwy Fl 11 & 12, New York NY 10003
Tel (212) 209-2500
SIC 5961 5621 5611 5661 5632 6794

JCREW GROUP INC p 780
770 Broadway Fl 11, New York NY 10003
Tel (212) 209-2500
SIC 5961 5621 5611 5632

■ LERNER NEW YORK HOLDING INC p 857
450 W 33rd St Fl 3, New York NY 10001
Tel (212) 736-1222 SIC 5621

■ LERNER NEW YORK INC p 857
330 W 34th St Fl 7, New York NY 10001
Tel (212) 884-2000 SIC 5621

LORD & TAYLOR LLC p 878
424 5th Ave, New York NY 10018
Tel (212) 391-3344
SIC 5621 5611 5632 5999

MAXMARA USA INC p 922
555 Madison Ave Fl 10, New York NY 10022
Tel (212) 536-6200 SIC 5621

MICHAEL KORS (USA) INC p 960
11 W 42nd St Fl 20, New York NY 10036
Tel (212) 201-8100 SIC 5137 5651 5621

▲ NEW YORK & CO INC p 1033
330 W 34th St Fl 9, New York NY 10001
Tel (212) 884-2000 SIC 5621

▲ PVH CORP p 1193
200 Madison Ave Bsmt 1, New York NY 10016
Tel (212) 381-3500
SIC 2321 2331 2253 3143 5621 5611

RAG & BONE HOLDINGS LLC p 1205
425 W 13th St Ofc 2, New York NY 10014
Tel (212) 982-3992 SIC 5621

SAKS & CO p 1271
611 5th Ave, New York NY 10022
Tel (212) 753-4000 SIC 5621 5311 5651

SAKS INC p 1271
12 E 49th St Fl 2, New York NY 10017
Tel (212) 940-5305
SIC 5311 5611 5621 5641

TLB HOLDINGS LLC p 1457
9 W 57th St, New York NY 10019
Tel (212) 796-8555
SIC 5961 5661 5632 5641 5621

TORY BURCH LLC p 1462
11 W 19th St Fl 7, New York NY 10011
Tel (212) 683-2323 SIC 5621

▲ VINCE HOLDING CORP p 1557
500 5th Ave Ste 20, New York NY 10110
Tel (212) 515-2600 SIC 5632 5611 5621

▲ CATO CORP p 267
8100 Denmark Rd, Charlotte NC 28273
Tel (704) 554-8510
SIC 5621 5632 5137 5699 5311 5641

WORTH BON INC p 1626
40 Francis Rd, Hendersonville NC 28792
Tel (828) 697-2216
SIC 2331 5621 2339 2335 2337 8741

VANITY SHOP OF GRAND FORKS INC p 1543
1001 25th St N, Fargo ND 58102
Tel (701) 282-0486 SIC 5621

▲ EXPRESS INC p 520
1 Express Dr, Columbus OH 43230
Tel (614) 474-4001 SIC 5621 5632 5611

■ EXPRESS LLC p 520
1 Express Dr, Columbus OH 43230
Tel (614) 474-4001 SIC 5621 5611

■ EXPRESS TOPCO LLC p 520
1 Express Dr, Columbus OH 43230
Tel (614) 474-4001 SIC 5621 5611

▲ L BRANDS INC p 833
3 Limited Pkwy, Columbus OH 43230
Tel (614) 415-7000
SIC 5632 5961 5621 5999

■ LANE BRYANT INC p 843
3344 Morse Xing, Columbus OH 43219
Tel (614) 476-9281 SIC 5621

▲ ABERCROMBIE & FITCH CO p 11
6301 Fitch Path, New Albany OH 43054
Tel (614) 283-6500
SIC 5611 5621 5641 5632 5651 5961

■ ABERCROMBIE & FITCH TRADING CO p 11
6301 Fitch Path, New Albany OH 43054
Tel (614) 283-6500
SIC 5136 5137 5641 5621 5611

LIMITED STORES LLC p 866
7775 Walton Pkwy Ste 400, New Albany OH 43054
Tel (614) 289-2200 SIC 5621 5941 5632

■ VICTORIAS SECRET DIRECT LLC p 1555
5 Limited Pkwy E, Reynoldsburg OH 43068
Tel (614) 577-7111 SIC 5961 5632 5621

■ VICTORIAS SECRET STORES LLC p 1555
4 Limited Pkwy E, Reynoldsburg OH 43068
Tel (614) 577-7111 SIC 5632 5621

DOTS LLC p 452
30300 Emerald Valley Pkwy, Solon OH 44139
Tel (440) 349-7900 SIC 5621

■ EXPRESS HOLDING LLC p 520
11431 W Airport Svc Rd, Swanton OH 43558
Tel (614) 474-4001 SIC 5621 5611

SAINT ANNS HOSPITAL AUXILIARY p 1268
500 S Cleveland Ave, Westerville OH 43081
Tel (614) 769-4459
SIC 5947 5621 5611 5992 5441

HANNA ANDERSSON LLC p 658
608 Ne 19th Ave, Portland OR 97232
Tel (503) 242-0920 SIC 5641 5621 5719

■ CATHERINES INC p 265
3750 State Rd, Bensalem PA 19020
Tel (215) 245-9100 SIC 5632 5621

■ CATHERINES STORES CORP p 265
3750 State Rd, Bensalem PA 19020
Tel (551) 777-6700 SIC 5632 5621

■ CHARMING SHOPPES INC p 290
3750 State Rd, Bensalem PA 19020
Tel (215) 245-9100 SIC 5961 5632 5621

■ CHARMING SHOPPES OF DELAWARE INC p 290
3750 State Rd, Bensalem PA 19020
Tel (215) 245-9100 SIC 5621 8741

JAG FOOTWEAR ACCESSORIES AND RETAIL CORP p 776
180 Rittenhouse Cir, Bristol PA 19007
Tel (215) 785-4000 *SIC* 5621

MELR INC p 941
250 Rittenhouse Cir, Bristol PA 19007
Tel (215) 785-4000 *SIC* 5621

DAVIDS BRIDAL INC p 415
1001 Washington St, Conshohocken PA 19428
Tel (610) 943-5000 *SIC* 5621

■ ANTHROPOLOGIE INC p 94
5000 S Broad St, Philadelphia PA 19112
Tel (215) 454-4421 *SIC* 5719 5621

DSI INC p 458
9401 Blue Grass Rd, Philadelphia PA 19114
Tel (215) 676-6000 *SIC* 5621

▲ URBAN OUTFITTERS INC p 1530
5000 S Broad St, Philadelphia PA 19112
Tel (215) 454-5500
SIC 5621 5611 5632 5661 5719 5137

▲ AMERICAN EAGLE OUTFITTERS INC p 71
77 Hot Metal St, Pittsburgh PA 15203
Tel (412) 432-3300
SIC 5621 5611 5661 5632

RUE21 INC p 1257
800 Commonwealth Dr, Warrendale PA 15086
Tel (724) 776-9780 *SIC* 5611 5621

■ PIER 1 LICENSING INC p 1147
100 Pier 1 Pl, Fort Worth TX 76102
Tel (817) 878-8000
SIC 5719 5712 5621 5632

▲ FRANCESCAS HOLDINGS CORP p 573
8760 Clay Rd, Houston TX 77080
Tel (713) 864-1358 *SIC* 5621 5632

■ K&G MENS CO INC p 799
6380 Rogerdale Rd, Houston TX 77072
Tel (281) 776-7000 *SIC* 5611 5621

■ MENS WEARHOUSE INC p 943
6380 Rogerdale Rd, Houston TX 77072
Tel (281) 776-7000
SIC 5611 5621 5632 5661 5699

▲ TAILORED BRANDS INC p 1421
6380 Rogerdale Rd, Houston TX 77072
Tel (281) 776-7000
SIC 5611 5621 5632 5661 5699

UNITED FASHIONS HOLDINGS INC p 1508
4629 Marco Dr, San Antonio TX 78218
Tel (210) 662-7140 *SIC* 5621 5641

UNITED FASHIONS OF TEXAS LLC p 1508
4629 Macro, San Antonio TX 78218
Tel (210) 662-7140 *SIC* 5611 5621 5651

DOWNEAST OUTFITTERS INC p 453
375 W Hope Ave, Salt Lake City UT 84115
Tel (801) 467-7520
SIC 5611 5621 5963 2512

CORNELL TRADING INC p 370
131 Battery St, Burlington VT 05401
Tel (802) 879-1271
SIC 5023 5137 5719 5621

EDDIE BAUER LLC p 477
10401 Ne 8th St Ste 500, Bellevue WA 98004
Tel (425) 755-6100 *SIC* 5611 5961 5621

AMCP RETAIL ACQUISITION CORP p 66
55 Scott Ave, Morgantown WV 26508
Tel (304) 292-6965 *SIC* 5611 5621

AMCP RETAIL HOLDINGS CORP p 66
55 Scott Ave, Morgantown WV 26508
Tel (304) 292-6965 *SIC* 5621 5611

▲ DULUTH HOLDINGS INC p 460
170 Countryside Dr, Belleville WI 53508
Tel (608) 424-1544 *SIC* 5961 5611 5621

▲ LANDS END INC p 843
1 Lands End Ln, Dodgeville WI 53595
Tel (608) 935-9341 *SIC* 5961 5611 5621

SIC 5632 Women's Access & Specialty Stores

BRIGHTON COLLECTIBLES LLC p 213
14022 Nelson Ave, City Of Industry CA 91746
Tel (626) 961-9381 *SIC* 5632

HOT TOPIC INC p 710
18305 San Jose Ave, City Of Industry CA 91748
Tel (626) 839-4681 *SIC* 2326 5632 5699

HUB DISTRIBUTING INC p 715
1260 Corona Pointe Ct, Corona CA 92879
Tel (951) 340-3149
SIC 5611 5621 5632 5137 5136 5094

▲ ROSS STORES INC p 1252
5130 Hacienda Dr, Dublin CA 94568
Tel (925) 965-4400
SIC 5651 5661 5944 5632 5611 5999

TECHSTYLE INC p 1432
800 Apollo St, El Segundo CA 90245
Tel (310) 683-0940
SIC 5961 5661 5632 5651

SEAL123 INC p 1296
26972 Burbank, Foothill Ranch CA 92610
Tel (949) 699-3900 *SIC* 5621 5632 5961

DRAPERS & DAMONS LLC p 455
9 Pasteur Ste 200, Irvine CA 92618
Tel (949) 784-3000 *SIC* 5961 5621 5632

■ SHEPLERS INC p 1315
15345 Barranca Pkwy, Irvine CA 92618
Tel (316) 946-3835
SIC 5699 5661 5961 5651 5632 5611

WET SEAL LLC p 1603
7555 Irvine Center Dr, Irvine CA 92618
Tel (949) 699-3900 *SIC* 5621 5632 5961

FOH GROUP INC p 563
6255 W Sunset Blvd # 2212, Los Angeles CA 90028
Tel (323) 466-5151
SIC 2341 2342 2339 5621 5632

FOREVER 21 INC p 567
3880 N Mission Rd, Los Angeles CA 90031
Tel (213) 741-5100 *SIC* 5632 5661 5621

METROPARK USA INC p 955
5750 Grace Pl, Los Angeles CA 90022
Tel (323) 622-3600 *SIC* 5632 5699

WILSHIRE PARTNERS p 1613
620 Newport Center Dr # 1100, Newport Beach CA 92660
Tel (800) 285-6038 *SIC* 5632 5961

MAX LEON INC p 922
3100 New York Dr, Pasadena CA 91107
Tel (626) 797-6886 *SIC* 2339 5632

▲ GAP INC p 591
2 Folsom St, San Francisco CA 94105
Tel (415) 427-0100
SIC 5651 5641 5632 5621 5611

WINDSOR FASHIONS INC p 1615
9603 John St, Santa Fe Springs CA 90670
Tel (323) 282-9000 *SIC* 5621 5632

CLAIRES BOUTIQUES INC p 321
11401 Pines Blvd, Pembroke Pines FL 33026
Tel (954) 438-0433
SIC 5632 5699 5999 5943 5947

CLAIRES STORES INC p 321
3 Sw 129th Ave, Pembroke Pines FL 33027
Tel (954) 433-3900 *SIC* 5632

▲ CITI TRENDS INC p 310
104 Coleman Blvd, Savannah GA 31408
Tel (912) 236-1561
SIC 5611 5621 5641 5632

▲ ULTA SALON COSMETICS & FRAGRANCE INC p 1500
1000 Remington Blvd # 120, Bolingbrook IL 60440
Tel (630) 410-4800 *SIC* 5999 5632 5961

CLAIRES INC p 321
2400 W Central Rd, Hoffman Estates IL 60192
Tel (847) 765-1100 *SIC* 5632 5947

PAYLESS INC p 1122
3231 Se 6th Ave, Topeka KS 66607
Tel (785) 233-5171 *SIC* 5661 5632

■ FILA USA INC p 542
930 Ridgebrook Rd Ste 200, Sparks MD 21152
Tel (410) 773-3000
SIC 5139 5131 5137 5611 5621 5632

TALBOTS INC p 1422
1 Talbots Dr Ste 1, Hingham MA 02043
Tel (781) 749-7600
SIC 5621 5137 5632 5641

J JILL GROUP INC p 771
4 Batterymarch Park, Quincy MA 02169
Tel (617) 376-4300
SIC 5961 5621 5661 5632

▲ CHRISTOPHER & BANKS CORP p 303
2400 Xenium Ln N, Plymouth MN 55441
Tel (763) 551-5000 *SIC* 5621 5632 5961

FREDERICKS OF HOLLYWOOD INC p 576
71 Homochitto St, Natchez MS 39120
Tel (323) 466-5151 *SIC* 5632 5961

▲ BUCKLE INC p 223
2407 W 24th St, Kearney NE 68845
Tel (308) 236-8491
SIC 5661 5632 5621 5611

■ ZAPPOS.COM INC p 1641
400 Stewart Ave Ste A, Las Vegas NV 89101
Tel (702) 943-7777
SIC 5661 4813 5632 5611

COLE HAAN LLC p 335
150 Ocean Rd, Greenland NH 03840
Tel (207) 846-2500 *SIC* 5651 5632

BURLINGTON COAT FACTORY HOLDINGS INC p 227
1830 N Route 130, Burlington NJ 08016
Tel (609) 387-7800
SIC 5651 5632 5719 5947 5712

ESCADA US SUBCO LLC p 509
26 Main St, Chatham NJ 07928
Tel (212) 852-5300
SIC 5137 5621 5632 5099

UBI LIQUIDATING CORP p 1498
300 Nixon Ln, Edison NJ 08837
Tel (201) 319-9093
SIC 5621 5641 5651 5137 5632

▲ ASCENA RETAIL GROUP INC p 115
933 Macarthur Blvd, Mahwah NJ 07430
Tel (551) 777-6700 *SIC* 5621 5632

■ DRESS BARN INC p 455
933 Macarthur Blvd, Mahwah NJ 07430
Tel (800) 373-7722 *SIC* 5621 5632

FERRAGAMO U S A INC p 538
700 Castle Rd, Secaucus NJ 07094
Tel (201) 553-6100
SIC 5139 5136 5137 5621 5632

BC INTERNATIONAL GROUP INC p 163
922 Riverview Dr, Totowa NJ 07512
Tel (973) 826-1140 *SIC* 5632

▲ STEVEN MADDEN LTD p 1388
5216 Barnett Ave, Long Island City NY 11104
Tel (718) 446-1800
SIC 3143 3144 3149 5632

■ ANN INC p 92
7 Times Sq Bsmt Sb4, New York NY 10036
Tel (212) 541-3300 *SIC* 5621 5632 5661

■ ANNTAYLOR INC p 92
7 Times Sq, New York NY 10036
Tel (212) 541-3300 *SIC* 5621 5632 5661

■ ANNTAYLOR RETAIL INC p 92
7 Times Sq, New York NY 10036
Tel (212) 541-3300 *SIC* 5621 5632 5661

BARNEYS INC p 156
575 5th Ave Fl 11, New York NY 10017
Tel (212) 450-8700
SIC 5611 5621 5632 5932 5947 6794

BERGDORF GOODMAN INC p 174
754 5th Ave, New York NY 10019
Tel (800) 558-1855 *SIC* 5621 5632 5611

BROOKS BROTHERS GROUP INC p 218
346 Madison Ave, New York NY 10017
Tel (212) 309-7765 *SIC* 5651 5632

CACHE INC p 235
256 W 38th St Fl 3, New York NY 10018
Tel (212) 575-3200 *SIC* 5632 5621 5961

CACHE OF VIRGINIA INC p 235
256 W 38th St Fl 3, New York NY 10018
Tel (212) 840-4226 *SIC* 5632 5621

CHANEL INC p 288
9 W 57th St Fl 44, New York NY 10019
Tel (212) 688-5055
SIC 5632 2844 5122 5944 5961 5999

CHINOS HOLDINGS INC p 301
770 Broadway, New York NY 10003
Tel (212) 209-2500
SIC 5961 5621 5611 5632 6794

CHINOS INTERMEDIATE HOLDINGS B INC p 301
770 Broadway, New York NY 10003
Tel (212) 209-2500
SIC 5961 5621 5611 5632 6794

DELIAS INC p 424
50 W 23rd St, New York NY 10010
Tel (212) 590-6200 *SIC* 5632 5611

DIESEL USA INC p 438
220 W 19th St Fl 5, New York NY 10011
Tel (212) 755-9200
SIC 5137 5136 5621 5632 5611

■ FOOT LOCKER SPECIALTY INC p 564
112 W 34th St Lbby 1, New York NY 10120
Tel (212) 720-3700 *SIC* 5632 5961 7311

GIORGIO ARMANI CORP p 612
450 W 15th St 3, New York NY 10011
Tel (212) 209-3500
SIC 5136 5137 5122 5611 5621 5632

GUCCI AMERICA INC p 645
195 Broadway Fl 12, New York NY 10007
Tel (212) 750-5220
SIC 5632 5948 5661 5611 5621 5137

J CREW OPERATING CORP p 770
770 Brdwy Fl 11 & 12, New York NY 10003
Tel (212) 209-2500
SIC 5961 5621 5611 5661 5632 6794

JCREW GROUP INC p 780
770 Broadway Fl 11, New York NY 10003
Tel (212) 209-2500
SIC 5961 5621 5611 5632

JONES GROUP INC p 792
1411 Broadway Fl 15, New York NY 10018
Tel (212) 642-3860
SIC 5632 5137 5139 5661 5641

■ KATE SPADE LLC p 804
2 Park Ave Fl 8, New York NY 10016
Tel (201) 295-6000 *SIC* 5137 5632

KCP HOLDCO INC p 806
603 W 50th St, New York NY 10019
Tel (212) 265-1500
SIC 3143 3171 5661 5632 5611

KENNETH COLE PRODUCTIONS INC p 811
603 W 50th St, New York NY 10019
Tel (212) 265-1500
SIC 3143 3144 3171 5661 5632 5611

LORD & TAYLOR LLC p 878
424 5th Ave, New York NY 10018
Tel (212) 391-3344
SIC 5621 5611 5632 5999

NINE WEST FOOTWEAR CORP p 1044
1411 Broadway Fl 20, New York NY 10018
Tel (800) 999-1877
SIC 3144 3171 5661 5632 5139

PRADA USA CORP p 1167
609 W 51st St, New York NY 10019
Tel (212) 307-9300
SIC 5136 5137 5139 5661 5632 8741

TLB HOLDINGS LLC p 1457
9 W 57th St, New York NY 10019
Tel (212) 796-8555
SIC 5961 5661 5632 5641 5621

■ TOMMY HILFIGER USA INC p 1459
601 W 26th St Rm 500, New York NY 10001
Tel (212) 840-8888
SIC 5611 5632 5641 5136 5137 5139

▲ VINCE HOLDING CORP p 1557
500 5th Ave Ste 20, New York NY 10110
Tel (212) 515-2600 *SIC* 5632 5611 5621

▲ CATO CORP p 267
8100 Denmark Rd, Charlotte NC 28273
Tel (704) 554-8510
SIC 5621 5632 5137 5699 5311 5641

▲ EXPRESS INC p 520
1 Express Dr, Columbus OH 43230
Tel (614) 474-4001 *SIC* 5621 5632 5611

■ INTIMATE BRANDS HOLDING LLC p 759
3 Limited Pkwy, Columbus OH 43230
Tel (614) 415-7000 *SIC* 5632

■ INTIMATE BRANDS INC p 759
3 Limited Pkwy, Columbus OH 43230
Tel (614) 415-7000 *SIC* 5632

▲ L BRANDS INC p 833
3 Limited Pkwy, Columbus OH 43230
Tel (614) 415-7000
SIC 5632 5961 5621 5999

▲ ABERCROMBIE & FITCH CO p 11
6301 Fitch Path, New Albany OH 43054
Tel (614) 283-6500
SIC 5611 5621 5641 5632 5651 5961

LIMITED STORES LLC p 866
7775 Walton Pkwy Ste 400, New Albany OH 43054
Tel (614) 289-2200 *SIC* 5621 5941 5632

■ VICTORIAS SECRET DIRECT LLC p 1555
5 Limited Pkwy E, Reynoldsburg OH 43068
Tel (614) 577-7111 *SIC* 5961 5632 5621

■ VICTORIAS SECRET STORES LLC p 1555
4 Limited Pkwy E, Reynoldsburg OH 43068
Tel (614) 577-7111 *SIC* 5632 5621

■ CATHERINES INC p 265
3750 State Rd, Bensalem PA 19020
Tel (215) 245-9100 *SIC* 5632 5621

■ CATHERINES STORES CORP p 265
3750 State Rd, Bensalem PA 19020
Tel (551) 777-6700 *SIC* 5632 5621

■ CHARMING SHOPPES INC p 290
3750 State Rd, Bensalem PA 19020
Tel (215) 245-9100 *SIC* 5961 5632 5621

▲ URBAN OUTFITTERS INC p 1530
5000 S Broad St, Philadelphia PA 19112
Tel (215) 454-5500
SIC 5621 5611 5632 5661 5719 5137

▲ AMERICAN EAGLE OUTFITTERS INC p 71
77 Hot Metal St, Pittsburgh PA 15203
Tel (412) 432-3300
SIC 5621 5611 5661 5632

■ PIER 1 LICENSING INC p 1147
100 Pier 1 Pl, Fort Worth TX 76102
Tel (817) 878-8000
SIC 5719 5712 5621 5632

EARTHBOUND HOLDING LLC p 469
4051 Freeport Pkwy Ste 400, Grapevine TX 76051
Tel (972) 248-0228 *SIC* 5632

CHARLIE CHARMING HOLDINGS INC p 290
5999 Savoy Dr, Houston TX 77036
Tel (713) 579-1936 *SIC* 5632

CHARMING CHARLIE LLC p 290
5999 Savoy Dr, Houston TX 77036
Tel (713) 579-1936 *SIC* 5632

▲ FRANCESCAS HOLDINGS CORP p 573
8760 Clay Rd, Houston TX 77080
Tel (713) 864-1358 *SIC* 5621 5632

■ MENS WEARHOUSE INC p 943
6380 Rogerdale Rd, Houston TX 77072
Tel (281) 776-7000
SIC 5611 5621 5632 5661 5699

▲ TAILORED BRANDS INC p 1421
6380 Rogerdale Rd, Houston TX 77072
Tel (281) 776-7000
SIC 5611 5621 5632 5661 5699

▲ FOSSIL GROUP INC p 570
901 S Central Expy, Richardson TX 75080
Tel (972) 234-2525
SIC 3873 5944 5094 5651 5632

SAN ANTONIO SHOE INC p 1275
1717 Sas Dr, San Antonio TX 78224
Tel (877) 727-7463
SIC 3131 5661 5139 5632 3144

▲ NORDSTROM INC p 1048
1617 6th Ave, Seattle WA 98101
Tel (206) 628-2111
SIC 5651 5661 5632 5611 5641 5961

SIC 5641 Children's & Infants' Clothing Stores

▲ DILLARDS INC p 439
1600 Cantrell Rd, Little Rock AR 72201
Tel (501) 376-5200
SIC 5311 5611 5621 5641 5712

▲ BOOT BARN HOLDINGS INC p 200
15345 Barranca Pkwy, Irvine CA 92618
Tel (949) 453-4400 *SIC* 5661 5641

▲ GUESS INC p 645
1444 S Alameda St, Los Angeles CA 90021
Tel (213) 765-3100
SIC 2325 2339 5611 5621 5641

▲ GAP INC p 591
2 Folsom St, San Francisco CA 94105
Tel (415) 427-0100
SIC 5651 5641 5632 5621 5611

GIRAFFE HOLDING INC p 613
500 Howard St, San Francisco CA 94105
Tel (415) 278-7000 *SIC* 5641

GYMBOREE CORP p 649
500 Howard St Fl 2, San Francisco CA 94105
Tel (415) 278-7000 *SIC* 5641

AMHERST NY BOBS INC p 85
160 Corporate Ct, Meriden CT 06450
Tel (203) 235-5775
SIC 5651 5611 5699 5621 5641 5661

BI RETAIL INC p 180
160 Corporate Ct, Meriden CT 06450
Tel (203) 235-5775
SIC 5651 5611 5699 5621 5641 5661

H C BOBS INC p 649
160 Corporate Ct, Meriden CT 06450
Tel (203) 235-5775
SIC 5651 5611 5699 5621 5641 5661

■ CARTERS RETAIL INC p 262
3438 Peachtree Rd Ne, Atlanta GA 30326
Tel (203) 926-5000 *SIC* 5641

■ WILLIAM CARTER CO p 1610
3438 Peachtree Rd Ne, Atlanta GA 30326
Tel (678) 791-1000 *SIC* 5641 5137

▲ CITI TRENDS INC p 310
104 Coleman Blvd, Savannah GA 31408
Tel (912) 236-1561
SIC 5611 5621 5641 5632

BROMENN SERVICE AUXILIARY GIFT SHOP p 217
Franklin Ave Virginia St, Normal IL 61761
Tel (309) 454-1400 *SIC* 5947 5641 5621

TALBOTS INC p 1422
1 Talbots Dr Ste 1, Hingham MA 02043
Tel (781) 749-7600
SIC 5621 5137 5632 5641

MARSHALL RETAIL GROUP LLC p 911
3755 W Sunset Rd Ste A, Las Vegas NV 89118
Tel (702) 385-5233
SIC 5661 5621 5641 5611

UBI LIQUIDATING CORP p 1498
300 Nixon Ln, Edison NJ 08837
Tel (201) 319-9093
SIC 5621 5641 5651 5137 5632

▲ CHILDRENS PLACE INC p 300
500 Plaza Dr Ste 400, Secaucus NJ 07094
Tel (201) 558-2400 *SIC* 5641 5651

TOYS "R" US INC p 1467
1 Geoffrey Way, Wayne NJ 07470
Tel (973) 617-3500
SIC 5945 5734 5999 5735 5641 5941

TOYS "R" US-DELAWARE INC p 1467
1 Geoffrey Way, Wayne NJ 07470
Tel (973) 617-3500 *SIC* 5945 5999 5641

■ BUY BUY BABY INC p 230
895 E Gate Blvd Ste 2, Garden City NY 11530
Tel (516) 507-3400 *SIC* 5641 5999 2023

HENRY MODELL & CO INC p 684
498 7th Ave Fl 20, New York NY 10018
Tel (212) 822-1000
SIC 5941 5661 5611 5621 5641 5961

JONES GROUP INC p 792
1411 Broadway Fl 15, New York NY 10018
Tel (212) 642-3860
SIC 5632 5137 5139 5661 5641

SAKS INC p 1271
12 E 49th St Fl 2, New York NY 10017
Tel (212) 940-5305
SIC 5311 5611 5621 5641

TLB HOLDINGS LLC p 1457
9 W 57th St, New York NY 10019
Tel (212) 796-8555
SIC 5961 5661 5632 5641 5621

■ TOMMY HILFIGER USA INC p 1459
601 W 26th St Rm 500, New York NY 10001
Tel (212) 840-8888
SIC 5611 5632 5641 5136 5137 5139

▲ CATO CORP p 267
8100 Denmark Rd, Charlotte NC 28273
Tel (704) 554-8510
SIC 5621 5632 5137 5699 5311 5641

▲ ABERCROMBIE & FITCH CO p 11
6301 Fitch Path, New Albany OH 43054
Tel (614) 283-6500
SIC 5611 5621 5641 5632 5651 5961

■ ABERCROMBIE & FITCH TRADING CO p 11
6301 Fitch Path, New Albany OH 43054
Tel (614) 283-6500
SIC 5136 5137 5641 5621 5611

■ TWEEN BRANDS INC p 1494
8323 Walton Pkwy, New Albany OH 43054
Tel (614) 775-3500 SIC 5641

HANNA ANDERSSON LLC p 658
608 Ne 19th Ave, Portland OR 97232
Tel (503) 242-0920 SIC 5641 5621 5719

UNITED FASHIONS HOLDINGS INC p 1508
4629 Marco Dr, San Antonio TX 78218
Tel (210) 662-7140 SIC 5621 5641

NAARTJIE CUSTOM KIDS INC p 1006
3676 W Ca Ave Ste D100, Salt Lake City UT 84104
Tel (801) 973-7988 SIC 5641

▲ NORDSTROM INC p 1048
1617 6th Ave, Seattle WA 98101
Tel (206) 628-2111
SIC 5651 5661 5632 5611 5641 5961

SIC 5651 Family Clothing Stores

FACTOR SALES INC p 523
676 N Archibald St, San Luis AZ 85349
Tel (928) 627-8033 SIC 5411 5651 5141

WEEBS INC p 1587
20 Rancho Del Mar, Aptos CA 95003
Tel (831) 688-8007 SIC 5651 5661

▲ ROSS STORES INC p 1252
5130 Hacienda Dr, Dublin CA 94568
Tel (925) 965-4400
SIC 5651 5661 5944 5632 5611 5999

TECHSTYLE INC p 1432
800 Apollo St, El Segundo CA 90245
Tel (310) 683-0940
SIC 5961 5661 5632 5651

J & M SALES INC p 770
15001 S Figueroa St, Gardena CA 90248
Tel (310) 324-9962
SIC 5651 6531 5311 5611 5621

NATIONAL STORES INC p 1016
15001 S Figueroa St, Gardena CA 90248
Tel (310) 324-9962 SIC 5651

■ SHEPLERS INC p 1315
15345 Barranca Pkwy, Irvine CA 92618
Tel (316) 946-3835
SIC 5699 5661 5961 5651 5632 5611

▲ TILLYS INC p 1453
10 Whatney, Irvine CA 92618
Tel (949) 609-5599 SIC 5651 5661

■ WORLD OF JEANS & TOPS p 1625
10 Whatney, Irvine CA 92618
Tel (949) 609-5599 SIC 5651

■ MOUNTAIN HARDWEAR INC p 994
1414 Harbour Way S, Richmond CA 94804
Tel (510) 558-3000 SIC 2399 2394 5651

■ BANANA REPUBLIC LLC p 149
2 Folsom St, San Francisco CA 94105
Tel (650) 952-4400 SIC 5651

▲ GAP INC p 591
2 Folsom St, San Francisco CA 94105
Tel (415) 427-0100
SIC 5651 5641 5632 5621 5611

■ OLD NAVY INC p 1081
2 Folsom St, San Francisco CA 94105
Tel (650) 952-4400 SIC 5651

▲ WALKING CO HOLDINGS INC p 1573
25 W Anapamu St, Santa Barbara CA 93101
Tel (805) 963-8727
SIC 5651 5961 5136 5137 5699

FYC APPAREL GROUP LLC p 586
30 Thompson Rd, Branford CT 06405
Tel (203) 481-2420
SIC 2331 2335 2337 5651

AMHERST NY BOBS INC p 85
160 Corporate Ct, Meriden CT 06450
Tel (203) 235-5775
SIC 5651 5611 5699 5621 5641 5661

BI RETAIL INC p 180
160 Corporate Ct, Meriden CT 06450
Tel (203) 235-5775
SIC 5651 5611 5699 5621 5641 5661

BS LIQUIDATING LLC p 222
160 Corporate Ct, Meriden CT 06450
Tel (203) 235-5775 SIC 5651

H C BOBS INC p 649
160 Corporate Ct, Meriden CT 06450
Tel (203) 235-5775
SIC 5651 5611 5699 5621 5641 5661

▲ SUN GORDMANS LP p 1400
5200 Town Center Cir # 600, Boca Raton FL 33486
Tel (561) 394-0550 SIC 5651 5963

BEALLS DEPARTMENT STORES INC p 165
1806 38th Ave E, Bradenton FL 34208
Tel (941) 747-2355 SIC 5311 5651 5947

BEALLS INC p 165
1806 13th Ave E, Bradenton FL 34208
Tel (941) 747-2355
SIC 5311 5719 5651 5947

BEALLS WEST GATE CORP p 165
1806 38th Ave E, Bradenton FL 34208
Tel (941) 744-4330 SIC 5651 5661 5719

BURKES OUTLET STORES INC p 227
1806 38th Ave E, Bradenton FL 34208
Tel (941) 747-2355 SIC 5651

▲ STEIN MART INC p 1385
1200 Riverplace Blvd # 1000, Jacksonville FL 32207
Tel (904) 346-1500 SIC 5311 5651

POMARE LTD p 1160
670 Auahi St Ste I03, Honolulu HI 96813
Tel (808) 524-3966 SIC 5651

WATSEKA RURAL KING SUPPLY INC p 1583
200 N Ernest Grove Pkwy, Watseka IL 60970
Tel (815) 432-3440
SIC 5999 5651 5251 5311

BOMGAARS SUPPLY INC p 199
1805 Zenith Dr, Sioux City IA 51103
Tel (712) 226-5000 SIC 5311 5999 5651

■ CONCORD BUYING GROUP INC p 354
770 Cochituate Rd, Framingham MA 01701
Tel (508) 390-4000 SIC 5651

■ MARMAXX OPERATING CORP p 909
770 Cochituate Rd, Framingham MA 01701
Tel (508) 390-1000 SIC 5311 5651

■ MARSHALLS OF MA INC p 911
770 Cochituate Rd, Framingham MA 01701
Tel (508) 390-1000 SIC 5651 5719

▲ TJX COMPANIES INC p 1457
770 Cochituate Rd Ste 1, Framingham MA 01701
Tel (508) 390-1000 SIC 5311 5651 5719

■ GORDMANS STORES INC p 625
1926 S 67th St, Omaha NE 68106
Tel (402) 691-4000 SIC 5651 5963

SUN GORDMANS LLC p 1400
1926 S 67th St, Omaha NE 68106
Tel (402) 691-4000 SIC 5651

COLE HAAN LLC p 335
150 Ocean Rd, Greenland NH 03840
Tel (207) 846-2500 SIC 5651 5632

BURLINGTON COAT FACTORY HOLDINGS INC p 227
1830 N Route 130, Burlington NJ 08016
Tel (609) 387-7800
SIC 5651 5632 5719 5947 5712

■ BURLINGTON COAT FACTORY REALTY OF MORROW INC p 227
1830 N Route 130, Burlington NJ 08016
Tel (609) 387-7800 SIC 5651

■ BURLINGTON COAT FACTORY WAREHOUSE OF MONMOUTH INC p 228
1830 N Route 130, Burlington NJ 08016
Tel (609) 387-7800 SIC 5651

UBI LIQUIDATING CORP p 1498
300 Nixon Ln, Edison NJ 08837
Tel (201) 319-9093
SIC 5621 5641 5651 5137 5632

■ RALPH LAUREN RETAIL INC p 1206
9 Polito Ave Fl 5, Lyndhurst NJ 07071
Tel (888) 475-7674 SIC 5651 5661 5719

■ LCI HOLDINGS INC p 849
5901 W Side Ave, North Bergen NJ 07047
Tel (201) 295-6300
SIC 5651 5136 5137 5094 5122 5944

▲ CHILDRENS PLACE INC p 300
500 Plaza Dr Ste 400, Secaucus NJ 07094
Tel (201) 558-2400 SIC 5641 5651

DAFFYS INC p 408
Daffys Way, Secaucus NJ 07094
Tel (201) 902-0800 SIC 5651

E & J LAWRENCE CORP p 465
85 Metro Way, Secaucus NJ 07094
Tel (201) 210-5577 SIC 5651

SYMS CORP p 1414
1 Syms Way, Secaucus NJ 07094
Tel (201) 902-9600 SIC 5651 5661

BARNEYS NEW YORK INC p 156
575 5th Ave Fl 11, New York NY 10017
Tel (212) 450-8700 SIC 5651

BROOKS BROTHERS GROUP INC p 218
346 Madison Ave, New York NY 10017
Tel (212) 309-7765 SIC 5651 5632

BROOKS BROTHERS INC p 218
346 Madison Ave, New York NY 10017
Tel (212) 682-8800 SIC 5611 5621 5651

■ CALVIN KLEIN INC p 243
205 W 39th St Lbby 2, New York NY 10018
Tel (212) 719-2600
SIC 5651 5137 5136 5611 5621 6794

H & M HENNES & MAURITZ LP p 649
110 5th Ave Fl 11, New York NY 10011
Tel (212) 564-9922 SIC 5651

▲ KATE SPADE & CO p 804
2 Park Ave Fl 8, New York NY 10016
Tel (212) 354-4900
SIC 2331 5651 5136 5137 5961

MICHAEL KORS (USA) INC p 960
11 W 42nd St Fl 20, New York NY 10036
Tel (212) 201-8100 SIC 5137 5651 5621

PRESIDIO INTERNATIONAL INC p 1172
450 W 15th St 4, New York NY 10011
Tel (212) 462-1100 SIC 5651 7379

SAKS & CO p 1271
611 5th Ave, New York NY 10022
Tel (212) 753-4000 SIC 5621 5311 5651

▲ ABERCROMBIE & FITCH CO p 11
6301 Fitch Path, New Albany OH 43054
Tel (614) 283-6500
SIC 5611 5621 5641 5632 5651 5961

■ VF OUTLET INC p 1553
801 Hill Ave Ste 1, Reading PA 19610
Tel (610) 378-0408 SIC 5651

HAMRICKS INC p 656
742 Peachoid Rd, Gaffney SC 29341
Tel (864) 489-6095
SIC 5651 2337 2331 2335 2339 5087

HAGGAR CLOTHING CO p 653
1507 Lbj Fwy Ste 100, Farmers Branch TX 75234
Tel (214) 352-8481
SIC 2325 2311 2321 5611 5651

■ SPECIALTY RETAILERS INC p 1356
2425 West Loop S Ste 110, Houston TX 77027
Tel (713) 331-4970 SIC 5651

▲ STAGE STORES INC p 1374
2425 West Loop S, Houston TX 77027
Tel (800) 579-2302 SIC 5651 5661

▲ FOSSIL GROUP INC p 570
901 S Central Expy, Richardson TX 75080
Tel (972) 234-2525
SIC 3873 5944 5094 5651 5632

UNITED FASHIONS OF TEXAS LLC p 1508
4629 Macro, San Antonio TX 78218
Tel (210) 662-7140 SIC 5611 5621 5651

UTAH NATIONAL SECURITY INC p 1536
2600 W 4700 S, Taylorsville UT 84129
Tel (801) 963-0397 SIC 5651

▲ NORDSTROM INC p 1048
1617 6th Ave, Seattle WA 98101
Tel (206) 628-2111
SIC 5651 5661 5632 5611 5641 5961

■ TOMMY BAHAMA GROUP INC p 1459
400 Fairview Ave N # 488, Seattle WA 98109
Tel (206) 622-8688
SIC 7389 5651 5136 5137

GABRIEL BROTHERS INC p 588
55 Scott Ave, Morgantown WV 26508
Tel (304) 292-6965 SIC 5651

GOODWILL RETAIL SERVICES INC p 625
5400 S 60th St, Greendale WI 53129
Tel (414) 847-4200 SIC 5651 4226

JOCKEY INTERNATIONAL DOMESTIC INC p 787
2300 60th St, Kenosha WI 53140
Tel (262) 658-8111 SIC 5651 5611

SIC 5661 Shoe Stores

■ HIBBETT SPORTING GOODS INC p 690
2700 Milan Ct, Birmingham AL 35211
Tel (205) 942-4292 SIC 5941 5661 5699

▲ HIBBETT SPORTS INC p 690
2700 Milan Ct, Birmingham AL 35211
Tel (205) 942-4292 SIC 5941 5661 5699

PACIFIC SUNWEAR STORES CORP p 1106
3450 E Miraloma Ave, Anaheim CA 92806
Tel (714) 414-4000
SIC 5611 5699 5661 5621 5999

WEEBS INC p 1587
20 Rancho Del Mar, Aptos CA 95003
Tel (831) 688-8007 SIC 5651 5661

MERCHANT OF TENNIS INC p 944
8737 Wilshire Blvd, Beverly Hills CA 90211
Tel (310) 228-4000
SIC 5941 5621 5661 5961 5999

▲ ROSS STORES INC p 1252
5130 Hacienda Dr, Dublin CA 94568
Tel (925) 965-4400
SIC 5651 5661 5944 5632 5611 5999

TECHSTYLE INC p 1432
800 Apollo St, El Segundo CA 90245
Tel (310) 683-0940
SIC 5961 5661 5632 5651

▲ BOOT BARN HOLDINGS INC p 200
15345 Barranca Pkwy, Irvine CA 92618
Tel (949) 453-4400 SIC 5661 5641

■ BOOT BARN INC p 200
11251 Beech Ave Ste 200, Irvine CA 92618
Tel (714) 288-8181 SIC 5699 5661

■ SHEPLERS INC p 1315
15345 Barranca Pkwy, Irvine CA 92618
Tel (316) 946-3835
SIC 5699 5661 5961 5651 5632 5611

▲ TILLYS INC p 1453
10 Whatney, Irvine CA 92618
Tel (949) 609-5599 SIC 5651 5661

EUROSTAR INC p 513
13425 S Figueroa St, Los Angeles CA 90061
Tel (310) 715-9300 SIC 5661

FOREVER 21 INC p 567
3880 N Mission Rd, Los Angeles CA 90031
Tel (213) 741-5100 SIC 5632 5661 5621

ROAD RUNNER SPORTS INC p 1240
5549 Copley Dr, San Diego CA 92111
Tel (858) 974-4200 SIC 5961 3949 5661

■ WALKING CO p 1573
25 W Anapamu St, Santa Barbara CA 93101
Tel (805) 963-8727 SIC 5661

▲ WEST MARINE INC p 1595
500 Westridge Dr, Watsonville CA 95076
Tel (831) 728-2700
SIC 5551 5961 5088 5611 5661 5621

▲ CROCS INC p 393
7477 Dry Creek Pkwy, Niwot CO 80503
Tel (303) 848-7000
SIC 3021 5139 3069 5661 2389

AMHERST NY BOBS INC p 85
160 Corporate Ct, Meriden CT 06450
Tel (203) 235-5775
SIC 5651 5611 5699 5621 5641 5661

BI RETAIL INC p 180
160 Corporate Ct, Meriden CT 06450
Tel (203) 235-5775
SIC 5651 5611 5699 5621 5641 5661

H C BOBS INC p 649
160 Corporate Ct, Meriden CT 06450
Tel (203) 235-5775
SIC 5651 5611 5699 5621 5641 5661

BEALLS OUTLET STORES INC p 165
1806 38th Ave E, Bradenton FL 34208
Tel (941) 747-2355
SIC 5611 5621 5661 5719

BEALLS WEST GATE CORP p 165
1806 38th Ave E, Bradenton FL 34208
Tel (941) 744-4330 SIC 5651 5661 5719

ANGELICA CORP p 91
1105 Lakewood Pkwy # 210, Alpharetta GA 30009
Tel (678) 823-4100 SIC 7213 5699 5661

▲ SHOE CARNIVAL INC p 1317
7500 E Columbia St, Evansville IN 47715
Tel (812) 867-6471 SIC 5661

▲ FINISH LINE INC p 543
3308 N Mitthoefer Rd, Indianapolis IN 46235
Tel (317) 899-1022 SIC 5661 5699 5941

SHOE SENSATION INC p 1317
253 America Pl, Jeffersonville IN 47130
Tel (812) 288-7659 SIC 5661

PAYLESS INC p 1122
3231 Se 6th Ave, Topeka KS 66607
Tel (785) 233-5171 SIC 5661 5632

PAYLESS SHOESOURCE INC p 1122
3231 Se 6th Ave, Topeka KS 66607
Tel (785) 233-5171 SIC 5661

■ SHEPLERS HOLDING CORP p 1315
6501 W Kellogg Dr, Wichita KS 67209
Tel (316) 946-3800 SIC 5699 5661

L L BEAN INC p 834
15 Casco St, Freeport ME 04033
Tel (207) 552-2000
SIC 5961 5621 5611 5941 5661 5948

OSC SPORTS INC p 1096
5 Bradley Dr, Westbrook ME 04092
Tel (207) 854-2794 SIC 5699 5661 5941

■ MACRO RETAILING LLC p 893
10365 Mount Savage Rd Nw, Cumberland MD 21502
Tel (301) 722-6563 SIC 5661

DTLR INC p 458
1300 Mercedes Dr, Hanover MD 21076
Tel (410) 850-5900 SIC 5611 5661

■ CONVERSE INC p 365
1 Love Joy Wharf, Boston MA 02114
Tel (978) 983-3300 SIC 5139 5661

REEBOK INTERNATIONAL LTD p 1217
1895 J W Foster Blvd, Canton MA 02021
Tel (781) 401-5000
SIC 3149 3143 3144 2329 2339 5661

J JILL GROUP INC p 771
4 Batterymarch Park, Quincy MA 02169
Tel (617) 376-4300
SIC 5961 5621 5661 5632

C & J CLARK AMERICA INC p 231
60 Tower Rd, Waltham MA 02451
Tel (617) 964-1222 SIC 3143 5139 5661

CLARKS AMERICAS INC p 322
60 Tower Rd, Waltham MA 02451
Tel (617) 796-5000 SIC 5661 5139

■ KEDS LLC p 807
500 Totten Pond Rd Ste 1, Waltham MA 02451
Tel (617) 824-6000 SIC 5139 5661

■ STRIDE RITE CHILDRENS GROUP LLC p 1393
500 Totten Pond Rd Ste 1, Waltham MA 02451
Tel (617) 824-6000 SIC 5139 5661

■ STRIDE RITE CORP p 1393
500 Totten Pond Rd Ste 1, Waltham MA 02451
Tel (617) 824-6000 SIC 5139 5661 3149

AMERICAN SPECIALTY RETAILING GROUP INC p 79
5607 New King Dr Ste 125, Troy MI 48098
Tel (248) 674-4991 SIC 5661 5941 5699

DUNHAMS ATHLEISURE CORP p 461
5607 New King Dr Ste 125, Troy MI 48098
Tel (248) 674-4991
SIC 5699 5661 5941 5961

TRADEHOME SHOE STORES INC p 1468
8300 97th St S, Cottage Grove MN 55016
Tel (651) 459-8600 SIC 5661

RED WING SHOE CO INC p 1216
314 Main St, Red Wing MN 55066
Tel (651) 388-8211
SIC 3143 3149 3144 3111 5661 3021

■ BG RETAIL LLC p 180
8300 Maryland Ave, Saint Louis MO 63105
Tel (314) 854-4000 SIC 5661

▲ CALERES INC p 238
8300 Maryland Ave, Saint Louis MO 63105
Tel (314) 854-4000 SIC 5661 5139

BASS PRO LLC p 159
2500 E Kearney St, Springfield MO 65898
Tel (417) 873-5000
SIC 5961 5941 5551 5661

▲ BUCKLE INC p 223
2407 W 24th St, Kearney NE 68845
Tel (308) 236-8491
SIC 5661 5632 5621 5611

MARSHALL RETAIL GROUP LLC p 911
3755 W Sunset Rd Ste A, Las Vegas NV 89118
Tel (702) 385-5233
SIC 5661 5621 5641 5611

■ ZAPPOS.COM INC p 1641
400 Stewart Ave Ste A, Las Vegas NV 89101
Tel (702) 943-7777
SIC 5661 4813 5632 5611

ECCO USA INC p 475
16 Delta Dr, Londonderry NH 03053
Tel (603) 537-7300 SIC 5139 5661

AEROGROUP INTERNATIONAL INC p 30
201 Meadow Rd, Edison NJ 08817
Tel (732) 985-6900 SIC 5139 5661

■ RALPH LAUREN RETAIL INC p 1206
9 Polito Ave Fl 5, Lyndhurst NJ 07071
Tel (888) 475-7674 SIC 5651 5661 5719

SYMS CORP p 1414
1 Syms Way, Secaucus NJ 07094
Tel (201) 902-9600 SIC 5651 5661

LOEHMANNS HOLDINGS INC p 874
2500 Halsey St Frnt 1, Bronx NY 10461
Tel (718) 409-2000 SIC 5621 5661 3171

DIVAL SAFETY EQUIPMENT INC p 443
1721 Niagara St, Buffalo NY 14207
Tel (716) 874-9060
SIC 5099 8748 8734 5047 5136 5661

■ **ANN INC** p 92
7 Times Sq Bsmt Sb4, New York NY 10036
Tel (212) 541-3300 SIC 5621 5632 5661

■ **ANNTAYLOR INC** p 92
7 Times Sq, New York NY 10036
Tel (212) 541-3300 SIC 5621 5632 5661

■ **ANNTAYLOR RETAIL INC** p 92
7 Times Sq, New York NY 10036
Tel (212) 541-3300 SIC 5621 5632 5661

DR JAYS INC p 454
15 W 37th St Fl 11, New York NY 10018
Tel (212) 239-3355 SIC 5611 5661

▲ **FOOT LOCKER INC** p 564
330 W 34th St, New York NY 10001
Tel (212) 720-3700
SIC 5661 5941 5961 6794

■ **FOOT LOCKER RETAIL INC** p 564
112 W 34th St Frnt 1, New York NY 10120
Tel (212) 465-9041 SIC 5661 5699

■ **GH BASS & CO** p 610
200 Madison Ave, New York NY 10016
Tel (212) 381-3900
SIC 3144 3143 3149 5661

GUCCI AMERICA INC p 645
195 Broadway Fl 12, New York NY 10007
Tel (212) 750-5220
SIC 5632 5948 5661 5611 5621 5137

HENRY MODELL & CO INC p 684
498 7th Ave Fl 20, New York NY 10018
Tel (212) 822-1000
SIC 5941 5661 5611 5621 5641 5961

J CREW OPERATING CORP p 770
770 Brdwy Fl 11 & 12, New York NY 10003
Tel (212) 209-2500
SIC 5961 5621 5611 5661 5632 6794

JONES GROUP INC p 792
1411 Broadway Fl 15, New York NY 10018
Tel (212) 642-3860
SIC 5632 5137 5139 5661 5641

KCP HOLDCO INC p 806
603 W 50th St, New York NY 10019
Tel (212) 265-1500
SIC 3143 3171 5661 5632 5611

KENNETH COLE PRODUCTIONS INC p 811
603 W 50th St, New York NY 10019
Tel (212) 265-1500
SIC 3143 3144 3171 5661 5632 5611

NINE WEST FOOTWEAR CORP p 1044
1411 Broadway Fl 20, New York NY 10018
Tel (800) 999-1877
SIC 3144 3171 5661 5632 5139

PRADA USA CORP p 1167
609 W 51st St, New York NY 10019
Tel (212) 307-9300
SIC 5136 5137 5139 5661 5632 8741

STUART WEITZMAN INC p 1394
50 W 57th St Fl 10, New York NY 10019
Tel (212) 582-9500 SIC 5661

TLB HOLDINGS LLC p 1457
9 W 57th St, New York NY 10019
Tel (212) 796-8555
SIC 5961 5661 5632 5641 5621

XSTELOS CORP p 1633
45 Rockefeller Plz # 2260, New York NY 10111
Tel (201) 934-2000 SIC 5661

RACK ROOM SHOES INC p 1203
8310 Technology Dr, Charlotte NC 28262
Tel (704) 547-9200 SIC 5661

SHOE SHOW INC p 1317
2201 Trinity Church Rd, Concord NC 28027
Tel (704) 782-4143 SIC 5661

SCHEELS ALL SPORTS INC p 1286
4550 15th Ave S, Fargo ND 58103
Tel (701) 364-0572
SIC 5661 5941 5699 5251 5261

▲ **DSW INC** p 458
810 Dsw Dr, Columbus OH 43219
Tel (614) 237-7100 SIC 5661

■ **DSW SHOE WAREHOUSE INC** p 458
4314 E 5th Ave, Columbus OH 43219
Tel (614) 237-7100 SIC 5661

■ **RETAIL VENTURES SERVICES INC** p 1228
4150 E 5th Ave, Columbus OH 43219
Tel (614) 238-4105 SIC 5661

■ **ELDER-BEERMAN STORES CORP** p 484
3155 Elbee Rd Ste 201, Moraine OH 45439
Tel (937) 296-2700 SIC 5311 5661 7389

■ **LEHIGH OUTFITTERS LLC** p 853
39 E Canal St, Nelsonville OH 45764
Tel (740) 753-1951 SIC 5661 5139

▲ **NIKE INC** p 1043
1 Sw Bowerman Dr, Beaverton OR 97005
Tel (503) 671-6453
SIC 3021 2329 2339 5139 5661 5136

■ **NIKE RETAIL SERVICES INC** p 1043
1 Sw Bowerman Dr, Beaverton OR 97005
Tel (503) 671-6453 SIC 5661 5699

KEEN INC p 807
515 Nw 13th Ave, Portland OR 97209
Tel (503) 402-1520 SIC 5139 5661

■ **ARAMARK UNIFORM & CAREER APPAREL GROUP INC** p 102
1101 Market St Ste 45, Philadelphia PA 19107
Tel (215) 238-3000
SIC 2337 2311 5699 5961 5661 5812

SNEAKER VILLA INC p 1335
1926 Arch St Fl 3, Philadelphia PA 19103
Tel (215) 279-5600 SIC 5699 5661

▲ **URBAN OUTFITTERS INC** p 1530
5000 S Broad St, Philadelphia PA 19112
Tel (215) 454-5500
SIC 5621 5611 5632 5661 5719 5137

▲ **AMERICAN EAGLE OUTFITTERS INC** p 71
77 Hot Metal St, Pittsburgh PA 15203
Tel (412) 432-3300
SIC 5621 5611 5661 5632

■ **GALYANS TRADING CO LLC** p 590
300 Industry Dr, Pittsburgh PA 15275
Tel (724) 273-3400 SIC 5941 5699 5661

IRON AGE HOLDINGS CORP p 764
3 Robinson Plz Ste 300, Pittsburgh PA 15205
Tel (412) 788-0888
SIC 5139 5661 3143 3144

▲ **GENESCO INC** p 602
1415 Murfreesboro Pike, Nashville TN 37217
Tel (615) 367-7000 SIC 5661 5139 5961

■ **GOLFSMITH INTERNATIONAL HOLDINGS INC** p 622
11000 N Interstate 35, Austin TX 78753
Tel (512) 837-8810
SIC 5941 5699 5661 5961

■ **MENS WEARHOUSE INC** p 943
6380 Rogerdale Rd, Houston TX 77072
Tel (281) 776-7000
SIC 5611 5621 5632 5661 5699

▲ **STAGE STORES INC** p 1374
2425 West Loop S, Houston TX 77027
Tel (800) 579-2302 SIC 5651 5661

▲ **TAILORED BRANDS INC** p 1421
6380 Rogerdale Rd, Houston TX 77072
Tel (281) 776-7000
SIC 5611 5621 5632 5661 5699

ACADEMY LTD p 13
1800 N Mason Rd, Katy TX 77449
Tel (281) 646-5200 SIC 5941 5699 5661

SAN ANTONIO SHOE INC p 1275
1717 Sas Dr, San Antonio TX 78224
Tel (877) 727-7463
SIC 3131 5661 5139 5632 3144

CAVENDER STORES LTD p 267
7820 S Broadway Ave, Tyler TX 75703
Tel (903) 509-9509 SIC 5699 5661

▲ **SPORTSMANS WAREHOUSE HOLDINGS INC** p 1360
7035 S High Tech Dr # 100, Midvale UT 84047
Tel (801) 566-6681 SIC 5941 5699 5661

■ **SPORTSMANS WAREHOUSE INC** p 1360
7035 S High Tech Dr, Midvale UT 84047
Tel (801) 566-6681 SIC 5941 5699 5661

S & K FAMOUS BRANDS INC p 1261
20 N 8th St, Richmond VA 23219
Tel (804) 827-1000 SIC 5611 5661

▲ **NORDSTROM INC** p 1048
1617 6th Ave, Seattle WA 98101
Tel (206) 628-2111
SIC 5651 5661 5632 5611 5641 5961

MASON COMPANIES INC p 916
1251 1st Ave, Chippewa Falls WI 54729
Tel (715) 720-4200 SIC 5961 5661

▲ **WEYCO GROUP INC** p 1603
333 W Estabrook Blvd # 1, Glendale WI 53212
Tel (414) 908-1600 SIC 5139 5661

ALLEN EDMONDS CORP p 53
201 E Seven Hills Rd, Port Washington WI 53074
Tel (262) 235-6000 SIC 3143 5661

ROGAN SHOES INC p 1246
1750 Ohio St, Racine WI 53405
Tel (262) 637-3613 SIC 5661

■ **EASTBAY INC** p 471
111 S 1st Ave, Wausau WI 54401
Tel (800) 826-2205 SIC 5699 5661 5941

■ **FOOTLOCKER.COM INC** p 564
111 S 1st Ave, Wausau WI 54401
Tel (715) 842-3890 SIC 5961 5661

SIC 5699 Apparel & Accessory Stores, Misc

■ **HIBBETT SPORTING GOODS INC** p 690
2700 Milan Ct, Birmingham AL 35211
Tel (205) 942-4292 SIC 5941 5661 5699

▲ **HIBBETT SPORTS INC** p 690
2700 Milan Ct, Birmingham AL 35211
Tel (205) 942-4292 SIC 5941 5661 5699

ASTRACO LLC p 122
1411 E Hidalgo Ave, Phoenix AZ 85040
Tel (602) 931-2981 SIC 5136 5699

FISHING HOLDINGS LLC p 552
927 Highway 178 N, Flippin AR 72634
Tel (870) 453-2222 SIC 3732 5699

PACIFIC SUNWEAR OF CALIFORNIA LLC p 1106
3450 E Miraloma Ave, Anaheim CA 92806
Tel (714) 414-4000 SIC 5611 5621 5699

PACIFIC SUNWEAR STORES CORP p 1106
3450 E Miraloma Ave, Anaheim CA 92806
Tel (714) 414-4000
SIC 5611 5699 5661 5621 5999

HOT TOPIC INC p 710
18305 San Jose Ave, City Of Industry CA 91748
Tel (626) 839-4681 SIC 2326 5632 5699

511 INC p 3
1360 Reynolds Ave Ste 101, Irvine CA 92614
Tel (949) 800-1511
SIC 5699 2231 5139 2393

■ **BOOT BARN INC** p 200
11251 Beech Ave Ste 200, Irvine CA 92618
Tel (714) 288-8181 SIC 5699 5661

■ **SHEPLERS INC** p 1315
15345 Barranca Pkwy, Irvine CA 92618
Tel (316) 946-3835
SIC 5699 5661 5961 5651 5632 5611

L A HEARNE CO p 833
512 Metz Rd, King City CA 93930
Tel (831) 385-5441
SIC 5191 0723 5699 4214 2048 5261

METROPARK USA INC p 955
5750 Grace Pl, Los Angeles CA 90022
Tel (323) 622-3600 SIC 5632 5699

▲ **WALKING CO HOLDINGS INC** p 1573
25 W Anapamu St, Santa Barbara CA 93101
Tel (805) 963-8727
SIC 5651 5961 5136 5137 5699

PATAGONIA WORKS p 1120
259 W Santa Clara St, Ventura CA 93001
Tel (805) 643-8616
SIC 5699 2339 2329 5961

AMHERST NY BOBS INC p 85
160 Corporate Ct, Meriden CT 06450
Tel (203) 235-5775
SIC 5651 5611 5699 5621 5641 5661

BI RETAIL INC p 180
160 Corporate Ct, Meriden CT 06450
Tel (203) 235-5775
SIC 5651 5611 5699 5621 5641 5661

EVEREST MERGER SUB INC p 514
160 Corporate Ct, Meriden CT 06450
Tel (203) 235-5775 SIC 5699

H C BOBS INC p 649
160 Corporate Ct, Meriden CT 06450
Tel (203) 235-5775
SIC 5651 5611 5699 5621 5641 5661

SME HOLDING CO LLC p 1332
160 Corporate Ct, Meriden CT 06450
Tel (603) 924-9571 SIC 5699 5941

SPORT CHALET LLC p 1359
160 Corporate Ct, Meriden CT 06450
Tel (818) 790-2717 SIC 5699

VINEYARD VINES LLC p 1558
181 Harbor Dr Fl 1, Stamford CT 06902
Tel (203) 661-1803
SIC 5136 5137 5699 5611 5621

FANATICS INC p 527
8100 Nations Way, Jacksonville FL 32256
Tel (904) 421-8143 SIC 5941 5699

PLANET HOLLYWOOD INTERNATIONAL INC p 1154
4700 Millenia Blvd # 400, Orlando FL 32839
Tel (407) 903-5500 SIC 5812 6794 5699

CLAIRES BOUTIQUES INC p 321
11401 Pines Blvd, Pembroke Pines FL 33026
Tel (954) 438-0433
SIC 5632 5699 5999 5943 5947

ANGELICA CORP p 91
1105 Lakewood Pkwy # 210, Alpharetta GA 30009
Tel (678) 823-4100 SIC 7213 5699 5661

HARP BUSINESS SERVICES INC p 662
2725 Northwoods Pkwy A2, Peachtree Corners GA 30071
Tel (678) 482-0675 SIC 2759 4225 5699

DNK SALES LLC p 446
949 Stephenson Rd Ste B, Stone Mountain GA 30087
Tel (678) 704-7300 SIC 6311 7291 5699

D&B SUPPLY CO p 407
3303 E Linden St, Caldwell ID 83605
Tel (208) 459-7446
SIC 5191 5699 5251 5261 5999 5531

EBHI HOLDINGS INC p 474
1000 Field Dr Ste 240, Lake Forest IL 60045
Tel (312) 251-3430
SIC 5611 5699 5941 5719 5947 5961

MAGID GLOVE & SAFETY MANUFACTURING CO LLC p 895
1300 Naperville Dr, Romeoville IL 60446
Tel (773) 384-2070
SIC 3151 2381 5699 3842 2326

▲ **FINISH LINE INC** p 543
3308 N Mitthoefer Rd, Indianapolis IN 46235
Tel (317) 899-1022 SIC 5661 5699 5941

■ **LIDS CORP** p 863
7555 Woodland Dr, Indianapolis IN 46278
Tel (888) 564-4287 SIC 5699

THEISENS INC p 1446
6201 Chavenelle Rd, Dubuque IA 52002
Tel (563) 556-4738
SIC 5531 5999 5699 5261

ITS GREEK TO ME INC p 768
520 Mccall Rd Ste A, Manhattan KS 66502
Tel (785) 537-8822
SIC 5136 5699 5137 5947 2759

■ **SHEPLERS HOLDING CORP** p 1315
6501 W Kellogg Dr, Wichita KS 67209
Tel (316) 946-3800 SIC 5699 5661

OSC SPORTS INC p 1096
5 Bradley Dr, Westbrook ME 04092
Tel (207) 854-2794 SIC 5699 5661 5941

CITY SPORTS INC p 320
77 N Washington St # 500, Boston MA 02114
Tel (617) 391-9100 SIC 5699

■ **CMRG APPAREL LLC** p 329
555 Turnpike St, Canton MA 02021
Tel (781) 828-9300 SIC 5699 2389

▲ **DESTINATION XL GROUP INC** p 432
555 Turnpike St, Canton MA 02021
Tel (781) 828-9300 SIC 5699

FAMILY CHRISTIAN STORES LLC p 526
5300 Patterson Ave Se, Grand Rapids MI 49530
Tel (616) 554-8700
SIC 5942 5735 5947 5699 8741

AMERICAN SPECIALTY RETAILING GROUP INC p 79
5607 New King Dr Ste 125, Troy MI 48098
Tel (248) 674-4991 SIC 5661 5941 5699

DUNHAMS ATHLEISURE CORP p 461
5607 New King Dr Ste 125, Troy MI 48098
Tel (248) 674-4991
SIC 5699 5661 5941 5961

■ **WILSONS HOUSE OF SUEDE INC** p 1614
7401 Boone Ave N, Brooklyn Park MN 55428
Tel (763) 391-4000 SIC 5699 5948

WILSONS LEATHER EXPERTS INC p 1614
7401 Boone Ave N, Brooklyn Park MN 55428
Tel (763) 391-4000 SIC 5699 5948

▲ **POLARIS INDUSTRIES INC** p 1159
2100 Highway 55, Medina MN 55340
Tel (763) 542-0500
SIC 3799 3751 3714 5699

RANCH AND HOME SUPPLY LLC p 1207
2311 N 7th Ave, Bozeman MT 59715
Tel (406) 586-8466
SIC 5699 5191 5531 5251

SPENCER SPIRIT HOLDINGS INC p 1358
6826 Black Horse Pike, Egg Harbor Township NJ 08234
Tel (609) 645-3300 SIC 5699 6719

FORMAN MILLS INC p 567
1070 Thomas Busch Mem Hwy, Pennsauken NJ 08110
Tel (856) 486-1447 SIC 5699

FASHION GALLERY INC p 531
1000 Pennsylvania Ave, Brooklyn NY 11207
Tel (718) 485-3000 SIC 5699

■ **FOOT LOCKER RETAIL INC** p 564
112 W 34th St Frnt 1, New York NY 10120
Tel (212) 465-9041 SIC 5661 5699

■ **MACYS MERCHANDISING GROUP INC** p 893
11 Penn Plz Fl 10, New York NY 10001
Tel (646) 429-6000 SIC 5699 5399

4004 INC p 3
12 Harbor Park Dr, Port Washington NY 11050
Tel (516) 829-4730 SIC 5699

TUXEDO JUNCTION INC p 1493
120 Earhart Dr, Williamsville NY 14221
Tel (716) 633-2400 SIC 5136 5699 7299

DONNIE SHONOBI BRAND NAME TRADEMARK COLLECTION CORP p 451
160 Town Park Dr, Advance NC 27006
Tel (336) 940-5682 SIC 5699 7389

▲ **CATO CORP** p 267
8100 Denmark Rd, Charlotte NC 28273
Tel (704) 554-8510
SIC 5621 5632 5137 5699 5311 5641

GOLD TOE MORETZ HOLDINGS CORP p 620
2121 Heilig Rd, Salisbury NC 28146
Tel (828) 464-0751 SIC 5136 5137 5699

SCHEELS ALL SPORTS INC p 1286
4550 15th Ave S, Fargo ND 58103
Tel (701) 364-0572
SIC 5661 5941 5699 5251 5261

■ **FECHHEIMER BROTHERS CO** p 533
4545 Malsbary Rd, Blue Ash OH 45242
Tel (513) 793-7819
SIC 2311 2337 2339 5699

TOTES ISOTONER HOLDINGS CORP p 1463
9655 International Blvd, West Chester OH 45246
Tel (513) 682-8200
SIC 2381 3151 2211 3021 5699

■ **NIKE RETAIL SERVICES INC** p 1043
1 Sw Bowerman Dr, Beaverton OR 97005
Tel (503) 671-6453 SIC 5661 5699

■ **SOREL CORP** p 1341
14375 Nw Science Park Dr, Portland OR 97229
Tel (503) 978-2300 SIC 5699

G I JOES INC p 587
9805 Sw Boeckman Rd, Wilsonville OR 97070
Tel (503) 682-2242
SIC 5941 5699 5531 5999

▲ **DICKS SPORTING GOODS INC** p 438
345 Court St, Coraopolis PA 15108
Tel (724) 273-3400 SIC 5941 5699

■ **ARAMARK UNIFORM & CAREER APPAREL GROUP INC** p 102
1101 Market St Ste 45, Philadelphia PA 19107
Tel (215) 238-3000
SIC 2337 2311 5699 5961 5661 5812

SNEAKER VILLA INC p 1335
1926 Arch St Fl 3, Philadelphia PA 19103
Tel (215) 279-5600 SIC 5699 5661

■ **GALYANS TRADING CO LLC** p 590
300 Industry Dr, Pittsburgh PA 15275
Tel (724) 273-3400 SIC 5941 5699 5661

■ **GENERAL NUTRITION CORP** p 601
300 6th Ave, Pittsburgh PA 15222
Tel (412) 288-4600
SIC 5499 5999 5941 5699 6794

SAMUEL VAZQUEZ p 1275
108 Calle Mendez Vigo E, Mayaguez PR 00680
Tel (787) 598-6107 SIC 5699

■ **KNIGHTS APPAREL INC** p 824
5475 N Blackstock Rd, Spartanburg SC 29303
Tel (864) 587-9690 SIC 5091 5699

▲ **TRACTOR SUPPLY CO** p 1468
5401 Virginia Way, Brentwood TN 37027
Tel (615) 440-4000
SIC 5999 5261 5251 5531 5699

■ **GOLFSMITH INTERNATIONAL HOLDINGS INC** p 622
11000 N Interstate 35, Austin TX 78753
Tel (512) 837-8810
SIC 5941 5699 5661 5961

■ **MENS WEARHOUSE INC** p 943
6380 Rogerdale Rd, Houston TX 77072
Tel (281) 776-7000
SIC 5611 5621 5632 5661 5699

▲ **TAILORED BRANDS INC** p 1421
6380 Rogerdale Rd, Houston TX 77072
Tel (281) 776-7000
SIC 5611 5621 5632 5661 5699

ACADEMY LTD p 13
1800 N Mason Rd, Katy TX 77449
Tel (281) 646-5200 SIC 5941 5699 5661

CAVENDER STORES LTD p 267
7820 S Broadway Ave, Tyler TX 75703
Tel (903) 509-9509 SIC 5699 5661

▲ **SPORTSMANS WAREHOUSE HOLDINGS INC** p 1360
7035 S High Tech Dr # 100, Midvale UT 84047
Tel (801) 566-6681 SIC 5941 5699 5661

■ **SPORTSMANS WAREHOUSE INC** p 1360
7035 S High Tech Dr, Midvale UT 84047
Tel (801) 566-6681 SIC 5941 5699 5661

CUSTOMINK LLC p 403
2910 District Ave Ste 100, Fairfax VA 22031
Tel (703) 891-2273 SIC 2759 5699 5941

AMARGOSA INC p 64
10401 Ne 8th St Ste 500, Bellevue WA 98004
Tel (425) 755-6100
SIC 5611 5699 5941 5719 5947 5961

EVERY EST HOLDINGS LLC p 514
10401 Ne 8th St Ste 500, Bellevue WA 98004
Tel (425) 755-6544 SIC 5699 5611 5961

RECREATIONAL EQUIPMENT INC p 1215
6750 S 228th St, Kent WA 98032
Tel (253) 395-3780
SIC 2329 3949 2399 5941 5961 5699

HELLY HANSEN (US) INC p 682
14218 Stewart Rd Ste 100a, Sumner WA 98390
Tel (800) 435-5901
SIC 5137 5699 2339 2329

■ EASTBAY INC p 471
111 S 1st Ave, Wausau WI 54401
Tel (800) 826-2205 SIC 5699 5661 5941

SIC 5712 Furniture Stores

GOODMANS INC p 624
1400 E Indian School Rd, Phoenix AZ 85014
Tel (602) 263-1110 SIC 5712 7389

ROOMSTORES OF PHOENIX LLC p 1249
3011 E Broadway Rd # 100, Phoenix AZ 85040
Tel (602) 268-1111 SIC 5712

SAM LEVITZ FURNITURE CO INC p 1274
3430 E 36th St, Tucson AZ 85713
Tel (520) 624-7443 SIC 5712

FURNITURE FACTORY OUTLET LLC p 585
6500 Jenny Lind Rd Spc A, Fort Smith AR 72908
Tel (918) 427-0241 SIC 5712 2515

▲ DILLARDS INC p 439
1600 Cantrell Rd, Little Rock AR 72201
Tel (501) 376-5200
SIC 5311 5611 5621 5641 5712

■ COST PLUS INC p 373
1201 Marina Village Pkwy # 100, Alameda CA 94501
Tel (510) 893-7300
SIC 5712 5713 5719 5947 5499 5921

▲ RESTORATION HARDWARE HOLDINGS INC p 1228
15 Koch Rd Ste K, Corte Madera CA 94925
Tel (415) 924-1005 SIC 5712

■ RESTORATION HARDWARE INC p 1228
15 Koch Rd Ste J, Corte Madera CA 94925
Tel (415) 924-1005 SIC 5712

LIVING SPACES FURNITURE LLC p 871
14501 Artesia Blvd, La Mirada CA 90638
Tel (714) 523-2000 SIC 5712 5021

DEARDENS p 420
700 S Main St, Los Angeles CA 90014
Tel (213) 362-9600
SIC 5712 5722 5731 5944

SCANDINAVIAN DESIGNS INC p 1286
2250 S Mcdowell Blvd Ext, Petaluma CA 94954
Tel (707) 778-1600 SIC 5712

SLEEP TRAIN INC p 1331
2205 Plaza Dr, Rocklin CA 95765
Tel (916) 751-4300 SIC 5712

JEROMES FURNITURE WAREHOUSE p 783
16960 Mesamint St, San Diego CA 92127
Tel (866) 633-4094 SIC 5712

MOR FURNITURE FOR LESS INC p 988
8996 Miramar Rd Ste 300, San Diego CA 92126
Tel (858) 547-1616 SIC 5712

PIVOT INTERIORS INC p 1152
3355 Scott Blvd Ste 110, Santa Clara CA 95054
Tel (408) 432-5600 SIC 5712 7389 7299

BIG SUR WATERBEDS INC p 182
5603 Brdwy, Denver CO 80216
Tel (303) 566-8700 SIC 5712 2515 2511

FURNITURE ROW LLC p 585
5641 Broadway, Denver CO 80216
Tel (303) 576-0787 SIC 5712

AMERICAN FURNITURE WAREHOUSE CO INC p 73
8820 American Way, Englewood CO 80112
Tel (303) 799-9044 SIC 5712

■ ETHAN ALLEN GLOBAL INC p 511
25 Lake Ave, Danbury CT 06810
Tel (203) 743-8000 SIC 5712

▲ ETHAN ALLEN INTERIORS INC p 511
Ethan Allen Dr, Danbury CT 06811
Tel (203) 743-8000 SIC 2511 2512 5712

■ ETHAN ALLEN RETAIL INC p 511
Ethan Allen Dr, Danbury CT 06811
Tel (203) 743-8000
SIC 5712 5719 5713 5231 2273

BDF HOLDING CORP p 164
428 Tolland Tpke, Manchester CT 06042
Tel (860) 474-1200 SIC 5712

BOBS DISCOUNT FURNITURE LLC p 196
428 Tolland Tpke, Manchester CT 06042
Tel (860) 474-1200 SIC 5712

IKEA HOLDING US INC p 731
1105 N Market St Ste 1044, Wilmington DE 19801
Tel (302) 655-4126 SIC 5021 5712

AMERICAN SIGNATURE HOME p 79
161 Brandon Town Ctr Dr, Brandon FL 33511
Tel (813) 315-1120 SIC 5712

PORPOISE POOL & PATIO INC p 1161
14480 62nd St N, Clearwater FL 33760
Tel (727) 531-8913
SIC 6794 5999 5712 5091

TRIVEST FUND III LP p 1483
550 S Dixie Hwy Ste 300, Coral Gables FL 33146
Tel (305) 858-2200 SIC 6799 5712

ROBB & STUCKY LIMITED LLLP p 1240
14550 Plantation Rd, Fort Myers FL 33912
Tel (239) 437-7997
SIC 5712 5713 5714 5231

EL DORADO FURNITURE CORP p 482
4200 Nw 167th St, Miami Gardens FL 33054
Tel (305) 624-9700 SIC 5712

WS BADCOCK CORP p 1628
205 Nw 2nd St, Mulberry FL 33860
Tel (863) 425-4921
SIC 5712 5713 5722 5731

FRENCH FURNITURE ORLANDO LLC p 578
901 Centr Flori Pkwy Unit, Orlando FL 32824
Tel (407) 270-1111 SIC 5712

KANE FURNITURE CORP p 802
5700 70th Ave N, Pinellas Park FL 33781
Tel (727) 545-9555 SIC 5712

BAERS FURNITURE CO INC p 144
1589 Nw 12th Ave, Pompano Beach FL 33069
Tel (954) 946-8001 SIC 5712

▲ HSN INC p 715
1 Hsn Dr, Saint Petersburg FL 33729
Tel (727) 872-1000 SIC 5961 5331 5712

RTG FURNITURE CORP p 1256
11540 E Us Highway 92, Seffner FL 33584
Tel (813) 623-5400 SIC 5712

RTG FURNITURE CORP OF GEORGIA p 1256
11540 E Us Highway 92, Seffner FL 33584
Tel (813) 623-5400 SIC 5712

RTG FURNITURE OF TEXAS LP p 1256
11540 E Us Highway 92, Seffner FL 33584
Tel (813) 628-9724 SIC 5712 5021

CITY FURNITURE INC p 312
6701 Hiatus Rd, Tamarac FL 33321
Tel (954) 597-2200 SIC 5712

▲ AARONS INC p 8
400 Galleria Pkwy Se # 300, Atlanta GA 30339
Tel (404) 231-0011
SIC 7359 5712 5731 5722 5932 6794

▲ HAVERTY FURNITURE COMPANIES INC p 668
780 Johnson Ferry Rd, Atlanta GA 30342
Tel (404) 443-2900
SIC 5712 5722 5713 5021

NATIONAL FURNITURE LIQUIDATORS I LLC p 1012
2865 Log Cabin Dr Se, Atlanta GA 30339
Tel (404) 872-7280 SIC 5021 5712 5932

WAREHOUSE HOME FURNISHINGS DISTRIBUTORS INC p 1575
1851 Telfair St, Dublin GA 31021
Tel (800) 456-0424 SIC 5712

WALTER E SMITHE FURNITURE INC p 1574
1251 W Thorndale Ave, Itasca IL 60143
Tel (800) 948-4263 SIC 5712

OLD HF LLC p 1081
1000 N Rohlwing Rd Ste 46, Lombard IL 60148
Tel (630) 261-3900 SIC 5712

■ OFFICEMAX CONTRACT INC p 1076
263 Shuman Blvd, Naperville IL 60563
Tel (630) 438-7800
SIC 5021 5112 5044 5111 5943 5712

EUROMARKET DESIGNS INC p 512
1250 Techny Rd, Northbrook IL 60062
Tel (847) 272-2888
SIC 5719 5947 5712 5961 2599

▲ HHGREGG INC p 689
4151 E 96th St, Indianapolis IN 46240
Tel (317) 848-8710 SIC 5731 5722 5712

KITTLES HOME FURNISHINGS CENTER INC p 822
8600 Allisonville Rd, Indianapolis IN 46250
Tel (317) 849-5300 SIC 5712 5719

■ NATIONAL OFFICE FURNITURE INC p 1014
1610 Royal St, Jasper IN 47549
Tel (812) 482-1600 SIC 5712

IVAN SMITH FURNITURE CO LLC p 769
5434 Technology Dr, Shreveport LA 71129
Tel (318) 688-1335 SIC 5712

■ WAYFAIR LLC p 1584
4 Copley Pl Ste 700, Boston MA 02116
Tel (617) 532-6100 SIC 5963 5712 5023

W B MASON CO INC p 1568
59 Center St, Brockton MA 02301
Tel (781) 794-8800 SIC 5712 5943

■ JORDANS FURNITURE INC p 793
450 Revolutionary Dr, East Taunton MA 02718
Tel (508) 828-4000 SIC 5712

▲ STAPLES INC p 1377
500 Staples Dr, Framingham MA 01702
Tel (508) 253-5000
SIC 5943 5999 7513 5961 5712

■ STAPLES INTERNATIONAL INC p 1378
500 Staples Dr, Framingham MA 01702
Tel (508) 253-5000
SIC 5943 5712 5044 5021 5112

CONVERTIBLE CASTLE INC p 365
308 E Main St, Norton MA 02766
Tel (800) 244-9350 SIC 5712

CARDIS DEPARTMENT STORE INC p 253
1 Furniture Way, Swansea MA 02777
Tel (508) 379-5000 SIC 5712

GARDNER WHITE FURNITURE CO INC p 592
4445 N Atlantic Blvd, Auburn Hills MI 48326
Tel (586) 774-8853 SIC 5712

▲ LA-Z-BOY INC p 836
1 La Z Boy Dr, Monroe MI 48162
Tel (734) 242-1444 SIC 2512 2511 5712

ART VAN FURNITURE INC p 113
6500 E 14 Mile Rd, Warren MI 48092
Tel (586) 939-2100 SIC 5712

SLUMBERLAND INC p 1331
3060 Centerville Rd, Little Canada MN 55117
Tel (651) 482-7500 SIC 5712

HOM FURNITURE INC p 703
10301 Woodcrest Dr Nw, Minneapolis MN 55433
Tel (763) 767-3600 SIC 5712

ROOM & BOARD INC p 1249
4600 Olson Memorial Hwy, Minneapolis MN 55422
Tel (763) 588-7525 SIC 5712

■ SELECT COMFORT RETAIL CORP p 1301
9800 59th Ave N, Minneapolis MN 55442
Tel (763) 551-7000 SIC 5712

▲ BEST BUY CO INC p 177
7601 Penn Ave S, Richfield MN 55423
Tel (612) 291-1000
SIC 5731 5734 5735 5712 5722

COLOR ART INTEGRATED INTERIORS LLC p 338
1325 N Warson Rd, Saint Louis MO 63132
Tel (314) 432-3000
SIC 5021 7641 5999 5712 5099 2521

■ NEBRASKA FURNITURE MART INC p 1023
700 S 72nd St, Omaha NE 68114
Tel (402) 397-6100
SIC 5712 5713 5722 5731 5734 5946

BURLINGTON COAT FACTORY HOLDINGS INC p 227
1830 N Route 130, Burlington NJ 08016
Tel (609) 387-7800
SIC 5651 5632 5719 5947 5712

CREST FURNITURE INC p 392
30 Tower Rd, Dayton NJ 08810
Tel (732) 355-9200 SIC 5712

AMERICAN FURNITURE RENTALS INC p 73
720 Hylton Rd, Pennsauken NJ 08110
Tel (856) 406-1200 SIC 7359 5712

HANOVER DIRECT INC p 658
1200 Harbor Blvd Fl 9, Weehawken NJ 07086
Tel (201) 863-7300
SIC 5712 5961 7389 2211 2221

SLEEPYS LLC p 1331
1000 S Oyster Bay Rd, Hicksville NY 11801
Tel (516) 861-8800 SIC 5712

SLEEPYS REORGANIZATION INC p 1331
1000 S Oyster Bay Rd, Hicksville NY 11801
Tel (516) 861-8800 SIC 5712

RAYMOURS FURNITURE CO INC p 1210
7248 Morgan Rd, Liverpool NY 13090
Tel (315) 453-2500 SIC 5712

ABC HOME FURNISHINGS INC p 10
888 Brdwy Fl 4, New York NY 10003
Tel (212) 473-3000 SIC 5712 5719 5023

P KAUFMANN INC p 1102
3 Park Ave, New York NY 10016
Tel (212) 292-2200
SIC 5131 5714 5712 2262

SAFAVIEH INC p 1265
40 Harbor Park Dr, Port Washington NY 11050
Tel (516) 945-1900 SIC 2273 5712

JENNIFER CONVERTIBLES INC p 782
335 Crossways Park Dr, Woodbury NY 11797
Tel (516) 496-1900 SIC 5712 6794 5021

LEVITZ FURNITURE CORP p 858
300 Crossways Park Dr, Woodbury NY 11797
Tel (516) 682-0481 SIC 5712

FURNITURE DISTRIBUTORS INC p 585
4524 South Blvd, Charlotte NC 28209
Tel (704) 523-3424 SIC 5712 5713 5722

MARSH FURNITURE CO p 911
1001 S Centennial St, High Point NC 27260
Tel (336) 884-7363 SIC 2434 5712 2421

VRUSH INDUSTRIES INC p 1566
118 N Wrenn St, High Point NC 27260
Tel (336) 886-7700
SIC 5045 5021 7379 3469 5712 7375

FURNITURELAND SOUTH INC p 585
5635 Riverdale Dr, Jamestown NC 27282
Tel (336) 822-3000 SIC 5712

BFI WIND DOWN INC p 179
815 Visionary St, Lenoir NC 28645
Tel (828) 759-8000 SIC 5712 2512

LUXURY HOME FURNISHINGS LLC p 887
130 S Merkle Rd, Columbus OH 43209
Tel (661) 631-0299 SIC 5712

SCHOTTENSTEIN STORES CORP p 1290
4300 E 5th Ave, Columbus OH 43219
Tel (614) 221-9200
SIC 5311 5712 5912 5999

VALUE CITY FURNITURE INC p 1542
4300 E 5th Ave, Columbus OH 43219
Tel (888) 751-8552 SIC 5712

MORRIS FURNITURE CO INC p 990
2377 Commerce Center Blvd, Fairborn OH 45324
Tel (937) 874-7100 SIC 5731 5722 5712

ARHAUS LLC p 108
51 E Hines Hill Rd, Hudson OH 44236
Tel (440) 439-7700 SIC 5712

■ CINMAR LLC p 308
5566 W Chester Rd, West Chester OH 45069
Tel (513) 603-1000 SIC 5961 5023 5712

WOLF FURNITURE ENTERPRISES INC p 1621
1620 N Tuckahoe St, Bellwood PA 16617
Tel (814) 742-4380
SIC 5712 5713 5722 5731 5719

IKEA NORTH AMERICA SERVICES LLC p 731
420 Alan Wood Rd, Conshohocken PA 19428
Tel (610) 834-0180 SIC 6794 5712

K INVESTMENTS LIMITED PARTNERSHIP p 799
1500 Sycamore Rd Ste 10, Montoursville PA 17754
Tel (570) 327-0111 SIC 7011 5521 5712

SAM LEVIN INC p 1274
301 Fitz Henry Rd, Smithton PA 15479
Tel (724) 872-2055 SIC 5712

PR RETAIL STORES INC p 1167
Edif Kodak Ave Campo, San Juan PR 00924
Tel (787) 641-8200
SIC 5311 5712 5722 5331

JLJ HOME FURNISHINGS LLC p 786
4776 Charlotte Hwy, Lancaster SC 29720
Tel (704) 239-8630 SIC 5712

BLATCHFORDS INC p 189
207 S Chicago St, Hot Springs SD 57747
Tel (605) 745-5173
SIC 5251 5712 5531 5947 5722

FURNITURE OUTLETS USA INC p 585
140 E Hinks Ln, Sioux Falls SD 57104
Tel (605) 336-5000 SIC 5712

H-HOME DIVISION HACKNEY HOME FURNISHINGS FAX O p 651
3036 Highway 11 S, Athens TN 37303
Tel (423) 745-9127 SIC 5712

FOUR HANDS LLC p 571
2090 Woodward St, Austin TX 78744
Tel (512) 371-7575 SIC 5023 5712

■ ENLINK MIDSTREAM INC p 500
2501 Cedar Springs Rd, Dallas TX 75201
Tel (214) 953-9500 SIC 1311 5712

FAMSA INC p 527
2727 Lyndon B Johnson Fwy, Dallas TX 75234
Tel (972) 993-5800 SIC 5722 5712

▲ TUESDAY MORNING CORP p 1490
6250 Lbj Fwy, Dallas TX 75240
Tel (972) 387-3562
SIC 5947 5719 5944 5948 5945 5712

▲ PIER 1 IMPORTS INC p 1147
100 Pier 1 Pl, Fort Worth TX 76102
Tel (817) 252-8000 SIC 5719 6794 5712

■ PIER 1 LICENSING INC p 1147
100 Pier 1 Pl, Fort Worth TX 76102
Tel (817) 878-8000
SIC 5719 5712 5621 5632

RBLS INC p 1211
502 Fountain Pkwy, Grand Prairie TX 75050
Tel (817) 633-6838 SIC 5712

MATTRESS FIRM HOLDING CORP p 921
10201 Main St, Houston TX 77025
Tel (713) 923-1090 SIC 5712

MATTRESS FIRM INC p 921
10201 Main St, Houston TX 77025
Tel (713) 923-1090 SIC 5712

MATTRESS GIANT CORP p 921
5815 Gulf Fwy, Houston TX 77023
Tel (713) 923-1090 SIC 5712

MATTRESS HOLDING CORP p 921
5815 Gulf Fwy, Houston TX 77023
Tel (713) 923-1090 SIC 5712

HILL COUNTRY FURNITURE PARTNERS LTD p 693
1431 Fm 1101, New Braunfels TX 78130
Tel (830) 515-1400 SIC 5712

LACKS VALLEY STORES LTD p 837
1300 San Patricia Dr, Pharr TX 78577
Tel (956) 702-3361 SIC 5712 5722

▲ CONNS INC p 358
4055 Technology Frst, The Woodlands TX 77381
Tel (936) 230-5899
SIC 5722 5731 5261 5712

■ RC WILLEY HOME FURNISHINGS p 1212
2301 S 300 W, Salt Lake City UT 84115
Tel (801) 461-3900 SIC 5712 5731 5722

▲ BASSETT FURNITURE INDUSTRIES INC p 159
3525 Fairystone Park Hwy, Bassett VA 24055
Tel (276) 629-6000
SIC 2511 2512 5021 5712

■ CORT BUSINESS SERVICES CORP p 373
15000 Conference Ste 440, Chantilly VA 20151
Tel (703) 968-8500 SIC 7359 5712 5932

ROWE FURNITURE CORP p 1253
2121 Gardner St, Elliston VA 24087
Tel (540) 444-7693 SIC 2512 5712

SCHEWEL FURNITURE CO INC p 1286
1031 Main St, Lynchburg VA 24504
Tel (434) 522-0200 SIC 5712 5722 5713

GRAND PIANO & FURNITURE CO p 630
4235 Electric Rd Ste 100, Roanoke VA 24018
Tel (540) 776-7000 SIC 5712 5021

HAYNES FURNITURE CO INC p 670
5324 Virginia Beach Blvd, Virginia Beach VA 23462
Tel (804) 276-1060 SIC 5713 5712

AMERICAN TV & APPLIANCE OF MADISON INC p 80
2404 W Beltline Hwy, Madison WI 53713
Tel (608) 515-5020 SIC 5731 5712 5722

FIRST SUPPLY LLC p 549
6800 Gisholt Dr, Monona WI 53713
Tel (608) 222-7799
SIC 5074 5078 5075 5712 5713

SIC 5713 Floor Covering Stores

E C BARTON & CO p 466
2929 Browns Ln, Jonesboro AR 72401
Tel (870) 932-6673 SIC 5031 5211 5713

■ COST PLUS INC p 373
1201 Marina Village Pkwy # 100, Alameda CA 94501
Tel (510) 893-7300
SIC 5712 5713 5719 5947 5499 5921

CARPETERIA FLOORING CENTERS LLC p 260
42212 10th St W Ste 2a, Lancaster CA 93534
Tel (661) 951-2200 SIC 5713

■ ETHAN ALLEN RETAIL INC p 511
Ethan Allen Dr, Danbury CT 06811
Tel (203) 743-8000
SIC 5712 5719 5713 5231 2273

■ DGPM INVESTMENTS INC p 435
300 E River Dr, East Hartford CT 06108
Tel (860) 528-9981
SIC 5044 5021 5713 1752

ROBB & STUCKY LIMITED LLLP p 1240
14550 Plantation Rd, Fort Myers FL 33912
Tel (239) 437-7997
SIC 5712 5713 5714 5231

WS BADCOCK CORP p 1628
205 Nw 2nd St, Mulberry FL 33860
Tel (863) 425-4921
SIC 5712 5713 5722 5731

ACOUSTI ENGINEERING CO OF FLORIDA p 18
4656 Sw 34th St, Orlando FL 32811
Tel (407) 425-3467 SIC 1742 5713

MASTER-TEC FLOORS INC p 918
3109 N T St, Pensacola FL 32505
Tel (850) 454-0008 SIC 1752 5713

▲ BMC STOCK HOLDINGS INC p 193
980 Hammond Dr Ste 500, Atlanta GA 30328
Tel (678) 222-1219
SIC 5211 2431 5031 5713 5251

▲ HAVERTY FURNITURE COMPANIES INC p 668
780 Johnson Ferry Rd, Atlanta GA 30342
Tel (404) 443-2900
SIC 5712 5722 5713 5021

US FLOORS INC p 1531
3580 Corporate Dr, Dalton GA 30721
Tel (706) 278-9491 SIC 5713

FLOOR AND DECOR OUTLETS OF AMERICA INC p 557
2233 Lake Park Dr Se # 400, Smyrna GA 30080
Tel (404) 471-1634 SIC 5713 1771

GREAT FLOORS LLC p 633
524 E Sherman Ave, Coeur D Alene ID 83814
Tel (208) 664-5405 SIC 1752 5713

EMPIRE TODAY LLC p 494
333 Northwest Ave, Northlake IL 60164
Tel (847) 583-5238 *SIC* 5713

STAR LUMBER & SUPPLY CO INC p 1378
325 S West St, Wichita KS 67213
Tel (316) 942-2221 *SIC* 5211 5713

TILE SHOP INC p 1453
14000 Carlson Pkwy, Plymouth MN 55441
Tel (763) 541-9720 *SIC* 5713 5023

■ **NEBRASKA FURNITURE MART INC** p 1023
700 S 72nd St, Omaha NE 68114
Tel (402) 397-6100
SIC 5712 5713 5722 5731 5734 5946

SOVEREIGN DISTRIBUTORS INC p 1353
2030 Springdale Rd, Cherry Hill NJ 08003
Tel (856) 489-4996 *SIC* 5713

CONGOLEUM CORP p 356
3500 Quakerbridge Rd, Trenton NJ 08619
Tel (609) 584-3000 *SIC* 3081 5713 8741

FURNITURE DISTRIBUTORS INC p 585
4524 South Blvd, Charlotte NC 28209
Tel (704) 523-3424 *SIC* 5712 5713 5722

■ **BMC EAST LLC** p 193
8020 Arco Corp Dr Ste 400, Raleigh NC 27617
Tel (919) 431-1000
SIC 5211 2431 5031 5713 5251

STOCK BUILDING SUPPLY HOLDINGS LLC p 1390
8020 Arco Corp Dr Ste 400, Raleigh NC 27617
Tel (919) 431-1000
SIC 5211 2431 5031 5713 5251

STANLEY STEEMER INTERNATIONAL INC p 1377
5800 Innovation Dr, Dublin OH 43016
Tel (614) 764-2007
SIC 7217 3635 6794 5713

DEGOL ORGANIZATION L P p 422
3229 Pleasant Valley Blvd, Altoona PA 16602
Tel (814) 941-7777
SIC 5031 5033 5211 5023 5713

WOLF FURNITURE ENTERPRISES INC p 1621
1620 N Tuckahoe St, Bellwood PA 16617
Tel (814) 742-4380
SIC 5712 5713 5722 5731 5719

FURNITURE MART USA INC p 585
140 E Hinks Ln, Sioux Falls SD 57104
Tel (605) 336-5000 *SIC* 7641 5713

■ **PIER 1 IMPORTS (US) INC** p 1147
100 Pier 1 Pl, Fort Worth TX 76102
Tel (817) 252-8000 *SIC* 5713 5719

FLOORS INC p 557
200 Bank St, Southlake TX 76092
Tel (817) 421-8787 *SIC* 5023 5713

SCHEWEL FURNITURE CO INC p 1286
1031 Main St, Lynchburg VA 24504
Tel (434) 522-0200 *SIC* 5712 5722 5713

HAYNES FURNITURE CO INC p 670
5324 Virginia Beach Blvd, Virginia Beach VA 23462
Tel (804) 276-1060 *SIC* 5713 5712

H J MARTIN & SON INC p 650
320 S Military Ave, Green Bay WI 54303
Tel (920) 494-3461
SIC 5713 1793 1522 1542 1742

FIRST SUPPLY LLC p 549
6800 Gisholt Dr, Monona WI 53713
Tel (608) 222-7799
SIC 5074 5078 5075 5712 5713

KUSSY INC p 832
1260 Huff Ln Ste B, Jackson WY 83001
Tel (307) 739-9465 *SIC* 1752 5713

SIC 5714 Drapery & Upholstery Stores

ANNAS LINENS INC p 92
3550 Hyland Ave, Costa Mesa CA 92626
Tel (714) 850-0504 *SIC* 5719 5714 5023

ROBB & STUCKY LIMITED LLLP p 1240
14550 Plantation Rd, Fort Myers FL 33912
Tel (239) 437-7997
SIC 5712 5713 5714 5231

FITZPATRICK COMPANIES INC p 553
705 Pleasant St, Lee MA 01238
Tel (413) 298-1610 *SIC* 5714 5021 5023

P KAUFMANN INC p 1102
3 Park Ave, New York NY 10016
Tel (212) 292-2200
SIC 5131 5714 5712 2262

SIC 5719 Home Furnishings Stores, Misc

MAYER ELECTRIC SUPPLY CO INC p 923
3405 4th Ave S, Birmingham AL 35222
Tel (205) 583-3500 *SIC* 5063 5719

■ **COST PLUS INC** p 373
1201 Marina Village Pkwy # 100, Alameda CA 94501
Tel (510) 893-7300
SIC 5712 5713 5719 5947 5499 5921

LAMPS PLUS INC p 841
20250 Plummer St, Chatsworth CA 91311
Tel (818) 886-5267 *SIC* 5719

ANNAS LINENS INC p 92
3550 Hyland Ave, Costa Mesa CA 92626
Tel (714) 850-0504 *SIC* 5719 5714 5023

Z GALLERIE LLC p 1640
1855 W 139th St, Gardena CA 90249
Tel (800) 358-8288 *SIC* 5719 5999

3 DAY BLINDS LLC p 2
167 Technology Dr, Irvine CA 92618
Tel (855) 569-0087 *SIC* 5719

■ **ONE KINGS LANE INC** p 1086
633 Folsom St Fl 2, San Francisco CA 94107
Tel (415) 489-9918 *SIC* 5719

■ **POTTERY BARN INC** p 1164
3250 Van Ness Ave, San Francisco CA 94109
Tel (415) 421-7900 *SIC* 5719

SHARPER IMAGE CORP p 1312
350 The Embarcadero Fl 6, San Francisco CA 94105
Tel (877) 714-7444
SIC 5731 5941 5999 5719 5945 5961

▲ **WILLIAMS-SONOMA INC** p 1612
3250 Van Ness Ave, San Francisco CA 94109
Tel (415) 421-7900
SIC 5719 5722 5261 5961

ASPEN ELECTRIC AND SUPPLY INC p 118
1890 Loggers Ln Unit C, Steamboat Springs CO 80487
Tel (970) 879-3905 *SIC* 5719 1731

■ **ETHAN ALLEN RETAIL INC** p 511
Ethan Allen Dr, Danbury CT 06811
Tel (203) 743-8000
SIC 5712 5719 5713 5231 2273

■ **DESIGN WITHIN REACH INC** p 432
711 Canal St Ste 3, Stamford CT 06902
Tel (203) 614-0600 *SIC* 5021 5719

HOLLANDER SLEEP PRODUCTS LLC p 700
6501 Congress Ave Ste 300, Boca Raton FL 33487
Tel (561) 997-6900 *SIC* 2392 2221 5719

BEALLS INC p 165
1806 13th Ave E, Bradenton FL 34208
Tel (941) 747-2355
SIC 5311 5719 5651 5947

BEALLS OUTLET STORES INC p 165
1806 38th Ave E, Bradenton FL 34208
Tel (941) 747-2355
SIC 5611 5621 5661 5719

BEALLS WEST GATE CORP p 165
1806 38th Ave E, Bradenton FL 34208
Tel (941) 744-4330 *SIC* 5651 5661 5719

DEL MAR DESIGNS INC p 423
1821 Holsonback Dr, Daytona Beach FL 32117
Tel (386) 767-1997 *SIC* 5719

OCEAN PROPERTIES LTD p 1073
1001 E Atl Ave Ste 202, Delray Beach FL 33483
Tel (603) 559-2100
SIC 7011 6552 1522 5719 5812 5813

TWIN-STAR INTERNATIONAL INC p 1495
1690 S Congress Ave # 210, Delray Beach FL 33445
Tel (561) 665-8084 *SIC* 5719

ATLANTA ORIENTAL FOOD WHOLESALE CO p 125
5600 Buford Hwy Ne, Atlanta GA 30340
Tel (770) 455-0770
SIC 5146 5421 5046 5719

EBHI HOLDINGS INC p 474
1000 Field Dr Ste 240, Lake Forest IL 60045
Tel (312) 251-3430
SIC 5611 5699 5941 5719 5947 5961

EUROMARKET DESIGNS INC p 512
1250 Techny Rd, Northbrook IL 60062
Tel (847) 272-2888
SIC 5719 5947 5712 5961 2599

WORLD KITCHEN LLC p 1625
9525 Bryn Mawr Ave # 300, Rosemont IL 60018
Tel (847) 233-8600
SIC 3229 3469 3365 3421 5719

SPRINGFIELD ELECTRIC SUPPLY CO p 1360
700 N 9th St, Springfield IL 62702
Tel (217) 788-2100 *SIC* 5063 5719

CENTRAL SUPPLY CO INC p 280
8900 E 30th St, Indianapolis IN 46219
Tel (317) 898-2411
SIC 5074 5063 5085 5719

■ **GREGG APPLIANCES INC** p 639
4151 E 96th St, Indianapolis IN 46240
Tel (317) 848-8710 *SIC* 5731 5722 5719

KITTLES HOME FURNISHINGS CENTER INC p 822
8600 Allisonville Rd, Indianapolis IN 46250
Tel (317) 849-5300 *SIC* 5712 5719

NEXT DAY BLINDS CORP p 1040
8251 Preston Ct Ste B, Jessup MD 20794
Tel (240) 568-8800
SIC 5023 2591 5719 1799

ORCHARD BRANDS CORP p 1093
138 Conant St Ste 3, Beverly MA 01915
Tel (978) 998-3800 *SIC* 5621 5611 5719

■ **HOMEGOODS INC** p 703
770 Cochituate Rd, Framingham MA 01701
Tel (508) 390-3199 *SIC* 5719

■ **MARSHALLS OF MA INC** p 911
770 Cochituate Rd, Framingham MA 01701
Tel (508) 390-1000 *SIC* 5651 5719

▲ **TJX COMPANIES INC** p 1457
770 Cochituate Rd Ste 1, Framingham MA 01701
Tel (508) 390-1000 *SIC* 5311 5651 5719

GRANITE CITY ELECTRIC SUPPLY CO INC p 631
19 Quincy Ave, Quincy MA 02169
Tel (617) 472-6500 *SIC* 5063 5719

W E AUBUCHON CO INC p 1568
95 Aubuchon Dr, Westminster MA 01473
Tel (978) 874-0521
SIC 5251 5211 5231 5719

ST LOUIS ELECTRIC SUPPLY INC p 1369
6801 Hoffman Ave, Saint Louis MO 63139
Tel (314) 645-9000 *SIC* 5063 5719

■ **HAYNEEDLE INC** p 670
9394 W Dodge Rd Ste 300, Omaha NE 68114
Tel (402) 715-3000
SIC 5943 5719 5945 5947

■ **INSTALLED BUILDING PRODUCTS LLC** p 747
62 King St, Auburn NH 03032
Tel (603) 645-1604
SIC 1781 5021 5719 2515

BURLINGTON COAT FACTORY HOLDINGS INC p 227
1830 N Route 130, Burlington NJ 08016
Tel (609) 387-7800
SIC 5651 5632 5719 5947 5712

■ **LUXURY LINENS OF NASHVILLE INC** p 887
1830 N Route 130, Burlington NJ 08016
Tel (609) 387-7800 *SIC* 5719

■ **RALPH LAUREN RETAIL INC** p 1206
9 Polito Ave Fl 5, Lyndhurst NJ 07071
Tel (888) 475-7674 *SIC* 5651 5661 5719

■ **MIKASA INC** p 968
1 Century Way, Secaucus NJ 07094
Tel (866) 645-2721 *SIC* 5023 5099 5719

▲ **BED BATH & BEYOND INC** p 167
650 Liberty Ave, Union NJ 07083
Tel (908) 688-0888 *SIC* 5719 5947 5999

▲ **LIFETIME BRANDS INC** p 864
1000 Stewart Ave, Garden City NY 11530
Tel (516) 683-6000 *SIC* 3421 5023 5719

■ **JANOVIC-PLAZA INC** p 777
3035 Thomson Ave, Long Island City NY 11101
Tel (718) 392-3999
SIC 5198 5231 5023 5719

ABC HOME FURNISHINGS INC p 10
888 Brdwy Fl 4, New York NY 10003
Tel (212) 473-3000 *SIC* 5712 5719 5023

■ **ICAHN ENTERPRISES HOLDINGS LP** p 726
767 5th Ave Fl 17, New York NY 10153
Tel (212) 702-4300
SIC 6512 5719 6211 5093

▲ **TIFFANY & CO** p 1453
200 5th Ave Bsmt 2, New York NY 10010
Tel (212) 755-8000
SIC 5944 5094 5719 5943 5999 5961

ONEIDA LTD p 1087
163 Kenwood Ave, Oneida NY 13421
Tel (315) 361-3000
SIC 5046 5719 5023 5094

ZWILLING JA HENCKELS LLC p 1645
270 Marble Ave, Pleasantville NY 10570
Tel (914) 749-3440 *SIC* 5023 5719

LIGHTING HOLDINGS INTERNATIONAL LLC p 865
4 Manhattanville Rd, Purchase NY 10577
Tel (845) 306-1850
SIC 3641 5719 5063 4225 3643 3229

FORTUNOFF FINE JEWELRY AND SILVERWARE INC p 570
70 Charles Lindbergh Blvd, Uniondale NY 11553
Tel (516) 222-7879 *SIC* 5944 5719

■ **KITCHEN COLLECTION LLC** p 822
71 E Water St, Chillicothe OH 45601
Tel (740) 773-9150 *SIC* 5719

▲ **NACCO INDUSTRIES INC** p 1006
5875 Landerbrook Dr # 300, Cleveland OH 44124
Tel (440) 229-5151
SIC 3634 1221 5719 3631

WASSERSTROM CO p 1580
477 S Front St, Columbus OH 43215
Tel (614) 737-8472
SIC 5087 3566 5021 5046 5112 5719

DOWN-LITE INTERNATIONAL INC p 453
8153 Duke Blvd, Mason OH 45040
Tel (513) 229-3696 *SIC* 2392 5719

PROVANTAGE LLC p 1185
7576 Freedom Ave Nw, North Canton OH 44720
Tel (330) 494-3781
SIC 5961 5719 5734 5045

DOLAN NORTHWEST LLC p 447
1919 Nw 19th Ave, Portland OR 97209
Tel (503) 221-1919 *SIC* 5063 5719

HANNA ANDERSSON LLC p 658
608 Ne 19th Ave, Portland OR 97232
Tel (503) 242-0920 *SIC* 5641 5621 5719

RODDA PAINT CO p 1246
6107 N Marine Dr Ste 3, Portland OR 97203
Tel (503) 521-4300
SIC 2851 5198 5023 5231 5719

WOLF FURNITURE ENTERPRISES INC p 1621
1620 N Tuckahoe St, Bellwood PA 16617
Tel (814) 742-4380
SIC 5712 5713 5722 5731 5719

LENOX HOLDINGS INC p 856
1414 Radcliffe St Fl 1, Bristol PA 19007
Tel (267) 525-7800
SIC 3229 3161 5719 5948

AMERICAN TEXTILE CO INC p 80
10 N Linden St, Duquesne PA 15110
Tel (412) 948-1020 *SIC* 5719 2392

FITZ AND FLOYD ENTERPRISES LLC p 553
3 Friends Ln Ste 300, Newtown PA 18940
Tel (800) 527-9550
SIC 5023 5199 5947 5719

■ **ANTHROPOLOGIE INC** p 94
5000 S Broad St, Philadelphia PA 19112
Tel (215) 454-4421 *SIC* 5719 5621

▲ **URBAN OUTFITTERS INC** p 1530
5000 S Broad St, Philadelphia PA 19112
Tel (215) 454-5500
SIC 5621 5611 5632 5661 5719 5137

■ **PFALTZGRAFF FACTORY STORES INC** p 1140
140 E Market St, York PA 17401
Tel (717) 848-5500 *SIC* 3269 5719

VVP HOLDINGS LLC p 1567
965 Ridge Lake Blvd # 300, Memphis TN 38120
Tel (901) 767-7111
SIC 5039 5013 1793 3231 3444 5719

TEAM TECHNOLOGIES INC p 1430
5949 Commerce Blvd, Morristown TN 37814
Tel (423) 587-2199
SIC 2844 5122 5719 3991

▲ **CONTAINER STORE GROUP INC** p 362
500 Freeport Pkwy, Coppell TX 75019
Tel (972) 538-6000 *SIC* 5719

■ **CONTAINER STORE INC** p 362
500 Freeport Pkwy Ste 100, Coppell TX 75019
Tel (972) 538-6000 *SIC* 5719

■ **HOUSEWARES HOLDING CO INC** p 711
14785 Preston Rd Ste 1100, Dallas TX 75254
Tel (440) 449-9600 *SIC* 3634 5719

▲ **TUESDAY MORNING CORP** p 1490
6250 Lbj Fwy, Dallas TX 75240
Tel (972) 387-3562
SIC 5947 5719 5944 5948 5945 5712

■ **TUESDAY MORNING INC** p 1490
6250 Lbj Fwy, Dallas TX 75240
Tel (972) 387-3562 *SIC* 5311 2392 5719

■ **PIER 1 IMPORTS (US) INC** p 1147
100 Pier 1 Pl, Fort Worth TX 76102
Tel (817) 252-8000 *SIC* 5713 5719

▲ **PIER 1 IMPORTS INC** p 1147
100 Pier 1 Pl, Fort Worth TX 76102
Tel (817) 252-8000 *SIC* 5719 6794 5712

■ **PIER 1 LICENSING INC** p 1147
100 Pier 1 Pl, Fort Worth TX 76102
Tel (817) 878-8000
SIC 5719 5712 5621 5632

▲ **AT HOME GROUP INC** p 123
1600 E Plano Pkwy, Plano TX 75074
Tel (972) 265-6227 *SIC* 5719 5945

■ **AT HOME STORES LLC** p 123
1600 E Plano Pkwy, Plano TX 75074
Tel (972) 265-6227
SIC 5719 5992 5999 5947 5945

GARDEN RIDGE CORP p 591
1600 E Plano Pkwy, Plano TX 75074
Tel (972) 265-6227 *SIC* 5719 5999 5945

GARDEN RIDGE HOLDINGS INC p 591
1600 E Plano Pkwy, Plano TX 75074
Tel (832) 391-7201
SIC 5719 5945 5992 5947 5999

DEALERS ELECTRICAL SUPPLY CO p 420
2320 Columbus Ave, Waco TX 76701
Tel (254) 756-7251 *SIC* 5063 5719

CORNELL TRADING INC p 370
131 Battery St, Burlington VT 05401
Tel (802) 879-1271
SIC 5023 5137 5719 5621

DOMINION ELECTRIC SUPPLY CO INC p 449
5053 Lee Hwy, Arlington VA 22207
Tel (703) 532-0741 *SIC* 5063 5719

AMARGOSA INC p 64
10401 Ne 8th St Ste 500, Bellevue WA 98004
Tel (425) 755-6100
SIC 5611 5699 5941 5719 5947 5961

SUR LA TABLE INC p 1408
6100 4th Ave S Ste 500, Seattle WA 98108
Tel (206) 613-6000 *SIC* 5719

HOMER LAUGHLIN CHINA CO p 704
672 Fiesta Dr, Newell WV 26050
Tel (304) 387-1300 *SIC* 3262 5719

SIC 5722 Household Appliance Stores

■ **MOBILE GAS SERVICE CORP** p 980
2828 Dauphin St, Mobile AL 36606
Tel (251) 476-2720 *SIC* 4924 5722

DEARDENS p 420
700 S Main St, Los Angeles CA 90014
Tel (213) 362-9600
SIC 5712 5722 5731 5944

▲ **WILLIAMS-SONOMA INC** p 1612
3250 Van Ness Ave, San Francisco CA 94109
Tel (415) 421-7900
SIC 5719 5722 5261 5961

■ **PETROLEUM HEAT AND POWER CO INC** p 1139
9 W Broad St Ste 3, Stamford CT 06902
Tel (800) 645-4328 *SIC* 5983 5172 5722

INTERBOND HOLDING CORP p 751
3200 Sw 42nd St, Fort Lauderdale FL 33312
Tel (954) 797-4000 *SIC* 7629 3699 5722

INTERBOND CORP OF AMERICA p 751
3200 Sw 42nd St, Hollywood FL 33020
Tel (954) 797-4000 *SIC* 5731 5722

WS BADCOCK CORP p 1628
205 Nw 2nd St, Mulberry FL 33860
Tel (863) 425-4921
SIC 5712 5713 5722 5731

▲ **AARONS INC** p 8
400 Galleria Pkwy Se # 300, Atlanta GA 30339
Tel (404) 231-0011
SIC 7359 5712 5731 5722 5932 6794

▲ **HAVERTY FURNITURE COMPANIES INC** p 668
780 Johnson Ferry Rd, Atlanta GA 30342
Tel (404) 443-2900
SIC 5712 5722 5713 5021

ABT ELECTRONICS INC p 13
1200 Milwaukee Ave, Glenview IL 60025
Tel (847) 967-8830 *SIC* 5722 5731

▲ **SEARS HOMETOWN AND OUTLET STORES INC** p 1297
5500 Trillium Blvd # 501, Hoffman Estates IL 60192
Tel (847) 286-2500 *SIC* 5251 5261 5722

■ **GREGG APPLIANCES INC** p 639
4151 E 96th St, Indianapolis IN 46240
Tel (317) 848-8710 *SIC* 5731 5722 5719

▲ **HHGREGG INC** p 689
4151 E 96th St, Indianapolis IN 46240
Tel (317) 848-8710 *SIC* 5731 5722 5712

SOUTHERN INDIANA WASTE SYSTEMS LLC p 1349
6108 Sable Mill Ct, Jeffersonville IN 47130
Tel (502) 935-1130 *SIC* 5722

■ **BGE HOME PRODUCTS AND SERVICES INC** p 180
1409 Tangier Dr Ste A, Baltimore MD 21220
Tel (410) 918-5600 *SIC* 5722

ABC APPLIANCE INC p 10
1 W Silverdome Indus Park, Pontiac MI 48342
Tel (248) 335-4222
SIC 5722 5731 5999 5065 5064 5063

▲ **APPLIANCE RECYCLING CENTERS OF AMERICA INC** p 99
175 Jackson Ave N Ste 102, Hopkins MN 55343
Tel (952) 930-9000 *SIC* 5722 4953

▲ **BEST BUY CO INC** p 177
7601 Penn Ave S, Richfield MN 55423
Tel (612) 291-1000
SIC 5731 5734 5735 5712 5722

BLOSSMAN COMPANIES INC p 190
809 Washington Ave, Ocean Springs MS 39564
Tel (228) 875-2261 *SIC* 5984 5722

AMERICAN RESIDENTIAL SERVICES OF INDIANA INC p 78
10403 Baur Blvd Ste E, Saint Louis MO 63132
Tel (314) 812-6000
SIC 1711 1731 1799 5722

SWAN SURFACES LLC p 1411
515 Olive St Ste 900, Saint Louis MO 63101
Tel (314) 231-8148 SIC 2541 5722 3431

■ **NEBRASKA FURNITURE MART INC** p 1023
700 S 72nd St, Omaha NE 68114
Tel (402) 397-6100
SIC 5712 5713 5722 5731 5734 5946

1 STOP ELECTRONICS CENTER INC p 1
1100 Coney Island Ave, Brooklyn NY 11230
Tel (718) 249-1211 SIC 5722 5021

MARTIN ATTEA p 912
1509 Clinton St, Buffalo NY 14206
Tel (716) 822-0378 SIC 5064 5722

A J RICHARD & SONS INC p 5
150 Price Pkwy, Farmingdale NY 11735
Tel (631) 843-4300 SIC 5722 5731

COLORADO PRIME OF PENNSYLVANIA INC p 339
1 Michael Ave, Farmingdale NY 11735
Tel (631) 694-1111 SIC 5421 5722

P C RICHARD & SON LONG ISLAND CORP p 1102
150 Price Pkwy, Farmingdale NY 11735
Tel (631) 843-4300 SIC 5722 5731 5064

PC RICHARD & SON INC p 1123
150 Price Pkwy, Farmingdale NY 11735
Tel (631) 843-4300
SIC 5722 5064 7629 7623

FACTORYOUTLETSTORE LLC p 524
1407 Broadway Rm 700, New York NY 10018
Tel (646) 367-6141 SIC 5722 5064

FURNITURE DISTRIBUTORS INC p 585
4524 South Blvd, Charlotte NC 28209
Tel (704) 523-3424 SIC 5712 5713 5722

▲ **LOWES COMPANIES INC** p 881
1000 Lowes Blvd, Mooresville NC 28117
Tel (704) 758-1000
SIC 5211 5031 5722 5064

■ **LOWES HOME CENTERS LLC** p 881
1605 Curtis Bridge Rd, Wilkesboro NC 28697
Tel (336) 658-4000
SIC 5211 5031 5722 5064

UNIVERSAL COMMERCE LLC p 1516
3939 Everhard Rd Nw, Canton OH 44709
Tel (800) 504-8105 SIC 5722

MORRIS FURNITURE CO INC p 990
2377 Commerce Center Blvd, Fairborn OH 45324
Tel (937) 874-7100 SIC 5731 5722 5712

HOUSE OF FABRICS INC p 711
5555 Darrow Rd, Hudson OH 44236
Tel (330) 656-2600 SIC 5949 5945 5722

■ **GAS CONNECTION LLC** p 593
9801 Se 82nd Ave, Portland OR 97086
Tel (503) 771-1750 SIC 5984 5722

WOLF FURNITURE ENTERPRISES INC p 1621
1620 N Tuckahoe St, Bellwood PA 16617
Tel (814) 742-4380
SIC 5712 5713 5722 5731 5719

■ **AMERIGAS INC** p 82
460 N Gulph Rd Ste 100, King Of Prussia PA 19406
Tel (610) 337-7000
SIC 5984 5172 5722 2911 2813

PR RETAIL STORES INC p 1167
Edif Kodak Ave Campo, San Juan PR 00924
Tel (787) 641-8200
SIC 5311 5712 5722 5331

BLATCHFORDS INC p 189
207 S Chicago St, Hot Springs SD 57747
Tel (605) 745-5173
SIC 5251 5712 5531 5947 5722

APPLIANCE PARTS DEPOT LP p 99
4754 Almond Ave, Dallas TX 75247
Tel (214) 631-6331 SIC 5064 5722

FAMSA INC p 527
2727 Lyndon B Johnson Fwy, Dallas TX 75234
Tel (972) 993-5800 SIC 5722 5712

VISTRA ENERGY CORP p 1562
1601 Bryan St, Dallas TX 75201
Tel (214) 812-4600 SIC 5722

LACKS VALLEY STORES LTD p 837
1300 San Patricia Dr, Pharr TX 78577
Tel (956) 702-3361 SIC 5712 5722

■ **RENT-A-CENTER FRANCHISING INTERNATIONAL INC** p 1224
5501 Headquarters Dr, Plano TX 75024
Tel (972) 403-4900 SIC 5722 5531

FRIEDRICH AIR CONDITIONING CO LTD p 579
10001 Reunion Pl Ste 500, San Antonio TX 78216
Tel (210) 546-0500 SIC 3585 5722

■ **CONN APPLIANCES INC** p 356
4055 Technology Frst, The Woodlands TX 77381
Tel (409) 832-1696
SIC 5722 5731 7629 6141 7359

▲ **CONNS INC** p 358
4055 Technology Frst, The Woodlands TX 77381
Tel (936) 230-5899
SIC 5722 5731 5261 5712

■ **RC WILLEY HOME FURNISHINGS** p 1212
2301 S 300 W, Salt Lake City UT 84115
Tel (801) 461-3900 SIC 5712 5731 5722

■ **HB PS HOLDING CO INC** p 671
4421 Waterfront Dr, Glen Allen VA 23060
Tel (804) 273-9777 SIC 5722

SCHEWEL FURNITURE CO INC p 1286
1031 Main St, Lynchburg VA 24504
Tel (434) 522-0200 SIC 5712 5722 5713

AMERICAN TV & APPLIANCE OF MADISON INC p 80
2404 W Beltline Hwy, Madison WI 53713
Tel (608) 515-5020 SIC 5731 5712 5722

SIC 5731 Radio, TV & Consumer Electronics Stores

MFG GALILEO COMPOSITES p 958
18361 Galileo Dr, Opp AL 36467
Tel (334) 493-0014 SIC 5731 3089

LINKUS ENTERPRISES LLC p 869
18631 Lloyd Ln, Anderson CA 96007
Tel (530) 229-9197 SIC 1623 5731 4813

▲ **PCM INC** p 1124
1940 E Mariposa Ave, El Segundo CA 90245
Tel (310) 354-5600
SIC 5734 5961 5731 5045

DEARDENS p 420
700 S Main St, Los Angeles CA 90014
Tel (213) 362-9600
SIC 5712 5722 5731 5944

SHARPER IMAGE CORP p 1312
350 The Embarcadero Fl 6, San Francisco CA 94105
Tel (877) 714-7444
SIC 5731 5941 5999 5719 5945 5961

FRYS ELECTRONICS INC p 582
600 E Brokaw Rd, San Jose CA 95112
Tel (408) 350-1484 SIC 5999 5734 5731

RENESAS ELECTRONICS AMERICA INC p 1223
2801 Scott Blvd, Santa Clara CA 95050
Tel (408) 588-6000
SIC 5065 8731 5731 5045 8711

ELECTRONICS ROW LLC p 486
10601 W I 70 Frntage Rd N, Wheat Ridge CO 80033
Tel (720) 728-5420 SIC 5731

HB COMMUNICATIONS INC p 671
60 Dodge Ave, North Haven CT 06473
Tel (203) 747-7174 SIC 5064 5065 5731

INTERBOND CORP OF AMERICA p 751
3200 Sw 42nd St, Hollywood FL 33020
Tel (954) 797-4000 SIC 5731 5722

WS BADCOCK CORP p 1628
205 Nw 2nd St, Mulberry FL 33860
Tel (863) 425-4921
SIC 5712 5713 5722 5731

▲ **AARONS INC** p 8
400 Galleria Pkwy Se # 300, Atlanta GA 30339
Tel (404) 231-0011
SIC 7359 5712 5731 5722 5932 6794

▲ **PC-TEL INC** p 1123
471 Brighton Ct, Bloomingdale IL 60108
Tel (630) 372-6800 SIC 5731 4812 7372

ABT ELECTRONICS INC p 13
1200 Milwaukee Ave, Glenview IL 60025
Tel (847) 967-8830 SIC 5722 5731

CELLULAR CONNECTION LLC p 274
525 Congressional Blvd, Carmel IN 46032
Tel (765) 651-2001
SIC 5065 1731 5999 5731

■ **GREGG APPLIANCES INC** p 639
4151 E 96th St, Indianapolis IN 46240
Tel (317) 848-8710 SIC 5731 5722 5719

▲ **HHGREGG INC** p 689
4151 E 96th St, Indianapolis IN 46240
Tel (317) 848-8710 SIC 5731 5722 5712

DSI DISTRIBUTING INC p 457
3601 109th St, Urbandale IA 50322
Tel (515) 276-9181 SIC 5063 5731

DIRECTECH HOLDING CO INC p 441
33 W 2nd St Ste 504, Maysville KY 41056
Tel (606) 564-0007 SIC 5731

EATELCORP LLC p 473
913 S Burnside Ave, Gonzales LA 70737
Tel (225) 621-4300 SIC 5731

BOSE CORP p 202
100 The Mountain, Framingham MA 01701
Tel (508) 879-7330 SIC 3651 5731

ABC APPLIANCE INC p 10
1 W Silverdome Indus Park, Pontiac MI 48342
Tel (248) 335-4222
SIC 5722 5731 5999 5065 5064 5063

VALEO RADAR SYSTEMS INC p 1539
150 Stephenson Hwy, Troy MI 48083
Tel (248) 619-8300 SIC 5731 3714

BERGQUIST CO p 174
18930 W 78th St, Chanhassen MN 55317
Tel (952) 835-2322
SIC 5731 5063 3645 3646 2822

▲ **BEST BUY CO INC** p 177
7601 Penn Ave S, Richfield MN 55423
Tel (612) 291-1000
SIC 5731 5734 5735 5712 5722

ORSCHELN FARM AND HOME LLC p 1096
1800 Overcenter Dr, Moberly MO 65270
Tel (800) 577-2580
SIC 5251 5999 5945 5731

■ **NEBRASKA FURNITURE MART INC** p 1023
700 S 72nd St, Omaha NE 68114
Tel (402) 397-6100
SIC 5712 5713 5722 5731 5734 5946

BEACH TRADING CO INC p 164
80 Carter Dr, Edison NJ 08817
Tel (800) 572-3224 SIC 3861 5731

DGL GROUP LTD p 435
195 Raritan Center Pkwy, Edison NJ 08837
Tel (718) 499-1000 SIC 5731 5065

▲ **TRANS WORLD ENTERTAINMENT CORP** p 1470
38 Corporate Cir, Albany NY 12203
Tel (518) 452-1242
SIC 5735 5731 5734 7841 5961

A J RICHARD & SONS INC p 5
150 Price Pkwy, Farmingdale NY 11735
Tel (631) 843-4300 SIC 5722 5731

P C RICHARD & SON LONG ISLAND CORP p 1102
150 Price Pkwy, Farmingdale NY 11735
Tel (631) 843-4300 SIC 5722 5731 5064

■ **VOXX ELECTRONICS CORP** p 1566
150 Marcus Blvd, Hauppauge NY 11788
Tel (631) 231-7750 SIC 5065 5731

SAM ASH MUSIC CORP p 1273
278 Duffy Ave Unit A, Hicksville NY 11801
Tel (516) 932-6400
SIC 5736 5731 5734 5961 7359 8741

B & H FOTO & ELECTRONICS CORP p 141
420 9th Ave, New York NY 10001
Tel (212) 239-7500 SIC 5946 5731 5961

PASS & SEYMOUR INC p 1119
50 Boyd Ave, Syracuse NY 13209
Tel (315) 468-6211 SIC 3643 5731

MORRIS FURNITURE CO INC p 990
2377 Commerce Center Blvd, Fairborn OH 45324
Tel (937) 874-7100 SIC 5731 5722 5712

AUDIO-TECHNICA US INC p 131
1221 Commerce Dr, Stow OH 44224
Tel (330) 686-2600 SIC 5065 5731

■ **FRED MEYER INC** p 576
3800 Se 22nd Ave, Portland OR 97202
Tel (503) 232-8844
SIC 5411 5311 5912 5211 5731 5944

■ **FRED MEYER STORES INC** p 576
3800 Se 22nd Ave, Portland OR 97202
Tel (503) 232-8844
SIC 5211 5411 5912 5731 5944

WOLF FURNITURE ENTERPRISES INC p 1621
1620 N Tuckahoe St, Bellwood PA 16617
Tel (814) 742-4380
SIC 5712 5713 5722 5731 5719

RS LEGACY CORP p 1255
300 Radioshack Cir, Fort Worth TX 76102
Tel (817) 415-3011 SIC 5731 5999 5734

■ **CONN APPLIANCES INC** p 356
4055 Technology Frst, The Woodlands TX 77381
Tel (409) 832-1696
SIC 5722 5731 7629 6141 7359

▲ **CONNS INC** p 358
4055 Technology Frst, The Woodlands TX 77381
Tel (936) 230-5899
SIC 5722 5731 5261 5712

▲ **ZAGG INC** p 1641
910 W Legacy Center Way, Midvale UT 84047
Tel (801) 263-0699 SIC 5731 6794

■ **RC WILLEY HOME FURNISHINGS** p 1212
2301 S 300 W, Salt Lake City UT 84115
Tel (801) 461-3900 SIC 5712 5731 5722

■ **AMAZON FULFILLMENT SERVICES INC** p 64
410 Terry Ave N, Seattle WA 98109
Tel (206) 266-1000
SIC 5735 5961 5731 5945

■ **AMAZON.COMDEDC LLC** p 65
410 Terry Ave N, Seattle WA 98109
Tel (206) 266-1000
SIC 5961 5735 5731 5945

CAR TOYS INC p 252
400 Fairview Ave N # 900, Seattle WA 98109
Tel (206) 443-2726 SIC 5731 5999

AMERICAN TV & APPLIANCE OF MADISON INC p 80
2404 W Beltline Hwy, Madison WI 53713
Tel (608) 515-5020 SIC 5731 5712 5722

SIC 5734 Computer & Software Stores

IT1 SOURCE LLC p 767
1860 W University Dr # 100, Tempe AZ 85281
Tel (480) 777-5995 SIC 5734

GOLDEN STAR TECHNOLOGY INC p 621
12881 166th St Ste 100, Cerritos CA 90703
Tel (562) 345-8700 SIC 5734 7378 5045

NEWEGG INC p 1037
17560 Rowland St, City Of Industry CA 91748
Tel (626) 271-9700 SIC 5734

▲ **PCM INC** p 1124
1940 E Mariposa Ave, El Segundo CA 90245
Tel (310) 354-5600
SIC 5734 5961 5731 5045

■ **PCM SALES INC** p 1124
1940 E Mariposa Ave, El Segundo CA 90245
Tel (310) 354-5600 SIC 5734

▲ **SYNNEX CORP** p 1415
44201 Nobel Dr, Fremont CA 94538
Tel (510) 656-3333 SIC 5734

■ **BLIZZARD ENTERTAINMENT INC** p 189
16215 Alton Pkwy, Irvine CA 92618
Tel (949) 955-1380 SIC 7372 5734 7819

CREATIVE LABS INC p 390
1901 Mccarthy Blvd, Milpitas CA 95035
Tel (408) 428-6600 SIC 5045 5734 3577

CLOUDERA INC p 327
1001 Page Mill Rd Bldg 3, Palo Alto CA 94304
Tel (650) 644-3900 SIC 7371 5734 8331

IDEALAB HOLDINGS LLC p 729
130 W Union St, Pasadena CA 91103
Tel (626) 585-6900 SIC 6799 5045 5734

PC SPECIALISTS INC p 1123
10240 Flanders Ct, San Diego CA 92121
Tel (858) 566-1900 SIC 5045 5734 7371

CALYPSO TECHNOLOGY INC p 243
595 Market St Ste 1800, San Francisco CA 94105
Tel (415) 817-2400 SIC 5734

FRYS ELECTRONICS INC p 582
600 E Brokaw Rd, San Jose CA 95112
Tel (408) 350-1484 SIC 5999 5734 5731

TRIGEM ENTERPRISES INC p 1480
2075 Zanker Rd, San Jose CA 95131
Tel (408) 943-9193 SIC 5734

HITACHI DATA SYSTEMS CORP p 696
2845 Lafayette St, Santa Clara CA 95050
Tel (408) 970-1000
SIC 5045 7378 7379 5734 4225 3571

■ **4 SURE.COM INC** p 3
55 Corporate Dr Ste 5, Trumbull CT 06611
Tel (203) 615-7000 SIC 5045 5734

CHAMPION SOLUTIONS GROUP INC p 287
791 Park Of Commerce Blvd, Boca Raton FL 33487
Tel (800) 771-7000 SIC 5045 5734

▲ **OFFICE DEPOT INC** p 1075
6600 N Military Trl, Boca Raton FL 33496
Tel (561) 438-4800
SIC 5943 5044 5734 5045

■ **LAWYERS TITLE INSURANCE CORP** p 848
601 Riverside Ave, Jacksonville FL 32204
Tel (888) 866-3684 SIC 6361 7372 5734

■ **TIGERDIRECT INC** p 1453
7795 W Flagler St Ste 35, Miami FL 33144
Tel (305) 415-2200 SIC 5961 5734

■ **RADIANT SYSTEMS INC** p 1204
3925 Brookside Pkwy, Alpharetta GA 30022
Tel (877) 794-7237 SIC 5734 7373

UNIVERSITY OF GEORGIA p 1521
415 Boyds Graduate Studie, Athens GA 30602
Tel (706) 542-2911 SIC 5734

GREENWAY HEALTH LLC p 638
100 Greenway Blvd, Carrollton GA 30117
Tel (877) 932-6301 SIC 5734

ALLIED BUSINESS SYSTEMS LLC p 56
4848 Mercer University Dr, Macon GA 31210
Tel (800) 727-7534 SIC 7371 5734

CLICK SALES INC p 326
917 S Lusk St Ste 200, Boise ID 83706
Tel (208) 472-9400 SIC 5734

MNJ TECHNOLOGIES DIRECT INC p 980
1025 Busch Pkwy, Buffalo Grove IL 60089
Tel (847) 634-0700 SIC 5734 5045 7373

▲ **CDW CORP** p 271
75 Tri State Intl, Lincolnshire IL 60069
Tel (847) 465-6000
SIC 5963 5045 5734 5961

■ **SYX DISTRIBUTION INC** p 1419
175 Ambassador Dr, Naperville IL 60540
Tel (516) 608-7000 SIC 5734

■ **CDW GOVERNMENT LLC** p 271
230 N Milwaukee Ave, Vernon Hills IL 60061
Tel (847) 465-6000 SIC 5961 5065 5734

CDW HOLDINGS LLC p 271
3 First National Pl, Vernon Hills IL 60061
Tel (847) 465-6000
SIC 5963 5045 5734 5961

SAYERS TECHNOLOGY LLC p 1285
825 Corporate Woods Pkwy, Vernon Hills IL 60061
Tel (847) 391-4802 SIC 5734 7378

JD BYRIDER SYSTEMS LLC p 780
12802 Hmlton Crssing Blvd, Carmel IN 46032
Tel (317) 249-3000
SIC 6794 5734 7538 7515 5521

BELL INDUSTRIES INC p 170
4400 W 96th St, Indianapolis IN 46268
Tel (866) 782-2355 SIC 7379 5734

INKCYCLE INC p 743
11100 W 82nd St, Lenexa KS 66214
Tel (913) 894-8387
SIC 3955 7699 7378 5045 8249 5734

RURAL TELEPHONE SERVICE CO INC p 1258
145 N Main St, Lenora KS 67645
Tel (785) 567-4281 SIC 4813 5734 5045

RAND WORLDWIDE SUBSIDIARY INC p 1207
11201 Difeld Blvd Ste 112, Owings Mills MD 21117
Tel (877) 726-3243
SIC 7379 7373 5045 5734

ROUNDTOWER NORTHEAST LLC p 1253
200 Quannapowitt Pkwy, Wakefield MA 01880
Tel (781) 621-8600 SIC 5734

LOWRY HOLDING CO INC p 882
9420 Maltby Rd, Brighton MI 48116
Tel (810) 229-7200
SIC 5045 2672 8742 7373 5044 5734

VISIONIT SUPPLIES AND SERVICES INC p 1561
3031 W Grand Blvd Ste 600, Detroit MI 48202
Tel (313) 664-5650 SIC 3577 3955 5734

OPEN SYSTEMS INTERNATIONAL INC p 1089
4101 Arrowhead Dr, Medina MN 55340
Tel (763) 551-0559 SIC 7371 5734

▲ **BEST BUY CO INC** p 177
7601 Penn Ave S, Richfield MN 55423
Tel (612) 291-1000
SIC 5731 5734 5735 5712 5722

■ **NEBRASKA FURNITURE MART INC** p 1023
700 S 72nd St, Omaha NE 68114
Tel (402) 397-6100
SIC 5712 5713 5722 5731 5734 5946

TOYS "R" US INC p 1467
1 Geoffrey Way, Wayne NJ 07470
Tel (973) 617-3500
SIC 5945 5734 5999 5735 5641 5941

▲ **TRANS WORLD ENTERTAINMENT CORP** p 1470
38 Corporate Cir, Albany NY 12203
Tel (518) 452-1242
SIC 5735 5731 5734 7841 5961

SAM ASH MUSIC CORP p 1273
278 Duffy Ave Unit A, Hicksville NY 11801
Tel (516) 932-6400
SIC 5736 5731 5734 5961 7359 8741

GENISYS SOFTWARE LTD p 604
1345 Ave Of The Americas, New York NY 10105
Tel (732) 635-7132 SIC 7371 7372 5734

SCHOOL OF VISUAL ARTS INC p 1290
209 E 23rd St Frnt 1, New York NY 10010
Tel (212) 592-2000 SIC 8221 5734 5999

SONY BROADBAND ENTERTAINMENT CORP p 1340
550 Madison Ave Fl 6, New York NY 10022
Tel (212) 833-6800
SIC 3652 7812 5734 7832 5735

TEKSERVE CORP p 1433
119 W 23rd St Frnt 1, New York NY 10011
Tel (212) 929-3645 SIC 7378 5734

■ **CINCINNATI BELL TECHNOLOGY SOLUTIONS INC** p 307
4600 Montgomery Rd # 400, Cincinnati OH 45212
Tel (513) 841-2287 SIC 7379 5734

STRATACACHE INC p 1392
2 Emmet St Ste 200, Dayton OH 45405
Tel (937) 224-0485 SIC 5734 4822

MICRO ELECTRONICS INC p 961
4119 Leap Rd, Hilliard OH 43026
Tel (614) 850-3000 SIC 5045 5734

PROVANTAGE LLC p 1185
7576 Freedom Ave Nw, North Canton OH 44720
Tel (330) 494-3781
SIC 5961 5719 5734 5045

■ **EPLUS TECHNOLOGY OF PENNSYLVANIA INC** p 505
130 Futura Dr, Pottstown PA 19464
Tel (610) 495-7800 SIC 5734 7378 8243

■ **SUNGARD BUSINESS SYSTEMS LLC** p 1402
680 E Swedesford Rd, Wayne PA 19087
Tel (484) 582-2000 SIC 7374 5734

■ EB INVESTMENT CORP p 474
931 S Matlack St, West Chester PA 19382
Tel (610) 430-8100 SIC 5734 5945

▲ AUTOZONE INC p 135
123 S Front St, Memphis TN 38103
Tel (901) 495-6500 SIC 5531 5734

■ WINCOR NIXDORF INC p 1615
12345 N Lamar Blvd # 200, Austin TX 78753
Tel (512) 676-5000 SIC 7379 5734 5251

■ COMPUSA INC p 352
14951 Dallas Pkwy, Dallas TX 75254
Tel (972) 982-4000 SIC 5734 5045 5961

LANYON SOLUTIONS INC p 844
717 N Harwood St Ste 2200, Dallas TX 75201
Tel (817) 226-5656 SIC 5734

RS LEGACY CORP p 1255
300 Radioshack Cir, Fort Worth TX 76102
Tel (817) 415-3011 SIC 5731 5999 5734

■ ELECTRONICS BOUTIQUE AMERICA INC p 486
625 Westport Pkwy, Grapevine TX 76051
Tel (817) 424-2000 SIC 5734

■ ELECTRONICS BOUTIQUE HOLDINGS CORP p 486
625 Westport Pkwy, Grapevine TX 76051
Tel (817) 424-2000 SIC 5734

■ ELECTRONICS BOUTIQUE OF AMERICA INC p 486
625 Westport Pkwy, Grapevine TX 76051
Tel (817) 424-2000 SIC 5734 5945

▲ GAMESTOP CORP p 590
625 Westport Pkwy, Grapevine TX 76051
Tel (817) 424-2000
SIC 5945 5734 5932 2721

VERIFINC CORP p 1549
12000 Westheimer Rd # 380, Houston TX 77077
Tel (832) 858-5548 SIC 7371 5734 5122

DET NORSKE VERITAS HOLDING (USA) INC p 433
1400 Ravello Rd, Katy TX 77449
Tel (281) 396-1000
SIC 8711 7389 5734 8741

▲ DELL TECHNOLOGIES INC p 425
1 Dell Way, Round Rock TX 78682
Tel (800) 289-3355 SIC 8731 5734

FC ORGANIZATIONAL PRODUCTS LLC p 532
2250 W Parkway Blvd, Salt Lake City UT 84119
Tel (801) 817-1776 SIC 5942 5734

■ EPLUS GROUP INC p 505
13595 Dulles Tech Dr, Herndon VA 20171
Tel (703) 984-8400 SIC 7377 5734 5045

■ EPLUS TECHNOLOGY INC p 505
13595 Dulles Tech Dr, Herndon VA 20171
Tel (703) 984-8400 SIC 5045 5734

ZONES INC p 1644
1102 15th St Sw Ste 102, Auburn WA 98001
Tel (253) 205-3000 SIC 7373 5734

NINTEX USA LLC p 1044
10900 Ne 8th St Ste 230, Bellevue WA 98004
Tel (425) 324-2455 SIC 5734

■ BIG FISH GAMES INC p 181
333 Elliott Ave W Ste 200, Seattle WA 98119
Tel (206) 213-5753 SIC 5734

PARAGON DEVELOPMENT SYSTEMS INC p 1113
13400 Bishops Ln Ste 190, Brookfield WI 53005
Tel (262) 569-5300 SIC 5734 7379

SIC 5735 Record & Prerecorded Tape Stores

G A M INC p 586
900 W Main St, Dothan AL 36301
Tel (334) 677-2108 SIC 7841 5735

■ BLOCKBUSTER LLC p 189
9601 S Meridian Blvd, Englewood CO 80112
Tel (702) 262-0703 SIC 7841 5735

FAMILY CHRISTIAN STORES LLC p 526
5300 Patterson Ave Se, Grand Rapids MI 49530
Tel (616) 554-8700
SIC 5942 5735 5947 5699 8741

▲ BEST BUY CO INC p 177
7601 Penn Ave S, Richfield MN 55423
Tel (612) 291-1000
SIC 5731 5734 5735 5712 5722

INSERRA SUPERMARKETS INC p 745
20 Ridge Rd Ste 1, Mahwah NJ 07430
Tel (201) 529-5900 SIC 5411 5735

TOYS "R" US INC p 1467
1 Geoffrey Way, Wayne NJ 07470
Tel (973) 617-3500
SIC 5945 5734 5999 5735 5641 5941

■ RECORD TOWN INC p 1215
38 Corporate Cir, Albany NY 12203
Tel (518) 452-1242 SIC 5735

▲ TRANS WORLD ENTERTAINMENT CORP p 1470
38 Corporate Cir, Albany NY 12203
Tel (518) 452-1242
SIC 5735 5731 5734 7841 5961

■ BARNES & NOBLE BOOKSELLERS INC p 155
1166 Ave Of Amer 18, New York NY 10036
Tel (212) 403-2580
SIC 5942 5994 5999 5735

SONY BROADBAND ENTERTAINMENT CORP p 1340
550 Madison Ave Fl 6, New York NY 10022
Tel (212) 833-6800
SIC 3652 7812 5734 7832 5735

MOVIE GALLERY INC p 995
9275 Sw Peyton Ln, Wilsonville OR 97070
Tel (503) 570-1700 SIC 7841 5735

▲ FAB UNIVERSAL CORP p 523
5001 Baum Blvd Ste 770, Pittsburgh PA 15213
Tel (412) 621-0902
SIC 7371 7372 5735 5942 5994 5099

LIFEWAY CHRISTIAN RESOURCES OF SOUTHERN BAPTIST CONVENTION p 865
1 Lifeway Plz, Nashville TN 37234
Tel (615) 251-2000
SIC 5942 5963 2731 5999 5735 5947

DRAW ANOTHER CIRCLE LLC p 455
3601 Plains Blvd, Amarillo TX 79102
Tel (806) 351-2300 SIC 5735

HASTINGS ENTERTAINMENT INC p 667
3601 Plains Blvd, Amarillo TX 79102
Tel (806) 351-2300 SIC 5735 5942 7841

■ AMAZON FULFILLMENT SERVICES INC p 64
410 Terry Ave N, Seattle WA 98109
Tel (206) 266-1000
SIC 5735 5961 5731 5945

■ AMAZON.COMDEDC LLC p 65
410 Terry Ave N, Seattle WA 98109
Tel (206) 266-1000
SIC 5961 5735 5731 5945

SIC 5736 Musical Instrument Stores

REDROCK PARTNERS LLC p 1217
8260 E Raintree Dr, Scottsdale AZ 85260
Tel (480) 596-5702
SIC 5944 5932 5736 5941 5999

■ DISNEY WORLDWIDE SERVICES INC p 443
500 S Buena Vista St, Burbank CA 91521
Tel (877) 466-6669 SIC 7812 5736

GUITAR CENTER HOLDINGS INC p 646
5795 Lindero Canyon Rd, Westlake Village CA 91362
Tel (818) 735-8800 SIC 5736

GUITAR CENTER INC p 646
5795 Lindero Canyon Rd, Westlake Village CA 91362
Tel (818) 735-8800 SIC 5736

GUITAR CENTER STORES INC p 646
5795 Lindero Canyon Rd, Westlake Village CA 91362
Tel (818) 735-8800 SIC 5736

CONN-SELMER INC p 356
600 Industrial Pkwy, Elkhart IN 46516
Tel (574) 522-1675 SIC 3931 5736

SWEETWATER SOUND INC p 1412
5501 Us Highway 30 W, Fort Wayne IN 46818
Tel (260) 432-8176 SIC 7389 5736 5999

SAM ASH MEGASTORES LLC p 1273
278 Duffy Ave Unit A, Hicksville NY 11801
Tel (516) 932-6400 SIC 5736

SAM ASH MUSIC CORP p 1273
278 Duffy Ave Unit A, Hicksville NY 11801
Tel (516) 932-6400
SIC 5736 5731 5734 5961 7359 8741

SAM ASH MUSIC CORP p 1273
278 Duffy Ave Unit A, Hicksville NY 11801
Tel (516) 932-6400 SIC 5099 5736

STEINWAY AND SONS p 1385
1 Steinway Pl, Long Island City NY 11105
Tel (718) 721-2600 SIC 3931 5736

STEINWAY INC p 1385
1 Steinway Pl, Long Island City NY 11105
Tel (718) 721-2600 SIC 3931 5736

MUSICIANS LIVEORG p 1002
77 Brookfield Dr, Elizabethtown PA 17022
Tel (717) 413-3265 SIC 5736 5961 7389

INMUSIC BRANDS INC p 744
200 Scenic View Dr, Cumberland RI 02864
Tel (401) 658-3131 SIC 5736

NUMARK INDUSTRIES LP p 1067
200 Scenic View Dr, Cumberland RI 02864
Tel (401) 658-3131 SIC 5736

SIC 5812 Eating Places

BIG JACK ULTIMATE HOLDINGS LP p 181
124 W Oxmoor Rd, Birmingham AL 35209
Tel (205) 945-8167 SIC 5812

C L P CORP p 232
121 Summit Pkwy, Birmingham AL 35209
Tel (205) 943-0417 SIC 5812

P J UNITED INC p 1102
2300 Resource Dr, Birmingham AL 35242
Tel (205) 981-7173 SIC 5812

WESFAM RESTAURANTS INC p 1593
206 Gates Ave Se, Huntsville AL 35801
Tel (256) 533-0211 SIC 5812

SOUTHERN FOODSERVICE MANAGEMENT INC p 1348
500 Office Park Dr # 210, Mountain Brk AL 35223
Tel (205) 871-8000 SIC 5812 5962

QUALITY RESTAURANT CONCEPTS LLC p 1197
601 Vestavia Pkwy # 1000, Vestavia AL 35216
Tel (205) 824-5060 SIC 5812

TACALA INC p 1421
4268 Cahaba Heights Ct, Vestavia AL 35243
Tel (205) 985-9626 SIC 5812

TACALA LLC p 1421
3750 Corporate Woods Dr, Vestavia AL 35242
Tel (205) 443-9600 SIC 5812

TACALA NORTH INC p 1421
4268 Cahaba Heights Ct, Vestavia AL 35243
Tel (205) 985-2364 SIC 5812

NANA MANAGEMENT SERVICES LLC p 1007
800 E Dimond Blvd 3-450, Anchorage AK 99515
Tel (907) 273-2400
SIC 5812 7349 7021 7033 7381

GILA RIVER GAMING ENTERPRISES p 611
5040 W Wildhorse Pass Blvd, Chandler AZ 85226
Tel (800) 946-4452 SIC 7993 5812

XANTERRA SOUTH RIM LLC p 1630
1 Main St, Grand Canyon AZ 86023
Tel (928) 638-2631 SIC 7011 5812

Q K INC p 1194
101 E Hopi Dr, Holbrook AZ 86025
Tel (928) 524-3680 SIC 5812

KSL ARIZONA HOLDINGS III INC p 831
2400 E Missouri Ave, Phoenix AZ 85016
Tel (602) 955-6600
SIC 7011 5812 7991 5813

MACAYO RESTAURANTS LLC p 892
1480 E Bethany Home Rd # 130, Phoenix AZ 85014
Tel (602) 264-1831 SIC 5813 5812 5149

PETER PIPER INC p 1138
4745 N 7th St Ste 350, Phoenix AZ 85014
Tel (480) 609-6400 SIC 5812 7993 6794

CHAI BAGEL CORP p 286
14431 N 73rd St, Scottsdale AZ 85260
Tel (480) 860-0475
SIC 5149 5461 5812 2052 2051

FAIRMONT SCOTTSDALE PRINCESS p 525
7575 E Princess Dr, Scottsdale AZ 85255
Tel (480) 585-4848 SIC 7011 5812 5813

KAHALA BRANDS LTD p 800
9311 E Via De Ventura, Scottsdale AZ 85258
Tel (480) 362-4800 SIC 5812 6794

▲ KONA GRILL INC p 827
7150 E Camelback Rd # 220, Scottsdale AZ 85251
Tel (480) 922-8100 SIC 5812 6794

PF CHANGS CHINA BISTRO INC p 1140
7676 E Pinnacle Peak Rd, Scottsdale AZ 85255
Tel (480) 888-3000 SIC 5812

PFCCB EDGEWATER LLC p 1140
7676 E Pinnacle Peak Rd, Scottsdale AZ 85255
Tel (480) 888-3000 SIC 5812

■ SHERATON PHOENICIAN CORP p 1315
6000 E Camelback Rd, Scottsdale AZ 85251
Tel (480) 941-8200
SIC 7011 5812 5813 7999 7992

SOUTHWEST FOODSERVICE EXCELLENCE LLC p 1352
9366 E Raintree Dr 101, Scottsdale AZ 85260
Tel (480) 551-6550 SIC 5812

STAR BUFFET INC p 1378
2501 N Hayden Rd Ste 103, Scottsdale AZ 85257
Tel (480) 425-0397 SIC 5812

SUNWEST RESTAURANT CONCEPTS INC p 1405
6360 E Thomas Rd Ste 100, Scottsdale AZ 85251
Tel (480) 659-1000 SIC 5812

WOK PARENT LLC p 1620
7676 E Pinnacle Peak Rd, Scottsdale AZ 85255
Tel (480) 888-3000 SIC 5812

DEGENCO MANAGEMENT LLC p 422
825 S 48th St, Tempe AZ 85281
Tel (480) 829-5090 SIC 5812

MJKL ENTERPRISES LLC p 978
5210 S Priest Dr, Tempe AZ 85283
Tel (480) 897-7777 SIC 5812

MOUNTAIN RANGE RESTAURANTS LLC p 994
825 S 48th St, Tempe AZ 85281
Tel (480) 829-5090 SIC 5812

PIZZA HUT OF ARIZONA INC p 1152
5902 E Pima St, Tucson AZ 85712
Tel (520) 838-5171 SIC 5812

CARROLL ELECTRIC COOPERATIVE CORP p 261
920 Highway 62 Spur, Berryville AR 72616
Tel (870) 423-2161 SIC 4911 5812

DIAMOND HOSPITALITY ENTERPRISES p 436
5 Mystic Isle Rd, Edgemont AR 72044
Tel (501) 723-5150 SIC 5812 5541 5411

K-MAC ENTERPRISES INC p 799
1820 S Zero St, Fort Smith AR 72901
Tel (479) 646-2053 SIC 5812

FOWLER FOODS INC p 572
139 Southwest Dr, Jonesboro AR 72401
Tel (870) 935-6984 SIC 5812

ARKANSAS STATE UNIVERSITY p 110
501 Woodlane St Ste 600, Little Rock AR 72201
Tel (870) 972-2024 SIC 5812

DIXIE RESTAURANTS INC p 445
1215 Rebsamen Park Rd, Little Rock AR 72202
Tel (501) 666-3494 SIC 5812 5813

FOURJAY LLC p 572
42 Parkstone Cir, North Little Rock AR 72116
Tel (501) 372-2000 SIC 5812

ATLANTA HILL RESTAURANT CORP p 125
4155 E La Palma Ave # 250, Anaheim CA 92807
Tel (714) 579-3900 SIC 5812

CARL KARCHER ENTERPRISES INC p 256
1200 N Harbor Blvd, Anaheim CA 92801
Tel (714) 776-8054 SIC 5812

SPECIALTY RESTAURANTS CORP p 1356
8191 E Kaiser Blvd, Anaheim CA 92808
Tel (714) 279-6100 SIC 5812 5813

■ WCO HOTELS INC p 1585
1150 W Magic Way, Anaheim CA 92802
Tel (323) 636-3251 SIC 7011 5812

BELL GARDENS BICYCLE CLUB INC p 170
888 Bicycle Casino Dr, Bell Gardens CA 90201
Tel (562) 806-4646 SIC 7999 5812

NORMS RESTAURANTS p 1049
17844 Lakewood Blvd, Bellflower CA 90706
Tel (562) 925-4026 SIC 5812

HILLSTONE RESTAURANT GROUP INC p 694
147 S Beverly Dr, Beverly Hills CA 90212
Tel (310) 385-7343 SIC 5812 5813

SNOW SUMMIT SKI CORP p 1336
880 Summit Blvd, Big Bear Lake CA 92315
Tel (909) 866-5766 SIC 7011 5812

■ DISNEY REGIONAL ENTERTAINMENT INC p 443
500 S Buena Vista St, Burbank CA 91521
Tel (818) 560-1000 SIC 7999 5812 5813

■ CHEESECAKE FACTORY RESTAURANTS INC p 292
26901 Malibu Hills Rd, Calabasas CA 91301
Tel (818) 871-3000 SIC 5812

▲ CHEESECAKE FACTORY INC p 292
26901 Malibu Hills Rd, Calabasas Hills CA 91301
Tel (818) 871-3000 SIC 5812 2051

BOHICA LIQUIDATION INC p 198
5942 Priestly Dr, Carlsbad CA 92008
Tel (760) 930-0456 SIC 5812

ISLANDS RESTAURANTS LP p 767
5750 Fleet St Ste 120, Carlsbad CA 92008
Tel (760) 268-1800 SIC 5812

RUBIOS RESTAURANTS INC p 1257
2200 Faraday Ave Ste 250, Carlsbad CA 92008
Tel (760) 929-8226 SIC 5812

CKE RESTAURANTS HOLDINGS INC p 320
6307 Carpinteria Ave A, Carpinteria CA 93013
Tel (805) 745-7500 SIC 5812 6794

SIERRA NEVADA BREWING CO p 1320
1075 E 20th St, Chico CA 95928
Tel (530) 893-3520 SIC 2082 5812

JACMAR COMPANIES p 775
300 Baldwin Park Blvd, City Of Industry CA 91746
Tel (800) 834-8806 SIC 5141 5812 6552

HARRIS FARMS INC p 663
29475 Fresno Coalinga Rd, Coalinga CA 93210
Tel (559) 884-2435
SIC 0191 0211 2011 7011 5812 5541

CALIFORNIA COMMERCE CLUB INC p 239
6131 Telegraph Rd, Commerce CA 90040
Tel (323) 721-2100 SIC 7011 5812

GOURMET FOODS INC p 627
2910 E Harcourt St, Compton CA 90221
Tel (310) 632-3300 SIC 5141 5812 2099

ROUND TABLE PIZZA INC p 1253
1320 Willow Pass Rd # 600, Concord CA 94520
Tel (925) 969-3900 SIC 5812 6794

L-O CORONADO HOTEL INC p 835
1500 Orange Ave, Coronado CA 92118
Tel (619) 435-6611
SIC 7011 5812 5813 5941

IL FORNAIO (AMERICA) CORP p 731
770 Tamalpais Dr Ste 400, Corte Madera CA 94925
Tel (415) 945-0500
SIC 5812 5813 5149 5461 2051

▲ EL POLLO LOCO HOLDINGS INC p 483
3535 Harbor Blvd Ste 100, Costa Mesa CA 92626
Tel (714) 599-5000 SIC 5812 6794

■ EL POLLO LOCO INC p 483
3535 Harbor Blvd Ste 100, Costa Mesa CA 92626
Tel (714) 599-5000 SIC 5812

■ EPL INTERMEDIATE INC p 505
3535 Harbor Blvd Ste 100, Costa Mesa CA 92626
Tel (714) 599-5000 SIC 5812

KINGS SEAFOOD CO LLC p 820
3185 Airway Ave Ste J, Costa Mesa CA 92626
Tel (310) 451-4595 SIC 5812

UNIVERSITY RESTAURANT GROUP INC p 1527
3185 Airway Ave Ste J, Costa Mesa CA 92626
Tel (714) 432-0400 SIC 5812 5813

REAL MEX RESTAURANTS INC p 1213
5660 Katella Ave Ste 200, Cypress CA 90630
Tel (562) 346-1020 SIC 5812

CHEVYS RESTAURANTS LLC p 296
2000 Powell St Ste 200, Emeryville CA 94608
Tel (510) 768-1400 SIC 5812

E-BRANDS RESTAURANTS LLC p 467
6475 Christie Ave Ste 300, Emeryville CA 94608
Tel (407) 226-1433 SIC 5812

▲ JAMBA INC p 776
6475 Christie Ave Ste 150, Emeryville CA 94608
Tel (510) 596-0100 SIC 5812 6794

■ JUICE CLUB INC p 797
6475 Christie Ave Ste 150, Emeryville CA 94608
Tel (510) 596-0100 SIC 5812 6794

JEM RESTAURANT MANAGEMENT CORP p 782
312 W Cromwell Ave, Fresno CA 93711
Tel (559) 435-9648 SIC 5812

▲ DINEEQUITY INC p 440
450 N Brand Blvd, Glendale CA 91203
Tel (818) 240-6055 SIC 5812 6794

EUREKA RESTAURANT GROUP LLC p 512
12101 Crenshaw Blvd, Hawthorne CA 90250
Tel (310) 331-8233 SIC 5812 8741

▲ BJS RESTAURANTS INC p 186
7755 Center Ave Ste 300, Huntington Beach CA 92647
Tel (714) 500-2400 SIC 5812

▲ HABIT RESTAURANTS INC p 651
17320 Red Hill Ave # 140, Irvine CA 92614
Tel (949) 851-8881 SIC 5812

■ HABIT RESTAURANTS LLC p 651
17320 Red Hill Ave # 140, Irvine CA 92614
Tel (949) 851-8881 SIC 5812

IN-N-OUT BURGERS p 735
4199 Campus Dr Ste 900, Irvine CA 92612
Tel (949) 509-6200 SIC 5812

■ TACO BELL CORP p 1421
1 Glen Bell Way, Irvine CA 92618
Tel (949) 863-4500 SIC 5812 6794

TRIMARAN POLLO PARTNERS LLC p 1480
3333 Michelson Dr, Irvine CA 92612
Tel (949) 399-2000 SIC 5812

■ YARD HOUSE RESTAURANTS LLC p 1635
7700 Irvine Center Dr # 300, Irvine CA 92618
Tel (800) 336-5336 SIC 5812

JACKSON RANCHERIA CASINO & HOTEL p 774
12222 New York Ranch Rd, Jackson CA 95642
Tel (209) 223-1677
SIC 7999 5812 7011 5813

MANCHA DEVELOPMENT CO LLC p 901
24422 Avenida De La Carlo, Laguna Hills CA 92653
Tel (951) 271-4100 SIC 5812

■ DEL TACO LLC p 423
25521 Commercentre Dr # 200, Lake Forest CA 92630
Tel (949) 462-9300 SIC 5812

■ DEL TACO HOLDINGS INC p 423
25521 Commercentre Dr # 200, Lake Forest CA 92630
Tel (949) 462-7324 SIC 5812

▲ DEL TACO RESTAURANTS INC p 423
25521 Commercentre Dr # 200, Lake Forest CA 92630
Tel (949) 462-9300 SIC 5812 6794

FOSTER POULTRY FARMS p 570
1000 Davis St, Livingston CA 95334
Tel (209) 394-6914
SIC 0254 2015 5812 0173 5191 4212

KNOX & ASSOCIATES LLC p 825
615 Candlewood Ct, Lodi CA 95242
Tel (209) 365-1567 SIC 8741 5812

ACAPULCO RESTAURANTS INC p 14
4001 Via Oro Ave Ste 200, Long Beach CA 90810
Tel (310) 513-7538 SIC 5812 5813

EL TORITO RESTAURANTS INC p 483
4001 Via Oro Ave Ste 200, Long Beach CA 90810
Tel (562) 346-1200 *SIC* 5812

AMERICAN RESTAURANT GROUP INC p 78
4410 El Camino Real # 201, Los Altos CA 94022
Tel (650) 949-6400 *SIC* 5812 5813

HARMAN MANAGEMENT CORP p 662
199 1st St Ste 212, Los Altos CA 94022
Tel (650) 941-5681 *SIC* 8741 5812 5046

AMERICAN GOLF CORP p 73
6080 Center Dr Ste 500, Los Angeles CA 90045
Tel (310) 664-4000
SIC 7997 7999 5812 5941 7992

CIMMS INC p 307
3061 Riverside Dr, Los Angeles CA 90039
Tel (323) 674-0203 *SIC* 5812

GRILL CONCEPTS-DC INC p 640
11661 San Vicente Blvd, Los Angeles CA 90049
Tel (310) 820-5559 *SIC* 5812

GRILL ON ALLEY THE INC p 640
11661 San Vicente Blvd # 404, Los Angeles CA 90049
Tel (310) 820-5559 *SIC* 5812

H&H CATERING LP p 651
6801 Hollywood Blvd, Los Angeles CA 90028
Tel (323) 491-1250 *SIC* 5812

INTERNATIONAL COFFEE & TEA LLC p 754
5700 Wilshire Blvd # 120, Los Angeles CA 90036
Tel (310) 237-2326 *SIC* 5812 5499 6794

MAMMOTH MOUNTAIN SKI AREA LLC p 900
10001 Minaret Rd, Mammoth Lakes CA 93546
Tel (760) 934-2571 *SIC* 7011 5812

PIATTI RESTAURANT CO LP p 1146
625 Rdwood Hwy Frntage Rd, Mill Valley CA 94941
Tel (415) 380-2511 *SIC* 5812

SIZZLER USA RESTAURANTS INC p 1328
25910 Acero Ste 350, Mission Viejo CA 92691
Tel (949) 273-4497 *SIC* 5812

OCAT INC p 1072
4306 Sisk Rd, Modesto CA 95356
Tel (209) 529-6802 *SIC* 5812

FRESH CHOICE LLC p 578
8371 Central Ave Ste A, Newark CA 94560
Tel (510) 857-1241 *SIC* 5812

RUBYS DINER INC p 1257
201 Shipyard Way Ste E, Newport Beach CA 92663
Tel (949) 644-7829 *SIC* 5812

DIANAS MEXICAN FOOD PRODUCTS INC p 437
16330 Pioneer Blvd, Norwalk CA 90650
Tel (562) 926-5802 *SIC* 2099 5812

NESTLE DREYERS ICE CREAM CO p 1026
5929 College Ave, Oakland CA 94618
Tel (510) 594-9466 *SIC* 5812 2024

BOSKOVICH FARMS INC p 202
711 Diaz Ave, Oxnard CA 93030
Tel (805) 487-2299 *SIC* 0723 5812 0161

CALIFORNIA PIZZA KITCHEN INC p 241
12181 Bluff Creek Dr Fl 5, Playa Vista CA 90094
Tel (310) 342-5000 *SIC* 5812

APEX RESTAURANT MANAGEMENT INC p 96
1024 Serpentine Ln # 101, Pleasanton CA 94566
Tel (925) 233-0006 *SIC* 5812

DOLAN FOSTER ENTERPRISES LLC p 447
5635 W Las Positas Blvd # 406, Pleasanton CA 94588
Tel (925) 621-2600 *SIC* 5812

MILITARY DELI & BAKERY SERVICES INC p 969
10600 N Trademark Pkwy, Rancho Cucamonga CA 91730
Tel (909) 373-1344 *SIC* 5812

■ RED ROBIN INTERNATIONAL p 1216
12271 Foothill Blvd, Rancho Cucamonga CA 91739
Tel (909) 803-2665 *SIC* 5812

PANDA EXPRESS INC p 1111
1683 Walnut Grove Ave, Rosemead CA 91770
Tel (626) 799-9898 *SIC* 5812

PANDA RESTAURANT GROUP INC p 1111
1683 Walnut Grove Ave, Rosemead CA 91770
Tel (626) 799-9898 *SIC* 5812

SAN BERNARDINO HILTON p 1276
285 E Hospitality Ln, San Bernardino CA 92408
Tel (909) 889-0133 *SIC* 7011 6512 5812

UNIVERSITY ENTERPRISES CORP AT CSUSB p 1518
5500 University Pkwy, San Bernardino CA 92407
Tel (909) 537-5929 *SIC* 5812 5942 8211

T W M INDUSTRIES p 1420
899 Cherry Ave, San Bruno CA 94066
Tel (650) 583-6491 *SIC* 5812

ATLAS HOTELS INC p 128
500 Hotel Cir N, San Diego CA 92108
Tel (619) 291-2232 *SIC* 7011 5812 5813

CAMBRIDGE INVESTMENTS LLC p 244
8745 Aero Dr Ste 306, San Diego CA 92123
Tel (858) 244-0419 *SIC* 5812

GARDEN FRESH HOLDINGS INC p 591
15822 Bernardo Center Dr A, San Diego CA 92127
Tel (858) 675-1600 *SIC* 5812

GARDEN FRESH RESTAURANT CORP p 591
15822 Bernardo Center Dr A, San Diego CA 92127
Tel (858) 675-1600 *SIC* 5812

▲ JACK IN BOX INC p 773
9330 Balboa Ave, San Diego CA 92123
Tel (858) 571-2121 *SIC* 5812 6794

PACIFIC SHELLFISH INC p 1106
5040 Cass St, San Diego CA 92109
Tel (858) 272-9940 *SIC* 5146 5421 5812

SMG-PREMIER FOOD SERVICES INC p 1333
8555 Aero Dr Ste 205, San Diego CA 92123
Tel (858) 621-5151 *SIC* 5812

ZOOLOGICAL SOCIETY OF SAN DIEGO p 1644
2920 Zoo Dr, San Diego CA 92101
Tel (619) 231-1515 *SIC* 8422 5812 5947

ANDRE-BOUDIN BAKERIES INC p 90
50 Francisco St Ste 200, San Francisco CA 94133
Tel (415) 882-1849
SIC 2051 5812 5961 5461

CPK HOLDINGS INC p 387
Embarcadero Ctr, San Francisco CA 94111
Tel (415) 983-2700 *SIC* 5812 6794

DELANCEY STREET FOUNDATION p 423
600 The Embarcadero, San Francisco CA 94107
Tel (415) 957-9800
SIC 8361 5199 8322 4212 5812

FLYNN RESTAURANT GROUP LLC p 562
225 Bush St Ste 1800, San Francisco CA 94104
Tel (415) 835-9700 *SIC* 5812

PASTA POMODORO INC p 1120
1550 Bryant St Ste 100, San Francisco CA 94103
Tel (415) 431-2681 *SIC* 5812

GHIRARDELLI CHOCOLATE CO p 610
1111 139th Ave, San Leandro CA 94578
Tel (510) 483-6970
SIC 5441 2066 5812 5149

GUCKENHEIMER ENTERPRISES INC p 645
1850 Gateway Dr Ste 500, San Mateo CA 94404
Tel (650) 592-3800 *SIC* 5812

PACPIZZA LLC p 1107
220 Porter Dr Ste 100, San Ramon CA 94583
Tel (925) 838-8567 *SIC* 5812

STRATEGIC RESTAURANTS ACQUISITION CO LLC p 1392
3000 Executive Pkwy, San Ramon CA 94583
Tel (925) 328-3300 *SIC* 5812

STRAW HAT COOPERATIVE CORP p 1393
18 Crow Canyon Ct Ste 150, San Ramon CA 94583
Tel (925) 837-3400 *SIC* 5812

E D D INVESTMENT CO p 466
14325 Iseli Rd, Santa Fe Springs CA 90670
Tel (562) 921-5410 *SIC* 5812

POLLYS INC p 1160
14325 Iseli Rd, Santa Fe Springs CA 90670
Tel (714) 773-9588 *SIC* 5812

COLONY CAPITAL LLC p 338
2450 Broadway Ste 600, Santa Monica CA 90404
Tel (310) 282-8820
SIC 6799 7999 7011 5813 5812

LUCKY STRIKE ENTERTAINMENT INC p 884
15260 Ventura Blvd # 1110, Sherman Oaks CA 91403
Tel (818) 933-3752 *SIC* 3949 5812 5813

HOFS HUT RESTAURANT INC p 699
2601 E Willow St, Signal Hill CA 90755
Tel (310) 406-6340 *SIC* 5812

HOFS HUT RESTAURANTS INC p 699
2601 E Willow St, Signal Hill CA 90755
Tel (562) 596-0200 *SIC* 5812

REDARHCS INC p 1216
4502 Georgetown Pl, Stockton CA 95207
Tel (209) 478-0234 *SIC* 5812

JERRYS FAMOUS DELI INC p 783
12711 Ventura Blvd # 400, Studio City CA 91604
Tel (818) 766-8311 *SIC* 5812

BAJA FRESH WESTLAKE VILLAGE INC p 145
100 Moody Ct Ste 200, Thousand Oaks CA 91360
Tel (805) 495-4704 *SIC* 5812

CLK INC p 327
72295 Manufacturing Rd, Thousand Palms CA 92276
Tel (760) 341-2992 *SIC* 5812

KINGS HAWAIIAN HOLDING CO INC p 820
19161 Harborgate Way, Torrance CA 90501
Tel (310) 755-7100 *SIC* 2051 5812

YOSHINOYA AMERICA INC p 1637
991 Knox St, Torrance CA 90502
Tel (310) 527-6060 *SIC* 5812

CHEVYS INC p 296
31100 Courthouse Dr, Union City CA 94587
Tel (510) 675-9620 *SIC* 5812 5813

WOOD RANCH BARBECUE AND GRILL INC p 1622
2835 Townsgate Rd Ste 200, Westlake Village CA 91361
Tel (805) 719-9000 *SIC* 5812

GRILL CONCEPTS INC p 640
6300 Canoga Ave Ste 600, Woodland Hills CA 91367
Tel (818) 251-7000 *SIC* 5812

DNC PARKS & RESORTS AT YOSEMITE INC p 446
9001 Village Dr, Yosemite Ntpk CA 95389
Tel (209) 372-1001
SIC 7011 5399 5812 5947 5541 4725

PIONEER RESTAURANTS LLC p 1151
7490 Clubhouse Rd Fl 2, Boulder CO 80301
Tel (720) 485-6841 *SIC* 5812

CRAFTWORKS RESTAURANTS & BREWERIES INC p 388
8001 Arista Pl Unit 500, Broomfield CO 80021
Tel (303) 664-4000 *SIC* 5812

▲ NOODLES & CO p 1047
520 Zang St Ste D, Broomfield CO 80021
Tel (720) 214-1900 *SIC* 5812

ROCK BOTTOM RESTAURANTS INC p 1243
8001 Arista Pl Unit 500, Broomfield CO 80021
Tel (303) 664-4000 *SIC* 5812 5813

BROADMOOR HOTEL INC p 215
1 Lake Ave, Colorado Springs CO 80906
Tel (719) 634-7711
SIC 7011 5812 5813 7992 7999 7389

W C S INC p 1568
1515 N Academy Blvd Ste 4, Colorado Springs CO 80909
Tel (719) 573-8557 *SIC* 5812

WENDYS OF COLORADO SPRINGS INC p 1592
1515 N Academy Blvd # 400, Colorado Springs CO 80909
Tel (719) 573-8557 *SIC* 5812

▲ CHIPOTLE MEXICAN GRILL INC p 301
1401 Wynkoop St Ste 500, Denver CO 80202
Tel (303) 595-4000 *SIC* 5812 5813

FIDELITY NEWPORT HOLDINGS LLC p 541
400 W 48th Ave, Denver CO 80216
Tel (303) 296-2121 *SIC* 5812 2051 6719

QUIZNOS CORP p 1200
7595 E Tech Way Ste 200, Denver CO 80237
Tel (720) 359-3300 *SIC* 6794 5812

SERVICE SYSTEMS ASSOCIATES INC p 1307
4699 Marion St, Denver CO 80216
Tel (417) 746-0242 *SIC* 5947 5812

BEP COLORADO RESTAURANTS LLC p 174
304 Inverness Way S # 305, Englewood CO 80112
Tel (303) 671-7333 *SIC* 5812

BAILEY CO LLLP p 145
601 Corporate Cir, Golden CO 80401
Tel (303) 384-0200 *SIC* 5812

ERIE COUNTY INVESTMENT CO p 508
601 Corporate Cir, Golden CO 80401
Tel (303) 384-0200
SIC 5812 6794 6531 6552 1542 1521

GIESEN RESTAURANT ENTERPRISES LLC p 611
10 E Belleview Way, Greenwood Village CO 80121
Tel (303) 761-7498 *SIC* 5812

PARKS XANTERRA & RESORTS INC p 1116
6312 S Fiddlers Green Cir 600n, Greenwood Village CO 80111
Tel (303) 600-3400 *SIC* 7011 5947 5812

▲ RED ROBIN GOURMET BURGERS INC p 1216
6312 S Fiddlers, Greenwood Village CO 80111
Tel (303) 846-6000 *SIC* 5812 6794

■ RED ROBIN INTERNATIONAL INC p 1216
6312 S Fiddlers Green Cir 200n, Greenwood Village CO 80111
Tel (303) 846-6000
SIC 5812 6794 5813 5087

XANTERRA HOLDING CORP p 1630
6312 S Fiddlers Green Cir # 600, Greenwood Village CO 80111
Tel (303) 600-3400 *SIC* 5812

BOSTON MARKET CORP p 203
14103 Denver West Pkwy # 100, Lakewood CO 80401
Tel (800) 340-2836 *SIC* 5812

BOSTON MARKET HOLDING CORP p 203
14103 Denver West Pkwy # 100, Lakewood CO 80401
Tel (303) 278-9500 *SIC* 5812

EINSTEIN AND NOAH CORP p 482
555 Zang St Ste 300, Lakewood CO 80228
Tel (303) 568-8000 *SIC* 5812

EINSTEIN NOAH RESTAURANT GROUP INC p 482
555 Zang St Ste 300, Lakewood CO 80228
Tel (303) 568-8000 *SIC* 5812 6794

■ QDOBA RESTAURANT CORP p 1194
7244 W Bonfils Ln, Lakewood CO 80226
Tel (720) 898-2300 *SIC* 5812 6794

TREFZ CORP p 1475
10 Middle St Ste 1701, Bridgeport CT 06604
Tel (203) 367-3621 *SIC* 5812 6531 8721

MRRC HOLD CO p 996
382 Greenwich Ave Apt 1, Greenwich CT 06830
Tel (203) 987-3500 *SIC* 5812

JH WHITNEY VI LP p 785
130 Main St, New Canaan CT 06840
Tel (203) 716-6100 *SIC* 6726 5812

VISTAR/VSA OF HARTFORD INC p 1562
175 Sullivan Ave, South Windsor CT 06074
Tel (860) 688-7702 *SIC* 5141 5812 8322

CENTERPLATE INC p 276
2187 Atlantic St, Stamford CT 06902
Tel (800) 698-6992
SIC 5812 7999 5947 7993

CENTERPLATE ULTIMATE HOLDINGS CORP p 276
2187 Atlantic St, Stamford CT 06902
Tel (800) 698-6992
SIC 5812 7999 5947 7993

VOLUME SERVICES INC p 1565
2187 Atlantic St Ste 6, Stamford CT 06902
Tel (203) 975-5900
SIC 5812 7999 5947 7993

CLYDE INC p 328
3236 M St Nw, Washington DC 20007
Tel (202) 333-9180 *SIC* 5812 5813

JUST ONE MORE RESTAURANT CORP p 797
1730 Rhode Island Ave Nw # 900, Washington DC 20036
Tel (202) 775-7256 *SIC* 5812 5813

BROCKWAY MORAN & PARTNERS INC p 216
225 Ne Mizner Blvd # 700, Boca Raton FL 33432
Tel (561) 750-2000 *SIC* 5812 3599 3728

■ PANTHERS BRHC LLC p 1111
501 E Camino Real, Boca Raton FL 33432
Tel (888) 543-1277 *SIC* 7011 5812 7997

SUN CAPITAL PARTNERS INC p 1400
5200 Town Center Cir # 600, Boca Raton FL 33486
Tel (561) 962-3400
SIC 6799 2672 2671 5812 5411 5311

APPLE INVESTORS GROUP LLC p 98
303 E Woolbright Rd, Boynton Beach FL 33435
Tel (888) 265-7402 *SIC* 5812

M & R UNITED INC p 889
402 High Point Dr Ste 101, Cocoa FL 32926
Tel (321) 631-0245 *SIC* 5812 5411

OCEAN PROPERTIES LTD p 1073
1001 E Atl Ave Ste 202, Delray Beach FL 33483
Tel (603) 559-2100
SIC 7011 6552 1522 5719 5812 5813

AMELIA ISLAND CO p 66
1423 Julia St, Fernandina Beach FL 32034
Tel (904) 261-6161
SIC 7011 6552 7992 7991 5812

▲ FLANIGANS ENTERPRISES INC p 554
5059 Ne 18th Ave, Fort Lauderdale FL 33334
Tel (954) 377-1961 *SIC* 5812 5921

GUMBYS PIZZA SYSTEMS INC p 647
3911 W Newberry Rd Ste C, Gainesville FL 32607
Tel (352) 338-7775 *SIC* 5812

BARBEQUE INTEGRATED INC p 154
4000 Hollywood Blvd, Hollywood FL 33021
Tel (407) 355-5800 *SIC* 5812

SEMINOLE TRIBE OF FLORIDA T V INC p 1303
3107 N State Road 7, Hollywood FL 33021
Tel (954) 966-6300 *SIC* 5812

FIREHOUSE SUBS INC p 543
3400-8 Kori Rd, Jacksonville FL 32257
Tel (904) 886-8300 *SIC* 5812

MORRIS HOLDINGS INC p 990
1650 County Road 210 W, Jacksonville FL 32259
Tel (904) 829-3946 *SIC* 5541 5812 5411

ORANGE LAKE COUNTRY CLUB INC p 1092
8505 W Irlo Bronson Hwy, Kissimmee FL 34747
Tel (407) 239-0000
SIC 7011 6552 7997 5812 5813

VILLAGES OF LAKE-SUMTER INC p 1557
1000 Lake Sumter Lndg, Lady Lake FL 32162
Tel (352) 753-2270
SIC 6552 1521 7997 5812 7389

MELTON MANAGEMENT INC p 941
6342 Lantana Rd, Lake Worth FL 33463
Tel (561) 641-6717 *SIC* 5812

ADH 702 INC p 22
203 Lookout Pl Ste A, Maitland FL 32751
Tel (407) 629-9311 *SIC* 5812

AREAS USA INC p 106
5301 Blue Lagoon Dr # 690, Miami FL 33126
Tel (305) 264-1709 *SIC* 5399 5812

BENIHANA INC p 173
21500 Biscayne Blvd # 100, Miami FL 33180
Tel (305) 593-0770 *SIC* 5812 6794

BURGER KING CAPITAL HOLDINGS LLC p 227
5505 Blue Lagoon Dr, Miami FL 33126
Tel (305) 378-3000 *SIC* 5812

BURGER KING CORP p 227
5505 Blue Lagoon Dr, Miami FL 33126
Tel (305) 378-3000 *SIC* 5812 6794

BURGER KING HOLDCO LLC p 227
5505 Blue Lagoon Dr, Miami FL 33126
Tel (305) 378-3000 *SIC* 5812

BURGER KING HOLDINGS INC p 227
5505 Blue Lagoon Dr, Miami FL 33126
Tel (305) 378-3000 *SIC* 5812 6794

BURGER KING WORLDWIDE INC p 227
5505 Blue Lagoon Dr, Miami FL 33126
Tel (305) 378-3000 *SIC* 5812

FONTAINEBLUEAU FLORIDA HOTEL LLC p 563
4441 Collins Ave, Miami FL 33140
Tel (305) 538-2000
SIC 6519 7011 5812 7991

HILTON INTERNATIONAL CO p 695
5201 Blue Lagoon Dr # 600, Miami FL 33126
Tel (305) 444-3444 *SIC* 7011 5812

INTERFOODS OF AMERICA INC p 752
9500 S Dadeland Blvd # 800, Miami FL 33156
Tel (305) 670-0746 *SIC* 5812 6794

INTERNATIONAL RESTAURANT MANAGEMENT GROUP INC p 756
4531 Pnc De Leon Blvd 3 Ste 300, Miami FL 33146
Tel (305) 476-1611 *SIC* 5812

KONING RESTAURANTS INTERNATIONAL LC p 827
15600 Nw 15th Ave, Miami FL 33169
Tel (305) 430-1200 *SIC* 5812

MAT CONCESSIONAIRE LLC p 918
860 Macarthur Cswy, Miami FL 33132
Tel (305) 929-0560 *SIC* 5812

MICCOSUKEE TRIBE OF INDIANS OF FLORIDA p 959
Sw 8th St & Us Hwy 41, Miami FL 33194
Tel (305) 223-8380
SIC 5812 5331 8412 5947 4489

POLLO OPERATIONS INC p 1160
7300 N Kendall Dr Fl 8, Miami FL 33156
Tel (305) 671-1225 *SIC* 5812

SAILORMEN INC p 1268
9500 S Dadeland Blvd # 800, Miami FL 33156
Tel (305) 670-4112 *SIC* 5812

TIM HORTONS USA INC p 1453
5505 Blue Lagoon Dr, Miami FL 33126
Tel (888) 376-4835 *SIC* 6794 5812

BAR HARBOR LOBSTER CO INC p 154
2000 Premier Row, Orlando FL 32809
Tel (407) 851-4001 *SIC* 5146 5812

BARNIES COFFEE & TEA CO INC p 156
29 S Orange Ave, Orlando FL 32801
Tel (407) 854-6600 *SIC* 5499 5812

BUCA INC p 222
4700 Millenia Blvd # 400, Orlando FL 32839
Tel (407) 903-5500 *SIC* 5812

▲ DARDEN RESTAURANTS INC p 412
1000 Darden Center Dr, Orlando FL 32837
Tel (407) 245-4000 *SIC* 5812

■ GMRI INC p 619
1000 Darden Center Dr, Orlando FL 32837
Tel (407) 245-4000 *SIC* 5812

HARD ROCK CAFE FOUNDATION INC p 660
6100 Old Park Ln Ste 100, Orlando FL 32835
Tel (407) 445-7625
SIC 5812 5813 7011 6794

HARD ROCK CAFE INTERNATIONAL (USA) INC p 660
6100 Old Park Ln Ste 100, Orlando FL 32835
Tel (407) 445-7625 *SIC* 5812

■ HYATT HOTELS OF FLORIDA INC p 723
9801 International Dr, Orlando FL 32819
Tel (407) 284-1234 *SIC* 7011 5812 5813

MILLERS ALE HOUSE INC p 971
5750 Major Blvd Ste 400, Orlando FL 32819
Tel (407) 547-1120 *SIC* 5812

PLANET HOLLYWOOD INTERNATIONAL INC p 1154
4700 Millenia Blvd # 400, Orlando FL 32839
Tel (407) 903-5500 *SIC* 5812 6794 5699

■ RARE HOSPITALITY INTERNATIONAL INC p 1209
7469 Brokerage Dr, Orlando FL 32809
Tel (407) 245-5042 *SIC* 5812

RED LOBSTER HOSPITALITY LLC p 1215
450 S Orange Ave Ste 800, Orlando FL 32801
Tel (407) 734-9000 *SIC* 5812

RED LOBSTER MANAGEMENT LLC p 1215
450 S Orange Ave Ste 800, Orlando FL 32801
Tel (407) 734-9000 *SIC* 5812

ROMACORP INC p 1248
11315 Corp Blvd Ste 100, Orlando FL 32817
Tel (214) 343-7800 *SIC* 5812

ROSEN 9939 INC p 1251
9840 International Dr, Orlando FL 32819
Tel (407) 996-9939
SIC 7011 5812 5813 7992 7389

ROSEN HOTELS AND RESORTS INC p 1251
9840 International Dr, Orlando FL 32819
Tel (407) 996-1706
SIC 7011 5812 5813 7389 8011 7992

■ UCF HOTEL VENTURE p 1499
6800 Lakewood Plaza Dr, Orlando FL 32819
Tel (407) 503-9000 *SIC* 7011 5813 5812

STONEWOOD HOLDINGS LLC p 1391
780 W Granada Blvd # 100, Ormond Beach FL 32174
Tel (386) 760-2282 *SIC* 5812

ITALIAN RESTAURANT p 767
1 S County Rd, Palm Beach FL 33480
Tel (561) 655-6611 *SIC* 5812

DUFFYS HOLDINGS INC p 459
4440 Pga Blvd Ste 201, Palm Beach Gardens FL 33410
Tel (561) 804-7676 *SIC* 5812

R H G ACQUISITION CORP p 1202
4440 Pga Blvd Ste 201, Palm Beach Gardens FL 33410
Tel (561) 804-7676 *SIC* 5812

EDGEWATER BEACH RESORT LLC p 477
11212 Front Beach Rd, Panama City FL 32407
Tel (850) 235-4044
SIC 1531 7011 5813 5812

FOLKS RESTAURANTS LTD p 563
508 Harmon Ave, Panama City FL 32401
Tel (850) 763-0501 *SIC* 5812

WENDCO CORP p 1591
220 W Garden St Ste 500, Pensacola FL 32502
Tel (850) 433-5425 *SIC* 5812

GA FOOD SERVICES OF PINELLAS COUNTY INC p 588
12200 32nd Ct N, Saint Petersburg FL 33716
Tel (727) 573-2211 *SIC* 2038 5812

ANGELINAS PIZZERIA & PASTA INC p 91
4005 E County Highway 30a, Santa Rosa Beach FL 32459
Tel (850) 231-2500 *SIC* 5812

SUNSHINE RESTAURANT MERGER SUB LLC p 1404
13650 Nw 8th St Ste 103, Sunrise FL 33325
Tel (305) 931-5454 *SIC* 5812

▲ BLOOMIN BRANDS INC p 190
2202 N West Shore Blvd # 500, Tampa FL 33607
Tel (813) 282-1225 *SIC* 5812

■ BONEFISH GRILL INC p 200
2202 N West Shore Blvd # 5, Tampa FL 33607
Tel (813) 282-1225 *SIC* 5812

■ CARRABBAS ITALIAN GRILL INC p 260
2202 N West Shore Blvd # 5, Tampa FL 33607
Tel (813) 288-8286 *SIC* 5812

CASUAL RESTAURANT CONCEPTS INC p 264
205 S Hoover Blvd Ste 402, Tampa FL 33609
Tel (813) 286-2006 *SIC* 5813 5812

CHECKERS DRIVE-IN RESTAURANTS INC p 292
4300 W Cypress St Ste 600, Tampa FL 33607
Tel (813) 283-7000 *SIC* 5812 6794

JTS ENTERPRISES OF TAMPA LIMITED p 796
4908 W Nassau St, Tampa FL 33607
Tel (813) 287-2231 *SIC* 5812

■ OS PRIME INC p 1096
2202 N West Shore Blvd # 50, Tampa FL 33607
Tel (813) 282-1225 *SIC* 5812

■ OSI RESTAURANT PARTNERS LLC p 1097
2202 N West Shore Blvd # 5, Tampa FL 33607
Tel (813) 282-1225 *SIC* 5812 5813

■ OUTBACK STEAKHOUSE OF FLORIDA LLC p 1098
2202 N West Shore Blvd # 500, Tampa FL 33607
Tel (813) 282-1225 *SIC* 5812

FIRST WATCH OF OHIO INC p 550
8027 Cooper Creek Blvd # 103, University Park FL 34201
Tel (941) 907-6657 *SIC* 5812

RREMC LLC p 1255
1800 Okeechobee Rd # 100, West Palm Beach FL 33409
Tel (561) 684-2101 *SIC* 5812

▲ RUTHS HOSPITALITY GROUP INC p 1260
1030 W Canton Ave Ste 100, Winter Park FL 32789
Tel (407) 333-7440 *SIC* 5812 6794

TM RESTAURANT GROUP LLC p 1457
6220 Shiloh Rd Ste 100, Alpharetta GA 30005
Tel (678) 679-1210 *SIC* 5812

ZAX INC p 1641
1040 Founders Blvd, Athens GA 30606
Tel (706) 353-8107 *SIC* 5812

ARBYS RESTAURANT GROUP p 103
1155 Perimeter Ctr, Atlanta GA 30338
Tel (678) 514-4100 *SIC* 5812

ARBYS RESTAURANT GROUP INC p 103
1155 Perimeter Ctr, Atlanta GA 30338
Tel (678) 514-4100 *SIC* 5812

ARG HOLDING CORP p 107
1180 Peachtree St Ne, Atlanta GA 30309
Tel (404) 591-5200 *SIC* 5812

ARG IH LLC p 107
1180 Peachtree St Ne, Atlanta GA 30309
Tel (404) 591-5200 *SIC* 5812

CAJUN OPERATING CO p 237
980 Hammond Dr Ste 1100, Atlanta GA 30328
Tel (770) 350-3800 *SIC* 5812

CHICK-FIL-A INC p 298
5200 Buffington Rd, Atlanta GA 30349
Tel (404) 765-8038 *SIC* 5812 8741

CONCESSIONS INTERNATIONAL LLC p 354
566 Wells St Sw, Atlanta GA 30312
Tel (404) 681-0300 *SIC* 5812 5963 5947

GOLDCO LLC p 620
100 Ashford Ctr N Ste 130, Atlanta GA 30338
Tel (334) 792-1267 *SIC* 5812

GPS HOSPITALITY LLC p 628
2100 Riveredge Pkwy # 850, Atlanta GA 30328
Tel (770) 933-5023 *SIC* 5812

HOOTERS OF AMERICA LLC p 706
1815 The Exchange Se, Atlanta GA 30339
Tel (770) 951-2040 *SIC* 5812 6794

▲ POPEYES LOUISIANA KITCHEN INC p 1161
400 Perimeter Ctr Ter, Atlanta GA 30346
Tel (404) 459-4450 *SIC* 5812 6794

ROYAL HOSPITALITY CORP p 1254
255 E Paces Ferry Rd Ne # 300, Atlanta GA 30305
Tel (404) 239-0329 *SIC* 6794 8741 5812

SYBRA LLC p 1413
1155 Perimeter Ctr # 1100, Atlanta GA 30338
Tel (678) 514-4100 *SIC* 5812

TEDS MONTANA GRILL INC p 1432
133 Luckie St Nw Ste 200, Atlanta GA 30303
Tel (404) 521-9796 *SIC* 5812

TEXAS WINGS INC p 1445
1815 The Exchange Se, Atlanta GA 30339
Tel (770) 799-2241 *SIC* 5812

■ TRIARC ACQUISITION LLC p 1478
1155 Perimeter Ctr, Atlanta GA 30338
Tel (678) 514-4101 *SIC* 5812

ELAN CHATEAU RESORTS LLC p 483
100 Rue Charlemagne Dr, Braselton GA 30517
Tel (678) 425-0900
SIC 2084 5812 7992 7011

FOUNTAINHEAD DEVELOPMENT LLC p 571
100 Rue Charlemagne Dr, Braselton GA 30517
Tel (770) 867-0903
SIC 7992 7991 5921 5812 7011

FRI HOLDING CO LLC p 579
4170 Ashford Dunwoody Rd, Brookhaven GA 30319
Tel (404) 865-3356 *SIC* 5812

PEZOLD MANAGEMENT ASSOCIATES INC p 1140
600 Brokstone Centre Pkwy, Columbus GA 31904
Tel (706) 576-6400 *SIC* 5812

SCHUSTER ENTERPRISES INC p 1291
3530 Macon Rd, Columbus GA 31907
Tel (706) 568-2657 *SIC* 5812

CLEAR GROUP LLC p 324
90 Summer Walk Ct, Covington GA 30016
Tel (404) 403-0274 *SIC* 5812

DEKALB FARMERS MARKET INC p 423
3000 E Ponce De Leon Ave, Decatur GA 30030
Tel (404) 377-6400
SIC 5431 5421 5461 5451 5921 5812

KURANI PIZZA INC p 832
2825 Breckinridge Blvd # 150, Duluth GA 30096
Tel (770) 923-2313 *SIC* 5812

KRYSTAL CO p 830
1455 Lincoln Pkwy E # 600, Dunwoody GA 30346
Tel (423) 757-1550 *SIC* 5812 6794

AMREST LLC p 86
2045 Attic Pkwy Nw, Kennesaw GA 30152
Tel (770) 850-8818 *SIC* 5812

HOPS GRILL & BAR INC p 706
Hancock At Washington St, Madison GA 30650
Tel (706) 342-4552 *SIC* 5813 5812

HERSCHEND ENTERTAINMENT CO LLC p 687
5445 Triangle Pkwy # 200, Norcross GA 30092
Tel (770) 441-1940 *SIC* 7999 5947 5812

WAFFLE HOUSE INC p 1571
5986 Financial Dr, Norcross GA 30071
Tel (770) 729-5700 *SIC* 5812 6794

FIVE STAR HOLDING CO INC p 553
248 Rollins Industrial Ct, Ringgold GA 30736
Tel (706) 937-5077
SIC 5962 5812 5963 2099

FCH ENTERPRISES INC p 533
1765 S King St, Honolulu HI 96826
Tel (808) 973-0877 *SIC* 5812

HAWAII FOODSERVICE ALLIANCE LLC p 669
2720 Waiwai Loop, Honolulu HI 96819
Tel (808) 839-2004 *SIC* 5141 5812

HAWAII PIZZA HUT INC p 669
828 Fort Street Mall # 130, Honolulu HI 96813
Tel (808) 566-3200 *SIC* 5812

■ HILTON HAWAIIAN VILLAGE LLC p 695
2005 Kalia Rd, Honolulu HI 96815
Tel (808) 949-4321 *SIC* 7011 5812 5813

HTH CORP p 715
1668 S King St Fl 2, Honolulu HI 96826
Tel (808) 469-4111 *SIC* 7011 5812 6512

KAZI FOODS CORP OF HAWAII p 805
560 N Nimitz Hwy Ste 214, Honolulu HI 96817
Tel (808) 550-4100 *SIC* 5812

KYO-YA HOTELS & RESORTS LP p 833
2255 Kalakaua Ave Fl 2, Honolulu HI 96815
Tel (808) 931-8600 *SIC* 7011 5812 5813

TD FOOD GROUP INC p 1429
828 Fort Street Mall # 130, Honolulu HI 96813
Tel (808) 566-3200 *SIC* 5812 6794

POLYNESIAN CULTURAL CENTER INC p 1160
55-370 Kamehameha Hwy, Laie HI 96762
Tel (808) 293-3000 *SIC* 7999 5812 5947

ES-O-EN CORP p 509
455 W Amity Rd, Meridian ID 83642
Tel (208) 888-6428 *SIC* 5812

TWINS INTERNATIONAL INC p 1495
2275 Half Day Rd Ste 300, Bannockburn IL 60015
Tel (847) 374-1200 *SIC* 5812

BIAGGIS RISTORANTE ITALIANO LLC p 181
1705 Clearwater Ave Ste A, Bloomington IL 61704
Tel (309) 664-2148 *SIC* 5812

MONICAL PIZZA CORP p 984
530 N Kinzie Ave, Bradley IL 60915
Tel (815) 937-1890 *SIC* 5812 6794

EASTERN ILLINOIS UNIVERSITY p 472
600 Lincoln Ave, Charleston IL 61920
Tel (217) 581-5000 *SIC* 8221 5812

EL-MILAGRO INC p 483
3050 W 26th St, Chicago IL 60623
Tel (773) 579-6120 *SIC* 2099 5812

FLAT OUT CRAZY LLC p 554
303 W Erie St Ste 600, Chicago IL 60654
Tel (312) 284-6500 *SIC* 8741 5812

FLYING FOOD FARE INC p 562
212 N Sangamon St Ste 1a, Chicago IL 60607
Tel (312) 243-2122 *SIC* 5812 5149 5947

FLYING FOOD GROUP INC p 562
212 N Sangamon St Ste 1a, Chicago IL 60607
Tel (312) 243-2122 *SIC* 5812

H GROUP HOLDING INC p 650
222 W Adams St Ste 250, Chicago IL 60606
Tel (312) 750-1234
SIC 4512 7011 5812 5813

LEONAS PIZZERIA INC p 856
3931 S Leavitt St, Chicago IL 60609
Tel (773) 843-0050 *SIC* 5812 5813

LETTUCE ENTERTAIN YOU ENTERPRISES INC p 857
5419 N Sheridan Rd, Chicago IL 60640
Tel (773) 878-7340 *SIC* 5812 8741

LETTUCE ENTERTAIN YOU TOO INC p 858
5419 N Sheridan Rd # 116, Chicago IL 60640
Tel (773) 878-7340 *SIC* 5812 5813

LEVY R & H LIMITED PARTNERSHIP p 858
980 N Michigan Ave # 400, Chicago IL 60611
Tel (312) 664-8200 *SIC* 5812

LUNAN CORP p 885
414 N Orleans St Ste 402, Chicago IL 60654
Tel (312) 645-9898 *SIC* 5812

MORTONS OF CHICAGO/BOCA RATON INC p 991
350 W Hubbard St, Chicago IL 60654
Tel (713) 850-1010 *SIC* 5812

ORGANICLIFE LLC p 1094
445 W Erie St Ste 110, Chicago IL 60654
Tel (312) 929-2005 *SIC* 5812

▲ POTBELLY CORP p 1164
111 N Canal St Ste 850, Chicago IL 60606
Tel (312) 951-0600 *SIC* 5812

PROTEIN BAR INC p 1185
200 N Lasalle Ste 1880, Chicago IL 60601
Tel (312) 300-2566 *SIC* 5812

TESTA PRODUCE INC p 1441
4555 S Racine Ave, Chicago IL 60609
Tel (312) 226-3237 *SIC* 5148 5812

COOPERS HAWK INTERMEDIATE HOLDING LLC p 367
5325 9th Ave, Countryside IL 60525
Tel (708) 839-2920
SIC 8741 2084 5182 5812

HEARTLAND HOME FOODS INC p 679
1400 Opus Pl Ste 900, Downers Grove IL 60515
Tel (800) 492-5592 *SIC* 5812 8741

TRI CITY FOODS OF ILLINOIS INC p 1476
1400 Opus Pl Ste 900, Downers Grove IL 60515
Tel (630) 598-3300 *SIC* 5812

■ MCDONALDS RESTAURANTS OF FLORIDA INC p 928
1 Mcdonalds Dr, Hinsdale IL 60523
Tel (630) 623-3000 *SIC* 5812

SHAMROCK CO p 1311
15 Spinning Wheel Rd # 110, Hinsdale IL 60521
Tel (630) 655-8274 *SIC* 5812

NORTHWESTERN LAKE FOREST HOSPITAL p 1060
660 N Westmoreland Rd, Lake Forest IL 60045
Tel (847) 234-0945
SIC 8062 5947 5932 5812

CLARK BRANDS LLC p 322
4200 Commerce Ct Ste 350, Lisle IL 60532
Tel (630) 355-8918
SIC 6794 7389 5541 5812

HEART OF AMERICA MANAGEMENT LLC p 678
1501 River Dr, Moline IL 61265
Tel (309) 797-9300 *SIC* 8741 5812 7011

R L C ENTERPRISES INC p 1202
155 Revere Dr Ste 5, Northbrook IL 60062
Tel (847) 498-7888 *SIC* 5812

▲ MCDONALDS CORP p 928
1 Mcdonalds Dr, Oak Brook IL 60523
Tel (630) 623-3000 *SIC* 5812 6794

■ MCDONALDS RESTAURANT OPERATIONS INC p 928
2111 Mcdonalds Dr, Oak Brook IL 60523
Tel (630) 623-3000 *SIC* 5812 8741

■ MCDONALDS RESTAURANTS OF ALASKA INC p 928
2111 Mcdonalds Dr, Oak Brook IL 60523
Tel (630) 623-3000 *SIC* 5812

■ MCDONALDS RESTAURANTS OF CALIFORNIA INC p 928
1 Mcdonalds Dr, Oak Brook IL 60523
Tel (630) 623-3000 *SIC* 5812

■ MCDONALDS RESTAURANTS OF COLORADO INC p 928
1 Mcdonalds Dr, Oak Brook IL 60523
Tel (630) 623-3000 *SIC* 5812

■ MCDONALDS RESTAURANTS OF CONNECTICUT INC p 928
1 Mcdonalds Dr, Oak Brook IL 60523
Tel (630) 623-3000 *SIC* 5812

■ MCDONALDS RESTAURANTS OF DISTRICT OF COLUMBIA INC p 928
1 Mcdonalds Dr, Oak Brook IL 60523
Tel (630) 623-3000 *SIC* 5812

■ MCDONALDS RESTAURANTS OF GEORGIA INC p 928
1 Mcdonalds Dr, Oak Brook IL 60523
Tel (630) 623-3000 *SIC* 5812

■ MCDONALDS RESTAURANTS OF ILLINOIS INC p 928
21 Mcdonalds Dr, Oak Brook IL 60523
Tel (630) 623-3000 *SIC* 5812

■ MCDONALDS RESTAURANTS OF INDIANA INC p 928
2111 Mcdonalds Dr, Oak Brook IL 60523
Tel (630) 623-3000 *SIC* 5812

■ MCDONALDS RESTAURANTS OF MARYLAND INC p 928
1 Mcdonalds Dr, Oak Brook IL 60523
Tel (630) 623-3000 *SIC* 5812

■ MCDONALDS RESTAURANTS OF MASSACHUSETTS INC p 928
1 Mcdonalds Dr, Oak Brook IL 60523
Tel (630) 623-3000 *SIC* 5812

■ MCDONALDS RESTAURANTS OF MICHIGAN INC p 928
1 Mcdonalds Dr, Oak Brook IL 60523
Tel (630) 623-3000 *SIC* 5812

■ MCDONALDS RESTAURANTS OF MINNESOTA INC p 928
1 Mcdonalds Dr, Oak Brook IL 60523
Tel (630) 623-3000 *SIC* 5812

■ MCDONALDS RESTAURANTS OF MISSOURI INC p 928
1 Mcdonalds Dr, Oak Brook IL 60523
Tel (630) 623-3000 *SIC* 5812

■ MCDONALDS RESTAURANTS OF NEVADA INC p 928
1 Mcdonalds Dr, Oak Brook IL 60523
Tel (630) 623-3000 *SIC* 5812

■ MCDONALDS RESTAURANTS OF NEW JERSEY INC p 928
1 Mcdonalds Dr, Oak Brook IL 60523
Tel (630) 623-3000 *SIC* 5812

■ MCDONALDS RESTAURANTS OF NEW YORK INC p 928
1 Mcdonalds Dr, Oak Brook IL 60523
Tel (630) 623-3000 *SIC* 5812

■ MCDONALDS RESTAURANTS OF NORTH CAROLINA INC p 928
1 Mcdonalds Dr, Oak Brook IL 60523
Tel (630) 623-3000 *SIC* 5812

■ MCDONALDS RESTAURANTS OF OHIO INC p 928
1 Mcdonalds Dr, Oak Brook IL 60523
Tel (630) 623-3000 *SIC* 5812

■ MCDONALDS RESTAURANTS OF OKLAHOMA INC p 928
1 Mcdonalds Dr, Oak Brook IL 60523
Tel (630) 623-3000 *SIC* 5812

■ MCDONALDS RESTAURANTS OF PENNSYLVANIA INC p 928
1 Mcdonalds Dr, Oak Brook IL 60523
Tel (630) 623-3000 *SIC* 5812

■ MCDONALDS RESTAURANTS OF SOUTH CAROLINA INC p 928
1 Mcdonalds Dr, Oak Brook IL 60523
Tel (630) 623-3000 *SIC* 5812

■ MCDONALDS RESTAURANTS OF TENNESSEE INC p 928
1 Mcdonalds Dr, Oak Brook IL 60523
Tel (630) 623-3000 *SIC* 5812

■ MCDONALDS RESTAURANTS OF TEXAS INC p 928
1 Mcdonalds Dr, Oak Brook IL 60523
Tel (630) 623-3000 *SIC* 5812

■ MCDONALDS RESTAURANTS OF VIRGINIA INC p 928
1 Mcdonalds Dr, Oak Brook IL 60523
Tel (630) 623-3000 *SIC* 5812

■ MCDONALDS RESTAURANTS OF WASHINGTON INC p 928
1 Mcdonalds Dr, Oak Brook IL 60523
Tel (630) 623-3000 *SIC* 5812 8741

■ MCDONALDS RESTAURANTS OF WISCONSIN INC p 928
1 Mcdonalds Dr, Oak Brook IL 60523
Tel (630) 623-3000 *SIC* 5812

■ MCDONALDS USA LLC p 928
2111 Mcdonalds Dr, Oak Brook IL 60523
Tel (630) 623-3000 *SIC* 5812

PORTILLOS HOT DOGS INC p 1163
2001 Spring Rd Ste 400, Oak Brook IL 60523
Tel (630) 954-3773 *SIC* 5812 5813

■ TRANS-PORTE INC p 1470
9399 W Higgins Rd, Rosemont IL 60018
Tel (847) 720-8000 *SIC* 5812

GONNELLA BAKING CO p 623
1117 Wiley Rd, Schaumburg IL 60173
Tel (312) 733-2020
SIC 2051 5812 2099 2038

BUFFINGTON HARBOR RIVERBOAT LLC p 224
21 Buffington Harbor Dr, Gary IN 46406
Tel (219) 977-9999 *SIC* 5812 7993

■ HORSESHOE HAMMOND LLC p 708
777 Casino Center Dr, Hammond IN 46320
Tel (866) 711-7463 *SIC* 7999 5947 5812

APPLE AMERICAN INDIANA LLC p 98
6515 E 82nd St Ste 109, Indianapolis IN 46250
Tel (317) 577-8334 *SIC* 5812 5813

BELL AMERICAN GROUP LLC p 169
8930 Bash St Ste L, Indianapolis IN 46256
Tel (317) 788-0374 *SIC* 5812

MCL INC p 930
2730 E 62nd St, Indianapolis IN 46220
Tel (317) 257-5425 *SIC* 5812

■ STEAK N SHAKE INC p 1384
36 S Pennsylvania St # 500, Indianapolis IN 46204
Tel (317) 633-4100 *SIC* 5812 6794

SERVUS p 1308
4201 Mannheim Rd Ste A, Jasper IN 47546
Tel (812) 482-3212 *SIC* 5812

BRAVOGRAND INC p 209
4220 Edison Lakes Pkwy # 300, Mishawaka IN 46545
Tel (574) 271-4600 *SIC* 5812

GRAYLING CORP p 632
4220 Edison Lkes Pkwy 100, Mishawaka IN 46545
Tel (856) 384-1212 *SIC* 5812 5813 6531

QUALITY DINING INC p 1197
4220 Edison Lakes Pkwy # 300, Mishawaka IN 46545
Tel (574) 271-4600 *SIC* 5812 6794

RESTAURANT MANAGEMENT CORP p 1228
1575 Adler Cir Ste C, Portage IN 46368
Tel (219) 764-3355 SIC 5812

HMR ACQUISITION CO INC p 698
1501 N Ironwood Dr, South Bend IN 46635
Tel (574) 272-5922 SIC 5812 5813

SOUTH BEND CHOCOLATE CO INC p 1343
3300 W Sample St Ste 110, South Bend IN 46619
Tel (574) 233-2577
SIC 5149 2066 5441 5812

PRAIRIE MEADOWS RACETRACK AND CASINO INC p 1167
1 Prairie Meadows Dr, Altoona IA 50009
Tel (515) 967-1000
SIC 7948 7993 7999 5947 5812 5813

■ **CASEYS MARKETING CO** p 263
1 Se Convenience Blvd, Ankeny IA 50021
Tel (515) 965-6100
SIC 5411 5172 5141 5812

RESTAURANTS RESOURCES INC p 1228
1805 State St Ste 201, Bettendorf IA 52722
Tel (563) 243-7571 SIC 5812

■ **AMERISTAR CASINO COUNCIL BLUFFS LLC** p 83
2200 River Rd, Council Bluffs IA 51501
Tel (712) 328-8888
SIC 7011 7991 5813 5812

PIZZA RANCH INC p 1153
204 19th St Se, Orange City IA 51041
Tel (712) 707-8800 SIC 5812 6794

IOWA 80 GROUP INC p 762
515 Sterling Dr, Walcott IA 52773
Tel (563) 468-5500
SIC 5541 5399 7542 5812

IOWA 80 TRUCKSTOP INC p 762
755 W Iowa 80 Rd I-80, Walcott IA 52773
Tel (563) 284-6961
SIC 5541 5399 7542 5812

■ **AMERICAN MULTI-CINEMA INC** p 76
1 Amc Way, Leawood KS 66211
Tel (913) 213-2000 SIC 7832 5812 8741

HOULIHANS RESTAURANTS INC p 711
8700 State Line Rd # 100, Leawood KS 66206
Tel (913) 901-2500 SIC 5812 5813

GENESH INC p 602
8831 Long St, Lenexa KS 66215
Tel (913) 492-0007 SIC 5812

HIGH PLAINS PIZZA INC p 690
7 W Parkway Blvd, Liberal KS 67901
Tel (620) 624-5638 SIC 5812

FQSR LLC p 573
8900 Indian Creek Pkwy # 100, Overland Park KS 66210
Tel (913) 469-1112 SIC 5812

NPC INTERNATIONAL HOLDINGS INC p 1064
7300 W 129th St, Overland Park KS 66213
Tel (913) 327-3109 SIC 5812

NPC INTERNATIONAL INC p 1064
7300 W 129th St, Overland Park KS 66213
Tel (913) 632-0300 SIC 5812

NPC RESTAURANT HOLDINGS LLC p 1064
7300 W 129th St, Overland Park KS 66213
Tel (913) 327-5555 SIC 5812 6794

ZANCANELLI MANAGEMENT CORP p 1641
11879 W 112th St Ste A, Overland Park KS 66210
Tel (913) 469-1112 SIC 5812

GOURMET SYSTEMS OF KANSAS INC p 627
4551 W 107th St Ste 100, Shawnee Mission KS 66207
Tel (913) 967-4000 SIC 5812 5813

RESTAURANT SERVICES INC p 1228
5877 Sw 29th St, Topeka KS 66614
Tel (785) 273-1805 SIC 5812

AMERICAN PIZZA PARTNERS LP p 77
7700 E Polo Dr, Wichita KS 67206
Tel (316) 634-1190 SIC 5812

▲ **AMERICAN RESTAURANT PARTNERS LP** p 78
3020 N Cypress St Ste 100, Wichita KS 67226
Tel (316) 634-1190 SIC 5812

APPLE CORPS LP p 98
1877 N Rock Rd, Wichita KS 67206
Tel (316) 683-2611 SIC 5812

CHAMPPS OPERATING CORP p 287
151 S Whittier St Ofc, Wichita KS 67207
Tel (800) 229-2118 SIC 5812 5813

FOX & HOUND RESTAURANT GROUP p 572
1421 N Waterfront Pkwy, Wichita KS 67206
Tel (316) 634-0505 SIC 5812

JS VENTURES INC p 795
2400 N Woodlawn Blvd # 230, Wichita KS 67220
Tel (316) 683-7799 SIC 5812

LDF FOOD GROUP INC p 849
10610 E 26th Cir N, Wichita KS 67226
Tel (316) 630-0677 SIC 5812

LONE STAR STEAKHOUSE & SALOON OF OHIO INC p 876
224 E Douglas Ave Ste 700, Wichita KS 67202
Tel (972) 295-8600 SIC 5812

RAGE ADMINISTRATIVE AND MARKETING SERVICES INC p 1205
1313 N Webb Rd Ste 200, Wichita KS 67206
Tel (316) 634-1888 SIC 5812

RESTAURANT MANAGEMENT CO OF WICHITA INC p 1228
7700 E Polo Dr, Wichita KS 67206
Tel (316) 634-1190 SIC 5812

TAVISTOCK RESTAURANTS LLC p 1426
2024 N Woodlawn St # 417, Wichita KS 67208
Tel (510) 594-4262 SIC 5812

RAFFERTYS INC p 1205
1750 Scottsville Rd Ste 2, Bowling Green KY 42104
Tel (270) 781-2834 SIC 5812 5813

WENDYS OF BOWLING GREEN INC p 1592
Store 3489 Store3489 St Sto, Bowling Green KY 42104
Tel (270) 782-6124 SIC 5812

APPLE SAUCE INC p 99
741 Centre View Blvd # 100, Crestview Hills KY 41017
Tel (859) 331-3900 SIC 5812

C J APPLE II INC p 232
741 Centre View Blvd # 100, Crestview Hills KY 41017
Tel (859) 331-3900 SIC 5812

COLUMBIA SUSSEX CORP p 342
740 Centre View Blvd, Crestview Hills KY 41017
Tel (859) 331-0091 SIC 7011 5812

CENTER COLLEGE p 275
600 W Walnut St, Danville KY 40422
Tel (859) 238-5369 SIC 5812

NEIGHBORHOOD RESTAURANTS INC p 1024
601 Main St Ste 102, Hazard KY 41701
Tel (606) 436-0736 SIC 5812

MAX ARNOLD & SONS LLC p 922
702 N Main St, Hopkinsville KY 42240
Tel (270) 885-8488
SIC 5171 5541 5411 5812

A & W RESTAURANTS INC p 4
1648 Mcgrathiana Pkwy # 380, Lexington KY 40511
Tel (859) 219-0019 SIC 5812 6794

A GREAT AMERICAN BRAND LLC p 5
1648 Mcgrathiana Pkwy, Lexington KY 40511
Tel (859) 219-0019 SIC 5812 6794

FAZOLIS RESTAURANTS LLC p 532
2470 Palumbo Dr, Lexington KY 40509
Tel (859) 268-1668 SIC 5812

SEED RESTAURANT GROUP INC p 1300
2470 Palumbo Dr, Lexington KY 40509
Tel (859) 268-1668 SIC 6794 5812

THOMAS AND KING INC p 1448
249 E Main St Ste 101, Lexington KY 40507
Tel (859) 254-2180 SIC 5812

THOMAS AND KING OF ARIZONA INC p 1448
249 E Main St Ste 101, Lexington KY 40507
Tel (859) 254-2180 SIC 5812 5813

YORKSHIRE GLOBAL RESTAURANTS INC p 1637
1648 Mcgrathiana Pkwy, Lexington KY 40511
Tel (859) 721-1328 SIC 5812

B F FT MYERS INC p 141
3309 Collins Ln, Louisville KY 40245
Tel (502) 254-7130 SIC 5812

B F SOUTH INC p 142
3309 Collins Ln, Louisville KY 40245
Tel (502) 254-7130 SIC 5812

■ **KENTUCKY FRIED CHICKEN CORP** p 812
1441 Gardiner Ln, Louisville KY 40213
Tel (502) 874-8300 SIC 5812 6794

■ **KENTUCKY FRIED CHICKEN OF LOUISVILLE INC** p 812
1441 Gardiner Ln, Louisville KY 40213
Tel (502) 874-8300 SIC 5812

■ **KFC CORP (DE)** p 816
1900 Colonel Sanders Ln, Louisville KY 40213
Tel (502) 874-8300 SIC 5812 6794

■ **KFC ENTERPRISES INC** p 816
1441 Gardiner Ln, Louisville KY 40213
Tel (502) 895-3227 SIC 5812

■ **KFC NATIONAL MANAGEMENT CO** p 816
1441 Gardiner Ln, Louisville KY 40213
Tel (502) 874-8300 SIC 5812

LONG JOHN SILVERS RESTAURANT INC p 876
1441 Gardiner Ln, Louisville KY 40213
Tel (502) 874-3000 SIC 5812 6794

▲ **PAPA JOHNS INTERNATIONAL INC** p 1112
2002 Papa Johns Blvd # 100, Louisville KY 40299
Tel (502) 261-7272 SIC 5812 6794 2099

■ **PAPA JOHNS INTERNATIONAL INC** p 1112
2002 Papa Johns Blvd # 100, Louisville KY 40299
Tel (502) 261-7272 SIC 5812

RESTAURANT SUPPLY CHAIN SOLUTIONS LLC p 1228
950 Breckenridge Ln # 300, Louisville KY 40207
Tel (502) 896-5900
SIC 5812 5046 5141 5149

RMD CORP p 1239
2509 Plantside Dr, Louisville KY 40299
Tel (502) 499-9991 SIC 5812 5813

■ **TEXAS ROADHOUSE HOLDINGS LLC** p 1444
6040 Dutchmans Ln Ste 400, Louisville KY 40205
Tel (502) 426-9984 SIC 5812 6794

▲ **TEXAS ROADHOUSE INC** p 1444
6040 Dutchmans Ln Ste 200, Louisville KY 40205
Tel (502) 426-9984 SIC 5812 6794

TUMBLEWEED INC p 1491
2301 River Rd Ste 200, Louisville KY 40206
Tel (502) 893-0323 SIC 5812

▲ **YUM BRANDS INC** p 1640
1441 Gardiner Ln, Louisville KY 40213
Tel (502) 874-8300 SIC 5812 6794

■ **YUM RESTAURANT SERVICES GROUP INC** p 1640
1900 Colonel Sanders Ln, Louisville KY 40213
Tel (502) 874-8300 SIC 5812

CHARTWELLS CATERING p 291
Cumberland Col Dining, Williamsburg KY 40769
Tel (606) 539-4358 SIC 5812

CCC HOLDING LLC p 269
3332 Partridge Ln Bldg A, Baton Rouge LA 70809
Tel (225) 368-3900 SIC 2095 5149 5812

PICCADILLY RESTAURANTS LLC p 1146
4150 S Shrwood Frest Blvd, Baton Rouge LA 70816
Tel (225) 293-9440 SIC 5812

RAISING CANES RESTAURANTS LLC p 1206
400 Convention St Ste 550, Baton Rouge LA 70802
Tel (225) 383-7400 SIC 5812

AMERICAS PIZZA CO LLC p 81
201 Rue De Jean Ste 200, Lafayette LA 70508
Tel (337) 806-1100 SIC 5812

EUREST SUPPORT SERVICES p 512
207 Towncenter Pkwy, Lafayette LA 70506
Tel (337) 233-9153 SIC 5812

TUNICA-BILOXI TRIBAL ECONOMIC DEVELOPMENT CORP p 1491
164 Yuroni Rd, Marksville LA 71351
Tel (318) 253-9767 SIC 5812

COPELANDS OF NEW ORLEANS INC p 368
2601 Severn Ave, Metairie LA 70002
Tel (504) 830-1000 SIC 5812 5813

B & G FOOD ENTERPRISES INC p 141
1430 Sandra St, Morgan City LA 70380
Tel (985) 384-3333 SIC 5812

B & G FOOD ENTERPRISES OF TEXAS LLC p 141
1430 Sandra St, Morgan City LA 70380
Tel (985) 384-3333 SIC 5812

SODEXO REMOTE SITES PARTNERSHIP p 1337
5749 Susitna Dr, New Orleans LA 70123
Tel (504) 733-5761 SIC 5812

GIFT COLLECTION INC p 611
6905 Rockledge Dr Fl 1, Bethesda MD 20817
Tel (240) 694-4100 SIC 6512 5812

HMSHOST CORP p 698
6905 Rockledge Dr Fl 1, Bethesda MD 20817
Tel (240) 694-4100
SIC 5812 5813 5994 5947

HOST INTERNATIONAL INC p 710
6905 Rockledge Dr Fl 1, Bethesda MD 20817
Tel (240) 694-4100
SIC 5812 5813 5994 5947

S & W MANAGEMENT INC p 1261
7070 Oakland Mills Rd, Columbia MD 21046
Tel (410) 720-6336 SIC 5812

DAVCO ACQUISITION HOLDING INC p 415
1657 Crofton Blvd, Crofton MD 21114
Tel (410) 721-3770 SIC 5812

DAVCO RESTAURANTS INC p 415
1657 Crofton Blvd, Crofton MD 21114
Tel (410) 721-3770 SIC 5812

LEMEK LLC p 855
8184 Lark Brown Rd # 101, Elkridge MD 21075
Tel (443) 552-0700 SIC 5812

■ **OVATIONS FOOD SERVICES LP** p 1099
21 Stadium Dr, Frederick MD 21703
Tel (301) 815-9935 SIC 5812

PLAMONDON ENTERPRISES INC p 1154
4991 New Design Rd # 109, Frederick MD 21703
Tel (301) 695-5051 SIC 5812 7011

SODEXO INC p 1337
9801 Washingtonian Blvd # 1, Gaithersburg MD 20878
Tel (301) 987-4000 SIC 5812 7349

SODEXO OPERATIONS LLC p 1337
9801 Washingtonian Blvd, Gaithersburg MD 20878
Tel (301) 987-4000 SIC 8741 5812 7349

NORDIC CORP p 1048
11019 Mccormick Rd # 320, Hunt Valley MD 21031
Tel (410) 771-1880 SIC 5812

SAGE DINING SERVICES INC p 1267
1402 York Rd Ste 100, Lutherville MD 21093
Tel (410) 339-3950 SIC 5812

SILVER DINER INC p 1323
12276 Rockville Pike, Rockville MD 20852
Tel (301) 770-2828 SIC 5812

JANJER ENTERPRISES INC p 777
12150 Tech Rd, Silver Spring MD 20904
Tel (301) 625-5920 SIC 5812 8721 8741

KING CANNON INC p 820
60 River St, Beverly MA 01915
Tel (978) 921-7438 SIC 5812

ABP CORP p 12
19 Fid Kennedy Ave, Boston MA 02210
Tel (617) 423-0629 SIC 5461 5812 2051

CHARLIE BROWNS ACQUISITION CORP p 290
1 Congress St Ste 113, Boston MA 02114
Tel (201) 842-3612 SIC 5812

COSI INC p 373
294 Washington St Ste 510, Boston MA 02108
Tel (857) 415-5000 SIC 5812 6794

DELAWARE NORTH COMPANIES INC - BOSTON p 424
100 Legends Way Ste 100, Boston MA 02114
Tel (617) 624-1000
SIC 5812 5994 6512 7311

■ **HST LESSEE BOSTON LLC** p 715
39 Dalton St, Boston MA 02199
Tel (617) 236-2000
SIC 7011 5812 7299 5813

LEGAL SEA FOODS LLC p 853
1 Seafood Way, Boston MA 02210
Tel (617) 530-9000 SIC 5812 5146 5961

SMITH & WOLLENSKY RESTAURANT GROUP INC p 1333
260 Franklin St Ste 240, Boston MA 02110
Tel (617) 600-3500 SIC 5812

URC LLC p 1530
100 Charles Park Rd, Boston MA 02132
Tel (617) 323-9200 SIC 5812 5813 6794

TAVISTOCK RESTAURANT GROUP p 1426
35 Braintree Hill Park # 1107, Braintree MA 02184
Tel (781) 817-4400 SIC 5812

BOSTON CULINARY GROUP INC p 202
55 Cambridge Pkwy Ste 200, Cambridge MA 02142
Tel (617) 225-0005 SIC 5812 5145

ALL SEASONS SERVICES INC p 51
5 Campanelli Cir Ste 200, Canton MA 02021
Tel (781) 828-2345 SIC 5962 5812

▲ **DUNKIN BRANDS GROUP INC** p 461
130 Royall St, Canton MA 02021
Tel (781) 737-3000
SIC 5461 5499 6794 5812

■ **DUNKIN BRANDS INC** p 461
130 Royall St, Canton MA 02021
Tel (781) 737-5200 SIC 5461 5812

DELOPS INC p 425
600 Providence Hwy, Dedham MA 02026
Tel (508) 697-7742 SIC 5812

PAPA GINOS HOLDINGS CORP p 1112
600 Providence Hwy, Dedham MA 02026
Tel (781) 461-1200 SIC 5812 6794

PAPA GINOS INC p 1112
600 Providence Hwy, Dedham MA 02026
Tel (781) 461-1200 SIC 5812

BOSTON-WYMAN INC p 203
110 Breeds Hill Rd Ste 8, Hyannis MA 02601
Tel (508) 778-5044 SIC 5812

NOT YOUR AVERAGE JOES INC p 1062
2 Granite Ave Ste 300, Milton MA 02186
Tel (774) 213-2800 SIC 5812

PR RESTAURANTS LLC p 1167
2150 Washington St # 125, Newton MA 02462
Tel (617) 581-6160 SIC 5461 5812

BERTUCCIS CORP p 176
155 Otis St Ste 3, Northborough MA 01532
Tel (508) 351-2500 SIC 5812

DDJ CAPITAL MANAGEMENT LLC p 419
130 Turner St Ste 600, Waltham MA 02453
Tel (781) 283-8500 SIC 6282 5094 5812

JW CHILDS ASSOCIATES LP p 798
500 Totten Pond Rd Ste 6, Waltham MA 02451
Tel (617) 753-1100 SIC 5812

FREEZE OPERATIONS HOLDING CORP p 577
1855 Boston Rd, Wilbraham MA 01095
Tel (413) 543-2445 SIC 5812 2024 5143

FRIENDLYS ICE CREAM LLC p 580
1855 Boston Rd, Wilbraham MA 01095
Tel (413) 731-4000 SIC 2024 5812

■ **FRIENDLYS MANUFACTURING AND RETAIL LLC** p 580
1855 Boston Rd, Wilbraham MA 01095
Tel (413) 731-4136 SIC 5812

FRIENDLYS RESTAURANTS LLC p 580
1855 Boston Rd, Wilbraham MA 01095
Tel (413) 731-4000 SIC 5812

99 BOSTON INC p 4
160 Olympia Ave, Woburn MA 01801
Tel (781) 933-8999 SIC 5812 5813

▲ **DOMINOS PIZZA INC** p 449
30 Frank Lloyd Wright Dr, Ann Arbor MI 48105
Tel (734) 930-3030 SIC 5812 5149 6794

■ **DOMINOS PIZZA LLC** p 449
30 Frank Lloyd Wright Dr, Ann Arbor MI 48105
Tel (734) 930-3030
SIC 5812 6794 5046 5149 8741 2045

MC DONALDS OF CALHOUN INC p 925
806 Columbia Ave W, Battle Creek MI 49015
Tel (269) 965-1402 SIC 5812 8742 6794

GREEKTOWN CASINO LLC p 636
555 E Lafayette Blvd, Detroit MI 48226
Tel (313) 223-2999 SIC 5812 7011

ILITCH HOLDINGS INC p 732
2211 Woodward Ave, Detroit MI 48201
Tel (313) 983-6000 SIC 7941 7922 5812

LITTLE CAESAR ENTERPRISES INC p 870
2211 Woodward Ave, Detroit MI 48201
Tel (313) 983-6000
SIC 5812 6794 5141 5046 8741

■ **MGM GRAND DETROIT LLC** p 958
1777 3rd St, Detroit MI 48226
Tel (313) 465-1777 SIC 7011 5812 7991

ANSARA RESTAURANT GROUP INC p 93
23925 Industrial Park Dr, Farmington Hills MI 48335
Tel (248) 848-9099 SIC 5812 5813

HAPPYS PIZZA CO p 659
30201 Orchrd Lke Rd 200, Farmington Hills MI 48334
Tel (248) 358-8888 SIC 5812

DORTCH ENTERPRISES LLC p 451
8487 Retreat Dr, Grand Blanc MI 48439
Tel (810) 771-4500 SIC 5812

BARFLY VENTURES LLC p 155
35 Oakes St Sw Ste 400, Grand Rapids MI 49503
Tel (616) 965-9780 SIC 5812

EXIT 76 CORP p 519
2696 Chicago Dr Sw, Grand Rapids MI 49519
Tel (616) 534-2181 SIC 5812

▲ **MERITAGE HOSPITALITY GROUP INC** p 949
45 Ottawa Ave Sw Ste 600, Grand Rapids MI 49503
Tel (616) 776-2600 SIC 5812 6794

■ **WEN OHIO LLC** p 1591
3310 Eagle Park Dr Ne, Grand Rapids MI 49525
Tel (616) 988-8751 SIC 5812

■ **WM LIMITED PARTNERSHIP - 1998** p 1620
45 Ottawa Ave Sw Ste 600, Grand Rapids MI 49503
Tel (616) 776-2600 SIC 5812

J STANTON DAVID & ASSOCIATES INC p 772
714 W Michigan Ave, Jackson MI 49201
Tel (517) 784-4094 SIC 5812

KING VENTURE INC p 820
17800 N Laurel Park Dr, Livonia MI 48152
Tel (248) 357-6182 SIC 5812

BELLEHOFF CORP p 170
405 S Mission St, Mount Pleasant MI 48858
Tel (989) 772-2902 SIC 5812

CENTRAL MICHIGAN UNIVERSITY p 279
1200 S Franklin St, Mount Pleasant MI 48859
Tel (989) 774-4000
SIC 8221 5942 4833 4832 5812

NORTHWIND INVESTMENTS INC p 1061
109 E Broadway St, Mount Pleasant MI 48858
Tel (989) 772-2600 SIC 5812

SAGINAW CHIPPEWA INDIAN TRIBE p 1268
7070 E Broadway Rd, Mount Pleasant MI 48858
Tel (989) 775-4000 SIC 5812

EMPLOYEES ONLY INC p 494
805 Oakwood Dr Ste 100, Rochester MI 48307
Tel (248) 276-0950 SIC 5812

MICHIGAN PIZZA HUT INC p 961
2053 Niles Rd, Saint Joseph MI 49085
Tel (269) 983-3888 SIC 5812

C A MUER CORP p 232
400 Galleria Ofc Ctr, Southfield MI 48034
Tel (248) 226-9400 SIC 5812

▲ **DIVERSIFIED RESTAURANT HOLDINGS INC** p 444
27680 Franklin Rd, Southfield MI 48034
Tel (248) 223-9160 SIC 5812 5813 6794

FORWARD CORP p 570
219 N Front St, Standish MI 48658
Tel (989) 846-4501
SIC 5411 5541 5172 5812

CONTINENTAL DISTRIBUTORS INC p 363
35710 Mound Rd, Sterling Heights MI 48310
Tel (586) 268-3835 SIC 5962 5812

GRAND TRAVERSE BAND ECONOMIC DEVELOPMENT CORP p 630
2331 N West Bay Shore Dr, Suttons Bay MI 49682
Tel (231) 534-8000 SIC 7011 7993 5812

HOSPITALITY WEST LLC p 710
745 S Garfield Ave Ste A, Traverse City MI 49686
Tel (231) 941-5052 SIC 5812

CHINA AUTOMOTIVE SYSTEMS INC p 301
2546 Elliott Dr, Troy MI 48083
Tel (248) 577-0353 SIC 5812

OLGAS KITCHEN INC p 1082
2125 Butterfield Dr # 301, Troy MI 48084
Tel (248) 362-0001 SIC 5812

BIG BOY RESTAURANTS INTERNATIONAL LLC p 181
4199 Marcy St, Warren MI 48091
Tel (586) 759-6000 SIC 5812 2099

OAK LANE GOLF COURSE INC p 1070
800 N Main St, Webberville MI 48892
Tel (517) 521-3900 SIC 7992 5812

CHIN LEEANN INC p 301
3600 American Blvd W # 52, Bloomington MN 55431
Tel (952) 896-3606 SIC 5812

MONGOLIAN OPERATING CO LLC p 984
200 E Travelers Trl # 235, Burnsville MN 55337
Tel (952) 288-2363 SIC 5812 6794

NORTHCOTT HOSPITALITY INTERNATIONAL LLC p 1054
250 Lake Dr E, Chanhassen MN 55317
Tel (952) 294-5100 SIC 7011 5812

JERRYS ENTERPRISES INC p 783
5125 Vernon Ave S, Edina MN 55436
Tel (952) 922-8335 SIC 5411 5812 5251

BORDER FOODS INC p 201
5425 Boone Ave N, Minneapolis MN 55428
Tel (763) 559-7338 SIC 5812

▲ BUFFALO WILD WINGS INC p 224
5500 Wayzata Blvd # 1600, Minneapolis MN 55416
Tel (952) 593-9943 SIC 5812 6794

CARIBOU COFFEE CO INC p 256
3900 Lake Breeze Ave, Minneapolis MN 55429
Tel (763) 592-2200 SIC 5812 5499 6794

CARLSON HOTELS LIMITED PARTNERSHIP p 257
Carlson Parkway 701 Twr St Carlson Parkw, Minneapolis MN 55459
Tel (763) 212-1000
SIC 6794 7011 5812 5813

DAMICO HOLDING CO p 410
275 Market St Ste 117, Minneapolis MN 55405
Tel (612) 374-1776 SIC 5812

■ GRANITE CITY FOOD & BREWERY LTD p 631
3500 Amrcn Blvd W Ste 450, Minneapolis MN 55431
Tel (952) 215-0660 SIC 5812 5813

■ INTERNATIONAL DAIRY QUEEN INC p 755
7505 Metro Blvd Ste 500, Minneapolis MN 55439
Tel (952) 830-0200 SIC 5812

NATH COMPANIES INC p 1009
900 American Blvd E # 300, Minneapolis MN 55420
Tel (952) 853-1400 SIC 5812

NATH MINNESOTA FRANCHISE GROUP INC p 1009
900 E 79th St Ste 300, Minneapolis MN 55420
Tel (952) 853-1400 SIC 5812 8741

CARLSON HOLDINGS INC p 257
701 Carlson Pkwy, Minnetonka MN 55305
Tel (763) 212-5000
SIC 7011 5812 6794 7389 4724

CARLSON INC p 258
701 Carlson Pkwy, Minnetonka MN 55305
Tel (763) 212-5000
SIC 7011 5812 6794 8742 8743 7389

▲ FAMOUS DAVES OF AMERICA INC p 527
12701 Whitewater Dr # 200, Minnetonka MN 55343
Tel (952) 294-1300 SIC 5812 6794

TAHER INC p 1421
5570 Smetana Dr, Minnetonka MN 55343
Tel (952) 945-0505 SIC 5812

REICHEL FOODS INC p 1220
3706 Enterprise Dr Sw, Rochester MN 55902
Tel (507) 289-7264
SIC 2011 5812 2013 0723

FOURCROWN INC p 572
434 Hale Ave N Ste 160, Saint Paul MN 55128
Tel (651) 714-0030 SIC 5812

■ SYSCO MINNESOTA INC p 1417
2400 County Road J, Saint Paul MN 55112
Tel (763) 785-9000 SIC 5141 5812 5813

PRAIRIE ISLAND INDIAN COMMUNITY p 1167
5636 Sturgeon Lake Rd, Welch MN 55089
Tel (800) 554-5473 SIC 7999 5812 7011

TREASURE ISLAND RESORT AND CASINO p 1475
5734 Sturgeon Lake Rd, Welch MN 55089
Tel (651) 388-6300 SIC 7999 7011 5812

TORGERSON PROPERTIES INC p 1461
103 15th Ave Nw Ste 200, Willmar MN 56201
Tel (320) 235-7207 SIC 7011 5812 5813

IMPERIAL PALACE OF MISSISSIPPI LLC p 734
850 Bayview Ave, Biloxi MS 39530
Tel (228) 432-3243
SIC 7011 5812 5813 7832

JACKIES INTERNATIONAL INC p 773
1554 W Peace St, Canton MS 39046
Tel (601) 855-0146 SIC 5812 7011

RETZER RESOURCES INC p 1229
1215 S Main St, Greenville MS 38701
Tel (662) 335-7138 SIC 5812

RPM PIZZA LLC p 1255
15384 5th St, Gulfport MS 39503
Tel (228) 832-4000 SIC 5812

WEST QUALITY FOOD SERVICE INC p 1595
220 N 16th Ave, Laurel MS 39440
Tel (601) 428-4791 SIC 5812

PEARL RIVER RESORT p 1126
13541 Highway 16 W, Philadelphia MS 39350
Tel (601) 663-4438 SIC 5812 8641

MCCLAIN SONICS INC p 926
425 Christine Dr, Ridgeland MS 39157
Tel (601) 914-3401 SIC 5812

■ OLYMPIA BALLYS LIMITED PARTNERSHIP p 1083
1450 Ballys Blvd, Robinsonville MS 38664
Tel (662) 357-1500
SIC 7999 7011 5813 5812

■ ROBINSON PROPERTY GROUP LIMITED PARTNERSHIP p 1242
1021 Casino Center Dr, Robinsonville MS 38664
Tel (662) 357-5500 SIC 7011 5813 5812

■ TUNICA ROADHOUSE CORP p 1491
13615 Old Highway 61 N, Robinsonville MS 38664
Tel (662) 363-4900
SIC 7999 7011 5813 5812

■ AMERISTAR CASINO VICKSBURG INC p 83
4116 Washington St, Vicksburg MS 39180
Tel (601) 638-1000 SIC 7999 7011 5812

BURGERS OZARK COUNTRY CURED HAMS INC p 227
32819 Highway 87, California MO 65018
Tel (573) 796-3134
SIC 5147 5812 2015 2013

MIDAMERICA HOTELS CORP p 964
105 S Mount Auburn Rd, Cape Girardeau MO 63703
Tel (573) 334-0546 SIC 5812

OPAA FOOD MANAGEMENT INC p 1089
100 Chesterfield Business, Chesterfield MO 63005
Tel (636) 812-0777 SIC 5812

■ APPLEBEES INTERNATIONAL INC p 99
8140 Ward Pkwy Ste 300, Kansas City MO 64114
Tel (913) 890-0100 SIC 5812 6794

HARRAHS MARYLAND HEIGHTS OPERATING CO INC p 663
777 Casino Center Dr, Maryland Heights MO 63043
Tel (314) 770-8100 SIC 7011 5813 5812

BISTATE BISTRO ASSOCIATES LP p 185
4 Boston Crest Ct, O Fallon MO 63366
Tel (636) 537-9777 SIC 5812

BREADS OF WORLD LLC p 209
2127 Innerbelt Business C, Saint Louis MO 63114
Tel (314) 965-3304 SIC 5812 5461

DRURY DEVELOPMENT CORP p 457
721 Emerson Rd Ste 200, Saint Louis MO 63141
Tel (314) 423-6698 SIC 6512 1542 5812

HARDEES RESTAURANTS LLC p 660
100 N Broadway Ste 1200, Saint Louis MO 63102
Tel (314) 259-6200 SIC 5812

▲ PANERA BREAD CO p 1111
3630 S Geyer Rd Ste 100, Saint Louis MO 63127
Tel (314) 984-1000 SIC 5812 5461 6794

■ PARADISE BAKERY & CAFES INC p 1113
3630 S Geyer Rd Ste 400, Saint Louis MO 63127
Tel (480) 889-5347 SIC 5812

PASTA HOUSE CO p 1120
700 N New Ballas Rd, Saint Louis MO 63141
Tel (314) 535-6644 SIC 5812 5813

SCHNUCK MARKETS INC p 1288
11420 Lackland Rd, Saint Louis MO 63146
Tel (314) 994-9900
SIC 5411 5912 5812 7841

RESTAURANT SYSTEMS INC p 1228
3880 W Battlefield St, Springfield MO 65807
Tel (417) 887-5929 SIC 5812

TRADITIONAL BAKERY INC p 1469
2040 W Vista St, Springfield MO 65807
Tel (417) 889-8282 SIC 5461 5812

TOWN PUMP INC p 1465
600 S Main St, Butte MT 59701
Tel (406) 497-6700
SIC 5541 5411 7993 6512 5812

BOSSELMAN INC p 202
3123 W Stolley Park Rd, Grand Island NE 68801
Tel (308) 381-2800
SIC 5541 5411 5812 7011 5172 5084

KWS INC p 833
3048 W Stolley Park Rd, Grand Island NE 68801
Tel (308) 382-1053 SIC 5812

CONCORD HOSPITALITY INC p 354
1701 Windhoek Dr, Lincoln NE 68512
Tel (402) 421-2551 SIC 5812 7011 7311

CONCORD NEIGHBORHOOD CORP p 355
1701 Windhoek Dr, Lincoln NE 68512
Tel (402) 421-2551 SIC 5812

GROWTH MANAGEMENT CORP p 642
3201 Pioneers Blvd # 112, Lincoln NE 68502
Tel (402) 488-8500 SIC 5812 5411

HORIZON FOOD SERVICE INC p 707
6101 S 58th St Ste B, Lincoln NE 68516
Tel (402) 421-6400 SIC 5812

HORIZON HOLDINGS INC p 707
6101 S 58th St Ste B, Lincoln NE 68516
Tel (402) 421-6400 SIC 5812

CUTCHALL MANAGEMENT CO INC p 403
13305 Birch Dr Ste 201, Omaha NE 68164
Tel (402) 558-3333 SIC 5812

DRM INC p 456
5324 N 134th Ave, Omaha NE 68164
Tel (402) 573-1216 SIC 5812

GODFATHERS PIZZA INC p 619
2808 N 108th St, Omaha NE 68164
Tel (402) 391-1452 SIC 5812 6794

ROBERTS DAIRY CO LLC p 1242
2901 Cuming St, Omaha NE 68131
Tel (402) 344-4321 SIC 2026 5812

SAPP BROS INC p 1281
9915 S 148th St, Omaha NE 68138
Tel (402) 895-7038 SIC 5812

SIMMONDS RESTAURANT MANAGEMENT INC p 1324
3730 S 149th St Ste 107, Omaha NE 68144
Tel (402) 493-2300 SIC 5812

ARIZONA CHARLIES INC p 108
740 S Decatur Blvd, Las Vegas NV 89107
Tel (702) 258-5200 SIC 7011 5812 5813

■ ARK LAS VEGAS RESTAURANT CORP p 109
3790 Las Vegas Blvd S, Las Vegas NV 89109
Tel (702) 207-4498 SIC 5812

■ CAESARS WORLD INC p 237
3570 Las Vegas Blvd S, Las Vegas NV 89109
Tel (702) 731-7110
SIC 7011 7999 5812 6552 5611 5621

GOLDEN NUGGET INC p 621
129 Fremont St, Las Vegas NV 89101
Tel (702) 385-7111 SIC 5812 7011

LAS-CAL CORP p 846
3225 S Rainbow Blvd # 102, Las Vegas NV 89146
Tel (702) 880-5818 SIC 5812

■ NEW CASTLE CORP p 1029
3850 Las Vegas Blvd S, Las Vegas NV 89109
Tel (702) 597-7777 SIC 5812 7011

■ RIO PROPERTIES INC p 1236
3700 W Flamingo Rd, Las Vegas NV 89103
Tel (702) 777-7777 SIC 7011 5812

■ VENETIAN CASINO RESORT LLC p 1547
3355 Las Vegas Blvd S, Las Vegas NV 89109
Tel (702) 414-1000
SIC 7011 5812 5813 7299

■ VICTORIA PARTNERS p 1555
3770 Las Vegas Blvd S, Las Vegas NV 89109
Tel (888) 529-4828
SIC 7011 5812 7299 5813

DONALD J LAUGHLIN p 450
1650 S Casino Dr Pmb 500, Laughlin NV 89029
Tel (702) 298-2535 SIC 7993 5812

■ HARRAHS LAUGHLIN LLC p 663
2900 S Casino Dr, Laughlin NV 89029
Tel (702) 298-4600 SIC 7011 5812

TEXAS GAMBLING HALL & HOTEL INC p 1443
2101 Texas Star Ln, North Las Vegas NV 89032
Tel (702) 631-1000 SIC 7011 7999 5812

ELDORADO RESORTS LLC p 484
345 N Virginia St, Reno NV 89501
Tel (775) 786-5700 SIC 7011 5812 5813

■ GOLDEN ROAD MOTOR INN INC p 621
3800 S Virginia St, Reno NV 89502
Tel (775) 335-4521
SIC 7011 5812 5813 7299

RECREATIONAL ENTERPRISES INC p 1215
345 N Virginia St, Reno NV 89501
Tel (775) 786-5700
SIC 7011 7999 5813 5812

MARGARITAS MANAGEMENT GROUP INC p 905
200 Griffin Rd Ste 1, Portsmouth NH 03801
Tel (603) 430-8905 SIC 5812

■ BALLYS PARK PLACE INC p 149
1721 Boardwalk, Atlantic City NJ 08401
Tel (609) 340-2000 SIC 6512 5812

MARINA ASSOCIATES LTD p 906
777 Harrahs Blvd, Atlantic City NJ 08401
Tel (609) 441-5000 SIC 7011 5812

AMERICAN HUTS INC p 74
350 Passaic Ave, Fairfield NJ 07004
Tel (973) 808-9525 SIC 5812

POMPTONIAN INC p 1161
3 Edison Pl Ste 5, Fairfield NJ 07004
Tel (973) 882-8070 SIC 5812

BRIAD CORP p 211
78 Okner Pkwy, Livingston NJ 07039
Tel (973) 597-6433 SIC 5812

BRIAD MAIN STREET INC p 211
78 Okner Pkwy, Livingston NJ 07039
Tel (973) 597-6433 SIC 5812

BRIAD RESTAURANT GROUP LLC p 211
78 Okner Pkwy, Livingston NJ 07039
Tel (973) 597-6433 SIC 5812

VILLA PIZZA INC p 1557
3 South St, Morristown NJ 07960
Tel (973) 285-4800 SIC 5812

BUGABOO CREEK HOLDINGS INC p 224
1450 Us Highway 22 Ste 4, Mountainside NJ 07092
Tel (908) 518-1800 SIC 5812

FERRARO FOODS INC p 538
287 S Randolphville Rd, Piscataway NJ 08854
Tel (732) 424-3400 SIC 5149 5812

LPG ENTERPRISES INC p 882
12854 Eastridge Dr Ne, Albuquerque NM 87112
Tel (505) 299-4155 SIC 5812

B & B CONSULTANTS INC p 141
750 N 17th St, Las Cruces NM 88005
Tel (575) 524-8998 SIC 5812

J & B RESTAURANT PARTNERS OF LONG ISLAND LLC p 769
4000 Veterans Memorial Hw, Bohemia NY 11716
Tel (631) 218-9067 SIC 5812

DELAWARE NORTH COMPANIES SPORTSERVICE INC p 424
250 Delaware Ave, Buffalo NY 14202
Tel (716) 858-5000 SIC 5812

DELAWARE NORTH COMPANIES TRAVEL HOSPITALITY SERVICES INC p 424
250 Delaware Ave Ste 3, Buffalo NY 14202
Tel (716) 858-5000 SIC 5812 5947 5813

DNC LANDMARK HOLDINGS LLC p 446
40 Fountain Plz, Buffalo NY 14202
Tel (716) 858-5000 SIC 5812

JETRO HOLDINGS LLC p 784
1506 132nd St, College Point NY 11356
Tel (718) 762-8700 SIC 5149 5141 5812

APPLE-METRO INC p 99
550 Mmaroneck Ave Ste 204, Harrison NY 10528
Tel (914) 777-2331 SIC 5812

WHITSONS FOOD SERVICE CORP p 1607
1800 Motor Pkwy, Islandia NY 11749
Tel (631) 424-2700 SIC 5812

▲ NATHANS FAMOUS INC p 1009
1 Jericho Plz Fl 2, Jericho NY 11753
Tel (516) 338-8500 SIC 5812 6794

AYCO CAFE p 140
25 British American Blvd, Latham NY 12110
Tel (518) 782-5080 SIC 5812

AMERICAN FOOD & VENDING CORP p 72
124 Metropolitan Park Dr, Liverpool NY 13088
Tel (315) 457-9950 SIC 5962 5812

SBARRO HOLDINGS LLC p 1285
401 Broadhollow Rd Ll10, Melville NY 11747
Tel (631) 715-4100 SIC 5812 6794

SBARRO INC p 1285
401 Broadhollow Rd Ll10, Melville NY 11747
Tel (631) 715-4100 SIC 5812 6794

APAX PARTNERS OF NEW YORK p 96
601 Lexington Ave Fl 53, New York NY 10022
Tel (212) 419-2447
SIC 6282 5399 5199 5812 5813

▲ ARK RESTAURANTS CORP p 109
85 5th Ave, New York NY 10003
Tel (212) 206-8800 SIC 5812 5813

CASTLE HARLAN PARTNERS III LP p 264
150 E 58th St Fl 38, New York NY 10155
Tel (212) 644-8600
SIC 5812 6282 6211 8732

CLAYTON DUBILIER & RICE INC p 323
375 Park Ave Fl 18, New York NY 10152
Tel (212) 407-5200 SIC 6799 3589 5812

CPS 1 REALTY LP p 387
768 5th Ave, New York NY 10019
Tel (212) 759-3000 SIC 7011 7299 5812

DEAN & DE LUCA BRANDS INC p 420
560 Broadway Frnt 2, New York NY 10012
Tel (212) 226-6800 SIC 5499 5812 2099

DEAN & DELUCA INC p 420
560 Broadway Frnt 2, New York NY 10012
Tel (212) 226-6800
SIC 5499 5812 5961 2099

METROMEDIA CO p 955
810 Seventh Ave Fl 29, New York NY 10019
Tel (212) 606-4437
SIC 5812 6794 4813 4911

NATIONAL RESTAURANTS MANAGEMENT INC p 1015
560 5th Ave Fl 3, New York NY 10036
Tel (212) 563-7440 SIC 5812 6531

NATIONAL RESTAURANTS MANAGEMENT INC p 1015
604 5th Ave Fl 5, New York NY 10020
Tel (212) 563-7440 SIC 5812

OAK HILL CAPITAL PARTNERS III LP p 1070
65 E 55th St Fl 32, New York NY 10022
Tel (212) 527-8400
SIC 5812 5813 7999 7993

▲ ONE GROUP HOSPITALITY INC p 1086
411 W 14th St Fl 3, New York NY 10014
Tel (212) 277-5301 SIC 5812

OTG EXP INC p 1097
352 Park Ave S Fl 10, New York NY 10010
Tel (212) 776-1478 SIC 5812

P&MCS HOLDING LLC p 1102
150 E 58th St, New York NY 10155
Tel (212) 644-8600 SIC 5812

PQ NEW YORK INC p 1166
50 Broad St Fl 12, New York NY 10004
Tel (212) 359-9000 SIC 5812

PRET A MANGER (USA) LIMITED p 1173
853 Broadway Ste 700, New York NY 10003
Tel (646) 728-0505 SIC 5812

RESTAURANT ASSOCIATES CORP p 1228
132 W 31st St Rm 601, New York NY 10001
Tel (212) 613-5500 SIC 5812

RESTAURANT ASSOCIATES LLC p 1228
132 W 31st St Rm 601, New York NY 10001
Tel (212) 613-5500 SIC 5812

ROSA MEXICANO MIAMI LLC p 1250
846 7th Ave Fl 4, New York NY 10019
Tel (212) 397-0666 SIC 5812

SENTINEL CAPITAL PARTNERS LLC p 1305
330 Madison Ave Fl 27, New York NY 10017
Tel (212) 688-3100 SIC 5812

▲ SHAKE SHACK INC p 1310
24 Union Sq E Fl 5, New York NY 10003
Tel (646) 747-7200 SIC 5812

SUNTORY INTERNATIONAL CORP p 1405
600 3rd Ave Fl 21, New York NY 10016
Tel (212) 891-6600
SIC 5149 2084 2086 5499 5812

TAXI HOLDINGS CORP p 1426
390 Park Ave, New York NY 10022
Tel (212) 318-9800 SIC 5812 6794

WELLSPRING CAPITAL MANAGEMENT LLC p 1591
390 Park Ave Fl 5, New York NY 10022
Tel (212) 318-9800 SIC 5812

WELLSPRING CAPITAL PARTNERS III LP p 1591
390 Park Ave Fl 5, New York NY 10022
Tel (212) 318-9800
SIC 5812 5813 7999 7993

WELLSPRING DISTRIBUTION INC p 1591
390 Park Ave Fl 5, New York NY 10022
Tel (212) 318-9800 SIC 6794 5812

WS MIDWAY HOLDINGS INC p 1628
390 Park Ave Fl 6, New York NY 10022
Tel (212) 318-9800
SIC 5812 5813 7999 7993

ONEIDA INDIAN NATION p 1087
2037 Dream Catcher Plz, Oneida NY 13421
Tel (315) 829-8900 SIC 5812

AUXILIARY SERVICES STATE UNIVERSITY COLLEGE AT OSWEGO INC p 135
7060 Route 104, Oswego NY 13126
Tel (315) 312-2106
SIC 5812 5942 5962 5441

CULINART INC p 400
175 Sunnyside Blvd # 200, Plainview NY 11803
Tel (516) 437-2700 SIC 5812

KESSLER FAMILY LLC p 814
410 White Spruce Blvd, Rochester NY 14623
Tel (585) 424-5277 SIC 5812

V & J NATIONAL AND UNITED ENTERPRISES LLC p 1538
1425 Mount Read Blvd # 1, Rochester NY 14606
Tel (585) 458-8140 SIC 5812

V & J NATIONAL ENTERPRISES LLC p 1538
1425 Mount Read Blvd # 1, Rochester NY 14606
Tel (585) 458-8140 SIC 5812

J & B RESTAURANT PARTNERS OF LONG ISLAND INC p 769
3385 Vtrans Mem Hwy Ste A, Ronkonkoma NY 11779
Tel (631) 218-9067 SIC 5812

FLIK INTERNATIONAL CORP p 557
2 International Dr Fl 2, Rye Brook NY 10573
Tel (914) 935-5300 SIC 8742 5812

■ **CARROLS CORP** p 261
968 James St, Syracuse NY 13203
Tel (315) 424-0513 SIC 5812

■ **CARROLS LLC** p 261
968 James St, Syracuse NY 13203
Tel (315) 424-0513 SIC 5812

▲ **CARROLS RESTAURANT GROUP INC** p 261
968 James St, Syracuse NY 13203
Tel (315) 424-0513 SIC 5812 6794

FIESTA RESTAURANT GROUP INC p 541
968 James St, Syracuse NY 13203
Tel (315) 424-0513 SIC 5812

LACKMANN FOOD SERVICE INC p 837
303 Crossways Park Dr, Woodbury NY 11797
Tel (516) 364-2300 SIC 5812

BILTMORE CO p 183
1 Lodge St, Asheville NC 28803
Tel (828) 225-6776 SIC 7999 5947 5812

GROVE PARK INN RESORT INC p 642
290 Macon Ave, Asheville NC 28804
Tel (828) 252-2711
SIC 7011 5812 5813 7992 7991 7299

OMNI GROVE PARK LLC p 1084
290 Macon Ave, Asheville NC 28804
Tel (828) 252-2711
SIC 7299 5812 7011 5813 7992 7991

FFC LIMITED PARTNERSHIP p 539
166 Southgate Dr Ste 10, Boone NC 28607
Tel (828) 262-1811 SIC 5812

TAR HEEL CAPITAL CORP NO 2 p 1424
166 Southgate Dr Ste 10, Boone NC 28607
Tel (828) 264-4221 SIC 5812

MORALE WELFARE RECREATION ACTIVITY p 988
1401 West Rd, Camp Lejeune NC 28547
Tel (910) 451-2861
SIC 5311 5812 8322 7999 9711

ALLIANCE DEVELOPMENT GROUP LLC p 54
301 S Tryon St Ste 1500, Charlotte NC 28282
Tel (704) 973-2950 SIC 5812 6552

BJ HOLDINGS CORP p 185
9432 Southern Pine Blvd, Charlotte NC 28273
Tel (704) 527-2675 SIC 5812 6794

BOJANGLES HOLDINGS INC p 198
9432 Southern Pine Blvd, Charlotte NC 28273
Tel (704) 527-2675 SIC 5812

▲ **BOJANGLES INC** p 198
9432 Southern Pine Blvd, Charlotte NC 28273
Tel (704) 527-2675 SIC 5812

■ **BOJANGLES RESTAURANTS INC** p 198
9432 Southern Pine Blvd, Charlotte NC 28273
Tel (704) 527-2675 SIC 5812 6794

CAROLINA RESTAURANT GROUP INC p 259
8040 Arrowridge Blvd # 100, Charlotte NC 28273
Tel (704) 525-3434 SIC 5812

COMPASS GROUP USA INC p 351
2400 Yorkmont Rd, Charlotte NC 28217
Tel (704) 329-4000 SIC 5812

COMPASS HOLDINGS INC p 351
2400 Yorkmont Rd, Charlotte NC 28217
Tel (704) 328-4000 SIC 5812 5962

FIREBIRDS INTERNATIONAL LLC p 543
13850 Balntyn Corp Pl # 450, Charlotte NC 28277
Tel (704) 944-5180 SIC 5812

TRUSTHOUSE SERVICES GROUP INC p 1488
4135 Southstream Blvd # 250, Charlotte NC 28217
Tel (704) 424-1071 SIC 5812

■ **SAGEBRUSH INC** p 1268
112 Main St, Claremont NC 28610
Tel (828) 459-0821 SIC 5812

BATTLEGROUND RESTAURANT GROUP INC p 160
1337 Winstead Pl, Greensboro NC 27408
Tel (336) 272-9355 SIC 5812

HAMS RESTAURANTS INC p 656
3017 W Gate City Blvd # 2, Greensboro NC 27403
Tel (336) 851-4800 SIC 5812 5813

PLATINUM CORRAL LLC p 1155
521 New Bridge St, Jacksonville NC 28540
Tel (910) 347-3971 SIC 5812

CLAREMONT RESTAURANT GROUP LLC p 321
129 Fast Ln, Mooresville NC 28117
Tel (704) 660-5939 SIC 5812

LUIHN FOOD SYSTEMS INC p 884
2950 Gateway Centre Blvd, Morrisville NC 27560
Tel (919) 850-0558 SIC 5812

PINEHURST LLC p 1149
80 Carolina Vista Dr, Pinehurst NC 28374
Tel (910) 295-6811
SIC 7011 7997 7992 5813 5812

APPLE GOLD INC p 98
164 Wind Chime Ct, Raleigh NC 27615
Tel (919) 846-2577 SIC 5812

GOLDEN CORRAL CORP p 620
5151 Glenwood Ave Ste 300, Raleigh NC 27612
Tel (919) 781-9310 SIC 5812

GREEN APPLE LLC p 636
164 Wind Chime Ct, Raleigh NC 27615
Tel (919) 846-2577 SIC 5812

INVESTORS MANAGEMENT CORP p 761
801 N West St, Raleigh NC 27603
Tel (919) 653-7499 SIC 5812 8741

NEW APPLE INC p 1029
170 Wind Chime Ct, Raleigh NC 27615
Tel (919) 870-0513 SIC 5812

BAY FOODS INC p 161
1021 Noell Ln, Rocky Mount NC 27804
Tel (252) 937-2000 SIC 5812

BODDIE-NOELL ENTERPRISES INC p 197
1021 Noell Ln, Rocky Mount NC 27804
Tel (252) 937-2000 SIC 5812 6552

ECPH MANAGEMENT INC p 476
2317 Professional Dr, Rocky Mount NC 27804
Tel (252) 443-4028 SIC 5812

GUARDIAN CORP p 645
3801 Sunset Ave Ste A, Rocky Mount NC 27804
Tel (252) 443-4101 SIC 5812

K & W CAFETERIAS INC p 798
1391 Plaza West Dr, Winston Salem NC 27103
Tel (336) 780-0526 SIC 5812

WILCOHESS LLC p 1608
5446 University Pkwy, Winston Salem NC 27105
Tel (336) 767-6280 SIC 5461 5812 5541

TRI-ENERGY COOPERATIVE p 1477
219 N 20th St, Bismarck ND 58501
Tel (701) 223-8707 SIC 5812 5541 5251

APPLE CORE ENTERPRISES INC p 98
1400 31st Ave Sw, Minot ND 58701
Tel (701) 838-2822 SIC 5812

HEIDMAN INC p 680
500 Grant St, Akron OH 44311
Tel (330) 535-8400 SIC 5812

FOOD FOLKS & FUN INC p 564
4354 Glendale Milford Rd, Blue Ash OH 45242
Tel (513) 769-4386 SIC 5812

AVALON FOODSERVICE INC p 135
1 Avalon Dr, Canal Fulton OH 44614
Tel (330) 854-4551
SIC 5142 5149 5169 5113 8322 5812

BISTRO MANAGEMENT INC p 185
5803 Mariemont Ave, Cincinnati OH 45227
Tel (513) 271-2349 SIC 5812

BUFFALO WINGS & RINGS LLC p 224
564 Old State Route 74 # 3, Cincinnati OH 45244
Tel (513) 831-9464 SIC 5812

CAROCO INC p 259
8635 Colerain Ave, Cincinnati OH 45251
Tel (513) 385-1244 SIC 5812

■ **FRISCHS OHIO INC** p 580
2800 Gilbert Ave, Cincinnati OH 45206
Tel (513) 961-2660 SIC 5812

FRISCHS RESTAURANTS INC p 580
2800 Gilbert Ave, Cincinnati OH 45206
Tel (513) 961-2660 SIC 5812

LAROSAS INC p 845
2334 Boudinot Ave, Cincinnati OH 45238
Tel (513) 347-5660
SIC 5812 6794 5141 5921

RESTAURANT MANAGEMENT INC p 1228
300 Main St, Cincinnati OH 45202
Tel (513) 362-8900 SIC 5812

APPLE AMERICAN LIMITED PARTNERSHIP OF OHIO p 98
8905 Lake Ave, Cleveland OH 44102
Tel (216) 961-6767 SIC 5812

APPLE AMERICAN LP OF INDIANA p 98
8905 Lake Ave Fl 2, Cleveland OH 44102
Tel (216) 961-6767 SIC 5812

MORGANS FOODS INC p 989
4829 Galaxy Pkwy Ste S, Cleveland OH 44128
Tel (216) 359-9000 SIC 5812

MORGANS RESTAURANT OF PENNSYLVANIA INC p 989
24200 Chagrin Blvd # 126, Cleveland OH 44122
Tel (216) 360-7500 SIC 5812

▲ **BRAVO BRIO RESTAURANT GROUP INC** p 209
777 Goodale Blvd Ste 100, Columbus OH 43212
Tel (614) 326-7944 SIC 5812

CAMERON MITCHELL RESTAURANTS LLC p 245
515 Park St, Columbus OH 43215
Tel (614) 621-3663 SIC 8741 5812

DAMONS INTERNATIONAL INC p 410
4645 Executive Dr, Columbus OH 43220
Tel (614) 442-7900 SIC 6794 8741 5812

DONATOS PIZZERIA LLC p 450
935 Taylor Station Rd, Columbus OH 43230
Tel (614) 864-2444 SIC 5812

OHIO STATE UNIVERSITY p 1078
Student Acade Servi Bldg, Columbus OH 43210
Tel (614) 292-6446 SIC 8221 5812

SBARRO LLC p 1285
1328 Dublin Rd Ste 21, Columbus OH 43215
Tel (614) 769-9911 SIC 5812

WHITE CASTLE SYSTEM INC p 1606
555 W Goodale St, Columbus OH 43215
Tel (614) 228-5781
SIC 5812 5142 2051 2013

G Z K INC p 587
660 Fame Rd, Dayton OH 45449
Tel (937) 461-7500 SIC 5812

THOMAS FIVE LTD p 1448
5131 Post Rd Ste 203, Dublin OH 43017
Tel (614) 764-9495 SIC 5812

▲ **WENDYS CO** p 1592
1 Dave Thomas Blvd, Dublin OH 43017
Tel (614) 764-3100 SIC 5812 6794

■ **WENDYS INTERNATIONAL LLC** p 1592
1 Dave Thomas Blvd, Dublin OH 43017
Tel (614) 764-3100 SIC 5812

■ **WENDYS OF DENVER INC** p 1592
4288 W Dblin Granville Rd, Dublin OH 43017
Tel (614) 764-3100 SIC 5812

■ **WENDYS OF NE FLORIDA INC** p 1592
4288 W Dblin Granville Rd, Dublin OH 43017
Tel (614) 764-3100 SIC 5812

■ **WENDYS OLD FASHIONED HAMBURGERS OF NEW YORK LLC** p 1592
4288 W Dblin Granville Rd, Dublin OH 43017
Tel (614) 764-3100 SIC 5812

■ **WENDYS RESTAURANTS LLC** p 1592
1 Dave Thomas Blvd, Dublin OH 43017
Tel (614) 764-3100 SIC 5812 6794

SKYLINE CHILI INC p 1330
4180 Thunderbird Ln, Fairfield OH 45014
Tel (513) 874-1188
SIC 5812 2038 6794 5149 2032

APPLE AMERICAN GROUP LLC p 98
6200 Oak Tree Blvd # 250, Independence OH 44131
Tel (216) 525-2775 SIC 5812

MIDLAND FOOD SERVICES LLC p 965
6200 Rockside Woods Blvd # 315, Independence OH 44131
Tel (216) 524-2251 SIC 5812

▲ **BOB EVANS FARMS INC** p 196
8111 Smiths Mill Rd, New Albany OH 43054
Tel (614) 491-2225
SIC 5812 2011 2099 2035

■ **BOB EVANS FARMS LLC** p 196
8111 Smiths Mill Rd, New Albany OH 43054
Tel (614) 491-2225 SIC 5812

B P L CORP p 142
27476 Holiday Ln, Perrysburg OH 43551
Tel (419) 874-1933 SIC 5812

BENNETT ENTERPRISES INC p 173
27476 Holiday Ln, Perrysburg OH 43551
Tel (419) 874-1933 SIC 7011 5812

DUTCHMAN HOSPITALITY GROUP INC p 463
4985 State Rte 515, Walnut Creek OH 44687
Tel (330) 893-2926 SIC 5812

AVI FOOD SYSTEMS INC p 137
2590 Elm Rd Ne, Warren OH 44483
Tel (330) 372-6000 SIC 5962 5812 8742

CADLE LIMITED LIABILITY CO p 236
3900 E Market St, Warren OH 44484
Tel (330) 856-3176 SIC 5812

COVELLI ENTERPRISES INC p 384
3900 E Market St Ste 1, Warren OH 44484
Tel (330) 856-3176 SIC 5812

SANESE SERVICES INC p 1279
2590 Elm Rd Ne, Warren OH 44483
Tel (614) 436-1234 SIC 5962 5812 7389

■ **TA OPERATING LLC** p 1420
24601 Center Ridge Rd # 200, Westlake OH 44145
Tel (440) 808-9100
SIC 5541 7538 5812 5411 6794

■ **TRAVELCENTERS OF AMERICA INC** p 1474
24601 Center Ridge Rd # 200, Westlake OH 44145
Tel (440) 808-9100
SIC 5541 7538 5812 5411

▲ **TRAVELCENTERS OF AMERICA LLC** p 1474
24601 Center Ridge Rd # 200, Westlake OH 44145
Tel (440) 808-9100 SIC 5541 5812 7538

DENN-OHIO LLC p 428
1002 Armstrong Dr, Willard OH 44890
Tel (419) 544-4030 SIC 5812

EATERIES INC p 473
1220 S Santa Fe Ave, Edmond OK 73003
Tel (480) 347-3800 SIC 5812 5813 6794

BRAUMS INC p 208
3000 Ne 63rd St, Oklahoma City OK 73121
Tel (405) 478-1656 SIC 5411 5812

M & D INDUSTRIES CORP p 888
2701 W I 44 Service Rd # 102, Oklahoma City OK 73112
Tel (405) 942-2936 SIC 5812

▲ **SONIC CORP** p 1340
300 Johnny Bench Dr, Oklahoma City OK 73104
Tel (405) 225-5000 SIC 5812 6794

■ **SONIC INDUSTRIES SERVICES INC** p 1340
300 Johnny Bench Dr # 400, Oklahoma City OK 73104
Tel (405) 225-5000 SIC 6794 5812

W H BRAUM INC p 1568
3000 Ne 63rd St, Oklahoma City OK 73121
Tel (405) 478-1656 SIC 5451 5812

MAZZIOS LLC p 924
4441 S 72nd East Ave, Tulsa OK 74145
Tel (918) 663-8880 SIC 5812 6794

UNITED STATES BEEF CORP p 1512
4923 E 49th St, Tulsa OK 74135
Tel (918) 665-0740 SIC 5812

KAIZEN RESTAURANTS INC p 801
16500 Nw Bethany Ct # 150, Beaverton OR 97006
Tel (214) 221-7599 SIC 5812

SHARIS MANAGEMENT CORP p 1312
9400 Sw Gemini Dr, Beaverton OR 97008
Tel (503) 605-4299 SIC 5812

PMD RESTAURANTS LLC p 1157
2117 Elkhorn Dr, Eugene OR 97408
Tel (541) 684-7655 SIC 5812

ELMERS RESTAURANTS INC p 489
8338 Ne Alderwood Rd, Portland OR 97220
Tel (503) 252-1485 SIC 6794 5812

MCCORMICK & SCHMICK HOLDING CORP p 927
720 Sw Washington St # 550, Portland OR 97205
Tel (800) 552-6379 SIC 5812

MCMENAMINS INC p 932
430 N Killingsworth St, Portland OR 97217
Tel (503) 223-0109 SIC 5813 5812

OSF INTERNATIONAL INC p 1096
0715 Sw Bancroft St, Portland OR 97239
Tel (503) 222-5375 SIC 5812 6794

MCGRATHS PUBLICK FISH HOUSE LLC p 929
1935 Davcor St Se, Salem OR 97302
Tel (503) 399-8456 SIC 5812

LEHIGH VALLEY RESTAURANT GROUP INC p 854
6802a Hamilton Blvd, Allentown PA 18106
Tel (610) 481-0436 SIC 5812

WOOD CO p 1622
6081 Hamilton Blvd, Allentown PA 18106
Tel (610) 366-5204 SIC 5812

FAMILY DINING INC p 526
1780 Swede Rd, Blue Bell PA 19422
Tel (610) 277-4200 SIC 5812

U S RESTAURANTS INC p 1497
1780 Swede Rd, Blue Bell PA 19422
Tel (610) 277-4200 SIC 5812

SUMMERWOOD CORP p 1398
14 Balligomingo Rd, Conshohocken PA 19428
Tel (610) 260-1500 SIC 5812

S&S CULINARY MANAGEMENT LLC p 1263
2 Woodland Dr, Dallas PA 18612
Tel (570) 675-8100 SIC 5812

HOSSS STEAK & SEA HOUSE INC p 710
170 Patchway Rd, Duncansville PA 16635
Tel (814) 695-7600 SIC 5812 5146 5046

PATTERSON-ERIE CORP p 1121
1250 Tower Ln Ste 1, Erie PA 16505
Tel (814) 455-8031 SIC 5812 6531 4522

NUTRITION INC p 1068
580 Wendel Rd Ste 100, Irwin PA 15642
Tel (724) 978-2100 SIC 5812 2099

TWOTON INC p 1495
1743 Rohrerstown Rd, Lancaster PA 17601
Tel (717) 569-5791 SIC 5812

UNIQUE VENTURES GROUP LLC p 1505
231 Chestnut St Ste 302, Meadville PA 16335
Tel (814) 337-6300 SIC 5812

■ **EMPIRE KOSHER POULTRY INC** p 493
Chicken Plant Rd, Mifflintown PA 17059
Tel (717) 436-5921 SIC 2015 5812

ROSE CASUAL DINING INC p 1250
826 Newtown Yardley Rd, Newtown PA 18940
Tel (215) 579-9220 SIC 5812

ROSE MANAGEMENT SERVICES p 1250
29 Friends Ln, Newtown PA 18940
Tel (215) 867-1802 SIC 5812

▲ **ARAMARK CORP** p 102
1101 Market St Ste 45, Philadelphia PA 19107
Tel (215) 238-3000 SIC 5812 7218 5136

■ **ARAMARK HEALTHCARE SUPPORT SERVICES OF TEXAS INC** p 102
1101 Market St, Philadelphia PA 19107
Tel (215) 238-3000 SIC 5812

■ **ARAMARK INTERMEDIATE HOLDCO CORP** p 102
1101 Market St Ste 45, Philadelphia PA 19107
Tel (215) 238-3000 SIC 5812 7218 5136

■ **ARAMARK SERVICES INC** p 102
1101 Market St Ste 45, Philadelphia PA 19107
Tel (215) 238-3000 SIC 5812 7218 5136

■ **ARAMARK SPORTS AND ENTERTAINMENT GROUP LLC** p 102
1101 Market St, Philadelphia PA 19107
Tel (215) 238-3000 SIC 5812

■ **ARAMARK UNIFORM & CAREER APPAREL GROUP INC** p 102
1101 Market St Ste 45, Philadelphia PA 19107
Tel (215) 238-3000
SIC 2337 2311 5699 5961 5661 5812

■ **HARRY M STEVENS INC OF NEW JERSEY** p 664
1101 Market St, Philadelphia PA 19107
Tel (215) 238-3000 SIC 5812

ABARTA INC p 9
200 Alpha Dr, Pittsburgh PA 15238
Tel (412) 963-6226
SIC 2086 2711 2721 5149 1382 5812

M & J MANAGEMENT CORP p 888
147 Delta Dr, Pittsburgh PA 15238
Tel (412) 963-6550 SIC 5812

P D M CO INC p 1102
185 Ferguson Ave, Shavertown PA 18708
Tel (570) 675-3636 SIC 5812

B M J FOODS PR INC p 142
Carr 175 Km 0 2 Bo Rio Ca St Ca, Caguas PR 00725
Tel (787) 286-7040 SIC 5812

CARIBBEAN RESTAURANTS LLC p 256
Rd 5 Km 27 4 Bldg 1, Catano PR 00962
Tel (787) 474-7777 SIC 5812

INTERNATIONAL RESTAURANT SERVICES INC p 756
Amelia Dist Ctr 23 Ema St, Guaynabo PR 00968
Tel (787) 273-3131 SIC 5813 5812

WENDCO OF PUERTO RICO INC p 1591
1155 Ave Ponce De Leon, San Juan PR 00907
Tel (787) 792-2001 SIC 5812

CENTRAARCHY RESTAURANT MANAGEMENT CO p 277
236 Albemarle Rd, Charleston SC 29407
Tel (843) 571-0096 SIC 5812

RO HO HO INC p 1240
1479 Tobias Gadson Blvd, Charleston SC 29407
Tel (877) 547-7272 SIC 5812

WHIT-MART INC p 1605
56 Wentworth St, Charleston SC 29401
Tel (843) 720-5010 SIC 5812

CALHOUN MANAGEMENT CORP p 238
108f Elm St, Clemson SC 29631
Tel (864) 624-9962 SIC 5812

JOHNSON FOOD SERVICES LLC p 791
Forney Smter St Bldg 3290, Columbia SC 29207
Tel (803) 782-1461 SIC 5812

SPINX CO INC p 1358
1414 E Washington St N, Greenville SC 29607
Tel (864) 233-5421 SIC 5541 5411 5812

FIRST SUN MANAGEMENT CORP p 549
127 Kiowa Ln, Piedmont SC 29673
Tel (864) 654-5099 SIC 5812

▲ **DENNYS CORP** p 428
203 E Main St, Spartanburg SC 29319
Tel (864) 597-8000 SIC 5812 6794

■ **DENNYS INC** p 428
2306 Reidville Rd, Spartanburg SC 29301
Tel (864) 597-8532 SIC 5812 6794

■ **DENNYS INC** p 428
203 E Main St P-73, Spartanburg SC 29319
Tel (864) 597-8000 SIC 5812

R L JORDAN OIL CO OF NORTH CAROLINA INC p 1202
1451 Fernwood Glendale Rd, Spartanburg SC 29307
Tel (864) 585-2784
SIC 5411 5172 5541 5812

CAFE ENTERPRISES INC p 237
4324 Wade Hampton Blvd B, Taylors SC 29687
Tel (864) 322-1331 SIC 5812

DAKOTA KING INC p 409
3800 W 53rd St, Sioux Falls SD 57106
Tel (605) 361-7714 SIC 5812

CRAFTWORKS RESTAURANTS & BREWERIES LLC p 388
201 W Main St Ste 301, Chattanooga TN 37408
Tel (423) 424-2000 SIC 5812

FIVE STAR FOOD SERVICE INC p 553
6005 Century Oaks Dr # 100, Chattanooga TN 37416
Tel (423) 490-4428 SIC 5962 5812 7389

JRN INC p 795
209 W 7th St, Columbia TN 38401
Tel (931) 381-3000 SIC 5812

DYNAMIC RESTAURANTS LLC p 464
313 E Mn St, Hendersonville TN 37075
Tel (615) 277-1234 SIC 5812

BROS MANAGEMENT INC p 218
2501 E Magnolia Ave, Knoxville TN 37914
Tel (865) 523-2157 SIC 5812

CFJ PROPERTIES LLC p 285
5508 Lonas Dr, Knoxville TN 37909
Tel (801) 624-1000 SIC 5541 5812 5411

COPPER CELLAR CORP p 368
3001 Industrial Pkwy E, Knoxville TN 37921
Tel (865) 673-3400 SIC 5812 5813

MID AMERICA CORP p 962
2812 N Broadway St, Knoxville TN 37917
Tel (865) 524-3477 SIC 5812

PENNANT FOODS LLC p 1129
310 Corporate Dr Ste 103, Knoxville TN 37923
Tel (865) 691-1393 SIC 5812

■ **REGAL CINEMAS CORP** p 1218
7132 Regal Ln, Knoxville TN 37918
Tel (865) 922-1123 SIC 7832 5812

SHONEYS OF KNOXVILLE INC p 1317
9720 Parkside Dr, Knoxville TN 37922
Tel (865) 690-6331 SIC 5812

■ **CBOCS TEXAS LLC** p 268
305 S Hartmann Dr, Lebanon TN 37087
Tel (615) 235-4096 SIC 5812

▲ **CRACKER BARREL OLD COUNTRY STORE INC** p 388
305 S Hartmann Dr, Lebanon TN 37087
Tel (615) 444-5533 SIC 5812 5947

▲ **RUBY TUESDAY INC** p 1257
150 W Church Ave, Maryville TN 37801
Tel (865) 379-5700 SIC 5812 5813 6794

CARLISLE LLC p 257
263 Wagner Pl, Memphis TN 38103
Tel (901) 526-5000 SIC 5812 8741 6531

■ **DOUBLETREE INC** p 452
755 Crossover Ln, Memphis TN 38117
Tel (901) 374-5000 SIC 7011 5812 5813

MARIE CALLENDER PIE SHOPS INC p 906
6075 Poplar Ave Ste 800, Memphis TN 38119
Tel (901) 766-6400 SIC 5812

MIRABILE INVESTMENT CORP p 974
1900 Whitten Rd, Memphis TN 38133
Tel (901) 873-1187 SIC 5812

PERKINS & MARIE CALLENDERS HOLDING INC p 1136
6075 Poplar Ave Ste 800, Memphis TN 38119
Tel (901) 766-6400 SIC 5812

PERKINS & MARIE CALLENDERS LLC p 1136
6075 Poplar Ave Ste 800, Memphis TN 38119
Tel (901) 766-6400 SIC 5812 6794

WENDELTA INC p 1592
263 Wagner Pl, Memphis TN 38103
Tel (901) 526-5000 SIC 5812

CHARTER FOODS INC p 291
5139 Old Highway 11e, Morristown TN 37814
Tel (423) 587-0690 SIC 5812

AMERICAN BLUE RIBBON HOLDINGS LLC p 69
3038 Sidco Dr, Nashville TN 37204
Tel (615) 256-8500 SIC 5812 6794

B F NASHVILLE INC p 141
1101 Kermit Dr Ste 310, Nashville TN 37217
Tel (615) 399-9700 SIC 5812

CAPTAIN DS LLC p 252
624 Grassmere Park Ste 30, Nashville TN 37211
Tel (615) 391-5461 SIC 5812

J ALEXANDERS HOLDINGS INC p 770
3401 West End Ave Ste 260, Nashville TN 37203
Tel (615) 250-1602 SIC 5812

■ **J ALEXANDERS LLC** p 770
3401 West End Ave Ste 260, Nashville TN 37203
Tel (615) 269-1900 SIC 5812

LOGANS ROADHOUSE INC p 874
3011 Armory Dr Ste 300, Nashville TN 37204
Tel (615) 885-9056 SIC 5812

LRI HOLDINGS INC p 882
3011 Armory Dr Ste 300, Nashville TN 37204
Tel (615) 885-9056 SIC 5812 6794

OCHARLEYS LLC p 1073
3038 Sidco Dr, Nashville TN 37204
Tel (615) 256-8500 SIC 5812

RESTAURANT MANAGEMENT GROUP p 1228
902 Murfreesboro Pike, Nashville TN 37217
Tel (423) 349-6204 SIC 5812

ROADHOUSE INTERMEDIATE INC p 1240
3011 Armory Dr Ste 300, Nashville TN 37204
Tel (615) 885-9056 SIC 5812

ROADHOUSE MIDCO INC p 1240
3011 Armory Dr Ste 300, Nashville TN 37204
Tel (615) 885-9056 SIC 5812 6794

ROADHOUSE PARENT INC p 1240
3011 Armory Dr Ste 300, Nashville TN 37204
Tel (615) 885-9056 SIC 5812 6794

SHONEYS NORTH AMERICA LLC p 1317
1717 Elm Hill Pike Ste B1, Nashville TN 37210
Tel (615) 231-2333 SIC 6794 8741 5812

GREAT AMERICAN DELI p 633
5828 Main St, Ooltewah TN 37363
Tel (423) 238-5492 SIC 5812

L&S SERVICES LLC p 834
501 W Broad St, Smithville TN 37166
Tel (615) 597-6278 SIC 5812

BL RESTAURANT OPERATIONS LLC p 186
4550 Beltway Dr, Addison TX 75001
Tel (972) 386-5567 SIC 5812 5813 6794

SOUPER SALAD INC p 1342
4004 Belt Line Rd Ste 100, Addison TX 75001
Tel (972) 761-1790 SIC 5812

CATERAIR HOLDINGS CORP p 265
524 E Lamar Blvd, Arlington TX 76011
Tel (817) 792-2100 SIC 5812

AUSTIN TACALA CORP p 133
500 N Capitl Of Texas Hwy, Austin TX 78746
Tel (512) 327-4654 SIC 5812

■ **BROSNA INC** p 218
5700 S Mo Pac Expy # 300, Austin TX 78749
Tel (512) 936-7600 SIC 5812

▲ **CHUYS HOLDINGS INC** p 305
1623 Toomey Rd, Austin TX 78704
Tel (512) 473-2783 SIC 5812

■ **CHUYS ON HWY 183 INC** p 305
1623 Toomey Rd, Austin TX 78704
Tel (512) 473-2783 SIC 5812

CHUYS OPCO INC p 305
1623 Toomey Rd, Austin TX 78704
Tel (512) 473-2783 SIC 5812

K & N MANAGEMENT INC p 798
11570 Research Blvd, Austin TX 78759
Tel (512) 418-0444 SIC 5411 5812

MGI HOLDINGS LP p 958
5912 Balcones Dr, Austin TX 78731
Tel (512) 459-4796 SIC 5812 6794

MR GATTIS LP p 996
5912 Balcones Dr Ste 200, Austin TX 78731
Tel (512) 459-4796 SIC 6794 5812

PISCES FOODS LP p 1152
5407 Parkcrest Dr Ste 200, Austin TX 78731
Tel (512) 452-5454 SIC 5812

SUCCESS FOODS MANAGEMENT GROUP LLC p 1396
4501 Springdale Rd, Austin TX 78723
Tel (512) 441-8900 SIC 8741 5812

DELI MANAGEMENT INC p 424
2400 Broadway St, Beaumont TX 77702
Tel (409) 838-1976 SIC 5812

E E R INC p 466
3000 W Cedar St, Beaumont TX 77702
Tel (409) 838-2002 SIC 5812

EMERALD FOODS INC p 491
6300 West Loop S, Bellaire TX 77401
Tel (713) 791-9167 SIC 5812

GULF COAST BROADCASTING CO p 646
409 S Staples St, Corpus Christi TX 78401
Tel (361) 886-6100 SIC 4833 5812

HART RESTAURANT MANAGEMENT INC p 665
108 N Mesquite St, Corpus Christi TX 78401
Tel (361) 882-4100 SIC 5812

■ **STRIPES LLC** p 1393
4433 Baldwin Blvd 9911, Corpus Christi TX 78408
Tel (361) 884-2463 SIC 5812

ANATOLE HOTEL INVESTORS L P p 88
2201 N Stemmons Fwy, Dallas TX 75207
Tel (214) 748-1200 SIC 7011 5813 5812

▲ **BRINKER INTERNATIONAL INC** p 213
6820 Lbj Fwy, Dallas TX 75240
Tel (972) 980-9917 SIC 5812 6794

■ **BRINKER RESTAURANT CORP** p 213
6820 Lbj Fwy, Dallas TX 75240
Tel (972) 980-9917 SIC 5812

BURCH MANAGEMENT CO INC p 226
10723 Composite Dr, Dallas TX 75220
Tel (214) 358-0055 SIC 8741 5813 5812

C C TEXAS INC p 232
3130 Lemmon Ave, Dallas TX 75204
Tel (214) 526-4664 SIC 5812

CARLSON RESTAURANTS INC p 258
19111 Dallas Pkwy, Dallas TX 75287
Tel (972) 662-5400 SIC 5812

CBC RESTAURANT CORP p 268
12700 Park Central Dr # 1300, Dallas TX 75251
Tel (972) 619-4100 SIC 5812 6794

■ **CHILIS INC** p 300
6820 Lbj Fwy, Dallas TX 75240
Tel (972) 980-9917 SIC 5812

▲ **CONCEPT DEVELOPMENT PARTNERS LLC** p 354
500 Crescent Ct Ste 250, Dallas TX 75201
Tel (214) 871-6819 SIC 6726 5812 5813

CONSOLIDATED RESTAURANT COMPANIES INC p 360
12200 N Stemmons Fwy, Dallas TX 75234
Tel (972) 241-5500 SIC 5812 6794

CONSOLIDATED RESTAURANT OPERATIONS INC p 360
12200 N Stemmons Fwy, Dallas TX 75234
Tel (972) 241-5500 SIC 5812 6794

CULINAIRE INTERNATIONAL INC p 400
8303 Elmbrook Dr, Dallas TX 75247
Tel (214) 754-1645 SIC 8742 5812 8741

▲ **DAVE & BUSTERS ENTERTAINMENT INC** p 415
2481 Manana Dr, Dallas TX 75220
Tel (214) 357-9588 SIC 5812 7993

■ **DAVE & BUSTERS HOLDINGS INC** p 415
2481 Manana Dr, Dallas TX 75220
Tel (214) 357-9588 SIC 5812

■ **DAVE & BUSTERS INC** p 415
2481 Manana Dr, Dallas TX 75220
Tel (214) 357-9588
SIC 5812 5813 7999 7993

DICKEYS BARBECUE RESTAURANTS INC p 438
4514 Cole Ave Ste 1015, Dallas TX 75205
Tel (972) 248-9899 SIC 5812

EL CHICO RESTAURANTS INC p 482
12200 N Stemmons Fwy, Dallas TX 75234
Tel (972) 241-5500 SIC 5812 6794 5046

▲ **FIESTA RESTAURANT GROUP INC** p 541
14800 Landmark Blvd # 500, Dallas TX 75254
Tel (972) 702-9300 SIC 5812 6794

FIREBIRD RESTAURANT GROUP LLC p 543
1845 Woodall Rodgers Fwy # 1100, Dallas TX 75201
Tel (972) 241-2171 SIC 5812

■ **FOGO DE CHAO CHURRASCARIA (LOS ANGELES) LLC** p 563
14881 Quorum Dr Ste 750, Dallas TX 75254
Tel (972) 361-6200 SIC 5812

▲ **FOGO DE CHAO INC** p 563
14881 Quorum Dr Ste 750, Dallas TX 75254
Tel (972) 960-9533 SIC 5812

HALLWOOD FINANCIAL LIMITED p 655
3710 Rawlins St Ste 1500, Dallas TX 75219
Tel (214) 523-1288 SIC 5812

KAINOS GP LLC p 800
2100 Mckinney Ave # 1600, Dallas TX 75201
Tel (214) 740-7300 SIC 5812

LE DUFF AMERICA INC p 849
12201 Merit Dr Ste 900, Dallas TX 75251
Tel (214) 540-1867 SIC 5812

LONE STAR FUND V (US) LP p 875
2711 N Haskell Ave # 1700, Dallas TX 75204
Tel (214) 754-8300 SIC 6799 5812

LSF5 WAGON HOLDINGS LLC p 883
2711 N Haskell Ave # 1700, Dallas TX 75204
Tel (214) 515-6824 SIC 5812 5813

MAC ACQUISITION OF KANSAS LLC p 891
6750 Lyndon B Johnson Fwy, Dallas TX 75240
Tel (972) 674-4300 SIC 5812

■ **MAGGIANOS INC** p 895
6820 Lyndon B Johnson Fwy, Dallas TX 75240
Tel (972) 980-9917 SIC 5812

■ **PEPPER DINING HOLDING CORP** p 1133
6820 Lyndon B Johnson Fwy, Dallas TX 75240
Tel (704) 943-5276 SIC 5812

■ **PEPPER DINING INC** p 1133
6820 Lyndon B Johnson Fwy, Dallas TX 75240
Tel (704) 943-5276 SIC 5812

■ **PIZZA HUT WEST INC** p 1153
14841 Dallas Pkwy Frnt, Dallas TX 75254
Tel (972) 338-7700 SIC 5812

SAXTON GROUP INC p 1285
7859 Walnut Hill Ln # 325, Dallas TX 75230
Tel (214) 373-3400 SIC 5812

SB RESTAURANT CO p 1285
18900 Dallas Pkwy Ste 125, Dallas TX 75287
Tel (800) 227-5454 SIC 5812 5813

SPAGHETTI WAREHOUSE RESTAURANTS INC p 1354
1815 N Market St, Dallas TX 75202
Tel (949) 336-5111 SIC 5812

SUN HOLDINGS INC p 1400
3318 Forest Ln Ste 300, Dallas TX 75234
Tel (972) 620-2287 SIC 5812

SWH MIMIS CAFE LLC p 1412
12201 Merit Dr Ste 900, Dallas TX 75251
Tel (866) 926-6636 SIC 5812

TEXAS DE BRAZIL (ADDISON) CORP p 1442
2952 N Stemmons Fwy, Dallas TX 75247
Tel (214) 615-2184 SIC 5812

TGI FRIDAYS INC p 1446
19111 Dallas Pkwy, Dallas TX 75287
Tel (972) 662-5400 SIC 5812 6794

TOP GOLF USA INC p 1460
8750 N Cntl Expy Ste 1200, Dallas TX 75231
Tel (214) 377-5053 SIC 7999 5812 5941

ROVIN INC p 1253
1332 Paisley St, Denton TX 76209
Tel (940) 383-0300 SIC 5812

PIZZA PROPERTIES LTD p 1153
4445 N Mesa St Ste 100, El Paso TX 79902
Tel (915) 544-8565 SIC 5812

TACO BUENO RESTAURANTS LP p 1421
1605 Lbj Fwy Ste 800, Farmers Branch TX 75234
Tel (800) 440-0778 SIC 5812 6794

RAZZOOS INC p 1211
2950 Texas Sage Trl, Fort Worth TX 76177
Tel (972) 233-6399 SIC 5812 5813

COTTON PATCH CAF LLC p 374
600 E Dallas Rd Ste 300, Grapevine TX 76051
Tel (817) 865-6500 SIC 5812

BUFFETS LLC p 224
120 Chula Vis, Hollywood Park TX 78232
Tel (651) 994-8608 SIC 5812 8741

CATALINA RESTAURANT GROUP INC p 264
120 Chula Vis, Hollywood Park TX 78232
Tel (760) 804-5750 SIC 5812

A 3 H FOODS LP p 4
13636 Breton Ridge St C, Houston TX 77070
Tel (832) 678-3590 SIC 5812

CLAIM JUMPER RESTAURANTS LLC p 321
1510 West Loop S, Houston TX 77027
Tel (949) 756-9001 SIC 5812

FSI DEVCO INC p 582
1510 West Loop S, Houston TX 77027
Tel (713) 850-1010 SIC 5812

FSI RESTAURANT DEVELOPMENT LIMITED p 582
1510 West Loop S, Houston TX 77027
Tel (713) 386-7176 SIC 5812

▲ **IGNITE RESTAURANT GROUP INC** p 730
10555 Richmond Ave # 100, Houston TX 77042
Tel (713) 366-7500 SIC 5812 6794

LANDRYS INC p 843
1510 West Loop S, Houston TX 77027
Tel (713) 850-1010 SIC 5812

LSRI HOLDINGS INC p 883
1510 West Loop S, Houston TX 77027
Tel (713) 850-1010 SIC 5812

▲ **LUBYS INC** p 884
13111 Nw Fwy Ste 600, Houston TX 77040
Tel (713) 329-6800 SIC 5812

■ **LUBYS RESTAURANTS LIMITED PARTNERSHIP** p 884
13111 Nw Fwy Ste 600, Houston TX 77040
Tel (713) 329-6800 SIC 5812

MAC PARENT LLC p 891
3100 S Gessner Rd Ste 125, Houston TX 77063
Tel (832) 649-2260 SIC 5812 6794

MCCORMICK & SCHMICK MANAGEMENT GROUP p 927
1510 West Loop S, Houston TX 77027
Tel (512) 836-0500 SIC 5812

MCCORMICK & SCHMICKS SEAFOOD RESTAURANTS INC p 927
1510 West Loop S, Houston TX 77027
Tel (800) 552-6379 SIC 5812

MEXICAN RESTAURANTS INC p 957
12000 Aerospace Ave # 400, Houston TX 77034
Tel (832) 300-5858 SIC 5812 6794 5046

MORTONS RESTAURANT GROUP INC p 991
1510 West Loop S, Houston TX 77027
Tel (713) 850-1010 SIC 5812

PAPPAS PARTNERS LP p 1112
6894 Southwest Fwy 1, Houston TX 77074
Tel (713) 869-7151 SIC 5812

PAPPAS RESTAURANTS INC p 1112
13939 Nw Fwy, Houston TX 77040
Tel (713) 869-0151 SIC 5812 5813

RAINFOREST CAFE INC p 1206
1510 West Loop S, Houston TX 77027
Tel (713) 850-1010 SIC 5812

▲ **RCI HOSPITALITY HOLDINGS INC** p 1212
10959 Cutten Rd, Houston TX 77066
Tel (281) 397-6730 SIC 5813 5812

RICE EPICUREAN MARKETS INC p 1232
5333 Gulfton St, Houston TX 77081
Tel (713) 662-7700 SIC 5411 5812

SALTGRASS INC p 1273
1510 West Loop S, Houston TX 77027
Tel (713) 850-1010 SIC 5812

WILLISTON HOLDINGS INC p 1612
12000 Aerospace Ave # 400, Houston TX 77034
Tel (832) 300-5858 SIC 5812 6794 5046

CEC ENTERTAINMENT INC p 272
1707 Market Pl Ste 200, Irving TX 75063
Tel (972) 258-8507 SIC 5812 7993 6794

CHEDDARS CASUAL CAFE INC p 292
2900 Ranch Trl, Irving TX 75063
Tel (214) 596-6700 SIC 5812

LSG SKY CHEFS USA INC p 883
6191 N State Highway 161 # 100, Irving TX 75038
Tel (972) 793-9000 SIC 5812 5962

ON BORDER CORP p 1085
2201 W Royal Ln Ste 240, Irving TX 75063
Tel (972) 499-3000 SIC 5812 5813

OTB ACQUISITION LLC p 1097
2201 W Royal Ln Ste 240, Irving TX 75063
Tel (972) 499-3000 SIC 5812

S C INTERNATIONAL SERVICES INC p 1262
6191 N State Highway 161 # 100, Irving TX 75038
Tel (972) 793-9000 SIC 5812 5962

SKY CHEFS INC p 1330
6191 N State Highway 161 # 100, Irving TX 75038
Tel (972) 793-9000 SIC 5812

TURBO RESTAURANT LLC p 1492
7750 N Macarthur Blvd 1, Irving TX 75063
Tel (972) 620-2287 SIC 5812

SOUTHERN MULTIFOODS INC p 1349
101 E Cherokee St, Jacksonville TX 75766
Tel (903) 586-1524 SIC 5812

FORD RESTAURANT GROUP INC p 566
1514 Ranch Road 620 S, Lakeway TX 78734
Tel (512) 263-0929 SIC 5812

FOOD CONCEPTS INTERNATIONAL INC p 564
4401 82nd St, Lubbock TX 79424
Tel (806) 785-8686 SIC 5812

D L ROGERS CORP p 407
5013 Davis Blvd, North Richland Hills TX 76180
Tel (817) 428-2077 SIC 5812 6552 6799

COASTAL RESTAURANTS GP LLC p 332
6340 Intl Pkwy Ste 300, Plano TX 75093
Tel (214) 443-1920 SIC 5812

■ **FRITO-LAY NORTH AMERICA INC** p 580
7701 Legacy Dr, Plano TX 75024
Tel (972) 334-7000
SIC 2096 2052 2013 5812 6794 2086

HOMESTYLE DINING LLC p 704
3701 W Plano Pkwy Ste 200, Plano TX 75075
Tel (972) 244-8900 SIC 5812 6794

LONE STAR STEAKHOUSE & SALOON OF KANSAS INC p 876
5055 W Park Blvd Ste 500, Plano TX 75093
Tel (972) 295-8600 SIC 5812

LONE STAR STEAKS INC p 876
5055 W Park Blvd Ste 500, Plano TX 75093
Tel (972) 295-8600 SIC 5812

MAIN EVENT ENTERTAINMENT LP p 897
6652 Pinecrest Dr Ste 100, Plano TX 75024
Tel (972) 406-2600 SIC 7929 5813 5812

OLD FRITO-LAY INC p 1080
7701 Legacy Dr, Plano TX 75024
Tel (972) 334-7000
SIC 2096 2052 2013 5812 6794 2086

■ **PIZZA HUT INC** p 1152
7100 Corporate Dr, Plano TX 75024
Tel (972) 338-7700 SIC 5812

■ **PIZZA HUT OF TITUSVILLE INC** p 1153
7100 Corporate Dr, Plano TX 75024
Tel (972) 338-7700 SIC 5812

▲ **ZOES KITCHEN INC** p 1644
5760 State Highway 121, Plano TX 75024
Tel (214) 436-8765 SIC 5812 6794

ZOES KITCHEN USA LLC p 1644
5760 State Highway 121 # 250, Plano TX 75024
Tel (214) 872-4141 SIC 5812

ROCKFISH SEAFOOD GRILL INC p 1244
801 E Campbell Rd Ste 300, Richardson TX 75081
Tel (214) 887-9400 SIC 5812 5813

FALCON HOLDINGS LLC p 526
1301 Solana Blvd Ste 2300, Roanoke TX 76262
Tel (817) 693-5151 SIC 5812

J & D RESTAURANT GROUP LLC p 769
1301 Solana Blvd Ste 2300, Roanoke TX 76262
Tel (817) 693-5119 SIC 5812

▲ **BIGLARI HOLDINGS INC** p 182
17802 W Ih 10 Ste 400, San Antonio TX 78257
Tel (210) 344-3400 SIC 5812 6794

BUFFET PARTNERS LP p 224
120 Chula Vis, San Antonio TX 78232
Tel (210) 403-3725 SIC 5812

BUFFETS HOLDINGS LLC p 224
120 Chula Vista Hollywood, San Antonio TX 78232
Tel (210) 403-3725 SIC 5812

FIRE MOUNTAIN RESTAURANTS LLC p 543
120 Chula Vis, San Antonio TX 78232
Tel (651) 994-8608 SIC 5812

HASSLOCHER ENTERPRISES INC p 667
8520 Crownhill Blvd, San Antonio TX 78209
Tel (210) 828-1493 SIC 5812 5142 6552

HOMETOWN BUFFET INC p 704
120 Chula Vis, San Antonio TX 78232
Tel (651) 994-8608 SIC 5812

JOJOS CALIFORNIA p 792
120 Chula Vis, San Antonio TX 78232
Tel (877) 225-4160 SIC 5812

MUY HAMBURGER PARTNERS LLC p 1003
17890 Blanco Rd Ste 401, San Antonio TX 78232
Tel (210) 408-2400 SIC 5812

■ **NATIONAL CONVENIENCE STORES INC** p 1011
6000 N Loop 1604 W, San Antonio TX 78249
Tel (830) 995-4303 SIC 5411 5812

OCB RESTAURANT CO LLC p 1072
120 Chula Vis, San Antonio TX 78232
Tel (210) 403-3725 SIC 5812

R&L FOODS INC p 1203
7550 W Interstate 10 # 508, San Antonio TX 78229
Tel (210) 433-3371 SIC 5812

RITA RESTAURANT CORP p 1236
120 Chula Vis, San Antonio TX 78232
Tel (210) 403-3725 SIC 5812 6794

RYANS RESTAURANT GROUP LLC p 1260
120 Chula Vis, San Antonio TX 78232
Tel (651) 994-8608 SIC 5812

WHATABURGER RESTAURANTS LLC p 1604
300 Concord Plaza Dr, San Antonio TX 78216
Tel (210) 476-6000 SIC 5812 6794

W DOUGLASS DISTRIBUTING LTD p 1568
325 E Forest Ave, Sherman TX 75090
Tel (903) 893-1181 SIC 5812

■ **DEL FRISCOS GRILLE OF TEXAS LLC** p 423
1200 E Southlake Blvd, Southlake TX 76092
Tel (817) 410-3777 SIC 5812 5813

■ **DEL FRISCOS OF NORTH CAROLINA INC** p 423
930 S Kimball Ave, Southlake TX 76092
Tel (817) 601-3421 SIC 5812

▲ **DEL FRISCOS RESTAURANT GROUP INC** p 423
920 S Kimball Ave Ste 100, Southlake TX 76092
Tel (817) 601-3421 SIC 5812 5813

HOUSTON FOODS INC p 712
4415 Highway 6, Sugar Land TX 77478
Tel (281) 201-2700 SIC 5812

POSADOS CAFE INC p 1163
204 W Main St, Tyler TX 75701
Tel (903) 534-1076 SIC 5812

SPEEDY STOP FOOD STORES LLC p 1358
8701 N Navarro St, Victoria TX 77904
Tel (361) 573-7662 SIC 5812 5541 5411

■ **PIZZA HUT OF UTAH INC** p 1153
76 N 100 E Ste 3, American Fork UT 84003
Tel (801) 756-9696 SIC 5812

ASC UTAH INC p 115
4000 Canyons Resort Dr, Park City UT 84098
Tel (435) 649-5400 SIC 7011 5812

SIZZLING PLATTER LLC p 1328
348 E Winchester St # 200, Salt Lake City UT 84107
Tel (801) 268-3400 SIC 5812

SLAYMAKER GROUP INC p 1331
404 E 4500 S Ste A12, Salt Lake City UT 84107
Tel (801) 261-3700 SIC 5812

VERMONT COUNTRY STORE INC p 1551
5650 Main St, Manchester Center VT 05255
Tel (802) 362-4667 SIC 5961 5399 5812

BEN & JERRYS HOMEMADE INC p 172
30 Community Dr Ste 1, South Burlington VT 05403
Tel (802) 846-1500 SIC 2024 5812 6794

■ **MT MANSFIELD CO INC** p 997
5781 Mountain Rd, Stowe VT 05672
Tel (802) 253-7311 SIC 6331 5812 5813

HIGHWAY SERVICE VENTURES INC p 692
100 Arbor Oak Dr Ste 305, Ashland VA 23005
Tel (804) 752-4966 SIC 5541 5411 5812

NEWCOMB ENTERPRISES INC JOHN p 1037
910 Triangle St, Blacksburg VA 24060
Tel (540) 552-7718 SIC 5812

SSP AMERICA INC p 1364
19465 Drfield Ave Ste 105, Lansdowne VA 20176
Tel (703) 723-7235 SIC 5812

MARS INC p 910
6885 Elm St, Mc Lean VA 22101
Tel (703) 821-4900
SIC 2044 2024 2066 2064 5812

WINTERGREEN RESORTS INC p 1617
11 Grassy Ridge Dr, Nellysford VA 22958
Tel (434) 325-8237 SIC 8721 7011 5812

SWEET FROG LLC p 1411
10800 Midlothian Tpke # 300, North Chesterfield VA 23235
Tel (804) 893-3151 SIC 5812 6794

GATE GOURMET US INC p 593
1880 Campus Commons Dr # 200, Reston VA 20191
Tel (703) 964-2300 SIC 5812 8742

GATEGROUP US HOLDING INC p 593
11710 Plaza America Dr # 800, Reston VA 20190
Tel (703) 964-2300 SIC 5812 8742

THOMPSON HOSPITALITY CORP p 1449
1741 Bus Ctr Dr Ste 200, Reston VA 20190
Tel (703) 757-5500 SIC 5812

THOMPSON HOSPITALITY SERVICES LLC p 1449
1741 Bus Ctr Dr Ste 200, Reston VA 20190
Tel (703) 757-5560 SIC 5812

CORNETT MANAGEMENT CO INC p 371
2120 Staples Mill Rd # 300, Richmond VA 23230
Tel (804) 678-9000 SIC 5812

DNC/MFS FOOD GROUP p 446
1 Richard E Byrd Trml Dr, Richmond VA 23250
Tel (804) 222-1227 SIC 5812

SHONEYS OF RICHMOND INC p 1317
7202 Glen Forest Dr # 104, Richmond VA 23226
Tel (804) 346-3414 SIC 5812

MARYLAND FOODS INC p 915
1960 Gallows Rd Ste 200, Vienna VA 22182
Tel (703) 827-0320 SIC 5812 5813

TEAM WASHINGTON INC p 1430
8381 Old Courthouse Rd # 100, Vienna VA 22182
Tel (703) 734-7080 SIC 5812

BURGERBUSTERS INC p 227
2242 W Great Neck Rd, Virginia Beach VA 23451
Tel (757) 412-0112 SIC 5812

PROFESSIONAL HOSPITALITY RESOURCES INC p 1180
932 Laskin Rd, Virginia Beach VA 23451
Tel (757) 491-3000 SIC 7011 7389 5812

COLONIAL WILLIAMSBURG FOUNDATION p 338
427 Franklin St Rm 212, Williamsburg VA 23185
Tel (757) 229-1000
SIC 5947 8412 5812 7011

MAD ANTHONYS INC p 893
10502 Ne 37th Cir Bldg 8, Kirkland WA 98033
Tel (425) 455-0732 SIC 5812 5813

RAM INTERNATIONAL LTD p 1206
10013 59th Ave Sw, Lakewood WA 98499
Tel (253) 588-1788 SIC 5812

EMERALD CITY PIZZA LLC p 491
12121 Harbour Rch Dr 20 Ste 200, Mukilteo WA 98275
Tel (425) 493-8077 SIC 5812

R U CORP p 1203
411 1st Ave S Ste 200n, Seattle WA 98104
Tel (206) 634-0550 SIC 5812 5813 5461

RESTAURANTS UNLIMITED INC p 1228
411 1st Ave S Ste 200, Seattle WA 98104
Tel (206) 634-0550 SIC 5812

■ **STARBUCKS COFFEE INTERNATIONAL INC** p 1378
2401 Utah Ave S Ste 800, Seattle WA 98134
Tel (206) 447-1575 SIC 5812

▲ **STARBUCKS CORP** p 1378
2401 Utah Ave S, Seattle WA 98134
Tel (206) 447-1575
SIC 5812 5499 5461 5149

PACIFIC BELLS LLC p 1104
111 W 39th St Ste A, Vancouver WA 98660
Tel (360) 694-7855 SIC 5812

▲ **PAPA MURPHYS HOLDINGS INC** p 1112
8000 Ne Parkway Dr # 350, Vancouver WA 98662
Tel (360) 260-7272 SIC 5812

HOMETOWN ENTERPRISES INC p 704
18815 139th Ave Ne Ste C, Woodinville WA 98072
Tel (425) 486-6336 SIC 5812

NORTHWEST RESTAURANTS INC p 1060
18815 139th Ave Ne Ste C, Woodinville WA 98072
Tel (425) 486-6336 SIC 5812

BRUCETON FARM SERVICE INC p 220
1768 Mileground Rd, Morgantown WV 26505
Tel (304) 291-6980
SIC 5411 5172 5999 5983 5812 2048

SNOWSHOE MOUNTAIN INC p 1336
10 Snowshoe Dr, Slatyfork WV 26291
Tel (304) 572-5601
SIC 8741 7011 5813 5812

FITZ VOGT & ASSOCIATES LTD p 553
21 Armory Dr Ste L-1, Wheeling WV 26003
Tel (603) 644-0117 SIC 5812 8742 7349

OGLEBAY RESORT CONFERENCE CENTER p 1076
Rr 88 Box N, Wheeling WV 26003
Tel (304) 243-4063 SIC 7011 7992 5812

UNITED COOPERATIVE p 1507
N7160 Raceway Rd, Beaver Dam WI 53916
Tel (920) 887-1756
SIC 5191 5171 5541 5153 5812

DORO INC p 451
3112 Golf Rd, Eau Claire WI 54701
Tel (715) 836-6800 SIC 5812

ROTTINGHAUS CO INC p 1252
510 Gillette St, La Crosse WI 54603
Tel (608) 784-2774 SIC 5812

PIZZA HUT OF SOUTHERN WISCONSIN INC p 1152
434 S Yellowstone Dr D, Madison WI 53719
Tel (608) 833-2113 SIC 5812

COUSINS SUBMARINES INC p 383
N83w13400 Leon Rd, Menomonee Falls WI 53051
Tel (262) 253-7700 SIC 5812

BINGO POTAWATOMI p 183
1721 W Canal St, Milwaukee WI 53233
Tel (414) 645-6888 SIC 7999 5812 5947

V & J EMPLOYMENT SERVICES INC p 1538
53223 W Brown Deer Rd, Milwaukee WI 53223
Tel (414) 365-9003 SIC 5812

V & J HOLDING COMPANIES INC p 1538
6933 W Brown Deer Rd Fl 2, Milwaukee WI 53223
Tel (414) 365-9003 SIC 5812

BRIDGEMAN FOODS II INC p 211
2025 Ws Branch Blvd, Oak Creek WI 53154
Tel (502) 254-7130 SIC 5812

COURTESY CORP p 383
2700 National Dr Ste 100, Onalaska WI 54650
Tel (608) 781-8080 SIC 5812

■ **DELLONA ENTERPRISES INC** p 425
S944 Christmas Mtn Rd, Wisconsin Dells WI 53965
Tel (608) 253-1000 SIC 7011 7992 5812

KALAHARI DEVELOPMENT LLC p 801
1305 Kalahari Dr, Wisconsin Dells WI 53965
Tel (608) 254-5466 SIC 7011 5812 5813

SIC 5813 Drinking Places

KSL ARIZONA HOLDINGS III INC p 831
2400 E Missouri Ave, Phoenix AZ 85016
Tel (602) 955-6600
SIC 7011 5812 7991 5813

MACAYO RESTAURANTS LLC p 892
1480 E Bethany Home Rd # 130, Phoenix AZ 85014
Tel (602) 264-1831 SIC 5813 5812 5149

FAIRMONT SCOTTSDALE PRINCESS p 525
7575 E Princess Dr, Scottsdale AZ 85255
Tel (480) 585-4848 SIC 7011 5812 5813

■ **SHERATON PHOENICIAN CORP** p 1315
6000 E Camelback Rd, Scottsdale AZ 85251
Tel (480) 941-8200
SIC 7011 5812 5813 7999 7992

DIXIE RESTAURANTS INC p 445
1215 Rebsamen Park Rd, Little Rock AR 72202
Tel (501) 666-3494 SIC 5812 5813

SPECIALTY RESTAURANTS CORP p 1356
8191 E Kaiser Blvd, Anaheim CA 92808
Tel (714) 279-6100 SIC 5812 5813

HILLSTONE RESTAURANT GROUP INC p 694
147 S Beverly Dr, Beverly Hills CA 90212
Tel (310) 385-7343 SIC 5812 5813

■ **DISNEY REGIONAL ENTERTAINMENT INC** p 443
500 S Buena Vista St, Burbank CA 91521
Tel (818) 560-1000 SIC 7999 5812 5813

L-O CORONADO HOTEL INC p 835
1500 Orange Ave, Coronado CA 92118
Tel (619) 435-6611
SIC 7011 5812 5813 5941

IL FORNAIO (AMERICA) CORP p 731
770 Tamalpais Dr Ste 400, Corte Madera CA 94925
Tel (415) 945-0500
SIC 5812 5813 5149 5461 2051

UNIVERSITY RESTAURANT GROUP INC p 1527
3185 Airway Ave Ste J, Costa Mesa CA 92626
Tel (714) 432-0400 SIC 5812 5813

JACKSON RANCHERIA CASINO & HOTEL p 774
12222 New York Ranch Rd, Jackson CA 95642
Tel (209) 223-1677
SIC 7999 5812 7011 5813

ACAPULCO RESTAURANTS INC p 14
4001 Via Oro Ave Ste 200, Long Beach CA 90810
Tel (310) 513-7538 SIC 5812 5813

AMERICAN RESTAURANT GROUP INC p 78
4410 El Camino Real # 201, Los Altos CA 94022
Tel (650) 949-6400 SIC 5812 5813

ATLAS HOTELS INC p 128
500 Hotel Cir N, San Diego CA 92108
Tel (619) 291-2232 SIC 7011 5812 5813

COLONY CAPITAL LLC p 338
2450 Broadway Ste 600, Santa Monica CA 90404
Tel (310) 282-8820
SIC 6799 7999 7011 5813 5812

JACKSON FAMILY WINES INC p 774
421 And 425 Aviation Blvd, Santa Rosa CA 95403
Tel (707) 544-4000 SIC 2084 0172 5813

LUCKY STRIKE ENTERTAINMENT INC p 884
15260 Ventura Blvd # 1110, Sherman Oaks CA 91403
Tel (818) 933-3752 SIC 3949 5812 5813

CHEVYS INC p 296
31100 Courthouse Dr, Union City CA 94587
Tel (510) 675-9620 SIC 5812 5813

ROCK BOTTOM RESTAURANTS INC p 1243
8001 Arista Pl Unit 500, Broomfield CO 80021
Tel (303) 664-4000 SIC 5812 5813

BROADMOOR HOTEL INC p 215
1 Lake Ave, Colorado Springs CO 80906
Tel (719) 634-7711
SIC 7011 5812 5813 7992 7999 7389

▲ **CHIPOTLE MEXICAN GRILL INC** p 301
1401 Wynkoop St Ste 500, Denver CO 80202
Tel (303) 595-4000 SIC 5812 5813

■ **RED ROBIN INTERNATIONAL INC** p 1216
6312 S Fiddlers Green Cir 200n, Greenwood Village CO 80111
Tel (303) 846-6000
SIC 5812 6794 5813 5087

XANTERRA SOUTH RIM LLC p 1630
6312 S Fiddlers Green Cir, Greenwood Village CO 80111
Tel (303) 600-3400 SIC 7011 5813 7999

CLYDE INC p 328
3236 M St Nw, Washington DC 20007
Tel (202) 333-9180 SIC 5812 5813

JUST ONE MORE RESTAURANT CORP p 797
1730 Rhode Island Ave Nw # 900, Washington DC 20036
Tel (202) 775-7256 SIC 5812 5813

OCEAN PROPERTIES LTD p 1073
1001 E Atl Ave Ste 202, Delray Beach FL 33483
Tel (603) 559-2100
SIC 7011 6552 1522 5719 5812 5813

ORANGE LAKE COUNTRY CLUB INC p 1092
8505 W Irlo Bronson Hwy, Kissimmee FL 34747
Tel (407) 239-0000
SIC 7011 6552 7997 5812 5813

HARD ROCK CAFE FOUNDATION INC p 660
6100 Old Park Ln Ste 100, Orlando FL 32835
Tel (407) 445-7625
SIC 5812 5813 7011 6794

■ **HYATT HOTELS OF FLORIDA INC** p 723
9801 International Dr, Orlando FL 32819
Tel (407) 284-1234 SIC 7011 5812 5813

ROSEN 9939 INC p 1251
9840 International Dr, Orlando FL 32819
Tel (407) 996-9939
SIC 7011 5812 5813 7992 7389

ROSEN HOTELS AND RESORTS INC p 1251
9840 International Dr, Orlando FL 32819
Tel (407) 996-1706
SIC 7011 5812 5813 7389 8011 7992

■ **UCF HOTEL VENTURE** p 1499
6800 Lakewood Plaza Dr, Orlando FL 32819
Tel (407) 503-9000 SIC 7011 5813 5812

EDGEWATER BEACH RESORT LLC p 477
11212 Front Beach Rd, Panama City FL 32407
Tel (850) 235-4044
SIC 1531 7011 5813 5812

CASUAL RESTAURANT CONCEPTS INC p 264
205 S Hoover Blvd Ste 402, Tampa FL 33609
Tel (813) 286-2006 SIC 5813 5812

■ **OSI RESTAURANT PARTNERS LLC** p 1097
2202 N West Shore Blvd # 5, Tampa FL 33607
Tel (813) 282-1225 SIC 5812 5813

LODGIAN INC p 873
2002 Summit Blvd Ste 300, Brookhaven GA 30319
Tel (404) 364-9400 SIC 7011 5813

HOPS GRILL & BAR INC p 706
Hancock At Washington St, Madison GA 30650
Tel (706) 342-4552 SIC 5813 5812

■ **HILTON HAWAIIAN VILLAGE LLC** p 695
2005 Kalia Rd, Honolulu HI 96815
Tel (808) 949-4321 SIC 7011 5812 5813

KYO-YA HOTELS & RESORTS LP p 833
2255 Kalakaua Ave Fl 2, Honolulu HI 96815
Tel (808) 931-8600 SIC 7011 5812 5813

H GROUP HOLDING INC p 650
222 W Adams St Ste 250, Chicago IL 60606
Tel (312) 750-1234
SIC 4512 7011 5812 5813

LEONAS PIZZERIA INC p 856
3931 S Leavitt St, Chicago IL 60609
Tel (773) 843-0050 SIC 5812 5813

LETTUCE ENTERTAIN YOU TOO INC p 858
5419 N Sheridan Rd # 116, Chicago IL 60640
Tel (773) 878-7340 SIC 5812 5813

PORTILLOS HOT DOGS INC p 1163
2001 Spring Rd Ste 400, Oak Brook IL 60523
Tel (630) 954-3773 SIC 5812 5813

APPLE AMERICAN INDIANA LLC p 98
6515 E 82nd St Ste 109, Indianapolis IN 46250
Tel (317) 577-8334 SIC 5812 5813

GRAYLING CORP p 632
4220 Edison Lkes Pkwy 100, Mishawaka IN 46545
Tel (856) 384-1212 SIC 5812 5813 6531

HMR ACQUISITION CO INC p 698
1501 N Ironwood Dr, South Bend IN 46635
Tel (574) 272-5922 SIC 5812 5813

PRAIRIE MEADOWS RACETRACK AND CASINO INC p 1167
1 Prairie Meadows Dr, Altoona IA 50009
Tel (515) 967-1000
SIC 7948 7993 7999 5947 5812 5813

■ **AMERISTAR CASINO COUNCIL BLUFFS LLC** p 83
2200 River Rd, Council Bluffs IA 51501
Tel (712) 328-8888
SIC 7011 7991 5813 5812

HOULIHANS RESTAURANTS INC p 711
8700 State Line Rd # 100, Leawood KS 66206
Tel (913) 901-2500 SIC 5812 5813

GOURMET SYSTEMS OF KANSAS INC p 627
4551 W 107th St Ste 100, Shawnee Mission KS 66207
Tel (913) 967-4000 SIC 5812 5813

CHAMPPS OPERATING CORP p 287
151 S Whittier St Ofc, Wichita KS 67207
Tel (800) 229-2118 SIC 5812 5813

RAFFERTYS INC p 1205
1750 Scottsville Rd Ste 2, Bowling Green KY 42104
Tel (270) 781-2834 SIC 5812 5813

THOMAS AND KING OF ARIZONA INC p 1448
249 E Main St Ste 101, Lexington KY 40507
Tel (859) 254-2180 SIC 5812 5813

RMD CORP p 1239
2509 Plantside Dr, Louisville KY 40299
Tel (502) 499-9991 SIC 5812 5813

COPELANDS OF NEW ORLEANS INC p 368
2601 Severn Ave, Metairie LA 70002
Tel (504) 830-1000 SIC 5812 5813

HMSHOST CORP p 698
6905 Rockledge Dr Fl 1, Bethesda MD 20817
Tel (240) 694-4100
SIC 5812 5813 5994 5947

HOST INTERNATIONAL INC p 710
6905 Rockledge Dr Fl 1, Bethesda MD 20817
Tel (240) 694-4100
SIC 5812 5813 5994 5947

■ **HST LESSEE BOSTON LLC** p 715
39 Dalton St, Boston MA 02199
Tel (617) 236-2000
SIC 7011 5812 7299 5813

URC LLC p 1530
100 Charles Park Rd, Boston MA 02132
Tel (617) 323-9200 SIC 5812 5813 6794

99 BOSTON INC p 4
160 Olympia Ave, Woburn MA 01801
Tel (781) 933-8999 SIC 5812 5813

ANSARA RESTAURANT GROUP INC p 93
23925 Industrial Park Dr, Farmington Hills MI 48335
Tel (248) 848-9099 SIC 5812 5813

GREENLEAF HOSPITALITY GROUP INC p 638
100 W Michigan Ave # 100, Kalamazoo MI 49007
Tel (269) 567-7691 SIC 7011 5813

▲ **DIVERSIFIED RESTAURANT HOLDINGS INC** p 444
27680 Franklin Rd, Southfield MI 48034
Tel (248) 223-9160 SIC 5812 5813 6794

CARLSON HOTELS LIMITED PARTNERSHIP p 257
Carlson Parkway 701 Twr St Carlson Parkw, Minneapolis MN 55459
Tel (763) 212-1000
SIC 6794 7011 5812 5813

■ **GRANITE CITY FOOD & BREWERY LTD** p 631
3500 Amrcn Blvd W Ste 450, Minneapolis MN 55431
Tel (952) 215-0660 SIC 5812 5813

■ **SYSCO MINNESOTA INC** p 1417
2400 County Road J, Saint Paul MN 55112
Tel (763) 785-9000 SIC 5141 5812 5813

TORGERSON PROPERTIES INC p 1461
103 15th Ave Nw Ste 200, Willmar MN 56201
Tel (320) 235-7207 *SIC* 7011 5812 5813

IMPERIAL PALACE OF MISSISSIPPI LLC p 734
850 Bayview Ave, Biloxi MS 39530
Tel (228) 432-3243
SIC 7011 5812 5813 7832

■ **OLYMPIA BALLYS LIMITED PARTNERSHIP** p 1083
1450 Ballys Blvd, Robinsonville MS 38664
Tel (662) 357-1500
SIC 7999 7011 5813 5812

■ **ROBINSON PROPERTY GROUP LIMITED PARTNERSHIP** p 1242
1021 Casino Center Dr, Robinsonville MS 38664
Tel (662) 357-5500 *SIC* 7011 5813 5812

■ **TUNICA ROADHOUSE CORP** p 1491
13615 Old Highway 61 N, Robinsonville MS 38664
Tel (662) 363-4900
SIC 7999 7011 5813 5812

HARRAHS MARYLAND HEIGHTS OPERATING CO INC p 663
777 Casino Center Dr, Maryland Heights MO 63043
Tel (314) 770-8100 *SIC* 7011 5813 5812

PASTA HOUSE CO p 1120
700 N New Ballas Rd, Saint Louis MO 63141
Tel (314) 535-6644 *SIC* 5812 5813

ARIZONA CHARLIES INC p 108
740 S Decatur Blvd, Las Vegas NV 89107
Tel (702) 258-5200 *SIC* 7011 5812 5813

GORDON BIERSCH BREWING CO p 626
10801 W Charleston Blvd # 600, Las Vegas NV 89135
Tel (702) 221-4475 *SIC* 5813

SILVERTON CASINO LLC p 1324
3333 Blue Diamond Rd, Las Vegas NV 89139
Tel (702) 263-7777 *SIC* 7011 7299 5813

■ **VENETIAN CASINO RESORT LLC** p 1547
3355 Las Vegas Blvd S, Las Vegas NV 89109
Tel (702) 414-1000
SIC 7011 5812 5813 7299

■ **VICTORIA PARTNERS** p 1555
3770 Las Vegas Blvd S, Las Vegas NV 89109
Tel (888) 529-4828
SIC 7011 5812 7299 5813

ELDORADO RESORTS LLC p 484
345 N Virginia St, Reno NV 89501
Tel (775) 786-5700 *SIC* 7011 5812 5813

■ **GOLDEN ROAD MOTOR INN INC** p 621
3800 S Virginia St, Reno NV 89502
Tel (775) 335-4521
SIC 7011 5812 5813 7299

RECREATIONAL ENTERPRISES INC p 1215
345 N Virginia St, Reno NV 89501
Tel (775) 786-5700
SIC 7011 7999 5813 5812

FABER COE & GREGG INC p 523
550 Madowlands Pkwy Ste 2, Secaucus NJ 07094
Tel (201) 330-1515 *SIC* 5994 5499 5813

DELAWARE NORTH COMPANIES TRAVEL HOSPITALITY SERVICES INC p 424
250 Delaware Ave Ste 3, Buffalo NY 14202
Tel (716) 858-5000 *SIC* 5812 5947 5813

APAX PARTNERS OF NEW YORK p 96
601 Lexington Ave Fl 53, New York NY 10022
Tel (212) 419-2447
SIC 6282 5399 5199 5812 5813

▲ **ARK RESTAURANTS CORP** p 109
85 5th Ave, New York NY 10003
Tel (212) 206-8800 *SIC* 5812 5813

OAK HILL CAPITAL PARTNERS III LP p 1070
65 E 55th St Fl 32, New York NY 10022
Tel (212) 527-8400
SIC 5812 5813 7999 7993

WELLSPRING CAPITAL PARTNERS III LP p 1591
390 Park Ave Fl 5, New York NY 10022
Tel (212) 318-9800
SIC 5812 5813 7999 7993

WS MIDWAY HOLDINGS INC p 1628
390 Park Ave Fl 6, New York NY 10022
Tel (212) 318-9800
SIC 5812 5813 7999 7993

GROVE PARK INN RESORT INC p 642
290 Macon Ave, Asheville NC 28804
Tel (828) 252-2711
SIC 7011 5812 5813 7992 7991 7299

OMNI GROVE PARK LLC p 1084
290 Macon Ave, Asheville NC 28804
Tel (828) 252-2711
SIC 7299 5812 7011 5813 7992 7991

HAMS RESTAURANTS INC p 656
3017 W Gate City Blvd # 2, Greensboro NC 27403
Tel (336) 851-4800 *SIC* 5812 5813

PINEHURST LLC p 1149
80 Carolina Vista Dr, Pinehurst NC 28374
Tel (910) 295-6811
SIC 7011 7997 7992 5813 5812

EATERIES INC p 473
1220 S Santa Fe Ave, Edmond OK 73003
Tel (480) 347-3800 *SIC* 5812 5813 6794

MCMENAMINS INC p 932
430 N Killingsworth St, Portland OR 97217
Tel (503) 223-0109 *SIC* 5813 5812

INTERNATIONAL RESTAURANT SERVICES INC p 756
Amelia Dist Ctr 23 Ema St, Guaynabo PR 00968
Tel (787) 273-3131 *SIC* 5813 5812

COPPER CELLAR CORP p 368
3001 Industrial Pkwy E, Knoxville TN 37921
Tel (865) 673-3400 *SIC* 5812 5813

▲ **RUBY TUESDAY INC** p 1257
150 W Church Ave, Maryville TN 37801
Tel (865) 379-5700 *SIC* 5812 5813 6794

■ **DOUBLETREE INC** p 452
755 Crossover Ln, Memphis TN 38117
Tel (901) 374-5000 *SIC* 7011 5812 5813

BL RESTAURANT OPERATIONS LLC p 186
4550 Beltway Dr, Addison TX 75001
Tel (972) 386-5567 *SIC* 5812 5813 6794

ANATOLE HOTEL INVESTORS L P p 88
2201 N Stemmons Fwy, Dallas TX 75207
Tel (214) 748-1200 *SIC* 7011 5813 5812

BURCH MANAGEMENT CO INC p 226
10723 Composite Dr, Dallas TX 75220
Tel (214) 358-0055 *SIC* 8741 5813 5812

▲ **CONCEPT DEVELOPMENT PARTNERS LLC** p 354
500 Crescent Ct Ste 250, Dallas TX 75201
Tel (214) 871-6819 *SIC* 6726 5812 5813

■ **DAVE & BUSTERS INC** p 415
2481 Manana Dr, Dallas TX 75220
Tel (214) 357-9588
SIC 5812 5813 7999 7993

LSF5 WAGON HOLDINGS LLC p 883
2711 N Haskell Ave # 1700, Dallas TX 75204
Tel (214) 515-6824 *SIC* 5812 5813

SB RESTAURANT CO p 1285
18900 Dallas Pkwy Ste 125, Dallas TX 75287
Tel (800) 227-5454 *SIC* 5812 5813

RAZZOOS INC p 1211
2950 Texas Sage Trl, Fort Worth TX 76177
Tel (972) 233-6399 *SIC* 5812 5813

PAPPAS RESTAURANTS INC p 1112
13939 Nw Fwy, Houston TX 77040
Tel (713) 869-0151 *SIC* 5812 5813

▲ **RCI HOSPITALITY HOLDINGS INC** p 1212
10959 Cutten Rd, Houston TX 77066
Tel (281) 397-6730 *SIC* 5813 5812

ON BORDER CORP p 1085
2201 W Royal Ln Ste 240, Irving TX 75063
Tel (972) 499-3000 *SIC* 5812 5813

GRAHAM BROTHERS ENTERTAINMENT INC p 628
6999 E Business 20, Odessa TX 79762
Tel (432) 362-0401 *SIC* 5813

MAIN EVENT ENTERTAINMENT LP p 897
6652 Pinecrest Dr Ste 100, Plano TX 75024
Tel (972) 406-2600 *SIC* 7929 5813 5812

ROCKFISH SEAFOOD GRILL INC p 1244
801 E Campbell Rd Ste 300, Richardson TX 75081
Tel (214) 887-9400 *SIC* 5812 5813

■ **DEL FRISCOS GRILLE OF TEXAS LLC** p 423
1200 E Southlake Blvd, Southlake TX 76092
Tel (817) 410-3777 *SIC* 5812 5813

▲ **DEL FRISCOS RESTAURANT GROUP INC** p 423
920 S Kimball Ave Ste 100, Southlake TX 76092
Tel (817) 601-3421 *SIC* 5812 5813

■ **MT MANSFIELD CO INC** p 997
5781 Mountain Rd, Stowe VT 05672
Tel (802) 253-7311 *SIC* 6331 5812 5813

MARYLAND FOODS INC p 915
1960 Gallows Rd Ste 200, Vienna VA 22182
Tel (703) 827-0320 *SIC* 5812 5813

MAD ANTHONYS INC p 893
10502 Ne 37th Cir Bldg 8, Kirkland WA 98033
Tel (425) 455-0732 *SIC* 5812 5813

R U CORP p 1203
411 1st Ave S Ste 200n, Seattle WA 98104
Tel (206) 634-0550 *SIC* 5812 5813 5461

SNOWSHOE MOUNTAIN INC p 1336
10 Snowshoe Dr, Slatyfork WV 26291
Tel (304) 572-5601
SIC 8741 7011 5813 5812

WHEELING ISLAND GAMING INC p 1605
1 S Stone St, Wheeling WV 26003
Tel (304) 232-5050 *SIC* 7948 7011 5813

KALAHARI DEVELOPMENT LLC p 801
1305 Kalahari Dr, Wisconsin Dells WI 53965
Tel (608) 254-5466 *SIC* 7011 5812 5813

SIC 5912 Drug & Proprietary Stores

BFW LIQUIDATION LLC p 179
1800 Intl Pk Dr Ste 500, Birmingham AL 35243
Tel (205) 853-2663 *SIC* 5411 5912 5921

SAAD ENTERPRISES INC p 1263
1515 S University Blvd, Mobile AL 36609
Tel (251) 343-9600
SIC 8082 5047 7352 5912 5621 8741

SUPER D DRUGS ACQUISITION CO p 1405
2100 Brookwood Dr, Little Rock AR 72202
Tel (501) 296-3300 *SIC* 5912

STEPHEN L LAFRANCE HOLDINGS INC p 1386
3017 N Midland Dr, Pine Bluff AR 71603
Tel (870) 535-5171 *SIC* 5912 6794

■ **STEPHEN L LAFRANCE PHARMACY INC** p 1386
3017 N Midland Dr, Pine Bluff AR 71603
Tel (870) 535-5171 *SIC* 5122 5912

■ **MODERNHEALTH SPECIALTY (PX) LLC** p 981
7373 Lincoln Way, Garden Grove CA 92841
Tel (818) 769-0313 *SIC* 5912

AIDS HEALTHCARE FOUNDATION p 37
6255 W Sunset Blvd Fl 21, Los Angeles CA 90028
Tel (323) 860-5200 *SIC* 5932 8093 5912

LUCILE SALTER PACKARD CHILDRENS HOSPITAL AT STANFORD p 884
725 Welch Rd, Palo Alto CA 94304
Tel (650) 497-8000 *SIC* 8069 8082 5912

SAFEWAY INC p 1267
5918 Stoneridge Mall Rd, Pleasanton CA 94588
Tel (925) 467-3000 *SIC* 5411 5912

SAN ANTONIO COMMUNITY HOSPITAL p 1275
999 San Bernardino Rd, Upland CA 91786
Tel (909) 985-2811 *SIC* 8062 5912

COMMUNITY MEMORIAL HEALTH SYSTEM p 349
147 N Brent St, Ventura CA 93003
Tel (805) 652-5011 *SIC* 5912

RALEYS p 1206
500 W Capitol Ave, West Sacramento CA 95605
Tel (916) 373-3333 *SIC* 5411 5912

■ **HEALTH NET OF CALIFORNIA INC** p 675
21281 Burbank Blvd Fl 4, Woodland Hills CA 91367
Tel (818) 676-6775
SIC 6324 8062 6311 6321 6331 5912

PHARMACA INTEGRATIVE PHARMACY INC p 1141
4940 Pearl East Cir # 301, Boulder CO 80301
Tel (303) 442-2304 *SIC* 5912

SISTERS OF CHARITY OF LEAVENWORTH HEALTH SYSTEM INC p 1327
500 Eldorado Blvd # 6300, Broomfield CO 80021
Tel (303) 813-5000 *SIC* 8062 8011 5912

WELLDYNERX INC p 1589
7472 S Tucson Way Ste 100, Centennial CO 80112
Tel (888) 479-2000 *SIC* 5122 5912

FAMILYMEDS GROUP INC p 527
312 Farmington Ave Ste B, Farmington CT 06032
Tel (888) 787-2800 *SIC* 5912

YALE-NEW HAVEN HEALTH SERVICES CORP p 1634
789 Howard Ave, New Haven CT 06519
Tel (888) 461-0106 *SIC* 5912 8721

■ **HAPPY HARRYS INC** p 659
326 Ruthar Dr, Newark DE 19711
Tel (302) 366-0335 *SIC* 5912

ADVENTIST HEALTH SYSTEM SUNBELT HEALTHCARE CORP p 27
900 Hope Way, Altamonte Springs FL 32714
Tel (407) 357-1000 *SIC* 5912

DEGC ENTERPRISES (US) INC p 422
14255 49th St N Ste 301, Clearwater FL 33762
Tel (727) 531-9161 *SIC* 5999 5912 5961

3801 FLAGLE SUPERMARKET LLC p 2
3801 W Flagler St, Coral Gables FL 33134
Tel (305) 846-9796 *SIC* 5411 5912

CONVEY HEALTH SOLUTIONS INC p 365
1 Financial Plz Fl 14, Fort Lauderdale FL 33394
Tel (954) 903-5000 *SIC* 5912 5999

SEDANOS MANAGEMENT INC p 1300
3140 W 76th St, Hialeah FL 33018
Tel (305) 824-1034 *SIC* 5411 5912

PAVILION HEALTH SERVICES INC p 1122
3563 Phillips Hwy Ste 106, Jacksonville FL 32207
Tel (904) 202-5887 *SIC* 5912

WINN-DIXIE STORES INC p 1616
8928 Prominence Pkwy # 200, Jacksonville FL 32256
Tel (904) 783-5000 *SIC* 5411 5541 5912

■ **NAVARRO DISCOUNT PHARMACIES LLC** p 1019
9675 Nw 117th Ave 202, Medley FL 33178
Tel (305) 805-1076 *SIC* 5912

TRIAD ISOTOPES INC p 1478
4205 Vineland Rd Ste L1, Orlando FL 32811
Tel (407) 872-8455 *SIC* 5912

CURANT INC p 401
11001 Roosevelt Blvd N # 1400, Saint Petersburg FL 33716
Tel (770) 437-8040 *SIC* 5912

DRUG SHOPPE INC p 457
4060 N Armenia Ave, Tampa FL 33607
Tel (813) 870-3939 *SIC* 5912

■ **PHARMERICA LONG-TERM CARE LLC** p 1141
3625 Queen Palm Dr, Tampa FL 33619
Tel (877) 975-2273
SIC 5912 5961 8082 5122

COMVEST INVESTMENT PARTNERS III LP p 353
525 Okeechobee Blvd # 1050, West Palm Beach FL 33401
Tel (561) 727-2000
SIC 4731 5912 5999 3652 8742 1731

COMVEST NATIONSHEALTH HOLDINGS LLC p 353
525 Okeechobee Blvd # 1050, West Palm Beach FL 33401
Tel (561) 727-2000 *SIC* 5912 5999

MARINER HEALTH CARE INC p 907
1 Ravinia Dr Ste 1500, Atlanta GA 30346
Tel (678) 443-7000
SIC 5912 8051 8093 8741 8062 3443

NATIONAL SENIOR CARE INC p 1016
1 Ravinia Dr Ste 1500, Atlanta GA 30346
Tel (678) 443-7000
SIC 5912 8051 8093 8741 8062 3443

PARADIES SHOPS LLC p 1113
2849 Paces Ferry Rd Se, Atlanta GA 30339
Tel (404) 344-7905
SIC 5947 5994 5621 5611 5912 5941

▲ **SUNLINK HEALTH SYSTEMS INC** p 1403
900 Cir 75 Pkwy Se # 650, Atlanta GA 30339
Tel (770) 933-7000 *SIC* 8062 8051 5912

DON QUIJOTE (USA) CO LTD p 450
801 Kaheka St, Honolulu HI 96814
Tel (808) 973-4800
SIC 5411 5331 6512 5912

ALBERTSONS COMPANIES INC p 46
250 E Parkcenter Blvd, Boise ID 83706
Tel (208) 395-6200 *SIC* 5912 5499

ALBERTSONS COMPANIES LLC p 46
250 E Parkcenter Blvd, Boise ID 83706
Tel (208) 395-6200 *SIC* 5912 5499

ALBERTSONS LLC p 46
250 E Parkcenter Blvd, Boise ID 83706
Tel (208) 395-6200 *SIC* 5499 5912

AMERICAN DRUG STORES LLC p 71
250 E Parkcenter Blvd, Boise ID 83706
Tel (208) 395-6200 *SIC* 5912

BROULIMS SUPER MARKET INC p 219
182 N State St, Rigby ID 83442
Tel (208) 745-9201 *SIC* 5912

OPTION CARE ENTERPRISES INC p 1090
3000 Lakeside Dr Ste 300n, Bannockburn IL 60015
Tel (847) 964-4950
SIC 8082 5122 6794 5912 8049

■ **BOND DRUG CO OF ILLINOIS LLC** p 200
200 Wilmot Rd, Deerfield IL 60015
Tel (847) 914-2500 *SIC* 5912

■ **WALGREEN ARIZONA DRUG CO** p 1572
200 Wilmot Rd, Deerfield IL 60015
Tel (847) 940-2500 *SIC* 5912

■ **WALGREEN CO** p 1572
200 Wilmot Rd, Deerfield IL 60015
Tel (847) 315-2500 *SIC* 5912

■ **WALGREEN EASTERN CO INC** p 1572
200 Wilmot Rd, Deerfield IL 60015
Tel (847) 940-2500 *SIC* 5912

■ **WALGREEN LOUISIANA CO INC** p 1572
200 Wilmot Rd, Deerfield IL 60015
Tel (847) 940-2500 *SIC* 5912

▲ **WALGREENS BOOTS ALLIANCE INC** p 1572
108 Wilmot Rd, Deerfield IL 60015
Tel (847) 315-2500 *SIC* 5912

NORTHSHORE UNIVERSITY HEALTHSYSTEM p 1058
1301 Central St, Evanston IL 60201
Tel (847) 570-5295 *SIC* 5912

■ **KMART CORP** p 824
3333 Beverly Rd, Hoffman Estates IL 60179
Tel (847) 286-2500 *SIC* 5311 5912 5399

NEW ALBERTSONS INC p 1029
150 E Pierce Rd Ste 200, Itasca IL 60143
Tel (630) 948-6000 *SIC* 5411 5912 5331

RIVERSIDE HEALTH SYSTEM p 1238
350 N Wall St, Kankakee IL 60901
Tel (815) 933-1671
SIC 8082 8062 5912 5047

RIVERSIDE MEDI-CENTER INC p 1238
350 N Wall St, Kankakee IL 60901
Tel (815) 933-1671 *SIC* 8082 5912 5999

ST JAMES HOSPITAL & HEALTH CENTERS INC p 1367
20201 Crawford Ave, Olympia Fields IL 60461
Tel (708) 747-4000 *SIC* 8062 5912

IV HEALTHCORP INC p 769
925 West St, Peru IL 61354
Tel (815) 223-3300 *SIC* 8062 8741 5912

GOSHEN HEALTH SYSTEM INC p 626
200 High Park Ave, Goshen IN 46526
Tel (574) 533-2141 *SIC* 5912

FOODS INC p 564
4343 Merle Hay Rd, Des Moines IA 50310
Tel (515) 278-1657 *SIC* 5912

HY-VEE INC p 723
5820 Westown Pkwy, West Des Moines IA 50266
Tel (515) 267-2800 *SIC* 5411 5912 5921

OLATHE HEALTH SYSTEM INC p 1080
20333 W 151st St, Olathe KS 66061
Tel (913) 791-4200 *SIC* 5912

REMKE MARKETS INC p 1222
1299 Cox Ave, Erlanger KY 41018
Tel (859) 594-3400 *SIC* 5912

▲ **PHARMERICA CORP** p 1141
1901 Campus Pl, Louisville KY 40299
Tel (502) 627-7000 *SIC* 5912 5122

SWLHS INC p 1413
1701 Oak Park Blvd, Lake Charles LA 70601
Tel (337) 494-3204 *SIC* 5912

LOUISIANA WHOLESALE DRUG CO INC p 880
2085 I 49 S Service Rd, Sunset LA 70584
Tel (337) 662-1040 *SIC* 5122 5912

HANNAFORD BROS CO LLC p 658
145 Pleasant Hill Rd, Scarborough ME 04074
Tel (207) 883-2911 *SIC* 5411 5912

GIANT FOOD LLC p 610
8301 Profess Pl Ste 115, Hyattsville MD 20785
Tel (301) 341-4100 *SIC* 5411 6512 5912

■ **CATAMARAN HEALTH SOLUTIONS LLC** p 264
800 King Farm Blvd # 300, Rockville MD 20850
Tel (301) 548-2900 *SIC* 5912 6411

■ **LYNNFIELD DRUG INC** p 888
12 Kent Way Ste 120, Byfield MA 01922
Tel (978) 499-1400 *SIC* 5912 5961

RELIANT MEDICAL GROUP INC p 1222
630 Plantation St, Worcester MA 01605
Tel (508) 368-5400 *SIC* 8011 7352 5912

▲ **SPARTANNASH CO** p 1355
850 76th St Sw, Byron Center MI 49315
Tel (616) 878-2000 *SIC* 5141 5411 5912

▲ **DIPLOMAT PHARMACY INC** p 441
4100 S Saginaw St Ste A, Flint MI 48507
Tel (888) 720-4450 *SIC* 5912

MEIJER COMPANIES LTD p 940
2929 Walker Ave Nw, Grand Rapids MI 49544
Tel (616) 453-6711 *SIC* 5311 5411 5912

MCLAREN PORT HURON p 931
1221 Pine Grove Ave, Port Huron MI 48060
Tel (810) 987-5000 *SIC* 5912

■ **BIOSCRIP PHARMACY INC** p 184
10050 Crosstown Cir # 300, Eden Prairie MN 55344
Tel (952) 979-3600 *SIC* 5912

DISTRIBUTION ALTERNATIVES INC p 443
435 Park Ct, Lino Lakes MN 55014
Tel (651) 636-9167 *SIC* 5122 5912

FAIRVIEW PHARMACY SERVICES LLC p 525
711 Kasota Ave Se, Minneapolis MN 55414
Tel (612) 672-5200 *SIC* 5912 5122

HENNEPIN HEALTHCARE SYSTEM INC p 683
701 Park Ave, Minneapolis MN 55415
Tel (612) 873-3000 *SIC* 8062 5912

PARK NICOLLET CLINIC p 1115
3800 Park Nicollet Blvd, Minneapolis MN 55416
Tel (952) 993-3123 *SIC* 8011 5912 5999

THRIFTY DRUG STORES INC p 1451
6055 Nathan Ln N Ste 200, Plymouth MN 55442
Tel (763) 513-4300 *SIC* 5912

B FOUR CORP p 142
3734 Pear St, Saint Joseph MO 64503
Tel (913) 321-4223 *SIC* 5912

ASCENSION HEALTH ALLIANCE p 116
4600 Edmundson Rd, Saint Louis MO 63134
Tel (314) 733-8000 *SIC* 5912

CHRISTIAN HOSPITAL NORTHEAST SURGERY CENTER p 303
11133 Dunn Rd, Saint Louis MO 63136
Tel (314) 355-2300 *SIC* 8742 8049 5912

DAUGHTERS OF CHARITY PROVINCE OF ST LOUISE p 414
4330 Olive St, Saint Louis MO 63108
Tel (314) 533-4770 *SIC* 8661 5912

▲ **EXPRESS SCRIPTS HOLDING CO** p 520
1 Express Way, Saint Louis MO 63121
Tel (314) 996-0900 *SIC* 5912 5961

SCHNUCK MARKETS INC p 1288
11420 Lackland Rd, Saint Louis MO 63146
Tel (314) 994-9900
SIC 5411 5912 5812 7841

CREIGHTON ALEGENT HEALTH p 391
12809 W Dodge Rd, Omaha NE 68154
Tel (402) 343-4300 SIC 5912

PAMIDA BRANDS HOLDING LLC p 1110
8800 F St, Omaha NE 68127
Tel (402) 493-4765 SIC 5331 5912

SHOPKO p 1318
8800 F St, Omaha NE 68127
Tel (402) 339-2400 SIC 5331 5912

SINGER SUPERMARKETS INC p 1326
20 Ridge Rd, Mahwah NJ 07430
Tel (201) 529-5900 SIC 5411 5912

COMMUNITY SURGICAL SUPPLY OF TOMS RIVER INC p 350
1390 Rte 37 W, Toms River NJ 08755
Tel (732) 349-2990 SIC 5047 7352 5912

PERLMART INC p 1136
954 Route 166 Ste 1, Toms River NJ 08753
Tel (732) 341-0700 SIC 5411 5912

L I C H CORP p 834
339 Hicks St, Brooklyn NY 11201
Tel (718) 780-1000 SIC 8062 8092 5912

PARKVIEW HEALTH SERVICES OF NEW YORK LLC p 1117
1770 Colvin Blvd, Buffalo NY 14223
Tel (716) 876-2323 SIC 5912

LEGEND HEALTH SYSTEMS INC p 853
1111 Broadhollow Rd # 319, Farmingdale NY 11735
Tel (631) 630-4713 SIC 5912

KPH HEALTHCARE SERVICES INC p 828
29 E Main St, Gouverneur NY 13642
Tel (315) 287-3600 SIC 5912

■ DUANE READE INC p 459
40 Wall St Fl 22, New York NY 10005
Tel (212) 273-5700 SIC 5912

■ DUANE READE SHAREHOLDERS LLC p 459
40 Wall St Fl 22, New York NY 10005
Tel (212) 273-5700 SIC 5912

■ READE DUANE HOLDINGS INC p 1213
40 Wall St Fl 22, New York NY 10005
Tel (212) 273-5700 SIC 5912

PARK RDG APOTHECARIES p 1115
89 Genesee St, Rochester NY 14611
Tel (585) 368-3928 SIC 5912

TOPS MARKETS LLC p 1461
6363 Main St, Williamsville NY 14221
Tel (716) 635-5000
SIC 5411 5141 5147 5148 5122 5912

▲ INGLES MARKETS INC p 743
2913 Us Highway 70, Black Mountain NC 28711
Tel (828) 669-2941
SIC 5411 5912 5541 2026 6512

DAVIDSON HEALTH CARE INC p 416
250 Hospital Dr, Lexington NC 27292
Tel (336) 248-5161 SIC 5912 8062

■ KDITRANSITION CO INC p 806
3220 Spring Forest Rd, Raleigh NC 27616
Tel (412) 828-1884 SIC 5912

SANFORD CLINIC NORTH p 1279
737 Broadway N, Fargo ND 58102
Tel (701) 234-2000 SIC 5912

▲ KROGER CO p 830
1014 Vine St Ste 1000, Cincinnati OH 45202
Tel (513) 762-4000
SIC 5411 5912 5541 5944

■ NEIGHBORCARE INC p 1024
201 E 4th St Ste 900, Cincinnati OH 45202
Tel (513) 719-2600
SIC 5122 5912 5047 7389

■ NEIGHBORCARE PHARMACY SERVICES INC p 1024
201 E 4th St Ste 900, Cincinnati OH 45202
Tel (513) 719-2600 SIC 5912

NCS HEALTHCARE INC p 1022
3201 Entp Pkwy Ste 220, Cleveland OH 44122
Tel (216) 514-3350
SIC 5122 8093 8049 8082 8742 5912

SCHOTTENSTEIN STORES CORP p 1290
4300 E 5th Ave, Columbus OH 43219
Tel (614) 221-9200
SIC 5311 5712 5912 5999

■ OHIO CVS STORES LLC p 1077
641 Graham Rd, Cuyahoga Falls OH 44221
Tel (330) 922-1298 SIC 5912

■ BUCKEYE DISCOUNT INC p 223
1020 Ford St, Maumee OH 43537
Tel (419) 893-9401 SIC 5912

ST LUKES HOSPITAL p 1370
5901 Monclova Rd, Maumee OH 43537
Tel (419) 893-5911 SIC 8062 5912

DISCOUNT DRUG MART INC p 442
211 Commerce Dr, Medina OH 44256
Tel (330) 725-2340
SIC 5912 5331 5411 5451 5122 8082

CORVALLIS CLINIC P C p 373
3680 Nw Samaritan Dr, Corvallis OR 97330
Tel (541) 754-1150 SIC 8011 5912

BI-MART ACQUISITION CORP p 180
220 Seneca Rd, Eugene OR 97402
Tel (541) 344-0681 SIC 5912 5399

LEGACY MOUNT HOOD MEDICAL CENTER p 852
24800 Se Stark St, Gresham OR 97030
Tel (503) 674-1122 SIC 8062 5912

MERLE WEST MEDICAL CENTER p 950
2865 Daggett Ave, Klamath Falls OR 97601
Tel (541) 882-6311 SIC 5912

■ FRED MEYER INC p 576
3800 Se 22nd Ave, Portland OR 97202
Tel (503) 232-8844
SIC 5411 5311 5912 5211 5731 5944

■ FRED MEYER STORES INC p 576
3800 Se 22nd Ave, Portland OR 97202
Tel (503) 232-8844
SIC 5211 5411 5912 5731 5944

SACRED HEART HEALTH CARE SYSTEM INC p 1265
421 Chew St, Allentown PA 18102
Tel (610) 776-4900 SIC 8741 5912

QUALITY LIFE SERVICES p 1197
612 N Main St Ste A, Butler PA 16001
Tel (724) 431-0770 SIC 5912 8051

■ HARCO INC p 660
30 Hunter Ln, Camp Hill PA 17011
Tel (717) 761-2633 SIC 5912

■ MAXI DRUG INC p 922
30 Hunter Ln, Camp Hill PA 17011
Tel (717) 761-2633 SIC 5912

▲ RITE AID CORP p 1236
30 Hunter Ln, Camp Hill PA 17011
Tel (717) 761-2633 SIC 5912 7384 5963

■ RITE AID OF KENTUCKY INC p 1236
30 Hunter Ln, Camp Hill PA 17011
Tel (717) 761-2633 SIC 5912

■ RITE AID OF MARYLAND INC p 1236
30 Hunter Ln, Camp Hill PA 17011
Tel (717) 761-2633 SIC 5912

■ RITE AID OF MICHIGAN INC p 1236
30 Hunter Ln, Camp Hill PA 17011
Tel (717) 761-2633 SIC 5912

■ RITE AID OF NEW JERSEY INC p 1236
30 Hunter Ln, Camp Hill PA 17011
Tel (717) 761-2633 SIC 5912

■ RITE AID OF NEW YORK INC p 1236
30 Hunter Ln, Camp Hill PA 17011
Tel (717) 761-2633 SIC 5912

■ RITE AID OF OHIO INC p 1236
30 Hunter Ln, Camp Hill PA 17011
Tel (717) 761-2633 SIC 5912

■ RITE AID OF PENNSYLVANIA INC p 1236
30 Hunter Ln, Camp Hill PA 17011
Tel (717) 761-2633 SIC 5912

■ RITE AID OF SOUTH CAROLINA INC p 1236
30 Hunter Ln, Camp Hill PA 17011
Tel (717) 761-2633 SIC 5912

■ RITE AID OF VIRGINIA INC p 1236
30 Hunter Ln, Camp Hill PA 17011
Tel (717) 761-2633 SIC 5912

■ RITE AID OF WEST VIRGINIA INC p 1236
30 Hunter Ln, Camp Hill PA 17011
Tel (717) 761-2633 SIC 5912

■ MILLENNIUM PHARMACY SYSTEMS LLC p 970
100 E Kensinger Dr # 500, Cranberry Township PA 16066
Tel (724) 940-2490 SIC 5912

HANOVER HEALTH CORP INC p 658
300 Highland Ave, Hanover PA 17331
Tel (717) 637-3711 SIC 8062 8011 5912

DIAMOND DRUGS INC p 436
645 Kolter Dr, Indiana PA 15701
Tel (724) 349-1111 SIC 5912 5999

HOME CARE PRODUCTS & PHARMACY p 703
1 Hospital Dr, Lewisburg PA 17837
Tel (570) 522-2000 SIC 5912 7352 5999

GENUARDIS FAMILY MARKETS LP p 605
301 E Germantown Pike, Norristown PA 19401
Tel (610) 277-6000 SIC 5912 5411

REDNERS MARKETS INC p 1217
3 Quarry Rd, Reading PA 19605
Tel (610) 926-3700 SIC 5411 5541 5912

TWIN TIER MANAGEMENT CORP p 1495
Guthrie Sq, Sayre PA 18840
Tel (570) 888-6666 SIC 8741 5912

WELLSPAN HEALTH p 1591
45 Monument Rd, York PA 17403
Tel (717) 851-2269 SIC 5912

■ WALGREEN OF SAN PATRICIO INC p 1572
580 Marginal Buchanan, Guaynabo PR 00966
Tel (787) 795-4200 SIC 5912

SPECIAL CARE PHARMACY SERVICES INC p 1355
1221 Ave Americo Miranda, San Juan PR 00921
Tel (787) 783-8579 SIC 5912 8082

■ CAREMARK PHC LLC p 255
695 George Washington Hwy, Lincoln RI 02865
Tel (401) 334-0069 SIC 8011 5912

■ ARBOR DRUGS INC p 103
1 Cvs Dr, Woonsocket RI 02895
Tel (401) 765-1500 SIC 5912

■ CVS CENTER INC p 404
1 Cvs Dr, Woonsocket RI 02895
Tel (401) 765-1500 SIC 5912

▲ CVS HEALTH CORP p 404
1 Cvs Dr, Woonsocket RI 02895
Tel (401) 765-1500 SIC 5912 5961 8099

■ CVS OF DC AND VA INC p 404
1 Cvs Dr, Woonsocket RI 02895
Tel (401) 765-1500 SIC 5912

■ CVS OF VIRGINIA INC p 404
1 Cvs Dr, Woonsocket RI 02895
Tel (401) 765-1500 SIC 5912

■ CVS PHARMACY INC p 404
1 Cvs Dr, Woonsocket RI 02895
Tel (401) 765-1500 SIC 5912 5122

■ CVS REVCO DS INC p 404
1 Cvs Dr, Woonsocket RI 02895
Tel (401) 765-1500 SIC 5912

■ LONGS DRUG STORES CALIFORNIA INC p 877
1 Cvs Dr, Woonsocket RI 02895
Tel (925) 937-1170 SIC 5912

■ LONGS DRUG STORES CORP p 877
1 Cvs Dr, Woonsocket RI 02895
Tel (401) 770-1830 SIC 5912 5961

■ MINUTECLINIC DIAGNOSTIC MEDICAL GROUP OF SAN DIEGO INC p 974
1 Cvs Dr, Woonsocket RI 02895
Tel (401) 765-1500 SIC 5912

■ NASHUA HOLLIS CVS INC p 1008
1 Cvs Dr, Woonsocket RI 02895
Tel (401) 765-1500 SIC 5912

■ PHARMACARE HOLDING CORP p 1141
1 Cvs Dr, Woonsocket RI 02895
Tel (401) 765-1500 SIC 5912

■ REVCO DISCOUNT DRUG CENTERS INC p 1229
1 Cvs Dr, Woonsocket RI 02895
Tel (401) 765-1500 SIC 5912

■ RHODE CVS ISLAND INC p 1231
1 Cvs Dr, Woonsocket RI 02895
Tel (401) 765-1500 SIC 5912

OPAL HOLDINGS LLC p 1089
208 Bi Lo Blvd, Greenville SC 29607
Tel (864) 213-2500 SIC 5411 5541 5912

AVERA ST LUKES p 137
305 S State St, Aberdeen SD 57401
Tel (605) 622-5000 SIC 8062 5912

LEWIS DRUGS INC p 858
2701 S Minn Ave Ste 1, Sioux Falls SD 57105
Tel (605) 367-2800 SIC 5912

■ TEL-DRUG INC p 1433
4901 N 4th Ave, Sioux Falls SD 57104
Tel (605) 809-8166 SIC 5912 5961

HAMILTON CHATTANOOGA COUNTY HOSPITAL AUTHORITY p 655
975 E 3rd St, Chattanooga TN 37403
Tel (423) 778-7000 SIC 5912

JACKSON CLINIC PHARMACY INC p 773
828 N Parkway, Jackson TN 38305
Tel (731) 422-0330 SIC 5912

JACKSON CLINIC PROFESSIONAL ASSOCIATION p 773
828 N Parkway, Jackson TN 38305
Tel (731) 422-0200 SIC 5912 8011 8062

▲ FREDS INC p 576
4300 New Getwell Rd, Memphis TN 38118
Tel (901) 365-8880
SIC 5331 5912 5199 6794

■ BASIC AMERICAN MEDICAL INC p 158
1 Park Plz, Nashville TN 37203
Tel (615) 344-9551 SIC 5912 2599 8093

MAXOR NATIONAL PHARMACY SERVICES LLC p 922
320 S Polk St Ste 900, Amarillo TX 79101
Tel (806) 324-5400 SIC 5912

AVT GROCERY INC p 139
777 Freeport Pkwy, Coppell TX 75019
Tel (972) 241-2184 SIC 5411 5912

CCS MEDICAL HOLDINGS INC p 270
1505 L B Johnson Fwy # 600, Farmers Branch TX 75234
Tel (972) 628-2100 SIC 5999 5912 5961

CCS MEDICAL INC p 270
1505 L B Johnson Fwy # 600, Farmers Branch TX 75234
Tel (972) 628-2100 SIC 5999 5912 5961

ACQUISITION VEHICLE TEXAS II LLC p 18
301 Commerce St Ste 3232, Fort Worth TX 76102
Tel (972) 915-2895 SIC 5411 5912

CYPRESS FAIRBANKS MEDICAL CENTER p 405
10655 Steepletop Dr, Houston TX 77065
Tel (281) 897-3172 SIC 5912

INDUS ENTERPRISES INC p 739
7051 Southwest Fwy, Houston TX 77074
Tel (713) 784-4335 SIC 5149 5194 5912

RANDALLS FOOD MARKETS INC p 1207
3663 Briarpark Dr, Houston TX 77042
Tel (713) 268-3500 SIC 5411 5912

TOM THUMB FOOD & DRUGS INC p 1459
3663 Briarpark Dr, Houston TX 77042
Tel (713) 268-3500
SIC 5411 5912 5499 6512 6552

GIBSON SALES LP p 611
2321a W Loop 281, Longview TX 75604
Tel (903) 297-0966 SIC 5912

KELSEY-SEYBOLD MEDICAL GROUP PLLC p 809
11511 Shadow Creek Pkwy, Pearland TX 77584
Tel (713) 442-0000 SIC 8011 5912

CROSSMARK INC p 394
5100 Legacy Dr, Plano TX 75024
Tel (469) 814-1000 SIC 5141 5912 7299

■ SMITHS FOOD & DRUG CENTERS INC p 1334
1550 S Redwood Rd, Salt Lake City UT 84104
Tel (801) 974-1400 SIC 5912 5499

HAGGEN INC p 653
2211 Rimland Dr Ste 300, Bellingham WA 98226
Tel (360) 733-8720 SIC 5411 5912

BARTELL DRUG CO p 157
4025 Delridge Way Sw # 400, Seattle WA 98106
Tel (206) 763-2626 SIC 5912

YOKES FOODS INC p 1636
3426 S University Rd, Spokane Valley WA 99206
Tel (509) 921-2292 SIC 5912

GENOA HEALTHCARE LLC p 604
18300 Cascade Ave S # 251, Tukwila WA 98188
Tel (800) 519-1139 SIC 5912

FRUTH INC p 582
4016 Ohio River Rd, Point Pleasant WV 25550
Tel (304) 675-1612 SIC 5912

AURORA PHARMACY INC p 132
12500 W Bluemound Rd # 201, Elm Grove WI 53122
Tel (262) 787-2136 SIC 5912

SHOPKO STORES OPERATING CO LLC p 1318
700 Pilgrim Way, Green Bay WI 54304
Tel (920) 429-2211 SIC 5311 5912 8042

GUNDERSEN LUTHERAN MEDICAL CENTER INC p 647
1900 South Ave, La Crosse WI 54601
Tel (608) 782-7300 SIC 8062 5912

CATHEDRAL SQUARE PHARMACY p 265
732 N Jackson St Ste 300, Milwaukee WI 53202
Tel (414) 277-6510 SIC 5912

EXTENDICARE HEALTH SERVICES INC p 521
111 W Michigan St, Milwaukee WI 53203
Tel (414) 908-6720 SIC 8051 7389 5912

LINDENGROVE INC p 868
13700 W National Ave # 9, New Berlin WI 53151
Tel (262) 797-4600 SIC 8051 5912

SIC 5921 Liquor Stores

BFW LIQUIDATION LLC p 179
1800 Intl Pk Dr Ste 500, Birmingham AL 35243
Tel (205) 853-2663 SIC 5411 5912 5921

SAFEWAY SELECT GIFT SOURCE INC p 1267
6401 A St, Anchorage AK 99518
Tel (907) 561-1944 SIC 5411 5141 5921

■ COST PLUS INC p 373
1201 Marina Village Pkwy # 100, Alameda CA 94501
Tel (510) 893-7300
SIC 5712 5713 5719 5947 5499 5921

BEVERAGES & MORE INC p 178
1401 Willow Pass Rd # 900, Concord CA 94520
Tel (925) 609-6000 SIC 5921 5499 5993

BEVMO HOLDINGS LLC p 179
1470 Civic Ct Ste 1600, Concord CA 94520
Tel (925) 609-6000 SIC 5921 5499 5993

WINE GROUP INC p 1616
4596 Tesla Rd, Livermore CA 94550
Tel (925) 456-2500 SIC 5921

TRADER JOES CO p 1469
800 S Shamrock Ave, Monrovia CA 91016
Tel (626) 599-3700 SIC 5411 5921

DFS GROUP LP p 435
525 Market St Fl 33, San Francisco CA 94105
Tel (415) 977-2701
SIC 5944 5948 5921 5993 5947 5999

WINE GROUP LLC p 1616
4596 S Tracy Blvd, Tracy CA 95377
Tel (415) 986-8700 SIC 5921

▲ FLANIGANS ENTERPRISES INC p 554
5059 Ne 18th Ave, Fort Lauderdale FL 33334
Tel (954) 377-1961 SIC 5812 5921

ABC LIQUORS INC p 10
8989 S Orange Ave, Orlando FL 32824
Tel (407) 851-0000 SIC 5921

SOUTHWEST GEORGIA OIL CO INC p 1352
1711 E Shotwell St, Bainbridge GA 39819
Tel (229) 246-1553
SIC 5171 5541 5411 5921

FOUNTAINHEAD DEVELOPMENT LLC p 571
100 Rue Charlemagne Dr, Braselton GA 30517
Tel (770) 867-0903
SIC 7992 7991 5921 5812 7011

DEKALB FARMERS MARKET INC p 423
3000 E Ponce De Leon Ave, Decatur GA 30030
Tel (404) 377-6400
SIC 5431 5421 5461 5451 5921 5812

MCDONALD OIL CO INC p 927
1700 Lukken Indus Dr W, Lagrange GA 30240
Tel (706) 884-6191 SIC 5541 5921 6519

C STEIN INC p 233
4719 S Market St, Boise ID 83705
Tel (208) 378-0550
SIC 5181 5182 5149 4941 5921

TREASURE ISLAND FOODS INC p 1475
3460 N Broadway St, Chicago IL 60657
Tel (773) 327-3880 SIC 5411 5921

SUNSET FOOD MART INC p 1404
777 Central Ave Ste 2, Highland Park IL 60035
Tel (847) 234-8380 SIC 5411 5921

HY-VEE INC p 723
5820 Westown Pkwy, West Des Moines IA 50266
Tel (515) 267-2800 SIC 5411 5912 5921

MOCKLER BEVERAGE CO p 980
11811 Reiger Rd, Baton Rouge LA 70809
Tel (225) 408-4283 SIC 5181 5921

RETAIL SERVICES & SYSTEMS INC p 1228
6600 Rockledge Dr Ste 150, Bethesda MD 20817
Tel (301) 795-1000 SIC 5921

MARTIGNETTI CORP p 912
500 John Hancock Rd, Taunton MA 02780
Tel (781) 278-2000 SIC 5182 5921

LRR FOOD INC p 882
850 76th St Sw, Grand Rapids MI 49518
Tel (810) 629-1383 SIC 5411 5921

POLLYS FOOD SERVICE INC p 1160
1821 Spring Arbor Rd, Jackson MI 49203
Tel (517) 787-5228 SIC 5411 5921

HOLLYWOOD HOLDING CO LLC p 701
2670 W Maple Rd, Troy MI 48084
Tel (248) 643-0309 SIC 5921 5141 5411

COBORNS INC p 333
1921 Coborn Blvd, Saint Cloud MN 56301
Tel (320) 252-4222 SIC 5411 5541 5921

FOODARAMA SUPERMARKETS INC p 564
922 State Route 33 Bldg 1, Freehold NJ 07728
Tel (732) 462-3120 SIC 5411 5261 5921

SAKER HOLDINGS CORP p 1271
922 State Route 33 Bldg 1, Freehold NJ 07728
Tel (732) 462-4700 SIC 5411 5261 5921

RONETCO SUPERMARKETS INC p 1249
1070 Us Highway 46 Ste 1, Ledgewood NJ 07852
Tel (973) 927-8300 SIC 5411 5921

GLASS GARDENS INC p 614
220 W Passaic St, Rochelle Park NJ 07662
Tel (201) 843-1424 SIC 5411 5921

▲ SOTHEBYS p 1341
1334 York Ave, New York NY 10021
Tel (212) 606-7000 SIC 6531 6111 5921

LAROSAS INC p 845
2334 Boudinot Ave, Cincinnati OH 45238
Tel (513) 347-5660
SIC 5812 6794 5141 5921

BRABHAM OIL CO INC p 206
525 Midway St, Bamberg SC 29003
Tel (803) 245-2471
SIC 5171 5541 5411 5921

CENTENNIAL BEVERAGE GROUP LLC p 275
4011 Commerce St, Dallas TX 75226
Tel (972) 668-7335 SIC 5921

SPECS FAMILY PARTNERS LTD p 1356
2410 Smith St, Houston TX 77006
Tel (713) 526-8787 SIC 5921

KWIK TRIP INC p 832
1626 Oak St, La Crosse WI 54603
Tel (608) 781-8988
SIC 5921 5993 5541 5983 5461

SIC 5932 Used Merchandise Stores

ALABAMA THRIFT STORES INC p 43
1125 Huffman Rd, Birmingham AL 35215
Tel (205) 856-1234 SIC 5331 5932

ATS OPERATING LLC p 129
1900 Crestwood Blvd, Irondale AL 35210
Tel (205) 215-9829 SIC 5932 5331

REDROCK PARTNERS LLC p 1217
8260 E Raintree Dr, Scottsdale AZ 85260
Tel (480) 596-5702
SIC 5944 5932 5736 5941 5999

AIDS HEALTHCARE FOUNDATION p 37
6255 W Sunset Blvd Fl 21, Los Angeles CA 90028
Tel (323) 860-5200 SIC 5932 8093 5912

SYAR INDUSTRIES INC p 1413
2301 Napa Vallejo Hwy, Napa CA 94558
Tel (707) 252-8711
SIC 5032 2951 0762 7992 5932

NORQUIST SALVAGE CORP INC p 1049
2151 Prof Dr Ste 200, Roseville CA 95661
Tel (916) 787-1070 SIC 5932

GOODWILL SOUTHERN CALIFORNIA p 625
8120 Palm Ln, San Bernardino CA 92410
Tel (909) 885-3831 SIC 5932 8331

GOODWILL INDUSTRIES OF ORANGE COUNTY CALIFORNIA p 625
410 N Fairview St, Santa Ana CA 92703
Tel (714) 547-6308 SIC 5932

EMANUEL MEDICAL CENTER AUXILLARY p 490
825 Delbon Ave, Turlock CA 95382
Tel (209) 667-4200 SIC 5932 5947 8699

DISCOVER GOODWILL OF SOUTHERN & WESTERN COLORADO p 442
1460 Grdn Of The Gods Rd, Colorado Springs CO 80907
Tel (719) 635-4483 SIC 5932 8331

GOODWILL INDUSTRIES OF SOUTHWEST FLORIDA INC p 625
5100 Tice St, Fort Myers FL 33905
Tel (239) 995-2106 SIC 5932 5087

HOSPICE TREASURE CHEST p 709
4266 Sunbeam Rd Ste 100, Jacksonville FL 32257
Tel (904) 596-6278 SIC 5932

GOODWILL INDUSTRIES-SUNCOAST INC p 625
10596 Gandy Blvd N, Saint Petersburg FL 33702
Tel (727) 523-1512 SIC 5932 8093

GOODWILL INDUSTRIES-SUNCOAST INC p 625
10596 Gandy Blvd N, Saint Petersburg FL 33702
Tel (727) 523-1512 SIC 7361 5932

▲ **AARONS INC** p 8
400 Galleria Pkwy Se # 300, Atlanta GA 30339
Tel (404) 231-0011
SIC 7359 5712 5731 5722 5932 6794

NATIONAL FURNITURE LIQUIDATORS I LLC p 1012
2865 Log Cabin Dr Se, Atlanta GA 30339
Tel (404) 872-7280 SIC 5021 5712 5932

GOODWILL OF NORTH GEORGIA INC p 625
2201 Lawrenceville Hwy, Decatur GA 30033
Tel (404) 420-9900 SIC 5932 8331

NORTHWESTERN LAKE FOREST HOSPITAL p 1060
660 N Westmoreland Rd, Lake Forest IL 60045
Tel (847) 234-0945
SIC 8062 5947 5932 5812

GOODWILL INDUSTRIES OF CENTRAL INDIANA INC p 624
1635 W Michigan St, Indianapolis IN 46222
Tel (317) 564-4313
SIC 5932 4783 8331 4953

GOODWILL INDUSTRIES INC p 624
553 Fairview Ave N, Saint Paul MN 55104
Tel (651) 379-5800
SIC 4953 8331 8322 5932 4226

GOTHAM TECHNOLOGY GROUP LLC p 626
1 Paragon Dr Ste 200, Montvale NJ 07645
Tel (201) 802-9600 SIC 5045 7361 5932

BARNEYS INC p 156
575 5th Ave Fl 11, New York NY 10017
Tel (212) 450-8700
SIC 5611 5621 5632 5932 5947 6794

1-800-PACK-RAT LLC p 1
11640 Northpark Dr 200, Wake Forest NC 27587
Tel (202) 362-0101 SIC 5932

GOODWILL INDUSTRIES OF NORTHWEST NORTH CAROLINA INC p 625
2701 University Pkwy, Winston Salem NC 27105
Tel (336) 724-3621 SIC 5932 8331

CHIC AND SIMPLE LLC p 297
573 Lancaster Ave, Berwyn PA 19312
Tel (610) 636-0686 SIC 5932

▲ **FIRSTCASH INC** p 550
690 E Lamar Blvd Ste 400, Arlington TX 76011
Tel (817) 460-3947 SIC 5932 6099

▲ **EZCORP INC** p 522
2500 Bee Caves Rd B1-200, Austin TX 78746
Tel (512) 314-3400 SIC 5932 6141

MS PAWN LIMITED PARTNERSHIP p 996
1901 Capital Pkwy, Austin TX 78746
Tel (512) 314-3400 SIC 5932 6141

■ **CASH AMERICA FINANCIAL SERVICES INC** p 263
1600 W 7th St, Fort Worth TX 76102
Tel (817) 335-1100 SIC 5932

CASH AMERICA INVESTMENTS INC p 263
1600 W 7th St, Fort Worth TX 76102
Tel (817) 335-1100 SIC 5932 6099

■ **FRONTIER MERGER SUB LLC** p 581
1600 W 7th St, Fort Worth TX 76102
Tel (800) 223-8738 SIC 5932 6099

▲ **GAMESTOP CORP** p 590
625 Westport Pkwy, Grapevine TX 76051
Tel (817) 424-2000
SIC 5945 5734 5932 2721

DESERET MANAGEMENT CORP p 432
55 N 300 W Ste 800, Salt Lake City UT 84101
Tel (801) 538-0651
SIC 4832 4833 5932 6512 6531 6411

■ **CORT BUSINESS SERVICES CORP** p 373
15000 Conference Ste 440, Chantilly VA 20151
Tel (703) 968-8500 SIC 7359 5712 5932

SAVERS INC p 1284
11400 Se 6th St Ste 220, Bellevue WA 98004
Tel (425) 462-1515 SIC 5932 5311 5331

TVI INC p 1494
11400 Se 6th St Ste 220, Bellevue WA 98004
Tel (425) 462-1515
SIC 5932 5251 5311 5331

SEATTLE GOODWILL INDUSTRIES INC p 1297
700 Dearborn Pl S, Seattle WA 98144
Tel (206) 329-1000 SIC 5932

GOODWILL INDUSTRIES OF NORTH CENTRAL WISCONSIN INC p 624
1800 Appleton Rd, Menasha WI 54952
Tel (920) 731-6601 SIC 5932 7389 8331

SIC 5941 Sporting Goods & Bicycle Stores

■ **HIBBETT SPORTING GOODS INC** p 690
2700 Milan Ct, Birmingham AL 35211
Tel (205) 942-4292 SIC 5941 5661 5699

▲ **HIBBETT SPORTS INC** p 690
2700 Milan Ct, Birmingham AL 35211
Tel (205) 942-4292 SIC 5941 5661 5699

REDROCK PARTNERS LLC p 1217
8260 E Raintree Dr, Scottsdale AZ 85260
Tel (480) 596-5702
SIC 5944 5932 5736 5941 5999

■ **VF OUTDOOR LLC** p 1553
2701 Harbor Bay Pkwy, Alameda CA 94502
Tel (510) 618-3500
SIC 2329 2339 3949 2394 2399 5941

MERCHANT OF TENNIS INC p 944
8737 Wilshire Blvd, Beverly Hills CA 90211
Tel (310) 228-4000
SIC 5941 5621 5661 5961 5999

L-O CORONADO HOTEL INC p 835
1500 Orange Ave, Coronado CA 92118
Tel (619) 435-6611
SIC 7011 5812 5813 5941

CHICKS SPORTING GOODS LLC p 298
979 S Village Oaks Dr, Covina CA 91724
Tel (626) 915-1685 SIC 5941

■ **BIG 5 CORP** p 181
2525 E El Segundo Blvd, El Segundo CA 90245
Tel (310) 536-0611 SIC 5941

▲ **BIG 5 SPORTING GOODS CORP** p 181
2525 E El Segundo Blvd, El Segundo CA 90245
Tel (310) 536-0611 SIC 5941

AMERICAN GOLF CORP p 73
6080 Center Dr Ste 500, Los Angeles CA 90045
Tel (310) 664-4000
SIC 7997 7999 5812 5941 7992

GREEN EQUITY INVESTORS IV LP p 637
11111 Santa Monica Blvd, Los Angeles CA 90025
Tel (310) 954-0444 SIC 5941

SLAP SHOT HOLDINGS CORP p 1331
11111 Santa Monica Blvd, Los Angeles CA 90025
Tel (310) 954-0444 SIC 5941

PEBBLE BEACH RESORT CO DBA LONE CYPRESS SHOP p 1126
2700 17 Mile Dr, Pebble Beach CA 93953
Tel (831) 647-7500
SIC 7011 7992 5941 7991

SHARPER IMAGE CORP p 1312
350 The Embarcadero Fl 6, San Francisco CA 94105
Tel (877) 714-7444
SIC 5731 5941 5999 5719 5945 5961

SPORTS AUTHORITY INC p 1359
1050 W Hampden Ave, Englewood CO 80110
Tel (303) 200-5050 SIC 5941

TSA STORES INC p 1489
1050 W Hampden Ave, Englewood CO 80110
Tel (303) 200-5050 SIC 5941 4832

■ **COLEMAN CO INC** p 336
1767 Denver West Blvd # 200, Golden CO 80401
Tel (316) 832-2653 SIC 3086 5941

FIT FOR LIFE LLC p 552
833 W S Boulder Rd Bldg G, Louisville CO 80027
Tel (303) 222-3600 SIC 5091 5941

SME HOLDING CO LLC p 1332
160 Corporate Ct, Meriden CT 06450
Tel (603) 924-9571 SIC 5699 5941

■ **ROBBYS SPORTING GOODS INC** p 1241
311 Manatee Ave W, Bradenton FL 34205
Tel (941) 748-0577 SIC 5941

FANATICS INC p 527
8100 Nations Way, Jacksonville FL 32256
Tel (904) 421-8143 SIC 5941 5699

MEADOWBROOK GOLF GROUP INC p 934
5385 Gateway Blvd Ste 12, Lakeland FL 33811
Tel (407) 589-7200
SIC 8742 8741 7992 5941

PARADIES SHOPS LLC p 1113
2849 Paces Ferry Rd Se, Atlanta GA 30339
Tel (404) 344-7905
SIC 5947 5994 5621 5611 5912 5941

EXCEPTIONAL INC p 517
111 Hana Hwy Ste 111, Kahului HI 96732
Tel (808) 877-6555 SIC 7363 5941 7361

EBHI HOLDINGS INC p 474
1000 Field Dr Ste 240, Lake Forest IL 60045
Tel (312) 251-3430
SIC 5611 5699 5941 5719 5947 5961

▲ **FINISH LINE INC** p 543
3308 N Mitthoefer Rd, Indianapolis IN 46235
Tel (317) 899-1022 SIC 5661 5699 5941

BROWNELLS INC p 220
200 S Front St, Montezuma IA 50171
Tel (641) 623-5401 SIC 5091 5941

CWI INC p 404
650 Three Springs Rd, Bowling Green KY 42104
Tel (270) 781-2718 SIC 5941

BUDSGUNSHOP.COM LLC p 224
1105 Industry Rd, Lexington KY 40505
Tel (859) 368-0371 SIC 5941

L L BEAN INC p 834
15 Casco St, Freeport ME 04033
Tel (207) 552-2000
SIC 5961 5621 5611 5941 5661 5948

OLYMPIA SPORT CENTER INC p 1083
5 Bradley Dr, Westbrook ME 04092
Tel (207) 854-2794 SIC 5941

OSC SPORTS INC p 1096
5 Bradley Dr, Westbrook ME 04092
Tel (207) 854-2794 SIC 5699 5661 5941

■ **TOP-FLITE GOLF CO** p 1460
425 Meadow St, Chicopee MA 01013
Tel (413) 536-1200 SIC 5941

DOVER SADDLERY INC p 453
525 Great Rd, Littleton MA 01460
Tel (978) 952-8062 SIC 5941

MICHIGAN SPORTING GOODS DISTRIBUTORS INC p 961
3070 Shaffer Ave Se, Grand Rapids MI 49512
Tel (616) 942-2600 SIC 5941

AMERICAN SPECIALTY RETAILING GROUP INC p 79
5607 New King Dr Ste 125, Troy MI 48098
Tel (248) 674-4991 SIC 5661 5941 5699

DUNHAMS ATHLEISURE CORP p 461
5607 New King Dr Ste 125, Troy MI 48098
Tel (248) 674-4991
SIC 5699 5661 5941 5961

GANDER MOUNTAIN CO p 590
180 5th St E Ste 1300, Saint Paul MN 55101
Tel (651) 325-4300 SIC 5941

BASS PRO GROUP LLC p 159
2500 E Kearney St, Springfield MO 65898
Tel (417) 873-5000 SIC 5941

BASS PRO LLC p 159
2500 E Kearney St, Springfield MO 65898
Tel (417) 873-5000
SIC 5961 5941 5551 5661

▲ **CABELAS INC** p 234
1 Cabelas Dr, Sidney NE 69162
Tel (308) 254-5505 SIC 5961 5941

TOYS "R" US INC p 1467
1 Geoffrey Way, Wayne NJ 07470
Tel (973) 617-3500
SIC 5945 5734 5999 5735 5641 5941

ALPIN HAUS SKI SHOP INC p 60
4850 State Highway 30, Amsterdam NY 12010
Tel (518) 843-4400 SIC 5561 5551 5941

▲ **FOOT LOCKER INC** p 564
330 W 34th St, New York NY 10001
Tel (212) 720-3700
SIC 5661 5941 5961 6794

HENRY MODELL & CO INC p 684
498 7th Ave Fl 20, New York NY 10018
Tel (212) 822-1000
SIC 5941 5661 5611 5621 5641 5961

PERFORMANCE DIRECT INC p 1135
1 Performance Way, Chapel Hill NC 27517
Tel (919) 933-9113 SIC 5961 5941

EUROPA SPORTS PRODUCTS INC p 513
11401 Granite St Ste H, Charlotte NC 28273
Tel (704) 405-2022 SIC 5122 5149 5941

SPORTS ENDEAVORS INC p 1359
431 Us Highway 70a E, Hillsborough NC 27278
Tel (919) 644-6800 SIC 5941

SCHEELS ALL SPORTS INC p 1286
4550 15th Ave S, Fargo ND 58103
Tel (701) 364-0572
SIC 5661 5941 5699 5251 5261

LIMITED STORES LLC p 866
7775 Walton Pkwy Ste 400, New Albany OH 43054
Tel (614) 289-2200 SIC 5621 5941 5632

■ **GOLF GALAXY GOLFWORKS INC** p 622
4820 Jacksontown Rd, Newark OH 43056
Tel (740) 328-4193
SIC 5091 2731 3949 5941

G I JOES INC p 587
9805 Sw Boeckman Rd, Wilsonville OR 97070
Tel (503) 682-2242
SIC 5941 5699 5531 5999

■ **DICKS MERCHANDISING & SUPPLY CHAIN INC** p 438
345 Court St, Coraopolis PA 15108
Tel (724) 723-3400 SIC 5941

▲ **DICKS SPORTING GOODS INC** p 438
345 Court St, Coraopolis PA 15108
Tel (724) 273-3400 SIC 5941 5699

■ **GOLF GALAXY INC** p 622
345 Court St, Coraopolis PA 15108
Tel (724) 273-3400 SIC 5941

■ **GALYANS TRADING CO LLC** p 590
300 Industry Dr, Pittsburgh PA 15275
Tel (724) 273-3400 SIC 5941 5699 5661

■ **GENERAL NUTRITION CORP** p 601
300 6th Ave, Pittsburgh PA 15222
Tel (412) 288-4600
SIC 5499 5999 5941 5699 6794

BUCKMANS INC p 223
105 Airport Rd, Pottstown PA 19464
Tel (610) 495-7495 SIC 5169 5941

SCHUYLKILL VALLEY SPORTS INC p 1291
118 Industrial Dr Ste 1, Pottstown PA 19464
Tel (610) 495-8813 SIC 5091 5941

ALLPLAYERS NETWORK INC p 58
4145 Belt Line Rd Ste 212, Addison TX 75001
Tel (214) 234-9770 SIC 5941

■ **GOLFSMITH INTERNATIONAL HOLDINGS INC** p 622
11000 N Interstate 35, Austin TX 78753
Tel (512) 837-8810
SIC 5941 5699 5661 5961

TOP GOLF USA INC p 1460
8750 N Cntl Expy Ste 1200, Dallas TX 75231
Tel (214) 377-5053 SIC 7999 5812 5941

RETAIL CONCEPTS INC p 1228
10560 Bissonnet St # 100, Houston TX 77099
Tel (281) 340-5000 SIC 5941

ACADEMY LTD p 13
1800 N Mason Rd, Katy TX 77449
Tel (281) 646-5200 SIC 5941 5699 5661

TEAM EXPRESS DISTRIBUTING LLC p 1429
5750 Northwest Pkwy # 100, San Antonio TX 78249
Tel (210) 525-9161 SIC 5941 5091

▲ **SPORTSMANS WAREHOUSE HOLDINGS INC** p 1360
7035 S High Tech Dr # 100, Midvale UT 84047
Tel (801) 566-6681 SIC 5941 5699 5661

■ **SPORTSMANS WAREHOUSE INC** p 1360
7035 S High Tech Dr, Midvale UT 84047
Tel (801) 566-6681 SIC 5941 5699 5661

■ **STRATTON CORP** p 1393
5 Village Lodge Rd, South Londonderry VT 05155
Tel (802) 297-2200
SIC 7011 7992 1531 6512 5941

ORVIS CO INC p 1096
178 Conservation Way, Sunderland VT 05250
Tel (802) 362-3622 SIC 5961 5941 3949

CUSTOMINK LLC p 403
2910 District Ave Ste 100, Fairfax VA 22031
Tel (703) 891-2273 SIC 2759 5699 5941

AMARGOSA INC p 64
10401 Ne 8th St Ste 500, Bellevue WA 98004
Tel (425) 755-6100
SIC 5611 5699 5941 5719 5947 5961

RECREATIONAL EQUIPMENT INC p 1215
6750 S 228th St, Kent WA 98032
Tel (253) 395-3780
SIC 2329 3949 2399 5941 5961 5699

▲ **ZUMIEZ INC** p 1645
4001 204th St Sw, Lynnwood WA 98036
Tel (425) 551-1500 SIC 5941

RAD POWER BIKES LLC p 1203
2622 Nw Market St Ste B, Seattle WA 98107
Tel (800) 939-0310 SIC 5941

JEAN NELL ENTERPRISES INC p 781
1 Nell Jean Sq 19, Beckley WV 25801
Tel (304) 253-0200 SIC 5941 5082 5091

JOHNSON HEALTH TECH NORTH AMERICA INC p 791
1600 Landmark Dr, Cottage Grove WI 53527
Tel (608) 839-1240 SIC 5091 5941

PACIFIC CYCLE INC p 1104
4902 Hammersley Rd, Madison WI 53711
Tel (608) 268-2468 SIC 5091 5941

TREK BICYCLE CORP p 1476
801 W Madison St, Waterloo WI 53594
Tel (920) 478-2191 SIC 5941 3429

■ **EASTBAY INC** p 471
111 S 1st Ave, Wausau WI 54401
Tel (800) 826-2205 SIC 5699 5661 5941

NATIONAL OUTDOOR LEADERSHIP SCHOOL p 1014
284 Lincoln St, Lander WY 82520
Tel (800) 710-6657 SIC 8299 5941

SIC 5942 Book Stores

BOOKS-A-MILLION INC p 200
402 Industrial Ln, Birmingham AL 35211
Tel (205) 942-3737
SIC 5942 5994 5947 5999

ASSOCIATED STUDENTS UCLA p 121
308 Westwood Plz, Los Angeles CA 90095
Tel (310) 825-4321 SIC 8399 5942

UNIVERSITY ENTERPRISES CORP AT CSUSB p 1518
5500 University Pkwy, San Bernardino CA 92407
Tel (909) 537-5929 SIC 5812 5942 8211

SAN FRANCISCO MUSEUM OF MODERN ART p 1276
151 3rd St, San Francisco CA 94103
Tel (415) 357-4035 SIC 8412 5942

▲ **CHEGG INC** p 292
3990 Freedom Cir, Santa Clara CA 95054
Tel (408) 855-5700 SIC 5942

NAVIGATORS p 1020
3820 N 30th St, Colorado Springs CO 80904
Tel (719) 598-1212 SIC 8661 7032 5942

■ **NATIONAL GALLERY OF ART** p 1012
6th And Csnttution Ave Nw, Washington DC 20565
Tel (202) 737-4215 SIC 5942 8412

■ **SCHOLASTIC BOOK FAIRS INC** p 1288
1080 Greenwood Blvd, Lake Mary FL 32746
Tel (407) 829-7300 SIC 5192 5199 5942

FLORIDA CONFERENCE ASSOCIATION OF SEVENTH-DAY ADVENTISTS p 557
655 N Wymore Rd, Winter Park FL 32789
Tel (407) 644-5000
SIC 8661 8211 5942 6513

PHOENIX INTERNATIONAL PUBLICATIONS INC p 1145
8501 W Higgins Rd Ste 300, Chicago IL 60631
Tel (312) 739-4400 SIC 5942 2731

FOLLETT CORP p 563
3 Westbrook Ctr Ste 200, Westchester IL 60154
Tel (708) 884-0000 SIC 5942 5192

FOLLETT HIGHER EDUCATION GROUP INC p 563
3 Westbrook Corp Ctr # 200, Westchester IL 60154
Tel (800) 365-5388 SIC 5942 5943 5947

VINCENNES UNIVERSITY p 1557
1002 N 1st St, Vincennes IN 47591
Tel (812) 888-8888 SIC 8221 5942

UNIVERSITY OF NEW ENGLAND p 1523
11 Hills Beach Rd, Biddeford ME 04005
Tel (207) 282-3025 SIC 8221 5942

FAMILY CHRISTIAN STORES LLC p 526
5300 Patterson Ave Se, Grand Rapids MI 49530
Tel (616) 554-8700
SIC 5942 5735 5947 5699 8741

CENTRAL MICHIGAN UNIVERSITY p 279
1200 S Franklin St, Mount Pleasant MI 48859
Tel (989) 774-4000
SIC 8221 5942 4833 4832 5812

MONTANA STATE UNIVERSITY-BILLINGS p 986
1500 University Dr, Billings MT 59101
Tel (406) 657-2011 SIC 4832 5942 8221

NBC ACQUISITION CORP p 1021
4700 S 19th St, Lincoln NE 68512
Tel (402) 421-7300 *SIC* 5192 5942

NEBRASKA BOOK CO INC p 1023
4700 S 19th St, Lincoln NE 68512
Tel (402) 421-7300 *SIC* 5942 5192 5961

NEBRASKA BOOK HOLDINGS INC p 1023
4700 S 19th St, Lincoln NE 68512
Tel (402) 421-0500
SIC 6719 5942 5192 5961

NEBRASKA BOOK INTERMEDIATE HOLDINGS INC p 1023
4701 S 19th St, Lincoln NE 68512
Tel (402) 421-7300
SIC 6719 5942 5192 5961

■ BARNES & NOBLE COLLEGE BOOKSELLERS LLC p 155
120 Mountainview Blvd A, Basking Ridge NJ 07920
Tel (908) 991-2665 *SIC* 5942 5943 5947

▲ BARNES & NOBLE EDUCATION INC p 156
120 Mountainview Blvd A, Basking Ridge NJ 07920
Tel (908) 991-2665 *SIC* 5942

ERIE COMMUNITY COLLEGE p 508
121 Ellicott St, Buffalo NY 14203
Tel (716) 842-2770 *SIC* 5942 8222

■ BARNES & NOBLE BOOKSELLERS INC p 155
1166 Ave Of Amer 18, New York NY 10036
Tel (212) 403-2580
SIC 5942 5994 5999 5735

▲ BARNES & NOBLE INC p 156
122 5th Ave Fl 2, New York NY 10011
Tel (212) 633-3300 *SIC* 5942 5961 5945

■ HARPERCOLLINS PUBLISHERS LLC p 663
195 Broadway Fl 2, New York NY 10007
Tel (212) 207-7000 *SIC* 5942 2731

JUILLIARD SCHOOL p 797
60 Lincoln Center Plz, New York NY 10023
Tel (212) 799-5000
SIC 8299 7911 5942 8221

MUSEUM OF MODERN ART p 1002
11 W 53rd St, New York NY 10019
Tel (212) 708-9400 *SIC* 8412 5942

RANDOM HOUSE LLC p 1208
1745 Broadway Frnt 3, New York NY 10019
Tel (212) 782-9000 *SIC* 5942 2731

AUXILIARY SERVICES STATE UNIVERSITY COLLEGE AT OSWEGO INC p 135
7060 Route 104, Oswego NY 13126
Tel (315) 312-2106
SIC 5812 5942 5962 5441

▲ FAB UNIVERSAL CORP p 523
5001 Baum Blvd Ste 770, Pittsburgh PA 15213
Tel (412) 621-0902
SIC 7371 7372 5735 5942 5994 5099

BRODART CO p 216
500 Arch St, Williamsport PA 17701
Tel (570) 326-2461
SIC 5192 5942 2752 2782 2789 2531

BOB JONES UNIVERSITY INC OF GREENVILLE S C p 196
1700 Wade Hampton Blvd, Greenville SC 29614
Tel (864) 242-5100
SIC 8221 8211 8231 8062 5942 0191

BETHEL UNIVERSITY p 178
325 Cherry Ave, Mc Kenzie TN 38201
Tel (731) 352-4000 *SIC* 8221 5942

GIDEONS INTERNATIONAL p 611
50 Century Blvd, Nashville TN 37214
Tel (615) 564-5000 *SIC* 8661 5942

LIFEWAY CHRISTIAN RESOURCES OF SOUTHERN BAPTIST CONVENTION p 865
1 Lifeway Plz, Nashville TN 37234
Tel (615) 251-2000
SIC 5942 5963 2731 5999 5735 5947

UNITED METHODIST PUBLISHING HOUSE p 1510
2222 Rosa L Parks Blvd, Nashville TN 37228
Tel (615) 749-6000
SIC 2731 5192 5942 2741 2721

HASTINGS ENTERTAINMENT INC p 667
3601 Plains Blvd, Amarillo TX 79102
Tel (806) 351-2300 *SIC* 5735 5942 7841

HALF PRICE BOOKS RECORDS MAGAZINES INC p 654
5803 E Northwest Hwy, Dallas TX 75231
Tel (214) 379-8000 *SIC* 5942 5192

TARRANT COUNTY COLLEGE DISTRICT p 1425
1500 Houston St, Fort Worth TX 76102
Tel (817) 515-5220 *SIC* 5942 8221

PON NORTH AMERICA INC p 1161
840 Gessner Rd Ste 950, Houston TX 77024
Tel (713) 365-2547 *SIC* 5942 5082

DESERET BOOK CO p 432
57 W South Temple, Salt Lake City UT 84101
Tel (801) 517-3294 *SIC* 5192 5942 2731

FC ORGANIZATIONAL PRODUCTS LLC p 532
2250 W Parkway Blvd, Salt Lake City UT 84119
Tel (801) 817-1776 *SIC* 5942 5734

SIC 5943 Stationery Stores

KELLY PAPER CO p 809
288 Brea Canyon Rd, Walnut CA 91789
Tel (909) 859-8200 *SIC* 5111 5943

■ CORPORATE EXPRESS US FINANCE INC p 372
1 Environmental Way, Broomfield CO 80021
Tel (303) 664-2000 *SIC* 5943

■ CORPORATE EXPRESS US INC p 372
1 Environmental Way, Broomfield CO 80021
Tel (303) 664-2000 *SIC* 5943

FRANCHISEE SHIPPING CENTER CO INC p 573
500 Bic Dr Bldg 3, Milford CT 06461
Tel (203) 301-0539 *SIC* 4731 5943

▲ OFFICE DEPOT INC p 1075
6600 N Military Trl, Boca Raton FL 33496
Tel (561) 438-4800
SIC 5943 5044 5734 5045

■ OFFICEMAX INC p 1076
6600 N Military Trl, Boca Raton FL 33496
Tel (630) 438-7800 *SIC* 5943 5021

■ OFFICE CLUB INC p 1075
2200 Germantown Rd, Delray Beach FL 33445
Tel (561) 438-4800 *SIC* 5943 5112

CLAIRES BOUTIQUES INC p 321
11401 Pines Blvd, Pembroke Pines FL 33026
Tel (954) 438-0433
SIC 5632 5699 5999 5943 5947

■ ESSENDANT MANAGEMENT SERVICES LLC p 510
1 Parkway N Ste 100, Deerfield IL 60015
Tel (847) 627-7000 *SIC* 5943 7373

■ QUILL CORP p 1200
100 Schelter Rd, Lincolnshire IL 60069
Tel (847) 634-6690 *SIC* 5943

■ OFFICEMAX CONTRACT INC p 1076
263 Shuman Blvd, Naperville IL 60563
Tel (630) 438-7800
SIC 5021 5112 5044 5111 5943 5712

CLOVER TECHNOLOGIES GROUP LLC p 328
4200 Columbus St, Ottawa IL 61350
Tel (815) 431-8100 *SIC* 5943 3861

FOLLETT HIGHER EDUCATION GROUP INC p 563
3 Westbrook Corp Ctr # 200, Westchester IL 60154
Tel (800) 365-5388 *SIC* 5942 5943 5947

W B MASON CO INC p 1568
59 Center St, Brockton MA 02301
Tel (781) 794-8800 *SIC* 5712 5943

CRANE & CO INC p 388
30 South St, Dalton MA 01226
Tel (617) 648-3714 *SIC* 2621 5943

■ STAPLES CONTRACT & COMMERCIAL INC p 1377
500 Staples Dr, Framingham MA 01702
Tel (508) 253-5000 *SIC* 5943

▲ STAPLES INC p 1377
500 Staples Dr, Framingham MA 01702
Tel (508) 253-5000
SIC 5943 5999 7513 5961 5712

■ STAPLES INTERNATIONAL INC p 1378
500 Staples Dr, Framingham MA 01702
Tel (508) 253-5000
SIC 5943 5712 5044 5021 5112

■ HAYNEEDLE INC p 670
9394 W Dodge Rd Ste 300, Omaha NE 68114
Tel (402) 715-3000
SIC 5943 5719 5945 5947

■ BARNES & NOBLE COLLEGE BOOKSELLERS LLC p 155
120 Mountainview Blvd A, Basking Ridge NJ 07920
Tel (908) 991-2665 *SIC* 5942 5943 5947

▲ TIFFANY & CO p 1453
200 5th Ave Bsmt 2, New York NY 10010
Tel (212) 755-8000
SIC 5944 5094 5719 5943 5999 5961

CARLTON CARDS RETAIL INC p 258
1 American Rd, Cleveland OH 44144
Tel (216) 252-7300 *SIC* 5947 5943

ACCO BRANDS USA LLC p 15
4751 Hempstead Station Dr, Kettering OH 45429
Tel (937) 495-6323 *SIC* 5943

ADMIRAL EXPRESS INC p 23
1823 N Yellowood Ave, Broken Arrow OK 74012
Tel (918) 249-4000 *SIC* 5112 5021 5943

MARDEL INC p 905
7727 Sw 44th St, Oklahoma City OK 73179
Tel (405) 745-1300 *SIC* 5999 5943

MYOFFICEPRODUCTS INC p 1004
22 Century Blvd Ste 420, Nashville TN 37214
Tel (615) 507-3515 *SIC* 5112 5943

CALENDAR HOLDINGS LLC p 238
6411 Burleson Rd, Austin TX 78744
Tel (512) 386-7220 *SIC* 5943 5945

SIC 5944 Jewelry Stores

REDROCK PARTNERS LLC p 1217
8260 E Raintree Dr, Scottsdale AZ 85260
Tel (480) 596-5702
SIC 5944 5932 5736 5941 5999

▲ ROSS STORES INC p 1252
5130 Hacienda Dr, Dublin CA 94568
Tel (925) 965-4400
SIC 5651 5661 5944 5632 5611 5999

▲ SPECTRUM GROUP INTERNATIONAL INC p 1357
1063 Mcgaw Ave Ste 250, Irvine CA 92614
Tel (949) 748-4800 *SIC* 7389 5094 5944

DEARDENS p 420
700 S Main St, Los Angeles CA 90014
Tel (213) 362-9600
SIC 5712 5722 5731 5944

■ UNIVERSAL STUDIOS INC p 1517
100 Universal City Plz, North Hollywood CA 91608
Tel (818) 777-1000
SIC 7812 3652 2741 5947 5944 5961

DFS GROUP LP p 435
525 Market St Fl 33, San Francisco CA 94105
Tel (415) 977-2701
SIC 5944 5948 5921 5993 5947 5999

■ UNIVERSAL CITY STUDIOS PRODUCTIONS LLLP LP p 1516
100 Universal City Plz, Universal City CA 91608
Tel (818) 777-1000
SIC 7812 3652 2741 5947 5944 5961

WESTERN STONE & METAL CORP p 1600
8085 S Chester St Ste 300, Centennial CO 80112
Tel (303) 792-3500 *SIC* 5944 5094

SIGNET US HOLDINGS INC p 1322
850 Library Ave, Newark DE 19711
Tel (302) 738-9652 *SIC* 5944

MP DIRECT INC p 995
4800 126th Ave N, Clearwater FL 33762
Tel (727) 572-8443 *SIC* 5094 5944 5091

MAUI DIVERS OF HAWAII LIMITED p 921
1520 Liona St, Honolulu HI 96814
Tel (808) 946-7979 *SIC* 3911 5944 5094

ULTRA STORES INC p 1501
122 S Michigan Ave # 800, Chicago IL 60603
Tel (312) 922-3800 *SIC* 5944

ROGERS ENTERPRISES INC p 1246
20821 S Cicero Ave, Matteson IL 60443
Tel (708) 679-7588 *SIC* 5944

ALBERT S SMYTH CO INC p 46
2020 York Rd, Lutherville Timonium MD 21093
Tel (410) 252-6666 *SIC* 5944 5961

■ HELZBERGS DIAMOND SHOPS INC p 682
1825 Swift Ave, Kansas City MO 64116
Tel (816) 842-7780 *SIC* 5944

SPENCER GIFTS LLC p 1358
6826 Black Horse Pike, Egg Harbor Township NJ 08234
Tel (609) 645-3300 *SIC* 5947 5944

■ LCI HOLDINGS INC p 849
5901 W Side Ave, North Bergen NJ 07047
Tel (201) 295-6300
SIC 5651 5136 5137 5094 5122 5944

CHANEL INC p 288
9 W 57th St Fl 44, New York NY 10019
Tel (212) 688-5055
SIC 5632 2844 5122 5944 5961 5999

▲ TIFFANY & CO p 1453
200 5th Ave Bsmt 2, New York NY 10010
Tel (212) 755-8000
SIC 5944 5094 5719 5943 5999 5961

■ VIVENDI UNIVERSAL ENTERTAINMENT LLLP p 1563
30 Rockefeller Plz, New York NY 10112
Tel (212) 664-4444
SIC 7812 3652 2741 5947 5944 5961

FORTUNOFF FINE JEWELRY AND SILVERWARE INC p 570
70 Charles Lindbergh Blvd, Uniondale NY 11553
Tel (516) 222-7879 *SIC* 5944 5719

REEDS JEWELERS INC p 1217
2525 S 17th St, Wilmington NC 28401
Tel (910) 350-3100 *SIC* 5944

▲ KROGER CO p 830
1014 Vine St Ste 1000, Cincinnati OH 45202
Tel (513) 762-4000
SIC 5411 5912 5541 5944

MARKS & MORGAN JEWELERS INC p 909
375 Ghent Rd, Fairlawn OH 44333
Tel (330) 668-5000 *SIC* 5944

SIGNET JEWELERS LIMITED p 1322
375 Ghent Rd, Fairlawn OH 44333
Tel (330) 668-5785 *SIC* 5944

STERLING INC p 1387
375 Ghent Rd, Fairlawn OH 44333
Tel (216) 867-1230 *SIC* 5944

SUAREZ CORP INDUSTRIES p 1395
7800 Whipple Ave Nw, North Canton OH 44720
Tel (330) 494-5504 *SIC* 5961 5944

COOPER & CO INC p 366
10179 Commerce Park Dr, West Chester OH 45246
Tel (513) 671-6067 *SIC* 5944

■ FRED MEYER INC p 576
3800 Se 22nd Ave, Portland OR 97202
Tel (503) 232-8844
SIC 5411 5311 5912 5211 5731 5944

■ FRED MEYER JEWELERS INC p 576
3800 Se 22nd Ave, Portland OR 97202
Tel (503) 232-8844 *SIC* 5944

■ FRED MEYER STORES INC p 576
3800 Se 22nd Ave, Portland OR 97202
Tel (503) 232-8844
SIC 5211 5411 5912 5731 5944

ALEX AND ANI LLC p 48
2000 Chapel View Blvd # 360, Cranston RI 02920
Tel (401) 633-1486 *SIC* 3915 5944

LUXURY BRAND HOLDINGS INC p 887
9 Ross Simons Dr, Cranston RI 02920
Tel (401) 463-3100 *SIC* 5944

COMMEMORATIVE BRANDS INC p 344
7211 Circle S Rd, Austin TX 78745
Tel (512) 444-0571 *SIC* 3911 5944 3961

▲ TUESDAY MORNING CORP p 1490
6250 Lbj Fwy, Dallas TX 75240
Tel (972) 387-3562
SIC 5947 5719 5944 5948 5945 5712

ZALE CANADA CO p 1641
901 W Walnut Hill Ln, Irving TX 75038
Tel (972) 580-4000 *SIC* 5944

ZALE CORP p 1641
901 W Walnut Hill Ln, Irving TX 75038
Tel (972) 580-4000 *SIC* 5944

ZALE DELAWARE INC p 1641
901 W Walnut Hill Ln, Irving TX 75038
Tel (972) 580-4000 *SIC* 5944

▲ FOSSIL GROUP INC p 570
901 S Central Expy, Richardson TX 75080
Tel (972) 234-2525
SIC 3873 5944 5094 5651 5632

■ BEN BRIDGE - JEWELER INC p 172
2901 3rd Ave Ste 200, Seattle WA 98121
Tel (206) 448-8800 *SIC* 5944 7631

▲ BLUE NILE INC p 192
411 1st Ave S Ste 700, Seattle WA 98104
Tel (206) 336-6700 *SIC* 5944

SIC 5945 Hobby, Toy & Game Store

BEVERLY FABRICS INC p 179
9019 Soquel Dr Ste 175, Aptos CA 95003
Tel (831) 684-4220 *SIC* 5945 5949

SKYROCKET TOYS LLC p 1330
12910 Culver Blvd Ste F, Los Angeles CA 90066
Tel (310) 822-6155 *SIC* 5945

SHARPER IMAGE CORP p 1312
350 The Embarcadero Fl 6, San Francisco CA 94105
Tel (877) 714-7444
SIC 5731 5941 5999 5719 5945 5961

AVALANCHE STRATEGIES LLC p 135
144 Dixon St, Selbyville DE 19975
Tel (302) 436-7060 *SIC* 5092 5945

FELD ENTERTAINMENT INC p 537
800 Feld Way, Palmetto FL 34221
Tel (941) 721-1200 *SIC* 7999 7929 5945

DICK BLICK CO p 438
1849 Green Bay Rd Ste 310, Highland Park IL 60035
Tel (847) 681-6800 *SIC* 5945

TOMY HOLDINGS INC p 1460
2015 Spring Rd Ste 400, Oak Brook IL 60523
Tel (630) 573-7200 *SIC* 5092 5945

SAINT-GOBAIN CORP p 1271
1 New Bond St, Worcester MA 01606
Tel (508) 795-5000 *SIC* 5945

U S TOY CO INC p 1497
13201 Arrington Rd, Grandview MO 64030
Tel (816) 761-5900 *SIC* 5049 5092 5945

ORSCHELN FARM AND HOME LLC p 1096
1800 Overcenter Dr, Moberly MO 65270
Tel (800) 577-2580
SIC 5251 5999 5945 5731

▲ BUILD-A-BEAR WORKSHOP INC p 224
1954 Innerbelt Bus Ctr Dr, Saint Louis MO 63114
Tel (314) 423-8000 *SIC* 5945 6794

■ HAYNEEDLE INC p 670
9394 W Dodge Rd Ste 300, Omaha NE 68114
Tel (402) 715-3000
SIC 5943 5719 5945 5947

AC MOORE ARTS & CRAFTS INC p 13
130 A C Moore Dr, Berlin NJ 08009
Tel (856) 768-4930 *SIC* 5945

AC MOORE INC p 13
130 A C Moore Dr, Berlin NJ 08009
Tel (856) 768-4930 *SIC* 5945

TOYS "R" US INC p 1467
1 Geoffrey Way, Wayne NJ 07470
Tel (973) 617-3500
SIC 5945 5734 5999 5735 5641 5941

TOYS "R" US-DELAWARE INC p 1467
1 Geoffrey Way, Wayne NJ 07470
Tel (973) 617-3500 *SIC* 5945 5999 5641

■ CORNING INTERNATIONAL CORP p 371
1 Riverfront Plz, Corning NY 14831
Tel (607) 974-9000 *SIC* 3229 5945

■ FISHER-PRICE INC p 552
636 Girard Ave, East Aurora NY 14052
Tel (716) 687-3000 *SIC* 5092 5945 3944

AI FRIEDMAN LP p 37
44 W 18th St Fl 4, New York NY 10011
Tel (212) 243-9000 *SIC* 5199 5945

▲ BARNES & NOBLE INC p 156
122 5th Ave Fl 2, New York NY 10011
Tel (212) 633-3300 *SIC* 5942 5961 5945

D E SHAW LAMINAR PORTFOLIOS LLC p 407
120 W 45th St Fl 22, New York NY 10036
Tel (212) 478-0000 *SIC* 6282 2392 5945

HOUSE OF FABRICS INC p 711
5555 Darrow Rd, Hudson OH 44236
Tel (330) 656-2600 *SIC* 5949 5945 5722

JO-ANN STORES HOLDINGS INC p 787
5555 Darrow Rd, Hudson OH 44236
Tel (888) 739-4120 *SIC* 5945 5949 5947

JO-ANN STORES LLC p 787
5555 Darrow Rd, Hudson OH 44236
Tel (330) 656-2600 *SIC* 5945 5949 5947

NEEDLE HOLDINGS INC p 1024
5555 Darrow Rd, Hudson OH 44236
Tel (330) 656-2600 *SIC* 5945

■ DARICE INC p 412
13000 Darice Pkwy 82, Strongsville OH 44149
Tel (440) 238-9150 *SIC* 5945 5193 5999

HOB-LOB LTD p 698
7707 Sw 44th St, Oklahoma City OK 73179
Tel (405) 745-1100
SIC 5945 5999 5949 5947

HOBBY LOBBY STORES INC p 699
7707 Sw 44th St, Oklahoma City OK 73179
Tel (855) 329-7060 *SIC* 5945

▲ FIVE BELOW INC p 553
1818 Market St Ste 2000, Philadelphia PA 19103
Tel (215) 546-7909 *SIC* 5331 5945

■ EB INVESTMENT CORP p 474
931 S Matlack St, West Chester PA 19382
Tel (610) 430-8100 *SIC* 5734 5945

CALENDAR HOLDINGS LLC p 238
6411 Burleson Rd, Austin TX 78744
Tel (512) 386-7220 *SIC* 5943 5945

▲ TUESDAY MORNING CORP p 1490
6250 Lbj Fwy, Dallas TX 75240
Tel (972) 387-3562
SIC 5947 5719 5944 5948 5945 5712

■ ELECTRONICS BOUTIQUE OF AMERICA INC p 486
625 Westport Pkwy, Grapevine TX 76051
Tel (817) 424-2000 *SIC* 5734 5945

▲ GAMESTOP CORP p 590
625 Westport Pkwy, Grapevine TX 76051
Tel (817) 424-2000
SIC 5945 5734 5932 2721

▲ CARBO CERAMICS INC p 252
575 N Dairy Ashford Rd # 30, Houston TX 77079
Tel (281) 921-6400
SIC 3291 5945 8742 7371

GRDG HOLDINGS LLC p 633
19411 Atrium Pl Ste 170, Houston TX 77084
Tel (281) 578-2334 *SIC* 5945

■ AARON BROTHERS INC p 8
8001 Ridgepoint Dr, Irving TX 75063
Tel (214) 492-6200 *SIC* 7699 5945

▲ MICHAELS COMPANIES INC p 960
8000 Bent Branch Dr, Irving TX 75063
Tel (972) 409-1300 *SIC* 5945 3999 2273

■ MICHAELS FINCO HOLDINGS LLC p 960
8000 Bent Branch Dr, Irving TX 75063
Tel (972) 409-1300 *SIC* 5945

■ MICHAELS FUNDING INC p 960
8000 Bent Branch Dr, Irving TX 75063
Tel (972) 409-1300 *SIC* 5945

MICHAELS HOLDINGS LLC p 960
8000 Bent Branch Dr, Irving TX 75063
Tel (972) 409-1300
SIC 5945 5999 5949 5947 5199 5099

■ MICHAELS STORES INC p 960
8000 Bent Branch Dr, Irving TX 75063
Tel (972) 409-1300
SIC 5945 5999 5949 5947 5199 5099

ABOUT TIME LTD p 12
7220 Bob Bullock Loop, Laredo TX 78041
Tel (956) 723-1198 *SIC* 5092 5945

▲ AT HOME GROUP INC p 123
1600 E Plano Pkwy, Plano TX 75074
Tel (972) 265-6227 *SIC* 5719 5945

■ AT HOME STORES LLC p 123
1600 E Plano Pkwy, Plano TX 75074
Tel (972) 265-6227
SIC 5719 5992 5999 5947 5945

GARDEN RIDGE CORP p 591
1600 E Plano Pkwy, Plano TX 75074
Tel (972) 265-6227 *SIC* 5719 5999 5945

GARDEN RIDGE HOLDINGS INC p 591
1600 E Plano Pkwy, Plano TX 75074
Tel (832) 391-7201
SIC 5719 5945 5992 5947 5999

PROVO CRAFT & NOVELTY INC p 1187
10855 S Rvr Frnt Pkwy # 400, South Jordan UT 84095
Tel (800) 937-7686
SIC 5092 5199 5945 5947

DENISE THRASHER p 428
959 E Axton Rd, Bellingham WA 98226
Tel (360) 223-4917 *SIC* 5945

■ AMAZON FULFILLMENT SERVICES INC p 64
410 Terry Ave N, Seattle WA 98109
Tel (206) 266-1000
SIC 5735 5961 5731 5945

■ AMAZON.COMDEDC LLC p 65
410 Terry Ave N, Seattle WA 98109
Tel (206) 266-1000
SIC 5961 5735 5731 5945

GLANT PACIFIC INC p 614
2230 4th Ave S, Seattle WA 98134
Tel (206) 628-6222
SIC 5949 5093 5094 5945

■ AMERICAN GIRL BRANDS LLC p 73
8400 Fairway Pl, Middleton WI 53562
Tel (608) 836-4848 *SIC* 5945 2731

SIC 5946 Camera & Photographic Sply Stores

DISTRICT PHOTO INC p 443
10501 Rhode Island Ave, Beltsville MD 20705
Tel (301) 595-5300 *SIC* 7384 5043 5946

■ NEBRASKA FURNITURE MART INC p 1023
700 S 72nd St, Omaha NE 68114
Tel (402) 397-6100
SIC 5712 5713 5722 5731 5734 5946

C & A MARKETING INC p 231
114 Tived Ln E, Edison NJ 08837
Tel (201) 881-1900
SIC 5065 8742 7384 5946 7359 7221

B & H FOTO & ELECTRONICS CORP p 141
420 9th Ave, New York NY 10001
Tel (212) 239-7500 *SIC* 5946 5731 5961

SIC 5947 Gift, Novelty & Souvenir Stores

BOOKS-A-MILLION INC p 200
402 Industrial Ln, Birmingham AL 35211
Tel (205) 942-3737
SIC 5942 5994 5947 5999

■ COST PLUS INC p 373
1201 Marina Village Pkwy # 100, Alameda CA 94501
Tel (510) 893-7300
SIC 5712 5713 5719 5947 5499 5921

UPPER DECK CO LLC p 1529
2251 Rutherford Rd, Carlsbad CA 92008
Tel (800) 873-7332 *SIC* 2752 5947

DRMC PROPERTIES INC p 456
11500 Brookshire Ave, Downey CA 90241
Tel (562) 904-5464 *SIC* 5947

SCHURMAN FINE PAPERS p 1291
500 Chadbourne Rd, Fairfield CA 94534
Tel (707) 425-8006
SIC 5113 2679 2771 5947

WONDERTREATS INC p 1622
2200 Lapham Dr, Modesto CA 95354
Tel (209) 521-8881 *SIC* 5199 5947

■ UNIVERSAL STUDIOS INC p 1517
100 Universal City Plz, North Hollywood CA 91608
Tel (818) 777-1000
SIC 7812 3652 2741 5947 5944 5961

SUMMIT MEDICAL CENTER p 1399
350 Hawthorne Ave, Oakland CA 94609
Tel (510) 655-4000 *SIC* 8062 8221 5947

ILLUMINATIONS.COM INC p 733
1736 Corporate Cir, Petaluma CA 94954
Tel (707) 776-2000 *SIC* 5961 5947

EVENT NETWORK INC p 513
9606 Aero Dr Ste 1000, San Diego CA 92123
Tel (858) 222-6100 *SIC* 5947

ZOOLOGICAL SOCIETY OF SAN DIEGO p 1644
2920 Zoo Dr, San Diego CA 92101
Tel (619) 231-1515 *SIC* 8422 5812 5947

DFS GROUP LP p 435
525 Market St Fl 33, San Francisco CA 94105
Tel (415) 977-2701
SIC 5944 5948 5921 5993 5947 5999

SAN FRANCISCO BASEBALL ASSOCIATES LLC p 1276
24 Willie Mays Plz, San Francisco CA 94107
Tel (415) 972-2000 *SIC* 7941 5947

EMANUEL MEDICAL CENTER AUXILLARY p 490
825 Delbon Ave, Turlock CA 95382
Tel (209) 667-4200 *SIC* 5932 5947 8699

■ UNIVERSAL CITY STUDIOS PRODUCTIONS LLLP LP p 1516
100 Universal City Plz, Universal City CA 91608
Tel (818) 777-1000
SIC 7812 3652 2741 5947 5944 5961

DNC PARKS & RESORTS AT YOSEMITE INC p 446
9001 Village Dr, Yosemite Ntpk CA 95389
Tel (209) 372-1001
SIC 7011 5399 5812 5947 5541 4725

C-USA INC p 234
1005 E Woodmen Rd, Colorado Springs CO 80920
Tel (719) 594-4100 *SIC* 5947 5961 2771

GENERAL NOVELTY LTD p 601
420 E 58th Ave Ste 200, Denver CO 80216
Tel (303) 292-5537 *SIC* 5947

SERVICE SYSTEMS ASSOCIATES INC p 1307
4699 Marion St, Denver CO 80216
Tel (417) 746-0242 *SIC* 5947 5812

PARKS XANTERRA & RESORTS INC p 1116
6312 S Fiddlers Green Cir 600n, Greenwood Village CO 80111
Tel (303) 600-3400 *SIC* 7011 5947 5812

SAVE CHILDREN FEDERATION INC p 1284
501 Kings Hwy E Ste 400, Fairfield CT 06825
Tel (203) 221-4000 *SIC* 8322 5947

CENTERPLATE INC p 276
2187 Atlantic St, Stamford CT 06902
Tel (800) 698-6992
SIC 5812 7999 5947 7993

CENTERPLATE ULTIMATE HOLDINGS CORP p 276
2187 Atlantic St, Stamford CT 06902
Tel (800) 698-6992
SIC 5812 7999 5947 7993

VOLUME SERVICES INC p 1565
2187 Atlantic St Ste 6, Stamford CT 06902
Tel (203) 975-5900
SIC 5812 7999 5947 7993

BEALLS DEPARTMENT STORES INC p 165
1806 38th Ave E, Bradenton FL 34208
Tel (941) 747-2355 *SIC* 5311 5651 5947

BEALLS INC p 165
1806 13th Ave E, Bradenton FL 34208
Tel (941) 747-2355
SIC 5311 5719 5651 5947

■ WALT DISNEY PARKS AND RESORTS US INC p 1574
1375 E Buena Vista Dr, Lake Buena Vista FL 32830
Tel (407) 824-2222 *SIC* 7996 7011 5947

MICCOSUKEE TRIBE OF INDIANS OF FLORIDA p 959
Sw 8th St & Us Hwy 41, Miami FL 33194
Tel (305) 223-8380
SIC 5812 5331 8412 5947 4489

PEARL PAINT CO INC p 1126
1033 E Oakland Park Blvd, Oakland Park FL 33334
Tel (954) 564-5700
SIC 5999 5199 7699 5112 5947 7311

CLAIRES BOUTIQUES INC p 321
11401 Pines Blvd, Pembroke Pines FL 33026
Tel (954) 438-0433
SIC 5632 5699 5999 5943 5947

BIGMOUTHBEN CONVENIENCE STORE LLC p 182
370 Auburn Ave Ne Ste A, Atlanta GA 30312
Tel (404) 331-3973 *SIC* 5411 5947

CONCESSIONS INTERNATIONAL LLC p 354
566 Wells St Sw, Atlanta GA 30312
Tel (404) 681-0300 *SIC* 5812 5963 5947

PARADIES SHOPS LLC p 1113
2849 Paces Ferry Rd Se, Atlanta GA 30339
Tel (404) 344-7905
SIC 5947 5994 5621 5611 5912 5941

HERSCHEND ENTERTAINMENT CO LLC p 687
5445 Triangle Pkwy # 200, Norcross GA 30092
Tel (770) 441-1940 *SIC* 7999 5947 5812

FOOD PANTRY LTD p 564
3536 Harding Ave Ste 500, Honolulu HI 96816
Tel (808) 732-5515 *SIC* 5411 5947

POLYNESIAN CULTURAL CENTER INC p 1160
55-370 Kamehameha Hwy, Laie HI 96762
Tel (808) 293-3000 *SIC* 7999 5812 5947

LTD COMMODITIES LLC p 883
2800 Lakeside Dr, Bannockburn IL 60015
Tel (847) 295-6058 *SIC* 5961 5947

FLYING FOOD FARE INC p 562
212 N Sangamon St Ste 1a, Chicago IL 60607
Tel (312) 243-2122 *SIC* 5812 5149 5947

WORLDS FINEST CHOCOLATE INC p 1626
4801 S Lawndale Ave, Chicago IL 60632
Tel (773) 847-4600 *SIC* 2066 5947

▲ FTD COMPANIES INC p 582
3113 Woodcreek Dr, Downers Grove IL 60515
Tel (630) 719-7800 *SIC* 5992 5947 5961

ADVENTIST MIDWEST HEALTH p 27
120 N Oak St, Hinsdale IL 60521
Tel (630) 856-9000 *SIC* 8062 5947 8011

CLAIRES INC p 321
2400 W Central Rd, Hoffman Estates IL 60192
Tel (847) 765-1100 *SIC* 5632 5947

ENESCO LLC p 498
225 Windsor Dr, Itasca IL 60143
Tel (630) 875-5300 *SIC* 5947

EBHI HOLDINGS INC p 474
1000 Field Dr Ste 240, Lake Forest IL 60045
Tel (312) 251-3430
SIC 5611 5699 5941 5719 5947 5961

NORTHWESTERN LAKE FOREST HOSPITAL p 1060
660 N Westmoreland Rd, Lake Forest IL 60045
Tel (847) 234-0945
SIC 8062 5947 5932 5812

■ FACTORY CARD & PARTY OUTLET CORP p 523
2727 W Diehl Rd, Naperville IL 60563
Tel (630) 579-2000 *SIC* 5947

BROMENN SERVICE AUXILIARY GIFT SHOP p 217
Franklin Ave Virginia St, Normal IL 61761
Tel (309) 454-1400 *SIC* 5947 5641 5621

EUROMARKET DESIGNS INC p 512
1250 Techny Rd, Northbrook IL 60062
Tel (847) 272-2888
SIC 5719 5947 5712 5961 2599

KIRLINS INC p 822
532 Maine St, Quincy IL 62301
Tel (217) 222-0813 *SIC* 5947

FOLLETT HIGHER EDUCATION GROUP INC p 563
3 Westbrook Corp Ctr # 200, Westchester IL 60154
Tel (800) 365-5388 *SIC* 5942 5943 5947

■ HORSESHOE HAMMOND LLC p 708
777 Casino Center Dr, Hammond IN 46320
Tel (866) 711-7463 *SIC* 7999 5947 5812

PRAIRIE MEADOWS RACETRACK AND CASINO INC p 1167
1 Prairie Meadows Dr, Altoona IA 50009
Tel (515) 967-1000
SIC 7948 7993 7999 5947 5812 5813

MERCY FLOWERS & GIFTS p 946
701 10th St Se, Cedar Rapids IA 52403
Tel (319) 398-6124 *SIC* 5992 5947

SOMEBODY CARES INC p 1339
57 N Court St, Fairfield IA 52556
Tel (641) 472-5352 *SIC* 5947 7699 5999

ITS GREEK TO ME INC p 768
520 Mccall Rd Ste A, Manhattan KS 66502
Tel (785) 537-8822
SIC 5136 5699 5137 5947 2759

MERCY REGIONAL HEALTH CENTRE AUXILLIARY p 948
1823 College Ave, Manhattan KS 66502
Tel (785) 776-2802 *SIC* 5947

TREES N TRENDS INC p 1475
3229 Benton Rd, Paducah KY 42003
Tel (270) 443-5100
SIC 5999 3999 5947 5193

OCHSNER CLINIC FOUNDATION p 1073
1514 Jefferson Hwy, New Orleans LA 70121
Tel (504) 842-3000 *SIC* 8062 5947

HMSHOST CORP p 698
6905 Rockledge Dr Fl 1, Bethesda MD 20817
Tel (240) 694-4100
SIC 5812 5813 5994 5947

HOST INTERNATIONAL INC p 710
6905 Rockledge Dr Fl 1, Bethesda MD 20817
Tel (240) 694-4100
SIC 5812 5813 5994 5947

FIDELITY INV CHARITABLE GIFT FUND p 540
200 Seaport Blvd Ste 1, Boston MA 02210
Tel (617) 392-8679 *SIC* 5947

WASH DEPOT AUTO CENTERS LP p 1577
435 Eastern Ave, Malden MA 02148
Tel (781) 324-2000 *SIC* 7542 5541 5947

FAMILY CHRISTIAN STORES LLC p 526
5300 Patterson Ave Se, Grand Rapids MI 49530
Tel (616) 554-8700
SIC 5942 5735 5947 5699 8741

MEMORIAL HEALTH CARE INC p 941
826 W King St, Owosso MI 48867
Tel (989) 725-8101 *SIC* 8641 5947

HALLMARK MARKETING CO LLC p 654
2501 Mcgee St, Kansas City MO 64108
Tel (816) 274-5111 *SIC* 5947 2542 7389

HALLMARK RETAIL LLC p 655
2440 Pershing Rd Ste 200, Kansas City MO 64108
Tel (816) 274-5878 *SIC* 5947

INDEPENDENT STAVE CO LLC p 737
1078 S Jefferson Ave, Lebanon MO 65536
Tel (417) 588-4151 *SIC* 2449 5947 2499

GLASS GALLERY LTD p 614
10300 Lake Bluff Dr, Saint Louis MO 63123
Tel (314) 416-4200 *SIC* 5947 5199

ARCHBISHOP BERGAN MERCY AUXILIARY p 104
7500 Mercy Rd, Omaha NE 68124
Tel (402) 398-6199 *SIC* 5947

■ HAYNEEDLE INC p 670
9394 W Dodge Rd Ste 300, Omaha NE 68114
Tel (402) 715-3000
SIC 5943 5719 5945 5947

BROOKSTONE CO INC p 218
1 Innovation Way, Merrimack NH 03054
Tel (866) 576-7337
SIC 5947 5399 5331 5961

BROOKSTONE HOLDINGS CORP p 218
1 Innovation Way, Merrimack NH 03054
Tel (603) 880-9500 *SIC* 5947 5961

BROOKSTONE INC p 218
1 Innovation Way, Merrimack NH 03054
Tel (603) 880-9500 *SIC* 5961 5947

■ BARNES & NOBLE COLLEGE BOOKSELLERS LLC p 155
120 Mountainview Blvd A, Basking Ridge NJ 07920
Tel (908) 991-2665 *SIC* 5942 5943 5947

BURLINGTON COAT FACTORY HOLDINGS INC p 227
1830 N Route 130, Burlington NJ 08016
Tel (609) 387-7800
SIC 5651 5632 5719 5947 5712

SPENCER GIFTS HOLDINGS INC p 1358
6826 Black Horse Pike, Egg Harbor Township NJ 08234
Tel (609) 645-3300 *SIC* 5947

SPENCER GIFTS LLC p 1358
6826 Black Horse Pike, Egg Harbor Township NJ 08234
Tel (609) 645-3300 *SIC* 5947 5944

HARCO INDUSTRIES INC USA p 660
333 S Van Brunt St, Englewood NJ 07631
Tel (201) 894-8941 *SIC* 5947

MUSEUM CO INC p 1002
695 Us Highway 46 Ste 400, Fairfield NJ 07004
Tel (973) 575-4446 *SIC* 5947

PALISADES GENERAL HOSPITAL GIFT SHOP p 1108
7600 River Rd, North Bergen NJ 07047
Tel (201) 854-5123 *SIC* 5947

■ PA ACQUISITION CORP p 1103
25 Green Pond Rd Ste 1, Rockaway NJ 07866
Tel (973) 453-8600 *SIC* 5947 7389

■ PARTY CITY CORP p 1119
25 Green Pond Rd Ste 1, Rockaway NJ 07866
Tel (973) 453-8600 *SIC* 6794 5947 7299

▲ BED BATH & BEYOND INC p 167
650 Liberty Ave, Union NJ 07083
Tel (908) 688-0888 *SIC* 5719 5947 5999

▲ ETSY INC p 512
117 Adams St, Brooklyn NY 11201
Tel (718) 855-7955 *SIC* 5961 5947 7319

DELAWARE NORTH COMPANIES TRAVEL HOSPITALITY SERVICES INC p 424
250 Delaware Ave Ste 3, Buffalo NY 14202
Tel (716) 858-5000 *SIC* 5812 5947 5813

▲ 1-800-FLOWERS.COM INC p 1
1 Old Country Rd Ste 500, Carle Place NY 11514
Tel (516) 237-6000 *SIC* 5992 5961 5947

■ AMSCAN HOLDINGS INC p 87
80 Grasslands Rd Ste 3, Elmsford NY 10523
Tel (914) 345-2020
SIC 5947 2679 3089 3069 6794

▲ PARTY CITY HOLDCO INC p 1119
80 Grasslands Rd, Elmsford NY 10523
Tel (914) 345-2020
SIC 5947 5963 5199 6794

■ PARTY CITY HOLDINGS INC p 1119
80 Grasslands Rd, Elmsford NY 10523
Tel (973) 453-8600 *SIC* 5947 6794

HUNTINGTON HOSPITAL AUXILIARY p 720
270 Park Ave, Huntington NY 11743
Tel (631) 351-2257 *SIC* 5947 5499 8322

MICHAEL C FINA CO INC p 960
3301 Hunters Point Ave, Long Island City NY 11101
Tel (212) 557-2500 *SIC* 5094 5947

BARNEYS INC p 156
575 5th Ave Fl 11, New York NY 10017
Tel (212) 450-8700
SIC 5611 5621 5632 5932 5947 6794

CHELSEY DIRECT LLC p 293
110 E 59th St, New York NY 10022
Tel (201) 863-7300 *SIC* 5961 5947 5611

GOLDMAN SACHS CHARITABLE GIFT FUND p 622
200 West St Fl 29, New York NY 10282
Tel (212) 902-4223 *SIC* 5947

HACHETTE DISTRIBUTION INC p 652
60 E 42nd St Ste 1940, New York NY 10165
Tel (212) 477-7373 *SIC* 5192 5994 5947

ORIENT EXPRESS HOTELS INC p 1094
441 Lexington Ave Rm 504, New York NY 10017
Tel (212) 302-5055
SIC 7011 3743 5947 6552

■ VIVENDI UNIVERSAL ENTERTAINMENT LLLP p 1563
30 Rockefeller Plz, New York NY 10112
Tel (212) 664-4444
SIC 7812 3652 2741 5947 5944 5961

BILTMORE CO p 183
1 Lodge St, Asheville NC 28803
Tel (828) 225-6776 *SIC* 7999 5947 5812

SOUTH EASTERN REGIONAL MEDICAL INC p 1344
300 W 27th St, Lumberton NC 28358
Tel (910) 671-5543 *SIC* 5947

CHRISTIAN AID MINISTRIES p 302
4464 State Rte 39 E, Berlin OH 44610
Tel (330) 893-2428 *SIC* 8661 5999 5947

CARLTON CARDS RETAIL INC p 258
1 American Rd, Cleveland OH 44144
Tel (216) 252-7300 *SIC* 5947 5943

CSA ST JOHN MINISTRIES p 397
29000 Center Ridge Rd, Cleveland OH 44145
Tel (440) 835-8000 *SIC* 5947

THIRTY-ONE GIFTS LLC p 1448
3425 Morse Xing, Columbus OH 43219
Tel (614) 414-4300 *SIC* 5947

THINGS REMEMBERED INC p 1448
5500 Avion Park Dr, Highland Heights OH 44143
Tel (440) 473-2000 *SIC* 7389 5947

JO-ANN STORES HOLDINGS INC p 787
5555 Darrow Rd, Hudson OH 44236
Tel (888) 739-4120 *SIC* 5945 5949 5947

JO-ANN STORES LLC p 787
5555 Darrow Rd, Hudson OH 44236
Tel (330) 656-2600 *SIC* 5945 5949 5947

SAINT ANNS HOSPITAL AUXILIARY p 1268
500 S Cleveland Ave, Westerville OH 43081
Tel (614) 769-4459
SIC 5947 5621 5611 5992 5441

HOB-LOB LTD p 698
7707 Sw 44th St, Oklahoma City OK 73179
Tel (405) 745-1100
SIC 5945 5999 5949 5947

LOVES TRAVEL STOPS & COUNTRY STORES INC p 881
10601 N Pennsylvania Ave, Oklahoma City OK 73120
Tel (405) 302-6500 *SIC* 5541 5411 5947

■ HARRY AND DAVID LLC p 664
2500 S Pacific Hwy, Medford OR 97501
Tel (541) 864-2500 *SIC* 5961 5947

FITZ AND FLOYD ENTERPRISES LLC p 553
3 Friends Ln Ste 300, Newtown PA 18940
Tel (800) 527-9550
SIC 5023 5199 5947 5719

FATIMA GIFT SHOP p 531
200 High Service Ave, North Providence RI 02904
Tel (401) 456-3448 *SIC* 5947

BLATCHFORDS INC p 189
207 S Chicago St, Hot Springs SD 57747
Tel (605) 745-5173
SIC 5251 5712 5531 5947 5722

▲ KIRKLANDS INC p 822
5310 Maryland Way, Brentwood TN 37027
Tel (615) 872-4800 SIC 5999 5947

▲ CRACKER BARREL OLD COUNTRY STORE INC p 388
305 S Hartmann Dr, Lebanon TN 37087
Tel (615) 444-5533 SIC 5812 5947

LIFEWAY CHRISTIAN RESOURCES OF SOUTHERN BAPTIST CONVENTION p 865
1 Lifeway Plz, Nashville TN 37234
Tel (615) 251-2000
SIC 5942 5963 2731 5999 5735 5947

LORIS GIFTS INC p 878
2125 Chenault Dr Ste 100, Carrollton TX 75006
Tel (972) 759-5000 SIC 5947 8099 5999

▲ TUESDAY MORNING CORP p 1490
6250 Lbj Fwy, Dallas TX 75240
Tel (972) 387-3562
SIC 5947 5719 5944 5948 5945 5712

MICHAELS HOLDINGS INC p 960
8000 Bent Branch Dr, Irving TX 75063
Tel (972) 409-1300
SIC 5945 5999 5949 5947 5199 5099

■ MICHAELS STORES INC p 960
8000 Bent Branch Dr, Irving TX 75063
Tel (972) 409-1300
SIC 5945 5999 5949 5947 5199 5099

■ AT HOME STORES LLC p 123
1600 E Plano Pkwy, Plano TX 75074
Tel (972) 265-6227
SIC 5719 5992 5999 5947 5945

GARDEN RIDGE HOLDINGS INC p 591
1600 E Plano Pkwy, Plano TX 75074
Tel (832) 391-7201
SIC 5719 5945 5992 5947 5999

PROVO CRAFT & NOVELTY INC p 1187
10855 S Rvr Frnt Pkwy # 400, South Jordan UT 84095
Tel (800) 937-7686
SIC 5092 5199 5945 5947

AMMARS INC p 85
710 S College Ave, Bluefield VA 24605
Tel (276) 322-4686 SIC 5947

SMITH MOUNTAIN INDUSTRIES OF VIRGINIA INC p 1333
1000 Dillard Dr, Forest VA 24551
Tel (800) 827-2231 SIC 5199 5947

COLONIAL WILLIAMSBURG FOUNDATION p 338
427 Franklin St Rm 212, Williamsburg VA 23185
Tel (757) 229-1000
SIC 5947 8412 5812 7011

AMARGOSA INC p 64
10401 Ne 8th St Ste 500, Bellevue WA 98004
Tel (425) 755-6100
SIC 5611 5699 5941 5719 5947 5961

BINGO POTAWATOMI p 183
1721 W Canal St, Milwaukee WI 53233
Tel (414) 645-6888 SIC 7999 5812 5947

SIC 5948 Luggage & Leather Goods Stores

DFS GROUP LP p 435
525 Market St Fl 33, San Francisco CA 94105
Tel (415) 977-2701
SIC 5944 5948 5921 5993 5947 5999

RANDA ACCESSORIES LEATHER GOODS LLC p 1207
5600 N River Rd Ste 500, Rosemont IL 60018
Tel (847) 292-8300 SIC 5136 5948 3172

L L BEAN INC p 834
15 Casco St, Freeport ME 04033
Tel (207) 552-2000
SIC 5961 5621 5611 5941 5661 5948

SAMSONITE LLC p 1274
575 West St Ste 110, Mansfield MA 02048
Tel (508) 851-1400 SIC 5948 5199

■ WILSONS HOUSE OF SUEDE INC p 1614
7401 Boone Ave N, Brooklyn Park MN 55428
Tel (763) 391-4000 SIC 5699 5948

WILSONS LEATHER EXPERTS INC p 1614
7401 Boone Ave N, Brooklyn Park MN 55428
Tel (763) 391-4000 SIC 5699 5948

WESTPORT CORP p 1602
331 Changebridge Rd Ste 3, Pine Brook NJ 07058
Tel (973) 575-0110 SIC 5948 5199

TUMI HOLDINGS INC p 1491
1001 Durham Ave Ste 1b, South Plainfield NJ 07080
Tel (908) 756-4400 SIC 3161 3172 5948

TUMI INC p 1491
1001 Durham Ave Ste 1b, South Plainfield NJ 07080
Tel (908) 756-4400 SIC 5199 5948 3161

GUCCI AMERICA INC p 645
195 Broadway Fl 12, New York NY 10007
Tel (212) 750-5220
SIC 5632 5948 5661 5611 5621 5137

LVMH MOET HENNESSY LOUIS VUITTON INC p 887
19 E 57th St, New York NY 10022
Tel (212) 931-2700 SIC 5948 5199

LENOX HOLDINGS INC p 856
1414 Radcliffe St Fl 1, Bristol PA 19007
Tel (267) 525-7800
SIC 3229 3161 5719 5948

▲ TUESDAY MORNING CORP p 1490
6250 Lbj Fwy, Dallas TX 75240
Tel (972) 387-3562
SIC 5947 5719 5944 5948 5945 5712

▲ TANDY LEATHER FACTORY INC p 1424
1900 Se Loop 820, Fort Worth TX 76140
Tel (817) 872-3200 SIC 5948 5199 3111

KING RANCH INC p 820
3 Riverway Ste 1600, Houston TX 77056
Tel (832) 681-5700
SIC 0212 2711 5083 5948

SIC 5949 Sewing, Needlework & Piece Goods Stores

BEVERLY FABRICS INC p 179
9019 Soquel Dr Ste 175, Aptos CA 95003
Tel (831) 684-4220 SIC 5945 5949

CAROLE FABRICS CORP p 259
633 Nw Frontage Rd, Augusta GA 30907
Tel (706) 863-4742
SIC 2221 2591 5131 5949 2392 2391

NICOLON CORP p 1043
365 S Holland Dr, Pendergrass GA 30567
Tel (706) 693-2226 SIC 2221 5949

HANCOCK FABRICS INC p 656
1 Fashion Way, Baldwyn MS 38824
Tel (662) 365-6000 SIC 5949

HOUSE OF FABRICS INC p 711
5555 Darrow Rd, Hudson OH 44236
Tel (330) 656-2600 SIC 5949 5945 5722

JO-ANN STORES HOLDINGS INC p 787
5555 Darrow Rd, Hudson OH 44236
Tel (888) 739-4120 SIC 5945 5949 5947

JO-ANN STORES LLC p 787
5555 Darrow Rd, Hudson OH 44236
Tel (330) 656-2600 SIC 5945 5949 5947

HOB-LOB LTD p 698
7707 Sw 44th St, Oklahoma City OK 73179
Tel (405) 745-1100
SIC 5945 5999 5949 5947

SPRINGS CREATIVE PRODUCTS GROUP LLC p 1361
300 Chatham Ave Ste 100, Rock Hill SC 29730
Tel (803) 324-6300 SIC 5949 2759

MICHAELS HOLDINGS LLC p 960
8000 Bent Branch Dr, Irving TX 75063
Tel (972) 409-1300
SIC 5945 5999 5949 5947 5199 5099

■ MICHAELS STORES INC p 960
8000 Bent Branch Dr, Irving TX 75063
Tel (972) 409-1300
SIC 5945 5999 5949 5947 5199 5099

RONILE INC p 1249
701 Orchard Ave, Rocky Mount VA 24151
Tel (540) 483-0261 SIC 2269 5949 2273

GLANT PACIFIC INC p 614
2230 4th Ave S, Seattle WA 98134
Tel (206) 628-6222
SIC 5949 5093 5094 5945

SIC 5961 Catalog & Mail-Order Houses

DMB ASSOCIATES INC p 445
7600 E Doubletree Ste 300, Scottsdale AZ 85258
Tel (480) 367-6874
SIC 5999 6512 5961 1542 3446

MERCHANT OF TENNIS INC p 944
8737 Wilshire Blvd, Beverly Hills CA 90211
Tel (310) 228-4000
SIC 5941 5621 5661 5961 5999

CENTRAL PURCHASING LLC p 280
3491 Mission Oaks Blvd, Camarillo CA 93012
Tel (805) 388-1000 SIC 5085 5961 5251

LAKESHORE EQUIPMENT CO INC p 840
2695 E Dominguez St, Carson CA 90895
Tel (310) 537-8600 SIC 5999 5961

▲ US AUTO PARTS NETWORK INC p 1531
16941 Keegan Ave, Carson CA 90746
Tel (310) 735-0085 SIC 5961

▲ PCM INC p 1124
1940 E Mariposa Ave, El Segundo CA 90245
Tel (310) 354-5600
SIC 5734 5961 5731 5045

▲ STAMPS.COM INC p 1375
1990 E Grand Ave, El Segundo CA 90245
Tel (310) 482-5800 SIC 7331 5961 4813

TECHSTYLE INC p 1432
800 Apollo St, El Segundo CA 90245
Tel (310) 683-0940
SIC 5961 5661 5632 5651

COLDWATER CREEK INC p 335
17000 Ventura Blvd # 300, Encino CA 91316
Tel (208) 263-2266 SIC 5621 5961

SEAL123 INC p 1296
26972 Burbank, Foothill Ranch CA 92610
Tel (949) 699-3900 SIC 5621 5632 5961

DRAPERS & DAMONS LLC p 455
9 Pasteur Ste 200, Irvine CA 92618
Tel (949) 784-3000 SIC 5961 5621 5632

FOX HEAD INC p 572
16752 Armstrong Ave, Irvine CA 92606
Tel (408) 776-8633 SIC 5136 5137 5961

■ SHEPLERS INC p 1315
15345 Barranca Pkwy, Irvine CA 92618
Tel (316) 946-3835
SIC 5699 5661 5961 5651 5632 5611

WET SEAL LLC p 1603
7555 Irvine Center Dr, Irvine CA 92618
Tel (949) 699-3900 SIC 5621 5632 5961

WILSHIRE PARTNERS p 1613
620 Newport Center Dr # 1100, Newport Beach CA 92660
Tel (800) 285-6038 SIC 5632 5961

■ UNIVERSAL STUDIOS INC p 1517
100 Universal City Plz, North Hollywood CA 91608
Tel (818) 777-1000
SIC 7812 3652 2741 5947 5944 5961

STARCREST PRODUCTS OF CALIFORNIA INC p 1379
3660 Brennan Ave # 1000, Perris CA 92599
Tel (951) 943-2011 SIC 5961

ILLUMINATIONS.COM INC p 733
1736 Corporate Cir, Petaluma CA 94954
Tel (707) 776-2000 SIC 5961 5947

CPL HOLDINGS LLC p 387
12181 Bluff Creek Dr # 250, Playa Vista CA 90094
Tel (310) 348-6800 SIC 5331 6719 5961

▲ NATURAL HEALTH TRENDS CORP p 1018
609 Deep Valley Dr # 390, Rllng Hls Est CA 90274
Tel (310) 541-0888 SIC 5122 5961

■ WAL-MART.COM USA LLC p 1572
850 Cherry Ave, San Bruno CA 94066
Tel (650) 837-5000 SIC 5961 5199

MERIDIAN RACK & PINION INC p 949
6740 Cobra Way Ste 200, San Diego CA 92121
Tel (858) 587-8777 SIC 5013 5961

NATIONAL PEN CORP p 1015
12121 Scripps Summit Dr # 200, San Diego CA 92131
Tel (858) 675-3000 SIC 5961

ROAD RUNNER SPORTS INC p 1240
5549 Copley Dr, San Diego CA 92111
Tel (858) 974-4200 SIC 5661 3949 5661

ANDRE-BOUDIN BAKERIES INC p 90
50 Francisco St Ste 200, San Francisco CA 94133
Tel (415) 882-1849
SIC 2051 5812 5961 5461

DEEM INC p 421
642 Harrison St Fl 2, San Francisco CA 94107
Tel (415) 590-8300 SIC 5961

EPANTRY LLC p 504
1770 Union St, San Francisco CA 94123
Tel (657) 444-7837 SIC 5961

SHARPER IMAGE CORP p 1312
350 The Embarcadero Fl 6, San Francisco CA 94105
Tel (877) 714-7444
SIC 5731 5941 5999 5719 5945 5961

▲ WILLIAMS-SONOMA INC p 1612
3250 Van Ness Ave, San Francisco CA 94109
Tel (415) 421-7900
SIC 5719 5722 5261 5961

▲ EBAY INC p 474
2065 Hamilton Ave, San Jose CA 95125
Tel (408) 376-7400 SIC 5961

▲ WALKING CO HOLDINGS INC p 1573
25 W Anapamu St, Santa Barbara CA 93101
Tel (805) 963-8727
SIC 5651 5961 5136 5137 5699

■ VIKING OFFICE PRODUCTS INC p 1557
3366 E Willow St, Signal Hill CA 90755
Tel (562) 490-1000
SIC 5112 5021 5045 5087 5043 5961

■ UNIVERSAL CITY STUDIOS PRODUCTIONS LLLP LP p 1516
100 Universal City Plz, Universal City CA 91608
Tel (818) 777-1000
SIC 7812 3652 2741 5947 5944 5961

ARVATO DIGITAL SERVICES LLC p 114
29011 Commerce Center Dr, Valencia CA 91355
Tel (661) 702-2700 SIC 5961 7389

PATAGONIA WORKS p 1120
259 W Santa Clara St, Ventura CA 93001
Tel (805) 643-8616
SIC 5699 2339 2329 5961

▲ WEST MARINE INC p 1595
500 Westridge Dr, Watsonville CA 95076
Tel (831) 728-2700
SIC 5551 5961 5088 5611 5661 5621

NOB HILL GENERAL STORE INC p 1046
500 W Capitol Ave, West Sacramento CA 95605
Tel (916) 373-3333 SIC 5411 5961

■ UNITED ONLINE INC p 1510
21255 Burbank Blvd # 400, Woodland Hills CA 91367
Tel (818) 287-3000 SIC 5961 7299

C-USA INC p 234
1005 E Woodmen Rd, Colorado Springs CO 80920
Tel (719) 594-4100 SIC 5947 5961 2771

▲ LIBERTY INTERACTIVE CORP p 862
12300 Liberty Blvd, Englewood CO 80112
Tel (720) 875-5300 SIC 4841 5961

■ LIBERTY INTERACTIVE LLC p 862
12300 Liberty Blvd, Englewood CO 80112
Tel (720) 875-5400
SIC 5961 4841 7819 4813

■ LIBERTY QVC HOLDING LLC p 862
12300 Liberty Blvd, Englewood CO 80112
Tel (484) 701-3777 SIC 4841 5961

■ SCHOLASTIC LIBRARY PUBLISHING INC p 1288
90 Sherman Tpke, Danbury CT 06816
Tel (203) 797-3500
SIC 2731 5963 5192 2721 5961 7371

MBI INC p 925
47 Richards Ave, Norwalk CT 06857
Tel (203) 853-2000 SIC 5961

■ PEPPERIDGE FARM INC p 1134
595 Westport Ave, Norwalk CT 06851
Tel (203) 846-7000
SIC 5963 2052 2099 2053 5961

AFFINION GROUP INC p 32
6 High Ridge Park Bldg A, Stamford CT 06905
Tel (203) 956-1000 SIC 7389 5961 6321

GENEVE CORP p 603
96 Cummings Point Rd, Stamford CT 06902
Tel (203) 358-8000 SIC 5961 3483 6282

LIVING SOCIAL INC p 871
1445 New York Ave Nw # 200, Washington DC 20005
Tel (877) 521-4191 SIC 5961

■ VITACOST.COM INC p 1562
5400 Broken Sound Blvd # 500, Boca Raton FL 33487
Tel (561) 982-4180 SIC 5961

DEGC ENTERPRISES (US) INC p 422
14255 49th St N Ste 301, Clearwater FL 33762
Tel (727) 531-9161 SIC 5999 5912 5961

BODY CENTRAL CORP p 197
6225 Powers Ave, Jacksonville FL 32217
Tel (904) 737-0811 SIC 5621 5961

TRADING CORP p 1469
5516 Scott View Ln, Lakeland FL 33813
Tel (754) 900-7666 SIC 5045 5961

■ TIGERDIRECT INC p 1453
7795 W Flagler St Ste 35, Miami FL 33144
Tel (305) 415-2200 SIC 5961 5734

PROFESSIONAL GOLFERS ASSOCIATION OF AMERICA INC p 1180
100 Avenue Of Champions, Palm Beach Gardens FL 33418
Tel (561) 624-8400 SIC 7941 5961

ATLS MEDICAL SUPPLY INC p 128
8881 Liberty Ln, Port Saint Lucie FL 34952
Tel (772) 398-5842 SIC 5961

■ LIBERTY HEALTHCARE GROUP INC p 861
8881 Liberty Ln, Port Saint Lucie FL 34952
Tel (772) 398-7257 SIC 5961

▲ HSN INC p 715
1 Hsn Dr, Saint Petersburg FL 33729
Tel (727) 872-1000 SIC 5961 5331 5712

■ HSN LLC p 715
1 Hsn Dr, Saint Petersburg FL 33729
Tel (727) 872-1000 SIC 5961

■ HSNI LLC p 715
1 Hsn Dr, Saint Petersburg FL 33729
Tel (727) 872-1000 SIC 5961

■ USANI SUB LLC p 1534
1 Hsn Dr, Saint Petersburg FL 33729
Tel (727) 872-1000 SIC 4833 5961

■ PHARMERICA LONG-TERM CARE LLC p 1141
3625 Queen Palm Dr, Tampa FL 33619
Tel (877) 975-2273
SIC 5912 5961 8082 5122

PURCHASING POWER LLC p 1192
1349 W Peachtree St Nw # 1100, Atlanta GA 30309
Tel (404) 609-5100 SIC 5961

LTD COMMODITIES LLC p 883
2800 Lakeside Dr, Bannockburn IL 60015
Tel (847) 295-6058 SIC 5961 5947

▲ ULTA SALON COSMETICS & FRAGRANCE INC p 1500
1000 Remington Blvd # 120, Bolingbrook IL 60440
Tel (630) 410-4800 SIC 5999 5632 5961

HOBBICO INC p 698
1608 Interstate Dr, Champaign IL 61822
Tel (217) 398-3630 SIC 5092 5961

▲ GRUBHUB INC p 642
111 W Washington St # 2100, Chicago IL 60602
Tel (877) 585-7878 SIC 5961

■ NEWARK ELECTRONICS CORP p 1037
300 S Riverside Plz, Chicago IL 60606
Tel (773) 784-5100 SIC 5065 5063 5961

■ CATAMARAN PBM OF ILLINOIS II INC p 264
1417 Lake Cook Rd Ste 100, Deerfield IL 60015
Tel (847) 374-2640 SIC 5961

SIMONTON HOLDINGS INC p 1325
520 Lake Cook Rd, Deerfield IL 60015
Tel (304) 428-8261
SIC 3089 5961 3086 5963

▲ FTD COMPANIES INC p 582
3113 Woodcreek Dr, Downers Grove IL 60515
Tel (630) 719-7800 SIC 5992 5947 5961

WINSTON BRANDS INC p 1617
2521 Busse Rd Fl 2, Elk Grove Village IL 60007
Tel (847) 350-5800 SIC 5961

DICK BLICK HOLDINGS INC p 438
1849 Green Bay Rd Ste 310, Highland Park IL 60035
Tel (847) 681-6800 SIC 5961

▲ SEARS HOLDINGS CORP p 1297
3333 Beverly Rd, Hoffman Estates IL 60179
Tel (847) 286-2500
SIC 5311 5411 5531 5961

INFINITY RESOURCES INC p 741
900 N Rohlwing Rd, Itasca IL 60143
Tel (630) 735-1000 SIC 5961

EBHI HOLDINGS INC p 474
1000 Field Dr Ste 240, Lake Forest IL 60045
Tel (312) 251-3430
SIC 5611 5699 5941 5719 5947 5961

▲ CDW CORP p 271
75 Tri State Intl, Lincolnshire IL 60069
Tel (847) 465-6000
SIC 5963 5045 5734 5961

BRADFORD EXCHANGE LTD p 206
9333 N Milwaukee Ave, Niles IL 60714
Tel (847) 966-2770 SIC 5961 5199

■ CAREMARK INTERNATIONAL LLC p 255
2211 Sanders Rd, Northbrook IL 60062
Tel (847) 559-4700
SIC 5961 6411 8099 8092 8093

■ CAREMARK LLC p 255
2211 Sanders Rd, Northbrook IL 60062
Tel (847) 559-4700
SIC 5961 6411 8099 8092 8093 8742

EUROMARKET DESIGNS INC p 512
1250 Techny Rd, Northbrook IL 60062
Tel (847) 272-2888
SIC 5719 5947 5712 5961 2599

■ CDW GOVERNMENT LLC p 271
230 N Milwaukee Ave, Vernon Hills IL 60061
Tel (847) 465-6000 SIC 5961 5065 5734

CDW HOLDINGS LLC p 271
3 First National Pl, Vernon Hills IL 60061
Tel (847) 465-6000
SIC 5963 5045 5734 5961

DIRECTBUY INC p 441
8450 Broadway, Merrillville IN 46410
Tel (219) 736-1100
SIC 5021 5064 5023 5961 6794 7299

STUMP PRINTING CO INC p 1395
101 Carroll Rd, South Whitley IN 46787
Tel (260) 723-5171
SIC 5199 2679 5961 2759

CAMPING WORLD INC p 246
650 Three Springs Rd, Bowling Green KY 42104
Tel (270) 781-2718 SIC 5561 5961

GALLS LLC p 590
1340 Russell Cave Rd, Lexington KY 40505
Tel (859) 266-7227 SIC 5961 5399 2395

▲ CAFEPRESS INC p 237
11909 Shelbyville Rd, Louisville KY 40243
Tel (502) 995-2268 SIC 4813 5961

PREMIERE INC p 1171
615 N Landry Dr, New Iberia LA 70563
Tel (337) 369-1000 SIC 5961

L L BEAN INC p 834
15 Casco St, Freeport ME 04033
Tel (207) 552-2000
SIC 5961 5621 5611 5941 5661 5948

LL BEAN INTERNATIONAL p 872
15 Casco St, Freeport ME 04033
Tel (207) 865-4761 *SIC* 5961

BLACKSTREET CAPITAL MANAGEMENT LLC p 188
5425 Wisconsin Ave # 701, Chevy Chase MD 20815
Tel (240) 223-1330
SIC 6726 5149 5145 5961

■ JOS A BANK CLOTHIERS INC p 793
500 Hanover Pike, Hampstead MD 21074
Tel (410) 239-2700 *SIC* 5611 5961

ALBERT S SMYTH CO INC p 46
2020 York Rd, Lutherville Timonium MD 21093
Tel (410) 252-6666 *SIC* 5944 5961

LEGAL SEA FOODS LLC p 853
1 Seafood Way, Boston MA 02210
Tel (617) 530-9000 *SIC* 5812 5146 5961

MUSEUM OF FINE ARTS p 1002
465 Huntington Ave, Boston MA 02115
Tel (617) 369-3861 *SIC* 8412 5961 8299

RUELALA INC p 1257
20 Channel Ctr St, Boston MA 02210
Tel (617) 695-7300 *SIC* 5961

▲ WAYFAIR INC p 1584
4 Copley Pl Ste 700, Boston MA 02116
Tel (617) 532-6100 *SIC* 5961

■ LYNNFIELD DRUG INC p 888
12 Kent Way Ste 120, Byfield MA 01922
Tel (978) 499-1400 *SIC* 5912 5961

▲ STAPLES INC p 1377
500 Staples Dr, Framingham MA 01702
Tel (508) 253-5000
SIC 5943 5999 7513 5961 5712

NORM THOMPSON OUTFITTERS INC p 1048
35 Village Rd Ste 500, Middleton MA 01949
Tel (503) 614-4600 *SIC* 5961

J JILL GROUP INC p 771
4 Batterymarch Park, Quincy MA 02169
Tel (617) 376-4300
SIC 5961 5621 5661 5632

JILL ACQUISITION LLC p 785
4 Batterymarch Park, Quincy MA 02169
Tel (617) 376-4300 *SIC* 5961 5621

DUNHAMS ATHLEISURE CORP p 461
5607 New King Dr Ste 125, Troy MI 48098
Tel (248) 674-4991
SIC 5699 5661 5941 5961

NORTHERN TOOL & EQUIPMENT CATALOG CO INC p 1057
2800 Southcross Dr W, Burnsville MN 55306
Tel (952) 894-9510 *SIC* 5961

NORTHERN TOOL & EQUIPMENT CO INC p 1057
2800 Southcross Dr W, Burnsville MN 55306
Tel (952) 894-9510 *SIC* 5961 5251

BLUESTEM BRANDS INC p 193
7075 Flying Cloud Dr, Eden Prairie MN 55344
Tel (952) 656-4037 *SIC* 5961

▲ EVINE LIVE INC p 515
6740 Shady Oak Rd, Eden Prairie MN 55344
Tel (952) 943-6000 *SIC* 5961

ROCKLER COMPANIES INC p 1245
4365 Willow Dr, Medina MN 55340
Tel (763) 478-8201 *SIC* 5251 5961 2721

LIBERTY DIVERSIFIED INTERNATIONAL INC p 861
5600 Highway 169 N, New Hope MN 55428
Tel (763) 536-6600
SIC 2653 2631 5112 2542 3089 5961

▲ CHRISTOPHER & BANKS CORP p 303
2400 Xenium Ln N, Plymouth MN 55441
Tel (763) 551-5000 *SIC* 5621 5632 5961

▲ TILE SHOP HOLDINGS INC p 1453
14000 Carlson Pkwy, Plymouth MN 55441
Tel (763) 852-2988 *SIC* 5211 5961 2891

■ BEST BUY STORES LP p 177
7601 Penn Ave S, Richfield MN 55423
Tel (612) 291-3979 *SIC* 5961

FREDERICKS OF HOLLYWOOD INC p 576
71 Homochitto St, Natchez MS 39120
Tel (323) 466-5151 *SIC* 5632 5961

▲ EXPRESS SCRIPTS HOLDING CO p 520
1 Express Way, Saint Louis MO 63121
Tel (314) 996-0900 *SIC* 5912 5961

■ EXPRESS SCRIPTS INC p 520
1 Express Way, Saint Louis MO 63121
Tel (314) 996-0900 *SIC* 5961

TRIAD CATALOG CO LLC p 1478
1100 N Lindbergh Blvd, Saint Louis MO 63132
Tel (314) 812-5200 *SIC* 5961

BASS PRO LLC p 159
2500 E Kearney St, Springfield MO 65898
Tel (417) 873-5000
SIC 5961 5941 5551 5661

NEBRASKA BOOK CO INC p 1023
4700 S 19th St, Lincoln NE 68512
Tel (402) 421-7300 *SIC* 5942 5192 5961

NEBRASKA BOOK HOLDINGS INC p 1023
4700 S 19th St, Lincoln NE 68512
Tel (402) 421-0500
SIC 6719 5942 5192 5961

NEBRASKA BOOK INTERMEDIATE HOLDINGS INC p 1023
4701 S 19th St, Lincoln NE 68512
Tel (402) 421-7300
SIC 6719 5942 5192 5961

■ OTC DIRECT INC p 1097
4206 S 108th St, Omaha NE 68137
Tel (402) 331-5511 *SIC* 5961

▲ CABELAS INC p 234
1 Cabelas Dr, Sidney NE 69162
Tel (308) 254-5505 *SIC* 5961 5941

BROOKSTONE CO INC p 218
1 Innovation Way, Merrimack NH 03054
Tel (866) 576-7337
SIC 5947 5399 5331 5961

BROOKSTONE HOLDINGS CORP p 218
1 Innovation Way, Merrimack NH 03054
Tel (603) 880-9500 *SIC* 5947 5961

BROOKSTONE INC p 218
1 Innovation Way, Merrimack NH 03054
Tel (603) 880-9500 *SIC* 5961 5947

▲ PC CONNECTION INC p 1123
730 Milford Rd, Merrimack NH 03054
Tel (603) 683-2000 *SIC* 5961

■ PC CONNECTION SALES CORP p 1123
730 Milford Rd, Merrimack NH 03054
Tel (603) 423-2000 *SIC* 5961 5045

EDMUND OPTICS INC p 478
101 E Gloucester Pike, Barrington NJ 08007
Tel (856) 547-3488 *SIC* 3211 5961

▲ BURLINGTON STORES INC p 228
2006 Route 130, Burlington NJ 08016
Tel (609) 387-7800 *SIC* 5311 5961

DR LEONARDS HEALTHCARE CORP p 454
100 Nixon Ln, Edison NJ 08837
Tel (732) 572-0900 *SIC* 5961

■ MEDCO HEALTH SOLUTIONS INC p 935
100 Parsons Pond Dr, Franklin Lakes NJ 07417
Tel (201) 269-3400 *SIC* 5961

ATLANTIC COAST MEDIA GROUP LLC p 126
100 Town Square Pl Fl 6, Jersey City NJ 07310
Tel (201) 942-3400 *SIC* 5961 5999

HABAND CO LLC p 651
1 International Blvd # 800, Mahwah NJ 07495
Tel (570) 383-3226 *SIC* 5961 5611

■ VITAMIN SHOPPE INDUSTRIES INC p 1562
2101 91st St, North Bergen NJ 07047
Tel (201) 868-5959 *SIC* 5961

VS PARENT INC p 1566
2101 91st St, North Bergen NJ 07047
Tel (201) 868-5959 *SIC* 5961 5499

▲ VITAMIN SHOPPE INC p 1562
300 Harmon Meadow Blvd # 2, Secaucus NJ 07094
Tel (201) 868-5959 *SIC* 5961 5499

IDEAVILLAGE PRODUCTS CORP p 729
155 Route 46 W Fl 4, Wayne NJ 07470
Tel (973) 826-8400 *SIC* 5961

HANOVER DIRECT INC p 658
1200 Harbor Blvd Fl 9, Weehawken NJ 07086
Tel (201) 863-7300
SIC 5712 5961 7389 2211 2221

800-JR CIGAR INC p 4
301 State Route 10, Whippany NJ 07981
Tel (973) 884-9555 *SIC* 5194 5993 5961

▲ TRANS WORLD ENTERTAINMENT CORP p 1470
38 Corporate Cir, Albany NY 12203
Tel (518) 452-1242
SIC 5735 5731 5734 7841 5961

■ REXALL SUNDOWN INC p 1230
110 Orville Dr, Bohemia NY 11716
Tel (631) 567-9500 *SIC* 5961 5122 2833

▲ ETSY INC p 512
117 Adams St, Brooklyn NY 11201
Tel (718) 855-7955 *SIC* 5961 5947 7319

▲ 1-800-FLOWERS.COM INC p 1
1 Old Country Rd Ste 500, Carle Place NY 11514
Tel (516) 237-6000 *SIC* 5992 5961 5947

SAM ASH MUSIC CORP p 1273
278 Duffy Ave Unit A, Hicksville NY 11801
Tel (516) 932-6400
SIC 5736 5731 5734 5961 7359 8741

AEON USA INC p 29
1 Penn Plz Fl 36, New York NY 10119
Tel (212) 946-8780
SIC 5621 5961 2211 2391

▲ AVON PRODUCTS INC p 139
777 3rd Ave, New York NY 10017
Tel (212) 282-5000
SIC 2844 3961 5961 5023 5137

B & H FOTO & ELECTRONICS CORP p 141
420 9th Ave, New York NY 10001
Tel (212) 239-7500 *SIC* 5946 5731 5961

▲ BARNES & NOBLE INC p 156
122 5th Ave Fl 2, New York NY 10011
Tel (212) 633-3300 *SIC* 5942 5961 5945

BLUE APRON INC p 190
5 Crosby St, New York NY 10013
Tel (888) 278-4349 *SIC* 5961

CACHE INC p 235
256 W 38th St Fl 3, New York NY 10018
Tel (212) 575-3200 *SIC* 5632 5621 5961

CHANEL INC p 288
9 W 57th St Fl 44, New York NY 10019
Tel (212) 688-5055
SIC 5632 2844 5122 5944 5961 5999

CHELSEY DIRECT LLC p 293
110 E 59th St, New York NY 10022
Tel (201) 863-7300 *SIC* 5961 5947 5611

CHINOS HOLDINGS INC p 301
770 Broadway, New York NY 10003
Tel (212) 209-2500
SIC 5961 5621 5611 5632 6794

CHINOS INTERMEDIATE HOLDINGS B INC p 301
770 Broadway, New York NY 10003
Tel (212) 209-2500
SIC 5961 5621 5611 5632 6794

DATA VISION COMPUTER VIDEO INC p 414
50 W 23rd St, New York NY 10010
Tel (212) 689-1111 *SIC* 5045 5961

DEAN & DELUCA INC p 420
560 Broadway Frnt 2, New York NY 10012
Tel (212) 226-6800
SIC 5499 5812 5961 2099

FILMED ENTERTAINMENT INC p 542
1 Penn Plz Fl 5, New York NY 10119
Tel (212) 596-2000 *SIC* 5961

▲ FOOT LOCKER INC p 564
330 W 34th St, New York NY 10001
Tel (212) 720-3700
SIC 5661 5941 5961 6794

■ FOOT LOCKER SPECIALTY INC p 564
112 W 34th St Lbby 1, New York NY 10120
Tel (212) 720-3700 *SIC* 5632 5961 7311

FULLBEAUTY BRANDS INC p 584
1 New York Plz Fl 13, New York NY 10004
Tel (212) 613-9500 *SIC* 5961 7389 5611

FULLBEAUTY BRANDS LP p 584
1 New York Plz Fl 13, New York NY 10004
Tel (212) 613-9500 *SIC* 5961

GILT GROUPE INC p 612
250 Vesey St Fl 21, New York NY 10281
Tel (877) 280-0545 *SIC* 5961

HENRY MODELL & CO INC p 684
498 7th Ave Fl 20, New York NY 10018
Tel (212) 822-1000
SIC 5941 5661 5611 5621 5641 5961

▲ IAC/INTERACTIVECORP p 725
555 W 18th St, New York NY 10011
Tel (212) 314-7300 *SIC* 7372 7375 5961

J CREW INC p 770
770 Broadway Fl 14, New York NY 10003
Tel (212) 209-8010 *SIC* 5961 5621 5611

J CREW OPERATING CORP p 770
770 Brdwy Fl 11 & 12, New York NY 10003
Tel (212) 209-2500
SIC 5961 5621 5611 5661 5632 6794

JCREW GROUP INC p 780
770 Broadway Fl 11, New York NY 10003
Tel (212) 209-2500
SIC 5961 5621 5611 5632

▲ KATE SPADE & CO p 804
2 Park Ave Fl 8, New York NY 10016
Tel (212) 354-4900
SIC 2331 5651 5136 5137 5961

LOCCITANE INC p 873
1430 Broadway Fl 2, New York NY 10018
Tel (212) 333-4880 *SIC* 5122 5999 5961

OXFORD UNIVERSITY PRESS LLC p 1101
198 Madison Ave Fl 8, New York NY 10016
Tel (212) 726-6000 *SIC* 2731 5961

RDA HOLDING CO p 1212
750 3rd Ave, New York NY 10017
Tel (914) 238-1000
SIC 2721 2731 5961 2741

▲ TIFFANY & CO p 1453
200 5th Ave Bsmt 2, New York NY 10010
Tel (212) 755-8000
SIC 5944 5094 5719 5943 5999 5961

TLB HOLDINGS LLC p 1457
9 W 57th St, New York NY 10019
Tel (212) 796-8555
SIC 5961 5661 5632 5641 5621

TRUSTED MEDIA BRANDS INC p 1487
750 3rd Ave Fl 3, New York NY 10017
Tel (914) 238-1000
SIC 2721 2731 5961 2741

■ VIVENDI UNIVERSAL ENTERTAINMENT LLLP p 1563
30 Rockefeller Plz, New York NY 10112
Tel (212) 664-4444
SIC 7812 3652 2741 5947 5944 5961

PUBLISHERS CLEARING HOUSE LLC p 1190
382 Channel Dr, Port Washington NY 11050
Tel (516) 883-5432 *SIC* 5961 8742

▲ SYSTEMAX INC p 1418
11 Harbor Park Dr, Port Washington NY 11050
Tel (516) 608-7000 *SIC* 5961 5046

■ ALPHABET HOLDING CO INC p 60
2100 Smithtown Ave, Ronkonkoma NY 11779
Tel (631) 200-2000
SIC 2833 5122 5499 5961

■ NBTY INC p 1021
2100 Smithtown Ave, Ronkonkoma NY 11779
Tel (631) 200-2000
SIC 2833 5122 5499 5961

PERFORMANCE DIRECT INC p 1135
1 Performance Way, Chapel Hill NC 27517
Tel (919) 933-9113 *SIC* 5961 5941

KAYSER-ROTH CORP p 805
102 Corporate Center Blvd, Greensboro NC 27408
Tel (336) 852-2030
SIC 2252 2251 5961 8741 3842

REPLACEMENTS LTD p 1224
1089 Knox Rd, Mc Leansville NC 27301
Tel (336) 697-3000 *SIC* 5961

■ MACYS.COM INC p 893
7 W 7th St, Cincinnati OH 45202
Tel (513) 579-7000 *SIC* 5961 5311

AMERIMARK DIRECT LLC p 82
6864 Engle Rd, Cleveland OH 44130
Tel (440) 826-1900 *SIC* 4226 5961 7331

AMERIMARK HOLDINGS LLC p 82
6864 Engle Rd, Cleveland OH 44130
Tel (440) 325-2000 *SIC* 5961 4226 7331

2CHECKOUT.COM INC p 2
855 Grandview Ave Ste 110, Columbus OH 43215
Tel (614) 921-2449 *SIC* 5961

▲ L BRANDS INC p 833
3 Limited Pkwy, Columbus OH 43230
Tel (614) 415-7000
SIC 5632 5961 5621 5999

MIDWEST TAPE LLC p 968
1417 Timber Wolf Dr, Holland OH 43528
Tel (419) 868-9370
SIC 7822 5099 8741 7389 5961 7374

■ HSN IMPROVEMENTS LLC p 715
16501 Rockside Rd, Maple Heights OH 44137
Tel (216) 662-6553 *SIC* 5961

▲ ABERCROMBIE & FITCH CO p 11
6301 Fitch Path, New Albany OH 43054
Tel (614) 283-6500
SIC 5611 5621 5641 5632 5651 5961

PROVANTAGE LLC p 1185
7576 Freedom Ave Nw, North Canton OH 44720
Tel (330) 494-3781
SIC 5961 5719 5734 5045

SUAREZ CORP INDUSTRIES p 1395
7800 Whipple Ave Nw, North Canton OH 44720
Tel (330) 494-5504 *SIC* 5961 5944

VITA-MIX CORP p 1562
8615 Usher Rd, Olmsted Twp OH 44138
Tel (440) 235-4840 *SIC* 5961 3556

■ VICTORIAS SECRET DIRECT HOLDING LLC p 1555
5 Limited Pkwy E, Reynoldsburg OH 43068
Tel (614) 577-7111 *SIC* 5961

■ VICTORIAS SECRET DIRECT LLC p 1555
5 Limited Pkwy E, Reynoldsburg OH 43068
Tel (614) 577-7111 *SIC* 5961 5632 5621

■ CINMAR LLC p 308
5566 W Chester Rd, West Chester OH 45069
Tel (513) 603-1000 *SIC* 5961 5023 5712

■ CORNERSTONE BRANDS INC p 371
5568 W Chester Rd, West Chester OH 45069
Tel (513) 603-1000 *SIC* 5961

QUIBIDS HOLDINGS LLC p 1199
1601 Nw Expwy St Ste 1500, Oklahoma City OK 73118
Tel (405) 253-3883 *SIC* 5961

■ HARRY & DAVID HOLDINGS INC p 664
2500 S Pacific Hwy, Medford OR 97501
Tel (541) 864-2362 *SIC* 5961 1541

■ HARRY AND DAVID LLC p 664
2500 S Pacific Hwy, Medford OR 97501
Tel (541) 864-2500 *SIC* 5961 5947

■ CHARMING SHOPPES INC p 290
3750 State Rd, Bensalem PA 19020
Tel (215) 245-9100 *SIC* 5961 5632 5621

KYNETIC LLC p 833
225 Washington St, Conshohocken PA 19428
Tel (484) 534-8100 *SIC* 8741 5961

MUSICIANS LIVEORG p 1002
77 Brookfield Dr, Elizabethtown PA 17022
Tel (717) 413-3265 *SIC* 5736 5961 7389

▲ NUTRISYSTEM INC p 1068
600 Office Center Dr, Fort Washington PA 19034
Tel (215) 706-5300 *SIC* 5961

■ GSI COMMERCE INC p 643
935 1st Ave, King Of Prussia PA 19406
Tel (610) 491-7000 *SIC* 5961 7371 7379

JAY GROUP INC p 779
700 Indian Springs Dr, Lancaster PA 17601
Tel (717) 285-6200
SIC 5961 7389 7331 7319 5199

■ ARAMARK UNIFORM & CAREER APPAREL GROUP INC p 102
1101 Market St Ste 45, Philadelphia PA 19107
Tel (215) 238-3000
SIC 2337 2311 5699 5961 5661 5812

■ COMCAST CABLE HOLDINGS LLC p 343
1500 Market St Ste Lmw 3, Philadelphia PA 19102
Tel (215) 665-1700 *SIC* 4841 7922 5961

W ATLEE BURPEE CO p 1568
300 Park Ave, Warminster PA 18974
Tel (215) 674-4900 *SIC* 0181 5961

BLAIR LLC p 188
220 Hickory St, Warren PA 16366
Tel (814) 723-3600 *SIC* 5961

■ QVC INC p 1201
1200 Wilson Dr, West Chester PA 19380
Tel (484) 701-1000 *SIC* 5961

▲ CVS HEALTH CORP p 404
1 Cvs Dr, Woonsocket RI 02895
Tel (401) 765-1500 *SIC* 5912 5961 8099

■ LONGS DRUG STORES CORP p 877
1 Cvs Dr, Woonsocket RI 02895
Tel (401) 770-1830 *SIC* 5912 5961

MIDCO COMMUNICATIONS INC p 964
3901 N Louise Ave, Sioux Falls SD 57107
Tel (605) 334-1200
SIC 8748 5961 7389 4812

■ TEL-DRUG INC p 1433
4901 N 4th Ave, Sioux Falls SD 57104
Tel (605) 809-8166 *SIC* 5912 5961

■ CAREMARK RX INC p 255
445 Great Circle Rd, Nashville TN 37228
Tel (615) 687-7400 *SIC* 5961

▲ GENESCO INC p 602
1415 Murfreesboro Pike, Nashville TN 37217
Tel (615) 367-7000 *SIC* 5661 5139 5961

■ GOLFSMITH INTERNATIONAL HOLDINGS INC p 622
11000 N Interstate 35, Austin TX 78753
Tel (512) 837-8810
SIC 5941 5699 5661 5961

■ COMPUSA INC p 352
14951 Dallas Pkwy, Dallas TX 75254
Tel (972) 982-4000 *SIC* 5734 5045 5961

NEIMAN MARCUS GROUP INC p 1025
1618 Main St, Dallas TX 75201
Tel (214) 743-7600 *SIC* 5311 5961

NEIMAN MARCUS GROUP LTD LLC p 1025
1618 Main St, Dallas TX 75201
Tel (214) 743-7600 *SIC* 5311 5961

CCS MEDICAL HOLDINGS INC p 270
1505 L B Johnson Fwy # 600, Farmers Branch TX 75234
Tel (972) 628-2100 *SIC* 5999 5912 5961

CCS MEDICAL INC p 270
1505 L B Johnson Fwy # 600, Farmers Branch TX 75234
Tel (972) 628-2100 *SIC* 5999 5912 5961

▲ J C PENNEY CO INC p 770
6501 Legacy Dr, Plano TX 75024
Tel (972) 431-1000 *SIC* 5311 5961

■ JC PENNEY CORP INC p 780
6501 Legacy Dr, Plano TX 75024
Tel (972) 431-1000 *SIC* 5311 5961

▲ TANDY BRANDS ACCESSORIES INC p 1424
501 N College St, Waxahachie TX 75165
Tel (214) 519-5200 *SIC* 3172 5961

1-800 CONTACTS INC p 1
261 W Data Dr, Draper UT 84020
Tel (801) 316-5000 *SIC* 5961 3851

▲ OVERSTOCK.COM INC p 1099
799 W Coliseum Way, Midvale UT 84047
Tel (801) 947-3100 *SIC* 5961

VERMONT COUNTRY STORE INC p 1551
5650 Main St, Manchester Center VT 05255
Tel (802) 362-4667 *SIC* 5961 5399 5812

KING ARTHUR FLOUR CO INC p 820
135 Us Route 5 S, Norwich VT 05055
Tel (802) 649-3881
SIC 5149 5961 5461 8299

ORVIS CO INC p 1096
178 Conservation Way, Sunderland VT 05250
Tel (802) 362-3622 *SIC* 5961 5941 3949

CRUTCHFIELD CORP p 396
1 Crutchfield Park, Charlottesville VA 22911
Tel (434) 817-1000 *SIC* 5961

PLOW & HEARTH LLC p 1156
7021 Wolftown Hood Rd, Madison VA 22727
Tel (540) 948-2272 *SIC* 5961 5251

ZONES PUBLIC SECTOR LLC p 1644
1102 15th St Sw Ste 102, Auburn WA 98001
Tel (253) 205-3000 *SIC* 5961

AMARGOSA INC p 64
10401 Ne 8th St Ste 500, Bellevue WA 98004
Tel (425) 755-6100
SIC 5611 5699 5941 5719 5947 5961

■ AMAZON COM DEDC LLC p 64
1227 124th Ave Ne Ste 200, Bellevue WA 98005
Tel (206) 266-5363 *SIC* 5961

EDDIE BAUER LLC p 477
10401 Ne 8th St Ste 500, Bellevue WA 98004
Tel (425) 755-6100 *SIC* 5611 5961 5621

EVEREST HOLDINGS LLC p 514
10401 Ne 8th St Ste 500, Bellevue WA 98004
Tel (425) 755-6544 *SIC* 5699 5611 5961

RECREATIONAL EQUIPMENT INC p 1215
6750 S 228th St, Kent WA 98032
Tel (253) 395-3780
SIC 2329 3949 2399 5941 5961 5699

■ AMAZON FULFILLMENT SERVICES INC p 64
410 Terry Ave N, Seattle WA 98109
Tel (206) 266-1000
SIC 5735 5961 5731 5945

▲ AMAZON.COM INC p 64
410 Terry Ave N, Seattle WA 98109
Tel (206) 266-1000 *SIC* 5961

■ AMAZON.COMDEDC LLC p 65
410 Terry Ave N, Seattle WA 98109
Tel (206) 266-1000
SIC 5961 5735 5731 5945

■ GETTY IMAGES INC p 609
605 5th Ave S Ste 400, Seattle WA 98104
Tel (206) 925-5000 *SIC* 5961

▲ NORDSTROM INC p 1048
1617 6th Ave, Seattle WA 98101
Tel (206) 628-2111
SIC 5651 5661 5632 5611 5641 5961

ZULILY INC p 1644
2601 Elliott Ave Ste 200, Seattle WA 98121
Tel (877) 779-5614 *SIC* 5961

■ ZULILY LLC p 1645
2601 Elliott Ave Ste 200, Seattle WA 98121
Tel (877) 779-5614 *SIC* 5961

WOODCRAFT SUPPLY LLC p 1622
1177 Rosemar Rd, Parkersburg WV 26105
Tel (304) 422-5412 *SIC* 5961 5251

▲ DULUTH HOLDINGS INC p 460
170 Countryside Dr, Belleville WI 53508
Tel (608) 424-1544 *SIC* 5961 5611 5621

MASON COMPANIES INC p 916
1251 1st Ave, Chippewa Falls WI 54729
Tel (715) 720-4200 *SIC* 5961 5661

▲ LANDS END INC p 843
1 Lands End Ln, Dodgeville WI 53595
Tel (608) 935-9341 *SIC* 5961 5611 5621

▲ SCHOOL SPECIALTY INC p 1290
W6316 Design Dr, Greenville WI 54942
Tel (920) 734-5712 *SIC* 5049 5021 5961

■ GHC SPECIALTY BRANDS LLC p 610
401 S Wright Rd, Janesville WI 53546
Tel (608) 754-2345 *SIC* 5961

▲ KOHLS CORP p 826
N56w17000 Ridgewood Dr, Menomonee Falls WI 53051
Tel (262) 703-7000 *SIC* 5311 5961

INTERNATIONAL COMMERCE & MARKETING CORP p 755
500 W Oklahoma Ave, Milwaukee WI 53207
Tel (414) 290-1500 *SIC* 5085 5961

COLONY BRANDS INC p 338
1112 7th Ave, Monroe WI 53566
Tel (608) 328-8400 *SIC* 5961 5143 2051

FOSTER AND SMITH INC p 570
2253 Air Park Rd, Rhinelander WI 54501
Tel (715) 369-3305 *SIC* 4813 5961

■ FOOTLOCKER.COM INC p 564
111 S 1st Ave, Wausau WI 54401
Tel (715) 842-3890 *SIC* 5961 5661

■ SIERRA TRADING POST INC p 1321
5025 Campstool Rd, Cheyenne WY 82007
Tel (307) 775-8050 *SIC* 5961

SIC 5962 Automatic Merchandising Machine Operators

BUFFALO ROCK CO p 224
111 Oxmoor Rd, Birmingham AL 35209
Tel (205) 942-3435 *SIC* 2086 5962 5149

COCA-COLA BOTTLING CO UNITED INC p 333
4600 E Lake Blvd, Birmingham AL 35217
Tel (205) 238-3300 *SIC* 2086 5962

SOUTHERN FOODSERVICE MANAGEMENT INC p 1348
500 Office Park Dr # 210, Mountain Brk AL 35223
Tel (205) 871-8000 *SIC* 5812 5962

GLACIER WATER SERVICES INC p 614
1385 Park Center Dr, Vista CA 92081
Tel (760) 560-1111 *SIC* 5962

NATIONAL ENTERTAINMENT NETWORK LLC p 1011
325 Interlocken Pkwy B, Broomfield CO 80021
Tel (303) 444-2559 *SIC* 5046 5962

NEN HOLDINGS INC p 1025
397 S Taylor Ave, Louisville CO 80027
Tel (303) 444-2559 *SIC* 5962

FIVE STAR HOLDING CO INC p 553
248 Rollins Industrial Ct, Ringgold GA 30736
Tel (706) 937-5077
SIC 5962 5812 5963 2099

A H MANAGEMENT GROUP INC p 5
1151 Rohlwing Rd, Rolling Meadows IL 60008
Tel (847) 342-8065
SIC 5962 7993 5963 7389 5046

MYRON GREEN CORP p 1005
8500 Shawnee Mission Pkwy, Merriam KS 66202
Tel (913) 384-4900 *SIC* 5962

MODERN DISTRIBUTORS INC p 981
817 W Columbia St, Somerset KY 42501
Tel (606) 679-1178
SIC 5194 5962 5145 5064

■ LOUISIANA COCA-COLA BOTTLING CO LIMITED p 880
5601 Citrus Blvd, New Orleans LA 70123
Tel (504) 818-7000 *SIC* 2086 5962

WM B REILY & CO INC p 1620
640 Magazine St, New Orleans LA 70130
Tel (504) 539-5200
SIC 2095 2035 2079 5962 5963 2099

ALL SEASONS SERVICES INC p 51
5 Campanelli Cir Ste 200, Canton MA 02021
Tel (781) 828-2345 *SIC* 5962 5812

CONTINENTAL DISTRIBUTORS INC p 363
35710 Mound Rd, Sterling Heights MI 48310
Tel (586) 268-3835 *SIC* 5962 5812

SUNSET STATION HOTEL AND CASINO p 1404
1301 W Sunset Rd, Henderson NV 89014
Tel (702) 547-7777 *SIC* 7011 5962 7389

ADVANCED BEVERAGE INC p 25
1835 Burnet Ave Ste 2, Union NJ 07083
Tel (908) 686-3666 *SIC* 5962

AMERICAN FOOD & VENDING CORP p 72
124 Metropolitan Park Dr, Liverpool NY 13088
Tel (315) 457-9950 *SIC* 5962 5812

AUXILIARY SERVICES STATE UNIVERSITY COLLEGE AT OSWEGO INC p 135
7060 Route 104, Oswego NY 13126
Tel (315) 312-2106
SIC 5812 5942 5962 5441

COMPASS HOLDINGS INC p 351
2400 Yorkmont Rd, Charlotte NC 28217
Tel (704) 328-4000 *SIC* 5812 5962

■ MILACRON INTERMEDIATE HOLDINGS INC p 968
3010 Disney St, Cincinnati OH 45209
Tel (513) 536-2000 *SIC* 5962 8741

AVI FOOD SYSTEMS INC p 137
2590 Elm Rd Ne, Warren OH 44483
Tel (330) 372-6000 *SIC* 5962 5812 8742

SANESE SERVICES INC p 1279
2590 Elm Rd Ne, Warren OH 44483
Tel (614) 436-1234 *SIC* 5962 5812 7389

■ ROCHESTER COCA COLA BOTTLING CORP p 1243
300 Oak St, Pittston PA 18640
Tel (570) 655-2874 *SIC* 2086 5962

FIVE STAR FOOD SERVICE INC p 553
6005 Century Oaks Dr # 100, Chattanooga TN 37416
Tel (423) 490-4428 *SIC* 5962 5812 7389

CUSTOM FOOD GROUP LP p 403
12221 Merit Dr Ste 975, Dallas TX 75251
Tel (214) 273-0500 *SIC* 5962

LSG SKY CHEFS USA INC p 883
6191 N State Highway 161 # 100, Irving TX 75038
Tel (972) 793-9000 *SIC* 5812 5962

S C INTERNATIONAL SERVICES INC p 1262
6191 N State Highway 161 # 100, Irving TX 75038
Tel (972) 793-9000 *SIC* 5812 5962

NOEL CORP p 1046
1001 S 1st St, Yakima WA 98901
Tel (509) 248-4545
SIC 2086 7389 4212 6512 4225 5962

SIC 5963 Direct Selling Establishments

BI-RITE RESTAURANT SUPPLY CO INC p 180
123 S Hill Dr, Brisbane CA 94005
Tel (415) 656-0187
SIC 5141 5147 5148 5023 5046 5963

SMART CIRCLE INTERNATIONAL LLC p 1332
4490 Von Karman Ave, Newport Beach CA 92660
Tel (949) 587-9207 *SIC* 5963

2100 FREEDOM INC p 1
625 N Grand Ave, Santa Ana CA 92701
Tel (714) 796-7000
SIC 2711 2721 7313 2741 5963 4813

FREEDOM COMMUNICATIONS INC p 576
625 N Grand Ave, Santa Ana CA 92701
Tel (714) 796-7000
SIC 2711 2721 7313 2741 5963

■ SCHOLASTIC LIBRARY PUBLISHING INC p 1288
90 Sherman Tpke, Danbury CT 06816
Tel (203) 797-3500
SIC 2731 5963 5192 2721 5961 7371

TAUNTON INC p 1426
63 S Main St, Newtown CT 06470
Tel (203) 426-8171
SIC 2721 2731 7812 5963

■ PEPPERIDGE FARM INC p 1134
595 Westport Ave, Norwalk CT 06851
Tel (203) 846-7000
SIC 5963 2052 2099 2053 5961

▲ SUN GORDMANS LP p 1400
5200 Town Center Cir # 600, Boca Raton FL 33486
Tel (561) 394-0550 *SIC* 5651 5963

■ SYSCO JACKSONVILLE INC p 1417
1501 Lewis Industrial Dr, Jacksonville FL 32254
Tel (904) 781-5070
SIC 5149 5147 5144 5963

DP DISTRIBUTION LLC p 454
9601 Nw 112th Ave, Medley FL 33178
Tel (305) 777-6108 *SIC* 5149 5963

■ QVC SAINT LUCIE INC p 1201
300 Nw Peacock Blvd, Port Saint Lucie FL 34986
Tel (772) 873-4300 *SIC* 5963

CONCESSIONS INTERNATIONAL LLC p 354
566 Wells St Sw, Atlanta GA 30312
Tel (404) 681-0300 *SIC* 5812 5963 5947

DS SERVICES OF AMERICA INC p 457
2300 Windy Ridge Pkwy Se 500n, Atlanta GA 30339
Tel (770) 933-1400 *SIC* 5963

FIVE STAR HOLDING CO INC p 553
248 Rollins Industrial Ct, Ringgold GA 30736
Tel (706) 937-5077
SIC 5962 5812 5963 2099

THOMAS MANAGEMENT CORP p 1449
700 E Franklin Rd, Meridian ID 83642
Tel (208) 884-5766 *SIC* 5963

■ PAMPERED CHEF LTD p 1110
140 N Swift Rd, Addison IL 60101
Tel (630) 261-8900 *SIC* 5963

PREFERRED MEAL SYSTEMS INC p 1169
5240 Saint Charles Rd, Berkeley IL 60163
Tel (309) 697-4550 *SIC* 5963

■ QUAKER SALES & DISTRIBUTION INC p 1196
555 W Monroe St, Chicago IL 60661
Tel (312) 821-1000 *SIC* 5963

SIMONTON HOLDINGS INC p 1325
520 Lake Cook Rd, Deerfield IL 60015
Tel (304) 428-8261
SIC 3089 5961 3086 5963

KRONOS FOODS CORP p 830
1 Kronos, Glendale Heights IL 60139
Tel (773) 847-2250
SIC 2013 2051 5141 5963

▲ CDW CORP p 271
75 Tri State Intl, Lincolnshire IL 60069
Tel (847) 465-6000
SIC 5963 5045 5734 5961

OBERWEIS DAIRY INC p 1072
951 Ice Cream Dr, North Aurora IL 60542
Tel (630) 801-6100 *SIC* 5963 5451

A H MANAGEMENT GROUP INC p 5
1151 Rohlwing Rd, Rolling Meadows IL 60008
Tel (847) 342-8065
SIC 5962 7993 5963 7389 5046

CDW HOLDINGS LLC p 271
3 First National Pl, Vernon Hills IL 60061
Tel (847) 465-6000
SIC 5963 5045 5734 5961

TREAT AMERICA MANAGEMENT CO LLC p 1475
8500 Shawnee Mission Pkwy # 100, Merriam KS 66202
Tel (913) 268-5800 *SIC* 5963

WM B REILY & CO INC p 1620
640 Magazine St, New Orleans LA 70130
Tel (504) 539-5200
SIC 2095 2035 2079 5962 5963 2099

PUBLISHERS CIRCULATION FULFILLMENT INC p 1190
502 Wshington Ave Ste 500, Towson MD 21204
Tel (410) 821-8614 *SIC* 5963

■ WAYFAIR LLC p 1584
4 Copley Pl Ste 700, Boston MA 02116
Tel (617) 532-6100 *SIC* 5963 5712 5023

AMWAY CORP p 87
7575 Fulton St E, Ada MI 49355
Tel (616) 787-6000 *SIC* 5963

J & B GROUP INC p 769
13200 43rd St Ne, Saint Michael MN 55376
Tel (763) 497-3913 *SIC* 6719 5963

HUSSMANN INTERNATIONAL INC p 721
12999 St Charles Rock Rd, Bridgeton MO 63044
Tel (314) 291-2000 *SIC* 3585 5963

▲ BERKSHIRE HATHAWAY INC p 175
3555 Farnam St Ste 1440, Omaha NE 68131
Tel (402) 346-1400
SIC 6331 6321 4911 4924 6531 5963

■ GORDMANS STORES INC p 625
1926 S 67th St, Omaha NE 68106
Tel (402) 691-4000 *SIC* 5651 5963

▲ PARTY CITY HOLDCO INC p 1119
80 Grasslands Rd, Elmsford NY 10523
Tel (914) 345-2020
SIC 5947 5963 5199 6794

■ SYSCO ALBANY LLC p 1416
1 Liebich Ln, Halfmoon NY 12065
Tel (518) 877-3200 *SIC* 5149 5963

ECONOMIST NEWSPAPER GROUP INC p 476
750 3rd Ave Fl 5, New York NY 10017
Tel (212) 541-0500 *SIC* 2721 7313 5963

HAVAS NORTH AMERICA INC p 668
200 Hudson St, New York NY 10013
Tel (212) 886-2000 *SIC* 7311 5963

CUTCO CORP p 403
1116 E State St, Olean NY 14760
Tel (716) 372-3111 *SIC* 5963 3421

■ BEF FOODS INC p 168
8111 Smiths Mill Rd, New Albany OH 43054
Tel (800) 272-7675 *SIC* 5963

▲ RITE AID CORP p 1236
30 Hunter Ln, Camp Hill PA 17011
Tel (717) 761-2633 *SIC* 5912 7384 5963

■ ARAMARK REFRESHMENT SERVICES LLC p 102
1101 Market St, Philadelphia PA 19107
Tel (215) 238-3000 *SIC* 5963

GFR MEDIA LLC p 610
50 Carr 165 Ste 1, Guaynabo PR 00968
Tel (787) 641-8000 *SIC* 4789 2711 5963

CHATTEM INC p 292
1715 W 38th St, Chattanooga TN 37409
Tel (423) 821-4571
SIC 2834 2844 2023 5963

FIVE STAR SERVICE GROUP INC p 553
6005 Century Oaks Dr # 100, Chattanooga TN 37416
Tel (423) 643-2600 *SIC* 5963

LIFEWAY CHRISTIAN RESOURCES OF SOUTHERN BAPTIST CONVENTION p 865
1 Lifeway Plz, Nashville TN 37234
Tel (615) 251-2000
SIC 5942 5963 2731 5999 5735 5947

MARY KAY HOLDING CORP p 914
16251 Dallas Pkwy, Addison TX 75001
Tel (972) 687-6300
SIC 5963 3961 3172 4724

MARY KAY INC p 914
16251 Dallas Pkwy, Addison TX 75001
Tel (972) 687-6300 *SIC* 5963

20/20 COMMUNICATIONS INC p 1
3575 Lone Star Cir # 200, Fort Worth TX 76177
Tel (817) 490-0100 *SIC* 5963

AFJ LLC p 33
1104 Country Hills Dr, Ogden UT 84403
Tel (801) 624-1000 *SIC* 5541 5963

DOWNEAST OUTFITTERS INC p 453
375 W Hope Ave, Salt Lake City UT 84115
Tel (801) 467-7520
SIC 5611 5621 5963 2512

MONAVIE LLC p 983
10855 S River Front Pkwy # 100, South Jordan UT 84095
Tel (801) 748-3100 *SIC* 5963

SMITHFIELD FARMLAND SALES CORP p 1333
111 Commerce St, Smithfield VA 23430
Tel (757) 357-3131 *SIC* 5147 8743 5963

REINHART FOODSERVICE LLC p 1221
1500 Saint James St, La Crosse WI 54603
Tel (608) 782-2660 *SIC* 5963

SIC 5983 Fuel Oil Dealers

COUGAR OIL INC p 374
1411 Water Ave, Selma AL 36703
Tel (334) 875-2023 *SIC* 5171 5983 5172

HARPEL OIL CO p 662
4204 E 105th Ave, Thornton CO 80233
Tel (303) 294-0767 *SIC* 5171 5983 5172

■ PETRO INC p 1139
9 W Broad St Ste 3, Stamford CT 06902
Tel (203) 325-5400 *SIC* 5983 7699

■ PETROLEUM HEAT AND POWER CO INC p 1139
9 W Broad St Ste 3, Stamford CT 06902
Tel (800) 645-4328 *SIC* 5983 5172 5722

MERCURY FUEL SERVICE INC p 945
43 Lafayette St, Waterbury CT 06708
Tel (203) 756-7284
SIC 5172 5541 5411 5983 1711 2911

HERRERA PETROLEUM CORP p 687
5209 Nw 74th Ave Ste 279, Miami FL 33166
Tel (786) 267-5467 *SIC* 5983

JACKSON OIL & SOLVENTS INC p 774
1970 Kentucky Ave, Indianapolis IN 46221
Tel (317) 481-2244
SIC 5172 5541 5983 5531

JOHN E RETZNER OIL CO INC p 788
630 S Adams St, Versailles IN 47042
Tel (812) 609-4178 *SIC* 5983

FARMERS UNION COOPERATIVE p 530
1913 County Road B32, Ossian IA 52161
Tel (563) 532-9381 *SIC* 5153 5261 5983

DEAD RIVER CO p 419
80 Exchange St Ste 3, Bangor ME 04401
Tel (207) 947-8641
SIC 6512 5172 5983 5541 5411

R H FOSTER ENERGY LLC p 1202
110 Mecaw Rd, Hampden ME 04444
Tel (207) 947-3835
SIC 5172 5541 5411 5983

FABIAN OIL INC p 523
15 Oak St, Oakland ME 04963
Tel (207) 465-7958
SIC 5541 5983 5984 5411

CN BROWN CO p 329
1 C N Brown Way, South Paris ME 04281
Tel (207) 743-9212 *SIC* 5411 5541 5983

CARROLL INDEPENDENT FUEL LLC p 261
2700 Loch Raven Rd, Baltimore MD 21218
Tel (410) 235-1066 *SIC* 5172 5983

WILLS GROUP INC p 1613
6355 Crain Hwy, La Plata MD 20646
Tel (301) 932-3600
SIC 5541 5983 5172 5411

JOHNSON OIL CO OF GAYLORD p 791
507 S Otsego Ave, Gaylord MI 49735
Tel (989) 732-6014 *SIC* 5171 5541 5983

WALTERS-DIMMICK PETROLEUM INC p 1574
1620 S Kalamazoo Ave, Marshall MI 49068
Tel (269) 781-4654
SIC 5541 5411 6512 5172 5171 5983

BEST OIL CO p 177
30 N 8th St, Cloquet MN 55720
Tel (218) 879-0201
SIC 5171 5172 5013 5983 5541 5411

UNITED FARMERS COOPERATIVE p 1508
705 E 4th St, Winthrop MN 55396
Tel (507) 237-2281
SIC 5153 5191 5983 5083

ON-SITE FUEL SERVICE INC p 1086
1089 Old Fannin Rd Ste A, Brandon MS 39047
Tel (601) 353-4142 *SIC* 5983

CITYSERVICEVALCON LLC p 320
640 W Montana St, Kalispell MT 59901
Tel (406) 755-4321 *SIC* 5172 5983

■ SUBURBAN PROPANE LP p 1396
240 State Route 10, Whippany NJ 07981
Tel (973) 887-5300 *SIC* 5983

MIRABITO HOLDINGS INC p 974
49 Court St Ste 1, Binghamton NY 13901
Tel (607) 561-2700
SIC 5172 4925 5541 5411 5983

S J FUEL CO INC p 1262
601 Union St, Brooklyn NY 11215
Tel (718) 855-6060 *SIC* 5983 1711

SLOMINS INC p 1331
125 Lauman Ln, Hicksville NY 11801
Tel (516) 932-7000 *SIC* 5983 1731 1711

TOWNSEND OIL CORP p 1466
64 Main St, Le Roy NY 14482
Tel (585) 768-8188 *SIC* 5171 5983

CAMBRIDGE PETROLEUM HOLDING INC p 244
31 S Plank Rd Unit 105, Newburgh NY 12550
Tel (516) 542-4900
SIC 5983 5541 5984 5172 5074

SUPERIOR PLUS ENERGY SERVICES INC p 1407
1870 Winton Rd S Ste 200, Rochester NY 14618
Tel (585) 328-3930 *SIC* 5171 5983

M SPIEGEL & SONS OIL CORP p 890
10 E Village Rd, Tuxedo Park NY 10987
Tel (845) 351-4700 *SIC* 5172 5983

HOP ENERGY HOLDINGS INC p 706
4 W Red Oak Ln Ste 310, White Plains NY 10604
Tel (914) 304-1300 *SIC* 5983

HOP ENERGY LLC p 706
4 W Red Oak Ln Ste 310, White Plains NY 10604
Tel (914) 304-1300 *SIC* 5983

PUGH OIL CO INC p 1191
701 Mcdowell Rd, Asheboro NC 27205
Tel (336) 629-2061
SIC 5172 5983 5541 5411 5149

SAMPSON-BLADEN OIL CO INC p 1274
510 Commerce St, Clinton NC 28328
Tel (910) 592-4177 *SIC* 5171 5411 5983

BUMGARNER OIL CO INC p 225
2004 Highland Ave Ne, Hickory NC 28601
Tel (828) 322-4377 *SIC* 5172 5983

MALLARD OIL CO p 899
1502 Dr Martin Luther, Kinston NC 28501
Tel (252) 527-0364 *SIC* 5171 5983 5984

EDEN OIL CO INC p 477
2507 Richardson Dr, Reidsville NC 27320
Tel (336) 349-8228 *SIC* 5171 5983

NEW DIXIE OIL CORP p 1029
1501 Marshall St, Roanoke Rapids NC 27870
Tel (252) 537-4118 *SIC* 5983

QUALITY OIL CO LLC p 1197
1540 Silas Creek Pkwy, Winston Salem NC 27127
Tel (336) 722-3441 *SIC* 5983 5541 7011

DUNCAN OIL CO p 461
849 Factory Rd, Dayton OH 45434
Tel (937) 426-5945
SIC 5172 5411 5983 1542

AIM LEASING CO p 38
1500 Trumbull Ave, Girard OH 44420
Tel (330) 759-0438
SIC 7513 7538 4212 5983

BAZELL OIL CO INC p 163
14371 State Route 328, Logan OH 43138
Tel (740) 385-5420 *SIC* 5172 5983

WESTERN RESERVE FARM COOPERATIVE INC p 1600
16003 E High St, Middlefield OH 44062
Tel (440) 632-0271 *SIC* 5191 5983 5211

LYKINS OIL CO p 887
5163 Wlfpn Plsnt Hl Rd, Milford OH 45150
Tel (513) 831-8820 *SIC* 5172 5983

JACK A ALLEN INC p 773
2105 Old State Route 7, Steubenville OH 43952
Tel (740) 282-4531
SIC 5172 5983 5541 5411

EARHART PETROLEUM INC p 468
1494 Lytle Rd, Troy OH 45373
Tel (937) 335-2928 *SIC* 5172 5541 5983

PORTS PETROLEUM CO INC p 1163
1337 Blachleyville Rd, Wooster OH 44691
Tel (330) 264-1885 *SIC* 5172 5983 5541

SANTMYER OIL CO INC p 1281
3000 Old Airport Rd, Wooster OH 44691
Tel (330) 262-6501
SIC 5172 5983 4212 5531

■ PETROLEUM MARKETERS INC p 1139
645 Hamilton St Ste 500, Allentown PA 18101
Tel (540) 772-4900 *SIC* 5983 5411

MARTIN OIL CO p 913
528 N 1st St, Bellwood PA 16617
Tel (814) 742-8438
SIC 5983 5171 5541 5411

BERKS PRODUCTS CORP p 175
167 Berks Products Dr, Leesport PA 19533
Tel (610) 374-5131
SIC 5031 3273 5983 5172 2439 1711

WORLEY & OBETZ INC p 1626
85 White Oak Rd, Manheim PA 17545
Tel (717) 665-6891 *SIC* 5983 5541

MOYER & SON INC p 995
113 E Reliance Rd, Souderton PA 18964
Tel (215) 799-2000
SIC 5191 5983 2875 0782 1711

WILLIAMS OIL CO INC p 1611
44 Reuter Blvd, Towanda PA 18848
Tel (570) 265-6673 *SIC* 5172 5983

DEARYBURY OIL & GAS INC p 420
2560 Southport Rd, Spartanburg SC 29302
Tel (864) 585-6226 *SIC* 5172 5983 4212

▲ WESTERN REFINING INC p 1599
123 W Mills Ave Ste 200, El Paso TX 79901
Tel (915) 534-1400 *SIC* 2911 5983

TWIN EAGLE RESOURCE MANAGEMENT LLC p 1495
8847 W Sam Houston Pkwy N, Houston TX 77040
Tel (713) 341-7332 *SIC* 4911 4924 5983

▲ CST BRANDS INC p 398
19500 Bulverde Rd Ste 100, San Antonio TX 78259
Tel (210) 692-5000 *SIC* 5983 5411

▲ TESORO CORP p 1440
19100 Ridgewood Pkwy, San Antonio TX 78259
Tel (210) 626-6000
SIC 2911 1311 5983 5984

BROOKSHIRE GROCERY CO INC p 218
1600 W Southwest Loop 323, Tyler TX 75701
Tel (903) 534-3000 *SIC* 5411 5983

CARDWELL DISTRIBUTING INC p 253
8137 S State St Bldg 1, Midvale UT 84047
Tel (801) 561-4251
SIC 5171 7549 5172 5983

DAVENPORT ENERGY INC p 415
108 Main St, Chatham VA 24531
Tel (434) 432-0251 *SIC* 5172 5983 5984

MILLER OIL CO INC p 970
1000 E City Hall Ave, Norfolk VA 23504
Tel (757) 623-6600
SIC 5411 5172 5983 7549

WOODFIN HEATING INC p 1623
1823 N Hamilton St, Richmond VA 23230
Tel (804) 730-4500
SIC 5172 5983 1711 7382

PARKER HOLDING CO INC p 1116
1428 W Danville St, South Hill VA 23970
Tel (434) 447-3146 *SIC* 5171 5541 5983

PARKER OIL CO INC p 1116
1428 W Danville St, South Hill VA 23970
Tel (434) 447-3146 *SIC* 5171 5541 5983

SKAGIT FARMERS SUPPLY p 1329
1833 Park Ln, Burlington WA 98233
Tel (360) 757-6053
SIC 5191 5172 5983 5451 5331 5261

WILSON OIL INC p 1614
95 Panel Way, Longview WA 98632
Tel (360) 575-9222 *SIC* 5541 5983 5172

BRUCETON FARM SERVICE INC p 220
1768 Mileground Rd, Morgantown WV 26505
Tel (304) 291-6980
SIC 5411 5172 5999 5983 5812 2048

KWIK TRIP INC p 832
1626 Oak St, La Crosse WI 54603
Tel (608) 781-8988
SIC 5921 5993 5541 5983 5461

JACOBUS ENERGY INC p 775
11815 W Bradley Rd, Milwaukee WI 53224
Tel (414) 577-0217 *SIC* 5983 5172

H WOLF EDWARD AND SONS INC p 651
414 Kettle Moraine Dr S, Slinger WI 53086
Tel (262) 644-5030 *SIC* 5983 5171

SCHIERL INC p 1287
2201 Madison St, Stevens Point WI 54481
Tel (715) 345-5060
SIC 5171 5014 5531 5983

HOPSON OIL CO INC p 706
1225 Whiterock Ave, Waukesha WI 53186
Tel (262) 542-5343 *SIC* 5171 5983 1711

SIC 5984 Liquefied Petroleum Gas Dealers

■ FLORIDA PUBLIC UTILITIES CO p 559
331 W Central Ave Ste 200, Winter Haven FL 33880
Tel (352) 447-2790 *SIC* 4911 4922 5984

HARRISON POULTRY INC p 664
107 Star St W, Bethlehem GA 30620
Tel (770) 867-9105
SIC 0254 2015 5984 2013 2011

■ GAS CO LLC p 593
745 Fort Street Mall # 1800, Honolulu HI 96813
Tel (808) 594-5530
SIC 4932 4925 5172 5984

■ MID PAC PETROLEUM LLC p 963
1132 Bishop St Ste 2500, Honolulu HI 96813
Tel (808) 535-5999 *SIC* 5984 5172

WHITE RIVER LLC p 1606
610 Church St, Loogootee IN 47553
Tel (812) 295-4835 *SIC* 5261 5984

FERRELL COMPANIES INC p 538
7500 College Blvd # 1000, Overland Park KS 66210
Tel (913) 661-1500 *SIC* 1311 5984

■ FERRELLGAS LP p 538
7500 College Blvd # 1000, Overland Park KS 66210
Tel (913) 661-1500 *SIC* 5984

FABIAN OIL INC p 523
15 Oak St, Oakland ME 04963
Tel (207) 465-7958
SIC 5541 5983 5984 5411

TRI-GAS & OIL CO INC p 1477
3941 Federalsburg Hwy, Federalsburg MD 21632
Tel (410) 754-2000 *SIC* 5172 5984 4731

CRYSTAL FLASH LIMITED PARTNERSHIP OF MICHIGAN p 396
1754 Alpine Ave Nw, Grand Rapids MI 49504
Tel (616) 363-4851 *SIC* 5172 5984

GRESHAM PETROLEUM CO p 639
415 Pershing Ave, Indianola MS 38751
Tel (662) 887-2160 *SIC* 5171 5984

SCOTT PETROLEUM CORP p 1293
102 Main St, Itta Bena MS 38941
Tel (662) 254-9024 *SIC* 5171 5984 5411

BLOSSMAN COMPANIES INC p 190
809 Washington Ave, Ocean Springs MS 39564
Tel (228) 875-2261 *SIC* 5984 5722

■ INERGY PROPANE LLC p 740
2 Brush Creek Blvd # 200, Kansas City MO 64112
Tel (816) 842-8181 *SIC* 5984 5172

■ HERITAGE OPERATING LP p 686
754 River Rock Dr, Helena MT 59602
Tel (406) 442-9759 *SIC* 5984 5172

TOWN AND COUNTRY SUPPLY ASSOCIATION p 1464
18 8th Ave, Laurel MT 59044
Tel (406) 628-6314
SIC 5984 5191 5411 5999

CVC HOLDING CO INC p 404
28 Industrial Way, Rochester NH 03867
Tel (603) 332-2080 *SIC* 5984

■ WELCO-CGI GAS TECHNOLOGIES LLC p 1588
425 Avenue P, Newark NJ 07105
Tel (973) 589-8795
SIC 5085 5169 5999 5984

▲ SUBURBAN PROPANE PARTNERS LP p 1396
240 Route 10 W, Whippany NJ 07981
Tel (973) 887-5300
SIC 5984 5172 4939 1711

CAMBRIDGE PETROLEUM HOLDING INC p 244
31 S Plank Rd Unit 105, Newburgh NY 12550
Tel (516) 542-4900
SIC 5983 5541 5984 5172 5074

MALLARD OIL CO p 899
1502 Dr Martin Luther, Kinston NC 28501
Tel (252) 527-0364 *SIC* 5171 5983 5984

LEGACY FARMERS COOPERATIVE p 852
6566 County Road 236, Findlay OH 45840
Tel (419) 423-2611
SIC 5153 5191 5984 2875 2048 2041

BECK SUPPLIERS INC p 167
1000 N Front St, Fremont OH 43420
Tel (419) 332-5527
SIC 5171 5541 5411 5984 1542

▲ GAS NATURAL INC p 593
8470 Station St, Mentor OH 44060
Tel (440) 974-3770
SIC 4924 4911 5172 5984

▲ NGL ENERGY PARTNERS LP p 1041
6120 S Yale Ave Ste 805, Tulsa OK 74136
Tel (918) 481-1119 *SIC* 5172 5984

■ GAS CONNECTION LLC p 593
9801 Se 82nd Ave, Portland OR 97086
Tel (503) 771-1750 *SIC* 5984 5722

ICHOR SYSTEMS INC p 727
9660 Sw Herman Rd, Tualatin OR 97062
Tel (503) 625-2251 *SIC* 3559 5984

■ AMERIGAS INC p 82
460 N Gulph Rd Ste 100, King Of Prussia PA 19406
Tel (610) 337-7000
SIC 5984 5172 5722 2911 2813

▲ AMERIGAS PARTNERS LP p 82
460 N Gulph Rd Ste 100, King Of Prussia PA 19406
Tel (610) 337-7000 *SIC* 5984 5172

■ AMERIGAS PROPANE INC p 82
460 N Gulph Rd Ste 100, King Of Prussia PA 19406
Tel (610) 337-7000 *SIC* 5984

■ AMERIGAS PROPANE LP p 82
460 N Gulph Rd Ste 100, King Of Prussia PA 19406
Tel (610) 337-7000 *SIC* 5984

■ TITAN PROPANE LLC p 1456
460 N Gulph Rd Ste 100, King Of Prussia PA 19406
Tel (610) 337-7000 *SIC* 5984 5172

▲ ENERGY TRANSFER PARTNERS LP p 498
8111 Westchester Dr # 600, Dallas TX 75225
Tel (214) 981-0700 *SIC* 4922 5984

■ INDEPENDENT PROPANE CO LLC p 737
2591 Dallas Pkwy Ste 105, Frisco TX 75034
Tel (972) 731-5454 *SIC* 5984 5172

▲ CRESTWOOD EQUITY PARTNERS LP p 392
700 Louisiana St Ste 2550, Houston TX 77002
Tel (832) 519-2200 *SIC* 5984 5172

MARTIN RESOURCE MANAGEMENT CORP p 913
4200 Stone Rd, Kilgore TX 75662
Tel (903) 983-6200
SIC 2911 4924 5984 5172

GIBSON ENERGY MARKETING LLC p 611
3819 Towne Crossing Blvd, Mesquite TX 75150
Tel (214) 461-5600 *SIC* 5172 5984

▲ TESORO CORP p 1440
19100 Ridgewood Pkwy, San Antonio TX 78259
Tel (210) 626-6000
SIC 2911 1311 5983 5984

SHERMAN V ALLEN INC p 1316
126 Post St, Rutland VT 05701
Tel (802) 775-7421
SIC 5172 5984 5411 4923

CHAMPLAIN OIL CO INC p 287
45 San Remo Dr, South Burlington VT 05403
Tel (802) 864-5380 *SIC* 5172 5984

DAVENPORT ENERGY INC p 415
108 Main St, Chatham VA 24531
Tel (434) 432-0251 *SIC* 5172 5983 5984

PROVISION PARTNERS COOPERATIVE p 1187
2327 W Veterans Pkwy, Marshfield WI 54449
Tel (715) 687-4443 *SIC* 5191 5984 5541

SIC 5989 Fuel Dealers, NEC

CARTER FUEL SYSTEMS LLC p 262
101 E Industrial Blvd, Logansport IN 46947
Tel (800) 342-6125 *SIC* 3714 5989

SIC 5992 Florists

CCC ASSOCIATES CO p 269
3601 Wetumpka Hwy, Montgomery AL 36110
Tel (334) 272-2140 *SIC* 5193 5992

FOREST LAWN MEMORIAL-PARK ASSOCIATION p 567
1712 S Glendale Ave, Glendale CA 91205
Tel (323) 254-3131 *SIC* 5992 6553 7261

FALCON FARMS INC p 526
2330 Nw 82nd Ave, Miami FL 33122
Tel (305) 477-8088 *SIC* 5992 5193

▲ FTD COMPANIES INC p 582
3113 Woodcreek Dr, Downers Grove IL 60515
Tel (630) 719-7800 *SIC* 5992 5947 5961

MERCY FLOWERS & GIFTS p 946
701 10th St Se, Cedar Rapids IA 52403
Tel (319) 398-6124 *SIC* 5992 5947

BACHMANS INC p 143
6010 Lyndale Ave S, Minneapolis MN 55419
Tel (612) 861-7600
SIC 5992 5261 0181 5193 7359

DIERBERGS INC p 438
16690 Swingley Ridge Rd # 300, Chesterfield MO 63017
Tel (636) 532-8884 *SIC* 5411 5992

▲ 1-800-FLOWERS.COM INC p 1
1 Old Country Rd Ste 500, Carle Place NY 11514
Tel (516) 237-6000 *SIC* 5992 5961 5947

FLORAL SPECIALTIES INC p 557
20601 Aurora Rd, Cleveland OH 44146
Tel (216) 475-2302 *SIC* 5992

SAINT ANNS HOSPITAL AUXILIARY p 1268
500 S Cleveland Ave, Westerville OH 43081
Tel (614) 769-4459
SIC 5947 5621 5611 5992 5441

■ AT HOME STORES LLC p 123
1600 E Plano Pkwy, Plano TX 75074
Tel (972) 265-6227
SIC 5719 5992 5999 5947 5945

GARDEN RIDGE HOLDINGS INC p 591
1600 E Plano Pkwy, Plano TX 75074
Tel (832) 391-7201
SIC 5719 5945 5992 5947 5999

STEIN GARDEN CENTERS INC p 1385
5400 S 27th St, Milwaukee WI 53221
Tel (414) 761-5400 *SIC* 5261 5992

SIC 5993 Tobacco Stores & Stands

■ FORREST CITY GROCERY CO p 568
3400 Commerce Rd, Forrest City AR 72335
Tel (870) 633-2044 *SIC* 5141 5993

BEVERAGES & MORE INC p 178
1401 Willow Pass Rd # 900, Concord CA 94520
Tel (925) 609-6000 *SIC* 5921 5499 5993

BEVMO HOLDINGS LLC p 179
1470 Civic Ct Ste 1600, Concord CA 94520
Tel (925) 609-6000 *SIC* 5921 5499 5993

DFS GROUP LP p 435
525 Market St Fl 33, San Francisco CA 94105
Tel (415) 977-2701
SIC 5944 5948 5921 5993 5947 5999

800-JR CIGAR INC p 4
301 State Route 10, Whippany NJ 07981
Tel (973) 884-9555 *SIC* 5194 5993 5961

FONTEM US INC p 563
1100 S Tryon St Ste 300, Charlotte NC 28203
Tel (888) 207-4588 *SIC* 2111 5993

CHEROKEE NATION ENTERTAINMENT LLC p 294
777 W Cherokee St, Catoosa OK 74015
Tel (918) 458-1696
SIC 7999 7011 7948 5541 5993

UNI-MARTS LLC p 1502
1155 Benner Pike 100, State College PA 16801
Tel (814) 234-6000
SIC 5411 5541 5993 6794 5172

KWIK TRIP INC p 832
1626 Oak St, La Crosse WI 54603
Tel (608) 781-8988
SIC 5921 5993 5541 5983 5461

SIC 5994 News Dealers & Newsstands

BOOKS-A-MILLION INC p 200
402 Industrial Ln, Birmingham AL 35211
Tel (205) 942-3737
SIC 5942 5994 5947 5999

PARADIES SHOPS LLC p 1113
2849 Paces Ferry Rd Se, Atlanta GA 30339
Tel (404) 344-7905
SIC 5947 5994 5621 5611 5912 5941

HMSHOST CORP p 698
6905 Rockledge Dr Fl 1, Bethesda MD 20817
Tel (240) 694-4100
SIC 5812 5813 5994 5947

HOST INTERNATIONAL INC p 710
6905 Rockledge Dr Fl 1, Bethesda MD 20817
Tel (240) 694-4100
SIC 5812 5813 5994 5947

DELAWARE NORTH COMPANIES INC - BOSTON p 424
100 Legends Way Ste 100, Boston MA 02114
Tel (617) 624-1000
SIC 5812 5994 6512 7311

FABER COE & GREGG INC p 523
550 Madowlands Pkwy Ste 2, Secaucus NJ 07094
Tel (201) 330-1515 *SIC* 5994 5499 5813

■ BARNES & NOBLE BOOKSELLERS INC p 155
1166 Ave Of Amer 18, New York NY 10036
Tel (212) 403-2580
SIC 5942 5994 5999 5735

HACHETTE DISTRIBUTION INC p 652
60 E 42nd St Ste 1940, New York NY 10165
Tel (212) 477-7373 *SIC* 5192 5994 5947

HDS RETAIL NORTH AMERICA LP p 673
60 E 42nd St Rm 3410, New York NY 10165
Tel (212) 477-7373 *SIC* 5994

▲ FAB UNIVERSAL CORP p 523
5001 Baum Blvd Ste 770, Pittsburgh PA 15213
Tel (412) 621-0902
SIC 7371 7372 5735 5942 5994 5099

TRIB TOTAL MEDIA INC p 1479
503 Martin Street D L C, Pittsburgh PA 15212
Tel (412) 321-6460 *SIC* 5994

NEWS GROUP INC p 1039
5130 Comm Pkwy, San Antonio TX 78218
Tel (210) 226-9333 *SIC* 5192 5994

SIC 5995 Optical Goods Stores

FOR EYES OPTICAL CO OF COCONUT GROVE INC p 565
285 W 74th Pl, Hialeah FL 33014
Tel (305) 557-9004 *SIC* 3851 5995

STANTON OPTICAL FLORIDA LLC p 1377
3801 S Congress Ave, Palm Springs FL 33461
Tel (561) 275-2020 *SIC* 5995

NATIONAL VISION INC p 1017
2435 Commerce Ave # 2200, Duluth GA 30096
Tel (770) 822-3600 *SIC* 5995 8042

AMERICAS BEST CONTACTS & EYEGLASSES INC p 81
296 Grayson Hwy, Lawrenceville GA 30046
Tel (770) 822-3600 *SIC* 5995

CONSOLIDATED VISION GROUP INC p 360
296 Grayson Hwy, Lawrenceville GA 30046
Tel (770) 822-3600 *SIC* 5995

OPTICSPLANET INC p 1090
3150 Commercial Ave, Northbrook IL 60062
Tel (847) 513-6190 *SIC* 5995 5049

GOLDEN OPTICAL CORP p 621
19800 W 8 Mile Rd, Southfield MI 48075
Tel (248) 354-7100 *SIC* 5995 6794

US VISION INC p 1533
1 Harmon Dr, Glendora NJ 08029
Tel (856) 227-8339 *SIC* 5995 3827

USV OPTICAL INC p 1536
1 Harmon Dr Glen Oaks, Glendora NJ 08029
Tel (856) 228-1000 *SIC* 5995 3851

LUXOTTICA US HOLDINGS CORP p 887
12 Harbor Park Dr, Port Washington NY 11050
Tel (516) 484-3800
SIC 5048 5099 5995 5999

EMPIRE VISION CENTER INC p 494
2921 Erie Blvd E, Syracuse NY 13224
Tel (315) 446-3145 SIC 5995

LUXOTTICA RETAIL NORTH AMERICA INC p 887
4000 Luxottica Pl, Mason OH 45040
Tel (513) 765-6000 SIC 5995

SUNGLASS HUT TRADING LLC p 1402
4000 Luxottica Pl, Mason OH 45040
Tel (513) 765-4001 SIC 5995

OPTICAL FOR EYES CO p 1090
1630 Walnut St, Philadelphia PA 19103
Tel (800) 367-3937 SIC 5995

EYE-MART EXPRESS INC p 522
13800 Senlac Dr Ste 200, Dallas TX 75234
Tel (972) 488-2002 SIC 5995

EYEMART EXPRESS LTD p 522
13800 Senlac Dr Ste 200, Dallas TX 75234
Tel (972) 488-2002 SIC 5995

EYEMART EXPRESS LLC p 522
13800 Senlac Dr Ste 200, Farmers Branch TX 75234
Tel (972) 488-2002 SIC 5995

ECCA HOLDINGS CORP p 475
175 E Houston St Fl 6, San Antonio TX 78205
Tel (210) 340-3531 SIC 5995 3851

VISIONWARE INC p 1561
11103 West Ave, San Antonio TX 78213
Tel (210) 340-3531 SIC 5995

VISIONWORKS OF AMERICA INC p 1561
175 E Houston St, San Antonio TX 78205
Tel (210) 340-3531 SIC 5995

SIC 5999 Misc Retail Stores, NEC

BOOKS-A-MILLION INC p 200
402 Industrial Ln, Birmingham AL 35211
Tel (205) 942-3737
SIC 5942 5994 5947 5999

AMERICAN PROMOTIONAL EVENTS INC p 78
4511 Helton Dr, Florence AL 35630
Tel (256) 284-1003 SIC 5092 5999

UNIVERSITY OF ALABAMA SYSTEM p 1519
401 Queen City Ave, Tuscaloosa AL 35401
Tel (205) 348-5861 SIC 5999

INTER-TEL TECHNOLOGIES INC p 751
1146 N Alma School Rd, Mesa AZ 85201
Tel (480) 858-9600
SIC 5999 1731 5065 3661 3577

LESLIES HOLDINGS INC p 857
3925 E Broadway Rd # 100, Phoenix AZ 85040
Tel (602) 366-3999 SIC 5999

LOFTIN EQUIPMENT CO p 874
2111 E Highland Ave # 255, Phoenix AZ 85016
Tel (800) 437-4376 SIC 5063 5084 5999

PETSMART INC p 1139
19601 N 27th Ave, Phoenix AZ 85027
Tel (623) 580-6100 SIC 5999 0742 0752

DMB ASSOCIATES INC p 445
7600 E Doubletree Ste 300, Scottsdale AZ 85258
Tel (480) 367-6874
SIC 5999 6512 5961 1542 3446

REDROCK PARTNERS LLC p 1217
8260 E Raintree Dr, Scottsdale AZ 85260
Tel (480) 596-5702
SIC 5944 5932 5736 5941 5999

■ **ELIZABETH ARDEN SALON-HOLDINGS INC** p 487
222 S Mill Ave Ste 201, Tempe AZ 85281
Tel (602) 864-8191 SIC 7231 5999 7299

■ **MOBILE STORAGE GROUP INC** p 980
7420 S Kyrene Rd Ste 101, Tempe AZ 85283
Tel (480) 894-6311 SIC 5999 7359

■ **RED DOOR SALONS INC** p 1215
222 S Mill Ave Ste 201, Tempe AZ 85281
Tel (480) 829-8191 SIC 7231 5999 7299

HANNAS CANDLE CO p 658
2700 S Armstrong Ave, Fayetteville AR 72701
Tel (479) 443-5467 SIC 3999 2844 5999

FARMERS SUPPLY ASSOCIATION p 530
16240 Highway 14 E, Harrisburg AR 72432
Tel (870) 578-2468
SIC 5191 5172 5261 5541 5999

■ **ALLTEL CORP** p 59
1001 Technology Dr, Little Rock AR 72223
Tel (866) 255-8357 SIC 4812 5999

■ **XETA TECHNOLOGIES INC** p 1631
4001 N Rodney Parham Rd, Little Rock AR 72212
Tel (800) 697-8153 SIC 3661 5999 7389

GREENWAY EQUIPMENT INC p 638
412 S Van Buren, Weiner AR 72479
Tel (870) 684-7740 SIC 5999 5082

PACIFIC SUNWEAR STORES CORP p 1106
3450 E Miraloma Ave, Anaheim CA 92806
Tel (714) 414-4000
SIC 5611 5699 5661 5621 5999

MERCHANT OF TENNIS INC p 944
8737 Wilshire Blvd, Beverly Hills CA 90211
Tel (310) 228-4000
SIC 5941 5621 5661 5961 5999

LAKESHORE EQUIPMENT CO INC p 840
2695 E Dominguez St, Carson CA 90895
Tel (310) 537-8600 SIC 5999 5961

BUILD.COM INC p 224
402 Otterson Dr Ste 100, Chico CA 95928
Tel (800) 375-3403 SIC 5074 5999

▲ **YOUNGEVITY INTERNATIONAL INC** p 1639
2400 Boswell Rd, Chula Vista CA 91914
Tel (619) 934-3980 SIC 5499 5999

CELLUPHONE INC p 274
6119 E Washington Blvd, Commerce CA 90040
Tel (323) 727-9131 SIC 5065 5999

▲ **ROSS STORES INC** p 1252
5130 Hacienda Dr, Dublin CA 94568
Tel (925) 965-4400
SIC 5651 5661 5944 5632 5611 5999

GUTHY-RENKER LLC p 648
100 N Sepulveda Blvd # 1600, El Segundo CA 90245
Tel (760) 773-9022
SIC 5099 7812 5999 7389

ART.COM INC p 113
2100 Powell St Fl 10th, Emeryville CA 94608
Tel (510) 879-4700 SIC 5999

Z GALLERIE LLC p 1640
1855 W 139th St, Gardena CA 90249
Tel (800) 358-8288 SIC 5719 5999

HAWAII BUSINESS EQUIPMENT INC p 668
2 Musick, Irvine CA 92618
Tel (949) 462-6000 SIC 5999 7629 5044

INFINITE RF HOLDINGS INC p 741
17802 Fitch, Irvine CA 92614
Tel (949) 261-1920 SIC 5999 6719

MX HOLDINGS US p 1004
153 Technology Dr Ste 200, Irvine CA 92618
Tel (949) 727-3277 SIC 1711 1731 5999

TCT MOBILE (US) INC p 1428
25 Edelman Ste 200, Irvine CA 92618
Tel (949) 892-2990 SIC 5999 5065

TOSHIBA BUSINESS SOLUTIONS (USA) INC p 1462
9740 Irvine Blvd, Irvine CA 92618
Tel (949) 462-6000 SIC 7629 5044 5999

APRIA HEALTHCARE LLC p 100
26220 Enterprise Ct, Lake Forest CA 92630
Tel (949) 616-2606 SIC 5047 7352 5999

LOMA LINDA UNIVERSITY HEALTH CARE p 875
11370 Anderson St # 3900, Loma Linda CA 92350
Tel (909) 558-2806
SIC 8062 8011 8051 5999

LOMA LINDA UNIVERSITY MEDICAL CENTER p 875
11234 Anderson St, Loma Linda CA 92354
Tel (909) 558-4000
SIC 8062 8011 8051 5999

▲ **VCA INC** p 1545
12401 W Olympic Blvd, Los Angeles CA 90064
Tel (310) 571-6500 SIC 0742 5999 5047

▲ **LANDEC CORP** p 842
3603 Haven Ave, Menlo Park CA 94025
Tel (650) 306-1650 SIC 2033 5148 5999

EXCELLIGENCE LEARNING CORP p 516
2 Lower Ragsda Dr Ste 200, Monterey CA 93940
Tel (831) 333-2000 SIC 3944 5999

ELF BEAUTY INC p 486
570 10th St, Oakland CA 94607
Tel (510) 778-7787 SIC 5999

NADONAH MEDICAL SUPPLY p 1006
5021 Columbia Way, Quartz Hill CA 93536
Tel (661) 718-3870 SIC 5999

CELLULAR 123 INC p 274
18414 Colima Rd Ste O, Rowland Heights CA 91748
Tel (626) 913-6788 SIC 5999

ANA GLOBAL LLC p 88
2360 Marconi Ct, San Diego CA 92154
Tel (619) 482-9990 SIC 2517 5999

HOME BREW MART INC p 703
9045 Carroll Way, San Diego CA 92121
Tel (858) 790-6900 SIC 2082 5999

PETCO ANIMAL SUPPLIES INC p 1137
10850 Via Frontera, San Diego CA 92127
Tel (858) 453-7845 SIC 0752 5199 5999

PETCO ANIMAL SUPPLIES STORES INC p 1137
9125 Rehco Rd, San Diego CA 92121
Tel (858) 453-7845 SIC 5999 0752 5199

PETCO HOLDINGS INC LLC p 1138
10850 Via Frontera, San Diego CA 92127
Tel (858) 453-7845 SIC 5999

ALIPHCOM p 50
99 Rhode Island St Fl 3, San Francisco CA 94103
Tel (415) 230-7600 SIC 5065 5999

BARE ESCENTUALS BEAUTY INC p 155
71 Stevenson St Fl 22, San Francisco CA 94105
Tel (415) 489-5000 SIC 5999

BARE ESCENTUALS INC p 155
71 Stevenson St Fl 22, San Francisco CA 94105
Tel (415) 489-5000 SIC 5999

DFS GROUP LP p 435
525 Market St Fl 33, San Francisco CA 94105
Tel (415) 977-2701
SIC 5944 5948 5921 5993 5947 5999

■ **POTTERY BARN KIDS INC** p 1164
3250 Van Ness Ave, San Francisco CA 94109
Tel (415) 421-7900 SIC 5999

SEPHORA USA INC p 1306
525 Market St Fl 32, San Francisco CA 94105
Tel (415) 284-3300 SIC 5999

SHARPER IMAGE CORP p 1312
350 The Embarcadero Fl 6, San Francisco CA 94105
Tel (877) 714-7444
SIC 5731 5941 5999 5719 5945 5961

WILBUR-ELLIS HOLDINGS II INC p 1608
345 California St Fl 27, San Francisco CA 94104
Tel (415) 772-4000 SIC 5999 5191 5169

FRYS ELECTRONICS INC p 582
600 E Brokaw Rd, San Jose CA 95112
Tel (408) 350-1484 SIC 5999 5734 5731

COSCO FIRE PROTECTION INC p 373
29222 Rancho Viejo Rd # 205, San Juan Capistrano CA 92675
Tel (714) 974-8770 SIC 1711 1731 5999

SONY MOBILE COMMUNICATIONS (USA) INC p 1341
2207 Bridgepoint Pkwy, San Mateo CA 94404
Tel (866) 766-9374 SIC 3663 5999

BLACKBERRY CORP p 187
3001 Bishop Dr, San Ramon CA 94583
Tel (972) 650-6126 SIC 5999 3661 4812

J D HEISKELL HOLDINGS LLC p 770
1939 Hillman St, Tulare CA 93274
Tel (559) 685-6100 SIC 5191 5999

GARTON TRACTOR INC p 592
2400 N Golden State Blvd, Turlock CA 95382
Tel (209) 632-3931 SIC 5999 5083

GUIRYS INC p 646
620 Canosa Ct, Denver CO 80204
Tel (720) 360-4840 SIC 5198 5231 5999

■ **QWEST BUSINESS & GOVERNMENT SERVICES INC** p 1201
1801 Calif St Ste 3800, Denver CO 80202
Tel (303) 391-8300
SIC 5999 1731 7629 7373 7371 7622

■ **ANIMAL HEALTH INTERNATIONAL INC** p 91
822 7th St Ste 740, Greeley CO 80631
Tel (970) 353-2600
SIC 5122 5047 5999 5191 5083 5154

▲ **PILGRIMS PRIDE CORP** p 1148
1770 Promontory Cir, Greeley CO 80634
Tel (970) 506-8000
SIC 2015 0254 0252 2048 5999

■ **PRAXAIR DISTRIBUTION INC** p 1167
39 Old Ridgebury Rd, Danbury CT 06810
Tel (203) 837-2000 SIC 2813 5084 5999

WW LIQUIDATION INC p 1629
60 Backus Ave, Danbury CT 06810
Tel (203) 546-6000 SIC 5074 5999 5211

ADVANCED CENTER FOR REHABILITATION MEDICINE INC p 25
24 Stevens St, Norwalk CT 06850
Tel (203) 852-2000 SIC 5999

NORTH AMERICAN MARKETING CORP p 1050
30 Waterchase Dr, Rocky Hill CT 06067
Tel (860) 649-3666 SIC 5999

▲ **INTERDIGITAL INC** p 752
200 Bellevue Pkwy Ste 300, Wilmington DE 19809
Tel (302) 281-3600 SIC 3663 5999 6794

JEUNESSE GLOBAL HOLDINGS LLC p 784
650 Douglas Ave Ste 1020, Altamonte Springs FL 32714
Tel (407) 215-7414 SIC 5999

PENTAIR AQUATIC ECO-SYSTEMS INC p 1131
2395 Apopka Blvd, Apopka FL 32703
Tel (407) 886-7575 SIC 5074 5999

DEGC ENTERPRISES (US) INC p 422
14255 49th St N Ste 301, Clearwater FL 33762
Tel (727) 531-9161 SIC 5999 5912 5961

LINCARE INC p 866
19387 Us Highway 19 N, Clearwater FL 33764
Tel (727) 530-7700 SIC 8082 5999

PORPOISE POOL & PATIO INC p 1161
14480 62nd St N, Clearwater FL 33760
Tel (727) 531-8913
SIC 6794 5999 5712 5091

ACCESS TELECOM GROUP INC p 15
1882 Nw 97th Ave, Doral FL 33172
Tel (305) 468-1955 SIC 5065 5999

JG BRANDS INC p 785
10530 Nw 26th St Ste F201, Doral FL 33172
Tel (786) 597-1554 SIC 5999

BODY CENTRAL STORES INC p 197
1883 W State Road 84 # 106, Fort Lauderdale FL 33315
Tel (904) 737-0811 SIC 5999

CONVEY HEALTH SOLUTIONS INC p 365
1 Financial Plz Fl 14, Fort Lauderdale FL 33394
Tel (954) 903-5000 SIC 5912 5999

■ **MAGNIFIQUE PARFUMES AND COSMETICS INC** p 896
5900 N Andrews Ave # 500, Fort Lauderdale FL 33309
Tel (954) 335-9100 SIC 5999

■ **PERFUMANIA INC** p 1135
5900 N Andrews Ave # 500, Fort Lauderdale FL 33309
Tel (866) 600-3600 SIC 5122 5999

MASTER PROTECTION HOLDINGS INC p 918
13050 Metro Pkwy Ste 1, Fort Myers FL 33966
Tel (239) 896-1680 SIC 7389 1711 5999

AV COOLING SOLUTIONS INC p 135
803 E Donegan Ave, Kissimmee FL 34744
Tel (407) 572-8739 SIC 5999

BUSINESS TELECOMMUNICATIONS SERVICES INC p 230
2620 Sw 27th Ave, Miami FL 33133
Tel (305) 358-5850 SIC 4813 5999 8748

PEARL PAINT CO INC p 1126
1033 E Oakland Park Blvd, Oakland Park FL 33334
Tel (954) 564-5700
SIC 5999 5199 7699 5112 5947 7311

DISCOVERY MARKETING AND DISTRIBUTING INC p 442
6505 Edgewater Dr, Orlando FL 32810
Tel (407) 523-0775 SIC 5999 7389

AUDIOLOGY DISTRIBUTION LLC p 131
10455 Riverside Dr, Palm Beach Gardens FL 33410
Tel (561) 478-8770 SIC 5999

CLAIRES BOUTIQUES INC p 321
11401 Pines Blvd, Pembroke Pines FL 33026
Tel (954) 438-0433
SIC 5632 5699 5999 5943 5947

▲ **PETMED EXPRESS INC** p 1139
1441 Sw 29th Ave, Pompano Beach FL 33069
Tel (954) 979-5995 SIC 5999 5122

PET SUPERMARKET INC p 1137
1100 International Pkwy # 200, Sunrise FL 33323
Tel (866) 434-1990 SIC 5999 3999 5199

AVI-SPL INC p 137
6301 Benjamin Rd Ste 101, Tampa FL 33634
Tel (866) 708-5034 SIC 7359 5999

COMVEST INVESTMENT PARTNERS III LP p 353
525 Okeechobee Blvd # 1050, West Palm Beach FL 33401
Tel (561) 727-2000
SIC 4731 5912 5999 3652 8742 1731

COMVEST NATIONSHEALTH HOLDINGS LLC p 353
525 Okeechobee Blvd # 1050, West Palm Beach FL 33401
Tel (561) 727-2000 SIC 5912 5999

■ **HOME DEPOT USA INC** p 703
2455 Paces Ferry Rd Se, Atlanta GA 30339
Tel (770) 433-8211 SIC 5023 5999

■ **AT&T MOBILITY LLC** p 123
1025 Lenox Park Blvd Ne, Brookhaven GA 30319
Tel (425) 580-6014 SIC 4812 4813 5999

MILNER INC p 972
5125 Peachtree Indus Blvd, Norcross GA 30092
Tel (770) 458-0999
SIC 7372 5999 7389 5065 5049 5044

LANIER WORLDWIDE INC p 844
4667 N Royal Atlanta Dr, Tucker GA 30084
Tel (770) 493-2100
SIC 5044 5999 7359 7629

NORCO INC p 1047
1125 W Amity Rd, Boise ID 83705
Tel (208) 336-1643
SIC 5084 5169 7352 5999 3548 2813

D&B SUPPLY CO p 407
3303 E Linden St, Caldwell ID 83605
Tel (208) 459-7446
SIC 5191 5699 5251 5261 5999 5531

LAND VIEW INC p 842
20504 4th St, Rupert ID 83350
Tel (208) 531-4100
SIC 2879 2873 2874 5999 5261 5169

E3 DIAGNOSTICS INC p 467
3333 N Kennicott Ave, Arlington Heights IL 60004
Tel (847) 459-1770 SIC 5999

CENTRAL ILLINOIS AG INC p 278
200 E Sharon St, Atlanta IL 61723
Tel (217) 648-2307 SIC 5999 7699

WALGREENS INFUSION SERVICES INC p 1573
3000 Lakeside Dr Ste 300n, Bannockburn IL 60015
Tel (312) 940-2500
SIC 8082 8011 8059 5999 5122

▲ **ULTA SALON COSMETICS & FRAGRANCE INC** p 1500
1000 Remington Blvd # 120, Bolingbrook IL 60440
Tel (630) 410-4800 SIC 5999 5632 5961

COBRA ELECTRONICS CORP p 333
6500 W Cortland St, Chicago IL 60707
Tel (773) 889-8870 SIC 5999

JORDAN INDUSTRIES INC p 793
1751 Lake Cook Rd Ste 550, Deerfield IL 60015
Tel (847) 945-5591
SIC 3621 3625 3714 3089 2759 5999

ARENDS HOGAN WALKER LLC p 106
27688 E 3200 North Rd, Dwight IL 60420
Tel (217) 388-7717 SIC 5999 5082

EFFINGHAM EQUITY p 480
201 W Roadway Ave, Effingham IL 62401
Tel (217) 342-4101 SIC 5999 5251

LIFT SOURCE INC p 865
1815 Landmeier Rd, Elk Grove Village IL 60007
Tel (847) 678-3450 SIC 5999 5084

DISCOUNT MEDIA PRODUCTS LLC p 442
845 N Church Ct, Elmhurst IL 60126
Tel (630) 834-3113 SIC 5065 5999

S & S AUTOMOTIVE INC p 1261
740 N Larch Ave, Elmhurst IL 60126
Tel (630) 279-1613
SIC 5013 5999 5065 1731

RIVERSIDE MEDI-CENTER INC p 1238
350 N Wall St, Kankakee IL 60901
Tel (815) 933-1671 SIC 8082 5912 5999

MEDLINE INDUSTRIES INC p 938
3 Lakes Dr, Northfield IL 60093
Tel (847) 949-5500 SIC 3841 5047 5999

CDS OFFICE SYSTEMS INC p 271
612 S Dirksen Pkwy, Springfield IL 62703
Tel (800) 367-1508
SIC 5044 5999 7629 7378 3861 3577

PROVEN BUSINESS SYSTEMS LLC p 1185
18450 Crossing Dr Ste D, Tinley Park IL 60487
Tel (708) 614-1770 SIC 5044 5999

PHONAK LLC p 1145
4520 Weaver Pkwy Ste 1, Warrenville IL 60555
Tel (630) 821-5000 SIC 3842 5999

WATSEKA RURAL KING SUPPLY INC p 1583
200 N Ernest Grove Pkwy, Watseka IL 60970
Tel (815) 432-3440
SIC 5999 5651 5251 5311

WHEATON FRANCISCAN SERVICES INC p 1604
26w 171 Roosevelt Rd, Wheaton IL 60189
Tel (414) 465-3000 SIC 8741 5999

CELLULAR CONNECTION LLC p 274
525 Congressional Blvd, Carmel IN 46032
Tel (765) 651-2001
SIC 5065 1731 5999 5731

SWEETWATER SOUND INC p 1412
5501 Us Highway 30 W, Fort Wayne IN 46818
Tel (260) 432-8176 SIC 7389 5736 5999

ECO-PAK p 476
9211 E Jackson St, Selma IN 47383
Tel (765) 287-2093 SIC 5999

WILLIAMS BROS HEALTH CARE PHARMACY INC p 1611
10 Williams Brothers Dr, Washington IN 47501
Tel (812) 254-2497
SIC 5047 7352 5999 5169 3999

■ **SILVERTOWNE LP** p 1324
120 E Union City Pike, Winchester IN 47394
Tel (765) 584-7481 SIC 5999 5094

S J SMITH CO INC p 1262
3707 W River Dr, Davenport IA 52802
Tel (563) 324-5237 SIC 5169 5084 5999

THEISENS INC p 1446
6201 Chavenelle Rd, Dubuque IA 52002
Tel (563) 556-4738
SIC 5531 5999 5699 5261

SOMEBODY CARES INC p 1339
57 N Court St, Fairfield IA 52556
Tel (641) 472-5352 SIC 5947 7699 5999

INNOVATIVE AG SERVICES CO p 744
2010 S Main St, Monticello IA 52310
Tel (319) 465-3501 SIC 5999

BOMGAARS SUPPLY INC p 199
1805 Zenith Dr, Sioux City IA 51103
Tel (712) 226-5000 SIC 5311 5999 5651

AGRI TRAILS COOP INC p 36
508 N Main St, Hope KS 67451
Tel (785) 366-7213 SIC 5999 5261

■ SPRINT COMMUNICATIONS INC p 1361
6200 Sprint Pkwy, Overland Park KS 66251
Tel (855) 848-3280 SIC 4813 4812 5999

SKC COMMUNICATION PRODUCTS LLC p 1329
8320 Hedge Lane Ter, Shawnee Mission KS 66227
Tel (913) 422-4222 SIC 5065 5999

KANEQUIP INC p 802
18035 E Us Highway 24, Wamego KS 66547
Tel (785) 456-2041 SIC 5999 5083

WICHITA STATE UNIVERSITY p 1608
1845 Fairmount St, Wichita KS 67260
Tel (316) 978-3040 SIC 5999

OUR LADY OF BELLEFONTE HOSPITAL INC p 1098
1000 Saint Christopher Dr, Ashland KY 41101
Tel (606) 833-3333
SIC 8062 8082 8011 5999

FAMILY ROOTS USA INC p 527
4211 Produce Rd, Louisville KY 40218
Tel (502) 964-0063 SIC 5999

TREES N TRENDS INC p 1475
3229 Benton Rd, Paducah KY 42003
Tel (270) 443-5100
SIC 5999 3999 5947 5193

NEILL CORP p 1024
303 S Pine St, Hammond LA 70403
Tel (985) 345-1085 SIC 5087 5999

TUNICA-BILOXI GAMING AUTHORITY p 1491
711 Paragon Pl, Marksville LA 71351
Tel (318) 253-1946 SIC 7011 7999 5999

ATG / USM HOLDINGS LLC p 124
101 Huntington Ave, Boston MA 02199
Tel (860) 257-3443 SIC 5999

■ RED THREAD SPACES LLC p 1216
101 Seaport Blvd Ste 600, Boston MA 02210
Tel (617) 439-4900
SIC 5999 5021 8712 5198

▲ STAPLES INC p 1377
500 Staples Dr, Framingham MA 01702
Tel (508) 253-5000
SIC 5943 5999 7513 5961 5712

■ YANKEE CANDLE CO INC p 1634
16 Yankee Candle Way, South Deerfield MA 01373
Tel (413) 665-8306 SIC 3999 2899 5999

■ YANKEE CANDLE INVESTMENTS LLC p 1634
16 Yankee Candle Way, South Deerfield MA 01373
Tel (413) 665-8306 SIC 3999 5999

■ YCC HOLDINGS LLC p 1635
16 Yankee Candle Way, South Deerfield MA 01373
Tel (413) 665-8306 SIC 3999 2899 5999

PSP STORES LLC p 1188
17197 N Laurel Park Dr, Livonia MI 48152
Tel (734) 793-6600 SIC 5999

USA SELLER CO LLC p 1534
17197 N Laurel Park Dr # 402, Livonia MI 48152
Tel (734) 793-6600 SIC 5999

FAMILY FARM & HOME INC p 526
900 3rd St Ste 302, Muskegon MI 49440
Tel (231) 722-8335
SIC 5999 5261 5149 5611 5211 5091

ABC APPLIANCE INC p 10
1 W Silverdome Indus Park, Pontiac MI 48342
Tel (248) 335-4222
SIC 5722 5731 5999 5065 5064 5063

WILLOW ENTERPRISES INC p 1613
1221 Pine Grove Ave, Port Huron MI 48060
Tel (810) 987-2064 SIC 8082 5999

WRIGHT & FILIPPIS INC p 1627
2845 Crooks Rd, Rochester Hills MI 48309
Tel (248) 829-8292 SIC 7352 5999

CITIZENS LLC p 311
870 S Main St, Vermontville MI 49096
Tel (517) 726-0514
SIC 5191 5153 5999 2041

PURITY CYLINDER GASES INC p 1192
2580 28th St Sw, Wyoming MI 49519
Tel (616) 532-2375
SIC 5085 7359 5999 7699

■ RURAL CELLULAR CORP p 1258
4133 Iowa St Ste 200, Alexandria MN 56308
Tel (320) 808-2111 SIC 4812 5999

DECOPAC INC p 421
3500 Thurston Ave Ste 200, Anoka MN 55303
Tel (763) 574-0091 SIC 5999

FEEDCO p 537
521 Wells St, Belgrade MN 56312
Tel (320) 254-8294 SIC 5999

CONVERGEONE HOLDINGS CORP p 365
3344 Highway 149, Eagan MN 55121
Tel (651) 994-6800 SIC 4813 5999 1731

CONVERGEONE INC p 365
3344 Highway 149, Eagan MN 55121
Tel (651) 994-6800 SIC 4813 5999 1731

RUNNING SUPPLY INC p 1258
901 Highway 59, Marshall MN 56258
Tel (507) 532-9566 SIC 5999

INVESTMENT RARITIES INC p 761
7850 Metro Pkwy Ste 121, Minneapolis MN 55425
Tel (952) 853-0700 SIC 5999

■ MCKESSON MEDICAL-SURGICAL MEDIMART INC p 930
8121 10th Ave N, Minneapolis MN 55427
Tel (763) 595-6000 SIC 5047 5999

MIRACLE-EAR INC p 974
5000 Cheshire Pkwy N # 1, Minneapolis MN 55446
Tel (763) 268-4000 SIC 5999

■ NEXTIRAONE LLC p 1040
5050 Lincoln Dr Ste 300, Minneapolis MN 55436
Tel (952) 352-4410
SIC 5065 7629 1731 5999 4813 4841

PARK NICOLLET CLINIC p 1115
3800 Park Nicollet Blvd, Minneapolis MN 55416
Tel (952) 993-3123 SIC 8011 5912 5999

SONUS-USA INC p 1340
5000 Cheshire Pkwy N # 1, Minneapolis MN 55446
Tel (763) 268-4065 SIC 5999

CULLIGAN SOFT WATER SERVICE CO p 400
6030 Culligan Way, Minnetonka MN 55345
Tel (952) 933-7200 SIC 5999 7389

TAYLOR GROUP INC p 1427
650 N Church Ave, Louisville MS 39339
Tel (662) 773-3421 SIC 7699 5999

BEAUTY BRANDS LLC p 166
4600 Madison Ave Ste 400, Kansas City MO 64112
Tel (816) 531-2266 SIC 5999 7231

ORSCHELN FARM AND HOME LLC p 1096
1800 Overcenter Dr, Moberly MO 65270
Tel (800) 577-2580
SIC 5251 5999 5945 5731

COLOR ART INTEGRATED INTERIORS LLC p 338
1325 N Warson Rd, Saint Louis MO 63132
Tel (314) 432-3000
SIC 5021 7641 5999 5712 5099 2521

TOWN AND COUNTRY SUPPLY ASSOCIATION p 1464
18 8th Ave, Laurel MT 59044
Tel (406) 628-6314
SIC 5984 5191 5411 5999

DUTTON-LAINSON CO p 463
451 W 2nd St, Hastings NE 68901
Tel (402) 463-6702
SIC 3531 5999 5063 5074

NEBCO INC p 1023
1815 Y St, Lincoln NE 68508
Tel (402) 434-1212
SIC 5999 3273 3272 3271 1442 4013

AG PROCESSING INC A COOPERATIVE p 33
12700 W Dodge Rd, Omaha NE 68154
Tel (402) 496-7809
SIC 5153 2075 2048 5999 0254

■ CUMMINS CENTRAL POWER LLC p 401
10088 S 136th St, Omaha NE 68138
Tel (402) 551-7678
SIC 5084 7538 5999 3519

BRADY INDUSTRIES INC p 207
7055 Lindell Rd, Las Vegas NV 89118
Tel (702) 876-3990
SIC 5169 5087 5999 5023 5064

GO WIRELESS INC p 619
9970 W Cheyenne Ave # 100, Las Vegas NV 89129
Tel (702) 853-6200 SIC 5999

■ CELLCO PARTNERSHIP p 273
1 Verizon Way, Basking Ridge NJ 07920
Tel (908) 306-7000 SIC 4812 5999 5065

LOCCITANE INC p 873
120 Herrod Blvd, Dayton NJ 08810
Tel (212) 696-9098 SIC 5999

E WALSH MANAGEMENT CORP p 467
45 Main St, Eatontown NJ 07724
Tel (732) 443-8100 SIC 5999 8082

EMPIRE TECHNOLOGIES LLC p 494
246 Industrial Way W # 1, Eatontown NJ 07724
Tel (732) 625-3200 SIC 5065 1731 5999

PCS WIRELESS LLC p 1124
11 Vreeland Rd, Florham Park NJ 07932
Tel (973) 805-7400 SIC 5065 5999

ATLANTIC COAST MEDIA GROUP LLC p 126
100 Town Square Pl Fl 6, Jersey City NJ 07310
Tel (201) 942-3400 SIC 5961 5999

BUTH-NA-BODHAIGE INC p 230
77 Deans Rhode Hall Rd, Monmouth Junction NJ 08852
Tel (732) 348-2152 SIC 5999

WE R WIRELESS INC p 1585
520 Fellowship Rd E508, Mount Laurel NJ 08054
Tel (443) 735-7500 SIC 5999

■ WELCO-CGI GAS TECHNOLOGIES LLC p 1588
425 Avenue P, Newark NJ 07105
Tel (973) 589-8795
SIC 5085 5169 5999 5984

STRATEGIC PRODUCTS AND SERVICES LLC p 1392
300 Littleton Rd Ste 200, Parsippany NJ 07054
Tel (973) 540-0600 SIC 5999

▲ BED BATH & BEYOND INC p 167
650 Liberty Ave, Union NJ 07083
Tel (908) 688-0888 SIC 5719 5947 5999

TOYS "R" US INC p 1467
1 Geoffrey Way, Wayne NJ 07470
Tel (973) 617-3500
SIC 5945 5734 5999 5735 5641 5941

TOYS "R" US-DELAWARE INC p 1467
1 Geoffrey Way, Wayne NJ 07470
Tel (973) 617-3500 SIC 5945 5999 5641

▲ PERFUMANIA HOLDINGS INC p 1135
35 Sawgrass Dr Ste 2, Bellport NY 11713
Tel (631) 866-4100 SIC 5122 5999

PETLAND DISCOUNTS INC p 1138
355 Crooked Hill Rd, Brentwood NY 11717
Tel (631) 273-6363 SIC 5999

GETYOURPERFUME.COM INC p 609
700 Columbia St Bldg 302, Brooklyn NY 11231
Tel (888) 264-2899 SIC 5999

CATHOLIC HEALTH SYSTEM INC p 266
144 Genesee St Fl 1, Buffalo NY 14203
Tel (716) 862-2400
SIC 8741 8062 5999 8051

MARY IMOGENE BASSETT HOSPITAL p 914
1 Atwell Rd, Cooperstown NY 13326
Tel (607) 547-3456 SIC 8011 8062 5999

CREATIVE ORTHOTICS & PROSTHETICS INC p 390
1300 College Ave Ste 1, Elmira NY 14901
Tel (607) 734-7215 SIC 3842 5999 5047

ZAHM & MATSON INC p 1641
1756 Lindquist Dr, Falconer NY 14733
Tel (716) 665-3110 SIC 5261 5999

PC RICHARD & SON LLC p 1123
150 Price Pkwy, Farmingdale NY 11735
Tel (631) 843-4300 SIC 5999

■ BUY BUY BABY INC p 230
895 E Gate Blvd Ste 2, Garden City NY 11530
Tel (516) 507-3400 SIC 5641 5999 2023

RELIANCE COMMUNICATIONS LLC p 1221
555 Wireless Blvd, Hauppauge NY 11788
Tel (631) 952-4800 SIC 5065 5999

PEARL ARTIST & CRAFT SUPPLY CORP p 1126
185 Merrick Rd, Lynbrook NY 11563
Tel (954) 564-5700 SIC 5999 5199

■ BARNES & NOBLE BOOKSELLERS INC p 155
1166 Ave Of Amer 18, New York NY 10036
Tel (212) 403-2580
SIC 5942 5994 5999 5735

BLISS WORLD LLC p 189
200 Vesey St Fl 25, New York NY 10281
Tel (212) 931-6383 SIC 5999

CHANEL INC p 288
9 W 57th St Fl 44, New York NY 10019
Tel (212) 688-5055
SIC 5632 2844 5122 5944 5961 5999

■ ESTEE LAUDER INC p 511
767 5th Ave Fl 37, New York NY 10153
Tel (212) 572-4200 SIC 2844 5999

IRVING PLACE CAPITAL LLC p 765
745 5th Ave Fl 7, New York NY 10151
Tel (212) 551-4500 SIC 5999 5099

LOCCITANE INC p 873
1430 Broadway Fl 2, New York NY 10018
Tel (212) 333-4880 SIC 5122 5999 5961

LORD & TAYLOR LLC p 878
424 5th Ave, New York NY 10018
Tel (212) 391-3344
SIC 5621 5611 5632 5999

METROPOLITAN MUSEUM OF ART p 956
1000 5th Ave, New York NY 10028
Tel (212) 535-7710 SIC 8412 5999

■ NEW AVON LLC p 1029
777 3rd Ave Fl 8, New York NY 10017
Tel (212) 282-8500 SIC 2844 5122 5999

REV HOLDINGS INC p 1229
466 Lexington Ave Fl 21, New York NY 10017
Tel (212) 527-4000
SIC 2844 3421 5122 5199 5999

REVLON HOLDINGS INC p 1229
237 Park Ave, New York NY 10017
Tel (212) 527-4000
SIC 2844 3421 5122 5199 5999

■ REVLON REAL ESTATE CORP p 1229
466 Lexington Ave Fl 13, New York NY 10017
Tel (212) 527-4000
SIC 5122 2844 3421 5199 5999

RGI GROUP INC p 1231
625 Madison Ave Frnt 4, New York NY 10022
Tel (212) 527-4000
SIC 2844 3421 5122 5199 5999

SCHOOL OF VISUAL ARTS INC p 1290
209 E 23rd St Frnt 1, New York NY 10010
Tel (212) 592-2000 SIC 8221 5734 5999

STUART WEITZMAN RETAIL STORES LLC p 1394
625 Madison Ave Frnt 3, New York NY 10022
Tel (212) 582-6388 SIC 7389 3171 5999

▲ TIFFANY & CO p 1453
200 5th Ave Bsmt 2, New York NY 10010
Tel (212) 755-8000
SIC 5944 5094 5719 5943 5999 5961

IMOBILE LLC p 734
207 Terminal Dr, Plainview NY 11803
Tel (516) 433-9300 SIC 5999

LUXOTTICA US HOLDINGS CORP p 887
12 Harbor Park Dr, Port Washington NY 11050
Tel (516) 484-3800
SIC 5048 5099 5995 5999

PERFUME WORLDWIDE INC p 1135
2020 Ocean Ave Unit A, Ronkonkoma NY 11779
Tel (516) 575-2499 SIC 5122 5999

BEST PLUMBING SUPPLY INC p 177
49 Route 138, Somers NY 10589
Tel (914) 232-2020 SIC 5074 5999

BYRAM HEALTHCARE CENTERS INC p 231
120 Bloomingdale Rd # 301, White Plains NY 10605
Tel (914) 286-2000 SIC 5999 5047

TRIBORO QUILT MANUFACTURING CORP p 1479
172 S Broadway Ste 100, White Plains NY 10605
Tel (914) 428-7551 SIC 5023 5999

POOL BUILDERS SUPPLY OF CAROLINAS INC p 1161
1124 Central Ave, Charlotte NC 28204
Tel (704) 375-7573 SIC 5091 5999

ABC PHONES OF NORTH CAROLINA INC p 10
1290 E Arlington Blvd B, Greenville NC 27858
Tel (252) 317-0388 SIC 5999

ADVANCED HOME CARE INC p 25
4001 Piedmont Pkwy, High Point NC 27265
Tel (336) 878-8950 SIC 8082 5999

CAROLINA CONTAINER CO p 259
909 Prospect St, High Point NC 27260
Tel (336) 883-7146 SIC 5999

BODY SHOP INC p 197
5036 One World Way, Wake Forest NC 27587
Tel (919) 554-4900 SIC 5999 6794 2844

FARMERS UNION OIL OF SOUTHERN VALLEY p 530
107 S Front St, Fairmount ND 58030
Tel (701) 474-5882 SIC 5999

HASCO MEDICAL INC p 667
810 Moe Dr, Akron OH 44310
Tel (214) 302-0930 SIC 5999 8082

TOWN AND COUNTRY CO-OP INC p 1464
813 Clark Ave, Ashland OH 44805
Tel (419) 281-2153 SIC 5541 5261 5999

CHRISTIAN AID MINISTRIES p 302
4464 State Rte 39 E, Berlin OH 44610
Tel (330) 893-2428 SIC 8661 5999 5947

KOENIG EQUIPMENT INC p 826
15213 State Route 274, Botkins OH 45306
Tel (937) 693-5000 SIC 5999 0782

MERCER LANDMARK INC p 944
426 W Market St, Celina OH 45822
Tel (419) 628-3093 SIC 5153 5999

MORGENTHALER MANAGEMENT PARTNERS VI LLC p 989
50 Public Sq Ste 2700, Cleveland OH 44113
Tel (216) 416-7500
SIC 1731 5065 7622 7373 5999

▲ L BRANDS INC p 833
3 Limited Pkwy, Columbus OH 43230
Tel (614) 415-7000
SIC 5632 5961 5621 5999

SCHOTTENSTEIN STORES CORP p 1290
4300 E 5th Ave, Columbus OH 43219
Tel (614) 221-9200
SIC 5311 5712 5912 5999

SARNOVA INC p 1282
5000 Tuttle Crossing Blvd, Dublin OH 43016
Tel (614) 760-5000 SIC 5999 5047

JD EQUIPMENT INC p 780
3979 Parkway Ln, Hilliard OH 43026
Tel (614) 527-8800 SIC 5999 5083

FAIRFIELD MEDICAL CENTER p 525
401 N Ewing St, Lancaster OH 43130
Tel (740) 687-8000 SIC 8062 7352 5999

CHRISTIAN AID MINISTRIES p 302
4464 State Route 39, Millersburg OH 44654
Tel (330) 893-2428 SIC 8322 5999

■ BATH & BODY WORKS LLC p 159
7 Limited Pkwy E, Reynoldsburg OH 43068
Tel (614) 856-6000 SIC 5999 2844

■ DARICE INC p 412
13000 Darice Pkwy 82, Strongsville OH 44149
Tel (440) 238-9150 SIC 5945 5193 5999

■ LAMRITE WEST INC p 841
14225 Pearl Rd, Strongsville OH 44136
Tel (440) 238-7318 SIC 5999 5199 5092

■ RGH ENTERPRISES INC p 1231
1810 Summit Commerce Park, Twinsburg OH 44087
Tel (330) 963-6998 SIC 5999 5047 8011

LIVINGSTON MACHINERY CO p 871
5201 S Highway 81, Chickasha OK 73018
Tel (405) 224-5056
SIC 5083 5999 7699 5261

PIONEER TELEPHONE COOPERATIVE INC p 1151
108 E Robberts Ave, Kingfisher OK 73750
Tel (405) 375-4111 SIC 5999

HOB-LOB LTD p 698
7707 Sw 44th St, Oklahoma City OK 73179
Tel (405) 745-1100
SIC 5945 5999 5949 5947

MARDEL INC p 905
7727 Sw 44th St, Oklahoma City OK 73179
Tel (405) 745-1300 SIC 5999 5943

STILLWATER MILLING CO LLC p 1390
512 E 6th Ave, Stillwater OK 74074
Tel (405) 372-2766 SIC 2048 5999

AHS OKLAHOMA HEALTH SYSTEM LLP p 37
110 W 7th St Ste 2540, Tulsa OK 74119
Tel (918) 579-1000
SIC 8062 8069 7352 6512 7389 5999

SAINT FRANCIS HOSPITAL INC p 1269
6161 S Yale Ave, Tulsa OK 74136
Tel (918) 502-2050 SIC 8062 7352 5999

COASTAL FARM HOLDINGS INC p 331
1355 Goldfish Farm Rd Se, Albany OR 97322
Tel (541) 967-3450 SIC 5999

TUALITY HEALTHCARE FOUNDATION INC p 1490
335 Se 8th Ave, Hillsboro OR 97123
Tel (503) 681-1850
SIC 8082 7374 6512 5999 7359

LEGACY VISITING NURSE ASSOCIATION p 852
815 Ne Davis St, Portland OR 97232
Tel (503) 220-1000 SIC 8399 5999 8082

G I JOES INC p 587
9805 Sw Boeckman Rd, Wilsonville OR 97070
Tel (503) 682-2242
SIC 5941 5699 5531 5999

CONNECT AMERICA.COM LLC p 356
1 Belmont Ave Fl 9, Bala Cynwyd PA 19004
Tel (610) 356-3307 SIC 5065 5999

ARMSTRONG HOLDINGS INC p 111
1 Armstrong Pl, Butler PA 16001
Tel (724) 283-0925 SIC 1731 5999 7382

AMERICAN HOMECARE SUPPLY LLC p 74
101 W Elm St Ste 210, Conshohocken PA 19428
Tel (484) 530-0880 SIC 5999 7352

ANTHONY & SYLVAN POOLS CORP p 94
3739 N Eastern Rd, Doylestown PA 18901
Tel (215) 489-5600 SIC 1799 5999

EXCELA HEALTH HOLDING CO INC p 516
532 W Pittsburgh St, Greensburg PA 15601
Tel (724) 832-4000
SIC 8062 8093 5999 7363 7322 8361

DIAMOND DRUGS INC p 436
645 Kolter Dr, Indiana PA 15701
Tel (724) 349-1111 SIC 5912 5999

HOOBER INC p 705
3452 Old Philadelphia Pike, Intercourse PA 17534
Tel (717) 768-8231 SIC 5999 7699 5083

HOME CARE PRODUCTS & PHARMACY p 703
1 Hospital Dr, Lewisburg PA 17837
Tel (570) 522-2000 SIC 5912 7352 5999

■ GENERAL NUTRITION CORP p 601
300 6th Ave, Pittsburgh PA 15222
Tel (412) 288-4600
SIC 5499 5999 5941 5699 6794

MAIN LINE HEALTH SYSTEM p 897
240 N Radnor Chester Rd, Radnor PA 19087
Tel (610) 225-6200
SIC 5999 8059 8361 8062

GUARDIAN PROTECTION SERVICES INC p 645
174 Thorn Hill Rd, Warrendale PA 15086
Tel (412) 788-2580 SIC 1731 5999 7382

COMMUNICATIONS TEST DESIGN INC p 347
1373 Enterprise Dr, West Chester PA 19380
Tel (610) 436-5203
SIC 7629 7378 5065 5999

■ CELLULAR COMMUNICATIONS OF PUERTO RICO INC p 274
103 Ave Ortegon, Guaynabo PR 00966
Tel (787) 397-1000 SIC 4812 5999

ION AUDIO LLC p 762
200 Scenic View Dr, Cumberland RI 02864
Tel (401) 658-3743 SIC 5999

■ SPERIAN PROTECTION USA INC p 1358
900 Douglas Pike, Smithfield RI 02917
Tel (401) 232-1200
SIC 3851 3842 2311 7218 5999

MEDICAL SERVICES OF AMERICA INC p 937
171 Monroe Ln, Lexington SC 29072
Tel (803) 957-0500
SIC 8082 8741 8011 8071 7352 5999

MERCOM CORP p 945
313 Commerce Dr, Pawleys Island SC 29585
Tel (843) 979-9957 SIC 5999

▲ KIRKLANDS INC p 822
5310 Maryland Way, Brentwood TN 37027
Tel (615) 872-4800 SIC 5999 5947

▲ TRACTOR SUPPLY CO p 1468
5401 Virginia Way, Brentwood TN 37027
Tel (615) 440-4000
SIC 5999 5261 5251 5531 5699

■ TRACTOR SUPPLY CO OF TEXAS LP p 1468
5401 Virginia Way, Brentwood TN 37027
Tel (877) 718-6750 SIC 5084 5999

NATIONAL SEATING & MOBILITY INC p 1016
320 Premier Ct S Ste 220, Franklin TN 37067
Tel (615) 595-1115 SIC 3842 5999

CELLULAR SALES OF KNOXVILLE INC p 274
9040 Executive Park Dr, Knoxville TN 37923
Tel (865) 584-7555 SIC 5999

■ HOUSECALL MEDICAL RESOURCES INC p 711
1400 Cntrpint Blvd St 100, Knoxville TN 37932
Tel (865) 689-7123 SIC 8082 8741 5999

■ CUMMINS MID-SOUTH LLC p 401
3770 S Perkins Rd, Memphis TN 38118
Tel (901) 577-0600 SIC 5999 5013

POWER & TELEPHONE SUPPLY CO p 1165
2673 Yale Ave, Memphis TN 38112
Tel (901) 324-6116 SIC 5063 5999

OLD TIME POTTERY LLC p 1081
480 River Rock Blvd, Murfreesboro TN 37128
Tel (615) 890-6060 SIC 5999 5023

LIFEWAY CHRISTIAN RESOURCES OF SOUTHERN BAPTIST CONVENTION p 865
1 Lifeway Plz, Nashville TN 37234
Tel (615) 251-2000
SIC 5942 5963 2731 5999 5735 5947

DOSKOCIL MANUFACTURING CO INC p 451
2300 E Randol Mill Rd, Arlington TX 76011
Tel (877) 738-6283 SIC 3999 5999

PETMATE HOLDINGS CO p 1138
2300 E Randol Mill Rd, Arlington TX 76011
Tel (817) 467-5116 SIC 3999 5999

■ MILLER SPRINGS MATERIALS LLC p 971
6218 State Highway 317, Belton TX 76513
Tel (254) 780-9959 SIC 5085 5999

COUFAL-PRATER EQUIPMENT LLC p 374
3110 W Highway 21, Bryan TX 77803
Tel (979) 822-7684 SIC 5999 7699 5082

LORIS GIFTS INC p 878
2125 Chenault Dr Ste 100, Carrollton TX 75006
Tel (972) 759-5000 SIC 5947 8099 5999

GHM CORP p 610
12700 Hillcrest Rd # 291, Dallas TX 75230
Tel (972) 840-1200
SIC 3448 1799 5999 5561

■ BEAUTY SYSTEMS GROUP LLC p 166
3001 Colorado Blvd, Denton TX 76210
Tel (940) 297-2000 SIC 5999 5122 5087

▲ SALLY BEAUTY HOLDINGS INC p 1273
3001 Colorado Blvd, Denton TX 76210
Tel (940) 898-7500 SIC 5999 5087

■ SALLY BEAUTY SUPPLY LLC p 1273
3001 Colorado Blvd, Denton TX 76210
Tel (940) 898-7500 SIC 5999 5122 5087

CCS MEDICAL HOLDINGS INC p 270
1505 L B Johnson Fwy # 600, Farmers Branch TX 75234
Tel (972) 628-2100 SIC 5999 5912 5961

CCS MEDICAL INC p 270
1505 L B Johnson Fwy # 600, Farmers Branch TX 75234
Tel (972) 628-2100 SIC 5999 5912 5961

RS LEGACY CORP p 1255
300 Radioshack Cir, Fort Worth TX 76102
Tel (817) 415-3011 SIC 5731 5999 5734

BEARCOM GROUP INC p 165
4009 Dist Dr Ste 200, Garland TX 75041
Tel (214) 340-8876 SIC 5999 5065

KIK INTERNATIONAL HOUSTON INC p 817
2921 Corder St, Houston TX 77054
Tel (713) 747-8710 SIC 5999

MUSEUM OF FINE ARTS OF HOUSTON p 1002
1001 Bissonnet St, Houston TX 77005
Tel (713) 639-7300 SIC 8412 5999

ELECTRICAL DISTRIBUTORS LLC p 485
2301 Century Cir, Irving TX 75062
Tel (469) 533-6250 SIC 5063 5999

MICHAELS HOLDINGS LLC p 960
8000 Bent Branch Dr, Irving TX 75063
Tel (972) 409-1300
SIC 5945 5999 5949 5947 5199 5099

■ MICHAELS STORES INC p 960
8000 Bent Branch Dr, Irving TX 75063
Tel (972) 409-1300
SIC 5945 5999 5949 5947 5199 5099

NOKIA SOLUTIONS AND NETWORKS US LLC p 1046
6000 Connection Dr, Irving TX 75039
Tel (972) 374-3000 SIC 3663 5999 4813

SCOOTER STORE LTD p 1293
1650 Independence Dr, New Braunfels TX 78132
Tel (877) 841-8159 SIC 5999

■ ARROW SYSTEMS INTEGRATION INC p 113
1820 Preston Park Blvd # 2800, Plano TX 75093
Tel (972) 462-5800 SIC 4813 1731 5999

■ AT HOME STORES LLC p 123
1600 E Plano Pkwy, Plano TX 75074
Tel (972) 265-6227
SIC 5719 5992 5999 5947 5945

GARDEN RIDGE CORP p 591
1600 E Plano Pkwy, Plano TX 75074
Tel (972) 265-6227 SIC 5719 5999 5945

GARDEN RIDGE HOLDINGS INC p 591
1600 E Plano Pkwy, Plano TX 75074
Tel (832) 391-7201
SIC 5719 5945 5992 5947 5999

■ SOUTHWESTERN BELL TELECOMMUNICATIONS INC p 1353
1651 N Collins Blvd, Richardson TX 75080
Tel (972) 705-7658 SIC 5065 5999

ZTE (USA) INC p 1644
2425 N Central Expy # 600, Richardson TX 75080
Tel (972) 671-8885 SIC 5065 5999

CAPSTONE COMMODITIES LLC p 251
1311 Chisholm Trl, Round Rock TX 78681
Tel (512) 671-6626 SIC 5191 5999

■ DAHILL OFFICE TECHNOLOGY CORP p 408
8200 W Interstate 10 # 400, San Antonio TX 78230
Tel (210) 805-8200 SIC 5999 3861 2759

GREAT WESTERN SUPPLY INC p 635
2626 Industrial Dr, Ogden UT 84401
Tel (801) 621-5412
SIC 5074 5051 5999 1711

INTERMOUNTAIN FARMERS ASSOCIATION p 753
1147 W 2100 S, South Salt Lake UT 84119
Tel (801) 972-2122 SIC 5999 5191

MAPLE MOUNTAIN GROUP INC p 903
588 S 2000 W, Springville UT 84663
Tel (801) 418-2000 SIC 5999

ROCKINGHAM CO-OPERATIVE FARM BUREAU INC p 1244
1040 S High St, Harrisonburg VA 22801
Tel (540) 434-3856 SIC 5999 5251

RIVERSIDE REGIONAL MEDIAL CENTER p 1238
500 J Clyde Morris Blvd, Newport News VA 23601
Tel (757) 856-7030 SIC 5999

EVERGREEN ENTERPRISES INC p 514
5915 Midlothian Tpke, Richmond VA 23225
Tel (804) 231-1800
SIC 3253 2399 5193 5999

■ ARCH WIRELESS INC p 104
6850 Versar Ctr Ste 420, Springfield VA 22151
Tel (703) 269-6850 SIC 5999 4812

■ AT&T GOVERNMENT SOLUTIONS INC p 123
1900 Gallows Rd Ste 105, Vienna VA 22182
Tel (703) 506-5000
SIC 5999 8742 7373 7371

CREATIVE HAIRDRESSERS INC p 390
1577 Spring Hill Rd # 600, Vienna VA 22182
Tel (703) 269-5400 SIC 5999 7231

CHRISTIAN BROADCASTING NETWORK INC p 302
977 Centerville Tpke, Virginia Beach VA 23463
Tel (757) 226-3030
SIC 8661 4833 4832 5999 4724

BEST FRIENDS PET CARE INC p 177
19717 62nd Ave S Ste F103, Kent WA 98032
Tel (253) 981-3998 SIC 0752 0742 5999

TWO RIVERS TERMINAL LLC p 1495
3300c N Glade Rd, Pasco WA 99301
Tel (509) 547-7776 SIC 5191 5999

AMAZON.COMINDC LLC p 65
440 Terry Ave N, Seattle WA 98109
Tel (206) 266-1000 SIC 4813 5999 7371

CARTOYS INC p 252
400 Fairview Ave N # 900, Seattle WA 98109
Tel (206) 443-2726 SIC 5731 5999

GROUP HEALTH COOPERATIVE p 641
320 Westlake Ave N # 100, Seattle WA 98109
Tel (206) 448-4141
SIC 6324 5999 8093 6321

WIRELESS ADVOCATES LLC p 1618
400 Fairview Ave N # 900, Seattle WA 98109
Tel (206) 428-2400 SIC 5999

BRUCETON FARM SERVICE INC p 220
1768 Mileground Rd, Morgantown WV 26505
Tel (304) 291-6980
SIC 5411 5172 5999 5983 5812 2048

BROWN COUNTY MSA CELLULAR LIMITED PARTNERSHIP p 219
1580 Mid Valley Dr, De Pere WI 54115
Tel (920) 339-4004 SIC 4812 5999

REINDERS INC p 1221
W227n6225 Sussex Rd, Sussex WI 53089
Tel (262) 786-3300
SIC 5191 5169 5074 5999 5083

FULL COMPASS SYSTEMS LTD p 584
9770 Silicon Prairie Pkwy, Verona WI 53593
Tel (608) 831-7330 SIC 5999

SIC 6011 Federal Reserve Banks

FEDERAL RESERVE BANK OF SAN FRANCISCO p 535
101 Market St, San Francisco CA 94105
Tel (415) 974-2000 SIC 6011

BOARD OF GOVERNORS OF FEDERAL RESERVE SYSTEM p 195
20th St Cnsttution Ave Nw, Washington DC 20551
Tel (202) 452-3000 SIC 6011

FEDERAL RESERVE BANK OF ATLANTA p 535
1000 Peachtree St Ne, Atlanta GA 30309
Tel (404) 498-8500 SIC 6011

FEDERAL RESERVE BANK OF CHICAGO p 535
230 S La Salle St Ste 1, Chicago IL 60604
Tel (312) 322-2128 SIC 6011

FEDERAL RESERVE BANK OF BOSTON p 535
600 Atlantic Ave, Boston MA 02210
Tel (617) 973-3000 SIC 6011

FEDERAL RESERVE BANK OF MINNEAPOLIS p 535
90 Hennepin Ave, Minneapolis MN 55401
Tel (612) 204-5000 SIC 6011

FEDERAL RESERVE BANK OF KANSAS CITY (INC) p 535
1 Memorial Dr, Kansas City MO 64198
Tel (816) 881-2000 SIC 6011

FEDERAL RESERVE BANK OF ST LOUIS p 535
1421 Dr Martin Luther, Saint Louis MO 63106
Tel (314) 444-8444 SIC 6011

FEDERAL RESERVE BANK OF NEW YORK p 535
33 Liberty St, New York NY 10045
Tel (212) 720-6130 SIC 6011

FEDERAL RESERVE BANK OF CLEVELAND p 535
1455 E 6th St, Cleveland OH 44114
Tel (216) 579-2000 SIC 6011

FEDERAL RESERVE BANK OF PHILADELPHIA (INC) p 535
100 N Independence Mall W, Philadelphia PA 19106
Tel (215) 574-6000 SIC 6011

FEDERAL RESERVE BANK DALLAS p 535
2200 N Pearl St, Dallas TX 75201
Tel (214) 922-6000 SIC 6011

SIC 6019 Central Reserve Depository, NEC

FEDERAL HOME LOAN BANK OF DES MOINES p 534
801 Walnut St Ste 200, Des Moines IA 50309
Tel (515) 281-1000 SIC 6019

FEDERAL HOME LOAN BANK p 534
1 Sw Sec Bnft Pl Ste 100, Topeka KS 66606
Tel (785) 233-0507 SIC 6019

FEDERAL HOME LOAN BANK OF BOSTON p 534
800 Boylston St Ste 900, Boston MA 02199
Tel (617) 292-9600 SIC 6111 6019

FEDERAL HOME LOAN BANK OF CINCINNATI p 534
600 Atrium Two # 2, Cincinnati OH 45201
Tel (513) 852-7500 SIC 6019

FEDERAL HOME LOAN BANK OF PITTSBURGH p 534
601 Grant St Ste 1000, Pittsburgh PA 15219
Tel (412) 288-3400 SIC 6019

FEDERAL HOME LOAN BANK - OFFICE OF FINANCE p 534
1818 Library St Ste 200, Reston VA 20190
Tel (703) 467-3600 SIC 6019

FEDERAL HOME LOAN BANK OF SEATTLE p 534
1001 4th Ave Ste 2600, Seattle WA 98154
Tel (206) 340-2421 SIC 6019

SIC 6021 National Commercial Banks

CADENCE BANK NA p 236
2100 3rd Ave N, Birmingham AL 35203
Tel (205) 326-2265 SIC 6021

COMPASS BANK p 350
15 20th St S Ste 100, Birmingham AL 35233
Tel (205) 297-1986 SIC 6021

FIRST NATIONAL BANK ALASKA p 548
101 W 36th Ave, Anchorage AK 99503
Tel (907) 777-4362 SIC 6021

■ CHASE BANKCARD SERVICES INC p 291
100 W University Dr, Tempe AZ 85281
Tel (480) 902-6000 SIC 6021 6022

BANK OF ENGLAND p 151
123 S Main St, England AR 72046
Tel (501) 842-2555 SIC 6022 6021

■ SIMMONS BANK p 1324
501 S Main St, Pine Bluff AR 71601
Tel (870) 541-1000 SIC 6021

▲ SIMMONS FIRST NATIONAL CORP p 1324
501 S Main St, Pine Bluff AR 71601
Tel (870) 541-1000 SIC 6021

▲ PACWEST BANCORP p 1107
9701 Wilshire Blvd # 700, Beverly Hills CA 90212
Tel (310) 887-8500 SIC 6021

▲ CU BANCORP p 399
15821 Ventura Blvd # 100, Encino CA 91436
Tel (818) 257-7700 SIC 6021 6712

▲ BANC OF CALIFORNIA INC p 149
18500 Von Karman Ave # 1100, Irvine CA 92612
Tel (949) 236-5436 SIC 6021

■ FARMERS & MERCHANTS BANK OF CENTRAL CALIFORNIA p 529
121 W Pine St, Lodi CA 95240
Tel (209) 367-2300 SIC 6022 6021

■ BANK OF HOPE p 151
3731 Wilshire Blvd # 400, Los Angeles CA 90010
Tel (213) 639-1700 SIC 6021

BBCN BANK p 163
3731 Wilshire Blvd # 1000, Los Angeles CA 90010
Tel (213) 251-2222 SIC 6021

CITY NATIONAL BANK p 312
555 S Flower St Ste 2500, Los Angeles CA 90071
Tel (310) 888-6000 SIC 6021 6022

▲ HANMI FINANCIAL CORP p 658
3660 Wilshire Blvd Penths Ste A, Los Angeles CA 90010
Tel (213) 382-2200 SIC 6021

▲ HOPE BANCORP INC p 706
3731 Wilshire Blvd, Los Angeles CA 90010
Tel (213) 639-1700 SIC 6021

■ CIT BANK NA p 309
75 N Fair Oaks Ave, Pasadena CA 91103
Tel (626) 535-4300 SIC 6021

MUFG UNION BANK NA p 999
400 California St, San Francisco CA 94104
Tel (212) 782-6800 SIC 6021

WACHOVIA A DIVISION OF WELLS F p 1570
420 Montgomery St, San Francisco CA 94104
Tel (415) 571-2832 SIC 6021

▲ WELLS FARGO & CO p 1590
420 Montgomery St Frnt, San Francisco CA 94104
Tel (866) 249-3302
SIC 6021 6022 6162 6141 7374

■ WELLS FARGO BANK NATIONAL ASSOCIATION p 1590
420 Montgomery St, San Francisco CA 94104
Tel (415) 396-7392 SIC 6021

WELLS FARGO FINANCING CORP p 1590
420 Montgomery St Frnt, San Francisco CA 94104
Tel (415) 222-4292 SIC 6022 6021

■ WFC HOLDINGS CORP p 1603
420 Montgomery St, San Francisco CA 94104
Tel (415) 396-7392 SIC 6021

▲ WESTAMERICA BANCORPORATION p 1596
1108 5th Ave, San Rafael CA 94901
Tel (707) 863-6000 SIC 6021

■ PACIFIC WESTERN BANK p 1106
456 Santa Monica Blvd, Santa Monica CA 90401
Tel (310) 458-1521 SIC 6021

FIRSTFED FINANCIAL CORP p 550
6320 Canoga Ave, Woodland Hills CA 91367
Tel (562) 618-0573 SIC 6021

AMERICAN NATIONAL BANK OF CHEYENNE INC p 76
3033 E 1st Ave Ste 300, Denver CO 80206
Tel (303) 394-5100 SIC 6021

■ COBIZ BANK p 332
821 17th St Ste 800, Denver CO 80202
Tel (303) 293-2265 SIC 6021

▲ COBIZ FINANCIAL INC p 333
821 17th St, Denver CO 80202
Tel (303) 312-3400 SIC 6021

FIRST NATIONAL BANK p 548
205 W Oak St, Fort Collins CO 80521
Tel (970) 482-4861 SIC 6021

▲ NATIONAL BANK HOLDINGS CORP p 1010
7800 E Orchard Rd Ste 300, Greenwood Village CO 80111
Tel (720) 529-3336 SIC 6021

FIRSTBANK p 550
10403 W Colfax Ave # 100, Lakewood CO 80215
Tel (303) 232-2000 SIC 6021

WOODLANDS COMMERCIAL BANK p 1623
10350 Park Meadows Dr, Lone Tree CO 80124
Tel (212) 257-4646 SIC 6021

■ RBS NATIONAL BANK p 1211
1000 Lafayette Blvd # 600, Bridgeport CT 06604
Tel (203) 551-7270 SIC 6021

▲ SYNCHRONY FINANCIAL p 1414
777 Long Ridge Rd, Stamford CT 06902
Tel (203) 585-2400 SIC 6021 7389

▲ WEBSTER FINANCIAL CORP p 1587
145 Bank St, Waterbury CT 06702
Tel (203) 578-2202 SIC 6021

▲ BANCORP INC p 150
409 Silverside Rd Ste 105, Wilmington DE 19809
Tel (302) 385-5000 SIC 6021

■ PNC BANCORP INC p 1158
300 Delaware Ave, Wilmington DE 19801
Tel (302) 427-5896 SIC 6021

▲ WSFS FINANCIAL CORP p 1628
500 Delaware Ave, Wilmington DE 19801
Tel (302) 792-6000 SIC 6021

NATIONAL CONSUMER COOPERATIVE BANK p 1011
2001 Penn Ave Nw Ste 625, Washington DC 20006
Tel (202) 349-7444 SIC 6021

■ CAPITAL BANK NA p 249
121 Alhambra Plz Ste 1601, Coral Gables FL 33134
Tel (305) 444-1660 SIC 6021

MERCANTIL COMMERCEBANK HOLDING CORP p 943
220 Alhambra Cir, Coral Gables FL 33134
Tel (305) 441-5555 SIC 6021 7389 8721

▲ CENTERSTATE BANKS INC p 276
42745 Highway 27, Davenport FL 33837
Tel (863) 419-7750 SIC 6021

PEOPLES TRUST INSURANCE CO p 1133
18 Peoples Trust Way, Deerfield Beach FL 33441
Tel (561) 988-9170 SIC 6411 6021

CITY NATIONAL BANK p 312
25 W Flagler St Fl 3, Miami FL 33130
Tel (305) 577-7333 SIC 6021

SABADELL UNITED BANK NATIONAL ASSOCIATION p 1263
1111 Brickell Ave, Miami FL 33131
Tel (305) 358-4334 SIC 6021

■ SUNTRUST BANKS OF FLORIDA INC p 1401
200 S Orange Ave, Orlando FL 32801
Tel (407) 237-4141 SIC 6021 6022

■ SEACOAST BANK OF FLORIDA INC p 1296
815 Colorado Ave Lbby, Stuart FL 34994
Tel (772) 221-2760 SIC 6021

SUPERIOR BANK p 1406
4350 W Cypress St Ste 102, Tampa FL 33607
Tel (813) 350-6728 SIC 6021

■ SUNTRUST BANK p 1405
303 Peachtree St Ne Fl 30, Atlanta GA 30308
Tel (877) 782-0175 SIC 6021

▲ SUNTRUST BANKS INC p 1405
303 Peachtree St Ne, Atlanta GA 30308
Tel (800) 786-8787
SIC 6021 6022 6211 6091 6282

■ SUNTRUST EQUITY FUNDING LLC p 1405
25 Park Pl Ne Lbby 2, Atlanta GA 30303
Tel (404) 477-6818 SIC 6021

▲ SYNOVUS FINANCIAL CORP p 1415
1111 Bay Ave Ste 500, Columbus GA 31901
Tel (706) 649-2311 SIC 6021 6022 7389

HSBC USA INC p 715
107 Iris Glen Dr Se, Conyers GA 30013
Tel (212) 525-5000 SIC 6021

■ AMERICAN BANKING CO p 68
225 S Main St, Moultrie GA 31768
Tel (229) 985-2222 SIC 6022 6021

BENEFICIAL CO LLC p 172
1421 W Shure Dr Ste 100, Arlington Heights IL 60004
Tel (708) 453-6502
SIC 6141 6351 6162 6021 6552 6311

■ **OLD SECOND NATIONAL BANK OF AURORA** p 1081
37 S River St, Aurora IL 60506
Tel (630) 844-3555 *SIC* 6021

BMO BANKCORP INC p 194
111 W Monroe St, Chicago IL 60603
Tel (312) 461-2121 *SIC* 6021 6211

BMO FINANCIAL CORP p 194
111 W Monroe St Ste 1200, Chicago IL 60603
Tel (312) 461-2121 *SIC* 6021 6082 6211

BYLINE BANK p 231
3639 N Broadway St, Chicago IL 60613
Tel (773) 244-7000 *SIC* 6022 6163 6021

HARRIS BMO BANK NATIONAL ASSOCIATION p 663
111 W Monroe St Ste 1200, Chicago IL 60603
Tel (312) 461-2323 *SIC* 6021

■ **NORTHERN TRUST CO** p 1057
50 S La Salle St, Chicago IL 60603
Tel (312) 630-6000 *SIC* 6021

■ **CITICORP DINERS CLUB INC** p 310
50 Northwest Point Blvd, Elk Grove Village IL 60007
Tel (847) 472-6041 *SIC* 6021

▲ **FIRST MIDWEST BANCORP INC** p 548
1 Pierce Pl Ste 1500w, Itasca IL 60143
Tel (630) 875-7450 *SIC* 6021

■ **FIRST MIDWEST BANK** p 548
1 Pierce Pl Ste 1500w, Itasca IL 60143
Tel (630) 875-7450 *SIC* 6021

MORTON COMMUNITY BANK INC p 991
721 W Jackson St, Morton IL 61550
Tel (309) 263-8126 *SIC* 6022 6021

■ **MB FINANCIAL BANK NA** p 924
6111 N River Rd Ste 800, Rosemont IL 60018
Tel (847) 653-4800 *SIC* 6021

AMERICAN CHARTERED BANK p 70
1199 E Higgins Rd, Schaumburg IL 60173
Tel (847) 517-5400 *SIC* 6022 6021

▲ **OLD NATIONAL BANCORP** p 1081
1 Main St, Evansville IN 47708
Tel (812) 464-1294 *SIC* 6021

■ **OLD NATIONAL BANK** p 1081
1 Main St, Evansville IN 47708
Tel (800) 731-2265 *SIC* 6021 6022

FIRST NATIONAL BANK AND TRUST p 548
2206 W Sycamore St, Kokomo IN 46901
Tel (765) 868-3551 *SIC* 6021

▲ **HORIZON BANCORP** p 707
515 Franklin St, Michigan City IN 46360
Tel (219) 879-0211 *SIC* 6021

■ **HORIZON BANK NATIONAL ASSOCIATION** p 707
515 Franklin St, Michigan City IN 46360
Tel (219) 873-2640 *SIC* 6021

▲ **FIRST MERCHANTS CORP** p 547
200 E Jackson St, Muncie IN 47305
Tel (765) 747-1500 *SIC* 6021 6331

■ **FIRST FINANCIAL BANK NA** p 546
1 First Financial Plz, Terre Haute IN 47807
Tel (812) 238-6000 *SIC* 6021

■ **FIDELITY ACCEPTANCE CORP** p 540
800 Walnut St, Des Moines IA 50309
Tel (515) 557-8279 *SIC* 6021

WELLS FARGO FINANCIAL CA INC p 1590
800 Walnut St, Des Moines IA 50309
Tel (515) 557-7401
SIC 6141 6153 6351 6159 6531 6021

■ **WELLS FARGO FINANCIAL SECURITY SERVICES INC** p 1590
800 Walnut St, Des Moines IA 50309
Tel (515) 243-2131
SIC 6141 6153 6351 6159 7374 6021

■ **WELLS FARGO IOWA NA** p 1591
666 Walnut St Ste 1400, Des Moines IA 50309
Tel (515) 245-3000 *SIC* 6021 7389

ARMED FORCES BANK NATIONAL ASSOCIATION p 111
320 Kansas Ave, Fort Leavenworth KS 66027
Tel (913) 682-9090 *SIC* 6021

INTRUST BANK NA p 760
105 N Main St, Wichita KS 67202
Tel (316) 383-1111 *SIC* 6021

▲ **FARMERS CAPITAL BANK CORP** p 529
202 W Main St Ste 100, Frankfort KY 40601
Tel (502) 227-1668 *SIC* 6021 7374 6411

■ **FIFTH THIRD BANK OF KENTUCKY INC** p 542
401 S 4th St Ste 1000, Louisville KY 40202
Tel (502) 562-5215 *SIC* 6021

■ **COMMUNITY TRUST BANK INC** p 350
346 N Mayo Trl, Pikeville KY 41501
Tel (606) 432-1414 *SIC* 6021

■ **COMMUNITY TRUST BANK** p 350
155 Main St, Whitesburg KY 41858
Tel (606) 633-0161 *SIC* 6022 6021

▲ **MIDSOUTH BANCORP INC** p 966
102 Versailles Blvd, Lafayette LA 70501
Tel (337) 237-8343 *SIC* 6021

■ **MIDSOUTH BANK NA** p 966
102 Versailles Blvd # 100, Lafayette LA 70501
Tel (337) 237-8343 *SIC* 6021

CRESCENT BANK & TRUST p 391
1100 Poydras St Ste 100, New Orleans LA 70163
Tel (504) 556-5950 *SIC* 6021

WHITNEY BANK p 1607
228 Saint Charles Ave # 228, New Orleans LA 70130
Tel (504) 586-7272 *SIC* 6021

▲ **CAMDEN NATIONAL CORP** p 245
2 Elm St, Camden ME 04843
Tel (207) 236-8821 *SIC* 6021 6733

■ **NATIONSBANK NA (INC)** p 1017
100 S Charles St Ste 207, Baltimore MD 21201
Tel (410) 605-5000 *SIC* 6021 6531

■ **FARMERS & MECHANICS BANK** p 529
110 Thomas Johnson Dr # 100, Frederick MD 21702
Tel (301) 694-4050 *SIC* 6021 6163

■ **SANDY SPRING BANK** p 1279
17801 Georgia Ave, Olney MD 20832
Tel (301) 774-6400 *SIC* 6021

■ **CITIZENS BANK OF MASSACHUSETTS** p 310
28 State St Fl 13, Boston MA 02109
Tel (617) 725-5900 *SIC* 6021

■ **SANTANDER HOLDINGS USA INC** p 1281
75 State St, Boston MA 02109
Tel (617) 346-7200 *SIC* 6021 6035

▲ **ALLY FINANCIAL INC** p 59
500 Woodward Ave Fl 1, Detroit MI 48226
Tel (866) 710-4623
SIC 6021 6153 6159 6311 6331 6162

CAPITOL BANCORP LTD p 250
200 N Washington Sq, Lansing MI 48933
Tel (517) 487-6555 *SIC* 6021

■ **COMERICA INSURANCE SERVICES INC** p 344
20700 Civic Center Dr # 290, Southfield MI 48076
Tel (248) 603-3600 *SIC* 6021

■ **TCF NATIONAL BANK** p 1428
1405 Xenium Ln N Ste 180, Minneapolis MN 55441
Tel (612) 661-8450 *SIC* 6021 6159

▲ **US BANCORP** p 1531
800 Nicollet Mall # 1500, Minneapolis MN 55402
Tel (651) 466-3000
SIC 6021 6022 6162 6091 6159 6411

■ **WELLS FARGO BUSINESS CREDIT INC** p 1590
730 2nd Ave S Fl 8, Minneapolis MN 55402
Tel (612) 673-8500 *SIC* 6021 6141

■ **WELLS FARGO FOUNDATION MINNESOTA** p 1590
N 9305-192, Minneapolis MN 55479
Tel (612) 667-1234 *SIC* 6021

STEARNS BANK NATIONAL ASSOCIATION p 1384
4191 2nd St S, Saint Cloud MN 56301
Tel (320) 253-6607 *SIC* 6021

▲ **TCF FINANCIAL CORP** p 1428
200 Lake St E, Wayzata MN 55391
Tel (952) 745-2760 *SIC* 6021

CITIZENS FINANCIAL CORP p 311
202 E Jackson St, Belzoni MS 39038
Tel (662) 746-6811 *SIC* 6022 6021 6141

▲ **TRUSTMARK CORP** p 1488
248 E Capitol St Ste 704, Jackson MS 39201
Tel (601) 208-5111 *SIC* 6021

■ **TRUSTMARK NATIONAL BANK** p 1488
248 E Capitol St Ste 704, Jackson MS 39201
Tel (601) 208-5111 *SIC* 6021

CADENCE FINANCIAL CORP p 236
301 E Main St, Starkville MS 39759
Tel (662) 323-1341 *SIC* 6021

LANDMARK BANK NATIONAL ASSOCIATION p 842
801 E Broadway, Columbia MO 65201
Tel (573) 449-3911 *SIC* 6021

■ **CBI-KANSAS INC** p 268
1000 Walnut St Fl 700, Kansas City MO 64106
Tel (816) 234-2000 *SIC* 6021

■ **UMB BANK NATIONAL ASSOCIATION** p 1501
1010 Grand Blvd Fl 3, Kansas City MO 64106
Tel (816) 842-2222 *SIC* 6021

▲ **UMB FINANCIAL CORP** p 1501
1010 Grand Blvd, Kansas City MO 64106
Tel (816) 860-7930 *SIC* 6021

■ **GREAT SOUTHERN BANK** p 634
14309 State Highway 13, Reeds Spring MO 65737
Tel (417) 888-5880 *SIC* 6021 4724 6712

FIRST BANKS INC p 545
135 N Meramec Ave, Saint Louis MO 63105
Tel (314) 854-4600 *SIC* 6021

■ **COMMERCE BANK (MO)** p 345
1345 E Battlefield St, Springfield MO 65804
Tel (417) 869-5411 *SIC* 6021

UNION BANK AND TRUST CO p 1504
3643 S 48th St, Lincoln NE 68506
Tel (402) 488-0941
SIC 6111 6029 6162 6021 6035 6022

AMERICAN NATIONAL BANK p 76
8990 W Dodge Rd Ste 1, Omaha NE 68114
Tel (402) 399-5000 *SIC* 6021

FIRST NATIONAL BANK OF OMAHA INC p 548
1620 Dodge St, Omaha NE 68197
Tel (402) 341-0500 *SIC* 6021

FIRST NATIONAL OF ILLINOIS INC p 548
1620 Dodge St, Omaha NE 68102
Tel (402) 991-6131 *SIC* 6021

■ **WELLS FARGO BANK NEBRASKA NA** p 1590
1919 Douglas St, Omaha NE 68102
Tel (402) 536-2022 *SIC* 6021

CREDIT ONE BANK NATIONAL ASSOCIATION p 390
585 Pilot Rd, Las Vegas NV 89119
Tel (702) 269-3900 *SIC* 6021

CREDIT ONE FINANCIAL p 390
585 Pilot Rd, Las Vegas NV 89119
Tel (702) 269-1000 *SIC* 6021

■ **WELLS FARGO BANK NEVADA NA** p 1590
3300 W Sahara Ave Frnt, Las Vegas NV 89102
Tel (702) 765-3593 *SIC* 6021

■ **CHARLES SCHWAB BANK NATIONAL ASSOCIATION** p 289
5190 Neil Rd Ste 100, Reno NV 89502
Tel (775) 689-6800 *SIC* 6021

TD BANK NA p 1428
1701 Marlton Pike E # 200, Cherry Hill NJ 08003
Tel (856) 751-2739 *SIC* 6021

TD EQUIPMENT FINANCE INC p 1429
1006 Astoria Blvd, Cherry Hill NJ 08003
Tel (856) 470-5741 *SIC* 6021

SUMITOMO MITSUI TRUST BANK (USA) INC p 1398
111 River St, Hoboken NJ 07030
Tel (201) 595-8900 *SIC* 6021

AMBOY BANCORPORATION p 65
3590 Us Highway 9, Old Bridge NJ 08857
Tel (732) 591-8700 *SIC* 6021

AMBOY BANK p 65
3590 Us Highway 9, Old Bridge NJ 08857
Tel (732) 721-4200 *SIC* 6021

▲ **FIRST BANK OF NEW JERSEY** p 545
2465 Kuser Rd, Trenton NJ 08690
Tel (609) 528-4400 *SIC* 6029 6021

FIRST CHOICE BANK p 545
669 Whitehead Rd, Trenton NJ 08648
Tel (609) 454-0338 *SIC* 6021

■ **SUN NATIONAL BANK** p 1400
226 W Landis Ave Ste 1, Vineland NJ 08360
Tel (800) 786-9066 *SIC* 6021

▲ **VALLEY NATIONAL BANCORP** p 1541
1455 Valley Rd Ste 3, Wayne NJ 07470
Tel (973) 305-8800 *SIC* 6021

■ **VALLEY NATIONAL BANK** p 1541
1455 Valley Rd Ste 3, Wayne NJ 07470
Tel (973) 696-4020 *SIC* 6021 6162

VNB MORTGAGE SERVICES INC p 1563
1720 Rte 23, Wayne NJ 07470
Tel (973) 696-2813 *SIC* 6021

■ **WELLS FARGO BANK NEW MEXICO NA** p 1590
200 Lomas Blvd Nw Ste 100, Albuquerque NM 87102
Tel (505) 765-5000 *SIC* 6021

■ **WELLS FARGO INC** p 1590
200 Lomas Blvd Nw Ste 100, Albuquerque NM 87102
Tel (505) 353-5000 *SIC* 6021

▲ **BRIDGE BANCORP INC** p 211
2200 Montauk Hwy, Bridgehampton NY 11932
Tel (631) 537-1000 *SIC* 6021

■ **BRIDGEHAMPTON NATIONAL BANK** p 211
2200 Montauk Hwy, Bridgehampton NY 11932
Tel (631) 602-3005 *SIC* 6021

■ **FIRST NIAGARA BANK NATIONAL ASSOCIATION** p 548
726 Exchange St Ste 618, Buffalo NY 14210
Tel (716) 625-7500 *SIC* 6021

HSBC NORTH AMERICA INC p 715
1 Hsbc Ctr Ste 1, Buffalo NY 14203
Tel (716) 841-2424
SIC 6021 6035 6221 6091 6211

■ **CANANDAIGUA NATIONAL BANK & TRUST CO** p 246
72 S Main St, Canandaigua NY 14424
Tel (585) 394-4260 *SIC* 6021

▲ **CANANDAIGUA NATIONAL CORP** p 246
72 S Main St, Canandaigua NY 14424
Tel (585) 394-4260 *SIC* 6021

▲ **COMMUNITY BANK SYSTEM INC** p 347
5790 Widewaters Pkwy # 1, De Witt NY 13214
Tel (315) 445-2282 *SIC* 6021

■ **FIRST NATIONAL BANK OF LONG ISLAND** p 548
10 Glen Head Rd, Glen Head NY 11545
Tel (516) 671-4900 *SIC* 6021

▲ **FIRST OF LONG ISLAND CORP** p 548
10 Glen Head Rd, Glen Head NY 11545
Tel (516) 671-4900 *SIC* 6021

▲ **ARROW FINANCIAL CORP** p 113
250 Glen St, Glens Falls NY 12801
Tel (518) 745-1000 *SIC* 6021

■ **GLENS FALLS NATIONAL BANK & TRUST CO** p 615
250 Glen St, Glens Falls NY 12801
Tel (518) 793-4121 *SIC* 6021

▲ **STERLING BANCORP** p 1386
400 Rella Blvd, Montebello NY 10901
Tel (845) 369-8040 *SIC* 6021

■ **CITIBANK NA** p 310
399 Park Ave Bsmt 1, New York NY 10022
Tel (212) 559-1000
SIC 6021 6153 6091 6099 6162

▲ **CITIGROUP INC** p 310
399 Park Ave, New York NY 10022
Tel (212) 559-1000
SIC 6021 6141 6331 6311 6321

DEUTSCHE BANK TRUST CO AMERICAS p 433
60 Wall St Bsmt 1, New York NY 10005
Tel (212) 250-2500 *SIC* 6021 6211

▲ **JPMORGAN CHASE & CO** p 795
270 Park Ave Fl 38, New York NY 10017
Tel (212) 270-6000
SIC 6021 6211 6162 6141

MUFG AMERICAS HOLDINGS CORP p 999
1251 Ave Of The Americas, New York NY 10020
Tel (212) 782-5911 *SIC* 6021

■ **NBC NEWS WORLDWIDE LLC** p 1021
30 Rockefeller Plz Fl 2, New York NY 10112
Tel (212) 664-4444
SIC 4832 4833 4841 6021 6531 7383

■ **NBC UNIVERSITY LLC** p 1021
30 Rockefeller Plz Fl 51, New York NY 10112
Tel (212) 664-4444
SIC 4832 4833 4841 6021 6531 7383

RBC USA HOLDCO CORP p 1211
3 World Financial Ctr, New York NY 10281
Tel (212) 858-7200 *SIC* 6712 6021 6022

SAFRA NATIONAL BANK OF NEW YORK p 1267
546 5th Ave, New York NY 10036
Tel (212) 382-9200 *SIC* 6021

STANDARD CHARTERED INTERNATIONAL (USA) LTD p 1375
200 Vesey St, New York NY 10285
Tel (212) 640-2000 *SIC* 6082 6021 6099

■ **STANLEY MORGAN DOMESTIC HOLDINGS INC** p 1377
1585 Broadway Lowr B, New York NY 10036
Tel (212) 761-4000 *SIC* 6021

STERLING BANCORP p 1386
650 5th Ave Ste 2406, New York NY 10019
Tel (212) 757-3300 *SIC* 6021

STERLING NATIONAL BANK p 1387
650 5th Ave Fl 4, New York NY 10019
Tel (212) 757-3300 *SIC* 6021

▲ **NBT BANCORP INC** p 1021
52 S Broad St, Norwich NY 13815
Tel (607) 337-2265 *SIC* 6021

■ **NBT BANK NA** p 1021
52 S Broad St, Norwich NY 13815
Tel (607) 337-2265 *SIC* 6021

■ **COMMUNITY BANK N A** p 347
5790 Widewaters Pkwy # 1, Syracuse NY 13214
Tel (315) 445-2282 *SIC* 6021

▲ **FINANCIAL INSTITUTIONS INC** p 542
220 Liberty St, Warsaw NY 14569
Tel (585) 786-1100 *SIC* 6021 7389

■ **COMMUNITYONE BANK NATIONAL ASSOCIATION** p 350
101 Sunset Ave, Asheboro NC 27203
Tel (336) 625-4012 *SIC* 6712 6021

▲ **BANK OF AMERICA CORP** p 151
100 N Tryon St Ste 220, Charlotte NC 28202
Tel (704) 386-5681
SIC 6021 6022 6211 6091 6162 6159

BANK OF AMERICA N A p 151
401 N Tryon St Ste 300, Charlotte NC 28202
Tel (800) 432-1000 *SIC* 6021

■ **BANK OF AMERICA NATIONAL ASSOCIATION** p 151
101 S Tryon St, Charlotte NC 28280
Tel (704) 386-5681 *SIC* 6021

▲ **CAPITAL BANK FINANCIAL CORP** p 249
4725 Piedmont Row Dr, Charlotte NC 28210
Tel (704) 554-5901 *SIC* 6021

COMMUNITYONE BANCORP p 350
1017 E Morehead St # 200, Charlotte NC 28204
Tel (336) 626-8300 *SIC* 6021

■ **WACHOVIA BANK NATIONAL ASSOCIATION** p 1570
301 S Tryon St, Charlotte NC 28282
Tel (704) 335-5878 *SIC* 6021

SQUARE 1 BANK p 1362
406 Blackwell St Ste 240, Durham NC 27701
Tel (919) 314-3040 *SIC* 6021

▲ **BNC BANCORP** p 194
3980 Premier Dr Ste 210, High Point NC 27265
Tel (336) 476-9200 *SIC* 6021

■ **BB&T CAPITAL TRUST IV** p 163
200 W 2nd St Ste 1800, Winston Salem NC 27101
Tel (336) 733-2000 *SIC* 6021

▲ **BB&T CORP** p 163
200 W 2nd St Ste 260, Winston Salem NC 27101
Tel (336) 733-2000
SIC 6021 6311 6035 6211

■ **BB&T INSURANCE HOLDINGS INC** p 163
200 W 2nd St, Winston Salem NC 27101
Tel (336) 733-2500 *SIC* 6021

■ **BRANCH BANKING AND TRUST CO** p 207
200 W 2nd St, Winston Salem NC 27101
Tel (336) 733-2000 *SIC* 6022 6021

■ **US BANK NATIONAL ASSOCIATION ND** p 1531
4325 17th Ave S, Fargo ND 58125
Tel (701) 461-0346 *SIC* 6021

ALERUS FINANCIAL NATIONAL ASSN p 48
2300 S Columbia Rd, Grand Forks ND 58201
Tel (701) 795-3200 *SIC* 6021

FIRSTMERIT BANK NATIONAL ASSOCIATION p 551
106 S Main St Fl 5, Akron OH 44308
Tel (330) 384-7201 *SIC* 6021

FIRSTMERIT CORP p 551
Iii Cascade Plz Fl 7, Akron OH 44308
Tel (330) 996-6300 *SIC* 6021

▲ **FIRST FINANCIAL BANCORP** p 546
255 E 5th St Ste 700, Cincinnati OH 45202
Tel (877) 322-9530 *SIC* 6021

■ **US BANK NATIONAL ASSOCIATION** p 1531
425 Walnut St Fl 1, Cincinnati OH 45202
Tel (513) 632-4234 *SIC* 6021

■ **CHARTER ONE BANK NATIONAL ASSOCIATION** p 291
1215 Superior Ave E # 245, Cleveland OH 44114
Tel (216) 277-5326 *SIC* 6021

■ **FIFTH THIRD BANK OF NORTHEASTERN OHIO** p 542
600 Superior Ave E Fl 5, Cleveland OH 44114
Tel (216) 274-5533 *SIC* 6021

■ **KEYBANC CAPITAL MARKETS INC** p 815
800 Superior Ave E # 1400, Cleveland OH 44114
Tel (800) 553-2240 *SIC* 6021 6211

■ **KEYBANK NATIONAL ASSOCIATION** p 815
127 Public Sq Ste 5600, Cleveland OH 44114
Tel (800) 539-2968 *SIC* 6021 6022 6159

▲ **KEYCORP** p 815
127 Public Sq, Cleveland OH 44114
Tel (216) 689-3000 *SIC* 6021 6141 6211

■ **PNC BANK NATIONAL ASSOCIATION** p 1158
1900 E 9th St Lowr Ll1, Cleveland OH 44114
Tel (877) 762-2000 *SIC* 6021

▲ **HUNTINGTON BANCSHARES INC** p 720
41 S High St, Columbus OH 43215
Tel (614) 480-8300 *SIC* 6021

■ **FIRST FINANCIAL BANK NATIONAL ASSOCIATION** p 546
300 High St Side, Hamilton OH 45011
Tel (513) 867-4700 *SIC* 6021

▲ **PEOPLES BANCORP INC** p 1132
138 Putnam St, Marietta OH 45750
Tel (740) 373-3155 *SIC* 6021

■ **PARK NATIONAL BANK** p 1115
50 N 3rd St, Newark OH 43055
Tel (740) 349-8451 *SIC* 6021

▲ **PARK NATIONAL CORP** p 1115
50 N 3rd St, Newark OH 43055
Tel (740) 349-8451 *SIC* 6021

■ **FIFTH THIRD BANK OF NORTHWESTERN OHIO NA** p 542
1 Seagate Ste 2200, Toledo OH 43604
Tel (419) 259-7820 *SIC* 6021

FIRST UNITED BANK AND TRUST CO p 550
1400 W Main St, Durant OK 74701
Tel (580) 924-2211 *SIC* 6022 6163 6021

■ BANK SNB p 152
608 S Main St, Stillwater OK 74074
Tel (405) 372-2230 SIC 6021 6163

▲ SOUTHWEST BANCORP INC p 1351
608 S Main St, Stillwater OK 74074
Tel (405) 742-1800 SIC 6021

▲ BOK FINANCIAL CORP p 198
320 S Boston Ave, Tulsa OK 74103
Tel (918) 588-6000 SIC 6021

■ BOKF NATIONAL ASSOCIATION p 198
1 One Williams Ctr Bsmt 1, Tulsa OK 74172
Tel (918) 588-6000 SIC 6021

■ UMPQUA BANK p 1501
445 Se Main St, Roseburg OR 97470
Tel (541) 440-3961 SIC 6021

■ NATIONAL PENN BANK p 1015
645 Hamilton St Ste 900, Allentown PA 18101
Tel (610) 705-9101 SIC 6021

■ FIRST NATIONAL BANK OF PENNSYLVANIA p 548
166 Main St, Greenville PA 16125
Tel (724) 588-6770 SIC 6021

■ FIRST COMMONWEALTH BANK p 545
601 Philadelphia St, Indiana PA 15701
Tel (724) 349-7220 SIC 6021

▲ FIRST COMMONWEALTH FINANCIAL CORP p 546
601 Philadelphia St, Indiana PA 15701
Tel (724) 349-7220 SIC 6021

▲ FULTON FINANCIAL CORP p 584
1 Penn Sq Ste 1, Lancaster PA 17602
Tel (717) 291-2411 SIC 6021

SUSQUEHANNA BANCSHARES INC p 1409
26 N Cedar St, Lititz PA 17543
Tel (717) 626-4721 SIC 6021

■ CITIZENS BANK OF PENNSYLVANIA p 310
130 N 18th St, Philadelphia PA 19103
Tel (267) 671-1000 SIC 6022 6021

■ BNY MELLON NATIONAL ASSOCIATION p 194
1 Mellon Center Ste 3831, Pittsburgh PA 15258
Tel (412) 234-5000 SIC 6021 6733

▲ FNB CORP p 562
1 N Shore Ctr 12 Fdral St, Pittsburgh PA 15212
Tel (800) 555-5455
SIC 6022 6021 6162 6411

■ PNC BANK NATIONAL ASSOCIATION p 1158
249 5th Ave Ste 1200, Pittsburgh PA 15222
Tel (412) 762-2000 SIC 6021

▲ PNC FINANCIAL SERVICES GROUP INC p 1158
300 5th Ave, Pittsburgh PA 15222
Tel (412) 762-2000
SIC 6021 6162 7389 6282 6211

■ UNIVEST BANK AND TRUST CO p 1527
14 N Main St, Souderton PA 18964
Tel (877) 723-5571 SIC 6021

▲ NORTHWEST BANCSHARES INC p 1059
100 Liberty St, Warren PA 16365
Tel (814) 726-2140 SIC 6021

■ SANTANDER BANCORP p 1281
B7 Calle Tabonuco Fl 18, Guaynabo PR 00968
Tel (787) 777-4100 SIC 6021 6411 6211

■ CITIZENS BANK NATIONAL ASSOCIATION p 310
1 Citizens Plz Ste 1, Providence RI 02903
Tel (401) 282-7000 SIC 6021

■ CERTUSBANK NATIONAL ASSOCIATION p 284
935 S Main St, Greenville SC 29601
Tel (864) 306-2540 SIC 6021

FIRST NATIONAL BANK p 548
307 E Hustan Ave, Fort Pierre SD 57532
Tel (605) 223-2521 SIC 6021

■ CITIBANK NATIONAL ASSOCIATION p 310
701 E 60th St N, Sioux Falls SD 57104
Tel (605) 331-2626 SIC 6021

■ NORWEST BANK SOUTH DAKOTA NATIONAL ASSOCIATION p 1061
101 N Phillips Ave Ste A, Sioux Falls SD 57104
Tel (605) 575-4900 SIC 6021

UNITED NATIONAL CORP p 1510
601 S Minnesota Ave, Sioux Falls SD 57104
Tel (605) 357-3001 SIC 6021

▲ WILSON BANK HOLDING CO p 1613
623 W Main St, Lebanon TN 37087
Tel (615) 444-2265 SIC 6021

▲ FIRST HORIZON NATIONAL CORP p 547
165 Madison Ave Fl 10, Memphis TN 38103
Tel (901) 523-4444 SIC 6021

■ FIRST TENNESSEE BANK NATIONAL ASSOCIATION p 549
165 Madison Ave, Memphis TN 38103
Tel (901) 523-4444 SIC 6021 6162

■ NATIONAL BANK OF COMMERCE p 1010
1 Commerce Sq, Memphis TN 38103
Tel (901) 523-3434
SIC 6021 6211 7374 6712

■ PINNACLE BANK p 1149
150 3rd Ave S Ste 900, Nashville TN 37201
Tel (615) 744-3700 SIC 6021

▲ PINNACLE FINANCIAL PARTNERS INC p 1149
150 3rd Ave S Ste 900, Nashville TN 37201
Tel (615) 744-3700 SIC 6021

■ SUNTRUST COMMUNITY DEVELOPMENT CORP p 1405
201 4th Ave N Ste 1700, Nashville TN 37219
Tel (615) 748-4000 SIC 6021

■ FIRST FINANCIAL BANK NATIONAL ASSOCIATION p 546
400 Pine St, Abilene TX 79601
Tel (325) 627-7000 SIC 6021

AMARILLO NATIONAL BANCORP INC p 64
Plaza One 410 S Taylor St # 1, Amarillo TX 79101
Tel (806) 378-8000 SIC 6021

AMARILLO NATIONAL BANK p 64
410 S Taylor St, Amarillo TX 79101
Tel (806) 349-9760 SIC 6021

COMMUNITYBANK OF TEXAS NATIONAL ASSOCIATION p 350
5999 Delaware St, Beaumont TX 77706
Tel (409) 861-7200
SIC 6163 6029 6022 6021

■ A PLAINSCAPITAL PRIMELENDING CO p 6
18111 Preston Rd Ste 900, Dallas TX 75252
Tel (800) 317-7463 SIC 6163 6021

BB&T p 163
8214 Westchester Dr # 100, Dallas TX 75225
Tel (214) 234-7750 SIC 6021

■ COMERICA BANK p 344
1717 Main St Ste 2100, Dallas TX 75201
Tel (214) 462-4000 SIC 6021

■ COMERICA BANK-TEXAS p 344
1601 Elm St, Dallas TX 75201
Tel (214) 462-6831 SIC 6021

▲ COMERICA INC p 344
1717 Main St Mc6404, Dallas TX 75201
Tel (214) 462-6831
SIC 6021 6022 6091 6082 6099 6141

■ TEXAS CAPITAL BANK NATIONAL ASSOCIATION p 1442
2000 Mckinney Ave Ste 700, Dallas TX 75201
Tel (214) 932-6600 SIC 6021

FIRST NATIONAL BANK p 548
100 W Cano St, Edinburg TX 78539
Tel (956) 380-8587 SIC 6021

UNITED CENTRAL BANK p 1507
4555 W Walnut St, Garland TX 75042
Tel (972) 487-1505 SIC 6021

AMEGY BANK NATIONAL ASSOCIATION p 66
4400 Post Oak Pkwy, Houston TX 77027
Tel (713) 235-8800 SIC 6021

CADENCE BANCORP LLC p 236
2800 Post Oak Blvd # 3800, Houston TX 77056
Tel (713) 871-4000 SIC 6021

ENCORE BANCSHARES INC p 496
9 Greenway Plz Ste 1000, Houston TX 77046
Tel (713) 787-3100 SIC 6021

ENCORE BANK p 496
9 Greenway Plz Ste 1000, Houston TX 77046
Tel (713) 787-3100 SIC 6021 6035

▲ GREEN BANCORP INC p 636
4000 Greenbriar St, Houston TX 77098
Tel (713) 275-8220 SIC 6021

■ ASSOCIATES FIRST CAPITAL CORP p 121
4000 Regent Blvd, Irving TX 75063
Tel (800) 922-6235
SIC 6162 6021 6141 6159 6153

AUSTIN BANCORP INC p 132
200 E Commerce St, Jacksonville TX 75766
Tel (903) 586-1526 SIC 6021 6211 6022

AUSTIN BANK TEXAS N A p 132
200 E Commerce St, Jacksonville TX 75766
Tel (903) 586-1526 SIC 6021

■ FIRST NATIONAL BANK TEXAS p 548
507 N Gray St, Killeen TX 76541
Tel (254) 554-6699 SIC 6021

LONE STAR NATIONAL BANCSHARES—TEXAS INC p 876
4500 N 10th St Ste 305, Mcallen TX 78504
Tel (956) 781-4321 SIC 6712 6021

LONE STAR NATIONAL BANK p 876
520 E Nolana Ave Ste 110, Mcallen TX 78504
Tel (956) 781-4321 SIC 6021

▲ INDEPENDENT BANK GROUP INC p 736
1600 Redbud Blvd Ste 400, Mckinney TX 75069
Tel (972) 548-9004 SIC 6021

LONE STAR NATIONAL BANK SHARES NEVEDA p 876
100 W Ferguson St, Pharr TX 78577
Tel (956) 781-4321 SIC 6021

BROADWAY BANCSHARES INC p 216
1177 Ne Loop 410, San Antonio TX 78209
Tel (210) 283-6500 SIC 6021

BROADWAY NATIONAL BANK p 216
1177 Ne Loop 410, San Antonio TX 78209
Tel (210) 283-6500 SIC 6021

▲ CULLEN/FROST BANKERS INC p 400
100 W Houston St, San Antonio TX 78205
Tel (210) 220-4011 SIC 6021 6411

■ FROST BANK p 581
100 W Houston St Ste 100, San Antonio TX 78205
Tel (210) 220-4011 SIC 6021

AMERICAN NATIONAL BANK OF TEXAS p 77
102 W Moore Ave Lbby, Terrell TX 75160
Tel (972) 524-3411 SIC 6021

WOODFOREST FINANCIAL GROUP INC p 1623
1330 Lake Robbins Dr # 150, The Woodlands TX 77380
Tel (832) 375-2000 SIC 6021

WOODFOREST NATIONAL BANK p 1623
25231 Grogans Mill Rd # 175, The Woodlands TX 77380
Tel (713) 455-7000 SIC 6021

FIRST VICTORIA NATIONAL BANK p 550
101 S Main St, Victoria TX 77901
Tel (361) 573-6321 SIC 6021

■ ALLY BANK p 59
6985 S Union Park Ctr # 435, Midvale UT 84047
Tel (801) 790-5005
SIC 6153 6021 6311 6331 6162

■ WEX INC p 1603
7090 S Union Park Ave # 350, Midvale UT 84047
Tel (801) 270-8166 SIC 6021

■ SALLIE MAE BANK p 1273
175 S West Temple Ste 600, Salt Lake City UT 84101
Tel (801) 320-3700 SIC 6021

UBS BANK USA p 1498
299 S Main St Ste 2275, Salt Lake City UT 84111
Tel (801) 532-2741 SIC 6021

■ ZB NATIONAL ASSOCIATION p 1641
1 S Main St, Salt Lake City UT 84133
Tel (801) 974-8800 SIC 6021

▲ ZIONS BANCORPORATION p 1643
1 S Main St Fl 15, Salt Lake City UT 84133
Tel (801) 844-7637 SIC 6022 6021

MERRICK BANK CORP p 950
10705 S Jordan Gtwy # 200, South Jordan UT 84095
Tel (801) 545-6600 SIC 6021

UNITED BANK p 1506
5350 Lee Hwy Ste 2, Arlington VA 22207
Tel (703) 534-1382 SIC 6021

■ FIRST COMMUNITY BANK p 546
1 Community Pl, Bluefield VA 24605
Tel (276) 326-9000 SIC 6021

■ FIRST COMMUNITY BANK NA p 546
29 College Dr, Bluefield VA 24605
Tel (304) 323-6300 SIC 6021

■ STELLAR ONE BANK p 1385
102 S Main St, Culpeper VA 22701
Tel (540) 382-4951 SIC 6021

■ CAPITAL ONE BANK p 250
1680 Capital One Dr, Mc Lean VA 22102
Tel (804) 967-1000 SIC 6021

▲ CAPITAL ONE FINANCIAL CORP p 250
1680 Capital One Dr, Mc Lean VA 22102
Tel (703) 720-1000 SIC 6021 6141

CAPITAL ONE FSB p 250
1680 Capital One Dr, Mc Lean VA 22102
Tel (610) 350-9074 SIC 6021

■ CAPITAL ONE NATIONAL ASSOCIATION p 250
1680 Capital One Dr, Mc Lean VA 22102
Tel (800) 655-2265 SIC 6021

■ CARDINAL BANK p 252
8270 Greensboro Dr # 100, Mc Lean VA 22102
Tel (703) 584-3400 SIC 6021 6162

▲ CARDINAL FINANCIAL CORP p 253
8270 Greensboro Dr # 500, Mc Lean VA 22102
Tel (703) 584-3400 SIC 6021 6211 8741

HSBC BANK USA NATIONAL ASSOCIATION p 714
1800 Tysons Blvd Ste 50, Mc Lean VA 22102
Tel (800) 975-4722 SIC 6021

▲ XENITH BANKSHARES INC p 1631
901 E Cary St Ste 1700, Richmond VA 23219
Tel (804) 433-2200 SIC 6021

▲ WASHINGTON FEDERAL INC p 1578
425 Pike St Ste 100, Seattle WA 98101
Tel (206) 624-7930 SIC 6021

AMERICANWEST BANK p 81
41 W Rverside Ave Ste 300, Spokane WA 99201
Tel (509) 232-1515 SIC 6021

▲ CITY HOLDING CO p 312
25 Gatewater Rd, Charleston WV 25313
Tel (304) 769-1100 SIC 6021

■ CITY NATIONAL BANK OF WEST VIRGINIA p 312
3601 Maccorkle Ave Se, Charleston WV 25304
Tel (304) 926-3301 SIC 6021

CITY NATIONAL BANK OF WEST VIRGINIA p 312
25 Gatewater Rd, Cross Lanes WV 25313
Tel (304) 769-1189 SIC 6021

▲ WESBANCO INC p 1593
2100 National Rd, Wheeling WV 26003
Tel (304) 234-9000 SIC 6021

■ ASSOCIATED BANK NATIONAL ASSOCIATION p 120
200 N Adams St, Green Bay WI 54301
Tel (920) 433-3200 SIC 6021 6211

JOHNSON BANK NA p 790
1 S Main St Ste 100, Janesville WI 53545
Tel (262) 639-6010 SIC 6021

JOHNSON FINANCIAL GROUP INC p 791
555 Main St Ste 400, Racine WI 53403
Tel (262) 619-2700
SIC 6022 6021 6712 6733 6311

SIC 6022 State Commercial Banks

■ REGIONS BANK p 1220
1901 5th Ave N, Birmingham AL 35203
Tel (205) 326-5300 SIC 6022

▲ REGIONS FINANCIAL CORP p 1220
1900 5th Ave N, Birmingham AL 35203
Tel (205) 581-7890 SIC 6022 6211 6282

▲ SERVISFIRST BANCSHARES INC p 1308
850 Shades Creek Pkwy, Mountain Brk AL 35209
Tel (205) 949-0302 SIC 6022

■ SERVISFIRST BANK p 1308
850 Shades Creek Pkwy, Mountain Brk AL 35209
Tel (205) 949-0302 SIC 6022

▲ NORTHRIM BANCORP INC p 1058
3111 C St, Anchorage AK 99503
Tel (907) 562-0062 SIC 6022 6282

▲ WESTERN ALLIANCE BANCORPORATION p 1597
1 E Wshington St Ste 1400, Phoenix AZ 85004
Tel (602) 389-3500 SIC 6022

■ CHASE BANKCARD SERVICES INC p 291
100 W University Dr, Tempe AZ 85281
Tel (480) 902-6000 SIC 6021 6022

■ CENTENNIAL BANK p 275
620 Chestnut St, Conway AR 72032
Tel (501) 328-4663 SIC 6022

▲ HOME BANCSHARES INC p 703
719 Harkrider St Ste 100, Conway AR 72032
Tel (501) 339-2929 SIC 6022

BANK OF ENGLAND p 151
123 S Main St, England AR 72046
Tel (501) 842-2555 SIC 6022 6021

ARVEST BANK p 114
1 N Mcilroy Ave, Fayetteville AR 72701
Tel (479) 575-1000 SIC 6022

▲ BANK OF OZARKS INC p 152
17901 Chenal Pkwy, Little Rock AR 72223
Tel (501) 978-2265 SIC 6022

FIRST SECURITY BANCORP p 549
314 N Spring St, Searcy AR 72143
Tel (501) 279-3400 SIC 6022

FIRST SECURITY BANK p 549
314 N Spring St, Searcy AR 72143
Tel (501) 279-3400 SIC 6022

LIBERTY BANK p 861
318 E Main St, Siloam Springs AR 72761
Tel (479) 524-8101 SIC 6022

CAPITALSOURCE BANK p 250
130 S State College Blvd, Brea CA 92821
Tel (714) 989-4600 SIC 6022

▲ TRICO BANCSHARES p 1479
63 Constitution Dr, Chico CA 95973
Tel (530) 898-0300 SIC 6022

VIB CORP p 1555
1498 W Main St, El Centro CA 92243
Tel (760) 352-5000 SIC 6022

■ CATHAY BANK p 265
9650 Flair Dr, El Monte CA 91731
Tel (626) 279-3698 SIC 6022

FREMONT BANK p 577
39150 Fremont Blvd, Fremont CA 94538
Tel (510) 505-5226 SIC 6022

▲ PACIFIC PREMIER BANCORP INC p 1105
17901 Von Karman Ave, Irvine CA 92614
Tel (949) 864-8000 SIC 6022

▲ FARMERS & MERCHANTS BANCORP p 529
111 W Pine St, Lodi CA 95240
Tel (209) 367-2300 SIC 6022

■ FARMERS & MERCHANTS BANK OF CENTRAL CALIFORNIA p 529
121 W Pine St, Lodi CA 95240
Tel (209) 367-2300 SIC 6022 6021

FARMERS & MERCHANTS BANK OF LONG BEACH p 529
302 Pine Ave, Long Beach CA 90802
Tel (562) 437-0011 SIC 6022 6029

BEVERLY HILLS BANCORP INC p 179
333 S Grand Ave Ste 4070, Los Angeles CA 90071
Tel (818) 223-8084 SIC 6022

■ CALIFORNIA UNITED BANK p 241
818 W 7th St Ste 220, Los Angeles CA 90017
Tel (213) 430-7000 SIC 6022

▲ CATHAY GENERAL BANCORP p 265
777 N Broadway, Los Angeles CA 90012
Tel (213) 625-4700 SIC 6022

CITY NATIONAL BANK p 312
555 S Flower St Ste 2500, Los Angeles CA 90071
Tel (310) 888-6000 SIC 6021 6022

GRANDPOINT BANK p 630
355 S Grand Ave Ste 2400, Los Angeles CA 90071
Tel (213) 626-0085 SIC 6022

■ HANMI BANK p 658
3660 Wilshire Blvd Ph A, Los Angeles CA 90010
Tel (213) 382-2200 SIC 6022

▲ PREFERRED BANK p 1169
601 S Figueroa St # 2900, Los Angeles CA 90017
Tel (213) 891-1188 SIC 6022

■ TCW GROUP INC p 1428
865 S Figueroa St # 2100, Los Angeles CA 90017
Tel (213) 244-0000 SIC 6022 6282 6211

UNION BANK FOUNDATION p 1504
445 S Figueroa St Ste 710, Los Angeles CA 90071
Tel (213) 236-5000 SIC 6022

UNION BANK OF CALIFORNIA p 1504
445 S Figueroa St Ste 710, Los Angeles CA 90071
Tel (213) 236-6444 SIC 6022

■ WELLS FARGO BANK LTD p 1590
333 S Grand Ave Ste 500, Los Angeles CA 90071
Tel (213) 253-6227 SIC 6022

WILSHIRE BANCORP INC p 1613
3200 Wilshire Blvd, Los Angeles CA 90010
Tel (213) 387-3200 SIC 6022

WILSHIRE BANK p 1613
3200 Wilshire Blvd Fl 10, Los Angeles CA 90010
Tel (213) 427-1000 SIC 6022

■ CITIZENS BUSINESS BANK p 310
701 N Haven Ave Ste 350, Ontario CA 91764
Tel (909) 980-4030 SIC 6022

▲ CVB FINANCIAL CORP p 404
701 N Haven Ave Ste 350, Ontario CA 91764
Tel (909) 980-4030 SIC 6022

COMMUNITY BANK p 347
460 Serra Madre Villa Ave, Pasadena CA 91107
Tel (626) 577-1700 SIC 6022 6029

▲ EAST WEST BANCORP INC p 471
135 N Los Robles Ave Fl 7, Pasadena CA 91101
Tel (626) 768-6000 SIC 6022

■ EAST WEST BANK p 471
135 N Ls Rbls Ave 100, Pasadena CA 91101
Tel (626) 768-6000 SIC 6022

RABOBANK NATIONAL ASSOCIATION p 1203
915 Highland Pointe Dr, Roseville CA 95678
Tel (760) 352-5000 SIC 6022

CALIFORNIA BANK & TRUST p 239
11622 El Camino Real # 200, San Diego CA 92130
Tel (858) 793-7400 SIC 6022

■ BANK OF WEST p 152
180 Montgomery St # 1400, San Francisco CA 94104
Tel (415) 765-4800 SIC 6022

▲ FIRST REPUBLIC BANK p 549
111 Pine St Ste Bsmt, San Francisco CA 94111
Tel (415) 392-1400 SIC 6022 6282 6162

▲ WELLS FARGO & CO p 1590
420 Montgomery St Frnt, San Francisco CA 94104
Tel (866) 249-3302
SIC 6021 6022 6162 6141 7374

WELLS FARGO FINANCING CORP p 1590
420 Montgomery St Frnt, San Francisco CA 94104
Tel (415) 222-4292 SIC 6022 6021

BRIDGE BANK NATIONAL ASSOCIATION p 211
55 Almaden Blvd Ste 200, San Jose CA 95113
Tel (408) 423-8500 SIC 6022 8742

▲ HERITAGE COMMERCE CORP p 686
150 Almaden Blvd Lbby, San Jose CA 95113
Tel (408) 947-6900 SIC 6022

■ WEST AMERICA BANK p 1593
1108 5th Ave, San Rafael CA 94901
Tel (707) 863-6113 SIC 6022

▲ SVB FINANCIAL GROUP p 1410
3003 Tasman Dr, Santa Clara CA 95054
Tel (408) 654-7400 SIC 6022

EXCHANGE BANK p 517
440 Aviation Blvd, Santa Rosa CA 95403
Tel (707) 524-3000 SIC 6036 8741 6022

BANK OF STOCKTON p 152
301 E Miner Ave, Stockton CA 95202
Tel (209) 929-1600 *SIC* 6022

MECHANICS BANK p 934
1111 Civic Dr Ste 333, Walnut Creek CA 94596
Tel (800) 797-6324 *SIC* 6022

▲ GUARANTY BANCORP p 644
1331 17th St Ste 200, Denver CO 80202
Tel (303) 296-9600 *SIC* 6022

■ GUARANTY BANK AND TRUST CO p 644
1331 17th St Lbby, Denver CO 80202
Tel (303) 298-6977 *SIC* 6022

VECTRA BANK COLORADO NA p 1546
2000 S Colorado Blvd Towe Tower, Denver CO 80222
Tel (720) 947-7700 *SIC* 6022

BANK OF COLORADO p 151
1609 E Harmony Rd, Fort Collins CO 80525
Tel (970) 206-1159 *SIC* 6022

ALPINE BANK p 60
2200 Grand Ave, Glenwood Springs CO 81601
Tel (970) 945-2424 *SIC* 6022

■ PEOPLES UNITED BANK NATIONAL ASSOCIATION p 1133
850 Main St Fl 6, Bridgeport CT 06604
Tel (203) 338-7171 *SIC* 6022

LIBERTY BANK p 861
315 Main St, Middletown CT 06457
Tel (860) 344-7200 *SIC* 6036 6163 6022

■ DISCOVER BANK p 442
502 E Market St, Greenwood DE 19950
Tel (302) 349-4512 *SIC* 6022

■ CITICORP DEL-LEASE INC p 310
1 Penns Way, New Castle DE 19721
Tel (302) 323-3801 *SIC* 6022 6311 6321

■ CHASE BANK USA NATIONAL ASSOCIATION p 291
200 White Clay Center Dr, Newark DE 19711
Tel (302) 634-1000 *SIC* 6022

■ MERCANTILE PENINSULA BANK p 944
1 W Church St, Selbyville DE 19975
Tel (302) 436-8236 *SIC* 6022

■ BANCORP BANK p 150
409 Silverside Rd Ste 105, Wilmington DE 19809
Tel (302) 385-5000 *SIC* 6022

■ COMENITY BANK p 344
1 Righter Pkwy Ste 100, Wilmington DE 19803
Tel (614) 729-4000 *SIC* 6022

HSBC BANK USA p 714
300 Delaware Ave Ste 1400, Wilmington DE 19801
Tel (302) 778-0169 *SIC* 6022

■ PNC BANK DELAWARE p 1158
222 Delaware Ave Lbby, Wilmington DE 19801
Tel (302) 655-7221 *SIC* 6022

■ PNC NATIONAL BANK OF DELAWARE p 1158
300 Bellevue Pkwy Ste 200, Wilmington DE 19809
Tel (302) 479-4529 *SIC* 6022

OCEAN BANK p 1072
780 Nw 42nd Ave Ste 300, Miami FL 33126
Tel (305) 448-2265 *SIC* 6022

TOTALBANK p 1463
100 Se 2nd St, Miami FL 33131
Tel (305) 982-3310 *SIC* 6022 6163

■ BANCO POPULAR NORTH AMERICA INC p 150
P.O. Box 4906, Miami Lakes FL 33014
Tel (847) 994-5400 *SIC* 6022

▲ BANKUNITED INC p 152
14817 Oak Ln, Miami Lakes FL 33016
Tel (305) 569-2000 *SIC* 6022

■ TIB FINANCIAL CORP p 1452
599 Tamiami Trl N Ste 101, Naples FL 34102
Tel (239) 263-3344 *SIC* 6022

■ SUNTRUST BANKS OF FLORIDA INC p 1401
200 S Orange Ave, Orlando FL 32801
Tel (407) 237-4141 *SIC* 6021 6022

▲ STONEGATE BANK p 1391
400 N Federal Hwy, Pompano Beach FL 33062
Tel (954) 315-5500 *SIC* 6022

▲ SEACOAST BANKING CORP OF FLORIDA p 1296
815 Colorado Ave, Stuart FL 34994
Tel (772) 287-4000 *SIC* 6022

■ CAPITAL CITY BANK p 249
217 N Monroe St, Tallahassee FL 32301
Tel (850) 402-7700 *SIC* 6022

▲ CAPITAL CITY BANK GROUP INC p 249
217 N Monroe St, Tallahassee FL 32301
Tel (850) 402-7000 *SIC* 6022

■ TRI-COUNTY BANK p 1477
350 E Wade St, Trenton FL 32693
Tel (352) 463-1547 *SIC* 6022

FIRST BANK OF PALM BEACHES p 545
415 5th St, West Palm Beach FL 33401
Tel (561) 651-7266 *SIC* 6022

▲ FCB FINANCIAL HOLDINGS INC p 532
2500 Weston Rd Ste 300, Weston FL 33331
Tel (954) 984-3313 *SIC* 6022

■ FLORIDA COMMUNITY BANK NA p 557
2500 Weston Rd Ste 300, Weston FL 33331
Tel (866) 764-0006 *SIC* 6022

■ CENTERSTATE BANK OF FLORIDA NATIONAL ASSOCIATION p 276
7722 State Road 544, Winter Haven FL 33881
Tel (863) 422-8990 *SIC* 6022

■ FIRST NATIONAL BANK OF POLK COUNTY INC p 548
7722 State Road 544 Fl 1, Winter Haven FL 33881
Tel (863) 422-8990 *SIC* 6022

MERCANTILE BANK p 943
1560 Orange Ave Ste 300, Winter Park FL 32789
Tel (407) 622-3528 *SIC* 6022

■ BANK OF NORTH GEORGIA p 152
8025 Westside Pkwy # 150, Alpharetta GA 30009
Tel (770) 569-9660 *SIC* 6022

■ CERTUSHOLDINGS INC p 284
1170 Peachtree St Nw 2400, Atlanta GA 30309
Tel (704) 973-3917 *SIC* 6022

COMMUNITY & SOUTHERN BANK p 347
3333 Rvrwood Pkwy Se # 350, Atlanta GA 30339
Tel (770) 832-3557 *SIC* 6022

▲ FIDELITY SOUTHERN CORP p 541
3490 Piedmont Rd Ne # 1550, Atlanta GA 30305
Tel (404) 639-6500 *SIC* 6022

■ STATE BANK AND TRUST CO p 1380
3399 Peachtree Rd Ne # 1900, Atlanta GA 30326
Tel (800) 414-4177 *SIC* 6022

▲ STATE BANK FINANCIAL CORP p 1380
3399 Peachtree Rd Ne, Atlanta GA 30326
Tel (404) 475-6599
SIC 6022 6712 6311 6141 6331

▲ SUNTRUST BANKS INC p 1405
303 Peachtree St Ne, Atlanta GA 30308
Tel (800) 786-8787
SIC 6021 6022 6211 6091 6282

■ UNITED COMMUNITY BANK p 1507
177 Highway 515 E, Blairsville GA 30512
Tel (706) 745-2151 *SIC* 6022

UNITED COMMUNITY BANKS INC p 1507
125 Highway 515 E, Blairsville GA 30512
Tel (581) 807-3041 *SIC* 6022

▲ UNITED COMMUNITY BANKS INC p 1507
125 Highway 515 E, Blairsville GA 30512
Tel (706) 781-2265 *SIC* 6022

■ SYNOVUS BANK p 1415
1148 Broadway, Columbus GA 31901
Tel (706) 649-4900 *SIC* 6022

▲ SYNOVUS FINANCIAL CORP p 1415
1111 Bay Ave Ste 500, Columbus GA 31901
Tel (706) 649-2311 *SIC* 6021 6022 7389

■ AMERICAN BANKING CO p 68
225 S Main St, Moultrie GA 31768
Tel (229) 985-2222 *SIC* 6022 6021

▲ AMERIS BANCORP p 83
310 1st St Se, Moultrie GA 31768
Tel (229) 890-1111 *SIC* 6022

■ AMERIS BANK p 83
310 1st St Se, Moultrie GA 31768
Tel (800) 845-5219 *SIC* 6022

■ BANK OF HAWAII p 151
130 Merchant St, Honolulu HI 96813
Tel (888) 643-3888 *SIC* 6022 6411 6211

▲ BANK OF HAWAII CORP p 151
130 Merchant St, Honolulu HI 96813
Tel (888) 643-3888 *SIC* 6022

■ CENTRAL PACIFIC BANK p 279
220 S King St, Honolulu HI 96813
Tel (808) 544-0500 *SIC* 6022

▲ CENTRAL PACIFIC FINANCIAL CORP p 279
220 S King St, Honolulu HI 96813
Tel (808) 544-0500 *SIC* 6022

■ FIRST HAWAIIAN BANK p 547
999 Bishop St Ste 3200, Honolulu HI 96813
Tel (808) 525-6340 *SIC* 6022

■ FIRST HAWAIIAN INC p 547
999 Bishop St Fl 29, Honolulu HI 96813
Tel (808) 525-7000 *SIC* 6022

▲ OLD SECOND BANCORP INC p 1081
37 S River St, Aurora IL 60506
Tel (630) 892-0202 *SIC* 6022

■ BARRINGTON BANK & TRUST CO NATIONAL ASSOCIATION p 157
201 S Hough St, Barrington IL 60010
Tel (847) 842-4500 *SIC* 6022

HEARTLAND BANK AND TRUST p 679
401 N Hershey Rd, Bloomington IL 61704
Tel (309) 662-4444 *SIC* 6022

BRIDGEVIEW BANK GROUP p 212
7940 S Harlem Ave, Bridgeview IL 60455
Tel (708) 594-7400 *SIC* 6022

■ BUSEY BANK p 229
100 W University Ave # 100, Champaign IL 61820
Tel (217) 365-4500 *SIC* 6022

▲ FIRST BUSEY CORP p 545
100 W University Ave, Champaign IL 61820
Tel (217) 365-4544 *SIC* 6022

BYLINE BANK p 231
3639 N Broadway St, Chicago IL 60613
Tel (773) 244-7000 *SIC* 6022 6163 6021

▲ NORTHERN TRUST CORP p 1057
50 S La Salle St, Chicago IL 60603
Tel (312) 630-6000 *SIC* 6022

▲ PRIVATEBANCORP INC p 1178
120 S Lasalle St Ste 400, Chicago IL 60603
Tel (312) 564-2000 *SIC* 6022

■ PRIVATEBANK AND TRUST CO p 1178
120 S La Salle St, Chicago IL 60603
Tel (312) 564-2000 *SIC* 6022

■ WINTRUST BANK p 1617
190 S La Salle St # 2200, Chicago IL 60603
Tel (773) 227-7074 *SIC* 6022

▲ MIDLAND STATES BANCORP INC p 966
1201 Network Centre Dr, Effingham IL 62401
Tel (217) 342-7321 *SIC* 6022

■ MIDLAND STATES BANK p 966
1201 Network Centre Dr, Effingham IL 62401
Tel (217) 342-2141 *SIC* 6022

FIRST AMERICAN BANK p 544
700 Busse Rd, Elk Grove Village IL 60007
Tel (847) 228-9300 *SIC* 6022

STANDARD BANK & TRUST CO (INC) p 1375
7800 W 95th St Ste 101, Hickory Hills IL 60457
Tel (708) 499-2062 *SIC* 6022

■ LAKE FOREST BANK AND TRUST CO p 839
727 N Bank Ln Fl 1, Lake Forest IL 60045
Tel (847) 234-2882 *SIC* 6022

WEST SUBURBAN BANCORP INC p 1595
711 Westmore Meyers Rd, Lombard IL 60148
Tel (630) 629-4200 *SIC* 6022

▲ QCR HOLDINGS INC p 1194
3551 7th St Ste 204, Moline IL 61265
Tel (309) 736-3584 *SIC* 6022

MORTON COMMUNITY BANK INC p 991
721 W Jackson St, Morton IL 61550
Tel (309) 263-8126 *SIC* 6022 6021

▲ DISCOVER FINANCIAL SERVICES p 442
2500 Lake Cook Rd, Riverwoods IL 60015
Tel (224) 405-0900 *SIC* 6022 6141 7389

COLE TAYLOR BANK p 336
9550 W Higgins Rd Fl 5, Rosemont IL 60018
Tel (847) 653-7000 *SIC* 6022

TAYLOR CAPITAL GROUP INC p 1427
9550 W Higgins Rd, Rosemont IL 60018
Tel (847) 653-7978 *SIC* 6022

▲ WINTRUST FINANCIAL CORP p 1617
9700 W Higgins Rd, Rosemont IL 60018
Tel (847) 939-9000 *SIC* 6022 6211 6282

AMERICAN CHARTERED BANK p 70
1199 E Higgins Rd, Schaumburg IL 60173
Tel (847) 517-5400 *SIC* 6022 6021

■ OLD NATIONAL BANK p 1081
1 Main St, Evansville IN 47708
Tel (800) 731-2265 *SIC* 6021 6022

▲ MAINSOURCE FINANCIAL GROUP INC p 898
2105 N State Road 3 Byp, Greensburg IN 47240
Tel (812) 663-0157 *SIC* 6022

FIRST BANCSHARES INC p 545
9701 Indpls Blvd, Highland IN 46322
Tel (219) 659-0043 *SIC* 6022

■ FIFTH THIRD BANK INDIANA p 542
251 N Illinois St # 1000, Indianapolis IN 46204
Tel (317) 383-2300 *SIC* 6022

■ GERMAN AMERICAN BANCORP p 608
711 Main St, Jasper IN 47546
Tel (812) 482-1314 *SIC* 6022

▲ GERMAN AMERICAN BANCORP INC p 608
711 Main St, Jasper IN 47546
Tel (812) 482-1314 *SIC* 6022

■ 1ST SOURCE BANK p 1
100 N Michigan St Ste 800, South Bend IN 46601
Tel (574) 235-2000 *SIC* 6022

▲ 1ST SOURCE CORP p 1
100 N Michigan St, South Bend IN 46601
Tel (574) 235-2000 *SIC* 6022

▲ FIRST FINANCIAL CORP p 546
1 First Financial Plz, Terre Haute IN 47807
Tel (812) 238-6000 *SIC* 6022

■ FIRST MERCHANTS BANK p 547
189 W Market St, Wabash IN 46992
Tel (260) 563-4116 *SIC* 6022

■ LAKE CITY BANK p 838
202 E Center St, Warsaw IN 46580
Tel (574) 267-6144 *SIC* 6022 6163

▲ LAKELAND FINANCIAL CORP p 840
202 E Center St, Warsaw IN 46580
Tel (574) 267-6144 *SIC* 6022

CENTIER BANK p 277
1500 119th St, Whiting IN 46394
Tel (219) 659-0043 *SIC* 6022

BANKERS TRUST CO p 152
453 7th St, Des Moines IA 50309
Tel (515) 245-2863 *SIC* 6022

■ DUBUQUE BANK AND TRUST CO p 459
1398 Central Ave, Dubuque IA 52001
Tel (563) 589-2000 *SIC* 6022

▲ HEARTLAND FINANCIAL USA INC p 679
1398 Central Ave, Dubuque IA 52001
Tel (563) 589-2000 *SIC* 6022

▲ HILLS BANCORPORATION p 694
131 Main St, Hills IA 52235
Tel (319) 679-2291 *SIC* 6022

■ HILLS BANK AND TRUST CO p 694
131 Main St, Hills IA 52235
Tel (319) 679-2291 *SIC* 6022

▲ MIDWESTONE FINANCIAL GROUP INC p 968
102 S Clinton St, Iowa City IA 52240
Tel (319) 356-5800 *SIC* 6022 6331

HILLCREST BANCSHARES INC p 693
11111 W 95th St, Shawnee Mission KS 66214
Tel (913) 492-7500 *SIC* 6022

INTRUST FINANCIAL CORP p 760
105 N Main St, Wichita KS 67202
Tel (316) 383-1111 *SIC* 6712 6022

■ FIFTH THIRD BANK OF NORTHERN KENTUCKY p 542
8100 Burlington Pike, Florence KY 41042
Tel (859) 283-8500 *SIC* 6022

CENTRAL BANK & TRUST CO p 277
300 W Vine St Ste 3, Lexington KY 40507
Tel (859) 253-6222 *SIC* 6022

▲ REPUBLIC BANCORP INC p 1225
601 W Market St Ste 100, Louisville KY 40202
Tel (502) 584-3600 *SIC* 6022

■ REPUBLIC BANK & TRUST CO INC p 1225
601 W Market St Ste 100, Louisville KY 40202
Tel (502) 584-3600 *SIC* 6022 6163

▲ STOCK YARDS BANCORP INC p 1390
1040 E Main St, Louisville KY 40206
Tel (502) 582-2571 *SIC* 6022

■ STOCK YARDS BANK & TRUST CO INC p 1390
1040 E Main St, Louisville KY 40206
Tel (502) 625-1790 *SIC* 6022

▲ COMMUNITY TRUST BANCORP INC p 350
346 N Mayo Trl, Pikeville KY 41501
Tel (606) 432-1414 *SIC* 6022

■ COMMUNITY TRUST BANK p 350
155 Main St, Whitesburg KY 41858
Tel (606) 633-0161 *SIC* 6022 6021

ORIGIN BANK p 1094
3921 Elm St, Choudrant LA 71227
Tel (318) 255-2222 *SIC* 6022

▲ IBERIABANK CORP p 726
200 W Congress St, Lafayette LA 70501
Tel (337) 521-4003 *SIC* 6022

CB&T HOLDING CORP p 268
1100 Poydras St Ste 1800, New Orleans LA 70163
Tel (504) 525-4381 *SIC* 6022

■ FIRST NBC BANK p 548
210 Baronne St Frnt, New Orleans LA 70112
Tel (504) 566-8000 *SIC* 6022

▲ FIRST NBC BANK HOLDING CO p 548
210 Baronne St, New Orleans LA 70112
Tel (504) 566-8000 *SIC* 6022

FIRSTRUST CORP p 551
909 Poydras St Ste 1700, New Orleans LA 70112
Tel (504) 584-5900 *SIC* 6022

GULF COAST BANK AND TRUST CO p 646
200 Saint Charles Ave, New Orleans LA 70130
Tel (504) 561-6100 *SIC* 6022

■ CAMDEN NATIONAL BANK (INC) p 244
2 Elm St, Camden ME 04843
Tel (207) 236-8821 *SIC* 6022

TD BANK US HOLDING CO p 1428
2 Portland Sq, Portland ME 04101
Tel (207) 761-8500 *SIC* 6022

■ CITIFINANCIAL CREDIT CO p 310
300 Saint Paul St Fl 3, Baltimore MD 21202
Tel (410) 332-3000
SIC 6141 6162 7389 6331 6159 6022

▲ EAGLE BANCORP INC p 467
7830 Old Georgtwn Rd Fl 3, Bethesda MD 20814
Tel (301) 986-1800 *SIC* 6022

■ EAGLEBANK p 468
7830 Old Georgtwn Rd Fl 3, Bethesda MD 20814
Tel (301) 986-1800 *SIC* 6022

■ INTERACTIVE DATA PRICING AND REFERENCE DATA LLC p 751
32 Crosby Dr, Bedford MA 01730
Tel (781) 687-8800 *SIC* 6022

■ BOSTON CO INC p 202
1 Boston Pl Ste 2100, Boston MA 02108
Tel (617) 722-7000 *SIC* 6022 6282

■ BOSTON PRIVATE BANK & TRUST CO p 203
10 Post Office Sq Lbby F, Boston MA 02109
Tel (617) 912-1931 *SIC* 6022

▲ BOSTON PRIVATE FINANCIAL HOLDINGS INC p 203
10 Post Office Sq, Boston MA 02109
Tel (617) 912-1900 *SIC* 6022 6722 6282

EASTERN BANK CORP p 471
265 Franklin St Fl 2, Boston MA 02110
Tel (617) 897-1100 *SIC* 6036 6022 6282

■ STATE STREET BANK AND TRUST CO p 1383
1 Lincoln St Fl 1, Boston MA 02111
Tel (617) 786-3000 *SIC* 6022

▲ STATE STREET CORP p 1383
1 Lincoln St, Boston MA 02111
Tel (617) 786-3000 *SIC* 6022 6282

▲ INDEPENDENT BANK CORP p 736
2036 Washington St, Hanover MA 02339
Tel (781) 878-6100 *SIC* 6022

▲ ENTERPRISE BANCORP INC p 502
222 Merrimack St, Lowell MA 01852
Tel (978) 459-9000 *SIC* 6022

■ ENTERPRISE BANK AND TRUST CO p 502
222 Merrimack St Fl 1, Lowell MA 01852
Tel (978) 459-9000 *SIC* 6022

▲ CENTURY BANCORP INC p 282
400 Mystic Ave, Medford MA 02155
Tel (781) 393-4160 *SIC* 6022

■ CENTURY BANK AND TRUST CO p 282
400 Mystic Ave, Medford MA 02155
Tel (781) 393-4677 *SIC* 6022

■ LSB CORP p 883
30 Massachusetts Ave # 8, North Andover MA 01845
Tel (978) 725-7500 *SIC* 6022

▲ BERKSHIRE HILLS BANCORP INC p 175
24 North St, Pittsfield MA 01201
Tel (413) 443-5601 *SIC* 6022 6411

■ ROCKLAND TRUST CO p 1245
288 Union St, Rockland MA 02370
Tel (781) 878-6100 *SIC* 6022

SALEM FIVE CENTS SAVINGS BANK p 1272
210 Essex St, Salem MA 01970
Tel (978) 745-5555 *SIC* 6022

CITIZENS BANK p 310
328 S Saginaw St Lbby, Flint MI 48502
Tel (810) 766-7500 *SIC* 6022 6159 6162

REPUBLIC BANK p 1225
328 S Saginaw St Lbby, Flint MI 48502
Tel (810) 257-2506 *SIC* 6022 6163 6029

■ FIFTH THIRD BANK p 541
1 Vandenberg Ctr Nw, Grand Rapids MI 49503
Tel (616) 653-5900 *SIC* 6022

▲ INDEPENDENT BANK CORP p 736
4200 E Beltline Ave Ne, Grand Rapids MI 49525
Tel (616) 527-5820 *SIC* 6022

▲ MERCANTILE BANK CORP p 943
310 Leonard St Nw, Grand Rapids MI 49504
Tel (616) 406-3000 *SIC* 6022

■ MERCANTILE BANK OF MICHIGAN p 943
310 Leonard St Nw, Grand Rapids MI 49504
Tel (616) 406-3000 *SIC* 6022

■ INDEPENDENT BANK CORP p 736
230 W Main St, Ionia MI 48846
Tel (616) 527-2400 *SIC* 6022

■ CHEMICAL BANK AND TRUST CO p 293
333 E Main St, Midland MI 48640
Tel (989) 631-9200 *SIC* 6022

▲ CHEMICAL FINANCIAL CORP p 293
235 E Main St, Midland MI 48640
Tel (989) 839-5350 *SIC* 6022

CRESTMARK BANK p 392
5480 Corporate Dr, Troy MI 48098
Tel (248) 641-5100 *SIC* 6022

TALMER BANK AND TRUST p 1423
2301 W Big Beaver Rd # 525, Troy MI 48084
Tel (248) 649-2301 *SIC* 6022

FRANDSEN FINANCIAL CORP p 574
4388 Round Lake Rd W, Arden Hills MN 55112
Tel (651) 242-5700 *SIC* 6022 6712

▲ US BANCORP p 1531
800 Nicollet Mall # 1500, Minneapolis MN 55402
Tel (651) 466-3000
SIC 6021 6022 6162 6091 6159 6411

MINNWEST CORP p 974
14820 Highway 7 Ste 200, Minnetonka MN 55345
Tel (952) 230-9800 *SIC* 6022

BREMER FINANCIAL CORP p 210
380 Sint Peter St Ste 500, Saint Paul MN 55102
Tel (800) 908-2265 *SIC* 6022 6712

OTTO BREMER FOUNDATION p 1098
30 7th St E Ste 2900, Saint Paul MN 55101
Tel (651) 227-8036 SIC 6732 6022

BANKPLUS p 152
202 E Jackson St, Belzoni MS 39038
Tel (601) 898-8300 SIC 6022

CITIZENS FINANCIAL CORP p 311
202 E Jackson St, Belzoni MS 39038
Tel (662) 746-6811 SIC 6022 6021 6141

▲ HANCOCK HOLDING CO p 657
2510 14th St, Gulfport MS 39501
Tel (228) 868-4000 SIC 6022

■ WHITNEY BANK p 1607
1 Hancock Plz Fl 7, Gulfport MS 39501
Tel (228) 868-4000 SIC 6022

M & F FIRST CORP p 888
134 W Washington St, Kosciusko MS 39090
Tel (662) 289-5121 SIC 6022

■ BANCORPSOUTH BANK p 150
201 S Spring St, Tupelo MS 38804
Tel (662) 680-2000 SIC 6022

▲ BANCORPSOUTH INC p 150
201 S Spring St, Tupelo MS 38804
Tel (662) 680-2000 SIC 6022

■ RENASANT BANK p 1223
209 Troy St, Tupelo MS 38804
Tel (662) 680-1001 SIC 6022 6162

FIRST STATE COMMUNITY BANK INC p 549
201 E Columbia St, Farmington MO 63640
Tel (573) 756-4547 SIC 6022

CENTRAL CAPITAL MARKETS p 277
238 Madison St, Jefferson City MO 65101
Tel (573) 634-1330 SIC 6022 6211

CENTRAL TRUST BANK p 280
238 Madison St, Jefferson City MO 65101
Tel (573) 634-1302 SIC 6022

▲ COMMERCE BANCSHARES INC p 344
1000 Walnut St, Kansas City MO 64106
Tel (816) 234-2000 SIC 6022 6311 6162

■ COMMERCE BANK p 345
1000 Walnut St Fl 700, Kansas City MO 64106
Tel (816) 234-2000 SIC 6022

■ NBH BANK p 1021
1111 Main St Ste 100, Kansas City MO 64105
Tel (816) 471-9800 SIC 6022

■ ENTERPRISE BANK & TRUST p 502
150 N Meramec Ave Ste 300, Saint Louis MO 63105
Tel (314) 725-5500 SIC 6022

▲ ENTERPRISE FINANCIAL SERVICES CORP p 502
150 N Meramec Ave Ste 350, Saint Louis MO 63105
Tel (314) 725-5500 SIC 6022

MISSISSIPPI VALLEY BANCSHARES INC p 976
13205 Manchester Rd, Saint Louis MO 63131
Tel (314) 543-3512 SIC 6022 6712

STUPP BROS INC p 1395
3800 Weber Rd, Saint Louis MO 63125
Tel (314) 638-5000 SIC 3441 3317 6022

▲ GREAT SOUTHERN BANCORP INC p 634
1451 E Battlefield St, Springfield MO 65804
Tel (417) 887-4400 SIC 6022

▲ FIRST INTERSTATE BANCSYSTEM INC p 547
401 N 31st St, Billings MT 59101
Tel (406) 255-5390 SIC 6022

■ FIRST INTERSTATE BANK p 547
401 N 31st St Bsmt, Billings MT 59101
Tel (406) 255-5000 SIC 6022

▲ GLACIER BANCORP INC p 613
49 Commons Loop, Kalispell MT 59901
Tel (406) 756-4200 SIC 6022

■ GLACIER BANK p 614
202 Mn St, Kalispell MT 59901
Tel (406) 756-4200 SIC 6022

STOCKMAN BANK OF MONTANA p 1390
700 Main St, Miles City MT 59301
Tel (406) 234-8420 SIC 6022

STOCKMAN FINANCIAL CORP p 1390
700 Main St, Miles City MT 59301
Tel (406) 234-8420 SIC 6022

PINNACLE BANCORP INC p 1149
1801 Burt St, Elkhorn NE 68022
Tel (402) 697-8666 SIC 6022 6712

UNION BANK AND TRUST CO p 1504
3643 S 48th St, Lincoln NE 68506
Tel (402) 488-0941
SIC 6111 6029 6162 6021 6035 6022

FIRST NATIONAL OF NEBRASKA INC p 548
1620 Dodge St, Omaha NE 68197
Tel (402) 341-0500 SIC 6022 6141 7371

BANK OF NEVADA p 151
2700 W Sahara Ave Ste 100, Las Vegas NV 89102
Tel (702) 248-4200 SIC 6022

NEVADA STATE BANK p 1028
750 E Warm Springs Rd # 240, Las Vegas NV 89119
Tel (702) 855-4575 SIC 6022

■ PEAPACK-GLADSTONE BANK p 1126
500 Hills Dr Ste 300, Bedminster NJ 07921
Tel (908) 234-0700 SIC 6022

■ CONNECTONE BANK p 357
301 Sylvan Ave Ste 1, Englewood NJ 07632
Tel (201) 816-8900 SIC 6022

▲ CONNECTONE BANCORP INC p 357
301 Sylvan Ave, Englewood Cliffs NJ 07632
Tel (201) 816-8900 SIC 6022

■ KEARNY BANK p 807
120 Passaic Ave, Fairfield NJ 07004
Tel (973) 244-4500 SIC 6022

HUDSON UNITED BANK p 717
1000 Macarthur Blvd, Mahwah NJ 07430
Tel (201) 236-2600 SIC 6141 6022

▲ MARLIN BUSINESS SERVICES CORP p 909
300 Fellowship Rd, Mount Laurel NJ 08054
Tel (888) 479-9111 SIC 7389 7359 6022

■ LAKELAND BANK p 839
2717 Route 23, Newfoundland NJ 07435
Tel (973) 697-2040 SIC 6022

▲ LAKELAND BANCORP INC p 839
250 Oak Ridge Rd, Oak Ridge NJ 07438
Tel (973) 697-2000 SIC 6022

▲ ORITANI FINANCIAL CORP p 1095
370 Pascack Rd, Twp Washinton NJ 07676
Tel (201) 664-5400 SIC 6022

▲ M&T BANK CORP p 890
1 M&T Plz Fl 5, Buffalo NY 14203
Tel (716) 635-4000 SIC 6022

■ MANUFACTURERS AND TRADERS TRUST CO p 903
1 M And T Plz, Buffalo NY 14203
Tel (716) 842-4200 SIC 6022

▲ TRUSTCO BANK CORP N Y p 1487
5 Sarnowski Dr, Glenville NY 12302
Tel (518) 377-3311 SIC 6022

▲ TOMPKINS FINANCIAL CORP p 1460
The Cmns, Ithaca NY 14851
Tel (607) 273-3210 SIC 6022

■ CAPITAL ONE BANK p 250
275 Broadhollow Rd, Melville NY 11747
Tel (631) 844-1376 SIC 6022

AMALGAMATED BANK p 64
275 7th Ave Lbby 2, New York NY 10001
Tel (212) 895-8988 SIC 6022

BANK LEUMI LE-ISRAEL CORP p 151
579 5th Ave Lbby 1, New York NY 10017
Tel (917) 542-2343 SIC 6022

BANK LEUMI USA p 151
579 5th Ave Frnt A, New York NY 10017
Tel (917) 542-2343 SIC 6022 7359

■ BANK OF AMERICA PVT WEALTH MANAGEMENT p 151
114 W 47th St Ste C-1, New York NY 10036
Tel (800) 878-7878
SIC 6282 6022 6099 6733

▲ BANK OF NEW YORK MELLON CORP p 151
225 Liberty St, New York NY 10281
Tel (212) 495-1784 SIC 6022

BESSEMER TRUST CO NA p 176
45 Rockefeller Plz 600b, New York NY 10111
Tel (212) 708-9100 SIC 6022

▲ CIT GROUP INC p 309
11 W 42nd St Fl 7, New York NY 10036
Tel (212) 461-5200
SIC 6022 6162 6159 6141

■ GOLDMAN SACHS BANK USA p 622
200 West St, New York NY 10282
Tel (212) 902-1000 SIC 6022

ISRAEL DISCOUNT BANK OF NEW YORK p 767
511 5th Ave, New York NY 10017
Tel (212) 551-8500 SIC 6022

MIZUHO BANK LTD p 978
1251 Ave Of The Americas, New York NY 10020
Tel (212) 282-3000 SIC 6022 6082 7359

RBC USA HOLDCO CORP p 1211
3 World Financial Ctr, New York NY 10281
Tel (212) 858-7200 SIC 6712 6021 6022

UTRECHT - AMERICA HOLDINGS INC p 1537
245 Park Ave Fl 36, New York NY 10167
Tel (212) 916-7800 SIC 6022

■ TRUSTCO BANK p 1487
1 Sarnowski Dr, Schenectady NY 12302
Tel (518) 344-7510 SIC 6022

■ FIVE STAR BANK p 553
220 Liberty St, Warsaw NY 14569
Tel (585) 786-3131 SIC 6022

■ NEW YORK COMMERCIAL BANK p 1034
615 Merrick Ave, Westbury NY 11590
Tel (800) 535-2269 SIC 6022

HUDSON VALLEY HOLDING CORP p 717
21 Scarsdale Rd, Yonkers NY 10707
Tel (914) 961-6100 SIC 6022

VANTAGESOUTH BANK p 1544
1005 High House Rd, Cary NC 27513
Tel (919) 460-7770 SIC 6022

▲ BANK OF AMERICA CORP p 151
100 N Tryon St Ste 220, Charlotte NC 28202
Tel (704) 386-5681
SIC 6021 6022 6211 6091 6162 6159

▲ PARK STERLING CORP p 1116
1043 E Morehead St # 111, Charlotte NC 28204
Tel (704) 716-2134 SIC 6022

SQUARE 1 FINANCIAL INC p 1362
406 Blackwell St Ste 240, Durham NC 27701
Tel (866) 355-0468 SIC 6022 6799

NEWBRIDGE BANCORP p 1037
1501 Highwoods Blvd # 400, Greensboro NC 27410
Tel (336) 369-0900 SIC 6022

NEWBRIDGE BANK p 1037
1501 Highwoods Blvd, Greensboro NC 27410
Tel (336) 248-6500 SIC 6022

SOUTHERN BANCSHARES (NC) INC p 1347
116 E Main St, Mount Olive NC 28365
Tel (919) 658-7000 SIC 6022

■ CAPITAL BANK CORP p 249
333 Fayetteville St, Raleigh NC 27601
Tel (919) 645-0868 SIC 6022

▲ FIRST CITIZENS BANCSHARES INC p 545
4300 Six Forks Rd, Raleigh NC 27609
Tel (919) 716-7000 SIC 6022

RBC BANCORPORATION (USA) p 1211
301 Fayetteville St, Raleigh NC 27601
Tel (252) 454-4400 SIC 6712 6022

VANTAGESOUTH BANCSHARES INC p 1544
3600 Glenwood Ave Ste 300, Raleigh NC 27612
Tel (919) 659-9000 SIC 6022

▲ YADKIN FINANCIAL CORP p 1633
3600 Glenwood Ave Ste 300, Raleigh NC 27612
Tel (919) 659-9000 SIC 6022

▲ FIRST BANCORP p 545
300 Sw Broad St, Southern Pines NC 28387
Tel (910) 246-2500 SIC 6022

■ YADKIN BANK p 1633
325 E Front St, Statesville NC 28677
Tel (704) 924-8815 SIC 6022

■ BANK OF NORTH CAROLINA p 151
831 Julian Ave, Thomasville NC 27360
Tel (336) 476-9200 SIC 6022

■ FIRST BANK p 545
341 N Main St, Troy NC 27371
Tel (910) 576-6171 SIC 6022

LIVE OAK BANCSHARES INC p 871
1741 Tiburon Dr, Wilmington NC 28403
Tel (910) 790-5867 SIC 6022

■ BRANCH BANKING AND TRUST CO p 207
200 W 2nd St, Winston Salem NC 27101
Tel (336) 733-2000 SIC 6022 6021

BELL BANK p 170
3100 13th Ave S, Fargo ND 58103
Tel (701) 298-1500 SIC 6022

STATE BANKSHARES INC p 1380
3100 13th Ave S, Fargo ND 58103
Tel (701) 298-1500 SIC 6022

FIRST INTERNATIONAL BANK AND TRUST p 547
100 N Main St, Watford City ND 58854
Tel (701) 232-1700 SIC 6022

▲ FIFTH THIRD BANCORP p 541
38 Fountain Square Plz, Cincinnati OH 45202
Tel (800) 972-3030 SIC 6022

■ FIFTH THIRD BANK p 541
38 Fountain Square Plz, Cincinnati OH 45202
Tel (800) 972-3030 SIC 6022

■ KEYBANK NATIONAL ASSOCIATION p 815
127 Public Sq Ste 5600, Cleveland OH 44114
Tel (800) 539-2968 SIC 6021 6022 6159

■ FIFTH THIRD BANK OF COLUMBUS OH p 542
21 E State St Fl 4, Columbus OH 43215
Tel (614) 744-7553 SIC 6022

■ JPMORGAN CHASE BANK NATIONAL ASSOCIATION p 795
1111 Polaris Pkwy, Columbus OH 43240
Tel (614) 436-3055
SIC 6022 6099 6799 6211 6162 7389

■ PEOPLES BANKING AND TRUST CO p 1132
138 Putnam St, Marietta OH 45750
Tel (740) 373-3155 SIC 6022

RCB BANK SERVICE INC p 1212
300 W Patti Page Blvd, Claremore OK 74017
Tel (918) 341-6150 SIC 6022

DURANT BANCORP INC p 462
1400 W Main St, Durant OK 74701
Tel (580) 924-2211 SIC 6022

FIRST UNITED BANK AND TRUST CO p 550
1400 W Main St, Durant OK 74701
Tel (580) 924-2211 SIC 6022 6163 6021

■ BANCFIRST p 149
101 N Broadway Ave # 1110, Oklahoma City OK 73102
Tel (405) 270-1000 SIC 6022

▲ BANCFIRST CORP p 149
101 N Broadway Ave # 1110, Oklahoma City OK 73102
Tel (405) 270-1086 SIC 6022

UNION BANK p 1504
4921 N May Ave, Oklahoma City OK 73112
Tel (405) 949-7200 SIC 6022

BANK OF OKLAHOMA FINANCIAL CORP p 152
6424 E 41st St, Tulsa OK 74135
Tel (918) 619-1578 SIC 6022

F & M BANK & TRUST CO p 522
1330 S Harvard Ave, Tulsa OK 74112
Tel (918) 744-1330 SIC 6022

■ BANK OF CASCADES p 151
1100 Nw Wall St, Bend OR 97703
Tel (541) 617-3500 SIC 6022

▲ CASCADE BANCORP p 262
1100 Nw Wall St, Bend OR 97703
Tel (541) 617-3500 SIC 6022

▲ UMPQUA HOLDINGS CORP p 1502
1 Sw Columbia St Ste 1200, Portland OR 97258
Tel (503) 727-4100 SIC 6035 6022

▲ BRYN MAWR BANK CORP p 221
801 W Lancaster Ave, Bryn Mawr PA 19010
Tel (610) 525-1700 SIC 6022

■ BRYN MAWR TRUST CO p 221
801 W Lancaster Ave, Bryn Mawr PA 19010
Tel (610) 581-4819 SIC 6022

■ CNB BANK p 330
1 S 2nd St, Clearfield PA 16830
Tel (814) 765-4577 SIC 6022

▲ CNB FINANCIAL CORP p 330
1 S 2nd St, Clearfield PA 16830
Tel (814) 765-9621 SIC 6022

METRO BANCORP INC p 954
3801 Paxton St, Harrisburg PA 17111
Tel (888) 937-0004 SIC 6022

CAPMARK BANK p 251
116 Welsh Rd, Horsham PA 19044
Tel (801) 569-4606 SIC 6022

■ S & T BANK p 1261
800 Philadelphia St, Indiana PA 15701
Tel (724) 349-1800 SIC 6022

▲ S&T BANCORP INC p 1263
800 Philadelphia St, Indiana PA 15701
Tel (800) 325-2265 SIC 6022

■ FULTON BANK NATIONAL ASSOCIATION p 584
1 Penn Sq Ste 1, Lancaster PA 17602
Tel (717) 581-3166 SIC 6022

METRO BANK p 954
1249 Market St, Lemoyne PA 17043
Tel (717) 972-2875 SIC 6022

■ SUSQUEHANNA BANK p 1409
9 E Main St, Lititz PA 17543
Tel (717) 627-1778 SIC 6022

■ CITIZENS BANK OF PENNSYLVANIA p 310
130 N 18th St, Philadelphia PA 19103
Tel (267) 671-1000 SIC 6022 6021

CUSTOMERS BANK p 403
99 Bridge St, Phoenixville PA 19460
Tel (610) 933-2000 SIC 6022

▲ FNB CORP p 562
1 N Shore Ctr 12 Fdral St, Pittsburgh PA 15212
Tel (800) 555-5455
SIC 6022 6021 6162 6411

▲ TRISTATE CAPITAL HOLDINGS INC p 1483
301 Grant St Ste 2700, Pittsburgh PA 15219
Tel (412) 304-0304 SIC 6022

▲ UNIVEST CORP OF PENNSYLVANIA p 1527
14 N Main St, Souderton PA 18964
Tel (215) 721-2400 SIC 6022 6282 6411

▲ CUSTOMERS BANCORP INC p 403
1015 Penn Ave Ste 103, Wyomissing PA 19610
Tel (610) 933-2000 SIC 6022

■ BANCO POPULAR DE PUERTO RICO (INC) p 150
Popular Ctr, San Juan PR 00918
Tel (787) 765-9800 SIC 6022 6159 6141

■ BANCO SANTANDER-PUERTO RICO INC p 150
207 Ave Ponce De Leon, San Juan PR 00917
Tel (787) 274-7200 SIC 6022

EUROBANCSHARES INC p 512
State Rd Pr 1 Km 24 5, San Juan PR 00926
Tel (787) 751-7340 SIC 6022

▲ FIRST BANCORP p 545
130 Mnoz Rvera Ave Fl 2, San Juan PR 00908
Tel (787) 729-8200 SIC 6022 6411

▲ OFG BANCORP p 1076
254 Ave Munoz Rivera Fl 8, San Juan PR 00918
Tel (787) 771-6800 SIC 6022

▲ POPULAR INC p 1161
209 Munoz Rivera, San Juan PR 00918
Tel (787) 765-9800 SIC 6022

■ RICO FIRSTBANK PUERTO p 1233
1519 Ave Ponce De Leon, San Juan PR 00909
Tel (787) 729-8200 SIC 6022

SCOTIABANK DE PUERTO RICO p 1293
290 Ave Jesus T Pinero, San Juan PR 00918
Tel (787) 766-4999 SIC 6022

▲ CITIZENS FINANCIAL GROUP INC p 311
1 Citizens Plz Ste 1, Providence RI 02903
Tel (401) 456-7000 SIC 6022

▲ WASHINGTON TRUST BANCORP INC p 1579
23 Broad St Fl 1, Westerly RI 02891
Tel (401) 348-1200 SIC 6022

■ WASHINGTON TRUST CO OF WESTERLY p 1579
23 Broad St Fl 1, Westerly RI 02891
Tel (401) 348-1200 SIC 6022

FIRST CITIZENS BANK AND TRUST CO INC p 545
1230 Main St, Columbia SC 29201
Tel (803) 733-2020 SIC 6022

■ SOUTH STATE BANK p 1345
520 Gervais St Ste 310, Columbia SC 29201
Tel (803) 771-2265 SIC 6022

▲ SOUTH STATE CORP p 1345
520 Gervais St Ste 310, Columbia SC 29201
Tel (800) 277-2175 SIC 6712 6022

DACOTAH BANK p 408
308 S Main St, Aberdeen SD 57401
Tel (605) 225-5611 SIC 6022

1ST FINANCIAL BANK USA p 1
331 Dakota Dunes Blvd, North Sioux City SD 57049
Tel (605) 232-9310 SIC 6022

▲ GREAT WESTERN BANCORP INC p 635
100 N Phillips Ave # 100, Sioux Falls SD 57104
Tel (605) 334-2548 SIC 6022

■ GREAT WESTERN BANK p 635
100 N Phillips Ave # 100, Sioux Falls SD 57104
Tel (605) 886-8401 SIC 6022

PREMIER BANKCARD HOLDINGS LLC p 1170
3820 N Louise Ave, Sioux Falls SD 57107
Tel (605) 357-3440 SIC 6022

■ WELLS FARGO FINANCIAL CARDS p 1590
3201 N 4th Ave, Sioux Falls SD 57104
Tel (605) 336-3933 SIC 6022

■ GREEN BANKSHARES INC p 636
100 N Main St, Greeneville TN 37743
Tel (704) 554-5901 SIC 6022

■ GREENBANK p 637
100 N Main St, Greeneville TN 37743
Tel (423) 639-5111 SIC 6022

■ WILSON BANK AND TRUST p 1613
623 W Main St, Lebanon TN 37087
Tel (615) 444-2265 SIC 6022

▲ FB FINANCIAL CORP p 532
211 Commerce St Ste 300, Nashville TN 37201
Tel (615) 313-0080 SIC 6022

■ FIFTH THIRD BANK NATIONAL ASSOCIATION p 542
424 Church St Ste 500, Nashville TN 37219
Tel (615) 687-3100 SIC 6022

■ FIRSTBANK p 550
211 Commerce St Ste 300, Nashville TN 37201
Tel (731) 968-4211 SIC 6022

▲ FIRST FINANCIAL BANKSHARES INC p 546
400 Pine St, Abilene TX 79601
Tel (325) 627-7155 SIC 6022

HAPPY STATE BANK p 659
701 S Taylor St Lb120, Amarillo TX 79101
Tel (806) 373-2265 SIC 6022

COMMUNITYBANK OF TEXAS NATIONAL ASSOCIATION p 350
5999 Delaware St, Beaumont TX 77706
Tel (409) 861-7200
SIC 6163 6029 6022 6021

▲ COMERICA INC p 344
1717 Main St Mc6404, Dallas TX 75201
Tel (214) 462-6831
SIC 6021 6022 6091 6082 6099 6141

▲ HILLTOP HOLDINGS INC p 694
200 Crescent Ct Ste 1330, Dallas TX 75201
Tel (214) 855-2177 SIC 6022 7389

■ PLAINSCAPITAL BANK p 1153
2323 Victory Ave Ste 1400, Dallas TX 75219
Tel (214) 252-4100 SIC 6022

▲ TEXAS CAPITAL BANCSHARES INC p 1442
2000 Mckinney Ave Ste 700, Dallas TX 75201
Tel (214) 932-6600 SIC 6022

▲ TRIUMPH BANCORP INC p 1483
12700 Park Central Dr # 1700, Dallas TX 75251
Tel (214) 365-6930 SIC 6022

■ PROSPERITY BANK p 1184
1301 N Mechanic St, El Campo TX 77437
Tel (979) 543-1426 SIC 6022

TIB - INDEPENDENT BANKERSBANK p 1452
11701 Luna Rd, Farmers Branch TX 75234
Tel (972) 650-6000 SIC 6022

NORTHSTAR BANK OF TEXAS p 1058
1300 S University Dr # 100, Fort Worth TX 76107
Tel (940) 591-1200 SIC 6022

▲ ALLEGIANCE BANCSHARES INC p 52
8847 W Sam Houston Pkwy N, Houston TX 77040
Tel (281) 894-3200 SIC 6022

BBVA COMPASS BANCSHARES INC p 163
2200 Post Oak Blvd Fl 18, Houston TX 77056
Tel (205) 297-3000 SIC 6022

▲ PROSPERITY BANCSHARES INC p 1184
4295 San Felipe St, Houston TX 77027
Tel (281) 269-7199 SIC 6022

■ STERLING BANCSHARES INC p 1386
2950 North Loop W # 1200, Houston TX 77092
Tel (713) 466-8300 SIC 6022

■ STERLING BANK p 1386
2550 North Loop W Ste 600, Houston TX 77092
Tel (713) 466-8300 SIC 6022

AUSTIN BANCORP INC p 132
200 E Commerce St, Jacksonville TX 75766
Tel (903) 586-1526 SIC 6021 6211 6022

▲ INTERNATIONAL BANCSHARES CORP p 754
1200 San Bernardo Ave, Laredo TX 78040
Tel (956) 722-7611 SIC 6022

■ INTERNATIONAL BANK OF COMMERCE p 754
1200 San Bernardo Ave, Laredo TX 78040
Tel (956) 722-7611 SIC 6022

TEXAS BANK & TRUST CO p 1442
300 E Whaley St, Longview TX 75601
Tel (903) 237-5500 SIC 6022

CITY BANK p 312
5219 City Bank Pkwy Fl 1, Lubbock TX 79407
Tel (806) 792-7101 SIC 6022

TEXAS REGIONAL DELAWARE INC p 1444
3900 N 10th St Fl 11, Mcallen TX 78501
Tel (956) 631-5400 SIC 6022 6541

■ LEGACYTEXAS BANK p 853
5851 Legacy Cir Ste 1200, Plano TX 75024
Tel (972) 578-5000 SIC 6022

▲ LEGACYTEXAS FINANCIAL GROUP INC p 853
5851 Legacy Cir, Plano TX 75024
Tel (972) 578-5000 SIC 6022

CITIZENS STATE BANK p 311
1709 N Grant St, Roma TX 78584
Tel (956) 849-2311 SIC 6022

AMERICAN BANK OF TEXAS p 68
2011 Texoma Pkwy Ste 101, Sherman TX 75090
Tel (903) 893-7555 SIC 6022

CITY BANK p 312
500 Main St, Silverton TX 79257
Tel (806) 823-2426 SIC 6022

▲ SOUTHSIDE BANCSHARES INC p 1351
1201 S Beckham Ave, Tyler TX 75701
Tel (903) 531-7111 SIC 6022

■ SOUTHSIDE BANK p 1351
1201 S Beckham Ave, Tyler TX 75701
Tel (903) 531-7111 SIC 6022

BMW BANK OF NORTH AMERICA p 194
2735 E Parleys Way # 301, Salt Lake City UT 84109
Tel (801) 461-6415 SIC 6022

■ COMENITY CAPITAL BANK p 344
2795 E Cottonwood Pkwy # 100, Salt Lake City UT 84121
Tel (801) 527-2272 SIC 6022

FJ MANAGEMENT INC p 553
185 S State St Ste 201, Salt Lake City UT 84111
Tel (801) 624-1000
SIC 5541 2911 5411 1382 6022

▲ ZIONS BANCORPORATION p 1643
1 S Main St Fl 15, Salt Lake City UT 84133
Tel (801) 844-7637 SIC 6022 6021

■ MORGAN STANLEY BANK p 989
680 W 10000 S Fl 2, South Jordan UT 84095
Tel (212) 761-4000 SIC 6022

▲ BURKE & HERBERT BANK & TRUST CO INC p 227
100 S Fairfax St, Alexandria VA 22314
Tel (703) 299-8491 SIC 6022

VIRGINIA COMMERCE BANCORP INC p 1558
5350 Lee Hwy, Arlington VA 22207
Tel (703) 534-0700 SIC 6022

▲ FIRST COMMUNITY BANCSHARES INC p 546
1 Community Pl, Bluefield VA 24605
Tel (276) 326-9000 SIC 6022

STELLARONE CORP p 1385
590 Peter Jefferson Pkwy, Charlottesville VA 22911
Tel (434) 964-2211 SIC 6022

MONARCH FINANCIAL HOLDINGS INC p 983
1435 Crossways Blvd, Chesapeake VA 23320
Tel (757) 389-5111 SIC 6022

CARTER BANK & TRUST p 261
1300 Kings Mountain Rd, Martinsville VA 24112
Tel (276) 656-1776 SIC 6022

▲ UNION BANKSHARES CORP p 1504
1051 E Cary St Ste 1200, Richmond VA 23219
Tel (804) 633-5031 SIC 6022

▲ TOWNEBANK p 1466
6001 Harbour View Blvd, Suffolk VA 23435
Tel (757) 638-6700 SIC 6022

■ UNITED BANK p 1506
2071 Chain Bridge Rd, Vienna VA 22182
Tel (703) 442-7118 SIC 6022

▲ C&F FINANCIAL CORP p 234
802 Main St, West Point VA 23181
Tel (804) 843-2360 SIC 6022

■ CITIZENS AND FARMERS BANK p 310
802 Main St, West Point VA 23181
Tel (804) 843-2360 SIC 6022

■ BOSTON PRIVATE BANK & TRUST CO p 203
10885 Ne 4th St Ste 100, Bellevue WA 98004
Tel (425) 586-5038 SIC 6022

WASHINGTON BANKING CO p 1577
450 Sw Bayshore Dr, Oak Harbor WA 98277
Tel (360) 679-3121 SIC 6022

■ HERITAGE BANK p 686
201 5th Ave Sw Ste 101, Olympia WA 98501
Tel (360) 943-1500 SIC 6022

▲ HOMESTREET INC p 704
601 Union St Ste 2000, Seattle WA 98101
Tel (206) 623-3050 SIC 6036 6022

AMERICANWEST BANCORPORATION p 81
41 W Riverside Ave Ste 300, Spokane WA 99201
Tel (509) 467-6993 SIC 6022

WASHINGTON TRUST BANK p 1579
717 W Sprague Ave Fl 7, Spokane WA 99201
Tel (509) 353-4204 SIC 6022

▲ COLUMBIA BANKING SYSTEM INC p 340
1301 A St, Tacoma WA 98402
Tel (253) 305-1900 SIC 6022

■ COLUMBIA STATE BANK p 342
1301 A St Ste 800, Tacoma WA 98402
Tel (253) 305-1900 SIC 6022

■ BANNER BANK p 152
10 S 1st Ave, Walla Walla WA 99362
Tel (800) 272-9933 SIC 6022

▲ BANNER CORP p 152
10 S 1st Ave, Walla Walla WA 99362
Tel (509) 527-3636 SIC 6022 6036

▲ UNITED BANKSHARES INC p 1506
500 Virginia St E, Charleston WV 25301
Tel (304) 424-8800 SIC 6022

▲ MVB FINANCIAL CORP p 1003
301 Virginia Ave, Fairmont WV 26554
Tel (304) 363-4800 SIC 6022

■ UNITED BANK INC p 1506
514 Market St, Parkersburg WV 26101
Tel (304) 424-8800 SIC 6022

■ WESBANCO BANK INC p 1593
1 Bank Plz, Wheeling WV 26003
Tel (304) 234-9000 SIC 6022

▲ ASSOCIATED BANC-CORP p 119
433 Main St, Green Bay WI 54301
Tel (920) 491-7500 SIC 6022

▲ FIRST BUSINESS FINANCIAL SERVICES INC p 545
401 Charmany Dr, Madison WI 53719
Tel (608) 238-8008 SIC 6022

■ BANK MUTUAL p 151
4949 W Brown Deer Rd, Milwaukee WI 53223
Tel (414) 354-1500
SIC 6036 6163 6029 6022

JOHNSON FINANCIAL GROUP INC p 791
555 Main St Ste 400, Racine WI 53403
Tel (262) 619-2700
SIC 6022 6021 6712 6733 6311

CITIZENS FIRST BANK p 311
101 S Main St, Viroqua WI 54665
Tel (608) 637-3133 SIC 6022

■ ASSOCIATED BANK NA p 120
303 S 1st Ave, Wittenberg WI 54499
Tel (715) 845-4301 SIC 6022

SIC 6029 Commercial Banks, NEC

■ TRI COUNTIES BANK p 1476
63 Constitution Dr, Chico CA 95973
Tel (530) 898-0300 SIC 6029 6163

▲ OPUS BANK p 1091
19900 Macarthur Blvd # 1200, Irvine CA 92612
Tel (949) 250-9800 SIC 6029

FARMERS & MERCHANTS BANK OF LONG BEACH p 529
302 Pine Ave, Long Beach CA 90802
Tel (562) 437-0011 SIC 6022 6029

COMMUNITY BANK p 347
460 Serra Madre Villa Ave, Pasadena CA 91107
Tel (626) 577-1700 SIC 6022 6029

■ SILICON VALLEY BANK p 1323
3003 Tasman Dr, Santa Clara CA 95054
Tel (408) 654-7400 SIC 6029

ROYAL BANK OF SCOTLAND PLC p 1254
600 Washington Blvd, Stamford CT 06901
Tel (203) 897-2700 SIC 6029

USAMERIBANK p 1534
4770 140th Ave N Ste 401, Clearwater FL 33762
Tel (727) 475-8780 SIC 6029

■ BANCO SANTANDER INTERNATIONAL p 150
1401 Brickell Ave Ste 200, Miami FL 33131
Tel (305) 530-2900 SIC 6029

■ FIDELITY BANK p 540
3 Corporate Blvd Ne # 110, Brookhaven GA 30329
Tel (404) 325-3935 SIC 6029

FIRST HAWAIIAN BANK p 547
2339 Kamehameha Hwy # 447, Honolulu HI 96819
Tel (808) 844-4444 SIC 6029

■ FIRST MERCHANTS BANK NATIONAL ASSOCIATION p 547
200 E Jackson St, Muncie IN 47305
Tel (765) 747-1500 SIC 6029

BANGOR SAVINGS BANK p 150
99 Franklin St, Bangor ME 04401
Tel (207) 942-3300 SIC 6029

COLUMBIA BANCORP p 340
7168 Columbia Gateway Dr, Columbia MD 21046
Tel (410) 872-9165 SIC 6029

■ EAST BOSTON SAVING BANK p 470
10 Meridian St, Boston MA 02128
Tel (617) 567-1500 SIC 6029 6141

■ CENTURY BANK AND TRUST CO p 282
102 Fellsway W, Somerville MA 02145
Tel (617) 629-0929 SIC 6029

REPUBLIC BANK p 1225
328 S Saginaw St Lbby, Flint MI 48502
Tel (810) 257-2506 SIC 6022 6163 6029

▲ RENASANT CORP p 1223
209 Troy St, Tupelo MS 38804
Tel (662) 680-1001 SIC 6029 6411

▲ CASS INFORMATION SYSTEMS INC p 263
12444 Powerscort Dr # 550, Saint Louis MO 63131
Tel (314) 506-5500 SIC 7389 7374 6029

HERITAGE GROUP INC p 686
1101 12th St, Aurora NE 68818
Tel (402) 694-3136 SIC 6029

UNION BANK AND TRUST CO p 1504
3643 S 48th St, Lincoln NE 68506
Tel (402) 488-0941
SIC 6111 6029 6162 6021 6035 6022

▲ PEAPACK-GLADSTONE FINANCIAL CORP p 1126
500 Hills Dr Ste 300, Bedminster NJ 07921
Tel (908) 234-0700 SIC 6029

■ PROVIDENT BANK p 1186
100 Wood Ave S Ste 119, Iselin NJ 08830
Tel (800) 448-7768 SIC 6036 6029

TD BANKNORTH NATIONAL ASSOCIATION p 1429
1000 Macarthur Blvd, Mahwah NJ 07430
Tel (201) 236-2680 SIC 6029

■ FULTON BANK OF NEW JERSEY p 584
533 Fellowship Rd Ste 250, Mount Laurel NJ 08054
Tel (856) 787-1997 SIC 6029 6163

▲ SUN BANCORP INC p 1400
350 Fellowship Rd Ste 101, Mount Laurel NJ 08054
Tel (856) 691-7700 SIC 6029

▲ FIRST BANK OF NEW JERSEY p 545
2465 Kuser Rd, Trenton NJ 08690
Tel (609) 528-4400 SIC 6029 6021

BANORTE USA CORP p 153
540 Madison Ave Fl 36, New York NY 10022
Tel (212) 484-5200 SIC 6029

COMMERZBANK AG p 345
225 Liberty St Fl 31, New York NY 10281
Tel (212) 266-7200 SIC 6029

DORAL FINANCIAL CORP p 451
200 Park Ave Ste 1700, New York NY 10166
Tel (646) 632-3700
SIC 6029 6162 6035 6211 6411

■ GOLDMAN SACHS BANK USA HOLDINGS LLC p 622
200 West St Bldg 200, New York NY 10282
Tel (212) 357-2882 SIC 6029

▲ SIGNATURE BANK p 1322
565 5th Ave Fl 8r, New York NY 10017
Tel (646) 822-1500 SIC 6029 7389

HUDSON VALLEY BANK p 717
21 Scarsdale Rd, Yonkers NY 10707
Tel (914) 961-6100 SIC 6029

AGCOUNTRY FARM CREDIT SERVICES ACA p 34
1900 44th St S, Fargo ND 58103
Tel (701) 235-9858 SIC 6029

■ HUNTINGTON NATIONAL BANK p 720
17 S High St Fl 1, Columbus OH 43215
Tel (614) 480-4293 SIC 6029

■ PREMIER BANK & TRUST NATIONAL ASSOCIATION p 1170
600 S Main St, North Canton OH 44720
Tel (330) 499-1900 SIC 6733 6029

■ TRISTATE CAPITAL BANK p 1483
301 Grant St Ste 2700, Pittsburgh PA 15219
Tel (412) 304-0304 SIC 6029

COMMUNITYBANK OF TEXAS NATIONAL ASSOCIATION p 350
5999 Delaware St, Beaumont TX 77706
Tel (409) 861-7200
SIC 6163 6029 6022 6021

EB ACQUISITION CO LLC p 474
200 Crescent Ct, Dallas TX 75201
Tel (214) 871-5151 SIC 6029

SWS GROUP INC p 1413
1201 Elm St Ste 3500, Dallas TX 75270
Tel (214) 859-1800 SIC 6211 6029

GREEN BANK NATIONAL ASSOCIATION p 636
4000 Greenbriar St, Houston TX 77098
Tel (713) 275-8200 SIC 6029

BEAL BANK p 165
6000 Legacy Dr, Plano TX 75024
Tel (469) 467-5000 SIC 6029

■ AMERICAN EXPRESS BANK FSB p 72
4315 S 2700 W, Salt Lake City UT 84184
Tel (801) 945-5000 SIC 6029

■ MEDALLION BANK p 935
1100 E 6600 S Ste 510, Salt Lake City UT 84121
Tel (801) 284-7065 SIC 6029

MONARCH BANK p 983
1435 Crossways Blvd, Chesapeake VA 23320
Tel (757) 222-2100 SIC 6029

FEDERAL RESERVE BANK OF RICHMOND p 535
701 E Byrd St Fl 2, Richmond VA 23219
Tel (804) 697-8000 SIC 6029

NEB CORP p 1023
130 S Main St, Fond Du Lac WI 54935
Tel (920) 921-7700 SIC 6029

■ BANK MUTUAL p 151
4949 W Brown Deer Rd, Milwaukee WI 53223
Tel (414) 354-1500
SIC 6036 6163 6029 6022

WATERSTONE BANK p 1582
11200 W Plank Ct, Wauwatosa WI 53226
Tel (414) 459-4211 SIC 6029

SIC 6035 Federal Savings Institutions

PFF BANCORP INC p 1140
2058 N Mills Ave Ste 139, Claremont CA 91711
Tel (213) 683-6393 SIC 6035

■ BANC OF CALIFORNIA NATIONAL ASSOCIATION p 149
18500 Von Karman Ave, Irvine CA 92612
Tel (877) 770-2262 SIC 6035

PACIFICTRUST BANK p 1106
18500 Von Karman Ave # 1100, Irvine CA 92612
Tel (949) 236-5211 SIC 6035

PACIFIC LIFECORP p 1105
700 Newport Center Dr, Newport Beach CA 92660
Tel (949) 219-3011
SIC 6371 6311 6321 6035 8111

ONEWEST BANK GROUP LLC p 1088
888 E Walnut St, Pasadena CA 91101
Tel (626) 535-4870 SIC 6035

▲ BOFI HOLDING INC p 197
4350 La Jolla Village Dr, San Diego CA 92122
Tel (858) 350-6200 SIC 6035

BURBANK LUTHER SAVINGS p 226
500 3rd St, Santa Rosa CA 95401
Tel (707) 578-9216 SIC 6036 6035

■ WEBSTER BANK NATIONAL ASSOCIATION p 1587
145 Bank St, Waterbury CT 06702
Tel (203) 578-2230 SIC 6035

BARCLAYS BANK DELAWARE p 154
100 S West St, Wilmington DE 19801
Tel (302) 255-8000 SIC 6035

■ ING BANK FSB p 742
802 Delaware Ave, Wilmington DE 19801
Tel (302) 658-2200 SIC 6035 6211

ING USA HOLDING CORP p 742
1 S Orange St, Wilmington DE 19801
Tel (302) 658-2200 SIC 6035

▲ THIRD FEDERAL SAVINGS p 1448
103 Foulk Rd Ste 101, Wilmington DE 19803
Tel (302) 661-2009 SIC 6035

■ WILMINGTON SAVINGS FUND SOCIETY p 1613
500 Delaware Ave Ste 500, Wilmington DE 19801
Tel (302) 792-6000 SIC 6035

■ BBX CAPITAL CORP p 163
401 E Las Olas Blvd, Fort Lauderdale FL 33301
Tel (954) 940-4000 SIC 6798 6035

▲ BFC FINANCIAL CORP p 179
401 E Las Olas Blvd # 800, Fort Lauderdale FL 33301
Tel (954) 940-4900 SIC 6035 6531 6552

■ FIRST INTERNATIONAL EXCHANGE GROUP p 547
2100 W Cypress Creek Rd, Fort Lauderdale FL 33309
Tel (954) 658-3464 SIC 6035 6531

■ EVERBANK p 513
501 Riverside Ave Fl 1, Jacksonville FL 32202
Tel (904) 623-8408 SIC 6035

▲ EVERBANK FINANCIAL CORP p 513
501 Riverside Ave, Jacksonville FL 32202
Tel (904) 281-6000 SIC 6035 7389

■ N A BANKUNITED p 1005
14817 Oak Ln, Miami Lakes FL 33016
Tel (305) 231-6400 SIC 6035 6163 6111

■ RAYMOND JAMES BANK NATIONAL ASSOCIATION p 1210
710 Carillon Pkwy, Saint Petersburg FL 33716
Tel (727) 567-8000 SIC 6035

■ RAYMOND JAMES FINANCIAL SERVICES INC p 1210
880 Carillon Pkwy, Saint Petersburg FL 33716
Tel (727) 567-1000
SIC 6211 6282 6712 6091 6035

HERITAGE FINANCIAL GROUP INC p 686
721 N Westover Blvd, Albany GA 31707
Tel (229) 420-0000 SIC 6035

■ AMERICAN SAVINGS BANK FSB p 79
915 Fort Street Mall, Honolulu HI 96813
Tel (808) 627-6900 SIC 6035

▲ HAWAIIAN ELECTRIC INDUSTRIES INC p 669
1001 Bishop St Ste 2900, Honolulu HI 96813
Tel (808) 543-5662 SIC 4911 6035

■ AMERICA SAVING BANK p 67
200 Kahelu Ave, Mililani HI 96789
Tel (808) 627-6900 SIC 6035

■ MB FINANCIAL BANK p 924
936 N Western Ave, Chicago IL 60622
Tel (773) 772-4500 SIC 6035

▲ MB FINANCIAL INC p 924
800 W Madison St, Chicago IL 60607
Tel (888) 422-6562 SIC 6035

■ MAINSOURCE BANK p 898
201 N Broadway St, Greensburg IN 47240
Tel (812) 663-4711 SIC 6035

■ METABANK p 952
121 E 5th St, Storm Lake IA 50588
Tel (712) 732-4117 SIC 6035

▲ CAPITOL FEDERAL FINANCIAL INC p 251
700 S Kansas Ave Fl 1, Topeka KS 66603
Tel (785) 235-1341 SIC 6035

■ CAPITOL FEDERAL SAVINGS BANK p 251
700 S Kansas Ave Fl 1, Topeka KS 66603
Tel (785) 235-1341 SIC 6035

FIDELITY FINANCIAL CORP p 540
100 E English St, Wichita KS 67202
Tel (316) 265-2261 SIC 6035

BANK OF KENTUCKY FINANCIAL CORP p 151
111 Lookout Farm Dr, Crestview Hills KY 41017
Tel (859) 371-2340 SIC 6035

ACACIA LIFE INSURANCE CO p 13
7315 Wisconsin Ave 1000w, Bethesda MD 20814
Tel (301) 280-1000
SIC 6311 6411 6035 6282 6211

■ CHEVY CHASE BANK FSB p 296
7501 Wisconsin Ave Fl 11, Bethesda MD 20814
Tel (240) 497-4101
SIC 6035 6411 6211 6519 6552 6719

▲ BROOKLINE BANCORP INC p 218
131 Clarendon St, Boston MA 02116
Tel (617) 425-4600 SIC 6035

■ SANTANDER BANK NA p 1281
28 State St Fl 5, Boston MA 02109
Tel (617) 757-3410 SIC 6035

■ SANTANDER HOLDINGS USA INC p 1281
75 State St, Boston MA 02109
Tel (617) 346-7200 SIC 6021 6035

▲ MERIDIAN BANCORP INC p 948
67 Prospect St, Peabody MA 01960
Tel (617) 567-1500 SIC 6035

■ BERKSHIRE BANK p 175
24 North St, Pittsfield MA 01201
Tel (413) 443-5601 SIC 6035

UNITED FINANCIAL BANCORP INC p 1508
95 Elm St, West Springfield MA 01089
Tel (413) 787-1700 SIC 6035

▲ FLAGSTAR BANCORP INC p 554
5151 Corporate Dr, Troy MI 48098
Tel (248) 312-2000 SIC 6035

■ **FLAGSTAR BANK FSB** p 554
5151 Corporate Dr, Troy MI 48098
Tel (248) 312-2000 SIC 6035

MIDCOUNTRY BANK p 964
Investors Bldg 7 Ste 103, Minneapolis MN 55402
Tel (952) 843-5200 SIC 6035

▲ **NASB FINANCIAL INC** p 1008
12498 S Us Highway 71, Grandview MO 64030
Tel (816) 765-2200 SIC 6035

■ **NORTH AMERICAN SAVINGS BANK FSB** p 1050
12498 S Us Highway 71, Grandview MO 64030
Tel (816) 765-2200 SIC 6035

■ **H&R BLOCK BANK** p 651
1 H And R Block Way, Kansas City MO 64105
Tel (888) 687-4722 SIC 6035

SCOTTRADE BANK p 1294
12800 Corp Hill Dr, Saint Louis MO 63131
Tel (314) 965-1555 SIC 6035

UNION BANK AND TRUST CO p 1504
3643 S 48th St, Lincoln NE 68506
Tel (402) 488-0941
SIC 6111 6029 6162 6021 6035 6022

MUTUAL OF OMAHA BANK p 1003
3333 Farnam St Ste 10, Omaha NE 68131
Tel (402) 351-5118 SIC 6035

CENLAR CAPITAL CORP p 275
425 Phillips Blvd, Ewing NJ 08618
Tel (609) 883-3900 SIC 6035

CENLAR FSB p 275
425 Phillips Blvd, Ewing NJ 08618
Tel (609) 883-3900 SIC 6035

COLUMBIA BANK p 340
19-01 State Rt 208, Fair Lawn NJ 07410
Tel (201) 796-3600 SIC 6035

■ **KEARNY BANK** p 807
120 Passaic Ave, Fairfield NJ 07004
Tel (973) 244-4500 SIC 6035

▲ **KEARNY FINANCIAL CORP** p 807
120 Passaic Ave, Fairfield NJ 07004
Tel (973) 244-4500 SIC 6035

KEARNY MHC p 807
120 Passaic Ave, Fairfield NJ 07004
Tel (973) 244-4500 SIC 6035

▲ **PROVIDENT FINANCIAL SERVICES INC** p 1186
239 Washington St, Jersey City NJ 07302
Tel (732) 590-9200 SIC 6035

HUDSON CITY BANCORP INC p 716
W80 Century Rd, Paramus NJ 07652
Tel (201) 967-1900 SIC 6035

HUDSON CITY SAVINGS BANK p 716
80 W Century Rd, Paramus NJ 07652
Tel (201) 967-1900 SIC 6035 6163

▲ **INVESTORS BANCORP INC** p 761
101 Jfk Pkwy Ste 3, Short Hills NJ 07078
Tel (973) 924-5100 SIC 6035

■ **OCEANFIRST BANK** p 1073
975 Hooper Ave, Toms River NJ 08753
Tel (732) 240-4500 SIC 6035

▲ **OCEANFIRST FINANCIAL CORP** p 1073
975 Hooper Ave, Toms River NJ 08753
Tel (732) 240-4500 SIC 6035

▲ **NORTHFIELD BANCORP INC** p 1057
581 Main St, Woodbridge NJ 07095
Tel (732) 499-7200 SIC 6035

▲ **DIME COMMUNITY BANCSHARES INC** p 440
209 Havemeyer St, Brooklyn NY 11211
Tel (718) 782-6200 SIC 6035

■ **DIME COMMUNITY BANK** p 440
209 Havemeyer St, Brooklyn NY 11211
Tel (718) 782-6200 SIC 6035

HSBC NORTH AMERICA INC p 715
1 Hsbc Ctr Ste 1, Buffalo NY 14203
Tel (716) 841-2424
SIC 6021 6035 6221 6091 6211

■ **FLUSHING BANK** p 561
220 Rxr Plz, Flushing NY 11354
Tel (718) 512-2929 SIC 6035 6163

■ **ASTORIA BANK** p 122
1 Astoria Federal Plz, Lake Success NY 11042
Tel (516) 535-9000 SIC 6035

■ **ALL POINTS CAPITAL CORP** p 51
275 Broadhollow Rd, Melville NY 11747
Tel (631) 531-2800 SIC 6035 6159

■ **STERLING NATIONAL BANK** p 1387
400 Rella Blvd Fl 3, Montebello NY 10901
Tel (845) 369-8040 SIC 6035

▲ **ASTORIA FINANCIAL CORP** p 122
1 Astoria Bank Plz, New Hyde Park NY 11042
Tel (516) 327-3000 SIC 6035

DORAL FINANCIAL CORP p 451
200 Park Ave Ste 1700, New York NY 10166
Tel (646) 632-3700
SIC 6029 6162 6035 6211 6411

▲ **E TRADE FINANCIAL CORP** p 467
1271 Ave Of The Americas, New York NY 10020
Tel (646) 521-4300 SIC 6211 6035

▲ **FLUSHING FINANCIAL CORP** p 561
220 Rxr Plz, Uniondale NY 11556
Tel (718) 961-5400 SIC 6035

▲ **HOMETRUST BANCSHARES INC** p 704
10 Woodfin St, Asheville NC 28801
Tel (828) 259-3939 SIC 6035

■ **GOLDEN WEST FINANCIAL CORP** p 621
301 S College St, Charlotte NC 28202
Tel (704) 374-6565 SIC 6035

■ **FIRST-CITIZENS BANK & TRUST CO** p 550
4300 Six Forks Rd, Raleigh NC 27609
Tel (919) 716-7000 SIC 6035

▲ **BB&T CORP** p 163
200 W 2nd St Ste 260, Winston Salem NC 27101
Tel (336) 733-2000
SIC 6021 6311 6035 6211

■ **TFS FINANCIAL CORP** p 1445
7007 Broadway Ave, Cleveland OH 44105
Tel (216) 441-6000 SIC 6035

■ **THIRD FEDERAL SAVINGS AND LOAN ASSOCIATION OF CLEVELAND** p 1448
7007 Broadway Ave, Cleveland OH 44105
Tel (800) 844-7333 SIC 6035

NATIONWIDE BANK p 1017
3 Nationwide Plz, Columbus OH 43215
Tel (800) 882-2822 SIC 6035

▲ **FIRST DEFIANCE FINANCIAL CORP** p 546
601 Clinton St, Defiance OH 43512
Tel (419) 782-5015
SIC 6035 6331 6321 6311

■ **FIRST FEDERAL BANK OF MIDWEST** p 546
601 Clinton St Ste 1, Defiance OH 43512
Tel (419) 782-5015 SIC 6035

N C B SAVINGS BANK FSB p 1005
139 S High St Ste 1, Hillsboro OH 45133
Tel (937) 393-4246 SIC 6035

■ **PEOPLES BANK** p 1132
138 Putnam St, Marietta OH 45750
Tel (740) 373-3155 SIC 6035

MIDFIRST BANK p 965
501 Nw Grand Blvd, Oklahoma City OK 73118
Tel (405) 767-7000 SIC 6035

MIDLAND FINANCIAL CO p 965
501 Nw Grand Blvd Ste 180, Oklahoma City OK 73118
Tel (405) 840-7600 SIC 6035 6162 6531

▲ **UMPQUA HOLDINGS CORP** p 1502
1 Sw Columbia St Ste 1200, Portland OR 97258
Tel (503) 727-4100 SIC 6035 6022

▲ **BENEFICIAL BANCORP INC** p 172
1818 Market St, Philadelphia PA 19103
Tel (215) 864-6000 SIC 6035

BENEFICIAL MUTUAL BANCORP INC p 172
1818 Market St, Philadelphia PA 19103
Tel (215) 864-6000 SIC 6035

DOLLAR BANK FEDERAL SAVINGS BANK p 448
401 Liberty Ave, Pittsburgh PA 15222
Tel (412) 261-4900 SIC 6035 7359

DOLLAR BANK LEASING CORP p 448
401 Liberty Ave Lobby, Pittsburgh PA 15222
Tel (412) 261-4900 SIC 6035 7359

NORTHWEST BANK p 1059
100 Liberty St, Warren PA 16365
Tel (814) 723-9696 SIC 6035

DORAL HOLDINGS DELAWARE LLC p 451
1451 Frnklin D Rsvelt Ave, San Juan PR 00920
Tel (787) 474-6700
SIC 6162 6035 6211 6411

■ **ORIENTAL BANK** p 1094
254 Ave Munoz Rivera, San Juan PR 00918
Tel (787) 771-6800
SIC 6035 7359 7515 6733

BANKNEWPORT p 152
184 John Clarke Rd, Middletown RI 02842
Tel (401) 846-3400 SIC 6035

FIRST FINANCIAL HOLDINGS INC p 547
2440 Mall Dr, North Charleston SC 29406
Tel (843) 529-5933 SIC 6035

▲ **META FINANCIAL GROUP INC** p 952
5501 S Broadband Ln, Sioux Falls SD 57108
Tel (605) 782-1767 SIC 6035

COLONIAL SAVINGS FA p 338
2600 West Fwy, Fort Worth TX 76102
Tel (817) 390-2000 SIC 6162 6035

ENCORE BANK p 496
9 Greenway Plz Ste 1000, Houston TX 77046
Tel (713) 787-3100 SIC 6021 6035

HOUSTON-GALVESTON AREA COUNCIL p 712
3555 Timmons Ln Ste 120, Houston TX 77027
Tel (713) 627-3200 SIC 6035

■ **WELLS FARGO BANK SOUTH CENTRAL NATIONAL ASSOCIATION** p 1590
2005 Taylor St, Houston TX 77007
Tel (713) 802-2717 SIC 6035

USAA CAPITAL CORP p 1534
9800 Fredericksburg Rd, San Antonio TX 78288
Tel (210) 498-2211
SIC 6035 6798 6722 7299 4813 4724

USAA FEDERAL SAVINGS BANK p 1534
10750 Mcdermott Fwy, San Antonio TX 78288
Tel (210) 498-2211 SIC 6035

■ **SYNCHRONY BANK** p 1414
170 W Election Rd Ste 125, Draper UT 84020
Tel (801) 619-4760 SIC 6035

■ **WASHINGTON FEDERAL NATIONAL ASSOCIATION** p 1578
425 Pike St, Seattle WA 98101
Tel (206) 624-7930 SIC 6035

▲ **WMI HOLDINGS CORP** p 1620
800 5th Ave Ste 4100, Seattle WA 98104
Tel (206) 432-8887 SIC 6035

STERLING SAVINGS BANK p 1387
111 N Wall St, Spokane WA 99201
Tel (509) 624-4121
SIC 6036 6162 6035 6141 6153

ANCHOR BANCORP WISCONSIN INC p 89
25 W Main St, Madison WI 53703
Tel (608) 252-8700 SIC 6035

■ **FPC FINANCIAL F S B** p 573
8402 Excelsior Dr, Madison WI 53717
Tel (608) 821-2000 SIC 6035

GUARANTY FINANCIAL MHC p 644
4000 W Brown Deer Rd, Milwaukee WI 53209
Tel (414) 362-4000 SIC 6035

■ **ASSOCIATED BANC-CORP** p 119
1305 Main St Ms7722, Stevens Point WI 54481
Tel (715) 341-0400 SIC 6035

▲ **WATERSTONE FINANCIAL INC** p 1582
11200 W Plank Ct, Wauwatosa WI 53226
Tel (414) 761-1000 SIC 6035

SIC 6036 Savings Institutions, Except Federal

BURBANK LUTHER SAVINGS p 226
500 3rd St, Santa Rosa CA 95401
Tel (707) 578-9216 SIC 6036 6035

EXCHANGE BANK p 517
440 Aviation Blvd, Santa Rosa CA 95403
Tel (707) 524-3000 SIC 6036 8741 6022

FIRSTBANK HOLDING CO p 550
12345 W Colfax Ave, Lakewood CO 80215
Tel (303) 232-3000 SIC 6036

UNION SAVINGS BANK p 1505
226 Main St, Danbury CT 06810
Tel (203) 830-4200 SIC 6036

■ **FARMINGTON BANK** p 530
1 Farm Glen Blvd, Farmington CT 06032
Tel (860) 676-4600 SIC 6036 6163

▲ **FIRST CONNECTICUT BANCORP INC** p 546
1 Farm Glen Blvd, Farmington CT 06032
Tel (860) 676-4600 SIC 6036

▲ **UNITED BANK** p 1506
45 Glastonbury Blvd # 200, Glastonbury CT 06033
Tel (860) 291-3600 SIC 6036

■ **ADVEST GROUP INC** p 27
90 State House Sq, Hartford CT 06103
Tel (860) 509-1000
SIC 6211 6036 6141 6153 6282

LIBERTY BANK p 861
315 Main St, Middletown CT 06457
Tel (860) 344-7200 SIC 6036 6163 6022

■ **UNITED BANK FOUNDATION CONNECTICUT INC** p 1506
25 Park St, Vernon Rockville CT 06066
Tel (860) 291-3705 SIC 6036

BRAND BANKING CO p 207
106 Crogan St, Lawrenceville GA 30046
Tel (770) 963-9224 SIC 6036

STATE FARM MUTUAL AUTOMOBILE INSURANCE CO p 1381
1 State Farm Plz, Bloomington IL 61710
Tel (309) 766-2311
SIC 6321 6311 6036 6331

■ **IBERIABANK** p 726
200 W Congress St, Lafayette LA 70501
Tel (800) 682-3231 SIC 6036 6163

■ **BROOKLINE BANK** p 218
131 Clarendon St, Boston MA 02116
Tel (617) 425-4625 SIC 6036

EASTERN BANK p 471
265 Franklin St Fl 2, Boston MA 02110
Tel (617) 897-1100 SIC 6036

EASTERN BANK CORP p 471
265 Franklin St Fl 2, Boston MA 02110
Tel (617) 897-1100 SIC 6036 6022 6282

HARBORONE BANK p 660
770 Oak St, Brockton MA 02301
Tel (508) 895-1000 SIC 6036

CAMBRIDGE FINANCIAL GROUP INC p 244
1374 Massachusetts Ave, Cambridge MA 02138
Tel (617) 864-8700 SIC 6036

MIDDLESEX BANCORP MHC p 965
6 Main St, Natick MA 01760
Tel (508) 653-0300 SIC 6036

MIDDLESEX SAVINGS BANK p 965
6 Main St, Natick MA 01760
Tel (508) 653-0300 SIC 6036

CAPE COD FIVE CENTS SAVINGS BANK p 248
19 West Rd, Orleans MA 02653
Tel (508) 240-0555 SIC 6036

FIRST BANK p 545
11901 Olive Blvd Stop 1, Saint Louis MO 63141
Tel (314) 995-8700 SIC 6036

BEAL BANK USA p 165
1970 Vlg Ctr Cir Ste 1, Las Vegas NV 89134
Tel (702) 242-8846 SIC 6036

USAA SAVINGS BANK p 1534
3773 Howard Hughes Pkwy, Las Vegas NV 89169
Tel (702) 862-8891 SIC 6036

■ **PROVIDENT BANK** p 1186
100 Wood Ave S Ste 119, Iselin NJ 08830
Tel (800) 448-7768 SIC 6036 6029

■ **CIT SMALL BUSINESS LENDING CORP** p 309
1 Cit Dr, Livingston NJ 07039
Tel (973) 740-5000 SIC 6036

INVESTORS BANCORP MHC p 761
101 Jfk Pkwy Ste 3, Short Hills NJ 07078
Tel (973) 376-5100 SIC 6036

■ **INVESTORS BANK** p 761
101 John F Kennedy Pkwy # 3, Short Hills NJ 07078
Tel (973) 376-5100 SIC 6036

■ **ORITANI BANK** p 1095
370 Pascack Rd, Twp Washinton NJ 07676
Tel (201) 664-5400 SIC 6036

APPLE BANK FOR SAVINGS p 98
1395 Northern Blvd, Manhasset NY 11030
Tel (516) 627-1800 SIC 6036

DEUTSCHE BANK SECURITIES INC p 433
60 Wall St Bsmt 1, New York NY 10005
Tel (212) 250-2500 SIC 6211 6036

EMIGRANT SAVINGS BANK p 493
5 E 42nd St Fl 5, New York NY 10017
Tel (212) 850-4000
SIC 6036 6311 6512 6514

FORESTERS FINANCIAL SERVICES p 567
40 Wall St Fl 10, New York NY 10005
Tel (212) 858-8000
SIC 6036 6211 6282 6311 8742 6153

RIDGEWOOD SAVINGS BANK p 1234
7102 Forest Ave Ste 1, Ridgewood NY 11385
Tel (718) 240-4800 SIC 6036

NORTHFIELD SAVINGS BANK p 1057
1731 Victory Blvd, Staten Island NY 10314
Tel (718) 448-1000 SIC 6036

▲ **NEW YORK COMMUNITY BANCORP INC** p 1034
615 Merrick Ave, Westbury NY 11590
Tel (516) 683-4100 SIC 6036

■ **NEW YORK COMMUNITY BANK** p 1035
615 Merrick Ave, Westbury NY 11590
Tel (516) 203-0010 SIC 6036

■ **PARK STERLING BANK** p 1116
1043 E Morehead St # 201, Charlotte NC 28204
Tel (704) 370-2444 SIC 6036

UNION SAVINGS BANK p 1505
8534 E Kemper Rd Fl 1, Cincinnati OH 45249
Tel (513) 489-1955 SIC 6036

▲ **UNITED COMMUNITY FINANCIAL CORP** p 1507
275 W Federal St, Youngstown OH 44503
Tel (330) 742-0500 SIC 6036

FIRSTRUST SAVINGS BANK p 551
15 E Ridge Pike Ste 400, Conshohocken PA 19428
Tel (610) 941-9898 SIC 6036

BENEFICIAL MUTUAL SAVINGS BANK p 172
1818 Market St Fl 8, Philadelphia PA 19103
Tel (888) 742-5272 SIC 6036

NORTHWEST BANCORP MHC p 1059
100 Liberty St, Warren PA 16365
Tel (814) 728-7260 SIC 6036

NORTHWEST BANCORP INC p 1059
100 Liberty St, Warren PA 16365
Tel (814) 726-2140 SIC 6036

BEAL FINANCIAL CORP p 165
6000 Legacy Dr, Plano TX 75024
Tel (469) 467-5000 SIC 6036

▲ **HEALTHEQUITY INC** p 677
15 W Scenic Pointe Dr # 100, Draper UT 84020
Tel (801) 727-1000
SIC 8399 6371 6036 6321 6282

CIT BANK p 309
2150 S 1300 E Ste 400, Salt Lake City UT 84106
Tel (801) 412-6800 SIC 6036

▲ **HERITAGE FINANCIAL CORP** p 686
201 5th Ave Sw, Olympia WA 98501
Tel (360) 943-1500 SIC 6036

■ **HOMESTREET BANK** p 704
601 Union St Ste 2000, Seattle WA 98101
Tel (206) 623-3050 SIC 6036

▲ **HOMESTREET INC** p 704
601 Union St Ste 2000, Seattle WA 98101
Tel (206) 623-3050 SIC 6036 6022

STERLING FINANCIAL CORP p 1387
111 N Wall St, Spokane WA 99201
Tel (509) 358-8097 SIC 6036

STERLING SAVINGS BANK p 1387
111 N Wall St, Spokane WA 99201
Tel (509) 624-4121
SIC 6036 6162 6035 6141 6153

▲ **BANNER CORP** p 152
10 S 1st Ave, Walla Walla WA 99362
Tel (509) 527-3636 SIC 6022 6036

ANCHORBANK FSB p 89
25 W Main St Lowr, Madison WI 53703
Tel (608) 252-8700 SIC 6036

■ **BANK MUTUAL** p 151
4949 W Brown Deer Rd, Milwaukee WI 53223
Tel (414) 354-1500
SIC 6036 6163 6029 6022

▲ **BANK MUTUAL CORP** p 151
4949 W Brown Deer Rd, Milwaukee WI 53223
Tel (414) 354-1500 SIC 6036

SIC 6061 Federal Credit Unions

ALASKA USA FEDERAL CREDIT UNION p 45
4000 Credit Union Dr, Anchorage AK 99503
Tel (907) 563-4567 SIC 6061 6163

LOGIX FEDERAL CREDIT UNION p 875
2340 N Hollywood Way, Burbank CA 91505
Tel (888) 718-5328 SIC 6061

KINECTA FEDERAL CREDIT UNION p 819
1440 Rosecrans Ave, Manhattan Beach CA 90266
Tel (310) 643-5400 SIC 6061

KINECTA FINANCIAL & INSURANCE SERVICES LLC p 819
1440 Rosecrans Ave, Manhattan Beach CA 90266
Tel (310) 643-5400 SIC 6061

FIRST TECHNOLOGY FEDERAL CREDIT UNION p 549
1335 Terra Bella Ave, Mountain View CA 94043
Tel (855) 855-8805 SIC 6061

PATELCO CREDIT UNION p 1120
5050 Hopyard Rd, Pleasanton CA 94588
Tel (800) 358-8228 SIC 6061

SCHOOLSFIRST FEDERAL CREDIT UNION p 1290
2115 N Broadway, Santa Ana CA 92706
Tel (714) 258-4000 SIC 6061

STAR ONE CREDIT UNION p 1378
1306 Bordeaux Dr, Sunnyvale CA 94089
Tel (408) 543-5202 SIC 6061

UNIFY FINANCIAL FEDERAL CREDIT UNION p 1503
1899 Western Way Ste 100, Torrance CA 90501
Tel (310) 536-5000 SIC 6061

TRAVIS CREDIT UNION p 1475
1 Travis Way, Vacaville CA 95687
Tel (707) 449-4000 SIC 6061

USA UNION INTERNATIONAL INC p 1534
26650 The Old Rd Ste 210, Valencia CA 91381
Tel (661) 286-8801 SIC 6061

ENT FEDERAL CREDIT UNION p 501
7250 Campus Dr Ste 200, Colorado Springs CO 80920
Tel (719) 574-1100 SIC 6061

BELLCO CREDIT UNION p 170
7600 E Orchard Rd 400n, Greenwood Village CO 80111
Tel (303) 689-7800 SIC 6061

BANK FUND STAFF FEDERAL CREDIT UNION p 150
1725 I St Nw Ste 150, Washington DC 20006
Tel (202) 212-6400 SIC 6061

NORTH BROWARD HOSPITAL DISTRICT FEDERAL CREDIT UNION p 1051
303 Se 17th St Ste 106, Fort Lauderdale FL 33316
Tel (954) 355-4400 SIC 6061

VYSTAR CREDIT UNION p 1568
4949 Blanding Blvd, Jacksonville FL 32210
Tel (904) 777-6000 SIC 6061

SUNCOAST CREDIT UNION p 1401
6801 E Hillsborough Ave, Tampa FL 33610
Tel (800) 999-5887 SIC 6062 6061

DELTA COMMUNITY CREDIT UNION p 426
1025 Virginia Ave, Atlanta GA 30354
Tel (404) 715-4725 SIC 6061 6163

ALLIANT CREDIT UNION FOUNDATION p 55
11545 W Touhy Ave, Chicago IL 60666
Tel (800) 328-1935 SIC 6062 6061

TOWER FEDERAL CREDIT UNION p 1464
7901 Sandy Spring Rd # 102, Laurel MD 20707
Tel (301) 490-6926 SIC 6163 6061

DIGITAL EMPLOYEES FEDERAL CREDIT UNION p 439
220 Donald Lynch Blvd, Marlborough MA 01752
Tel (508) 263-6700 SIC 6061

MICHIGAN STATE UNIVERSITY FEDERAL CREDIT UNION p 961
3777 West Rd, East Lansing MI 48823
Tel (517) 333-2424 SIC 6061

UNITED FEDERAL CREDIT UNION p 1508
2807 S State St, Saint Joseph MI 49085
Tel (888) 982-1400 SIC 6061 6163

WINGS FINANCIAL CREDIT UNION p 1616
14985 Glazier Ave Ste 100, Saint Paul MN 55124
Tel (952) 997-8000 SIC 6061 6282

■ MPB CORP p 995
7 Optical Ave, Keene NH 03431
Tel (603) 352-0310 SIC 3562 6061

HACKNSCK HSPTL EMPLYS FDRL CRDT UN (INC) p 652
241 Moore St, Hackensack NJ 07601
Tel (201) 996-2000 SIC 6061

STATE EMPLOYEES FEDERAL CREDIT UNION p 1380
575 Broadway, Albany NY 12207
Tel (518) 452-8183 SIC 6061

STATE EMPLOYEES FEDERAL CREDIT UNION p 1380
700 Patroon Creek Blvd, Albany NY 12206
Tel (518) 452-8183 SIC 6061

BETHPAGE FEDERAL CREDIT UNION INC p 178
899 S Oyster Bay Rd, Bethpage NY 11714
Tel (516) 349-6700 SIC 6061

VISIONS FEDERAL CREDIT UNION p 1561
24 Mckinley Ave, Endicott NY 13760
Tel (607) 754-7900 SIC 6061

TEACHERS FEDERAL CREDIT UNION p 1429
100 Hauppauge, Hauppauge NY 11788
Tel (631) 698-7000 SIC 6061

NORTH SHORE LIJ HEALTH SYSTEM FEDERAL CREDIT UNION p 1053
350 Jericho Tpke Ste 103, Jericho NY 11753
Tel (516) 301-3040 SIC 6061

UNITED NATIONS FEDERAL CREDIT UNION p 1510
2401 44th Rd, Long Island City NY 11101
Tel (347) 686-6000 SIC 6061

HUDSON VALLEY FEDERAL CREDIT UNION p 717
137 Boardman Rd, Poughkeepsie NY 12603
Tel (845) 463-3011 SIC 6061

ESL FEDERAL CREDIT UNION p 509
225 Chestnut St, Rochester NY 14604
Tel (585) 336-1000 SIC 6061

COASTAL FEDERAL CREDIT UNION p 331
1000 Saint Albans Dr, Raleigh NC 27609
Tel (919) 420-8000 SIC 6061

TINKER FEDERAL CREDIT UNION p 1455
4140 W I 40 Service Rd, Oklahoma City OK 73108
Tel (405) 732-0324 SIC 6061

CITADEL FEDERAL CREDIT UNION INC p 309
520 Eagleview Blvd, Exton PA 19341
Tel (610) 380-6000 SIC 6061

MEMBERS 1ST FEDERAL CREDIT UNION p 941
5000 Louise Dr, Mechanicsburg PA 17055
Tel (717) 697-1161 SIC 6061

POLICE AND FIRE FEDERAL CREDIT UNION (INC) p 1159
901 Arch St, Philadelphia PA 19107
Tel (215) 931-0300 SIC 6061 6163

FOUNDERS FEDERAL CREDIT UNION p 571
607 N Main St, Lancaster SC 29720
Tel (803) 283-5958 SIC 6061

NAVY ARMY COMMUNITY CREDIT UNION p 1020
2730 Rodd Field Rd, Corpus Christi TX 78414
Tel (361) 986-4500 SIC 6061

AMERICAN AIRLINES FEDERAL CREDIT UNION INC p 67
4151 Amon Carter Blvd, Fort Worth TX 76155
Tel (817) 963-6000 SIC 6061

FIRST SERVICE CREDIT UNION p 549
9621 W Sam Houston Pkwy N, Houston TX 77064
Tel (832) 688-1000 SIC 6061

SECURITY SERVICE CUSO LLC p 1299
16211 La Cantera Pkwy, San Antonio TX 78256
Tel (210) 476-4151 SIC 6061 7381

SECURITY SERVICE FEDERAL CREDIT UNION p 1299
15000 W Interstate 10, San Antonio TX 78249
Tel (210) 476-4000 SIC 6061

RANDOLPH-BROOKS FEDERAL CREDIT UNION p 1208
1600 E Court St, Seguin TX 78155
Tel (210) 945-3300 SIC 6061

PENTAGON FEDERAL CREDIT UNION p 1131
2930 Eisenhower Ave, Alexandria VA 22314
Tel (800) 247-5626 SIC 6061

NAVY FEDERAL CREDIT UNION p 1020
820 Follin Ln Se, Vienna VA 22180
Tel (703) 255-8000 SIC 6061

BOEING EMPLOYEES CREDIT UNION p 197
12770 Gateway Dr S, Tukwila WA 98168
Tel (206) 439-5700 SIC 6062 6061

SIC 6062 State Credit Unions

DESERT SCHOOLS FEDERAL CREDIT UNION p 432
148 N 48th St, Phoenix AZ 85034
Tel (602) 433-7000 SIC 6062

SAFE CREDIT UNION p 1265
2295 Iron Point Rd # 100, Folsom CA 95630
Tel (916) 979-7233 SIC 6062

WESCOM CENTRAL CREDIT UNION p 1593
123 S Marengo Ave, Pasadena CA 91101
Tel (888) 493-7266 SIC 6062

GOLDEN 1 CREDIT UNION p 620
8945 Cal Center Dr, Sacramento CA 95826
Tel (916) 732-2900 SIC 6062

SAN DIEGO COUNTY CREDIT UNION INC p 1276
6545 Sequence Dr, San Diego CA 92121
Tel (877) 732-2848 SIC 6062

BANK FUND STAFF FCU p 150
1725 I St Nw Ste 300, Washington DC 20006
Tel (202) 429-9180 SIC 6062

BANK-FUND STAFF FEDERAL CREDIT UNION p 152
1722 I St Nw Ste 200, Washington DC 20006
Tel (202) 458-4350 SIC 6062

SPACE COAST CREDIT UNION p 1354
8045 N Wickham Rd, Melbourne FL 32940
Tel (321) 259-6219 SIC 6062

SUNCOAST CREDIT UNION p 1401
6801 E Hillsborough Ave, Tampa FL 33610
Tel (800) 999-5887 SIC 6062 6061

GEORGIAS OWN CREDIT UNION p 608
1155 Peachtree St Ne # 400, Atlanta GA 30309
Tel (404) 874-1166 SIC 6062

ALLIANT CREDIT UNION FOUNDATION p 55
11545 W Touhy Ave, Chicago IL 60666
Tel (800) 328-1935 SIC 6062 6061

CITIZENS EQUITY FIRST CREDIT UNION p 311
5401 W Everett M Dirksen, Peoria IL 61607
Tel (309) 633-3603 SIC 6062

BAXTER CREDIT UNION p 160
340 N Milwaukee Ave, Vernon Hills IL 60061
Tel (847) 522-8600 SIC 6062

VERIDIAN CREDIT UNION p 1549
1827 Ansborough Ave, Waterloo IA 50701
Tel (319) 236-5600 SIC 6062 6163

COMMUNITYAMERICA CREDIT UNION p 350
9777 Ridge Dr, Lenexa KS 66219
Tel (913) 905-7000 SIC 6062 6163

STATE EMPLOYEES CREDIT UNION OF MARYLAND INC p 1380
971 Corporate Blvd # 100, Linthicum Heights MD 21090
Tel (410) 487-7920 SIC 6062

LAKE MICHIGAN CREDIT UNION p 839
4027 Lake Dr Se Ste 100, Grand Rapids MI 49546
Tel (616) 242-9790 SIC 6062

MUNICIPAL CREDIT UNION p 1000
2 Lafayette St Frnt D, New York NY 10007
Tel (212) 238-3300 SIC 6062

STATE EMPLOYEES CREDIT UNION p 1380
119 N Salisbury St, Raleigh NC 27603
Tel (919) 839-5000 SIC 6062

WRIGHT-PATT CREDIT UNION INC p 1627
3560 Pentagon Blvd, Beavercreek OH 45431
Tel (937) 912-7000 SIC 6062

TINKER FEDERAL CREDIT UNION p 1455
5101 W 6th Ave, Stillwater OK 74074
Tel (405) 707-7440 SIC 6062

ONPOINT COMMUNITY CREDIT UNION p 1088
2701 Nw Vaughn St Ste 800, Portland OR 97210
Tel (503) 228-8255 SIC 6062

PENNSYLVANIA STATE EMPLOYEES CREDIT UNION p 1130
1500 Elmerton Ave, Harrisburg PA 17110
Tel (800) 237-7328 SIC 6062 9199

EASTMAN CREDIT UNION p 473
2021 Meadowview Ln # 200, Kingsport TN 37660
Tel (423) 229-8200 SIC 6062

CTECU p 399
4800 Fournace Pl, Bellaire TX 77401
Tel (713) 432-0038 SIC 6062

GECU p 597
1225 Airway Blvd, El Paso TX 79925
Tel (915) 778-9221 SIC 6062

TEXAS DOW EMPLOYEES CREDIT UNION p 1443
1001 Fm 2004 Rd, Lake Jackson TX 77566
Tel (979) 297-1154 SIC 6062

VIEWPOINT BANK NA p 1556
1309 W 15th St Ste 210, Plano TX 75075
Tel (972) 578-5000 SIC 6062

SAN ANTONIO FEDERAL CREDIT UNION p 1275
6061 W Ih 10 Fl 3, San Antonio TX 78201
Tel (210) 258-1414 SIC 6062

AMERICA FIRST CREDIT UNION p 67
1344 W 4675 S Ste 130, Ogden UT 84405
Tel (801) 627-0900 SIC 6062

MOUNTAIN AMERICA FEDERAL CREDIT UNION p 994
7181 S Campus View Dr, West Jordan UT 84084
Tel (801) 325-6228 SIC 6062

VIRGINIA CREDIT UNION INC p 1558
7500 Boulder View Dr, North Chesterfield VA 23225
Tel (804) 323-6800 SIC 6062 6163

WASHINGTON STATE EMPLOYEES CREDIT UNION p 1579
330 Union Ave Se, Olympia WA 98501
Tel (360) 943-7911 SIC 6062

NUMERICA CREDIT UNION p 1067
14610 E Sprague Ave, Spokane Valley WA 99216
Tel (509) 535-7613 SIC 6062

BOEING EMPLOYEES CREDIT UNION p 197
12770 Gateway Dr S, Tukwila WA 98168
Tel (206) 439-5700 SIC 6062 6061

SUMMIT CREDIT UNION p 1398
2424 Rimrock Rd, Madison WI 53713
Tel (608) 244-2400 SIC 6062

LANDMARK CREDIT UNION p 842
5445 S Westridge Dr, New Berlin WI 53151
Tel (262) 796-4500 SIC 6062

SIC 6081 Foreign Banks, Branches & Agencies

ANZ LIMITED PARTNERSHIP p 94
1177 Ave Of The Americas, New York NY 10036
Tel (212) 801-9800 SIC 6081

STANDARD AMERICAS INC p 1375
520 Madison Ave Fl 28, New York NY 10022
Tel (212) 407-5000 SIC 6081 6082

SIC 6082 Foreign Trade & Intl Banks

INTER-AMERICAN DEVELOPMENT BANK p 751
1300 New York Ave Nw, Washington DC 20577
Tel (202) 623-1000 SIC 6082

INTERNATIONAL BANK FOR RECONSTRUCTION & DEVELOPMENT (INC) p 754
1818 H St Nw, Washington DC 20433
Tel (202) 473-1000 SIC 6082

INTERNATIONAL FINANCE CORP p 755
1818 H St Nw, Washington DC 20433
Tel (202) 458-2454 SIC 6082

INTERNATIONAL MONETARY FUND p 756
700 19th St Nw, Washington DC 20431
Tel (202) 623-7000 SIC 6082

WORLD BANK GROUP p 1624
1818 H St Nw, Washington DC 20433
Tel (202) 473-1000 SIC 6082

TFS RT INC p 1445
20807 Biscayne Blvd # 203, Aventura FL 33180
Tel (416) 240-8404 SIC 6082

BMO FINANCIAL CORP p 194
111 W Monroe St Ste 1200, Chicago IL 60603
Tel (312) 461-2121 SIC 6021 6082 6211

■ STATE STREET HOLDING CO LLC p 1383
225 Franklin St Lbby 1, Boston MA 02110
Tel (617) 664-1029 SIC 6082

■ BANK OF NEW YORK MELLON p 151
225 Liberty St, New York NY 10281
Tel (212) 495-1784
SIC 6153 6211 6282 6082

DEXIA CREDIT LOCAL (INC) p 434
445 Park Ave Fl 8, New York NY 10022
Tel (212) 515-7000 SIC 6082

HVB AMERICA INC p 722
150 E 42nd St Fl 29, New York NY 10017
Tel (212) 672-6000 SIC 6082

MIZUHO BANK LTD p 978
1251 Ave Of The Americas, New York NY 10020
Tel (212) 282-3000 SIC 6022 6082 7359

STANDARD AMERICAS INC p 1375
520 Madison Ave Fl 28, New York NY 10022
Tel (212) 407-5000 SIC 6081 6082

STANDARD CHARTERED INTERNATIONAL (USA) LTD p 1375
200 Vesey St, New York NY 10285
Tel (212) 640-2000 SIC 6082 6021 6099

▲ COMERICA INC p 344
1717 Main St Mc6404, Dallas TX 75201
Tel (214) 462-6831
SIC 6021 6022 6091 6082 6099 6141

SIC 6091 Nondeposit Trust Facilities

CAPITAL GROUP COMPANIES INC p 249
333 S Hope St Fl 55, Los Angeles CA 90071
Tel (213) 486-9200
SIC 6282 6091 6722 8741

■ SUNAMERICA INC p 1401
1 Sun America Ctr Fl 38, Los Angeles CA 90067
Tel (310) 772-6000
SIC 6091 6311 6211 6282 6411 6371

▲ CHARLES SCHWAB CORP p 289
211 Main St Fl 17, San Francisco CA 94105
Tel (415) 667-7000
SIC 6211 6091 6282 7389

INDUSTRIAL INCOME TRUST INC p 740
518 17th St Ste 17, Denver CO 80202
Tel (303) 228-2200 SIC 6091

UBS SECURITIES LLC p 1498
677 Washington Blvd, Stamford CT 06901
Tel (203) 719-3000
SIC 6211 6221 6289 6311 6091 6282

■ RAYMOND JAMES FINANCIAL SERVICES INC p 1210
880 Carillon Pkwy, Saint Petersburg FL 33716
Tel (727) 567-1000
SIC 6211 6282 6712 6091 6035

▲ SUNTRUST BANKS INC p 1405
303 Peachtree St Ne, Atlanta GA 30308
Tel (800) 786-8787
SIC 6021 6022 6211 6091 6282

SECURITY BENEFIT LIFE INSURANCE CO p 1299
1 Sw Security Benefit Pl, Topeka KS 66636
Tel (785) 438-3000
SIC 6311 6722 6091 6211 8748

▲ LPL FINANCIAL HOLDINGS INC p 882
75 State St Ste 2401, Boston MA 02109
Tel (617) 423-3644 SIC 6211 6282 6091

▲ US BANCORP p 1531
800 Nicollet Mall # 1500, Minneapolis MN 55402
Tel (651) 466-3000
SIC 6021 6022 6162 6091 6159 6411

HSBC NORTH AMERICA INC p 715
1 Hsbc Ctr Ste 1, Buffalo NY 14203
Tel (716) 841-2424
SIC 6021 6035 6221 6091 6211

■ BEAR STEARNS COMPANIES LLC p 165
383 Madison Ave, New York NY 10179
Tel (212) 272-2000
SIC 6211 6282 6221 6099 6091 6289

BROWN BROTHERS HARRIMAN & CO p 219
140 Brdwy, New York NY 10005
Tel (212) 483-1818 SIC 6091 6211

■ CITIBANK NA p 310
399 Park Ave Bsmt 1, New York NY 10022
Tel (212) 559-1000
SIC 6021 6153 6091 6099 6162

▲ BANK OF AMERICA CORP p 151
100 N Tryon St Ste 220, Charlotte NC 28202
Tel (704) 386-5681
SIC 6021 6022 6211 6091 6162 6159

OREGON HEALTH & SCIENCE UNIVERSITY FOUNDATION INC p 1093
1121 Sw Salmon St Ste 100, Portland OR 97205
Tel (503) 228-1730
SIC 8399 6091 8733 6732

■ CONCORD EFS INC p 354
7000 Goodlett Farms Pkwy # 300, Cordova TN 38016
Tel (901) 371-8000
SIC 6099 7389 6091 5044

■ NETSPEND CORP p 1027
701 Brazos St, Austin TX 78701
Tel (512) 532-8200 SIC 6091

▲ COMERICA INC p 344
1717 Main St Mc6404, Dallas TX 75201
Tel (214) 462-6831
SIC 6021 6022 6091 6082 6099 6141

■ MERRILL LYNCH COMMODITIES INC p 950
20 Greenway Plz Ste 950, Houston TX 77046
Tel (832) 681-5904 SIC 6211 6091

SIC 6099 Functions Related To Deposit Banking, NEC

■ CONTINENTAL EXCHANGE SOLUTIONS INC p 363
7001 Village Dr Ste 200, Buena Park CA 90621
Tel (562) 345-2100 SIC 6099

▲ BLACKHAWK NETWORK HOLDINGS INC p 187
6220 Stoneridge Mall Rd, Pleasanton CA 94588
Tel (925) 226-9990 SIC 6099

■ BLACKHAWK NETWORK INC p 187
6220 Stoneridge Mall Rd, Pleasanton CA 94588
Tel (925) 226-9990 SIC 6099

CU COOPERATIVE SYSTEMS INC p 399
9692 Haven Ave, Rancho Cucamonga CA 91730
Tel (909) 948-2500 SIC 6099

■ XOOM CORP p 1632
425 Market St Fl 12, San Francisco CA 94105
Tel (415) 777-4800 SIC 6099

CONTINENTAL CURRENCY SERVICES INC p 363
1108 E 17th St, Santa Ana CA 92701
Tel (714) 569-0300 SIC 6099

TARBELL FINANCIAL CORP p 1424
1403 N Tustin Ave Ste 380, Santa Ana CA 92705
Tel (714) 972-0988 SIC 6163 6531 6099

▲ WESTERN UNION CO p 1600
12500 Belford Ave, Englewood CO 80112
Tel (866) 405-5012 SIC 6099

■ WESTERN UNION FINANCIAL SERVICES INC p 1600
12510 Belford Ave M22b3, Englewood CO 80112
Tel (720) 332-1000 SIC 6099

FIRST DATA HOLDINGS INC p 546
5775 Dtc Blvd Ste 100, Greenwood Village CO 80111
Tel (303) 967-8000
SIC 6099 7375 7389 6153

■ INTEGRATED PAYMENT SYSTEMS INC p 749
6200 S Quebec St Ste 320b, Greenwood Village CO 80111
Tel (402) 951-7008 SIC 6099

■ CONCORD CORPORATE SERVICES INC p 354
1100 Carr Rd, Wilmington DE 19809
Tel (302) 791-8200 SIC 6099

TEMPUS INC p 1436
1201 New York Ave Nw # 300, Washington DC 20005
Tel (800) 834-2497 SIC 6099

■ WESTERN UNION BUSINESS SOLUTIONS (USA) LLC p 1600
1152 15th St Nw Ste 700, Washington DC 20005
Tel (202) 408-1200 SIC 6099

GARDA CL TECHNICAL SERVICES INC p 591
700 S Federal Hwy Ste 300, Boca Raton FL 33432
Tel (561) 939-7000 SIC 6099 7381

■ FIRST DATA MERCHANT SERVICES CORP p 546
5565 Glenridge Connector, Atlanta GA 30342
Tel (404) 890-3000
SIC 7374 7389 7375 6153 6099

INCOMM HOLDINGS INC p 735
250 Williams St Nw Fl 5, Atlanta GA 30303
Tel (770) 240-6100 SIC 6099

INTERACTIVE COMMUNICATIONS INTERNATIONAL INC p 751
250 Williams St Nw # 5000, Atlanta GA 30303
Tel (770) 240-6100 SIC 6099

■ VALUED SERVICES ACQUISITIONS CO LLC p 1542
5 Concrs Pkwy Ne Ste 1000, Atlanta GA 30328
Tel (678) 593-1300 SIC 6099

■ INTERCEPT INC p 751
3150 Holcomb Bridge Rd, Norcross GA 30071
Tel (770) 248-9600 SIC 6099 7374

PENDUM LLC p 1128
558 W Lamont Rd, Elmhurst IL 60126
Tel (800) 422-6835 SIC 6099 7381

▲ EURONET WORLDWIDE INC p 512
3500 College Blvd, Leawood KS 66211
Tel (913) 327-4200 SIC 6099 7372 4813

QC FINANCIAL SERVICES INC p 1194
9401 Indian Creek Pkwy # 1500, Shawnee Mission KS 66210
Tel (913) 439-1100 SIC 6141 6099

UNIVERSAL COMPANIES INC p 1516
2824 N Ohio St, Wichita KS 67219
Tel (316) 832-0151
SIC 5171 5541 6512 8741 6099 2992

PAYMENT ALLIANCE INTERNATIONAL INC p 1122
1 Paragon Ctr 6060 Dutchm, Louisville KY 40205
Tel (502) 212-4000 SIC 6099

■ MONEYGRAM PAYMENT SYSTEMS INC p 984
1550 Utica Ave S Ste 100, Minneapolis MN 55416
Tel (952) 591-3000 SIC 6099 7389
■ WORLDS FOREMOST BANK p 1626
1 Cabelas Dr, Sidney NE 69162
Tel (402) 323-4300 SIC 6099
■ EVERI PAYMENTS INC p 515
7250 S Tenaya Way Ste 100, Las Vegas NV 89113
Tel (702) 855-3000 SIC 7389 6099
KALDI MANAGEMENT INC p 801
4824 Winterset Dr Ste 100, Las Vegas NV 89130
Tel (702) 340-7283 SIC 6099
NEXXAR GROUP INC p 1041
580 Sylvan Ave Ste Ma, Englewood Cliffs NJ 07632
Tel (201) 477-6045 SIC 6099
ICAP CAPITAL MARKETS LLC p 726
1100 Plaza Five, Jersey City NJ 07311
Tel (212) 732-6900 SIC 6099
▲ AMERICAN EXPRESS CO p 72
200 Vesey St, New York NY 10285
Tel (212) 640-2000
SIC 6141 7389 6282 6099 6311 6211
■ BANK OF AMERICA PVT WEALTH MANAGEMENT p 151
114 W 47th St Ste C-1, New York NY 10036
Tel (800) 878-7878
SIC 6282 6022 6099 6733
■ BEAR STEARNS COMPANIES LLC p 165
383 Madison Ave, New York NY 10179
Tel (212) 272-2000
SIC 6211 6282 6221 6099 6091 6289
■ CITIBANK NA p 310
399 Park Ave Bsmt 1, New York NY 10022
Tel (212) 559-1000
SIC 6021 6153 6091 6099 6162
CLEARING HOUSE PAYMENTS CO L L C p 324
1114 Avenue Of The Americ, New York NY 10036
Tel (212) 612-9200 SIC 6099
■ CURRENEX INC p 402
1230 Ave Of, New York NY 10020
Tel (212) 340-1780 SIC 6099
■ FIDUCIARY TRUST CO INTERNATIONAL p 541
280 Park Ave, New York NY 10017
Tel (212) 632-3000 SIC 6099
▲ FIRST DATA CORP p 546
225 Liberty St Fl 29, New York NY 10281
Tel (800) 735-3362 SIC 7389 6099 6153
▲ FXCM INC p 586
55 Water St Fl 50, New York NY 10041
Tel (646) 432-2986 SIC 6211 6099
FXDIRECTDEALER LLC p 586
7 World Trade Ctr 32nd, New York NY 10007
Tel (212) 266-0700 SIC 6099
JLL PARTNERS INC p 786
450 Lexington Ave Fl 31, New York NY 10017
Tel (212) 286-8600 SIC 6799 6099
STANDARD CHARTERED INTERNATIONAL (USA) LTD p 1375
200 Vesey St, New York NY 10285
Tel (212) 640-2000 SIC 6082 6021 6099
TRAVELEX CURRENCY SERVICES INC p 1474
122 E 42nd St Rm 2800, New York NY 10168
Tel (212) 363-6206 SIC 6099
■ MASTERCARD INTERNATIONAL INC p 918
2000 Purchase St, Purchase NY 10577
Tel (914) 249-2000 SIC 7389 6099
PAY-O-MATIC CORP p 1122
160 Oak Dr, Syosset NY 11791
Tel (516) 496-4900 SIC 6099 7381 7999
ALLIED CASH HOLDINGS LLC p 56
7755 Montgomery Rd # 400, Cincinnati OH 45236
Tel (305) 371-3141 SIC 6099
CNG FINANCIAL CORP p 330
7755 Montgomery Rd # 400, Cincinnati OH 45236
Tel (513) 336-7735 SIC 6099
■ JPMORGAN CHASE BANK NATIONAL ASSOCIATION p 795
1111 Polaris Pkwy, Columbus OH 43240
Tel (614) 436-3055
SIC 6022 6099 6799 6211 6162 7389
BUCKEYE CHECK CASHING INC p 223
6785 Bobcat Way Ste 200, Dublin OH 43016
Tel (614) 798-5900 SIC 6099
CHECKSMART FINANCIAL CO p 292
6785 Bobcat Way Ste 200, Dublin OH 43016
Tel (614) 798-5900 SIC 6099
COLUMBIA HOUSING/PNC INSTITUTIONAL FUND XX LIMITED PARTNERSHIP p 341
121 Sw Morrison St # 1300, Portland OR 97204
Tel (503) 808-1300 SIC 6099
MONETARY MANAGEMENT OF CA INC p 984
1436 Lancaster Ave, Berwyn PA 19312
Tel (610) 296-3400 SIC 6099
DFC GLOBAL CORP p 435
74 E Swedesford Rd # 150, Malvern PA 19355
Tel (610) 296-3400 SIC 6099 6141
DFG WORLD INC p 435
74 E Swedesford Rd, Malvern PA 19355
Tel (610) 296-3400 SIC 6099
DOLLAR FINANCIAL GROUP INC p 448
74 E Swedesford Rd, Malvern PA 19355
Tel (610) 296-3400 SIC 6099 8721
CHECK INTO CASH INC p 292
201 Keith St Sw Ste 80, Cleveland TN 37311
Tel (423) 479-2400 SIC 6099
■ CONCORD EFS INC p 354
7000 Goodlett Farms Pkwy # 300, Cordova TN 38016
Tel (901) 371-8000
SIC 6099 7389 6091 5044
■ ELECTRONIC FUNDS SOURCE LLC p 485
3100 West End Ave # 1150, Nashville TN 37203
Tel (888) 824-7378 SIC 7371 6099
DOLEX DOLLAR EXPRESS INC p 448
700 Highlander Blvd # 450, Arlington TX 76015
Tel (817) 548-4700 SIC 6099
▲ FIRSTCASH INC p 550
690 E Lamar Blvd Ste 400, Arlington TX 76011
Tel (817) 460-3947 SIC 5932 6099
APEX CLEARING CORP p 96
350 N Paul St Ste 1300, Dallas TX 75201
Tel (214) 765-1100
SIC 6099 7389 4813 6289
▲ COMERICA INC p 344
1717 Main St Mc6404, Dallas TX 75201
Tel (214) 462-6831
SIC 6021 6022 6091 6082 6099 6141
▲ MONEYGRAM INTERNATIONAL INC p 984
2828 N Harwood St Fl 15, Dallas TX 75201
Tel (214) 999-7552 SIC 6099
CASH AMERICA INVESTMENTS INC p 263
1600 W 7th St, Fort Worth TX 76102
Tel (817) 335-1100 SIC 5932 6099
■ FRONTIER MERGER SUB LLC p 581
1600 W 7th St, Fort Worth TX 76102
Tel (800) 223-8738 SIC 5932 6099
BANCOMER TRANSFER SERVICES INC p 150
16825 Northchase Dr Ste 1, Houston TX 77060
Tel (281) 765-1500 SIC 6099
ACE CASH EXPRESS INC p 16
1231 Greenway Dr Ste 600, Irving TX 75038
Tel (972) 550-5000 SIC 7323 6099
GSC ENTERPRISES INC p 643
130 Hillcrest Dr, Sulphur Springs TX 75482
Tel (903) 885-7621 SIC 5141 6099
AIRLINES REPORTING CORP p 40
3000 Wilson Blvd Ste 300, Arlington VA 22201
Tel (703) 816-8000 SIC 7389 6099 7374
MONEYTREE INC p 984
6720 Fort Dent Way # 230, Tukwila WA 98188
Tel (888) 516-6643 SIC 6099
WERCS p 1592
400 E 1st St Ste 100, Casper WY 82601
Tel (307) 235-6200
SIC 6211 6163 6411 6321 6531 6099

SIC 6111 Federal Credit Agencies

JOE WHEELER EMC p 787
25700 Al Highway 24, Trinity AL 35673
Tel (256) 552-2300 SIC 6111
■ HOMEQ SERVICING CORP p 703
4837 Watt Ave, North Highlands CA 95660
Tel (916) 339-6192
SIC 6162 6163 6111 6159
FEDERAL HOME LOAN BANK OF SAN FRANCISCO p 534
600 California St, San Francisco CA 94108
Tel (415) 616-1000 SIC 6111
YOSEMITE FARM CREDIT ACA p 1637
806 W Monte Vista Ave, Turlock CA 95382
Tel (209) 667-2366 SIC 6111
COBANK ACB p 332
6340 S Fiddlers Green Cir, Greenwood Village CO 80111
Tel (303) 740-6527 SIC 6111 7359 6159
▲ SLM CORP p 1331
300 Continental Dr Ste 1s, Newark DE 19713
Tel (302) 451-0200 SIC 6111 6141 7322
▲ FEDERAL AGRICULTURAL MORTGAGE CORP p 533
1999 K St Nw Fl 4, Washington DC 20006
Tel (202) 872-7700 SIC 6111 6159
▲ FEDERAL NATIONAL MORTGAGE ASSOCIATION p 535
3900 Wisconsin Ave Nw, Washington DC 20016
Tel (202) 752-7000 SIC 6111
■ N A BANKUNITED p 1005
14817 Oak Ln, Miami Lakes FL 33016
Tel (305) 231-6400 SIC 6035 6163 6111
FEDERAL HOME LOAN BANK OF ATLANTA p 534
1475 Peachtree St Ne # 400, Atlanta GA 30309
Tel (404) 888-8000 SIC 6111
PROMMIS SOLUTIONS LLC p 1183
400 Northridge Rd, Atlanta GA 30350
Tel (800) 275-7171 SIC 6111
GEORGIA FARM BUREAU FEDERATION INC p 607
1620 Bass Rd, Macon GA 31210
Tel (478) 474-8411
SIC 6111 5154 8699 5191
FEDERAL HOME LOAN BANK OF CHICAGO p 534
200 E Randolph St # 1700, Chicago IL 60601
Tel (312) 565-5700 SIC 6111
FARM CREDIT ILLINOIS ACA p 528
1100 Farm Credit Dr, Mahomet IL 61853
Tel (217) 590-2222 SIC 6159 6153 6111
INDIANA SECONDARY MARKET FOR EDUCATION LOANS INC p 738
11595 N Meridian St # 200, Carmel IN 46032
Tel (317) 715-9000 SIC 6111
FEDERAL HOME LOAN BANK OF INDIANAPOLIS p 534
8250 Wdfld Xing Blvd, Indianapolis IN 46240
Tel (317) 465-0200 SIC 6111
IOWA STUDENT LOAN LIQUIDITY CORP p 763
6775 Vista Dr, West Des Moines IA 50266
Tel (515) 243-5626 SIC 6111 6141
FEDERAL HOME LOAN BANK OF BOSTON p 534
800 Boylston St Ste 900, Boston MA 02199
Tel (617) 292-9600 SIC 6111 6019
MASSACHUSETTS EDUCATIONAL FINANCING AUTHORITY p 916
160 Federal St Fl 4, Boston MA 02110
Tel (617) 224-4800 SIC 6111
MASSACHUSETTS HIGHER EDUCATION ASSISTANCE CORP p 917
100 Cambridge St Ste 1600, Boston MA 02114
Tel (617) 728-4507 SIC 6111
AGSTAR FINANCIAL SERVICES ACA p 36
1921 Premier Dr, Mankato MN 56001
Tel (507) 387-4174 SIC 6111
ECMC GROUP INC p 475
111 Washington Ave S # 1400, Minneapolis MN 55401
Tel (651) 325-3652 SIC 6111
EDUCATIONAL CREDIT MANAGEMENT CORP p 479
111 Wshngton Ave Ste 1400, Minneapolis MN 55401
Tel (651) 221-0566 SIC 6111
MISSOURI HIGHER EDUCATION LOAN AUTHORITY p 976
633 Spirit Dr, Chesterfield MO 63005
Tel (636) 733-3700 SIC 6111
■ NELNET STUDENT LOAN CORP-1 p 1025
121 S 13th St Ste 301, Lincoln NE 68508
Tel (402) 458-2370 SIC 6111
UNION BANK AND TRUST CO p 1504
3643 S 48th St, Lincoln NE 68506
Tel (402) 488-0941
SIC 6111 6029 6162 6021 6035 6022
FEDERAL HOME LOAN BANK OF NEW YORK p 534
101 Park Ave Fl 5, New York NY 10178
Tel (212) 441-6616 SIC 6111
▲ SOTHEBYS p 1341
1334 York Ave, New York NY 10021
Tel (212) 606-7000 SIC 6531 6111 5921
TRAXYS NORTH AMERICA LLC p 1475
825 3rd Ave Fl 9, New York NY 10022
Tel (212) 918-8000 SIC 6111 7389
AMERICAN EDUCATIONAL SERVICES CORP p 71
1200 N 7th St, Harrisburg PA 17102
Tel (717) 720-2700 SIC 6111
AGFIRST FARM CREDIT BANK p 34
1901 Main St, Columbia SC 29201
Tel (803) 799-5000 SIC 6111
SOUTH CAROLINA STUDENT LOAN CORP p 1343
8906 Two Notch Rd, Columbia SC 29223
Tel (803) 798-0916 SIC 6111
EDFINANCIAL SERVICES LLC p 477
298 N Seven Oaks Dr, Knoxville TN 37922
Tel (865) 342-5500 SIC 6111
FARM CREDIT BANK OF TEXAS p 528
4801 Plaza On The Lk # 1200, Austin TX 78746
Tel (512) 330-9060 SIC 6111
FEDERAL HOME LOAN BANK OF DALLAS p 534
8500 Freeport Pkwy # 600, Irving TX 75063
Tel (214) 441-8500 SIC 6111
TEXAS GUARANTEED STUDENT LOAN CORP p 1443
301 Sundance Pkwy, Round Rock TX 78681
Tel (512) 219-5700 SIC 6111
■ MARLIN BUSINESS BANK p 909
2795 E Cottonwood Pkwy # 120, Salt Lake City UT 84121
Tel (888) 479-9111 SIC 6111
▲ FEDERAL HOME LOAN MORTGAGE CORP p 534
8200 Jones Branch Dr, Mc Lean VA 22102
Tel (703) 903-2000 SIC 6111
■ NAVIENT SOLUTIONS INC p 1020
2001 Edmund Halley Dr, Reston VA 20191
Tel (703) 810-3000 SIC 6111
NORTHWEST FARM CREDIT SERVICES p 1059
2001 S Flint Rd, Spokane WA 99224
Tel (509) 838-2429 SIC 6111

SIC 6141 Personal Credit Institutions

■ PALM HARBOR HOMES INC p 1109
1001 N Central Ave # 800, Phoenix AZ 85004
Tel (602) 256-6263 SIC 2452 5211 6141
▲ AMERICAS CAR-MART INC p 81
802 Se Plaza Ave Ste 200, Bentonville AR 72712
Tel (479) 464-9944 SIC 5521 6141
AMERICAN FINANCIAL NETWORK INC p 72
10 Pointe Dr Ste 330, Brea CA 92821
Tel (909) 606-3905 SIC 6141
BALBOA CAPITAL CORP p 147
575 Anton Blvd Fl 12, Costa Mesa CA 92626
Tel (949) 756-0800 SIC 6141
HYUNDAI MOTOR AMERICA p 724
10550 Talbert Ave, Fountain Valley CA 92708
Tel (714) 965-3000 SIC 5511 6141 6153
HYUNDAI CAPITAL AMERICA p 724
3161 Michelson Dr # 1900, Irvine CA 92612
Tel (714) 965-3000 SIC 6141
■ WELLS FARGO DEALER SERVICES INC p 1590
23 Pasteur, Irvine CA 92618
Tel (949) 727-1002 SIC 6141
GENERAL BUSINESS CREDIT p 599
110 E 9th St Ste A1126, Los Angeles CA 90079
Tel (213) 244-9500 SIC 6141
CASHCALL INC p 263
1 City Blvd W Ste 102, Orange CA 92868
Tel (949) 752-4600 SIC 6141
▲ GREEN DOT CORP p 637
3465 E Foothill Blvd # 100, Pasadena CA 91107
Tel (626) 765-2000 SIC 6141 7389
COMMERCE WEST INSURANCE CO p 345
6130 Stoneridge Mall Rd # 400, Pleasanton CA 94588
Tel (925) 730-6400 SIC 6141
■ B OF I FEDERAL BANK p 142
4350 La Jolla Village Dr # 140, San Diego CA 92122
Tel (858) 350-6200 SIC 6141 6163
■ BANKAMERICA FINANCIAL INC p 152
315 Montgomery St, San Francisco CA 94104
Tel (415) 622-3521 SIC 6153 6141 6282
▲ WELLS FARGO & CO p 1590
420 Montgomery St Frnt, San Francisco CA 94104
Tel (866) 249-3302
SIC 6021 6022 6162 6141 7374
REDWOOD CREDIT UNION p 1217
3033 Cleveland Ave # 100, Santa Rosa CA 95403
Tel (707) 545-4000 SIC 6141
WESTLEND FINANCING INC p 1601
15260 Ventura Blvd # 710, Sherman Oaks CA 91403
Tel (818) 385-7500 SIC 6162 6141
AMERICAN HONDA FINANCE CORP p 74
20800 Madrona Ave, Torrance CA 90503
Tel (310) 972-2239 SIC 6141
TOYOTA MOTOR CREDIT CORP p 1466
19001 S Western Ave, Torrance CA 90501
Tel (310) 468-1310 SIC 6141
■ GENERAL ELECTRIC CAPITAL SERVICES INC p 600
3135 Easton Tpke, Fairfield CT 06828
Tel (203) 373-2211
SIC 6159 6141 7359 6162
■ ADVEST GROUP INC p 27
90 State House Sq, Hartford CT 06103
Tel (860) 509-1000
SIC 6211 6036 6141 6153 6282
■ AMG FUNDS LLC p 85
800 Connecticut Ave Ste 2, Norwalk CT 06854
Tel (203) 299-3500 SIC 6141
■ GENERAL ELECTRIC CAPITAL CORP p 600
901 Main Ave, Norwalk CT 06851
Tel (203) 840-6300 SIC 6159 6141 7359
■ GE CAPITAL MONTGOMERY WARD p 595
3135 Easton Tpke, Stamford CT 06927
Tel (203) 357-4000 SIC 6141
▲ SLM CORP p 1331
300 Continental Dr Ste 1s, Newark DE 19713
Tel (302) 451-0200 SIC 6111 6141 7322
▲ NICHOLAS FINANCIAL INC p 1042
2454 N Mcmullen Booth Rd, Clearwater FL 33759
Tel (727) 726-0763 SIC 6141
WORLD OMNI FINANCIAL CORP p 1625
190 Jim Moran Blvd, Deerfield Beach FL 33442
Tel (954) 429-2200 SIC 6141 6159
CARIBBEAN FINANCIAL GROUP INC p 256
20807 Biscayne Blvd # 200, Miami FL 33180
Tel (305) 933-6601 SIC 6141
HAMILTON RISK MANAGEMENT CO p 655
3155 Nw 77th Ave, Miami FL 33122
Tel (305) 716-6000
SIC 6331 7323 6141 6541 6411
CNL FINANCIAL GROUP INC p 330
450 S Orange Ave Ste 300, Orlando FL 32801
Tel (407) 650-1000 SIC 6141 6719
■ WYNDHAM VACATION RESORTS INC p 1630
6277 Sea Harbor Dr # 400, Orlando FL 32821
Tel (407) 370-5200 SIC 6531 6141
■ SMART CHOICE AUTOMOTIVE GROUP INC p 1332
5130 S Washington Ave, Titusville FL 32780
Tel (321) 269-9680 SIC 5521 3714 6141
FEDELITY FEDERAL BANK & TRUST p 533
205 Datura St, West Palm Beach FL 33401
Tel (561) 803-9900 SIC 6141
GREENSKY LLC p 638
5565 Glenridge Connector, Atlanta GA 30342
Tel (404) 832-4000 SIC 6141
▲ STATE BANK FINANCIAL CORP p 1380
3399 Peachtree Rd Ne, Atlanta GA 30326
Tel (404) 475-6599
SIC 6022 6712 6311 6141 6331
INSURANCE HOUSE INC p 748
1904 Leland Dr Se, Marietta GA 30067
Tel (770) 952-0080 SIC 6331 6411 6141
TITLEMAX OF TEXAS INC p 1456
15 Bull St Ste 200, Savannah GA 31401
Tel (912) 525-2675 SIC 6141
TMX FINANCE LLC p 1458
15 Bull St Ste 200, Savannah GA 31401
Tel (912) 525-2675 SIC 6141
1ST FRANKLIN FINANCIAL CORP p 1
135 E Tugalo St, Toccoa GA 30577
Tel (706) 886-7571 SIC 6141
BENEFICIAL CO LLC p 172
1421 W Shure Dr Ste 100, Arlington Heights IL 60004
Tel (708) 453-6502
SIC 6141 6351 6162 6021 6552 6311
HSBC FINANCE CORP p 714
1421 W Shure Dr Ste 100, Arlington Heights IL 60004
Tel (224) 880-7000 SIC 6141
AVANT INC p 136
222 N Lsalle St Ste 1700, Chicago IL 60601
Tel (312) 448-8685 SIC 6141
■ GE HEALTHCARE FINANCIAL SERVICES INC p 596
500 W Monroe St Fl 19, Chicago IL 60661
Tel (312) 697-3999 SIC 6141
■ HARLEY-DAVIDSON FINANCIAL SERVICES INC p 661
222 W Adams St Ste 2000, Chicago IL 60606
Tel (312) 368-9501 SIC 6141 6411
▲ KEMPER CORP p 809
1 E Wacker Dr, Chicago IL 60601
Tel (312) 661-4600
SIC 6331 6321 6311 6141
LIBERTY HAMPSHIRE CO LLC p 861
227 W Monroe St, Chicago IL 60606
Tel (312) 827-0100 SIC 6141
■ CITICORP CREDIT SERVICES INC p 310
50 Northwest Point Blvd, Elk Grove Village IL 60007
Tel (847) 597-3000
SIC 7374 7389 7379 6141
■ WELLS FARGO COMMERCIAL DISTRIBUTION FINANCE LLC p 1590
5595 Trillium Blvd, Hoffman Estates IL 60192
Tel (847) 747-6800 SIC 6153 6159 6141
HOUSEHOLD FINANCE CORP p 711
2700 Sanders Rd, Prospect Heights IL 60070
Tel (847) 790-1590
SIC 6141 6162 6351 6153 6159 6311
HOUSEHOLD REALTY CORP p 711
2700 Sanders Rd Fl 1, Prospect Heights IL 60070
Tel (847) 790-1590 SIC 6141
HSBC INVESTMENTS (NORTH AMERICA) INC p 715
2700 Sanders Rd, Prospect Heights IL 60070
Tel (847) 564-5000
SIC 6141 7389 6351 6159 6162 6311
▲ DISCOVER FINANCIAL SERVICES p 442
2500 Lake Cook Rd, Riverwoods IL 60015
Tel (224) 405-0900 SIC 6022 6141 7389

▲ ONE MAIN FINANCIAL SERVICES p 1086
601 Nw 2nd St, Evansville IN 47708
Tel (800) 961-5577 SIC 6141 6351 6331

■ ONEMAIN HOLDINGS INC p 1087
601 Nw 2nd St, Evansville IN 47708
Tel (812) 424-8031 SIC 6141

■ SPRINGLEAF FINANCE CORP p 1361
601 Nw 2nd St, Evansville IN 47708
Tel (812) 424-8031 SIC 6141

WELLS FARGO FINANCIAL CA INC p 1590
800 Walnut St, Des Moines IA 50309
Tel (515) 557-7401
SIC 6141 6153 6351 6159 6531 6021

■ WELLS FARGO FINANCIAL SECURITY SERVICES INC p 1590
800 Walnut St, Des Moines IA 50309
Tel (515) 243-2131
SIC 6141 6153 6351 6159 7374 6021

■ JOHN DEERE FINANCIAL SERVICES INC p 788
6400 Nw 86th St, Johnston IA 50131
Tel (515) 267-3000 SIC 6141

IOWA STUDENT LOAN LIQUIDITY CORP p 763
6775 Vista Dr, West Des Moines IA 50266
Tel (515) 243-5626 SIC 6111 6141

QC HOLDINGS INC p 1194
9401 Indian Creek Pkwy # 1500, Overland Park KS 66210
Tel (866) 660-2243 SIC 6141 7389

QC FINANCIAL SERVICES INC p 1194
9401 Indian Creek Pkwy # 1500, Shawnee Mission KS 66210
Tel (913) 439-1100 SIC 6141 6099

FORCHT GROUP OF KENTUCKY LLC p 565
200 S Kentucky Ave, Corbin KY 40701
Tel (606) 528-9600 SIC 6141

FARM CREDIT MID-AMERICA p 528
1601 Ups Dr, Louisville KY 40223
Tel (502) 420-3700 SIC 6159 6141

AFFIRMATIVE LLC p 32
2900 Westfork Dr Ste 600, Baton Rouge LA 70827
Tel (225) 928-9000 SIC 6311 6141

REPUBLIC FINANCE LLC p 1225
7031 Commerce Cir Ste 100, Baton Rouge LA 70809
Tel (225) 927-0005 SIC 6141

■ CITIFINANCIAL CREDIT CO p 310
300 Saint Paul St Fl 3, Baltimore MD 21202
Tel (410) 332-3000
SIC 6141 6162 7389 6331 6159 6022

■ ONEMAIN FINANCIAL GROUP LLC p 1087
100 Intl Dr 15000, Baltimore MD 21202
Tel (855) 663-6246 SIC 6141

ELEMENT VEHICLE MANAGEMENT SERVICES GROUP LLC p 486
940 Ridgebrook Rd, Sparks MD 21152
Tel (410) 771-1900 SIC 6141

CHELSEA PETROLEUM PRODUCTS HOLDINGS LLC p 293
200 Clarendon St Fl 55, Boston MA 02116
Tel (617) 531-6300 SIC 6141

■ EAST BOSTON SAVING BANK p 470
10 Meridian St, Boston MA 02128
Tel (617) 567-1500 SIC 6029 6141

▲ FORD MOTOR CO p 565
1 American Rd, Dearborn MI 48126
Tel (313) 322-3000
SIC 3711 3713 3714 6153 6141 7515

■ FORD MOTOR CREDIT CO LLC p 565
1 American Rd, Dearborn MI 48126
Tel (313) 322-3000 SIC 6159 6141

■ ALLY INSURANCE HOLDINGS INC p 59
500 Woodward Ave Fl 1, Detroit MI 48226
Tel (888) 737-8460 SIC 6331 6141

H W KAUFMAN FINANCIAL GROUP INC p 651
30833 Northwestern Hwy, Farmington Hills MI 48334
Tel (248) 932-9000 SIC 6141 6719

ROUTEONE LLC p 1253
31500 Nrthwstrn Hwy 200, Farmington Hills MI 48334
Tel (866) 768-8301 SIC 6141 7379

▲ CREDIT ACCEPTANCE CORP p 390
25505 W 12 Mile Rd # 2300, Southfield MI 48034
Tel (248) 353-2700 SIC 6141

ASSET ACCEPTANCE HOLDINGS LLC p 119
320 E Big Beaver Rd, Troy MI 48083
Tel (586) 939-9600 SIC 6141

ASSET ACCEPTANCE LLC p 119
320 E Big Beaver Rd, Troy MI 48083
Tel (586) 939-9600 SIC 6141

■ WELLS FARGO BUSINESS CREDIT INC p 1590
730 2nd Ave S Fl 8, Minneapolis MN 55402
Tel (612) 673-8500 SIC 6021 6141

CITIZENS FINANCIAL CORP p 311
202 E Jackson St, Belzoni MS 39038
Tel (662) 746-6811 SIC 6022 6021 6141

MILLER TRANSPORTERS EMPLOYEES p 971
5500 Highway 80 W, Jackson MS 39209
Tel (601) 922-8331 SIC 6141

FIRST HERITAGE CREDIT CORP p 547
605 Crescent Blvd Ste 101, Ridgeland MS 39157
Tel (601) 952-0635 SIC 6141

▲ NELNET INC p 1025
121 S 13th St Ste 100, Lincoln NE 68508
Tel (402) 458-2370 SIC 6141 7389

FIRST NATIONAL OF NEBRASKA INC p 548
1620 Dodge St, Omaha NE 68197
Tel (402) 341-0500 SIC 6022 6141 7371

▲ CONSUMER PORTFOLIO SERVICES INC p 361
3800 Howard Hughes Pkwy, Las Vegas NV 89169
Tel (949) 753-6800 SIC 6141

DIAMOND RESORTS CORP p 437
10600 W Charleston Blvd, Las Vegas NV 89135
Tel (702) 684-8000 SIC 7041 6141 8741

DIAMOND RESORTS HOLDINGS LLC p 437
10600 W Charleston Blvd, Las Vegas NV 89135
Tel (877) 787-0906 SIC 7011 6141 8741

HUDSON UNITED BANK p 717
1000 Macarthur Blvd, Mahwah NJ 07430
Tel (201) 236-2600 SIC 6141 6022

▲ AMERICAN EXPRESS CO p 72
200 Vesey St, New York NY 10285
Tel (212) 640-2000
SIC 6141 7389 6282 6099 6311 6211

▲ CIT GROUP INC p 309
11 W 42nd St Fl 7, New York NY 10036
Tel (212) 461-5200
SIC 6022 6162 6159 6141

▲ CITIGROUP INC p 310
399 Park Ave, New York NY 10022
Tel (212) 559-1000
SIC 6021 6141 6331 6311 6321

DB USA CORP p 418
60 Wall St, New York NY 10005
Tel (212) 250-2500 SIC 6141 6153

DEUTSCHE BANK AMERICAS HOLDING CORP p 433
60 Wall St, New York NY 10005
Tel (212) 250-2500 SIC 6141 6153 6211

▲ JPMORGAN CHASE & CO p 795
270 Park Ave Fl 38, New York NY 10017
Tel (212) 270-6000
SIC 6021 6211 6162 6141

■ SPH GROUP LLC p 1358
590 Madison Ave, New York NY 10022
Tel (212) 520-2300 SIC 6141

■ SPH SERVICES INC p 1358
590 Madison Ave Fl 32, New York NY 10022
Tel (212) 520-2300 SIC 6141

▲ STEEL PARTNERS HOLDINGS LP p 1384
590 Madison Ave Rm 3202, New York NY 10022
Tel (212) 520-2300
SIC 3479 3497 1381 6141

MACK TRUCKS INC p 892
7825 National Service Rd, Greensboro NC 27409
Tel (336) 291-9001
SIC 3711 3714 5012 6141 6153 7538

AXCESS FINANCIAL SERVICES INC p 140
7755 Montgomery Rd # 400, Cincinnati OH 45236
Tel (513) 336-7735 SIC 6141

▲ KEYCORP p 815
127 Public Sq, Cleveland OH 44114
Tel (216) 689-3000 SIC 6021 6141 6211

■ MACYS CREDIT AND CUSTOMER SERVICES INC p 893
9111 Duke Blvd, Mason OH 45040
Tel (513) 398-5221 SIC 7389 7322 6141

MTD HOLDINGS INC p 997
5965 Grafton Rd, Valley City OH 44280
Tel (330) 225-2600
SIC 3524 3544 3469 6141

PAPE GROUP INC p 1112
355 Goodpasture Island Rd # 300, Eugene OR 97401
Tel (541) 334-3400
SIC 5084 5082 7699 6141 5599 4581

DFC GLOBAL CORP p 435
74 E Swedesford Rd # 150, Malvern PA 19355
Tel (610) 296-3400 SIC 6099 6141

■ POPULAR FINANCE INC p 1161
326 Salud St El El Senorial Cond, Ponce PR 00716
Tel (787) 844-2760 SIC 6141

■ BANCO POPULAR DE PUERTO RICO (INC) p 150
Popular Ctr, San Juan PR 00918
Tel (787) 765-9800 SIC 6022 6159 6141

▲ REGIONAL MANAGEMENT CORP p 1219
509 W Butler Rd, Greenville SC 29607
Tel (864) 422-8011 SIC 7389 6141

SOUTHERN MANAGEMENT CORP p 1349
101 N Main St Ste 600, Greenville SC 29601
Tel (864) 233-9033 SIC 6141

▲ WORLD ACCEPTANCE CORP p 1624
108 Frederick St, Greenville SC 29607
Tel (864) 298-9800 SIC 6141

ADVANCE AMERICA CASH ADVANCE CENTERS INC p 24
135 N Church St, Spartanburg SC 29306
Tel (864) 342-5600 SIC 6141 6153

EAGLE US SUB INC p 468
135 N Church St, Spartanburg SC 29306
Tel (864) 515-5600 SIC 6141 6153

SECURITY FINANCE CORP OF SPARTANBURG p 1299
181 Security Pl, Spartanburg SC 29307
Tel (864) 582-8193 SIC 6141

SECURITY GROUP INC p 1299
181 Security Pl, Spartanburg SC 29307
Tel (864) 582-8193 SIC 6141

STUDENT LOAN FINANCE CORP p 1394
124 S 1st St, Aberdeen SD 57401
Tel (605) 622-4400 SIC 6141

PIONEER CREDIT CO p 1150
1870 Executive Park Nw, Cleveland TN 37312
Tel (423) 476-6511 SIC 6141

NISSAN MOTOR ACCEPTANCE CORP p 1044
1 Nissan Way, Franklin TN 37067
Tel (615) 725-1000 SIC 6141

NISSAN NORTH AMERICA INC p 1044
1 Nissan Way, Franklin TN 37067
Tel (615) 725-1000
SIC 5012 8711 8734 6141 8741 3711

■ PRIMUS AUTOMOTIVE FINANCIAL SERVICES INC p 1176
9009 Carothers Pkwy, Franklin TN 37067
Tel (800) 374-7000 SIC 6141

EDUCATIONAL FUNDING OF SOUTH INC p 479
12700 Kingston Pike, Knoxville TN 37934
Tel (865) 342-0684 SIC 6141

■ CLAYTON HOMES INC p 323
5000 Clayton Rd, Maryville TN 37804
Tel (865) 380-3000
SIC 2451 5271 6141 6351 6331

■ VANDERBILT MORTGAGE AND FINANCE INC p 1543
500 Alcoa Trl, Maryville TN 37804
Tel (865) 380-3000 SIC 6141

PERMANENT GENERAL ASSURANCE CORP p 1136
2636 Elm Hill Pike # 510, Nashville TN 37214
Tel (615) 744-1351 SIC 6331 6411 6141

▲ EZCORP INC p 522
2500 Bee Caves Rd B1-200, Austin TX 78746
Tel (512) 314-3400 SIC 5932 6141

MS PAWN LIMITED PARTNERSHIP p 996
1901 Capital Pkwy, Austin TX 78746
Tel (512) 314-3400 SIC 5932 6141

▲ COMERICA INC p 344
1717 Main St Mc6404, Dallas TX 75201
Tel (214) 462-6831
SIC 6021 6022 6091 6082 6099 6141

■ SANTANDER CONSUMER USA HOLDINGS INC p 1281
1601 Elm St Ste 800, Dallas TX 75201
Tel (214) 634-1110 SIC 6141

■ SANTANDER CONSUMER USA INC FOUNDATION p 1281
8585 N Stemmons Fwy, Dallas TX 75247
Tel (214) 634-1110 SIC 6141

■ AMERICREDIT FINANCIAL SERVICES INC p 82
801 Cherry St Ste 3500, Fort Worth TX 76102
Tel (817) 302-7000 SIC 6141

ELEVATE CREDIT INC p 486
4150 Intl Plz Ste 300, Fort Worth TX 76109
Tel (817) 928-1500 SIC 6141

■ GENERAL MOTORS FINANCIAL CO INC p 601
801 Cherry St Ste 3500, Fort Worth TX 76102
Tel (817) 302-7000 SIC 6141

■ AIG LIFE HOLDINGS INC p 38
2929 Allen Pkwy, Houston TX 77019
Tel (713) 522-1111
SIC 6311 6321 6331 6141 6162 6153

▲ GROUP 1 AUTOMOTIVE INC p 641
800 Gessner Rd Ste 500, Houston TX 77024
Tel (713) 647-5700
SIC 5511 6141 7538 7532 5531

■ ASSOCIATES CORP OF NORTH AMERICA p 121
250 E John Carpenter Fwy, Irving TX 75062
Tel (972) 652-4000
SIC 6141 6153 6159 6311 6321 6331

■ ASSOCIATES FIRST CAPITAL CORP p 121
4000 Regent Blvd, Irving TX 75063
Tel (800) 922-6235
SIC 6162 6021 6141 6159 6153

■ CITI FINANCIAL AUTO p 309
250 E John Carpenter Fwy, Irving TX 75062
Tel (972) 652-4000 SIC 6141

COTTONWOOD FINANCIAL ADMINISTRATIVE SERVICES LLC p 374
1901 Gateway Dr Ste 200, Irving TX 75038
Tel (972) 753-0822 SIC 6141

■ CAPITAL ONE AUTO FINANCE INC p 250
7933 Preston Rd, Plano TX 75024
Tel (800) 946-0332 SIC 6141

WESTERN-SHAMROCK CORP p 1600
801 S Abe St Ste 2a, San Angelo TX 76903
Tel (325) 653-6814 SIC 6141 6159 6153

■ CONN APPLIANCES INC p 356
4055 Technology Frst, The Woodlands TX 77381
Tel (409) 832-1696
SIC 5722 5731 7629 6141 7359

PROG FINANCE LLC p 1180
11629 S 700 E Ste 200, Draper UT 84020
Tel (877) 898-1970 SIC 6141

■ PITNEY BOWES BANK INC p 1152
1245 E Brickyard Rd # 250, Salt Lake City UT 84106
Tel (801) 832-4440 SIC 6141

NATIONAL RURAL UTILITIES COOPERATIVE FINANCE CORP p 1016
20701 Cooperative Way, Dulles VA 20166
Tel (703) 467-1800 SIC 6141 6159

VOLKSWAGEN GROUP OF AMERICA INC p 1564
2200 Ferdinand Porsche Dr, Herndon VA 20171
Tel (703) 364-7000
SIC 5511 5012 5013 6153 6141 4899

VW CREDIT INC p 1567
2200 Ferdinand Porsche Dr, Herndon VA 20171
Tel (248) 340-5000 SIC 6141

▲ CAPITAL ONE FINANCIAL CORP p 250
1680 Capital One Dr, Mc Lean VA 22102
Tel (703) 720-1000 SIC 6021 6141

■ CAPITAL ONE SERVICES LLC p 250
1680 Capital One Dr, Mc Lean VA 22102
Tel (703) 720-1000 SIC 6141

▲ CARMAX INC p 258
12800 Tuckahoe Creek Pkwy, Richmond VA 23238
Tel (804) 747-0422 SIC 5521 5511 6141

■ GENWORTH NORTH AMERICA CORP p 605
6620 W Broad St Bldg 3, Richmond VA 23230
Tel (804) 281-6000 SIC 6141

TIDEWATER FINANCE CO p 1452
6520 Indian River Rd, Virginia Beach VA 23464
Tel (757) 579-6444 SIC 6141

STERLING SAVINGS BANK p 1387
111 N Wall St, Spokane WA 99201
Tel (509) 624-4121
SIC 6036 6162 6035 6141 6153

AMFAM INC p 85
6000 American Pkwy, Madison WI 53783
Tel (608) 249-2111 SIC 6331 6311 6141

CATHOLIC KNIGHTS INSURANCE SOCIETY INC p 267
1100 W Wells St Ste 1, Milwaukee WI 53233
Tel (414) 273-6266
SIC 6311 6411 6211 6141

▲ HARLEY-DAVIDSON INC p 661
3700 W Juneau Ave, Milwaukee WI 53208
Tel (414) 342-4680
SIC 3751 6153 6141 6411 6399

SIC 6153 Credit Institutions, Short-Term Business

HYUNDAI MOTOR AMERICA p 724
10550 Talbert Ave, Fountain Valley CA 92708
Tel (714) 965-3000 SIC 5511 6141 6153

UNITED CALIFORNIA DISCOUNT CORP p 1506
2200 E Route 66 Ste 102, Glendora CA 91740
Tel (909) 394-5400 SIC 6153

▲ ENCORE CAPITAL GROUP INC p 496
3111 Camino Del Rio N # 103, San Diego CA 92108
Tel (877) 445-4581 SIC 6153

■ MIDLAND CREDIT MANAGEMENT INC p 965
3111 Camino Del Rio N, San Diego CA 92108
Tel (877) 240-2377 SIC 6153

NATIONAL FUNDING INC p 1012
9820 Towne Centre Dr # 200, San Diego CA 92121
Tel (888) 576-4685 SIC 6153 6159 7389

■ BANKAMERICA FINANCIAL INC p 152
315 Montgomery St, San Francisco CA 94104
Tel (415) 622-3521 SIC 6153 6141 6282

▲ LENDINGCLUB CORP p 855
71 Stevenson St Ste 300, San Francisco CA 94105
Tel (415) 632-5600 SIC 6153

FIRST DATA HOLDINGS INC p 546
5775 Dtc Blvd Ste 100, Greenwood Village CO 80111
Tel (303) 967-8000
SIC 6099 7375 7389 6153

CPI CARD GROUP INC p 387
10368 W Centennial Rd A, Littleton CO 80127
Tel (303) 973-9311 SIC 6153

■ ADVEST GROUP INC p 27
90 State House Sq, Hartford CT 06103
Tel (860) 509-1000
SIC 6211 6036 6141 6153 6282

BANKERS HEALTHCARE GROUP LLC p 152
10234 W State Road 84, Davie FL 33324
Tel (954) 384-9119 SIC 6153

PROSPERITY FUNDING INC p 1184
200 S Andrews Ave 201c, Fort Lauderdale FL 33301
Tel (919) 954-0232 SIC 6153

LSQ FUNDING GROUP LC p 883
2600 Lucien Way Ste 100, Maitland FL 32751
Tel (407) 206-0022 SIC 6153

LSQ GROUP LLC p 883
2600 Lucien Way Ste 100, Maitland FL 32751
Tel (407) 206-0022 SIC 6153

EXPOCREDIT LLC p 520
1450 Brickell Ave # 2660, Miami FL 33131
Tel (305) 347-9222 SIC 6153

■ LENNAR FINANCIAL SERVICES LLC p 855
700 Nw 107th Ave Ste 400, Miami FL 33172
Tel (305) 559-4000
SIC 6162 6153 6361 6411 7382

ACTION CAPITAL CORP p 19
230 Peachtree St Nw # 810, Atlanta GA 30303
Tel (404) 524-3181 SIC 6153

■ FIRST DATA MERCHANT SERVICES CORP p 546
5565 Glenridge Connector, Atlanta GA 30342
Tel (404) 890-3000
SIC 7374 7389 7375 6153 6099

KABBAGE INC p 799
730 Peachtree St Ne # 350, Atlanta GA 30308
Tel (855) 278-7084 SIC 6153

■ BANC ONE FINANCIAL LLC p 149
1 Chase Tower, Chicago IL 60670
Tel (312) 732-5531 SIC 6211 6153

■ BUSINESS PROPERTY LENDING INC p 229
500 W Monroe St, Chicago IL 60661
Tel (312) 441-7000
SIC 6153 6799 6162 6159

PAYONEER INC p 1122
5300 Katrine Ave, Downers Grove IL 60515
Tel (331) 777-2622 SIC 6153

LENDING SOLUTIONS INC p 855
2200 Point Blvd Ste 110, Elgin IL 60123
Tel (847) 844-2200 SIC 6153 7389

■ WELLS FARGO COMMERCIAL DISTRIBUTION FINANCE LLC p 1590
5595 Trillium Blvd, Hoffman Estates IL 60192
Tel (847) 747-6800 SIC 6153 6159 6141

SNAP-ON CREDIT LLC p 1335
950 Technology Way # 301, Libertyville IL 60048
Tel (847) 782-7700 SIC 6153

■ NAVISTAR INC p 1020
2701 Navistar Dr, Lisle IL 60532
Tel (331) 332-5000
SIC 3711 3714 3519 6153 6159 6331

FARM CREDIT ILLINOIS ACA p 528
1100 Farm Credit Dr, Mahomet IL 61853
Tel (217) 590-2222 SIC 6159 6153 6111

HOUSEHOLD FINANCE CORP p 711
2700 Sanders Rd, Prospect Heights IL 60070
Tel (847) 790-1590
SIC 6141 6162 6351 6153 6159 6311

■ DFS CORPORATE SERVICES LLC p 435
2500 Lake Cook Rd 2, Riverwoods IL 60015
Tel (224) 405-0900 SIC 6153

■ ADESA CORP LLC p 22
13085 Hamilton Crossing B, Carmel IN 46032
Tel (317) 249-4550 SIC 5012 6153

■ AUTOMOTIVE FINANCE CORP p 134
13085 H Croining Blvd 3 Ste 300, Carmel IN 46032
Tel (317) 815-9645 SIC 6153

▲ KAR AUCTION SERVICES INC p 804
13085 Hmlton Crssing Blvd, Carmel IN 46032
Tel (800) 923-3725 SIC 5012 6153 5521

KAR HOLDINGS II LLC p 804
13085 Hamil Cross Blvd St Ste 500, Carmel IN 46032
Tel (317) 815-1100 SIC 5012 6153

■ SPRINGLEAF FINANCE INC p 1361
601 Nw 2nd St, Evansville IN 47708
Tel (812) 424-8031
SIC 6153 6351 6331 7389

WELLS FARGO FINANCIAL CA INC p 1590
800 Walnut St, Des Moines IA 50309
Tel (515) 557-7401
SIC 6141 6153 6351 6159 6531 6021

■ WELLS FARGO FINANCIAL SECURITY SERVICES INC p 1590
800 Walnut St, Des Moines IA 50309
Tel (515) 243-2131
SIC 6141 6153 6351 6159 7374 6021

■ DEERE CREDIT INC p 422
6400 Nw 86th St, Johnston IA 50131
Tel (515) 224-2800 *SIC* 6153

SHAMROCK TRADING CORP p 1311
9300 Metcalf Ave, Overland Park KS 66212
Tel (913) 310-2200
SIC 4731 6153 8742 7323

▲ FORD MOTOR CO p 565
1 American Rd, Dearborn MI 48126
Tel (313) 322-3000
SIC 3711 3713 3714 6153 6141 7515

▲ ALLY FINANCIAL INC p 59
500 Woodward Ave Fl 1, Detroit MI 48226
Tel (866) 710-4623
SIC 6021 6153 6159 6311 6331 6162

TD AUTO FINANCE LLC p 1428
27777 Inkster Rd, Farmington Hills MI 48334
Tel (248) 427-6800 *SIC* 6153 5511

■ ASSET ACCEPTANCE CAPITAL CORP p 119
320 E Big Beaver Rd, Troy MI 48083
Tel (800) 505-5166 *SIC* 6153 7322

CAPITAL FOR MERCHANTS LLC p 249
250 Stephenson Hwy, Troy MI 48083
Tel (248) 269-6000 *SIC* 6153

NORTH AMERICAN BANCARD LLC p 1049
250 Stephenson Hwy, Troy MI 48083
Tel (800) 226-2273 *SIC* 6153

FINANCIAL HOLDING CORP p 542
1055 Broadway Blvd Fl 11, Kansas City MO 64105
Tel (816) 391-2000 *SIC* 6411 6311 6153

IPFS CORP p 763
1055 Broadway Blvd Fl 11, Kansas City MO 64105
Tel (816) 627-0500 *SIC* 6153

■ EMERSON ELECTRIC OVERSEAS FINANCE CORP p 492
8000 W Florissant Ave, Saint Louis MO 63136
Tel (314) 553-2000 *SIC* 6153

■ JOHN DEERE CAPITAL CORP p 788
10587 Double R Blvd # 100, Reno NV 89521
Tel (775) 786-5527 *SIC* 6153

■ PSEG ENERGY HOLDINGS LLC p 1188
80 Park Plz Ste 3, Newark NJ 07102
Tel (973) 430-7000 *SIC* 6153 6512

■ IBM CREDIT LLC p 726
1 North Castle Dr, Armonk NY 10504
Tel (914) 765-1900 *SIC* 6153 6159

CITICORP NORTH AMERICA INC p 310
450 Mamaroneck Ave Ste A, Harrison NY 10528
Tel (914) 899-7000 *SIC* 6153 6159

▲ NEWTEK BUSINESS SERVICES INC p 1039
1981 Marcus Ave Ste C130, New Hyde Park NY 11042
Tel (212) 356-9500 *SIC* 6153 7374 4813

■ AIG FUNDING INC p 37
70 Pine St Fl 50, New York NY 10270
Tel (212) 770-7000 *SIC* 6411 6153

■ AMERICAN EXPRESS CREDIT CORP p 72
200 Vesey St, New York NY 10285
Tel (866) 572-4944 *SIC* 6153

AMERICAN INDUSTRIAL ACQUISITION CORP p 74
250 Park Ave Fl 7, New York NY 10177
Tel (212) 572-4853 *SIC* 6211 6153

■ BANK OF NEW YORK MELLON p 151
225 Liberty St, New York NY 10281
Tel (212) 495-1784
SIC 6153 6211 6282 6082

CAN CAPITAL INC p 246
414 W 14th St Fl 3, New York NY 10014
Tel (914) 725-9301 *SIC* 6153

▲ CAPITAL ON DECK INC p 250
1400 Broadway Fl 25, New York NY 10018
Tel (888) 269-4246 *SIC* 6153

■ CIT GROUP/COMMERCIAL SERVICES INC p 309
11 W 42nd St Fl 11, New York NY 10036
Tel (212) 461-5200 *SIC* 6153

■ CITIBANK NA p 310
399 Park Ave Bsmt 1, New York NY 10022
Tel (212) 559-1000
SIC 6021 6153 6091 6099 6162

DB USA CORP p 418
60 Wall St, New York NY 10005
Tel (212) 250-2500 *SIC* 6141 6153

DEUTSCHE BANK AMERICAS HOLDING CORP p 433
60 Wall St, New York NY 10005
Tel (212) 250-2500 *SIC* 6141 6153 6211

EXPRESS TRADE CAPITAL INC p 520
1410 Broadway Fl 26, New York NY 10018
Tel (212) 997-0155 *SIC* 6153 4731

▲ FIRST DATA CORP p 546
225 Liberty St Fl 29, New York NY 10281
Tel (800) 735-3362 *SIC* 7389 6099 6153

FORESTERS FINANCIAL SERVICES p 567
40 Wall St Fl 10, New York NY 10005
Tel (212) 858-8000
SIC 6036 6211 6282 6311 8742 6153

■ GOLDMAN SACHS & CO p 622
200 West St Bldg 200, New York NY 10282
Tel (212) 346-5440
SIC 6211 6221 6282 6153

JORDACHE LIMITED p 793
1400 Broadway Rm 1404b, New York NY 10018
Tel (212) 944-1330 *SIC* 5137 5136 6153

MERCHANT CASH AND CAPITAL LLC p 944
460 Park Ave S Fl 10, New York NY 10016
Tel (212) 545-3180 *SIC* 6153 7389

MOET HENNESSY USA INC p 982
85 10th Ave Fl 2, New York NY 10011
Tel (212) 888-7575
SIC 0172 2844 6153 5182 5122

NYLIFE LLC p 1069
51 Madison Ave, New York NY 10010
Tel (212) 576-7000
SIC 6282 6211 6733 6153

▲ PJT PARTNERS INC p 1153
280 Park Ave Fl 16, New York NY 10017
Tel (212) 364-7800 *SIC* 6282 6153

ROSENTHAL & ROSENTHAL INC p 1251
1370 Broadway, New York NY 10018
Tel (212) 356-1400 *SIC* 6153

SOLVATION INC p 1339
885 3rd Ave Fl 34, New York NY 10022
Tel (212) 888-5500 *SIC* 6153 1611 3272

VOIP GUARDIAN LLC p 1564
405 E 56th St Apt 3g, New York NY 10022
Tel (212) 421-0888 *SIC* 6153

PUBLIC LOAN CO INC p 1189
300 Plaza Dr, Vestal NY 13850
Tel (607) 584-5274 *SIC* 6153

MACK TRUCKS INC p 892
7825 National Service Rd, Greensboro NC 27409
Tel (336) 291-9001
SIC 3711 3714 5012 6141 6153 7538

LIVE OAK BANKING CO p 871
1741 Tiburon Dr, Wilmington NC 28403
Tel (910) 790-5867 *SIC* 6153

DAIMLER TRUCKS REMARKETING CORP p 408
4747 N Channel Ave, Portland OR 97217
Tel (503) 745-8000 *SIC* 6153

ROCKWELL FUNDING LLC p 1245
310 Maple Ave Ste L04, Barrington RI 02806
Tel (401) 466-4755 *SIC* 6153

SHERMAN FINANCIAL GROUP LLC p 1316
200 Meeting St Ste 206, Charleston SC 29401
Tel (212) 922-1616 *SIC* 6153 6726

ADVANCE AMERICA CASH ADVANCE CENTERS INC p 24
135 N Church St, Spartanburg SC 29306
Tel (864) 342-5600 *SIC* 6141 6153

EAGLE US SUB INC p 468
135 N Church St, Spartanburg SC 29306
Tel (864) 515-5600 *SIC* 6141 6153

NBT INC p 1021
813 Ridge Lake Blvd, Memphis TN 38120
Tel (901) 818-3309 *SIC* 6153

AFFILIATED FOODS INC p 32
1401 W Farmers Ave, Amarillo TX 79118
Tel (806) 345-7773
SIC 5141 2026 2051 5149 6153

■ NETSPEND HOLDINGS INC p 1027
701 Brazos St Ste 1300, Austin TX 78701
Tel (512) 532-8200 *SIC* 6153

■ CHASE PAYMENTECH SOLUTIONS LLC p 291
14221 Dallas Pkwy Bldg 2, Dallas TX 75254
Tel (214) 849-3000 *SIC* 6153 7389

APEX CAPITAL CORP p 96
6000 Western Pl Ste 1000, Fort Worth TX 76107
Tel (800) 511-6022 *SIC* 6153

FIRST AMERICAN PAYMENT SYSTEMS LP p 544
100 Throckmorton St # 1800, Fort Worth TX 76102
Tel (817) 317-9100 *SIC* 6153

■ AIG LIFE HOLDINGS INC p 38
2929 Allen Pkwy, Houston TX 77019
Tel (713) 522-1111
SIC 6311 6321 6331 6141 6162 6153

■ TELECHECK SERVICES INC p 1434
5251 Westheimr Rd B100, Houston TX 77056
Tel (713) 331-7600 *SIC* 7389 7374 6153

■ ASSOCIATES CORP OF NORTH AMERICA p 121
250 E John Carpenter Fwy, Irving TX 75062
Tel (972) 652-4000
SIC 6141 6153 6159 6311 6321 6331

■ ASSOCIATES FIRST CAPITAL CORP p 121
4000 Regent Blvd, Irving TX 75063
Tel (800) 922-6235
SIC 6162 6021 6141 6159 6153

CALIBER FUNDING LLC p 239
6031 Connection Dr # 200, Irving TX 75039
Tel (866) 373-2968 *SIC* 6153

CALIBER HOME LOANS INC p 239
3701 Regent Blvd, Irving TX 75063
Tel (800) 401-6587 *SIC* 6153

■ EXETER FINANCE CORP p 519
222 Las Colinas Blvd W, Irving TX 75039
Tel (214) 572-8276 *SIC* 6153

WESTERN-SHAMROCK CORP p 1600
801 S Abe St Ste 2a, San Angelo TX 76903
Tel (325) 653-6814 *SIC* 6141 6159 6153

LEAVITT GROUP ENTERPRISES INC p 850
216 S 200 W, Cedar City UT 84720
Tel (435) 586-1555 *SIC* 6153 8741 6411

TETRA FINANCIAL GROUP LLC p 1441
6995 S Union Park Ctr # 400, Cottonwood Heights UT 84047
Tel (801) 748-2200 *SIC* 6153

■ ALLY BANK p 59
6985 S Union Park Ctr # 435, Midvale UT 84047
Tel (801) 790-5005
SIC 6153 6021 6311 6331 6162

VOLKSWAGEN GROUP OF AMERICA INC p 1564
2200 Ferdinand Porsche Dr, Herndon VA 20171
Tel (703) 364-7000
SIC 5511 5012 5013 6153 6141 4899

■ PACCAR FINANCIAL CORP p 1103
777 106th Ave Ne, Bellevue WA 98004
Tel (425) 468-7100 *SIC* 6153

▲ PACCAR INC p 1103
777 106th Ave Ne, Bellevue WA 98004
Tel (425) 468-7400
SIC 3711 3714 3713 3537 5013 6153

STERLING SAVINGS BANK p 1387
111 N Wall St, Spokane WA 99201
Tel (509) 624-4121
SIC 6036 6162 6035 6141 6153

▲ HARLEY-DAVIDSON INC p 661
3700 W Juneau Ave, Milwaukee WI 53208
Tel (414) 342-4680
SIC 3751 6153 6141 6411 6399

■ METAVANTE CORP p 953
4900 W Brown Deer Rd, Milwaukee WI 53223
Tel (904) 438-6000 *SIC* 7374 8742 6153

SIC 6159 Credit Institutions, Misc Business

AMADA AMERICA INC p 64
7025 Firestone Blvd, Buena Park CA 90621
Tel (714) 739-2111 *SIC* 5084 6159

MITSUBISHI MOTORS NORTH AMERICA INC p 978
6400 Katella Ave, Cypress CA 90630
Tel (714) 799-4730
SIC 5511 5013 6159 6512

FRESNO TRUCK CENTER p 579
2727 E Central Ave, Fresno CA 93725
Tel (559) 486-4310
SIC 5511 5521 5531 5012 5013 6159

AERCAP US GLOBAL AVIATION LLC p 30
10250 Constellation Blvd, Los Angeles CA 90067
Tel (310) 788-1999 *SIC* 3721 4581 6159

CAPITALSOURCE INC p 250
633 W 5th St Ste 33, Los Angeles CA 90071
Tel (213) 443-7700 *SIC* 6159

■ HOMEQ SERVICING CORP p 703
4837 Watt Ave, North Highlands CA 95660
Tel (916) 339-6192
SIC 6162 6163 6111 6159

▲ WILLIS LEASE FINANCE CORP p 1612
773 San Marin Dr Ste 2215, Novato CA 94945
Tel (415) 408-4700 *SIC* 6159 5084

ALLIANCE FUNDING GROUP p 54
3745 W Chapman Ave # 200, Orange CA 92868
Tel (714) 940-0653 *SIC* 6159

■ MENLO WORLDWIDE FORWARDING INC p 943
1 Lagoon Dr Ste 400, Redwood City CA 94065
Tel (650) 596-9600
SIC 4513 4215 4522 4731 6159 6351

FARM CREDIT WEST ACA p 529
1478 Stone Point Dr # 450, Roseville CA 95661
Tel (916) 724-4800 *SIC* 6159

NATIONAL FUNDING INC p 1012
9820 Towne Centre Dr # 200, San Diego CA 92121
Tel (888) 576-4685 *SIC* 6153 6159 7389

AMERICAN AGCREDIT FLCA p 67
400 Aviation Blvd Ste 100, Santa Rosa CA 95403
Tel (707) 545-1200 *SIC* 6159

TOYOTA MOTOR SALES USA INC p 1467
19001 S Western Ave, Torrance CA 90501
Tel (310) 468-4000 *SIC* 6159 5012 3711

CHG-MERIDIAN US HOLDING INC p 296
21800 Oxnard St Ste 400, Woodland Hills CA 91367
Tel (818) 702-1800
SIC 7377 6159 5045 7378

COBANK ACB p 332
6340 S Fiddlers Green Cir, Greenwood Village CO 80111
Tel (303) 740-6527 *SIC* 6111 7359 6159

REPUBLIC FINANCIAL CORP p 1225
5251 Dtc Pkwy Ste 300, Greenwood Village CO 80111
Tel (800) 596-3608 *SIC* 6726 6159

■ GENERAL ELECTRIC CAPITAL SERVICES INC p 600
3135 Easton Tpke, Fairfield CT 06828
Tel (203) 373-2211
SIC 6159 6141 7359 6162

KANDERS & CO INC p 802
2 Sound View Dr Ste 3, Greenwich CT 06830
Tel (203) 552-9600 *SIC* 6159

■ SOUTHERN NEW ENGLAND TELECOMMUNICATIONS CORP p 1349
2 Science Park, New Haven CT 06511
Tel (203) 771-5200
SIC 4813 4812 5065 6159 2741 4822

■ GENERAL ELECTRIC CAPITAL CORP p 600
901 Main Ave, Norwalk CT 06851
Tel (203) 840-6300 *SIC* 6159 6141 7359

■ PHILIP MORRIS CAPITAL CORP p 1143
225 High Ridge Rd Ste 300, Stamford CT 06905
Tel (203) 348-1350 *SIC* 6159

■ B WILLIAMS HOLDING CORP p 142
1403 Foulk Rd Ste 200, Wilmington DE 19803
Tel (302) 656-8596
SIC 3579 3661 3861 7359 7629 6159

▲ FEDERAL AGRICULTURAL MORTGAGE CORP p 533
1999 K St Nw Fl 4, Washington DC 20006
Tel (202) 872-7700 *SIC* 6111 6159

WORLD OMNI FINANCIAL CORP p 1625
190 Jim Moran Blvd, Deerfield Beach FL 33442
Tel (954) 429-2200 *SIC* 6141 6159

SCOTT-MCRAE AUTOMOTIVE GROUP INC p 1294
701 Riverside Park Pl # 120, Jacksonville FL 32204
Tel (904) 354-4000 *SIC* 5511 7515 6159

BTS GROUP INC p 222
2620 Sw 27th Ave, Miami FL 33133
Tel (305) 358-5850 *SIC* 6159

▲ AGCO CORP p 34
4205 River Green Pkwy, Duluth GA 30096
Tel (770) 813-9200 *SIC* 3523 6159

■ ASBURY AUTOMOTIVE ATLANTA LLC p 115
3039 Premiere Pkwy # 900, Duluth GA 30097
Tel (404) 622-1921
SIC 5511 7515 5013 6159 5521

AGSOUTH FARM CREDIT ACA p 36
26 S Main St, Statesboro GA 30458
Tel (912) 764-9091 *SIC* 6159

■ AT&T TELEHOLDINGS INC p 123
30 S Wacker Dr Fl 34, Chicago IL 60606
Tel (800) 257-0902
SIC 4813 4812 2741 5065 6159 7382

■ BUSINESS PROPERTY LENDING INC p 229
500 W Monroe St, Chicago IL 60661
Tel (312) 441-7000
SIC 6153 6799 6162 6159

■ MARMON INDUSTRIAL LLC p 909
181 W Madison St Fl 26, Chicago IL 60602
Tel (312) 372-9500
SIC 3743 4741 3589 6159 3965 3492

PRITZKER ORGANIZATION LLC p 1178
71 S Wacker Dr Fl 47, Chicago IL 60606
Tel (312) 873-4900 *SIC* 6159

MEREX TECHNOLOGY LEASING CORP p 948
570 Lake Cook Rd Ste 300, Deerfield IL 60015
Tel (847) 940-1200 *SIC* 6159 5045

MERIDIAN GROUP INTERNATIONAL INC p 948
9 Parkway N Ste 500, Deerfield IL 60015
Tel (847) 940-1200 *SIC* 8742 6159

MERIDIAN LEASING CORP p 949
9 Parkway N Ste 500, Deerfield IL 60015
Tel (847) 964-2700 *SIC* 6159

■ WELLS FARGO COMMERCIAL DISTRIBUTION FINANCE LLC p 1590
5595 Trillium Blvd, Hoffman Estates IL 60192
Tel (847) 747-6800 *SIC* 6153 6159 6141

■ KNOWLES ELECTRONICS HOLDINGS INC p 825
1151 Maplewood Dr, Itasca IL 60143
Tel (630) 250-5100
SIC 3679 3625 3651 8731 6159

▲ CAMPING WORLD HOLDINGS INC p 246
250 Parkway Dr Ste 270, Lincolnshire IL 60069
Tel (847) 808-3000 *SIC* 7513 6159 7539

■ NAVISTAR INC p 1020
2701 Navistar Dr, Lisle IL 60532
Tel (331) 332-5000
SIC 3711 3714 3519 6153 6159 6331

▲ NAVISTAR INTERNATIONAL CORP p 1020
2701 Navistar Dr, Lisle IL 60532
Tel (331) 332-5000
SIC 3711 3714 3713 3519 6159

FARM CREDIT ILLINOIS ACA p 528
1100 Farm Credit Dr, Mahomet IL 61853
Tel (217) 590-2222 *SIC* 6159 6153 6111

▲ DEERE & CO p 422
1 John Deere Pl, Moline IL 61265
Tel (309) 765-8000
SIC 3523 3531 3524 6159

■ FIRST INSURANCE FUNDING CORP p 547
450 Skokie Blvd Ste 1000, Northbrook IL 60062
Tel (847) 374-3000 *SIC* 6159

HOUSEHOLD FINANCE CORP p 711
2700 Sanders Rd, Prospect Heights IL 60070
Tel (847) 790-1590
SIC 6141 6162 6351 6153 6159 6311

HSBC INVESTMENTS (NORTH AMERICA) INC p 715
2700 Sanders Rd, Prospect Heights IL 60070
Tel (847) 564-5000
SIC 6141 7389 6351 6159 6162 6311

ROBERT V ROHRMAN INC p 1241
750 E Golf Rd, Schaumburg IL 60173
Tel (847) 884-6632 *SIC* 5511 6159

ALLIED SOLUTIONS LLC p 57
1320 City Center Dr # 300, Carmel IN 46032
Tel (317) 706-7600 *SIC* 6321 6351 6159

NEXTGEAR CAPITAL INC p 1040
11799 N College Ave, Carmel IN 46032
Tel (317) 571-3721 *SIC* 6159

■ ANTHEM INSURANCE COMPANIES INC p 94
120 Monument Cir Ste 200, Indianapolis IN 46204
Tel (317) 488-6000
SIC 6324 6411 6321 6331 6159 7371

AEGON US HOLDING CORP p 29
4333 Edgewood Rd Ne, Cedar Rapids IA 52499
Tel (319) 355-8511
SIC 6311 6321 6351 6159

GREATAMERICA FINANCIAL SERVICES CORP p 635
625 1st St Se Ste 800, Cedar Rapids IA 52401
Tel (319) 365-8000 *SIC* 6159

WELLS FARGO FINANCIAL CA INC p 1590
800 Walnut St, Des Moines IA 50309
Tel (515) 557-7401
SIC 6141 6153 6351 6159 6531 6021

■ WELLS FARGO FINANCIAL LEASING INC p 1590
800 Walnut St, Des Moines IA 50309
Tel (515) 557-4000 *SIC* 6159

■ WELLS FARGO FINANCIAL SECURITY SERVICES INC p 1590
800 Walnut St, Des Moines IA 50309
Tel (515) 243-2131
SIC 6141 6153 6351 6159 7374 6021

■ AGCO FINANCE LLC p 34
8001 Birchwood Ct C, Johnston IA 50131
Tel (515) 251-2800 *SIC* 6159

MURPHY-HOFFMAN CO p 1001
11120 Tomahawk Creek Pkwy, Leawood KS 66211
Tel (816) 483-6444
SIC 5012 7513 7538 6159 5511

FARM CREDIT MID-AMERICA p 528
1601 Ups Dr, Louisville KY 40223
Tel (502) 420-3700 *SIC* 6159 6141

■ CITIFINANCIAL CREDIT CO p 310
300 Saint Paul St Fl 3, Baltimore MD 21202
Tel (410) 332-3000
SIC 6141 6162 7389 6331 6159 6022

MIDATLANTIC FARM CREDIT p 964
45 Aileron Ct, Westminster MD 21157
Tel (410) 848-1033 *SIC* 6159

SCHOONER CAPITAL LLC p 1290
60 South St, Boston MA 02111
Tel (617) 963-5200 *SIC* 6159

ERVIN INDUSTRIES INC p 508
3893 Research Park Dr, Ann Arbor MI 48108
Tel (734) 769-4600 *SIC* 3291 6159

■ FORD MOTOR CREDIT CO LLC p 565
1 American Rd, Dearborn MI 48126
Tel (313) 322-3000 *SIC* 6159 6141

▲ **ALLY FINANCIAL INC** p 59
500 Woodward Ave Fl 1, Detroit MI 48226
Tel (866) 710-4623
SIC 6021 6153 6159 6311 6331 6162

MERCEDES-BENZ FINANCIAL SERVICES USA LLC p 944
36455 Corporate Dr, Farmington Hills MI 48331
Tel (248) 991-6700 *SIC* 6159

CITIZENS BANK p 310
328 S Saginaw St Lbby, Flint MI 48502
Tel (810) 766-7500 *SIC* 6022 6159 6162

■ **GELCO CORP** p 598
3 Capital Dr, Eden Prairie MN 55344
Tel (952) 828-1000 *SIC* 6159

■ **TCF NATIONAL BANK** p 1428
1405 Xenium Ln N Ste 180, Minneapolis MN 55441
Tel (612) 661-8450 *SIC* 6021 6159

▲ **US BANCORP** p 1531
800 Nicollet Mall # 1500, Minneapolis MN 55402
Tel (651) 466-3000
SIC 6021 6022 6162 6091 6159 6411

W D LARSON COMPANIES LTD INC p 1568
10700 Lyndale Ave S Ste A, Minneapolis MN 55420
Tel (952) 888-4934
SIC 5012 5013 7538 6159

BEDIVERE INSURANCE CO p 168
605 Hwy 169th N Ste 800, Plymouth MN 55441
Tel (952) 852-2431
SIC 6331 6282 6159 7389

FARM CREDIT FOUNDATIONS WELFARE BENEFITS p 528
30 7th St E, Saint Paul MN 55101
Tel (651) 282-8347 *SIC* 6159

■ **WELLS FARGO EQUIPMENT FINANCE INC** p 1590
2345 Rice St Ste 230, Saint Paul MN 55113
Tel (612) 667-9876 *SIC* 6159

STAPLE COTTON CO-OPERATIVE ASSOCIATION p 1377
214 W Market St, Greenwood MS 38930
Tel (662) 453-6231 *SIC* 5159 4221 6159

FARM CREDIT SERVICES OF AMERICA PCA/FLCA p 528
5015 S 118th St, Omaha NE 68137
Tel (800) 884-3276 *SIC* 6159

GL CAPITAL PARTNERS LLC p 613
350 Main St Ste 8, Bedminster NJ 07921
Tel (928) 526-2735 *SIC* 6159

■ **HEWLETT-PACKARD FINANCIAL SERVICES CO** p 688
200 Connell Dr Ste 5000, Berkeley Heights NJ 07922
Tel (908) 288-9315 *SIC* 6159 7389

SIEMENS FINANCIAL SERVICES INC p 1320
170 Wood Ave S Fl 1, Iselin NJ 08830
Tel (609) 954-2489 *SIC* 6159

■ **CIT FINANCE LLC** p 309
1 Cit Dr, Livingston NJ 07039
Tel (973) 740-5000 *SIC* 6159

■ **CIT FINANCIAL USA INC** p 309
1 Cit Dr, Livingston NJ 07039
Tel (973) 740-5000 *SIC* 6159

CANON FINANCIAL SERVICES INC p 247
158 Gaither Dr Ste 200, Mount Laurel NJ 08054
Tel (856) 813-1000 *SIC* 6159 7389

ATLAS COPCO USA HOLDINGS INC p 128
7 Campus Dr Ste 200, Parsippany NJ 07054
Tel (973) 397-3432 *SIC* 6722 6159 7699

VOLVO CARS OF NORTH AMERICA LLC p 1565
1 Volvo Dr, Rockleigh NJ 07647
Tel (201) 768-7300
SIC 5511 5013 6159 7515 3714

■ **IBM CREDIT LLC** p 726
1 North Castle Dr, Armonk NY 10504
Tel (914) 765-1900 *SIC* 6153 6159

CITICORP NORTH AMERICA INC p 310
450 Mamaroneck Ave Ste A, Harrison NY 10528
Tel (914) 899-7000 *SIC* 6153 6159

■ **ALL POINTS CAPITAL CORP** p 51
275 Broadhollow Rd, Melville NY 11747
Tel (631) 531-2800 *SIC* 6035 6159

AVENUE CAPITAL GROUP LLC p 136
399 Park Ave Fl 6, New York NY 10022
Tel (212) 878-3500 *SIC* 6282 6159

▲ **CIT GROUP INC** p 309
11 W 42nd St Fl 7, New York NY 10036
Tel (212) 461-5200
SIC 6022 6162 6159 6141

■ **CONTINENTAL CORP** p 363
111 8th Ave, New York NY 10011
Tel (212) 440-3000
SIC 6331 6351 6321 6159 8741 6411

■ **COWEN HOLDINGS INC** p 385
599 Lexington Ave Fl 26, New York NY 10022
Tel (212) 562-1000 *SIC* 6211 6159

CREDIT AGRICOLE AMERICA SERVICES INC p 390
1301 Ave Of The Americas, New York NY 10019
Tel (212) 261-7000 *SIC* 6159

HARTZ GROUP INC p 666
667 Madison Ave Fl 24, New York NY 10065
Tel (212) 308-3336
SIC 6512 6552 6531 6159

ROTHSCHILD NORTH AMERICA INC p 1252
1251 Ave Of The Ave Fl 51, New York NY 10020
Tel (212) 403-3500
SIC 6211 6159 8742 6221 6282 8741

MITSUI CHEMICALS AMERICA INC p 978
800 Westchester Ave N607, Rye Brook NY 10573
Tel (914) 253-0777
SIC 2821 2865 3082 8731 5169 6159

▲ **BANK OF AMERICA CORP** p 151
100 N Tryon St Ste 220, Charlotte NC 28202
Tel (704) 386-5681
SIC 6021 6022 6211 6091 6162 6159

VNA HOLDING INC p 1563
7825 National Service Rd, Greensboro NC 27409
Tel (336) 393-4890
SIC 6159 3713 5012 5013

OHIO MACHINERY CO p 1077
3993 E Royalton Rd, Broadview Heights OH 44147
Tel (440) 526-6200
SIC 7513 6159 7699 5082 7353

■ **KEYBANK NATIONAL ASSOCIATION** p 815
127 Public Sq Ste 5600, Cleveland OH 44114
Tel (800) 539-2968 *SIC* 6021 6022 6159

BMW FINANCIAL SERVICES NA LLC p 194
5550 Britton Pkwy, Hilliard OH 43026
Tel (614) 718-6900 *SIC* 6159

REYNOLDS AND REYNOLDS CO p 1230
1 Reynolds Way, Kettering OH 45430
Tel (937) 485-2000 *SIC* 7373 6159

ELEMENT FLEET MANAGEMENT (US) CORP p 486
655 Business Center Dr, Horsham PA 19044
Tel (267) 960-4000 *SIC* 6159

RICOH USA INC p 1233
70 Valley Stream Pkwy, Malvern PA 19355
Tel (610) 296-8000
SIC 5044 5065 7359 5112 7334 6159

LEAF COMMERCIAL CAPITAL INC p 850
2005 Market St Fl 14, Philadelphia PA 19103
Tel (800) 819-5556 *SIC* 6159 7359

DE LAGE LANDEN FINANCIAL SERVICES INC p 419
1111 Old Eagle School Rd, Wayne PA 19087
Tel (610) 386-5000 *SIC* 6159

■ **BANCO POPULAR DE PUERTO RICO (INC)** p 150
Popular Ctr, San Juan PR 00918
Tel (787) 765-9800 *SIC* 6022 6159 6141

GREENBAX ENTERPRISES INC p 637
884 Johnnie Dodds Blvd B, Mount Pleasant SC 29464
Tel (866) 891-1195 *SIC* 7389 6159 6512

■ **CATERPILLAR FINANCIAL SERVICES CORP** p 265
2120 West End Ave, Nashville TN 37203
Tel (615) 341-1000 *SIC* 6159

NEELY COBLE CO p 1024
319 Fesslers Ln, Nashville TN 37210
Tel (615) 244-8900 *SIC* 6159

HIGHLANDER PARTNERS LP p 691
300 Crescent Ct Ste 550, Dallas TX 75201
Tel (214) 245-5000 *SIC* 6159

■ **FIRST SIERRA FINANCIAL INC** p 549
600 Travis St Ste 7050, Houston TX 77002
Tel (713) 221-8822 *SIC* 6159

MOSSY HOLDING CO INC p 992
12150 Old Katy Rd, Houston TX 77079
Tel (281) 558-9970 *SIC* 5511 6159 7532

■ **ASSOCIATES CORP OF NORTH AMERICA** p 121
250 E John Carpenter Fwy, Irving TX 75062
Tel (972) 652-4000
SIC 6141 6153 6159 6311 6321 6331

■ **ASSOCIATES FIRST CAPITAL CORP** p 121
4000 Regent Blvd, Irving TX 75063
Tel (800) 922-6235
SIC 6162 6021 6141 6159 6153

■ **ATLANTIC AVIATION CORP** p 125
6652 Pinecrest Dr Ste 300, Plano TX 75024
Tel (972) 905-2500
SIC 4581 5088 5172 6331 6159 4522

WESTERN-SHAMROCK CORP p 1600
801 S Abe St Ste 2a, San Angelo TX 76903
Tel (325) 653-6814 *SIC* 6141 6159 6153

■ **ZIONS CREDIT CORP** p 1643
310 S Main St Ste 1300, Salt Lake City UT 84101
Tel (801) 524-2230 *SIC* 6159

NATIONAL RURAL UTILITIES COOPERATIVE FINANCE CORP p 1016
20701 Cooperative Way, Dulles VA 20166
Tel (703) 467-1800 *SIC* 6141 6159

ROLLS-ROYCE NORTH AMERICA (USA) HOLDINGS CO p 1247
1875 Explorer St Ste 200, Reston VA 20190
Tel (703) 834-1700
SIC 5088 8741 6159 3724

FARM CREDIT OF VIRGINIAS ACA p 528
106 Sangers Ln, Staunton VA 24401
Tel (540) 899-0989 *SIC* 6159

JX ENTERPRISES INC p 798
1320 Walnut Ridge Dr, Hartland WI 53029
Tel (800) 810-3410
SIC 5012 5511 7538 6159 7513

LAKESIDE INTERNATIONAL LLC p 840
11000 W Silver Spring Dr, Milwaukee WI 53225
Tel (414) 353-4800
SIC 5511 5531 7538 7532 6159 7513

CNH INDUSTRIAL CAPITAL LLC p 330
5729 Washington Ave, Mount Pleasant WI 53406
Tel (262) 636-6011 *SIC* 6159

CASE CONSTRUCTION EQUIPMENT INC p 263
700 State St, Racine WI 53404
Tel (262) 636-6011 *SIC* 6159 3531 3523

CNH INDUSTRIAL AMERICA LLC p 330
700 St St, Racine WI 53404
Tel (262) 636-6011 *SIC* 3523 3531 6159

SIC 6162 Mortgage Bankers & Loan Correspondents

FISHER FINANCIAL GROUP INC p 552
3303 E Baseline Rd # 113, Gilbert AZ 85234
Tel (480) 461-1111 *SIC* 6162

L & G MORTGAGEBANC INC p 833
8151 E Evans Rd Ste 10, Scottsdale AZ 85260
Tel (408) 905-5140 *SIC* 6162

ON Q FINANCIAL INC p 1086
4800 N Scottsdale Rd, Scottsdale AZ 85251
Tel (480) 444-7100 *SIC* 6282 6162

PRIVATE NATIONAL MORTGAGE ACCEPTANCE CO LLC p 1178
6101 Condor Dr, Agoura Hills CA 91301
Tel (818) 224-7401 *SIC* 6162

RPM MORTGAGE INC p 1255
3240 Stone Valley Rd W, Alamo CA 94507
Tel (925) 295-9300 *SIC* 6162

JMJ FINANCIAL GROUP p 786
26800 Aliso Viejo Pkwy # 200, Aliso Viejo CA 92656
Tel (949) 340-6336 *SIC* 6162

■ **COUNTRYWIDE FINANCIAL CORP** p 375
4500 Park Granada, Calabasas CA 91302
Tel (818) 225-3000
SIC 6162 6211 6361 6411 6163 6799

AMERICAN FINANCIAL NETWORK INC p 72
3110 Chino Ave Ste 290, Chino CA 91710
Tel (909) 606-3905 *SIC* 6162

STEARNS LENDING LLC p 1384
555 Anton Blvd Ste 300, Costa Mesa CA 92626
Tel (714) 513-7777 *SIC* 6162

SIERRA PACIFIC MORTGAGE CO INC p 1321
1180 Iron Point Rd # 200, Folsom CA 95630
Tel (916) 932-1700 *SIC* 6162

LOANDEPOT.COM LLC p 872
26642 Towne Centre Dr, Foothill Ranch CA 92610
Tel (949) 474-1322 *SIC* 6162

▲ **CALATLANTIC GROUP INC** p 238
15360 Barranca Pkwy, Irvine CA 92618
Tel (949) 789-1600
SIC 1531 1521 6162 6541

FINANCE AMERICA LLC p 542
1901 Main St Ste 150, Irvine CA 92614
Tel (949) 440-1000 *SIC* 6162 6163

■ **SAND CANYON CORP** p 1278
7595 Irvine Center Dr # 100, Irvine CA 92618
Tel (949) 727-9425 *SIC* 6163 6162

NORTH COAST MORTGAGE CO p 1052
80 E Sir Francis Drake Bl, Larkspur CA 94939
Tel (415) 461-2070 *SIC* 6162

▲ **CBRE GROUP INC** p 269
400 S Hope St Ste 25, Los Angeles CA 90071
Tel (213) 613-3333 *SIC* 6531 6162 8742

▲ **KB HOME** p 806
10990 Wilshire Blvd Fl 5, Los Angeles CA 90024
Tel (310) 231-4000 *SIC* 1531 6351 6162

REALTY FINANCE CORP p 1214
895 Dove St Ste 210, Newport Beach CA 92660
Tel (949) 296-3280 *SIC* 6162

■ **HOMEQ SERVICING CORP** p 703
4837 Watt Ave, North Highlands CA 95660
Tel (916) 339-6192
SIC 6162 6163 6111 6159

FIRST MORTGAGE CORP p 548
1131 W 6th St Ste 300, Ontario CA 91762
Tel (909) 595-1996 *SIC* 6162

■ **FULL SPECTRUM LENDING INC** p 584
35 N Lake Ave Fl 3, Pasadena CA 91101
Tel (626) 584-2220 *SIC* 6162 6163

■ **E-LOAN INC** p 467
6230 Stoneridge Mall Rd, Pleasanton CA 94588
Tel (925) 847-6200 *SIC* 6163 6162

CENTRAL VALLEY MORTGAGE SERVICE INC p 280
1987 W Orange Ave, Porterville CA 93257
Tel (559) 782-8011 *SIC* 6162

AMERICAN PACIFIC MORTGAGE CORP p 77
3000 Lava Ridge Ct # 200, Roseville CA 95661
Tel (916) 960-1325 *SIC* 6162

PARAMOUNT EQUITY MORTGAGE LLC p 1114
8781 Sierra College Blvd, Roseville CA 95661
Tel (916) 290-9999 *SIC* 6162

GUILD MORTGAGE CO p 646
5898 Copley Dr Fl 4, San Diego CA 92111
Tel (800) 283-8823 *SIC* 6162 6733

PLAZA HOME MORTGAGE INC p 1156
4820 Eastgate Mall # 100, San Diego CA 92121
Tel (858) 346-1200 *SIC* 6162

▲ **FIRST REPUBLIC BANK** p 549
111 Pine St Ste Bsmt, San Francisco CA 94111
Tel (415) 392-1400 *SIC* 6022 6282 6162

▲ **WELLS FARGO & CO** p 1590
420 Montgomery St Frnt, San Francisco CA 94104
Tel (866) 249-3302
SIC 6021 6022 6162 6141 7374

AMERIQUEST MORTGAGE CO p 83
2677 N Main St Ste 140, Santa Ana CA 92705
Tel (714) 732-9100 *SIC* 6162

GRUBB & ELLIS CO p 642
1551 N Tustin Ave Ste 300, Santa Ana CA 92705
Tel (714) 667-8252 *SIC* 6531 8742 6162

▲ **REAL INDUSTRY INC** p 1213
15301 Ventura Blvd # 400, Sherman Oaks CA 91403
Tel (805) 435-1255 *SIC* 5063 6162

WESTLEND FINANCING INC p 1601
15260 Ventura Blvd # 710, Sherman Oaks CA 91403
Tel (818) 385-7500 *SIC* 6162 6141

■ **COUNTRYWIDE HOME LOANS INC** p 375
225 W Hillcrest Dr, Thousand Oaks CA 91360
Tel (818) 225-3000 *SIC* 6162

BROKER SOLUTIONS INC p 217
14511 Myford Rd Ste 100, Tustin CA 92780
Tel (800) 450-2010 *SIC* 8742 6162

PENNYMAC FINANCIAL SERVICES INC p 1131
3043 Townsgate Rd, Westlake Village CA 91361
Tel (818) 224-7442 *SIC* 6162 6282

RYLAND GROUP INC p 1261
3011 Townsgate Rd Ste 200, Westlake Village CA 91361
Tel (805) 367-3800 *SIC* 1531 1521 6162

CITYWIDE FINANCIAL INC p 320
13731 E Mississippi Ave, Aurora CO 80012
Tel (303) 365-4050 *SIC* 6162

▲ **MDC HOLDINGS INC** p 933
4350 S Monaco St Ste 500, Denver CO 80237
Tel (303) 773-1100 *SIC* 1521 6162 7389

■ **PULTE MORTGAGE LLC** p 1192
7390 S Iola St, Englewood CO 80112
Tel (303) 740-8800 *SIC* 6162

CHERRY CREEK MORTGAGE CO INC p 294
7600 E Orchard Rd 250n, Greenwood Village CO 80111
Tel (303) 320-4040 *SIC* 6162

SPECIALIZED LOAN SERVICING LLC p 1356
8742 Lucent Blvd Ste 300, Highlands Ranch CO 80129
Tel (720) 241-7200 *SIC* 6162

WJ BRADLEY MORTGAGE CAPITAL LLC p 1619
10940 S Parker Rd Ste 506, Parker CO 80134
Tel (303) 825-5670 *SIC* 6162

■ **GENERAL ELECTRIC CAPITAL SERVICES INC** p 600
3135 Easton Tpke, Fairfield CT 06828
Tel (203) 373-2211
SIC 6159 6141 7359 6162

PM HOLDINGS INC p 1157
1 American Row, Hartford CT 06103
Tel (860) 403-5000
SIC 6411 6162 6722 6282 6211 6552

ELLINGTON FINANCIAL LLC p 488
53 Forest Ave, Old Greenwich CT 06870
Tel (203) 698-1200 *SIC* 6162

■ **CITICORP BANKING CORP** p 310
1 Penns Way, New Castle DE 19721
Tel (302) 323-3140 *SIC* 6162

FEDERAL HOME LOAN ADMINISTRATION INC p 534
1201 N Orange St Ste 600, Wilmington DE 19801
Tel (855) 345-2669 *SIC* 6162

TOUSA INC p 1464
4000 Hollywood Blvd # 555, Hollywood FL 33021
Tel (954) 364-4000
SIC 1521 1522 6162 6541

■ **EVERHOME MORTGAGE CO** p 515
301 W Bay St Ste 2600, Jacksonville FL 32202
Tel (904) 281-6000 *SIC* 6162

■ **LENNAR FINANCIAL SERVICES LLC** p 855
700 Nw 107th Ave Ste 400, Miami FL 33172
Tel (305) 559-4000
SIC 6162 6153 6361 6411 7382

NATIONWIDE TITLE CLEARING INC p 1018
2100 Alt 19, Palm Harbor FL 34683
Tel (727) 771-4000 *SIC* 6162 6541

MORTGAGE INVESTORS CORP p 991
6090 Central Ave, Saint Petersburg FL 33707
Tel (727) 347-1930 *SIC* 6162

FLORIDA HOUSING FINANCE CORP p 559
227 N Bronough St # 5000, Tallahassee FL 32301
Tel (850) 488-4197 *SIC* 6162

▲ **WALTER INVESTMENT MANAGEMENT CORP** p 1574
3000 Bayport Dr Ste 1100, Tampa FL 33607
Tel (813) 421-7600 *SIC* 6162

■ **OPTEUM FINANCIAL SERVICES LLC** p 1090
3305 Flamingo Dr, Vero Beach FL 32963
Tel (772) 231-1245 *SIC* 6162

▲ **OCWEN FINANCIAL CORP** p 1074
1661 Worthington Rd # 100, West Palm Beach FL 33409
Tel (561) 682-8000 *SIC* 6162

■ **OCWEN LOAN SERVICING LLC** p 1074
1661 Worthington Rd # 100, West Palm Beach FL 33409
Tel (561) 682-8000 *SIC* 6162

ALTISOURCE SOLUTIONS INC p 62
1000 Abernathy Rd Ste 200, Atlanta GA 30328
Tel (770) 612-7007 *SIC* 6162

HEALTH CARE CAPITAL INC p 674
2 Ravinia Dr Ste 1350, Atlanta GA 30346
Tel (770) 393-3355 *SIC* 6162 8051 8741

■ **PULTE HOME CORP** p 1192
3350 Peachtree Rd Ne # 150, Atlanta GA 30326
Tel (248) 647-2750 *SIC* 1531 6552 6162

▲ **PULTEGROUP INC** p 1192
3350 Peachtree Rd Ne # 150, Atlanta GA 30326
Tel (404) 978-6400 *SIC* 1531 6552 6162

HLSS MANAGEMENT LLC p 697
2002 Summit Blvd Fl 6, Brookhaven GA 30319
Tel (561) 682-7561 *SIC* 6162

LENDMARK FINANCIAL SERVICES LLC p 855
2118 Usher St Nw, Covington GA 30014
Tel (678) 625-6500 *SIC* 6162

BENEFICIAL CO LLC p 172
1421 W Shure Dr Ste 100, Arlington Heights IL 60004
Tel (708) 453-6502
SIC 6141 6351 6162 6021 6552 6311

■ **BUSINESS PROPERTY LENDING INC** p 229
500 W Monroe St, Chicago IL 60661
Tel (312) 441-7000
SIC 6153 6799 6162 6159

BYLINE BANCORP INC p 231
180 N La Salle St Ste 300, Chicago IL 60601
Tel (773) 843-7800 *SIC* 6712 6162

GUARANTEED RATE INC p 644
3940 N Ravenswood Ave, Chicago IL 60613
Tel (866) 934-7283 *SIC* 6162

DOVENMUEHLE MORTGAGE INC p 452
1 Corporate Dr Ste 360, Lake Zurich IL 60047
Tel (847) 550-7300 *SIC* 6162 6411

INLAND REAL ESTATE GROUP OF COMPANIES p 743
2901 Butterfield Rd, Oak Brook IL 60523
Tel (630) 218-8000
SIC 6513 6512 6162 6282 1522 1542

HOUSEHOLD FINANCE CORP p 711
2700 Sanders Rd, Prospect Heights IL 60070
Tel (847) 790-1590
SIC 6141 6162 6351 6153 6159 6311

HSBC INVESTMENTS (NORTH AMERICA) INC p 715
2700 Sanders Rd, Prospect Heights IL 60070
Tel (847) 564-5000
SIC 6141 7389 6351 6159 6162 6311

■ **HOMESERVICES OF ILLINOIS LLC** p 704
1370 Meadow Rd, Skokie IL 60076
Tel (847) 853-5000 *SIC* 6162

■ **MOREQUITY INC** p 988
7116 Eagle Crest Blvd, Evansville IN 47715
Tel (800) 345-0187 *SIC* 6162

▲ **STONEGATE MORTGAGE CORP** p 1391
9190 Priority Way West Dr, Indianapolis IN 46240
Tel (317) 663-5100 *SIC* 6162

■ **PRINCIPAL LIFE INSURANCE CO** p 1177
711 High St, Des Moines IA 50392
Tel (515) 247-5111
SIC 6311 6211 6162 6321 6411

■ **WELLS FARGO HOME MORTGAGE INC** p 1590
1 Home Campus, Des Moines IA 50328
Tel (515) 324-3707 *SIC* 6162

■ **MIDLAND LOAN SERVICES A DIVISION OF PNC BANK NATIONAL ASSOCIATION** p 965
10851 Mastin St Ste 700, Overland Park KS 66210
Tel (913) 253-9000 *SIC* 6162

SPEEDY CASH HOLDINGS CORP p 1358
3527 N Ridge Rd, Wichita KS 67205
Tel (316) 722-3801 *SIC* 6162

MAINE STATE HOUSING AUTHORITY p 898
353 Water St, Augusta ME 04330
Tel (207) 626-4600 *SIC* 6162

RESIDENTIAL MORTGAGE SERVICES INC p 1226
24 Christopher Toppi Dr, South Portland ME 04106
Tel (207) 675-3609 *SIC* 6162

■ **CITIFINANCIAL CREDIT CO** p 310
300 Saint Paul St Fl 3, Baltimore MD 21202
Tel (410) 332-3000
SIC 6141 6162 7389 6331 6159 6022

▲ **LEGG MASON INC** p 853
100 International Dr, Baltimore MD 21202
Tel (410) 539-0000 *SIC* 6282 6211 6162

■ **ONEMAIN FINANCIAL HOLDINGS LLC** p 1087
100 Intl Dr Ste 15000, Baltimore MD 21202
Tel (410) 332-3000 *SIC* 6162 6163

▲ **NEWSTAR FINANCIAL INC** p 1039
500 Boylston St Ste 1250, Boston MA 02116
Tel (617) 848-2500 *SIC* 6162

▲ **ALLY FINANCIAL INC** p 59
500 Woodward Ave Fl 1, Detroit MI 48226
Tel (866) 710-4623
SIC 6021 6153 6159 6311 6331 6162

QUICKEN LOANS INC p 1199
1050 Woodward Ave, Detroit MI 48226
Tel (734) 805-5000 *SIC* 6162

CITIZENS BANK p 310
328 S Saginaw St Lbby, Flint MI 48502
Tel (810) 766-7500 *SIC* 6022 6159 6162

VAN DYK MORTGAGE CORP p 1542
2449 Camelot Ct Se, Grand Rapids MI 49546
Tel (616) 940-3000 *SIC* 6162 6163

AMERIFIRST FINANCIAL CORP p 82
950 Trade Centre Way # 400, Portage MI 49002
Tel (269) 324-4240 *SIC* 6162

ROSS MORTGAGE CORP p 1252
2075 W Big Beaver Rd # 700, Troy MI 48084
Tel (248) 968-1800 *SIC* 6162

FIVE BROTHERS MORTGAGE CO SERVICES AND SECURING INC p 553
12220 E 13 Mile Rd, Warren MI 48093
Tel (586) 772-7600 *SIC* 6162

CAPMARK FINANCE INC p 251
7075 Flying Cloud Dr, Eden Prairie MN 55344
Tel (215) 328-4622 *SIC* 6162

▲ **US BANCORP** p 1531
800 Nicollet Mall # 1500, Minneapolis MN 55402
Tel (651) 466-3000
SIC 6021 6022 6162 6091 6159 6411

■ **WELLS FARGO FUNDING INC** p 1590
2701 Wells Fargo Way Fl 5, Minneapolis MN 55467
Tel (800) 328-5074 *SIC* 6162

DITECH FINANCIAL LLC p 443
345 Sint Peter St Ste 300, Saint Paul MN 55102
Tel (651) 293-4800 *SIC* 6162

■ **NORTHLAND CO** p 1057
385 Washington St, Saint Paul MN 55102
Tel (800) 328-5972 *SIC* 6331 6162 6531

■ **RENASANT BANK** p 1223
209 Troy St, Tupelo MS 38804
Tel (662) 680-1001 *SIC* 6022 6162

▲ **COMMERCE BANCSHARES INC** p 344
1000 Walnut St, Kansas City MO 64106
Tel (816) 234-2000 *SIC* 6022 6311 6162

■ **NOVASTAR MORTGAGE LLC** p 1063
2114 Central St Ste 600, Kansas City MO 64108
Tel (816) 237-7000 *SIC* 6162

■ **CITIMORTGAGE INC** p 310
1000 Technology Dr, O Fallon MO 63368
Tel (636) 261-2484 *SIC* 6162

■ **FIRST COLLATERAL SERVICES INC** p 545
1000 Technology Dr, O Fallon MO 63368
Tel (813) 604-8143 *SIC* 6162

UNION BANK AND TRUST CO p 1504
3643 S 48th St, Lincoln NE 68506
Tel (402) 488-0941
SIC 6111 6029 6162 6021 6035 6022

PROFICIO MORTGAGE VENTURES LLC p 1180
2225 Village Walk Dr # 200, Henderson NV 89052
Tel (407) 476-2400 *SIC* 6162

REGENCY MORTGAGE CORP p 1219
26 Londonderry Tpke, Hooksett NH 03106
Tel (603) 669-5626 *SIC* 6162

ADAMAR GARAGE CORP p 21
Brighton Avenue Boardwalk, Atlantic City NJ 08401
Tel (609) 340-4000 *SIC* 6162

■ **CHASE MANHATTAN MORTGAGE CORP** p 291
343 Thornall St Ste 7, Edison NJ 08837
Tel (732) 205-0600 *SIC* 6162

HOMEBRIDGE FINANCIAL SERVICES INC p 703
194 Wood Ave S Fl 9, Iselin NJ 08830
Tel (201) 498-9300 *SIC* 6162

FRANKLIN CREDIT HOLDING CORP p 575
101 Hudson St Fl 25, Jersey City NJ 07302
Tel (201) 604-1800 *SIC* 6163 6162

AMERICAN NEIGHBOURHOOD MORTGAGE ACCEPTANCE CO LLC p 77
700 E Gate Dr Ste 400, Mount Laurel NJ 08054
Tel (856) 252-1506 *SIC* 6162

FREEDOM MORTGAGE CORP p 576
907 Pleasant Valley Ave # 3, Mount Laurel NJ 08054
Tel (866) 759-8624 *SIC* 6162

■ **PHH MORTGAGE CORP** p 1142
1 Mortgage Way, Mount Laurel NJ 08054
Tel (866) 946-0081 *SIC* 6162

▲ **HOVNANIAN ENTERPRISES INC** p 713
110 W Front St, Red Bank NJ 07701
Tel (732) 747-7800
SIC 1521 1531 1522 6162 6361

SUTHERLAND ASSET MANAGEMENT CORP p 1409
2 Bridge Ave Ste 322, Red Bank NJ 07701
Tel (732) 978-7518 *SIC* 6162

NEW JERSEY HOUSING AND MORTGAGE FINANCE AGENCY CJ p 1031
637 S Clinton Ave, Trenton NJ 08611
Tel (609) 278-7400 *SIC* 6162 9199

■ **VALLEY NATIONAL BANK** p 1541
1455 Valley Rd Ste 3, Wayne NJ 07470
Tel (973) 696-4020 *SIC* 6021 6162

■ **M&TMORTGAGE CORP** p 890
1 Fountain Plz, Buffalo NY 14203
Tel (716) 842-5445 *SIC* 6162

SENECA MORTGAGE SERVICING LLC p 1303
611 Jamison Rd Ste 1201, Elma NY 14059
Tel (716) 204-3601 *SIC* 6162

MORTGAGE SOURCE LLC p 991
600 Old Country Rd Rm 210, Garden City NY 11530
Tel (516) 487-3111 *SIC* 6162

BARCLAYS CAPITAL REAL ESTATE HOLDINGS INC p 155
1301 Ave Of The Americas, New York NY 10019
Tel (212) 581-1628 *SIC* 6162

■ **CB RICHARD ELLIS REAL ESTATE SERVICES LLC** p 268
200 Park Ave Fl 19, New York NY 10166
Tel (212) 984-8000 *SIC* 6531 6162

▲ **CIT GROUP INC** p 309
11 W 42nd St Fl 7, New York NY 10036
Tel (212) 461-5200
SIC 6022 6162 6159 6141

■ **CITIBANK NA** p 310
399 Park Ave Bsmt 1, New York NY 10022
Tel (212) 559-1000
SIC 6021 6153 6091 6099 6162

COURT SQUARE CAPITAL LIMITED p 383
55 E 52nd St Rm 3400, New York NY 10055
Tel (212) 752-6110 *SIC* 8743 6162

DORAL FINANCIAL CORP p 451
200 Park Ave Ste 1700, New York NY 10166
Tel (646) 632-3700
SIC 6029 6162 6035 6211 6411

▲ **JPMORGAN CHASE & CO** p 795
270 Park Ave Fl 38, New York NY 10017
Tel (212) 270-6000
SIC 6021 6211 6162 6141

▲ **LADDER CAPITAL CORP** p 837
345 Park Ave Fl 8, New York NY 10154
Tel (212) 715-3170 *SIC* 6798 6162

■ **MERRILL LYNCH GROUP INC** p 950
4 World Financial Ctr # 4, New York NY 10080
Tel (646) 855-5000 *SIC* 6282 6162

■ **MORGAN STANLEY MORTGAGE CAPITAL HOLDINGS LLC** p 989
1585 Broadway Lowr B, New York NY 10036
Tel (212) 761-4000 *SIC* 6162

SHELLPOINT PARTNERS LLC p 1314
140 E 45th St Fl 37, New York NY 10017
Tel (212) 850-7700 *SIC* 6162 7389

▲ **TIPTREE FINANCIAL INC** p 1455
780 3rd Ave Fl 21, New York NY 10017
Tel (212) 446-1400
SIC 6162 6282 6311 6798

■ **WELLS FARGO CAPITAL FINANCE LLC** p 1590
100 Park Ave Fl 3, New York NY 10017
Tel (212) 840-2000 *SIC* 6162 7389

NORTHPOINT MORTGAGE CORP p 1057
10002 101st Ave, Ozone Park NY 11416
Tel (718) 641-7000 *SIC* 6162

▲ **BANK OF AMERICA CORP** p 151
100 N Tryon St Ste 220, Charlotte NC 28202
Tel (704) 386-5681
SIC 6021 6022 6211 6091 6162 6159

■ **BANK OF AMERICA MORTGAGE SECURITIES INC** p 151
101 S Tryon St Ste 1000, Charlotte NC 28280
Tel (704) 386-5681 *SIC* 6162 6163

■ **WACHOVIA MORTGAGE CORP** p 1570
201 S College St Fl 16, Charlotte NC 28244
Tel (704) 374-6161 *SIC* 6162 6411

■ **JPMORGAN CHASE BANK NATIONAL ASSOCIATION** p 795
1111 Polaris Pkwy, Columbus OH 43240
Tel (614) 436-3055
SIC 6022 6099 6799 6211 6162 7389

▲ **M/I HOMES INC** p 890
3 Easton Oval Ste 500, Columbus OH 43219
Tel (614) 418-8000 *SIC* 1531 6162

NATIONS LENDING CORP p 1017
4 Summit Park Dr Ste 200, Independence OH 44131
Tel (440) 842-4817 *SIC* 6162 6163

■ **OLD REPUBLIC TITLE CO OF NORTHERN OHIO LLC** p 1081
6480 Rckside Woods Blvd S, Independence OH 44131
Tel (216) 524-5700 *SIC* 6411 6162 6211

■ **NATIONAL CITY MORTGAGE INC** p 1010
3232 Newmark Dr, Miamisburg OH 45342
Tel (937) 910-1200 *SIC* 6162

AMERICAN MORTGAGE SERVICE CO p 76
7324 Kingsgate Way Ste C, West Chester OH 45069
Tel (513) 452-4120 *SIC* 6162

ADFITECH INC p 22
3001 Technology Dr, Edmond OK 73013
Tel (800) 880-0456 *SIC* 6162

MIDLAND FINANCIAL CO p 965
501 Nw Grand Blvd Ste 180, Oklahoma City OK 73118
Tel (405) 840-7600 *SIC* 6035 6162 6531

KLAMATH FALLS INTERCOMMUNITY HOSPITAL AUTHORITY p 823
2865 Daggett Ave, Klamath Falls OR 97601
Tel (541) 883-6150 *SIC* 6162

BERKADIA COMMERCIAL MORTGAGE LLC p 174
323 Norristown Rd Ste 300, Ambler PA 19002
Tel (215) 328-3200 *SIC* 6162

GATEWAY FUNDING DIVERSIFIED MORTGAGE SERVICES LP p 593
300 Welsh Rd, Horsham PA 19044
Tel (215) 591-0222 *SIC* 6162

■ **GMAC MORTGAGE LLC** p 618
4 Walnut Grove Dr, Horsham PA 19044
Tel (215) 682-1000 *SIC* 6162

▲ **FNB CORP** p 562
1 N Shore Ctr 12 Fdral St, Pittsburgh PA 15212
Tel (800) 555-5455
SIC 6022 6021 6162 6411

HANNA HOLDINGS INC p 658
1090 Freeport Rd Ste 1a, Pittsburgh PA 15238
Tel (412) 967-9000 *SIC* 6531 6162 6361

HFF HOLDINGS LLC p 689
1 Oxford Ctr, Pittsburgh PA 15219
Tel (412) 281-8714 *SIC* 6162

▲ **HFF INC** p 689
301 Grant St Ste 1100, Pittsburgh PA 15219
Tel (412) 281-8714 *SIC* 6162

▲ **PNC FINANCIAL SERVICES GROUP INC** p 1158
300 5th Ave, Pittsburgh PA 15222
Tel (412) 762-2000
SIC 6021 6162 7389 6282 6211

NEW PENN FINANCIAL LLC p 1032
4000 Chemical Rd Ste 200, Plymouth Meeting PA 19462
Tel (484) 594-1000 *SIC* 6162

DORAL HOLDINGS DELAWARE LLC p 451
1451 Frnkln D Rsvelt Ave, San Juan PR 00920
Tel (787) 474-6700
SIC 6162 6035 6211 6411

EMBRACE HOME LOANS INC p 490
25 Enterprise Ctr, Middletown RI 02842
Tel (401) 846-3100 *SIC* 6162

■ **FIRST TENNESSEE BANK NATIONAL ASSOCIATION** p 549
165 Madison Ave, Memphis TN 38103
Tel (901) 523-4444 *SIC* 6021 6162

HARPETH FINANCIAL SERVICES LLC p 663
100 Oceanside Dr, Nashville TN 37204
Tel (615) 341-5900 *SIC* 6162

■ **HOMEWARD RESIDENTIAL INC** p 704
16675 Addison Rd, Addison TX 75001
Tel (877) 304-3100 *SIC* 6162

■ **DHI MORTGAGE CO LTD** p 435
10700 Pecan Park Blvd # 450, Austin TX 78750
Tel (512) 502-0545 *SIC* 6162

ALACRITY LENDING CO p 43
6209 Colleyville Blvd, Colleyville TX 76034
Tel (817) 481-1500 *SIC* 6162

▲ **NATIONSTAR MORTGAGE HOLDINGS INC** p 1017
8950 Cypress Waters Blvd, Coppell TX 75019
Tel (469) 549-2000 *SIC* 6162

■ **NATIONSTAR MORTGAGE LLC** p 1017
8950 Cypress Waters Blvd, Coppell TX 75019
Tel (469) 549-2000 *SIC* 6162

▲ **AMERICAN REALTY INVESTORS INC** p 78
1603 Lbj Fwy Ste 800, Dallas TX 75234
Tel (469) 522-4200
SIC 6798 6162 6513 6512

■ **CENTEX CORP** p 277
2728 N Harwood St Ste 200, Dallas TX 75201
Tel (214) 981-5000
SIC 1531 2451 6162 1542 1541 1522

■ **CENTEX FINANCIAL SERVICES LLC** p 277
2728 N Harwood St, Dallas TX 75201
Tel (214) 981-5000 *SIC* 6162

UNION STREET MORTGAGE p 1505
4403 N Beltwood Pkwy, Dallas TX 75244
Tel (866) 499-3411 *SIC* 6162

COLONIAL SAVINGS FA p 338
2600 West Fwy, Fort Worth TX 76102
Tel (817) 390-2000 *SIC* 6162 6035

▲ **DR HORTON INC** p 454
301 Commerce St Ste 500, Fort Worth TX 76102
Tel (817) 390-8200 *SIC* 1531 6162

■ **AIG LIFE HOLDINGS INC** p 38
2929 Allen Pkwy, Houston TX 77019
Tel (713) 522-1111
SIC 6311 6321 6331 6141 6162 6153

AMERICUS MORTGAGE CORP p 82
6110 Pinemont Dr Ste 215, Houston TX 77092
Tel (713) 684-0725 *SIC* 6162

CORNERSTONE HOME LENDING INC p 371
1177 West Loop S Ste 200, Houston TX 77027
Tel (713) 599-2895 *SIC* 6162

■ **HOLLIDAY FENOGLIO FOWLER LP** p 701
9 Greenway Plz Ste 700, Houston TX 77046
Tel (713) 852-3500 *SIC* 6162

LITTON LOAN SERVICING LP p 871
4828 Loop Central Dr # 104, Houston TX 77081
Tel (713) 960-9676 *SIC* 6162

■ **US HOME CORP** p 1532
10707 Clay Rd, Houston TX 77041
Tel (305) 559-4000 *SIC* 1531 6162 6552

■ **ASSOCIATES FIRST CAPITAL CORP** p 121
4000 Regent Blvd, Irving TX 75063
Tel (800) 922-6235
SIC 6162 6021 6141 6159 6153

■ **METLIFE HOME LOANS LLC** p 954
7880 Bent Branch Dr # 100, Irving TX 75063
Tel (214) 441-4000 *SIC* 6162

■ **SAXON MORTGAGE SERVICES INC** p 1284
3701 Regent Blvd Ste 100, Irving TX 75063
Tel (972) 570-6000 *SIC* 6162

■ **EMC MORTGAGE LLC** p 490
2780 Lake Vista Dr, Lewisville TX 75067
Tel (214) 626-2735 *SIC* 6162

■ **NATIONSTAR CAPITAL CORP** p 1017
350 Highland Dr, Lewisville TX 75067
Tel (469) 549-2000 *SIC* 6162

W R STARKEY MORTGAGE LLP p 1569
6101 W Plano Pkwy, Plano TX 75093
Tel (972) 599-5510 *SIC* 6162

SOUTHWEST BUSINESS CORP p 1351
9311 San Pedro Ave # 600, San Antonio TX 78216
Tel (210) 525-1241 *SIC* 6411 6162 6282

CITY FIRST MORTGAGE SERVICES LLC p 312
750 S Main St Ste 104, Bountiful UT 84010
Tel (801) 299-1770 *SIC* 6162

CASTLE & COOKE MORTGAGE LLC p 264
13751 S Wadsworth Park Dr # 101, Draper UT 84020
Tel (866) 461-7101 *SIC* 6162

■ **ALLY BANK** p 59
6985 S Union Park Ctr # 435, Midvale UT 84047
Tel (801) 790-5005
SIC 6153 6021 6311 6331 6162

FIRST MANHATTAN FUNDING LLC p 547
261 E Broadway Ste 255, Salt Lake City UT 84111
Tel (801) 643-3022 *SIC* 6162

▲ **SECURITY NATIONAL FINANCIAL CORP** p 1299
5300 S 360 W Ste 250, Salt Lake City UT 84123
Tel (801) 264-1060 *SIC* 6311 6531 6162

SPS HOLDINGS CORP p 1362
3815 S West Temple, Salt Lake City UT 84115
Tel (801) 293-1883 *SIC* 6162 6798

SELECT PORTFOLIO SERVICING INC p 1301
3217 Decker Lake Dr, West Valley City UT 84119
Tel (800) 258-8602 *SIC* 6162

UTAH HOUSING CORP p 1536
2479 S Lake Park Blvd, West Valley City UT 84120
Tel (801) 902-8200 *SIC* 6211 6162

▲ **ARLINGTON ASSET INVESTMENT CORP** p 110
1001 19th St N Ste 1900, Arlington VA 22209
Tel (703) 373-0200 *SIC* 6798 6162

■ **WASHINGTONFIRST MORTGAGE CORP** p 1579
12700 Fair Lakes Cir, Fairfax VA 22033
Tel (703) 564-9100 *SIC* 6162

■ **CARDINAL BANK** p 252
8270 Greensboro Dr # 100, Mc Lean VA 22102
Tel (703) 584-3400 *SIC* 6021 6162

▲ **NVR INC** p 1068
11700 Plaza America Dr # 500, Reston VA 20190
Tel (703) 956-4000 *SIC* 1531 6162

■ **SUNTRUST MORTGAGE INC** p 1405
901 Semmes Ave, Richmond VA 23224
Tel (804) 291-0740 *SIC* 6162

VIRGINIA HOUSING DEVELOPMENT AUTHORITY p 1559
601 S Belvidere St, Richmond VA 23220
Tel (804) 780-0789 *SIC* 6162

STERLING SAVINGS BANK p 1387
111 N Wall St, Spokane WA 99201
Tel (509) 624-4121
SIC 6036 6162 6035 6141 6153

CONSUMER LOAN SERVICES LLC p 361
811 Monitor St, La Crosse WI 54603
Tel (877) 791-1257 *SIC* 6162

FAIRWAY INDEPENDENT MORTGAGE CORP p 525
4801 S Biltmore Ln, Madison WI 53718
Tel (608) 837-4800 *SIC* 6162

SIC 6163 Loan Brokers

ALASKA USA FEDERAL CREDIT UNION p 45
4000 Credit Union Dr, Anchorage AK 99503
Tel (907) 563-4567 *SIC* 6061 6163

PIONEER TITLE AGENCY INC p 1151
580 E Wilcox Dr, Sierra Vista AZ 85635
Tel (520) 459-4100 *SIC* 6361 6163

■ **FIRST AMERICAN MORTGAGE SOLUTIONS LLC** p 544
30005 Ladyface Ct, Agoura Hills CA 91301
Tel (800) 333-4510 *SIC* 6163

PENNYMAC CORP p 1131
27001 Agoura Rd, Agoura Hills CA 91301
Tel (818) 878-8416 *SIC* 6163

■ **COUNTRYWIDE FINANCIAL CORP** p 375
4500 Park Granada, Calabasas CA 91302
Tel (818) 225-3000
SIC 6162 6211 6361 6411 6163 6799

■ **TRI COUNTIES BANK** p 1476
63 Constitution Dr, Chico CA 95973
Tel (530) 898-0300 *SIC* 6029 6163

FINANCE AMERICA LLC p 542
1901 Main St Ste 150, Irvine CA 92614
Tel (949) 440-1000 *SIC* 6162 6163

■ **SAND CANYON CORP** p 1278
7595 Irvine Center Dr # 100, Irvine CA 92618
Tel (949) 727-9425 *SIC* 6163 6162

TOPA EQUITIES LTD p 1460
1800 Ave Of The Ste 1400, Los Angeles CA 90067
Tel (310) 203-9199 *SIC* 6163 5181 7538

■ **HOMEQ SERVICING CORP** p 703
4837 Watt Ave, North Highlands CA 95660
Tel (916) 339-6192
SIC 6162 6163 6111 6159

AMERIQUEST CAPITAL CORP p 83
1100 W Twn Cntry Rd R, Orange CA 92868
Tel (714) 564-0600 *SIC* 6163

■ **FULL SPECTRUM LENDING INC** p 584
35 N Lake Ave Fl 3, Pasadena CA 91101
Tel (626) 584-2220 *SIC* 6162 6163

■ **E-LOAN INC** p 467
6230 Stoneridge Mall Rd, Pleasanton CA 94588
Tel (925) 847-6200 *SIC* 6163 6162

■ B OF I FEDERAL BANK p 142
4350 La Jolla Village Dr # 140, San Diego CA 92122
Tel (858) 350-6200 *SIC* 6141 6163

PROSPER MARKETPLACE INC p 1184
221 Main St Fl 3, San Francisco CA 94105
Tel (415) 593-5400 *SIC* 6163

TARBELL FINANCIAL CORP p 1424
1403 N Tustin Ave Ste 380, Santa Ana CA 92705
Tel (714) 972-0988 *SIC* 6163 6531 6099

PROSPECT MORTGAGE LLC p 1184
15301 Ventura Blvd D300, Sherman Oaks CA 91403
Tel (818) 981-0606 *SIC* 6163

LENDERLIVE NETWORK INC p 855
710 S Ash St Ste 200, Denver CO 80246
Tel (303) 226-8000 *SIC* 4813 6163

■ FARMINGTON BANK p 530
1 Farm Glen Blvd, Farmington CT 06032
Tel (860) 676-4600 *SIC* 6036 6163

LIBERTY BANK p 861
315 Main St, Middletown CT 06457
Tel (860) 344-7200 *SIC* 6036 6163 6022

▲ NAVIENT CORP p 1020
123 S Justison St Ste 300, Wilmington DE 19801
Tel (302) 283-8000 *SIC* 6211 6163

PARAMOUNT FUNDING GROUP INC p 1114
212 E Ocean Ave, Lantana FL 33462
Tel (561) 586-6290 *SIC* 6163

▲ LENNAR CORP p 855
700 Nw 107th Ave Ste 400, Miami FL 33172
Tel (305) 559-4000 *SIC* 1531 6552 6163

TOTALBANK p 1463
100 Se 2nd St, Miami FL 33131
Tel (305) 982-3310 *SIC* 6022 6163

■ N A BANKUNITED p 1005
14817 Oak Ln, Miami Lakes FL 33016
Tel (305) 231-6400 *SIC* 6035 6163 6111

AMERISAVE MORTGAGE CORP p 83
3350 Peachtree Rd Ne # 1000, Atlanta GA 30326
Tel (866) 970-7283 *SIC* 6163

DELTA COMMUNITY CREDIT UNION p 426
1025 Virginia Ave, Atlanta GA 30354
Tel (404) 715-4725 *SIC* 6061 6163

BYLINE BANK p 231
3639 N Broadway St, Chicago IL 60613
Tel (773) 244-7000 *SIC* 6022 6163 6021

■ ENOVA FINANCIAL HOLDINGS LLC p 500
200 W Jackson Blvd # 2400, Chicago IL 60606
Tel (312) 568-4200 *SIC* 6163

MADISON CAPITAL FUNDING LLC p 894
30 S Wacker Dr Ste 3700, Chicago IL 60606
Tel (312) 596-6900 *SIC* 6163

■ LAKE CITY BANK p 838
202 E Center St, Warsaw IN 46580
Tel (574) 267-6144 *SIC* 6022 6163

■ SPECIALTY BLENDING CO LLC p 1356
1000 Wenig Rd Ne, Cedar Rapids IA 52402
Tel (319) 298-3360 *SIC* 6163

HALO GROUP INC p 655
814 33rd St, Des Moines IA 50312
Tel (515) 974-6908 *SIC* 6163

IOWA FINANCE AUTHORITY p 762
2015 Grand Ave Ste 200, Des Moines IA 50312
Tel (515) 725-4900 *SIC* 6163

VERIDIAN CREDIT UNION p 1549
1827 Ansborough Ave, Waterloo IA 50701
Tel (319) 236-5600 *SIC* 6062 6163

COMMUNITYAMERICA CREDIT UNION p 350
9777 Ridge Dr, Lenexa KS 66219
Tel (913) 905-7000 *SIC* 6062 6163

■ REPUBLIC BANK & TRUST CO INC p 1225
601 W Market St Ste 100, Louisville KY 40202
Tel (502) 584-3600 *SIC* 6022 6163

■ IBERIABANK p 726
200 W Congress St, Lafayette LA 70501
Tel (800) 682-3231 *SIC* 6036 6163

■ ONEMAIN FINANCIAL HOLDINGS LLC p 1087
100 Intl Dr Ste 15000, Baltimore MD 21202
Tel (410) 332-3000 *SIC* 6162 6163

FIELDSTONE MORTGAGE CO p 541
5094 Dorsey Hall Dr # 104, Ellicott City MD 21042
Tel (410) 772-7217 *SIC* 6163

■ FARMERS & MECHANICS BANK p 529
110 Thomas Johnson Dr # 100, Frederick MD 21702
Tel (301) 694-4050 *SIC* 6021 6163

■ FIRST NATIONWIDE MORTGAGE CORP p 548
5280 Corporate Dr, Frederick MD 21703
Tel (301) 791-8108 *SIC* 6163

TOWER FEDERAL CREDIT UNION p 1464
7901 Sandy Spring Rd # 102, Laurel MD 20707
Tel (301) 490-6926 *SIC* 6163 6061

FIRST HOME MORTGAGE CORP p 547
5355 Nottingham Dr # 130, Nottingham MD 21236
Tel (877) 933-3100 *SIC* 6163

MARTHAS VINEYARD MORTGAGE CO LLC p 912
107 Beach Rd Ste 101, Vineyard Haven MA 02568
Tel (508) 696-1801 *SIC* 6163

CALM INC p 242
102 Elm St, Walpole MA 02081
Tel (508) 850-4100 *SIC* 6163

REPUBLIC BANK p 1225
328 S Saginaw St Lbby, Flint MI 48502
Tel (810) 257-2506 *SIC* 6022 6163 6029

VAN DYK MORTGAGE CORP p 1542
2449 Camelot Ct Se, Grand Rapids MI 49546
Tel (616) 940-3000 *SIC* 6162 6163

UNITED FEDERAL CREDIT UNION p 1508
2807 S State St, Saint Joseph MI 49085
Tel (888) 982-1400 *SIC* 6061 6163

JONES FINANCIAL COMPANIES LLLP p 792
12555 Manchester Rd, Saint Louis MO 63131
Tel (314) 515-2000 *SIC* 6211 6411 6163

FRANKLIN CREDIT HOLDING CORP p 575
101 Hudson St Fl 25, Jersey City NJ 07302
Tel (201) 604-1800 *SIC* 6163 6162

■ FULTON BANK OF NEW JERSEY p 584
533 Fellowship Rd Ste 250, Mount Laurel NJ 08054
Tel (856) 787-1997 *SIC* 6029 6163

HUDSON CITY SAVINGS BANK p 716
80 W Century Rd, Paramus NJ 07652
Tel (201) 967-1900 *SIC* 6035 6163

AMERICAN FINANCIAL RESOURCES INC p 72
9 Sylvan Way Ste 310, Parsippany NJ 07054
Tel (973) 983-5626 *SIC* 6163

■ FLUSHING BANK p 561
220 Rxr Plz, Flushing NY 11354
Tel (718) 512-2929 *SIC* 6035 6163

CONSUMER HOME MORTGAGE INC p 361
115 Broadhollow Rd, Melville NY 11747
Tel (631) 547-6840 *SIC* 6163

■ N Y MCG INC p 1006
1 Battery Park Plz Fl 26, New York NY 10004
Tel (212) 972-3600 *SIC* 6163

NEW YORK MORTGAGE TRUST INC p 1035
275 Madison Ave Fl 32, New York NY 10016
Tel (212) 792-0107 *SIC* 6798 6163

■ BANK OF AMERICA MORTGAGE SECURITIES INC p 151
101 S Tryon St Ste 1000, Charlotte NC 28280
Tel (704) 386-5681 *SIC* 6162 6163

▲ LENDINGTREE INC p 855
11115 Rushmore Dr, Charlotte NC 28277
Tel (704) 541-5351 *SIC* 6163 6531

NATIONS LENDING CORP p 1017
4 Summit Park Dr Ste 200, Independence OH 44131
Tel (440) 842-4817 *SIC* 6162 6163

WESTFIELD BANCORP INC p 1601
2 Park Cir, Westfield Center OH 44251
Tel (330) 887-8112 *SIC* 6163

FIRST UNITED BANK AND TRUST CO p 550
1400 W Main St, Durant OK 74701
Tel (580) 924-2211 *SIC* 6022 6163 6021

GATEWAY MORTGAGE GROUP LLC p 594
244 S Gateway Pl, Jenks OK 74037
Tel (918) 712-9000 *SIC* 6163

■ BANK SNB p 152
608 S Main St, Stillwater OK 74074
Tel (405) 372-2230 *SIC* 6021 6163

POLICE AND FIRE FEDERAL CREDIT UNION (INC) p 1159
901 Arch St, Philadelphia PA 19107
Tel (215) 931-0300 *SIC* 6061 6163

URBAN LENDING SOLUTIONS p 1530
1001 Liberty Ave Ste 1050, Pittsburgh PA 15222
Tel (412) 325-7046 *SIC* 6163

ACCESS GROUP INC p 14
10 N High St Fl 4, West Chester PA 19380
Tel (484) 653-3300 *SIC* 6163

EAST RIVER ELECTRIC POWER COOPERATIVE INC p 470
211 S Harth Ave, Madison SD 57042
Tel (605) 256-4536 *SIC* 4911 6163

FIRST AMERICAN HOLDING INC p 544
2504 Cross Winds Ln, Chattanooga TN 37421
Tel (423) 894-8783 *SIC* 6163

COMMUNITYBANK OF TEXAS NATIONAL ASSOCIATION p 350
5999 Delaware St, Beaumont TX 77706
Tel (409) 861-7200
SIC 6163 6029 6022 6021

TBA INSURANCE GROUP LIMITED PARTNERSHIP p 1427
1900 L Don Dodson Dr, Bedford TX 76021
Tel (817) 265-2000 *SIC* 6331 6163

■ A PLAINSCAPITAL PRIMELENDING CO p 6
18111 Preston Rd Ste 900, Dallas TX 75252
Tel (800) 317-7463 *SIC* 6163 6021

EVERETT FINANCIAL INC p 514
14801 Quorum Dr Ste 300, Dallas TX 75254
Tel (214) 340-5225 *SIC* 6163

AMSTAR MORTGAGE CORP p 87
10851 Scarsdale Blvd # 800, Houston TX 77089
Tel (281) 481-9040 *SIC* 6163

ARK-LA-TEX FINANCIAL SERVICES LLC p 109
5160 Tennyson Pkwy 2000w, Plano TX 75024
Tel (972) 398-7676 *SIC* 6163

■ VALERO REFINING CO-NEW JERSEY p 1539
1 Valero Way, San Antonio TX 78249
Tel (210) 345-2000 *SIC* 2911 6163

ACADEMY MORTGAGE CORP p 13
339 W 13490 S, Draper UT 84020
Tel (801) 233-7237 *SIC* 6163

PRIMARY RESIDENTIAL MORTGAGE INC p 1174
1480 N 2200 W, Salt Lake City UT 84116
Tel (801) 596-8707 *SIC* 6163

VIRGINIA CREDIT UNION INC p 1558
7500 Boulder View Dr, North Chesterfield VA 23225
Tel (804) 323-6800 *SIC* 6062 6163

COBALT MORTGAGE INC p 332
11241 Slater Ave Ne # 110, Kirkland WA 98033
Tel (425) 605-3100 *SIC* 6163

■ BANK MUTUAL p 151
4949 W Brown Deer Rd, Milwaukee WI 53223
Tel (414) 354-1500
SIC 6036 6163 6029 6022

LANDLOVERS LLC p 842
1833 Executive Dr Ste 105, Oconomowoc WI 53066
Tel (262) 560-9786 *SIC* 6163

WINTERTHUR U S HOLDINGS INC p 1617
1 General Dr, Sun Prairie WI 53596
Tel (608) 837-4440 *SIC* 6411 6163

WERCS p 1592
400 E 1st St Ste 100, Casper WY 82601
Tel (307) 235-6200
SIC 6211 6163 6411 6321 6531 6099

SIC 6211 Security Brokers & Dealers

▲ REGIONS FINANCIAL CORP p 1220
1900 5th Ave N, Birmingham AL 35203
Tel (205) 581-7890 *SIC* 6022 6211 6282

■ STERNE AGEE & LEACH INC p 1387
800 Shades Creek Pkwy, Birmingham AL 35209
Tel (205) 226-3397 *SIC* 6211

■ SAGEPOINT FINANCIAL INC p 1268
2800 N Central Ave # 2100, Phoenix AZ 85004
Tel (602) 744-3000 *SIC* 6311 6211

SI HOLDINGS INC p 1319
111 Center St, Little Rock AR 72201
Tel (501) 688-8400 *SIC* 6211

STEPHENS CAPITAL PARTNERS LLC p 1386
111 Center St Ste 200, Little Rock AR 72201
Tel (800) 643-9691 *SIC* 6211

STEPHENS INC p 1386
111 Center St Ste 200, Little Rock AR 72201
Tel (501) 377-2000 *SIC* 6211

GORES GROUP LLC p 626
9800 Wilshire Blvd, Beverly Hills CA 90212
Tel (310) 209-3010 *SIC* 6211

■ COUNTRYWIDE FINANCIAL CORP p 375
4500 Park Granada, Calabasas CA 91302
Tel (818) 225-3000
SIC 6162 6211 6361 6411 6163 6799

LERETA LLC p 857
1123 Park View Dr, Covina CA 91724
Tel (626) 543-1765 *SIC* 6211 6541 6361

ARES MANAGEMENT HOLDINGS LP p 107
2000 Avenue Of The Stars, Los Angeles CA 90067
Tel (310) 201-4100 *SIC* 6211

DATA ANALYSIS INC p 413
12655 Beatrice St, Los Angeles CA 90066
Tel (310) 448-6800 *SIC* 6211 2711 7374

FREEMAN SPOGLI & CO LLC p 577
11100 Santa Monica Blvd # 1900, Los Angeles CA 90025
Tel (310) 444-1822 *SIC* 6211

GOLD PARENT LP p 620
11111 Santa Monica Blvd, Los Angeles CA 90025
Tel (310) 954-0444 *SIC* 6211

GREEN EQUITY INVESTORS III L P p 637
11111 Santa Monica Blvd # 2000, Los Angeles CA 90025
Tel (310) 954-0444 *SIC* 6211

▲ HOULIHAN LOKEY INC p 711
10250 Constellation Blvd # 5, Los Angeles CA 90067
Tel (310) 553-8871 *SIC* 6211 6282

LEAR CAPITAL INC p 850
1990 S Bundy Dr Ste 600, Los Angeles CA 90025
Tel (310) 571-0190 *SIC* 6211

LEONARD GREEN & PARTNERS LP p 856
11111 Santa Monica Blvd # 2000, Los Angeles CA 90025
Tel (310) 954-0444 *SIC* 6211

■ OAKTREE CAPITAL MANAGEMENT LP p 1071
333 S Grand Ave Ste 2800, Los Angeles CA 90071
Tel (213) 830-6300 *SIC* 6282 6722 6211

■ SUNAMERICA INC p 1401
1 Sun America Ctr Fl 38, Los Angeles CA 90067
Tel (310) 772-6000
SIC 6091 6311 6211 6282 6411 6371

■ SUNAMERICA INVESTMENTS INC p 1401
1 Sun America Ctr Fl 37, Los Angeles CA 90067
Tel (310) 772-6000
SIC 8741 6211 6282 7311

■ TCW GROUP INC p 1428
865 S Figueroa St # 2100, Los Angeles CA 90017
Tel (213) 244-0000 *SIC* 6022 6282 6211

■ TRUST CO OF WEST p 1487
865 S Figueroa St # 1800, Los Angeles CA 90017
Tel (213) 244-0000 *SIC* 6211

WEDBUSH SECURITIES INC p 1587
1000 Wilshire Blvd # 900, Los Angeles CA 90017
Tel (213) 688-8000 *SIC* 6211

ATRIUM CAPITAL CORP p 129
3000 Sand Hill Rd 2-130, Menlo Park CA 94025
Tel (650) 233-7878 *SIC* 6211

SILVER LAKE PARTNERS II LP p 1323
2775 Sand Hill Rd Ste 100, Menlo Park CA 94025
Tel (650) 233-8120 *SIC* 6726 6211

WINDJAMMER CAPITAL INVESTORS III LLC p 1615
610 Newport Center Dr # 1100, Newport Beach CA 92660
Tel (949) 706-9989 *SIC* 6211

PLETHORA BUSINESSES p 1156
2117 W Orangewood Ave A, Orange CA 92868
Tel (714) 255-8862 *SIC* 6211

BROADREACH CAPITAL PARTNERS LLC p 215
248 Homer Ave, Palo Alto CA 94301
Tel (650) 331-2500 *SIC* 6211

■ FRANKLIN TEMPLETON INVESTOR SERVICES LLC p 575
3344 Quality Dr, Rancho Cordova CA 95670
Tel (916) 463-1500 *SIC* 6211 6282

FIRST ALLIED SECURITIES INC p 544
655 W Broadway Fl 11, San Diego CA 92101
Tel (619) 702-9600 *SIC* 6211

FORESTERS EQUITY SERVICES INC p 567
6640 Lusk Blvd Ste A202, San Diego CA 92121
Tel (858) 550-4844 *SIC* 6211

■ LPL FINANCIAL LLC p 882
4707 Executive Dr, San Diego CA 92121
Tel (800) 877-7210 *SIC* 6211

■ LPL HOLDINGS INC p 882
4707 Executive Dr, San Diego CA 92121
Tel (858) 450-9606 *SIC* 6211

BABCOCK & BROWN HOLDINGS INC p 143
1 Pier Ste 3, San Francisco CA 94111
Tel (415) 512-1515 *SIC* 6211

BBAM LLC p 163
50 California St Fl 14, San Francisco CA 94111
Tel (415) 512-1515 *SIC* 6211

BTIG LLC p 222
600 Montgomery St Fl 6, San Francisco CA 94111
Tel (415) 248-2200 *SIC* 6211

CALERA CAPITAL MANAGEMENT INC p 238
580 California St # 2200, San Francisco CA 94104
Tel (415) 632-5200 *SIC* 6211

■ CHARLES SCHWAB & CO INC p 289
211 Main St Fl 17, San Francisco CA 94105
Tel (415) 636-7000 *SIC* 6211

▲ CHARLES SCHWAB CORP p 289
211 Main St Fl 17, San Francisco CA 94105
Tel (415) 667-7000
SIC 6211 6091 6282 7389

GOLDEN GATE CAPITAL LP p 620
1 Embarcadero Ctr Fl 39, San Francisco CA 94111
Tel (415) 983-2700 *SIC* 6211

■ JMP GROUP INC p 786
600 Montgomery St # 1100, San Francisco CA 94111
Tel (415) 835-8900 *SIC* 6211

▲ JMP GROUP LLC p 786
600 Montgomery St # 1100, San Francisco CA 94111
Tel (415) 835-8900 *SIC* 6211

■ JP MORGAN H&Q PRINCIPALS LP p 794
560 Mission St Fl 2, San Francisco CA 94105
Tel (415) 315-5000
SIC 6211 6799 6282 7389

PARKSIDE LENDING LLC p 1117
1130 Howard St, San Francisco CA 94103
Tel (415) 771-3700 *SIC* 6211

■ SCHWAB HOLDINGS INC p 1291
211 Main St, San Francisco CA 94105
Tel (415) 636-7000 *SIC* 6211

FOX PAINE & CO LLC p 572
2105 Woodside Rd Ste D, Woodside CA 94062
Tel (650) 235-2075 *SIC* 6211

▲ ROYAL GOLD INC p 1254
1660 Wynkoop St Ste 1000, Denver CO 80202
Tel (303) 573-1660 *SIC* 6211

GREAT-WEST LIFE & ANNUITY INSURANCE CO p 635
8515 E Orchard Rd, Greenwood Village CO 80111
Tel (303) 737-3000 *SIC* 6211 6311

GWFS EQUITIES INC p 648
8515 E Orchard Rd, Greenwood Village CO 80111
Tel (303) 737-3817 *SIC* 6211

GWL&A FINANCIAL INC p 648
8515 E Orchard Rd, Greenwood Village CO 80111
Tel (303) 737-3000 *SIC* 6211 6311

FRANCO-NEVADA US CORP p 574
1745 Shea Center Dr # 310, Highlands Ranch CO 80129
Tel (303) 317-6335 *SIC* 6211

BRYNWOOD PARTNERS VII LP p 222
8 Sound Shore Dr Ste 265, Greenwich CT 06830
Tel (203) 622-1790 *SIC* 6211

CATTERTON PARTNERS CORP p 267
599 W Putnam Ave, Greenwich CT 06830
Tel (203) 629-4901 *SIC* 6211

GENERAL ATLANTIC CORP p 599
3 Pickwick Plz Ste 200, Greenwich CT 06830
Tel (203) 629-8600 *SIC* 6211

■ IBG LLC p 726
1 Pickwick Plz, Greenwich CT 06830
Tel (203) 618-5800 *SIC* 6211 8732

▲ INTERACTIVE BROKERS GROUP INC p 751
1 Pickwick Plz, Greenwich CT 06830
Tel (203) 618-5800 *SIC* 6211

■ INTERACTIVE BROKERS LLC p 751
2 Pickwick Plz Ste 210, Greenwich CT 06830
Tel (203) 618-5700 *SIC* 6211

LAUREN HOLDING INC p 847
781 North St, Greenwich CT 06831
Tel (239) 514-7329 *SIC* 6211

STARWOOD CAPITAL GROUP LLC p 1379
591 W Putnam Ave, Greenwich CT 06830
Tel (203) 422-7700 *SIC* 6211

WEEDEN & CO LP p 1587
145 Mason St, Greenwich CT 06830
Tel (203) 861-7670 *SIC* 6211

■ ADVEST GROUP INC p 27
90 State House Sq, Hartford CT 06103
Tel (860) 509-1000
SIC 6211 6036 6141 6153 6282

PM HOLDINGS INC p 1157
1 American Row, Hartford CT 06103
Tel (860) 403-5000
SIC 6411 6162 6722 6282 6211 6552

WHITNEY & CO LLC p 1607
130 Main St, New Canaan CT 06840
Tel (203) 716-6100 *SIC* 6211

CRT CAPITAL GROUP LLC p 396
262 Harbor Dr Fl 2, Stamford CT 06902
Tel (203) 569-6400 *SIC* 6211

RBS HOLDINGS USA INC p 1211
600 Washington Blvd, Stamford CT 06901
Tel (203) 897-2700 *SIC* 6211

RBS SECURITIES INC p 1211
600 Washington Blvd, Stamford CT 06901
Tel (203) 897-2700 *SIC* 6282 6211

STAMFORD CAPITAL GROUP INC p 1375
1266 E Main St Ste 700r, Stamford CT 06902
Tel (800) 977-7837 *SIC* 2741 6211

UBS ENERGY LLC p 1498
677 Washington Blvd, Stamford CT 06901
Tel (203) 719-3000 *SIC* 6211 6799

UBS SECURITIES LLC p 1498
677 Washington Blvd, Stamford CT 06901
Tel (203) 719-3000
SIC 6211 6221 6289 6311 6091 6282

UBS SECURITIES LLC p 1498
677 Washington Blvd, Stamford CT 06901
Tel (203) 719-3000 *SIC* 6211 6282

■ HARTFORD EQUITY SALES CO INC p 665
200 Hopmeadow St, Weatogue CT 06089
Tel (860) 843-8213 *SIC* 6211

▲ COMPASS DIVERSIFIED HOLDINGS p 351
61 Wilton Rd Ste 2, Westport CT 06880
Tel (203) 221-1703 *SIC* 6211

■ STERNOCANDLELAMP HOLDINGS INC p 1388
61 Wilton Rd Ste 2, Westport CT 06880
Tel (203) 221-1703 *SIC* 6211

■ VOYA INVESTMENT TRUST CO p 1566
1 Orange Way, Windsor CT 06095
Tel (860) 580-4646 *SIC* 6211 6282

BARCLAYS FINANCIAL CORP p 155
125 S West St, Wilmington DE 19801
Tel (302) 622-8990 *SIC* 7389 6282 6211

CAWSL ENTERPRISES INC p 268
3411 Silverside Rd, Wilmington DE 19810
Tel (302) 478-6160 *SIC* 6211

■ **ING BANK FSB** p 742
802 Delaware Ave, Wilmington DE 19801
Tel (302) 658-2200 SIC 6035 6211

▲ **NAVIENT CORP** p 1020
123 S Justison St Ste 300, Wilmington DE 19801
Tel (302) 283-8000 SIC 6211 6163

ASTRA CAPITAL MANAGEMENT LLC p 122
1900 K St Nw Ste 1130, Washington DC 20006
Tel (202) 779-9044 SIC 6211

CAPITOL PARTNERS I LP p 251
1808 I St Nw Ste 200, Washington DC 20006
Tel (202) 955-7960 SIC 8082 6211

REVOLUTION LLC p 1229
1717 Rhode Island Ave Nw # 1000, Washington DC 20036
Tel (202) 776-1400 SIC 6211 7514

THAYER CAPITAL PARTNERS LP p 1446
1455 Penn Ave Nw Ste 350, Washington DC 20004
Tel (202) 371-0150 SIC 6211

BAYVIEW FINANCIAL HOLDINGS LP p 162
4425 Ponce De Leon Blvd # 500, Coral Gables FL 33146
Tel (305) 854-8880 SIC 6211

BAYVIEW LENDING GROUP LLC p 163
4425 P De Leon Blvd Fl 3, Coral Gables FL 33146
Tel (305) 854-8880 SIC 6211

■ **TEMPLETON WORLDWIDE INC** p 1436
500 E Broward Blvd # 900, Fort Lauderdale FL 33394
Tel (954) 527-7500
SIC 6211 6282 8742 8748

HIG CAPITAL INC p 690
1450 Brickell Ave # 3100, Miami FL 33131
Tel (305) 379-2322 SIC 8742 6211

HIG CAPITAL LLC p 690
1450 Brickell Ave Fl 31, Miami FL 33131
Tel (305) 379-2322 SIC 6211

HIG CAPITAL MANAGEMENT INC p 690
1450 Brickell Ave Fl 31, Miami FL 33131
Tel (305) 379-2322 SIC 6211

HIG CAPITAL PARTNERS III LP p 690
1450 Brickell Ave # 3100, Miami FL 33131
Tel (305) 379-2322
SIC 6211 5084 7352 7699 8748 3842

▲ **LADENBURG THALMANN FINANCIAL SERVICES INC** p 837
4400 Biscayne Blvd Fl 12, Miami FL 33137
Tel (305) 572-4100 SIC 6211 6282

JACOBS INVESTMENTS INC p 775
11770 Us Highway 1 # 600, North Palm Beach FL 33408
Tel (561) 776-6050 SIC 6211 7011

TRADESTATION GROUP INC p 1469
8050 Sw 10th St Ste 4000, Plantation FL 33324
Tel (954) 652-7000 SIC 6211

AEGON USA SECURITIES INC p 29
570 Carillon Pkwy, Saint Petersburg FL 33716
Tel (727) 299-1800 SIC 6211

■ **RAYMOND JAMES & ASSOCIATES INC** p 1210
880 Carillon Pkwy, Saint Petersburg FL 33716
Tel (727) 567-1000 SIC 6211 6722 8741

▲ **RAYMOND JAMES FINANCIAL INC** p 1210
880 Carillon Pkwy, Saint Petersburg FL 33716
Tel (727) 567-1000 SIC 6211

■ **RAYMOND JAMES FINANCIAL SERVICES INC** p 1210
880 Carillon Pkwy, Saint Petersburg FL 33716
Tel (727) 567-1000
SIC 6211 6282 6712 6091 6035

GUNNALLEN FINANCIAL INC p 648
5002 W Waters Ave, Tampa FL 33634
Tel (800) 713-4046 SIC 6211

PALM BEACH CAPITAL FUND I LP p 1109
525 S Flagler Dr Ste 208, West Palm Beach FL 33401
Tel (561) 659-9022 SIC 6211

■ **FINANCIAL SERVICE CORP** p 543
2300 Windy Ridge Pkwy Se 1100s, Atlanta GA 30339
Tel (770) 916-6500
SIC 6722 6411 8742 6211

FORMATION CAPITAL LLC p 567
3500 Lenox Rd Ne Ste 510, Atlanta GA 30326
Tel (770) 754-9660 SIC 6211 8742

■ **FSC CORP** p 582
2300 Windy Ridge Pkwy Se # 1100, Atlanta GA 30339
Tel (770) 916-6500
SIC 6722 6411 8742 6211

■ **FSC SECURITIES CORP** p 582
2300 Windy Ridge Pkwy Se # 1100, Atlanta GA 30339
Tel (770) 916-6500 SIC 6411 6211

JP TURNER & CO LLC p 795
1 Buckhead Plz 3060, Atlanta GA 30305
Tel (404) 479-8300 SIC 6211

NCP 2 LP p 1022
3060 Peachtree Rd Nw # 780, Atlanta GA 30305
Tel (404) 504-4080 SIC 6211

▲ **SUNTRUST BANKS INC** p 1405
303 Peachtree St Ne, Atlanta GA 30308
Tel (800) 786-8787
SIC 6021 6022 6211 6091 6282

■ **VOYA INVESTMENT MANAGEMENT CO LLC** p 1566
5780 Powers Ferry Rd, Atlanta GA 30327
Tel (770) 980-5100 SIC 6211

■ **VOYA INVESTMENT MANAGEMENT LLC** p 1566
5780 Powers Ferry Rd, Atlanta GA 30327
Tel (770) 980-5100 SIC 6211

HSBC SECURITIES (USA) INC p 715
107 Iris Glen Dr Se, Conyers GA 30013
Tel (212) 525-5000 SIC 6211

■ **BANK OF HAWAII** p 151
130 Merchant St, Honolulu HI 96813
Tel (888) 643-3888 SIC 6022 6411 6211

ADVANCED EQUITIES FINANCIAL CORP p 25
200 S Wacker Dr Ste 3200, Chicago IL 60606
Tel (312) 377-5300 SIC 6211

■ **BANC ONE CAPITAL MARKETS INC** p 149
1 Bank One Plz, Chicago IL 60670
Tel (800) 992-7169 SIC 6211 6282

■ **BANC ONE FINANCIAL LLC** p 149
1 Chase Tower, Chicago IL 60670
Tel (312) 732-5531 SIC 6211 6153

BMO BANKCORP INC p 194
111 W Monroe St, Chicago IL 60603
Tel (312) 461-2121 SIC 6021 6211

BMO FINANCIAL CORP p 194
111 W Monroe St Ste 1200, Chicago IL 60603
Tel (312) 461-2121 SIC 6021 6082 6211

■ **CHICAGO BOARD OPTIONS EXCHANGE INC** p 297
400 S La Salle St Fl 1, Chicago IL 60605
Tel (312) 786-5600 SIC 6211 6231

CITADEL LLC p 309
131 S Dearborn St Ste 200, Chicago IL 60603
Tel (312) 395-2100 SIC 6211

LINCOLN INTERNATIONAL LLC p 867
500 W Madison St Ste 3900, Chicago IL 60661
Tel (312) 580-8339 SIC 6211

MESIROW FINANCIAL HOLDINGS INC p 951
353 N Clark St Lowr Level, Chicago IL 60654
Tel (312) 595-6000
SIC 6211 6282 6531 6552 6411

MESIROW FINANCIAL INC p 951
353 N Clark St Lowr Level, Chicago IL 60654
Tel (312) 595-6000 SIC 6211

NESBITT BURNS SECURITIES INC p 1026
115 S La Salle St Ste 20w, Chicago IL 60603
Tel (312) 461-6220 SIC 6211

NUVEEN INVESTMENTS INC p 1068
333 W Wacker Dr, Chicago IL 60606
Tel (312) 917-7700 SIC 6282 6211

NUVEEN JOHN & CO INC (DEL) p 1068
333 W Wacker Dr Fl 33, Chicago IL 60606
Tel (312) 917-7700 SIC 6211 8742

PEAK6 INVESTMENTS LP p 1126
141 W Jackson Blvd # 500, Chicago IL 60604
Tel (312) 362-2401 SIC 6211

PFINGSTEN PARTNERS LLC p 1140
300 N Lasalle St 5400, Chicago IL 60654
Tel (312) 222-8707
SIC 5065 6211 3679 3578

RJ OBRIEN & ASSOCIATES LLC p 1239
222 S Riverside Plz # 1200, Chicago IL 60606
Tel (312) 373-5000 SIC 6221 6211

ROSENTHAL COLLINS GROUP LLC p 1251
216 W Jackson Blvd # 400, Chicago IL 60606
Tel (312) 460-9200
SIC 6221 6289 6231 6211

UBS ASSET MANAGEMENT (AMERICAS) INC p 1498
1 N Wacker Dr Ste 3700, Chicago IL 60606
Tel (312) 525-4111 SIC 6211

WATER STREET HEALTHCARE PARTNERS LLC p 1581
333 W Wacker Dr Ste 2800, Chicago IL 60606
Tel (312) 506-2900 SIC 6211

WILLIAM BLAIR & CO LLC p 1610
222 W Adams St Ste 2900, Chicago IL 60606
Tel (312) 236-1600 SIC 6211

WOLVERINE TRADING LLC p 1621
175 W Jackson Blvd # 200, Chicago IL 60604
Tel (312) 884-4000 SIC 6211

GCG FINANCIAL INC p 595
3 Parkway N Ste 500, Deerfield IL 60015
Tel (847) 457-3000 SIC 6411 8742 6211

TRICOR PACIFIC CAPITAL PARTNERS (FUND IV) US LP p 1479
1 Westminster Pl Ste 100n, Lake Forest IL 60045
Tel (847) 295-4410 SIC 6211

▲ **CALAMOS ASSET MANAGEMENT INC** p 238
2020 Calamos Ct Ofc, Naperville IL 60563
Tel (630) 245-7200 SIC 6211 6282

■ **CALAMOS INVESTMENTS LLC** p 238
2020 Calamos Ct Ofc, Naperville IL 60563
Tel (630) 245-7200 SIC 6211 6282

INLAND REAL ESTATE INVESTMENT CORP p 743
2901 Butterfield Rd, Oak Brook IL 60523
Tel (630) 218-8000 SIC 6211 6798

INLAND SECURITIES CORP p 744
2901 Butterfield Rd, Oak Brook IL 60523
Tel (630) 218-8000 SIC 6211

BCS FINANCIAL CORP p 164
2 Mid America Plz, Oakbrook Terrace IL 60181
Tel (630) 472-7700 SIC 6331 6311 6211

▲ **WINTRUST FINANCIAL CORP** p 1617
9700 W Higgins Rd, Rosemont IL 60018
Tel (847) 939-9000 SIC 6022 6211 6282

■ **AMERICAN GENERAL LIFE INSURANCE** p 73
1 Franklin Sq, Springfield IL 62703
Tel (217) 528-2011 SIC 6411 6321 6211

FIRST TRUST PORTFOLIOS LP p 550
120 E Liberty Dr Ste 400, Wheaton IL 60187
Tel (800) 621-1675 SIC 6211

COOK GROUP INC p 365
750 N Daniels Way, Bloomington IN 47404
Tel (812) 339-2235
SIC 3841 3821 3845 6411 6512 6211

AMERICAN UNITED MUTUAL INSURANCE HOLDING CO p 81
1 American Sq, Indianapolis IN 46282
Tel (317) 285-1877
SIC 6211 6311 6371 6351 6331

ALLIED GROUP INC p 56
1100 Locust St, Des Moines IA 50391
Tel (515) 280-4211 SIC 6331 6211 5112

■ **PRINCIPAL LIFE INSURANCE CO** p 1177
711 High St, Des Moines IA 50392
Tel (515) 247-5111
SIC 6311 6211 6162 6321 6411

CAMBRIDGE INVESTMENT RESEARCH INC p 244
1776 Pleasant Plain Rd, Fairfield IA 52556
Tel (641) 472-5100 SIC 6211

FARM BUREAU PROPERTY & CASUALTY INSURANCE CO p 528
5400 University Ave, West Des Moines IA 50266
Tel (515) 225-5400 SIC 6411 2711 6211

▲ **WADDELL & REED FINANCIAL INC** p 1571
6300 Lamar Ave, Overland Park KS 66202
Tel (913) 236-2000 SIC 6211 6282 6411

■ **WADDELL & REED FINANCIAL SERVICES INC** p 1571
6300 Lamar Ave, Overland Park KS 66202
Tel (913) 236-2000
SIC 6722 6311 6211 6531

■ **WADDELL & REED INC** p 1571
6300 Lamar Ave, Shawnee Mission KS 66202
Tel (913) 236-2000
SIC 6282 6211 6289 6411

■ **WADDELL & REED INVESTMENT MANAGEMENT CO** p 1571
6300 Lamar Ave, Shawnee Mission KS 66202
Tel (913) 236-2000 SIC 6211

SECURITY BENEFIT CORP p 1299
1 Sw Security Benefit Pl, Topeka KS 66636
Tel (785) 438-3000 SIC 6211

SECURITY BENEFIT GROUP INC p 1299
1 Sw Security Benefit Pl, Topeka KS 66636
Tel (785) 438-3000 SIC 6211 7311 6411

SECURITY BENEFIT LIFE INSURANCE CO p 1299
1 Sw Security Benefit Pl, Topeka KS 66636
Tel (785) 438-3000
SIC 6311 6722 6091 6211 8748

ROSS ACQUISITION CO p 1251
3380 Langley Dr, Hebron KY 41048
Tel (859) 538-8000 SIC 5145 6211

J J B HILLIARD W L LYONS LLC p 771
500 W Jefferson St # 700, Louisville KY 40202
Tel (502) 588-8400 SIC 6211

CARI INVESTMENT CO LLC p 256
222 N Vermont St, Covington LA 70433
Tel (985) 635-6009
SIC 6211 4424 3731 5146

BROWN ADVISORY LLC p 219
901 S Bond St Ste 400, Baltimore MD 21231
Tel (410) 537-5487 SIC 6211

EDUCATION AFFILIATES LLC p 479
5204 Campbell Blvd Ste A, Baltimore MD 21236
Tel (410) 633-2929 SIC 8222 6211

▲ **LEGG MASON INC** p 853
100 International Dr, Baltimore MD 21202
Tel (410) 539-0000 SIC 6282 6211 6162

STERLING PARTNERS LLC p 1387
650 S Exeter St Ste 1000, Baltimore MD 21202
Tel (443) 703-1700 SIC 6211

ACACIA LIFE INSURANCE CO p 13
7315 Wisconsin Ave 1000w, Bethesda MD 20814
Tel (301) 280-1000
SIC 6311 6411 6035 6282 6211

■ **CHEVY CHASE BANK FSB** p 296
7501 Wisconsin Ave Fl 11, Bethesda MD 20814
Tel (240) 497-4101
SIC 6035 6411 6211 6519 6552 6719

ARLINGTON CAPITAL PARTNERS LP p 110
5425 Wisconsin Ave # 200, Chevy Chase MD 20815
Tel (202) 337-7500 SIC 6726 6211

BERKSHIRE PARTNERS LLC p 175
200 Clarendon St Ste 3500, Boston MA 02116
Tel (617) 227-0050 SIC 6211 6726 8741

CHARLESBANK CAPITAL PARTNERS LLC p 289
200 Clarendon St Fl 54, Boston MA 02116
Tel (617) 619-5400 SIC 6211

FIDELITY CAPITAL INVESTORS INC p 540
82 Devonshire St, Boston MA 02109
Tel (617) 563-7000 SIC 6282 6211

FIDELITY INVESTMENTS INSTITUTIONAL OPERATIONS CO INC p 540
245 Summer St Ste 1100, Boston MA 02210
Tel (617) 563-7000 SIC 6282 6211

FMR CORP p 562
82 Devonshire St, Boston MA 02109
Tel (617) 563-7000 SIC 6211

FMR LLC p 562
245 Summer St, Boston MA 02210
Tel (617) 563-7000
SIC 6282 6211 6799 6552 6531

▲ **LPL FINANCIAL HOLDINGS INC** p 882
75 State St Ste 2401, Boston MA 02109
Tel (617) 423-3644 SIC 6211 6282 6091

MASSACHUSETTS FINANCIAL SERVICES CO p 917
111 Huntington Ave, Boston MA 02199
Tel (617) 954-5000 SIC 6282 6211 6289

NATIONAL FINANCIAL SERVICES LLC p 1012
200 Seaport Blvd Ste 630, Boston MA 02210
Tel (800) 471-0382 SIC 6211 6411 6282

■ **OMGEO LLC** p 1084
55 Thomson Pl, Boston MA 02210
Tel (877) 664-3625 SIC 6211

PARTHENON CAPITAL PARTNERS p 1118
1 Federal St Fl 21, Boston MA 02110
Tel (617) 960-4000 SIC 6211

PUTNAM INTERMEDIATE GOVERNMENT INCOME TRUST p 1193
1 Post Office Sq, Boston MA 02109
Tel (617) 292-1000 SIC 6211

QUALIFIED HOUSING TAX CREDITS LP V p 1196
101 Arch St Fl 16, Boston MA 02110
Tel (617) 439-3911 SIC 6211 6531

COMPUTERSHARE INC p 353
250 Royall St, Canton MA 02021
Tel (781) 575-2000 SIC 6289 6211

INVESTORS CAPITAL HOLDINGS LLC p 761
6 Kimball Ln Ste 150, Lynnfield MA 01940
Tel (781) 246-7982 SIC 6211 6282

BOSTON FINANCIAL DATA SERVICES INC p 202
2000 Crown Colony Dr, Quincy MA 02169
Tel (617) 483-5000 SIC 6211 6289 6282

COMMONWEALTH EQUITY SERVICES LLP p 346
29 Sawyer Rd Ste 2, Waltham MA 02453
Tel (781) 398-0401 SIC 6211 6282 6221

■ **ALLMERICA FINANCIAL LIFE INSURANCE AND ANNUITY** p 58
440 Lincoln St, Worcester MA 01653
Tel (508) 855-1000 SIC 6411 6211

FIRST ALLMERICA FINANCIAL LIFE INSURANCE CO p 544
440 Lincoln St, Worcester MA 01653
Tel (508) 855-1000 SIC 6411 6211 6324

JACKSON NATIONAL LIFE INSURANCE CO INC p 774
1 Corporate Way, Lansing MI 48951
Tel (517) 381-5500
SIC 6311 6282 6211 6411

MEADOWBROOK INSURANCE GROUP INC p 934
26255 American Dr, Southfield MI 48034
Tel (248) 358-1100 SIC 6411 6211

■ **OPPENHEIMER & CO INC** p 1090
3310 W Big Beaver Rd # 205, Troy MI 48084
Tel (248) 637-8300 SIC 6211

DAIN RAUSCHER INC p 408
60 S 6th St Ste 700, Minneapolis MN 55402
Tel (704) 377-4300 SIC 6211

EBERSEN INC p 474
7401 Central Ave Ne Ste 2, Minneapolis MN 55432
Tel (763) 572-2661
SIC 4911 1521 6211 1382 4731 8711

GOLDNER HAWN JOHNSON & MORRISON INC p 622
3700 Wells Fargo Ctr # 90, Minneapolis MN 55402
Tel (612) 338-5912 SIC 6211

▲ **PIPER JAFFRAY COMPANIES** p 1151
800 Nicollet Mall Ste 800, Minneapolis MN 55402
Tel (612) 303-6000 SIC 6211

RBC CAPITAL MARKETS LLC p 1211
60 S 6th St Ste 700, Minneapolis MN 55402
Tel (612) 371-2711
SIC 6211 6512 6513 6282

THRIVENT FINANCIAL FOR LUTHERANS FOUNDATION p 1451
625 4th Ave S, Minneapolis MN 55415
Tel (920) 734-5721
SIC 6311 6321 8742 6411 6211

DENMISS LLC p 428
1368 Old Fannin Rd # 100, Brandon MS 39047
Tel (601) 919-1757 SIC 6211 6531

CENTRAL CAPITAL MARKETS p 277
238 Madison St, Jefferson City MO 65101
Tel (573) 634-1330 SIC 6022 6211

CNS CORP p 330
500 E 9th St, Kansas City MO 64106
Tel (816) 842-6300 SIC 6211 6311 4724

■ **H&R BLOCK GROUP INC** p 651
4400 Main St, Kansas City MO 64111
Tel (816) 854-3000 SIC 6211 8721 8742

HUNT MIDWEST ENTERPRISES INC p 719
8300 Ne Underground Dr # 100, Kansas City MO 64161
Tel (816) 455-2500 SIC 6552 1422 6211

EDWARD D JONES & CO LP p 479
12555 Manchester Rd, Saint Louis MO 63131
Tel (314) 515-2000 SIC 6211

JONES FINANCIAL COMPANIES LLLP p 792
12555 Manchester Rd, Saint Louis MO 63131
Tel (314) 515-2000 SIC 6211 6411 6163

PEABODY INVESTMENTS CORP p 1125
701 Market St, Saint Louis MO 63101
Tel (314) 342-3400 SIC 6211

SCOTTRADE INC p 1294
12800 Corporate Hill Dr, Saint Louis MO 63131
Tel (314) 965-1555 SIC 6211

▲ **STIFEL FINANCIAL CORP** p 1389
501 N Broadway, Saint Louis MO 63102
Tel (314) 342-2000 SIC 6211 6719

■ **STIFEL NICOLAUS & CO INC** p 1389
501 N Broadway, Saint Louis MO 63102
Tel (314) 342-2000 SIC 6211

■ **WELLS FARGO ADVISORS LLC** p 1590
1 N Jefferson Ave, Saint Louis MO 63103
Tel (314) 955-3000 SIC 6211

DA DAVIDSON & CO p 407
8 3rd St N, Great Falls MT 59401
Tel (406) 727-4200 SIC 6211

DA DAVIDSON COMPANIES p 407
8 3rd St N, Great Falls MT 59401
Tel (406) 727-4200 SIC 6211 6733 8741

■ **TD AMERITRADE INC** p 1428
1005 N Ameritrade Pl, Bellevue NE 68005
Tel (402) 970-7000 SIC 6211

AMERITAS LIFE INSURANCE CORP p 84
5900 O St, Lincoln NE 68510
Tel (402) 467-1122 SIC 6371 6311 6211

MUTUAL OF OMAHA INSURANCE CO p 1003
Mutual Of Omaha Plaza, Omaha NE 68175
Tel (402) 342-7600 SIC 6311 6211 8748

■ **TD AMERITRADE CLEARING INC** p 1428
200 S 108th Ave, Omaha NE 68154
Tel (402) 331-2744 SIC 6211

▲ **TD AMERITRADE HOLDING CORP** p 1428
200 S 108th Ave, Omaha NE 68154
Tel (402) 331-7856 SIC 6211

REAL PROPERTY SERVICES CORP p 1214
9960 W Chynne Ave Ste 110, North Las Vegas NV 89030
Tel (702) 313-3700 SIC 6531 6211

▲ **GAIN CAPITAL HOLDINGS INC** p 589
135 Route 202 206, Bedminster NJ 07921
Tel (908) 731-0700 SIC 6211 6221

HUMC HOLDCO LLC p 718
308 Willow Ave, Hoboken NJ 07030
Tel (201) 418-1000 SIC 6211

FRED ALGER MANAGEMENT INC p 575
600 Plaza One, Jersey City NJ 07311
Tel (201) 547-3600 SIC 6282 6211 6799

ICAP SERVICES NORTH AMERICA LLC p 726
1100 Plaza Five Fl 12, Jersey City NJ 07311
Tel (212) 341-9900 SIC 6211

▲ **KCG HOLDINGS INC** p 806
545 Washington Blvd, Jersey City NJ 07310
Tel (201) 222-9400 SIC 6211 6282

■ **KNIGHT CAPITAL AMERICAS LP** p 824
545 Washington Blvd Ste 1, Jersey City NJ 07310
Tel (800) 544-7508 SIC 6211

■ **KNIGHT CAPITAL GROUP INC** p 824
545 Washington Blvd Ste 1, Jersey City NJ 07310
Tel (201) 222-9400 SIC 6211 6282

■ **PERSHING LLC** p 1137
95 Chrstopher Columbus Dr, Jersey City NJ 07302
Tel (201) 413-2078 SIC 6211

REDI GLOBAL TECHNOLOGIES LLC p 1216
30 Hudson St, Jersey City NJ 07302
Tel (212) 357-3840 SIC 6211

UBS FINANCIAL SERVICES INC p 1498
499 Washington Blvd, Jersey City NJ 07310
Tel (201) 318-5900 SIC 6211

ABSCO LTD CORP p 12
2740 Rte 10 E Ste 205, Morris Plains NJ 07950
Tel (973) 402-2148
SIC 6351 6411 6211 6282

■ **REALOGY SERVICES GROUP LLC** p 1214
3001 Leadenhall Rd, Mount Laurel NJ 08054
Tel (856) 914-8500 SIC 6531 6211

■ **TITLE RESOURCE GROUP LLC** p 1456
3001 Leadenhall Rd, Mount Laurel NJ 08054
Tel (856) 914-8500 SIC 6541 6211

■ **PRUCO SECURITIES LLC** p 1187
751 Broad St, Newark NJ 07102
Tel (800) 235-7637
SIC 6321 6331 6211 6282 8071

▲ **PRUDENTIAL FINANCIAL INC** p 1187
751 Broad St, Newark NJ 07102
Tel (973) 802-6000
SIC 6311 6321 6331 6211 6552

▲ **BFI CO LLC** p 179
300 Frank W Burr Blvd # 21, Teaneck NJ 07666
Tel (201) 329-7300 SIC 6211

THORNBURG INVESTMENT MANAGEMENT p 1450
2300 N Ridgetop Rd, Santa Fe NM 87506
Tel (505) 984-0200 SIC 6211

■ **JP MORGAN CLEARING CORP** p 794
1 Metrotech Ctr N Lbby 4, Brooklyn NY 11201
Tel (212) 272-1000 SIC 6289 6211

HSBC NORTH AMERICA INC p 715
1 Hsbc Ctr Ste 1, Buffalo NY 14203
Tel (716) 841-2424
SIC 6021 6035 6221 6091 6211

BUTLER CAPITAL CORP p 230
60 Cuttermill Rd Ste 214, Great Neck NY 11021
Tel (212) 980-0606 SIC 6211

SCHONFELD SECURITIES LLC p 1288
2 Jericho Plz Ste 300, Jericho NY 11753
Tel (646) 735-3180 SIC 6211

KOHLBERG & CO LLC p 826
111 Radio Circle Dr, Mount Kisco NY 10549
Tel (914) 241-7430 SIC 6726 6211

ACCESS INDUSTRIES INC p 14
730 5th Ave Fl 20, New York NY 10019
Tel (212) 247-6400 SIC 6211

AEA INVESTORS LP p 28
666 5th Ave Fl 36, New York NY 10103
Tel (212) 644-5900 SIC 6282 6211

▲ **AMBAC FINANCIAL GROUP INC** p 65
1 State St Fl 15, New York NY 10004
Tel (212) 658-7470 SIC 6211

▲ **AMERICAN EXPRESS CO** p 72
200 Vesey St, New York NY 10285
Tel (212) 640-2000
SIC 6141 7389 6282 6099 6311 6211

AMERICAN INDUSTRIAL ACQUISITION CORP p 74
250 Park Ave Fl 7, New York NY 10177
Tel (212) 572-4853 SIC 6211 6153

AMHERST PIERPONT SECURITIES LLC p 85
245 Park Ave Fl 15, New York NY 10167
Tel (203) 428-2500 SIC 6211

ARETEC GROUP INC p 107
405 Park Ave Fl 12, New York NY 10022
Tel (866) 904-2988 SIC 6211 6282 6722

■ **AXA FINANCIAL INC** p 139
1290 Ave Of The Am Fl Con, New York NY 10104
Tel (212) 554-1234
SIC 6311 6211 6552 6531 6371 6221

■ **BANK OF NEW YORK MELLON** p 151
225 Liberty St, New York NY 10281
Tel (212) 495-1784
SIC 6153 6211 6282 6082

BARCLAYS CAPITAL INC p 155
745 7th Ave, New York NY 10019
Tel (212) 526-7000 SIC 6211

BARCLAYS USA INC p 155
200 Park Ave Fl 3w, New York NY 10166
Tel (212) 412-4000 SIC 6211

■ **BEAR STEARNS COMPANIES LLC** p 165
383 Madison Ave, New York NY 10179
Tel (212) 272-2000
SIC 6211 6282 6221 6099 6091 6289

▲ **BGC PARTNERS INC** p 180
499 Park Ave, New York NY 10022
Tel (212) 610-2200 SIC 6211

▲ **BLACKROCK CAPITAL INVESTMENT CORP** p 188
40 E 52nd St, New York NY 10022
Tel (212) 810-5800 SIC 6211

▲ **BLACKROCK INC** p 188
55 E 52nd St Fl 11, New York NY 10055
Tel (212) 810-5300 SIC 6282 6211

■ **BLACKSTONE GROUP HOLDINGS LLC** p 188
345 Park Ave Ste 1100, New York NY 10154
Tel (212) 583-5000 SIC 6211

▲ **BLACKSTONE GROUP L P** p 188
345 Park Ave Ste 1100, New York NY 10154
Tel (212) 583-5000 SIC 6282 6211

BLOOMBERG TRADEBOOK LLC p 190
731 Lexington Ave, New York NY 10022
Tel (212) 617-7070 SIC 6211

■ **BNP PARIBAS NORTH AMERICA INC** p 194
787 7th Ave Fl 27, New York NY 10019
Tel (212) 841-2000 SIC 6211

■ **BNP PARIBAS SECURITIES CORP** p 194
787 7th Ave Fl 27, New York NY 10019
Tel (212) 841-3000 SIC 6211

BROWN BROTHERS HARRIMAN & CO p 219
140 Brdwy, New York NY 10005
Tel (212) 483-1818 SIC 6091 6211

C I B C OPPENHEIMER HOLDINGS INC p 232
425 Lexington Ave Fl 5, New York NY 10017
Tel (212) 856-4000 SIC 6211

CANTOR FITZGERALD & CO INC p 248
110 E 59th St Fl 5, New York NY 10022
Tel (212) 938-5000 SIC 6211

CANTOR FITZGERALD SECURITIES CORP p 248
499 Park Ave, New York NY 10022
Tel (212) 938-5000 SIC 6211

CASTLE HARLAN PARTNERS III LP p 264
150 E 58th St Fl 38, New York NY 10155
Tel (212) 644-8600
SIC 5812 6282 6211 8732

CENTERBRIDGE PARTNERS LP p 276
375 Park Ave Fl 13, New York NY 10152
Tel (212) 672-5000 SIC 6282 6211

CIBC DELAWARE HOLDINGS INC p 306
300 Madison Ave Bsmt C2, New York NY 10017
Tel (212) 856-4000 SIC 6211

CIBC WORLD MARKETS CORP p 306
425 Lexington Ave Bsmt C2, New York NY 10017
Tel (212) 667-7000 SIC 6211 6311 6531

■ **CITIGROUP FINANCIAL PRODUCTS INC** p 310
388 Greenwich St, New York NY 10013
Tel (212) 816-6000 SIC 6211

■ **CITIGROUP GLOBAL MARKETS HOLDINGS INC** p 310
388 Greenwich St, New York NY 10013
Tel (212) 816-6000 SIC 6211

■ **CITIGROUP GLOBAL MARKETS INC** p 310
388 Greenwich St Fl 18, New York NY 10013
Tel (212) 816-6000 SIC 6211 6221 6282

CLAYTON DUBILIER & RICE LLC p 323
375 Park Ave Fl 18, New York NY 10152
Tel (212) 407-5200 SIC 6719 6726 6211

COMPUTERSHARE INVESTOR SERVICES LLC p 353
1290 Ave Of The Americas, New York NY 10104
Tel (312) 588-4700 SIC 6289 6211 6282

CONVERGEX GROUP LLC p 365
1633 Broadway Ste 1300, New York NY 10019
Tel (212) 468-7500 SIC 6211

CORINTHIAN CAPITAL GROUP LLC p 370
601 Lexington Ave Rm 5901, New York NY 10022
Tel (212) 920-2300 SIC 6211

■ **COWEN AND CO LLC** p 385
599 Lexington Ave Fl 19, New York NY 10022
Tel (646) 562-1000 SIC 6211

▲ **COWEN GROUP INC** p 385
599 Lexington Ave, New York NY 10022
Tel (212) 845-7900 SIC 6211 6722

■ **COWEN HOLDINGS INC** p 385
599 Lexington Ave Fl 26, New York NY 10022
Tel (212) 562-1000 SIC 6211 6159

CREDIT AGRICOLE GLOBALPARTNERS INC p 390
1301 Ave Of The Americas, New York NY 10019
Tel (212) 261-7000 SIC 6211

CREDIT SUISSE (USA) INC p 390
11 Madison Ave Frnt 1, New York NY 10010
Tel (212) 325-2000 SIC 6211 6282 6799

CREDIT SUISSE ASSET MANAGEMENT LLC p 390
11 Madison Ave Bsmt 1b, New York NY 10010
Tel (212) 325-2000 SIC 6211

CREDIT SUISSE SECURITIES (USA) LLC p 391
11 Madison Ave Bsmt 1b, New York NY 10010
Tel (212) 325-2000 SIC 6211

CRESTVIEW PARTNERS LP p 392
667 Madison Ave Fl 10, New York NY 10065
Tel (212) 906-0700 SIC 6211

D E SHAW INVESTMENTS LP p 407
1166 Avenue Of The Americ, New York NY 10036
Tel (212) 478-0000 SIC 6211

D L J MERCHANT BANKING PARTNERS I I LP p 407
11 Madison Ave, New York NY 10010
Tel (212) 325-2000 SIC 6211

DAIWA CAPITAL MARKETS AMERICA HOLDINGS INC p 409
32 Old Slip Fl 14, New York NY 10005
Tel (212) 612-7000 SIC 6211

▲ **DEPOSITORY TRUST & CLEARING CORP** p 431
55 Water St Ste Conc3, New York NY 10041
Tel (212) 855-1000 SIC 6289 6211 7389

DEUTSCHE BANK AMERICAS HOLDING CORP p 433
60 Wall St, New York NY 10005
Tel (212) 250-2500 SIC 6141 6153 6211

DEUTSCHE BANK SECURITIES INC p 433
60 Wall St Bsmt 1, New York NY 10005
Tel (212) 250-2500 SIC 6211 6036

DEUTSCHE BANK TRUST CO AMERICAS p 433
60 Wall St Bsmt 1, New York NY 10005
Tel (212) 250-2500 SIC 6021 6211

DEUTSCHE BANK US FINANCIAL MARKETS HOLDING CORP p 433
60 Wall St Bsmt 1, New York NY 10005
Tel (212) 250-2500 SIC 6211

DORAL FINANCIAL CORP p 451
200 Park Ave Ste 1700, New York NY 10166
Tel (646) 632-3700
SIC 6029 6162 6035 6211 6411

■ **DREYFUS CORP** p 456
200 Park Ave Fl 7east, New York NY 10166
Tel (212) 922-6000 SIC 6211 6282

■ **DREYFUS SERVICE ORGANIZATION INC** p 456
200 Park Ave, New York NY 10166
Tel (212) 922-6000 SIC 6211

DUFF & PHELPS CORP p 459
55 E 52nd St Fl 31, New York NY 10055
Tel (212) 871-2000 SIC 6282 6211

▲ **ETRADE FINANCIAL CORP** p 467
1271 Ave Of The Americas, New York NY 10020
Tel (646) 521-4300 SIC 6211 6035

EOS PARTNERS LP p 504
320 Park Ave Rm 900, New York NY 10022
Tel (212) 832-5800 SIC 6211

EVERCORE LP p 514
55 E 52nd St Fl 35, New York NY 10055
Tel (212) 857-3100 SIC 6282 6211

▲ **EVERCORE PARTNERS INC** p 514
55 E 52nd St Fl 35, New York NY 10055
Tel (212) 857-3100 SIC 6282 6211

EVERGREEN CAPITAL LP p 514
21st Fl 551 5th Ave, New York NY 10176
Tel (914) 400-4277 SIC 6211

FENWAY PARTNERS LLC p 537
152 W 57th St Fl 5927, New York NY 10019
Tel (212) 698-9400 SIC 6211

FIRST INVESTORS CORP p 547
40 Wall St Fl 10, New York NY 10005
Tel (212) 858-8000 SIC 6282 6211

FITZGERALD CANTOR L P p 553
499 Park Ave, New York NY 10022
Tel (212) 938-5000 SIC 6211

FORESTERS FINANCIAL SERVICES p 567
40 Wall St Fl 10, New York NY 10005
Tel (212) 858-8000
SIC 6036 6211 6282 6311 8742 6153

FOREX CAPITAL MARKETS LLC p 567
55 Water St Fl 50, New York NY 10041
Tel (646) 355-0839 SIC 6211

FORSTMANN LITTLE & CO p 568
767 5th Ave Fl 4, New York NY 10153
Tel (212) 355-5656 SIC 7991 6211

FOUNDERS EQUITY INC p 571
711 5th Ave Ste 501, New York NY 10022
Tel (212) 829-0900 SIC 6211

FX ALLIANCE INC p 586
3 Times Sq, New York NY 10036
Tel (646) 268-9900 SIC 6231 6211

▲ **FXCM INC** p 586
55 Water St Fl 50, New York NY 10041
Tel (646) 432-2986 SIC 6211 6099

■ **GFI GROUP INC** p 610
55 Water St, New York NY 10041
Tel (212) 968-4100 SIC 6211

■ **GOLDMAN SACHS & CO** p 622
200 West St Bldg 200, New York NY 10282
Tel (212) 346-5440
SIC 6211 6221 6282 6153

■ **GOLDMAN SACHS (ASIA) LLC** p 622
200 West St Bldg 200, New York NY 10282
Tel (212) 902-1000 SIC 6211 6282 6722

▲ **GOLDMAN SACHS GROUP INC** p 622
200 West St Bldg 200, New York NY 10282
Tel (212) 902-1000 SIC 6211 6282

▲ **GREENHILL & CO INC** p 638
300 Park Ave Fl 23, New York NY 10022
Tel (212) 389-1500 SIC 6211

■ **HIGHBRIDGE CAPITAL MANAGEMENT LLC** p 691
40 W 57th St Fl 33, New York NY 10019
Tel (212) 287-5496 SIC 6211

■ **ICAHN ENTERPRISES HOLDINGS LP** p 726
767 5th Ave Fl 17, New York NY 10153
Tel (212) 702-4300
SIC 6512 5719 6211 5093

ICV PARTNERS p 728
810 7th Ave Ste 3501, New York NY 10019
Tel (212) 455-9600 SIC 6282 6211

INSTINET CORP p 747
1095 Avenue Of The, New York NY 10036
Tel (212) 310-9500 SIC 6211 7379

▲ **INTL FCSTONE INC** p 759
708 3rd Ave Rm 1500, New York NY 10017
Tel (212) 485-3500 SIC 6282 6211 6289

▲ **INVESTMENT TECHNOLOGY GROUP INC** p 761
165 Broadway, New York NY 10006
Tel (212) 588-4000 SIC 6211

■ **ITG INC** p 768
1 Liberty Plz Fl 4, New York NY 10006
Tel (212) 588-4000 SIC 6211

■ **J P MORGAN ASSET MANAGEMENT INC** p 772
270 Park Ave Fl 12, New York NY 10017
Tel (212) 270-6000 SIC 6211 6282

JANE STREET GROUP LLC p 777
250 Vesey St, New York NY 10281
Tel (646) 759-6000 SIC 6211

JASPER PARENT LLC p 778
9 W 57th St Ste 3100, New York NY 10019
Tel (212) 796-8500 SIC 6211

■ **JEFFERIES GROUP LLC** p 781
520 Madison Ave, New York NY 10022
Tel (212) 284-2550 SIC 6211

■ **JEFFERIES LLC** p 781
520 Madison Ave Fl 10, New York NY 10022
Tel (212) 284-2300 SIC 6211

■ **JP MORGAN SECURITIES LLC** p 795
383 Madison Ave Fl 9, New York NY 10179
Tel (212) 272-2000 SIC 6211 6282 6289

▲ **JPMORGAN CHASE & CO** p 795
270 Park Ave Fl 38, New York NY 10017
Tel (212) 270-6000
SIC 6021 6211 6162 6141

■ **KBW LLC** p 806
787 7th Ave Fl 4, New York NY 10019
Tel (212) 887-7777 SIC 6211

■ **KEEFE BRUYETTE & WOODS INC** p 807
787 7th Ave Fl 4, New York NY 10019
Tel (212) 887-7777 SIC 6211

KENNER & CO INC p 811
437 Madison Ave Ste 3601, New York NY 10022
Tel (212) 319-2300 SIC 6211

LAZ-MD HOLDINGS LLC p 848
30 Rockefeller Plz, New York NY 10112
Tel (212) 632-6000 SIC 6211 6221

LAZARD FRERES & CO LLC p 849
30 Rockefeller Plz, New York NY 10112
Tel (212) 632-6000 SIC 6211

LAZARD GROUP LLC p 849
30 Rockefeller Plz, New York NY 10112
Tel (212) 632-6000 SIC 6282 6211

▲ **LEUCADIA NATIONAL CORP** p 858
520 Madison Ave Bsmt A, New York NY 10022
Tel (212) 460-1900
SIC 6798 6211 1382 2011 2426

LINCOLNSHIRE MANAGEMENT INC p 868
780 3rd Ave Rm 4000, New York NY 10017
Tel (212) 319-3633 SIC 6211 7389 3599

MACQUARIE CAPITAL (USA) INC p 893
125 W 55th St Frnt 3, New York NY 10019
Tel (212) 231-1000 SIC 6211

MACQUARIE HOLDINGS (USA) INC p 893
125 W 55th St Fl 8, New York NY 10019
Tel (212) 231-1000 SIC 6211

▲ **MARKETAXESS HOLDINGS INC** p 908
299 Park Ave Fl 10, New York NY 10171
Tel (212) 813-6000 SIC 6211

MAXIM GROUP LLC p 922
405 Lexington Ave Fl 2, New York NY 10174
Tel (212) 895-3500 SIC 6211

■ **MERRILL LYNCH INTERNATIONAL INC** p 950
4 Wrld Fncl Ctr Fl 12, New York NY 10281
Tel (646) 855-5000 SIC 6211

■ **MERRILL LYNCH INVESTMENT MANAGEMENT INC** p 950
225 Liberty St Fl C1056, New York NY 10281
Tel (212) 449-1000 SIC 6211 6282

■ **MERRILL LYNCH PIERCE FENNER & SMITH INC** p 950
111 8th Ave, New York NY 10011
Tel (800) 637-7455 SIC 6211 6411

MF GLOBAL HOLDINGS LTD p 957
142 W 57th St Ste 401, New York NY 10019
Tel (646) 568-8114 SIC 6211

MF GLOBAL HOLDINGS USA INC p 957
717 5th Ave Fl 11, New York NY 10022
Tel (212) 589-6200 SIC 6211

MISTRAL EQUITY PARTNERS LP p 976
650 5th Ave Fl 31, New York NY 10019
Tel (212) 616-9600 SIC 6211

MIZUHO SECURITIES USA INC p 978
320 Park Ave Fl 12, New York NY 10022
Tel (212) 282-3000 SIC 6211

MONY LIFE INSURANCE CO p 987
1740 Broadway, New York NY 10019
Tel (800) 487-6669
SIC 6411 6321 6211 6282 6531

▲ **MORGAN STANLEY** p 988
1585 Broadway, New York NY 10036
Tel (212) 761-4000 SIC 6211 6282

■ **MORGAN STANLEY & CO LLC** p 989
1585 Broadway, New York NY 10036
Tel (212) 761-4000 SIC 6211

■ **MORGAN STANLEY DEAN WITTER & CO** p 989
1585 Broadway Lowr B, New York NY 10036
Tel (212) 761-4000 SIC 6211

■ **MORGAN STANLEY SMITH BARNEY HOLDINGS LLC** p 989
1585 Broadway, New York NY 10036
Tel (212) 761-4000 SIC 6211

■ **NATHAN & LEWIS SECURITIES INC** p 1009
260 Madison Ave Ste 11, New York NY 10016
Tel (212) 413-4553 SIC 6211

NEUBERGER BERMAN GROUP LLC p 1028
605 3rd Ave Fl 21, New York NY 10158
Tel (212) 476-9000 SIC 6282 6211 6722

NEUBERGER BERMAN LLC p 1028
605 3rd Ave Fl 21, New York NY 10158
Tel (212) 476-9000 SIC 6282 6211 6722

■ **NL HOLDING CORP (DEL)** p 1045
260 Madison Ave Ste 11, New York NY 10016
Tel (212) 354-8800 SIC 6211 6411

NOMURA HOLDING AMERICA INC p 1047
309 W 49th St, New York NY 10019
Tel (212) 667-9300 SIC 6211

NOMURA SECURITIES INTERNATIONAL INC p 1047
Worldwide Plaza 309 W 49t, New York NY 10019
Tel (212) 667-9000 SIC 6211

NYLIFE LLC p 1069
51 Madison Ave, New York NY 10010
Tel (212) 576-7000
SIC 6282 6211 6733 6153

ODYSSEY INVESTMENT PARTNERS LLC p 1075
590 Madison Ave Fl 39, New York NY 10022
Tel (212) 351-7900 SIC 6211

■ **OPPENHEIMER & CO INC** p 1090
85 Broad St Bldg 85, New York NY 10004
Tel (212) 668-8000 SIC 6211

▲ **OPPENHEIMER HOLDINGS INC** p 1090
85 Broad St, New York NY 10004
Tel (212) 668-8000 SIC 6211 6712 6722

PALLADIUM EQUITY PARTNERS III LP p 1108
1270 Ave Of The, New York NY 10020
Tel (212) 218-5150 SIC 6211 6799

■ **PARIBAS PROPERTIES INC** p 1114
787 7th Ave Fl 33, New York NY 10019
Tel (212) 841-3000
SIC 6211 6221 6799 8742

PEM HOLDING CO INC p 1128
800 3rd Ave Fl 40, New York NY 10022
Tel (212) 446-9300 SIC 6211 3429 3621

PMI GROUP INC p 1157
350 5th Ave, New York NY 10118
Tel (925) 658-7878 SIC 6351 6211

RAV INVESTIGATIVE & SECURITIES SERVICES LTD p 1209
347 W 36th St, New York NY 10018
Tel (212) 447-7777 SIC 6211

RBC CAPITAL MARKETS LLC p 1211
200 Vesey St Fl 6, New York NY 10281
Tel (212) 858-7000 SIC 6211

REDI HOLDINGS LLC p 1216
80 Pine St Fl 27, New York NY 10005
Tel (212) 419-9696 SIC 6211

RIPPLEWOOD HOLDINGS LLC p 1236
1 Rockefeller Plz Fl 10, New York NY 10020
Tel (212) 218-2705 SIC 7389 6211

ROTHSCHILD INC p 1252
1251 Avenue Of The Americ, New York NY 10020
Tel (212) 403-3500 SIC 6282 6211

ROTHSCHILD NORTH AMERICA INC p 1252
1251 Ave Of The Ave Fl 51, New York NY 10020
Tel (212) 403-3500
SIC 6211 6159 8742 6221 6282 8741

ROYAL ALLIANCE ASSOCIATES INC p 1254
1 Wrld Fncl Ctr Fl 14, New York NY 10281
Tel (212) 786-0235 SIC 6211

SANDLER ONEILL & PARTNERS LP p 1278
1251 Ave Of Americas 6t, New York NY 10020
Tel (212) 466-7800 SIC 6211

SCHRODER US HOLDINGS INC p 1290
875 3rd Ave Fl 21, New York NY 10022
Tel (212) 641-3800
SIC 6282 6719 6211 6799

SG AMERICAS SECURITIES HOLDINGS LLC p 1310
245 Park Ave Fl 5, New York NY 10167
Tel (212) 278-6000 SIC 6211

SG AMERICAS SECURITIES LLC p 1310
245 Park Ave, New York NY 10167
Tel (212) 278-6000 SIC 6211

SK CAPITAL PARTNERS LP p 1328
400 Park Ave Ste 820, New York NY 10022
Tel (212) 826-2700 SIC 6211

STABILIS CAPITAL MANAGEMENT LP p 1374
767 5th Ave Fl 12, New York NY 10153
Tel (212) 256-8970 SIC 6211

STANDARD CHARTERED HOLDINGS INC p 1375
1095 Ave Of The Americas, New York NY 10036
Tel (212) 667-0700 SIC 6221 6211 6531

SYCAMORE PARTNERS MANAGEMENT LP p 1413
9 W 57th St Ste 3100, New York NY 10019
Tel (212) 796-8500 SIC 6211

THOR EQUITIES LLC p 1450
25 W 39th St Fl 11, New York NY 10018
Tel (212) 529-5055 SIC 6531 6211 6282

TIAA-CREF INDIVIDUAL & INSTITUTIONAL SERVICES LLC p 1452
730 3rd Ave Ste 2a, New York NY 10017
Tel (212) 490-9000 SIC 6211

TINICUM CAPITAL PARTNERS II LP p 1455
800 3rd Ave Fl 40, New York NY 10022
Tel (212) 446-9300 SIC 6211 3429 3621

■TRADEWEB MARKETS LLC p 1469
1177 Avenues Of The Am, New York NY 10036
Tel (646) 430-6000 SIC 6211

TRADITION (NORTH AMERICA) INC p 1469
255 Greenwich St Fl 4, New York NY 10007
Tel (212) 791-4500 SIC 6211

TRIMARAN FUND MANAGEMENT LLC p 1480
1325 Ave Of The Flr 34, New York NY 10019
Tel (212) 616-3700 SIC 6211

TULLETT PREBON AMERICAS CORP p 1491
199 Water St Fl 17, New York NY 10038
Tel (212) 208-2000 SIC 6211 7373

UBS FINANCIAL SERVICES INC p 1498
1285 Ave Of The Americas, New York NY 10019
Tel (212) 713-2000 SIC 6211 6282

UBS REAL ESTATE SECURITIES INC p 1498
1285 Av Of Amrc Fl Sconc1, New York NY 10019
Tel (212) 713-2000 SIC 6211

VERONIS SUHLER & ASSOCIATES INC p 1551
55 E 52nd St Fl 33, New York NY 10055
Tel (212) 935-4990 SIC 6211

▲VIRTU FINANCIAL INC p 1560
900 3rd Ave Fl 29, New York NY 10022
Tel (212) 418-0100 SIC 6211

▲VOYA FINANCIAL INC p 1566
230 Park Ave Fl 14, New York NY 10169
Tel (212) 309-8200
SIC 6311 6411 6282 6211 7389

WARBURG PINCUS LLC p 1575
450 Lexington Ave, New York NY 10017
Tel (212) 878-0600 SIC 6799 6211

WENDEL NORTH AMERICA LLC p 1591
152 W 57th St Fl 55, New York NY 10019
Tel (212) 557-5100 SIC 6211

WICKS GROUP OF COMPANIES LLC (DE CORP) p 1608
400 Park Ave Fl 12a, New York NY 10022
Tel (212) 838-2100 SIC 6211 6282

ZURICH FINANCE (USA) INC p 1645
1 Liberty Plz Ste 2800, New York NY 10006
Tel (917) 534-4500 SIC 6211

DKM LTD p 445
2515 South Rd, Poughkeepsie NY 12601
Tel (212) 661-4600 SIC 6211

■ MORGAN STANLEY SMITH BARNEY LLC p 989
2000 Westchester Ave, Purchase NY 10577
Tel (914) 225-5510 SIC 6211

XEROX CAPITAL SERVICES LLC p 1631
100 S Clinton Ave Fl 18, Rochester NY 14604
Tel (585) 423-3805 SIC 6211

GABELLI & CO INC p 588
1 Corporate Ctr, Rye NY 10580
Tel (914) 921-3700 SIC 6211 6282

GABELLI GROUP CAPITAL PARTNERS INC p 588
555 Theodore Fremd Ave C300, Rye NY 10580
Tel (914) 921-3700 SIC 6211 6282

GABELLI SECURITIES INC p 588
1 Corporate Ctr 401, Rye NY 10580
Tel (914) 921-3700 SIC 6211

GRANT CADARET & CO INC p 631
1 Lincoln Rd Fl 5, Syracuse NY 13212
Tel (315) 471-2191 SIC 6211

▲ BANK OF AMERICA CORP p 151
100 N Tryon St Ste 220, Charlotte NC 28202
Tel (704) 386-5681
SIC 6021 6022 6211 6091 6162 6159

CAROUSEL CAPITAL CO LLC p 260
201 N Tryon St Ste 2450, Charlotte NC 28202
Tel (704) 372-2040 SIC 6211

■ EVEREN CAPITAL CORP p 514
301 S College St, Charlotte NC 28202
Tel (704) 374-6565 SIC 6211

■WACHOVIA INVESTMENT HOLDINGS LLC p 1570
201 S College St Ste 500, Charlotte NC 28244
Tel (704) 374-2584 SIC 6211

■WELLS FARGO SECURITIES LLC p 1591
301 S Tryon St, Charlotte NC 28282
Tel (312) 920-9177 SIC 6211

▲ BB&T CORP p 163
200 W 2nd St Ste 260, Winston Salem NC 27101
Tel (336) 733-2000
SIC 6021 6311 6035 6211

MCM CAPITAL PARTNERS p 932
25201 Chagrin Blvd # 360, Beachwood OH 44122
Tel (216) 514-1840 SIC 6211

WESTERN & SOUTHERN FINANCIAL GROUP INC p 1597
400 Broadway St, Cincinnati OH 45202
Tel (866) 832-7719 SIC 6211

WESTERN & SOUTHERN LIFE INSURANCE CO p 1597
400 Broadway St, Cincinnati OH 45202
Tel (513) 629-1800 SIC 6211

WESTERN & SOUTHERN MUTUAL HOLDING CO p 1597
400 Broadway St, Cincinnati OH 45202
Tel (866) 832-7719 SIC 6211

■ KEYBANC CAPITAL MARKETS INC p 815
800 Superior Ave E # 1400, Cleveland OH 44114
Tel (800) 553-2240 SIC 6021 6211

▲ KEYCORP p 815
127 Public Sq, Cleveland OH 44114
Tel (216) 689-3000 SIC 6021 6141 6211

■ BROADSTREET PARTNERS INC p 215
580 N 4th St Ste 450, Columbus OH 43215
Tel (614) 993-3009 SIC 6211

CORPORATE FINANCE ASSOCIATES OF COLUMBUS INC p 372
671 Camden Yard Ct, Columbus OH 43235
Tel (614) 457-9219 SIC 8742 7389 6211

■ JPMORGAN CHASE BANK NATIONAL ASSOCIATION p 795
1111 Polaris Pkwy, Columbus OH 43240
Tel (614) 436-3055
SIC 6022 6099 6799 6211 6162 7389

NATIONWIDE FINANCIAL INSTITUTION DISTRIBUTORS AGENCY INC p 1017
1 W Nationwide Blvd 2-0501, Columbus OH 43215
Tel (614) 249-6825 SIC 6211

■ CINCINNATI INSURANCE CO p 307
6200 S Gilmore Rd, Fairfield OH 45014
Tel (513) 870-2000
SIC 6311 6331 6321 6211

■ OLD REPUBLIC TITLE CO OF NORTHERN OHIO LLC p 1081
6480 Rockside Woods Blvd S, Independence OH 44131
Tel (216) 524-5700 SIC 6411 6162 6211

UNIVERSITY OF OKLAHOMA FOUNDATION INC p 1524
100 W Timberdell Rd Rm 1, Norman OK 73019
Tel (405) 321-1174 SIC 6211

SUSQUEHANNA INTERNATIONAL GROUP LLP p 1409
401 E City Ave Ste 220, Bala Cynwyd PA 19004
Tel (610) 617-2600 SIC 6211

NATIONWIDE LIFE INSURANCE CO OF AMERICA p 1018
1000 Chesterbrook Blvd, Berwyn PA 19312
Tel (610) 407-1717 SIC 6411 6211 6719

■ PLANCO FINANCIAL SERVICES INC p 1154
1500 Liberty Ridge Dr # 100, Chesterbrook PA 19087
Tel (610) 695-9500 SIC 6211 6311

■ EXCO RESOURCES (PA) LLC p 517
260 Executive Dr Ste 100, Cranberry Township PA 16066
Tel (724) 720-2500
SIC 1382 1381 1311 8741 6211

■ GMAC MORTGAGE SECURITIES INC p 619
1100 Virginia Dr, Fort Washington PA 19034
Tel (215) 682-1000 SIC 6211

LINCOLN INVESTMENT PLANNING LLC p 867
601 Office Center Dr # 200, Fort Washington PA 19034
Tel (215) 887-8111 SIC 6211 6282

■ GMAC MORTGAGE GROUP LLC p 618
4 Walnut Grove Dr, Horsham PA 19044
Tel (215) 682-1000 SIC 6211

HORNOR TOWNSEND & KENT INC p 708
600 Dresher Rd, Horsham PA 19044
Tel (215) 957-7300 SIC 6211

■ SEI PRIVATE TRUST CO p 1300
1 Freedom Valley Dr, Oaks PA 19456
Tel (610) 676-1000 SIC 6733 6211

JANNEY MONTGOMERY SCOTT LLC p 777
1717 Arch St Fl 16, Philadelphia PA 19103
Tel (215) 665-6000 SIC 6211

▲ PNC FINANCIAL SERVICES GROUP INC p 1158
300 5th Ave, Pittsburgh PA 15222
Tel (412) 762-2000
SIC 6021 6162 7389 6282 6211

ST JOHN HOLDINGS INC p 1367
320 King Of Prussia Rd, Radnor PA 19087
Tel (610) 964-8702 SIC 6211

■ PRUDENTIAL TRUST CO p 1187
30 Ed Preate Dr, Scranton PA 18507
Tel (570) 341-6000 SIC 6282 6722 6211

■ SANTANDER BANCORP p 1281
B7 Calle Tabonuco Fl 18, Guaynabo PR 00968
Tel (787) 777-4100 SIC 6021 6411 6211

DORAL HOLDINGS DELAWARE LLC p 451
1451 Frnklin D Rsvelt Ave, San Juan PR 00920
Tel (787) 474-6700
SIC 6162 6035 6211 6411

PROVIDENCE EQUITY PARTNERS INC p 1185
100 Westminster St # 1800, Providence RI 02903
Tel (401) 751-1700 SIC 6211

SRA COMPANIES INC p 1362
50 Kennedy Plz 18, Providence RI 02903
Tel (401) 277-1000 SIC 6211

FIRST TENN BROKERAGE p 549
4990 Poplar Ave Fl 3, Memphis TN 38117
Tel (901) 818-6000 SIC 6211

■ NATIONAL BANK OF COMMERCE p 1010
1 Commerce Sq, Memphis TN 38103
Tel (901) 523-3434
SIC 6021 6211 7374 6712

VINING-SPARKS IBG LIMITED PARTNERSHIP p 1558
775 Ridge Lake Blvd # 200, Memphis TN 38120
Tel (901) 766-3000 SIC 6211

WUNDERLICH SECURITIES INC p 1628
6000 Poplar Ave Ste 150, Memphis TN 38119
Tel (901) 251-1330 SIC 6211

■ AMERICAN PHYSICIANS SERVICE GROUP INC p 77
1221 S Mo Pac Expy # 200, Austin TX 78746
Tel (512) 328-0888
SIC 6282 8741 6411 6211

FIRST SOUTHWEST CO p 549
325 N Saint Paul St # 800, Dallas TX 75201
Tel (214) 953-4000 SIC 6211

HIGHLAND CAPITAL MANAGEMENT LP p 691
300 Crescent Ct Ste 700, Dallas TX 75201
Tel (972) 628-4100 SIC 6211

■ HILLTOP SECURITIES HOLDINGS LLC p 694
200 Crescent Ct Ste 1330, Dallas TX 75201
Tel (214) 855-2177 SIC 6211

■ HILLTOP SECURITIES INC p 694
1201 Elm St Ste 3500, Dallas TX 75270
Tel (214) 859-1800 SIC 6211

LONE STAR FUNDS p 875
2711 N Haskell Ave # 1700, Dallas TX 75204
Tel (214) 754-8300 SIC 6211

ORIX USA CORP p 1095
1717 Main St Ste 1100, Dallas TX 75201
Tel (214) 237-2000 SIC 6211 6282

PARALLEL INVESTMENT PARTNERS LLC p 1113
3889 Maple Ave Ste 220, Dallas TX 75219
Tel (214) 740-3600 SIC 6211

SWS GROUP INC p 1413
1201 Elm St Ste 3500, Dallas TX 75270
Tel (214) 859-1800 SIC 6211 6029

WINGSPAN PORTFOLIO HOLDINGS INC p 1616
18451 Dallas Pkwy Ste 100, Dallas TX 75287
Tel (469) 737-2441 SIC 6211

FIRST COMMAND FINANCIAL PLANNING INC p 545
1 Firstcomm Plz, Fort Worth TX 76109
Tel (817) 731-8621 SIC 6311 6211

TEXAS ENERGY FUTURE HOLDINGS LIMITED PARTNERSHIP p 1443
301 Commerce St Ste 3300, Fort Worth TX 76102
Tel (817) 871-4000 SIC 4911 6211

FRIEDKIN COMPANIES INC p 579
1345 Enclave Pkwy, Houston TX 77077
Tel (713) 580-3300 SIC 5012 6211

▲ MAIN STREET CAPITAL CORP p 898
1300 Post Oak Blvd, Houston TX 77056
Tel (713) 350-6000 SIC 6211

■ MERRILL LYNCH COMMODITIES INC p 950
20 Greenway Plz Ste 950, Houston TX 77046
Tel (832) 681-5904 SIC 6211 6091

VITOL INC p 1563
2925 Richmond Ave Ste 11, Houston TX 77098
Tel (713) 230-1000 SIC 6211

AUSTIN BANCORP INC p 132
200 E Commerce St, Jacksonville TX 75766
Tel (903) 586-1526 SIC 6021 6211 6022

■ SOUTHWEST ROYALTIES INC p 1352
6 Desta Dr Ste 2100, Midland TX 79705
Tel (432) 688-3008 SIC 1311 6211 1389

KESTRA INVESTMENT SERVICES LLC p 814
1250 Capital Of Texas Hwy, West Lake Hills TX 78746
Tel (512) 697-6940 SIC 6211

UTAH HOUSING CORP p 1536
2479 S Lake Park Blvd, West Valley City UT 84120
Tel (801) 902-8200 SIC 6211 6162

▲ FBR & CO p 532
1300 17th St N, Arlington VA 22209
Tel (703) 312-9500 SIC 6211

▲ MARKEL CORP p 908
4521 Highwoods Pkwy, Glen Allen VA 23060
Tel (804) 747-0136 SIC 6331 6211

▲ CARDINAL FINANCIAL CORP p 253
8270 Greensboro Dr # 500, Mc Lean VA 22102
Tel (703) 584-3400 SIC 6021 6211 8741

DAVENPORT & CO LLC p 415
901 E Cary St Ste 1200, Richmond VA 23219
Tel (804) 780-2000 SIC 6211 6282

■ GENWORTH LIFE AND ANNUITY INSURANCE CO p 605
6610 W Broad St, Richmond VA 23230
Tel (804) 281-6000 SIC 6311 6211

■ SCOTT & STRINGFELLOW LLC p 1293
901 E Byrd St Ste 300, Richmond VA 23219
Tel (804) 643-1811 SIC 6211

■WACHOVIA SECURITIES FINANCIAL HOLDINGS LLC p 1570
901 E Byrd St Ste 500, Richmond VA 23219
Tel (804) 782-4174 SIC 6211

ATLANTIC BAY MORTGAGE GROUP LLC p 126
596 Lynnhven Pkwy Ste 102, Virginia Beach VA 23452
Tel (757) 498-6789 SIC 6211

FRANK RUSSELL CO p 574
1301 2nd Ave Fl 18, Seattle WA 98101
Tel (206) 505-7877 SIC 6282 6211 6722

INTERNATIONAL INDUSTRIES INC p 755
210 Larry Joe Harless Dr, Gilbert WV 25621
Tel (304) 664-3227 SIC 6211

■ UNITED BROKERAGE SERVICES INC p 1506
514 Market St, Parkersburg WV 26101
Tel (304) 424-8781 SIC 6211

■ASSOCIATED BANK NATIONAL ASSOCIATION p 120
200 N Adams St, Green Bay WI 54301
Tel (920) 433-3200 SIC 6021 6211

■AMERIPRISE FINANCIAL SERVICES INC p 83
500 2nd St S Ste 101, La Crosse WI 54601
Tel (608) 783-2639
SIC 6282 6411 6211 8742

GREAT LAKES FINANCIAL MANAGEMENT GROUP INC p 633
2033 Marinette Ave, Marinette WI 54143
Tel (715) 732-9955
SIC 6211 8742 6282 6411

CATHOLIC FINANCIAL SERVICES CORP p 266
1100 W Wells St Ste 1, Milwaukee WI 53233
Tel (414) 278-6550 SIC 6311 6211

CATHOLIC KNIGHTS INSURANCE SOCIETY INC p 267
1100 W Wells St Ste 1, Milwaukee WI 53233
Tel (414) 273-6266
SIC 6311 6411 6211 6141

MASON WELLS BUYOUT FUND II LIMITED PARTNERSHIP p 916
411 E Wisconsin Ave, Milwaukee WI 53202
Tel (414) 727-6400
SIC 3594 3492 3593 6211

CORNERSTONE ADVISORS p 370
2711 Stewart Ave, Wausau WI 54401
Tel (715) 849-3697 SIC 6211

WERCS p 1592
400 E 1st St Ste 100, Casper WY 82601
Tel (307) 235-6200
SIC 6211 6163 6411 6321 6531 6099

SIC 6221 Commodity Contracts Brokers & Dealers

RIDA INTERNATIONAL INVESTMENTS LLC p 1234
1774 S Barranca Ave, Glendora CA 91740
Tel (626) 712-4776 SIC 6221

PANASONIC PROCUREMENT CORP OF AMERICA p 1111
20000 Mariner Ave Ste 200, Torrance CA 90503
Tel (310) 783-4100 SIC 6221

GRIDIRON TRADING MANAGEMENT CO LLC p 640
81 Hemlock Hill Rd, New Canaan CT 06840
Tel (704) 872-5231 SIC 6221

BOEHRINGER INGELHEIM CORP p 197
900 Ridgebury Rd, Ridgefield CT 06877
Tel (203) 798-9988 SIC 2834 6221

COFCO AMERICAS RESOURCES CORP p 334
4 Stamford Plz, Stamford CT 06902
Tel (203) 658-2820
SIC 6221 5153 5149 2099

FREEPOINT COMMODITIES LLC p 577
58 Commerce Rd, Stamford CT 06902
Tel (203) 542-6000 SIC 6221

GERALD HOLDINGS LLC p 608
680 Washington Blvd Fl 9, Stamford CT 06901
Tel (203) 609-8550 SIC 6221

GLENCORE LTD p 615
301 Tresser Blvd Fl 14, Stamford CT 06901
Tel (203) 328-4900 SIC 6221

UBS SECURITIES LLC p 1498
677 Washington Blvd, Stamford CT 06901
Tel (203) 719-3000
SIC 6211 6221 6289 6311 6091 6282

LD COMMODITIES CITRUS HOLDINGS LLC p 849
40 Danbury Rd, Wilton CT 06897
Tel (203) 761-2000 SIC 6221

LOUIS DREYFUS CO LLC p 879
40 Danbury Rd, Wilton CT 06897
Tel (402) 844-2680 SIC 6221

LOUIS DREYFUS HOLDING CO INC p 879
10 Westport Rd Ste 200, Wilton CT 06897
Tel (203) 761-2000
SIC 6221 5153 6512 6531 1311

LOUIS DREYFUS US LLC p 879
40 Danbury Rd, Wilton CT 06897
Tel (203) 761-2000 SIC 6221

ZUAGGUA PARTNERS LLC p 1644
4321 Nw 15th Ave, Fort Lauderdale FL 33309
Tel (772) 501-3594 SIC 6221

DESA AGI LLC p 431
1450 Brickell Ave # 2080, Miami FL 33131
Tel (786) 315-4680 SIC 6221

SUCDEN AMERICAS CORP p 1396
701 Brickell Ave Ste 1200, Miami FL 33131
Tel (305) 374-4440 SIC 6221

HELM FERTILIZER CORP (FLORIDA) p 682
401 E Jackson St Ste 1400, Tampa FL 33602
Tel (813) 621-8846 SIC 5191 6221

■ GENON NORTH AMERICA LLC p 604
1155 Perimeter Ctr # 100, Atlanta GA 30338
Tel (678) 579-5000 SIC 4924 4911 6221

INTERSTATE NATIONAL DEALER SERVICES INC p 758
6120 Powers Ferry Rd S, Atlanta GA 30339
Tel (678) 894-3500 SIC 6399 6221

■ **ADM INVESTOR SERVICES INC** p 23
141 W Jackson Blvd 2100a, Chicago IL 60604
Tel (312) 242-7000 *SIC* 6221

RJ OBRIEN & ASSOCIATES LLC p 1239
222 S Riverside Plz # 1200, Chicago IL 60606
Tel (312) 373-5000 *SIC* 6221 6211

ROSENTHAL COLLINS GROUP LLC p 1251
216 W Jackson Blvd # 400, Chicago IL 60606
Tel (312) 460-9200
SIC 6221 6289 6231 6211

▲ **SEABOARD CORP** p 1295
9000 W 67th St, Merriam KS 66202
Tel (913) 676-8800
SIC 2011 0133 4412 6221 0723 0213

LANSING TRADE GROUP LLC p 844
10975 Benson Dr Ste 400, Overland Park KS 66210
Tel (913) 748-3000 *SIC* 5153 6221

KOCH RESOURCES LLC p 826
4111 E 37th St N, Wichita KS 67220
Tel (316) 828-5500 *SIC* 6221 2911

CAMPBELL & CO INC p 245
2850 Quarry Lake Dr # 302, Baltimore MD 21209
Tel (410) 413-2600 *SIC* 6221

CAMPBELL FUND TRUST p 245
2850 Quarry Lake Dr, Baltimore MD 21209
Tel (410) 413-2600 *SIC* 6221

COMMONWEALTH EQUITY SERVICES LLP p 346
29 Sawyer Rd Ste 2, Waltham MA 02453
Tel (781) 398-0401 *SIC* 6211 6282 6221

US COMMODITIES LLC p 1531
730 2nd Ave S Ste 700, Minneapolis MN 55402
Tel (612) 486-3800 *SIC* 5191 6221

■ **FCSTONE GROUP INC** p 533
1251 Nw Briarcliff Pkwy, Kansas City MO 64116
Tel (816) 410-7120 *SIC* 6221

ENERFO USA INC p 497
16934 Frances St Ste 105, Omaha NE 68130
Tel (402) 401-6300 *SIC* 6221

GAVILON GRAIN LLC p 594
1331 Capitol Ave, Omaha NE 68102
Tel (402) 889-4000
SIC 6221 5153 4221 4226

■ **NGL CRUDE LOGISTICS LLC** p 1041
1299 Farnam St Ste 120, Omaha NE 68102
Tel (402) 889-4000 *SIC* 6221 5153

▲ **GAIN CAPITAL HOLDINGS INC** p 589
135 Route 202 206, Bedminster NJ 07921
Tel (908) 731-0700 *SIC* 6211 6221

HSBC NORTH AMERICA INC p 715
1 Hsbc Ctr Ste 1, Buffalo NY 14203
Tel (716) 841-2424
SIC 6021 6035 6221 6091 6211

ACT COMMODITIES INC p 19
437 Madison Ave Fl 19c, New York NY 10022
Tel (415) 741-2290 *SIC* 6221

■ **AXA FINANCIAL INC** p 139
1290 Ave Of The Am Fl Con, New York NY 10104
Tel (212) 554-1234
SIC 6311 6211 6552 6531 6371 6221

■ **BEAR STEARNS COMPANIES LLC** p 165
383 Madison Ave, New York NY 10179
Tel (212) 272-2000
SIC 6211 6282 6221 6099 6091 6289

■ **CITIGROUP GLOBAL MARKETS INC** p 310
388 Greenwich St Fl 18, New York NY 10013
Tel (212) 816-6000 *SIC* 6211 6221 6282

■ **GOLDMAN SACHS & CO** p 622
200 West St Bldg 200, New York NY 10282
Tel (212) 346-5440
SIC 6211 6221 6282 6153

HARTREE PARTNERS LP p 666
1185 Avenue Of The Americ, New York NY 10036
Tel (212) 536-8915 *SIC* 6221 5172

LAZ-MD HOLDINGS LLC p 848
30 Rockefeller Plz, New York NY 10112
Tel (212) 632-6000 *SIC* 6211 6221

■ **MORGAN STANLEY CAPITAL GROUP INC** p 989
1585 Broadway, New York NY 10036
Tel (212) 761-4000 *SIC* 6221

■ **NEW YORK MERCANTILE EXCHANGE INC** p 1035
1 N End Ave Frnt, New York NY 10282
Tel (212) 299-2000 *SIC* 6221

■ **PARIBAS PROPERTIES INC** p 1114
787 7th Ave Fl 33, New York NY 10019
Tel (212) 841-3000
SIC 6211 6221 6799 8742

ROTHSCHILD NORTH AMERICA INC p 1252
1251 Ave Of The Ave Fl 51, New York NY 10020
Tel (212) 403-3500
SIC 6211 6159 8742 6221 6282 8741

STANDARD CHARTERED HOLDINGS INC p 1375
1095 Ave Of The Americas, New York NY 10036
Tel (212) 667-0700 *SIC* 6221 6211 6531

MACQUARIE ENERGY LLC p 893
500 Dallas St 31, Houston TX 77002
Tel (713) 275-6100 *SIC* 6221

RCMA AMERICAS INC p 1212
150 Boush St Ste 1000, Norfolk VA 23510
Tel (757) 627-4000 *SIC* 5199 6221

ABILENE MOTOR EXPRESS p 11
1700 Willis Rd, North Chesterfield VA 23237
Tel (804) 275-0224 *SIC* 4213 6221 4212

SIC 6231 Security & Commodity Exchanges

■ **INTERCONTINENTAL EXCHANGE INC** p 752
1415 Moonstone, Brea CA 92821
Tel (770) 857-4700 *SIC* 6231

▲ **INTERCONTINENTAL EXCHANGE INC** p 752
5660 New Northside Dr # 300, Atlanta GA 30328
Tel (770) 857-4700 *SIC* 6231

■ **BOARD OF TRADE OF CITY OF CHICAGO** p 195
141 W Jackson Blvd 756, Chicago IL 60604
Tel (312) 435-3500 *SIC* 6231

▲ **CBOE HOLDINGS INC** p 269
400 S Lasalle St, Chicago IL 60605
Tel (312) 786-5600 *SIC* 6231

■ **CBOT HOLDINGS INC** p 269
141 W Jackson Blvd, Chicago IL 60604
Tel (312) 435-3500 *SIC* 6231

■ **CHICAGO BOARD OPTIONS EXCHANGE INC** p 297
400 S La Salle St Fl 1, Chicago IL 60605
Tel (312) 786-5600 *SIC* 6211 6231

■ **CHICAGO MERCANTILE EXCHANGE INC** p 297
20 S Wacker Dr, Chicago IL 60606
Tel (312) 930-1000 *SIC* 6231

▲ **CME GROUP INC** p 329
20 S Wacker Dr, Chicago IL 60606
Tel (312) 930-1000 *SIC* 6231

IMC-CHICAGO LLC p 733
233 S Wacker Dr Ste 4300, Chicago IL 60606
Tel (312) 244-3300 *SIC* 6231

ROSENTHAL COLLINS GROUP LLC p 1251
216 W Jackson Blvd # 400, Chicago IL 60606
Tel (312) 460-9200
SIC 6221 6289 6231 6211

BATS GLOBAL MARKETS INC p 159
8050 Marshall Dr Ste 120, Lenexa KS 66214
Tel (913) 815-7000 *SIC* 6231

FX ALLIANCE INC p 586
3 Times Sq, New York NY 10036
Tel (646) 268-9900 *SIC* 6231 6211

INSTINET GROUP LLC p 747
Worldwide Plz 309 W 49th, New York NY 10019
Tel (212) 310-9500 *SIC* 6231

■ **INTERNATIONAL SECURITIES EXCHANGE HOLDINGS INC** p 756
60 Broad St Fl 26, New York NY 10004
Tel (212) 943-2400 *SIC* 6231

INTERNATIONAL SECURITIES EXCHANGE LLC p 756
60 Broad St Fl 26, New York NY 10004
Tel (212) 943-2400 *SIC* 6231

■ **NASDAQ CORPORATE SOLUTIONS LLC** p 1008
1 Liberty Plz Ste 4900, New York NY 10006
Tel (212) 231-5369 *SIC* 6231

▲ **NASDAQ INC** p 1008
1 Liberty Plz Ste 4900, New York NY 10006
Tel (212) 401-8700 *SIC* 6231 8742

■ **NEW YORK STOCK EXCHANGE LLC** p 1036
11 Wall St Fl 6, New York NY 10005
Tel (212) 656-3000 *SIC* 6231

■ **NYMEX HOLDINGS INC** p 1069
1 N End Ave Rm 1215, New York NY 10282
Tel (212) 299-2000 *SIC* 6231

■ **NYSE EURONEXT HOLDINGS LLC** p 1069
11 Wall St, New York NY 10005
Tel (212) 656-3000 *SIC* 6231

■ **NYSE GROUP INC** p 1069
11 Wall St, New York NY 10005
Tel (212) 656-3000 *SIC* 6231 6289

SIG STRUCTURED PRODUCTS LLLP p 1321
401 E City Ave Ste 220, Bala Cynwyd PA 19004
Tel (610) 617-2600 *SIC* 6231

■ **NASDAQ OMX PHLX LLC** p 1008
1900 Market St Fl 2, Philadelphia PA 19103
Tel (215) 496-5000 *SIC* 6231

SIC 6282 Investment Advice

▲ **REGIONS FINANCIAL CORP** p 1220
1900 5th Ave N, Birmingham AL 35203
Tel (205) 581-7890 *SIC* 6022 6211 6282

▲ **NORTHRIM BANCORP INC** p 1058
3111 C St, Anchorage AK 99503
Tel (907) 562-0062 *SIC* 6022 6282

ON Q FINANCIAL INC p 1086
4800 N Scottsdale Rd, Scottsdale AZ 85251
Tel (480) 444-7100 *SIC* 6282 6162

CALIBER CAPITAL GROUP LLC p 239
5900 Katella Ave Ste A101, Cypress CA 90630
Tel (714) 507-1998 *SIC* 6282 8111

CETERA FINANCIAL GROUP INC p 284
200 N Sepulveda Blvd # 1200, El Segundo CA 90245
Tel (800) 879-8100 *SIC* 7389 6282

AMERICAN REALTY ASSOCIATES INC p 78
801 N Brand Blvd Ste 800, Glendale CA 91203
Tel (818) 545-1152 *SIC* 6282

MARLIN EQUITY PARTNERS LLC p 909
338 Pier Ave, Hermosa Beach CA 90254
Tel (310) 364-0100 *SIC* 6282

CREDO 180 CAPITAL PARTNERS p 391
5405 Alton Pkwy 5a, Irvine CA 92604
Tel (949) 274-4405 *SIC* 6282 7373

■ **QUADION LLC** p 1196
17651 Armstrong Ave, Irvine CA 92614
Tel (714) 546-0990 *SIC* 6282

▲ **ARES MANAGEMENT LP** p 107
2000 Avenue Of The Stars, Los Angeles CA 90067
Tel (310) 201-4100 *SIC* 6282

BALMORAL FUNDS LLC p 149
11150 Santa Monica Blvd, Los Angeles CA 90025
Tel (310) 473-3065 *SIC* 6282

CALTIUS PARTNERS IV LP p 243
11766 Wilshire Blvd # 850, Los Angeles CA 90025
Tel (310) 996-9585 *SIC* 6282

CAPITAL GROUP COMPANIES INC p 249
333 S Hope St Fl 55, Los Angeles CA 90071
Tel (213) 486-9200
SIC 6282 6091 6722 8741

CAPITAL RESEARCH AND MANAGEMENT CO p 250
333 S Hope St Fl 55, Los Angeles CA 90071
Tel (213) 486-9200 *SIC* 6282

▲ **HOULIHAN LOKEY INC** p 711
10250 Constellation Blvd # 5, Los Angeles CA 90067
Tel (310) 553-8871 *SIC* 6211 6282

OAKTREE CAPITAL GROUP HOLDINGS LP p 1071
333 S Grand Ave Fl 28, Los Angeles CA 90071
Tel (213) 830-6300 *SIC* 6282

▲ **OAKTREE CAPITAL GROUP LLC** p 1071
333 S Grand Ave Ste 2800, Los Angeles CA 90071
Tel (213) 830-6300 *SIC* 6282

■ **OAKTREE CAPITAL MANAGEMENT LP** p 1071
333 S Grand Ave Ste 2800, Los Angeles CA 90071
Tel (213) 830-6300 *SIC* 6282 6722 6211

■ **SUNAMERICA INC** p 1401
1 Sun America Ctr Fl 38, Los Angeles CA 90067
Tel (310) 772-6000
SIC 6091 6311 6211 6282 6411 6371

■ **SUNAMERICA INVESTMENTS INC** p 1401
1 Sun America Ctr Fl 37, Los Angeles CA 90067
Tel (310) 772-6000
SIC 8741 6211 6282 7311

■ **TCW GROUP INC** p 1428
865 S Figueroa St # 2100, Los Angeles CA 90017
Tel (213) 244-0000 *SIC* 6022 6282 6211

ALLIANZ GLOBAL INVESTORS OF AMERICA LP p 55
680 Nwport Ctr Dr Ste 250, Newport Beach CA 92660
Tel (949) 219-2200 *SIC* 6282

PACIFIC INVESTMENT MANAGEMENT CO LLC p 1105
650 Nwport Ctr Dr Ste 100, Newport Beach CA 92660
Tel (949) 720-6000 *SIC* 6282

PACIFIC LIFE FUND ADVISORS LLC p 1105
700 Newport Center Dr, Newport Beach CA 92660
Tel (800) 800-7646 *SIC* 6282

SABAL FINANCIAL GROUP LP p 1263
4675 Macarthur Ct Fl 15, Newport Beach CA 92660
Tel (949) 255-2660 *SIC* 6282

■ **WESTERN ASSET MANAGEMENT CO** p 1597
385 E Colorado Blvd # 250, Pasadena CA 91101
Tel (626) 844-9265 *SIC* 6282

■ **FRANKLIN TEMPLETON INVESTOR SERVICES LLC** p 575
3344 Quality Dr, Rancho Cordova CA 95670
Tel (916) 463-1500 *SIC* 6211 6282

BRANDES INVESTMENT PARTNERS INC p 208
11988 El Cmino Real Ste 6, San Diego CA 92130
Tel (858) 755-0239 *SIC* 6282

AMERICAN INDUSTRIAL PARTNERS LP p 74
1 Maritime Plz Ste 1925, San Francisco CA 94111
Tel (415) 788-7354 *SIC* 6282

■ **BANKAMERICA FINANCIAL INC** p 152
315 Montgomery St, San Francisco CA 94104
Tel (415) 622-3521 *SIC* 6153 6141 6282

■ **BLACKROCK GLOBAL INVESTORS** p 188
400 Howard St, San Francisco CA 94105
Tel (415) 670-2000 *SIC* 6282

▲ **CHARLES SCHWAB CORP** p 289
211 Main St Fl 17, San Francisco CA 94105
Tel (415) 667-7000
SIC 6211 6091 6282 7389

▲ **FIRST REPUBLIC BANK** p 549
111 Pine St Ste Bsmt, San Francisco CA 94111
Tel (415) 392-1400 *SIC* 6022 6282 6162

■ **JP MORGAN H&Q PRINCIPALS LP** p 794
560 Mission St Fl 2, San Francisco CA 94105
Tel (415) 315-5000
SIC 6211 6799 6282 7389

■ **KKR FINANCIAL HOLDINGS LLC** p 822
555 California St Fl 50, San Francisco CA 94104
Tel (415) 315-3620 *SIC* 6798 6282

VIKING ASSET MANAGEMENT LLC p 1556
505 Sansome St Ste 1275, San Francisco CA 94111
Tel (415) 981-5300 *SIC* 6282

■ **FRANKLIN ADVISERS INC** p 574
1 Franklin Pkwy, San Mateo CA 94403
Tel (650) 312-2000 *SIC* 6282

■ **FRANKLIN TEMPLETON SERVICES LLC** p 575
1 Franklin Pkwy, San Mateo CA 94403
Tel (650) 312-3000 *SIC* 6282

STONE CANYON INDUSTRIES LLC p 1391
1250 4th St, Santa Monica CA 90401
Tel (310) 570-4869 *SIC* 6282

▲ **FINANCIAL ENGINES INC** p 542
1050 Enterprise Way Fl 3, Sunnyvale CA 94089
Tel (408) 498-6000 *SIC* 8742 6282 6411

PENNYMAC FINANCIAL SERVICES INC p 1131
3043 Townsgate Rd, Westlake Village CA 91361
Tel (818) 224-7442 *SIC* 6162 6282

AMERICAN GUARANTY MORTGAGE LLC p 73
2000 S Colo Blvd Ste 3700, Denver CO 80222
Tel (303) 577-7210 *SIC* 6282

■ **JANUS CAPITAL CORP** p 777
151 Detroit St, Denver CO 80206
Tel (303) 333-3863 *SIC* 6282

▲ **JANUS CAPITAL GROUP INC** p 778
151 Detroit St, Denver CO 80206
Tel (303) 333-3863 *SIC* 6282 8741

STURM FINANCIAL GROUP INC p 1395
3033 E 1st Ave Ste 300, Denver CO 80206
Tel (303) 394-5023 *SIC* 6282

BRYNWOOD PARTNERS II LIMITED PARTNERSHIP p 222
8 Sound Shore Dr Ste 265, Greenwich CT 06830
Tel (203) 622-1790 *SIC* 6282 4731

BRYNWOOD PARTNERS V LIMITED PARTNERSHIP p 222
8 Sound Shore Dr Ste 265, Greenwich CT 06830
Tel (203) 622-1790
SIC 6282 1751 3442 5031 3354

▲ **FIFTH STREET ASSET MANAGEMENT INC** p 541
777 W Putnam Ave Ste 3, Greenwich CT 06830
Tel (203) 681-3600 *SIC* 6282

JACOBS PRIVATE EQUITY LLC p 775
350 Round Hill Rd, Greenwich CT 06831
Tel (203) 413-4000 *SIC* 4731 6282 6726

TUDOR INVESTMENT CORP p 1490
1275 King St, Greenwich CT 06831
Tel (203) 863-6700 *SIC* 6282

WEXFORD CAPITAL LP p 1603
411 W Putnam Ave Ste 125, Greenwich CT 06830
Tel (203) 862-7000
SIC 8741 6282 1221 1222

■ **ADVEST GROUP INC** p 27
90 State House Sq, Hartford CT 06103
Tel (860) 509-1000
SIC 6211 6036 6141 6153 6282

■ **HARTFORD INVESTMENT MANAGEMENT CO** p 665
1 Hartford Plz, Hartford CT 06155
Tel (860) 297-6700 *SIC* 6282

PM HOLDINGS INC p 1157
1 American Row, Hartford CT 06103
Tel (860) 403-5000
SIC 6411 6162 6722 6282 6211 6552

VIRTUS PARTNERS INC p 1560
100 Pearl St Fl 9, Hartford CT 06103
Tel (860) 403-5000 *SIC* 6282

AFFINION GROUP HOLDINGS INC p 32
6 High Ridge Park Bldg A, Stamford CT 06905
Tel (203) 956-1000 *SIC* 8611 6282 8748

GE ASSET MANAGEMENT INC p 595
1600 Summer St Ste 3, Stamford CT 06905
Tel (203) 326-2300 *SIC* 6282

GENEVE CORP p 603
96 Cummings Point Rd, Stamford CT 06902
Tel (203) 358-8000 *SIC* 5961 3483 6282

RBS SECURITIES INC p 1211
600 Washington Blvd, Stamford CT 06901
Tel (203) 897-2700 *SIC* 6282 6211

SAC CAPITAL ADVISORS LP p 1264
72 Cummings Point Rd, Stamford CT 06902
Tel (203) 890-2000 *SIC* 6282

UBS SECURITIES LLC p 1498
677 Washington Blvd, Stamford CT 06901
Tel (203) 719-3000 *SIC* 6211 6282

UBS SECURITIES LLC p 1498
677 Washington Blvd, Stamford CT 06901
Tel (203) 719-3000
SIC 6211 6221 6289 6311 6091 6282

XL GLOBAL SERVICES INC p 1632
70 Seaview Ave Ste 7, Stamford CT 06902
Tel (203) 964-5200 *SIC* 6331 6282 6351

BRIDGEWATER ASSOCIATES LP p 212
1 Glendinning Pl, Westport CT 06880
Tel (203) 226-3030 *SIC* 6282 8742

COMMON FUND FOR NONPROFIT ORGANIZATIONS p 345
15 Old Danbury Rd Ste 200, Wilton CT 06897
Tel (203) 563-5000 *SIC* 6282

SIRIUSDECISIONS INC p 1327
187 Danbury Rd, Wilton CT 06897
Tel (203) 665-4000 *SIC* 6282 8742

■ **VOYA INVESTMENT TRUST CO** p 1566
1 Orange Way, Windsor CT 06095
Tel (860) 580-4646 *SIC* 6211 6282

■ **CIGNA HOLDINGS INC** p 306
590 Naamans Rd, Claymont DE 19703
Tel (215) 761-1000
SIC 6311 6321 6331 6512 6514 6282

BARCLAYS FINANCIAL CORP p 155
125 S West St, Wilmington DE 19801
Tel (302) 622-8990 *SIC* 7389 6282 6211

▲ **CARLYLE GROUP L P** p 258
1001 Pennsylvania Ave Nw 220s, Washington DC 20004
Tel (202) 729-5626 *SIC* 6726 6282

■ **CARLYLE INVESTMENT MANAGEMENT LLC** p 258
1001 Pennsylvania Ave Nw, Washington DC 20004
Tel (202) 729-5385 *SIC* 6282

■ **TEMPLETON INTERNATIONAL INC** p 1436
300 Se 2nd St Ste 600, Fort Lauderdale FL 33301
Tel (954) 527-7500 *SIC* 6282

■ **TEMPLETON WORLDWIDE INC** p 1436
500 E Broward Blvd # 900, Fort Lauderdale FL 33394
Tel (954) 527-7500
SIC 6211 6282 8742 8748

▲ **LADENBURG THALMANN FINANCIAL SERVICES INC** p 837
4400 Biscayne Blvd Fl 12, Miami FL 33137
Tel (305) 572-4100 *SIC* 6211 6282

■ **RAYMOND JAMES FINANCIAL SERVICES INC** p 1210
880 Carillon Pkwy, Saint Petersburg FL 33716
Tel (727) 567-1000
SIC 6211 6282 6712 6091 6035

DAYHAGAN FINANCIAL RJFS p 417
1000 S Tamiami Trl, Sarasota FL 34236
Tel (941) 330-1702 *SIC* 6282

▲ **AFFILIATED MANAGERS GROUP INC** p 32
777 S Flagler Dr, West Palm Beach FL 33401
Tel (800) 345-1100 *SIC* 6722 6282

EQUICORP PARTNERS LLC p 506
75 14th St Ne Unit 4610, Atlanta GA 30309
Tel (404) 442-1530 *SIC* 6282

▲ **INVESCO LTD** p 761
1555 Peachtree St Ne 18, Atlanta GA 30309
Tel (404) 892-0896 *SIC* 6282

▲ **SUNTRUST BANKS INC** p 1405
303 Peachtree St Ne, Atlanta GA 30308
Tel (800) 786-8787
SIC 6021 6022 6211 6091 6282

■ **SYNOVUS TRUST CO NA** p 1415
1148 Broadway, Columbus GA 31901
Tel (706) 649-2311 *SIC* 6733 6282

AMERICAN MEDICAL ASSOCIATION INC p 76
330 N Wabash Ave # 39300, Chicago IL 60611
Tel (312) 464-5000
SIC 8621 2721 6321 6282

■ **BANC ONE CAPITAL MARKETS INC** p 149
1 Bank One Plz, Chicago IL 60670
Tel (800) 992-7169 *SIC* 6211 6282

CHRISTIAN BROTHERS INVESTMENT SERVICES INC p 302
20 N Wacker Dr Ste 2000, Chicago IL 60606
Tel (312) 526-3343 *SIC* 6282

ELECTRICAL INSURANCE TRUSTEES p 485
221 N La Salle St Ste 200, Chicago IL 60601
Tel (312) 782-5442 *SIC* 6371 6282

■ ENVESTNET ASSET MANAGEMENT INC p 503
35 E Wacker Dr Ste 2400, Chicago IL 60601
Tel (312) 827-2800 *SIC* 6282

▲ ENVESTNET INC p 503
35 E Wacker Dr Ste 2400, Chicago IL 60601
Tel (312) 827-2800 *SIC* 7389 6282 7372

■ JONES LANG LASALLE AMERICAS INC p 792
200 E Randolph St # 4300, Chicago IL 60601
Tel (312) 782-5800 *SIC* 6282 1542

MESIROW FINANCIAL HOLDINGS INC p 951
353 N Clark St Lowr Level, Chicago IL 60654
Tel (312) 595-6000
SIC 6211 6282 6531 6552 6411

▲ MORNINGSTAR INC p 989
22 W Washington St # 600, Chicago IL 60602
Tel (312) 696-6000 *SIC* 6282 6722 7375

NUVEEN INVESTMENTS INC p 1068
333 W Wacker Dr, Chicago IL 60606
Tel (312) 917-7700 *SIC* 6282 6211

PPM AMERICA INC p 1166
225 W Wacker Dr Ste 1200, Chicago IL 60606
Tel (312) 634-2500 *SIC* 6282

RJ OBRIEN HOLDINGS INC p 1239
222 S Riverside Plz # 900, Chicago IL 60606
Tel (312) 373-5000 *SIC* 6282

ZACKS INVESTMENT RESEARCH INC p 1640
10 S Riverside Plz # 1600, Chicago IL 60606
Tel (312) 630-9880 *SIC* 6282

▲ ARTHUR J GALLAGHER & CO p 114
2 Pierce Pl, Itasca IL 60143
Tel (630) 773-3800 *SIC* 6411 6282 8741

▲ CALAMOS ASSET MANAGEMENT INC p 238
2020 Calamos Ct Ofc, Naperville IL 60563
Tel (630) 245-7200 *SIC* 6211 6282

■ CALAMOS INVESTMENTS LLC p 238
2020 Calamos Ct Ofc, Naperville IL 60563
Tel (630) 245-7200 *SIC* 6211 6282

INLAND REAL ESTATE GROUP OF COMPANIES p 743
2901 Butterfield Rd, Oak Brook IL 60523
Tel (630) 218-8000
SIC 6513 6512 6162 6282 1522 1542

▲ WINTRUST FINANCIAL CORP p 1617
9700 W Higgins Rd, Rosemont IL 60018
Tel (847) 939-9000 *SIC* 6022 6211 6282

■ LINCOLN FINANCIAL ADVISORS CORP p 867
1300 S Clinton St, Fort Wayne IN 46802
Tel (800) 237-3813
SIC 6311 6282 8748 8742

■ LINCOLN NATIONAL INVESTMENT COMPANIES INC p 867
200 E Berry St, Fort Wayne IN 46802
Tel (260) 455-2000 *SIC* 6282 6722

AEGON USA INVESTMENT MANAGEMENT LLC p 29
4333 Edgewood Rd Ne, Cedar Rapids IA 52499
Tel (319) 398-8511 *SIC* 6282

■ PRINCIPAL INTERNATIONAL INC p 1177
711 High St, Des Moines IA 50392
Tel (515) 247-5013
SIC 6282 6311 6321 6331

▲ WADDELL & REED FINANCIAL INC p 1571
6300 Lamar Ave, Overland Park KS 66202
Tel (913) 236-2000 *SIC* 6211 6282 6411

■ WADDELL & REED INC p 1571
6300 Lamar Ave, Shawnee Mission KS 66202
Tel (913) 236-2000
SIC 6282 6211 6289 6411

BROWN ADVISORY HOLDINGS INC p 219
901 S Bond St Ste 400, Baltimore MD 21231
Tel (410) 537-5400 *SIC* 6282

▲ LEGG MASON INC p 853
100 International Dr, Baltimore MD 21202
Tel (410) 539-0000 *SIC* 6282 6211 6162

▲ T ROWE PRICE GROUP INC p 1420
100 E Pratt St, Baltimore MD 21202
Tel (410) 345-2000 *SIC* 6282

ACACIA LIFE INSURANCE CO p 13
7315 Wisconsin Ave 1000w, Bethesda MD 20814
Tel (301) 280-1000
SIC 6311 6411 6035 6282 6211

DANFORTH ASSOCIATES INC p 411
20 Wight Ave Ste 155, Cockeysville MD 21030
Tel (781) 235-9100 *SIC* 6282

AEW CAPITAL MANAGEMENT LP p 32
2 Seaport Ln, Boston MA 02210
Tel (617) 951-0812 *SIC* 6282 6798

BAIN CAPITAL LP p 145
200 Clarendon St, Boston MA 02116
Tel (617) 516-2000 *SIC* 6282

BARINGS LLC p 155
470 Atlantic Ave Fl 9, Boston MA 02210
Tel (617) 225-3800 *SIC* 6282

■ BOSTON CO INC p 202
1 Boston Pl Ste 2100, Boston MA 02108
Tel (617) 722-7000 *SIC* 6022 6282

▲ BOSTON PRIVATE FINANCIAL HOLDINGS INC p 203
10 Post Office Sq, Boston MA 02109
Tel (617) 912-1900 *SIC* 6022 6722 6282

CAMBRIDGE ASSOCIATES LLC p 244
125 High St Ste 1505, Boston MA 02110
Tel (617) 457-7500 *SIC* 6282

EASTERN BANK CORP p 471
265 Franklin St Fl 2, Boston MA 02110
Tel (617) 897-1100 *SIC* 6036 6022 6282

▲ EATON VANCE CORP p 473
2 International Pl # 1400, Boston MA 02110
Tel (617) 482-8260 *SIC* 6282

■ EATON VANCE MANAGEMENT INC p 474
2 International Pl # 1400, Boston MA 02110
Tel (617) 482-8260 *SIC* 6282

■ EVERGREEN INVESTMENT MANAGEMENT CO LLC p 514
200 Berkeley St Ste 22, Boston MA 02116
Tel (617) 210-3200 *SIC* 6282

FIDELITY CAPITAL INVESTORS INC p 540
82 Devonshire St, Boston MA 02109
Tel (617) 563-7000 *SIC* 6282 6211

FIDELITY INVESTMENTS INSTITUTIONAL OPERATIONS CO INC p 540
245 Summer St Ste 1100, Boston MA 02210
Tel (617) 563-7000 *SIC* 6282 6211

FIDELITY MANAGEMENT & RESEARCH CO p 540
1 Federal St Fl 33, Boston MA 02110
Tel (603) 791-5000 *SIC* 6282

FIDELITY MANAGEMENT TRUST CO p 540
82 Devonshire St, Boston MA 02109
Tel (617) 563-7000 *SIC* 6282

FIDELITY/WTC INC p 541
82 Devonshire St, Boston MA 02109
Tel (617) 563-8300 *SIC* 6282

FMR LLC p 562
245 Summer St, Boston MA 02210
Tel (617) 563-7000
SIC 6282 6211 6799 6552 6531

GRANTHAM MAYO VAN OTTERLOO & CO LLC p 631
40 Rowes Wharf Ste 600, Boston MA 02110
Tel (617) 330-7500 *SIC* 6282 6722

JOHN HANCOCK SIGNATURE SERVICES INC p 789
101 Huntington Ave Fl 3, Boston MA 02199
Tel (617) 375-4708 *SIC* 6289 6282

LOOMIS SAYLES & CO LP p 877
1 Financial Ctr Fl 34, Boston MA 02111
Tel (617) 482-2451 *SIC* 6282

▲ LPL FINANCIAL HOLDINGS INC p 882
75 State St Ste 2401, Boston MA 02109
Tel (617) 423-3644 *SIC* 6211 6282 6091

MASSACHUSETTS FINANCIAL SERVICES CO p 917
111 Huntington Ave, Boston MA 02199
Tel (617) 954-5000 *SIC* 6282 6211 6289

NATIONAL FINANCIAL SERVICES LLC p 1012
200 Seaport Blvd Ste 630, Boston MA 02210
Tel (800) 471-0382 *SIC* 6211 6411 6282

NATIXIS GLOBAL ASSET MANAGEMENT LP p 1018
399 Boylston St, Boston MA 02116
Tel (617) 449-2100 *SIC* 6282 8742

NEPC LLC p 1026
255 State St Ste 600, Boston MA 02109
Tel (617) 314-3176 *SIC* 6411 6282

PIONEER INVESTMENT MANAGEMENT INC p 1150
60 State St, Boston MA 02109
Tel (617) 742-7825 *SIC* 6282

PIONEER INVESTMENT MANAGEMENT USA INC p 1151
60 State St Ste 700, Boston MA 02109
Tel (617) 742-7825 *SIC* 6722 6282

PUTNAM INVESTMENTS p 1193
1 Post Office Sq, Boston MA 02109
Tel (617) 292-1000 *SIC* 6722 6282 6726

▲ STATE STREET CORP p 1383
1 Lincoln St, Boston MA 02111
Tel (617) 786-3000 *SIC* 6022 6282

THOMAS H LEE ADVISORS II LP p 1448
100 Federal St, Boston MA 02110
Tel (617) 227-1050 *SIC* 6282

WELLINGTON MANAGEMENT GROUP LLP p 1589
280 Congress St, Boston MA 02210
Tel (617) 951-5000 *SIC* 6282

■ GRAVITY FINANCIAL LLC p 632
1 New Boston Dr Ste 7, Canton MA 02021
Tel (781) 828-7800 *SIC* 6282

INVESTORS CAPITAL HOLDINGS LLC p 761
6 Kimball Ln Ste 150, Lynnfield MA 01940
Tel (781) 246-7982 *SIC* 6211 6282

BOSTON FINANCIAL DATA SERVICES INC p 202
2000 Crown Colony Dr, Quincy MA 02169
Tel (617) 483-5000 *SIC* 6211 6289 6282

MASSACHUSETTS MUTUAL LIFE INSURANCE CO p 917
1295 State St, Springfield MA 01111
Tel (413) 788-8411
SIC 6321 6324 6411 6282

COMMONWEALTH EQUITY SERVICES LLP p 346
29 Sawyer Rd Ste 2, Waltham MA 02453
Tel (781) 398-0401 *SIC* 6211 6282 6221

DDJ CAPITAL MANAGEMENT LLC p 419
130 Turner St Ste 600, Waltham MA 02453
Tel (781) 283-8500 *SIC* 6282 5094 5812

■ EAGLE INVESTMENT SYSTEMS LLC p 468
45 William St Ste 200, Wellesley MA 02481
Tel (781) 943-2200
SIC 6722 6282 8721 7372

SUN LIFE ASSURANCE CO OF CANADA (US) p 1400
1 Sun Life Park, Wellesley MA 02481
Tel (781) 237-6030 *SIC* 6311 6282

■ SPRINGSTONE FINANCIAL LLC p 1361
1700 W Park Dr Ste 310, Westborough MA 01581
Tel (800) 630-1663 *SIC* 6282

ROCKBRIDGE GROWTH EQUITY LLC p 1243
1078 Woodward Ave, Detroit MI 48226
Tel (313) 373-7000 *SIC* 6282

JACKSON NATIONAL LIFE INSURANCE CO INC p 774
1 Corporate Way, Lansing MI 48951
Tel (517) 381-5500
SIC 6311 6282 6211 6411

HANTZ GROUP INC p 659
26200 American Dr Ste 500, Southfield MI 48034
Tel (248) 304-2855 *SIC* 6282

UNITED SHORE FINANCIAL SERVICES LLC p 1511
1414 E Maple Rd Fl 5, Troy MI 48083
Tel (248) 647-8590 *SIC* 6282

▲ AMERIPRISE FINANCIAL INC p 83
55 Ameriprise Fincl Ctr, Minneapolis MN 55474
Tel (612) 671-3131
SIC 6282 7389 6411 6311

RBC CAPITAL MARKETS LLC p 1211
60 S 6th St Ste 700, Minneapolis MN 55402
Tel (612) 371-2711
SIC 6211 6512 6513 6282

RBC DAIN RAUSCHER LENDING SERVICES INC p 1211
60 S 6th Strreet, Minneapolis MN 55402
Tel (612) 371-2941 *SIC* 6282

■ TARGET CAPITAL CORP p 1425
1000 Nicollet Mall, Minneapolis MN 55403
Tel (612) 304-6073 *SIC* 6282

BEDIVERE INSURANCE CO p 168
605 Hwy 169th N Ste 800, Plymouth MN 55441
Tel (952) 852-2431
SIC 6331 6282 6159 7389

WINGS FINANCIAL CREDIT UNION p 1616
14985 Glazier Ave Ste 100, Saint Paul MN 55124
Tel (952) 997-8000 *SIC* 6061 6282

AMERICAN CENTURY COMPANIES INC p 70
430 W 7th St, Kansas City MO 64105
Tel (816) 531-5575 *SIC* 6282

AMERICAN CENTURY INVESTMENT MANAGEMENT INC p 70
4500 Main St, Kansas City MO 64111
Tel (816) 531-5575 *SIC* 6722 6282

■ INVESTORS FIDUCIARY TRUST CO p 761
801 Pennsylvania Ave, Kansas City MO 64105
Tel (816) 871-4100 *SIC* 6722 6733 6282

NISA INVESTMENT ADVISORS INC p 1044
101 S Hanley Rd Ste 1700, Saint Louis MO 63105
Tel (314) 721-1900 *SIC* 6722 6282

TIAA-CREF TRUST CO FSB p 1452
1 Metropolitan Sq, Saint Louis MO 63102
Tel (314) 588-9738 *SIC* 7389 6282

FRED ALGER MANAGEMENT INC p 575
600 Plaza One, Jersey City NJ 07311
Tel (201) 547-3600 *SIC* 6282 6211 6799

▲ KCG HOLDINGS INC p 806
545 Washington Blvd, Jersey City NJ 07310
Tel (201) 222-9400 *SIC* 6211 6282

■ KNIGHT CAPITAL GROUP INC p 824
545 Washington Blvd Ste 1, Jersey City NJ 07310
Tel (201) 222-9400 *SIC* 6211 6282

LORD ABBETT & CO LLC p 878
90 Hudson St Fl 10, Jersey City NJ 07302
Tel (201) 827-2000 *SIC* 6282

ABSCO LTD CORP p 12
2740 Rte 10 E Ste 205, Morris Plains NJ 07950
Tel (973) 402-2148
SIC 6351 6411 6211 6282

■ PGIM INC p 1140
655 Broad St, Newark NJ 07102
Tel (973) 802-6791 *SIC* 6411 6799 6282

■ PRUCO SECURITIES LLC p 1187
751 Broad St, Newark NJ 07102
Tel (800) 235-7637
SIC 6321 6331 6211 6282 8071

■ PRUDENTIAL HOLDINGS LLC p 1187
751 Broad St, Newark NJ 07102
Tel (973) 802-6000 *SIC* 6282 6321 6324

■ PRUDENTIAL INSURANCE CO OF AMERICA p 1187
751 Broad St, Newark NJ 07102
Tel (973) 802-6000
SIC 6311 6371 6282 6722

BESSEMER GROUP INC p 176
100 Woodbridge Center Dr, Woodbridge NJ 07095
Tel (732) 694-5500 *SIC* 6282

■ FLEET/NORSTAR EMPLOYEES BENEFIT SERVICES INC p 555
1 Peter Kiernan Plz, Albany NY 12207
Tel (518) 956-1007 *SIC* 6282

SAW MILL CAPITAL LLC p 1284
555 Pleasantville Rd 220s, Briarcliff Manor NY 10510
Tel (914) 741-2426 *SIC* 6726 6282

MANNING & NAPIER ADVISORS LLC p 902
290 Woodcliff Dr Ste 300, Fairport NY 14450
Tel (800) 551-0224 *SIC* 6282 8742 7375

▲ MANNING & NAPIER INC p 902
290 Woodcliff Dr Ste 300, Fairport NY 14450
Tel (585) 325-6880 *SIC* 6282 8742 6722

DIVERSIFIED RETIREMENT CORP p 444
440 Mamaroneck Ave, Harrison NY 10528
Tel (914) 627-3000 *SIC* 6282

AMERICAN CAPITAL PARTNERS LLC p 69
205 Oser Ave, Hauppauge NY 11788
Tel (631) 851-0918 *SIC* 6282

■ CITICORP SELECT INVESTMENTS INC p 310
1 Court Sq Fl 24, Long Island City NY 11101
Tel (212) 559-1000 *SIC* 6282

21ST CENTURY ONCOLOGY INVESTMENTS LLC p 2
245 Park Ave Fl 41, New York NY 10167
Tel (239) 931-7275 *SIC* 6282

■ A C S HUMAN RESOURCES SOLUTIONS INC p 5
112 W 34th St Ste 605, New York NY 10120
Tel (212) 685-7981 *SIC* 8742 6282

AEA INVESTORS LP p 28
666 5th Ave Fl 36, New York NY 10103
Tel (212) 644-5900 *SIC* 6282 6211

■ ALLIANCEBERNSTEIN CORP p 55
1345 Ave Of The Americas, New York NY 10105
Tel (212) 969-1000 *SIC* 6282

■ ALLIANCEBERNSTEIN HOLDING LP p 55
1345 Ave Of The Americas, New York NY 10105
Tel (212) 969-1000 *SIC* 6282

■ ALLIANCEBERNSTEIN LP p 55
1345 Ave Of The Americas, New York NY 10105
Tel (212) 969-1000 *SIC* 6282

▲ AMERICAN EXPRESS CO p 72
200 Vesey St, New York NY 10285
Tel (212) 640-2000
SIC 6141 7389 6282 6099 6311 6211

▲ AMERICAN INTERNATIONAL GROUP INC p 75
175 Water St Rm 1800, New York NY 10038
Tel (212) 770-7000
SIC 6331 6321 6311 6324 6411 6282

ANGEL HOLDINGS LLC p 91
245 Park Ave, New York NY 10167
Tel (212) 692-2000 *SIC* 6282

ANGELO GORDON & CO LP p 91
245 Park Ave Fl 24, New York NY 10167
Tel (212) 692-2000 *SIC* 6282

APAX PARTNERS LP p 96
601 Lexington Ave Fl 53, New York NY 10022
Tel (212) 753-6300 *SIC* 6282

APAX PARTNERS OF NEW YORK p 96
601 Lexington Ave Fl 53, New York NY 10022
Tel (212) 419-2447
SIC 6282 5399 5199 5812 5813

▲ APOLLO GLOBAL MANAGEMENT LLC p 97
9 W 57th St Fl 43, New York NY 10019
Tel (212) 515-3200 *SIC* 6726 6282 6799

ARETEC GROUP INC p 107
405 Park Ave Fl 12, New York NY 10022
Tel (866) 904-2988 *SIC* 6211 6282 6722

AVENUE CAPITAL GROUP LLC p 136
399 Park Ave Fl 6, New York NY 10022
Tel (212) 878-3500 *SIC* 6282 6159

■ AXA EQUITABLE LIFE INSURANCE CO p 139
1290 Avenue Of The Americ, New York NY 10104
Tel (212) 554-1234 *SIC* 6311 6411 6282

■ BANK OF AMERICA PVT WEALTH MANAGEMENT p 151
114 W 47th St Ste C-1, New York NY 10036
Tel (800) 878-7878
SIC 6282 6022 6099 6733

■ BANK OF NEW YORK MELLON p 151
225 Liberty St, New York NY 10281
Tel (212) 495-1784
SIC 6153 6211 6282 6082

■ BEAR STEARNS COMPANIES LLC p 165
383 Madison Ave, New York NY 10179
Tel (212) 272-2000
SIC 6211 6282 6221 6099 6091 6289

■ BLACKROCK FINANCIAL MANAGEMENT INC p 188
40 E 52nd St Fl 2, New York NY 10022
Tel (212) 810-5300 *SIC* 6282

■ BLACKROCK HOLDCO 2 INC p 188
40 E 52nd St, New York NY 10022
Tel (212) 754-5300 *SIC* 6282

▲ BLACKROCK INC p 188
55 E 52nd St Fl 11, New York NY 10055
Tel (212) 810-5300 *SIC* 6282 6211

▲ BLACKSTONE GROUP L P p 188
345 Park Ave Ste 1100, New York NY 10154
Tel (212) 583-5000 *SIC* 6282 6211

■ BUCK CONSULTANTS LLC p 222
485 Lexington Ave Fl 10, New York NY 10017
Tel (212) 330-1000 *SIC* 8742 6282 2741

CASTLE HARLAN PARTNERS III LP p 264
150 E 58th St Fl 38, New York NY 10155
Tel (212) 644-8600
SIC 5812 6282 6211 8732

CENTERBRIDGE PARTNERS LP p 276
375 Park Ave Fl 13, New York NY 10152
Tel (212) 672-5000 *SIC* 6282 6211

CHARTERHOUSE GROUP INC p 291
535 Madison Ave Fl 28, New York NY 10022
Tel (212) 584-3200 *SIC* 8741 6799 6282

■ CITIGROUP GLOBAL MARKETS INC p 310
388 Greenwich St Fl 18, New York NY 10013
Tel (212) 816-6000 *SIC* 6211 6221 6282

▲ COHEN & STEERS INC p 334
280 Park Ave Fl 10w, New York NY 10017
Tel (212) 832-3232 *SIC* 6282

COMPUTERSHARE INVESTOR SERVICES LLC p 353
1290 Ave Of The Americas, New York NY 10104
Tel (312) 588-4700 *SIC* 6289 6211 6282

CREDIT SUISSE (USA) INC p 390
11 Madison Ave Frnt 1, New York NY 10010
Tel (212) 325-2000 *SIC* 6211 6282 6799

D E SHAW LAMINAR PORTFOLIOS LLC p 407
120 W 45th St Fl 22, New York NY 10036
Tel (212) 478-0000 *SIC* 6282 2392 5945

DRA ADVISORS LLC p 455
220 E 42nd St Fl 27, New York NY 10017
Tel (212) 697-4740 *SIC* 6282

■ DREYFUS CORP p 456
200 Park Ave Fl 7east, New York NY 10166
Tel (212) 922-6000 *SIC* 6211 6282

DUFF & PHELPS CORP p 459
55 E 52nd St Fl 31, New York NY 10055
Tel (212) 871-2000 *SIC* 6282 6211

ELLIOTT ASSOCIATES LP p 488
712 5th Ave Fl 36, New York NY 10019
Tel (212) 586-9431 *SIC* 6282 1382

EVERCORE LP p 514
55 E 52nd St Fl 35, New York NY 10055
Tel (212) 857-3100 *SIC* 6282 6211

▲ EVERCORE PARTNERS INC p 514
55 E 52nd St Fl 35, New York NY 10055
Tel (212) 857-3100 *SIC* 6282 6211

FIRST EAGLE INVESTMENT MANAGEMENT LLC p 546
1345 Ave Of The Americas, New York NY 10105
Tel (212) 698-3300 *SIC* 6282

FIRST INVESTORS CORP p 547
40 Wall St Fl 10, New York NY 10005
Tel (212) 858-8000 *SIC* 6282 6211

FIRSTMARK CAPITAL LLC p 551
100 5th Ave Fl 3, New York NY 10011
Tel (212) 792-2200 *SIC* 6282

FORESTERS FINANCIAL SERVICES p 567
40 Wall St Fl 10, New York NY 10005
Tel (212) 858-8000
SIC 6036 6211 6282 6311 8742 6153

▲ FORTRESS INVESTMENT GROUP LLC p 570
1345 Avenue, New York NY 10105
Tel (212) 798-6100 *SIC* 6282

GARRISON INVESTMENT GROUP LP p 592
1290 Avenue OfThe Americ, NewYork NY 10104
Tel (212) 372-9500 SIC 6282

GENNX360 CAPITAL PARTNERS LP p 604
590 Madison Ave Fl 27, NewYork NY 10022
Tel (212) 257-6772 SIC 6282

GERSON LEHRMAN GROUP INC p 609
60 E 42nd St Fl 3, NewYork NY 10165
Tel (212) 223-0839 SIC 6282

■ GOLDMAN SACHS & CO p 622
200 West St Bldg 200, NewYork NY 10282
Tel (212) 346-5440
SIC 6211 6221 6282 6153

■ GOLDMAN SACHS (ASIA) LLC p 622
200 West St Bldg 200, NewYork NY 10282
Tel (212) 902-1000 SIC 6211 6282 6722

▲ GOLDMAN SACHS GROUP INC p 622
200 West St Bldg 200, NewYork NY 10282
Tel (212) 902-1000 SIC 6211 6282

GOODE PARTNERS LLC p 624
767 3rd Ave Fl 22, NewYork NY 10017
Tel (646) 722-9450 SIC 6282

GUARDIAN LIFE INSURANCE CO OF AMERICA p 645
7 Hanover Sq Fl 14, NewYork NY 10004
Tel (212) 598-8000
SIC 6311 6371 6324 6321 6722 6282

ICV PARTNERS p 728
810 7th Ave Ste 3501, NewYork NY 10019
Tel (212) 455-9600 SIC 6282 6211

▲ INTL FCSTONE INC p 759
708 3rd Ave Rm 1500, NewYork NY 10017
Tel (212) 485-3500 SIC 6282 6211 6289

INVESTCORP INTERNATIONAL HOLDINGS INC p 761
280 Park Ave Fl 36, NewYork NY 10017
Tel (212) 599-4700 SIC 6282

INVESTCORP SERVICES INC p 761
280 Park Ave Fl 36, NewYork NY 10017
Tel (212) 599-4700 SIC 6282

■ J P MORGAN ASSET MANAGEMENT INC p 772
270 Park Ave Fl 12, NewYork NY 10017
Tel (212) 270-6000 SIC 6211 6282

■ JP MORGAN SECURITIES LLC p 795
383 Madison Ave Fl 9, NewYork NY 10179
Tel (212) 272-2000 SIC 6211 6282 6289

▲ KKR & CO LP p 822
9 W 57th St Ste 4200, NewYork NY 10019
Tel (212) 750-8300 SIC 6282 6799

LAZARD GROUP LLC p 849
30 Rockefeller Plz, NewYork NY 10112
Tel (212) 632-6000 SIC 6282 6211

MACQUARIE INFRASTRUCTURE PARTNERS II INTERNATIONAL LP p 893
125 W 55th St, NewYork NY 10019
Tel (212) 231-1310 SIC 6282

MARATHON ASSET MANAGEMENT LP p 904
1 Bryant Park Fl 38, NewYork NY 10036
Tel (212) 500-3000 SIC 6282

▲ MARSH & MCLENNAN COMPANIES INC p 910
1166 Avenue OfThe Americ, NewYork NY 10036
Tel (212) 345-5000 SIC 6411 6282 8742

■ MARSH LLC p 911
1166 Avenue OfThe Americ, NewYork NY 10036
Tel (212) 345-5000 SIC 6411 6282 8742

■ MARSH USA INC p 911
1166 Ave OfThe Americas, NewYork NY 10036
Tel (212) 345-6000
SIC 6411 6331 6351 6282

■ MERCER INVESTMENT CONSULTING INC p 944
1166 Ave OfThe Americas, NewYork NY 10036
Tel (212) 345-7000 SIC 6282

■ MERRILL LYNCH GROUP INC p 950
4 World Financial Ctr # 4, NewYork NY 10080
Tel (646) 855-5000 SIC 6282 6162

■ MERRILL LYNCH INVESTMENT MANAGEMENT INC p 950
225 Liberty St Fl C1056, NewYork NY 10281
Tel (212) 449-1000 SIC 6211 6282

▲ MOELIS & CO p 981
399 Park Ave Fl 5, NewYork NY 10022
Tel (212) 883-3800 SIC 6282

■ MOELIS & CO LLC p 981
399 Park Ave Fl 5, NewYork NY 10022
Tel (212) 883-3800 SIC 6733 6282

MONY LIFE INSURANCE CO p 987
1740 Broadway, NewYork NY 10019
Tel (800) 487-6669
SIC 6411 6321 6211 6282 6531

▲ MOODYS CORP p 987
250 Greenwich St, NewYork NY 10007
Tel (212) 553-0300 SIC 7323 6282

▲ MORGAN STANLEY p 988
1585 Broadway, NewYork NY 10036
Tel (212) 761-4000 SIC 6211 6282

■ MORGAN STANLEY INVESTMENT MANAGEMENT INC p 989
1585 Broadway, NewYork NY 10036
Tel (888) 454-3965 SIC 6282

▲ MSCI INC p 996
250 Greenwich St Fl 49, NewYork NY 10007
Tel (212) 804-3900
SIC 7389 7371 6282 8742

NEUBERGER BERMAN GROUP LLC p 1028
605 3rd Ave Fl 21, NewYork NY 10158
Tel (212) 476-9000 SIC 6282 6211 6722

NEUBERGER BERMAN LLC p 1028
605 3rd Ave Fl 21, NewYork NY 10158
Tel (212) 476-9000 SIC 6282 6211 6722

NEW YORK LIFE INSURANCE CO p 1035
51 Madison Ave Bsmt 1b, NewYork NY 10010
Tel (212) 576-7000 SIC 6311 6321 6282

NFP CORP p 1041
340 Madison Ave Fl 21, NewYork NY 10173
Tel (212) 301-4000 SIC 6411 7389 6282

▲ NORTHSTAR ASSET MANAGEMENT GROUP INC p 1058
399 Park Ave Fl 18, NewYork NY 10022
Tel (212) 547-2600 SIC 8741 6531 6282

NYLIFE LLC p 1069
51 Madison Ave, NewYork NY 10010
Tel (212) 576-7000
SIC 6282 6211 6733 6153

OCH-ZIFF CAPITAL MANAGEMENT GROUP LLC p 1073
9 W 57th St, NewYork NY 10019
Tel (212) 790-0000 SIC 6282

ONE ROCK CAPITAL PARTNERS LLC p 1086
30 Rockefeller Plz # 5400, NewYork NY 10112
Tel (212) 605-6000 SIC 6282

ONEX INVESTMENT CORP p 1088
712 5th Ave Fl 40, NewYork NY 10019
Tel (212) 582-2211 SIC 6799 6282

OPPENHEIMER FUNDS p 1090
2 Wrld Fncl Ctr Ste 1100, NewYork NY 10281
Tel (212) 323-0200 SIC 6289 6282

OPPENHEIMERFUNDS INC p 1090
2 Wrld Fncl Ctr Fl 14, NewYork NY 10281
Tel (303) 768-3200 SIC 6282 6289

PERELLA WEINBERG PARTNERS GROUP LP p 1135
767 5th Ave Fl 3, NewYork NY 10153
Tel (212) 287-3200 SIC 6282

PERMIRA ADVISERS LLC p 1136
320 Park Ave Fl 33, NewYork NY 10022
Tel (212) 386-7480 SIC 6282

■ PJT PARTNERS HOLDINGS LP p 1153
280 Park Ave Fl 15w, NewYork NY 10017
Tel (212) 364-7800 SIC 6282

▲ PJT PARTNERS INC p 1153
280 Park Ave Fl 16, NewYork NY 10017
Tel (212) 364-7800 SIC 6282 6153

RENAISSANCE TECHNOLOGIES LLC p 1223
800 3rd Ave Fl 33, NewYork NY 10022
Tel (212) 821-1502 SIC 6722 6282

RESURGENCE ASSET MANAGEMENT LLC p 1228
1185 Av OfThe Amer Fl 18, NewYork NY 10036
Tel (212) 710-5001
SIC 6282 2865 2821 2869 2861 2819

RHONE GROUP LLC p 1232
630 5th Ave Ste 2710, NewYork NY 10111
Tel (212) 218-6700 SIC 6282

RIPPLEWOOD INVESTMENTS LLC p 1236
920 Broadway Fl 6, NewYork NY 10010
Tel (212) 218-2705 SIC 6282

ROBECO USA INC p 1241
909 3rd Ave, NewYork NY 10022
Tel (212) 908-9500 SIC 6282

ROTHSCHILD INC p 1252
1251 Avenue OfThe Americ, NewYork NY 10020
Tel (212) 403-3500 SIC 6282 6211

ROTHSCHILD NORTH AMERICA INC p 1252
1251 Ave OfThe Ave Fl 51, NewYork NY 10020
Tel (212) 403-3500
SIC 6211 6159 8742 6221 6282 8741

▲ S&P GLOBAL INC p 1263
55 Water St Ste Conc2, NewYork NY 10041
Tel (212) 438-1000 SIC 7323 6282

SCHRODER US HOLDINGS INC p 1290
875 3rd Ave Fl 21, NewYork NY 10022
Tel (212) 641-3800
SIC 6282 6719 6211 6799

SOROS FUND MANAGEMENT LLC p 1341
250 W 55th St Fl 28, NewYork NY 10019
Tel (212) 872-1054 SIC 6282

■ STANDARD & POORS FINANCIAL SERVICES LLC p 1375
55 Water St Fl 49, NewYork NY 10041
Tel (212) 438-2000 SIC 6282

STARR INSURANCE HOLDINGS INC p 1379
399 Park Ave Rm 1702, NewYork NY 10022
Tel (646) 227-6300 SIC 6282 6411

THOR EQUITIES LLC p 1450
25 W 39th St Fl 11, NewYork NY 10018
Tel (212) 529-5055 SIC 6531 6211 6282

THREE CITIES RESEARCH INC p 1450
37 W 20th St Ste 908, NewYork NY 10011
Tel (212) 838-9660 SIC 6282

▲ TIPTREE FINANCIAL INC p 1455
780 3rd Ave Fl 21, NewYork NY 10017
Tel (212) 446-1400
SIC 6162 6282 6311 6798

TORCHLIGHT INVESTORS LLC p 1461
475 5th Ave Fl 10, NewYork NY 10017
Tel (212) 883-2800 SIC 6722 6282

TOWERBROOK CAPITAL PARTNERS LP p 1464
65 E 55th St Fl 27, NewYork NY 10022
Tel (212) 699-2200 SIC 6282

UBS FINANCIAL SERVICES INC p 1498
1285 Ave OfThe Americas, NewYork NY 10019
Tel (212) 713-2000 SIC 6211 6282

VICTORY CAPITAL HOLDINGS INC p 1555
667 Madison Ave Fl 10, NewYork NY 10065
Tel (212) 906-0746 SIC 6282 6722

VNU MARKETING INFORMATION INC p 1564
770 Broadway Fl 15, NewYork NY 10003
Tel (646) 654-5011
SIC 8732 6282 7374 5045

VONTOBEL ASSET MANAGEMENT INC p 1565
1540 Broadway Fl 38, NewYork NY 10036
Tel (212) 415-7000 SIC 6282

▲ VOYA FINANCIAL INC p 1566
230 Park Ave Fl 14, NewYork NY 10169
Tel (212) 309-8200
SIC 6311 6411 6282 6211 7389

▲ W P CAREY INC p 1569
50 Rockefeller Plz Fl 2, NewYork NY 10020
Tel (212) 492-1100 SIC 6531 6282

WICKS GROUP OF COMPANIES LLC (DE CORP) p 1608
400 Park Ave Fl 12a, NewYork NY 10022
Tel (212) 838-2100 SIC 6211 6282

GABELLI & CO INC p 588
1 Corporate Ctr, Rye NY 10580
Tel (914) 921-3700 SIC 6211 6282

GABELLI GROUP CAPITAL PARTNERS INC p 588
555 Theodore Fremd Ave C300, Rye NY 10580
Tel (914) 921-3700 SIC 6211 6282

■ GAMCO ASSET MANAGEMENT INC p 590
401 Theodore Fremd Ave, Rye NY 10580
Tel (914) 921-5000 SIC 6282

▲ GAMCO ASSET MANAGEMENT INC p 590
1 Corporate Ctr, Rye NY 10580
Tel (914) 921-3700 SIC 6282

■ AYCO CO L P p 140
321 Broadway, Saratoga Springs NY 12866
Tel (518) 886-4000
SIC 6411 6282 8742 7291

A G HOME HEALTH LLC p 5
700 White Plains Rd # 275, Scarsdale NY 10583
Tel (914) 722-9000 SIC 6282

FORESTLAND GROUP LLC p 567
1512 E Franklin St # 104, Chapel Hill NC 27514
Tel (919) 929-2497 SIC 6282

VICTORY CAPITAL MANAGEMENT INC p 1555
4900 Tiedeman Rd Fl 4, Brooklyn OH 44144
Tel (216) 898-2400 SIC 6282

CNG FINANCIAL CORP p 330
7755 Montgomery Rd # 400, Cincinnati OH 45236
Tel (513) 336-7735 SIC 6282

FORT WASHINGTON INVESTMENT ADVISORS INC p 569
303 Broadway St Ste 1100, Cincinnati OH 45202
Tel (513) 361-7600 SIC 6282

CENTRIC FINANCIAL GROUP LLC p 281
4016 Townsfair Way # 202, Columbus OH 43219
Tel (614) 824-6100 SIC 6311 6282 6321

▲ DIAMOND HILL INVESTMENT GROUP INC p 436
325 John H Mcconnell Blvd # 200, Columbus OH 43215
Tel (614) 255-3333 SIC 6282

■ JPMORGAN INVESTMENT ADVISORS INC p 795
1111 Polaris Pkwy, Columbus OH 43240
Tel (614) 248-5800 SIC 6282

RED CAPITAL GROUP LLC p 1215
10 W Broad St Ste 1510, Columbus OH 43215
Tel (614) 857-1400 SIC 6282

UNITED RETIREMENT PLAN CONSULTANTS INC p 1511
545 Metro Pl S Ste 240, Dublin OH 43017
Tel (614) 923-8822 SIC 6411 6282

LINCOLN INVESTMENT PLANNING LLC p 867
601 Office Center Dr # 200, Fort Washington PA 19034
Tel (215) 887-8111 SIC 6211 6282

ABERDEEN ASSET MANAGEMENT INC p 11
1735 Market St Fl 32, Philadelphia PA 19103
Tel (215) 405-5700 SIC 6282

■ BRANDYWINE GLOBAL INVESTMENT MANAGEMENT LLC p 208
2929 Arch St Ste 700, Philadelphia PA 19104
Tel (215) 609-3500 SIC 6282

FS INVESTMENT CORP II p 582
Cira Centre 2929 Arch St Cira Cent, Philadelphia PA 19104
Tel (215) 495-1150 SIC 6282

▲ FEDERATED INVESTORS INC p 536
1001 Liberty Ave Ste 2100, Pittsburgh PA 15222
Tel (412) 288-1900 SIC 6282 6722

■ FEDERATED INVESTORS SERVICES CORP p 536
1001 Liberty Ave Ste 2100, Pittsburgh PA 15222
Tel (412) 288-1900 SIC 6722 6282

▲ PNC FINANCIAL SERVICES GROUP INC p 1158
300 5th Ave, Pittsburgh PA 15222
Tel (412) 762-2000
SIC 6021 6162 7389 6282 6211

▲ LINCOLN NATIONAL CORP p 867
150 N Rad Chester Rd A305 Ste A, Radnor PA 19087
Tel (484) 583-1400
SIC 6311 6321 6371 6722 6411 6282

■ PRUDENTIAL TRUST CO p 1187
30 Ed Preate Dr, Scranton PA 18507
Tel (570) 341-6000 SIC 6282 6722 6211

▲ UNIVEST CORP OF PENNSYLVANIA p 1527
14 N Main St, Souderton PA 18964
Tel (215) 721-2400 SIC 6022 6282 6411

SAFEGUARD INTERNATIONAL FUND LP p 1266
435 Devon Park Dr Ste 200, Wayne PA 19087
Tel (610) 254-4110 SIC 6282

ORIANNA HEALTH SYSTEMS p 1094
2723 Summer Oaks Dr, Bartlett TN 38134
Tel (901) 937-7994 SIC 6282 8051

SERVICE GROUP INVESTMENTS LLC p 1307
6005 Century Oaks Dr # 100, Chattanooga TN 37416
Tel (423) 643-2600 SIC 6282

■ MBNA TECHNOLOGY INC p 925
16001 Dallas Pkwy, Addison TX 75001
Tel (972) 233-7101 SIC 7374 6282

■ AMERICAN PHYSICIANS SERVICE GROUP INC p 77
1221 S Mo Pac Expy # 200, Austin TX 78746
Tel (512) 328-0888
SIC 6282 8741 6411 6211

FORD FINANCIAL FUND II LP p 565
200 Crescent Ct, Dallas TX 75201
Tel (214) 871-5151 SIC 6282 6799 7389

ORIX USA CORP p 1095
1717 Main St Ste 1100, Dallas TX 75201
Tel (214) 237-2000 SIC 6211 6282

▲ WESTWOOD HOLDINGS GROUP INC p 1603
200 Crescent Ct Ste 1200, Dallas TX 75201
Tel (214) 756-6900 SIC 6282

LUTHER KING CAPITAL MANAGEMENT CORP p 886
301 Commerce St Ste 1600, Fort Worth TX 76102
Tel (817) 429-6256 SIC 6282

PINNACLE SUMMER INVESTMENTS INC p 1150
600 Travis St Ste 5800, Houston TX 77002
Tel (781) 749-7409 SIC 6282 8741

PACIFIC UNION FINANCIAL LLC p 1106
8900 Freeport Pkwy Ste 150, Irving TX 75063
Tel (800) 809-0421 SIC 6282

SOUTHWEST BUSINESS CORP p 1351
9311 San Pedro Ave # 600, San Antonio TX 78216
Tel (210) 525-1241 SIC 6411 6162 6282

PROPHET EQUITY LP p 1184
1460 Main St Ste 200, Southlake TX 76092
Tel (817) 898-1500 SIC 6282

▲ HEALTHEQUITY INC p 677
15 W Scenic Pointe Dr # 100, Draper UT 84020
Tel (801) 727-1000
SIC 8399 6371 6036 6321 6282

RELATIVITY CAPITAL LLC p 1221
1655 Fort Myer Dr Fl 7, Arlington VA 22209
Tel (703) 812-3020 SIC 6282 4581

CFA INSTITUTE p 285
915 E High St, Charlottesville VA 22902
Tel (434) 951-5499 SIC 8621 6282 8221

DAVENPORT & CO LLC p 415
901 E Cary St Ste 1200, Richmond VA 23219
Tel (804) 780-2000 SIC 6211 6282

FISHER INVESTMENTS INC p 552
5525 Nw Fisher Creek Dr, Camas WA 98607
Tel (888) 823-9566 SIC 6282

EVERGREEN PACIFIC PARTNERS MANAGEMENT CO INC p 514
1700 7th Ave Ste 2300, Seattle WA 98101
Tel (206) 262-4709 SIC 7389 6282

FRANK RUSSELL CO p 574
1301 2nd Ave Fl 18, Seattle WA 98101
Tel (206) 505-7877 SIC 6282 6211 6722

■ AMERIPRISE FINANCIAL SERVICES INC p 83
500 2nd St S Ste 101, La Crosse WI 54601
Tel (608) 783-2639
SIC 6282 6411 6211 8742

GREAT LAKES FINANCIAL MANAGEMENT GROUP INC p 633
2033 Marinette Ave, Marinette WI 54143
Tel (715) 732-9955
SIC 6211 8742 6282 6411

ARTISAN PARTNERS ASSET MANAGEMENT INC p 114
875 E Wscnsin Ave Ste 800, Milwaukee WI 53202
Tel (414) 390-6100 SIC 6282

EVERETT SMITH GROUP LTD p 514
330 E Kilbourn Ave # 1400, Milwaukee WI 53202
Tel (414) 223-1560 SIC 3111 6282

SIC 6289 Security & Commodity Svcs, NEC

UBS SECURITIES LLC p 1498
677 Washington Blvd, Stamford CT 06901
Tel (203) 719-3000
SIC 6211 6221 6289 6311 6091 6282

SECURITIES INVESTOR PROTECTION CORP p 1299
1667 K St Nw Ste 1000, Washington DC 20006
Tel (202) 371-8300 SIC 6289

ABN AMRO CLEARING CHICAGO LLC p 12
175 W Jackson Blvd # 400, Chicago IL 60604
Tel (312) 604-8000 SIC 6289

COMPUTERSHARE LLC p 353
2 N La Salle St Ste 200, Chicago IL 60602
Tel (312) 588-4992 SIC 6289

OPTIONS CLEARING CORP p 1090
1 N Wacker Dr Fl 5, Chicago IL 60606
Tel (312) 322-6200 SIC 6289

ROSENTHAL COLLINS GROUP LLC p 1251
216 W Jackson Blvd # 400, Chicago IL 60606
Tel (312) 460-9200
SIC 6221 6289 6231 6211

NST HOLDINGS GROUP INC p 1065
3620 Paoli Pike Ste 8, Floyds Knobs IN 47119
Tel (812) 248-9273 SIC 6289

■ WADDELL & REED INC p 1571
6300 Lamar Ave, Shawnee Mission KS 66202
Tel (913) 236-2000
SIC 6282 6211 6289 6411

IGLOO HOLDINGS CORP p 730
32 Crosby Dr, Bedford MA 01730
Tel (781) 687-8500 SIC 6289 7375

IGLOO INTERMEDIATE CORP p 730
32 Crosby Dr, Bedford MA 01730
Tel (781) 687-8500 SIC 6289 7375

■ INTERACTIVE DATA CORP p 751
32 Crosby Dr, Bedford MA 01730
Tel (781) 687-8500 SIC 6289 7375

JOHN HANCOCK SIGNATURE SERVICES INC p 789
101 Huntington Ave Fl 3, Boston MA 02199
Tel (617) 375-4708 SIC 6289 6282

MASSACHUSETTS FINANCIAL SERVICES CO p 917
111 Huntington Ave, Boston MA 02199
Tel (617) 954-5000 SIC 6282 6211 6289

PUTNAM INVESTOR SERVICES INC p 1193
1 Post Office Sq Ste 500, Boston MA 02109
Tel (617) 292-1000 SIC 6289

COMPUTERSHARE INC p 353
250 Royall St, Canton MA 02021
Tel (781) 575-2000 SIC 6289 6211

MADISON SECURITY GROUP INC p 894
31 Kirk St, Lowell MA 01852
Tel (978) 459-5911 SIC 6289

BOSTON FINANCIAL DATA SERVICES INC p 202
2000 Crown Colony Dr, Quincy MA 02169
Tel (617) 483-5000 SIC 6211 6289 6282

AMERICAN STOCK TRANSFER & TRUST CO LLC p 80
6201 15th Ave, Brooklyn NY 11219
Tel (718) 921-8200 SIC 6289

■ JP MORGAN CLEARING CORP p 794
1 Metrotech Ctr N Lbby 4, Brooklyn NY 11201
Tel (212) 272-1000 SIC 6289 6211

■ BEAR STEARNS COMPANIES LLC p 165
383 Madison Ave, New York NY 10179
Tel (212) 272-2000
SIC 6211 6282 6221 6099 6091 6289

COMPUTERSHARE INVESTOR SERVICES LLC p 353
1290 Ave Of The Americas, New York NY 10104
Tel (312) 588-4700 SIC 6289 6211 6282

▲ DEPOSITORY TRUST & CLEARING CORP p 431
55 Water St Ste Conc3, New York NY 10041
Tel (212) 855-1000 SIC 6289 6211 7389

■ DEPOSITORY TRUST CO INC p 431
55 Water St Ste Conc4, New York NY 10041
Tel (212) 855-1000 SIC 6289

FITCH GROUP INC p 552
33 Whitehall St, New York NY 10004
Tel (212) 908-0500 SIC 6289

FITCH RATINGS INC p 552
33 Whitehall St, New York NY 10004
Tel (212) 612-7726 SIC 6289

▲ INTL FCSTONE INC p 759
708 3rd Ave Rm 1500, New York NY 10017
Tel (212) 485-3500 SIC 6282 6211 6289

■ JP MORGAN SECURITIES LLC p 795
383 Madison Ave Fl 9, New York NY 10179
Tel (212) 272-2000 SIC 6211 6282 6289

MARKIT NORTH AMERICA INC p 909
620 8th Ave Fl 35, New York NY 10018
Tel (212) 931-4900 SIC 6289

■ NYSE GROUP INC p 1069
11 Wall St, New York NY 10005
Tel (212) 656-3000 SIC 6231 6289

OPPENHEIMER FUNDS p 1090
2 Wrld Fncl Ctr Ste 1100, New York NY 10281
Tel (212) 323-0200 SIC 6289 6282

OPPENHEIMERFUNDS INC p 1090
2 Wrld Fncl Ctr Fl 14, New York NY 10281
Tel (303) 768-3200 SIC 6282 6289

■ STANDARD & POORS SECURITIES EVALUATIONS INC p 1375
55 Water St Fl 44, New York NY 10041
Tel (212) 438-3388 SIC 7323 6289

TEMCO SERVICE INDUSTRIES INC p 1436
417 5th Ave Fl 9, New York NY 10016
Tel (212) 889-6353 SIC 7349 7342 6289

■ PPL SERVICES CORP p 1166
2 N 9th St, Allentown PA 18101
Tel (610) 774-5151 SIC 6289 4911

APEX CLEARING CORP p 96
350 N Paul St Ste 1300, Dallas TX 75201
Tel (214) 765-1100
SIC 6099 7389 4813 6289

PENSON WORLDWIDE INC p 1131
1700 Pacific Ave Ste 1400, Dallas TX 75201
Tel (214) 765-1100 SIC 6289

■ UNITED STATES LIME & MINERALS INC p 1513
5429 Lbj Fwy Ste 230, Dallas TX 75240
Tel (972) 991-8400 SIC 1422 3274 6289

SIC 6311 Life Insurance Carriers

PROTECTIVE LIFE CORP p 1185
2801 Highway 280 S Ofc, Birmingham AL 35223
Tel (205) 268-1000
SIC 6311 6321 6351 6411

PROTECTIVE LIFE INSURANCE CO p 1185
2801 Highway 280 S, Birmingham AL 35223
Tel (205) 268-1000 SIC 6311 6411 7389

▲ NATIONAL SECURITY GROUP INC p 1016
661 Davis St E, Elba AL 36323
Tel (334) 897-2273 SIC 6311 6331

■ LIBERTY NATIONAL LIFE INSURANCE CO p 862
100 Cncourse Pkwy Ste 350, Hoover AL 35244
Tel (205) 325-2722 SIC 6321 6311

LINCOLN HERITAGE LIFE INSURANCE CO p 867
4343 E Camelback Rd # 400, Phoenix AZ 85018
Tel (800) 750-6404 SIC 6311 6411

LONDEN INSURANCE GROUP INC p 875
4343 E Camelback Rd # 400, Phoenix AZ 85018
Tel (602) 957-1650 SIC 6311 6321 8741

■ OXFORD LIFE INSURANCE CO INC p 1101
2721 N Central Ave Fl 5, Phoenix AZ 85004
Tel (602) 263-6666 SIC 6311 6321

■ SAGEPOINT FINANCIAL INC p 1268
2800 N Central Ave # 2100, Phoenix AZ 85004
Tel (602) 744-3000 SIC 6311 6211

SAGICOR LIFE INSURANCE CO p 1268
4343 N Scottsdale Rd # 300, Scottsdale AZ 85251
Tel (480) 425-5100 SIC 6311

JD MELLBERG FINANCIAL p 780
3067 W Ina Rd Ste 105, Tucson AZ 85741
Tel (520) 731-9000 SIC 6311

USABLE LIFE p 1534
17500 Chenal Pkwy, Little Rock AR 72223
Tel (800) 648-0271 SIC 6311 6321

■ SUNAMERICA ANNUITY AND LIFE ASSURANCE CO p 1401
1 Sun America Ctr, Los Angeles CA 90067
Tel (310) 772-6000 SIC 6311

■ SUNAMERICA INC p 1401
1 Sun America Ctr Fl 38, Los Angeles CA 90067
Tel (310) 772-6000
SIC 6091 6311 6211 6282 6411 6371

■ SUNAMERICA LIFE INSURANCE CO p 1401
1 Sun America Ctr Fl 36, Los Angeles CA 90067
Tel (310) 772-6000 SIC 6311

TRANSAMERICA OCCIDENTAL LIFE INSURANCE CO p 1470
1150 S Olive St Fl 23, Los Angeles CA 90015
Tel (213) 742-2111
SIC 6311 6371 6321 6324 6799

TRANSAMERICA SERVICE CO INC p 1470
1150 S Olive St, Los Angeles CA 90015
Tel (213) 742-2111 SIC 6311

PACIFIC LIFE & ANNUITY CO p 1105
700 Newport Center Dr, Newport Beach CA 92660
Tel (949) 219-3011 SIC 6311 6411

PACIFIC LIFE INSURANCE CO p 1105
700 Newport Center Dr, Newport Beach CA 92660
Tel (949) 219-3011
SIC 6311 6371 6321 7359

PACIFIC LIFECORP p 1105
700 Newport Center Dr, Newport Beach CA 92660
Tel (949) 219-3011
SIC 6371 6311 6321 6035 8111

PACIFIC MUTUAL HOLDING CO p 1105
700 Newport Center Dr, Newport Beach CA 92660
Tel (949) 219-3011 SIC 6371 6311 6321

ASSOCIATED INDEMNITY CORP p 120
1465 N Mcdowell Blvd # 100, Petaluma CA 94954
Tel (415) 899-2000
SIC 6311 6321 6331 6351

BLUE SHIELD OF CALIFORNIA LIFE & HEALTH INSURANCE CO p 192
50 Beale St Ste 2000, San Francisco CA 94105
Tel (415) 229-5000 SIC 6311 6321

TRANSAMERICA FINANCE CORP p 1470
600 Montgomery St Fl 16, San Francisco CA 94111
Tel (415) 983-4000 SIC 6311

■ CENTURY-NATIONAL INSURANCE CO p 282
16650 Sherman Way, Van Nuys CA 91406
Tel (818) 760-0880 SIC 6311

FARMERS INSURANCE EXCHANGE p 529
6301 Owensmouth Ave # 300, Woodland Hills CA 91367
Tel (323) 932-3200 SIC 6311

■ HEALTH NET INC p 675
21650 Oxnard St Fl 25, Woodland Hills CA 91367
Tel (818) 676-6000 SIC 6324 6311

■ HEALTH NET OF CALIFORNIA INC p 675
21281 Burbank Blvd Fl 4, Woodland Hills CA 91367
Tel (818) 676-6775
SIC 6324 8062 6311 6321 6331 5912

LIFECARE ASSURANCE CO INC p 864
21600 Oxnard St Fl 16, Woodland Hills CA 91367
Tel (818) 887-4436 SIC 6321 6411 6311

JACKSON NATIONAL LIFE DISTRIBUTORS LLC p 774
7601 E Technology Way, Denver CO 80237
Tel (303) 488-3518 SIC 6311

MASTERS INSURANCE AGENCY INC p 918
9785 Maroon Cir Ste 340, Englewood CO 80112
Tel (303) 814-1596 SIC 6411 6331 6311

GREAT-WEST LIFE & ANNUITY INSURANCE CO p 635
8515 E Orchard Rd, Greenwood Village CO 80111
Tel (303) 737-3000 SIC 6211 6311

GREAT-WEST LIFECO US INC p 635
8515 E Orchard Rd, Greenwood Village CO 80111
Tel (303) 737-3000 SIC 6311

GWL&A FINANCIAL INC p 648
8515 E Orchard Rd, Greenwood Village CO 80111
Tel (303) 737-3000 SIC 6211 6311

▲ CIGNA CORP p 306
900 Cottage Grove Rd, Bloomfield CT 06002
Tel (860) 226-6000
SIC 6324 6311 6351 6321

■ CIGNA HEALTH AND LIFE INSURANCE CO p 306
900 Cottage Grove Rd, Bloomfield CT 06002
Tel (860) 226-6000 SIC 6311

■ CONNECTICUT GENERAL CORP p 357
900 Cottage Grove Rd, Bloomfield CT 06002
Tel (860) 226-6000 SIC 6311 6321

■ CONNECTICUT GENERAL LIFE INSURANCE CO p 357
900 Cottage Grove Rd, Bloomfield CT 06002
Tel (860) 226-6000 SIC 6311 6321

■ DISCOVER RE MANAGERS INC p 442
5 Batterson Park Rd, Farmington CT 06032
Tel (860) 674-2660 SIC 6311

▲ W R BERKLEY CORP p 1569
475 Steamboat Rd Fl 1, Greenwich CT 06830
Tel (203) 629-3000
SIC 6331 6321 6351 6311

■ AHP HOLDINGS INC p 37
151 Farmington Ave, Hartford CT 06156
Tel (860) 273-0123 SIC 6321 6311 8011

■ CIGNA RE CORP p 306
900 Cottage Grove Rd, Hartford CT 06152
Tel (860) 726-6000 SIC 6311 6321

CM LIFE INSURANCE CO INC p 328
140 Garden St, Hartford CT 06105
Tel (860) 987-2676 SIC 6311

▲ HARTFORD FINANCIAL SERVICES GROUP INC p 665
1 Hartford Plz, Hartford CT 06155
Tel (860) 547-5000
SIC 6331 6311 6351 6321

■ HARTFORD FIRE INSURANCE CO (INC) p 665
1 Hartford Plz, Hartford CT 06115
Tel (860) 547-5000
SIC 6411 6311 6351 7373

■ HARTFORD LIFE AND ACCIDENT INSURANCE CO INC p 665
1 Hartford Plz, Hartford CT 06115
Tel (860) 547-5000 SIC 6311

PHOENIX LIFE INSURANCE CO p 1145
1 American Row, Hartford CT 06103
Tel (860) 403-5000 SIC 6311

■ TRI STATE BUSINESS SYSTEMS INC p 1477
1 Tower Sq, Hartford CT 06183
Tel (860) 277-0111 SIC 6311 6321

■ UNITEDHEALTHCARE INSURANCE CO p 1515
185 Asylum St, Hartford CT 06103
Tel (860) 702-5000 SIC 6311 6321

WILTON RE US HOLDINGS INC p 1614
20 Glover Ave Ste 4, Norwalk CT 06850
Tel (203) 762-4400 SIC 6311

WILTON REASSURANCE CO p 1614
20 Glover Ave Ste 4, Norwalk CT 06850
Tel (203) 762-4400 SIC 6311

■ HARTFORD HOLDINGS INC p 665
200 Hopmeadow St, Simsbury CT 06070
Tel (860) 547-5000 SIC 6311

■ HARTFORD LIFE INC p 665
200 Hopmeadow St, Simsbury CT 06070
Tel (860) 547-5000 SIC 6311

■ INDEPENDENCE HOLDING CO p 736
96 Cummings Point Rd, Stamford CT 06902
Tel (203) 358-8000 SIC 6311 6321

ODYSSEY REINSURANCE CO p 1075
300 Stamford Pl Ste 700, Stamford CT 06902
Tel (203) 965-0004
SIC 6411 6361 6331 6324 6311

UBS SECURITIES LLC p 1498
677 Washington Blvd, Stamford CT 06901
Tel (203) 719-3000
SIC 6211 6221 6289 6311 6091 6282

■ HARTFORD LIFE AND ANNUITY INSURANCE CO p 665
200 Hopmeadow St, Weatogue CT 06089
Tel (860) 547-5000 SIC 6311 6321

ALLIANZ OF AMERICA INC p 56
55 Greens Farms Rd Ste 1, Westport CT 06880
Tel (203) 221-8500 SIC 6311 6331

■ VOYA RETIREMENT INSURANCE AND ANNUITY CO p 1566
1 Orange Way, Windsor CT 06095
Tel (860) 580-4646 SIC 6311

■ CIGNA GLOBAL HOLDINGS INC p 306
590 Naamans Rd, Claymont DE 19703
Tel (302) 797-3469 SIC 6311 6512 6411

■ CIGNA HOLDINGS INC p 306
590 Naamans Rd, Claymont DE 19703
Tel (215) 761-1000
SIC 6311 6321 6331 6512 6514 6282

■ CITICORP DEL-LEASE INC p 310
1 Penns Way, New Castle DE 19721
Tel (302) 323-3801 SIC 6022 6311 6321

■ CMH CAPITAL INC p 329
1105 N Market St Ste 1300, Wilmington DE 19801
Tel (302) 651-7947
SIC 6719 2451 6515 6311

ULLICO INC p 1500
1625 I St Nw Fl 5, Washington DC 20006
Tel (202) 682-0900 SIC 6311 6321

LUMBERMENS UNDERWRITING ALLIANCE p 885
1905 Nw Corporate Blvd, Boca Raton FL 33431
Tel (561) 994-1900 SIC 6331 6411 6311

■ AMERICAN HERITAGE LIFE INSURANCE CO INC p 74
1776 Amercn Heritg Lf Dr, Jacksonville FL 32224
Tel (904) 992-1776 SIC 6321 6311 6351

■ AMERICAN HERITAGE LIFE INVESTMENT CORP p 74
1776 Amercn Heritg Lf Dr, Jacksonville FL 32224
Tel (904) 992-1776
SIC 6311 6321 6351 7374

DIVERSIFIED HEALTH SERVICES INC p 444
4800 Deerwood Campus Pkwy, Jacksonville FL 32246
Tel (904) 791-6111 SIC 6311

WESTCOR LAND TITLE INSURANCE CO p 1597
875 Cncrse Pkwy S Ste 200, Maitland FL 32751
Tel (407) 629-5842 SIC 6311

■ AMERICAN BANKERS INSURANCE GROUP INC p 68
11222 Quail Roost Dr, Miami FL 33157
Tel (305) 253-2244
SIC 6331 6311 6351 6321 6324

■ AMERICAN BANKERS LIFE ASSURANCE CO OF FLORIDA p 68
11222 Quail Roost Dr, Miami FL 33157
Tel (305) 253-2244 SIC 6311

WESTERN RESERVE LIFE ASSURANCE CO p 1600
570 Carillon Pkwy, Saint Petersburg FL 33716
Tel (727) 299-1800 SIC 6311

CITIZENS PROPERTY INSURANCE CORP p 311
2101 Maryland Cir, Tallahassee FL 32303
Tel (888) 685-1555 SIC 6311

AAA AUTO CLUB SOUTH INC p 7
1515 N West Shore Blvd, Tampa FL 33607
Tel (813) 289-5000
SIC 4724 6331 8699 6311

■ SOUTHLAND LIFE INSURANCE CO p 1351
5780 Powers Ferry Rd, Atlanta GA 30327
Tel (770) 980-5100 SIC 6311

▲ STATE BANK FINANCIAL CORP p 1380
3399 Peachtree Rd Ne, Atlanta GA 30326
Tel (404) 475-6599
SIC 6022 6712 6311 6141 6331

■ VOYA AMERICA EQUITIES INC p 1566
5780 Powers Ferry Rd, Atlanta GA 30327
Tel (612) 372-5432 SIC 6311 6411

▲ ATLANTIC AMERICAN CORP p 125
4370 Peachtree Rd Ne # 200, Brookhaven GA 30319
Tel (404) 266-5500 SIC 6311 6321 6331

▲ AFLAC INC p 33
1932 Wynnton Rd, Columbus GA 31999
Tel (706) 323-3431 SIC 6321 6311

■ AMERICAN FAMILY LIFE ASSURANCE CO OF COLUMBUS p 72
1932 Wynnton Rd, Columbus GA 31999
Tel (706) 323-3431 SIC 6311

PRIMERICA LIFE INSURANCE CO p 1175
1 Primerica Pkwy, Duluth GA 30099
Tel (770) 381-1000 SIC 6311

COMPDENT OF GEORGIA INC p 351
100 Mansell Ct E Ste 400, Roswell GA 30076
Tel (770) 998-8936 SIC 6324 6311

DNK SALES LLC p 446
949 Stephenson Rd Ste B, Stone Mountain GA 30087
Tel (678) 704-7300 SIC 6311 7291 5699

PACIFIC GUARDIAN LIFE INSURANCE CO LIMITED p 1104
1440 Kalani St Ste 1700, Honolulu HI 96817
Tel (808) 942-6541 SIC 6311 6321

UNITED HERITAGE FINANCIAL GROUP INC p 1509
707 E United Heritage Ct, Meridian ID 83642
Tel (208) 493-6100 SIC 6311

UNITED HERITAGE LIFE INSURANCE CO p 1509
707 E Untd Heritage Ct # 130, Meridian ID 83642
Tel (208) 475-0932 SIC 6311

BENEFICIAL CO LLC p 172
1421 W Shure Dr Ste 100, Arlington Heights IL 60004
Tel (708) 453-6502
SIC 6141 6351 6162 6021 6552 6311

COUNTRY LIFE INSURANCE CO p 375
1701 Towanda Ave, Bloomington IL 61701
Tel (309) 557-3000 SIC 6311 6321

ILLINOIS AGRICULTURAL ASSOCIATION p 732
1701 Towanda Ave, Bloomington IL 61701
Tel (309) 557-2111
SIC 8611 6722 8742 6311 7514

STATE FARM LIFE INSURANCE CO INC p 1381
1 State Farm Plz, Bloomington IL 61701
Tel (309) 766-2311 SIC 6311

STATE FARM MUTUAL AUTOMOBILE INSURANCE CO p 1381
1 State Farm Plz, Bloomington IL 61710
Tel (309) 766-2311
SIC 6321 6311 6036 6331

AON BENFIELD FAC INC p 94
200 E Randolph St Fl 15, Chicago IL 60601
Tel (312) 381-5300 SIC 6321 6311

AON GROUP INC p 95
200 E Randolph St Fl 5, Chicago IL 60601
Tel (312) 381-2738 SIC 6311 8742 6411

■ BANKERS LIFE & CASUALTY CO p 152
111 E Wacker Dr Ste 2100, Chicago IL 60601
Tel (312) 396-6000 SIC 6321 6311 6324

■ CELTIC GROUP INC p 274
233 S Wacker Dr Ste 700, Chicago IL 60606
Tel (312) 332-5401 SIC 6321 6311

■ CELTIC INSURANCE CO p 274
233 S Wacker Dr Ste 700, Chicago IL 60606
Tel (312) 332-5401 SIC 6311

■ CNA FINANCIAL CORP p 329
333 S Wabash Ave Ste 300, Chicago IL 60604
Tel (312) 822-5000 SIC 6411 6331 6311

COMBINED INSURANCE CO OF AMERICA p 343
200 E Randolph St Lbby 10, Chicago IL 60601
Tel (800) 225-4500 SIC 6321 6311

HCSC INSURANCE SERVICES CO p 672
300 E Randolph St, Chicago IL 60601
Tel (312) 653-6000 SIC 6311

▲ KEMPER CORP p 809
1 E Wacker Dr, Chicago IL 60601
Tel (312) 661-4600
SIC 6331 6321 6311 6141

NORTH AMERICAN CO FOR LIFE & HEALTH INSURANCE p 1049
525 W Van Buren St # 1200, Chicago IL 60607
Tel (312) 648-7600 SIC 6311 6321

SAMMONS FINANCIAL GROUP INC p 1274
525 W Van Buren St # 1200, Chicago IL 60607
Tel (312) 648-7600 SIC 6311

THOMA CRESSEY BRAVO INC p 1448
300 N La Salle Dr # 4350, Chicago IL 60654
Tel (312) 254-3300
SIC 6799 8711 6311 6321 6531 7373

■ VALLEY FORGE LIFE INSURANCE CO INC p 1540
333 S Wabash Ave, Chicago IL 60604
Tel (312) 822-5000 SIC 6321 6311

GUARANTEE TRUST LIFE INSURANCE CO p 644
1275 Milwaukee Ave # 100, Glenview IL 60025
Tel (847) 699-0600 SIC 6321 6311

TRUSTMARK INSURANCE CO (MUTUAL) p 1488
400 N Field Dr, Lake Forest IL 60045
Tel (847) 283-4145 SIC 6321 6311

AON CONSULTING WORLDWIDE INC p 95
100 Half Day Rd 2, Lincolnshire IL 60069
Tel (312) 381-4800
SIC 6311 6321 6331 8742 6411 6351

JOHN DEERE INSURANCE GROUP INC p 788
3400 80th St, Moline IL 61265
Tel (309) 765-8000 SIC 6331 6321 6311

CATHOLIC ORDER OF FORESTERS INC p 267
355 Shuman Blvd, Naperville IL 60563
Tel (630) 983-4900 SIC 6311

ILONA FINANCIAL GROUP INC p 733
1807 S Washington St, Naperville IL 60565
Tel (630) 699-6147 SIC 6311

▲ ALLSTATE CORP p 58
2775 Sanders Rd, Northbrook IL 60062
Tel (847) 402-5000
SIC 6411 6351 6311 6371

■ ALLSTATE LIFE INSURANCE CO p 58
3075 Sanders Rd, Northbrook IL 60062
Tel (847) 402-5000 SIC 6411 6311

MTL INSURANCE CO p 998
1200 Jorie Blvd Ste 100, Oak Brook IL 60523
Tel (630) 990-1000 SIC 6311

B C S LIFE INSURANCE CO (INC) p 141
2 Mid America Plz Ste 200, Oakbrook Terrace IL 60181
Tel (630) 472-7700 SIC 6321 6311

BCS FINANCIAL CORP p 164
2 Mid America Plz, Oakbrook Terrace IL 60181
Tel (630) 472-7700 SIC 6331 6311 6211

HORTON GROUP INC p 708
10320 Orland Pkwy, Orland Park IL 60467
Tel (708) 845-3000
SIC 6411 6331 6321 6311

▲ FARMERS AUTOMOBILE INSURANCE ASSOCIATION (INC) p 529
2505 Court St, Pekin IL 61558
Tel (309) 346-1161 SIC 6411 6311

■ **FARMERS AUTOMOBILE MANAGEMENT CORP** p 529
2505 Court St, Pekin IL 61554
Tel (309) 346-1161 SIC 6311 6321

■ **PEKIN LIFE INSURANCE CO** p 1128
2505 Court St, Pekin IL 61554
Tel (309) 346-1161 SIC 6311 6321

ILLINOIS MUTUAL LIFE INSURANCE CO p 732
300 Sw Adams St, Peoria IL 61634
Tel (309) 674-8255 SIC 6321 6311

HOUSEHOLD FINANCE CORP p 711
2700 Sanders Rd, Prospect Heights IL 60070
Tel (847) 790-1590
SIC 6141 6162 6351 6153 6159 6311

HSBC INVESTMENTS (NORTH AMERICA) INC p 715
2700 Sanders Rd, Prospect Heights IL 60070
Tel (847) 564-5000
SIC 6141 7389 6351 6159 6162 6311

MODERN WOODMEN OF AMERICA p 981
1701 1st Ave, Rock Island IL 61201
Tel (309) 793-5537 SIC 6311

ROYAL NEIGHBORS OF AMERICA p 1254
230 16th St, Rock Island IL 61201
Tel (309) 788-4561 SIC 6411 6311

■ **AMERICAN GENERAL ASSURANCE CO** p 73
1000 E Wdfield Rd Ste 300, Schaumburg IL 60173
Tel (847) 517-6000 SIC 6311

■ **FEDERAL KEMPER LIFE ASSURANCE CO** p 535
1600 Mcconnor Pkwy, Schaumburg IL 60173
Tel (847) 874-4000 SIC 6311

ZURICH HOLDING CO OF AMERICA INC p 1645
1299 Zurich Way, Schaumburg IL 60196
Tel (847) 605-6000
SIC 6311 6331 6321 6324 6719

▲ **HORACE MANN EDUCATORS CORP** p 706
1 Horace Mann Plz, Springfield IL 62715
Tel (217) 789-2500 SIC 6311 6331 6411

LINCOLN HERITAGE LIFE INSURANCE CO p 867
920 S Spring St, Springfield IL 62704
Tel (602) 957-1650 SIC 6311

■ **TEACHERS INSURANCE CO INC** p 1429
1 Horace Mann Plz, Springfield IL 62715
Tel (217) 789-2500 SIC 6311

FORETHOUGHT LIFE INSURANCE CO p 567
1 Forethought Ctr, Batesville IN 47006
Tel (812) 934-7139 SIC 6311

■ **CICH INC** p 306
11825 N Pennsylvania St, Carmel IN 46032
Tel (317) 817-6100 SIC 6311

▲ **CNO FINANCIAL GROUP INC** p 330
11825 N Pennsylvania St, Carmel IN 46032
Tel (317) 817-6100 SIC 6311 6321 6331

CONSECO VARIABLE INSURANCE CO p 358
11825 N Pennsylvania St, Carmel IN 46032
Tel (317) 817-6100 SIC 6311

■ **WASHINGTON NATIONAL INSURANCE CO** p 1578
11815 N Pennsylvania St, Carmel IN 46032
Tel (317) 817-4100 SIC 6311 6321

WILCO LIFE INSURANCE CO p 1608
11825 N Pennsylvania St, Carmel IN 46032
Tel (317) 817-6100 SIC 6311

■ **MERIT LIFE INSURANCE CO** p 949
601 Nw 2nd St Unit 1, Evansville IN 47708
Tel (812) 424-8031 SIC 6311

■ **CHINA FW INC** p 301
1300 S Clinton St, Fort Wayne IN 46802
Tel (260) 455-2000 SIC 6311

■ **LINCOLN FINANCIAL ADVISORS CORP** p 867
1300 S Clinton St, Fort Wayne IN 46802
Tel (800) 237-3813
SIC 6311 6282 8748 8742

AMERICAN UNITED LIFE INSURANCE CO INC p 81
1 American Sq Ste 368, Indianapolis IN 46282
Tel (317) 285-1877 SIC 6371 6311 6321

AMERICAN UNITED MUTUAL INSURANCE HOLDING CO p 81
1 American Sq, Indianapolis IN 46282
Tel (317) 285-1877
SIC 6211 6311 6371 6351 6331

■ **ANTHEM SOUTHEAST INC** p 94
120 Monument Cir Ste 200, Indianapolis IN 46204
Tel (317) 488-6000 SIC 6411 6311 6321

■ **GOLDEN RULE FINANCIAL CORP** p 621
7440 Woodland Dr, Indianapolis IN 46278
Tel (317) 297-4123 SIC 6321 6311

■ **GOLDEN RULE INSURANCE CO** p 621
7440 Woodland Dr, Indianapolis IN 46278
Tel (317) 297-4123 SIC 6321 6311

GUGGENHEIM LIFE AND ANNUITY CO p 645
401 Penn Pkwy Ste 300, Indianapolis IN 46280
Tel (317) 574-6213 SIC 6311

ONEAMERICA FINANCIAL PARTNERS INC p 1087
1 American Sq, Indianapolis IN 46282
Tel (317) 285-1877 SIC 6371 6311 6321

STATE LIFE INSURANCE CO p 1381
1 American Sq, Indianapolis IN 46282
Tel (317) 285-2300 SIC 6311 6321

UNITED FARM FAMILY LIFE INSURANCE CO p 1508
225 S East St Ste 144, Indianapolis IN 46202
Tel (317) 692-7200 SIC 6311 6411

AEGON US HOLDING CORP p 29
4333 Edgewood Rd Ne, Cedar Rapids IA 52499
Tel (319) 355-8511
SIC 6311 6321 6351 6159

AEGON USA LLC p 29
4333 Edgewood Rd Ne, Cedar Rapids IA 52499
Tel (319) 355-8511 SIC 6311

CADET HOLDING CORP p 236
4333 Edgewood Rd Ne, Cedar Rapids IA 52499
Tel (319) 398-8511 SIC 6311

COMMONWEALTH GENERAL CORP p 346
4333 Edgewood Rd Ne, Cedar Rapids IA 52499
Tel (502) 560-2000 SIC 6311

TRANSAMERICA ADVISORS LIFE INSURANCE CO p 1470
4333 Edgewood Rd Ne, Cedar Rapids IA 52499
Tel (800) 346-3677 SIC 6311

TRANSAMERICA CORP p 1470
4333 Edgewood Rd Ne, Cedar Rapids IA 52499
Tel (319) 398-8511 SIC 6311

TRANSAMERICA LIFE INSURANCE CO p 1470
4333 Edgewood Rd Ne, Cedar Rapids IA 52499
Tel (319) 398-8511 SIC 6371 6311

TRANSAMERICA PREMIER LIFE INSURANCE CO p 1470
4333 Edgewood Rd Ne, Cedar Rapids IA 52499
Tel (319) 355-8511 SIC 6311 6321

■ **UNITED FIRE & CASUALTY CO** p 1508
118 2nd Ave Se, Cedar Rapids IA 52401
Tel (319) 399-5700 SIC 6331 6311 6321

▲ **UNITED FIRE GROUP INC** p 1508
118 2nd Ave Se, Cedar Rapids IA 52401
Tel (319) 399-5700 SIC 6411 6311

■ **UNITED LIFE INSURANCE CO INC** p 1510
118 2nd Ave Se, Cedar Rapids IA 52401
Tel (319) 399-5700 SIC 6311

E M C NATIONAL LIFE MUTUAL HOLDING CO p 466
699 Walnut St, Des Moines IA 50309
Tel (515) 225-8197 SIC 6311

EMC NATIONAL LIFE CO p 491
699 Walnut St Ste 1100, Des Moines IA 50309
Tel (515) 237-2000 SIC 6311 6411

▲ **EMPLOYERS MUTUAL CASUALTY CO** p 494
717 Mulberry St, Des Moines IA 50309
Tel (515) 280-2511
SIC 6411 6321 6311 6519

■ **FIDELITY & GUARANTY LIFE** p 540
601 Locust St Fl 2, Des Moines IA 50309
Tel (800) 445-6758 SIC 6311

▲ **PRINCIPAL FINANCIAL GROUP INC** p 1177
711 High St, Des Moines IA 50392
Tel (515) 247-5111
SIC 6321 6799 6722 6311

■ **PRINCIPAL FINANCIAL SERVICES INC** p 1177
711 High St, Des Moines IA 50392
Tel (515) 247-5111 SIC 6311

■ **PRINCIPAL GLOBAL INVESTORS LLC** p 1177
801 Grand Ave, Des Moines IA 50309
Tel (515) 247-6582 SIC 6311

■ **PRINCIPAL INTERNATIONAL INC** p 1177
711 High St, Des Moines IA 50392
Tel (515) 247-5013
SIC 6282 6311 6321 6331

■ **PRINCIPAL LIFE INSURANCE CO** p 1177
711 High St, Des Moines IA 50392
Tel (515) 247-5111
SIC 6311 6211 6162 6321 6411

▲ **AMERICAN EQUITY INVESTMENT LIFE HOLDING CO** p 71
6000 Westown Pkwy, West Des Moines IA 50266
Tel (515) 221-0002 SIC 6311

■ **AMERICAN EQUITY INVESTMENT LIFE INSURANCE CO** p 71
5000 Westown Pkwy Ste 440, West Des Moines IA 50266
Tel (515) 221-0002 SIC 6311

ATHENE ANNUITY AND LIFE CO p 124
7700 Mills Civic Pkwy, West Des Moines IA 50266
Tel (888) 266-8489 SIC 6311

ATHENE USA CORP p 124
7700 Mills Civic Pkwy, West Des Moines IA 50266
Tel (515) 342-3413 SIC 6311

▲ **FBL FINANCIAL GROUP INC** p 532
5400 University Ave, West Des Moines IA 50266
Tel (515) 225-5400 SIC 6311 6411

GUIDEONE INC p 645
1111 Ashworth Rd, West Des Moines IA 50265
Tel (515) 267-5000 SIC 6311

HOMESTEADERS LIFE CO p 704
5700 Westown Pkwy Ofc, West Des Moines IA 50266
Tel (515) 440-7777 SIC 6311

IOWA FARM BUREAU FEDERATION p 762
5400 University Ave, West Des Moines IA 50266
Tel (515) 225-5400
SIC 8699 5154 6311 6321 6411

SCOR GLOBAL LIFE USA REINSURANCE CO p 1293
11625 Rosewood St Ste 300, Leawood KS 66211
Tel (913) 901-4600 SIC 6311 6321

SWISS RE AMERICA HOLDING CORP p 1412
5200 Metcalf Ave, Overland Park KS 66202
Tel (913) 676-5200 SIC 6331 6311

SWISS REINSURANCE AMERICA CORP p 1413
5200 Metcalf Ave, Overland Park KS 66202
Tel (913) 676-5200 SIC 6311

■ **WADDELL & REED FINANCIAL SERVICES INC** p 1571
6300 Lamar Ave, Overland Park KS 66202
Tel (913) 236-2000
SIC 6722 6311 6211 6531

ZURICH AGENCY SERVICES INC p 1645
7045 College Blvd, Overland Park KS 66211
Tel (913) 339-1000 SIC 6331 6311

SECURITY BENEFIT LIFE INSURANCE CO p 1299
1 Sw Security Benefit Pl, Topeka KS 66636
Tel (785) 438-3000
SIC 6311 6722 6091 6211 8748

AFFIRMATIVE LLC p 32
2900 Westfork Dr Ste 600, Baton Rouge LA 70827
Tel (225) 928-9000 SIC 6311 6141

STARMOUNT LIFE INSURANCE CO INC p 1379
8485 Goodwood Blvd, Baton Rouge LA 70806
Tel (225) 400-9100 SIC 6311

PAN-AMERICAN LIFE INSURANCE GROUP INC p 1110
601 Poydras St Ste 1000, New Orleans LA 70130
Tel (504) 566-1300 SIC 6311 7389

AEGON DIRECT MARKETING SERVICES INC p 29
100 Light St Fl B1, Baltimore MD 21202
Tel (410) 685-5500 SIC 6311 8011

■ **FIDELITY & GUARANTY LIFE INSURANCE CO** p 540
1001 Fleet St Fl 7, Baltimore MD 21202
Tel (410) 895-0100 SIC 6311

FIRST AUSA LIFE INSURANCE CO p 545
1111 N Charles St, Baltimore MD 21201
Tel (410) 576-4571 SIC 6311

ACACIA LIFE INSURANCE CO p 13
7315 Wisconsin Ave 1000w, Bethesda MD 20814
Tel (301) 280-1000
SIC 6311 6411 6035 6282 6211

BANNER LIFE INSURANCE CO p 153
3275 Bennett Creek Ave, Frederick MD 21704
Tel (301) 279-4800 SIC 6311 6411

LEGAL & GENERAL AMERICA INC p 853
3275 Bennett Creek Ave, Frederick MD 21704
Tel (800) 638-8428 SIC 6411 6311

BALTIMORE LIFE INSURANCE CO INC p 149
10075 Red Run Blvd # 175, Owings Mills MD 21117
Tel (410) 581-6600 SIC 6311

UNION LABOR LIFE INSURANCE CO p 1504
8403 Colesville Rd # 1000, Silver Spring MD 20910
Tel (202) 682-0900
SIC 6311 6321 6324 6371

FIRST STATE MANAGEMENT GROUP INC p 549
141 Tremont St Ste 1200, Boston MA 02111
Tel (617) 526-7600 SIC 6311

JOHN HANCOCK FINANCIAL SERVICES INC p 788
200 Clarendon St, Boston MA 02116
Tel (617) 572-6000
SIC 6311 6351 6411 6371 6321

LIBERTY SPAIN INSURANCE GROUP LLC p 862
175 Berkeley St, Boston MA 02116
Tel (617) 357-9500 SIC 6311

BOSTON MUTUAL LIFE INSURANCE CO p 203
120 Royall St Ste 1, Canton MA 02021
Tel (781) 828-7000 SIC 6311

COMMONWEALTH ANNUITY & LIFE INSURANCE p 345
132 Turnpike Rd Ste 210, Southborough MA 01772
Tel (508) 460-2400 SIC 6311

MASSMUTUAL INTERNATIONAL LLC p 917
1295 State St, Springfield MA 01111
Tel (413) 788-8411 SIC 6311

DELAWARE LIFE HOLDINGS LLC p 424
1601 Trapelo Rd Ste 30, Waltham MA 02451
Tel (877) 253-2323 SIC 6311

SUN LIFE ASSURANCE CO OF CANADA (US) p 1400
1 Sun Life Park, Wellesley MA 02481
Tel (781) 237-6030 SIC 6311 6282

SUN LIFE FINANCIAL (US) SERVICES CO INC p 1400
1 Sun Life Executive Park, Wellesley MA 02481
Tel (781) 237-6030 SIC 6311

SUN LIFE OF CANADA (US) HOLDINGS INC p 1400
1 Sun Life Park, Wellesley MA 02481
Tel (781) 237-6030 SIC 6311

SAVINGS BANK LIFE INSURANCE CO OF MASSACHUSETTS p 1284
1 Linscott Rd, Woburn MA 01801
Tel (781) 938-3500 SIC 6311

▲ **HANOVER INSURANCE GROUP INC** p 658
440 Lincoln St, Worcester MA 01653
Tel (508) 855-1000 SIC 6331 6311

■ **OPUS INVESTMENT MANAGEMENT INC** p 1091
440 Lincoln St, Worcester MA 01653
Tel (508) 855-1000
SIC 6311 6321 6324 6351 6722

■ **PAUL REVERE LIFE INSURANCE CO** p 1121
1 Mercantile St, Worcester MA 01608
Tel (508) 366-8707 SIC 6311 6321

■ **UNUM INSURANCE CO** p 1528
1 Mercantile St, Worcester MA 01608
Tel (508) 366-8707 SIC 6311

GLEANER LIFE INSURANCE SOCIETY INC p 614
5200 W Us Highway 223, Adrian MI 49221
Tel (517) 263-2244 SIC 6311

ALLIANCE HEALTH AND LIFE INSURANCE CO p 54
2850 W Grand Blvd Fl 5, Detroit MI 48202
Tel (313) 872-8100 SIC 6311

▲ **ALLY FINANCIAL INC** p 59
500 Woodward Ave Fl 1, Detroit MI 48226
Tel (866) 710-4623
SIC 6021 6153 6159 6311 6331 6162

GERBER LIFE INSURANCE CO p 608
1311 Mmroneck Ave Ste 350, Fremont MI 49412
Tel (800) 704-2180 SIC 6311 6321

LIGHTHOUSE INSURANCE GROUP INC p 865
877 E 16th St, Holland MI 49423
Tel (616) 392-6900
SIC 6411 6331 6321 6311

JACKSON NATIONAL LIFE INSURANCE CO INC p 774
1 Corporate Way, Lansing MI 48951
Tel (517) 381-5500
SIC 6311 6282 6211 6411

MICHIGAN FARM BUREAU FINANCIAL CORP p 961
7373 W Saginaw Hwy, Lansing MI 48917
Tel (517) 323-7000 SIC 6311 6331

AAA LIFE INSURANCE CO p 7
17900 N Laurel Park Dr, Livonia MI 48152
Tel (734) 779-2600 SIC 6311

AMERICAN COMMUNITY MUTUAL INSURANCE CO p 70
39201 7 Mile Rd, Livonia MI 48152
Tel (734) 591-9000 SIC 6321 6311

ALLIANZ LIFE INSURANCE CO OF NORTH AMERICA p 56
5701 Golden Hills Dr, Minneapolis MN 55416
Tel (763) 765-6500 SIC 6311

▲ **AMERIPRISE FINANCIAL INC** p 83
55 Ameriprise Fincl Ctr, Minneapolis MN 55474
Tel (612) 671-3131
SIC 6282 7389 6411 6311

■ **RELIASTAR LIFE INSURANCE CO** p 1222
20 Washington Ave S, Minneapolis MN 55401
Tel (612) 372-5432 SIC 6311 6321 6324

■ **RIVERSOURCE LIFE INSURANCE CO** p 1238
1099 Ameriprise Fincl Ctr, Minneapolis MN 55474
Tel (612) 671-3131 SIC 6311 6321

THRIVENT FINANCIAL FOR LUTHERANS FOUNDATION p 1451
625 4th Ave S, Minneapolis MN 55415
Tel (920) 734-5721
SIC 6311 6321 8742 6411 6211

■ **METRAHEALTH CARE MANAGEMENT CORP** p 954
9900 Bren Rd E, Minnetonka MN 55343
Tel (952) 936-1300 SIC 6321 6311

FEDERATED LIFE INSURANCE CO p 536
121 E Park Sq, Owatonna MN 55060
Tel (507) 455-5200 SIC 6311

FEDERATED MUTUAL INSURANCE CO p 536
121 E Park Sq, Owatonna MN 55060
Tel (507) 455-5200 SIC 6331 6321 6311

MINNESOTA LIFE INSURANCE CO p 973
400 And 401 Robert St N, Saint Paul MN 55101
Tel (478) 314-3189 SIC 6311

MINNESOTA MUTUAL COMPANIES INC p 973
400 Robert St N Ste A, Saint Paul MN 55101
Tel (651) 665-3500 SIC 6311

▲ **REINSURANCE GROUP OF AMERICA INC** p 1221
16600 Swingley Ridge Rd, Chesterfield MO 63017
Tel (636) 736-7000 SIC 6311 6321 6411

SHELTER MUTUAL INSURANCE CO p 1315
1817 W Broadway, Columbia MO 65218
Tel (573) 445-8441 SIC 6331 6311

AMERICO LIFE INC p 81
300 W 11th St, Kansas City MO 64105
Tel (816) 391-2000 SIC 6311 6321 6331

CNS CORP p 330
500 E 9th St, Kansas City MO 64106
Tel (816) 842-6300 SIC 6211 6311 4724

▲ **COMMERCE BANCSHARES INC** p 344
1000 Walnut St, Kansas City MO 64106
Tel (816) 234-2000 SIC 6022 6311 6162

FINANCIAL HOLDING CORP p 542
1055 Broadway Blvd Fl 11, Kansas City MO 64105
Tel (816) 391-2000 SIC 6411 6311 6153

GREAT SOUTHERN LIFE INSURANCE CO p 634
300 W 11th St, Kansas City MO 64105
Tel (816) 391-2000 SIC 6311

KANSAS CITY LIFE INSURANCE CO p 802
3520 Broadway Blvd, Kansas City MO 64111
Tel (816) 753-7000 SIC 6311 6411

OZARK NATIONAL LIFE INSURANCE CO p 1101
500 E 9th St, Kansas City MO 64106
Tel (314) 664-4389 SIC 6311 6321

UNITED FIDELITY LIFE INSURANCE CO INC p 1508
1055 Broadway Blvd Ste Ph, Kansas City MO 64105
Tel (816) 391-2000 SIC 6311

■ **GENERAL AMERICAN LIFE INSURANCE CO** p 599
13045 Tesson Ferry Rd, Saint Louis MO 63128
Tel (314) 843-8700 SIC 6411 6311

■ **GENERAL AMERICAN MUTUAL HOLDING CO** p 599
700 Market St, Saint Louis MO 63101
Tel (314) 231-1700 SIC 6311

JOHN M QUALY p 789
701 Market St Ste 1070, Saint Louis MO 63101
Tel (314) 231-3931 SIC 6411 6311

■ **UNION NATIONAL LIFE INSURANCE CO** p 1504
12115 Lackland Rd, Saint Louis MO 63146
Tel (877) 710-5081 SIC 6311

AMERITAS HOLDING CO p 84
5900 O St, Lincoln NE 68510
Tel (402) 467-1122 SIC 6311

AMERITAS LIFE INSURANCE CORP p 84
5900 O St, Lincoln NE 68510
Tel (402) 467-1122 SIC 6371 6311 6211

AMERITAS MUTUAL HOLDING CO p 84
5900 O St, Lincoln NE 68510
Tel (402) 467-1122 SIC 6311

ASG INC p 116
1526 K St, Lincoln NE 68508
Tel (402) 476-6500 SIC 6321 6311

ASSURITY SECURITY GROUP INC p 122
1526 K St, Lincoln NE 68508
Tel (402) 476-6500 SIC 6321 6311

SECURITY FINANCIAL LIFE INSURANCE CO p 1299
4000 Pine Lake Rd, Lincoln NE 68516
Tel (402) 434-9500 SIC 6311

BLUE CROSS & BLUE SHIELD OF NEBRASKA p 191
1919 Aksarben Dr, Omaha NE 68180
Tel (402) 982-7000 SIC 6324 6311

MUTUAL OF OMAHA INSURANCE CO p 1003
Mutual Of Omaha Plaza, Omaha NE 68175
Tel (402) 342-7600 SIC 6311 6211 8748

■ **NATIONAL INDEMNITY CO (INC)** p 1013
1314 Douglas St Ste 1400, Omaha NE 68102
Tel (402) 916-3000 SIC 6331 6411 6311

PHYSICIANS LIFE INSURANCE CO p 1145
2600 Dodge St, Omaha NE 68131
Tel (402) 633-1000 SIC 6311

PHYSICIANS MUTUAL INSURANCE CO p 1145
2600 Dodge St, Omaha NE 68131
Tel (402) 633-1000 SIC 6321 6311

SILVERSTONE GROUP INC p 1324
11516 Miracle Hills Dr # 100, Omaha NE 68154
Tel (402) 964-5400
SIC 6371 6311 8742 6411

UNITED OF OMAHA LIFE INSURANCE CO p 1510
Mutual Of Omaha Plaza, Omaha NE 68175
Tel (402) 342-7600 *SIC* 6311 6321 6324

WOODMEN INSURANCE AGENCY INC p 1623
1700 Farnam St Ste 840, Omaha NE 68102
Tel (402) 342-1890 *SIC* 6311

WOODMEN OF WORLD LIFE INSURANCE SOCIETY AND/OR OMAHA WOODMEN LIFE INSURANCE SOCIETY p 1623
1700 Farnam St Ste 840, Omaha NE 68102
Tel (402) 342-1890 *SIC* 6311

■ SIERRA HEALTH AND LIFE INSURANCE CO INC p 1320
2720 N Tenaya Way, Las Vegas NV 89128
Tel (702) 242-7700 *SIC* 6311

■ SIERRA HEALTH SERVICES INC p 1320
2720 N Tenaya Way, Las Vegas NV 89128
Tel (702) 242-7000
SIC 6324 6311 8082 8741 8093

DIRECTORS INVESTMENT GROUP INC p 442
955 S Virginia St Ste 116, Reno NV 89502
Tel (775) 329-3311 *SIC* 6311

NEW JERSEY RE-INSURANCE CO p 1031
301 Sullivan Way, Ewing NJ 08628
Tel (609) 883-1300 *SIC* 6311 6331

IPFS CORP p 763
101 Hudson St Fl 33, Jersey City NJ 07302
Tel (201) 557-4625 *SIC* 6311

CRUM & FORSTER INC p 396
305 Madison Ave, Morristown NJ 07960
Tel (973) 490-6600
SIC 6311 6321 6331 6411

■ PRUCO LIFE INSURANCE CO p 1187
213 Washington St, Newark NJ 07102
Tel (973) 802-6000 *SIC* 6311 6411

■ PRUCO LIFE INSURANCE CO OF NEW JERSEY p 1187
213 Washington St, Newark NJ 07102
Tel (973) 802-6000 *SIC* 6311

▲ PRUDENTIAL FINANCIAL INC p 1187
751 Broad St, Newark NJ 07102
Tel (973) 802-6000
SIC 6311 6321 6331 6211 6552

■ PRUDENTIAL INSURANCE CO OF AMERICA p 1187
751 Broad St, Newark NJ 07102
Tel (973) 802-6000
SIC 6311 6371 6282 6722

MERRILL LYNCH INSURANCE GROUP INC p 950
1700 American Blvd, Pennington NJ 08534
Tel (609) 274-5351 *SIC* 6311

■ MUNICH RE AMERICA BROKERS INC p 1000
685 College Rd E, Princeton NJ 08540
Tel (609) 243-4900 *SIC* 6321 6311

■ MUNICH REINSURANCE AMERICA INC p 1000
555 College Rd E, Princeton NJ 08540
Tel (609) 243-4200 *SIC* 6331 6311

LIFE RE CORP p 863
175 King St, Armonk NY 10504
Tel (914) 828-8500 *SIC* 6311 6321

SR CORPORATE SOLUTIONS AMERICA HOLDING CORP p 1362
175 King St, Armonk NY 10504
Tel (914) 828-8000 *SIC* 6331 6311

SECURITY MUTUAL LIFE INSURANCE CO OF NEW YORK p 1299
100 Court St, Binghamton NY 13901
Tel (607) 723-3551 *SIC* 6311 6321

AMERICAN TRANSIT INSURANCE CO INC p 80
1 Metrotech Ctr Fl 7, Brooklyn NY 11201
Tel (212) 857-8200 *SIC* 6321 6331 6311

ELECTRICAL EMPLOYERS SELF INSURANCE SAFETY PLAN p 485
15811 Jewel Ave, Fresh Meadows NY 11365
Tel (718) 591-2000 *SIC* 6311

TRANSAMERICA FINANCIAL LIFE INSURANCE CO p 1470
440 Mamaroneck Ave, Harrison NY 10528
Tel (319) 355-8511 *SIC* 6311

COMPANION LIFE INSURANCE CO p 350
888 Veterans Hwy Ste 515, Hauppauge NY 11788
Tel (866) 371-8905 *SIC* 6311

COMBINED LIFE INSURANCE CO OF NEW YORK INC p 343
11 British American Blvd # 2, Latham NY 12110
Tel (518) 220-9333 *SIC* 6321 6311

UTICA MUTUAL INSURANCE CO p 1537
180 Genesee St, New Hartford NY 13413
Tel (315) 734-2000 *SIC* 6331 6311

ADVISOR GROUP INC p 28
1 World Financial Ctr, New York NY 10281
Tel (866) 673-1550 *SIC* 6311

■ AIG PROPERTY CASUALTY INC p 38
175 Water St Fl 5, New York NY 10038
Tel (212) 458-5000 *SIC* 6331 6321 6311

▲ AMERICAN EXPRESS CO p 72
200 Vesey St, New York NY 10285
Tel (212) 640-2000
SIC 6141 7389 6282 6099 6311 6211

▲ AMERICAN INTERNATIONAL GROUP INC p 75
175 Water St Rm 1800, New York NY 10038
Tel (212) 770-7000
SIC 6331 6321 6311 6324 6411 6282

ARCH CAPITAL GROUP (US) INC p 104
1 Liberty Plz Fl 53, New York NY 10006
Tel (212) 651-6500 *SIC* 6311 6321

▲ ASSURANT INC p 121
28 Liberty St Fl 41, New York NY 10005
Tel (212) 859-7000 *SIC* 6311 6399 6331

ASSURED GUARANTY US HOLDINGS INC p 122
31 W 52nd St Fl 26, New York NY 10019
Tel (212) 974-0100 *SIC* 6311

■ AXA EQUITABLE LIFE INSURANCE CO p 139
1290 Avenue Of The Americ, New York NY 10104
Tel (212) 554-1234 *SIC* 6311 6411 6282

■ AXA FINANCIAL INC p 139
1290 Ave Of The Am Fl Con, New York NY 10104
Tel (212) 554-1234
SIC 6311 6211 6552 6531 6371 6221

CHURCH PENSION GROUP SERVICES CORP p 305
19 E 34th St Fl 3, New York NY 10016
Tel (212) 592-1800
SIC 6371 6321 6311 6331 2731

CIBC WORLD MARKETS CORP p 306
425 Lexington Ave Bsmt C2, New York NY 10017
Tel (212) 667-7000 *SIC* 6211 6311 6531

▲ CITIGROUP INC p 310
399 Park Ave, New York NY 10022
Tel (212) 559-1000
SIC 6021 6141 6331 6311 6321

EMIGRANT SAVINGS BANK p 493
5 E 42nd St Fl 5, New York NY 10017
Tel (212) 850-4000
SIC 6036 6311 6512 6514

FORESTERS FINANCIAL SERVICES p 567
40 Wall St Fl 10, New York NY 10005
Tel (212) 858-8000
SIC 6036 6211 6282 6311 8742 6153

GUARDIAN INSURANCE & ANNUITY CO INC p 645
7 Hanover Sq, New York NY 10004
Tel (212) 598-8000 *SIC* 6311 6371

GUARDIAN LIFE INSURANCE CO OF AMERICA p 645
7 Hanover Sq Fl 14, New York NY 10004
Tel (212) 598-8000
SIC 6311 6371 6324 6321 6722 6282

▲ HRG GROUP INC p 714
450 Park Ave Fl 29, New York NY 10022
Tel (212) 906-8555
SIC 3691 3634 3999 6311

HUDSON INSURANCE CO p 716
100 William St Fl 5, New York NY 10038
Tel (212) 978-2800 *SIC* 6311

▲ LOEWS CORP p 874
667 Madison Ave Fl 7, New York NY 10065
Tel (212) 521-2000
SIC 6331 6311 1381 4922 7011

▲ METLIFE INC p 954
200 Park Ave Fl 1200, New York NY 10166
Tel (212) 578-9500 *SIC* 6311 6321 6331

MUTUAL OF AMERICA CORP p 1003
320 Park Ave Fl 5, New York NY 10022
Tel (212) 224-1147 *SIC* 6311 7389

MUTUAL OF AMERICA LIFE INSURANCE CO p 1003
320 Park Ave Fl 5, New York NY 10022
Tel (212) 224-1600 *SIC* 6311

NEW YORK LIFE INSURANCE CO p 1035
51 Madison Ave Bsmt 1b, New York NY 10010
Tel (212) 576-7000 *SIC* 6311 6321 6282

PROSPERITY LIFE INSURANCE GROUP p 1184
650 Madison Ave Fl 26, New York NY 10022
Tel (212) 223-5627 *SIC* 6311

QBE INSURANCE CORP p 1194
88 Pine St Fl 16, New York NY 10005
Tel (212) 422-1212 *SIC* 6311 6321

■ SEABURY & SMITH (DELAWARE) INC p 1296
1166 Ave Of The Americas, New York NY 10036
Tel (212) 345-9049
SIC 6411 6331 6321 6311

TEACHERS INSURANCE AND ANNUITY ASSOCIATION OF AMERICA p 1429
730 3rd Ave Ste 2a, New York NY 10017
Tel (212) 490-9000 *SIC* 6311

TEACHERS INSURANCE AND ANNUITY ASSOCIATION-COLLEGE RETIREMENT EQUITIES FUND p 1429
730 3rd Ave Ste 2a, New York NY 10017
Tel (212) 490-9000 *SIC* 6311

▲ TIPTREE FINANCIAL INC p 1455
780 3rd Ave Fl 21, New York NY 10017
Tel (212) 446-1400
SIC 6162 6282 6311 6798

■ USL SEPARATE ACCOUNT USL VL-R p 1535
1 World Fin Ctr, New York NY 10281
Tel (800) 874-8743 *SIC* 6311 6321

▲ VOYA FINANCIAL INC p 1566
230 Park Ave Fl 14, New York NY 10169
Tel (212) 309-8200
SIC 6311 6411 6282 6211 7389

ATHENE ANNUITY & LIFE ASSURANCE CO OF NEW YORK p 124
69 Lydecker St, Nyack NY 10960
Tel (845) 358-2300 *SIC* 6311

PRESIDENTIAL LIFE CORP p 1172
69 Lydecker St, Nyack NY 10960
Tel (845) 358-2300 *SIC* 6311

ULYSSES CAREMARK HOLDING CORP p 1501
44 S Broadway Fl 12f, White Plains NY 10601
Tel (914) 934-5200 *SIC* 6311 6321

▲ UNIVERSAL AMERICAN CORP p 1516
44 S Broadway Ste 1200, White Plains NY 10601
Tel (914) 934-5200 *SIC* 6311 6321 6324

RAYCOM SPORTS NETWORK INC p 1210
1900 W Morehead St, Charlotte NC 28208
Tel (704) 378-4400
SIC 6311 6321 6324 6411 4832 4833

▲ SONIC FINANCIAL CORP p 1340
5401 E Independence Blvd, Charlotte NC 28212
Tel (704) 536-5600 *SIC* 7948 6321 6311

NORTH CAROLINA FARM BUREAU INSURANCE AGENCY INC p 1051
5301 Glenwood Ave, Raleigh NC 27612
Tel (919) 782-1705 *SIC* 6331 6411 6311

▲ BB&T CORP p 163
200 W 2nd St Ste 260, Winston Salem NC 27101
Tel (336) 733-2000
SIC 6021 6311 6035 6211

SUMMA INSURANCE CO INC p 1398
10 N Main St, Akron OH 44308
Tel (800) 996-8411 *SIC* 6321 6311

■ MIDLAND-GUARDIAN CO p 966
7000 Midland Blvd, Amelia OH 45102
Tel (513) 943-7100 *SIC* 6311 6331

▲ AMERICAN FINANCIAL GROUP INC p 72
301 E 4th St, Cincinnati OH 45202
Tel (513) 579-2121 *SIC* 6331 6311 6321

INTEGRITY LIFE INSURANCE CO p 750
400 Broadway St, Cincinnati OH 45202
Tel (513) 362-8000 *SIC* 6311

■ LOYAL AMERICAN LIFE INSURANCE CO p 882
250 E 5th St Fl 8, Cincinnati OH 45202
Tel (800) 633-6752 *SIC* 6311

UNION CENTRAL LIFE INSURANCE CO p 1504
1876 Waycross Rd, Cincinnati OH 45240
Tel (866) 696-7478 *SIC* 6311 6321

■ PROGRESSIVE BAYSIDE INSURANCE CO p 1181
6300 Wilson Mills Rd, Cleveland OH 44143
Tel (440) 395-4460 *SIC* 6311

CENTRIC FINANCIAL GROUP LLC p 281
4016 Townsfair Way # 202, Columbus OH 43219
Tel (614) 824-6100 *SIC* 6311 6282 6321

MOTORISTS LIFE INSURANCE CO p 993
471 E Broad St Ste 200, Columbus OH 43215
Tel (614) 225-8211 *SIC* 6311

NATIONWIDE FINANCIAL SERVICES INC p 1017
1 Nationwide Plz, Columbus OH 43215
Tel (614) 249-7111 *SIC* 6311 6411 8742

NATIONWIDE MUTUAL INSURANCE CO p 1018
1 Nationwide Plz, Columbus OH 43215
Tel (614) 249-7111
SIC 6331 6311 6321 6531

▲ FIRST DEFIANCE FINANCIAL CORP p 546
601 Clinton St, Defiance OH 43512
Tel (419) 782-5015
SIC 6035 6331 6321 6311

▲ CINCINNATI FINANCIAL CORP p 307
6200 S Gilmore Rd, Fairfield OH 45014
Tel (513) 870-2000 *SIC* 6311 6411

■ CINCINNATI INSURANCE CO p 307
6200 S Gilmore Rd, Fairfield OH 45014
Tel (513) 870-2000
SIC 6311 6331 6321 6211

■ CINCINNATI LIFE INSURANCE CO p 307
6200 S Gilmore Rd, Fairfield OH 45014
Tel (513) 870-2000 *SIC* 6311

OHIO CASUALTY INSURANCE CO p 1077
9450 Seward Rd, Fairfield OH 45014
Tel (800) 843-6446 *SIC* 6331 6311

OHIO NATIONAL FINANCIAL SERVICES INC p 1077
1 Financial Way Ste 100, Montgomery OH 45242
Tel (513) 794-6100 *SIC* 6311

OHIO NATIONAL MUTUAL HOLDINGS INC p 1078
1 Financial Way Ste 100, Montgomery OH 45242
Tel (513) 794-6100 *SIC* 6311

AMERICAN FIDELITY ASSURANCE CO p 72
9000 Cameron Pkwy, Oklahoma City OK 73114
Tel (405) 523-2000 *SIC* 6321 6311

AMERICAN FIDELITY CORP p 72
2000 Classen Ctr Blvd, Oklahoma City OK 73106
Tel (405) 523-2000 *SIC* 6321 6311

AMERICAN FIDELITY GENERAL AGENCY INC p 72
9000 Cameron Pkwy, Oklahoma City OK 73114
Tel (405) 523-2000 *SIC* 6321 6311

■ GLOBE LIFE & ACCIDENT INSURANCE CO p 618
204 N Robinson Ave, Oklahoma City OK 73102
Tel (972) 540-6542 *SIC* 6311 6321

STANCORP MORTGAGE INVESTORS LLC p 1375
19225 Nw Tanasbourne Dr, Hillsboro OR 97124
Tel (503) 321-7785 *SIC* 6311

PRECOA LLC p 1169
13221 Sw 68th Pkwy # 100, Portland OR 97223
Tel (503) 244-7755 *SIC* 6311

STANCORP FINANCIAL GROUP INC p 1375
1100 Sw 6th Ave, Portland OR 97204
Tel (971) 321-7000 *SIC* 6311 6321

STANDARD INSURANCE CO p 1376
920 Sw 6th Ave Ste 1100, Portland OR 97204
Tel (971) 321-7000 *SIC* 6311 6321 6411

■ PLANCO FINANCIAL SERVICES INC p 1154
1500 Liberty Ridge Dr # 100, Chesterbrook PA 19087
Tel (610) 695-9500 *SIC* 6211 6311

PEOPLES BENEFIT LIFE INSURANCE CO p 1132
300 Eagleview Blvd, Exton PA 19341
Tel (610) 648-5000 *SIC* 6311 6321

COVENTRY FIRST LLC p 384
7111 Valley Green Rd, Fort Washington PA 19034
Tel (877) 836-8300 *SIC* 6311

COVENTRY GROUP INC p 384
7111 Valley Green Rd # 320, Fort Washington PA 19034
Tel (215) 233-5100 *SIC* 6311

■ OLD REPUBLIC INSURANCE CO p 1081
133 Oakland Ave, Greensburg PA 15601
Tel (724) 838-5400 *SIC* 6411 6321 6311

HARLEYSVILLE MUTUAL INSURANCE CO p 662
355 Maple Ave, Harleysville PA 19438
Tel (215) 256-5000 *SIC* 6311 6331

PENN MUTUAL LIFE INSURANCE CO p 1129
600 Dresher Rd, Horsham PA 19044
Tel (215) 956-8000 *SIC* 6311

■ EASTERN INSURANCE HOLDINGS INC p 472
25 Race Ave, Lancaster PA 17603
Tel (717) 239-1641 *SIC* 6311 6331

VETERANS LIFE INSURANCE CO INC p 1553
20 Moores Rd, Malvern PA 19355
Tel (610) 648-5000 *SIC* 6311 6321

NATIONAL SLOVAK SOCIETY OF USA INC p 1016
351 Valley Brook Rd, Mc Murray PA 15317
Tel (724) 731-0094 *SIC* 6311

■ CIGNA LIFE INSURANCE CO OF NEW YORK p 306
Two Liberty Place, Philadelphia PA 19192
Tel (215) 761-2355 *SIC* 6321 6311

■ COLONIAL PENN LIFE INSURANCE CO p 338
399 Market St, Philadelphia PA 19181
Tel (215) 928-8000 *SIC* 6321 6311

■ LIFE INSURANCE CO OF NORTH AMERICA p 863
1601 Chestnut St, Philadelphia PA 19192
Tel (215) 761-1000 *SIC* 6321 6311

PHILADELPHIA CONTRIBUTIONSHIP FOR INSURANCE OF HOUSES FROM LOSS BY FIRE p 1142
212 S 4th St, Philadelphia PA 19106
Tel (215) 627-1752
SIC 6331 6311 7382 6321

RELIANCE STANDARD LIFE INSURANCE CO p 1222
2001 Market St Ste 1500, Philadelphia PA 19103
Tel (267) 256-3500 *SIC* 6311 6321

GBU FINANCIAL LIFE p 595
4254 Saw Mill Run Blvd, Pittsburgh PA 15227
Tel (412) 884-5100 *SIC* 6311

HM INSURANCE GROUP INC p 697
120 5th Ave, Pittsburgh PA 15222
Tel (412) 544-1000 *SIC* 6311 6371

▲ LINCOLN NATIONAL CORP p 867
150 N Rad Chester Rd A305 Ste A, Radnor PA 19087
Tel (484) 583-1400
SIC 6311 6321 6371 6722 6411 6282

■ VOYA INSURANCE AND ANNUITY CO p 1566
1475 Dunwoody Dr, West Chester PA 19380
Tel (610) 425-3400 *SIC* 6311

▲ TRIPLE-S MANAGEMENT CORP p 1482
1441 Ave Fd Roosevelt, San Juan PR 00920
Tel (787) 749-4949 *SIC* 6324 6311 6321

■ VIDA TRIPLE-S INC p 1556
1052 Ave Munoz Rivera, San Juan PR 00927
Tel (800) 980-7651 *SIC* 6311

AMWINS GROUP BENEFITS INC p 87
50 Whitecap Dr, North Kingstown RI 02852
Tel (877) 739-3330 *SIC* 6311 6321

BRUCE SEIBELS GROUP INC p 220
1501 Lady St, Columbia SC 29201
Tel (803) 748-2000 *SIC* 6331 6321 6311

■ COLONIAL LIFE & ACCIDENT INSURANCE CO INC p 337
1200 Colonial Life Blvd W, Columbia SC 29210
Tel (803) 798-7000 *SIC* 6321 6311

MIDLAND NATIONAL LIFE INSURANCE CO p 966
1 Sammons Plz, Sioux Falls SD 57193
Tel (605) 335-5700 *SIC* 6311

■ AMERICAN GENERAL LIFE & ACCIDENT INSURANCE CO p 73
2000 American General Way, Brentwood TN 37027
Tel (800) 265-5054 *SIC* 6311

■ PROVIDENT LIFE & ACCIDENT INSURANCE CO p 1186
1 Fountain Sq Ste 1, Chattanooga TN 37402
Tel (423) 755-1011 *SIC* 6311 6321

▲ UNUM GROUP p 1528
1 Fountain Sq, Chattanooga TN 37402
Tel (423) 294-1011
SIC 6321 6324 6311 6371

AMERICAN INCOME LIFE p 74
8820 Trinity Rd, Cordova TN 38018
Tel (901) 748-5584 *SIC* 6311

■ DIRECT GENERAL CORP p 441
1281 Murfreesboro Pike # 150, Nashville TN 37217
Tel (615) 399-4700
SIC 6311 6321 6331 6411

■ CICA LIFE INSURANCE CO OF AMERICA p 306
400 E Anderson Ln, Austin TX 78752
Tel (512) 836-9730 *SIC* 6311

▲ CITIZENS INC p 311
400 E Anderson Ln Ste 600, Austin TX 78752
Tel (512) 837-7100 *SIC* 6311 6321

▲ NATIONAL WESTERN LIFE INSURANCE CO p 1017
850 E Anderson Ln, Austin TX 78752
Tel (512) 836-1010 *SIC* 6311

SHA LLC p 1310
12940 N Hwy 183, Austin TX 78750
Tel (512) 257-6000 *SIC* 6324 6311 6321

GERMANIA FARM MUTUAL INSURANCE ASSOCIATION p 609
507 Highway 290 E, Brenham TX 77833
Tel (979) 836-5224 *SIC* 6311 6331

■ REPUBLIC COMPANIES INC p 1225
5525 Lyndon B Johnson Fwy, Dallas TX 75240
Tel (972) 788-6001 *SIC* 6321 6311 6331

SAMMONS ENTERPRISES INC p 1274
5949 Sherry Ln Ste 1900, Dallas TX 75225
Tel (214) 210-5000 *SIC* 5084 6311

SOUTHWESTERN FINANCIAL SERVICES CORP p 1353
12001 N Cntl Expy Ste 800, Dallas TX 75243
Tel (800) 792-4368 *SIC* 6311

FIRST COMMAND FINANCIAL PLANNING INC p 545
1 Firstcomm Plz, Fort Worth TX 76109
Tel (817) 731-8621 *SIC* 6311 6211

▲ HALLMARK FINANCIAL SERVICES INC p 654
777 Main St Ste 1000, Fort Worth TX 76102
Tel (817) 348-1600 *SIC* 6411 6311

PENN TREATY AMERICAN CORP p 1129
2500 Legacy Dr Ste 130, Frisco TX 75034
Tel (469) 287-7044 *SIC* 6311

▲ AMERICAN NATIONAL INSURANCE CO INC p 77
1 Moody Plz Fl 18, Galveston TX 77550
Tel (409) 763-4661
SIC 6351 6311 6321 6324 6331

■ STANDARD LIFE & ACCIDENT INSURANCE CO INC p 1376
1 Moody Plz, Galveston TX 77550
Tel (409) 766-6036 SIC 6324 6311

■ AIG LIFE HOLDINGS INC p 38
2929 Allen Pkwy, Houston TX 77019
Tel (713) 522-1111
SIC 6311 6321 6331 6141 6162 6153

■ ALDERWOODS (DELAWARE) INC p 47
1929 Allen Pkwy, Houston TX 77019
Tel (713) 522-5141 SIC 7261 6553 6311

■ AMERICAN GENERAL LIFE INSURANCE CO p 73
2727 Allen Pkwy Ste A, Houston TX 77019
Tel (713) 522-1111 SIC 6311

■ AMERICAN GENERAL LIFE INSURANCE CO p 73
10700 Northwest Fwy # 300, Houston TX 77092
Tel (713) 522-1111 SIC 6311

CENTRAL UNITED LIFE INSURANCE CO INC p 280
10777 Northwest Fwy # 100, Houston TX 77092
Tel (713) 529-0045 SIC 6311

FORETHOUGHT FINANCIAL GROUP INC p 567
3200 Southwest Fwy # 1300, Houston TX 77027
Tel (713) 599-0405 SIC 6311

HCC INSURANCE HOLDINGS INC p 672
13403 Northwest Fwy, Houston TX 77040
Tel (713) 690-7300 SIC 6311 6321 6331

RELIANCE STANDARD LIFE INSURANCE CO OF TEXAS p 1222
7600 W Tidwell Rd Ste 111, Houston TX 77040
Tel (713) 468-2603 SIC 6311 6321

■ VARIABLE ANNUITY LIFE INSURANCE CO (INC) p 1544
2929 Allen Pkwy, Houston TX 77019
Tel (713) 522-1111 SIC 6311

■ ASSOCIATES CORP OF NORTH AMERICA p 121
250 E John Carpenter Fwy, Irving TX 75062
Tel (972) 652-4000
SIC 6141 6153 6159 6311 6321 6331

▲ INSPERITY INC p 746
19001 Crescent Springs Dr, Kingwood TX 77339
Tel (281) 358-8986
SIC 8742 7363 7361 6311

▲ TORCHMARK CORP p 1461
3700 S Stonebridge Dr, Mckinney TX 75070
Tel (972) 569-4000 SIC 6321 6311

■ UNITED AMERICAN INSURANCE CO p 1506
3700 S Stonebridge Dr, Mckinney TX 75070
Tel (800) 331-2512 SIC 6321 6311

HEALTHMARKETS INC p 677
9151 Blvd 256, North Richland Hills TX 76180
Tel (817) 255-3100 SIC 6311 6321

HEALTHMARKETS LLC p 677
9151 Boulevard 26, North Richland Hills TX 76180
Tel (817) 255-3100 SIC 6311 6321

J C PENNEY LIFE INSURANCE CO p 770
2700 W Plano Pkwy, Plano TX 75075
Tel (972) 881-6000 SIC 6311 6321

BLUE CROSS AND BLUE SHIELD OF TEXAS INC p 191
1001 E Lookout Dr, Richardson TX 75082
Tel (972) 766-6900 SIC 6324 6311

CATHOLIC LIFE INSURANCE p 267
1635 Ne Loop 410 Ste 300, San Antonio TX 78209
Tel (210) 828-9921 SIC 6311 6411

UNITED SERVICES AUTOMOBILE ASSOCIATION p 1511
9800 Fredericksburg Rd, San Antonio TX 78288
Tel (210) 498-2211 SIC 6331 6311 6351

USAA LIFE INSURANCE CO p 1534
9800 Fredericksburg Rd, San Antonio TX 78288
Tel (210) 498-2211 SIC 6331 6311

■ AMERICAN INCOME LIFE INSURANCE CO INC p 74
1200 Wooded Acres Dr, Waco TX 76710
Tel (254) 741-5701 SIC 6311

TEXAS LIFE INSURANCE CO p 1444
900 Washington Ave # 400, Waco TX 76701
Tel (254) 752-6521 SIC 6311

■ ALLY BANK p 59
6985 S Union Park Ctr # 435, Midvale UT 84047
Tel (801) 790-5005
SIC 6153 6021 6311 6331 6162

BENEFICIAL LIFE INSURANCE CO p 172
55 N 300 W Ste 375, Salt Lake City UT 84101
Tel (801) 933-1272 SIC 6311

EQUITABLE LIFE & CASUALTY INSURANCE CO p 506
3 Triad Ctr, Salt Lake City UT 84180
Tel (801) 579-3400 SIC 6411 6311

▲ SECURITY NATIONAL FINANCIAL CORP p 1299
5300 S 360 W Ste 250, Salt Lake City UT 84123
Tel (801) 264-1060 SIC 6311 6531 6162

NATIONAL LIFE HOLDING CO p 1014
1 National Life Dr, Montpelier VT 05604
Tel (802) 229-3333 SIC 6311 6321

NATIONAL LIFE INSURANCE CO p 1014
1 National Life Dr, Montpelier VT 05604
Tel (802) 229-3333 SIC 6311

NLV FINANCIAL CORP p 1045
1 National Life Dr, Montpelier VT 05604
Tel (802) 229-3333 SIC 6311 6321

■ GE FINANCIAL ASSURANCE HOLDINGS INC p 596
6604 W Broad St, Richmond VA 23230
Tel (804) 281-6000 SIC 6311

▲ GENWORTH FINANCIAL INC p 605
6620 W Broad St Ste 270, Richmond VA 23230
Tel (804) 281-6000 SIC 6311 6371 6351

■ GENWORTH LIFE AND ANNUITY INSURANCE CO p 605
6610 W Broad St, Richmond VA 23230
Tel (804) 281-6000 SIC 6311 6211

■ GENWORTH LIFE INSURANCE CO p 605
6620 W Broad St, Richmond VA 23230
Tel (804) 281-6000 SIC 6311

SHENANDOAH LIFE INSURANCE CO p 1315
4415 Pheasant Ridge Rd # 300, Roanoke VA 24014
Tel (540) 985-4400 SIC 6311

SYMETRA FINANCIAL CORP p 1414
777 108th Ave Ne Ste 1200, Bellevue WA 98004
Tel (425) 256-8000 SIC 6311 6411

SYMETRA LIFE INSURANCE CO p 1414
777 108th Ave Ne Ste 1200, Bellevue WA 98004
Tel (877) 796-3872 SIC 6311 6324 6411

MUTUAL OF ENUMCLAW INSURANCE CO p 1003
1460 Wells St, Enumclaw WA 98022
Tel (360) 825-2591 SIC 6331 6311

FARMERS NEW WORLD LIFE INSURANCE CO INC p 530
3003 77th Ave Se, Mercer Island WA 98040
Tel (206) 232-1093 SIC 6311 6411

SAFECO CORP p 1266
1001 4th Ave Ste 800, Seattle WA 98185
Tel (206) 545-5000
SIC 6411 6311 6321 6324 6351

■ AMERICAN MEDICAL SECURITY GROUP INC PAC p 76
3100 Ams Blvd, Green Bay WI 54313
Tel (920) 661-1111 SIC 6321 6311

■ HUMANA INSURANCE CO p 718
1100 Employers Blvd, Green Bay WI 54344
Tel (502) 580-1000 SIC 6311 6321

■ UNITEDHEALTHCARE LIFE INSURANCE CO p 1515
3100 Ams Blvd, Green Bay WI 54313
Tel (800) 232-5432
SIC 6411 6324 6311 8322

AMERICAN FAMILY MUTUAL INSURANCE CO INC p 72
6000 American Pkwy, Madison WI 53783
Tel (608) 249-2111 SIC 6331 6311

AMFAM INC p 85
6000 American Pkwy, Madison WI 53783
Tel (608) 249-2111 SIC 6331 6311 6141

CMFG LIFE INSURANCE CO p 329
5910 Mineral Point Rd, Madison WI 53705
Tel (800) 356-2644 SIC 6321 6311

CUNA MUTUAL GROUP p 401
5910 Mineral Point Rd, Madison WI 53705
Tel (608) 238-5851
SIC 6331 6311 6351 6411 7515

NATIONAL GUARDIAN LIFE INSURANCE CO (INC) p 1013
2 E Gilman St Stop 1, Madison WI 53703
Tel (608) 257-5611 SIC 6311

WEA INSURANCE CORP p 1585
45 Nob Hill Rd, Madison WI 53713
Tel (608) 276-4000 SIC 6324 6311 6321

■ ALDEN JOHN LIFE INSURANCE CO p 47
501 W Michigan St, Milwaukee WI 53203
Tel (414) 271-3011 SIC 6311

■ AMERICAN GENERAL LIFE BROKERAGE GROUP p 73
1200 N Mayfair Rd Ste 300, Milwaukee WI 53226
Tel (414) 443-5800 SIC 6311 6411

CATHOLIC FINANCIAL SERVICES CORP p 266
1100 W Wells St Ste 1, Milwaukee WI 53233
Tel (414) 278-6550 SIC 6311 6211

CATHOLIC KNIGHTS INSURANCE SOCIETY INC p 267
1100 W Wells St Ste 1, Milwaukee WI 53233
Tel (414) 273-6266
SIC 6311 6411 6211 6141

■ FORTIS INSURANCE CO p 569
501 W Michigan St, Milwaukee WI 53203
Tel (262) 646-4633 SIC 6311 6321

NORTHWESTERN MUTUAL LIFE INSURANCE CO p 1060
720 E Wisconsin Ave, Milwaukee WI 53202
Tel (414) 271-1444 SIC 6311 6321 7389

JOHNSON FINANCIAL GROUP INC p 791
555 Main St Ste 400, Racine WI 53403
Tel (262) 619-2700
SIC 6022 6021 6712 6733 6311

SENTRY INSURANCE A MUTUAL CO p 1305
1800 Northpoint Dr, Stevens Point WI 54481
Tel (715) 346-6000
SIC 6331 6311 6411 6321

EMPLOYERS INSURANCE OF WAUSAU A MUTUAL CO p 494
2000 Westwood Dr, Wausau WI 54401
Tel (715) 845-5211 SIC 6331 6311

WAUSAU SERVICE CORP p 1583
2000 Westwood Dr, Wausau WI 54401
Tel (715) 845-5211 SIC 6331 6311

SIC 6321 Accident & Health Insurance

▲ PROASSURANCE CORP p 1178
100 Brookwood Pl Ste 500, Birmingham AL 35209
Tel (205) 877-4400 SIC 6351 6321

PROTECTIVE LIFE CORP p 1185
2801 Highway 280 S Ofc, Birmingham AL 35223
Tel (205) 268-1000
SIC 6311 6321 6351 6411

BLUE CROSS & BLUE SHIELD OF ALABAMA p 191
450 Riverchase Pkwy E, Hoover AL 35244
Tel (205) 988-2200 SIC 6321 6324

■ LIBERTY NATIONAL LIFE INSURANCE CO p 862
100 Cncourse Pkwy Ste 350, Hoover AL 35244
Tel (205) 325-2722 SIC 6321 6311

HEALTH CHOICE ARIZONA INC p 674
410 N 44th St Ste 900, Phoenix AZ 85008
Tel (480) 968-6866 SIC 6321 6411

LONDEN INSURANCE GROUP INC p 875
4343 E Camelback Rd # 400, Phoenix AZ 85018
Tel (602) 957-1650 SIC 6311 6321 8741

■ OXFORD LIFE INSURANCE CO INC p 1101
2721 N Central Ave Fl 5, Phoenix AZ 85004
Tel (602) 263-6666 SIC 6311 6321

BLUE ADVANTAGE ADMINISTRATORS OF ARKANSAS p 190
320 W Capitol Ave Ste 500, Little Rock AR 72201
Tel (501) 378-3600 SIC 6321

USABLE LIFE p 1534
17500 Chenal Pkwy, Little Rock AR 72223
Tel (800) 648-0271 SIC 6311 6321

AUTO CLUB ENTERPRISES p 133
3333 Fairview Rd Msa451, Costa Mesa CA 92626
Tel (714) 850-5111 SIC 6321

■ OPTUMRX INC p 1091
2300 Main St, Irvine CA 92614
Tel (714) 825-3600 SIC 6324 6321

■ MOLINA HEALTHCARE OF CALIFORNIA PARTNER PLAN INC p 982
200 Oceangate Ste 100, Long Beach CA 90802
Tel (562) 435-3666 SIC 6321 8011

JOHN HANCOCK LIFE INSURANCE CO (USA) p 788
865 S Figueroa St # 3320, Los Angeles CA 90017
Tel (213) 689-0813
SIC 7389 6351 6371 6321

TRANSAMERICA OCCIDENTAL LIFE INSURANCE CO p 1470
1150 S Olive St Fl 23, Los Angeles CA 90015
Tel (213) 742-2111
SIC 6311 6371 6321 6324 6799

DOCTORS CO AN INTERINSURANCE EXCHANGE p 447
185 Greenwood Rd, Napa CA 94558
Tel (707) 226-0100 SIC 6321

PACIFIC LIFE INSURANCE CO p 1105
700 Newport Center Dr, Newport Beach CA 92660
Tel (949) 219-3011
SIC 6311 6371 6321 7359

PACIFIC LIFECORP p 1105
700 Newport Center Dr, Newport Beach CA 92660
Tel (949) 219-3011
SIC 6371 6311 6321 6035 8111

PACIFIC MUTUAL HOLDING CO p 1105
700 Newport Center Dr, Newport Beach CA 92660
Tel (949) 219-3011 SIC 6371 6311 6321

FIREMANS FUND INSURANCE CO p 543
777 San Marin Dr Ste 2160, Novato CA 94945
Tel (415) 899-2000 SIC 6331 6351 6321

ASSOCIATED INDEMNITY CORP p 120
1465 N Mcdowell Blvd # 100, Petaluma CA 94954
Tel (415) 899-2000
SIC 6311 6321 6331 6351

SAN FRANCISCO REINSURANCE CO p 1276
1465 N Mcdowell Blvd, Petaluma CA 94954
Tel (415) 899-2000 SIC 6321

INLAND EMPIRE HEALTH PLAN p 743
10801 6th St Ste 120, Rancho Cucamonga CA 91730
Tel (909) 890-2000 SIC 6321 6324

WESTERN HEALTH ADVANTAGE p 1598
2349 Gateway Oaks Dr # 100, Sacramento CA 95833
Tel (916) 567-1950 SIC 6321

BLUE SHIELD OF CALIFORNIA LIFE & HEALTH INSURANCE CO p 192
50 Beale St Ste 2000, San Francisco CA 94105
Tel (415) 229-5000 SIC 6311 6321

21ST CENTURY LIFE AND HEALTH CO INC p 1
21600 Oxnard St Ste 1500, Woodland Hills CA 91367
Tel (818) 887-4436 SIC 6321

■ HEALTH NET OF CALIFORNIA INC p 675
21281 Burbank Blvd Fl 4, Woodland Hills CA 91367
Tel (818) 676-6775
SIC 6324 8062 6311 6321 6331 5912

LIFECARE ASSURANCE CO INC p 864
21600 Oxnard St Fl 16, Woodland Hills CA 91367
Tel (818) 887-4436 SIC 6321 6411 6311

ROCKY MOUNTAIN HEALTH MAINTENANCE ORGANIZATION INC p 1245
2775 Crossroads Blvd, Grand Junction CO 81506
Tel (970) 243-7050 SIC 6321

M&C HOTEL INTERESTS INC p 890
6560 Greenwood Plaza Blvd # 300, Greenwood Village CO 80111
Tel (303) 779-2000
SIC 8741 8712 6321 6331 7389

RICHFIELD HOLDINGS INC p 1233
5775 Dtc Blvd Ste 300, Greenwood Village CO 80111
Tel (303) 220-2000
SIC 6321 8712 7389 6331 7011

GLOBAL HEALTHCARE EXCHANGE LLC p 616
1315 W Century Dr Ste 100, Louisville CO 80027
Tel (720) 887-7000 SIC 6321

▲ CIGNA CORP p 306
900 Cottage Grove Rd, Bloomfield CT 06002
Tel (860) 226-6000
SIC 6324 6311 6351 6321

■ CONNECTICUT GENERAL CORP p 357
900 Cottage Grove Rd, Bloomfield CT 06002
Tel (860) 226-6000 SIC 6311 6321

■ CONNECTICUT GENERAL LIFE INSURANCE CO p 357
900 Cottage Grove Rd, Bloomfield CT 06002
Tel (860) 226-6000 SIC 6311 6321

▲ W R BERKLEY CORP p 1569
475 Steamboat Rd Fl 1, Greenwich CT 06830
Tel (203) 629-3000
SIC 6331 6321 6351 6311

■ AETNA HEALTH HOLDINGS LLC p 31
151 Farmington Ave, Hartford CT 06156
Tel (860) 273-0123 SIC 6324 6411 6321

▲ AETNA INC p 31
151 Farmington Ave, Hartford CT 06156
Tel (860) 273-0123
SIC 6324 6321 6371 8011

■ AETNA LIFE INSURANCE CO INC p 31
151 Farmington Ave, Hartford CT 06156
Tel (860) 273-0123 SIC 6324 6321 8011

■ AHP HOLDINGS INC p 37
151 Farmington Ave, Hartford CT 06156
Tel (860) 273-0123 SIC 6321 6311 8011

■ CIGNA RE CORP p 306
900 Cottage Grove Rd, Hartford CT 06152
Tel (860) 726-6000 SIC 6311 6321

▲ HARTFORD FINANCIAL SERVICES GROUP INC p 665
1 Hartford Plz, Hartford CT 06155
Tel (860) 547-5000
SIC 6331 6311 6351 6321

■ TRAVELERS CASUALTY CO OF CONNECTICUT p 1474
1 Tower Sq, Hartford CT 06183
Tel (860) 277-0111 SIC 6331 6351 6321

TRAVELERS COMPANIES FOUNDATION INC p 1474
1 Tower Sq, Hartford CT 06183
Tel (860) 842-5075 SIC 6321

■ TRI STATE BUSINESS SYSTEMS INC p 1477
1 Tower Sq, Hartford CT 06183
Tel (860) 277-0111 SIC 6311 6321

■ UNITEDHEALTHCARE INSURANCE CO p 1515
185 Asylum St, Hartford CT 06103
Tel (860) 702-5000 SIC 6311 6321

AFFINION GROUP INC p 32
6 High Ridge Park Bldg A, Stamford CT 06905
Tel (203) 956-1000 SIC 7389 5961 6321

■ GENERAL REINSURANCE CORP p 602
120 Long Ridge Rd, Stamford CT 06902
Tel (203) 328-5000
SIC 6331 6351 6411 6321

■ GENERAL STAR INDEMNITY CO p 602
695 Main St Ste 1, Stamford CT 06901
Tel (203) 328-5000 SIC 6321

■ INDEPENDENCE HOLDING CO p 736
96 Cummings Point Rd, Stamford CT 06902
Tel (203) 358-8000 SIC 6311 6321

XL AMERICA INC p 1632
70 Seaview Ave Ste 7, Stamford CT 06902
Tel (203) 964-5200 SIC 6411 6321 6351

XL SPECIALTY INSURANCE CO p 1632
70 Seaview Ave Ste 5, Stamford CT 06902
Tel (800) 622-7311 SIC 6321

■ HARTFORD LIFE AND ANNUITY INSURANCE CO p 665
200 Hopmeadow St, Weatogue CT 06089
Tel (860) 547-5000 SIC 6311 6321

■ CIGNA HOLDINGS INC p 306
590 Naamans Rd, Claymont DE 19703
Tel (215) 761-1000
SIC 6311 6321 6331 6512 6514 6282

■ CITICORP DEL-LEASE INC p 310
1 Penns Way, New Castle DE 19721
Tel (302) 323-3801 SIC 6022 6311 6321

■ AMERICAN LIFE INSURANCE CO p 75
1 Alico Plz, Wilmington DE 19801
Tel (302) 594-2000 SIC 6411 6321 6324

DELPHI FINANCIAL GROUP INC p 425
1105 N Market St Ste 1230, Wilmington DE 19801
Tel (302) 478-5142 SIC 6321

HIGHMARKS INC p 692
800 Delaware Ave Ste 900, Wilmington DE 19801
Tel (302) 421-3000 SIC 6321

ULLICO INC p 1500
1625 I St Nw Fl 5, Washington DC 20006
Tel (202) 682-0900 SIC 6311 6321

■ AMERICAN HERITAGE LIFE INSURANCE CO INC p 74
1776 Amercn Heritg Lf Dr, Jacksonville FL 32224
Tel (904) 992-1776 SIC 6321 6311 6351

■ AMERICAN HERITAGE LIFE INVESTMENT CORP p 74
1776 Amercn Heritg Lf Dr, Jacksonville FL 32224
Tel (904) 992-1776
SIC 6311 6321 6351 7374

ASSUREDPARTNERS GULF COAST INSURANCE AGENCY LLC p 122
200 Colonial Center Pkwy, Lake Mary FL 32746
Tel (407) 804-5222 SIC 6321

■ UNITED HEALTHCARE OF FLORIDA INC p 1509
495 N Keller Rd Ste 200, Maitland FL 32751
Tel (407) 659-6900 SIC 6321

■ AMERICAN BANKERS INSURANCE GROUP INC p 68
11222 Quail Roost Dr, Miami FL 33157
Tel (305) 253-2244
SIC 6331 6311 6351 6321 6324

■ NEIGHBORHOOD HEALTH PARTNERSHIP INC p 1024
7600 Nw 19th St Ste 100, Miami FL 33126
Tel (305) 715-2200 SIC 6324 6321

■ SIMPLY HEALTHCARE HOLDINGS INC p 1325
9250 W Flagler St Ste 600, Miami FL 33174
Tel (877) 915-0551 SIC 6321 6719

■ SIMPLY HEALTHCARE PLANS INC p 1325
9250 W Flagler St Ste 600, Miami FL 33174
Tel (305) 408-5700 SIC 6321

BUPA INSURANCE CO p 226
17901 Old Cutler Rd, Palmetto Bay FL 33157
Tel (305) 275-1400 SIC 6321

FLORIDA HEALTHY KIDS CORP p 558
661 E Jefferson St # 200, Tallahassee FL 32301
Tel (850) 701-6160 SIC 6321

PHYSICIANS UNITED PLAN INC p 1146
2020 Capital Cir Se 310, Tallahassee FL 32301
Tel (888) 827-5787 SIC 6321

■ BLUE CROSS AND BLUE SHIELD OF GEORGIA INC p 191
3350 Peachtree Rd Ne # 300, Atlanta GA 30326
Tel (404) 842-8000 SIC 6324 6321

■ RSUI GROUP INC p 1256
945 E Paces Ferry Rd Ne # 1800, Atlanta GA 30326
Tel (404) 231-2366 SIC 6331 6321

▲ ATLANTIC AMERICAN CORP p 125
4370 Peachtree Rd Ne # 200, Brookhaven GA 30319
Tel (404) 266-5500 SIC 6311 6321 6331

▲AFLAC INC p 33
1932 Wynnton Rd, Columbus GA 31999
Tel (706) 323-3431 *SIC* 6321 6311

HAWAII MEDICAL SERVICE ASSOCIATION p 669
818 Keeaumoku St Ste 200, Honolulu HI 96814
Tel (808) 948-6111 *SIC* 6321 6324

PACIFIC GUARDIAN LIFE INSURANCE CO LIMITED p 1104
1440 Kalani St Ste 1700, Honolulu HI 96817
Tel (808) 942-6541 *SIC* 6311 6321

BLUE CROSS OF IDAHO CARE PLUS INC p 192
3000 E Pine Ave, Meridian ID 83642
Tel (208) 345-4550 *SIC* 6321

BLUE CROSS OF IDAHO HEALTH SERVICE INC p 192
3000 E Pine Ave, Meridian ID 83642
Tel (208) 331-7408 *SIC* 6321

COUNTRY LIFE INSURANCE CO p 375
1701 Towanda Ave, Bloomington IL 61701
Tel (309) 557-3000 *SIC* 6311 6321

STATE FARM MUTUAL AUTOMOBILE INSURANCE CO p 1381
1 State Farm Plz, Bloomington IL 61710
Tel (309) 766-2311
SIC 6321 6311 6036 6331

■AMERICAN IMAGING MANAGEMENT INC p 74
8600 W Bryn Mawr Ave 800s, Chicago IL 60631
Tel (773) 864-4600 *SIC* 6321

AMERICAN MEDICAL ASSOCIATION INC p 76
330 N Wabash Ave # 39300, Chicago IL 60611
Tel (312) 464-5000
SIC 8621 2721 6321 6282

AON BENFIELD FAC INC p 94
200 E Randolph St Fl 15, Chicago IL 60601
Tel (312) 381-5300 *SIC* 6321 6311

B C S INSURANCE CO p 141
676 N Saint Clair St # 1500, Chicago IL 60611
Tel (312) 371-6006 *SIC* 6321

■BANKERS LIFE & CASUALTY CO p 152
111 E Wacker Dr Ste 2100, Chicago IL 60601
Tel (312) 396-6000 *SIC* 6321 6311 6324

■CELTIC GROUP INC p 274
233 S Wacker Dr Ste 700, Chicago IL 60606
Tel (312) 332-5401 *SIC* 6321 6311

COMBINED INSURANCE CO OF AMERICA p 343
200 E Randolph St Lbby 10, Chicago IL 60601
Tel (800) 225-4500 *SIC* 6321 6311

CONTINENTAL ASSURANCE CO p 362
333 S Wabash Ave Fl 43, Chicago IL 60604
Tel (312) 822-5000 *SIC* 6411 6371 6321

DESTINY HEALTH INC p 432
200 W Monroe St Ste 1900, Chicago IL 60606
Tel (312) 224-7100 *SIC* 6321 8399

HEALTH CARE SERVICE CORP A MUTUAL LEGAL RESERVE CO p 674
300 E Randolph St Fl 4, Chicago IL 60601
Tel (312) 653-6000 *SIC* 6324 6321 6411

HEALTH CARE SERVICE CORP ILLINOIS STATE PAC NFP p 674
300 E Randolph St Fl 4, Chicago IL 60601
Tel (312) 653-6000 *SIC* 6321

▲KEMPER CORP p 809
1 E Wacker Dr, Chicago IL 60601
Tel (312) 661-4600
SIC 6331 6321 6311 6141

NORTH AMERICAN CO FOR LIFE & HEALTH INSURANCE p 1049
525 W Van Buren St # 1200, Chicago IL 60607
Tel (312) 648-7600 *SIC* 6311 6321

THOMA CRESSEY BRAVO INC p 1448
300 N La Salle Dr # 4350, Chicago IL 60654
Tel (312) 254-3300
SIC 6799 8711 6311 6321 6531 7373

■VALLEY FORGE LIFE INSURANCE CO INC p 1540
333 S Wabash Ave, Chicago IL 60604
Tel (312) 822-5000 *SIC* 6321 6311

■FIRST HEALTH GROUP CORP p 547
3200 Highland Ave, Downers Grove IL 60515
Tel (630) 737-7900
SIC 8742 6324 6321 6411

GUARANTEE TRUST LIFE INSURANCE CO p 644
1275 Milwaukee Ave # 100, Glenview IL 60025
Tel (847) 699-0600 *SIC* 6321 6311

TRUSTMARK INSURANCE CO (MUTUAL) p 1488
400 N Field Dr, Lake Forest IL 60045
Tel (847) 283-4145 *SIC* 6321 6311

TRUSTMARK LIFE INSURANCE CO p 1488
400 N Field Dr, Lake Forest IL 60045
Tel (847) 615-1500 *SIC* 6321

AON CONSULTING WORLDWIDE INC p 95
100 Half Day Rd 2, Lincolnshire IL 60069
Tel (312) 381-4800
SIC 6311 6321 6331 8742 6411 6351

JOHN DEERE INSURANCE GROUP INC p 788
3400 80th St, Moline IL 61265
Tel (309) 765-8000 *SIC* 6331 6321 6311

HALLMARK SERVICES CORP p 655
1000 E Warrenville Rd # 400, Naperville IL 60563
Tel (630) 328-4400 *SIC* 6321

■RSA MEDICAL LLC p 1255
2135 City Gate Ln Ste 600, Naperville IL 60563
Tel (630) 416-7150 *SIC* 6321

B C S LIFE INSURANCE CO (INC) p 141
2 Mid America Plz Ste 200, Oakbrook Terrace IL 60181
Tel (630) 472-7700 *SIC* 6321 6311

HORTON GROUP INC p 708
10320 Orland Pkwy, Orland Park IL 60467
Tel (708) 845-3000
SIC 6411 6331 6321 6311

■FARMERS AUTOMOBILE MANAGEMENT CORP p 529
2505 Court St, Pekin IL 61554
Tel (309) 346-1161 *SIC* 6311 6321

■PEKIN LIFE INSURANCE CO p 1128
2505 Court St, Pekin IL 61554
Tel (309) 346-1161 *SIC* 6311 6321

▲CATERPILLAR INC p 265
100 Ne Adams St, Peoria IL 61629
Tel (309) 675-1000
SIC 3531 3519 3511 6531 6321 6331

ILLINOIS MUTUAL LIFE INSURANCE CO p 732
300 Sw Adams St, Peoria IL 61634
Tel (309) 674-8255 *SIC* 6321 6311

ZURICH HOLDING CO OF AMERICA INC p 1645
1299 Zurich Way, Schaumburg IL 60196
Tel (847) 605-6000
SIC 6311 6331 6321 6324 6719

■AMERICAN GENERAL LIFE INSURANCE p 73
1 Franklin Sq, Springfield IL 62703
Tel (217) 528-2011 *SIC* 6411 6321 6211

HEALTH ALLIANCE MEDICAL PLANS INC p 674
301 S Vine St, Urbana IL 61801
Tel (217) 337-8000 *SIC* 6321 6324

ALLIED SOLUTIONS LLC p 57
1320 City Center Dr # 300, Carmel IN 46032
Tel (317) 706-7600 *SIC* 6321 6351 6159

▲CNO FINANCIAL GROUP INC p 330
11825 N Pennsylvania St, Carmel IN 46032
Tel (317) 817-6100 *SIC* 6311 6321 6331

■SENIOR CONSECO HEALTH INSURANCE CO p 1304
11825 N Pennsylvania St, Carmel IN 46032
Tel (317) 817-6100 *SIC* 6321

■WASHINGTON NATIONAL INSURANCE CO p 1578
11815 N Pennsylvania St, Carmel IN 46032
Tel (317) 817-4100 *SIC* 6311 6321

PHYSICIANS HEALTH PLAN OF NORTHERN INDIANA INC p 1145
8101 W Jefferson Blvd, Fort Wayne IN 46804
Tel (260) 432-6690 *SIC* 6321 8011 6411

EVERENCE ASSOCIATION INC p 514
1110 N Main St, Goshen IN 46528
Tel (574) 533-9511 *SIC* 6321

AMERICAN UNITED LIFE INSURANCE CO INC p 81
1 American Sq Ste 368, Indianapolis IN 46282
Tel (317) 285-1877 *SIC* 6371 6311 6321

■ANTHEM HOLDING CORP p 93
120 Monument Cir Ste 200, Indianapolis IN 46204
Tel (317) 488-6000 *SIC* 6321

▲ANTHEM INC p 93
120 Monument Cir Ste 200, Indianapolis IN 46204
Tel (317) 488-6000 *SIC* 6324 6321

■ANTHEM INSURANCE COMPANIES INC p 94
120 Monument Cir Ste 200, Indianapolis IN 46204
Tel (317) 488-6000
SIC 6324 6411 6321 6331 6159 7371

■ANTHEM SOUTHEAST INC p 94
120 Monument Cir Ste 200, Indianapolis IN 46204
Tel (317) 488-6000 *SIC* 6411 6311 6321

■CERULEAN COMPANIES INC p 284
120 Monument Cir Ste 200, Indianapolis IN 46204
Tel (317) 488-6000 *SIC* 6321

■GOLDEN RULE FINANCIAL CORP p 621
7440 Woodland Dr, Indianapolis IN 46278
Tel (317) 297-4123 *SIC* 6321 6311

■GOLDEN RULE INSURANCE CO p 621
7440 Woodland Dr, Indianapolis IN 46278
Tel (317) 297-4123 *SIC* 6321 6311

METHODIST HEALTH GROUP INC p 953
1701 Senate Blvd, Indianapolis IN 46202
Tel (317) 962-2000 *SIC* 8062 6321

ONEAMERICA FINANCIAL PARTNERS INC p 1087
1 American Sq, Indianapolis IN 46282
Tel (317) 285-1877 *SIC* 6371 6311 6321

STATE LIFE INSURANCE CO p 1381
1 American Sq, Indianapolis IN 46282
Tel (317) 285-2300 *SIC* 6311 6321

AEGON US HOLDING CORP p 29
4333 Edgewood Rd Ne, Cedar Rapids IA 52499
Tel (319) 355-8511
SIC 6311 6321 6351 6159

TRANSAMERICA INSURANCE CORP p 1470
4333 Edgewood Rd Ne, Cedar Rapids IA 52499
Tel (319) 355-4883 *SIC* 6321

TRANSAMERICA PREMIER LIFE INSURANCE CO p 1470
4333 Edgewood Rd Ne, Cedar Rapids IA 52499
Tel (319) 355-8511 *SIC* 6311 6321

■UNITED FIRE & CASUALTY CO p 1508
118 2nd Ave Se, Cedar Rapids IA 52401
Tel (319) 399-5700 *SIC* 6331 6311 6321

AMERICAN ENTERPRISE MUTUAL HOLDING CO p 71
601 6th Ave, Des Moines IA 50309
Tel (515) 245-2000 *SIC* 6321 6411

■EMC INSURANCE GROUP INC p 490
717 Mulberry St, Des Moines IA 50309
Tel (515) 345-2902 *SIC* 6331 6351 6321

▲EMPLOYERS MUTUAL CASUALTY CO p 494
717 Mulberry St, Des Moines IA 50309
Tel (515) 280-2511
SIC 6411 6321 6311 6519

▲PRINCIPAL FINANCIAL GROUP INC p 1177
711 High St, Des Moines IA 50392
Tel (515) 247-5111
SIC 6321 6799 6722 6311

■PRINCIPAL INTERNATIONAL INC p 1177
711 High St, Des Moines IA 50392
Tel (515) 247-5013
SIC 6282 6311 6321 6331

■PRINCIPAL LIFE INSURANCE CO p 1177
711 High St, Des Moines IA 50392
Tel (515) 247-5111
SIC 6311 6211 6162 6321 6411

WELLMARK INC p 1589
1331 Grand Ave, Des Moines IA 50309
Tel (515) 376-4500 *SIC* 6324 6411 6321

DELTA DENTAL OF IOWA p 426
9000 Northpark Dr, Johnston IA 50131
Tel (515) 331-4594 *SIC* 6321

CUNA MUTUAL LIFE INSURANCE CO p 401
2000 Heritage Way, Waverly IA 50677
Tel (319) 352-4090 *SIC* 6411 6321 8742

HMA INC p 697
3001 Westown Pkwy Stop 1, West Des Moines IA 50266
Tel (515) 223-6800 *SIC* 6411 6321 8742

IOWA FARM BUREAU FEDERATION p 762
5400 University Ave, West Des Moines IA 50266
Tel (515) 225-5400
SIC 8699 5154 6311 6321 6411

■UNION SECURITY INSURANCE CO p 1505
6941 Vista Dr, West Des Moines IA 50266
Tel (651) 361-4000 *SIC* 6321 6324

SCOR GLOBAL LIFE USA REINSURANCE CO p 1293
11625 Rosewood St Ste 300, Leawood KS 66211
Tel (913) 901-4600 *SIC* 6311 6321

BLUE CROSS AND BLUE SHIELD OF KANSAS INC p 191
1133 Sw Topeka Blvd, Topeka KS 66629
Tel (785) 291-7000 *SIC* 6321 6324

BLUEGRASS FAMILY HEALTH p 193
651 Perimeter Dr Ste 300, Lexington KY 40517
Tel (859) 269-4475 *SIC* 6321 6411

■HUMANA GOVERNMENT BUSINESS INC p 718
305 N Hurstbourne Pkwy 1b, Louisville KY 40222
Tel (502) 318-0935 *SIC* 6321

■HUMANA HEALTH PLAN OF KANSAS INC p 718
500 W Main St Ste 300, Louisville KY 40202
Tel (502) 580-1000 *SIC* 6324 6321

▲HUMANA INC p 718
500 W Main St Ste 300, Louisville KY 40202
Tel (502) 580-1000 *SIC* 6324 6321 6411

■HUMANA INSURANCE CO OF KENTUCKY p 718
500 W Main St Ste 300, Louisville KY 40202
Tel (502) 580-1000 *SIC* 6321 8741

■HUMCO INC p 718
500 W Main St Ste 300, Louisville KY 40202
Tel (502) 580-1000 *SIC* 6321

LOUISIANA HEALTH SERVICE AND INDEMNITY CO p 880
5525 Reitz Ave, Baton Rouge LA 70809
Tel (225) 295-3307 *SIC* 6321 6324 6411

■UNUM LIFE INSURANCE CO OF AMERICA p 1528
2211 Congress St, Portland ME 04122
Tel (207) 575-2211 *SIC* 6321

■BRAVO HEALTH LLC p 209
3601 Odonnell St, Baltimore MD 21224
Tel (800) 235-9188 *SIC* 6321

AVEMCO CORP p 136
8490 Progress Dr Ste 100, Frederick MD 21701
Tel (301) 694-5700
SIC 6331 6321 6399 6411 7372

AVEMCO INSURANCE CO p 136
8490 Progress Dr Ste 100, Frederick MD 21701
Tel (301) 694-5700 *SIC* 6321 6331

MERITUS HEALTH INC p 949
11116 Medical Campus Rd, Hagerstown MD 21742
Tel (301) 790-8000 *SIC* 6321

CAREFIRST BLUECHOICE INC p 254
10455 Mill Run Cir, Owings Mills MD 21117
Tel (202) 479-8000 *SIC* 6321 8011 6411

UNION LABOR LIFE INSURANCE CO p 1504
8403 Colesville Rd # 1000, Silver Spring MD 20910
Tel (202) 682-0900
SIC 6311 6321 6324 6371

CHESAPEAKE EMPLOYERS INSURANCE CO p 295
8722 Loch Raven Blvd, Towson MD 21286
Tel (410) 494-2000 *SIC* 6321

BLUE CROSS AND BLUE SHIELD OF MASSACHUSETTS INC p 191
101 Huntington Ave # 1300, Boston MA 02199
Tel (617) 246-5000 *SIC* 6321 8741 6324

JOHN HANCOCK FINANCIAL SERVICES INC p 788
200 Clarendon St, Boston MA 02116
Tel (617) 572-6000
SIC 6311 6351 6411 6371 6321

LIBERTY MUTUAL GROUP INC p 862
175 Berkeley St, Boston MA 02116
Tel (617) 357-9500
SIC 6331 6321 6351 7389

LIBERTY MUTUAL INSURANCE CO p 862
175 Berkeley St, Boston MA 02116
Tel (617) 357-9500
SIC 6331 6321 6351 7389

LMHC MASSACHUSETTS HOLDINGS INC p 872
175 Berkeley St, Boston MA 02116
Tel (617) 357-9500
SIC 6331 6321 6351 7389

PROMUTUAL GROUP INC p 1183
1 Financial Ctr Fl 13, Boston MA 02111
Tel (617) 330-1755 *SIC* 6321 8742

■SAFETY INDEMNITY INSURANCE CO INC p 1266
20 Custom House St # 400, Boston MA 02110
Tel (617) 951-0600 *SIC* 6321

BERKSHIRE LIFE INSURANCE CO OF AMERICA p 175
700 South St, Pittsfield MA 01201
Tel (413) 395-4321 *SIC* 6321

MASSACHUSETTS MUTUAL LIFE INSURANCE CO p 917
1295 State St, Springfield MA 01111
Tel (413) 788-8411
SIC 6321 6324 6411 6282

■OPUS INVESTMENT MANAGEMENT INC p 1091
440 Lincoln St, Worcester MA 01653
Tel (508) 855-1000
SIC 6311 6321 6324 6351 6722

■PAUL REVERE LIFE INSURANCE CO p 1121
1 Mercantile St, Worcester MA 01608
Tel (508) 366-8707 *SIC* 6311 6321

BLUE CROSS AND BLUE SHIELD OF MICHIGAN p 191
600 E Lafayette Blvd, Detroit MI 48226
Tel (313) 225-9000 *SIC* 6321 6324

MICHIGAN EDUCATION SPECIAL SERVICES ASSOCIATION p 961
1475 Kendale Blvd, East Lansing MI 48823
Tel (517) 332-2581 *SIC* 6411 6321

HEALTHPLUS INSURANCE CO p 677
2050 S Linden Rd, Flint MI 48532
Tel (810) 230-2000 *SIC* 6321

GERBER LIFE INSURANCE CO p 608
1311 Mmroneck Ave Ste 350, Fremont MI 49412
Tel (800) 704-2180 *SIC* 6311 6321

LIGHTHOUSE INSURANCE GROUP INC p 865
877 E 16th St, Holland MI 49423
Tel (616) 392-6900
SIC 6411 6331 6321 6311

PHYSICIANS HEALTH PLAN OF MID-MICHIGAN INC p 1145
1400 E Michigan Ave, Lansing MI 48912
Tel (517) 364-8400 *SIC* 8011 6321

AMERICAN COMMUNITY MUTUAL INSURANCE CO p 70
39201 7 Mile Rd, Livonia MI 48152
Tel (734) 591-9000 *SIC* 6321 6311

UPPER PENINSULA HEALTH PLAN LLC p 1529
853 W Washington St, Marquette MI 49855
Tel (906) 225-7500 *SIC* 6321 6411

■SPECIALTY BENEFITS LLC p 1356
11000 Optum Cir, Eden Prairie MN 55344
Tel (866) 427-6845 *SIC* 6321

AON BENFIELD INC p 94
5600 W 83rd St Ste 1100, Minneapolis MN 55437
Tel (866) 280-3720 *SIC* 6321

■RELIASTAR LIFE INSURANCE CO p 1222
20 Washington Ave S, Minneapolis MN 55401
Tel (612) 372-5432 *SIC* 6311 6321 6324

■RIVERSOURCE LIFE INSURANCE CO p 1238
1099 Ameriprise Fincl Ctr, Minneapolis MN 55474
Tel (612) 671-3131 *SIC* 6311 6321

THRIVENT FINANCIAL FOR LUTHERANS FOUNDATION p 1451
625 4th Ave S, Minneapolis MN 55415
Tel (920) 734-5721
SIC 6311 6321 8742 6411 6211

■METRAHEALTH CARE MANAGEMENT CORP p 954
9900 Bren Rd E, Minnetonka MN 55343
Tel (952) 936-1300 *SIC* 6321 6311

■UNITED HEALTHCARE SERVICES INC p 1509
9700 Health Care Ln, Minnetonka MN 55343
Tel (952) 936-1300 *SIC* 6321

▲UNITEDHEALTH GROUP INC p 1515
9900 Bren Rd E Ste 300w, Minnetonka MN 55343
Tel (952) 936-1300 *SIC* 6324 6411 6321

FEDERATED MUTUAL INSURANCE CO p 536
121 E Park Sq, Owatonna MN 55060
Tel (507) 455-5200 *SIC* 6331 6321 6311

BCBSM INC p 163
3535 Blue Cross Rd, Saint Paul MN 55122
Tel (651) 662-8000 *SIC* 6321 6324

■ST PAUL FIRE AND MARINE INSURANCE CO p 1372
385 Washington St, Saint Paul MN 55102
Tel (651) 221-7911
SIC 6331 6351 6321 6411

▲REINSURANCE GROUP OF AMERICA INC p 1221
16600 Swingley Ridge Rd, Chesterfield MO 63017
Tel (636) 736-7000 *SIC* 6311 6321 6411

MISSOURI CONSOLIDATED HEALTH CARE PLAN p 976
832 Weathered Rock Ct, Jefferson City MO 65101
Tel (573) 751-8881 *SIC* 6321

AMERICO LIFE INC p 81
300 W 11th St, Kansas City MO 64105
Tel (816) 391-2000 *SIC* 6311 6321 6331

BLUE CROSS AND BLUE SHIELD OF KANSAS CITY p 191
2301 Main St, Kansas City MO 64108
Tel (816) 395-2222 *SIC* 6321

OZARK NATIONAL LIFE INSURANCE CO p 1101
500 E 9th St, Kansas City MO 64106
Tel (314) 664-4389 *SIC* 6311 6321

GOVERNMENT EMPLOYEES HEALTH ASSOCIATION INC p 627
310 Ne Mulberry St, Lees Summit MO 64086
Tel (816) 257-5500 *SIC* 6321

BLUE CROSS AND BLUE SHIELD OF MISSOURI INC p 191
1831 Chestnut St, Saint Louis MO 63103
Tel (314) 923-4444 *SIC* 6321

DELTA DENTAL OF MISSOURI p 426
12399 Gravois Rd Fl 2, Saint Louis MO 63127
Tel (314) 656-3000 *SIC* 6324 6321

■UNITED INSURANCE CO OF AMERICA p 1509
12115 Lackland Rd, Saint Louis MO 63146
Tel (314) 819-4300 *SIC* 6411 6321 6331

HEALTH SYSTEMS INC p 676
1220 N Main St, Sikeston MO 63801
Tel (573) 481-9625 *SIC* 6321 8011 8322

ASG INC p 116
1526 K St, Lincoln NE 68508
Tel (402) 476-6500 *SIC* 6321 6311

ASSURITY SECURITY GROUP INC p 122
1526 K St, Lincoln NE 68508
Tel (402) 476-6500 *SIC* 6321 6311

▲ BERKSHIRE HATHAWAY INC p 175
3555 Farnam St Ste 1440, Omaha NE 68131
Tel (402) 346-1400
SIC 6331 6321 4911 4924 6531 5963

PHYSICIANS MUTUAL INSURANCE CO p 1145
2600 Dodge St, Omaha NE 68131
Tel (402) 633-1000 *SIC* 6321 6311

UNITED OF OMAHA LIFE INSURANCE CO p 1510
Mutual Of Omaha Plaza, Omaha NE 68175
Tel (402) 342-7600 *SIC* 6311 6321 6324

PALISADES SAFETY INSURANCE AGENCY INC p 1108
200 Connell Dr, Berkeley Heights NJ 07922
Tel (908) 790-7800 *SIC* 6321

PXRE CORP p 1193
379 Thornall St Ste 2, Edison NJ 08837
Tel (973) 321-3590 *SIC* 6331 6324 6321

HORIZON NJ HEALTH p 707
210 Silvia St, Ewing NJ 08628
Tel (609) 718-9001 *SIC* 6321

EVEREST REINSURANCE HOLDINGS INC p 514
477 Martinsville Rd, Liberty Corner NJ 07938
Tel (908) 604-3000 *SIC* 6411 6331 6321

CRUM & FORSTER HOLDINGS CORP p 396
305 Madison Ave, Morristown NJ 07960
Tel (973) 490-6600 *SIC* 6331 6321 6351

CRUM & FORSTER INC p 396
305 Madison Ave, Morristown NJ 07960
Tel (973) 490-6600
SIC 6311 6321 6331 6411

HORIZON HEALTHCARE SERVICES INC p 707
3 Penn Plz E Ste 1, Newark NJ 07105
Tel (973) 466-4000 *SIC* 6324 6411 6321

■ PRUCO SECURITIES LLC p 1187
751 Broad St, Newark NJ 07102
Tel (800) 235-7637
SIC 6321 6331 6211 6282 8071

▲ PRUDENTIAL FINANCIAL INC p 1187
751 Broad St, Newark NJ 07102
Tel (973) 802-6000
SIC 6311 6321 6331 6211 6552

■ PRUDENTIAL HOLDINGS LLC p 1187
751 Broad St, Newark NJ 07102
Tel (973) 802-6000 *SIC* 6282 6321 6324

■ AETNA HEALTH INC (NJ) p 31
9 Entin Rd, Parsippany NJ 07054
Tel (973) 244-3500 *SIC* 6324 6321

■ MUNICH RE AMERICA BROKERS INC p 1000
685 College Rd E, Princeton NJ 08540
Tel (609) 243-4900 *SIC* 6321 6311

CHUBB CAPITAL CORP p 304
15 Mountainview Rd, Warren NJ 07059
Tel (908) 903-2000 *SIC* 6321

■ AMERICAN FAMILY LIFE ASSURANCE CO OF NY (INC) p 72
22 Corporate Woods Blvd, Albany NY 12211
Tel (518) 438-0764 *SIC* 6321

LIFE RE CORP p 863
175 King St, Armonk NY 10504
Tel (914) 828-8500 *SIC* 6311 6321

SECURITY MUTUAL LIFE INSURANCE CO OF NEW YORK p 1299
100 Court St, Binghamton NY 13901
Tel (607) 723-3551 *SIC* 6311 6321

AMERICAN TRANSIT INSURANCE CO INC p 80
1 Metrotech Ctr Fl 7, Brooklyn NY 11201
Tel (212) 857-8200 *SIC* 6321 6331 6311

UNIVERA COMMUNITY HEALTH CARE p 1516
205 Park Club Ln Fl 2, Buffalo NY 14221
Tel (585) 454-1700 *SIC* 6321

COOK MARAN & ASSOCIATES INC p 366
461 Pantigo Rd, East Hampton NY 11937
Tel (631) 324-1440 *SIC* 6321

COMBINED LIFE INSURANCE CO OF NEW YORK INC p 343
11 British American Blvd # 2, Latham NY 12110
Tel (518) 220-9333 *SIC* 6321 6311

■ METROPOLITAN LIFE INSURANCE CO (INC) p 956
2701 Queens Plz N Ste 1, Long Island City NY 11101
Tel (212) 578-2211
SIC 6411 6324 6331 6321 6531

AJB VENTURES INC p 41
10 Walter Ln, Manhasset NY 11030
Tel (516) 365-6690 *SIC* 6321

■ AIG PROPERTY CASUALTY INC p 38
175 Water St Fl 5, New York NY 10038
Tel (212) 458-5000 *SIC* 6331 6321 6311

■ AIU INSURANCE CO p 41
175 Water St Fl 24, New York NY 10038
Tel (212) 770-7000 *SIC* 6331 6321

▲ AMERICAN INTERNATIONAL GROUP INC p 75
175 Water St Rm 1800, New York NY 10038
Tel (212) 770-7000
SIC 6331 6321 6311 6324 6411 6282

■ AMIC HOLDINGS INC p 85
485 Madison Ave Fl 14, New York NY 10022
Tel (212) 355-4141 *SIC* 6321 6411

ARCH CAPITAL GROUP (US) INC p 104
1 Liberty Plz Fl 53, New York NY 10006
Tel (212) 651-6500 *SIC* 6311 6321

CHURCH PENSION GROUP SERVICES CORP p 305
19 E 34th St Fl 3, New York NY 10016
Tel (212) 592-1800
SIC 6371 6321 6311 6331 2731

▲ CITIGROUP INC p 310
399 Park Ave, New York NY 10022
Tel (212) 559-1000
SIC 6021 6141 6331 6311 6321

CLARENDON NATIONAL INSURANCE CO (MD CORP) p 321
411 5th Ave Fl 5, New York NY 10016
Tel (212) 790-9700
SIC 6321 1542 1541 7011

■ CONTINENTAL CORP p 363
111 8th Ave, New York NY 10011
Tel (212) 440-3000
SIC 6331 6351 6321 6159 8741 6411

GLOBAL REINSURANCE CORP OF AMERICA p 617
125 Broad St Lbby 5, New York NY 10004
Tel (212) 754-7500 *SIC* 6321

GUARDIAN LIFE INSURANCE CO OF AMERICA p 645
7 Hanover Sq Fl 14, New York NY 10004
Tel (212) 598-8000
SIC 6311 6371 6324 6321 6722 6282

■ HEALTH PLUS PREPAID HEALTH SERVICES PLAN INC p 675
9 Pine St Fl 14, New York NY 10005
Tel (718) 532-1011 *SIC* 6321 6324 8741

HEALTHFIRST HEALTH PLAN OF NEW JERSEY INC p 677
25 Broadway Fl 9, New York NY 10004
Tel (212) 801-6000 *SIC* 6321

HEALTHFIRST PHSP INC p 677
100 Church St Fl 17, New York NY 10007
Tel (212) 801-6000 *SIC* 6321

HHC FOUNDATION OF NEW YORK CITY INC p 689
160 Water St Fl 10, New York NY 10038
Tel (646) 458-2810 *SIC* 6321

▲ METLIFE INC p 954
200 Park Ave Fl 1200, New York NY 10166
Tel (212) 578-9500 *SIC* 6311 6321 6331

MONY LIFE INSURANCE CO p 987
1740 Broadway, New York NY 10019
Tel (800) 487-6669
SIC 6411 6321 6211 6282 6531

NEW YORK LIFE INSURANCE CO p 1035
51 Madison Ave Bsmt 1b, New York NY 10010
Tel (212) 576-7000 *SIC* 6311 6321 6282

QBE HOLDINGS INC p 1194
88 Pine St, New York NY 10005
Tel (212) 422-1212 *SIC* 6321 6411

QBE INSURANCE CORP p 1194
88 Pine St Fl 16, New York NY 10005
Tel (212) 422-1212 *SIC* 6311 6321

■ SEABURY & SMITH (DELAWARE) INC p 1296
1166 Ave Of The Americas, New York NY 10036
Tel (212) 345-9049
SIC 6411 6331 6321 6311

SENIOR HEALTH PARTNERS INC p 1304
100 Church St Fl 17, New York NY 10007
Tel (646) 273-4610 *SIC* 6321

STARR COMPANIES p 1379
399 Park Ave Rm 1700, New York NY 10022
Tel (646) 227-6300 *SIC* 6321

STARR INDEMNITY & LIABILITY CO p 1379
399 Park Ave Rm 1700, New York NY 10022
Tel (646) 227-6300 *SIC* 6321

▲ TRAVELERS COMPANIES INC p 1474
485 Lexington Ave, New York NY 10017
Tel (917) 778-6000 *SIC* 6331 6351 6321

■ USL SEPARATE ACCOUNT USL VL-R p 1535
1 World Fin Ctr, New York NY 10281
Tel (800) 874-8743 *SIC* 6311 6321

VIDACARE INC p 1556
248 W 35th St Fl 7, New York NY 10001
Tel (917) 637-3780 *SIC* 6321

■ WELLCHOICE INC p 1589
1 Liberty Pl, New York NY 10038
Tel (212) 476-1000 *SIC* 6321

EXCELLUS HEALTH PLAN INC p 517
165 Court St, Rochester NY 14647
Tel (585) 454-1700 *SIC* 6321

LIFETIME HEALTHCARE INC p 864
165 Court St, Rochester NY 14647
Tel (585) 454-1700 *SIC* 6324 6321

ADMINISTRATORS FOR PROFESSIONS INC p 23
1800 N Blvd, Roslyn NY 11576
Tel (516) 365-6690 *SIC* 6321

PHYSICIANS RECIPROCAL INSURERS p 1146
1800 Northern Blvd, Roslyn NY 11576
Tel (516) 365-6690 *SIC* 6321

HUDSON HEALTH PLAN INC p 716
303 S Broadway Ste 321, Tarrytown NY 10591
Tel (800) 339-4557 *SIC* 6321

ULYSSES CAREMARK HOLDING CORP p 1501
44 S Broadway Fl 12f, White Plains NY 10601
Tel (914) 934-5200 *SIC* 6311 6321

▲ UNIVERSAL AMERICAN CORP p 1516
44 S Broadway Ste 1200, White Plains NY 10601
Tel (914) 934-5200 *SIC* 6311 6321 6324

■ METLIFE INSURANCE CO USA p 954
11225 N Community Hse Rd, Charlotte NC 28277
Tel (980) 949-3626
SIC 6411 6321 6331 6324

RAYCOM SPORTS NETWORK INC p 1210
1900 W Morehead St, Charlotte NC 28208
Tel (704) 378-4400
SIC 6311 6321 6324 6411 4832 4833

▲ SONIC FINANCIAL CORP p 1340
5401 E Independence Blvd, Charlotte NC 28212
Tel (704) 536-5600 *SIC* 7948 6321 6311

■ LINCOLN NATIONAL LIFE INSURANCE CO p 867
100 N Greene St, Greensboro NC 27401
Tel (336) 691-3000 *SIC* 6411 6321 6324

SDM&R INC p 1295
3625 N Elm St, Greensboro NC 27455
Tel (336) 272-7161 *SIC* 6321

NORIDIAN MUTUAL INSURANCE CO p 1048
4510 13th Ave S, Fargo ND 58121
Tel (701) 282-1100 *SIC* 8399 6321 6324

SUMMA INSURANCE CO INC p 1398
10 N Main St, Akron OH 44308
Tel (800) 996-8411 *SIC* 6321 6311

■ AMERICAN MODERN INSURANCE GROUP INC p 76
7000 Midland Blvd, Amelia OH 45102
Tel (513) 943-7100 *SIC* 6411 6321

AULTCARE INSURANCE CO p 131
2600 6th St Sw, Canton OH 44710
Tel (330) 363-6360 *SIC* 6321

▲ AMERICAN FINANCIAL GROUP INC p 72
301 E 4th St, Cincinnati OH 45202
Tel (513) 579-2121 *SIC* 6331 6311 6321

■ PENNSYLVANIA CO INC p 1130
1 E 4th St, Cincinnati OH 45202
Tel (513) 579-2121 *SIC* 6321

UNION CENTRAL LIFE INSURANCE CO p 1504
1876 Waycross Rd, Cincinnati OH 45240
Tel (866) 696-7478 *SIC* 6311 6321

CENTRIC FINANCIAL GROUP LLC p 281
4016 Townsfair Way # 202, Columbus OH 43219
Tel (614) 824-6100 *SIC* 6311 6282 6321

NATIONWIDE CORP p 1017
1 Nationwide Plz, Columbus OH 43215
Tel (614) 249-7111 *SIC* 6411 6321

NATIONWIDE MUTUAL INSURANCE CO p 1018
1 Nationwide Plz, Columbus OH 43215
Tel (614) 249-7111
SIC 6331 6311 6321 6531

CARESOURCE MANAGEMENT GROUP CO p 255
230 N Main St, Dayton OH 45402
Tel (937) 224-3300 *SIC* 6321

▲ FIRST DEFIANCE FINANCIAL CORP p 546
601 Clinton St, Defiance OH 43512
Tel (419) 782-5015
SIC 6035 6331 6321 6311

■ CINCINNATI INSURANCE CO p 307
6200 S Gilmore Rd, Fairfield OH 45014
Tel (513) 870-2000
SIC 6311 6331 6321 6211

■ PROGRESSIVE CASUALTY INSURANCE CO p 1181
6300 Wilson Mills Rd, Mayfield Village OH 44143
Tel (440) 461-5000
SIC 6331 6351 6411 6321

AMERICAN FIDELITY ASSURANCE CO p 72
9000 Cameron Pkwy, Oklahoma City OK 73114
Tel (405) 523-2000 *SIC* 6321 6311

AMERICAN FIDELITY CORP p 72
2000 Classen Ctr Blvd, Oklahoma City OK 73106
Tel (405) 523-2000 *SIC* 6321 6311

AMERICAN FIDELITY GENERAL AGENCY INC p 72
9000 Cameron Pkwy, Oklahoma City OK 73114
Tel (405) 523-2000 *SIC* 6321 6311

■ GLOBE LIFE & ACCIDENT INSURANCE CO p 618
204 N Robinson Ave, Oklahoma City OK 73102
Tel (972) 540-6542 *SIC* 6311 6321

■ MIDLANDS MANAGEMENT CORP p 966
3817 Nw Expwy Ste 1000, Oklahoma City OK 73112
Tel (405) 840-0074 *SIC* 6411 6331 6321

CAMBIA HEALTH SOLUTIONS INC p 243
100 Sw Market St, Portland OR 97201
Tel (503) 225-5336 *SIC* 6321 6411 6324

LIFEWISE HEALTH PLAN OF OREGON p 865
2020 Sw 4th Ave Ste 1000, Portland OR 97201
Tel (503) 295-6707 *SIC* 6321

MODA HEALTH PLAN INC p 980
601 Sw 2nd Ave, Portland OR 97204
Tel (503) 228-6554 *SIC* 6321

REGENCE BLUECROSS BLUESHIELD OF OREGON p 1218
100 Sw Market St, Portland OR 97201
Tel (503) 225-5336 *SIC* 6321

STANCORP FINANCIAL GROUP INC p 1375
1100 Sw 6th Ave, Portland OR 97204
Tel (971) 321-7000 *SIC* 6311 6321

STANDARD INSURANCE CO p 1376
920 Sw 6th Ave Ste 1100, Portland OR 97204
Tel (971) 321-7000 *SIC* 6311 6321 6411

COW CREEK BAND OF UMPQUA TRIBE OF INDIANS p 385
2371 Ne Stephens St, Roseburg OR 97470
Tel (541) 957-8945 *SIC* 9131 6321 7999

REGENCE HMO OREGON INC p 1218
201 High St Se, Salem OR 97301
Tel (503) 364-4868 *SIC* 6321

SAIF CORP p 1268
400 High St Se, Salem OR 97312
Tel (503) 373-8000 *SIC* 6321 8111 6331

PACIFICSOURCE HEALTH PLANS p 1106
110 International Way, Springfield OR 97477
Tel (541) 686-1242 *SIC* 6321

PENN TREATY NETWORK AMERICA INSURANCE CO p 1129
3440 Lehigh St Ste 4, Allentown PA 18103
Tel (800) 362-0700 *SIC* 6321

TMG HEALTH INC p 1457
100 Four Falls Corporate, Conshohocken PA 19428
Tel (610) 878-9111 *SIC* 6321

EMPLOYEE BENEFIT TR OF EASTERN PA p 494
6 Danforth Dr, Easton PA 18045
Tel (610) 515-6412 *SIC* 6351 8699 6321

PEOPLES BENEFIT LIFE INSURANCE CO p 1132
300 Eagleview Blvd, Exton PA 19341
Tel (610) 648-5000 *SIC* 6311 6321

■ OLD REPUBLIC INSURANCE CO p 1081
133 Oakland Ave, Greensburg PA 15601
Tel (724) 838-5400 *SIC* 6411 6321 6311

CAPITAL BLUE CROSS p 249
2500 Elmerton Ave, Harrisburg PA 17177
Tel (717) 541-7000 *SIC* 6321

VETERANS LIFE INSURANCE CO INC p 1553
20 Moores Rd, Malvern PA 19355
Tel (610) 648-5000 *SIC* 6311 6321

NOVITAS SOLUTIONS INC p 1063
2020 Tech Pkwy Ste 100, Mechanicsburg PA 17050
Tel (717) 526-3459 *SIC* 6321

ACE AMERICAN INSURANCE CO p 16
436 Walnut St, Philadelphia PA 19106
Tel (215) 640-1000 *SIC* 6321 6331 6351

ACE PROPERTY AND CASUALTY INSURANCE CO p 16
2 Liberty Pl 2 Liberty Place, Philadelphia PA 19102
Tel (215) 761-1000 *SIC* 6321 6331 6351

ACE USA INC p 16
436 Walnut St, Philadelphia PA 19106
Tel (215) 923-5352 *SIC* 6411 6321 6351

AMERIHEALTH ADMINISTRATORS INC p 82
1900 Market St Ofc 624, Philadelphia PA 19103
Tel (215) 657-8900 *SIC* 6321

AMERIHEALTH CARITAS HEALTH PLAN p 82
200 Stevens Dr, Philadelphia PA 19113
Tel (215) 937-8000 *SIC* 6321

CENTURY INDEMNITY CO p 282
1601 Chestnut St, Philadelphia PA 19192
Tel (215) 761-1000 *SIC* 6321 6331 6351

■ CIGNA LIFE INSURANCE CO OF NEW YORK p 306
Two Liberty Place, Philadelphia PA 19192
Tel (215) 761-2355 *SIC* 6321 6311

■ COLONIAL PENN LIFE INSURANCE CO p 338
399 Market St, Philadelphia PA 19181
Tel (215) 928-8000 *SIC* 6321 6311

COMPSERVICES INC p 352
1717 Arch St Fl 45, Philadelphia PA 19103
Tel (215) 587-1829 *SIC* 6321

CSAA AFFINITY INSURANCE CO p 397
2040 Market St, Philadelphia PA 19103
Tel (215) 864-5000 *SIC* 6331 6321

INAMAR LTD p 735
1601 Chestnut St, Philadelphia PA 19192
Tel (215) 640-1000 *SIC* 6321

INDEPENDENCE HEALTH GROUP INC p 736
1901 Market St, Philadelphia PA 19103
Tel (215) 241-2400 *SIC* 6321

INDEPENDENCE HOSPITAL INDEMNITY PLAN INC p 736
1901 Market St, Philadelphia PA 19103
Tel (215) 241-2400 *SIC* 6321

■ LIFE INSURANCE CO OF NORTH AMERICA p 863
1601 Chestnut St, Philadelphia PA 19192
Tel (215) 761-1000 *SIC* 6321 6311

MERCY HEALTH PLAN INC p 946
200 Stevens Dr Ste 350, Philadelphia PA 19113
Tel (215) 937-8000 *SIC* 6324 6321

PHILADELPHIA CONTRIBUTIONSHIP FOR INSURANCE OF HOUSES FROM LOSS BY FIRE p 1142
212 S 4th St, Philadelphia PA 19106
Tel (215) 627-1752
SIC 6331 6311 7382 6321

RELIANCE STANDARD LIFE INSURANCE CO p 1222
2001 Market St Ste 1500, Philadelphia PA 19103
Tel (267) 256-3500 *SIC* 6311 6321

HIGHMARK INC p 692
120 5th Ave, Pittsburgh PA 15222
Tel (412) 544-7000
SIC 6321 6324 6411 6512

HM HEALTH SOLUTIONS INC p 697
120 5th Ave, Pittsburgh PA 15222
Tel (412) 544-7226 *SIC* 8099 6321

UPMC HEALTH PLAN INC p 1528
600 Grant St Fl 24, Pittsburgh PA 15219
Tel (412) 454-7642 *SIC* 6321

▲ LINCOLN NATIONAL CORP p 867
150 N Rad Chester Rd A305 Ste A, Radnor PA 19087
Tel (484) 583-1400
SIC 6311 6321 6371 6722 6411 6282

ALLONE HEALTH RESOURCES INC p 58
100 N Penna Ave, Wilkes Barre PA 18701
Tel (877) 720-7770 *SIC* 6321

■ TRIPLE-S ADVANTAGE INC p 1482
1 Calle 1 Fl 3, Guaynabo PR 00968
Tel (787) 620-1919 *SIC* 6321

■ TRIPLE - S SALUD INC p 1482
1441 Ave Fd Roosevelt, San Juan PR 00920
Tel (787) 749-4949 *SIC* 6321

▲ TRIPLE-S MANAGEMENT CORP p 1482
1441 Ave Fd Roosevelt, San Juan PR 00920
Tel (787) 749-4949 *SIC* 6324 6311 6321

AMWINS GROUP BENEFITS INC p 87
50 Whitecap Dr, North Kingstown RI 02852
Tel (877) 739-3330 *SIC* 6311 6321

BLUE CROSS BLUE SHIELD OF SOUTH CAROLINA p 192
I-20 Alpine Rd, Columbia SC 29219
Tel (803) 788-3860 *SIC* 6321

BRUCE SEIBELS GROUP INC p 220
1501 Lady St, Columbia SC 29201
Tel (803) 748-2000 *SIC* 6331 6321 6311

■ COLONIAL LIFE & ACCIDENT INSURANCE CO INC p 337
1200 Colonial Life Blvd W, Columbia SC 29210
Tel (803) 798-7000 *SIC* 6321 6311

■ PROVIDENT LIFE & ACCIDENT INSURANCE CO p 1186
1 Fountain Sq Ste 1, Chattanooga TN 37402
Tel (423) 755-1011 *SIC* 6311 6321

▲ UNUM GROUP p 1528
1 Fountain Sq, Chattanooga TN 37402
Tel (423) 294-1011
SIC 6321 6324 6311 6371

■ CHSPSC p 304
4000 Meridian Blvd, Franklin TN 37067
Tel (615) 465-7000 *SIC* 8062 6321

■ DIRECT GENERAL CORP p 441
1281 Murfreesboro Pike # 150, Nashville TN 37217
Tel (615) 399-4700
SIC 6311 6321 6331 6411

■ NEWQUEST LLC p 1038
44 Vantage Way Ste 300, Nashville TN 37228
Tel (615) 291-7000 *SIC* 6321

▲ CITIZENS INC p 311
400 E Anderson Ln Ste 600, Austin TX 78752
Tel (512) 837-7100 *SIC* 6311 6321

SHA LLC p 1310
12940 N Hwy 183, Austin TX 78750
Tel (512) 257-6000 *SIC* 6324 6311 6321

TEXAS MEDICAL LIABILITY TRUST p 1444
901 S Mo Pac Expy V500, Austin TX 78746
Tel (512) 425-5800 *SIC* 6321

■ REPUBLIC COMPANIES INC p 1225
5525 Lyndon B Johnson Fwy, Dallas TX 75240
Tel (972) 788-6001 *SIC* 6321 6311 6331

■ CITI ASSURANCE SERVICES INC p 309
3001 Meacham Blvd Ste 100, Fort Worth TX 76137
Tel (817) 348-7500 *SIC* 6321 6411

USHEALTH ADMINISTRATORS LLC p 1535
300 Burnett St Ste 200, Fort Worth TX 76102
Tel (817) 878-3307 *SIC* 6321

▲ AMERICAN NATIONAL INSURANCE CO INC p 77
1 Moody Plz Fl 18, Galveston TX 77550
Tel (409) 763-4661
SIC 6351 6311 6321 6324 6331

■ AMERICAN NATIONAL LIFE INSURANCE CO OF TEXAS p 77
1 Moody Plz Fl 8, Galveston TX 77550
Tel (409) 763-4661 *SIC* 6411 6321

■ AIG LIFE HOLDINGS INC p 38
2929 Allen Pkwy, Houston TX 77019
Tel (713) 522-1111
SIC 6311 6321 6331 6141 6162 6153

HCC INSURANCE HOLDINGS INC p 672
13403 Northwest Fwy, Houston TX 77040
Tel (713) 690-7300 *SIC* 6311 6321 6331

RELIANCE STANDARD LIFE INSURANCE CO OF TEXAS p 1222
7800 W Tidwell Rd Ste 111, Houston TX 77040
Tel (713) 468-2603 *SIC* 6311 6321

■ ASSOCIATES CORP OF NORTH AMERICA p 121
250 E John Carpenter Fwy, Irving TX 75062
Tel (972) 652-4000
SIC 6141 6153 6159 6311 6321 6331

▲ TORCHMARK CORP p 1461
3700 S Stonebridge Dr, Mckinney TX 75070
Tel (972) 569-4000 *SIC* 6321 6311

■ UNITED AMERICAN INSURANCE CO p 1506
3700 S Stonebridge Dr, Mckinney TX 75070
Tel (800) 331-2512 *SIC* 6321 6311

HEALTHMARKETS INC p 677
9151 Blvd 256, North Richland Hills TX 76180
Tel (817) 255-3100 *SIC* 6311 6321

HEALTHMARKETS LLC p 677
9151 Boulevard 26, North Richland Hills TX 76180
Tel (817) 255-3100 *SIC* 6311 6321

J C PENNEY LIFE INSURANCE CO p 770
2700 W Plano Pkwy, Plano TX 75075
Tel (972) 881-6000 *SIC* 6311 6321

■ HUMANA HEALTH PLAN INC p 718
8431 Fredericksburg Rd # 340, San Antonio TX 78229
Tel (210) 615-5100 *SIC* 6324 6321 8011

USAA GENERAL AGENCY INC p 1534
9800 Fredericksburg Rd, San Antonio TX 78288
Tel (210) 456-1800 *SIC* 6331 6321

USAA INSURANCE AGENCY INC p 1534
9800 Fredericksburg Rd B-2e, San Antonio TX 78288
Tel (210) 498-2211 *SIC* 6331 6321 8742

▲ HEALTHEQUITY INC p 677
15 W Scenic Pointe Dr # 100, Draper UT 84020
Tel (801) 727-1000
SIC 8399 6371 6036 6321 6282

SELECTHEALTH BENEFIT ASSURANCE p 1302
5381 S Green St, Murray UT 84123
Tel (801) 442-5000 *SIC* 6321

SELECTHEALTH INC p 1302
5381 S Green St, Murray UT 84123
Tel (801) 442-5000 *SIC* 6321

BLUE CROSS AND BLUE SHIELD OF VERMONT p 192
445 Industrial Ln, Montpelier VT 05602
Tel (802) 223-6131 *SIC* 6321

NATIONAL LIFE HOLDING CO p 1014
1 National Life Dr, Montpelier VT 05604
Tel (802) 229-3333 *SIC* 6311 6321

NLV FINANCIAL CORP p 1045
1 National Life Dr, Montpelier VT 05604
Tel (802) 229-3333 *SIC* 6311 6321

PIEDMONT COMMUNITY HEALTH PLAN INC p 1146
2316 Atherholt Rd, Lynchburg VA 24501
Tel (434) 947-4463 *SIC* 6321

DELTA DENTAL OF VIRGINIA p 426
4818 Starkey Rd, Roanoke VA 24018
Tel (540) 989-8000 *SIC* 6411 6321

UNIGARD INC p 1503
2125 158th Ct Ne, Bellevue WA 98008
Tel (425) 641-4321 *SIC* 6321 6331

PREMERA BLUE CROSS p 1170
7001 220th St Sw Bldg 1, Mountlake Terrace WA 98043
Tel (425) 670-4000 *SIC* 6321

GROUP HEALTH COOPERATIVE p 641
320 Westlake Ave N # 100, Seattle WA 98109
Tel (206) 448-4141
SIC 6324 5999 8093 6321

SAFECO CORP p 1266
1001 4th Ave Ste 800, Seattle WA 98185
Tel (206) 545-5000
SIC 6411 6311 6321 6324 6351

■ UNITEDHEALTHCARE OF WASHINGTON INC p 1515
1111 3rd Ave Ste 1100, Seattle WA 98101
Tel (206) 236-2500 *SIC* 6324 6321

BRICKSTREET MUTUAL INSURANCE CO p 211
400 Quarrier St, Charleston WV 25301
Tel (304) 941-1000 *SIC* 6321 6331

CAPITAL AREA SERVICE CO INC p 249
200 Kanawha Blvd E, Charleston WV 25301
Tel (304) 346-3800 *SIC* 6324 6321

HIGHMARK BLUE CROSS BLUE SHIELD WEST VIRGINIA p 692
614 Market St, Parkersburg WV 26101
Tel (304) 424-7700 *SIC* 6321

LAKELAND CARE DISTRICT p 839
N6654 Rolling Meadows Dr, Fond Du Lac WI 54937
Tel (920) 906-5100 *SIC* 6321

■ AMERICAN MEDICAL SECURITY GROUP INC PAC p 76
3100 Ams Blvd, Green Bay WI 54313
Tel (920) 661-1111 *SIC* 6321 6311

■ HUMANA INSURANCE CO p 718
1100 Employers Blvd, Green Bay WI 54344
Tel (502) 580-1000 *SIC* 6311 6321

CMFG LIFE INSURANCE CO p 329
5910 Mineral Point Rd, Madison WI 53705
Tel (800) 356-2644 *SIC* 6321 6311

ST MARYS HOSPITAL MEDICAL CENTER AUXILIARY (INC) p 1371
700 S Park St, Madison WI 53715
Tel (608) 251-6100 *SIC* 6321

WEA INSURANCE CORP p 1585
45 Nob Hill Rd, Madison WI 53713
Tel (608) 276-4000 *SIC* 6324 6311 6321

■ FORTIS INSURANCE CO p 569
501 W Michigan St, Milwaukee WI 53203
Tel (262) 646-4633 *SIC* 6311 6321

NORTHWESTERN MUTUAL LIFE INSURANCE CO p 1060
720 E Wisconsin Ave, Milwaukee WI 53202
Tel (414) 271-1444 *SIC* 6311 6321 7389

■ TIME INSURANCE CO p 1454
501 W Michigan St, Milwaukee WI 53203
Tel (414) 271-3011 *SIC* 6321

■ UNITEDHEALTHCARE OF WISCONSIN INC p 1515
10701 W Research Dr, Milwaukee WI 53226
Tel (414) 443-4060 *SIC* 6324 6411 6321

SENTRY INSURANCE A MUTUAL CO p 1305
1800 Northpoint Dr, Stevens Point WI 54481
Tel (715) 346-6000
SIC 6331 6311 6411 6321

SENTRY LIFE INSURANCE CO p 1305
1800 Northpoint Dr, Stevens Point WI 54481
Tel (715) 346-6000 *SIC* 6411 6321

WERCS p 1592
400 E 1st St Ste 100, Casper WY 82601
Tel (307) 235-6200
SIC 6211 6163 6411 6321 6531 6099

BLUE CROSS & BLUE SHIELD OF WYOMING p 191
4000 House Ave, Cheyenne WY 82001
Tel (307) 634-1393 *SIC* 6321

SIC 6324 Hospital & Medical Svc Plans Carriers

CAHABA GOVERNMENT BENEFIT ADMINISTRATORS LLC p 237
500 Corporate Pkwy, Birmingham AL 35242
Tel (205) 220-1900 *SIC* 6324

■ UNITED HEALTHCARE OF ALABAMA INC p 1509
33 Inverness Center Pkwy # 350, Birmingham AL 35242
Tel (205) 437-8500 *SIC* 6324

BLUE CROSS & BLUE SHIELD OF ALABAMA p 191
450 Riverchase Pkwy E, Hoover AL 35244
Tel (205) 988-2200 *SIC* 6321 6324

ARIZONA DENTAL INSURANCE SERVICE INC p 108
5656 W Talavi Blvd, Glendale AZ 85306
Tel (602) 588-3617 *SIC* 6324 6411

BLUE CROSS AND BLUE SHIELD OF ARIZONA INC p 191
2444 W Las Palmaritas Dr, Phoenix AZ 85021
Tel (602) 864-4100 *SIC* 6324

BLUECROSS AND BLUESHIELD OF AZ p 193
2410 W Royal Palm Rd, Phoenix AZ 85021
Tel (602) 864-4100 *SIC* 6324

■ CIGNA HEALTHCARE OF ARIZONA INC p 306
25500 N Norterra Dr, Phoenix AZ 85085
Tel (623) 587-4402 *SIC* 6324

MERCY MARICOPA INTEGRATED CARE p 947
4350 E Cotton Center Blvd D, Phoenix AZ 85040
Tel (602) 453-8308 *SIC* 6324

USA MANAGED HEALTH & WELLNESS RESOURCES GROUP INC p 1534
7301 N 16th St Ste 201, Phoenix AZ 85020
Tel (602) 371-3860 *SIC* 6324 6411

■ HEALTH NET OF ARIZONA INC p 675
1230 W Washington St # 401, Tempe AZ 85281
Tel (602) 286-9242 *SIC* 6324

NEXTMED HOLDINGS LLC p 1041
6339 E Speedway Blvd, Tucson AZ 85710
Tel (520) 323-8732 *SIC* 6324

USABLE MUTUAL INSURANCE CO p 1534
601 S Gaines St, Little Rock AR 72201
Tel (501) 378-2000 *SIC* 6324 6411

DELTA DENTAL PLAN OF ARKANSAS INC p 426
1513 Country Club Rd, Sherwood AR 72120
Tel (501) 992-1666 *SIC* 6324

ALAMEDA ALLIANCE FOR HEALTH p 44
1240 S Loop Rd, Alameda CA 94502
Tel (510) 747-4555 *SIC* 6324

■ SAFEGUARD HEALTH ENTERPRISES INC p 1266
95 Enterprise Ste 100, Aliso Viejo CA 92656
Tel (949) 425-4300 *SIC* 6324

■ UNICARE LIFE & HEALTH INSURANCE CO p 1502
5151 Camino Ruiz Ste A, Camarillo CA 93012
Tel (888) 742-2505 *SIC* 6411 6324

■ PACIFICARE HEALTH SYSTEMS LLC p 1106
5995 Plaza Dr, Cypress CA 90630
Tel (714) 952-1121 *SIC* 6324

■ UHC OF CALIFORNIA p 1500
5995 Plaza Dr, Cypress CA 90630
Tel (714) 952-1121 *SIC* 6324 8732

PARTNERSHIP HEALTH PLAN OF CALIFORNIA p 1118
4665 Business Center Dr, Fairfield CA 94534
Tel (707) 863-4100 *SIC* 6324

HEALTH PLAN OF SAN JOAQUIN p 675
7751 S Manthey Rd, French Camp CA 95231
Tel (209) 942-6300 *SIC* 6324

■ CIGNA HEALTHCARE OF CALIFORNIA INC p 306
400 N Brand Blvd Ste 400, Glendale CA 91203
Tel (818) 500-6262 *SIC* 6324

LIBERTY DENTAL PLAN OF CALIFORNIA INC p 861
340 Commerce Ste 100, Irvine CA 92602
Tel (949) 223-0007 *SIC* 6324

■ OPTUMRX INC p 1091
2300 Main St, Irvine CA 92614
Tel (714) 825-3600 *SIC* 6324 6321

▲ MOLINA HEALTHCARE INC p 982
200 Oceangate Ste 100, Long Beach CA 90802
Tel (562) 435-3666 *SIC* 8011 6324

SCAN HEALTH PLAN p 1286
3800 Kilroy Airport Way # 100, Long Beach CA 90806
Tel (562) 989-5100 *SIC* 6324

SENIOR CARE ACTION NETWORK FOUNDATION p 1303
3800 Kilroy Airport Way, Long Beach CA 90806
Tel (562) 989-5100 *SIC* 6324

LOCAL INITIATIVE HEALTH AUTHORITY FOR LOS ANGELES COUNTY p 872
1055 W 7th St Fl 11, Los Angeles CA 90017
Tel (213) 694-1250 *SIC* 6324

TRANSAMERICA OCCIDENTAL LIFE INSURANCE CO p 1470
1150 S Olive St Fl 23, Los Angeles CA 90015
Tel (213) 742-2111
SIC 6311 6371 6321 6324 8799

KAISER FOUNDATION HEALTH PLAN INC p 800
1 Kaiser Plz, Oakland CA 94612
Tel (510) 271-5800 *SIC* 6324

SOUTHERN CALIFORNIA PERMANENTE MEDICAL GROUP p 1347
393 Walnut Dr, Pasadena CA 91107
Tel (626) 405-5704 *SIC* 6324

INTER-VALLEY HEALTH PLAN INC p 751
300 S Park Ave Ste 300, Pomona CA 91766
Tel (909) 623-6333 *SIC* 6324 8011

■ HEALTH NET FEDERAL SERVICES LLC p 675
2025 Aerojet Rd, Rancho Cordova CA 95742
Tel (916) 935-5000 *SIC* 6324

VISION SERVICE PLAN p 1561
3333 Quality Dr, Rancho Cordova CA 95670
Tel (916) 851-5000 *SIC* 6324 5048

INLAND EMPIRE HEALTH PLAN p 743
10801 6th St Ste 120, Rancho Cucamonga CA 91730
Tel (909) 890-2000 *SIC* 6321 6324

SHARP HEALTH PLAN p 1312
8520 Tech Way Ste 200, San Diego CA 92123
Tel (858) 499-8300 *SIC* 6324

SHARP HEALTHCARE p 1312
8695 Spectrum Center Blvd, San Diego CA 92123
Tel (858) 499-4000 *SIC* 8062 8741 6324

CALIFORNIA PHYSICIANS SERVICE p 241
50 Beale St Bsmt 2, San Francisco CA 94105
Tel (415) 229-5000 *SIC* 6324

DELTA DENTAL OF CALIFORNIA p 426
100 1st St Fl 4, San Francisco CA 94105
Tel (415) 972-8300 *SIC* 6324

ON LOK SENIOR HEALTH SERVICES p 1086
1333 Bush St, San Francisco CA 94109
Tel (415) 292-8888 *SIC* 6324 8082

SANTA CLARA VALLEY MEDICAL CENTER p 1280
751 S Bascom Ave, San Jose CA 95128
Tel (408) 885-5000 *SIC* 8062 6324

■ MANAGED HEALTH NETWORK p 900
2370 Kerner Blvd, San Rafael CA 94901
Tel (415) 460-8168
SIC 6324 8099 8093 8011

■ MHN SERVICES p 959
2370 Kerner Blvd, San Rafael CA 94901
Tel (415) 460-8300
SIC 6324 8011 8742 8322

■ AETNA HEALTH OF CALIFORNIA INC p 31
2409 Camino Ramon, San Ramon CA 94583
Tel (925) 543-9000 *SIC* 6324

■ PACIFICARE HEALTH PLAN ADMINISTRATORS INC p 1106
3120 W Lake Center Dr, Santa Ana CA 92704
Tel (714) 825-5200 *SIC* 6324

■ BLUE CROSS OF CALIFORNIA p 192
4553 La Tienda Rd, Westlake Village CA 91362
Tel (805) 557-6050 *SIC* 6324 6411

■ WELLPOINT CALIFORNIA SERVICES INC p 1589
4553 La Tienda Rd, Westlake Village CA 91362
Tel (805) 557-6655 *SIC* 6324

■ HEALTH NET INC p 675
21650 Oxnard St Fl 25, Woodland Hills CA 91367
Tel (818) 676-6000 *SIC* 6324 6311

■ HEALTH NET OF CALIFORNIA INC p 675
21281 Burbank Blvd Fl 4, Woodland Hills CA 91367
Tel (818) 676-6775
SIC 6324 8062 6311 6321 6331 5912

COLORADO DENTAL SERVICE INC p 338
4582 S Ulster St Ste 800, Denver CO 80237
Tel (303) 741-9300 *SIC* 6324

KAISER FOUNDATION HEALTH PLAN OF COLORADO p 800
10350 E Dakota Ave, Denver CO 80247
Tel (866) 239-1677 *SIC* 6324

■ CIGNA HEALTHCARE OF COLORADO INC p 306
8525 E Orchard Rd, Greenwood Village CO 80111
Tel (303) 305-1000 *SIC* 6324

▲ CIGNA CORP p 306
900 Cottage Grove Rd, Bloomfield CT 06002
Tel (860) 226-6000
SIC 6324 6311 6351 6321

■ CIGNA HEALTH CORP p 306
900 Cottage Grove Rd, Bloomfield CT 06002
Tel (860) 226-6000 *SIC* 6324

■ CIGNA HEALTHCARE OF CONNECTICUT INC p 306
900 Cottage Grove Rd, Bloomfield CT 06002
Tel (860) 226-2300 *SIC* 6324

CONNECTICARE INC p 356
175 Scott Swamp Rd, Farmington CT 06032
Tel (860) 674-5700 *SIC* 6324

■ AETNA HEALTH HOLDINGS LLC p 31
151 Farmington Ave, Hartford CT 06156
Tel (860) 273-0123 *SIC* 6324 6411 6321

■ AETNA HEALTH INC p 31
151 Farmington Ave, Hartford CT 06156
Tel (800) 872-3862 *SIC* 6324

■ AETNA HEALTH MANAGEMENT INC p 31
151 Farmington Ave, Hartford CT 06156
Tel (860) 273-0123 *SIC* 6324

▲ AETNA INC p 31
151 Farmington Ave, Hartford CT 06156
Tel (860) 273-0123
SIC 6324 6321 6371 8011

■ AETNA LIFE INSURANCE CO INC p 31
151 Farmington Ave, Hartford CT 06156
Tel (860) 273-0123 *SIC* 6324 6321 8011

ODYSSEY REINSURANCE CO p 1075
300 Stamford Pl Ste 700, Stamford CT 06902
Tel (203) 965-0004
SIC 6411 6361 6331 6324 6311

■ OXFORD HEALTH PLANS (CT) INC p 1101
48 Monroe Tpke, Trumbull CT 06611
Tel (203) 459-9100 *SIC* 6324

■ OXFORD HEALTH PLANS (NY) INC p 1101
48 Monroe Tpke, Trumbull CT 06611
Tel (203) 459-9100 *SIC* 6324

■ OXFORD HEALTH PLANS INC p 1101
48 Monroe Tpke, Trumbull CT 06611
Tel (203) 459-9100 *SIC* 6324

■ AMERICAN LIFE INSURANCE CO p 75
1 Alico Plz, Wilmington DE 19801
Tel (302) 594-2000 *SIC* 6411 6321 6324

PREFERRED MEDICAL PLAN INC p 1169
4950 Sw 8th St Fl 4, Coral Gables FL 33134
Tel (305) 324-5585 *SIC* 6324

AVMED INC p 138
4300 Nw 89th Blvd Fl 2, Gainesville FL 32606
Tel (352) 372-8400 *SIC* 6324

FLORIDA HEALTH CARE PLAN INC p 558
1340 Ridgewood Ave, Holly Hill FL 32117
Tel (386) 615-4022 *SIC* 6324

HIP ADMINISTRATORS OF FLORIDA INC p 695
3251 Hollywood Blvd # 401, Hollywood FL 33021
Tel (954) 893-6400 *SIC* 6324

BLUE CROSS AND BLUE SHIELD OF FLORIDA INC p 191
4800 Deerwood Campus Pkwy, Jacksonville FL 32246
Tel (904) 905-0000 *SIC* 6324

HEALTH OPTIONS INC p 675
4800 Deerwood Campus Pkwy, Jacksonville FL 32246
Tel (904) 564-5700 *SIC* 6324

■ AMERICAN BANKERS INSURANCE GROUP INC p 68
11222 Quail Roost Dr, Miami FL 33157
Tel (305) 253-2244
SIC 6331 6311 6351 6321 6324

■ NEIGHBORHOOD HEALTH PARTNERSHIP INC p 1024
7600 Nw 19th St Ste 100, Miami FL 33126
Tel (305) 715-2200 *SIC* 6324 6321

■ CIGNA DENTAL HEALTH INC p 306
300 Nw 82nd Ave Ste 700, Plantation FL 33324
Tel (954) 514-6600 *SIC* 6324

SOLSTICE BENEFITS INC p 1339
7901 Sw 6th Ct Ste 400, Plantation FL 33324
Tel (954) 370-1700 *SIC* 6324

HEALTH FIRST HEALTH PLANS INC p 674
6450 Us Highway 1, Rockledge FL 32955
Tel (321) 434-5600 *SIC* 6324

HEALTH FIRST INC p 674
6450 Us Highway 1, Rockledge FL 32955
Tel (321) 434-4300
SIC 8062 8011 8082 8069 7991 6324

■ CIGNA HEALTHCARE OF FLORIDA INC p 306
2701 N Rocky Point Dr # 178, Rocky Point FL 33607
Tel (215) 761-1000 *SIC* 6324

■ COVENTRY HEALTH PLAN OF FLORIDA INC p 385
1340 Concord Ter, Sunrise FL 33323
Tel (954) 858-3000 *SIC* 6324

■ AMERIGROUP FLORIDA INC p 82
4200 W Cypress St 900-1000, Tampa FL 33607
Tel (813) 830-6900 *SIC* 6324

CITRUS HEALTH CARE INC p 311
101 S Hoover Blvd Ste 100, Tampa FL 33609
Tel (813) 490-7931 *SIC* 6324

▲ WELLCARE HEALTH PLANS INC p 1589
8735 Henderson Rd, Tampa FL 33634
Tel (813) 290-6200 *SIC* 6324

HEALTHPORT INC p 677
925 North Point Pkwy # 350, Alpharetta GA 30005
Tel (770) 360-1700 *SIC* 6324 7373 7374

■ BLUE CROSS AND BLUE SHIELD OF GEORGIA INC p 191
3350 Peachtree Rd Ne # 300, Atlanta GA 30326
Tel (404) 842-8000 *SIC* 6324 6321

KAISER FOUNDATION HEALTH PLAN OF GEORGIA INC p 800
3495 Piedmont Rd Ne # 9, Atlanta GA 30305
Tel (404) 364-7000 SIC 6324

■ **PEACH STATE HEALTH PLAN INC** p 1125
1100 Circle 75 Pkwy Se # 1100, Atlanta GA 30339
Tel (678) 556-2300 SIC 6324

COMPDENT OF GEORGIA INC p 351
100 Mansell Ct E Ste 400, Roswell GA 30076
Tel (770) 998-8936 SIC 6324 6311

HAWAII DENTAL SERVICE p 668
700 Bishop St Ste 700, Honolulu HI 96813
Tel (808) 521-1431 SIC 6324

HAWAII MEDICAL SERVICE ASSOCIATION p 669
818 Keeaumoku St Ste 200, Honolulu HI 96814
Tel (808) 948-6111 SIC 6321 6324

DELTA DENTAL PLAN OF IDAHO INC p 426
555 E Parkcenter Blvd, Boise ID 83706
Tel (208) 489-3580 SIC 6324 8021

REGENCE BLUESHIELD OF IDAHO INC p 1218
1602 21st Ave, Lewiston ID 83501
Tel (208) 743-0320 SIC 6324

■ **AETNA HEALTH OF ILLINOIS INC** p 31
100 N Riverside Plz Fl 20, Chicago IL 60606
Tel (312) 928-3000 SIC 6324

■ **BANKERS LIFE & CASUALTY CO** p 152
111 E Wacker Dr Ste 2100, Chicago IL 60601
Tel (312) 396-6000 SIC 6321 6311 6324

BLUE CROSS & BLUE SHIELD ASSOCIATION p 191
225 N Michigan Ave Fl 5, Chicago IL 60601
Tel (312) 297-6000 SIC 8621 6324

■ **CIGNA HEALTHCARE OF ILLINOIS INC** p 306
525 W Monroe St Ste 1800, Chicago IL 60661
Tel (312) 496-5340 SIC 6324

■ **HARMONY HEALTH SYSTEMS INC** p 662
200 W Adams St Ste 800, Chicago IL 60606
Tel (312) 372-3471 SIC 6324 8011

HEALTH CARE SERVICE CORP A MUTUAL LEGAL RESERVE CO p 674
300 E Randolph St Fl 4, Chicago IL 60601
Tel (312) 653-6000 SIC 6324 6321 6411

■ **FIRST HEALTH GROUP CORP** p 547
3200 Highland Ave, Downers Grove IL 60515
Tel (630) 737-7900
SIC 8742 6324 6321 6411

CORESOURCE INC p 370
400 N Field Dr, Lake Forest IL 60045
Tel (847) 615-1500 SIC 6324 6411

■ **UNITED HEALTHCARE OF ILLINOIS INC** p 1509
550 Warrenville Rd # 300, Lisle IL 60532
Tel (630) 725-7204 SIC 6324

DENTAL NETWORK OF AMERICA LLC p 429
701 E 22nd St Ste 300, Lombard IL 60148
Tel (630) 691-0290 SIC 6324

■ **UNITEDHEALTHCARE SERVICES CO OF RIVER VALLEY INC** p 1515
1300 River Dr Ste 200, Moline IL 61265
Tel (952) 936-1300 SIC 6324

DELTA DENTAL OF ILLINOIS p 426
111 Shuman Blvd Ste 100, Naperville IL 60563
Tel (630) 718-4700 SIC 6324

ZURICH HOLDING CO OF AMERICA INC p 1645
1299 Zurich Way, Schaumburg IL 60196
Tel (847) 605-6000
SIC 6311 6331 6321 6324 6719

HEALTH ALLIANCE MEDICAL PLANS INC p 674
301 S Vine St, Urbana IL 61801
Tel (217) 337-8000 SIC 6321 6324

ADVANTAGE HEALTH SOLUTIONS INC p 26
9045 River Rd Ste 200, Indianapolis IN 46240
Tel (317) 573-2700 SIC 6324

AMERICAN HEALTH NETWORK OF INDIANA INC p 73
10689 N Pennsylvna St # 200, Indianapolis IN 46280
Tel (317) 580-6314 SIC 6324 8011

▲ **ANTHEM INC** p 93
120 Monument Cir Ste 200, Indianapolis IN 46204
Tel (317) 488-6000 SIC 6324 6321

■ **ANTHEM INSURANCE COMPANIES INC** p 94
120 Monument Cir Ste 200, Indianapolis IN 46204
Tel (317) 488-6000
SIC 6324 6411 6321 6331 6159 7371

■ **ASSOCIATED GROUP INC** p 120
120 Monument Cir Ste 200, Indianapolis IN 46204
Tel (317) 488-6000 SIC 6324

EQUIAN LLC p 506
5975 Castle Crk Pkwy 10 Ste 100, Indianapolis IN 46250
Tel (800) 962-6831 SIC 6324

INDIANA UNIVERSITY HEALTH INC p 739
1701 Senate Blvd, Indianapolis IN 46202
Tel (317) 962-2000 SIC 8062 6324

M-PLAN INC p 890
8802 N Meridian St # 100, Indianapolis IN 46260
Tel (317) 963-9700 SIC 6324 6411

MDWISE INC p 933
1200 Madison Ave Ste 400, Indianapolis IN 46225
Tel (317) 630-2828 SIC 6324

STANDARD LIFE INSURANCE CO OF INDIANA p 1376
10689 N Pennsylvna St # 200, Indianapolis IN 46280
Tel (317) 574-6201 SIC 6324

■ **PORTER HEALTH SERVICES INC** p 1162
814 Laporte Ave, Valparaiso IN 46383
Tel (219) 477-1013 SIC 6324

AMERICAN REPUBLIC INSURANCE CO p 78
601 6th Ave, Des Moines IA 50309
Tel (515) 245-2000 SIC 6324

WELLMARK INC p 1589
1331 Grand Ave, Des Moines IA 50309
Tel (515) 376-4500 SIC 6324 6411 6321

■ **UNION SECURITY INSURANCE CO** p 1505
6941 Vista Dr, West Des Moines IA 50266
Tel (651) 361-4000 SIC 6321 6324

■ **COVENTRY HEALTH CARE OF KANSAS INC** p 385
9401 Indian Creek Pkwy # 1300, Overland Park KS 66210
Tel (800) 969-3343 SIC 6324 8011

BLUE CROSS AND BLUE SHIELD OF KANSAS INC p 191
1133 Sw Topeka Blvd, Topeka KS 66629
Tel (785) 291-7000 SIC 6321 6324

DELTA DENTAL OF KANSAS INC p 426
1619 N Waterfront Pkwy, Wichita KS 67206
Tel (316) 264-4511 SIC 6324

■ **PREFERRED HEALTH SYSTEMS INC** p 1169
8535 E 21st St N, Wichita KS 67206
Tel (316) 609-2345 SIC 6324

DELTA DENTAL OF KENTUCKY INC p 426
10100 Linn Station Rd # 700, Louisville KY 40223
Tel (502) 736-5000 SIC 6324

■ **HUMANA HEALTH PLAN OF KANSAS INC** p 718
500 W Main St Ste 300, Louisville KY 40202
Tel (502) 580-1000 SIC 6324 6321

▲ **HUMANA INC** p 718
500 W Main St Ste 300, Louisville KY 40202
Tel (502) 580-1000 SIC 6324 6321 6411

UNIVERSITY HEALTHCARE INC p 1519
5100 Cmmerce Crossings Dr, Louisville KY 40229
Tel (800) 691-5566 SIC 6324

GENERAL HEALTH SYSTEM p 601
8585 Picardy Ave, Baton Rouge LA 70809
Tel (225) 387-7000 SIC 8741 6324

GENERAL HEALTH SYSTEM MANAGEMENT INC p 601
8585 Picardy Ave, Baton Rouge LA 70809
Tel (225) 237-1700 SIC 6324

HMO OF LOUISIANA INC p 698
5525 Reitz Ave, Baton Rouge LA 70809
Tel (225) 295-3307 SIC 6324

LOUISIANA HEALTH SERVICE AND INDEMNITY CO p 880
5525 Reitz Ave, Baton Rouge LA 70809
Tel (225) 295-3307 SIC 6321 6324 6411

■ **COVENTRY HEALTH CARE INC** p 385
6720 Rockledge Dr 700b, Bethesda MD 20817
Tel (301) 581-0600 SIC 6324

UNION HOSPITAL OF CECIL COUNTY HEALTH SERVICES INC p 1504
106 Bow St, Elkton MD 21921
Tel (410) 392-7009 SIC 6324 8062

CAREFIRST INC p 254
10455 Mill Run Cir, Owings Mills MD 21117
Tel (301) 805-5005 SIC 6324

CAREFIRST OF MARYLAND INC p 254
10455 Mill Run Cir, Owings Mills MD 21117
Tel (410) 581-3000 SIC 6324

GROUP HOSPITALIZATION AND MEDICAL SERVICES INC p 641
10455 Mill Run Cir, Owings Mills MD 21117
Tel (202) 479-8000 SIC 6324

KAISER FOUNDATION HEALTH PLAN OF MID-ATLANTIC STATES INC p 800
2101 E Jefferson St, Rockville MD 20852
Tel (301) 816-2424 SIC 6324

■ **MID ATLANTIC MEDICAL SERVICES LLC** p 962
800 King Farm Blvd # 600, Rockville MD 20850
Tel (301) 990-3844 SIC 6324

UNION LABOR LIFE INSURANCE CO p 1504
8403 Colesville Rd # 1000, Silver Spring MD 20910
Tel (202) 682-0900
SIC 6311 6321 6324 6371

CARROLL COUNTY HEALTH SERVICES CORP p 261
200 Memorial Ave, Westminster MD 21157
Tel (410) 848-3000 SIC 6324

BLUE CROSS AND BLUE SHIELD OF MASSACHUSETTS INC p 191
101 Huntington Ave # 1300, Boston MA 02199
Tel (617) 246-5000 SIC 6321 8741 6324

BOSTON MEDICAL CENTER HEALTH PLAN INC p 203
2 Copley Pl Ste 600, Boston MA 02116
Tel (617) 748-6000 SIC 6324

DENTAQUEST VENTURES LLC p 429
465 Medford St Ste 150, Boston MA 02129
Tel (617) 886-1818 SIC 6324

DENTAL SERVICE OF MASSACHUSETTS INC p 429
465 Medford St Ste 150, Charlestown MA 02129
Tel (617) 886-1000 SIC 6324

MEDICAL WEST COMMUNITY HEALTH p 937
444 Montgomery St, Chicopee MA 01020
Tel (413) 598-7440 SIC 6324

BAYSTATE HEALTH SYSTEM HEALTH SERVICES INC p 162
280 Chestnut St, Springfield MA 01199
Tel (413) 794-9939
SIC 8741 8062 6324 6512

HEALTH NEW ENGLAND INC p 675
1 Monarch Pl Ste 1500, Springfield MA 01144
Tel (413) 787-4000 SIC 6324

MASSACHUSETTS MUTUAL LIFE INSURANCE CO p 917
1295 State St, Springfield MA 01111
Tel (413) 788-8411
SIC 6321 6324 6411 6282

PRIVATE HEALTHCARE SYSTEMS INC p 1178
1100 Winter St Ste 2300, Waltham MA 02451
Tel (781) 895-7500 SIC 6324

TUFTS ASSOCIATED HEALTH PLANS INC p 1491
705 Mount Auburn St, Watertown MA 02472
Tel (617) 972-9400 SIC 6324

HARVARD PILGRIM HEALTH CARE INC p 666
93 Worcester St, Wellesley MA 02481
Tel (781) 263-6000 SIC 6324

FALLON COMMUNITY HEALTH PLAN INC p 526
10 Chestnut St Ste 800, Worcester MA 01608
Tel (508) 799-2100 SIC 6324

FIRST ALLMERICA FINANCIAL LIFE INSURANCE CO p 544
440 Lincoln St, Worcester MA 01653
Tel (508) 855-1000 SIC 6411 6211 6324

■ **OPUS INVESTMENT MANAGEMENT INC** p 1091
440 Lincoln St, Worcester MA 01653
Tel (508) 855-1000
SIC 6311 6321 6324 6351 6722

GATEWAY COMMUNITY HEALTH p 593
7457 M E Cad Blvd Ste 200, Clarkston MI 48348
Tel (313) 262-5050 SIC 6324

BLUE CROSS AND BLUE SHIELD OF MICHIGAN p 191
600 E Lafayette Blvd, Detroit MI 48226
Tel (313) 225-9000 SIC 6321 6324

HEALTH ALLIANCE PLAN OF MICHIGAN p 674
2850 W Grand Blvd, Detroit MI 48202
Tel (313) 872-8100 SIC 6324 8011 8099

HEALTHPLUS OF MICHIGAN INC p 677
2050 S Linden Rd, Flint MI 48532
Tel (810) 230-2000 SIC 6324

PRIORITY HEALTH MANAGED BENEFITS INC p 1177
1231 E Beltline Ave Ne, Grand Rapids MI 49525
Tel (616) 942-0954 SIC 6324

DELTA DENTAL PLAN OF MICHIGAN INC p 426
4100 Okemos Rd, Okemos MI 48864
Tel (517) 349-6000 SIC 6324

BLUE CARE NETWORK OF MICHIGAN p 191
20500 Civic Center Dr, Southfield MI 48076
Tel (248) 799-6400 SIC 6324

SELECTCARE INC p 1301
2401 W Big Beaver Rd, Troy MI 48084
Tel (248) 358-2560 SIC 6324 8741

■ **CIGNA BEHAVIORAL HEALTH INC** p 306
11095 Viking Dr Ste 350, Eden Prairie MN 55344
Tel (952) 996-2000 SIC 6324

■ **OPTUM INC** p 1090
11000 Optum Cir, Eden Prairie MN 55344
Tel (952) 936-1300 SIC 6324

■ **OPTUMHEALTH HOLDINGS LLC** p 1090
13625 Technology Dr, Eden Prairie MN 55344
Tel (763) 595-3200 SIC 6324 8741 6411

■ **OPTUMHEALTH CARE SOLUTIONS INC** p 1090
6300 Olson Memorial Hwy, Golden Valley MN 55427
Tel (877) 801-3507 SIC 6324 7374 8999

■ **COLLABORATIVE CARE HOLDINGS LLC** p 336
9900 Bren Rd E, Hopkins MN 55343
Tel (952) 936-1300 SIC 6324

■ **OVATIONS INC** p 1099
9900 Bren Rd E Ste 300w, Hopkins MN 55343
Tel (952) 936-1300 SIC 6324

■ **RELIASTAR LIFE INSURANCE CO** p 1222
20 Washington Ave S, Minneapolis MN 55401
Tel (612) 372-5432 SIC 6311 6321 6324

UCARE MINNESOTA p 1498
500 Stinson Blvd, Minneapolis MN 55413
Tel (612) 676-6500 SIC 6324

▲ **UNITEDHEALTH GROUP INC** p 1515
9900 Bren Rd E Ste 300w, Minnetonka MN 55343
Tel (952) 936-1300 SIC 6324 6411 6321

AWARE INTEGRATED INC p 139
3535 Blue Cross Rd, Saint Paul MN 55122
Tel (651) 662-8000 SIC 6324

BCBSM INC p 163
3535 Blue Cross Rd, Saint Paul MN 55122
Tel (651) 662-8000 SIC 6321 6324

■ **DECARE DENTAL LLC** p 420
3560 Delta Dental Dr, Saint Paul MN 55122
Tel (800) 371-6561 SIC 6324 8621

BLUE CROSS & BLUE SHIELD OF MISSISSIPPI A MUTUAL INSURANCE CO p 191
3545 Lakeland Dr, Jackson MS 39232
Tel (601) 932-3704 SIC 6324

■ **MERCY HEALTH PLANS INC** p 946
14528 South Outer 40 Rd # 100, Chesterfield MO 63017
Tel (314) 214-2384 SIC 6324

■ **MAGELLAN HEALTHCARE INC** p 895
14100 Magellan Plz, Maryland Heights MO 63043
Tel (410) 953-1000 SIC 6324

■ **UNITED HEALTHCARE OF MIDWEST INC** p 1509
13655 Riverport Dr, Maryland Heights MO 63043
Tel (314) 592-7000 SIC 8741 6324

▲ **CENTENE CORP** p 275
7700 Forsyth Blvd Ste 800, Saint Louis MO 63105
Tel (314) 725-4477 SIC 6324 8011 8099

■ **COVENTRY HEALTH CARE OF MISSOURI INC** p 385
550 Maryville Centre Dr # 300, Saint Louis MO 63141
Tel (314) 506-1700 SIC 6324

DELTA DENTAL OF MISSOURI p 426
12399 Gravois Rd Fl 2, Saint Louis MO 63127
Tel (314) 656-3000 SIC 6324 6321

■ **ALLEGIANCE BENEFIT PLAN MANAGEMENT INC** p 52
2806 S Grfield St Ste 101, Missoula MT 59801
Tel (406) 523-3122 SIC 6324

BLUE CROSS & BLUE SHIELD OF NEBRASKA p 191
1919 Aksarben Dr, Omaha NE 68180
Tel (402) 982-7000 SIC 6324 6311

UNITED OF OMAHA LIFE INSURANCE CO p 1510
Mutual Of Omaha Plaza, Omaha NE 68175
Tel (402) 342-7600 SIC 6311 6321 6324

■ **SIERRA HEALTH SERVICES INC** p 1320
2720 N Tenaya Way, Las Vegas NV 89128
Tel (702) 242-7000
SIC 6324 6311 8082 8741 8093

DELTA DENTAL PLAN OF NEW HAMPSHIRE INC p 426
1 Delta Dr, Concord NH 03301
Tel (800) 537-1715 SIC 6324 8021

■ **HEALTHSOURCE INC** p 677
2 College Park Dr, Hooksett NH 03106
Tel (603) 268-7000 SIC 6324 8741 8011

PXRE CORP p 1193
379 Thornall St Ste 2, Edison NJ 08837
Tel (973) 321-3590 SIC 6331 6324 6321

INNOVACARE SERVICES CO LLC p 744
173 Bridge Plz N, Fort Lee NJ 07024
Tel (201) 969-2300
SIC 6324 8011 8741 8742

■ **ADMIRAL INSURANCE CO** p 23
1000 Howard Blvd Ste 300, Mount Laurel NJ 08054
Tel (856) 429-9200 SIC 6331 6411 6324

HORIZON HEALTHCARE SERVICES INC p 707
3 Penn Plz E Ste 1, Newark NJ 07105
Tel (973) 466-4000 SIC 6324 6411 6321

■ **PRUDENTIAL HOLDINGS LLC** p 1187
751 Broad St, Newark NJ 07102
Tel (973) 802-6000 SIC 6282 6321 6324

■ **AETNA HEALTH INC (NJ)** p 31
9 Entin Rd, Parsippany NJ 07054
Tel (973) 244-3500 SIC 6324 6321

■ **QUALCARE ALLIANCE NETWORKS INC** p 1196
30 Knightsbridge Rd # 530, Piscataway NJ 08854
Tel (732) 562-0833 SIC 6324

DELTA DENTAL PLAN OF NEW MEXICO INC p 426
2500 La Blvd Ne Ste 600, Albuquerque NM 87110
Tel (505) 883-4777 SIC 6324

AFFINITY HEALTH PLAN INC p 32
1776 Eastchester Rd # 202, Bronx NY 10461
Tel (718) 794-7700 SIC 6324

BROOKDALE UNIVERSITY HOSPITAL & MEDICAL CENTER p 217
1 Brookdale Plz, Brooklyn NY 11212
Tel (718) 240-5000 SIC 8011 6324

ELDERPLAN INC p 484
6323 7th Ave Ste 3, Brooklyn NY 11220
Tel (800) 353-3765 SIC 6324

HEALTHNOW NEW YORK INC p 677
257 W Genesee St, Buffalo NY 14202
Tel (716) 887-6900 SIC 6324 6411

INDEPENDENT HEALTH CORP p 736
511 Farber Lakes Dr Ste 2, Buffalo NY 14221
Tel (716) 631-3001 SIC 6324

■ **METROPOLITAN LIFE INSURANCE CO (INC)** p 956
2701 Queens Plz N Ste 1, Long Island City NY 11101
Tel (212) 578-2211
SIC 6411 6324 6331 6321 6531

VYTRA HEALTH PLANS LONG ISLAND INC p 1568
395 N Service Rd Ste 110, Melville NY 11747
Tel (631) 694-4000 SIC 6324

▲ **AMERICAN INTERNATIONAL GROUP INC** p 75
175 Water St Rm 1800, New York NY 10038
Tel (212) 770-7000
SIC 6331 6321 6311 6324 6411 6282

■ **AMERIGROUP NEW YORK LLC** p 82
360 W 31st St Fl 5, New York NY 10001
Tel (212) 372-6900 SIC 6324

AMIDA CARE INC p 85
225 W 34th St Fl 2, New York NY 10122
Tel (646) 757-7000 SIC 6324

EMBLEMHEALTH INC p 490
55 Water St Ste Conc1, New York NY 10041
Tel (646) 447-5000 SIC 6324

GROUP HEALTH INC p 641
441 9th Ave Frnt, New York NY 10001
Tel (212) 615-0000 SIC 6324

GUARDIAN LIFE INSURANCE CO OF AMERICA p 645
7 Hanover Sq Fl 14, New York NY 10004
Tel (212) 598-8000
SIC 6311 6371 6324 6321 6722 6282

■ **HEALTH PLUS PREPAID HEALTH SERVICES PLAN INC** p 675
9 Pine St Fl 14, New York NY 10005
Tel (718) 532-1011 SIC 6321 6324 8741

INDEPENDENCE CARE SYSTEMS INC p 736
257 Park Ave S Fl 2, New York NY 10010
Tel (212) 584-2500 SIC 8322 6324

METROPLUS HEALTH PLAN INC p 955
160 Water St Fl 3, New York NY 10038
Tel (212) 788-3648 SIC 6324

MONROE PLAN FOR MEDICAL CARE INC p 985
1120 Pittsford Victor Rd, Pittsford NY 14534
Tel (585) 244-5550 SIC 6324

BLUE CROSS & BLUE SHIELD OF ROCHESTER p 191
165 Court St, Rochester NY 14647
Tel (585) 454-1700 SIC 6324

LIFETIME HEALTHCARE INC p 864
165 Court St, Rochester NY 14647
Tel (585) 454-1700 SIC 6324 6321

HEALTHPLEX INC p 677
333 Earle Ovington Blvd # 300, Uniondale NY 11553
Tel (516) 542-2200 SIC 6324

▲ **UNIVERSAL AMERICAN CORP** p 1516
44 S Broadway Ste 1200, White Plains NY 10601
Tel (914) 934-5200 SIC 6311 6321 6324

INDEPENDENT HEALTH ASSOCIATION INC p 736
511 Farber Lakes Dr Ste 2, Williamsville NY 14221
Tel (716) 631-3001 SIC 6324

■ **METLIFE INSURANCE CO USA** p 954
11225 N Community Hse Rd, Charlotte NC 28277
Tel (980) 949-3626
SIC 6411 6321 6331 6324

RAYCOM SPORTS NETWORK INC p 1210
1900 W Morehead St, Charlotte NC 28208
Tel (704) 378-4400
SIC 6311 6321 6324 6411 4832 4833

BLUE CROSS AND BLUE SHIELD NORTH CAROLINA p 191
4615 University Dr, Durham NC 27707
Tel (919) 489-7431 SIC 6324

■ **LINCOLN NATIONAL LIFE INSURANCE CO** p 867
100 N Greene St, Greensboro NC 27401
Tel (336) 691-3000 SIC 6411 6321 6324

■ **UNITEDHEALTHCARE OF NORTH CAROLINA INC** p 1515
2307 W Cone Blvd Ste 200, Greensboro NC 27408
Tel (336) 540-2000 SIC 6324

■ **COVENTRY HEALTH CARE OF CAROLINAS INC** p 385
2801 Slater Rd Ste 200, Morrisville NC 27560
Tel (919) 337-1800 SIC 6324

FIRSTCAROLINACARE INSURANCE CO p 550
42 Memorial Dr, Pinehurst NC 28374
Tel (910) 715-8100 SIC 6324

NOVANT HEALTH INC p 1062
3333 Silas Creek Pkwy, Winston Salem NC 27103
Tel (336) 718-5000 SIC 6324

PARTNERS NATIONAL HEALTH PLANS OF NORTH CAROLINA INC p 1118
5660 University Pkwy, Winston Salem NC 27105
Tel (336) 760-4822 SIC 6324

NORIDIAN HEALTHCARE SOLUTIONS LLC p 1048
900 42nd St S, Fargo ND 58103
Tel (701) 277-6500 SIC 6324

NORIDIAN MUTUAL INSURANCE CO p 1048
4510 13th Ave S, Fargo ND 58121
Tel (701) 282-1100 SIC 8399 6321 6324

AULTCARE CORP p 131
2600 6th St Sw, Canton OH 44710
Tel (330) 363-6360 SIC 6324

MEDICAL MUTUAL OF OHIO p 937
2060 E 9th St Frnt Ste, Cleveland OH 44115
Tel (216) 687-7000 SIC 6324

■ **UNITED HEALTHCARE OF OHIO INC** p 1509
9200 Worthington Rd, Columbus OH 43085
Tel (614) 410-7000 SIC 6324

DELTA DENTAL PLAN OF OHIO INC p 426
5600 Blazer Pkwy Ste 150, Dublin OH 43017
Tel (614) 776-2300 SIC 6324

HEALTH PLAN OF UPPER OHIO VALLEY INC p 675
52160 National Rd E, Saint Clairsville OH 43950
Tel (740) 695-3585 SIC 6324 8082

DCP HOLDING CO p 418
100 Crowne Point Pl, Sharonville OH 45241
Tel (513) 554-1100 SIC 6324

FAMILY HEALTH PLAN INC p 527
2200 Jefferson Ave Fl 6, Toledo OH 43604
Tel (419) 241-6501 SIC 6324 8011

PROMEDICA HEALTH SYSTEMS INC p 1183
1801 Richards Rd, Toledo OH 43607
Tel (419) 469-3800
SIC 8062 6324 8351 8741

PAULS VALLEY HOSPITAL AUTHORITY p 1122
100 Valley Dr, Pauls Valley OK 73075
Tel (405) 238-5501 SIC 6324 8062

COMMUNITY CARE HMO INC p 347
218 W 6th St Ste 700, Tulsa OK 74119
Tel (918) 594-5200 SIC 6324

COMMUNITYCARE MANAGED HEALTHCARE PLANS OF OKLAHOMA INC p 350
218 W 6th St, Tulsa OK 74119
Tel (918) 594-5200 SIC 6324

COMPREHENSIVE MEDICAL CARE AFFILIATES INC p 352
218 W 6th St Ste 704, Tulsa OK 74119
Tel (918) 594-5202 SIC 6324

CAMBIA HEALTH SOLUTIONS INC p 243
100 Sw Market St, Portland OR 97201
Tel (503) 225-5336 SIC 6321 6411 6324

KAISER FOUNDATION HEALTH PLAN OF NORTHWEST p 800
500 Ne Multnomah St # 100, Portland OR 97232
Tel (503) 813-2440 SIC 6324

OREGON DENTAL SERVICE p 1093
601 Sw 2nd Ave Ste 900, Portland OR 97204
Tel (503) 228-6554 SIC 6324

PROVIDENCE HEALTH PLAN p 1186
10126 Sw Park Way, Portland OR 97225
Tel (503) 574-5000 SIC 6324

■ **HEALTH NET HEALTH PLAN OF OREGON INC** p 675
13221 Sw 68th Pkwy Ste 20, Tigard OR 97223
Tel (503) 213-5000 SIC 6324 8011

CORRECTIONAL MEDICAL CARE INC p 372
980 Harvest Dr Ste 202, Blue Bell PA 19422
Tel (215) 542-5800 SIC 6324 8742

UNITED CONCORDIA COMPANIES INC p 1507
4401 Deer Path Rd, Harrisburg PA 17110
Tel (717) 260-6800 SIC 6324

PENNSYLVANIA DENTAL SERVICE CORP p 1130
1 Delta Dr, Mechanicsburg PA 17055
Tel (717) 766-8500 SIC 6324 8021

AMERIHEALTH INC p 82
1901 Market St Fl 32, Philadelphia PA 19103
Tel (215) 241-3019 SIC 6411 6324 8748

INDEPENDENCE BLUE CROSS LLC p 736
1901 Market St Fl 32, Philadelphia PA 19103
Tel (215) 241-2400 SIC 6324 6411 8748

KEYSTONE FAMILY HEALTH PLAN p 815
200 Stevens Dr, Philadelphia PA 19113
Tel (215) 937-8000 SIC 6324

KEYSTONE HEALTH PLAN EAST INC p 815
1901 Market St Ste 1000, Philadelphia PA 19103
Tel (215) 241-2001 SIC 6324 8011

MERCY HEALTH PLAN INC p 946
200 Stevens Dr Ste 350, Philadelphia PA 19113
Tel (215) 937-8000 SIC 6324 6321

COMMUNITY CARE BEHAVIORAL HEALTH ORGANIZATION p 347
339 6th Ave Ste 1300, Pittsburgh PA 15222
Tel (412) 454-2120 SIC 6324

GATEWAY HEALTH PLAN INC p 593
600 Grant St Fl 41, Pittsburgh PA 15219
Tel (412) 255-4640 SIC 6324

GATEWAY HEALTH PLAN LP p 594
4 Gateway Ctr 444, Pittsburgh PA 15222
Tel (412) 255-4640 SIC 6324

HIGHMARK INC p 692
120 5th Ave, Pittsburgh PA 15222
Tel (412) 544-7000
SIC 6321 6324 6411 6512

POTTSTOWN AREA HEALTH & WELLNESS FOUNDATION p 1164
152 E High St Ste 500, Pottstown PA 19464
Tel (610) 323-2006 SIC 6324

WASHINGTON HEALTH CARE SERVICES INC p 1578
155 Wilson Ave, Washington PA 15301
Tel (724) 225-7000 SIC 6324

MEDECISION INC p 935
550 E Swedesford Rd # 220, Wayne PA 19087
Tel (484) 588-0102 SIC 6324 7371

HMO OF NORTHEASTERN PENNSYLVANIA INC p 698
19 N Main St, Wilkes Barre PA 18711
Tel (570) 200-4300 SIC 6324

HOSPITAL ESPANOL AUXILIO MUTUO DE PUERTO RICO INC p 709
Ave Ponce De Leon, San Juan PR 00918
Tel (787) 758-2000 SIC 6324

MEDICARE MUCHO MAS HOLDINGS INC p 937
Torrechardon 350 Av Chard 350th Avenue, San Juan PR 00918
Tel (787) 622-3000 SIC 6324

MMM HEALTHCARE LLC p 979
350 Ave Carlos Chardon # 500, San Juan PR 00918
Tel (787) 622-3000 SIC 6324

▲ **TRIPLE-S MANAGEMENT CORP** p 1482
1441 Ave Fd Roosevelt, San Juan PR 00920
Tel (787) 749-4949 SIC 6324 6311 6321

■ **CDMI LLC** p 271
130 Bellevue Ave Unit 201, Newport RI 02840
Tel (401) 619-5210 SIC 6324

BLUE CROSS & BLUE SHIELD OF RHODE ISLAND p 191
500 Exchange St, Providence RI 02903
Tel (401) 459-1000 SIC 6324

DELTA DENTAL OF RHODE ISLAND p 426
10 Charles St Ste 100, Providence RI 02904
Tel (401) 752-6246 SIC 6324 8021

■ **UNITEDHEALTHCARE OF NEW ENGLAND INC** p 1515
475 Kilvert St Ste 310, Warwick RI 02886
Tel (401) 737-6900 SIC 6324

PALMETTO GBA LLC p 1109
17 Technology Cir, Columbia SC 29203
Tel (803) 735-1034 SIC 6324

TRAILBLAZER HEALTH ENTERPRISES LLC p 1469
I-20 At Alpine Road, Columbia SC 29219
Tel (803) 788-4138 SIC 6324

■ **CIGNA HEALTHCARE OF SOUTH CAROLINA INC** p 306
146 Fairchild St Ste 100, Daniel Island SC 29492
Tel (800) 949-0325 SIC 6324

ONLIFE HEALTH INC p 1088
9020 Overlook Blvd # 300, Brentwood TN 37027
Tel (615) 844-2100 SIC 6324

■ **QUORUM HEALTH RESOURCES LLC** p 1201
1573 Mallory Ln 200, Brentwood TN 37027
Tel (615) 371-7979
SIC 8742 8741 8082 8231 6324

TAKE CARE EMPLOYER SOLUTIONS LLC p 1422
5500 Maryland Way Ste 200, Brentwood TN 37027
Tel (615) 665-9500 SIC 6324

■ **UNITED HEALTHCARE OF TENNESSEE INC** p 1509
10 Cadillac Dr Ste 200, Brentwood TN 37027
Tel (615) 372-3622 SIC 6324

BLUECROSS BLUESHIELD OF TENNESSEE INC p 193
1 Cameron Hill Cir, Chattanooga TN 37402
Tel (423) 535-5600 SIC 6324

▲ **UNUM GROUP** p 1528
1 Fountain Sq, Chattanooga TN 37402
Tel (423) 294-1011
SIC 6321 6324 6311 6371

MEDSOLUTIONS INC p 938
730 Cool Springs Blvd # 250, Franklin TN 37067
Tel (615) 468-0600 SIC 6324 8322

■ **CARITEN INSURANCE CO** p 256
2160 Lakeside Centre Way # 200, Knoxville TN 37922
Tel (865) 470-7470 SIC 6324

UNIVERSITY HEALTH SYSTEM INC p 1519
9000 Executive Park Dr D240, Knoxville TN 37923
Tel (865) 251-3700 SIC 6324 8011

DELTA DENTAL OF TENNESSEE p 426
240 Venture Cir, Nashville TN 37228
Tel (615) 255-3175 SIC 6324

■ **HEALTHSPRING INC** p 678
530 Great Circle Rd, Nashville TN 37228
Tel (615) 291-7000 SIC 6324

■ **HEALTHSPRING USA LLC** p 678
44 Vantage Way Ste 300, Nashville TN 37228
Tel (615) 291-7000 SIC 6324

■ **VANGUARD HEALTH SYSTEMS INC** p 1543
20 Burton Hills Blvd # 100, Nashville TN 37215
Tel (615) 665-6000 SIC 8062 6324

■ **CENPATICO BEHAVIORAL HEALTH LLC** p 275
12515-8 Res Blvd Ste 400, Austin TX 78759
Tel (512) 406-7200 SIC 6324

SHA LLC p 1310
12940 N Hwy 183, Austin TX 78750
Tel (512) 257-6000 SIC 6324 6311 6321

■ **UNITED TEACHER ASSOCIATES INC** p 1514
11200 Lakeline Blvd, Austin TX 78717
Tel (512) 451-2224 SIC 6324

TRAILBLAZER HEALTH ENTERPRISES LLC p 1469
8330 L B Johnson Fwy 10 Ste 100, Dallas TX 75243
Tel (469) 372-2000 SIC 6324

CAREINGTON INTERNATIONAL CORP p 255
7400 Gaylord Pkwy, Frisco TX 75034
Tel (972) 335-6970 SIC 6324 6411

▲ **AMERICAN NATIONAL INSURANCE CO INC** p 77
1 Moody Plz Fl 18, Galveston TX 77550
Tel (409) 763-4661
SIC 6351 6311 6321 6324 6331

■ **STANDARD LIFE & ACCIDENT INSURANCE CO INC** p 1376
1 Moody Plz, Galveston TX 77550
Tel (409) 766-6036 SIC 6324 6311

TEXAS CHILDRENS HEALTH PLAN INC p 1442
1919 S Braeswood Blvd, Houston TX 77030
Tel (832) 824-2939 SIC 6324

■ **TRIUMPH HEALTHCARE HOLDINGS INC** p 1483
7333 North Fwy Ste 500, Houston TX 77076
Tel (713) 699-8879 SIC 6324

HEALTHSMART PREFERRED CARE II LP p 677
2002 W Loop 289 Ste 103, Lubbock TX 79407
Tel (806) 473-2500 SIC 6324

BLUE CROSS AND BLUE SHIELD OF TEXAS INC p 191
1001 E Lookout Dr, Richardson TX 75082
Tel (972) 766-6900 SIC 6324 6311

■ **HUMANA HEALTH PLAN INC** p 718
8431 Fredericksburg Rd # 340, San Antonio TX 78229
Tel (210) 615-5100 SIC 6324 6321 8011

HVHC INC p 722
175 E Houston St, San Antonio TX 78205
Tel (210) 340-3531 SIC 6324

REGENCE BLUECROSS BLUESHIELD OF UTAH p 1218
2890 E Cottonwood Pkwy, Salt Lake City UT 84121
Tel (801) 942-9205 SIC 6324

■ **INNOVATION HEALTH PLAN INC** p 744
3130 Fairview Park Dr # 300, Falls Church VA 22042
Tel (703) 914-2925 SIC 6324

BEACON HEALTH OPTIONS INC p 164
240 Corporate Blvd # 100, Norfolk VA 23502
Tel (757) 459-5100 SIC 6324 8322 6411

SENTARA HEALTHCARE p 1305
6015 Poplar Hall Dr, Norfolk VA 23502
Tel (757) 455-7976 SIC 8062 6324

■ **AMERICHOICE CORP** p 81
12018 Sunrise Valley Dr # 400, Reston VA 20191
Tel (571) 262-8933 SIC 6324

■ **ANTHEM HEALTH PLANS OF VIRGINIA INC** p 93
2015 Staples Mill Rd, Richmond VA 23230
Tel (804) 354-7000 SIC 6324

■ **SOUTHEAST SERVICES INC** p 1346
2015 Staples Mill Rd, Richmond VA 23230
Tel (804) 354-7000 SIC 6324

■ **AMERIGROUP CORP** p 82
4425 Corp Ln Ste 160, Virginia Beach VA 23462
Tel (757) 473-2737 SIC 6324

OPTIMA HEALTH PLAN p 1090
4417 Corp Ln Ste 150, Virginia Beach VA 23462
Tel (757) 552-7401 SIC 6324

SYMETRA LIFE INSURANCE CO p 1414
777 108th Ave Ne Ste 1200, Bellevue WA 98004
Tel (877) 796-3872 SIC 6311 6324 6411

COMMUNITY HEALTH NETWORK OF WASHINGTON p 348
720 Olive Way Ste 300, Seattle WA 98101
Tel (206) 521-8833 SIC 6324

COMMUNITY HEALTH PLAN OF WASHINGTON p 348
720 Olive Way Ste 300, Seattle WA 98101
Tel (206) 521-8833 SIC 6324

DELTA DENTAL OF WASHINGTON p 426
9706 4th Ave Ne Ste 100, Seattle WA 98115
Tel (206) 522-2300 SIC 6324

FIRST CHOICE HEALTH NETWORK INC p 545
600 University St # 1400, Seattle WA 98101
Tel (206) 292-8255 SIC 6324

GROUP HEALTH COOPERATIVE p 641
320 Westlake Ave N # 100, Seattle WA 98109
Tel (206) 448-4141
SIC 6324 5999 8093 6321

REGENCE BLUESHIELD p 1218
1800 9th Ave Ste 200, Seattle WA 98101
Tel (206) 340-6600 SIC 6324

SAFECO CORP p 1266
1001 4th Ave Ste 800, Seattle WA 98185
Tel (206) 545-5000
SIC 6411 6311 6321 6324 6351

TRUPANION INC p 1487
6100 4th Ave S Ste 200, Seattle WA 98108
Tel (855) 727-9079 SIC 6324 8011

■ **UNITEDHEALTHCARE OF WASHINGTON INC** p 1515
1111 3rd Ave Ste 1100, Seattle WA 98101
Tel (206) 236-2500 SIC 6324 6321

COLUMBIA UNITED PROVIDERS INC p 342
19120 Se 34th St Ste 201, Vancouver WA 98683
Tel (360) 891-1520 SIC 6324

CAPITAL AREA SERVICE CO INC p 249
200 Kanawha Blvd E, Charleston WV 25301
Tel (304) 346-3800 SIC 6324 6321

LUTHER MIDELFORT MAYO HEALTH SYSTEM p 886
733 W Clairemont Ave, Eau Claire WI 54701
Tel (715) 838-5353 SIC 6324 8011

■ **AMERICAN MEDICAL SECURITY INC** p 76
3100 Ams Blvd, Green Bay WI 54313
Tel (920) 661-1111 SIC 6324

■ **UNITEDHEALTHCARE LIFE INSURANCE CO** p 1515
3100 Ams Blvd, Green Bay WI 54313
Tel (800) 232-5432
SIC 6411 6324 6311 8322

GROUP HEALTH CO-OPERATIVE OF SOUTH CENTRAL WISCONSIN p 641
1265 John Q Hammons Dr # 200, Madison WI 53717
Tel (608) 251-4156 SIC 6324

WEA INSURANCE CORP p 1585
45 Nob Hill Rd, Madison WI 53713
Tel (608) 276-4000 SIC 6324 6311 6321

WEA INSURANCE CORP p 1585
45 Nob Hill Rd, Madison WI 53713
Tel (608) 276-4000 SIC 6324

NETWORK PLAN OF WISCONSIN INC p 1028
1570 Midway Pl, Menasha WI 54952
Tel (920) 720-1200 SIC 6324

DENTAQUEST LLC p 429
12121 Corporate Pkwy, Mequon WI 53092
Tel (262) 241-7140 SIC 6324

■ **UNITEDHEALTHCARE OF WISCONSIN INC** p 1515
10701 W Research Dr, Milwaukee WI 53226
Tel (414) 443-4060 SIC 6324 6411 6321

WISCONSIN PHYSICIANS SERVICE INSURANCE CORP p 1619
1717 W Broadway, Monona WI 53713
Tel (608) 221-4711 SIC 6324

UNITY HEALTH PLANS INSURANCE CORP p 1515
840 Carolina St, Sauk City WI 53583
Tel (608) 643-2491 SIC 6324

DELTA DENTAL OF WISCONSIN INC p 426
2801 Hoover Rd, Stevens Point WI 54481
Tel (715) 344-6087 SIC 6324

■ **UMR INC** p 1502
11 Scott St, Wausau WI 54403
Tel (800) 826-9781 SIC 6324 8748

SIC 6331 Fire, Marine & Casualty Insurance

■ **HILSTAR INSURANCE CO** p 694
2201 4th Ave N, Birmingham AL 35203
Tel (205) 870-4000 SIC 6331

■ **INFINITY CASUALTY INSURANCE CO** p 741
2201 4th Ave N, Birmingham AL 35203
Tel (205) 870-4000 SIC 6331

■ **INFINITY GROUP INC** p 741
2201 4th Ave N, Birmingham AL 35203
Tel (205) 870-4000 SIC 6331

■ **INFINITY INSURANCE CO** p 741
2201 4th Ave N, Birmingham AL 35203
Tel (205) 870-4000 SIC 6331

▲ **INFINITY PROPERTY AND CASUALTY CORP** p 741
3700 Colonnade Pkwy # 600, Birmingham AL 35243
Tel (205) 870-4000 SIC 6331

■ **INFINITY STANDARD INSURANCE CO** p 741
2201 4th Ave N, Birmingham AL 35203
Tel (205) 870-4000 SIC 6331

▲ **NATIONAL SECURITY GROUP INC** p 1016
661 Davis St E, Elba AL 36323
Tel (334) 897-2273 SIC 6311 6331

ALFA CORP p 49
2108 E South Blvd, Montgomery AL 36116
Tel (334) 288-3900 SIC 6331 6411 7389

ALFA GENERAL INSURANCE CORP p 49
2108 E South Blvd, Montgomery AL 36116
Tel (334) 288-0375 SIC 6331

ALFA INSURANCE CORP p 49
2108 E South Blvd, Montgomery AL 36116
Tel (334) 277-6942 SIC 6331

ALFA MUTUAL GENERAL INSURANCE CO p 49
2108 E South Blvd, Montgomery AL 36116
Tel (334) 288-3900 SIC 6331

ALASKA NATIONAL INSURANCE CO p 45
7001 Jewel Lake Rd, Anchorage AK 99502
Tel (907) 248-2642 SIC 6331 6351

UKPEAGVIK INUPIAT CORP p 1500
1250 Agvik St, Barrow AK 99723
Tel (907) 852-4460
SIC 1542 6512 6331 1389 4449

COPPERPOINT MUTUAL INSURANCE CO p 368
3030 N 3rd St Ste 110, Phoenix AZ 85012
Tel (602) 631-2300 SIC 6331

■ **REPWEST INSURANCE CO** p 1226
2721 N Central Ave Fl 8, Phoenix AZ 85004
Tel (602) 263-6755 SIC 6331

AMERICAN RELIABLE INSURANCE CO p 78
8655 E Via De Ventura E200, Scottsdale AZ 85258
Tel (480) 483-8666 SIC 6331

SCOTTSDALE INSURANCE CO p 1294
8877 N Gainey Center Dr, Scottsdale AZ 85258
Tel (480) 365-4000 SIC 6331

SERVICES GROUP OF AMERICA INC p 1308
16100 N 71st St Ste 500, Scottsdale AZ 85254
Tel (480) 927-4000
SIC 5141 5148 6331 6552

■ **CALIFORNIA AUTOMOBILE INSURANCE CO** p 239
555 W Imperial Hwy, Brea CA 92821
Tel (714) 232-8669 SIC 6331

■ **MERCURY CASUALTY CO** p 945
555 W Imperial Hwy, Brea CA 92821
Tel (323) 937-1060 SIC 6331 6351

ALLIANZ GLOBAL RISKS US INSURANCE CO p 55
2350 W Empire Ave, Burbank CA 91504
Tel (818) 260-7500 SIC 6331

WESTERN GENERAL HOLDING CO p 1598
5230 Las Virgenes Rd # 100, Calabasas CA 91302
Tel (818) 880-9070 SIC 6331

WESTERN GENERAL INSURANCE CO INC p 1598
5230 Las Virgenes Rd, Calabasas CA 91302
Tel (818) 880-9070 SIC 6331

COMMERCIAL CARRIERS INSURANCE AGENCY INC p 345
12641 166th St, Cerritos CA 90703
Tel (562) 404-4900 *SIC* 6331

UNIFIED GROCERS INC p 1503
5200 Sheila St, Commerce CA 90040
Tel (323) 264-5200 *SIC* 5141 6331

AAA NORTHERN CALIFORNIA NEVADA AND UTAH p 7
1900 Powell St Ste 1200, Emeryville CA 94608
Tel (510) 596-3669 *SIC* 6331 8699

KRAMER-WILSON CO INC p 829
6345 Balboa Blvd Ste 190, Encino CA 91316
Tel (818) 760-0880 *SIC* 6331

■ REPUBLIC INDEMNITY CO OF AMERICA p 1225
15821 Ventura Blvd # 370, Encino CA 91436
Tel (818) 990-9860 *SIC* 6331

WESTERN GROWERS ASSURANCE TRUST p 1598
17620 Fitch, Irvine CA 92614
Tel (800) 777-7898 *SIC* 6331

TRISTAR INSURANCE GROUP INC p 1482
100 Oceangate Ste 700, Long Beach CA 90802
Tel (562) 495-6600 *SIC* 6331 8741

▲ MERCURY GENERAL CORP p 945
4484 Wilshire Blvd, Los Angeles CA 90010
Tel (323) 937-1060 *SIC* 6331 6411

■ MERCURY INSURANCE CO p 945
4484 Wilshire Blvd, Los Angeles CA 90010
Tel (323) 937-1060 *SIC* 6331

■ MERCURY INSURANCE SERVICES LLC p 945
4484 Wilshire Blvd, Los Angeles CA 90010
Tel (323) 937-1060 *SIC* 6331

CALIFORNIA CAPITAL INSURANCE CO p 239
2300 Garden Rd, Monterey CA 93940
Tel (831) 233-5500 *SIC* 6331

H & H AGENCY INC p 649
20351 Sw Acacia St, Newport Beach CA 92660
Tel (949) 260-8840 *SIC* 6331

FIREMANS FUND INSURANCE CO p 543
777 San Marin Dr Ste 2160, Novato CA 94945
Tel (415) 899-2000 *SIC* 6331 6351 6321

AMERICAN INSURANCE CO INC p 75
1465 N Mcdowell Blvd, Petaluma CA 94954
Tel (415) 899-2000 *SIC* 6331

ASSOCIATED INDEMNITY CORP p 120
1465 N Mcdowell Blvd # 100, Petaluma CA 94954
Tel (415) 899-2000
SIC 6311 6321 6331 6351

■ ARROWHEAD GENERAL INSURANCE AGENCY INC p 113
701 B St Ste 2100, San Diego CA 92101
Tel (619) 881-8600 *SIC* 6331 6411

GOLDEN EAGLE INSURANCE CORP p 620
525 B St Ste 1300, San Diego CA 92101
Tel (619) 744-6000 *SIC* 6331

ICW GROUP HOLDINGS INC p 728
11455 El Camino Real, San Diego CA 92130
Tel (858) 350-2400 *SIC* 6331 6411

INSURANCE CO OF WEST p 748
15025 Innovation Dr, San Diego CA 92128
Tel (858) 350-2400 *SIC* 6331

WAWANESA GENERAL INSURANCE CO p 1584
9050 Friars Rd Ste 200, San Diego CA 92108
Tel (619) 285-6020 *SIC* 6331

NORCAL MUTUAL INSURANCE CO INC p 1047
560 Davis St Fl 2, San Francisco CA 94111
Tel (415) 397-9703 *SIC* 6411 6331

STATE COMPENSATION INSURANCE FUND INC p 1380
333 Bush St Fl 8, San Francisco CA 94104
Tel (888) 782-8338 *SIC* 6331

CALIFORNIA CASUALTY INDEMNITY EXCHANGE p 239
1900 Almeda De Las Pulgas, San Mateo CA 94403
Tel (650) 574-4000 *SIC* 6331

CALIFORNIA CASUALTY MANAGEMENT CO p 239
1900 Almeda De Las Pulgas, San Mateo CA 94403
Tel (650) 574-4000 *SIC* 6331 8741

CALIFORNIA STATE AUTOMOBILE ASSOCIATION INTER-INSURANCE BUREAU p 241
1276 S California Blvd, Walnut Creek CA 94596
Tel (925) 287-7600 *SIC* 6331

■ PACIFIC COMPENSATION INSURANCE CO p 1104
1 Baxter Way Ste 170, Westlake Village CA 91362
Tel (818) 575-8500 *SIC* 6331

FARMERS GROUP INC p 529
6301 Owensmouth Ave, Woodland Hills CA 91367
Tel (323) 932-3200 *SIC* 6331

■ HEALTH NET OF CALIFORNIA INC p 675
21281 Burbank Blvd Fl 4, Woodland Hills CA 91367
Tel (818) 676-6775
SIC 6324 8062 6311 6321 6331 5912

ZENITH INSURANCE CO p 1642
21255 Califa St, Woodland Hills CA 91367
Tel (818) 713-1000 *SIC* 6331

ZENITH NATIONAL INSURANCE CORP p 1642
21255 Califa St, Woodland Hills CA 91367
Tel (818) 713-1000 *SIC* 6331

PINNACOL ASSURANCE p 1150
7501 E Lowry Blvd, Denver CO 80230
Tel (303) 361-4000 *SIC* 6331

MASTERS INSURANCE AGENCY INC p 918
9785 Maroon Cir Ste 340, Englewood CO 80112
Tel (303) 814-1596 *SIC* 6411 6331 6311

M&C HOTEL INTERESTS INC p 890
6560 Greenwood Plaza Blvd # 300, Greenwood Village CO 80111
Tel (303) 779-2000
SIC 8741 8712 6321 6331 7389

RICHFIELD HOLDINGS INC p 1233
5775 Dtc Blvd Ste 300, Greenwood Village CO 80111
Tel (303) 220-2000
SIC 6321 8712 7389 6331 7011

BEAZLEY INSURANCE CO INC p 166
30 Batterson Park Rd, Farmington CT 06032
Tel (860) 677-3700 *SIC* 6331

■ BERKLEY REGIONAL INSURANCE CO p 175
475 Steamboat Rd Fl 1, Greenwich CT 06830
Tel (203) 629-3000 *SIC* 6331

PARTNER REINSURANCE CO OF US p 1118
1 Greenwich Plz Fl 3, Greenwich CT 06830
Tel (203) 622-1279 *SIC* 6331

▲ W R BERKLEY CORP p 1569
475 Steamboat Rd Fl 1, Greenwich CT 06830
Tel (203) 629-3000
SIC 6331 6321 6351 6311

■ AUTOMOBILE INSURANCE CO OF HARTFORD CONNECTICUT p 134
1 Tower Sq, Hartford CT 06183
Tel (860) 277-0111 *SIC* 6331

■ CHARTER OAK FIRE INSURANCE CO p 291
1 Tower Sq, Hartford CT 06183
Tel (860) 277-0111 *SIC* 6351 6331

■ HARTFORD CASUALTY INSURANCE CO p 665
690 Asylum Ave, Hartford CT 06155
Tel (860) 547-5000 *SIC* 6411 6331

▲ HARTFORD FINANCIAL SERVICES GROUP INC p 665
1 Hartford Plz, Hartford CT 06155
Tel (860) 547-5000
SIC 6331 6311 6351 6321

■ HARTFORD STEAM BOILER INSPECTION AND INSURANCE CO p 665
1 State St Fl 5-12, Hartford CT 06103
Tel (860) 722-1866
SIC 6331 8711 7373 8742

■ HSB GROUP INC p 714
1 State St, Hartford CT 06102
Tel (860) 722-1866
SIC 6331 6411 6799 8711 8742

■ PHOENIX INSURANCE CO p 1145
1 Tower Sq, Hartford CT 06183
Tel (860) 277-0111 *SIC* 6351 6331

■ STANDARD FIRE INSURANCE CO p 1376
1 Tower Ave, Hartford CT 06120
Tel (860) 277-0111 *SIC* 6331

■ TRAVELERS CASUALTY CO OF CONNECTICUT p 1474
1 Tower Sq, Hartford CT 06183
Tel (860) 277-0111 *SIC* 6331 6351 6321

■ TRAVELERS COMMERCIAL CASUALTY CO p 1474
1 Tower Sq, Hartford CT 06183
Tel (860) 277-0111 *SIC* 6351 6331

■ TRAVELERS INDEMNITY CO p 1474
1 Tower Sq, Hartford CT 06183
Tel (860) 277-0111 *SIC* 6411 6331

■ TRAVELERS INDEMNITY CO OF CONNECTICUT p 1474
1 Tower Sq, Hartford CT 06183
Tel (860) 548-9948 *SIC* 6411 6331

■ TWIN CITY FIRE INSURANCE CO p 1495
1 Hartford Plz, Hartford CT 06115
Tel (860) 547-5000 *SIC* 6331

■ GENERAL RE CORP p 602
120 Long Ridge Rd, Stamford CT 06902
Tel (203) 352-3000 *SIC* 6331

■ GENERAL REINSURANCE CORP p 602
120 Long Ridge Rd, Stamford CT 06902
Tel (203) 328-5000
SIC 6331 6351 6411 6321

GENEVE HOLDINGS INC p 603
96 Cummings Point Rd, Stamford CT 06902
Tel (203) 358-8000 *SIC* 3462 6331

▲ NAVIGATORS GROUP INC p 1020
400 Atlantic St Fl 8, Stamford CT 06901
Tel (203) 905-6090 *SIC* 6331 6351

ODYSSEY REINSURANCE CO p 1075
300 Stamford Pl Ste 700, Stamford CT 06902
Tel (203) 965-0004
SIC 6411 6361 6331 6324 6311

XL GLOBAL SERVICES INC p 1632
70 Seaview Ave Ste 7, Stamford CT 06902
Tel (203) 964-5200 *SIC* 6331 6282 6351

ALLIANZ OF AMERICA INC p 56
55 Greens Farms Rd Ste 1, Westport CT 06880
Tel (203) 221-8500 *SIC* 6311 6331

WESTPORT INSURANCE CORP p 1602
2 Waterside Xing Ste 200, Windsor CT 06095
Tel (860) 902-7201 *SIC* 6331 6411

■ CIGNA HOLDINGS INC p 306
590 Naamans Rd, Claymont DE 19703
Tel (215) 761-1000
SIC 6311 6321 6331 6512 6514 6282

AAA CLUB ALLIANCE INC p 7
1 River Pl, Wilmington DE 19801
Tel (302) 299-4700
SIC 8699 6331 6351 6512 4724

NUCLEAR ELECTRIC INSURANCE LIMITED p 1066
1201 N Market St Ste 1100, Wilmington DE 19801
Tel (302) 888-3000 *SIC* 6331

■ GEICO INDEMNITY CO p 597
One Geico Plaza, Washington DC 20047
Tel (301) 986-3000 *SIC* 6331 6411

LUMBERMENS UNDERWRITING ALLIANCE p 885
1905 Nw Corporate Blvd, Boca Raton FL 33431
Tel (561) 994-1900 *SIC* 6331 6411 6311

NATIONAL COUNCIL ON COMPENSATION INSURANCE INC p 1011
901 Peninsula Corp Cir, Boca Raton FL 33487
Tel (561) 893-1000 *SIC* 6331

NCCI HOLDINGS INC p 1021
901 Peninsula Corp Cir, Boca Raton FL 33487
Tel (561) 893-1000 *SIC* 6331

▲ HERITAGE INSURANCE HOLDINGS INC p 686
2600 Mccormick Dr Ste 300, Clearwater FL 33759
Tel (727) 362-7200 *SIC* 6331

■ MERCURY INSURANCE CO OF FLORIDA p 945
1901 Ulmerton Rd Fl 6, Clearwater FL 33762
Tel (727) 561-4000 *SIC* 6331

BRISTOL WEST HOLDINGS INC p 214
5701 Stirling Rd, Davie FL 33314
Tel (954) 316-5200 *SIC* 6331

GUARANTEE INSURANCE GROUP INC p 644
401 E Las Olas Blvd # 1540, Fort Lauderdale FL 33301
Tel (954) 670-2900 *SIC* 6411 6331

TOWER HILL INSURANCE GROUP INC p 1464
7201 Nw 11th Pl, Gainesville FL 32605
Tel (352) 332-8800 *SIC* 6331 7371

■ BLACK KNIGHT FINANCIAL SERVICES LLC p 187
601 Riverside Ave, Jacksonville FL 32204
Tel (904) 854-8100
SIC 6361 6331 6531 8741

■ BLACK KNIGHT HOLDINGS INC p 187
601 Riverside Ave, Jacksonville FL 32204
Tel (904) 854-8100
SIC 6361 6331 6531 8741

▲ FIDELITY NATIONAL FINANCIAL INC p 540
601 Riverside Ave Fl 4, Jacksonville FL 32204
Tel (904) 854-8100
SIC 6361 6331 6531 8741 3699

NGM INSURANCE CO p 1041
4601 Touchton Rd E # 3400, Jacksonville FL 32246
Tel (904) 380-7282 *SIC* 6331

■ SERVICELINK HOLDINGS LLC p 1307
601 Riverside Ave Bldg 5, Jacksonville FL 32204
Tel (904) 854-8100
SIC 6361 6331 6531 8741 3699

STILLWATER INSURANCE SERVICES INC p 1389
4905 Belfort Rd Ste 110, Jacksonville FL 32256
Tel (904) 997-7336 *SIC* 6331

■ SUMMIT CONSULTING LLC p 1398
2310 Commerce Point Dr, Lakeland FL 33801
Tel (863) 665-6060 *SIC* 6331 6411

■ AMERICAN BANKERS INSURANCE CO OF FLORIDA p 68
11222 Quail Roost Dr, Miami FL 33157
Tel (305) 253-2244 *SIC* 6411 6331

■ AMERICAN BANKERS INSURANCE GROUP INC p 68
11222 Quail Roost Dr, Miami FL 33157
Tel (305) 253-2244
SIC 6331 6311 6351 6321 6324

HAMILTON RISK MANAGEMENT CO p 655
3155 Nw 77th Ave, Miami FL 33122
Tel (305) 716-6000
SIC 6331 7323 6141 6541 6411

US SECURITY INSURANCE CO p 1533
3155 Nw 77th Ave, Miami FL 33122
Tel (305) 716-6100 *SIC* 6331

■ PROGRESSIVE BAYSIDE INSURANCE CO p 1181
4030 Crescent Park Dr B, Riverview FL 33578
Tel (813) 487-1000 *SIC* 6331

■ PROGRESSIVE SOUTHEASTERN INSURANCE CO INC p 1182
4030 Crescent Park Dr B, Riverview FL 33578
Tel (813) 487-1000 *SIC* 6331

AMERICAN STRATEGIC INSURANCE CORP p 80
1 Asi Way N, Saint Petersburg FL 33702
Tel (727) 821-8765 *SIC* 6331

BANKERS INSURANCE CO p 152
11101 Roosevelt Blvd N, Saint Petersburg FL 33716
Tel (727) 823-4000 *SIC* 6331

FCCI GROUP INC p 533
6300 University Pkwy, Sarasota FL 34240
Tel (941) 907-3224 *SIC* 6331

FCCI INSURANCE CO p 533
6300 University Pkwy, Sarasota FL 34240
Tel (941) 907-3224 *SIC* 6331

FCCI MUTUAL INSURANCE HOLDING CO p 533
6300 University Pkwy, Sarasota FL 34240
Tel (941) 907-3224 *SIC* 6331

BROADSPIRE SERVICES INC p 215
1391 Nw 136th Ave, Sunrise FL 33323
Tel (954) 452-4000 *SIC* 8099 6331

▲ FEDERATED NATIONAL HOLDING CO p 536
14050 Nw 14th St Ste 180, Sunrise FL 33323
Tel (954) 581-9993 *SIC* 6331 6411

ONECIS INSURANCE CO p 1087
1601 Sawgrs Corp Pkwy, Sunrise FL 33323
Tel (954) 236-8100 *SIC* 7389 6331

AAA AUTO CLUB SOUTH INC p 7
1515 N West Shore Blvd, Tampa FL 33607
Tel (813) 289-5000
SIC 4724 6331 8699 6311

AMERICAN INTEGRITY INSURANCE GROUP LLC p 75
5426 Bay Center Dr # 650, Tampa FL 33609
Tel (813) 880-7000 *SIC* 6331

▲ HCI GROUP INC p 672
5300 W Cypress St Ste 100, Tampa FL 33607
Tel (813) 849-9500 *SIC* 6331 6411

LYKES BROS INC p 887
400 N Tampa St Ste 1900, Tampa FL 33602
Tel (813) 223-3911 *SIC* 0174 6331

PMSI LLC p 1157
175 Kelsey Ln, Tampa FL 33619
Tel (813) 626-7788 *SIC* 6331

AXIS SPECIALTY US SERVICES INC p 140
11680 Great Oaks Way # 500, Alpharetta GA 30022
Tel (678) 746-9000 *SIC* 6331

■ AMERICAN SECURITY INSURANCE CO p 79
260 Interstate N Cir Se, Atlanta GA 30339
Tel (770) 763-1000 *SIC* 6331

■ MUNICH AMERICAN REASSURANCE CO PAC INC p 1000
56 Perimeter Ctr E # 200, Atlanta GA 30346
Tel (770) 350-3200 *SIC* 6331

OMNI INSURANCE CO p 1084
2018 Powers Ferry Rd Se # 100, Atlanta GA 30339
Tel (770) 952-4500 *SIC* 6331

OMNI INSURANCE GROUP INC p 1085
20018 Powers Ferry Rd, Atlanta GA 30339
Tel (770) 952-4500 *SIC* 6331

■ RSUI GROUP INC p 1256
945 E Paces Ferry Rd Ne # 1800, Atlanta GA 30326
Tel (404) 231-2366 *SIC* 6331 6321

▲ STATE BANK FINANCIAL CORP p 1380
3399 Peachtree Rd Ne, Atlanta GA 30326
Tel (404) 475-6599
SIC 6022 6712 6311 6141 6331

▲ ATLANTIC AMERICAN CORP p 125
4370 Peachtree Rd Ne # 200, Brookhaven GA 30319
Tel (404) 266-5500 *SIC* 6311 6321 6331

CRAWFORD & CO p 389
1001 Summit Blvd Ste 500, Brookhaven GA 30319
Tel (404) 300-1000
SIC 6411 8111 8099 6331

INSURANCE HOUSE INC p 748
1904 Leland Dr Se, Marietta GA 30067
Tel (770) 952-0080 *SIC* 6331 6411 6141

FIRST INSURANCE CO OF HAWAII LTD p 547
1100 Ward Ave, Honolulu HI 96814
Tel (808) 527-7777 *SIC* 6331 6411

ISLAND INSURANCE CO LIMITED p 766
1022 Bethel St, Honolulu HI 96813
Tel (808) 564-8200 *SIC* 6331 6411

FARM BUREAU MUTUAL INSURANCE CO OF IDAHO p 528
275 Tierra Vista Dr, Pocatello ID 83201
Tel (208) 232-7914 *SIC* 6331

STATE FARM MUTUAL AUTOMOBILE INSURANCE CO p 1381
1 State Farm Plz, Bloomington IL 61710
Tel (309) 766-2311
SIC 6321 6311 6036 6331

■ CNA FINANCIAL CORP p 329
333 S Wabash Ave Ste 300, Chicago IL 60604
Tel (312) 822-5000 *SIC* 6411 6331 6311

■ CNA FOUNDATION p 329
333 S Wabash Ave Fl 1, Chicago IL 60604
Tel (312) 822-5000 *SIC* 6331

■ CONTINENTAL CASUALTY CO INC p 363
333 S Wabash Ave Ste 300, Chicago IL 60604
Tel (312) 822-5000 *SIC* 6331

▲ KEMPER CORP p 809
1 E Wacker Dr, Chicago IL 60601
Tel (312) 661-4600
SIC 6331 6321 6311 6141

■ NATIONAL FIRE INSURANCE CO OF HARTFORD p 1012
Cna Plz, Chicago IL 60604
Tel (312) 822-5000 *SIC* 6331

■ EVANSTON INSURANCE CO p 513
10 Parkway N Ste 100, Deerfield IL 60015
Tel (847) 572-6000 *SIC* 6351 6331

▲ ATLAS FINANCIAL HOLDINGS INC p 128
150 Northwest Point Blvd # 3, Elk Grove Village IL 60007
Tel (847) 472-6700 *SIC* 6331

AON CONSULTING WORLDWIDE INC p 95
100 Half Day Rd 2, Lincolnshire IL 60069
Tel (312) 381-4800
SIC 6311 6321 6331 8742 6411 6351

■ NAVISTAR INC p 1020
2701 Navistar Dr, Lisle IL 60532
Tel (331) 332-5000
SIC 3711 3714 3519 6153 6159 6331

AMERICAN MANUFACTURERS MUTUAL INSURANCE CO p 75
1 Kemper Dr, Long Grove IL 60047
Tel (847) 320-2000 *SIC* 6331

JOHN DEERE INSURANCE GROUP INC p 788
3400 80th St, Moline IL 61265
Tel (309) 765-8000 *SIC* 6331 6321 6311

■ ST PAUL PROTECTIVE INSURANCE CO p 1372
Allstate S Barrington Plz, Northbrook IL 60062
Tel (847) 402-5000 *SIC* 6331

BCS FINANCIAL CORP p 164
2 Mid America Plz, Oakbrook Terrace IL 60181
Tel (630) 472-7700 *SIC* 6331 6311 6211

SIRVA INC p 1327
1 Parkview Plz, Oakbrook Terrace IL 60181
Tel (630) 570-3047
SIC 4213 4214 4731 7513 6331

SIRVA WORLDWIDE INC p 1327
1 Parkview Plz Ste 300, Oakbrook Terrace IL 60181
Tel (630) 570-3047
SIC 4213 4214 4731 7513 6331

HORTON GROUP INC p 708
10320 Orland Pkwy, Orland Park IL 60467
Tel (708) 845-3000
SIC 6411 6331 6321 6311

▲ CATERPILLAR INC p 265
100 Ne Adams St, Peoria IL 61629
Tel (309) 675-1000
SIC 3531 3519 3511 6531 6321 6331

■ RLI INSURANCE CO (INC) p 1239
9025 N Lindbergh Dr, Peoria IL 61615
Tel (309) 692-1000 *SIC* 6331

■ BITUMINOUS CASUALTY CORP p 185
320 18th St, Rock Island IL 61201
Tel (309) 786-5401 *SIC* 6331

XL SPECIALTY INSURANCE CO p 1632
10 N Martingale Rd # 220, Schaumburg IL 60173
Tel (847) 517-2990 *SIC* 6351 6331

ZURICH AMERICAN INSURANCE CO p 1645
1299 Zurich Way, Schaumburg IL 60196
Tel (800) 987-3373 *SIC* 6331

ZURICH HOLDING CO OF AMERICA INC p 1645
1299 Zurich Way, Schaumburg IL 60196
Tel (847) 605-6000
SIC 6311 6331 6321 6324 6719

ZURICH SERVICES CORP p 1645
1299 Zurich Way, Schaumburg IL 60196
Tel (847) 605-6000 *SIC* 6331

■ ALLEGIANCE INSURANCE CO p 53
1 Horace Mann Plz, Springfield IL 62715
Tel (217) 789-2500 *SIC* 6331

▲ HORACE MANN EDUCATORS CORP p 706
1 Horace Mann Plz, Springfield IL 62715
Tel (217) 789-2500 *SIC* 6311 6331 6411

■ HORACE MANN PROPERTY & CASUALTY INSURANCE CO p 706
1 Horace Mann Plz, Springfield IL 62715
Tel (217) 789-2500 SIC 6331

▲ BALDWIN & LYONS INC p 147
111 Congressional Blvd # 500, Carmel IN 46032
Tel (317) 636-9800 SIC 6331 6411

▲ CNO FINANCIAL GROUP INC p 330
11825 N Pennsylvania St, Carmel IN 46032
Tel (317) 817-6100 SIC 6311 6321 6331

▲ ONE MAIN FINANCIAL SERVICES p 1086
601 Nw 2nd St, Evansville IN 47708
Tel (800) 961-5577 SIC 6141 6351 6331

■ SPRINGLEAF FINANCE INC p 1361
601 Nw 2nd St, Evansville IN 47708
Tel (812) 424-8031
SIC 6153 6351 6331 7389

BROTHERHOOD MUTUAL INSURANCE CO p 219
6400 Brotherhood Way, Fort Wayne IN 46825
Tel (260) 482-8668 SIC 6331

NORTH AMERICAN VAN LINES INC p 1050
5001 Us Highway 30 W, Fort Wayne IN 46818
Tel (260) 429-1682
SIC 4213 4731 4214 6331 7389 4212

AMERICAN ECONOMY INSURANCE CO INC p 71
500 N Meridian St, Indianapolis IN 46204
Tel (317) 423-9920 SIC 6331

AMERICAN UNITED MUTUAL INSURANCE HOLDING CO p 81
1 American Sq, Indianapolis IN 46282
Tel (317) 285-1877
SIC 6211 6311 6371 6351 6331

■ ANTHEM INSURANCE COMPANIES INC p 94
120 Monument Cir Ste 200, Indianapolis IN 46204
Tel (317) 488-6000
SIC 6324 6411 6321 6331 6159 7371

MERIDIAN CITIZENS MUTUAL INSURANCE CO p 948
2955 N Meridian St, Indianapolis IN 46208
Tel (317) 931-7000 SIC 6331

UNITED FARM FAMILY MUTUAL INSURANCE CO p 1508
225 S East St, Indianapolis IN 46202
Tel (317) 692-7200 SIC 6331

▲ FIRST MERCHANTS CORP p 547
200 E Jackson St, Muncie IN 47305
Tel (765) 747-1500 SIC 6021 6331

PHARMACISTS MUTUAL INSURANCE CO p 1141
808 Highway 18 W, Algona IA 50511
Tel (515) 295-2461 SIC 6331

■ ADDISON INSURANCE CO p 22
118 2nd Ave Se, Cedar Rapids IA 52401
Tel (319) 399-5700 SIC 6331

■ UNITED FIRE & CASUALTY CO p 1508
118 2nd Ave Se, Cedar Rapids IA 52401
Tel (319) 399-5700 SIC 6331 6311 6321

■ BITCO CORP p 185
3700 Market Square Cir, Davenport IA 52807
Tel (309) 786-5401 SIC 6411 6331

■ BITCO NATIONAL INSURANCE CO p 185
3700 Market Square Cir, Davenport IA 52807
Tel (309) 786-5401 SIC 6331

ALLIED GROUP INC p 56
1100 Locust St, Des Moines IA 50391
Tel (515) 280-4211 SIC 6331 6211 5112

ALLIED PROPERTY AND CASUALTY INSURANCE CO p 56
1100 Locust St, Des Moines IA 50391
Tel (515) 280-4211 SIC 6331

■ EMC INSURANCE GROUP INC p 490
717 Mulberry St, Des Moines IA 50309
Tel (515) 345-2902 SIC 6331 6351 6321

■ PRINCIPAL INTERNATIONAL INC p 1177
711 High St, Des Moines IA 50392
Tel (515) 247-5013
SIC 6282 6311 6321 6331

▲ MIDWESTONE FINANCIAL GROUP INC p 968
102 S Clinton St, Iowa City IA 52240
Tel (319) 356-5800 SIC 6022 6331

■ CONTINENTAL WESTERN INSURANCE CO p 364
11201 Douglas Ave, Urbandale IA 50322
Tel (515) 473-3000 SIC 6331

FARMERS MUTUAL HAIL INSURANCE CO OF IOWA p 529
6785 Westown Pkwy, West Des Moines IA 50266
Tel (515) 282-9104 SIC 6331

GUIDEONE AMERICA INSURANCE CO p 645
1111 Ashworth Rd, West Des Moines IA 50265
Tel (515) 267-5000 SIC 6331

GUIDEONE MUTUAL INSURANCE CO p 645
1111 Ashworth Rd, West Des Moines IA 50265
Tel (515) 267-5000 SIC 6331

IMT INSURANCE CO p 735
4445 Corporate Dr Ste 100, West Des Moines IA 50266
Tel (515) 327-2777 SIC 6331 7374

FEDERATED RURAL ELECTRIC INSURANCE EXCHANGE p 536
11875 W 85th St, Lenexa KS 66214
Tel (913) 541-0150 SIC 6331

FARM BUREAU MUTUAL INSURANCE CO INC p 528
2627 Kfb Plz, Manhattan KS 66503
Tel (785) 587-6000 SIC 6331

FARMERS ALLIANCE MUTUAL INSURANCE CO p 529
1122 N Main St, Mcpherson KS 67460
Tel (620) 241-2200 SIC 6331

SWISS RE AMERICA HOLDING CORP p 1412
5200 Metcalf Ave, Overland Park KS 66202
Tel (913) 676-5200 SIC 6331 6311

SWISS RE SOLUTIONS HOLDING CORP p 1413
5200 Metcalf Ave, Overland Park KS 66202
Tel (913) 676-5200 SIC 6331

WESTPORT INSURANCE CORP p 1602
5200 Metcalf Ave, Overland Park KS 66202
Tel (913) 676-5270 SIC 6331

ZURICH AGENCY SERVICES INC p 1645
7045 College Blvd, Overland Park KS 66211
Tel (913) 339-1000 SIC 6331 6311

FIRST EXCESS AND REINSURANCE CORP p 546
6329 Glenwood St Ste 300, Shawnee Mission KS 66202
Tel (913) 676-5524 SIC 6331

KENTUCKY EMPLOYERS MUTUAL INSURANCE AUTHORITY p 812
250 W Main St Ste 900, Lexington KY 40507
Tel (859) 425-7800 SIC 6331

■ AUDUBON INSURANCE CO p 131
4000 S Shrwd Frst Blvd Ste 401, Baton Rouge LA 70816
Tel (225) 293-5900 SIC 6331 6411

LOUISIANA WORKERS COMPENSATION CORP p 880
2237 S Acadian Thruway, Baton Rouge LA 70808
Tel (225) 924-7788 SIC 6331

▲ AMERISAFE INC p 83
2301 Highway 190 W, Deridder LA 70634
Tel (337) 463-9052 SIC 6331

GRAY & CO INC p 632
3625 N I 10 Service Rd W, Metairie LA 70002
Tel (504) 888-7790 SIC 6331

IMPERIAL MANAGEMENT CORP p 734
4670 I 49 N Service Rd, Opelousas LA 70570
Tel (337) 942-5691 SIC 6331

MAINE EMPLOYERS MUTUAL INSURANCE CO p 898
261 Commercial St, Portland ME 04101
Tel (207) 791-3300 SIC 6331

MMG INSURANCE CO p 979
44 Maysville Rd, Presque Isle ME 04769
Tel (207) 764-6611 SIC 6331

■ CITIFINANCIAL CREDIT CO p 310
300 Saint Paul St Fl 3, Baltimore MD 21202
Tel (410) 332-3000
SIC 6141 6162 7389 6331 6159 6022

HARFORD MUTUAL INSURANCE CO p 661
200 N Main St, Bel Air MD 21014
Tel (410) 879-2360 SIC 6331

AVEMCO CORP p 136
8490 Progress Dr Ste 100, Frederick MD 21701
Tel (301) 694-5700
SIC 6331 6321 6399 6411 7372

AVEMCO INSURANCE CO p 136
8490 Progress Dr Ste 100, Frederick MD 21701
Tel (301) 694-5700 SIC 6321 6331

BRETHREN MUTUAL INSURANCE CO p 210
149 N Edgewood Dr, Hagerstown MD 21740
Tel (800) 621-4264 SIC 6331 6411

BAY STATE INSURANCE CO p 161
95 River Rd, Andover MA 01810
Tel (978) 475-3300 SIC 6331

MERRIMACK MUTUAL FIRE INSURANCE CO p 950
95 River Rd, Andover MA 01810
Tel (978) 475-3300 SIC 6331

HELMSMAN MANAGEMENT SERVICES LLC p 682
175 Berkeley St, Boston MA 02116
Tel (857) 224-1970 SIC 6331

■ LEXINGTON INSURANCE CO p 859
99 High St Fl 23, Boston MA 02110
Tel (617) 330-1100 SIC 6331

LIBERTY INSURANCE CORP p 862
175 Berkeley St, Boston MA 02116
Tel (617) 357-9500 SIC 6331

LIBERTY INTERNATIONAL HOLDINGS INC p 862
175 Berkeley St, Boston MA 02116
Tel (617) 357-9500 SIC 6331

LIBERTY MUTUAL FIRE INSURANCE CO INC p 862
175 Berkeley St, Boston MA 02116
Tel (617) 357-9500 SIC 6331

LIBERTY MUTUAL GROUP INC p 862
175 Berkeley St, Boston MA 02116
Tel (617) 357-9500
SIC 6331 6321 6351 7389

LIBERTY MUTUAL HOLDING CO INC p 862
175 Berkeley St, Boston MA 02116
Tel (617) 357-9500 SIC 6331 6351 7389

LIBERTY MUTUAL HOLDING CORP p 862
175 Berkeley St, Boston MA 02116
Tel (617) 357-9500 SIC 6331

LIBERTY MUTUAL INSURANCE CO p 862
175 Berkeley St, Boston MA 02116
Tel (617) 357-9500
SIC 6331 6321 6351 7389

LMHC MASSACHUSETTS HOLDINGS INC p 872
175 Berkeley St, Boston MA 02116
Tel (617) 357-9500
SIC 6331 6321 6351 7389

MEDICAL PROFESSIONAL MUTUAL INSURANCE CO p 937
1 Financial Ctr Fl 13, Boston MA 02111
Tel (800) 225-6168 SIC 6331

PLYMOUTH ROCK ASSURANCE CORP p 1157
695 Atlantic Ave Fl 7, Boston MA 02111
Tel (866) 353-6292 SIC 6331

PLYMOUTH ROCK CO INC p 1157
695 Atlantic Ave, Boston MA 02111
Tel (617) 720-1620 SIC 6331

RHODE ISLAND JOINT REINSURANCE ASSOC p 1232
2 Center Plz Ste 700, Boston MA 02108
Tel (617) 723-3800 SIC 6331

■ SAFETY INSURANCE CO p 1266
20 Custom House St # 400, Boston MA 02110
Tel (617) 951-0600 SIC 6331

▲ SAFETY INSURANCE GROUP INC p 1266
20 Custom House St # 400, Boston MA 02110
Tel (617) 951-0600 SIC 6331 6411

WHITE MOUNTAINS CAPITAL INC p 1606
265 Franklin St Ste 500, Boston MA 02110
Tel (617) 330-5310 SIC 6331

ASSOCIATED INDUSTRIES OF MASSACHUSETTS MUTUAL INSURANCE CO p 120
54 3rd Ave, Burlington MA 01803
Tel (781) 221-1600 SIC 6331

ONEBEACON INSURANCE GROUP LLC p 1087
150 Royall St, Canton MA 02021
Tel (781) 332-7000 SIC 6331

ARBELLA MUTUAL INSURANCE CO p 102
1100 Crown Colony Dr, Quincy MA 02169
Tel (617) 328-2800 SIC 6411 6331

QUINCY MUTUAL FIRE INSURANCE CO INC p 1200
57 Washington St, Quincy MA 02169
Tel (617) 770-5100 SIC 6331 6411

COMMERCE INSURANCE CO p 345
211 Main St, Webster MA 01570
Tel (508) 943-9000 SIC 6331

MAPFRE USA CORP p 903
211 Main St, Webster MA 01570
Tel (508) 943-9000 SIC 6331

■ HANOVER INSURANCE CO p 658
440 Lincoln St, Worcester MA 01653
Tel (508) 853-7200 SIC 6331 6351

▲ HANOVER INSURANCE GROUP INC p 658
440 Lincoln St, Worcester MA 01653
Tel (508) 855-1000 SIC 6331 6311

FOREMOST AFFINITY SERVICES INC p 566
5600 Beechtree Ln Se, Caledonia MI 49316
Tel (616) 942-3000 SIC 6331

FOREMOST CORP OF AMERICA p 566
5600 Beechtree Ln Se, Caledonia MI 49316
Tel (616) 942-3000 SIC 6331

FOREMOST FINANCIAL SERVICES CORP p 566
5600 Beechtree Ln Se, Caledonia MI 49316
Tel (616) 956-3501 SIC 6331

FOREMOST INSURANCE CO p 566
5600 Beechtree Ln Se, Caledonia MI 49316
Tel (616) 942-3000 SIC 6331

FOREMOST LLOYDS OF TEXAS p 566
5600 Beechtree Ln Se, Caledonia MI 49316
Tel (616) 942-3000 SIC 6331

AUTO CLUB INSURANCE ASSOCIATION CO p 133
1 Auto Club Dr, Dearborn MI 48126
Tel (313) 336-1234 SIC 6331

▲ ALLY FINANCIAL INC p 59
500 Woodward Ave Fl 1, Detroit MI 48226
Tel (866) 710-4623
SIC 6021 6153 6159 6311 6331 6162

■ ALLY INSURANCE HOLDINGS INC p 59
500 Woodward Ave Fl 1, Detroit MI 48226
Tel (888) 737-8460 SIC 6331 6141

AMERISURE INSURANCE CO p 84
26777 Halsted Rd Lbby, Farmington Hills MI 48331
Tel (248) 615-9000 SIC 6331

AMERISURE MUTUAL INSURANCE CO p 84
26777 Halsted Rd Lbby, Farmington Hills MI 48331
Tel (248) 615-9000 SIC 6331

BURNS & WILCOX LTD p 228
120 Kaufm Finan Cente 30, Farmington Hills MI 48334
Tel (248) 932-9000 SIC 6331 6411

FRANKENMUTH MUTUAL INSURANCE CO INC p 574
1 Mutual Ave, Frankenmuth MI 48787
Tel (989) 652-6121 SIC 6331

SPECTRUM HEALTH HOSPITALS p 1357
100 Michigan St Ne Mc-498, Grand Rapids MI 49503
Tel (616) 391-1774
SIC 8062 6351 8082 6331

LIGHTHOUSE INSURANCE GROUP INC p 865
877 E 16th St, Holland MI 49423
Tel (616) 392-6900
SIC 6411 6331 6321 6311

■ CITIZENS INSURANCE CO OF AMERICA p 311
808 N Highlander Way, Howell MI 48843
Tel (517) 546-2160 SIC 6331

■ CITIZENS INSURANCE CO OF MIDWEST p 311
808 N Highlander Way, Howell MI 48843
Tel (517) 546-2160 SIC 6331

ACCIDENT FUND HOLDINGS INC p 15
200 N Grand Ave, Lansing MI 48933
Tel (866) 206-5851 SIC 6331

AUTO-OWNERS INSURANCE CO p 133
6101 Anacapri Blvd, Lansing MI 48917
Tel (517) 323-1200 SIC 6331

AUTO-OWNERS LIFE INSURANCE CO p 133
6101 Anacapri Blvd, Lansing MI 48917
Tel (517) 323-1200 SIC 6411 6331

FARM BUREAU MUTUAL INSURANCE CO OF MICHIGAN p 528
7373 W Saginaw Hwy, Lansing MI 48917
Tel (517) 323-7000 SIC 6331

MICHIGAN FARM BUREAU FINANCIAL CORP p 961
7373 W Saginaw Hwy, Lansing MI 48917
Tel (517) 323-7000 SIC 6311 6331

OWNERS INSURANCE CO p 1100
6101 Anacapri Blvd, Lansing MI 48917
Tel (517) 323-1200 SIC 6411 6331

MAIPF p 898
17456 N Laurel Park Dr # 130, Livonia MI 48152
Tel (734) 464-1100 SIC 6331

■ DIGITAL LEASH LLC p 439
39500 High Pointe Blvd # 250, Novi MI 48375
Tel (877) 775-3274 SIC 6331 6411

FIRST MERCURY FINANCIAL CORP p 548
26600 Telegraph Rd, Southfield MI 48033
Tel (248) 358-4010 SIC 6331

FIRST MERCURY INSURANCE CO p 548
26600 Telegraph Rd, Southfield MI 48033
Tel (248) 358-4010 SIC 6331

■ MOTORS INSURANCE CORP p 993
300 Galleria Officentre # 201, Southfield MI 48034
Tel (248) 263-6000 SIC 6331

LAKE HARLEYSVILLE STATES INSURANCE CO p 839
600 E Front St Ste 200, Traverse City MI 49686
Tel (231) 946-6390 SIC 6331

SFM MUTUAL INSURANCE CO p 1310
3500 Amrcn Blvd W Ste 700, Bloomington MN 55431
Tel (952) 838-4200 SIC 6331

MENDOTA INSURANCE CO p 943
2805 Dodd Rd Ste 300, Eagan MN 55121
Tel (800) 422-0792 SIC 6331

WESTERN NATIONAL MUTUAL INSURANCE CO INC p 1599
5350 W 78th St, Minneapolis MN 55439
Tel (952) 835-5350 SIC 6331

FEDERATED MUTUAL INSURANCE CO p 536
121 E Park Sq, Owatonna MN 55060
Tel (507) 455-5200 SIC 6331 6321 6311

FEDERATED SERVICE INSURANCE CO p 536
121 E Park Sq, Owatonna MN 55060
Tel (507) 455-5200 SIC 6331

BEDIVERE INSURANCE CO p 168
605 Hwy 169th N Ste 800, Plymouth MN 55441
Tel (952) 852-2431
SIC 6331 6282 6159 7389

▲ ONEBEACON INSURANCE GROUP LTD p 1087
605 Highway 169 N Ste 800, Plymouth MN 55441
Tel (952) 852-2431 SIC 6331

NAU COUNTRY INSURANCE CO p 1019
7333 Sunwood Dr Nw, Ramsey MN 55303
Tel (763) 323-0175 SIC 6331

■ JUPITER HOLDINGS INC p 797
1285 Northland Dr, Saint Paul MN 55120
Tel (952) 681-3005 SIC 6331

■ NORTHFIELD INSURANCE CO p 1057
385 Washington St, Saint Paul MN 55102
Tel (651) 310-4100 SIC 6331

■ NORTHLAND CO p 1057
385 Washington St, Saint Paul MN 55102
Tel (800) 328-5972 SIC 6331 6162 6531

■ NORTHLAND INSURANCE CO p 1057
385 Washington St, Saint Paul MN 55102
Tel (651) 310-4100 SIC 6331

■ ST PAUL FIRE AND MARINE INSURANCE CO p 1372
385 Washington St, Saint Paul MN 55102
Tel (651) 221-7911
SIC 6331 6351 6321 6411

■ ST PAUL GUARDIAN INSURANCE CO p 1372
385 Washington St, Saint Paul MN 55102
Tel (651) 221-7911 SIC 6331

■ ST PAUL SURPLUS LINES INSURANCE CO p 1372
385 Washington St, Saint Paul MN 55102
Tel (651) 310-7911 SIC 6331

MISSISSIPPI FARM BUREAU MUTUAL INSURANCE CO p 975
6311 Ridgewood Rd, Jackson MS 39211
Tel (601) 957-3200 SIC 6331

COLUMBIA MUTUAL INSURANCE CO INC p 341
2102 Whitegate Dr, Columbia MO 65202
Tel (573) 474-6193 SIC 6331

MISSOURI EMPLOYERS MUTUAL INSURANCE CO p 976
101 N Keene St, Columbia MO 65201
Tel (573) 499-9714 SIC 6331

SHELTER MUTUAL INSURANCE CO p 1315
1817 W Broadway, Columbia MO 65218
Tel (573) 445-8441 SIC 6331 6311

AMERICO LIFE INC p 81
300 W 11th St, Kansas City MO 64105
Tel (816) 391-2000 SIC 6311 6321 6331

CLUB EXCHANGE CORP p 328
12901 N 40 Dr, Saint Louis MO 63141
Tel (314) 523-6976 SIC 6331

SAFETY NATIONAL CASUALTY CORP p 1266
1832 Schuetz Rd, Saint Louis MO 63146
Tel (314) 995-5300 SIC 6331

■ UNITED INSURANCE CO OF AMERICA p 1509
12115 Lackland Rd, Saint Louis MO 63146
Tel (314) 819-4300 SIC 6411 6321 6331

MONTANA STATE FUND p 986
855 Front St, Helena MT 59601
Tel (406) 444-6500 SIC 6331

AON NATIONAL FLOOD SERVICES INC p 95
555 Corporate Dr, Kalispell MT 59901
Tel (406) 756-8656 SIC 6331

■ APPLIED UNDERWRITERS INC p 100
10805 Old Mill Rd, Omaha NE 68154
Tel (402) 342-4900
SIC 6331 8721 8741 8742

▲ BERKSHIRE HATHAWAY INC p 175
3555 Farnam St Ste 1440, Omaha NE 68131
Tel (402) 346-1400
SIC 6331 6321 4911 4924 6531 5963

■ COLUMBIA INSURANCE CO p 341
3024 Harney St, Omaha NE 68131
Tel (402) 536-3000 SIC 6331

■ NATIONAL INDEMNITY CO (INC) p 1013
1314 Douglas St Ste 1400, Omaha NE 68102
Tel (402) 916-3000 SIC 6331 6411 6311

■ GREAT WEST CASUALTY p 634
1100 W 29th St, South Sioux City NE 68776
Tel (402) 494-2411 SIC 6331

■ GREAT WEST CASUALTY CO p 634
1100 W 29th St, South Sioux City NE 68776
Tel (402) 494-2411 SIC 6331

■ EMPLOYERS GROUP INC p 494
9790 Gateway Dr, Reno NV 89521
Tel (775) 327-6000 SIC 6331

▲ EMPLOYERS HOLDINGS INC p 494
10375 Professional Cir, Reno NV 89521
Tel (888) 682-6671 SIC 6331

■ **EMPLOYERS INSURANCE CO OF NEVADA** p 494
10375 Professional Cir, Reno NV 89521
Tel (775) 327-2700 *SIC* 6331

■ **CHARTIS US INC** p 291
1 Executive Park Dr, Bedford NH 03110
Tel (603) 645-7000 *SIC* 6331

CONCORD GENERAL MUTUAL INSURANCE CO p 354
4 Bouton St, Concord NH 03301
Tel (603) 224-4086 *SIC* 6331

PEERLESS INSURANCE CO p 1127
62 Maple Ave, Keene NH 03431
Tel (603) 352-3221 *SIC* 6331

TIG HOLDINGS INC p 1453
250 Commercial St # 5000, Manchester NH 03101
Tel (603) 656-2200 *SIC* 6331

TIG INSURANCE CO p 1453
250 Commercial St # 5000, Manchester NH 03101
Tel (603) 656-2200 *SIC* 6331

TIG INSURANCE GROUP p 1453
250 Commercial St # 5000, Manchester NH 03101
Tel (603) 656-2200 *SIC* 6331

▲ **SELECTIVE INSURANCE GROUP INC** p 1302
40 Wantage Ave, Branchville NJ 07890
Tel (973) 948-3000 *SIC* 6331

CUMBERLAND MUTUAL FIRE INSURANCE CO (INC) p 400
633 Shiloh Pike, Bridgeton NJ 08302
Tel (856) 451-4050 *SIC* 6331 6411

PXRE CORP p 1193
379 Thornall St Ste 2, Edison NJ 08837
Tel (973) 321-3590 *SIC* 6331 6324 6321

PXRE REINSURANCE CO p 1193
379 Thornall St Ste 2, Edison NJ 08837
Tel (732) 906-9157 *SIC* 6331

NEW JERSEY MANUFACTURERS INSURANCE CO p 1031
301 Sullivan Way, Ewing NJ 08628
Tel (609) 883-1300 *SIC* 6331

NEW JERSEY RE-INSURANCE CO p 1031
301 Sullivan Way, Ewing NJ 08628
Tel (609) 883-1300 *SIC* 6311 6331

VALIDUS SPECIALTY INC p 1540
400 Parsons Pond Dr, Franklin Lakes NJ 07417
Tel (201) 847-8600 *SIC* 6331

ARCH INSURANCE GROUP INC p 104
Harborside 3 210 Hudson S, Jersey City NJ 07311
Tel (201) 743-4000 *SIC* 6331 6351

EVEREST REINSURANCE CO p 514
477 Martinsville Rd, Liberty Corner NJ 07938
Tel (908) 604-3000 *SIC* 6331

EVEREST REINSURANCE HOLDINGS INC p 514
477 Martinsville Rd, Liberty Corner NJ 07938
Tel (908) 604-3000 *SIC* 6411 6331 6321

CRUM & FORSTER HOLDINGS CORP p 396
305 Madison Ave, Morristown NJ 07960
Tel (973) 490-6600 *SIC* 6331 6321 6351

CRUM & FORSTER INC p 396
305 Madison Ave, Morristown NJ 07960
Tel (973) 490-6600
SIC 6311 6321 6331 6411

NORTH RIVER INSURANCE CO p 1053
305 Madison Ave, Morristown NJ 07960
Tel (973) 490-6600 *SIC* 6331

PROSIGHT SPECIALTY INSURANCE GROUP INC p 1184
412 Mount Kemble Ave 300c, Morristown NJ 07960
Tel (973) 532-1900 *SIC* 6351 6331

UNITED STATES FIRE INSURANCE CO p 1513
305 Madison Ave, Morristown NJ 07960
Tel (973) 490-6600 *SIC* 6331

■ **ADMIRAL INSURANCE CO** p 23
1000 Howard Blvd Ste 300, Mount Laurel NJ 08054
Tel (856) 429-9200 *SIC* 6331 6411 6324

■ **PRUCO SECURITIES LLC** p 1187
751 Broad St, Newark NJ 07102
Tel (800) 235-7637
SIC 6321 6331 6211 6282 8071

▲ **PRUDENTIAL FINANCIAL INC** p 1187
751 Broad St, Newark NJ 07102
Tel (973) 802-6000
SIC 6311 6321 6331 6211 6552

WESTERN WORLD INSURANCE GROUP INC p 1600
300 Kimball Dr Ste 500, Parsippany NJ 07054
Tel (201) 847-8600 *SIC* 6331

■ **MUNICH HEALTH NORTH AMERICA INC** p 1000
555 College Rd E, Princeton NJ 08540
Tel (609) 243-4200 *SIC* 6331

■ **MUNICH RE AMERICA CORP** p 1000
555 College Rd E, Princeton NJ 08540
Tel (609) 243-4200 *SIC* 6331

■ **MUNICH REINSURANCE AMERICA INC** p 1000
555 College Rd E, Princeton NJ 08540
Tel (609) 243-4200 *SIC* 6331 6311

■ **MUNICH-AMERICAN HOLDING CORP** p 1000
555 College Rd E, Princeton NJ 08540
Tel (609) 243-4876 *SIC* 6331

CHUBB CORP p 304
15 Mountainview Rd, Warren NJ 07059
Tel (908) 903-2000 *SIC* 6331

CHUBB GROUP OF INSURANCE COMPANIES p 304
15 Mountainview Rd, Warren NJ 07059
Tel (908) 903-2000 *SIC* 6331

MITSUI SUMITOMO INSURANCE CO OF AMERICA p 978
15 Independence Blvd 1100a, Warren NJ 07059
Tel (908) 604-2900 *SIC* 6331

NEW MEXICO MUTUAL CASUALTY CO p 1032
3900 Singer Blvd Ne, Albuquerque NM 87109
Tel (800) 788-8851 *SIC* 6331

SR CORPORATE SOLUTIONS AMERICA HOLDING CORP p 1362
175 King St, Armonk NY 10504
Tel (914) 828-8000 *SIC* 6331 6311

SWISS REINSURANCE AMERICA CORP p 1413
175 King St, Armonk NY 10504
Tel (914) 828-8000 *SIC* 6331

AMERICAN TRANSIT INSURANCE CO INC p 80
1 Metrotech Ctr Fl 7, Brooklyn NY 11201
Tel (212) 857-8200 *SIC* 6321 6331 6311

MERCHANTS INSURANCE GROUP p 945
250 Main St, Buffalo NY 14202
Tel (716) 849-3333 *SIC* 6331

MERCHANTS MUTUAL INSURANCE CO p 945
240 Main St, Buffalo NY 14202
Tel (716) 849-3333 *SIC* 6331

NEW YORK CENTRAL MUTUAL FIRE INSURANCE CO p 1034
1899 Central Plz E, Edmeston NY 13335
Tel (607) 965-8321 *SIC* 6331

■ **FARM FAMILY HOLDINGS INC** p 529
344 Route 9w, Glenmont NY 12077
Tel (518) 431-5000 *SIC* 6331

STATE WIDE INSURANCE CO INC p 1383
20 Main St, Hempstead NY 11550
Tel (516) 564-8000 *SIC* 6331

■ **METROPOLITAN LIFE INSURANCE CO (INC)** p 956
2701 Queens Plz N Ste 1, Long Island City NY 11101
Tel (212) 578-2211
SIC 6411 6324 6331 6321 6531

PREFERRED MUTUAL INSURANCE CO p 1169
1 Preferred Way, New Berlin NY 13411
Tel (607) 847-6161 *SIC* 6331

GRAPHIC ARTS MUTUAL INSURANCE CO INC p 631
180 Genesee St, New Hartford NY 13413
Tel (315) 734-2000 *SIC* 6331

UTICA MUTUAL INSURANCE CO p 1537
180 Genesee St, New Hartford NY 13413
Tel (315) 734-2000 *SIC* 6331 6311

UTICA NATIONAL INSURANCE GROUP p 1537
180 Genesee St, New Hartford NY 13413
Tel (315) 734-2000 *SIC* 6331 6411

■ **AIG PROPERTY CASUALTY INC** p 38
175 Water St Fl 5, New York NY 10038
Tel (212) 458-5000 *SIC* 6331 6321 6311

■ **AIU INSURANCE CO** p 41
175 Water St Fl 24, New York NY 10038
Tel (212) 770-7000 *SIC* 6331 6321

▲ **ALLEGHANY CORP** p 52
7 Times Sq Tower, New York NY 10036
Tel (212) 752-1356 *SIC* 6331 6411 6531

■ **ALLEGHANY INSURANCE HOLDINGS LLC** p 52
7 Times Sq Tower Fl 17, New York NY 10152
Tel (212) 752-1356 *SIC* 6331

AMERICAN EUROPEAN GROUP INC p 72
605 3rd Ave Fl 9, New York NY 10158
Tel (212) 355-3310 *SIC* 6331

■ **AMERICAN HOME ASSURANCE CO INC** p 74
70 Pine St Fl 1, New York NY 10005
Tel (212) 770-7000 *SIC* 6331 7371

▲ **AMERICAN INTERNATIONAL GROUP INC** p 75
175 Water St Rm 1800, New York NY 10038
Tel (212) 770-7000
SIC 6331 6321 6311 6324 6411 6282

▲ **AMTRUST FINANCIAL SERVICES INC** p 87
59 Maiden Ln Fl 43, New York NY 10038
Tel (212) 220-7120 *SIC* 6331

▲ **ASSURANT INC** p 121
28 Liberty St Fl 41, New York NY 10005
Tel (212) 859-7000 *SIC* 6311 6399 6331

CHURCH PENSION GROUP SERVICES CORP p 305
19 E 34th St Fl 3, New York NY 10016
Tel (212) 592-1800
SIC 6371 6321 6311 6331 2731

▲ **CITIGROUP INC** p 310
399 Park Ave, New York NY 10022
Tel (212) 559-1000
SIC 6021 6141 6331 6311 6321

COFACE NORTH AMERICA HOLDING CO p 334
1350 Broadway Rm 615, New York NY 10018
Tel (212) 389-6500 *SIC* 6331

CONDOR 3 CORP p 355
120 Broadway Ste 31, New York NY 10271
Tel (212) 655-2000 *SIC* 6331

■ **CONTINENTAL CORP** p 363
111 8th Ave, New York NY 10011
Tel (212) 440-3000
SIC 6331 6351 6321 6159 8741 6411

LIBERTY INTERNATIONAL UNDERWRITERS USA p 862
55 Water St Fl 23, New York NY 10041
Tel (212) 208-4100 *SIC* 6331

▲ **LOEWS CORP** p 874
667 Madison Ave Fl 7, New York NY 10065
Tel (212) 521-2000
SIC 6331 6311 1381 4922 7011

MAGNA CARTA COMPANIES INC p 895
1 Park Ave Fl 15, New York NY 10016
Tel (212) 591-9500 *SIC* 6331

■ **MARSH USA INC** p 911
1166 Ave Of The Americas, New York NY 10036
Tel (212) 345-6000
SIC 6411 6331 6351 6282

▲ **METLIFE INC** p 954
200 Park Ave Fl 1200, New York NY 10166
Tel (212) 578-9500 *SIC* 6311 6321 6331

MITSUI SUMITOMO INSURANCE CO OF AMERICA p 978
560 Lexington Ave Fl 20, New York NY 10022
Tel (212) 446-3600 *SIC* 6331

MSIG HOLDINGS (AMERICAS) INC p 997
560 Lexington Ave Fl 20, New York NY 10022
Tel (212) 446-3600 *SIC* 8741 6331

■ **NATIONAL UNION FIRE INSURANCE CO OF PITTSBURGH PA** p 1016
70 Pine St Fl 50, New York NY 10005
Tel (631) 692-4545 *SIC* 6331

■ **NEW HAMPSHIRE INSURANCE CO** p 1030
70 Pine St Fl 23, New York NY 10005
Tel (212) 770-7000 *SIC* 6331

PMI MORTGAGE INSURANCE CO p 1157
350 5th Ave, New York NY 10118
Tel (925) 658-7878 *SIC* 6351 6331

SCOR REINSURANCE CO p 1293
199 Water St Fl 21, New York NY 10038
Tel (212) 884-9000 *SIC* 6331

■ **SEABURY & SMITH (DELAWARE) INC** p 1296
1166 Ave Of The Americas, New York NY 10036
Tel (212) 345-9049
SIC 6411 6331 6321 6311

SIRIUS AMERICA INSURANCE CO p 1326
140 Broadway Fl 32, New York NY 10005
Tel (212) 312-2500 *SIC* 6331

SOMPO AMERICA INSURANCE SERVICES LLC p 1339
777 3rd Ave Fl 24, New York NY 10017
Tel (212) 416-1200 *SIC* 6331

STARR TECHNICAL RISKS AGENCY INC p 1379
90 Park Ave Fl 9, New York NY 10016
Tel (646) 227-6301 *SIC* 6331

TOYOTA TSUSHO AMERICA INC p 1467
805 3rd Ave Fl 17, New York NY 10022
Tel (212) 355-3600
SIC 5051 5013 4225 6331 5153

■ **TRANSATLANTIC HOLDINGS INC** p 1470
80 Pine St Fl 9, New York NY 10005
Tel (212) 365-2200 *SIC* 6331

■ **TRANSATLANTIC REINSURANCE CO** p 1471
1 Liberty Plz Fl 17, New York NY 10006
Tel (212) 365-2200 *SIC* 6331

▲ **TRAVELERS COMPANIES INC** p 1474
485 Lexington Ave, New York NY 10017
Tel (917) 778-6000 *SIC* 6331 6351 6321

LANCER INSURANCE CO p 842
1 Fairchild Ct Ste 200, Plainview NY 11803
Tel (541) 472-0950 *SIC* 6331

MUELLER SERVICES INC p 998
63 Main St, Tonawanda NY 14150
Tel (716) 691-4344 *SIC* 6331

FIRST FINANCIAL INSURANCE CO INC p 547
238 International Rd, Burlington NC 27215
Tel (336) 586-2500 *SIC* 6331

INTERNATIONAL FINANCIAL GROUP INC p 755
238 International Rd, Burlington NC 27215
Tel (336) 586-2500 *SIC* 6331

NORTH CAROLINA INSURANCE UNDERWRITING ASSOCIATION p 1051
5651 Dillard Dr, Cary NC 27518
Tel (919) 821-1299 *SIC* 6331

ARROWOOD INDEMNITY CO p 113
3600 Arco Corporate Dr, Charlotte NC 28273
Tel (704) 522-2000 *SIC* 6331

ARROWPOINT CAPITAL CORP p 113
3600 Arco Corporate Dr, Charlotte NC 28273
Tel (704) 522-2000 *SIC* 6331

■ **METLIFE INSURANCE CO USA** p 954
11225 N Community Hse Rd, Charlotte NC 28277
Tel (980) 949-3626
SIC 6411 6321 6331 6324

MCM CORP p 932
702 Oberlin Rd Ste 300, Raleigh NC 27605
Tel (919) 833-1600 *SIC* 6331

NORTH CAROLINA FARM BUREAU INSURANCE AGENCY INC p 1051
5301 Glenwood Ave, Raleigh NC 27612
Tel (919) 782-1705 *SIC* 6331 6411 6311

OCCIDENTAL FIRE & CASUALTY CO OF NORTH CAROLINA p 1072
702 Oberlin Rd Ste 300, Raleigh NC 27605
Tel (919) 833-1600 *SIC* 6331

■ **AMERICAN MODERN HOME INSURANCE CO** p 76
7000 Midland Blvd, Amelia OH 45102
Tel (513) 943-7100 *SIC* 6331

■ **MIDLAND CO** p 965
7000 Midland Blvd, Amelia OH 45102
Tel (513) 947-5503 *SIC* 6331 4449

■ **MIDLAND-GUARDIAN CO** p 966
7000 Midland Blvd, Amelia OH 45102
Tel (513) 943-7100 *SIC* 6311 6331

■ **HAMILTON MUTUAL INSURANCE CO** p 655
11311 Cornell Park Dr # 500, Blue Ash OH 45242
Tel (513) 221-6010 *SIC* 6331

OHIO MUTUAL INSURANCE CO p 1077
1725 Hopley Ave, Bucyrus OH 44820
Tel (419) 562-3011 *SIC* 6411 6331

CELINA MUTUAL INSURANCE CO p 273
1 Insurance Sq, Celina OH 45822
Tel (419) 586-5181 *SIC* 6331

▲ **AMERICAN FINANCIAL GROUP INC** p 72
301 E 4th St, Cincinnati OH 45202
Tel (513) 579-2121 *SIC* 6331 6311 6321

■ **GREAT AMERICAN INSURANCE CO** p 633
301 E 4th St Ste 2800, Cincinnati OH 45202
Tel (513) 369-5000 *SIC* 6331

■ **AMTRUST NORTH AMERICA INC** p 87
800 Superior Ave E # 2100, Cleveland OH 44114
Tel (216) 328-6100 *SIC* 6331 6411

■ **DRIVE INSURANCE HOLDINGS INC** p 456
6300 Wilson Mills Rd, Cleveland OH 44143
Tel (440) 461-5000 *SIC* 6331 6351

■ **PROGRESSIVE AGENCY INC** p 1181
6300 Wilson Mills Rd, Cleveland OH 44143
Tel (440) 461-5000 *SIC* 6331

■ **PROGRESSIVE AMERICAN INSURANCE CO** p 1181
6300 Wilson Mills Rd, Cleveland OH 44143
Tel (440) 461-5000 *SIC* 6331

■ **PROGRESSIVE CHOICE INSURANCE CO** p 1181
6300 Wilson Mills Rd, Cleveland OH 44143
Tel (440) 461-5000 *SIC* 6331

■ **PROGRESSIVE DIRECT INSURANCE CO** p 1181
6300 Wilson Mills Rd, Cleveland OH 44143
Tel (440) 461-5000 *SIC* 6331

■ **PROGRESSIVE MARATHON INSURANCE CO INC** p 1181
6300 Wilson Mills Rd, Cleveland OH 44143
Tel (888) 223-3558 *SIC* 6331

■ **PROGRESSIVE MAX INSURANCE CO** p 1181
6300 Wilson Mills Rd, Cleveland OH 44143
Tel (440) 461-5000 *SIC* 6331 6411

■ **PROGRESSIVE NORTHWESTERN INSURANCE CO** p 1181
6300 Wilson Mills Rd, Cleveland OH 44143
Tel (440) 461-5000 *SIC* 6331

■ **PROGRESSIVE PREFERRED INSURANCE CO** p 1182
6300 Wilson Mills Rd, Cleveland OH 44143
Tel (216) 464-8000 *SIC* 6331

■ **PROGRESSIVE SELECT INSURANCE CO** p 1182
6300 Wilson Mills Rd, Cleveland OH 44143
Tel (440) 461-5000 *SIC* 6331

■ **PROGRESSIVE SPECIALTY INSURANCE CO** p 1182
6300 Wilson Mills Rd, Cleveland OH 44143
Tel (440) 461-5000 *SIC* 6331

■ **UNITED FINANCIAL CASUALTY CO INC** p 1508
6300 Wilson Mills Rd, Cleveland OH 44143
Tel (440) 461-5000 *SIC* 6331

AMERICAN COMMERCE INSURANCE CO p 70
3590 Twin Creeks Dr, Columbus OH 43204
Tel (614) 272-6951 *SIC* 6331 6351

GRANGE MUTUAL CASUALTY CO p 630
671 S High St, Columbus OH 43206
Tel (614) 445-2900 *SIC* 6331

MOTORISTS COMMERCIAL MUTUAL INSURANCE CO p 993
471 E Broad St Bsmt, Columbus OH 43215
Tel (614) 225-8211 *SIC* 6331

MOTORISTS MUTUAL INSURANCE CO p 993
471 E Broad St Ste 200, Columbus OH 43215
Tel (614) 225-8211 *SIC* 6331

NATIONWIDE MUTUAL INSURANCE CO p 1018
1 Nationwide Plz, Columbus OH 43215
Tel (614) 249-7111
SIC 6331 6311 6321 6531

OHIO BUREAU OF WORKERS COMPENSATION p 1077
30 W Spring St Fl 2-29, Columbus OH 43215
Tel (614) 644-6292 *SIC* 6331 9199

PERSONAL SERVICE INSURANCE CO p 1137
2760 Airport Dr Ste 130, Columbus OH 43219
Tel (800) 282-9416 *SIC* 6331

SAFE AUTO INSURANCE GROUP INC p 1265
4 Easton Oval, Columbus OH 43219
Tel (614) 231-0200 *SIC* 6331 6411

■ **STATE AUTO FINANCIAL CORP** p 1380
518 E Broad St, Columbus OH 43215
Tel (614) 464-5000 *SIC* 6331

■ **STATE AUTO PROPERTY AND CASUALTY INSURANCE CO** p 1380
518 E Broad St, Columbus OH 43215
Tel (614) 464-5000 *SIC* 6331

▲ **STATE AUTOMOBILE MUTUAL INSURANCE CO INC** p 1380
518 E Broad St, Columbus OH 43215
Tel (614) 464-5000 *SIC* 6331 6411 6351

▲ **FIRST DEFIANCE FINANCIAL CORP** p 546
601 Clinton St, Defiance OH 43512
Tel (419) 782-5015
SIC 6035 6331 6321 6311

■ **CINCINNATI INDEMINTY CO** p 307
6200 S Gilmore Rd, Fairfield OH 45014
Tel (513) 870-2000 *SIC* 6331

■ **CINCINNATI INSURANCE CO** p 307
6200 S Gilmore Rd, Fairfield OH 45014
Tel (513) 870-2000
SIC 6311 6331 6321 6211

OHIO CASUALTY CORP p 1077
9450 Seward Rd, Fairfield OH 45014
Tel (513) 603-2400 *SIC* 6331

OHIO CASUALTY INSURANCE CO p 1077
9450 Seward Rd, Fairfield OH 45014
Tel (800) 843-6446 *SIC* 6331 6311

INDIANA INSURANCE CO p 738
6281 Tri Ridge Blvd # 1, Loveland OH 45140
Tel (816) 216-5313 *SIC* 6331

■ **PROGRESSIVE CASUALTY INSURANCE CO** p 1181
6300 Wilson Mills Rd, Mayfield Village OH 44143
Tel (440) 461-5000
SIC 6331 6351 6411 6321

▲ **PROGRESSIVE CORP** p 1181
6300 Wilson Mills Rd, Mayfield Village OH 44143
Tel (440) 461-5000 *SIC* 6331 6351

OHIO NATIONAL LIFE INSURANCE CO p 1078
1 Financial Way Ste 100, Montgomery OH 45242
Tel (513) 794-6100 *SIC* 6331

■ **NATIONAL INTERSTATE CORP** p 1013
3250 Interstate Dr, Richfield OH 44286
Tel (330) 659-8900 *SIC* 6331 6411

■ **NATIONAL INTERSTATE INSURANCE CO** p 1013
3250 Interstate Dr, Richfield OH 44286
Tel (330) 659-8900 *SIC* 6331

CENTRAL MUTUAL INSURANCE CO p 279
800 S Washington St, Van Wert OH 45891
Tel (419) 238-1010 *SIC* 6331

OHIO FARMERS INSURANCE CO p 1077
1 Park Cir, Westfield Center OH 44251
Tel (800) 243-0210 *SIC* 6411 6331

WESTFIELD INSURANCE CO p 1601
1 Park Cir, Westfield Center OH 44251
Tel (800) 243-0210 *SIC* 6411 6331

WESTERN RESERVE GROUP p 1600
1685 Cleveland Rd, Wooster OH 44691
Tel (330) 262-9060 SIC 6331

AMERICAN FARMERS & RANCHERS MUTUAL INSURANCE CO p 72
4400 Will Rogers Pkwy, Oklahoma City OK 73108
Tel (405) 218-5400 SIC 6331

■ **AMERICAN MERCURY INSURANCE CO** p 76
7301 Nw Expressway # 200, Oklahoma City OK 73132
Tel (405) 621-6509 SIC 6411 6331

COMPSOURCE MUTUAL INSURANCE CO p 352
1901 N Walnut Ave, Oklahoma City OK 73105
Tel (405) 232-7663 SIC 6331

■ **MIDLANDS MANAGEMENT CORP** p 966
3817 Nw Expwy Ste 1000, Oklahoma City OK 73112
Tel (405) 840-0074 SIC 6411 6331 6321

OKLAHOMA FARM BUREAU MUTUAL INSURANCE CO p 1079
2501 N Stiles Ave, Oklahoma City OK 73105
Tel (405) 523-2300 SIC 6331 6351

■ **MID-CONTINENT CASUALTY CO** p 963
1437 S Boulder Ave # 200, Tulsa OK 74119
Tel (918) 587-7221 SIC 6331

OREGON MUTUAL INSURANCE CO INC p 1093
400 Ne Baker St, Mcminnville OR 97128
Tel (503) 472-2141 SIC 6331

LIBERTY NORTHWEST INSURANCE CORP p 862
650 Ne Holladay St, Portland OR 97232
Tel (503) 239-5800 SIC 6331

NORTH PACIFIC INSURANCE CO p 1053
1 Liberty Ctr, Portland OR 97232
Tel (503) 239-5800 SIC 6331

SAIF CORP p 1268
400 High St Se, Salem OR 97312
Tel (503) 373-8000 SIC 6321 8111 6331

NATIONAL PENN BANCSHARES INC p 1015
645 Hamilton St Ste 1100, Allentown PA 18101
Tel (800) 822-3321 SIC 6331

AMERICAN INSURANCE SERVICE INC p 75
3 Bala Plz E Ste 300, Bala Cynwyd PA 19004
Tel (610) 664-1500 SIC 6411 6331

DIAMOND STATE INSURANCE CO p 437
3 Bala Plz E Ste 300, Bala Cynwyd PA 19004
Tel (610) 664-1500 SIC 6331 6411

PHILADELPHIA CONSOLIDATED HOLDING CORP p 1142
1 Bala Plz Ste 100, Bala Cynwyd PA 19004
Tel (610) 617-7900 SIC 6331

PHILADELPHIA INSURANCE CO p 1143
231 Sint Asphs Rd Ste 100, Bala Cynwyd PA 19004
Tel (877) 438-7459 SIC 6331 6411

UNITED NATIONAL INSURANCE CO p 1510
3 Bala Plz E Ste 300, Bala Cynwyd PA 19004
Tel (610) 664-1500 SIC 6331

AMERICAN INDEPENDENT INSURANCE CO INC p 74
1400 Union Meeting Rd # 250, Blue Bell PA 19422
Tel (610) 832-4940 SIC 6331 6411

■ **PENNSYLVANIA MANUFACTURERS ASSOCIATION INSURANCE CO** p 1130
380 Sentry Pkwy, Blue Bell PA 19422
Tel (610) 397-5000 SIC 6331

■ **PENNSYLVANIA MANUFACTURERS INDEMNITY CO** p 1130
380 Sentry Pkwy, Blue Bell PA 19422
Tel (610) 397-5000 SIC 6331

■ **PMA COMPANIES INC** p 1157
380 Sentry Pkwy Ste 200, Blue Bell PA 19422
Tel (610) 397-5298 SIC 6331

INDEPENDENT INSURANCE INVESTMENTS INC p 736
1000 River Rd Ste 300, Conshohocken PA 19428
Tel (610) 832-4940 SIC 6331 6411

ERIE FAMILY LIFE INSURANCE CO INC p 508
100 Erie Insurance Pl, Erie PA 16530
Tel (814) 870-2000 SIC 6331

ERIE INSURANCE EXCHANGE ACTIVITIES ASSOCIATION INC p 508
100 Erie Insurance Pl, Erie PA 16530
Tel (800) 458-0811 SIC 6331

HARLEYSVILLE GROUP INC p 662
355 Maple Ave, Harleysville PA 19438
Tel (215) 256-9773 SIC 6331 6411

HARLEYSVILLE MUTUAL INSURANCE CO p 662
355 Maple Ave, Harleysville PA 19438
Tel (215) 256-5000 SIC 6331 6331

PENNSYLVANIA NATIONAL MUTUAL CASUALTY INSURANCE CO p 1130
2 N 2nd St Ste 2, Harrisburg PA 17101
Tel (717) 230-8200 SIC 6331

GRUNDY WORLDWIDE INC p 642
400 Horsham Rd Ste 150, Horsham PA 19044
Tel (888) 647-8639 SIC 6331

MUTUAL BENEFIT INSURANCE CO p 1003
409 Penn St, Huntingdon PA 16652
Tel (814) 643-3000 SIC 6331

■ **EASTERN INSURANCE HOLDINGS INC** p 472
25 Race Ave, Lancaster PA 17603
Tel (717) 239-1641 SIC 6311 6331

■ **ATLANTIC STATES INSURANCE CO** p 127
1195 River Rd, Marietta PA 17547
Tel (717) 426-1931 SIC 6331

▲ **DONEGAL GROUP INC** p 450
1195 River Rd, Marietta PA 17547
Tel (717) 426-1931 SIC 6331

■ **DONEGAL MUTUAL INSURANCE CO** p 450
1195 River Rd, Marietta PA 17547
Tel (717) 426-1931 SIC 6331

ACE AMERICAN INSURANCE CO p 16
436 Walnut St, Philadelphia PA 19106
Tel (215) 640-1000 SIC 6321 6331 6351

ACE PROPERTY AND CASUALTY INSURANCE CO p 16
2 Liberty Pl 2 Liberty Place, Philadelphia PA 19102
Tel (215) 761-1000 SIC 6321 6331 6351

CENTURY INDEMNITY CO p 282
1601 Chestnut St, Philadelphia PA 19192
Tel (215) 761-1000 SIC 6321 6331 6351

CHUBB US HOLDING INC p 304
1601 Chestnut St, Philadelphia PA 19192
Tel (215) 640-1000 SIC 6411 6331

CSAA AFFINITY INSURANCE CO p 397
2040 Market St, Philadelphia PA 19103
Tel (215) 864-5000 SIC 6331 6321

■ **EXCALIBUR REINSURANCE CORP** p 516
1735 Market St Fl 30, Philadelphia PA 19103
Tel (215) 665-5000 SIC 6331

INA CORP p 735
1601 Chestnut St Ste 1, Philadelphia PA 19192
Tel (215) 761-1000 SIC 6331

PENNSYLVANIA LUMBERMENS MUTUAL INSURANCE CO p 1130
2005 Market St Ste 1200, Philadelphia PA 19103
Tel (800) 752-1895 SIC 6331

PHILADELPHIA CONTRIBUTIONSHIP FOR INSURANCE OF HOUSES FROM LOSS BY FIRE p 1142
212 S 4th St, Philadelphia PA 19106
Tel (215) 627-1752
SIC 6331 6311 7382 6321

■ **GUARD INSURANCE GROUP INC** p 645
16 S River St, Wilkes Barre PA 18702
Tel (570) 825-9900 SIC 6331

LINCOLN GENERAL INSURANCE CO p 867
3501 Concord Rd Ste 120, York PA 17402
Tel (717) 757-0000 SIC 6331

COOPERATIVA DE SEGUROS MULTIPLES DE PUERTO RICO p 367
Expreso Ls America Y Mira, San Juan PR 00927
Tel (787) 758-8585 SIC 6331 6351

AFFILIATED FM INSURANCE CO p 32
270 Central Ave, Johnston RI 02919
Tel (401) 275-3000 SIC 6512 6331

FACTORY MUTUAL INSURANCE CO p 524
270 Central Ave, Johnston RI 02919
Tel (401) 275-3000 SIC 6331 8711 6512

AMICA MUTUAL INSURANCE CO p 85
100 Amica Way, Lincoln RI 02865
Tel (800) 992-6422 SIC 6331

BEACON MUTUAL INSURANCE CO p 165
1 Beacon Ctr Ste 100, Warwick RI 02886
Tel (401) 825-2667 SIC 6331

■ **METROPOLITAN GROUP PROPERTIES & CASUALTY** p 956
700 Quaker Ln, Warwick RI 02886
Tel (401) 827-2400 SIC 6331 6351

SOUTH CAROLINA FARM BUREAU MUTUAL INSURANCE CO (INC) p 1343
724 Knox Abbott Dr, Cayce SC 29033
Tel (803) 796-6700 SIC 6331

BRUCE SEIBELS GROUP INC p 220
1501 Lady St, Columbia SC 29201
Tel (803) 748-2000 SIC 6331 6321 6311

SUSSEX INSURANCE CO p 1409
221 Dawson Rd, Columbia SC 29223
Tel (803) 735-0672 SIC 6331

CANAL INSURANCE CO p 246
400 E Stone Ave, Greenville SC 29601
Tel (800) 452-6911 SIC 6331

TENNESSEE FARMERS MUTUAL INSURANCE CO p 1438
147 Bear Creek Pike, Columbia TN 38401
Tel (877) 876-2222 SIC 6331

■ **CLAYTON HOMES INC** p 323
5000 Clayton Rd, Maryville TN 37804
Tel (865) 380-3000
SIC 2451 5271 6141 6351 6331

■ **DIRECT GENERAL CORP** p 441
1281 Murfreesboro Pike # 150, Nashville TN 37217
Tel (615) 399-4700
SIC 6311 6321 6331 6411

▲ **FIRST ACCEPTANCE CORP** p 544
3813 Green Hills Vlg Dr, Nashville TN 37215
Tel (615) 844-2800 SIC 6331 6531

NEW ASURION CORP p 1029
648 Grassmere Park, Nashville TN 37211
Tel (615) 837-3000 SIC 6331

PERMANENT GENERAL ASSURANCE CORP p 1136
2636 Elm Hill Pike # 510, Nashville TN 37214
Tel (615) 744-1351 SIC 6331 6411 6141

NEW AFFIRMATIVE LLC p 1029
4450 Sojourn Dr Ste 500, Addison TX 75001
Tel (972) 728-6300 SIC 6331

AGRILOGIC INSURANCE SERVICES LLC p 36
1000 Ballpark Way Ste 314, Arlington TX 76011
Tel (888) 245-6442 SIC 6331

SERVICE LLOYDS INSURANCE CO p 1307
6907 N Capital Of Texas, Austin TX 78731
Tel (512) 343-0600 SIC 6331

TEXAS MUTUAL INSURANCE CO p 1444
6210 E Hwy 290, Austin TX 78723
Tel (512) 322-3800 SIC 6331

STATE NATIONAL INSURANCE CO INC p 1381
1900 L Don Dodson Dr, Bedford TX 76021
Tel (817) 265-2000 SIC 6331

TBA INSURANCE GROUP LIMITED PARTNERSHIP p 1427
1900 L Don Dodson Dr, Bedford TX 76021
Tel (817) 265-2000 SIC 6331 6163

GERMANIA FARM MUTUAL INSURANCE ASSOCIATION p 609
507 Highway 290 E, Brenham TX 77833
Tel (979) 836-5224 SIC 6311 6331

PRONTO GENERAL AGENCY LTD p 1183
805 Media Luna St Ste 100, Brownsville TX 78520
Tel (956) 574-9787 SIC 6331 6361 7291

■ **EMPLOYERS GENERAL INSURANCE GROUP INC** p 494
1700 Pacific Ave Ste 1600, Dallas TX 75201
Tel (214) 665-6100 SIC 6331 8742

▲ **GAINSCO INC** p 589
3333 Lee Pkwy Ste 1200, Dallas TX 75219
Tel (972) 629-4301 SIC 6331

■ **MGA INSURANCE CO INC** p 958
3333 Lee Pkwy, Dallas TX 75219
Tel (972) 629-4301 SIC 6331

■ **REPUBLIC COMPANIES INC** p 1225
5525 Lyndon B Johnson Fwy, Dallas TX 75240
Tel (972) 788-6001 SIC 6321 6311 6331

REPUBLIC INSURANCE CO INC p 1225
5525 Lyndon B Johnson Fwy, Dallas TX 75240
Tel (972) 788-6001 SIC 6331

■ **REPUBLIC UNDERWRITERS INSURANCE CO** p 1226
5525 Lbj Fwy, Dallas TX 75240
Tel (972) 788-6001 SIC 6331

■ **TRINITY UNIVERSAL INSURANCE CO** p 1482
12790 Merit Dr Ste 400, Dallas TX 75251
Tel (312) 661-4930 SIC 6331

▲ **AMERICAN NATIONAL INSURANCE CO INC** p 77
1 Moody Plz Fl 18, Galveston TX 77550
Tel (409) 763-4661
SIC 6351 6311 6321 6324 6331

■ **AIG LIFE HOLDINGS INC** p 38
2929 Allen Pkwy, Houston TX 77019
Tel (713) 522-1111
SIC 6311 6321 6331 6141 6162 6153

HCC INSURANCE HOLDINGS INC p 672
13403 Northwest Fwy, Houston TX 77040
Tel (713) 690-7300 SIC 6311 6321 6331

HIGHLANDS INSURANCE GROUP INC p 691
10370 Richmond Ave, Houston TX 77042
Tel (713) 952-0665 SIC 6331 6351

HOUSTON CASUALTY CO p 712
13403 Northwest Fwy, Houston TX 77040
Tel (713) 462-1000 SIC 6331

HOUSTON INTERNATIONAL INSURANCE GROUP LTD p 712
800 Gessner Rd Ste 600, Houston TX 77024
Tel (713) 935-4800 SIC 6331

■ **ALLSTATE TEXAS LLOYDS** p 58
8711 Freeport Pkwy, Irving TX 75063
Tel (847) 402-3029 SIC 6331

■ **ASSOCIATES CORP OF NORTH AMERICA** p 121
250 E John Carpenter Fwy, Irving TX 75062
Tel (972) 652-4000
SIC 6141 6153 6159 6311 6321 6331

■ **UNION STANDARD INSURANCE GROUP LLC** p 1505
222 Las Colinas Blvd W # 1300, Irving TX 75039
Tel (972) 719-2400 SIC 6331

IRONSHORE SPECIALTY INSURANCE CO p 765
2850 Lake Vista Dr # 150, Lewisville TX 75067
Tel (646) 826-6600 SIC 6331

■ **ATLANTIC AVIATION CORP** p 125
6652 Pinecrest Dr Ste 300, Plano TX 75024
Tel (972) 905-2500
SIC 4581 5088 5172 6331 6159 4522

ARGO GROUP US INC p 107
10101 Reunion Pl Ste 500, San Antonio TX 78216
Tel (210) 321-8400 SIC 6331

ARGONAUT INSURANCE CO INC p 107
10101 Reunion Pl Ste 500, San Antonio TX 78216
Tel (210) 321-8400 SIC 6331

UNITED SERVICES AUTOMOBILE ASSOCIATION p 1511
9800 Fredericksburg Rd, San Antonio TX 78288
Tel (210) 498-2211 SIC 6331 6311 6351

USAA GENERAL AGENCY INC p 1534
9800 Fredericksburg Rd, San Antonio TX 78288
Tel (210) 456-1800 SIC 6331 6321

USAA INSURANCE AGENCY INC p 1534
9800 Fredericksburg Rd B-2e, San Antonio TX 78288
Tel (210) 498-2211 SIC 6331 6321 8742

USAA LIFE INSURANCE CO p 1534
9800 Fredericksburg Rd, San Antonio TX 78288
Tel (210) 498-2211 SIC 6331 6311

■ **ALLY BANK** p 59
6985 S Union Park Ctr # 435, Midvale UT 84047
Tel (801) 790-5005
SIC 6153 6021 6311 6331 6162

BEAR RIVER MUTUAL INSURANCE CO p 165
778 E Winchester St, Salt Lake City UT 84107
Tel (801) 267-5000 SIC 6331 6411

WORKERS COMPENSATION FUND p 1624
100 W Towne Ridge Pkwy, Sandy UT 84070
Tel (385) 351-8000 SIC 6331

VERMONT MUTUAL INSURANCE CO p 1551
89 State St, Montpelier VT 05602
Tel (802) 223-2341 SIC 6331

■ **MT MANSFIELD CO INC** p 997
5781 Mountain Rd, Stowe VT 05672
Tel (802) 253-7311 SIC 6331 5812 5813

■ **BOAT AMERICA CORP** p 196
880 S Pickett St, Alexandria VA 22304
Tel (703) 823-0984 SIC 6331

■ **ESSEX INSURANCE CO** p 510
4521 Highwoods Pkwy, Glen Allen VA 23060
Tel (804) 273-1400 SIC 6331

▲ **MARKEL CORP** p 908
4521 Highwoods Pkwy, Glen Allen VA 23060
Tel (804) 747-0136 SIC 6331 6211

UNIGARD INC p 1503
2125 158th Ct Ne, Bellevue WA 98008
Tel (425) 641-4321 SIC 6321 6331

UNIGARD INSURANCE CO p 1503
15800 Northup Way, Bellevue WA 98008
Tel (425) 641-4321 SIC 6331

UNIGARD PACIFIC INSURANCE CO p 1503
15800 Northup Way, Bellevue WA 98008
Tel (425) 644-5236 SIC 6331 6411

MUTUAL OF ENUMCLAW INSURANCE CO p 1003
1460 Wells St, Enumclaw WA 98022
Tel (360) 825-2591 SIC 6331 6311

FIRST NATIONAL INSURANCE CO OF AMERICA p 548
4333 Rootland Ave Ne, Seattle WA 98185
Tel (206) 545-5000 SIC 6331

PEMCO MUTUAL INSURANCE CO p 1128
1300 Dexter Ave N, Seattle WA 98109
Tel (425) 712-7700 SIC 6331

SEABRIGHT HOLDINGS INC p 1296
1111 3rd Ave Ste 1450, Seattle WA 98101
Tel (206) 269-8500 SIC 6331

BRICKSTREET MUTUAL INSURANCE CO p 211
400 Quarrier St, Charleston WV 25301
Tel (304) 941-1000 SIC 6321 6331

SECURA INSURANCE A MUTUAL CO (INC) p 1298
2401 S Memorial Dr, Appleton WI 54915
Tel (920) 739-3161 SIC 6331

■ **AMERIPRISE BANK FSB** p 83
3500 Packerland Dr, De Pere WI 54115
Tel (920) 330-5835 SIC 6331

AMERICAN FAMILY MUTUAL INSURANCE CO INC p 72
6000 American Pkwy, Madison WI 53783
Tel (608) 249-2111 SIC 6331 6311

AMFAM INC p 85
6000 American Pkwy, Madison WI 53783
Tel (608) 249-2111 SIC 6331 6311 6141

CUNA MUTUAL GROUP p 401
5910 Mineral Point Rd, Madison WI 53705
Tel (608) 238-5851
SIC 6331 6311 6351 6411 7515

MIDVALE INDEMNITY CO p 966
6000 American Pkwy, Madison WI 53783
Tel (847) 320-2000 SIC 6331 8099

■ **PROGRESSIVE NORTHERN INSURANCE CO** p 1181
44 E Mifflin St, Madison WI 53703
Tel (440) 461-5000 SIC 6331

■ **CAPITOL INDEMNITY CORP** p 251
1600 Aspen Cmns Ste 400, Middleton WI 53562
Tel (608) 829-4200 SIC 6331 6351

■ **CAPITOL TRANSAMERICA CORP** p 251
1600 Aspen Cmns Ste 400, Middleton WI 53562
Tel (608) 829-4200 SIC 6331 6351

JEWELERS MUTUAL INSURANCE CO p 784
24 Jewelers Park Dr, Neenah WI 54956
Tel (800) 558-6411 SIC 6331

A ACUITY MUTUAL INSURANCE CO p 4
2800 S Taylor Dr, Sheboygan WI 53081
Tel (920) 458-9131 SIC 6411 6331

DAIRYLAND INSURANCE CO p 409
1800 Northpoint Dr, Stevens Point WI 54481
Tel (715) 346-6000 SIC 6331

SENTRY INSURANCE A MUTUAL CO p 1305
1800 Northpoint Dr, Stevens Point WI 54481
Tel (715) 346-6000
SIC 6331 6311 6411 6321

VIKING INSURANCE CO OF WISCONSIN p 1557
1800 Northpoint Dr, Stevens Point WI 54481
Tel (715) 346-6000 SIC 6331

QBE AMERICAS INC p 1194
1 General Dr, Sun Prairie WI 53596
Tel (608) 837-4440 SIC 6331

QBE INVESTMENTS (NORTH AMERICA) INC p 1194
1 General Dr, Sun Prairie WI 53596
Tel (608) 837-4440 SIC 6331

■ **FIDELITY & GUARANTY INSURANCE UNDERWRITERS INC** p 540
20800 Swenson Dr Ste 300, Waukesha WI 53186
Tel (414) 784-5530 SIC 6331

EMPLOYERS INSURANCE OF WAUSAU A MUTUAL CO p 494
2000 Westwood Dr, Wausau WI 54401
Tel (715) 845-5211 SIC 6331 6311

WAUSAU SERVICE CORP p 1583
2000 Westwood Dr, Wausau WI 54401
Tel (715) 845-5211 SIC 6331 6311

WEST BEND MUTUAL INSURANCE CO p 1593
1900 S 18th Ave, West Bend WI 53095
Tel (262) 334-5571 SIC 6331

SIC 6351 Surety Insurance Carriers

▲ **PROASSURANCE CORP** p 1178
100 Brookwood Pl Ste 500, Birmingham AL 35209
Tel (205) 877-4400 SIC 6351 6321

PROTECTIVE LIFE CORP p 1185
2801 Highway 280 S Ofc, Birmingham AL 35223
Tel (205) 268-1000
SIC 6311 6321 6351 6411

▲ **TRIAD GUARANTY INC** p 1478
1900 Crestwood Blvd, Irondale AL 35210
Tel (205) 951-4012 SIC 6351

ALASKA NATIONAL INSURANCE CO p 45
7001 Jewel Lake Rd, Anchorage AK 99502
Tel (907) 248-2642 SIC 6331 6351

■ **MERCURY CASUALTY CO** p 945
555 W Imperial Hwy, Brea CA 92821
Tel (323) 937-1060 SIC 6331 6351

■ **FIRST AMERICAN HOME BUYERS PROTECTION CORP** p 544
8521 Fallbrook Ave # 340, Canoga Park CA 91304
Tel (818) 781-5050 SIC 6351

CAP-MPT p 248
333 S Hope St Fl 8, Los Angeles CA 90071
Tel (213) 473-8600 SIC 6351

JOHN HANCOCK LIFE INSURANCE CO (USA) p 788
865 S Figueroa St # 3320, Los Angeles CA 90017
Tel (213) 689-0813
SIC 7389 6351 6371 6321

▲ **KB HOME** p 806
10990 Wilshire Blvd Fl 5, Los Angeles CA 90024
Tel (310) 231-4000 SIC 1531 6351 6162

FIREMANS FUND INSURANCE CO p 543
777 San Marin Dr Ste 2160, Novato CA 94945
Tel (415) 899-2000 SIC 6331 6351 6321

ASSOCIATED INDEMNITY CORP p 120
1465 N Mcdowell Blvd # 100, Petaluma CA 94954
Tel (415) 899-2000
SIC 6311 6321 6331 6351

NATIONAL SURETY CORP p 1016
1465 N Mcdowell Blvd # 100, Petaluma CA 94954
Tel (415) 899-2000 *SIC* 6351

■ MENLO WORLDWIDE FORWARDING INC p 943
1 Lagoon Dr Ste 400, Redwood City CA 94065
Tel (650) 596-9600
SIC 4513 4215 4522 4731 6159 6351

▲ FIRST AMERICAN FINANCIAL CORP p 544
1 First American Way, Santa Ana CA 92707
Tel (714) 250-3000 *SIC* 6361 6351

HOME BUYERS WARRANTY CORP p 703
10375 E Harvard Ave # 100, Denver CO 80231
Tel (720) 747-6000 *SIC* 6351 1531

▲ CIGNA CORP p 306
900 Cottage Grove Rd, Bloomfield CT 06002
Tel (860) 226-6000
SIC 6324 6311 6351 6321

▲ W R BERKLEY CORP p 1569
475 Steamboat Rd Fl 1, Greenwich CT 06830
Tel (203) 629-3000
SIC 6331 6321 6351 6311

■ CHARTER OAK FIRE INSURANCE CO p 291
1 Tower Sq, Hartford CT 06183
Tel (860) 277-0111 *SIC* 6351 6331

▲ HARTFORD FINANCIAL SERVICES GROUP INC p 665
1 Hartford Plz, Hartford CT 06155
Tel (860) 547-5000
SIC 6331 6311 6351 6321

■ HARTFORD FIRE INSURANCE CO (INC) p 665
1 Hartford Plz, Hartford CT 06115
Tel (860) 547-5000
SIC 6411 6311 6351 7373

■ PHOENIX INSURANCE CO p 1145
1 Tower Sq, Hartford CT 06183
Tel (860) 277-0111 *SIC* 6351 6331

■ TRAVELERS CASUALTY AND SURETY CO p 1474
1 Tower Sq 8ms, Hartford CT 06183
Tel (860) 277-0111 *SIC* 6411 6351

■ TRAVELERS CASUALTY AND SURETY CO OF AMERICA p 1474
1 Tower Sq 2ms, Hartford CT 06183
Tel (860) 277-0111 *SIC* 6411 6351

■ TRAVELERS CASUALTY CO OF CONNECTICUT p 1474
1 Tower Sq, Hartford CT 06183
Tel (860) 277-0111 *SIC* 6331 6351 6321

■ TRAVELERS COMMERCIAL CASUALTY CO p 1474
1 Tower Sq, Hartford CT 06183
Tel (860) 277-0111 *SIC* 6351 6331

■ GENERAL REINSURANCE CORP p 602
120 Long Ridge Rd, Stamford CT 06902
Tel (203) 328-5000
SIC 6331 6351 6411 6321

▲ NAVIGATORS GROUP INC p 1020
400 Atlantic St Fl 8, Stamford CT 06901
Tel (203) 905-6090 *SIC* 6331 6351

XL AMERICA INC p 1632
70 Seaview Ave Ste 7, Stamford CT 06902
Tel (203) 964-5200 *SIC* 6411 6321 6351

XL GLOBAL SERVICES INC p 1632
70 Seaview Ave Ste 7, Stamford CT 06902
Tel (203) 964-5200 *SIC* 6331 6282 6351

AAA CLUB ALLIANCE INC p 7
1 River Pl, Wilmington DE 19801
Tel (302) 299-4700
SIC 8699 6331 6351 6512 4724

HERD ENTERPRISES INC p 685
3500 N 28th Ter, Hollywood FL 33020
Tel (954) 920-9774 *SIC* 6351

■ AMERICAN HERITAGE LIFE INSURANCE CO INC p 74
1776 Amercn Heritg Lf Dr, Jacksonville FL 32224
Tel (904) 992-1776 *SIC* 6321 6311 6351

■ AMERICAN HERITAGE LIFE INVESTMENT CORP p 74
1776 Amercn Heritg Lf Dr, Jacksonville FL 32224
Tel (904) 992-1776
SIC 6311 6321 6351 7374

■ AMERICAN BANKERS INSURANCE GROUP INC p 68
11222 Quail Roost Dr, Miami FL 33157
Tel (305) 253-2244
SIC 6331 6311 6351 6321 6324

CROSS COUNTRY HOME HOLDINGS INC p 393
1625 Nw 136th Ave Ste 200, Sunrise FL 33323
Tel (954) 835-1900 *SIC* 6351

CROSS COUNTRY HOME SERVICES INC p 393
1625 Nw 136th Ave Ste 200, Sunrise FL 33323
Tel (954) 835-1900 *SIC* 6351

MAG MUTUAL INSURANCE AGENCY LLC p 895
3525 Piedmont Rd Ne 8-600, Atlanta GA 30305
Tel (404) 842-5600 *SIC* 6351 6411

BENEFICIAL CO LLC p 172
1421 W Shure Dr Ste 100, Arlington Heights IL 60004
Tel (708) 453-6502
SIC 6141 6351 6162 6021 6552 6311

ISMIE MUTUAL INSURANCE CO p 767
20 N Michigan Ave Ste 700, Chicago IL 60602
Tel (312) 782-2749 *SIC* 6351

▲ OLD REPUBLIC INTERNATIONAL CORP p 1081
307 N Michigan Ave, Chicago IL 60601
Tel (312) 346-8100 *SIC* 6351

VIRGINIA SURETY CO INC p 1560
175 W Jackson Blvd Fl 11, Chicago IL 60604
Tel (312) 356-3000 *SIC* 6351 6399

WARRANTY GROUP INC p 1576
175 W Jackson Blvd Fl 11, Chicago IL 60604
Tel (312) 356-3000 *SIC* 6351 6399

■ EVANSTON INSURANCE CO p 513
10 Parkway N Ste 100, Deerfield IL 60015
Tel (847) 572-6000 *SIC* 6351 6331

■ MARKEL MIDWEST p 908
10 Parkway N Ste 100, Deerfield IL 60015
Tel (847) 572-6000 *SIC* 6351

HSBC NORTH AMERICA HOLDINGS INC p 715
452 5th Ave 7, Lake Forest IL 60045
Tel (224) 544-4400 *SIC* 6351

AON CONSULTING WORLDWIDE INC p 95
100 Half Day Rd 2, Lincolnshire IL 60069
Tel (312) 381-4800
SIC 6311 6321 6331 8742 6411 6351

▲ ALLSTATE CORP p 58
2775 Sanders Rd, Northbrook IL 60062
Tel (847) 402-5000
SIC 6411 6351 6311 6371

HOUSEHOLD FINANCE CORP p 711
2700 Sanders Rd, Prospect Heights IL 60070
Tel (847) 790-1590
SIC 6141 6162 6351 6153 6159 6311

HSBC INVESTMENTS (NORTH AMERICA) INC p 715
2700 Sanders Rd, Prospect Heights IL 60070
Tel (847) 564-5000
SIC 6141 7389 6351 6159 6162 6311

XL SPECIALTY INSURANCE CO p 1632
10 N Martingale Rd # 220, Schaumburg IL 60173
Tel (847) 517-2990 *SIC* 6351 6331

ZFUS SERVICES LLC p 1643
1299 Zurich Way, Schaumburg IL 60196
Tel (847) 605-6000 *SIC* 6351

ALLIED SOLUTIONS LLC p 57
1320 City Center Dr # 300, Carmel IN 46032
Tel (317) 706-7600 *SIC* 6321 6351 6159

▲ ONE MAIN FINANCIAL SERVICES p 1086
601 Nw 2nd St, Evansville IN 47708
Tel (800) 961-5577 *SIC* 6141 6351 6331

■ SPRINGLEAF FINANCE INC p 1361
601 Nw 2nd St, Evansville IN 47708
Tel (812) 424-8031
SIC 6153 6351 6331 7389

■ MEDICAL PROTECTIVE CO p 937
5814 Reed Rd, Fort Wayne IN 46835
Tel (260) 485-9622 *SIC* 6351 6411

■ MEDPRO GROUP INC p 938
5814 Reed Rd, Fort Wayne IN 46835
Tel (800) 463-3776 *SIC* 6351

AMERICAN UNITED MUTUAL INSURANCE HOLDING CO p 81
1 American Sq, Indianapolis IN 46282
Tel (317) 285-1877
SIC 6211 6311 6371 6351 6331

AEGON US HOLDING CORP p 29
4333 Edgewood Rd Ne, Cedar Rapids IA 52499
Tel (319) 355-8511
SIC 6311 6321 6351 6159

■ EMC INSURANCE GROUP INC p 490
717 Mulberry St, Des Moines IA 50309
Tel (515) 345-2902 *SIC* 6331 6351 6321

WELLS FARGO FINANCIAL CA INC p 1590
800 Walnut St, Des Moines IA 50309
Tel (515) 557-7401
SIC 6141 6153 6351 6159 6531 6021

■ WELLS FARGO FINANCIAL SECURITY SERVICES INC p 1590
800 Walnut St, Des Moines IA 50309
Tel (515) 243-2131
SIC 6141 6153 6351 6159 7374 6021

MERCHANTS BONDING CO (MUTUAL) p 944
6700 Westown Pkwy, West Des Moines IA 50266
Tel (515) 243-8171 *SIC* 6351

ALTRADIUS CREDIT INSURANCE INC p 62
230 Schilling Cir Ste 240, Hunt Valley MD 21031
Tel (410) 568-3850 *SIC* 6351

MEDICAL MUTUAL LIABILITY INSURANCE SOCIETY OF MARYLAND p 937
225 International Cir # 300, Hunt Valley MD 21030
Tel (410) 785-0050 *SIC* 6351

EULER HERMES ACI HOLDING INC p 512
800 Red Brook Blvd # 400, Owings Mills MD 21117
Tel (410) 753-0753 *SIC* 7322 6351 6719

EULER HERMES NORTH AMERICA INSURANCE CO p 512
800 Red Brook Blvd, Owings Mills MD 21117
Tel (410) 753-0753 *SIC* 6351 6411

JOHN HANCOCK FINANCIAL SERVICES INC p 788
200 Clarendon St, Boston MA 02116
Tel (617) 572-6000
SIC 6311 6351 6411 6371 6321

LIBERTY MUTUAL GROUP INC p 862
175 Berkeley St, Boston MA 02116
Tel (617) 357-9500
SIC 6331 6321 6351 7389

LIBERTY MUTUAL HOLDING CO INC p 862
175 Berkeley St, Boston MA 02116
Tel (617) 357-9500 *SIC* 6331 6351 7389

LIBERTY MUTUAL INSURANCE CO p 862
175 Berkeley St, Boston MA 02116
Tel (617) 357-9500
SIC 6331 6321 6351 7389

LMHC MASSACHUSETTS HOLDINGS INC p 872
175 Berkeley St, Boston MA 02116
Tel (617) 357-9500
SIC 6331 6321 6351 7389

■ HANOVER INSURANCE CO p 658
440 Lincoln St, Worcester MA 01653
Tel (508) 853-7200 *SIC* 6331 6351

■ OPUS INVESTMENT MANAGEMENT INC p 1091
440 Lincoln St, Worcester MA 01653
Tel (508) 855-1000
SIC 6311 6321 6324 6351 6722

SPECTRUM HEALTH HOSPITALS p 1357
100 Michigan St Ne Mc-498, Grand Rapids MI 49503
Tel (616) 391-1774
SIC 8062 6351 8082 6331

■ HOMESERVICES OF AMERICA INC p 704
333 S 7th St Fl 27, Minneapolis MN 55402
Tel (612) 336-5900 *SIC* 6351 6361

■ ST PAUL FIRE AND MARINE INSURANCE CO p 1372
385 Washington St, Saint Paul MN 55102
Tel (651) 221-7911
SIC 6331 6351 6321 6411

CATHOLIC MUTUAL RELIEF SOCIETY OF AMERICA p 267
10843 Old Mill Rd, Omaha NE 68154
Tel (402) 551-8765 *SIC* 6351

■ SELECTIVE INSURANCE CO OF AMERICA p 1302
40 Wantage Ave, Branchville NJ 07890
Tel (973) 948-3000 *SIC* 6411 6351

ARCH INSURANCE GROUP INC p 104
Harborside 3 210 Hudson S, Jersey City NJ 07311
Tel (201) 743-4000 *SIC* 6331 6351

ABSCO LTD CORP p 12
2740 Rte 10 E Ste 205, Morris Plains NJ 07950
Tel (973) 402-2148
SIC 6351 6411 6211 6282

CRUM & FORSTER HOLDINGS CORP p 396
305 Madison Ave, Morristown NJ 07960
Tel (973) 490-6600 *SIC* 6331 6321 6351

PROSIGHT SPECIALTY INSURANCE GROUP INC p 1184
412 Mount Kemble Ave 300c, Morristown NJ 07960
Tel (973) 532-1900 *SIC* 6351 6331

INTERNATIONAL FIDELITY INSURANCE CO p 755
1111 Raymond Blvd Fl 20, Newark NJ 07102
Tel (973) 286-7911 *SIC* 6351

WESTERN WORLD INSURANCE CO p 1600
300 Kimball Dr Ste 500, Parsippany NJ 07054
Tel (201) 847-8600 *SIC* 6351

■ CONTINENTAL CORP p 363
111 8th Ave, New York NY 10011
Tel (212) 440-3000
SIC 6331 6351 6321 6159 8741 6411

ENDURANCE ASSURANCE CORP p 496
750 3rd Ave Fl 1819, New York NY 10017
Tel (212) 471-2800 *SIC* 6351

FINANCIAL GUARANTY INSURANCE CO p 542
521 5th Ave Fl 15, New York NY 10175
Tel (212) 312-3000 *SIC* 6351

FINANCIAL SECURITY ASSURANCE HOLDINGS LTD p 542
31 W 52nd St, New York NY 10019
Tel (212) 826-0100 *SIC* 6351

FINANCIAL SECURITY ASSURANCE INTERNATIONAL INC p 542
350 Park Ave Fl 13, New York NY 10022
Tel (212) 826-0100 *SIC* 6351

LAZARD ASSET MANAGEMENT LLC p 848
30 Rockefeller Plz Fl 57, New York NY 10112
Tel (212) 632-1890 *SIC* 6351

■ MARSH USA INC p 911
1166 Ave Of The Americas, New York NY 10036
Tel (212) 345-6000
SIC 6411 6331 6351 6282

PMI GROUP INC p 1157
350 5th Ave, New York NY 10118
Tel (925) 658-7878 *SIC* 6351 6211

PMI MORTGAGE INSURANCE CO p 1157
350 5th Ave, New York NY 10118
Tel (925) 658-7878 *SIC* 6351 6331

▲ TRAVELERS COMPANIES INC p 1474
485 Lexington Ave, New York NY 10017
Tel (917) 778-6000 *SIC* 6331 6351 6321

▲ MBIA INC p 925
1 Manhattanville Rd # 301, Purchase NY 10577
Tel (914) 273-4545 *SIC* 6351

▲ INVESTORS TITLE CO p 762
121 N Columbia St, Chapel Hill NC 27514
Tel (919) 968-2200 *SIC* 6361 6351

■ UNITED GUARANTY CORP p 1509
230 N Elm St Ste 1200, Greensboro NC 27401
Tel (336) 373-0232 *SIC* 6351

■ UNITED GUARANTY INSURANCE CO p 1509
230 N Elm St Ste 1200, Greensboro NC 27401
Tel (336) 373-0232 *SIC* 6351

■ UNITED GUARANTY RESIDENTIAL INSURANCE CO p 1509
230 N Elm St, Greensboro NC 27401
Tel (336) 373-0232 *SIC* 6351

■ GENWORTH MORTGAGE INSURANCE CORP p 605
8325 Six Forks Rd, Raleigh NC 27615
Tel (919) 846-4100 *SIC* 6351 8741

■ REPUBLIC MORTGAGE INSURANCE CO INC p 1225
101 N Cherry St Ste 101, Winston Salem NC 27101
Tel (336) 661-0015 *SIC* 6351

■ DRIVE INSURANCE HOLDINGS INC p 456
6300 Wilson Mills Rd, Cleveland OH 44143
Tel (440) 461-5000 *SIC* 6331 6351

AMERICAN COMMERCE INSURANCE CO p 70
3590 Twin Creeks Dr, Columbus OH 43204
Tel (614) 272-6951 *SIC* 6331 6351

▲ STATE AUTOMOBILE MUTUAL INSURANCE CO INC p 1380
518 E Broad St, Columbus OH 43215
Tel (614) 464-5000 *SIC* 6331 6411 6351

■ PROGRESSIVE CASUALTY INSURANCE CO p 1181
6300 Wilson Mills Rd, Mayfield Village OH 44143
Tel (440) 461-5000
SIC 6331 6351 6411 6321

▲ PROGRESSIVE CORP p 1181
6300 Wilson Mills Rd, Mayfield Village OH 44143
Tel (440) 461-5000 *SIC* 6331 6351

OKLAHOMA FARM BUREAU MUTUAL INSURANCE CO p 1079
2501 N Stiles Ave, Oklahoma City OK 73105
Tel (405) 523-2300 *SIC* 6331 6351

GLOBAL INDEMNITY GROUP INC p 616
3 Bala Plz Ste 300, Bala Cynwyd PA 19004
Tel (610) 664-1500 *SIC* 6351

EMPLOYEE BENEFIT TR OF EASTERN PA p 494
6 Danforth Dr, Easton PA 18045
Tel (610) 515-6412 *SIC* 6351 8699 6321

ACE AMERICAN INSURANCE CO p 16
436 Walnut St, Philadelphia PA 19106
Tel (215) 640-1000 *SIC* 6321 6331 6351

ACE PROPERTY AND CASUALTY INSURANCE CO p 16
2 Liberty Pl 2 Liberty Place, Philadelphia PA 19102
Tel (215) 761-1000 *SIC* 6321 6331 6351

ACE USA INC p 16
436 Walnut St, Philadelphia PA 19106
Tel (215) 923-5352 *SIC* 6411 6321 6351

CENTURY INDEMNITY CO p 282
1601 Chestnut St, Philadelphia PA 19192
Tel (215) 761-1000 *SIC* 6321 6331 6351

RADIAN ASSET ASSURANCE INC p 1204
1601 Market St Fl 5, Philadelphia PA 19103
Tel (212) 983-3100 *SIC* 6351

▲ RADIAN GROUP INC p 1204
1601 Market St Fl 12, Philadelphia PA 19103
Tel (215) 231-1000 *SIC* 6351

■ RADIAN GUARANTY INC p 1204
1601 Market St Fl 5, Philadelphia PA 19103
Tel (215) 564-6600 *SIC* 6351

COOPERATIVA DE SEGUROS MULTIPLES DE PUERTO RICO p 367
Expreso Ls America Y Mira, San Juan PR 00927
Tel (787) 758-8585 *SIC* 6331 6351

■ METROPOLITAN GROUP PROPERTIES & CASUALTY p 956
700 Quaker Ln, Warwick RI 02886
Tel (401) 827-2400 *SIC* 6331 6351

■ SUREWEST FINANCIAL CORP p 1408
101 S Phillips Ave, Sioux Falls SD 57104
Tel (605) 336-0850 *SIC* 6351

■ WESTERN SURETY CO p 1600
101 S Reid St Ste 300, Sioux Falls SD 57103
Tel (605) 336-0850 *SIC* 6351

■ CLAYTON HOMES INC p 323
5000 Clayton Rd, Maryville TN 37804
Tel (865) 380-3000
SIC 2451 5271 6141 6351 6331

■ AMERICAN HOME SHIELD CORP p 74
889 Ridge Lake Blvd, Memphis TN 38120
Tel (901) 597-8000 *SIC* 6351

■ AMERICAN HOME SHIELD INSPECTION SERVICES INC p 74
860 Ridge Lake Blvd # 101, Memphis TN 38120
Tel (901) 537-8000 *SIC* 6351

■ SERVICEMASTER CONSUMER SERVICES LIMITED PARTNERSHIP p 1307
889 Ridge Lake Blvd Fl 2, Memphis TN 38120
Tel (901) 597-7574 *SIC* 0782 6351 7349

TI EMPLOYEES HEALTH BENEFIT TRUST p 1452
7839 Churchill Way, Dallas TX 75251
Tel (972) 995-3333 *SIC* 6351

▲ AMERICAN NATIONAL INSURANCE CO INC p 77
1 Moody Plz Fl 18, Galveston TX 77550
Tel (409) 763-4661
SIC 6351 6311 6321 6324 6331

HIGHLANDS INSURANCE GROUP INC p 691
10370 Richmond Ave, Houston TX 77042
Tel (713) 952-0665 *SIC* 6331 6351

AMERICAN HOMESTAR CORP p 74
2450 S Shore Blvd Ste 300, League City TX 77573
Tel (281) 334-9700
SIC 2451 4213 5271 6351 6515

UNITED SERVICES AUTOMOBILE ASSOCIATION p 1511
9800 Fredericksburg Rd, San Antonio TX 78288
Tel (210) 498-2211 *SIC* 6331 6311 6351

COLONY INSURANCE CO p 338
8720 Stony Point Pkwy # 400, Richmond VA 23235
Tel (804) 560-2000 *SIC* 6351

▲ GENWORTH FINANCIAL INC p 605
6620 W Broad St Ste 270, Richmond VA 23230
Tel (804) 281-6000 *SIC* 6311 6371 6351

PARKER SMITH & FEEK INC p 1116
2233 112th Ave Ne, Bellevue WA 98004
Tel (425) 709-3600 *SIC* 6411 6351 8748

SAFECO CORP p 1266
1001 4th Ave Ste 800, Seattle WA 98185
Tel (206) 545-5000
SIC 6411 6311 6321 6324 6351

CUNA MUTUAL GROUP p 401
5910 Mineral Point Rd, Madison WI 53705
Tel (608) 238-5851
SIC 6331 6311 6351 6411 7515

■ CAPITOL INDEMNITY CORP p 251
1600 Aspen Cmns Ste 400, Middleton WI 53562
Tel (608) 829-4200 *SIC* 6331 6351

■ CAPITOL TRANSAMERICA CORP p 251
1600 Aspen Cmns Ste 400, Middleton WI 53562
Tel (608) 829-4200 *SIC* 6331 6351

■ M G I C MORTGAGE INSURANCE CORP p 889
250 E Kilbourn Ave, Milwaukee WI 53202
Tel (414) 347-6480 *SIC* 6351

▲ MGIC INVESTMENT CORP p 958
250 E Kilbourn Ave, Milwaukee WI 53202
Tel (414) 347-6480 *SIC* 6351 6411

■ MORTGAGE GUARANTY INSURANCE CORP p 991
270 E Kilbourn Ave, Milwaukee WI 53202
Tel (414) 347-6480 *SIC* 6351

■ MORTGAGE GUARANTY REINSURANCE CORP p 991
250 E Kilbourn Ave 270, Milwaukee WI 53202
Tel (414) 347-6480 *SIC* 6351

SIC 6361 Title Insurance

PIONEER TITLE AGENCY INC p 1151
580 E Wilcox Dr, Sierra Vista AZ 85635
Tel (520) 459-4100 *SIC* 6361 6163

MOTHER LODE HOLDING CO p 992
189 Fulweiler Ave, Auburn CA 95603
Tel (530) 887-2410 *SIC* 6361 6531 7389

PLACER TITLE CO p 1153
189 Fulweiler Ave, Auburn CA 95603
Tel (530) 887-2410 *SIC* 6361

■ LAWYERS TITLE CO p 848
7530 N Glenoaks Blvd, Burbank CA 91504
Tel (818) 767-0425 *SIC* 6361 6531

■ COUNTRYWIDE FINANCIAL CORP p 375
4500 Park Granada, Calabasas CA 91302
Tel (818) 225-3000
SIC 6162 6211 6361 6411 6163 6799

■ FIRST AMERICAN TITLE GUARANTY CO p 544
1355 Willow Way Ste 100, Concord CA 94520
Tel (925) 356-7000 *SIC* 6361 6531

■ NORTH AMERICAN ASSET DEVELOPMENT CORP p 1049
1855 Gateway Blvd Ste 650, Concord CA 94520
Tel (925) 935-5599 *SIC* 6361 6531

■ NORTH AMERICAN TITLE CO INC p 1050
1855 Gateway Blvd Ste 600, Concord CA 94520
Tel (925) 935-5599 *SIC* 6361 6531

LERETA LLC p 857
1123 Park View Dr, Covina CA 91724
Tel (626) 543-1765 *SIC* 6211 6541 6361

■ OLD REPUBLIC TITLE CO p 1081
101 N Brand Blvd Ste 1400, Glendale CA 91203
Tel (818) 240-1936 *SIC* 6361

■ STEWART TITLE OF CALIFORNIA INC p 1389
525 N Brand Blvd Ste 100, Glendale CA 91203
Tel (818) 291-9145 *SIC* 6361

WFG NATIONAL TITLE INSURANCE CO p 1603
700 N Brand Blvd Ste 1100, Glendale CA 91203
Tel (818) 476-4000 *SIC* 6361

■ FIDELITY NATIONAL TITLE INSURANCE CO p 541
3220 El Camino Real, Irvine CA 92602
Tel (949) 622-4600
SIC 6361 8741 6541 6531

■ EXPERIENCE 1 INC p 520
5000 Birch St Ste 300, Newport Beach CA 92660
Tel (949) 475-3752 *SIC* 6361 6531

■ TICOR TITLE CO OF CALIFORNIA p 1452
1500 Quail St Ste 300, Newport Beach CA 92660
Tel (714) 289-7100 *SIC* 6361

■ TICOR TITLE INSURANCE CO INC p 1452
131 N El Molino Ave, Pasadena CA 91101
Tel (616) 302-3121 *SIC* 6361

■ OLD REPUBLIC TITLE CO p 1081
275 Battery St Ste 1500, San Francisco CA 94111
Tel (415) 421-3500 *SIC* 6361 6531

■ OLD REPUBLIC TITLE HOLDING CO INC p 1081
275 Battery St Ste 1500, San Francisco CA 94111
Tel (415) 421-3500 *SIC* 6361 6531 5045

▲ FIRST AMERICAN FINANCIAL CORP p 544
1 First American Way, Santa Ana CA 92707
Tel (714) 250-3000 *SIC* 6361 6351

FIRST AMERICAN MORTGAGE SERVICES p 544
3 First American Way, Santa Ana CA 92707
Tel (714) 250-4210 *SIC* 6361

■ FIRST AMERICAN TITLE CO INC p 544
1 First American Way, Santa Ana CA 92707
Tel (505) 881-3300 *SIC* 6361

■ FIRST AMERICAN TITLE INSURANCE CO p 544
1 First American Way, Santa Ana CA 92707
Tel (800) 854-3643 *SIC* 6361

ORANGE COAST TITLE CO OF SOUTHERN CALIFORNIA p 1092
640 N Tustin Ave Ste 106, Santa Ana CA 92705
Tel (714) 558-2836 *SIC* 7389 6361 6541

■ CHICAGO TITLE INSURANCE CO p 297
4050 Calle Real, Santa Barbara CA 93110
Tel (805) 565-6900 *SIC* 6361

ALLIANT NATIONAL TITLE INSURANCE CO INC p 55
1831 Lefthand Cir Ste G, Longmont CO 80501
Tel (303) 682-9800 *SIC* 6361

ODYSSEY REINSURANCE CO p 1075
300 Stamford Pl Ste 700, Stamford CT 06902
Tel (203) 965-0004
SIC 6411 6361 6331 6324 6311

■ BLACK KNIGHT FINANCIAL SERVICES LLC p 187
601 Riverside Ave, Jacksonville FL 32204
Tel (904) 854-8100
SIC 6361 6331 6531 8741

■ BLACK KNIGHT HOLDINGS INC p 187
601 Riverside Ave, Jacksonville FL 32204
Tel (904) 854-8100
SIC 6361 6331 6531 8741

■ CHICAGO TITLE INSURANCE CO p 297
601 Riverside Ave, Jacksonville FL 32204
Tel (904) 854-8100 *SIC* 6361

■ FIDELITY NATIONAL EUROPE LLC p 540
601 Riverside Ave Fl 4, Jacksonville FL 32204
Tel (904) 854-8100 *SIC* 6361

▲ FIDELITY NATIONAL FINANCIAL INC p 540
601 Riverside Ave Fl 4, Jacksonville FL 32204
Tel (904) 854-8100
SIC 6361 6331 6531 8741 3699

■ LAWYERS TITLE INSURANCE CORP p 848
601 Riverside Ave, Jacksonville FL 32204
Tel (888) 866-3684 *SIC* 6361 7372 5734

■ SERVICELINK HOLDINGS LLC p 1307
601 Riverside Ave Bldg 5, Jacksonville FL 32204
Tel (904) 854-8100
SIC 6361 6331 6531 8741 3699

■ LENNAR FINANCIAL SERVICES LLC p 855
700 Nw 107th Ave Ste 400, Miami FL 33172
Tel (305) 559-4000
SIC 6162 6153 6361 6411 7382

■ NORTH AMERICAN TITLE GROUP INC p 1050
700 Nw 107th Ave Ste 300, Miami FL 33172
Tel (305) 552-1102 *SIC* 6361

ATTORNEYS TITLE INSURANCE FUND INC p 129
6545 Corp Center Blvd # 100, Orlando FL 32822
Tel (407) 240-3863 *SIC* 6361

TITLE GUARANTY OF HAWAII INC p 1456
235 Queen St Fl 2nd, Honolulu HI 96813
Tel (808) 533-6261 *SIC* 6361

FUTURE FOUNDATION INC p 585
380 E Parkcenter Blvd # 230, Boise ID 83706
Tel (208) 336-0150 *SIC* 3354 5013 6361

■ CHICAGO TITLE AND TRUST CO p 297
10 S La Salle St Ste 3100, Chicago IL 60603
Tel (312) 223-2000 *SIC* 6361

■ CHICAGO TITLE INSURANCE CO p 297
10 S Lasalle St Ste 2850, Chicago IL 60603
Tel (312) 223-2402 *SIC* 6411 6361

NATIONAL EQUITY TITLE AGENCY INC p 1011
415 N La Salle Dr Ste 202, Chicago IL 60654
Tel (312) 782-4290 *SIC* 6361

■ OLD REPUBLIC MORTGAGE GUARANTEE GROUP INC p 1081
307 N Michigan Ave # 1400, Chicago IL 60601
Tel (312) 346-8100 *SIC* 6361

■ OLD REPUBLIC SECURITY HOLDINGS INC p 1081
307 N Michigan Ave # 1400, Chicago IL 60601
Tel (312) 346-8100 *SIC* 6411 6361

■ OLD REPUBLIC SURETY GROUP INC p 1081
307 N Michigan Ave # 1400, Chicago IL 60601
Tel (312) 346-8100 *SIC* 6411 6361

■ OLD REPUBLIC TITLE INSURANCE GROUP INC (DEL) p 1081
307 N Michigan Ave # 1400, Chicago IL 60601
Tel (312) 346-8100 *SIC* 6361 6531

PROFESSIONAL NATIONAL TITLE NETWORK p 1180
70 W Madison St Ste 1600, Chicago IL 60602
Tel (312) 621-1105 *SIC* 6361

NETCO INC (IL) p 1027
7501 Lemont Rd Ste 305, Woodridge IL 60517
Tel (312) 782-4290 *SIC* 6361

MERIDIAN TITLE CORP p 949
202 S Michigan St Ste 300, South Bend IN 46601
Tel (574) 232-5845 *SIC* 6361

■ ALLEGAN METROPOLITAN TITLE AGENCY p 52
400 Water St Ste 100, Rochester MI 48307
Tel (248) 656-8686 *SIC* 6361

■ HOMESERVICES OF AMERICA INC p 704
333 S 7th St Fl 27, Minneapolis MN 55402
Tel (612) 336-5900 *SIC* 6351 6361

■ OLD REPUBLIC NATIONAL TITLE HOLDING CO p 1081
400 2nd Ave S, Minneapolis MN 55401
Tel (612) 371-1111 *SIC* 6361

■ OLD REPUBLIC NATIONAL TITLE INSURANCE CO p 1081
400 2nd Ave S, Minneapolis MN 55401
Tel (612) 371-1111 *SIC* 6361

SURETY TITLE CO LLC p 1408
11 Eves Dr Ste 150, Marlton NJ 08053
Tel (856) 988-8900 *SIC* 6361 6541

▲ HOVNANIAN ENTERPRISES INC p 713
110 W Front St, Red Bank NJ 07701
Tel (732) 747-7800
SIC 1521 1531 1522 6162 6361

■ FIDELITY NATIONAL TITLE INSURANCE CO OF NEW YORK p 541
1 Pak Ave Ste 1402, New York NY 10016
Tel (904) 854-8100 *SIC* 6361

■ FIRST AMERICAN TITLE INSURANCE CO OF NEW YORK p 544
666 3rd Ave Fl 5, New York NY 10017
Tel (646) 487-5640 *SIC* 6361

■ STEWART TITLE INSURANCE CO p 1389
300 E 42nd St Fl 10, New York NY 10017
Tel (212) 922-0050 *SIC* 6361

■ TITLEVEST AGENCY OF NEW YORK INC p 1456
44 Wall St Fl 10, New York NY 10005
Tel (212) 757-5800 *SIC* 6361

▲ INVESTORS TITLE CO p 762
121 N Columbia St, Chapel Hill NC 27514
Tel (919) 968-2200 *SIC* 6361 6351

■ INVESTORS TITLE INSURANCE CO p 762
121 N Columbia St, Chapel Hill NC 27514
Tel (919) 968-2200 *SIC* 6361

■ MIDLAND TITLE SECURITY INC p 966
1111 Superior Ave E # 700, Cleveland OH 44114
Tel (216) 241-6045 *SIC* 6361

MORTGAGE INFORMATION SERVICES INC p 991
4877 Galaxy Pkwy Ste I, Cleveland OH 44128
Tel (216) 514-7480 *SIC* 6361 6531

WFG NATIONAL TITLE INSURANCE CO INC p 1603
12909 Sw 68th Pkwy # 350, Portland OR 97223
Tel (503) 387-3636 *SIC* 6361

WILLISTON FINANCIAL GROUP LLC p 1612
12909 Sw 68th Pkwy # 350, Portland OR 97223
Tel (503) 387-3636 *SIC* 6361

■ SERVICELINK NLS LLC p 1307
1400 Cherrington Pkwy, Moon Township PA 15108
Tel (800) 777-8759 *SIC* 6361

HANNA HOLDINGS INC p 658
1090 Freeport Rd Ste 1a, Pittsburgh PA 15238
Tel (412) 967-9000 *SIC* 6531 6162 6361

HYLANT GROUP p 724
8 Cadillac Dr Ste 230, Brentwood TN 37027
Tel (615) 732-6500 *SIC* 6361

INDEPENDENCE TITLE CO p 736
5900 Sheph Mount Cove Bld, Austin TX 78730
Tel (512) 372-8455 *SIC* 6361

PRONTO GENERAL AGENCY LTD p 1183
805 Media Luna St Ste 100, Brownsville TX 78520
Tel (956) 574-9787 *SIC* 6331 6361 7291

■ ALAMO TITLE HOLDING CO p 44
6200 Colleyville Blvd, Colleyville TX 76034
Tel (817) 428-6996 *SIC* 6361

■ STEWART TITLE NORTH TEXAS INC p 1389
15950 Dallas Pkwy Ste 100, Dallas TX 75248
Tel (972) 386-9898 *SIC* 6361 6541

■ TITLE RESOURCES GUARANTY CO p 1456
8111 L B Johnson Fwy 12 Ste 1200, Dallas TX 75251
Tel (972) 644-6500 *SIC* 6361

■ FIRST AMERICAN TITLE INSURANCE CO OF TEXAS p 544
1500 S Dairy Ashford Rd # 300, Houston TX 77077
Tel (281) 588-2200 *SIC* 6361

▲ STEWART INFORMATION SERVICES CORP p 1389
1980 Post Oak Blvd, Houston TX 77056
Tel (713) 625-8100 *SIC* 6361 8742 7389

■ STEWART TITLE CO p 1389
1980 Post Oak Blvd Ste 80, Houston TX 77056
Tel (713) 625-8100
SIC 6361 7389 8713 8742 6541

■ STEWART TITLE GUARANTY CO p 1389
1980 Post Oak Blvd Ste 61, Houston TX 77056
Tel (713) 625-8100 *SIC* 6361 6541

TEXAS AMERICAN TITLE CO p 1442
2000 Bering Dr Ste 900, Houston TX 77057
Tel (713) 988-9999 *SIC* 6361 8111

C-III CAPITAL PARTNERS LLC p 234
5221 N O Connor Blvd, Irving TX 75039
Tel (972) 868-5300
SIC 6519 6726 6361 6411

CAPITAL TITLE OF TEXAS LLC p 250
2400 Dallas Pkwy Ste 560, Plano TX 75093
Tel (972) 682-2700 *SIC* 6361

■ ALAMO TITLE CO p 44
18618 Tuscany Stone, San Antonio TX 78258
Tel (210) 490-1313 *SIC* 6361

■ ALAMO TITLE INSURANCE CO p 44
434 N Loop 1604 W # 2204, San Antonio TX 78232
Tel (210) 499-5872 *SIC* 6361

■ COMMONWEALTH LAND TITLE INSURANCE CO p 346
201 Cncourse Blvd Ste 200, Glen Allen VA 23059
Tel (904) 854-8100 *SIC* 6361

SIC 6371 Pension, Health & Welfare Funds

SELF-INSURED SCHOOLS OF CALIFORNIA p 1302
1300 17th St 5, Bakersfield CA 93301
Tel (661) 636-4000 *SIC* 6371

SCREEN ACTORS GUILD-PRODUCERS ADMINISTRATIVE CORP p 1294
3601 W Olive Ave Ste 200, Burbank CA 91505
Tel (818) 954-9400 *SIC* 6371

SOUTHERN CAL UNITED FOOD & COMMERCIAL WORKERS UNIONS & FOOD EMPLOYERS PENSION TRUST FUND p 1347
6425 Katella Ave, Cypress CA 90630
Tel (714) 220-2297 *SIC* 6371

DIRECTORS GUILD OF AMERICA - PRODUCER PENSION AND HEALTH PLANS p 442
5055 Wilshire Blvd # 600, Los Angeles CA 90036
Tel (323) 866-2200 *SIC* 6371

JOHN HANCOCK LIFE INSURANCE CO (USA) p 788
865 S Figueroa St # 3320, Los Angeles CA 90017
Tel (213) 689-0813
SIC 7389 6351 6371 6321

■ SUNAMERICA INC p 1401
1 Sun America Ctr Fl 38, Los Angeles CA 90067
Tel (310) 772-6000
SIC 6091 6311 6211 6282 6411 6371

TRANSAMERICA OCCIDENTAL LIFE INSURANCE CO p 1470
1150 S Olive St Fl 23, Los Angeles CA 90015
Tel (213) 742-2111
SIC 6311 6371 6321 6324 6799

PACIFIC LIFE INSURANCE CO p 1105
700 Newport Center Dr, Newport Beach CA 92660
Tel (949) 219-3011
SIC 6311 6371 6321 7359

PACIFIC LIFECORP p 1105
700 Newport Center Dr, Newport Beach CA 92660
Tel (949) 219-3011
SIC 6371 6311 6321 6035 8111

PACIFIC MUTUAL HOLDING CO p 1105
700 Newport Center Dr, Newport Beach CA 92660
Tel (949) 219-3011 *SIC* 6371 6311 6321

LOS ANGELES COUNTY EMPLOYEES RETIREMENT ASSOCIATION p 878
300 N Lake Ave Ste 720, Pasadena CA 91101
Tel (626) 564-6000 *SIC* 6371

CALIFORNIA PUBLIC EMPLOYEES RETIREMENT SYSTEM p 241
400 Q St, Sacramento CA 95811
Tel (916) 795-3000 *SIC* 6371 9441

MOTION PICTURE INDUSTRY HEALTH PLAN p 992
11365 Ventura Blvd, Studio City CA 91604
Tel (818) 769-0007 *SIC* 6371

MOTION PICTURE INDUSTRY PENSION & HEALTH PLANS p 992
11365 Ventura Blvd # 300, Studio City CA 91604
Tel (818) 769-0007 *SIC* 6371

CALIFORNIA STATE TEACHERS RETIREMENT SYSTEM p 241
100 Waterfront Pl, West Sacramento CA 95605
Tel (800) 228-5453 *SIC* 6371 9441

▲ AETNA INC p 31
151 Farmington Ave, Hartford CT 06156
Tel (860) 273-0123
SIC 6324 6321 6371 8011

TRI STATE JOINT FUND p 1477
25 Research Dr, Milford CT 06460
Tel (203) 876-3100 *SIC* 6371

NEMOURS FOUNDATION PENSION PLAN p 1025
10140 Centurion Pkwy N, Jacksonville FL 32256
Tel (904) 697-4100 *SIC* 6371

NECA IBEW FAMILY MEDICAL CARE PLAN p 1023
410 Chickamauga Ave # 301, Rossville GA 30741
Tel (877) 937-9602 *SIC* 6371

UNITE HERE HEALTH p 1506
711 N Commons Dr, Aurora IL 60504
Tel (630) 236-5100 *SIC* 6371

INTER LOCAL PENSION FUND INC p 751
455 Kehoe Blvd Ste 100, Carol Stream IL 60188
Tel (630) 752-8400 *SIC* 6371

■ BSWIFT LLC p 222
10 S Riverside Plz # 1100, Chicago IL 60606
Tel (312) 261-5750 *SIC* 6371 7373

CONTINENTAL ASSURANCE CO p 362
333 S Wabash Ave Fl 43, Chicago IL 60604
Tel (312) 822-5000 *SIC* 6411 6371 6321

ELECTRICAL INSURANCE TRUSTEES p 485
221 N La Salle St Ste 200, Chicago IL 60601
Tel (312) 782-5442 *SIC* 6371 6282

LOCAL 25 SEIU WELFARE FUND p 872
111 E Wacker Dr Ste 1700, Chicago IL 60601
Tel (312) 240-1600 *SIC* 6371

PIPE FITTERS RETIREMENT FUND LOCAL 597 p 1151
45 N Ogden Ave Fl 1, Chicago IL 60607
Tel (312) 829-4191 *SIC* 6371

MIDWEST OPERATING ENGINEERS FRINGE BENEFIT FUND p 967
6150 Joliet Rd, Countryside IL 60525
Tel (708) 482-0589 *SIC* 6371

WESPATH BENEFITS AND INVESTMENTS p 1593
1901 Chestnut Ave, Glenview IL 60025
Tel (847) 869-4550 *SIC* 6371

ZENITH AMERICAN SOLUTIONS INC p 1642
18861 90th Ave Ste A, Mokena IL 60448
Tel (312) 649-1200 *SIC* 6371

▲ ALLSTATE CORP p 58
2775 Sanders Rd, Northbrook IL 60062
Tel (847) 402-5000
SIC 6411 6351 6311 6371

ILLINOIS MUNICIPAL RETIREMENT FUND p 732
2211 York Rd Ste 500, Oak Brook IL 60523
Tel (630) 368-1010 *SIC* 6371

CENTRAL STATES SOUTHEAST & SOUTHWEST AREAS HEALTH & WELFARE FUND p 280
9377 W Higgins Rd, Rosemont IL 60018
Tel (847) 518-9800 *SIC* 6371

CENTRAL STATES SOUTHEAST AND SOUTHWEST AREAS PENSION FUND p 280
9377 W Higgins Rd Fl 2, Rosemont IL 60018
Tel (847) 518-9800 *SIC* 6371

■ OPTUMRX PBM OF ILLINOIS INC p 1091
1600 Mcconnor Pkwy, Schaumburg IL 60173
Tel (224) 231-1743 *SIC* 6371

TEACHERS RETIREMENT SYSTEM OF STATE OF ILLINOIS p 1429
2815 W Washington St # 200, Springfield IL 62702
Tel (217) 753-0370 *SIC* 6371 9199

LABORERS PENSION & WELFARE FUNDS p 836
11465 W Cermak Rd, Westchester IL 60154
Tel (708) 562-0200 *SIC* 6371

AMERICAN UNITED LIFE INSURANCE CO INC p 81
1 American Sq Ste 368, Indianapolis IN 46282
Tel (317) 285-1877 *SIC* 6371 6311 6321

AMERICAN UNITED MUTUAL INSURANCE HOLDING CO p 81
1 American Sq, Indianapolis IN 46282
Tel (317) 285-1877
SIC 6211 6311 6371 6351 6331

KEY BENEFIT ADMINISTRATORS INC p 814
8330 Allison Pointe Trl, Indianapolis IN 46250
Tel (317) 284-7100 *SIC* 6371

ONEAMERICA FINANCIAL PARTNERS INC p 1087
1 American Sq, Indianapolis IN 46282
Tel (317) 285-1877 *SIC* 6371 6311 6321

INDIANA LABORERS WELFARE FUND p 738
413 Swan St, Terre Haute IN 47807
Tel (812) 238-2551 *SIC* 6371

TRANSAMERICA LIFE INSURANCE CO p 1470
4333 Edgewood Rd Ne, Cedar Rapids IA 52499
Tel (319) 398-8511 *SIC* 6371 6311

BOILERMAKER BLACKSMITH NATIONAL PENSION TRUST p 198
754 Minnesota Ave Ste 522, Kansas City KS 66101
Tel (913) 342-6555 *SIC* 6371

BAKERY & CONFECTIONERY UNION & INDUSTRY INTERNATIONAL PENSION FUND p 147
10401 Conn Ave Ste 210, Kensington MD 20895
Tel (301) 468-3700 *SIC* 6371

NATIONAL AUTOMATIC SPRINKLER INDUSTRY WELFARE FUND p 1010
8000 Corporate Dr, Landover MD 20785
Tel (301) 577-1700 *SIC* 8741 6371

NATIONAL ELECTRICAL BENEFIT FUND p 1011
2400 Res Blvd Ste 500, Rockville MD 20850
Tel (301) 556-4300 *SIC* 6371

UNION LABOR LIFE INSURANCE CO p 1504
8403 Colesville Rd # 1000, Silver Spring MD 20910
Tel (202) 682-0900
SIC 6311 6321 6324 6371

JOHN HANCOCK FINANCIAL SERVICES INC p 788
200 Clarendon St, Boston MA 02116
Tel (617) 572-6000
SIC 6311 6351 6411 6371 6321

TEAMSTERS UNION 25 HEALTH SERVICES & INSURANCE PLAN p 1430
16 Sever St, Boston MA 02129
Tel (617) 241-9220 *SIC* 6371

MASSACHUSETTS LABORERS HEALTH AND WELFARE FUND p 917
14 New England Exec Park, Burlington MA 01803
Tel (781) 238-0700 *SIC* 6371

MICHIGAN CONFERENCE OF TEAMSTERS WELFARE FUND p 960
2700 Trumbull St, Detroit MI 48216
Tel (313) 964-2400 *SIC* 6371

MUNICIPAL EMPLOYEES RETIREMENT SYSTEM OF MICHIGAN p 1000
1134 Municipal Way, Lansing MI 48917
Tel (517) 703-9030 *SIC* 6371

BOARD OF PENSIONS OF EVANGELICAL LUTHERAN CHURCH IN AMERICA p 195
800 Marquette Ave # 1050, Minneapolis MN 55402
Tel (612) 333-7651 *SIC* 6371

ST PAUL TEACHERS RETMNT FUND ASSN p 1372
1619 Dayton Ave Ste 309, Saint Paul MN 55104
Tel (651) 642-2550 *SIC* 6371

AMERITAS LIFE INSURANCE CORP p 84
5900 O St, Lincoln NE 68510
Tel (402) 467-1122 *SIC* 6371 6311 6211

SILVERSTONE GROUP INC p 1324
11516 Miracle Hills Dr # 100, Omaha NE 68154
Tel (402) 964-5400
SIC 6371 6311 8742 6411

NORTHERN NEW ENGLAND BENEFIT TRUST p 1056
51 Goffstown Rd Ste 2, Manchester NH 03102
Tel (603) 669-4771 *SIC* 6371

NEW JERSEY CARPENTERS PENSION FUND p 1031
91 Fieldcrest Ave, Edison NJ 08837
Tel (732) 417-3900 *SIC* 6371

UFCW NATIONAL HEALTH AND WELFARE FUND p 1499
66 Grand Ave Ste A, Englewood NJ 07631
Tel (201) 569-8802 *SIC* 6371

■ PRUDENTIAL INSURANCE CO OF AMERICA p 1187
751 Broad St, Newark NJ 07102
Tel (973) 802-6000
SIC 6311 6371 6282 6722

UNITED WELFARE FUND p 1515
13850 Queens Blvd, Briarwood NY 11435
Tel (718) 658-4848 *SIC* 6371

1199 SEIU NATIONAL BENEFIT FUND p 1
330 W 42nd St Fl 8, New York NY 10036
Tel (646) 473-6300 *SIC* 6371

AFTRA HEALTH & RETIREMENT FUND (INC) p 33
261 Madison Ave Fl 7, New York NY 10016
Tel (212) 499-4800 *SIC* 6371 8111

■ AXA FINANCIAL INC p 139
1290 Ave Of The Am Fl Con, New York NY 10104
Tel (212) 554-1234
SIC 6311 6211 6552 6531 6371 6221

CARPENTERS WELFARE BENEFIT FUND OF NEW YORK CITY (INC) p 260
395 Hudson St Fl 9, New York NY 10014
Tel (212) 366-7300 *SIC* 6371

CHURCH PENSION GROUP SERVICES CORP p 305
19 E 34th St Fl 3, New York NY 10016
Tel (212) 592-1800
SIC 6371 6321 6311 6331 2731

DISTRICT COUNCIL 37 BENEFITS FUND TRUST p 443
125 Barclay St Bsmt B, New York NY 10007
Tel (917) 716-2097 *SIC* 6371

GUARDIAN INSURANCE & ANNUITY CO INC p 645
7 Hanover Sq, New York NY 10004
Tel (212) 598-8000 *SIC* 6311 6371

GUARDIAN LIFE INSURANCE CO OF AMERICA p 645
7 Hanover Sq Fl 14, New York NY 10004
Tel (212) 598-8000
SIC 6311 6371 6324 6321 6722 6282

MASON TENDER DISTRICT COUNCIL TRUST FUND p 916
520 8th Ave Rm 600, New York NY 10018
Tel (212) 452-9700 *SIC* 6371

MONOMOY CAPITAL PARTNERS LLC p 984
142 W 57th St Fl 17, New York NY 10019
Tel (212) 699-4000 *SIC* 6371

NEW YORK STATE COURT OFFICERS ASSOCIATION SECURITY BENEFIT FUND p 1036
321 Broadway Ste 600, New York NY 10007
Tel (212) 608-1124 *SIC* 6371

NYC DISTRICT COUNCIL OF CARPENTERS WELFARE FUND p 1069
395 Hudson St Lbby 3, New York NY 10014
Tel (212) 366-7300 *SIC* 6371

UNITED FEDERATION OF TEACHERS WELFARE FUND p 1508
52 Broadway Lowr, New York NY 10004
Tel (212) 539-0500 *SIC* 6371

PENTEGRA SERVICES INC p 1132
701 Westchester Ave 320e, White Plains NY 10604
Tel (800) 872-3473 *SIC* 6371

■ GREAT AMERICAN FINANCIAL RESOURCES INC p 633
250 E 5th St Ste 1000, Cincinnati OH 45202
Tel (513) 333-5300 *SIC* 6371

OHIO OPERATING ENGINEERS HEALTH & WELFARE FUND p 1078
1180 Dublin Rd, Columbus OH 43215
Tel (614) 488-0708 *SIC* 6371

OHIO PUBLIC EMPLOYEES RETIREMENT SYSTEM p 1078
277 E Town St, Columbus OH 43215
Tel (614) 228-8471 *SIC* 6371 9441

SCHOOL EMPLOYEES RETIREMENT SYSTEM OF OHIO p 1290
300 E Broad St Ste 100, Columbus OH 43215
Tel (614) 222-5853 *SIC* 6371 9441

STATE TEACHERS RETIREMENT SYSTEM OF OHIO p 1383
275 E Broad St, Columbus OH 43215
Tel (614) 227-4090 *SIC* 6371

SHEET METAL WORKERS LOCAL 124 p 1313
3717 Nw 63rd St Ste 100, Oklahoma City OK 73116
Tel (405) 848-4848 *SIC* 6371

ASCENSUS INC p 116
200 Dryden Rd E Ste 1000, Dresher PA 19025
Tel (215) 648-8000 *SIC* 6371

PUBLIC SCHOOL EMPLOYEES RETIREMENT SYSTEM p 1189
5 N 5th St, Harrisburg PA 17101
Tel (717) 720-4734 *SIC* 6371 9441

BOARD OF PENSIONS OF PRESBYTERIAN CHURCH USA p 195
2000 Market St Fl 4, Philadelphia PA 19103
Tel (800) 773-7752 *SIC* 6371

CARPENTERS HEALTH AND WELFARE FUND p 260
1811 Spring Garden St # 1, Philadelphia PA 19130
Tel (215) 568-0430 *SIC* 6371

HM INSURANCE GROUP INC p 697
120 5th Ave, Pittsburgh PA 15222
Tel (412) 544-1000 *SIC* 6311 6371

LABORERS COMBINED FUNDS OF WESTERN PENNSYLVANIA p 836
12 8th St, Pittsburgh PA 15222
Tel (412) 263-0900 *SIC* 6371

▲ LINCOLN NATIONAL CORP p 867
150 N Radnor Chester Rd A305 Ste A, Radnor PA 19087
Tel (484) 583-1400
SIC 6311 6321 6371 6722 6411 6282

▲ UNUM GROUP p 1528
1 Fountain Sq, Chattanooga TN 37402
Tel (423) 294-1011
SIC 6321 6324 6311 6371

EMPLOYEES RETIREMENT SYSTEM OF TEXAS p 494
200 E 18th St, Austin TX 78701
Tel (512) 867-7199 *SIC* 6371 9441

■ SCHWAB RETIREMENT PLAN SERVICES CO p 1291
12401 Res Blvd Bldg 2, Austin TX 78759
Tel (512) 344-3000 *SIC* 6371

▲ HEALTHEQUITY INC p 677
15 W Scenic Pointe Dr # 100, Draper UT 84020
Tel (801) 727-1000
SIC 8399 6371 6036 6321 6282

UNION PACIFIC RAILROAD EMPLOYES HEALTH SYSTEMS p 1505
1040 N 2200 W Ste 200, Salt Lake City UT 84116
Tel (801) 595-4300 *SIC* 6371

UTAH RETIREMENT SYSTEMS p 1536
540 E 200 S, Salt Lake City UT 84102
Tel (801) 366-7700 *SIC* 6371

FAIRFAX COUNTY WATER AUTHORITY WELFARE BENEFIT TRUST p 524
8570 Executive Park Ave, Fairfax VA 22031
Tel (703) 698-5600 *SIC* 6371

▲ GENWORTH FINANCIAL INC p 605
6620 W Broad St Ste 270, Richmond VA 23230
Tel (804) 281-6000 *SIC* 6311 6371 6351

NORTHWEST ADMINISTRATORS INC p 1059
2323 Eastlake Ave E, Seattle WA 98102
Tel (206) 329-4900 *SIC* 6371

SIC 6399 Insurance Carriers, NEC

■ UNITRIN DIRECT INSURANCE CO p 1515
80 Blue Ravine Rd Ste 200, Folsom CA 95630
Tel (760) 603-3276 *SIC* 6399

AMERICAN CONTRACTORS INDEMNITY CO p 70
601 S Figueroa St # 1600, Los Angeles CA 90017
Tel (213) 330-1309 *SIC* 6399

FEDERAL DEPOSIT INSURANCE CORP p 534
550 17th St Nw, Washington DC 20429
Tel (877) 275-3342 *SIC* 6399 9311

US ASSURE INC p 1531
8230 Nations Way, Jacksonville FL 32256
Tel (904) 398-3907 *SIC* 6399

PRIDE AIR CONDITIONING & APPLIANCE INC p 1174
2150 Nw 18th St, Pompano Beach FL 33069
Tel (954) 977-7433 *SIC* 6399 7623

HEALTHPLAN HOLDINGS INC p 677
3501 E Frontage Rd, Tampa FL 33607
Tel (813) 289-1000 *SIC* 6399

INFOSYS MCCAMISH SYSTEMS LLC p 742
6425 Powers Ferry Rd, Atlanta GA 30339
Tel (770) 690-1500 *SIC* 6399 7373

INTERSTATE NATIONAL DEALER SERVICES INC p 758
6120 Powers Ferry Rd S, Atlanta GA 30339
Tel (678) 894-3500 *SIC* 6399 6221

TWG HOLDINGS INC p 1494
175 W Jackson Blvd Fl 11, Chicago IL 60604
Tel (312) 356-3000 *SIC* 6399 8721 6411

TWG WARRANTY GROUP INC p 1494
175 W Jackson Blvd Fl 11, Chicago IL 60604
Tel (312) 356-3000 *SIC* 6399 8721 6411

VIRGINIA SURETY CO INC p 1560
175 W Jackson Blvd Fl 11, Chicago IL 60604
Tel (312) 356-3000 *SIC* 6351 6399

WARRANTY GROUP INC p 1576
175 W Jackson Blvd Fl 11, Chicago IL 60604
Tel (312) 356-3000 *SIC* 6351 6399

AVEMCO CORP p 136
8490 Progress Dr Ste 100, Frederick MD 21701
Tel (301) 694-5700
SIC 6331 6321 6399 6411 7372

SECURIAN FINANCIAL GROUP INC p 1298
400 Robert St N Ste A, Saint Paul MN 55101
Tel (651) 665-3500 *SIC* 7389 6399

CHUBB & SON INC p 304
15 Mountainview Rd, Warren NJ 07059
Tel (908) 903-2000 *SIC* 6399

▲ ASSURANT INC p 121
28 Liberty St Fl 41, New York NY 10005
Tel (212) 859-7000 *SIC* 6311 6399 6331

SYNCORA GUARANTEE INC p 1414
135 W 50th St Fl 20, New York NY 10020
Tel (212) 478-3400 *SIC* 6399

■ AMT WARRANTY CORP p 87
5800 Lombardo Ctr Ste 150, Seven Hills OH 44131
Tel (212) 220-7120 *SIC* 6399

ASURION LLC p 123
648 Grassmere Park # 300, Nashville TN 37211
Tel (615) 837-3000 *SIC* 6399

■ WARRANTECH CORP p 1576
2200 Highway 121, Bedford TX 76021
Tel (817) 785-6601 *SIC* 6399

DRISCOLL CHILDRENS HEALTH PLAN p 456
615 N Uppr Brdwy 1621, Corpus Christi TX 78401
Tel (361) 694-6432 *SIC* 8011 6399

▲ HARLEY-DAVIDSON INC p 661
3700 W Juneau Ave, Milwaukee WI 53208
Tel (414) 342-4680
SIC 3751 6153 6141 6411 6399

SIC 6411 Insurance Agents, Brokers & Svc

■ CRC INSURANCE SERVICES INC p 390
1 Metroplex Dr Ste 400, Birmingham AL 35209
Tel (205) 870-7790 *SIC* 6411

■ HIGHLAND CAPITAL BROKERAGE INC p 691
3535 Grandview Pkwy Ste 6, Birmingham AL 35243
Tel (205) 263-4400 *SIC* 6411

HIGHLAND CAPITAL HOLDING CORP p 691
3535 Grandview Pkwy # 600, Birmingham AL 35243
Tel (205) 263-4400 *SIC* 6411

■ INFINITY INSURANCE AGENCY INC p 741
2201 4th Ave N, Birmingham AL 35203
Tel (205) 870-4000 *SIC* 6411

■ MCGRIFF SEIBELS & WILLIAMS INC p 929
2211 7th Ave S, Birmingham AL 35233
Tel (205) 252-9871 *SIC* 6411

PROTECTIVE LIFE CORP p 1185
2801 Highway 280 S Ofc, Birmingham AL 35223
Tel (205) 268-1000
SIC 6311 6321 6351 6411

PROTECTIVE LIFE INSURANCE CO p 1185
2801 Highway 280 S, Birmingham AL 35223
Tel (205) 268-1000 *SIC* 6311 6411 7389

STATE FARM INSURANCE p 1381
100 State Farm Pkwy, Birmingham AL 35209
Tel (205) 916-6000 *SIC* 6411

■ AGENTS ALLIANCE INSURANCE CO p 34
3800 Sollie Rd, Mobile AL 36619
Tel (251) 665-2418 *SIC* 6411

PILOT CATASTROPHE SERVICES INC p 1148
1055 Hillcrest Rd, Mobile AL 36695
Tel (251) 607-7700 *SIC* 6411

ALFA CORP p 49
2108 E South Blvd, Montgomery AL 36116
Tel (334) 288-3900 *SIC* 6331 6411 7389

ALFA MUTUAL FIRE INSURANCE CO p 49
2108 E South Blvd, Montgomery AL 36116
Tel (334) 288-3900 *SIC* 6411

ALFA MUTUAL INSURANCE CO p 49
2108 E South Blvd, Montgomery AL 36116
Tel (334) 613-4639 *SIC* 6411

ALASKA NATIONAL CORP p 45
7001 Jewel Lake Rd, Anchorage AK 99502
Tel (907) 248-2642 *SIC* 6411

ARIZONA DENTAL INSURANCE SERVICE INC p 108
5656 W Talavi Blvd, Glendale AZ 85306
Tel (602) 588-3617 *SIC* 6324 6411

M & O AGENCIES INC p 888
1835 S Extension Rd, Mesa AZ 85210
Tel (480) 730-4920 *SIC* 6411

FARMERS INSURANCE CO OF ARIZONA p 529
16001 N 28th Ave, Phoenix AZ 85053
Tel (602) 863-8100 *SIC* 6411 8741

HEALTH CHOICE ARIZONA INC p 674
410 N 44th St Ste 900, Phoenix AZ 85008
Tel (480) 968-6866 *SIC* 6321 6411

LINCOLN HERITAGE LIFE INSURANCE CO p 867
4343 E Camelback Rd # 400, Phoenix AZ 85018
Tel (800) 750-6404 *SIC* 6311 6411

MATRIX ABSENCE MANAGEMENT INC p 920
2421 W Peoria Ave Ste 200, Phoenix AZ 85029
Tel (602) 866-2333 *SIC* 6411

ROGERS BENEFIT GROUP INC p 1246
5110 N 40th St Ste 234, Phoenix AZ 85018
Tel (612) 332-8866 *SIC* 6411

■ SECURITY TITLE AGENCY INC p 1299
3636 N Central Ave # 140, Phoenix AZ 85012
Tel (602) 230-6271 *SIC* 6411 6541

SPENCE DRISCOLL & CO LLC p 1358
5050 N 40th St Ste 350, Phoenix AZ 85018
Tel (602) 957-7155 *SIC* 6411

USA MANAGED HEALTH & WELLNESS RESOURCES GROUP INC p 1534
7301 N 16th St Ste 201, Phoenix AZ 85020
Tel (602) 371-3860 *SIC* 6324 6411

LOVITT & TOUCHE INC p 881
7202 E Rosewood St # 200, Tucson AZ 85710
Tel (520) 722-3000 *SIC* 6411

■ REGIONS INSURANCE GROUP p 1220
1500 Riverfront Dr # 200, Little Rock AR 72202
Tel (501) 661-4800 *SIC* 6411

USABLE MUTUAL INSURANCE CO p 1534
601 S Gaines St, Little Rock AR 72201
Tel (501) 378-2000 *SIC* 6324 6411

RITTER AGRIBUSINESS p 1237
10 Elm St, Marked Tree AR 72365
Tel (870) 336-7310 *SIC* 6411

PINNACLE BUSINESS SOLUTIONS INC p 1149
515 W Pershing Blvd, North Little Rock AR 72114
Tel (501) 210-9000 *SIC* 6411 7371

■ PACIFIC COMPENSATION CORP p 1104
30301 Agoura Rd Ste 100, Agoura Hills CA 91301
Tel (818) 575-8500 *SIC* 6411

VETERINARY PET INSURANCE SERVICES INC p 1553
1800 E Emperi Hwy Ste 145, Brea CA 92821
Tel (714) 989-0555 *SIC* 6411

FCE BENEFIT ADMINISTRATORS INC p 533
887 Mitten Rd Ste 200, Burlingame CA 94010
Tel (650) 341-0306 *SIC* 6411

■ COUNTRYWIDE FINANCIAL CORP p 375
4500 Park Granada, Calabasas CA 91302
Tel (818) 225-3000
SIC 6162 6211 6361 6411 6163 6799

■ UNICARE LIFE & HEALTH INSURANCE CO p 1502
5151 Camino Ruiz Ste A, Camarillo CA 93012
Tel (888) 742-2505 *SIC* 6411 6324

G I A A INC p 587
1155 Eugenia Pl, Carpinteria CA 93013
Tel (805) 566-9191 *SIC* 6411

■ AIS MANAGEMENT LLC p 41
17785 Center Court Dr N # 250, Cerritos CA 90703
Tel (562) 345-4247 *SIC* 6411

NNA SERVICES LLC p 1045
9350 De Soto Ave, Chatsworth CA 91311
Tel (818) 739-4071 *SIC* 6411

FREEWAY INSURANCE p 577
10801 Walker St Ste 250, Cypress CA 90630
Tel (714) 252-2500 *SIC* 6411

■ MULLIN TBG INSURANCE AGENCY SERVICES LLC p 999
100 N Sepulveda Blvd, El Segundo CA 90245
Tel (310) 203-8770 *SIC* 6411

TEAMSTER BENEFIT TRUST p 1430
39420 Liberty St Ste 260, Fremont CA 94538
Tel (510) 796-4676 *SIC* 8631 6411

DIBUDUO & DEFENDIS INSURANCE BROKERS LLC p 437
6873 N West Ave, Fresno CA 93711
Tel (559) 432-0222 *SIC* 6411

JAMES G PARKER INSURANCE ASSOCIATES p 776
1753 E Fir Ave, Fresno CA 93720
Tel (559) 222-7722 *SIC* 6411

DMA CLAIMS INC p 445
330 N Brand Blvd Ste 230, Glendale CA 91203
Tel (323) 342-6800 *SIC* 6411

■ EMPLOYERS COMPENSATION INSURANCE CO INC p 494
500 N Brand Blvd Ste 800, Glendale CA 91203
Tel (818) 549-4600 *SIC* 6411

CONFIE SEGUROS HOLDING CO p 356
7711 Center Ave Ste 200, Huntington Beach CA 92647
Tel (714) 252-2649 *SIC* 6411

CONFIE SEGUROS INC p 356
7711 Center Ave Ste 200, Huntington Beach CA 92647
Tel (714) 252-2500 *SIC* 6411

FREEWAY INSURANCE SERVICES INC p 577
7711 Center Ave Ste 200, Huntington Beach CA 92647
Tel (714) 252-2500 *SIC* 6411

■ MOLINA INFORMATION SYSTEMS LLC p 982
200 Oceangate Ste 100, Long Beach CA 90802
Tel (916) 561-8540 *SIC* 6411

AUTOMOBILE CLUB OF SOUTHERN CALIFORNIA p 134
2601 S Figueroa St, Los Angeles CA 90007
Tel (213) 741-3686 *SIC* 6411 8699

BROWN AND RIDING INSURANCE SERVICES INC p 219
777 S Figueroa St # 2550, Los Angeles CA 90017
Tel (213) 452-7060 *SIC* 6411

FARMERS INSURANCE GROUP p 529
6301 Owensmouth Ave, Los Angeles CA 90010
Tel (888) 327-6335 *SIC* 6411

FARMERS SERVICES LLC p 530
4680 Wilshire Blvd, Los Angeles CA 90010
Tel (323) 932-3200 *SIC* 6411

FIRE INSURANCE EXCHANGE p 543
4680 Wilshire Blvd, Los Angeles CA 90010
Tel (323) 932-3200 *SIC* 6411

HUB INTERNATIONAL OF CALIFORNIA INC p 716
6701 Center Dr W Ste 1500, Los Angeles CA 90045
Tel (310) 568-5900 *SIC* 6411

LOCKTON COMPANIES LLC - PACIFIC SERIES p 873
725 S Figueroa St Fl 35, Los Angeles CA 90017
Tel (213) 689-0500 *SIC* 6411

■ MARSH RISK & INSURANCE SERVICES INC p 911
777 S Figueroa St # 2200, Los Angeles CA 90017
Tel (213) 624-5555 *SIC* 6411

▲ MERCURY GENERAL CORP p 945
4484 Wilshire Blvd, Los Angeles CA 90010
Tel (323) 937-1060 *SIC* 6331 6411

■ SAFG RETIREMENT SERVICES INC p 1267
1 Sun America Ctr Fl 36, Los Angeles CA 90067
Tel (310) 772-6000 *SIC* 6411

SULLIVAN GJ & ASSOCIATES INC p 1397
800 W 6th St Ste 1800, Los Angeles CA 90017
Tel (213) 626-1000 *SIC* 6411

■ SUNAMERICA INC p 1401
1 Sun America Ctr Fl 38, Los Angeles CA 90067
Tel (310) 772-6000
SIC 6091 6311 6211 6282 6411 6371

U B O C INSURANCE INC p 1497
445 S Figueroa St, Los Angeles CA 90071
Tel (213) 236-7700 *SIC* 6411

▲ EHEALTH INC p 481
440 E Middlefield Rd, Mountain View CA 94043
Tel (650) 584-2700 *SIC* 6411

DOCTORS MANAGEMENT CO p 447
185 Greenwood Rd, Napa CA 94558
Tel (707) 226-0100 *SIC* 6411

RISK MANAGEMENT SOLUTIONS INC p 1236
7575 Gateway Blvd, Newark CA 94560
Tel (510) 505-2500 *SIC* 6794 6411

ALLIANT INSURANCE SERVICES INC p 55
1301 Dove St Ste 200, Newport Beach CA 92660
Tel (949) 756-0271 *SIC* 6411 8748

PACIFIC LIFE & ANNUITY CO p 1105
700 Newport Center Dr, Newport Beach CA 92660
Tel (949) 219-3011 *SIC* 6311 6411

CHOICE ADMINISTRATORS INSURANCE SERVICES INC p 302
721 S Parker St Ste 200, Orange CA 92868
Tel (714) 542-4200 SIC 6411

CONEXIS BENEFIT ADMINISTRATORS LP p 355
721 S Parker St Ste 300, Orange CA 92868
Tel (714) 835-5006 SIC 6411

WORD & BROWN INSURANCE ADMINISTRATORS INC p 1624
721 S Parker St Ste 300, Orange CA 92868
Tel (714) 835-5006 SIC 6411

BOLTON & CO p 199
3475 E Foothill Blvd # 100, Pasadena CA 91107
Tel (626) 799-7000 SIC 6411

UNITED AGENCIES INC p 1506
301 E Colo Blvd Ste 200, Pasadena CA 91101
Tel (626) 564-2670 SIC 6411

■ WESCO FINANCIAL CORP p 1593
301 E Colo Blvd Ste 300, Pasadena CA 91101
Tel (626) 585-6700 SIC 7359 6411 7389

HUB INTERNATIONAL INSURANCE SERVICES INC p 716
3390 University Ave # 300, Riverside CA 92501
Tel (951) 788-8500 SIC 6411

ACCLAMATION INSURANCE MANAGEMENT SERVICES p 15
10445 Old Placerville Rd, Sacramento CA 95827
Tel (916) 563-1900 SIC 6411

GO WEST INSURANCE SERVICES INC p 619
2386 Fair Oaks Blvd Ste 2, Sacramento CA 95825
Tel (916) 487-1102 SIC 6411

INTERWEST INSURANCE SERVICES INC p 759
3636 American River Dr # 2, Sacramento CA 95864
Tel (916) 488-3100 SIC 6411

■ AIG DIRECT INSURANCE SERVICES INC p 37
9640 Gran Rdge Dr Ste 200, San Diego CA 92123
Tel (858) 309-3000 SIC 6411

AMERICAN SPECIALTY HEALTH INC p 79
10221 Wateridge Cir # 201, San Diego CA 92121
Tel (858) 754-2000 SIC 6411

■ ARROWHEAD GENERAL INSURANCE AGENCY INC p 113
701 B St Ste 2100, San Diego CA 92101
Tel (619) 881-8600 SIC 6331 6411

■ ARROWHEAD MANAGEMENT CO p 113
701 B St Ste 2100, San Diego CA 92101
Tel (800) 669-1889 SIC 6411 8741

■ BARNEY & BARNEY INC p 156
9171 Twne Cntre Dr 500, San Diego CA 92122
Tel (800) 321-4696 SIC 6411

ICW GROUP HOLDINGS INC p 728
11455 El Camino Real, San Diego CA 92130
Tel (858) 350-2400 SIC 6331 6411

C V STARR & CO p 233
101 2nd St Ste 2500, San Francisco CA 94105
Tel (415) 216-4000 SIC 6411

CROUSE AND ASSOCIATES INSURANCE BROKERS INC p 394
100 Pine St Ste 2500, San Francisco CA 94111
Tel (415) 982-3870 SIC 6411

DELTA DENTAL INSURANCE CO p 426
100 1st St Fl 4, San Francisco CA 94105
Tel (415) 972-8400 SIC 6411

EDGEWOOD PARTNERS INSURANCE CENTER p 478
135 Main St 21f, San Francisco CA 94105
Tel (415) 356-3900 SIC 6411

■ ESURANCE INSURANCE SERVICES INC p 511
650 Davis St, San Francisco CA 94111
Tel (415) 875-4500 SIC 6411

NORCAL MUTUAL INSURANCE CO INC p 1047
560 Davis St Fl 2, San Francisco CA 94111
Tel (415) 397-9703 SIC 6411 6331

S F ADMINISTRATORS INC p 1262
642 Harrison St 306, San Francisco CA 94107
Tel (415) 777-3707 SIC 6411

SELECTQUOTE INSURANCE SERVICES p 1302
595 Market St Fl 10, San Francisco CA 94105
Tel (415) 543-7338 SIC 6411

SQUARETRADE INC p 1362
360 3rd St Fl 6, San Francisco CA 94107
Tel (415) 541-1000 SIC 6411

WOODRUFF-SAWYER & CO p 1623
50 California St Fl 12, San Francisco CA 94111
Tel (415) 391-2141 SIC 6411

YOURPEOPLE INC p 1639
303 2nd St Ste 401, San Francisco CA 94107
Tel (415) 798-9086 SIC 6411 7372

ABD INSURANCE & FINANCIAL SERVICES INC p 10
3 Waters Park Dr Ste 100, San Mateo CA 94403
Tel (650) 488-8565 SIC 6411

ANDREINI & CO p 90
220 W 20th Ave, San Mateo CA 94403
Tel (650) 573-1111 SIC 6411

EXTEND HEALTH INC p 521
2929 Campus Dr Ste 400, San Mateo CA 94403
Tel (650) 288-4800 SIC 6411

LISI INC p 870
1600 W Hillsdale Blvd # 100, San Mateo CA 94402
Tel (650) 348-4131 SIC 6411

CLAIMS SERVICES GROUP LLC p 321
6111 Bollinger Canyon Rd, San Ramon CA 94583
Tel (925) 866-1100 SIC 6411

■ OLD REPUBLIC HOME PROTECTION CO INC p 1081
2 Annabel Ln Ste 112, San Ramon CA 94583
Tel (925) 866-1500 SIC 6411

K2 INSURANCE SERVICES LLC p 799
514 Via De La Valle Ste 3, Solana Beach CA 92075
Tel (858) 866-8966 SIC 6411

▲ FINANCIAL ENGINES INC p 542
1050 Enterprise Way Fl 3, Sunnyvale CA 94089
Tel (408) 498-6000 SIC 8742 6282 6411

KEENAN & ASSOCIATES p 807
2355 Crenshaw Blvd # 200, Torrance CA 90501
Tel (310) 212-3344 SIC 6411

CARL WARREN & CO p 256
17862 17th St Ste 111, Tustin CA 92780
Tel (800) 572-6900 SIC 6411

ASCENSION INSURANCE INC p 116
1277 Treat Blvd Ste 400, Walnut Creek CA 94597
Tel (800) 404-4969 SIC 6411

CSAA INSURANCE EXCHANGE p 397
3055 Oak Rd, Walnut Creek CA 94597
Tel (800) 922-8228 SIC 6411

HEFFERNAN INSURANCE BROKERS p 680
1350 Carlback Ave, Walnut Creek CA 94596
Tel (925) 934-8500 SIC 6411

PORTAL INSURANCE AGENCY INC p 1162
1277 Treat Blvd Ste 650, Walnut Creek CA 94597
Tel (925) 937-8787 SIC 6411

■ BLUE CROSS OF CALIFORNIA p 192
4553 La Tienda Rd, Westlake Village CA 91362
Tel (805) 557-6050 SIC 6324 6411

WARNER PACIFIC INSURANCE SERVICES INC p 1576
32110 Agoura Rd, Westlake Village CA 91361
Tel (408) 298-4049 SIC 6411

21ST CENTURY INSURANCE CO p 1
6301 Owensmouth Ave, Woodland Hills CA 91367
Tel (877) 310-5687 SIC 6411

LIFECARE ASSURANCE CO INC p 864
21600 Oxnard St Fl 16, Woodland Hills CA 91367
Tel (818) 887-4436 SIC 6321 6411 6311

▲ BIOSCRIP INC p 184
1600 Broadway Ste 700, Denver CO 80202
Tel (720) 697-5200 SIC 8059 6411

KRG CAPITAL PARTNERS LLC p 830
1800 Larimer St Ste 2200, Denver CO 80202
Tel (303) 390-5001 SIC 6726 8742 6411

LAND TITLE GUARANTEE CO INC p 842
3033 E 1st Ave Ste 600, Denver CO 80206
Tel (303) 321-1880 SIC 6411

▲ RE/MAX HOLDINGS INC p 1212
5075 S Syracuse St, Denver CO 80237
Tel (303) 770-5531 SIC 6531 6411

MASTERS INSURANCE AGENCY INC p 918
9785 Maroon Cir Ste 340, Englewood CO 80112
Tel (303) 814-1596 SIC 6411 6331 6311

USI COLORADO LLC p 1535
6501 S Fiddlers Ste 100, Greenwood Village CO 80111
Tel (800) 873-8500 SIC 6411

EBERL CLAIMS SERVICE LLC p 474
7276 W Mansfield Ave, Lakewood CO 80235
Tel (303) 988-6286 SIC 6411

▲ PEOPLES UNITED FINANCIAL INC p 1133
850 Main St, Bridgeport CT 06604
Tel (203) 338-7171 SIC 6411

ALLIED WORLD ASSURANCE INC p 57
1690 New Britain Ave B, Farmington CT 06032
Tel (860) 284-1300 SIC 6411

PARTNERRE US CORP p 1118
1 Greenwich Plz, Greenwich CT 06830
Tel (203) 485-4200 SIC 6411

SECURITY CAPITAL CORP p 1299
8 Greenwich Office Park # 2, Greenwich CT 06831
Tel (203) 625-0770 SIC 6411 8211

■ AETNA HEALTH HOLDINGS LLC p 31
151 Farmington Ave, Hartford CT 06156
Tel (860) 273-0123 SIC 6324 6411 6321

■ FARMINGTON CASUALTY CO p 530
1 Tower Sq, Hartford CT 06183
Tel (860) 277-0111 SIC 6411

■ HARTFORD ACCIDENT & INDEMNITY CO p 665
1 Hartford Plz, Hartford CT 06155
Tel (860) 547-5000 SIC 6411

■ HARTFORD CASUALTY INSURANCE CO p 665
690 Asylum Ave, Hartford CT 06155
Tel (860) 547-5000 SIC 6411 6331

■ HARTFORD FIRE INSURANCE CO (INC) p 665
1 Hartford Plz, Hartford CT 06115
Tel (860) 547-5000
SIC 6411 6311 6351 7373

■ HARTFORD INSURANCE CO OF ILLINOIS p 665
690 Asylum Ave, Hartford CT 06105
Tel (860) 547-5000 SIC 6411

■ HSB GROUP INC p 714
1 State St, Hartford CT 06102
Tel (860) 722-1866
SIC 6331 6411 6799 8711 8742

PHL VARIABLE INSURANCE CO p 1144
1 American Row, Hartford CT 06115
Tel (860) 253-1000 SIC 6411

PHOENIX COMPANIES INC p 1144
1 American Row, Hartford CT 06103
Tel (860) 403-5000 SIC 6411

PM HOLDINGS INC p 1157
1 American Row, Hartford CT 06103
Tel (860) 403-5000
SIC 6411 6162 6722 6282 6211 6552

■ TRAVELERS CASUALTY AND SURETY CO p 1474
1 Tower Sq 8ms, Hartford CT 06183
Tel (860) 277-0111 SIC 6411 6351

■ TRAVELERS CASUALTY AND SURETY CO OF AMERICA p 1474
1 Tower Sq 2ms, Hartford CT 06183
Tel (860) 277-0111 SIC 6411 6351

■ TRAVELERS CASUALTY INSURANCE CO OF AMERICA p 1474
1 Tower Sq, Hartford CT 06183
Tel (860) 277-0111 SIC 6411

■ TRAVELERS COMMERCIAL INSURANCE CO p 1474
1 Tower Sq, Hartford CT 06183
Tel (860) 548-9948 SIC 6411

■ TRAVELERS INDEMNITY CO p 1474
1 Tower Sq, Hartford CT 06183
Tel (860) 277-0111 SIC 6411 6331

■ TRAVELERS INDEMNITY CO OF AMERICA INC p 1474
1 Tower Sq, Hartford CT 06183
Tel (860) 277-0111 SIC 6411 6531

■ TRAVELERS INDEMNITY CO OF CONNECTICUT p 1474
1 Tower Sq, Hartford CT 06183
Tel (860) 548-9948 SIC 6411 6331

■ TRAVELERS PERSONAL SECURITY INSURANCE CO p 1474
1 Tower Sq, Hartford CT 06183
Tel (860) 277-0111 SIC 6411

■ TRAVELERS PROPERTY CASUALTY CORP p 1474
1 Tower Sq 8ms, Hartford CT 06183
Tel (860) 277-0111 SIC 6411

UNITED PACIFIC INSURANCE CO p 1510
1 Tower Sq, Hartford CT 06183
Tel (860) 277-0995 SIC 6411

FUTURITY FIRST INSURANCE GROUP INC p 586
101 Centerpoint Dr # 208, Middletown CT 06457
Tel (860) 838-4800 SIC 6411

KNIGHTS OF COLUMBUS p 824
1 Columbus Plz Ste 1700, New Haven CT 06510
Tel (203) 752-4000 SIC 6411 8641

■ PRUDENTIAL ANNUITIES DISTRIBUTORS INC p 1187
1 Corporate Dr, Shelton CT 06484
Tel (203) 926-1888 SIC 6411

■ PRUDENTIAL ANNUITIES INC p 1187
1 Corporate Dr Ste 800, Shelton CT 06484
Tel (203) 926-1888 SIC 6411 8741

■ PRUDENTIAL ANNUITIES LIFE ASSURANCE CORP p 1187
1 Corporate Dr Ste 800, Shelton CT 06484
Tel (203) 926-1888 SIC 6411

WILLIAM RAVEIS REAL ESTATE INC p 1611
7 Trap Falls Rd, Shelton CT 06484
Tel (203) 926-1090 SIC 6411

CHUBB EXECUTIVE RISK INC p 304
82 Hopmeadow St, Simsbury CT 06070
Tel (860) 408-2000 SIC 6411

FINIAL REINSURANCE CO p 543
100 Stamford Pl Ste 201, Stamford CT 06902
Tel (203) 564-5273 SIC 6411

GENERAL ELECTRIC INSURANCE PLAN TRUST p 600
1070 High Ridge Rd, Stamford CT 06905
Tel (203) 326-2300 SIC 6411

■ GENERAL REINSURANCE CORP p 602
120 Long Ridge Rd, Stamford CT 06902
Tel (203) 328-5000
SIC 6331 6351 6411 6321

ODYSSEY RE HOLDINGS CORP p 1075
300 Stamford Pl, Stamford CT 06902
Tel (203) 977-8000 SIC 6411

ODYSSEY REINSURANCE CO p 1075
300 Stamford Pl Ste 700, Stamford CT 06902
Tel (203) 965-0004
SIC 6411 6361 6331 6324 6311

XL AMERICA INC p 1632
70 Seaview Ave Ste 7, Stamford CT 06902
Tel (203) 964-5200 SIC 6411 6321 6351

XL GLOBAL SERVICES INC p 1632
70 Seaview Ave Ste 7, Stamford CT 06902
Tel (203) 964-5200 SIC 6411

■ HARTFORD LIFE INSURANCE CO p 665
200 Hopmeadow St, Weatogue CT 06089
Tel (860) 547-5000 SIC 6411

WESTPORT INSURANCE CORP p 1602
2 Waterside Xing Ste 200, Windsor CT 06095
Tel (860) 902-7201 SIC 6331 6411

■ CIGNA GLOBAL HOLDINGS INC p 306
590 Naamans Rd, Claymont DE 19703
Tel (302) 797-3469 SIC 6311 6512 6411

21ST CENTURY NORTH AMERICA INSURANCE CO p 2
3 Beaver Valley Rd, Wilmington DE 19803
Tel (877) 310-5687 SIC 6411

■ AMERICAN LIFE INSURANCE CO p 75
1 Alico Plz, Wilmington DE 19801
Tel (302) 594-2000 SIC 6411 6321 6324

LEXISNEXIS RISK ASSETS INC p 859
1105 N Market St Ste 501, Wilmington DE 19801
Tel (770) 752-6000
SIC 6411 7375 8721 7323

■ GEICO CORP p 597
1 Geico Plz, Washington DC 20076
Tel (301) 986-3000 SIC 6411

■ GEICO GENERAL INSURANCE CO p 597
1 Geico Plz, Washington DC 20076
Tel (301) 986-3000 SIC 6411

■ GEICO INDEMNITY CO p 597
One Geico Plaza, Washington DC 20047
Tel (301) 986-3000 SIC 6331 6411

LABORERS-EMPLOYERS BENEFIT PLAN COLLECTION TRUST p 836
905 16th St Nw, Washington DC 20006
Tel (202) 393-7344 SIC 6411

FLORIDA PENINSULA HOLDINGS LLC p 559
903 Nw 65th St Ste 200, Boca Raton FL 33487
Tel (561) 210-0370 SIC 6411

ICAN BENEFIT GROUP LLC p 726
5300 Broken Sound Blvd Nw, Boca Raton FL 33487
Tel (800) 530-4226 SIC 6411

LUMBERMENS UNDERWRITING ALLIANCE p 885
1905 Nw Corporate Blvd, Boca Raton FL 33431
Tel (561) 994-1900 SIC 6331 6411 6311

AMERILIFE GROUP LLC p 82
2650 Mccormick Dr Ste 100, Clearwater FL 33759
Tel (727) 726-0726 SIC 6411

BOUCHARD INSURANCE INC p 204
101 Starcrest Dr, Clearwater FL 33765
Tel (727) 447-6481 SIC 6411

■ HULL & CO INC p 718
1815 Griffin Rd Ste 300, Dania Beach FL 33004
Tel (954) 920-6790 SIC 6411

BRISTOL WEST INSURANCE SERVICE INC p 214
5701 Stirling Rd, Davie FL 33314
Tel (954) 316-5200 SIC 6411

▲ BROWN & BROWN INC p 219
220 S Ridgewood Ave # 180, Daytona Beach FL 32114
Tel (386) 252-9601 SIC 6411

PEOPLES TRUST INSURANCE CO p 1133
18 Peoples Trust Way, Deerfield Beach FL 33441
Tel (561) 988-9170 SIC 6411 6021

GUARANTEE INSURANCE GROUP INC p 644
401 E Las Olas Blvd # 1540, Fort Lauderdale FL 33301
Tel (954) 670-2900 SIC 6411 6331

▲ PATRIOT NATIONAL INC p 1121
401 E Las Olas Blvd # 1650, Fort Lauderdale FL 33301
Tel (954) 670-2900 SIC 6411

SEITLIN & CO p 1301
1000 Corp Dr Ste 400, Fort Lauderdale FL 33334
Tel (305) 591-0090 SIC 6411 8742

▲ UNIVERSAL INSURANCE HOLDINGS INC p 1517
1110 W Coml Blvd Ste 100, Fort Lauderdale FL 33309
Tel (954) 958-1200 SIC 6411

FLORIDA FARM BUREAU GENERAL INSURANCE CO p 558
5700 Sw 34th St, Gainesville FL 32608
Tel (352) 378-1321 SIC 6411

AON RISK SERVICES INC OF FLORIDA p 95
13901 Sutton Park Dr S # 360, Jacksonville FL 32224
Tel (904) 724-2001 SIC 6411

■ FORTEGRA FINANCIAL CORP p 569
10151 Deerwood Park Blvd # 330, Jacksonville FL 32256
Tel (866) 961-9529 SIC 6411

■ KEMPER INDEPENDENCE INSURANCE CO p 810
12926 Gran Bay Pkwy W, Jacksonville FL 32258
Tel (904) 245-5600 SIC 6411

MAIN STREET AMERICA GROUP INC p 897
4601 Touchton Rd E # 3300, Jacksonville FL 32246
Tel (904) 642-3000 SIC 6411

ASSUREDPARTNERS INC p 122
200 Colonial Center Pkwy, Lake Mary FL 32746
Tel (407) 804-5222 SIC 6411

■ SUMMIT CONSULTING LLC p 1398
2310 Commerce Point Dr, Lakeland FL 33801
Tel (863) 665-6060 SIC 6331 6411

INSURANCE OFFICE OF AMERICA INC p 748
1855 W State Road 434, Longwood FL 32750
Tel (407) 788-3000 SIC 6411

■ AMERICAN BANKERS INSURANCE CO OF FLORIDA p 68
11222 Quail Roost Dr, Miami FL 33157
Tel (305) 253-2244 SIC 6411 6331

HAMILTON RISK MANAGEMENT CO p 655
3155 Nw 77th Ave, Miami FL 33122
Tel (305) 716-6000
SIC 6331 7323 6141 6541 6411

■ LENNAR FINANCIAL SERVICES LLC p 855
700 Nw 107th Ave Ste 400, Miami FL 33172
Tel (305) 559-4000
SIC 6162 6153 6361 6411 7382

UNITED AUTOMOBILE INSURANCE GROUP INC p 1506
3909 Ne 163rd St Ste 308, Miami FL 33160
Tel (305) 940-5022 SIC 6411

AMERICAN MANAGED CARE LLC p 75
100 Central Ave Ste 200, Saint Petersburg FL 33701
Tel (866) 690-4842 SIC 6411

BANKERS FINANCIAL CORP p 152
11101 Roosevelt Blvd N, Saint Petersburg FL 33716
Tel (727) 823-4000 SIC 6411

BANKERS INSURANCE GROUP INC p 152
11101 Roosevelt Blvd N, Saint Petersburg FL 33716
Tel (727) 823-4000 SIC 6411

BANKERS INTERNATIONAL FINANCIAL CORP p 152
11101 Roosevelt Blvd N, Saint Petersburg FL 33716
Tel (727) 823-4000 SIC 6411

FCCI INSURANCE GROUP INC p 533
6300 University Pkwy, Sarasota FL 34240
Tel (941) 907-2515 SIC 6411

FCCI SERVICES INC p 533
6300 University Pkwy, Sarasota FL 34240
Tel (941) 556-3345 SIC 6411

FINANCIAL INSURANCE MANAGEMENT CORP p 542
1440 Main St, Sarasota FL 34236
Tel (941) 952-5522 SIC 6411 8742

UNIVERSAL INSURANCE MANAGERS INC p 1517
101 Paramount Dr Ste 220, Sarasota FL 34232
Tel (941) 378-8851 SIC 6411

▲ FEDERATED NATIONAL HOLDING CO p 536
14050 Nw 14th St Ste 180, Sunrise FL 33323
Tel (954) 581-9993 SIC 6331 6411

TEAM FOCUS INSURANCE GROUP LLC p 1429
1300 Sawgrs Corp Pkwy # 300, Sunrise FL 33323
Tel (954) 331-4800 SIC 6719 6411

AUTO CLUB SOUTH INSURANCE CO p 133
14055 Riveredge Dr # 500, Tampa FL 33637
Tel (800) 289-1325 SIC 6411

▲ HCI GROUP INC p 672
5300 W Cypress St Ste 100, Tampa FL 33607
Tel (813) 849-9500 SIC 6331 6411

HEALTH E SYSTEMS LLC p 674
5100 W Lemon St Ste 311, Tampa FL 33609
Tel (813) 463-1235 SIC 6411

▲ HEALTH INSURANCE INNOVATIONS INC p 675
15438 N Florida Ave # 201, Tampa FL 33613
Tel (877) 376-5831 SIC 6411

MATRIX HEALTHCARE SERVICES INC p 920
3111 W Dr Martin, Tampa FL 33607
Tel (813) 247-2077 SIC 6411

WILLIS OF FLORIDA INC p 1612
4211 W Boy Scout Blvd # 4, Tampa FL 33607
Tel (813) 281-2095 *SIC* 6411

■ **FIRST GUARD INSURANCE CO** p 547
200 Nokomis Ave S Fl 4, Venice FL 34285
Tel (941) 485-6210 *SIC* 6411

■ **BRIGHTSTAR DEVICE PROTECTION LLC** p 213
2325 Lkeview Pkwy Ste 700, Alpharetta GA 30009
Tel (843) 548-0120 *SIC* 6411

PRIME RISK PARTNERS INC p 1175
2475 Northwinds Pkwy, Alpharetta GA 30009
Tel (770) 856-9332 *SIC* 6411

SOUTHERN INSURANCE UNDERWRITERS INC p 1349
4500 Mansell Rd, Alpharetta GA 30022
Tel (678) 498-4500 *SIC* 6411

ACCESS INSURANCE HOLDINGS INC p 14
3 Ravinia Dr Ste 400, Atlanta GA 30346
Tel (770) 234-3631 *SIC* 6411

■ **BEECHER CARLSON HOLDINGS INC** p 168
6 Concourse Pkwy Ste 2300, Atlanta GA 30328
Tel (404) 460-1400 *SIC* 6411

■ **FINANCIAL SERVICE CORP** p 543
2300 Windy Ridge Pkwy Se 1100s, Atlanta GA 30339
Tel (770) 916-6500
SIC 6722 6411 8742 6211

■ **FSC CORP** p 582
2300 Windy Ridge Pkwy Se # 1100, Atlanta GA 30339
Tel (770) 916-6500
SIC 6722 6411 8742 6211

■ **FSC SECURITIES CORP** p 582
2300 Windy Ridge Pkwy Se # 1100, Atlanta GA 30339
Tel (770) 916-6500 *SIC* 6411 6211

GEORGIA BANKERS ASSOCIATION INSURANCE TRUST INC p 607
50 Hurt Plz Se Ste 1050, Atlanta GA 30303
Tel (404) 522-1501 *SIC* 6411

GEORGIA BANKERS ASSOCIATION INSURANCE TRUST INC p 607
50 Hurt Plz Se Ste 1050, Atlanta GA 30303
Tel (404) 522-1501 *SIC* 6411

HBW INSURANCE SERVICES LLC p 671
4501 Circ 75 Pkwy Sef6200, Atlanta GA 30339
Tel (678) 742-6300 *SIC* 6411

MAG MUTUAL INSURANCE AGENCY LLC p 895
3525 Piedmont Rd Ne 8-600, Atlanta GA 30305
Tel (404) 842-5600 *SIC* 6351 6411

MARTIN ENGLE & ASSOCIATES INC p 912
5565 Glenridge Connector # 900, Atlanta GA 30342
Tel (678) 553-4400 *SIC* 6411

■ **QBE FIRST INSURANCE AGENCY INC** p 1194
210 Interstate North Pkwy, Atlanta GA 30339
Tel (770) 690-8400 *SIC* 6411

■ **SAFE-GUARD PRODUCTS INTERNATIONAL LLC** p 1266
2 Concourse Pkwy Ste 500, Atlanta GA 30328
Tel (404) 816-3221 *SIC* 6411

SWETT & CRAWFORD OF GEORGIA INC p 1412
3350 Riverwood Pkwy Se # 1100, Atlanta GA 30339
Tel (404) 240-5200 *SIC* 6411

■ **VOYA AMERICA EQUITIES INC** p 1566
5780 Powers Ferry Rd, Atlanta GA 30327
Tel (612) 372-5432 *SIC* 6311 6411

CRAWFORD & CO p 389
1001 Summit Blvd Ste 500, Brookhaven GA 30319
Tel (404) 300-1000
SIC 6411 8111 8099 6331

CRAWFORD & CO HEALTHCARE MANAGEMENT INC p 389
1001 Summit Blvd, Brookhaven GA 30319
Tel (404) 256-0830 *SIC* 6411

AMERISURE MUTUAL INSURANCE CO p 84
2160 Satellite Blvd # 200, Duluth GA 30097
Tel (770) 813-3300 *SIC* 6411

GROUP RESOURCES INC p 642
3080 Premiere Pkwy # 100, Duluth GA 30097
Tel (770) 623-8383 *SIC* 6411

■ **PRIMERICA FINANCIAL SERVICES INC** p 1175
3120 Breckinridge Blvd, Duluth GA 30099
Tel (800) 544-5445 *SIC* 6411

▲ **PRIMERICA INC** p 1175
1 Primerica Pkwy, Duluth GA 30099
Tel (770) 381-1000 *SIC* 6411

BRECKENRIDGE IS INC p 209
245 Townpark Dr Nw # 200, Kennesaw GA 30144
Tel (678) 322-3536 *SIC* 6411

HCC LIFE INSURANCE CO p 672
225 Townpark Dr Nw # 145, Kennesaw GA 30144
Tel (770) 973-9851 *SIC* 6411

GEORGIA FARM BUREAU MUTUAL INSURANCE CO p 607
1620 Bass Rd, Macon GA 31210
Tel (478) 474-0679 *SIC* 6411

INSURANCE HOUSE INC p 748
1904 Leland Dr Se, Marietta GA 30067
Tel (770) 952-0080 *SIC* 6331 6411 6141

AUTOMOBILE PROTECTION CORP-APCO p 134
6010 Atlantic Blvd, Norcross GA 30071
Tel (678) 225-1001 *SIC* 6411

YOUNG MCLARENS INTERNATIONAL INC p 1638
5555 Triangle Pkwy # 200, Norcross GA 30092
Tel (770) 448-4680 *SIC* 6411

CUSTARD INSURANCE ADJUSTERS INC p 402
4875 Avalon Ridge Pkwy, Peachtree Corners GA 30071
Tel (770) 263-6800 *SIC* 6411

GRESHAM WOFTAM INC p 639
1 Gresham Lndg, Stockbridge GA 30281
Tel (770) 389-1600 *SIC* 6411

SWETT & CRAWFORD GROUP INC p 1412
7230 Mcginnis Ferry Rd # 300, Suwanee GA 30024
Tel (404) 240-5200 *SIC* 6411

J SMITH LANIER & CO p 772
300 W 10th St, West Point GA 31833
Tel (706) 645-2211 *SIC* 6411

■ **BANK OF HAWAII** p 151
130 Merchant St, Honolulu HI 96813
Tel (888) 643-3888 *SIC* 6022 6411 6211

FIRST INSURANCE CO OF HAWAII LTD p 547
1100 Ward Ave, Honolulu HI 96814
Tel (808) 527-7777 *SIC* 6331 6411

ISLAND INSURANCE CO LIMITED p 766
1022 Bethel St, Honolulu HI 96813
Tel (808) 564-8200 *SIC* 6331 6411

ALLIANCE TITLE & ESCROW CORP p 55
380 E Parkcenter Blvd # 105, Boise ID 83706
Tel (208) 388-8881 *SIC* 6411

CC SERVICES INC p 269
1701 Towanda Ave, Bloomington IL 61701
Tel (309) 821-3372 *SIC* 8742 6411

COUNTRY MUTUAL INSURANCE CO INC p 375
1701 Towanda Ave, Bloomington IL 61701
Tel (309) 821-3000 *SIC* 6411

STATE FARM BANK FSB p 1380
1 State Farm Plz E 6, Bloomington IL 61701
Tel (877) 734-2265 *SIC* 6411

STATE FARM FIRE AND CASUALTY CO p 1380
Three State Frm Plz S H-4, Bloomington IL 61710
Tel (309) 766-2311 *SIC* 6411

STATE FARM FLORIDA INSURANCE CO p 1380
1 State Farm Plaza D 2, Bloomington IL 61701
Tel (309) 766-2311 *SIC* 6411

STATE FARM GENERAL INSURANCE CO INC p 1380
1 State Farm Plz, Bloomington IL 61701
Tel (309) 766-2311 *SIC* 6411

STATE FARM LIFE AND ACCIDENT ASSURANCE CO (INC) p 1381
1 State Farm Plz, Bloomington IL 61701
Tel (309) 766-2311 *SIC* 6411

■ **AMERICAN CASUALTY CO OF READING PENNSYLVANIA INC** p 70
333 S Wabash Ave Fl 22, Chicago IL 60604
Tel (312) 822-5000 *SIC* 6411

AON CORP p 95
200 E Randolph St, Chicago IL 60601
Tel (312) 381-1000 *SIC* 6411 8742

AON GROUP INC p 95
200 E Randolph St Fl 5, Chicago IL 60601
Tel (312) 381-2738 *SIC* 6311 8742 6411

AON RISK SERVICES COMPANIES INC p 95
200 E Randolph St Fl 14, Chicago IL 60601
Tel (312) 381-1000 *SIC* 6411 8111

AON SOLUTIONS INC p 95
200 E Randolph St, Chicago IL 60601
Tel (312) 381-1000 *SIC* 6411

AON US HOLDINGS INC p 95
200 E Randolph St, Chicago IL 60601
Tel (312) 381-1000 *SIC* 6411 6799 8741

■ **CHICAGO TITLE INSURANCE CO** p 297
10 S Lasalle St Ste 2850, Chicago IL 60603
Tel (312) 223-2402 *SIC* 6411 6361

■ **CNA FINANCIAL CORP** p 329
333 S Wabash Ave Ste 300, Chicago IL 60604
Tel (312) 822-5000 *SIC* 6411 6331 6311

■ **CNA SURETY CORP** p 330
333 S Wabash Ave Ste 41s, Chicago IL 60604
Tel (312) 822-5000 *SIC* 6411

CONTINENTAL ASSURANCE CO p 362
333 S Wabash Ave Fl 43, Chicago IL 60604
Tel (312) 822-5000 *SIC* 6411 6371 6321

■ **FIDELITY & CASUALTY CO OF NEW YORK** p 540
333 S Wabash Ave Fl 1, Chicago IL 60604
Tel (312) 822-5000 *SIC* 6411

■ **HARLEY-DAVIDSON FINANCIAL SERVICES INC** p 661
222 W Adams St Ste 2000, Chicago IL 60606
Tel (312) 368-9501 *SIC* 6141 6411

HEALTH CARE SERVICE CORP A MUTUAL LEGAL RESERVE CO p 674
300 E Randolph St Fl 4, Chicago IL 60601
Tel (312) 653-6000 *SIC* 6324 6321 6411

HUB INTERNATIONAL LIMITED p 716
300 N La Salle Dr Ste 17, Chicago IL 60654
Tel (312) 596-7522 *SIC* 6411

HUB INTERNATIONAL MIDWEST LTD p 716
55 E Jackson Blvd 1400a, Chicago IL 60604
Tel (312) 922-5000 *SIC* 6411

HUB INTERNATIONAL OF ILLINOIS LIMITED p 716
300 N Lslle St Fl 17, Chicago IL 60654
Tel (312) 922-5000 *SIC* 6411

LLOYDS ILLINOIS INC p 872
181 W Madison St Ste 3870, Chicago IL 60602
Tel (312) 407-6200 *SIC* 6411

MAGNUM INSURANCE AGENCY CO INC p 896
4259 N Western Ave, Chicago IL 60618
Tel (773) 539-2102 *SIC* 6411

MARSH MCLENNAN p 911
540 W Madison St Ste 1200, Chicago IL 60661
Tel (312) 627-6000 *SIC* 6411

MESIROW FINANCIAL HOLDINGS INC p 951
353 N Clark St Lowr Level, Chicago IL 60654
Tel (312) 595-6000
SIC 6211 6282 6531 6552 6411

NEAR NORTH NATIONAL GROUP INC p 1023
875 N Michigan Ave # 3100, Chicago IL 60611
Tel (312) 867-0064 *SIC* 6411

NORTHWEST INSURANCE NETWORK INC p 1060
515 N State St Ste 2100, Chicago IL 60654
Tel (312) 427-1777 *SIC* 6411

■ **OLD REPUBLIC SECURITY HOLDINGS INC** p 1081
307 N Michigan Ave # 1400, Chicago IL 60601
Tel (312) 346-8100 *SIC* 6411 6361

■ **OLD REPUBLIC SURETY GROUP INC** p 1081
307 N Michigan Ave # 1400, Chicago IL 60601
Tel (312) 346-8100 *SIC* 6411 6361

■ **TRANSPORTATION INSURANCE CO** p 1472
333 S Wabash Ave, Chicago IL 60604
Tel (312) 822-5000 *SIC* 6411

TWG HOLDINGS INC p 1494
175 W Jackson Blvd Fl 11, Chicago IL 60604
Tel (312) 356-3000 *SIC* 6399 8721 6411

TWG WARRANTY GROUP INC p 1494
175 W Jackson Blvd Fl 11, Chicago IL 60604
Tel (312) 356-3000 *SIC* 6399 8721 6411

■ **WELLS FARGO INSURANCE SERVICES INC** p 1590
230 W Monroe St Ste 1950, Chicago IL 60606
Tel (312) 685-4122 *SIC* 6411

■ **WELLS FARGO INSURANCE SERVICES USA INC** p 1591
150 N Michigan Ave # 3900, Chicago IL 60601
Tel (866) 294-2571 *SIC* 6411

WIRTZ CORP p 1618
680 N Lake Shore Dr # 1900, Chicago IL 60611
Tel (312) 943-7000
SIC 5181 5182 6513 6512 7011 6411

CANNON COCHRAN MANAGEMENT SERVICES INC p 247
2 E Main St Towne Ctr, Danville IL 61832
Tel (217) 446-1089 *SIC* 6411

GCG FINANCIAL INC p 595
3 Parkway N Ste 500, Deerfield IL 60015
Tel (847) 457-3000 *SIC* 6411 8742 6211

■ **FIRST HEALTH GROUP CORP** p 547
3200 Highland Ave, Downers Grove IL 60515
Tel (630) 737-7900
SIC 8742 6324 6321 6411

■ **FIRST HEALTH STRATEGIES INC** p 547
3200 Highland Ave, Downers Grove IL 60515
Tel (630) 737-7900 *SIC* 6411

▲ **ARTHUR J GALLAGHER & CO** p 114
2 Pierce Pl, Itasca IL 60143
Tel (630) 773-3800 *SIC* 6411 6282 8741

■ **ARTHUR J GALLAGHER & CO (ILLINOIS)** p 114
2 Pierce Pl Ste 100, Itasca IL 60143
Tel (630) 773-3800 *SIC* 6411

■ **GALLAGHER BASSETT SERVICES INC** p 589
2 Pierce Pl Ste 100, Itasca IL 60143
Tel (630) 773-3800 *SIC* 6411 8741

■ **GALLAGHER BENEFIT SERVICES INC** p 589
2 Pierce Pl, Itasca IL 60143
Tel (630) 773-3800 *SIC* 6411

■ **RISK PLACEMENT SERVICES INC** p 1236
2 Pierce Pl Fl 25, Itasca IL 60143
Tel (630) 773-3800 *SIC* 6411

CORESOURCE INC p 370
400 N Field Dr, Lake Forest IL 60045
Tel (847) 615-1500 *SIC* 6324 6411

DOVENMUEHLE MORTGAGE INC p 452
1 Corporate Dr Ste 360, Lake Zurich IL 60047
Tel (847) 550-7300 *SIC* 6162 6411

AON CONSULTING WORLDWIDE INC p 95
100 Half Day Rd 2, Lincolnshire IL 60069
Tel (312) 381-4800
SIC 6311 6321 6331 8742 6411 6351

AMERICAN MOTORISTS INSURANCE CO p 76
1 Kemper Dr, Long Grove IL 60047
Tel (847) 320-2000 *SIC* 6411

AMERICAN PROTECTION INSURANCE CO INC p 78
1 Kemper Dr, Long Grove IL 60047
Tel (847) 320-2000 *SIC* 6411

VERICLAIM INC p 1549
1833 Cntre Pt Cir Ste 139, Naperville IL 60563
Tel (630) 245-7000 *SIC* 6411

▲ **ALLSTATE CORP** p 58
2775 Sanders Rd, Northbrook IL 60062
Tel (847) 402-5000
SIC 6411 6351 6311 6371

■ **ALLSTATE DISTRIBUTORS LLC** p 58
2775 Sanders Rd, Northbrook IL 60062
Tel (847) 402-5000 *SIC* 6411

■ **ALLSTATE INDEMNITY CO** p 58
2775 Sanders Rd F9, Northbrook IL 60062
Tel (847) 402-5000 *SIC* 6411

■ **ALLSTATE INSURANCE CO** p 58
2775 Sanders Rd, Northbrook IL 60062
Tel (847) 402-5000 *SIC* 6411

■ **ALLSTATE LIFE INSURANCE CO** p 58
3075 Sanders Rd, Northbrook IL 60062
Tel (847) 402-5000 *SIC* 6411 6311

■ **ALLSTATE NON INSURANCE HOLDINGS INC** p 58
2775 Sanders Rd Ste D, Northbrook IL 60062
Tel (847) 402-5000 *SIC* 6411

■ **CAREMARK INTERNATIONAL LLC** p 255
2211 Sanders Rd, Northbrook IL 60062
Tel (847) 559-4700
SIC 5961 6411 8099 8092 8093

■ **CAREMARK LLC** p 255
2211 Sanders Rd, Northbrook IL 60062
Tel (847) 559-4700
SIC 5961 6411 8099 8092 8093 8742

HORTON GROUP INC p 708
10320 Orland Pkwy, Orland Park IL 60467
Tel (708) 845-3000
SIC 6411 6331 6321 6311

▲ **FARMERS AUTOMOBILE INSURANCE ASSOCIATION (INC)** p 529
2505 Court St, Pekin IL 61558
Tel (309) 346-1161 *SIC* 6411 6311

■ **PEKIN INSURANCE** p 1128
2505 Court St, Pekin IL 61558
Tel (888) 735-4611 *SIC* 6411

PEARL & ASSOCIATES LTD p 1126
1200 E Glen Ave, Peoria IL 61616
Tel (309) 688-9000 *SIC* 6411

▲ **RLI CORP** p 1239
9025 N Lindbergh Dr, Peoria IL 61615
Tel (309) 692-1000 *SIC* 6411

ROYAL NEIGHBORS OF AMERICA p 1254
230 16th St, Rock Island IL 61201
Tel (309) 788-4561 *SIC* 6411 6311

CHRISTIAN BROTHERS EMPLOYEE BENEFIT TRUST p 302
1205 Windham Pkwy, Romeoville IL 60446
Tel (630) 378-2900 *SIC* 6411

AMERICAN FARM BUREAU INSURANCE SERVICES INC p 72
1501 E Wdfeld Rd Ste 300w, Schaumburg IL 60173
Tel (847) 969-2900 *SIC* 6411

ASSURANCE AGENCY LTD p 121
1750 E Golf Rd, Schaumburg IL 60173
Tel (847) 944-9087 *SIC* 6411

ROANOKE COMPANIES INC p 1240
1475 E Woodfield Rd, Schaumburg IL 60173
Tel (847) 969-1420 *SIC* 6411

ROANOKE INSURANCE GROUP INC p 1240
1475 E Wdfield Rd Ste 500, Schaumburg IL 60173
Tel (847) 969-1420 *SIC* 6411

ZURICH NORTH AMERICA INC p 1645
1299 Zurich Way, Schaumburg IL 60196
Tel (800) 987-3373 *SIC* 6411

■ **AMERICAN GENERAL LIFE INSURANCE** p 73
1 Franklin Sq, Springfield IL 62703
Tel (217) 528-2011 *SIC* 6411 6321 6211

▲ **HORACE MANN EDUCATORS CORP** p 706
1 Horace Mann Plz, Springfield IL 62715
Tel (217) 789-2500 *SIC* 6311 6331 6411

■ **HORACE MANN LIFE INSURANCE CO** p 706
1 Horace Mann Plz, Springfield IL 62715
Tel (217) 789-2500 *SIC* 6411

■ **HORACE MANN SERVICE CORP** p 706
1 Horace Mann Plz, Springfield IL 62715
Tel (217) 789-2500 *SIC* 6411

COOK GROUP INC p 365
750 N Daniels Way, Bloomington IN 47404
Tel (812) 339-2235
SIC 3841 3821 3845 6411 6512 6211

▲ **BALDWIN & LYONS INC** p 147
111 Congressional Blvd # 500, Carmel IN 46032
Tel (317) 636-9800 *SIC* 6331 6411

■ **CNO SERVICES LLC** p 330
11825 N Pennsylvania St, Carmel IN 46032
Tel (317) 817-6100 *SIC* 6411

SHEPHERD INSURANCE LLC p 1315
111 Congressional Blvd # 100, Carmel IN 46032
Tel (317) 846-5554 *SIC* 6411

NATIONAL CATASTROPHE ADJUSTERS INC p 1010
9725 Windermere Blvd, Fishers IN 46037
Tel (317) 915-8888 *SIC* 6411

ASH BROKERAGE CORP p 116
888 S Harrison St, Fort Wayne IN 46802
Tel (260) 459-0823 *SIC* 6411

■ **FIRST PENN-PACIFIC LIFE INSURANCE CO** p 548
1300 S Clinton St, Fort Wayne IN 46802
Tel (260) 455-6408 *SIC* 6411

■ **LINCOLN NATIONAL LIFE INSURANCE CO** p 867
1300 S Clinton St, Fort Wayne IN 46802
Tel (260) 455-2000 *SIC* 6411

■ **LINCOLN NATIONAL RISK MANAGEMENT INC** p 867
1670 Magnavox Way, Fort Wayne IN 46804
Tel (260) 455-2000 *SIC* 6411

■ **MEDICAL PROTECTIVE CO** p 937
5814 Reed Rd, Fort Wayne IN 46835
Tel (260) 485-9622 *SIC* 6351 6411

PHYSICIANS HEALTH PLAN OF NORTHERN INDIANA INC p 1145
8101 W Jefferson Blvd, Fort Wayne IN 46804
Tel (260) 432-6690 *SIC* 6321 8011 6411

■ **ANTHEM INSURANCE COMPANIES INC** p 94
120 Monument Cir Ste 200, Indianapolis IN 46204
Tel (317) 488-6000
SIC 6324 6411 6321 6331 6159 7371

■ **ANTHEM SOUTHEAST INC** p 94
120 Monument Cir Ste 200, Indianapolis IN 46204
Tel (317) 488-6000 *SIC* 6411 6311 6321

INDIANA FARM BUREAU INC p 738
225 S East St, Indianapolis IN 46202
Tel (317) 692-7851 *SIC* 6411

M-PLAN INC p 890
8802 N Meridian St # 100, Indianapolis IN 46260
Tel (317) 963-9700 *SIC* 6324 6411

ONEAMERICA RETIREMENT SERVICES LLC p 1087
1 American Sq, Indianapolis IN 46282
Tel (317) 285-1877 *SIC* 6411

ONI RISK PARTNERS INC p 1088
600 E 96th St Ste 400, Indianapolis IN 46240
Tel (317) 706-9500 *SIC* 6411

UNITED FARM FAMILY LIFE INSURANCE CO p 1508
225 S East St Ste 144, Indianapolis IN 46202
Tel (317) 692-7200 *SIC* 6311 6411

TRUENORTH COMPANIES LC p 1486
500 1st St Se, Cedar Rapids IA 52401
Tel (319) 364-5193 *SIC* 6411

▲ **UNITED FIRE GROUP INC** p 1508
118 2nd Ave Se, Cedar Rapids IA 52401
Tel (319) 399-5700 *SIC* 6411 6311

■ **BITCO CORP** p 185
3700 Market Square Cir, Davenport IA 52807
Tel (309) 786-5401 *SIC* 6411 6331

AMCO INSURANCE CO p 65
1100 Locust St, Des Moines IA 50391
Tel (515) 280-4211 *SIC* 6411

AMERICAN ENTERPRISE MUTUAL HOLDING CO p 71
601 6th Ave, Des Moines IA 50309
Tel (515) 245-2000 *SIC* 6321 6411

EMC NATIONAL LIFE CO p 491
699 Walnut St Ste 1100, Des Moines IA 50309
Tel (515) 237-2000 *SIC* 6311 6411

■ **EMC REINSURANCE CO** p 491
717 Mulberry St, Des Moines IA 50309
Tel (515) 345-4541 *SIC* 6411

▲ **EMPLOYERS MUTUAL CASUALTY CO** p 494
717 Mulberry St, Des Moines IA 50309
Tel (515) 280-2511
SIC 6411 6321 6311 6519

FARMLAND MUTUAL INSURANCE CO INC p 530
1100 Locust St, Des Moines IA 50391
Tel (515) 508-3300 SIC 6411

■ PRINCIPAL LIFE INSURANCE CO p 1177
711 High St, Des Moines IA 50392
Tel (515) 247-5111
SIC 6311 6211 6162 6321 6411

WELLMARK INC p 1589
1331 Grand Ave, Des Moines IA 50309
Tel (515) 376-4500 SIC 6324 6411 6321

COTTINGHAM & BUTLER INC p 374
800 Main St, Dubuque IA 52001
Tel (800) 793-5235 SIC 6411

GRINNELL MUTUAL REINSURANCE CO p 641
4215 Highway 146, Grinnell IA 50112
Tel (641) 269-8000 SIC 6411

IOWA BANKERS BENEFIT PLAN p 762
8800 Nw 62nd Ave, Johnston IA 50131
Tel (515) 286-4300 SIC 6411

CUNA MUTUAL LIFE INSURANCE CO p 401
2000 Heritage Way, Waverly IA 50677
Tel (319) 352-4090 SIC 6411 6321 8742

EQUITRUST LIFE INSURANCE CO INC p 506
7100 Westown Pkwy Ste 200, West Des Moines IA 50266
Tel (888) 400-5759 SIC 6411

FARM BUREAU MULTI-STATE SERVICES INC p 528
5400 University Ave, West Des Moines IA 50266
Tel (515) 225-5400 SIC 6411

FARM BUREAU PROPERTY & CASUALTY INSURANCE CO p 528
5400 University Ave, West Des Moines IA 50266
Tel (515) 225-5400 SIC 6411 2711 6211

▲ FBL FINANCIAL GROUP INC p 532
5400 University Ave, West Des Moines IA 50266
Tel (515) 225-5400 SIC 6311 6411

GUIDEONE MUTUAL INSURANCE CO p 645
1111 Ashworth Rd, West Des Moines IA 50265
Tel (515) 267-5000 SIC 6411

HMA INC p 697
3001 Westown Pkwy Stop 1, West Des Moines IA 50266
Tel (515) 223-6800 SIC 6411 6321 8742

HOLMES MURPHY AND ASSOCIATES LLC p 701
3001 Westown Pkwy, West Des Moines IA 50266
Tel (800) 247-7756 SIC 6411

HY-VEE AND AFFILIATES BENEFIT PLAN AND TRUST p 723
5820 Westown Pkwy, West Des Moines IA 50266
Tel (515) 267-2800 SIC 6411

IOWA FARM BUREAU FEDERATION p 762
5400 University Ave, West Des Moines IA 50266
Tel (515) 225-5400
SIC 8699 5154 6311 6321 6411

■ MARSH AFFINITY GROUP SERVICES p 910
12421 Meredith Dr, West Des Moines IA 50398
Tel (515) 243-1900 SIC 6411

■ LABONE INC p 836
10101 Renner Blvd, Lenexa KS 66219
Tel (913) 888-1770 SIC 8071 6411

ASCENSION INSURANCE INC p 116
9225 Indian Creek Pkwy # 700, Overland Park KS 66210
Tel (816) 842-1332 SIC 6411

GREAT-WEST FINANCIAL RETIREMENT PLAN SERVICES LLC p 635
11500 Outlook St, Overland Park KS 66211
Tel (847) 857-3000 SIC 6411

■ OVERLAND SOLUTIONS INC p 1099
10975 Grandview Dr # 400, Overland Park KS 66210
Tel (913) 451-3222 SIC 6411

▲ WADDELL & REED FINANCIAL INC p 1571
6300 Lamar Ave, Overland Park KS 66202
Tel (913) 236-2000 SIC 6211 6282 6411

BROOKE HOLDINGS INC p 217
205 F St, Phillipsburg KS 67661
Tel (785) 543-3199 SIC 6411

■ WADDELL & REED INC p 1571
6300 Lamar Ave, Shawnee Mission KS 66202
Tel (913) 236-2000
SIC 6282 6211 6289 6411

SECURITY BENEFIT GROUP INC p 1299
1 Sw Security Benefit Pl, Topeka KS 66636
Tel (785) 438-3000 SIC 6211 7311 6411

CORKEN STEEL PRODUCTS CO p 370
7920 Kentucky Dr, Florence KY 41042
Tel (859) 291-4664
SIC 5075 3444 5051 8742 6411

▲ FARMERS CAPITAL BANK CORP p 529
202 W Main St Ste 100, Frankfort KY 40601
Tel (502) 227-1668 SIC 6021 7374 6411

BLUEGRASS FAMILY HEALTH p 193
651 Perimeter Dr Ste 300, Lexington KY 40517
Tel (859) 269-4475 SIC 6321 6411

AMERICAN INCOME LIFE INSURANCE p 74
10000 Shelbyville Rd # 211, Louisville KY 40223
Tel (812) 280-1360 SIC 6411

ASSURED NL INSURANCE AGENCY INC p 122
2305 River Rd, Louisville KY 40206
Tel (502) 894-2100 SIC 6411

CHURCHILL INSURANCE ASSOCIATES INC p 305
1700 Eastpoint Pkwy, Louisville KY 40223
Tel (502) 244-1343 SIC 6411

▲ HUMANA INC p 718
500 W Main St Ste 300, Louisville KY 40202
Tel (502) 580-1000 SIC 6324 6321 6411

KENTUCKY FARM BUREAU INSURANCE AGENCY INC p 812
9201 Bunsen Pkwy, Louisville KY 40220
Tel (502) 495-5000 SIC 6411

KENTUCKY FARM BUREAU MUTUAL INSURANCE CO p 812
9201 Bunsen Pkwy, Louisville KY 40220
Tel (502) 495-5000 SIC 6411

NL OF KY INC p 1045
2305 River Rd, Louisville KY 40206
Tel (502) 894-2100 SIC 6411

SHPS HOLDINGS INC p 1319
9200 Shelbyville Rd # 100, Louisville KY 40222
Tel (502) 267-4900 SIC 6411 8742

TROVER SOLUTIONS INC p 1485
9390 Bunsen Pkwy, Louisville KY 40220
Tel (502) 214-1340 SIC 6411 7322

UNDERWRITERS SAFETY AND CLAIMS INC p 1502
1700 Eastpoint Pkwy, Louisville KY 40223
Tel (502) 244-1343 SIC 6411

UNIVERSITY HEALTH CARE INC p 1518
5100 Cmmerce Crossings Dr, Louisville KY 40229
Tel (502) 585-7900 SIC 8011 6411

■ AUDUBON INSURANCE CO p 131
4000 S Shrwd Frst Blvd Ste 401, Baton Rouge LA 70816
Tel (225) 293-5900 SIC 6331 6411

LOUISIANA FARM BUREAU CASUALTY INSURANCE CO p 880
9516 Airline Hwy, Baton Rouge LA 70815
Tel (225) 922-6200 SIC 6411

LOUISIANA HEALTH SERVICE AND INDEMNITY CO p 880
5525 Reitz Ave, Baton Rouge LA 70809
Tel (225) 295-3307 SIC 6321 6324 6411

GILSBAR INC p 612
2100 Covington Centre, Covington LA 70433
Tel (985) 892-3520 SIC 6411

F A RICHARD & ASSOCIATES INC p 522
1625 W Causeway Approach, Mandeville LA 70471
Tel (985) 624-8383 SIC 6411

CROSS FINANCIAL CORP p 393
491 Main St, Bangor ME 04401
Tel (207) 947-7345 SIC 6411

DARLINGS p 412
96 Parkway S Unit 1, Brewer ME 04412
Tel (207) 992-1720 SIC 5511 6411

T D BANKNORTH INSURANCE GROUP p 1419
75 John Roberts Rd Bldg C, South Portland ME 04106
Tel (207) 239-3500 SIC 6411

AON RISK SERVICES INC OF MARYLAND p 95
500 E Pratt St, Baltimore MD 21202
Tel (410) 547-2800 SIC 6411

RIGGS COUNSELMAN MICHAELS & DOWNES INC p 1234
555 Fairmount Ave, Baltimore MD 21286
Tel (410) 339-7263 SIC 6411

ACACIA LIFE INSURANCE CO p 13
7315 Wisconsin Ave 1000w, Bethesda MD 20814
Tel (301) 280-1000
SIC 6311 6411 6035 6282 6211

B F SAUL CO p 141
7501 Wisconsin Ave, Bethesda MD 20814
Tel (301) 986-6000 SIC 6531 6411

■ CHEVY CHASE BANK FSB p 296
7501 Wisconsin Ave Fl 11, Bethesda MD 20814
Tel (240) 497-4101
SIC 6035 6411 6211 6519 6552 6719

■ GOVERNMENT EMPLOYEES INSURANCE CO INC p 627
5260 Western Ave, Chevy Chase MD 20815
Tel (301) 986-2500 SIC 6411

AVEMCO CORP p 136
8490 Progress Dr Ste 100, Frederick MD 21701
Tel (301) 694-5700
SIC 6331 6321 6399 6411 7372

BANNER LIFE INSURANCE CO p 153
3275 Bennett Creek Ave, Frederick MD 21704
Tel (301) 279-4800 SIC 6311 6411

LEGAL & GENERAL AMERICA INC p 853
3275 Bennett Creek Ave, Frederick MD 21704
Tel (800) 638-8428 SIC 6411 6311

BRETHREN MUTUAL INSURANCE CO p 210
149 N Edgewood Dr, Hagerstown MD 21740
Tel (800) 621-4264 SIC 6331 6411

PDP GROUP INC p 1125
10909 Mccormick Rd, Hunt Valley MD 21031
Tel (410) 584-2000 SIC 6411

▲ SANDY SPRING BANCORP INC p 1279
17801 Georgia Ave, Olney MD 20832
Tel (301) 774-6400 SIC 6411

CAREFIRST BLUECHOICE INC p 254
10455 Mill Run Cir, Owings Mills MD 21117
Tel (202) 479-8000 SIC 6321 8011 6411

EULER HERMES NORTH AMERICA INSURANCE CO p 512
800 Red Brook Blvd, Owings Mills MD 21117
Tel (410) 753-0753 SIC 6351 6411

■ CATAMARAN HEALTH SOLUTIONS LLC p 264
800 King Farm Blvd # 300, Rockville MD 20850
Tel (301) 548-2900 SIC 5912 6411

■ CLAIMS ADMINISTRATION CORP p 321
15400 Calhoun Dr Ste 300, Rockville MD 20855
Tel (301) 762-5806 SIC 6411

SPECIAL AGENTS MUTUAL BENEFIT ASSOCIATION INC p 1355
11301 Old Georgetown Rd, Rockville MD 20852
Tel (301) 984-1440 SIC 6411

KELLY & ASSOCIATES INSURANCE GROUP INC p 809
1 Kelly Way, Sparks Glencoe MD 21152
Tel (410) 527-3400 SIC 6411

■ AIR WORLDWIDE CORP p 39
131 Dartmouth St Ste 401, Boston MA 02116
Tel (617) 267-6645 SIC 6411

ALLIED WORLD ASSURANCE CO (US) INC p 57
2 Liberty Sq Fl 11, Boston MA 02109
Tel (857) 288-6000 SIC 6411

ARBELLA INC p 102
101 Arch St Ste 1860, Boston MA 02110
Tel (617) 328-2800 SIC 6411

FIDELITY WELFARE BENEFIT PLANS VEBA TRUST p 541
82 Devonshire St, Boston MA 02109
Tel (617) 563-1428 SIC 6411

HANCOCK NATURAL RESOURCE GROUP INC p 657
197 Clarendon St, Boston MA 02116
Tel (617) 747-1600 SIC 6411

HOMESITE GROUP INC p 704
1 Federal St Ste 400, Boston MA 02110
Tel (617) 832-1300 SIC 6411

JOHN HANCOCK FINANCIAL SERVICES INC p 788
200 Clarendon St, Boston MA 02116
Tel (617) 572-6000
SIC 6311 6351 6411 6371 6321

JOHN HANCOCK MANULIFE p 788
197 Clarendon St Fl 4, Boston MA 02116
Tel (617) 663-3000 SIC 6411

NATIONAL FINANCIAL SERVICES LLC p 1012
200 Seaport Blvd Ste 630, Boston MA 02210
Tel (800) 471-0382 SIC 6211 6411 6282

NEPC LLC p 1026
255 State St Ste 600, Boston MA 02109
Tel (617) 314-3176 SIC 6411 6282

■ NEW ENGLAND LIFE INSURANCE CO p 1030
501 Boylston St Ste 1, Boston MA 02116
Tel (617) 578-2000 SIC 6411

RSC INSURANCE BROKERAGE INC p 1255
160 Federal St, Boston MA 02110
Tel (617) 330-5700 SIC 6411

▲ SAFETY INSURANCE GROUP INC p 1266
20 Custom House St # 400, Boston MA 02110
Tel (617) 951-0600 SIC 6331 6411

■ THOMAS BLACK CORP p 1448
20 Custom House St # 400, Boston MA 02110
Tel (617) 951-0600 SIC 6411

■ WILLIAM GALLAGHER ASSOCIATES INSURANCE BROKERS INC p 1610
470 Atlantic Ave Fl 13, Boston MA 02210
Tel (617) 261-6700 SIC 6411 8742

MIB GROUP INC p 959
50 Braintree Hill Park # 400, Braintree MA 02184
Tel (781) 751-6000 SIC 6411

HEALTH ALLIANCE WITH PHYSICIAN p 674
60 Hospital Rd, Leominster MA 01453
Tel (978) 466-2000 SIC 6411

ONEBEACON INSURANCE CO p 1087
11 Norfolk St, Mansfield MA 02048
Tel (781) 332-7000 SIC 6411

NORTHLAND INVESTMENT CORP p 1057
2150 Washington St # 300, Newton MA 02462
Tel (617) 965-7100 SIC 6799 6411 6531

▲ BERKSHIRE HILLS BANCORP INC p 175
24 North St, Pittsfield MA 01201
Tel (413) 443-5601 SIC 6022 6411

ARBELLA MUTUAL INSURANCE CO p 102
1100 Crown Colony Dr, Quincy MA 02169
Tel (617) 328-2800 SIC 6411 6331

ARBELLA PROTECTION INSURANCE CO INC p 102
1100 Crown Colony Dr, Quincy MA 02169
Tel (617) 328-2800 SIC 6411

QUINCY MUTUAL FIRE INSURANCE CO INC p 1200
57 Washington St, Quincy MA 02169
Tel (617) 770-5100 SIC 6331 6411

MASSACHUSETTS MUTUAL LIFE INSURANCE CO p 917
1295 State St, Springfield MA 01111
Tel (413) 788-8411
SIC 6321 6324 6411 6282

CITATION INSURANCE CO p 309
211 Main St, Webster MA 01570
Tel (508) 943-9000 SIC 6411

HEALTH PLANS INC p 675
1500 W Park Dr Ste 330, Westborough MA 01581
Tel (508) 752-2480 SIC 6411

AMERICAN FLORIST SUPPLY INC p 72
1 Progress Way, Wilmington MA 01887
Tel (978) 658-2400 SIC 6411

■ ALLMERICA FINANCIAL LIFE INSURANCE AND ANNUITY p 58
440 Lincoln St, Worcester MA 01653
Tel (508) 855-1000 SIC 6411 6211

FIRST ALLMERICA FINANCIAL LIFE INSURANCE CO p 544
440 Lincoln St, Worcester MA 01653
Tel (508) 855-1000 SIC 6411 6211 6324

AAA INSURANCE OF MICHIGAN p 7
6751 Dixie Hwy Ste 103, Clarkston MI 48346
Tel (248) 620-9120 SIC 6411

AON CONSULTING (MICHIGAN) INC p 94
400 Renaissance Ctr Lbby, Detroit MI 48243
Tel (313) 393-7888 SIC 6411

MICHIGAN EDUCATION SPECIAL SERVICES ASSOCIATION p 961
1475 Kendale Blvd, East Lansing MI 48823
Tel (517) 332-2581 SIC 6411 6321

AJK ENTERPRISES INC p 41
30833 Northwestern Hwy, Farmington Hills MI 48334
Tel (248) 932-9000 SIC 6411

AMERISURE INC p 84
26777 Halsted Rd Lbby, Farmington Hills MI 48331
Tel (248) 615-9000 SIC 6411

BURNS & WILCOX LTD p 228
120 Kaufm Finan Cente 30, Farmington Hills MI 48334
Tel (248) 932-9000 SIC 6331 6411

PIONEER STATE MUTUAL INSURANCE CO p 1151
1510 N Elms Rd, Flint MI 48532
Tel (810) 733-2300 SIC 6411

HASTINGS MUTUAL INSURANCE CO p 667
404 E Woodlawn Ave, Hastings MI 49058
Tel (800) 442-8277 SIC 6411

LIGHTHOUSE INSURANCE GROUP INC p 865
877 E 16th St, Holland MI 49423
Tel (616) 392-6900
SIC 6411 6331 6321 6311

AUTO-OWNERS LIFE INSURANCE CO p 133
6101 Anacapri Blvd, Lansing MI 48917
Tel (517) 323-1200 SIC 6411 6331

FARM BUREAU GENERAL INSURANCE CO OF MICHIGAN p 528
7373 W Saginaw Hwy, Lansing MI 48917
Tel (517) 323-7000 SIC 6411

JACKSON NATIONAL LIFE INSURANCE CO INC p 774
1 Corporate Way, Lansing MI 48951
Tel (517) 381-5500
SIC 6311 6282 6211 6411

OWNERS INSURANCE CO p 1100
6101 Anacapri Blvd, Lansing MI 48917
Tel (517) 323-1200 SIC 6411 6331

UPPER PENINSULA HEALTH PLAN LLC p 1529
853 W Washington St, Marquette MI 49855
Tel (906) 225-7500 SIC 6321 6411

■ DIGITAL LEASH LLC p 439
39500 High Pointe Blvd # 250, Novi MI 48375
Tel (877) 775-3274 SIC 6331 6411

■ PROGRESSIVE MICHIGAN INSURANCE CO p 1181
46333 Five Mile Rd 100, Plymouth MI 48170
Tel (734) 456-5742 SIC 6411

NGS AMERICAN INC p 1041
27575 Harper Ave, Saint Clair Shores MI 48081
Tel (586) 552-4656 SIC 6411 8741

MEADOWBROOK INC p 934
26255 American Dr, Southfield MI 48034
Tel (248) 358-1100 SIC 6411

MEADOWBROOK INSURANCE GROUP INC p 934
26255 American Dr, Southfield MI 48034
Tel (248) 358-1100 SIC 6411 6211

US HEALTH HOLDINGS LTD p 1532
8220 Irving Rd, Sterling Heights MI 48312
Tel (586) 693-4400 SIC 6411

HAGERTY INSURANCE AGENCY INC p 652
141 Rvers Edge Dr Ste 200, Traverse City MI 49684
Tel (231) 947-6868 SIC 6411

■ PROCTOR FINANCIAL INC p 1179
5225 Crooks Rd, Troy MI 48098
Tel (248) 269-5700 SIC 6411

NORTH STAR GENERAL INSURANCE CO p 1054
269 Barstad Rd S, Cottonwood MN 56229
Tel (507) 423-6262 SIC 6411

NORTH STAR MUTUAL INSURANCE CO INC p 1054
269 Barstad Rd S, Cottonwood MN 56229
Tel (507) 423-6262 SIC 6411

PRIME THERAPEUTICS LLC p 1175
1305 Corporate Center Dr, Eagan MN 55121
Tel (612) 777-4000 SIC 8741 6411 2834

LONG TERM CARE GROUP INC p 876
11000 Prairie Lakes Dr, Eden Prairie MN 55344
Tel (952) 516-6800 SIC 6411

■ OPTUMHEALTH HOLDINGS LLC p 1090
13625 Technology Dr, Eden Prairie MN 55344
Tel (763) 595-3200 SIC 6324 8741 6411

INFORMATION PROVIDERS INC p 742
33 10th Ave S Ste 301, Hopkins MN 55343
Tel (952) 938-1400 SIC 6411

▲ AMERIPRISE FINANCIAL INC p 83
55 Ameriprise Fincl Ctr, Minneapolis MN 55474
Tel (612) 671-3131
SIC 6282 7389 6411 6311

■ BERKLEY RISK ADMINISTRATION CO LLC p 175
222 S 9th St Ste 2700, Minneapolis MN 55402
Tel (612) 766-3000 SIC 6411 3052 3432

HAYS GROUP INC p 670
80 S 8th St Ste 700, Minneapolis MN 55402
Tel (612) 347-8377 SIC 6411

NORTH STAR RESOURCE GROUP p 1054
2701 University Ave Se # 300, Minneapolis MN 55414
Tel (612) 617-6000 SIC 6411

■ RJF AGENCIES INC p 1239
7225 Northland Dr N, Minneapolis MN 55428
Tel (763) 746-8000 SIC 6411

THRIVENT FINANCIAL FOR LUTHERANS FOUNDATION p 1451
625 4th Ave S, Minneapolis MN 55415
Tel (920) 734-5721
SIC 6311 6321 8742 6411 6211

▲ US BANCORP p 1531
800 Nicollet Mall # 1500, Minneapolis MN 55402
Tel (651) 466-3000
SIC 6021 6022 6162 6091 6159 6411

■ US BANCORP INFORMATION SERVICES INC p 1531
800 Nicollet Mall, Minneapolis MN 55402
Tel (651) 466-3000 SIC 6411

■ WELLS FARGO INSURANCE SERVICES OF MINNESOTA INC p 1590
400 Highway 169 S Ste 800, Minneapolis MN 55426
Tel (952) 563-0600 SIC 6411

■ ASSOCIATED FINANCIAL GROUP LLC p 120
12600 Whitewater Dr # 100, Minnetonka MN 55343
Tel (952) 945-0200 SIC 6411

▲ UNITEDHEALTH GROUP INC p 1515
9900 Bren Rd E Ste 300w, Minnetonka MN 55343
Tel (952) 936-1300 SIC 6324 6411 6321

CATHOLIC UNITED FINANCIAL p 267
3499 Lexington Ave N, Saint Paul MN 55126
Tel (651) 490-0170 SIC 8641 6411

■ ST PAUL FIRE AND MARINE INSURANCE CO p 1372
385 Washington St, Saint Paul MN 55102
Tel (651) 221-7911
SIC 6331 6351 6321 6411

TRAVELERS INSURANCE COMPANIES p 1474
385 Washington St, Saint Paul MN 55102
Tel (651) 310-7911 SIC 6411

SOUTHERN FARM BUREAU LIFE INSURANCE CO INC p 1348
1401 Livingston Ln, Jackson MS 39213
Tel (601) 981-7422 SIC 6411

SOUTHERN FARM BUREAU CASUALTY INSURANCE CO p 1348
1800 E County Line Rd, Ridgeland MS 39157
Tel (601) 957-3200 SIC 6411

■ BANCORPSOUTH INSURANCE SERVICES INC p 150
201 W Main St Fl 2, Tupelo MS 38804
Tel (662) 680-2000 SIC 6411

▲ RENASANT CORP p 1223
209 Troy St, Tupelo MS 38804
Tel (662) 680-1001 SIC 6029 6411

▲ REINSURANCE GROUP OF AMERICA INC p 1221
16600 Swingley Ridge Rd, Chesterfield MO 63017
Tel (636) 736-7000 SIC 6311 6321 6411

■ VANLINER GROUP INC p 1544
1 Premier Dr, Fenton MO 63026
Tel (636) 343-9889 SIC 6411 8742

ASURION PROTECTION SERVICES LLC p 123
8880 Ward Pkwy Fl 5, Kansas City MO 64114
Tel (816) 237-3000 SIC 6411

FINANCIAL HOLDING CORP p 542
1055 Broadway Blvd Fl 11, Kansas City MO 64105
Tel (816) 391-2000 SIC 6411 6311 6153

FORREST T JONES & CO INC p 568
3130 Brdwy Blvd, Kansas City MO 64111
Tel (816) 756-1060 SIC 6411

KANSAS CITY LIFE INSURANCE CO p 802
3520 Broadway Blvd, Kansas City MO 64111
Tel (816) 753-7000 SIC 6311 6411

LOCKTON INC p 873
444 W 47th St Ste 900, Kansas City MO 64112
Tel (816) 960-9000 SIC 6411

ASCENSION HEALTH INSURANCE LTD p 116
4600 Edmundson Rd, Saint Louis MO 63134
Tel (314) 733-8000 SIC 6411

CHARLES L CRANE AGENCY CO p 289
100 N Broadway Ste 900, Saint Louis MO 63102
Tel (314) 241-8700 SIC 6411

■ COMMONWEALTH MUTUAL p 346
12115 Lackland Rd, Saint Louis MO 63146
Tel (314) 644-1255 SIC 6411

CONCORDIA HEALTH PLAN p 355
1333 S Kirkwood Rd, Saint Louis MO 63122
Tel (314) 965-9917 SIC 6411

DANIEL & HENRY CO p 411
1001 Highlands Plaza Dr W # 500, Saint Louis MO 63110
Tel (314) 421-1525 SIC 6411

■ GENERAL AMERICAN LIFE INSURANCE CO p 599
13045 Tesson Ferry Rd, Saint Louis MO 63128
Tel (314) 843-8700 SIC 6411 6311

JOHN M QUALY p 789
701 Market St Ste 1070, Saint Louis MO 63101
Tel (314) 231-3931 SIC 6411 6311

JONES FINANCIAL COMPANIES LLLP p 792
12555 Manchester Rd, Saint Louis MO 63131
Tel (314) 515-2000 SIC 6211 6411 6163

■ UNITED INSURANCE CO OF AMERICA p 1509
12115 Lackland Rd, Saint Louis MO 63146
Tel (314) 819-4300 SIC 6411 6321 6331

■ AMERICAN NATIONAL PROPERTY AND CASUALTY CO p 77
1949 E Snshine Corp Cntre, Springfield MO 65804
Tel (417) 887-0220 SIC 6411

■ AMERICAN NATIONAL PROPERTY AND CASUALTY INSURANCE CO p 77
1949 E Snshine Corp Cntre, Springfield MO 65899
Tel (417) 887-0220 SIC 6411

PAYNEWEST INSURANCE INC p 1122
3289 Gabel Rd, Billings MT 59102
Tel (406) 238-1900 SIC 6411

FRINGE BENEFIT RESOURCES p 580
1730 Alder Dr, Great Falls MT 59404
Tel (406) 268-1721 SIC 6411

ROSE LANE HOME p 1250
1005 N 8th St, Loup City NE 68853
Tel (308) 745-0303 SIC 8051 6411

■ FIRSTCOMP INSURANCE CO p 550
222 S 15th St Ste 1500n, Omaha NE 68102
Tel (888) 500-3344 SIC 6411

MUTUAL OF OMAHA HEALTH PLANS INC p 1003
3301 Dodge St, Omaha NE 68131
Tel (402) 342-7600 SIC 6411

■ NATIONAL INDEMNITY CO (INC) p 1013
1314 Douglas St Ste 1400, Omaha NE 68102
Tel (402) 916-3000 SIC 6331 6411 6311

■ NATIONAL LIABILITY & FIRE INSURANCE CO p 1014
3024 Harney St, Omaha NE 68131
Tel (402) 536-3000 SIC 6411

■ PAYFLEX HOLDINGS INC p 1122
10802 Farnam Dr Ste 100, Omaha NE 68154
Tel (800) 284-4885 SIC 6411

■ PAYFLEX SYSTEMS USA INC p 1122
10802 Farnam Dr Ste 100, Omaha NE 68154
Tel (402) 345-0666 SIC 6411

SILVERSTONE GROUP INC p 1324
11516 Miracle Hills Dr # 100, Omaha NE 68154
Tel (402) 964-5400
SIC 6371 6311 8742 6411

LIBERTY-USA CORP p 863
62 Maple Ave, Keene NH 03431
Tel (603) 352-3221 SIC 6411

NATIONAL GRANGE MUTUAL INSURANCE CO p 1012
55 West St, Keene NH 03431
Tel (603) 358-6517 SIC 6411

NETHERLANDS INSURANCE CO p 1027
62 Maple Ave, Keene NH 03431
Tel (603) 352-3221 SIC 6411

NEW JERSEY PROPERTY LIABILITY INSURANCE GUARANTY ASSOCIATION p 1031
222 Mount Airy Rd, Basking Ridge NJ 07920
Tel (908) 953-9533 SIC 6411

■ AIG CLAIM SERVICES INC p 37
100 Connell Dr Ste 2100, Berkeley Heights NJ 07922
Tel (973) 402-2800 SIC 6411 8111

■ SELECTIVE INSURANCE CO OF AMERICA p 1302
40 Wantage Ave, Branchville NJ 07890
Tel (973) 948-3000 SIC 6411 6351

CUMBERLAND MUTUAL FIRE INSURANCE CO (INC) p 400
633 Shiloh Pike, Bridgeton NJ 08302
Tel (856) 451-4050 SIC 6331 6411

AEGIS INSURANCE SERVICES INC p 29
1 Meadowlands Plz Ste 300, East Rutherford NJ 07073
Tel (201) 508-2600 SIC 6411

COFACE NORTH AMERICA INC p 334
Suite 3 Bldg 100, Hightstown NJ 08520
Tel (609) 469-0400 SIC 6411

TOWER GROUP INC p 1464
800 Plaza Two 8, Jersey City NJ 07311
Tel (212) 655-2000 SIC 6411

MADISON TITLE AGENCY LLC p 894
1125 Ocean Ave Ste 1, Lakewood NJ 08701
Tel (732) 905-9400 SIC 6411

BENECARD SERVICES INC p 172
3131 Princeton Pike 2-B103, Lawrenceville NJ 08648
Tel (609) 219-0400 SIC 6411

EVEREST REINSURANCE HOLDINGS INC p 514
477 Martinsville Rd, Liberty Corner NJ 07938
Tel (908) 604-3000 SIC 6411 6331 6321

■ AIG TECHNOLOGIES INC p 38
2 Peach Tree Hill Rd, Livingston NJ 07039
Tel (973) 597-0285 SIC 8742 6411 7374

CONNER STRONG & BUCKELEW COMPANIES INC p 358
401 Route 73 N Ste 300, Marlton NJ 08053
Tel (877) 861-3220 SIC 6411

ABSCO LTD CORP p 12
2740 Rte 10 E Ste 205, Morris Plains NJ 07950
Tel (973) 402-2148
SIC 6351 6411 6211 6282

ARCH REINSURANCE CO p 104
445 South St Ste 220, Morristown NJ 07960
Tel (973) 898-9575 SIC 6411

CRUM & FORSTER INC p 396
305 Madison Ave, Morristown NJ 07960
Tel (973) 490-6600
SIC 6311 6321 6331 6411

FAIRFAX INC p 524
305 Madison Ave, Morristown NJ 07960
Tel (973) 490-6600 SIC 6411

■ ADMIRAL INSURANCE CO p 23
1000 Howard Blvd Ste 300, Mount Laurel NJ 08054
Tel (856) 429-9200 SIC 6331 6411 6324

HORIZON HEALTHCARE SERVICES INC p 707
3 Penn Plz E Ste 1, Newark NJ 07105
Tel (973) 466-4000 SIC 6324 6411 6321

■ PGIM INC p 1140
655 Broad St, Newark NJ 07102
Tel (973) 802-6791 SIC 6411 6799 6282

■ PRUCO LIFE INSURANCE CO p 1187
213 Washington St, Newark NJ 07102
Tel (973) 802-6000 SIC 6311 6411

FOX HILL HOLDINGS INC p 572
99 Cherry Hill Rd, Parsippany NJ 07054
Tel (212) 734-1525 SIC 6411

■ GLOBAL AEROSPACE INC p 615
1 Sylvan Way Ste 3, Parsippany NJ 07054
Tel (973) 490-8500 SIC 6411

SOUTHERN CALIFORNIA RISK MANAGEMENT ASSOCIATES INC p 1347
99 Cherry Hill Rd Ste 102, Parsippany NJ 07054
Tel (973) 541-1330 SIC 6411

YORK RISK SERVICES GROUP INC p 1637
1 Upper Pond Bldg F, Parsippany NJ 07054
Tel (973) 404-1200 SIC 6411

HIGH POINT SAFETY AND INSURANCE MANAGEMENT CORP p 691
331 Newman Springs Rd # 304, Red Bank NJ 07701
Tel (732) 978-6000 SIC 6411

■ CITI INVESTOR SERVICES INC p 310
105 Eisenhower Pkwy Ste 2, Roseland NJ 07068
Tel (973) 461-2500 SIC 6411 7374

CRUMP GROUP INC p 396
105 Eisenhower Pkwy Fl 4, Roseland NJ 07068
Tel (973) 461-2100 SIC 6411

FEDERAL INSURANCE CO p 535
15 Mountainview Rd, Warren NJ 07059
Tel (908) 903-2000 SIC 6411

■ BOLLINGER INC p 198
200 Jefferson Park, Whippany NJ 07981
Tel (800) 526-1379 SIC 6411

MERCK AND CO INC EMPLOYEE BENEFITS TRUST p 945
1 Merck Dr, Whitehouse Station NJ 08889
Tel (908) 423-1000 SIC 6411

COLUMBIAN MUTUAL LIFE INSURANCE CO INC p 342
4704 Vestal Pkwy E, Binghamton NY 13902
Tel (607) 724-2472 SIC 6411

USI SERVICE CORP p 1535
555 Plsntvlle Rd Ste 160s, Briarcliff Manor NY 10510
Tel (914) 747-6300 SIC 6411

FIRST NIAGARA FINANCIAL GROUP INC p 548
726 Exchange St Ste 618, Buffalo NY 14210
Tel (716) 819-5500 SIC 6411

■ FIRST NIAGARA RISK MANAGEMENT INC p 548
726 Exchange St Ste 900, Buffalo NY 14210
Tel (716) 819-5500 SIC 6411

HEALTHNOW NEW YORK INC p 677
257 W Genesee St, Buffalo NY 14202
Tel (716) 887-6900 SIC 6324 6411

LAWLEY SERVICE INC p 847
361 Delaware Ave, Buffalo NY 14202
Tel (716) 849-8618 SIC 6411

MAPFRE INSURANCE CO p 903
901 Franklin Ave, Garden City NY 11530
Tel (516) 564-8000 SIC 6411

SHELTERPOINT GROUP INC p 1315
600 Northern Blvd Ste 310, Great Neck NY 11021
Tel (516) 829-8100 SIC 6411

■ METLIFE INVESTORS DISTRIBUTION CO p 954
1 Met Life Plz, Long Island City NY 11101
Tel (212) 578-2211 SIC 6411

■ METROPOLITAN LIFE INSURANCE CO (INC) p 956
2701 Queens Plz N Ste 1, Long Island City NY 11101
Tel (212) 578-2211
SIC 6411 6324 6331 6321 6531

MORSTAN GENERAL INSURANCE AGENCY INC p 991
600 Community Dr, Manhasset NY 11030
Tel (516) 488-4747 SIC 6411

INTERBORO MANAGEMENT INC p 751
155 Mineola Blvd, Mineola NY 11501
Tel (516) 213-0286 SIC 6411

UTICA NATIONAL INSURANCE GROUP p 1537
180 Genesee St, New Hartford NY 13413
Tel (315) 734-2000 SIC 6331 6411

A T I C MANAGEMENT CORP DE CORP p 6
275 7th Ave Fl 3, New York NY 10001
Tel (212) 857-8200 SIC 6411

■ AIG CAPITAL CORP p 37
70 Pine St Fl 11, New York NY 10270
Tel (908) 679-3150 SIC 6411 6799

■ AIG FUNDING INC p 37
70 Pine St Fl 50, New York NY 10270
Tel (212) 770-7000 SIC 6411 6153

■ AIG GLOBAL ASSET MANAGEMENT HOLDINGS CORP p 37
111 8th Ave, New York NY 10011
Tel (212) 709-6100 SIC 6722 6411

■ AIG GLOBAL INVESTMENT CORP p 37
175 Water St Fl 18, New York NY 10038
Tel (212) 770-7000 SIC 6722 6411

■ AIG GLOBAL REAL ESTATE INVESTMENT CORP p 37
32 Old Slip Fl 28, New York NY 10005
Tel (646) 857-2300 SIC 6512 6411

■ AIG PROPERTY CASUALTY CO p 38
70 Pine St Fl 1, New York NY 10005
Tel (800) 551-0824 SIC 6411

▲ ALLEGHANY CORP p 52
7 Times Sq Tower, New York NY 10036
Tel (212) 752-1356 SIC 6331 6411 6531

▲ AMERICAN INTERNATIONAL GROUP INC p 75
175 Water St Rm 1800, New York NY 10038
Tel (212) 770-7000
SIC 6331 6321 6311 6324 6411 6282

■ AMIC HOLDINGS INC p 85
485 Madison Ave Fl 14, New York NY 10022
Tel (212) 355-4141 SIC 6321 6411

ASSURED GUARANTY CORP p 122
31 W 52nd St Fl 26, New York NY 10019
Tel (212) 974-0100 SIC 6411

■ AXA EQUITABLE LIFE INSURANCE CO p 139
1290 Avenue Of The Americ, New York NY 10104
Tel (212) 554-1234 SIC 6311 6411 6282

CHUBB GROUP HOLDINGS INC p 304
1133 Ave Of The Americas, New York NY 10036
Tel (212) 827-4400 SIC 6411

■ CONTINENTAL CORP p 363
111 8th Ave, New York NY 10011
Tel (212) 440-3000
SIC 6331 6351 6321 6159 8741 6411

COUNTRY-WIDE INSURANCE CO p 375
40 Wall St Fl 13, New York NY 10005
Tel (212) 514-7000 SIC 6411

CRYSTAL FRANK & CO INC p 397
32 Old Slip, New York NY 10005
Tel (212) 344-2444 SIC 6411

DEWITT STERN GROUP INC p 434
420 Lexington Ave Rm 2700, New York NY 10170
Tel (212) 867-3550 SIC 6411

DONALD J FAGER & ASSOCIATES INC p 450
2 Park Ave Fl 25, New York NY 10016
Tel (212) 576-9800 SIC 6411

DORAL FINANCIAL CORP p 451
200 Park Ave Ste 1700, New York NY 10166
Tel (646) 632-3700
SIC 6029 6162 6035 6211 6411

ENDURANCE SERVICES LIMITED p 497
750 3rd Ave 210, New York NY 10017
Tel (212) 471-2800 SIC 6411

FEINBERG GRADUATE SCHOOL OF WEIZMANN INSTITUTE OF SCIENCE p 537
633 3rd Ave Fl 20, New York NY 10017
Tel (212) 895-7900 SIC 6411

FGIC CORP p 539
125 Park Ave Fl 5, New York NY 10017
Tel (212) 312-3000 SIC 6411 7389

FRENKEL BENEFITS LLC p 578
350 Hudson St Fl 4, New York NY 10014
Tel (212) 488-0200 SIC 6411

GREATER NEW YORK MUTUAL INSURANCE CO p 635
200 Madison Ave Frnt 2, New York NY 10016
Tel (212) 683-9700 SIC 6411

■ GUY CARPENTER & CO LLC p 648
1166 Ave Of The Americas, New York NY 10036
Tel (917) 937-3000 SIC 6411 8742 8732

HISCOX INC p 696
520 Madison Ave Rm 3200, New York NY 10022
Tel (914) 273-7400 SIC 6411

HUB INTERNATIONAL GROUP NORTHEAST INC p 716
5 Bryant Park Fl 4, New York NY 10018
Tel (212) 338-2000 SIC 6411

INTEGRO LTD p 750
1 State St Fl 9, New York NY 10004
Tel (212) 295-8000 SIC 6411

INTEGRO USA INC p 750
1 State St Fl 9, New York NY 10004
Tel (212) 295-8000 SIC 6411

INVIVA INC p 762
434 Hudson St Apt 2, New York NY 10014
Tel (212) 741-9322 SIC 6411

IRONSHORE SERVICES INC p 765
1 State St Fl 8, New York NY 10004
Tel (646) 826-6600 SIC 6411

K2 INTELLIGENCE LLC p 799
845 3rd Ave Fl 15, New York NY 10022
Tel (212) 694-7000 SIC 6411

▲ MARSH & MCLENNAN COMPANIES INC p 910
1166 Avenue Of The Americ, New York NY 10036
Tel (212) 345-5000 SIC 6411 6282 8742

■ MARSH LLC p 911
1166 Avenue Of The Americ, New York NY 10036
Tel (212) 345-5000 SIC 6411 6282 8742

■ MARSH USA INC p 911
1166 Ave Of The Americas, New York NY 10036
Tel (212) 345-6000
SIC 6411 6331 6351 6282

■ MERRILL LYNCH PIERCE FENNER & SMITH INC p 950
111 8th Ave, New York NY 10011
Tel (800) 637-7455 SIC 6211 6411

■ METLIFE GROUP INC p 954
1095 Ave Of The Americas, New York NY 10036
Tel (800) 638-5433 SIC 6411

■ METROPOLITAN INSURANCE & ANNUITY CO p 956
1 Madison Ave Lbby, New York NY 10010
Tel (212) 578-2211 SIC 6411

■ MONY GROUP INC p 987
1740 Broadway Ste 202, New York NY 10019
Tel (212) 708-2000 SIC 6411

MONY LIFE INSURANCE CO p 987
1740 Broadway, New York NY 10019
Tel (800) 487-6669
SIC 6411 6321 6211 6282 6531

▲ NATIONAL GENERAL HOLDINGS CORP p 1012
59 Maiden Ln Fl 38, New York NY 10038
Tel (212) 380-9500 SIC 6411

NATIONAL GENERAL INSURANCE p 1012
59 Maiden Ln Fl 38, New York NY 10038
Tel (212) 380-9477 SIC 6411

NFP CORP p 1041
340 Madison Ave Fl 21, New York NY 10173
Tel (212) 301-4000 SIC 6411 7389 6282

■ NL HOLDING CORP (DEL) p 1045
260 Madison Ave Ste 11, New York NY 10016
Tel (212) 354-8800 SIC 6211 6411

PAINTING INDUSTRY INSURANCE FUND p 1108
45 W 14th St Fl 5, New York NY 10011
Tel (212) 255-2950 SIC 6411

PALLADIUM EQUITY PARTNERS IV LP p 1108
1270 Ave Of The Americas, New York NY 10020
Tel (212) 218-5150 SIC 6411

QBE HOLDINGS INC p 1194
88 Pine St, New York NY 10005
Tel (212) 422-1212 SIC 6321 6411

SCOR US CORP p 1293
199 Water St Fl 21, New York NY 10038
Tel (212) 884-9667 SIC 6411

■ SEABURY & SMITH (DELAWARE) INC p 1296
1166 Ave Of The Americas, New York NY 10036
Tel (212) 345-9049
SIC 6411 6331 6321 6311

STARR INSURANCE HOLDINGS INC p 1379
399 Park Ave Rm 1702, New York NY 10022
Tel (646) 227-6300 SIC 6282 6411

TOKIO MARINE AMERICA p 1458
230 Park Ave Fl 2, New York NY 10169
Tel (212) 297-6600 SIC 6411

TOWER INSURANCE CO OF NEW YORK p 1464
120 Broadway Ste 31, New York NY 10271
Tel (212) 655-2000 SIC 6411

VOIP GUARDIAN PARTNERS I LLC p 1564
405 E 56th St Apt 3g, New York NY 10022
Tel (212) 421-0888 SIC 6411

▲ VOYA FINANCIAL INC p 1566
230 Park Ave Fl 14, New York NY 10169
Tel (212) 309-8200
SIC 6311 6411 6282 6211 7389

WILLIS NORTH AMERICA INC p 1612
200 Liberty St Fl 7, New York NY 10281
Tel (212) 915-8888
SIC 6411 8742 8999 8748

WILLIS OF NEW YORK INC p 1612
335 Madison Ave Fl 20, New York NY 10017
Tel (212) 938-2439 SIC 6411

WILLIS OF NEW YORK INC p 1612
200 Liberty St, New York NY 10281
Tel (212) 915-8888 SIC 6411

MARSHALL & STERLING ENTERPRISES INC p 911
110 Main St Ste 4, Poughkeepsie NY 12601
Tel (845) 454-0800 SIC 6411

FIRST SECURITY BENEFIT LIFE INSURANCE AND ANNUITY CO OF NEW YORK p 549
800 Westchester Ave N641, Rye Brook NY 10573
Tel (914) 697-4748 SIC 6411

■ AYCO CO L P p 140
321 Broadway, Saratoga Springs NY 12866
Tel (518) 886-4000
SIC 6411 6282 8742 7291

POMCO INC p 1160
2425 James St, Syracuse NY 13206
Tel (315) 432-9171 SIC 6411

USI INC p 1535
200 Summit Lake Dr # 350, Valhalla NY 10595
Tel (914) 747-6300 SIC 6411

USI INSURANCE SERVICES LLC p 1535
200 Summit Lake Dr, Valhalla NY 10595
Tel (914) 749-8500 SIC 6411

GREAT-WEST LIFE & ANNUITY INSURANCE CO OF NEW YORK p 635
50 Main St, White Plains NY 10606
Tel (914) 682-3611 SIC 6411

■ MARSH & MCLENNAN AGENCY LLC p 910
360 Hamilton Ave Ste 930, White Plains NY 10601
Tel (914) 397-1600 SIC 6411

■ STERLING & STERLING LLC p 1386
135 Crossways Park Dr # 300, Woodbury NY 11797
Tel (516) 487-0300 SIC 6411

■ TAPCO UNDERWRITERS INC p 1424
3060 S Church St, Burlington NC 27215
Tel (336) 584-8892 SIC 6411

JAMES RIVER GROUP INC p 777
1414 Raleigh Rd Ste 405, Chapel Hill NC 27517
Tel (919) 883-4171 SIC 6411

ALLEN TATE CO INC p 53
6700 Fairview Rd, Charlotte NC 28210
Tel (704) 365-6910 SIC 6411

AMWINS GROUP INC p 87
4725 Piedmont Row Dr # 600, Charlotte NC 28210
Tel (704) 749-2700 SIC 6411 8748

■ BANC OF AMERICA MORTGAGE CAPITAL CORP p 149
100 N Tryon St Ste 4700, Charlotte NC 28202
Tel (800) 876-4496 SIC 6411

■ METLIFE INSURANCE CO USA p 954
11225 N Community Hse Rd, Charlotte NC 28277
Tel (980) 949-3626
SIC 6411 6321 6331 6324

RAYCOM SPORTS NETWORK INC p 1210
1900 W Morehead St, Charlotte NC 28208
Tel (704) 378-4400
SIC 6311 6321 6324 6411 4832 4833

■ WACHOVIA MORTGAGE CORP p 1570
201 S College St Fl 16, Charlotte NC 28244
Tel (704) 374-6161 SIC 6162 6411

■ LINCOLN NATIONAL LIFE INSURANCE CO p 867
100 N Greene St, Greensboro NC 27401
Tel (336) 691-3000 SIC 6411 6321 6324

REGED INC p 1218
2100 Gateway Centre Blvd # 200, Morrisville NC 27560
Tel (919) 653-5200 SIC 6411

■ BB&T INSURANCE SERVICES INC p 163
3605 Glenwood Ave Ste 190, Raleigh NC 27612
Tel (919) 716-9907 SIC 6411

G4S COMPLIANCE & INVESTIGATIONS INC p 588
910 Paverstone Dr, Raleigh NC 27615
Tel (800) 927-0456 SIC 6411

NORTH CAROLINA FARM BUREAU INSURANCE AGENCY INC p 1051
5301 Glenwood Ave, Raleigh NC 27612
Tel (919) 782-1705 SIC 6331 6411 6311

■ NATIONAL GENERAL MANAGEMENT CORP p 1012
5630 University Pkwy, Winston Salem NC 27105
Tel (336) 435-3164 SIC 6411

■ AMERICAN MODERN INSURANCE GROUP INC p 76
7000 Midland Blvd, Amelia OH 45102
Tel (513) 943-7100 SIC 6411 6321

OHIO MUTUAL INSURANCE CO p 1077
1725 Hopley Ave, Bucyrus OH 44820
Tel (419) 562-3011 SIC 6411 6331

■ AMTRUST NORTH AMERICA INC p 87
800 Superior Ave E # 2100, Cleveland OH 44114
Tel (216) 328-6100 SIC 6331 6411

AON RISK SERVICES NORTHEAST INC p 95
1660 W 2nd St, Cleveland OH 44113
Tel (216) 621-8100 SIC 6411

DAWSON INSURANCE INC p 417
1340 Depot St Ste 300, Cleveland OH 44116
Tel (440) 333-9000 SIC 6411

JAMES B OSWALD CO p 776
1100 Superior Ave E # 1500, Cleveland OH 44114
Tel (216) 367-8787 SIC 6411

■ PROGRESSIVE HAWAII INSURANCE CORP p 1181
6300 Wilson Mills Rd, Cleveland OH 44143
Tel (440) 461-5000 SIC 6411

■ PROGRESSIVE MAX INSURANCE CO p 1181
6300 Wilson Mills Rd, Cleveland OH 44143
Tel (440) 461-5000 SIC 6331 6411

■ PROGRESSIVE PREMIER INSURANCE CO OF ILLINOIS p 1182
6300 Wilson Mills Rd W33, Cleveland OH 44143
Tel (440) 461-5000 SIC 6411

MILBANK INSURANCE CO p 968
518 E Broad St, Columbus OH 43215
Tel (614) 464-5000 SIC 6411

NATIONWIDE CORP p 1017
1 Nationwide Plz, Columbus OH 43215
Tel (614) 249-7111 SIC 6411 6321

NATIONWIDE FINANCIAL SERVICES INC p 1017
1 Nationwide Plz, Columbus OH 43215
Tel (614) 249-7111 SIC 6311 6411 8742

NATIONWIDE INSURANCE CO OF FLORIDA p 1018
2 Nationwide Plz, Columbus OH 43215
Tel (614) 249-7111 SIC 6411

NATIONWIDE LIFE AND ANNUITY INSURANCE CO p 1018
1 W Nationwide Blvd # 100, Columbus OH 43215
Tel (614) 249-7111 SIC 6411

NATIONWIDE LIFE INSURANCE CO p 1018
1 Nationwide Plz, Columbus OH 43215
Tel (877) 669-6877 SIC 6411

NATIONWIDE MUTUAL FIRE INSURANCE CO p 1018
1 W Nationwide Blvd # 100, Columbus OH 43215
Tel (614) 249-7111 SIC 6411

SAFE AUTO INSURANCE CO p 1265
4 Easton Oval, Columbus OH 43219
Tel (614) 231-0200 SIC 6411

SAFE AUTO INSURANCE GROUP INC p 1265
4 Easton Oval, Columbus OH 43219
Tel (614) 231-0200 SIC 6331 6411

SAFELITE GROUP INC p 1266
7400 Safelite Way, Columbus OH 43235
Tel (614) 210-9000 SIC 7536 3231 6411

SCOTTSDALE INSURANCE CO p 1294
1 Nationwide Plz 13207, Columbus OH 43215
Tel (480) 365-4000 SIC 6411

▲ STATE AUTOMOBILE MUTUAL INSURANCE CO INC p 1380
518 E Broad St, Columbus OH 43215
Tel (614) 464-5000 SIC 6331 6411 6351

■ BROWER INSURANCE AGENCY LLC p 219
409 E Monu Ave Ste 400, Dayton OH 45402
Tel (937) 228-4135 SIC 6411

■ METLIFE AUTO & HOME INSURANCE AGENCY INC p 954
9797 Springboro Pike, Dayton OH 45448
Tel (815) 266-5301 SIC 6411

COMPMANAGEMENT INC p 351
6377 Emerald Pkwy, Dublin OH 43016
Tel (614) 376-5300 SIC 6411

FRANK GATES COMPANIES INC p 574
5000 Bradenton Ave, Dublin OH 43017
Tel (614) 793-8000 SIC 8742 6411

UNITED RETIREMENT PLAN CONSULTANTS INC p 1511
545 Metro Pl S Ste 240, Dublin OH 43017
Tel (614) 923-8822 SIC 6411 6282

▲ CINCINNATI FINANCIAL CORP p 307
6200 S Gilmore Rd, Fairfield OH 45014
Tel (513) 870-2000 SIC 6311 6411

■ OLD REPUBLIC TITLE CO OF NORTHERN OHIO LLC p 1081
6480 Rckside Woods Blvd S, Independence OH 44131
Tel (216) 524-5700 SIC 6411 6162 6211

■ PROGRESSIVE CASUALTY INSURANCE CO p 1181
6300 Wilson Mills Rd, Mayfield Village OH 44143
Tel (440) 461-5000
SIC 6331 6351 6411 6321

OHIO NATIONAL LIFE ASSURANCE CORP p 1077
1 Financial Way Ste 100, Montgomery OH 45242
Tel (513) 794-6100 SIC 6411

LICKING MEMORIAL HEALTH SYSTEMS p 863
1320 W Main St, Newark OH 43055
Tel (740) 348-4000 SIC 8741 6411

■ NATIONAL INTERSTATE CORP p 1013
3250 Interstate Dr, Richfield OH 44286
Tel (330) 659-8900 SIC 6331 6411

■ HUNTINGTON INSURANCE INC p 720
519 Madison Ave, Toledo OH 43604
Tel (419) 720-7900 SIC 6411

HYLANT GROUP INC p 724
811 Madison Ave Fl 11, Toledo OH 43604
Tel (419) 255-1020 SIC 6411

■ ENVISION PHARMACEUTICAL SERVICES LLC p 504
2181 E Aurora Rd Ste 201, Twinsburg OH 44087
Tel (330) 405-8080 SIC 6411

ALL AMERICA INSURANCE CO INC p 51
800 S Washington St, Van Wert OH 45891
Tel (419) 238-1010 SIC 6411

■ HARRINGTON HEALTH SERVICES INC p 663
780 Brooksedge Plaza Dr, Westerville OH 43081
Tel (614) 212-7000 SIC 6411

HELIOS p 681
250 Progressive Way, Westerville OH 43082
Tel (614) 794-3300 SIC 6411

OHIO FARMERS INSURANCE CO p 1077
1 Park Cir, Westfield Center OH 44251
Tel (800) 243-0210 SIC 6411 6331

WESTFIELD INSURANCE CO p 1601
1 Park Cir, Westfield Center OH 44251
Tel (800) 243-0210 SIC 6411 6331

FORGE INDUSTRIES INC p 567
4450 Market St, Youngstown OH 44512
Tel (330) 782-8301
SIC 5085 3566 3599 3531 6411 7699

PACESETTER CLAIMS SERVICE INC p 1103
2871 N Highway 167, Catoosa OK 74015
Tel (918) 665-8887 SIC 6411

■ AMERICAN MERCURY INSURANCE CO p 76
7301 Nw Expressway # 200, Oklahoma City OK 73132
Tel (405) 621-6509 SIC 6411 6331

DELTA DENTAL PLAN OF OKLAHOMA p 426
16 Nw 63rd St Ste 301, Oklahoma City OK 73116
Tel (405) 607-2100 SIC 6411

INSURICA p 748
5100 N Classen Blvd # 300, Oklahoma City OK 73118
Tel (405) 556-2205 SIC 6411

■ MIDLANDS MANAGEMENT CORP p 966
3817 Nw Expwy Ste 1000, Oklahoma City OK 73112
Tel (405) 840-0074 SIC 6411 6331 6321

NORTH AMERICAN INSURANCE AGENCY INC p 1050
5101 Classen Cir, Oklahoma City OK 73118
Tel (405) 523-2100 SIC 6411

FARMERS INSURANCE p 529
23175 Nw Bennett St, Hillsboro OR 97124
Tel (503) 372-2000 SIC 6411

CAMBIA HEALTH SOLUTIONS INC p 243
100 Sw Market St, Portland OR 97201
Tel (503) 225-5336 SIC 6321 6411 6324

FAMILYCARE MEDICAL CLINICS INC p 527
825 Ne Multnomah St # 300, Portland OR 97232
Tel (503) 222-3205 SIC 6411

GREAT NORTHERN STAFF ADMINISTRATORS LLC p 634
6915 Sw Mcdam Ave Ste 245, Portland OR 97219
Tel (503) 972-1944 SIC 6411

STANDARD INSURANCE CO p 1376
920 Sw 6th Ave Ste 1100, Portland OR 97204
Tel (971) 321-7000 SIC 6311 6321 6411

CITY COUNTY INSURANCE SERVICES p 312
1212 Court St Ne, Salem OR 97301
Tel (503) 763-3800 SIC 6411 8111

■ ABE ENTERCOM HOLDINGS LLC p 10
401 E City Ave Ste 809, Bala Cynwyd PA 19004
Tel (404) 239-7211 SIC 6411

AMERICAN INSURANCE SERVICE INC p 75
3 Bala Plz E Ste 300, Bala Cynwyd PA 19004
Tel (610) 664-1500 SIC 6411 6331

DIAMOND STATE INSURANCE CO p 437
3 Bala Plz E Ste 300, Bala Cynwyd PA 19004
Tel (610) 664-1500 SIC 6331 6411

MAGUIRE INSURANCE AGENCY INC p 897
1 Bala Plz Ste Ll34, Bala Cynwyd PA 19004
Tel (610) 617-7900 SIC 6411

PHILADELPHIA INDEMNITY INSURANCE CO p 1142
1 Bala Plz Ste 100, Bala Cynwyd PA 19004
Tel (610) 642-8400 SIC 6411

PHILADELPHIA INSURANCE CO p 1143
231 Sint Asphs Rd Ste 100, Bala Cynwyd PA 19004
Tel (877) 438-7459 SIC 6331 6411

TOKIO MARINE SPECIALTY INSURANCE CO p 1458
1 Bala Plz Ste 100, Bala Cynwyd PA 19004
Tel (610) 206-7822 SIC 6411

NATIONWIDE LIFE INSURANCE CO OF AMERICA p 1018
1000 Chesterbrook Blvd, Berwyn PA 19312
Tel (610) 407-1717 SIC 6411 6211 6719

AMERICAN INDEPENDENT INSURANCE CO INC p 74
1400 Union Meeting Rd # 250, Blue Bell PA 19422
Tel (610) 832-4940 SIC 6331 6411

INDEPENDENT INSURANCE INVESTMENTS INC p 736
1000 River Rd Ste 300, Conshohocken PA 19428
Tel (610) 832-4940 SIC 6331 6411

▲ ERIE INSURANCE GROUP EMPLOYEES p 508
100 Erie Insurance Pl, Erie PA 16530
Tel (814) 870-2000 SIC 6411 8741

XL ENVIRONMENTAL INC p 1632
505 Eagleview Blvd # 100, Exton PA 19341
Tel (800) 327-1414 SIC 6411 8748

CEI GROUP INC p 272
4850 E Street Rd Ste 200, Feasterville Trevose PA 19053
Tel (215) 364-5600 SIC 6411 7532

■ OLD REPUBLIC INSURANCE CO p 1081
133 Oakland Ave, Greensburg PA 15601
Tel (724) 838-5400 SIC 6411 6321 6311

HARLEYSVILLE GROUP INC p 662
355 Maple Ave, Harleysville PA 19438
Tel (215) 256-9773 SIC 6331 6411

■ CRUMP LIFE INSURANCE SERVICES INC p 396
4135 N Front St, Harrisburg PA 17110
Tel (717) 657-2740 SIC 6411

PA EMPLOYEES BENEFIT TRUST FUND (INC) p 1103
150 S 43rd St Ste 1, Harrisburg PA 17111
Tel (717) 561-4750 SIC 6411

PARTNERS SPECIALTY GROUP LLC p 1118
100 Tournament Dr Ste 214, Horsham PA 19044
Tel (484) 322-0400 SIC 6411

MEDRISK INC p 938
2701 Renaissance Blvd, King Of Prussia PA 19406
Tel (610) 768-5812 SIC 6411

CONSOLIDATED SERVICES GROUP INC p 360
1555 Bustard Rd Ste 100, Lansdale PA 19446
Tel (215) 661-0500 SIC 6411

NATIONAL ELEVATOR INDUSTRY HEALTH BENEFIT PLAN p 1011
19 Campus Blvd Ste 200, Newtown Square PA 19073
Tel (610) 325-9100 SIC 6411

ACE USA INC p 16
436 Walnut St, Philadelphia PA 19106
Tel (215) 923-5352 SIC 6411 6321 6351

AMERIHEALTH INC p 82
1901 Market St Fl 32, Philadelphia PA 19103
Tel (215) 241-3019 SIC 6411 6324 8748

BENEFICIAL SAVINGS BANK MHC p 173
1818 Market St Fl 8, Philadelphia PA 19103
Tel (215) 864-6000 SIC 6411

CHUBB US HOLDING INC p 304
1601 Chestnut St, Philadelphia PA 19192
Tel (215) 640-1000 SIC 6411 6331

ESIS INC p 509
436 Walnut St, Philadelphia PA 19106
Tel (215) 640-1000 SIC 6411

INA CHUBB HOLDINGS INC p 735
436 Walnut St, Philadelphia PA 19106
Tel (215) 640-1000 SIC 6411

INDEPENDENCE BLUE CROSS LLC p 736
1901 Market St Fl 32, Philadelphia PA 19103
Tel (215) 241-2400 SIC 6324 6411 8748

LOMBARD INTERNATIONAL AGENCY INC p 875
1 Liberty Pl Ste 1650, Philadelphia PA 19103
Tel (484) 530-4800 SIC 6411

WESTCHESTER FIRE INSURANCE CO INC p 1596
436 Walnut St, Philadelphia PA 19106
Tel (215) 640-1000 SIC 6411

A A A EAST CENTRAL p 4
5900 Baum Blvd Ste 2, Pittsburgh PA 15206
Tel (412) 362-3300 SIC 6411

▲ FNB CORP p 562
1 N Shore Ctr 12 Fdral St, Pittsburgh PA 15212
Tel (800) 555-5455
SIC 6022 6021 6162 6411

HIGHMARK INC p 692
120 5th Ave, Pittsburgh PA 15222
Tel (412) 544-7000
SIC 6321 6324 6411 6512

▲ LINCOLN NATIONAL CORP p 867
150 N Rad Chester Rd A305 Ste A, Radnor PA 19087
Tel (484) 583-1400
SIC 6311 6321 6371 6722 6411 6282

▲ UNIVEST CORP OF PENNSYLVANIA p 1527
14 N Main St, Souderton PA 18964
Tel (215) 721-2400 SIC 6022 6282 6411

CSI HOLDINGS INC p 397
4850 E Street Rd Ste 230, Trevose PA 19053
Tel (215) 357-4400 SIC 6411 7532

GENEX SERVICES LLC p 603
440 E Swedesford Rd # 1000, Wayne PA 19087
Tel (610) 964-5100 SIC 6411

■ SIGNAL p 1321
676 E Swedesford Rd # 300, Wayne PA 19087
Tel (610) 975-8901 SIC 6411

PAGNOTTI ENTERPRISES INC p 1107
46 Public Sq Ste 600, Wilkes Barre PA 18701
Tel (570) 825-8700 SIC 6411 1231 4841

ASPLUNDH TREE EXPERT CO p 119
708 Blair Mill Rd, Willow Grove PA 19090
Tel (215) 784-4200
SIC 0783 1629 1623 1611 6411

LOOMIS CO p 877
850 N Park Rd, Wyomissing PA 19610
Tel (610) 374-4040 SIC 6411 8742

ARTHUR J GLATFELTER AGENCY INC p 114
183 Leaders Heights Rd, York PA 17402
Tel (717) 741-0911 SIC 6411 8742

■ SANTANDER BANCORP p 1281
B7 Calle Tabonuco Fl 18, Guaynabo PR 00968
Tel (787) 777-4100 SIC 6021 6411 6211

UNIVERSAL GROUP INC p 1517
Calle 1 Lote 10 Metro Ofc St Cal, Guaynabo PR 00968
Tel (787) 793-7202 SIC 6411

DORAL HOLDINGS DELAWARE LLC p 451
1451 Frnklin D Rsvelt Ave, San Juan PR 00920
Tel (787) 474-6700
SIC 6162 6035 6211 6411

▲ FIRST BANCORP p 545
130 Mnoz Rvera Ave Fl 2, San Juan PR 00908
Tel (787) 729-8200 SIC 6022 6411

MAPFRE PRAICO CORP p 903
297 Ave Chardon Urb Tres, San Juan PR 00918
Tel (787) 250-6500 SIC 6411

MEDICAL CARD SYSTEM INC p 936
Mcs Plaza 255 Ponce St Mcs Pla, San Juan PR 00917
Tel (787) 758-2500 SIC 6411

AAA NORTHEAST p 7
110 Royal Little Dr, Providence RI 02904
Tel (401) 868-2000 SIC 8699 6411 4724

NEIGHBORHOOD HEALTH PLAN OF RHODE ISLAND p 1024
299 Promenade St, Providence RI 02908
Tel (401) 459-6000 SIC 6411

■ METROPOLITAN PROPERTY AND CASUALTY INSURANCE CO p 956
700 Quaker Ln, Warwick RI 02886
Tel (401) 827-2400 SIC 6411

■ CVS CAREMARK PART D SERVICES LLC p 404
1 Cvs Dr, Woonsocket RI 02895
Tel (401) 770-3317 SIC 6411

BRUCE SEIBELS & CO p 220
1501 Lady St, Columbia SC 29201
Tel (803) 748-2000 SIC 6411

■ CONTINENTAL AMERICAN INSURANCE CO p 362
1600 Williams St, Columbia SC 29201
Tel (803) 256-6265 SIC 6411

PLANNED ADMINISTRATORS INC p 1154
17 Technology Cir E2ag, Columbia SC 29203
Tel (803) 462-0151 SIC 6411

DELTA DENTAL PLAN OF SOUTH DAKOTA p 426
720 N Euclid Ave, Pierre SD 57501
Tel (605) 224-7345 SIC 6411

■ AGC LIFE INSURANCE CO p 34
American General Ctr, Brentwood TN 37027
Tel (615) 749-1000 SIC 6411

SEDGWICK CLAIMS MANAGEMENT SERVICES INC p 1300
1100 Ridgeway Loop Rd # 200, Memphis TN 38120
Tel (901) 415-7400 SIC 6411

■ SEDGWICK JAMES INC p 1300
1000 Ridgeway Loop Rd # 4, Memphis TN 38120
Tel (901) 415-7400 SIC 6411

ASURION INSURANCE SERVICES INC p 123
648 Grassmere Park # 300, Nashville TN 37211
Tel (615) 837-3000 SIC 6411

CGS ADMINISTRATORS LLC p 286
2 Vantage Way, Nashville TN 37228
Tel (615) 244-5600 SIC 6411

■ DIRECT GENERAL CORP p 441
1281 Murfreesboro Pike # 150, Nashville TN 37217
Tel (615) 399-4700
SIC 6311 6321 6331 6411

■ DIRECT GENERAL INSURANCE AGENCY INC p 441
1281 Murfreesboro Pike, Nashville TN 37217
Tel (615) 226-2550 SIC 6411

■ DIRECT GENERAL INSURANCE CO p 441
1281 Murfreesboro Pike # 150, Nashville TN 37217
Tel (615) 399-4700 SIC 6411

PERMANENT GENERAL ASSURANCE CORP p 1136
2636 Elm Hill Pike # 510, Nashville TN 37214
Tel (615) 744-1351 SIC 6331 6411 6141

PERMANENT GENERAL COMPANIES INC p 1136
2636 Elm Hill Pike # 510, Nashville TN 37214
Tel (615) 242-1961 SIC 6411

WILLIS ADMINISTRATIVE SERVICES CORP p 1612
26 Century Blvd Ste 101, Nashville TN 37214
Tel (615) 872-3000 SIC 6411

WILLIS OF TENNESSEE INC p 1612
26 Century Blvd Ste 101, Nashville TN 37214
Tel (615) 872-3000 SIC 6411

NAUTILUS GROUP p 1019
15305 Dallas Pkwy Ste 950, Addison TX 75001
Tel (972) 720-6600 SIC 6411

ALL WEB LEADS INC p 51
7300 Rm Ste 100, Austin TX 78730
Tel (512) 349-7900 SIC 6411

■ AMERICAN PHYSICIANS SERVICE GROUP INC p 77
1221 S Mo Pac Expy # 200, Austin TX 78746
Tel (512) 328-0888
SIC 6282 8741 6411 6211

BOON GROUP INC p 200
6300 Bridge Point Pkwy 3-500, Austin TX 78730
Tel (512) 339-4441 SIC 6411

■ FROST INSURANCE AGENCY INC p 582
201 Lavaca St Apt 621, Austin TX 78701
Tel (512) 473-4520 SIC 6411

MC CARTY CORP p 925
13494 Pond Springs Rd, Austin TX 78729
Tel (512) 331-1344 SIC 1541 6411

TEXAS DEPARTMENT OF INSURANCE p 1443
333 Guadalupe St Ste 2, Austin TX 78701
Tel (512) 463-6169 SIC 6411 9651

GERMANIA INSURANCE CO p 609
507 Highway 290 E, Brenham TX 77833
Tel (979) 886-5224 SIC 6411

ANCO INSURANCE MANAGERS INC p 89
1111 Briarcrest Dr, Bryan TX 77802
Tel (979) 776-2626 SIC 6411

AAA TEXAS LLC p 7
1225 Freeport Pkwy, Coppell TX 75019
Tel (469) 221-8285 SIC 6411

BENEFITMALL INC p 173
4851 Freeway Ste 100, Dallas TX 75244
Tel (469) 791-3300 SIC 6411 8742 7375

■ CHARTER INDEMNITY CO p 291
8360 Lyndon B Johnson Fwy # 400, Dallas TX 75243
Tel (972) 690-5500 SIC 6411

GROUP & PENSION ADMINISTRATORS INC p 641
12770 Merit Dr Ste 200, Dallas TX 75251
Tel (972) 238-7900 SIC 6411

■ SHOOTING STAR p 1318
8144 Walnut Hill Ln Fl 16, Dallas TX 75231
Tel (972) 770-1600 SIC 6411 8741

STATE FARM LLOYDS INC p 1381
17301 Preston Rd, Dallas TX 75252
Tel (972) 732-5000 SIC 6411

FRED LOYA INSURANCE AGENCY INC p 576
1800 N Lee Trevino Dr # 100, El Paso TX 79936
Tel (915) 595-0595 SIC 6411

■ CITI ASSURANCE SERVICES INC p 309
3001 Meacham Blvd Ste 100, Fort Worth TX 76137
Tel (817) 348-7500 SIC 6321 6411

▲ HALLMARK FINANCIAL SERVICES INC p 654
777 Main St Ste 1000, Fort Worth TX 76102
Tel (817) 348-1600 SIC 6411 6311

HIGGINBOTHAM INSURANCE AGENCY MCKINNEY INC p 690
500 W 13th St Ste 200, Fort Worth TX 76102
Tel (817) 336-2377 SIC 6411

HIGGINBOTHAM INSURANCE GROUP INC p 690
500 W 13th St Ste 200, Fort Worth TX 76102
Tel (800) 728-2374 SIC 6411

US HEALTH GROUP INC p 1532
300 Burnett St Ste 200, Fort Worth TX 76102
Tel (817) 878-3300 SIC 6411

CAREINGTON INTERNATIONAL CORP p 255
7400 Gaylord Pkwy, Frisco TX 75034
Tel (972) 335-6970 SIC 6324 6411

CLA USA INC p 321
9300 Wade Blvd Ste 100, Frisco TX 75035
Tel (214) 472-5000 SIC 6411

■ AMERICAN NATIONAL LIFE INSURANCE CO OF TEXAS p 77
1 Moody Plz Fl 8, Galveston TX 77550
Tel (409) 763-4661 SIC 6411 6321

■ AMERICAN GENERAL LIFE INSURANCE CO OF DELAWARE p 73
2727 Allen Pkwy Ste A, Houston TX 77019
Tel (713) 522-1111 SIC 6411

AON RISK SERVICES SOUTHWEST INC p 95
5555 San Felipe St # 1500, Houston TX 77056
Tel (832) 476-6000 SIC 6411

BOWEN MICLETTE & BRITT INSURANCE AGENCY LLC p 204
1111 North Loop W Ste 400, Houston TX 77008
Tel (713) 802-6100 SIC 6411

FAIRMONT SPECIALTY INSURANCE MANAGERS INC p 525
11490 Westheimer Rd # 300, Houston TX 77077
Tel (713) 954-8100 SIC 6411

GROUP MANAGEMENT 0002 LLC p 642
1321 Upland Dr 3966, Houston TX 77043
Tel (716) 998-3386 SIC 6411

GULF STATES FINANCIAL SERVICES INC p 647
1375 Enclave Pkwy, Houston TX 77077
Tel (713) 580-3000 SIC 6411

HOUSTON SERIES OF LOCKTON COMPANIES LLC p 712
5847 San Felipe St # 320, Houston TX 77057
Tel (713) 458-5200 SIC 6411

JOHN L WORTHAM & SON LP p 789
2727 Allen Pkwy, Houston TX 77019
Tel (713) 526-3366 SIC 6411

■ WESTERN NATIONAL LIFE INSURANCE CO p 1599
2929 Allen Pkwy Ste 3800, Houston TX 77019
Tel (713) 522-1111 SIC 6411

C-III CAPITAL PARTNERS LLC p 234
5221 N O Connor Blvd, Irving TX 75039
Tel (972) 868-5300
SIC 6519 6726 6361 6411

DEEP SOUTH HOLDING INC p 421
7701 Las Colinas Rdg # 600, Irving TX 75063
Tel (214) 493-4200 SIC 6411

ETHOS GROUP INC p 511
5215 N O Connor Blvd # 1450, Irving TX 75039
Tel (972) 331-1000 SIC 6411

FLUOR EMPLOYEE BENEFIT TRUST p 561
6700 Las Colinas Blvd, Irving TX 75039
Tel (469) 398-7000 SIC 6411

G2 SECURE STAFF LLC p 588
400 Las Colinas Blvd E # 750, Irving TX 75039
Tel (972) 915-6979 SIC 6411 4789 4729

TEXAS WASATCH INSURANCE SERVICES LP p 1444
100 E Royal Ln Ste 320, Irving TX 75039
Tel (214) 838-5500 SIC 6411 6799

CUNNINGHAM LINDSEY US INC p 401
405 State Highway 121 Byp A100, Lewisville TX 75067
Tel (214) 488-5139 SIC 6411

K & S GROUP INC p 798
18601 Lyndn B Jhnsn 420, Mesquite TX 75150
Tel (214) 234-8871 SIC 6411

INSPHERE INSURANCE SOLUTIONS INC p 746
9151 Boulevard 26, North Richland Hills TX 76180
Tel (817) 255-3100 SIC 6411

■ REPUBLIC TITLE OF TEXAS INC p 1226
2701 W Plano Pkwy Ste 100, Plano TX 75075
Tel (972) 578-8611
SIC 6411 7372 6531 6541

CATHOLIC LIFE INSURANCE p 267
1635 Ne Loop 410 Ste 300, San Antonio TX 78209
Tel (210) 828-9921 SIC 6311 6411

▲ CULLEN/FROST BANKERS INC p 400
100 W Houston St, San Antonio TX 78205
Tel (210) 220-4011 SIC 6021 6411

EEMPLOYERS SOLUTIONS INC p 480
12211 Huebner Rd, San Antonio TX 78230
Tel (210) 495-1171 SIC 8742 6411

SOUTHWEST BUSINESS CORP p 1351
9311 San Pedro Ave # 600, San Antonio TX 78216
Tel (210) 525-1241 SIC 6411 6162 6282

TRIDENT INSURANCE SERVICES LLC p 1479
175 E Houston St Ste 1300, San Antonio TX 78205
Tel (210) 342-8808 SIC 6411

TEXAS FARM BUREAU MUTUAL INSURANCE CO p 1443
7420 Fish Pond Rd, Waco TX 76710
Tel (254) 772-3030 SIC 6411

■ COLT INTERNATIONAL LLC p 339
300 Flint Ridge Rd, Webster TX 77598
Tel (281) 280-2100 SIC 6411 5172

LEAVITT GROUP ENTERPRISES INC p 850
216 S 200 W, Cedar City UT 84720
Tel (435) 586-1555 SIC 6153 8741 6411

CLYDE COMPANIES INC p 328
730 N 1500 W, Orem UT 84057
Tel (801) 802-6900 SIC 1611 5031 6411

BEAR RIVER MUTUAL INSURANCE CO p 165
778 E Winchester St, Salt Lake City UT 84107
Tel (801) 267-5000 SIC 6331 6411

DESERET MANAGEMENT CORP p 432
55 N 300 W Ste 800, Salt Lake City UT 84101
Tel (801) 538-0651
SIC 4832 4833 5932 6512 6531 6411

EQUITABLE LIFE & CASUALTY INSURANCE CO p 506
3 Triad Ctr, Salt Lake City UT 84180
Tel (801) 579-3400 SIC 6411 6311

FRED A MORETON & CO p 575
101 S 200 E Ste 300, Salt Lake City UT 84111
Tel (801) 531-1234 SIC 6411

NAVY MUTUAL AID ASSOCIATION p 1020
Henderson Hall, 29, Arlington VA 22212
Tel (703) 945-1440 SIC 8641 6411

AMERICAN ARMED FORCES MUTUAL AID ASSOCIATION p 68
102 Sheridan Ave, Fort Myer VA 22211
Tel (800) 522-5221 SIC 6411

■ BERKLEY MID-ATLANTIC GROUP LLC p 175
4820 Lake Brook Dr # 300, Glen Allen VA 23060
Tel (804) 285-2700 SIC 6411

■ MAGELLAN MEDICAID ADMINISTRATION INC p 895
11013 W Broad St Ste 500, Glen Allen VA 23060
Tel (804) 548-0100
SIC 7374 8093 6411 8741

■ MARKEL INSURANCE CO p 908
4600 Cox Rd Ste 100, Glen Allen VA 23060
Tel (800) 431-1270 SIC 6411

■ MARKEL SERVICE INC p 908
4600 Cox Rd Ste 100, Glen Allen VA 23060
Tel (804) 747-0136 SIC 6411

ARMFIELD HARRISON & THOMAS INC p 111
20 S King St Ste 300, Leesburg VA 20175
Tel (703) 777-2341 SIC 6411

■ GENWORTH FINANCIAL CAPITAL INC p 605
700 Main St, Lynchburg VA 24504
Tel (434) 845-0911 SIC 6411

BEACON HEALTH OPTIONS INC p 164
240 Corporate Blvd # 100, Norfolk VA 23502
Tel (757) 459-5100 SIC 6324 8322 6411

HENDERSON & PHILLIPS INC p 682
101 W Main St Ste 900, Norfolk VA 23510
Tel (757) 625-1800 SIC 6411

AGA (VIRGINIA) INC p 34
9950 Mayland Dr, Richmond VA 23233
Tel (804) 285-3300 SIC 6411 4724

ALLIANZ GLOBAL ASSISTANCE (AGA) SERVICE CO p 55
9950 Mayland Dr, Richmond VA 23233
Tel (800) 628-4908 SIC 6411

HILB GROUP LLC p 692
8720 Stony Point Pkwy # 125, Richmond VA 23235
Tel (804) 414-6501 SIC 6411

DELTA DENTAL OF VIRGINIA p 426
4818 Starkey Rd, Roanoke VA 24018
Tel (540) 989-8000 SIC 6411 6321

NATIONAL ELECTRONICS WARRANTY LLC p 1011
22894 Pacific Blvd, Sterling VA 20166
Tel (703) 375-8100 SIC 6411

EFINANCIAL LLC p 480
13810 Se Eastgate Way # 300, Bellevue WA 98005
Tel (800) 482-6616 SIC 6411

HEALTH CARE MANAGEMENT ADMINISTRATORS INC p 674
220 120th Ave Ne, Bellevue WA 98005
Tel (425) 462-1000 SIC 6411

PARKER SMITH & FEEK INC p 1116
2233 112th Ave Ne, Bellevue WA 98004
Tel (425) 709-3600 SIC 6411 6351 8748

SYMETRA FINANCIAL CORP p 1414
777 108th Ave Ne Ste 1200, Bellevue WA 98004
Tel (425) 256-8000 SIC 6311 6411

SYMETRA LIFE INSURANCE CO p 1414
777 108th Ave Ne Ste 1200, Bellevue WA 98004
Tel (877) 796-3872 SIC 6311 6324 6411

UNIGARD PACIFIC INSURANCE CO p 1503
15800 Northup Way, Bellevue WA 98008
Tel (425) 644-5236 SIC 6331 6411

■ STERLING LIFE INSURANCE CO p 1387
2219 Rimland Dr Ste 100, Bellingham WA 98226
Tel (360) 647-9080 SIC 6411

FARMERS NEW WORLD LIFE INSURANCE CO INC p 530
3003 77th Ave Se, Mercer Island WA 98040
Tel (206) 232-1093 SIC 6311 6411

ALTIG INTERNATIONAL INC p 62
15440 Bel Red Rd, Redmond WA 98052
Tel (425) 885-2838 SIC 6411

CHP OF WASHINGTON p 302
720 Olive Way Ste 300, Seattle WA 98101
Tel (206) 521-8833 SIC 6411

PHYSICIANS INSURANCE A MUTUAL CO p 1145
1301 2nd Ave Ste 2700, Seattle WA 98101
Tel (206) 343-7300 SIC 6411

SAFECO ADMINISTRATIVE SERVICES INC p 1266
1001 4th Ave, Seattle WA 98154
Tel (206) 545-5000 SIC 6411

SAFECO CORP p 1266
1001 4th Ave Ste 800, Seattle WA 98185
Tel (206) 545-5000
SIC 6411 6311 6321 6324 6351

SAFECO INSURANCE CO OF AMERICA p 1266
1001 4th Ave Ste 800, Seattle WA 98185
Tel (206) 545-5000 SIC 6411

HEALTHCARE RESOURCE GROUP INC p 676
12610 E Mirabeau Pkwy # 900, Spokane Valley WA 99216
Tel (509) 209-2000
SIC 6411 7322 8742 8721

MIDDLETON BRATRUD INSURANCE BROKERS INC p 965
1201 Pacific Ave Ste 1000, Tacoma WA 98402
Tel (253) 759-2200 SIC 6411

■ WELLS FARGO INSURANCE SERVICES OF WEST VIRGINIA INC p 1591
1 Hillcrest Dr E, Charleston WV 25311
Tel (304) 346-0611 SIC 6411

INSURANCE CLAIMS MANAGEMENT INC p 748
404 S Barstow St, Eau Claire WI 54701
Tel (715) 830-6000 SIC 6411

SOCIETY INSURANCE A MUTUAL CO p 1336
150 Camelot Dr, Fond Du Lac WI 54935
Tel (920) 922-1220 SIC 6411

■ UNITEDHEALTHCARE LIFE INSURANCE CO p 1515
3100 Ams Blvd, Green Bay WI 54313
Tel (800) 232-5432
SIC 6411 6324 6311 8322

■ AMERIPRISE FINANCIAL SERVICES INC p 83
500 2nd St S Ste 101, La Crosse WI 54601
Tel (608) 783-2639
SIC 6282 6411 6211 8742

AMERICAN FAMILY LIFE INSURANCE CO p 72
6000 American Pkwy, Madison WI 53783
Tel (608) 249-2111 SIC 6411

CUNA MUTUAL GROUP p 401
5910 Mineral Point Rd, Madison WI 53705
Tel (608) 238-5851
SIC 6331 6311 6351 6411 7515

CUNA MUTUAL INSURANCE AGENCY INC p 401
5910 Mineral Point Rd, Madison WI 53705
Tel (608) 238-5851 SIC 6411

M3 INSURANCE SOLUTIONS INC p 891
828 John Nolen Dr, Madison WI 53713
Tel (608) 273-0655 SIC 6411

RURAL MUTUAL INSURANCE CO p 1258
1241 John Q Hammons Dr # 200, Madison WI 53717
Tel (608) 836-5525 SIC 6411

WISCONSIN EDUCATION ASSOCIATION INSURANCE TRUST p 1618
45 Nob Hill Rd, Madison WI 53713
Tel (608) 276-4000 SIC 6411

GREAT LAKES FINANCIAL MANAGEMENT GROUP INC p 633
2033 Marinette Ave, Marinette WI 54143
Tel (715) 732-9955
SIC 6211 8742 6282 6411

CHURCH MUTUAL INSURANCE CO p 305
3000 Schuster Ln, Merrill WI 54452
Tel (715) 536-5577 SIC 6411

■ AMERICAN GENERAL LIFE BROKERAGE GROUP p 73
1200 N Mayfair Rd Ste 300, Milwaukee WI 53226
Tel (414) 443-5800 SIC 6311 6411

CATHOLIC KNIGHTS INSURANCE SOCIETY INC p 267
1100 W Wells St Ste 1, Milwaukee WI 53233
Tel (414) 273-6266
SIC 6311 6411 6211 6141

▲ HARLEY-DAVIDSON INC p 661
3700 W Juneau Ave, Milwaukee WI 53208
Tel (414) 342-4680
SIC 3751 6153 6141 6411 6399

■ MARSHALL & SWIFT/BOECKH LLC p 911
10001 W Innovation Dr # 102, Milwaukee WI 53226
Tel (262) 780-2800 SIC 6411

▲ MGIC INVESTMENT CORP p 958
250 E Kilbourn Ave, Milwaukee WI 53202
Tel (414) 347-6480 SIC 6351 6411

NORTHWESTERN MUTUAL WEALTH MANAGEMENT CO p 1061
611 E Wisconsin Ave, Milwaukee WI 53202
Tel (206) 623-8801 SIC 6411

RYAN ROBERTSON AND ASSOCIATES INC p 1260
330 E Kilbourn Ave # 650, Milwaukee WI 53202
Tel (414) 271-3575 SIC 6411

■ UNITEDHEALTHCARE OF WISCONSIN INC p 1515
10701 W Research Dr, Milwaukee WI 53226
Tel (414) 443-4060 SIC 6324 6411 6321

A ACUITY MUTUAL INSURANCE CO p 4
2800 S Taylor Dr, Sheboygan WI 53081
Tel (920) 458-9131 SIC 6411 6331

SENTRY INSURANCE A MUTUAL CO p 1305
1800 Northpoint Dr, Stevens Point WI 54481
Tel (715) 346-6000
SIC 6331 6311 6411 6321

SENTRY LIFE INSURANCE CO p 1305
1800 Northpoint Dr, Stevens Point WI 54481
Tel (715) 346-6000 SIC 6411 6321

■ TRAVEL GUARD GROUP INC p 1473
3300 Business Park Dr, Stevens Point WI 54482
Tel (715) 345-0505 SIC 6411

WINTERTHUR U S HOLDINGS INC p 1617
1 General Dr, Sun Prairie WI 53596
Tel (608) 837-4440 SIC 6411 6163

■ MARKEL AMERICAN INSURANCE CO p 908
N14w23800 Stone Ridge Dr # 300, Waukesha WI 53188
Tel (262) 548-9880 SIC 6411

WERCS p 1592
400 E 1st St Ste 100, Casper WY 82601
Tel (307) 235-6200
SIC 6211 6163 6411 6321 6531 6099

SIC 6512 Operators Of Nonresidential Bldgs

INFIRMARY HEALTH SYSTEM INC p 741
5 Mobile Infirmary Cir, Mobile AL 36607
Tel (251) 435-3030
SIC 8062 6512 1542 7322 5047 7389

CALISTA CORP p 242
5015 Bus Pk Blvd Ste 3000, Anchorage AK 99503
Tel (907) 279-5516 SIC 6512 7363 2711

UKPEAGVIK INUPIAT CORP p 1500
1250 Agvik St, Barrow AK 99723
Tel (907) 852-4460
SIC 1542 6512 6331 1389 4449

GOLDBELT INC p 620
3025 Clinton Dr Ste 100, Juneau AK 99801
Tel (907) 790-4990 SIC 4489 6512

BASHAS INC p 158
22402 S Basha Rd, Chandler AZ 85248
Tel (480) 883-6131
SIC 5411 5149 5148 5147 6512

W M GRACE COS INC p 1569
7575 N 16th St Ste 1, Phoenix AZ 85020
Tel (602) 956-8254 SIC 1542 6512 7011

DMB ASSOCIATES INC p 445
7600 E Doubletree Ste 300, Scottsdale AZ 85258
Tel (480) 367-6874
SIC 5999 6512 5961 1542 3446

COULSON OIL CO INC p 374
1434 Pike Ave 38, North Little Rock AR 72114
Tel (501) 376-4222
SIC 5172 5541 5411 6512

ESKATON p 509
5105 Manzanita Ave Ste D, Carmichael CA 95608
Tel (916) 334-0296 SIC 6512 8051

MITSUBISHI MOTORS NORTH AMERICA INC p 978
6400 Katella Ave, Cypress CA 90630
Tel (714) 799-4730
SIC 5511 5013 6159 6512

■ CALMAT CO p 242
500 N Brand Blvd Ste 500, Glendale CA 91203
Tel (818) 553-8821
SIC 2951 1442 1429 3273 6512 6552

■ INSIGNIA/ESG HOTEL PARTNERS INC p 746
11150 Santa Monica Blvd # 220, Los Angeles CA 90025
Tel (310) 765-2600 SIC 6512

INTERNATIONAL CHURCH OF FOURSQUARE GOSPEL p 754
1910 W Sunset Blvd # 200, Los Angeles CA 90026
Tel (213) 989-4234
SIC 8661 6512 7032 8211 8221

▲ READING INTERNATIONAL INC p 1213
6100 Center Dr Ste 900, Los Angeles CA 90045
Tel (213) 235-2240
SIC 7832 7922 6512 6531

WESTFIELD AMERICA INC p 1600
2049 Century Park E Fl 41, Los Angeles CA 90067
Tel (310) 478-4456 SIC 6512

WESTFIELD LLC p 1601
2049 Century Park E # 4100, Los Angeles CA 90067
Tel (813) 926-4600 SIC 6512

SAN BERNARDINO HILTON p 1276
285 E Hospitality Ln, San Bernardino CA 92408
Tel (909) 889-0133 SIC 7011 6512 5812

PACIFICA COMPANIES LLC p 1106
1775 Hancock St Ste 200, San Diego CA 92110
Tel (619) 296-9000 SIC 6798 6512

SAN DIEGO CONVENTION CENTER CORP INC p 1276
111 W Harbor Dr, San Diego CA 92101
Tel (619) 525-5000 SIC 6512

CANADIAN AMERICAN OIL CO INC p 246
444 Divisadero St 100, San Francisco CA 94117
Tel (415) 621-8676 SIC 5541 6512 6552

HARBOR VIEW HOLDINGS INC p 660
433 California St Fl 7, San Francisco CA 94104
Tel (415) 982-7777
SIC 1522 1521 6512 8741

PACIFIC UNION CO p 1106
1 Letterman Dr Ste 300, San Francisco CA 94129
Tel (415) 929-7100 SIC 6552 6512 6531

GREEN VALLEY CORP p 637
777 N 1st St Fl 5, San Jose CA 95112
Tel (408) 287-0246 SIC 1542 1522 6512

LAVIDA COMMUNITIES INC p 847
500 Stevens Ave Ste 100, Solana Beach CA 92075
Tel (858) 792-9300
SIC 6513 6512 6531 6553

SENIOR RESOURCE GROUP LLC p 1304
500 Stevens Ave Ste 100, Solana Beach CA 92075
Tel (858) 792-9300
SIC 6513 6512 6531 6553

JF SHEA CONSTRUCTION INC p 785
655 Brea Canyon Rd, Walnut CA 91789
Tel (909) 595-4397 SIC 1521 1622 6512

FURNITURE LOW LLC p 585
1333 E 37th Ave, Denver CO 80205
Tel (303) 371-8560 SIC 6512

■ QWEST BUSINESS RESOURCES INC p 1201
1005 17th St, Denver CO 80202
Tel (303) 896-5025 SIC 7389 6512

■ A E PROPERTIES INC p 5
1 Tower Sq, Hartford CT 06183
Tel (860) 277-1295 SIC 6512

CARABETTA ENTERPRISES INC p 252
200 Pratt St Ofc, Meriden CT 06450
Tel (203) 237-7400
SIC 1522 1542 1521 6512

LOUIS DREYFUS HOLDING CO INC p 879
10 Westport Rd Ste 200, Wilton CT 06897
Tel (203) 761-2000
SIC 6221 5153 6512 6531 1311

■ CIGNA GLOBAL HOLDINGS INC p 306
590 Naamans Rd, Claymont DE 19703
Tel (302) 797-3469 SIC 6311 6512 6411

■ CIGNA HOLDINGS INC p 306
590 Naamans Rd, Claymont DE 19703
Tel (215) 761-1000
SIC 6311 6321 6331 6512 6514 6282

AAA CLUB ALLIANCE INC p 7
1 River Pl, Wilmington DE 19801
Tel (302) 299-4700
SIC 8699 6331 6351 6512 4724

■ BROTHERS PROPERTY CORP p 219
2 Alhambra Plz Ste 1280, Coral Gables FL 33134
Tel (305) 285-1035 SIC 6512

TURNBERRY ASSOCIATES p 1492
19501 Biscayne Blvd # 3400, Miami FL 33180
Tel (305) 937-6262 SIC 6512 6552

GRAHAM COMPANIES p 628
6843 Main St, Miami Lakes FL 33014
Tel (305) 821-1130
SIC 1531 7011 0212 6552 6512 2711

SUNBEAM TELEVISION CORP p 1401
1401 79th Street Cswy, North Bay Village FL 33141
Tel (305) 751-6692 SIC 4833 6512

CASTLE MANAGEMENT INC p 264
12270 Sw 3rd St Ste 200, Plantation FL 33325
Tel (800) 337-5850 SIC 6512

▲ ST JOE CO p 1367
133 S Watersound Pkwy A, Watersound FL 32461
Tel (850) 231-6400
SIC 6531 6552 6512 0811 0851

LANE SERVICES LLC p 843
303 Perimeter Ctr N # 200, Atlanta GA 30346
Tel (678) 681-7200 SIC 6512

ROBERT W WOODRUFF ARTS CENTER INC p 1241
1280 Peachtree St Ne, Atlanta GA 30309
Tel (404) 733-4200
SIC 7929 8412 6512 8299

SHIVERS TRADING & OPERATING CO p 1317
725 Broad St, Augusta GA 30901
Tel (706) 724-0851
SIC 2711 2721 2731 4832 7312 6512

WINTER GROUP OF COMPANIES INC p 1617
191 Peachtree St Ne, Peachtree Corners GA 30071
Tel (404) 588-3300
SIC 1541 1542 1799 6512

C-E MINERALS INC p 234
100 Mansell Ct E Ste 615, Roswell GA 30076
Tel (770) 225-7900
SIC 1099 1446 3295 6512

▲ ALEXANDER & BALDWIN INC p 49
822 Bishop St, Honolulu HI 96813
Tel (808) 525-6611 SIC 6512 2062

DON QUIJOTE (USA) CO LTD p 450
801 Kaheka St, Honolulu HI 96814
Tel (808) 973-4800
SIC 5411 5331 6512 5912

ELITE PACIFIC PROPERTIES LLC p 487
4211 Waialae Ave Ste 106, Honolulu HI 96816
Tel (808) 589-2040 SIC 6512 6531

HTH CORP p 715
1668 S King St Fl 2, Honolulu HI 96826
Tel (808) 469-4111 SIC 7011 5812 6512

ISLAND HOLDINGS INC p 766
1022 Bethel St Fl 4, Honolulu HI 96813
Tel (808) 531-1311 SIC 6512

■ KAPALUA LAND CO LTD p 803
1000 Kapalua Dr, Lahaina HI 96761
Tel (808) 669-5622 SIC 6552 6512

LANAI RESORTS LLC p 841
1311 Fraser Ave, Lanai City HI 96763
Tel (808) 565-3000 SIC 6552 6512

AMBERJACK LTD p 65
3 State Farm Plz, Bloomington IL 61791
Tel (309) 766-6920 SIC 6512 6513

HOMETOWN AMERICA LLC p 704
150 N Wacker Dr Ste 2800, Chicago IL 60606
Tel (312) 604-7500 SIC 6512

■ ILLINOIS BELL TELEPHONE CO p 732
225 W Randolph St Fl LI, Chicago IL 60606
Tel (618) 344-9077 SIC 4813 8721 6512

▲ JONES LANG LASALLE INC p 792
200 E Randolph St # 4300, Chicago IL 60601
Tel (312) 782-5800 SIC 6512 6531

KATO KAGAKU CO LTD p 804
151 E Wacker Dr, Chicago IL 60601
Tel (312) 565-1234 SIC 6512 7011

SINAI HEALTH SYSTEM p 1326
1500 S Fairfield Ave, Chicago IL 60608
Tel (773) 542-2000 SIC 6512 8741

WIRTZ CORP p 1618
680 N Lake Shore Dr # 1900, Chicago IL 60611
Tel (312) 943-7000
SIC 5181 5182 6513 6512 7011 6411

D D G INC p 407
1955 Shermer Rd Ste 300, Northbrook IL 60062
Tel (847) 412-0277 SIC 3317 2511 6512

INLAND REAL ESTATE GROUP OF COMPANIES p 743
2901 Butterfield Rd, Oak Brook IL 60523
Tel (630) 218-8000
SIC 6513 6512 6162 6282 1522 1542

SWEDISHAMERICAN HEALTH SYSTEM CORP p 1411
1401 E State St, Rockford IL 61104
Tel (815) 968-4400
SIC 8743 6512 8742 8099 8082 8062

MCII HOLDINGS INC p 930
1700 E Golf Rd, Schaumburg IL 60173
Tel (866) 624-2622 SIC 6512

COOK GROUP INC p 365
750 N Daniels Way, Bloomington IN 47404
Tel (812) 339-2235
SIC 3841 3821 3845 6411 6512 6211

EAGLE CARE p 467
6900 Gray Rd, Indianapolis IN 46237
Tel (317) 788-2500 SIC 6512

■ MALL AT MONTGOMERYVILLE LP p 899
115 W Washington St, Indianapolis IN 46204
Tel (215) 362-1600 SIC 6512

▲ SIMON PROPERTY GROUP INC p 1325
225 W Washington St, Indianapolis IN 46204
Tel (317) 636-1600 SIC 6798 6512

■ SIMON PROPERTY GROUP LP p 1325
225 W Washington St, Indianapolis IN 46204
Tel (317) 636-1600 SIC 6798 6512

JASPER ENGINE EXCHANGE INC p 778
815 Wernsing Rd, Jasper IN 47546
Tel (812) 482-1041 SIC 3714 7538 6512

MERCY HOSPITAL IOWA CITY IOWA INC p 947
500 E Market St, Iowa City IA 52245
Tel (319) 339-0300
SIC 8062 8011 6512 8399

HEALTH CARE INC p 674
1701 E 23rd Ave, Hutchinson KS 67502
Tel (620) 665-2000 SIC 8062 7352 6512

FOLEY INDUSTRIES INC p 563
1550 S West St, Wichita KS 67213
Tel (316) 943-4211
SIC 5082 5084 7353 6512

MURFIN DRILLING CO INC p 1001
250 N Water St Ste 300, Wichita KS 67202
Tel (316) 267-3241
SIC 1381 1382 5082 6512 6514

UNIVERSAL COMPANIES INC p 1516
2824 N Ohio St, Wichita KS 67219
Tel (316) 832-0151
SIC 5171 5541 6512 8741 6099 2992

CORPOREX REALTY & INVESTMENT LLC p 372
100 E Riverctr Ste 1100, Covington KY 41011
Tel (859) 292-5500
SIC 1542 6531 6552 8741 6512

AFFILIATED HEALTHCARE SYSTEMS p 32
931 Union St, Bangor ME 04401
Tel (207) 973-6720
SIC 5047 8071 8741 7322 6512

DEAD RIVER CO p 419
80 Exchange St Ste 3, Bangor ME 04401
Tel (207) 947-8641
SIC 6512 5172 5983 5541 5411

BROADWAY SERVICES INC p 216
3709 E Monument St, Baltimore MD 21205
Tel (410) 563-6900
SIC 7349 7381 7521 6512 4119

B F SAUL REAL ESTATE INVESTMENT TRUST p 141
7501 Wscnsin Ave Ste 1500, Bethesda MD 20814
Tel (301) 657-2619 SIC 6512 6513

GIFT COLLECTION INC p 611
6905 Rockledge Dr Fl 1, Bethesda MD 20817
Tel (240) 694-4100 SIC 6512 5812

MANIKEN LLC p 901
8621 Robert Fulton Dr # 100, Columbia MD 21046
Tel (410) 290-1400 SIC 6512

■ ROUSE CO LP p 1253
10221 Wincopin Cir # 300, Columbia MD 21044
Tel (410) 992-6000 SIC 6798 6512

GIANT FOOD LLC p 610
8301 Profess Pl Ste 115, Hyattsville MD 20785
Tel (301) 341-4100 SIC 5411 6512 5912

HBW PROPERTIES INC p 671
1055 1st St Ste 200, Rockville MD 20850
Tel (301) 424-2900 SIC 1542 6512 6531

DELAWARE NORTH COMPANIES INC - BOSTON p 424
100 Legends Way Ste 100, Boston MA 02114
Tel (617) 624-1000
SIC 5812 5994 6512 7311

MASSACHUSETTS PORT AUTHORITY p 917
1 Harborside Dr Ste 200s, Boston MA 02128
Tel (617) 561-1600
SIC 4581 4491 6799 6512 4785

NEWTON-WELLESLEY HEALTH CARE SYSTEM INC p 1039
2014 Washington St, Newton MA 02462
Tel (617) 243-6000 SIC 8741 7374 6512

BAYSTATE HEALTH SYSTEM HEALTH SERVICES INC p 162
280 Chestnut St, Springfield MA 01199
Tel (413) 794-9939
SIC 8741 8062 6324 6512

CUMMINGS FOUNDATION INC p 401
200 W Cummings Park, Woburn MA 01801
Tel (781) 935-8000 SIC 8361 6512

■ FORD HOLDINGS LLC p 565
American Rd, Dearborn MI 48121
Tel (313) 845-5338 SIC 6552 6512

■ FORD MOTOR LAND DEVELOPMENT CORP p 566
330 Town Center Dr # 1100, Dearborn MI 48126
Tel (313) 323-3100 SIC 6512 6552

LANSING MALL LIMITED PARTNERSHIP p 844
5330 W Saginaw Hwy, Lansing MI 48917
Tel (517) 321-0145 SIC 6512 7311

HOWARD TERNES PACKAGING CO p 713
35275 Industrial Rd, Livonia MI 48150
Tel (734) 793-4130 SIC 4783 6512 6552

WALTERS-DIMMICK PETROLEUM INC p 1574
1620 S Kalamazoo Ave, Marshall MI 49068
Tel (269) 781-4654
SIC 5541 5411 6512 5172 5171 5983

DIVERSIFIED MOTEL PROPERTIES LIMITED PARTNERSHIP p 444
2305 W Superior St, Duluth MN 55806
Tel (218) 723-8433 SIC 6512

LUTHER HOLDING CO p 886
3701 Alabama Ave S, Minneapolis MN 55416
Tel (763) 593-5755
SIC 5511 7515 7513 6512 6552 5611

RBC CAPITAL MARKETS LLC p 1211
60 S 6th St Ste 700, Minneapolis MN 55402
Tel (612) 371-2711
SIC 6211 6512 6513 6282

RYAN COMPANIES US INC p 1260
50 S 10th St Ste 300, Minneapolis MN 55403
Tel (612) 492-4000
SIC 1542 1541 6552 6512 1522

BURD & FLETCHER CO p 226
5151 E Geospace Dr, Independence MO 64056
Tel (816) 257-0291 SIC 2657 2752 6512

SAINT LUKES HOSPITAL OF KANSAS CITY p 1270
4401 Wornall Rd, Kansas City MO 64111
Tel (816) 932-2000
SIC 8062 8742 8011 6512 8082 7322

DASH MULTI-CORP INC p 413
2500 Adie Rd, Maryland Heights MO 63043
Tel (314) 432-3200
SIC 2821 3069 6512 5169 7359

DRURY DEVELOPMENT CORP p 457
721 Emerson Rd Ste 200, Saint Louis MO 63141
Tel (314) 423-6698 SIC 6512 1542 5812

RH MONTGOMERY PROPERTIES INC p 1231
214 N Scott St, Sikeston MO 63801
Tel (573) 471-1113 SIC 6512

TOWN PUMP INC p 1465
600 S Main St, Butte MT 59701
Tel (406) 497-6700
SIC 5541 5411 7993 6512 5812

CRETE CARRIER CORP p 392
400 Nw 56th St, Lincoln NE 68528
Tel (402) 475-9521 SIC 4213 4212 6512

■ PARBALL CORP p 1114
3655 Las Vegas Blvd S, Las Vegas NV 89109
Tel (702) 967-4111
SIC 7011 7999 6512 7521 7211

AMERICAN CASINO & ENTERTAINMENT PROPERTIES LLC p 70
1900 S Casino Dr, Laughlin NV 89029
Tel (702) 298-5111 SIC 6512 7011

LAUGHLIN RECREATIONAL ENTERPRISES INC p 847
1650 S Casino Dr, Laughlin NV 89029
Tel (702) 298-2535 SIC 6512

■ BALLYS PARK PLACE INC p 149
1721 Boardwalk, Atlantic City NJ 08401
Tel (609) 340-2000 SIC 6512 5812

TRUMP TAJ MAHAL REALTY CORP p 1487
1000 Boardwalk, Atlantic City NJ 08401
Tel (609) 449-1000 SIC 6512

CONNELL CO p 357
200 Connell Dr Ste 4100, Berkeley Heights NJ 07922
Tel (908) 673-3700
SIC 6552 6512 7359 5082

SSNYC INC p 1364
80 Washington St, Hoboken NJ 07030
Tel (201) 216-1500 SIC 4731 6512

ISS TMC SERVICES INC p 767
81 Dorsa Ave, Livingston NJ 07039
Tel (973) 740-0032 SIC 6512 7349 7699

NEW JERSEY SPORTS & EXPOSITION AUTHORITY p 1031
1 Dekorte Park Plz, Lyndhurst NJ 07071
Tel (201) 460-1700 SIC 8641 7941 6512

■ PSEG ENERGY HOLDINGS LLC p 1188
80 Park Plz Ste 3, Newark NJ 07102
Tel (973) 430-7000 SIC 6153 6512

■ DCH AUTO GROUP (USA) INC p 418
955 Route 9 N, South Amboy NJ 08879
Tel (732) 727-9168
SIC 5511 7515 6512 6514

TOYS "R" US PROPERTY CO II LLC p 1467
1 Geoffrey Way, Wayne NJ 07470
Tel (973) 617-3500 SIC 6512

EXCAVATORS 731 PROPERTY CORP p 516
3411 35th Ave, Astoria NY 11106
Tel (718) 706-0720 SIC 6512

JAZZY ELECTRONICS CORP p 779
1600 63rd St, Brooklyn NY 11204
Tel (718) 236-8000 SIC 6512 5064 3651

PYRAMID WALDEN CO LP p 1194
1 Walden Galleria, Buffalo NY 14225
Tel (315) 422-7000 SIC 6512

METROPLEX HOLDINGS INC p 955
15 Commerce Dr S, Harriman NY 10926
Tel (845) 781-5000 SIC 6512 5149 5087

RESOURCE CENTER p 1227
200 Dunham Ave, Jamestown NY 14701
Tel (716) 661-4829
SIC 8093 6513 6512 8052

■ AIG GLOBAL REAL ESTATE INVESTMENT CORP p 37
32 Old Slip Fl 28, New York NY 10005
Tel (646) 857-2300 SIC 6512 8411

BERTELSMANN INC p 176
1745 Broadway Fl 20, New York NY 10019
Tel (212) 782-1000
SIC 2731 2721 7819 3652 6512

DURST ORGANIZATION INC p 463
1 Bryant Park Fl 49, New York NY 10036
Tel (212) 257-6600 SIC 6512

EMIGRANT SAVINGS BANK p 493
5 E 42nd St Fl 5, New York NY 10017
Tel (212) 850-4000
SIC 6036 6311 6512 6514

GFI MANAGEMENT SERVICES INC p 610
50 Brdwy 140 Brdwy 41, New York NY 10004
Tel (212) 668-1444 SIC 6513 6512

HARTZ GROUP INC p 666
667 Madison Ave Fl 24, New York NY 10065
Tel (212) 308-3336
SIC 6512 6552 6531 6159

■ HILTON NEW YORK p 695
1335 Ave Of The Americas, New York NY 10019
Tel (212) 586-7000 SIC 6512

■ ICAHN ENTERPRISES HOLDINGS LP p 726
767 5th Ave Fl 17, New York NY 10153
Tel (212) 702-4300
SIC 6512 5719 6211 5093

KOP KLINE PLAZA LLC p 827
450 Lexington Ave Fl 13, New York NY 10017
Tel (212) 661-9890 SIC 6512

KUSHNER COMPANIES INC p 832
666 5th Ave Fl 15, New York NY 10103
Tel (212) 527-7000
SIC 1521 6513 6531 6512 1522 1531

LEFRAK ORGANIZATION INC p 852
40 W 57th St Fl 23, New York NY 10019
Tel (212) 707-6600 SIC 6513 6512

ND PROPERTIES INC p 1022
730 3rd Ave Ste 15485, New York NY 10017
Tel (800) 842-2252 SIC 6512

PORT AUTHORITY OF NEW YORK & NEW JERSEY p 1162
4 World Trade Ctr 150, New York NY 10007
Tel (212) 435-7000
SIC 4581 4785 6512 4491 4111

ROCKEFELLER GROUP INTERNATIONAL INC p 1244
1221 Avenue Of The Americ, New York NY 10020
Tel (212) 282-2000 SIC 6512 6552 4813

ROLEX INDUSTRIES INC p 1247
665 5th Ave Fl 6, New York NY 10022
Tel (212) 758-7700 SIC 5094 7631 6512

SHUBERT FOUNDATION INC p 1319
234 W 44th St Fl 6, New York NY 10036
Tel (212) 944-3777 SIC 8699 6512

SHUBERT ORGANIZATION INC p 1319
234 W 44th St Fl 6, New York NY 10036
Tel (212) 944-3700 SIC 6512 7922

UNITED CHARITIES p 1507
633 3rd Ave Fl 10, New York NY 10017
Tel (212) 614-5393 SIC 6512

COMMUNITY PROVIDERS INC p 350
75 Beekman St, Plattsburgh NY 12901
Tel (518) 561-2000 SIC 8062 8741 6512

INTERNATIONAL UNION OF OPERATING ENGINEERS LOCAL 30 p 757
11506 Myrtle Ave, Richmond Hill NY 11418
Tel (718) 847-8484 SIC 8631 6512

EJ DEL MONTE CORP p 482
909 Linden Ave Ste 1, Rochester NY 14625
Tel (585) 586-3121
SIC 6552 8741 6512 6799 7011

LIFETIME ASSISTANCE INC p 864
425 Paul Rd, Rochester NY 14624
Tel (585) 247-2255 SIC 8322 6512

PYRAMID MANAGEMENT GROUP INC p 1193
4 Clinton Sq, Syracuse NY 13202
Tel (315) 422-7000 SIC 6531 6512

▲ INGLES MARKETS INC p 743
2913 Us Highway 70, Black Mountain NC 28711
Tel (828) 669-2941
SIC 5411 5912 5541 2026 6512

COC PROPERTIES INC p 333
110 Mackenan Dr Ste 300, Cary NC 27511
Tel (919) 462-1100 SIC 6512 5541 5411

CHILDRESS KLEIN PROPERTIES INC p 300
301 S College St Ste 2800, Charlotte NC 28202
Tel (704) 342-9000 SIC 6552 6512 6531

■ HORIZON LINES HOLDING CORP p 707
2550 W Tyvola Rd Ste 530, Charlotte NC 28217
Tel (704) 973-7000 SIC 4731 6512

KOURY CORP p 828
2275 Vanstory St Ste 200, Greensboro NC 27403
Tel (336) 299-9200 SIC 6512 6513

B V HEDRICK GRAVEL & SAND CO p 142
120 1/2 N Church St, Salisbury NC 28144
Tel (704) 633-5982
SIC 1442 7359 6512 3273 1541 1542

PHILLIPS EDISON - ARC SHOPPING CENTER REIT INC p 1144
11501 Northlake Dr Fl 1, Cincinnati OH 45249
Tel (513) 554-1110 SIC 6512

AT HOLDINGS CORP p 123
23555 Euclid Ave, Cleveland OH 44117
Tel (216) 692-6000 SIC 3724 3728 6512

CAVALIERS HOLDINGS LLC p 267
1 Center Ct, Cleveland OH 44115
Tel (216) 420-2000 SIC 7941 6512

FOREST CITY ENTERPRISES LP p 566
50 Public Sq Ste 1100, Cleveland OH 44113
Tel (216) 621-6060 SIC 6512 6513 6552

FOREST CITY PROPERTIES LLC p 566
50 Public Sq Ste 1360, Cleveland OH 44113
Tel (216) 621-6060 SIC 6512 6513

GARLAND INDUSTRIES INC p 592
3800 E 91st St, Cleveland OH 44105
Tel (216) 641-7500 SIC 2952 6512 8712

PARK CORP p 1115
6200 Riverside Dr, Cleveland OH 44135
Tel (216) 267-4870
SIC 3547 1711 3443 5084 6512 7999

PUBCO CORP p 1189
3830 Kelley Ave, Cleveland OH 44114
Tel (216) 881-5300 SIC 3531 6512 3955

COLUMBUS ASSOCIATION FOR PERFORMING ARTS p 342
55 E State St, Columbus OH 43215
Tel (614) 469-1045 SIC 6512

GARDNER INC p 592
3641 Interchange Rd, Columbus OH 43204
Tel (614) 351-1325 SIC 5084 6512

GLIMCHER REALTY TRUST p 615
180 E Broad St Fl 20, Columbus OH 43215
Tel (614) 621-9000 SIC 6512

OKLAHOMA PUBLISHING CO OF OKLAHOMA p 1080
9000 N Brdwy, Oklahoma City OK 73114
Tel (405) 475-3311
SIC 2711 1311 6512 7375 2752

AHS OKLAHOMA HEALTH SYSTEM LLP p 37
110 W 7th St Ste 2540, Tulsa OK 74119
Tel (918) 579-1000
SIC 8062 8069 7352 6512 7389 5999

▲ HELMERICH & PAYNE INC p 682
1437 S Boulder Ave # 1400, Tulsa OK 74119
Tel (918) 742-5531 SIC 1381 1389 6512

QUIKTRIP CORP p 1200
4705 S 129th East Ave, Tulsa OK 74134
Tel (918) 615-7700
SIC 5411 5541 5172 2099 5141 6512

ST JOHN HEALTH SYSTEM INC p 1367
1923 S Utica Ave, Tulsa OK 74104
Tel (918) 744-2180
SIC 7991 6512 7389 8361 8071 8062

KEZI INC p 816
2975 Chad Dr, Eugene OR 97408
Tel (541) 485-5611 SIC 4833 6512 4813

TUALITY HEALTHCARE FOUNDATION INC p 1490
335 Se 8th Ave, Hillsboro OR 97123
Tel (503) 681-1850
SIC 8082 7374 6512 5999 7359

GANNETT FLEMING AFFILIATES INC p 590
207 Senate Ave, Camp Hill PA 17011
Tel (717) 763-7211 SIC 8711 7374 6512

TOUCHPOINT INC p 1463
210 N Brinton Lake Rd, Concordville PA 19331
Tel (610) 459-4000 SIC 6512 3452

SMG HOLDINGS INC p 1332
300 Cnshohckn State Rd # 450, Conshohocken PA 19428
Tel (610) 729-7900 SIC 6512 8742 7922

GEISINGER HEALTH SYSTEM FOUNDATION p 597
100 N Academy Ave, Danville PA 17822
Tel (570) 271-6461 SIC 8741 6512 7699

NEW WERNER HOLDING CO INC p 1033
93 Werner Rd, Greenville PA 16125
Tel (724) 588-2000
SIC 3499 3355 3089 3446 2499 6512

CROWN HOLDING CO p 395
Pasquerilla Plz, Johnstown PA 15901
Tel (814) 536-4441 SIC 6512

CMI HOLDING CORP p 329
1555 Bustard Rd, Kulpsville PA 19443
Tel (215) 361-9000 SIC 5411 6512

LIBERTY PROPERTY LIMITED PARTNERSHIP p 862
500 Chesterfield Pkwy, Malvern PA 19355
Tel (610) 648-1700 SIC 6512

HORIZON HOUSE INC p 707
120 S 30th St, Philadelphia PA 19104
Tel (215) 386-3838
SIC 8361 6512 8322 8093

■ SPECTRUM ARENA LIMITED PARTNERSHIP p 1357
3601 S Broad St, Philadelphia PA 19148
Tel (215) 389-9524 SIC 6512 7941

GENCO OF LEBANON INC p 598
100 Papercraft Park, Pittsburgh PA 15238
Tel (412) 820-3747 SIC 6512

HIGHMARK INC p 692
120 5th Ave, Pittsburgh PA 15222
Tel (412) 544-7000
SIC 6321 6324 6411 6512

DIGIORGIO MUSHROOM CORP p 439
1161 Park Rd, Reading PA 19605
Tel (610) 926-2139
SIC 2033 5148 2037 6512

READING HEALTH SYSTEM p 1213
6th Ave And Spruce St, Reading PA 19611
Tel (610) 988-8000
SIC 8062 6512 8093 8721 8011 7219

READING HOSPITAL p 1213
6th And Spruce St, Reading PA 19611
Tel (484) 628-8000 SIC 8062 6512

SUSQUEHANNA PFALTZGRAFF CO INC p 1409
140 E Market St, York PA 17401
Tel (717) 848-5500 SIC 4832 4841 6512

GATEWAY WOODSIDE INC p 594
100 Midway Rd Ste 14, Cranston RI 02920
Tel (401) 942-2800 SIC 6512

AFFILIATED FM INSURANCE CO p 32
270 Central Ave, Johnston RI 02919
Tel (401) 275-3000 SIC 6512 6331

FACTORY MUTUAL INSURANCE CO p 524
270 Central Ave, Johnston RI 02919
Tel (401) 275-3000 SIC 6331 8711 6512

GILBANE INC p 611
7 Jackson Walkway, Providence RI 02903
Tel (401) 456-5800
SIC 1541 1542 8741 6513 6512

GREENBAX ENTERPRISES INC p 637
884 Johnnie Dodds Blvd B, Mount Pleasant SC 29464
Tel (866) 891-1195 SIC 7389 6159 6512

BURROUGHS & CHAPIN CO INC p 228
8800 Marina Pkwy, Myrtle Beach SC 29572
Tel (843) 448-5123
SIC 6552 6515 6519 6512

MYRTLE BEACH FARMS CO INC p 1005
8820 Marina Pkwy, Myrtle Beach SC 29572
Tel (843) 448-5123 SIC 6552 7996 6512

KENCO GROUP INC p 810
2001 Rverside Dr Ste 3100, Chattanooga TN 37406
Tel (423) 622-1113 SIC 4225 6512

SAINT THOMAS HEALTH SERVICES INC p 1271
4220 Harding Pike, Nashville TN 37205
Tel (615) 222-2111 SIC 6512 6513 7011

OLYMPUS REAL ESTATE CORP p 1083
5080 Spectrum Dr, Addison TX 75001
Tel (972) 980-2200 SIC 7011 6512

▲ AMERICAN REALTY INVESTORS INC p 78
1603 Lbj Fwy Ste 800, Dallas TX 75234
Tel (469) 522-4200
SIC 6798 6162 6513 6512

ENCORE ENTERPRISES INC p 496
5005 L B Johnson Fwy 12 Ste 1200, Dallas TX 75244
Tel (214) 259-7009 SIC 6531 6512

■ HOWARD HUGHES CORP p 713
13355 Noel Rd Fl 22, Dallas TX 75240
Tel (702) 791-4000 SIC 6552 6512 7992

■ TENET HEALTHSYSTEM MEDICAL INC p 1437
1445 Ross Ave Ste 1400, Dallas TX 75202
Tel (469) 893-2000 SIC 8062 8063 6512

■ TRAMMELL CROW CENTRAL TEXAS LTD p 1469
2001 Ross Ave Ste 325, Dallas TX 75201
Tel (214) 267-0400 SIC 6799 6552 6512

■ TRAMMELL CROW CO p 1469
2100 Mckinney Ave Ste 900, Dallas TX 75201
Tel (214) 863-3000 SIC 6512

TRAMMELL CROW RESIDENTIAL CO p 1469
3819 Maple Ave, Dallas TX 75219
Tel (214) 922-8400 SIC 6513 6512 6531

LIVE NATION MUSIC GROUP TEXAS INC p 871
2000 West Loop S Ste 1300, Houston TX 77027
Tel (713) 693-8152 SIC 7922 6512

METRO NATIONAL CORP p 955
945 Bunker Hill Rd # 400, Houston TX 77024
Tel (713) 973-6400 SIC 6512 6531 6722

TOM THUMB FOOD & DRUGS INC p 1459
3663 Briarpark Dr, Houston TX 77042
Tel (713) 268-3500
SIC 5411 5912 5499 6512 6552

TRANSWESTERN COMMERCIAL SERVICES LLC p 1473
1900 West Loop S Ste 1300, Houston TX 77027
Tel (713) 270-7000 SIC 6512

VENTECH INC p 1548
1149 Ellsworth Dr Ofc, Pasadena TX 77506
Tel (713) 477-0201
SIC 8711 3491 5084 6512

LYND CO p 887
8000 W Interstate 10 # 1200, San Antonio TX 78230
Tel (210) 798-8114 SIC 6513 6512

PRESIDIAN DESTINATIONS LTD p 1172
9000 Tesoro Dr Ste 300, San Antonio TX 78217
Tel (210) 646-8811 SIC 6512

■ ULTRAMAR DIAMOND SHAMROCK INC p 1501
6000 N Loop 1604 W, San Antonio TX 78249
Tel (210) 627-2003 SIC 6512

UNIVERSITY HEALTH SYSTEM p 1518
355 Spencer Ln Ste 2, San Antonio TX 78201
Tel (210) 358-9185 SIC 8011 6512

SCOTT & WHITE MEMORIAL HOSPITAL p 1293
2401 S 31st St, Temple TX 76508
Tel (254) 724-2111
SIC 8062 6512 7352 7363

■ WOODLANDS OPERATING CO L P p 1623
24 Waterway Ave Ste 1100, The Woodlands TX 77380
Tel (281) 719-6100
SIC 6552 7997 7389 6513 6512

DESERET MANAGEMENT CORP p 432
55 N 300 W Ste 800, Salt Lake City UT 84101
Tel (801) 538-0651
SIC 4832 4833 5932 6512 6531 6411

GARFF ENTERPRISES INC p 592
405 S Main St Ste 1200, Salt Lake City UT 84111
Tel (801) 257-3400 SIC 5511 6512

■ STRATTON CORP p 1393
5 Village Lodge Rd, South Londonderry VT 05155
Tel (802) 297-2200
SIC 7011 7992 1531 6512 5941

K-VA-T FOOD STORES INC p 799
1 Food City Cir E, Abingdon VA 24210
Tel (800) 826-8451 SIC 5411 5141 6512

RELIANT ASSET MANAGEMENT LLC p 1222
2900 S Quincy St Ste 300a, Arlington VA 22206
Tel (703) 820-2900 SIC 6512

SHAMIN HOTELS INC p 1311
2000 Ware Btm Spring Rd, Chester VA 23836
Tel (804) 777-9000
SIC 7011 8051 6512 6513

THALHIMER INC MORTON G p 1446
11100 W Broad St, Glen Allen VA 23060
Tel (804) 648-5881
SIC 1542 6531 6799 6513 6512

AIRLINE PILOTS ASSOCIATION INTERNATIONAL p 40
1625 Massachusetts Ave Nw, Herndon VA 20172
Tel (703) 689-2270 SIC 8631 6512

ECK ENTERPRISES INC p 475
1405 W Main St, Richmond VA 23220
Tel (804) 359-5781 SIC 5063 6512

DIAMOND PARKING SERVICES LLC p 437
605 1st Ave Ste 600, Seattle WA 98104
Tel (206) 284-2732 SIC 7521 6512

PINNACLE REALTY MANAGEMENT CO p 1150
2801 Alaskan Way Ste 200, Seattle WA 98121
Tel (206) 215-9700
SIC 6531 8741 6513 6512 1522

WASHINGTON REAL ESTATE HOLDINGS LLC p 1578
600 University St # 2820, Seattle WA 98101
Tel (206) 613-5300 SIC 6512

NOEL CORP p 1046
1001 S 1st St, Yakima WA 98901
Tel (509) 248-4545
SIC 2086 7389 4212 6512 4225 5962

■ PARK MOUNTAINEER INC p 1115
Hc 2, Chester WV 26034
Tel (304) 387-8300
SIC 7999 7011 7389 6512

VHC INC p 1553
3090 Holmgren Way, Green Bay WI 54304
Tel (920) 336-7278
SIC 1731 1542 1541 1521 1711 6512

SIC 6513 Operators Of Apartment Buildings

COLONIAL PROPERTIES TRUST p 338
2101 6th Ave N Ste 750, Birmingham AL 35203
Tel (205) 250-8700
SIC 6798 6552 6531 6513

TUNGLAND CORP p 1491
4747 N 7th St Ste 300, Phoenix AZ 85014
Tel (602) 224-5052 SIC 6513

TUCSON MEDICAL CENTER p 1490
5301 E Grant Rd, Tucson AZ 85712
Tel (520) 327-5461
SIC 8062 8051 6513 8741

ERC PROPERTIES INC p 507
4107 Massard Rd, Fort Smith AR 72903
Tel (479) 478-5103 SIC 1522 6552 6513

PATH FINDER SCHOOLS INC p 1120
425 E Trickey Ln, Jacksonville AR 72076
Tel (501) 982-0528 SIC 6513

CBM 2012 A CALIFORNIA LIMITED PARTNERSHIP p 268
1010 Racquet Club Dr # 108, Auburn CA 95603
Tel (530) 823-2477
SIC 1531 1522 6513 6531 8741

■ SKILLED HEALTHCARE LLC p 1330
27442 Portola Pkwy # 200, Foothill Ranch CA 92610
Tel (949) 282-5800 SIC 8051 6513 5122

IRVINE APARTMENT COMMUNITIES LP p 765
110 Innovation Dr, Irvine CA 92617
Tel (949) 720-5600 SIC 6513 6552 6798

LONGWOOD MANAGEMENT CORP p 877
4032 Wilshire Blvd Fl 6, Los Angeles CA 90010
Tel (213) 389-6900 SIC 8742 6513

ESSEX PORTFOLIO LP p 510
925 E Meadow Dr, Palo Alto CA 94303
Tel (650) 494-3700 SIC 6798 6513

■ AAH HUDSON LP p 8
1255 N Hudson Ave, Pasadena CA 91104
Tel (626) 794-9179 SIC 6513

ST ELIZABETH COMMUNITY HOSPITAL p 1366
2550 Sster Mary Clumba Dr, Red Bluff CA 96080
Tel (530) 529-7760 SIC 8062 6513

SUTTER HEALTH p 1410
2200 River Plaza Dr, Sacramento CA 95833
Tel (916) 733-8800
SIC 8062 8051 8011 6513

ALL HALLOWS PRESERVATION LP p 51
54 Navy Rd, San Francisco CA 94124
Tel (415) 285-3909 SIC 6513

BAYVIEW PRESERVATION LP p 163
5 Commer Ct, San Francisco CA 94124
Tel (415) 285-7344 SIC 6513

INVEST WEST FINANCIAL CORP p 761
1933 Cliff Dr Ste 1, Santa Barbara CA 93109
Tel (805) 957-0095 SIC 6726 6513

LAVIDA COMMUNITIES INC p 847
500 Stevens Ave Ste 100, Solana Beach CA 92075
Tel (858) 792-9300
SIC 6513 6512 6531 6553

SENIOR RESOURCE GROUP LLC p 1304
500 Stevens Ave Ste 100, Solana Beach CA 92075
Tel (858) 792-9300
SIC 6513 6512 6531 6553

ARVADA HOUSE PRESERVATION LIMITED PARTNERSHIP p 114
10175 W 58th Pl Apt 402, Arvada CO 80004
Tel (303) 423-8872 SIC 6513

MANAGEMENT SENIOR LLC MORNINGSTAR p 900
7555 E Hampden Ave # 501, Denver CO 80231
Tel (303) 750-5522 SIC 6513

ARCHSTONE COMMUNITIES LLC p 105
9200 E Panorama Cir # 400, Englewood CO 80112
Tel (303) 708-5959 SIC 6798 6513

TALCOTT GARDENS LIMITED PARTNERSHIP p 1422
135 West St, New Britain CT 06051
Tel (860) 229-9554 SIC 6513

■ SUNRISE CONNECTICUT AVENUE ASSISTED LIVING LLC p 1403
5111 Connecticut Ave Nw, Washington DC 20008
Tel (202) 966-8020 SIC 6513

CHRISTIAN AND MISSIONARY ALLIANCE FOUNDATION INC p 302
15101 Shell Point Blvd, Fort Myers FL 33908
Tel (239) 466-1111 SIC 6513 8051 8059

CONCORD MANAGEMENT CO INC p 354
1551 Sandspur Rd, Maitland FL 32751
Tel (407) 741-8600 SIC 6513

LNR PROPERTY LLC p 872
1601 Washington Ave # 800, Miami Beach FL 33139
Tel (305) 695-5500 SIC 6513

FLORIDA CONFERENCE ASSOCIATION OF SEVENTH-DAY ADVENTISTS p 557
655 N Wymore Rd, Winter Park FL 32789
Tel (407) 644-5000
SIC 8661 8211 5942 6513

POST APARTMENT HOMES LP p 1163
4401 Northsde Pkwy 800, Atlanta GA 30327
Tel (404) 846-5000 SIC 6798 6513

AMBLING MANAGEMENT CO LLC p 65
348 Enterprise Dr, Valdosta GA 31601
Tel (866) 777-7228
SIC 1522 6552 6531 6513

AMBERJACK LTD p 65
3 State Farm Plz, Bloomington IL 61791
Tel (309) 766-6920 SIC 6512 6513

CT ASSOCIATES OF ILLINOIS LP p 399
2061 N Campbell Ave Ofc, Chicago IL 60647
Tel (773) 486-3666 SIC 6531 6513

NORTHWESTERN MEMORIAL HEALTHCARE p 1060
251 E Huron St Ste 3-710, Chicago IL 60611
Tel (312) 926-2000
SIC 8082 6513 7389 8099

PULLMAN WHEEL WORKS ASSOCIATES p 1191
901 E 104th St Ste 2, Chicago IL 60628
Tel (773) 785-1300 SIC 6513

WATERTON ASSOCIATES LLC p 1582
30 S Wacker Dr Ste 3600, Chicago IL 60606
Tel (312) 948-4500 SIC 6513 6798

WIRTZ CORP p 1618
680 N Lake Shore Dr # 1900, Chicago IL 60611
Tel (312) 943-7000
SIC 5181 5182 6513 6512 7011 6411

LUTHERAN SOCIAL SERVICES OF ILLINOIS p 886
1001 E Touhy Ave Ste 50, Des Plaines IL 60018
Tel (847) 635-4600 SIC 8322 6514 6513

STANDARD WESTWOOD VENTURE LP p 1376
2200 1st St Ste A, Moline IL 61265
Tel (309) 797-4327 SIC 6513

INLAND REAL ESTATE GROUP OF COMPANIES p 743
2901 Butterfield Rd, Oak Brook IL 60523
Tel (630) 218-8000
SIC 6513 6512 6162 6282 1522 1542

LIFELINK HOUSING CORP p 864
1900 Spring Rd Ste 300, Oak Brook IL 60523
Tel (630) 368-0817 SIC 6513

CARDON & ASSOCIATES INC p 253
2749 E Covenanter Dr, Bloomington IN 47401
Tel (812) 332-2265 SIC 8741 6513 8742

GENE B GLICK CO INC p 598
8801 River Crossing Blvd # 200, Indianapolis IN 46240
Tel (317) 469-0400 SIC 1522 6531 6513

COMMONWEALTH HEALTH CORP INC p 346
800 Park St, Bowling Green KY 42101
Tel (270) 745-1500 SIC 8062 6513

CALIFORNIA SQUARE LIMITED PARTNERSHIP p 241
1600 Garland Ave, Louisville KY 40210
Tel (502) 589-9034 SIC 6513

MAINE MEDICAL CENTER p 898
22 Bramhall St, Portland ME 04102
Tel (207) 662-0111 SIC 8062 8071 6513

CHARLESTOWN COMMUNITY INC p 290
719 Maiden Choice Ln, Baltimore MD 21228
Tel (410) 737-8830 SIC 6513 8051

B F SAUL REAL ESTATE INVESTMENT TRUST p 141
7501 Wscnsin Ave Ste 1500, Bethesda MD 20814
Tel (301) 657-2619 SIC 6512 6513

OXFORD-COLUMBIA ASSOCIATES A MARYLAND LIMITED PARTNERSHIP p 1101
6531 Quiet Hours, Columbia MD 21045
Tel (410) 381-1906 SIC 6513

BOZZUTO & ASSOCIATES INC p 205
6406 Ivy Ln Ste 700, Greenbelt MD 20770
Tel (301) 220-0100 SIC 6513 1522 6552

WINN WB MANAGEMENT CO LLC p 1616
6 Faneuil Hall Market Pl # 500, Boston MA 02109
Tel (617) 742-4500 SIC 6513

WINNRESIDENTIAL LIMITED PARTNERSHIP p 1616
6 Faneuil Hall Market Pl, Boston MA 02109
Tel (617) 742-4500 SIC 6513

CONTINENTAL WINGATE CO INC p 364
1 Charles River Pl, Needham MA 02494
Tel (781) 707-9000 SIC 6513 8051

WORCESTER EPISCOPAL HOUSING CO LIMITED PARTNERSHIP p 1624
6 Wachusett St, Worcester MA 01609
Tel (508) 757-1133 SIC 6513

MCKINLEY INC p 930
320 N Main St Ste 200, Ann Arbor MI 48104
Tel (734) 769-8520 SIC 6513

BEACON HILL PRESERVATION LIMITED DIVIDEND HOUSING ASSOCIATION LIMITED PARTNERSHIP p 164
32 E Carleton Rd, Hillsdale MI 49242
Tel (517) 437-2177 SIC 6513

SENIOR RELATED WORLD LLC p 1304
5600 Mall Dr W, Lansing MI 48917
Tel (517) 321-5058 SIC 6513

SUNTREE-OXFORD ASSOCIATES LIMITED DIVIDEND HOUSING ASSOCIATION p 1405
1100 Sunview Dr, Saint Johns MI 48879
Tel (989) 224-8910 SIC 6513

HARTMAN AND TYNER INC p 666
24700 W 12 Mile Rd, Southfield MI 48034
Tel (248) 352-2010 SIC 6513 6531

SINGH MANAGEMENT CO INC p 1326
7125 Orchard Lake Rd # 200, West Bloomfield MI 48322
Tel (248) 865-1600 SIC 6531 6513 8742

AUGUSTANA CARE p 131
1007 E 14th St, Minneapolis MN 55404
Tel (612) 238-5101 SIC 6513 8051

NORTH RIDGE SKILLED LLC p 1053
5430 Boone Ave N, Minneapolis MN 55428
Tel (763) 592-3000 SIC 6513 8051

RBC CAPITAL MARKETS LLC p 1211
60 S 6th St Ste 700, Minneapolis MN 55402
Tel (612) 371-2711
SIC 6211 6512 6513 6282

WINTER GARDEN PRESERVATION LP p 1617
5708 Kingsbury Pl, Saint Louis MO 63112
Tel (314) 361-0251 SIC 6513

MARINA CLUB CONDOMINIUM p 906
655 Absecon Blvd Ste B, Atlantic City NJ 08401
Tel (609) 348-0040 SIC 6513

CHURCHILL CORPORATE SERVICES INC p 305
56 Utter Ave, Hawthorne NJ 07506
Tel (973) 636-9400 SIC 6513 7389

INTERSTATE REALTY MANAGEMENT CO INC p 758
3 E Stow Rd, Marlton NJ 08053
Tel (856) 596-0500 SIC 6531 6513

■ **SUNBRIDGE RETIREMENT CARE ASSOCIATES INC** p 1401
101 Sun Ave Ne, Albuquerque NM 87109
Tel (505) 821-3355 SIC 6513 3842

CENTRAL TOWERS PRESERVATION LP p 280
400 Central Ave Ste 1, Albany NY 12206
Tel (518) 438-6834 SIC 6513

JEWISH HOME AND HOSPITAL p 784
100 W Kingsbridge Rd # 100, Bronx NY 10468
Tel (718) 579-0420 SIC 6513 6531

RIVERBAY CORP p 1237
2049 Bartow Ave, Bronx NY 10475
Tel (718) 320-3300 SIC 6513

STARRETT CITY ASSOCIATES LP p 1379
1230 Pa Ave Ste 1, Brooklyn NY 11239
Tel (718) 240-4112 SIC 6513

STARRETT CITY INC p 1379
1230 Pa Ave Ste 1, Brooklyn NY 11239
Tel (718) 642-8700 SIC 6513

BUFFALO VILLAGE ASSOC 190 CAROLINA BUF p 224
190 Carolina St, Buffalo NY 14201
Tel (716) 847-6313 SIC 6513

RESOURCE CENTER p 1227
200 Dunham Ave, Jamestown NY 14701
Tel (716) 661-4829
SIC 8093 6513 6512 8052

BRE RETAIL CENTERS HOLDINGS LP p 209
345 Park Ave, New York NY 10154
Tel (212) 583-5000 SIC 6513 6722

GFI MANAGEMENT SERVICES INC p 610
50 Brdwy 140 Brdwy 41, New York NY 10004
Tel (212) 668-1444 SIC 6513 6512

HELMSLEY ENTERPRISES INC p 682
230 Park Ave Rm 659, New York NY 10169
Tel (212) 679-3600 SIC 6513 8742 1522

HELP USA INC p 682
115 E 13th St, New York NY 10003
Tel (212) 400-7000 SIC 6513 8322

KUSHNER COMPANIES INC p 832
666 5th Ave Fl 15, New York NY 10103
Tel (212) 527-7000
SIC 1521 6513 6531 6512 1522 1531

LEFRAK ORGANIZATION INC p 852
40 W 57th St Fl 23, New York NY 10019
Tel (212) 707-6600 SIC 6513 6512

SOUTHPORT MEWS HOUSING PRESERVATION p 1351
50 S Main St, Port Chester NY 10573
Tel (914) 937-1681 SIC 6513

PJ HOUSING PRESERVATION LP p 1153
230 Jersey Ave, Port Jervis NY 12771
Tel (845) 856-7677 SIC 6513

HOME PROPERTIES LIMITED PARTNERSHIP p 703
850 Clinton Sq, Rochester NY 14604
Tel (585) 546-4900 SIC 6513

BELL PARTNERS INC p 170
300 N Greene St Ste 1000, Greensboro NC 27401
Tel (336) 232-1900 SIC 6513

KOURY CORP p 828
2275 Vanstory St Ste 200, Greensboro NC 27403
Tel (336) 299-9200 SIC 6512 6513

ALLIANCE TOWERS LLC p 55
350 S Arch Ave Apt 106, Alliance OH 44601
Tel (330) 823-1063 SIC 6513

ANTIOCH PRESERVATION LP p 94
8920 Carnegie Ave, Cleveland OH 44106
Tel (216) 721-6100 SIC 6513

FOREST CITY ENTERPRISES LP p 566
50 Public Sq Ste 1100, Cleveland OH 44113
Tel (216) 621-6060 SIC 6512 6513 6552

FOREST CITY PROPERTIES LLC p 566
50 Public Sq Ste 1360, Cleveland OH 44113
Tel (216) 621-6060 SIC 6512 6513

MENORAH PARK CENTER FOR SENIOR LIVING BET MOSHAV ZEKENIM HADATI p 943
27100 Cedar Rd, Cleveland OH 44122
Tel (216) 831-6500 SIC 8051 6513 8322

NATIONAL CHURCH RESIDENCES p 1010
2333 N Bank Dr, Columbus OH 43220
Tel (614) 451-2151
SIC 6531 6513 8051 8059

HCF MANAGEMENT INC p 672
1100 Shawnee Rd, Lima OH 45805
Tel (419) 999-2010 SIC 8051 6513

PINEWOOD PLACE APARTMENTS p 1149
1210 Collingwood Blvd, Toledo OH 43604
Tel (419) 243-1413 SIC 6513

INTEGRIS RURAL HEALTHCARE OF OKLAHOMA INC p 749
3300 Nw Expwy, Oklahoma City OK 73112
Tel (405) 951-2277 SIC 8062 6513

IDA TOWER p 728
1010 12th St, Altoona PA 16601
Tel (814) 944-4055 SIC 6513

RICHLIEU ASSOCIATES p 1233
3338 Richlieu Rd, Bensalem PA 19020
Tel (215) 639-2800 SIC 6513

■ **GMH COMMUNITIES TRUST** p 619
10 Campus Blvd, Newtown Square PA 19073
Tel (610) 355-8000 SIC 6798 6513 8742

MADLYN AND LEONARD ABRAMSON CENTER FOR JEWISH LIFE p 894
1425 Horsham Rd, North Wales PA 19454
Tel (215) 371-3000 SIC 8051 8069 6513

PRESBYTERIAN SENIORCARE p 1171
1215 Hulton Rd, Oakmont PA 15139
Tel (412) 828-5600
SIC 8051 8052 6513 8741

UNIVERSITY PLAZA ASSOCIATES p 1527
3901 Market St Ofc B, Philadelphia PA 19104
Tel (215) 386-0351 SIC 6513

MC WIL GROUP LTD p 925
209 N Beaver St, York PA 17401
Tel (717) 854-7857
SIC 8059 8051 8069 6513 8742 6552

WILMAC CORP p 1613
209 N Beaver St, York PA 17401
Tel (717) 854-7857
SIC 8059 8051 8069 6513 8742 6552

MEMORIAL HOSPITAL p 942
111 Brewster St, Pawtucket RI 02860
Tel (401) 729-2000 SIC 8062 6513

GILBANE INC p 611
7 Jackson Walkway, Providence RI 02903
Tel (401) 456-5800
SIC 1541 1542 8741 6513 6512

LANDAU APARTMENTS LIMITED PARTNERSHIP p 842
1321 S Broad St, Clinton SC 29325
Tel (864) 833-3215 SIC 6513

RELATED CLINTON MANOR LLC p 1221
100 Clinton St, Clinton SC 29325
Tel (864) 833-3836 SIC 6531 6513

RELATED NEWBERRY ARMS LLC p 1221
186 Newberry Arms, Newberry SC 29108
Tel (803) 276-4053 SIC 6513

SAINT THOMAS HEALTH SERVICES INC p 1271
4220 Harding Pike, Nashville TN 37205
Tel (615) 222-2111 SIC 6512 6513 7011

HIGH PLAINS BAPTIST HOSPITAL INC p 690
1600 Wallace Blvd, Amarillo TX 79106
Tel (806) 358-5800 SIC 8062 6513 8051

PLEASANT HILL PRESERVATION LP p 1156
2501 Anken Dr Ofc, Austin TX 78741
Tel (512) 447-7244 SIC 6513

▲ **AMERICAN REALTY INVESTORS INC** p 78
1603 Lbj Fwy Ste 800, Dallas TX 75234
Tel (469) 522-4200
SIC 6798 6162 6513 6512

■ **CAPITAL SENIOR LIVING INC** p 250
14160 Dallas Pkwy Ste 300, Dallas TX 75254
Tel (972) 770-5600 SIC 6513

MILESTONE MANAGEMENTS LLC p 969
5429 Lyndon B Johnson Fwy # 800, Dallas TX 75240
Tel (214) 561-1200 SIC 6513

TRAMMELL CROW RESIDENTIAL CO p 1469
3819 Maple Ave, Dallas TX 75219
Tel (214) 922-8400 SIC 6513 6512 6531

GREYSTAR MANAGEMENT SERVICES LP p 639
750 Bering Dr Ste 300, Houston TX 77057
Tel (713) 966-5000 SIC 6513 6531 1522

JPI LIFESTYLE APARTMENT COMMUNITIES LP p 795
600 Las Colinas Blvd E, Irving TX 75039
Tel (972) 556-1700 SIC 6513 6552

VILLAGE OF KAUFMAN p 1557
421 E 7th St, Kaufman TX 75142
Tel (972) 962-7328 SIC 6513

LYND CO p 887
8000 W Interstate 10 # 1200, San Antonio TX 78230
Tel (210) 798-8114 SIC 6513 6512

■ **WOODLANDS OPERATING CO L P** p 1623
24 Waterway Ave Ste 1100, The Woodlands TX 77380
Tel (281) 719-6100
SIC 6552 7997 7389 6513 6512

BRIDGE INVESTMENT GROUP PARTNERS LLC p 211
5295 S Commerce Dr # 100, Salt Lake City UT 84107
Tel (801) 716-4500 SIC 6513 6531

HHHUNT CORP p 689
800 Hethwood Blvd, Blacksburg VA 24060
Tel (540) 552-3515 SIC 6513

HHHUNT PROPERTY MANAGEMENT INC p 689
800 Hethwood Blvd, Blacksburg VA 24060
Tel (540) 552-3515 SIC 6513

CREVENNA OAKS PRESERVATION LP p 392
11550 Oak Bluff Ct, Burke VA 22015
Tel (703) 323-7964 SIC 6513 7389

SHAMIN HOTELS INC p 1311
2000 Ware Btm Spring Rd, Chester VA 23836
Tel (804) 777-9000
SIC 7011 8051 6512 6513

BARCELO CRESTLINE CORP p 154
3950 University Dr # 301, Fairfax VA 22030
Tel (571) 529-6000 SIC 6513 6531

THALHIMER INC MORTON G p 1446
11100 W Broad St, Glen Allen VA 23060
Tel (804) 648-5881
SIC 1542 6531 6799 6513 6512

■ **SUNRISE SENIOR LIVING LLC** p 1404
7902 Westpark Dr, Mc Lean VA 22102
Tel (703) 273-7500 SIC 6513

CITY LINE APTS p 312
155a Mytilene Dr, Newport News VA 23605
Tel (757) 838-5553 SIC 6513

CARRIAGE HOUSE PRESERVATION LP p 260
135 W Old St, Petersburg VA 23803
Tel (804) 733-6225 SIC 6513

LANDMARK APARTMENT TRUST INC p 842
4901 Dickens Rd Ste 101, Richmond VA 23230
Tel (804) 237-1335 SIC 6798 6513

PROVIDENCE HEALTH & SERVICES-WASHINGTON p 1186
1801 Lind Ave Sw 9016, Renton WA 98057
Tel (425) 525-3355
SIC 8062 8051 8052 6513 8069

PINNACLE REALTY MANAGEMENT CO p 1150
2801 Alaskan Way Ste 200, Seattle WA 98121
Tel (206) 215-9700
SIC 6531 8741 6513 6512 1522

R D MERRILL CO p 1202
1938 Frview Ave E Ste 300, Seattle WA 98102
Tel (206) 676-5600 SIC 6513

VIRGINIA MASON MEDICAL CENTER p 1559
1100 9th Ave, Seattle WA 98101
Tel (206) 223-6600
SIC 8011 8051 6513 8062

EVERGREEN HEALTHCARE INC p 514
4601 Ne 77th Ave Ste 300, Vancouver WA 98662
Tel (360) 892-6472
SIC 8051 6513 8059 8741

HOLLAND RESIDENTIAL LLC p 700
1111 Main St Ste 700, Vancouver WA 98660
Tel (360) 694-7888 SIC 6513 8741

CAPITOL LAKES RETIREMENT COMMUNITY p 251
110 S Henry St, Madison WI 53703
Tel (608) 283-2000
SIC 6513 8051 8052 8361

■ **SOUTHERN ASSISTED LIVING INC** p 1347
6737 W Wa St Ste 2300, Milwaukee WI 53214
Tel (414) 588-0431 SIC 6513

SIC 6514 Operators Of Dwellings, Except Apartments

RUSSELL LANDS INC p 1259
2544 Willow Point Rd, Alexander City AL 35010
Tel (256) 329-0835
SIC 5211 6514 4493 7997 7011

SHEE ATIKA INC p 1313
315 Lincoln St Ste 300, Sitka AK 99835
Tel (907) 747-3534 SIC 6514 6552

■ **SHAPELL INDUSTRIES LLC** p 1311
8383 Wilshire Blvd # 700, Beverly Hills CA 90211
Tel (323) 655-7330 SIC 6552 6514 1522

■ **CIGNA HOLDINGS INC** p 306
590 Naamans Rd, Claymont DE 19703
Tel (215) 761-1000
SIC 6311 6321 6331 6512 6514 6282

LUTHERAN SOCIAL SERVICES OF ILLINOIS p 886
1001 E Touhy Ave Ste 50, Des Plaines IL 60018
Tel (847) 635-4600 SIC 8322 6514 6513

MURFIN DRILLING CO INC p 1001
250 N Water St Ste 300, Wichita KS 67202
Tel (316) 267-3241
SIC 1381 1382 5082 6512 6514

■ **DCH AUTO GROUP (USA) INC** p 418
955 Route 9 N, South Amboy NJ 08879
Tel (732) 727-9168
SIC 5511 7515 6512 6514

EMIGRANT SAVINGS BANK p 493
5 E 42nd St Fl 5, New York NY 10017
Tel (212) 850-4000
SIC 6036 6311 6512 6514

J & R ASSOCIATES p 770
14803 Holland Rd, Brookpark OH 44142
Tel (440) 250-4080 SIC 1542 8361 6514

HAMOT HEALTH FOUNDATION p 656
201 State St, Erie PA 16550
Tel (814) 877-7020 SIC 8741 8062 6514

SIC 6515 Operators of Residential Mobile Home Sites

■ **CAREFREE COMMUNITIES INC** p 254
6991 E Camelback Rd B310, Scottsdale AZ 85251
Tel (480) 423-5700 SIC 6515

■ **CMH CAPITAL INC** p 329
1105 N Market St Ste 1300, Wilmington DE 19801
Tel (302) 651-7947
SIC 6719 2451 6515 6311

HOMETOWN AMERICA MANAGEMENT CORP p 704
150 N Wacker Dr Ste 2800, Chicago IL 60606
Tel (312) 604-7500 SIC 6515

■ **MHC OPERATING LIMITED PARTNERSHIP** p 959
2 N Riverside Plz Ste 800, Chicago IL 60606
Tel (312) 279-1400 SIC 6515 6531

BURROUGHS & CHAPIN CO INC p 228
8800 Marina Pkwy, Myrtle Beach SC 29572
Tel (843) 448-5123
SIC 6552 6515 6519 6512

AMERICAN HOMESTAR CORP p 74
2450 S Shore Blvd Ste 300, League City TX 77573
Tel (281) 334-9700
SIC 2451 4213 5271 6351 6515

KING COUNTY HOUSING AUTHORITY p 820
401 37th St Se, Auburn WA 98002
Tel (206) 205-8837 SIC 6515

SIC 6519 Lessors Of Real Estate, NEC

COOK INLET REGION INC p 366
725 E Fireweed Ln Ste 800, Anchorage AK 99503
Tel (907) 274-8638
SIC 6552 1382 1389 6519 4832 4833

KONIAG INC p 827
3800 Cntrpoint Dr Ste 502, Kodiak AK 99615
Tel (907) 486-2530 SIC 6552 6519 6719

RIMROCK PARTNERS LLC p 1235
2415 E Camelback Rd # 700, Phoenix AZ 85016
Tel (602) 954-7085 SIC 6531 6519 6552

OWL COMPANIES p 1100
4695 Macarthur Ct Ste 950, Newport Beach CA 92660
Tel (949) 797-2000 SIC 8331 6519 4911

▲ **AEROJET ROCKETDYNE HOLDINGS INC** p 30
2001 Aerojet Rd, Rancho Cordova CA 95742
Tel (916) 355-4000
SIC 3812 3764 3769 6552 6519

CARMEL PARTNERS INC p 258
1000 Sansome St 1, San Francisco CA 94111
Tel (415) 273-2900 SIC 6531 6519

NATIONAL GOLF PROPERTIES LLC p 1012
2951 28th St Ste 3000, Santa Monica CA 90405
Tel (310) 664-4000 SIC 6519 8111

■ **FRONTIER FLORIDA LLC** p 581
401 Merritt 7, Norwalk CT 06851
Tel (813) 483-2011
SIC 4813 6519 8721 5065 7629

■ **SBA SENIOR FINANCE II LLC** p 1285
8051 Congress Ave Ste 100, Boca Raton FL 33487
Tel (561) 995-7670 SIC 6519

■ **SENIOR SBA FINANCE INC** p 1304
8051 Congress Ave Ste 100, Boca Raton FL 33487
Tel (561) 995-7670 SIC 4899 6519

■ **RESORTQUEST INTERNATIONAL INC** p 1227
8955 Us Highway 98 W # 203, Destin FL 32550
Tel (850) 837-4774 SIC 7011 6519

▲ **ALICO INC** p 50
10070 Daniels Interstate, Fort Myers FL 33913
Tel (239) 226-2000
SIC 0174 0212 0133 6519

■ **PATRIOT TRANSPORTATION INC** p 1121
200 W Forsyth St Ste 700, Jacksonville FL 32202
Tel (904) 356-6110 SIC 4213 6531 6519

FONTAINEBLEAU FLORIDA HOTEL LLC p 563
4441 Collins Ave, Miami FL 33140
Tel (305) 538-2000
SIC 6519 7011 5812 7991

ATKINS NORTH AMERICA HOLDINGS CORP p 125
4030 W Boy Scout Blvd, Tampa FL 33607
Tel (813) 282-7275 SIC 8712 6519 8711

SEVEN-ONE-SEVEN PARKING SERVICES INC p 1309
1410 N Florida Ave, Tampa FL 33602
Tel (813) 228-7722
SIC 7299 6519 7521 4119 8742

ALTISOURCE HOLDINGS LLC p 62
1000 Abernathy Rd, Atlanta GA 30328
Tel (877) 839-7118 SIC 6794 6519

MCDONALD OIL CO INC p 927
1700 Lukken Indus Dr W, Lagrange GA 30240
Tel (706) 884-6191 SIC 5541 5921 6519

CIRI DEVELOPMENT CORP p 308
1425 Higham St, Idaho Falls ID 83402
Tel (208) 528-8718 SIC 6519 6552

NAVY PIER INC p 1020
600 E Grand Ave Ste 134, Chicago IL 60611
Tel (312) 595-5333 SIC 6519 7999

ACA SPARROW CORP p 13
2937 N Kenwood Ave Apt B, Indianapolis IN 46208
Tel (317) 920-1374 SIC 6519

▲ **EMPLOYERS MUTUAL CASUALTY CO** p 494
717 Mulberry St, Des Moines IA 50309
Tel (515) 280-2511
SIC 6411 6321 6311 6519

ABCM CORP p 10
1320 4th St Ne, Hampton IA 50441
Tel (641) 456-5636 SIC 8741 6519 7011

HANNAFORD BROTHERS CO p 658
145 Pleasant Hill Rd, Scarborough ME 04074
Tel (207) 883-2911 SIC 5411 6519

BF SAUL PROPERTY CO p 179
7501 Wisconsin Ave, Bethesda MD 20814
Tel (301) 986-6000
SIC 6531 6519 1542 1522

■ **CHEVY CHASE BANK FSB** p 296
7501 Wisconsin Ave Fl 11, Bethesda MD 20814
Tel (240) 497-4101
SIC 6035 6411 6211 6519 6552 6719

▲ **RAMCO-GERSHENSON PROPERTIES TRUST** p 1207
31500 Northwestern Hwy, Farmington Hills MI 48334
Tel (248) 350-9900 SIC 6798 6519

ROBERT A WILLIAMS ENTERPRISES p 1241
3701 Central Ave Ne, Minneapolis MN 55421
Tel (763) 788-1113 SIC 5541 6519

BUFFALO SERVICES INC p 224
747 S Broadway St, Mccomb MS 39648
Tel (601) 684-7702
SIC 5172 5411 6519 4212

CNL HOLDINGS LLC p 330
430 W 7th St Ste 219001, Kansas City MO 64105
Tel (407) 650-1000 SIC 6519

GLOBE HOLDING CO LLC p 618
37 Loudon Rd, Pittsfield NH 03263
Tel (603) 435-8323 SIC 6519

ALLSUP ENTERPRISES INC p 58
2112 N Thornton St, Clovis NM 88101
Tel (575) 769-2311
SIC 5411 5541 4832 6519 5171

■ **FRONTIER CALIFORNIA INC** p 581
140 West St, New York NY 10007
Tel (212) 395-1000
SIC 4813 6519 8721 5065 1731 7629

■ VIACOM SONGS INC p 1554
1515 Broadway Lbby, New York NY 10036
Tel (212) 258-6000
SIC 6531 6519 7359 7941 7812 2731

■ HIGHWOODS REALTY LIMITED PARTNERSHIP p 692
3100 Smoketree Ct Ste 600, Raleigh NC 27604
Tel (919) 872-4924 SIC 6519 6531 6798

DAKOTA COAL CO p 409
1717 E Interstate Ave, Bismarck ND 58503
Tel (701) 223-0441 SIC 6519 7353 3274

LEATHERS ENTERPRISES INC p 850
255 Depot St, Fairview OR 97024
Tel (503) 661-1244 SIC 5541 6519

BERWIND CORP p 176
3000 Ctr Sq W 1500 Mkt St 1500 W, Philadelphia PA 19102
Tel (215) 563-2800
SIC 6519 5052 4789 3625 3669 2899

▲ GAMING AND LEISURE PROPERTIES INC p 590
845 Berkshire Blvd, Wyomissing PA 19610
Tel (610) 401-2900 SIC 6519

K I INVESTMENTS INC p 799
Ave 65 De Infntria St1179, San Juan PR 00924
Tel (787) 622-0600 SIC 6519 5012 5511

BURROUGHS & CHAPIN CO INC p 228
8800 Marina Pkwy, Myrtle Beach SC 29572
Tel (843) 448-5123
SIC 6552 6515 6519 6512

H Q GLOBAL HOLDINGS INC p 650
15305 Dallas Pkwy Ste 400, Addison TX 75001
Tel (972) 361-8100 SIC 6519 7389

HQ GLOBAL WORKPLACES INC p 714
15305 Dallas Pkwy Ste 400, Addison TX 75001
Tel (972) 361-8100 SIC 6519 7389

▲ SUNOCO LP p 1403
8020 Park Ln Ste 200, Dallas TX 75231
Tel (214) 981-0700 SIC 5172 6519 5541

■ MARATHON INTERNATIONAL OIL CO p 904
5555 San Felipe St # 2796, Houston TX 77056
Tel (713) 629-6600 SIC 1311 1382 6519

■ SUSSER PETROLEUM PROPERTY CO LLC p 1409
555 E Airtex Dr, Houston TX 77073
Tel (832) 234-3600 SIC 5172 6519

C-III CAPITAL PARTNERS LLC p 234
5221 N O Connor Blvd, Irving TX 75039
Tel (972) 868-5300
SIC 6519 6726 6361 6411

■ VERIZON NORTHWEST INC p 1550
600 Hidden Rdg, Irving TX 75038
Tel (972) 718-5600
SIC 4813 6519 8721 5065 7629

SNOWBIRD LTD p 1336
State Rd 210, Snowbird UT 84092
Tel (801) 742-2222 SIC 1531 6519

SIC 6531 Real Estate Agents & Managers

COLONIAL PROPERTIES TRUST p 338
2101 6th Ave N Ste 750, Birmingham AL 35203
Tel (205) 250-8700
SIC 6798 6552 6531 6513

■ REALTYSOUTH ADMIN OFFICE p 1214
2501 20th Pl S Ste 400, Birmingham AL 35223
Tel (205) 325-1397 SIC 6531

ALASKA RAILROAD CORP p 45
327 W Ship Creek Ave, Anchorage AK 99501
Tel (907) 265-2494 SIC 4011 6531

NATIONWIDE HOMES INC p 1018
1100 London Bridge Rd G102, Lake Havasu City AZ 86404
Tel (928) 453-6600 SIC 1521 6531

ALLIANCE RESIDENTIAL LLC p 55
2415 E Camelback Rd # 600, Phoenix AZ 85016
Tel (602) 778-2800 SIC 6531

RIMROCK PARTNERS LLC p 1235
2415 E Camelback Rd # 700, Phoenix AZ 85016
Tel (602) 954-7085 SIC 6531 6519 6552

■ HUNT CORP p 719
6720 N Scottsdale Rd # 300, Scottsdale AZ 85253
Tel (480) 368-4755 SIC 1541 6531 6552

SUN HEALTH CORP p 1400
14719 W Grand Ave Ste 113, Surprise AZ 85374
Tel (623) 876-5350
SIC 8062 8051 8082 7361 8733 6531

▲ DELTIC TIMBER CORP p 427
210 E Elm St, El Dorado AR 71730
Tel (870) 881-9400
SIC 0811 2411 6531 8741

CBM 2012 A CALIFORNIA LIMITED PARTNERSHIP p 268
1010 Racquet Club Dr # 108, Auburn CA 95603
Tel (530) 823-2477
SIC 1531 1522 6513 6531 8741

MOTHER LODE HOLDING CO p 992
189 Fulweiler Ave, Auburn CA 95603
Tel (530) 887-2410 SIC 6361 6531 7389

▲ KENNEDY-WILSON HOLDINGS INC p 811
151 El Camino Dr, Beverly Hills CA 90212
Tel (310) 887-6400 SIC 6531 6799

■ LAWYERS TITLE CO p 848
7530 N Glenoaks Blvd, Burbank CA 91504
Tel (818) 767-0425 SIC 6361 6531

OBAYASHI USA LLC p 1072
577 Airport Blvd Ste 600, Burlingame CA 94010
Tel (650) 952-4910 SIC 6531

▲ MARCUS & MILLICHAP INC p 905
23975 Park Sorrento # 400, Calabasas CA 91302
Tel (818) 212-2250 SIC 6531

GRAND PACIFIC RESORTS INC p 630
5900 Pasteur Ct Ste 200, Carlsbad CA 92008
Tel (760) 431-8500 SIC 6531 7011

■ FIRST AMERICAN TITLE GUARANTY CO p 544
1355 Willow Way Ste 100, Concord CA 94520
Tel (925) 356-7000 SIC 6361 6531

■ NORTH AMERICAN ASSET DEVELOPMENT CORP p 1049
1855 Gateway Blvd Ste 650, Concord CA 94520
Tel (925) 935-5599 SIC 6361 6531

■ NORTH AMERICAN TITLE CO INC p 1050
1855 Gateway Blvd Ste 600, Concord CA 94520
Tel (925) 935-5599 SIC 6361 6531

FPI MANAGEMENT INC p 573
800 Iron Point Rd, Folsom CA 95630
Tel (916) 357-5300 SIC 6531

PROFESSIONAL COMMUNITY MANAGEMENT OF CALIFORNIA p 1180
27051 Towne Centre Dr # 200, Foothill Ranch CA 92610
Tel (800) 369-7260 SIC 6531

STEELWAVE INC p 1385
4000 E 3rd Ave Ste 600, Foster City CA 94404
Tel (650) 571-2200 SIC 6552 8741 6531

STEELWAVE LLC p 1385
4000 E 3rd Ave Ste 500, Foster City CA 94404
Tel (650) 571-2200 SIC 6552 8741 6531

J & M SALES INC p 770
15001 S Figueroa St, Gardena CA 90248
Tel (310) 324-9962
SIC 5651 6531 5311 5611 5621

UNITED EL SEGUNDO INC p 1508
17311 S Main St, Gardena CA 90248
Tel (310) 323-3992 SIC 5172 6531

■ BRER AFFILIATES INC p 210
18500 Von Karman Ave # 400, Irvine CA 92612
Tel (949) 794-7900 SIC 6794 6531

DAHN CORP p 408
18552 Macarthur Blvd # 495, Irvine CA 92612
Tel (949) 752-1282 SIC 1531 6531 4225

■ FIDELITY NATIONAL TITLE INSURANCE CO p 541
3220 El Camino Real, Irvine CA 92602
Tel (949) 622-4600
SIC 6361 8741 6541 6531

FIRST TEAM REAL ESTATE - ORANGE COUNTY p 549
108 Pacifica Ste 300, Irvine CA 92618
Tel (888) 236-1943 SIC 6531

MONTAGE HOTELS & RESORTS LLC p 986
1 Ada Ste 250, Irvine CA 92618
Tel (949) 715-5002 SIC 6531

■ PACIFIC PREMIER BANK p 1105
17901 Von Karman Ave, Irvine CA 92614
Tel (714) 431-4000 SIC 6531

PARKING CONCEPTS INC p 1116
12 Mauchly Ste I, Irvine CA 92618
Tel (949) 753-7525 SIC 6531

■ RELS LLC p 1222
40 Pacifica Ste 900, Irvine CA 92618
Tel (949) 214-1000 SIC 6531 7323

TEN-X LLC p 1436
1 Mauchly, Irvine CA 92618
Tel (949) 859-2777 SIC 6531

▲ PICO HOLDINGS INC p 1146
7979 Ivanhoe Ave Ste 300, La Jolla CA 92037
Tel (888) 389-3222 SIC 6531

LAGUNA WOODS VILLAGE p 838
24351 El Toro Rd, Laguna Beach CA 92653
Tel (949) 597-4267 SIC 6531

RETIREMENT HOUSING FOUNDATION INC p 1229
911 N Studebaker Rd # 100, Long Beach CA 90815
Tel (562) 257-5100 SIC 6531

▲ CBRE GROUP INC p 269
400 S Hope St Ste 25, Los Angeles CA 90071
Tel (213) 613-3333 SIC 6531 6162 8742

■ CBRE INC p 269
400 S Hope St Ste 25, Los Angeles CA 90071
Tel (310) 477-5876 SIC 6726 6531

LOWE ENTERPRISES INC p 881
11777 San Vicente Blvd # 900, Los Angeles CA 90049
Tel (310) 820-6661 SIC 6531 6552

OAKTREE REAL ESTATE OPPORTUNITIES FUND V GP LP p 1071
333 S Grand Ave Fl 28, Los Angeles CA 90071
Tel (213) 830-6300 SIC 6531

R & B REALTY GROUP A CALIFORNIA LIMITED PARTNERSHIP p 1201
2222 Corinth Ave, Los Angeles CA 90064
Tel (800) 888-0808 SIC 7021 6531

R & B REALTY GROUP LP p 1201
2222 Corinth Ave, Los Angeles CA 90064
Tel (310) 478-1021 SIC 6531

▲ READING INTERNATIONAL INC p 1213
6100 Center Dr Ste 900, Los Angeles CA 90045
Tel (213) 235-2240
SIC 7832 7922 6512 6531

THOMAS PROPERTIES GROUP INC p 1449
515 S Flower St Ste 600, Los Angeles CA 90071
Tel (213) 613-1900 SIC 6531

VOLUNTEERS OF AMERICA OF LOS ANGELES p 1565
3600 Wilshire Blvd # 1500, Los Angeles CA 90010
Tel (213) 389-1500 SIC 8322 6531

■ COLDWELL BANKER RESIDENTIAL BROKERAGE CO p 335
27271 Las Ramblas, Mission Viejo CA 92691
Tel (949) 367-1800 SIC 6531

■ COLDWELL BANKER RESIDENTIAL REAL ESTATE p 335
27271 Las Ramblas, Mission Viejo CA 92691
Tel (949) 367-1800 SIC 6531

PLAZA MANOR PRESERVATION LP p 1156
2615 E Plaza Blvd, National City CA 91950
Tel (619) 475-2125 SIC 6531

■ EXPERIENCE 1 INC p 520
5000 Birch St Ste 300, Newport Beach CA 92660
Tel (949) 475-3752 SIC 6361 6531

IRVINE CO LLC p 765
550 Newport Center Dr # 160, Newport Beach CA 92660
Tel (949) 720-2000
SIC 6552 6531 0174 0191 4841

KOLL MANAGEMENT SERVICES INC p 826
4343 Von Karman Ave # 150, Newport Beach CA 92660
Tel (949) 833-3030 SIC 6531 8741

MARCUS & MILLICHAP CO p 905
777 S California Ave, Palo Alto CA 94304
Tel (650) 494-1400 SIC 6531

MARCUS & MILLICHAP REAL ESTATE INVESTMENT SERVICES OF INDIANA INC p 905
2626 Hanover St, Palo Alto CA 94304
Tel (650) 494-1400 SIC 6531

USA PROPERTIES FUND INC p 1534
3200 Douglas Blvd Ste 200, Roseville CA 95661
Tel (916) 773-6060 SIC 6552 6531

AMERICAN PROPERTY-MANAGEMENT CORP p 78
8910 University Center Ln # 100, San Diego CA 92122
Tel (858) 964-5500 SIC 6531

BIOMED REALTY LP p 184
17190 Bernardo Center Dr, San Diego CA 92128
Tel (858) 485-9840 SIC 6798 6531

CARMEL PARTNERS INC p 258
1000 Sansome St 1, San Francisco CA 94111
Tel (415) 273-2900 SIC 6531 6519

CUSHMAN & WAKEFIELD OF CALIFORNIA INC p 402
1 Maritime Plz Ste 900, San Francisco CA 94111
Tel (408) 275-6730 SIC 6531

JOHN STEWART CO p 789
1388 Sutter St Ste 1100, San Francisco CA 94109
Tel (213) 833-1860 SIC 6531 6552 6726

LEMBI GROUP INC p 855
2101 Market St, San Francisco CA 94114
Tel (415) 861-1111 SIC 6531

■ OLD REPUBLIC TITLE CO p 1081
275 Battery St Ste 1500, San Francisco CA 94111
Tel (415) 421-3500 SIC 6361 6531

■ OLD REPUBLIC TITLE HOLDING CO INC p 1081
275 Battery St Ste 1500, San Francisco CA 94111
Tel (415) 421-3500 SIC 6361 6531 5045

PACIFIC UNION CO p 1106
1 Letterman Dr Ste 300, San Francisco CA 94129
Tel (415) 929-7100 SIC 6552 6512 6531

SWINERTON INC p 1412
260 Townsend St, San Francisco CA 94107
Tel (415) 421-2980
SIC 1542 1541 6531 1522

■ URS HOLDINGS INC p 1530
600 Montgomery St Fl 25, San Francisco CA 94111
Tel (415) 774-2700
SIC 8711 7389 6531 8249 4581

HOUSING AUTHORITY OF COUNTY OF SANTA CLARA p 711
505 W Julian St, San Jose CA 95110
Tel (408) 275-8770 SIC 6531

▲ SJW CORP p 1328
110 W Taylor St, San Jose CA 95110
Tel (408) 279-7800 SIC 4941 6531

HATCH REALTY GROUP INC p 667
1611 Lodi Ave, San Mateo CA 94401
Tel (650) 438-2444 SIC 6531

F M TARBELL CO p 522
1403 N Tustin Ave Ste 380, Santa Ana CA 92705
Tel (714) 972-0988 SIC 6531

GRUBB & ELLIS CO p 642
1551 N Tustin Ave Ste 300, Santa Ana CA 92705
Tel (714) 667-8252 SIC 6531 8742 6162

GRUBB & ELLIS MANAGEMENT SERVICES INC p 642
1551 N Tustin Ave Ste 300, Santa Ana CA 92705
Tel (412) 201-8200 SIC 6531

TARBELL FINANCIAL CORP p 1424
1403 N Tustin Ave Ste 380, Santa Ana CA 92705
Tel (714) 972-0988 SIC 6163 6531 6099

■ MOVE INC p 995
3315 Scott Blvd Ste 250, Santa Clara CA 95054
Tel (408) 558-7100 SIC 6531

SANTA CRUZ SEASIDE CO INC p 1280
400 Beach St, Santa Cruz CA 95060
Tel (831) 423-5590
SIC 7996 7011 7933 6531

▲ LIMONEIRA CO p 866
1141 Cummings Rd Ofc, Santa Paula CA 93060
Tel (805) 525-5541
SIC 0723 0174 0179 6531 6799

LAVIDA COMMUNITIES INC p 847
500 Stevens Ave Ste 100, Solana Beach CA 92075
Tel (858) 792-9300
SIC 6513 6512 6531 6553

SENIOR RESOURCE GROUP LLC p 1304
500 Stevens Ave Ste 100, Solana Beach CA 92075
Tel (858) 792-9300
SIC 6513 6512 6531 6553

GRUPE CO p 642
3255 W March Ln Ste 400, Stockton CA 95219
Tel (209) 473-6000 SIC 6531 1542

URBAN SETTLEMENT SERVICES LLC p 1530
11802 Ridge Pkwy Ste 200, Broomfield CO 80021
Tel (303) 996-8900 SIC 6531

▲ INTRAWEST RESORTS HOLDINGS INC p 760
1621 18th St Ste 300, Denver CO 80202
Tel (303) 749-8200 SIC 7011 7999 6531

MERCY HOUSING INC p 947
1999 Broadway Ste 1000, Denver CO 80202
Tel (303) 830-3300 SIC 1522 6531

NEW ERA REALTY INC p 1030
2441 Eliot St, Denver CO 80211
Tel (303) 248-3519 SIC 6531

▲ RE/MAX HOLDINGS INC p 1212
5075 S Syracuse St, Denver CO 80237
Tel (303) 770-5531 SIC 6531 6411

■ RE/MAX LLC p 1212
5075 S Syracuse St, Denver CO 80237
Tel (303) 770-5531 SIC 6531

ERIE COUNTY INVESTMENT CO p 508
601 Corporate Cir, Golden CO 80401
Tel (303) 384-0200
SIC 5812 6794 6531 6552 1542 1521

KENTWOOD DTC LLC p 813
5690 Dtc Blvd Ste 600w, Greenwood Village CO 80111
Tel (303) 773-3399 SIC 6531 7389

■ UNITED DOMINION REALTY LP p 1508
1745 Shea Center Dr # 200, Highlands Ranch CO 80129
Tel (720) 283-6120 SIC 6531

ST VINCENTS DEVELOPMENT INC p 1373
2800 Main St, Bridgeport CT 06606
Tel (203) 576-6000 SIC 8399 6531

TREFZ CORP p 1475
10 Middle St Ste 1701, Bridgeport CT 06604
Tel (203) 367-3621 SIC 5812 6531 8721

▲ CONNECTICUT WATER SERVICE INC p 357
93 W Main St, Clinton CT 06413
Tel (860) 669-8636 SIC 4941 6531 1623

■ TRAVELERS INDEMNITY CO OF AMERICA INC p 1474
1 Tower Sq, Hartford CT 06183
Tel (860) 277-0111 SIC 6411 6531

■ CLAYTON HOLDINGS LLC p 323
100 Beard Sawmill Rd # 200, Shelton CT 06484
Tel (203) 926-5600 SIC 8741 7389 6531

LOUIS DREYFUS HOLDING CO INC p 879
10 Westport Rd Ste 200, Wilton CT 06897
Tel (203) 761-2000
SIC 6221 5153 6512 6531 1311

CASSIDY TURLEY INC p 264
2101 L St Nw Ste 700, Washington DC 20037
Tel (202) 463-2100 SIC 6531

DOUGLAS DEVELOPMENT CORP p 452
702 H St Nw Ste 400, Washington DC 20001
Tel (202) 638-6300 SIC 6552 6531

HOLLADAY CORP p 700
3400 Idaho Ave Nw Ste 400, Washington DC 20016
Tel (202) 362-2400 SIC 1522 6531

R G A INC p 1202
1001 G St Nw Ste 700w, Washington DC 20001
Tel (202) 393-1999 SIC 6552 7521 6531

REAL ESTATE IN REAL TIME INC p 1213
100 Lakeshore Dr Ste 96, Altamonte Springs FL 32714
Tel (321) 312-0748 SIC 6531 1542 1522

■ BLUEGREEN CORP p 193
4960 Conference Way N # 100, Boca Raton FL 33431
Tel (561) 912-8000 SIC 6531 6552

▲ WCI COMMUNITIES INC p 1585
24301 Walden Center Dr, Bonita Springs FL 34134
Tel (239) 947-2600 SIC 1531 6531

CODINA PARTNERS LLC p 333
135 San Lorenzo Ave # 750, Coral Gables FL 33146
Tel (305) 529-1300
SIC 6552 6531 1521 8742

KW PROPERTY MANAGEMENT LLC p 832
8200 Nw 33rd St Ste 300, Doral FL 33122
Tel (305) 476-9188 SIC 6531

▲ BFC FINANCIAL CORP p 179
401 E Las Olas Blvd # 800, Fort Lauderdale FL 33301
Tel (954) 940-4900 SIC 6035 6531 6552

■ FIRST INTERNATIONAL EXCHANGE GROUP p 547
2100 W Cypress Creek Rd, Fort Lauderdale FL 33309
Tel (954) 658-3464 SIC 6035 6531

FIRST SERVICE RESIDENTIAL FLORIDA INC p 549
2950 N 28th Ter, Hollywood FL 33020
Tel (954) 925-8200 SIC 6531

■ BLACK KNIGHT FINANCIAL SERVICES LLC p 187
601 Riverside Ave, Jacksonville FL 32204
Tel (904) 854-8100
SIC 6361 6331 6531 8741

■ BLACK KNIGHT HOLDINGS INC p 187
601 Riverside Ave, Jacksonville FL 32204
Tel (904) 854-8100
SIC 6361 6331 6531 8741

DIOCESE OF ST AUGUSTINE INC p 440
11625 Old St Augustine Rd, Jacksonville FL 32258
Tel (904) 824-2806 SIC 8661 6531

▲ FIDELITY NATIONAL FINANCIAL INC p 540
601 Riverside Ave Fl 4, Jacksonville FL 32204
Tel (904) 854-8100
SIC 6361 6331 6531 8741 3699

■ PATRIOT TRANSPORTATION INC p 1121
200 W Forsyth St Ste 700, Jacksonville FL 32202
Tel (904) 356-6110 SIC 4213 6531 6519

■ SERVICELINK HOLDINGS LLC p 1307
601 Riverside Ave Bldg 5, Jacksonville FL 32204
Tel (904) 854-8100
SIC 6361 6331 6531 8741 3699

VESTA PROPERTY SERVICES INC p 1552
1021 Oak St, Jacksonville FL 32204
Tel (904) 355-1831 SIC 6722 6531

VILLAGES OPERATING CO p 1557
1020 Lake Sumter Lndg, Lady Lake FL 32162
Tel (352) 753-2270 SIC 6531

OAKLEY TRANSPORT INC p 1071
101 Abc Rd, Lake Wales FL 33859
Tel (863) 638-1435 SIC 4213 6531

K NEAL PATRICK & ASSOCIATES INC p 799
8210 Lakewood Ranch Blvd, Lakewood Ranch FL 34202
Tel (941) 328-1111 SIC 6531

CONCORD MANAGEMENT LTD p 354
1551 Sandspur Rd, Maitland FL 32751
Tel (407) 741-8600 SIC 6531

4701 NORTH MERIDIAN LLC p 3
4218 Ne 22nd Ave Fl 2, Miami FL 33137
Tel (305) 573-3900 *SIC* 6531

PHINEAS CORP p 1144
9040 Sw 72nd St, Miami FL 33173
Tel (305) 596-9040 *SIC* 8361 8399 6531

ADVANTA REALTY LLC p 26
3956 Town Ctr Blvd 329, Orlando FL 32837
Tel (407) 697-6604 *SIC* 6531

CENTRAL FLORIDA INVESTMENTS INC p 278
5601 Windhover Dr Ofc, Orlando FL 32819
Tel (407) 354-3040 *SIC* 6552 7011 6531

▲ MARRIOTT VACATIONS WORLDWIDE CORP p 910
6649 Westwood Blvd, Orlando FL 32821
Tel (407) 206-6000 *SIC* 6531 7011

■ SVO MANAGEMENT INC p 1410
9002 San Marco Ct, Orlando FL 32819
Tel (407) 239-3100 *SIC* 6531

TEMPUS RESORTS INTERNATIONAL LTD p 1436
7345 Greenbriar Pkwy, Orlando FL 32819
Tel (407) 363-1717 *SIC* 7011 6531

■ WYNDHAM VACATION RESORTS INC p 1630
6277 Sea Harbor Dr # 400, Orlando FL 32821
Tel (407) 370-5200 *SIC* 6531 6141

■ INTERVAL HOLDING CO INC p 759
6262 Sunset Dr Fl 6, South Miami FL 33143
Tel (305) 666-1861 *SIC* 8699 8721 6531

■ HORIZON BAY MANAGEMENT LLC p 707
5426 Bay Center Dr # 600, Tampa FL 33609
Tel (813) 287-3900 *SIC* 8611 6531 1522

HOLDING CO OF VILLAGES INC p 700
1000 Lake Sumter Lndg, The Villages FL 32162
Tel (352) 753-2270 *SIC* 6531

▲ ST JOE CO p 1367
133 S Watersound Pkwy A, Watersound FL 32461
Tel (850) 231-6400
SIC 6531 6552 6512 0811 0851

■ CEMETERY MANAGEMENT INC p 274
1201 S Orlando Ave # 365, Winter Park FL 32789
Tel (407) 740-7000 *SIC* 6553 6531

CORTLAND IMPROVEMENTS LLC p 373
3424 Peachtree Rd Ne # 300, Atlanta GA 30326
Tel (404) 965-3988 *SIC* 6531

GABLES RESIDENTIAL SERVICES INC p 588
3399 Peachtree Rd Ne # 600, Atlanta GA 30326
Tel (404) 923-5500 *SIC* 6531

INDUSTRIAL DEVELOPMENTS INTERNATIONAL LLC p 739
1100 Peachtree S, Atlanta GA 30309
Tel (404) 479-4000 *SIC* 6552 6531

KAJIMA USA INC p 801
3475 Piedmont Rd Ne, Atlanta GA 30305
Tel (404) 564-3900
SIC 1542 1541 6531 1522 6552 1622

LEGAL ACQUISITIONS SUPPORT SERVICES LLC p 853
1170 Peachtree St Ne # 1200, Atlanta GA 30309
Tel (404) 546-7290 *SIC* 6531

LION GABLES REALTY LIMITED PARTNERSHIP p 869
3399 Peachtree Rd Ne, Atlanta GA 30326
Tel (404) 923-5500 *SIC* 6531

POST PROPERTIES INC p 1164
4401 Northside Pkwy Nw # 800, Atlanta GA 30327
Tel (404) 846-5000 *SIC* 6798 6531

■ POST SERVICES LLC p 1164
4401 Northside Pkwy Nw # 800, Atlanta GA 30327
Tel (404) 846-5000 *SIC* 6531

RENTPATH INC p 1224
950 E Paces Ferry Rd Ne # 2600, Atlanta GA 30326
Tel (678) 421-3000 *SIC* 6531

RESOURCE HEALTHCARE OF AMERICA INC p 1227
1819 Peachtree Rd Ne # 520, Atlanta GA 30309
Tel (404) 364-2900 *SIC* 6531

TRIMONT REAL ESTATE ADVISORS INC p 1480
3424 Peachtree Rd Ne # 2200, Atlanta GA 30326
Tel (404) 420-5600 *SIC* 6531

▲ WESTROCK CO p 1602
504 Thrasher St, Norcross GA 30071
Tel (678) 291-7456
SIC 2631 2899 3699 6531

BUILDER SUPPORT SERVICES INC p 224
4125 Atlanta Rd Se, Smyrna GA 30080
Tel (770) 907-3400 *SIC* 1531 6531

BLAKEWOOD PROPERTIES ASSOCIATES p 188
620 E Olliff St, Statesboro GA 30458
Tel (912) 764-3330 *SIC* 6531

AMBLING MANAGEMENT CO LLC p 65
348 Enterprise Dr, Valdosta GA 31601
Tel (866) 777-7228
SIC 1522 6552 6531 6513

■ ALEXANDER & BALDWIN LLC p 49
822 Bishop St, Honolulu HI 96813
Tel (808) 525-6611
SIC 6531 0133 0179 6552

■ AMFAC HAWAII LLC A HAWAII LIMITED LIABILITY CO p 85
700 Bishop St Ste 2002, Honolulu HI 96813
Tel (808) 543-8900
SIC 6531 6552 0133 0179

ELITE PACIFIC PROPERTIES LLC p 487
4211 Waialae Ave Ste 106, Honolulu HI 96816
Tel (808) 589-2040 *SIC* 6512 6531

ISLAND PALM COMMUNITIES LLC p 766
215 Duck Rd Bldg 950, Schofield Barracks HI 96857
Tel (808) 275-3100 *SIC* 6531

CITY POINT REALTY LLC p 319
1275 N Clybourn Ave, Chicago IL 60610
Tel (312) 255-1500 *SIC* 6531

CT ASSOCIATES OF ILLINOIS LP p 399
2061 N Campbell Ave Ofc, Chicago IL 60647
Tel (773) 486-3666 *SIC* 6531 6513

CUSHMAN & WAKEFIELD INC p 402
77 W Wacker Dr Ste 1800, Chicago IL 60601
Tel (312) 424-8000 *SIC* 6531 8742 8732

▲ EQUITY LIFESTYLE PROPERTIES INC p 507
2 N Riverside Plz Ste 800, Chicago IL 60606
Tel (312) 279-1400 *SIC* 6798 6531

HABITAT CO LLC p 651
350 W Hubbard St Ste 500, Chicago IL 60654
Tel (312) 955-0413 *SIC* 6531

▲ JONES LANG LASALLE INC p 792
200 E Randolph St # 4300, Chicago IL 60601
Tel (312) 782-5800 *SIC* 6512 6531

LASALLE INCOME & GROWTH FUND IV p 846
200 E Randolph St Fl 44, Chicago IL 60601
Tel (312) 228-2087 *SIC* 6531

■ LASALLE INVESTMENT MANAGEMENT INC p 846
333 W Wacker Dr Ste 2000, Chicago IL 60606
Tel (312) 782-5800 *SIC* 6531

MERCHANDISE MART PROPERTIES INC p 944
222 Merchandise Mart Plz # 470, Chicago IL 60654
Tel (312) 527-4141 *SIC* 6531

MESIROW FINANCIAL HOLDINGS INC p 951
353 N Clark St Lowr Level, Chicago IL 60654
Tel (312) 595-6000
SIC 6211 6282 6531 6552 6411

■ MHC OPERATING LIMITED PARTNERSHIP p 959
2 N Riverside Plz Ste 800, Chicago IL 60606
Tel (312) 279-1400 *SIC* 6515 6531

■ OLD REPUBLIC TITLE INSURANCE GROUP INC (DEL) p 1081
307 N Michigan Ave # 1400, Chicago IL 60601
Tel (312) 346-8100 *SIC* 6361 6531

THOMA CRESSEY BRAVO INC p 1448
300 N La Salle Dr # 4350, Chicago IL 60654
Tel (312) 254-3300
SIC 6799 8711 6311 6321 6531 7373

TERRA COTTA HOLDINGS CO p 1439
3703 S Il Route 31, Crystal Lake IL 60012
Tel (815) 459-2400 *SIC* 3499 3398 6531

■ SEARS HOLDINGS MANAGEMENT CORP p 1297
3333 Beverly Rd, Hoffman Estates IL 60179
Tel (847) 286-2500 *SIC* 6531 6719

SHAWNEE VILLAGE PRESERVATION LP p 1313
1304 W Boulevard St, Marion IL 62959
Tel (618) 997-5365 *SIC* 6531

HILCO INC p 692
5 Revere Dr Ste 430, Northbrook IL 60062
Tel (847) 714-1288 *SIC* 7389 6531

GREAT LAKES REIT p 634
823 Commerce Dr Ste 300, Oak Brook IL 60523
Tel (708) 848-5216 *SIC* 6798 6531

▲ CATERPILLAR INC p 265
100 Ne Adams St, Peoria IL 61629
Tel (309) 675-1000
SIC 3531 3519 3511 6531 6321 6331

BEAVERS HOLDINGS LLC p 166
3550 Hobson Rd Fl 3, Woodridge IL 60517
Tel (630) 963-2736 *SIC* 8741 6531

▲ VECTREN CORP p 1546
1 Vectren Sq, Evansville IN 47708
Tel (812) 491-4000
SIC 4924 4911 1241 1623 6531

GENE B GLICK CO INC p 598
8801 River Crossing Blvd # 200, Indianapolis IN 46240
Tel (317) 469-0400 *SIC* 1522 6531 6513

VISIONARY ENTERPRISES INC p 1561
6626 E 75th St Ste 100, Indianapolis IN 46250
Tel (317) 621-4000 *SIC* 6531 8742 8093

GRAYLING CORP p 632
4220 Edison Lkes Pkwy 100, Mishawaka IN 46545
Tel (856) 384-1212 *SIC* 5812 5813 6531

MCCOLLY REALTORS INC p 927
850 Deer Creek Dr, Schererville IN 46375
Tel (219) 322-5508 *SIC* 6531

THOMPSON THRIFT CONSTRUCTION INC p 1449
901 Wabash Ave Ste 300, Terre Haute IN 47807
Tel (812) 235-5959 *SIC* 1542 6531

HEDGES ASSOCIATES INC p 680
5408 Blairs Forest Way Ne, Cedar Rapids IA 52402
Tel (319) 378-8760 *SIC* 6531

■ BERKSHIRE HATHAWAY ENERGY CO p 175
666 Grand Ave Ste 500, Des Moines IA 50309
Tel (515) 242-4300 *SIC* 4911 4924 6531

■ PPW HOLDINGS LLC p 1166
666 Grand Ave Ste 500, Des Moines IA 50309
Tel (515) 242-4300 *SIC* 4911 4924 6531

WELLS FARGO FINANCIAL CA INC p 1590
800 Walnut St, Des Moines IA 50309
Tel (515) 557-7401
SIC 6141 6153 6351 6159 6531 6021

QUALITY GROUP OF COMPANIES LLC p 1197
12851 Foster St Ste 205, Overland Park KS 66213
Tel (913) 814-9988 *SIC* 6531

■ WADDELL & REED FINANCIAL SERVICES INC p 1571
6300 Lamar Ave, Overland Park KS 66202
Tel (913) 236-2000
SIC 6722 6311 6211 6531

CORPOREX REALTY & INVESTMENT LLC p 372
100 E Riverctr Ste 1100, Covington KY 41011
Tel (859) 292-5500
SIC 1542 6531 6552 8741 6512

LATTER & BLUM INC p 846
430 Notre Dame St, New Orleans LA 70130
Tel (504) 525-1311 *SIC* 6531

■ NATIONSBANK NA (INC) p 1017
100 S Charles St Ste 207, Baltimore MD 21201
Tel (410) 605-5000 *SIC* 6021 6531

B F SAUL CO p 141
7501 Wisconsin Ave, Bethesda MD 20814
Tel (301) 986-6000 *SIC* 6531 6411

BF SAUL PROPERTY CO p 179
7501 Wisconsin Ave, Bethesda MD 20814
Tel (301) 986-6000
SIC 6531 6519 1542 1522

▲ MARRIOTT INTERNATIONAL INC p 910
10400 Fernwood Rd, Bethesda MD 20817
Tel (301) 380-3000 *SIC* 7011 6794 6531

JBG PROPERTIES INC p 779
4445 Willard Ave Ste 400, Chevy Chase MD 20815
Tel (240) 333-3600 *SIC* 6531 6552

CLAMPETT INDUSTRIES LLC p 321
10461 Mill Run Cir # 1100, Owings Mills MD 21117
Tel (410) 785-6200 *SIC* 8748 6531

DOUGLAS REALTY LLC p 452
8096 Edwin Raynor Blvd C, Pasadena MD 21122
Tel (410) 255-3690 *SIC* 6531

HBW PROPERTIES INC p 671
1055 1st St Ste 200, Rockville MD 20850
Tel (301) 424-2900 *SIC* 1542 6512 6531

C&W FACILITY SERVICES INC p 234
275 Grove St Ste 3-200, Auburndale MA 02466
Tel (617) 527-5222 *SIC* 7349 6531

BEACON COMPANIES INC p 164
2 Center Plz Ste 700, Boston MA 02108
Tel (617) 574-1100 *SIC* 1522 6531 1542

BEACON RESIDENTIAL MANAGEMENT LIMITED PARTNERSHIP p 165
2 Center Plz Ste 700, Boston MA 02108
Tel (617) 574-1100 *SIC* 6531

CRESA PARTNERS LLC p 391
200 State St Ste 13a, Boston MA 02109
Tel (617) 758-6000 *SIC* 8742 6531

FIRST STEP REALTY INC p 549
1620 Commonwealth Ave, Boston MA 02135
Tel (617) 264-4900 *SIC* 6531

FMR LLC p 562
245 Summer St, Boston MA 02210
Tel (617) 563-7000
SIC 6282 6211 6799 6552 6531

QUALIFIED HOUSING TAX CREDITS LP V p 1196
101 Arch St Fl 16, Boston MA 02110
Tel (617) 439-3911 *SIC* 6211 6531

WINN MANAGEMENT CO LLC p 1616
6 Faneuil Hall Market Pl # 500, Boston MA 02109
Tel (617) 742-4501 *SIC* 6531

WINNCOMPANIES LLC p 1616
6 Faneuil Hall Market Pl, Boston MA 02109
Tel (617) 742-4500 *SIC* 6531

BRIGHTON MARINE HEALTH CENTER INC p 213
77 Warren St Fl 7, Brighton MA 02135
Tel (617) 562-5222 *SIC* 6531

BARRETT SOTHEBYS INTERNATIONAL REALTY p 157
33 Walden St, Concord MA 01742
Tel (978) 369-6453 *SIC* 6531

WESTMINSTER PRESERVATION LP p 1601
1307 Pawtucket Blvd, Lowell MA 01854
Tel (212) 506-5885 *SIC* 6531

NORTHLAND INVESTMENT CORP p 1057
2150 Washington St # 300, Newton MA 02462
Tel (617) 965-7100 *SIC* 6799 6411 6531

MASSMUTUAL MORTGAGE FINANCE LLC p 917
1295 State St, Springfield MA 01111
Tel (413) 788-8411 *SIC* 6531

VILLAGE GREEN MANAGEMENT CLEARING CO p 1557
30833 Northwestern Hwy, Farmington Hills MI 48334
Tel (248) 851-9800 *SIC* 6531

P M GROUP INC p 1102
1050 Corporate Office Dr, Milford MI 48381
Tel (248) 529-2000 *SIC* 6531 1522 6552

HARTMAN AND TYNER INC p 666
24700 W 12 Mile Rd, Southfield MI 48034
Tel (248) 352-2010 *SIC* 6513 6531

REAL ESTATE ONE INC p 1213
25800 Northwestern Hwy # 100, Southfield MI 48075
Tel (248) 208-2900 *SIC* 6531

SINGH MANAGEMENT CO INC p 1326
7125 Orchard Lake Rd # 200, West Bloomfield MI 48322
Tel (248) 865-1600 *SIC* 6531 6513 8742

■ OTTER TAIL POWER CO p 1098
215 S Cascade St, Fergus Falls MN 56537
Tel (218) 739-8200 *SIC* 3699 4953 6531

CARLSON HOTELS MANAGEMENT CORP p 258
701 Tower Carlson Pkwy, Hopkins MN 55305
Tel (763) 212-5000 *SIC* 6794 6531 6552

POHLAD COMPANIES p 1159
60 S 6th St Ste 3700, Minneapolis MN 55402
Tel (612) 661-3700
SIC 8742 7929 6531 5013 7549 7379

OPUS HOLDING LLC p 1091
10350 Bren Rd W, Minnetonka MN 55343
Tel (952) 656-4444 *SIC* 6531

RADISSON HOTELS INTERNATIONAL INC p 1204
701 Carlson Pkwy, Minnetonka MN 55305
Tel (763) 212-5000
SIC 7011 6794 6552 6531 8742 7389

SILVER BAY REALTY TRUST CORP p 1323
3300 Fernbrook Ln N, Plymouth MN 55447
Tel (952) 358-4400 *SIC* 6798 6531 1521

■ NORTHLAND CO p 1057
385 Washington St, Saint Paul MN 55102
Tel (800) 328-5972 *SIC* 6331 6162 6531

DENMISS LLC p 428
1368 Old Fannin Rd # 100, Brandon MS 39047
Tel (601) 919-1757 *SIC* 6211 6531

YARCO CO INC p 1635
7920 Ward Pkwy, Kansas City MO 64114
Tel (816) 561-4240 *SIC* 6552 6531

■ COLDWELL BANKER GUNDAKER REAL ESTATE SCHOOL p 335
2458 Old Dorsett Rd, Maryland Heights MO 63043
Tel (314) 298-5000 *SIC* 6531

NORTHPOINT DEVELOPMENT LLC p 1057
4825 Nw 41st St Ste 500, Riverside MO 64150
Tel (816) 888-7380 *SIC* 6552 6531

CASSIDY TURLEY COMMERCIAL REAL ESTATE SERVICES INC p 264
7700 Forsyth Blvd Ste 900, Saint Louis MO 63105
Tel (314) 862-7100 *SIC* 6531

PROVISION LIVING LLC p 1187
1630 Des Peres Rd Ste 310, Saint Louis MO 63131
Tel (314) 238-3800 *SIC* 6531

HEALTH FACILITIES MANAGEMENT CORP p 674
731 N Main St, Sikeston MO 63801
Tel (573) 471-1276 *SIC* 6531

▲ BERKSHIRE HATHAWAY INC p 175
3555 Farnam St Ste 1440, Omaha NE 68131
Tel (402) 346-1400
SIC 6331 6321 4911 4924 6531 5963

REAL PROPERTY SERVICES CORP p 1214
9960 W Chynne Ave Ste 110, North Las Vegas NV 89030
Tel (702) 313-3700 *SIC* 6531 6211

CLEARCAPITAL.COM INC p 324
300 E 2nd St Ste 1405, Reno NV 89501
Tel (775) 470-5656 *SIC* 6531

NORTHPOINT PROPERTY MANAGEMENT LLC p 1058
55 Lake St Ste 4, Nashua NH 03060
Tel (603) 594-2300 *SIC* 8641 6531

FLAGSHIP RESORT DEVELOPMENT CORP p 554
60 N Maine Ave, Atlantic City NJ 08401
Tel (609) 347-3524 *SIC* 6531 7011

HADDAD ORGANIZATION LTD p 652
90 E 5th St Ste 1, Bayonne NJ 07002
Tel (201) 339-0665 *SIC* 6531

TRYKO PARTNERS LLC p 1489
575 Route 70 Fl 2, Brick NJ 08723
Tel (732) 961-9991 *SIC* 6531 8051

ERA RIZZO REALTY LLC p 507
244 Us Highway 46 Ste 6, Fairfield NJ 07004
Tel (973) 575-1155 *SIC* 6531

SAINT BARNABAS REALTY DEVELOP CORP p 1268
94 Old Short Hills Rd, Livingston NJ 07039
Tel (732) 923-8072 *SIC* 6531

■ NRT COMMERCIAL UTAH LLC p 1064
175 Park Ave, Madison NJ 07940
Tel (973) 407-6880 *SIC* 6531

■ REALOGY GROUP LLC p 1214
175 Park Ave, Madison NJ 07940
Tel (973) 407-2000
SIC 6531 6794 7389 6541

▲ REALOGY HOLDINGS CORP p 1214
175 Park Ave, Madison NJ 07940
Tel (973) 407-2000
SIC 6531 6794 7389 6541

■ REALOGY INTERMEDIATE HOLDINGS LLC p 1214
175 Park Ave, Madison NJ 07940
Tel (973) 407-0000
SIC 6531 6794 7389 6541

INTERSTATE REALTY MANAGEMENT CO INC p 758
3 E Stow Rd, Marlton NJ 08053
Tel (856) 596-0500 *SIC* 6531 6513

WEICHERT CO p 1587
1625 State Route 10, Morris Plains NJ 07950
Tel (973) 984-1400 *SIC* 6531

RREEF REGENCY PARK LLC p 1255
64 Regency Dr, Mount Holly NJ 08060
Tel (856) 848-6700 *SIC* 6531

▲ PHH CORP p 1142
1 Mortgage Way, Mount Laurel NJ 08054
Tel (856) 917-1744 *SIC* 6531 8741

■ REALOGY SERVICES GROUP LLC p 1214
3001 Leadenhall Rd, Mount Laurel NJ 08054
Tel (856) 914-8500 *SIC* 6531 6211

▲ WYNDHAM WORLDWIDE CORP p 1630
22 Sylvan Way, Parsippany NJ 07054
Tel (973) 753-6000
SIC 7011 8741 7389 6531

EDGEWOOD PROPERTIES INC p 478
1260 Stelton Rd, Piscataway NJ 08854
Tel (732) 985-1900 *SIC* 6552 6531

■ K HOVNANIAN COMPANIES OF NEW YORK INC p 798
10 Rte 35, Red Bank NJ 07701
Tel (732) 747-7800 *SIC* 6531

HARTZ MOUNTAIN INDUSTRIES INC p 666
400 Plaza Dr Ste 400, Secaucus NJ 07094
Tel (201) 348-1200 *SIC* 6531

GARDEN HOMES INC p 591
820 Morris Tpke Ste 301, Short Hills NJ 07078
Tel (973) 467-5000 *SIC* 1531 6531

GARDEN PROPERTIES CORP p 591
820 Morris Tpke, Short Hills NJ 07078
Tel (973) 467-5000 *SIC* 6531

SOMERS RELATED POINT LLC p 1339
50 Mays Landing Rd # 226, Somers Point NJ 08244
Tel (609) 927-0441 *SIC* 7299 6531

KENNEDY HEALTH CARE FOUNDATION INC p 811
18 E Laurel Rd, Stratford NJ 08084
Tel (856) 661-5100
SIC 6733 4119 8051 6531 7361 8721

TMST INC p 1458
125 Lincoln Ave Ste 100, Santa Fe NM 87501
Tel (505) 989-1900 *SIC* 6531 6798

JEWISH HOME AND HOSPITAL p 784
100 W Kingsbridge Rd # 100, Bronx NY 10468
Tel (718) 579-0420 *SIC* 6513 6531

ELLICOTT DEVELOPMENT OF BUFFALO LLC p 488
295 Main St Rm 210, Buffalo NY 14203
Tel (716) 854-0060 *SIC* 1522 1542 6531

ELMWOOD SQUARE PRESERVATION LP p 489
505 Elmwood Ave, Buffalo NY 14222
Tel (716) 881-6662 *SIC* 6531

WIN-SUM SKI CORP p 1614
6557 Holiday Valley Rd, Ellicottville NY 14731
Tel (716) 699-2345 *SIC* 7011 7997 6531

RELATED COMPANIES L P p 1221
40 W Point Hwy, Highland Falls NY 10928
Tel (845) 446-4966 SIC 6531

■ METROPOLITAN LIFE INSURANCE CO (INC) p 956
2701 Queens Plz N Ste 1, Long Island City NY 11101
Tel (212) 578-2211
SIC 6411 6324 6331 6321 6531

95TH IH ASSOCIATES LLC p 4
238 E 95th St, New York NY 10128
Tel (212) 996-0646 SIC 6531

▲ ALLEGHANY CORP p 52
7 Times Sq Tower, New York NY 10036
Tel (212) 752-1356 SIC 6331 6411 6531

■ APOLLO MANAGEMENT LP p 97
9 W 57th St Fl 43, New York NY 10019
Tel (212) 515-3200 SIC 6799 6531

■ AXA FINANCIAL INC p 139
1290 Ave Of The Am Fl Con, New York NY 10104
Tel (212) 554-1234
SIC 6311 6211 6552 6531 6371 6221

■ BLACKHAWK PARENT LLC p 187
345 Park Ave, New York NY 10154
Tel (212) 583-5000 SIC 6798 6531

BLACKSTONE REAL ESTATE PARTNERS VI LP p 188
345 Park Ave, New York NY 10154
Tel (212) 583-5000 SIC 8741 6531

CARNEGIE HALL CORP p 258
881 Sventh Ave At 57th St, New York NY 10019
Tel (212) 903-9600 SIC 7922 6531

■ CB RICHARD ELLIS REAL ESTATE SERVICES LLC p 268
200 Park Ave Fl 19, New York NY 10166
Tel (212) 984-8000 SIC 6531 6162

CENTURY 21 INC p 281
21 Cortlandt St, New York NY 10007
Tel (212) 227-9092 SIC 6531

CIBC WORLD MARKETS CORP p 306
425 Lexington Ave Bsmt C2, New York NY 10017
Tel (212) 667-7000 SIC 6211 6311 6531

■ CORCORAN GROUP INC p 368
660 Madison Ave Fl 11, New York NY 10065
Tel (212) 355-3550 SIC 6531

CUSHMAN & WAKEFIELD HOLDINGS INC p 402
1290 Ave Of The Americas, New York NY 10104
Tel (212) 841-7500 SIC 6531 8742 8732

HARTZ GROUP INC p 666
667 Madison Ave Fl 24, New York NY 10065
Tel (212) 308-3336
SIC 6512 6552 6531 6159

HELMSLEY-NOYES CO LLC p 682
230 Park Ave Rm 659, New York NY 10169
Tel (212) 679-6772 SIC 6531

▲ ICAHN ENTERPRISES LP p 726
767 5th Ave Ste 4700, New York NY 10153
Tel (212) 702-4300
SIC 6722 3714 7999 3743 5093 6531

INVESTCORP INTERNATIONAL INC p 761
280 Park Ave Fl 36, New York NY 10017
Tel (212) 599-4700 SIC 6531

ITRIA LLC p 768
333 7th Ave Fl 18, New York NY 10001
Tel (212) 644-4555 SIC 6531

KBF AMSTERDAM PARTNERS p 806
189 W 89th St, New York NY 10024
Tel (212) 712-2661 SIC 6531

KUSHNER COMPANIES INC p 832
666 5th Ave Fl 15, New York NY 10103
Tel (212) 527-7000
SIC 1521 6513 6531 6512 1522 1531

LIGHTSTONE GROUP LLC p 865
460 Park Ave Rm 1300, New York NY 10022
Tel (212) 616-9969 SIC 6531

MONY LIFE INSURANCE CO p 987
1740 Broadway, New York NY 10019
Tel (800) 487-6669
SIC 6411 6321 6211 6282 6531

NATIONAL RESTAURANTS MANAGEMENT INC p 1015
560 5th Ave Fl 3, New York NY 10036
Tel (212) 563-7440 SIC 5812 6531

■ NBC NEWS WORLDWIDE LLC p 1021
30 Rockefeller Plz Fl 2, New York NY 10112
Tel (212) 664-4444
SIC 4832 4833 4841 6021 6531 7383

■ NBC UNIVERSITY LLC p 1021
30 Rockefeller Plz Fl 51, New York NY 10112
Tel (212) 664-4444
SIC 4832 4833 4841 6021 6531 7383

NEW WATER STREET CORP p 1033
55 Water St Ste Conc6, New York NY 10041
Tel (212) 422-1320 SIC 6531

NEW YORK REIT INC p 1036
405 Park Ave Fl 14, New York NY 10022
Tel (212) 415-6500 SIC 6531

■ NEWMARK & CO REAL ESTATE INC p 1038
125 Park Ave, New York NY 10017
Tel (212) 372-2000 SIC 6531

▲ NORTHSTAR ASSET MANAGEMENT GROUP INC p 1058
399 Park Ave Fl 18, New York NY 10022
Tel (212) 547-2600 SIC 8741 6531 6282

PARAMOUNT GROUP INC p 1114
1633 Broadway Ste 1801, New York NY 10019
Tel (212) 974-1450 SIC 6552 6531

RECKSON OPERATING PARTNERSHIP LP p 1214
420 Lexington Ave, New York NY 10170
Tel (212) 594-2700 SIC 6531

RELATED COMPANIES INC p 1221
511 W 33rd St Rm 200, New York NY 10001
Tel (212) 801-1000 SIC 6552 6531

RELATED COMPANIES L P p 1221
60 Columbus Cir, New York NY 10023
Tel (212) 421-5333 SIC 6552 6531

RELATED MANAGEMENT CORP p 1221
423 W 55th St, New York NY 10019
Tel (212) 319-1200 SIC 6531

ROCKEFELLER GROUP INC p 1244
1221 Ave Of The Am Flr 17, New York NY 10020
Tel (212) 282-2000 SIC 6531 7389

SAVILLS AMERICA LIMITED p 1284
399 Park Ave Fl 11, New York NY 10022
Tel (212) 326-1000 SIC 6531 6799

SAVILLS STUDLEY INC p 1284
399 Park Ave Fl 11, New York NY 10022
Tel (212) 326-1000 SIC 6531 6799

SILVERPEAK REAL ESTATE PARTNERS LP p 1324
909 3rd Ave Fl 30, New York NY 10022
Tel (212) 716-2000 SIC 6531

SIMPSON THACHER & BARTLETT LLP p 1325
425 Lexington Ave Fl 15, New York NY 10017
Tel (212) 455-2000 SIC 8111 6531

▲ SOTHEBYS p 1341
1334 York Ave, New York NY 10021
Tel (212) 606-7000 SIC 5999 6531 6111 5921

STANDARD CHARTERED HOLDINGS INC p 1375
1095 Ave Of The Americas, New York NY 10036
Tel (212) 667-0700 SIC 6221 6211 6531

STARR INTERNATIONAL CO INC p 1379
399 Park Ave Fl 8, New York NY 10022
Tel (646) 227-6300 SIC 6531

TERRA HOLDINGS LLC p 1439
770 Lexington Ave Rm 301, New York NY 10065
Tel (212) 508-7200 SIC 6531

THOR EQUITIES LLC p 1450
25 W 39th St Fl 11, New York NY 10018
Tel (212) 529-5055 SIC 6531 6211 6282

TIAA REAL ESTATE ACCOUNT p 1452
730 3rd Ave, New York NY 10017
Tel (212) 490-9000 SIC 6531

TISHMAN SPEYER PROPERTIES LP p 1456
45 Rockefeller Plz Conc1, New York NY 10111
Tel (212) 715-0300 SIC 6531 6552

TOWN RESIDENTIAL LLC p 1465
33 Irving Pl Frnt 1, New York NY 10003
Tel (212) 557-6500 SIC 6531

TRUMP ORGANIZATION INC p 1487
725 5th Ave Bsmt A, New York NY 10022
Tel (212) 832-2000 SIC 6531 7922 6794

■ VIACOM SONGS INC p 1554
1515 Broadway Lbby, New York NY 10036
Tel (212) 258-6000
SIC 6531 6519 7359 7941 7812 2731

▲ W P CAREY INC p 1569
50 Rockefeller Plz Fl 2, New York NY 10020
Tel (212) 492-1100 SIC 6531 6282

CONIFER REALTY LLC p 356
1000 University Ave # 500, Rochester NY 14607
Tel (585) 324-0500 SIC 6531

PYRAMID MANAGEMENT GROUP INC p 1193
4 Clinton Sq, Syracuse NY 13202
Tel (315) 422-7000 SIC 6531 6512

LUTHERAN HOME ALBEMARLE PROPERTY INC p 886
24724 S Business 52, Albemarle NC 28001
Tel (704) 982-8191 SIC 6531

DIVI HOTELS MARKETING INC p 444
6320 Quadrangle Dr # 210, Chapel Hill NC 27517
Tel (919) 419-3484 SIC 7011 7999 6531

CAMPUS CREST COMMUNITIES INC p 246
2100 Rexford Rd Ste 300, Charlotte NC 28211
Tel (704) 496-2500 SIC 6798 6552 6531

CHILDRESS KLEIN PROPERTIES INC p 300
301 S College St Ste 2800, Charlotte NC 28202
Tel (704) 342-9000 SIC 6552 6512 6531

▲ LENDINGTREE INC p 855
11115 Rushmore Dr, Charlotte NC 28277
Tel (704) 541-5351 SIC 6163 6531

LINCOLN HARRIS LLC p 867
4725 Piedmont Row Dr, Charlotte NC 28210
Tel (704) 331-0917 SIC 6531 6552

JOMARSHE INVESTMENT GROUP INC p 792
1617 Nc Highway 66 S # 201, Kernersville NC 27284
Tel (336) 992-0200 SIC 6531

■ HIGHWOODS REALTY LIMITED PARTNERSHIP p 692
3100 Smoketree Ct Ste 600, Raleigh NC 27604
Tel (919) 872-4924 SIC 6519 6531 6798

YORK PROPERTIES INC OF RALEIGH p 1637
1900 Cameron St, Raleigh NC 27605
Tel (919) 821-1350 SIC 6552 6531

SIBCY CLINE INC p 1319
8044 Montgomery Rd # 300, Cincinnati OH 45236
Tel (513) 984-4100 SIC 6531

FC CONTINENTAL LANDLORD LLC p 532
50 Public Sq Ste 1360, Cleveland OH 44113
Tel (216) 621-6060 SIC 6531

FOREST CITY COMMERCIAL MANAGEMENT INC p 566
50 Public Sq Ste 1410, Cleveland OH 44113
Tel (216) 621-6060 SIC 6531

MORTGAGE INFORMATION SERVICES INC p 991
4877 Galaxy Pkwy Ste I, Cleveland OH 44128
Tel (216) 514-7480 SIC 6361 6531

NESCO INC p 1026
6140 Parkland Blvd # 110, Cleveland OH 44124
Tel (440) 461-6000
SIC 3535 3541 3544 8711 6531

REALTY ONE INC p 1214
800 W Saint Clair Ave, Cleveland OH 44113
Tel (216) 328-2500 SIC 6531

NATIONAL CHURCH RESIDENCES p 1010
2333 N Bank Dr, Columbus OH 43220
Tel (614) 451-2151
SIC 6531 6513 8051 8059

NATIONWIDE MUTUAL INSURANCE CO p 1018
1 Nationwide Plz, Columbus OH 43215
Tel (614) 249-7111
SIC 6331 6311 6321 6531

REAL LIVING INC p 1213
77 E Nationwide Blvd, Columbus OH 43215
Tel (614) 221-7400 SIC 6531

MILLER-VALENTINE OPERATIONS INC p 971
137 N Main St Ste 900, Dayton OH 45402
Tel (937) 293-0900 SIC 6552 6531

▲ REX AMERICAN RESOURCES CORP p 1229
7720 Paragon Rd, Dayton OH 45459
Tel (937) 276-3931 SIC 2869 6531

ALLYEAR SERVICES LLC p 51
270 Amherst Rd, Lima OH 45806
Tel (419) 296-1699 SIC 6531

RE/MAX CONSULTANT GROUP p 1212
6650 Walnut St, New Albany OH 43054
Tel (614) 855-2822 SIC 6531

MRI SOFTWARE LLC p 996
28925 Fountain Pkwy, Solon OH 44139
Tel (800) 327-8770 SIC 7374 7371 6531

AMERICAN BULK COMMODITIES INC p 69
8063 Southern Blvd, Youngstown OH 44512
Tel (330) 758-0841
SIC 4212 7532 6531 7363

MIDLAND FINANCIAL CO p 965
501 Nw Grand Blvd Ste 180, Oklahoma City OK 73118
Tel (405) 840-7600 SIC 6035 6162 6531

MCGRAW DAVISSON STEWART INC p 929
4105 S Rockford Ave, Tulsa OK 74105
Tel (918) 592-6000 SIC 6531

VIGOR INDUSTRIAL LLC p 1556
5555 N Channel Ave # 71, Portland OR 97217
Tel (503) 247-1777 SIC 3731 3599 6531

PATTERSON-ERIE CORP p 1121
1250 Tower Ln Ste 1, Erie PA 16505
Tel (814) 455-8031 SIC 5812 6531 4522

HORST GROUP INC p 708
320 Granite Run Dr, Lancaster PA 17601
Tel (717) 560-1919 SIC 1542 1541 6531

BALFOUR BEATTY COMMUNITIES LLC p 147
1 Country View Rd Ste 100, Malvern PA 19355
Tel (610) 355-8100 SIC 6531

BALFOUR BEATTY INVESTMENTS INC p 148
1 Country View Rd Ste 100, Malvern PA 19355
Tel (610) 355-8100
SIC 6531 8748 1731 8999 8741

BALFOUR BEATTY MILITARY HOUSING MANAGEMENT LLC p 148
1 Country View Rd Ste 100, Malvern PA 19355
Tel (610) 355-8100 SIC 6531

WESTMORELAND REALTY CORP p 1602
1428 Delberts Dr, Monongahela PA 15063
Tel (724) 258-9009 SIC 6531

G M H COMMUNITIES LP p 587
10 Campus Blvd, Newtown Square PA 19073
Tel (610) 355-8000 SIC 6531

PENNSYLVANIA REAL ESTATE INVESTMENT TRUST p 1130
200 S Broad St, Philadelphia PA 19102
Tel (215) 875-0700 SIC 6798 6531

RESOURCE AMERICA INC p 1227
1 Crescent Dr Ste 203, Philadelphia PA 19112
Tel (215) 546-5005 SIC 6531 6722 7359

HANNA HOLDINGS INC p 658
1090 Freeport Rd Ste 1a, Pittsburgh PA 15238
Tel (412) 967-9000 SIC 6531 6162 6361

PENSKE REALTY INC p 1131
Green Hls Rr 10, Reading PA 19607
Tel (610) 775-6000 SIC 6531

NEWPORT HEALTH CARE CORP p 1038
11 Friendship St, Newport RI 02840
Tel (401) 846-6400 SIC 8062 6531 6732

PICERNE INVESTMENT CORP p 1146
75 Lambert Lind Hwy # 300, Warwick RI 02886
Tel (401) 732-3700
SIC 6552 6531 1521 1522 1542

GREYSTAR REAL ESTATE PARTNERS LLC p 639
18 Broad St Ste 300, Charleston SC 29401
Tel (843) 579-9400 SIC 6531

OSHAUGHNESSY REALTY CO INC p 1096
4024 Salt Pointe Pkwy, Charleston SC 29405
Tel (843) 202-2016 SIC 6531

RELATED CLINTON MANOR LLC p 1221
100 Clinton St, Clinton SC 29325
Tel (864) 833-3836 SIC 6531 6513

SANDS PROPERTIES INC p 1278
201 74th Ave N, Myrtle Beach SC 29572
Tel (843) 449-4431 SIC 6531

▲ NATIONAL AMERICAN UNIVERSITY HOLDINGS INC p 1009
5301 S Highway 16 Ste 200, Rapid City SD 57701
Tel (605) 721-5220 SIC 8221 6531 1531

CARLISLE LLC p 257
263 Wagner Pl, Memphis TN 38103
Tel (901) 526-5000 SIC 5812 8741 6531

■ CB RICHARD ELLIS MEMPHIS LLC p 268
2620 Thousand Oaks Blvd # 4000, Memphis TN 38118
Tel (901) 528-1000 SIC 6531 8742

LRC EAGLES LANDING GP LLC p 882
555 Perkins Ext, Memphis TN 38117
Tel (901) 435-7716 SIC 6798 6531

SOUTH PLAZA CO p 1344
100 Peabody Pl Ste 1400, Memphis TN 38103
Tel (901) 260-7400 SIC 6531

▲ FIRST ACCEPTANCE CORP p 544
3813 Green Hills Vlg Dr, Nashville TN 37215
Tel (615) 844-2800 SIC 6331 6531

HARDAWAY GROUP INC p 660
615 Main St, Nashville TN 37206
Tel (615) 254-5461
SIC 1542 1541 1522 6531

MAIN STREET OPERATING CO INC p 898
615 Main St, Nashville TN 37206
Tel (615) 254-5461
SIC 1542 1541 1521 6531

REGUS CORP p 1220
15305 Dallas Pkwy Ste 400, Addison TX 75001
Tel (972) 361-8100 SIC 7363 7389 6531

▲ AMERICAN CAMPUS COMMUNITIES INC p 69
12700 Hill Country Blvd, Austin TX 78738
Tel (512) 732-1000 SIC 6798 6531

■ AMERICAN CAMPUS COMMUNITIES OPERATING PARTNERSHIP LP p 69
12700 Hill Country Blvd, Austin TX 78738
Tel (512) 732-1000 SIC 6531

▲ FORESTAR GROUP INC p 567
6300 Fm 2244 Rd Bldg 500, Austin TX 78746
Tel (512) 433-5200 SIC 6531 1382

HOMEAWAY INC p 703
1011 W 5th St Ste 300, Austin TX 78703
Tel (512) 684-1100 SIC 6531 7389 7375

KELLER WILLIAMS REALTY INC p 808
1221 S Mo Pac Expy # 400, Austin TX 78746
Tel (512) 327-3070 SIC 6531

■ SUSSER CO LTD p 1409
4545 Ayers St, Corpus Christi TX 78415
Tel (361) 883-6321 SIC 6531

ASSOCIATIONS INC p 121
5401 N Central Expy # 300, Dallas TX 75205
Tel (214) 953-3009 SIC 6531

CAS RESIDENTIAL LLC p 262
1201 Elm St Ste 1600, Dallas TX 75270
Tel (214) 965-6000 SIC 6531

ENCORE ENTERPRISES INC p 496
5005 L B Johnson Fwy 12 Ste 1200, Dallas TX 75244
Tel (214) 259-7009 SIC 6531 6512

HALL FINANCIAL GROUP LTD p 654
2323 Ross Ave Ste 200, Dallas TX 75201
Tel (972) 377-1100 SIC 6552 6531

HILLWOOD DEVELOPMENT CORP p 694
3090 Olive St Ste 300, Dallas TX 75219
Tel (214) 303-5535 SIC 6552 6531

LINCOLN PROPERTY CO p 868
2000 Mckinney Ave # 1000, Dallas TX 75201
Tel (214) 740-3300 SIC 6531

ROSEWOOD CORP p 1251
2101 Cedar Springs Rd # 1600, Dallas TX 75201
Tel (214) 849-9000 SIC 6531 7382

SILVERLEAF RESORTS INC p 1324
1201 Elm St Ste 4600, Dallas TX 75270
Tel (214) 631-1166 SIC 6531

SMART CITY LOCATING INC p 1332
5555 Smu Blvd, Dallas TX 75206
Tel (214) 586-0519 SIC 6531

THR PROPERTY MANAGEMENT LP p 1450
1201 Elm St Ste 1600, Dallas TX 75270
Tel (214) 965-6053 SIC 6531

TRAMMELL CROW RESIDENTIAL CO p 1469
3819 Maple Ave, Dallas TX 75219
Tel (214) 922-8400 SIC 6513 6512 6531

WESTDALE ASSET MANAGEMENT LTD p 1597
3100 Monticello Ave # 600, Dallas TX 75205
Tel (214) 515-7000 SIC 6531

WILLIAM DAVIS REALTY WOODLANDS LLC p 1610
17732 Creston Rd, Dallas TX 75252
Tel (214) 621-9689 SIC 6531

HUNT BUILDING CO LTD p 718
4401 N Mesa St Ste 201, El Paso TX 79902
Tel (915) 533-1122
SIC 1522 6531 1542 7389

HUNT COMPANIES INC p 718
4401 N Mesa St, El Paso TX 79902
Tel (915) 533-1122 SIC 1522 6531 1542

CAMDEN DEVELOPMENT INC p 244
11 Greenway Plz Ste 2400, Houston TX 77046
Tel (713) 354-2500 SIC 6531 6552

GREYSTAR MANAGEMENT SERVICES LP p 639
750 Bering Dr Ste 300, Houston TX 77057
Tel (713) 966-5000 SIC 6513 6531 1522

MAXXAM INC p 923
1330 Post Oak Blvd # 2000, Houston TX 77056
Tel (832) 251-5960 SIC 6531 7948

METRO NATIONAL CORP p 955
945 Bunker Hill Rd # 400, Houston TX 77024
Tel (713) 973-6400 SIC 6512 6531 6722

OIL & GAS ASSET CLEARINGHOUSE LP p 1079
1235 North Loop W Ste 500, Houston TX 77008
Tel (281) 873-4600 SIC 6531

PM REALTY GROUP LP p 1157
1000 Main St Ste 2400, Houston TX 77002
Tel (713) 209-5800 SIC 6531

■ SOLUTIONSTAR HOLDINGS LLC p 1339
750 Hwy 121 Byp Ste 100, Lewisville TX 75067
Tel (888) 321-2192 SIC 6531

ONYX SERVICES LLC p 1088
22971 Keith Dr, New Caney TX 77357
Tel (281) 577-5131 SIC 6531

▲ CINEMARK HOLDINGS INC p 307
3900 Dallas Pkwy Ste 500, Plano TX 75093
Tel (972) 665-1000 SIC 6531

▲ GREEN BRICK PARTNERS INC p 636
2805 Dallas Pkwy Ste 400, Plano TX 75093
Tel (469) 573-6755 SIC 1531 6531

■ REPUBLIC TITLE OF TEXAS INC p 1226
2701 W Plano Pkwy Ste 100, Plano TX 75075
Tel (972) 578-8611
SIC 6411 7372 6531 6541

CURTIS C GUNN INC p 402
227 Broadway St, San Antonio TX 78205
Tel (210) 472-2501 SIC 5511 6531

SNOWBIRD CORP p 1336
3165 E Millrock Dr # 150, Holladay UT 84121
Tel (801) 742-2222 SIC 6531 7011

BRIDGE INVESTMENT GROUP PARTNERS LLC p 211
5295 S Commerce Dr # 100, Salt Lake City UT 84107
Tel (801) 716-4500 SIC 6513 6531

DESERET MANAGEMENT CORP p 432
55 N 300 W Ste 800, Salt Lake City UT 84101
Tel (801) 538-0651
SIC 4832 4833 5932 6512 6531 6411

▲ SECURITY NATIONAL FINANCIAL CORP p 1299
5300 S 360 W Ste 250, Salt Lake City UT 84123
Tel (801) 264-1060 SIC 6311 6531 6162

VOLUNTEERS OF AMERICA INC p 1565
1660 Duke St Ste 100, Alexandria VA 22314
Tel (703) 341-5000 SIC 8322 6531

LONG & FOSTER COMPANIES INC p 876
14501 George Carter Way # 1, Chantilly VA 20151
Tel (888) 462-9111 SIC 6531 6794

DALY SEVEN INC p 410
4829 Riverside Dr, Danville VA 24541
Tel (434) 822-2161 SIC 8741 1522 6531

BARCELO CRESTLINE CORP p 154
3950 University Dr # 301, Fairfax VA 22030
Tel (571) 529-6000 SIC 6513 6531

ONE UP ENTERPRISES INC p 1086
7777 Lsburg Pike Ste 302s, Falls Church VA 22043
Tel (703) 448-7333
SIC 2731 2711 2092 6531

GET SOLD REALTY INC p 609
1171 Cntl Pk Blvd Ste 200, Fredericksburg VA 22401
Tel (540) 371-7653 SIC 6531

THALHIMER INC MORTON G p 1446
11100 W Broad St, Glen Allen VA 23060
Tel (804) 648-5881
SIC 1542 6531 6799 6513 6512

WOLSELEY REAL ESTATE INC p 1621
618 Bland Blvd, Newport News VA 23602
Tel (757) 874-7795 SIC 6531

LANDMARK MEDIA ENTERPRISES LLC p 843
150 Granby St, Norfolk VA 23510
Tel (757) 351-7000
SIC 2711 5045 2721 6531

MASTIN KIRKLAND BOLLING INC p 918
3801 Electric Rd, Roanoke VA 24018
Tel (540) 989-4555 SIC 6531

SOUTHERN MANAGEMENT CORP p 1349
1950 Old Gallows Rd # 600, Vienna VA 22182
Tel (703) 902-2000 SIC 6531

JOHN L SCOTT INC p 789
1700 Nw Gilman Blvd # 300, Issaquah WA 98027
Tel (425) 392-1211 SIC 6531 6794

CLUB WORLDMARK p 328
9805 Willows Rd Ne, Redmond WA 98052
Tel (425) 498-2500 SIC 6531

AMERICAN MANAGEMENT SERVICES WEST LLC p 75
2801 Alaskan Way Ste 200, Seattle WA 98121
Tel (206) 215-9700 SIC 6531

COLLIERS INTERNATIONAL PROPERTY CONSULTANTS INC p 337
601 Union St Ste 3320, Seattle WA 98101
Tel (206) 695-4200 SIC 6531

COLLIERS INTERNATIONAL WA LLC p 337
601 Union St Ste 3320, Seattle WA 98101
Tel (206) 223-0866 SIC 6531

KIDDER MATHEWS LLC p 817
601 Union St Ste 4720, Seattle WA 98101
Tel (206) 296-9600 SIC 6531

MERRILL GARDENS LLC p 950
1938 Frview Ave E Ste 300, Seattle WA 98102
Tel (206) 676-5300 SIC 6531

PINNACLE REALTY MANAGEMENT CO p 1150
2801 Alaskan Way Ste 200, Seattle WA 98121
Tel (206) 215-9700
SIC 6531 8741 6513 6512 1522

VULCAN INC p 1567
505 5th Ave S Ste 900, Seattle WA 98104
Tel (206) 342-2000 SIC 6531 6722 7941

▲ ZILLOW GROUP INC p 1643
1301 2nd Ave Fl 31, Seattle WA 98101
Tel (206) 470-7000 SIC 7372 6531 4813

SCAFCO CORP p 1285
2800 E Main Ave, Spokane WA 99202
Tel (509) 343-9000
SIC 3523 5065 6531 3444

MCFARLAND CASCADE HOLDINGS INC p 928
1640 E Marc St, Tacoma WA 98421
Tel (253) 572-3033 SIC 2491 6552 6531

HOLLAND PARTNERS ROCK CREEK LANDING LLC p 700
1111 Main St Ste 700, Vancouver WA 98660
Tel (360) 694-7888 SIC 6531

JERRY ERWIN ASSOCIATES INC p 783
12115 Ne 99th St Ste 1800, Vancouver WA 98682
Tel (800) 254-9442 SIC 6552 6531

PAYMENT SERVICE NETWORK INC p 1122
2901 International Ln # 100, Madison WI 53704
Tel (608) 442-5100 SIC 7389 6531 8721

AA MANAGEMENT GROUP INC p 7
411 E Wisconsin Ave # 1900, Milwaukee WI 53202
Tel (414) 271-7240 SIC 6531 7389

AMERICAN APPRAISAL ASSOCIATES INC p 68
411 E Wisconsin Ave # 1900, Milwaukee WI 53202
Tel (630) 541-4650 SIC 8748 7389 6531

GORMAN & CO INC p 626
200 N Main St, Oregon WI 53575
Tel (608) 835-3900 SIC 6552 6531

WERCS p 1592
400 E 1st St Ste 100, Casper WY 82601
Tel (307) 235-6200
SIC 6211 6163 6411 6321 6531 6099

TEAM REAL ESTATE INC p 1430
601 Broadway St, Rock Springs WY 82901
Tel (307) 362-1275 SIC 6531

SIC 6541 Title Abstract Offices

■ SECURITY TITLE AGENCY INC p 1299
3636 N Central Ave # 140, Phoenix AZ 85012
Tel (602) 230-6271 SIC 6411 6541

LERETA LLC p 857
1123 Park View Dr, Covina CA 91724
Tel (626) 543-1765 SIC 6211 6541 6361

▲ CALATLANTIC GROUP INC p 238
15360 Barranca Pkwy, Irvine CA 92618
Tel (949) 789-1600
SIC 1531 1521 6162 6541

■ FIDELITY NATIONAL TITLE INSURANCE CO p 541
3220 El Camino Real, Irvine CA 92602
Tel (949) 622-4600
SIC 6361 8741 6541 6531

ALLIANCE INSPECTION MANAGEMENT LLC p 54
330 Golden Shore Ste 400, Long Beach CA 90802
Tel (562) 432-5050 SIC 6541

■ TITLE365 CO p 1456
5000 Birch St Ste 300, Newport Beach CA 92660
Tel (877) 365-9365 SIC 6541

ORANGE COAST TITLE CO OF SOUTHERN CALIFORNIA p 1092
640 N Tustin Ave Ste 106, Santa Ana CA 92705
Tel (714) 558-2836 SIC 7389 6361 6541

TOUSA INC p 1464
4000 Hollywood Blvd # 555, Hollywood FL 33021
Tel (954) 364-4000
SIC 1521 1522 6162 6541

HAMILTON RISK MANAGEMENT CO p 655
3155 Nw 77th Ave, Miami FL 33122
Tel (305) 716-6000
SIC 6331 7323 6141 6541 6411

NATIONWIDE TITLE CLEARING INC p 1018
2100 Alt 19, Palm Harbor FL 34683
Tel (727) 771-4000 SIC 6162 6541

TITLEONE EXCHANGE CO p 1456
1101 W River St Ste 201, Boise ID 83702
Tel (208) 424-8511 SIC 6541

TITLE SOURCE INC p 1456
662 Woodward Ave, Detroit MI 48226
Tel (888) 848-5355 SIC 6541

■ REALOGY GROUP LLC p 1214
175 Park Ave, Madison NJ 07940
Tel (973) 407-2000
SIC 6531 6794 7389 6541

▲ REALOGY HOLDINGS CORP p 1214
175 Park Ave, Madison NJ 07940
Tel (973) 407-2000
SIC 6531 6794 7389 6541

■ REALOGY INTERMEDIATE HOLDINGS LLC p 1214
175 Park Ave, Madison NJ 07940
Tel (973) 407-0000
SIC 6531 6794 7389 6541

SURETY TITLE CO LLC p 1408
11 Eves Dr Ste 150, Marlton NJ 08053
Tel (856) 988-8900 SIC 6361 6541

■ TITLE RESOURCE GROUP LLC p 1456
3001 Leadenhall Rd, Mount Laurel NJ 08054
Tel (856) 914-8500 SIC 6541 6211

■ STEWART TITLE NORTH TEXAS INC p 1389
15950 Dallas Pkwy Ste 100, Dallas TX 75248
Tel (972) 386-9898 SIC 6361 6541

■ STEWART TITLE CO p 1389
1980 Post Oak Blvd Ste 80, Houston TX 77056
Tel (713) 625-8100
SIC 6361 7389 8713 8742 6541

■ STEWART TITLE GUARANTY CO p 1389
1980 Post Oak Blvd Ste 61, Houston TX 77056
Tel (713) 625-8100 SIC 6361 6541

TEXAS REGIONAL DELAWARE INC p 1444
3900 N 10th St Fl 11, Mcallen TX 78501
Tel (956) 631-5400 SIC 6022 6541

■ REPUBLIC TITLE OF TEXAS INC p 1226
2701 W Plano Pkwy Ste 100, Plano TX 75075
Tel (972) 578-8611
SIC 6411 7372 6531 6541

SIC 6552 Land Subdividers & Developers

COLONIAL PROPERTIES TRUST p 338
2101 6th Ave N Ste 750, Birmingham AL 35203
Tel (205) 250-8700
SIC 6798 6552 6531 6513

EBSCO INDUSTRIES INC p 474
5724 Highway 280 E, Birmingham AL 35242
Tel (205) 991-6600
SIC 7389 2782 3949 7375 2721 6552

COOK INLET REGION INC p 366
725 E Fireweed Ln Ste 800, Anchorage AK 99503
Tel (907) 274-8638
SIC 6552 1382 1389 6519 4832 4833

TATITLEK CORP p 1426
561 E 36th Ave, Anchorage AK 99503
Tel (907) 278-4000 SIC 0811 6552 7361

TYONEK NATIVE CORP p 1496
1689 C St Ste 219, Anchorage AK 99501
Tel (907) 272-0707 SIC 6552

KONIAG INC p 827
3800 Cntrpoint Dr Ste 502, Kodiak AK 99615
Tel (907) 486-2530 SIC 6552 6519 6719

SHEE ATIKA INC p 1313
315 Lincoln St Ste 300, Sitka AK 99835
Tel (907) 747-3534 SIC 6514 6552

ACHEN-GARDNER INC p 17
550 S 79th St, Chandler AZ 85226
Tel (480) 940-1300
SIC 1611 1542 1521 1751 6552

KITCHELL CORP p 822
1707 E Highland Ave # 100, Phoenix AZ 85016
Tel (602) 264-4411
SIC 1542 1541 1521 8711 5078 6552

▲ PINNACLE WEST CAPITAL CORP p 1150
400 N 5th St, Phoenix AZ 85004
Tel (602) 250-1000 SIC 4911 6552

RIMROCK PARTNERS LLC p 1235
2415 E Camelback Rd # 700, Phoenix AZ 85016
Tel (602) 954-7085 SIC 6531 6519 6552

■ DEL WEBB COMMUNITIES INC p 423
15333 N Pima Rd Ste 300, Scottsdale AZ 85260
Tel (602) 808-8000 SIC 6552

■ DEL WEBB CORP p 423
15111 N Pima Rd, Scottsdale AZ 85260
Tel (480) 391-6000 SIC 6552

DESERT MOUNTAIN PROPERTIES LIMITED PARTNERSHIP p 432
37700 N Desert Mtn Pkwy, Scottsdale AZ 85262
Tel (480) 595-4000 SIC 6552 7997

■ HUNT CORP p 719
6720 N Scottsdale Rd # 300, Scottsdale AZ 85253
Tel (480) 368-4755 SIC 1541 6531 6552

SERVICES GROUP OF AMERICA INC p 1308
16100 N 71st St Ste 500, Scottsdale AZ 85254
Tel (480) 927-4000
SIC 5141 5148 6331 6552

TROON GOLF LLC p 1484
15044 N Scottsdale Rd # 300, Scottsdale AZ 85254
Tel (480) 606-1000 SIC 8741 6552

ERC PROPERTIES INC p 507
4107 Massard Rd, Fort Smith AR 72903
Tel (479) 478-5103 SIC 1522 6552 6513

■ LENNAR HOMES OF CALIFORNIA INC p 855
25 Enterprise Ste 400, Aliso Viejo CA 92656
Tel (949) 349-8000 SIC 1521 6552

G&L REALTY CORP LLC p 587
439 N Bedford Dr, Beverly Hills CA 90210
Tel (310) 273-9930 SIC 6552

■ SHAPELL INDUSTRIES LLC p 1311
8383 Wilshire Blvd # 700, Beverly Hills CA 90211
Tel (323) 655-7330 SIC 6552 6514 1522

JACMAR COMPANIES p 775
300 Baldwin Park Blvd, City Of Industry CA 91746
Tel (800) 834-8806 SIC 5141 5812 6552

GOLDRICH & KEST INDUSTRIES LLC p 622
5150 Overland Ave, Culver City CA 90230
Tel (310) 204-2050 SIC 6552

STEELWAVE INC p 1385
4000 E 3rd Ave Ste 600, Foster City CA 94404
Tel (650) 571-2200 SIC 6552 8741 6531

STEELWAVE LLC p 1385
4000 E 3rd Ave Ste 500, Foster City CA 94404
Tel (650) 571-2200 SIC 6552 8741 6531

■ CALMAT CO p 242
500 N Brand Blvd Ste 500, Glendale CA 91203
Tel (818) 553-8821
SIC 2951 1442 1429 3273 6512 6552

IRVINE APARTMENT COMMUNITIES LP p 765
110 Innovation Dr, Irvine CA 92617
Tel (949) 720-5600 SIC 6513 6552 6798

SARES REGIS GROUP p 1282
18802 Bardeen Ave, Irvine CA 92612
Tel (949) 756-5959 SIC 6552

HANCOCK PARK ASSOCIATES II LP p 657
10350 Santa Monica Blvd # 295, Los Angeles CA 90025
Tel (310) 228-6900 SIC 6552

LOWE ENTERPRISES INC p 881
11777 San Vicente Blvd # 900, Los Angeles CA 90049
Tel (310) 820-6661 SIC 6531 6552

UNICOM GLOBAL INC p 1502
15535 San Fernando Mssion, Mission Hills CA 91345
Tel (818) 838-0606
SIC 8732 6552 7389 7371

EUREKA REALTY PARTNERS INC p 512
4100 Macarthur Blvd # 200, Newport Beach CA 92660
Tel (949) 224-4100 SIC 6552

IRVINE CO LLC p 765
550 Newport Center Dr # 160, Newport Beach CA 92660
Tel (949) 720-2000
SIC 6552 6531 0174 0191 4841

MAKAR PROPERTIES LLC p 899
4100 Macarthur Blvd # 150, Newport Beach CA 92660
Tel (949) 255-1100 SIC 6552 1542

VI LLC INTEGRAL PARTNERS p 1554
3 San Joaquin Plz Ste 100, Newport Beach CA 92660
Tel (949) 720-3612 SIC 6552

■ WILLIAM LYON HOMES INC p 1610
4695 Macarthur Ct Ste 800, Newport Beach CA 92660
Tel (949) 833-3600 SIC 6552

AGUA CALIENTE BAND OF CAHUILLA INDIANS p 36
5401 Dinah Shore Dr, Palm Springs CA 92264
Tel (760) 699-6800 SIC 8699 6552 7999

J G BOSWELL CO p 771
101 W Walnut St, Pasadena CA 91103
Tel (626) 356-7492 SIC 0131 6552

▲ AEROJET ROCKETDYNE HOLDINGS INC p 30
2001 Aerojet Rd, Rancho Cordova CA 95742
Tel (916) 355-4000
SIC 3812 3764 3769 6552 6519

USA PROPERTIES FUND INC p 1534
3200 Douglas Blvd Ste 200, Roseville CA 95661
Tel (916) 773-6060 SIC 6552 6531

AMERICAN NEWLAND COMMUNITIES LP p 77
9820 Towne Centre Dr # 100, San Diego CA 92121
Tel (858) 455-7503 SIC 6552

OLIVERMCMILLAN LLC p 1082
733 8th Ave, San Diego CA 92101
Tel (619) 321-1111 SIC 6552

CANADIAN AMERICAN OIL CO INC p 246
444 Divisadero St 100, San Francisco CA 94117
Tel (415) 621-8676 SIC 5541 6512 6552

■ EDAW INC p 477
300 California St Fl 5, San Francisco CA 94104
Tel (415) 955-2800 SIC 6552 0781

JOHN STEWART CO p 789
1388 Sutter St Ste 1100, San Francisco CA 94109
Tel (213) 833-1860 SIC 6531 6552 6726

PACIFIC UNION CO p 1106
1 Letterman Dr Ste 300, San Francisco CA 94129
Tel (415) 929-7100 SIC 6552 6512 6531

■ UCP INC p 1499
99 Almaden Blvd Ste 400, San Jose CA 95113
Tel (408) 207-9499 SIC 1521 1531 6552

■ TUTOR-SALIBA CORP p 1493
15901 Olden St, Sylmar CA 91342
Tel (818) 362-8391
SIC 1542 1629 7353 1799 6552

PEAK 7 LLC p 1125
100 S Main St, Breckenridge CO 80424
Tel (888) 783-8883 SIC 6552

▲ VAIL RESORTS INC p 1538
390 Interlocken Cres, Broomfield CO 80021
Tel (303) 404-1800 SIC 7011 6552

■ PROLOGIS p 1183
4545 Airport Way, Denver CO 80239
Tel (303) 375-9292 SIC 6798 6552

ERIE COUNTY INVESTMENT CO p 508
601 Corporate Cir, Golden CO 80401
Tel (303) 384-0200
SIC 5812 6794 6531 6552 1542 1521

PM HOLDINGS INC p 1157
1 American Row, Hartford CT 06103
Tel (860) 403-5000
SIC 6411 6162 6722 6282 6211 6552

WESLEYAN UNIVERSITY p 1593
45 Wyllys Ave, Middletown CT 06459
Tel (860) 685-2000 SIC 8221 6552

ENSIGN-BICKFORD INDUSTRIES INC p 501
125 Pwder Frest Dr Fl 3, Simsbury CT 06070
Tel (860) 843-2000
SIC 3764 2047 2835 3829 2499 6552

BUCCINI/POLLIN GROUP INC p 222
322 A St Ste 300, Wilmington DE 19801
Tel (302) 691-2100 SIC 6552

DONOHOE COMPANIES INC p 451
2101 Wisconsin Ave Nw, Washington DC 20007
Tel (202) 333-0880 SIC 6552 1542

DOUGLAS DEVELOPMENT CORP p 452
702 H St Nw Ste 400, Washington DC 20001
Tel (202) 638-6300 SIC 6552 6531

QUADRANGLE DEVELOPMENT CORP p 1196
1001 G St Nw Ste 700w, Washington DC 20001
Tel (202) 667-0014 SIC 6552

R G A INC p 1202
1001 G St Nw Ste 700w, Washington DC 20001
Tel (202) 393-1999 SIC 6552 7521 6531

■ BLUEGREEN CORP p 193
4960 Conference Way N # 100, Boca Raton FL 33431
Tel (561) 912-8000 SIC 6531 6552

CODINA PARTNERS LLC p 333
135 San Lorenzo Ave # 750, Coral Gables FL 33146
Tel (305) 529-1300
SIC 6552 6531 1521 8742

FLORIDA EAST COAST INDUSTRIES LLC p 558
2855 S Le Jeune Rd Fl 4, Coral Gables FL 33134
Tel (305) 520-2300 SIC 6552

OCEAN PROPERTIES LTD p 1073
1001 E Atl Ave Ste 202, Delray Beach FL 33483
Tel (603) 559-2100
SIC 7011 6552 1522 5719 5812 5813

AMELIA ISLAND CO p 66
1423 Julia St, Fernandina Beach FL 32034
Tel (904) 261-6161
SIC 7011 6552 7992 7991 5812

▲ BFC FINANCIAL CORP p 179
401 E Las Olas Blvd # 800, Fort Lauderdale FL 33301
Tel (954) 940-4900 SIC 6035 6531 6552

LA PLAYA BEACH ASSOCIATES LLC p 835
1000 E Hllandale Bch Blvd, Hallandale Beach FL 33009
Tel (954) 668-2505 SIC 6552

▲ RAYONIER INC p 1210
225 Water St Ste 1400, Jacksonville FL 32202
Tel (904) 357-9100
SIC 6798 5099 6552 5031

GOSPEL OF PEACE INC p 626
215 Celebration Pl # 200, Kissimmee FL 34747
Tel (321) 939-4700 SIC 6552

ORANGE LAKE COUNTRY CLUB INC p 1092
8505 W Irlo Bronson Hwy, Kissimmee FL 34747
Tel (407) 239-0000
SIC 7011 6552 7997 5812 5813

VILLAGES OF LAKE-SUMTER INC p 1557
1000 Lake Sumter Lndg, Lady Lake FL 32162
Tel (352) 753-2270
SIC 6552 1521 7997 5812 7389

▲ LENNAR CORP p 855
700 Nw 107th Ave Ste 400, Miami FL 33172
Tel (305) 559-4000 SIC 1531 6552 6163

TURNBERRY ASSOCIATES p 1492
19501 Biscayne Blvd # 3400, Miami FL 33180
Tel (305) 937-6262 SIC 6512 6552

▲ VECTOR GROUP LTD p 1546
4400 Biscayne Blvd Fl 10, Miami FL 33137
Tel (305) 579-8000 SIC 2111 6552

■ VGR HOLDING LLC p 1553
4400 S Biscayne Blvd # 10, Miami FL 33131
Tel (305) 579-8000 SIC 2111 6552

GRAHAM COMPANIES p 628
6843 Main St, Miami Lakes FL 33014
Tel (305) 821-1130 SIC 6552

GRAHAM COMPANIES p 628
6843 Main St, Miami Lakes FL 33014
Tel (305) 821-1130
SIC 1531 7011 0212 6552 6512 2711

ON TOP OF WORLD COMMUNITIES INC p 1086
8445 Sw 80th St, Ocala FL 34481
Tel (352) 854-3600 SIC 6552 1522

CENTRAL FLORIDA INVESTMENTS INC p 278
5601 Windhover Dr Ofc, Orlando FL 32819
Tel (407) 354-3040 SIC 6552 7011 6531

■ HILTON GRAND VACATIONS CO LLC p 695
5323 Millenia Lakes Blvd # 400, Orlando FL 32839
Tel (407) 722-3100 SIC 6552

A DUDA & SONS INC p 5
1200 Duda Trl, Oviedo FL 32765
Tel (407) 365-2111
SIC 0161 5148 2033 0133 6552 0174

■ DIVOSTA HOMES LP p 444
4500 Pga Blvd Ste 400, Palm Beach Gardens FL 33418
Tel (561) 691-9050 SIC 6552

PEOPLES FIRST PROPERTIES INC p 1132
1002 W 23rd St Ste 400, Panama City FL 32405
Tel (850) 769-8981 SIC 1522 6552

▲ ST JOE CO p 1367
133 S Watersound Pkwy A, Watersound FL 32461
Tel (850) 231-6400
SIC 6531 6552 6512 0811 0851

CREATIVE CHOICE HOMES INC p 390
8895 N Military Trl 206e, West Palm Beach FL 33410
Tel (561) 627-7988 *SIC* 6552 4813

FANJUL CORP p 527
1 N Clematis St Ste 200, West Palm Beach FL 33401
Tel (561) 655-6303
SIC 0133 2061 2099 6552

HOLDER CORP p 700
3300 Cumberland Blvd Se # 400, Atlanta GA 30339
Tel (770) 988-3000 *SIC* 6552 1542

INDUSTRIAL DEVELOPMENTS INTERNATIONAL LLC p 739
1100 Peachtree S, Atlanta GA 30309
Tel (404) 479-4000 *SIC* 6552 6531

INTEGRAL GROUP LLC p 748
191 Peachtree St Ne # 4100, Atlanta GA 30303
Tel (404) 224-1860
SIC 6552 8748 6798 6799 6722

KAJIMA REAL ESTATE DEVELOPMENT INC p 801
3475 Pdmn Rd Ne Ste 1600, Atlanta GA 30305
Tel (404) 564-3900 *SIC* 6552

KAJIMA USA INC p 801
3475 Piedmont Rd Ne, Atlanta GA 30305
Tel (404) 564-3900
SIC 1542 1541 6531 1522 6552 1622

PLACE PROPERTIES LP p 1153
3445 Peachtree Rd Ne # 1400, Atlanta GA 30326
Tel (404) 495-7500 *SIC* 6552

■ PULTE HOME CORP p 1192
3350 Peachtree Rd Ne # 150, Atlanta GA 30326
Tel (248) 647-2750 *SIC* 1531 6552 6162

▲ PULTEGROUP INC p 1192
3350 Peachtree Rd Ne # 150, Atlanta GA 30326
Tel (404) 978-6400 *SIC* 1531 6552 6162

WATKINS ASSOCIATED INDUSTRIES INC p 1582
1958 Monroe Dr Ne, Atlanta GA 30324
Tel (404) 872-3841 *SIC* 4213 6552

FLOURNOY DEVELOPMENT CO p 560
900 Brookstone Ctr Pkwy, Columbus GA 31904
Tel (706) 324-4000 *SIC* 6552 1522 8741

■ LINGER LONGER DEVELOPMENT CO p 869
100 Linger Longer Rd, Greensboro GA 30642
Tel (888) 298-3119 *SIC* 6552 7997

AMBLING MANAGEMENT CO LLC p 65
348 Enterprise Dr, Valdosta GA 31601
Tel (866) 777-7228
SIC 1522 6552 6531 6513

■ ALEXANDER & BALDWIN LLC p 49
822 Bishop St, Honolulu HI 96813
Tel (808) 525-6611
SIC 6531 0133 0179 6552

■ AMFAC HAWAII LLC A HAWAII LIMITED LIABILITY CO p 85
700 Bishop St Ste 2002, Honolulu HI 96813
Tel (808) 543-8900
SIC 6531 6552 0133 0179

MARYL GROUP INC p 914
55 Merchant St Ste 2000, Honolulu HI 96813
Tel (808) 545-2920 *SIC* 6552 1542

■ SCHULER HOMES INC p 1290
828 Fort Street Mall 4th, Honolulu HI 96813
Tel (808) 521-5661 *SIC* 6552

HUALALAI INVESTORS LLC p 715
100 Kaupulehu Dr, Kailua Kona HI 96740
Tel (808) 325-8400 *SIC* 6552

■ KAPALUA LAND CO LTD p 803
1000 Kapalua Dr, Lahaina HI 96761
Tel (808) 669-5622 *SIC* 6552 6512

LANAI RESORTS LLC p 841
1311 Fraser Ave, Lanai City HI 96763
Tel (808) 565-3000 *SIC* 6552 6512

CIRI DEVELOPMENT CORP p 308
1425 Higham St, Idaho Falls ID 83402
Tel (208) 528-8718 *SIC* 6519 6552

BENEFICIAL CO LLC p 172
1421 W Shure Dr Ste 100, Arlington Heights IL 60004
Tel (708) 453-6502
SIC 6141 6351 6162 6021 6552 6311

BARRINGTON VENTURE HOLDING CO LLC p 157
6000 Garlands Ln Ste 120, Barrington IL 60010
Tel (847) 756-3000 *SIC* 6552

CC INDUSTRIES INC p 269
222 N La Salle St # 1000, Chicago IL 60601
Tel (312) 855-4000 *SIC* 6552

MCHUGH ENTERPRISES INC p 929
1737 S Michigan Ave, Chicago IL 60616
Tel (312) 986-8000
SIC 1542 1522 1622 1771 1742 6552

MESIROW FINANCIAL HOLDINGS INC p 951
353 N Clark St Lowr Level, Chicago IL 60654
Tel (312) 595-6000
SIC 6211 6282 6531 6552 6411

ARMON INC p 111
2265 Carlson Dr, Northbrook IL 60062
Tel (847) 498-4800 *SIC* 1711 7515 6552

■ KENNY INDUSTRIES INC p 811
2215 Sanders Rd Ste 400, Northbrook IL 60062
Tel (847) 919-8200
SIC 1611 1622 1629 1623 1541 6552

MCSHANE DEVELOPMENT CO LLC p 932
9500 Bryn Mawr Ave, Rosemont IL 60018
Tel (847) 292-4300 *SIC* 6552

WHITE LODGING SERVICES CORP p 1606
701 E 83rd Ave Ste 17, Merrillville IN 46410
Tel (219) 472-2900 *SIC* 8741 6552

WHITECO INDUSTRIES INC p 1606
1000 E 80th Pl Ste 700n, Merrillville IN 46410
Tel (219) 769-6601
SIC 7312 7011 7922 6552 7374 3993

JACOBSON WAREHOUSE CO INC p 775
3811 Dixon St, Des Moines IA 50313
Tel (515) 265-6171
SIC 4226 4221 4225 8741 6552 4783

LODGING ENTERPRISES LLC p 874
8080 E Central Ave # 180, Wichita KS 67206
Tel (316) 630-6300 *SIC* 7011 8741 6552

CORPOREX REALTY & INVESTMENT LLC p 372
100 E Riverctr Ste 1100, Covington KY 41011
Tel (859) 292-5500
SIC 1542 6531 6552 8741 6512

HISTORIC RESTORATION INC p 696
812 Gravier St Apt 200, New Orleans LA 70112
Tel (504) 493-6129 *SIC* 6552

AMERICAN TRADING AND PRODUCTION CORP p 80
1 South St Ste 2800, Baltimore MD 21202
Tel (410) 347-7150 *SIC* 6552

SHELTER DEVELOPMENT LLC p 1314
218 N Charles St Ste 220, Baltimore MD 21201
Tel (410) 962-0595 *SIC* 6552

■ CHEVY CHASE BANK FSB p 296
7501 Wisconsin Ave Fl 11, Bethesda MD 20814
Tel (240) 497-4101
SIC 6035 6411 6211 6519 6552 6719

CLARK ENTERPRISES INC p 322
7500 Old Georgetown Rd # 7, Bethesda MD 20814
Tel (301) 657-7100
SIC 6552 4832 7359 1521 1542 6726

JBG PROPERTIES INC p 779
4445 Willard Ave Ste 400, Chevy Chase MD 20815
Tel (240) 333-3600 *SIC* 6531 6552

SODEXO MANAGEMENT INC p 1337
9801 Washingtonian Blvd, Gaithersburg MD 20878
Tel (301) 987-4000 *SIC* 8741 6552

BOZZUTO & ASSOCIATES INC p 205
6406 Ivy Ln Ste 700, Greenbelt MD 20770
Tel (301) 220-0100 *SIC* 6513 1522 6552

CITADEL LAND INC p 309
1802 Brightseat Rd # 600, Landover MD 20785
Tel (301) 683-6498 *SIC* 6552

FMR LLC p 562
245 Summer St, Boston MA 02210
Tel (617) 563-7000
SIC 6282 6211 6799 6552 6531

NEW ENGLAND DEVELOPMENT INC p 1030
75 Park Plz Ste 3, Boston MA 02116
Tel (617) 965-8700 *SIC* 6552

WDC DEVELOPMENT ASSOCIATES LP p 1585
6 Faneuil Hall Market Pl, Boston MA 02109
Tel (617) 742-4500 *SIC* 6552

CHELSEA INDUSTRIES INC p 293
46a Glen Ave, Newton MA 02459
Tel (617) 232-6060 *SIC* 6552

■ FORD HOLDINGS LLC p 565
American Rd, Dearborn MI 48121
Tel (313) 845-5338 *SIC* 6552 6512

■ FORD MOTOR LAND DEVELOPMENT CORP p 566
330 Town Center Dr # 1100, Dearborn MI 48126
Tel (313) 323-3100 *SIC* 6512 6552

BEZTAK CO (INC) p 179
31731 Northwstrn Hwy 25 Ste 250W, Farmington Hills MI 48334
Tel (248) 855-5400 *SIC* 6552

GRANGER ASSOCIATES INC p 630
16980 Wood Rd, Lansing MI 48906
Tel (517) 372-2800 *SIC* 4953 1794 6552

HOWARD TERNES PACKAGING CO p 713
35275 Industrial Rd, Livonia MI 48150
Tel (734) 793-4130 *SIC* 4783 6512 6552

P M GROUP INC p 1102
1050 Corporate Office Dr, Milford MI 48381
Tel (248) 529-2000 *SIC* 6531 1522 6552

▲ ALLETE INC p 53
30 W Superior St, Duluth MN 55802
Tel (218) 279-5000
SIC 4931 4924 4941 1231 6552

CARLSON HOTELS MANAGEMENT CORP p 258
701 Tower Carlson Pkwy, Hopkins MN 55305
Tel (763) 212-5000 *SIC* 6794 6531 6552

LUTHER HOLDING CO p 886
3701 Alabama Ave S, Minneapolis MN 55416
Tel (763) 593-5755
SIC 5511 7515 7513 6512 6552 5611

RYAN COMPANIES US INC p 1260
50 S 10th St Ste 300, Minneapolis MN 55403
Tel (612) 492-4000
SIC 1542 1541 6552 6512 1522

RADISSON HOTELS INTERNATIONAL INC p 1204
701 Carlson Pkwy, Minnetonka MN 55305
Tel (763) 212-5000
SIC 7011 6794 6552 6531 8742 7389

HUNT MIDWEST ENTERPRISES INC p 719
8300 Ne Underground Dr # 100, Kansas City MO 64161
Tel (816) 455-2500 *SIC* 6552 1422 6211

YARCO CO INC p 1635
7920 Ward Pkwy, Kansas City MO 64114
Tel (816) 561-4240 *SIC* 6552 6531

NORTHPOINT DEVELOPMENT LLC p 1057
4825 Nw 41st St Ste 500, Riverside MO 64150
Tel (816) 888-7380 *SIC* 6552 6531

J H BERRA HOLDING CO INC p 771
5091 Baumgartner Rd, Saint Louis MO 63129
Tel (314) 487-5617 *SIC* 6552

AMERICAN WEST HOMES INC p 81
250 Pilot Rd Ste 140, Las Vegas NV 89119
Tel (702) 736-6434 *SIC* 6552

■ CAESARS WORLD INC p 237
3570 Las Vegas Blvd S, Las Vegas NV 89109
Tel (702) 731-7110
SIC 7011 7999 5812 6552 5611 5621

■ HUGHES CORP p 717
10801 W Charleston Blvd # 300, Las Vegas NV 89135
Tel (702) 791-4000 *SIC* 6552

CONNELL CO p 357
200 Connell Dr Ste 4100, Berkeley Heights NJ 07922
Tel (908) 673-3700
SIC 6552 6512 7359 5082

KAPLAN AT OLD BRIDGE INC p 803
433 River Rd, Highland Park NJ 08904
Tel (732) 846-5900 *SIC* 6552

▲ PRUDENTIAL FINANCIAL INC p 1187
751 Broad St, Newark NJ 07102
Tel (973) 802-6000
SIC 6311 6321 6331 6211 6552

EDGEWOOD PROPERTIES INC p 478
1260 Stelton Rd, Piscataway NJ 08854
Tel (732) 985-1900 *SIC* 6552 6531

■ K HOVNANIAN HOLDINGS NJ LLC p 798
110 W Front St, Red Bank NJ 07701
Tel (732) 747-7800 *SIC* 6552

TRITEC BUILDING CO INC p 1483
45 Research Way Ste 100, East Setauket NY 11733
Tel (631) 751-0300 *SIC* 6552 8742

■ AXA FINANCIAL INC p 139
1290 Ave Of The Am Fl Con, New York NY 10104
Tel (212) 554-1234
SIC 6311 6211 6552 6531 6371 6221

BROADSTONE GROUP INC p 215
156 W 56th St Ste 1604, New York NY 10019
Tel (212) 333-2100 *SIC* 6552 7011 8741

HARTZ GROUP INC p 666
667 Madison Ave Fl 24, New York NY 10065
Tel (212) 308-3336
SIC 6512 6552 6531 6159

LEND LEASE (US) INC p 855
250 Civic Center Dr, New York NY 10166
Tel (212) 592-6700 *SIC* 6799 6552

ORIENT EXPRESS HOTELS INC p 1094
441 Lexington Ave Rm 504, New York NY 10017
Tel (212) 302-5055
SIC 7011 3743 5947 6552

PARAMOUNT GROUP INC p 1114
1633 Broadway Ste 1801, New York NY 10019
Tel (212) 974-1450 *SIC* 6552 6531

RELATED COMPANIES INC p 1221
511 W 33rd St Rm 200, New York NY 10001
Tel (212) 801-1000 *SIC* 6552 6531

RELATED COMPANIES L P p 1221
60 Columbus Cir, New York NY 10023
Tel (212) 421-5333 *SIC* 6552 6531

ROCKEFELLER GROUP INTERNATIONAL INC p 1244
1221 Avenue Of The Americ, New York NY 10020
Tel (212) 282-2000 *SIC* 6512 6552 4813

ROCKROSE DEVELOPMENT CORP p 1245
15 E 26th St Fl 7, New York NY 10010
Tel (212) 847-3700 *SIC* 6552

STARRETT CORP p 1379
70 E 55th St Fl 7, New York NY 10022
Tel (212) 350-9909 *SIC* 6552

SYCAMORE PARTNERS LLC p 1413
9 W 57th St Ste 3100, New York NY 10019
Tel (212) 796-8500 *SIC* 6552

■ TISHMAN REALTY & CONSTRUCTION CO INC p 1456
100 Park Ave Fl 5, New York NY 10017
Tel (212) 708-6800 *SIC* 8741 6552

TISHMAN SPEYER PROPERTIES LP p 1456
45 Rockefeller Plz Conc1, New York NY 10111
Tel (212) 715-0300 *SIC* 6531 6552

■ ORANGE AND ROCKLAND UTILITIES INC p 1091
1 Blue Hill Plz Ste 20, Pearl River NY 10965
Tel (845) 352-6000
SIC 4924 4911 1311 6552

EJ DEL MONTE CORP p 482
909 Linden Ave Ste 1, Rochester NY 14625
Tel (585) 586-3121
SIC 6552 8741 6512 6799 7011

ALLIANCE DEVELOPMENT GROUP LLC p 54
301 S Tryon St Ste 1500, Charlotte NC 28282
Tel (704) 973-2950 *SIC* 5812 6552

CAMPUS CREST COMMUNITIES INC p 246
2100 Rexford Rd Ste 300, Charlotte NC 28211
Tel (704) 496-2500 *SIC* 6798 6552 6531

CHILDRESS KLEIN PROPERTIES INC p 300
301 S College St Ste 2800, Charlotte NC 28202
Tel (704) 342-9000 *SIC* 6552 6512 6531

CRESCENT RESOURCES LLC p 391
227 W Trade St Ste 1000, Charlotte NC 28202
Tel (980) 321-6000 *SIC* 6552

LINCOLN HARRIS LLC p 867
4725 Piedmont Row Dr, Charlotte NC 28210
Tel (704) 331-0917 *SIC* 6531 6552

YORK PROPERTIES INC OF RALEIGH p 1637
1900 Cameron St, Raleigh NC 27605
Tel (919) 821-1350 *SIC* 6552 6531

BODDIE-NOELL ENTERPRISES INC p 197
1021 Noell Ln, Rocky Mount NC 27804
Tel (252) 937-2000 *SIC* 5812 6552

SANFORD CONTRACTORS INC p 1279
628 Rocky Fork Church Rd, Sanford NC 27332
Tel (919) 775-7882
SIC 1611 1622 1629 6552 1794 1623

REQ/JQH HOLDINGS INC p 1226
4243 Hunt Rd Ste 2, Blue Ash OH 45242
Tel (513) 891-1066 *SIC* 8741 6552

TP MECHANICAL CONTRACTORS INC p 1467
1500 Kemper Meadow Dr, Cincinnati OH 45240
Tel (513) 851-8881 *SIC* 6552

FOREST CITY ENTERPRISES LP p 566
50 Public Sq Ste 1100, Cleveland OH 44113
Tel (216) 621-6060 *SIC* 6512 6513 6552

GEORGE J IGEL & CO INC p 606
2040 Alum Creek Dr, Columbus OH 43207
Tel (614) 445-8421 *SIC* 1794 1623 6552

MILLER-VALENTINE OPERATIONS INC p 971
137 N Main St Ste 900, Dayton OH 45402
Tel (937) 293-0900 *SIC* 6552 6531

CARTER-JONES COMPANIES INC p 262
601 Tallmadge Rd, Kent OH 44240
Tel (330) 673-6100 *SIC* 5211 5031 6552

AMERICANA DEVELOPMENT INC p 81
7095 Americana Pkwy, Reynoldsburg OH 43068
Tel (614) 866-9803 *SIC* 6552

■ MAGNUM MANAGEMENT CORP p 897
1 Cedar Point Dr, Sandusky OH 44870
Tel (419) 627-2334 *SIC* 4785 6552 7996

RESORTS GROUP INC p 1227
Rr 209, Bushkill PA 18324
Tel (570) 588-6661 *SIC* 7011 6552

MARONDA INC p 910
11 Timberglen Dr, Imperial PA 15126
Tel (724) 695-1200 *SIC* 6552 1521

ONEILL PROPERTIES GROUP LP p 1087
2701 Renaissance Blvd # 4, King Of Prussia PA 19406
Tel (610) 337-5560 *SIC* 6552

MC WIL GROUP LTD p 925
209 N Beaver St, York PA 17401
Tel (717) 854-7857
SIC 8059 8051 8069 6513 8742 6552

WILMAC CORP p 1613
209 N Beaver St, York PA 17401
Tel (717) 854-7857
SIC 8059 8051 8069 6513 8742 6552

CESAR CASTILLO INC p 284
Km 21 1 Pr 1 Rr 1, Guaynabo PR 00971
Tel (787) 999-1616 *SIC* 5122 6552

PICERNE INVESTMENT CORP p 1146
75 Lambert Lind Hwy # 300, Warwick RI 02886
Tel (401) 732-3700
SIC 6552 6531 1521 1522 1542

BEACH CO p 164
211 King St Ste 300, Charleston SC 29401
Tel (843) 722-2615 *SIC* 6552 8741 1542

GREENWOOD MILLS INC p 639
300 Morgan Ave, Greenwood SC 29646
Tel (864) 227-2121
SIC 2211 2221 2241 2261 2262 6552

KIAWAH RESORT ASSOCIATES p 816
245 Gardners Cir, Johns Island SC 29455
Tel (843) 768-3400 *SIC* 6552

BURROUGHS & CHAPIN CO INC p 228
8800 Marina Pkwy, Myrtle Beach SC 29572
Tel (843) 448-5123
SIC 6552 6515 6519 6512

MYRTLE BEACH FARMS CO INC p 1005
8820 Marina Pkwy, Myrtle Beach SC 29572
Tel (843) 448-5123 *SIC* 6552 7996 6512

LAND SOUTHERN CO LLC p 842
1550 W Mcewen Dr Ste 200, Franklin TN 37067
Tel (615) 778-3150 *SIC* 6552

DOUBLE DIAMOND - DELAWARE INC p 452
5495 Belt Line Rd Ste 200, Dallas TX 75254
Tel (214) 706-9831 *SIC* 6552 7992

DOUBLE DIAMOND INC p 452
5495 Belt Line Rd Ste 200, Dallas TX 75254
Tel (214) 706-9801 *SIC* 6552

HALL FINANCIAL GROUP LTD p 654
2323 Ross Ave Ste 200, Dallas TX 75201
Tel (972) 377-1100 *SIC* 6552 6531

HILLWOOD DEVELOPMENT CORP p 694
3090 Olive St Ste 300, Dallas TX 75219
Tel (214) 303-5535 *SIC* 6552 6531

■ HOWARD HUGHES CORP p 713
13355 Noel Rd Fl 22, Dallas TX 75240
Tel (702) 791-4000 *SIC* 6552 6512 7992

LPC COMMERCIAL SERVICES INC p 882
2000 Mckinney Ave # 1000, Dallas TX 75201
Tel (202) 513-6710 *SIC* 6552

■ TRAMMELL CROW CENTRAL TEXAS LTD p 1469
2001 Ross Ave Ste 325, Dallas TX 75201
Tel (214) 267-0400 *SIC* 6799 6552 6512

CAMAC INTERNATIONAL CORP p 243
1330 Post Oak Blvd Ste 22, Houston TX 77056
Tel (713) 965-5100
SIC 8711 6552 1382 8741 1389

CAMCORP INTERESTS LTD p 244
10410 Wndamere Lakes Blvd, Houston TX 77065
Tel (281) 671-9000 *SIC* 1521 6798 6552

CAMDEN DEVELOPMENT INC p 244
11 Greenway Plz Ste 2400, Houston TX 77046
Tel (713) 354-2500 *SIC* 6531 6552

HINES INTERESTS LIMITED PARTNERSHIP p 695
2800 Post Oak Blvd # 4800, Houston TX 77056
Tel (713) 621-8000 *SIC* 6552

TOM THUMB FOOD & DRUGS INC p 1459
3663 Briarpark Dr, Houston TX 77042
Tel (713) 268-3500
SIC 5411 5912 5499 6512 6552

■ US HOME CORP p 1532
10707 Clay Rd, Houston TX 77041
Tel (305) 559-4000 *SIC* 1531 6162 6552

JPI INVESTMENT CO LP p 795
600 Las Colinas Blvd E # 1800, Irving TX 75039
Tel (972) 556-1700 *SIC* 6552

JPI LIFESTYLE APARTMENT COMMUNITIES LP p 795
600 Las Colinas Blvd E, Irving TX 75039
Tel (972) 556-1700 *SIC* 6513 6552

■ PULTE HOMES OF TEXAS LP p 1192
4800 Regent Blvd Ste 100, Irving TX 75063
Tel (972) 304-2800 *SIC* 6552 1521

PERCHERON SERVICES p 1134
1904 W Grand Pkwy N, Katy TX 77449
Tel (832) 300-6400 *SIC* 6552

D L ROGERS CORP p 407
5013 Davis Blvd, North Richland Hills TX 76180
Tel (817) 428-2077 *SIC* 5812 6552 6799

HASSLOCHER ENTERPRISES INC p 667
8520 Crownhill Blvd, San Antonio TX 78209
Tel (210) 828-1493 *SIC* 5812 5142 6552

USAA REAL ESTATE CO p 1534
9830 Colonnade Blvd # 600, San Antonio TX 78230
Tel (210) 641-8400 *SIC* 6552

YANTIS CORP p 1635
3611 Paesanos Pkwy # 300, San Antonio TX 78231
Tel (210) 655-3780
SIC 1623 1611 1622 1629 6552 1521

■ **WOODLANDS OPERATING CO L P** p 1623
24 Waterway Ave Ste 1100, The Woodlands TX 77380
Tel (281) 719-6100
SIC 6552 7997 7389 6513 6512

JAS D EASTON INC p 778
5215 W Wiley Post Way # 130, Salt Lake City UT 84116
Tel (801) 526-6211 SIC 3949 5091 6552

PETERSON COMPANIES L C p 1138
12500 Fair Lakes Cir # 400, Fairfax VA 22033
Tel (703) 631-7570 SIC 6552

S W RODGERS CO INC p 1263
5816 Wellington Rd, Gainesville VA 20155
Tel (703) 591-8400
SIC 1611 1799 6552 1771 1623

LANDOR INTERNATIONAL INC p 843
2120 Staples Mill Rd # 300, Richmond VA 23230
Tel (804) 346-8200 SIC 6552 8741 4724

ARMADA/HOFFLER PROPERTIES LLC p 110
222 Central Park Ave # 2100, Virginia Beach VA 23462
Tel (757) 366-4000 SIC 6552

OPUS NORTHWEST LLC p 1091
2025 1st Ave Ph B, Seattle WA 98121
Tel (425) 467-2701 SIC 6552 1542

MCFARLAND CASCADE HOLDINGS INC p 928
1640 E Marc St, Tacoma WA 98421
Tel (253) 572-3033 SIC 2491 6552 6531

JERRY ERWIN ASSOCIATES INC p 783
12115 Ne 99th St Ste 1800, Vancouver WA 98682
Tel (800) 254-9442 SIC 6552 6531

WILKINSON CORP p 1609
212 N Naches Ave, Yakima WA 98901
Tel (866) 914-2403 SIC 6552

RAYMOND MANAGEMENT CO INC p 1210
8333 Greenway Blvd # 200, Middleton WI 53562
Tel (608) 833-4100 SIC 6552 8741 7011

GORMAN & CO INC p 626
200 N Main St, Oregon WI 53575
Tel (608) 835-3900 SIC 6552 6531

OMEGA PROBE INC p 1084
308 Southwest Dr, Cheyenne WY 82007
Tel (877) 323-2201 SIC 7371 6552

JACKSON HOLE MOUNTAIN RESORT CORP p 774
3395 Cody Ln, Teton Village WY 83025
Tel (307) 733-2292 SIC 7999 6552

SIC 6553 Cemetery Subdividers & Developers

FOREST LAWN MEMORIAL-PARK ASSOCIATION p 567
1712 S Glendale Ave, Glendale CA 91205
Tel (323) 254-3131 SIC 5992 6553 7261

■ **SKYLAWN** p 1330
32992 Mission Blvd, Hayward CA 94544
Tel (510) 471-3363 SIC 6553 7261

LAVIDA COMMUNITIES INC p 847
500 Stevens Ave Ste 100, Solana Beach CA 92075
Tel (858) 792-9300
SIC 6513 6512 6531 6553

SENIOR RESOURCE GROUP LLC p 1304
500 Stevens Ave Ste 100, Solana Beach CA 92075
Tel (858) 792-9300
SIC 6513 6512 6531 6553

ROSE HILLS CO p 1250
3888 Workman Mill Rd, Whittier CA 90601
Tel (562) 699-0921 SIC 6553

ROSE HILLS HOLDINGS CORP p 1250
3888 Workman Mill Rd, Whittier CA 90601
Tel (562) 699-0921 SIC 6553

■ **NATIONAL CEMETERY ADMINISTRATION** p 1010
810 Vrmont Ave Nw Ste 427, Washington DC 20420
Tel (800) 827-1000 SIC 6553 9451

■ **CEMETERY MANAGEMENT INC** p 274
1201 S Orlando Ave # 365, Winter Park FL 32789
Tel (407) 740-7000 SIC 6553 6531

CATHOLIC DIOCESE OF ROCKFORD p 266
555 Colman Center Dr, Rockford IL 61108
Tel (815) 399-4300
SIC 8661 8322 8361 8211 6553

ABBEY LAFAYETTE p 9
2 Avenue De Lafayette, Boston MA 02111
Tel (617) 542-7373 SIC 6553

CATHOLIC DIOCESE OF KANSAS CITY-ST JOSEPH p 266
850 Main St, Kansas City MO 64105
Tel (816) 756-1850
SIC 8661 8211 8351 8361 6553

STONEMOR GP LLC p 1391
3600 Horizon Blvd Ste 100, Feasterville Trevose PA 19053
Tel (215) 826-2947 SIC 6553

CATHOLIC SOCIAL SERVICES OF DIOCESE OF SCRANTON INC p 267
516 Fig St, Scranton PA 18505
Tel (570) 207-2283
SIC 8661 2711 8211 8322 6553

▲ **STONEMOR PARTNERS LP** p 1391
3600 Horizon Blvd Ste 100, Trevose PA 19053
Tel (215) 826-2800 SIC 6553 7261

■ **ALDERWOODS (DELAWARE) INC** p 47
1929 Allen Pkwy, Houston TX 77019
Tel (713) 522-5141 SIC 7261 6553 6311

▲ **CARRIAGE SERVICES INC** p 260
3040 Post Oak Blvd # 300, Houston TX 77056
Tel (713) 332-8400 SIC 7261 6553

■ **SCI SHARED RESOURCES LLC** p 1292
1929 Allen Pkwy, Houston TX 77019
Tel (713) 522-5141 SIC 7261 6553

SIC 6712 Offices Of Bank Holding Co's

SKBHC HOLDINGS LLC p 1329
8723 E Via De Commercio, Scottsdale AZ 85258
Tel (480) 393-0562 SIC 6712

ARVEST BANK GROUP INC p 114
913 W Monroe Ave, Lowell AR 72745
Tel (479) 750-1400 SIC 6712

▲ **CU BANCORP** p 399
15821 Ventura Blvd # 100, Encino CA 91436
Tel (818) 257-7700 SIC 6021 6712

FREMONT BANCORPORATION p 577
39150 Fremont Blvd, Fremont CA 94538
Tel (510) 792-2300 SIC 6712

OCEAN BANKSHARES INC p 1073
780 Nw 42nd Ave Ste 626, Miami FL 33126
Tel (305) 442-2660 SIC 6712

■ **RAYMOND JAMES FINANCIAL SERVICES INC** p 1210
880 Carillon Pkwy, Saint Petersburg FL 33716
Tel (727) 567-1000
SIC 6211 6282 6712 6091 6035

INTOWN HOLDING CO LLC p 759
2727 Paces Fery Rd 2 1200, Atlanta GA 30339
Tel (770) 799-5000 SIC 6712

▲ **STATE BANK FINANCIAL CORP** p 1380
3399 Peachtree Rd Ne, Atlanta GA 30326
Tel (404) 475-6599
SIC 6022 6712 6311 6141 6331

COMMUNITY BANKSHARES INC p 347
400 N Main St, Cornelia GA 30531
Tel (706) 778-3900 SIC 6712

AQUILEX LLC p 101
2225 Skyland Ct, Norcross GA 30071
Tel (404) 869-6677 SIC 6712

BYLINE BANCORP INC p 231
180 N La Salle St Ste 300, Chicago IL 60601
Tel (773) 843-7800 SIC 6712 6162

FIRST AMERICAN BANK CORP (DEL) p 544
1650 Lewis Ave, Elk Grove Village IL 60007
Tel (847) 228-5505 SIC 6712

FOUNDERS GROUP INC p 571
6825 W 111th St, Worth IL 60482
Tel (708) 448-6500 SIC 6712

STAR FINANCIAL GROUP INC p 1378
127 W Berry St Fl 2, Fort Wayne IN 46802
Tel (260) 467-5500 SIC 6712

■ **REMY INTERNATIONAL HOLDINGS INC** p 1223
600 Corporation Dr, Pendleton IN 46064
Tel (765) 778-6499 SIC 6712

PEOPLES BANK p 1132
4831 W 6th St, Lawrence KS 66049
Tel (785) 842-4004 SIC 6712

VALLEY VIEW BANCSHARES INC p 1541
7500 W 95th St, Shawnee Mission KS 66212
Tel (913) 381-3311 SIC 6712

INTRUST FINANCIAL CORP p 760
105 N Main St, Wichita KS 67202
Tel (316) 383-1111 SIC 6712 6022

COMMUNITY TRUST FINANCIAL CORP p 350
1511 N Trenton St, Ruston LA 71270
Tel (318) 255-2222 SIC 6712

BANGOR BANCORP MHC p 150
3 State St, Bangor ME 04401
Tel (207) 942-5211 SIC 6712

TD BANKNORTH LEASING CORP p 1428
70 Gray Rd, Falmouth ME 04105
Tel (207) 317-4616 SIC 6712

CB HOLDING CORP p 268
1 Congress St Ste 113, Boston MA 02114
Tel (617) 720-2994 SIC 6712

SALEM FIVE BANCORP p 1272
210 Essex St, Salem MA 01970
Tel (978) 745-5555 SIC 6712

FRANDSEN FINANCIAL CORP p 574
4388 Round Lake Rd W, Arden Hills MN 55112
Tel (651) 242-5700 SIC 6022 6712

RAINEY ROAD HOLDINGS INC p 1205
15600 37th Ave N Ste 100, Minneapolis MN 55446
Tel (763) 541-1410 SIC 6712

BREMER FINANCIAL CORP p 210
380 Sint Peter St Ste 500, Saint Paul MN 55102
Tel (800) 908-2265 SIC 6022 6712

COMMUNITY BANCSHARES OF MISSISSIPPI INC p 347
1255 W Government St, Brandon MS 39042
Tel (601) 825-4323 SIC 6712

BANCPLUS CORP p 150
1068 Highland Colony Pkwy, Ridgeland MS 39157
Tel (601) 898-8300 SIC 6712

CENTRAL BANCOMPANY INC p 277
238 Madison St, Jefferson City MO 65101
Tel (573) 634-1234 SIC 6712

DICKINSON FINANCIAL CORP II p 438
1111 Main St Ste 1600, Kansas City MO 64105
Tel (816) 472-5244 SIC 6712

■ **GREAT SOUTHERN BANK** p 634
14309 State Highway 13, Reeds Spring MO 65737
Tel (417) 888-5880 SIC 6021 4724 6712

MISSISSIPPI VALLEY BANCSHARES INC p 976
13205 Manchester Rd, Saint Louis MO 63131
Tel (314) 543-3512 SIC 6022 6712

PINNACLE BANCORP INC p 1149
1801 Burt St, Elkhorn NE 68022
Tel (402) 697-8666 SIC 6022 6712

■ **MERCK HOLDINGS LLC** p 945
1 Merck Dr, Whitehouse Station NJ 08889
Tel (908) 423-1000 SIC 2834 6712

■ **WILMINGTON TRUST CORP** p 1613
1 M And T Plz Ste 1, Buffalo NY 14203
Tel (302) 651-1000 SIC 6712

BARCLAYS GROUP US INC p 155
745 7th Ave, New York NY 10019
Tel (212) 412-4000 SIC 6712

CREDIT SUISSE HOLDINGS (USA) INC p 390
11 Madison Ave Bsmt 1b, New York NY 10010
Tel (646) 935-0299 SIC 6712

FLAVORS HOLDINGS INC p 555
35 E 62nd St, New York NY 10065
Tel (212) 572-8677 SIC 2869 6712

NEW OMAHA HOLDINGS LP p 1032
9 W 57th St Ste 4200, New York NY 10019
Tel (212) 750-8300 SIC 6712

▲ **OPPENHEIMER HOLDINGS INC** p 1090
85 Broad St, New York NY 10004
Tel (212) 668-8000 SIC 6211 6712 6722

RBC USA HOLDCO CORP p 1211
3 World Financial Ctr, New York NY 10281
Tel (212) 858-7200 SIC 6712 6021 6022

NWL HOLDINGS INC p 1068
111 Hempstead Tpke, West Hempstead NY 11552
Tel (516) 489-3300 SIC 6712

■ **COMMUNITYONE BANK NATIONAL ASSOCIATION** p 350
101 Sunset Ave, Asheboro NC 27203
Tel (336) 625-4012 SIC 6712 6021

FIDELITY BANCSHARES (NC) INC p 540
100 S Main St, Fuquay Varina NC 27526
Tel (919) 552-2242 SIC 6712

RBC BANCORPORATION (USA) p 1211
301 Fayetteville St, Raleigh NC 27601
Tel (252) 454-4400 SIC 6712 6022

INTERBANK INC p 751
4921 N May Ave, Oklahoma City OK 73112
Tel (580) 928-5511 SIC 6712

PENN NATIONAL HOLDING CORP p 1129
2 N 2nd St Ste 2, Harrisburg PA 17101
Tel (717) 234-4941 SIC 6712

▲ **SOUTH STATE CORP** p 1345
520 Gervais St Ste 310, Columbia SC 29201
Tel (800) 277-2175 SIC 6712 6022

DACOTAH BANKS INC p 408
401 S Main St Ste 212, Aberdeen SD 57401
Tel (605) 225-1300 SIC 6712

■ **NATIONAL BANK OF COMMERCE** p 1010
1 Commerce Sq, Memphis TN 38103
Tel (901) 523-3434
SIC 6021 6211 7374 6712

INDEPENDENT BANKERS FINANCIAL CORP p 736
11701 Luna Rd, Farmers Branch TX 75234
Tel (972) 650-6000 SIC 6712

SOUTH PLAINS FINANCIAL INC p 1344
5219 City Bank Pkwy # 55, Lubbock TX 79407
Tel (806) 792-7101 SIC 6712

LONE STAR NATIONAL BANCSHARES – TEXAS INC p 876
4500 N 10th St Ste 305, Mcallen TX 78504
Tel (956) 781-4321 SIC 6712 6021

■ **NEW GALVESTON CO** p 1030
100 W Houston St, San Antonio TX 78205
Tel (210) 220-4011 SIC 6712

ANB CORP p 89
102 W Moore Ave Lbby Lbby, Terrell TX 75160
Tel (972) 563-2611 SIC 6712

ANB HOLDING CO LTD p 89
102 W Moore Ave, Terrell TX 75160
Tel (972) 524-3411 SIC 6712

EXTRACO CORP p 521
1700 N Vly Mills Dr Ste 1, Waco TX 76710
Tel (254) 776-0330 SIC 6712

WTB FINANCIAL CORP p 1628
717 W Sprague Ave Fl 7, Spokane WA 99201
Tel (509) 353-4204 SIC 6712

CPL INDUSTRIES INC p 387
1111 Cedar Creek Rd, Grafton WI 53024
Tel (262) 377-2210 SIC 6712

JOHNSON FINANCIAL GROUP INC p 791
555 Main St Ste 400, Racine WI 53403
Tel (262) 619-2700
SIC 6022 6021 6712 6733 6311

SIC 6719 Offices Of Holding Co's, NEC

SOUTHERN STORE FIXTURES INC p 1350
275 Drexel Rd Se, Bessemer AL 35022
Tel (205) 428-4800 SIC 6719

■ **HEALTHSOUTH HOME HEALTH HOLDINGS INC** p 677
3660 Grandview Pkwy, Birmingham AL 35243
Tel (205) 967-7116 SIC 8099 8082 6719

■ **SANMINA-SCI SYSTEMS (ALABAMA) INC** p 1280
13000 Memorial Pkwy Sw, Huntsville AL 35803
Tel (256) 882-4800 SIC 6719

COLUMBIA SOUTHERN EDUCATION GROUP INC p 341
21982 University Ln, Orange Beach AL 36561
Tel (251) 943-2273 SIC 6719

WKW ERBSLOEH NORTH AMERICA HOLDING INC p 1620
103 Parkway E, Pell City AL 35125
Tel (205) 338-4242 SIC 6719

CHUGACH GOVERNMENT SOLUTIONS LLC p 305
3800 Cntrpint Dr Ste 1200, Anchorage AK 99503
Tel (907) 563-8866 SIC 6719

■ **G C I HOLDINGS INC** p 586
2550 Denali St Ste 1000, Anchorage AK 99503
Tel (907) 265-5600 SIC 6719

KONIAG DEVELOPMENT CO LLC p 827
3800 Centerpoint Dr # 502, Anchorage AK 99503
Tel (907) 561-2668 SIC 8741 6719

KONIAG INC p 827
3800 Cntrpoint Dr Ste 502, Kodiak AK 99615
Tel (907) 486-2530 SIC 6552 6519 6719

■ **CYPRUS CLIMAX METALS CO** p 405
333 N Central Ave, Phoenix AZ 85004
Tel (928) 473-7000 SIC 6719

■ **SLC OPERATING LIMITED PARTNERSHIP** p 1331
2231 E Camelback Rd # 400, Phoenix AZ 85016
Tel (602) 852-3900 SIC 6719

NCU HOLDINGS LLC p 1022
10000 E University Dr, Prescott Valley AZ 86314
Tel (928) 541-7777 SIC 6719

■ **AMERICA WEST HOLDINGS CORP** p 67
111 W Rio Salado Pkwy, Tempe AZ 85281
Tel (480) 693-0800 SIC 6719

MEDPLAST LLC p 938
405 W Geneva Dr, Tempe AZ 85282
Tel (480) 553-6400 SIC 6719

SSW HOLDING CO INC p 1364
3501 Tulsa St, Fort Smith AR 72903
Tel (479) 646-1651 SIC 3496 6719

LIFE AND SPECIALTY VENTURES LLC p 863
17500 Chenal Pkwy Ste 500, Little Rock AR 72223
Tel (501) 378-2910 SIC 6719

STEPHENS LLC p 1386
111 Center St Ste 200, Little Rock AR 72201
Tel (501) 377-2000 SIC 6719

GGC ACQUISITION HOLDINGS CORP p 610
3450 E Miraloma Ave, Anaheim CA 92806
Tel (714) 414-4000 SIC 6719

STURGEON SERVICES INTERNATIONAL INC p 1395
3511 Gilmore Ave, Bakersfield CA 93308
Tel (661) 322-4408 SIC 6719

PROJECT BOAT HOLDINGS LLC p 1182
360 N Crescent Dr Bldg S, Beverly Hills CA 90210
Tel (310) 712-1850 SIC 6719

PROJECT SKYLINE INTERMEDIATE HOLDING CORP p 1182
360 N Crescent Dr Bldg S, Beverly Hills CA 90210
Tel (310) 712-1850 SIC 6719

HANERGY HOLDING AMERICA INC p 657
1350 Bayshore Hwy Ste 825, Burlingame CA 94010
Tel (650) 288-3722 SIC 4911 6719

PT-1 HOLDINGS LLC p 1189
720 Portal St, Cotati CA 94931
Tel (707) 665-4295 SIC 6719

CHRISTIE DIGITAL SYSTEMS INC p 303
10550 Camden Dr, Cypress CA 90630
Tel (714) 236-8610 SIC 3861 6719

HCO HOLDING I CORP p 672
999 N Sepulveda Blvd, El Segundo CA 90245
Tel (323) 583-5000 SIC 6719

DRYBAR HOLDINGS LLC p 457
125 Technology Dr Ste 150, Irvine CA 92618
Tel (310) 776-6330 SIC 6719

INFINITE RF HOLDINGS INC p 741
17802 Fitch, Irvine CA 92614
Tel (949) 261-1920 SIC 5999 6719

■ **MISSION ENERGY HOLDING CO** p 975
2600 Michelson Dr # 1700, Irvine CA 92612
Tel (949) 752-5588 SIC 6719

JOHN S FREY ENTERPRISES p 789
1900 E 64th St, Los Angeles CA 90001
Tel (323) 583-4061 SIC 3441 3444 6719

NEST PARENT INC p 1026
10877 Wilshire Blvd, Los Angeles CA 90024
Tel (310) 551-0101 SIC 6719

US MERCHANTS FINANCIAL GROUP INC p 1532
1118 S La Cienega Blvd, Los Angeles CA 90035
Tel (310) 855-1946 SIC 6719

YUCAIPA COMPANIES LLC p 1640
9130 W Sunset Blvd, Los Angeles CA 90069
Tel (310) 789-7200 SIC 8748 6719 6726

AEROSPACE PARTS HOLDINGS INC p 31
610 Nwport Ctr Dr Ste 950, Newport Beach CA 92660
Tel (949) 877-3630 SIC 6719

SYMPHONY TECHNOLOGY GROUP LLC p 1414
2475 Hanover St, Palo Alto CA 94304
Tel (650) 935-9500 SIC 8748 6719

CPL HOLDINGS LLC p 387
12181 Bluff Creek Dr # 250, Playa Vista CA 90094
Tel (310) 348-6800 SIC 5331 6719 5961

LEISURE SPORTS INC p 854
4670 Willow Rd Ste 100, Pleasanton CA 94588
Tel (925) 600-1966 SIC 6719

PARK WEST COMPANIES INC p 1116
22421 Gilberto Ste A, Rcho Sta Marg CA 92688
Tel (949) 546-8300 SIC 0782 1629 6719

BIOTIX HOLDINGS INC p 184
9880 Mesa Rim Rd, San Diego CA 92121
Tel (858) 875-7681 SIC 6719

SUNROAD HOLDING CORP p 1404
4445 Estgate Mall Ste 400, San Diego CA 92121
Tel (858) 362-8500 SIC 6719

HEALD CAPITAL LLC p 673
601 Montgomery St Fl 14, San Francisco CA 94111
Tel (415) 808-1400 SIC 6719

STEELRIVER INFRASTRUCTURE PARTNERS LP p 1384
1 Letterman Dr, San Francisco CA 94129
Tel (415) 512-1515 SIC 6719

SUNBEAM GP LLC p 1401
1 Maritime Plz, San Francisco CA 94111
Tel (615) 665-1283 SIC 6719

■ **EARTHBOUND HOLDINGS III LLC** p 469
1721 San Juan Hwy, San Juan Bautista CA 95045
Tel (831) 623-7880 SIC 0723 2099 6719

WH ACQUISITIONS INC p 1604
800 Concar Dr Ste 100, San Mateo CA 94402
Tel (650) 358-5000 SIC 5084 6719

ALLIED UNIVERSAL HOLDCO LLC p 57
1551 N Tustin Ave Ste 650, Santa Ana CA 92705
Tel (714) 619-9700 SIC 6719 7381

ALLIED UNIVERSAL TOPCO LLC p 57
1551 N Tustin Ave, Santa Ana CA 92705
Tel (714) 619-9700 SIC 6719 7381 7349

FREEDOM COMMUNICATIONS HOLDINGS INC p 576
625 N Grand Ave, Santa Ana CA 92701
Tel (714) 796-7000
SIC 6719 2711 4813 2721

KPC HEALTHCARE INC p 828
1301 N Tustin Ave, Santa Ana CA 92705
Tel (714) 953-3652 SIC 8062 6719

BUTLER AMERICA HOLDINGS INC p 230
3820 State St Ste A, Santa Barbara CA 93105
Tel (805) 884-9538 SIC 6719

MARVELL TECHNOLOGY GROUP LTD p 914
5488 Marvell Ln, Santa Clara CA 95054
Tel (408) 222-2500 *SIC* 6719

OOYALA HOLDINGS INC p 1089
4750 Patrick Henry Dr, Santa Clara CA 95054
Tel (650) 961-3400 *SIC* 7812 6719

FUTURIS GLOBAL HOLDINGS LLC p 586
233 Wilshire Blvd Ste 800, Santa Monica CA 90401
Tel (510) 771-2333 *SIC* 6719

BSI HOLDINGS INC p 222
2495 Uravan St, Aurora CO 80011
Tel (303) 371-2200
SIC 6719 3589 5093 3715 3823 5051

GRAEBEL HOLDINGS INC p 628
16346 Airport Cir, Aurora CO 80011
Tel (303) 214-6683 *SIC* 4213 4225 6719

■ BOULDER BRANDS INC p 204
1600 Pearl St Ste 300, Boulder CO 80302
Tel (303) 652-0521 *SIC* 2096 6719

CRAFTWORKS RESTAURANTS & BREWERIES GROUP INC p 388
8001 Arista Pl Unit 500, Broomfield CO 80021
Tel (623) 878-8822 *SIC* 6719

FIDELITY NEWPORT HOLDINGS LLC p 541
400 W 48th Ave, Denver CO 80216
Tel (303) 296-2121 *SIC* 5812 2051 6719

■ JANUS INTERNATIONAL HOLDING LLC p 778
151 Detroit St, Denver CO 80206
Tel (303) 333-3863 *SIC* 6719

OPTIV INC p 1090
1125 17th St Ste 1700, Denver CO 80202
Tel (303) 298-0600
SIC 5045 5065 6719 7381

VOICE MEDIA GROUP INC p 1564
969 N Broadway, Denver CO 80203
Tel (303) 296-7744 *SIC* 6719

■ GAMBRO INC p 590
9540 Maroon Cir Unit 400, Englewood CO 80112
Tel (800) 525-2623 *SIC* 6719

TERUMO BCT HOLDING CORP p 1440
10811 W Collins Ave, Lakewood CO 80215
Tel (303) 232-6800 *SIC* 3841 6719

GLOBAL EMPLOYMENT HOLDINGS INC p 616
10375 Park Meadows Dr # 475, Littleton CO 80124
Tel (303) 216-9500 *SIC* 7363 6719

LONGVIEW HOLDING CORP p 877
43 Arch St, Greenwich CT 06830
Tel (203) 869-6734 *SIC* 6719 1389

ROCKWOOD SERVICE CORP p 1245
43 Arch St, Greenwich CT 06830
Tel (203) 869-6734 *SIC* 6719

EASTERN OUTFITTERS LLC p 472
160 Corporate Ct, Meriden CT 06450
Tel (203) 235-5775 *SIC* 5611 6719

CRIUS ENERGY LLC p 393
535 Connecticut Ave # 400, Norwalk CT 06854
Tel (203) 663-5089 *SIC* 6719 1731

GALATA CHEMICALS HOLDING CO LLC p 589
464 Heritage Rd Ste 1, Southbury CT 06488
Tel (203) 236-9000 *SIC* 5169 6719

DMG INFORMATION INC p 446
46 Southfield Ave Ste 400, Stamford CT 06902
Tel (203) 973-2940 *SIC* 6719 1731 8748

■ GE CAPITAL INTERNATIONAL HOLDINGS CORP p 595
260 Long Ridge Rd, Stamford CT 06927
Tel (203) 357-4000 *SIC* 6719

LEGRAND HOLDING INC p 853
60 Woodlawn St, West Hartford CT 06110
Tel (860) 233-6251 *SIC* 3643 6719

■ CEHI ACQUISITION CORP p 272
61 Wilton Rd Ste 2, Westport CT 06880
Tel (203) 221-1703 *SIC* 4959 6719

LOUIS DREYFUS CO HOLDING INC p 879
40 Danbury Rd Ste 3, Wilton CT 06897
Tel (203) 761-2000 *SIC* 6719

ALSTOM INC p 61
200 Great Pond Dr, Windsor CT 06095
Tel (866) 257-8664 *SIC* 4911 6719

■ VOYA HOLDINGS INC p 1566
1 Orange Way, Windsor CT 06095
Tel (860) 580-4646 *SIC* 6719

QPS HOLDINGS LLC p 1195
3 Innovation Way Ste 240, Newark DE 19711
Tel (302) 369-5601 *SIC* 6719

■ ADP ATLANTIC LLC p 24
800 Delaware Ave Ste 601, Wilmington DE 19801
Tel (302) 657-4060 *SIC* 6719

■ CMH CAPITAL INC p 329
1105 N Market St Ste 1300, Wilmington DE 19801
Tel (302) 651-7947
SIC 6719 2451 6515 6311

■ ERI INVESTMENTS INC p 507
801 N West St Fl 2, Wilmington DE 19801
Tel (302) 656-8089 *SIC* 6719

EXCO INC p 517
1007 N Orange St, Wilmington DE 19801
Tel (905) 477-3065 *SIC* 6719

JUMIO HOLDINGS INC p 797
2711 Centerville Rd # 400, Wilmington DE 19808
Tel (650) 424-8545 *SIC* 6719 7371

LABWARE HOLDINGS INC p 836
3 Mill Rd Ste 102, Wilmington DE 19806
Tel (302) 658-8444 *SIC* 7371 7372 6719

■ PITNEY BOWES INTERNATIONAL HOLDINGS INC p 1152
801 N West St Fl 2, Wilmington DE 19801
Tel (302) 656-8595 *SIC* 6719

REED ELSEVIER US HOLDINGS INC p 1217
1105 N Market St Ste 501, Wilmington DE 19801
Tel (302) 427-2672
SIC 2721 7999 8748 6719

■ CARLYLE PARTNERS III LP p 258
1001 Penn Ave Nw Ste 220, Washington DC 20004
Tel (202) 347-2626 *SIC* 6719

MECCANICA HOLDINGS USA INC p 934
1625 I St Nw Fl 12, Washington DC 20006
Tel (202) 292-2620 *SIC* 6719

WINCHESTER ACQUISITION HOLDINGS CORP p 1614
1111 19th St Nw, Washington DC 20036
Tel (202) 463-4860 *SIC* 6719

ACCOUNTABLE HEALTHCARE HOLDINGS CORP p 15
999 Nw 51st St Ste 210, Boca Raton FL 33431
Tel (561) 235-7813 *SIC* 6719

GEO CORRECTIONS HOLDINGS INC p 605
1 Park Pl, Boca Raton FL 33487
Tel (432) 267-7911 *SIC* 6719

SUNTECK HOLDINGS LLC p 1405
6413 Congress Ave Ste 260, Boca Raton FL 33487
Tel (561) 988-9456 *SIC* 4731 6719

PODS HOLDINGS INC p 1159
5585 Rio Vista Dr, Clearwater FL 33760
Tel (727) 538-6300 *SIC* 6719

SHC HOLDING INC p 1313
311 Park Place Blvd, Clearwater FL 33759
Tel (727) 533-9700 *SIC* 6719

SUNCOAST CARING COMMUNITY INC p 1401
5771 Roosevelt Blvd, Clearwater FL 33760
Tel (727) 586-4432 *SIC* 6719

M & R HIGH POINT HOLDINGS INC p 889
402 High Point Dr Ste 101, Cocoa FL 32926
Tel (321) 631-0245 *SIC* 6719

ALVACO TRADING CO p 63
12301 Nw 39th St, Coral Springs FL 33065
Tel (800) 852-8089 *SIC* 6719

ALTADIS HOLDINGS USA INC p 61
5900 N Andrews Ave # 1100, Fort Lauderdale FL 33309
Tel (954) 772-9000 *SIC* 6719

RESORT MARKETING HOLDINGS INC p 1227
2419 E Commercial Blvd, Fort Lauderdale FL 33308
Tel (954) 630-9449 *SIC* 7011 6719

DIVERSIFIED SERVICE OPTIONS INC p 444
532 Riverside Ave, Jacksonville FL 32202
Tel (904) 791-6305 *SIC* 6719

FLORIDA EAST COAST HOLDINGS CORP p 558
7411 Fullerton St Ste 300, Jacksonville FL 32256
Tel (800) 342-1131 *SIC* 6719

D+H USA HOLDINGS INC p 407
605 Crescent Executive Ct # 600, Lake Mary FL 32746
Tel (407) 804-6600 *SIC* 6719

HIGH-TECH INSTITUTE HOLDINGS INC p 691
3383 N State Road 7, Lauderdale Lakes FL 33319
Tel (602) 328-2800 *SIC* 6719

ALL AMERICAN GROUP HOLDINGS LLC p 51
1450 Brickell Ave # 3100, Miami FL 33131
Tel (305) 379-2322 *SIC* 6719

BEST DOCTORS INSURANCE HOLDINGS LLC p 177
5201 Blue Lagoon Dr # 300, Miami FL 33126
Tel (305) 269-2521 *SIC* 8011 6719

■ SIMPLY HEALTHCARE HOLDINGS INC p 1325
9250 W Flagler St Ste 600, Miami FL 33174
Tel (877) 915-0551 *SIC* 6321 6719

COMPUPAY HOLDINGS CORP p 352
3450 Lakeside Dr Ste 400, Miramar FL 33027
Tel (469) 791-3300 *SIC* 6719

CNL FINANCIAL GROUP INC p 330
450 S Orange Ave Ste 300, Orlando FL 32801
Tel (407) 650-1000 *SIC* 6141 6719

■ KROGER SPECIALTY PHARMACY HOLDINGS I INC p 830
6435 Hazeltine National, Orlando FL 32822
Tel (626) 932-1600 *SIC* 6719

UNR HOLDINGS INC p 1528
301 E Pine St, Orlando FL 32801
Tel (407) 210-6541 *SIC* 6719

■ ADVANCED DISPOSAL SERVICES SOUTH LLC p 25
90 Fort Wade Rd Ste 200, Ponte Vedra FL 32081
Tel (904) 737-7900 *SIC* 4953 6719

CUNNINGHAM LINDSEY US INC p 401
3030 N Rocky Point Dr W # 530, Rocky Point FL 33607
Tel (813) 830-7100 *SIC* 6719

ANDERSON GROUP LLC p 90
111 2nd Ave Ne Ste 105, Saint Petersburg FL 33701
Tel (248) 645-8000 *SIC* 6799 6719

ALLIANCE ENTERTAINMENT HOLDING CORP p 54
1401 Nw 136th Ave Ste 100, Sunrise FL 33323
Tel (954) 255-4000 *SIC* 5199 6719

TEAM FOCUS INSURANCE GROUP LLC p 1429
1300 Sawgrs Corp Pkwy # 300, Sunrise FL 33323
Tel (954) 331-4800 *SIC* 6719 6411

■ KFORCE GOVERNMENT HOLDINGS INC p 816
1001 E Palm Ave, Tampa FL 33605
Tel (813) 552-5000 *SIC* 6719

TRIBRIDGE HOLDINGS LLC p 1479
4830 W Kennedy Blvd # 890, Tampa FL 33609
Tel (813) 287-8887 *SIC* 6719

■ MANITOWOC FOODSERVICE COMPANIES LLC p 902
2227 Welbilt Blvd, Trinity FL 34655
Tel (727) 375-7010 *SIC* 6719

COMVEST VELOCITY ACQUISITION I LLC p 354
525 Okeechobee Blvd # 1050, West Palm Beach FL 33401
Tel (561) 727-2000 *SIC* 6719

AGC AMERICA INC p 34
11175 Cicero Dr Ste 400, Alpharetta GA 30022
Tel (404) 446-4200
SIC 6719 3211 2869 5169 3229

AXIS SPECIALTY US HOLDINGS INC p 140
11680 Great Oaks Way # 500, Alpharetta GA 30022
Tel (678) 746-9000 *SIC* 6719

MAGNITUDE PARENT HOLDINGS LLC p 896
200 N Point Ctr E Ste 200, Alpharetta GA 30022
Tel (678) 323-2500 *SIC* 6719

GEORGIA-PACIFIC HOLDINGS LLC p 608
133 Peachtree St Ne # 4810, Atlanta GA 30303
Tel (404) 652-4000 *SIC* 6719

INTERRA GROUP INC p 757
400 Interstate N Pkwy Ste, Atlanta GA 30339
Tel (770) 612-8101 *SIC* 5141 6719

■ MEAD PACKAGING INTERNATIONAL INC p 933
3423 Piedmont Rd Ne, Atlanta GA 30305
Tel (404) 875-2711 *SIC* 6719

■ NATIONAL GENERAL LENDER SERVICES INC p 1012
210 Interstate N Pkwy, Atlanta GA 30339
Tel (770) 690-8400 *SIC* 6719

ROYAL CAPITAL CORP p 1254
255 E Paces Ferry Rd Ne # 300, Atlanta GA 30305
Tel (404) 239-0808 *SIC* 6719

SUN SUITES INTERESTS LLLP p 1400
4770 S Atlanta Rd Se, Atlanta GA 30339
Tel (404) 350-9990 *SIC* 6719

TIN LIZZYS CONSOLIDATED LLC p 1455
2030 Powers Ferry Rd Se, Atlanta GA 30339
Tel (678) 681-9503 *SIC* 6719

NRD HOLDINGS LLC p 1064
625 Dekalb Ste 100, Decatur GA 30033
Tel (404) 499-1960 *SIC* 6719

COLUMBIAN INTERNATIONAL CHEMICALS CORP p 342
1800 W Oak Commons Ct, Marietta GA 30062
Tel (770) 792-9400 *SIC* 6719

PEDIATRIC SERVICES HOLDING CORP p 1127
3720 Da Vinci Ct, Norcross GA 30092
Tel (770) 441-1580 *SIC* 8082 6719

TMX FINANCE HOLDINGS INC p 1458
15 Bull St Ste 200, Savannah GA 31401
Tel (912) 525-2675 *SIC* 6719

■ KOKO OHA INVESTMENTS INC p 826
1100 Alakea St Fl 8, Honolulu HI 96813
Tel (808) 535-5999 *SIC* 5172 6719

PT HOLDINGS LLC p 1189
1150 N Swift Rd Ste A, Addison IL 60101
Tel (800) 438-8898
SIC 5084 5046 7699 6719

BWAY INTERMEDIATE CO INC p 231
3 First National Plz, Chicago IL 60602
Tel (312) 895-1000 *SIC* 6719

COVERIS HOLDING CORP p 385
8600 W Bryn Mawr Ave, Chicago IL 60631
Tel (773) 877-3300 *SIC* 6719 2673 2631

CT TECHNOLOGIES HOLDINGS INC p 399
875 N Michigan Ave, Chicago IL 60611
Tel (770) 360-1700 *SIC* 6719

DRW HOLDINGS LLC p 457
540 W Madison St Ste 2500, Chicago IL 60661
Tel (312) 542-1000 *SIC* 6719

HOME PRODUCTS INTERNATIONAL INC p 703
4501 W 47th St, Chicago IL 60632
Tel (773) 890-1010 *SIC* 6719

ITR CONCESSION CO HOLDINGS LLC p 768
8801 S Anthony Ave, Chicago IL 60617
Tel (312) 552-7100 *SIC* 4785 6719

MADISON INDUSTRIES HOLDINGS LLC p 894
500 W Madison St Ste 3890, Chicago IL 60661
Tel (312) 277-0156
SIC 6719 5051 3443 3316

OXFORD CAPITAL GROUP LLC p 1101
350 W Hubbard St Ste 440, Chicago IL 60654
Tel (312) 755-9500 *SIC* 6719

OXFORD CAPITAL PARTNERS INC p 1101
350 W Hubbard St Ste 440, Chicago IL 60654
Tel (312) 755-9500 *SIC* 6719

PLS GROUP INC p 1156
1 S Wacker Dr Fl 36, Chicago IL 60606
Tel (312) 491-7300 *SIC* 6719

RIVERBED HOLDINGS INC p 1237
300 N La Salle Dr # 4350, Chicago IL 60654
Tel (312) 254-3300 *SIC* 6719

THYSSENKRUPP NORTH AMERICA INC p 1451
111 W Jackson Blvd # 2400, Chicago IL 60604
Tel (312) 525-2800 *SIC* 6719 3714

VPC PIZZA HOLDINGS LLC p 1566
227 W Monroe St, Chicago IL 60606
Tel (312) 701-1777 *SIC* 6719

STERIGENICS HOLDINGS LLC p 1386
3 Parkway N Ste 100n, Deerfield IL 60015
Tel (847) 607-6060 *SIC* 6719

NEOVIA LOGISTICS SERVICES LLC p 1026
2001 Bttrfeld Rd Ste 1400, Downers Grove IL 60515
Tel (469) 513-7000 *SIC* 6719

■ ATKORE INTERNATIONAL HOLDINGS INC p 125
16100 Lathrop Ave, Harvey IL 60426
Tel (708) 225-2051
SIC 6719 3441 1791 3446 3448 3496

■ SEARS HOLDINGS MANAGEMENT CORP p 1297
3333 Beverly Rd, Hoffman Estates IL 60179
Tel (847) 286-2500 *SIC* 6531 6719

CCBC INC p 269
1 Mi Jack Way, Homewood IL 60430
Tel (708) 206-0500 *SIC* 6719

GRABBER HOLDINGS LLC p 628
1 Dot Way, Mount Sterling IL 62353
Tel (217) 773-4411 *SIC* 5072 5211 6719

VIANT HOLDINGS INC p 1554
535 E Diehl Rd Ste 100, Naperville IL 60563
Tel (630) 649-5000 *SIC* 6719

GARVEY GROUP LLC p 593
7400 N Lehigh Ave, Niles IL 60714
Tel (847) 647-1900 *SIC* 6719

AMARI METALS EUROPE LTD p 64
555 Skokie Blvd Ste 555, Northbrook IL 60062
Tel (847) 480-4690 *SIC* 6719

HENLEY MANAGEMENT CO p 683
555 Skokie Blvd Ste 555, Northbrook IL 60062
Tel (847) 480-4690 *SIC* 6719

INLAND BANCORP INC p 743
2805 Butterfield Rd # 370, Oak Brook IL 60523
Tel (630) 218-8000 *SIC* 6719

PSI ACQUISITION INC p 1188
1901 S Meyers Rd Ste 400, Oakbrook Terrace IL 60181
Tel (630) 691-1490 *SIC* 6719

HELIX ACQUISITION HOLDINGS INC p 681
9501 Tech Blvd Ste 401, Rosemont IL 60018
Tel (847) 349-5760 *SIC* 6719

MW INDUSTRIES INC p 1004
9501 Tech Blvd Ste 401, Rosemont IL 60018
Tel (847) 349-5760 *SIC* 6719 5085

MWI HOLDINGS INC p 1004
9501 Tech Blvd Ste 401, Rosemont IL 60018
Tel (847) 349-5760 *SIC* 6719

ZURICH HOLDING CO OF AMERICA INC p 1645
1299 Zurich Way, Schaumburg IL 60196
Tel (847) 605-6000
SIC 6311 6331 6321 6324 6719

HEICO HOLDING INC p 680
27501 Bella Vista Pkwy, Warrenville IL 60555
Tel (630) 353-5000 *SIC* 6719

PETTIBONE LLC p 1140
27501 Bella Vista Pkwy, Warrenville IL 60555
Tel (630) 353-5000 *SIC* 6719

ARMOR PARENT CORP p 111
7140 Office Cir, Evansville IN 47715
Tel (812) 962-5000 *SIC* 6719

■ LUTHERAN HEALTH NETWORK OF INDIANA LLC p 886
2123 Lincolnway Ct, Fort Wayne IN 46819
Tel (260) 479-3550 *SIC* 6719

PHOENIX GROUP INC p 1145
164 S Park Blvd, Greenwood IN 46143
Tel (317) 884-3600 *SIC* 8742 6719

CENTAUR HOLDINGS LLC p 275
111 Monument Cir, Indianapolis IN 46204
Tel (317) 656-8787 *SIC* 6719

COUNTRYMARK COOPERATIVE HOLDING CORP p 375
225 S East St Ste 144, Indianapolis IN 46202
Tel (800) 808-3170
SIC 5172 2911 1382 1311 6719

LDI LTD LLC p 849
54 Monument Cir Ste 800, Indianapolis IN 46204
Tel (317) 237-5400 *SIC* 6719

MATERIALS PROCESSING INC p 919
3500 Depauw Blvd, Indianapolis IN 46268
Tel (317) 803-3010 *SIC* 6719

VERTELLUS SPECIALTIES HOLDINGS CORP p 1552
201 N Illinois St # 1800, Indianapolis IN 46204
Tel (317) 247-8141 *SIC* 2865 6719

■ VECTREN ENERGY SERVICES CORP p 1546
4655 Rosebud Ln, Newburgh IN 47630
Tel (812) 492-3723
SIC 8711 8742 8748 6719

KW SERVICES LLC p 832
3801 Voorde Dr Ste B, South Bend IN 46628
Tel (574) 232-2051 *SIC* 6719 1799 5063

METROGROUP HOLDING LLC p 955
1805 E Washington St, Mount Pleasant IA 52641
Tel (319) 385-5135 *SIC* 6719

EBY GROUP INC p 474
13795 S Mur Len Rd # 301, Olathe KS 66062
Tel (913) 782-3200 *SIC* 6719

QUALITY TECHNOLOGY SERVICES HOLDING LLC p 1197
12851 Foster St Ste 205, Overland Park KS 66213
Tel (913) 814-9988 *SIC* 6719

■ BEECHCRAFT HOLDINGS LLC p 168
10511 E Central Ave, Wichita KS 67206
Tel (316) 676-7111 *SIC* 3721 3728 6719

MVP HOLDINGS LLC p 1003
8301 E 21st St N Ste 370, Wichita KS 67206
Tel (316) 262-2819 *SIC* 6719

HOUCHENS INDUSTRIES INC p 711
700 Church St, Bowling Green KY 42101
Tel (270) 843-3252 *SIC* 6719

POMEROY GROUP HOLDINGS INC p 1160
1020 Petersburg Rd, Hebron KY 41048
Tel (859) 586-6000
SIC 7373 7374 7361 6719

LOGO HOLDINGS II CORP p 875
626 W Main St, Louisville KY 40202
Tel (502) 637-5443 *SIC* 6719 7336

SGS INTERNATIONAL LLC p 1310
626 W Main St Ste 500, Louisville KY 40202
Tel (502) 637-5443 *SIC* 6719

■ H&J CAPITAL LLC p 651
8485 Goodwood Blvd, Baton Rouge LA 70806
Tel (225) 926-2888 *SIC* 6719

LAITRAM LLC p 838
220 Laitram Ln, Harahan LA 70123
Tel (504) 733-6000
SIC 3535 3556 7359 3446 6719

ALL ABOARD AMERICA HOLDINGS INC p 50
2838 Touro St, New Orleans LA 70122
Tel (800) 356-6831
SIC 6719 4141 4131 4119 4111

CONNECTION EDUCATION INC p 357
1001 Fleet St Fl 5, Baltimore MD 21202
Tel (443) 529-1000 *SIC* 6719

M-L HOLDINGS CO p 890
4601 Washington Blvd, Baltimore MD 21227
Tel (410) 242-6500 *SIC* 5082 6719

■ CHEVY CHASE BANK FSB p 296
7501 Wisconsin Ave Fl 11, Bethesda MD 20814
Tel (240) 497-4101
SIC 6035 6411 6211 6519 6552 6719

PALISADES ASSOCIATES HOLDING INC p 1108
9140 Vendome Dr, Bethesda MD 20817
Tel (301) 469-7564 *SIC* 6719

SUMMIT HOLDING ONE CORP p 1399
10330 Old Columbia Rd, Columbia MD 21046
Tel (410) 312-6000 *SIC* 6719

GXS HOLDINGS INC p 649
100 Edison Park Dr, Gaithersburg MD 20878
Tel (301) 340-5370 *SIC* 6719

EULER HERMES ACI HOLDING INC p 512
800 Red Brook Blvd # 400, Owings Mills MD 21117
Tel (410) 753-0753 *SIC* 7322 6351 6719

REMEDI SENIORCARE HOLDING CORP p 1222
1 Olympic Pl Ste 600, Towson MD 21204
Tel (443) 927-8400 *SIC* 6719

CCC ACQUISITION HOLDINGS INC p 269
200 Clarendon St Ste 4000, Boston MA 02116
Tel (617) 516-2000 *SIC* 6719 2821

COMMUNITY INTERVENTION SERVICES INC p 349
500 Boylston St Ste 1350, Boston MA 02116
Tel (617) 262-8455 *SIC* 6719

CONNELL LIMITED PARTNERSHIP p 358
1 International Pl Fl 31, Boston MA 02110
Tel (617) 737-2700
SIC 3443 3444 3341 3544 6719

DOUBLE EAGLE PARENT INC p 452
75 State St Fl 29, Boston MA 02109
Tel (617) 951-0555 *SIC* 6719

RF1 HOLDING CO p 1231
400 Nickerson Rd, Marlborough MA 01752
Tel (855) 294-3800 *SIC* 3674 6719

HMG HOLDING CORP p 698
920 Winter St, Waltham MA 02451
Tel (781) 699-9000 *SIC* 8741 6719

MA INDUSTRIAL JV LLC p 891
5683 Hines Dr, Ann Arbor MI 48108
Tel (734) 585-9500 *SIC* 3585 3679 6719

NEAPCO HOLDINGS LLC p 1023
6735 Haggerty Rd, Belleville MI 48111
Tel (734) 447-1380
SIC 3568 3714 6719 6799

BELFOR HOLDINGS INC p 169
185 Oakland Ave Ste 300, Birmingham MI 48009
Tel (248) 594-1144 *SIC* 6719

GREEKTOWN SUPERHOLDINGS INC p 636
555 E Lafayette Blvd, Detroit MI 48226
Tel (313) 223-2999 *SIC* 6719

SOAVE ENTERPRISES LLC p 1336
3400 E Lafayette St, Detroit MI 48207
Tel (313) 567-7000 *SIC* 6719

EJ AMERICAS LLC p 482
301 Spring St, East Jordan MI 49727
Tel (231) 536-2261 *SIC* 6719 3321

H W KAUFMAN FINANCIAL GROUP INC p 651
30833 Northwestern Hwy, Farmington Hills MI 48334
Tel (248) 932-9000 *SIC* 6141 6719

VILLAGE GREEN HOLDING LLC p 1557
30833 Northwestern Hwy # 300, Farmington Hills MI 48334
Tel (248) 851-9600 *SIC* 6719

DAWN FOODS INC p 416
3333 Sargent Rd, Jackson MI 49201
Tel (517) 789-4400
SIC 2053 2045 3556 5046 6719

■ **MPS HOLDCO INC** p 995
5800 W Grand River Ave, Lansing MI 48906
Tel (517) 886-2526 *SIC* 6719

ROCK HOLDINGS INC p 1243
20555 Victor Pkwy, Livonia MI 48152
Tel (313) 373-7700 *SIC* 6719

■ **DOW CORNING SILICON ENERGY SYSTEMS INC** p 453
2200 Salzburg St, Midland MI 48640
Tel (989) 496-4000 *SIC* 6719

ADIENT HOLDING MEXICO LLC p 22
49200 Halyard Dr, Plymouth MI 48170
Tel (414) 220-8900 *SIC* 6719

ADIENT INC p 22
49200 Halyard Dr, Plymouth MI 48170
Tel (414) 220-8900 *SIC* 6719

A RAYMOND CORPORATE NORTH AMERICA INC p 6
2350 Austin Ave Ste 200, Rochester Hills MI 48309
Tel (248) 853-2500 *SIC* 5085 3469 6719

WABASH INTERMEDIATE HOLDING CORP p 1570
3155 W Big Beaver Rd # 209, Troy MI 48084
Tel (248) 220-5400 *SIC* 6719

MINNESOTA AVIATION LLC p 973
805 Enterprise Dr E Ste H, Belle Plaine MN 56011
Tel (651) 681-3900 *SIC* 6719

LTF HOLDINGS INC p 883
2902 Corporate Pl, Chanhassen MN 55317
Tel (952) 380-0303 *SIC* 6719

CERIDIAN HCM HOLDING INC p 283
3311 E Old Shakopee Rd, Minneapolis MN 55425
Tel (952) 853-8100 *SIC* 6719 7374

MMIC GROUP INC p 979
7701 France Ave S Ste 500, Minneapolis MN 55435
Tel (952) 838-6700 *SIC* 6719

■ **VISANT HOLDING CORP** p 1561
3601 Minnesota Dr Ste 400, Minneapolis MN 55435
Tel (914) 595-8200
SIC 2741 2759 3911 6719

■ **MFI HOLDING CORP** p 958
301 Carlson Pkwy Ste 400, Minnetonka MN 55305
Tel (952) 258-4000 *SIC* 6719 0252

■ **MICHAEL FOODS GROUP INC** p 960
301 Carlson Pkwy Ste 400, Minnetonka MN 55305
Tel (952) 258-4000
SIC 0252 2015 5144 5143 5148 6719

J & B GROUP INC p 769
13200 43rd St Ne, Saint Michael MN 55376
Tel (763) 497-3913 *SIC* 6719 5963

ROSENBAUER MOTORS LLC p 1251
5181 260th St, Wyoming MN 55092
Tel (651) 408-9304 *SIC* 6719

HOOD COMPANIES INC p 705
623 N Main St Ste 300, Hattiesburg MS 39401
Tel (601) 582-1545 *SIC* 3086 2952 6719

DEWEY CORP p 434
5500 Highway 80 W, Jackson MS 39209
Tel (601) 922-8331 *SIC* 4213 6719

PROGRESSIVE PIPELINE HOLDINGS LLC p 1182
12340 Oitman Meridian Hwy, Meridian MS 39301
Tel (601) 693-8777 *SIC* 6719 1623

PRETIUM HOLDING LLC p 1173
15450 South Outer 40 Rd, Chesterfield MO 63017
Tel (314) 727-8200 *SIC* 6719

RHC HOLDING CORP p 1231
281 Lotus Dr, Jackson MO 63755
Tel (573) 204-0373 *SIC* 6719

INERGY HOLDINGS LP p 740
2 Brush Creek Blvd # 200, Kansas City MO 64112
Tel (816) 842-8181 *SIC* 5172 6719

KCS HOLDINGS LLC p 806
8001 Nw 106th St, Kansas City MO 64153
Tel (515) 266-4100 *SIC* 6719

NIDEC AMERICAS HOLDING CORP p 1043
8050 W Florissant Ave, Saint Louis MO 63136
Tel (314) 595-8000 *SIC* 3625 3594 6719

PEABODY HOLDING CO LLC p 1125
701 Market St Ste 700, Saint Louis MO 63101
Tel (314) 342-3400
SIC 1221 1222 5052 2873 6719

▲ **STIFEL FINANCIAL CORP** p 1389
501 N Broadway, Saint Louis MO 63102
Tel (314) 342-2000 *SIC* 6211 6719

TIERPOINT SPOKANE ONE & TWO LLC p 1453
520 Maryville Centre Dr, Saint Louis MO 63141
Tel (314) 315-9372 *SIC* 6719

VJCS HOLDINGS INC p 1563
8515 Page Ave, Saint Louis MO 63114
Tel (314) 427-1000 *SIC* 6719 2844

WATLOW ELECTRIC MANUFACTURING HOLDINGS CO p 1582
12001 Lackland Rd, Saint Louis MO 63146
Tel (314) 878-4600 *SIC* 6719

WATERLOO HOLDINGS INC p 1582
1500 Waterloo Dr, Sedalia MO 65301
Tel (660) 826-0960 *SIC* 3429 6719

WATERLOO HOLDINGS LLC p 1582
1500 Waterloo Dr, Sedalia MO 65301
Tel (660) 826-0960 *SIC* 6719

PROVIDENCE CORP p 1185
500 W Broadway St, Missoula MT 59802
Tel (406) 543-7271 *SIC* 6719

MEAD HOLDING CO INC p 933
2218 11th St, Columbus NE 68601
Tel (402) 564-5225 *SIC* 6719 5211

NBC HOLDINGS CORP p 1021
4700 S 19th St, Lincoln NE 68512
Tel (402) 421-7300 *SIC* 5192 6719

NEBRASKA BOOK HOLDINGS INC p 1023
4700 S 19th St, Lincoln NE 68512
Tel (402) 421-0500
SIC 6719 5942 5192 5961

NEBRASKA BOOK INTERMEDIATE HOLDINGS INC p 1023
4701 S 19th St, Lincoln NE 68512
Tel (402) 421-7300
SIC 6719 5942 5192 5961

■ **ASPEN HOLDINGS INC** p 118
222 S 15th St Ste 1500n, Omaha NE 68102
Tel (402) 926-0099 *SIC* 6719

FASTENER HOLDINGS INC p 531
10840 Harney St, Omaha NE 68154
Tel (402) 593-5300 *SIC* 6719

GAVILON HOLDINGS LLC p 594
1331 Capitol Ave, Omaha NE 68102
Tel (402) 889-4000 *SIC* 6719

SKO GROUP HOLDING LLC p 1330
8800 F St, Omaha NE 68127
Tel (920) 429-2211 *SIC* 6719

CITY CENTER HOLDINGS LLC p 312
3950 Las Vegas Blvd S, Las Vegas NV 89119
Tel (702) 632-9800 *SIC* 6719

T H ONE INC p 1419
3773 Howard Hughes Pkwy 350n, Las Vegas NV 89169
Tel (702) 734-3700 *SIC* 6719

XPRESS HOLDINGS INC p 1633
3993 Howard Hughes Pkwy # 250, Las Vegas NV 89169
Tel (702) 866-6001 *SIC* 6719 4213

ST JOSEPHS HOSPITAL CORPORATE SERVICES p 1369
172 Kinsley St, Nashua NH 03060
Tel (603) 882-3000 *SIC* 6719

EMR (USA HOLDINGS) INC p 495
143 Harding Ave Ste 1, Bellmawr NJ 08031
Tel (856) 365-7500 *SIC* 6719

UNION GRAPHICS INC p 1504
350 Michele Pl, Carlstadt NJ 07072
Tel (201) 372-1000 *SIC* 6719

PAPPAS LASSONDE HOLDINGS INC p 1112
1 Collins Dr Ste 200, Carneys Point NJ 08069
Tel (856) 455-1000 *SIC* 2033 6719

TRIDEC AQUISITION CO INC p 1479
800 Federal Blvd, Carteret NJ 07008
Tel (732) 750-9000 *SIC* 6719

EUROHEALTH (USA) INC p 512
401 Industrial Way W, Eatontown NJ 07724
Tel (732) 542-1191 *SIC* 6719

SPENCER SPIRIT HOLDINGS INC p 1358
6826 Black Horse Pike, Egg Harbor Township NJ 08234
Tel (609) 645-3300 *SIC* 5699 6719

CHRIST HOSPITAL HEALTH SERVICES CORP p 302
176 Palisade Ave, Jersey City NJ 07306
Tel (201) 795-8200 *SIC* 6719

ST GEORGE WAREHOUSE OF DELAWARE INC p 1367
5 Logistics Dr, Kearny NJ 07032
Tel (973) 578-8400 *SIC* 6719

VERITEXT LEGAL SOLUTIONS p 1550
290 W Mount Pleasant Ave, Livingston NJ 07039
Tel (973) 410-4040 *SIC* 6719 7338

HEALTHSTAR COMMUNICATIONS INC p 678
1000 Wyckoff Ave Ste 202, Mahwah NJ 07430
Tel (201) 560-5370 *SIC* 7372 7311 6719

SUEZ WATER INC p 1396
461 From Rd Ste 400, Paramus NJ 07652
Tel (201) 767-9300 *SIC* 6719 4941 4952

CHEMTRADE GCC HOLDING CO p 293
90 E Halsey Rd, Parsippany NJ 07054
Tel (973) 515-0900 *SIC* 6719 2819

FARREN INTERNATIONAL LLC p 530
1578 Sussex Tpke, Randolph NJ 07869
Tel (800) 253-3203 *SIC* 4213 1796 6719

WARNER CHILCOTT CORP p 1576
100 Enterprise Dr Ste 280, Rockaway NJ 07866
Tel (862) 261-7000 *SIC* 2834 6719

SGS US HOLDING INC p 1310
201 Route 17, Rutherford NJ 07070
Tel (201) 508-3000 *SIC* 8734 6719 7389

■ **BED N BATH STORES INC** p 167
650 Liberty Ave Ste 2, Union NJ 07083
Tel (908) 688-0888 *SIC* 6719

ARA HOLDINGS INC p 102
4300 San Mateo Blvd Ne, Albuquerque NM 87110
Tel (505) 881-8074 *SIC* 6719

ACOMA BUSINESS ENTERPRISES p 18
I 40 Exit 102, Pueblo Of Acoma NM 87034
Tel (888) 759-2489 *SIC* 6719 5154

BBHI HOLDINGS LLC p 163
1111 Stewart Ave, Bethpage NY 11714
Tel (516) 803-2300 *SIC* 6719

VWRE HOLDINGS INC p 1567
105 Orville Dr, Bohemia NY 11716
Tel (631) 567-9500 *SIC* 6719 5499

GRAPHIC CONTROLS HOLDINGS INC p 631
400 Exchange St, Buffalo NY 14204
Tel (716) 853-7500 *SIC* 2752 2679 6719

KNIA HOLDINGS INC p 824
110 Hopkins St, Buffalo NY 14220
Tel (914) 241-7430 *SIC* 6719

PII HOLDINGS INC p 1147
2150 Elmwood Ave, Buffalo NY 14207
Tel (716) 876-9951 *SIC* 3089 3822 6719

MARIETTA HOLDING CORP INC p 906
37 Huntington St, Cortland NY 13045
Tel (607) 753-6746 *SIC* 6719 2841

ADECCO INC p 22
175 Broadhollow Rd # 200, Melville NY 11747
Tel (631) 391-5776 *SIC* 6719

KPLT HOLDINGS INC p 828
111 Radio Circle Dr, Mount Kisco NY 10549
Tel (914) 241-7430 *SIC* 6719

AFI PARTNERS LLC p 33
158 Mercer St Frnt 2, New York NY 10012
Tel (212) 938-0016 *SIC* 6719

▲ **ALJ REGIONAL HOLDINGS INC** p 50
244 Madison Ave, New York NY 10016
Tel (212) 883-0083 *SIC* 6719

ASP BLADE INTERMEDIATE HOLDINGS INC p 118
299 Park Ave Fl 34, New York NY 10171
Tel (212) 476-8000 *SIC* 3531 3523 6719

■ **BLACKSTONE CAPITAL PARTNERS V LP** p 188
345 Park Ave, New York NY 10154
Tel (212) 583-5000 *SIC* 6719

C V STARR & CO INC p 233
90 Park Ave Fl 7, New York NY 10016
Tel (212) 230-5050 *SIC* 6719

CALCEUS TOPCO INC p 238
601 Lexington Ave, New York NY 10022
Tel (212) 753-6300 *SIC* 6719

CALCEUS TOPCO LP p 238
601 Lexington Ave, New York NY 10022
Tel (212) 753-6300 *SIC* 6719

CANADIAN IMPERIAL HOLDINGS INC p 246
425 Lexington Ave Bsmt C2, New York NY 10017
Tel (212) 856-4000 *SIC* 6719

CASTLE HARLAN PARTNERS IV LP p 264
150 E 58th St Fl 38, New York NY 10155
Tel (212) 644-8600 *SIC* 6799 6719

CLAYTON DUBILIER & RICE LLC p 323
375 Park Ave Fl 18, New York NY 10152
Tel (212) 407-5200 *SIC* 6719 6726 6211

CLOTHESLINE HOLDINGS INC p 327
399 Park Ave Fl 15, New York NY 10022
Tel (212) 607-8450 *SIC* 6719

COLUMBIA LAKE ACQUISITION HOLDINGS INC p 341
9 W 57th St Fl 43, New York NY 10019
Tel (212) 515-3450 *SIC* 6719

CORPORATE RISK HOLDINGS LLC p 372
600 3rd Ave Fl 4, New York NY 10016
Tel (212) 896-2001
SIC 6719 8748 7375 7389

DAKOTA PARENT INC p 409
9 W 57th St Fl 43, New York NY 10019
Tel (212) 515-3200 *SIC* 6719

DAYCO GLOBAL HOLDING CORP p 417
111 8th Ave, New York NY 10011
Tel (716) 689-4972 *SIC* 6719

EUROMONEY US HOLDINGS LP p 512
225 Park Ave S Fl 7, New York NY 10003
Tel (212) 224-3300 *SIC* 6719

HMAN INTERMEDIATE HOLDINGS CORP p 697
245 Park Ave Fl 16, New York NY 10167
Tel (513) 851-4900 *SIC* 6719 5072 7699

HUDSON LEASECO LLC p 716
356 W 58th St, New York NY 10019
Tel (212) 247-2353 *SIC* 6719

■ **INTERFINANCIAL INC** p 752
28 Liberty St Fl 41, New York NY 10005
Tel (212) 859-7000 *SIC* 6719

INTERSECTION MEDIA HOLDINGS INC p 757
10 Hudson Yards Fl 26, New York NY 10001
Tel (212) 644-6200 *SIC* 7312 6719

KPI CAPITAL HOLDINGS INC p 828
437 Madison Ave Fl 36, New York NY 10022
Tel (479) 443-1455 *SIC* 6719 3363 3312

KPI HOLDINGS INC p 828
437 Madison Ave Fl 36, New York NY 10022
Tel (479) 443-1455 *SIC* 6719 3363 3312

■ **NATIONAL HOLDINGS CORP** p 1013
410 Park Ave Fl 14, New York NY 10022
Tel (212) 417-8000 *SIC* 6719

■ **PARAMOUNT COMMUNICATIONS ACQUISITION CORP** p 1114
1515 Broadway Lbby, New York NY 10036
Tel (212) 258-6000 *SIC* 6719

PATRIOT INTERMEDIATE HOLDINGS B CORP p 1120
340 Madison Ave, New York NY 10173
Tel (212) 301-4000 *SIC* 6719

PLUS ONE HOLDINGS INC p 1157
77 Water St Fl 15, New York NY 10005
Tel (212) 269-2896 *SIC* 6719

SCHRODER US HOLDINGS INC p 1290
875 3rd Ave Fl 21, New York NY 10022
Tel (212) 641-3800
SIC 6282 6719 6211 6799

SENECA MORTGAGE INVESTMENTS LP p 1303
375 Park Ave Ste 3401, New York NY 10152
Tel (888) 601-6718 *SIC* 6799 6719

■ **SPF HOLDINGS II LLC** p 1358
9 W 57th St Ste 4200, New York NY 10019
Tel (212) 750-8300
SIC 2033 5149 6719 2099

SWISS POST US HOLDINGS INC p 1412
10 E 40th St Fl 9, New York NY 10016
Tel (212) 204-0900 *SIC* 6719

TRIANGLE PRIVATE HOLDINGS I LLC p 1478
601 Lexington Ave Fl 59, New York NY 10022
Tel (212) 231-0095 *SIC* 6719

■ **WHITEHALL STREET INTERNATIONAL REAL ESTATE LIMITED PARTNERSHIP 2001** p 1606
85 Broad St, New York NY 10004
Tel (212) 902-1000 *SIC* 6719

WLR RECOVERY ASSOCIATES II LLC p 1620
1166 Ave Of The Americas, New York NY 10036
Tel (212) 826-1100 *SIC* 6719

WLR RECOVERY FUND II LP p 1620
1166 6th Ave, New York NY 10036
Tel (212) 278-9821 *SIC* 6719 3714

INTEGRAMED HOLDING CORP p 749
2 Manhattanville Rd, Purchase NY 10577
Tel (914) 253-8000 *SIC* 6719

GLICK LLC p 615
415 W Main St, Rochester NY 14608
Tel (716) 235-1595 *SIC* 6719

PALMER FAMILY OF COMPANIES INC p 1109
900 Jefferson Rd Ste 1000, Rochester NY 14623
Tel (585) 424-3210 *SIC* 6719

NOCO INC p 1046
2440 Sheridan Dr Ste 202, Tonawanda NY 14150
Tel (716) 833-6626
SIC 2992 6719 5172 4924

U C A HOLDINGS INC p 1497
1 W Pack Sq Ste 305, Asheville NC 28801
Tel (828) 210-8120 *SIC* 6719

GK HOLDINGS INC p 613
9000 Regency Pkwy Ste 500, Cary NC 27518
Tel (800) 268-7737 *SIC* 6719

POSITEC TOOL CORP p 1163
10130 Perimeter Pkwy # 300, Charlotte NC 28216
Tel (704) 599-3711 *SIC* 5072 6719

URGENT CARES OF AMERICA HOLDINGS LLC p 1530
935 Shotwell Rd Ste 108, Clayton NC 27520
Tel (919) 550-0821 *SIC* 6719 8011

S&D COFFEE HOLDING CO p 1263
300 Concord Pkwy S, Concord NC 28027
Tel (704) 782-3121
SIC 6719 2095 5149 2086

CONSTELLIS HOLDINGS LLC p 361
850 Puddin Ridge Rd, Moyock NC 27958
Tel (252) 435-2488 *SIC* 6719

PORT CITY JAVA INC p 1162
101 Portwatch Way, Wilmington NC 28412
Tel (910) 796-6646 *SIC* 6719

A T WILLIAMS OIL CO p 6
5446 University Pkwy, Winston Salem NC 27105
Tel (336) 767-9883 *SIC* 6719

SHAZZAM INC p 1313
1001 25th St N, Fargo ND 58102
Tel (701) 237-3330 *SIC* 6719

■ **VARISTAR CORP** p 1545
4334 18th Ave S Ste 200, Fargo ND 58103
Tel (701) 232-6414
SIC 6719 4899 1623 5047 1731 4213

BETCO CORP p 177
400 Van Camp Rd, Bowling Green OH 43402
Tel (419) 241-2156 *SIC* 6719

HEXPOL HOLDING INC p 688
14330 Kinsman Rd, Burton OH 44021
Tel (440) 834-4644 *SIC* 6719

AMPAC HOLDINGS LLC p 86
12025 Tricon Rd, Cincinnati OH 45246
Tel (513) 671-1777
SIC 2673 2677 3081 2674 6719

CNG HOLDINGS INC p 330
7755 Montgomery Rd # 400, Cincinnati OH 45236
Tel (513) 336-7735 *SIC* 6719

■ **GREAT AMERICAN HOLDING INC** p 633
301 E 4th St, Cincinnati OH 45202
Tel (513) 369-3000 *SIC* 6719

HMAN GROUP HOLDINGS INC p 697
10590 Hamilton Ave, Cincinnati OH 45231
Tel (513) 851-4900 *SIC* 6719 5072 7699

■ **HEXION HOLDINGS LLC** p 688
180 E Broad St, Columbus OH 43215
Tel (614) 225-4000 *SIC* 6719

IBP CORP HOLDINGS INC p 726
495 S High St Ste 50, Columbus OH 43215
Tel (614) 692-6360 *SIC* 1742 6719

NEW SBARRO INTERMEDIATE HOLDINGS INC p 1033
1328 Dublin Rd, Columbus OH 43215
Tel (614) 769-9911 *SIC* 6719

DAYTON LAMINA CORP p 417
500 Progress Rd, Dayton OH 45449
Tel (937) 859-5111 *SIC* 3544 6719

DRT HOLDINGS INC p 457
618 Greenmount Blvd, Dayton OH 45419
Tel (937) 298-7391 *SIC* 6719

LION GROUP INC p 869
7200 Poe Ave Ste 400, Dayton OH 45414
Tel (937) 898-1949 SIC 6719

MISUMI INVESTMENT USA CORP p 976
500 Progress Rd, Dayton OH 45449
Tel (937) 859-5111 SIC 6719 3544

■ **CITADEL PLASTICS HOLDINGS INC** p 309
3637 Ridgewood Rd, Fairlawn OH 44333
Tel (330) 666-3751 SIC 6719

MMH AMERICAS INC p 979
4401 Gateway Blvd, Springfield OH 45502
Tel (414) 764-6200 SIC 3536 5084 6719

■ **AKRON BRASS HOLDING CORP** p 42
343 Venture Blvd, Wooster OH 44691
Tel (330) 264-5678 SIC 3647 3699 6719

CHICKASAW NATION INDUSTRIES INC p 298
2600 John Saxon Blvd # 100, Norman OK 73071
Tel (405) 253-8200 SIC 6719

ASCENT RESOURCES LLC p 116
3501 Nw 63rd St, Oklahoma City OK 73116
Tel (405) 608-5544 SIC 1382 6719

MAXCESS INTERNATIONAL CORP p 922
222 W Memorial Rd, Oklahoma City OK 73114
Tel (405) 755-1600 SIC 3554 3565 6719

MAXCESS INTERNATIONAL HOLDING CORP p 922
222 W Memorial Rd, Oklahoma City OK 73114
Tel (405) 755-1600 SIC 3554 3565 6719

AJINOMOTO NORTH AMERICA HOLDINGS INC p 41
7124 N Marine Dr, Portland OR 97203
Tel (503) 505-5783
SIC 5142 6719 2038 2037

NATIONWIDE LIFE INSURANCE CO OF AMERICA p 1018
1000 Chesterbrook Blvd, Berwyn PA 19312
Tel (610) 407-1717 SIC 6411 6211 6719

B BRAUN OF AMERICA INC p 141
824 12th Ave, Bethlehem PA 18018
Tel (610) 691-5400 SIC 6719 3841

RC LONESTAR INC p 1212
100 Brodhead Rd Ste 230, Bethlehem PA 18017
Tel (610) 882-5000 SIC 6719

SERVICE ELECTRIC CABLE TV INC p 1307
2200 Avenue A Ste 101, Bethlehem PA 18017
Tel (610) 865-9100 SIC 4841 6719

PRIMETALS TECHNOLOGIES USA HOLDINGS INC p 1175
501 Technology Dr, Canonsburg PA 15317
Tel (724) 514-8500 SIC 5084 6719

DFI HOLDINGS LLC p 435
3179 Deer Creek Rd, Collegeville PA 19426
Tel (610) 584-5836 SIC 6719

NEH INC p 1024
Airport Ofc Pk Bl 2 400 R, Coraopolis PA 15108
Tel (412) 299-7200 SIC 3313 6719

CONSOLIDATED GLASS HOLDINGS INC p 359
500 Grant Ave Ste 201, East Butler PA 16029
Tel (866) 412-6977
SIC 5039 3211 6719 1793

GAMESA TECHNOLOGY CORP INC p 590
1150 Northbrook Dr # 300, Feasterville Trevose PA 19053
Tel (215) 710-3100 SIC 6719 3621

■ **KENNAMETAL HOLDINGS EUROPE INC** p 810
1600 Technology Way, Latrobe PA 15650
Tel (724) 539-5000 SIC 6719

QMES LLC p 1195
122 Mill Rd Ste A130, Phoenixville PA 19460
Tel (610) 630-6357 SIC 5047 6719

DQE HOLDINGS LLC p 454
411 7th Ave Ste 3, Pittsburgh PA 15219
Tel (412) 393-7100 SIC 6719

PREFERRED SANDS LLC p 1169
1 Radnor Corp Ctr 1-101, Radnor PA 19087
Tel (610) 834-1969 SIC 6719

QLIK PARENT INC p 1195
150 N Radnor Chester Rd, Radnor PA 19087
Tel (888) 828-9768 SIC 6719 7371

M&Q HOLDINGS LLC p 890
3 Earl Ave, Schuylkill Haven PA 17972
Tel (570) 385-4991 SIC 3089 6719

LUBE HOLDINGS INC p 883
101 Chestnut Ave, Sharon PA 16146
Tel (724) 981-3123 SIC 6719

RHODES HOLDCO INC p 1232
800 Commonwealth Dr # 100, Warrendale PA 15086
Tel (724) 776-9780 SIC 6719

■ **SIGNAL HOLDINGS LLC** p 1322
676 E Swedesford Rd # 300, Wayne PA 19087
Tel (610) 341-1300 SIC 6719

■ **SYNTHES INC** p 1416
1302 Wrights Ln E, West Chester PA 19380
Tel (610) 647-9700 SIC 3841 3842 6719

ATHENE ANNUITY & LIFE ASSURANCE CO p 124
2000 Wade Hampton Blvd, Greenville SC 29615
Tel (864) 609-1000 SIC 6719

LOUIS BERGER SERVICES INC p 879
80 International Dr # 130, Greenville SC 29615
Tel (864) 385-7500 SIC 6719

RANGER AEROSPACE LLC p 1208
128 Millport Cir Ste 200, Greenville SC 29607
Tel (864) 329-9000 SIC 6719

COVERIS KEY HOLDINGS LLC p 385
345 Cedar Springs Ave, Spartanburg SC 29302
Tel (864) 596-7300 SIC 2673 2631 6719

NORTHERN GROWERS LLC p 1056
48416 144th St, Big Stone City SD 57216
Tel (605) 862-7902 SIC 6719

CAPELLA HOLDINGS INC p 248
103 Continental Pl # 200, Brentwood TN 37027
Tel (615) 844-9800 SIC 8062 6719

PROPEX HOLDING LLC p 1184
1110 Market St Ste 300, Chattanooga TN 37402
Tel (800) 621-1273
SIC 6719 2221 2297 2262 2211

DYK AUTOMOTIVE LLC p 464
1900 Exeter Rd Ste 200, Germantown TN 38138
Tel (763) 478-2360 SIC 6719

ARS INVESTMENT HOLDINGS LLC p 113
965 Ridge Lake Blvd # 201, Memphis TN 38120
Tel (901) 271-9700 SIC 6719

BRYCE CORP p 221
4505 Old Lamar Ave, Memphis TN 38118
Tel (901) 369-4400 SIC 6719

■ **CDRSVM HOLDING LLC** p 271
860 Ridge Lake Blvd, Memphis TN 38120
Tel (901) 597-1400 SIC 6719

SEDGWICK CMS HOLDINGS INC p 1300
1100 Ridgeway Loop Rd # 200, Memphis TN 38120
Tel (901) 415-7400 SIC 6719

TRUGREEN HOLDING CORP p 1486
1790 Kirby Pkwy Ste 300, Memphis TN 38138
Tel (901) 251-4002 SIC 0782 6719

ARIZONA II MERGER CORP p 109
15 Burton Hills Blvd, Nashville TN 37215
Tel (615) 665-1283 SIC 6719

■ **ELARA HOLDINGS INC** p 483
1281 Murfreesboro Pike, Nashville TN 37217
Tel (615) 366-3723 SIC 6719

NORTH AMERICAN STAMPING GROUP LLC p 1050
119 Kirby Dr, Portland TN 37148
Tel (615) 323-0500 SIC 3469 6719

UANT VENTURES LLP p 1498
612 E Lamar Blvd Ste 700, Arlington TX 76011
Tel (817) 543-4905 SIC 6719

CRCI HOLDINGS INC p 390
4301 Westbank Dr A-250, Austin TX 78746
Tel (512) 327-9200 SIC 6719

ROC HOLDINGS LLC p 1242
191 Energy Way, Bridgeport TX 76426
Tel (940) 683-0159 SIC 1794 1731 6719

HILITE INDUSTRIES INC p 692
1671 S Broadway St, Carrollton TX 75006
Tel (972) 242-2116 SIC 6719

TRAFIGURA CORPUS CHRISTI HOLDINGS INC p 1469
7002 Marvin L Berry Rd, Corpus Christi TX 78409
Tel (361) 884-4000 SIC 6719

ALLFLEX USA INC p 53
2805 E 14th St, Dallas TX 75261
Tel (972) 456-3686 SIC 6719

DATASPAN HOLDINGS INC p 414
1245 Viceroy Dr, Dallas TX 75247
Tel (214) 905-1882 SIC 6719 7375

■ **DEAN DAIRY HOLDINGS LLC** p 420
2515 Mckinney Ave # 1100, Dallas TX 75201
Tel (214) 303-3400 SIC 6719 2026

EMR GOLD RECYCLING LLC p 495
4305 S Lamar St, Dallas TX 75215
Tel (214) 421-0247 SIC 5093 6719

GENERAL HEALTH SERVICES CORP p 601
7515 Grnvlle Ave Ste 1000, Dallas TX 75231
Tel (214) 345-8345 SIC 6719

GOLDS HOLDING CORP p 622
4001 Maple Ave Ste 200, Dallas TX 75219
Tel (214) 574-4653 SIC 6719

JBRE HOLDINGS LLC p 779
8150 N Central Expy, Dallas TX 75206
Tel (214) 276-5504 SIC 7539 6719

■ **PIM HIGHLAND HOLDING LLC** p 1148
14185 Dallas Pkwy # 1100, Dallas TX 75254
Tel (972) 778-9452 SIC 6719

SUPERMEDIA LLC p 1407
2200 W Airfield Dr, Dfw Airport TX 75261
Tel (972) 453-7000 SIC 2741 6719

NOVA USA INC p 1062
500 W Overland Ave # 300, El Paso TX 79901
Tel (915) 594-1618 SIC 6719

VARSITY BRANDS HOLDING CO INC p 1545
1901 Diplomat Dr, Farmers Branch TX 75234
Tel (972) 406-7162 SIC 5091 7299 6719

CARLILE BANCSHARES INC p 257
201 Main St Ste 1320, Fort Worth TX 76102
Tel (817) 877-4440 SIC 6719

EIGER HOLDCO LLC p 481
301 Commerce St Ste 1600, Fort Worth TX 76102
Tel (817) 332-3235 SIC 6719

TPG CAPITAL MANAGEMENT LP p 1467
301 Commerce St Ste 3300, Fort Worth TX 76102
Tel (817) 871-4000
SIC 6726 3674 6799 3993 6719

SES HOLDINGS LLC p 1308
114 E Foreline St, Gainesville TX 76240
Tel (940) 668-0251 SIC 6719 5084

INTEGRACARE HOLDINGS INC p 748
2559 Sw Grapevine Pkwy, Grapevine TX 76051
Tel (817) 310-4999 SIC 6719

VALLEY BAPTIST HEALTH SYSTEM p 1540
2101 Pease St, Harlingen TX 78550
Tel (956) 389-1100 SIC 6719

AMERICAN AIR LIQUIDE HOLDINGS INC p 67
2700 Post Oak Blvd, Houston TX 77056
Tel (713) 624-8000 SIC 2813 6719

ASPIRE HOLDINGS LLC p 118
811 Main St Ste 2100, Houston TX 77002
Tel (713) 307-8700 SIC 6719

BRACE INC p 206
14950 Heathrow Forest Pkw, Houston TX 77032
Tel (281) 749-1020 SIC 6719

■ **BUCKEYE TEXAS PARTNERS HOLDINGS LLC** p 223
1 Greenway Plz Ste 600, Houston TX 77046
Tel (832) 615-8600 SIC 6719

■ **BUCKEYE TEXAS PARTNERS LLC** p 223
1 Greenway Plz Ste 600, Houston TX 77046
Tel (832) 615-8600 SIC 6719 4491

CJ HOLDING CO p 320
3990 Rogerdale Rd, Houston TX 77042
Tel (713) 325-6086 SIC 6719

■ **EL PASO HOLDCO LLC** p 483
1001 Louisiana St, Houston TX 77002
Tel (713) 420-2600 SIC 6719

FRAMEWORK CAPITAL PARTNERS LLC p 573
1700 Post Oak Blvd, Houston TX 77056
Tel (713) 826-9351 SIC 6719

GSE HOLDING INC p 643
19103 Gundle Rd, Houston TX 77073
Tel (281) 443-8564 SIC 3081 6719

PARK PLAZA HOSPITAL p 1115
5209 Chenevert St, Houston TX 77004
Tel (713) 527-5000 SIC 6719

RELIANCE HOLDING USA INC p 1221
2000 W Sam Houston Pkwy S # 700, Houston TX 77042
Tel (713) 430-8700 SIC 6719

SAE TOWERS HOLDINGS LLC p 1265
16945 Northchase Dr # 1910, Houston TX 77060
Tel (281) 763-2282 SIC 6719

SHELF DRILLING DISTRIBUTION LTD p 1314
1 Riverway, Houston TX 77056
Tel (713) 457-8220 SIC 6719

TRICON ENERGY INC p 1479
777 Post Oak Blvd Ste 550, Houston TX 77056
Tel (713) 963-0066 SIC 6719

TRIPLE-S STEEL HOLDINGS INC p 1482
6000 Jensen Dr, Houston TX 77026
Tel (713) 697-7105 SIC 5051 6719

VALERUS FIELD SOLUTIONS HOLDINGS LLC p 1540
919 Milam St Ste 1000, Houston TX 77002
Tel (713) 744-6100 SIC 1382 6719

ACM NEWSPAPERS HOLDINGS LLC p 17
7301 State Highway 161, Irving TX 75039
Tel (214) 691-4066 SIC 6719

▲ **FORTERRA US HOLDINGS LLC** p 569
511 E John Carpenter Fwy, Irving TX 75062
Tel (469) 284-8678 SIC 6719

S A ICTS-U INC p 1261
545 E John Carpenter Fwy, Irving TX 75062
Tel (972) 719-9180 SIC 6719

SOURCEHOV HOLDINGS INC p 1342
2701 E Grauwyler Rd, Irving TX 75061
Tel (972) 821-4000 SIC 6719

W-INDUSTRIES OF TEXAS LLC p 1569
11500 Charles Rd, Jersey Village TX 77041
Tel (713) 466-9463 SIC 6719

CALIBER HOLDINGS CORP p 239
401 E Corp Dr Ste 150, Lewisville TX 75057
Tel (469) 948-9500 SIC 6719

APPLIED-CLEVELAND HOLDINGS INC p 100
2735 State Highway 322, Longview TX 75603
Tel (918) 358-5735 SIC 6719 7389

RIP GRIFFIN TRUCK SERVICE CENTER INC p 1236
4710 4th St, Lubbock TX 79416
Tel (806) 795-8785 SIC 6719

JORDAN HEALTHCARE HOLDINGS INC p 793
412 Texas Highway 37 S, Mount Vernon TX 75457
Tel (903) 537-2445 SIC 6719 8082

HILL COUNTRY HOLDINGS LLC p 693
1431 Fm 1101, New Braunfels TX 78130
Tel (830) 515-1400 SIC 6719

DAY STAR RESTAURANT GROUP INC p 417
5055 W Park Blvd Ste 500, Plano TX 75093
Tel (972) 295-8600 SIC 6719

■ **LINEAGE POWER HOLDINGS INC** p 869
601 Shiloh Rd, Plano TX 75074
Tel (974) 244-9288 SIC 6719

■ **SK HOLDING CO INC** p 1328
5400 Legacy Dr Cluster Ii, Plano TX 75024
Tel (972) 265-2000 SIC 6719

GROTHUES BROTHERS HOLDINGS LTD p 641
2651 Sw Military Dr, San Antonio TX 78224
Tel (830) 569-1131 SIC 5031 5211 6719

MINER HOLDING CO INC p 973
11827 Tech Com Rd Ste 115, San Antonio TX 78233
Tel (830) 627-8600 SIC 1799 6719

■ **THERMON HOLDING CORP** p 1447
100 Thermon Dr, San Marcos TX 78666
Tel (512) 396-5801 SIC 6719

LIBERTYTOWN USA 2 INC p 863
13131 Dairy Ashford Rd # 230, Sugar Land TX 77478
Tel (832) 295-5024 SIC 6719

CENTRAL FREIGHT LINES INC p 278
5601 W Waco Dr, Waco TX 76710
Tel (254) 772-2120 SIC 6719 4213

MID VALLEY HEALTH SYSTEM p 963
1401 E 8th St, Weslaco TX 78596
Tel (956) 969-5112 SIC 6719

SUMMERTIME HOLDING CORP p 1398
1301 Solana Blvd Ste 2100, Westlake TX 76262
Tel (817) 961-2100 SIC 6719 7371

MORINDA BIOACTIVES INC p 989
737 E 1180 S, American Fork UT 84003
Tel (801) 234-1000 SIC 6719

MARITZCX HOLDINGS LLC p 907
3451 N Triumph Blvd, Lehi UT 84043
Tel (385) 695-2800 SIC 8742 6719

APX PARENT HOLDCO INC p 101
4931 N 300 W, Provo UT 84604
Tel (801) 377-9111
SIC 6719 3822 1711 8711 5065 5074

SNOWBIRD HOLDINGS LLC p 1336
2721 E Kelly Ln, Salt Lake City UT 84117
Tel (801) 277-2840 SIC 6719

MACK GROUP INC p 892
608 Warm Brook Rd, Arlington VT 05250
Tel (802) 375-2511 SIC 3089 3577 6719

NORTH AMERICA SEKISUI HOUSE LLC p 1049
2001 Jefferson Davis Hwy, Arlington VA 22202
Tel (703) 740-0229 SIC 6719

PAE HOLDING CORP p 1107
1320 N Courthouse Rd # 800, Arlington VA 22201
Tel (703) 717-6000 SIC 6719 8742 8711

VENCORE HOLDING CORP p 1547
15052 Conference Ctr Dr, Chantilly VA 20151
Tel (571) 313-6000
SIC 6719 8711 8733 3812 7372

GREENBRIER INC p 637
200 Carlton Rd, Charlottesville VA 22902
Tel (434) 817-2611 SIC 6719

DEWBERRY COMPANIES INC p 434
8401 Arlington Blvd, Fairfax VA 22031
Tel (703) 849-0100 SIC 6719

■ **GENERAL DYNAMICS GOVERNMENT SYSTEMS CORP** p 600
2941 Fairview Park Dr, Falls Church VA 22042
Tel (703) 876-3000 SIC 6719

ADSUMMA GROUP INC p 24
1431 Cedar Ave, Mc Lean VA 22101
Tel (703) 883-0404 SIC 6719

FHC HEALTH SYSTEMS INC p 539
240 Corporate Blvd # 100, Norfolk VA 23502
Tel (757) 459-5100 SIC 6719

■ **NEXTEL FINANCE CO** p 1040
2001 Edmund Halley Dr, Reston VA 20191
Tel (703) 433-4000 SIC 4812 6719

AGA SERVICE CO p 34
2805 N Parham Rd, Richmond VA 23294
Tel (804) 285-3300 SIC 6719

JAMES C JUSTICE COMPANIES INC p 776
302 S Jefferson St # 400, Roanoke VA 24011
Tel (540) 776-7890 SIC 6719

TRIPLE-I HOLDINGS LLC p 1482
7400 Fullerton Rd Ste 210, Springfield VA 22153
Tel (703) 635-7088 SIC 7379 6719

DARKA HOLDINGS LLC p 412
1528 Taylor Farm Rd # 105, Virginia Beach VA 23453
Tel (757) 689-4400 SIC 6719

SHAPE TECHNOLOGIES GROUP INC p 1311
23500 64th Ave S, Kent WA 98032
Tel (253) 246-3200 SIC 6719

CALLISON ARCHITECTURE HOLDING LLC p 242
1420 5th Ave Ste 2400, Seattle WA 98101
Tel (206) 623-4646 SIC 6719

CATALYST PAPER HOLDINGS INC p 264
2200 6th Ave Ste 800, Seattle WA 98121
Tel (604) 247-4018 SIC 6719

SOUND INPATIENT PHYSICIANS HOLDINGS LLC p 1342
1498 Pacific Ave Ste 400, Tacoma WA 98402
Tel (253) 682-1710 SIC 8011 6719

VOITH HOLDING INC p 1564
2200 N Roemer Rd, Appleton WI 54911
Tel (920) 731-7724
SIC 5131 3554 2221 6719

M10 INC p 890
817 W Main St, Brownsville WI 53006
Tel (920) 583-3132 SIC 6719

FOTH & VAN DYKE LLC p 571
2121 Innovation Ct # 100, De Pere WI 54115
Tel (920) 497-2500 SIC 6719

SPECIALTY RETAIL SHOPS HOLDING CORP p 1356
700 Pilgrim Way, Green Bay WI 54304
Tel (920) 429-2211 SIC 6719

KSPG HOLDING USA INC p 831
1731 Industrial Pkwy N, Marinette WI 54143
Tel (715) 732-0181 SIC 3592 3714 6719

BAIRD FINANCIAL CORP p 145
777 E Wisconsin Ave, Milwaukee WI 53202
Tel (414) 765-3500 SIC 6719

BAIRD HOLDING CO p 145
777 E Wisconsin Ave, Milwaukee WI 53202
Tel (414) 765-3500 SIC 6719

JOHNSON CONTROLS HOLDING CO INC p 791
5757 N Green Bay Ave, Milwaukee WI 53209
Tel (414) 524-1200 SIC 6719

ROBERT W BAIRD & CO INC p 1241
777 E Wisconsin Ave Fl 29, Milwaukee WI 53202
Tel (414) 765-3500 SIC 6719

PHMH HOLDING CO p 1144
315 W Forest Hill Ave, Oak Creek WI 53154
Tel (414) 764-6200 SIC 3625 6719

STI HOLDINGS INC p 1389
416 S Academy St, Stoughton WI 53589
Tel (608) 873-2500 SIC 6719

FISHER-BARTON INC p 552
576 Bluemound Road 53188, Watertown WI 53094
Tel (920) 261-0131 SIC 6719

M C HOLDINGS INC p 889
5709 Education Dr Apt 205, Cheyenne WY 82009
Tel (307) 514-1510 SIC 6719 7389

SIC 6722 Management Investment Offices

ZILLIONAIRE EMPRESS DANIELLE BERHANE MANAGEMENT FIRM p 1643
8549 Wilshire Blvd # 817, Beverly Hills CA 90211
Tel (310) 461-9923 SIC 6722

FILM MUSICIANS SECONDARY MARKETS FUND p 542
15910 Ventura Blvd # 900, Encino CA 91436
Tel (818) 755-7777 SIC 8741 6722

ALTURA HOLDINGS LLC p 63
1335 S Acacia Ave, Fullerton CA 92831
Tel (714) 948-8400 SIC 6722

CAPITAL GROUP COMPANIES INC p 249
333 S Hope St Fl 55, Los Angeles CA 90071
Tel (213) 486-9200
SIC 6282 6091 6722 8741

■ **OAKTREE CAPITAL MANAGEMENT LP** p 1071
333 S Grand Ave Ste 2800, Los Angeles CA 90071
Tel (213) 830-6300 SIC 6282 6722 6211

ABSOLUTE RETURN PORTFOLIO p 13
700 Newport Center Dr, Newport Beach CA 92660
Tel (800) 800-7646 SIC 6722

■ **ADVENT SOFTWARE INC** p 27
600 Townsend St Fl 5, San Francisco CA 94103
Tel (415) 543-7696
SIC 7371 7373 7372 6722

■ **BLACKROCK INSTITUTIONAL TRUST CO NATIONAL ASSOCIATION** p 188
400 Howard St, San Francisco CA 94105
Tel (415) 597-2000 SIC 6722

DODGE & COX p 447
555 California St Fl 40, San Francisco CA 94104
Tel (415) 981-1710 SIC 6722

VALUEACT CAPITAL MANAGEMENT LP p 1542
1 Letterman Dr Bldg D, San Francisco CA 94129
Tel (415) 249-1232 SIC 6722

VISTA EQUITY PARTNERS FUND VI-A LP p 1562
4 Embarcadero Ctr Fl 20, San Francisco CA 94111
Tel (415) 765-6500 SIC 6722

▲ FRANKLIN RESOURCES INC p 575
1 Franklin Pkwy, San Mateo CA 94403
Tel (650) 312-2000 SIC 6722 6726

UNIVERSITY OF COLORADO HOSPITALS RETIREMENT PLAN p 1521
2400 S Peoria St Ste 100, Aurora CO 80014
Tel (720) 848-4011 SIC 6722

GE FOUNDATION p 596
3135 Easton Tpke, Fairfield CT 06828
Tel (203) 373-3216 SIC 6722

DKR CAPITAL INC p 445
10 Glenville St Ste 5, Greenwich CT 06831
Tel (203) 324-8352 SIC 6722

CONNING & CO p 358
1 Financial Plz Fl 13, Hartford CT 06103
Tel (860) 299-2100 SIC 6722

PM HOLDINGS INC p 1157
1 American Row, Hartford CT 06103
Tel (860) 403-5000
SIC 6411 6162 6722 6282 6211 6552

DKR OASIS MANAGEMENT CO LP p 445
1281 E Main St Ste 3, Stamford CT 06902
Tel (203) 324-8400 SIC 6722

H S B C OVERSEAS CORP (DE) p 650
300 Delaware Ave Ste 1400, Wilmington DE 19801
Tel (302) 657-8400 SIC 6722

ACON INVESTMENTS LLC p 18
1133 Conn Ave Nw Ste 700, Washington DC 20036
Tel (202) 454-1100 SIC 6722

INTERNATIONAL CITY MANAGEMENT ASSOCIATION RETIREMENT CORP p 754
777 N Capitol St Ne # 600, Washington DC 20002
Tel (202) 962-4600 SIC 7389 6722

THAYER-BLUM FUNDING III LLC p 1446
1455 Penn Ave Nw Ste 350, Washington DC 20004
Tel (202) 371-0150 SIC 6722 3672 3577

VESTA PROPERTY SERVICES INC p 1552
1021 Oak St, Jacksonville FL 32204
Tel (904) 355-1831 SIC 6722 6531

■ RAYMOND JAMES & ASSOCIATES INC p 1210
880 Carillon Pkwy, Saint Petersburg FL 33716
Tel (727) 567-1000 SIC 6211 6722 8741

▲ AFFILIATED MANAGERS GROUP INC p 32
777 S Flagler Dr, West Palm Beach FL 33401
Tel (800) 345-1100 SIC 6722 6282

■ FINANCIAL SERVICE CORP p 543
2300 Windy Ridge Pkwy Se 1100s, Atlanta GA 30339
Tel (770) 916-6500
SIC 6722 6411 8742 6211

■ FSC CORP p 582
2300 Windy Ridge Pkwy Se # 1100, Atlanta GA 30339
Tel (770) 916-6500
SIC 6722 6411 8742 6211

INTEGRAL GROUP LLC p 748
191 Peachtree St Ne # 4100, Atlanta GA 30303
Tel (404) 224-1860
SIC 6552 8748 6798 6799 6722

ILLINOIS AGRICULTURAL ASSOCIATION p 732
1701 Towanda Ave, Bloomington IL 61701
Tel (309) 557-2111
SIC 8611 6722 8742 6311 7514

MADISON DEARBORN PARTNERS LLC p 894
70 W Madison St Ste 4600, Chicago IL 60602
Tel (312) 895-1000 SIC 6726 6722

▲ MORNINGSTAR INC p 989
22 W Washington St # 600, Chicago IL 60602
Tel (312) 696-6000 SIC 6282 6722 7375

MIDWEST OPERATING ENGINEERS WELFARE FUND p 967
6150 Joliet Rd, Countryside IL 60525
Tel (708) 482-7300 SIC 6722

SILVER OAK SERVICES PARTNERS LLC p 1324
1560 Sherman Ave Ste 1200, Evanston IL 60201
Tel (847) 492-1700 SIC 6722

ROUNDTABLE HEALTHCARE PARTNERS LP p 1253
272 E Deerpath Ste 350, Lake Forest IL 60045
Tel (847) 482-9275 SIC 6722 3699 2834

■ LINCOLN NATIONAL INVESTMENT COMPANIES INC p 867
200 E Berry St, Fort Wayne IN 46802
Tel (260) 455-2000 SIC 6282 6722

GIT-N-GO CONVENIENCE STORES INC p 613
2716 Indianola Ave, Des Moines IA 50315
Tel (515) 288-8565 SIC 5411 5541 6722

▲ PRINCIPAL FINANCIAL GROUP INC p 1177
711 High St, Des Moines IA 50392
Tel (515) 247-5111
SIC 6321 6799 6722 6311

BOILERMAKERS NATIONAL HEALTH AND WELFARE FUND p 198
754 Minnesota Ave Ste 424, Kansas City KS 66101
Tel (866) 342-6555 SIC 6722

■ WADDELL & REED FINANCIAL SERVICES INC p 1571
6300 Lamar Ave, Overland Park KS 66202
Tel (913) 236-2000
SIC 6722 6311 6211 6531

SECURITY BENEFIT LIFE INSURANCE CO p 1299
1 Sw Security Benefit Pl, Topeka KS 66636
Tel (785) 438-3000
SIC 6311 6722 6091 6211 8748

ABRY PARTNERS VI LP p 12
111 Huntington Ave Fl 30, Boston MA 02199
Tel (617) 859-2959 SIC 6722

▲ BOSTON PRIVATE FINANCIAL HOLDINGS INC p 203
10 Post Office Sq, Boston MA 02109
Tel (617) 912-1900 SIC 6022 6722 6282

GORDON BROTHERS GROUP LLC p 626
800 Boylston St Ste 27, Boston MA 02199
Tel (888) 424-1903 SIC 6722

GRANTHAM MAYO VAN OTTERLOO & CO LLC p 631
40 Rowes Wharf Ste 600, Boston MA 02110
Tel (617) 330-7500 SIC 6282 6722

HARVARD MANAGEMENT CO INC p 666
600 Atlantic Ave Ste 15, Boston MA 02210
Tel (617) 720-6526 SIC 8741 6722

MFS INVESTMENT MANAGEMENT FOUNDATION INC p 958
111 Huntington Ave # 200, Boston MA 02199
Tel (800) 343-2829 SIC 6722

NORTHEAST INVESTORS TRUST p 1055
125 High St Ste 1801, Boston MA 02110
Tel (857) 263-8100 SIC 6722

PIONEER INVESTMENT MANAGEMENT USA INC p 1151
60 State St Ste 700, Boston MA 02109
Tel (617) 742-7825 SIC 6722 6282

PUTNAM INVESTMENTS p 1193
1 Post Office Sq, Boston MA 02109
Tel (617) 292-1000 SIC 6722 6282 6726

■ EAGLE INVESTMENT SYSTEMS LLC p 468
45 William St Ste 200, Wellesley MA 02481
Tel (781) 943-2200
SIC 6722 6282 8721 7372

■ OPUS INVESTMENT MANAGEMENT INC p 1091
440 Lincoln St, Worcester MA 01653
Tel (508) 855-1000
SIC 6311 6321 6324 6351 6722

PINE RIVER CAPITAL MANAGEMENT LP p 1149
601 Carlson Pkwy Ste 330, Minnetonka MN 55305
Tel (612) 238-3300 SIC 6722

AMERICAN CENTURY INVESTMENT MANAGEMENT INC p 70
4500 Main St, Kansas City MO 64111
Tel (816) 531-5575 SIC 6722 6282

■ INVESTORS FIDUCIARY TRUST CO p 761
801 Pennsylvania Ave, Kansas City MO 64105
Tel (816) 871-4100 SIC 6722 6733 6282

FORSYTH BALDWIN LLC p 568
8040 Forsyth Blvd, Saint Louis MO 63105
Tel (314) 726-2152 SIC 6722

FORSYTH CAPITAL INVESTORS LLC p 568
8040 Forsyth Blvd, Saint Louis MO 63105
Tel (314) 726-2152 SIC 6722

NISA INVESTMENT ADVISORS INC p 1044
101 S Hanley Rd Ste 1700, Saint Louis MO 63105
Tel (314) 721-1900 SIC 6722 6282

GAVILON INTERMEDIATE HOLDINGS LLC p 594
1331 Capitol Ave, Omaha NE 68102
Tel (402) 889-4000 SIC 6722

MUTUAL OF OMAHA MARKETING CORP p 1003
3301 Dodge St, Omaha NE 68131
Tel (402) 342-7600 SIC 6722

■ LINCOLN FINANCIAL SECURITIES CORP p 867
1 Granite Pl, Concord NH 03301
Tel (603) 226-5000 SIC 6722

FORBES MANAGEMENT CO INC p 565
499 Washington Blvd Fl 9, Jersey City NJ 07310
Tel (212) 620-2200 SIC 6722

■ PRUDENTIAL INSURANCE CO OF AMERICA p 1187
751 Broad St, Newark NJ 07102
Tel (973) 802-6000
SIC 6311 6371 6282 6722

ATLAS COPCO USA HOLDINGS INC p 128
7 Campus Dr Ste 200, Parsippany NJ 07054
Tel (973) 397-3432 SIC 6722 6159 7699

COMPOSTELA FUND OF ROMAN CATHOLIC DIOCESE OF BROOKLYN NEW YORK p 352
75 Greene Ave, Brooklyn NY 11238
Tel (718) 623-5231 SIC 6722

▲ MANNING & NAPIER INC p 902
290 Woodcliff Dr Ste 300, Fairport NY 14450
Tel (585) 325-6880 SIC 6282 8742 6722

■ AIG GLOBAL ASSET MANAGEMENT HOLDINGS CORP p 37
111 8th Ave, New York NY 10011
Tel (212) 709-6100 SIC 6722 6411

■ AIG GLOBAL INVESTMENT CORP p 37
175 Water St Fl 18, New York NY 10038
Tel (212) 770-7000 SIC 6722 6411

■ AIG HIGHSTAR CAPITAL LP p 38
277 Park Ave Fl 45, New York NY 10172
Tel (646) 857-8700 SIC 6722 4491

ARETEC GROUP INC p 107
405 Park Ave Fl 12, New York NY 10022
Tel (866) 904-2988 SIC 6211 6282 6722

ARSENAL CAPITAL PARTNERS LP p 113
100 Park Ave Fl 31, New York NY 10017
Tel (212) 771-1717 SIC 6722

BRE RETAIL CENTERS HOLDINGS LP p 209
345 Park Ave, New York NY 10154
Tel (212) 583-5000 SIC 6513 6722

BRE SELECT HOTELS CORP p 209
345 Park Ave, New York NY 10154
Tel (212) 583-5000 SIC 6722

▲ CERBERUS CAPITAL MANAGEMENT LP p 283
875 3rd Ave, New York NY 10022
Tel (212) 891-2100
SIC 6722 6726 5031 5211

■ CIFC CORP p 306
250 Park Ave Ste 400, New York NY 10177
Tel (212) 624-1200 SIC 6722

■ CIFC LLC p 306
250 Park Ave Ste 400, New York NY 10177
Tel (212) 624-1200 SIC 6722

■ CLARION PARTNERS LLC p 322
230 Park Ave Fl 12, New York NY 10169
Tel (212) 883-2500 SIC 6722

▲ COWEN GROUP INC p 385
599 Lexington Ave, New York NY 10022
Tel (212) 845-7900 SIC 6211 6722

FALCONHEAD CAPITAL LLC p 526
645 Madison Ave Fl 9, New York NY 10022
Tel (212) 634-3304 SIC 6722 3812

FALCONHEAD CAPITAL PARTNERS II LP p 526
450 Park Ave Bsmt, New York NY 10022
Tel (212) 634-3304 SIC 6722 7221 7335

GLOBAL CAPITAL RESOURCES GROUP LLC p 616
1201 Broadway Ste 608, New York NY 10001
Tel (646) 221-1898 SIC 6722

■ GOLDMAN SACHS (ASIA) LLC p 622
200 West St Bldg 200, New York NY 10282
Tel (212) 902-1000 SIC 6211 6282 6722

■ GSO CAPITAL PARTNERS LP p 643
345 Park Ave Ste 1100, New York NY 10154
Tel (212) 583-5000 SIC 6722 7389

GUARDIAN LIFE INSURANCE CO OF AMERICA p 645
7 Hanover Sq Fl 14, New York NY 10004
Tel (212) 598-8000
SIC 6311 6371 6324 6321 6722 6282

▲ ICAHN ENTERPRISES LP p 726
767 5th Ave Ste 4700, New York NY 10153
Tel (212) 702-4300
SIC 6722 3714 7999 3743 5093 6531

JF LEHMAN & CO INC p 785
110 E 59th St Fl 27, New York NY 10022
Tel (212) 634-0100 SIC 6722

JLL PARTNERS FUND IV LP p 786
450 Lexington Ave Fl 31, New York NY 10017
Tel (212) 286-8600 SIC 6722

■ JP MORGAN INVESTMENT MANAGEMENT INC p 794
270 Park Ave Fl 12, New York NY 10017
Tel (212) 483-2323 SIC 6722

KPS CAPITAL PARTNERS LP p 829
485 Lexington Ave Fl 31, New York NY 10017
Tel (212) 338-5100
SIC 3541 6722 3545 5084

NEUBERGER & BERMAN PARTNERS FUND INC p 1028
605 3rd Ave Fl 21, New York NY 10158
Tel (212) 476-8800 SIC 6722

NEUBERGER BERMAN GROUP LLC p 1028
605 3rd Ave Fl 21, New York NY 10158
Tel (212) 476-9000 SIC 6282 6211 6722

NEUBERGER BERMAN LLC p 1028
605 3rd Ave Fl 21, New York NY 10158
Tel (212) 476-9000 SIC 6282 6211 6722

▲ OPPENHEIMER HOLDINGS INC p 1090
85 Broad St, New York NY 10004
Tel (212) 668-8000 SIC 6211 6712 6722

■ PRUDENTIAL SECURITIES GROUP INC p 1187
199 Water St, New York NY 10038
Tel (212) 778-1000 SIC 6722

▲ PZENA INVESTMENT MANAGEMENT INC p 1194
320 Park Ave Fl 8, New York NY 10022
Tel (212) 355-1600 SIC 6722

RENAISSANCE TECHNOLOGIES LLC p 1223
800 3rd Ave Fl 33, New York NY 10022
Tel (212) 821-1502 SIC 6722 6282

TENEX CAPITAL MANAGEMENT LP p 1437
60 E 42nd St Rm 5230, New York NY 10165
Tel (212) 457-1138 SIC 6722

TORCHLIGHT INVESTORS LLC p 1461
475 5th Ave Fl 10, New York NY 10017
Tel (212) 883-2800 SIC 6722 6282

VICTORY CAPITAL HOLDINGS INC p 1555
667 Madison Ave Fl 10, New York NY 10065
Tel (212) 906-0746 SIC 6282 6722

Z CAPITAL GROUP LLC p 1640
1330 Avenue Of The Americ, New York NY 10019
Tel (212) 595-8400 SIC 6722

TEAMSTERS NEW YORK STATE CONFERENCE p 1430
151 Northern Concourse # 1, Syracuse NY 13212
Tel (315) 455-9790 SIC 6722

TIAA CREF INVESTMENT MANAGEMENT LLC p 1452
8500 Andrew Carnegie Blvd, Charlotte NC 28262
Tel (704) 595-1000 SIC 6726 6722

▲ KKR PRA INVESTORS LP p 822
4130 Parklake Ave Ste 400, Raleigh NC 27612
Tel (919) 786-8200 SIC 6722 6726

PROAMPAC HOLDINGS INC p 1178
12025 Tricon Rd, Cincinnati OH 45246
Tel (513) 671-1777 SIC 6722

PROAMPAC INTERMEDIATE INC p 1178
12025 Tricon Rd, Cincinnati OH 45246
Tel (513) 671-1777 SIC 6722

■ KEYBANK EB MANAGED GUARANTEED INVESTMENT CONTRACT FUND p 815
127 Public Sq, Cleveland OH 44114
Tel (216) 689-3000 SIC 6722

OHIO CARPENTERS PENSION FUND p 1077
3611 Chester Ave, Cleveland OH 44114
Tel (330) 652-3475 SIC 6722

DIRECTIONAL CAPITAL LLC p 441
355 Richmond Rd Ste 8, Richmond Heights OH 44143
Tel (216) 261-3000 SIC 6722

VANGUARD FIDUCIARY TRUST CO INC p 1543
100 Vanguard Blvd, Malvern PA 19355
Tel (610) 669-6000 SIC 6722

VANGUARD GROUP INC p 1543
100 Vanguard Blvd, Malvern PA 19355
Tel (610) 669-1000 SIC 6722

▲ SEI INVESTMENTS CO p 1300
1 Freedom Valley Dr, Oaks PA 19456
Tel (610) 676-1000 SIC 6722 8742

BERWIND CONSOLIDATED HOLDINGS INC p 176
3000 Ctr Sq W 1500 Mkt St 1500 W, Philadelphia PA 19102
Tel (215) 563-2800 SIC 6722

FS ENERGY AND POWER FUND p 582
Cira Centre 2929 Arch St Cira Cent, Philadelphia PA 19104
Tel (215) 495-1150 SIC 6722

FS INVESTMENT CORP p 582
201 Rouse Blvd, Philadelphia PA 19112
Tel (215) 495-1150 SIC 6726 6722

RESOURCE AMERICA INC p 1227
1 Crescent Dr Ste 203, Philadelphia PA 19112
Tel (215) 546-5005 SIC 6531 6722 7359

▲ FEDERATED INVESTORS INC p 536
1001 Liberty Ave Ste 2100, Pittsburgh PA 15222
Tel (412) 288-1900 SIC 6282 6722

■ FEDERATED INVESTORS SERVICES CORP p 536
1001 Liberty Ave Ste 2100, Pittsburgh PA 15222
Tel (412) 288-1900 SIC 6722 6282

▲ LINCOLN NATIONAL CORP p 867
150 N Rad Chester Rd A305 Ste A, Radnor PA 19087
Tel (484) 583-1400
SIC 6311 6321 6371 6722 6411 6282

■ PRUDENTIAL TRUST CO p 1187
30 Ed Preate Dr, Scranton PA 18507
Tel (570) 341-6000 SIC 6282 6722 6211

DIMENSIONAL FUND ADVISORS LP p 440
6300 Fm 2244 Rd Bldg 1, Austin TX 78746
Tel (512) 306-7400 SIC 6722

■ ASHFORD HOSPITALITY LIMITED PARTNERSHIP p 117
14185 Dallas Pkwy # 1100, Dallas TX 75254
Tel (972) 778-9452 SIC 6722

ENERGY SPECTRUM PARTNERS VI LP p 498
5956 Sherry Ln Ste 900, Dallas TX 75225
Tel (214) 987-6100 SIC 6722

ACCELERATE HOLDINGS CORP p 14
301 Commerce St Ste 3300, Fort Worth TX 76102
Tel (817) 871-4000 SIC 6722

TPG PARTNERS LP p 1467
301 Commerce St Ste 3300, Fort Worth TX 76102
Tel (817) 871-4000 SIC 6722

ASCEND PERFORMANCE MATERIALS HOLDINGS INC p 115
1010 Travis St Ste 900, Houston TX 77002
Tel (713) 315-5700 SIC 6722

■ INVESCO AIM ADVISORS INC p 761
11 Greenway Plz Ste 2500, Houston TX 77046
Tel (713) 626-1919 SIC 6722

METRO NATIONAL CORP p 955
945 Bunker Hill Rd # 400, Houston TX 77024
Tel (713) 973-6400 SIC 6512 6531 6722

USAA CAPITAL CORP p 1534
9800 Fredericksburg Rd, San Antonio TX 78288
Tel (210) 498-2211
SIC 6035 6798 6722 7299 4813 4724

INSIGHT EQUITY A P X L P p 746
1400 Civic Pl Ste 250, Southlake TX 76092
Tel (817) 488-7775
SIC 6722 3441 3443 3556 3714 5171

INSIGHT EQUITY ACQUISITION CO LLC p 746
1400 Civic Pl Ste 250, Southlake TX 76092
Tel (817) 354-2715
SIC 2911 6722 3851 3441

INSIGHT EQUITY LP p 746
1400 Civic Pl Ste 250, Southlake TX 76092
Tel (817) 488-7775
SIC 6722 3441 3443 3556 3714 5171

UNIVERSITY OF VIRGINIA INVESTMENT MANAGEMENT CO p 1526
Fontain 560 Ray C Hunt Dr, Charlottesville VA 22903
Tel (434) 924-4245 SIC 6722

FRANK RUSSELL CO p 574
1301 2nd Ave Fl 18, Seattle WA 98101
Tel (206) 505-7877 SIC 6282 6211 6722

VULCAN INC p 1567
505 5th Ave S Ste 900, Seattle WA 98104
Tel (206) 342-2000 SIC 6531 6722 7941

LUBAR & CO INC p 883
700 N Water St Ste 1200, Milwaukee WI 53202
Tel (414) 291-9000 SIC 6722

SIC 6726 Unit Investment Trusts, Face-Amount Certificate Offices

HARBERT MANAGEMENT CORP p 659
2100 3rd Ave N Ste 600, Birmingham AL 35203
Tel (205) 987-5500 SIC 6726 6799

PLATINUM EQUITY LLC p 1155
360 N Crescent Dr Bldg S, Beverly Hills CA 90210
Tel (310) 712-1850 SIC 6726

PLATINUM EQUITY PARTNERS LLC p 1155
360 N Crescent Dr, Beverly Hills CA 90210
Tel (310) 712-1850 SIC 6726

AURORA CAPITAL PARTNERS LP p 132
10877 Wilshire Blvd # 2100, Los Angeles CA 90024
Tel (310) 551-0101 SIC 6726

■ CBRE INC p 269
400 S Hope St Ste 25, Los Angeles CA 90071
Tel (310) 477-5876 SIC 6726 6531

CREO CAPITAL PARTNERS LLC p 391
12400 Walsh Ave Ste 1100, Los Angeles CA 90066
Tel (310) 230-8600 SIC 6726

YUCAIPA COMPANIES LLC p 1640
9130 W Sunset Blvd, Los Angeles CA 90069
Tel (310) 789-7200 SIC 8748 6719 6726

SILVER LAKE PARTNERS II LP p 1323
2775 Sand Hill Rd Ste 100, Menlo Park CA 94025
Tel (650) 233-8120 SIC 6726 6211

IDEALAB p 729
130 W Union St, Pasadena CA 91103
Tel (626) 356-3654 SIC 5511 6726

SCHAUMBOND GROUP INC p 1286
225 S Lake Ave Ste 300, Pasadena CA 91101
Tel (626) 215-4998 SIC 6726

HELLMAN & FRIEDMAN LLC p 681
1 Maritime Plz Fl 12, San Francisco CA 94111
Tel (415) 788-5111 SIC 6726

JOHN STEWART CO p 789
1388 Sutter St Ste 1100, San Francisco CA 94109
Tel (213) 833-1860 SIC 6531 6552 6726

RED LOBSTER SEAFOOD CO LLC p 1215
1 Embarcadero Ctr Fl 39, San Francisco CA 94111
Tel (415) 983-2706 *SIC* 6726

TOMAHAWK ACQUISITION LLC p 1459
150 California St Fl 19, San Francisco CA 94111
Tel (415) 765-6500 *SIC* 6726 7371

VECTOR TALENT II LLC p 1546
1 Market St Ste 2300, San Francisco CA 94105
Tel (415) 293-5000 *SIC* 6726

VISTA EQUITY PARTNERS LLC p 1562
4 Embarcadero Ctr # 2000, San Francisco CA 94111
Tel (415) 765-6500 *SIC* 6726

▲ FRANKLIN RESOURCES INC p 575
1 Franklin Pkwy, San Mateo CA 94403
Tel (650) 312-2000 *SIC* 6722 6726

INVEST WEST FINANCIAL CORP p 761
1933 Cliff Dr Ste 1, Santa Barbara CA 93109
Tel (805) 957-0095 *SIC* 6726 6513

TENNENBAUM CAPITAL PARTNERS LLC p 1438
2951 28th St Ste 1000, Santa Monica CA 90405
Tel (310) 396-5451 *SIC* 6726

GREY MOUNTAIN PARTNERS LLC p 639
1470 Walnut St Ste 400, Boulder CO 80302
Tel (303) 449-5692 *SIC* 6726

KRG CAPITAL PARTNERS LLC p 830
1800 Larimer St Ste 2200, Denver CO 80202
Tel (303) 390-5001 *SIC* 6726 8742 6411

REPUBLIC FINANCIAL CORP p 1225
5251 Dtc Pkwy Ste 300, Greenwood Village CO 80111
Tel (800) 596-3608 *SIC* 6726 6159

▲ FIFTH STREET FINANCE CORP p 541
777 W Putnam Ave Ste 3, Greenwich CT 06830
Tel (203) 681-3600 *SIC* 6726

JACOBS PRIVATE EQUITY LLC p 775
350 Round Hill Rd, Greenwich CT 06831
Tel (203) 413-4000 *SIC* 4731 6282 6726

SILVER POINT CAPITAL LIMITED PARTNERSHIP p 1324
2 Greenwich Plz, Greenwich CT 06830
Tel (203) 542-4200 *SIC* 8741 6726

STONE POINT CAPITAL LLC p 1391
20 Horseneck Ln Ste 1, Greenwich CT 06830
Tel (203) 862-2900 *SIC* 6726

TICC CAPITAL CORP p 1452
8 Sound Shore Dr Ste 255, Greenwich CT 06830
Tel (203) 983-5275 *SIC* 6726

GRIDIRON CAPITAL LLC p 640
220 Elm St Fl 2, New Canaan CT 06840
Tel (203) 972-1100 *SIC* 6726

JH WHITNEY VI LP p 785
130 Main St, New Canaan CT 06840
Tel (203) 716-6100 *SIC* 6726 5812

ALINDA CAPITAL PARTNERS LLC p 50
1266 E Main St Ste 700r, Stamford CT 06902
Tel (203) 930-3800 *SIC* 6726

■ COMPASS GROUP DIVERSIFIED HOLDINGS LLC p 351
60 One Wilton Rd Fl 2, Westport CT 06880
Tel (203) 221-1703 *SIC* 6726

ATLAS MANAGEMENT INC p 128
103 Foulk Rd, Wilmington DE 19803
Tel (302) 576-2749 *SIC* 6726

▲ CARLYLE GROUP L P p 258
1001 Pennsylvania Ave Nw 220s, Washington DC 20004
Tel (202) 729-5626 *SIC* 6726 6282

PORTFOLIO LOGIC LLC p 1163
600 New Hampshire Ave Nw 9f, Washington DC 20037
Tel (202) 266-6519 *SIC* 6726 8741

IAP GLOBAL SERVICES LLC p 725
7315 N Atlantic Ave, Cape Canaveral FL 32920
Tel (321) 784-7100 *SIC* 6726

NAVIGATION CAPITAL PARTNERS INC p 1020
3060 Peachtree Rd Nw, Atlanta GA 30305
Tel (404) 504-4070 *SIC* 6726

NOBLE INVESTMENT GROUP LLC p 1046
3424 Peachtree Rd Ne # 2000, Atlanta GA 30326
Tel (404) 262-9660 *SIC* 6726

ROARK CAPITAL GROUP INC p 1240
1180 Peachtree St Ne # 2500, Atlanta GA 30309
Tel (404) 591-5200
SIC 6726 3993 7331 6794 5261

MID OAKS INVESTMENTS LLC p 963
750 W Lake Cook Rd # 460, Buffalo Grove IL 60089
Tel (847) 215-3475 *SIC* 6726 3089

ARBOR PRIVATE INVESTMENT CO LLC p 103
676 N Michigan Ave # 3410, Chicago IL 60611
Tel (312) 981-3770 *SIC* 6726

▲ GOLUB CAPITAL BDC INC p 622
150 S Wacker Dr Ste 800, Chicago IL 60606
Tel (312) 205-5050 *SIC* 6726

GTCR GOLDER RAUNER LLC p 644
300 N La Salle Dr # 5600, Chicago IL 60654
Tel (312) 329-0225 *SIC* 6726

GUGGENHEIM CAPITAL LLC p 645
227 W Monroe St Ste 4900, Chicago IL 60606
Tel (312) 827-0100 *SIC* 6726

■ JPMORGAN CAPITAL CORP p 795
55 W Monroe St, Chicago IL 60603
Tel (614) 248-5800 *SIC* 8748 6726

LINDEN LLC p 868
111 S Wacker Dr Ste 3350, Chicago IL 60606
Tel (312) 506-5657 *SIC* 6726

MADISON DEARBORN PARTNERS LLC p 894
70 W Madison St Ste 4600, Chicago IL 60602
Tel (312) 895-1000 *SIC* 6726 6722

THAYER LODGING GROUP INC p 1446
1997 Annapolis Exchange P, Annapolis MD 21401
Tel (410) 268-0515 *SIC* 6799 6726

▲ AMERICAN CAPITAL LTD p 69
2 Bethesda Metro Ctr # 14, Bethesda MD 20814
Tel (301) 951-6122 *SIC* 6726

CLARK ENTERPRISES INC p 322
7500 Old Georgetown Rd # 7, Bethesda MD 20814
Tel (301) 657-7100
SIC 6552 4832 7359 1521 1542 6726

ARLINGTON CAPITAL PARTNERS LP p 110
5425 Wisconsin Ave # 200, Chevy Chase MD 20815
Tel (202) 337-7500 *SIC* 6726 6211

BLACKSTREET CAPITAL MANAGEMENT LLC p 188
5425 Wisconsin Ave # 701, Chevy Chase MD 20815
Tel (240) 223-1330
SIC 6726 5149 5145 5961

ADVENT INTERNATIONAL CORP p 27
75 State St Ste 2900, Boston MA 02109
Tel (617) 951-0555 *SIC* 6726

ADVENT INTERNATIONAL GPE VII LLC p 27
75 State St Fl 29, Boston MA 02109
Tel (617) 951-9493 *SIC* 6726

AUDAX GROUP LP p 130
101 Huntington Ave # 2450, Boston MA 02199
Tel (617) 859-1500 *SIC* 6726 3646

BERKSHIRE PARTNERS LLC p 175
200 Clarendon St Ste 3500, Boston MA 02116
Tel (617) 227-0050 *SIC* 6211 6726 8741

FIDESSA BUY-SIDE INC p 541
160 Federal St, Boston MA 02110
Tel (617) 235-1000 *SIC* 6726 8742

OLD MUTUAL (US) HOLDINGS INC p 1081
200 Clarendon St Fl 53, Boston MA 02116
Tel (617) 369-7300 *SIC* 6726

PUTNAM INVESTMENTS p 1193
1 Post Office Sq, Boston MA 02109
Tel (617) 292-1000 *SIC* 6722 6282 6726

▲ THL CREDIT INC p 1448
100 Federal St Fl 31, Boston MA 02110
Tel (800) 450-4424 *SIC* 6726

WESTON PRESIDIO CAPITAL MANAGEMENT II LP p 1602
200 Clarendon St Fl 50, Boston MA 02116
Tel (617) 988-2500 *SIC* 6726

KRONOS ACQUISITION CORP p 830
297 Billerica Rd, Chelmsford MA 01824
Tel (978) 250-9800 *SIC* 7372 7373 6726

BLACKFORD CAPITAL LLC p 187
190 Monroe Ave Nw Ste 6, Grand Rapids MI 49503
Tel (616) 233-3101 *SIC* 6726

■ AMERIPRISE CERTIFICATE CO p 83
1099 Ameriprise Fincl Ctr, Minneapolis MN 55474
Tel (612) 671-3131 *SIC* 6726

WAITT MEDIA INC p 1571
1125 S 103rd St Ste 425, Omaha NE 68124
Tel (402) 697-8000 *SIC* 6726

SAW MILL CAPITAL LLC p 1284
555 Pleasantville Rd 220s, Briarcliff Manor NY 10510
Tel (914) 741-2426 *SIC* 6726 6282

KOHLBERG & CO LLC p 826
111 Radio Circle Dr, Mount Kisco NY 10549
Tel (914) 241-7430 *SIC* 6726 6211

AMERICAN INDUSTRIAL PARTNERS CAPITAL FUND IV (PARALLEL) LP p 74
330 Madison Ave Fl 28, New York NY 10017
Tel (212) 627-2360 *SIC* 6726

▲ APOLLO GLOBAL MANAGEMENT LLC p 97
9 W 57th St Fl 43, New York NY 10019
Tel (212) 515-3200 *SIC* 6726 6282 6799

▲ APOLLO INVESTMENT CORP p 97
9 W 57th St Fl 43, New York NY 10019
Tel (212) 515-3450 *SIC* 6726

▲ ARES CAPITAL CORP p 107
245 Park Ave Fl 44, New York NY 10167
Tel (212) 750-7300 *SIC* 6726

BLUE WOLF CAPITAL FUND II LP p 192
1 Liberty Plz Fl 52, New York NY 10006
Tel (212) 488-1340 *SIC* 6726

■ BNP PARIBAS ASSET MANAGEMENT INC p 194
200 Park Ave Rm 4520, New York NY 10166
Tel (212) 681-3000 *SIC* 6726

BRUCKMANN ROSSER SHERRILL & CO INC p 220
126 E 56th St Fl 29, New York NY 10022
Tel (212) 521-3700 *SIC* 6726

CCMP CAPITAL ADVISORS LP p 270
277 Park Ave Fl 27, New York NY 10172
Tel (212) 600-9600 *SIC* 6726

CENTRE PARTNERS MANAGEMENT LLC p 281
825 3rd Ave Fl 40, New York NY 10022
Tel (212) 332-5800 *SIC* 6726 5112

▲ CERBERUS CAPITAL MANAGEMENT LP p 283
875 3rd Ave, New York NY 10022
Tel (212) 891-2100
SIC 6722 6726 5031 5211

■ CERBERUS PARTNERS LP p 283
450 Park Ave Fl 28, New York NY 10022
Tel (212) 421-2600 *SIC* 6726

CI CAPITAL PARTNERS LLC p 305
500 Park Ave Fl 8, New York NY 10022
Tel (212) 752-1850 *SIC* 6726

CLAYTON DUBILIER & RICE LLC p 323
375 Park Ave Fl 18, New York NY 10152
Tel (212) 407-5200 *SIC* 6719 6726 6211

■ GOLDMAN SACHS BDC INC p 622
200 West St Bldg 200, New York NY 10282
Tel (212) 902-1000 *SIC* 6726

GREEN LIGHT CAPITAL INC p 637
140 E 45th St Fl 24, New York NY 10017
Tel (212) 922-9370 *SIC* 6726

■ HARBINGER OM LLC p 659
450 Park Ave Fl 27, New York NY 10022
Tel (212) 906-8555 *SIC* 6726

HARLAN CASTLE INC p 661
150 E 58th St Fl 38, New York NY 10155
Tel (212) 644-8600 *SIC* 6726

INCEPTION PARENT INC p 735
9 W 57th St Fl 43, New York NY 10019
Tel (212) 515-3200 *SIC* 6726

JORDAN CO L P p 793
399 Park Ave Fl 30, New York NY 10022
Tel (212) 572-0800 *SIC* 6726

■ KOHLBERG KRAVIS ROBERTS & CO LP p 826
9 W 57th St Ste 4200, New York NY 10019
Tel (212) 750-8300 *SIC* 6726

LIGHTYEAR CAPITAL LLC p 865
9 W 57th St, New York NY 10019
Tel (212) 328-0555 *SIC* 6726

MEDLEY CAPITAL CORP p 938
375 Park Ave Fl 33, New York NY 10152
Tel (212) 759-0777 *SIC* 6726

METALMARK CAPITAL LLC p 952
1177 Ave Of The Americas, New York NY 10036
Tel (212) 823-1900 *SIC* 6726

MOELIS CAPITAL PARTNERS LLC p 982
399 Park Ave Fl 5, New York NY 10022
Tel (212) 883-3800 *SIC* 6726

NEW MOUNTAIN CAPITAL I LLC p 1032
787 7th Ave Fl 49, New York NY 10019
Tel (212) 720-0300 *SIC* 6726

NEW MOUNTAIN CAPITAL LLC p 1032
787 7th Ave Fl 49, New York NY 10019
Tel (212) 720-0300 *SIC* 6726

NEW MOUNTAIN FINANCE CORP p 1032
787 7th Ave Fl 48, New York NY 10019
Tel (212) 720-0300 *SIC* 6726

NEW SENIOR INVESTMENT GROUP INC p 1033
1345 Avenue Of The Americ, New York NY 10105
Tel (212) 479-3140 *SIC* 6726

NM Z PARENT INC p 1045
787 7th Ave Fl 49, New York NY 10019
Tel (212) 720-0300
SIC 6726 2841 2879 2842

OEP CAPITAL ADVISORS LP p 1075
510 Madison Ave Fl 19, New York NY 10022
Tel (212) 277-1552 *SIC* 6726

ONE EQUITY PARTNERS LLC p 1086
320 Park Ave Fl 18, New York NY 10022
Tel (212) 794-3434 *SIC* 6726 8748

PENNANTPARK INVESTMENT CORP p 1129
590 Madison Ave Fl 15, New York NY 10022
Tel (212) 905-1000 *SIC* 6726

PLATINUM PARTNERS VALUE ARBITRAGE FUND LP p 1155
250 W 55th St Fl 14, New York NY 10019
Tel (212) 581-0500 *SIC* 6726

▲ PROSPECT CAPITAL CORP p 1184
10 E 40th St Fl 42, New York NY 10016
Tel (212) 448-0702 *SIC* 6726

▲ VSS-CAMBIUM HOLDINGS III LLC p 1567
55 E 52nd St Fl 33, New York NY 10055
Tel (212) 308-2281 *SIC* 6726

APOLLO INVESTMENT FUND VI LP p 97
1 Manhattanville Rd # 201, Purchase NY 10577
Tel (914) 694-8000 *SIC* 6726

■ APOLLO SVF MANAGEMENT LP p 97
1 Manhattanville Rd # 201, Purchase NY 10577
Tel (914) 694-8000 *SIC* 6726

■ APOLLO VALUE MANAGEMENT LP p 97
2 Mnhttnvlle Rd Fl 2, Purchase NY 10577
Tel (914) 694-8000 *SIC* 6726

■ GABELLI FUNDS LLC p 588
1 Corporate Ctr, Rye NY 10580
Tel (914) 921-5105 *SIC* 6726 3993

COMPASS GROUP USA INVESTMENTS LLP p 351
2400 Yorkmont Rd, Charlotte NC 28217
Tel (704) 328-4000 *SIC* 6726

FALFURRIAS CAPITAL PARTNERS LP p 526
100 N Tryon St Ste 4100, Charlotte NC 28202
Tel (704) 371-3220 *SIC* 6726

TIAA CREF INVESTMENT MANAGEMENT LLC p 1452
8500 Andrew Carnegie Blvd, Charlotte NC 28262
Tel (704) 595-1000 *SIC* 6726 6722

▲ KKR PRA INVESTORS LP p 822
4130 Parklake Ave Ste 400, Raleigh NC 27612
Tel (919) 786-8200 *SIC* 6722 6726

■ AIRBORNE ACQUISITION INC p 39
30500 Aurora Rd Ste 100, Solon OH 44139
Tel (216) 438-6111 *SIC* 6726

FS INVESTMENT CORP p 582
201 Rouse Blvd, Philadelphia PA 19112
Tel (215) 495-1150 *SIC* 6726 6722

SHERMAN FINANCIAL GROUP LLC p 1316
200 Meeting St Ste 206, Charleston SC 29401
Tel (212) 922-1616 *SIC* 6153 6726

INTELLIGENT INVESTMENTS LLC p 750
1010 Park Dr, Myrtle Beach SC 29577
Tel (980) 989-4016 *SIC* 6726 7389

BLUE SAGE CAPITAL LP p 192
114 W 7th St Ste 820, Austin TX 78701
Tel (512) 536-1900 *SIC* 6726

▲ CONCEPT DEVELOPMENT PARTNERS LLC p 354
500 Crescent Ct Ste 250, Dallas TX 75201
Tel (214) 871-6819 *SIC* 6726 5812 5813

LONE STAR FUND IV (US) LP p 875
2711 N Haskell Ave, Dallas TX 75204
Tel (214) 754-8300 *SIC* 6726

UNITED INVESTMENT LTD p 1509
11700 Preston Rd 660-388, Dallas TX 75230
Tel (214) 632-9531 *SIC* 6726

WINGATE PARTNERS V LP p 1616
750 N Saint Paul St # 1200, Dallas TX 75201
Tel (214) 720-1313 *SIC* 6726 3448

NOVARIA GROUP LLC p 1062
6300 Ridglea Pl Ste 800, Fort Worth TX 76116
Tel (817) 381-3810 *SIC* 6726

TPG CAPITAL MANAGEMENT LP p 1467
301 Commerce St Ste 3300, Fort Worth TX 76102
Tel (817) 871-4000
SIC 6726 3674 6799 3993 6719

TPG SPECIALTY LENDING INC p 1467
301 Commerce St Ste 3300, Fort Worth TX 76102
Tel (817) 871-4000 *SIC* 6726

WHITE DEER ENERGY LP II p 1606
700 Louisiana St Ste 4770, Houston TX 77002
Tel (713) 581-6900 *SIC* 6726

C-III CAPITAL PARTNERS LLC p 234
5221 N O Connor Blvd, Irving TX 75039
Tel (972) 868-5300
SIC 6519 6726 6361 6411

INSIGHT EQUITY HOLDINGS LLC p 746
1400 Civic Pl Ste 250, Southlake TX 76092
Tel (817) 488-7775
SIC 6726 3851 2911 3441

■ PERPETUAL CAPITAL PARTNERS LLC p 1137
1000 Wilson Blvd Ste 2700, Arlington VA 22209
Tel (703) 647-8709 *SIC* 6726

HENDRICKS HOLDING CO INC p 683
690 3rd St Ste 300, Beloit WI 53511
Tel (608) 362-8981 *SIC* 6726

SIC 6732 Education, Religious & Charitable Trusts

ARIZONA COMMUNITY FOUNDATION INC p 108
2201 E Camelback Rd # 405, Phoenix AZ 85016
Tel (928) 348-9649 *SIC* 6732

ARIZONA STATE UNIVERSITY FOUNDATION FOR A NEW AMERICAN UNIVE p 109
300 E University Dr, Tempe AZ 85281
Tel (480) 965-3759 *SIC* 6732

HEIFER PROJECT INTERNATIONAL INC p 681
1 World Ave, Little Rock AR 72202
Tel (501) 907-2600 *SIC* 8399 6732 9532

CALIFORNIA COMMUNITY FOUNDATION p 239
221 S Figueroa St Ste 400, Los Angeles CA 90012
Tel (213) 413-4130 *SIC* 6732

UCLA FOUNDATION p 1499
10920 Wilshire Blvd # 200, Los Angeles CA 90024
Tel (310) 794-3193 *SIC* 6732

ORANGE COUNTY COMMUNITY FOUNDATION p 1092
4041 Macarthur Blvd # 510, Newport Beach CA 92660
Tel (949) 553-4202 *SIC* 6732

ASIA FOUNDATION p 117
465 California St Fl 9, San Francisco CA 94104
Tel (415) 982-4640 *SIC* 6732

JAMES IRVINE FOUNDATION p 776
1 Bush St Fl 8, San Francisco CA 94104
Tel (415) 777-2244 *SIC* 6732

PENINSULA COMMUNITY FOUNDATION p 1129
1700 S El Camino Real # 300, San Mateo CA 94402
Tel (650) 358-9369 *SIC* 6732

DENVER FOUNDATION p 429
55 Madison St Ste 800, Denver CO 80206
Tel (303) 300-1790 *SIC* 6732

HARTFORD FOUNDATION FOR PUBLIC GIVING p 665
10 Columbus Blvd Fl 8, Hartford CT 06106
Tel (860) 548-1888 *SIC* 6732 8733

■ LEGAL SERVICES CORP p 853
3333 K St Nw Ste 1, Washington DC 20007
Tel (202) 295-1500 *SIC* 6732 9199

NOT FOR PROFIT HOSPITAL CORP p 1062
1310 Southern Ave Se, Washington DC 20032
Tel (202) 574-6024 *SIC* 6732

CHILDRENS TRUST p 300
3150 Sw 3rd Ave Fl 8, Miami FL 33129
Tel (305) 571-5700 *SIC* 6732

UNIVERSITY OF GEORGIA RESEARCH FOUNDATION INC p 1521
310 E Campus Rd 409, Athens GA 30602
Tel (706) 542-5939 *SIC* 6732

COMMUNITY FOUNDATION FOR GREATER ATLANTA INC p 348
191 Peachtree St Ne # 1000, Atlanta GA 30303
Tel (404) 688-5525 *SIC* 6732

HEALTH SCHOLARSHIPS INC p 675
1005 Boulder Dr, Gray GA 31032
Tel (478) 742-6569 *SIC* 6732

DECATUR MEMORIAL FOUNDATION p 420
2300 N Edward St, Decatur IL 62526
Tel (217) 876-8121 *SIC* 6732

KANSAS UNIVERSITY ENDOWMENT ASSOCIATION p 803
1891 Constant Ave, Lawrence KS 66047
Tel (785) 832-7400 *SIC* 6732

ANNE ARUNDEL MEDICAL CENTER INC p 92
2001 Medical Pkwy, Annapolis MD 21401
Tel (443) 481-1000 *SIC* 8062 8093 6732

CLINTON HEALTH ACCESS INITIATIVE INC p 327
383 Dorchester Ave # 400, Boston MA 02127
Tel (617) 774-0110 *SIC* 6732

MOTT CHARLES STEWART FOUNDATION INC p 993
503 S Saginaw St Ste 1200, Flint MI 48502
Tel (810) 238-5651 *SIC* 6732

DOW HERBERT H & GRACE A FOUNDATION p 453
1809 Eastman Ave, Midland MI 48640
Tel (989) 631-2677 *SIC* 6732

KRESGE FOUNDATION p 829
3215 W Big Beaver Rd, Troy MI 48084
Tel (248) 643-9630 *SIC* 6732

MC KNIGHT FOUNDATION p 925
710 S 2nd St Ste 400, Minneapolis MN 55401
Tel (612) 333-4220 *SIC* 6732

MINNEAPOLIS FOUNDATION p 973
80 S 8th St Ste 800, Minneapolis MN 55402
Tel (612) 672-3878 *SIC* 6732

OTTO BREMER FOUNDATION p 1098
30 7th St E Ste 2900, Saint Paul MN 55101
Tel (651) 227-8036 *SIC* 6732 6022

GREATER KANSAS CITY COMMUNITY FOUNDATION AND AFFILIATED TRUSTS p 635
1055 Broadway Blvd # 130, Kansas City MO 64105
Tel (816) 842-0944 *SIC* 6732 7941

U B FOUNDATION ACTIVITIES INC p 1497
101 Center For Tommorrow, Buffalo NY 14260
Tel (716) 645-3013 *SIC* 6732

ALFRED P SLOAN FOUNDATION p 50
45 Rockefeller Plz # 2200, New York NY 10111
Tel (212) 649-1649 *SIC* 6732

CLARK FOUNDATION p 322
1 Rockefeller Plz Fl 31, New York NY 10020
Tel (212) 977-6900 *SIC* 6732

COMMUNITY FUNDS INC p 348
2 Park Ave Fl 24, New York NY 10016
Tel (212) 686-0010 SIC 6732

FORD FOUNDATION p 565
320 E 43rd St Fl 4, New York NY 10017
Tel (212) 573-5370 SIC 6732

JEWISH COMMUNAL FUND p 784
575 Madison Ave Ste 703, New York NY 10022
Tel (212) 752-8277 SIC 6732

NEW YORK COMMUNITY TRUST AND COMMUNITY FUNDS INC p 1035
909 3rd Ave Fl 22, New York NY 10022
Tel (212) 686-0010 SIC 6732

SURDNA FOUNDATION INC p 1408
330 Madison Ave Fl 30, New York NY 10017
Tel (212) 557-0010 SIC 6732 8742

WALLACE FOUNDATION p 1573
5 Penn Plz Fl 7, New York NY 10001
Tel (212) 251-9700 SIC 6732

SAMARITANS PURSE p 1274
801 Bamboo Rd, Boone NC 28607
Tel (828) 262-1980 SIC 8322 6732

GREATER CINCINNATI FOUNDATION p 635
200 W 4th St Fl 1, Cincinnati OH 45202
Tel (513) 241-2880 SIC 6732

CLEVELAND FOUNDATION p 325
1422 Euclid Ave Ste 1300, Cleveland OH 44115
Tel (216) 861-3810 SIC 6732

OREGON STATE UNIVERSITY FOUNDATION INC p 1094
850 Sw 35th St, Corvallis OR 97333
Tel (541) 737-4218 SIC 6732

OREGON HEALTH & SCIENCE UNIVERSITY FOUNDATION INC p 1093
1121 Sw Salmon St Ste 100, Portland OR 97205
Tel (503) 228-1730
SIC 8399 6091 8733 6732

GLENMEDE CORP p 615
1650 Market St Ste 1200, Philadelphia PA 19103
Tel (215) 419-6000 SIC 6733 6732

PEW CHARITABLE TRUSTS p 1140
2005 Market St Fl 28, Philadelphia PA 19103
Tel (215) 575-9050 SIC 8732 6732

WILLIAM PENN FOUNDATION p 1611
2 Logan Sq Fl 11, Philadelphia PA 19103
Tel (215) 988-1830 SIC 6732

HEINZ ENDOWMENTS p 681
625 Liberty Ave Fl 30, Pittsburgh PA 15222
Tel (412) 281-5777 SIC 6732

PITTSBURGH FOUNDATION p 1152
5 Ppg Pl Ste 250, Pittsburgh PA 15222
Tel (412) 391-5122 SIC 6732

NEWPORT HEALTH CARE CORP p 1038
11 Friendship St, Newport RI 02840
Tel (401) 846-6400 SIC 8062 6531 6732

TEXAS A&M FOUNDATION p 1442
401 George Bush Dr, College Station TX 77840
Tel (979) 845-8161 SIC 6732 8399

BROWN FOUNDATION INC p 219
2217 Welch St, Houston TX 77019
Tel (713) 523-6867 SIC 6732

DONORS TRUST INC p 451
1800 Diagonal Rd Ste 280, Alexandria VA 22314
Tel (703) 535-3563 SIC 6732 8733

WORLD VISION INC p 1625
34834 Weyerhaeuser Way S, Federal Way WA 98001
Tel (253) 815-1000 SIC 6732

VIRGINIA WEST UNIVERSITY FOUNDATION INC p 1560
1 Waterfront Pl Fl 7, Morgantown WV 26501
Tel (304) 293-3708 SIC 6732

SIC 6733 Trusts Except Educational, Religious & Charitable

ALASKA PERMANENT FUND CORP p 45
801 W 10th St Ste 302, Juneau AK 99801
Tel (907) 796-1500 SIC 6733

CALIFORNIAS VALUED TRUST p 242
520 E Herndon Ave, Fresno CA 93720
Tel (559) 437-2960 SIC 6733

CARPENTER FUNDS ADMINISTRATIVE OFFICE OF NORTHERN CALIFORNIA INC p 260
265 Hegenberger Rd # 100, Oakland CA 94621
Tel (510) 639-3996 SIC 6733

OPERATING ENGINEERS HEALTH & WELFARE FUND p 1089
100 Corson St, Pasadena CA 91103
Tel (626) 356-1000 SIC 6733

CAHP HEALTH BENEFITS TRUST p 237
2030 V St, Sacramento CA 95818
Tel (916) 732-2155 SIC 6733

GUILD MORTGAGE CO p 646
5898 Copley Dr Fl 4, San Diego CA 92111
Tel (800) 283-8823 SIC 6162 6733

KELLY CAPITAL GROUP INC p 809
12730 High Bluff Dr # 250, San Diego CA 92130
Tel (619) 687-5000 SIC 6733

SHOPCORE PROPERTIES LP p 1318
17140 Bernardo Center Dr, San Diego CA 92128
Tel (858) 613-1800 SIC 6733

RETA TRUST p 1228
1255 Battery St Ste 450, San Francisco CA 94111
Tel (415) 546-9300 SIC 6733

2100 TRUST LLC p 1
625 N Grand Ave, Santa Ana CA 92701
Tel (877) 469-7344 SIC 6733

VARNER FAMILY LIMITED PARTNERSHIP p 1545
5900 E Lerdo Hwy, Shafter CA 93263
Tel (661) 399-1163 SIC 6733

MANAGEMENT TRUST ASSOCIATION INC p 900
15661 Red Hill Ave # 201, Tustin CA 92780
Tel (714) 285-2626 SIC 6733

UNIVERSITY OF COLORADO HEALTH AND WELFARE TRUST p 1521
1800 N Grant St Ste 800, Denver CO 80203
Tel (303) 860-5600 SIC 6733

HARRIS DENISE ANN TRUST p 663
301 W Bay St Ste 1417, Jacksonville FL 32202
Tel (888) 504-0994 SIC 6733

TREMAYNE ANTONIO WILLIAMS GLOBAL ESTATE ENTRUST TRUST p 1476
12955 Walsingham Rd # 197, Largo FL 33774
Tel (727) 218-0199 SIC 6733

CORPORATE CAPITAL TRUST INC p 372
450 S Orange Ave, Orlando FL 32801
Tel (866) 933-1960 SIC 6733

KSF INTERMEDIATE CORP p 831
11780 Us Highway 1 400n, Palm Beach Gardens FL 33408
Tel (866) 726-2272 SIC 6733

ATLANTIC TRUST CO NA p 127
1555 Peachtree St Ne # 1100, Atlanta GA 30309
Tel (404) 881-3400 SIC 6733

ROBERT W WOODRUFF FOUNDATION INC p 1241
191 Peachtree St Ne, Atlanta GA 30303
Tel (404) 522-6755 SIC 6733

■ **SYNOVUS TRUST CO NA** p 1415
1148 Broadway, Columbus GA 31901
Tel (706) 649-2311 SIC 6733 6282

W W GRAINGER INC GROUP BENEFIT TRUST I p 1569
100 Grainger Pkwy, Lake Forest IL 60045
Tel (847) 535-1096 SIC 6733

WYNNCHURCH CAPITAL LTD p 1630
6250 N Rver Rd Ste 10-100, Rosemont IL 60018
Tel (847) 604-6100 SIC 6733 6799

■ **SPRINGLEAF MORTGAGE LOAN TRUST 2012-2** p 1361
601 Nw 2nd St, Evansville IN 47708
Tel (812) 424-8031 SIC 6733

NORTH OAKS HEALTH SYSTEM FOUNDATION p 1053
15790 Paul Vega Md Dr, Hammond LA 70403
Tel (985) 345-2700 SIC 6733

▲ **CAMDEN NATIONAL CORP** p 245
2 Elm St, Camden ME 04843
Tel (207) 236-8821 SIC 6021 6733

PRESIDENT AND TRUSTEES OF COLBY COLLEGE p 1172
4120 Mayflower Hl, Waterville ME 04901
Tel (207) 859-4127 SIC 6733

BOSTON FOUNDATION INC p 202
75 Arlington St Fl 10, Boston MA 02116
Tel (617) 338-1700 SIC 6733

CONSOLIDATED EDISON MASTER RETIREE HEALTH VEBA TRUST FOR WEEKLY EES p 359
P.O. Box 5100, Boston MA 02206
Tel (617) 664-9564 SIC 6733

■ **MELLON TRUST OF NEW ENGLAND NA** p 941
1 Boston Pl Fl 8, Boston MA 02108
Tel (617) 722-7000 SIC 6733

MILFORD REGIONAL HEALTHCARE FOUNDATION INC p 969
14 Prospect St, Milford MA 01757
Tel (508) 473-1190 SIC 6733 8082 8011

MORTON HOSPITAL AND MEDICAL CENTER INC p 991
88 Washington St, Taunton MA 02780
Tel (508) 828-7000 SIC 6733 8062

ELECTRO SWITCH BUSINESS TRUST p 485
775 Pleasant St Ste 1, Weymouth MA 02189
Tel (781) 335-1195 SIC 6733

3M EMPLOYEES WELFARE BENEFITS ASSOCIATION TRUST II p 2
3m Center Bldg 224, Saint Paul MN 55144
Tel (651) 737-3201 SIC 6733

ST PAUL ELECTRICAL ADMINISTRATIVE SERVICES CORP p 1372
1330 Conway St Ste 130, Saint Paul MN 55106
Tel (651) 772-8746 SIC 6733

■ **INVESTORS FIDUCIARY TRUST CO** p 761
801 Pennsylvania Ave, Kansas City MO 64105
Tel (816) 871-4100 SIC 6722 6733 6282

ASCENSION HEALTH WELFARE BENEFITS TRUST p 116
11775 Borman Dr Ste 200, Saint Louis MO 63146
Tel (314) 733-8648 SIC 6733

JOHN Q HAMMONS RVOCTR 12281989 p 789
300 S John Q Hammons Pkwy # 9, Springfield MO 65806
Tel (417) 864-4300 SIC 7011 6733

DA DAVIDSON COMPANIES p 407
8 3rd St N, Great Falls MT 59401
Tel (406) 727-4200 SIC 6211 6733 8741

TEACHERS HEALTH TRUST p 1429
2950 E Rochelle Ave, Las Vegas NV 89121
Tel (702) 866-6133 SIC 6733

PRUDENTIAL WELFARE BENEFITS TRUST p 1187
751 Broad St Fl 18, Newark NJ 07102
Tel (973) 802-7490 SIC 6733

ROCHE EMPLOYEE WELFARE BENEFIT TRUST p 1243
340 Kingsland St, Nutley NJ 07110
Tel (973) 235-5000 SIC 6733

PRINCETON HEALTHCARE SYSTEM HOLDING INC p 1177
1 Plainsboro Rd, Plainsboro NJ 08536
Tel (609) 497-4190 SIC 6733

KENNEDY HEALTH CARE FOUNDATION INC p 811
18 E Laurel Rd, Stratford NJ 08084
Tel (856) 661-5100
SIC 6733 4119 8051 6531 7361 8721

■ **TOMPKINS TRUST CO** p 1460
110 N Tioga St, Ithaca NY 14850
Tel (607) 257-1909 SIC 6733

1199 SEIU NATIONAL BENEFIT FUND FOR HEALTH AND HUMAN SERVICE EMPLOYEES p 1
P.O. Box 842, New York NY 10108
Tel (646) 473-6020 SIC 6733

AMERICAN REALTY CAPITAL OPERATING PARTNERSHIP II LP p 78
405 Park Ave Fl 15, New York NY 10022
Tel (212) 415-6500 SIC 6733

■ **BANK OF AMERICA PVT WEALTH MANAGEMENT** p 151
114 W 47th St Ste C-1, New York NY 10036
Tel (800) 878-7878
SIC 6282 6022 6099 6733

BP PRUDHOE BAY ROYALTY TRUST INC p 206
101 Barclay St, New York NY 10007
Tel (212) 815-6908 SIC 6733

GOVERNORS ISLAND CORP p 627
10 South St Frnt Slip7, New York NY 10004
Tel (212) 440-2200 SIC 6733

JPMORGAN CHASE VEBA TRUST FOR RETIREE p 795
1 Chase Manhattan Plz, New York NY 10005
Tel (212) 552-2992 SIC 6733

LEONA M AND HARRY B HELMSLEY CHARITABLE TRUST p 856
230 Park Ave, New York NY 10169
Tel (212) 679-3600 SIC 6733

MATLINPATTERSON GLOBAL ADVISERS LLC p 920
520 Madison Ave Fl 35, New York NY 10022
Tel (212) 651-9500 SIC 6733

■ **MOELIS & CO LLC** p 981
399 Park Ave Fl 5, New York NY 10022
Tel (212) 883-3800 SIC 6733 6282

NYLIFE LLC p 1069
51 Madison Ave, New York NY 10010
Tel (212) 576-7000
SIC 6282 6211 6733 6153

UNITY HEALTH SYSTEM FOUNDATION p 1515
1555 Long Pond Rd, Rochester NY 14626
Tel (585) 723-7050 SIC 6733

BRANCH BANKING AND TRUST CO HEALTH CARE PLAN p 207
P.O. Box 1215, Winston Salem NC 27102
Tel (336) 733-2411 SIC 6733

PROCTER AND GAMBLE RETIREE BENEFIT TRUST p 1179
2 Procter And Gamble Plz, Cincinnati OH 45202
Tel (513) 698-4501 SIC 6733

■ **PREMIER BANK & TRUST NATIONAL ASSOCIATION** p 1170
600 S Main St, North Canton OH 44720
Tel (330) 499-1900 SIC 6733 6029

CAMERON ENTERPRISES A LIMITED PARTNERSHIP p 245
9000 Cameron Pkwy, Oklahoma City OK 73114
Tel (405) 523-2000 SIC 6733

HARRISON ELECTRICAL WORKERS TRUSTS p 664
1220 Sw Morrison St # 300, Portland OR 97205
Tel (503) 224-0048 SIC 6733

■ **SEI PRIVATE TRUST CO** p 1300
1 Freedom Valley Dr, Oaks PA 19456
Tel (610) 676-1000 SIC 6733 6211

GLENMEDE CORP p 615
1650 Market St Ste 1200, Philadelphia PA 19103
Tel (215) 419-6000 SIC 6733 6732

■ **BNY MELLON NATIONAL ASSOCIATION** p 194
1 Mellon Center Ste 3831, Pittsburgh PA 15258
Tel (412) 234-5000 SIC 6021 6733

■ **ORIENTAL BANK** p 1094
254 Ave Munoz Rivera, San Juan PR 00918
Tel (787) 771-6800
SIC 6035 7359 7515 6733

SANDRIDGE PERMIAN TRUST p 1278
919 Congress Ave, Austin TX 78701
Tel (512) 236-6599 SIC 6733

TEXAS COUNTY AND DISTRICT RETIREMENT SYSTEM p 1442
901 S Mopac, Austin TX 78746
Tel (512) 328-8889 SIC 6733

ASHFORD HOSPITALITY TRUST INC p 117
14185 Dallas Pkwy # 1100, Dallas TX 75254
Tel (972) 490-9600 SIC 6798 6733

LONE STAR REAL ESTATE FUND (US) LP p 876
2711 N Haskell Ave, Dallas TX 75204
Tel (214) 754-8300 SIC 6733

MA ACQUISITION CO LLC p 891
501 Galveston St, Wichita Falls TX 76301
Tel (940) 397-2100 SIC 6733

RETIREE HEALTH PLAN AND TRUST FOR CERTAIN EMPOF AIR LINE PILOTS ASSNINTL p 1228
535 Herndon Pkwy, Herndon VA 20170
Tel (703) 689-4238 SIC 6733

SEIU HEALTHCARE NW HEALTH BENEFITS TRUST p 1301
215 Columbia St Ste 300, Seattle WA 98104
Tel (425) 771-7359 SIC 6733

WESTERN CONFERENCE OF TEAMSTERS PENSION TRUST FUND p 1597
2323 Eastlake Ave E, Seattle WA 98102
Tel (206) 329-4900 SIC 6733

VEBA TRUST FOR PUBLIC EMPLOYEES IN NORTHWEST p 1546
906 W 2nd Ave, Spokane WA 99201
Tel (509) 838-5571 SIC 6733

BELOIT MEMORIAL HOSPITAL FOUNDATION INC p 171
1969 W Hart Rd, Beloit WI 53511
Tel (608) 363-5724 SIC 6733

MARSHALL & ILSLEY TRUST CO NATIONAL ASSOCIATION p 911
111 E Kilbourn Ave # 200, Milwaukee WI 53202
Tel (414) 287-8700 SIC 6733

JOHNSON FINANCIAL GROUP INC p 791
555 Main St Ste 400, Racine WI 53403
Tel (262) 619-2700
SIC 6022 6021 6712 6733 6311

SIC 6792 Oil Royalty Traders

GLOBAL FINANCIAL MANAGEMENT SERVICES LLC p 616
925 S Federal Hwy Ste 375, Boca Raton FL 33432
Tel (561) 347-5500 SIC 6792

MATCON TRADING CORP p 919
2020 Ponce De Leon Blvd # 1204, Coral Gables FL 33134
Tel (305) 442-6333 SIC 6792 2951

APEX HOLDING CO p 96
8235 Forsyth Blvd Ste 400, Saint Louis MO 63105
Tel (314) 889-9600 SIC 6792 4412 4226

MODERN AG PRODUCTS LTD p 981
1655 Louisiana St, Beaumont TX 77701
Tel (409) 833-2665 SIC 7359 6792 0161

SIC 6794 Patent Owners & Lessors

EXPRESS OIL CHANGE LLC p 520
1880 Southpark Dr, Hoover AL 35244
Tel (205) 945-1771 SIC 7549 7538 6794

PETER PIPER INC p 1138
4745 N 7th St Ste 350, Phoenix AZ 85014
Tel (480) 609-6400 SIC 5812 7993 6794

BRER SERVICES INC p 210
16260 N 71st St, Scottsdale AZ 85254
Tel (949) 794-7900 SIC 6794

KAHALA BRANDS LTD p 800
9311 E Via De Ventura, Scottsdale AZ 85258
Tel (480) 362-4800 SIC 5812 6794

▲ **KONA GRILL INC** p 827
7150 E Camelback Rd # 220, Scottsdale AZ 85251
Tel (480) 922-8100 SIC 5812 6794

STEPHEN L LAFRANCE HOLDINGS INC p 1386
3017 N Midland Dr, Pine Bluff AR 71603
Tel (870) 535-5171 SIC 5912 6794

■ **DISNEY ENTERPRISES INC** p 443
500 S Buena Vista St, Burbank CA 91521
Tel (818) 560-1000
SIC 7812 6794 5331 7996 7941

■ **WALT DISNEY MUSIC CO** p 1574
500 S Buena Vista St, Burbank CA 91521
Tel (818) 560-1000 SIC 6794

▲ **CALLAWAY GOLF CO** p 242
2180 Rutherford Rd, Carlsbad CA 92008
Tel (760) 931-1771
SIC 3949 2329 2339 6794

JENNY CRAIG INC p 782
5770 Fleet St, Carlsbad CA 92008
Tel (760) 696-4000
SIC 7299 6794 5149 5499

CKE RESTAURANTS HOLDINGS INC p 320
6307 Carpinteria Ave A, Carpinteria CA 93013
Tel (805) 745-7500 SIC 5812 6794

ROUND TABLE PIZZA INC p 1253
1320 Willow Pass Rd # 600, Concord CA 94520
Tel (925) 969-3900 SIC 5812 6794

▲ **EL POLLO LOCO HOLDINGS INC** p 483
3535 Harbor Blvd Ste 100, Costa Mesa CA 92626
Tel (714) 599-5000 SIC 5812 6794

▲ **JAMBA INC** p 776
6475 Christie Ave Ste 150, Emeryville CA 94608
Tel (510) 596-0100 SIC 5812 6794

■ **JUICE CLUB INC** p 797
6475 Christie Ave Ste 150, Emeryville CA 94608
Tel (510) 596-0100 SIC 5812 6794

▲ **DINEEQUITY INC** p 440
450 N Brand Blvd, Glendale CA 91203
Tel (818) 240-6055 SIC 5812 6794

■ **BRER AFFILIATES INC** p 210
18500 Von Karman Ave # 400, Irvine CA 92612
Tel (949) 794-7900 SIC 6794 6531

BROOKFIELD RELOCATION INC p 217
3333 Michelson Dr # 1000, Irvine CA 92612
Tel (949) 794-7900 SIC 6794

FITNESS INTERNATIONAL LLC p 553
3161 Michelson Dr Ste 600, Irvine CA 92612
Tel (949) 255-7200 SIC 7991 6794

PACIFIC DENTAL SERVICES INC p 1104
17000 Red Hill Ave, Irvine CA 92614
Tel (714) 845-8500 SIC 8021 6794

■ **TACO BELL CORP** p 1421
1 Glen Bell Way, Irvine CA 92618
Tel (949) 863-4500 SIC 5812 6794

▲ **DEL TACO RESTAURANTS INC** p 423
25521 Commercentre Dr # 200, Lake Forest CA 92630
Tel (949) 462-9300 SIC 5812 6794

INTERNATIONAL COFFEE & TEA LLC p 754
5700 Wilshire Blvd # 120, Los Angeles CA 90036
Tel (310) 237-2326 SIC 5812 5499 6794

▲ **RENTECH INC** p 1224
10880 Wilshire Blvd # 1101, Los Angeles CA 90024
Tel (310) 571-9800 SIC 2999 2873 6794

RISK MANAGEMENT SOLUTIONS INC p 1236
7575 Gateway Blvd, Newark CA 94560
Tel (510) 505-2500 SIC 6794 6411

▲ **ACACIA RESEARCH CORP** p 13
520 Newport Center Dr # 1200, Newport Beach CA 92660
Tel (949) 480-8300 SIC 6794

FRANDELI GROUP LLC p 574
20377 Sw Acacia St # 200, Newport Beach CA 92660
Tel (714) 450-7660 SIC 6794

TODAI FRANCHISING LLC p 1458
19481 San Jose Ave, Rowland Heights CA 91748
Tel (909) 869-7727 SIC 6794

▲ **JACK IN BOX INC** p 773
9330 Balboa Ave, San Diego CA 92123
Tel (858) 571-2121 SIC 5812 6794

▲ **QUALCOMM INC** p 1196
5775 Morehouse Dr, San Diego CA 92121
Tel (858) 587-1121 SIC 3674 7372 6794

■ **QUALCOMM INTERNATIONAL INC** p 1196
5775 Morehouse Dr, San Diego CA 92121
Tel (858) 587-1121 SIC 6794

■ **QUALCOMM TECHNOLOGIES INC** p 1196
5775 Morehouse Dr, San Diego CA 92121
Tel (858) 587-1121 SIC 3674 7372 6794

CPK HOLDINGS INC p 387
Embarcadero Ctr, San Francisco CA 94111
Tel (415) 983-2700 SIC 5812 6794

▲ **DOLBY LABORATORIES INC** p 447
1275 Market St, San Francisco CA 94103
Tel (415) 558-0200 SIC 3663 6794

▲ **RPX CORP** p 1255
1 Market Plz Ste 800, San Francisco CA 94105
Tel (866) 779-7641 SIC 6794 8741

■ **TESSERA TECHNOLOGIES INC** p 1441
3025 Orchard Pkwy, San Jose CA 95134
Tel (408) 321-6000 SIC 6794 3674

▲ **RAMBUS INC** p 1207
1050 Entp Way Ste 700, Sunnyvale CA 94089
Tel (408) 462-8000 SIC 3674 6794

SUNKIST GROWERS INC p 1402
27770 N Entertainment Dr # 120, Valencia CA 91355
Tel (818) 986-4800
SIC 5148 2033 2037 2899 6794 5046

LUND BROWN ENTERPRISES LLC p 885
7490 Clubhouse Rd Ste 200, Boulder CO 80301
Tel (303) 530-2900 SIC 6794

MRS FIELDS COMPANIES INC p 996
8001 Arista Pl Unit 600, Broomfield CO 80021
Tel (720) 599-3374 SIC 6794 5461

MRS FIELDS HOLDING CO INC p 996
8001 Arista Pl Unit 600, Broomfield CO 80021
Tel (720) 599-3350 SIC 5461 6794

QUIZNOS CORP p 1200
7595 E Tech Way Ste 200, Denver CO 80237
Tel (720) 359-3300 SIC 6794 5812

ERIE COUNTY INVESTMENT CO p 508
601 Corporate Cir, Golden CO 80401
Tel (303) 384-0200
SIC 5812 6794 6531 6552 1542 1521

▲ **RED ROBIN GOURMET BURGERS INC** p 1216
6312 S Fiddlers, Greenwood Village CO 80111
Tel (303) 846-6000 SIC 5812 6794

■ **RED ROBIN INTERNATIONAL INC** p 1216
6312 S Fiddlers Green Cir 200n, Greenwood Village CO 80111
Tel (303) 846-6000
SIC 5812 6794 5813 5087

EINSTEIN NOAH RESTAURANT GROUP INC p 482
555 Zang St Ste 300, Lakewood CO 80228
Tel (303) 568-8000 SIC 5812 6794

■ **QDOBA RESTAURANT CORP** p 1194
7244 W Bonfils Ln, Lakewood CO 80226
Tel (720) 898-2300 SIC 5812 6794

CAPRICORN INVESTORS II LP p 251
30 E Elm St, Greenwich CT 06830
Tel (203) 861-6600 SIC 2676 5461 6794

NORTH CASTLE PARTNERS LLC p 1051
183 E Putnam Ave, Greenwich CT 06830
Tel (203) 485-0216
SIC 7299 6794 5149 5499

▲ **INTERDIGITAL INC** p 752
200 Bellevue Pkwy Ste 300, Wilmington DE 19809
Tel (302) 281-3600 SIC 3663 5999 6794

CAREY INTERNATIONAL INC p 255
4530 Wscnsin Ave Nw Ste 5, Washington DC 20016
Tel (202) 895-1200 SIC 4119 6794

PODS ENTERPRISES LLC p 1158
5585 Rio Vista Dr, Clearwater FL 33760
Tel (727) 538-6300 SIC 4225 6794

PORPOISE POOL & PATIO INC p 1161
14480 62nd St N, Clearwater FL 33760
Tel (727) 531-8913
SIC 6794 5999 5712 5091

CNA HOLDING CORP p 329
350 Sw 12th Ave, Deerfield Beach FL 33442
Tel (561) 922-2500 SIC 7349 6794

COVERALL NORTH AMERICA INC p 385
350 Sw 12th Ave, Deerfield Beach FL 33442
Tel (561) 922-2500 SIC 6794 7349

■ **HERTZ CORP** p 687
8501 Williams Rd, Estero FL 33928
Tel (239) 301-7000
SIC 7514 7515 7513 7359 5521 6794

SFN GROUP INC p 1310
2050 Spectrum Blvd, Fort Lauderdale FL 33309
Tel (954) 308-7600 SIC 6794 7363

ADECCO USA INC p 22
10151 Deerwood Bldg 200, Jacksonville FL 32256
Tel (904) 359-4710
SIC 7363 7361 8742 6794

BENIHANA INC p 173
21500 Biscayne Blvd # 100, Miami FL 33180
Tel (305) 593-0770 SIC 5812 6794

BURGER KING CORP p 227
5505 Blue Lagoon Dr, Miami FL 33126
Tel (305) 378-3000 SIC 5812 6794

BURGER KING HOLDINGS INC p 227
5505 Blue Lagoon Dr, Miami FL 33126
Tel (305) 378-3000 SIC 5812 6794

INTERFOODS OF AMERICA INC p 752
9500 S Dadeland Blvd # 800, Miami FL 33156
Tel (305) 670-0746 SIC 5812 6794

TIM HORTONS USA INC p 1453
5505 Blue Lagoon Dr, Miami FL 33126
Tel (888) 376-4835 SIC 6794 5812

HARD ROCK CAFE FOUNDATION INC p 660
6100 Old Park Ln Ste 100, Orlando FL 32835
Tel (407) 445-7625
SIC 5812 5813 7011 6794

PLANET HOLLYWOOD INTERNATIONAL INC p 1154
4700 Millenia Blvd # 400, Orlando FL 32839
Tel (407) 903-5500 SIC 5812 6794 5699

MIDAS INC p 964
4300 Tbc Way, Palm Beach Gardens FL 33410
Tel (630) 438-3000 SIC 7533 6794

VALPAK DIRECT MARKETING SYSTEMS INC p 1542
805 Exe Ctr Dr W, Saint Petersburg FL 33702
Tel (727) 399-3175 SIC 7331 6794

INTERIM HEALTHCARE INC p 752
1601 Swgrs Corp Pkwy # 100, Sunrise FL 33323
Tel (800) 338-7786 SIC 6794 7363 8082

BUDDYS NEWCO LLC p 223
6608 E Adamo Dr, Tampa FL 33619
Tel (813) 623-5461 SIC 7359 6794

CHECKERS DRIVE-IN RESTAURANTS INC p 292
4300 W Cypress St Ste 600, Tampa FL 33607
Tel (813) 283-7000 SIC 5812 6794

▲ **RUTHS HOSPITALITY GROUP INC** p 1260
1030 W Canton Ave Ste 100, Winter Park FL 32789
Tel (407) 333-7440 SIC 5812 6794

EXECUTRAIN CORP p 518
2500 Northwinds Pkwy # 460, Alpharetta GA 30009
Tel (770) 667-7700 SIC 6794 8243

▲ **AARONS INC** p 8
400 Galleria Pkwy Se # 300, Atlanta GA 30339
Tel (404) 231-0011
SIC 7359 5712 5731 5722 5932 6794

ALTISOURCE HOLDINGS LLC p 62
1000 Abernathy Rd, Atlanta GA 30328
Tel (877) 839-7118 SIC 6794 6519

FOCUS BRANDS INC p 562
5620 Glenridge Dr, Atlanta GA 30342
Tel (404) 255-3250 SIC 5461 5143 6794

GLOBAL FRANCHISE GROUP LLC p 616
5555 Glenridge Connector # 850, Atlanta GA 30342
Tel (770) 514-4500 SIC 5461 6794

HOOTERS OF AMERICA LLC p 706
1815 The Exchange Se, Atlanta GA 30339
Tel (770) 951-2040 SIC 5812 6794

INTERCONTINENTAL HOTELS GROUP RESOURCES INC p 752
3 Ravinia Dr Ste 100, Atlanta GA 30346
Tel (770) 604-5000 SIC 7011 8741 6794

▲ **POPEYES LOUISIANA KITCHEN INC** p 1161
400 Perimeter Ctr Ter, Atlanta GA 30346
Tel (404) 459-4450 SIC 5812 6794

ROARK CAPITAL GROUP INC p 1240
1180 Peachtree St Ne # 2500, Atlanta GA 30309
Tel (404) 591-5200
SIC 6726 3993 7331 6794 5261

ROYAL HOSPITALITY CORP p 1254
255 E Paces Ferry Rd Ne # 300, Atlanta GA 30305
Tel (404) 239-0329 SIC 6794 8741 5812

SIX CONTINENTS HOTELS INC p 1328
3 Ravinia Dr Ste 100, Atlanta GA 30346
Tel (770) 604-2000 SIC 7011 6794 8741

KRYSTAL CO p 830
1455 Lincoln Pkwy E # 600, Dunwoody GA 30346
Tel (423) 757-1550 SIC 5812 6794

AMERICAN LUBEFAST LLC p 75
1550 N Brown Rd Ste 140, Lawrenceville GA 30043
Tel (770) 995-6312 SIC 6794 7549

MDSA LLC p 933
650 Engineering Dr, Norcross GA 30092
Tel (770) 448-3900 SIC 5013 6794

WAFFLE HOUSE INC p 1571
5986 Financial Dr, Norcross GA 30071
Tel (770) 729-5700 SIC 5812 6794

TD FOOD GROUP INC p 1429
828 Fort Street Mall # 130, Honolulu HI 96813
Tel (808) 566-3200 SIC 5812 6794

OPTION CARE ENTERPRISES INC p 1090
3000 Lakeside Dr Ste 300n, Bannockburn IL 60015
Tel (847) 964-4950
SIC 8082 5122 6794 5912 8049

MONICAL PIZZA CORP p 984
530 N Kinzie Ave, Bradley IL 60915
Tel (815) 937-1890 SIC 5812 6794

▲ **HYATT HOTELS CORP** p 723
71 S Wacker Dr Ste 1000, Chicago IL 60606
Tel (312) 750-1234 SIC 7011 6794

CLARK BRANDS LLC p 322
4200 Commerce Ct Ste 350, Lisle IL 60532
Tel (630) 355-8918
SIC 6794 7389 5541 5812

▲ **MCDONALDS CORP** p 928
1 Mcdonalds Dr, Oak Brook IL 60523
Tel (630) 623-3000 SIC 5812 6794

JD BYRIDER SYSTEMS LLC p 780
12802 Hmlton Crssing Blvd, Carmel IN 46032
Tel (317) 249-3000
SIC 6794 5734 7538 7515 5521

■ **STEAK N SHAKE INC** p 1384
36 S Pennsylvania St # 500, Indianapolis IN 46204
Tel (317) 633-4100 SIC 5812 6794

DIRECTBUY INC p 441
8450 Broadway, Merrillville IN 46410
Tel (219) 736-1100
SIC 5021 5064 5023 5961 6794 7299

QUALITY DINING INC p 1197
4220 Edison Lakes Pkwy # 300, Mishawaka IN 46545
Tel (574) 271-4600 SIC 5812 6794

BRIDGESTONE BANDAG LLC p 211
2000 Bandag Dr, Muscatine IA 52761
Tel (563) 262-2511
SIC 7534 3559 5014 3011 7549 6794

PIZZA RANCH INC p 1153
204 19th St Se, Orange City IA 51041
Tel (712) 707-8800 SIC 5812 6794

NPC RESTAURANT HOLDINGS LLC p 1064
7300 W 129th St, Overland Park KS 66213
Tel (913) 327-5555 SIC 5812 6794

TACO TICO INC p 1421
505 S Broadway Ave # 205, Wichita KS 67202
Tel (316) 683-6621 SIC 6794

A & W RESTAURANTS INC p 4
1648 Mcgrathiana Pkwy # 380, Lexington KY 40511
Tel (859) 219-0019 SIC 5812 6794

A GREAT AMERICAN BRAND LLC p 5
1648 Mcgrathiana Pkwy, Lexington KY 40511
Tel (859) 219-0019 SIC 5812 6794

SEED RESTAURANT GROUP INC p 1300
2470 Palumbo Dr, Lexington KY 40509
Tel (859) 268-1668 SIC 6794 5812

■ **KENTUCKY FRIED CHICKEN CORP** p 812
1441 Gardiner Ln, Louisville KY 40213
Tel (502) 874-8300 SIC 5812 6794

■ **KFC CORP (DE)** p 816
1900 Colonel Sanders Ln, Louisville KY 40213
Tel (502) 874-8300 SIC 5812 6794

LONG JOHN SILVERS RESTAURANT INC p 876
1441 Gardiner Ln, Louisville KY 40213
Tel (502) 874-3000 SIC 5812 6794

▲ **PAPA JOHNS INTERNATIONAL INC** p 1112
2002 Papa Johns Blvd # 100, Louisville KY 40299
Tel (502) 261-7272 SIC 5812 6794 2099

■ **TEXAS ROADHOUSE HOLDINGS LLC** p 1444
6040 Dutchmans Ln Ste 400, Louisville KY 40205
Tel (502) 426-9984 SIC 5812 6794

▲ **TEXAS ROADHOUSE INC** p 1444
6040 Dutchmans Ln Ste 200, Louisville KY 40205
Tel (502) 426-9984 SIC 5812 6794

▲ **YUM BRANDS INC** p 1640
1441 Gardiner Ln, Louisville KY 40213
Tel (502) 874-8300 SIC 5812 6794

CROWN CENTRAL PETROLEUM CORP p 395
1 N Charles St Ste 2100, Baltimore MD 21201
Tel (410) 539-7400 SIC 2911 5171 6794

▲ **MARRIOTT INTERNATIONAL INC** p 910
10400 Fernwood Rd, Bethesda MD 20817
Tel (301) 380-3000 SIC 7011 6794 6531

RENAISSANCE HOTEL OPERATING CO INC p 1223
10400 Fernwood Rd, Bethesda MD 20817
Tel (301) 380-3000 SIC 7011 8741 6794

DASH IN FOOD STORES INC p 413
6355 Crain Hwy, La Plata MD 20646
Tel (301) 932-3600 SIC 5541 5411 6794

COSI INC p 373
294 Washington St Ste 510, Boston MA 02108
Tel (857) 415-5000 SIC 5812 6794

URC LLC p 1530
100 Charles Park Rd, Boston MA 02132
Tel (617) 323-9200 SIC 5812 5813 6794

▲ **DUNKIN BRANDS GROUP INC** p 461
130 Royall St, Canton MA 02021
Tel (781) 737-3000
SIC 5461 5499 6794 5812

COPYRIGHT CLEARANCE CENTER INC p 368
222 Rosewood Dr Fl 10, Danvers MA 01923
Tel (978) 750-8400 SIC 6794 7375

PAPA GINOS HOLDINGS CORP p 1112
600 Providence Hwy, Dedham MA 02026
Tel (781) 461-1200 SIC 5812 6794

▲ **DOMINOS PIZZA INC** p 449
30 Frank Lloyd Wright Dr, Ann Arbor MI 48105
Tel (734) 930-3030 SIC 5812 5149 6794

■ **DOMINOS PIZZA LLC** p 449
30 Frank Lloyd Wright Dr, Ann Arbor MI 48105
Tel (734) 930-3030
SIC 5812 6794 5046 5149 8741 2045

MC DONALDS OF CALHOUN INC p 925
806 Columbia Ave W, Battle Creek MI 49015
Tel (269) 965-1402 SIC 5812 8742 6794

LITTLE CAESAR ENTERPRISES INC p 870
2211 Woodward Ave, Detroit MI 48201
Tel (313) 983-6000
SIC 5812 6794 5141 5046 8741

▲ **MERITAGE HOSPITALITY GROUP INC** p 949
45 Ottawa Ave Sw Ste 600, Grand Rapids MI 49503
Tel (616) 776-2600 SIC 5812 6794

▲ **DIVERSIFIED RESTAURANT HOLDINGS INC** p 444
27680 Franklin Rd, Southfield MI 48034
Tel (248) 223-9160 SIC 5812 5813 6794

GOLDEN OPTICAL CORP p 621
19800 W 8 Mile Rd, Southfield MI 48075
Tel (248) 354-7100 SIC 5995 6794

ABRA AUTO BODY & GLASS LP p 12
7225 Northland Dr N # 210, Brooklyn Park MN 55428
Tel (651) 487-2470 SIC 6794 7532

MONGOLIAN OPERATING CO LLC p 984
200 E Travelers Trl # 235, Burnsville MN 55337
Tel (952) 288-2363 SIC 5812 6794

▲ **REGIS CORP** p 1220
7201 Metro Blvd, Edina MN 55439
Tel (952) 947-7777 SIC 7231 7299 6794

CARLSON HOTELS MANAGEMENT CORP p 258
701 Tower Carlson Pkwy, Hopkins MN 55305
Tel (763) 212-5000 SIC 6794 6531 6552

JACOBS INDUSTRIES INC p 775
8096 Excelsior Blvd, Hopkins MN 55343
Tel (612) 339-9500
SIC 2841 2087 2099 2844 5084 6794

▲ **BUFFALO WILD WINGS INC** p 224
5500 Wayzata Blvd # 1600, Minneapolis MN 55416
Tel (952) 593-9943 SIC 5812 6794

CARIBOU COFFEE CO INC p 256
3900 Lake Breeze Ave, Minneapolis MN 55429
Tel (763) 592-2200 SIC 5812 5499 6794

CARLSON HOTELS LIMITED PARTNERSHIP p 257
Carlson Parkway 701 Twr St Carlson Parkw, Minneapolis MN 55459
Tel (763) 212-1000
SIC 6794 7011 5812 5813

CARLSON HOLDINGS INC p 257
701 Carlson Pkwy, Minnetonka MN 55305
Tel (763) 212-5000
SIC 7011 5812 6794 7389 4724

CARLSON INC p 258
701 Carlson Pkwy, Minnetonka MN 55305
Tel (763) 212-5000
SIC 7011 5812 6794 8742 8743 7389

▲ **FAMOUS DAVES OF AMERICA INC** p 527
12701 Whitewater Dr # 200, Minnetonka MN 55343
Tel (952) 294-1300 SIC 5812 6794

RADISSON HOTELS INTERNATIONAL INC p 1204
701 Carlson Pkwy, Minnetonka MN 55305
Tel (763) 212-5000
SIC 7011 6794 6552 6531 8742 7389

■ **APPLEBEES INTERNATIONAL INC** p 99
8140 Ward Pkwy Ste 300, Kansas City MO 64114
Tel (913) 890-0100 SIC 5812 6794

▲ **H&R BLOCK INC** p 651
1 H&R Block Way, Kansas City MO 64105
Tel (816) 854-3000 SIC 7291 6794

K-STATE-MRI BIODEFENSE COALITION LLC p 799
425 Volker Blvd, Kansas City MO 64110
Tel (816) 753-7600 SIC 6794

MRIGLOBAL p 996
425 Volker Blvd, Kansas City MO 64110
Tel (816) 753-7600 SIC 8731 6794

▲ **BUILD-A-BEAR WORKSHOP INC** p 224
1954 Innerbelt Bus Ctr Dr, Saint Louis MO 63114
Tel (314) 423-8000 SIC 5945 6794

▲ **PANERA BREAD CO** p 1111
3630 S Geyer Rd Ste 100, Saint Louis MO 63127
Tel (314) 984-1000 SIC 5812 5461 6794

KAMPGROUNDS OF AMERICA INC p 802
550 N 31st St Ste 400, Billings MT 59101
Tel (406) 248-8135 SIC 6794 7033

GODFATHERS PIZZA INC p 619
2808 N 108th St, Omaha NE 68164
Tel (402) 391-1452 SIC 5812 6794

■ **VF SPORTSWEAR INC** p 1553
545 Wshngton Blvd Fl 8, Jersey City NJ 07310
Tel (212) 541-5757
SIC 2329 2384 5136 5137 5611 6794

■ **REALOGY GROUP LLC** p 1214
175 Park Ave, Madison NJ 07940
Tel (973) 407-2000
SIC 6531 6794 7389 6541

▲ **REALOGY HOLDINGS CORP** p 1214
175 Park Ave, Madison NJ 07940
Tel (973) 407-2000
SIC 6531 6794 7389 6541

■ **REALOGY INTERMEDIATE HOLDINGS LLC** p 1214
175 Park Ave, Madison NJ 07940
Tel (973) 407-0000
SIC 6531 6794 7389 6541

■ **HERTZ INVESTORS INC** p 687
225 Brae Blvd, Park Ridge NJ 07656
Tel (201) 307-2000
SIC 7514 7515 7513 7359 5521 6794

▲ **AVIS BUDGET GROUP INC** p 138
6 Sylvan Way Ste 1, Parsippany NJ 07054
Tel (973) 496-4700 SIC 7514 7513 6794

■ **SUPER 8 WORLDWIDE INC** p 1405
22 Sylvan Way Fl 3, Parsippany NJ 07054
Tel (850) 973-3331 SIC 6794

■ **PARTY CITY CORP** p 1119
25 Green Pond Rd Ste 1, Rockaway NJ 07866
Tel (973) 453-8600 SIC 6794 5947 7299

ASPEN DENTAL MANAGEMENT INC p 118
281 Sanders Creek Pkwy, East Syracuse NY 13057
Tel (315) 454-6000 SIC 8021 8072 6794

■ **AMSCAN HOLDINGS INC** p 87
80 Grasslands Rd Ste 3, Elmsford NY 10523
Tel (914) 345-2020
SIC 5947 2679 3089 3069 6794

▲ **PARTY CITY HOLDCO INC** p 1119
80 Grasslands Rd, Elmsford NY 10523
Tel (914) 345-2020
SIC 5947 5963 5199 6794

■ **PARTY CITY HOLDINGS INC** p 1119
80 Grasslands Rd, Elmsford NY 10523
Tel (973) 453-8600 SIC 5947 6794

▲ **NATHANS FAMOUS INC** p 1009
1 Jericho Plz Fl 2, Jericho NY 11753
Tel (516) 338-8500 SIC 5812 6794

ADO STAFFING INC p 23
175 Broadhollow Rd, Melville NY 11747
Tel (631) 844-7800 SIC 7363 6794

SBARRO HOLDINGS LLC p 1285
401 Broadhollow Rd Ll10, Melville NY 11747
Tel (631) 715-4100 SIC 5812 6794

SBARRO INC p 1285
401 Broadhollow Rd Ll10, Melville NY 11747
Tel (631) 715-4100 SIC 5812 6794

■ **ABC INC** p 10
77 W 66th St Rm 100, New York NY 10023
Tel (212) 456-7777
SIC 4833 4832 7812 6794 2711 2721

AUTHENTIC BRANDS GROUP LLC p 133
1411 Broadway Fl 4, New York NY 10018
Tel (212) 760-2410 SIC 6794

BARNEYS INC p 156
575 5th Ave Fl 11, New York NY 10017
Tel (212) 450-8700
SIC 5611 5621 5632 5932 5947 6794

BROADCAST MUSIC INC p 215
250 Greenwich St, New York NY 10007
Tel (212) 220-3000 SIC 6794

BTF/CFI INC p 222
144 W 38th St, New York NY 10018
Tel (212) 993-0300
SIC 6794 7991 5621 5411

■ **CALVIN KLEIN INC** p 243
205 W 39th St Lbby 2, New York NY 10018
Tel (212) 719-2600
SIC 5651 5137 5136 5611 5621 6794

CHINOS HOLDINGS INC p 301
770 Broadway, New York NY 10003
Tel (212) 209-2500
SIC 5961 5621 5611 5632 6794

CHINOS INTERMEDIATE HOLDINGS B INC p 301
770 Broadway, New York NY 10003
Tel (212) 209-2500
SIC 5961 5621 5611 5632 6794

CRUNCH LLC p 396
220 W 19th St, New York NY 10011
Tel (212) 993-0300 SIC 7991 6794

▲ FOOT LOCKER INC p 564
330 W 34th St, New York NY 10001
Tel (212) 720-3700
SIC 5661 5941 5961 6794

GIRL SCOUTS OF UNITED STATES OF AMERICA p 613
420 5th Ave Fl 13, New York NY 10018
Tel (212) 852-8000
SIC 8641 5137 6794 2721

HILTON HOTELS HOLDINGS CORP p 695
345 Park Ave, New York NY 10154
Tel (212) 583-5000 *SIC* 7011 6794

■ HISTORIC TW INC p 696
75 Rockefeller Plz, New York NY 10019
Tel (212) 484-8000
SIC 3652 6794 2741 7812 4841 2721

HUGO BOSS USA INC p 717
55 Water St Fl 48, New York NY 10041
Tel (212) 940-0600
SIC 2311 2325 2337 5136 5611 6794

▲ ICONIX BRAND GROUP INC p 728
1450 Broadway Fl 3, New York NY 10018
Tel (212) 730-0030 *SIC* 6794 3143 3144

INFORMATION BUILDERS INC p 741
2 Penn Plz Fl 28, New York NY 10121
Tel (212) 736-4433 *SIC* 7373 6794

J CREW OPERATING CORP p 770
770 Brdwy Fl 11 & 12, New York NY 10003
Tel (212) 209-2500
SIC 5961 5621 5611 5661 5632 6794

MAJOR LEAGUE BASEBALL PROPERTIES INC p 899
245 Park Ave Fl 34, New York NY 10167
Tel (212) 931-7800 *SIC* 6794 4833 8748

■ MARVEL ENTERTAINMENT LLC p 913
135 W 50th St Fl 7, New York NY 10020
Tel (212) 576-4000
SIC 2721 6794 3944 7929

METROMEDIA CO p 955
810 Seventh Ave Fl 29, New York NY 10019
Tel (212) 606-4437
SIC 5812 6794 4813 4911

▲ SCHOLASTIC CORP p 1288
557 Broadway Lbby 1, New York NY 10012
Tel (212) 343-6100
SIC 2731 2721 7372 7812 6794 7311

TAXI HOLDINGS CORP p 1426
390 Park Ave, New York NY 10022
Tel (212) 318-9800 *SIC* 5812 6794

TRUMP ORGANIZATION INC p 1487
725 5th Ave Bsmt A, New York NY 10022
Tel (212) 832-2000 *SIC* 6531 7922 6794

WARNER MUSIC GROUP CORP p 1576
1633 Broadway, New York NY 10019
Tel (212) 275-2000 *SIC* 3652 6794

WELLSPRING DISTRIBUTION INC p 1591
390 Park Ave Fl 5, New York NY 10022
Tel (212) 318-9800 *SIC* 6794 5812

▲ CARROLS RESTAURANT GROUP INC p 261
968 James St, Syracuse NY 13203
Tel (315) 424-0513 *SIC* 5812 6794

■ SHERATON CORP p 1315
1111 Westchester Ave, White Plains NY 10604
Tel (800) 328-6242 *SIC* 7011 8741 6794

JENNIFER CONVERTIBLES INC p 782
335 Crossways Park Dr, Woodbury NY 11797
Tel (516) 496-1900 *SIC* 5712 6794 5021

BJ HOLDINGS CORP p 185
9432 Southern Pine Blvd, Charlotte NC 28273
Tel (704) 527-2675 *SIC* 5812 6794

■ BOJANGLES RESTAURANTS INC p 198
9432 Southern Pine Blvd, Charlotte NC 28273
Tel (704) 527-2675 *SIC* 5812 6794

■ OHIO MATTRESS CO LICENSING AND COMPONENTS GROUP p 1077
1 Office Parkway Rd, Trinity NC 27370
Tel (336) 861-3500 *SIC* 2515 6794

BODY SHOP INC p 197
5036 One World Way, Wake Forest NC 27587
Tel (919) 554-4900 *SIC* 5999 6794 2844

PHYSICIANS WEIGHT LOSS CENTERS OF AMERICA INC p 1146
395 Springside Dr, Akron OH 44333
Tel (330) 666-7952 *SIC* 5141 5122 6794

LAROSAS INC p 845
2334 Boudinot Ave, Cincinnati OH 45238
Tel (513) 347-5660
SIC 5812 6794 5141 5921

DAMONS INTERNATIONAL INC p 410
4645 Executive Dr, Columbus OH 43220
Tel (614) 442-7900 *SIC* 6794 8741 5812

STANLEY STEEMER INTERNATIONAL INC p 1377
5800 Innovation Dr, Dublin OH 43016
Tel (614) 764-2007
SIC 7217 3635 6794 5713

▲ WENDYS CO p 1592
1 Dave Thomas Blvd, Dublin OH 43017
Tel (614) 764-3100 *SIC* 5812 6794

■ WENDYS RESTAURANTS LLC p 1592
1 Dave Thomas Blvd, Dublin OH 43017
Tel (614) 764-3100 *SIC* 5812 6794

SKYLINE CHILI INC p 1330
4180 Thunderbird Ln, Fairfield OH 45014
Tel (513) 874-1188
SIC 5812 2038 6794 5149 2032

CORNWELL QUALITY TOOLS CO p 371
667 Seville Rd, Wadsworth OH 44281
Tel (330) 336-3506 *SIC* 5085 3423 6794

■ TA OPERATING LLC p 1420
24601 Center Ridge Rd # 200, Westlake OH 44145
Tel (440) 808-9100
SIC 5541 7538 5812 5411 6794

EATERIES INC p 473
1220 S Santa Fe Ave, Edmond OK 73003
Tel (480) 347-3800 *SIC* 5812 5813 6794

EXPRESS SERVICES INC p 520
9701 Boardwalk Blvd, Oklahoma City OK 73162
Tel (405) 840-5000 *SIC* 7363 6794 7361

▲ SONIC CORP p 1340
300 Johnny Bench Dr, Oklahoma City OK 73104
Tel (405) 225-5000 *SIC* 5812 6794

■ SONIC INDUSTRIES SERVICES INC p 1340
300 Johnny Bench Dr # 400, Oklahoma City OK 73104
Tel (405) 225-5000 *SIC* 6794 5812

■ DOLLAR THRIFTY AUTOMOTIVE GROUP INC p 448
5330 E 31st St, Tulsa OK 74135
Tel (918) 660-7700 *SIC* 6794 7514

MAZZIOS LLC p 924
4441 S 72nd East Ave, Tulsa OK 74145
Tel (918) 663-8880 *SIC* 5812 6794

■ THRIFTY INC p 1451
5310 E 31st St Ste 100, Tulsa OK 74135
Tel (918) 665-3930
SIC 6794 7515 7514 7513

ELMERS RESTAURANTS INC p 489
8338 Ne Alderwood Rd, Portland OR 97220
Tel (503) 252-1485 *SIC* 6794 5812

OSF INTERNATIONAL INC p 1096
0715 Sw Bancroft St, Portland OR 97239
Tel (503) 222-5375 *SIC* 5812 6794

IKEA NORTH AMERICA SERVICES LLC p 731
420 Alan Wood Rd, Conshohocken PA 19428
Tel (610) 834-0180 *SIC* 6794 5712

NEW HORIZONS WORLDWIDE INC p 1031
100 4 Falls Corporate Ctr # 408, Conshohocken PA 19428
Tel (888) 236-3625 *SIC* 6794 8243

AUNTIE ANNES INC p 131
48-50 W Chestnut St # 200, Lancaster PA 17603
Tel (717) 435-1435 *SIC* 6794 2051 5461

ZAUSNER FOODS CORP p 1641
400 S Custer Ave, New Holland PA 17557
Tel (717) 355-8505 *SIC* 2022 2032 6794

■ CDI CORP p 271
1735 Market St Ste 200, Philadelphia PA 19103
Tel (215) 569-2200
SIC 7363 8711 7361 6794

■ GENERAL NUTRITION CORP p 601
300 6th Ave, Pittsburgh PA 15222
Tel (412) 288-4600
SIC 5499 5999 5941 5699 6794

GIANT EAGLE INC p 610
101 Kappa Dr, Pittsburgh PA 15238
Tel (800) 362-8899
SIC 5411 5141 5147 5148 5143 6794

UNI-MARTS LLC p 1502
1155 Benner Pike 100, State College PA 16801
Tel (814) 234-6000
SIC 5411 5541 5993 6794 5172

MUZAK LLC p 1003
3318 Lakemont Blvd, Fort Mill SC 29708
Tel (803) 396-3000 *SIC* 7389 6794

▲ DENNYS CORP p 428
203 E Main St, Spartanburg SC 29319
Tel (864) 597-8000 *SIC* 5812 6794

■ DENNYS INC p 428
2306 Reidville Rd, Spartanburg SC 29301
Tel (864) 597-8532 *SIC* 5812 6794

ADMINISTRATIVE RESOURCES INC p 23
801 Sunset Dr F1, Johnson City TN 37604
Tel (423) 283-0296
SIC 8721 8741 8742 6794

ATWORK FRANCHISE INC p 130
3215 W Gov J Sevier Hwy, Knoxville TN 37920
Tel (865) 609-6911 *SIC* 6794 8742 8721

RADIO SYSTEMS CORP p 1204
10427 Petsafe Way, Knoxville TN 37932
Tel (865) 777-5404 *SIC* 0752 1799 6794

▲ RUBY TUESDAY INC p 1257
150 W Church Ave, Maryville TN 37801
Tel (865) 379-5700 *SIC* 5812 5813 6794

▲ FREDS INC p 576
4300 New Getwell Rd, Memphis TN 38118
Tel (901) 365-8880
SIC 5331 5912 5199 6794

PERKINS & MARIE CALLENDERS LLC p 1136
6075 Poplar Ave Ste 800, Memphis TN 38119
Tel (901) 766-6400 *SIC* 5812 6794

PROMUS HOTEL CORP p 1183
755 Crossover Ln, Memphis TN 38117
Tel (901) 374-5000 *SIC* 7011 8741 6794

■ PROMUS HOTELS LLC p 1183
755 Crossover Ln, Memphis TN 38117
Tel (719) 265-6600 *SIC* 7011 8741 6794

■ PROMUS OPERATING CO INC p 1183
755 Crossover Ln, Memphis TN 38117
Tel (901) 374-5000 *SIC* 7011 8741 6794

AMERICAN BLUE RIBBON HOLDINGS LLC p 69
3038 Sidco Dr, Nashville TN 37204
Tel (615) 256-8500 *SIC* 5812 6794

LRI HOLDINGS INC p 882
3011 Armory Dr Ste 300, Nashville TN 37204
Tel (615) 885-9056 *SIC* 5812 6794

ROADHOUSE MIDCO INC p 1240
3011 Armory Dr Ste 300, Nashville TN 37204
Tel (615) 885-9056 *SIC* 5812 6794

ROADHOUSE PARENT INC p 1240
3011 Armory Dr Ste 300, Nashville TN 37204
Tel (615) 885-9056 *SIC* 5812 6794

SHONEYS NORTH AMERICA LLC p 1317
1717 Elm Hill Pike Ste B1, Nashville TN 37210
Tel (615) 231-2333 *SIC* 6794 8741 5812

BL RESTAURANT OPERATIONS LLC p 186
4550 Beltway Dr, Addison TX 75001
Tel (972) 386-5567 *SIC* 5812 5813 6794

MGI HOLDINGS LP p 958
5912 Balcones Dr, Austin TX 78731
Tel (512) 459-4796 *SIC* 5812 6794

MOOD MEDIA NORTH AMERICA LIMITED p 987
1703 W 5th St Ste 600, Austin TX 78703
Tel (512) 380-8500 *SIC* 6794 7389

MR GATTIS LP p 996
5912 Balcones Dr Ste 200, Austin TX 78731
Tel (512) 459-4796 *SIC* 6794 5812

▲ BRINKER INTERNATIONAL INC p 213
6820 Lbj Fwy, Dallas TX 75240
Tel (972) 980-9917 *SIC* 5812 6794

CBC RESTAURANT CORP p 268
12700 Park Central Dr # 1300, Dallas TX 75251
Tel (972) 619-4100 *SIC* 5812 6794

CONSOLIDATED RESTAURANT COMPANIES INC p 360
12200 N Stemmons Fwy, Dallas TX 75234
Tel (972) 241-5500 *SIC* 5812 6794

CONSOLIDATED RESTAURANT OPERATIONS INC p 360
12200 N Stemmons Fwy, Dallas TX 75234
Tel (972) 241-5500 *SIC* 5812 6794

EL CHICO RESTAURANTS INC p 482
12200 N Stemmons Fwy, Dallas TX 75234
Tel (972) 241-5500 *SIC* 5812 6794 5046

▲ FIESTA RESTAURANT GROUP INC p 541
14800 Landmark Blvd # 500, Dallas TX 75254
Tel (972) 702-9300 *SIC* 5812 6794

TGI FRIDAYS INC p 1446
19111 Dallas Pkwy, Dallas TX 75287
Tel (972) 662-5400 *SIC* 5812 6794

HAGGAR CORP p 653
1507 Lyndon B Johnson Fwy, Farmers Branch TX 75234
Tel (214) 352-8481
SIC 2325 2311 2321 5611 6794

TACO BUENO RESTAURANTS LP p 1421
1605 Lbj Fwy Ste 800, Farmers Branch TX 75234
Tel (800) 440-0778 *SIC* 5812 6794

▲ PIER 1 IMPORTS INC p 1147
100 Pier 1 Pl, Fort Worth TX 76102
Tel (817) 252-8000 *SIC* 5719 6794 5712

▲ IGNITE RESTAURANT GROUP INC p 730
10555 Richmond Ave # 100, Houston TX 77042
Tel (713) 366-7500 *SIC* 5812 6794

MAC PARENT LLC p 891
3100 S Gessner Rd Ste 125, Houston TX 77063
Tel (832) 649-2260 *SIC* 5812 6794

MEXICAN RESTAURANTS INC p 957
12000 Aerospace Ave # 400, Houston TX 77034
Tel (832) 300-5858 *SIC* 5812 6794 5046

WILLISTON HOLDINGS INC p 1612
12000 Aerospace Ave # 400, Houston TX 77034
Tel (832) 300-5858 *SIC* 5812 6794 5046

7-ELEVEN INC p 3
3200 Hackberry Rd, Irving TX 75063
Tel (972) 828-0711 *SIC* 5411 6794

CEC ENTERTAINMENT INC p 272
1707 Market Pl Ste 200, Irving TX 75063
Tel (972) 258-8507 *SIC* 5812 7993 6794

GOLDS GYM INTERNATIONAL INC p 622
125 E J Carpentr Fwy 13, Irving TX 75062
Tel (972) 444-8527 *SIC* 7991 6794

■ LA QUINTA LLC p 836
909 Hidden Rdg Ste 600, Irving TX 75038
Tel (214) 492-6600 *SIC* 7011 6794 8741

■ FRITO-LAY NORTH AMERICA INC p 580
7701 Legacy Dr, Plano TX 75024
Tel (972) 334-7000
SIC 2096 2052 2013 5812 6794 2086

HOMESTYLE DINING LLC p 704
3701 W Plano Pkwy Ste 200, Plano TX 75075
Tel (972) 244-8900 *SIC* 5812 6794

OLD FRITO-LAY INC p 1080
7701 Legacy Dr, Plano TX 75024
Tel (972) 334-7000
SIC 2096 2052 2013 5812 6794 2086

▲ RENT-A-CENTER INC p 1224
5501 Headquarters Dr, Plano TX 75024
Tel (972) 801-1100 *SIC* 7359 6794

▲ ZOES KITCHEN INC p 1644
5760 State Highway 121, Plano TX 75024
Tel (214) 436-8765 *SIC* 5812 6794

▲ BIGLARI HOLDINGS INC p 182
17802 W Ih 10 Ste 400, San Antonio TX 78257
Tel (210) 344-3400 *SIC* 5812 6794

RITA RESTAURANT CORP p 1236
120 Chula Vis, San Antonio TX 78232
Tel (210) 403-3725 *SIC* 5812 6794

WHATABURGER RESTAURANTS LLC p 1604
300 Concord Plaza Dr, San Antonio TX 78216
Tel (210) 476-6000 *SIC* 5812 6794

▲ ZAGG INC p 1641
910 W Legacy Center Way, Midvale UT 84047
Tel (801) 263-0699 *SIC* 5731 6794

BIOFIRE DEFENSE LLC p 183
79 W 4500 S Ste 14, Salt Lake City UT 84107
Tel (801) 262-3592 *SIC* 3829 3826 6794

YOUNG ELECTRIC SIGN CO INC p 1638
2401 S Foothill Dr, Salt Lake City UT 84109
Tel (801) 464-4600
SIC 3993 7359 1799 6794

BEN & JERRYS HOMEMADE INC p 172
30 Community Dr Ste 1, South Burlington VT 05403
Tel (802) 846-1500 *SIC* 2024 5812 6794

LONG & FOSTER COMPANIES INC p 876
14501 George Carter Way # 1, Chantilly VA 20151
Tel (888) 462-9111 *SIC* 6531 6794

HILTON GLOBAL HOLDINGS LLC p 694
7930 Jones Branch Dr # 1100, Mc Lean VA 22102
Tel (703) 883-1000 *SIC* 6794 7011

▲ HILTON WORLDWIDE HOLDINGS INC p 695
7930 Jones Branch Dr # 100, Mc Lean VA 22102
Tel (703) 883-1000 *SIC* 7011 6794

■ PARK HOTELS & RESORTS INC p 1115
7930 Jones Branch Dr # 700, Mc Lean VA 22102
Tel (703) 883-1000 *SIC* 7011 6794

SWEET FROG LLC p 1411
10800 Midlothian Tpke # 300, North Chesterfield VA 23235
Tel (804) 893-3151 *SIC* 5812 6794

JOHN L SCOTT INC p 789
1700 Nw Gilman Blvd # 300, Issaquah WA 98027
Tel (425) 392-1211 *SIC* 6531 6794

■ IDSC HOLDINGS LLC p 729
2801 80th St, Kenosha WI 53143
Tel (262) 656-5200
SIC 3423 3559 7372 6794 5013 3546

WISCONSIN ALUMNI RESEARCH FOUNDATION p 1618
614 Walnut St Fl 13, Madison WI 53726
Tel (608) 263-2500 *SIC* 6799 6794

SIC 6798 Real Estate Investment Trusts

COLONIAL PROPERTIES TRUST p 338
2101 6th Ave N Ste 750, Birmingham AL 35203
Tel (205) 250-8700
SIC 6798 6552 6531 6513

MPT OPERATING PARTNERSHIP LP p 996
3500 Colonnade Pkwy # 540, Birmingham AL 35243
Tel (205) 969-3755 *SIC* 6798

CAPELLA HEALTH HOLDINGS LLC p 248
1000 Urban Center Dr # 501, Vestavia AL 35242
Tel (205) 969-3455 *SIC* 6798 8062

MEDICAL PROPERTIES TRUST INC p 937
1000 Urban Center Dr # 501, Vestavia AL 35242
Tel (205) 969-3755 *SIC* 6798

KOYITLOTSINA LIMITED p 828
1603 College Rd Ste 2, Fairbanks AK 99709
Tel (907) 452-8119 *SIC* 6798 8744 7349

▲ VEREIT INC p 1549
2325 E Camelback Rd, Phoenix AZ 85016
Tel (800) 606-3610 *SIC* 6798

COLONY STARWOOD HOMES p 338
8665 E Hartford Dr # 200, Scottsdale AZ 85255
Tel (480) 362-9760 *SIC* 6798

GLOBAL AGGREGATE LLC p 615
8901 E Mountain View Rd, Scottsdale AZ 85258
Tel (480) 414-9400 *SIC* 6798 7389 5045

HEALTHCARE TRUST OF AMERICA INC p 676
16435 N Scottsdale Rd, Scottsdale AZ 85254
Tel (480) 998-3478 *SIC* 6798

SPIRIT REALTY CAPITAL INC p 1359
16767 N Perimeter Dr # 210, Scottsdale AZ 85260
Tel (480) 606-0820 *SIC* 6798

STORE CAPITAL CORP p 1391
8501 E Prnceaz Dr Ste 190, Scottsdale AZ 85255
Tel (480) 256-1100 *SIC* 6798

▲ AMERICAN HOMES 4 RENT p 74
30601 Agoura Rd Ste 200, Agoura Hills CA 91301
Tel (805) 413-5300 *SIC* 6798

▲ SUNSTONE HOTEL INVESTORS INC p 1404
120 Vantis Dr Ste 350, Aliso Viejo CA 92656
Tel (949) 330-4000 *SIC* 6798

JAMIESON-HILL A GENERAL PARTNERSHIP p 777
3101 State Rd, Bakersfield CA 93308
Tel (661) 393-7000 *SIC* 5541 6798

DART TRANSPORTATION SERVICE A CORP p 413
1430 S Eastman Ave Ste 1, Commerce CA 90023
Tel (323) 981-8205 *SIC* 6798 7513

MISSION WEST PROPERTIES INC p 975
10050 Bandley Dr, Cupertino CA 95014
Tel (408) 725-0700 *SIC* 6798

▲ PS BUSINESS PARKS INC p 1187
701 Western Ave, Glendale CA 91201
Tel (818) 244-8080 *SIC* 6798

▲ PUBLIC STORAGE p 1190
701 Western Ave, Glendale CA 91201
Tel (818) 244-8080 *SIC* 6798 4225

▲ HCP INC p 672
1920 Main St Ste 1200, Irvine CA 92614
Tel (949) 407-0700 *SIC* 6798

▲ IMPAC MORTGAGE HOLDINGS INC p 734
19500 Jamboree Rd, Irvine CA 92612
Tel (949) 475-3600 *SIC* 6798

IRVINE APARTMENT COMMUNITIES LP p 765
110 Innovation Dr, Irvine CA 92617
Tel (949) 720-5600 *SIC* 6513 6552 6798

SABRA HEALTH CARE REIT INC p 1264
18500 Von Karman Ave # 550, Irvine CA 92612
Tel (949) 255-7100 *SIC* 6798

STEADFAST INCOME REIT INC p 1384
18100 Von Karman Ave # 500, Irvine CA 92612
Tel (949) 852-0700 *SIC* 6798

STRATEGIC STORAGE TRUST INC p 1392
111 Corporate Dr Ste 120, Ladera Ranch CA 92694
Tel (949) 429-6600 *SIC* 6798

▲ COLONY CAPITAL INC p 338
515 S Flower St Fl 44, Los Angeles CA 90071
Tel (310) 282-8820 *SIC* 6798

▲ HUDSON PACIFIC PROPERTIES INC p 717
11601 Wilshire Blvd Fl 6, Los Angeles CA 90025
Tel (310) 445-5700 *SIC* 6798

▲ KILROY REALTY CORP p 818
12200 W Olympic Blvd # 200, Los Angeles CA 90064
Tel (310) 481-8400 *SIC* 6798

KILROY REALTY LP p 818
12200 W Olympic Blvd # 200, Los Angeles CA 90064
Tel (310) 481-8400 *SIC* 6798

MPG OFFICE TRUST INC p 995
355 S Grand Ave Ste 3300, Los Angeles CA 90071
Tel (213) 626-3300 *SIC* 6798

PRIME ADMINISTRATION LLC p 1174
357 S Curson Ave, Los Angeles CA 90036
Tel (323) 549-7155 *SIC* 6798

REXFORD INDUSTRIAL REALTY INC p 1230
11620 Wilshire Blvd # 1000, Los Angeles CA 90025
Tel (310) 966-1680 *SIC* 6798

▲ REDWOOD TRUST INC p 1217
1 Belvedere Pl Ste 300, Mill Valley CA 94941
Tel (415) 389-7373 *SIC* 6798

PENNYMAC MORTGAGE INVESTMENT TRUST p 1131
6101 Condor Dr, Moorpark CA 93021
Tel (818) 224-7442 *SIC* 6798

IRVINE EASTGATE OFFICE II LLC p 765
550 Newport Center Dr, Newport Beach CA 92660
Tel (949) 720-2000 *SIC* 6798

KBS REAL ESTATE INVESTMENT TRUST III INC p 806
620 Newport Center Dr # 1300, Newport Beach CA 92660
Tel (949) 417-6500 *SIC* 6798

KBS STRATEGIC OPPORTUNITY REIT INC p 806
620 Newport Center Dr, Newport Beach CA 92660
Tel (949) 417-6500 *SIC* 6798

ESSEX PORTFOLIO LP p 510
925 E Meadow Dr, Palo Alto CA 94303
Tel (650) 494-3700 *SIC* 6798 6513

ALEXANDRIA REAL ESTATE EQUITIES INC p 49
385 E Colo Blvd Ste 299, Pasadena CA 91101
Tel (626) 578-0777 *SIC* 6798

ACCREDITED HOME LENDERS HOLDING CO p 15
15253 Ave Of Science, San Diego CA 92128
Tel (858) 676-2100 *SIC* 6798

AMERICAN ASSETS TRUST INC p 68
11455 El Camino Real # 200, San Diego CA 92130
Tel (858) 350-2600 *SIC* 6798

BIOMED REALTY LP p 184
17190 Bernardo Center Dr, San Diego CA 92128
Tel (858) 485-9840 *SIC* 6798 6531

BIOMED REALTY TRUST INC p 184
17190 Bernardo Center Dr, San Diego CA 92128
Tel (858) 485-9840 *SIC* 6798

EXCEL TRUST INC p 516
17140 Bernardo Center Dr, San Diego CA 92128
Tel (858) 613-1800 *SIC* 6798

PACIFICA COMPANIES LLC p 1106
1775 Hancock St Ste 200, San Diego CA 92110
Tel (619) 296-9000 *SIC* 6798 6512

▲ REALTY INCOME CORP p 1214
11995 El Camino Real, San Diego CA 92130
Tel (858) 284-5000 *SIC* 6798

▲ RETAIL OPPORTUNITY INVESTMENTS CORP p 1228
8905 Towne Centre Dr # 108, San Diego CA 92122
Tel (858) 677-0900 *SIC* 6798

BRE PROPERTIES INC p 209
525 Market St Fl 4, San Francisco CA 94105
Tel (415) 445-6530 *SIC* 6798

▲ DIGITAL REALTY TRUST INC p 439
4 Embarcadero Ctr # 3200, San Francisco CA 94111
Tel (415) 738-6500 *SIC* 6798

■ KKR FINANCIAL HOLDINGS LLC p 822
555 California St Fl 50, San Francisco CA 94104
Tel (415) 315-3620 *SIC* 6798 6282

▲ PROLOGIS INC p 1183
Bay 1 Pier 1, San Francisco CA 94111
Tel (415) 394-9000 *SIC* 6798

■ PROLOGIS LP p 1183
Bay 1 Pier 1, San Francisco CA 94111
Tel (415) 394-9000 *SIC* 6798 6799

TERRENO REALTY CORP p 1440
101 Montgomery St Ste 200, San Francisco CA 94104
Tel (415) 655-4580 *SIC* 6798

ESSEX PROPERTY TRUST INC p 510
1100 Park Pl Ste 200, San Mateo CA 94403
Tel (650) 655-7800 *SIC* 6798

ANWORTH MORTGAGE ASSET CORP p 94
1299 Ocean Ave Fl 2, Santa Monica CA 90401
Tel (310) 255-4493 *SIC* 6798

DOUGLAS EMMETT INC p 452
808 Wilshire Blvd Ste 200, Santa Monica CA 90401
Tel (310) 255-7700 *SIC* 6798

▲ MACERICH CO p 892
401 Wilshire Blvd Ste 700, Santa Monica CA 90401
Tel (310) 394-6000 *SIC* 6798

▲ LTC PROPERTIES INC p 883
2829 Townsgate Rd Ste 350, Westlake Village CA 91361
Tel (805) 981-8655 *SIC* 6798

AIMCO PROPERTIES LP p 38
4582 S Ulster St Ste 1100, Denver CO 80237
Tel (303) 757-8101 *SIC* 6798

■ AIMCO-GP INC p 38
4582 S Ulster St Ste 1100, Denver CO 80237
Tel (303) 757-8101 *SIC* 6798

■ AIMCO-LP TRUST p 38
4582 S Ulster St Ste 1100, Denver CO 80237
Tel (303) 757-8101 *SIC* 6798

▲ APARTMENT INVESTMENT & MANAGEMENT CO p 96
4582 S Ulster St Ste 1100, Denver CO 80237
Tel (303) 757-8101 *SIC* 6798

■ CORESITE LLC p 369
1001 17th St Ste 500, Denver CO 80202
Tel (866) 777-2673 *SIC* 6798

▲ CORESITE REALTY CORP p 369
1001 17th St Ste 500, Denver CO 80202
Tel (866) 777-2673 *SIC* 6798

DCT INDUSTRIAL TRUST INC p 419
518 17th St Ste 800, Denver CO 80202
Tel (303) 597-2400 *SIC* 6798

DIVIDEND CAPITAL DIVERSIFIED PROPERTY FUND INC p 444
518 17th St Ste 1200, Denver CO 80202
Tel (303) 228-2200 *SIC* 6798

■ PROLOGIS p 1183
4545 Airport Way, Denver CO 80239
Tel (303) 375-9292 *SIC* 6798 6552

YES MANAGEMENT p 1635
1900 16th St Ste 950, Denver CO 80202
Tel (303) 483-7300 *SIC* 6798

ARCHSTONE COMMUNITIES LLC p 105
9200 E Panorama Cir # 400, Englewood CO 80112
Tel (303) 708-5959 *SIC* 6798 6513

NATIONAL STORAGE AFFILIATES TRUST p 1016
5200 Dtc Pkwy Ste 200, Greenwood Village CO 80111
Tel (720) 630-2600 *SIC* 6798

▲ UDR INC p 1499
1745 Shea Center Dr # 200, Highlands Ranch CO 80129
Tel (720) 283-6120 *SIC* 6798

STARWOOD PROPERTY TRUST INC p 1379
591 W Putnam Ave, Greenwich CT 06830
Tel (203) 422-7700 *SIC* 6798

▲ URSTADT BIDDLE PROPERTIES INC p 1530
321 Railroad Ave Ste 5, Greenwich CT 06830
Tel (203) 863-8200 *SIC* 6798

■ G E COMMERCIAL FINANCE REAL ESTATE p 586
292 Long Ridge Rd, Stamford CT 06902
Tel (203) 373-2211 *SIC* 6798

▲ DUPONT FABROS TECHNOLOGY INC p 462
1212 New York Ave Nw # 900, Washington DC 20005
Tel (202) 728-0044 *SIC* 6798 7374

■ DUPONT FABROS TECHNOLOGY LP p 462
1212 New York Ave Nw # 900, Washington DC 20005
Tel (202) 728-0044 *SIC* 6798

JER PARTNERS LLC p 783
1250 Conn Ave Nw Ste 700, Washington DC 20036
Tel (703) 714-8000 *SIC* 6798

▲ WASHINGTON REAL ESTATE INVESTMENT TRUST p 1579
1775 Eye St Nw Ste 1000, Washington DC 20006
Tel (202) 774-3200 *SIC* 6798

CRT PROPERTIES INC p 396
225 Ne Mizner Blvd # 300, Boca Raton FL 33432
Tel (561) 395-9666 *SIC* 6798

GABLES REALTY LIMITED PARTNERSHIP p 588
225 Ne Mizner Blvd # 400, Boca Raton FL 33432
Tel (561) 997-9700 *SIC* 6798

GEO GROUP INC p 605
621 Nw 53rd St Ste 700, Boca Raton FL 33487
Tel (561) 893-0101 *SIC* 6798

■ BBX CAPITAL CORP p 163
401 E Las Olas Blvd, Fort Lauderdale FL 33301
Tel (954) 940-4000 *SIC* 6798 6035

▲ RAYONIER INC p 1210
225 Water St Ste 1400, Jacksonville FL 32202
Tel (904) 357-9100
SIC 6798 5099 6552 5031

▲ REGENCY CENTERS CORP p 1218
1 Independent Dr Ste 114, Jacksonville FL 32202
Tel (904) 598-7000 *SIC* 6798

■ REGENCY CENTERS LP p 1218
1 Independent Dr Ste 114, Jacksonville FL 32202
Tel (904) 598-7000 *SIC* 6798

CNL HEALTHCARE PROPERTIES INC p 330
450 S Orange Ave, Orlando FL 32801
Tel (407) 650-1000 *SIC* 6798

CNL LIFESTYLE PROPERTIES INC p 330
450 S Orange Ave, Orlando FL 32801
Tel (407) 650-1000 *SIC* 6798

▲ NATIONAL RETAIL PROPERTIES INC p 1015
450 S Orange Ave Ste 900, Orlando FL 32801
Tel (407) 265-7348 *SIC* 6798

PARKWAY PROPERTIES INC p 1117
390 N Orange Ave Ste 2400, Orlando FL 32801
Tel (407) 650-0593 *SIC* 6798

SENTIO HEALTHCARE PROPERTIES INC p 1305
189 S Orange Ave Ste 1700, Orlando FL 32801
Tel (407) 999-7679 *SIC* 6798

▲ XENIA HOTELS & RESORTS INC p 1631
200 S Orange Ave Ste 2700, Orlando FL 32801
Tel (407) 317-6950 *SIC* 6798

ZRAIM INVESTMENTS LLC p 1644
400 Sunny Isles Blvd # 190, Sunny Isles Beach FL 33160
Tel (718) 708-0065 *SIC* 6798

CARTER VALIDUS MISSION CRITICAL REIT INC p 262
4890 W Kennedy Blvd # 650, Tampa FL 33609
Tel (813) 287-0101 *SIC* 6798

ARMOUR RESIDENTIAL REIT INC p 111
3001 Ocean Dr Ste 201, Vero Beach FL 32963
Tel (772) 617-4340 *SIC* 6798

▲ CHATHAM LODGING TRUST p 291
222 Lakeview Ave Ste 200, West Palm Beach FL 33401
Tel (561) 802-4477 *SIC* 6798

ARCAPITA INC p 103
1180 Peachtree St Ne # 3000, Atlanta GA 30309
Tel (404) 920-9000 *SIC* 6798

COLUMBIA PROPERTY TRUST INC p 341
1 Glenlake Pkwy Ste 1200, Atlanta GA 30328
Tel (404) 465-2200 *SIC* 6798

▲ COUSINS PROPERTIES INC p 383
191 Peachtree St Ne # 500, Atlanta GA 30303
Tel (404) 407-1000 *SIC* 6798

INTEGRAL GROUP LLC p 748
191 Peachtree St Ne # 4100, Atlanta GA 30303
Tel (404) 224-1860
SIC 6552 8748 6798 6799 6722

INVESCO AGENCY SECURITIES INC p 761
1360 Peachtree St Ne # 600, Atlanta GA 30309
Tel (404) 892-0896 *SIC* 6798

INVESCO MORTGAGE CAPITAL INC p 761
1555 Peachtree St Ne, Atlanta GA 30309
Tel (404) 892-0896 *SIC* 6798

POST APARTMENT HOMES LP p 1163
4401 Northside Pkwy 800, Atlanta GA 30327
Tel (404) 846-5000 *SIC* 6798 6513

POST PROPERTIES INC p 1164
4401 Northside Pkwy Nw # 800, Atlanta GA 30327
Tel (404) 846-5000 *SIC* 6798 6531

▲ PREFERRED APARTMENT COMMUNITIES INC p 1169
3284 Northside Pkwy Nw # 150, Atlanta GA 30327
Tel (770) 818-4100 *SIC* 6798

MERRY LAND PROPERTIES LLC p 950
209 7th St Ste 300, Augusta GA 30901
Tel (706) 722-6756 *SIC* 6798

▲ PIEDMONT OFFICE REALTY TRUST INC p 1147
11695 Johns Creek Pkwy, Johns Creek GA 30097
Tel (770) 418-8800 *SIC* 6798

■ AMLI RESIDENTIAL PROPERTIES LP p 85
141 W Jackson Blvd # 300, Chicago IL 60604
Tel (312) 283-4700 *SIC* 6798

AVIV REIT INC p 138
303 W Madison St Ste 2400, Chicago IL 60606
Tel (312) 855-0930 *SIC* 6798

CARE CAPITAL PROPERTIES INC p 254
191 N Wacker Dr Ste 1200, Chicago IL 60606
Tel (312) 881-4700 *SIC* 6798

EQUITY COMMONWEALTH p 506
2 N Riverside Plz Ste 600, Chicago IL 60606
Tel (312) 646-2800 *SIC* 6798

▲ EQUITY LIFESTYLE PROPERTIES INC p 507
2 N Riverside Plz Ste 800, Chicago IL 60606
Tel (312) 279-1400 *SIC* 6798 6531

EQUITY RESIDENTIAL p 507
2 N Rverside Plz Ste 1100, Chicago IL 60606
Tel (312) 474-1300 *SIC* 6798

ERP OPERATING LIMITED PARTNERSHIP p 508
2 N Riverside Plz Ste 400, Chicago IL 60606
Tel (312) 474-1300 *SIC* 6798

FIRST INDUSTRIAL LP p 547
311 S Wacker Dr Ste 3900, Chicago IL 60606
Tel (312) 344-4300 *SIC* 6798

FIRST INDUSTRIAL REALTY TRUST INC p 547
311 S Wacker Dr Ste 3900, Chicago IL 60606
Tel (312) 344-4300 *SIC* 6798

▲ GENERAL GROWTH PROPERTIES INC p 601
110 N Wacker Dr, Chicago IL 60606
Tel (312) 960-5000 *SIC* 6798

■ GGP INC p 610
110 N Wacker Dr, Chicago IL 60606
Tel (312) 960-5000 *SIC* 6798

GREEN COURTE PARTNERS LLC p 637
303 W Madison St Ste 1500, Chicago IL 60606
Tel (847) 615-1631 *SIC* 6798

PLS FINANCIAL SERVICES INC p 1156
1 S Wacker Dr Fl 36, Chicago IL 60606
Tel (312) 491-7300 *SIC* 7389 6798

STRATEGIC HOTELS & RESORTS INC p 1392
200 W Madison St Ste 1700, Chicago IL 60606
Tel (312) 658-5000 *SIC* 6798

▲ VENTAS INC p 1547
353 N Clark St Ste 3300, Chicago IL 60654
Tel (877) 483-6827 *SIC* 6798

WATERTON ASSOCIATES LLC p 1582
30 S Wacker Dr Ste 3600, Chicago IL 60606
Tel (312) 948-4500 *SIC* 6513 6798

GREAT LAKES REIT p 634
823 Commerce Dr Ste 300, Oak Brook IL 60523
Tel (708) 848-5216 *SIC* 6798 6531

INLAND DIVERSIFIED REAL ESTATE TRUST INC p 743
2901 Butterfield Rd, Oak Brook IL 60523
Tel (630) 218-8000 *SIC* 6798

INLAND REAL ESTATE INVESTMENT CORP p 743
2901 Butterfield Rd, Oak Brook IL 60523
Tel (630) 218-8000 *SIC* 6211 6798

INVENTRUST PROPERTIES CORP p 761
2809 Butterfield Rd, Oak Brook IL 60523
Tel (855) 377-0510 *SIC* 6798

IRC RETAIL CENTERS LLC p 764
814 Commerce Dr Ste 300, Oak Brook IL 60523
Tel (877) 206-5656 *SIC* 6798

▲ RETAIL PROPERTIES OF AMERICA INC p 1228
2021 Spring Rd Ste 200, Oak Brook IL 60523
Tel (630) 634-4200 *SIC* 6798

DUKE REALTY CORP p 460
600 E 96th St Ste 100, Indianapolis IN 46240
Tel (317) 808-6000 *SIC* 6798 1542

DUKE REALTY LIMITED PARTNERSHIP p 460
600 E 96th St Ste 100, Indianapolis IN 46240
Tel (317) 808-6000 *SIC* 6798

KITE REALTY GROUP TRUST p 822
30 S Meridian St Ste 1100, Indianapolis IN 46204
Tel (317) 577-5600 *SIC* 6798

▲ SIMON PROPERTY GROUP INC p 1325
225 W Washington St, Indianapolis IN 46204
Tel (317) 636-1600 *SIC* 6798 6512

■ SIMON PROPERTY GROUP LP p 1325
225 W Washington St, Indianapolis IN 46204
Tel (317) 636-1600 *SIC* 6798 6512

SPG-FCM VENTURES LLC p 1358
225 W Washington St, Indianapolis IN 46204
Tel (317) 636-1600 *SIC* 6798

CORPOREX COMPANIES LLC p 372
100 E Rivercntr Blvd 11 Ste 1100, Covington KY 41011
Tel (859) 292-5500 *SIC* 6798

▲ LAMAR ADVERTISING CO p 841
5321 Corporate Blvd, Baton Rouge LA 70808
Tel (225) 926-1000 *SIC* 7312 6798

▲ CHESAPEAKE LODGING TRUST p 295
1997 Annapolis Exch Pkwy, Annapolis MD 21401
Tel (410) 972-4140 *SIC* 6798

▲ AGNC INVESTMENT CORP p 35
2 Bethesda Metro Ctr # 12, Bethesda MD 20814
Tel (301) 968-9315 *SIC* 6798

▲ DIAMONDROCK HOSPITALITY CO p 437
3 Bethesda Metro Ctr # 1500, Bethesda MD 20814
Tel (240) 744-1150 *SIC* 6798

FIRST POTOMAC REALTY TRUST p 549
7600 Wisconsin Ave # 1100, Bethesda MD 20814
Tel (301) 986-9200 *SIC* 6798

▲ HOST HOTELS & RESORTS INC p 710
6903 Rockledge Dr # 1500, Bethesda MD 20817
Tel (240) 744-1000 *SIC* 6798 7011

■ HOST HOTELS & RESORTS LP p 710
6903 Rockledge Dr # 1500, Bethesda MD 20817
Tel (240) 744-1000 *SIC* 6798 7011

LASALLE HOTEL PROPERTIES p 846
7550 Wisconsin Ave # 100, Bethesda MD 20814
Tel (301) 941-1500 *SIC* 6798

▲ MTGE INVESTMENT CORP p 998
2 Bethesda Metro Ctr # 14, Bethesda MD 20814
Tel (301) 968-9220 *SIC* 6798

PEBBLEBROOK HOTEL TRUST p 1126
7315 Wisconsin Ave 1100w, Bethesda MD 20814
Tel (240) 507-1300 *SIC* 6798

RLJ LODGING TRUST p 1239
3 Bethesda Metro Ctr, Bethesda MD 20814
Tel (301) 280-7777 *SIC* 6798

▲ SAUL CENTERS INC p 1283
7501 Wisconsin Ave 1500e, Bethesda MD 20814
Tel (301) 986-6200 *SIC* 6798

MILLS CORP p 971
5425 Wisconsin Ave # 300, Chevy Chase MD 20815
Tel (301) 968-6000 *SIC* 6798

CORPORATE OFFICE PROPERTIES TRUST p 372
6711 Columbia Gateway Dr, Columbia MD 21046
Tel (443) 285-5400 *SIC* 6798

■ ROUSE CO LP p 1253
10221 Wincopin Cir # 300, Columbia MD 21044
Tel (410) 992-6000 *SIC* 6798 6512

▲ OMEGA HEALTHCARE INVESTORS INC p 1084
200 International Cir # 3500, Hunt Valley MD 21030
Tel (410) 427-1700 *SIC* 6798

▲ FEDERAL REALTY INVESTMENT TRUST p 535
1626 E Jefferson St, Rockville MD 20852
Tel (301) 998-8100 *SIC* 6798

AEW CAPITAL MANAGEMENT LP p 32
2 Seaport Ln, Boston MA 02210
Tel (617) 951-0812 *SIC* 6282 6798

■ BOSTON PROPERTIES INC p 203
800 Boylston St Ste 1900, Boston MA 02199
Tel (617) 236-3300 *SIC* 6798

■ BOSTON PROPERTIES LIMITED PARTNERSHIP p 203
800 Boylston St Ste 1900, Boston MA 02199
Tel (617) 236-3300 *SIC* 6798

CNL HOSPITALITY PROPERTIES II INC p 330
1 Post Office Sq Ste 3100, Boston MA 02109
Tel (617) 964-8389 *SIC* 6798

▲ IRON MOUNTAIN INC p 764
1 Federal St Fl 7, Boston MA 02110
Tel (617) 535-4766
SIC 4226 8741 7375 6798

▲ STAG INDUSTRIAL INC p 1374
1 Federal St Fl 23, Boston MA 02110
Tel (617) 574-4777 *SIC* 6798

GOVERNMENT PROPERTIES INCOME TRUST p 627
255 Washington St Ste 300, Newton MA 02458
Tel (617) 219-1440 *SIC* 6798

▲ HOSPITALITY PROPERTIES TRUST p 710
255 Washington St Ste 300, Newton MA 02458
Tel (617) 964-8389 *SIC* 6798

SELECT INCOME REIT p 1301
255 Washington St Ste 300, Newton MA 02458
Tel (617) 796-8303 *SIC* 6798

SENIOR HOUSING PROPERTIES TRUST p 1304
255 Washington St Ste 300, Newton MA 02458
Tel (617) 796-8350 *SIC* 6798

▲ FRANKLIN STREET PROPERTIES CORP p 575
401 Edgewater Pl Ste 200, Wakefield MA 01880
Tel (781) 557-1300 *SIC* 6798

CYS INVESTMENTS INC p 406
500 Totten Pond Rd Ste 6, Waltham MA 02451
Tel (617) 639-0440 *SIC* 6798

▲ TAUBMAN CENTERS INC p 1426
200 E Long Lake Rd # 300, Bloomfield Hills MI 48304
Tel (248) 258-6800 *SIC* 6798

▲ RAMCO-GERSHENSON PROPERTIES TRUST p 1207
31500 Northwestern Hwy, Farmington Hills MI 48334
Tel (248) 350-9900 *SIC* 6798 6519

▲ SUN COMMUNITIES INC p 1400
27777 Franklin Rd Ste 200, Southfield MI 48034
Tel (248) 208-2500 *SIC* 6798 2451

■ WACHOVIA PREFERRED FUNDING CORP p 1570
90 S 7th St Fl 13, Minneapolis MN 55402
Tel (855) 825-1437 *SIC* 6798

SILVER BAY REALTY TRUST CORP p 1323
3300 Fernbrook Ln N, Plymouth MN 55447
Tel (952) 358-4400 *SIC* 6798 6531 1521

▲ EASTGROUP PROPERTIES INC p 473
190 E Capitol St Ste 400, Jackson MS 39201
Tel (601) 354-3555 *SIC* 6798

EPR PROPERTIES p 505
909 Walnut St Ste 200, Kansas City MO 64106
Tel (816) 472-1700 *SIC* 6798

INTERNATIONAL MARKET CENTERS INC p 756
475 S Grand Central Pkwy, Las Vegas NV 89106
Tel (702) 599-9621 *SIC* 6798

WALTERS GROUP p 1574
2030 E Flamingo Rd # 290, Las Vegas NV 89119
Tel (702) 450-8001 *SIC* 6798

▲ MACK-CALI REALTY CORP p 892
343 Thornall St, Edison NJ 08837
Tel (732) 590-1000 *SIC* 6798

▲ ALEXANDERS INC p 49
210 E Rte 4, Paramus NJ 07652
Tel (201) 587-8541 *SIC* 6798

MACK-CALI REALTY L P p 892
4 Becker Farm Rd Ste 104, Roseland NJ 07068
Tel (973) 577-2472 *SIC* 6798

TMST INC p 1458
125 Lincoln Ave Ste 100, Santa Fe NM 87501
Tel (505) 989-1900 *SIC* 6531 6798

▲ GETTY REALTY CORP p 609
2 Jericho Plz Ste 110, Jericho NY 11753
Tel (516) 478-5400 *SIC* 6798

▲ KIMCO REALTY CORP p 818
3333 New Hyde Park Rd # 100, New Hyde Park NY 11042
Tel (516) 869-9000 *SIC* 6798

AG MORTGAGE INVESTMENT TRUST INC p 33
245 Park Ave Fl 26, New York NY 10167
Tel (212) 692-2000 *SIC* 6798

■ AMERICAN REALTY CAPITAL HEALTHCARE TRUST INC p 78
1065 Ave Of The Amer # 23, New York NY 10018
Tel (212) 415-6500 *SIC* 6798

▲ANNALY CAPITAL MANAGEMENT INC p 92
1211 Ave Of The Americas, New York NY 10036
Tel (212) 696-0100 SIC 6798

APOLLO COMMERCIAL REAL ESTATE FINANCE INC p 97
9 W 57th St Fl 43, New York NY 10019
Tel (212) 515-3200 SIC 6798

APOLLO RESIDENTIAL MORTGAGE INC p 97
9 W 57th St Fl 43, New York NY 10019
Tel (212) 515-3200 SIC 6798

APPLE REIT SIX INC p 99
345 Park Ave, New York NY 10154
Tel (804) 344-8121 SIC 6798

ARES COMMERCIAL REAL ESTATE CORP p 107
245 Park Ave Fl 42, New York NY 10167
Tel (212) 750-7300 SIC 6798

■BLACKHAWK PARENT LLC p 187
345 Park Ave, New York NY 10154
Tel (212) 583-5000 SIC 6798 6531

BLACKSTONE MORTGAGE TRUST INC p 188
345 Park Ave Fl 42, New York NY 10154
Tel (212) 655-0220 SIC 6798

BRIXMOR LLC p 215
450 Lexington Ave Fl 13, New York NY 10017
Tel (212) 869-3000 SIC 6798

BRIXMOR PROPERTY GROUP INC p 215
450 Lexington Ave Fl 13, New York NY 10017
Tel (212) 869-3000 SIC 6798

■CAPLEASE INC p 251
1065 Avenue Of The Americ, New York NY 10018
Tel (212) 217-6300 SIC 6798

CAREY WATERMARK INVESTORS INC p 255
50 Rockefeller Plz, New York NY 10020
Tel (212) 492-1100 SIC 6798 7011

▲CHIMERA INVESTMENT CORP p 300
520 Madison Ave Rm 3200, New York NY 10022
Tel (646) 454-3759 SIC 6798

■CORPORATE PROPERTY ASSOCIATES 15 INC p 372
50 Rockefeller Plz, New York NY 10020
Tel (212) 492-1100 SIC 6798

CORPORATE PROPERTY ASSOCIATES 16 - GLOBAL INC p 372
50 Rockefeller Plz Fl 2, New York NY 10020
Tel (212) 492-1100 SIC 6798

CORPORATE PROPERTY ASSOCIATES 17 - GLOBAL INC p 372
50 Rockefeller Plz Fl 2, New York NY 10020
Tel (212) 492-1100 SIC 6798

CORPORATE PROPERTY INVESTORS p 372
305 E 47th St, New York NY 10017
Tel (212) 421-8200 SIC 6798

EMPIRE STATE REALTY TRUST INC p 493
60 E 42nd St, New York NY 10165
Tel (212) 687-8700 SIC 6798

▲EQUITY ONE INC p 507
410 Park Ave Ste 1220, New York NY 10022
Tel (212) 796-1760 SIC 6798

▲FAB HOLDINGS I LP p 523
250 Park Ave Fl 4, New York NY 10177
Tel (212) 624-1200 SIC 6798

GRAMERCY PROPERTY TRUST p 629
521 5th Ave Fl 30, New York NY 10175
Tel (212) 297-1000 SIC 6798

GRAMERCY PROPERTY TRUST INC p 629
521 5th Ave Fl 30, New York NY 10175
Tel (212) 297-1000 SIC 6798

HEALTHCARE TRUST INC p 676
405 Park Ave Fl 15, New York NY 10022
Tel (215) 449-3638 SIC 6798

▲ISTAR INC p 767
1114 Ave Of The Americas, New York NY 10036
Tel (212) 930-9400 SIC 6798

■KKR FUND HOLDINGS LP p 822
9 W 57th St Fl 41, New York NY 10019
Tel (212) 230-9742 SIC 6798

▲LADDER CAPITAL CORP p 837
345 Park Ave Fl 8, New York NY 10154
Tel (212) 715-3170 SIC 6798 6162

▲LEUCADIA NATIONAL CORP p 858
520 Madison Ave Bsmt A, New York NY 10022
Tel (212) 460-1900
SIC 6798 6211 1382 2011 2426

LEXINGTON REALTY TRUST p 859
1 Penn Plz Ste 4015, New York NY 10119
Tel (212) 692-7200 SIC 6798

MFA FINANCIAL INC p 957
350 Park Ave Fl 20, New York NY 10022
Tel (212) 207-6400 SIC 6798

▲NEW RESIDENTIAL INVESTMENT CORP p 1033
1345 Ave Americas, New York NY 10105
Tel (212) 798-3150 SIC 6798

NEW YORK MORTGAGE TRUST INC p 1035
275 Madison Ave Fl 32, New York NY 10016
Tel (212) 792-0107 SIC 6798 6163

▲NEWCASTLE INVESTMENT CORP p 1037
1345 Avenue Of America Flr 46, New York NY 10105
Tel (212) 798-6100 SIC 6798

NORTHSTAR HEALTHCARE INCOME INC p 1059
399 Park Ave Fl 18, New York NY 10022
Tel (212) 547-2600 SIC 6798

NORTHSTAR REALTY EUROPE CORP p 1059
399 Park Ave Fl 18, New York NY 10022
Tel (212) 547-2600 SIC 6798

NORTHSTAR REALTY FINANCE CORP p 1059
399 Park Ave Fl 18, New York NY 10022
Tel (212) 319-8801 SIC 6798

▲NORTHSTAR REALTY FINANCE CORP p 1059
399 Park Ave Fl 18, New York NY 10022
Tel (212) 547-2600 SIC 6798

▲OUTFRONT MEDIA INC p 1099
405 Lexington Ave Fl 17, New York NY 10174
Tel (212) 297-6400 SIC 7312 7319 6798

▲RESOURCE CAPITAL CORP p 1227
712 5th Ave Fl 12, New York NY 10019
Tel (212) 506-3870 SIC 6798

SL GREEN OPERATING PARTNERSHIP LP p 1330
420 Lexington Ave Rm 1800, New York NY 10170
Tel (212) 594-2700 SIC 6798

▲SL GREEN REALTY CORP p 1330
420 Lexington Ave Rm 1824, New York NY 10170
Tel (212) 594-2700 SIC 6798

▲TIPTREE FINANCIAL INC p 1455
780 3rd Ave Fl 21, New York NY 10017
Tel (212) 446-1400
SIC 6162 6282 6311 6798

TRZ HOLDINGS II INC p 1489
3 World Financial Ctr, New York NY 10281
Tel (212) 693-8150 SIC 6798

▲TWO HARBORS INVESTMENT CORP p 1495
590 Madison Ave Fl 3600, New York NY 10022
Tel (612) 629-2500 SIC 6798

▲URBAN EDGE PROPERTIES p 1530
888 7th Ave Ste 602, New York NY 10106
Tel (212) 956-2556 SIC 6798

VORNADO REALTY TRUST p 1565
888 7th Ave Fl 44, New York NY 10106
Tel (212) 894-7000 SIC 6798

▲CEDAR REALTY TRUST INC p 272
44 S Bayles Ave Ste 304, Port Washington NY 11050
Tel (516) 767-6492 SIC 6798

HOME PROPERTIES INC p 703
300 Clinton Sq, Rochester NY 14604
Tel (585) 546-4900 SIC 6798

▲ACADIA REALTY TRUST p 13
411 Theodore Fremd Ave # 300, Rye NY 10580
Tel (914) 288-8100 SIC 6798

ARBOR REALTY TRUST INC p 103
333 Earle Ovington Blvd # 900, Uniondale NY 11553
Tel (516) 506-4200 SIC 6798

RXR REALTY p 1260
625 Rxr Plz, Uniondale NY 11556
Tel (516) 506-6000 SIC 6798

▲LIFE STORAGE INC p 864
6467 Main St, Williamsville NY 14221
Tel (716) 633-1850 SIC 6798

■SOVRAN ACQUISITION LIMITED PARTNERSHIP p 1353
6467 Main St, Williamsville NY 14221
Tel (716) 633-1850 SIC 6798

CAMPUS CREST COMMUNITIES INC p 246
2100 Rexford Rd Ste 300, Charlotte NC 28211
Tel (704) 496-2500 SIC 6798 6552 6531

■ESH HOSPITALITY INC p 509
11525 N Community Hse Rd, Charlotte NC 28277
Tel (980) 345-1600 SIC 6798

▲TANGER FACTORY OUTLET CENTERS INC p 1424
3200 Northline Ave # 360, Greensboro NC 27408
Tel (336) 292-3010 SIC 6798

■TANGER PROPERTIES LIMITED PARTNERSHIP p 1424
3200 Northline Ave # 360, Greensboro NC 27408
Tel (336) 292-3010 SIC 6798

▲HIGHWOODS PROPERTIES INC p 692
3100 Smoketree Ct Ste 600, Raleigh NC 27604
Tel (919) 872-4924 SIC 6798

■HIGHWOODS REALTY LIMITED PARTNERSHIP p 692
3100 Smoketree Ct Ste 600, Raleigh NC 27604
Tel (919) 872-4924 SIC 6519 6531 6798

HATTERAS FINANCIAL CORP p 668
751 W 4th St Ste 400, Winston Salem NC 27101
Tel (336) 760-9347 SIC 6798

INVESTORS REAL ESTATE TRUST p 761
1400 31st Ave Sw Ste 60, Minot ND 58701
Tel (701) 837-4738 SIC 6798

▲DDR CORP p 419
3300 Enterprise Pkwy, Beachwood OH 44122
Tel (216) 755-5500 SIC 6798

PHILLIPS EDISON-ARC GROCERY CENTER REIT II INC p 1144
11501 Northlake Dr, Cincinnati OH 45249
Tel (513) 554-1110 SIC 6798

PROFILL HOLDINGS LLC p 1180
255 W Crescentville Rd, Cincinnati OH 45246
Tel (513) 742-4000
SIC 5199 5136 5137 6798

FOREST CITY REALTY TRUST INC p 566
50 Public Sq, Cleveland OH 44113
Tel (216) 621-6060 SIC 6798

▲WASHINGTON PRIME GROUP INC p 1578
180 E Broad St, Columbus OH 43215
Tel (614) 621-9000 SIC 6798

■WP GLIMCHER INC p 1627
180 E Broad St Fl 21, Columbus OH 43215
Tel (614) 621-9000 SIC 6798

ASSOCIATED ESTATES REALTY CORP p 120
1 Aec Pkwy, Richmond Heights OH 44143
Tel (216) 261-5000 SIC 6798 1531

■BREWER HOLDCO INC p 210
4500 Dorr St, Toledo OH 43615
Tel (419) 247-2800 SIC 6798

▲WELLTOWER INC p 1591
4500 Dorr St, Toledo OH 43615
Tel (419) 247-2800 SIC 6798

HERSHA HOSPITALITY TRUST p 687
44 Hersha Dr, Harrisburg PA 17102
Tel (717) 236-4400 SIC 6798

CUBESMART p 399
5 Old Lancaster Rd, Malvern PA 19355
Tel (610) 535-5000 SIC 6798

CUBESMART LP p 399
5 Old Lancaster Rd, Malvern PA 19355
Tel (610) 535-5700 SIC 4225 6798

LIBERTY PROPERTY TRUST p 862
500 Chesterfield Pkwy, Malvern PA 19355
Tel (610) 648-1700 SIC 6798

■GMH COMMUNITIES TRUST p 619
10 Campus Blvd, Newtown Square PA 19073
Tel (610) 355-8000 SIC 6798 6513 8742

INDEPENDENCE REALTY TRUST INC p 736
2929 Arch St Ste 1650, Philadelphia PA 19104
Tel (215) 243-9000 SIC 6798

LUMINENT MORTGAGE CAPITAL INC p 885
1 Commerce Sq, Philadelphia PA 19103
Tel (215) 564-5900 SIC 6798

PENNSYLVANIA REAL ESTATE INVESTMENT TRUST p 1130
200 S Broad St, Philadelphia PA 19102
Tel (215) 875-0700 SIC 6798 6531

RAIT FINANCIAL TRUST p 1206
2 Logan Sq Fl 23, Philadelphia PA 19103
Tel (215) 243-9000 SIC 6798

RESOURCE REAL ESTATE OPPORTUNITY REIT INC p 1227
1 Crescent Dr Ste 203, Philadelphia PA 19112
Tel (215) 231-7050 SIC 6798

BRANDYWINE OPERATING PARTNERSHIP LP p 208
555 E Lancaster Ave # 100, Radnor PA 19087
Tel (610) 325-5600 SIC 6798

BRANDYWINE REALTY TRUST p 208
555 E Lancaster Ave # 100, Radnor PA 19087
Tel (610) 325-5600 SIC 6798

▲J G WENTWORTH CO p 771
201 King Of Prussia Rd # 501, Radnor PA 19087
Tel (484) 434-2300 SIC 7389 6798

EDENS & AVANT INC p 477
1221 Main St Ste 1000, Columbia SC 29201
Tel (803) 779-4420 SIC 6798

NPI PROPERTY MANAGEMENT CORP p 1064
55 Beattie Pl, Greenville SC 29601
Tel (864) 239-1000 SIC 6798

▲CBL & ASSOCIATES PROPERTIES INC p 268
2030 Hamilton Place Blvd, Chattanooga TN 37421
Tel (423) 855-0001 SIC 6798

■MID-AMERICA APARTMENTS LP p 963
6584 Poplar Ave, Germantown TN 38138
Tel (866) 620-1130 SIC 6798

W2007 GRACE ACQUISITION I INC p 1569
7700 Wolf River Blvd, Germantown TN 38138
Tel (901) 759-6000 SIC 6798

EDUCATION REALTY TRUST INC p 479
999 Shady Grove Rd S # 600, Memphis TN 38120
Tel (901) 259-2500 SIC 6798

LRC EAGLES LANDING GP LLC p 882
555 Perkins Ext, Memphis TN 38117
Tel (901) 435-7716 SIC 6798 6531

▲MID-AMERICA APARTMENT COMMUNITIES INC p 963
6584 Poplar Ave, Memphis TN 38138
Tel (901) 682-6600 SIC 6798

▲NATIONAL HEALTH INVESTORS INC p 1013
222 Robert Rose Dr, Murfreesboro TN 37129
Tel (615) 890-9100 SIC 6798

▲CORECIVIC INC p 369
10 Burton Hills Blvd, Nashville TN 37215
Tel (615) 263-3000
SIC 6798 8744 8361 8299

HEALTHCARE REALTY TRUST INC p 676
3310 West End Ave Ste 700, Nashville TN 37203
Tel (615) 269-8175 SIC 6798

RYMAN HOSPITALITY PROPERTIES INC p 1261
1 Gaylord Dr, Nashville TN 37214
Tel (615) 316-6000 SIC 6798 7011

▲AMERICAN CAMPUS COMMUNITIES INC p 69
12700 Hill Country Blvd, Austin TX 78738
Tel (512) 732-1000 SIC 6798 6531

▲SUMMIT HOTEL PROPERTIES INC p 1399
12600 Hill Country Blvd, Austin TX 78738
Tel (512) 538-2300 SIC 6798

KWIK CHEK REAL ESTATE TRUST INC p 832
2207 N Center St, Bonham TX 75418
Tel (903) 583-7481 SIC 6798

▲CYRUSONE INC p 406
1649 W Frankford Rd, Carrollton TX 75007
Tel (972) 350-0060 SIC 6798

▲AMERICAN REALTY INVESTORS INC p 78
1603 Lbj Fwy Ste 800, Dallas TX 75234
Tel (469) 522-4200
SIC 6798 6162 6513 6512

ASHFORD HOSPITALITY PRIME INC p 117
14185 Dallas Pkwy # 1100, Dallas TX 75254
Tel (972) 490-9600 SIC 6798

ASHFORD HOSPITALITY TRUST INC p 117
14185 Dallas Pkwy # 1100, Dallas TX 75254
Tel (972) 490-9600 SIC 6798 6733

▲CAPSTEAD MORTGAGE CORP p 251
8401 N Central Expy # 800, Dallas TX 75225
Tel (214) 874-2323 SIC 6798

CIM COMMERCIAL TRUST CORP p 307
17950 Preston Rd Ste 600, Dallas TX 75252
Tel (972) 349-3200 SIC 6798

▲HOWARD HUGHES CORP p 713
13355 Noel Rd Fl 22, Dallas TX 75240
Tel (214) 741-7744 SIC 6798

INFRAREIT INC p 742
1807 Ross Ave Fl 4, Dallas TX 75201
Tel (214) 855-6700 SIC 6798

L S F 5 ACCREDITED INVESTMENTS LLC p 834
717 N Harwood St Ste 2200, Dallas TX 75201
Tel (214) 754-8300 SIC 6798

LSREF LODGING INVESTMENTS LLC p 883
2711 N Haskell Ave, Dallas TX 75204
Tel (214) 754-8300 SIC 6798

SPIRIT REALTY CAPITAL INC p 1359
2727 N Harwood St Ste 300, Dallas TX 75201
Tel (480) 606-0820 SIC 6798

TIER REIT INC p 1452
5950 Sherry Ln Ste 700, Dallas TX 75225
Tel (972) 483-2400 SIC 6798

▲TRANSCONTINENTAL REALTY INVESTORS INC p 1471
1603 Lbj Fwy Ste 800, Dallas TX 75234
Tel (469) 522-4200 SIC 6798

CRESCENT REAL ESTATE EQUITIES CO p 391
777 Main St Ste 2260, Fort Worth TX 76102
Tel (817) 321-2100 SIC 6798

CRESCENT REAL ESTATE HOLDINGS LLC p 391
777 Main St Ste 2260, Fort Worth TX 76102
Tel (817) 321-2100 SIC 6798

UNITED DEVELOPMENT FUNDING IV p 1507
1301 Municipal Way # 100, Grapevine TX 76051
Tel (214) 370-8960 SIC 6798

CAMCORP INTERESTS LTD p 244
10410 Wndamere Lakes Blvd, Houston TX 77065
Tel (281) 671-9000 SIC 1521 6798 6552

CAMDEN PROPERTY TRUST p 245
11 Greenway Plz Ste 2400, Houston TX 77046
Tel (713) 354-2500 SIC 6798

▲CROWN CASTLE INTERNATIONAL CORP p 395
1220 Augusta Dr Ste 600, Houston TX 77057
Tel (713) 570-3000
SIC 6798 4899 7622 4812

CROWN CASTLE INTERNATIONAL CORP p 395
1220 Augusta Dr Ste 600, Houston TX 77057
Tel (713) 570-3000
SIC 4899 7622 4812 6798

HINES GLOBAL REIT INC p 695
2800 Post Oak Blvd # 5000, Houston TX 77056
Tel (888) 220-6121 SIC 6798

HINES REAL ESTATE INVESTMENT TRUST INC p 695
2800 Post Oak Blvd # 4800, Houston TX 77056
Tel (713) 621-8000 SIC 6798

▲WEINGARTEN REALTY INVESTORS p 1588
2600 Citadel Plaza Dr # 125, Houston TX 77008
Tel (713) 866-6000 SIC 6798

FELCOR LODGING TRUST INC p 537
545 E John Carpenter Fwy # 1300, Irving TX 75062
Tel (972) 444-4900 SIC 6798

MONOGRAM RESIDENTIAL TRUST INC p 984
5800 Gran Pkwy Ste 1000, Plano TX 75024
Tel (469) 250-5500 SIC 6798

USAA CAPITAL CORP p 1534
9800 Fredericksburg Rd, San Antonio TX 78288
Tel (210) 498-2211
SIC 6035 6798 6722 7299 4813 4724

▲EXTRA SPACE STORAGE INC p 521
2795 E Cottonwood Pkwy # 400, Salt Lake City UT 84121
Tel (801) 365-4600 SIC 6798

SPS HOLDINGS CORP p 1362
3815 S West Temple, Salt Lake City UT 84115
Tel (801) 293-1883 SIC 6162 6798

ALTISOURCE RESIDENTIAL CORP p 62
36c Strand St, Christiansted VI 00820
Tel (340) 692-1055 SIC 6798

▲ARLINGTON ASSET INVESTMENT CORP p 110
1001 19th St N Ste 1900, Arlington VA 22209
Tel (703) 373-0200 SIC 6798 6162

▲AVALONBAY COMMUNITIES INC p 136
671 N Glebe Rd Ste 800, Arlington VA 22203
Tel (703) 329-6300 SIC 6798

▲DYNEX CAPITAL INC p 465
4991 Lake Brook Dr # 100, Glen Allen VA 23060
Tel (804) 217-5800 SIC 6798

■SAXON CAPITAL INC p 1284
4860 Cox Rd Ste 300, Glen Allen VA 23060
Tel (804) 270-1468 SIC 6798

■UNITED DOMINION REALTY TRUST INC p 1508
4510 Cox Rd Ste 105, Glen Allen VA 23060
Tel (804) 290-4705 SIC 6798

CAPITAL AUTOMOTIVE REAL ESTATE SERVICES INC p 249
8270 Greensboro Dr # 950, Mc Lean VA 22102
Tel (703) 288-3075 SIC 6798

▲GLADSTONE COMMERCIAL CORP p 614
1521 Westbranch Dr # 200, Mc Lean VA 22102
Tel (703) 287-5800 SIC 6798

JER INVESTORS TRUST INC p 783
1650 Tysons Blvd Ste 1600, Mc Lean VA 22102
Tel (703) 714-8000 SIC 6798

APPLE HOSPITALITY REIT INC p 98
814 E Main St, Richmond VA 23219
Tel (804) 344-8121 SIC 6798

APPLE REIT EIGHT INC p 99
14 E Main St, Richmond VA 23219
Tel (804) 344-8121 SIC 6798

APPLE REIT TEN INC p 99
814 E Main St, Richmond VA 23219
Tel (804) 344-8121 SIC 6798

LANDMARK APARTMENT TRUST INC p 842
4901 Dickens Rd Ste 101, Richmond VA 23230
Tel (804) 237-1335 SIC 6798 6513

▲ARMADA HOFFLER PROPERTIES INC p 110
222 Central Park Ave # 2100, Virginia Beach VA 23462
Tel (757) 366-4000 SIC 6798

▲SOTHERLY HOTELS INC p 1342
410 W Francis St, Williamsburg VA 23185
Tel (757) 229-5648 SIC 6798

PLUM CREEK TIMBER CO INC p 1156
601 Union St Ste 3100, Seattle WA 98101
Tel (206) 467-3600 SIC 6798 1311

▲WEYERHAEUSER CO p 1603
220 Occidental Ave S, Seattle WA 98104
Tel (253) 924-2345
SIC 6798 0811 2411 2435 2611 2621

▲POTLATCH CORP p 1164
601 W 1st Ave Ste 1600, Spokane WA 99201
Tel (509) 835-1500 SIC 0831 6798

PHYSICIANS REALTY TRUST p 1146
309 N Water St Ste 500, Milwaukee WI 53202
Tel (414) 367-5600 SIC 6798

SIC 6799 Investors, NEC

HARBERT CORP p 659
2100 3rd Ave N Ste 600, Birmingham AL 35203
Tel (205) 987-5500 SIC 4911 6799

HARBERT MANAGEMENT CORP p 659
2100 3rd Ave N Ste 600, Birmingham AL 35203
Tel (205) 987-5500 SIC 6726 6799

ALEUT CORP p 48
4000 Old Seward Hwy # 300, Anchorage AK 99503
Tel (907) 561-4300 SIC 6799 1542 8742

OUZINKIE NATIVE CORP p 1099
500 Main St, Ouzinkie AK 99644
Tel (907) 680-2208 *SIC* 6799

AMERICAN RESIDENTIAL PROPERTIES LLC p 78
7033 E Greenway Pkwy # 210, Scottsdale AZ 85254
Tel (480) 474-4800 *SIC* 6799

▲ BEAR STATE FINANCIAL HOLDINGS LLC p 165
900 S Shackleford Rd # 200, Little Rock AR 72211
Tel (501) 320-4862 *SIC* 6799

■ FLUOR DANIEL ASIA INC p 561
3 Polaris Way, Aliso Viejo CA 92656
Tel (949) 349-2000 *SIC* 6799

■ FLUOR DANIEL VENTURE GROUP INC p 561
1 Enterprise, Aliso Viejo CA 92656
Tel (949) 349-2000 *SIC* 6799

▲ KENNEDY-WILSON HOLDINGS INC p 811
151 El Camino Dr, Beverly Hills CA 90212
Tel (310) 887-6400 *SIC* 6531 6799

LEVINE LEICHTMAN CAPITAL PARTNERS INC p 858
335 N Maple Dr Ste 130, Beverly Hills CA 90210
Tel (310) 275-5335 *SIC* 6799

CRIMSON CAPITAL SILICON VALLEY p 392
1000 Marina Blvd Ste 105, Brisbane CA 94005
Tel (650) 325-8673 *SIC* 6799 3429

■ COUNTRYWIDE FINANCIAL CORP p 375
4500 Park Granada, Calabasas CA 91302
Tel (818) 225-3000
SIC 6162 6211 6361 6411 6163 6799

WESTAR CAPITAL ASSOCIATES II LLC p 1596
949 S Coast Dr Ste 170, Costa Mesa CA 92626
Tel (714) 481-5160 *SIC* 6799 3089

HGGC LLC p 689
1950 University Ave # 350, East Palo Alto CA 94303
Tel (650) 321-4910 *SIC* 6799

KRUSE INVESTMENT CO INC p 830
31120 W St, Goshen CA 93227
Tel (559) 302-1000 *SIC* 6799

■ ARES MANAGEMENT LLC p 107
2000 Avenue Of The Stars, Los Angeles CA 90067
Tel (310) 201-4100 *SIC* 6799

GRANDPOINT CAPITAL INC p 630
333 S Grand Ave Ste 4250, Los Angeles CA 90071
Tel (213) 542-4410 *SIC* 6799

OAKTREE HOLDINGS INC p 1071
333 S Grand Ave Ste 2800, Los Angeles CA 90071
Tel (213) 830-6300 *SIC* 6799

OCM REAL ESTATE OPPORTUNITIES FUND II LP p 1074
333 S Grand Ave Fl 28, Los Angeles CA 90071
Tel (213) 830-6300 *SIC* 6799

OPENGATE CAPITAL LLC p 1089
10250 Constellation Blvd, Los Angeles CA 90067
Tel (310) 432-7000 *SIC* 2721 6799 8621

P-WAVE HOLDINGS LLC p 1102
10877 Wilshire Blvd, Los Angeles CA 90024
Tel (310) 209-3010 *SIC* 6799

TRANSAMERICA OCCIDENTAL LIFE INSURANCE CO p 1470
1150 S Olive St Fl 23, Los Angeles CA 90015
Tel (213) 742-2111
SIC 6311 6371 6321 6324 6799

TRANSOM CAPITAL GROUP LLC p 1472
10990 Wilshire Blvd # 440, Los Angeles CA 90024
Tel (424) 293-2818 *SIC* 6799

VANCE STREET CAPITAL LLC p 1543
11150 Santa Monica Blvd # 750, Los Angeles CA 90025
Tel (310) 231-7100 *SIC* 6799

■ MARINE HOLDING US CORP p 906
6000 Condor Dr, Moorpark CA 93021
Tel (805) 529-2000 *SIC* 6799

KBS REAL ESTATE INVESTMENT TRUST II INC p 806
800 Nwport Ctr Dr Ste 700, Newport Beach CA 92660
Tel (949) 417-6500 *SIC* 6799

WINDJAMMER CAPITAL INVESTORS IV LP p 1615
610 Newport Center Dr, Newport Beach CA 92660
Tel (919) 706-9989 *SIC* 6799

ALTAMONT CAPITAL PARTNERS LLC p 62
400 Hamilton Ave Ste 230, Palo Alto CA 94301
Tel (650) 264-7750 *SIC* 6799

▲ HERCULES CAPITAL INC p 685
400 Hamilton Ave Ste 310, Palo Alto CA 94301
Tel (650) 289-3060 *SIC* 6799

IDEALAB HOLDINGS LLC p 729
130 W Union St, Pasadena CA 91103
Tel (626) 585-6900 *SIC* 6799 5045 5734

GOLDEN INTERNATIONAL p 621
36720 Palmdale Rd, Rancho Mirage CA 92270
Tel (760) 568-1912 *SIC* 6799

■ EDISON MISSION GROUP INC p 478
2244 Walnut Grove Ave, Rosemead CA 91770
Tel (626) 302-2222
SIC 4931 6799 1629 1531

MCMILLIN COMMUNITIES INC p 932
2750 Womble Rd Ste 200, San Diego CA 92106
Tel (619) 561-5275 *SIC* 6799

MEDIMPACT HOLDINGS INC p 938
10181 Scripps Gateway Ct, San Diego CA 92131
Tel (858) 566-2727 *SIC* 6799

SAN DIEGO COUNTY CAPITAL ASSET LEASING C p 1276
1600 Pacific Hwy Ste 163, San Diego CA 92101
Tel (336) 733-2728 *SIC* 6799

FILLMORE CAPITAL PARTNERS LLC p 542
4 Embarcadero Ctr Ste 710, San Francisco CA 94111
Tel (415) 834-1477 *SIC* 6799

FRANCISCO PARTNERS MANAGEMENT LP p 574
1 Letterman Dr Ste 410, San Francisco CA 94129
Tel (415) 418-2900 *SIC* 6799 7372

GENSTAR CAPITAL LLC p 604
4 Embarcadero Ctr # 1900, San Francisco CA 94111
Tel (415) 834-2350 *SIC* 6799

GRYPHON INVESTORS INC p 643
1 Maritime Plz Ste 2300, San Francisco CA 94111
Tel (415) 217-7400 *SIC* 6799

HORIZON HOLDINGS LLC p 707
1 Bush St Ste 650, San Francisco CA 94104
Tel (415) 788-2000 *SIC* 6799 2053

■ JP MORGAN H&Q PRINCIPALS LP p 794
560 Mission St Fl 2, San Francisco CA 94105
Tel (415) 315-5000
SIC 6211 6799 6282 7389

■ PROLOGIS LP p 1183
Bay 1 Pier 1, San Francisco CA 94111
Tel (415) 394-9000 *SIC* 6798 6799

VISTA EQUITY PARTNERS FUND III LP p 1562
4 Embarcadero Ctr # 2000, San Francisco CA 94111
Tel (415) 765-6500 *SIC* 6799

■ CHEVRON INVESTOR INC p 296
6001 Bollinger Canyon Rd, San Ramon CA 94583
Tel (925) 842-1000 *SIC* 6799

CLEARLAKE CAPITAL GROUP LP p 324
233 Wilshire Blvd Ste 800, Santa Monica CA 90401
Tel (310) 400-8800 *SIC* 6799

COLONY CAPITAL LLC p 338
2450 Broadway Ste 600, Santa Monica CA 90404
Tel (310) 282-8820
SIC 6799 7999 7011 5813 5812

SHAPCO INC p 1311
1666 20th St Ste 100, Santa Monica CA 90404
Tel (310) 264-1666 *SIC* 5051 3317 6799

TCP CAPITAL CORP p 1428
2951 28th St Ste 1000, Santa Monica CA 90405
Tel (310) 566-1000 *SIC* 6799

▲ LIMONEIRA CO p 866
1141 Cummings Rd Ofc, Santa Paula CA 93060
Tel (805) 525-5541
SIC 0723 0174 0179 6531 6799

ACOUSTIC VENTURES LLC p 18
1775 N Sherman St # 2300, Denver CO 80203
Tel (303) 573-7011 *SIC* 6799

KSL CAPITAL PARTNERS LLC p 831
100 Saint Paul St Ste 800, Denver CO 80206
Tel (720) 284-6400 *SIC* 6799

PLATTE RIVER VENTURES LLC p 1155
200 Fillmore St Ste 200, Denver CO 80206
Tel (303) 292-7300 *SIC* 6799

TUCANOS DEVELOPMENT LLC p 1490
12345 W Alameda Pkwy, Lakewood CO 80228
Tel (303) 237-1340 *SIC* 6799

FIRST RESERVE XII ADVISORS LLC p 549
1 Lafayette Pl Ste 3, Greenwich CT 06830
Tel (203) 661-6601 *SIC* 6799

GENERAL ATLANTIC LLC p 599
600 Steamboat Rd Ste 105, Greenwich CT 06830
Tel (203) 629-8600 *SIC* 6799

LITTLEJOHN & CO LLC p 871
8 Sound Shore Dr Ste 303, Greenwich CT 06830
Tel (203) 552-3500 *SIC* 6799

WEEDEN INVESTORS LIMITED PARTNERSHIP p 1587
145 Mason St, Greenwich CT 06830
Tel (203) 861-7600 *SIC* 6799

■ HSB GROUP INC p 714
1 State St, Hartford CT 06102
Tel (860) 722-1866
SIC 6331 6411 6799 8711 8742

INVERNESS MANAGEMENT LLC p 761
21 Locust Ave Ste 1d, New Canaan CT 06840
Tel (203) 966-4177 *SIC* 6799

J H WHITNEY CAPITAL PARTNERS LLC p 771
130 Main St, New Canaan CT 06840
Tel (203) 716-6100 *SIC* 6799

ATLANTIC STREET CAPITAL MANAGEMENT LLC p 127
281 Tresser Blvd Fl 6, Stamford CT 06901
Tel (203) 428-3150 *SIC* 6799

CLEARVIEW CAPITAL LLC p 324
1010 Washington Blvd # 1, Stamford CT 06901
Tel (203) 698-2777 *SIC* 6799

OLYMPUS PARTNERS LP p 1083
1 Station Pl Ste 4, Stamford CT 06902
Tel (203) 353-5900 *SIC* 6799

SAC CAPITAL ADVISORS LLC p 1264
72 Cummings Point Rd, Stamford CT 06902
Tel (203) 890-2000 *SIC* 6799

■ SECURITY CAPITAL GROUP INC p 1299
292 Long Ridge Rd, Stamford CT 06902
Tel (203) 373-2211 *SIC* 6799 8742

UBS ENERGY LLC p 1498
677 Washington Blvd, Stamford CT 06901
Tel (203) 719-3000 *SIC* 6211 6799

JAB BEECH INC p 773
2200 Pennsylvania Ave Nw, Washington DC 20037
Tel (516) 537-1040 *SIC* 6799

▲ LINDBLAD EXPEDITIONS HOLDINGS INC p 868
509 7th St Nw, Washington DC 20004
Tel (202) 654-7060 *SIC* 6799

HART JEFFREY GROUP INC p 665
4400 N Federal Hwy, Boca Raton FL 33431
Tel (561) 997-2238 *SIC* 8732 6799

SUN CAPITAL PARTNERS INC p 1400
5200 Town Center Cir # 600, Boca Raton FL 33486
Tel (561) 962-3400
SIC 6799 2672 2671 5812 5411 5311

EMPIRE INVESTMENT HOLDINGS LLC p 493
1220 Malaga Ave, Coral Gables FL 33134
Tel (305) 403-1111 *SIC* 6799

TRIVEST FUND III LP p 1483
550 S Dixie Hwy Ste 300, Coral Gables FL 33146
Tel (305) 858-2200 *SIC* 6799 5712

■ NEXTERA ENERGY CAPITAL HOLDINGS INC p 1040
700 Universe Blvd, Juno Beach FL 33408
Tel (561) 694-6311 *SIC* 6799

BAYSIDE CAPITAL INC p 162
1450 Brickell Ave Fl 31, Miami FL 33131
Tel (305) 379-8686 *SIC* 6799

SURGERY CENTER HOLDINGS INC p 1408
1450 Brickell Ave Fl 31, Miami FL 33131
Tel (813) 514-9571 *SIC* 6799

AMERICAN INVESTMENT GROUP p 75
1549 Ne 123rd St, North Miami FL 33161
Tel (561) 714-6157 *SIC* 6799

PALM BEACH CAPITAL FUND II LP p 1109
180 Royal Palm Way, Palm Beach FL 33480
Tel (561) 659-9022 *SIC* 6799 2621

ANDERSON GROUP LLC p 90
111 2nd Ave Ne Ste 105, Saint Petersburg FL 33701
Tel (248) 645-8000 *SIC* 6799 6719

COMVEST PARTNERS p 353
525 Okeechobee Blvd # 1050, West Palm Beach FL 33401
Tel (561) 727-2000 *SIC* 6799

ARGONNE CAPITAL GROUP LLC p 107
3060 Peachtree Rd Nw # 400, Atlanta GA 30305
Tel (404) 364-2984 *SIC* 6799

EQUITY MSOUTH PARTNERS L P p 507
3050 Peachtree Rd Nw, Atlanta GA 30305
Tel (404) 816-3255 *SIC* 6799 7363

HOTEL EQUITIES INC p 710
41 Perimeter Ctr E # 510, Atlanta GA 30346
Tel (770) 934-2170 *SIC* 6799 8741

INTEGRAL GROUP LLC p 748
191 Peachtree St Ne # 4100, Atlanta GA 30303
Tel (404) 224-1860
SIC 6552 8748 6798 6799 6722

LOR INC p 878
2170 Piedmont Rd Ne, Atlanta GA 30324
Tel (404) 486-5600 *SIC* 6799 5084 3443

■ PENNINGTON SEED INC p 1130
1280 Atlanta Hwy, Madison GA 30650
Tel (706) 342-1234
SIC 5261 2873 5191 6799 0723

KLOCKNER USA HOLDING INC p 823
500 Colonial Center Pkwy # 500, Roswell GA 30076
Tel (678) 259-8800 *SIC* 6799 5051

AON US HOLDINGS INC p 95
200 E Randolph St, Chicago IL 60601
Tel (312) 381-1000 *SIC* 6411 6799 8741

BDT CAPITAL PARTNERS LLC p 164
401 N Michigan Ave # 3100, Chicago IL 60611
Tel (312) 660-7311 *SIC* 6799

BEECKEN PETTY OKEEFE & CO LLC p 168
131 S Dearborn St Ste 122, Chicago IL 60603
Tel (312) 435-0300 *SIC* 6799 3841

■ BUSINESS PROPERTY LENDING INC p 229
500 W Monroe St, Chicago IL 60661
Tel (312) 441-7000
SIC 6153 6799 6162 6159

CHICAGO GROWTH PARTNERS II LP p 297
222 Merchandise Mart Plz # 1871, Chicago IL 60654
Tel (312) 698-6300 *SIC* 6799

CIVC PARTNERS LP p 320
191 N Wacker Dr Ste 1100, Chicago IL 60606
Tel (312) 521-2000 *SIC* 8742 6799

ECHELON CAPITAL LLC p 475
121 W Wacker Dr, Chicago IL 60601
Tel (312) 263-0263 *SIC* 6799

GEM REALTY CAPITAL INC p 598
900 N Michigan Ave # 1450, Chicago IL 60611
Tel (312) 915-2900 *SIC* 6799

HARRIS WILLIAM & CO INC p 664
191 N Wacker Dr Ste 1500, Chicago IL 60606
Tel (312) 621-0590 *SIC* 6799 3317

LAKE CAPITAL MANAGEMENT LLC p 838
676 N Michigan Ave # 3900, Chicago IL 60611
Tel (312) 640-7050 *SIC* 6799

NOVA CAPITAL MANAGEMENT USA LLC p 1062
401 N Michigan Ave # 1200, Chicago IL 60611
Tel (312) 822-3380 *SIC* 6799

THOMA BRAVO LLC p 1448
300 N La Salle Dr # 4350, Chicago IL 60654
Tel (312) 254-3300 *SIC* 6799

THOMA CRESSEY BRAVO INC p 1448
300 N La Salle Dr # 4350, Chicago IL 60654
Tel (312) 254-3300
SIC 6799 8711 6311 6321 6531 7373

URBAN PENNSYLVANIA INVESTMENT MEMBER LLC p 1530
445 N Wells St Ste 200, Chicago IL 60654
Tel (312) 222-0777 *SIC* 6799

VWR INVESTORS INC p 1567
3 First National Plz, Chicago IL 60602
Tel (610) 386-1700 *SIC* 6799

WHI CAPITAL PARTNERS p 1605
191 N Wacker Dr Ste 1500, Chicago IL 60606
Tel (312) 621-0590 *SIC* 6799 3317

WIND POINT PARTNERS LP p 1615
676 N Michigan Ave # 3700, Chicago IL 60611
Tel (312) 255-4800 *SIC* 6799 7363 3089

WIND POINT PARTNERS VI LP p 1615
676 N Michigan Ave # 3700, Chicago IL 60611
Tel (312) 255-4800
SIC 6799 2542 2541 3429

■ KNOWLES INTERMEDIATE HOLDING INC p 825
1151 Maplewood Dr, Itasca IL 60143
Tel (630) 250-5100 *SIC* 6799

WILLIS STEIN & PARTNERS MANAGEMENT III LLC p 1612
1033 Skokie Blvd Ste 360, Northbrook IL 60062
Tel (312) 422-2400
SIC 6799 3479 2721 8721

WYNNCHURCH CAPITAL LTD p 1630
6250 N River Rd Ste 10-100, Rosemont IL 60018
Tel (847) 604-6100 *SIC* 6733 6799

▲ PRINCIPAL FINANCIAL GROUP INC p 1177
711 High St, Des Moines IA 50392
Tel (515) 247-5111
SIC 6321 6799 6722 6311

BURRUS INVESTMENT GROUP INC p 229
401 Veterans Memrl, Metairie LA 70005
Tel (504) 455-7600 *SIC* 6799

PAN-AMERICAN LIFE MUTUAL HOLDING CO p 1110
601 Poydras St Ste 1000, New Orleans LA 70130
Tel (877) 939-4550 *SIC* 6799

THAYER LODGING GROUP INC p 1446
1997 Annapolis Exchange P, Annapolis MD 21401
Tel (410) 268-0515 *SIC* 6799 6726

■ T ROWE PRICE ASSOCIATES INC p 1420
100 E Pratt St, Baltimore MD 21202
Tel (410) 345-2000 *SIC* 6799

PERSEUS LLC p 1137
4350 East West Hwy # 202, Bethesda MD 20814
Tel (301) 652-3200 *SIC* 6799

JBG COMPANIES L L C p 779
4445 Willard Ave, Chevy Chase MD 20815
Tel (240) 333-3600 *SIC* 6799

ABRY PARTNERS LLC p 12
888 Boylston St Ste 1600, Boston MA 02199
Tel (617) 375-8800 *SIC* 6799

ARCLIGHT CAPITAL HOLDINGS LLC p 105
200 Clarendon St Fl 55, Boston MA 02116
Tel (617) 531-6300 *SIC* 6799

ARCLIGHT CAPITAL PARTNERS LLC p 105
200 Clarendon St Fl 55, Boston MA 02116
Tel (617) 531-6300 *SIC* 6799

BAIN CAPITAL PARTNERS LLC p 145
200 Clarendon St, Boston MA 02116
Tel (617) 516-2000 *SIC* 6799

■ BANCBOSTON CAPITAL INC p 149
100 Federal St Ste 1m, Boston MA 02110
Tel (617) 434-2509 *SIC* 6799

FMR LLC p 562
245 Summer St, Boston MA 02210
Tel (617) 563-7000
SIC 6282 6211 6799 6552 6531

MASSACHUSETTS PORT AUTHORITY p 917
1 Harborside Dr Ste 200s, Boston MA 02128
Tel (617) 561-1600
SIC 4581 4491 6799 6512 4785

SUMMIT PARTNERS LP p 1399
222 Berkeley St Fl 18, Boston MA 02116
Tel (617) 824-1000 *SIC* 6799

TA ASSOCIATES p 1420
200 Clarendon St Ste 5600, Boston MA 02116
Tel (617) 574-6700 *SIC* 6799

TA ASSOCIATES MANAGEMENT LP p 1420
200 Clarendon St Fl 56, Boston MA 02116
Tel (617) 574-6700 *SIC* 6799

WESTON PRESIDIO INC p 1602
200 Clarendon St Ste 5000, Boston MA 02116
Tel (617) 988-2500
SIC 6799 3944 2519 3085

WATERMILL VENTURES LTD p 1582
1 Cranberry Hl 750, Lexington MA 02421
Tel (781) 891-6660 *SIC* 6799

NORTHLAND INVESTMENT CORP p 1057
2150 Washington St # 300, Newton MA 02462
Tel (617) 965-7100 *SIC* 6799 6411 6531

NSF INTERNATIONAL HOLDINGS p 1065
789 N Dixboro Rd, Ann Arbor MI 48105
Tel (734) 769-8010 *SIC* 6799

NEAPCO HOLDINGS LLC p 1023
6735 Haggerty Rd, Belleville MI 48111
Tel (734) 447-1380
SIC 3568 3714 6719 6799

PENSKE TRANSPORTATION HOLDINGS CORP p 1131
13400 W Outer Dr, Detroit MI 48239
Tel (313) 592-7311 *SIC* 6799

DIALOGDIRECT LLC p 436
13700 Oakland St, Highland Park MI 48203
Tel (313) 957-5100 *SIC* 6799 8742

MD INVESTORS CORP p 933
47659 Halyard Dr, Plymouth MI 48170
Tel (734) 207-6200 *SIC* 6799

BLUESTEM GROUP INC p 193
7505 Flying Cloud Dr, Eden Prairie MN 55344
Tel (952) 656-3700 *SIC* 6799 7389

TONKA BAY EQUITY PARTNERS LLC p 1460
301 Carlson Pkwy Ste 325, Hopkins MN 55305
Tel (952) 345-2030 *SIC* 6799

NORTH CENTRAL EQUITY LLC p 1051
60 S 6th St Ste 2535, Minneapolis MN 55402
Tel (612) 465-0260 *SIC* 6799 4813

■ NORWEST VENTURE CAPITAL MANAGEMENT INC p 1061
80 S 8th St Ste 3600, Minneapolis MN 55402
Tel (612) 215-1600 *SIC* 6799

SPELL CAPITAL PARTNERS FUND III FOR QUALIFIED PURCHASERS LP p 1358
222 S 9th St Ste 2880, Minneapolis MN 55402
Tel (612) 371-9650 *SIC* 6799

▲ WAYZATA INVESTMENT PARTNERS LLC p 1584
701 Lake St E Ste 300, Wayzata MN 55391
Tel (952) 345-0700 *SIC* 6799

PRESIDENT CASINOS INC p 1172
1000 N Lnor K Slivan Blvd, Saint Louis MO 63102
Tel (314) 622-3000 *SIC* 6799

COLEEN M MCCORMICK p 336
415 Center St Dakota Pl, Ulysses NE 68669
Tel (402) 549-2778 *SIC* 8748 6799

SAGEBRUSH ENTERPRISES INC p 1267
4730 S Fort Apache Rd, Las Vegas NV 89147
Tel (702) 873-5338
SIC 1522 1542 7992 6799

FRED ALGER MANAGEMENT INC p 575
600 Plaza One, Jersey City NJ 07311
Tel (201) 547-3600 *SIC* 6282 6211 6799

NEW YORK LIFE INVESTMENT MANAGEMENT LLC p 1035
30 Hudson St, Jersey City NJ 07302
Tel (973) 394-3000 *SIC* 6799

■ PGIM INC p 1140
655 Broad St, Newark NJ 07102
Tel (973) 802-6791 *SIC* 6411 6799 6282

SAMSUNG C&T AMERICA INC p 1275
105 Challenger Rd Fl 3, Ridgefield Park NJ 07660
Tel (201) 229-4000 *SIC* 5169 6799 8742

ENERGY CAPITAL PARTNERS II LLC p 497
51 John F Kennedy Pkwy # 200, Short Hills NJ 07078
Tel (973) 671-6100 *SIC* 6799 4953 8711

KOHLBERG TE INVESTORS VII-B LP p 826
111 Radio Circle Dr, Mount Kisco NY 10549
Tel (914) 241-7430 *SIC* 6799

ACF INDUSTRIES HOLDING CORP p 17
767 5th Ave, New York NY 10153
Tel (212) 702-4363
SIC 3743 4741 4789 6799

ACQUISITION HOLDINGS SUBSIDIARY I LLC p 18
1177 Ave Of The Americas, New York NY 10036
Tel (212) 715-8000 *SIC* 6799

■ **AIG CAPITAL CORP** p 37
70 Pine St Fl 11, New York NY 10270
Tel (908) 679-3150 *SIC* 6411 6799

AIP LLC p 38
330 Madison Ave Fl 28, New York NY 10017
Tel (212) 627-2360 *SIC* 6799

AIP/AEROSPACE HOLDINGS LLC p 38
330 Madison Ave Fl 28, New York NY 10017
Tel (212) 916-8142 *SIC* 3721 6799

▲ **AMERICAN SECURITIES LLC** p 79
299 Park Ave Fl 34, New York NY 10171
Tel (212) 476-8000 *SIC* 6799

▲ **APOLLO GLOBAL MANAGEMENT LLC** p 97
9 W 57th St Fl 43, New York NY 10019
Tel (212) 515-3200 *SIC* 6726 6282 6799

■ **APOLLO MANAGEMENT LP** p 97
9 W 57th St Fl 43, New York NY 10019
Tel (212) 515-3200 *SIC* 6799 6531

AQUILINE CAPITAL PARTNERS LLC p 102
535 Madison Ave Fl 24, New York NY 10022
Tel (212) 624-9500 *SIC* 6799

■ **AREA PROPERTY PARTNERS L P** p 106
245 Park Ave Fl 44, New York NY 10167
Tel (212) 515-3400 *SIC* 6799

ARLON FOOD AND AGRICULTURE PARTNERS LP p 110
277 Park Ave, New York NY 10172
Tel (212) 207-5200 *SIC* 6799

ASSET CHURCHILL MANAGEMENT LLC p 119
430 Park Ave Ste 701, New York NY 10022
Tel (212) 478-9207 *SIC* 6799

AVISTA CAPITAL HOLDINGS LP p 138
65 E 55th St Fl 18, New York NY 10022
Tel (212) 593-6900 *SIC* 6799

BEHRMAN CAPITAL LP p 168
126 E 56th St Fl 27, New York NY 10022
Tel (212) 980-5419 *SIC* 6799

BKH ACQUISITION HOLDCO I LLC p 186
150 E 58th St Bsmt, New York NY 10155
Tel (787) 474-7762 *SIC* 6799

BRE SPADE VOTECO LLC p 209
345 Park Ave Fl 42, New York NY 10154
Tel (212) 583-5000 *SIC* 6799

BRERA CAPITAL PARTNERS LLC p 210
244 5th Ave, New York NY 10001
Tel (212) 230-5495 *SIC* 6799

CASTLE HARLAN PARTNERS IV LP p 264
150 E 58th St Fl 38, New York NY 10155
Tel (212) 644-8600 *SIC* 6799 6719

CCMP CAPITAL INVESTORS III LP p 270
245 Park Ave Fl 16, New York NY 10167
Tel (212) 600-9600 *SIC* 6799

CDPQ US INC p 271
1211 6th Ave Ste 3001, New York NY 10036
Tel (212) 596-6300 *SIC* 6799

CENTERBRIDGE CAPITAL PARTNERS LP p 276
375 Park Ave Fl 12, New York NY 10152
Tel (212) 672-5000 *SIC* 6799

CENTRE LANE PARTNERS LLC p 281
60 E 42nd St Ste 1250, New York NY 10165
Tel (646) 843-0710 *SIC* 6799

CHARTERHOUSE GROUP INC p 291
535 Madison Ave Fl 28, New York NY 10022
Tel (212) 584-3200 *SIC* 8741 6799 6282

CIRCLE PEAK CAPITAL MANAGEMENT LLC p 308
1325 Ave Of The Americas, New York NY 10019
Tel (646) 230-8812 *SIC* 2053 6799

■ **CITIGROUP VENTURE CAPITAL INTERNATIONAL DE CORP** p 310
731 Lexington Ave Fl 21, New York NY 10022
Tel (212) 559-5099 *SIC* 6799

CLARION CAPITAL PARTNERS LLC p 321
527 Madison Ave Fl 10, New York NY 10022
Tel (212) 821-0111 *SIC* 6799

CLAYTON DUBILIER & RICE INC p 323
375 Park Ave Fl 18, New York NY 10152
Tel (212) 407-5200 *SIC* 6799 3589 5812

CORAL REEF CAPITAL GROUP LLC p 368
757 3rd Ave, New York NY 10017
Tel (646) 599-9680 *SIC* 6799 1081

COURT SQUARE CAPITAL PARTNERS LP p 383
55 E 52nd St Rm 3400, New York NY 10055
Tel (212) 752-6110 *SIC* 6799 2731 2721

CREDIT SUISSE (USA) INC p 390
11 Madison Ave Frnt 1, New York NY 10010
Tel (212) 325-2000 *SIC* 6211 6282 6799

FIRST ATLANTIC CAPITAL LTD p 545
135 E 57th St Rear, New York NY 10022
Tel (212) 750-0300 *SIC* 6799

FLOW TRADERS US LLC p 560
1140 Avenue Of Americas, New York NY 10036
Tel (917) 210-5000 *SIC* 6799

FOCUS FINANCIAL PARTNERS LLC p 562
825 3rd Ave Fl 27, New York NY 10022
Tel (646) 519-2456 *SIC* 6799

GMACCH INVESTOR LLC p 619
9 W 57th St, New York NY 10019
Tel (212) 750-8300 *SIC* 6799

GOLDBERG LINDSAY & CO LLC p 620
630 5th Ave Fl 30, New York NY 10111
Tel (212) 651-1100 *SIC* 6799 8711 8712

HARVEST PARTNERS LP p 666
280 Park Ave Fl 25w, New York NY 10017
Tel (212) 599-6300 *SIC* 6799 7349

HOCHTIEF USA INC p 699
375 Hudson St Fl 6, New York NY 10014
Tel (212) 229-6000
SIC 1542 1541 1522 8741 8742 6799

IFM GLOBAL INFRASTRUCTURE FUND p 730
114 W 47th St Fl 26, New York NY 10036
Tel (212) 784-2260 *SIC* 6799 1623

JLL PARTNERS INC p 786
450 Lexington Ave Fl 31, New York NY 10017
Tel (212) 286-8600 *SIC* 6799 6099

KINDERHOOK INDUSTRIES LLC p 819
521 5th Ave Fl 34, New York NY 10175
Tel (212) 201-6780 *SIC* 6799

▲ **KKR & CO LP** p 822
9 W 57th St Ste 4200, New York NY 10019
Tel (212) 750-8300 *SIC* 6282 6799

LEND LEASE (US) INC p 855
250 Civic Center Dr, New York NY 10166
Tel (212) 592-6700 *SIC* 6799 6552

LINDSAY GOLDBERG LLC p 868
630 5th Ave Fl 30, New York NY 10111
Tel (212) 651-1100 *SIC* 6799

MONOMOY CAPITAL PARTNERS LP p 984
142 W 57th St Fl 17, New York NY 10019
Tel (212) 699-4000 *SIC* 6799

ONEX INVESTMENT CORP p 1088
712 5th Ave Fl 40, New York NY 10019
Tel (212) 582-2211 *SIC* 6799 6282

P O I ACQUISITION I INC p 1102
375 Park Ave Ste 1202, New York NY 10152
Tel (212) 418-1700 *SIC* 6799

PALLADIUM EQUITY PARTNERS III LP p 1108
1270 Ave Of The, New York NY 10020
Tel (212) 218-5150 *SIC* 6211 6799

■ **PARIBAS PROPERTIES INC** p 1114
787 7th Ave Fl 33, New York NY 10019
Tel (212) 841-3000
SIC 6211 6221 6799 8742

PRIME SECURITY SERVICES BORROWER LLC p 1175
9 W 57th St Fl 43, New York NY 10019
Tel (212) 515-3200
SIC 6799 7382 3699 7381

PSILOS GROUP MANAGERS LLC p 1188
1 Liberty Plz Ste 2301, New York NY 10006
Tel (212) 242-8844 *SIC* 6799 8059

RHONE CAPITAL LLC p 1232
45 Rockefeller Plz # 2710, New York NY 10111
Tel (212) 218-6700 *SIC* 6799

RIPPLEWOOD ADVISORS LLC p 1236
920 Broadway Fl 6, New York NY 10010
Tel (212) 218-2705 *SIC* 6799

RIVERSIDE PARTNERS LLC p 1238
45 Rockefeller Plz # 400, New York NY 10111
Tel (212) 265-6575 *SIC* 6799

ROUSE PROPERTIES LLC p 1253
1114 Avenue Of The Americ, New York NY 10036
Tel (212) 608-5108 *SIC* 6799

RUDER FINN GROUP INC p 1257
301 E 57th St, New York NY 10022
Tel (212) 593-5838 *SIC* 8743 6799 8741

SAGARD CAPITAL PARTNERS LP p 1267
280 Park Ave Fl 3ny, New York NY 10017
Tel (203) 629-6700 *SIC* 6799

SAVILLS AMERICA LIMITED p 1284
399 Park Ave Fl 11, New York NY 10022
Tel (212) 326-1000 *SIC* 6531 6799

SAVILLS STUDLEY INC p 1284
399 Park Ave Fl 11, New York NY 10022
Tel (212) 326-1000 *SIC* 6531 6799

SCHRODER US HOLDINGS INC p 1290
875 3rd Ave Fl 21, New York NY 10022
Tel (212) 641-3800
SIC 6282 6719 6211 6799

SENECA MORTGAGE INVESTMENTS LP p 1303
375 Park Ave Ste 3401, New York NY 10152
Tel (888) 601-6718 *SIC* 6799 6719

SIRIS CAPITAL GROUP LLC p 1326
601 Lexington Ave Rm 5901, New York NY 10022
Tel (212) 231-0095 *SIC* 6799

SK CAPITAL PARTNERS II LP p 1328
400 Park Ave Ste 820, New York NY 10022
Tel (212) 826-2700 *SIC* 6799

SK TITAN HOLDINGS LLC p 1329
400 Park Ave, New York NY 10022
Tel (212) 826-2700 *SIC* 6799

SKY ACQUISITION LLC p 1330
345 Park Ave, New York NY 10154
Tel (212) 583-5000 *SIC* 6799

SNOW PHIPPS GROUP LLC p 1336
667 Madison Ave Fl 18, New York NY 10065
Tel (212) 508-3300 *SIC* 6799

SOLAR CAPITAL LTD p 1338
500 Park Ave Fl 3, New York NY 10022
Tel (212) 993-1670 *SIC* 6799

SOUTHPORT LANE MANAGEMENT LLC p 1351
350 Madison Ave Fl 21, New York NY 10017
Tel (212) 729-3247 *SIC* 6799

TAILWIND MANAGEMENT LP p 1421
485 Lexington Ave Rm 2300, New York NY 10017
Tel (212) 271-3800 *SIC* 6799

THIRD POINT LLC p 1448
390 Park Ave Fl 18, New York NY 10022
Tel (212) 715-3880 *SIC* 6799

VERITAS CAPITAL MANAGEMENT LLC p 1549
9 W 57th St Fl 29, New York NY 10019
Tel (212) 415-6700 *SIC* 6799

VESTAR CAPITAL PARTNERS INC p 1552
245 Park Ave Rm 4100, New York NY 10167
Tel (212) 351-1600 *SIC* 6799

VIRTU FINANCIAL LLC p 1560
645 Madison Ave Fl 16, New York NY 10022
Tel (212) 418-0100 *SIC* 6799

WARBURG PINCUS LLC p 1575
450 Lexington Ave, New York NY 10017
Tel (212) 878-0600 *SIC* 6799 6211

WARBURG PINCUS PRIVATE EQUITY VIII LP p 1575
450 Lexington Ave, New York NY 10017
Tel (212) 878-0600 *SIC* 6799

WASSERSTEIN & CO LP p 1580
1185 Avenue Of The Americ, New York NY 10036
Tel (212) 702-5600 *SIC* 6799 2721 2741

WASSERSTEIN COSMOS CO-INVEST LP p 1580
1301 Ave Of The Americas, New York NY 10019
Tel (212) 702-5600 *SIC* 6799

WASSERSTEIN HOLDINGS LLC p 1580
1301 Avenue Of The Americ, New York NY 10019
Tel (212) 702-5600 *SIC* 6799 2721 2741

WELSH CARSON ANDERSON & STOWE VI LP p 1591
320 Park Ave Fl 25, New York NY 10022
Tel (212) 893-9500 *SIC* 6799

WICKS COMMUNICATIONS & MEDIA PARTNERS III LP p 1608
405 Park Ave Ste 702, New York NY 10022
Tel (212) 838-2100 *SIC* 6799

EJ DEL MONTE CORP p 482
909 Linden Ave Ste 1, Rochester NY 14625
Tel (585) 586-3121
SIC 6552 8741 6512 6799 7011

DUNES POINT CAPITAL LLC p 461
411 Theodore Fremd Ave # 125, Rye NY 10580
Tel (914) 967-1390 *SIC* 6799

GREENBRIAR EQUITY GROUP LLC p 637
555 Theodore Fremd Ave A201, Rye NY 10580
Tel (914) 925-9600 *SIC* 4789 6799

FAISON ENTERPRISES INC p 526
121 W Trade St Fl 27, Charlotte NC 28202
Tel (704) 972-2500 *SIC* 6799

PAMLICO CAPITAL MANAGEMENT LP p 1110
150 N College St Ste 2400, Charlotte NC 28202
Tel (704) 374-6100 *SIC* 6799

SPANGLER COMPANIES INC p 1354
1110 E Morehead St, Charlotte NC 28204
Tel (704) 372-4500 *SIC* 6799

DPX HOLDINGS INC p 454
4307 Emperor Blvd Ste 140, Durham NC 27703
Tel (919) 226-3200 *SIC* 6799

SQUARE 1 FINANCIAL INC p 1362
406 Blackwell St Ste 240, Durham NC 27701
Tel (866) 355-0468 *SIC* 6022 6799

RHF INVESTMENTS INC p 1231
401 11th St Nw, Hickory NC 28601
Tel (828) 326-8350 *SIC* 6799

WEINBERG CAPITAL GROUP INC p 1588
5005 Rockside Rd Ste 1140, Cleveland OH 44131
Tel (216) 503-8307 *SIC* 6799

■ **JPMORGAN CHASE BANK NATIONAL ASSOCIATION** p 795
1111 Polaris Pkwy, Columbus OH 43240
Tel (614) 436-3055
SIC 6022 6099 6799 6211 6162 7389

COMMUNITY CHOICE FINANCIAL INC p 347
6785 Bobcat Way, Dublin OH 43016
Tel (614) 798-5900 *SIC* 6799

NM GROUP GLOBAL LLC p 1045
161 Greenfield St, Tiffin OH 44883
Tel (419) 447-5211 *SIC* 3542 3599 6799

KLINGBEIL CAPITAL MANAGEMENT LLC p 823
500 W Wilson Bridge Rd, Worthington OH 43085
Tel (614) 396-4919 *SIC* 6799 8741

ENDEAVOUR CAPITAL FUND LIMITED PARTNERSHIP p 496
920 Sw 6th Ave Ste 1400, Portland OR 97204
Tel (503) 223-2721 *SIC* 4213 4731 6799

■ **OLLIES BARGAIN OUTLET INC** p 1082
6295 Allentown Blvd Ste 1, Harrisburg PA 17112
Tel (717) 657-8243 *SIC* 6799

■ **OLLIES HOLDINGS INC** p 1082
6295 Allentown Blvd Ste 1, Harrisburg PA 17112
Tel (717) 657-2300 *SIC* 6799

GRAHAM PARTNERS INC p 629
3811 West Chester Pike # 200, Newtown Square PA 19073
Tel (610) 408-0500 *SIC* 8742 6799

■ **COMCAST INTERACTIVE CAPITAL LP** p 343
1701 John F Kennedy Blvd, Philadelphia PA 19103
Tel (215) 981-8450 *SIC* 6799

VERSA CAPITAL MANAGEMENT LLC p 1551
2929 Arch St Ste 1650, Philadelphia PA 19104
Tel (215) 609-3400 *SIC* 6799

■ **PNC INVESTMENTS LLC** p 1158
620 Liberty Ave Bsmt, Pittsburgh PA 15222
Tel (800) 762-6111 *SIC* 6799

MILESTONE PARTNERS MANAGEMENT CO LP p 969
555 E Lancaster Ave, Radnor PA 19087
Tel (610) 526-2700 *SIC* 6799

NATCO INDUSTRIES INC DEL p 1009
150 Thorn Hill Rd, Warrendale PA 15086
Tel (724) 776-4857 *SIC* 6799

NAUTIC PARTNERS LLC p 1019
100 Westminster St # 1220, Providence RI 02903
Tel (401) 278-6770 *SIC* 6799 7629

DHW LEASING LLC p 435
230 S Phillips Ave # 202, Sioux Falls SD 57104
Tel (605) 330-9414 *SIC* 6799

SMSA PALESTINE ACQUISITION CORP p 1334
174 E Fm 1830, Argyle TX 76226
Tel (972) 233-0300 *SIC* 6799

ABRAMS INTERNATIONAL INC p 12
111 Congress Ave Ste 2400, Austin TX 78701
Tel (512) 322-4000
SIC 1611 1622 1629 6799 7359 8742

AUSTIN VENTURES LP p 133
300 W 6th St Ste 2300, Austin TX 78701
Tel (512) 485-1900 *SIC* 6799 2038

F & H ACQUISITION CORP p 522
200 Crescent Ct Ste 1400, Dallas TX 75201
Tel (214) 661-7474 *SIC* 6799

FORD FINANCIAL FUND II LP p 565
200 Crescent Ct, Dallas TX 75201
Tel (214) 871-5151 *SIC* 6282 6799 7389

HUNT CONSOLIDATED INC p 718
1900 N Akard St, Dallas TX 75201
Tel (214) 978-8000
SIC 6799 1311 2911 1382 0212

LONE STAR FUND V (US) LP p 875
2711 N Haskell Ave # 1700, Dallas TX 75204
Tel (214) 754-8300 *SIC* 6799 5812

NEWCASTLE CAPITAL MANAGEMENT LP p 1037
200 Crescent Ct Ste 1400, Dallas TX 75201
Tel (317) 704-6000 *SIC* 6799

ROSEWOOD PRIVATE INVESTMENTS INC p 1251
2101 Cedar Springs Rd # 1600, Dallas TX 75201
Tel (214) 849-9000 *SIC* 6799 3423

RRH CORP p 1255
1900 N Akard St, Dallas TX 75201
Tel (214) 978-8000
SIC 1382 1311 2911 0212 6799

■ **TRAMMELL CROW CENTRAL TEXAS LTD** p 1469
2001 Ross Ave Ste 325, Dallas TX 75201
Tel (214) 267-0400 *SIC* 6799 6552 6512

TRANSITION CAPITAL PARTNERS LP p 1472
2100 Mckinney Ave # 1501, Dallas TX 75201
Tel (214) 978-3800 *SIC* 6799

WILLIAM HERBERT HUNT TRUST ESTATE p 1610
1601 Elm St Ste 3900, Dallas TX 75201
Tel (214) 880-8400 *SIC* 8742 6799

TPG CAPITAL MANAGEMENT LP p 1467
301 Commerce St Ste 3300, Fort Worth TX 76102
Tel (817) 871-4000
SIC 6726 3674 6799 3993 6719

BURROW GLOBAL LLC p 228
6200 Savoy Dr Ste 800, Houston TX 77036
Tel (713) 963-0930 *SIC* 1542 6799

EDF TRADING NORTH AMERICA LLC p 477
4700 W Sam Houston Pkwy N, Houston TX 77041
Tel (281) 781-0333 *SIC* 6799

FERTITTA GROUP INC p 538
1510 West Loop S, Houston TX 77027
Tel (713) 850-1010 *SIC* 6799

L E SIMMONS & ASSOCIATES INC p 834
600 Travis St Ste 6600, Houston TX 77002
Tel (713) 227-7888 *SIC* 6799

LEE SUMMER HOLDINGS LLC p 851
600 Travis St Ste 5800, Houston TX 77002
Tel (713) 993-4610 *SIC* 6799

STERLING GROUP L P p 1387
9 Greenway Plz Ste 2400, Houston TX 77046
Tel (713) 877-8257 *SIC* 6799

■ **TARGA RESOURCES LLC** p 1425
1000 Louisiana St # 4300, Houston TX 77002
Tel (713) 873-1000 *SIC* 1389 6799

TRAFIGURA TRADING LLC p 1469
1401 Mckinney St Ste 1500, Houston TX 77010
Tel (832) 203-6400 *SIC* 6799

TEXAS WASATCH INSURANCE SERVICES LP p 1444
100 E Royal Ln Ste 320, Irving TX 75039
Tel (214) 838-5500 *SIC* 6411 6799

D L ROGERS CORP p 407
5013 Davis Blvd, North Richland Hills TX 76180
Tel (817) 428-2077 *SIC* 5812 6552 6799

LSF5 CACTUS LLC p 883
5055 W Park Blvd Ste 500, Plano TX 75093
Tel (281) 830-0055 *SIC* 6799

▲ **NEXEO SOLUTIONS INC** p 1040
3 Waterway Square Pl # 1000, The Woodlands TX 77380
Tel (281) 297-0700 *SIC* 6799

REX-HIDE INC p 1230
705 S Lyons Ave, Tyler TX 75702
Tel (903) 593-7387
SIC 3061 3069 2891 6799

US GOLD INC p 1532
299 S Main St Ste 1800, Salt Lake City UT 84111
Tel (800) 607-4600 *SIC* 6799

THALHIMER INC MORTON G p 1446
11100 W Broad St, Glen Allen VA 23060
Tel (804) 648-5881
SIC 1542 6531 6799 6513 6512

FRAZIER MANAGEMENT LLC p 575
601 Union St Ste 3200, Seattle WA 98101
Tel (206) 621-7200 *SIC* 6799

MARUHA CAPITAL INVESTMENT INC p 913
2101 4th Ave Ste 1700, Seattle WA 98121
Tel (206) 382-0640 *SIC* 6799 2091

HOSPITALITY INVESTMENTS LIMITED PARTNERSHIP p 710
3808 N Sullivan Rd # 34, Spokane Valley WA 99216
Tel (509) 928-3736 *SIC* 6799

WISCONSIN ALUMNI RESEARCH FOUNDATION p 1618
614 Walnut St Fl 13, Madison WI 53726
Tel (608) 263-2500 *SIC* 6799 6794

MASON WELLS INC p 916
411 E Wisconsin Ave # 1280, Milwaukee WI 53202
Tel (414) 727-6400 *SIC* 6799

SIC 7011 Hotels, Motels & Tourist Courts

RUSSELL LANDS INC p 1259
2544 Willow Point Rd, Alexander City AL 35010
Tel (256) 329-0835
SIC 5211 6514 4493 7997 7011

PCH HOTELS AND RESORTS INC p 1124
11 N Water St Ste 8290, Mobile AL 36602
Tel (251) 338-5600 *SIC* 7011

BRISTOL BAY NATIVE CORP p 214
111 W 16th Ave Ste 400, Anchorage AK 99501
Tel (907) 563-0013 *SIC* 7011

TANADGUSIX CORP p 1424
615 E 82nd Ave Ste 200, Anchorage AK 99518
Tel (907) 278-2312 *SIC* 1796 7011 7359

NANA REGIONAL CORP INC p 1007
3150 C St Ste 150, Kotzebue AK 99752
Tel (907) 442-3301 *SIC* 7011

XANTERRA SOUTH RIM LLC p 1630
1 Main St, Grand Canyon AZ 86023
Tel (928) 638-2631 SIC 7011 5812

TOHONO OODHAM GAMING ENTERPRISE p 1458
1100 W Pima Mine Rd, Green Valley AZ 85614
Tel (520) 342-3000 SIC 7999 7011

11111 NORTH 7TH STREET PROPERTY LLC p 1
11111 N 7th St, Phoenix AZ 85020
Tel (602) 866-7500 SIC 7011

ABR PROPERTY LLC p 12
2400 E Missouri Ave, Phoenix AZ 85016
Tel (602) 955-6600 SIC 7011

KSL ARIZONA HOLDINGS III INC p 831
2400 E Missouri Ave, Phoenix AZ 85016
Tel (602) 955-6600
SIC 7011 5812 7991 5813

■ **POINTE HILTON SQUAW PEAK RESORT** p 1159
7677 N 16th St, Phoenix AZ 85020
Tel (602) 997-2626 SIC 7011

W M GRACE COS INC p 1569
7575 N 16th St Ste 1, Phoenix AZ 85020
Tel (602) 956-8254 SIC 1542 6512 7011

FAIRMONT SCOTTSDALE PRINCESS p 525
7575 E Princess Dr, Scottsdale AZ 85255
Tel (480) 585-4848 SIC 7011 5812 5813

PHOENICIAN RESORT p 1144
6000 E Camelback Rd, Scottsdale AZ 85251
Tel (480) 941-8200 SIC 7011

■ **SHERATON PHOENICIAN CORP** p 1315
6000 E Camelback Rd, Scottsdale AZ 85251
Tel (480) 941-8200
SIC 7011 5812 5813 7999 7992

ZC MANAGEMENT LLC p 1641
8600 E Rockcliff Rd, Tucson AZ 85750
Tel (520) 749-9655 SIC 7011

SUNSTONE HOTEL PROPERTIES INC p 1404
120 Vantis Dr Ste 350, Aliso Viejo CA 92656
Tel (949) 330-4000 SIC 7011

MAKAR ANAHEIM LLC p 899
777 W Convention Way, Anaheim CA 92802
Tel (714) 740-4431 SIC 7011

■ **WCO HOTELS INC** p 1585
1150 W Magic Way, Anaheim CA 92802
Tel (323) 636-3251 SIC 7011 5812

■ **HILTON INNS INC** p 695
9336 Civic Center Dr, Beverly Hills CA 90210
Tel (310) 278-4321 SIC 7011

SNOW SUMMIT SKI CORP p 1336
880 Summit Blvd, Big Bear Lake CA 92315
Tel (909) 866-5766 SIC 7011 5812

CACHE CREEK CASINO RESORT p 235
14455 State Highway 16, Brooks CA 95606
Tel (530) 796-3118 SIC 7011

▲ **WALT DISNEY CO** p 1574
500 S Buena Vista St, Burbank CA 91521
Tel (818) 560-1000
SIC 4833 4841 7011 7996 7812 2731

AVIARA FSRC ASSOCIATES LIMITED p 138
7100 Aviara Resort Dr, Carlsbad CA 92011
Tel (760) 603-6800 SIC 7011

AVIARA RESORT ASSOCIATES LIMITED PARTNERSHIP A CALIFORNIA LIMITED PARTNERSHIP p 138
7100 Aviara Resort Dr, Carlsbad CA 92011
Tel (760) 448-1234 SIC 7011

GRAND PACIFIC RESORTS INC p 630
5900 Pasteur Ct Ste 200, Carlsbad CA 92008
Tel (760) 431-8500 SIC 6531 7011

HARRIS FARMS INC p 663
29475 Fresno Coalinga Rd, Coalinga CA 93210
Tel (559) 884-2435
SIC 0191 0211 2011 7011 5812 5541

CHUKCHANSI GOLD RESORT & CASINO p 305
711 Lucky Ln, Coarsegold CA 93614
Tel (866) 794-6946 SIC 7011

CALIFORNIA COMMERCE CLUB INC p 239
6131 Telegraph Rd, Commerce CA 90040
Tel (323) 721-2100 SIC 7011 5812

L-O CORONADO HOTEL INC p 835
1500 Orange Ave, Coronado CA 92118
Tel (619) 435-6611
SIC 7011 5812 5813 5941

■ **SANSPAN CORP** p 1280
1500 Orange Ave, Coronado CA 92118
Tel (619) 435-6611 SIC 7011

CPH MONARCH HOTEL LLC p 387
1 Monarch Beach Resort, Dana Point CA 92629
Tel (949) 234-3200 SIC 7011

AVANTI HOSPITALS LLC p 136
222 N Splvd Blvd Ste 950, El Segundo CA 90245
Tel (310) 356-0550 SIC 7011

RPD HOTELS 18 LLC p 1255
2361 Rosecrans Ave # 150, El Segundo CA 90245
Tel (213) 746-1531 SIC 7011

OLS HOTELS & RESORTS LP p 1083
16000 Ventura Blvd # 1010, Encino CA 91436
Tel (818) 905-8280 SIC 7011

WELK GROUP INC p 1589
8860 Lawrence Welk Dr, Escondido CA 92026
Tel (760) 749-3000 SIC 7011 5099

JACKSON RANCHERIA CASINO & HOTEL p 774
12222 New York Ranch Rd, Jackson CA 95642
Tel (209) 223-1677
SIC 7999 5812 7011 5813

COPLEY PRESS INC p 368
7776 Ivanhoe Ave, La Jolla CA 92037
Tel (858) 454-0411 SIC 7383 2711 7011

KSL RECREATION MANAGEMENT OPERATIONS LLC p 831
50905 Avenida Bermudas, La Quinta CA 92253
Tel (760) 564-8000 SIC 7992 7011

BARONA RESORT & CASINO p 156
1932 Wildcat Canyon Rd, Lakeside CA 92040
Tel (619) 443-2300 SIC 7011

TACHI PALACE HOTEL & CASINO p 1421
17225 Jersey Ave, Lemoore CA 93245
Tel (559) 924-7751 SIC 7011

CARPENTERS SOUTHWEST ADMINISTRATIVE CORP p 260
533 S Fremont Ave, Los Angeles CA 90071
Tel (213) 386-8590 SIC 7011

STOCKBRIDGE/SBE HOLDINGS LLC p 1390
5900 Wilshire Blvd # 3100, Los Angeles CA 90036
Tel (323) 655-8000 SIC 7011

MAMMOTH MOUNTAIN SKI AREA LLC p 900
10001 Minaret Rd, Mammoth Lakes CA 93546
Tel (760) 934-2571 SIC 7011 5812

TARSADIA HOTELS p 1425
620 Newport Center Dr # 1400, Newport Beach CA 92660
Tel (949) 610-8000 SIC 7011

PARK MANAGEMENT GROUP LLC p 1115
1825 Gillespie Way Ste 101, North Hollywood CA 91601
Tel (404) 350-9990 SIC 7011

SPA RESORT CASINO p 1353
401 E Amado Rd, Palm Springs CA 92262
Tel (888) 999-1995 SIC 7011

I CYPRESS CO p 725
1700 17 Mile Dr, Pebble Beach CA 93953
Tel (831) 647-7500 SIC 7011

PEBBLE BEACH RESORT CO DBA LONE CYPRESS SHOP p 1126
2700 17 Mile Dr, Pebble Beach CA 93953
Tel (831) 647-7500
SIC 7011 7992 5941 7991

LONG POINT DEVELOPMENT LLC p 876
100 Terranea Way, Rancho Palos Verdes CA 90275
Tel (310) 265-2800 SIC 7011

SAN BERNARDINO HILTON p 1276
285 E Hospitality Ln, San Bernardino CA 92408
Tel (909) 889-0133 SIC 7011 6512 5812

EVOLUTION HOSPITALITY LLC p 515
1211 Puerta Del Sol # 170, San Clemente CA 92673
Tel (949) 325-1350 SIC 8741 7011

ATLAS HOTELS INC p 128
500 Hotel Cir N, San Diego CA 92108
Tel (619) 291-2232 SIC 7011 5812 5813

C N L HOTEL DEL PARTNERS LP p 233
1500 Orange Ave, San Diego CA 92118
Tel (619) 522-8299 SIC 7011

PACIFICA HOSTS INC p 1106
1775 Hancock St Ste 200, San Diego CA 92110
Tel (619) 296-9000 SIC 7011

MASON STREET OPCO LLC p 916
950 Mason St, San Francisco CA 94108
Tel (415) 772-5000 SIC 7011

MILLBRAE WCP HOTEL I LLC p 970
335 Powell St, San Francisco CA 94102
Tel (415) 397-7000 SIC 7011

WEST SAN CARLOS HOTEL PARTNERS LLC p 1595
282 Almaden Blvd, San Jose CA 95113
Tel (408) 998-0400 SIC 7011

PRINCESS CRUISE LINES LTD p 1176
24305 Town Center Dr, Santa Clarita CA 91355
Tel (661) 753-0000 SIC 4481 4725 7011

SANTA CRUZ SEASIDE CO INC p 1280
400 Beach St, Santa Cruz CA 95060
Tel (831) 423-5590
SIC 7996 7011 7933 6531

COLONY CAPITAL LLC p 338
2450 Broadway Ste 600, Santa Monica CA 90404
Tel (310) 282-8820
SIC 6799 7999 7011 5813 5812

WINDSOR CAPITAL GROUP INC p 1615
3250 Ocean Park Blvd # 350, Santa Monica CA 90405
Tel (310) 566-1100 SIC 7011

CHUMASH CASINO RESORT p 305
3400 E Highway 246, Santa Ynez CA 93460
Tel (805) 686-0855 SIC 7999 7011

PECHANGA DEVELOPMENT CORP p 1126
45000 Pechanga Pkwy, Temecula CA 92592
Tel (951) 695-4655 SIC 7011 7929 7999

DNC PARKS & RESORTS AT YOSEMITE INC p 446
9001 Village Dr, Yosemite Ntpk CA 95389
Tel (209) 372-1001
SIC 7011 5399 5812 5947 5541 4725

SAGE CLIENT 283 LLC p 1267
3155 S Vaughn Way, Aurora CO 80014
Tel (303) 595-7200 SIC 7011 8741

VAIL CORP p 1538
390 Interlocken Cres # 1000, Broomfield CO 80021
Tel (303) 404-1800 SIC 7011

▲ **VAIL RESORTS INC** p 1538
390 Interlocken Cres, Broomfield CO 80021
Tel (303) 404-1800 SIC 7011 6552

BROADMOOR HOTEL INC p 215
1 Lake Ave, Colorado Springs CO 80906
Tel (719) 634-7711
SIC 7011 5812 5813 7992 7999 7389

▲ **CENTURY CASINOS INC** p 282
455 E Pikes Peak Ave # 210, Colorado Springs CO 80903
Tel (719) 527-8300 SIC 7011 7929 7999

CROWNE PLAZA DENVER p 396
1450 Glenarm Pl, Denver CO 80202
Tel (303) 573-1450 SIC 7011

▲ **INTRAWEST RESORTS HOLDINGS INC** p 760
1621 18th St Ste 300, Denver CO 80202
Tel (303) 749-8200 SIC 7011 7999 6531

SAGE HOSPITALITY RESOURCES LLC p 1267
1575 Welton St Ste 300, Denver CO 80202
Tel (303) 595-7200 SIC 7011

DESTINATION RESIDENCES LLC p 432
10333 E Dry Creek Rd, Englewood CO 80112
Tel (303) 799-3830 SIC 7011 8741

STONEBRIDGE REALTY ADVISORS INC p 1391
9100 E Panorama Dr # 300, Englewood CO 80112
Tel (303) 785-3100 SIC 7011

M&C HOTEL INTERESTS INC p 890
7600 E Orchard Rd 230s, Greenwood Village CO 80111
Tel (303) 779-2000 SIC 7011

PARKS XANTERRA & RESORTS INC p 1116
6312 S Fiddlers Green Cir 600n, Greenwood Village CO 80111
Tel (303) 600-3400 SIC 7011 5947 5812

RICHFIELD HOLDINGS INC p 1233
5775 Dtc Blvd Ste 300, Greenwood Village CO 80111
Tel (303) 220-2000
SIC 6321 8712 7389 6331 7011

XANTERRA INC p 1630
6312 S Fiddlers Green Cir 600n, Greenwood Village CO 80111
Tel (303) 600-3400 SIC 7011

XANTERRA SOUTH RIM LLC p 1630
6312 S Fiddlers Green Cir, Greenwood Village CO 80111
Tel (303) 600-3400 SIC 7011 5813 7999

HEI HOSPITALITY LLC p 680
101 Merritt 7 Corp, Norwalk CT 06851
Tel (203) 849-8844 SIC 7011

CAMBRIDGE HOTEL MANAGEMENT LLC p 244
2 Crporate Driveshelton, Shelton CT 06484
Tel (203) 925-8370 SIC 7011

NEW CASTLE HOTELS LLC p 1029
2 Corporate Dr Ste 154, Shelton CT 06484
Tel (203) 925-8370 SIC 7011 8741 8742

■ **STARWOOD HOTELS & RESORTS WORLDWIDE LLC** p 1379
1 Star Pt, Stamford CT 06902
Tel (203) 964-6000 SIC 7011 8741

MOHEGAN SUN CASINO p 982
1 Mohegan Sun Blvd, Uncasville CT 06382
Tel (888) 226-7711 SIC 7011

MOHEGAN TRIBAL GAMING AUTHORITY p 982
1 Mohegan Sun Blvd, Uncasville CT 06382
Tel (860) 862-0777 SIC 7011

MTIC LLC p 998
1 Mohegan Sun Blvd, Uncasville CT 06382
Tel (860) 862-6100 SIC 7011

SAINT MARYS HEALTH SYSTEM INC p 1270
56 Franklin St, Waterbury CT 06706
Tel (203) 709-6000 SIC 8062 7011

▲ **DOVER DOWNS GAMING & ENTERTAINMENT INC** p 453
1131 N Dupont Hwy, Dover DE 19901
Tel (302) 674-4600
SIC 7929 7999 7011 7948

TUCSON HOTELS LP p 1490
2711 Centerville Rd # 400, Wilmington DE 19808
Tel (678) 830-2438 SIC 7011

YOUNG MENS CHRISTIAN ASSOCIATION OF WILMINGTON DELAWARE p 1639
100 W 10th St Ste 1100, Wilmington DE 19801
Tel (302) 221-9622 SIC 7997 7011

FORGE CO p 567
1050 Thmas Jfferson St Nw, Washington DC 20007
Tel (202) 295-8100 SIC 7521 7011

ROBERT CO INC J E p 1241
1250 Connecticut Ave Nw # 700, Washington DC 20036
Tel (703) 714-8000 SIC 7011

WILLARD HOTEL p 1610
1401 Pennsylvania Ave Nw, Washington DC 20004
Tel (202) 628-9100 SIC 7011

■ **BOCA RESORTS INC** p 197
501 E Camino Real, Boca Raton FL 33432
Tel (888) 543-1277 SIC 7011

BRE SELECT HOTELS OPERATING LLC p 209
501 E Camino Real, Boca Raton FL 33432
Tel (973) 503-9733 SIC 7011

BRE/BATON OPERATING LESSEE LLC p 209
501 E Camino Real, Boca Raton FL 33432
Tel (561) 447-3000 SIC 7011 7997

■ **PANTHERS BRHC LLC** p 1111
501 E Camino Real, Boca Raton FL 33432
Tel (888) 543-1277 SIC 7011 5812 7997

CLUB MED INC (A CAYMAN ISLANDS CORP) p 328
75 Valencia Ave Fl 12, Coral Gables FL 33134
Tel (305) 925-9000 SIC 7011

OCEAN PROPERTIES LTD p 1073
1001 E Atl Ave Ste 202, Delray Beach FL 33483
Tel (603) 559-2100
SIC 7011 6552 1522 5719 5812 5813

■ **RESORTQUEST INTERNATIONAL INC** p 1227
8955 Us Highway 98 W # 203, Destin FL 32550
Tel (850) 837-4774 SIC 7011 6519

■ **RESORTQUEST REAL ESTATE OF FLORIDA INC** p 1227
35000 Emerald Coast Pkwy, Destin FL 32541
Tel (850) 837-3700 SIC 7011 8741

▲ **CARNIVAL CORP** p 259
3655 Nw 87th Ave, Doral FL 33178
Tel (305) 599-2600 SIC 4481 4725 7011

A V AMELIA ISLAND PLANTATION p 6
39 Beach Lagoon Rd, Fernandina Beach FL 32034
Tel (904) 261-6161 SIC 7011

AMELIA ISLAND CO p 66
1423 Julia St, Fernandina Beach FL 32034
Tel (904) 261-6161
SIC 7011 6552 7992 7991 5812

RESORT MARKETING HOLDINGS INC p 1227
2419 E Commercial Blvd, Fort Lauderdale FL 33308
Tel (954) 630-9449 SIC 7011 6719

SEMINOLE HARD ROCK HOTEL & CASINO p 1302
1 Seminole Way, Fort Lauderdale FL 33314
Tel (954) 327-7625 SIC 7011

SEMINOLE TRIBE OF FLORIDA HARD ROCK p 1302
1 Seminole Way, Fort Lauderdale FL 33314
Tel (954) 327-7625 SIC 7011

INNISFREE HOTELS INC p 744
113 Bay Bridge Dr, Gulf Breeze FL 32561
Tel (850) 934-3609 SIC 7011

DIPLOMAT PROPERTIES LIMITED PARTNERSHIP p 441
3555 S Ocean Dr, Hollywood FL 33019
Tel (954) 602-6000 SIC 7011 7997

ORANGE LAKE COUNTRY CLUB INC p 1092
8505 W Irlo Bronson Hwy, Kissimmee FL 34747
Tel (407) 239-0000
SIC 7011 6552 7997 5812 5813

WALT DISNEY ATTRACTIONS p 1574
1500 Epcot Resorts Blvd, Lake Buena Vista FL 32830
Tel (407) 934-4000 SIC 7011 7299

■ **WALT DISNEY PARKS AND RESORTS US INC** p 1574
1375 E Buena Vista Dr, Lake Buena Vista FL 32830
Tel (407) 824-2222 SIC 7996 7011 5947

WALT DISNEY WORLD SWAN AND DOLPHIN p 1574
1500 Epcot Resorts Blvd, Lake Buena Vista FL 32830
Tel (407) 934-4000 SIC 7011

CLUB MED SALES INC p 328
6505 Blue Lagoon Dr # 225, Miami FL 33126
Tel (305) 925-9000
SIC 4724 4725 7011 8741

FONTAINEBLEUAU FLORIDA HOTEL LLC p 563
4441 Collins Ave, Miami FL 33140
Tel (305) 538-2000
SIC 6519 7011 5812 7991

HILTON INTERNATIONAL CO p 695
5201 Blue Lagoon Dr # 600, Miami FL 33126
Tel (305) 444-3444 SIC 7011 5812

GRAHAM COMPANIES p 628
6843 Main St, Miami Lakes FL 33014
Tel (305) 821-1130
SIC 1531 7011 0212 6552 6512 2711

DRIFTWOOD HOSPITALITY MANAGEMENT LLC p 456
11770 Us Highway 1 # 202, North Palm Beach FL 33408
Tel (561) 833-9979 SIC 7011

JACOBS INVESTMENTS INC p 775
11770 Us Highway 1 # 600, North Palm Beach FL 33408
Tel (561) 776-6050 SIC 6211 7011

BELV PARTNERS LP p 171
9801 International Dr, Orlando FL 32819
Tel (407) 352-4000 SIC 7011

CENTRAL FLORIDA INVESTMENTS INC p 278
5601 Windhover Dr Ofc, Orlando FL 32819
Tel (407) 354-3040 SIC 6552 7011 6531

HARD ROCK CAFE FOUNDATION INC p 660
6100 Old Park Ln Ste 100, Orlando FL 32835
Tel (407) 445-7625
SIC 5812 5813 7011 6794

■ **HYATT HOTELS OF FLORIDA INC** p 723
9801 International Dr, Orlando FL 32819
Tel (407) 284-1234 SIC 7011 5812 5813

KESSLER ENTERPRISE INC p 813
4901 Vineland Rd Ste 650, Orlando FL 32811
Tel (407) 996-9999 SIC 8741 7011

■ **MARRIOTT CORP** p 910
4040 Central Florida Pkwy, Orlando FL 32837
Tel (407) 206-2300 SIC 7011

■ **MARRIOTT OWNERSHIP RESORTS INC** p 910
6649 W Wood Blvd Ste 500, Orlando FL 32821
Tel (863) 688-7700 SIC 7011

■ **MARRIOTT RESORTS HOSPITALITY CORP** p 910
6649 W Wood Blvd Ste 500, Orlando FL 32821
Tel (407) 206-6000 SIC 7011

▲ **MARRIOTT VACATIONS WORLDWIDE CORP** p 910
6649 Westwood Blvd, Orlando FL 32821
Tel (407) 206-6000 SIC 6531 7011

■ **MSR HOTELS & RESORTS INC** p 997
450 S Orange Ave, Orlando FL 32801
Tel (407) 650-1000 SIC 7011

ROSEN 9939 INC p 1251
9840 International Dr, Orlando FL 32819
Tel (407) 996-9939
SIC 7011 5812 5813 7992 7389

ROSEN HOTELS AND RESORTS INC p 1251
9840 International Dr, Orlando FL 32819
Tel (407) 996-1706
SIC 7011 5812 5813 7389 8011 7992

TEMPUS RESORTS INTERNATIONAL LTD p 1436
7345 Greenbriar Pkwy, Orlando FL 32819
Tel (407) 363-1717 SIC 7011 6531

■ **UCF HOTEL VENTURE** p 1499
6800 Lakewood Plaza Dr, Orlando FL 32819
Tel (407) 503-9000 SIC 7011 5813 5812

EDGEWATER BEACH RESORT LLC p 477
11212 Front Beach Rd, Panama City FL 32407
Tel (850) 235-4044
SIC 1531 7011 5813 5812

BAYBEACH HOTELS LLC p 161
51 Gulf Breeze Pkwy, Pensacola FL 32507
Tel (850) 932-2214 SIC 7011

KERZNER INTERNATIONAL NORTH AMERICA INC p 813
1000 S Pine Island Rd, Plantation FL 33324
Tel (954) 809-2000 SIC 7011

ATRIUM HOSPITALITY LP p 129
12735 Morris Road Ext # 400, Alpharetta GA 30004
Tel (678) 762-0005 SIC 7011

DAVIDSON HOTEL CO p 416
1 Ravinia Dr Ste 1600, Atlanta GA 30346
Tel (678) 349-0909 SIC 8741 7011

DAVIDSON HOTEL CO LLC p 416
1 Ravinia Dr Ste 1600, Atlanta GA 30346
Tel (901) 821-4117 SIC 7011

DAVIDSON HOTEL PARTNERS LP p 416
1 Ravinia Dr Ste 1600, Atlanta GA 30346
Tel (901) 761-4664 SIC 7011

INTER-CONTINENTAL HOTELS CORP p 751
3 Ravinia Dr Ste 100, Atlanta GA 30346
Tel (770) 604-5000 SIC 7011

INTERCONTINENTAL HOTELS GROUP RESOURCES INC p 752
3 Ravinia Dr Ste 100, Atlanta GA 30346
Tel (770) 604-5000 SIC 7011 8741 6794

INTOWN HOSPITALITY INVESTORS LP p 759
980 Hammond Dr Ste 1400, Atlanta GA 30328
Tel (770) 799-5000 SIC 7011

JAMESON INNS INC p 777
41 Perimeter Ctr E # 4100, Atlanta GA 30346
Tel (770) 512-0462 SIC 7011 1522

SIX CONTINENTS HOTELS INC p 1328
3 Ravinia Dr Ste 100, Atlanta GA 30346
Tel (770) 604-2000 SIC 7011 6794 8741

ELAN CHATEAU RESORTS LLC p 483
100 Rue Charlemagne Dr, Braselton GA 30517
Tel (678) 425-0900
SIC 2084 5812 7992 7011

FOUNTAINHEAD DEVELOPMENT LLC p 571
100 Rue Charlemagne Dr, Braselton GA 30517
Tel (770) 867-0903
SIC 7992 7991 5921 5812 7011

LODGIAN INC p 873
2002 Summit Blvd Ste 300, Brookhaven GA 30319
Tel (404) 364-9400 SIC 7011 5813

SEA ISLAND ACQUISITION LP p 1295
100 Cloister Dr, Sea Island GA 31561
Tel (912) 638-3611 SIC 7011 0781 7992

SEA ISLAND ACQUISITIONS LLC p 1295
100 Cloister Dr, Sea Island GA 31561
Tel (912) 638-3611 SIC 7011

SEA ISLAND CO p 1295
100 Cloister Dr, Sea Island GA 31561
Tel (888) 732-4752 SIC 7011 0781 7992

LANGDALE CO p 844
1202 Madison Hwy, Valdosta GA 31601
Tel (229) 242-7450
SIC 2421 2491 7011 7699 5031 5171

■ **AQUA HOTELS AND RESORTS INC** p 101
1850 Ala Moana Blvd, Honolulu HI 96815
Tel (808) 943-9291 SIC 7011

■ **AQUA-ASTON HOSPITALITY LLC** p 101
2155 Kalakaua Ave Fl 5, Honolulu HI 96815
Tel (808) 931-1400 SIC 7389 7011

■ **HILTON HAWAIIAN VILLAGE LLC** p 695
2005 Kalia Rd, Honolulu HI 96815
Tel (808) 949-4321 SIC 7011 5812 5813

HTH CORP p 715
1668 S King St Fl 2, Honolulu HI 96826
Tel (808) 469-4111 SIC 7011 5812 6512

KYO-YA HOTELS & RESORTS LP p 833
2255 Kalakaua Ave Fl 2, Honolulu HI 96815
Tel (808) 931-8600 SIC 7011 5812 5813

OUTRIGGER HOTELS HAWAII p 1099
2375 Kuhio Ave Fl 4, Honolulu HI 96815
Tel (808) 921-6510 SIC 7011

ROBERTS HAWAII INC p 1242
680 Iwilei Rd Ste 700, Honolulu HI 96817
Tel (808) 523-7750
SIC 4119 4724 7011 4489

KAWAILOA DEVELOPMENT LLP p 805
1571 Poipu Rd Ste 3063, Koloa HI 96756
Tel (808) 742-1234 SIC 7011 7992

■ **MAUI OPERATING LLC** p 921
2365 Kaanapali Pkwy, Lahaina HI 96761
Tel (808) 661-2588 SIC 7011 7389

HAGADONE INVESTMENT CO INC p 652
111 S 1st St, Coeur D Alene ID 83814
Tel (208) 667-3431 SIC 2711 7011

SUN VALLEY CO p 1401
1 Sun Valley Rd, Sun Valley ID 83353
Tel (208) 622-4111 SIC 7011 7996

SCOTT KRAMER p 1293
Hwy 95, Worley ID 83876
Tel (800) 523-2464 SIC 7011

CLASSIC RIVERDALE INC p 323
200 W Madison St Ste 3700, Chicago IL 60606
Tel (312) 803-8800 SIC 7011

H GROUP HOLDING INC p 650
222 W Adams St Ste 250, Chicago IL 60606
Tel (312) 750-1234
SIC 4512 7011 5812 5813

■ **HYATT CORP** p 723
150 N Riverside Plz, Chicago IL 60606
Tel (312) 750-1234 SIC 7011

■ **HYATT EQUITIES LLC** p 723
71 S Wacker Dr Fl 14, Chicago IL 60606
Tel (312) 750-1234 SIC 7011

▲ **HYATT HOTELS CORP** p 723
71 S Wacker Dr Ste 1000, Chicago IL 60606
Tel (312) 750-1234 SIC 7011 6794

■ **HYATT HOTELS MANAGEMENT CORP** p 723
71 S Wacker Dr Ste 1000, Chicago IL 60606
Tel (312) 750-1234 SIC 7011

■ **HYATT INTERNATIONAL CORP** p 723
71 S Wacker Dr 12, Chicago IL 60606
Tel (312) 750-1234 SIC 7011

JOHN D AND CATHERINE T MACARTHUR FOUNDATION p 788
140 S Dearborn St, Chicago IL 60603
Tel (312) 332-0101 SIC 7011

KATO KAGAKU CO LTD p 804
151 E Wacker Dr, Chicago IL 60601
Tel (312) 565-1234 SIC 6512 7011

METROPOLITAN PIER AND EXPOSITION AUTHORITY p 956
301 Ecermak Rd Fl 5, Chicago IL 60616
Tel (312) 791-7000 SIC 7389 7999 7011

■ **SELECT HOTELS GROUP LLC** p 1301
71 S Wacker Dr, Chicago IL 60606
Tel (312) 750-1234 SIC 7011

SWISSOTEL MANAGEMENT CORP p 1413
323 E Wacker Dr, Chicago IL 60601
Tel (312) 565-0565 SIC 7011

THOR PALMER HOUSE HOTEL LLC p 1450
17 E Monroe St Lbby 10, Chicago IL 60603
Tel (312) 726-7500 SIC 7011

WIRTZ CORP p 1618
680 N Lake Shore Dr # 1900, Chicago IL 60611
Tel (312) 943-7000
SIC 5181 5182 6513 6512 7011 6411

YOUNG MENS CHRISTIAN ASSOCIATION OF CHICAGO p 1638
1030 W Van Buren St, Chicago IL 60607
Tel (312) 932-1200
SIC 8641 7011 8351 8699 8322 7999

RAYNOR MFG CO p 1210
1101 E River Rd, Dixon IL 61021
Tel (815) 288-1431
SIC 3442 7011 3699 2431

CASINO QUEEN INC p 263
200 Front St, East Saint Louis IL 62201
Tel (618) 874-5000 SIC 7999 7011

HEART OF AMERICA MANAGEMENT LLC p 678
1501 River Dr, Moline IL 61265
Tel (309) 797-9300 SIC 8741 5812 7011

LANE CLEARWATER LIMITED PARTNERSHIP p 843
1200 Shermer Rd, Northbrook IL 60062
Tel (847) 498-6650 SIC 7011

FIRST HOSPITALITY GROUP INC p 547
10275 W Higgins Rd # 300, Rosemont IL 60018
Tel (847) 299-9040 SIC 7011

MONTCLAIR HOTELS MB LLC p 986
6600 Mannheim Rd, Rosemont IL 60018
Tel (847) 457-3900 SIC 7011

PORTFOLIO HOTELS & RESORTS LLC p 1162
601 Oakmont Ln Ste 420, Westmont IL 60559
Tel (630) 366-2018 SIC 7011

■ **CAESARS RIVERBOAT CASINO LLC** p 237
11999 Casino Center Dr Se, Elizabeth IN 47117
Tel (812) 969-6000 SIC 7011

■ **AZTAR INDIANA GAMING CO LLC** p 140
421 Nw Riverside Dr, Evansville IN 47708
Tel (812) 433-4000 SIC 7011

FRENCH LICK SPRINGS RESORT INC p 578
8670 W State Road 56, French Lick IN 47432
Tel (888) 936-9360 SIC 7011

MAJESTIC HOLDCO LLC p 898
1 Buffington Harbor Dr, Gary IN 46406
Tel (702) 388-2400 SIC 7011

CENTAUR ACQUISITION LLC p 275
111 Monument Cir Ste 777, Indianapolis IN 46204
Tel (317) 656-8787 SIC 7011 7948

■ **INDIANA GAMING CO LP** p 738
777 Hollywood Blvd, Lawrenceburg IN 47025
Tel (812) 539-8000 SIC 7011

WHITECO INDUSTRIES INC p 1606
1000 E 80th Pl Ste 700n, Merrillville IN 46410
Tel (219) 769-6601
SIC 7312 7011 7922 6552 7374 3993

■ **AMERISTAR CASINO COUNCIL BLUFFS LLC** p 83
2200 River Rd, Council Bluffs IA 51501
Tel (712) 328-8888
SIC 7011 7991 5813 5812

■ **HARVEYS IOWA MANAGEMENT CO INC** p 667
1 Harrahs Blvd, Council Bluffs IA 51501
Tel (712) 329-6000 SIC 7011

■ **PENINSULA GAMING LLC** p 1129
301 Bell St, Dubuque IA 52001
Tel (563) 690-4975 SIC 7999 7011

PENINSULA GAMING PARTNERS LLC p 1129
600 Star Brewery Dr # 110, Dubuque IA 52001
Tel (563) 690-4975 SIC 7999 7011

ABCM CORP p 10
1320 4th St Ne, Hampton IA 50441
Tel (641) 456-5636 SIC 8741 6519 7011

LODGING ENTERPRISES LLC p 874
8080 E Central Ave # 180, Wichita KS 67206
Tel (316) 630-6300 SIC 7011 8741 6552

COMMONWEALTH HOTELS LLC p 346
100 E Rivercenter Blvd # 1050, Covington KY 41011
Tel (859) 392-2264 SIC 7011 8741

COLUMBIA SUSSEX CORP p 342
740 Centre View Blvd, Crestview Hills KY 41017
Tel (859) 331-0091 SIC 7011 5812

TROPICANA ENTERTAINMENT INTERMEDIATE HOLDINGS LLC p 1484
740 Centre View Blvd, Crestview Hills KY 41017
Tel (859) 578-1100 SIC 7011

AL J SCHNEIDER CO p 43
325 W Main St Ste 1800, Louisville KY 40202
Tel (502) 584-5984 SIC 7011 5031

■ **HORSESHOE ENTERTAINMENT** p 708
711 Horseshoe Blvd, Bossier City LA 71111
Tel (318) 742-0711 SIC 7011

GOLDEN NUGGET LLC p 621
2550 Golden Nugget Blvd, Lake Charles LA 70601
Tel (337) 508-7777 SIC 7011

■ **PNK (LAKE CHARLES) LLC** p 1158
777 Ave Lauberge, Lake Charles LA 70601
Tel (337) 395-7777 SIC 7011

■ **ST CHARLES GAMING CO INC** p 1365
100 Lake St, Lake Charles LA 70607
Tel (337) 430-0711 SIC 7011

TUNICA-BILOXI GAMING AUTHORITY p 1491
711 Paragon Pl, Marksville LA 71351
Tel (318) 253-1946 SIC 7011 7999 5999

JAZZ CASINO CO L L C p 779
8 Canal St, New Orleans LA 70130
Tel (504) 525-6260 SIC 7011

ELDORADO CASINO SHREVEPORT JOINT VENTURE p 484
451 Clyde Fant Pkwy, Shreveport LA 71101
Tel (877) 602-0711 SIC 7011

■ **ISLE OF CAPRI LAKE CHARLES** p 767
100 Westlake Ave, Westlake LA 70669
Tel (337) 430-2400 SIC 7011

PORTLAND HOTEL GARDEN INN p 1163
145 Jetport Blvd, Portland ME 04102
Tel (207) 828-1117 SIC 7011

HOTEL ACQUISITION CO LLC p 710
1997 Annapolis Exch Pkwy, Annapolis MD 21401
Tel (410) 268-0515 SIC 8741 7011

■ **COURTYARD MANAGEMENT CORP** p 383
10400 Fernwood Rd, Bethesda MD 20817
Tel (301) 380-3000 SIC 7011

CROSSROADS HOSPITALITY CO LLC p 394
6430 Rockland Dr, Bethesda MD 20817
Tel (301) 581-5900 SIC 7011

▲ **HOST HOTELS & RESORTS INC** p 710
6903 Rockledge Dr # 1500, Bethesda MD 20817
Tel (240) 744-1000 SIC 6798 7011

■ **HOST HOTELS & RESORTS LP** p 710
6903 Rockledge Dr # 1500, Bethesda MD 20817
Tel (240) 744-1000 SIC 6798 7011

HOST MARRIOTT SERVICES INC p 710
6711 Democracy Blvd, Bethesda MD 20817
Tel (240) 344-1000 SIC 7011

LODGING RLJ TRUST L P p 874
3 Bethesda Metro Ctr # 1000, Bethesda MD 20814
Tel (301) 280-7777 SIC 7011

▲ **MARRIOTT INTERNATIONAL INC** p 910
10400 Fernwood Rd, Bethesda MD 20817
Tel (301) 380-3000 SIC 7011 6794 6531

■ **MARRIOTT WORLDWIDE CORP** p 910
10400 Fernwood Rd, Bethesda MD 20817
Tel (301) 634-5100 SIC 7011

■ **RC MARRIOTT II INC** p 1212
10400 Fernwood Rd, Bethesda MD 20817
Tel (301) 333-3333 SIC 7011

RENAISSANCE HOTEL OPERATING CO INC p 1223
10400 Fernwood Rd, Bethesda MD 20817
Tel (301) 380-3000 SIC 7011 8741 6794

■ **RESIDENCE INN BY MARRIOTT LLC** p 1226
10400 Fernwood Rd, Bethesda MD 20817
Tel (301) 380-3000 SIC 7011

■ **RITZ-CARLTON HOTEL CO LLC** p 1237
4445 Willard Ave Ste 800, Chevy Chase MD 20815
Tel (301) 547-4700 SIC 7011

PLAMONDON ENTERPRISES INC p 1154
4991 New Design Rd # 109, Frederick MD 21703
Tel (301) 695-5051 SIC 5812 7011

CHESAPEAKE HOSPITALITY LLC p 295
6404 Ivy Ln Ste 800, Greenbelt MD 20770
Tel (301) 474-3307 SIC 7011

MARYLAND HOSPITALITY INC p 915
6411 Ivy Ln Ste 510, Greenbelt MD 20770
Tel (301) 474-3307 SIC 7011 8741 8742

▲ **CHOICE HOTELS INTERNATIONAL INC** p 302
1 Choice Hotels Cir, Rockville MD 20850
Tel (301) 592-5000 SIC 7011 7373

COMFORT CALIFORNIA INC p 344
10750 Columbia Pike # 300, Silver Spring MD 20901
Tel (301) 592-3800 SIC 7011

SUNBURST HOSPITALITY CORP p 1401
10750 Columbia Pike # 300, Silver Spring MD 20901
Tel (301) 592-3800 SIC 8741 7011

■ **HST LESSEE BOSTON LLC** p 715
39 Dalton St, Boston MA 02199
Tel (617) 236-2000
SIC 7011 5812 7299 5813

PYRAMID ADVISORS LLC p 1193
1 Post Office Sq Ste 1950, Boston MA 02109
Tel (617) 202-2033 SIC 7011

BRAINTREE HOTEL OPERATOR INC p 207
215 Wood Rd, Braintree MA 02184
Tel (781) 380-3300 SIC 7011

LINCHRIS HOTEL CORP p 866
269 Hanover St Ste 2, Hanover MA 02339
Tel (781) 826-8824 SIC 7011

■ **HPT TRS IHG-2 INC** p 714
255 Washington St Ste 300, Newton MA 02458
Tel (617) 964-8389 SIC 7011

SONESTA INTERNATIONAL HOTELS CORP p 1340
255 Washington St Ste 270, Newton MA 02458
Tel (770) 923-1775 SIC 7011

BOYNE USA INC p 205
1 Boyne Mountain Rd, Boyne Falls MI 49713
Tel (231) 549-6000 SIC 7011 7992 7032

GREEKTOWN CASINO LLC p 636
555 E Lafayette Blvd, Detroit MI 48226
Tel (313) 223-2999 SIC 5812 7011

■ **MGM GRAND DETROIT LLC** p 958
1777 3rd St, Detroit MI 48226
Tel (313) 465-1777 SIC 7011 5812 7991

GREENLEAF HOSPITALITY GROUP INC p 638
100 W Michigan Ave # 100, Kalamazoo MI 49007
Tel (269) 567-7691 SIC 7011 5813

ROMULUS KEWADIN CASINO LLC p 1249
2186 Shunk Rd, Sault Sainte Marie MI 49783
Tel (906) 632-0530 SIC 7011

GRAND TRAVERSE BAND ECONOMIC DEVELOPMENT CORP p 630
2331 N West Bay Shore Dr, Suttons Bay MI 49682
Tel (231) 534-8000 SIC 7011 7993 5812

NORTHCOTT HOSPITALITY INTERNATIONAL LLC p 1054
250 Lake Dr E, Chanhassen MN 55317
Tel (952) 294-5100 SIC 7011 5812

CARLSON HOTELS LIMITED PARTNERSHIP p 257
Carlson Parkway 701 Twr St Carlson Parkw, Minneapolis MN 55459
Tel (763) 212-1000
SIC 6794 7011 5812 5813

CARLSON HOLDINGS INC p 257
701 Carlson Pkwy, Minnetonka MN 55305
Tel (763) 212-5000
SIC 7011 5812 6794 7389 4724

CARLSON INC p 258
701 Carlson Pkwy, Minnetonka MN 55305
Tel (763) 212-5000
SIC 7011 5812 6794 8742 8743 7389

RADISSON HOTELS INTERNATIONAL INC p 1204
701 Carlson Pkwy, Minnetonka MN 55305
Tel (763) 212-5000
SIC 7011 6794 6552 6531 8742 7389

SMSC GAMING ENTERPRISE p 1334
2400 Mystic Lake Blvd, Prior Lake MN 55372
Tel (952) 445-9000 SIC 7999 7011

PRAIRIE ISLAND INDIAN COMMUNITY p 1167
5636 Sturgeon Lake Rd, Welch MN 55089
Tel (800) 554-5473 SIC 7999 5812 7011

TREASURE ISLAND RESORT AND CASINO p 1475
5734 Sturgeon Lake Rd, Welch MN 55089
Tel (651) 388-6300 SIC 7999 7011 5812

TORGERSON PROPERTIES INC p 1461
103 15th Ave Nw Ste 200, Willmar MN 56201
Tel (320) 235-7207 SIC 7011 5812 5813

■ **BEAU RIVAGE RESORTS INC** p 166
875 Beach Blvd, Biloxi MS 39530
Tel (228) 386-7111 SIC 7011

IMPERIAL PALACE OF MISSISSIPPI LLC p 734
850 Bayview Ave, Biloxi MS 39530
Tel (228) 432-3243
SIC 7011 5812 5813 7832

■ **RIVERBOAT CORP OF MISSISSIPPI** p 1237
151 Beach Blvd, Biloxi MS 39530
Tel (228) 435-5400 SIC 7011

JACKIES INTERNATIONAL INC p 773
1554 W Peace St, Canton MS 39046
Tel (601) 855-0146 SIC 5812 7011

GRAND CASINOS INC p 629
3300 W Beach Blvd, Gulfport MS 39501
Tel (228) 314-2100 SIC 7011

GULFSIDE CASINO PARTNERSHIP DBA p 647
3300 W Beach Blvd, Gulfport MS 39501
Tel (228) 832-5374 SIC 7011

MMI HOTEL GROUP INC p 979
1000 Red Fern Pl, Jackson MS 39232
Tel (601) 936-3666 SIC 7011

CHOCTAW RESORT DEVELOPMENT ENTERPRISE p 302
Highway 16 W, Philadelphia MS 39350
Tel (866) 447-3275 SIC 7011

■ **BL DEVELOPMENT CORP** p 186
13615 Old Highway 61 N, Robinsonville MS 38664
Tel (662) 357-3097 SIC 7011

■ **BOYD TUNICA INC** p 205
1477 Csno Strip Res Blvd, Robinsonville MS 38664
Tel (662) 363-0711 SIC 7011

MAJESTIC MISSISSIPPI LLC p 899
711 Lucky Ln, Robinsonville MS 38664
Tel (662) 363-5825 SIC 7011

■ **OLYMPIA BALLYS LIMITED PARTNERSHIP** p 1083
1450 Ballys Blvd, Robinsonville MS 38664
Tel (662) 357-1500
SIC 7999 7011 5813 5812

■ **ROBINSON PROPERTY GROUP LIMITED PARTNERSHIP** p 1242
1021 Casino Center Dr, Robinsonville MS 38664
Tel (662) 357-5500 SIC 7011 5813 5812

■ **TUNICA ROADHOUSE CORP** p 1491
13615 Old Highway 61 N, Robinsonville MS 38664
Tel (662) 363-4900
SIC 7999 7011 5813 5812

■ **AMERISTAR CASINO VICKSBURG INC** p 83
4116 Washington St, Vicksburg MS 39180
Tel (601) 638-1000 SIC 7999 7011 5812

■ **AMERISTAR CASINO KANSAS CITY INC** p 83
3200 Ameristar Dr, Kansas City MO 64161
Tel (816) 414-7000 SIC 7011 7999

HARRAHS MARYLAND HEIGHTS OPERATING CO INC p 663
777 Casino Center Dr, Maryland Heights MO 63043
Tel (314) 770-8100 SIC 7011 5813 5812

■ **ST LOUIS GAMING VENTURES LLC** p 1369
777 Casino Center Dr, Maryland Heights MO 63043
Tel (314) 770-7629 SIC 7999 7011

■ **MISSOURI GAMING CO** p 976
777 Nw Argosy Pkwy, Riverside MO 64150
Tel (816) 746-3171 SIC 7999 7011

■ **AMERISTAR CASINO ST CHARLES INC** p 83
1 Ameristar Blvd, Saint Charles MO 63301
Tel (636) 949-7777 SIC 7999 7011

DRURY HOTELS CO LLC p 457
721 Emerson Rd Ste 400, Saint Louis MO 63141
Tel (314) 429-2255 SIC 7011

▲ **ISLE OF CAPRI CASINOS INC** p 767
600 Emerson Rd Ste 300, Saint Louis MO 63141
Tel (314) 813-9200 SIC 7011 7948

ATRIUM HOTELS INC p 129
300 S John Q Hammons Pkwy # 900, Springfield MO 65806
Tel (417) 864-4300 SIC 7011

HAMMONS INC p 656
300 S John Q Hammons Pkwy # 900, Springfield MO 65806
Tel (417) 864-4300 SIC 7011

JOHN Q HAMMONS HOTELS MANAGEMENT LLC p 789
300 S John Q Hammons Pkwy # 900, Springfield MO 65806
Tel (471) 864-7333 SIC 7011

JOHN Q HAMMONS RVOCTR 12281989 p 789
300 S John Q Hammons Pkwy # 9, Springfield MO 65806
Tel (417) 864-4300 SIC 7011 6733

▲ **PEAK RESORTS INC** p 1126
17409 Hidden Valley Dr, Wildwood MO 63025
Tel (636) 938-7474 SIC 7992 7999 7011

CONFEDERATED SALISH & KOOTENAI TRIBES INC p 355
42487 Complex Blvd, Pablo MT 59855
Tel (406) 675-2700 SIC 7011

BOSSELMAN INC p 202
3123 W Stolley Park Rd, Grand Island NE 68801
Tel (308) 381-2800
SIC 5541 5411 5812 7011 5172 5084

CONCORD HOSPITALITY INC p 354
1701 Windhoek Dr, Lincoln NE 68512
Tel (402) 421-2551 SIC 5812 7011 7311

SUPERTEL HOSPITALITY MANAGEMENT INC p 1407
1800 W Pswalk Ave Ste 200, Norfolk NE 68701
Tel (402) 371-2520 SIC 7011

WINNEBAGO TRIBE OF NEBRASKA p 1616
100 Bluff Ave, Winnebago NE 68071
Tel (402) 878-3100 SIC 7011

GREEN VALLEY RANCH GAMING LLC p 637
2300 Paseo Verde Pkwy, Henderson NV 89052
Tel (702) 617-7777 SIC 7011

LV GAMING VENTURES LLC p 887
12300 Las Vegas Blvd S, Henderson NV 89044
Tel (702) 797-1000 SIC 7011 7991

■ LVGV LLC p 887
12300 Las Vegas Blvd S, Henderson NV 89044
Tel (702) 797-1000 SIC 7011 7991

MARNELL SHER GAMING LLC p 909
12300 Las Vegas Blvd S, Henderson NV 89044
Tel (702) 797-1000 SIC 7011

SUNSET STATION HOTEL AND CASINO p 1404
1301 W Sunset Rd, Henderson NV 89014
Tel (702) 547-7777 SIC 7011 5962 7389

PRIMADONNA CO LLC p 1174
31900 Las Vegas Blvd S, Jean NV 89019
Tel (702) 386-7867 SIC 7011

PRIMM VALLEY RESORT AND CASINO p 1176
31900 Las Vegas Blvd S, Jean NV 89019
Tel (702) 679-5160 SIC 7011

■ ACE GAMING LLC p 16
8918 Spanish Ridge Ave, Las Vegas NV 89148
Tel (702) 401-5931 SIC 7011

AFFINITY GAMING p 32
3755 Breakthrough Way # 300, Las Vegas NV 89135
Tel (702) 341-2400 SIC 7011

AFFINITY GAMING FINANCE CORP p 32
3755 Breakthrough Way # 300, Las Vegas NV 89135
Tel (702) 341-2400 SIC 7011 7999

ALLADDIN GAMING LLC p 51
3667 Las Vegas Blvd S, Las Vegas NV 89109
Tel (702) 785-5555 SIC 7011

AMERICAN CASINO & ENTERTAINMENT PROPERTIES LLC p 69
2000 Las Vegas Blvd S, Las Vegas NV 89104
Tel (702) 383-5242 SIC 7011

AMERISTAR CASINOS INC p 83
3773 Howard Hughes Pkwy # 490, Las Vegas NV 89169
Tel (702) 567-7000 SIC 7011

ARIZONA CHARLIES INC p 108
740 S Decatur Blvd, Las Vegas NV 89107
Tel (702) 258-5200 SIC 7011 5812 5813

BOULDER STATION INC p 204
4111 Boulder Hwy, Las Vegas NV 89121
Tel (702) 432-7777 SIC 7011 7389

▲ BOYD GAMING CORP p 205
3883 Howard Hughes Pkwy Flr 9, Las Vegas NV 89169
Tel (702) 792-7200 SIC 7011

▲ CAESARS ACQUISITION CO p 237
1 Caesars Palace Dr, Las Vegas NV 89109
Tel (702) 407-6000 SIC 7011

▲ CAESARS ENTERTAINMENT CORP p 237
1 Caesars Palace Dr, Las Vegas NV 89109
Tel (702) 407-6000 SIC 7011 7999

■ CAESARS GROWTH PARTNERS LLC p 237
1 Caesars Palace Dr, Las Vegas NV 89109
Tel (702) 407-6586 SIC 7011

■ CAESARS PALACE CORP p 237
3570 Las Vegas Blvd S, Las Vegas NV 89109
Tel (702) 731-7110 SIC 7011

■ CAESARS WORLD INC p 237
3570 Las Vegas Blvd S, Las Vegas NV 89109
Tel (702) 731-7110
SIC 7011 7999 5812 6552 5611 5621

■ CALIFORNIA HOTEL AND CASINO p 240
12 E Ogden Ave, Las Vegas NV 89101
Tel (702) 385-1222 SIC 7011

CANNERY CASINO RESORTS LLC p 247
9107 W Russell Rd, Las Vegas NV 89148
Tel (702) 507-5700 SIC 7011

CHINA ENERGY CORP p 301
6130 Elton Ave, Las Vegas NV 89107
Tel (702) 998-8146 SIC 7011

■ CIRCUS CIRCUS CASINOS INC p 308
2880 Las Vegas Blvd S, Las Vegas NV 89109
Tel (702) 734-0410 SIC 7011

■ COAST HOTELS & CASINOS INC p 331
4500 W Tropicana Ave, Las Vegas NV 89103
Tel (702) 367-7111 SIC 7011

■ COAST HOTELS AND CASINOS INC p 331
4500 W Tropicana Ave, Las Vegas NV 89103
Tel (702) 365-7111 SIC 7011

COLONY RESORTS LVH ACQUISITIONS LLC p 338
3000 Paradise Rd, Las Vegas NV 89109
Tel (702) 732-5111 SIC 7011

■ DESERT PALACE INC p 432
1 Caesars Palace Dr, Las Vegas NV 89109
Tel (702) 407-6269 SIC 7011

DIAMOND RESORTS HOLDINGS LLC p 437
10600 W Charleston Blvd, Las Vegas NV 89135
Tel (877) 787-0906 SIC 7011 6141 8741

DIAMOND RESORTS INTERNATIONAL INC p 437
10600 W Charleston Blvd, Las Vegas NV 89135
Tel (702) 798-8840 SIC 7011

DIAMOND RESORTS MANAGEMENT INC p 437
10600 W Charleston Blvd, Las Vegas NV 89135
Tel (702) 240-9712 SIC 7011

FITZGERALDS GAMING CORP p 553
301 Fremont St Fl 12, Las Vegas NV 89101
Tel (702) 388-2400 SIC 7011

FITZGERALDS LAS VEGAS INC p 553
301 Fremont St, Las Vegas NV 89101
Tel (702) 388-2224 SIC 7011

FP HOLDINGS LP p 573
4321 W Flamingo Rd, Las Vegas NV 89103
Tel (702) 942-7777 SIC 7011

▲ FULL HOUSE RESORTS INC p 584
4670 S Fort Apache Rd # 190, Las Vegas NV 89147
Tel (702) 221-7800 SIC 7011 7993

GAUGHAN SOUTH LLC p 594
9777 Las Vegas Blvd S, Las Vegas NV 89183
Tel (702) 796-7111 SIC 7011

■ GOLDEN NUGGET FINANCE CORP p 621
129 Fremont St, Las Vegas NV 89101
Tel (702) 385-7111 SIC 7011

GOLDEN NUGGET INC p 621
129 Fremont St, Las Vegas NV 89101
Tel (702) 385-7111 SIC 5812 7011

HARD ROCK HOTEL HOLDINGS LLC p 660
4455 Paradise Rd, Las Vegas NV 89169
Tel (702) 693-5000 SIC 7011

HARD ROCK HOTEL INC p 660
4455 Paradise Rd, Las Vegas NV 89169
Tel (702) 693-5000 SIC 7011

HRHH HOTEL/CASINO LLC p 714
4455 Paradise Rd, Las Vegas NV 89169
Tel (702) 693-5000 SIC 7011

IKE GAMING INC p 731
600 Fremont St, Las Vegas NV 89101
Tel (702) 385-5200 SIC 7011

LAS VEGAS RESORT HOLDINGS LLC p 845
2535 Las Vegas Blvd S, Las Vegas NV 89109
Tel (702) 761-7702 SIC 7011

▲ LAS VEGAS SANDS CORP p 845
3355 Las Vegas Blvd S, Las Vegas NV 89109
Tel (702) 414-1000 SIC 7011

■ LAS VEGAS SANDS LLC p 845
3355 Las Vegas Blvd S, Las Vegas NV 89109
Tel (702) 414-1000 SIC 7011

MAJESTIC STAR CASINO LLC p 899
5524 S Fort Apache Rd # 120, Las Vegas NV 89148
Tel (702) 386-0226 SIC 7011

■ MANDALAY RESORT GROUP p 901
3950 Las Vegas Blvd S, Las Vegas NV 89119
Tel (702) 693-7120 SIC 7011 7999 7996

■ MGM GRAND HOTEL LLC p 958
3799 Las Vegas Blvd S, Las Vegas NV 89109
Tel (702) 891-1111 SIC 7011

▲ MGM RESORTS INTERNATIONAL p 958
3600 Las Vegas Blvd S, Las Vegas NV 89109
Tel (702) 693-7120 SIC 7011

■ MH INC p 958
3950 Las Vegas Blvd S, Las Vegas NV 89119
Tel (702) 693-7120 SIC 7011

■ MIRAGE CASINO-HOTEL p 974
3400 Las Vegas Blvd S, Las Vegas NV 89109
Tel (702) 791-7111 SIC 7011

■ MIRAGE RESORTS INC p 974
3400 Las Vegas Blvd S, Las Vegas NV 89109
Tel (702) 791-7111 SIC 7011

▲ NEVADA GOLD & CASINOS INC p 1028
133 E Warm Springs Rd # 102, Las Vegas NV 89119
Tel (702) 685-1000 SIC 7011

NEVADA PROPERTY 1 LLC p 1028
3708 Las Vegas Blvd S, Las Vegas NV 89109
Tel (702) 698-7000 SIC 7011

■ NEW CASTLE CORP p 1029
3850 Las Vegas Blvd S, Las Vegas NV 89109
Tel (702) 597-7777 SIC 5812 7011

■ NEW YORK - NEW YORK HOTEL & CASINO LLC p 1033
3790 Las Vegas Blvd S, Las Vegas NV 89109
Tel (702) 740-6969 SIC 7011 7996

PALACE STATION HOTEL & CASINO INC p 1108
2411 W Sahara Ave, Las Vegas NV 89102
Tel (702) 367-2411 SIC 7011

■ PARBALL CORP p 1114
3655 Las Vegas Blvd S, Las Vegas NV 89109
Tel (702) 967-4111
SIC 7011 7999 6512 7521 7211

■ PARIS LAS VEGAS p 1115
3655 Las Vegas Blvd S, Las Vegas NV 89109
Tel (702) 946-7000 SIC 7011

PINNACLE ENTERTAINMENT INC p 1149
3980 Howard Hughes Pkwy, Las Vegas NV 89169
Tel (702) 541-7777 SIC 7999 7011

PLAZA HOTEL & CASINO LLC p 1156
1 S Main St, Las Vegas NV 89101
Tel (702) 386-2110 SIC 7011

■ RAMPARTS INC p 1207
3900 Las Vegas Blvd S, Las Vegas NV 89119
Tel (702) 262-4000 SIC 7011

RED ROCK RESORTS INC p 1216
1505 S Pavilion Center Dr, Las Vegas NV 89135
Tel (702) 495-3000 SIC 7011

■ RIO HOTEL & CASINO INC p 1236
3700 W Flamingo Rd, Las Vegas NV 89103
Tel (702) 777-7777 SIC 7011 7997

■ RIO PROPERTIES INC p 1236
3700 W Flamingo Rd, Las Vegas NV 89103
Tel (702) 777-7777 SIC 7011 5812

RIVIERA HOLDINGS CORP p 1239
2901 Las Vegas Blvd S, Las Vegas NV 89109
Tel (702) 794-9237 SIC 7011

■ SAM-WILL INC p 1274
200 Fremont St, Las Vegas NV 89101
Tel (702) 385-3232 SIC 7011

SANTA FE STATION INC p 1280
4949 N Rancho Dr, Las Vegas NV 89130
Tel (702) 658-4900 SIC 7011

SILVERTON CASINO LLC p 1324
3333 Blue Diamond Rd, Las Vegas NV 89139
Tel (702) 263-7777 SIC 7011 7299 5813

STATION CASINOS INC p 1383
4949 N Rancho Dr, Las Vegas NV 89130
Tel (702) 658-4900 SIC 7011

STATION CASINOS INC p 1383
1505 S Pavilion Center Dr, Las Vegas NV 89135
Tel (702) 495-3000 SIC 8741 7993 7011

STATION CASINOS LLC p 1383
1505 S Pavilion Center Dr, Las Vegas NV 89135
Tel (702) 495-3000 SIC 7011

STATION VOTECO LLC p 1383
1505 S Pavilion Center Dr, Las Vegas NV 89135
Tel (702) 495-3000 SIC 7011

STRATOSPHERE GAMING LLC p 1392
2000 Las Vegas Blvd S, Las Vegas NV 89104
Tel (702) 380-7777 SIC 7011

STRATOSPHERE LLC p 1393
2000 Las Vegas Blvd S, Las Vegas NV 89104
Tel (702) 380-7777 SIC 7011 7999

TREASURE ISLAND LLC p 1475
3300 Las Vegas Blvd S, Las Vegas NV 89109
Tel (702) 894-7111 SIC 7011 7231

TROPICANA ENTERTAINMENT HOLDINGS LLC p 1484
3930 Howard Hughes Pkwy, Las Vegas NV 89169
Tel (702) 589-3900 SIC 7011

■ TROPICANA ENTERTAINMENT INC p 1484
8345 W Sunset Rd Ste 300, Las Vegas NV 89113
Tel (702) 589-3900 SIC 7011 7999

TROPICANA ENTERTAINMENT LLC p 1484
3930 Howard Hughes Pkwy # 400, Las Vegas NV 89169
Tel (702) 589-3900 SIC 7011

■ TROPICANA LAS VEGAS INC p 1484
3801 Las Vegas Blvd S, Las Vegas NV 89109
Tel (702) 739-2222 SIC 7011

■ TROPICANA ST LOUIS LLC p 1484
3930 Howard Hughes Pkwy # 4, Las Vegas NV 89169
Tel (702) 589-3900 SIC 7011

■ VENETIAN CASINO RESORT LLC p 1547
3355 Las Vegas Blvd S, Las Vegas NV 89109
Tel (702) 414-1000
SIC 7011 5812 5813 7299

■ VICTORIA PARTNERS p 1555
3770 Las Vegas Blvd S, Las Vegas NV 89109
Tel (888) 529-4828
SIC 7011 5812 7299 5813

WESTGATE LAS VEGAS RESORT LLC p 1601
3000 Paradise Rd, Las Vegas NV 89109
Tel (702) 732-5111 SIC 7011

WESTGATE LVH LLC p 1601
3000 Paradise Rd, Las Vegas NV 89109
Tel (702) 732-5111 SIC 7011

■ WYNN LAS VEGAS LLC p 1630
3131 Las Vegas Blvd S, Las Vegas NV 89109
Tel (702) 770-7555 SIC 7011

■ WYNN RESORTS HOLDINGS LLC p 1630
3131 Las Vegas Blvd S, Las Vegas NV 89109
Tel (702) 770-7555 SIC 7011

▲ WYNN RESORTS LIMITED p 1630
3131 Las Vegas Blvd S, Las Vegas NV 89109
Tel (702) 770-7555 SIC 7011

AMERICAN CASINO & ENTERTAINMENT PROPERTIES LLC p 70
1900 S Casino Dr, Laughlin NV 89029
Tel (702) 298-5111 SIC 6512 7011

■ HARRAHS LAUGHLIN LLC p 663
2900 S Casino Dr, Laughlin NV 89029
Tel (702) 298-4600 SIC 7011 5812

RIVER PALMS RESORT CASINO p 1237
2121 S Casino Dr, Laughlin NV 89029
Tel (702) 298-2242 SIC 7011

TROPICANA EXPRESS INC p 1484
2121 S Casino Dr, Laughlin NV 89029
Tel (702) 299-0306 SIC 7011

EPIC RESORTS - SCOTTSDALE LINKS RESORT LLC p 505
3865 W Cheyenne Ave, North Las Vegas NV 89032
Tel (610) 992-0100 SIC 7011

TEXAS GAMBLING HALL & HOTEL INC p 1443
2101 Texas Star Ln, North Las Vegas NV 89032
Tel (702) 631-1000 SIC 7011 7999 5812

TEXAS STATION GAMBLING HALL & HOTEL INC p 1444
2101 Texas Star Ln, North Las Vegas NV 89032
Tel (702) 631-1000 SIC 7011 7993

■ CC-RENO LLC p 269
500 N Sierra St, Reno NV 89503
Tel (775) 328-9469 SIC 7011

■ CIRCUS AND ELDORADO JOINT VENTURE LLC p 308
407 N Virginia St, Reno NV 89501
Tel (777) 329-4777 SIC 7011

▲ ELDORADO RESORTS INC p 484
100 W Liberty St Ste 1150, Reno NV 89501
Tel (775) 328-0100 SIC 7011

ELDORADO RESORTS LLC p 484
345 N Virginia St, Reno NV 89501
Tel (775) 786-5700 SIC 7011 5812 5813

■ GOLDEN ROAD MOTOR INN INC p 621
3800 S Virginia St, Reno NV 89502
Tel (775) 335-4521
SIC 7011 5812 5813 7299

GRAND SIERRA RESORT CORP p 630
2500 2nd St, Reno NV 89595
Tel (800) 501-2651 SIC 7011

MEI-GSR HOLDINGS LLC p 940
2500 2nd St, Reno NV 89595
Tel (775) 789-2000 SIC 7011

▲ MONARCH CASINO & RESORT INC p 983
3800 S Virginia St, Reno NV 89502
Tel (775) 335-4600 SIC 7011

PEPPERMILL CASINOS INC p 1134
90 W Grove St Ste 600, Reno NV 89509
Tel (775) 689-8900 SIC 7011 7999

RECREATIONAL ENTERPRISES INC p 1215
345 N Virginia St, Reno NV 89501
Tel (775) 786-5700
SIC 7011 7999 5813 5812

SIERRA DEVELOPMENT CO p 1320
38 E 2nd St, Reno NV 89501
Tel (775) 323-1046 SIC 7011

SPARKS NUGGET INC p 1354
1100 Nugget Ave, Sparks NV 89431
Tel (775) 356-3300 SIC 7011

■ HARVEYS CASINO RESORTS p 667
Hwy 50 & Stateline Ave, Stateline NV 89449
Tel (775) 588-2411 SIC 7011

ATLANTIC CITY SHOWBOAT INC p 126
801 Boardwalk, Atlantic City NJ 08401
Tel (609) 343-4000 SIC 7011

■ BALLYS PARK PLACE INC p 149
1900 Pacific Ave, Atlantic City NJ 08401
Tel (609) 340-2000 SIC 7011

■ CAESARS NEW JERSEY INC p 237
2100 Pacific Ave, Atlantic City NJ 08401
Tel (609) 348-4411 SIC 7011

DGMB CASINO LLC p 435
1133 Boardwalk, Atlantic City NJ 08401
Tel (800) 772-9000 SIC 7011

FLAGSHIP RESORT DEVELOPMENT CORP p 554
60 N Maine Ave, Atlantic City NJ 08401
Tel (609) 347-3524 SIC 6531 7011

■ HARRAHS ATLANTIC CITY OPERATING CO LLC p 663
777 Harrahs Blvd, Atlantic City NJ 08401
Tel (609) 441-5000 SIC 7011

MARINA ASSOCIATES LTD p 906
777 Harrahs Blvd, Atlantic City NJ 08401
Tel (609) 441-5000 SIC 7011 5812

MARINA DISTRICT DEVELOPMENT CO LLC p 906
1 Borgata Way, Atlantic City NJ 08401
Tel (609) 317-1000 SIC 7011

MARINA DISTRICT FINANCE CO INC p 906
1 Borgata Way, Atlantic City NJ 08401
Tel (609) 317-1000 SIC 7011

RAMADA NEW JERSEY HOLDINGS CORP p 1206
Brighton Ave Boardwalk, Atlantic City NJ 08401
Tel (609) 340-4000 SIC 7011

RESORTS CASINO HOTEL p 1227
1133 Boardwalk, Atlantic City NJ 08401
Tel (609) 344-6000 SIC 7011

REVEL ENTERTAINMENT GROUP LLC p 1229
500 Boardwalk, Atlantic City NJ 08401
Tel (609) 340-0003 SIC 7011

SHOWBOAT INC p 1319
801 Boardwalk, Atlantic City NJ 08401
Tel (609) 343-4000 SIC 7011

■ TROPICANA ATLANTIC CITY CORP p 1484
2831 Boardwalk, Atlantic City NJ 08401
Tel (609) 340-4000 SIC 7011

TROPICANA ENTERTAINMENT INC p 1484
2831 Brighton Ave, Atlantic City NJ 08401
Tel (609) 340-4000 SIC 7011

TRUMP ENTERTAINMENT RESORTS INC p 1487
1000 Boardwalk, Atlantic City NJ 08401
Tel (609) 449-5534 SIC 7011 7999

TRUMP TAJ MAHAL ASSOCIATES LLC p 1487
1000 Boardwalk, Atlantic City NJ 08401
Tel (609) 345-4045 SIC 7011

■ SYSCO GUEST SUPPLY LLC p 1417
4301 Us Highway 1 Ste 300, Monmouth Junction NJ 08852
Tel (609) 514-9696
SIC 5122 2844 5131 5139 7011 8741

■ DOLCE INTERNATIONAL HOLDINGS INC p 448
22 Sylvan Way, Parsippany NJ 07054
Tel (201) 307-8700 SIC 7011 8741

■ DOLCE INTERNATIONAL HOSPITALITY LLC p 448
22 Sylvan Way, Parsippany NJ 07054
Tel (201) 307-8700 SIC 7011

■ RESORT CONDOMINIUMS INTERNATIONAL LLC p 1227
1 Sylvan Way, Parsippany NJ 07054
Tel (973) 753-6667 SIC 7011

■ WYNDHAM HOTEL GROUP LLC p 1629
22 Sylvan Way, Parsippany NJ 07054
Tel (973) 753-6000 SIC 7011

WYNDHAM INTERNATIONAL INC p 1630
22 Sylvan Way, Parsippany NJ 07054
Tel (973) 753-6000 SIC 7011 8741

▲ WYNDHAM WORLDWIDE CORP p 1630
22 Sylvan Way, Parsippany NJ 07054
Tel (973) 753-6000
SIC 7011 8741 7389 6531

LAGUNA DEVELOPMENT CORP p 838
14500 Central Ave Sw I40, Albuquerque NM 87121
Tel (505) 352-7877 SIC 7011 5411

INN OF MOUNTAIN GODS RESORT AND CASINO p 744
287 Carrizo Canyon Rd, Mescalero NM 88340
Tel (575) 464-7777 SIC 7999 7011

DELAWARE NORTH COMPANIES INC p 424
250 Delaware Ave, Buffalo NY 14202
Tel (716) 858-5000
SIC 5461 7011 7993 7999

DELAWARE NORTH COMPANIES PARKS & RESORTS INC p 424
250 Delaware Ave Ste 3, Buffalo NY 14202
Tel (716) 858-5000 SIC 7011

HAMISTER GROUP LLC p 655
10 Lafayette Sq Ste 1900, Buffalo NY 14203
Tel (716) 839-4000 SIC 7011 8052 8741

HART HOTELS INC p 665
617 Dingens St Ste 4, Buffalo NY 14206
Tel (716) 893-6551 SIC 7011

ST LAWRENCE UNIVERSITY p 1369
23 Romoda Dr, Canton NY 13617
Tel (315) 229-5011 SIC 8221 7011

WIN-SUM SKI CORP p 1614
6557 Holiday Valley Rd, Ellicottville NY 14731
Tel (716) 699-2345 SIC 7011 7997 6531

BRYANSTON GROUP INC p 221
1886 State Route 52 52, Hopewell Junction NY 12533
Tel (845) 223-3603 SIC 7011

AB STABLE LLC p 9
301 Park Ave, New York NY 10022
Tel (212) 355-3000 SIC 7011

ACCOR BUSINESS AND LEISURE NORTH AMERICA INC p 15
245 Park Ave, New York NY 10167
Tel (972) 360-9000 SIC 7011

BREF HR LLC p 209
250 Vesey St Fl 15, New York NY 10281
Tel (212) 417-7265 SIC 7011

BREF HR MANAGEMENT LLC p 209
250 Vesey St Fl 11, New York NY 10281
Tel (212) 417-7265 SIC 7011

BROADSTONE GROUP INC p 215
156 W 56th St Ste 1604, New York NY 10019
Tel (212) 333-2100 SIC 6552 7011 8741

CAREY WATERMARK INVESTORS INC p 255
50 Rockefeller Plz, New York NY 10020
Tel (212) 492-1100 SIC 6798 7011

CLARENDON NATIONAL INSURANCE CO (MD CORP) p 321
411 5th Ave Fl 5, New York NY 10016
Tel (212) 790-9700
SIC 6321 1542 1541 7011

CMP I OWNER-T LLC p 329
399 Park Ave Fl 18, New York NY 10022
Tel (212) 547-2609 SIC 7011

CPS 1 REALTY LP p 387
768 5th Ave, New York NY 10019
Tel (212) 759-3000 SIC 7011 7299 5812

GRACE I W2007 LLC p 628
85 Broad St Fl 15, New York NY 10004
Tel (212) 902-1000 SIC 7011

HILTON HOTELS HOLDINGS CORP p 695
345 Park Ave, New York NY 10154
Tel (212) 583-5000 SIC 7011 6794

HUDSON HOTEL BAR p 716
356 W 58th St, New York NY 10019
Tel (212) 554-6000 SIC 7011

INTERNATIONAL HOTEL MANAGEMENT SERVICES INC p 755
2 E 61st St, New York NY 10065
Tel (212) 838-8000 SIC 7011

▲ **LOEWS CORP** p 874
667 Madison Ave Fl 7, New York NY 10065
Tel (212) 521-2000
SIC 6331 6311 1381 4922 7011

■ **LOEWS HOTELS HOLDING CORP** p 874
667 Madison Ave, New York NY 10065
Tel (212) 521-2000 SIC 7011

LOTTE HOTEL NEW YORK PALACE LLC p 879
455 Madison Ave, New York NY 10022
Tel (212) 888-7000 SIC 7011

▲ **MORGANS HOTEL GROUP CO** p 989
475 10th Ave Fl 11, New York NY 10018
Tel (212) 277-4100 SIC 7011

MORGANS HOTEL GROUP MANAGEMENT LLC p 989
475 10th Ave Fl 11, New York NY 10018
Tel (212) 277-4100 SIC 7011

NEVADA MEZZ 1 LLC p 1028
60 Wall St, New York NY 10005
Tel (702) 314-3265 SIC 7011

ORIENT EXPRESS HOTELS INC p 1094
441 Lexington Ave Rm 504, New York NY 10017
Tel (212) 302-5055
SIC 7011 3743 5947 6552

W2007/ACEP MANAGERS VOTECO LLC p 1569
85 Broad St, New York NY 10004
Tel (212) 902-1000 SIC 7011 7999

WIND HOTELS HOLDINGS INC p 1615
345 Park Ave, New York NY 10154
Tel (212) 583-5000 SIC 7011 8741

HAMLET HOLDING LLC p 656
2 Manhattanville Rd, Purchase NY 10577
Tel (914) 694-8000 SIC 7011 7999

EJ DEL MONTE CORP p 482
909 Linden Ave Ste 1, Rochester NY 14625
Tel (585) 586-3121
SIC 6552 8741 6512 6799 7011

HUDSON HOTELS CORP p 716
400 Linden Oaks Ste 120, Rochester NY 14625
Tel (585) 419-4000 SIC 7011 8741

■ **SHERATON CORP** p 1315
1111 Westchester Ave, White Plains NY 10604
Tel (800) 328-6242 SIC 7011 8741 6794

WESTIN HOTELS LIMITED PARTNERSHIP p 1601
1111 Westchester Ave, White Plains NY 10604
Tel (617) 532-4600 SIC 7011

GROVE PARK INN RESORT INC p 642
290 Macon Ave, Asheville NC 28804
Tel (828) 252-2711
SIC 7011 5812 5813 7992 7991 7299

OMNI GROVE PARK LLC p 1084
290 Macon Ave, Asheville NC 28804
Tel (828) 252-2711
SIC 7299 5812 7011 5813 7992 7991

DIVI HOTELS MARKETING INC p 444
6320 Quadrangle Dr # 210, Chapel Hill NC 27517
Tel (919) 419-3484 SIC 7011 7999 6531

■ **ESA 2007 OPERATING LESSEE LLC** p 509
11525 N Cmnity Hse Rd R, Charlotte NC 28277
Tel (980) 345-1600 SIC 7011

▲ **EXTENDED STAY AMERICA INC** p 521
11525 N Community House, Charlotte NC 28277
Tel (980) 345-1600 SIC 7011

■ **HVM LLC** p 722
11525 N Community House, Charlotte NC 28277
Tel (980) 345-1600 SIC 7011

TRIBAL CASINO GAMING ENTERPRISES p 1479
777 Casino Dr, Cherokee NC 28719
Tel (877) 811-0777 SIC 7011

PINEHURST LLC p 1149
80 Carolina Vista Dr, Pinehurst NC 28374
Tel (910) 295-6811
SIC 7011 7997 7992 5813 5812

ALLIANCE HOSPITALITY MANAGEMENT LLC p 54
215 N Boylan Ave, Raleigh NC 27603
Tel (919) 791-1801 SIC 7011

CONCORD HOSPITALITY ENTERPRISES CO p 354
11410 Common Oaks Dr, Raleigh NC 27614
Tel (919) 455-2900 SIC 7011

QUALITY OIL CO LLC p 1197
1540 Silas Creek Pkwy, Winston Salem NC 27127
Tel (336) 722-3441 SIC 5983 5541 7011

TMI HOSPITALITY LP p 1457
4850 32nd Ave S, Fargo ND 58104
Tel (701) 235-1060 SIC 7011

RED ROOF INNS INC p 1216
605 S Front St Ste 150, Columbus OH 43215
Tel (614) 744-2600 SIC 7011

SALT FORK RESORT CLUB INC p 1273
74978 Broadhead Rd, Kimbolton OH 43749
Tel (740) 498-8116 SIC 7011 7997

BENNETT ENTERPRISES INC p 173
27476 Holiday Ln, Perrysburg OH 43551
Tel (419) 874-1933 SIC 7011 5812

LMN DEVELOPMENT LLC p 872
7000 Kalahari Dr, Sandusky OH 44870
Tel (419) 433-7200 SIC 7011 7996 5091

CHEROKEE NATION ENTERTAINMENT LLC p 294
777 W Cherokee St, Catoosa OK 74015
Tel (918) 458-1696
SIC 7999 7011 7948 5541 5993

21C OKC LLC p 1
900 W Main St, Oklahoma City OK 73106
Tel (502) 882-6243 SIC 7011

CITIZEN POTAWATOMI NATION p 310
1601 Gordon Cooper Dr, Shawnee OK 74801
Tel (405) 275-3121
SIC 7992 5411 7011 8412

SOUTHERN HOSPITALITY INC p 1348
3202 1st St, Woodward OK 73801
Tel (580) 256-7600 SIC 7011

JUBITZ CORP p 796
33 Ne Middlefield Rd, Portland OR 97211
Tel (503) 283-1111
SIC 5541 4789 5014 7011

CONFEDERATED TRIBES OF WARM SPRINGS RESERVATION OF OREGON p 356
1233 Veterans St, Warm Springs OR 97761
Tel (541) 553-1161 SIC 7011 4832 0811

■ **SANDS BETHWORKS GAMING LLC** p 1278
77 Sands Blvd, Bethlehem PA 18015
Tel (877) 726-3777 SIC 7011

RESORTS GROUP INC p 1227
Rr 209, Bushkill PA 18324
Tel (570) 588-6661 SIC 7011 6552

■ **CHESTER DOWNS AND MARINA LLC** p 295
777 Harrahs Blvd, Chester PA 19013
Tel (484) 490-1800 SIC 7011

BUSHKILL GROUP INC p 229
1008 Sand Hill Creek Rd, East Stroudsburg PA 18302
Tel (570) 588-6661 SIC 7011

■ **PRESQUE ISLE DOWNS INC** p 1172
8199 Perry Hwy, Erie PA 16509
Tel (814) 860-8999 SIC 7011

SCOTTS PEEK N PEAK LLC p 1294
2225 Downs Dr, Erie PA 16509
Tel (814) 868-9518 SIC 7011 7992

44 NEW ENGLAND MANAGEMENT CO p 3
450 Friendship Rd, Harrisburg PA 17111
Tel (717) 412-5500 SIC 7011

HERSHA HOSPITALITY MANAGEMENT LP p 687
44 Hersha Dr Fl 1, Harrisburg PA 17102
Tel (717) 412-5500 SIC 7011

HERSHEY ENTERTAINMENT & RESORTS CO p 687
27 W Chocolate Ave # 100, Hershey PA 17033
Tel (717) 534-3131 SIC 7011 7996

EPIC RESORTS LLC p 505
1150 1st Ave Ste 900, King Of Prussia PA 19406
Tel (610) 992-0100 SIC 7011

K INVESTMENTS LIMITED PARTNERSHIP p 799
1500 Sycamore Rd Ste 10, Montoursville PA 17754
Tel (570) 327-0111 SIC 7011 5521 5712

TUTHILL CORP p 1493
1660 Blue Mountain Dr, Palmerton PA 18071
Tel (610) 826-7700 SIC 7011

OXFORD DEVELOPMENT CO INC p 1101
301 Grant St Ste 4500, Pittsburgh PA 15219
Tel (412) 261-1500 SIC 7011

■ **HOLLYWOOD CASINO CORP** p 701
825 Berkshire Blvd # 200, Reading PA 19610
Tel (610) 373-2400 SIC 7011 8741

SHANER HOTEL GROUP LIMITED PARTNERSHIP p 1311
1965 Waddle Rd, State College PA 16803
Tel (814) 234-4460 SIC 7011

■ **GOLD MERGER SUB LLC** p 620
845 Berkshire Blvd # 200, Wyomissing PA 19610
Tel (610) 401-2900 SIC 7999 7011

▲ **PENN NATIONAL GAMING INC** p 1129
825 Berkshire Blvd # 200, Wyomissing PA 19610
Tel (610) 373-2400 SIC 7011 7948

■ **DORADO BEACH HOTEL CORP** p 451
Km 12 7 Rr 693, Dorado PR 00646
Tel (787) 796-1234 SIC 7011

EL CONQUISTADOR PARTNERSHIP LPSE (DE) p 482
1000 Ave El Conquistador, Fajardo PR 00738
Tel (787) 863-1000 SIC 7011

RIO MAR RESORT- WHG HOTEL PROPERTY LLC p 1236
6000 Rio Mar Blvd, Rio Grande PR 00745
Tel (787) 888-6000 SIC 7011

UTGR INC p 1536
100 Twin River Rd, Lincoln RI 02865
Tel (401) 723-3200 SIC 7011

JOHNSON & WALES UNIVERSITY INC p 790
8 Abbott Park Pl, Providence RI 02903
Tel (401) 598-1000 SIC 7011

INTERSTATE MANAGEMENT & INVESTMENT CORP p 758
1 Surrey Ct, Columbia SC 29212
Tel (803) 772-2629 SIC 7011

COLFIN JIH AHI OPCO LLC p 336
109 Enterprise Ct, Greenwood SC 29649
Tel (864) 942-0002 SIC 7011

KIAWAH ISLAND INN CO p 816
1 Sanctuary Beach Dr, Johns Island SC 29455
Tel (843) 768-6000 SIC 7011

LEGACY BUSINESS SOLUTIONS LLC p 852
1144 Shine Ave, Myrtle Beach SC 29577
Tel (843) 945-4358 SIC 7011

DELUXE MOTEL p 427
2700 N Main St, Sumter SC 29153
Tel (803) 469-0236 SIC 7011

REGENCY MIDWEST VENTURES LIMITED PARTNERSHIP p 1219
3211 W Sencore Dr, Sioux Falls SD 57107
Tel (605) 334-2371 SIC 7011

SUMMIT GROUP INC p 1398
2701 S Minn Ave Ste 6, Sioux Falls SD 57105
Tel (512) 538-2300 SIC 7011

■ **DOUBLETREE INC** p 452
755 Crossover Ln, Memphis TN 38117
Tel (901) 374-5000 SIC 7011 5812 5813

■ **PARK HOTELS & RESORTS INC** p 1115
755 Crossover Ln, Memphis TN 38117
Tel (901) 374-5000 SIC 7011

PROMUS HOTEL CORP p 1183
755 Crossover Ln, Memphis TN 38117
Tel (901) 374-5000 SIC 7011 8741 6794

■ **PROMUS HOTELS LLC** p 1183
755 Crossover Ln, Memphis TN 38117
Tel (719) 265-6600 SIC 7011 8741 6794

■ **PROMUS OPERATING CO INC** p 1183
755 Crossover Ln, Memphis TN 38117
Tel (901) 374-5000 SIC 7011 8741 6794

CENTRAL SHARED SERVICES LLC p 280
1 Park Plz, Nashville TN 37203
Tel (615) 344-5228 SIC 7011

■ **GAYLORD OPRYLAND USA INC** p 594
2800 Opryland Dr, Nashville TN 37214
Tel (615) 889-1000 SIC 7011

RYMAN HOSPITALITY PROPERTIES INC p 1261
1 Gaylord Dr, Nashville TN 37214
Tel (615) 316-6000 SIC 6798 7011

SAINT THOMAS HEALTH SERVICES INC p 1271
4220 Harding Pike, Nashville TN 37205
Tel (615) 222-2111 SIC 6512 6513 7011

ACCOR NORTH AMERICA INC p 15
5055 Kelle Sprin Rd Ste 2, Addison TX 75001
Tel (972) 360-9000 SIC 7011

OLYMPUS REAL ESTATE CORP p 1083
5080 Spectrum Dr, Addison TX 75001
Tel (972) 980-2200 SIC 7011 6512

■ **SUMMIT HOTEL OP LP** p 1399
12600 Hill Country Blvd, Austin TX 78738
Tel (512) 538-2300 SIC 7011

G6 HOSPITALITY LLC p 588
4001 International Pkwy, Carrollton TX 75007
Tel (972) 360-9000 SIC 7011

■ **HILTON RESERVATIONS WORLDWIDE LLC** p 695
2050 Chenault Dr, Carrollton TX 75006
Tel (972) 770-6100 SIC 7011

IBL LIMITED LLC p 726
4001 International Pkwy, Carrollton TX 75007
Tel (972) 360-9000 SIC 7011

MOTEL 6 OPERATING LP p 992
4001 Intl Pkwy Ste 500, Carrollton TX 75007
Tel (972) 360-9000 SIC 7011

ANATOLE HOTEL INVESTORS L P p 88
2201 N Stemmons Fwy, Dallas TX 75207
Tel (214) 748-1200 SIC 7011 5813 5812

BAYLOR HEALTH ENTERPRISES LP p 162
411 N Washington Ave # 7200, Dallas TX 75246
Tel (214) 820-2492 SIC 5122 7011 7991

■ **CLUBCORP USA INC** p 328
3030 Lyndon B Johnson Fwy, Dallas TX 75234
Tel (972) 243-6191 SIC 7011 7997

DALLAS MARKET CENTER DEVELOPMENT CO LTD p 410
2201 N Stemmons Fwy, Dallas TX 75207
Tel (214) 748-1200 SIC 7011

OMNI HOTELS CORP p 1084
4001 Maple Ave Ste 500, Dallas TX 75219
Tel (972) 730-6664 SIC 7011

OMNI HOTELS MANAGEMENT CORP p 1084
4001 Maple Ave Ste 500, Dallas TX 75219
Tel (972) 871-5600 SIC 7011

REMINGTON HOSPITALITY SERVICES p 1222
14185 Dallas Pkwy # 1150, Dallas TX 75254
Tel (972) 980-2700 SIC 7011

REMINGTON LODGING & HOSPITALITY LLC p 1222
14185 Dallas Pkwy # 1150, Dallas TX 75254
Tel (972) 980-2700 SIC 7011

TEXAS WESTERN MANAGEMENT PARTNERS LP p 1445
13747 Montfort Dr Ste 115, Dallas TX 75240
Tel (469) 385-6248 SIC 7011

TRT DEVELOPMENT CO - CCB p 1485
4001 Maple Ave Ste 600, Dallas TX 75219
Tel (800) 809-6664 SIC 7011

TRT HOLDINGS INC p 1485
4001 Maple Ave Ste 600, Dallas TX 75219
Tel (214) 283-8500 SIC 7011 7991 1382

1859-HISTORIC HOTELS LTD p 1
2302 Post Office St # 500, Galveston TX 77550
Tel (409) 763-8536 SIC 7011

GAL-TEX HOTEL CORP p 589
2302 Pstoffice St Ste 500, Galveston TX 77550
Tel (409) 763-8536 SIC 7011 8741

MOODY GARDENS INC p 987
1 Hope Blvd, Galveston TX 77554
Tel (409) 744-4673
SIC 8412 8422 7999 7011

ASSET PLUS CORP p 119
950 Corbindale Rd Ste 300, Houston TX 77024
Tel (713) 782-5800 SIC 7011

▲ **CIVEO CORP** p 320
333 Clay St Ste 4980, Houston TX 77002
Tel (713) 510-2400 SIC 7011

■ **CIVEO US HOLDINGS LLC** p 320
333 Clay St Ste 4980, Houston TX 77002
Tel (713) 510-2400 SIC 7011

LANDRYS GAMING INC p 843
1510 West Loop S, Houston TX 77027
Tel (713) 850-1010 SIC 7011

RAINTREE RESORTS INTERNATIONAL INC p 1206
10000 Memorial Dr Ste 480, Houston TX 77024
Tel (713) 613-2800 SIC 7011

RUSHLAKE HOTELS (USA) INC p 1259
333 Clay St Ste 4980, Houston TX 77002
Tel (713) 759-0790 SIC 7011

SEATTLE AIRPORT HOSPITALITY LLC p 1297
5847 San Felipe St # 4650, Houston TX 77057
Tel (713) 787-6222 SIC 7011

SEDKO GROUP INC p 1300
5847 San Felipe St # 4650, Houston TX 77057
Tel (713) 782-9100 SIC 7011

VISTA HOST INC p 1562
10370 Richmond Ave # 150, Houston TX 77042
Tel (713) 267-5800 SIC 7011

WRRH INVESTMENTS LP p 1628
5747 San Felipe St # 4650, Houston TX 77057
Tel (713) 782-9100 SIC 7011

FELCOR LODGING LIMITED PARTNERSHIP p 537
545 E John Carpenter Fwy # 1300, Irving TX 75062
Tel (972) 444-4900 SIC 7011

FOUR SEASONS RESORT & CLUB p 572
4150 N Macarthur Blvd, Irving TX 75038
Tel (972) 717-0700 SIC 7011

▲ **LA QUINTA HOLDINGS INC** p 836
909 Hidden Rdg Ste 600, Irving TX 75038
Tel (214) 492-6600 SIC 7011

■ **LA QUINTA LLC** p 836
909 Hidden Rdg Ste 600, Irving TX 75038
Tel (214) 492-6600 SIC 7011 6794 8741

■ **LQ MANAGEMENT LLC** p 882
909 Hidden Rdg Ste 600, Irving TX 75038
Tel (214) 492-6600 SIC 7011

TRT HOTEL CO LLC p 1485
420 Decker Dr, Irving TX 75062
Tel (972) 730-6664 SIC 7011

W2005 WYN HOTELS LP p 1569
545 E J Carpntr Fwy 140, Irving TX 75062
Tel (972) 444-9700 SIC 7011

US-LAS COLINAS LIMITED PARTNERSHIP p 1533
9830 Colonnade Blvd # 600, San Antonio TX 78230
Tel (210) 498-0626 SIC 7011 7997

SNOWBIRD CORP p 1336
3165 E Millrock Dr # 150, Holladay UT 84121
Tel (801) 742-2222 SIC 6531 7011

ASC UTAH INC p 115
4000 Canyons Resort Dr, Park City UT 84098
Tel (435) 649-5400 SIC 7011 5812

PACIFIC GROUP RESORTS INC p 1104
1389 Center Dr Ste 200, Park City UT 84098
Tel (435) 241-7000 SIC 7011

POWDR CORP p 1164
1790 Bonanza Dr Ste W201, Park City UT 84060
Tel (435) 647-5490 SIC 7011

GRAND AMERICA HOTELS & RESORTS INC p 629
555 S Main St, Salt Lake City UT 84111
Tel (801) 596-5717 SIC 7011

SINCLAIR COMPANIES p 1326
550 E South Temple, Salt Lake City UT 84102
Tel (801) 363-5100
SIC 2911 4612 1382 5541 7011 0212

SNOWBIRD RESORT LLC p 1336
9385 S Snowbird Center Dr, Snowbird UT 84092
Tel (801) 933-4670 SIC 7011

KILLINGTON/PICO SKI RESORT PARTNERS LLC p 818
4763 Killington Rd, Killington VT 05751
Tel (802) 422-3333 SIC 7011

■ **STRATTON CORP** p 1393
5 Village Lodge Rd, South Londonderry VT 05155
Tel (802) 297-2200
SIC 7011 7992 1531 6512 5941

INTERSTATE HOTELS & RESORTS INC p 758
4501 Fairfax Dr Ste 500, Arlington VA 22203
Tel (703) 387-3100 SIC 7011

SHAMIN HOTELS INC p 1311
2000 Ware Btm Spring Rd, Chester VA 23836
Tel (804) 777-9000
SIC 7011 8051 6512 6513

CRESCENT HOTELS & RESORTS LLC p 391
10306 Eaton Pl Ste 430, Fairfax VA 22030
Tel (703) 279-7820 SIC 7011

BH HOTELS HOLDCO LLC p 180
7930 Jones Branch Dr, Mc Lean VA 22102
Tel (703) 883-1000 SIC 7011

■ **DOUBLETREE LLC** p 452
7930 Jones Branch Dr, Mc Lean VA 22102
Tel (703) 883-1000 SIC 7011

■ **EMBASSY SUITES CLUB NO 1 INC** p 490
7930 Jones Branch Dr, Mc Lean VA 22102
Tel (703) 883-1000 SIC 7011

■ **HILTON GARDEN INNS MANAGEMENT LLC** p 694
7930 Jones Branch Dr, Mc Lean VA 22102
Tel (703) 448-6100 SIC 7011

HILTON GLOBAL HOLDINGS LLC p 694
7930 Jones Branch Dr # 1100, Mc Lean VA 22102
Tel (703) 883-1000 SIC 6794 7011

■ **HILTON HAWAII CORP** p 695
7930 Jones Branch Dr, Mc Lean VA 22102
Tel (703) 883-1000 SIC 7011

■ **HILTON HOTELS HOLDINGS LLC** p 695
7930 Jones Branch Dr, Mc Lean VA 22102
Tel (703) 883-1000 SIC 7011

■ **HILTON ILLINOIS HOLDINGS LLC** p 695
7930 Jones Branch Dr, Mc Lean VA 22102
Tel (703) 883-1000 SIC 7011

▲ **HILTON WORLDWIDE HOLDINGS INC** p 695
7930 Jones Branch Dr # 100, Mc Lean VA 22102
Tel (703) 883-1000 SIC 7011 6794

■ **HLT ESP INTERNATIONAL FRANCHISE LLC** p 697
7930 Jones Branch Dr, Mc Lean VA 22102
Tel (703) 883-1000 SIC 7011

■ PARK HOTELS & RESORTS INC p 1115
7930 Jones Branch Dr # 700, Mc Lean VA 22102
Tel (703) 883-1000 SIC 7011 6794

WINTERGREEN RESORTS INC p 1617
11 Grassy Ridge Dr, Nellysford VA 22958
Tel (434) 325-8237 SIC 8721 7011 5812

APPLE REIT EIGHT INC p 99
814 E Main St, Richmond VA 23219
Tel (804) 344-8121 SIC 7011

APPLE REIT SEVEN INC p 99
814 E Main St, Richmond VA 23219
Tel (804) 344-8121 SIC 7011

PROFESSIONAL HOSPITALITY RESOURCES INC p 1180
932 Laskin Rd, Virginia Beach VA 23451
Tel (757) 491-3000 SIC 7011 7389 5812

COLONIAL WILLIAMSBURG FOUNDATION p 338
427 Franklin St Rm 212, Williamsburg VA 23185
Tel (757) 229-1000
SIC 5947 8412 5812 7011

COASTAL HOTEL GROUP INC p 331
15375 Se 30th Pl Ste 290, Bellevue WA 98007
Tel (206) 388-0400 SIC 7011

HOTEL GROUP INC p 710
201 5th Ave S Ste 200, Edmonds WA 98020
Tel (425) 771-1788 SIC 7011

NOBLE HOUSE HOTELS & RESORTS LTD p 1046
600 6th St S, Kirkland WA 98033
Tel (425) 827-8737 SIC 7011

TULALIP RESORT CASINO p 1491
10200 Quil Ceda Blvd, Quil Ceda Village WA 98271
Tel (360) 716-6000 SIC 7011

AMERICAN MOTELS ACQUISITION CO LLC p 76
2101 4th Ave Ste 1020, Seattle WA 98121
Tel (206) 443-3550 SIC 7011

SQUAXIN ISLAND TRIBE OF SQUAXIN ISLAND RESERVATION p 1362
10 Se Squaxin Ln, Shelton WA 98584
Tel (360) 426-9781
SIC 5411 5146 7011 0132

SNOQUALMIE ENTERTAINMENT p 1336
37500 Se North Bend Way, Snoqualmie WA 98065
Tel (425) 888-1234 SIC 7993 7011

▲ RED LION HOTELS CORP p 1215
201 W North River Dr # 100, Spokane WA 99201
Tel (509) 459-6100 SIC 7011

■ RED LION HOTELS HOLDINGS INC p 1215
201 W North River Dr # 100, Spokane WA 99201
Tel (509) 459-6100 SIC 7011

■ RL VENTURE LLC p 1239
201 W North River Dr # 100, Spokane WA 99201
Tel (509) 459-6100 SIC 7011

DOW HOTEL CO LLC p 453
16400 Southcenter Pkwy # 208, Tukwila WA 98188
Tel (206) 575-3600 SIC 7011

■ MTR GAMING GROUP INC p 998
Hc 2 Box S, Chester WV 26034
Tel (304) 387-8000 SIC 7011 7948

■ PARK MOUNTAINEER INC p 1115
Hc 2, Chester WV 26034
Tel (304) 387-8300
SIC 7999 7011 7389 6512

SNOWSHOE MOUNTAIN INC p 1336
10 Snowshoe Dr, Slatyfork WV 26291
Tel (304) 572-5601
SIC 8741 7011 5813 5812

OGLEBAY RESORT CONFERENCE CENTER p 1076
Rr 88 Box N, Wheeling WV 26003
Tel (304) 243-4063 SIC 7011 7992 5812

WHEELING ISLAND GAMING INC p 1605
1 S Stone St, Wheeling WV 26003
Tel (304) 232-5050 SIC 7948 7011 5813

GREENBRIER HOTEL CORP p 637
300 W Main St, Wht Sphr Spgs WV 24986
Tel (304) 536-1110 SIC 7011

FORTNEY HOSPITALITY GROUP INC p 570
308 3rd St S, La Crosse WI 54601
Tel (608) 784-1225 SIC 7011

GREAT WOLF RESORTS HOLDINGS INC p 635
525 Junction Rd Ste 6000, Madison WI 53717
Tel (608) 662-4700 SIC 7011

RAYMOND MANAGEMENT CO INC p 1210
8333 Greenway Blvd # 200, Middleton WI 53562
Tel (608) 833-4100 SIC 6552 8741 7011

▲ MARCUS CORP p 905
100 E Wisconsin Ave # 1, Milwaukee WI 53202
Tel (414) 905-1000 SIC 7011 7833

■ MARCUS HOTELS INC p 905
100 E Wisconsin Ave, Milwaukee WI 53202
Tel (414) 905-1200 SIC 7011

■ DELLONA ENTERPRISES INC p 425
S944 Christmas Mtn Rd, Wisconsin Dells WI 53965
Tel (608) 253-1000 SIC 7011 7992 5812

KALAHARI DEVELOPMENT LLC p 801
1305 Kalahari Dr, Wisconsin Dells WI 53965
Tel (608) 254-5466 SIC 7011 5812 5813

NEWPAGE WISCONSIN SYSTEM INC p 1038
111 W Jackson St, Wisconsin Rapids WI 54495
Tel (715) 422-3111
SIC 2621 2611 2653 7011

■ GRAND TETON LODGE CO p 630
Highway 89 5 Mls N Moran, Moran WY 83013
Tel (307) 543-2811 SIC 7011

SIC 7021 Rooming & Boarding Houses

COLLEGIATE HOUSING FOUNDA p 337
409 Johnson Ave, Fairhope AL 36532
Tel (251) 928-9340 SIC 7021

NANA MANAGEMENT SERVICES LLC p 1007
800 E Dimond Blvd 3-450, Anchorage AK 99515
Tel (907) 273-2400
SIC 5812 7349 7021 7033 7381

R & B REALTY GROUP A CALIFORNIA LIMITED PARTNERSHIP p 1201
2222 Corinth Ave, Los Angeles CA 90064
Tel (800) 888-0808 SIC 7021 6531

WORLDWIDE CORPORATE HOUSING LP p 1626
2222 Corinth Ave, Los Angeles CA 90064
Tel (877) 902-0832 SIC 7021

UNIVERSITY OF CHICAGO p 1520
1414 E 59th St, Chicago IL 60637
Tel (773) 753-2270 SIC 7021

MELWOOD-WERNER HOUSING INC p 941
6188 Oxon Hill Rd, Oxon Hill MD 20745
Tel (301) 982-6207 SIC 7021

YMCA OF NORTH SHORE INC p 1636
245 Cabot St, Beverly MA 01915
Tel (978) 922-0990
SIC 7021 8322 8351 7999 7032

SIC 7032 Sporting & Recreational Camps

YOUNG MENS CHRISTIAN ASSOCIATION OF BIRMINGHAM p 1638
2101 4th Ave N, Birmingham AL 35203
Tel (205) 801-9622
SIC 7991 8641 8351 7032

INTERNATIONAL CHURCH OF FOURSQUARE GOSPEL p 754
1910 W Sunset Blvd # 200, Los Angeles CA 90026
Tel (213) 989-4234
SIC 8661 6512 7032 8211 8221

YOUNG MENS CHRISTIAN ASSOCIATION OF SAN FRANCISCO p 1639
50 California St Ste 650, San Francisco CA 94111
Tel (415) 777-9622
SIC 8641 7991 8351 7032 8322

YMCA OF SILICON VALLEY p 1636
80 Saratoga Ave, Santa Clara CA 95051
Tel (408) 351-6400
SIC 8641 7991 8351 7032 8322

NAVIGATORS p 1020
3820 N 30th St, Colorado Springs CO 80904
Tel (719) 598-1212 SIC 8661 7032 5942

YOUNG LIFE p 1638
420 N Cascade Ave, Colorado Springs CO 80903
Tel (719) 381-1800 SIC 8661 7032

YMCA OF METROPOLITAN HARTFORD INC p 1636
50 State House Sq Fl 2, Hartford CT 06103
Tel (860) 522-9622 SIC 8641 7032 7997

YOUNG MENS CHRISTIAN ASSOCIATION OF SUNCOAST p 1639
2469 Enterprise Rd, Clearwater FL 33763
Tel (312) 932-1200
SIC 8641 7991 8351 7032 8322

YOUNG MENS CHRISTIAN ASSOCIATION OF METROPOLITAN ATLANTA INC p 1638
100 Edgewood Ave Ne, Atlanta GA 30303
Tel (404) 588-9622
SIC 8641 7991 8351 7032 8322

YOUNG MENS CHRISTIAN ASSOCIATION OF WICHITA KANSAS p 1639
402 N Market St, Wichita KS 67202
Tel (316) 219-9622
SIC 8641 7991 8351 7032 8322

YOUNG MENS CHRISTIAN ASSOCIATION OF GREATER LOUISVILLE p 1638
545 S 2nd St, Louisville KY 40202
Tel (502) 587-9622
SIC 8641 7991 8351 7032 8322

YMCA OF NORTH SHORE INC p 1636
245 Cabot St, Beverly MA 01915
Tel (978) 922-0990
SIC 7021 8322 8351 7999 7032

YMCA OF GREATER BOSTON INC p 1636
316 Huntington Ave Ste 1, Boston MA 02115
Tel (617) 536-6950
SIC 8641 7991 8351 7032 8322

OLD COLONY Y p 1080
320 Main St, Brockton MA 02301
Tel (508) 583-2155
SIC 8641 7991 8351 7032 8322

BOYNE USA INC p 205
1 Boyne Mountain Rd, Boyne Falls MI 49713
Tel (231) 549-6000 SIC 7011 7992 7032

YOUNG MENS CHRISTIAN ASSOCIATION OF GREATER NEW YORK p 1638
5 W 63rd St Fl 6, New York NY 10023
Tel (212) 630-9600
SIC 8641 7991 8351 7032 8322

CAMPGROUP LLC p 246
4 New King St Ste 130, White Plains NY 10604
Tel (914) 997-2177 SIC 7032

■ STEEL EXCEL INC p 1384
1133 Westchester Ave N-222, White Plains NY 10604
Tel (914) 461-1300 SIC 1389 7353 7032

YOUNG MEN S CHRISTIAN ASSOCIATION OF GREATER CHARLOTTE p 1638
400 E Morehead St, Charlotte NC 28202
Tel (704) 716-6200 SIC 7032 8641

YMCA OF NORTHWEST NORTH CAROLINA p 1636
301 N Main St Ste 1900, Winston Salem NC 27101
Tel (336) 777-8055
SIC 8641 7991 8351 7032 8322

YOUNG MENS CHRISTIAN ASSOCIATION OF GREATER DAYTON p 1638
118 W St Ste 300, Dayton OH 45402
Tel (937) 223-5201
SIC 8641 7991 8351 7032 8322

YOUNG MENS CHRISTIAN ASSOCIATION OF GREATER TOLEDO p 1638
1500 N Superior St Fl 2, Toledo OH 43604
Tel (419) 729-8135
SIC 8641 7991 8351 7032 8322

YMCA GREATER BRANDYWINE p 1636
1 E Chestnut St, West Chester PA 19380
Tel (610) 643-9622
SIC 8641 7991 8351 7032 8322

GREATER PROVIDENCE YOUNG MENS CHRISTIAN ASSOCIATION p 636
371 Pine St, Providence RI 02903
Tel (401) 521-9622
SIC 8641 7991 8351 7032 8322

YMCA OF METROPOLITAN CHATTANOOGA p 1636
301 W 6th St, Chattanooga TN 37402
Tel (423) 266-3766
SIC 8641 7991 8351 7032 8322

YOUNG MENS CHRISTIAN ASSOCIATION OF MIDDLE TENNESSEE p 1638
1000 Church St, Nashville TN 37203
Tel (615) 259-9622
SIC 8641 7991 8351 7032 8322

YOUNG MENS CHRISTIAN ASSOCIATION OF METROPOLITAN p 1638
601 N Akard St, Dallas TX 75201
Tel (214) 880-9622
SIC 8641 7991 8351 7032 8322

YOUNG MENS CHRISTIAN ASSOCIATION OF GREATER HOUSTON AREA INC p 1638
2600 North Loop W Ste 300, Houston TX 77092
Tel (713) 659-5566
SIC 8641 7991 8351 7032 8322

YOUNG MENS CHRISTIAN ASSOCIATION OF GREATER RICHMOND p 1638
2 W Franklin St, Richmond VA 23220
Tel (804) 644-9622
SIC 8641 7991 8351 7032 8322

YOUNG MENS CHRISTIAN ASSOCIATION OF PIERCE AND KITSAP COUNTY p 1639
4717 S 19th St Ste 201, Tacoma WA 98405
Tel (253) 534-7800
SIC 8699 7991 7032 8322

INTERVARSITY CHRISTIAN FELLOWSHIP/USA p 759
635 Science Dr, Madison WI 53711
Tel (608) 274-9001 SIC 8661 2731 7032

YOUNG MENS CHRISTIAN ASSOCIATION OF METROPOLITAN MILWAUKEE INC p 1638
161 W Wisconsin Ave, Milwaukee WI 53203
Tel (414) 291-9622
SIC 8641 7991 8351 7032 8322

SIC 7033 Trailer Parks & Camp Sites

NANA MANAGEMENT SERVICES LLC p 1007
800 E Dimond Blvd 3-450, Anchorage AK 99515
Tel (907) 273-2400
SIC 5812 7349 7021 7033 7381

SOMMERS CO p 1339
1000 Sommers Blvd, Richmond Hill GA 31324
Tel (800) 654-6466 SIC 5172 5541 7033

KAMPGROUNDS OF AMERICA INC p 802
550 N 31st St Ste 400, Billings MT 59101
Tel (406) 248-8135 SIC 6794 7033

SIC 7041 Membership-Basis Hotels

MEDIEVAL TIMES ENTERTAINMENT INC p 938
7662 Beach Blvd, Buena Park CA 90620
Tel (714) 523-1100 SIC 7041 7996

AIRBNB INC p 39
888 Brannan St Ste 400, San Francisco CA 94103
Tel (415) 800-5959 SIC 7041

■ STARWOOD VACATION SERVICES INC p 1379
8801 Vistana Centre Dr, Orlando FL 32821
Tel (407) 903-4640 SIC 7041

FLAGLER SYSTEM INC p 554
1 S County Rd, Palm Beach FL 33480
Tel (561) 655-6611 SIC 7041 7997

DIAMOND RESORTS CORP p 437
10600 W Charleston Blvd, Las Vegas NV 89135
Tel (702) 684-8000 SIC 7041 6141 8741

FILLMORE HOSPITALITY LLC p 542
250 W Old Wilson Bridge R, Worthington OH 43085
Tel (614) 781-1420 SIC 7041

SIC 7211 Power Laundries, Family & Commercial

ANGELICA TEXTILE SERVICES INC p 91
1105 Lakewood Pkwy # 210, Alpharetta GA 30009
Tel (678) 823-4100 SIC 7213 7211

SHARED SERVICE SYSTEMS INC p 1312
1725 S 20th St, Omaha NE 68108
Tel (402) 536-5300
SIC 5047 5142 7211 5149 5113 7218

■ PARBALL CORP p 1114
3655 Las Vegas Blvd S, Las Vegas NV 89109
Tel (702) 967-4111
SIC 7011 7999 6512 7521 7211

COINMACH CORP p 335
303 Sunnyside Blvd # 70, Plainview NY 11803
Tel (516) 349-8555
SIC 7215 7359 5087 5064 7211 8741

BORDER APPAREL LAUNDRY LTD p 201
6969 Industrial Ave, El Paso TX 79915
Tel (915) 772-7170 SIC 2326 7211

SIC 7213 Linen Sply

MISSION LINEN SUPPLY p 975
717 E Yanonali St, Santa Barbara CA 93103
Tel (805) 730-3620 SIC 7218 7213

SYNERGY HEALTH NORTH AMERICA INC p 1415
401 E Jackson St Ste 3100, Tampa FL 33602
Tel (813) 891-9550 SIC 5047 7213

ANGELICA CORP p 91
1105 Lakewood Pkwy # 210, Alpharetta GA 30009
Tel (678) 823-4100 SIC 7213 5699 5661

ANGELICA TEXTILE SERVICES INC p 91
1105 Lakewood Pkwy # 210, Alpharetta GA 30009
Tel (678) 823-4100 SIC 7213 7211

DOMESTIC LINEN SUPPLY AND LAUNDRY CO p 448
30555 Northwestern Hwy, Farmington Hills MI 48334
Tel (248) 737-2000 SIC 7213

AMERIPRIDE SERVICES INC p 83
10801 Wayzata Blvd # 100, Hopkins MN 55305
Tel (800) 750-4628 SIC 7213 7218

▲ G&K SERVICES INC p 587
5995 Opus Pkwy Ste 500, Minnetonka MN 55343
Tel (952) 912-5500 SIC 7218 7213 7219

MISSION OF NEVADA INC p 975
1 W Mayflower Ave, North Las Vegas NV 89030
Tel (702) 639-2500 SIC 7213

■ CINTAS CORP NO 1 p 308
6800 Cintas Blvd, Mason OH 45040
Tel (513) 459-1200
SIC 7213 5136 5137 7549

SUMMIT SERVICES GROUP INC p 1399
3220 Tillman Dr Ste 300, Bensalem PA 19020
Tel (215) 639-4274 SIC 7213 7349

PHILADELPHIA BUNZL p 1142
10814 Northeast Ave, Philadelphia PA 19116
Tel (215) 969-0600
SIC 5087 5023 5113 7213

TTS INC p 1490
333 N Sam Houston Pkwy E, Houston TX 77060
Tel (281) 716-2000 SIC 7213

ALSCO INC p 61
505 E South Temple, Salt Lake City UT 84102
Tel (801) 328-8831 SIC 7213

SIC 7215 Coin Operated Laundries & Cleaning

COINMACH CORP p 335
303 Sunnyside Blvd # 70, Plainview NY 11803
Tel (516) 349-8555
SIC 7215 7359 5087 5064 7211 8741

COINMACH HOLDINGS LLC p 335
1017 E Morehead St # 100, Charlotte NC 28204
Tel (704) 375-1947 SIC 7215

COINMACH LAUNDRY CORP p 335
1017 E Morehead St # 100, Charlotte NC 28204
Tel (704) 375-1947 SIC 7215

SIC 7217 Carpet & Upholstery Cleaning

STANLEY STEEMER INTERNATIONAL INC p 1377
5800 Innovation Dr, Dublin OH 43016
Tel (614) 764-2007
SIC 7217 3635 6794 5713

IH SERVICES INC p 730
127 Tanner Rd, Greenville SC 29607
Tel (864) 297-3748 SIC 7349 5014 7217

MASTERCORP INC p 918
3505 N Main St, Crossville TN 38555
Tel (931) 484-1752 SIC 7349 7217

CLEAN POWER LLC p 324
124 N 121st St, Milwaukee WI 53226
Tel (414) 302-3000 SIC 7349 7217

SIC 7218 Industrial Launderers

■ ARAMARK UNIFORM & CAREER APPAREL LLC p 102
115 N First St Ste 203, Burbank CA 91502
Tel (818) 973-3700 SIC 7218

PRUDENTIAL OVERALL SUPPLY p 1187
1661 Alton Pkwy, Irvine CA 92606
Tel (949) 250-4855 SIC 7218

MISSION LINEN SUPPLY p 975
717 E Yanonali St, Santa Barbara CA 93103
Tel (805) 730-3620 SIC 7218 7213

GENESIS HEALTH SYSTEM p 603
1227 E Rusholme St, Davenport IA 52803
Tel (563) 421-1000 SIC 8741 8399 7218

GEA NORTH AMERICA INC p 597
9165 Rumsey Rd, Columbia MD 21045
Tel (410) 997-8700 SIC 7218

▲ UNIFIRST CORP p 1503
68 Jonspin Rd, Wilmington MA 01887
Tel (978) 658-8888 SIC 7218 2326

AMERIPRIDE SERVICES INC p 83
10801 Wayzata Blvd # 100, Hopkins MN 55305
Tel (800) 750-4628 SIC 7213 7218

▲ G&K SERVICES INC p 587
5995 Opus Pkwy Ste 500, Minnetonka MN 55343
Tel (952) 912-5500 SIC 7218 7213 7219

SHARED SERVICE SYSTEMS INC p 1312
1725 S 20th St, Omaha NE 68108
Tel (402) 536-5300
SIC 5047 5142 7211 5149 5113 7218

BOTNICK/5 VENTURES INC p 203
159 Front St 163, Binghamton NY 13905
Tel (607) 723-8971 SIC 5511 7218

COYNE INTERNATIONAL ENTERPRISES CORP p 387
140 Cortland Ave, Syracuse NY 13202
Tel (315) 475-1626 SIC 7218

▲ CINTAS CORP p 308
6800 Cintas Blvd, Cincinnati OH 45262
Tel (513) 459-1200
SIC 7218 2337 2326 5084

■ CINTAS R US INC p 308
6800 Cintas Blvd, Cincinnati OH 45262
Tel (513) 459-1200 SIC 7218

■ CINTAS CORP NO 3 p 308
6800 Cintas Blvd, Mason OH 45040
Tel (513) 459-1200 SIC 7218

■ CINTAS-RUS LP p 308
6800 Cintas Blvd, Mason OH 45040
Tel (513) 459-1200 SIC 7218

▲ ARAMARK CORP p 102
1101 Market St Ste 45, Philadelphia PA 19107
Tel (215) 238-3000 SIC 5812 7218 5136

■ ARAMARK INTERMEDIATE HOLDCO CORP p 102
1101 Market St Ste 45, Philadelphia PA 19107
Tel (215) 238-3000 SIC 5812 7218 5136

■ ARAMARK SERVICES INC p 102
1101 Market St Ste 45, Philadelphia PA 19107
Tel (215) 238-3000 SIC 5812 7218 5136

■ SPERIAN PROTECTION USA INC p 1358
900 Douglas Pike, Smithfield RI 02917
Tel (401) 232-1200
SIC 3851 3842 2311 7218 5999

SIC 7219 Laundry & Garment Svcs, NEC

MERCY HOSPITAL INC p 947
271 Carew St, Springfield MA 01104
Tel (413) 748-9000
SIC 8062 8071 8011 7219 8748

▲ G&K SERVICES INC p 587
5995 Opus Pkwy Ste 500, Minnetonka MN 55343
Tel (952) 912-5500 SIC 7218 7213 7219

FIRSTHEALTH OF CAROLINAS INC p 550
155 Memorial Dr, Pinehurst NC 28374
Tel (910) 715-1000
SIC 8062 8093 8051 8021 7991 7219

READING HEALTH SYSTEM p 1213
6th Ave And Spruce St, Reading PA 19611
Tel (610) 988-8000
SIC 8062 6512 8093 8721 8011 7219

SIC 7221 Photographic Studios, Portrait

LIFETOUCH CHURCH DIRECTORIES AND PORTRAITS INC p 865
11000 Viking Dr Ste 400, Eden Prairie MN 55344
Tel (952) 826-4000 SIC 7221 2741

LIFETOUCH INC p 865
11000 Viking Dr, Eden Prairie MN 55344
Tel (952) 826-4000 SIC 7221 7812 2741

LIFETOUCH NATIONAL SCHOOL STUDIOS INC p 865
11000 Viking Dr Ste 300, Eden Prairie MN 55344
Tel (952) 826-4000 SIC 7221

LIFETOUCH PORTRAIT STUDIOS INC p 865
11000 Viking Dr, Eden Prairie MN 55344
Tel (952) 826-4335 SIC 7221

■ VISANT CORP p 1560
3601 Minnesota Dr Ste 400, Minneapolis MN 55435
Tel (914) 595-8200
SIC 3911 2741 2389 7221

C & A MARKETING INC p 231
114 Tived Ln E, Edison NJ 08837
Tel (201) 881-1900
SIC 5065 8742 7384 5946 7359 7221

FALCONHEAD CAPITAL PARTNERS II LP p 526
450 Park Ave Bsmt, New York NY 10022
Tel (212) 634-3304 SIC 6722 7221 7335

OLAN MILLS INC p 1080
735 Broad St Ste 218, Chattanooga TN 37402
Tel (423) 622-5141 SIC 7221 2752

SANDIS DINER LLC p 1278
704 Ayers St, Corpus Christi TX 78404
Tel (361) 334-3850 SIC 7221

TPP ACQUISITION INC p 1467
1155 Kas Dr Ste 180, Richardson TX 75081
Tel (972) 265-7600 SIC 7221

SIC 7231 Beauty Shops

■ ELIZABETH ARDEN SALON-HOLDINGS INC p 487
222 S Mill Ave Ste 201, Tempe AZ 85281
Tel (602) 864-8191 SIC 7231 5999 7299

■ RED DOOR SALONS INC p 1215
222 S Mill Ave Ste 201, Tempe AZ 85281
Tel (480) 829-8191 SIC 7231 5999 7299

GINO MORENA ENTERPRISES LLC p 612
111 Starlite St, South San Francisco CA 94080
Tel (800) 227-6905 SIC 7231

CHICAGO 29 INC p 297
7328 Pine Valley St, Bradenton FL 34202
Tel (419) 621-9002 SIC 7231

■ MARIO TRICOCIS HAIR SALON & DAY SPA p 907
900 N Michigan Ave # 1850, Chicago IL 60611
Tel (800) 874-2624 SIC 7231

■ AVEDA CORP p 136
4000 Pheasant Ridge Dr Ne, Blaine MN 55449
Tel (763) 783-4250 SIC 2844 7231

▲ REGIS CORP p 1220
7201 Metro Blvd, Edina MN 55439
Tel (952) 947-7777 SIC 7231 7299 6794

HAIRSTYLISTS MANAGEMENT SYSTEMS INC p 653
12700 Industrial Park Blv, Minneapolis MN 55441
Tel (763) 550-1332 SIC 7231

■ SUPERCUTS INC p 1406
7201 Metro Blvd, Minneapolis MN 55439
Tel (952) 947-7777 SIC 7231

BEAUTY BRANDS LLC p 166
4600 Madison Ave Ste 400, Kansas City MO 64112
Tel (816) 531-2266 SIC 5999 7231

MARIANNA INDUSTRIES INC p 906
11222 I St Ste A, Omaha NE 68137
Tel (402) 593-0211 SIC 5122 2844 7231

TREASURE ISLAND LLC p 1475
3300 Las Vegas Blvd S, Las Vegas NV 89109
Tel (702) 894-7111 SIC 7011 7231

BURMAX CO INC p 228
28 Barretts Ave, Holtsville NY 11742
Tel (631) 447-8700 SIC 5087 7231

GRUPO EDUK INC p 643
Marginal Rd 20 Km 2 3, Guaynabo PR 00966
Tel (787) 982-3000
SIC 8249 8244 8243 8222 7231

INSTITUTO DE BANCA Y COMERCIO INC p 747
56 Carr 20, Guaynabo PR 00966
Tel (787) 982-3000
SIC 8249 8244 8243 8222 7231

DIRECT BEAUTY INC p 441
33 Estate Fryndendahl, St Thomas VI 00802
Tel (340) 775-4612 SIC 7231

CREATIVE HAIRDRESSERS INC p 390
1577 Spring Hill Rd # 600, Vienna VA 22182
Tel (703) 269-5400 SIC 5999 7231

RATNER COMPANIES LC p 1209
1577 Spring Hill Rd # 500, Vienna VA 22182
Tel (703) 269-5400 SIC 7231

RED DOOR SALONS INC p 1215
8075 Leesburg Pike # 110, Vienna VA 22182
Tel (602) 760-2519 SIC 7231

GENE JUAREZ SALONS LLC p 598
3633 136th Pl Se Ste 200, Bellevue WA 98006
Tel (425) 748-1400 SIC 7231

GJS HOLDING LLC p 613
3633 136th Pl Se Ste 200, Bellevue WA 98006
Tel (425) 748-1400 SIC 7231

SIC 7261 Funeral Svcs & Crematories

FOREST LAWN MEMORIAL-PARK ASSOCIATION p 567
1712 S Glendale Ave, Glendale CA 91205
Tel (323) 254-3131 SIC 5992 6553 7261

■ SKYLAWN p 1330
32992 Mission Blvd, Hayward CA 94544
Tel (510) 471-3363 SIC 6553 7261

KEYSTONE GROUP HOLDINGS INC p 815
4901 Vineland Rd Ste 350, Orlando FL 32811
Tel (813) 225-4650 SIC 7389 7261

■ STEWART ENTERPRISES INC p 1389
1333 S Clearview Pkwy, New Orleans LA 70121
Tel (504) 729-1400 SIC 7261 5087

■ KEYSTONE AMERICA INC p 815
2685 Henderson Dr, Jacksonville NC 28546
Tel (910) 347-2595 SIC 7261

■ YORK GROUP INC p 1637
2 N Shore Ctr, Pittsburgh PA 15212
Tel (412) 995-1600 SIC 7261

▲ STONEMOR PARTNERS LP p 1391
3600 Horizon Blvd Ste 100, Trevose PA 19053
Tel (215) 826-2800 SIC 6553 7261

■ ALDERWOODS (DELAWARE) INC p 47
1929 Allen Pkwy, Houston TX 77019
Tel (713) 522-5141 SIC 7261 6553 6311

▲ CARRIAGE SERVICES INC p 260
3040 Post Oak Blvd # 300, Houston TX 77056
Tel (713) 332-8400 SIC 7261 6553

■ SCI FUNERAL SERVICES OF NEW YORK INC p 1292
1929 Allen Pkwy, Houston TX 77019
Tel (713) 522-5141 SIC 7261

■ SCI SHARED RESOURCES LLC p 1292
1929 Allen Pkwy, Houston TX 77019
Tel (713) 522-5141 SIC 7261 6553

▲ SERVICE CORP INTERNATIONAL p 1307
1929 Allen Pkwy, Houston TX 77019
Tel (713) 522-5141 SIC 7261

SIC 7291 Tax Return Preparation Svcs

ADVANTEDGE BUSINESS GROUP LLC p 27
9777 Pyramid Ct Ste 220, Englewood CO 80112
Tel (303) 734-9424 SIC 8741 7291 7363

THOMSON REUTERS (GRC) INC p 1449
2711 Centerville Rd # 400, Wilmington DE 19808
Tel (212) 227-7357
SIC 7291 8111 8721 8733 8741

DNK SALES LLC p 446
949 Stephenson Rd Ste B, Stone Mountain GA 30087
Tel (678) 704-7300 SIC 6311 7291 5699

RSM US LLP p 1256
1 S Wacker Dr Ste 800, Chicago IL 60606
Tel (312) 634-3400 SIC 8721 8742 7291

▲ H&R BLOCK INC p 651
1 H&R Block Way, Kansas City MO 64105
Tel (816) 854-3000 SIC 7291 6794

■ AYCO CO L P p 140
321 Broadway, Saratoga Springs NY 12866
Tel (518) 886-4000
SIC 6411 6282 8742 7291

PREMIUM TRANSPORTATION STAFFING INC p 1171
190 Highland Dr, Medina OH 44256
Tel (330) 722-7974 SIC 7291 7363

PRONTO GENERAL AGENCY LTD p 1183
805 Media Luna St Ste 100, Brownsville TX 78520
Tel (956) 574-9787 SIC 6331 6361 7291

RYAN LLC p 1260
13155 Noel Rd Ste 100, Dallas TX 75240
Tel (972) 934-0022 SIC 8721 7291 7389

▲ LIBERTY TAX INC p 862
1716 Corp Landing Pkwy, Virginia Beach VA 23454
Tel (757) 493-8855 SIC 7291

SIC 7299 Miscellaneous Personal Svcs, NEC

COLLEGIATE HOUSING FOUNDATION p 337
409 Johnson Ave, Fairhope AL 36532
Tel (251) 304-0055 SIC 7299

■ HYPERCOM CORP p 724
8888 E Raintree Dr # 300, Scottsdale AZ 85260
Tel (480) 642-5000
SIC 3578 7372 7299 5065

■ ELIZABETH ARDEN SALON-HOLDINGS INC p 487
222 S Mill Ave Ste 201, Tempe AZ 85281
Tel (602) 864-8191 SIC 7231 5999 7299

■ RED DOOR SALONS INC p 1215
222 S Mill Ave Ste 201, Tempe AZ 85281
Tel (480) 829-8191 SIC 7231 5999 7299

▲ NETSOL TECHNOLOGIES INC p 1027
24025 Park Sorrento # 410, Calabasas CA 91302
Tel (818) 222-9195 SIC 7372 7373 7299

JENNY CRAIG INC p 782
5770 Fleet St, Carlsbad CA 92008
Tel (760) 696-4000
SIC 7299 6794 5149 5499

JENNY CRAIG WEIGHT LOSS CENTERS INC p 782
5770 Fleet St, Carlsbad CA 92008
Tel (760) 696-4000 SIC 7299 7991

CP OPCO LLC p 387
901 W Hillcrest Blvd, Inglewood CA 90301
Tel (310) 966-4900 SIC 7299

▲ CORELOGIC INC p 369
40 Pacifica Ste 900, Irvine CA 92618
Tel (949) 214-1000
SIC 7323 7299 8742 8732

VALET PARKING SERVICE A CALIFORNIA LTD PARTNERSHIP p 1540
6933 Hollywood Blvd, Los Angeles CA 90028
Tel (323) 465-5873 SIC 7521 7299

HITACHI CONSULTING SOFTWARE SERVICES INC p 696
8000 Jarvis Ave Ste 130, Newark CA 94560
Tel (510) 742-4100 SIC 7299 7371

HITACHI DATA SYSTEMS HOLDING CORP p 696
2845 Lafayette St, Santa Clara CA 95050
Tel (408) 970-1000 SIC 7299

PIVOT INTERIORS INC p 1152
3355 Scott Blvd Ste 110, Santa Clara CA 95054
Tel (408) 432-5600 SIC 5712 7389 7299

▲ TRUECAR INC p 1486
120 Broadway Ste 200, Santa Monica CA 90401
Tel (800) 200-2000 SIC 5012 7299

RANDALL FOODS INC p 1207
2905 E 50th St, Vernon CA 90058
Tel (323) 261-6565 SIC 5147 7299

■ UNITED ONLINE INC p 1510
21255 Burbank Blvd # 400, Woodland Hills CA 91367
Tel (818) 287-3000 SIC 5961 7299

IHS GLOBAL INC p 731
15 Inverness Way E, Englewood CO 80112
Tel (303) 790-0600
SIC 7299 8732 8748 7375 7373

IHS HOLDING INC p 731
15 Inverness Way E, Englewood CO 80112
Tel (303) 790-0600
SIC 7299 8732 8748 7375

IHS INC p 731
15 Inverness Way E, Englewood CO 80112
Tel (303) 790-0600
SIC 7299 8732 8748 7375

▲ GAIA INC p 589
833 W South Boulder Rd, Louisville CO 80027
Tel (303) 222-3600 SIC 7299 7812 7999

NORTH CASTLE PARTNERS LLC p 1051
183 E Putnam Ave, Greenwich CT 06830
Tel (203) 485-0216
SIC 7299 6794 5149 5499

FORT LAUDERDALE TRANSPORTATION INC p 569
1330 Se 4th Ave Ste D, Fort Lauderdale FL 33316
Tel (954) 524-6500 SIC 7299 4789

TAX DEFENSE NETWORK LLC p 1426
9000 Southside Blvd # 11000, Jacksonville FL 32256
Tel (904) 421-4410 SIC 7299

WALT DISNEY ATTRACTIONS p 1574
1500 Epcot Resorts Blvd, Lake Buena Vista FL 32830
Tel (407) 934-4000 SIC 7011 7299

KENT SECURITY SERVICES INC p 812
14600 Biscayne Blvd, North Miami FL 33181
Tel (305) 919-9400 SIC 7381 7299

SEVEN-ONE-SEVEN PARKING SERVICES INC p 1309
1410 N Florida Ave, Tampa FL 33602
Tel (813) 228-7722
SIC 7299 6519 7521 4119 8742

AMERIPARK LLC p 82
3200 Cobb Galleria Pkwy # 299, Atlanta GA 30339
Tel (404) 364-0342 SIC 7521 7299

APARTMENTTIME COM LLC p 96
2025 Peachtree Rd Ne, Atlanta GA 30309
Tel (404) 961-0603 SIC 7299

INTELLIGENT CONSUMER HOLDINGS LLC p 750
980 Hammond Dr Ste 1000, Atlanta GA 30328
Tel (404) 260-2200 SIC 7299

TRUSTWAVE CORP p 1488
70 W Madison St Ste 1050, Chicago IL 60602
Tel (312) 873-7500 SIC 7299 7373

DIRECTBUY INC p 441
8450 Broadway, Merrillville IN 46410
Tel (219) 736-1100
SIC 5021 5064 5023 5961 6794 7299

CIRI - STROUP INC p 308
1 Park Pl Ste 200, Annapolis MD 21401
Tel (410) 267-6111 SIC 7299

JW HOME IMPROVEMENT LLC p 798
849 Quince Orch, Gaithersburg MD 20878
Tel (703) 899-3129 SIC 7299

■ AECOM GOVERNMENT SERVICES INC p 28
20501 Seneca Meadows Pkwy, Germantown MD 20876
Tel (703) 921-1600
SIC 4959 4173 4581 7299

■ HST LESSEE BOSTON LLC p 715
39 Dalton St, Boston MA 02199
Tel (617) 236-2000
SIC 7011 5812 7299 5813

WW GROUP INC p 1629
28555 Orchard Lake Rd # 100, Farmington Hills MI 48334
Tel (248) 553-8555 SIC 7299

▲ REGIS CORP p 1220
7201 Metro Blvd, Edina MN 55439
Tel (952) 947-7777 SIC 7231 7299 6794

SILVERTON CASINO LLC p 1324
3333 Blue Diamond Rd, Las Vegas NV 89139
Tel (702) 263-7777 SIC 7011 7299 5813

■ VENETIAN CASINO RESORT LLC p 1547
3355 Las Vegas Blvd S, Las Vegas NV 89109
Tel (702) 414-1000
SIC 7011 5812 5813 7299

■ VICTORIA PARTNERS p 1555
3770 Las Vegas Blvd S, Las Vegas NV 89109
Tel (888) 529-4828
SIC 7011 5812 7299 5813

■ GOLDEN ROAD MOTOR INN INC p 621
3800 S Virginia St, Reno NV 89502
Tel (775) 335-4521
SIC 7011 5812 5813 7299

■ PARTY CITY CORP p 1119
25 Green Pond Rd Ste 1, Rockaway NJ 07866
Tel (973) 453-8600 SIC 6794 5947 7299

SOMERS RELATED POINT LLC p 1339
50 Mays Landing Rd # 226, Somers Point NJ 08244
Tel (609) 927-0441 SIC 7299 6531

FERRANDINO & SON INC p 538
71 Carolyn Blvd, Farmingdale NY 11735
Tel (866) 571-4609
SIC 1542 0781 3531 7299

FUN STATION ASSOCIATES INC p 585
40 Rocklyn Ave, Lynbrook NY 11563
Tel (516) 599-7757 SIC 7299 7999

CPS 1 REALTY LP p 387
768 5th Ave, New York NY 10019
Tel (212) 759-3000 SIC 7011 7299 5812

▲ WEIGHT WATCHERS INTERNATIONAL INC p 1588
675 Ave Americas Fl 6, New York NY 10010
Tel (212) 589-2700 SIC 7299 7991

▲ XO GROUP INC p 1632
195 Broadway Fl 25, New York NY 10007
Tel (212) 219-8555 SIC 7299

RUBIES COSTUME CO INC p 1257
12008 Jamaica Ave, Richmond Hill NY 11418
Tel (718) 846-1008 SIC 2389 7299

TUXEDO JUNCTION INC p 1493
120 Earhart Dr, Williamsville NY 14221
Tel (716) 633-2400 SIC 5136 5699 7299

GROVE PARK INN RESORT INC p 642
290 Macon Ave, Asheville NC 28804
Tel (828) 252-2711
SIC 7011 5812 5813 7992 7991 7299

OMNI GROVE PARK LLC p 1084
290 Macon Ave, Asheville NC 28804
Tel (828) 252-2711
SIC 7299 5812 7011 5813 7992 7991

JF ACQUISITION LLC p 785
1330 Saint Marys St # 210, Raleigh NC 27605
Tel (757) 857-5700 SIC 5084 1799 7299

PARKING SOLUTIONS INC p 1116
353 W Nationwide Blvd, Columbus OH 43215
Tel (614) 469-7000 SIC 7299

PCCW TELESERVICES (US) INC p 1124
5200 Rings Rd, Dublin OH 43017
Tel (614) 652-6300 SIC 7389 7299

UHDE CORP OF AMERICA p 1500
1370 Wash Pike Ste 510, Bridgeville PA 15017
Tel (412) 257-8277 SIC 8711 7299

■ MATCH GROUP INC p 919
8750 N Cntl Expy Ste 1400, Dallas TX 75231
Tel (214) 576-9352 SIC 7299 7374

VARSITY BRANDS HOLDING CO INC p 1545
1901 Diplomat Dr, Farmers Branch TX 75234
Tel (972) 406-7162 SIC 5091 7299 6719

EPCO HOLDINGS INC p 504
1100 Louisiana St Fl 10, Houston TX 77002
Tel (713) 880-6500 SIC 7299

CROSSMARK INC p 394
5100 Legacy Dr, Plano TX 75024
Tel (469) 814-1000 SIC 5141 5912 7299

USAA CAPITAL CORP p 1534
9800 Fredericksburg Rd, San Antonio TX 78288
Tel (210) 498-2211
SIC 6035 6798 6722 7299 4813 4724

CSS CORP p 398
11778 S Election Rd # 160, Draper UT 84020
Tel (801) 619-4014 SIC 7299

VIRGINIA TECH FOUNDATION INC p 1560
902 Prices Fork Rd, Blacksburg VA 24060
Tel (540) 231-2861 SIC 7299

■ CSRA SYSTEMS AND SOLUTIONS LLC p 398
15000 Conference Ctr Dr, Chantilly VA 20151
Tel (703) 641-2213 SIC 7299

■ HISTORIC AOL LLC p 696
22000 Aol Way, Dulles VA 20166
Tel (703) 265-1000 SIC 4813 7299

RETAIL DATA LLC p 1228
11013 W Broad St Ste 300, Glen Allen VA 23060
Tel (804) 678-7500 SIC 7299

■ COINSTAR LLC p 335
1800 114th Ave Se, Bellevue WA 98004
Tel (425) 943-8000 SIC 7299 7841

INDEPENDENT PHARMACY COOPERATIVE p 736
1550 Columbus St, Sun Prairie WI 53590
Tel (608) 825-9556 SIC 5122 7299

SIC 7311 Advertising Agencies

BEST WESTERN INTERNATIONAL INC p 177
6201 N 24th Pkwy, Phoenix AZ 85016
Tel (602) 957-4200
SIC 7389 7311 5046 8743

IGNITED LLC p 730
2150 Park Pl Ste 100, El Segundo CA 90245
Tel (310) 773-3100 SIC 7311

KATCH p 804
2381 Rosecrans Ave # 400, El Segundo CA 90245
Tel (310) 219-6200 SIC 7311

BDS MARKETING INC p 164
10 Holland, Irvine CA 92618
Tel (949) 472-6700 SIC 7311 8743 8732

LOCAL CORP p 872
7555 Irvine Center Dr, Irvine CA 92618
Tel (949) 784-0800 SIC 7311

▲ RUBICON PROJECT INC p 1257
12181 Bluff Creek Dr Fl 4, Los Angeles CA 90094
Tel (310) 207-0272 SIC 7311

■ SUNAMERICA INVESTMENTS INC p 1401
1 Sun America Ctr Fl 37, Los Angeles CA 90067
Tel (310) 772-6000
SIC 8741 6211 6282 7311

HUGH DUNCAN & ASSOCIATES INC p 717
26908 Mlibu Cove Colny Dr, Malibu CA 90265
Tel (310) 457-7432 SIC 7311

OPENX TECHNOLOGIES INC p 1089
888 E Walnut St Fl 2, Pasadena CA 91101
Tel (855) 673-6948 SIC 7311

▲ YUME INC p 1640
1204 Middlefield Rd, Redwood City CA 94063
Tel (650) 591-9400 SIC 7311

IMAGE ONE MARKETING GROUP INC p 733
11956 Bernardo Plaza Dr # 525, San Diego CA 92128
Tel (858) 673-8299 *SIC* 7311 5199

▲TRADE DESK INC p 1468
42 N Chestnut St, Ventura CA 93001
Tel (805) 585-3434 *SIC* 7311

■ REACHLOCAL INC p 1213
21700 Oxnard St Ste 1600, Woodland Hills CA 91367
Tel (818) 274-0260 *SIC* 7311 7375

■ CRISPIN PORTER & BOGUSKY LLC p 392
6450 Gunpark Dr, Boulder CO 80301
Tel (303) 628-5100 *SIC* 7311

▲ NATIONAL CINEMEDIA INC p 1010
9110 E Nichols Ave # 200, Centennial CO 80112
Tel (303) 792-3600 *SIC* 7311 7389

■ NATIONAL CINEMEDIA LLC p 1010
9110 E Nichols Ave # 200, Centennial CO 80112
Tel (303) 792-3600 *SIC* 7311

■ INTEGER GROUP L L C p 748
7245 W Alaska Dr, Lakewood CO 80226
Tel (303) 393-3000 *SIC* 7311 8742 8743

VESTIS RETAIL GROUP LLC p 1552
160 Corporate Ct, Meriden CT 06450
Tel (203) 235-5775 *SIC* 7311

■ ZIMMERMAN ADVERTISING LLC p 1643
6600 N Andrews Ave # 200, Fort Lauderdale FL 33309
Tel (954) 644-4000 *SIC* 7311

PEARL PAINT CO INC p 1126
1033 E Oakland Park Blvd, Oakland Park FL 33334
Tel (954) 564-5700
SIC 5999 5199 7699 5112 5947 7311

TRIAD DIGITAL MEDIA LLC p 1478
100 Carillon Pkwy Ste 100, Saint Petersburg FL 33716
Tel (727) 231-5041 *SIC* 7311

ALEXANDER GALLO HOLDINGS LLC p 49
101 Marietta St Nw # 2700, Atlanta GA 30303
Tel (404) 495-0777 *SIC* 7311

■ YP ADVERTISING & PUBLISHING LLC p 1639
2247 Northlake Pkwy, Tucker GA 30084
Tel (678) 406-5523 *SIC* 2741 7313 7311

▲ GROUPON INC p 642
600 W Chicago Ave Ste 400, Chicago IL 60654
Tel (312) 334-1579 *SIC* 7311 7319

LEO BURNETT CO INC p 856
35 W Wacker Dr Fl 21, Chicago IL 60601
Tel (312) 220-5959 *SIC* 7311 3993

MARKETING STORE WORLDWIDE L L C p 908
55 W Monroe St Fl 14, Chicago IL 60603
Tel (312) 614-4600 *SIC* 7311 8742

STARCOM MEDIAVEST GROUP INC p 1379
35 W Wacker Dr Fl 9, Chicago IL 60601
Tel (312) 220-3535 *SIC* 7311

GENERAL YELLOW PAGES CONSULTANTS INC p 602
222 Ne Monroe St Ste 800, Peoria IL 61602
Tel (309) 677-0400 *SIC* 7311

▲ANGIES LIST INC p 91
1030 E Washington St, Indianapolis IN 46202
Tel (888) 888-5478 *SIC* 7311

YELLOWBOOK CO INC p 1635
6300 C St Sw, Cedar Rapids IA 52404
Tel (319) 366-1100 *SIC* 7311

WOODWARD COMMUNICATIONS INC p 1623
801 Bluff St, Dubuque IA 52001
Tel (563) 588-5611
SIC 2711 2741 4832 2752 7311

SECURITY BENEFIT GROUP INC p 1299
1 Sw Security Benefit Pl, Topeka KS 66636
Tel (785) 438-3000 *SIC* 6211 7311 6411

ARNOLD WORLDWIDE LLC p 112
10 Summer St Ste 600, Boston MA 02110
Tel (617) 587-8000 *SIC* 7311 8743

DELAWARE NORTH COMPANIES INC - BOSTON p 424
100 Legends Way Ste 100, Boston MA 02114
Tel (617) 624-1000
SIC 5812 5994 6512 7311

■ INDEPENDENT ADVERTISING INC p 736
53 State St, Boston MA 02109
Tel (617) 437-1600
SIC 7311 7331 7389 8732

EXTREME REACH INC p 521
75 2nd Ave Ste 720, Needham Heights MA 02494
Tel (781) 577-2016 *SIC* 7311

MONSTER WORLDWIDE INC p 985
133 Boston Post Rd, Weston MA 02493
Tel (978) 461-8000 *SIC* 7311 7361

PROJECT WORLDWIDE INC p 1182
3600 Giddings Rd, Auburn Hills MI 48326
Tel (248) 475-8863 *SIC* 7311

TEAMDETROIT LLC p 1430
550 Town Center Dr, Dearborn MI 48126
Tel (313) 615-2000 *SIC* 7311

CAPITAL SALES CO p 250
1471 E 9 Mile Rd, Hazel Park MI 48030
Tel (248) 542-4400 *SIC* 5141 7311

LANSING MALL LIMITED PARTNERSHIP p 844
5330 W Saginaw Hwy, Lansing MI 48917
Tel (517) 321-0145 *SIC* 6512 7311

■ DONER PARTNERS LLC p 450
25900 Northwestern Hwy, Southfield MI 48075
Tel (248) 354-9700 *SIC* 7311

VML INC p 1563
250 Nw Richards Rd # 255, Kansas City MO 64116
Tel (816) 283-0700 *SIC* 7311 7373 8742

CONCORD HOSPITALITY INC p 354
1701 Windhoek Dr, Lincoln NE 68512
Tel (402) 421-2551 *SIC* 5812 7011 7311

WHITE ROSE INC p 1606
380 Middlesex Ave, Carteret NJ 07008
Tel (732) 541-5555
SIC 5141 5143 5142 5122 7311 8721

VISION PROMOTIONS INC p 1561
81 Hobart St, Hackensack NJ 07601
Tel (908) 333-4213 *SIC* 7311

HEALTHSTAR COMMUNICATIONS INC p 678
1000 Wyckoff Ave Ste 202, Mahwah NJ 07430
Tel (201) 560-5370 *SIC* 7372 7311 6719

ELITELUCK.COM INC p 487
10510 62nd Rd Apt 1d, Forest Hills NY 11375
Tel (718) 938-1203 *SIC* 7311

AEGIS LIFESTYLE INC p 29
32 Aveune Of The Americas, New York NY 10013
Tel (212) 366-3400 *SIC* 7311 7389 8743

ALIXPARTNERS LLP p 50
909 3rd Ave Fl 30, New York NY 10022
Tel (212) 490-2500 *SIC* 7311

■ BBDO WORLDWIDE INC p 163
1285 Ave Of The Amer, New York NY 10019
Tel (212) 459-5000 *SIC* 7311

■ CMGRP INC p 329
909 3rd Ave, New York NY 10022
Tel (212) 445-8000
SIC 8743 7311 7319 8742

■ COMCAST SPOTLIGHT p 343
5 Times Sq, New York NY 10036
Tel (212) 278-8156 *SIC* 7311

■ DAS HOLDINGS INC p 413
437 Madison Ave, New York NY 10022
Tel (212) 415-3700 *SIC* 7311

■ DDB WORLDWIDE COMMUNICATIONS GROUP INC p 419
437 Madison Ave Fl 11, New York NY 10022
Tel (212) 415-2000 *SIC* 7311

■ DEUTSCH INC p 433
6 E 78th St, New York NY 10075
Tel (212) 981-7600 *SIC* 7311

EURO RSCG LATINO p 512
350 Hudson St Fl 6, New York NY 10014
Tel (212) 345-6383 *SIC* 7311

FCB INTERNATIONAL LLC p 532
100 W 23rd St Frnt, New York NY 10011
Tel (212) 885-3000 *SIC* 7311

■ FCB WORLDWIDE INC p 532
100 W 33rd St Fl 5, New York NY 10001
Tel (212) 885-3000 *SIC* 7311 8743

■ FOOT LOCKER SPECIALTY INC p 564
112 W 34th St Lbby 1, New York NY 10120
Tel (212) 720-3700 *SIC* 5632 5961 7311

GREY GLOBAL GROUP LLC p 639
200 5th Ave Bsmt B, New York NY 10010
Tel (212) 546-2000 *SIC* 7311

HAVAS HEALTH INC p 668
200 Madison Ave, New York NY 10016
Tel (212) 532-1000 *SIC* 7311

HAVAS NORTH AMERICA INC p 668
200 Hudson St, New York NY 10013
Tel (212) 886-2000 *SIC* 7311 5963

ICROSSING INC p 728
300 W 57th St Fl 20f, New York NY 10019
Tel (212) 649-3900 *SIC* 8742 7311

▲ INTERPUBLIC GROUP OF COMPANIES INC p 757
909 3rd Ave Fl 7, New York NY 10022
Tel (212) 704-1200 *SIC* 7311 8742

J WALTER THOMPSON CO LLC p 772
466 Lexington Ave Ste 6r, New York NY 10017
Tel (212) 210-7000 *SIC* 7311

J WALTER THOMPSON USA LLC p 772
466 Lexington Ave Ste 6r, New York NY 10017
Tel (212) 210-7000 *SIC* 7311

KIRSHENBAUM BOND SENECAL & PARTNERS LLC p 822
160 Varick St Fl 4, New York NY 10013
Tel (646) 336-9400 *SIC* 7311

■ MCCANN WORLDGROUP LLC p 926
622 3rd Ave Ste 3, New York NY 10017
Tel (646) 865-5000 *SIC* 7311 7319

■ MCCANN-ERICKSON USA INC p 926
622 3rd Ave Fl 16, New York NY 10017
Tel (646) 865-2000 *SIC* 8732 7311

▲ MDC PARTNERS INC p 933
745 5th Ave Fl 19, New York NY 10151
Tel (646) 429-1800 *SIC* 7311 8748

■ MEDIABRANDS WORLDWIDE INC p 936
100 W 33rd St, New York NY 10001
Tel (212) 605-7000 *SIC* 7319 7311

MEDIAOCEAN LLC p 936
45 W 18th St, New York NY 10011
Tel (212) 633-8100 *SIC* 7371 7311

MKTG INC p 979
32 Avenue Of The Americas # 20, New York NY 10013
Tel (212) 366-3400 *SIC* 7311 7389 8743

MMS USA INVESTMENTS INC p 979
41 Madison Ave, New York NY 10010
Tel (212) 463-2000 *SIC* 7311

■ MOMENTUM-NA INC p 983
250 Hudson St Fl 2, New York NY 10013
Tel (646) 638-5400 *SIC* 8743 7311 8732

NEW YORK INTERCONNECT L L C p 1035
530 5th Ave Fl 6, New York NY 10036
Tel (212) 382-5300 *SIC* 7311

OGILVY & MATHER WORLDWIDE INC p 1076
636 11th Ave, New York NY 10036
Tel (212) 237-4000
SIC 7311 7812 7375 8742

OGILVY GROUP LLC p 1076
636 11th Ave, New York NY 10036
Tel (212) 237-4000
SIC 7311 8743 8748 7336 7361 8732

■ OMD USA LLC p 1084
195 Broadway, New York NY 10007
Tel (212) 590-7100 *SIC* 7311

▲ OMNICOM GROUP INC p 1085
437 Madison Ave, New York NY 10022
Tel (212) 415-3600 *SIC* 7311

■ OMNICOM MEDIA GROUP p 1085
195 Broadway Fl 12, New York NY 10007
Tel (212) 590-7100 *SIC* 7311

PUBLICIS INC p 1190
1675 Broadway Fl 2, New York NY 10019
Tel (212) 279-5000 *SIC* 7311

■ R/GA MEDIA GROUP INC p 1203
450 W 33rd St Fl 12, New York NY 10001
Tel (212) 946-4000
SIC 7374 7336 7375 7311

RUDER FINN INC p 1257
425 E 53rd St, New York NY 10022
Tel (212) 593-6400 *SIC* 8743 7311 2752

RUN INC p 1258
375 Hudson St Fl 8, New York NY 10014
Tel (212) 244-3200 *SIC* 7311 7319

SAATCHI & SAATCHI ADVERTISING GROUP INC p 1263
355 Park Ave S, New York NY 10010
Tel (212) 229-6403 *SIC* 7311

▲ SCHOLASTIC CORP p 1288
557 Broadway Lbby 1, New York NY 10012
Tel (212) 343-6100
SIC 2731 2721 7372 7812 6794 7311

SSCG GROUP LLC p 1363
220 E 42nd St, New York NY 10017
Tel (212) 907-4300 *SIC* 7311

■ TBWA CHIAT/DAY INC p 1427
488 Madison Ave Fl 7, New York NY 10022
Tel (212) 804-1000 *SIC* 7311 8743

■ TBWA WORLDWIDE INC p 1427
488 Madison Ave, New York NY 10022
Tel (212) 804-1000 *SIC* 7311

TMP WORLDWIDE ADVERTISING & COMMUNICATIONS LLC p 1457
125 Broad St Fl 10, New York NY 10004
Tel (646) 613-2000 *SIC* 7311

▲ TREMOR VIDEO INC p 1476
1501 Broadway Fl 8, New York NY 10036
Tel (646) 723-5300 *SIC* 7311

■ TRUE NORTH COMMUNICATIONS INC p 1486
1114 Ave Of The Americas, New York NY 10036
Tel (212) 704-1200 *SIC* 7311

WPP CLAPTON SQUARE LLC p 1627
100 Park Ave Fl 4, New York NY 10017
Tel (212) 632-2200 *SIC* 7311

WPP GROUP HOLDINGS LLC p 1627
100 Park Ave Fl 4, New York NY 10017
Tel (212) 632-2200 *SIC* 7311

WPP GROUP US INVESTMENTS INC p 1627
100 Park Ave, New York NY 10017
Tel (212) 632-2200 *SIC* 7311

WPP GROUP USA INC p 1627
100 Park Ave Fl 4, New York NY 10017
Tel (212) 632-2200 *SIC* 7311

WPP GROUP USA INC p 1627
100 Park Ave, New York NY 10017
Tel (212) 632-2200 *SIC* 7311

XAXIS LLC p 1631
132 W 31st St Fl 9, New York NY 10001
Tel (646) 259-4200 *SIC* 7311

■ CONCENTRIX CORP p 354
3750 Monroe Ave, Pittsford NY 14534
Tel (585) 218-5300 *SIC* 7379 7331 7311

■ GATEHOUSE MEDIA LLC p 593
175 Sullys Trl Ste 300, Pittsford NY 14534
Tel (585) 598-0030 *SIC* 2711 7311 2759

▲ MAXPOINT INTERACTIVE INC p 923
3020 Carrington Mill Blvd, Morrisville NC 27560
Tel (800) 916-9960 *SIC* 7311 8711

D & S CREATIVE COMMUNICATIONS INC p 406
140 Park Ave E, Mansfield OH 44902
Tel (419) 524-6699
SIC 7311 2752 2791 2789

■ L M BERRY AND CO p 834
3170 Kettering Blvd, Moraine OH 45439
Tel (937) 296-2121 *SIC* 7311 2741

KENNEDY WIEDEN INC p 811
224 Nw 13th Ave, Portland OR 97209
Tel (503) 937-7000 *SIC* 7311

LIN TV CORP p 866
1 W Exchange St Ste 305, Providence RI 02903
Tel (401) 454-2880 *SIC* 4833 7311

PIGGLY WIGGLY CAROLINA CO INC p 1147
176 Croghan Spur Ste 400, Charleston SC 29407
Tel (843) 554-9880
SIC 7311 5411 5148 5141 2752 1542

■ ERWIN-PENLAND INC p 508
125 E Broad St Ste 300, Greenville SC 29601
Tel (864) 271-0500 *SIC* 7311

■ GSD&M IDEA CITY LLC p 643
828 W 6th St, Austin TX 78703
Tel (512) 242-4736 *SIC* 7311

▲ RETAILMENOT INC p 1228
301 Congress Ave Ste 700, Austin TX 78701
Tel (512) 777-2970 *SIC* 7311

SIZMEK INC p 1328
500 W 5th St Ste 900, Austin TX 78701
Tel (512) 469-5900 *SIC* 7311

■ CPM-US LLC p 387
1999 Bryan St Ste 3200, Dallas TX 75201
Tel (800) 648-0722 *SIC* 7311

MOROCH HOLDINGS INC p 989
3625 N Hall St Ste 1100, Dallas TX 75219
Tel (214) 520-9700 *SIC* 7311

RICHARDS GROUP INC p 1232
2801 N Cntl Expy Ste 100, Dallas TX 75204
Tel (214) 891-5700 *SIC* 7311

DEX MEDIA INC p 434
2200 W Airfield Dr, Dfw Airport TX 75261
Tel (972) 453-7000 *SIC* 2741 7311

GREENLEAF ADVERTISING & MEDIA INC p 638
601 Silveron Ste 200, Flower Mound TX 75028
Tel (972) 899-8750 *SIC* 7311

IVIE & ASSOCIATES INC p 769
601 Silveron Ste 200, Flower Mound TX 75028
Tel (972) 899-5000 *SIC* 7311

PRO-MARK INC p 1178
845 Overland St, North Salt Lake UT 84054
Tel (801) 299-5500 *SIC* 7311 7336

PAPPAS GROUP LLC p 1112
4100 Fairfax Dr Ste 400, Arlington VA 22203
Tel (703) 349-7221 *SIC* 7311

■ MARTIN AGENCY INC p 912
1 Shockoe Plz, Richmond VA 23219
Tel (804) 649-1496
SIC 7331 7311 8743 7313

SIC 7312 Outdoor Advertising Svcs

■ CLEAR CHANNEL OUTDOOR INC p 324
2325 E Camelback Rd # 400, Phoenix AZ 85016
Tel (602) 381-5700 *SIC* 7312

SHIVERS TRADING & OPERATING CO p 1317
725 Broad St, Augusta GA 30901
Tel (706) 724-0851
SIC 2711 2721 2731 4832 7312 6512

ADAMS OUTDOOR ADVERTISING LIMITED PARTNERSHIP p 21
500 Colonial Center Pkwy, Roswell GA 30076
Tel (770) 333-0399 *SIC* 7312

WHITECO INDUSTRIES INC p 1606
1000 E 80th Pl Ste 700n, Merrillville IN 46410
Tel (219) 769-6601
SIC 7312 7011 7922 6552 7374 3993

▲ LAMAR ADVERTISING CO p 841
5321 Corporate Blvd, Baton Rouge LA 70808
Tel (225) 926-1000 *SIC* 7312 6798

■ LAMAR MEDIA CORP p 841
5321 Corporate Blvd, Baton Rouge LA 70808
Tel (225) 926-1000 *SIC* 7312

LAMAR TEXAS LIMITED PARTNERSHIP p 841
5321 Corporate Blvd, Baton Rouge LA 70808
Tel (800) 235-2627 *SIC* 7312

ALLOY INC p 58
151 W 26th St Fl 11, New York NY 10001
Tel (609) 655-8878
SIC 8743 8742 7331 7312

■ BORDERFREE INC p 201
292 Madison Ave, New York NY 10017
Tel (212) 299-3500 *SIC* 8742 4731 7312

■ CBS CORP p 269
51 W 52nd St Bsmt 1, New York NY 10019
Tel (212) 975-4321
SIC 4833 4832 7312 2731

■ CBS RADIO INC p 269
1271 Ave Of The Amer 44, New York NY 10020
Tel (212) 314-9200 *SIC* 4832 7312

INTERSECTION MEDIA HOLDINGS INC p 757
10 Hudson Yards Fl 26, New York NY 10001
Tel (212) 644-6200 *SIC* 7312 6719

▲ OUTFRONT MEDIA INC p 1099
405 Lexington Ave Fl 17, New York NY 10174
Tel (212) 297-6400 *SIC* 7312 7319 6798

■ OUTFRONT MEDIA LLC p 1099
405 Lexington Ave, New York NY 10174
Tel (212) 297-6400 *SIC* 7312

■ CLEAR CHANNEL OUTDOOR HOLDINGS INC p 324
200 E Basse Rd Ste 100, San Antonio TX 78209
Tel (210) 832-3700 *SIC* 7312 7999

■ IHEARTCOMMUNICATIONS INC p 731
200 E Basse Rd, San Antonio TX 78209
Tel (210) 822-2828 *SIC* 4832 4833 7312

▲ IHEARTMEDIA INC p 731
200 E Basse Rd Ste 100, San Antonio TX 78209
Tel (210) 822-2828 *SIC* 4832 7312

■ ACKERLEY VENTURES INC p 17
1301 5th Ave Ste 3525, Seattle WA 98101
Tel (206) 624-2888
SIC 7941 4833 4832 7319 7312

DERSE INC p 431
3800 W Canal St, Milwaukee WI 53208
Tel (414) 257-2000 *SIC* 3993 7312

SIC 7313 Radio, TV & Publishers Adv Reps

1105 MEDIA INC p 1
9201 Oakdale Ave Ste 101, Chatsworth CA 91311
Tel (818) 814-5200
SIC 7313 7389 2721 2741 8748

DELUXE ENTERTAINMENT SERVICES GROUP INC p 427
2400 W Empire Ave, Los Angeles CA 90027
Tel (323) 462-6171 *SIC* 7819 7313

■ FOX TELEVISION STATIONS LLC p 573
1999 S Bundy Dr, Los Angeles CA 90025
Tel (310) 584-2000 *SIC* 4833 7313

■ SAN DIEGO UNION-TRIBUNE LLC p 1276
600 B St, San Diego CA 92101
Tel (619) 299-3131 *SIC* 2711 7313 7383

2100 FREEDOM INC p 1
625 N Grand Ave, Santa Ana CA 92701
Tel (714) 796-7000
SIC 2711 2721 7313 2741 5963 4813

FREEDOM COMMUNICATIONS INC p 576
625 N Grand Ave, Santa Ana CA 92701
Tel (714) 796-7000
SIC 2711 2721 7313 2741 5963

BEACHBODY LLC p 164
3301 Exposition Blvd Fl 3, Santa Monica CA 90404
Tel (310) 883-9000 *SIC* 7313 7999

▲ DEMAND MEDIA INC p 427
1655 26th St, Santa Monica CA 90404
Tel (310) 656-6253 *SIC* 7313 7336

■ JACOR BROADCASTING OF COLORADO INC p 775
4695 S Monaco St, Denver CO 80237
Tel (303) 631-2933 *SIC* 7313

■ TELEMUNDO COMMUNICATIONS GROUP INC p 1434
2290 W 8th Ave, Hialeah FL 33010
Tel (305) 884-8200 *SIC* 4833 7313

COX MEDIA GROUP LLC p 386
6205 Pachtree Dunwoody Rd, Atlanta GA 30328
Tel (678) 645-0000
SIC 4833 4832 7922 7313

COX MEDIA LLC p 386
1400 Lake Hearn Dr Ne, Brookhaven GA 30319
Tel (404) 843-5000 *SIC* 4841 7313

■ YP ADVERTISING & PUBLISHING LLC p 1639
2247 Northlake Pkwy, Tucker GA 30084
Tel (678) 406-5523 *SIC* 2741 7313 7311

■ YP HOLDINGS LLC p 1639
2247 Northlake Pkwy Fl 10, Tucker GA 30084
Tel (866) 570-8863 SIC 7374 7389 7313

■ CARS.COM LLC p 261
175 W Jackson Blvd Fl 8, Chicago IL 60604
Tel (312) 601-5000 SIC 7313

■ CHICAGO TRIBUNE NEWSPAPERS INC p 298
435 N Michigan Ave # 200, Chicago IL 60611
Tel (312) 222-3232 SIC 7313

DANIEL J EDELMAN HOLDINGS INC p 411
200 E Randolph St Fl 63, Chicago IL 60601
Tel (312) 240-3000 SIC 7313 8743

DANIEL J EDELMAN INC p 411
200 E Randolph St Fl 63, Chicago IL 60601
Tel (312) 240-3000 SIC 7313 8743

COMMERCIAL PRINT GROUP INC p 345
1750 Northway Dr, North Mankato MN 56003
Tel (507) 625-2828 SIC 7313

MARCO TECHNOLOGIES LLC p 905
4510 Heatherwood Rd, Saint Cloud MN 56301
Tel (320) 259-3000
SIC 7371 4813 7313 7812

CMW HOLDCO INC p 329
20000 Horizon Way Ste 600, Mount Laurel NJ 08054
Tel (267) 443-2547 SIC 7313

NEPTUNE HOLDING US CORP p 1026
6 Corporate Center Dr, Melville NY 11747
Tel (516) 803-2265 SIC 7313 7929

■ LOCAL MEDIA GROUP INC p 873
40 Mulberry St, Middletown NY 10940
Tel (845) 341-1100 SIC 2711 7313

CPX INTERACTIVE HOLDINGS LLC p 388
1441 Broadway Fl 18, New York NY 10018
Tel (646) 863-8309 SIC 7313

ECONOMIST NEWSPAPER GROUP INC p 476
750 3rd Ave Fl 5, New York NY 10017
Tel (212) 541-0500 SIC 2721 7313 5963

KANTAR MEDIA INTELLIGENCES INC p 803
11 Madison Ave Fl 12, New York NY 10010
Tel (800) 497-8450 SIC 7313

■ KATZ MEDIA GROUP INC p 805
125 W 55th St Fl 11, New York NY 10019
Tel (212) 315-0956 SIC 7313

■ KATZ MILLENNIUM SALES & MARKETING INC p 805
125 W 55th St Frnt 3, New York NY 10019
Tel (212) 424-6000 SIC 7313

MLB ADVANCED MEDIA LP p 979
75 9th Ave Fl 5, New York NY 10011
Tel (212) 485-3444 SIC 4841 7313 7929

PENTON MEDIA INC p 1132
1166 Avenue Of The Americ, New York NY 10036
Tel (212) 204-4200
SIC 2721 7389 7313 7375

▲ TRAVELZOO INC p 1475
590 Madison Ave Rm 3700, New York NY 10022
Tel (212) 484-4900 SIC 7313 7373

XAXIS INC p 1631
132 W 31st St Fl 9, New York NY 10001
Tel (212) 629-7173 SIC 7319 7313

▲ A H BELO CORP p 5
508 Young St, Dallas TX 75202
Tel (214) 977-8222 SIC 2711 7313

HOUSTON LIVESTOCK SHOW AND RODEO INC p 712
8334 Nrg Park, Houston TX 77054
Tel (832) 667-1000 SIC 7313

MULTI-VIEW INC p 999
7701 Las Colinas Rdg, Irving TX 75063
Tel (972) 402-7070 SIC 7313

■ MARTIN AGENCY INC p 912
1 Shockoe Plz, Richmond VA 23219
Tel (804) 649-1496
SIC 7331 7311 8743 7313

▲ MARCHEX INC p 905
520 Pike St Ste 2000, Seattle WA 98101
Tel (206) 331-3300 SIC 7313

SIC 7319 Advertising, NEC

KSL MEDIA INC p 831
15910 Ventura Blvd # 900, Encino CA 91436
Tel (212) 468-3395 SIC 7319

QUALITY CUSTOM DISTRIBUTION SERVICES INC p 1197
18301 Von Karman Ave, Irvine CA 92612
Tel (949) 252-2000 SIC 5087 7319

▲ QUOTIENT TECHNOLOGY INC p 1201
400 Logue Ave, Mountain View CA 94043
Tel (650) 605-4600 SIC 7319

■ CBS INTERACTIVE INC p 269
235 2nd St, San Francisco CA 94105
Tel (415) 344-2000 SIC 7319 7375 4832

CHECKOUT HOLDING CORP p 292
1 Maritime Plz Ste 1200, San Francisco CA 94111
Tel (415) 788-5111 SIC 7319

AFFINION GROUP LLC p 32
6 High Ridge Park Bldg A, Stamford CT 06905
Tel (203) 956-1000
SIC 8699 8748 7319 7331

■ ICON HOLDING CORP p 727
107 Elm St Fl 15, Stamford CT 06902
Tel (203) 328-2300 SIC 7389 7319

■ ICON INTERNATIONAL INC p 728
4 Stamford Plz 15th, Stamford CT 06902
Tel (203) 328-2300 SIC 7389 7319

■ NEWS AMERICA MARKETING IN-STORE SERVICES LLC p 1039
20 Westport Rd Ste 320, Wilton CT 06897
Tel (203) 563-6600 SIC 7319

AMERICAN CHEMICAL SOCIETY p 70
1155 16th St Nw, Washington DC 20036
Tel (202) 872-4600 SIC 8621 7319

CUSTOMIZED DISTRIBUTION LLC p 403
5545 Shawland Rd, Jacksonville FL 32254
Tel (904) 783-0848 SIC 5141 7319

CATALINA MARKETING CORP p 264
200 Carillon Pkwy, Saint Petersburg FL 33716
Tel (727) 579-5000 SIC 7319

▲ GROUPON INC p 642
600 W Chicago Ave Ste 400, Chicago IL 60654
Tel (312) 334-1579 SIC 7311 7319

MITTERA GROUP INC p 978
1312 Locust St Ste 202, Des Moines IA 50309
Tel (515) 343-5353 SIC 2752 7319

■ MILLENNIAL MEDIA INC p 970
2400 Boston St Ste 300, Baltimore MD 21224
Tel (410) 522-8705 SIC 7319 7371

CARAT FUSION INC p 252
1 South Sta 300, Boston MA 02110
Tel (617) 449-4100 SIC 7319

SANCTUS LLC p 1278
348 E Maple Rd, Birmingham MI 48009
Tel (248) 594-2396 SIC 8741 7319 8742

VALASSIS COMMUNICATIONS INC p 1539
19975 Victor Pkwy, Livonia MI 48152
Tel (734) 591-3000 SIC 7319 7331 7372

ECM PUBLISHERS INC p 475
4095 Coon Rapids Blvd Nw, Minneapolis MN 55433
Tel (763) 712-2400
SIC 2711 2741 7319 2789 2752

▲ ETSY INC p 512
117 Adams St, Brooklyn NY 11201
Tel (718) 855-7955 SIC 5961 5947 7319

CARAT USA INC p 252
150 E 42nd St, New York NY 10017
Tel (212) 591-9100 SIC 7319

■ CMGRP INC p 329
909 3rd Ave, New York NY 10022
Tel (212) 445-8000
SIC 8743 7311 7319 8742

▲ EVERYDAY HEALTH INC p 515
345 Hudson St Rm 1600, New York NY 10014
Tel (646) 728-9500 SIC 8099 7319

GROUP M WORLDWIDE LLC p 642
498 7th Ave, New York NY 10018
Tel (212) 297-7000 SIC 7319

HORIZON MEDIA INC p 707
75 Varick St Ste 1404, New York NY 10013
Tel (212) 220-5000 SIC 7319

IGNITIONONE INC p 730
200 Park Ave Fl 27, New York NY 10166
Tel (888) 744-6483 SIC 7319

■ MCCANN WORLDGROUP LLC p 926
622 3rd Ave Ste 3, New York NY 10017
Tel (646) 865-5000 SIC 7311 7319

MEDIA PLANNING GROUP USA LLC p 936
200 Hudson St, New York NY 10013
Tel (646) 587-5000 SIC 7319

■ MEDIABRANDS WORLDWIDE INC p 936
100 W 33rd St, New York NY 10001
Tel (212) 605-7000 SIC 7319 7311

MINDSHARE USA LLC p 972
498 Fashion Ave, New York NY 10018
Tel (212) 297-7000 SIC 7319

▲ OUTFRONT MEDIA INC p 1099
405 Lexington Ave Fl 17, New York NY 10174
Tel (212) 297-6400 SIC 7312 7319 6798

RUN INC p 1258
375 Hudson St Fl 8, New York NY 10014
Tel (212) 244-3200 SIC 7311 7319

UBM LLC p 1498
2 Penn Plz Fl 15, New York NY 10121
Tel (516) 562-5085
SIC 2721 2711 7319 7389

■ UNIVERSAL MCCANN WORLDWIDE INC p 1517
100 W 33rd St Fl 5, New York NY 10001
Tel (212) 494-4700 SIC 7319

XAXIS INC p 1631
132 W 31st St Fl 9, New York NY 10001
Tel (212) 629-7173 SIC 7319 7313

ZENITH MEDIA SERVICES INC p 1642
299 W Houston St Fl 11, New York NY 10014
Tel (212) 989-3034 SIC 7319

■ ZIFF DAVIS LLC p 1643
28 E 28th St Fl 11-R, New York NY 10016
Tel (212) 503-3500 SIC 7319

ACTIVE MEDIA SERVICES INC p 20
1 Blue Hill Plz Ste 1705, Pearl River NY 10965
Tel (845) 735-1700 SIC 7319 4731 4789

GLOBAL CONTACT SERVICES LLC p 616
118b S Main St B, Salisbury NC 28144
Tel (704) 647-9672 SIC 7319 7389

INNOMARK COMMUNICATIONS LLC p 744
3005 W Tech Blvd, Miamisburg OH 45342
Tel (513) 285-1040 SIC 7319

JAY GROUP INC p 779
700 Indian Springs Dr, Lancaster PA 17601
Tel (717) 285-6200
SIC 5961 7389 7331 7319 5199

MOOD MEDIA CORP p 987
1703 W 5th St Ste 600, Austin TX 78703
Tel (800) 345-5000 SIC 7319 7389

RTU INC p 1256
1445 Langham Creek Dr, Houston TX 77084
Tel (800) 247-4793 SIC 7319 2752

■ ACKERLEY VENTURES INC p 17
1301 5th Ave Ste 3525, Seattle WA 98101
Tel (206) 624-2888
SIC 7941 4833 4832 7319 7312

RAZORFISH LLC p 1211
424 2nd Ave W, Seattle WA 98119
Tel (206) 816-8800 SIC 7375 7319

CYGNUS BUSINESS MEDIA INC p 405
1233 Janesville Ave, Fort Atkinson WI 53538
Tel (920) 563-6388 SIC 2721 7389 7319

SIC 7322 Adjustment & Collection Svcs

INFIRMARY HEALTH SYSTEM INC p 741
5 Mobile Infirmary Cir, Mobile AL 36607
Tel (251) 435-3030
SIC 8062 6512 1542 7322 5047 7389

SOUTHERN MEDICAL HEALTH SYSTEMS INC p 1349
3632 Dauphin St Ste 101b, Mobile AL 36608
Tel (251) 460-5280
SIC 8741 8011 7374 7322

NATIONWIDE CREDIT INC p 1017
1225 W Washington St # 300, Tempe AZ 85281
Tel (800) 456-4729 SIC 7322

■ PERFORMANT RECOVERY INC p 1135
333 N Canyons Pkwy # 100, Livermore CA 94551
Tel (209) 858-3994 SIC 7322 8742 7371

PIERPASS INC p 1147
444 W Ocean Blvd Ste 700, Long Beach CA 90802
Tel (562) 437-9112 SIC 8399 7322

SQUARETWO FINANCIAL CORP p 1362
4340 S Monaco St Fl 2, Denver CO 80237
Tel (877) 844-5715 SIC 7322

▲ SLM CORP p 1331
300 Continental Dr Ste 1s, Newark DE 19713
Tel (302) 451-0200 SIC 6111 6141 7322

FLORIDA CLINICAL PRACTICE ASSOCIATION INC p 557
1329 Sw 16th St Ste 4250, Gainesville FL 32608
Tel (352) 265-8017 SIC 7322

ENHANCED RECOVERY CO LLC p 499
8014 Bayberry Rd, Jacksonville FL 32256
Tel (904) 371-1005 SIC 7322

IQOR US INC p 764
1 Progress Plz Ste 170, Saint Petersburg FL 33701
Tel (866) 657-2057 SIC 7322

CONVERGENT RESOURCES INC p 365
555 N Point Ctr E Ste 175, Alpharetta GA 30022
Tel (770) 512-3670 SIC 7322

■ MCKESSON TECHNOLOGIES INC p 930
11475 Great Oaks Way # 400, Alpharetta GA 30022
Tel (404) 338-6000
SIC 7374 8741 8721 7322 7373

AFNI INC p 33
404 Brock Dr, Bloomington IL 61701
Tel (309) 828-5226 SIC 8742 7322

■ KAPSTONE RECEIVABLES LLC p 804
1101 Skokie Blvd Ste 300, Northbrook IL 60062
Tel (270) 393-2559 SIC 7322

AHC p 36
121 Ne Jefferson Ave # 100, Peoria IL 61602
Tel (888) 568-3137 SIC 7322

CBE GROUP INC p 268
1309 Technology Pkwy, Cedar Falls IA 50613
Tel (319) 234-6686 SIC 7322 8742

■ ENCORE RECEIVABLE MANAGEMENT INC p 496
400 N Rogers Rd, Olathe KS 66062
Tel (913) 782-3333 SIC 7322

TROVER SOLUTIONS INC p 1485
9390 Bunsen Pkwy, Louisville KY 40220
Tel (502) 214-1340 SIC 6411 7322

AFFILIATED HEALTHCARE SYSTEMS p 32
931 Union St, Bangor ME 04401
Tel (207) 973-6720
SIC 5047 8071 8741 7322 6512

CENTRAL MAINE HEALTH VENTURES INC p 279
300 Main St, Lewiston ME 04240
Tel (207) 795-0111
SIC 8049 8052 7322 8011

EULER HERMES ACI HOLDING INC p 512
800 Red Brook Blvd # 400, Owings Mills MD 21117
Tel (410) 753-0753 SIC 7322 6351 6719

■ ASSET ACCEPTANCE CAPITAL CORP p 119
320 E Big Beaver Rd, Troy MI 48083
Tel (800) 505-5166 SIC 6153 7322

ALLIED INTERSTATE LLC p 56
12755 Hwy 55 Ste 300, Plymouth MN 55441
Tel (973) 630-5720 SIC 7322

I C SYSTEM INC p 725
444 Highway 96 E, Saint Paul MN 55127
Tel (651) 483-8201 SIC 7322

SAINT LUKES HOSPITAL OF KANSAS CITY p 1270
4401 Wornall Rd, Kansas City MO 64111
Tel (816) 932-2000
SIC 8062 8742 8011 6512 8082 7322

INTEGRITY SOLUTION SERVICES INC p 750
20 Corporate Hills Dr, Saint Charles MO 63301
Tel (636) 530-7985 SIC 8748 7322

HEARTLAND HEALTH p 679
5325 Faraon St, Saint Joseph MO 64506
Tel (816) 271-6000 SIC 8062 7322 8721

■ OUTSOURCE GROUP INC p 1099
3 Cityplace Dr Ste 690, Saint Louis MO 63141
Tel (314) 692-6500 SIC 7322

FIRSTSOURCE ADVANTAGE LLC p 551
205 Bryant Woods S, Amherst NY 14228
Tel (716) 564-4400 SIC 7322

■ PIONEER CREDIT RECOVERY INC p 1150
26 Edward St, Arcade NY 14009
Tel (585) 492-1234 SIC 7322

INTELLIRISK MANAGEMENT CORP p 750
335 Madison Ave Fl 27, New York NY 10017
Tel (646) 274-3030 SIC 7322

CARDWORKS INC p 254
101 Crossways Park Dr W, Woodbury NY 11797
Tel (516) 576-0404 SIC 7322 7389

CBC COMPANIES INC p 268
250 E Broad St Fl 21, Columbus OH 43215
Tel (614) 222-4343 SIC 7322

■ MACYS CREDIT AND CUSTOMER SERVICES INC p 893
9111 Duke Blvd, Mason OH 45040
Tel (513) 398-5221 SIC 7389 7322 6141

RECEIVABLE MANAGEMENT SERVICES CORP p 1214
240 Emery St, Bethlehem PA 18015
Tel (484) 242-4000 SIC 7322

RECEIVABLE MANAGEMENT SERVICES INTERNATIONAL INC p 1214
240 Emery St, Bethlehem PA 18015
Tel (484) 242-4000 SIC 7322

TRANSWORLD SYSTEMS INC p 1473
500 Virginia Dr Ste 514, Fort Washington PA 19034
Tel (703) 757-0977 SIC 7322

EXCELA HEALTH HOLDING CO INC p 516
532 W Pittsburgh St, Greensburg PA 15601
Tel (724) 832-4000
SIC 8062 8093 5999 7363 7322 8361

EGS FINANCIAL CARE INC p 481
507 Prudential Rd, Horsham PA 19044
Tel (877) 217-4423 SIC 7322

COLLECTION & CONSULTING FINANCIAL SERVICES INC p 336
2948 Reed St Ste 100, Philadelphia PA 19146
Tel (215) 463-3477 SIC 7322

ALLIANCEONE INC p 55
4850 E Street Rd Ste 300, Trevose PA 19053
Tel (215) 354-5500 SIC 7322

ALLTRAN FINANCIAL LP p 59
5800 N Course Dr, Houston TX 77072
Tel (800) 568-0399 SIC 7322

GC SERVICES LIMITED PARTNERSHIP p 595
6330 Gulfton St, Houston TX 77081
Tel (713) 777-4441 SIC 7322 7389

▲ HMS HOLDINGS CORP p 698
5615 High Point Dr # 100, Irving TX 75038
Tel (214) 453-3000 SIC 7322

EXPERT GLOBAL SOLUTIONS INC p 520
5085 W Park Blvd Ste 300, Plano TX 75093
Tel (800) 252-3996 SIC 7322

■ PRA GOVERNMENT SERVICES LLC p 1167
120 Corporate Blvd # 100, Norfolk VA 23502
Tel (757) 519-9300 SIC 7322

▲ PRA GROUP INC p 1167
120 Corporate Blvd # 100, Norfolk VA 23502
Tel (888) 772-7326 SIC 7322

■ CSC CREDIT SERVICES INC p 397
1775 Tysons Blvd, Tysons VA 22102
Tel (703) 876-1000 SIC 7323 7322

HEALTHCARE RESOURCE GROUP INC p 676
12610 E Mirabeau Pkwy # 900, Spokane Valley WA 99216
Tel (509) 209-2000
SIC 6411 7322 8742 8721

CHILDRENS HOSPITAL AND HEALTH SYSTEM INC p 299
8915 W Connell Ave, Milwaukee WI 53226
Tel (414) 266-2000
SIC 8069 8082 7389 7322

SIC 7323 Credit Reporting Svcs

EXPERIAN INFORMATION SOLUTIONS INC p 520
475 Anton Blvd, Costa Mesa CA 92626
Tel (714) 830-7000 SIC 7323

▲ CORELOGIC INC p 369
40 Pacifica Ste 900, Irvine CA 92618
Tel (949) 214-1000
SIC 7323 7299 8742 8732

■ RELS LLC p 1222
40 Pacifica Ste 900, Irvine CA 92618
Tel (949) 214-1000 SIC 6531 7323

EXPERIAN CORP p 519
475 Anton Blvd, Santa Ana CA 92704
Tel (714) 830-7000 SIC 7323

LEXISNEXIS RISK ASSETS INC p 859
1105 N Market St Ste 501, Wilmington DE 19801
Tel (770) 752-6000
SIC 6411 7375 8721 7323

TRG HOLDINGS LLC p 1476
1700 Penn Ave Nw Ste 560, Washington DC 20006
Tel (202) 289-9898 SIC 7323

HAMILTON RISK MANAGEMENT CO p 655
3155 Nw 77th Ave, Miami FL 33122
Tel (305) 716-6000
SIC 6331 7323 6141 6541 6411

▲ EQUIFAX INC p 506
1550 Peachtree St Nw, Atlanta GA 30309
Tel (404) 885-8000
SIC 7323 7389 8732 8741

■ EQUIFAX INFORMATION SERVICES LLC p 506
1550 Peachtree St Ne, Atlanta GA 30309
Tel (404) 885-8000 SIC 7323

FIRST ADVANTAGE CORP p 544
1 Concourse Pkwy Ste 200, Atlanta GA 30328
Tel (800) 888-5773
SIC 7323 8742 7372 7389 7381

▲ TRANSUNION p 1473
555 W Adams St Fl 1, Chicago IL 60661
Tel (312) 985-2000 SIC 7323

■ TRANSUNION INTERACTIVE INC p 1473
555 W Adams St, Chicago IL 60661
Tel (805) 782-8282 SIC 7323

■ TRANSUNION INTERMEDIATE HOLDINGS INC p 1473
555 W Adams St Fl 2, Chicago IL 60661
Tel (312) 258-1717 SIC 7323

SHAMROCK TRADING CORP p 1311
9300 Metcalf Ave, Overland Park KS 66212
Tel (913) 310-2200
SIC 4731 6153 8742 7323

▲ DUN & BRADSTREET CORP p 461
103 Jfk Pkwy, Short Hills NJ 07078
Tel (973) 921-5500 SIC 7323

■ DUN & BRADSTREET INC p 461
103 Jfk Pkwy, Short Hills NJ 07078
Tel (973) 921-5500 SIC 7323

■ DUN & BRADSTREET INTERNATIONAL LTD p 461
103 Jfk Pkwy, Short Hills NJ 07078
Tel (973) 921-5500 SIC 7323 8741

■ MOODYS ANALYTICS INC p 987
250 Greenwich St 7w, New York NY 10007
Tel (415) 874-6368 SIC 7323

▲ MOODYS CORP p 987
250 Greenwich St, New York NY 10007
Tel (212) 553-0300 SIC 7323 6282

■ MOODYS INVESTORS SERVICE INC p 987
250 Greenwich St, New York NY 10007
Tel (212) 553-0300 SIC 7323

▲ S&P GLOBAL INC p 1263
55 Water St Ste Conc2, New York NY 10041
Tel (212) 438-1000 SIC 7323 6282

■ STANDARD & POORS SECURITIES EVALUATIONS INC p 1375
55 Water St Fl 44, New York NY 10041
Tel (212) 438-3388 SIC 7323 6289

CBCINNOVIS INC p 268
8 Parkway Ctr, Pittsburgh PA 15220
Tel (412) 503-9254 SIC 7323

ACE CASH EXPRESS INC p 16
1231 Greenway Dr Ste 600, Irving TX 75038
Tel (972) 550-5000 SIC 7323 6099

▲ INTERSECTIONS INC p 757
3901 Stonecroft Blvd, Chantilly VA 20151
Tel (703) 488-6100 SIC 7323

▲ COMPUTER SCIENCES CORP p 353
1775 Tysons Blvd, Tysons VA 22102
Tel (703) 245-9675
SIC 7376 7374 7379 7373 7323

■ CSC CREDIT SERVICES INC p 397
1775 Tysons Blvd, Tysons VA 22102
Tel (703) 876-1000 SIC 7323 7322

SIC 7331 Direct Mail Advertising Svcs

▲ STAMPS.COM INC p 1375
1990 E Grand Ave, El Segundo CA 90245
Tel (310) 482-5800 SIC 7331 5961 4813

KP LLC p 828
13951 Washington Ave, San Leandro CA 94578
Tel (510) 346-0729
SIC 2752 7334 7331 7374 7389 8742

ADVANSTAR COMMUNICATIONS INC p 26
2501 Colorado Ave Ste 280, Santa Monica CA 90404
Tel (310) 857-7500 SIC 7389 2721 7331

AFFINION GROUP LLC p 32
6 High Ridge Park Bldg A, Stamford CT 06905
Tel (203) 956-1000
SIC 8699 8748 7319 7331

VALASSIS DIRECT MAIL INC p 1539
1 Targeting Ctr, Windsor CT 06095
Tel (800) 437-0479 SIC 7331

AGORA MARKETING SOLUTIONS INC p 35
8285 Bryan Dairy Rd # 150, Largo FL 33777
Tel (727) 369-2700 SIC 7331 7389

V P HOLDINGS INC p 1538
8605 Largo Lakes Dr, Largo FL 33773
Tel (727) 393-1270 SIC 7331

■ CONNEXTIONS INC p 358
9395 S John Young Pkwy, Orlando FL 32819
Tel (407) 926-2411 SIC 7379 7331

COX TARGET MEDIA INC p 386
1 Valpak Ave N, Saint Petersburg FL 33716
Tel (727) 399-3000
SIC 7331 8741 8742 2759

VALPAK DIRECT MARKETING SYSTEMS INC p 1542
805 Exe Ctr Dr W, Saint Petersburg FL 33702
Tel (727) 399-3175 SIC 7331 6794

ROARK CAPITAL GROUP INC p 1240
1180 Peachtree St Ne # 2500, Atlanta GA 30309
Tel (404) 591-5200
SIC 6726 3993 7331 6794 5261

■ CHICAGO TRIBUNE CO p 298
435 N Michigan Ave # 200, Chicago IL 60611
Tel (312) 222-3232
SIC 2711 7383 7389 7331

CISION US INC p 309
130 E Randolph St Fl 7, Chicago IL 60601
Tel (312) 922-2400 SIC 7389 2741 7331

▲ RR DONNELLEY & SONS CO p 1255
35 W Wacker Dr Ste 3650, Chicago IL 60601
Tel (312) 326-8000
SIC 2754 2759 2752 2732 7331 7336

SOURCELINK ACQUISITION LLC p 1342
500 Park Blvd Ste 1425, Itasca IL 60143
Tel (866) 947-6872 SIC 7374 7331

ANTHONY WAYNE REHABILITATION CENTER FOR HANDICAPPED AND BLIND INC p 94
8515 Bluffton Rd, Fort Wayne IN 46809
Tel (260) 744-6145
SIC 8331 7331 3441 3412 2449 2448

■ ACCENT MARKETING SERVICES LLC p 14
4550 Town Center Blvd, Jeffersonville IN 47130
Tel (812) 941-1112 SIC 7331 7389 8748

METROGROUP CORP p 955
1805 E Washington St, Mount Pleasant IA 52641
Tel (319) 385-5135 SIC 7331 7389

AGORA INC p 35
14 W Mount Vernon Pl, Baltimore MD 21201
Tel (410) 783-8499 SIC 2741 7331

MERKLE GROUP INC p 950
7001 Columbia Gateway Dr, Columbia MD 21046
Tel (443) 542-4000 SIC 7331

ENVELOPES UNLIMITED INC p 503
649 N Horners Ln, Rockville MD 20850
Tel (301) 424-3300 SIC 2759 7331

■ INDEPENDENT ADVERTISING INC p 736
53 State St, Boston MA 02109
Tel (617) 437-1600
SIC 7311 7331 7389 8732

■ SALESLINK CORP p 1272
425 Medford St, Charlestown MA 02129
Tel (617) 886-4800 SIC 7379 8744 7331

■ CONSTANT CONTACT INC p 360
1601 Trapelo Rd Ste 329, Waltham MA 02451
Tel (781) 472-8100 SIC 7373 4813 7331

VALASSIS COMMUNICATIONS INC p 1539
19975 Victor Pkwy, Livonia MI 48152
Tel (734) 591-3000 SIC 7319 7331 7372

INSTANT WEB LLC p 747
7951 Powers Blvd, Chanhassen MN 55317
Tel (952) 474-0961 SIC 7331

INSTANT WEB LLC p 747
7951 Powers Blvd, Chanhassen MN 55317
Tel (952) 474-0961 SIC 7331

UNITED MAILING INC p 1510
1001 Park Rd, Chanhassen MN 55317
Tel (952) 474-0961 SIC 7331 2759 8732

ADVANSTAR HOLDINGS CORP p 26
131 W 1st St, Duluth MN 55802
Tel (218) 740-7200 SIC 7389 2721 7331

JAPS-OLSON CO p 778
7500 Excelsior Blvd, St Louis Park MN 55426
Tel (952) 932-9393
SIC 2752 7331 2791 2759

■ BROADRIDGE CUSTOMER COMMUNICATIONS CENTRAL LLC p 215
2600 Southwest Blvd, Kansas City MO 64108
Tel (816) 221-1234 SIC 7331

■ BROADRIDGE CUSTOMER COMMUNICATIONS LLC p 215
2600 Southwest Blvd, Kansas City MO 64108
Tel (816) 221-1234
SIC 7389 2759 7374 7331 2752 7336

▲ DST SYSTEMS INC p 458
333 W 11th St, Kansas City MO 64105
Tel (816) 435-1000
SIC 7374 7371 7331 7372

HENRY WURST INC p 684
1331 Saline St, North Kansas City MO 64116
Tel (816) 701-0825 SIC 2752 7331

ANSIRA PARTNERS INC p 93
2300 Locust St, Saint Louis MO 63103
Tel (314) 783-2300 SIC 7389 7331

■ OMAHA WORLD-HERALD CO p 1084
1314 Douglas St Ste 700, Omaha NE 68102
Tel (402) 444-1000 SIC 2711 7331

INFOGROUP INC p 741
1020 E 1st St, Papillion NE 68046
Tel (402) 836-4500 SIC 7331

HIBBERT CO p 690
400 Pennington Ave, Trenton NJ 08618
Tel (609) 392-0478 SIC 7331 7389

NORTH AMERICAN COMMUNICATIONS INC p 1049
7 Edgemont Rd, Katonah NY 10536
Tel (914) 273-8620 SIC 7331

ALLOY INC p 58
151 W 26th St Fl 11, New York NY 10001
Tel (609) 655-8878
SIC 8743 8742 7331 7312

THOMAS PUBLISHING CO LLC p 1449
5 Penn Plz Fl 9, New York NY 10001
Tel (212) 695-0500
SIC 2741 2721 7374 7331

VSS-AHC CONSOLIDATED HOLDINGS CORP p 1567
350 Park Ave Fl 7, New York NY 10022
Tel (212) 935-4990 SIC 7389 2721 7331

■ CONCENTRIX CORP p 354
3750 Monroe Ave, Pittsford NY 14534
Tel (585) 218-5300 SIC 7379 7331 7311

A W S INC p 7
1275 Lakeside Ave E, Cleveland OH 44114
Tel (216) 861-0250
SIC 8331 7374 7334 7331

AMERIMARK DIRECT LLC p 82
6864 Engle Rd, Cleveland OH 44130
Tel (440) 826-1900 SIC 4226 5961 7331

AMERIMARK HOLDINGS LLC p 82
6864 Engle Rd, Cleveland OH 44130
Tel (440) 325-2000 SIC 5961 4226 7331

JAY GROUP INC p 779
700 Indian Springs Dr, Lancaster PA 17601
Tel (717) 285-6200
SIC 5961 7389 7331 7319 5199

WINDWARD PRINT STAR INC p 1616
14950 Hethrw Frst Pkwy # 120, Houston TX 77032
Tel (281) 821-5522
SIC 2752 2791 2796 7335 7336 7331

HOV SERVICES INC p 712
2701 E Grauwyler Rd, Irving TX 75061
Tel (248) 837-7100
SIC 7374 7334 7389 2752 7331 7379

▲ HARTE HANKS INC p 665
9601 Mcallister Fwy # 610, San Antonio TX 78216
Tel (210) 829-9000 SIC 7331 7372

DIDLAKE INC p 438
8641 Breeden Ave Ste 101, Manassas VA 20110
Tel (703) 361-4195
SIC 8331 7331 7349 7334

SERVICESOURCE INC p 1308
10467 White Granite Dr # 100, Oakton VA 22124
Tel (703) 461-6000 SIC 8331 7331

■ MARTIN AGENCY INC p 912
1 Shockoe Plz, Richmond VA 23219
Tel (804) 649-1496
SIC 7331 7311 8743 7313

FGS-WI LLC p 539
1101 S Janesville St, Milton WI 53563
Tel (608) 373-6500 SIC 2752 7331

SIC 7334 Photocopying & Duplicating Svcs

KP LLC p 828
13951 Washington Ave, San Leandro CA 94578
Tel (510) 346-0729
SIC 2752 7334 7331 7374 7389 8742

COMPEX LEGAL SERVICES INC p 351
325 Maple Ave, Torrance CA 90503
Tel (310) 782-1801 SIC 8111 7338 7334

■ AMERICAN REPROGRAPHICS CO LLC p 78
1981 N Broadway Ste 385, Walnut Creek CA 94596
Tel (925) 949-5100 SIC 8744 7334

▲ ARC DOCUMENT SOLUTIONS INC p 103
1981 N Broadway Ste 385, Walnut Creek CA 94596
Tel (925) 949-5100
SIC 7334 7335 7374 7372

NOVITEX ENTERPRISE SOLUTIONS INC p 1063
300 First Stamford Pl # 2, Stamford CT 06902
Tel (844) 668-4839 SIC 7334 8741

T & T REPROGRAPHICS INC p 1419
5100 Newport Dr Ste 1, Rolling Meadows IL 60008
Tel (847) 398-5855 SIC 7334

LAKE COUNTY PRESS INC p 838
98 Noll St, Waukegan IL 60085
Tel (847) 336-4333 SIC 2791 7334

SOURCECORP HEALTHSERVE RADIOLOGY INC p 1342
602 N English Station Rd, Louisville KY 40223
Tel (502) 244-0035 SIC 7334 8748 8721

SBI INC p 1285
8500 Valcour Ave, Saint Louis MO 63123
Tel (314) 615-2000
SIC 5199 5122 7334 5084

A W S INC p 7
1275 Lakeside Ave E, Cleveland OH 44114
Tel (216) 861-0250
SIC 8331 7374 7334 7331

LEHIGH BLUE PRINT CO INC p 853
2000 Butler St, Easton PA 18042
Tel (610) 253-3303 SIC 7334

RICOH USA INC p 1233
70 Valley Stream Pkwy, Malvern PA 19355
Tel (610) 296-8000
SIC 5044 5065 7359 5112 7334 6159

EDM AMERICAS INC p 478
10 Ed Preate Dr, Moosic PA 18507
Tel (800) 852-9809
SIC 4226 7389 7334 8741

PACE RESOURCES INC p 1103
140 E Market St Fl 2, York PA 17401
Tel (717) 852-1300
SIC 2752 5049 7334 2789

▲ FEDEX CORP p 536
942 Shady Grove Rd S, Memphis TN 38120
Tel (901) 818-7500
SIC 4513 4512 4213 4215 7334

CORPSOURCE HOLDINGS LLC p 372
2701 E Grauwyler Rd, Irving TX 75061
Tel (866) 321-5854 SIC 7375 7334 7374

HOV SERVICES INC p 712
2701 E Grauwyler Rd, Irving TX 75061
Tel (248) 837-7100
SIC 7374 7334 7389 2752 7331 7379

SOURCECORP INC p 1342
2701 E Grauwyler Rd, Irving TX 75061
Tel (866) 321-5854 SIC 7375 7334 7374

■ FEDEX OFFICE AND PRINT SERVICES INC p 536
7900 Legacy Dr, Plano TX 75024
Tel (214) 550-7000 SIC 7334

DIDLAKE INC p 438
8641 Breeden Ave Ste 101, Manassas VA 20110
Tel (703) 361-4195
SIC 8331 7331 7349 7334

SIC 7335 Commercial Photography

▲ ARC DOCUMENT SOLUTIONS INC p 103
1981 N Broadway Ste 385, Walnut Creek CA 94596
Tel (925) 949-5100
SIC 7334 7335 7374 7372

ICONIC GROUP INC p 728
3490 Martin Hurst Rd, Tallahassee FL 32312
Tel (800) 628-4509 SIC 7335

BELAIR HD STUDIOS LLC p 169
2233 S Throop St, Chicago IL 60608
Tel (312) 254-5188 SIC 7335 2711

FALCONHEAD CAPITAL PARTNERS II LP p 526
450 Park Ave Bsmt, New York NY 10022
Tel (212) 634-3304 SIC 6722 7221 7335

SHUTTERSTOCK INC p 1319
350 5th Ave Fl 21, New York NY 10118
Tel (646) 766-1855 SIC 7374 7335

WINDWARD PRINT STAR INC p 1616
14950 Hethrw Frst Pkwy # 120, Houston TX 77032
Tel (281) 821-5522
SIC 2752 2791 2796 7335 7336 7331

BRANDED ENTERTAINMENT NETWORK INC p 208
710 2nd Ave Ste 200, Seattle WA 98104
Tel (206) 373-6000 SIC 7335

SIC 7336 Commercial Art & Graphic Design

4 OVER LLC p 3
5900 San Fernando Rd D, Glendale CA 91202
Tel (818) 246-1170 SIC 2759 7336

■ MADISON/GRAHAM COLOR GRAPHICS INC p 894
150 N Myers St, Los Angeles CA 90033
Tel (323) 261-7171 SIC 2752 7336 2796

▲ DEMAND MEDIA INC p 427
1655 26th St, Santa Monica CA 90404
Tel (310) 656-6253 SIC 7313 7336

LIGHTSOURCE CREATIVE SERVICES INC p 865
121 La Porte Ave, Fort Collins CO 80524
Tel (970) 224-2806 SIC 7336

GERBER SCIENTIFIC LLC p 608
24 Indl Pk Rd W, Tolland CT 06084
Tel (860) 871-8082
SIC 3993 7336 3851 7372 3577

GRAPHIC CENTER GROUP CORP p 631
2150 Coral Way Fl 1, Coral Gables FL 33145
Tel (305) 961-1649 SIC 7372 7336

CREST FOODS CO INC p 392
905 Main St, Ashton IL 61006
Tel (800) 435-6972 SIC 2023 7336

▲ RR DONNELLEY & SONS CO p 1255
35 W Wacker Dr Ste 3650, Chicago IL 60601
Tel (312) 326-8000
SIC 2754 2759 2752 2732 7331 7336

PREGIS HOLDING I CORP p 1170
1650 Lake Cook Rd Ste 400, Deerfield IL 60015
Tel (847) 597-2200 SIC 2671 5199 7336

LOGO HOLDINGS II CORP p 875
626 W Main St, Louisville KY 40202
Tel (502) 637-5443 SIC 6719 7336

SOUTHERN GRAPHICS INC p 1348
626 W Main St, Louisville KY 40202
Tel (502) 637-5443 SIC 7336 7389

VOMELA SPECIALTY CO p 1565
274 Fillmore Ave E, Saint Paul MN 55107
Tel (651) 228-2200 SIC 7336 2396 2752

■ BROADRIDGE CUSTOMER COMMUNICATIONS LLC p 215
2600 Southwest Blvd, Kansas City MO 64108
Tel (816) 221-1234
SIC 7389 2759 7374 7331 2752 7336

NEW YORK CITY GEOGRAPHIC DISTRICT 24 p 1034
9850 50th Ave, Corona NY 11368
Tel (718) 592-3357 SIC 7336

■ INTERBRAND CORP p 751
130 5th Ave Fl 4, New York NY 10011
Tel (212) 798-7500 SIC 8742 7336

OGILVY GROUP LLC p 1076
636 11th Ave, New York NY 10036
Tel (212) 237-4000
SIC 7311 8743 8748 7336 7361 8732

■ R/GA MEDIA GROUP INC p 1203
450 W 33rd St Fl 12, New York NY 10001
Tel (212) 946-4000
SIC 7374 7336 7375 7311

KEEN LIVE INC p 807
2789 W Main St Ste 4, Wappingers Falls NY 12590
Tel (845) 790-0813 SIC 7336

NS FLEXIBLES LLC p 1064
2619 Phoenix Dr, Greensboro NC 27406
Tel (336) 292-9911 SIC 2671 7336 2759

SHAMROCK COMPANIES INC p 1311
24090 Detroit Rd, Westlake OH 44145
Tel (440) 899-9510
SIC 5112 5199 7336 7389 2754 2395

WINDWARD PRINT STAR INC p 1616
14950 Hethrw Frst Pkwy # 120, Houston TX 77032
Tel (281) 821-5522
SIC 2752 2791 2796 7335 7336 7331

PRO-MARK INC p 1178
845 Overland St, North Salt Lake UT 84054
Tel (801) 299-5500 SIC 7311 7336

KELLER INC p 808
N216 State Highway 55, Kaukauna WI 54130
Tel (920) 766-5795 SIC 1542 1541 7336

SIC 7338 Secretarial & Court Reporting Svcs

SOFTSCRIPT INC p 1337
2215 Campus Dr, El Segundo CA 90245
Tel (310) 451-2110 SIC 7338

COMPEX LEGAL SERVICES INC p 351
325 Maple Ave, Torrance CA 90503
Tel (310) 782-1801 SIC 8111 7338 7334

WINCORP INTERNATIONAL INC p 1615
10025 Nw 116th Way Ste 14, Medley FL 33178
Tel (305) 887-1294
SIC 5191 5083 5199 7338 5144

ESQUIRE DEPOSITION SERVICES LLC p 510
2700 Centennial Twr, Atlanta GA 30303
Tel (404) 495-0777 SIC 7338

IMEDX INC p 733
3560 Lenox Rd Ne Ste 3000, Atlanta GA 30326
Tel (404) 418-0096 SIC 7338

■ NUANCE TRANSCRIPTION SERVICES INC p 1066
1 Glenlake Pkwy Ste 800, Atlanta GA 30328
Tel (800) 205-7047 SIC 7338

CCH INC p 270
2700 Lake Cook Rd, Riverwoods IL 60015
Tel (847) 267-7000
SIC 2721 2731 7389 7338 8732 7371

L B & B ASSOCIATES INC p 833
9891 Broken Land Pkwy # 400, Columbia MD 21046
Tel (301) 621-3944
SIC 8744 7338 4225 8742 8748 4581

PERRY JOHNSON & ASSOCIATES INC p 1137
1489 W Warm Springs Rd, Henderson NV 89014
Tel (800) 803-6330 SIC 7338

VERITEXT LEGAL SOLUTIONS p 1550
290 W Mount Pleasant Ave, Livingston NJ 07039
Tel (973) 410-4040 SIC 6719 7338

SP WIND DOWN INC p 1353
9009 Carothers Pkwy # 303, Franklin TN 37067
Tel (615) 261-1500 SIC 7338

SPHERIS HOLDING III INC p 1358
720 Cool Springs Blvd, Franklin TN 37067
Tel (615) 261-1500 SIC 7338

TOTAL EMED INC p 1462
9009 Carothers Pkwy # 303, Franklin TN 37067
Tel (615) 261-1500 SIC 7338

SIC 7342 Disinfecting & Pest Control Svcs

COOKS PEST CONTROL INC p 366
1741 5th Ave Se Ste A, Decatur AL 35601
Tel (256) 355-3285 SIC 7342

TRULY NOLEN OF AMERICA INC p 1486
3636 E Speedway Blvd, Tucson AZ 85716
Tel (800) 528-3442 SIC 7342

CLARK PEST CONTROL OF STOCKTON INC p 322
555 N Guild Ave, Lodi CA 95240
Tel (209) 368-7152 SIC 7342

MASSEY SERVICES INC p 917
315 Groveland St, Orlando FL 32804
Tel (407) 645-2500 SIC 7342

ARROW EXTERMINATORS INC p 113
8613 Roswell Rd Bldg 4, Atlanta GA 30350
Tel (770) 993-8705
SIC 1742 7342 1521 1542

■ ORKIN LLC p 1095
2170 Piedmont Rd Ne, Atlanta GA 30324
Tel (404) 888-2000 SIC 7342

▲ ROLLINS INC p 1247
2170 Piedmont Rd Ne, Atlanta GA 30324
Tel (404) 888-2000 SIC 7342

PACKERS HOLDINGS LLC p 1107
1010 E Washington St # 202, Mount Pleasant IA 52641
Tel (800) 881-9558 SIC 7342 7349

RESIDEX LLC p 1226
46495 Humboldt Dr, Novi MI 48377
Tel (855) 737-4339
SIC 5191 7342 0781 0782

▲ ECOLAB INC p 476
370 Wabasha St N, Saint Paul MN 55102
Tel (800) 232-6522 SIC 2841 2842 7342

TEMCO SERVICE INDUSTRIES INC p 1436
417 5th Ave Fl 9, New York NY 10016
Tel (212) 889-6353 *SIC* 7349 7342 6289

STERITECH GROUP INC p 1386
6701 Carmel Rd Ste 300, Charlotte NC 28226
Tel (704) 544-1900 *SIC* 7342 8721

DCS SANITATION MANAGEMENT INC p 419
7864 Camargo Rd, Cincinnati OH 45243
Tel (513) 891-4980 *SIC* 7349 7342

▲ SCOTTS MIRACLE-GRO CO p 1294
14111 Scottslawn Rd, Marysville OH 43040
Tel (937) 644-0011 *SIC* 3542 0782 7342

RENTOKIL NORTH AMERICA INC p 1224
1125 Berkshire Blvd # 150, Wyomissing PA 19610
Tel (610) 372-9700 *SIC* 7342 0781 5191

TERMINIX SERVICE INC p 1439
3618 Fernandina Rd, Columbia SC 29210
Tel (803) 772-1783 *SIC* 7342

■ SERVICEMASTER CO LLC p 1307
860 Ridge Lake Blvd Fl 3, Memphis TN 38120
Tel (901) 597-1400
SIC 7349 7342 1711 1731 7641

▲ SERVICEMASTER GLOBAL HOLDINGS INC p 1308
860 Ridge Lake Blvd, Memphis TN 38120
Tel (901) 597-1400 *SIC* 7342 7629 7641

SERVICEMASTER HOLDING CORP p 1308
860 Ridge Lake Blvd, Memphis TN 38120
Tel (901) 597-1400
SIC 0782 7342 1711 1731 7349 7641

■ TERMINIX INTERNATIONAL CO LIMITED PARTNERSHIP p 1439
860 Ridge Lake Blvd, Memphis TN 38120
Tel (901) 766-1400 *SIC* 7342 7389

■ TERMINIX INTERNATIONAL INC p 1439
860 Ridge Lake Blvd # 101, Memphis TN 38120
Tel (901) 766-1100 *SIC* 7342

■ CENTEX HOME SERVICES CO LLC p 277
2728 N Harwood St Ste 200, Dallas TX 75201
Tel (214) 981-5000 *SIC* 7342

■ HOMETEAM PEST DEFENSE INC p 704
3100 Mckinnon St Ste 120, Dallas TX 75201
Tel (214) 665-8700 *SIC* 7342

S C JOHNSON & SON INC p 1262
1525 Howe St, Racine WI 53403
Tel (262) 260-2000
SIC 2842 2844 2879 2865 7342 7349

SIC 7349 Building Cleaning & Maintenance Svcs, NEC

LS1 LLC p 883
331 1st Ave N, Birmingham AL 35204
Tel (205) 251-9249 *SIC* 7349

LS1 LLC p 883
331 1st Ave N, Birmingham AL 35204
Tel (205) 251-9249 *SIC* 7349

BALDWIN JANITORIAL & PAPER LLC p 147
18260 County Road 12 S, Foley AL 36535
Tel (251) 943-7570 *SIC* 7349

G & R MINERAL SERVICES INC p 586
2355 Alton Rd, Irondale AL 35210
Tel (205) 956-7300 *SIC* 7349 7699

NANA MANAGEMENT SERVICES LLC p 1007
800 E Dimond Blvd 3-450, Anchorage AK 99515
Tel (907) 273-2400
SIC 5812 7349 7021 7033 7381

KOYITLOTSINA LIMITED p 828
1603 College Rd Ste 2, Fairbanks AK 99709
Tel (907) 452-8119 *SIC* 6798 8744 7349

HOTEL CLEANING SERVICES INC p 710
9609 N 22nd Ave, Phoenix AZ 85021
Tel (602) 588-0864 *SIC* 7349

PARAMOUNT BUILDING SOLUTIONS LLC p 1114
10235 S 51st St Ste 185, Phoenix AZ 85044
Tel (480) 348-1177 *SIC* 7349

■ FLUOR INDUSTRIAL SERVICES INC p 561
1 Enterprise, Aliso Viejo CA 92656
Tel (949) 439-2000 *SIC* 7349

ACME BUILDING MAINTENANCE CO INC p 17
941 Catherine St, Alviso CA 95002
Tel (408) 263-5911 *SIC* 7349

CHIRO INC p 301
2260 S Vista Ave, Bloomington CA 92316
Tel (909) 879-1160 *SIC* 5087 7349 5169

UNISERVE FACILITIES SERVICES CORP p 1505
2363 S Atlantic Blvd, Commerce CA 90040
Tel (213) 533-1000 *SIC* 7349

SERVICON SYSTEMS INC p 1308
3965 Landmark St, Culver City CA 90232
Tel (310) 204-5040 *SIC* 8744 7349 1771

WSA GROUP INC p 1628
19208 S Vermont Ave 200, Gardena CA 90248
Tel (310) 743-3000 *SIC* 7381 7349

Q C S BUILDING SERVICES INC p 1194
41619 Palermo Ct, Lancaster CA 93536
Tel (661) 267-6211 *SIC* 7349

MAINTENANCE STAFF INC p 898
122 W 8th St, Long Beach CA 90813
Tel (562) 493-3982 *SIC* 7349

■ ABM JANITORIAL SERVICES - SOUTHWEST INC p 12
5300 S Eastern Ave, Los Angeles CA 90040
Tel (323) 720-4020 *SIC* 7349

■ ABM PARKING SERVICES INC p 12
1150 S Olive St Fl 19, Los Angeles CA 90015
Tel (213) 284-7600 *SIC* 7521 7349

SBM MANAGEMENT SERVICES LP p 1285
5241 Arnold Ave, Mcclellan CA 95652
Tel (866) 855-2211 *SIC* 7349

SBM SITE SERVICES LLC p 1285
5241 Arnold Ave, Mcclellan CA 95652
Tel (916) 922-7600 *SIC* 7349

SOMERS BUILDING MAINTENANCE INC p 1339
5241 Arnold Ave, Mcclellan CA 95652
Tel (916) 922-3300 *SIC* 7349

MERCHANTS BUILDING MAINTENANCE CO p 944
1190 Monterey Pass Rd, Monterey Park CA 91754
Tel (323) 881-6701 *SIC* 7349

BERGENSONS PROPERTY SERVICES INC p 174
3605 Ocean Ranch Blvd # 200, Oceanside CA 92056
Tel (760) 631-5111 *SIC* 7349

EXCEL BUILDING SERVICES LLC p 516
1061 Serpentine Ln Ste H, Pleasanton CA 94566
Tel (650) 755-0900 *SIC* 7349

PRIDE INDUSTRIES p 1174
10030 Foothills Blvd, Roseville CA 95747
Tel (916) 788-2100 *SIC* 4226 7349 3679

■ AMERICAN BUILDING MAINTENANCE CO OF ILLINOIS INC p 69
420 Taylor St 200, San Francisco CA 94102
Tel (415) 351-4386 *SIC* 7349

■ AMERICAN BUILDING MAINTENANCE CO OF NEW YORK p 69
101 California St, San Francisco CA 94111
Tel (415) 733-4000 *SIC* 7349

■ AMERICAN BUILDING MAINTENANCE CO-WEST (INC) p 69
75 Broadway Ste 111, San Francisco CA 94111
Tel (415) 733-4000 *SIC* 7349

■ AMTECH SERVICES INC p 87
420 Taylor St 200, San Francisco CA 94102
Tel (415) 733-4000 *SIC* 7349 8742

■ BONDED MAINTENANCE CO p 200
75 Broadway Ste 111, San Francisco CA 94111
Tel (415) 733-4000 *SIC* 7349

CROWN BUILDING MAINTENANCE CO p 395
868 Folsom St, San Francisco CA 94107
Tel (415) 981-8070 *SIC* 7349 8711

FLAGSHIP ENTERPRISES HOLDING INC p 554
1050 N 5th St Ste E, San Jose CA 95112
Tel (408) 977-0155 *SIC* 7349

FLAGSHIP FACILITY SERVICES INC p 554
1050 N 5th St Ste E, San Jose CA 95112
Tel (408) 977-0155 *SIC* 7349

ALLIED UNIVERSAL TOPCO LLC p 57
1551 N Tustin Ave, Santa Ana CA 92705
Tel (714) 619-9700 *SIC* 6719 7381 7349

UNIVERSAL BUILDING MAINTENANCE LLC p 1516
1551 N Tustin Ave Ste 650, Santa Ana CA 92705
Tel (714) 619-9700 *SIC* 7349

UNIVERSAL SERVICES OF AMERICA LP p 1517
1551 N Tustin Ave, Santa Ana CA 92705
Tel (714) 619-9700 *SIC* 7381 7349

DMS FACILITY SERVICES INC p 446
1040 Arroyo Dr, South Pasadena CA 91030
Tel (626) 305-8500 *SIC* 7349

DMS FACILITY SERVICES LLC p 446
1040 Arroyo Dr, South Pasadena CA 91030
Tel (626) 305-8500 *SIC* 8711 7349 0781

GLOBAL BUILDING SERVICES INC p 616
25129 The Old Rd Ste 102, Stevenson Ranch CA 91381
Tel (661) 288-5733 *SIC* 7349

RESOURCE COLLECTION INC p 1227
3771 W 242nd St Ste 205, Torrance CA 90505
Tel (310) 219-3272
SIC 7349 7381 0782 3564

AMERI-KLEEN p 67
119 W Beach St, Watsonville CA 95076
Tel (831) 722-8888 *SIC* 7349

AFFINECO LLC p 32
855 Main St Ste 900, Bridgeport CT 06604
Tel (203) 878-0638 *SIC* 7349 7382

UNITED SERVICES OF AMERICA INC p 1511
855 Main St Ste 900, Bridgeport CT 06604
Tel (203) 878-0638 *SIC* 7349

PRITCHARD INDUSTRIES (NEW ENGLAND) INC p 1178
111 Court St, New Haven CT 06511
Tel (203) 624-3200 *SIC* 7349

▲ EMCOR GROUP INC p 491
301 Merritt 7 Fl 6, Norwalk CT 06851
Tel (203) 849-7800 *SIC* 1731 1711 7349

CNA HOLDING CORP p 329
350 Sw 12th Ave, Deerfield Beach FL 33442
Tel (561) 922-2500 *SIC* 7349 6794

COVERALL NORTH AMERICA INC p 385
350 Sw 12th Ave, Deerfield Beach FL 33442
Tel (561) 922-2500 *SIC* 6794 7349

ROYAL SERVICES INC p 1254
4526 Lenox Ave, Jacksonville FL 32205
Tel (904) 386-6436 *SIC* 7349 7371

AMERICAN SALES AND MANAGEMENT ORGANIZATION LLC p 79
7200 Corp Ctr Dr Ste 206, Miami FL 33126
Tel (305) 269-2700 *SIC* 7382 7349 7363

HARVARD MAINTENANCE INC p 666
2 S Biscayne Blvd # 3650, Miami FL 33131
Tel (305) 351-7300 *SIC* 7349

SUNSHINE CLEANING SYSTEMS INC p 1404
3445 Ne 12th Ter, Oakland Park FL 33334
Tel (954) 772-0884 *SIC* 7349

SHAMROCK ACQUISITION CORP p 1311
10540 Belcher Rd S, Seminole FL 33777
Tel (727) 209-0553 *SIC* 7349

AETNA MAINTENANCE INC p 31
101 E Kennedy Blvd G102, Tampa FL 33602
Tel (813) 621-6878 *SIC* 7349

DIVERSIFIED MAINTENANCE SYSTEMS LLC p 444
5110 Sunforest Dr Ste 250, Tampa FL 33634
Tel (800) 351-1557 *SIC* 7349

BURKS COMPANIES p 227
191 Peachtree St Ne # 800, Atlanta GA 30303
Tel (404) 589-4600
SIC 1752 5085 7349 4953 8999

ICS CONTRACT SERVICES LLC p 728
1251 Marietta Blvd Nw, Atlanta GA 30318
Tel (404) 367-8286 *SIC* 7349

SIZEMORE INC p 1328
2116 Walton Way, Augusta GA 30904
Tel (706) 736-1456 *SIC* 7381 7363 7349

KIMCO FACILITY SERVICES LLC p 818
6055 Lakeside Commons Dr, Macon GA 31210
Tel (478) 752-7000 *SIC* 7349

PROFESSIONAL SYSTEMS LLC p 1180
6055 Lakeside Ste 440, Macon GA 31210
Tel (478) 752-7000 *SIC* 7349 7361

AQUILEX HOLDINGS LLC p 101
2225 Skyland Ct, Norcross GA 30071
Tel (678) 728-9100 *SIC* 7349

INITIAL CONTRACT SERVICES INC p 743
1780 Corporate Dr Ste 440, Norcross GA 30093
Tel (678) 812-3079 *SIC* 7349

US SECURITY ASSOCIATES HOLDINGS INC p 1533
200 Mansell Ct E Fl 5, Roswell GA 30076
Tel (770) 625-1500 *SIC* 7381 7349

US SECURITY HOLDINGS INC p 1533
200 Mansell Ct E Ste 500, Roswell GA 30076
Tel (770) 625-1400 *SIC* 7381 7349

VARSITY CONTRACTORS INC p 1545
315 S 5th Ave, Pocatello ID 83201
Tel (208) 232-8598 *SIC* 7349

FCC ENTERPRISES INC p 533
1641 Barclay Blvd, Buffalo Grove IL 60089
Tel (847) 279-7360 *SIC* 7349

A B M INC p 5
180 N Lasalle St Ste 1700, Chicago IL 60601
Tel (312) 469-1643 *SIC* 7349

CARYLON CORP p 262
2500 W Arthington St, Chicago IL 60612
Tel (312) 666-7700
SIC 7699 1629 7349 8748 4959

PROSPECT AIRPORT SERVICES INC p 1184
2130 S Wolf Rd Fl 2, Des Plaines IL 60018
Tel (847) 299-3636 *SIC* 4581 7349

■ ARAMARK MANAGEMENT SERVICES LIMITED PARTNERSHIP p 102
2300 Warrenville Rd, Downers Grove IL 60515
Tel (630) 271-2000 *SIC* 7349

CAPITAL BUILDING SERVICES GROUP INC p 249
540 Capital Dr Ste 100, Lake Zurich IL 60047
Tel (847) 847-3800 *SIC* 7349

MILLARD GROUP INC p 969
7301 N Cicero Ave, Lincolnwood IL 60712
Tel (847) 674-4100 *SIC* 7349

VONACHEN SERVICES INC p 1565
8900 N Pioneer Rd, Peoria IL 61615
Tel (309) 691-6202
SIC 7349 4731 8741 7361

LACOSTA INC p 837
440 W Bonner Rd, Wauconda IL 60084
Tel (847) 526-9556 *SIC* 7349

A & R JANITORIAL SERVICE INC p 4
10127 W Roosevelt Rd, Westchester IL 60154
Tel (708) 656-8300 *SIC* 7349

EXECUTIVE MANAGEMENT SERVICES OF INDIANA INC p 517
4177 N Ems Blvd, Indianapolis IN 46250
Tel (317) 813-1490 *SIC* 7349

GSF USA INC p 643
2701 Fortune Cir E Ste D, Indianapolis IN 46241
Tel (317) 262-4958 *SIC* 7349

PACKERS HOLDINGS LLC p 1107
1010 E Washington St # 202, Mount Pleasant IA 52641
Tel (800) 881-9558 *SIC* 7342 7349

CITY WIDE HOLDING CO INC p 320
15447 W 100th Ter, Lenexa KS 66219
Tel (913) 888-5700
SIC 1542 1522 5087 7349

CORPORATE CLEANING SYSTEMS INC p 372
3370 Turfway Rd Ste 190, Erlanger KY 41018
Tel (859) 371-5252 *SIC* 7349

DIVISIONS INC p 444
1 Riverfront Pl Ste 500, Newport KY 41071
Tel (859) 448-9730 *SIC* 7349

TURNER INDUSTRIAL MAINTENANCE LLC p 1492
8687 United Plaza Blvd, Baton Rouge LA 70809
Tel (225) 922-5050 *SIC* 7349

UNITED SITE SERVICES OF MISSISSIPPI LLC p 1511
9486 Highway 23, Belle Chasse LA 70037
Tel (866) 356-5615 *SIC* 7349

OMNI ENERGY SERVICES CORP p 1084
4500 Ne Evangeline Trwy, Carencro LA 70520
Tel (337) 896-6664 *SIC* 1382 1389 7349

ABACUS CORP p 9
610 Gusryan St, Baltimore MD 21224
Tel (410) 633-1900 *SIC* 7381 7363 7349

BROADWAY SERVICES INC p 216
3709 E Monument St, Baltimore MD 21205
Tel (410) 563-6900
SIC 7349 7381 7521 6512 4119

ECO GSI CONSTRUCTION AND MAINTENANCE LLC p 475
6917 Arlington Rd, Bethesda MD 20814
Tel (240) 832-8035 *SIC* 7349

RED COATS INC p 1215
4520 East West Hwy # 200, Bethesda MD 20814
Tel (301) 654-4360 *SIC* 7349 7381

UNITED STATES SERVICE INDUSTRIES INC p 1514
4340 East West Hwy # 204, Bethesda MD 20814
Tel (202) 783-2030 *SIC* 7349

CBMC CAPITAL BUILDING MAINTENANCE CORP p 268
5018 College Ave, College Park MD 20740
Tel (301) 277-8000 *SIC* 7349

SODEXHO INC p 1337
9801 Washingtonian Blvd # 1, Gaithersburg MD 20878
Tel (301) 987-4000 *SIC* 5812 7349

SODEXO OPERATIONS LLC p 1337
9801 Washingtonian Blvd, Gaithersburg MD 20878
Tel (301) 987-4000 *SIC* 8741 5812 7349

GALI SERVICE INDUSTRIES INC p 589
12312 Wilkins Ave Ste 100, Rockville MD 20852
Tel (301) 986-8890 *SIC* 7349

INTEGRATED SERVICE MANAGEMENT LLC p 749
12312 Wilkins Ave, Rockville MD 20852
Tel (703) 480-2671 *SIC* 7349

UNITED SITE SERVICES OF MARYLAND INC p 1511
3250 Old Washington Rd, Waldorf MD 20602
Tel (301) 396-8501 *SIC* 7349

C&W FACILITY SERVICES INC p 234
275 Grove St Ste 3-200, Auburndale MA 02466
Tel (617) 527-5222 *SIC* 7349 6531

DTZ GOVERNMENT SERVICES INC p 458
275 Grove St Ste 3-200, Auburndale MA 02466
Tel (617) 527-5222 *SIC* 7349

UG2 LLC p 1499
1 International Pl # 1402, Boston MA 02110
Tel (617) 279-8100 *SIC* 7349

SUBURBAN CONTRACT CLEANING INC p 1396
65 Bay State Dr Ste 4, Braintree MA 02184
Tel (781) 356-4400 *SIC* 7349

AMERICAN CLEANING CO INC p 70
94 Lincoln St, Brighton MA 02135
Tel (617) 562-4000 *SIC* 7349

CLEANING SERVICE GROUP INC p 324
230 North St, Danvers MA 01923
Tel (978) 750-8900 *SIC* 7349

JANITRONICS INC p 777
29 Sawyer Rd Ste 11, Waltham MA 02453
Tel (781) 647-5570 *SIC* 7349

SYLVANIA LIGHTING SERVICES CORP p 1414
200 Ballardvale St, Wilmington MA 01887
Tel (978) 570-3000 *SIC* 7349

TPG HOLDINGS LLC p 1467
719 Griswold St Ste 2100, Detroit MI 48226
Tel (313) 496-3500 *SIC* 7349

CARAVAN FACILITIES MANAGEMENT LLC p 252
1400 Weiss St Ste 1, Saginaw MI 48602
Tel (989) 239-2126 *SIC* 7349

GDI FACILITY SERVICES INC p 595
24300 Southfield Rd # 220, Southfield MI 48075
Tel (248) 483-3170 *SIC* 7349

GDI SERVICES INC p 595
24300 Southfield Rd # 220, Southfield MI 48075
Tel (248) 483-3170 *SIC* 7349

ISS WORLDWIDE p 767
1225 E 18th St, Kansas City MO 64108
Tel (816) 421-8088 *SIC* 7349 7381

4M BUILDING SOLUTIONS INC p 3
2827 Clark Ave, Saint Louis MO 63103
Tel (314) 535-2100 *SIC* 7349

■ ABM INDUSTRIES INC p 12
500 S Ewing Ave Ste A, Saint Louis MO 63103
Tel (314) 241-1975 *SIC* 7349

INTERSTATE CLEANING CORP p 758
1566 N Warson Rd, Saint Louis MO 63132
Tel (314) 428-0566 *SIC* 7349

FBG SERVICE CORP p 532
407 S 27th Ave, Omaha NE 68131
Tel (402) 346-4422 *SIC* 7349

DON HENRY JR & SONS p 450
Rr Box 12a, Plainfield NH 03781
Tel (603) 298-8551 *SIC* 7349

C&H INDUSTRIAL SERVICES INC p 234
542 Penny St, Franklinville NJ 08322
Tel (856) 875-8152 *SIC* 7349 1542

BRAVO BUILDING SERVICES INC p 209
29 King George Rd, Green Brook NJ 08812
Tel (732) 465-0707 *SIC* 7349

ISS TMC SERVICES INC p 767
81 Dorsa Ave, Livingston NJ 07039
Tel (973) 740-0032 *SIC* 6512 7349 7699

ALLAN INDUSTRIES INC p 51
270 Us Highway 46 Ste E, Rockaway NJ 07866
Tel (973) 586-9400 *SIC* 1521 7349 1799

RONELL INDUSTRIES INC p 1249
298 Cox St, Roselle NJ 07203
Tel (908) 245-5255 *SIC* 7349 2842

CONTROL BUILDING SERVICES INC p 364
333 Meadowlands Pkwy Fl 1, Secaucus NJ 07094
Tel (201) 864-1900 *SIC* 7349 0782

USI SERVICES GROUP INC p 1535
51 Progress St, Union NJ 07083
Tel (973) 376-6000 *SIC* 7349

ACA INDUSTRIES INC p 13
385 W Main St, Babylon NY 11702
Tel (631) 587-2485 *SIC* 7349

NORTH AMERICAN INDUSTRIAL SERVICES INC p 1050
1240 Saratoga Rd, Ballston Spa NY 12020
Tel (518) 885-1820 *SIC* 7349

WHELANS INTERNATIONAL CO INC p 1605
163 Keyland Ct, Bohemia NY 11716
Tel (631) 244-6962 *SIC* 7349

WHITE GLOVE PLACEMENT INC p 1606
630 Flushing Ave Fl 2, Brooklyn NY 11206
Tel (718) 387-8181 *SIC* 7349

AMERICAN INDUSTRIAL CLEANING CO INC p 74
10 Chelsea Pl, Great Neck NY 11021
Tel (516) 482-8424 *SIC* 7349

MARK GOLDEN MAINTENANCE LTD INC p 907
420 Doughty Blvd Ste 4, Inwood NY 11096
Tel (516) 239-3400 *SIC* 7349 5087

▲ ABM INDUSTRIES INC p 12
1 Liberty Plz Fl Con1, New York NY 10006
Tel (212) 297-0200
SIC 7349 7521 7381 8711

■ ABM ONSITE SERVICES INC p 12
1 Liberty Plz Fl 7, New York NY 10006
Tel (212) 497-0600
SIC 7349 7381 7521 8711

BUILDING MAINTENANCE SERVICE LLC p 225
11 Penn Plz, New York NY 10001
Tel (212) 714-0004 *SIC* 7349

■ **FOREST ELECTRIC CORP** p 566
1375 Broadway Fl 7, New York NY 10018
Tel (212) 318-1500 *SIC* 1731 7349

GUARDIAN SERVICE INDUSTRIES INC p 645
161 Ave Of The Amer, New York NY 10013
Tel (212) 645-9500 *SIC* 7349

HARVEST PARTNERS LP p 666
280 Park Ave Fl 25w, New York NY 10017
Tel (212) 599-6300 *SIC* 6799 7349

PRITCHARD INDUSTRIES INC p 1178
1120 Ave Of The Amrcs 17r, New York NY 10036
Tel (212) 382-2295 *SIC* 7349

QUALITY BUILDING SERVICES CORP p 1196
801 2nd Ave Fl 8, New York NY 10017
Tel (212) 883-0009 *SIC* 7349

TEMCO SERVICE INDUSTRIES INC p 1436
417 5th Ave Fl 9, New York NY 10016
Tel (212) 889-6353 *SIC* 7349 7342 6289

HURLEY OF AMERICA INC p 721
803 Linden Ave Ste 3, Rochester NY 14625
Tel (781) 438-7830 *SIC* 7349 7382

TRIANGLE SERVICES INC p 1478
10 5th St Ste 200, Valley Stream NY 11581
Tel (516) 561-1700
SIC 7349 4581 1799 7382

A & A MAINTENANCE ENTERPRISE INC p 4
965 Midland Ave, Yonkers NY 10704
Tel (914) 969-0009
SIC 7349 1721 1542 4959 0782

WALLICO MAINTENANCE GROUP LLC p 1573
965 Midland Ave, Yonkers NY 10704
Tel (914) 595-0664 *SIC* 7349

GCA SERVICES GROUP OF NORTH CAROLINA INC p 595
1 Centerview Dr Ste 109, Greensboro NC 27407
Tel (336) 294-9411 *SIC* 7349 7363

BUDD GROUP INC p 223
2325 S Stratford Rd, Winston Salem NC 27103
Tel (336) 765-9324 *SIC* 0781 7349

VIUS SERVICES CORP p 1563
9395 Kenwood Rd Ste 200, Blue Ash OH 45242
Tel (513) 731-3590 *SIC* 7349 8741 3714

DCS SANITATION MANAGEMENT INC p 419
7864 Camargo Rd, Cincinnati OH 45243
Tel (513) 891-4980 *SIC* 7349 7342

CHEMICAL SOLVENTS INC p 293
3751 Jennings Rd, Cleveland OH 44109
Tel (216) 741-9310
SIC 5169 7349 3471 2992

GCA SERVICES GROUP INC p 595
1350 Euclid Ave Ste 1500, Cleveland OH 44115
Tel (216) 535-4900 *SIC* 7349

BLANCHARD VALLEY HEALTH SYSTEM p 188
1900 S Main St, Findlay OH 45840
Tel (419) 423-4500 *SIC* 8741 7349

MPW INDUSTRIAL SERVICES GROUP INC p 996
9711 Lancaster Rd, Hebron OH 43025
Tel (740) 927-8790 *SIC* 7349 8744 3589

MPW INDUSTRIAL SERVICES INC p 996
9711 Lancaster Rd, Hebron OH 43025
Tel (800) 827-8790 *SIC* 7349

C & K INDUSTRIAL SERVICES INC p 231
5617 E Schaaf Rd, Independence OH 44131
Tel (216) 642-0055 *SIC* 4959 7349

KELLERMEYER BERGENSONS SERVICES LLC p 808
1575 Henthorne Dr, Maumee OH 43537
Tel (419) 867-4300 *SIC* 7349

▲ **MATRIX SERVICE CO** p 920
5100 E Skelly Dr Ste 700, Tulsa OK 74135
Tel (918) 838-8822
SIC 1542 1623 7349 8711

▲ **HEALTHCARE SERVICES GROUP INC** p 676
3220 Tillman Dr Ste 300, Bensalem PA 19020
Tel (215) 639-4274 *SIC* 8059 7349 8049

SUMMIT SERVICES GROUP INC p 1399
3220 Tillman Dr Ste 300, Bensalem PA 19020
Tel (215) 639-4274 *SIC* 7213 7349

CROTHALL SERVICES GROUP p 394
1500 Liberty Ridge Dr # 210, Chesterbrook PA 19087
Tel (610) 576-5100 *SIC* 7349

LAUREL HOLDINGS INC p 847
111 Roosevelt Blvd, Johnstown PA 15906
Tel (814) 533-5777
SIC 4941 5063 3599 4724 7349

GDI SERVICES INC p 595
780 5th Ave Ste 115, King Of Prussia PA 19406
Tel (610) 584-0888 *SIC* 7349

MATRIX LLC p 920
780 5th Ave Ste 115, King Of Prussia PA 19406
Tel (607) 766-0700 *SIC* 7349

XANITOS INC p 1630
3809 West Chester Pike # 210, Newtown Square PA 19073
Tel (484) 654-2300 *SIC* 7349

■ **ARAMARK FACILITY SERVICES LLC** p 102
1101 Market St, Philadelphia PA 19107
Tel (215) 238-3000 *SIC* 7349

ELLIOTT-LEWIS CORP p 488
2900 Black Lake Pl, Philadelphia PA 19154
Tel (215) 698-4400 *SIC* 1711 7349 7353

ASSOCIATED CLEANING CONSULTANTS AND SERVICES INC p 120
431 Davidson Rd, Pittsburgh PA 15239
Tel (412) 795-9200 *SIC* 7349 8742

ST MORITZ BUILDING SERVICES INC p 1372
4616 Clairton Blvd, Pittsburgh PA 15236
Tel (412) 885-2100 *SIC* 7349 5087

BUDGET MAINTENANCE CONCRETE SERVICES INC p 224
135 Walnut St, Pottstown PA 19464
Tel (610) 323-7702 *SIC* 5087 7349

NATIONAL BUILDING MAINTENANCE CORP p 1010
855 Ave Hostos, Ponce PR 00716
Tel (787) 290-7020 *SIC* 7349 5169

AMERICAN SERVICES INC p 79
1300 Rutherford Rd, Greenville SC 29609
Tel (864) 292-7450 *SIC* 7381 7349 7363

GREENWOOD INC p 639
160 Milestone Way Ste A, Greenville SC 29615
Tel (864) 288-5510 *SIC* 1541 7349

IH SERVICES INC p 730
127 Tanner Rd, Greenville SC 29607
Tel (864) 297-3748 *SIC* 7349 5014 7217

DEFENDER SERVICES INC p 422
9031 Garners Ferry Rd, Hopkins SC 29061
Tel (803) 776-4220 *SIC* 7349 7361 7382

DIVERSCO HOLDINGS INC p 443
105 Diversco Dr, Spartanburg SC 29307
Tel (864) 579-3420 *SIC* 7381 7349

THOMPSON CONSTRUCTION GROUP INC p 1449
100 N Main St, Sumter SC 29150
Tel (803) 773-8005
SIC 7349 1711 1721 1541

ERMC II LP p 508
1 Park Pl 6148, Chattanooga TN 37421
Tel (423) 899-2753 *SIC* 7349 7382

ERMC III PROPERTY MANAGEMENT CO LLC p 508
6148 Lee Hwy Ste 300, Chattanooga TN 37421
Tel (423) 899-2753 *SIC* 7349

■ **SOUTHERN MANAGEMENT CORP** p 1349
5751 Uptain Rd Ste 408, Chattanooga TN 37411
Tel (423) 510-0010 *SIC* 7349

MASTERCORP INC p 918
3505 N Main St, Crossville TN 38555
Tel (931) 484-1752 *SIC* 7349 7217

SERVPRO INTELLECTUAL PROPERTY INC p 1308
801 Industrial Blvd, Gallatin TN 37066
Tel (615) 451-0200 *SIC* 7349 8741 5087

SOUTHEAST SERVICE CORP p 1346
1845 Midpark Rd Ste 201, Knoxville TN 37921
Tel (865) 546-8880 *SIC* 7349

■ **MERRY MAIDS LIMITED PARTNERSHIP** p 950
860 Ridge Lake Blvd Fl 3, Memphis TN 38120
Tel (901) 597-8100 *SIC* 7349

■ **SERVICEMASTER CO LLC** p 1307
860 Ridge Lake Blvd Fl 3, Memphis TN 38120
Tel (901) 597-1400
SIC 7349 7342 1711 1731 7641

■ **SERVICEMASTER CONSUMER SERVICES LIMITED PARTNERSHIP** p 1307
889 Ridge Lake Blvd Fl 2, Memphis TN 38120
Tel (901) 597-7574 *SIC* 0782 6351 7349

SERVICEMASTER HOLDING CORP p 1308
860 Ridge Lake Blvd, Memphis TN 38120
Tel (901) 597-1400
SIC 0782 7342 1711 1731 7349 7641

STRATOS INC p 1392
66 N Main St, Memphis TN 38103
Tel (901) 683-0064 *SIC* 7349

SMS HOLDINGS CORP p 1334
7135 Charlotte Pike # 100, Nashville TN 37209
Tel (615) 399-1839 *SIC* 7349

YATES SERVICES LLC p 1635
983 Nissan Dr, Smyrna TN 37167
Tel (615) 459-1701 *SIC* 7349

JANI-KING INTERNATIONAL INC p 777
16885 Dallas Pkwy, Addison TX 75001
Tel (972) 991-0900 *SIC* 7349

HOSPITAL HOUSEKEEPING SYSTEMS INC p 709
811 Barton Springs Rd # 300, Austin TX 78704
Tel (512) 478-1888 *SIC* 7349

HOSPITAL HOUSEKEEPING SYSTEMS LLC p 709
216 E 4th St, Austin TX 78701
Tel (512) 478-1888 *SIC* 7349

KINGS BAY SERVICES GROUP LLC p 820
3755 S Cptl Of Tx Hwy # 35, Austin TX 78704
Tel (931) 241-1183 *SIC* 7349

PROFESSIONAL CONTRACT SERVICES INC p 1180
718 W Fm 1626 Bldg 100, Austin TX 78748
Tel (512) 358-8887 *SIC* 7349

HYDROCHEM LLC p 723
900 Georgia Ave, Deer Park TX 77536
Tel (713) 393-5600 *SIC* 7349

INTERSTATE RESTORATION LLC p 758
3401 Quorum Dr Ste 300, Fort Worth TX 76137
Tel (817) 293-0035 *SIC* 1542 1522 7349

BMS ENTERPRISES INC p 194
5718 Airport Fwy, Haltom City TX 76117
Tel (877) 730-1948 *SIC* 7349

■ **ABM JANITORIAL SERVICES INC** p 12
1111 Fannin St Ste 1500, Houston TX 77002
Tel (713) 654-8924 *SIC* 7349

AZTEC FACILITY SERVICES INC p 140
11000 S Wilcrest Dr Ste 1, Houston TX 77099
Tel (281) 668-9000 *SIC* 7349

BROCK HOLDINGS III INC p 216
10343 Sam Houston Park Dr, Houston TX 77064
Tel (281) 807-8200 *SIC* 1721 7349

MUNDY CONTRACT MAINTENANCE INC p 1000
11150 S Wilcrest Dr # 300, Houston TX 77099
Tel (281) 530-8711 *SIC* 7349

PRITCHARD INDUSTRIES SOUTHWEST INC p 1178
4040 Directors Row, Houston TX 77092
Tel (713) 957-1387 *SIC* 7349

PRESTIGE MAINTENANCE USA LTD p 1173
1808 10th St Ste 300, Plano TX 75074
Tel (800) 321-4773 *SIC* 7349

ISS FACILITY SERVICES HOLDING INC p 767
1019 Central Pkwy N # 100, San Antonio TX 78232
Tel (210) 495-6021 *SIC* 7349

ISS HOLDING INC p 767
1019 Central Pkwy N # 100, San Antonio TX 78232
Tel (210) 495-6021 *SIC* 7349

MANAGEMENT & TRAINING CORP p 900
500 N Market Place Dr # 100, Centerville UT 84014
Tel (801) 693-2600
SIC 8744 8331 7349 8741 8249

TWO GUYS SERVICE LLC p 1495
45662 Terminal Dr, Dulles VA 20166
Tel (703) 481-0222 *SIC* 7349 1541

CAVALIER MAINTENANCE SERVICES INC p 267
2722 Merrilee Dr Ste 300, Fairfax VA 22031
Tel (703) 849-1100 *SIC* 7349

P & R ENTERPRISES INC p 1102
5681 Columbia Pike # 101, Falls Church VA 22041
Tel (703) 379-2018 *SIC* 7349

■ **NORTHROP GRUMMAN ENTERPRISE MANAGEMENT SERVICES CORP** p 1058
2340 Dulles Corner Blvd, Herndon VA 20171
Tel (703) 713-4000
SIC 8741 8744 4731 8331 7349

DIDLAKE INC p 438
8641 Breeden Ave Ste 101, Manassas VA 20110
Tel (703) 361-4195
SIC 8331 7331 7349 7334

FITZ VOGT & ASSOCIATES LTD p 553
21 Armory Dr Ste L-1, Wheeling WV 26003
Tel (603) 644-0117 *SIC* 5812 8742 7349

GOODWILL INDUSTRIES OF SOUTHEASTERN WISCONSIN INC p 625
5400 S 60th St, Greendale WI 53129
Tel (414) 847-4200 *SIC* 8331 7349

KAISER CONTRACT CLEANING SPECIALISTS LLC p 800
3691 Prism Ln, Kieler WI 53812
Tel (608) 568-3413 *SIC* 7349

CLEAN POWER LLC p 324
124 N 121st St, Milwaukee WI 53226
Tel (414) 302-3000 *SIC* 7349 7217

S C JOHNSON & SON INC p 1262
1525 Howe St, Racine WI 53403
Tel (262) 260-2000
SIC 2842 2844 2879 2865 7342 7349

SIC 7352 Medical Eqpt Rental & Leasing

■ **GADSDEN REGIONAL MEDICAL CENTER LLC** p 589
1007 Goodyear Ave, Gadsden AL 35903
Tel (256) 494-4000
SIC 8062 8082 8011 7352

SAAD ENTERPRISES INC p 1263
1515 S University Blvd, Mobile AL 36609
Tel (251) 343-9600
SIC 8082 5047 7352 5912 5621 8741

FOUNDERS HEALTHCARE LLC p 571
4601 E Hilton Ave Ste 100, Phoenix AZ 85034
Tel (800) 636-2123 *SIC* 7352

APRIA HEALTHCARE LLC p 100
26220 Enterprise Ct, Lake Forest CA 92630
Tel (949) 616-2606 *SIC* 5047 7352 5999

TERUMO BCT INC p 1440
10811 W Collins Ave, Lakewood CO 80215
Tel (303) 232-6800
SIC 8733 3842 3845 5047 7352 7699

BAYCARE HOME CARE INC p 161
8452 118th Ave, Largo FL 33773
Tel (727) 394-6461 *SIC* 8082 7352

HIG CAPITAL PARTNERS III LP p 690
1450 Brickell Ave # 3100, Miami FL 33131
Tel (305) 379-2322
SIC 6211 5084 7352 7699 8748 3842

UNIVITA OF FLORIDA INC p 1528
15800 Sw 25th St, Miramar FL 33027
Tel (305) 826-0244 *SIC* 5047 7352

ROTECH HEALTHCARE INC p 1252
3600 Vineland Rd Ste 114, Orlando FL 32811
Tel (407) 822-4600 *SIC* 7352

NORCO INC p 1047
1125 W Amity Rd, Boise ID 83705
Tel (208) 336-1643
SIC 5084 5169 7352 5999 3548 2813

▲ **HILL-ROM HOLDINGS INC** p 693
2 Prudential Plz Ste 4100, Chicago IL 60601
Tel (312) 819-7200 *SIC* 3841 7352

■ **HILL-ROM CO INC** p 693
1069 State Road 46 E, Batesville IN 47006
Tel (812) 934-7777 *SIC* 7352

■ **HILL-ROM INC** p 693
1069 State Route 46 E, Batesville IN 47006
Tel (812) 934-7777 *SIC* 7352 2599

WILLIAMS BROS HEALTH CARE PHARMACY INC p 1611
10 Williams Brothers Dr, Washington IN 47501
Tel (812) 254-2497
SIC 5047 7352 5999 5169 3999

HEALTH CARE INC p 674
1701 E 23rd Ave, Hutchinson KS 67502
Tel (620) 665-2000 *SIC* 8062 7352 6512

MEDICAL SPECIALTIES DISTRIBUTORS LLC p 937
800 Technology Center Dr # 3, Stoughton MA 02072
Tel (781) 344-6000 *SIC* 5047 7352

RELIANT MEDICAL GROUP INC p 1222
630 Plantation St, Worcester MA 01605
Tel (508) 368-5400 *SIC* 8011 7352 5912

WRIGHT & FILIPPIS INC p 1627
2845 Crooks Rd, Rochester Hills MI 48309
Tel (248) 829-8292 *SIC* 7352 5999

UNIVERSAL HOSPITAL SERVICES INC p 1517
6625 W 78th St Ste 300, Minneapolis MN 55439
Tel (952) 893-3200 *SIC* 7352

■ **D B INDUSTRIES INC** p 406
3833 Sala Way, Red Wing MN 55066
Tel (651) 388-8282 *SIC* 5099 5084 7352

SKAGGS COMMUNITY HOSPITAL ASSOCIATION p 1329
251 Skaggs Rd, Branson MO 65616
Tel (417) 335-7000
SIC 8062 8082 8011 7352 8051

KALISPELL REGIONAL HEALTHCARE SYSTEM p 801
310 Sunnyview Ln, Kalispell MT 59901
Tel (406) 752-8991
SIC 8051 8011 4522 7352

COMMUNITY SURGICAL SUPPLY OF TOMS RIVER INC p 350
1390 Rte 37 W, Toms River NJ 08755
Tel (732) 349-2990 *SIC* 5047 7352 5912

AMBERCARE CORP p 65
420 N Main St, Belen NM 87002
Tel (505) 861-0060
SIC 8082 8361 5047 7352

UHS HOLDCO INC p 1500
383 Madison Ave Fl 40, New York NY 10179
Tel (212) 272-2000 *SIC* 7352 5047

ALTRU HEALTH SYSTEM p 63
1200 S Columbia Rd, Grand Forks ND 58201
Tel (701) 780-5000
SIC 7352 8011 8062 8063

FAIRFIELD MEDICAL CENTER p 525
401 N Ewing St, Lancaster OH 43130
Tel (740) 687-8000 *SIC* 8062 7352 5999

ST RITAS MEDICAL CENTER p 1373
730 W Market St, Lima OH 45801
Tel (419) 227-3361 *SIC* 8062 7352

AHS OKLAHOMA HEALTH SYSTEM LLP p 37
110 W 7th St Ste 2540, Tulsa OK 74119
Tel (918) 579-1000
SIC 8062 8069 7352 6512 7389 5999

SAINT FRANCIS HOSPITAL INC p 1269
6161 S Yale Ave, Tulsa OK 74136
Tel (918) 502-2050 *SIC* 8062 7352 5999

AMERICAN HOMECARE SUPPLY LLC p 74
101 W Elm St Ste 210, Conshohocken PA 19428
Tel (484) 530-0880 *SIC* 5999 7352

CHARLES COLE MEMORIAL HOSPITAL p 289
1001 E 2nd St, Coudersport PA 16915
Tel (814) 274-9300 *SIC* 7352 8069 8051

HOME CARE PRODUCTS & PHARMACY p 703
1 Hospital Dr, Lewisburg PA 17837
Tel (570) 522-2000 *SIC* 5912 7352 5999

GUTHRIE HEALTHCARE SYSTEM p 648
1 Guthrie Sq Ste B, Sayre PA 18840
Tel (570) 888-6666 *SIC* 8011 7352 8741

MEDICAL SERVICES OF AMERICA INC p 937
171 Monroe Ln, Lexington SC 29072
Tel (803) 957-0500
SIC 8082 8741 8011 8071 7352 5999

CHIRON HOLDINGS INC p 301
12930 W Interstate 10, San Antonio TX 78249
Tel (210) 524-9000 *SIC* 2599 7352

KCI USA INC p 806
12930 W Interstate 10, San Antonio TX 78249
Tel (800) 275-4524 *SIC* 7352 3842 5047

SCOTT & WHITE MEMORIAL HOSPITAL p 1293
2401 S 31st St, Temple TX 76508
Tel (254) 724-2111
SIC 8062 6512 7352 7363

UINTAH BASIN MEDICAL CENTER p 1500
250 W 300 N, Roosevelt UT 84066
Tel (435) 725-2008
SIC 8062 8082 7352 8092 8361

RUTLAND REGIONAL HEALTH SERVICES p 1260
160 Allen St, Rutland VT 05701
Tel (802) 775-7111 *SIC* 8062 7352 8059

NORCO INC p 1047
101 E Stuart Rd, Bellingham WA 98226
Tel (360) 746-0826 *SIC* 7352

NORCO INC p 1047
3030 Hoyt Ave, Everett WA 98201
Tel (425) 205-4200 *SIC* 7352

BELLIN HEALTH SYSTEMS INC p 170
744 S Webster Ave, Green Bay WI 54301
Tel (920) 433-3500 *SIC* 8062 8063 7352

SIC 7353 Heavy Construction Eqpt Rental & Leasing

EMPIRE SOUTHWEST LLC p 493
1725 S Country Club Dr, Mesa AZ 85210
Tel (480) 633-4000 *SIC* 5082 7353 7699

WHITEMAN FAMILY CORP p 1606
1725 S Country Club Dr, Mesa AZ 85210
Tel (480) 633-4413
SIC 5082 5083 7353 7699 7359 5012

ROAD MACHINERY LLC p 1240
4710 E Elwood St Ste 6, Phoenix AZ 85040
Tel (602) 256-5128
SIC 5082 7359 7699 7353 7629

SUNSTATE EQUIPMENT CO LLC p 1404
5552 E Washington St, Phoenix AZ 85034
Tel (602) 275-2398 *SIC* 7359 7353

RSC EQUIPMENT RENTAL INC p 1255
6929 E Greenway Pkwy # 200, Scottsdale AZ 85254
Tel (480) 905-3300 *SIC* 7353

HUGG AND HALL EQUIPMENT CO p 717
7201 Scott Hamilton Dr, Little Rock AR 72209
Tel (501) 562-1262
SIC 5084 5082 7353 7699 5083 3531

PACIFIC PROCESS SYSTEMS INC p 1105
7401 Rosedale Hwy, Bakersfield CA 93308
Tel (661) 321-9681 *SIC* 1389 7353 5082

QUINN CO p 1200
10006 Rose Hills Rd, City Of Industry CA 90601
Tel (562) 463-4000
SIC 5082 5083 5084 7353

QUINN GROUP INC p 1200
10006 Rose Hills Rd, City Of Industry CA 90601
Tel (562) 463-4000
SIC 5084 5082 7353 7359

BRAGG INVESTMENT CO INC p 207
6251 N Paramount Blvd, Long Beach CA 90805
Tel (562) 984-2400 *SIC* 7389 7353 1791

IRWIN INDUSTRIES INC p 765
1580 W Carson St, Long Beach CA 90810
Tel (310) 233-3000
SIC 1629 1731 1796 7353 1542

NATIONAL BUSINESS GROUP INC p 1010
15319 Chatsworth St, Mission Hills CA 91345
Tel (818) 221-6000
SIC 7353 5039 7359 3496 7519

NATIONAL CONSTRUCTION RENTALS INC p 1011
15319 Chatsworth St, Mission Hills CA 91345
Tel (818) 221-6000 *SIC* 7353

MCGUIRE AND HESTER p 929
9009 Railroad Ave, Oakland CA 94603
Tel (510) 632-7676 *SIC* 1623 7353

HAWTHORNE MACHINERY CO p 670
16945 Camino San Bernardo, San Diego CA 92127
Tel (858) 674-7000
SIC 7353 7699 5082 7359

BECHTEL CONSTRUCTION OPERATIONS INC p 167
50 Beale St Bsmt 1, San Francisco CA 94105
Tel (415) 768-1234
SIC 1541 1629 1623 8741 7353

PETERSON POWER SYSTEMS INC p 1138
2828 Teagarden St, San Leandro CA 94577
Tel (510) 618-2921 *SIC* 5084 7353

■ **WASTE MANAGEMENT COLLECTION AND RECYCLING INC** p 1580
1800 S Grand Ave, Santa Ana CA 92705
Tel (714) 637-3010 *SIC* 7353 4953

■ **TUTOR-SALIBA CORP** p 1493
15901 Olden St, Sylmar CA 91342
Tel (818) 362-8391
SIC 1542 1629 7353 1799 6552

WAGNER EQUIPMENT CO p 1571
18000 Smith Rd, Aurora CO 80011
Tel (303) 739-3000 *SIC* 5082 7699 7353

FMH MATERIAL HANDLING SOLUTIONS INC p 562
4105 Globeville Rd, Denver CO 80216
Tel (303) 292-5438 *SIC* 5084 7353 5013

SUPERIOR PRODUCTS DISTRIBUTORS INC p 1407
1403 Meriden Waterbury Rd, Milldale CT 06467
Tel (860) 621-3621
SIC 5074 5032 5082 7353

■ **UNITED RENTALS (NORTH AMERICA) INC** p 1511
100 Frist Stamford 700, Stamford CT 06902
Tel (203) 622-3131 *SIC* 7353 7359 5084

▲ **UNITED RENTALS INC** p 1511
100 1st Stamford Pl # 700, Stamford CT 06902
Tel (203) 622-3131 *SIC* 7359 7353

KELLY TRACTOR CO p 809
8255 Nw 58th St, Doral FL 33166
Tel (305) 592-5360
SIC 5082 5083 7359 7353 5084 7699

PANTROPIC POWER INC p 1112
8205 Nw 58th St, Doral FL 33166
Tel (305) 477-3329
SIC 5084 5085 5063 7353

LINDER INDUSTRIAL MACHINERY CO p 868
1601 S Frontage Rd # 100, Plant City FL 33563
Tel (813) 754-2727 *SIC* 5082 7353

RING POWER CORP p 1235
500 World Commerce Pkwy, Saint Augustine FL 32092
Tel (904) 201-7400 *SIC* 5082 5084 7353

YANCEY BROS CO p 1634
330 Lee Industrial Blvd # 1, Austell GA 30168
Tel (770) 941-2424
SIC 5082 5084 7699 7353

BRAMBLES USA INC (DEL) p 207
180 Technology Pkwy # 600, Norcross GA 30092
Tel (770) 776-1900
SIC 4953 4212 7353 8741 7359

HAWTHORNE PACIFIC CORP p 670
94-025 Farrington Hwy, Waipahu HI 96797
Tel (808) 676-0227 *SIC* 5084 7353

ASSOCIATED MATERIAL HANDLING INDUSTRIES INC p 120
133 N Swift Rd, Addison IL 60101
Tel (630) 588-8800 *SIC* 5084 7699 7353

ESSEX RENTAL CORP p 510
1110 W Lake Cook Rd # 220, Buffalo Grove IL 60089
Tel (847) 215-6500 *SIC* 7353 5082

PATTEN INDUSTRIES INC p 1121
635 W Lake St, Elmhurst IL 60126
Tel (630) 279-4400 *SIC* 5084 5082 7353

LANCO INTERNATIONAL INC p 842
3111 167th St, Hazel Crest IL 60429
Tel (708) 596-5200
SIC 3531 8711 5084 3536 7353 3537

ROLAND MACHINERY CO p 1247
816 N Dirksen Pkwy, Springfield IL 62702
Tel (217) 789-7711 *SIC* 7353 5082

ROAD BUILDERS MACHINERY & SUPPLY CO INC p 1240
1001 S 7th St, Kansas City KS 66105
Tel (913) 371-3822 *SIC* 5082 7353 7699

APAC-KANSAS INC p 95
7415 W 130th St Ste 300, Overland Park KS 66213
Tel (913) 371-1003
SIC 1611 1771 2951 7353 1622

BERRY COMPANIES INC p 176
3223 N Hydraulic St, Wichita KS 67219
Tel (316) 838-3321
SIC 5082 7353 7699 5084

EBY CORP p 474
2525 E 36th Cir N, Wichita KS 67219
Tel (316) 268-3500
SIC 1629 1623 1622 1541 1542 7353

FOLEY INDUSTRIES INC p 563
1550 S West St, Wichita KS 67213
Tel (316) 943-4211
SIC 5082 5084 7353 6512

BRAMCO INC p 207
1801 Watterson Trl, Louisville KY 40299
Tel (502) 493-4300 *SIC* 5082 7353

RUDD EQUIPMENT CO INC p 1257
4344 Poplar Level Rd, Louisville KY 40213
Tel (502) 456-4050 *SIC* 5082 7353

■ **INTERNATIONAL SNUBBING SERVICES LLC** p 756
190 Industries Ln, Arnaudville LA 70512
Tel (337) 754-7233 *SIC* 1389 7353

DEEP SOUTH CRANE AND RIGGING LLC p 421
15324 Airline Hwy, Baton Rouge LA 70817
Tel (225) 753-4371 *SIC* 7353

■ **SUPERIOR ENERGY SERVICES LLC** p 1406
5801 Highway 90 E, Broussard LA 70518
Tel (337) 714-4545 *SIC* 1389 7353

FRANCIS DRILLING FLUIDS LTD p 573
240 Jasmine Rd, Crowley LA 70526
Tel (337) 783-8685 *SIC* 5169 1389 7353

LOUISIANA CRANE & CONSTRUCTION LLC p 880
1045 Highway 190, Eunice LA 70535
Tel (337) 550-6217 *SIC* 7389 7353 1623

FRANKS CASING CREW & RENTAL TOOLS INC p 575
700 E Verot School Rd, Lafayette LA 70508
Tel (337) 233-0303 *SIC* 7353 1389

SCOTT EQUIPMENT CO LLC p 1293
1000 M L King Jr Dr J, Monroe LA 71203
Tel (318) 387-4160 *SIC* 7353 5082

LOUISIANA MACHINERY CO LLC p 880
3799 W Airline Hwy, Reserve LA 70084
Tel (985) 536-1121 *SIC* 5082 7699 7353

SOUTHWORTH-MILTON INC p 1353
100 Quarry Dr, Milford MA 01757
Tel (508) 634-3400 *SIC* 5082 7353

SATELLITE SHELTERS INC p 1283
2530 Xenium Ln N Ste 150, Minneapolis MN 55441
Tel (763) 553-1900 *SIC* 1542 7353

STRIBLING EQUIPMENT LLC p 1393
408 Highway 49 S, Richland MS 39218
Tel (601) 939-1000 *SIC* 5082 7353

ERB EQUIPMENT CO INC p 507
200 Erb Industrial Dr, Fenton MO 63026
Tel (636) 349-0200 *SIC* 5082 7353 5084

WASHINGTON CORPS p 1577
101 International Dr, Missoula MT 59808
Tel (406) 523-1300
SIC 5082 7353 4213 8741

CASHMAN EQUIPMENT CO p 263
3300 Saint Rose Pkwy, Henderson NV 89052
Tel (702) 649-8777
SIC 5084 5063 7353 7699

AHERN RENTALS INC p 36
1401 Mineral Ave, Las Vegas NV 89106
Tel (702) 362-0623 *SIC* 7353

NEW-COM INC p 1036
6600 Amelia Earhart Ct B, Las Vegas NV 89119
Tel (702) 642-3331 *SIC* 7353

■ **XYLEM DEWATERING SOLUTIONS INC** p 1633
84 Floodgate Rd, Bridgeport NJ 08014
Tel (410) 243-4900 *SIC* 7353 3561 5084

J F KIELY CONSTRUCTION CO INC p 771
700 Mcclellan St, Long Branch NJ 07740
Tel (732) 222-4400 *SIC* 1623 7353

FOLEY INC p 563
855 Centennial Ave, Piscataway NJ 08854
Tel (732) 885-5555 *SIC* 5082 7699 7353

BINDER MACHINERY CO INC p 183
2820 Hamilton Blvd, South Plainfield NJ 07080
Tel (908) 561-9000
SIC 5082 5084 7353 7699

TRACEY ROAD EQUIPMENT INC p 1468
6803 Manlius Center Rd, East Syracuse NY 13057
Tel (315) 437-1471
SIC 5082 5012 7353 7699 5013

MONROE TRACTOR & IMPLEMENT CO INC p 985
1001 Lehigh Station Rd, Henrietta NY 14467
Tel (585) 334-3867 *SIC* 5082 5083 7353

TRANSERVICE LEASE CORP p 1471
5 Dakota Dr, New Hyde Park NY 11042
Tel (800) 645-8018
SIC 7699 7539 4212 7353

DIAMOND CASTLE HOLDINGS LLC p 436
280 Pk Ave Fl 25 E Tower, New York NY 10017
Tel (212) 300-1900 *SIC* 7353 7699 5082

MARUBENI AUTO & CONSTRUCTION MACHINERY (AMERICA) INC p 913
450 Lexington Ave, New York NY 10017
Tel (212) 450-0447 *SIC* 5082 7353 7699

■ **STEEL EXCEL INC** p 1384
1133 Westchester Ave N-222, White Plains NY 10604
Tel (914) 461-1300 *SIC* 1389 7353 7032

ASHTEAD US HOLDINGS INC p 117
401 S Tryon St, Charlotte NC 28202
Tel (803) 578-5811 *SIC* 7353 7359 5082

CAROLINA TRACTOR & EQUIPMENT CO INC p 259
9000 Statesville Rd, Charlotte NC 28269
Tel (704) 596-6700
SIC 5082 5084 5013 7353 7359 7629

SOUTHEAST INDUSTRIAL EQUIPMENT INC p 1346
12200 Steele Creek Rd, Charlotte NC 28273
Tel (704) 363-6432 *SIC* 7353 7359 5084

C P BUCKNER STEEL ERECTION INC p 233
4732 S Nc Highway 54, Graham NC 27253
Tel (336) 376-8888 *SIC* 1791 7353

■ **SOUTHERN INDUSTRIAL CONSTRUCTORS INC** p 1349
6101 Triangle Dr, Raleigh NC 27617
Tel (919) 782-4600
SIC 1629 1799 1731 1796 1791 7353

DAKOTA COAL CO p 409
1717 E Interstate Ave, Bismarck ND 58503
Tel (701) 223-0441 *SIC* 6519 7353 3274

RDO CONSTRUCTION EQUIPMENT CO p 1212
2000 Industrial Dr, Bismarck ND 58501
Tel (701) 223-5798 *SIC* 5082 5084 7353

BUTLER MACHINERY CO p 230
3401 33rd St S, Fargo ND 58104
Tel (701) 298-1700 *SIC* 5082 7353 7699

RDO EQUIPMENT CO p 1212
700 7th St S, Fargo ND 58103
Tel (701) 239-8700
SIC 5083 5082 5084 7699 7359 7353

OHIO MACHINERY CO p 1077
3993 E Royalton Rd, Broadview Heights OH 44147
Tel (440) 526-6200
SIC 7513 6159 7699 5082 7353

ALL ERECTION & CRANE RENTAL CORP p 51
4700 Acorn Dr, Cleveland OH 44131
Tel (216) 524-6550 *SIC* 7353 7359

COLUMBUS EQUIPMENT CO p 342
2323 Performance Way, Columbus OH 43207
Tel (614) 437-0352 *SIC* 5082 7353

F & M MAFCO INC p 522
9149 Dry Fork Rd, Harrison OH 45030
Tel (513) 367-2151
SIC 5085 5072 7353 5082

KIRBY - SMITH MACHINERY INC p 821
6715 W Reno Ave, Oklahoma City OK 73127
Tel (888) 861-0219 *SIC* 7353 5082 7692

SAMSON INVESTMENT CO p 1274
2 W 2nd St Ste 1500, Tulsa OK 74103
Tel (918) 583-1791 *SIC* 1311 7353 5082

GILES & RANSOME INC p 612
2975 Galloway Rd, Bensalem PA 19020
Tel (215) 639-4300 *SIC* 5082 5084 7353

ANDERSON EQUIPMENT CO p 90
1000 Washington Pike, Bridgeville PA 15017
Tel (412) 343-2300
SIC 5082 7699 7353 5531

■ **MAXIM CRANE WORKS HOLDINGS INC** p 922
1225 Wash Pike Ste 100, Bridgeville PA 15017
Tel (412) 504-0200 *SIC* 7353 7359

■ **MAXIM CRANE WORKS LP** p 922
1225 Wash Pike Ste 100, Bridgeville PA 15017
Tel (412) 504-0200 *SIC* 7353

MODERN GROUP LTD p 981
2501 Durham Rd, Bristol PA 19007
Tel (215) 943-9100 *SIC* 5084 7353 7699

MODERN HANDLING EQUIPMENT CO p 981
2501 Durham Rd Ste G, Bristol PA 19007
Tel (215) 943-9100 *SIC* 5084 7353

▲ **HARSCO CORP** p 664
350 Poplar Church Rd, Camp Hill PA 17011
Tel (717) 763-7064
SIC 7359 7353 5082 3443 3585 4789

CLEVELAND BROTHERS HOLDINGS INC p 325
5300 Paxton St, Harrisburg PA 17111
Tel (717) 564-2121
SIC 7353 5082 5084 7629

LIFT INC p 865
3745 Hempland Rd, Mountville PA 17554
Tel (717) 295-1800 *SIC* 5084 7353

BECKWITH MACHINERY CO INC p 167
4565 William Penn Hwy, Murrysville PA 15668
Tel (724) 327-1300
SIC 5082 5084 7629 7353

ELLIOTT-LEWIS CORP p 488
2900 Black Lake Pl, Philadelphia PA 19154
Tel (215) 698-4400 *SIC* 1711 7349 7353

DANELLA COMPANIES INC p 411
2290 Butler Pike, Plymouth Meeting PA 19462
Tel (610) 828-6200
SIC 7513 7353 8711 1623 8748

DIMEO CONSTRUCTION CO p 440
75 Chapman St, Providence RI 02905
Tel (401) 781-9800 *SIC* 1542 1522 7353

AME INC p 66
2467 Coltharp Rd, Fort Mill SC 29715
Tel (803) 548-7766 *SIC* 1541 7353 3443

ASHTEAD HOLDINGS LLC p 117
2341 Deerfield Dr, Fort Mill SC 29715
Tel (803) 578-5811 *SIC* 7353 7359 5082

SUNBELT RENTALS INC p 1401
2341 Deerfield Dr, Fort Mill SC 29715
Tel (803) 578-5811 *SIC* 7359 7353

■ **AMERICAN EQUIPMENT CO INC** p 71
2106 Anderson Rd, Greenville SC 29611
Tel (864) 295-7800
SIC 7699 7359 5082 7353

BLANCHARD MACHINERY CO p 188
3151 Charleston Hwy, West Columbia SC 29172
Tel (803) 791-7100 *SIC* 5082 7353

POWER EQUIPMENT CO p 1165
3300 Alcoa Hwy, Knoxville TN 37920
Tel (865) 577-5563 *SIC* 5082 3531 7353

THOMPSON MACHINERY COMMERCE CORP p 1449
1245 Bridgestone Pkwy, La Vergne TN 37086
Tel (615) 256-2424 *SIC* 5082 7353

BARNHART CRANE AND RIGGING CO p 156
2163 Airways Blvd, Memphis TN 38114
Tel (901) 775-3000 *SIC* 7353 4213 1796

HEAVY MACHINES INC p 680
3926 E Raines Rd, Memphis TN 38118
Tel (901) 260-2200
SIC 5082 7699 7353 3531 5063

CHARLES BLALOCK & SONS INC p 289
409 Robert Henderson Rd, Sevierville TN 37862
Tel (865) 429-5902
SIC 1611 7353 3271 3255 2951

PETROSMITH EQUIPMENT LP p 1139
7435 Us Highway 277 S, Abilene TX 79606
Tel (325) 691-1085 *SIC* 5084 7353

J-W ENERGY CO p 772
15505 Wright Brothers Dr, Addison TX 75001
Tel (972) 233-8191
SIC 1311 7353 3533 1381

FGI GROUP INC p 539
3901 S Lamar Blvd Ste 100, Austin TX 78704
Tel (512) 448-9898
SIC 1542 1541 1794 1611 7353 1711

FTS INTERNATIONAL MANUFACTURING LLC p 583
777 Main St Ste 2900, Fort Worth TX 76102
Tel (817) 850-8004 *SIC* 5082 7353 5211

FTS INTERNATIONAL SERVICES LLC p 583
777 Main St Ste 2900, Fort Worth TX 76102
Tel (817) 850-1008
SIC 3561 8711 7353 4225

ALLIS-CHALMERS ENERGY INC p 58
12101 Cutten Rd, Houston TX 77066
Tel (281) 301-2600 *SIC* 1381 1389 7353

■ **DNOW LP** p 446
7402 N Eldridge Pkwy, Houston TX 77041
Tel (281) 823-4700 *SIC* 5084 7353 3533

ENVENTURE GLOBAL TECHNOLOGY INC p 503
15995 N Barkers Landing R, Houston TX 77079
Tel (281) 552-2200 *SIC* 7353

EQUIPMENT DEPOT LTD p 506
840 Gessner Rd Ste 950, Houston TX 77024
Tel (713) 365-2547
SIC 5083 5084 7359 7699 7353

■ **EXTERRAN ENERGY SOLUTIONS LP** p 521
263 N Sam Houston Pkwy E, Houston TX 77060
Tel (281) 836-7000 *SIC* 7353

■ **EXTERRAN INC** p 521
16666 Northchase Dr, Houston TX 77060
Tel (281) 836-7000 *SIC* 7353 5084

■ **EXTERRAN TRINIDAD LLC** p 521
12001 N Huston Rosslyn Rd, Houston TX 77086
Tel (281) 921-9337 *SIC* 7353 5084 1389

FRANKS INTERNATIONAL LLC p 575
10260 Westheimer Rd, Houston TX 77042
Tel (281) 966-7300 *SIC* 1382 7353

KEANE GROUP HOLDINGS LLC p 807
11200 Westheimer Rd # 900, Houston TX 77042
Tel (713) 960-0381 *SIC* 1381 7353 4212

NABORS INTERNATIONAL INC p 1006
515 W Greens Rd Ste 600, Houston TX 77067
Tel (281) 874-0035 *SIC* 1381 7353

NABORS WELL SERVICES LTD p 1006
515 W Greens Rd Ste 1200, Houston TX 77067
Tel (281) 874-0035 *SIC* 1389 7353

OIL PATCH GROUP INC p 1079
11767 Katy Fwy Ste 510a, Houston TX 77079
Tel (832) 300-0000 *SIC* 1389 7353

OLD GES INC p 1080
11757 Katy Fwy Ste 700, Houston TX 77079
Tel (281) 598-6830
SIC 1389 7353 3599 7359 1382

▲ **PARKER DRILLING CO** p 1116
5 Greenway Plz Ste 100, Houston TX 77046
Tel (281) 406-2000 *SIC* 1381 7353

PARMAN CAPITAL GROUP LLC p 1117
1000 La St Ste 5900, Houston TX 77002
Tel (713) 751-2700 *SIC* 1389 7353

■ **SESI LLC** p 1308
1001 Louisiana St, Houston TX 77002
Tel (504) 587-7374 *SIC* 7353 1389

STEWART & STEVENSON LLC p 1389
1000 La St Ste 5900, Houston TX 77002
Tel (713) 751-2600
SIC 5084 5082 3533 7353

STEWART & STEVENSON POWER PRODUCTS LLC p 1389
1000 La St Ste 5900, Houston TX 77002
Tel (713) 751-2600
SIC 1389 5084 5082 3533 7353

▲ **SUPERIOR ENERGY SERVICES INC** p 1406
1001 La St Ste 2900, Houston TX 77002
Tel (713) 654-2200 *SIC* 1389 3533 7353

■ **TESCO CORP (US)** p 1440
11330 Clay Rd Ste 350, Houston TX 77041
Tel (713) 359-7000
SIC 7353 5082 1389 1381

TEXAS UNITED CORP p 1444
4800 San Felipe St, Houston TX 77056
Tel (713) 877-1793
SIC 1479 2819 4619 2899 3299 7353

TNT CRANE & RIGGING INC p 1458
925 S Loop W, Houston TX 77054
Tel (713) 644-6113 *SIC* 7353 1611

W-H ENERGY SERVICES LLC p 1569
2000 W Sam Houston Pkwy S # 500, Houston TX 77042
Tel (713) 969-1000 *SIC* 1389 7353

VERMEER EQUIPMENT OF TEXAS INC p 1551
3025 State Highway 161, Irving TX 75062
Tel (972) 255-3500 *SIC* 5082 7699 7353

ASSOCIATED SUPPLY CO INC p 121
2102 E Slaton Rd, Lubbock TX 79404
Tel (806) 745-2000 *SIC* 5084 5082 7353

▲ **NATURAL GAS SERVICES GROUP INC** p 1018
508 W Wall St Ste 550, Midland TX 79701
Tel (432) 262-2700 *SIC* 7353 3563

HOLT TEXAS LTD p 702
5665 Se Loop 410, San Antonio TX 78222
Tel (210) 648-1111
SIC 3531 5082 7353 7699

▲ **PIONEER ENERGY SERVICES CORP** p 1150
1250 Ne Loop 410 Ste 1000, San Antonio TX 78209
Tel (855) 884-0575 *SIC* 1381 7353

DARR EQUIPMENT LP p 412
350 Bank St, Southlake TX 76092
Tel (254) 420-2650
SIC 5084 7353 5013 4959

BLUELINE RENTAL LLC p 193
8401 New Trils Dr Ste 150, The Woodlands TX 77381
Tel (832) 299-7515 *SIC* 7353 4789

WHEELER MACHINERY CO p 1605
4901 W 2100 S, Salt Lake City UT 84120
Tel (801) 974-0511
SIC 5082 5084 7359 7353

WASHINGTON TRACTOR INC p 1579
2700 136th Avenue Ct E, Sumner WA 98390
Tel (253) 863-4436
SIC 3523 5083 5261 7699 7353

SIC 7359 Equipment Rental & Leasing, NEC

TANADGUSIX CORP p 1424
615 E 82nd Ave Ste 200, Anchorage AK 99518
Tel (907) 278-2312 *SIC* 1796 7011 7359

MITEL (DELAWARE) INC p 977
1146 N Alma School Rd, Mesa AZ 85201
Tel (480) 449-8900
SIC 3661 5045 4813 5065 1731 7359

MITEL NETWORKS INC p 977
1146 N Alma School Rd, Mesa AZ 85201
Tel (480) 961-9000
SIC 3661 7359 1731 7373

WHITEMAN FAMILY CORP p 1606
1725 S Country Club Dr, Mesa AZ 85210
Tel (480) 633-4413
SIC 5082 5083 7353 7699 7359 5012

■ **BROWNING-FERRIS INDUSTRIES INC** p 220
18500 N Allied Way # 100, Phoenix AZ 85054
Tel (480) 627-2700 *SIC* 4953 4959 7359

▲ **MOBILE MINI INC** p 980
4646 E Van Buren St # 400, Phoenix AZ 85008
Tel (480) 894-6311
SIC 4225 3448 3441 3412 7359

ROAD MACHINERY LLC p 1240
4710 E Elwood St Ste 6, Phoenix AZ 85040
Tel (602) 256-5128
SIC 5082 7359 7699 7353 7629

SUNSTATE EQUIPMENT CO LLC p 1404
5552 E Washington St, Phoenix AZ 85034
Tel (602) 275-2398 *SIC* 7359 7353

■ **U-HAUL INTERNATIONAL INC** p 1498
2727 N Central Ave, Phoenix AZ 85004
Tel (602) 263-6011
SIC 7513 7519 7359 5531 4226 8741

■ **MOBILE STORAGE GROUP INC** p 980
7420 S Kyrene Rd Ste 101, Tempe AZ 85283
Tel (480) 894-6311 *SIC* 5999 7359

KALIL BOTTLING CO p 801
931 S Highland Ave, Tucson AZ 85719
Tel (520) 624-1788 *SIC* 2086 7359

BEARDEN LEASING CO LTD p 165
111 S Plum St, Bearden AR 71720
Tel (870) 687-2246 *SIC* 7359 0811

NABHOLZ INC p 1006
612 Garland St, Conway AR 72032
Tel (501) 505-5800 *SIC* 5084 7359

SR BRAY LLC p 1362
1210 N Red Gum St, Anaheim CA 92806
Tel (714) 765-7551 *SIC* 1731 7359

QUINN GROUP INC p 1200
10006 Rose Hills Rd, City Of Industry CA 90601
Tel (562) 463-4000
SIC 5084 5082 7353 7359

YALE/CHASE EQUIPMENT AND SERVICES INC p 1634
2615 Pellissier Pl, City Of Industry CA 90601
Tel (562) 463-8000 *SIC* 5084 7699 7359

S & S TOOL & SUPPLY INC p 1261
2700 Maxwell Way, Fairfield CA 94534
Tel (925) 335-4000
SIC 5085 7699 5072 7359

METRIC EQUIPMENT SALES INC p 954
25841 Industrial Blvd # 200, Hayward CA 94545
Tel (510) 264-0887
SIC 5065 5084 7359 3825

AFTER-PARTY6 INC p 33
901 W Hillcrest Blvd, Inglewood CA 90301
Tel (310) 966-4900 *SIC* 7359

CLASSIC PARTY RENTALS INC p 323
901 W Hillcrest Blvd, Inglewood CA 90301
Tel (310) 966-4900 *SIC* 7359

▲ **MCGRATH RENTCORP** p 929
5700 Las Positas Rd, Livermore CA 94551
Tel (925) 606-9200 *SIC* 7359 5084

AUDIO VISUAL SERVICES GROUP INC p 131
111 Ocean Beach Blvd Ste 1110, Long Beach CA 90802
Tel (562) 366-0620 *SIC* 7389 7812 7359

PSAV HOLDINGS LLC p 1188
111 W Ocean Blvd Ste 1110, Long Beach CA 90802
Tel (562) 366-0138 *SIC* 7359

▲ **AIR LEASE CORP** p 38
2000 Avenue Of The Stars 1000n, Los Angeles CA 90067
Tel (310) 553-0555 *SIC* 7359 7389

INTERNATIONAL LEASE FINANCE CORP p 755
10250 Constellation Blvd, Los Angeles CA 90067
Tel (310) 788-1999 *SIC* 7359 8741 5599

NATIONAL BUSINESS GROUP INC p 1010
15319 Chatsworth St, Mission Hills CA 91345
Tel (818) 221-6000
SIC 7353 5039 7359 3496 7519

PACIFIC LIFE INSURANCE CO p 1105
700 Newport Center Dr, Newport Beach CA 92660
Tel (949) 219-3011
SIC 6311 6371 6321 7359

▲ **GENERAL FINANCE CORP** p 600
39 E Union St Ste 206, Pasadena CA 91103
Tel (626) 584-9722 *SIC* 7359 5085

■ **WESCO FINANCIAL CORP** p 1593
301 E Colo Blvd Ste 300, Pasadena CA 91101
Tel (626) 585-6700 *SIC* 7359 6411 7389

HOC HOLDINGS INC p 699
7310 Pacific Ave, Pleasant Grove CA 95668
Tel (916) 921-8950
SIC 5082 5084 5083 7359

HOLT OF CALIFORNIA p 702
7310 Pacific Ave, Pleasant Grove CA 95668
Tel (916) 991-8200
SIC 5082 5084 5083 7359

SOLIGENT HOLDINGS INC p 1338
1500 Valley House Dr, Rohnert Park CA 94928
Tel (707) 992-3100 *SIC* 5074 7359 1711

HAWTHORNE MACHINERY CO p 670
16945 Camino San Bernardo, San Diego CA 92127
Tel (858) 674-7000
SIC 7353 7699 5082 7359

▲ **CAI INTERNATIONAL INC** p 237
1 Market Plz Ste 900, San Francisco CA 94105
Tel (415) 788-0100 *SIC* 7359

AIRCRAFT FINANCE TRUST p 40
2401 Kerner Blvd, San Rafael CA 94901
Tel (415) 485-4500 *SIC* 7359

MARBORG INDUSTRIES p 904
728 E Yanonali St, Santa Barbara CA 93103
Tel (805) 963-1852
SIC 4953 7359 7699 4212

RAYMOND HANDLING SOLUTIONS INC p 1210
9939 Norwalk Blvd, Santa Fe Springs CA 90670
Tel (562) 944-8067 *SIC* 5084 7699 7359

BAKERCORP p 146
3020 Old Ranch Pkwy # 220, Seal Beach CA 90740
Tel (562) 430-6262 *SIC* 7359

AVAD LLC p 135
5805 Sepulvda Blvd # 750, Sherman Oaks CA 91411
Tel (818) 742-4800 *SIC* 5065 7359

CR&R INC p 388
11292 Western Ave, Stanton CA 90680
Tel (714) 826-9049 *SIC* 4953 4212 7359

ELECTRO RENT CORP p 485
6060 Sepulveda Blvd # 300, Van Nuys CA 91411
Tel (818) 786-2525
SIC 7359 7377 5065 5045

PANAVISION INC p 1111
6101 Variel Ave, Woodland Hills CA 91367
Tel (818) 316-1000
SIC 7359 3861 3648 5063

UNITED STATES WELDING INC p 1514
600 S Santa Fe Dr, Denver CO 80223
Tel (303) 777-2475
SIC 5169 5084 5085 5047 7359

COBANK ACB p 332
6340 S Fiddlers Green Cir, Greenwood Village CO 80111
Tel (303) 740-6527 *SIC* 6111 7359 6159

■ **KEY EQUIPMENT FINANCE INC** p 814
1000 S Mccaslin Blvd, Superior CO 80027
Tel (800) 539-2968 *SIC* 7359

■ **GENERAL ELECTRIC CAPITAL SERVICES INC** p 600
3135 Easton Tpke, Fairfield CT 06828
Tel (203) 373-2211
SIC 6159 6141 7359 6162

NEOPOST USA INC p 1026
478 Wheelers Farms Rd, Milford CT 06461
Tel (203) 301-3400 *SIC* 3579 7359 7629

■ **GENERAL ELECTRIC CAPITAL CORP** p 600
901 Main Ave, Norwalk CT 06851
Tel (203) 840-6300 *SIC* 6159 6141 7359

▲ **AIRCASTLE LIMITED** p 40
300 1st Stamford Pl 9a, Stamford CT 06902
Tel (203) 504-1020 *SIC* 7359

▲ **PITNEY BOWES INC** p 1152
3001 Summer St Ste 3, Stamford CT 06905
Tel (203) 356-5000
SIC 3579 7359 3661 8744 7372

■ **UNITED RENTALS (NORTH AMERICA) INC** p 1511
100 Frist Stamford 700, Stamford CT 06902
Tel (203) 622-3131 *SIC* 7353 7359 5084

▲ **UNITED RENTALS INC** p 1511
100 1st Stamford Pl # 700, Stamford CT 06902
Tel (203) 622-3131 *SIC* 7359 7353

■ **B WILLIAMS HOLDING CORP** p 142
1403 Foulk Rd Ste 200, Wilmington DE 19803
Tel (302) 656-8596
SIC 3579 3661 3861 7359 7629 6159

BARLOWORLD USA INC p 155
1105 N Market St Ste 1300, Wilmington DE 19801
Tel (302) 427-2765 *SIC* 5084 7699 7359

▲ **HERC HOLDINGS INC** p 685
27500 Riverview Ctr Blvd, Bonita Springs FL 34134
Tel (239) 301-1000 *SIC* 7359

■ **HERC RENTALS INC** p 685
27500 Rverview Ctr Bldg 7, Bonita Springs FL 34134
Tel (239) 301-1001 *SIC* 7359

AERSALE HOLDINGS INC p 31
121 Alhambra Plz Ste 1700, Coral Gables FL 33134
Tel (305) 764-3200 *SIC* 5088 7359

KELLY TRACTOR CO p 809
8255 Nw 58th St, Doral FL 33166
Tel (305) 592-5360
SIC 5082 5083 7359 7353 5084 7699

▲ **NEFF CORP** p 1024
3750 Nw 87th Ave Ste 400, Doral FL 33178
Tel (305) 513-3350 *SIC* 7359

■ **HERTZ CORP** p 687
8501 Williams Rd, Estero FL 33928
Tel (239) 301-7000
SIC 7514 7515 7513 7359 5521 6794

AVI-SPL INC p 137
6301 Benjamin Rd Ste 101, Tampa FL 33634
Tel (866) 708-5034 *SIC* 7359 5999

BUDDYS NEWCO LLC p 223
6608 E Adamo Dr, Tampa FL 33619
Tel (813) 623-5461 *SIC* 7359 6794

FLORIDA LIFT SYSTEMS LLC p 559
115 S 78th St, Tampa FL 33619
Tel (904) 764-7662 *SIC* 5084 7359 7699

■ **AUTOTOTE SYSTEMS INC** p 135
1500 Bluegrass Lakes Pkwy, Alpharetta GA 30004
Tel (770) 664-3700
SIC 3578 7373 7359 8711

CHEP (USA) INC p 294
5897 Windward Pkwy, Alpharetta GA 30005
Tel (770) 379-6900 *SIC* 7359

▲ **AARONS INC** p 8
400 Galleria Pkwy Se # 300, Atlanta GA 30339
Tel (404) 231-0011
SIC 7359 5712 5731 5722 5932 6794

TOSCA SERVICES LLC p 1462
303 Peachtree Center Ave, Atlanta GA 30303
Tel (920) 569-5335 *SIC* 7359 5144

AIRGAS CARBONIC INC p 40
2530 Sever Rd Ste 300, Lawrenceville GA 30043
Tel (770) 717-2210 *SIC* 2813 7359 5088

BROWN INTEGRATED LOGISTICS INC p 219
6908 Chapman Rd, Lithonia GA 30058
Tel (770) 482-6521
SIC 4225 4213 4731 7359

BRAMBLES USA INC (DEL) p 207
180 Technology Pkwy # 600, Norcross GA 30092
Tel (770) 776-1900
SIC 4953 4212 7353 8741 7359

MCSI INC p 933
2975 Northwoods Pkwy, Peachtree Corners GA 30071
Tel (770) 441-5263 *SIC* 1731 5065 7359

LANIER WORLDWIDE INC p 844
4667 N Royal Atlanta Dr, Tucker GA 30084
Tel (770) 493-2100
SIC 5044 5999 7359 7629

■ **WASHINGTON GROUP INTERNATIONAL INC** p 1578
1 Morrison Knudsen Plz, Boise ID 83729
Tel (208) 386-5000 *SIC* 7359

WESTERN AIRCRAFT INC p 1597
4300 S Kennedy St, Boise ID 83705
Tel (208) 338-1800
SIC 5088 4581 7359 5172

ALUMA SYSTEMS p 63
1020 Anita Ave, Antioch IL 60002
Tel (847) 838-4366 *SIC* 7359

▲ **GATX CORP** p 594
222 W Adams St, Chicago IL 60606
Tel (312) 621-6200 *SIC* 4741 7359 4491

GENERAL ELECTRIC RAILCAR SERVICES CORP p 600
161 N Clark St Fl 7, Chicago IL 60601
Tel (312) 853-5000
SIC 7359 3743 4789 3462

HINCKLEY & SCHMITT INC p 695
6055 S Harlem Ave, Chicago IL 60638
Tel (773) 586-8600 *SIC* 2086 5149 7359

NATIONAL EQUIPMENT SERVICES INC p 1011
8420 W Bryn Mawr Ave, Chicago IL 60631
Tel (773) 695-3999 *SIC* 7359

NES RENTALS HOLDINGS INC p 1026
8420 W Bryn Mawr Ave # 310, Chicago IL 60631
Tel (773) 695-3999 *SIC* 7359 7699 5082

AUDIO VISUAL SERVICES GROUP INC p 131
5100 River Rd Ste 300, Schiller Park IL 60176
Tel (847) 222-9800 *SIC* 7359

PSAV INC p 1188
5100 River Rd Ste 300, Schiller Park IL 60176
Tel (847) 222-9800 *SIC* 7371 7359

INDECK POWER EQUIPMENT CO p 736
1111 Willis Ave, Wheeling IL 60090
Tel (847) 541-8300 *SIC* 5084 5074 7359

▲ **AAR CORP** p 8
1100 N Wood Dale Rd, Wood Dale IL 60191
Tel (630) 227-2000
SIC 3724 4581 3537 5599 7359

GKN NORTH AMERICA SERVICES INC p 613
2715 Davey Rd Ste 300, Woodridge IL 60517
Tel (630) 972-9300 *SIC* 3714 5013 7359

SCHILLI LEASING INC p 1287
6358 W Us Highway 24, Remington IN 47977
Tel (888) 233-1919 *SIC* 7513 7359

AGRI INDUSTRIES INC p 36
700 Se Dalbey Dr, Ankeny IA 50021
Tel (515) 964-2200 *SIC* 5153 7359

■ **R K DIXON CO** p 1202
5700 Utica Ridge Rd, Davenport IA 52807
Tel (563) 344-9100 *SIC* 5044 7629 7359

STATE UNIVERSITY OF IOWA FOUNDATION p 1383
1 W Park Rd, Iowa City IA 52242
Tel (319) 335-3305 *SIC* 8399 7371 7359

MUSCO CORP p 1002
100 1st Ave W, Oskaloosa IA 52577
Tel (641) 676-1746
SIC 7359 3648 3646 3641 3545 3423

G W VAN KEPPEL CO p 587
1801 N 9th St, Kansas City KS 66101
Tel (913) 281-4800
SIC 5082 7699 5084 7359

INTEGRATED HEALTHCARE SYSTEMS INC p 749
3311 E Murdock St, Wichita KS 67208
Tel (316) 689-9111 *SIC* 7359

CARDINAL CARRYOR INC p 252
1055 Grade Ln, Louisville KY 40213
Tel (502) 363-6641
SIC 5084 7699 7359 5085 3535

▲ **H&E EQUIPMENT SERVICES INC** p 651
7500 Pecue Ln, Baton Rouge LA 70809
Tel (225) 298-5200 *SIC* 7359 5082

TURNER INDUSTRIES GROUP LLC p 1493
8687 United Plaza Blvd, Baton Rouge LA 70809
Tel (225) 922-5050 *SIC* 7359 7699

LAITRAM LLC p 838
220 Laitram Ln, Harahan LA 70123
Tel (504) 733-6000
SIC 3535 3556 7359 3446 6719

GULFSTREAM SERVICES INC p 647
103 Dickson Rd, Houma LA 70363
Tel (985) 868-0303 *SIC* 1382 7359

WILLIAMS SCOTSMAN INC p 1611
901 S Bond St Ste 600, Baltimore MD 21231
Tel (410) 931-6000
SIC 1531 1541 5039 7359

CLARK ENTERPRISES INC p 322
7500 Old Georgetown Rd # 7, Bethesda MD 20814
Tel (301) 657-7100
SIC 6552 4832 7359 1521 1542 6726

C & T A CO INC p 231
11535 Hopewell Rd, Hagerstown MD 21740
Tel (800) 458-3835
SIC 5541 5172 7359 7699

R H WHITE COMPANIES INC p 1202
41 Central St, Auburn MA 01501
Tel (508) 832-3295
SIC 1629 7359 1522 1521

CONTINENTAL RESOURCES INC p 363
175 Middlesex Tpke Ste 1, Bedford MA 01730
Tel (781) 275-0850
SIC 5045 5065 7377 7359 7378 7629

■ **DOBLE ENGINEERING CO** p 447
85 Walnut St, Watertown MA 02472
Tel (617) 926-4900
SIC 3825 7359 3829 3826

NORTHLAND INDUSTRIAL TRUCK CO INC p 1057
6 Jonspin Rd, Wilmington MA 01887
Tel (978) 658-5900 *SIC* 5084 7699 7359

GKN NORTH AMERICA INC p 613
2200 N Opdyke Rd, Auburn Hills MI 48326
Tel (248) 296-7200 *SIC* 3714 5013 7359

MORRISON INDUSTRIES INC p 990
1825 Monroe Ave Nw, Grand Rapids MI 49505
Tel (616) 447-3838 *SIC* 5084 7699 7359

■ **ROFAN SERVICES INC** p 1246
2030 Dow Ctr, Midland MI 48674
Tel (989) 636-6943 *SIC* 7359

PURITY CYLINDER GASES INC p 1192
2580 28th St Sw, Wyoming MI 49519
Tel (616) 532-2375
SIC 5085 7359 5999 7699

GENESIS p 602
1273 W Derrynane St, Le Center MN 56057
Tel (507) 357-6868 *SIC* 7359

BACHMANS INC p 143
6010 Lyndale Ave S, Minneapolis MN 55419
Tel (612) 861-7600
SIC 5992 5261 0181 5193 7359

METRO SALES INC p 955
1640 E 78th St, Minneapolis MN 55423
Tel (612) 861-4000
SIC 5044 5112 5065 7359

AMERICAN CRYSTAL SUGAR CO p 70
101 3rd St N, Moorhead MN 56560
Tel (218) 236-4326 *SIC* 2063 7359

SWANK AUDIO VISUALS LLC p 1411
639 Gravois Bluffs Blvd E, Fenton MO 63026
Tel (636) 680-9000 *SIC* 7359

COGENT INC p 334
318 Brdwy St, Kansas City MO 64105
Tel (816) 221-0650 *SIC* 5084 5082 7359

DASH MULTI-CORP INC p 413
2500 Adie Rd, Maryland Heights MO 63043
Tel (314) 432-3200
SIC 2821 3069 6512 5169 7359

J S LEASING CO INC p 772
1441 Hampton Ave, Saint Louis MO 63139
Tel (314) 647-7529 *SIC* 7359

NU WAY CONCRETE FORMS INC p 1066
4190 Hoffmeister Ave, Saint Louis MO 63125
Tel (573) 893-8786
SIC 5032 5051 5072 7359

WIESE HOLDING CO p 1608
1445 Woodson Rd, Saint Louis MO 63132
Tel (314) 997-4444 *SIC* 5084 7359

■ **XTRA CORP** p 1633
7911 Forsyth Blvd Ste 600, Saint Louis MO 63105
Tel (314) 719-0300 *SIC* 7359

T-L IRRIGATION CO p 1420
151 E Hwy 6 And Ab Rd, Hastings NE 68901
Tel (402) 462-4128
SIC 3523 3561 3479 7359

■ **CONWAY TECHNOLOGY GROUP LLC** p 365
10 Capitol St, Nashua NH 03063
Tel (603) 889-1665
SIC 5044 5065 7699 7359

CONNELL CO p 357
200 Connell Dr Ste 4100, Berkeley Heights NJ 07922
Tel (908) 673-3700
SIC 6552 6512 7359 5082

C & A MARKETING INC p 231
114 Tived Ln E, Edison NJ 08837
Tel (201) 881-1900
SIC 5065 8742 7384 5946 7359 7221

EASTERN LIFT TRUCK CO INC p 472
549 E Linwood Ave, Maple Shade NJ 08052
Tel (856) 779-8880 *SIC* 5084 7699 7359

▲ **MARLIN BUSINESS SERVICES CORP** p 909
300 Fellowship Rd, Mount Laurel NJ 08054
Tel (888) 479-9111 *SIC* 7389 7359 6022

■ **HERTZ INVESTORS INC** p 687
225 Brae Blvd, Park Ridge NJ 07656
Tel (201) 307-2000
SIC 7514 7515 7513 7359 5521 6794

AMERICAN FURNITURE RENTALS INC p 73
720 Hylton Rd, Pennsauken NJ 08110
Tel (856) 406-1200 *SIC* 7359 5712

TRAC INTERMODAL LLC p 1468
750 College Rd E, Princeton NJ 08540
Tel (609) 452-8900 *SIC* 7359 3715 5012

PARTY RENTAL LTD p 1119
275 North St, Teterboro NJ 07608
Tel (201) 727-4700 *SIC* 7359

RAYMOND CORP p 1210
22 S Canal St, Greene NY 13778
Tel (607) 656-2311 *SIC* 3537 3535 7359

SAM ASH MUSIC CORP p 1273
278 Duffy Ave Unit A, Hicksville NY 11801
Tel (516) 932-6400
SIC 5736 5731 5734 5961 7359 8741

BAKERCORP INTERNATIONAL HOLDINGS INC p 146
320 Park Ave, New York NY 10022
Tel (212) 386-7480 *SIC* 7359

BANK LEUMI USA p 151
579 5th Ave Frnt A, New York NY 10017
Tel (917) 542-2343 *SIC* 6022 7359

MIZUHO BANK LTD p 978
1251 Ave Of The Americas, New York NY 10020
Tel (212) 282-3000 *SIC* 6022 6082 7359

PX HOLDING CORP p 1193
35 E 62nd St, New York NY 10065
Tel (212) 688-9000 *SIC* 7359 3861 3648

SAFWAY HOLDINGS LLC p 1267
280 Park Ave Fl 38, New York NY 10017
Tel (212) 351-7900 *SIC* 7359 5082 1799

■ **VERIZON NEW YORK INC** p 1550
140 West St, New York NY 10007
Tel (212) 395-1000 SIC 4813 7359

■ **VIACOM SONGS INC** p 1554
1515 Broadway Lbby, New York NY 10036
Tel (212) 258-6000
SIC 6531 6519 7359 7941 7812 2731

COINMACH CORP p 335
303 Sunnyside Blvd # 70, Plainview NY 11803
Tel (516) 349-8555
SIC 7215 7359 5087 5064 7211 8741

▲ **ATLAS AIR WORLDWIDE HOLDINGS INC** p 127
2000 Westchester Ave, Purchase NY 10577
Tel (914) 701-8000 SIC 4522 4512 7359

TAL INTERNATIONAL CONTAINER CORP p 1422
100 Manhattanville Rd # 13, Purchase NY 10577
Tel (914) 251-9000 SIC 7359

TAL INTERNATIONAL GROUP INC p 1422
100 Manhattanville Rd # 13, Purchase NY 10577
Tel (914) 251-9000 SIC 7359 5085 4412

ASHTEAD US HOLDINGS INC p 117
401 S Tryon St, Charlotte NC 28202
Tel (803) 578-5811 SIC 7353 7359 5082

CAROLINA TRACTOR & EQUIPMENT CO INC p 259
9000 Statesville Rd, Charlotte NC 28269
Tel (704) 596-6700
SIC 5082 5084 5013 7353 7359 7629

SOUTHEAST INDUSTRIAL EQUIPMENT INC p 1346
12200 Steele Creek Rd, Charlotte NC 28273
Tel (704) 363-6432 SIC 7353 7359 5084

ARC3 GASES INC p 103
1636 Us Highway 301 S, Dunn NC 28334
Tel (910) 892-4016
SIC 2813 5084 5169 7359 7692

MICROLEASE INC p 962
9221 Globe Center Dr # 105, Morrisville NC 27560
Tel (866) 520-0200 SIC 7359

B V HEDRICK GRAVEL & SAND CO p 142
120 1/2 N Church St, Salisbury NC 28144
Tel (704) 633-5982
SIC 1442 7359 6512 3273 1541 1542

RDO EQUIPMENT CO p 1212
700 7th St S, Fargo ND 58103
Tel (701) 239-8700
SIC 5083 5082 5084 7699 7359 7353

TOWLIFT INC p 1464
1395 Valley Belt Rd, Brooklyn Heights OH 44131
Tel (216) 749-6800 SIC 5084 7699 7359

BUDCO GROUP INC p 223
1100 Gest St, Cincinnati OH 45203
Tel (513) 621-6111 SIC 7359

ALL ERECTION & CRANE RENTAL CORP p 51
4700 Acorn Dr, Cleveland OH 44131
Tel (216) 524-6550 SIC 7353 7359

SUMMA HOLDINGS INC p 1398
8223 Brecksville Rd # 100, Cleveland OH 44141
Tel (440) 838-4700
SIC 2542 3462 3569 7359 3728

■ **NETJETS INC** p 1027
4111 Bridgeway Ave, Columbus OH 43219
Tel (614) 239-5500 SIC 4522 5088 7359

WMOG INC p 1620
122 S Wilson Ave, Fremont OH 43420
Tel (419) 334-3801 SIC 1541 7359 1611

TUALITY HEALTHCARE FOUNDATION INC p 1490
335 Se 8th Ave, Hillsboro OR 97123
Tel (503) 681-1850
SIC 8082 7374 6512 5999 7359

ERICKSON INC p 507
5550 Sw Mcdam Ave Ste 200, Portland OR 97239
Tel (503) 505-5800
SIC 7363 4581 3721 7359 5599 3728

MODULAR SPACE CORP p 981
1200 W Swedesford Rd Fl 2, Berwyn PA 19312
Tel (610) 232-1200 SIC 7359 1542

■ **MAXIM CRANE WORKS HOLDINGS INC** p 922
1225 Wash Pike Ste 100, Bridgeville PA 15017
Tel (412) 504-0200 SIC 7353 7359

▲ **HARSCO CORP** p 664
350 Poplar Church Rd, Camp Hill PA 17011
Tel (717) 763-7064
SIC 7359 7353 5082 3443 3585 4789

TMS INTERNATIONAL CORP p 1457
12 Monongahela Ave, Glassport PA 15045
Tel (412) 678-6141
SIC 3312 4731 3399 7359 4213

TMS INTERNATIONAL HOLDING CORP p 1457
12 Monongahela Ave, Glassport PA 15045
Tel (412) 678-6141
SIC 3312 4731 3399 7359 4213

TMS INTERNATIONAL LLC p 1458
12 Monongahela Ave, Glassport PA 15045
Tel (412) 678-6141
SIC 3312 4731 3399 7359 4213

STABLER COMPANIES INC p 1374
635 Lucknow Rd, Harrisburg PA 17110
Tel (717) 236-9307
SIC 5032 3089 7359 3531 1611 3648

RICOH USA INC p 1233
70 Valley Stream Pkwy, Malvern PA 19355
Tel (610) 296-8000
SIC 5044 5065 7359 5112 7334 6159

BOLTTECH MANNINGS INC p 199
501 Mosside Blvd, North Versailles PA 15137
Tel (724) 872-4873
SIC 3546 5072 3599 7359 3545 3423

LEAF COMMERCIAL CAPITAL INC p 850
2005 Market St Fl 14, Philadelphia PA 19103
Tel (800) 819-5556 SIC 6159 7359

RESOURCE AMERICA INC p 1227
1 Crescent Dr Ste 203, Philadelphia PA 19112
Tel (215) 546-5005 SIC 6531 6722 7359

DOLLAR BANK FEDERAL SAVINGS BANK p 448
401 Liberty Ave, Pittsburgh PA 15222
Tel (412) 261-4900 SIC 6035 7359

DOLLAR BANK LEASING CORP p 448
401 Liberty Ave Lobby, Pittsburgh PA 15222
Tel (412) 261-4900 SIC 6035 7359

■ **ORIENTAL BANK** p 1094
254 Ave Munoz Rivera, San Juan PR 00918
Tel (787) 771-6800
SIC 6035 7359 7515 6733

ASHTEAD HOLDINGS LLC p 117
2341 Deerfield Dr, Fort Mill SC 29715
Tel (803) 578-5811 SIC 7353 7359 5082

SUNBELT RENTALS INC p 1401
2341 Deerfield Dr, Fort Mill SC 29715
Tel (803) 578-5811 SIC 7359 7353

SUNBELT RENTALS INDUSTRIAL SERVICES LLC p 1401
2341 Deerfield Dr, Fort Mill SC 29715
Tel (803) 578-5811 SIC 7359

■ **AMERICAN EQUIPMENT CO INC** p 71
2106 Anderson Rd, Greenville SC 29611
Tel (864) 295-7800
SIC 7699 7359 5082 7353

LILLY CO p 866
3613 Knight Arnold Rd, Memphis TN 38118
Tel (901) 363-6000
SIC 5084 7699 7359 5046

NEXAIR LLC p 1039
1385 Corporate Ave, Memphis TN 38132
Tel (901) 396-5050
SIC 5169 5084 7699 7359

ABRAMS INTERNATIONAL INC p 12
111 Congress Ave Ste 2400, Austin TX 78701
Tel (512) 322-4000
SIC 1611 1622 1629 6799 7359 8742

FLARE INDUSTRIES LLC p 554
16310 Bratton Ln Ste 350, Austin TX 78728
Tel (512) 836-9473
SIC 3822 7359 3694 2899 1711 3569

MODERN AG PRODUCTS LTD p 981
1655 Louisiana St, Beaumont TX 77701
Tel (409) 833-2665 SIC 7359 6792 0161

MODERN GROUP LTD p 981
1655 Louisiana St, Beaumont TX 77701
Tel (800) 231-8198 SIC 7359 3441

BROCK HOLDINGS I LLC p 216
10343 Sam Houston Park Dr # 200, Houston TX 77064
Tel (281) 807-8200 SIC 1721 1799 7359

CARRUTH-DOGGETT INC p 261
7110 North Fwy, Houston TX 77076
Tel (713) 675-7000 SIC 5084 7359 7699

DELTA RIGGING & TOOLS INC p 427
125 Mccarty St, Houston TX 77029
Tel (713) 512-1700 SIC 7359 2298 3496

EQUIPMENT DEPOT LTD p 506
840 Gessner Rd Ste 950, Houston TX 77024
Tel (713) 365-2547
SIC 5083 5084 7359 7699 7353

▲ **EXTERRAN CORP** p 521
4444 Brittmoore Rd, Houston TX 77041
Tel (281) 836-7000 SIC 7359

HIGHWAY TECHNOLOGIES INC p 692
6811 Dixie Dr, Houston TX 77087
Tel (713) 845-1800 SIC 1622 7359

HOOVER GROUP INC p 706
2135 Highway 6 S, Houston TX 77077
Tel (800) 844-8683
SIC 3496 3412 3443 3089 7359 3411

J D FIELDS & CO INC p 770
55 Waugh Dr Ste 1250, Houston TX 77007
Tel (281) 558-7199 SIC 5051 7359 3443

OLD GES INC p 1080
11757 Katy Fwy Ste 700, Houston TX 77079
Tel (281) 598-6830
SIC 1389 7353 3599 7359 1382

■ **COMPRESSOR SYSTEMS INC** p 352
3809 S Fm 1788, Midland TX 79706
Tel (432) 563-1170 SIC 7359 7699 3563

WARREN EQUIPMENT CO p 1577
10325 Younger Rd, Midland TX 79706
Tel (432) 571-8462
SIC 5082 5084 7699 3563 7359

BAKERCORP INTERNATIONAL INC p 146
7800 Dallas Pkwy Ste 500, Plano TX 75024
Tel (888) 882-4895 SIC 7359

▲ **RENT-A-CENTER INC** p 1224
5501 Headquarters Dr, Plano TX 75024
Tel (972) 801-1100 SIC 7359 6794

■ **SAFETY-KLEEN SYSTEMS INC** p 1266
2600 N Central Expy # 400, Richardson TX 75080
Tel (972) 265-2000
SIC 3559 7359 5172 4212 7389 5085

■ **CONN APPLIANCES INC** p 356
4055 Technology Frst, The Woodlands TX 77381
Tel (409) 832-1696
SIC 5722 5731 7629 6141 7359

MITY-LITE INC p 978
1301 W 400 N, Orem UT 84057
Tel (801) 224-0589 SIC 2531 2522 7359

WHEELER MACHINERY CO p 1605
4901 W 2100 S, Salt Lake City UT 84120
Tel (801) 974-0511
SIC 5082 5084 7359 7353

YOUNG ELECTRIC SIGN CO INC p 1638
2401 S Foothill Dr, Salt Lake City UT 84109
Tel (801) 464-4600
SIC 3993 7359 1799 6794

■ **CORT BUSINESS SERVICES CORP** p 373
15000 Conference Ste 440, Chantilly VA 20151
Tel (703) 968-8500 SIC 7359 5712 5932

NORTHWEST CASCADE INC p 1059
10412 John Bananola Way E, Puyallup WA 98374
Tel (253) 848-2371
SIC 1623 7359 7699 3272 1711

EMERALD SERVICES INC p 491
7343 E Marginal Way S, Seattle WA 98108
Tel (206) 430-7795
SIC 4953 7699 2911 8748 7359

GLENN DISTRIBUTOR INC p 615
1301 N Wenatchee Ave, Wenatchee WA 98801
Tel (509) 663-7173 SIC 5172 5541 7359

DOLSEN COMPANIES p 448
301 N 3rd St, Yakima WA 98901
Tel (509) 248-2831
SIC 0241 0211 2086 7359

▲ **ACTUANT CORP** p 20
N86w12500 Westbrook Xing, Menomonee Falls WI 53051
Tel (262) 293-1500
SIC 3593 3492 3594 3625 7359

SIC 7361 Employment Agencies

ONIN STAFFING LLC p 1088
1 Perimeter Park S 450n, Birmingham AL 35243
Tel (205) 298-7233 SIC 7361

CHUGACH ALASKA CORP p 304
3800 Cntrpint Dr Ste 1200, Anchorage AK 99503
Tel (907) 563-8866
SIC 8744 4959 7361 0851 7373

TATITLEK CORP p 1426
561 E 36th Ave, Anchorage AK 99503
Tel (907) 278-4000 SIC 0811 6552 7361

BANNER HEALTH p 153
2901 N Central Ave # 160, Phoenix AZ 85012
Tel (602) 747-4000
SIC 8062 8051 8082 7361 8011 8093

SUN HEALTH CORP p 1400
14719 W Grand Ave Ste 113, Surprise AZ 85374
Tel (623) 876-5350
SIC 8062 8051 8082 7361 8733 6531

TRAVEL NURSE ACROSS AMERICA LLC p 1473
5020 Northshore Dr Ste 2, North Little Rock AR 72118
Tel (501) 663-5288 SIC 7361

ESPARZA ENTERPRISES INC p 509
3851 Fruitvale Ave Ste A, Bakersfield CA 93308
Tel (661) 831-0002 SIC 7361 7363

DIVERSE STAFFING INC p 443
1800 E Lambert Rd Ste 100, Brea CA 92821
Tel (714) 482-0499 SIC 7361

▲ **ON ASSIGNMENT INC** p 1085
26745 Malibu Hills Rd, Calabasas CA 91301
Tel (818) 878-7900 SIC 7363 7361

A P R CONSULTING INC p 6
1370 Valley Vista Dr # 280, Diamond Bar CA 91765
Tel (909) 396-5375 SIC 7361 7379

CHIPTON-ROSS INC (WISCONSIN) p 301
343 Main St, El Segundo CA 90245
Tel (310) 414-7800 SIC 7361

SOLVIS STAFFING SERVICES INC p 1339
500 La Terraza Blvd # 110, Escondido CA 92025
Tel (858) 230-8920 SIC 7361

HOWROYD-WRIGHT EMPLOYMENT AGENCY INC p 714
327 W Broadway, Glendale CA 91204
Tel (818) 240-8688 SIC 7361

KIMCO STAFFING SERVICES INC p 818
17872 Cowan, Irvine CA 92614
Tel (949) 331-1199 SIC 7361

DENSO PRODUCTS AND SERVICES AMERICAS INC p 429
3900 Via Oro Ave, Long Beach CA 90810
Tel (310) 834-6352
SIC 5013 7361 5075 3714

CAREER GROUP INC p 254
10100 Santa Monica Blvd # 900, Los Angeles CA 90067
Tel (310) 277-8188 SIC 7361

▲ **KORN/FERRY INTERNATIONAL** p 828
1900 Avenue Stars, Los Angeles CA 90067
Tel (310) 552-1834 SIC 8742 7361

TEAM-ONE EMPLOYMENT SPECIALISTS LLC p 1430
2999 Overland Ave Ste 212, Los Angeles CA 90064
Tel (310) 481-4482 SIC 7361

TEAM-ONE STAFFING SERVICES INC p 1430
10801 National Blvd # 104, Los Angeles CA 90064
Tel (310) 481-4480 SIC 7361

▲ **ROBERT HALF INTERNATIONAL INC** p 1241
2884 Sand Hill Rd Ste 200, Menlo Park CA 94025
Tel (650) 234-6000
SIC 7363 7361 8748 8721

NOVA MANAGEMENT INC p 1062
660 Camino Aguajito # 300, Monterey CA 93940
Tel (831) 373-4544 SIC 8711 7361

CONTEMPORARY SERVICES CORP p 362
17101 Superior St, Northridge CA 91325
Tel (818) 885-5150 SIC 7361

STAFFCHEX INC p 1374
790 The City Dr S Ste 180, Orange CA 92868
Tel (714) 912-7500 SIC 7361

CORNERSTONE STAFFING SOLUTIONS INC p 371
7020 Koll Center Pkwy, Pleasanton CA 94566
Tel (925) 426-6900 SIC 7361

RAMCO ENTERPRISES LP p 1207
320 Airport Blvd, Salinas CA 93905
Tel (831) 758-5272 SIC 0171 7361 0723

EPLICA INC p 505
2355 Northside Dr Ste 120, San Diego CA 92108
Tel (619) 260-2000 SIC 7363 7361

GARICH INC p 592
6336 Greenwich Dr Ste A, San Diego CA 92122
Tel (858) 453-1331 SIC 7361 8742

■ **NURSEFINDERS LLC** p 1067
12400 High Bluff Dr, San Diego CA 92130
Tel (858) 314-7427
SIC 7361 8082 7363 8049

SE SCHER CORP p 1295
665 3rd St Ste 415, San Francisco CA 94107
Tel (415) 431-8826 SIC 7361

40 HRS INC p 3
1669 Flanigan Dr, San Jose CA 95121
Tel (408) 414-0158 SIC 7361

▲ **TRINET GROUP INC** p 1480
1100 San Leandro Blvd # 300, San Leandro CA 94577
Tel (510) 352-5000 SIC 7361 8721

CHILDCARE CAREERS LLC p 298
1700 S El Camino Real # 201, San Mateo CA 94402
Tel (650) 372-0211 SIC 7363 7361

VOLUNTEERS OF AMERICA p 1565
2100 N Broadway Ste 300, Santa Ana CA 92706
Tel (714) 426-9834 SIC 8322 7361 9531

BUTLER AMERICA LLC p 230
3820 State St Ste B, Santa Barbara CA 93105
Tel (203) 926-2700 SIC 8711 8748 7361

ATR INTERNATIONAL INC p 129
1230 Oakmead Pkwy Ste 110, Sunnyvale CA 94085
Tel (408) 328-8000 SIC 7361

ACT 1 GROUP INC p 19
1999 W 190th St, Torrance CA 90504
Tel (310) 532-1529 SIC 7361 8741

■ **ALPINE ACCESS INC** p 60
1290 N Broadway Ste 1400, Denver CO 80203
Tel (303) 850-3700 SIC 7361 8742 8748

ARGUS OF COLORADO INC p 108
720 S Colorado Blvd 600n, Denver CO 80246
Tel (303) 322-4100 SIC 8082 7361

IQNAVIGATOR INC p 764
6465 Greenwood Plaza Blvd, Greenwood Village CO 80111
Tel (303) 563-1500 SIC 7371 7361

▲ **COMMAND CENTER INC** p 344
3609 S Wadsworth Blvd # 250, Lakewood CO 80235
Tel (866) 464-5844 SIC 7361

MONROE STAFFING SERVICES LLC p 985
35 Nutmeg Dr Ste 250, Trumbull CT 06611
Tel (203) 268-8624 SIC 7361

COMPASS GROUP INTERNATIONAL LLC p 351
61 Wilton Rd Ste 2, Westport CT 06880
Tel (203) 221-1703 SIC 7361 7363

■ **ONWARD HEALTHCARE INC** p 1088
64 Danbury Rd Ste 100, Wilton CT 06897
Tel (203) 834-3000 SIC 7361

SERVICEXPRESS CORP p 1308
120 N Ray St, Georgetown DE 19947
Tel (302) 856-3500 SIC 7361

NRI INC p 1064
1015 18th St Nw Ste 710, Washington DC 20036
Tel (202) 466-4670 SIC 7363 7361

SPECIAL COUNSEL p 1355
1400 I St Nw Ste 325, Washington DC 20005
Tel (202) 737-3436 SIC 7363 8111 7361

AMERICAN TRAVELER STAFFING PROFESSIONALS LLC p 80
1615 S Federal Hwy # 300, Boca Raton FL 33432
Tel (561) 391-1811 SIC 7363 7361

CAREERS USA INC p 254
6501 Congress Ave Ste 200, Boca Raton FL 33487
Tel (561) 995-7000 SIC 7361

▲ **CROSS COUNTRY HEALTHCARE INC** p 393
6551 Pk Of Cmmrce Blvd Nw, Boca Raton FL 33487
Tel (561) 998-2232 SIC 7361 7363

P2P STAFFING CORP p 1103
5810 Coral Ridge Dr # 250, Coral Springs FL 33076
Tel (954) 656-8600 SIC 7361

LIFE CARE HOME HEALTH SERVICES CORP p 863
4723 W Atl Ave Ste 21, Delray Beach FL 33445
Tel (561) 272-5866 SIC 8082 7361

■ **KAPLAN INC** p 803
6301 Kaplan Univ Ave, Fort Lauderdale FL 33309
Tel (212) 492-5800
SIC 8299 7361 7372 2731

TECHNISOURCE INC p 1431
2050 Spectrum Blvd, Fort Lauderdale FL 33309
Tel (954) 308-7600 SIC 7363 5045 7361

ADECCO USA INC p 22
10151 Deerwood Bldg 200, Jacksonville FL 32256
Tel (904) 359-4710
SIC 7363 7361 8742 6794

CSI COMPANIES INC p 397
9995 Gate Pkwy N Ste 100, Jacksonville FL 32246
Tel (904) 338-9515 SIC 7361

MPS GROUP INC p 995
10151 Deerwood Park Blvd 200-400, Jacksonville FL 32256
Tel (904) 360-2000 SIC 7363 8742 7361

GL STAFFING SERVICES INC p 613
1709 Banks Rd Bldg A, Margate FL 33063
Tel (954) 973-8350 SIC 7361

RESOURCE EMPLOYMENT SOLUTIONS LLC p 1227
5900 Lake Ellenor Dr # 100, Orlando FL 32809
Tel (866) 412-6535 SIC 7361 7363

HALIFAX HOME HEALTH p 654
3800 Woodbriar Trl, Port Orange FL 32129
Tel (386) 322-4700 SIC 8082 7361

GOODWILL INDUSTRIES-SUNCOAST INC p 625
10596 Gandy Blvd N, Saint Petersburg FL 33702
Tel (727) 523-1512 SIC 7361 5932

ACCUIRE LLC p 16
2001 Thomasville Rd, Tallahassee FL 32308
Tel (850) 893-7710 SIC 7361

▲ **KFORCE INC** p 816
1001 E Palm Ave, Tampa FL 33605
Tel (813) 552-5000 SIC 7363 7361

KFORCE SERVICES CORP p 816
1001 E Palm Ave, Tampa FL 33605
Tel (813) 552-3734 SIC 7361

JACKSON HEALTHCARE LLC p 774
2655 Northwinds Pkwy, Alpharetta GA 30009
Tel (770) 643-5500 SIC 7361

■ **DAL GLOBAL SERVICES LLC** p 409
980 Virginia Ave 4th, Atlanta GA 30354
Tel (404) 715-4300
SIC 7361 8331 7382 5088

EMPLOYBRIDGE HOLDING CO p 494
1040 Crown Pointe Pkwy # 1040, Atlanta GA 30338
Tel (770) 671-1900 SIC 7361

RANDSTAD NORTH AMERICA INC p 1208
3625 Cumberland Blvd Se, Atlanta GA 30339
Tel (770) 937-7000 SIC 7363 7361

RANDSTAD US LP p 1208
3625 Cumberland Blvd Se, Atlanta GA 30339
Tel (770) 937-7000 SIC 7361 7363

STAFFING SOLUTIONS SOUTHWEST INC p 1374
1040 Crown Pointe Pkwy, Atlanta GA 30338
Tel (678) 443-4200 SIC 7361 7363

MANAGEMENT ANALYSIS & UTILIZATION INC p 900
501 Greene St Ste 100, Augusta GA 30901
Tel (706) 722-6806 SIC 7361

IG STAFFING HOLDINGS LLC p 730
4170 Ashford Dnwody Rd Ne, Brookhaven GA 30319
Tel (404) 257-7900 SIC 7361

INSIGHT GLOBAL LLC p 746
4170 Ashford Dunwoody 250, Brookhaven GA 30319
Tel (404) 257-7900 SIC 7361

MAGIC WORKFORCE SOLUTIONS LLC p 895
840 Ernest W Barrett Pkwy, Kennesaw GA 30144
Tel (770) 420-4759 SIC 7361

PROFESSIONAL SYSTEMS LLC p 1180
6055 Lakeside Ste 440, Macon GA 31210
Tel (478) 752-7000 SIC 7349 7361

PP&A-GA CORP p 1166
5425 Peachtree Pkwy, Norcross GA 30092
Tel (678) 906-2806 SIC 7361

SULLIVAN GROUP p 1397
37 W Fairmont Ave # 100, Savannah GA 31406
Tel (912) 352-3800 SIC 7361

EXCEPTIONAL INC p 517
111 Hana Hwy Ste 111, Kahului HI 96732
Tel (808) 877-6555 SIC 7363 5941 7361

ACCRETIVE SOLUTIONS OPERATING CORP p 16
1 S Wacker Dr Ste 950, Chicago IL 60606
Tel (312) 994-4600 SIC 8721 7363 7361

■ **CAREERBUILDER LLC** p 254
200 N La Salle St # 1100, Chicago IL 60601
Tel (773) 527-3600 SIC 7361

HARBORQUEST INC p 660
14 E Jackson Blvd # 1210, Chicago IL 60604
Tel (312) 612-7600 SIC 7363 4119 7361

▲ **HEIDRICK & STRUGGLES INTERNATIONAL INC** p 680
233 S Wacker Dr Ste 4900, Chicago IL 60606
Tel (312) 496-1200 SIC 7361

■ **PEOPLESCOUT INC** p 1133
860 W Evergreen Ave, Chicago IL 60642
Tel (312) 915-0505 SIC 7361

PROFESSIONAL NURSING INC p 1180
325 N Wells St Ste 900, Chicago IL 60654
Tel (312) 527-1839 SIC 7361 7363

SMX LLC p 1335
860 W Evergreen Ave, Chicago IL 60642
Tel (312) 915-0900 SIC 7361

UNITED TEMPS INC p 1514
1550 S Ind Ave Ste 300, Chicago IL 60605
Tel (312) 922-8558 SIC 7361

ALTERNATIVE STAFFING INC p 62
5620 W Cermak Rd, Cicero IL 60804
Tel (708) 652-3636 SIC 7361

MESSINA GROUP INC p 951
200 S Prospect Ave, Park Ridge IL 60068
Tel (847) 825-8000 SIC 7361 7379

VONACHEN SERVICES INC p 1565
8900 N Pioneer Rd, Peoria IL 61615
Tel (309) 691-6202
SIC 7349 4731 8741 7361

UNISTAFF PRO INC p 1505
344 E Irving Park Rd, Roselle IL 60172
Tel (708) 450-1600 SIC 7361

EMPLOYCO USA II INC p 494
350 E Ogden Ave, Westmont IL 60559
Tel (630) 920-0000 SIC 7361

PLUS GROUP INC p 1157
7425 Janes Ave Ste 201, Woodridge IL 60517
Tel (630) 515-0500 SIC 7361 7363

ELWOOD STAFFING SERVICES INC p 490
4111 Central Ave, Columbus IN 47203
Tel (812) 372-6200 SIC 7361

ABC EMPLOYMENT HOLDINGS LLC p 10
6610 N Shadeland Ave, Indianapolis IN 46220
Tel (866) 674-7678 SIC 7361

PEOPLELINK LLC p 1132
431 E Colfax Ave Ste 200, South Bend IN 46617
Tel (574) 232-5400 SIC 7361

ACCESS DIRECT TELEMARKETING SERVICES INC p 14
4515 20th Ave Sw Ste B, Cedar Rapids IA 52404
Tel (319) 390-8900 SIC 7389 7361

SNI COMPANIES p 1335
4500 Westown Pkwy Ste 120, West Des Moines IA 50266
Tel (727) 577-4294 SIC 7361

GRAFTON INC p 628
4501 College Blvd Ste 160, Leawood KS 66211
Tel (913) 498-0701 SIC 7363 7361

POMEROY GROUP HOLDINGS INC p 1160
1020 Petersburg Rd, Hebron KY 41048
Tel (859) 586-6000
SIC 7373 7374 7361 6719

POMEROY IT SOLUTIONS SALES CO INC p 1160
1020 Petersburg Rd, Hebron KY 41048
Tel (859) 586-0600 SIC 7373 7374 7361

LOFTON CORP p 874
9414 Interline Ave, Baton Rouge LA 70809
Tel (225) 924-0200 SIC 7361

WORKPLACE STAFFING SOLUTIONS LLC p 1624
13055 Hwy 1, Larose LA 70373
Tel (985) 798-5111 SIC 7363 7361

ADVANTAGE MEDICAL PROFESSIONALS LLC p 26
3340 Severn Ave Ste 320, Metairie LA 70002
Tel (504) 456-0073 SIC 7361 7363

UP PROFESSIONAL SOLUTIONS LLC p 1528
1100 Poydras St Ste 1300, New Orleans LA 70163
Tel (800) 245-8274 SIC 7361 7363

CADDO PARISH COMMISSION p 236
525 Marshall St, Shreveport LA 71101
Tel (318) 226-6891 SIC 7361

YORK HOSPITAL p 1637
15 Hospital Dr, York ME 03909
Tel (207) 351-2023
SIC 8062 8051 8069 7361

CARE SOURCE LLC p 254
9114 Philadelphia Rd # 214, Baltimore MD 21237
Tel (410) 391-2627 SIC 7361

ALLEGIS GLOBAL SOLUTIONS INC p 53
7312 Parkway Dr, Hanover MD 21076
Tel (410) 579-3000 SIC 7361

ALLEGIS GROUP INC p 53
7301 Parkway Dr, Hanover MD 21076
Tel (410) 579-3000 SIC 7361

AQUENT LLC p 101
501 Boylston St Ste 3, Boston MA 02116
Tel (617) 535-5000 SIC 7361

BEACON HILL STAFFING GROUP LLC p 164
152 Bowdoin St, Boston MA 02108
Tel (617) 326-4000 SIC 7361

RENAISSANCE WORLDWIDE INC p 1223
711 Boylston St, Boston MA 02116
Tel (617) 535-5000
SIC 7363 8742 7379 7361 8748 7371

HARVARD STUDENT AGENCIES INC p 666
67 Mount Auburn St, Cambridge MA 02138
Tel (617) 495-3030 SIC 7361

ADVANTAGE RESOURCING AMERICA INC p 26
220 Norwood Park S, Norwood MA 02062
Tel (781) 251-8000 SIC 7361

MONSTER WORLDWIDE INC p 985
133 Boston Post Rd, Weston MA 02493
Tel (978) 461-8000 SIC 7311 7361

RANDSTAD PROFESSIONALS US LP p 1208
150 Presidential Way Fl 4, Woburn MA 01801
Tel (781) 213-1500 SIC 7361

RANDSTAD TECHNOLOGIES LP p 1208
150 Presidential Way # 300, Woburn MA 01801
Tel (781) 938-1910 SIC 7361

GONZALEZ CONTRACT SERVICES INC p 623
1670 Highwood E, Pontiac MI 48340
Tel (248) 548-6010 SIC 7361

RCO ENGINEERING INC p 1212
29200 Calahan Rd, Roseville MI 48066
Tel (586) 774-0100
SIC 3714 3089 3365 7361 3325 2531

RAPID GLOBAL BUSINESS SOLUTIONS INC p 1208
1200 Stephenson Hwy, Troy MI 48083
Tel (248) 589-1135 SIC 8711 7371 7361

SCHOENECKERS INC p 1288
7630 Bush Lake Rd, Edina MN 55439
Tel (952) 835-4800 SIC 8742 7361

ATTERRO INC p 129
730 2nd Ave S Ste 520, Minneapolis MN 55402
Tel (612) 373-2600 SIC 7363 7361

COUGHLAN COMPANIES INC p 374
1710 Roe Crest Dr, North Mankato MN 56003
Tel (507) 345-8100 SIC 7361 1741

CONSUMER DIRECTIONS INC p 361
425 E Saint Germain St # 200, Saint Cloud MN 56304
Tel (320) 420-3423 SIC 7361 8721

ATLAS STAFFING INC p 128
189 7th Pl E, Saint Paul MN 55101
Tel (651) 222-5894 SIC 7363 7361

HIMAGINE SOLUTIONS INC p 695
600 Emerson Rd Ste 225, Saint Louis MO 63141
Tel (314) 627-5135 SIC 8741 7361

ADVANCE SERVICES INC p 25
112 S Birch St, Norfolk NE 68701
Tel (402) 371-5733 SIC 7361

■ **CLP HOLDINGS CORP** p 328
10539 Prof Cir St 200, Reno NV 89521
Tel (775) 321-8000 SIC 7363 7361

SURGE RESOURCES INC p 1408
920 Candia Rd, Manchester NH 03109
Tel (603) 623-0007 SIC 8742 7361 7363

STAFF HUNTERS p 1374
1 Nh Ave Ste 125, Portsmouth NH 03801
Tel (603) 766-4909 SIC 7361

ON TIME STAFFING LLC p 1086
535 Route 38 Ste 412, Cherry Hill NJ 08002
Tel (866) 333-3007 SIC 7361

BOWLES CORPORATE SERVICES INC p 204
335 Broad St, Clifton NJ 07013
Tel (973) 773-0699 SIC 7381 7389 7361

CAREER NETWORK AFFILIATES INC p 254
38 Ivanhoe Dr, Manalapan NJ 07726
Tel (732) 972-3000 SIC 7361

GOTHAM TECHNOLOGY GROUP LLC p 626
1 Paragon Dr Ste 200, Montvale NJ 07645
Tel (201) 802-9600 SIC 5045 7361 5932

TR BRYANT ASSOCIATES INC p 1468
377 Hoes Ln, Piscataway NJ 08854
Tel (732) 981-0440 SIC 7363 7361

KENNEDY HEALTH CARE FOUNDATION INC p 811
18 E Laurel Rd, Stratford NJ 08084
Tel (856) 661-5100
SIC 6733 4119 8051 6531 7361 8721

COWORX STAFFING SERVICES LLC p 386
1375 Plainfield Ave Ste 1, Watchung NJ 07069
Tel (908) 757-5300 SIC 7361 8721

EXCEL STAFFING COMPANIES LLC p 516
2100 Osuna Rd Ne Ste 100, Albuquerque NM 87113
Tel (505) 262-1871 SIC 7361 7363

PRO CORP p 1178
999 Stewart Ave Ste 100, Bethpage NY 11714
Tel (516) 437-3300 SIC 7363 7361

PRO UNLIMITED GLOBAL SOLUTIONS INC p 1178
999 Stewart Ave Ste 100, Bethpage NY 11714
Tel (516) 437-3300 SIC 7363 7361

■ **BRACOR INC** p 206
346 Delaware Ave, Buffalo NY 14202
Tel (716) 856-7500 SIC 8082 8071 7361

▲ **COMPUTER TASK GROUP INC** p 353
800 Delaware Ave, Buffalo NY 14209
Tel (716) 882-8000 SIC 7371 7379 7361

ADECCO EMPLOYMENT SERVICES INC p 22
175 Broadhollow Rd, Melville NY 11747
Tel (631) 844-7100 SIC 7363 7361

STAR MULTI CARE SERVICES INC p 1378
115 Broadhollow Rd # 275, Melville NY 11747
Tel (631) 423-6689 SIC 8082 7361

ATC STAFFING SERVICES INC p 124
1983 Marcus Ave Ste E122, New Hyde Park NY 11042
Tel (516) 326-1396 SIC 7361 8093 8011

ACCESS STAFFING LLC p 15
360 Lexington Ave Fl 8, New York NY 10017
Tel (212) 687-5440 SIC 7361

CORE STAFFING SERVICES INC p 369
40 Wall St Ste 1600, New York NY 10005
Tel (212) 766-1222 SIC 7361

CTPARTNERS EXECUTIVE SEARCH INC p 399
1166 Avenue Of The Amrcs, New York NY 10036
Tel (212) 588-3500 SIC 7361

▲ **DHI GROUP INC** p 435
1040 Avenue Of The Amrcas, New York NY 10018
Tel (212) 725-6550 SIC 7361 4813 7375

FORREST SOLUTIONS INC p 568
19 W 44th St Fl 9, New York NY 10036
Tel (212) 986-3600 SIC 7361

▲ **HUDSON GLOBAL INC** p 716
1325 Avenue Of The Americ, New York NY 10019
Tel (212) 351-7300 SIC 7361 7363

OGILVY GROUP LLC p 1076
636 11th Ave, New York NY 10036
Tel (212) 237-4000
SIC 7311 8743 8748 7336 7361 8732

RUSSELL REYNOLDS ASSOCIATES INC p 1259
200 Park Ave Fl 23, New York NY 10166
Tel (212) 309-1089 SIC 7361

SOLOMON-PAGE GROUP LLC p 1338
260 Madison Ave Fl 3, New York NY 10016
Tel (212) 403-6100 SIC 7361

SYMPHONY TALENT LLC p 1414
45 Rockefeller Plz # 659, New York NY 10111
Tel (212) 999-9000 SIC 7372 7361

TEACH FOR AMERICA INC p 1429
25 Broadway Fl 12, New York NY 10004
Tel (212) 279-2080 SIC 7361

THERACARE OF NEW YORK INC p 1447
116 W 32nd St Fl 8, New York NY 10001
Tel (212) 564-2350 SIC 8093 7361

TRI-STATE EMPLOYMENT SERVICE INC p 1477
160 Broadway Fl 15, New York NY 10038
Tel (212) 346-7960 SIC 7361

KEENA STAFF INC p 807
2 Progress Blvd, Queensbury NY 12804
Tel (518) 793-9825 SIC 7361 7363

NATIONAL HOME HEALTH CARE CORP p 1013
700 White Plains Rd Ste 2, Scarsdale NY 10583
Tel (914) 722-9000 SIC 8082 7361

SHOW PROS ENTERTAINMENT SERVICES INC p 1318
514 Springbrook Rd Ste A, Charlotte NC 28217
Tel (704) 525-3784 SIC 7363 7361

SET AND SERVICE RESOURCES LLC p 1308
8303 Six Forks Rd Ste 207, Raleigh NC 27615
Tel (919) 787-5571 SIC 7361

RESOURCE CO INC p 1227
1292 S Stratford Rd, Winston Salem NC 27103
Tel (336) 896-1000 SIC 7363 7361

RIGHT HUMAN RESOURCE CONSULTANTS INC p 1234
4445 Lake Forest Dr # 470, Blue Ash OH 45242
Tel (513) 733-1313 SIC 8742 7361

BELFLEX STAFFING NETWORK LLC p 169
11591 Goldcoast Dr, Cincinnati OH 45249
Tel (513) 488-8588 SIC 7361 7363

STAFFMARK HOLDINGS INC p 1374
201 E 4th St Ste 800, Cincinnati OH 45202
Tel (513) 651-1111 SIC 7361 7363

STAFFMARK INVESTMENT LLC p 1374
201 E 4th St Ste 800, Cincinnati OH 45202
Tel (513) 651-3600 SIC 7361

JOBSOHIO p 787
41 S High St, Columbus OH 43215
Tel (614) 224-6446 SIC 7361

TRADESMEN INTERNATIONAL LLC p 1469
9760 Shepard Rd, Macedonia OH 44056
Tel (440) 349-3432 SIC 7361

MANCAN INC p 901
48 1st St Nw, Massillon OH 44647
Tel (330) 832-4595 SIC 7361

■ **HEARTLAND EMPLOYMENT SERVICES LLC** p 679
333 N Summit St, Toledo OH 43604
Tel (419) 252-5743 SIC 7361

JOB 1 USA p 787
701 Jefferson Ave Ste 202, Toledo OH 43604
Tel (419) 255-5005 SIC 7381 7363 7361

RUMPF CORP p 1258
701 Jefferson Ave Ste 201, Toledo OH 43604
Tel (419) 255-5005 SIC 7361 7363 7381

DMD INC p 446
1309 W Detroit St, Broken Arrow OK 74012
Tel (918) 250-5521 SIC 7361

ADDISON GROUP L L C p 22
901 N Lincoln Blvd # 305, Oklahoma City OK 73104
Tel (405) 235-6700 SIC 7361 8742

EXPRESS SERVICES INC p 520
9701 Boardwalk Blvd, Oklahoma City OK 73162
Tel (405) 840-5000 SIC 7363 6794 7361

STATE OF OKLAHOMA p 1382
421 Nw 13th St Ste 220, Oklahoma City OK 73103
Tel (405) 521-2342 SIC 7361

GDH CONSULTING INC p 595
4200 E Skelly Dr Ste 650, Tulsa OK 74135
Tel (918) 392-1600 SIC 7379 7361 7371

CERTIFIED PERSONNEL SERVICE AGENCY INC p 284
10201 N Mcalister Rd, La Grande OR 97850
Tel (541) 963-6678 SIC 7361

DEPAUL INDUSTRIES p 430
4950 Ne Martin Luther Ki, Portland OR 97211
Tel (503) 281-1289 SIC 7361 8331

NORTHWEST STAFFING RESOURCES INC p 1060
851 Sw 6th Ave Ste 300, Portland OR 97204
Tel (503) 323-9190 SIC 7363 7361

DAY & ZIMMERMANN NPS INC p 417
1827 Freedom Rd Ste 101, Lancaster PA 17601
Tel (717) 299-3754 SIC 7361

MCCALLION TEMPS INC p 926
601 N Bthlhem Pike Bldg A, Montgomeryville PA 18936
Tel (215) 855-8000 SIC 7363 7361

▲ **MASTECH DIGITAL INC** p 918
1305 Cherrington Pkwy # 400, Moon Township PA 15108
Tel (412) 787-2100 SIC 7361 7371

■ **CDI CORP** p 271
1735 Market St Ste 200, Philadelphia PA 19103
Tel (215) 569-2200
SIC 7363 8711 7361 6794

▲ **CDI CORP** p 271
1735 Market St Ste 200, Philadelphia PA 19103
Tel (215) 569-2200
SIC 8711 7371 7373 7376 7361 7363

SYSTEM ONE HOLDINGS LLC p 1418
12 Federal St Ste 205, Pittsburgh PA 15212
Tel (412) 995-1900 SIC 7361

JUDGE GROUP INC p 796
151 S Warner Rd Ste 100, Wayne PA 19087
Tel (610) 667-7700 SIC 7373 7361 7379

KENEXA CORP p 810
650 E Swedesford Rd # 200, Wayne PA 19087
Tel (877) 971-9171 SIC 7361 7371

JMM SERVICES INC p 786
1431 N George St, York PA 17404
Tel (717) 848-1100 SIC 7361

TRADESOURCE INC p 1469
205 Hallene Rd Unit 211, Warwick RI 02886
Tel (401) 384-6148
SIC 7361 1751 1711 1731 1742 1721

SOI HOLDINGS INC p 1337
3023 Hsbc Way Ste 100, Fort Mill SC 29707
Tel (704) 523-2191 SIC 7361

DEFENDER SERVICES INC p 422
9031 Garners Ferry Rd, Hopkins SC 29061
Tel (803) 776-4220 SIC 7349 7361 7382

■ **DHI HOLDINGS INC** p 435
105 Diversco Dr, Spartanburg SC 29307
Tel (864) 579-3420 SIC 7361

DIRECT AUCTION SERVICES LLC p 441
101 Jessica Lauren Ct, Hendersonville TN 37075
Tel (678) 570-3493
SIC 5012 7539 7549 7542 7361

COUNTRYWIDE HR p 375
135 Fox Rd Ste F, Knoxville TN 37922
Tel (877) 257-6662 SIC 8721 7361

ALLIED STAFFING INC p 57
4400 Buffalo Gap Rd # 4500, Abilene TX 79606
Tel (325) 695-5822 SIC 7361 7363

■ **BG STAFFING LLC** p 180
14900 Landmark Blvd, Dallas TX 75254
Tel (972) 692-2400 SIC 7361

DRIVING MOMENTUM USA INC p 456
2025 Irving Blvd Ste 102, Dallas TX 75207
Tel (214) 651-1031 SIC 7361

PINNACLE LIGHT INDUSTRIAL LLC p 1150
5501 Lyndon B Johnson Fwy Fw600, Dallas TX 75240
Tel (214) 740-2443 SIC 7361

T & T STAFF MANAGEMENT INC p 1419
511 Executive Center Blvd, El Paso TX 79902
Tel (915) 771-0393 SIC 7361

BURNETT COMPANIES CONSOLIDATED INC p 228
9800 Richmond Ave Ste 800, Houston TX 77042
Tel (713) 977-4777 SIC 7361 8243

PDS TECH INC p 1125
300 E John Carpenter Fwy # 700, Irving TX 75062
Tel (214) 647-9600 SIC 7361

WORKWAY INC p 1624
105 Decker Ct Ste 560, Irving TX 75062
Tel (972) 514-1547 SIC 7361

▲ **INSPERITY INC** p 746
19001 Crescent Springs Dr, Kingwood TX 77339
Tel (281) 358-8986
SIC 8742 7363 7361 6311

ITSQUEST INC p 768
4505 82nd St Ste 3, Lubbock TX 79424
Tel (806) 785-9100 SIC 7361

AM-MEX PRODUCTS INC p 63
3801 W Military Hwy, Mcallen TX 78503
Tel (956) 631-7916 SIC 3714 7361 3672

MEADOR STAFFING SERVICES INC p 934
722a Fairmont Pkwy, Pasadena TX 77504
Tel (713) 941-0616 SIC 7361 7363

TREND PERSONNEL SERVICES INC p 1476
2701 Sunset Ridge Dr, Rockwall TX 75032
Tel (214) 553-5505 SIC 7361

HAWKINS ASSOCIATES INC p 669
909 Ne Loop 410 Ste 104, San Antonio TX 78209
Tel (210) 349-9911 SIC 7363 7361

TALENTNET INC p 1422
2219 Sawdust Rd Ste 603, Spring TX 77380
Tel (844) 825-3686 SIC 7361

TECHNOLOGY TRANSFER INC p 1432
16969 N Texas Ave Ste 400, Webster TX 77598
Tel (281) 488-7961 SIC 7361 7379

SHC SERVICES INC p 1313
1640 Redstone Center Dr # 200, Park City UT 84098
Tel (435) 645-0788 SIC 7361

ISI HR INC p 766
859 W South Jordan Pkwy # 77, South Jordan UT 84095
Tel (801) 984-0252 SIC 7361

STG INTERNATIONAL INC p 1389
99 Canal Center Plz # 500, Alexandria VA 22314
Tel (571) 970-3729 SIC 7361

■ **APEX SYSTEMS LLC** p 96
4400 Cox Rd Ste 100, Glen Allen VA 23060
Tel (804) 254-2600 SIC 7363 7361

■ **DYNCORP INTERNATIONAL INC** p 465
1700 Old Meadow Rd, Mc Lean VA 22102
Tel (571) 722-0210
SIC 8741 7371 7381 7361 7363

FRIENDS & CO p 580
1760 Reston Pkwy Ste 200, Reston VA 20190
Tel (703) 796-0333 SIC 7361

PEOPLE TECH GROUP INC p 1132
601108 Ave Ne Ste 310, Bellevue WA 98004
Tel (425) 880-7981 SIC 7361

WAFERTECH LLC p 1571
5509 Nw Parker St, Camas WA 98607
Tel (360) 817-3000 SIC 3674 7361

LABOR READY SOUTHWEST INC p 836
1015 A St Unit A, Tacoma WA 98402
Tel (800) 610-8920 SIC 7361

▲ **BARRETT BUSINESS SERVICES INC** p 157
8100 Ne Parkway Dr # 200, Vancouver WA 98662
Tel (360) 828-0700 SIC 7361 8742

PRN HEALTH SERVICES INC p 1178
740 Ford St Ste A, Kimberly WI 54136
Tel (920) 830-8811 SIC 7361 7363

■ **EXPERIS US INC** p 520
100 W Manpower Pl, Milwaukee WI 53212
Tel (414) 961-1000 SIC 7361

▲ **MANPOWERGROUP INC** p 903
100 W Manpower Pl, Milwaukee WI 53212
Tel (414) 961-1000 SIC 7363 7361

SIC 7363 Help Supply Svcs

SKILSTAF INC p 1330
860 Airport Dr, Alexander City AL 35010
Tel (256) 234-6208 SIC 7363

■ **TECHNICAL STAFFING RESOURCES LLC** p 1431
10 Inverness Center Pkwy, Birmingham AL 35242
Tel (205) 437-7100 SIC 8711 7363

AVIATION & MISSILE SOLUTIONS LLC p 138
1000 Explorer Blvd Nw, Huntsville AL 35806
Tel (256) 713-5900 SIC 7363

AUTOMATION PERSONNEL SERVICES INC p 134
401 Southgate Dr, Pelham AL 35124
Tel (205) 733-3700 SIC 7363

WARREN AVERETT COMPANIES LLC p 1576
2500 Acton Rd Ste 200, Vestavia AL 35243
Tel (205) 979-4100
SIC 8721 8741 7363 8742

CALISTA CORP p 242
5015 Bus Pk Blvd Ste 3000, Anchorage AK 99503
Tel (907) 279-5516 SIC 6512 7363 2711

SWAN EMPLOYER SERVICES p 1411
1306 E 74th Ave Ste 200, Anchorage AK 99518
Tel (907) 344-7926 SIC 7363 8721

YUKON-KUSKOKWIM HEALTH CORP p 1640
829 Hospin Hwy Ste 329, Bethel AK 99559
Tel (907) 543-6300
SIC 8062 7363 8069 8093 8042 8021

■ **HONEYWELL AEROSPACE INC** p 705
1944 E Sky Harbor Cir N, Phoenix AZ 85034
Tel (602) 365-3099 SIC 3812 7363 7699

TERAMAR STAFFING INC p 1439
1075 N 51st Ave Ste 102, Phoenix AZ 85043
Tel (602) 288-0500 SIC 7363

STANDARDAERO BUSINESS AVIATION SERVICES LLC p 1376
6710 N Scottsdale Rd, Scottsdale AZ 85253
Tel (480) 377-3100 SIC 7363

MERCY MEDICAL SERVICES INC p 948
5401 Ellsworth Rd, Fort Smith AR 72903
Tel (479) 314-6060 SIC 7363

CONTINENTAL LABOR RESOURCES INC p 363
900 Mohawk St Ste 120, Bakersfield CA 93309
Tel (661) 635-0335 SIC 7363

ESPARZA ENTERPRISES INC p 509
3851 Fruitvale Ave Ste A, Bakersfield CA 93308
Tel (661) 831-0002 SIC 7361 7363

SOURCE ONE STAFFING LLC p 1342
5312 Irwindale Ave Ste 1h, Baldwin Park CA 91706
Tel (626) 337-0560 SIC 7363

NES HOLDINGS INC p 1026
39 Main St, Belvedere Tiburon CA 94920
Tel (415) 435-4591 SIC 7363

▲ **ON ASSIGNMENT INC** p 1085
26745 Malibu Hills Rd, Calabasas CA 91301
Tel (818) 878-7900 SIC 7363 7361

TEG STAFFING INC p 1432
2604 El Camino Real Ste B, Carlsbad CA 92008
Tel (619) 584-3444 SIC 7363

UNITED STAFFING SOLUTIONS INC p 1512
12069 Jefferson Blvd, Culver City CA 90230
Tel (310) 305-9999 SIC 7363

CORPORATE PERSONNEL NETWORK INC p 372
3552 Green Ave Ste 200, La Habra CA 90631
Tel (562) 493-1503 SIC 7363

HALLMARK AVIATION SERVICES LP p 654
5757 W Century Blvd # 860, Los Angeles CA 90045
Tel (310) 215-0701 SIC 7363

MEDICAL MANAGEMENT CONSULTANTS INC p 937
8150 Beverly Blvd, Los Angeles CA 90048
Tel (310) 659-3835
SIC 7363 8742 8748 8721

▲ **ROBERT HALF INTERNATIONAL INC** p 1241
2884 Sand Hill Rd Ste 200, Menlo Park CA 94025
Tel (650) 234-6000
SIC 7363 7361 8748 8721

ROTH STAFFING COMPANIES LP p 1252
450 N State College Blvd, Orange CA 92868
Tel (714) 939-8600 SIC 7363

STAR H-R p 1378
3820 Cypress Dr Ste 2, Petaluma CA 94954
Tel (707) 762-4447 SIC 7363

CAMEO GLOBAL INC p 245
4695 Chabot Dr Ste 101, Pleasanton CA 94588
Tel (925) 479-7800
SIC 7373 7371 7379 7363 4813 8742

STENO EMPLOYMENT SERVICES INC p 1385
8560 Vineyard Ave Ste 208, Rancho Cucamonga CA 91730
Tel (909) 476-1404 SIC 7363

FLEXCARE LLC p 556
990 Reserve Dr Ste 200, Roseville CA 95678
Tel (866) 564-3589 SIC 7363

▲ **AMN HEALTHCARE SERVICES INC** p 85
12400 High Bluff Dr, San Diego CA 92130
Tel (866) 871-8519 SIC 7363

CPM LTD INC p 387
1855 1st Ave Ste 300, San Diego CA 92101
Tel (619) 237-9900 SIC 7363

EPLICA INC p 505
2355 Northside Dr Ste 120, San Diego CA 92108
Tel (619) 260-2000 SIC 7363 7361

GO-STAFF INC p 619
8798 Complex Dr, San Diego CA 92123
Tel (858) 292-8562 SIC 7363 8721

■ **NURSEFINDERS LLC** p 1067
12400 High Bluff Dr, San Diego CA 92130
Tel (858) 314-7427
SIC 7361 8082 7363 8049

■ **RX PRO HEALTH LLC** p 1260
12400 High Bluff Dr, San Diego CA 92130
Tel (858) 369-4050 SIC 7363

TEGP INC p 1432
2375 Northside Dr Ste 360, San Diego CA 92108
Tel (619) 584-3408 SIC 7363

CHILDCARE CAREERS LLC p 298
1700 S El Camino Real # 201, San Mateo CA 94402
Tel (650) 372-0211 SIC 7363 7361

SURGICAL STAFF INC p 1409
120 Saint Matthews Ave, San Mateo CA 94401
Tel (650) 558-3999 SIC 7363

IMPCO TECHNOLOGIES INC p 734
3030 S Susan St, Santa Ana CA 92704
Tel (714) 656-1200 SIC 3714 3592 7363

BUTLER INTERNATIONAL INC p 230
3820 State St Ste A, Santa Barbara CA 93105
Tel (805) 882-2200 SIC 7363 8742

BUTLER SERVICE GROUP INC p 230
3820 State St Ste A, Santa Barbara CA 93105
Tel (201) 891-5312
SIC 7363 8711 8748 3661 7538

EMPLOYBRIDGE LLC p 494
3820 State St, Santa Barbara CA 93105
Tel (805) 882-2200 SIC 7363

COAST PERSONNEL SERVICES INC p 331
2295 De La Cruz Blvd, Santa Clara CA 95050
Tel (408) 653-2100 SIC 7363

WEST VALLEY ENGINEERING INC p 1596
390 Potrero Ave, Sunnyvale CA 94085
Tel (408) 735-1420 SIC 7363

JOHN MUIR PHYSICIAN NETWORK p 789
1450 Treat Blvd, Walnut Creek CA 94597
Tel (925) 296-9700
SIC 8062 8069 8093 7363

ADVANTEDGE BUSINESS GROUP LLC p 27
9777 Pyramid Ct Ste 220, Englewood CO 80112
Tel (303) 734-9424 SIC 8741 7291 7363

CENTER PARTNERS INC p 276
4401 Innovation Dr, Fort Collins CO 80525
Tel (970) 206-9000 SIC 7379 8742 7363

■ **ENVISION HEALTHCARE CORP** p 504
6363 S Fiddlers Green Cir # 1400, Greenwood Village CO 80111
Tel (303) 495-1200 SIC 4119 7363

GLOBAL EMPLOYMENT HOLDINGS INC p 616
10375 Park Meadows Dr # 475, Littleton CO 80124
Tel (303) 216-9500 SIC 7363 6719

GLOBAL EMPLOYMENT SOLUTIONS INC p 616
10375 Park Meadows Dr # 475, Littleton CO 80124
Tel (303) 216-9500 SIC 7363

EXCLUSIVE STAFFING LTD p 517
8774 Yates Dr Ste 210, Westminster CO 80031
Tel (303) 430-1700 SIC 7363

COMPASS GROUP INTERNATIONAL LLC p 351
61 Wilton Rd Ste 2, Westport CT 06880
Tel (203) 221-1703 SIC 7361 7363

INTEGRITY STAFFING SOLUTIONS INC p 750
700 Prides Xing 300, Newark DE 19713
Tel (302) 661-8770 SIC 7363

NRI INC p 1064
1015 18th St Nw Ste 710, Washington DC 20036
Tel (202) 466-4670 SIC 7363 7361

SPECIAL COUNSEL p 1355
1400 I St Nw Ste 325, Washington DC 20005
Tel (202) 737-3436 SIC 7363 8111 7361

ACCOUNTABLE HEALTHCARE STAFFING INC p 15
999 Yamato Rd Ste 210, Boca Raton FL 33431
Tel (561) 235-7810 SIC 7363

AMERICAN TRAVELER STAFFING PROFESSIONALS LLC p 80
1615 S Federal Hwy # 300, Boca Raton FL 33432
Tel (561) 391-1811 SIC 7363 7361

▲ **CROSS COUNTRY HEALTHCARE INC** p 393
6551 Pk Of Cmmrce Blvd Nw, Boca Raton FL 33487
Tel (561) 998-2232 SIC 7361 7363

DCR WORKFORCE INC p 418
7795 Nw Beacon Sq 201, Boca Raton FL 33487
Tel (561) 998-3737 SIC 7379 7363 8742

EMPLOYEE LEASING SOLUTIONS INC p 494
1401 Manatee Ave W # 600, Bradenton FL 34205
Tel (941) 746-6567 SIC 7363

TAD PGS INC p 1421
1001 3rd Ave W Ste 460, Bradenton FL 34205
Tel (941) 746-4434 SIC 7363

WORKFORCE BUSINESS SERVICES INC p 1624
1401 Manatee Ave W # 600, Bradenton FL 34205
Tel (941) 746-6567 SIC 7363

HALIFAX STAFFING INC p 654
303 N Clyde Morris Blvd, Daytona Beach FL 32114
Tel (386) 226-4560 SIC 7363

SFN GROUP INC p 1310
2050 Spectrum Blvd, Fort Lauderdale FL 33309
Tel (954) 308-7600 SIC 6794 7363

SFN PROFESSIONAL SERVICES LLC p 1310
2050 Spectrum Blvd, Fort Lauderdale FL 33309
Tel (954) 938-7600 SIC 7363

TECHNISOURCE INC p 1431
2050 Spectrum Blvd, Fort Lauderdale FL 33309
Tel (954) 308-7600 SIC 7363 5045 7361

21ST CENTURY ONCOLOGY INC p 2
2270 Colonial Blvd, Fort Myers FL 33907
Tel (239) 931-7333 SIC 8011 7363

PAYROLL MANAGEMENT INC p 1123
348 Miracle Strip Pkwy Sw # 39, Fort Walton Beach FL 32548
Tel (850) 243-5604 SIC 7363

DSK GROUP INC p 458
6715 W Grver Clvland Blvd, Homosassa FL 34446
Tel (352) 628-9800 SIC 7363

ADECCO USA INC p 22
10151 Deerwood Bldg 200, Jacksonville FL 32256
Tel (904) 359-4710
SIC 7363 7361 8742 6794

AMERI-FORCE INC p 67
9485 Regency Square Blvd, Jacksonville FL 32225
Tel (904) 633-9918 SIC 7363

MPS GROUP INC p 995
10151 Deerwood Park Blvd 200-400, Jacksonville FL 32256
Tel (904) 360-2000 SIC 7363 8742 7361

SPECIAL COUNSEL INC p 1355
10201 Centurion Pkwy N, Jacksonville FL 32256
Tel (904) 360-2251 SIC 7363

AMERICAN SALES AND MANAGEMENT ORGANIZATION LLC p 79
7200 Corp Ctr Dr Ste 206, Miami FL 33126
Tel (305) 269-2700 SIC 7382 7349 7363

APC WORKFORCE SOLUTIONS LLC p 96
420 S Orange Ave Ste 600, Orlando FL 32801
Tel (407) 770-6161 SIC 7363

JACKSON NURSE PROFESSIONALS LLC p 774
3452 Lake Lynda Dr # 200, Orlando FL 32817
Tel (205) 968-7500 SIC 7363

RESOURCE EMPLOYMENT SOLUTIONS LLC p 1227
5900 Lake Ellenor Dr # 100, Orlando FL 32809
Tel (866) 412-6535 SIC 7361 7363

INTERIM HEALTHCARE INC p 752
1601 Swgrs Corp Pkwy # 100, Sunrise FL 33323
Tel (800) 338-7786 SIC 6794 7363 8082

■ **GRANITE SERVICES INTERNATIONAL INC** p 631
201 N Franklin St # 1000, Tampa FL 33602
Tel (813) 242-7400 SIC 7363

▲ **KFORCE INC** p 816
1001 E Palm Ave, Tampa FL 33605
Tel (813) 552-5000 SIC 7363 7361

WORKERS TEMPORARY STAFFING INC p 1624
5050 W Lemon St Ste 200, Tampa FL 33609
Tel (813) 637-2220 SIC 7363

WTS ACQUISITION CORP p 1628
5050 W Lemon St, Tampa FL 33609
Tel (813) 637-2220 SIC 7363

AMERICAN STAFF MANAGEMENT INC p 79
27613 Cashford Cir # 102, Wesley Chapel FL 33544
Tel (813) 994-1200 SIC 7363

OASIS OUTSOURCING INC p 1071
2054 Vista Pkwy Ste 300, West Palm Beach FL 33411
Tel (561) 227-6500 SIC 8721 8742 7363

PERSONNEL SERVICES INC p 1137
2260 Palm Bch Lks 210, West Palm Beach FL 33409
Tel (561) 965-7070 SIC 7363

CRDENTIA CORP p 390
1964 Howell Branch Rd # 103, Winter Park FL 32792
Tel (520) 327-2651 SIC 7363

▲ **DLH HOLDINGS CORP** p 445
3565 Piedmont Rd Ne, Atlanta GA 30305
Tel (770) 554-3545 SIC 7363 8742

EB SUBHOLDINGS I INC p 474
1040 Crown Pointe Pkwy, Atlanta GA 30338
Tel (770) 671-1900 SIC 7363

EMPLOYBRIDGE SOUTHWEST LLC p 494
3050 Peachtree Rd Nw, Atlanta GA 30305
Tel (404) 816-3255 SIC 7363

EQUITY MSOUTH PARTNERS L P p 507
3050 Peachtree Rd Nw, Atlanta GA 30305
Tel (404) 816-3255 SIC 6799 7363

PRINCIPLE SOLUTIONS GROUP LLC p 1177
5 Concourse Pkwy Ste 2700, Atlanta GA 30328
Tel (770) 399-4500 SIC 7363

RANDSTAD NORTH AMERICA INC p 1208
3625 Cumberland Blvd Se, Atlanta GA 30339
Tel (770) 937-7000 SIC 7363 7361

RANDSTAD US LP p 1208
3625 Cumberland Blvd Se, Atlanta GA 30339
Tel (770) 937-7000 SIC 7361 7363

STAFFING SOLUTIONS OF CENTRAL TEXAS INC p 1374
1040 Crown Pointe Pkwy, Atlanta GA 30338
Tel (770) 671-1900 SIC 7363

STAFFING SOLUTIONS SOUTHWEST INC p 1374
1040 Crown Pointe Pkwy, Atlanta GA 30338
Tel (678) 443-4200 SIC 7361 7363

SIZEMORE INC p 1328
2116 Walton Way, Augusta GA 30904
Tel (706) 736-1456 SIC 7381 7363 7349

ALLSTAFF MANAGEMENT INC p 58
6650 Sugarloaf Pkwy # 300, Duluth GA 30097
Tel (770) 339-0000 SIC 7363

STAFFING CONCEPTS INTERNATIONAL OF GEORGIA INC p 1374
2435 Tech Center Pkwy, Lawrenceville GA 30043
Tel (770) 623-9143 SIC 7363

EXCEPTIONAL INC p 517
111 Hana Hwy Ste 111, Kahului HI 96732
Tel (808) 877-6555 SIC 7363 5941 7361

EMPLOYERS RESOURCE MANAGEMENT CO p 494
1301 S Vista Ave Ste 200, Boise ID 83705
Tel (208) 376-3000 SIC 7363

EXTREME STAFFING OF IDAHO LLC p 521
651 Blue Lakes Blvd N, Twin Falls ID 83301
Tel (208) 733-5627 SIC 7363

ANDY FRAIN SERVICES INC p 91
761 Shoreline Dr, Aurora IL 60504
Tel (630) 820-3820 SIC 7381 7363

ALTERNATIVE RESOURCES CORP p 62
600 Hart Rd Ste 300, Barrington IL 60010
Tel (847) 381-6701 SIC 7363

HUMAN FACTORS APPLICATIONS INC p 718
1000 Burr Ridge Pkwy, Burr Ridge IL 60527
Tel (630) 850-6900 SIC 7363 8748

ACCRETIVE SOLUTIONS OPERATING CORP p 16
1 S Wacker Dr Ste 950, Chicago IL 60606
Tel (312) 994-4600 SIC 8721 7363 7361

ADDISON PROFESSIONAL FINANCIAL SEARCH LLC p 22
125 S Wacker Dr Fl 27, Chicago IL 60606
Tel (312) 424-0300 SIC 7363

ELITE LABOR SERVICES LTD p 487
1400 W Hubbard St Ste 2, Chicago IL 60642
Tel (773) 235-3000 SIC 7363

HARBORQUEST INC p 660
14 E Jackson Blvd # 1210, Chicago IL 60604
Tel (312) 612-7600 SIC 7363 4119 7361

PROFESSIONAL NURSING INC p 1180
325 N Wells St Ste 900, Chicago IL 60654
Tel (312) 527-1839 SIC 7361 7363

■ **STAFF MANAGEMENT SOLUTIONS LLC** p 1374
860 W Evergreen Ave, Chicago IL 60642
Tel (312) 915-0900 SIC 7363 8741

UNIFIED MANAGEMENT CORP p 1503
1 E Wacker Dr Ste 3504, Chicago IL 60601
Tel (312) 828-9480 SIC 7363

WIND POINT PARTNERS LP p 1615
676 N Michigan Ave # 3700, Chicago IL 60611
Tel (312) 255-4800 SIC 6799 7363 3089

■ **PLANETECHS LLC** p 1154
1520 Kensington Rd # 311, Oak Brook IL 60523
Tel (630) 468-1766 SIC 7363

SIERRA SYSTEMS INC p 1321
200 S Prospect Ave, Park Ridge IL 60068
Tel (847) 384-2000 SIC 7363

ANDREWS STAFFING INC p 90
1834 Walden Office Sq # 150, Schaumburg IL 60173
Tel (847) 995-9300 SIC 7363

JOHNSON SERVICE GROUP INC p 791
1 E Oakhill Dr Ste 200, Westmont IL 60559
Tel (630) 655-3500 SIC 7363 8711

CLEARSTAFF INC p 324
7501 Lemont Rd Ste 220, Woodridge IL 60517
Tel (630) 985-0100 SIC 7363

PLUS GROUP INC p 1157
7425 Janes Ave Ste 201, Woodridge IL 60517
Tel (630) 515-0500 SIC 7361 7363

TRANSPORT DRIVERS INC p 1472
3540 Seven Bridges Dr # 300, Woodridge IL 60517
Tel (630) 766-2721 SIC 7363

GRAFTON INC p 628
4501 College Blvd Ste 160, Leawood KS 66211
Tel (913) 498-0701 SIC 7363 7361

FAVORITE HEALTHCARE STAFFING INC p 531
7255 W 98th Ter Ste 150, Overland Park KS 66212
Tel (913) 383-9733 SIC 7363

RES-CARE INC p 1226
9901 Linn Station Rd, Louisville KY 40223
Tel (502) 394-2100 SIC 8052 8331 7363

HUTCO INC p 722
114 Park Center Dr, Broussard LA 70518
Tel (337) 837-5594 SIC 7363

PERFORMANCE ENERGY SERVICES LLC p 1135
132 Valhi Lagoon Xing, Houma LA 70360
Tel (985) 868-4895 SIC 1623 1389 7363

ACADIANA HEALTH CARE OF LOUISIANA INC p 14
101 La Rue France Ste 300, Lafayette LA 70508
Tel (337) 232-5044 SIC 7363

SCHUMACHER GROUP OF DELAWARE INC p 1291
200 Corporate Blvd # 201, Lafayette LA 70508
Tel (337) 237-1915 SIC 7363

WORKPLACE STAFFING SOLUTIONS LLC p 1624
13055 Hwy 1, Larose LA 70373
Tel (985) 798-5111 SIC 7363 7361

ADVANTAGE MEDICAL PROFESSIONALS LLC p 26
3340 Severn Ave Ste 320, Metairie LA 70002
Tel (504) 456-0073 SIC 7361 7363

UP PROFESSIONAL SOLUTIONS LLC p 1528
1100 Poydras St Ste 1300, New Orleans LA 70163
Tel (800) 245-8274 SIC 7361 7363

ADVANTAGE HUMAN RESOURCING INC p 26
401 Thomas Rd Ste 2, West Monroe LA 71292
Tel (318) 324-8060 SIC 7363

ABACUS CORP p 9
610 Gusryan St, Baltimore MD 21224
Tel (410) 633-1900 SIC 7381 7363 7349

■ **INFORMATION NETWORK SYSTEMS INC** p 742
700 N Frederick Ave, Gaithersburg MD 20879
Tel (301) 240-7000 SIC 7373 7363

AEROTEK INC p 31
7301 Parkway Dr, Hanover MD 21076
Tel (410) 694-5100 SIC 7363 8748 8711

PAY STAFF p 1122
700 King Farm Blvd # 300, Rockville MD 20850
Tel (301) 527-0655 SIC 7363 8721

■ **OXFORD GLOBAL RESOURCES LLC** p 1101
100 Cummings Ctr Ste 206c, Beverly MA 01915
Tel (978) 236-1182 SIC 7363 8748

RENAISSANCE WORLDWIDE INC p 1223
711 Boylston St, Boston MA 02116
Tel (617) 535-5000
SIC 7363 8742 7379 7361 8748 7371

TRI VENTURES INC p 1477
711 Boylston St, Boston MA 02116
Tel (617) 535-5000 SIC 7363

ENTEGEE INC p 501
70 Blanchard Rd Ste 102, Burlington MA 01803
Tel (781) 221-5800 SIC 7363 5045

▲ **TRC COMPANIES INC** p 1475
650 Suffolk St, Lowell MA 01854
Tel (978) 970-5600
SIC 7363 8734 7382 8748

HIRE THINKING INC p 695
220 Norwood Park S Ste 1, Norwood MA 02062
Tel (781) 251-8000 SIC 7363

TECHNICAL AID CORP p 1431
220 Norwood Park S Ste 2, Norwood MA 02062
Tel (781) 251-8000 SIC 7363

EMPLOYMENT TRADITIONS INC p 494
10045 E Rivershore Dr Se, Alto MI 49302
Tel (616) 891-9194 SIC 7363

MSX INTERNATIONAL INC p 997
500 Woodward Ave Ste 2150, Detroit MI 48226
Tel (248) 829-6300
SIC 8748 7363 8742 8711

VISION INFORMATION TECHNOLOGIES INC p 1561
3031 W Grand Blvd Ste 600, Detroit MI 48202
Tel (313) 664-5650 SIC 7363 7379

POCH STAFFING INC p 1158
5555 Gull Rd Ste 300, Kalamazoo MI 49048
Tel (810) 229-2033 SIC 7363

ACRO SERVICE CORP p 18
39209 6 Mile Rd Ste 250, Livonia MI 48152
Tel (734) 591-1100 SIC 7363 7371

ACRO STAFFING INC p 18
39209 W Six Ste 250, Livonia MI 48152
Tel (734) 542-4204 SIC 7363

ANCHOR STAFFING INC p 89
39209 6 Mile Rd Ste 250, Livonia MI 48152
Tel (734) 591-1100 SIC 7363

ARCADIA SERVICES INC p 103
20750 Civic Center Dr # 100, Southfield MI 48076
Tel (248) 352-7530 SIC 7363 8082

BARTECH GROUP INC p 157
27777 Franklin Rd Ste 600, Southfield MI 48034
Tel (201) 970-0605 SIC 7363

ICONMA LLC p 728
850 Stephenson Hwy, Troy MI 48083
Tel (248) 583-1930 SIC 7363

▲ **KELLY SERVICES INC** p 809
999 W Big Beaver Rd, Troy MI 48084
Tel (248) 362-4444 SIC 7363

POPULUS GROUP LLC p 1161
850 Stephenson Hwy, Troy MI 48083
Tel (248) 581-1100 SIC 7363

ATTERRO INC p 129
730 2nd Ave S Ste 520, Minneapolis MN 55402
Tel (612) 373-2600 SIC 7363 7361

SYNICO STAFFING LLC p 1415
3033 Excelsior Blvd # 495, Minneapolis MN 55416
Tel (612) 926-6000 SIC 7363

ATLAS STAFFING INC p 128
189 7th Pl E, Saint Paul MN 55101
Tel (651) 222-5894 SIC 7363 7361

MIDWEST STAFFING GROUP INC p 968
162 Pennsylvania Ave W, Saint Paul MN 55103
Tel (651) 641-0442 SIC 7363

PYRAMID HOMEMAKER SERVICES INC p 1193
18 N Main St, Cape Girardeau MO 63701
Tel (573) 339-1864 SIC 7363

HEALTHCARE SERVICES OF OZARKS INC p 676
3660 S National Ave, Springfield MO 65807
Tel (417) 882-4170 SIC 7363 8082

■ **DRIVERS MANAGEMENT LLC** p 456
14507 Frontier Rd, Omaha NE 68138
Tel (402) 895-6640 SIC 7363

■ **CLP HOLDINGS CORP** p 328
10539 Prof Cir St 200, Reno NV 89521
Tel (775) 321-8000 SIC 7363 7361

HAT LIMITED PARTNERSHIP p 667
63 Keystone Ave Ste 202, Reno NV 89503
Tel (775) 328-6020 SIC 7363

SURGE RESOURCES INC p 1408
920 Candia Rd, Manchester NH 03109
Tel (603) 623-0007 SIC 8742 7361 7363

APOLLO PROFESSIONAL SOLUTIONS INC p 97
29 Stiles Rd Ste 302, Salem NH 03079
Tel (866) 277-3343 SIC 7363

J&J STAFFING RESOURCES INC p 772
1814 Marlton Pike E # 210, Cherry Hill NJ 08003
Tel (856) 751-5050 SIC 7363

N J PROTOCALL INC p 1005
1 Mall Dr Ste 100, Cherry Hill NJ 08002
Tel (856) 667-9003 SIC 7363

TEKMARK GLOBAL SOLUTIONS LLC p 1433
100 Metroplex Dr Ste 102, Edison NJ 08817
Tel (732) 572-5400 SIC 7379 7371 7363

NATIONAL RETAIL SYSTEMS INC p 1015
2820 16th St, North Bergen NJ 07047
Tel (201) 330-1900 SIC 7363

LOVING HANDS LTD p 881
676 Winters Ave Ste 1, Paramus NJ 07652
Tel (201) 265-3523 SIC 7363 8082

▲ **RCM TECHNOLOGIES INC** p 1212
2500 Mcclellan Ave # 350, Pennsauken NJ 08109
Tel (856) 356-4500
SIC 8711 8748 7373 8049 7363

TR BRYANT ASSOCIATES INC p 1468
377 Hoes Ln, Piscataway NJ 08854
Tel (732) 981-0440 SIC 7363 7361

JID TRANSPORTATION LLC p 785
158 61st St Apt 2, West New York NJ 07093
Tel (201) 362-0841 SIC 3713 4212 7363

EXCEL STAFFING COMPANIES LLC p 516
2100 Osuna Rd Ne Ste 100, Albuquerque NM 87113
Tel (505) 262-1871 SIC 7361 7363

■ **SHG SERVICES INC** p 1316
101 Sun Ave Ne, Albuquerque NM 87109
Tel (505) 468-4973 SIC 7363

EMPLOYER SERVICES CORP p 494
20 Pineview Dr Ste 3, Amherst NY 14228
Tel (716) 691-4455 SIC 7363 8721

COMFORCE TELECOM INC p 344
999 Stewart Ave, Bethpage NY 11714
Tel (516) 437-3300 SIC 7363

PRO CORP p 1178
999 Stewart Ave Ste 100, Bethpage NY 11714
Tel (516) 437-3300 SIC 7363 7361

PRO UNLIMITED GLOBAL SOLUTIONS INC p 1178
999 Stewart Ave Ste 100, Bethpage NY 11714
Tel (516) 437-3300 SIC 7363 7361

ALCOTT GROUP INC p 47
71 Executive Blvd Ste 1, Farmingdale NY 11735
Tel (631) 420-0100 SIC 7363

■ **FLIGHTSAFETY INTERNATIONAL INC** p 556
Marine Air Terminal, Flushing NY 11371
Tel (718) 565-4100 SIC 7363

ADECCO EMPLOYMENT SERVICES INC p 22
175 Broadhollow Rd, Melville NY 11747
Tel (631) 844-7100 SIC 7363 7361

ADO STAFFING INC p 23
175 Broadhollow Rd, Melville NY 11747
Tel (631) 844-7800 SIC 7363 6794

LLOYD STAFFING INC p 872
445 Broadhollow Rd # 119, Melville NY 11747
Tel (631) 777-7600 SIC 7363

ATC HEALTHCARE SERVICES INC p 124
1983 Marcus Ave Ste E122, New Hyde Park NY 11042
Tel (516) 345-9928 SIC 7363

AIR INDIA LIMITED p 38
570 Lexington Ave Rm 1401, New York NY 10022
Tel (212) 407-1400 SIC 7363

CORPORATE RESOURCE SERVICES INC p 372
160 Broadway Rm 1300, New York NY 10038
Tel (646) 443-2380 SIC 7363 8742

ENSEMBLE PARENT LLC p 500
345 Park Ave, New York NY 10154
Tel (212) 583-5000 SIC 7363 8741

FUEL SYSTEMS SOLUTIONS INC p 583
780 3rd Ave Fl 25, New York NY 10017
Tel (646) 502-7170 SIC 3714 3592 7363

▲ **HUDSON GLOBAL INC** p 716
1325 Avenue Of The Americ, New York NY 10019
Tel (212) 351-7300 SIC 7361 7363

IPSOFT INC p 764
17 State St Fl 14, New York NY 10004
Tel (888) 477-6388
SIC 7376 7363 7374 8742

MEDECINS SANS FRONTIERES USA INC p 935
333 7th Ave Fl 2, New York NY 10001
Tel (212) 679-6800 SIC 8399 7363

NEXTSOURCE INC p 1041
1040 Avenue Of The Americ, New York NY 10018
Tel (212) 736-5870 SIC 7363 8741

▲ **STAFFING 360 SOLUTIONS INC** p 1374
641 Lexington Ave, New York NY 10022
Tel (646) 507-5710 SIC 7363

▲ **VOLT INFORMATION SCIENCES INC** p 1564
1133 Avenue Of The Americ, New York NY 10036
Tel (212) 704-2400 SIC 7363 4813 4899

VOLT MANAGEMENT CORP p 1565
1133 Ave Of The Americas, New York NY 10036
Tel (212) 704-2400 SIC 7363

KEENA STAFF INC p 807
2 Progress Blvd, Queensbury NY 12804
Tel (518) 793-9825 SIC 7361 7363

▲ **PAYCHEX INC** p 1122
911 Panorama Trl S, Rochester NY 14625
Tel (585) 385-6666 SIC 8721 7363

STAFF LEASING OF CENTRAL NEW YORK INC p 1374
149 Northern Concourse # 3, Syracuse NY 13212
Tel (315) 641-3600 SIC 7363 8721

SUPERIOR WORKFORCE SOLUTIONS INC p 1407
250 International Dr, Williamsville NY 14221
Tel (716) 631-8310 SIC 7363

INSOURCE PERFORMANCE SOLUTIONS LLC p 746
5601 77 Center Dr Ste 240, Charlotte NC 28217
Tel (704) 643-3232 SIC 7363

SHOW PROS ENTERTAINMENT SERVICES INC p 1318
514 Springbrook Rd Ste A, Charlotte NC 28217
Tel (704) 525-3784 SIC 7363 7361

FREIGHT HANDLERS INC p 577
310 N Judd Pkwy Ne, Fuquay Varina NC 27526
Tel (919) 552-3157 SIC 4731 7363

CAROMONT MEDICAL GROUP INC p 260
2525 Court Dr, Gastonia NC 28054
Tel (704) 671-7483 SIC 7363

GCA SERVICES GROUP OF NORTH CAROLINA INC p 595
1 Centerview Dr Ste 109, Greensboro NC 27407
Tel (336) 294-9411 SIC 7349 7363

ZEN HRO INC p 1642
110 Hepler St Ste E, Kernersville NC 27284
Tel (877) 569-8660 SIC 7363 8742

DEBBIES STAFFING SERVICES INC p 420
4431 Cherry St Ste 50, Winston Salem NC 27105
Tel (336) 744-2393 SIC 7363

RESOURCE CO INC p 1227
1292 S Stratford Rd, Winston Salem NC 27103
Tel (336) 896-1000 SIC 7363 7361

BELCAN LLC p 169
10200 Anderson Way, Blue Ash OH 45242
Tel (513) 891-0972 SIC 7363 8711

BELCAN SERVICES GROUP LIMITED PARTNERSHIP p 169
10200 Anderson Way, Blue Ash OH 45242
Tel (513) 891-0972 SIC 7363

BELFLEX STAFFING NETWORK LLC p 169
11591 Goldcoast Dr, Cincinnati OH 45249
Tel (513) 488-8588 SIC 7361 7363

STAFFMARK HOLDINGS INC p 1374
201 E 4th St Ste 800, Cincinnati OH 45202
Tel (513) 651-1111 SIC 7361 7363

AREA TEMPS INC p 106
1228 Euclid Ave Ste 1115, Cleveland OH 44115
Tel (216) 781-5350 SIC 7363

▲ **CBIZ INC** p 268
6050 Oak Tree Blvd # 500, Cleveland OH 44131
Tel (216) 447-9000 SIC 8742 7389 7363

TRANSPORTATION UNLIMITED INC p 1473
3740 Carnegie Ave Ste 101, Cleveland OH 44115
Tel (216) 426-0088 SIC 7363 4213 4212

SPHERION OF LIMA INC p 1358
216 N Elizabeth St, Lima OH 45801
Tel (419) 224-8367 SIC 7363

MARCOR ENTERPRISES INC p 905
190 Highland Dr, Medina OH 44256
Tel (330) 722-7974 SIC 7363

PREMIUM TRANSPORTATION STAFFING INC p 1171
190 Highland Dr, Medina OH 44256
Tel (330) 722-7974 SIC 7291 7363

CHI HEALTH AT HOME p 296
1700 Edison Dr Ste 300, Milford OH 45150
Tel (513) 576-0262 SIC 7363 8093

JOB 1 USA p 787
701 Jefferson Ave Ste 202, Toledo OH 43604
Tel (419) 255-5005 SIC 7381 7363 7361

RUMPF CORP p 1258
701 Jefferson Ave Ste 201, Toledo OH 43604
Tel (419) 255-5005 SIC 7361 7363 7381

TSL LTD p 1489
5217 Monroe St Ste A1, Toledo OH 43623
Tel (419) 843-3200 SIC 7363

AMERICAN BULK COMMODITIES INC p 69
8063 Southern Blvd, Youngstown OH 44512
Tel (330) 758-0841
SIC 4212 7532 6531 7363

EXPRESS SERVICES INC p 520
9701 Boardwalk Blvd, Oklahoma City OK 73162
Tel (405) 840-5000 SIC 7363 6794 7361

ERICKSON INC p 507
5550 Sw Mcdam Ave Ste 200, Portland OR 97239
Tel (503) 505-5800
SIC 7363 4581 3721 7359 5599 3728

NORTHWEST STAFFING RESOURCES INC p 1060
851 Sw 6th Ave Ste 300, Portland OR 97204
Tel (503) 323-9190 SIC 7363 7361

STARPLEX CORP p 1379
12722 Ne Airport Way, Portland OR 97230
Tel (503) 222-5957 SIC 7381 7363 7999

DELTA-T GROUP INC p 427
950 E Haverford Rd # 200, Bryn Mawr PA 19010
Tel (610) 527-0830 SIC 7363

EXCELA HEALTH HOLDING CO INC p 516
532 W Pittsburgh St, Greensburg PA 15601
Tel (724) 832-4000
SIC 8062 8093 5999 7363 7322 8361

CLEARPEO LLC p 324
2080 Cabot Blvd W Ste 202, Langhorne PA 19047
Tel (215) 701-9400 SIC 7363

MCCALLION TEMPS INC p 926
601 N Bthlhem Pike Bldg A, Montgomeryville PA 18936
Tel (215) 855-8000 SIC 7363 7361

■ **CDI CORP** p 271
1735 Market St Ste 200, Philadelphia PA 19103
Tel (215) 569-2200
SIC 7363 8711 7361 6794

▲ **CDI CORP** p 271
1735 Market St Ste 200, Philadelphia PA 19103
Tel (215) 569-2200
SIC 8711 7371 7373 7376 7361 7363

■ **RIGHT MANAGEMENT INC** p 1234
1600 Jf Kennedy Blvd # 610, Philadelphia PA 19103
Tel (952) 837-0955 SIC 7363

YOH SERVICES LLC p 1636
1500 Spring Garden St, Philadelphia PA 19130
Tel (215) 656-2650 SIC 7363

CARIBBEAN TEMPORARY SERVICES INC p 256
1431 Ave Ponce De Leon, San Juan PR 00907
Tel (787) 724-5643 SIC 7363

QUILL.COM p 1200
300 Arbor Lake Dr # 1200, Columbia SC 29223
Tel (803) 333-8300 SIC 7363

AMERICAN SERVICES INC p 79
1300 Rutherford Rd, Greenville SC 29609
Tel (864) 292-7450 SIC 7381 7349 7363

PINNACLE STAFFING INC p 1150
127 Tanner Rd, Greenville SC 29607
Tel (864) 297-4212 SIC 7363

ALLIED TRANSPORTATION SERVICES INC p 57
1533 Nw 2nd St, Madison SD 57042
Tel (877) 241-6237 SIC 7363 4731

▲ **TEAM HEALTH HOLDINGS INC** p 1430
265 Brookview Centre Way, Knoxville TN 37919
Tel (865) 693-1000 SIC 7363 8741

GUARDSMARK HOLDINGS INC p 645
22 S 2nd St, Memphis TN 38103
Tel (901) 522-6000 SIC 7363

PROFESSIONAL PERSONNEL SERVICE INC p 1180
3815 Highway 66 S Ste 4, Rogersville TN 37857
Tel (423) 764-1334 SIC 7363

ALLIED STAFFING INC p 57
4400 Buffalo Gap Rd # 4500, Abilene TX 79606
Tel (325) 695-5822 SIC 7361 7363

REGUS CORP p 1220
15305 Dallas Pkwy Ste 400, Addison TX 75001
Tel (972) 361-8100 SIC 7363 7389 6531

BRADFORD HOLDING CO INC p 206
4646 Corona Dr Ste 105, Corpus Christi TX 78411
Tel (361) 852-6392 SIC 7363

G BRADFORD CO INC p 586
4646 Corona Dr Ste 100, Corpus Christi TX 78411
Tel (361) 852-6392 SIC 7363

UNIQUE RISK AND ADMINISTRATIVE SERVICES (US) INC p 1505
4646 Corona Dr Ste 105, Corpus Christi TX 78411
Tel (361) 852-6392 SIC 7363

UNIQUE STAFF LEASING I LTD p 1505
4646 Corona Dr Ste 105, Corpus Christi TX 78411
Tel (361) 852-6392 SIC 7363

UNIQUE STAFF LEASING III LTD p 1505
4646 Corona Dr Ste 105, Corpus Christi TX 78411
Tel (361) 852-6392 SIC 7363

■ **EMCARE HOLDINGS INC** p 491
13737 Noel Rd Ste 1600, Dallas TX 75240
Tel (214) 712-2000 SIC 7363

■ **EMCARE INC** p 491
13737 Noel Rd Ste 1600, Dallas TX 75240
Tel (214) 712-2000 SIC 7363

INTREPID USA INC p 760
4055 Valley View Ln # 500, Dallas TX 75244
Tel (214) 445-3750 SIC 7363 8082

SNELLING STAFFING LLC p 1335
4055 Valley View Ln # 700, Dallas TX 75244
Tel (972) 239-7575 SIC 7363

STAFF ONE INC p 1374
8111 Lndn B Jnsn Fwy 13 Ste 1350, Dallas TX 75251
Tel (214) 461-1140 SIC 7363

▲ **WILHELMINA INTERNATIONAL INC** p 1609
200 Crescent Ct Ste 1400, Dallas TX 75201
Tel (214) 661-7488 SIC 7363

SUPREME ENTERPRISES INC p 1408
204 N Ector Dr, Euless TX 76039
Tel (817) 267-6090 SIC 7363

SMITH TEMPORARIES INC p 1333
1200 Summit Ave Ste 518, Fort Worth TX 76102
Tel (817) 332-5882 SIC 7363

CORPORATE SERVICES GROUP HOLDINGS INC p 372
10740 N Gessner Rd # 400, Houston TX 77064
Tel (713) 438-1411 SIC 7363

DRIVING MOMENTUM INC p 456
17024 Butte Creek Rd # 107, Houston TX 77090
Tel (281) 893-3390 SIC 7363

GULF COAST REGIONAL BLOOD CENTER p 646
1400 La Concha Ln, Houston TX 77054
Tel (713) 790-1200 SIC 8099 7371 7363

MAGNUM STAFFING SERVICES INC p 897
2900 Smith St Ste 250, Houston TX 77006
Tel (713) 658-0068 SIC 7363

TEXAS STAFFING SERVICES INC p 1444
3000 Richmond Ave Ste 120, Houston TX 77098
Tel (713) 522-4800 SIC 7363

STAFF FORCE INC p 1374
419 Mason Park Blvd, Katy TX 77450
Tel (281) 492-6044 SIC 7363

■ **INSPERITY HOLDINGS INC** p 746
19001 Crescent Springs Dr, Kingwood TX 77339
Tel (281) 358-8986 SIC 7363

▲ **INSPERITY INC** p 746
19001 Crescent Springs Dr, Kingwood TX 77339
Tel (281) 358-8986
SIC 8742 7363 7361 6311

MEADOR STAFFING SERVICES INC p 934
722a Fairmont Pkwy, Pasadena TX 77504
Tel (713) 941-0616 SIC 7361 7363

■ **VICEROY INC** p 1555
3225 Pasadena Blvd, Pasadena TX 77503
Tel (713) 475-4518
SIC 1629 3443 1796 8742 8748 7363

▲ **BG STAFFING INC** p 180
5850 Granite Pkwy Ste 730, Plano TX 75024
Tel (972) 692-2400 SIC 7363

CHRONIC DISEASE FUND p 304
6900 Dallas Pkwy Ste 200, Plano TX 75024
Tel (972) 608-7175 SIC 7363

ADVANCED TEMPORARIES INC p 26
5139 Fredericksburg Rd, San Antonio TX 78229
Tel (903) 561-0927 SIC 7363

HAWKINS ASSOCIATES INC p 669
909 Ne Loop 410 Ste 104, San Antonio TX 78209
Tel (210) 349-9911 SIC 7363 7361

METHODIST HEALTHCARE MINISTRIES OF SOUTH TEXAS INC p 953
4507 Medical Dr, San Antonio TX 78229
Tel (210) 692-0234 SIC 8011 7363

GAS UNLIMITED INC p 593
2277 Plaza Dr Ste 270, Sugar Land TX 77479
Tel (281) 295-5600 SIC 7363

SCOTT & WHITE MEMORIAL HOSPITAL p 1293
2401 S 31st St, Temple TX 76508
Tel (254) 724-2111
SIC 8062 6512 7352 7363

CHG HEALTHCARE SERVICES INC p 296
6440 S Millrock Dr # 175, Salt Lake City UT 84121
Tel (801) 930-3000 SIC 7363

INNOVATIVE STAFFING INC p 745
859 W South Jordan Pkwy # 77, South Jordan UT 84095
Tel (801) 984-0252 SIC 7363

TRANSFORCE INC p 1471
5520 Cherokee Ave Ste 200, Alexandria VA 22312
Tel (703) 838-5580 SIC 7363

SWISSPORT CORP p 1413
45025 Aviation Dr Ste 350, Dulles VA 20166
Tel (703) 742-4300 SIC 7363

■ **APEX SYSTEMS LLC** p 96
4400 Cox Rd Ste 100, Glen Allen VA 23060
Tel (804) 254-2600 SIC 7363 7361

■ **DYNCORP INTERNATIONAL INC** p 465
1700 Old Meadow Rd, Mc Lean VA 22102
Tel (571) 722-0210
SIC 8741 7371 7381 7361 7363

PROGRESSIVE NURSING STAFFERS OF VIRGINIA INC p 1181
5531 Hempstead Way Ste B, Springfield VA 22151
Tel (703) 750-3991 *SIC* 7363

■ LABOR READY MIDWEST INC p 836
1015 A St Unit A, Tacoma WA 98402
Tel (253) 383-9101 *SIC* 7363

■ LABOR READY NORTHWEST INC p 836
P.O. Box 2910, Tacoma WA 98401
Tel (253) 383-9101 *SIC* 7363

■ LABOR READY SOUTHEAST III LP p 836
1015 A St Unit A, Tacoma WA 98402
Tel (253) 383-9101 *SIC* 7363

■ LABOR READY SOUTHEAST INC p 836
1016 S 28th St, Tacoma WA 98409
Tel (253) 383-9101 *SIC* 7363

▲ TRUEBLUE INC p 1486
1015 A St, Tacoma WA 98402
Tel (253) 383-9101 *SIC* 7363

PRN HEALTH SERVICES INC p 1178
740 Ford St Ste A, Kimberly WI 54136
Tel (920) 830-8811 *SIC* 7361 7363

■ MANPOWER INC OF NEW YORK p 902
100 W Manpower Pl, Milwaukee WI 53212
Tel (414) 961-1000 *SIC* 7363

▲ MANPOWERGROUP INC p 903
100 W Manpower Pl, Milwaukee WI 53212
Tel (414) 961-1000 *SIC* 7363 7361

SIC 7371 Custom Computer Programming Svcs

COMMAND ALKON INC p 344
1800 Intl Pk Dr Ste 400, Birmingham AL 35243
Tel (205) 879-3282 *SIC* 7371 5045

CAMBER CORP p 243
670 Discovery Dr Nw, Huntsville AL 35806
Tel (256) 922-0200 *SIC* 8731 7371

■ CAS INC p 262
100 Quality Cir Nw, Huntsville AL 35806
Tel (256) 922-4200 *SIC* 8711 7371

▲ COMPUTER PROGRAMS AND SYSTEMS INC p 353
6600 Wall St, Mobile AL 36695
Tel (251) 639-8100 *SIC* 7373 7371

SSI GROUP INC p 1363
4721 Morrison Dr, Mobile AL 36609
Tel (251) 345-0000 *SIC* 7371 7372

SEALASKA CORP p 1296
1 Sealaska Plz Ste 400, Juneau AK 99801
Tel (907) 586-1512
SIC 5099 8744 7371 8748 1542

INFUSION SOFTWARE INC p 742
1260 S Spectrum Blvd, Chandler AZ 85286
Tel (480) 807-0644 *SIC* 7379 7371

AFS TECHNOLOGIES INC p 33
2141 E Highland Ave # 100, Phoenix AZ 85016
Tel (602) 522-8282 *SIC* 7371

ASPECT SOFTWARE INC p 118
2325 E Camelback Rd # 700, Phoenix AZ 85016
Tel (978) 250-7900 *SIC* 7371

■ EFUNDS CORP p 481
4900 N Scottsdale Rd # 1000, Scottsdale AZ 85251
Tel (602) 431-2700 *SIC* 7374 7372 7371

JDA SOFTWARE GROUP INC p 780
15059 N Scottsdale Rd # 400, Scottsdale AZ 85254
Tel (480) 308-3000 *SIC* 7371

JDA SOFTWARE INC p 780
15059 N Scottsdale Rd # 400, Scottsdale AZ 85254
Tel (480) 308-3000 *SIC* 7371 7373

RP CROWN PARENT LLC p 1255
15059 N Scottsdale Rd # 400, Scottsdale AZ 85254
Tel (480) 308-3000 *SIC* 7371

YAM SPECIAL HOLDINGS INC p 1634
15475 N 84th St, Scottsdale AZ 85260
Tel (480) 505-8800 *SIC* 7371

■ COMSYS INFORMATION TECHNOLOGY SERVICES LLC p 353
2050 E Asu Cir Ste 120, Tempe AZ 85284
Tel (877) 626-6797 *SIC* 7371 7374

■ SUNQUEST INFORMATION SYSTEMS INC p 1403
250 S Williams Blvd, Tucson AZ 85711
Tel (520) 570-2000 *SIC* 7373 7371

▲ ACXIOM CORP p 21
601 E 3rd St, Little Rock AR 72201
Tel (501) 252-1000 *SIC* 7374 7375 7371

PINNACLE BUSINESS SOLUTIONS INC p 1149
515 W Pershing Blvd, North Little Rock AR 72114
Tel (501) 210-9000 *SIC* 6411 7371

UST GLOBAL INC p 1535
5 Polaris Way, Aliso Viejo CA 92656
Tel (949) 716-8757 *SIC* 7371

■ TIVO SOLUTIONS INC p 1456
2160 Gold St, Alviso CA 95002
Tel (408) 519-9100 *SIC* 7371

UNICOM SYSTEMS INC p 1502
1143 Summit Dr, Beverly Hills CA 90210
Tel (818) 838-0606 *SIC* 7371

■ DISNEY INTERACTIVE STUDIOS INC p 443
500 S Buena Vista St, Burbank CA 91521
Tel (818) 560-1000 *SIC* 7371

▲ IXIA p 769
26601 Agoura Rd, Calabasas CA 91302
Tel (818) 871-1800 *SIC* 3825 7371

PROLIFICS INC p 1182
24025 Park Sorrento # 450, Calabasas CA 91302
Tel (212) 267-7722 *SIC* 7379 7371

■ TETRA TECH EMC INC p 1441
100 Camino Ruiz, Camarillo CA 93012
Tel (805) 484-9082 *SIC* 8711 7371

VOICELOTS INC p 1564
350 Budd Ave Apt J5, Campbell CA 95008
Tel (408) 802-4047 *SIC* 7371 7389

X.COMMERCE INC p 1630
54 N Central Ave Ste 200, Campbell CA 95008
Tel (310) 954-8012 *SIC* 7371

SYSPRO IMPACT SOFTWARE INC p 1418
959 S Coast Dr Ste 100, Costa Mesa CA 92626
Tel (714) 437-1000 *SIC* 5045 7372 7371

▲ CALLIDUS SOFTWARE INC p 242
4140 Dublin Blvd Ste 400, Dublin CA 94568
Tel (925) 251-2200 *SIC* 7371 7372

■ WYLE INC p 1629
1960 E Grand Ave Ste 900, El Segundo CA 90245
Tel (310) 563-6800 *SIC* 8711 7371 8731

■ WYLE SERVICES CORP p 1629
1960 E Grand Ave Ste 900, El Segundo CA 90245
Tel (310) 563-6800 *SIC* 8711 7371

■ GRACENOTE INC p 628
2000 Powell St Ste 1500, Emeryville CA 94608
Tel (510) 428-7200 *SIC* 7371

■ PIXAR p 1152
1200 Park Ave, Emeryville CA 94608
Tel (510) 922-3000 *SIC* 7812 7372 7371

IC COMPLIANCE LLC p 726
1065 E Hillsdale Blvd # 300, Foster City CA 94404
Tel (650) 378-4150 *SIC* 7371 8721

KOFAX INC p 826
15211 Laguna Canyon Rd, Irvine CA 92618
Tel (949) 783-1000 *SIC* 3577 7371

SAGE SOFTWARE HOLDINGS INC p 1267
6561 Irvine Center Dr, Irvine CA 92618
Tel (866) 530-7243 *SIC* 7372 7371

THOMAS GALLAWAY CORP p 1448
100 Spectrum Center Dr # 700, Irvine CA 92618
Tel (949) 716-9500 *SIC* 7371 5045

VISION SOLUTIONS INC p 1561
15300 Barranca Pkwy # 100, Irvine CA 92618
Tel (949) 253-6500 *SIC* 7371 7373

■ PERFORMANT RECOVERY INC p 1135
333 N Canyons Pkwy # 100, Livermore CA 94551
Tel (209) 858-3994 *SIC* 7322 8742 7371

■ CONTINENTAL GRAPHICS CORP p 363
4060 N Lakewood Blvd, Long Beach CA 90808
Tel (714) 503-4200
SIC 3724 7371 7372 7374

▲ DSP GROUP INC p 458
161 S San Antonio Rd # 10, Los Altos CA 94022
Tel (408) 986-4300 *SIC* 3674 7371

RIOT GAMES INC p 1236
12333 W Olympic Blvd, Los Angeles CA 90064
Tel (310) 828-7953 *SIC* 7371 7993

SENTINEL ACQUISITION HOLDINGS INC p 1305
2000 Avenue Of The Stars, Los Angeles CA 90067
Tel (310) 201-4100 *SIC* 7371 7379

▲ GLOBAL EAGLE ENTERTAINMENT INC p 616
4553 Glencoe Ave Ste 200, Marina Del Rey CA 90292
Tel (310) 437-6000 *SIC* 4899 7371 4813

CYBERNET SOFTWARE SYSTEMS INC p 404
1900 Mccarthy Blvd # 210, Milpitas CA 95035
Tel (408) 615-5700 *SIC* 7371

■ SILICON GRAPHICS INTERNATIONAL CORP p 1323
900 N Mccarthy Blvd, Milpitas CA 95035
Tel (669) 900-8000 *SIC* 3577 7371

UNICOM GLOBAL INC p 1502
15535 San Fernando Mssion, Mission Hills CA 91345
Tel (818) 838-0606
SIC 8732 6552 7389 7371

ACHIEVO CORP p 17
1400 Terra Bella Ave E, Mountain View CA 94043
Tel (925) 498-8864 *SIC* 7371

▲ ALPHABET INC p 60
1600 Amphitheatre Pkwy, Mountain View CA 94043
Tel (650) 253-0000 *SIC* 7371

▲ SYNOPSYS INC p 1415
690 E Middlefield Rd, Mountain View CA 94043
Tel (650) 584-5000 *SIC* 7371

VERITAS TECHNOLOGIES LLC p 1550
500 E Middlefield Rd, Mountain View CA 94043
Tel (650) 933-1000 *SIC* 7371 7375

VERITAS US INC p 1550
500 E Middlefield Rd, Mountain View CA 94043
Tel (650) 933-1000 *SIC* 7371

HITACHI CONSULTING SOFTWARE SERVICES INC p 696
8000 Jarvis Ave Ste 130, Newark CA 94560
Tel (510) 742-4100 *SIC* 7299 7371

VM SERVICES INC p 1563
6701 Mowry Ave, Newark CA 94560
Tel (510) 744-3720 *SIC* 7371

CLOUDERA INC p 327
1001 Page Mill Rd Bldg 3, Palo Alto CA 94304
Tel (650) 644-3900 *SIC* 7371 5734 8331

HEWLETT PACKARD p 688
3000 Hanover St, Palo Alto CA 94304
Tel (650) 857-1501 *SIC* 7371

JUMIO CORP p 797
268 Lambert Ave, Palo Alto CA 94306
Tel (650) 424-8545 *SIC* 7371

PALANTIR TECHNOLOGIES INC p 1108
100 Hamilton Ave Ste 300, Palo Alto CA 94301
Tel (650) 815-0200 *SIC* 7371

TIBCO SOFTWARE INC p 1452
3303 Hillview Ave, Palo Alto CA 94304
Tel (650) 846-1000 *SIC* 7371 7373

■ VMWARE INC p 1563
3401 Hillview Ave, Palo Alto CA 94304
Tel (650) 427-1000 *SIC* 7371 7375

CAMEO GLOBAL INC p 245
4695 Chabot Dr Ste 101, Pleasanton CA 94588
Tel (925) 479-7800
SIC 7373 7371 7379 7363 4813 8742

■ DOCUMENTUM INC p 447
6801 Koll Center Pkwy, Pleasanton CA 94566
Tel (925) 600-6800 *SIC* 7372 7371

▲ ELLIE MAE INC p 488
4420 Rosewood Dr Ste 500, Pleasanton CA 94588
Tel (925) 227-7000 *SIC* 7371

▲ VEEVA SYSTEMS INC p 1546
4280 Hacienda Dr, Pleasanton CA 94588
Tel (925) 452-6500 *SIC* 7372 7371 7379

▲ WORKDAY INC p 1624
6230 Stoneridge Mall Rd, Pleasanton CA 94588
Tel (925) 951-9000 *SIC* 7371

■ ARICENT INC p 108
303 Twin Dolphin Dr # 600, Redwood City CA 94065
Tel (650) 632-4310 *SIC* 7371

■ DIGITAL INSIGHT CORP p 439
1300 Seaport Blvd Ste 300, Redwood City CA 94063
Tel (818) 879-1010 *SIC* 7375 7372 7371

▲ IMPERVA INC p 735
3400 Bridge Pkwy Ste 200, Redwood City CA 94065
Tel (650) 345-9000 *SIC* 7371

▲ N MODEL INC p 1005
1600 Seaport Blvd Ste 400, Redwood City CA 94063
Tel (650) 610-4600 *SIC* 7371

■ OC ACQUISITION LLC p 1072
500 Oracle Pkwy, Redwood City CA 94065
Tel (650) 506-7000 *SIC* 7371 7372

▲ QUALYS INC p 1198
1600 Bridge Pkwy Ste 201, Redwood City CA 94065
Tel (650) 801-6100 *SIC* 7371 7372

SABA SOFTWARE INC p 1263
2400 Bridge Pkwy, Redwood City CA 94065
Tel (650) 581-2500 *SIC* 7372 7371

■ RESPONSYS INC p 1228
1100 Grundy Ln Ste 300, San Bruno CA 94066
Tel (650) 745-1700 *SIC* 7371 7372

MARKLOGIC CORP p 909
999 Skyway Rd Ste 200, San Carlos CA 94070
Tel (650) 655-2300 *SIC* 7371

DEALERSOCKET INC p 420
100 Avenida La Pata, San Clemente CA 92673
Tel (949) 900-0300 *SIC* 7371

DAYBREAK GAME CO LLC p 417
15051 Avenue Of Science, San Diego CA 92128
Tel (858) 577-3100 *SIC* 7371

■ MITCHELL INTERNATIONAL INC p 977
6220 Greenwich Dr, San Diego CA 92122
Tel (858) 368-7000 *SIC* 7371

▲ NOVATEL WIRELESS INC p 1063
9645 Scranton Rd Ste 205, San Diego CA 92121
Tel (858) 812-3400 *SIC* 3661 7371

PC SPECIALISTS INC p 1123
10240 Flanders Ct, San Diego CA 92121
Tel (858) 566-1900 *SIC* 5045 5734 7371

TRITECH SOFTWARE SYSTEMS p 1483
9477 Waples St Ste 100, San Diego CA 92121
Tel (858) 799-7000 *SIC* 7371

■ ADVENT SOFTWARE INC p 27
600 Townsend St Fl 5, San Francisco CA 94103
Tel (415) 543-7696
SIC 7371 7373 7372 6722

AMBER HOLDING INC p 65
150 California St, San Francisco CA 94111
Tel (415) 765-6500 *SIC* 7371

APPDYNAMICS INC p 98
303 2nd St Ste N450, San Francisco CA 94107
Tel (415) 442-8400 *SIC* 7371

APPIRIO INC p 98
760 Market St Ste 1150, San Francisco CA 94102
Tel (415) 663-4433 *SIC* 7371 7379

BIRST INC p 185
45 Fremont St Ste 1800, San Francisco CA 94105
Tel (415) 766-4800 *SIC* 7371

FINANCIALFORCE.COM INC p 543
595 Market St Ste 2700, San Francisco CA 94105
Tel (866) 743-2220 *SIC* 7371

FUSIONSTORM p 585
2 Bryant St Ste 150, San Francisco CA 94105
Tel (415) 623-2626
SIC 7379 7371 7374 7376

GLOBANT LLC p 618
875 Howard St Fl 3, San Francisco CA 94103
Tel (877) 798-8104 *SIC* 7371

▲ GLU MOBILE INC p 618
500 Howard St Ste 300, San Francisco CA 94105
Tel (415) 800-6100 *SIC* 7371 3944

KABAM INC p 799
795 Folsom St Fl 6, San Francisco CA 94107
Tel (415) 391-0817 *SIC* 7371

MULESOFT INC p 999
77 Geary St Fl 400, San Francisco CA 94108
Tel (415) 229-2009 *SIC* 7371

TOMAHAWK ACQUISITION LLC p 1459
150 California St Fl 19, San Francisco CA 94111
Tel (415) 765-6500 *SIC* 6726 7371

■ TOWNS END STUDIOS LLC p 1466
699 8th St, San Francisco CA 94103
Tel (415) 802-7936 *SIC* 7371

■ ALTERA CORP p 62
101 Innovation Dr, San Jose CA 95134
Tel (408) 544-7000 *SIC* 3674 7371

■ APIGEE CORP p 96
10 Almaden Blvd Ste 1600, San Jose CA 95113
Tel (408) 343-7300 *SIC* 7371

■ BEA SYSTEMS INC p 164
2315 N 1st St, San Jose CA 95131
Tel (650) 506-7000 *SIC* 7371 7372

BRISTLECONE INC p 213
10 Almaden Blvd Ste 600, San Jose CA 95113
Tel (650) 386-4000 *SIC* 7371 8742

E-INFOCHIPS INC p 467
2025 Gateway Pl Ste 270, San Jose CA 95110
Tel (408) 496-1882 *SIC* 7371 7373

FLEXTRONICS HOLDING USA INC p 556
2090 Fortune Dr, San Jose CA 95131
Tel (408) 576-7000
SIC 3672 3679 7371 3825

FORESCOUT TECHNOLOGIES INC p 566
190 W Tasman Dr, San Jose CA 95134
Tel (408) 213-3191 *SIC* 7371

GLOBALLOGIC INC p 617
1741 Tech Dr Ste 400, San Jose CA 95110
Tel (408) 273-8900 *SIC* 7371 7379 7373

■ MICROSEMI SOC CORP p 962
3870 N 1st St, San Jose CA 95134
Tel (408) 643-6000 *SIC* 3674 7371

▲ PDF SOLUTIONS INC p 1124
333 W San Carlos St # 700, San Jose CA 95110
Tel (408) 280-7900 *SIC* 7371

■ SILICON IMAGE INC p 1323
2115 Onel Dr, San Jose CA 95131
Tel (408) 616-4000 *SIC* 3674 7371

ZSCALER INC p 1644
110 Rose Orchard Way, San Jose CA 95134
Tel (408) 533-0288 *SIC* 7371

REVENUE PROCESSING SOLUTIONS INC p 1229
28293 Via Del Mar, San Juan Capistrano CA 92675
Tel (949) 481-9080 *SIC* 7371 7389

OSISOFT LLC p 1097
1600 Alvarado St, San Leandro CA 94577
Tel (510) 297-5800 *SIC* 7372 7371 7373

MARKETO INC p 908
901 Mariners Island Blvd, San Mateo CA 94404
Tel (650) 376-2300 *SIC* 7371 7372

▲ QAD INC p 1194
100 Innovation Pl, Santa Barbara CA 93108
Tel (805) 566-6000 *SIC* 7372 7371

YARDI SYSTEMS INC p 1635
430 S Fairview Ave, Santa Barbara CA 93117
Tel (805) 699-2040 *SIC* 7371

AVAYA INC p 136
4655 Great America Pkwy, Santa Clara CA 95054
Tel (908) 953-6000 *SIC* 3661 7372 7371

INFOBLOX INC p 741
3111 Coronado Dr, Santa Clara CA 95054
Tel (408) 986-4000 *SIC* 7374 7371 7379

MERA SOFTWARE SERVICES INC p 943
2350 Mission College Blvd # 340, Santa Clara CA 95054
Tel (650) 703-7226 *SIC* 7371

OOYALA INC p 1089
4750 Patrick Henry Dr, Santa Clara CA 95054
Tel (650) 961-3400 *SIC* 7371

▲ PALO ALTO NETWORKS INC p 1110
4401 Great America Pkwy, Santa Clara CA 95054
Tel (408) 753-4000 *SIC* 3577 7371

TAVANT TECHNOLOGIES INC p 1426
3965 Freedom Cir Ste 750, Santa Clara CA 95054
Tel (408) 519-5400 *SIC* 7371

SUCCESSFACTORS INC p 1396
1 Tower Pl Fl 11, South San Francisco CA 94080
Tel (800) 845-0395 *SIC* 7371

AEDAN INC p 29
27447, Sun City CA 92586
Tel (889) 272-5505
SIC 7371 7381 8733 3812 7382

■ ARUBA NETWORKS INC p 114
1344 Crossman Ave, Sunnyvale CA 94089
Tel (408) 227-4500 *SIC* 3577 3663 7371

GOOD TECHNOLOGY CORP p 624
430 N Mary Ave Ste 200, Sunnyvale CA 94085
Tel (408) 212-7500 *SIC* 7371 7382

HCL AMERICA INC p 672
330 Potrero Ave, Sunnyvale CA 94085
Tel (408) 733-0480 *SIC* 7376 7371 8741

▲ PROOFPOINT INC p 1183
892 Ross Dr, Sunnyvale CA 94089
Tel (408) 517-4710 *SIC* 7371

XORIANT CORP p 1632
1248 Reamwood Ave, Sunnyvale CA 94089
Tel (408) 743-4427 *SIC* 7379 7371

▲ BLACKLINE INC p 187
21300 Victory Blvd Fl 12, Woodland Hills CA 91367
Tel (818) 223-9008 *SIC* 7371

WEBROOT INC p 1586
385 Interlocken Cres # 800, Broomfield CO 80021
Tel (303) 442-3813 *SIC* 7371

INTELLIGENT SOFTWARE SOLUTIONS USA LLC p 750
5450 Tech Center Dr # 400, Colorado Springs CO 80919
Tel (719) 452-7000 *SIC* 7371

ALL COPY PRODUCTS INC p 51
4141 Colorado Blvd, Denver CO 80216
Tel (303) 373-1105 *SIC* 5044 5112 7371

PETROLEUM PLACE INC p 1139
1670 Broadway Ste 2800, Denver CO 80202
Tel (303) 515-5400 *SIC* 4813 7371

■ POLICY STUDIES INC p 1159
1515 Wynkoop St Ste 400, Denver CO 80202
Tel (303) 863-0900 *SIC* 8741 8742 7371

■ PSI SERVICES HOLDING INC p 1188
1515 Wynkoop St Ste 400, Denver CO 80202
Tel (303) 863-0900
SIC 8741 8742 7371 8748

■ QWEST BUSINESS & GOVERNMENT SERVICES INC p 1201
1801 Calif St Ste 3800, Denver CO 80202
Tel (303) 391-8300
SIC 5999 1731 7629 7373 7371 7622

SYNERGY SERVICES INC p 1415
4601 Dtc Blvd Ste 650, Denver CO 80237
Tel (303) 468-2070 *SIC* 7371

IQNAVIGATOR INC p 764
6465 Greenwood Plaza Blvd, Greenwood Village CO 80111
Tel (303) 563-1500 *SIC* 7371 7361

JONES INTERNATIONAL LTD p 792
300 E Mineral Ave Ste 5, Littleton CO 80122
Tel (303) 792-3111
SIC 4832 4841 7371 7372

DOT HILL SYSTEMS CORP p 452
1351 S Sunset St, Longmont CO 80501
Tel (303) 845-3200 *SIC* 3572 7371

ROGUE WAVE SOFTWARE INC p 1246
1315 W Century Dr Ste 150, Louisville CO 80027
Tel (303) 473-9118 *SIC* 7371 7372

GENPACT INTERNATIONAL INC p 604
42 Old Ridgebury Rd Ste 1, Danbury CT 06810
Tel (203) 730-5100 *SIC* 7371

■ **SCHOLASTIC LIBRARY PUBLISHING INC** p 1288
90 Sherman Tpke, Danbury CT 06816
Tel (203) 797-3500
SIC 2731 5963 5192 2721 5961 7371

OPUS INSPECTION INC p 1091
7 Kripes Rd, East Granby CT 06026
Tel (860) 392-2100 *SIC* 7371

DATA-MAIL INC p 414
240 Hartford Ave, Newington CT 06111
Tel (860) 666-0399 *SIC* 7371

TOWERS WATSON PENNSYLVANIA INC p 1464
263 Tresser Blvd Ste 700, Stamford CT 06901
Tel (203) 326-5400 *SIC* 8742 7371

GERBER TECHNOLOGY LLC p 608
24 Industrial Park Rd W, Tolland CT 06084
Tel (860) 871-8082 *SIC* 3559 7371

TRIPLE POINT TECHNOLOGY INC p 1482
57 Greens Farms Rd, Westport CT 06880
Tel (203) 291-7979 *SIC* 7371

▲ **SS&C TECHNOLOGIES HOLDINGS INC** p 1363
80 Lamberton Rd, Windsor CT 06095
Tel (860) 298-4500 *SIC* 7372 7371

■ **SS&C TECHNOLOGIES INC** p 1363
80 Lamberton Rd, Windsor CT 06095
Tel (860) 298-4500 *SIC* 7372 7371 8741

JUMIO HOLDINGS INC p 797
2711 Centerville Rd # 400, Wilmington DE 19808
Tel (650) 424-8545 *SIC* 6719 7371

LABWARE HOLDINGS INC p 836
3 Mill Rd Ste 102, Wilmington DE 19806
Tel (302) 658-8444 *SIC* 7371 7372 6719

SEVERN TRENT (DEL) INC p 1309
1011 Centre Rd Ste 320, Wilmington DE 19805
Tel (302) 427-5990 *SIC* 3589 7371 8741

GRYPHON TECHNOLOGIES LC p 643
80 M St Se Ste 600, Washington DC 20003
Tel (202) 617-2004
SIC 8741 8711 8731 7371

PACE AMERICAS LLC p 1103
3701 Fau Blvd Ste 200, Boca Raton FL 33431
Tel (561) 995-6000 *SIC* 7371 5065

SOFT COMPUTER CONSULTANTS INC p 1337
5400 Tech Data Dr, Clearwater FL 33760
Tel (727) 789-0100 *SIC* 7373 7371

MAGIC LEAP INC p 895
1855 Griffin Rd Ste B454, Dania Beach FL 33004
Tel (954) 889-7010 *SIC* 7371

AMADEUS AMERICAS INC p 64
3470 Nw 82nd Ave Ste 1000, Doral FL 33122
Tel (305) 499-6000 *SIC* 7371

AMADEUS NORTH AMERICA INC p 64
3470 Nw 82nd Ave Ste 1000, Doral FL 33122
Tel (305) 499-6613 *SIC* 7371 8322

■ **INTCOMEX INC** p 748
3505 Nw 107th Ave Ste 1, Doral FL 33178
Tel (305) 477-6230 *SIC* 7371 5045

■ **TYBRIN CORP** p 1496
1030 Titan Ct, Fort Walton Beach FL 32547
Tel (850) 337-2500 *SIC* 7371

SUMTOTAL SYSTEMS LLC p 1399
2850 Nw 43rd St Ste 150, Gainesville FL 32606
Tel (352) 264-2800 *SIC* 7371

TOWER HILL INSURANCE GROUP INC p 1464
7201 Nw 11th Pl, Gainesville FL 32605
Tel (352) 332-8800 *SIC* 6331 7371

BEELINE.COM INC p 168
12724 Gran Bay Pkwy W # 200, Jacksonville FL 32258
Tel (904) 527-5700 *SIC* 7371

■ **CSX TECHNOLOGY INC** p 398
550 Water St, Jacksonville FL 32202
Tel (904) 633-1000 *SIC* 7371

MODIS INC p 981
10151 Deerwood Pkwy Bldg, Jacksonville FL 32256
Tel (904) 360-2300 *SIC* 7371

ROYAL SERVICES INC p 1254
4526 Lenox Ave, Jacksonville FL 32205
Tel (904) 386-6436 *SIC* 7349 7371

ELANDIA INTERNATIONAL INC p 483
8333 Nw 53rd St Ste 400, Miami FL 33166
Tel (305) 415-8830
SIC 4813 4899 7371 5044

ANSWER GROUP INC p 93
7562 Southgate Blvd, North Lauderdale FL 33068
Tel (954) 720-4002 *SIC* 7371 8748

LAKEVIEW CENTER INC p 840
1221 W Lakeview Ave, Pensacola FL 32501
Tel (850) 432-1222
SIC 8069 8093 7389 7371 7373

MAINLINE INFORMATION SYSTEMS INC p 898
1700 Summit Lake Dr, Tallahassee FL 32317
Tel (850) 219-5000 *SIC* 7373 7379 7371

■ **VERIZON DATA SERVICES INC** p 1550
1 E Telecom Pkwy, Tampa FL 33637
Tel (212) 395-1000 *SIC* 7374 7371

MEDASSETS NET REVENUE SYSTEMS LLC p 935
200 N Point Ctr E Ste 400, Alpharetta GA 30022
Tel (678) 248-8200 *SIC* 8742 7371

PYRAMID CONSULTING INC p 1193
11100 Atlantis Pl, Alpharetta GA 30022
Tel (678) 514-3500 *SIC* 7379 7371

ROLTA INTERNATIONAL INC p 1248
5865 N Point Pkwy Ste 300, Alpharetta GA 30022
Tel (678) 942-5000 *SIC* 7389 7371 7372

■ **AIRWATCH LLC** p 41
1155 Perimeter Ctr # 100, Atlanta GA 30338
Tel (470) 247-4312 *SIC* 7371

■ **AWS HOLDINGS LLC** p 139
1155 Perimeter Ctr # 100, Atlanta GA 30338
Tel (404) 478-7500 *SIC* 7371

BYERS ENGINEERING CO p 231
6285 Barfield Rd Fl 4, Atlanta GA 30328
Tel (404) 843-1000 *SIC* 8711 7371

CHARTER GLOBAL INC p 291
7000 Central Pkwy # 1100, Atlanta GA 30328
Tel (888) 326-9933 *SIC* 7371

CLOUD SHERPAS INC p 327
3525 Piedmont Rd Ne 8-710, Atlanta GA 30305
Tel (404) 665-3556 *SIC* 7371

NIIT TECHNOLOGIES INC p 1043
1050 Crown Pinte Pkwy 5th # 5, Atlanta GA 30338
Tel (770) 551-9494 *SIC* 7379 7371

▲ **NUMEREX CORP** p 1067
400 Interstate North Pkwy, Atlanta GA 30339
Tel (770) 693-5950 *SIC* 3669 7371

■ **SECUREWORKS CORP** p 1298
1 Concrse Pkwy Ne Ste 500, Atlanta GA 30328
Tel (404) 327-6339 *SIC* 7371

■ **SECUREWORKS INC** p 1298
1 Concourse Pkwy Ste 500, Atlanta GA 30328
Tel (770) 396-5767 *SIC* 7371

SOFTTEK INTEGRATION SYSTEMS INC p 1337
2002 Summit Blvd Ste 300, Brookhaven GA 30319
Tel (404) 460-5040 *SIC* 7379 7371 7373

GREENWAY HEALTH p 638
100 Greenway Blvd, Carrollton GA 30117
Tel (770) 836-3100 *SIC* 7373 7371

JOHN H HARLAND CO p 788
2939 Miller Rd, Decatur GA 30035
Tel (770) 593-5050
SIC 2782 2752 2761 7371 7379

AMERICAN CYBERSYSTEMS INC p 71
2400 Meadowbrook Pkwy, Duluth GA 30096
Tel (770) 493-5588 *SIC* 7373 7371 7372

▲ **EBIX INC** p 474
1 Ebix Way Ste 100, Duluth GA 30097
Tel (678) 281-2020 *SIC* 7371 7372

▲ **NCR CORP** p 1022
3097 Satellite Blvd # 100, Duluth GA 30096
Tel (937) 445-5000
SIC 3575 3578 7379 7374 7371

PEACHTREE SOFTWARE INC p 1125
1715 N Brown Rd, Lawrenceville GA 30043
Tel (770) 682-1542 *SIC* 7372 7371

ALLIED BUSINESS SYSTEMS LLC p 56
4848 Mercer University Dr, Macon GA 31210
Tel (800) 727-7534 *SIC* 7371 5734

■ **ISAAC FAIR CORP** p 766
3550 Engrg Dr Ste 200, Norcross GA 30092
Tel (770) 810-8000 *SIC* 7371

■ **S1 CORP** p 1263
705 Westech Dr, Norcross GA 30092
Tel (678) 966-9499 *SIC* 7372 7371

CCC INFORMATION SERVICES INC p 269
222 Mchds Mart Plz 900, Chicago IL 60654
Tel (312) 222-4636 *SIC* 7371

GREEN COUCH CORP p 636
231 S La Salle St Fl 8, Chicago IL 60604
Tel (312) 263-1177 *SIC* 7379 7371

HERE NORTH AMERICA LLC p 685
425 W Randolph St, Chicago IL 60606
Tel (312) 894-7000 *SIC* 7371

QUINNOX INC p 1200
400 N Michigan Ave # 1300, Chicago IL 60611
Tel (630) 548-4800 *SIC* 7379 7371

SILKROAD TECHNOLOGY INC p 1323
100 S Wacker Dr Ste 425, Chicago IL 60606
Tel (866) 329-3363 *SIC* 7371

TRADING TECHNOLOGIES INTERNATIONAL INC p 1469
222 S Riverside Plz # 1000, Chicago IL 60606
Tel (312) 476-1000 *SIC* 7371

FLEXERA HOLDINGS LP p 556
300 Park Blvd Ste 500, Itasca IL 60143
Tel (847) 466-4000 *SIC* 7371 7372

FLEXERA SOFTWARE LLC p 556
300 Park Blvd Ste 500, Itasca IL 60143
Tel (847) 466-4000 *SIC* 7371 7372

ZENSAR TECHNOLOGIES INC p 1642
1415 W 22nd St Ste 925, Oak Brook IL 60523
Tel (630) 928-1518 *SIC* 7371

▲ **VASCO DATA SECURITY INTERNATIONAL INC** p 1545
1901 S Meyers Rd Ste 210, Oakbrook Terrace IL 60181
Tel (630) 932-8844 *SIC* 7373 7371

PROBIDDER LLC p 1178
945 E Kenilworth Ave, Palatine IL 60074
Tel (847) 962-3140 *SIC* 8742 7371

CCH INC p 270
2700 Lake Cook Rd, Riverwoods IL 60015
Tel (847) 267-7000
SIC 2721 2731 7389 7338 8732 7371

CAPGEMINI FINANCIAL SERVICES INTERNATIONAL INC p 248
6400 Shafer Ct Ste 100, Rosemont IL 60018
Tel (847) 384-6100 *SIC* 7371

PSAV INC p 1188
5100 River Rd Ste 300, Schiller Park IL 60176
Tel (847) 222-9800 *SIC* 7371 7359

LEVI RAY & SHOUP INC p 858
2401 W Monroe St, Springfield IL 62704
Tel (217) 793-3800 *SIC* 7371 5045 7379

APPLIED SYSTEMS INC p 100
200 Applied Pkwy, University Park IL 60484
Tel (708) 534-5575 *SIC* 7371 7372

■ **ANTHEM INSURANCE COMPANIES INC** p 94
120 Monument Cir Ste 200, Indianapolis IN 46204
Tel (317) 488-6000
SIC 6324 6411 6321 6331 6159 7371

APTEAN HOLDINGS INC p 101
450 E 96th St Ste 300, Indianapolis IN 46240
Tel (317) 249-1700 *SIC* 7371 5045

■ **HAVERSTICK CONSULTING INC** p 668
8770 Guion Rd Ste A, Indianapolis IN 46268
Tel (317) 218-1700 *SIC* 7371 7373

■ **INTERACTIVE INTELLIGENCE INC** p 751
7601 Interactive Way, Indianapolis IN 46278
Tel (800) 267-1364 *SIC* 7372 7371

PARAGON MEDICAL INC p 1113
8 Matchett Dr, Pierceton IN 46562
Tel (574) 594-2140 *SIC* 3089 3841 7371

STONERIVER INC p 1391
222 3rd Ave Se Ste 405, Cedar Rapids IA 52401
Tel (319) 378-5773 *SIC* 7371

STATE UNIVERSITY OF IOWA FOUNDATION p 1383
1 W Park Rd, Iowa City IA 52242
Tel (319) 335-3305 *SIC* 8399 7371 7359

EPIQ SYSTEMS INC p 505
501 Kansas Ave, Kansas City KS 66105
Tel (913) 621-9500 *SIC* 7371 8748

LEXMARK ENTERPRISE SOFTWARE LLC p 860
8900 Renner Blvd, Lenexa KS 66219
Tel (913) 422-7525 *SIC* 7371 7372

▲ **NIC INC** p 1042
25501 W Valley Pkwy # 300, Olathe KS 66061
Tel (877) 234-3468 *SIC* 7371

NETSMART TECHNOLOGIES INC p 1027
4950 College Blvd, Overland Park KS 66211
Tel (913) 327-7444 *SIC* 7371 7372

PRAXIS ENGINEERING TECHNOLOGIES INC p 1168
135 Natl Bus Pkwy, Annapolis Junction MD 20701
Tel (301) 490-4299 *SIC* 7371

■ **MILLENNIAL MEDIA INC** p 970
2400 Boston St Ste 300, Baltimore MD 21224
Tel (410) 522-8705 *SIC* 7319 7371

SAFENET HOLDING CORP p 1266
4690 Millennium Dr, Belcamp MD 21017
Tel (410) 931-7500 *SIC* 7371

SAFENET INC p 1266
4690 Millennium Dr # 400, Belcamp MD 21017
Tel (410) 931-7500 *SIC* 7371

ASRC AEROSPACE CORP p 119
7000 Muirkirk Meadows Dr # 100, Beltsville MD 20705
Tel (301) 837-5500
SIC 3812 7371 7373 5088

VOCUS INC p 1564
12051 Indian Creek Ct, Beltsville MD 20705
Tel (301) 459-2590 *SIC* 7371 7372

DIGITAL MANAGEMENT LLC p 439
6550 Rock Spring Dr Fl 7, Bethesda MD 20817
Tel (240) 223-4800 *SIC* 7371

GETWELLNETWORK INC p 609
7700 Old Georgetown Rd # 4, Bethesda MD 20814
Tel (240) 482-3200 *SIC* 7371

▲ **INOVALON HOLDINGS INC** p 745
4321 Collington Rd # 100, Bowie MD 20716
Tel (301) 809-4000 *SIC* 7371 7374 7372

MIL CORP p 968
4000 Mitchellville Rd R, Bowie MD 20716
Tel (301) 805-8500
SIC 7371 7373 7374 7375 7376 8711

TENABLE NETWORK SECURITY INC p 1436
7021 Columbia Gateway Dr # 200, Columbia MD 21046
Tel (410) 872-0555 *SIC* 7372 7371

▲ **BROADSOFT INC** p 215
9737 Washingtonian Blvd # 350, Gaithersburg MD 20878
Tel (301) 977-9440 *SIC* 7372 7371 8748

MDA INFORMATION SYSTEMS LLC p 933
820 W Diamond Ave Ste 300, Gaithersburg MD 20878
Tel (240) 833-8200 *SIC* 7371

■ **OAO CORP** p 1071
700 N Frederick Ave, Gaithersburg MD 20879
Tel (301) 240-7000
SIC 7371 8711 3823 3559

SGT INC p 1310
7701 Greenbelt Rd Ste 400, Greenbelt MD 20770
Tel (301) 614-8600 *SIC* 7371 7373 7376

SMARTRONIX INC p 1332
44150 Smartronix Way, Hollywood MD 20636
Tel (301) 373-6000 *SIC* 7371 8731 7373

CLIENT NETWORK SERVICES INC p 326
2277 Research Blvd, Rockville MD 20850
Tel (301) 634-4600 *SIC* 7371 7373 7379

INFINITE COMPUTER SOLUTIONS INC p 740
15201 Diamondback Dr # 125, Rockville MD 20850
Tel (301) 355-7760 *SIC* 7379 7371

INFOSYS PUBLIC SERVICES INC p 742
800 King Farm Blvd # 505, Rockville MD 20850
Tel (301) 354-8600 *SIC* 7371 7374 8742

WESTAT INC p 1596
1600 Research Blvd, Rockville MD 20850
Tel (301) 251-1500
SIC 8732 7371 7373 8741 8742 8999

ZENIMAX MEDIA INC p 1642
1370 Piccard Dr Ste 120, Rockville MD 20850
Tel (301) 948-2200 *SIC* 7371

SOCIAL & SCIENTIFIC SYSTEMS INC p 1336
8757 Georgia Ave Ste 1200, Silver Spring MD 20910
Tel (301) 628-3000 *SIC* 7374 7371

▲ **SEACHANGE INTERNATIONAL INC** p 1296
50 Nagog Park, Acton MA 01720
Tel (978) 897-0100 *SIC* 3663 7822 7371

▲ **ASPEN TECHNOLOGY INC** p 118
20 Crosby Dr, Bedford MA 01730
Tel (781) 221-6400 *SIC* 7371 7372

▲ **PROGRESS SOFTWARE CORP** p 1181
14 Oak Park Dr, Bedford MA 01730
Tel (781) 280-4000 *SIC* 7372 7371

EMPIRIX INC p 494
600 Technology Park Dr # 1, Billerica MA 01821
Tel (978) 313-7000 *SIC* 7371 8734

▲ **ENERNOC INC** p 498
1 Marina Park Dr Ste 400, Boston MA 02210
Tel (617) 224-9900 *SIC* 7371

NTT DATA INTERNATIONAL SERVICES INC p 1066
100 City Sq, Boston MA 02129
Tel (800) 745-3263 *SIC* 7371 7372

RENAISSANCE WORLDWIDE INC p 1223
711 Boylston St, Boston MA 02116
Tel (617) 535-5000
SIC 7363 8742 7379 7361 8748 7371

SAPIENT CORP p 1281
131 Dartmouth St Ste 301, Boston MA 02116
Tel (617) 621-0200
SIC 7373 7374 7371 8742

TUFTS MEDICAL CENTER INC p 1491
800 Washington St, Boston MA 02111
Tel (617) 636-5000
SIC 8062 7371 8742 8741

TUFTS MEDICAL CENTER PARENT INC p 1491
800 Washington St, Boston MA 02111
Tel (617) 636-5000 *SIC* 8062 7371

CHARLES RIVER DEVELOPMENT INC p 289
700 District Ave Ste 400, Burlington MA 01803
Tel (781) 238-0099 *SIC* 7371

CHARLES RIVER SYSTEMS INC p 289
700 District Ave Ste 400, Burlington MA 01803
Tel (781) 238-0099 *SIC* 7371

■ **DEMANDWARE INC** p 427
5 Wall St Fl 2, Burlington MA 01803
Tel (888) 553-9216 *SIC* 7371 7372

SOPHOS INC p 1341
3 Van De Graaff Dr Ste 2, Burlington MA 01803
Tel (781) 494-5800 *SIC* 7371

■ **VIECORE FEDERAL SYSTEMS DIVISION INC** p 1556
1 Wayside Rd, Burlington MA 01803
Tel (781) 565-5000 *SIC* 7371

IGATE AMERICAS INC p 730
1 Broadway Fl 13, Cambridge MA 02142
Tel (617) 914-8000 *SIC* 7371 7373

INTERSYSTEMS CORP p 758
1 Memorial Dr Ste 6, Cambridge MA 02142
Tel (617) 621-0600 *SIC* 7371

▲ **PEGASYSTEMS INC** p 1127
1 Rogers St, Cambridge MA 02142
Tel (617) 374-9600 *SIC* 7379 7371 7372

■ **RAYTHEON BBN TECHNOLOGIES CORP** p 1210
10 Moulton St, Cambridge MA 02138
Tel (617) 873-3052 *SIC* 7371 7374 7373

■ **EMC CORP** p 490
176 South St, Hopkinton MA 01748
Tel (508) 435-1000
SIC 3572 7372 7371 3577

▲ **WATERS CORP** p 1582
34 Maple St, Milford MA 01757
Tel (508) 478-2000
SIC 3826 3829 7371 7372

MATHWORKS INC p 920
3 Apple Hill Dr, Natick MA 01760
Tel (508) 647-7000 *SIC* 7371 3823 8222

▲ **PTC INC** p 1189
140 Kendrick St, Needham MA 02494
Tel (781) 370-5000 *SIC* 7372 7373 7371

■ **NEWBURYPORT HOLDINGS INC** p 1037
4 Middle St Ste 226, Newburyport MA 01950
Tel (781) 246-8234 *SIC* 7371

■ **KEYW CORP** p 816
250 Clark St, North Andover MA 01845
Tel (978) 682-7767 *SIC* 7371 8713 7389

COMPUTER MERCHANT LTD p 353
95 Longwater Cir, Norwell MA 02061
Tel (781) 878-1070 *SIC* 7379 7371

■ **EDGEWATER TECHNOLOGY** p 477
200 Harvard Mill Sq # 210, Wakefield MA 01880
Tel (781) 246-3343 *SIC* 7371

XURA INC p 1633
200 Quannapowitt Pkwy, Wakefield MA 01880
Tel (781) 246-9000 *SIC* 7371

3DS ACQUISITION CORP p 2
175 Wyman St, Waltham MA 02451
Tel (781) 810-5011 *SIC* 7371

CAMBRIDGE COMPUTER SERVICES INC p 244
271 Waverley Oaks Rd # 301, Waltham MA 02452
Tel (781) 250-3000
SIC 5045 7373 7371 7379

CARBON BLACK INC p 252
1100 Winter St Fl 4, Waltham MA 02451
Tel (617) 393-7400 *SIC* 7371 7379

■ **CSC CONSULTING INC** p 397
404 Wyman St Ste 355, Waltham MA 02451
Tel (781) 890-7446 *SIC* 7373 7371 8742

DASSAULT SYSTEMES AMERICAS CORP p 413
175 Wyman St, Waltham MA 02451
Tel (781) 810-3000 *SIC* 7371

DASSAULT SYSTEMES SOLIDWORKS CORP p 413
175 Wyman St, Waltham MA 02451
Tel (781) 810-3000 *SIC* 7371

▲ **LIONBRIDGE TECHNOLOGIES INC** p 870
1050 Winter St Ste 2300, Waltham MA 02451
Tel (781) 434-6000 *SIC* 7389 7374 7371

ROCKET SOFTWARE INC p 1244
77 4th Ave Ste 101, Waltham MA 02451
Tel (781) 577-4323 *SIC* 7371

SALARY.COM LLC p 1272
610 Lincoln St Ste 200, Waltham MA 02451
Tel (781) 989-9488 *SIC* 7371 7375

ECLINICAL WORKS LLC p 475
2 Technology Dr, Westborough MA 01581
Tel (508) 366-8301 *SIC* 7371

ECLINICALWORKS LLC p 475
2 Technology Dr, Westborough MA 01581
Tel (508) 475-0450 *SIC* 7371

▲ **VIRTUSA CORP** p 1560
2000 W Park Dr Ste 300, Westborough MA 01581
Tel (508) 389-7300 *SIC* 7371 7379

CORPORATE CONSULTING GROUP INC p 372
133 Boston Post Rd 15, Weston MA 02493
Tel (978) 461-8000 *SIC* 7371

▲ **MONOTYPE IMAGING HOLDINGS INC** p 985
600 Unicorn Park Dr, Woburn MA 01801
Tel (781) 970-6000 *SIC* 7371 7372

V2SOFT INC p 1538
300 Enterprise Ct Ste 100, Bloomfield Hills MI 48302
Tel (248) 904-1705 *SIC* 7371

BURTEK HOLDINGS INC p 229
50325 Patricia St, Chesterfield MI 48051
Tel (586) 421-8000 *SIC* 7371 3812 8711

■TWEDDLE GROUP INC p 1494
24700 Maplehurst Dr, Clinton Township MI 48036
Tel (586) 307-3700
SIC 2732 2791 2752 2759 2741 7371

BARDEN COMPANIES INC p 155
400 Renaissance Ctr # 2400, Detroit MI 48243
Tel (313) 496-2900 *SIC* 7371 7372

COMPUWARE CORP p 353
1 Campus Martius Fl 4, Detroit MI 48226
Tel (313) 227-7300 *SIC* 7372 7371

COMPUWARE HOLDINGS LLC p 353
1 Campus Martius, Detroit MI 48226
Tel (313) 227-7300 *SIC* 7371

HCL GLOBAL SYSTEMS INC p 672
24543 Indoplex Cir # 220, Farmington Hills MI 48335
Tel (248) 473-0720 *SIC* 7379 7371

ACRO SERVICE CORP p 18
39209 6 Mile Rd Ste 250, Livonia MI 48152
Tel (734) 591-1100 *SIC* 7363 7371

WORKFORCE SOFTWARE LLC p 1624
38705 7 Mile Rd Ste 300, Livonia MI 48152
Tel (734) 542-4100 *SIC* 7372 7371

NETLINK SOFTWARE GROUP AMERICA INC p 1027
999 Tech Row, Madison Heights MI 48071
Tel (248) 204-8803 *SIC* 7379 7371

KONVISSER CUSTOM SOFTWARE p 827
5109 Deer Run Cir, Orchard Lake MI 48323
Tel (248) 682-0717 *SIC* 7371

ALTIMETRIK CORP p 62
1000 Town Ctr Ste 700, Southfield MI 48075
Tel (248) 281-2500 *SIC* 7371

EPITEC INC p 505
24800 Denso Dr Ste 150, Southfield MI 48033
Tel (248) 353-6800
SIC 7371 7379 7373 8748 8711

IWKA HOLDING CORP p 769
6600 Center Dr, Sterling Heights MI 48312
Tel (586) 795-2000
SIC 3549 5084 7371 8711

RAPID GLOBAL BUSINESS SOLUTIONS INC p 1208
1200 Stephenson Hwy, Troy MI 48083
Tel (248) 589-1135 *SIC* 8711 7371 7361

▲SYNTEL INC p 1416
525 E Big Beaver Rd # 300, Troy MI 48083
Tel (248) 619-2800 *SIC* 7371 7372 8748

REVSPRING INC p 1229
29241 Beck Rd, Wixom MI 48393
Tel (248) 567-7300 *SIC* 7371 7375

NXTRANET CORP p 1068
1500 Mcandrews Rd W, Burnsville MN 55337
Tel (952) 808-5554 *SIC* 7371

▲DATALINK CORP p 414
10050 Crosstown Cir # 500, Eden Prairie MN 55344
Tel (952) 944-3462 *SIC* 5045 7371 7373

■OPTUMINSIGHT INC p 1091
11000 Optum Cir, Eden Prairie MN 55344
Tel (952) 833-7100
SIC 7371 7375 8742 8741

OPEN SYSTEMS INTERNATIONAL INC p 1089
4101 Arrowhead Dr, Medina MN 55340
Tel (763) 551-0559 *SIC* 7371 5734

ANALYSTS INTERNATIONAL CORP p 88
7700 France Ave S Ste 200, Minneapolis MN 55435
Tel (952) 835-5900 *SIC* 7371 7379

CALABRIO INC p 238
400 1st Ave N Ste 300, Minneapolis MN 55401
Tel (763) 592-4600 *SIC* 5045 7371

CLIFTONLARSONALLEN LLP p 326
220 S 6th St Ste 300, Minneapolis MN 55402
Tel (612) 376-4620 *SIC* 8742 7371 8721

HIGHJUMP SOFTWARE INC p 691
5600 W 83rd St Ste 600, Minneapolis MN 55437
Tel (952) 947-4088 *SIC* 7371

MOBILESOFT TECHNOLOGY INC p 980
100 Washington Ave S, Minneapolis MN 55401
Tel (612) 460-4700 *SIC* 7371

NEWSCYCLE SOLUTIONS INC p 1039
7900 Intl Dr Ste 800, Minneapolis MN 55425
Tel (651) 639-0662 *SIC* 7371

OPEN ACCESS TECHNOLOGY INTERNATIONAL INC p 1089
3660 Technology Dr, Minneapolis MN 55418
Tel (763) 201-2000 *SIC* 7371 8711

SPANLINK COMMUNICATIONS INC p 1354
5940 Golden Hills Dr, Minneapolis MN 55416
Tel (763) 971-2000 *SIC* 7373 7371

WOLTERS KLUWER FINANCIAL SERVICES INC p 1621
100 S 5th St Ste 700, Minneapolis MN 55402
Tel (612) 656-7700 *SIC* 7371

▲DIGI INTERNATIONAL INC p 438
11001 Bren Rd E, Minnetonka MN 55343
Tel (952) 912-3444
SIC 3577 3575 7374 7371

MARCO TECHNOLOGIES LLC p 905
4510 Heatherwood Rd, Saint Cloud MN 56301
Tel (320) 259-3000
SIC 7371 4813 7313 7812

RUSH SERVICE CO INC p 1258
1314 19th Ave, Meridian MS 39301
Tel (601) 483-0011 *SIC* 8741 7371

AMDOCS INC p 66
1390 Timberlake Manor Pkw, Chesterfield MO 63017
Tel (314) 212-7000 *SIC* 7372 7371 7373

ROSE INTERNATIONAL INC p 1250
16401 Swingley Ridge Rd, Chesterfield MO 63017
Tel (636) 812-4000 *SIC* 7371 8748

ACLARA TECHNOLOGIES LLC p 17
945 Hornet Dr, Hazelwood MO 63042
Tel (314) 895-6400
SIC 3824 3825 3829 7371 7373

METER READINGS HOLDING LLC p 953
945 Hornet Dr, Hazelwood MO 63042
Tel (561) 394-0550
SIC 3824 3825 3829 7371 7373

■CERNER DHT INC p 284
2800 Rock Creek Pkwy, Kansas City MO 64117
Tel (816) 221-1024 *SIC* 8742 7372 7371

▲DST SYSTEMS INC p 458
333 W 11th St, Kansas City MO 64105
Tel (816) 435-1000
SIC 7374 7371 7331 7372

DAUGHERTY SYSTEMS INC p 414
3 Cityplace Dr Ste 400, Saint Louis MO 63141
Tel (314) 432-8200
SIC 7379 7371 8742 7373 7372

KELLY MITCHELL GROUP INC p 809
8229 Maryland Ave, Saint Louis MO 63105
Tel (314) 727-1700 *SIC* 7371 7373

▲PERFICIENT INC p 1135
555 Maryville Univ Dr 6, Saint Louis MO 63141
Tel (314) 529-3600 *SIC* 7371

■INFORMATION TECHNOLOGY INC p 742
1345 Old Cheney Rd, Lincoln NE 68512
Tel (402) 423-2682
SIC 5045 7373 7374 7371

FIRST NATIONAL OF NEBRASKA INC p 548
1620 Dodge St, Omaha NE 68197
Tel (402) 341-0500 *SIC* 6022 6141 7371

AMADEUS HOSPITALITY AMERICAS INC p 64
75 Nh Ave Ste 300, Portsmouth NH 03801
Tel (603) 436-7500 *SIC* 7371

NMTI HOLDINGS INC p 1045
75 Nh Ave, Portsmouth NH 03801
Tel (603) 427-5794 *SIC* 7371

CEGEDIM INC p 272
1425 Us Highway 206, Bedminster NJ 07921
Tel (908) 443-2000 *SIC* 7371 7372

IGATE CORP p 730
100 Somerset Corp Blvd # 5000, Bridgewater NJ 08807
Tel (908) 219-8050 *SIC* 7371 7374 7389

IGATE TECHNOLOGIES INC p 730
100 Somerset Corp Blvd # 5000, Bridgewater NJ 08807
Tel (908) 219-8050 *SIC* 7371

▲SYNCHRONOSS TECHNOLOGIES INC p 1414
200 Crossing Blvd Fl 8, Bridgewater NJ 08807
Tel (866) 620-3940 *SIC* 7371 4813

ZENTRY LLC p 1642
200 Crossing Blvd Fl 8, Bridgewater NJ 08807
Tel (866) 620-3940 *SIC* 7371

WORLDWIDE INFORMATION SYSTEMS LLC p 1626
360 Central Ave 2051, Clark NJ 07066
Tel (908) 272-9430 *SIC* 7371

MGL AMERICAS INC p 958
1249 S River Rd Ste 102, Cranbury NJ 08512
Tel (609) 235-9632 *SIC* 7379 7371

■ARICENT US INC p 108
1 Tower Center Blvd Fl 18, East Brunswick NJ 08816
Tel (732) 514-6654 *SIC* 7371

WIPRO LLC p 1618
2 Tower Center Blvd # 2200, East Brunswick NJ 08816
Tel (732) 509-1664 *SIC* 7371

BIRLASOFT INC p 185
399 Thornall St Ste 8, Edison NJ 08837
Tel (732) 287-5000 *SIC* 7371

TEKMARK GLOBAL SOLUTIONS LLC p 1433
100 Metroplex Dr Ste 102, Edison NJ 08817
Tel (732) 572-5400 *SIC* 7379 7371 7363

TRIGYN TECHNOLOGIES INC p 1480
100 Metroplex Dr Ste 101, Edison NJ 08817
Tel (732) 777-0050 *SIC* 7371 7379

DAMCO SOLUTIONS INC p 410
3240 E Estate St Ext, Hamilton NJ 08619
Tel (609) 632-0350 *SIC* 7371

AVEPOINT INC p 137
3 Plaza Ten, Jersey City NJ 07311
Tel (201) 793-1111 *SIC* 7371

FUNDTECH CORP p 585
30 Montgomery St Ste 501, Jersey City NJ 07302
Tel (201) 324-0203 *SIC* 7372 7371

OPERA SOLUTIONS LLC p 1089
10 Exchange Pl Fl 11, Jersey City NJ 07302
Tel (646) 520-4320 *SIC* 7371

ARTECH INFORMATION SYSTEMS LLC p 114
360 Mount Kemble Ave # 2, Morristown NJ 07960
Tel (973) 998-2500 *SIC* 7371 7379

COLLABERA INC p 336
25 Airport Rd, Morristown NJ 07960
Tel (973) 889-5200 *SIC* 7371

COLLABERA TECHNOLOGIES p 336
25 Airport Rd, Morristown NJ 07960
Tel (973) 889-5200 *SIC* 7371

■MAJESCO p 898
412 Mount Kemble Ave 110c, Morristown NJ 07960
Tel (973) 461-5200 *SIC* 7372 7371

DIALOGIC INC p 436
4 Gatehall Dr, Parsippany NJ 07054
Tel (973) 967-6000 *SIC* 3661 3577 7371

AEQUOR TECHNOLOGIES INC p 30
377 Hoes Ln Ste 300, Piscataway NJ 08854
Tel (732) 494-4999 *SIC* 7371

MARLABS INC p 909
1 Corporate Pl S Fl 3, Piscataway NJ 08854
Tel (732) 694-1000 *SIC* 7371

■POLARIS CONSULTING & SERVICES LTD p 1159
20 Corporate Pl S, Piscataway NJ 08854
Tel (732) 590-8100 *SIC* 7371

TELCORDIA TECHNOLOGIES INC p 1433
444 Hoes Ln, Piscataway NJ 08854
Tel (732) 699-6800 *SIC* 7371 7373 8742

COMPUNNEL SOFTWARE GROUP INC p 352
103 Morgan Ln Ste 102, Plainsboro NJ 08536
Tel (609) 606-9010 *SIC* 7371

SAMSUNG SDS AMERICA INC p 1275
100 Challenger Rd, Ridgefield Park NJ 07660
Tel (201) 229-4456 *SIC* 7372 7371

CGI AMS p 285
75 Livingston Ave Ste 202, Roseland NJ 07068
Tel (972) 788-0400
SIC 7379 8748 7374 7371

SHI INTERNATIONAL CORP p 1316
290 Davidson Ave, Somerset NJ 08873
Tel (732) 764-8888 *SIC* 7371 7374

▲COGNIZANT TECHNOLOGY SOLUTIONS CORP p 334
500 Frank W Burr Blvd, Teaneck NJ 07666
Tel (201) 801-0233 *SIC* 7371 7379 7372

NESS TECHNOLOGIES INC p 1026
300 Frank W Burr Blvd, Teaneck NJ 07666
Tel (201) 488-7222 *SIC* 7371

PEARSON EDUCATION INC p 1126
1 Lake St, Upper Saddle River NJ 07458
Tel (201) 236-7000 *SIC* 7371

SYNCSORT INC p 1415
50 Tice Blvd Ste 250, Woodcliff Lake NJ 07677
Tel (877) 700-0970 *SIC* 7371

▲INTERNATIONAL BUSINESS MACHINES CORP p 754
1 New Orchard Rd Ste 1, Armonk NY 10504
Tel (914) 499-1900
SIC 7379 7371 3571 3572 3674

AMPLIFY EDUCATION INC p 86
55 Washington St Ste 900, Brooklyn NY 11201
Tel (212) 213-8177 *SIC* 7371 8299

▲COMPUTER TASK GROUP INC p 353
800 Delaware Ave, Buffalo NY 14209
Tel (716) 882-8000 *SIC* 7371 7379 7361

▲SYNACOR INC p 1414
40 La Riviere Dr Ste 300, Buffalo NY 14202
Tel (716) 853-1362 *SIC* 7371 7374

SAAB SENSIS CORP p 1263
85 Collamer Crossings, East Syracuse NY 13057
Tel (315) 445-0550 *SIC* 3699 7371 3728

CURRIER MCCABE & ASSOCIATES INC p 402
700 Troy Schenectady Rd, Latham NY 12110
Tel (518) 783-9003 *SIC* 7371 7379

ANALYSIS & DESIGN APPLICATION CO LTD p 88
60 Broadhollow Rd, Melville NY 11747
Tel (631) 549-2300 *SIC* 7371

■VERINT ACQUISITION LLC p 1549
330 S Service Rd Ste 108, Melville NY 11747
Tel (631) 962-9600 *SIC* 7371

ACTIMIZE INC p 19
1359 Broadway Fl 5, New York NY 10018
Tel (212) 643-4600 *SIC* 7371

■AMERICAN HOME ASSURANCE CO INC p 74
70 Pine St Fl 1, New York NY 10005
Tel (212) 770-7000 *SIC* 6331 7371

▲CINEDIGM CORP p 307
902 Broadway Fl 9, New York NY 10010
Tel (212) 206-8600 *SIC* 7384 7389 7371

COMPUTER GENERATED SOLUTIONS INC p 352
200 Vesey St Fl 27, New York NY 10281
Tel (212) 408-3800
SIC 7373 7379 7371 8243

COMVERSE INC p 353
810 7th Ave Fl 32, New York NY 10019
Tel (212) 739-1060 *SIC* 7371

COMVERSE TECHNOLOGY INC p 353
810 7th Ave, New York NY 10019
Tel (212) 739-1000 *SIC* 7372 7371

DANUBE PRIVATE HOLDINGS II LLC p 412
601 Lexington Ave, New York NY 10022
Tel (212) 231-0095 *SIC* 7371

DATAART SOLUTIONS INC p 414
475 Park Ave S Fl 15, New York NY 10016
Tel (212) 378-4108 *SIC* 7371

■DAVIS ZIFF PUBLISHING INC p 416
28 E 28th St Fl 10, New York NY 10016
Tel (212) 503-3500 *SIC* 2721 2731 7371

FIDESSA CORP p 541
17 State St Fl 18, New York NY 10004
Tel (212) 269-9000 *SIC* 7371

GENISYS SOFTWARE LTD p 604
1345 Ave Of The Americas, New York NY 10105
Tel (732) 635-7132 *SIC* 7371 7372 5734

INFOR INC p 741
641 Ave Of The Americas # 4, New York NY 10011
Tel (646) 336-1700 *SIC* 7371 7372

INFOR LUX BOND CO p 741
641 Ave Of The Americas, New York NY 10011
Tel (646) 336-1700 *SIC* 7371 7372 8748

▲LIVEPERSON INC p 871
475 10th Ave Fl 5, New York NY 10018
Tel (212) 609-4200 *SIC* 7371 4813

MEDIAOCEAN LLC p 936
45 W 18th St, New York NY 10011
Tel (212) 633-8100 *SIC* 7371 7311

MMETRO.COM LLC p 979
568 Broadway Rm 507, New York NY 10012
Tel (646) 786-1938 *SIC* 7371

MPHASIS CORP p 995
460 Park Ave S Rm 1101, New York NY 10016
Tel (212) 686-6655 *SIC* 7371

▲MSCI INC p 996
250 Greenwich St Fl 49, New York NY 10007
Tel (212) 804-3900
SIC 7389 7371 6282 8742

■NYNEX INFORMATION SOLUTIONS GROUP INC p 1069
1095 Ave Of The Amer Fl 7, New York NY 10036
Tel (212) 395-1000 *SIC* 8732 7371 7379

REVAL.COM INC p 1229
420 5th Ave Fl 5, New York NY 10018
Tel (212) 393-1313 *SIC* 7371

SQUARESPACE INC p 1362
225 Varick St Fl 12, New York NY 10014
Tel (646) 580-3456 *SIC* 7371

▲TAKE-TWO INTERACTIVE SOFTWARE INC p 1422
622 Broadway Fl 6, New York NY 10012
Tel (646) 536-2842 *SIC* 7371 7372

TRANSPERFECT GLOBAL INC p 1472
3 Park Ave Fl 39, New York NY 10016
Tel (212) 689-5555 *SIC* 7389 7371 8748

VEXOS INC p 1553
60 E 42nd St Ste 1400, New York NY 10165
Tel (646) 843-0710 *SIC* 7371

VITECH SYSTEMS GROUP INC p 1563
401 Park Ave S Fl 12, New York NY 10016
Tel (212) 868-0900 *SIC* 7371

WALL STREET SYSTEMS SERVICES CORP p 1573
1345 Ave Of The, New York NY 10105
Tel (212) 809-7200 *SIC* 7371

ODYSSEY GROUP OF COMPANIES p 1075
11 Overlook Way, Setauket NY 11733
Tel (631) 751-8400
SIC 7373 3577 7371 1731

■SYSTEMS MADE SIMPLE INC p 1419
149 Northern Concourse # 1, Syracuse NY 13212
Tel (315) 455-3200 *SIC* 7371 8742

OPENLINK FINANCIAL LLC p 1089
1502 Rxr Plz Fl 15w, Uniondale NY 11556
Tel (516) 227-6600 *SIC* 7371 7372 8742

■CONSTELLA GROUP LLC p 360
2605 Meridian Pkwy # 200, Durham NC 27713
Tel (919) 544-8500
SIC 7371 8742 7375 8748 8731 8071

FREUDENBERG IT LP p 579
601 Keystone Park Dr # 600, Morrisville NC 27560
Tel (919) 321-0254 *SIC* 7371

TEKELEC GLOBAL INC p 1433
5200 Paramount Pkwy, Morrisville NC 27560
Tel (919) 460-5500 *SIC* 3661 3825 7371

TITAN PRIVATE HOLDINGS I LLC p 1456
5200 Paramount Pkwy, Morrisville NC 27560
Tel (919) 460-5500 *SIC* 3661 3825 7371

JENNE INC p 782
33665 Chester Rd, Avon OH 44011
Tel (440) 835-0040 *SIC* 7371 7382

■INTELLIGRATED SYSTEMS INC p 750
7901 Innovation Way, Mason OH 45040
Tel (866) 936-7300 *SIC* 3535 5084 7371

■INTELLIGRATED SYSTEMS LLC p 750
7901 Innovation Way, Mason OH 45040
Tel (513) 701-7300 *SIC* 3535 5084 7371

▲TERADATA CORP p 1439
10000 Innovation Dr, Miamisburg OH 45342
Tel (866) 548-8348
SIC 3571 3572 7372 7371

■KEITHLEY INSTRUMENTS INC p 808
28775 Aurora Rd, Solon OH 44139
Tel (440) 248-0400 *SIC* 3825 3823 7371

MRI SOFTWARE LLC p 996
28925 Fountain Pkwy, Solon OH 44139
Tel (800) 327-8770 *SIC* 7374 7371 6531

▲PAYCOM SOFTWARE INC p 1122
7501 W Memorial Rd, Oklahoma City OK 73142
Tel (405) 722-6900 *SIC* 8721 7371 7372

CHICKASAW HOLDING CO p 298
124 W Vinita Ave, Sulphur OK 73086
Tel (580) 622-2111 *SIC* 4813 7371 5065

GDH CONSULTING INC p 595
4200 E Skelly Dr Ste 650, Tulsa OK 74135
Tel (918) 392-1600 *SIC* 7379 7361 7371

■TRIPWIRE INC p 1482
101 Sw Main St Ste 1500, Portland OR 97204
Tel (503) 276-7500 *SIC* 7371

COMPUTER AID INC p 352
1390 Ridgeview Dr Ste 300, Allentown PA 18104
Tel (610) 530-5000 *SIC* 7371

■ALLIANCE CONSULTING GLOBAL HOLDINGS INC p 54
181 Washington St Ste 350, Conshohocken PA 19428
Tel (610) 234-4301 *SIC* 7371

■MASTECH DIGITAL TECHNOLOGIES INC p 918
1305 Cherrington Pkwy, Coraopolis PA 15108
Tel (412) 787-2100 *SIC* 7371

LOBAR INC p 872
1 Old Mill Rd, Dillsburg PA 17019
Tel (717) 432-9728
SIC 1541 1542 8741 1629 1731 7371

HIGHPOINT SOLUTIONS LLC p 692
301 E Germantown Pike # 1, East Norriton PA 19401
Tel (610) 233-2700 *SIC* 7371

CI&T INC p 305
630 Freedom Bus Ctr Dr # 300, King Of Prussia PA 19406
Tel (610) 482-4810 *SIC* 7371

■GSI COMMERCE INC p 643
935 1st Ave, King Of Prussia PA 19406
Tel (610) 491-7000 *SIC* 5961 7371 7379

▲MASTECH DIGITAL INC p 918
1305 Cherrington Pkwy # 400, Moon Township PA 15108
Tel (412) 787-2100 *SIC* 7361 7371

■ALLIANCE GLOBAL SERVICES INC p 54
41 University Dr Ste 202, Newtown PA 18940
Tel (610) 234-4301 *SIC* 7371

▲EPAM SYSTEMS INC p 504
41 University Dr Ste 202, Newtown PA 18940
Tel (267) 759-9000 *SIC* 7371 8742

SAP AMERICA INC p 1281
3999 West Chester Pike, Newtown Square PA 19073
Tel (610) 661-1000 *SIC* 7371

PENCOR SERVICES INC p 1128
613 3rd Street Palmerton, Palmerton PA 18071
Tel (610) 826-2115
SIC 2711 7371 4813 4841

▲CDI CORP p 271
1735 Market St Ste 200, Philadelphia PA 19103
Tel (215) 569-2200
SIC 8711 7371 7373 7376 7361 7363

▲FAB UNIVERSAL CORP p 523
5001 Baum Blvd Ste 770, Pittsburgh PA 15213
Tel (412) 621-0902
SIC 7371 7372 5735 5942 5994 5099

MANAGEMENT SCIENCE ASSOCIATES INC p 900
6565 Penn Ave, Pittsburgh PA 15206
Tel (412) 362-2000 *SIC* 8742 7371

▲ EMTEC INC p 495
150 N Radnor, Radnor PA 19087
Tel (973) 376-4242 SIC 7371 7379

QLIK PARENT INC p 1195
150 N Radnor Chester Rd, Radnor PA 19087
Tel (888) 828-9768 SIC 6719 7371

QLIKTECHNOLOGIES INC p 1195
150 N Radnor Chester Rd, Radnor PA 19087
Tel (866) 616-4960 SIC 7374 7371

KENEXA CORP p 810
650 E Swedesford Rd # 200, Wayne PA 19087
Tel (877) 971-9171 SIC 7361 7371

MEDECISION INC p 935
550 E Swedesford Rd # 220, Wayne PA 19087
Tel (484) 588-0102 SIC 6324 7371

GTECH HOLDINGS CORP p 644
10 Memorial Blvd Ste 101, Providence RI 02903
Tel (401) 392-1000 SIC 7999 7371

■ BENEFITFOCUS INC p 173
1016 Woods Crossing Rd, Greenville SC 29607
Tel (864) 234-2827 SIC 7371

LIFE CYCLE ENGINEERING INC p 863
4360 Corporate Rd Ste 100, North Charleston SC 29405
Tel (843) 744-7110
SIC 7371 7373 7376 7379 8711

MEDHOST OF TENNESSEE INC p 935
6550 Carothers Pkwy # 100, Franklin TN 37067
Tel (615) 761-1000 SIC 7371

MMODAL SERVICES INC p 979
5000 Meridian Blvd # 200, Franklin TN 37067
Tel (615) 261-1500 SIC 7372 7371

■ ELECTRONIC FUNDS SOURCE LLC p 485
3100 West End Ave # 1150, Nashville TN 37203
Tel (888) 824-7378 SIC 7371 6099

▲ HEALTHSTREAM INC p 678
209 10th Ave S Ste 450, Nashville TN 37203
Tel (615) 301-3100 SIC 7372 7371

QUALIFACTS SYSTEMS INC p 1196
200 2nd Ave S, Nashville TN 37201
Tel (615) 386-6755 SIC 7373 7371

ACTIVANT SOLUTIONS HOLDINGS INC p 19
804 Las Cimas Pkwy, Austin TX 78746
Tel (512) 328-2300 SIC 7371

EMBARCADERO TECHNOLOGIES INC p 490
10801 N Mopac Expy 1-100, Austin TX 78759
Tel (415) 834-3131 SIC 7371 7372

KASASA LTD p 804
4516 Seton Center Pkwy, Austin TX 78759
Tel (512) 418-9590 SIC 7371 7373 7379

PLANVIEW INC p 1154
12301 Research Blvd 5-100, Austin TX 78759
Tel (512) 346-8600 SIC 7371 8748 8742

SOFTSERVE INC p 1337
111 Congress Ave, Austin TX 78701
Tel (512) 516-8880 SIC 7371

SPREDFAST INC p 1360
200 W Cesar Chavez St # 600, Austin TX 78701
Tel (512) 823-2320 SIC 7371

■ THOMSON REUTERS (TAX & ACCOUNTING) INC p 1450
2395 Midway Rd, Carrollton TX 75006
Tel (800) 431-9025 SIC 2721 7371

COMPAREX USA INC p 350
600 N Pearl St Ste 1960, Dallas TX 75201
Tel (972) 734-5223 SIC 5045 7371

ENTRUST INC p 503
5430 Lyndon B Johnson Fwy, Dallas TX 75240
Tel (972) 728-0447 SIC 7371

MODEST BILLIONAIRES LLC p 981
3815 Martha Ln, Dallas TX 75229
Tel (972) 672-0755 SIC 7374 7371 7389

ADI WORLDLINK LLC p 22
3880 Parkwood Blvd # 204, Frisco TX 75034
Tel (972) 671-3434 SIC 7371

BMC SOFTWARE INC p 193
2103 Citywest Blvd # 2100, Houston TX 77042
Tel (713) 918-8800 SIC 7372 7371

▲ CARBO CERAMICS INC p 252
575 N Dairy Ashford Rd # 30, Houston TX 77079
Tel (281) 921-6400
SIC 3291 5945 8742 7371

GULF COAST REGIONAL BLOOD CENTER p 646
1400 La Concha Ln, Houston TX 77054
Tel (713) 790-1200 SIC 8099 7371 7363

IDERA INC p 729
2950 North Loop W Ste 700, Houston TX 77092
Tel (713) 523-4433 SIC 7371 7372

■ LANDMARK GRAPHICS CORP p 843
2107 Citywest Blvd Bldg 2, Houston TX 77042
Tel (713) 839-2000 SIC 7371 7373

NETIQ CORP p 1027
515 Post Oak Blvd # 1000, Houston TX 77027
Tel (713) 548-1700 SIC 7372 7371

▲ PROS HOLDINGS INC p 1184
3100 Main St Ste 900, Houston TX 77002
Tel (713) 335-5151 SIC 7371 7372

REYNOLDS AND REYNOLDS CO p 1230
6700 Hollister St, Houston TX 77040
Tel (713) 718-1800 SIC 7371

SHELL INFORMATION TECHNOLOGY INTERNATIONAL INC p 1314
910 Louisiana St, Houston TX 77002
Tel (855) 697-4355 SIC 8742 7371

SUMMIT CONSOLIDATION GROUP INC p 1398
10497 Town Cntry Way 3, Houston TX 77024
Tel (713) 554-2244 SIC 7373 7371 4813

VERIFINC CORP p 1549
12000 Westheimer Rd # 380, Houston TX 77077
Tel (832) 858-5548 SIC 7371 5734 5122

■ HP ENTERPRISE SERVICES LLC p 714
5400 Legacy Dr, Plano TX 75024
Tel (972) 604-6000 SIC 7374 7371 8742

■ RETALIX USA INC p 1228
6100 Tennyson Pkwy # 150, Plano TX 75024
Tel (469) 241-8400 SIC 7371

ELECTRONIC TRANSACTION CONSULTANTS CORP p 486
1705 N Plano Rd, Richardson TX 75081
Tel (972) 470-5873 SIC 7371

INFOVISION INC p 742
800 E Campbell Rd Ste 388, Richardson TX 75081
Tel (972) 234-0058 SIC 8711 7371

▲ REALPAGE INC p 1214
2201 Lakeside Blvd, Richardson TX 75082
Tel (972) 820-3000 SIC 7371

RACKSPACE HOSTING INC p 1203
1 Fanatical Pl, San Antonio TX 78218
Tel (210) 312-4000
SIC 7371 7374 7382 4813

GRAVICK GROUP LLC p 632
4985 Fm 1017, San Isidro TX 78588
Tel (956) 330-5676 SIC 8742 7371 7389

■ SABRE GLBL INC p 1264
3150 Sabre Dr, Southlake TX 76092
Tel (682) 605-1000
SIC 7375 7371 7374 7389 8748

SOLERA HOLDINGS INC p 1338
1301 Solana Blvd Ste 2100, Westlake TX 76262
Tel (817) 961-2100 SIC 7371

SOLERA LLC p 1338
1301 Solana Blvd Ste 2100, Westlake TX 76262
Tel (817) 961-2100 SIC 7371

SUMMERTIME HOLDING CORP p 1398
1301 Solana Blvd Ste 2100, Westlake TX 76262
Tel (817) 961-2100 SIC 6719 7371

PDX INC p 1125
101 S Jim Wright Fwy # 100, White Settlement TX 76108
Tel (817) 246-6760 SIC 7371

SIRSI CORP p 1327
3300 N Ashton Blvd # 500, Lehi UT 84043
Tel (801) 223-5200 SIC 7371

WORKFRONT INC p 1624
3301 N Thank Way Ste 100, Lehi UT 84043
Tel (801) 373-3266 SIC 7371

SOFTWARE FORENSICS INC p 1337
384 S 400 W Ste 200, Lindon UT 84042
Tel (801) 377-5410 SIC 7371 8243

UTAH STATE UNIVERSITY RESEARCH FOUNDATION p 1536
1695 N Research Pkwy, North Logan UT 84341
Tel (435) 713-3400
SIC 8711 8734 8733 7371

■ OMNITURE LLC p 1085
550 E Tmpngos Cle Bldng G, Orem UT 84097
Tel (801) 722-7000 SIC 7371

QUALTRICS LLC p 1198
333 River Park Dr, Provo UT 84604
Tel (801) 374-6682 SIC 7371

LANDESK SOFTWARE INC p 842
698 W 10000 S Ste 500, South Jordan UT 84095
Tel (801) 208-1500 SIC 7371

■ IDX SYSTEMS CORP p 729
40 Idx Dr, South Burlington VT 05403
Tel (802) 658-2664 SIC 7371

■ CACI INC - FEDERAL p 235
1100 N Glebe Rd Ste 200, Arlington VA 22201
Tel (703) 841-7800
SIC 7373 7372 7371 8711

▲ CACI INTERNATIONAL INC p 235
1100 N Glebe Rd Ste 200, Arlington VA 22201
Tel (703) 841-7800 SIC 7373 4899 7371

■ CACI-ISS INC p 236
1100 N Glebe Rd Ste 200, Arlington VA 22201
Tel (703) 841-7800 SIC 7371

PHACIL INC p 1141
800 N Glebe Rd Ste 700, Arlington VA 22203
Tel (703) 526-1800 SIC 7379 7371

■ PRO-TELLIGENT LLC p 1178
1320 N Courthouse Rd # 600, Arlington VA 22201
Tel (703) 387-2100 SIC 7371 7379

▲ ROSETTA STONE INC p 1251
1621 N Kent St Ste 1200, Arlington VA 22209
Tel (703) 387-5800 SIC 7372 4813 7371

THALES USA INC p 1446
2733 Crystal Dr, Arlington VA 22202
Tel (703) 413-6029
SIC 5065 3699 3679 3841 8711 7371

SAAB NORTH AMERICA INC p 1263
20700 Loudoun County Pkwy # 152, Ashburn VA 20147
Tel (703) 406-7277 SIC 5088 3699 7371

■ APPTIS HOLDINGS INC p 100
4800 Westfields Blvd # 1, Chantilly VA 20151
Tel (703) 745-6016 SIC 7371

■ GE INTELLIGENT PLATFORMS INC p 596
2500 Austin Dr, Charlottesville VA 22911
Tel (434) 978-5000 SIC 3625 3674 7371

HARRIS TECHNICAL SERVICES CORP p 664
21000 Atl Blvd Ste 300, Dulles VA 20166
Tel (703) 610-4200
SIC 7371 7379 8711 3577

ASM RESEARCH LLC p 118
4050 Legato Rd Ste 1100, Fairfax VA 22033
Tel (703) 645-0420 SIC 7371 8731

CAMBER GOVERNMENT SOLUTIONS INC p 243
12730 Fair Lakes Cir, Fairfax VA 22033
Tel (703) 653-8000 SIC 7371 7379

ECS FEDERAL LLC p 476
2750 Prosperity Ave # 600, Fairfax VA 22031
Tel (703) 270-1540 SIC 7371 7379 8742

ELLUCIAN INC p 489
4375 Fair Lakes Ct, Fairfax VA 22033
Tel (407) 660-1199 SIC 7371 7373

INFORELIANCE CORP p 741
4050 Legato Rd Ste 700, Fairfax VA 22033
Tel (703) 246-9360 SIC 7371

SALIENT CRGT HOLDINGS INC p 1272
4000 Legato Rd Ste 600, Fairfax VA 22033
Tel (703) 891-8200 SIC 7371 8748

SALIENT FEDERAL SOLUTIONS INC p 1272
4000 Legato Rd Ste 600, Fairfax VA 22033
Tel (703) 891-8200 SIC 7371

■ VANGENT INC p 1543
3211 Jermantown Rd, Fairfax VA 22030
Tel (703) 995-2666
SIC 8748 7371 7372 7373 7374 7376

■ ACENTIA LLC p 17
3130 Frview Pk Dr Ste 800, Falls Church VA 22042
Tel (703) 712-4000 SIC 7371

■ CSC COVANSYS CORP p 397
3170 Fairview Park Dr, Falls Church VA 22042
Tel (703) 876-1000 SIC 7371

■ CSRA LLC p 398
3170 Fairview Park Dr, Falls Church VA 22042
Tel (703) 876-1000
SIC 7371 8733 7376 7374 7379

EOIR TECHNOLOGIES INC p 504
10300 Spotsylvania Ave, Fredericksburg VA 22408
Tel (540) 834-4888
SIC 8711 7371 8731 8742

ANALEX CORP p 88
3076 Centreville Rd # 200, Herndon VA 20171
Tel (703) 880-2800 SIC 7371

■ CONTENT EPLUS SERVICES INC p 362
13595 Dulles Tech Dr, Herndon VA 20171
Tel (703) 984-8400 SIC 7371

■ CUBIC GLOBAL DEFENSE INC p 399
205 Van Buren St Ste 310, Herndon VA 20170
Tel (703) 821-8930
SIC 7379 7371 7373 8711

DELTEK INC p 427
2291 Wood Oak Dr Ste 100, Herndon VA 20171
Tel (703) 734-8606 SIC 7371 7379

DLT SOLUTIONS HOLDINGS INC p 445
13861 Sunrise Valley Dr # 400, Herndon VA 20171
Tel (800) 262-4358 SIC 7371

DRS GLOBAL ENTERPRISE SOLUTIONS INC p 457
12930 Worldgate Dr, Herndon VA 20170
Tel (703) 896-7100 SIC 7371 8731

■ RAYTHEON BLACKBIRD TECHNOLOGIES INC p 1211
13900 Lincoln Park Dr # 400, Herndon VA 20171
Tel (703) 796-1420 SIC 7371 7382

SOTERA DEFENSE SOLUTIONS INC p 1341
2121 Coop Way Ste 400, Herndon VA 20171
Tel (703) 230-8200 SIC 7371 7379

DIGITAL INTELLIGENCE SYSTEMS LLC p 439
8270 Greensboro Dr # 1000, Mc Lean VA 22102
Tel (703) 752-7900 SIC 7373 7371

■ DYNCORP p 465
1700 Old Meadow Rd, Mc Lean VA 22102
Tel (571) 722-0210
SIC 7373 7371 7374 7375 8744 4581

■ DYNCORP INTERNATIONAL INC p 465
1700 Old Meadow Rd, Mc Lean VA 22102
Tel (571) 722-0210
SIC 8741 7371 7381 7361 7363

■ IMMIXGROUP INC p 734
8444 Westpark Dr Ste 200, Mc Lean VA 22102
Tel (703) 752-0610 SIC 7371 7379

TWD & ASSOCIATES INC p 1494
1751 Pinnacle Dr Ste 900, Mc Lean VA 22102
Tel (703) 820-9777 SIC 7371

APPIAN CORP p 98
11955 Democracy Dr # 1700, Reston VA 20190
Tel (703) 442-8844 SIC 7379 7371

■ CONTACT SOLUTIONS LLC p 362
11950 Democracy Dr # 250, Reston VA 20190
Tel (703) 480-1620 SIC 7379 7371 7389

▲ LEIDOS HOLDINGS INC p 854
11951 Freedom Dr Ste 500, Reston VA 20190
Tel (571) 526-6000
SIC 8731 7371 7373 8742 3674

SERCO SERVICES INC p 1306
1818 Library St Ste 1000, Reston VA 20190
Tel (703) 939-6000 SIC 7371

SOFTWARE AG USA INC p 1337
11700 Plaza America Dr # 700, Reston VA 20190
Tel (703) 860-5050 SIC 7371

▲ MICROSTRATEGY INC p 962
1850 Towers Crescent Plz # 700, Tysons Corner VA 22182
Tel (703) 848-8600 SIC 7372 7371

ACTIONET INC p 19
2600 Park Twr Dr Ste 1000, Vienna VA 22180
Tel (703) 204-0090
SIC 7379 7373 7372 7371

■ AT&T GOVERNMENT SOLUTIONS INC p 123
1900 Gallows Rd Ste 105, Vienna VA 22182
Tel (703) 506-5000
SIC 5999 8742 7373 7371

▲ BSQUARE CORP p 222
110 110th Ave Ne Ste 300, Bellevue WA 98004
Tel (425) 519-5900 SIC 7371 8711

CONCUR TECHNOLOGIES INC p 355
601 108th Ave Ne Ste 1000, Bellevue WA 98004
Tel (425) 702-8808 SIC 7372 7371

▲ ITRON INC p 768
2111 N Molter Rd, Liberty Lake WA 99019
Tel (509) 924-9900 SIC 3829 7371

▲ MICROSOFT CORP p 962
1 Microsoft Way, Redmond WA 98052
Tel (425) 882-8080
SIC 7372 7371 3577 7375

PACTERA TECHNOLOGIES NA INC p 1107
14980 Ne 31st Way Ste 120, Redmond WA 98052
Tel (425) 233-8578 SIC 7371 8742

WORLD WIDE TECHNOLOGY p 1625
26017 Se 23rd Pl, Sammamish WA 98075
Tel (425) 269-2678 SIC 7371

AMAZON.COMINDC LLC p 65
440 Terry Ave N, Seattle WA 98109
Tel (206) 266-1000 SIC 4813 5999 7371

ATTACHMATE CORP p 129
705 5th Ave S Ste 1000, Seattle WA 98104
Tel (206) 217-7100 SIC 7373 7371 7372

ATTACHMATE GROUP INC p 129
705 5th Ave S Ste 1100, Seattle WA 98104
Tel (206) 217-7100 SIC 7371 7372 7373

NORTHLAND TELECOMMUNICATIONS CORP p 1057
101 Stewart St Ste 700, Seattle WA 98101
Tel (206) 621-1351 SIC 4841 7371

▲ REALNETWORKS INC p 1214
1501 1st Ave S Ste 600, Seattle WA 98134
Tel (206) 674-2700 SIC 7371 7372

■ ZILLOW INC p 1643
1301 2nd Ave Fl 31, Seattle WA 98101
Tel (206) 470-7000 SIC 7371 8742

TEKNETIX INC p 1433
2501 Garfield Ave, Parkersburg WV 26101
Tel (304) 489-3600 SIC 3672 7371

▲ CONNECTURE INC p 357
18500 W Corp Dr Ste 250, Brookfield WI 53045
Tel (262) 432-8282 SIC 7371

▲ FISERV INC p 551
255 Fiserv Dr, Brookfield WI 53045
Tel (262) 879-5000 SIC 7374 7371

PROGRESSIVE ENTERPRISES HOLDINGS INC p 1181
250 N Sunny Slope Rd # 110, Brookfield WI 53005
Tel (262) 207-2101 SIC 7371

STONERIVER INC p 1391
250 N Sunny Slope Rd # 110, Brookfield WI 53005
Tel (262) 207-2101 SIC 7371

ALDRICH CHEMICAL CO LLC p 48
6000 N Teutonia Ave, Milwaukee WI 53209
Tel (414) 438-3850
SIC 2869 2819 3821 7371 2741

EPIC SYSTEMS CORP p 505
1979 Milky Way, Verona WI 53593
Tel (608) 271-9000 SIC 7371

OMEGA PROBE INC p 1084
308 Southwest Dr, Cheyenne WY 82007
Tel (877) 323-2201 SIC 7371 6552

SIC 7372 Prepackaged Software

INTERGRAPH CORP p 752
305 Intergraph Way, Madison AL 35758
Tel (256) 730-2000 SIC 7372 7373 7379

SSI GROUP INC p 1363
4721 Morrison Dr, Mobile AL 36609
Tel (251) 345-0000 SIC 7371 7372

AXWAY INC p 140
6811 E Mayo Blvd Ste 400, Phoenix AZ 85054
Tel (480) 627-1800 SIC 7372

ENGHOUSE INTERACTIVE INC p 498
2095 W Pinnacle Peak Rd, Phoenix AZ 85027
Tel (602) 789-2800
SIC 3571 3661 3663 7372 7374

■ EFUNDS CORP p 481
4900 N Scottsdale Rd # 1000, Scottsdale AZ 85251
Tel (602) 431-2700 SIC 7374 7372 7371

■ HYPERCOM CORP p 724
8888 E Raintree Dr # 300, Scottsdale AZ 85260
Tel (480) 642-5000
SIC 3578 7372 7299 5065

▲ LIMELIGHT NETWORKS INC p 866
222 S Mill Ave Ste 800, Tempe AZ 85281
Tel (602) 850-5000 SIC 7372 7375

■ WIND RIVER SYSTEMS INC p 1615
500 Wind River Way, Alameda CA 94501
Tel (510) 748-4100 SIC 7372 7373

QUEST SOFTWARE INC p 1199
4 Polaris Way, Aliso Viejo CA 92656
Tel (949) 754-8000 SIC 7373 7372 7379

▲ RINGCENTRAL INC p 1235
20 Davis Dr, Belmont CA 94002
Tel (650) 472-4100 SIC 7372 4899

▲ NETSOL TECHNOLOGIES INC p 1027
24025 Park Sorrento # 410, Calabasas CA 91302
Tel (818) 222-9195 SIC 7372 7373 7299

▲ BARRACUDA NETWORKS INC p 156
3175 Winchester Blvd, Campbell CA 95008
Tel (408) 342-5400 SIC 7372 7373

■ APPLIED BIOSYSTEMS LLC p 99
5791 Van Allen Way, Carlsbad CA 92008
Tel (760) 638-5000 SIC 3826 7372

■ ENTROPIC COMMUNICATIONS LLC p 503
5966 La Place Ct Ste 100, Carlsbad CA 92008
Tel (858) 768-3600 SIC 3674 7372

FILENET CORP p 542
3565 Harbor Blvd, Costa Mesa CA 92626
Tel (800) 345-3638 SIC 7373 7372

SYSPRO IMPACT SOFTWARE INC p 1418
959 S Coast Dr Ste 100, Costa Mesa CA 92626
Tel (714) 437-1000 SIC 5045 7372 7371

▲ APPLE INC p 98
1 Infinite Loop, Cupertino CA 95014
Tel (408) 996-1010
SIC 3663 3571 3575 3577 3651 7372

GENESYS TELECOMMUNICATIONS LABORATORIES INC p 603
2001 Junipero Serra Blvd, Daly City CA 94014
Tel (650) 466-1100 SIC 7372

▲ CALLIDUS SOFTWARE INC p 242
4140 Dublin Blvd Ste 400, Dublin CA 94568
Tel (925) 251-2200 SIC 7371 7372

SYBASE INC p 1413
1 Sybase Dr, Dublin CA 94568
Tel (925) 236-5000 SIC 7372

■ TALEO CORP p 1422
4140 Dublin Blvd Ste 400, Dublin CA 94568
Tel (925) 452-3000 SIC 7372

■ PIXAR p 1152
1200 Park Ave, Emeryville CA 94608
Tel (510) 922-3000 SIC 7812 7372 7371

▲ TUBEMOGUL INC p 1490
1250 53rd St Ste 2, Emeryville CA 94608
Tel (510) 653-0126 SIC 7372

▲ GUIDEWIRE SOFTWARE INC p 646
1001 E Hillsdale Blvd # 800, Foster City CA 94404
Tel (650) 357-9100 SIC 7372

▲ QUINSTREET INC p 1200
950 Tower Ln Ste 600, Foster City CA 94404
Tel (650) 578-7700 SIC 7389 7372

ZUORA INC p 1645
1051 E Hillsdale Blvd # 600, Foster City CA 94404
Tel (800) 425-1281 SIC 7372

AGILITY LOGISTICS CORP p 35
240 Commerce, Irvine CA 92602
Tel (714) 617-6300
SIC 4731 8742 7372 1381

■ BLIZZARD ENTERTAINMENT INC p 189
16215 Alton Pkwy, Irvine CA 92618
Tel (949) 955-1380 SIC 7372 5734 7819

EAGLE TOPCO LP p 468
18200 Von Karman Ave, Irvine CA 92612
Tel (949) 585-4329 SIC 7372

EGL HOLDCO INC p 481
18200 Von Karman Ave # 1000, Irvine CA 92612
Tel (800) 678-7423 SIC 7372

KOFAX LIMITED p 826
15211 Laguna Canyon Rd, Irvine CA 92618
Tel (949) 783-1000 SIC 7372

▲ QUALITY SYSTEMS INC p 1197
18111 Von Karman Ave # 700, Irvine CA 92612
Tel (949) 255-2600 SIC 7372 7373

SAGE SOFTWARE HOLDINGS INC p 1267
6561 Irvine Center Dr, Irvine CA 92618
Tel (866) 530-7243 SIC 7372 7371

■ CONTINENTAL GRAPHICS CORP p 363
4060 N Lakewood Blvd, Long Beach CA 90808
Tel (714) 503-4200
SIC 3724 7371 7372 7374

GLADIATOR CORP p 614
2882 Sand Hill Rd Ste 280, Menlo Park CA 94025
Tel (650) 233-2900 SIC 7372

■ KAY TECHNOLOGY HOLDINGS INC p 805
2500 Sand Hill Rd Ste 300, Menlo Park CA 94025
Tel (650) 289-2481 SIC 7372

▲ FIREEYE INC p 543
1440 Mccarthy Blvd, Milpitas CA 95035
Tel (408) 321-6300 SIC 7372

▲ INTUIT INC p 760
2700 Coast Ave, Mountain View CA 94043
Tel (650) 944-6000 SIC 7372

▲ MOBILEIRON INC p 980
415 E Middlefield Rd, Mountain View CA 94043
Tel (650) 919-8100 SIC 7372

▲ SYMANTEC CORP p 1414
350 Ellis St, Mountain View CA 94043
Tel (650) 527-8000 SIC 7372 7379

MSCSOFTWARE CORP p 997
4675 Macarthur Ct Ste 900, Newport Beach CA 92660
Tel (714) 540-8900 SIC 7372

TZ HOLDINGS LP p 1496
567 San Nicolas Dr # 120, Newport Beach CA 92660
Tel (949) 719-2200 SIC 7372

ACTIAN CORP p 19
2300 Geng Rd Ste 150, Palo Alto CA 94303
Tel (650) 587-5500 SIC 7373 7372

ADAPTIVE INSIGHTS INC p 21
3350 W Byshore Rd Ste 200, Palo Alto CA 94303
Tel (800) 303-6346 SIC 7372

ARIBA INC p 108
3420 Hillview Ave Bldg 3, Palo Alto CA 94304
Tel (650) 849-4000 SIC 7372

▲ HEWLETT PACKARD ENTERPRISE CO p 688
3000 Hanover St, Palo Alto CA 94304
Tel (650) 857-5817 SIC 7372 7379 3572

▲ HP INC p 714
1501 Page Mill Rd, Palo Alto CA 94304
Tel (650) 857-1501
SIC 3571 7372 3861 3577 3572 3575

▲ JIVE SOFTWARE INC p 786
325 Lytton Ave Ste 200, Palo Alto CA 94301
Tel (650) 319-1920 SIC 7372

MAXIMUS HOLDINGS INC p 922
2475 Hanover St, Palo Alto CA 94304
Tel (650) 935-9500 SIC 7372

MEDALLIA INC p 935
395 Page Mill Rd Ste 100, Palo Alto CA 94306
Tel (650) 321-3000 SIC 7372 8732

■ MERCURY INTERACTIVE LLC p 945
3000 Hanover St, Palo Alto CA 94304
Tel (650) 857-1501 SIC 7372

METRICSTREAM INC p 954
2600 E Bayshore Rd, Palo Alto CA 94303
Tel (650) 620-2900 SIC 7372

▲ VARIAN MEDICAL SYSTEMS INC p 1544
3100 Hansen Way, Palo Alto CA 94304
Tel (650) 493-4000 SIC 3845 3844 7372

▲ GUIDANCE SOFTWARE INC p 645
1055 E Colo Blvd Ste 400, Pasadena CA 91106
Tel (626) 229-9191 SIC 7372 3572

■ DOCUMENTUM INC p 447
6801 Koll Center Pkwy, Pleasanton CA 94566
Tel (925) 600-6800 SIC 7372 7371

▲ VEEVA SYSTEMS INC p 1546
4280 Hacienda Dr, Pleasanton CA 94588
Tel (925) 452-6500 SIC 7372 7371 7379

ZOHO CORP p 1644
4141 Hacienda Dr, Pleasanton CA 94588
Tel (925) 924-9500 SIC 7372

▲ BOX INC p 205
900 Jefferson Ave, Redwood City CA 94063
Tel (877) 729-4269 SIC 7372

■ DIGITAL INSIGHT CORP p 439
1300 Seaport Blvd Ste 300, Redwood City CA 94063
Tel (818) 879-1010 SIC 7375 7372 7371

▲ ELECTRONIC ARTS INC p 485
209 Redwood Shores Pkwy, Redwood City CA 94065
Tel (650) 628-1500 SIC 7372

INFORMATICA LLC p 741
2100 Seaport Blvd, Redwood City CA 94063
Tel (650) 385-5000 SIC 7372

■ OC ACQUISITION LLC p 1072
500 Oracle Pkwy, Redwood City CA 94065
Tel (650) 506-7000 SIC 7371 7372

■ ORACLE AMERICA INC p 1091
500 Oracle Pkwy, Redwood City CA 94065
Tel (650) 506-7000
SIC 3571 7379 7373 7372 3674

▲ ORACLE CORP p 1091
500 Oracle Pkwy, Redwood City CA 94065
Tel (650) 506-7000
SIC 7372 7379 8243 3571 3674

■ ORACLE SYSTEMS CORP p 1091
500 Oracle Pkwy, Redwood City CA 94065
Tel (650) 506-7000 SIC 7372 7379 8243

■ ORACLE USA INC p 1091
500 Oracle Pkwy, Redwood City CA 94065
Tel (650) 506-7000 SIC 7372

▲ QUALYS INC p 1198
1600 Bridge Pkwy Ste 201, Redwood City CA 94065
Tel (650) 801-6100 SIC 7371 7372

SABA SOFTWARE INC p 1263
2400 Bridge Pkwy, Redwood City CA 94065
Tel (650) 581-2500 SIC 7372 7371

▲ SUPPORT.COM INC p 1408
900 Chesapeake Dr Fl 2, Redwood City CA 94063
Tel (650) 556-9440 SIC 7374 7372

HITACHI SOLUTIONS AMERICA LTD p 697
851 Traeger Ave Ste 200, San Bruno CA 94066
Tel (650) 615-7600 SIC 5045 7372 7373

■ RESPONSYS INC p 1228
1100 Grundy Ln Ste 300, San Bruno CA 94066
Tel (650) 745-1700 SIC 7371 7372

CHECK POINT SOFTWARE TECHNOLOGIES INC p 292
959 Skyway Rd Ste 300, San Carlos CA 94070
Tel (800) 429-4391 SIC 7372

■ ROVI CORP p 1253
2 Circle Star Way, San Carlos CA 94070
Tel (408) 562-8400 SIC 7372

AUDATEX NORTH AMERICA INC p 130
15030 Ave Of Ste 100, San Diego CA 92128
Tel (858) 946-1900 SIC 7372

▲ CUBIC CORP p 399
9333 Balboa Ave, San Diego CA 92123
Tel (858) 277-6780 SIC 3812 3699 7372

DASSAULT SYSTEMES BIOVIA CORP p 413
5005 Wateridge Vista Dr # 2, San Diego CA 92121
Tel (858) 799-5000 SIC 7372

OMNITRACS MIDCO LLC p 1085
10182 Telesis Ct Ste 100, San Diego CA 92121
Tel (858) 651-5812 SIC 7372

▲ QUALCOMM INC p 1196
5775 Morehouse Dr, San Diego CA 92121
Tel (858) 587-1121 SIC 3674 7372 6794

■ QUALCOMM TECHNOLOGIES INC p 1196
5775 Morehouse Dr, San Diego CA 92121
Tel (858) 587-1121 SIC 3674 7372 6794

■ SMART-TEK AUTOMATED SERVICES INC p 1332
11838 Bernardo Plaza Ct # 250, San Diego CA 92128
Tel (858) 798-1644 SIC 7372

■ ADOBE MACROMEDIA SOFTWARE LLC p 23
601 Townsend St, San Francisco CA 94103
Tel (415) 832-2000 SIC 7372

■ ADVENT SOFTWARE INC p 27
600 Townsend St Fl 5, San Francisco CA 94103
Tel (415) 543-7696
SIC 7371 7373 7372 6722

FRANCISCO PARTNERS LP p 574
1 Letterman Dr Bldg C, San Francisco CA 94129
Tel (415) 418-2900 SIC 7373 7372

FRANCISCO PARTNERS MANAGEMENT LP p 574
1 Letterman Dr Ste 410, San Francisco CA 94129
Tel (415) 418-2900 SIC 6799 7372

▲ MCKESSON CORP p 930
1 Post St Fl 18, San Francisco CA 94104
Tel (415) 983-8300
SIC 5122 5047 5199 7372

▲ NEW RELIC INC p 1033
188 Spear St Ste 1200, San Francisco CA 94105
Tel (650) 777-7600 SIC 7372

▲ SALESFORCE.COM INC p 1272
1 Market Ste 300, San Francisco CA 94105
Tel (415) 901-7000 SIC 7372 7375

▲ SPLUNK INC p 1359
250 Brannan St, San Francisco CA 94107
Tel (415) 848-8400 SIC 7372

▲ SQUARE INC p 1362
1455 Market St Ste 600, San Francisco CA 94103
Tel (415) 375-3176 SIC 7372

▲ TWILIO INC p 1494
645 Harrison St Fl 3, San Francisco CA 94107
Tel (415) 390-2337 SIC 7372 4812

UBER TECHNOLOGIES INC p 1498
1455 Market St Fl 4, San Francisco CA 94103
Tel (415) 986-2715 SIC 7372

YOURPEOPLE INC p 1639
303 2nd St Ste 401, San Francisco CA 94107
Tel (415) 798-9086 SIC 6411 7372

▲ ZENDESK INC p 1642
1019 Market St, San Francisco CA 94103
Tel (415) 418-7506 SIC 7372

▲ ZYNGA INC p 1645
699 8th St, San Francisco CA 94103
Tel (855) 449-9642 SIC 7372 7374

▲ 8X8 INC p 4
2125 Onel Dr, San Jose CA 95131
Tel (408) 727-1885 SIC 4813 7372

▲ ADOBE SYSTEMS INC p 23
345 Park Ave, San Jose CA 95110
Tel (408) 536-6000 SIC 7372

■ BEA SYSTEMS INC p 164
2315 N 1st St, San Jose CA 95131
Tel (650) 506-7000 SIC 7371 7372

▲ CADENCE DESIGN SYSTEMS INC p 236
2655 Seely Ave Bldg 5, San Jose CA 95134
Tel (408) 943-1234 SIC 7372

▲ EXTREME NETWORKS INC p 521
145 Rio Robles, San Jose CA 95134
Tel (408) 579-2800 SIC 3661 7373 7372

▲ FAIR ISAAC CORP p 524
181 Metro Dr Ste 700, San Jose CA 95110
Tel (408) 535-1500 SIC 7372 8748 7389

■ MICROSEMI FREQUENCY AND TIME CORP p 962
3870 N 1st St, San Jose CA 95134
Tel (408) 428-6993 SIC 3625 7372

▲ SILVER SPRING NETWORKSINC p 1324
230 W Tasman Dr, San Jose CA 95134
Tel (669) 770-4000 SIC 4899 7372

▲ SUPER MICRO COMPUTER INC p 1405
980 Rock Ave, San Jose CA 95131
Tel (408) 503-8000 SIC 3571 3572 7372

▲ SYNAPTICS INC p 1414
1251 Mckay Dr, San Jose CA 95131
Tel (408) 904-1100 SIC 3577 7372

■ VERIFONE INC p 1549
88 W Plumeria Dr, San Jose CA 95134
Tel (408) 232-7800
SIC 3578 7372 3577 3575 8711 3643

▲ VERIFONE SYSTEMS INC p 1549
88 W Plumeria Dr, San Jose CA 95134
Tel (408) 232-7800 SIC 3578 7372

▲ XILINX INC p 1631
2100 Logic Dr, San Jose CA 95124
Tel (408) 559-7778 SIC 3672 3674 7372

OSISOFT LLC p 1097
1600 Alvarado St, San Leandro CA 94577
Tel (510) 297-5800 SIC 7372 7371 7373

▲ MINDBODY INC p 972
4051 Broad St Ste 220, San Luis Obispo CA 93401
Tel (877) 755-4279 SIC 7372 8741

ACTUATE CORP p 20
951 Mariners Island Blvd # 600, San Mateo CA 94404
Tel (650) 645-3000 SIC 7372

▲ COUPA SOFTWARE INC p 383
1855 S Grant St Fl 4, San Mateo CA 94402
Tel (650) 931-3200 SIC 7372

▲ GOPRO INC p 625
3000 Clearview Way, San Mateo CA 94402
Tel (650) 332-7600 SIC 3861 7372

MARKETO INC p 908
901 Mariners Island Blvd, San Mateo CA 94404
Tel (650) 376-2300 SIC 7371 7372

■ NETSUITE INC p 1027
2955 Campus Dr Ste 100, San Mateo CA 94403
Tel (650) 627-1000 SIC 7372

▲ AUTODESK INC p 134
111 Mcinnis Pkwy, San Rafael CA 94903
Tel (415) 507-5000 SIC 7372

■ FAIR ISAAC INTERNATIONAL CORP p 524
200 Smith Ranch Rd, San Rafael CA 94903
Tel (415) 446-6000 SIC 7372

▲ FIVE9 INC p 553
4000 Executive Pkwy # 400, San Ramon CA 94583
Tel (925) 201-2000 SIC 7372

▲ UNIVERSAL ELECTRONICS INC p 1516
201 Sandpointe Ave # 800, Santa Ana CA 92707
Tel (714) 918-9500 SIC 3651 3625 7372

▲ QAD INC p 1194
100 Innovation Pl, Santa Barbara CA 93108
Tel (805) 566-6000 SIC 7372 7371

▲ AGILENT TECHNOLOGIES INC p 35
5301 Stevens Creek Blvd, Santa Clara CA 95051
Tel (408) 345-8886 SIC 3825 3826 7372

AVAYA HOLDINGS CORP p 136
4655 Great America Pkwy, Santa Clara CA 95054
Tel (908) 953-6000 SIC 3661 7372

AVAYA INC p 136
4655 Great America Pkwy, Santa Clara CA 95054
Tel (908) 953-6000 SIC 3661 7372 7371

■ FILEMAKER INC p 542
5201 Patrick Henry Dr, Santa Clara CA 95054
Tel (408) 987-7000 SIC 7372

▲ GIGAMON INC p 611
3300 Olcott St, Santa Clara CA 95054
Tel (408) 831-4000 SIC 7372 3577

HORTONWORKS INC p 708
5470 Great America Pkwy, Santa Clara CA 95054
Tel (408) 916-4121 SIC 7372

▲ INTEL CORP p 750
2200 Mission College Blvd, Santa Clara CA 95054
Tel (408) 765-8080 SIC 3674 3577 7372

■ KANA SOFTWARE INC p 802
2550 Walsh Ave Ste 120, Santa Clara CA 95051
Tel (650) 614-8300 SIC 7372

■ MCAFEE INC p 925
2821 Mission College Blvd, Santa Clara CA 95054
Tel (408) 346-3832 SIC 7372

■ MCAFEE SECURITY LLC p 925
2821 Mission College Blvd, Santa Clara CA 95054
Tel (866) 622-3911 SIC 7372

▲ SERVICENOW INC p 1308
2225 Lawson Ln, Santa Clara CA 95054
Tel (408) 501-8550 SIC 7379 7372

▲ ACTIVISION BLIZZARD INC p 20
3100 Ocean Park Blvd, Santa Monica CA 90405
Tel (310) 255-2000 SIC 7372

■ ACTIVISION PUBLISHING INC p 20
3100 Ocean Park Blvd, Santa Monica CA 90405
Tel (310) 255-2000 SIC 7372

▲ CORNERSTONE ONDEMAND INC p 371
1601 Cloverfield Blvd 620s, Santa Monica CA 90404
Tel (310) 752-0200 SIC 7372

XAVIENT INFORMATION SYSTEMS INC p 1630
2125 N Madera Rd Ste B, Simi Valley CA 93065
Tel (805) 955-4111 SIC 7372

■ BLUE COAT INC p 191
384 Santa Trinita Ave, Sunnyvale CA 94085
Tel (408) 220-2200 SIC 7372

■ BLUE COAT SYSTEMS LLC p 191
384 Santa Trinita Ave, Sunnyvale CA 94085
Tel (408) 220-2200 SIC 7372

▲ FORTINET INC p 569
899 Kifer Rd, Sunnyvale CA 94086
Tel (408) 235-7700 SIC 7372

▲ INFINERA CORP p 740
140 Caspian Ct, Sunnyvale CA 94089
Tel (408) 572-5200 SIC 3661 7372

■ INTERWOVEN INC p 759
1140 Enterprise Way, Sunnyvale CA 94089
Tel (312) 580-9100 SIC 7372

▲ JUNIPER NETWORKS INC p 797
1133 Innovation Way, Sunnyvale CA 94089
Tel (408) 745-2000 SIC 3577 7372

▲ NETAPP INC p 1027
495 E Java Dr, Sunnyvale CA 94089
Tel (408) 822-6000 SIC 3572 7373 7372

▲ SHORETEL INC p 1318
960 Stewart Dr, Sunnyvale CA 94085
Tel (408) 331-3300 SIC 3661 3663 7372

SNAP INC p 1335
63 Market St, Venice CA 90291
Tel (310) 399-3339 SIC 7372

▲ ARC DOCUMENT SOLUTIONS INC p 103
1981 N Broadway Ste 385, Walnut Creek CA 94596
Tel (925) 949-5100
SIC 7334 7335 7374 7372

THQ INC p 1450
21900 Burbank Blvd # 100, Woodland Hills CA 91367
Tel (818) 591-1310 SIC 7372

LOGRHYTHM INC p 875
4780 Pearl East Cir, Boulder CO 80301
Tel (303) 245-9074 SIC 7372

■ RALLY SOFTWARE DEVELOPMENT CORP p 1206
3333 Walnut St, Boulder CO 80301
Tel (303) 565-2800 SIC 7372

CHERWELL SOFTWARE LLC p 294
10125 Federal Dr Ste 100, Colorado Springs CO 80908
Tel (719) 386-7000 SIC 7372

FOUR WINDS INTERACTIVE LLC p 572
1221 N Broadway, Denver CO 80203
Tel (877) 204-6679 SIC 7372

■ STARTEK USA INC p 1379
8200 E Maplewood Ave # 100, Greenwood Village CO 80111
Tel (303) 262-4150 SIC 7372 7379 5045

JONES INTERNATIONAL LTD p 792
300 E Mineral Ave Ste 5, Littleton CO 80122
Tel (303) 792-3111
SIC 4832 4841 7371 7372

ROGUE WAVE SOFTWARE INC p 1246
1315 W Century Dr Ste 150, Louisville CO 80027
Tel (303) 473-9118 SIC 7371 7372

■ HARPOON ACQUISITION CORP p 663
455 Winding Brook Dr, Glastonbury CT 06033
Tel (860) 815-5736 SIC 7372 7373

■ OPEN SOLUTIONS LLC p 1089
455 Winding Brook Dr # 101, Glastonbury CT 06033
Tel (860) 815-5000 SIC 7372 7373

▲ TANGOE INC p 1424
35 Executive Blvd, Orange CT 06477
Tel (203) 859-9300 SIC 7372

▲ PITNEY BOWES INC p 1152
3001 Summer St Ste 3, Stamford CT 06905
Tel (203) 356-5000
SIC 3579 7359 3661 8744 7372

GERBER SCIENTIFIC LLC p 608
24 Indl Pk Rd W, Tolland CT 06084
Tel (860) 871-8082
SIC 3993 7336 3851 7372 3577

▲ SS&C TECHNOLOGIES HOLDINGS INC p 1363
80 Lamberton Rd, Windsor CT 06095
Tel (860) 298-4500 SIC 7372 7371

■ SS&C TECHNOLOGIES INC p 1363
80 Lamberton Rd, Windsor CT 06095
Tel (860) 298-4500 SIC 7372 7371 8741

LABWARE HOLDINGS INC p 836
3 Mill Rd Ste 102, Wilmington DE 19806
Tel (302) 658-8444 SIC 7371 7372 6719

▲ ADVISORY BOARD CO p 28
2445 M St Nw Ste 500, Washington DC 20037
Tel (202) 266-5600 SIC 8732 8741 7372

BLACKBOARD INC p 187
1111 19th St Nw, Washington DC 20036
Tel (202) 463-4860 SIC 7372

▲ COGENT COMMUNICATIONS HOLDINGS INC p 334
2450 N St Nw, Washington DC 20037
Tel (202) 295-4200 SIC 4813 7372

■ TEKTRONIX TEXAS LLC p 1433
2200 Penn Ave Nw Ste 800w, Washington DC 20037
Tel (202) 828-0850 SIC 7372

MODERNIZING MEDICINE INC p 981
3600 Fau Blvd Ste 202, Boca Raton FL 33431
Tel (561) 544-0906 SIC 7372

PRO UNLIMITED INC p 1178
7777 Glades Rd Ste 208, Boca Raton FL 33434
Tel (561) 994-9500 SIC 8741 7372

GRAPHIC CENTER GROUP CORP p 631
2150 Coral Way Fl 1, Coral Gables FL 33145
Tel (305) 961-1649 SIC 7372 7336

▲ CITRIX SYSTEMS INC p 311
851 W Cypress Creek Rd, Fort Lauderdale FL 33309
Tel (954) 267-3000 SIC 7372

INTERMEDIX CORP p 753
6451 N Federal Hwy # 1000, Fort Lauderdale FL 33308
Tel (954) 308-8700 SIC 7372

■ KAPLAN INC p 803
6301 Kaplan Univ Ave, Fort Lauderdale FL 33309
Tel (212) 492-5800
SIC 8299 7361 7372 2731

▲ BLACK KNIGHT FINANCIAL SERVICES INC p 187
601 Riverside Ave, Jacksonville FL 32204
Tel (904) 854-5100 SIC 7372

■ FIS FINANCIAL SYSTEMS LLC p 551
601 Riverside Ave, Jacksonville FL 32204
Tel (904) 438-6000 SIC 7374 7372

■ **LAWYERS TITLE INSURANCE CORP** p 848
601 Riverside Ave, Jacksonville FL 32204
Tel (888) 866-3684 SIC 6361 7372 5734

▲ **WEB.COM GROUP INC** p 1586
12808 Gran Bay Pkwy W, Jacksonville FL 32258
Tel (904) 680-6600 SIC 7372 7374

D+H USA CORP p 407
605 Crescent Executive Ct # 600, Lake Mary FL 32746
Tel (407) 804-6600 SIC 7372

▲ **ACI WORLDWIDE INC** p 17
3520 Kraft Rd Ste 300, Naples FL 34105
Tel (239) 403-4600 SIC 7372 5045

ASG TECHNOLOGIES GROUP INC p 116
708 Goodlette Rd N, Naples FL 34102
Tel (239) 435-2200 SIC 7372

KONY INC p 827
7380 W Sand Lake Rd # 390, Orlando FL 32819
Tel (407) 730-5669 SIC 7372

SARASOTA COUNTY PUBLIC HOSPITAL DISTRICT p 1282
1700 S Tamiami Trl, Sarasota FL 34239
Tel (941) 917-9000 SIC 8062 7372

▲ **ULTIMATE SOFTWARE GROUP INC** p 1501
2000 Ultimate Way, Weston FL 33326
Tel (800) 432-1729 SIC 7372

INFOR (US) INC p 741
13560 Morris Rd Ste 4100, Alpharetta GA 30004
Tel (678) 319-8000 SIC 7372

ROLTA INTERNATIONAL INC p 1248
5865 N Point Pkwy Ste 300, Alpharetta GA 30022
Tel (678) 942-5000 SIC 7389 7371 7372

■ **VERINT AMERICAS INC** p 1549
800 North Point Pkwy, Alpharetta GA 30005
Tel (770) 754-1900 SIC 7372

ABB ENTERPRISE SOFTWARE INC p 9
400 Perimeter Ctr Ter 5, Atlanta GA 30346
Tel (678) 830-1000 SIC 7372

▲ **AMERICAN SOFTWARE INC** p 79
470 E Paces Ferry Rd Ne, Atlanta GA 30305
Tel (404) 261-4381 SIC 7372

BCD TRAVEL USA LLC p 164
6 Concourse Pkwy Ste 2400, Atlanta GA 30328
Tel (678) 441-5200 SIC 4724 7372

CDC SOFTWARE HOLDINGS INC p 270
Two Cncourse Pkwy Ste 800, Atlanta GA 39901
Tel (770) 351-9600 SIC 7372 7379 8243

FIRST ADVANTAGE CORP p 544
1 Concourse Pkwy Ste 200, Atlanta GA 30328
Tel (800) 888-5773
SIC 7323 8742 7372 7389 7381

▲ **MANHATTAN ASSOCIATES INC** p 901
2300 Windy Ridge Pkwy Se 1000n, Atlanta GA 30339
Tel (770) 955-7070 SIC 7373 7372 5045

PREMIERE GLOBAL SERVICES INC p 1171
3280 Peachtree Rd Ne # 1000, Atlanta GA 30305
Tel (404) 262-8400 SIC 7372 7389

SAGE SOFTWARE INC p 1267
271 17th St Nw Ste 1100, Atlanta GA 30363
Tel (866) 996-7243 SIC 7372

AMERICAN CYBERSYSTEMS INC p 71
2400 Meadowbrook Pkwy, Duluth GA 30096
Tel (770) 493-5588 SIC 7373 7371 7372

▲ **EBIX INC** p 474
1 Ebix Way Ste 100, Duluth GA 30097
Tel (678) 281-2020 SIC 7371 7372

PEACHTREE SOFTWARE INC p 1125
1715 N Brown Rd, Lawrenceville GA 30043
Tel (770) 682-1542 SIC 7372 7371

MILNER INC p 972
5125 Peachtree Indus Blvd, Norcross GA 30092
Tel (770) 458-0999
SIC 7372 5999 7389 5065 5049 5044

▲ **S1 CORP** p 1263
705 Westech Dr, Norcross GA 30092
Tel (678) 966-9499 SIC 7372 7371

ARRIS GROUP INC p 112
3871 Lakefield Dr Ste 300, Suwanee GA 30024
Tel (678) 473-2907
SIC 7372 3663 3357 7373 3661

ARRIS TECHNOLOGY INC p 113
3871 Lakefield Dr, Suwanee GA 30024
Tel (678) 473-2907 SIC 7372 3825

▲ **PAYLOCITY HOLDING CORP** p 1122
3850 N Wilke Rd, Arlington Heights IL 60004
Tel (847) 463-3200 SIC 7372

▲ **PC-TEL INC** p 1123
471 Brighton Ct, Bloomingdale IL 60108
Tel (630) 372-6800 SIC 5731 4812 7372

▲ **ALLSCRIPTS HEALTHCARE SOLUTIONS INC** p 58
222 Merchandise Mart Plz, Chicago IL 60654
Tel (312) 506-1200 SIC 7372

▲ **ENVESTNET INC** p 503
35 E Wacker Dr Ste 2400, Chicago IL 60601
Tel (312) 827-2800 SIC 7389 6282 7372

INFORMATION RESOURCES INC p 742
150 N Clinton St, Chicago IL 60661
Tel (312) 726-1221 SIC 7372

▲ **INNERWORKINGS INC** p 744
600 W Chicago Ave Ste 850, Chicago IL 60654
Tel (312) 642-3700 SIC 2752 7374 7372

SPSS INC p 1362
200 W Madison St Ste 2300, Chicago IL 60606
Tel (312) 651-3000 SIC 7372

SYSTEM SOFTWARE ASSOCIATES INC DEL p 1418
500 W Madison St Ste 1600, Chicago IL 60661
Tel (312) 258-6000 SIC 7372 7373

TRUSTWAVE HOLDINGS INC p 1488
70 W Madison St Ste 1050, Chicago IL 60602
Tel (312) 750-0950 SIC 7373 7372

■ **TEXTURA CORP** p 1445
1405 Lake Cook Rd, Deerfield IL 60015
Tel (866) 839-8872 SIC 7372

▲ **CDK GLOBAL INC** p 271
1950 Hassell Rd, Hoffman Estates IL 60169
Tel (847) 397-1700 SIC 7372

FLEXERA HOLDINGS LP p 556
300 Park Blvd Ste 500, Itasca IL 60143
Tel (847) 466-4000 SIC 7371 7372

FLEXERA SOFTWARE LLC p 556
300 Park Blvd Ste 500, Itasca IL 60143
Tel (847) 466-4000 SIC 7371 7372

IFS NORTH AMERICA INC p 730
300 Park Blvd Ste 555, Itasca IL 60143
Tel (888) 437-4968 SIC 7372 7379 8243

APPLIED SYSTEMS INC p 100
200 Applied Pkwy, University Park IL 60484
Tel (708) 534-5575 SIC 7371 7372

■ **EXACTTARGET INC** p 516
20 N Meridian St Ste 200, Indianapolis IN 46204
Tel (317) 423-3928 SIC 7372

▲ **HURCO COMPANIES INC** p 721
1 Technology Way, Indianapolis IN 46268
Tel (317) 293-5309 SIC 3823 7372

INTERACTIVE INTELLIGENCE GROUP INC p 751
7601 Interactive Way, Indianapolis IN 46278
Tel (317) 872-3000 SIC 7372

■ **INTERACTIVE INTELLIGENCE INC** p 751
7601 Interactive Way, Indianapolis IN 46278
Tel (800) 267-1364 SIC 7372 7371

▲ **WORKIVA INC** p 1624
2900 University Blvd, Ames IA 50010
Tel (888) 275-3125 SIC 7372

▲ **EURONET WORLDWIDE INC** p 512
3500 College Blvd, Leawood KS 66211
Tel (913) 327-4200 SIC 6099 7372 4813

LEXMARK ENTERPRISE SOFTWARE LLC p 860
8900 Renner Blvd, Lenexa KS 66219
Tel (913) 422-7525 SIC 7371 7372

MEDIWARE INFORMATION SYSTEMS INC p 938
11711 W 79th St, Lenexa KS 66214
Tel (913) 307-1000 SIC 7372

NETSMART TECHNOLOGIES INC p 1027
4950 College Blvd, Overland Park KS 66211
Tel (913) 327-7444 SIC 7371 7372

VOCUS INC p 1564
12051 Indian Creek Ct, Beltsville MD 20705
Tel (301) 459-2590 SIC 7371 7372

▲ **INOVALON HOLDINGS INC** p 745
4321 Collington Rd # 100, Bowie MD 20716
Tel (301) 809-4000 SIC 7371 7374 7372

■ **MICROS SYSTEMS INC** p 962
7031 Columbia Gateway Dr # 1, Columbia MD 21046
Tel (443) 285-6000
SIC 7373 7372 3577 3578

NIELSEN AUDIO INC p 1043
7000 Columbia Gateway Dr # 200, Columbia MD 21046
Tel (410) 312-8000 SIC 8732 7372

PEAK-RYZEX INC p 1126
10330 Old Columbia Rd # 102, Columbia MD 21046
Tel (410) 312-6000 SIC 7378 5045 7372

TENABLE NETWORK SECURITY INC p 1436
7021 Columbia Gateway Dr # 200, Columbia MD 21046
Tel (410) 872-0555 SIC 7372 7371

AVEMCO CORP p 136
8490 Progress Dr Ste 100, Frederick MD 21701
Tel (301) 694-5700
SIC 6331 6321 6399 6411 7372

▲ **BROADSOFT INC** p 215
9737 Washingtonian Blvd # 350, Gaithersburg MD 20878
Tel (301) 977-9440 SIC 7372 7371 8748

GXS GROUP INC p 649
9711 Washingtonian Blvd, Gaithersburg MD 20878
Tel (301) 340-4000 SIC 7372

■ **LEIDOS GOVERNMENT SERVICES INC** p 854
700 N Frederick Ave, Gaithersburg MD 20879
Tel (856) 486-5156
SIC 7379 7373 7374 7372

▲ **KEYW HOLDING CORP** p 816
7740 Milestone Pkwy # 400, Hanover MD 21076
Tel (443) 733-1600
SIC 7373 7372 8731 7375

▲ **2U INC** p 2
8201 Corporate Dr Ste 900, Landover MD 20785
Tel (301) 892-4350 SIC 7372 8748 8299

RAND WORLDWIDE INC p 1207
11201 Dlfeld Blvd Ste 112, Owings Mills MD 21117
Tel (410) 581-8080 SIC 7372 7373

MICRO FOCUS (US) INC p 961
700 King Farm Blvd # 125, Rockville MD 20850
Tel (301) 838-5000 SIC 7372

ACME PACKET INC p 18
100 Crosby Dr, Bedford MA 01730
Tel (781) 328-4400 SIC 7372

▲ **ASPEN TECHNOLOGY INC** p 118
20 Crosby Dr, Bedford MA 01730
Tel (781) 221-6400 SIC 7371 7372

▲ **PROGRESS SOFTWARE CORP** p 1181
14 Oak Park Dr, Bedford MA 01730
Tel (781) 280-4000 SIC 7372 7371

■ **RSA SECURITY LLC** p 1255
174 Middlesex Tpke, Bedford MA 01730
Tel (781) 515-5000 SIC 3577 7372 7373

▲ **BRIGHTCOVE INC** p 213
290 Congress St Fl 4, Boston MA 02210
Tel (888) 882-1880 SIC 4813 7372

▲ **CARBONITE INC** p 252
2 Avenue De Lafayette # 2, Boston MA 02111
Tel (617) 587-1100 SIC 7372 7374

JENZABAR INC p 783
101 Huntington Ave # 2200, Boston MA 02199
Tel (617) 492-9099 SIC 7372

▲ **LOGMEIN INC** p 875
320 Summer St Ste 100, Boston MA 02210
Tel (781) 638-9050 SIC 7372 7379

NTT DATA INTERNATIONAL SERVICES INC p 1066
100 City Sq, Boston MA 02129
Tel (800) 745-3263 SIC 7371 7372

▲ **RAPID7 INC** p 1208
100 Summer St Fl 13, Boston MA 02110
Tel (617) 247-1717 SIC 7372

▲ **AVID TECHNOLOGY INC** p 138
75 Network Dr, Burlington MA 01803
Tel (978) 640-6789 SIC 3861 7372

■ **DEMANDWARE INC** p 427
5 Wall St Fl 2, Burlington MA 01803
Tel (888) 553-9216 SIC 7371 7372

▲ **ENDURANCE INTERNATIONAL GROUP HOLDINGS INC** p 497
10 Corporate Dr Ste 300, Burlington MA 01803
Tel (781) 852-3200 SIC 7372

▲ **NUANCE COMMUNICATIONS INC** p 1066
1 Wayside Rd, Burlington MA 01803
Tel (781) 565-5000 SIC 7372

▲ **AKAMAI TECHNOLOGIES INC** p 42
150 Broadway Ste 100, Cambridge MA 02142
Tel (617) 444-3000 SIC 7372 7374

▲ **HUBSPOT INC** p 716
25 1st St Ste 200, Cambridge MA 02141
Tel (888) 482-7768 SIC 7372

▲ **PEGASYSTEMS INC** p 1127
1 Rogers St, Cambridge MA 02142
Tel (617) 374-9600 SIC 7379 7371 7372

QUICKBASE INC p 1199
150 Cambridgepark Dr # 500, Cambridge MA 02140
Tel (855) 725-2293 SIC 7372

UNICOM ENGINEERING INC p 1502
25 Dan Rd, Canton MA 02021
Tel (781) 332-1000 SIC 3572 7372

KRONOS ACQUISITION CORP p 830
297 Billerica Rd, Chelmsford MA 01824
Tel (978) 250-9800 SIC 7372 7373 6726

KRONOS INC p 830
297 Billerica Rd, Chelmsford MA 01824
Tel (978) 250-9800 SIC 7372 7373

KRONOS PARENT CORP p 830
297 Billerica Rd, Chelmsford MA 01824
Tel (978) 250-9800 SIC 7372 7373

▲ **MERCURY SYSTEMS INC** p 945
201 Riverneck Rd, Chelmsford MA 01824
Tel (978) 256-1300 SIC 3672 7372

ZOLL MEDICAL CORP p 1644
269 Mill Rd, Chelmsford MA 01824
Tel (978) 421-9100 SIC 3845 7372

■ **EMC CORP** p 490
176 South St, Hopkinton MA 01748
Tel (508) 435-1000
SIC 3572 7372 7371 3577

IMPRIVATA INC p 735
10 Maguire Rd Ste 125, Lexington MA 02421
Tel (781) 674-2700 SIC 7372 7382

▲ **CSP INC** p 398
175 Cabot St Ste 210, Lowell MA 01854
Tel (978) 663-7598 SIC 3577 7372 7373

STRATUS TECHNOLOGIES INC p 1393
5 Mill Main Pl Ste 500, Maynard MA 01754
Tel (978) 461-7000 SIC 7372

▲ **WATERS CORP** p 1582
34 Maple St, Milford MA 01757
Tel (508) 478-2000
SIC 3826 3829 7371 7372

▲ **PTC INC** p 1189
140 Kendrick St, Needham MA 02494
Tel (781) 370-5000 SIC 7372 7373 7371

DYNATRACE LLC p 464
404 Wyman St Ste 500, Waltham MA 02451
Tel (781) 530-1000 SIC 7372 5045

NETCRACKER TECHNOLOGY CORP p 1027
95 Sawyer Rd, Waltham MA 02453
Tel (781) 419-3300 SIC 7372

▲ **ATHENAHEALTH INC** p 124
311 Arsenal St Ste 14, Watertown MA 02472
Tel (617) 402-1000 SIC 7372

■ **EAGLE INVESTMENT SYSTEMS LLC** p 468
45 William St Ste 200, Wellesley MA 02481
Tel (781) 943-2200
SIC 6722 6282 8721 7372

MEDICAL INFORMATION TECHNOLOGY INC p 937
Meditech Cir, Westwood MA 02090
Tel (781) 821-3000 SIC 7372

▲ **MONOTYPE IMAGING HOLDINGS INC** p 985
600 Unicorn Park Dr, Woburn MA 01801
Tel (781) 970-6000 SIC 7371 7372

BARDEN COMPANIES INC p 155
400 Renaissance Ctr # 2400, Detroit MI 48243
Tel (313) 496-2900 SIC 7371 7372

COMPUWARE CORP p 353
1 Campus Martius Fl 4, Detroit MI 48226
Tel (313) 227-7300 SIC 7372 7371

■ **MCKESSON PHARMACY SYSTEMS LLC** p 930
30881 Schoolcraft Rd, Livonia MI 48150
Tel (734) 421-0260 SIC 7372 5122

VALASSIS COMMUNICATIONS INC p 1539
19975 Victor Pkwy, Livonia MI 48152
Tel (734) 591-3000 SIC 7319 7331 7372

WORKFORCE SOFTWARE LLC p 1624
38705 7 Mile Rd Ste 300, Livonia MI 48152
Tel (734) 542-4100 SIC 7372 7371

▲ **SYNTEL INC** p 1416
525 E Big Beaver Rd # 300, Troy MI 48083
Tel (248) 619-2800 SIC 7371 7372 8748

EDMENTUM INC p 478
5600 W 83rd St 3008200, Bloomington MN 55437
Tel (800) 447-5286 SIC 7372

SCANTRON CORP p 1286
1313 Lone Oak Rd, Eagan MN 55121
Tel (651) 683-6000
SIC 3577 7372 2752 3575 2761

HELP/SYSTEMS LLC p 682
6455 City West Pkwy, Eden Prairie MN 55344
Tel (952) 933-0609 SIC 7372

KROLL ONTRACK LLC p 830
9023 Columbine Rd, Eden Prairie MN 55347
Tel (952) 937-5161 SIC 7374 7372

SMEAD MANUFACTURING CO INC p 1332
600 Smead Blvd, Hastings MN 55033
Tel (651) 437-4111
SIC 2675 7372 2789 2759 2752 2542

NCS PEARSON INC p 1022
5601 Green Valley Dr # 220, Minneapolis MN 55437
Tel (952) 681-3000
SIC 3577 7372 7374 8748 7379

▲ **SPS COMMERCE INC** p 1362
333 S 7th St Ste 1000, Minneapolis MN 55402
Tel (612) 435-9400 SIC 7374 7372

▲ **PATTERSON COMPANIES INC** p 1121
1031 Mendota Heights Rd, Saint Paul MN 55120
Tel (651) 686-1600
SIC 5047 5112 7372 7699 2834

ENTRUST DATACARD CORP p 503
1187 Park Pl, Shakopee MN 55379
Tel (952) 933-1223
SIC 3579 3089 7373 7372

AMDOCS INC p 66
1390 Timberlake Manor Pkw, Chesterfield MO 63017
Tel (314) 212-7000 SIC 7372 7371 7373

■ **CERNER DHT INC** p 284
2800 Rock Creek Pkwy, Kansas City MO 64117
Tel (816) 221-1024 SIC 8742 7372 7371

▲ **DST SYSTEMS INC** p 458
333 W 11th St, Kansas City MO 64105
Tel (816) 435-1000
SIC 7374 7371 7331 7372

DAUGHERTY SYSTEMS INC p 414
3 Cityplace Dr Ste 400, Saint Louis MO 63141
Tel (314) 432-8200
SIC 7379 7371 8742 7373 7372

■ **ACI WORLDWIDE CORP** p 17
6060 Coventry Dr, Elkhorn NE 68022
Tel (402) 390-7600 SIC 7372 5045

▲ **WEST CORP** p 1594
11808 Miracle Hills Dr, Omaha NE 68154
Tel (402) 963-1200
SIC 7389 7372 4813 7374

■ **BALLY TECHNOLOGIES INC** p 148
6601 Bermuda Rd, Las Vegas NV 89119
Tel (770) 420-2388
SIC 3999 7999 7993 7372

SKILLSOFT CORP p 1330
107 Northeastern Blvd, Nashua NH 03062
Tel (603) 821-3715 SIC 7372

SSI INVESTMENTS I LIMITED p 1364
107 Northeastern Blvd, Nashua NH 03062
Tel (603) 324-3000 SIC 7372

SSI INVESTMENTS II LIMITED p 1364
107 Northeastern Blvd, Nashua NH 03062
Tel (603) 324-3000 SIC 7372

▲ **BOTTOMLINE TECHNOLOGIES (DE) INC** p 204
325 Corporate Dr Ste 300, Portsmouth NH 03801
Tel (603) 436-0700 SIC 7372

CEGEDIM INC p 272
1425 Us Highway 206, Bedminster NJ 07921
Tel (908) 443-2000 SIC 7371 7372

PREMIER HEALTHCARE EXCHANGE CORP p 1170
2 Crossroads Dr Ste 101b, Bedminster NJ 07921
Tel (908) 658-3535 SIC 7372

FUNDTECH CORP p 585
30 Montgomery St Ste 501, Jersey City NJ 07302
Tel (201) 324-0203 SIC 7372 7371

U S TECH SOLUTIONS INC p 1497
10 Exchange Pl Ste 1820, Jersey City NJ 07302
Tel (201) 524-9600 SIC 7379 7372

HEALTHSTAR COMMUNICATIONS INC p 678
1000 Wyckoff Ave Ste 202, Mahwah NJ 07430
Tel (201) 560-5370 SIC 7372 7311 6719

■ **MAJESCO** p 898
412 Mount Kemble Ave 110c, Morristown NJ 07960
Tel (973) 461-5200 SIC 7372 7371

ALCATEL-LUCENT USA INC p 47
600 Mountain Ave Ste 700, New Providence NJ 07974
Tel (908) 582-3275 SIC 7372 3674

NICE SYSTEMS INC p 1042
461 From Rd Ste 103, Paramus NJ 07652
Tel (201) 964-2600
SIC 7372 7382 1731 8741

▲ **MISTRAS GROUP INC** p 976
195 Clarksville Rd Ste 2, Princeton Junction NJ 08550
Tel (609) 716-4000
SIC 8711 7372 3829 3825

SAMSUNG SDS AMERICA INC p 1275
100 Challenger Rd, Ridgefield Park NJ 07660
Tel (201) 229-4456 SIC 7372 7371

■ **CARDINAL HEALTH SYSTEMS INC** p 253
14 Schoolhouse Rd, Somerset NJ 08873
Tel (732) 537-6544 SIC 7372 2834

▲ **MEDICAL TRANSCRIPTION BILLING CORP** p 937
7 Clyde Rd, Somerset NJ 08873
Tel (732) 873-5133 SIC 7372

▲ **COGNIZANT TECHNOLOGY SOLUTIONS CORP** p 334
500 Frank W Burr Blvd, Teaneck NJ 07666
Tel (201) 801-0233 SIC 7371 7379 7372

▲ **COMMVAULT SYSTEMS INC** p 350
1 Commvault Way, Tinton Falls NJ 07724
Tel (732) 870-4000 SIC 7373 7372 7376

▲ **COMMERCEHUB INC** p 345
201 Fuller Rd Fl 6, Albany NY 12203
Tel (518) 810-0700 SIC 7372

■ **PAETEC COMMUNICATIONS INC** p 1107
600 Willowbrook Office Pa, Fairport NY 14450
Tel (585) 340-2500 SIC 4813 7375 7372

FLEXTRADE SYSTEMS INC p 556
111 Great Neck Rd Ste 314, Great Neck NY 11021
Tel (516) 627-8993 SIC 7372

ARCSERVE (USA) LLC p 106
1 Ca Plz, Islandia NY 11749
Tel (866) 576-9742 SIC 7372

■ **CBORD GROUP INC** p 269
950 Danby Rd Ste 100c, Ithaca NY 14850
Tel (607) 257-2410 SIC 7372 5045

▲ **HENRY SCHEIN INC** p 684
135 Duryea Rd, Melville NY 11747
Tel (631) 843-5500 SIC 5047 5122 7372

▲ **VERINT SYSTEMS INC** p 1549
175 Broadhollow Rd # 100, Melville NY 11747
Tel (631) 962-9600 SIC 7382 7372

▲ **PARTECHNOLOGY CORP** p 1113
8383 Seneca Tpke Ste 2, New Hartford NY 13413
Tel (315) 738-0600 SIC 7372 7832

▲ **BROADRIDGE FINANCIAL SOLUTIONS INC** p 215
5 Dakota Dr Ste 300, New Hyde Park NY 11042
Tel (516) 472-5400 SIC 7374 7372

■ **BLUE WOLF GROUP LLC** p 192
11 E 26th St Fl 21, New York NY 10010
Tel (866) 455-9653 SIC 7372

▲ **CA INC** p 234
520 Madison Ave Fl 22, New York NY 10022
Tel (800) 225-5224 SIC 7372 8742

CLAYTON DUBILIER & RICE FUND V LIMITED PARTNERSHIP p 323
375 Park Ave Fl 18, New York NY 10152
Tel (212) 407-5200
SIC 3825 3661 3812 3577 3575 7372

COMVERSE TECHNOLOGY INC p 353
810 7th Ave, New York NY 10019
Tel (212) 739-1000 SIC 7372 7371

DILIGENT CORP p 439
1385 Brdwy Fl 19, New York NY 10018
Tel (212) 741-8181 SIC 7372

▲ **FUSION TELECOMMUNICATIONS INTERNATIONAL INC** p 585
420 Lexington Ave Rm 1718, New York NY 10170
Tel (212) 201-2400 SIC 7372 4813

GENISYS SOFTWARE LTD p 604
1345 Ave Of The Americas, New York NY 10105
Tel (732) 635-7132 SIC 7371 7372 5734

GENPACT LIMITED p 604
1155 Avenue Of The Americ, New York NY 10036
Tel (212) 896-6600 SIC 8741 7372

▲ **IAC/INTERACTIVECORP** p 725
555 W 18th St, New York NY 10011
Tel (212) 314-7300 SIC 7372 7375 5961

INFOR INC p 741
641 Ave Of The Americas # 4, New York NY 10011
Tel (646) 336-1700 SIC 7371 7372

INFOR LUX BOND CO p 741
641 Ave Of The Americas, New York NY 10011
Tel (646) 336-1700 SIC 7371 7372 8748

▲ **INTRALINKS HOLDINGS INC** p 760
150 E 42nd St Fl 8, New York NY 10017
Tel (212) 543-7700 SIC 7372 7382

▲ **MEDIDATA SOLUTIONS INC** p 937
350 Hudson St Fl 9, New York NY 10014
Tel (212) 918-1800 SIC 7372

▲ **MIDAS MEDICI GROUP HOLDINGS INC** p 964
445 Park Ave Frnt 5, New York NY 10022
Tel (212) 792-0920 SIC 7372

MISYS INTERNATIONAL BANKING SYSTEMS INC p 976
1180 Avenue Of The Amer, New York NY 10036
Tel (914) 428-7200 SIC 7378 7372

OMX (US) INC p 1085
140 Broadway Fl 25, New York NY 10005
Tel (646) 428-2800 SIC 7372

▲ **SCHOLASTIC CORP** p 1288
557 Broadway Lbby 1, New York NY 10012
Tel (212) 343-6100
SIC 2731 2721 7372 7812 6794 7311

■ **SCHOLASTIC INC** p 1288
557 Broadway Lbby 1, New York NY 10012
Tel (800) 724-6527
SIC 2731 2721 7372 7812

■ **SIMON & SCHUSTER INC** p 1324
1230 Ave Of The Americas, New York NY 10020
Tel (212) 698-7000
SIC 2731 2741 7372 8732

SPRINKLR INC p 1361
29 W 35th St Fl 7, New York NY 10001
Tel (917) 933-7800 SIC 8742 7372

SYMPHONY TALENT LLC p 1414
45 Rockefeller Plz # 659, New York NY 10111
Tel (212) 999-9000 SIC 7372 7361

▲ **TAKE-TWO INTERACTIVE SOFTWARE INC** p 1422
622 Broadway Fl 6, New York NY 10012
Tel (646) 536-2842 SIC 7371 7372

■ **THOMSON REUTERS CORP** p 1450
3 Times Sq Lbby Mailroom, New York NY 10036
Tel (646) 223-4000
SIC 2741 8111 7372 7383

▲ **VARONIS SYSTEMS INC** p 1545
1250 Broadway Fl 29, New York NY 10001
Tel (877) 292-8767 SIC 7372

▲ **NEULION INC** p 1028
1600 Old Country Rd, Plainview NY 11803
Tel (516) 622-8300 SIC 4841 7372

OPENLINK FINANCIAL LLC p 1089
1502 Rxr Plz Fl 15w, Uniondale NY 11556
Tel (516) 227-6600 SIC 7371 7372 8742

SAS INSTITUTE INC p 1282
100 Sas Campus Dr, Cary NC 27513
Tel (919) 677-8000 SIC 8243 7372

■ **GOODRICH CORP** p 624
4 Coliseum Ctr 2730 W, Charlotte NC 28217
Tel (704) 423-7000 SIC 7372 3724 3728

SCHAEFER SYSTEMS INTERNATIONAL INC p 1286
10021 Westlake Dr, Charlotte NC 28273
Tel (704) 944-4500
SIC 3089 5046 5084 5099 7372

▲ **CHANNELADVISOR CORP** p 288
3025 Carringtn Ml Blvd # 500, Morrisville NC 27560
Tel (919) 228-4700 SIC 7372

SCIQUEST INC p 1292
3020 Carrington Mill Blvd # 100, Morrisville NC 27560
Tel (919) 659-2100 SIC 7372

SCIQUEST PARENT LLC p 1292
3020 Carrington Mill Blvd, Morrisville NC 27560
Tel (919) 659-2100 SIC 7372

■ **ALLSCRIPTS HEALTHCARE LLC** p 58
8529 Six Forks Rd, Raleigh NC 27615
Tel (919) 847-8102 SIC 7372

▲ **RED HAT INC** p 1215
100 E Davie St, Raleigh NC 27601
Tel (919) 754-3700 SIC 7372

STERLING COMMERCE LLC p 1387
4600 Lakehurst Ct, Dublin OH 43016
Tel (614) 798-2192 SIC 7372

ONX ACQUISITION LLC p 1088
5910 Landerbrook Dr # 250, Mayfield Heights OH 44124
Tel (440) 569-2300 SIC 7372 7379

■ **TMW SYSTEMS INC** p 1458
6085 Parkland Blvd, Mayfield Heights OH 44124
Tel (216) 831-6606 SIC 7372

■ **ESKO-GRAPHICS INC** p 509
8535 Gander Creek Dr, Miamisburg OH 45342
Tel (937) 454-1721 SIC 5084 7372

▲ **TERADATA CORP** p 1439
10000 Innovation Dr, Miamisburg OH 45342
Tel (866) 548-8348
SIC 3571 3572 7372 7371

HYLAND SOFTWARE INC p 724
28500 Clemens Rd, Westlake OH 44145
Tel (440) 788-5000 SIC 7372

TURNING TECHNOLOGIES LLC p 1493
255 W Federal St, Youngstown OH 44503
Tel (330) 746-3015 SIC 7372

▲ **PAYCOM SOFTWARE INC** p 1122
7501 W Memorial Rd, Oklahoma City OK 73142
Tel (405) 722-6900 SIC 8721 7371 7372

■ **CASCADE MICROTECH INC** p 262
9100 Sw Gemini Dr, Beaverton OR 97008
Tel (503) 601-1000 SIC 3825 3674 7372

SERENA SOFTWARE INC p 1306
2345 Nw Amberbrook Dr # 200, Beaverton OR 97006
Tel (650) 481-3400 SIC 7372

▲ **RADISYS CORP** p 1204
5435 Ne Dawson Creek Dr, Hillsboro OR 97124
Tel (503) 615-1100 SIC 3825 7374 7372

■ **RENTRAK CORP** p 1224
7700 Ne Ambassador Pl # 300, Portland OR 97220
Tel (503) 284-7581 SIC 7372

WEBTRENDS INC p 1587
555 Sw Oak St Ste 300, Portland OR 97204
Tel (503) 294-7025 SIC 7372

VERTEX INC p 1552
1041 Old Cassatt Rd, Berwyn PA 19312
Tel (610) 640-4200 SIC 7372

▲ **ANSYS INC** p 93
2600 Ansys Dr, Canonsburg PA 15317
Tel (724) 746-3304 SIC 7372

■ **FIS DATA SYSTEMS INC** p 551
200 Campus Dr, Collegeville PA 19426
Tel (484) 582-2000 SIC 7374 7372

■ **FIS SYSTEMS INTERNATIONAL INC** p 551
200 Campus Dr, Collegeville PA 19426
Tel (484) 582-2000 SIC 7372

ANALYTICAL GRAPHICS INC p 88
220 Valley Creek Blvd, Exton PA 19341
Tel (610) 981-8000 SIC 7372

BENTLEY SYSTEMS INC p 173
685 Stockton Dr, Exton PA 19341
Tel (610) 458-5000 SIC 7372 7373

INTERNET PIPELINE INC p 757
222 Valley Creek Blvd # 300, Exton PA 19341
Tel (484) 348-6555 SIC 7372

ADVERTISING SPECIALTY INSTITUTE INC p 27
4800 E Street Rd Ste 100a, Feasterville Trevose PA 19053
Tel (215) 953-4000 SIC 2721 7372

■ **THOMSON REUTERS (SCIENTIFIC) LLC** p 1450
1500 Spring Garden St # 400, Philadelphia PA 19130
Tel (215) 386-0100 SIC 2741 7372

WOLTERS KLUWER HEALTH INC p 1621
2001 Market St Lbby 1, Philadelphia PA 19103
Tel (215) 521-8300
SIC 2721 2731 2741 7372 8748

▲ **FAB UNIVERSAL CORP** p 523
5001 Baum Blvd Ste 770, Pittsburgh PA 15213
Tel (412) 621-0902
SIC 7371 7372 5735 5942 5994 5099

■ **VOCOLLECT INC** p 1564
703 Rodi Rd, Pittsburgh PA 15235
Tel (412) 829-8145 SIC 3577 3571 7372

BUSINESS & DECISION NORTH AMERICA INC p 229
900 W Valley Rd Ste 1000, Wayne PA 19087
Tel (610) 230-2500 SIC 7372

■ **FIS SG LLC** p 551
680 E Swedesford Rd, Wayne PA 19087
Tel (484) 582-5400 SIC 7372 7374

■ **SUNGARD CAPITAL CORP II** p 1402
680 E Swedesford Rd, Wayne PA 19087
Tel (484) 582-2000 SIC 7372 7374

■ **SUNGARD HOLDCO LLC** p 1402
680 E Swedesford Rd, Wayne PA 19087
Tel (484) 582-2000 SIC 7372 7374

■ **SUNGARD HOLDING CORP** p 1402
680 E Swedesford Rd, Wayne PA 19087
Tel (888) 332-2564 SIC 7372 7374

IGT GLOBAL SOLUTIONS CORP p 730
10 Memorial Blvd, Providence RI 02903
Tel (401) 392-1000
SIC 7999 3575 7372 7378 2752 7374

SCHNEIDER ELECTRIC IT CORP p 1287
132 Fairgrounds Rd, West Kingston RI 02892
Tel (401) 789-5735
SIC 3629 3612 3677 3585 7372 2542

▲ **BENEFITFOCUS INC** p 173
100 Benefitfocus Way, Daniel Island SC 29492
Tel (843) 849-7476 SIC 7372

▲ **BLACKBAUD INC** p 187
2000 Daniel Island Dr, Daniel Island SC 29492
Tel (843) 216-6200 SIC 7372 8748

WYNIT DISTRIBUTION LLC p 1630
2 W Washington St Ste 500, Greenville SC 29601
Tel (864) 605-9920
SIC 5045 5043 5046 5199 7372

▲ **3D SYSTEMS CORP** p 2
333 Three D Systems Cir, Rock Hill SC 29730
Tel (803) 326-3900 SIC 3577 7372

▲ **DAKTRONICS INC** p 409
201 Daktronics Dr, Brookings SD 57006
Tel (605) 692-0200 SIC 3993 7372

EXPERIAN HEALTH INC p 519
720 Cool Springs Blvd, Franklin TN 37067
Tel (615) 661-5657 SIC 7372 8399

MMODAL SERVICES INC p 979
5000 Meridian Blvd # 200, Franklin TN 37067
Tel (615) 261-1500 SIC 7372 7371

▲ **HEALTHSTREAM INC** p 678
209 10th Ave S Ste 450, Nashville TN 37203
Tel (615) 301-3100 SIC 7372 7371

HEALTHTECH HOLDINGS INC p 678
3102 West End Ave Ste 400, Nashville TN 37203
Tel (615) 383-7300 SIC 7372

ACCRUENT LLC p 16
11500 Alterra Pkwy # 110, Austin TX 78758
Tel (512) 861-0726 SIC 7372

▲ **BAZAARVOICE INC** p 163
10901 Stonelake Blvd, Austin TX 78759
Tel (512) 551-6000 SIC 7372

EMBARCADERO TECHNOLOGIES INC p 490
10801 N Mopac Expy 1-100, Austin TX 78759
Tel (415) 834-3131 SIC 7371 7372

EPICOR SOFTWARE CORP p 505
804 Las Cimas Pkwy, Austin TX 78746
Tel (512) 328-2300 SIC 7372

■ **FORCEPOINT LLC** p 565
10900 Stonelake Blvd, Austin TX 78759
Tel (858) 320-8000 SIC 7372

▲ **NATIONAL INSTRUMENTS CORP** p 1013
11500 N Mopac Expy, Austin TX 78759
Tel (512) 338-9119 SIC 7372

▲ **Q2 HOLDINGS INC** p 1194
13785 Res Blvd Ste 150, Austin TX 78750
Tel (512) 275-0072 SIC 7372

SAILPOINT TECHNOLOGIES INC p 1268
11305 Four Points Dr 2-100, Austin TX 78726
Tel (512) 346-2000 SIC 7372

SHI/GOVERNMENT SOLUTIONS INC p 1316
1301 St Mo Pac Expy Ste, Austin TX 78746
Tel (512) 634-8100 SIC 5045 7372

SOLARWINDS HOLDINGS INC p 1338
7171 Southwest Pkwy # 400, Austin TX 78735
Tel (512) 682-9300 SIC 7372

SOLARWINDS INC p 1338
7171 Southwest Pkwy # 400, Austin TX 78735
Tel (512) 682-9300 SIC 7372

■ **WEBSENSE LLC** p 1586
10900 Stonelake Blvd, Austin TX 78759
Tel (858) 320-8000 SIC 7372

■ **CAMBIUM LEARNING GROUP INC** p 244
17855 Dallas Pkwy Ste 400, Dallas TX 75287
Tel (214) 932-9500 SIC 8299 8211 7372

I2 TECHNOLOGIES INC p 725
11701 Luna Rd, Dallas TX 75234
Tel (469) 357-1000 SIC 7372

BMC SOFTWARE INC p 193
2103 Citywest Blvd # 2100, Houston TX 77042
Tel (713) 918-8800 SIC 7372 7371

BOXER PARENT CO INC p 205
2101 Citywest Blvd, Houston TX 77042
Tel (713) 918-8800 SIC 7372

IDERA INC p 729
2950 North Loop W Ste 700, Houston TX 77092
Tel (713) 523-4433 SIC 7371 7372

▲ **ION GEOPHYSICAL CORP** p 762
2105 Citywest Blvd # 900, Houston TX 77042
Tel (281) 933-3339 SIC 7372 3829

NETIQ CORP p 1027
515 Post Oak Blvd # 1000, Houston TX 77027
Tel (713) 548-1700 SIC 7372 7371

▲ **PROS HOLDINGS INC** p 1184
3100 Main St Ste 900, Houston TX 77002
Tel (713) 335-5151 SIC 7371 7372

■ **PROS INC** p 1184
3100 Main St Ste 900, Houston TX 77002
Tel (713) 335-5151 SIC 7372

■ **HEALTH MANAGEMENT SYSTEMS INC** p 675
5615 High Point Dr # 100, Irving TX 75038
Tel (214) 453-3000 SIC 7374 7372

PRESIDIO NETWORKED SOLUTIONS GROUP LLC p 1172
1955 Lakeway Dr Ste 220, Lewisville TX 75057
Tel (469) 549-3800 SIC 5045 7372 7373

NTT DATA INC p 1065
5601 Gran Pkwy Ste 1000, Plano TX 75024
Tel (800) 745-3263 SIC 7373 7372 7379

■ **REPUBLIC TITLE OF TEXAS INC** p 1226
2701 W Plano Pkwy Ste 100, Plano TX 75075
Tel (972) 578-8611
SIC 6411 7372 6531 6541

SIEMENS PRODUCT LIFECYCLE MANAGEMENT SOFTWARE INC p 1320
5800 Granite Pkwy Ste 600, Plano TX 75024
Tel (972) 987-3000 SIC 7372

▲ **TYLER TECHNOLOGIES INC** p 1496
5101 Tennyson Pkwy, Plano TX 75024
Tel (972) 713-3700 SIC 7372

■ **UGS CAPITAL CORP** p 1500
5800 Gran Pkwy Ste 600, Plano TX 75024
Tel (972) 987-3000 SIC 7372

■ **DELL INC** p 425
1 Dell Way, Round Rock TX 78682
Tel (512) 338-4400
SIC 3571 3572 3575 3577 7372 7379

■ **DENALI INTERMEDIATE INC** p 428
1 Dell Way, Round Rock TX 78682
Tel (713) 627-0933
SIC 3571 3572 3577 7372

▲ **HARTE HANKS INC** p 665
9601 Mcallister Fwy # 610, San Antonio TX 78216
Tel (210) 829-9000 SIC 7331 7372

▲ **CONTROL4 CORP** p 364
11734 S Election Rd, Draper UT 84020
Tel (801) 523-3100 SIC 3679 7372

ABOUT TIME TECHNOLOGIES LLC p 12
58 N 1100 W Apt 2, Payson UT 84651
Tel (801) 465-8181 SIC 5045 7372 7375

NOVELL INC p 1063
1800 Novell Pl, Provo UT 84606
Tel (801) 861-4272 SIC 7372

INCONTACT INC p 735
75 W Towne Ridge Pkwy # 1, Sandy UT 84070
Tel (801) 320-3200 SIC 7372 4813

■ **CACI INC - FEDERAL** p 235
1100 N Glebe Rd Ste 200, Arlington VA 22201
Tel (703) 841-7800
SIC 7373 7372 7371 8711

■ **OPOWER INC** p 1090
1515 N Courthouse Rd Fl 8, Arlington VA 22201
Tel (703) 778-4544 SIC 7372

▲ **ROSETTA STONE INC** p 1251
1621 N Kent St Ste 1200, Arlington VA 22209
Tel (703) 387-5800 SIC 7372 4813 7371

■ **ROSETTA STONE INTL LTD** p 1251
1919 N Lynn St Fl 7, Arlington VA 22209
Tel (540) 236-7719 SIC 7372

■ **MCI COMMUNICATIONS CORP** p 929
22001 Loudoun County Pkwy, Ashburn VA 20147
Tel (703) 886-5600
SIC 4813 4812 4822 7372

■ **MCI INTERNATIONAL INC** p 929
22001 Loudoun County Pkwy, Ashburn VA 20147
Tel (703) 886-5600
SIC 4813 4812 4822 7372

SRA COMPANIES INC p 1362
15036 Conference Ctr Dr, Chantilly VA 20151
Tel (703) 803-1500 SIC 7372 8742

VENCORE HOLDING CORP p 1547
15052 Conference Ctr Dr, Chantilly VA 20151
Tel (571) 313-6000
SIC 6719 8711 8733 3812 7372

VENCORE INC p 1547
15052 Conference Ctr Dr, Chantilly VA 20151
Tel (571) 313-6000
SIC 8711 8733 3812 7372

■ **ORBITAL SCIENCES CORP** p 1092
45101 Warp Dr, Dulles VA 20166
Tel (703) 406-5000 SIC 3812 4899 7372

CGI TECHNOLOGIES AND SOLUTIONS INC p 286
11325 Random Hills Rd, Fairfax VA 22030
Tel (703) 267-8000
SIC 7379 7373 7372 7389

■ **VANGENT INC** p 1543
3211 Jermantown Rd, Fairfax VA 22030
Tel (703) 995-2666
SIC 8748 7371 7372 7373 7374 7376

■ **ROSETTA STONE LTD** p 1251
135 W Market St, Harrisonburg VA 22801
Tel (540) 432-6166 SIC 7372

▲ **EPLUS INC** p 505
13595 Dulles Tech Dr, Herndon VA 20171
Tel (703) 984-8400
SIC 5045 7377 7379 7372

CORCENTRIC COLLECTIVE BUSINESS SYSTEM CORP p 368
7927 Jones Branch Dr # 3200, Mc Lean VA 22102
Tel (703) 790-7272 SIC 7372

■ **NORTHROP GRUMMAN INFORMATION TECHNOLOGY INC** p 1058
7575 Colshire Dr, Mc Lean VA 22102
Tel (703) 556-1000 SIC 7373 7372 8733

▲ **COMSCORE INC** p 353
11950 Democracy Dr # 600, Reston VA 20190
Tel (703) 438-2000 SIC 7372

QUADRAMED CORP p 1196
12110 Sunset Hills Rd # 600, Reston VA 20190
Tel (703) 709-2300 SIC 7372

SOFTWARE AG INC p 1337
11700 Plaza America Dr # 700, Reston VA 20190
Tel (703) 860-5050 SIC 7372

▲ **VERISIGN INC** p 1549
12061 Bluemont Way, Reston VA 20190
Tel (703) 948-3200 SIC 7375 7372

▲ **SPOK HOLDINGS INC** p 1359
6850 Versar Ctr Ste 420, Springfield VA 22151
Tel (800) 611-8488 SIC 4812 4822 7372

CVENT INC p 404
1765 Grnsboro Stn Pl Fl 7, Tysons Corner VA 22102
Tel (703) 226-3500 SIC 7372

▲ **MICROSTRATEGY INC** p 962
1850 Towers Crescent Plz # 700, Tysons Corner VA 22182
Tel (703) 848-8600 SIC 7372 7371

ACTIONET INC p 19
2600 Park Twr Dr Ste 1000, Vienna VA 22180
Tel (703) 204-0090
SIC 7379 7373 7372 7371

▲ **APPTIO INC** p 100
11100 Ne 8th St Ste 600, Bellevue WA 98004
Tel (425) 453-5861 SIC 7372

CONCUR TECHNOLOGIES INC p 355
601 108th Ave Ne Ste 1000, Bellevue WA 98004
Tel (425) 702-8808 SIC 7372 7371

BITTITAN INC p 185
3933 Lk Wa Blvd Ne # 200, Kirkland WA 98033
Tel (206) 428-6030 SIC 7372

▲ **MICROSOFT CORP** p 962
1 Microsoft Way, Redmond WA 98052
Tel (425) 882-8080
SIC 7372 7371 3577 7375

PHYSIO-CONTROL INC p 1146
11811 Willows Rd Ne, Redmond WA 98052
Tel (425) 867-4000
SIC 3841 3845 7699 7372

ATTACHMATE CORP p 129
705 5th Ave S Ste 1000, Seattle WA 98104
Tel (206) 217-7100 *SIC* 7373 7371 7372

ATTACHMATE GROUP INC p 129
705 5th Ave S Ste 1100, Seattle WA 98104
Tel (206) 217-7100 *SIC* 7371 7372 7373

■ COBALT GROUP INC p 332
605 5th Ave S Ste 800, Seattle WA 98104
Tel (206) 269-6363 *SIC* 7372

▲ F5 NETWORKS INC p 523
401 Elliott Ave W Ste 500, Seattle WA 98119
Tel (206) 272-5555 *SIC* 7373 7372

▲ REALNETWORKS INC p 1214
1501 1st Ave S Ste 600, Seattle WA 98134
Tel (206) 674-2700 *SIC* 7371 7372

▲ TABLEAU SOFTWARE INC p 1420
837 N 34th St Ste 200, Seattle WA 98103
Tel (206) 633-3400 *SIC* 7372

WATCHGUARD TECHNOLOGIES INC p 1581
505 5th Ave S Ste 500, Seattle WA 98104
Tel (206) 613-6600 *SIC* 7372

▲ ZILLOW GROUP INC p 1643
1301 2nd Ave Fl 31, Seattle WA 98101
Tel (206) 470-7000 *SIC* 7372 6531 4813

■ FISERV CIR INC p 551
255 Fiserv Dr, Brookfield WI 53045
Tel (262) 879-5000 *SIC* 7374 7372 7373

■ IDSC HOLDINGS LLC p 729
2801 80th St, Kenosha WI 53143
Tel (262) 656-5200
SIC 3423 3559 7372 6794 5013 3546

RENAISSANCE LEARNING INC p 1223
2911 Peach St, Wisconsin Rapids WI 54494
Tel (715) 424-4242 *SIC* 7372 5072

SIC 7373 Computer Integrated Systems Design

AVOCENT CORP p 138
4991 Corporate Dr Nw, Huntsville AL 35805
Tel (256) 430-4000 *SIC* 3575 3577 7373

COLSA CORP p 339
6728 Odyssey Dr Nw, Huntsville AL 35806
Tel (256) 964-5361
SIC 8731 7373 8744 8711

INTERGRAPH CORP p 752
305 Intergraph Way, Madison AL 35758
Tel (256) 730-2000 *SIC* 7372 7373 7379

▲ COMPUTER PROGRAMS AND SYSTEMS INC p 353
6600 Wall St, Mobile AL 36695
Tel (251) 639-8100 *SIC* 7373 7371

CHUGACH ALASKA CORP p 304
3800 Cntrpint Dr Ste 1200, Anchorage AK 99503
Tel (907) 563-8866
SIC 8744 4959 7361 0851 7373

MITEL NETWORKS INC p 977
1146 N Alma School Rd, Mesa AZ 85201
Tel (480) 961-9000
SIC 3661 7359 1731 7373

ASPECT SOFTWARE GROUP HOLDINGS LTD p 118
2325 E Camelback Rd # 700, Phoenix AZ 85016
Tel (602) 282-1500 *SIC* 7373

CLIMATEC LLC p 326
2851 W Kathleen Rd, Phoenix AZ 85053
Tel (602) 944-3330 *SIC* 1731 7373

GHA TECHNOLOGIES INC p 610
8998 E Raintree Dr, Scottsdale AZ 85260
Tel (480) 951-6865 *SIC* 7373

■ GO DADDY OPERATING CO LLC p 619
14455 N Hayden Rd Ste 219, Scottsdale AZ 85260
Tel (480) 505-8877 *SIC* 7373 7374

▲ GODADDY INC p 619
14455 N Hayden Rd Ste 100, Scottsdale AZ 85260
Tel (480) 505-8800 *SIC* 7373 4813

JDA SOFTWARE INC p 780
15059 N Scottsdale Rd # 400, Scottsdale AZ 85254
Tel (480) 308-3000 *SIC* 7371 7373

FRONTIER TECHNOLOGY LLC p 581
8160 S Hardy Dr Ste 101, Tempe AZ 85284
Tel (480) 366-2000 *SIC* 7373

■ SUNQUEST INFORMATION SYSTEMS INC p 1403
250 S Williams Blvd, Tucson AZ 85711
Tel (520) 570-2000 *SIC* 7373 7371

■ WIND RIVER SYSTEMS INC p 1615
500 Wind River Way, Alameda CA 94501
Tel (510) 748-4100 *SIC* 7372 7373

QUEST SOFTWARE INC p 1199
4 Polaris Way, Aliso Viejo CA 92656
Tel (949) 754-8000 *SIC* 7373 7372 7379

MORPHOTRAK LLC p 990
5515 E La Palma Ave # 100, Anaheim CA 92807
Tel (714) 238-2000 *SIC* 7373

▲ NETSOL TECHNOLOGIES INC p 1027
24025 Park Sorrento # 410, Calabasas CA 91302
Tel (818) 222-9195 *SIC* 7372 7373 7299

▲ BARRACUDA NETWORKS INC p 156
3175 Winchester Blvd, Campbell CA 95008
Tel (408) 342-5400 *SIC* 7372 7373

GROUPWARE TECHNOLOGY INC p 642
541 Division St, Campbell CA 95008
Tel (408) 540-0090 *SIC* 7373 5045

FILENET CORP p 542
3565 Harbor Blvd, Costa Mesa CA 92626
Tel (800) 345-3638 *SIC* 7373 7372

▲ NANTWORKS LLC p 1007
9920 Jefferson Blvd, Culver City CA 90232
Tel (310) 405-7539 *SIC* 7373

R SYSTEMS INC p 1202
5000 Windplay Dr Ste 5, El Dorado Hills CA 95762
Tel (916) 939-9696 *SIC* 7379 7373 7374

INFONET SERVICES CORP p 741
2160 E Grand Ave, El Segundo CA 90245
Tel (310) 335-2859 *SIC* 4813 7373 7375

FUJITSU FRONTECH NORTH AMERICA INC p 584
27121 Towne Centre Dr # 100, Foothill Ranch CA 92610
Tel (949) 855-5500 *SIC* 7373

MILESTONE TECHNOLOGIES INC p 969
3101 Skyway Ct, Fremont CA 94539
Tel (510) 651-2454 *SIC* 7373 7374

SASCO ELECTRIC INC p 1283
2750 Moore Ave, Fullerton CA 92833
Tel (714) 870-0217 *SIC* 7373 1731

CREDO 180 CAPITAL PARTNERS p 391
5405 Alton Pkwy 5a, Irvine CA 92604
Tel (949) 274-4405 *SIC* 6282 7373

▲ QUALITY SYSTEMS INC p 1197
18111 Von Karman Ave # 700, Irvine CA 92612
Tel (949) 255-2600 *SIC* 7372 7373

VISION SOLUTIONS INC p 1561
15300 Barranca Pkwy # 100, Irvine CA 92618
Tel (949) 253-6500 *SIC* 7371 7373

SCHNEIDER ELECTRIC SOFTWARE LLC p 1288
26561 Rancho Pkwy S, Lake Forest CA 92630
Tel (949) 727-3200 *SIC* 7373

INTERNET CORP FOR ASSIGNED NAMES AND NUMBERS p 757
12025 Waterfront Dr # 300, Los Angeles CA 90094
Tel (310) 823-9358 *SIC* 7373

INFOGAIN CORP p 741
485 Alberto Way Ste 100, Los Gatos CA 95032
Tel (408) 355-6000
SIC 7379 7373 8742 8748 7374 1731

▲ AEROHIVE NETWORKS INC p 30
1011 Mccarthy Blvd, Milpitas CA 95035
Tel (408) 510-6100 *SIC* 7373

BELL INTEGRATOR INC p 170
800 W El Camino Real, Mountain View CA 94040
Tel (650) 603-0988 *SIC* 7373 7389

■ HARMAN CONNECTED SERVICES HOLDING CORP p 662
636 Ellis St, Mountain View CA 94043
Tel (650) 623-9400 *SIC* 7373

SIGMANET INC p 1321
4290 E Brickell St, Ontario CA 91761
Tel (909) 230-7500 *SIC* 5045 7373

CB TECHNOLOGIES INC p 268
750 The City Dr S Ste 225, Orange CA 92868
Tel (714) 573-7733 *SIC* 7379 7373

ACTIAN CORP p 19
2300 Geng Rd Ste 150, Palo Alto CA 94303
Tel (650) 587-5500 *SIC* 7373 7372

TIBCO SOFTWARE INC p 1452
3303 Hillview Ave, Palo Alto CA 94304
Tel (650) 846-1000 *SIC* 7371 7373

TPUSA - FHCS INC p 1468
215 N Marengo Ave Ste 160, Pasadena CA 91101
Tel (213) 873-5100 *SIC* 7376 7373

CAMEO GLOBAL INC p 245
4695 Chabot Dr Ste 101, Pleasanton CA 94588
Tel (925) 479-7800
SIC 7373 7371 7379 7363 4813 8742

■ ORACLE AMERICA INC p 1091
500 Oracle Pkwy, Redwood City CA 94065
Tel (650) 506-7000
SIC 3571 7379 7373 7372 3674

QUEST MEDIA & SUPPLIES INC p 1199
5822 Roseville Rd, Sacramento CA 95842
Tel (916) 338-7070 *SIC* 7373

HITACHI SOLUTIONS AMERICA LTD p 697
851 Traeger Ave Ste 200, San Bruno CA 94066
Tel (650) 615-7600 *SIC* 5045 7372 7373

BAE SYSTEMS NATIONAL SECURITY SOLUTIONS INC p 144
10920 Technology Pl, San Diego CA 92127
Tel (858) 592-5000 *SIC* 3825 7373 3812

■ INTEGRAL SYSTEMS INC p 748
4820 Estgate Mall Ste 200, San Diego CA 92121
Tel (443) 539-5330 *SIC* 7373

UPWIND SOLUTIONS INC p 1530
4863 Shawline St Ste A, San Diego CA 92111
Tel (866) 927-3142 *SIC* 7374 4931 7373

■ ADVENT SOFTWARE INC p 27
600 Townsend St Fl 5, San Francisco CA 94103
Tel (415) 543-7696
SIC 7371 7373 7372 6722

DOCUSIGN INC p 447
221 Main St Ste 1000, San Francisco CA 94105
Tel (415) 489-4940 *SIC* 7373

DOCUSIGN INC p 447
221 Main St Ste 1000, San Francisco CA 94105
Tel (415) 489-4940 *SIC* 7373

FRANCISCO PARTNERS LP p 574
1 Letterman Dr Bldg C, San Francisco CA 94129
Tel (415) 418-2900 *SIC* 7373 7372

IXONOS USA LIMITED p 769
85 2nd St, San Francisco CA 94105
Tel (949) 278-1354 *SIC* 7373 8731

▲ A10 NETWORKS INC p 7
3 W Plumeria Dr, San Jose CA 95134
Tel (408) 325-8668 *SIC* 7373

E-INFOCHIPS INC p 467
2025 Gateway Pl Ste 270, San Jose CA 95110
Tel (408) 496-1882 *SIC* 7371 7373

▲ EXTREME NETWORKS INC p 521
145 Rio Robles, San Jose CA 95134
Tel (408) 579-2800 *SIC* 3661 7373 7372

GLOBALLOGIC INC p 617
1741 Tech Dr Ste 400, San Jose CA 95110
Tel (408) 273-8900 *SIC* 7371 7379 7373

NAGARRO INC p 1006
2001 Gateway Pl Ste 100w, San Jose CA 95110
Tel (408) 436-6170 *SIC* 7373

■ NORTHROP GRUMMAN SPACE & MISSION SYSTEMS CORP p 1058
6377 San Ignacio Ave, San Jose CA 95119
Tel (703) 280-2900
SIC 7373 3663 3661 3812 3761

▲ NUTANIX INC p 1067
1740 Tech Dr Ste 150, San Jose CA 95110
Tel (408) 216-8360 *SIC* 7373

QCT LLC p 1194
1010 Rincon Cir, San Jose CA 95131
Tel (510) 270-6111 *SIC* 7373

▲ UBIQUITI NETWORKS INC p 1498
2580 Orchard Pkwy, San Jose CA 95131
Tel (408) 942-3085 *SIC* 7373

OSISOFT LLC p 1097
1600 Alvarado St, San Leandro CA 94577
Tel (510) 297-5800 *SIC* 7372 7371 7373

APTTUS CORP p 101
1400 Fashion Island Blvd # 100, San Mateo CA 94404
Tel (650) 445-7700 *SIC* 7373

KEYNOTE LLC p 815
777 Mariners Island Blvd, San Mateo CA 94404
Tel (650) 376-3033 *SIC* 7374 7373

GLODYNE TECHNOSERVE INC p 618
2700 Augustine Dr Ste 190, Santa Clara CA 95054
Tel (408) 340-5017 *SIC* 7373

MOBILEUM INC p 980
2880 Lakeside Dr Ste 135, Santa Clara CA 95054
Tel (408) 844-6600 *SIC* 4899 7373

■ SONICWALL LLC p 1340
5455 Great America Pkwy, Santa Clara CA 95054
Tel (800) 509-1265 *SIC* 7373

FUJITSU AMERICA INC p 583
1250 E Arques Ave, Sunnyvale CA 94085
Tel (408) 746-6000 *SIC* 7373

FUJITSU NORTH AMERICA HOLDINGS INC p 584
1250 E Arques Ave, Sunnyvale CA 94085
Tel (408) 737-5600 *SIC* 7373

▲ NETAPP INC p 1027
495 E Java Dr, Sunnyvale CA 94089
Tel (408) 822-6000 *SIC* 3572 7373 7372

▲ YAHOO INC p 1633
701 First Ave, Sunnyvale CA 94089
Tel (408) 349-3300 *SIC* 7373 7375

VECTOR RESOURCES INC p 1546
3530 Voyager St, Torrance CA 90503
Tel (310) 436-1000 *SIC* 1731 3651 7373

CHG-MERIDIAN USA CORP p 296
21800 Oxnard St Ste 400, Woodland Hills CA 91367
Tel (818) 702-1800 *SIC* 7373

GORES ENT HOLDINGS INC p 626
6260 Lookout Rd, Boulder CO 80301
Tel (303) 531-3100 *SIC* 3577 7373 3357

▲ LEVEL 3 COMMUNICATIONS INC p 858
1025 Eldorado Blvd, Broomfield CO 80021
Tel (720) 888-1000 *SIC* 4813 7373 7374

■ LEVEL 3 COMMUNICATIONS LLC p 858
1025 Eldorado Blvd, Broomfield CO 80021
Tel (720) 888-2750 *SIC* 4813 7373

■ MCDATA SERVICES CORP p 927
4 Brocade Pkwy, Broomfield CO 80021
Tel (720) 558-8000 *SIC* 7373 3572

ACCELLOS INC p 14
90 S Cascade Ave Ste 1200, Colorado Springs CO 80903
Tel (719) 433-7000 *SIC* 7373

GLOBAL TECHNOLOGY RESOURCES INC p 617
990 S Broadway Ste 300, Denver CO 80209
Tel (303) 455-8800 *SIC* 7373

■ QWEST BUSINESS & GOVERNMENT SERVICES INC p 1201
1801 Calif St Ste 3800, Denver CO 80202
Tel (303) 391-8300
SIC 5999 1731 7629 7373 7371 7622

IHS GLOBAL INC p 731
15 Inverness Way E, Englewood CO 80112
Tel (303) 790-0600
SIC 7299 8732 8748 7375 7373

■ TRIZETTO CORP p 1483
9655 Maroon Cir, Englewood CO 80112
Tel (303) 495-7000 *SIC* 7373 8742

▲ CIBER INC p 306
6312 S Fiddlers Green Cir 320n, Greenwood Village CO 80111
Tel (303) 220-0100 *SIC* 7373 7379

■ WEST SAFETY SERVICES p 1595
1601 Dry Creek Dr, Longmont CO 80503
Tel (402) 963-1200 *SIC* 7373

■ HARPOON ACQUISITION CORP p 663
455 Winding Brook Dr, Glastonbury CT 06033
Tel (860) 815-5736 *SIC* 7372 7373

■ OPEN SOLUTIONS LLC p 1089
455 Winding Brook Dr # 101, Glastonbury CT 06033
Tel (860) 815-5000 *SIC* 7372 7373

■ HARTFORD FIRE INSURANCE CO (INC) p 665
1 Hartford Plz, Hartford CT 06115
Tel (860) 547-5000
SIC 6411 6311 6351 7373

■ HARTFORD STEAM BOILER INSPECTION AND INSURANCE CO p 665
1 State St Fl 5-12, Hartford CT 06103
Tel (860) 722-1866
SIC 6331 8711 7373 8742

TELAID INDUSTRIES INC p 1433
13 W Main St, Niantic CT 06357
Tel (860) 739-4461 *SIC* 7373

SONALYSTS INC p 1339
215 Parkway N, Waterford CT 06385
Tel (860) 442-4355
SIC 8711 7373 8748 8732 3993

■ VERIZON DELAWARE LLC p 1550
901 N Tatnall St Fl 2, Wilmington DE 19801
Tel (302) 571-1571
SIC 4813 4812 7373 2741

AKIRA TECHNOLOGIES INC p 42
1747 Penn Ave Nw Ste 600, Washington DC 20006
Tel (202) 517-7187 *SIC* 7373 7379

CHESAPEAKE MANAGEMENT SERVICES INC p 295
1629 K St Nw Ste 300, Washington DC 20006
Tel (202) 600-7678 *SIC* 7373

TRANS DIGITAL TECHNOLOGIES LIMITED LIABILITY CO p 1470
1255 23rd St Nw Ste 100, Washington DC 20037
Tel (571) 730-7029 *SIC* 7373

CAMPUS MANAGEMENT CORP p 246
5201 Congress Ave C220, Boca Raton FL 33487
Tel (561) 923-2500 *SIC* 7373 8741

DCR SYSTEM HOUSE INC p 418
7795 Nw Beacon Sq Blvd, Boca Raton FL 33487
Tel (561) 998-3737 *SIC* 7373

■ MOREDIRECT INC p 988
1001 Yamato Rd Ste 200, Boca Raton FL 33431
Tel (561) 237-3300 *SIC* 5045 7373 7376

SOFT COMPUTER CONSULTANTS INC p 1337
5400 Tech Data Dr, Clearwater FL 33760
Tel (727) 789-0100 *SIC* 7373 7371

■ MASTEC NETWORK SOLUTIONS LLC p 918
806 S Douglas Rd Fl 11, Coral Gables FL 33134
Tel (866) 545-1782 *SIC* 4812 7373

■ MASTEC NETWORK SOLUTIONS LLC p 918
806 S Douglas Rd Fl 11, Coral Gables FL 33134
Tel (866) 545-1782 *SIC* 4812 7373

IDEA INTEGRATION CORP p 728
12724 Gran Bay Pkwy W, Jacksonville FL 32258
Tel (877) 727-8234 *SIC* 7373

LAKEVIEW CENTER INC p 840
1221 W Lakeview Ave, Pensacola FL 32501
Tel (850) 432-1222
SIC 8069 8093 7389 7371 7373

MAINLINE INFORMATION SYSTEMS INC p 898
1700 Summit Lake Dr, Tallahassee FL 32317
Tel (850) 219-5000 *SIC* 7373 7379 7371

CAE USA INC p 236
4908 Tampa West Blvd, Tampa FL 33634
Tel (813) 885-7481
SIC 3699 7373 8299 8249 8711

MCS OF TAMPA INC p 932
8510 Sunstate St, Tampa FL 33634
Tel (813) 872-0217
SIC 1731 7373 4813 7378

■ AUTOTOTE SYSTEMS INC p 135
1500 Bluegrass Lakes Pkwy, Alpharetta GA 30004
Tel (770) 664-3700
SIC 3578 7373 7359 8711

HEALTHPORT INC p 677
925 North Point Pkwy # 350, Alpharetta GA 30005
Tel (770) 360-1700 *SIC* 6324 7373 7374

LIAISON TECHNOLOGIES INC p 861
3157 Royal Dr Ste 200, Alpharetta GA 30022
Tel (770) 642-5000 *SIC* 7373

■ MCKESSON INFORMATION SOLUTIONS LLC p 930
5995 Windward Pkwy, Alpharetta GA 30005
Tel (404) 338-6000 *SIC* 7373

■ MCKESSON TECHNOLOGIES INC p 930
11475 Great Oaks Way # 400, Alpharetta GA 30022
Tel (404) 338-6000
SIC 7374 8741 8721 7322 7373

■ RADIANT SYSTEMS INC p 1204
3925 Brookside Pkwy, Alpharetta GA 30022
Tel (877) 794-7237 *SIC* 5734 7373

SPORTECH RACING LLC p 1359
1095 Windward Ridge Pkwy, Alpharetta GA 30005
Tel (678) 566-1021 *SIC* 7373

AVANGATE INC p 136
3500 Lenox Rd Ne Ste 710, Atlanta GA 30326
Tel (650) 249-5280 *SIC* 7373

■ DELTA TECHNOLOGY LLC p 427
1001 International Blvd, Atlanta GA 30354
Tel (404) 714-1500 *SIC* 7373

INFOSYS MCCAMISH SYSTEMS LLC p 742
6425 Powers Ferry Rd, Atlanta GA 30339
Tel (770) 690-1500 *SIC* 6399 7373

▲ INTERNAP CORP p 754
1 Ravinia Dr Ste 1300, Atlanta GA 30346
Tel (404) 302-9700 *SIC* 7373 7375

▲ MANHATTAN ASSOCIATES INC p 901
2300 Windy Ridge Pkwy Se 1000n, Atlanta GA 30339
Tel (770) 955-7070 *SIC* 7373 7372 5045

■ XEROX STATE HEALTHCARE LLC p 1631
9040 Roswell Rd Ste 700, Atlanta GA 30350
Tel (678) 352-7200 *SIC* 7373

TRANSCENTRA INC p 1471
4855 Peachtree Industrial, Berkeley Lake GA 30092
Tel (678) 728-2500 *SIC* 7373

SOFTTEK INTEGRATION SYSTEMS INC p 1337
2002 Summit Blvd Ste 300, Brookhaven GA 30319
Tel (404) 460-5040 *SIC* 7379 7371 7373

GREENWAY HEALTH p 638
100 Greenway Blvd, Carrollton GA 30117
Tel (770) 836-3100 *SIC* 7373 7371

AMERICAN CYBERSYSTEMS INC p 71
2400 Meadowbrook Pkwy, Duluth GA 30096
Tel (770) 493-5588 *SIC* 7373 7371 7372

■ EMS TECHNOLOGIES INC p 495
660 Engineering Dr, Norcross GA 30092
Tel (770) 263-9200 *SIC* 3663 7373

PROSYS INFORMATION SYSTEMS INC p 1185
6575 The Corners Pkwy # 300, Norcross GA 30092
Tel (678) 268-1300 *SIC* 5045 7373

DYNAMIX GROUP INC p 464
1905 Woodstock Rd # 4150, Roswell GA 30075
Tel (770) 643-8877 *SIC* 7373 8731

ARRIS GROUP INC p 112
3871 Lakefield Dr Ste 300, Suwanee GA 30024
Tel (678) 473-2907
SIC 7372 3663 3357 7373 3661

QUALITY TECHNOLOGY SERVICES LLC p 1197
300 Satellite Blvd Nw, Suwanee GA 30024
Tel (678) 546-0064
SIC 7373 4813 7378 7374

MITUTOYO AMERICA CORP p 978
965 Corporate Blvd, Aurora IL 60502
Tel (630) 820-9666 *SIC* 5084 7373

MNJ TECHNOLOGIES DIRECT INC p 980
1025 Busch Pkwy, Buffalo Grove IL 60089
Tel (847) 634-0700 *SIC* 5734 5045 7373

■ BSWIFT LLC p 222
10 S Riverside Plz # 1100, Chicago IL 60606
Tel (312) 261-5750 *SIC* 6371 7373

FIELDGLASS INC p 541
111 N Canal St Ste 600, Chicago IL 60606
Tel (312) 763-4800 SIC 7373

■ MERGE HEALTHCARE INC p 948
71 S Wacker Dr Ste 2, Chicago IL 60606
Tel (312) 565-6868 SIC 7373 3841

SYSTEM SOFTWARE ASSOCIATES INC DEL p 1418
500 W Madison St Ste 1600, Chicago IL 60661
Tel (312) 258-6000 SIC 7372 7373

THOMA CRESSEY BRAVO INC p 1448
300 N La Salle Dr # 4350, Chicago IL 60654
Tel (312) 254-3300
SIC 6799 8711 6311 6321 6531 7373

TRUSTWAVE CORP p 1488
70 W Madison St Ste 1050, Chicago IL 60602
Tel (312) 873-7500 SIC 7299 7373

TRUSTWAVE HOLDINGS INC p 1488
70 W Madison St Ste 1050, Chicago IL 60602
Tel (312) 750-0950 SIC 7373 7372

■ ESSENDANT MANAGEMENT SERVICES LLC p 510
1 Parkway N Ste 100, Deerfield IL 60015
Tel (847) 627-7000 SIC 5943 7373

▲ RICHARDSON ELECTRONICS LTD p 1232
40w267 Keslinger Rd, Lafox IL 60147
Tel (630) 208-2316 SIC 5065 7373 3671

MOL (AMERICA) INC p 982
700 E Bttrfeld Rd Ste 250, Lombard IL 60148
Tel (630) 424-3480 SIC 4731 7373 4412

VELOCITEL INC p 1547
1033 Skokie Blvd Ste 320, Northbrook IL 60062
Tel (224) 757-0001 SIC 7373 8712

COSATECH INC p 373
1415 W 22nd St Towe Flr, Oak Brook IL 60523
Tel (630) 684-2331 SIC 7373

▲ VASCO DATA SECURITY INTERNATIONAL INC p 1545
1901 S Meyers Rd Ste 210, Oakbrook Terrace IL 60181
Tel (630) 932-8844 SIC 7373 7371

CAPGEMINI FINANCIAL SERVICES USA INC p 249
6400 Shafer Ct Ste 100, Rosemont IL 60018
Tel (847) 384-6100 SIC 7373

FORSYTHE TECHNOLOGY INC p 568
7770 Frontage Rd, Skokie IL 60077
Tel (847) 213-7000 SIC 7377 5045 7373

FORSYTHE/MCARTHUR ASSOCIATES INC p 568
7770 Frontage Rd, Skokie IL 60077
Tel (847) 213-7000 SIC 7377 7373 5045

CORE BTS INC p 369
10201 N Illinois St # 240, Indianapolis IN 46290
Tel (317) 566-6200 SIC 7373

■ HAVERSTICK CONSULTING INC p 668
8770 Guion Rd Ste A, Indianapolis IN 46268
Tel (317) 218-1700 SIC 7371 7373

ALEXANDER OPEN SYSTEMS INC p 49
12980 Foster St Ste 300, Overland Park KS 66213
Tel (913) 307-2300
SIC 5045 7373 8748 7376 3577 1731

POMEROY GROUP HOLDINGS INC p 1160
1020 Petersburg Rd, Hebron KY 41048
Tel (859) 586-6000
SIC 7373 7374 7361 6719

POMEROY IT SOLUTIONS INC p 1160
1020 Petersburg Rd, Hebron KY 41048
Tel (859) 586-0600 SIC 7373 5045 7378

POMEROY IT SOLUTIONS SALES CO INC p 1160
1020 Petersburg Rd, Hebron KY 41048
Tel (859) 586-0600 SIC 7373 7374 7361

SENTURE LLC p 1305
460 Industrial Blvd, London KY 40741
Tel (606) 878-4205
SIC 7379 7389 7374 7373 8742

■ TELECOMMUNICATION SYSTEMS INC p 1434
275 West St, Annapolis MD 21401
Tel (410) 263-7616 SIC 7373 4899

ASRC AEROSPACE CORP p 119
7000 Muirkirk Meadows Dr # 100, Beltsville MD 20705
Tel (301) 837-5500
SIC 3812 7371 7373 5088

FIDELIS CYBERSECURITY INC p 540
4416 East West Hwy # 310, Bethesda MD 20814
Tel (617) 275-8800 SIC 7373

MIL CORP p 968
4000 Mitchellville Rd R, Bowie MD 20716
Tel (301) 805-8500
SIC 7371 7373 7374 7375 7376 8711

■ MICROS SYSTEMS INC p 962
7031 Columbia Gateway Dr # 1, Columbia MD 21046
Tel (443) 285-6000
SIC 7373 7372 3577 3578

FORCE 3 LLC p 565
2151 Priest Bridge Dr # 7, Crofton MD 21114
Tel (301) 261-0204 SIC 7373 5045 3571

PRESIDIO NETWORKED SOLUTIONS LLC p 1172
8161 Maple Lawn Blvd # 150, Fulton MD 20759
Tel (301) 313-2000 SIC 7373

■ INFORMATION NETWORK SYSTEMS INC p 742
700 N Frederick Ave, Gaithersburg MD 20879
Tel (301) 240-7000 SIC 7373 7363

■ LEIDOS GOVERNMENT SERVICES INC p 854
700 N Frederick Ave, Gaithersburg MD 20879
Tel (856) 486-5156
SIC 7379 7373 7374 7372

■ VISION TECHNOLOGIES INC p 1561
530 Mccormick Dr Ste G, Glen Burnie MD 21061
Tel (410) 424-2183 SIC 7373

SGT INC p 1310
7701 Greenbelt Rd Ste 400, Greenbelt MD 20770
Tel (301) 614-8600 SIC 7371 7373 7376

▲ CIENA CORP p 306
7035 Ridge Rd, Hanover MD 21076
Tel (410) 694-5700 SIC 3661 7373

▲ KEYW HOLDING CORP p 816
7740 Milestone Pkwy # 400, Hanover MD 21076
Tel (443) 733-1600
SIC 7373 7372 8731 7375

PHILLIPS CORP p 1144
7390 Coca Cola Dr Ste 200, Hanover MD 21076
Tel (800) 878-4747 SIC 5084 7373 3542

TEKSYSTEMS INC p 1433
7437 Race Rd, Hanover MD 21076
Tel (410) 540-7700 SIC 7379 7376 7373

SMARTRONIX INC p 1332
44150 Smartronix Way, Hollywood MD 20636
Tel (301) 373-6000 SIC 7371 8731 7373

RAND WORLDWIDE INC p 1207
11201 Dlfeld Blvd Ste 112, Owings Mills MD 21117
Tel (410) 581-8080 SIC 7372 7373

RAND WORLDWIDE SUBSIDIARY INC p 1207
11201 Dlfeld Blvd Ste 112, Owings Mills MD 21117
Tel (877) 726-3243
SIC 7379 7373 5045 5734

▲ CHOICE HOTELS INTERNATIONAL INC p 302
1 Choice Hotels Cir, Rockville MD 20850
Tel (301) 592-5000 SIC 7011 7373

CLIENT NETWORK SERVICES INC p 326
2277 Research Blvd, Rockville MD 20850
Tel (301) 634-4600 SIC 7371 7373 7379

WESTAT INC p 1596
1600 Research Blvd, Rockville MD 20850
Tel (301) 251-1500
SIC 8732 7371 7373 8741 8742 8999

CGI INFORMATION SYSTEMS & MANAGEMENT CONSULTANTS INC p 286
600 Federal St, Andover MA 01810
Tel (978) 946-3000 SIC 7374 3577 7373

■ DYNAMICS RESEARCH CORP p 464
2 Tech Dr, Andover MA 01810
Tel (978) 289-1500 SIC 7373 7379 8711

■ RSA SECURITY LLC p 1255
174 Middlesex Tpke, Bedford MA 01730
Tel (781) 515-5000 SIC 3577 7372 7373

GETRONICS USA INC p 609
290 Concord Rd, Billerica MA 01821
Tel (978) 625-5000 SIC 7378 7373 7379

SAPIENT CORP p 1281
131 Dartmouth St Ste 301, Boston MA 02116
Tel (617) 621-0200
SIC 7373 7374 7371 8742

SEVONE INC p 1309
800 Boylston St Bsmt 5, Boston MA 02199
Tel (617) 982-7700 SIC 7373

EGENERA INC p 481
80 Central St Ste 300, Boxborough MA 01719
Tel (978) 206-6300 SIC 7373 1731 8741

IGATE AMERICAS INC p 730
1 Broadway Fl 13, Cambridge MA 02142
Tel (617) 914-8000 SIC 7371 7373

■ RAYTHEON BBN TECHNOLOGIES CORP p 1210
10 Moulton St, Cambridge MA 02138
Tel (617) 873-3052 SIC 7371 7374 7373

BULL HN INFORMATION SYSTEMS INC p 225
285 Billerica Rd Ste 200, Chelmsford MA 01824
Tel (978) 294-6000 SIC 5045 7373

KRONOS ACQUISITION CORP p 830
297 Billerica Rd, Chelmsford MA 01824
Tel (978) 250-9800 SIC 7372 7373 6726

KRONOS INC p 830
297 Billerica Rd, Chelmsford MA 01824
Tel (978) 250-9800 SIC 7372 7373

KRONOS PARENT CORP p 830
297 Billerica Rd, Chelmsford MA 01824
Tel (978) 250-9800 SIC 7372 7373

▲ CSP INC p 398
175 Cabot St Ste 210, Lowell MA 01854
Tel (978) 663-7598 SIC 3577 7372 7373

▲ PTC INC p 1189
140 Kendrick St, Needham MA 02494
Tel (781) 370-5000 SIC 7372 7373 7371

GETRONICS US OPERATIONS INC p 609
100 Ames Pond Dr Ste 99, Tewksbury MA 01876
Tel (978) 625-5000 SIC 7373

WORLDWIDE TECHSERVICES LLC p 1626
836 North St Unit 5, Tewksbury MA 01876
Tel (978) 848-9000 SIC 7373 7375

CAMBRIDGE COMPUTER SERVICES INC p 244
271 Waverley Oaks Rd # 301, Waltham MA 02452
Tel (781) 250-3000
SIC 5045 7373 7371 7379

■ CONSTANT CONTACT INC p 360
1601 Trapelo Rd Ste 329, Waltham MA 02451
Tel (781) 472-8100 SIC 7373 4813 7331

■ CSC CONSULTING INC p 397
404 Wyman St Ste 355, Waltham MA 02451
Tel (781) 890-7446 SIC 7373 7371 8742

NWN CORP p 1068
271 Waverley Oaks Rd # 302, Waltham MA 02452
Tel (781) 472-3400 SIC 7373

▲ NETSCOUT SYSTEMS INC p 1027
310 Littleton Rd, Westford MA 01886
Tel (978) 614-4000 SIC 7373 3577

▲ SONUS NETWORKS INC p 1340
4 Technology Park Dr, Westford MA 01886
Tel (978) 614-8100 SIC 7373

LOWRY HOLDING CO INC p 882
9420 Maltby Rd, Brighton MI 48116
Tel (810) 229-7200
SIC 5045 2672 8742 7373 5044 5734

EPITEC INC p 505
24800 Denso Dr Ste 150, Southfield MI 48033
Tel (248) 353-6800
SIC 7371 7379 7373 8748 8711

▲ DATALINK CORP p 414
10050 Crosstown Cir # 500, Eden Prairie MN 55344
Tel (952) 944-3462 SIC 5045 7371 7373

■ HEALTHLAND INC p 677
1600 Utica Ave S Ste 300, Minneapolis MN 55416
Tel (612) 787-3120 SIC 7373 5045

SPANLINK COMMUNICATIONS INC p 1354
5940 Golden Hills Dr, Minneapolis MN 55416
Tel (763) 971-2000 SIC 7373 7371

■ PEOPLENET COMMUNICATIONS CORP p 1132
4400 Baker Rd, Minnetonka MN 55343
Tel (952) 908-6200 SIC 7373 3663 4812

ERGOTRON INC p 507
1181 Trapp Rd Ste 100, Saint Paul MN 55121
Tel (651) 681-7600 SIC 7373 3577

ENTRUST DATACARD CORP p 503
1187 Park Pl, Shakopee MN 55379
Tel (952) 933-1223
SIC 3579 3089 7373 7372

VSS LLC p 1567
382 Galleria Pkwy Ste 400, Madison MS 39110
Tel (601) 853-8550 SIC 5045 7373

GKR SYSTEMS INC p 613
860 Centre St, Ridgeland MS 39157
Tel (601) 956-5440 SIC 5045 7373

AMDOCS INC p 66
1390 Timberlake Manor Pkw, Chesterfield MO 63017
Tel (314) 212-7000 SIC 7372 7371 7373

ACLARA TECHNOLOGIES LLC p 17
945 Hornet Dr, Hazelwood MO 63042
Tel (314) 895-6400
SIC 3824 3825 3829 7371 7373

METER READINGS HOLDING LLC p 953
945 Hornet Dr, Hazelwood MO 63042
Tel (561) 394-0550
SIC 3824 3825 3829 7371 7373

▲ CERNER CORP p 284
2800 Rock Creek Pkwy, Kansas City MO 64117
Tel (816) 201-1024 SIC 7373

VML INC p 1563
250 Nw Richards Rd # 255, Kansas City MO 64116
Tel (816) 283-0700 SIC 7311 7373 8742

▲ JACK HENRY & ASSOCIATES INC p 773
663 W Highway 60, Monett MO 65708
Tel (417) 235-6652 SIC 7373

DAUGHERTY SYSTEMS INC p 414
3 Cityplace Dr Ste 400, Saint Louis MO 63141
Tel (314) 432-8200
SIC 7379 7371 8742 7373 7372

KELLY MITCHELL GROUP INC p 809
8229 Maryland Ave, Saint Louis MO 63105
Tel (314) 727-1700 SIC 7371 7373

■ TALX CORP p 1423
11432 Lackland Rd, Saint Louis MO 63146
Tel (314) 214-7000 SIC 7373 7379 7389

SAVVIS INC p 1284
1 Solutions Pkwy, Town And Country MO 63017
Tel (314) 628-7000
SIC 7373 7379 4813 7375

■ INFORMATION TECHNOLOGY INC p 742
1345 Old Cheney Rd, Lincoln NE 68512
Tel (402) 423-2682
SIC 5045 7373 7374 7371

RIMINI STREET INC p 1235
3993 Howard Hughes Pkwy, Las Vegas NV 89169
Tel (702) 839-9671 SIC 7379 7373

▲ SCIENTIFIC GAMES CORP p 1292
6650 El Camino Rd, Las Vegas NV 89118
Tel (702) 897-7150 SIC 7999 7373

TRAX INTERNATIONAL CORP p 1475
8337 W Sunset Rd Ste 250, Las Vegas NV 89113
Tel (702) 216-4455
SIC 7373 8711 7376 8742 8744

■ ENTERASYS NETWORKS INC p 501
9 Northstern Blvd Ste 300, Salem NH 03079
Tel (603) 952-5000
SIC 3577 7373 3357 5045

WORLDCOM EXCHANGE INC p 1625
43 Northwestern Dr, Salem NH 03079
Tel (603) 893-0900 SIC 7373 5045 7379

TYCO ELECTRONICS SUBSEA COMMUNICATIONS LLC p 1496
250 Industrial Way W, Eatontown NJ 07724
Tel (732) 578-7000
SIC 3661 5063 7373 1731 8999

EMDEON CORP p 491
669 River Dr Ste 240, Elmwood Park NJ 07407
Tel (201) 703-3400 SIC 7373 3089

ACUATIVE CORP p 20
30 Two Bridges Rd Ste 240, Fairfield NJ 07004
Tel (862) 926-5600 SIC 7373 5065 1731

ONE DIVERSIFIED LLC p 1086
37 Market St, Kenilworth NJ 07033
Tel (908) 245-4833
SIC 5099 7373 4899 8711

COMPUTER HORIZONS CORP p 353
2001 Us Highway 46 # 310, Parsippany NJ 07054
Tel (973) 257-5030 SIC 7373

▲ RCM TECHNOLOGIES INC p 1212
2500 Mcclellan Ave # 350, Pennsauken NJ 08109
Tel (856) 356-4500
SIC 8711 8748 7373 8049 7363

TELCORDIA TECHNOLOGIES INC p 1433
444 Hoes Ln, Piscataway NJ 08854
Tel (732) 699-6800 SIC 7371 7373 8742

SIEMENS CORPORATE RESEARCH INC p 1320
755 College Rd E, Princeton NJ 08540
Tel (609) 734-6500 SIC 8731 7373

▲ WAYSIDE TECHNOLOGY GROUP INC p 1584
1157 Shrewsbury Ave, Shrewsbury NJ 07702
Tel (732) 389-8950 SIC 5045 7373 7379

HIGH POINT SOLUTIONS INC p 691
5 Gail Ct, Sparta NJ 07871
Tel (973) 940-0040 SIC 5045 7373

▲ COMMVAULT SYSTEMS INC p 350
1 Commvault Way, Tinton Falls NJ 07724
Tel (732) 870-4000 SIC 7373 7372 7376

CORE TECHNOLOGY SOLUTIONS LIMITED LIABILITY CO p 369
80 S Jefferson Rd, Whippany NJ 07981
Tel (973) 588-4533 SIC 7379 7373

CONVERGENCE TECHNOLOGIES INC p 365
80 State St, Albany NY 12207
Tel (914) 697-7669 SIC 7373

▲ NAPCO SECURITY TECHNOLOGIES INC p 1007
333 Bayview Ave, Amityville NY 11701
Tel (631) 842-9400
SIC 3669 3699 3429 1731 7373

NFRASTRUCTURE TECHNOLOGIES LLC p 1041
5 Enterprise Ave, Halfmoon NY 12065
Tel (518) 664-3899 SIC 7373

CUSTOM COMPUTER SPECIALISTS INC p 403
70 Suffolk Ct Ste 100, Hauppauge NY 11788
Tel (800) 598-8989 SIC 7379 7373 7378

FUTURE TECH ENTERPRISE INC p 585
101 Colin Dr Unit 8, Holbrook NY 11741
Tel (631) 472-5500 SIC 7373

■ TELXON CORP p 1435
1 Zebra Plz, Holtsville NY 11742
Tel (631) 738-2400 SIC 3571 7373 3663

■ PARTECH INC p 1118
8383 Seneca Tpke Ste 2, New Hartford NY 13413
Tel (315) 738-0600 SIC 7373

DEALERTRACK TECHNOLOGIES INC p 420
1111 Marcus Ave Ste M04, New Hyde Park NY 11042
Tel (516) 734-3600 SIC 7373

COMPUTER GENERATED SOLUTIONS INC p 352
200 Vesey St Fl 27, New York NY 10281
Tel (212) 408-3800
SIC 7373 7379 7371 8243

DIMENSION DATA NORTH AMERICA INC p 440
1 Penn Plz Ste 1600, New York NY 10119
Tel (212) 613-1220 SIC 7373

INFORMATION BUILDERS INC p 741
2 Penn Plz Fl 28, New York NY 10121
Tel (212) 736-4433 SIC 7373 6794

▲ NEW MEDIA INVESTMENT GROUP INC p 1032
1345 Avenue Of The Americ, New York NY 10105
Tel (212) 479-3160 SIC 2711 7373

PRESIDIO INC p 1172
1 Penn Plz Ste 2832, New York NY 10119
Tel (212) 324-4398 SIC 7373

PRIDE CAPITAL PARTNERS LLC p 1174
420 Lexington Ave Rm 2903, New York NY 10170
Tel (212) 235-5300 SIC 7373

SHOREGROUP INC p 1318
460 W 35th St, New York NY 10001
Tel (212) 736-2915 SIC 7373

T2 COMPUTING INC p 1420
119 W 23rd St Ste 206, New York NY 10011
Tel (212) 220-9600 SIC 7373 7379

▲ TRAVELZOO INC p 1475
590 Madison Ave Rm 3700, New York NY 10022
Tel (212) 484-4900 SIC 7313 7373

TULLETT PREBON AMERICAS CORP p 1491
199 Water St Fl 17, New York NY 10038
Tel (212) 208-2000 SIC 6211 7373

SANDATA HOLDINGS INC p 1278
26 Harbor Park Dr, Port Washington NY 11050
Tel (516) 484-4400 SIC 7374 7373

■ GLOBAL CROSSING BANDWIDTH INC p 616
200 Meridian Centre Blvd # 130, Rochester NY 14618
Tel (212) 920-8201 SIC 4813 7373 7374

ODYSSEY GROUP OF COMPANIES p 1075
11 Overlook Way, Setauket NY 11733
Tel (631) 751-8400
SIC 7373 3577 7371 1731

ISLAND COMPUTER PRODUCTS INC p 766
20 Clifton Ave, Staten Island NY 10305
Tel (718) 556-6700
SIC 5045 7373 7379 7378

ERGONOMIC GROUP INC p 507
609 Cantiague Rock Rd # 3, Westbury NY 11590
Tel (516) 746-7777
SIC 5045 7373 7374 7376 7379

VELOCITY TECHNOLOGY SOLUTIONS INC p 1547
1901 Roxborough Rd 4, Charlotte NC 28211
Tel (646) 884-6600 SIC 7373

■ POWERSECURE INC p 1166
1609 Heritage Commerce Ct, Wake Forest NC 27587
Tel (919) 556-3056 SIC 7373

▲ CINCINNATI BELL INC p 307
221 E 4th St Ste 700, Cincinnati OH 45202
Tel (513) 397-9900
SIC 4813 7373 7374 7379

CINCOM SYSTEMS INC p 307
55 Merchant St Ste 100, Cincinnati OH 45246
Tel (513) 612-2300 SIC 7373

▲ CONVERGYS CORP p 365
201 E 4th St, Cincinnati OH 45202
Tel (513) 723-7000 SIC 7374 7373

INFOTELECOM HOLDINGS LLC p 742
75 Erieview Plz Fl 4, Cleveland OH 44114
Tel (216) 373-4811 SIC 4813 7373

MORGENTHALER MANAGEMENT PARTNERS VI LLC p 989
50 Public Sq Ste 2700, Cleveland OH 44113
Tel (216) 416-7500
SIC 1731 5065 7622 7373 5999

CORBUS LLC p 368
1129 Miamisbrg Cntrvle Rd Ste, Dayton OH 45449
Tel (937) 226-7724 SIC 8741 7373

ROLTA ADVIZEX TECHNOLOGIES LLC p 1248
6480 S Rockside Woods, Independence OH 44131
Tel (216) 901-1818 SIC 7373

REYNOLDS AND REYNOLDS CO p 1230
1 Reynolds Way, Kettering OH 45430
Tel (937) 485-2000 SIC 7373 6159

CONTINGENT NETWORK SERVICES LLC p 364
4400 Port Union Rd, West Chester OH 45011
Tel (513) 616-5773 SIC 7379 7373

STRUCTURED COMMUNICATION SYSTEMS INC p 1394
12901 Se 97th Ave Ste 400, Clackamas OR 97015
Tel (503) 513-9979 SIC 7373 5045

▲ MENTOR GRAPHICS CORP p 943
8005 Sw Boeckman Rd, Wilsonville OR 97070
Tel (503) 685-7000 SIC 7373

▲ UNISYS CORP p 1506
801 Lakeview Dr Ste 100, Blue Bell PA 19422
Tel (215) 986-4011
SIC 7373 7378 7379 3571 3572

AESYNT INC p 31
500 Cranberry Woods Dr # 400, Cranberry Township PA 16066
Tel (724) 741-8000 *SIC* 7373

BENTLEY SYSTEMS INC p 173
685 Stockton Dr, Exton PA 19341
Tel (610) 458-5000 *SIC* 7372 7373

■ TRANSCORE HOLDINGS INC p 1471
3721 Tecport Dr, Harrisburg PA 17111
Tel (717) 561-5812 *SIC* 7373

ELLUCIAN CO LP p 489
4 Country View Rd, Malvern PA 19355
Tel (610) 647-5930 *SIC* 7373 8741

IGATE INC p 730
1305 Cherrington Pkwy, Moon Township PA 15108
Tel (412) 787-2100 *SIC* 7373

APPLABS TECHNOLOGIES PVT LTD p 98
1515 Market St Ste 1110, Philadelphia PA 19102
Tel (215) 563-9396 *SIC* 7373

▲ CDI CORP p 271
1735 Market St Ste 200, Philadelphia PA 19103
Tel (215) 569-2200
SIC 8711 7371 7373 7376 7361 7363

▲ ACTUA CORP p 20
555 E Lancaster Ave # 640, Radnor PA 19087
Tel (610) 727-6900 *SIC* 7373

JUDGE GROUP INC p 796
151 S Warner Rd Ste 100, Wayne PA 19087
Tel (610) 667-7700 *SIC* 7373 7361 7379

ATRION INC p 129
125 Metro Center Blvd, Warwick RI 02886
Tel (401) 736-6400 *SIC* 7373 5065

GOWER CORP p 627
355 Woodruff Rd Ste 101, Greenville SC 29607
Tel (864) 458-3114 *SIC* 3535 5051 7373

LIFE CYCLE ENGINEERING INC p 863
4360 Corporate Rd Ste 100, North Charleston SC 29405
Tel (843) 744-7110
SIC 7371 7373 7376 7379 8711

TOLT SOLUTIONS INC p 1459
3550 Rutherford Rd, Taylors SC 29687
Tel (864) 322-4200
SIC 8748 7379 7374 7373

STERLING COMPUTERS CORP p 1387
600 Stevens Port Dr, Dakota Dunes SD 57049
Tel (605) 242-4000 *SIC* 7373

JANUS GLOBAL OPERATIONS LLC p 778
2229 Old Highway 95, Lenoir City TN 37771
Tel (865) 988-6063
SIC 4959 7381 7373 7379 8742

QUALIFACTS SYSTEMS INC p 1196
200 2nd Ave S, Nashville TN 37201
Tel (615) 386-6755 *SIC* 7373 7371

▲ DIGITAL TURBINE INC p 439
1300 Guadalupe St Ste 302, Austin TX 78701
Tel (512) 387-7717 *SIC* 7373

KASASA LTD p 804
4516 Seton Center Pkwy, Austin TX 78759
Tel (512) 418-9590 *SIC* 7371 7373 7379

M&A TECHNOLOGY INC p 890
2045 Chenault Dr, Carrollton TX 75006
Tel (972) 490-5803 *SIC* 5045 7373

ATOS ORIGIN INC p 128
18062 Fm 529 Rd Ste 215, Cypress TX 77433
Tel (914) 881-3000
SIC 7373 7374 7376 7379

COMPUCOM SYSTEMS HOLDING LLC p 352
7171 Forest Ln, Dallas TX 75230
Tel (972) 856-3600
SIC 7373 5045 7378 8748

■ MEDIA RECOVERY p 936
5501 L B Johnson Fwy 350, Dallas TX 75240
Tel (800) 660-3586 *SIC* 7373

SIGNWAREHOUSE INC p 1322
2614 Texoma Dr, Denison TX 75020
Tel (903) 462-7700 *SIC* 7373

ECOMMERCE INDUSTRIES INC p 476
4400 Alliance Gateway Fwy # 154, Fort Worth TX 76177
Tel (682) 831-0827 *SIC* 7373

■ LANDMARK GRAPHICS CORP p 843
2107 Citywest Blvd Bldg 2, Houston TX 77042
Tel (713) 839-2000 *SIC* 7371 7373

NETVERSANT SOLUTIONS LLC p 1028
9750 W Sam Houston Pkwy N # 100, Houston TX 77064
Tel (800) 540-2739 *SIC* 7373 8999 7381

SUMMIT CONSOLIDATION GROUP INC p 1398
10497 Town Cntry Way 3, Houston TX 77024
Tel (713) 554-2244 *SIC* 7373 7371 4813

SQS USA INC p 1362
545 E John Carpenter Fwy, Irving TX 75062
Tel (630) 596-6001 *SIC* 7373

PRESIDIO NETWORKED SOLUTIONS GROUP LLC p 1172
1955 Lakeway Dr Ste 220, Lewisville TX 75057
Tel (469) 549-3800 *SIC* 5045 7372 7373

ETECH GLOBAL SERVICES LLC p 511
1903 Berry Dr, Nacogdoches TX 75964
Tel (936) 559-2200
SIC 7389 8742 7373 8741 8721 7374

COMPUCOM SYSTEMS INC p 352
8383 Dominion Pkwy, Plano TX 75024
Tel (972) 856-3600
SIC 7373 5045 7378 8748

NTT DATA INC p 1065
5601 Gran Pkwy Ste 1000, Plano TX 75024
Tel (800) 745-3263 *SIC* 7373 7372 7379

■ SOFTWARE SPECTRUM INC p 1337
3480 Lotus Dr, Plano TX 75075
Tel (469) 443-3900 *SIC* 5045 7373

■ RAYTHEON E-SYSTEMS INC p 1211
1727 Cityline Dr, Richardson TX 75082
Tel (972) 205-9374
SIC 3663 3812 7373 3575 4581 3721

GENESIS NETWORKS ENTERPRISES LLC p 603
600 N Loop 1604 E, San Antonio TX 78232
Tel (210) 489-6600 *SIC* 7373

SIGMA SOLUTIONS GP INC p 1321
607 E Sonterra Blvd # 250, San Antonio TX 78258
Tel (210) 348-9876 *SIC* 7373 7379

SIGMA TECHNOLOGY SOLUTIONS INC p 1321
607 E Sonterra Blvd # 250, San Antonio TX 78258
Tel (888) 895-0495 *SIC* 7373

SIRIUS COMPUTER SOLUTIONS INC p 1327
10100 Reunion Pl Ste 500, San Antonio TX 78216
Tel (210) 369-8000 *SIC* 7373 5045

ACCESSDATA GROUP INC p 15
588 W 400 S Ste 350, Lindon UT 84042
Tel (801) 377-5410 *SIC* 7373

CATAPULT TECHNOLOGY LTD p 265
11 Canal Center Plz Fl 2, Alexandria VA 22314
Tel (240) 482-2100 *SIC* 7373 8742

DCS CORP p 418
6909 Metro Park Dr # 500, Alexandria VA 22310
Tel (571) 227-6000 *SIC* 7373

NES ASSOCIATES LLC p 1026
6400 Beulah St Ste 100, Alexandria VA 22310
Tel (703) 224-2600 *SIC* 7373

■ CACI ENTERPRISE SOLUTIONS INC p 235
1100 N Glebe Rd Ste 200, Arlington VA 22201
Tel (703) 841-7800 *SIC* 7373

■ CACI INC - FEDERAL p 235
1100 N Glebe Rd Ste 200, Arlington VA 22201
Tel (703) 841-7800
SIC 7373 7372 7371 8711

▲ CACI INTERNATIONAL INC p 235
1100 N Glebe Rd Ste 200, Arlington VA 22201
Tel (703) 841-7800 *SIC* 7373 4899 7371

■ CACI TECHNOLOGIES INC p 236
1100 N Glebe Rd Ste 200, Arlington VA 22201
Tel (703) 841-7800 *SIC* 7373 8711

SIEMENS GOVERNMENT TECHNOLOGIES INC p 1320
2231 Crystal Dr Ste 700, Arlington VA 22202
Tel (703) 860-1574
SIC 8711 7373 7376 7379 8712 7378

■ SIX3 SYSTEMS HOLDINGS II INC p 1328
1100 N Glebe Rd, Arlington VA 22201
Tel (703) 841-7800 *SIC* 7373

▲ TELOS CORP p 1435
19886 Ashburn Rd, Ashburn VA 20147
Tel (703) 724-3800 *SIC* 7373

AMERICAN SYSTEMS CORP p 80
14151 Pk Madow Dr Ste 500, Chantilly VA 20151
Tel (703) 968-6300
SIC 8711 1731 8742 7373

IRON BOW HOLDINGS INC p 764
4800 Westfields Blvd # 300, Chantilly VA 20151
Tel (703) 279-3000 *SIC* 7379 7373

■ SRA INTERNATIONAL INC p 1362
15036 Conference Ctr Dr, Chantilly VA 20151
Tel (703) 803-1500 *SIC* 7373 8748

BAZON-COX AND ASSOCIATES INC p 163
1244 Executive Blvd B113, Chesapeake VA 23320
Tel (757) 410-2128 *SIC* 7373

CGI TECHNOLOGIES AND SOLUTIONS INC p 286
11325 Random Hills Rd, Fairfax VA 22030
Tel (703) 267-8000
SIC 7379 7373 7372 7389

ELLUCIAN INC p 489
4375 Fair Lakes Ct, Fairfax VA 22033
Tel (407) 660-1199 *SIC* 7371 7373

■ GENERAL DYNAMICS INFORMATION TECHNOLOGY INC p 600
3211 Jermantown Rd, Fairfax VA 22030
Tel (703) 995-8700 *SIC* 7379 8711 7373

▲ MANTECH INTERNATIONAL CORP p 903
12015 Lee Jackson Hwy, Fairfax VA 22033
Tel (703) 218-6000 *SIC* 7373 8711 7379

■ MANTECH SYSTEMS ENGINEERING CORP p 903
12015 Lee Jackson Hwy, Fairfax VA 22033
Tel (703) 218-6000 *SIC* 7373 8711

■ MANTECH TELECOMMUNICATIONS AND INFORMATION SYSTEMS CORP p 903
12015 Lee Jackson Mem Hwy, Fairfax VA 22033
Tel (703) 218-6000 *SIC* 7373

SALIENT CRGT INC p 1272
4000 Legato Rd Ste 600, Fairfax VA 22033
Tel (703) 891-8200 *SIC* 7373 8748

■ SIGNAL SOLUTIONS LLC p 1322
3211 Jermantown Rd # 700, Fairfax VA 22030
Tel (703) 205-0500
SIC 8711 7379 7374 4813 7373 8731

STANLEY ASSOCIATES INC p 1377
12601 Fair Lakes Cir, Fairfax VA 22033
Tel (703) 227-6000 *SIC* 7373

STANLEY INC p 1377
12601 Fair Lakes Cir, Fairfax VA 22033
Tel (703) 684-1125 *SIC* 7373

■ VANGENT INC p 1543
3211 Jermantown Rd, Fairfax VA 22030
Tel (703) 995-2666
SIC 8748 7371 7372 7373 7374 7376

■ XEROX STATE & LOCAL SOLUTIONS INC p 1631
8260 Willow Oaks Crprt, Fairfax VA 22031
Tel (202) 378-2804 *SIC* 7373

▲ CSRA INC p 398
3170 Fairview Park Dr, Falls Church VA 22042
Tel (703) 641-2000 *SIC* 7373

■ MANTECH GRAY HAWK SYSTEMS INC p 903
7799 Leesburg Pike 700s, Falls Church VA 22043
Tel (703) 610-9232 *SIC* 7373 7378

■ STAR SECOND MERGER SUB LLC p 1378
3170 Fairview Park Dr, Falls Church VA 22042
Tel (703) 876-1000 *SIC* 7373 8748

APEX EPUBLISHING DATA SERVICES LLC p 96
198 Van Buren St Ste 120, Herndon VA 20170
Tel (703) 709-3000 *SIC* 7373

■ CUBIC GLOBAL DEFENSE INC p 399
205 Van Buren St Ste 310, Herndon VA 20170
Tel (703) 821-8930
SIC 7379 7371 7373 8711

DLT MERGERCO LLC p 445
2411 Dulles Corner Park, Herndon VA 20171
Tel (800) 262-4358 *SIC* 7373

DLT SOLUTIONS LLC p 445
2411 Dulles Corner Park # 800, Herndon VA 20171
Tel (703) 709-7172 *SIC* 7373

ELECTRONIC WARFARE ASSOCIATES INC p 486
13873 Park Center Rd # 500, Herndon VA 20171
Tel (703) 904-5700
SIC 7373 7374 3672 3699 3643 3441

■ NTT DATA SERVICES FEDERAL GOVERNMENT INC p 1066
13880 Dulles Corner Ln, Herndon VA 20171
Tel (703) 289-8000 *SIC* 8711 7373 7374

PROGENY SYSTEMS CORP p 1180
9500 Innovation Dr, Manassas VA 20110
Tel (703) 368-6107 *SIC* 7373

DIGITAL INTELLIGENCE SYSTEMS LLC p 439
8270 Greensboro Dr # 1000, Mc Lean VA 22102
Tel (703) 752-7900 *SIC* 7373 7371

■ DYNCORP p 465
1700 Old Meadow Rd, Mc Lean VA 22102
Tel (571) 722-0210
SIC 7373 7371 7374 7375 8744 4581

■ NORTHROP GRUMMAN INFORMATION TECHNOLOGY INC p 1058
7575 Colshire Dr, Mc Lean VA 22102
Tel (703) 556-1000 *SIC* 7373 7372 8733

NOVETTA SOLUTIONS LLC p 1063
7921 Jones Branch Dr # 500, Mc Lean VA 22102
Tel (571) 282-3000 *SIC* 7373

SALIENT FEDERAL-SGIS INC p 1272
8255 Greensboro Dr # 400, Mc Lean VA 22102
Tel (703) 891-8200 *SIC* 7373 8711 7382

▲ SCIENCE APPLICATIONS INTERNATIONAL CORP p 1292
1710 Saic Dr Ste B, Mc Lean VA 22102
Tel (703) 676-6942 *SIC* 7373 7374

■ SIX3 SYSTEMS INC p 1328
1430 Spring Hill Rd # 525, Mc Lean VA 22102
Tel (703) 442-6650 *SIC* 7373

SMS DATA PRODUCTS GROUP INC p 1334
1751 Pinnacle Dr Ste 1200, Mc Lean VA 22102
Tel (703) 288-8100 *SIC* 5045 7373

STRATEGIC RESOURCES INC p 1392
7927 Jones Branch Dr 600w, Mc Lean VA 22102
Tel (703) 749-3040 *SIC* 8742 8748 7373

■ TITAN II INC p 1456
4101 Washington Ave, Newport News VA 23607
Tel (757) 380-2000
SIC 3728 3761 7373 3721 4581 3812

APOGEN TECHNOLOGIES INC p 97
11091 Sunset Hills Rd # 200, Reston VA 20190
Tel (703) 644-6433 *SIC* 7373 7379

■ CACI NSS INC p 236
11955 Freedom Dr Fl 2, Reston VA 20190
Tel (703) 434-4000 *SIC* 7373 8711

▲ LEIDOS HOLDINGS INC p 854
11951 Freedom Dr Ste 500, Reston VA 20190
Tel (571) 526-6000
SIC 8731 7371 7373 8742 3674

■ LEIDOS INC p 854
11951 Freedom Dr Ste 500, Reston VA 20190
Tel (571) 526-6000 *SIC* 8731 7373

▲ NCI INC p 1022
11730 Plaza America Dr # 700, Reston VA 20190
Tel (703) 707-6900 *SIC* 7373 8711

■ NCI INFORMATION SYSTEMS INC p 1022
11730 Plaza America Dr # 700, Reston VA 20190
Tel (703) 707-6900 *SIC* 7373

■ SCITOR HOLDINGS INC p 1292
12010 Sunset Hills Rd # 800, Reston VA 20190
Tel (703) 481-5892 *SIC* 7382 5065 7373

VENCORE SERVICES AND SOLUTIONS INC p 1547
1835 Alexander Bell Dr, Reston VA 20191
Tel (703) 391-7017 *SIC* 7379 7373 3812

▲ COMPUTER SCIENCES CORP p 353
1775 Tysons Blvd, Tysons VA 22102
Tel (703) 245-9675
SIC 7376 7374 7379 7373 7323

ACTIONET INC p 19
2600 Park Twr Dr Ste 1000, Vienna VA 22180
Tel (703) 204-0090
SIC 7379 7373 7372 7371

■ AT&T GOVERNMENT SOLUTIONS INC p 123
1900 Gallows Rd Ste 105, Vienna VA 22182
Tel (703) 506-5000
SIC 5999 8742 7373 7371

SLAIT PARTNERS INC p 1331
100 Landmark Sq, Virginia Beach VA 23452
Tel (757) 313-6500
SIC 5045 3571 8748 7373

ZONES INC p 1644
1102 15th St Sw Ste 102, Auburn WA 98001
Tel (253) 205-3000 *SIC* 7373 5734

EAGLE GROUP SYSTEMS INC p 468
230 Grant Rd, East Wenatchee WA 98802
Tel (509) 665-0319
SIC 4214 4119 4522 7373 7374 8741

CUBIC GLOBAL DEFENSE INC p 399
400 Union Ave Se Ste 300, Olympia WA 98501
Tel (360) 493-6275
SIC 7373 8744 8711 7376 8748 8741

ATTACHMATE CORP p 129
705 5th Ave S Ste 1000, Seattle WA 98104
Tel (206) 217-7100 *SIC* 7373 7371 7372

ATTACHMATE GROUP INC p 129
705 5th Ave S Ste 1100, Seattle WA 98104
Tel (206) 217-7100 *SIC* 7371 7372 7373

▲ F5 NETWORKS INC p 523
401 Elliott Ave W Ste 500, Seattle WA 98119
Tel (206) 272-5555 *SIC* 7373 7372

SLALOM LLC p 1331
821 2nd Ave Ste 1900, Seattle WA 98104
Tel (206) 374-4200 *SIC* 8742 7373

■ FISERV CIR INC p 551
255 Fiserv Dr, Brookfield WI 53045
Tel (262) 879-5000 *SIC* 7374 7372 7373

■ CDW TECHNOLOGIES LLC p 271
5520 Research Park Dr, Fitchburg WI 53711
Tel (608) 288-3000 *SIC* 7373 4813

■ WAUSAU FINANCIAL SYSTEMS INC p 1583
400 Westwood Dr, Wausau WI 54401
Tel (715) 359-0427 *SIC* 7373

SIC 7374 Data & Computer Processing & Preparation

NCP SOLUTIONS LLC p 1022
5200 E Lake Blvd, Birmingham AL 35217
Tel (205) 849-5200 *SIC* 7374

SOUTHERN MEDICAL HEALTH SYSTEMS INC p 1349
3632 Dauphin St Ste 101b, Mobile AL 36608
Tel (251) 460-5280
SIC 8741 8011 7374 7322

■ AMERICAN TRAFFIC SOLUTIONS INC p 80
1150 N Alma School Rd, Mesa AZ 85201
Tel (480) 443-7000 *SIC* 7374 1731 5084

ENGHOUSE INTERACTIVE INC p 498
2095 W Pinnacle Peak Rd, Phoenix AZ 85027
Tel (602) 789-2800
SIC 3571 3661 3663 7372 7374

■ EFUNDS CORP p 481
4900 N Scottsdale Rd # 1000, Scottsdale AZ 85251
Tel (602) 431-2700 *SIC* 7374 7372 7371

■ GO DADDY OPERATING CO LLC p 619
14455 N Hayden Rd Ste 219, Scottsdale AZ 85260
Tel (480) 505-8877 *SIC* 7373 7374

PEGASUS SOLUTIONS INC p 1127
14000 N Pima Rd Ste 200, Scottsdale AZ 85260
Tel (480) 624-6000 *SIC* 7374

■ COMSYS INFORMATION TECHNOLOGY SERVICES LLC p 353
2050 E Asu Cir Ste 120, Tempe AZ 85284
Tel (877) 626-6797 *SIC* 7371 7374

▲ ACXIOM CORP p 21
601 E 3rd St, Little Rock AR 72201
Tel (501) 252-1000 *SIC* 7374 7375 7371

■ TELOGIS INC p 1435
20 Enterprise Ste 100, Aliso Viejo CA 92656
Tel (949) 389-5500 *SIC* 7374

DATADIRECT NETWORKS INC p 414
9351 Deering Ave, Chatsworth CA 91311
Tel (818) 700-7600 *SIC* 3572 7374

SONY PICTURES IMAGEWORKS INC p 1341
9050 Washington Blvd, Culver City CA 90232
Tel (310) 840-8000 *SIC* 7374

R SYSTEMS INC p 1202
5000 Windplay Dr Ste 5, El Dorado Hills CA 95762
Tel (916) 939-9696 *SIC* 7379 7373 7374

INTERNET BRANDS INC p 757
909 N Sepulveda Blvd # 11, El Segundo CA 90245
Tel (310) 280-4000 *SIC* 7374

■ CYBERSOURCE CORP p 405
900 Metro Center Blvd, Foster City CA 94404
Tel (650) 432-7350 *SIC* 7374

■ HYVE SOLUTIONS CORP p 724
44201 Nobel Dr, Fremont CA 94538
Tel (864) 349-4415 *SIC* 7374

MAGPIE INTERNET COMMUNICATIONS CORP p 897
2762 Bayview Dr, Fremont CA 94538
Tel (510) 344-1200 *SIC* 4813 7379 7374

MILESTONE TECHNOLOGIES INC p 969
3101 Skyway Ct, Fremont CA 94539
Tel (510) 651-2454 *SIC* 7373 7374

HIRERIGHT LLC p 695
3349 Michelson Dr Ste 150, Irvine CA 92612
Tel (949) 428-5800 *SIC* 7375 7374

■ LPS REAL ESTATE GROUP INC p 882
2050 Main St Ste 400, Irvine CA 92614
Tel (949) 681-4700 *SIC* 7374

■ CONTINENTAL GRAPHICS CORP p 363
4060 N Lakewood Blvd, Long Beach CA 90808
Tel (714) 503-4200
SIC 3724 7371 7372 7374

■ XEROX EDUCATION SERVICES LLC p 1631
2277 E 220th St, Long Beach CA 90810
Tel (310) 830-9847 *SIC* 7374

DATA ANALYSIS INC p 413
12655 Beatrice St, Los Angeles CA 90066
Tel (310) 448-6800 *SIC* 6211 2711 7374

INFOGAIN CORP p 741
485 Alberto Way Ste 100, Los Gatos CA 95032
Tel (408) 355-6000
SIC 7379 7373 8742 8748 7374 1731

■ VITESSE LLC p 1563
1601 Willow Rd, Menlo Park CA 94025
Tel (650) 543-4800 *SIC* 7374

■ PAYPAL GLOBAL HOLDINGS INC p 1122
303 Bryant St, Mountain View CA 94041
Tel (408) 967-1000 *SIC* 7374 4813

REGULUS GROUP LLC p 1220
860 Latour Ct, Napa CA 94558
Tel (707) 259-7100 *SIC* 7374

▲ SUPPORT.COM INC p 1408
900 Chesapeake Dr Fl 2, Redwood City CA 94063
Tel (650) 556-9440 *SIC* 7374 7372

▲ TIVO CORP p 1456
2 Circle Way, San Carlos CA 94070
Tel (408) 562-8400 *SIC* 7374 7929

GENERAL ATOMIC TECHNOLOGIES CORP p 599
3550 General Atomics Ct, San Diego CA 92121
Tel (858) 455-3000
SIC 8731 3829 3443 7374 3499 2819

SAN DIEGO DATA PROCESSING CORP INC p 1276
202 C St Fl 3, San Diego CA 92101
Tel (858) 581-9600 SIC 7374

UPWIND SOLUTIONS INC p 1530
4863 Shawline St Ste A, San Diego CA 92111
Tel (866) 927-3142 SIC 7374 4931 7373

FUSIONSTORM p 585
2 Bryant St Ste 150, San Francisco CA 94105
Tel (415) 623-2626
SIC 7379 7371 7374 7376

▲ MARIN SOFTWARE INC p 906
123 Mission St Fl 27, San Francisco CA 94105
Tel (415) 399-2580 SIC 7374

MERCHANT SERVICES INC p 944
1 S Van Ness Ave Fl 5, San Francisco CA 94103
Tel (817) 725-0900 SIC 7374

MICRO HOLDING CORP p 961
1 Maritime Plz Fl 12, San Francisco CA 94111
Tel (415) 788-5111 SIC 7374 7389

■ STUBHUB INC p 1394
199 Fremont St Fl 4, San Francisco CA 94105
Tel (415) 222-8400 SIC 7374 7999 7922

■ TRULIA INC p 1486
535 Mission St Fl 7, San Francisco CA 94105
Tel (415) 648-4358 SIC 7374

▲ WELLS FARGO & CO p 1590
420 Montgomery St Frnt, San Francisco CA 94104
Tel (866) 249-3302
SIC 6021 6022 6162 6141 7374

▲ ZYNGA INC p 1645
699 8th St, San Francisco CA 94103
Tel (855) 449-9642 SIC 7372 7374

▲ PAYPAL HOLDINGS INC p 1123
2211 N 1st St, San Jose CA 95131
Tel (408) 967-1000 SIC 4813 7374

■ PAYPAL INC p 1123
2211 N 1st St, San Jose CA 95131
Tel (877) 981-2163 SIC 4813 7374

KP LLC p 828
13951 Washington Ave, San Leandro CA 94578
Tel (510) 346-0729
SIC 2752 7334 7331 7374 7389 8742

KEYNOTE LLC p 815
777 Mariners Island Blvd, San Mateo CA 94404
Tel (650) 376-3033 SIC 7374 7373

INFOBLOX INC p 741
3111 Coronado Dr, Santa Clara CA 95054
Tel (408) 986-4000 SIC 7374 7371 7379

TASKUS INC p 1426
3233 Donald, Santa Monica CA 90405
Tel (888) 400-8275 SIC 7374

▲ ARC DOCUMENT SOLUTIONS INC p 103
1981 N Broadway Ste 385, Walnut Creek CA 94596
Tel (925) 949-5100
SIC 7334 7335 7374 7372

▲ LEVEL 3 COMMUNICATIONS INC p 858
1025 Eldorado Blvd, Broomfield CO 80021
Tel (720) 888-1000 SIC 4813 7373 7374

TRANSFIRST LLC p 1471
12202 Airport Way Ste 100, Broomfield CO 80021
Tel (800) 654-9256 SIC 7374

▲ CSG SYSTEMS INTERNATIONAL INC p 397
9555 Maroon Cir, Englewood CO 80112
Tel (303) 200-2000 SIC 7374

▲ LIBERTY TRIPADVISOR HOLDINGS INC p 862
12300 Liberty Blvd, Englewood CO 80112
Tel (720) 875-5200 SIC 7374

▲ STARTEK INC p 1379
8200 E Maplewood Ave # 100, Greenwood Village CO 80111
Tel (303) 262-4500 SIC 7374 7379 8742

CIRCLE GRAPHICS INC p 308
120 9th Ave Ste B, Longmont CO 80501
Tel (303) 532-2370 SIC 2759 7374

INSURITY INC p 748
170 Huyshope Ave, Hartford CT 06106
Tel (866) 476-2606 SIC 7374

▲ FACTSET RESEARCH SYSTEMS INC p 524
601 Merritt 7, Norwalk CT 06851
Tel (203) 810-1000 SIC 7374

▲ XEROX CORP p 1631
45 Glover Ave Ste 700, Norwalk CT 06850
Tel (203) 968-3000
SIC 3861 3579 3577 7629 7378 7374

CONNECTICUT ON-LINE COMPUTER CENTER INC p 357
100 Executive Blvd Ste 1, Southington CT 06489
Tel (860) 678-0444 SIC 7374

■ J P MORGAN SERVICES INC p 772
500 Stanton Christiana Rd, Newark DE 19713
Tel (302) 634-1000 SIC 7374 8741

INVENSIS INC p 761
1000 N West St Ste 1200, Wilmington DE 19801
Tel (302) 351-3509 SIC 7374

▲ DUPONT FABROS TECHNOLOGY INC p 462
1212 New York Ave Nw # 900, Washington DC 20005
Tel (202) 728-0044 SIC 6798 7374

NAYLOR LLC p 1020
5950 Nw 1st Pl, Gainesville FL 32607
Tel (800) 369-6220 SIC 2759 7374

■ AMERICAN HERITAGE LIFE INVESTMENT CORP p 74
1776 Amercn Heritg Lf Dr, Jacksonville FL 32224
Tel (904) 992-1776
SIC 6311 6321 6351 7374

■ BLACK KNIGHT INFOSERV LLC p 187
601 Riverside Ave, Jacksonville FL 32204
Tel (904) 854-5100 SIC 7389 7374

■ FIDELITY INFORMATION SERVICES LLC p 540
601 Riverside Ave, Jacksonville FL 32204
Tel (888) 323-0310 SIC 7374

▲ FIDELITY NATIONAL INFORMATION SERVICES INC p 541
601 Riverside Ave, Jacksonville FL 32204
Tel (904) 438-6000 SIC 7389 7374

■ FIS FINANCIAL SYSTEMS LLC p 551
601 Riverside Ave, Jacksonville FL 32204
Tel (904) 438-6000 SIC 7374 7372

■ FIS WEALTH MANAGEMENT SERVICES INC p 551
601 Riverside Ave, Jacksonville FL 32204
Tel (904) 854-5000 SIC 7389 7374

■ METAVANTE HOLDINGS LLC p 953
601 Riverside Ave, Jacksonville FL 32204
Tel (904) 438-6000 SIC 3578 5049 7374

▲ WEB.COM GROUP INC p 1586
12808 Gran Bay Pkwy W, Jacksonville FL 32258
Tel (904) 680-6600 SIC 7372 7374

RELIANT INVENTORY GROUP LLC p 1222
2601 S Byshr Dr Ste 725, Miami FL 33133
Tel (786) 268-4520 SIC 7374

TELEFONICA USA p 1434
1111 Brickell Ave # 1000, Miami FL 33131
Tel (305) 925-5300 SIC 7375 7374 4813

■ TIME CUSTOMER SERVICE INC p 1454
1 N Dale Mabry Hwy # 150, Tampa FL 33609
Tel (813) 878-6427 SIC 7389 7374

■ VERIZON DATA SERVICES INC p 1550
1 E Telecom Pkwy, Tampa FL 33637
Tel (212) 395-1000 SIC 7374 7371

ALTEGRA HEALTH INC p 62
1725 N Commerce Pkwy, Weston FL 33326
Tel (305) 779-6070 SIC 7374

■ CHECKFREE SERVICES CORP p 292
2900 Westside Pkwy, Alpharetta GA 30004
Tel (678) 375-3000 SIC 7374

HEALTHPORT INC p 677
925 North Point Pkwy # 350, Alpharetta GA 30005
Tel (770) 360-1700 SIC 6324 7373 7374

■ MCKESSON TECHNOLOGIES INC p 930
11475 Great Oaks Way # 400, Alpharetta GA 30022
Tel (404) 338-6000
SIC 7374 8741 8721 7322 7373

■ ELAVON INC p 483
2 Cncourse Pkwy Ste 800, Atlanta GA 30328
Tel (678) 731-5000 SIC 7375 7374

■ FIRST DATA MERCHANT SERVICES CORP p 546
5565 Glenridge Connector, Atlanta GA 30342
Tel (404) 890-3000
SIC 7374 7389 7375 6153 6099

■ SILVERPOP SYSTEMS INC p 1324
6303 Barfield Rd, Atlanta GA 30328
Tel (404) 348-9600 SIC 7374

■ SYMCOR INC p 1414
3399 Peachtree Rd Ne # 850, Atlanta GA 30326
Tel (404) 504-0100 SIC 7374

TRAVELPORT LP p 1475
300 Galleria Pkwy Se, Atlanta GA 30339
Tel (770) 563-7400 SIC 7374

WORLDPAY US INC p 1626
600 Morgan Falls Rd # 260, Atlanta GA 30350
Tel (770) 396-1616 SIC 7374

■ NDCHEALTH CORP p 1022
1564 Northeast Expy Ne, Brookhaven GA 30329
Tel (404) 728-2000 SIC 7374 8742

▲ TOTAL SYSTEM SERVICES INC p 1463
1 Tsys Way, Columbus GA 31901
Tel (706) 644-6081 SIC 7374

■ MACYS SYSTEMS AND TECHNOLOGY INC p 893
5985 State Bridge Rd, Duluth GA 30097
Tel (678) 474-2000 SIC 7374

▲ NCR CORP p 1022
3097 Satellite Blvd # 100, Duluth GA 30096
Tel (937) 445-5000
SIC 3575 3578 7379 7374 7371

BLUE EAGLE HOLDINGS LP p 192
6465 E Johns Xing, Johns Creek GA 30097
Tel (678) 584-4000 SIC 7389 7374 8742

RADIAL SOUTH LP p 1204
6465 E Johns Xing, Johns Creek GA 30097
Tel (678) 584-4000 SIC 7389 7374 8742

ACS ACQUISITION CORP p 18
6575 The Corners Pkwy, Norcross GA 30092
Tel (678) 268-1300 SIC 5045 7374

■ CHECKFREE INVESTMENT CORP p 292
4411 E Jones Bridge Rd, Norcross GA 30092
Tel (678) 375-3000 SIC 7374

■ INTERCEPT INC p 751
3150 Holcomb Bridge Rd, Norcross GA 30071
Tel (770) 248-9600 SIC 6099 7374

PROSYS INC p 1185
6575 The Corners Pkwy # 300, Norcross GA 30092
Tel (678) 268-1300 SIC 5045 7374

QUALITY TECHNOLOGY SERVICES LLC p 1197
300 Satellite Blvd Nw, Suwanee GA 30024
Tel (678) 546-0064
SIC 7373 4813 7378 7374

■ YP HOLDINGS LLC p 1639
2247 Northlake Pkwy Fl 10, Tucker GA 30084
Tel (866) 570-8863 SIC 7374 7389 7313

▲ INNERWORKINGS INC p 744
600 W Chicago Ave Ste 850, Chicago IL 60654
Tel (312) 642-3700 SIC 2752 7374 7372

■ CITICORP CREDIT SERVICES INC p 310
50 Northwest Point Blvd, Elk Grove Village IL 60007
Tel (847) 597-3000
SIC 7374 7389 7379 6141

NORTHWESTERN UNIVERSITY INFORMATION TECHNOLOGIES p 1061
1800 Sherman Ave Ste 7, Evanston IL 60201
Tel (847) 467-1766 SIC 4813 7374 4812

SOURCELINK ACQUISITION LLC p 1342
500 Park Blvd Ste 1425, Itasca IL 60143
Tel (866) 947-6872 SIC 7374 7331

MU SIGMA INC p 998
3400 Dundee Rd Ste 160, Northbrook IL 60062
Tel (847) 919-0445 SIC 7378 7374

URSCHEL LABORATORIES INC p 1530
1200 Cutting Edge Dr, Chesterton IN 46304
Tel (219) 464-4811 SIC 3556 7374

WHITECO INDUSTRIES INC p 1606
1000 E 80th Pl Ste 700n, Merrillville IN 46410
Tel (219) 769-6601
SIC 7312 7011 7922 6552 7374 3993

CDS GLOBAL INC p 271
1901 Bell Ave Ste 19, Des Moines IA 50315
Tel (866) 897-7987 SIC 7389 7375 7374

■ WELLS FARGO FINANCIAL SECURITY SERVICES INC p 1590
800 Walnut St, Des Moines IA 50309
Tel (515) 243-2131
SIC 6141 6153 6351 6159 7374 6021

SHAZAM INC p 1313
6700 Pioneer Pkwy, Johnston IA 50131
Tel (515) 288-2828 SIC 7374

IMT INSURANCE CO p 735
4445 Corporate Dr Ste 100, West Des Moines IA 50266
Tel (515) 327-2777 SIC 6331 7374

QTS REALTY TRUST INC p 1195
12851 Foster St, Overland Park KS 66213
Tel (913) 814-9988 SIC 7375 7374

QUALITYTECH LP p 1197
12851 Foster St, Overland Park KS 66213
Tel (877) 787-3282 SIC 7374

XCELLENCE INC p 1631
5800 Foxridge Dr Ste 406, Shawnee Mission KS 66202
Tel (913) 362-8662 SIC 7374

▲ FARMERS CAPITAL BANK CORP p 529
202 W Main St Ste 100, Frankfort KY 40601
Tel (502) 227-1668 SIC 6021 7374 6411

POMEROY GROUP HOLDINGS INC p 1160
1020 Petersburg Rd, Hebron KY 41048
Tel (859) 586-6000
SIC 7373 7374 7361 6719

POMEROY IT SOLUTIONS SALES CO INC p 1160
1020 Petersburg Rd, Hebron KY 41048
Tel (859) 586-0600 SIC 7373 7374 7361

SENTURE LLC p 1305
460 Industrial Blvd, London KY 40741
Tel (606) 878-4205
SIC 7379 7389 7374 7373 8742

■ BA MERCHANT SERVICES p 143
1231 Durrett Ln, Louisville KY 40213
Tel (502) 315-2000 SIC 7374

■ BA MERCHANT SERVICES LLC p 143
1231 Durrett Ln, Louisville KY 40213
Tel (502) 315-2000 SIC 7374

COMPUTER SERVICES INC p 353
3901 Technology Dr, Paducah KY 42001
Tel (800) 545-4274 SIC 7374

CMC AMERICAS INC p 328
4354 S Shrwd Forst Bl 175, Baton Rouge LA 70816
Tel (225) 296-8440 SIC 7374 7379

AMERITOX LIMITED PARTNERSHIP p 84
300 E Lombard St Ste 1610, Baltimore MD 21202
Tel (443) 220-0115 SIC 7374 8734 8731

▲ INOVALON HOLDINGS INC p 745
4321 Collington Rd # 100, Bowie MD 20716
Tel (301) 809-4000 SIC 7371 7374 7372

MIL CORP p 968
4000 Mitchellville Rd R, Bowie MD 20716
Tel (301) 805-8500
SIC 7371 7373 7374 7375 7376 8711

GXS INC p 649
9711 Washingtonian Blvd # 5, Gaithersburg MD 20878
Tel (301) 340-4000 SIC 7374

■ LEIDOS ASPEN SYSTEMS CORP p 854
700 N Frederick Ave, Gaithersburg MD 20879
Tel (301) 240-7000 SIC 7374 7379 7389

■ LEIDOS GOVERNMENT SERVICES INC p 854
700 N Frederick Ave, Gaithersburg MD 20879
Tel (856) 486-5156
SIC 7379 7373 7374 7372

INFOSYS PUBLIC SERVICES INC p 742
800 King Farm Blvd # 505, Rockville MD 20850
Tel (301) 354-8600 SIC 7371 7374 8742

SOCIAL & SCIENTIFIC SYSTEMS INC p 1336
8757 Georgia Ave Ste 1200, Silver Spring MD 20910
Tel (301) 628-3000 SIC 7374 7371

CGI INFORMATION SYSTEMS & MANAGEMENT CONSULTANTS INC p 286
600 Federal St, Andover MA 01810
Tel (978) 946-3000 SIC 7374 3577 7373

MORPHOTRUST USA LLC p 990
296 Concord Rd Ste 300, Billerica MA 01821
Tel (978) 215-2400 SIC 7374 8711

▲ CARBONITE INC p 252
2 Avenue De Lafayette # 2, Boston MA 02111
Tel (617) 587-1100 SIC 7372 7374

SAPIENT CORP p 1281
131 Dartmouth St Ste 301, Boston MA 02116
Tel (617) 621-0200
SIC 7373 7374 7371 8742

■ TRILLIUM SOFTWARE INC p 1480
17 New England Executive, Burlington MA 01803
Tel (978) 901-0000 SIC 7374

▲ AKAMAI TECHNOLOGIES INC p 42
150 Broadway Ste 100, Cambridge MA 02142
Tel (617) 444-3000 SIC 7372 7374

■ RAYTHEON BBN TECHNOLOGIES CORP p 1210
10 Moulton St, Cambridge MA 02138
Tel (617) 873-3052 SIC 7371 7374 7373

■ TRIPADVISOR INC p 1482
400 1st Ave, Needham MA 02494
Tel (781) 800-5000 SIC 4724 7374

■ TRIPADVISOR LLC p 1482
400 1st Ave, Needham MA 02494
Tel (781) 800-5000 SIC 7374

NEWTON-WELLESLEY HEALTH CARE SYSTEM INC p 1039
2014 Washington St, Newton MA 02462
Tel (617) 243-6000 SIC 8741 7374 6512

ACTIFIO INC p 19
333 Wyman St Ste 30, Waltham MA 02451
Tel (781) 790-7676 SIC 7374

▲ LIONBRIDGE TECHNOLOGIES INC p 870
1050 Winter St Ste 2300, Waltham MA 02451
Tel (781) 434-6000 SIC 7389 7374 7371

PLEX SYSTEMS INC p 1156
900 Tower Dr Ste 1400, Troy MI 48098
Tel (248) 391-8001 SIC 7374

■ THOMSON REUTERS APPLICATIONS INC p 1450
610 Opperman Dr, Eagan MN 55123
Tel (651) 687-7000 SIC 7374

KROLL ONTRACK LLC p 830
9023 Columbine Rd, Eden Prairie MN 55347
Tel (952) 937-5161 SIC 7374 7372

■ OPTUMHEALTH CARE SOLUTIONS INC p 1090
6300 Olson Memorial Hwy, Golden Valley MN 55427
Tel (877) 801-3507 SIC 6324 7374 8999

CERIDIAN HCM HOLDING INC p 283
3311 E Old Shakopee Rd, Minneapolis MN 55425
Tel (952) 853-8100 SIC 6719 7374

NCS PEARSON INC p 1022
5601 Green Valley Dr # 220, Minneapolis MN 55437
Tel (952) 681-3000
SIC 3577 7372 7374 8748 7379

RBC CAPITAL MARKETS CORP p 1211
60 S 6th St Ste 700, Minneapolis MN 55402
Tel (612) 371-2711 SIC 7374

▲ SPS COMMERCE INC p 1362
333 S 7th St Ste 1000, Minneapolis MN 55402
Tel (612) 435-9400 SIC 7374 7372

■ WELLS FARGO SERVICES INC p 1591
255 2nd Ave S, Minneapolis MN 55401
Tel (612) 667-1234 SIC 7374

▲ DIGI INTERNATIONAL INC p 438
11001 Bren Rd E, Minnetonka MN 55343
Tel (952) 912-3444
SIC 3577 3575 7374 7371

MERRILL COMMUNICATIONS LLC p 950
1 Merrill Cir, Saint Paul MN 55108
Tel (651) 646-4501 SIC 7374 7389

AMERICAN CENTURY SERVICES CORP p 70
4500 Main St, Kansas City MO 64111
Tel (816) 531-5575 SIC 7374 8741

■ BROADRIDGE CUSTOMER COMMUNICATIONS LLC p 215
2600 Southwest Blvd, Kansas City MO 64108
Tel (816) 221-1234
SIC 7389 2759 7374 7331 2752 7336

▲ DST SYSTEMS INC p 458
333 W 11th St, Kansas City MO 64105
Tel (816) 435-1000
SIC 7374 7371 7331 7372

NATIONAL INFORMATION SOLUTIONS COOPERATIVE INC p 1013
1 Innovation Cir, Lake Saint Louis MO 63367
Tel (636) 755-2300 SIC 7374

SYSTEMS & SERVICES TECHNOLOGIES INC p 1418
4315 Pickett Rd, Saint Joseph MO 64503
Tel (800) 392-8308 SIC 7374

▲ CASS INFORMATION SYSTEMS INC p 263
12444 Powerscort Dr # 550, Saint Louis MO 63131
Tel (314) 506-5500 SIC 7389 7374 6029

CEQUEL DATA CENTERS LP p 283
520 Maryville Centre Dr # 300, Saint Louis MO 63141
Tel (314) 965-2020 SIC 7374

TIERPOINT LLC p 1453
520 Maryville Centre Dr # 300, Saint Louis MO 63141
Tel (314) 594-1300 SIC 7374

■ CSG SYSTEMS INC p 397
18020 Burt St, Elkhorn NE 68022
Tel (402) 431-7000 SIC 7374

■ INFORMATION TECHNOLOGY INC p 742
1345 Old Cheney Rd, Lincoln NE 68512
Tel (402) 423-2682
SIC 5045 7373 7374 7371

■ FIRST DATA RESOURCES LLC p 546
6855 Pacific St, Omaha NE 68106
Tel (303) 967-8000 SIC 7374 7389 7375

■ FIRST DATA TECHNOLOGIES INC p 546
6902 Pine St, Omaha NE 68106
Tel (402) 222-5679 SIC 7374

▲ WEST CORP p 1594
11808 Miracle Hills Dr, Omaha NE 68154
Tel (402) 963-1200
SIC 7389 7372 4813 7374

CAMP SYSTEMS INTERNATIONAL INC p 245
11 Continental Blvd Ste C, Merrimack NH 03054
Tel (603) 595-0030 SIC 7374

IGATE CORP p 730
100 Somerset Corp Blvd # 5000, Bridgewater NJ 08807
Tel (908) 219-8050 SIC 7371 7374 7389

AMERIQUEST INC p 83
457 Haddonfield Rd # 220, Cherry Hill NJ 08002
Tel (630) 925-7681 SIC 7374

▲ INNODATA INC p 744
3 University Plz, Hackensack NJ 07601
Tel (201) 371-8000 SIC 7374

DATAPIPE INC p 414
10 Exchange Pl, Jersey City NJ 07302
Tel (201) 792-1918 SIC 7374

PRINCETON INFORMATION LTD p 1177
100 Plaza Ten Ste 1101h, Jersey City NJ 07311
Tel (201) 604-9900 SIC 7374 7379

INFOCROSSING INC p 741
2 Christie Hts, Leonia NJ 07605
Tel (201) 840-4700 SIC 7374

■ AIG TECHNOLOGIES INC p 38
2 Peach Tree Hill Rd, Livingston NJ 07039
Tel (973) 597-0285 SIC 8742 6411 7374

■ **ADP FINANCIAL INFORMATION SERVICES INC** p 24
110 W Park Dr, Mount Laurel NJ 08054
Tel (856) 787-8000 SIC 7374

■ **INNOVEX INC** p 745
10 Waterview Blvd Ste 100, Parsippany NJ 07054
Tel (973) 257-4500 SIC 8734 8999 7374

▲ **AUTOMATIC DATA PROCESSING INC** p 134
1 Adp Blvd Ste 1, Roseland NJ 07068
Tel (973) 974-5000 SIC 7374

CGI AMS p 285
75 Livingston Ave Ste 202, Roseland NJ 07068
Tel (972) 788-0400
SIC 7379 8748 7374 7371

■ **CITI INVESTOR SERVICES INC** p 310
105 Eisenhower Pkwy Ste 2, Roseland NJ 07068
Tel (973) 461-2500 SIC 6411 7374

SHI INTERNATIONAL CORP p 1316
290 Davidson Ave, Somerset NJ 08873
Tel (732) 764-8888 SIC 7371 7374

■ **IMAGE SOLUTIONS INC** p 733
100 S Jefferson Rd # 300, Whippany NJ 07981
Tel (973) 560-0404 SIC 7374

AFTERDARKK MEDIA SOLUTIONS LLC p 33
271 Beach 135th St, Belle Harbor NY 11694
Tel (347) 244-6619 SIC 7374

▲ **SYNACOR INC** p 1414
40 La Riviere Dr Ste 300, Buffalo NY 14202
Tel (716) 853-1362 SIC 7371 7374

AJILON LLC p 41
175 Broadhollow Rd, Melville NY 11747
Tel (631) 844-7800 SIC 7379 8742 7374

▲ **BROADRIDGE FINANCIAL SOLUTIONS INC** p 215
5 Dakota Dr Ste 300, New Hyde Park NY 11042
Tel (516) 472-5400 SIC 7374 7372

■ **BROADRIDGE OUTPUT SOLUTIONS INC** p 215
5 Dakota Dr Ste 300, New Hyde Park NY 11042
Tel (516) 472-5400 SIC 7374

DEALERTRACK INC p 420
1111 Marcus Ave Ste M04, New Hyde Park NY 11042
Tel (516) 734-3600 SIC 7374

▲ **NEWTEK BUSINESS SERVICES INC** p 1039
1981 Marcus Ave Ste C130, New Hyde Park NY 11042
Tel (212) 356-9500 SIC 6153 7374 4813

■ **AOL INC** p 94
770 Broadway Fl 4, New York NY 10003
Tel (212) 652-6400 SIC 7374

■ **CERBERUS LP LLC** p 283
875 3rd Ave Fl 11, New York NY 10022
Tel (212) 891-2100 SIC 7389 7374

IPSOFT INC p 764
17 State St Fl 14, New York NY 10004
Tel (888) 477-6388
SIC 7376 7363 7374 8742

IQOR HOLDINGS INC p 764
1 Progress Plz, New York NY 10017
Tel (866) 657-2057 SIC 7374

KDDI AMERICA INC p 806
825 3rd Ave Fl 3, New York NY 10022
Tel (212) 295-1200
SIC 4813 7375 7374 8743

MARKIT GROUP LIMITED p 908
620 8th Ave Fl 35, New York NY 10018
Tel (212) 931-4900 SIC 7374

NTT DATA INTERNATIONAL LLC p 1066
45 W 36th St Fl 7, New York NY 10018
Tel (212) 355-5585 SIC 7374

■ **R/GA MEDIA GROUP INC** p 1203
450 W 33rd St Fl 12, New York NY 10001
Tel (212) 946-4000
SIC 7374 7336 7375 7311

RELX INC p 1222
230 Park Ave, New York NY 10169
Tel (212) 309-8100
SIC 2721 2731 7389 7374 8748

SHUTTERSTOCK INC p 1319
350 5th Ave Fl 21, New York NY 10118
Tel (646) 766-1855 SIC 7374 7335

THOMAS PUBLISHING CO LLC p 1449
5 Penn Plz Fl 9, New York NY 10001
Tel (212) 695-0500
SIC 2741 2721 7374 7331

TRIDENT PRIVATE HOLDINGS I LLC p 1479
601 Lexington Ave 59thf, New York NY 10022
Tel (212) 231-0095 SIC 4813 7374

VERITAS CAPITAL FUND II L P p 1549
590 Madison Ave Ste 3501, New York NY 10022
Tel (212) 415-6700 SIC 8742 7374

VNU MARKETING INFORMATION INC p 1564
770 Broadway Fl 15, New York NY 10003
Tel (646) 654-5011
SIC 8732 6282 7374 5045

SANDATA HOLDINGS INC p 1278
26 Harbor Park Dr, Port Washington NY 11050
Tel (516) 484-4400 SIC 7374 7373

CARESTREAM HEALTH INC p 255
150 Verona St, Rochester NY 14608
Tel (585) 627-1800 SIC 8011 7374

■ **GLOBAL CROSSING BANDWIDTH INC** p 616
200 Meridian Centre Blvd # 130, Rochester NY 14618
Tel (212) 920-8201 SIC 4813 7373 7374

ERGONOMIC GROUP INC p 507
609 Cantiague Rock Rd # 3, Westbury NY 11590
Tel (516) 746-7777
SIC 5045 7373 7374 7376 7379

GUTHY-RENKER FULFILLMENT SERVICES LLC p 648
1845 Brevard Rd, Arden NC 28704
Tel (828) 684-4300 SIC 7389 7374

TRIAD GROUP INC p 1478
623 W Main St, Yadkinville NC 27055
Tel (336) 679-8852 SIC 8051 5047 7374

▲ **CINCINNATI BELL INC** p 307
221 E 4th St Ste 700, Cincinnati OH 45202
Tel (513) 397-9900
SIC 4813 7373 7374 7379

▲ **CONVERGYS CORP** p 365
201 E 4th St, Cincinnati OH 45202
Tel (513) 723-7000 SIC 7374 7373

A W S INC p 7
1275 Lakeside Ave E, Cleveland OH 44114
Tel (216) 861-0250
SIC 8331 7374 7334 7331

MIDWEST TAPE LLC p 968
1417 Timber Wolf Dr, Holland OH 43528
Tel (419) 868-9370
SIC 7822 5099 8741 7389 5961 7374

MRI SOFTWARE LLC p 996
28925 Fountain Pkwy, Solon OH 44139
Tel (800) 327-8770 SIC 7374 7371 6531

■ **VANTIV HOLDING LLC** p 1544
8500 Governors Hill Dr, Symmes Twp OH 45249
Tel (513) 358-6192 SIC 7374

■ **VANTIV LLC** p 1544
8500 Governors Hill Dr, Symmes Twp OH 45249
Tel (877) 713-5964 SIC 7374

▲ **RADISYS CORP** p 1204
5435 Ne Dawson Creek Dr, Hillsboro OR 97124
Tel (503) 615-1100 SIC 3825 7374 7372

TUALITY HEALTHCARE FOUNDATION INC p 1490
335 Se 8th Ave, Hillsboro OR 97123
Tel (503) 681-1850
SIC 8082 7374 6512 5999 7359

SDI INC p 1295
1414 Radcliffe St Ste 300, Bristol PA 19007
Tel (215) 633-1900
SIC 7374 7389 8711 8748

GANNETT FLEMING AFFILIATES INC p 590
207 Senate Ave, Camp Hill PA 17011
Tel (717) 763-7211 SIC 8711 7374 6512

1&1 INTERNET INC p 1
701 Lee Rd Ste 300, Chesterbrook PA 19087
Tel (877) 461-2631 SIC 7374 4813 4822

■ **FIS DATA SYSTEMS INC** p 551
200 Campus Dr, Collegeville PA 19426
Tel (484) 582-2000 SIC 7374 7372

DATABANK IMX LLC p 414
620 Freedom Business Ctr, King Of Prussia PA 19406
Tel (610) 233-0251 SIC 7374 5044

PRWT SERVICES INC p 1187
1835 Market St Ste 800, Philadelphia PA 19103
Tel (215) 563-7698 SIC 7374

QLIKTECHNOLOGIES INC p 1195
150 N Radnor Chester Rd, Radnor PA 19087
Tel (866) 616-4960 SIC 7374 7371

■ **FIS EPROCESS INTELLIGENCE LLC** p 551
680 E Swedesford Rd, Wayne PA 19087
Tel (888) 601-2361 SIC 7374 5045

■ **FIS SG LLC** p 551
680 E Swedesford Rd, Wayne PA 19087
Tel (484) 582-5400 SIC 7372 7374

SUNGARD AVAILABILITY SERVICES LP p 1402
680 E Swedesford Rd, Wayne PA 19087
Tel (484) 582-2000 SIC 7374

■ **SUNGARD BUSINESS SYSTEMS LLC** p 1402
680 E Swedesford Rd, Wayne PA 19087
Tel (484) 582-2000 SIC 7374 5734

■ **SUNGARD CAPITAL CORP II** p 1402
680 E Swedesford Rd, Wayne PA 19087
Tel (484) 582-2000 SIC 7372 7374

■ **SUNGARD HOLDCO LLC** p 1402
680 E Swedesford Rd, Wayne PA 19087
Tel (484) 582-2000 SIC 7372 7374

■ **SUNGARD HOLDING CORP** p 1402
680 E Swedesford Rd, Wayne PA 19087
Tel (888) 332-2564 SIC 7372 7374

IGT GLOBAL SOLUTIONS CORP p 730
10 Memorial Blvd, Providence RI 02903
Tel (401) 392-1000
SIC 7999 3575 7372 7378 2752 7374

J M SMITH CORP p 771
101 W Saint John St # 305, Spartanburg SC 29306
Tel (864) 542-9419 SIC 5122 7374

TOLT SOLUTIONS INC p 1459
3550 Rutherford Rd, Taylors SC 29687
Tel (864) 322-4200
SIC 8748 7379 7374 7373

COMDATA HOLDINGS CORP p 344
5301 Maryland Way, Brentwood TN 37027
Tel (615) 370-7000 SIC 7374 7389 7375

COMDATA NETWORK INC p 344
5301 Maryland Way, Brentwood TN 37027
Tel (615) 370-7405 SIC 7374

MMODAL INC p 979
5000 Meridian Blvd # 200, Franklin TN 37067
Tel (888) 840-4050 SIC 7374

■ **NATIONAL BANK OF COMMERCE** p 1010
1 Commerce Sq, Memphis TN 38103
Tel (901) 523-3434
SIC 6021 6211 7374 6712

BEAGLE PARENT CORP p 165
3055 Lebanon Pike # 1000, Nashville TN 37214
Tel (615) 932-3000 SIC 7374

CHANGE HEALTHCARE HOLDINGS INC p 288
3055 Lebanon Pike # 1000, Nashville TN 37214
Tel (615) 932-3000 SIC 7374

CHANGE HEALTHCARE OPERATIONS LLC p 288
3055 Lebanon Pike # 1000, Nashville TN 37214
Tel (615) 932-3000 SIC 7374 8741 8099

HCA INFORMATION SERVICES INC p 672
2555 Park Plz, Nashville TN 37203
Tel (615) 344-9551 SIC 7374

MEDIFAX-EDI LLC p 938
26 Century Blvd, Nashville TN 37214
Tel (615) 932-3226 SIC 7374 7389

■ **MBNA TECHNOLOGY INC** p 925
16001 Dallas Pkwy, Addison TX 75001
Tel (972) 233-7101 SIC 7374 6282

ATOS ORIGIN INC p 128
18062 Fm 529 Rd Ste 215, Cypress TX 77433
Tel (914) 881-3000
SIC 7373 7374 7376 7379

■ **ACS ENTERPRISE SOLUTIONS INC** p 19
2828 N Haskell Ave, Dallas TX 75204
Tel (214) 841-6111 SIC 7374

■ **ACS IMAGE SOLUTIONS INC** p 19
3988 N Central Expy, Dallas TX 75204
Tel (214) 818-3000
SIC 7389 5112 7374 7375

HITACHI CONSULTING CORP p 696
14643 Dallas Pkwy Ste 800, Dallas TX 75254
Tel (214) 665-7000 SIC 7379 7374

■ **MATCH GROUP INC** p 919
8750 N Cntl Expy Ste 1400, Dallas TX 75231
Tel (214) 576-9352 SIC 7299 7374

MODEST BILLIONAIRES LLC p 981
3815 Martha Ln, Dallas TX 75229
Tel (972) 672-0755 SIC 7374 7371 7389

PERSEUS HOLDING CORP p 1137
8350 N Central Expy, Dallas TX 75206
Tel (214) 234-4000 SIC 7374

■ **SAFEGUARD BUSINESS SYSTEMS INC** p 1266
8585 N Stemmons Fwy, Dallas TX 75247
Tel (214) 640-3916
SIC 7374 2759 5112 5045

SOFTLAYER TECHNOLOGIES INC p 1337
14001 Dallas Pkwy M100, Dallas TX 75240
Tel (214) 442-0600 SIC 7374 4813

■ **XEROX BUSINESS SERVICES LLC** p 1631
2828 N Haskell Ave Fl 1, Dallas TX 75204
Tel (214) 841-6111 SIC 7374 7375 7389

■ **XEROX COMMERCIAL SOLUTIONS LLC** p 1631
2828 N Haskell Ave Fl 9, Dallas TX 75204
Tel (214) 841-6111 SIC 7374

DATAMARK INC p 414
123 W Mills Ave Ste 400, El Paso TX 79901
Tel (915) 778-1944 SIC 7374

GENPACT p 604
2004 Bassett Ave Pmb 2500, El Paso TX 79901
Tel (915) 225-2500 SIC 7374

AMERICAN INFOSOURCE LP p 74
5847 San Felipe St # 1200, Houston TX 77057
Tel (713) 532-8977 SIC 7374

GEOKINETICS INC p 606
1500 Citywest Blvd # 800, Houston TX 77042
Tel (713) 850-7600 SIC 1382 7374

■ **TELECHECK SERVICES INC** p 1434
5251 Westheimr Rd B100, Houston TX 77056
Tel (713) 331-7600 SIC 7389 7374 6153

CORPSOURCE HOLDINGS LLC p 372
2701 E Grauwyler Rd, Irving TX 75061
Tel (866) 321-5854 SIC 7375 7334 7374

■ **HEALTH MANAGEMENT SYSTEMS INC** p 675
5615 High Point Dr # 100, Irving TX 75038
Tel (214) 453-3000 SIC 7374 7372

HOV SERVICES INC p 712
2701 E Grauwyler Rd, Irving TX 75061
Tel (248) 837-7100
SIC 7374 7334 7389 2752 7331 7379

MOSAIC SALES SOLUTIONS US OPERATING CO LLC p 992
220 Las Colinas Blvd E, Irving TX 75039
Tel (972) 870-4800 SIC 8742 8743 7374

SOURCECORP INC p 1342
2701 E Grauwyler Rd, Irving TX 75061
Tel (866) 321-5854 SIC 7375 7334 7374

ETECH GLOBAL SERVICES LLC p 511
1903 Berry Dr, Nacogdoches TX 75964
Tel (936) 559-2200
SIC 7389 8742 7373 8741 8721 7374

■ **EDS ELECTRONIC FINANCIAL SERVICES INC** p 478
5400 Legacy Dr, Plano TX 75024
Tel (972) 378-6985 SIC 7374

■ **HP ENTERPRISE SERVICES LLC** p 714
5400 Legacy Dr, Plano TX 75024
Tel (972) 604-6000 SIC 7374 7371 8742

RACKSPACE HOSTING INC p 1203
1 Fanatical Pl, San Antonio TX 78218
Tel (210) 312-4000
SIC 7371 7374 7382 4813

■ **SABRE GLBL INC** p 1264
3150 Sabre Dr, Southlake TX 76092
Tel (682) 605-1000
SIC 7375 7371 7374 7389 8748

FAIRFIELD INDUSTRIES INC p 525
1111 Gillingham Ln, Sugar Land TX 77478
Tel (281) 275-7627
SIC 7374 3829 1382 3429

ANCESTRY.COM INC p 89
1300 W Traverse Pkwy, Lehi UT 84043
Tel (801) 705-7000 SIC 7374

ANCESTRY.COM LLC p 89
1300 W Traverse Pkwy, Lehi UT 84043
Tel (801) 705-7000 SIC 7374

ANCESTRY.COM HOLDINGS LLC p 89
360 W 4800 N, Provo UT 84604
Tel (801) 705-7000 SIC 7374 7375

■ **ACS COMMERCIAL SOLUTIONS INC** p 18
510 W Parkland Dr, Sandy UT 84070
Tel (801) 567-5000 SIC 7374 7389

DEALER DOT COM INC p 419
1 Howard St, Burlington VT 05401
Tel (888) 894-8989 SIC 7374

AIRLINES REPORTING CORP p 40
3000 Wilson Blvd Ste 300, Arlington VA 22201
Tel (703) 816-8000 SIC 7389 6099 7374

■ **SNL FINANCIAL LC** p 1335
1 Snl Plz, Charlottesville VA 22902
Tel (434) 977-1600 SIC 7374

AIRLINE TARIFF PUBLISHING CO p 40
45005 Aviation Dr Ste 400, Dulles VA 20166
Tel (703) 661-7400 SIC 2721 7374 2731

GIESECKE & DEVRIENT MOBILE SECURITY AMERICA INC p 611
45925 Horseshoe Dr, Dulles VA 20166
Tel (703) 480-2100
SIC 7382 3089 5045 7374

■ **SIGNAL SOLUTIONS LLC** p 1322
3211 Jermantown Rd # 700, Fairfax VA 22030
Tel (703) 205-0500
SIC 8711 7379 7374 4813 7373 8731

■ **VANGENT INC** p 1543
3211 Jermantown Rd, Fairfax VA 22030
Tel (703) 995-2666
SIC 8748 7371 7372 7373 7374 7376

■ **CSRA LLC** p 398
3170 Fairview Park Dr, Falls Church VA 22042
Tel (703) 876-1000
SIC 7371 8733 7376 7374 7379

■ **MAGELLAN MEDICAID ADMINISTRATION INC** p 895
11013 W Broad St Ste 500, Glen Allen VA 23060
Tel (804) 548-0100
SIC 7374 8093 6411 8741

APEX DATA SERVICES INC p 96
198 Van Buren St Ste 200, Herndon VA 20170
Tel (703) 709-3000 SIC 7374

ELECTRONIC WARFARE ASSOCIATES INC p 486
13873 Park Center Rd # 500, Herndon VA 20171
Tel (703) 904-5700
SIC 7373 7374 3672 3699 3643 3441

■ **NETWORK SOLUTIONS LLC** p 1028
13861 Sunrise Valley Dr # 300, Herndon VA 20171
Tel (703) 668-4600
SIC 7375 7389 4813 7374

■ **NTT DATA SERVICES FEDERAL GOVERNMENT INC** p 1066
13880 Dulles Corner Ln, Herndon VA 20171
Tel (703) 289-8000 SIC 8711 7373 7374

PARAGON SYSTEMS INC p 1113
13655 Dulles Tech Dr # 100, Herndon VA 20171
Tel (703) 263-7176 SIC 7381 7382 7374

■ **DYNCORP** p 465
1700 Old Meadow Rd, Mc Lean VA 22102
Tel (571) 722-0210
SIC 7373 7371 7374 7375 8744 4581

▲ **SCIENCE APPLICATIONS INTERNATIONAL CORP** p 1292
1710 Saic Dr Ste B, Mc Lean VA 22102
Tel (703) 676-6942 SIC 7373 7374

DOMINION ENTERPRISES p 449
150 Granby St Ste 150, Norfolk VA 23510
Tel (757) 351-7000 SIC 7374 2721 2741

TNS INC p 1458
10740 Parkridge Blvd # 100, Reston VA 20191
Tel (703) 453-8300 SIC 4813 7374

TRANSACTION NETWORK SERVICES INC p 1470
10740 Parkridge Blvd # 100, Reston VA 20191
Tel (703) 453-8300 SIC 4813 7389 7374

▲ **COMPUTER SCIENCES CORP** p 353
1775 Tysons Blvd, Tysons VA 22102
Tel (703) 245-9675
SIC 7376 7374 7379 7373 7323

▲ **BLUCORA INC** p 190
10900 Ne 8th St Ste 800, Bellevue WA 98004
Tel (425) 201-6100 SIC 7375 7374

VERTAFORE INC p 1552
11724 Ne 195th St, Bothell WA 98011
Tel (425) 402-1000 SIC 7374

EAGLE GROUP SYSTEMS INC p 468
230 Grant Rd, East Wenatchee WA 98802
Tel (509) 665-0319
SIC 4214 4119 4522 7373 7374 8741

SCHREINER CORP p 1290
28210 Se 440th St, Enumclaw WA 98022
Tel (253) 736-5774 SIC 7374

▲ **RIGHTSIDE GROUP LTD** p 1234
5808 Lake Washington Blvd, Kirkland WA 98033
Tel (425) 298-2500 SIC 7374 7375

■ **FISERV CIR INC** p 551
255 Fiserv Dr, Brookfield WI 53045
Tel (262) 879-5000 SIC 7374 7372 7373

▲ **FISERV INC** p 551
255 Fiserv Dr, Brookfield WI 53045
Tel (262) 879-5000 SIC 7374 7371

■ **FISERV SOLUTIONS LLC** p 551
255 Fiserv Dr, Brookfield WI 53045
Tel (262) 879-5000 SIC 7374 2754 5084

F DOHMEN CO p 522
190 N Milwaukee St, Milwaukee WI 53202
Tel (414) 299-4913 SIC 5122 5045 7374

■ **METAVANTE CORP** p 953
4900 W Brown Deer Rd, Milwaukee WI 53223
Tel (904) 438-6000 SIC 7374 8742 6153

SC DATA CENTER INC p 1285
1112 7th Ave, Monroe WI 53566
Tel (608) 328-8600 SIC 7374

CS ESTATE INC p 397
N7w22025 Johnson Dr, Waukesha WI 53186
Tel (262) 953-3500 SIC 3841 3663 7374

SIC 7375 Information Retrieval Svcs

EBSCO INDUSTRIES INC p 474
5724 Highway 280 E, Birmingham AL 35242
Tel (205) 991-6600
SIC 7389 2782 3949 7375 2721 6552

ENTERPRISE CONSULTING SOLUTIONS INC p 502
15458 N 28th Ave, Phoenix AZ 85053
Tel (623) 207-5600 SIC 7375

▲ **LIMELIGHT NETWORKS INC** p 866
222 S Mill Ave Ste 800, Tempe AZ 85281
Tel (602) 850-5000 SIC 7372 7375

▲ **ACXIOM CORP** p 21
601 E 3rd St, Little Rock AR 72201
Tel (501) 252-1000 SIC 7374 7375 7371

INFONET SERVICES CORP p 741
2160 E Grand Ave, El Segundo CA 90245
Tel (310) 335-2859 SIC 4813 7373 7375

▲ AUTOBYTEL INC p 133
18872 Macarthur Blvd # 200, Irvine CA 92612
Tel (949) 225-4500 SIC 7375

■ CORELOGIC SOLUTIONS LLC p 369
40 Pacifica Ste 900, Irvine CA 92618
Tel (949) 214-1000 SIC 7375

HIRERIGHT LLC p 695
3349 Michelson Dr Ste 150, Irvine CA 92612
Tel (949) 428-5800 SIC 7375 7374

ACCESS INFORMATION MANAGEMENT SHARED SERVICES LLC p 14
6818 Patterson Pass Rd A, Livermore CA 94550
Tel (925) 461-5352 SIC 7375

▲ PERFORMANT FINANCIAL CORP p 1135
333 N Canyons Pkwy # 100, Livermore CA 94551
Tel (925) 960-4800 SIC 7375

RETRIEVEX ACQUISITION CORP II p 1229
6818 Patterson Pass Rd, Livermore CA 94550
Tel (925) 583-0100 SIC 4226 7375

▲ FACEBOOK INC p 523
1 Hacker Way Bldg 10, Menlo Park CA 94025
Tel (650) 543-4800 SIC 7375

■ GOOGLE INC p 625
1600 Amphitheatre Pkwy, Mountain View CA 94043
Tel (650) 253-0000 SIC 4813 7375

■ GOOGLE INTERNATIONAL LLC p 625
1600 Amphitheatre Pkwy, Mountain View CA 94043
Tel (650) 253-0000 SIC 4813 7375

▲ LINKEDIN CORP p 869
2029 Stierlin Ct Ste 200, Mountain View CA 94043
Tel (650) 687-3600 SIC 7375

VERITAS TECHNOLOGIES LLC p 1550
500 E Middlefield Rd, Mountain View CA 94043
Tel (650) 933-1000 SIC 7371 7375

■ IAC SEARCH & MEDIA INC p 725
555 12th St Ste 500, Oakland CA 94607
Tel (510) 985-7400 SIC 7375

■ VMWARE INC p 1563
3401 Hillview Ave, Palo Alto CA 94304
Tel (650) 427-1000 SIC 7371 7375

■ GTT COMMUNICATIONS (MP) INC p 644
6800 Koll Center Pkwy # 200, Pleasanton CA 94566
Tel (925) 201-2500 SIC 4813 7375

■ DIGITAL INSIGHT CORP p 439
1300 Seaport Blvd Ste 300, Redwood City CA 94063
Tel (818) 879-1010 SIC 7375 7372 7371

■ MCCLATCHY NEWSPAPERS INC p 926
2100 Q St, Sacramento CA 95816
Tel (916) 321-1000 SIC 2711 2759 7375

■ CBS INTERACTIVE INC p 269
235 2nd St, San Francisco CA 94105
Tel (415) 344-2000 SIC 7319 7375 4832

PINTEREST INC p 1150
808 Brannan St, San Francisco CA 94103
Tel (650) 561-5407 SIC 7375

▲ SALESFORCE.COM INC p 1272
1 Market Ste 300, San Francisco CA 94105
Tel (415) 901-7000 SIC 7372 7375

▲ TWITTER INC p 1495
1355 Market St Ste 900, San Francisco CA 94103
Tel (415) 222-9670 SIC 7375

▲ YELP INC p 1635
140 New Montgomery St # 900, San Francisco CA 94105
Tel (415) 908-3801 SIC 7375

EDMUNDS HOLDING CO p 478
1620 26th St Ste 400s, Santa Monica CA 90404
Tel (310) 309-6300 SIC 7375

▲ YAHOO INC p 1633
701 First Ave, Sunnyvale CA 94089
Tel (408) 349-3300 SIC 7373 7375

■ CONVERSANT LLC p 365
30699 Russell Ranch Rd # 250, Westlake Village CA 91362
Tel (818) 575-4500 SIC 7375 4813

■ REACHLOCAL INC p 1213
21700 Oxnard St Ste 1600, Woodland Hills CA 91367
Tel (818) 274-0260 SIC 7311 7375

■ QWEST CYBERSOLUTIONS LLC p 1201
1801 California St # 3800, Denver CO 80202
Tel (303) 296-2787 SIC 7375

IHS GLOBAL INC p 731
15 Inverness Way E, Englewood CO 80112
Tel (303) 790-0600
SIC 7299 8732 8748 7375 7373

IHS HOLDING INC p 731
15 Inverness Way E, Englewood CO 80112
Tel (303) 790-0600
SIC 7299 8732 8748 7375

IHS INC p 731
15 Inverness Way E, Englewood CO 80112
Tel (303) 790-0600
SIC 7299 8732 8748 7375

FIRST DATA HOLDINGS INC p 546
5775 Dtc Blvd Ste 100, Greenwood Village CO 80111
Tel (303) 967-8000
SIC 6099 7375 7389 6153

DATTO INC p 414
101 Merritt 7 Ste 7, Norwalk CT 06851
Tel (203) 665-6423 SIC 7375

▲ PRICELINE GROUP INC p 1174
800 Connecticut Ave 3w01, Norwalk CT 06854
Tel (203) 299-8000 SIC 4724 7375

LEXISNEXIS RISK ASSETS INC p 859
1105 N Market St Ste 501, Wilmington DE 19801
Tel (770) 752-6000
SIC 6411 7375 8721 7323

■ COGENT COMMUNICATIONS INC p 334
2450 N St Nw, Washington DC 20037
Tel (202) 295-4200 SIC 4813 7375

▲ COSTAR GROUP INC p 374
1331 L St Nw Ste 2, Washington DC 20005
Tel (202) 346-6500 SIC 7375

QUICKTEST INC p 1199
1061 E Indiantown Rd # 300, Jupiter FL 33477
Tel (561) 748-0931 SIC 7375

TELEFONICA USA p 1434
1111 Brickell Ave # 1000, Miami FL 33131
Tel (305) 925-5300 SIC 7375 7374 4813

CIOX HEALTH LLC p 308
925 North Point Pkwy # 350, Alpharetta GA 30005
Tel (800) 367-1500 SIC 7375

■ ELAVON INC p 483
2 Cncourse Pkwy Ste 800, Atlanta GA 30328
Tel (678) 731-5000 SIC 7375 7374

■ FIRST DATA MERCHANT SERVICES CORP p 546
5565 Glenridge Connector, Atlanta GA 30342
Tel (404) 890-3000
SIC 7374 7389 7375 6153 6099

▲ INTERNAP CORP p 754
1 Ravinia Dr Ste 1300, Atlanta GA 30346
Tel (404) 302-9700 SIC 7373 7375

▲ MORNINGSTAR INC p 989
22 W Washington St # 600, Chicago IL 60602
Tel (312) 696-6000 SIC 6282 6722 7375

CDS GLOBAL INC p 271
1901 Bell Ave Ste 19, Des Moines IA 50315
Tel (866) 897-7987 SIC 7389 7375 7374

QTS REALTY TRUST INC p 1195
12851 Foster St, Overland Park KS 66213
Tel (913) 814-9988 SIC 7375 7374

▲ WEX INC p 1603
97 Darling Ave, South Portland ME 04106
Tel (207) 773-8171 SIC 7389 7375

MIL CORP p 968
4000 Mitchellville Rd R, Bowie MD 20716
Tel (301) 805-8500
SIC 7371 7373 7374 7375 7376 8711

UNITED COMMUNICATIONS GROUP LIMITED PARTNERSHIP p 1507
9737 Washingtonian Blvd # 500, Gaithersburg MD 20878
Tel (301) 287-2700 SIC 2721 7375

▲ KEYW HOLDING CORP p 816
7740 Milestone Pkwy # 400, Hanover MD 21076
Tel (443) 733-1600
SIC 7373 7372 8731 7375

▲ TECHTARGET INC p 1432
275 Grove St Ste 1-150, Auburndale MA 02466
Tel (617) 431-9200 SIC 7375

IGLOO HOLDINGS CORP p 730
32 Crosby Dr, Bedford MA 01730
Tel (781) 687-8500 SIC 6289 7375

IGLOO INTERMEDIATE CORP p 730
32 Crosby Dr, Bedford MA 01730
Tel (781) 687-8500 SIC 6289 7375

■ INTERACTIVE DATA CORP p 751
32 Crosby Dr, Bedford MA 01730
Tel (781) 687-8500 SIC 6289 7375

▲ IRON MOUNTAIN INC p 764
1 Federal St Fl 7, Boston MA 02110
Tel (617) 535-4766
SIC 4226 8741 7375 6798

COPYRIGHT CLEARANCE CENTER INC p 368
222 Rosewood Dr Fl 10, Danvers MA 01923
Tel (978) 750-8400 SIC 6794 7375

EBSCO PUBLISHING INC p 474
10 Estes St, Ipswich MA 01938
Tel (978) 356-6500
SIC 2741 7375 2731 2721

WORLDWIDE TECHSERVICES LLC p 1626
836 North St Unit 5, Tewksbury MA 01876
Tel (978) 848-9000 SIC 7373 7375

SALARY.COM LLC p 1272
610 Lincoln St Ste 200, Waltham MA 02451
Tel (781) 989-9488 SIC 7371 7375

PROQUEST LLC p 1184
789 E Eisenhower Pkwy, Ann Arbor MI 48108
Tel (734) 761-4700 SIC 7375

GALE GROUP INC p 589
27500 Drake Rd, Farmington Hills MI 48331
Tel (248) 699-4253 SIC 7375

REVSPRING INC p 1229
29241 Beck Rd, Wixom MI 48393
Tel (248) 567-7300 SIC 7371 7375

■ WEST PUBLISHING CORP p 1595
610 620 Opperman Dr, Eagan MN 55123
Tel (651) 687-7000 SIC 7375

■ OPTUMINSIGHT INC p 1091
11000 Optum Cir, Eden Prairie MN 55344
Tel (952) 833-7100
SIC 7371 7375 8742 8741

DOLAN LLC p 447
222 S 9th St Ste 2300, Minneapolis MN 55402
Tel (612) 317-9420
SIC 7375 2741 2711 2752

BIRCH TELECOM INC p 185
2323 Grand Blvd Ste 925, Kansas City MO 64108
Tel (816) 300-3000 SIC 4813 7375 4812

■ SAVVIS COMMUNICATIONS CORP p 1284
1 Solutions Pkwy, Town And Country MO 63017
Tel (314) 628-7000 SIC 4813 7375

SAVVIS INC p 1284
1 Solutions Pkwy, Town And Country MO 63017
Tel (314) 628-7000
SIC 7373 7379 4813 7375

■ FIRST DATA RESOURCES LLC p 546
6855 Pacific St, Omaha NE 68106
Tel (303) 967-8000 SIC 7374 7389 7375

TELVENT DTN LLC p 1435
9110 W Dodge Rd Ste 100, Omaha NE 68114
Tel (402) 390-2328 SIC 7375

■ AT&T CORP p 123
1 At&T Way, Bedminster NJ 07921
Tel (800) 403-3302 SIC 4813 4822 7375

■ INSURANCE SERVICES OFFICE INC p 748
545 Washington Blvd Fl 12, Jersey City NJ 07310
Tel (201) 469-2000 SIC 7375

ISO SERVICES INC p 767
545 Washington Blvd Fl 12, Jersey City NJ 07310
Tel (201) 469-2000 SIC 7375

▲ VERISK ANALYTICS INC p 1549
545 Washington Blvd, Jersey City NJ 07310
Tel (201) 469-2000 SIC 7375

■ FACTIVA INC p 523
4300 N Rt 1 820 Ridge Rd, Monmouth Junction NJ 08852
Tel (609) 627-2000 SIC 7375

TRAVELPORT LLC p 1474
6 Campus Dr Ste 1, Parsippany NJ 07054
Tel (770) 563-7400 SIC 7375

RCN TELECOM SERVICES LLC p 1212
650 College Rd E Ste 3100, Princeton NJ 08540
Tel (609) 452-8197 SIC 4841 7375 4813

■ COMCAST CABLEVISION OF NEW JERSEY INC p 343
800 Rahway Ave, Union NJ 07083
Tel (908) 206-8640 SIC 4841 1731 7375

MANNING & NAPIER ADVISORS LLC p 902
290 Woodcliff Dr Ste 300, Fairport NY 14450
Tel (800) 551-0224 SIC 6282 8742 7375

■ PAETEC COMMUNICATIONS INC p 1107
600 Willowbrook Office Pa, Fairport NY 14450
Tel (585) 340-2500 SIC 4813 7375 7372

ADVENTITY INC p 27
444 Park Ave S Ste 1202, New York NY 10016
Tel (212) 404-2468 SIC 7375 8742 8732

CORPORATE RISK HOLDINGS LLC p 372
600 3rd Ave Fl 4, New York NY 10016
Tel (212) 896-2001
SIC 6719 8748 7375 7389

▲ DHI GROUP INC p 435
1040 Avenue Of The Amrcas, New York NY 10018
Tel (212) 725-6550 SIC 7361 4813 7375

▲ IAC/INTERACTIVECORP p 725
555 W 18th St, New York NY 10011
Tel (212) 314-7300 SIC 7372 7375 5961

■ INTRALINKS INC p 760
150 E 42nd St Fl 8, New York NY 10017
Tel (212) 543-7700 SIC 4899 7375

KDDI AMERICA INC p 806
825 3rd Ave Fl 3, New York NY 10022
Tel (212) 295-1200
SIC 4813 7375 7374 8743

▲ NEW YORK TIMES CO p 1036
620 8th Ave, New York NY 10018
Tel (212) 556-1234
SIC 2711 4832 4833 7383 7375

▲ NEWS CORP p 1039
1211 Ave Of The Americas, New York NY 10036
Tel (212) 416-3400 SIC 2711 2731 7375

OGILVY & MATHER WORLDWIDE INC p 1076
636 11th Ave, New York NY 10036
Tel (212) 237-4000
SIC 7311 7812 7375 8742

PENTON MEDIA INC p 1132
1166 Avenue Of The Americ, New York NY 10036
Tel (212) 204-4200
SIC 2721 7389 7313 7375

■ R/GA MEDIA GROUP INC p 1203
450 W 33rd St Fl 12, New York NY 10001
Tel (212) 946-4000
SIC 7374 7336 7375 7311

RAKUTEN MARKETING LLC p 1206
215 Park Ave S Fl 9, New York NY 10003
Tel (646) 943-8200 SIC 8742 7375

STERLING INFOSYSTEMS INC p 1387
1 State St Fl Plaza24, New York NY 10004
Tel (800) 899-2272 SIC 7375 7381

■ THOMSON REUTERS (MARKETS) LLC p 1450
3 Times Sq Lbby Mailroom, New York NY 10036
Tel (646) 223-4000 SIC 7375

▲ WEBMD HEALTH CORP p 1586
395 Hudson St, New York NY 10014
Tel (212) 624-3700 SIC 7375 4813

■ WEBMD LLC p 1586
395 Hudson St Lbby 3, New York NY 10014
Tel (212) 624-3700 SIC 7375

▲ PREMIER INC p 1170
13034 Balntyn Corp Pl, Charlotte NC 28277
Tel (704) 357-0022 SIC 8742 7375

■ CONSTELLA GROUP LLC p 360
2605 Meridian Pkwy # 200, Durham NC 27713
Tel (919) 544-8500
SIC 7371 8742 7375 8748 8731 8071

TOSHIBA GLOBAL COMMERCE SOLUTIONS INC p 1462
3901 S Miami Blvd, Durham NC 27703
Tel (984) 444-7153 SIC 8742 7375

VRUSH INDUSTRIES INC p 1566
118 N Wrenn St, High Point NC 27260
Tel (336) 886-7700
SIC 5045 5021 7379 3469 5712 7375

▲ E W SCRIPPS CO p 467
312 Walnut St Ste 2800, Cincinnati OH 45202
Tel (513) 977-3000
SIC 4841 2711 4833 7375

OCLC ONLINE COMPUTER LIBRARY CENTER INCORPORATE p 1074
6565 Kilgour Pl, Dublin OH 43017
Tel (614) 764-6000 SIC 7375

LEXISNEXIS GROUP p 859
9443 Springboro Pike, Miamisburg OH 45342
Tel (937) 865-6800 SIC 7375 2741

OKLAHOMA PUBLISHING CO OF OKLAHOMA p 1080
9000 N Brdwy, Oklahoma City OK 73114
Tel (405) 475-3311
SIC 2711 1311 6512 7375 2752

RADIAL INC p 1204
935 1st Ave, King Of Prussia PA 19406
Tel (610) 491-7000
SIC 3149 5139 5091 5136 5137 7375

VERTICAL SCREEN INC p 1552
251 Veterans Way, Warminster PA 18974
Tel (215) 396-9870 SIC 7375

COMDATA HOLDINGS CORP p 344
5301 Maryland Way, Brentwood TN 37027
Tel (615) 370-7000 SIC 7374 7389 7375

SITEL OPERATING CORP p 1328
3102 West End Ave Ste 900, Nashville TN 37203
Tel (615) 301-7100 SIC 7389 7375

SITEL WORLDWIDE CORP p 1328
3102 West End Ave Ste 900, Nashville TN 37203
Tel (615) 301-7100 SIC 7389 7375

HOMEAWAY INC p 703
1011 W 5th St Ste 300, Austin TX 78703
Tel (512) 684-1100 SIC 6531 7389 7375

MILLER ENVIRONMENTAL SERVICES LLC p 970
401 Navigation Blvd, Corpus Christi TX 78408
Tel (361) 289-9800 SIC 4953 7375

■ ACS IMAGE SOLUTIONS INC p 19
3988 N Central Expy, Dallas TX 75204
Tel (214) 818-3000
SIC 7389 5112 7374 7375

BENEFITMALL INC p 173
4851 Freeway Ste 100, Dallas TX 75244
Tel (469) 791-3300 SIC 6411 8742 7375

DATASPAN HOLDINGS INC p 414
1245 Viceroy Dr, Dallas TX 75247
Tel (214) 905-1882 SIC 6719 7375

DATASPAN INC p 414
1245 Viceroy Dr, Dallas TX 75247
Tel (800) 660-3586 SIC 5045 7375

■ HOTELS.COM LP p 710
5400 Lyndon B Johnson Fwy # 500, Dallas TX 75240
Tel (214) 361-7311 SIC 7389 7375

■ XEROX BUSINESS SERVICES LLC p 1631
2828 N Haskell Ave Fl 1, Dallas TX 75204
Tel (214) 841-6111 SIC 7374 7375 7389

CORPSOURCE HOLDINGS LLC p 372
2701 E Grauwyler Rd, Irving TX 75061
Tel (866) 321-5854 SIC 7375 7334 7374

■ EPSILON DATA MANAGEMENT LLC p 505
6021 Connection Dr, Irving TX 75039
Tel (972) 582-9600 SIC 7375

■ SIRIUS XM CONNECTED VEHICLE SERVICES INC p 1327
8550 Freeport Pkwy, Irving TX 75063
Tel (972) 753-6200 SIC 7375

SOURCECORP INC p 1342
2701 E Grauwyler Rd, Irving TX 75061
Tel (866) 321-5854 SIC 7375 7334 7374

▲ SABRE CORP p 1264
3150 Sabre Dr, Southlake TX 76092
Tel (682) 605-1000 SIC 4724 7375

■ SABRE GLBL INC p 1264
3150 Sabre Dr, Southlake TX 76092
Tel (682) 605-1000
SIC 7375 7371 7374 7389 8748

ABOUT TIME TECHNOLOGIES LLC p 12
58 N 1100 W Apt 2, Payson UT 84651
Tel (801) 465-8181 SIC 5045 7372 7375

ANCESTRY US HOLDINGS INC p 89
360 W 4800 N, Provo UT 84604
Tel (801) 705-7000 SIC 7375

ANCESTRY.COM HOLDINGS LLC p 89
360 W 4800 N, Provo UT 84604
Tel (801) 705-7000 SIC 7374 7375

■ NETWORK SOLUTIONS LLC p 1028
13861 Sunrise Valley Dr # 300, Herndon VA 20171
Tel (703) 668-4600
SIC 7375 7389 4813 7374

SIDERA NETWORKS INC p 1319
196 Van Buren St Ste 250, Herndon VA 20170
Tel (703) 434-8500 SIC 4841 4813 7375

■ DYNCORP p 465
1700 Old Meadow Rd, Mc Lean VA 22102
Tel (571) 722-0210
SIC 7373 7371 7374 7375 8744 4581

▲ GANNETT CO INC p 590
7950 Jones Branch Dr, Mc Lean VA 22102
Tel (703) 854-6000 SIC 2711 7375

▲ VERISIGN INC p 1549
12061 Bluemont Way, Reston VA 20190
Tel (703) 948-3200 SIC 7375 7372

▲ NEUSTAR INC p 1028
21575 Ridgetop Cir, Sterling VA 20166
Tel (571) 434-5400 SIC 7375 4899

▲ BLUCORA INC p 190
10900 Ne 8th St Ste 800, Bellevue WA 98004
Tel (425) 201-6100 SIC 7375 7374

▲ RIGHTSIDE GROUP LTD p 1234
5808 Lake Washington Blvd, Kirkland WA 98033
Tel (425) 298-2500 SIC 7374 7375

▲ MICROSOFT CORP p 962
1 Microsoft Way, Redmond WA 98052
Tel (425) 882-8080
SIC 7372 7371 3577 7375

RAZORFISH LLC p 1211
424 2nd Ave W, Seattle WA 98119
Tel (206) 816-8800 SIC 7375 7319

IOD INC p 762
1030 Ontario Rd, Green Bay WI 54311
Tel (920) 469-5000 SIC 7375

SIC 7376 Computer Facilities Management Svcs

CHENEGA CORP p 294
3000 C St Ste 301, Anchorage AK 99503
Tel (907) 277-5706
SIC 8744 7379 7376 3629 8742

TPUSA - FHCS INC p 1468
215 N Marengo Ave Ste 160, Pasadena CA 91101
Tel (213) 873-5100 SIC 7376 7373

RAGINGWIRE DATA CENTERS INC p 1205
1200 Striker Ave, Sacramento CA 95834
Tel (916) 286-3000 SIC 7376

FUSIONSTORM p 585
2 Bryant St Ste 150, San Francisco CA 94105
Tel (415) 623-2626
SIC 7379 7371 7374 7376

HCL AMERICA INC p 672
330 Potrero Ave, Sunnyvale CA 94085
Tel (408) 733-0480 SIC 7376 7371 8741

■ VECTRUS SYSTEMS CORP p 1546
655 Space Center Dr, Colorado Springs CO 80915
Tel (719) 591-3600 SIC 8744 7376

■ **MOREDIRECT INC** p 988
1001 Yamato Rd Ste 200, Boca Raton FL 33431
Tel (561) 237-3300 SIC 5045 7373 7376
ONEPATH SYSTEMS LLC p 1088
2053 Franklin Way Se, Marietta GA 30067
Tel (678) 695-5500
SIC 7389 8744 7378 7376 7382
ALEXANDER OPEN SYSTEMS INC p 49
12980 Foster St Ste 300, Overland Park KS 66213
Tel (913) 307-2300
SIC 5045 7373 8748 7376 3577 1731
QUALITY TECHNOLOGY SERVICES LLC p 1197
12851 Foster St, Overland Park KS 66213
Tel (913) 814-9988 SIC 7376 8741
MIL CORP p 968
4000 Mitchellville Rd R, Bowie MD 20716
Tel (301) 805-8500
SIC 7371 7373 7374 7375 7376 8711
SGT INC p 1310
7701 Greenbelt Rd Ste 400, Greenbelt MD 20770
Tel (301) 614-8600 SIC 7371 7373 7376
TEKSYSTEMS INC p 1433
7437 Race Rd, Hanover MD 21076
Tel (410) 540-7700 SIC 7379 7376 7373
TRAX INTERNATIONAL CORP p 1475
8337 W Sunset Rd Ste 250, Las Vegas NV 89113
Tel (702) 216-4455
SIC 7373 8711 7376 8742 8744
▲ **COMMVAULT SYSTEMS INC** p 350
1 Commvault Way, Tinton Falls NJ 07724
Tel (732) 870-4000 SIC 7373 7372 7376
IPSOFT INC p 764
17 State St Fl 14, New York NY 10004
Tel (888) 477-6388
SIC 7376 7363 7374 8742
ERGONOMIC GROUP INC p 507
609 Cantiague Rock Rd # 3, Westbury NY 11590
Tel (516) 746-7777
SIC 5045 7373 7374 7376 7379
▲ **CDI CORP** p 271
1735 Market St Ste 200, Philadelphia PA 19103
Tel (215) 569-2200
SIC 8711 7371 7373 7376 7361 7363
LIFE CYCLE ENGINEERING INC p 863
4360 Corporate Rd Ste 100, North Charleston SC 29405
Tel (843) 744-7110
SIC 7371 7373 7376 7379 8711
ATOS ORIGIN INC p 128
18062 Fm 529 Rd Ste 215, Cypress TX 77433
Tel (914) 881-3000
SIC 7373 7374 7376 7379
■ **ACS HEALTH CARE INC** p 19
2828 N Haskell Ave, Dallas TX 75204
Tel (214) 841-6111 SIC 7376 8742
LASON INC p 846
11850 Hempstead Rd # 270, Houston TX 77092
Tel (713) 957-0800 SIC 7376
■ **PEROT SYSTEMS CORP** p 1137
2300 W Plano Pkwy, Plano TX 75075
Tel (972) 577-0000 SIC 7376 7379
SIEMENS GOVERNMENT TECHNOLOGIES INC p 1320
2231 Crystal Dr Ste 700, Arlington VA 22202
Tel (703) 860-1574
SIC 8711 7373 7376 7379 8712 7378
■ **VANGENT INC** p 1543
3211 Jermantown Rd, Fairfax VA 22030
Tel (703) 995-2666
SIC 8748 7371 7372 7373 7374 7376
■ **CSRA LLC** p 398
3170 Fairview Park Dr, Falls Church VA 22042
Tel (703) 876-1000
SIC 7371 8733 7376 7374 7379
■ **CSRA INFORMATION SYSTEMS LLC** p 398
13857 Mclearen Rd, Herndon VA 20171
Tel (703) 818-4000 SIC 7376
▲ **COMPUTER SCIENCES CORP** p 353
1775 Tysons Blvd, Tysons VA 22102
Tel (703) 245-9675
SIC 7376 7374 7379 7373 7323
CUBIC GLOBAL DEFENSE INC p 399
400 Union Ave Se Ste 300, Olympia WA 98501
Tel (360) 493-6275
SIC 7373 8744 8711 7376 8748 8741

SIC 7377 Computer Rental & Leasing

INSIGHT INVESTMENTS CORP p 746
611 Anton Blvd Ste 700, Costa Mesa CA 92626
Tel (714) 939-2300 SIC 7377 5045
INSIGHT INVESTMENTS LLC p 746
611 Anton Blvd Ste 700, Costa Mesa CA 92626
Tel (714) 939-2300 SIC 7377 5045
ABF DATA SYSTEMS INC p 11
9020 Kenamar Dr Ste 201, San Diego CA 92121
Tel (858) 547-8300 SIC 5045 7377
ELECTRO RENT CORP p 485
6060 Sepulveda Blvd # 300, Van Nuys CA 91411
Tel (818) 786-2525
SIC 7359 7377 5065 5045
CHG-MERIDIAN US HOLDING INC p 296
21800 Oxnard St Ste 400, Woodland Hills CA 91367
Tel (818) 702-1800
SIC 7377 6159 5045 7378
PGA RESORT & SPA p 1140
1555 Palm Beach Lks, West Palm Beach FL 33401
Tel (561) 686-2000
SIC 8741 7377 7513 7515
FORSYTHE TECHNOLOGY INC p 568
7770 Frontage Rd, Skokie IL 60077
Tel (847) 213-7000 SIC 7377 5045 7373
FORSYTHE/MCARTHUR ASSOCIATES INC p 568
7770 Frontage Rd, Skokie IL 60077
Tel (847) 213-7000 SIC 7377 7373 5045
CONTINENTAL RESOURCES INC p 363
175 Middlesex Tpke Ste 1, Bedford MA 01730
Tel (781) 275-0850
SIC 5045 5065 7377 7359 7378 7629
DATA SALES CO INC p 413
3450 W Burnsville Pkwy, Burnsville MN 55337
Tel (952) 890-8838 SIC 5045 7377
CSI LEASING INC p 398
9990 Old Olive Street Rd # 101, Saint Louis MO 63141
Tel (314) 997-4934 SIC 7377 5045
■ **IBM WORLD TRADE CORP** p 726
1 New Orchard Rd Ste 1, Armonk NY 10504
Tel (914) 765-1900
SIC 3571 3577 7377 7379
SUTTON HOLDING CORP p 1410
2330 Interstate 30, Mesquite TX 75150
Tel (972) 755-8200 SIC 7377
VAR RESOURCES LLC p 1544
2330 Interstate 30, Mesquite TX 75150
Tel (972) 755-8200 SIC 7377
■ **EPLUS GROUP INC** p 505
13595 Dulles Tech Dr, Herndon VA 20171
Tel (703) 984-8400 SIC 7377 5734 5045
▲ **EPLUS INC** p 505
13595 Dulles Tech Dr, Herndon VA 20171
Tel (703) 984-8400
SIC 5045 7377 7379 7372

SIC 7378 Computer Maintenance & Repair

DATA EXCHANGE CORP p 413
3600 Via Pescador, Camarillo CA 93012
Tel (805) 388-1711 SIC 5045 7378
GOLDEN STAR TECHNOLOGY INC p 621
12881 166th St Ste 100, Cerritos CA 90703
Tel (562) 345-8700 SIC 5734 7378 5045
COMPUTER CONSULTING OPERATIONS SPECIALISTS INC p 352
600 Corporate Pointe # 1010, Culver City CA 90230
Tel (310) 568-5000
SIC 4813 4899 5045 7378
BROADWAY TYPEWRITER CO INC p 216
1055 6th Ave Ste 101, San Diego CA 92101
Tel (619) 645-0253 SIC 5045 7378
HITACHI DATA SYSTEMS CORP p 696
2845 Lafayette St, Santa Clara CA 95050
Tel (408) 970-1000
SIC 5045 7378 7379 5734 4225 3571
CHG-MERIDIAN US HOLDING INC p 296
21800 Oxnard St Ste 400, Woodland Hills CA 91367
Tel (818) 702-1800
SIC 7377 6159 5045 7378
▲ **XEROX CORP** p 1631
45 Glover Ave Ste 700, Norwalk CT 06850
Tel (203) 968-3000
SIC 3861 3579 3577 7629 7378 7374
MCS OF TAMPA INC p 932
8510 Sunstate St, Tampa FL 33634
Tel (813) 872-0217
SIC 1731 7373 4813 7378
APTOS INC p 101
945 E Paces Ferry Rd Ne, Atlanta GA 30326
Tel (866) 493-7037
SIC 5044 5045 7378 7699
ONEPATH SYSTEMS LLC p 1088
2053 Franklin Way Se, Marietta GA 30067
Tel (678) 695-5500
SIC 7389 8744 7378 7376 7382
QUALITY TECHNOLOGY SERVICES LLC p 1197
300 Satellite Blvd Nw, Suwanee GA 30024
Tel (678) 546-0064
SIC 7373 4813 7378 7374
SENTINEL TECHNOLOGIES INC p 1305
2550 Warrenville Rd, Downers Grove IL 60515
Tel (630) 769-4300 SIC 7378 1731
MU SIGMA INC p 998
3400 Dundee Rd Ste 160, Northbrook IL 60062
Tel (847) 919-0445 SIC 7378 7374
ADVANCED TECHNOLOGY SERVICES INC p 26
8201 N University St # 1, Peoria IL 61615
Tel (309) 693-4000 SIC 7699 7629 7378
CDS OFFICE SYSTEMS INC p 271
612 S Dirksen Pkwy, Springfield IL 62703
Tel (800) 367-1508
SIC 5044 5999 7629 7378 3861 3577
SAYERS TECHNOLOGY LLC p 1285
825 Corporate Woods Pkwy, Vernon Hills IL 60061
Tel (847) 391-4802 SIC 5734 7378
INKCYCLE INC p 743
11100 W 82nd St, Lenexa KS 66214
Tel (913) 894-8387
SIC 3955 7699 7378 5045 8249 5734
POMEROY IT SOLUTIONS INC p 1160
1020 Petersburg Rd, Hebron KY 41048
Tel (859) 586-0600 SIC 7373 5045 7378
PEAK-RYZEX INC p 1126
10330 Old Columbia Rd # 102, Columbia MD 21046
Tel (410) 312-6000 SIC 7378 5045 7372
CONTINENTAL RESOURCES INC p 363
175 Middlesex Tpke Ste 1, Bedford MA 01730
Tel (781) 275-0850
SIC 5045 5065 7377 7359 7378 7629
GETRONICS USA INC p 609
290 Concord Rd, Billerica MA 01821
Tel (978) 625-5000 SIC 7378 7373 7379
BULL DATA SYSTEMS INC p 225
285 Billerica Rd Ste 200, Chelmsford MA 01824
Tel (978) 294-6000 SIC 3571 3577 7378
PLUMCHOICE INC p 1157
900 Chelmsford St Ofc 1, Lowell MA 01851
Tel (866) 811-3321 SIC 7378
■ **PCG PARENT CORP** p 1124
4 Technology Dr, Peabody MA 01960
Tel (978) 538-8000
SIC 5045 5065 4953 5093 7378
■ **PCG TRADING LLC** p 1124
4 Technology Dr, Peabody MA 01960
Tel (978) 538-8000
SIC 5045 5065 4953 5093 7378
WHALLEY COMPUTER ASSOCIATES INC p 1604
1 Whalley Way, Southwick MA 01077
Tel (413) 569-4200 SIC 5045 7378
SEI INC p 1300
3854 Broadmoor Ave Se # 101, Grand Rapids MI 49512
Tel (616) 698-2221 SIC 7378
EXPRESSPOINT TECHNOLOGY SERVICES INC p 521
10900 Wayzata Blvd # 800, Hopkins MN 55305
Tel (763) 543-6000
SIC 5045 7379 7699 8741 7389 7378
CUSTOM COMPUTER SPECIALISTS INC p 403
70 Suffolk Ct Ste 100, Hauppauge NY 11788
Tel (800) 598-8989 SIC 7379 7373 7378
ETRALI NORTH AMERICA LLC p 512
1500 Broadway Ste 708, New York NY 10036
Tel (212) 418-9328 SIC 5045 7378 1731
MISYS INTERNATIONAL BANKING SYSTEMS INC p 976
1180 Avenue Of The Amer, New York NY 10036
Tel (914) 428-7200 SIC 7378 7372
TEKSERVE CORP p 1433
119 W 23rd St Frnt 1, New York NY 10011
Tel (212) 929-3645 SIC 7378 5734
ISLAND COMPUTER PRODUCTS INC p 766
20 Clifton Ave, Staten Island NY 10305
Tel (718) 556-6700
SIC 5045 7373 7379 7378
SMS SYSTEMS MAINTENANCE SERVICES INC p 1334
10420 Harris Oak Blvd C, Charlotte NC 28269
Tel (704) 921-1620 SIC 7378
PARK PLACE TECHNOLOGIES LLC p 1115
5910 Landerbrook Dr # 300, Mayfield Heights OH 44124
Tel (877) 778-8707 SIC 7378
EMERSON NETWORK POWER LIEBERT SERVICES INC p 492
610 Executive Campus Dr, Westerville OH 43082
Tel (614) 841-6400 SIC 7378
▲ **UNISYS CORP** p 1506
801 Lakeview Dr Ste 100, Blue Bell PA 19422
Tel (215) 986-4011
SIC 7373 7378 7379 3571 3572
DECISIONONE CORP p 421
426 W Lancaster Ave, Devon PA 19333
Tel (610) 296-6000 SIC 7378
■ **EPLUS TECHNOLOGY OF PENNSYLVANIA INC** p 505
130 Futura Dr, Pottstown PA 19464
Tel (610) 495-7800 SIC 5734 7378 8243
COMMUNICATIONS TEST DESIGN INC p 347
1373 Enterprise Dr, West Chester PA 19380
Tel (610) 436-5203
SIC 7629 7378 5065 5999
■ **COMPAQ COMPUTER CARIBBEAN INC** p 350
1 Calle Sonata 3, Guaynabo PR 00969
Tel (787) 781-0505 SIC 5045 7378
IGT GLOBAL SOLUTIONS CORP p 730
10 Memorial Blvd, Providence RI 02903
Tel (401) 392-1000
SIC 7999 3575 7372 7378 2752 7374
COMPUCOM SYSTEMS HOLDING LLC p 352
7171 Forest Ln, Dallas TX 75230
Tel (972) 856-3600
SIC 7373 5045 7378 8748
SMS INFOCOMM CORP p 1334
4051 N Highway 121 # 100, Grapevine TX 76051
Tel (972) 906-7800 SIC 7378
CSAT SOLUTIONS LP p 397
4949 Windfern Rd, Houston TX 77041
Tel (713) 934-5200 SIC 7378
PCPC DIRECT LTD p 1124
10690 Shadow Wood Dr # 132, Houston TX 77043
Tel (713) 984-8808 SIC 5045 7378 7379
PCPC INC p 1124
10690 Shadow Wood Dr # 132, Houston TX 77043
Tel (713) 984-8808 SIC 5045 7378 7379
COMPUCOM SYSTEMS INC p 352
8383 Dominion Pkwy, Plano TX 75024
Tel (972) 856-3600
SIC 7373 5045 7378 8748
SIEMENS GOVERNMENT TECHNOLOGIES INC p 1320
2231 Crystal Dr Ste 700, Arlington VA 22202
Tel (703) 860-1574
SIC 8711 7373 7376 7379 8712 7378
■ **MANTECH GRAY HAWK SYSTEMS INC** p 903
7799 Leesburg Pike 700s, Falls Church VA 22043
Tel (703) 610-9232 SIC 7373 7378
■ **SPACELABS HEALTHCARE (WASHINGTON) INC** p 1354
35301 Se Center St, Snoqualmie WA 98065
Tel (425) 396-3300
SIC 3845 3841 3575 7699 7378
■ **SPACELABS HEALTHCARE INC** p 1354
35301 Se Center St, Snoqualmie WA 98065
Tel (425) 396-3302
SIC 3841 3845 3575 7699 7378

SIC 7379 Computer Related Svcs, NEC

SYSTEM STUDIES & SIMULATION INC p 1418
615 Discovery Dr Nw, Huntsville AL 35806
Tel (256) 539-1700 SIC 3761 7379 8711
INTERGRAPH CORP p 752
305 Intergraph Way, Madison AL 35758
Tel (256) 730-2000 SIC 7372 7373 7379
ALUTIIQ PACIFIC LLC p 63
3909 Arctic Blvd Ste 500, Anchorage AK 99503
Tel (907) 222-9500 SIC 8742 7379
CHENEGA CORP p 294
3000 C St Ste 301, Anchorage AK 99503
Tel (907) 277-5706
SIC 8744 7379 7376 3629 8742
INFUSION SOFTWARE INC p 742
1260 S Spectrum Blvd, Chandler AZ 85286
Tel (480) 807-0644 SIC 7379 7371
▲ **AVNET INC** p 138
2211 S 47th St, Phoenix AZ 85034
Tel (480) 643-2000 SIC 5065 5045 7379
▲ **INSIGHT ENTERPRISES INC** p 746
201 N Central Ave, Phoenix AZ 85004
Tel (480) 333-3000 SIC 5045 7379 5065
IO DATA CENTERS LLC p 762
615 N 48th St, Phoenix AZ 85008
Tel (480) 513-8500 SIC 7379
GODADDY.COM LLC p 619
14455 N Hayden Rd Ste 219, Scottsdale AZ 85260
Tel (480) 505-8800 SIC 7379
QUEST SOFTWARE INC p 1199
4 Polaris Way, Aliso Viejo CA 92656
Tel (949) 754-8000 SIC 7373 7372 7379
TOOLOW INC p 1460
4273 Reids Way, Berkeley CA 94704
Tel (408) 694-2361 SIC 7379
PROLIFICS APPLICATION SERVICES INC p 1182
24025 Park Sorrento # 405, Calabasas CA 91302
Tel (646) 201-4967 SIC 7379
PROLIFICS INC p 1182
24025 Park Sorrento # 450, Calabasas CA 91302
Tel (212) 267-7722 SIC 7379 7371
24/7 CUSTOMER INC p 2
910 E Hamilton Ave # 240, Campbell CA 95008
Tel (650) 385-2247 SIC 7379
A P R CONSULTING INC p 6
1370 Valley Vista Dr # 280, Diamond Bar CA 91765
Tel (909) 396-5375 SIC 7361 7379
R SYSTEMS INC p 1202
5000 Windplay Dr Ste 5, El Dorado Hills CA 95762
Tel (916) 939-9696 SIC 7379 7373 7374
VISIONARY INTEGRATION PROFESSIONALS LLC p 1561
80 Iron Point Cir Ste 100, Folsom CA 95630
Tel (916) 608-8320 SIC 8742 7379
INTELLISWIFT SOFTWARE INC p 750
2201 Walnut Ave Ste 180, Fremont CA 94538
Tel (510) 490-9240 SIC 7379
MAGPIE INTERNET COMMUNICATIONS CORP p 897
2762 Bayview Dr, Fremont CA 94538
Tel (510) 344-1200 SIC 4813 7379 7374
PENGUIN COMPUTING INC p 1128
45800 Northport Loop W, Fremont CA 94538
Tel (415) 954-2800 SIC 5045 7379
CYLANCE INC p 405
18201 Von Karman Ave # 700, Irvine CA 92612
Tel (949) 375-3380 SIC 3825 7379
NEUDESIC LLC p 1028
100 Spectrum Center Dr # 1200, Irvine CA 92618
Tel (949) 754-4500 SIC 7379
SYNOPTEK INC p 1415
19520 Jamboree Rd Ste 110, Irvine CA 92612
Tel (949) 241-8600 SIC 7379
SENTINEL ACQUISITION HOLDINGS INC p 1305
2000 Avenue Of The Stars, Los Angeles CA 90067
Tel (310) 201-4100 SIC 7371 7379
INFOGAIN CORP p 741
485 Alberto Way Ste 100, Los Gatos CA 95032
Tel (408) 355-6000
SIC 7379 7373 8742 8748 7374 1731
ADVANTECH CORP p 27
380 Fairview Way, Milpitas CA 95035
Tel (408) 519-3800 SIC 5045 7379
▲ **SYMANTEC CORP** p 1414
350 Ellis St, Mountain View CA 94043
Tel (650) 527-8000 SIC 7372 7379
CB TECHNOLOGIES INC p 268
750 The City Dr S Ste 225, Orange CA 92868
Tel (714) 573-7733 SIC 7379 7373
▲ **HEWLETT PACKARD ENTERPRISE CO** p 688
3000 Hanover St, Palo Alto CA 94304
Tel (650) 857-5817 SIC 7372 7379 3572
CAMEO GLOBAL INC p 245
4695 Chabot Dr Ste 101, Pleasanton CA 94588
Tel (925) 479-7800
SIC 7373 7371 7379 7363 4813 8742
▲ **VEEVA SYSTEMS INC** p 1546
4280 Hacienda Dr, Pleasanton CA 94588
Tel (925) 452-6500 SIC 7372 7371 7379
■ **ORACLE AMERICA INC** p 1091
500 Oracle Pkwy, Redwood City CA 94065
Tel (650) 506-7000
SIC 3571 7379 7373 7372 3674
▲ **ORACLE CORP** p 1091
500 Oracle Pkwy, Redwood City CA 94065
Tel (650) 506-7000
SIC 7372 7379 8243 3571 3674
■ **ORACLE SYSTEMS CORP** p 1091
500 Oracle Pkwy, Redwood City CA 94065
Tel (650) 506-7000 SIC 7372 7379 8243
▲ **ROCKET FUEL INC** p 1244
1900 Seaport Blvd, Redwood City CA 94063
Tel (650) 595-1300 SIC 7379
APPIRIO INC p 98
760 Market St Ste 1150, San Francisco CA 94102
Tel (415) 663-4433 SIC 7371 7379
FUSIONSTORM p 585
2 Bryant St Ste 150, San Francisco CA 94105
Tel (415) 623-2626
SIC 7379 7371 7374 7376
VECTOR STEALTH HOLDINGS II LLC p 1546
456 Montgomery St Fl 19, San Francisco CA 94104
Tel (415) 293-5000 SIC 7379
ACER AMERICA CORP p 17
333 W San Carlos St, San Jose CA 95110
Tel (408) 533-7700 SIC 7379
▲ **CISCO SYSTEMS INC** p 309
170 W Tasman Dr, San Jose CA 95134
Tel (408) 526-4000 SIC 3577 7379
GLOBALLOGIC INC p 617
1741 Tech Dr Ste 400, San Jose CA 95110
Tel (408) 273-8900 SIC 7371 7379 7373
TAOS MOUNTAIN LLC p 1424
121 Daggett Dr, San Jose CA 95134
Tel (408) 324-2800 SIC 7379
OPEN TEXT INC p 1089
951 Mariners Island Blvd # 7, San Mateo CA 94404
Tel (650) 645-3000 SIC 7379

NHR NEWCO HOLDINGS LLC p 1042
6500 Hollister Ave # 210, Santa Barbara CA 93117
Tel (800) 230-6638 *SIC* 5045 5065 7379

HITACHI DATA SYSTEMS CORP p 696
2845 Lafayette St, Santa Clara CA 95050
Tel (408) 970-1000
SIC 5045 7378 7379 5734 4225 3571

INCEDO INC p 735
2350 Mission College Blvd, Santa Clara CA 95054
Tel (408) 531-6040 *SIC* 7379

INFOBLOX INC p 741
3111 Coronado Dr, Santa Clara CA 95054
Tel (408) 986-4000 *SIC* 7374 7371 7379

▲ SERVICENOW INC p 1308
2225 Lawson Ln, Santa Clara CA 95054
Tel (408) 501-8550 *SIC* 7379 7372

TRIANZ p 1478
3979 Freedom Cir Ste 210, Santa Clara CA 95054
Tel (408) 387-5800 *SIC* 7379

XORIANT CORP p 1632
1248 Reamwood Ave, Sunnyvale CA 94089
Tel (408) 743-4427 *SIC* 7379 7371

HOSTING.COM INC p 710
900 Suth Broadway Ste 400, Denver CO 80209
Tel (720) 389-3800 *SIC* 7379

OPTIV SECURITY INC p 1090
1125 17th St Ste 1700, Denver CO 80202
Tel (888) 732-9406
SIC 5045 7379 7382 5065

CENTER PARTNERS INC p 276
4401 Innovation Dr, Fort Collins CO 80525
Tel (970) 206-9000 *SIC* 7379 8742 7363

▲ CIBER INC p 306
6312 S Fiddlers Green Cir 320n, Greenwood Village CO 80111
Tel (303) 220-0100 *SIC* 7373 7379

▲ STARTEK INC p 1379
8200 E Maplewood Ave # 100, Greenwood Village CO 80111
Tel (303) 262-4500 *SIC* 7374 7379 8742

■ STARTEK USA INC p 1379
8200 E Maplewood Ave # 100, Greenwood Village CO 80111
Tel (303) 262-4150 *SIC* 7372 7379 5045

▲ INFORMATION SERVICES GROUP INC p 742
281 Tresser Blvd Ste 901, Stamford CT 06901
Tel (203) 517-3100 *SIC* 8742 7379

MTM TECHNOLOGIES INC p 998
4 High Ridge Park Ste 102, Stamford CT 06905
Tel (203) 588-1981 *SIC* 5045 7379

AKIRA TECHNOLOGIES INC p 42
1747 Penn Ave Nw Ste 600, Washington DC 20006
Tel (202) 517-7187 *SIC* 7373 7379

DCR WORKFORCE INC p 418
7795 Nw Beacon Sq 201, Boca Raton FL 33487
Tel (561) 998-3737 *SIC* 7379 7363 8742

UNITED DATA TECHNOLOGIES INC p 1507
8825 Nw 21st Ter, Doral FL 33172
Tel (305) 882-0435 *SIC* 7379

SIGNATURE CONSULTANTS LLC p 1322
200 W Cypress Creek Rd # 400, Fort Lauderdale FL 33309
Tel (954) 677-1020 *SIC* 7379 8742

■ RAYTHEON CYBER SOLUTIONS INC p 1211
1220 N Hwy A1a Ste 123, Indialantic FL 32903
Tel (321) 253-7841 *SIC* 7379

■ CONNEXTIONS INC p 358
9395 S John Young Pkwy, Orlando FL 32819
Tel (407) 926-2411 *SIC* 7379 7331

CHETU INC p 295
10167 W Sunrise Blvd # 200, Plantation FL 33322
Tel (954) 342-5676 *SIC* 7379

MAINLINE INFORMATION SYSTEMS INC p 898
1700 Summit Lake Dr, Tallahassee FL 32317
Tel (850) 219-5000 *SIC* 7373 7379 7371

■ SYKES ACQUISITION LLC p 1413
400 N Ashley Dr, Tampa FL 33602
Tel (813) 274-1000 *SIC* 7379

▲ SYKES ENTERPRISES INC p 1413
400 N Ashley Dr Ste 2800, Tampa FL 33602
Tel (813) 274-1000 *SIC* 7379 7389

PYRAMID CONSULTING INC p 1193
11100 Atlantis Pl, Alpharetta GA 30022
Tel (678) 514-3500 *SIC* 7379 7371

CDC SOFTWARE HOLDINGS INC p 270
Two Cncourse Pkwy Ste 800, Atlanta GA 39901
Tel (770) 351-9600 *SIC* 7372 7379 8243

DATA BLUE LLC p 413
1117 Perimeter Ctr, Atlanta GA 30338
Tel (727) 412-8470 *SIC* 7379

IDHASOFT INC p 729
6 Concourse Pkwy Ste 500, Atlanta GA 30328
Tel (770) 248-2999 *SIC* 7379

NIIT TECHNOLOGIES INC p 1043
1050 Crown Pinte Pkwy 5th # 5, Atlanta GA 30338
Tel (770) 551-9494 *SIC* 7379 7371

NORTH HIGHLAND CO LLC p 1052
3333 Piedmont Rd Ne # 1000, Atlanta GA 30305
Tel (404) 233-1015 *SIC* 8742 7379

SOFTWARE PARADIGMS INTERNATIONAL GROUP LLC p 1337
5 Concourse Pkwy Ste 500, Atlanta GA 30328
Tel (770) 904-7720 *SIC* 7379

SOFTTEK INTEGRATION SYSTEMS INC p 1337
2002 Summit Blvd Ste 300, Brookhaven GA 30319
Tel (404) 460-5040 *SIC* 7379 7371 7373

■ VERIZON TELEMATICS INC p 1550
2002 Summit Blvd Ste 1800, Brookhaven GA 30319
Tel (404) 573-5800 *SIC* 7379 4813

JOHN H HARLAND CO p 788
2939 Miller Rd, Decatur GA 30035
Tel (770) 593-5050
SIC 2782 2752 2761 7371 7379

INTRALOT INC p 760
11360 Technology Cir, Duluth GA 30097
Tel (678) 473-7200 *SIC* 7379

▲ NCR CORP p 1022
3097 Satellite Blvd # 100, Duluth GA 30096
Tel (937) 445-5000
SIC 3575 3578 7379 7374 7371

ASAP SOLUTIONS GROUP LLC p 115
3885 Holcomb Bridge Rd, Norcross GA 30092
Tel (770) 246-1718 *SIC* 7379 8742

S & A COMPUTER SERVICES INC p 1261
1125 Northmeadow Pkwy # 120, Roswell GA 30076
Tel (770) 569-2828 *SIC* 7379

ARINSO INTERNATIONAL INC p 108
3965 Johns Creek Ct Ste A, Suwanee GA 30024
Tel (678) 259-0500 *SIC* 7379

ACCENTURE INC p 14
161 N Clark St Ste 1100, Chicago IL 60601
Tel (312) 737-8842 *SIC* 7379 7389 8742

ACCENTURE LLC p 14
161 N Clark St Ste 1100, Chicago IL 60601
Tel (312) 693-0161 *SIC* 7379 7389 8742

GREEN COUCH CORP p 636
231 S La Salle St Fl 8, Chicago IL 60604
Tel (312) 263-1177 *SIC* 7379 7371

HERE HOLDING CORP p 685
425 W Randolph St, Chicago IL 60606
Tel (312) 894-7000 *SIC* 7379

QUINNOX INC p 1200
400 N Michigan Ave # 1300, Chicago IL 60611
Tel (630) 548-4800 *SIC* 7379 7371

■ SIMPLER NORTH AMERICA LLC p 1325
1 N Dearborn St Ste 1400, Chicago IL 60602
Tel (312) 533-3500 *SIC* 8742 7379

WRAPPORTS LLC p 1627
350 N Orleans St 10thf, Chicago IL 60654
Tel (312) 321-3000 *SIC* 7379 2711

■ T-SYSTEMS NORTH AMERICA INC p 1420
1901 Butterfield Rd # 700, Downers Grove IL 60515
Tel (630) 493-6100 *SIC* 7379 8748

YASH TECHNOLOGIES INC p 1635
605 17th Ave, East Moline IL 61244
Tel (309) 755-0433 *SIC* 7379

ENRIQUE MENDOZA p 500
2350 Nantucket Ln, Elgin IL 60123
Tel (630) 364-1808 *SIC* 7379 5045

■ CITICORP CREDIT SERVICES INC p 310
50 Northwest Point Blvd, Elk Grove Village IL 60007
Tel (847) 597-3000
SIC 7374 7389 7379 6141

IFS NORTH AMERICA INC p 730
300 Park Blvd Ste 555, Itasca IL 60143
Tel (888) 437-4968 *SIC* 7372 7379 8243

MAKE CORP p 899
1 S 450 Smmit Ave Ste 165, Oakbrook Terrace IL 60181
Tel (630) 376-0646 *SIC* 7379

TELVENT USA LLC p 1435
1415 S Roselle Rd, Palatine IL 60067
Tel (717) 944-5460 *SIC* 7379 8748

MESSINA GROUP INC p 951
200 S Prospect Ave, Park Ridge IL 60068
Tel (847) 825-8000 *SIC* 7361 7379

FORSYTHE SOLUTIONS GROUP INC p 568
7770 Frontage Rd, Skokie IL 60077
Tel (847) 213-7000 *SIC* 7379

LEVI RAY & SHOUP INC p 858
2401 W Monroe St, Springfield IL 62704
Tel (217) 793-3800 *SIC* 7371 5045 7379

BELL INDUSTRIES INC p 170
4400 W 96th St, Indianapolis IN 46268
Tel (866) 782-2355 *SIC* 7379 5734

BELL TECHLOGIX INC p 170
4400 W 96th St, Indianapolis IN 46268
Tel (317) 333-7777 *SIC* 7379

BUCHER AND CHRISTIAN CONSULTING INC p 222
9777 N College Ave, Indianapolis IN 46280
Tel (317) 493-2000 *SIC* 7379

TECHNICAL YOUTH LLC p 1431
8365 Keystone Xing # 104, Indianapolis IN 46240
Tel (317) 475-0079 *SIC* 7379

■ CLOUDBLUE TECHNOLOGIES INC p 327
501 Airtech Pkwy, Plainfield IN 46168
Tel (866) 437-4258 *SIC* 7379

SOFTWARE INFORMATION SYSTEMS LLC p 1337
165 Barr St, Lexington KY 40507
Tel (859) 977-4747 *SIC* 5045 7379

SENTURE LLC p 1305
460 Industrial Blvd, London KY 40741
Tel (606) 878-4205
SIC 7379 7389 7374 7373 8742

CMC AMERICAS INC p 328
4354 S Shrwd Forst Bl 175, Baton Rouge LA 70816
Tel (225) 296-8440 *SIC* 7374 7379

GREENPAGES INC p 638
33 Badgers Is W, Kittery ME 03904
Tel (207) 439-7310 *SIC* 7379

ASRC FEDERAL HOLDING CO LLC p 119
7000 Muirkirk Meadows Dr # 100, Beltsville MD 20705
Tel (301) 345-4500 *SIC* 7379

PRIMUS SOLUTIONS LLC p 1176
7000 Muirkirk Meadows Dr # 100, Beltsville MD 20705
Tel (301) 345-5500 *SIC* 7379

■ LEIDOS ASPEN SYSTEMS CORP p 854
700 N Frederick Ave, Gaithersburg MD 20879
Tel (301) 240-7000 *SIC* 7374 7379 7389

■ LEIDOS GOVERNMENT SERVICES INC p 854
700 N Frederick Ave, Gaithersburg MD 20879
Tel (856) 486-5156
SIC 7379 7373 7374 7372

■ ACTERNA LLC p 19
20250 Century Blvd # 100, Germantown MD 20874
Tel (301) 353-1550
SIC 3669 7379 3825 5065 3679 8734

OAO TECHNOLOGY SOLUTIONS INC p 1071
7500 Greenway Center Dr # 150, Greenbelt MD 20770
Tel (301) 486-0400 *SIC* 7379

TEKSYSTEMS INC p 1433
7437 Race Rd, Hanover MD 21076
Tel (410) 540-7700 *SIC* 7379 7376 7373

RAND WORLDWIDE SUBSIDIARY INC p 1207
11201 Dlfeld Blvd Ste 112, Owings Mills MD 21117
Tel (877) 726-3243
SIC 7379 7373 5045 5734

CLIENT NETWORK SERVICES INC p 326
2277 Research Blvd, Rockville MD 20850
Tel (301) 634-4600 *SIC* 7371 7373 7379

INFINITE COMPUTER SOLUTIONS INC p 740
15201 Diamondback Dr # 125, Rockville MD 20850
Tel (301) 355-7760 *SIC* 7379 7371

AUTOMATED RESOURCE MANAGEMENT ASSOCIATES INC p 134
962 Wayne Ave Ste 320, Silver Spring MD 20910
Tel (301) 587-7077 *SIC* 7379

ADAMS COMMUNICATION & ENGINEERING TECHNOLOGY INC p 21
11637 Terrace Dr Ste 201, Waldorf MD 20602
Tel (301) 861-5000 *SIC* 7379

■ DYNAMICS RESEARCH CORP p 464
2 Tech Dr, Andover MA 01810
Tel (978) 289-1500 *SIC* 7373 7379 8711

ONPROCESS TECHNOLOGY INC p 1088
200 Homer Ave, Ashland MA 01721
Tel (508) 520-2711 *SIC* 7379

GETRONICS USA INC p 609
290 Concord Rd, Billerica MA 01821
Tel (978) 625-5000 *SIC* 7378 7373 7379

▲ LOGMEIN INC p 875
320 Summer St Ste 100, Boston MA 02210
Tel (781) 638-9050 *SIC* 7372 7379

RENAISSANCE WORLDWIDE INC p 1223
711 Boylston St, Boston MA 02116
Tel (617) 535-5000
SIC 7363 8742 7379 7361 8748 7371

▲ PEGASYSTEMS INC p 1127
1 Rogers St, Cambridge MA 02142
Tel (617) 374-9600 *SIC* 7379 7371 7372

■ SALESLINK CORP p 1272
425 Medford St, Charlestown MA 02129
Tel (617) 886-4800 *SIC* 7379 8744 7331

COMPUTER MERCHANT LTD p 353
95 Longwater Cir, Norwell MA 02061
Tel (781) 878-1070 *SIC* 7379 7371

VITALIZE CONSULTING SOLUTIONS INC p 1562
248 Main St Ste 101, Reading MA 01867
Tel (781) 670-1000 *SIC* 8082 7379

▲ EDGEWATER TECHNOLOGY INC p 477
200 Harvard Mill Sq # 210, Wakefield MA 01880
Tel (781) 246-3343 *SIC* 7379 8742

CAMBRIDGE COMPUTER SERVICES INC p 244
271 Waverley Oaks Rd # 301, Waltham MA 02452
Tel (781) 250-3000
SIC 5045 7373 7371 7379

CARBON BLACK INC p 252
1100 Winter St Fl 4, Waltham MA 02451
Tel (617) 393-7400 *SIC* 7371 7379

■ MODUSLINK CORP p 981
1601 Trapelo Rd Ste 170, Waltham MA 02451
Tel (781) 663-5000 *SIC* 7379 7389 5045

▲ MODUSLINK GLOBAL SOLUTIONS INC p 981
1601 Trapelo Rd Ste 170, Waltham MA 02451
Tel (781) 663-5000 *SIC* 7379

▲ VIRTUSA CORP p 1560
2000 W Park Dr Ste 300, Westborough MA 01581
Tel (508) 389-7300 *SIC* 7371 7379

NETECH CORP p 1027
6355 E Paris Ave Se, Caledonia MI 49316
Tel (212) 324-4398 *SIC* 7379

VISION INFORMATION TECHNOLOGIES INC p 1561
3031 W Grand Blvd Ste 600, Detroit MI 48202
Tel (313) 664-5650 *SIC* 7363 7379

HCL GLOBAL SYSTEMS INC p 672
24543 Indoplex Cir # 220, Farmington Hills MI 48335
Tel (248) 473-0720 *SIC* 7379 7371

ROUTEONE LLC p 1253
31500 Nrthwstrn Hwy 200, Farmington Hills MI 48334
Tel (866) 768-8301 *SIC* 6141 7379

OPEN SYSTEMS TECHNOLOGIES DE LLC p 1089
605 Seward Ave Nw Ste 101, Grand Rapids MI 49504
Tel (616) 574-3500 *SIC* 7379

NETLINK SOFTWARE GROUP AMERICA INC p 1027
999 Tech Row, Madison Heights MI 48071
Tel (248) 204-8803 *SIC* 7379 7371

EPITEC INC p 505
24800 Denso Dr Ste 150, Southfield MI 48033
Tel (248) 353-6800
SIC 7371 7379 7373 8748 8711

STEFANINI INC p 1385
27335 W 11 Mile Rd, Southfield MI 48033
Tel (248) 357-2866 *SIC* 7379

TECHNOSOFT CORP p 1432
28411 Northwestern Hwy # 640, Southfield MI 48034
Tel (248) 603-2600 *SIC* 7379

HTC GLOBAL SERVICES INC p 715
3270 W Big Beaver Rd # 100, Troy MI 48084
Tel (248) 786-2500 *SIC* 7379

EXPRESSPOINT TECHNOLOGY SERVICES INC p 521
10900 Wayzata Blvd # 800, Hopkins MN 55305
Tel (763) 543-6000
SIC 5045 7379 7699 8741 7389 7378

ABILITY NETWORK INC p 11
100 N 6th St Ste 900a, Minneapolis MN 55403
Tel (612) 460-4301 *SIC* 7379

ANALYSTS INTERNATIONAL CORP p 88
7700 France Ave S Ste 200, Minneapolis MN 55435
Tel (952) 835-5900 *SIC* 7371 7379

■ GEEK SQUAD INC p 597
1213 Washington Ave N, Minneapolis MN 55401
Tel (952) 544-0377 *SIC* 7379

NCS PEARSON INC p 1022
5601 Green Valley Dr # 220, Minneapolis MN 55437
Tel (952) 681-3000
SIC 3577 7372 7374 8748 7379

■ NORSTAN INC p 1049
5050 Lincoln Dr Ste 300, Minneapolis MN 55436
Tel (952) 352-4000
SIC 7389 3661 8748 7379

POHLAD COMPANIES p 1159
60 S 6th St Ste 3700, Minneapolis MN 55402
Tel (612) 661-3700
SIC 8742 7929 6531 5013 7549 7379

VOLT SYSTEMS LLC p 1565
618 Spirit Dr, Chesterfield MO 63005
Tel (636) 393-8658 *SIC* 7379

DAUGHERTY SYSTEMS INC p 414
3 Cityplace Dr Ste 400, Saint Louis MO 63141
Tel (314) 432-8200
SIC 7379 7371 8742 7373 7372

■ TALX CORP p 1423
11432 Lackland Rd, Saint Louis MO 63146
Tel (314) 214-7000 *SIC* 7373 7379 7389

SAVVIS INC p 1284
1 Solutions Pkwy, Town And Country MO 63017
Tel (314) 628-7000
SIC 7373 7379 4813 7375

■ BH MEDIA GROUP HOLDINGS INC p 180
Omaha World Herald Bldg 1, Omaha NE 68102
Tel (402) 444-1000 *SIC* 2711 7379

■ BH MEDIA GROUP INC p 180
Omaha Wrld Hrld Bldg 1314, Omaha NE 68102
Tel (402) 444-1000 *SIC* 2711 7379

PROKARMA INC p 1182
222 S 15th St Ste 505n, Omaha NE 68102
Tel (877) 527-6226 *SIC* 7379

SOLUTIONARY INC p 1339
9420 Underwood Ave # 300, Omaha NE 68114
Tel (402) 361-3000 *SIC* 7379

RIMINI STREET INC p 1235
3993 Howard Hughes Pkwy, Las Vegas NV 89169
Tel (702) 839-9671 *SIC* 7379 7373

RED RIVER COMPUTER CO INC p 1216
21 Water St Ste 500, Claremont NH 03743
Tel (603) 298-5293 *SIC* 7379

WORLDCOM EXCHANGE INC p 1625
43 Northwestern Dr, Salem NH 03079
Tel (603) 893-0900 *SIC* 7373 5045 7379

MGL AMERICAS INC p 958
1249 S River Rd Ste 102, Cranbury NJ 08512
Tel (609) 235-9632 *SIC* 7379 7371

■ QUADRANT 4 CONSULTING INC p 1196
1246 S River Rd Ste 102, Cranbury NJ 08512
Tel (609) 799-3762 *SIC* 7379

LARSEN & TOUBRO INFOTECH LIMITED p 845
2035 State Route 27 # 3000, Edison NJ 08817
Tel (732) 248-6111 *SIC* 7379

TEKMARK GLOBAL SOLUTIONS LLC p 1433
100 Metroplex Dr Ste 102, Edison NJ 08817
Tel (732) 572-5400 *SIC* 7379 7371 7363

TRIGYN TECHNOLOGIES INC p 1480
100 Metroplex Dr Ste 101, Edison NJ 08817
Tel (732) 777-0050 *SIC* 7371 7379

ZSL INC p 1644
85 State Route 27, Edison NJ 08820
Tel (877) 800-0975 *SIC* 7379

HEXAWARE TECHNOLOGIES INC p 688
101 Wood Ave S Ste 600, Iselin NJ 08830
Tel (609) 409-6950 *SIC* 7379

PRINCETON INFORMATION LTD p 1177
100 Plaza Ten Ste 1101h, Jersey City NJ 07311
Tel (201) 604-9900 *SIC* 7374 7379

U S TECH SOLUTIONS INC p 1497
10 Exchange Pl Ste 1820, Jersey City NJ 07302
Tel (201) 524-9600 *SIC* 7379 7372

WIPRO DATA CENTER AND CLOUD SERVICES INC p 1618
2 Christie Hts, Leonia NJ 07605
Tel (201) 840-4772 *SIC* 7379

CONTENT CRITICAL SOLUTIONS INC p 362
121 Moonachie Ave, Moonachie NJ 07074
Tel (201) 528-2777 *SIC* 7379

ARTECH INFORMATION SYSTEMS LLC p 114
360 Mount Kemble Ave # 2, Morristown NJ 07960
Tel (973) 998-2500 *SIC* 7371 7379

IMS HEALTH INC p 735
100 Ims Dr, Parsippany NJ 07054
Tel (203) 448-4600 *SIC* 7379

■ RCM TECHNOLOGIES (USA) INC p 1212
2500 Mcclellan Ave # 350, Pennsauken NJ 08109
Tel (856) 356-4500 *SIC* 8742 7379 8711

NITYO INFOTECH CORP p 1045
666 Plainsboro Rd Ste 210, Plainsboro NJ 08536
Tel (609) 799-5959 *SIC* 7379

NAVITAS INC p 1020
502 Carnegie Ctr Ste 100, Princeton NJ 08540
Tel (609) 720-1002 *SIC* 7379

CGI AMS p 285
75 Livingston Ave Ste 202, Roseland NJ 07068
Tel (972) 788-0400
SIC 7379 8748 7374 7371

ZT GROUP INTL INC p 1644
333 Meadowlands Pkwy Fl 2, Secaucus NJ 07094
Tel (201) 559-1000 *SIC* 7379

▲ WAYSIDE TECHNOLOGY GROUP INC p 1584
1157 Shrewsbury Ave, Shrewsbury NJ 07702
Tel (732) 389-8950 *SIC* 5045 7373 7379

▲ COGNIZANT TECHNOLOGY SOLUTIONS CORP p 334
500 Frank W Burr Blvd, Teaneck NJ 07666
Tel (201) 801-0233 *SIC* 7371 7379 7372

CORE TECHNOLOGY SOLUTIONS LIMITED LIABILITY CO p 369
80 S Jefferson Rd, Whippany NJ 07981
Tel (973) 588-4533 *SIC* 7379 7373

■ IBM WORLD TRADE CORP p 726
1 New Orchard Rd Ste 1, Armonk NY 10504
Tel (914) 765-1900
SIC 3571 3577 7377 7379

▲ INTERNATIONAL BUSINESS MACHINES CORP p 754
1 New Orchard Rd Ste 1, Armonk NY 10504
Tel (914) 499-1900
SIC 7379 7371 3571 3572 3674

▲ COMPUTER TASK GROUP INC p 353
800 Delaware Ave, Buffalo NY 14209
Tel (716) 882-8000 SIC 7371 7379 7361

CUSTOM COMPUTER SPECIALISTS INC p 403
70 Suffolk Ct Ste 100, Hauppauge NY 11788
Tel (800) 598-8989 SIC 7379 7373 7378

CURRIER MCCABE & ASSOCIATES INC p 402
700 Troy Schenectady Rd, Latham NY 12110
Tel (518) 783-9003 SIC 7371 7379

AJILON LLC p 41
175 Broadhollow Rd, Melville NY 11747
Tel (631) 844-7800 SIC 7379 8742 7374

AP CARIB HOLDING LTD p 95
9 W 57th St Fl 43, New York NY 10019
Tel (212) 515-3202 SIC 8741 8748 7379

ASI SYSTEM INTEGRATION INC p 117
48 W 37th St Fl 4, New York NY 10018
Tel (212) 695-7970 SIC 7379

AXELON SERVICES CORP p 140
44 Wall St Fl 18, New York NY 10005
Tel (877) 711-8700 SIC 7379

CAP GEMINI AMERICA INC p 248
623 5th Ave Fl 33, New York NY 10022
Tel (917) 934-8000 SIC 7379

CAPGEMINI NORTH AMERICA INC p 249
623 5th Ave Fl 33, New York NY 10022
Tel (212) 314-8000 SIC 7379

COMPUTER GENERATED SOLUTIONS INC p 352
200 Vesey St Fl 27, New York NY 10281
Tel (212) 408-3800
SIC 7373 7379 7371 8243

FAREPORTAL INC p 528
135 W 50th St Ste 500, New York NY 10020
Tel (646) 738-7813 SIC 7379

GENESIS CORP p 602
950 3rd Ave Ste 2702, New York NY 10022
Tel (212) 688-5522 SIC 7379 8742

GLOBAL DATA PUBLICATIONS INC p 616
441 Lexington Ave Fl 3, New York NY 10017
Tel (646) 395-5460 SIC 7379 8732 8748

INSTINET CORP p 747
1095 Avenue Of The, New York NY 10036
Tel (212) 310-9500 SIC 6211 7379

ITHAKA HARBORS INC p 768
2 Rector St Fl 18, New York NY 10006
Tel (212) 500-2600 SIC 7379

MEDIAMATH INC p 936
4 World Trade Ctr, New York NY 10007
Tel (646) 840-4200 SIC 7379

■ NYNEX INFORMATION SOLUTIONS GROUP INC p 1069
1095 Ave Of The Amer Fl 7, New York NY 10036
Tel (212) 395-1000 SIC 8732 7371 7379

OAK HILL CAPITAL PARTNERS LP p 1070
65 E 55th St Fl 32, New York NY 10022
Tel (212) 527-8400 SIC 7379

PRESIDIO INTERNATIONAL INC p 1172
450 W 15th St 4, New York NY 10011
Tel (212) 462-1100 SIC 5651 7379

STROZ FRIEDBERG LLC p 1394
32 Avenue Of The Americas # 1, New York NY 10013
Tel (212) 981-6540 SIC 7379

T2 COMPUTING INC p 1420
119 W 23rd St Ste 206, New York NY 10011
Tel (212) 220-9600 SIC 7373 7379

TATA AMERICA INTERNATIONAL CORP p 1426
101 Park Ave Rm 2603, New York NY 10178
Tel (212) 557-8038 SIC 7379

■ CONCENTRIX CORP p 354
3750 Monroe Ave, Pittsford NY 14534
Tel (585) 218-5300 SIC 7379 7331 7311

ATOS IT SOLUTIONS AND SERVICES INC p 128
2500 Westchester Ave Fl 3, Purchase NY 10577
Tel (914) 881-3000 SIC 7379

ISLAND COMPUTER PRODUCTS INC p 766
20 Clifton Ave, Staten Island NY 10305
Tel (718) 556-6700
SIC 5045 7373 7379 7378

ERGONOMIC GROUP INC p 507
609 Cantiague Rock Rd # 3, Westbury NY 11590
Tel (516) 746-7777
SIC 5045 7373 7374 7376 7379

VRUSH INDUSTRIES INC p 1566
118 N Wrenn St, High Point NC 27260
Tel (336) 886-7700
SIC 5045 5021 7379 3469 5712 7375

▲ CINCINNATI BELL INC p 307
221 E 4th St Ste 700, Cincinnati OH 45202
Tel (513) 397-9900
SIC 4813 7373 7374 7379

■ CINCINNATI BELL TECHNOLOGY SOLUTIONS INC p 307
4600 Montgomery Rd # 400, Cincinnati OH 45212
Tel (513) 841-2287 SIC 7379 5734

ITELLIGENCE INC p 768
10856 Reed Hartman Hwy, Cincinnati OH 45242
Tel (513) 956-2000 SIC 7379

PENTON BUSINESS MEDIA INC p 1132
1100 Superior Ave E Fl 8, Cleveland OH 44114
Tel (216) 696-7000 SIC 2741 7379

ONX ACQUISITION LLC p 1088
5910 Landerbrook Dr # 250, Mayfield Heights OH 44124
Tel (440) 569-2300 SIC 7372 7379

SOGETI USA LLC p 1337
10100 Innovation Dr # 200, Miamisburg OH 45342
Tel (937) 291-8100 SIC 7379

INTERNATIONAL COMMUNICATIONS EXCHANGE CORP p 755
4033 Ellery Ave, Moraine OH 45439
Tel (937) 296-9605 SIC 8748 7379

CONTINGENT NETWORK SERVICES LLC p 364
4400 Port Union Rd, West Chester OH 45011
Tel (513) 616-5773 SIC 7379 7373

HITACHI COMPUTER PRODUCTS (AMERICA) INC p 696
1800 E Imhoff Rd, Norman OK 73071
Tel (405) 360-5500 SIC 3577 3572 7379

GDH CONSULTING INC p 595
4200 E Skelly Dr Ste 650, Tulsa OK 74135
Tel (918) 392-1600 SIC 7379 7361 7371

▲ UNISYS CORP p 1506
801 Lakeview Dr Ste 100, Blue Bell PA 19422
Tel (215) 986-4011
SIC 7373 7378 7379 3571 3572

SICOM SYSTEMS INC p 1319
4434 Progress Meadow Dr, Doylestown PA 18902
Tel (215) 489-2500 SIC 5045 3578 7379

■ GSI COMMERCE INC p 643
935 1st Ave, King Of Prussia PA 19406
Tel (610) 491-7000 SIC 5961 7371 7379

COMMUNICATION CABLE CO p 346
140 Quaker Ln, Malvern PA 19355
Tel (610) 644-5155 SIC 5045 7379

■ BELL ATLANTIC GLOBAL WIRELESS INC p 170
1717 Arch St Fl 33, Philadelphia PA 19103
Tel (215) 246-9494
SIC 4813 4812 5065 7379

OPEN SYSTEMS TECHNOLOGIES INC p 1089
1818 Market St Ste 2510, Philadelphia PA 19103
Tel (215) 399-5800 SIC 7379

NITYO INFOTECH CORP p 1045
2652 Hidden Valley Rd # 103, Pittsburgh PA 15241
Tel (412) 894-9054 SIC 7379

▲ EMTEC INC p 495
150 N Radnor, Radnor PA 19087
Tel (973) 376-4242 SIC 7371 7379

JUDGE GROUP INC p 796
151 S Warner Rd Ste 100, Wayne PA 19087
Tel (610) 667-7700 SIC 7373 7361 7379

▲ EVERTEC INC p 515
Km 1/3 Rr 176, San Juan PR 00926
Tel (787) 759-9999
SIC 8741 8748 7379 8721

LIFE CYCLE ENGINEERING INC p 863
4360 Corporate Rd Ste 100, North Charleston SC 29405
Tel (843) 744-7110
SIC 7371 7373 7376 7379 8711

TOLT SOLUTIONS INC p 1459
3550 Rutherford Rd, Taylors SC 29687
Tel (864) 322-4200
SIC 8748 7379 7374 7373

LPS INTEGRATION INC p 882
5300 Virginia Way Ste 100, Brentwood TN 37027
Tel (866) 706-7904 SIC 5045 7379

JANUS GLOBAL OPERATIONS LLC p 778
2229 Old Highway 95, Lenoir City TN 37771
Tel (865) 988-6063
SIC 4959 7381 7373 7379 8742

LUMENATE TECHNOLOGIES LP p 885
16633 Dallas Pkwy Ste 450, Addison TX 75001
Tel (972) 248-8999 SIC 7379

KASASA LTD p 804
4516 Seton Center Pkwy, Austin TX 78759
Tel (512) 418-9590 SIC 7371 7373 7379

■ WINCOR NIXDORF INC p 1615
12345 N Lamar Blvd # 200, Austin TX 78753
Tel (512) 676-5000 SIC 7379 5734 5251

ATOS ORIGIN INC p 128
18062 Fm 529 Rd Ste 215, Cypress TX 77433
Tel (914) 881-3000
SIC 7373 7374 7376 7379

HITACHI CONSULTING CORP p 696
14643 Dallas Pkwy Ste 800, Dallas TX 75254
Tel (214) 665-7000 SIC 7379 7374

COMPUGEN SYSTEMS INC p 352
5847 San Felipe St # 1700, Houston TX 77057
Tel (713) 821-1739 SIC 7379

PCPC DIRECT LTD p 1124
10690 Shadow Wood Dr # 132, Houston TX 77043
Tel (713) 984-8808 SIC 5045 7378 7379

PCPC INC p 1124
10690 Shadow Wood Dr # 132, Houston TX 77043
Tel (713) 984-8808 SIC 5045 7378 7379

PREDICTIF SOLUTIONS p 1169
8588 Katy Fwy Ste 435, Houston TX 77024
Tel (713) 457-7471 SIC 7379

HOV SERVICES INC p 712
2701 E Grauwyler Rd, Irving TX 75061
Tel (248) 837-7100
SIC 7374 7334 7389 2752 7331 7379

RJR CONSULTING GROUP INC p 1239
707 Dover Park Trl # 200, Mansfield TX 76063
Tel (817) 992-0124 SIC 7379

NTT DATA INC p 1065
5601 Gran Pkwy Ste 1000, Plano TX 75024
Tel (800) 745-3263 SIC 7373 7372 7379

■ PEROT SYSTEMS CORP p 1137
2300 W Plano Pkwy, Plano TX 75075
Tel (972) 577-0000 SIC 7376 7379

VERTEX BUSINESS SERVICES LLC p 1552
501 W Pres G Bush Hwy 3, Richardson TX 75080
Tel (214) 576-1000 SIC 7379

■ DELL INC p 425
1 Dell Way, Round Rock TX 78682
Tel (512) 338-4400
SIC 3571 3572 3575 3577 7372 7379

SIGMA SOLUTIONS GP INC p 1321
607 E Sonterra Blvd # 250, San Antonio TX 78258
Tel (210) 348-9876 SIC 7373 7379

■ ISG INFORMATION SERVICES GROUP AMERICAS INC p 766
25025 N I 45 Ste 225, The Woodlands TX 77380
Tel (281) 465-5700 SIC 7379

TECHNOLOGY TRANSFER INC p 1432
16969 N Texas Ave Ste 400, Webster TX 77598
Tel (281) 488-7961 SIC 7361 7379

CALIBRE SYSTEMS INC p 239
6354 Walker Ln Ste 300, Alexandria VA 22310
Tel (703) 797-8500 SIC 7379 8748

MODERN TECHNOLOGY SOLUTIONS INC p 981
5285 Shawnee Rd Ste 400, Alexandria VA 22312
Tel (703) 564-3800
SIC 8711 8742 8731 7379

ACCENTURE FEDERAL SERVICES LLC p 14
800 N Glebe Rd Ste 300, Arlington VA 22203
Tel (703) 947-2000 SIC 8742 7379

PHACIL INC p 1141
800 N Glebe Rd Ste 700, Arlington VA 22203
Tel (703) 526-1800 SIC 7379 7371

■ PRO-TELLIGENT LLC p 1178
1320 N Courthouse Rd # 600, Arlington VA 22201
Tel (703) 387-2100 SIC 7371 7379

■ SAVVIS FEDERAL SYSTEMS INC p 1284
4250 Fairfax Dr, Arlington VA 22203
Tel (703) 667-6000 SIC 4813 7379

SIEMENS GOVERNMENT TECHNOLOGIES INC p 1320
2231 Crystal Dr Ste 700, Arlington VA 22202
Tel (703) 860-1574
SIC 8711 7373 7376 7379 8712 7378

ENGINEERING SOLUTIONS & PRODUCTS LLC p 499
14566 Lee Rd, Chantilly VA 20151
Tel (571) 375-1400
SIC 8711 7379 4813 8742 8748

IRON BOW HOLDINGS INC p 764
4800 Westfields Blvd # 300, Chantilly VA 20151
Tel (703) 279-3000 SIC 7379 7373

NJVC LLC p 1045
14295 Park Meadow Dr, Chantilly VA 20151
Tel (703) 429-9000 SIC 7379

HARRIS TECHNICAL SERVICES CORP p 664
21000 Atl Blvd Ste 300, Dulles VA 20166
Tel (703) 610-4200
SIC 7371 7379 8711 3577

CAMBER GOVERNMENT SOLUTIONS INC p 243
12730 Fair Lakes Cir, Fairfax VA 22033
Tel (703) 653-8000 SIC 7371 7379

CGI FEDERAL INC p 285
12601 Fair Lakes Cir, Fairfax VA 22033
Tel (703) 227-6000 SIC 7379 7389 8999

CGI TECHNOLOGIES AND SOLUTIONS INC p 286
11325 Random Hills Rd, Fairfax VA 22030
Tel (703) 267-8000
SIC 7379 7373 7372 7389

ECS FEDERAL LLC p 476
2750 Prosperity Ave # 600, Fairfax VA 22031
Tel (703) 270-1540 SIC 7371 7379 8742

■ GENERAL DYNAMICS INFORMATION TECHNOLOGY INC p 600
3211 Jermantown Rd, Fairfax VA 22030
Tel (703) 995-8700 SIC 7379 8711 7373

■ KFORCE GOVERNMENT SOLUTIONS INC p 816
2677 Prosperity Ave # 100, Fairfax VA 22031
Tel (703) 245-7350 SIC 7379

▲ MANTECH INTERNATIONAL CORP p 903
12015 Lee Jackson Hwy, Fairfax VA 22033
Tel (703) 218-6000 SIC 7373 8711 7379

■ SIGNAL SOLUTIONS LLC p 1322
3211 Jermantown Rd # 700, Fairfax VA 22030
Tel (703) 205-0500
SIC 8711 7379 7374 4813 7373 8731

TEOCO CORP p 1439
12150 Monu Dr Ste 400, Fairfax VA 22033
Tel (703) 322-9200 SIC 7379

APTARA INC p 101
3110 Frview Pk Dr Ste 900, Falls Church VA 22042
Tel (703) 352-0001 SIC 7379

■ CSRA LLC p 398
3170 Fairview Park Dr, Falls Church VA 22042
Tel (703) 876-1000
SIC 7371 8733 7376 7374 7379

■ CUBIC GLOBAL DEFENSE INC p 399
205 Van Buren St Ste 310, Herndon VA 20170
Tel (703) 821-8930
SIC 7379 7371 7373 8711

DELTEK INC p 427
2291 Wood Oak Dr Ste 100, Herndon VA 20171
Tel (703) 734-8606 SIC 7371 7379

▲ EPLUS INC p 505
13595 Dulles Tech Dr, Herndon VA 20171
Tel (703) 984-8400
SIC 5045 7377 7379 7372

SOTERA DEFENSE SOLUTIONS INC p 1341
2121 Coop Way Ste 400, Herndon VA 20171
Tel (703) 230-8200 SIC 7371 7379

OBERON ASSOCIATES INC p 1072
9700 Capital Ct Ste 301, Manassas VA 20110
Tel (703) 365-8801 SIC 7379

CELERITY IT LLC p 273
8401 Greensboro Dr # 500, Mc Lean VA 22102
Tel (703) 848-1900 SIC 7379

COGNOSANTE LLC p 334
8200 Greensboro Dr # 1200, Mc Lean VA 22102
Tel (703) 206-6000 SIC 7379 8748

■ IMMIXGROUP INC p 734
8444 Westpark Dr Ste 200, Mc Lean VA 22102
Tel (703) 752-0610 SIC 7371 7379

PREFERRED SYSTEMS SOLUTIONS INC p 1169
7925 Jones Branch Dr # 6200, Mc Lean VA 22102
Tel (703) 663-2777 SIC 7379

TVAR SOLUTIONS LLC p 1494
1320 Old Chain Bridge Rd # 445, Mc Lean VA 22101
Tel (703) 635-3900 SIC 5045 7379 3571

ACE INFO SOLUTIONS INC p 16
11490 Commerce Park Dr # 340, Reston VA 20191
Tel (703) 391-2800 SIC 7379

APOGEN TECHNOLOGIES INC p 97
11091 Sunset Hills Rd # 200, Reston VA 20190
Tel (703) 644-6433 SIC 7373 7379

APPIAN CORP p 98
11955 Democracy Dr # 1700, Reston VA 20190
Tel (703) 442-8844 SIC 7379 7371

■ CONTACT SOLUTIONS LLC p 362
11950 Democracy Dr # 250, Reston VA 20190
Tel (703) 480-1620 SIC 7379 7371 7389

HEADSTRONG CORP p 673
11921 Freedom Dr Ste 550, Reston VA 20190
Tel (703) 272-6761 SIC 7379 8999

PRAGMATICS INC p 1167
1761 Business Center Dr # 110, Reston VA 20190
Tel (703) 890-8500 SIC 7379

SI INTERNATIONAL ZEN TECHNOLOGY INC p 1319
1818 Library St, Reston VA 20190
Tel (703) 939-6671 SIC 7379

VENCORE SERVICES AND SOLUTIONS INC p 1547
1835 Alexander Bell Dr, Reston VA 20191
Tel (703) 391-7017 SIC 7379 7373 3812

INFORMATION INNOVATORS INC p 742
7400 Fullerton Rd Ste 210, Springfield VA 22153
Tel (703) 635-7088 SIC 7379

TRIPLE-I HOLDINGS LLC p 1482
7400 Fullerton Rd Ste 210, Springfield VA 22153
Tel (703) 635-7088 SIC 7379 6719

▲ COMPUTER SCIENCES CORP p 353
1775 Tysons Blvd, Tysons VA 22102
Tel (703) 245-9675
SIC 7376 7374 7379 7373 7323

ALVAREZ LLC p 63
8251 Greensboro Dr # 230, Tysons Corner VA 22102
Tel (301) 830-4020
SIC 8742 8741 7379 5044

ACTIONET INC p 19
2600 Park Twr Dr Ste 1000, Vienna VA 22180
Tel (703) 204-0090
SIC 7379 7373 7372 7371

MICROTECHNOLOGIES LLC p 962
8330 Boone Blvd Ste 600, Vienna VA 22182
Tel (703) 891-1073 SIC 7379

INTELLECTUAL VENTURES LLC p 750
3150 139th Ave Se Ste 500, Bellevue WA 98005
Tel (425) 467-2300 SIC 7379

PARALLELS INC p 1113
110 110th Ave Ne Ste 410, Bellevue WA 98004
Tel (425) 728-8239 SIC 7379

SHAPE TECHNOLOGIES GROUP PARENT HOLDINGS INC p 1311
23500 64th Ave S, Kent WA 98032
Tel (253) 850-3500 SIC 7379

AVANADE INC p 136
818 Stewart St Ste 400, Seattle WA 98101
Tel (206) 239-5600 SIC 7379 8742

▲ CRAY INC p 389
901 5th Ave Ste 1000, Seattle WA 98164
Tel (206) 701-2000 SIC 3571 7379

PARAGON DEVELOPMENT SYSTEMS INC p 1113
13400 Bishops Ln Ste 190, Brookfield WI 53005
Tel (262) 569-5300 SIC 5734 7379

SIC 7381 Detective & Armored Car Svcs

SECURITY ENGINEERS INC p 1299
1617 3rd Ave N, Birmingham AL 35203
Tel (205) 251-0566 SIC 7381

DOTHAN SECURITY INC p 452
600 W Adams St, Dothan AL 36303
Tel (334) 793-5720 SIC 7381

DYNAMIC SECURITY INC p 464
1102 Woodward Ave, Muscle Shoals AL 35661
Tel (256) 383-5798 SIC 7381

NANA DEVELOPMENT CORP p 1007
909 W 9th Ave, Anchorage AK 99501
Tel (907) 265-4100 SIC 7381 1389

NANA MANAGEMENT SERVICES LLC p 1007
800 E Dimond Blvd 3-450, Anchorage AK 99515
Tel (907) 273-2400
SIC 5812 7349 7021 7033 7381

ANDREWS INTERNATIONAL INC p 90
455 N Moss St, Burbank CA 91502
Tel (818) 487-4060 SIC 7381

ARMOR DOMAIN INC p 111
235 Westlake Ctr Pmb 518, Daly City CA 94015
Tel (415) 637-1817 SIC 7381

CONSTRUCTION PROTECTIVE SERVICES INC p 361
436 W Walnut St, Gardena CA 90248
Tel (800) 257-5512 SIC 7381 7382

CPS SECURITY SOLUTIONS INC p 388
436 W Walnut St, Gardena CA 90248
Tel (310) 818-1030 SIC 7381

WSA GROUP INC p 1628
19208 S Vermont Ave 200, Gardena CA 90248
Tel (310) 743-3000 SIC 7381 7349

GARDA CL WEST INC p 591
1612 W Pico Blvd, Los Angeles CA 90015
Tel (213) 383-3611 SIC 7381

PROFESSIONAL SECURITY CONSULTANTS p 1180
11454 San Vicente Blvd # 2, Los Angeles CA 90049
Tel (310) 207-7729 SIC 7381 7382

WORLDWIDE SECURITY ASSOCIATES INC p 1626
10311 S La Cienega Blvd, Los Angeles CA 90045
Tel (310) 743-3000 SIC 7381

GUARD-SYSTEMS INC p 645
1190 Monterey Pass Rd, Monterey Park CA 91754
Tel (626) 443-0031 SIC 7381

INTER-CON SECURITY SYSTEMS INC p 751
210 S De Lacey Ave # 200, Pasadena CA 91105
Tel (626) 535-2200 SIC 7381

ELITE SHOW SERVICES INC p 487
2878 Camino Del Rio S # 260, San Diego CA 92108
Tel (619) 574-1589 SIC 7381

■ AMERICAN COMMERCIAL SECURITY SERVICES INC p 70
420 Taylor St Fl 2, San Francisco CA 94102
Tel (415) 856-1020 SIC 7381

STEELE INTERNATIONAL INC p 1384
1 Sansome St Ste 3500, San Francisco CA 94104
Tel (415) 781-4300 SIC 7381 8742 8748

ALLIED UNIVERSAL HOLDCO LLC p 57
1551 N Tustin Ave Ste 650, Santa Ana CA 92705
Tel (714) 619-9700 SIC 6719 7381

ALLIED UNIVERSAL TOPCO LLC p 57
1551 N Tustin Ave, Santa Ana CA 92705
Tel (714) 619-9700 *SIC* 6719 7381 7349

GUARDSMARK LLC p 645
1551 N Tustin Ave Ste 650, Santa Ana CA 92705
Tel (714) 619-9700 *SIC* 7381 8742 2721

SHIELD SECURITY INC p 1316
1551 N Tustin Ave Ste 650, Santa Ana CA 92705
Tel (714) 210-1501 *SIC* 7381

UNIVERSAL PROTECTION GP LLC p 1517
1551 N Tustin Ave Ste 650, Santa Ana CA 92705
Tel (714) 619-9700 *SIC* 7381

UNIVERSAL PROTECTION SERVICE LP p 1517
1551 N Tustin Ave Ste 650, Santa Ana CA 92705
Tel (714) 619-9700 *SIC* 7381

UNIVERSAL SERVICES OF AMERICA LP p 1517
1551 N Tustin Ave, Santa Ana CA 92705
Tel (714) 619-9700 *SIC* 7381 7349

AEDAN INC p 29
27447, Sun City CA 92586
Tel (888) 272-5505
SIC 7371 7381 8733 3812 7382

RESOURCE COLLECTION INC p 1227
3771 W 242nd St Ste 205, Torrance CA 90505
Tel (310) 219-3272
SIC 7349 7381 0782 3564

OFFDUTYOFFICERS.COM p 1075
2365 La Mirada Dr, Vista CA 92081
Tel (888) 408-5900 *SIC* 7381 8742

HSS INC p 715
900 S Broadway Ste 100, Denver CO 80209
Tel (303) 603-3000 *SIC* 8082 7381 7382

OPTIV INC p 1090
1125 17th St Ste 1700, Denver CO 80202
Tel (303) 298-0600
SIC 5045 5065 6719 7381

LANDMARK EVENT STAFFING SERVICES INC p 842
4131 Harbor Walk Dr, Fort Collins CO 80525
Tel (714) 293-4248 *SIC* 7381 7389

ADT CORP p 24
1501 Yamato Rd, Boca Raton FL 33431
Tel (561) 988-3600 *SIC* 7381 7382 3699

ADT HOLDINGS INC p 24
1501 Nw 51st St, Boca Raton FL 33431
Tel (888) 298-9274 *SIC* 7381 1731

ATI SYSTEMS INTERNATIONAL INC p 124
2000 Nw Corp Blvd Ste 101, Boca Raton FL 33431
Tel (561) 939-7000 *SIC* 7381 4513 4215

GARDA CL TECHNICAL SERVICES INC p 591
700 S Federal Hwy Ste 300, Boca Raton FL 33432
Tel (561) 939-7000 *SIC* 6099 7381

TYCO INTEGRATED SECURITY LLC p 1496
4700 Exchange Ct Ste 300, Boca Raton FL 33431
Tel (561) 226-8201 *SIC* 7382 7381 1731

MARKSMAN SECURITY CORP p 909
1700 Nw 49th St Ste 110, Fort Lauderdale FL 33309
Tel (954) 771-9755 *SIC* 7382 7381

G4S HOLDING ONE INC p 588
1395 University Blvd, Jupiter FL 33458
Tel (561) 622-5656
SIC 7381 7382 8744 8748 8742

G4S SECURE SOLUTIONS (USA) INC p 588
1395 University Blvd, Jupiter FL 33458
Tel (561) 622-5656
SIC 7381 8744 8748 8742

G4S SECURE SOLUTIONS INTERNATIONAL INC p 588
1395 University Blvd, Jupiter FL 33458
Tel (561) 622-5656 *SIC* 7382 7381

G4S TECHNOLOGY HOLDINGS (USA) INC p 588
1395 University Blvd, Jupiter FL 33458
Tel (561) 622-5656 *SIC* 7381

KENT SECURITY SERVICES INC p 812
14600 Biscayne Blvd, North Miami FL 33181
Tel (305) 919-9400 *SIC* 7381 7299

CENTERRA GROUP LLC p 276
7121 Fairway Dr Ste 301, Palm Beach Gardens FL 33418
Tel (561) 472-0600 *SIC* 7381 8744

FIRST ADVANTAGE CORP p 544
1 Concourse Pkwy Ste 200, Atlanta GA 30328
Tel (800) 888-5773
SIC 7323 8742 7372 7389 7381

SECURAMERICA LLC p 1298
3399 Peachtree Rd Ne # 1050, Atlanta GA 30326
Tel (404) 926-4222 *SIC* 7381

SIZEMORE INC p 1328
2116 Walton Way, Augusta GA 30904
Tel (706) 736-1456 *SIC* 7381 7363 7349

ANDREWS INTERNATIONAL p 90
200 Mansell Ct E Ste 500, Roswell GA 30076
Tel (661) 775-8400 *SIC* 7381

US SECURITY ASSOCIATES HOLDINGS INC p 1533
200 Mansell Ct E Fl 5, Roswell GA 30076
Tel (770) 625-1500 *SIC* 7381 7349

US SECURITY ASSOCIATES INC p 1533
200 Mansell Ct E Ste 500, Roswell GA 30076
Tel (770) 625-1500 *SIC* 7381

US SECURITY HOLDINGS INC p 1533
200 Mansell Ct E Ste 500, Roswell GA 30076
Tel (770) 625-1400 *SIC* 7381 7349

ANDY FRAIN SERVICES INC p 91
761 Shoreline Dr, Aurora IL 60504
Tel (630) 820-3820 *SIC* 7381 7363

COVENANT AVIATION SECURITY LLC p 384
400 Quadrangle Dr Ste A, Bolingbrook IL 60440
Tel (630) 771-0800 *SIC* 7381

COVENANT SECURITY SERVICES LTD p 384
400 Quadrangle Dr Ste A, Bolingbrook IL 60440
Tel (630) 771-0800 *SIC* 7381

COVENANT SERVICES WORLDWIDE LLC p 384
400 Quadrangle Dr Ste A, Bolingbrook IL 60440
Tel (630) 771-0800 *SIC* 7381

PENDUM LLC p 1128
558 W Lamont Rd, Elmhurst IL 60126
Tel (800) 422-6835 *SIC* 6099 7381

A & R SECURITY SERVICES INC p 4
600 Holiday Plaza Dr # 500, Matteson IL 60443
Tel (708) 389-3830 *SIC* 7381

IPC INTERNATIONAL CORP p 763
10255 W Hggi, Rosemont IL 60018
Tel (847) 444-2000
SIC 7381 8742 2389 3199

PER MAR SECURITY AND RESEARCH CORP p 1134
1910 E Kimberly Rd, Davenport IA 52807
Tel (563) 359-3200
SIC 8732 7381 5099 7389 7382

LOFTON SECURITY SERVICE INC p 874
9405 Interline Ave, Baton Rouge LA 70809
Tel (225) 906-2200 *SIC* 7381

VINSON GUARD SERVICE INC p 1558
955 Howard Ave, New Orleans LA 70113
Tel (504) 525-0591 *SIC* 7381

WEISER SECURITY SERVICES INC p 1588
3939 Tulane Ave 300, New Orleans LA 70119
Tel (504) 586-4712 *SIC* 7381

ABACUS CORP p 9
610 Gusryan St, Baltimore MD 21224
Tel (410) 633-1900 *SIC* 7381 7363 7349

BROADWAY SERVICES INC p 216
3709 E Monument St, Baltimore MD 21205
Tel (410) 563-6900
SIC 7349 7381 7521 6512 4119

RED COATS INC p 1215
4520 East West Hwy # 200, Bethesda MD 20814
Tel (301) 654-4360 *SIC* 7349 7381

KNIGHT PROTECTIVE SERVICE INC p 824
6411 Ivy Ln Ste 320, Greenbelt MD 20770
Tel (301) 808-4669 *SIC* 7381

DUNBAR ARMORED INC p 461
50 Schilling Rd, Hunt Valley MD 21031
Tel (410) 584-9800 *SIC* 7381

COASTAL INTERNATIONAL SECURITY INC p 332
6101 Fallard Dr, Upper Marlboro MD 20772
Tel (703) 339-0233 *SIC* 7381

APOLLO SECURITY INTERNATIONAL INC p 97
2150 Bston Providence Hwy, Walpole MA 02081
Tel (508) 660-1197 *SIC* 7381 8748

GUARDIAN GUARD SERVICES INC p 645
18000 W 8 Mile Rd, Southfield MI 48075
Tel (248) 423-1000 *SIC* 7381

PRUDENTIAL SECURITY INC p 1187
20600 Eureka Rd Ste 900, Taylor MI 48180
Tel (734) 286-6000 *SIC* 7381

DECO INC p 421
11156 Zealand Ave N, Champlin MN 55316
Tel (763) 576-9572 *SIC* 7381

AMERICAN SECURITY LLC p 79
1717 University Ave W, Saint Paul MN 55104
Tel (651) 644-1155 *SIC* 7381

ISS WORLDWIDE p 767
1225 E 18th St, Kansas City MO 64108
Tel (816) 421-8088 *SIC* 7349 7381

SIGNAL 88 FRANCHISE GROUP INC p 1322
3880 S 149th St Ste 102, Omaha NE 68144
Tel (877) 498-8494 *SIC* 7381

SIGNAL 88 LLC p 1322
3880 S 149th St Ste 102, Omaha NE 68144
Tel (877) 498-8494 *SIC* 7381

BOWLES CORPORATE SERVICES INC p 204
335 Broad St, Clifton NJ 07013
Tel (973) 773-0699 *SIC* 7381 7389 7361

GATEWAY SECURITY INC p 594
604 Market St 608, Newark NJ 07105
Tel (973) 465-8006 *SIC* 7381

SECURITAS HOLDINGS INC p 1298
9 Campus Dr Ste 1, Parsippany NJ 07054
Tel (973) 267-5300 *SIC* 7381

SECURITAS SECURITY SERVICES USA INC p 1299
9 Campus Dr, Parsippany NJ 07054
Tel (973) 267-5300 *SIC* 7381

SECURITAS SERVICES INC p 1299
9 Campus Dr Ste 1, Parsippany NJ 07054
Tel (973) 267-5300 *SIC* 7381

SOS SECURITY INC p 1341
1915 Us Highway 46 Ste 1, Parsippany NJ 07054
Tel (973) 402-6600 *SIC* 7381

SOS SECURITY LLC p 1341
1915 Us Highway 46, Parsippany NJ 07054
Tel (973) 402-6600 *SIC* 7381

SILVER STAR SOLUTIONS-KNIGHT PROTECTIVE SERVICE-JOINT VENTURE LLC p 1324
59 Osceola Rd, Wayne NJ 07470
Tel (201) 847-9148 *SIC* 7381

AKAL SECURITY INC p 42
7 Infinity Loop, Espanola NM 87532
Tel (505) 753-7832 *SIC* 7381

LANCE INVESTIGATION SERVICE INC p 841
1438 Boston Rd, Bronx NY 10460
Tel (718) 893-1400 *SIC* 7381 1731

FJC SECURITY SERVICES INC p 553
275 Jericho Tpke, Floral Park NY 11001
Tel (516) 328-6000 *SIC* 7381

▲ABM INDUSTRIES INC p 12
1 Liberty Plz Fl Con1, New York NY 10006
Tel (212) 297-0200
SIC 7349 7521 7381 8711

■ABM ONSITE SERVICES INC p 12
1 Liberty Plz Fl 7, New York NY 10006
Tel (212) 497-0600
SIC 7349 7381 7521 8711

ELITE INVESTIGATIONS LTD p 487
538 W 29th St, New York NY 10001
Tel (212) 629-3131 *SIC* 7381

KROLL LLC p 830
600 3rd Ave Fl 4, New York NY 10016
Tel (212) 593-1000
SIC 7381 8742 8748 7389

MC ROBERTS CORP p 925
87 Nassau St, New York NY 10038
Tel (212) 425-2500 *SIC* 7381

MCROBERTS PROTECTIVE AGENCY INC p 932
42 Broadway Ste 1836, New York NY 10004
Tel (732) 886-0990 *SIC* 7381 1731

PRIME SECURITY SERVICES BORROWER LLC p 1175
9 W 57th St Fl 43, New York NY 10019
Tel (212) 515-3200
SIC 6799 7382 3699 7381

SPARTAN SECURITY SERVICES INC p 1355
417 5th Ave Fl 9, New York NY 10016
Tel (212) 251-7888 *SIC* 7381

STERLING INFOSYSTEMS INC p 1387
1 State St Fl Plaza24, New York NY 10004
Tel (800) 899-2272 *SIC* 7375 7381

SAFE ENVIRONMENT BUSINESS SOLUTIONS INC p 1266
8 Revolutionary Rd, Ossining NY 10562
Tel (914) 741-1000 *SIC* 7381

STRATEGIC SECURITY CORP p 1392
4 Higbie Dr, Smithtown NY 11787
Tel (212) 509-0547 *SIC* 7381

PAY-O-MATIC CORP p 1122
160 Oak Dr, Syosset NY 11791
Tel (516) 496-4900 *SIC* 6099 7381 7999

SUMMIT SECURITY SERVICES INC p 1399
390 Rxr Plz Lobbyl, Uniondale NY 11556
Tel (516) 240-2400 *SIC* 7381

SUNSTATES SECURITY LLC p 1404
7011 Albert Pick Rd Ste B, Greensboro NC 27409
Tel (336) 664-6944 *SIC* 7381

ALLEGIANCE SECURITY GROUP LLC p 53
2900 Arendell St Ste 18, Morehead City NC 28557
Tel (252) 247-1138 *SIC* 7381

SSA HOLDINGS II LLC p 1363
1207 Arendell St Ste C, Morehead City NC 28557
Tel (252) 808-3185 *SIC* 7381

■ SSA SECURITY INC p 1363
5447 Hwy 70 W Ste 200, Morehead City NC 28557
Tel (252) 808-3185 *SIC* 7381

SAFEGUARD PROPERTIES LLC p 1266
7887 Safeguard Cir, Cleveland OH 44125
Tel (216) 739-2900 *SIC* 8741 7382 7381

TENABLE PROTECTIVE SERVICES INC p 1437
2423 Payne Ave, Cleveland OH 44114
Tel (216) 361-0002 *SIC* 7381

AWP INC p 139
826 Overholt Rd, Kent OH 44240
Tel (330) 644-0655 *SIC* 7381

JOB 1 USA p 787
701 Jefferson Ave Ste 202, Toledo OH 43604
Tel (419) 255-5005 *SIC* 7381 7363 7361

RUMPF CORP p 1258
701 Jefferson Ave Ste 201, Toledo OH 43604
Tel (419) 255-5005 *SIC* 7361 7363 7381

STARPLEX CORP p 1379
12722 Ne Airport Way, Portland OR 97230
Tel (503) 222-5957 *SIC* 7381 7363 7999

ALLIED SECURITY HOLDINGS LLC p 57
161 Washington St Ste 600, Conshohocken PA 19428
Tel (484) 351-1300 *SIC* 7381 7382

ALLIED SECURITY LLC p 57
161 Washington St, Conshohocken PA 19428
Tel (610) 239-1100 *SIC* 7381

ALLIEDBARTON AEROSPACE AND DEFENSE SERVICES LLC p 57
161 Washington St Ste 600, Conshohocken PA 19428
Tel (484) 351-1300 *SIC* 7381 7382

ALLIEDBARTON SECURITY SERVICES LLC p 57
8 Tower Bridge 161 Wshgtn, Conshohocken PA 19428
Tel (610) 239-1100 *SIC* 7381

SPECTAGUARD ACQUISITION LLC p 1356
161 Washington St Ste 600, Conshohocken PA 19428
Tel (484) 351-1300 *SIC* 7381

SPECTAGUARD HOLDING CORP p 1356
161 Washington St Ste 600, Conshohocken PA 19428
Tel (610) 239-1100 *SIC* 7381

UNIVERSAL PROTECTION SERVICE LLC p 1517
161 Washington St Ste 600, Conshohocken PA 19428
Tel (704) 334-4751 *SIC* 7381

US INVESTIGATIONS SERVICES LLC p 1532
125 Lincoln Ave, Grove City PA 16127
Tel (724) 458-1750 *SIC* 7381

DAY & ZIMMERMANN GROUP INC p 417
1500 Spring Garden St # 900, Philadelphia PA 19130
Tel (215) 299-8000
SIC 8711 8712 8741 7381 7382 3489

DAY & ZIMMERMANN LLC CO p 417
1500 Spring Garden St # 900, Philadelphia PA 19130
Tel (215) 299-8000 *SIC* 7381

ST MORITZ SECURITY SERVICES INC p 1372
4600 Clairton Blvd, Pittsburgh PA 15236
Tel (412) 885-3144 *SIC* 7381

GENESIS SECURITY SERVICE p 603
5900 Ave Isla Verde L, Carolina PR 00979
Tel (787) 701-2830 *SIC* 7381

CAPITOL SECURITY POLICE INC p 251
703 Calle Victor Lopez, San Juan PR 00909
Tel (787) 727-1700 *SIC* 7381

RANGER AMERICAN OF PUERTO RICO INC p 1208
605 Calle Lodi, San Juan PR 00924
Tel (787) 999-6060 *SIC* 1731 7382 7381

ST JAMES SECURITY SERVICES INC p 1367
1604 Ave Ponce De Leon, San Juan PR 00909
Tel (787) 754-8448 *SIC* 7381

AMERICAN SECURITY OF GREENVILLE LLC p 79
1300 Rutherford Rd, Greenville SC 29609
Tel (864) 292-7450 *SIC* 7381

AMERICAN SERVICES INC p 79
1300 Rutherford Rd, Greenville SC 29609
Tel (864) 292-7450 *SIC* 7381 7349 7363

DIVERSCO HOLDINGS INC p 443
105 Diversco Dr, Spartanburg SC 29307
Tel (864) 579-3420 *SIC* 7381 7349

METROPOLITAN SECURITY SERVICES INC p 956
100 E 10th St Ste 400, Chattanooga TN 37402
Tel (423) 702-8200 *SIC* 7381

MURRAY GUARD INC p 1001
58 Murray Guard Dr, Jackson TN 38305
Tel (731) 668-3400 *SIC* 7381

JANUS GLOBAL OPERATIONS LLC p 778
2229 Old Highway 95, Lenoir City TN 37771
Tel (865) 988-6063
SIC 4959 7381 7373 7379 8742

NATION WIDE SERVICES INC p 1009
223 Sequoyah Rd, Loudon TN 37774
Tel (248) 355-0500 *SIC* 7381

CENTRAL DEFENSE SERVICES LLC p 278
6084 Apple Tree Dr Ste 1, Memphis TN 38115
Tel (901) 322-9554 *SIC* 7381

IMPERIAL GUARD AND DETECTIVE SERVICES INC p 734
2555 Poplar Ave, Memphis TN 38112
Tel (866) 840-2066 *SIC* 7381

SMITH PROTECTIVE SERVICES INC p 1333
4440 Beltway Dr, Addison TX 75001
Tel (972) 960-8481 *SIC* 7381

ASSET PROTECTION & SECURITY SERVICES LP p 119
5502 Burnham Dr, Corpus Christi TX 78413
Tel (361) 906-1552 *SIC* 7381

PAE APPLIED TECHNOLOGIES LLC p 1107
6500 West Fwy Ste 600, Fort Worth TX 76116
Tel (817) 737-1500
SIC 8741 8711 8744 4581 7381

LOOMIS ARMORED US LLC p 877
2500 Citywest Blvd # 2300, Houston TX 77042
Tel (713) 435-6700 *SIC* 7381 4789

NETVERSANT SOLUTIONS LLC p 1028
9750 W Sam Houston Pkwy N # 100, Houston TX 77064
Tel (800) 540-2739 *SIC* 7373 8999 7381

ISS MANAGEMENT & FINANCE CO INC p 767
1019 Central Pkwy N Ste 1, San Antonio TX 78232
Tel (210) 495-6021 *SIC* 7381

SECURITY SERVICE CUSO LLC p 1299
16211 La Cantera Pkwy, San Antonio TX 78256
Tel (210) 476-4151 *SIC* 6061 7381

M V M INC p 890
44620 Guilford Dr Ste 150, Ashburn VA 20147
Tel (571) 223-4500 *SIC* 7381 8741

ANDREWS INTERNATIONAL INC p 90
5870 Trinity Pkwy Ste 300, Centreville VA 20120
Tel (703) 592-1400 *SIC* 7381

CHENEGA INTEGRATED SYSTEMS LLC p 294
14295 Pk Madow Dr Ste 400, Chantilly VA 20151
Tel (571) 291-8500 *SIC* 7381 7382 8331

OMNIPLEX WORLD SERVICES CORP p 1085
14151 Park Meadow Dr # 300, Chantilly VA 20151
Tel (703) 652-3100 *SIC* 7381

▲ COMMAND SECURITY CORP p 344
512 Herndon Pkwy Ste A, Herndon VA 20170
Tel (703) 464-4735 *SIC* 7381

PARAGON SYSTEMS INC p 1113
13655 Dulles Tech Dr # 100, Herndon VA 20171
Tel (703) 263-7176 *SIC* 7381 7382 7374

SECURITY CONSULTANTS GROUP INC p 1299
13655 Dulles Tech Dr, Herndon VA 20171
Tel (703) 263-7176 *SIC* 7381

■ DYNCORP INTERNATIONAL INC p 465
1700 Old Meadow Rd, Mc Lean VA 22102
Tel (571) 722-0210
SIC 8741 7371 7381 7361 7363

GW CONSULTING INC p 648
1760 Old Madow Rd Ste 400, Mc Lean VA 22102
Tel (703) 253-8080 *SIC* 7381

SECURIGUARD INC p 1298
6858 Old Dominion Dr # 307, Mc Lean VA 22101
Tel (703) 821-6777 *SIC* 7381 8744

TRIPLE CANOPY INC p 1482
12018 Sunrise Valley Dr # 140, Reston VA 20191
Tel (703) 673-5000 *SIC* 7381 8748

▲ BRINKS CO p 213
1801 Bayberry Ct Ste 400, Richmond VA 23226
Tel (804) 289-9600 *SIC* 7382 7381

■ BRINKS INC p 213
1801 Bayberry Ct Ste 400, Richmond VA 23226
Tel (804) 289-9600 *SIC* 7381

SECURITAS CRITICAL INFRASTRUCTURE SERVICES INC p 1298
6850 Versar Ctr Ste 400, Springfield VA 22151
Tel (703) 750-1098 *SIC* 7381

SIC 7382 Security Systems Svcs

US TACTICAL RESPONSE AND INFORMATION SERVICE LLC p 1533
2 N Jackson St Ste 605, Montgomery AL 36104
Tel (888) 315-1113 *SIC* 7382

▲ LIFELOCK INC p 864
60 E Rio Salado Pkwy # 400, Tempe AZ 85281
Tel (480) 682-5100 *SIC* 7382

FIRST ALARM p 544
1111 Estates Dr, Aptos CA 95003
Tel (831) 476-1111 *SIC* 7382

PELCO INC p 1128
3500 Pelco Way, Clovis CA 93612
Tel (559) 292-1981 *SIC* 3663 7382

CONSTRUCTION PROTECTIVE SERVICES INC p 361
436 W Walnut St, Gardena CA 90248
Tel (800) 257-5512 *SIC* 7381 7382

STAFF PRO INC p 1374
15272 Jason Cir, Huntington Beach CA 92649
Tel (714) 230-7200 *SIC* 7382 8741

GORES RADIO HOLDINGS LLC p 626
10877 Wilshire Blvd # 1805, Los Angeles CA 90024
Tel (310) 209-3010 *SIC* 3699 7382

PROFESSIONAL SECURITY CONSULTANTS p 1180
11454 San Vicente Blvd # 2, Los Angeles CA 90049
Tel (310) 207-7729 *SIC* 7381 7382

BAY ALARM CO p 160
60 Berry Dr, Pacheco CA 94553
Tel (925) 935-1100 *SIC* 1731 7382 5063

▲ KRATOS DEFENSE & SECURITY SOLUTIONS INC p 829
4820 Estgate Mall Ste 200, San Diego CA 92121
Tel (858) 812-7300
SIC 3761 8711 8744 7382

SWANN COMMUNICATIONS USA INC p 1411
12636 Clark St, Santa Fe Springs CA 90670
Tel (562) 777-2551 *SIC* 5045 7382

AEDAN INC p 29
27447, Sun City CA 92586
Tel (888) 272-5505
SIC 7371 7381 8733 3812 7382

GOOD TECHNOLOGY CORP p 624
430 N Mary Ave Ste 200, Sunnyvale CA 94085
Tel (408) 212-7500 *SIC* 7371 7382

HSS INC p 715
900 S Broadway Ste 100, Denver CO 80209
Tel (303) 603-3000 *SIC* 8082 7381 7382

OPTIV SECURITY INC p 1090
1125 17th St Ste 1700, Denver CO 80202
Tel (888) 732-9406
SIC 5045 7379 7382 5065

▲ ASCENT CAPITAL GROUP INC p 116
5251 Dtc Pkwy Ste 1000, Greenwood Village CO 80111
Tel (303) 628-5600 *SIC* 3822 7382

AFFINECO LLC p 32
855 Main St Ste 900, Bridgeport CT 06604
Tel (203) 878-0638 *SIC* 7349 7382

ADT CORP p 24
1501 Yamato Rd, Boca Raton FL 33431
Tel (561) 988-3600 *SIC* 7381 7382 3699

ADT LLC p 24
1501 Yamato Rd, Boca Raton FL 33431
Tel (561) 988-3600 *SIC* 7382

RED HAWK FIRE & SECURITY LLC p 1215
5100 Town Center Cir # 350, Boca Raton FL 33486
Tel (561) 672-3737 *SIC* 3699 7382

SENSORMATIC ELECTRONICS LLC p 1305
6600 Congress Ave, Boca Raton FL 33487
Tel (561) 912-6000 *SIC* 7382

SIMPLEXGRINNELL LP p 1325
4700 Exchange Ct, Boca Raton FL 33431
Tel (561) 988-7200
SIC 5087 1711 3669 7382

TYCO INTEGRATED SECURITY LLC p 1496
4700 Exchange Ct Ste 300, Boca Raton FL 33431
Tel (561) 226-8201 *SIC* 7382 7381 1731

MARKSMAN SECURITY CORP p 909
1700 Nw 49th St Ste 110, Fort Lauderdale FL 33309
Tel (954) 771-9755 *SIC* 7382 7381

G4S HOLDING ONE INC p 588
1395 University Blvd, Jupiter FL 33458
Tel (561) 622-5656
SIC 7381 7382 8744 8748 8742

G4S SECURE SOLUTIONS INTERNATIONAL INC p 588
1395 University Blvd, Jupiter FL 33458
Tel (561) 622-5656 *SIC* 7382 7381

RONCO CONSULTING CORP p 1249
1395 University Blvd, Jupiter FL 33458
Tel (571) 551-2934 *SIC* 1794 7389 7382

AMERICAN SALES AND MANAGEMENT ORGANIZATION LLC p 79
7200 Corp Ctr Dr Ste 206, Miami FL 33126
Tel (305) 269-2700 *SIC* 7382 7349 7363

■ LENNAR FINANCIAL SERVICES LLC p 855
700 Nw 107th Ave Ste 400, Miami FL 33172
Tel (305) 559-4000
SIC 6162 6153 6361 6411 7382

■ DAL GLOBAL SERVICES LLC p 409
980 Virginia Ave 4th, Atlanta GA 30354
Tel (404) 715-4300
SIC 7361 8331 7382 5088

ONEPATH SYSTEMS LLC p 1088
2053 Franklin Way Se, Marietta GA 30067
Tel (678) 695-5500
SIC 7389 8744 7378 7376 7382

BATTELLE ENERGY ALLIANCE LLC p 159
2525 Fremont Ave, Idaho Falls ID 83402
Tel (208) 533-7606 *SIC* 8731 7382

SIEMENS INDUSTRY INC p 1320
1000 Deerfield Pkwy, Buffalo Grove IL 60089
Tel (847) 215-1000
SIC 3822 5063 3669 1731 7382 3625

■ AT&T TELEHOLDINGS INC p 123
30 S Wacker Dr Fl 34, Chicago IL 60606
Tel (800) 257-0902
SIC 4813 4812 2741 5065 6159 7382

■ STANLEY CONVERGENT SECURITY SOLUTIONS INC p 1377
55 Shuman Blvd Ste 900, Naperville IL 60563
Tel (630) 245-7100 *SIC* 7382

PROTECTION ONE INC p 1185
1267 Windham Pkwy, Romeoville IL 60446
Tel (877) 938-2214 *SIC* 7382

CONVERGINT TECHNOLOGIES LLC p 365
1 Commerce Dr, Schaumburg IL 60173
Tel (847) 620-5000 *SIC* 7382

ELECTRONIC TECHNOLOGIES CORP USA p 486
11819 N Pennsylvania St, Carmel IN 46032
Tel (317) 810-3177 *SIC* 5065 5063 7382

DEFENDERS INC p 422
3750 Priority Way S Dr, Indianapolis IN 46240
Tel (317) 810-4720 *SIC* 7382

PER MAR SECURITY AND RESEARCH CORP p 1134
1910 E Kimberly Rd, Davenport IA 52807
Tel (563) 359-3200
SIC 8732 7381 5099 7389 7382

PROTECTION ONE ALARM MONITORING INC p 1185
1035 N 3rd St Ste 101, Lawrence KS 66044
Tel (785) 856-5500 *SIC* 7382

ELECTRIC & WATER PLANT BOARD OF CITY OF FRANKFORT KY p 484
317 W 2nd St, Frankfort KY 40601
Tel (502) 352-4372
SIC 4941 4911 7382 5063 4841 4813

ALARM SECURITY GROUP LLC p 44
12301 Kiln Ct Ste A, Beltsville MD 20705
Tel (301) 623-4000 *SIC* 7382

BFPE INTERNATIONAL INC p 179
7512 Connelley Dr, Hanover MD 21076
Tel (410) 768-2200 *SIC* 1731 7382 7389

■ AMERICAN SCIENCE AND ENGINEERING INC p 79
829 Middlesex Tpke, Billerica MA 01821
Tel (978) 262-8700 *SIC* 7389 8734 7382

■ IRON MOUNTAIN/PACIFIC RECORDS MANAGEMENT INC p 765
1 Federal St, Boston MA 02110
Tel (617) 357-4455 *SIC* 7382

IMPRIVATA INC p 735
10 Maguire Rd Ste 125, Lexington MA 02421
Tel (781) 674-2700 *SIC* 7372 7382

▲ TRC COMPANIES INC p 1475
650 Suffolk St, Lowell MA 01854
Tel (978) 970-5600
SIC 7363 8734 7382 8748

SIMPLEX TIME RECORDER LLC p 1325
50 Technology Dr, Westminster MA 01441
Tel (978) 731-2500 *SIC* 7382 3669 1711

CORPORATE SECURITY SOLUTIONS INC p 372
8066 Fulton St E, Ada MI 49301
Tel (616) 248-3372 *SIC* 7382

PARSONS ELECTRIC LLC p 1118
5960 Main St Ne, Minneapolis MN 55432
Tel (763) 571-8000 *SIC* 1731 7382 8711

WRIGHT-HENNEPIN SECURITY CORP p 1627
6800 Electric Dr, Rockford MN 55373
Tel (763) 477-3664
SIC 1731 1711 7382 5063 4911

WHELAN SECURITY CO p 1605
1699 S Hanley Rd Ste 350, Saint Louis MO 63144
Tel (314) 644-3227 *SIC* 7382

G4S SECURE INTEGRATION LLC p 588
1299 Farnam St Ste 1300, Omaha NE 68102
Tel (402) 233-7700 *SIC* 1623 7382

NICE SYSTEMS INC p 1042
461 From Rd Ste 103, Paramus NJ 07652
Tel (201) 964-2600
SIC 7372 7382 1731 8741

▲ VERINT SYSTEMS INC p 1549
175 Broadhollow Rd # 100, Melville NY 11747
Tel (631) 962-9600 *SIC* 7382 7372

▲ INTRALINKS HOLDINGS INC p 760
150 E 42nd St Fl 8, New York NY 10017
Tel (212) 543-7700 *SIC* 7372 7382

PRIME SECURITY SERVICES BORROWER LLC p 1175
9 W 57th St Fl 43, New York NY 10019
Tel (212) 515-3200
SIC 6799 7382 3699 7381

HURLEY OF AMERICA INC p 721
803 Linden Ave Ste 3, Rochester NY 14625
Tel (781) 438-7830 *SIC* 7349 7382

■ GE POWER & WATER p 596
1 River Rd Bldg 5-419, Schenectady NY 12345
Tel (518) 385-2211 *SIC* 7382 5063

TRIANGLE SERVICES INC p 1478
10 5th St Ste 200, Valley Stream NY 11581
Tel (516) 561-1700
SIC 7349 4581 1799 7382

MB HAYNES CORP p 925
187 Deaverview Rd, Asheville NC 28806
Tel (828) 254-6141
SIC 1542 1623 1711 7382

JENNE INC p 782
33665 Chester Rd, Avon OH 44011
Tel (440) 835-0040 *SIC* 7371 7382

SAFEGUARD PROPERTIES LLC p 1266
7887 Safeguard Cir, Cleveland OH 44125
Tel (216) 739-2900 *SIC* 8741 7382 7381

SECURITAS ELECTRONIC SECURITY INC p 1298
1790 Graybill Rd Ste 100, Uniontown OH 44685
Tel (855) 331-0359 *SIC* 7382

BANK EQUIPMENT SYSTEMS INC p 150
8086 S Yale Ave Ste 103, Tulsa OK 74136
Tel (918) 630-4133 *SIC* 7382

CENTRAL SECURITY GROUP INC p 280
2448 E 81st St Ste 4300, Tulsa OK 74137
Tel (918) 491-3151 *SIC* 7382

GEO W KISTLER INC p 605
2210 City Line Rd, Bethlehem PA 18017
Tel (610) 266-7100
SIC 5063 7382 5087 7389

ARMSTRONG HOLDINGS INC p 111
1 Armstrong Pl, Butler PA 16001
Tel (724) 283-0925 *SIC* 1731 5999 7382

ALLIED SECURITY HOLDINGS LLC p 57
161 Washington St Ste 600, Conshohocken PA 19428
Tel (484) 351-1300 *SIC* 7381 7382

ALLIEDBARTON AEROSPACE AND DEFENSE SERVICES LLC p 57
161 Washington St Ste 600, Conshohocken PA 19428
Tel (484) 351-1300 *SIC* 7381 7382

HERLEY INDUSTRIES INC p 686
3061 Industry Dr, Lancaster PA 17603
Tel (717) 397-2777 *SIC* 7382

ADT SECURITY SERVICES INC p 24
2450 Blvd Of The Generals, Norristown PA 19403
Tel (800) 423-9637 *SIC* 7382

DAY & ZIMMERMANN GROUP INC p 417
1500 Spring Garden St # 900, Philadelphia PA 19130
Tel (215) 299-8000
SIC 8711 8712 8741 7381 7382 3489

PHILADELPHIA CONTRIBUTIONSHIP FOR INSURANCE OF HOUSES FROM LOSS BY FIRE p 1142
212 S 4th St, Philadelphia PA 19106
Tel (215) 627-1752
SIC 6331 6311 7382 6321

INTERTECH SECURITY GROUP LLC p 759
1501 Preble Ave Ste 6, Pittsburgh PA 15233
Tel (724) 742-4900 *SIC* 7382

GUARDIAN PROTECTION SERVICES INC p 645
174 Thorn Hill Rd, Warrendale PA 15086
Tel (412) 788-2580 *SIC* 1731 5999 7382

VECTOR SECURITY INC p 1546
2000 Ericsson Dr Ste 250, Warrendale PA 15086
Tel (724) 741-2200 *SIC* 7382 1731

WILKES UNIVERSITY SECURITY DEPARTMENT p 1609
84 W South St, Wilkes Barre PA 18766
Tel (570) 408-4999 *SIC* 7382

RANGER AMERICAN OF PUERTO RICO INC p 1208
605 Calle Lodi, San Juan PR 00924
Tel (787) 999-6060 *SIC* 1731 7382 7381

ALLIANCE SECURITY INC p 55
85 Garfield Ave, Cranston RI 02920
Tel (877) 746-2559 *SIC* 7382

HORRY TELEPHONE COOPERATIVE INC p 708
3480 Highway 701 N, Conway SC 29526
Tel (843) 365-2151 *SIC* 4813 4841 7382

DEFENDER SERVICES INC p 422
9031 Garners Ferry Rd, Hopkins SC 29061
Tel (803) 776-4220 *SIC* 7349 7361 7382

ERMC II LP p 508
1 Park Pl 6148, Chattanooga TN 37421
Tel (423) 899-2753 *SIC* 7349 7382

■ CONSOLIDATED NUCLEAR SECURITY LLC p 360
2373 Farm To Market Rd, Amarillo TX 79120
Tel (806) 477-3000 *SIC* 7382

SCIS AIR SECURITY CORP p 1292
1521 N Cooper St Ste 300, Arlington TX 76011
Tel (817) 792-4500 *SIC* 5063 7382

■ MONITRONICS INTERNATIONAL INC p 984
1990 Wittington Pl, Dallas TX 75234
Tel (972) 243-7443 *SIC* 7382 1731

ROSEWOOD CORP p 1251
2101 Cedar Springs Rd # 1600, Dallas TX 75201
Tel (214) 849-9000 *SIC* 6531 7382

ABM SECURITY SERVICES INC p 12
3800 Buffalo Speedway # 325, Houston TX 77098
Tel (713) 928-5344 *SIC* 7382

BROADVIEW SECURITY INC p 215
8880 Esters Blvd, Irving TX 75063
Tel (972) 871-3500 *SIC* 7382

RACKSPACE HOSTING INC p 1203
1 Fanatical Pl, San Antonio TX 78218
Tel (210) 312-4000
SIC 7371 7374 7382 4813

APX GROUP HOLDINGS INC p 101
4931 N 300 W, Provo UT 84604
Tel (801) 377-9111
SIC 7382 5065 3822 1711

SECURE MISSION SOLUTIONS INC p 1298
5875 Trinity Pkwy Ste 300, Centreville VA 20120
Tel (703) 230-2804 *SIC* 7382

SECURE MISSION SOLUTIONS LLC p 1298
5875 Trinity Pkwy Ste 300, Centreville VA 20120
Tel (703) 245-1300 *SIC* 7382

CHENEGA INTEGRATED SYSTEMS LLC p 294
14295 Pk Madow Dr Ste 400, Chantilly VA 20151
Tel (571) 291-8500 *SIC* 7381 7382 8331

OBERTHUR TECHNOLOGIES OF AMERICA CORP p 1072
4250 Pleasant Valley Rd, Chantilly VA 20151
Tel (703) 263-0100
SIC 3089 7382 3953 3578 3499

SOC LLC p 1336
15002 Northridge Dr # 100, Chantilly VA 20151
Tel (703) 955-5700 *SIC* 7382 1731

GIESECKE & DEVRIENT MOBILE SECURITY AMERICA INC p 611
45925 Horseshoe Dr, Dulles VA 20166
Tel (703) 480-2100
SIC 7382 3089 5045 7374

PARAGON SYSTEMS INC p 1113
13655 Dulles Tech Dr # 100, Herndon VA 20171
Tel (703) 263-7176 *SIC* 7381 7382 7374

■ RAYTHEON BLACKBIRD TECHNOLOGIES INC p 1211
13900 Lincoln Park Dr # 400, Herndon VA 20171
Tel (703) 796-1420 *SIC* 7371 7382

SALIENT FEDERAL-SGIS INC p 1272
8255 Greensboro Dr # 400, Mc Lean VA 22102
Tel (703) 891-8200 *SIC* 7373 8711 7382

ACADEMI LLC p 13
12018 Sunrise Valley Dr # 140, Reston VA 20191
Tel (252) 435-2488 *SIC* 7382 8742

INDYNE INC p 740
11800 Sunrise Valley Dr # 250, Reston VA 20191
Tel (703) 903-6900 *SIC* 8744 8748 7382

■ SCITOR HOLDINGS INC p 1292
12010 Sunset Hills Rd # 800, Reston VA 20190
Tel (703) 481-5892 *SIC* 7382 5065 7373

▲ BRINKS CO p 213
1801 Bayberry Ct Ste 400, Richmond VA 23226
Tel (804) 289-9600 *SIC* 7382 7381

WOODFIN HEATING INC p 1623
1823 N Hamilton St, Richmond VA 23230
Tel (804) 730-4500
SIC 5172 5983 1711 7382

▲ ALARM.COM HOLDINGS INC p 44
8281 Greensboro Dr # 100, Tysons Corner VA 22102
Tel (877) 389-4033 *SIC* 7382

COCHRAN INC p 333
12500 Aurora Ave N Main, Seattle WA 98133
Tel (206) 367-1900 *SIC* 1731 7382

SIC 7383 News Syndicates

COPLEY PRESS INC p 368
7776 Ivanhoe Ave, La Jolla CA 92037
Tel (858) 454-0411 *SIC* 7383 2711 7011

CONNEXITY INC p 358
12200 W Olympic Blvd # 300, Los Angeles CA 90064
Tel (310) 571-1235 *SIC* 4813 7383

■ SAN DIEGO UNION-TRIBUNE LLC p 1276
600 B St, San Diego CA 92101
Tel (619) 299-3131 *SIC* 2711 7313 7383

■ CHICAGO TRIBUNE CO p 298
435 N Michigan Ave # 200, Chicago IL 60611
Tel (312) 222-3232
SIC 2711 7383 7389 7331

ASSOCIATED PRESS p 121
450 W 33rd St Fl 16, New York NY 10001
Tel (212) 621-1500 *SIC* 7383 4822

BLOOMBERG LP p 190
731 Lexington Ave Fl Ll2, New York NY 10022
Tel (212) 318-2000 *SIC* 7383

HEARST CORP p 678
300 W 57th St Fl 42, New York NY 10019
Tel (212) 649-2000
SIC 2721 2731 2711 4832 4833 7383

■ NBC NEWS WORLDWIDE LLC p 1021
30 Rockefeller Plz Fl 2, New York NY 10112
Tel (212) 664-4444
SIC 4832 4833 4841 6021 6531 7383

■ NBC UNIVERSITY LLC p 1021
30 Rockefeller Plz Fl 51, New York NY 10112
Tel (212) 664-4444
SIC 4832 4833 4841 6021 6531 7383

▲ NEW YORK TIMES CO p 1036
620 8th Ave, New York NY 10018
Tel (212) 556-1234
SIC 2711 4832 4833 7383 7375

PR NEWSWIRE ASSOCIATION LLC p 1167
350 Hudson St Fl 3, New York NY 10014
Tel (800) 776-8090 *SIC* 7383

■ REUTERS AMERICA LLC p 1229
3 Times Sq, New York NY 10036
Tel (646) 223-4000 *SIC* 7383

■ THOMSON REUTERS CORP p 1450
3 Times Sq Lbby Mailroom, New York NY 10036
Tel (646) 223-4000
SIC 2741 8111 7372 7383

SIC 7384 Photofinishing Labs

TECHNICOLOR THOMSON GROUP INC p 1431
2233 N Ontario St Ste 300, Burbank CA 91504
Tel (818) 260-3600 *SIC* 7819 7384

▲ SHUTTERFLY INC p 1319
2800 Bridge Pkwy Ste 100, Redwood City CA 94065
Tel (650) 610-5200 *SIC* 7384

MILLERS INC p 971
610 E Jefferson St, Pittsburg KS 66762
Tel (620) 231-8050 *SIC* 7384

DISTRICT PHOTO INC p 443
10501 Rhode Island Ave, Beltsville MD 20705
Tel (301) 595-5300 *SIC* 7384 5043 5946

C & A MARKETING INC p 231
114 Tived Ln E, Edison NJ 08837
Tel (201) 881-1900
SIC 5065 8742 7384 5946 7359 7221

▲ CINEDIGM CORP p 307
902 Broadway Fl 9, New York NY 10010
Tel (212) 206-8600 *SIC* 7384 7389 7371

■ EASTMAN KODAK CO p 473
343 State St, Rochester NY 14650
Tel (585) 724-4000 *SIC* 3861 3577 7384

FUJICOLOR PROCESSING INC p 583
120 White Plains Rd # 400, Tarrytown NY 10591
Tel (914) 220-4700 *SIC* 7384

FUJIFILM NORTH AMERICA CORP p 583
200 Summit Lake Dr Fl 2, Valhalla NY 10595
Tel (914) 789-8100
SIC 7384 5043 5065 3695 2673 3861

QUALEX INC p 1196
4020 Stirrup Creek Dr # 100, Durham NC 27703
Tel (919) 484-3500 *SIC* 7384

▲ RITE AID CORP p 1236
30 Hunter Ln, Camp Hill PA 17011
Tel (717) 761-2633 *SIC* 5912 7384 5963

SIC 7389 Business Svcs, NEC

■ PROGRESS RAIL SERVICES CORP p 1181
1600 Progress Dr, Albertville AL 35950
Tel (256) 593-1260 *SIC* 4789 7389

AUBURN UNIVERSITY FOUNDATION p 130
317 S College St, Auburn AL 36849
Tel (334) 844-1124 *SIC* 7389 8641

■ AGEE STERNE GROUP INC p 34
800 Shades Creek Pkwy # 700, Birmingham AL 35209
Tel (205) 949-3500 *SIC* 7389

EBSCO INDUSTRIES INC p 474
5724 Highway 280 E, Birmingham AL 35242
Tel (205) 991-6600
SIC 7389 2782 3949 7375 2721 6552

PROTECTIVE LIFE INSURANCE CO p 1185
2801 Highway 280 S, Birmingham AL 35223
Tel (205) 268-1000 *SIC* 6311 6411 7389

GTEL HOLDINGS INC p 644
2609 Cameron St, Mobile AL 36607
Tel (251) 479-4500 *SIC* 3661 7389

INFIRMARY HEALTH SYSTEM INC p 741
5 Mobile Infirmary Cir, Mobile AL 36607
Tel (251) 435-3030
SIC 8062 6512 1542 7322 5047 7389

ALFA CORP p 49
2108 E South Blvd, Montgomery AL 36116
Tel (334) 288-3900 *SIC* 6311 6411 7389

CONSTELLIUM METAL PROCUREMENT LLC p 361
2415 Rosedale St Ste H, Muscle Shoals AL 35661
Tel (256) 443-7435 SIC 7389

AHTNA INC p 37
110 W 38th Ave Ste 100, Anchorage AK 99503
Tel (907) 868-8250
SIC 1629 7389 1542 1521

■ GCI INC p 595
2550 Denali St Ste 1000, Anchorage AK 99503
Tel (907) 868-5400 SIC 7389

■ SCIENCE APPLICATIONS INTERNATIONAL CORP p 1292
1049 W 5th Ave, Anchorage AK 99501
Tel (907) 792-2700 SIC 7389

DIGI-KEY CORP p 439
1393 E Powell Way, Chandler AZ 85249
Tel (480) 294-5709 SIC 7389

CITY OF GLENDALE MUNICIPAL PROPERTY CORP p 315
5850 W Glendale Ave, Glendale AZ 85301
Tel (623) 930-2820 SIC 7389

BEST WESTERN INTERNATIONAL INC p 177
6201 N 24th Pkwy, Phoenix AZ 85016
Tel (602) 957-4200
SIC 7389 7311 5046 8743

BURNS CONSULTING INC p 228
15414 N 7th St 8122, Phoenix AZ 85022
Tel (602) 993-3070 SIC 8742 7389

GOODMANS INC p 624
1400 E Indian School Rd, Phoenix AZ 85014
Tel (602) 263-1110 SIC 5712 7389

SHASTA INDUSTRIES INC p 1312
6031 N 16th St, Phoenix AZ 85016
Tel (602) 532-3750
SIC 1799 1771 5169 7389 3088 5091

SYNERGY SOLUTIONS INC p 1415
3141 N 3rd Ave Ste C100, Phoenix AZ 85013
Tel (602) 296-1600 SIC 7389

▲ VIAD CORP p 1554
1850 N Central Ave # 1900, Phoenix AZ 85004
Tel (602) 207-1000 SIC 7389

DWW AZ INC p 464
7875 E Frank Lloyd Wright, Scottsdale AZ 85260
Tel (480) 778-2440 SIC 7389

GLOBAL AGGREGATE LLC p 615
8901 E Mountain View Rd, Scottsdale AZ 85258
Tel (480) 414-9400 SIC 6798 7389 5045

■ RURAL/METRO CORP p 1258
8465 N Pima Rd, Scottsdale AZ 85258
Tel (480) 606-3886 SIC 4119 7389

■ RURAL/METRO CORP p 1258
8465 N Pima Rd, Scottsdale AZ 85258
Tel (480) 606-3345 SIC 4119 7389

■ WP ROCKET HOLDINGS INC p 1627
8465 N Pima Rd, Scottsdale AZ 85258
Tel (800) 352-2309 SIC 4119 7389

BRIDGECREST ACCEPTANCE CORP p 211
1720 W Rio Salado Pkwy, Tempe AZ 85281
Tel (602) 770-1940 SIC 7389

CYRACOM INTERNATIONAL INC p 406
5780 N Swan Rd, Tucson AZ 85718
Tel (520) 745-9447 SIC 7389

ROYSTON HOLDING LLC p 1255
111 Center St Ste 2500, Little Rock AR 72201
Tel (770) 735-3456 SIC 7389 1751 2542

VESTCOM INTERNATIONAL INC p 1552
2800 Cantrell Rd Ste 400, Little Rock AR 72202
Tel (501) 663-0100 SIC 8742 7389

■ XETA TECHNOLOGIES INC p 1631
4001 N Rodney Parham Rd, Little Rock AR 72212
Tel (800) 697-8153 SIC 3661 5999 7389

CENTRAL STATES MANUFACTURING INC p 280
302 Jane Pl, Lowell AR 72745
Tel (479) 770-0188 SIC 3353 3448 7389

HERITAGE CO INC p 686
2402 Wildwood Ave Ste 500, North Little Rock AR 72120
Tel (501) 835-9111 SIC 7389 2721

ARSG INC p 113
3870 E Eagle Dr, Anaheim CA 92807
Tel (714) 666-6650 SIC 7389

MOTHER LODE HOLDING CO p 992
189 Fulweiler Ave, Auburn CA 95603
Tel (530) 887-2410 SIC 6361 6531 7389

▲ LIVE NATION ENTERTAINMENT INC p 871
9348 Civic Center Dr Lbby, Beverly Hills CA 90210
Tel (310) 867-7000 SIC 7922 7389 7941

MAGIC JOHNSON ENTERPRISES INC p 895
9100 Wilshire Blvd 700e, Beverly Hills CA 90212
Tel (310) 247-2033 SIC 8743 7389

■ RIA ENVIA INC p 1232
6565 Knott Ave, Buena Park CA 90620
Tel (714) 543-8448 SIC 7389

WARNER BROS RECORDS INC p 1576
3300 Warner Blvd, Burbank CA 91505
Tel (818) 953-3378 SIC 7389

GARCOA INC p 591
26135 Mureau Rd Ste 100, Calabasas CA 91302
Tel (818) 225-0375 SIC 7389

VOICELOTS INC p 1564
350 Budd Ave Apt J5, Campbell CA 95008
Tel (408) 802-4047 SIC 7371 7389

ACCOUNT CONTROL TECHNOLOGY HOLDINGS INC p 15
6918 Owensmouth Ave, Canoga Park CA 91303
Tel (818) 712-4999 SIC 7389

1105 MEDIA INC p 1
9201 Oakdale Ave Ste 101, Chatsworth CA 91311
Tel (818) 814-5200
SIC 7313 7389 2721 2741 8748

CHICO CSU RESEARCH FOUNDATION p 298
Csuc Bldg 25 Ste 203, Chico CA 95929
Tel (530) 898-6811 SIC 7389

CONCEPT GREEN ENERGY SOLUTIONS INC p 354
13824 Yorba Ave, Chino CA 91710
Tel (855) 459-6535 SIC 7389 5211

QUETICO LLC p 1199
5521 Schaefer Ave, Chino CA 91710
Tel (909) 628-6200 SIC 5199 7389

COACHELLA VALLEY WATER DISTRICT p 331
85995 Avenue 52, Coachella CA 92236
Tel (760) 398-2651
SIC 4941 4971 4952 7389

ERNEST PACKAGING SOLUTIONS INC p 508
5777 Smithway St, Commerce CA 90040
Tel (800) 233-7788 SIC 5113 5199 7389

ROMAN JAMES DESIGN BUILD INC p 1249
3535 E Coast Hwy 145, Corona Del Mar CA 92625
Tel (949) 375-8618 SIC 7389

VOLCOM LLC p 1564
1740 Monrovia Ave, Costa Mesa CA 92627
Tel (949) 646-2175
SIC 7389 2253 7822 5136 5137

KIRSCHENMAN ENTERPRISES SALES LP p 822
12826 Edison Hwy, Edison CA 93220
Tel (661) 366-5736 SIC 7389

CETERA FINANCIAL GROUP INC p 284
200 N Sepulveda Blvd # 1200, El Segundo CA 90245
Tel (800) 879-8100 SIC 7389 6282

GUTHY-RENKER LLC p 648
100 N Sepulveda Blvd # 1600, El Segundo CA 90245
Tel (760) 773-9022
SIC 5099 7812 5999 7389

PROLOGIC REDEMPTION SOLUTIONS INC p 1182
2121 Rosecrans Ave, El Segundo CA 90245
Tel (310) 322-7774 SIC 7389

▲ QUINSTREET INC p 1200
950 Tower Ln Ste 600, Foster City CA 94404
Tel (650) 578-7700 SIC 7389 7372

▲ VISA INC p 1560
900 Metro Center Blvd, Foster City CA 94404
Tel (650) 432-3200 SIC 7389

■ VISA INTERNATIONAL SERVICE ASSOCIATION p 1560
900 Metro Center Blvd, Foster City CA 94404
Tel (650) 432-3200 SIC 7389

■ VISA USA INC p 1560
900 Metro Center Blvd, Foster City CA 94404
Tel (650) 432-3200 SIC 7389

SCRIP ADVANTAGE INC p 1294
4273 W Richert Ave # 110, Fresno CA 93722
Tel (559) 320-0052 SIC 7389

■ YP.COM LLC p 1639
611 N Brand Blvd Fl 3, Glendale CA 91203
Tel (818) 937-5500 SIC 7389

ALORICA INC p 59
5 Park Plz Ste 1100, Irvine CA 92614
Tel (949) 527-4600 SIC 7389

CONSOLIDATED FIRE PROTECTION LLC p 359
153 Technology Dr Ste 200, Irvine CA 92618
Tel (949) 727-3277 SIC 7389

CORPORATE RISK HOLDINGS III INC p 372
3349 Michelson Dr Ste 150, Irvine CA 92612
Tel (949) 428-5839 SIC 7389

▲ RESOURCES CONNECTION INC p 1227
17101 Armstrong Ave, Irvine CA 92614
Tel (714) 430-6400 SIC 8742 7389 8721

▲ SPECTRUM GROUP INTERNATIONAL INC p 1357
1063 Mcgaw Ave Ste 250, Irvine CA 92614
Tel (949) 748-4800 SIC 7389 5094 5944

SIEGESECURE LLC p 1320
111 Lindbergh Ave Ste E, Livermore CA 94551
Tel (925) 963-6548 SIC 7389

AUDIO VISUAL SERVICES GROUP INC p 131
111 Ocean Beach Blvd Ste 1110, Long Beach CA 90802
Tel (562) 366-0620 SIC 7389 7812 7359

BRAGG INVESTMENT CO INC p 207
6251 N Paramount Blvd, Long Beach CA 90805
Tel (562) 984-2400 SIC 7389 7353 1791

▲ AIR LEASE CORP p 38
2000 Avenue Of The Stars 1000n, Los Angeles CA 90067
Tel (310) 553-0555 SIC 7359 7389

CAPITOL RECORDS LLC p 251
1750 Vine St, Los Angeles CA 90028
Tel (213) 462-6252 SIC 7389 8999

JOHN HANCOCK LIFE INSURANCE CO (USA) p 788
865 S Figueroa St # 3320, Los Angeles CA 90017
Tel (213) 689-0813
SIC 7389 6351 6371 6321

MAURICIO ESPINOSA p 921
3523 Division St, Los Angeles CA 90065
Tel (909) 253-9108 SIC 7389

VXI GLOBAL SOLUTIONS LLC p 1567
220 W 1st St Fl 3, Los Angeles CA 90012
Tel (213) 739-4720 SIC 7389

WEDBUSH INC p 1587
1000 Wilshire Blvd # 900, Los Angeles CA 90017
Tel (213) 688-8080 SIC 7389

■ DUN & BRADSTREET EMERGING BUSINESSES CORP p 461
22761 Pacific Coast Hwy # 226, Malibu CA 90265
Tel (310) 456-8271 SIC 7389

CORNERSTONE RESEARCH INC p 371
1000 El Camino Real # 250, Menlo Park CA 94025
Tel (650) 853-1660 SIC 8748 7389

■ FACEBOOK PAYMENTS INC p 523
1601 Willow Rd, Menlo Park CA 94025
Tel (650) 690-3038 SIC 7389

UNICOM GLOBAL INC p 1502
15535 San Fernando Mssion, Mission Hills CA 91345
Tel (818) 838-0606
SIC 8732 6552 7389 7371

LANGUAGE LINE HOLDINGS INC p 844
1 Lower Ragsdale Dr # 2, Monterey CA 93940
Tel (831) 648-5800 SIC 7389

PRODUCT DEVELOPMENT CORP p 1179
20 Ragsdale Dr Ste 100, Monterey CA 93940
Tel (831) 333-1100 SIC 7389

BELL INTEGRATOR INC p 170
800 W El Camino Real, Mountain View CA 94040
Tel (650) 603-0988 SIC 7373 7389

XCELLERATEHR LLC p 1631
702 Civic Center Dr, Oceanside CA 92054
Tel (602) 571-2187 SIC 7389

▲ GREEN DOT CORP p 637
3465 E Foothill Blvd # 100, Pasadena CA 91107
Tel (626) 765-2000 SIC 6141 7389

■ WESCO FINANCIAL CORP p 1593
301 E Colo Blvd Ste 300, Pasadena CA 91101
Tel (626) 585-6700 SIC 7359 6411 7389

DIABLO VALLEY COLLEGE FOUNDATION p 436
321 Golf Club Rd, Pleasant Hill CA 94523
Tel (925) 685-1230 SIC 7389 8221

IRONPLANET INC p 765
3825 Hopyard Rd Ste 250, Pleasanton CA 94588
Tel (925) 225-8600 SIC 7389

PURPLE COMMUNICATIONS INC p 1193
595 Menlo Dr, Rocklin CA 95765
Tel (888) 600-4780 SIC 4812 7389

CLUB DEMONSTRATION SERVICES INC p 328
9555 Chesapeake Dr # 100, San Diego CA 92123
Tel (858) 581-8700 SIC 7389

NATIONAL FUNDING INC p 1012
9820 Towne Centre Dr # 200, San Diego CA 92121
Tel (888) 576-4685 SIC 6153 6159 7389

■ UPS STORE INC p 1529
6060 Cornerstone Ct W, San Diego CA 92121
Tel (858) 455-8800 SIC 7389 8742 4783

■ WIS p 1618
9265 Sky Park Ct Ste 100, San Diego CA 92123
Tel (858) 565-8111 SIC 7389

▲ CHARLES SCHWAB CORP p 289
211 Main St Fl 17, San Francisco CA 94105
Tel (415) 667-7000
SIC 6211 6091 6282 7389

HELLMUTH OBATA & KASSABAUM INC p 682
1 Bush St Ste 200, San Francisco CA 94104
Tel (415) 243-0555
SIC 8712 8711 8742 7389 0781

IGP INDUSTRIES LLC p 730
101 Mission St Ste 1500, San Francisco CA 94105
Tel (415) 882-4550 SIC 7389

■ JP MORGAN H&Q PRINCIPALS LP p 794
560 Mission St Fl 2, San Francisco CA 94105
Tel (415) 315-5000
SIC 6211 6799 6282 7389

MICRO HOLDING CORP p 961
1 Maritime Plz Fl 12, San Francisco CA 94111
Tel (415) 788-5111 SIC 7374 7389

■ OPENTABLE INC p 1089
1 Montgomery St Ste 700, San Francisco CA 94104
Tel (415) 344-4200 SIC 7389

SAN FRANCISCO FOUNDATION p 1276
1 Embarcadero Ctr # 4150, San Francisco CA 94111
Tel (415) 733-8500 SIC 7389

■ URS HOLDINGS INC p 1530
600 Montgomery St Fl 25, San Francisco CA 94111
Tel (415) 774-2700
SIC 8711 7389 6531 8249 4581

■ CISCO WEBEX LLC p 309
170 W Tasman Dr, San Jose CA 95134
Tel (408) 435-7000 SIC 7389 4813

▲ FAIR ISAAC CORP p 524
181 Metro Dr Ste 700, San Jose CA 95110
Tel (408) 535-1500 SIC 7372 8748 7389

TRANS-PAK INC p 1470
520 Marburg Way, San Jose CA 95133
Tel (408) 254-0500 SIC 7389

EMERALD EXPOSITIONS LLC p 491
31910 Del Obispo St # 200, San Juan Capistrano CA 92675
Tel (949) 226-5700 SIC 7389

REVENUE PROCESSING SOLUTIONS INC p 1229
28293 Via Del Mar, San Juan Capistrano CA 92675
Tel (949) 481-9080 SIC 7371 7389

KP LLC p 828
13951 Washington Ave, San Leandro CA 94578
Tel (510) 346-0729
SIC 2752 7334 7331 7374 7389 8742

ORANGE COAST TITLE CO OF SOUTHERN CALIFORNIA p 1092
640 N Tustin Ave Ste 106, Santa Ana CA 92705
Tel (714) 558-2836 SIC 7389 6361 6541

PIVOT INTERIORS INC p 1152
3355 Scott Blvd Ste 110, Santa Clara CA 95054
Tel (408) 432-5600 SIC 5712 7389 7299

ADVANSTAR COMMUNICATIONS INC p 26
2501 Colorado Ave Ste 280, Santa Monica CA 90404
Tel (310) 857-7500 SIC 7389 2721 7331

UNIVERSAL MUSIC GROUP INC p 1517
2220 Colorado Ave, Santa Monica CA 90404
Tel (310) 865-4000 SIC 7389 2741

TRAFFIC MANAGEMENT INC p 1469
2435 Lemon Ave, Signal Hill CA 90755
Tel (562) 595-4278 SIC 7389 8741

KOOS MANUFACTURING INC p 827
2741 Seminole Ave, South Gate CA 90280
Tel (323) 249-1000 SIC 7389

AMERICAN MERCHANTS INC p 76
3279 Laurel Canyon Blvd, Studio City CA 91604
Tel (818) 505-1040 SIC 7389

MERCURY AIR GROUP INC p 945
2780 Skypark Dr Ste 300, Torrance CA 90505
Tel (310) 602-3770 SIC 5172 7389 4581

ARVATO DIGITAL SERVICES LLC p 114
29011 Commerce Center Dr, Valencia CA 91355
Tel (661) 702-2700 SIC 5961 7389

VICTOR ELEMENTARY SCHOOL DISTRICT FINANCING CORP p 1555
15579 Eighth St, Victorville CA 92395
Tel (760) 245-1691 SIC 8699 7389

IPAYMENT HOLDINGS INC p 763
30721 Russell Ranch Rd # 200, Westlake Village CA 91362
Tel (310) 436-5294 SIC 7389

IPAYMENT INC p 763
30721 Russell Ranch Rd # 200, Westlake Village CA 91362
Tel (212) 802-7200 SIC 7389

▲ B RILEY FINANCIAL INC p 142
21860 Burbank Blvd, Woodland Hills CA 91367
Tel (818) 884-3737 SIC 7389

IMG p 733
4560 Dorinda Rd, Yorba Linda CA 92887
Tel (714) 974-1700 SIC 7389

ASCENDA USA INC p 116
14001 E Iliff Ave Ste 500, Aurora CO 80014
Tel (720) 399-2050 SIC 7389

RICOH PRODUCTION PRINT SOLUTIONS LLC p 1233
6300 Diagonal Hwy, Boulder CO 80301
Tel (303) 924-9348 SIC 7389

IMPACT TELECOM LLC p 734
9000 E Nichols Ave # 230, Centennial CO 80112
Tel (866) 557-8919 SIC 7389

▲ NATIONAL CINEMEDIA INC p 1010
9110 E Nichols Ave # 200, Centennial CO 80112
Tel (303) 792-3600 SIC 7311 7389

BROADMOOR HOTEL INC p 215
1 Lake Ave, Colorado Springs CO 80906
Tel (719) 634-7711
SIC 7011 5812 5813 7992 7999 7389

TIMS AIRBRUSH LLC p 1455
10490 Vaughn Way, Commerce City CO 80022
Tel (303) 944-9497 SIC 8999 7389

▲ MDC HOLDINGS INC p 933
4350 S Monaco St Ste 500, Denver CO 80237
Tel (303) 773-1100 SIC 1521 6162 7389

P2 ACQUISITION LLC p 1103
216 16th St Ste 1700, Denver CO 80202
Tel (303) 390-9400 SIC 7389

P2 NEWCO INC p 1103
216 16th St Ste 1700, Denver CO 80202
Tel (303) 390-9400 SIC 7389

■ QWEST BUSINESS RESOURCES INC p 1201
1005 17th St, Denver CO 80202
Tel (303) 896-5025 SIC 7389 6512

VALIANT PRODUCTS CORP p 1540
2727 W 5th Ave, Denver CO 80204
Tel (303) 892-1234
SIC 5131 5023 7389 2511 2599 1752

▲ TELETECH HOLDINGS INC p 1435
9197 S Peoria St, Englewood CO 80112
Tel (303) 397-8100 SIC 7389

■ TELETECH SERVICES CORP p 1435
9197 S Peoria St, Englewood CO 80112
Tel (303) 397-8100 SIC 7389

LANDMARK EVENT STAFFING SERVICES INC p 842
4131 Harbor Walk Dr, Fort Collins CO 80525
Tel (714) 293-4248 SIC 7381 7389

FIRST DATA HOLDINGS INC p 546
5775 Dtc Blvd Ste 100, Greenwood Village CO 80111
Tel (303) 967-8000
SIC 6099 7375 7389 6153

KENTWOOD DTC LLC p 813
5690 Dtc Blvd Ste 600w, Greenwood Village CO 80111
Tel (303) 773-3399 SIC 6531 7389

M&C HOTEL INTERESTS INC p 890
6560 Greenwood Plaza Blvd # 300, Greenwood Village CO 80111
Tel (303) 779-2000
SIC 8741 8712 6321 6331 7389

RICHFIELD HOLDINGS INC p 1233
5775 Dtc Blvd Ste 300, Greenwood Village CO 80111
Tel (303) 220-2000
SIC 6321 8712 7389 6331 7011

SUMMIT SLICKLINE INC p 1399
20701 County Road 50, La Salle CO 80645
Tel (970) 397-1808 SIC 1389 7389

MAVERICK PUMP SERVICES LLC p 921
9791 Titan Park Cir, Littleton CO 80125
Tel (303) 981-8349 SIC 7389

PARKVIEW HEALTH SYSTEM INC p 1117
400 W 16th St, Pueblo CO 81003
Tel (719) 584-4000 SIC 8062 7389

NEXUS BIOENERGY INC p 1041
3026 Castle Peak Ave, Superior CO 80027
Tel (720) 318-2339 SIC 4939 7389 8731

LUTHERAN MEDICAL CENTER p 886
8300 W 38th Ave, Wheat Ridge CO 80033
Tel (303) 425-4500
SIC 8011 7389 8082 8331

TRIPLE "R" TRAFFIC CONTROL & BARRICADE RENTAL "LLC p 1482
509 Scott Ave Ste 106, Woodland Park CO 80863
Tel (720) 641-8099 SIC 7389

AMERICAN CUSTOMER CARE INC p 71
225 N Main St Fl 5, Bristol CT 06010
Tel (800) 267-0686 SIC 7389

MARK FACEY & CO p 907
225 N Main St Ste 500, Bristol CT 06010
Tel (800) 237-0938 SIC 7389

■ CARTUS CORP p 262
40 Apple Ridge Rd, Danbury CT 06810
Tel (203) 205-3400 SIC 7389

TONTINE CAPITAL PARTNERS LIMITED PARTNERSHIP p 1460
55 Railroad Ave Ste 103, Greenwich CT 06830
Tel (203) 769-2000 SIC 7389

CCMC CORP p 270
282 Washington St, Hartford CT 06106
Tel (860) 545-9490 SIC 8069 7389 8299

HIGHER ONE HOLDINGS INC p 691
115 Munson St, New Haven CT 06511
Tel (203) 776-7776 SIC 7389

HIGHER ONE INC p 691
115 Munson St, New Haven CT 06511
Tel (203) 776-7776 SIC 7389

VERTRUE LLC p 1552
20 Glover Ave, Norfolk CT 06058
Tel (203) 324-7635 *SIC* 7389

■ CLAYTON HOLDINGS LLC p 323
100 Beard Sawmill Rd # 200, Shelton CT 06484
Tel (203) 926-5600 *SIC* 8741 7389 6531

AFFINION GROUP INC p 32
6 High Ridge Park Bldg A, Stamford CT 06905
Tel (203) 956-1000 *SIC* 7389 5961 6321

■ ICON HOLDING CORP p 727
107 Elm St Fl 15, Stamford CT 06902
Tel (203) 328-2300 *SIC* 7389 7319

■ ICON INTERNATIONAL INC p 728
4 Stamford Plz 15th, Stamford CT 06902
Tel (203) 328-2300 *SIC* 7389 7319

▲ PROVIDENCE SERVICE CORP p 1186
700 Canal St Ste 3, Stamford CT 06902
Tel (203) 307-2800 *SIC* 8322 8742 7389

RON WEBER AND ASSOCIATES INC p 1249
1127 High Ridge Rd, Stamford CT 06905
Tel (203) 268-1725 *SIC* 7389

▲ SYNCHRONY FINANCIAL p 1414
777 Long Ridge Rd, Stamford CT 06902
Tel (203) 585-2400 *SIC* 6021 7389

COTIVITI USA LLC p 374
50 Danbury Rd, Wilton CT 06897
Tel (203) 529-2000 *SIC* 7389

AUGUST TECHNIC CORP CO p 131
8 The Grn Ste 4934, Dover DE 19901
Tel (302) 223-5215 *SIC* 5065 5045 7389

ILC DOVER LP p 731
1 Moonwalker Rd, Frederica DE 19946
Tel (302) 335-3911 *SIC* 3842 3721 7389

BARCLAYS FINANCIAL CORP p 155
125 S West St, Wilmington DE 19801
Tel (302) 622-8990 *SIC* 7389 6282 6211

CORP SERVICE CO INC p 371
2711 Centerville Rd # 400, Wilmington DE 19808
Tel (302) 636-5400 *SIC* 7389

■ DU PONT FOREIGN SALES CORP p 459
974 Centre Rd, Wilmington DE 19805
Tel (302) 774-1000 *SIC* 7389

■ FIA CARD SERVICES NATIONAL ASSOCIATION p 539
1100 N King St, Wilmington DE 19884
Tel (800) 362-6255 *SIC* 7389

■ MBNA MARKETING SYSTEMS INC p 925
1100 N King St, Wilmington DE 19884
Tel (302) 456-8588 *SIC* 7389

ACON SUZO-HAPP LLC p 18
1133 Conn Ave Nw Ste 700, Washington DC 20036
Tel (202) 454-1100 *SIC* 7389

CORP FOR TRAVEL PROMOTION p 371
1725 I St Nw Ste 800, Washington DC 20006
Tel (202) 536-2060 *SIC* 7389

GOOD BUDDY BUDDY GOOD LLC p 623
300 Anacostia Rd Se # 103, Washington DC 20019
Tel (240) 532-0031 *SIC* 7389

HW HOLDCO LLC p 722
1 Thomas Cir Nw Ste 600, Washington DC 20005
Tel (202) 452-0800 *SIC* 2721 7389

INTERNATIONAL CITY MANAGEMENT ASSOCIATION RETIREMENT CORP p 754
777 N Capitol St Ne # 600, Washington DC 20002
Tel (202) 962-4600 *SIC* 7389 6722

▲ LIQUIDITY SERVICES INC p 870
1920 L St Nw Fl 6, Washington DC 20036
Tel (202) 467-6868 *SIC* 7389

NEW VENTURE FUND p 1033
1201 Conn Ave Nw Ste 300, Washington DC 20036
Tel (202) 595-1061 *SIC* 7389

PARALYZED VETERANS OF AMERICA p 1114
801 18th St Nw Frnt 1, Washington DC 20006
Tel (202) 872-1300 *SIC* 8399 7389 8641

■ PHI SERVICE CO p 1142
701 9th St Nw, Washington DC 20001
Tel (202) 872-2000 *SIC* 7389

TRG CUSTOMER SOLUTIONS INC p 1476
1700 Penn Ave Nw Ste 560, Washington DC 20006
Tel (202) 289-9898 *SIC* 7389

WILL PERKINS INC p 1609
1250 24th St Nw Ste 800, Washington DC 20037
Tel (312) 755-0770 *SIC* 8712 7389

TFP INTERNATIONAL INC p 1445
20807 Biscayne Blvd # 203, Aventura FL 33180
Tel (786) 279-2900 *SIC* 7389

TRADE FINANCE SOLUTIONS INC p 1468
20807 Biscayne Blvd # 203, Aventura FL 33180
Tel (786) 279-2900 *SIC* 7389

MERCANTIL COMMERCEBANK HOLDING CORP p 943
220 Alhambra Cir, Coral Gables FL 33134
Tel (305) 441-5555 *SIC* 6021 7389 8721

FLORIDA HOSPITAL MEMORIAL FOUNDATION p 558
305 Memorial Medical Pkwy # 212, Daytona Beach FL 32117
Tel (386) 615-4144 *SIC* 7389

ANSA MCAL (US) INC p 93
11403 Nw 39th St, Doral FL 33178
Tel (305) 599-8766 *SIC* 7389 4731

CHIQUITA BRANDS LLC p 301
2051 Se 35th St, Fort Lauderdale FL 33316
Tel (954) 453-1201
SIC 0175 0174 0179 0161 5148 7389

RESOLVE MARINE GROUP INC p 1227
1510 Se 17th St Ste 400, Fort Lauderdale FL 33316
Tel (954) 764-8700
SIC 4499 4492 4491 4412 7389

MASTER PROTECTION HOLDINGS INC p 918
13050 Metro Pkwy Ste 1, Fort Myers FL 33966
Tel (239) 896-1680 *SIC* 7389 1711 5999

CAMBRIDGE INTEGRATED SERVICES GROUP INC p 244
7369 Sheridan St Ste 301, Hollywood FL 33024
Tel (954) 966-4772 *SIC* 8742 7389

■ BLACK KNIGHT INFOSERV LLC p 187
601 Riverside Ave, Jacksonville FL 32204
Tel (904) 854-5100 *SIC* 7389 7374

▲ EVERBANK FINANCIAL CORP p 513
501 Riverside Ave, Jacksonville FL 32202
Tel (904) 281-6000 *SIC* 6035 7389

▲ FIDELITY NATIONAL INFORMATION SERVICES INC p 541
601 Riverside Ave, Jacksonville FL 32204
Tel (904) 438-6000 *SIC* 7389 7374

■ FIS WEALTH MANAGEMENT SERVICES INC p 551
601 Riverside Ave, Jacksonville FL 32204
Tel (904) 854-5000 *SIC* 7389 7374

ONE CALL MEDICAL INC p 1086
841 Prudential Dr Ste 900, Jacksonville FL 32207
Tel (904) 646-0199 *SIC* 8742 7389

RONCO CONSULTING CORP p 1249
1395 University Blvd, Jupiter FL 33458
Tel (571) 551-2934 *SIC* 1794 7389 7382

UNITED SPACE ALLIANCE LLC p 1512
Launch Equipment Support, Kennedy Space Center FL 32899
Tel (321) 861-0733 *SIC* 7389

VILLAGES OF LAKE-SUMTER INC p 1557
1000 Lake Sumter Lndg, Lady Lake FL 32162
Tel (352) 753-2270
SIC 6552 1521 7997 5812 7389

BUNKERS INTERNATIONAL CORP p 226
1071 S Sun Dr Ste 3, Lake Mary FL 32746
Tel (407) 328-7757 *SIC* 7389 5172

AGORA MARKETING SOLUTIONS INC p 35
8285 Bryan Dairy Rd # 150, Largo FL 33777
Tel (727) 369-2700 *SIC* 7331 7389

GLOBAL RESPONSE CORP p 617
777 S State Road 7, Margate FL 33068
Tel (954) 973-7300 *SIC* 7389

INDEPENDENT PURCHASING COOPERATIVE INC p 737
9200 S Dadeland Blvd # 800, Miami FL 33156
Tel (305) 670-0041 *SIC* 7389

SHAMI MEDIA GROUP INC p 1311
1395 Brickell Ave Ste 800, Miami FL 33131
Tel (347) 549-2710 *SIC* 7389

INKTEL HOLDINGS CORP p 743
13975 Nw 58th Ct, Miami Lakes FL 33014
Tel (305) 523-1100 *SIC* 7389

ALLIED CONVENTION SERVICE INC p 56
2502 Lake Orange Dr, Orlando FL 32837
Tel (407) 851-0261 *SIC* 7389

DISCOVERY MARKETING AND DISTRIBUTING INC p 442
6505 Edgewater Dr, Orlando FL 32810
Tel (407) 523-0775 *SIC* 5999 7389

ISI DESIGN AND INSTALLATION SOLUTIONS INC p 766
6321 Emperor Dr Ste 201, Orlando FL 32809
Tel (407) 872-1865
SIC 7389 1752 1799 1751

KEYSTONE GROUP HOLDINGS INC p 815
4901 Vineland Rd Ste 350, Orlando FL 32811
Tel (813) 225-4650 *SIC* 7389 7261

ROSEN 9939 INC p 1251
9840 International Dr, Orlando FL 32819
Tel (407) 996-9939
SIC 7011 5812 5813 7992 7389

ROSEN HOTELS AND RESORTS INC p 1251
9840 International Dr, Orlando FL 32819
Tel (407) 996-1706
SIC 7011 5812 5813 7389 8011 7992

WESTGATE RESORTS LTD p 1601
5601 Windhover Dr, Orlando FL 32819
Tel (407) 351-3350 *SIC* 7389

LAKEVIEW CENTER INC p 840
1221 W Lakeview Ave, Pensacola FL 32501
Tel (850) 432-1222
SIC 8069 8093 7389 7371 7373

C3/CUSTOMERCONTACTCHANNELS INC p 234
1200 S Pine Island Rd # 200, Plantation FL 33324
Tel (954) 849-0622 *SIC* 7389

DHL EXPRESS (USA) INC p 435
1210 S Pine Island Rd, Plantation FL 33324
Tel (954) 888-7000 *SIC* 4513 7389 4731

STAR GLOBE NETWORK ENTERPRISES INC p 1378
1331 Nw 80th Ter, Plantation FL 33322
Tel (561) 771-2053 *SIC* 7389

INTERACTIVE RESPONSE TECHNOLOGIES INC p 751
895 Sw 30th Ave Ste 201, Pompano Beach FL 33069
Tel (954) 484-4973 *SIC* 7389

■ FIDELITY NATIONAL GLOBAL CARD SERVICES INC p 541
11601 Roosevelt Blvd N, Saint Petersburg FL 33716
Tel (727) 556-9000 *SIC* 7389

FIRST CONTACT LLC p 546
200 Central Ave Ste 600, Saint Petersburg FL 33701
Tel (727) 369-0850 *SIC* 7389

PSCU INC p 1188
560 Carillon Pkwy, Saint Petersburg FL 33716
Tel (727) 572-8822 *SIC* 7389

■ RENZ NICHOLS FAMILY LIMITED PARTNERSHIP p 1224
11601 Roosevelt Blvd N, Saint Petersburg FL 33716
Tel (727) 573-7848 *SIC* 7389

WIGINTON CORP p 1608
699 Aero Ln, Sanford FL 32771
Tel (407) 585-3200 *SIC* 1711 7699 7389

▲ SUPERIOR UNIFORM GROUP INC p 1407
10055 Seminole Blvd, Seminole FL 33772
Tel (727) 397-9611 *SIC* 2389 3999 7389

BUREAU VERITAS HOLDINGS INC p 226
1601 Sawgrass Corporate S Ste 400, Sunrise FL 33323
Tel (954) 835-9309
SIC 7389 8748 8711 8742

BUREAU VERITAS NORTH AMERICA INC p 227
1601 Sawgrs Corp Pkwy, Sunrise FL 33323
Tel (954) 236-8100
SIC 7389 8748 8734 8711 8742

ONECIS INSURANCE CO p 1087
1601 Sawgrs Corp Pkwy, Sunrise FL 33323
Tel (954) 236-8100 *SIC* 7389 6331

▲ SYKES ENTERPRISES INC p 1413
400 N Ashley Dr Ste 2800, Tampa FL 33602
Tel (813) 274-1000 *SIC* 7379 7389

■ TIME CUSTOMER SERVICE INC p 1454
1 N Dale Mabry Hwy # 150, Tampa FL 33609
Tel (813) 878-6427 *SIC* 7389 7374

WOLF RETAIL SOLUTIONS I INC p 1621
2801 W Busch Blvd Ste 101, Tampa FL 33618
Tel (813) 280-2946 *SIC* 7389

FULL SAIL LLC p 584
3300 University Blvd, Winter Park FL 32792
Tel (407) 679-0100 *SIC* 8222 7389

■ CHECKFREE CORP p 292
2900 Westside Pkwy, Alpharetta GA 30004
Tel (678) 375-3000 *SIC* 7389

LANDIS+GYR HOLDCO2 LLC p 842
30000 Mill Creek Ave, Alpharetta GA 30022
Tel (678) 258-1500 *SIC* 7389

ROLTA INTERNATIONAL INC p 1248
5865 N Point Pkwy Ste 300, Alpharetta GA 30022
Tel (678) 942-5000 *SIC* 7389 7371 7372

■ SCIENTIFIC GAMES INTERNATIONAL INC p 1292
1500 Bluegrass Lakes Pkwy, Alpharetta GA 30004
Tel (770) 664-3700 *SIC* 7389 7999

■ UPS WORLDWIDE LOGISTICS INC p 1529
12380 Morris Rd, Alpharetta GA 30005
Tel (678) 746-4100 *SIC* 7389

AMERICOLD LOGISTICS LLC p 82
10 Glenlake Pkwy Ste 324, Atlanta GA 30328
Tel (678) 441-1400
SIC 4222 4899 8742 7389

CBEYOND INC p 268
320 Interstate N Pkwy 500, Atlanta GA 30339
Tel (678) 424-2400
SIC 4813 7389 4899 1731

CONSOLIDATED CONTAINER HOLDINGS LLC p 359
3101 Towercreek Pkwy Se P, Atlanta GA 30339
Tel (678) 742-4600 *SIC* 2671 7389 5113

COX ENTERPRISES INC p 386
6205 Pachtree Dunwoody Rd, Atlanta GA 30328
Tel (678) 645-0000
SIC 4841 4813 2711 4833 7389 4832

DOCUMENT TECHNOLOGIES LLC p 447
2 Ravinia Dr Ste 850, Atlanta GA 30346
Tel (770) 390-2700 *SIC* 7389

▲ EQUIFAX INC p 506
1550 Peachtree St Nw, Atlanta GA 30309
Tel (404) 885-8000
SIC 7323 7389 8732 8741

EXAMWORKS INC p 516
3280 Peachtree Rd Ne # 2625, Atlanta GA 30305
Tel (404) 952-2400 *SIC* 7389

FIRST ADVANTAGE CORP p 544
1 Concourse Pkwy Ste 200, Atlanta GA 30328
Tel (800) 888-5773
SIC 7323 8742 7372 7389 7381

■ FIRST DATA MERCHANT SERVICES CORP p 546
5565 Glenridge Connector, Atlanta GA 30342
Tel (404) 890-3000
SIC 7374 7389 7375 6153 6099

▲ GLOBAL PAYMENTS INC p 617
10 Glenlake Pkwy N Tower, Atlanta GA 30328
Tel (770) 829-8000 *SIC* 7389

■ GRAPHIC PACKAGING INTERNATIONAL INC p 632
1500 Riveredge Pkwy # 100, Atlanta GA 30328
Tel (770) 240-7200 *SIC* 2657 2631 7389

GSMA LTD p 643
1000 Abernathy Rd Ste 450, Atlanta GA 30328
Tel (678) 281-6600 *SIC* 7389

H J RUSSELL & CO p 650
171 17th St Nw Ste 1600, Atlanta GA 30363
Tel (404) 330-1000
SIC 1542 8741 7389 8742

INTERIOR LOGIC GROUP INC p 753
3050 Peachtree Rd Nw, Atlanta GA 30305
Tel (770) 560-7186 *SIC* 7389

ISD HOLDINGS INC p 766
4715 Frederick Dr Sw, Atlanta GA 30336
Tel (404) 691-7400
SIC 7389 2542 2759 2752

MILLER ZELL INC p 971
6100 Fulton Indus Blvd Sw, Atlanta GA 30336
Tel (404) 691-7400
SIC 7389 2542 2759 2752

NEXXLINX CORP INC p 1041
3565 Piedmont Rd Ne 2-104, Atlanta GA 30305
Tel (877) 747-0658 *SIC* 7389 8742

PREMIERE GLOBAL SERVICES INC p 1171
3280 Peachtree Rd Ne # 1000, Atlanta GA 30305
Tel (404) 262-8400 *SIC* 7372 7389

■ ROLLINS SUPPLY INC p 1247
2170 Piedmont Rd Ne, Atlanta GA 30324
Tel (404) 888-2000 *SIC* 7389

SHEPARD EXPOSITION SERVICES INC p 1315
1424 Hills Pl Nw, Atlanta GA 30318
Tel (404) 720-8600 *SIC* 7389

■ UNITED PARCEL SERVICE INC (OH) p 1510
55 Glenlake Pkwy, Atlanta GA 30328
Tel (404) 828-6000 *SIC* 7389

■ UPS LOGISTICS GROUP INC p 1529
55 Glenlake Pkwy, Atlanta GA 30328
Tel (678) 746-4100
SIC 7389 7513 4731 4513

■ WACHOVIA OPERATIONAL SERVICES LLC (NORTH CAROLINA) p 1570
191 Peachtree St Ne Fl 31, Atlanta GA 30303
Tel (404) 332-5000 *SIC* 7389

AUBREY SILVEY ENTERPRISES INC p 130
371 Hamp Jones Rd, Carrollton GA 30117
Tel (770) 834-0738
SIC 1629 1541 3643 7389 3699 5063

▲ SYNOVUS FINANCIAL CORP p 1415
1111 Bay Ave Ste 500, Columbus GA 31901
Tel (706) 649-2311 *SIC* 6021 6022 7389

WHATLEY OIL AND AUTO PARTS CO p 1604
598 Blakely St, Cuthbert GA 39840
Tel (229) 732-2611 *SIC* 5171 5013 7389

SOUTHEAST TESTING & ENGINEERING INC p 1346
2870 N Berkeley Lk Rd Nw, Duluth GA 30096
Tel (678) 377-1234 *SIC* 7389

HEALTH SYSTEMS FACILITIES INC p 676
1005 Boulder Dr, Gray GA 31032
Tel (478) 621-2100 *SIC* 7389

INNVISION HOSPITALITY INC p 745
504 Carver Rd, Griffin GA 30224
Tel (888) 875-6202 *SIC* 5131 5021 7389

ROYSTON LLC p 1255
1 Pickroy Rd, Jasper GA 30143
Tel (770) 735-3456 *SIC* 7389 2542 1751

BLUE EAGLE HOLDINGS LP p 192
6465 E Johns Xing, Johns Creek GA 30097
Tel (678) 584-4000 *SIC* 7389 7374 8742

RADIAL SOUTH LP p 1204
6465 E Johns Xing, Johns Creek GA 30097
Tel (678) 584-4000 *SIC* 7389 7374 8742

RYLA INC p 1261
2120 Barrett Park Dr Nw, Kennesaw GA 30144
Tel (678) 322-5000 *SIC* 7389

MIDCOUNTRY FINANCIAL CORP p 964
201 2nd St Ste 950, Macon GA 31201
Tel (478) 746-8222 *SIC* 7389

BENEVIS LLC p 173
1090 Northchase Pkwy Se, Marietta GA 30067
Tel (770) 916-9000 *SIC* 8741 7389

ONEPATH SYSTEMS LLC p 1088
2053 Franklin Way Se, Marietta GA 30067
Tel (678) 695-5500
SIC 7389 8744 7378 7376 7382

▲ FLEETCOR TECHNOLOGIES INC p 555
5445 Triangle Pkwy # 400, Norcross GA 30092
Tel (770) 449-0479 *SIC* 7389

■ FLEETCOR TECHNOLOGIES OPERATING CO LLC p 555
655 Engineering Dr # 300, Norcross GA 30092
Tel (770) 449-0479 *SIC* 7389

MILNER INC p 972
5125 Peachtree Indus Blvd, Norcross GA 30092
Tel (770) 458-0999
SIC 7372 5999 7389 5065 5049 5044

CRYSTAL DIAMOND BRANDS INC p 396
3000 Tremont Rd, Savannah GA 31405
Tel (912) 651-5112 *SIC* 7389 2099

ALLISON-SMITH CO LLC p 58
1869 S Cobb Indus Blvd Se, Smyrna GA 30082
Tel (404) 351-6430 *SIC* 1731 7389

■ YP HOLDINGS LLC p 1639
2247 Northlake Pkwy Fl 10, Tucker GA 30084
Tel (866) 570-8863 *SIC* 7374 7389 7313

■ AQUA-ASTON HOSPITALITY LLC p 101
2155 Kalakaua Ave Fl 5, Honolulu HI 96815
Tel (808) 931-1400 *SIC* 7389 7011

■ MAUI OPERATING LLC p 921
2365 Kaanapali Pkwy, Lahaina HI 96761
Tel (808) 661-2588 *SIC* 7011 7389

SYNCREON TECHNOLOGY (USA) LLC p 1415
1200 N Greenbriar Dr, Addison IL 60101
Tel (630) 261-3100 *SIC* 7389 4222

ADVERTISING RESOURCES INC p 27
11601 S Central Ave, Alsip IL 60803
Tel (708) 293-1926 *SIC* 7389

GRIFFITH FOODS INTERNATIONAL INC p 640
1 Griffith Ctr, Alsip IL 60803
Tel (708) 371-0900 *SIC* 2099 7389

▲ WESTELL TECHNOLOGIES INC p 1597
750 N Commons Dr, Aurora IL 60504
Tel (630) 898-2500 *SIC* 3661 4813 7389

PREFERRED RISK INSURANCE SERVICES INC p 1169
6640 S Cicero Ave Ste 400, Bedford Park IL 60638
Tel (708) 552-2424 *SIC* 7389

BROOKFIELD GLOBAL RELOCATION SERVICES LLC p 217
150 Harvester Dr Ste 201, Burr Ridge IL 60527
Tel (630) 972-2250 *SIC* 7389

A EPSTEIN AND SONS INTERNATIONAL INC p 5
600 W Fulton St Ste 800, Chicago IL 60661
Tel (312) 454-9100
SIC 8711 8712 7389 1542 1541 8742

ACCENTURE INC p 14
161 N Clark St Ste 1100, Chicago IL 60601
Tel (312) 737-8842 *SIC* 7379 7389 8742

ACCENTURE LLC p 14
161 N Clark St Ste 1100, Chicago IL 60601
Tel (312) 693-0161 *SIC* 7379 7389 8742

■ AMERITECH SERVICES INC p 84
208 S Lasalle St Ste 814, Chicago IL 60604
Tel (847) 248-2000
SIC 7389 4225 8742 8721

CHICAGO CHARTER SCHOOL FOUNDATION p 297
11 E Adams St Ste 600, Chicago IL 60603
Tel (312) 455-7890 *SIC* 7389

■ CHICAGO TRIBUNE CO p 298
435 N Michigan Ave # 200, Chicago IL 60611
Tel (312) 222-3232
SIC 2711 7383 7389 7331

CISION US INC p 309
130 E Randolph St Fl 7, Chicago IL 60601
Tel (312) 922-2400 *SIC* 7389 2741 7331

CZARNOWSKI DISPLAY SERVICE INC p 406
2287 S Blue Island Ave, Chicago IL 60608
Tel (773) 247-1500 *SIC* 7389

DELOITTE CORPORATE FINANCE LLC p 425
111 S Wacker Dr, Chicago IL 60606
Tel (312) 486-1400 *SIC* 7389

▲ ENOVA INTERNATIONAL INC p 500
175 W Jackson Blvd Fl 10, Chicago IL 60604
Tel (312) 568-4200 *SIC* 7389

▲ ENVESTNET INC p 503
35 E Wacker Dr Ste 2400, Chicago IL 60601
Tel (312) 827-2800 *SIC* 7389 6282 7372

■ EXELON BUSINESS SERVICES CO LLC p 518
10 S Dearborn St, Chicago IL 60603
Tel (800) 483-3220 *SIC* 7389

FORWARD SPACE LLC p 570
1142 N North Branch St, Chicago IL 60642
Tel (312) 942-1100 *SIC* 5021 7389

GTCR VALOR COMPANIES INC p 644
300 N La Salle Dr # 5600, Chicago IL 60654
Tel (312) 382-2200 *SIC* 7389

■ JT CO INC p 796
7401 S Cicero Ave, Chicago IL 60629
Tel (773) 838-3400 *SIC* 7389

LIVINGSTON INTERNATIONAL INC p 871
141 W Jackson Blvd 1510a, Chicago IL 60604
Tel (630) 766-0202 *SIC* 7389

METROPOLITAN PIER AND EXPOSITION AUTHORITY p 956
301 Ecermak Rd Fl 5, Chicago IL 60616
Tel (312) 791-7000 *SIC* 7389 7999 7011

NORTHWESTERN MEMORIAL HEALTHCARE p 1060
251 E Huron St Ste 3-710, Chicago IL 60611
Tel (312) 926-2000
SIC 8082 6513 7389 8099

PERKINS & WILL GROUP LTD p 1136
410 N Michigan Ave # 1600, Chicago IL 60611
Tel (312) 755-0770 *SIC* 8712 7389

PLS FINANCIAL SERVICES INC p 1156
1 S Wacker Dr Fl 36, Chicago IL 60606
Tel (312) 491-7300 *SIC* 7389 6798

REWARDS NETWORK INC p 1229
2 N Riverside Plz # 200, Chicago IL 60606
Tel (312) 756-0021 *SIC* 7389

ROADSAFE TRAFFIC SYSTEMS INC p 1240
8750 W Bryn Mawr Ave # 400, Chicago IL 60631
Tel (773) 724-3300 *SIC* 1721 1611 7389

■ WEST UNIFIED COMMUNICATIONS SERVICES INC p 1596
8420 W Bryn Mawr Ave # 1100, Chicago IL 60631
Tel (773) 399-1600 *SIC* 7389

HOWARD G BUFFETT FOUNDATION p 713
145 N Merchant St Apt 1, Decatur IL 62523
Tel (217) 429-3988 *SIC* 7389

BAXALTA US INC p 160
1 Baxter Pkwy, Deerfield IL 60015
Tel (224) 948-2000 *SIC* 7389

NCH MARKETING SERVICES INC p 1022
155 N Pfingsten Rd # 200, Deerfield IL 60015
Tel (847) 317-9039 *SIC* 7389

STERIGENICS US LLC p 1386
3 Parkway N Ste 100n, Deerfield IL 60015
Tel (847) 607-6060 *SIC* 7389

■ FLORISTS TRANSWORLD DELIVERY INC p 560
3113 Woodcreek Dr, Downers Grove IL 60515
Tel (630) 719-7800 *SIC* 5193 7389 2771

■ FTD GROUP INC p 582
3113 Woodcreek Dr, Downers Grove IL 60515
Tel (630) 719-7800 *SIC* 5193 7389

■ FTD INC p 582
3113 Woodcreek Dr, Downers Grove IL 60515
Tel (630) 719-7800 *SIC* 5193 7389

LENDING SOLUTIONS INC p 855
2200 Point Blvd Ste 110, Elgin IL 60123
Tel (847) 844-2200 *SIC* 6153 7389

QUANTUM PLASTICS LLC p 1198
1000 Davis Rd, Elgin IL 60123
Tel (847) 695-9700 *SIC* 7389

■ CITICORP CREDIT SERVICES INC p 310
50 Northwest Point Blvd, Elk Grove Village IL 60007
Tel (847) 597-3000
SIC 7374 7389 7379 6141

HOWE-OTTO INC p 713
951 E 3300 North Rd, Farmer City IL 61842
Tel (309) 928-9730 *SIC* 0116 0115 7389

PEACOCK FOODS LLC p 1125
1800 Averill Rd, Geneva IL 60134
Tel (630) 845-9400 *SIC* 4783 7389

ROUND GROUND METALS INC p 1252
4825 Turnberry Dr, Hanover Park IL 60133
Tel (630) 539-5300 *SIC* 5051 7389

HENRICKSEN & CO INC p 683
1101 W Thorndale Ave, Itasca IL 60143
Tel (630) 250-9090 *SIC* 5021 7389

REYNOLDS CONSUMER PRODUCTS HOLDINGS INC p 1230
1900 W Field Ct, Lake Forest IL 60045
Tel (847) 482-3050 *SIC* 7389

CLARK BRANDS LLC p 322
4200 Commerce Ct Ste 350, Lisle IL 60532
Tel (630) 355-8918
SIC 6794 7389 5541 5812

FOOTPRINT ACQUISITION LLC p 564
2200 Western Ct Ste 150, Lisle IL 60532
Tel (630) 324-3400 *SIC* 7389

CIMCO RESOURCES INC p 307
1616 Windsor Rd, Loves Park IL 61111
Tel (815) 986-7211 *SIC* 5093 7389

GROUP O INC p 642
4905 77th Ave E, Milan IL 61264
Tel (309) 736-8100
SIC 8742 7389 4226 5085

HILCO INC p 692
5 Revere Dr Ste 430, Northbrook IL 60062
Tel (847) 714-1288 *SIC* 7389 6531

STERIGENICS INTERNATIONAL LLC p 1386
2015 Spring Rd Ste 650, Oak Brook IL 60523
Tel (630) 928-1700 *SIC* 7389

UNION PARTNERS I LLC p 1505
1400 16th St Ste 250, Oak Brook IL 60523
Tel (630) 822-7000 *SIC* 8741 7389

HGS (USA) LLC p 689
1901 E War Memorial Dr, Peoria IL 61614
Tel (309) 679-4261 *SIC* 7389

ONE CALL LOCATORS LTD p 1086
60 State St Ste 201, Peoria IL 61602
Tel (309) 673-2851 *SIC* 7389

SUPERIOR CONSOLIDATED INDUSTRIES INC p 1406
801 Sw Jefferson Ave, Peoria IL 61605
Tel (309) 677-5980 *SIC* 7389 1721

STERLING LUMBER CO p 1387
501 E 151st St, Phoenix IL 60426
Tel (708) 388-2223 *SIC* 5031 7389 2448

HSBC INVESTMENTS (NORTH AMERICA) INC p 715
2700 Sanders Rd, Prospect Heights IL 60070
Tel (847) 564-5000
SIC 6141 7389 6351 6159 6162 6311

CCH INC p 270
2700 Lake Cook Rd, Riverwoods IL 60015
Tel (847) 267-7000
SIC 2721 2731 7389 7338 8732 7371

▲ DISCOVER FINANCIAL SERVICES p 442
2500 Lake Cook Rd, Riverwoods IL 60015
Tel (224) 405-0900 *SIC* 6022 6141 7389

ANDERSONBRECON INC p 90
4545 Assembly Dr, Rockford IL 61109
Tel (815) 484-8900 *SIC* 7389

A H MANAGEMENT GROUP INC p 5
1151 Rohlwing Rd, Rolling Meadows IL 60008
Tel (847) 342-8065
SIC 5962 7993 5963 7389 5046

ROSEMONT EXPOSITION SERVICES INC p 1251
9291w Bryn Mawr Ave, Rosemont IL 60018
Tel (847) 696-2208 *SIC* 7389

TRIMEGA PURCHASING ASSOCIATION p 1480
5600 N River Rd Ste 700, Rosemont IL 60018
Tel (847) 699-3330 *SIC* 7389

POWER PACKAGING INC p 1165
525 Dunham Rd Ste 3, Saint Charles IL 60174
Tel (630) 377-3838 *SIC* 7389

MIDSTATES VIDEO CORP p 966
1022 E Adams St, Springfield IL 62703
Tel (217) 544-8433 *SIC* 7389 7841

VISUAL PAK CO p 1562
1909 S Waukegan Rd, Waukegan IL 60085
Tel (847) 689-1000 *SIC* 7389

HERITAGE MANAGEMENT GROUP INC p 686
2384 Glebe St, Carmel IN 46032
Tel (317) 569-0877 *SIC* 7389

ZOTEC SOLUTIONS INC p 1644
11460 N Meridian St Ste X, Carmel IN 46032
Tel (317) 848-2815 *SIC* 7389

■ SPRINGLEAF FINANCE INC p 1361
601 Nw 2nd St, Evansville IN 47708
Tel (812) 424-8031
SIC 6153 6351 6331 7389

STRATOSPHERE QUALITY LLC p 1393
12024 Exit 5 Pkwy, Fishers IN 46037
Tel (317) 578-1455 *SIC* 7389

CADILLAC COFFEE CO p 236
7221 Innovation Blvd, Fort Wayne IN 46818
Tel (248) 545-2266 *SIC* 5149 7389

NORTH AMERICAN VAN LINES INC p 1050
5001 Us Highway 30 W, Fort Wayne IN 46818
Tel (260) 429-1682
SIC 4213 4731 4214 6331 7389 4212

▲ STEEL DYNAMICS INC p 1384
7575 W Jefferson Blvd, Fort Wayne IN 46804
Tel (260) 969-3500 *SIC* 3312 3316 7389

SWEETWATER SOUND INC p 1412
5501 Us Highway 30 W, Fort Wayne IN 46818
Tel (260) 432-8176 *SIC* 7389 5736 5999

CLOSURE SYSTEMS INTERNATIONAL HOLDINGS INC p 327
7702 Woodland Dr Ste 200, Indianapolis IN 46278
Tel (317) 876-0173 *SIC* 7389

COMMUNITY HEALTH NETWORK FOUNDATION INC p 348
7321 Shadeland Sta # 100, Indianapolis IN 46256
Tel (317) 621-1282 *SIC* 7389

HERITAGE ENVIRONMENTAL SERVICES INC p 686
7901 W Morris St, Indianapolis IN 46231
Tel (317) 243-0811
SIC 5093 4213 8731 7389 1799 8711

HERITAGE ENVIRONMENTAL SERVICES LLC p 686
7901 W Morris St, Indianapolis IN 46231
Tel (317) 243-0811
SIC 5093 4213 8731 7389 1799 8711

KOORSEN FIRE & SECURITY INC p 827
2719 N Arlington Ave, Indianapolis IN 46218
Tel (317) 542-1800
SIC 5099 7389 5199 5063 1731

■ ACCENT MARKETING SERVICES LLC p 14
4550 Town Center Blvd, Jeffersonville IN 47130
Tel (812) 941-1112 *SIC* 7331 7389 8748

LOUISIANA DOCK CO LLC p 880
1701 Utica Pike, Jeffersonville IN 47130
Tel (812) 288-0100 *SIC* 7389

ROYAL ADHESIVES AND SEALANTS LLC p 1254
2001 W Washington St, South Bend IN 46628
Tel (574) 246-5000 *SIC* 2891 7389 8711

CROSS OVER LLC p 393
621 Alta Vista Dr, Carroll IA 51401
Tel (712) 790-4549 *SIC* 8733 7389

ACCESS DIRECT TELEMARKETING SERVICES INC p 14
4515 20th Ave Sw Ste B, Cedar Rapids IA 52404
Tel (319) 390-8900 *SIC* 7389 7361

RUFFALO NOEL LEVITZ LLC p 1257
1025 Kirkwood Pkwy Sw, Cedar Rapids IA 52404
Tel (800) 876-1117 *SIC* 7389

WEST SIDE UNLIMITED CORP p 1595
4201 16th Ave Sw, Cedar Rapids IA 52404
Tel (319) 390-4466 *SIC* 4213 7389

PER MAR SECURITY AND RESEARCH CORP p 1134
1910 E Kimberly Rd, Davenport IA 52807
Tel (563) 359-3200
SIC 8732 7381 5099 7389 7382

CDS GLOBAL INC p 271
1901 Bell Ave Ste 19, Des Moines IA 50315
Tel (866) 897-7987 *SIC* 7389 7375 7374

■ WELLS FARGO IOWA NA p 1591
666 Walnut St Ste 1400, Des Moines IA 50309
Tel (515) 245-3000 *SIC* 6021 7389

STAR OF DAVID ARMS INDUSTRIES INC p 1378
304 Se 2nd St Apt B, Grimes IA 50111
Tel (888) 491-0307 *SIC* 3484 7389

METROGROUP CORP p 955
1805 E Washington St, Mount Pleasant IA 52641
Tel (319) 385-5135 *SIC* 7331 7389

KANSAS STATE UNIVERSITY FOUNDATION INC p 803
1800 Kimball Ave Ste 200, Manhattan KS 66502
Tel (785) 532-6266 *SIC* 7389

TSVC INC p 1489
18001 W 106th St Ste 300, Olathe KS 66061
Tel (913) 599-6886 *SIC* 7389

ASH GROVE MATERIALS CORP p 117
11011 Cody St Ste 300, Overland Park KS 66210
Tel (913) 345-2030
SIC 3273 3272 1411 7389 4212

QC HOLDINGS INC p 1194
9401 Indian Creek Pkwy # 1500, Overland Park KS 66210
Tel (866) 660-2243 *SIC* 6141 7389

SANDEN NORTH AMERICA INC p 1278
9900 Pflumm Rd Ste 22, Shawnee Mission KS 66215
Tel (913) 888-6667 *SIC* 7389

CITY OF FRANKFORT p 315
1200 Kentucky Ave, Frankfort KY 40601
Tel (502) 875-8500 *SIC* 7389

SENTURE LLC p 1305
460 Industrial Blvd, London KY 40741
Tel (606) 878-4205
SIC 7379 7389 7374 7373 8742

DERBY INDUSTRIES LLC p 431
4451 Robards Ln, Louisville KY 40218
Tel (502) 451-7373
SIC 4225 7389 4222 4226

HILLIARD-LYONS INC p 693
500 W Jefferson St # 700, Louisville KY 40202
Tel (502) 588-8400 *SIC* 7389

HL FINANCIAL SERVICES LLC p 697
500 W Jefferson St, Louisville KY 40202
Tel (502) 588-8400 *SIC* 7389

NORTON HEALTHCARE FOUNDATION INC p 1061
4967 Us Highway 42 # 100, Louisville KY 40222
Tel (502) 629-8000 *SIC* 7389

■ NPC GROUP INC p 1064
5100 Interchange Way, Louisville KY 40229
Tel (312) 627-6000 *SIC* 7389

SOUTHERN GRAPHICS INC p 1348
626 W Main St, Louisville KY 40202
Tel (502) 637-5443 *SIC* 7336 7389

DIRECTECH OF KENTUCKY INC p 441
33 W 2nd St Ste 504, Maysville KY 41056
Tel (606) 564-0007 *SIC* 7389

VERST GROUP LOGISTICS INC p 1552
300 Shorland Dr, Walton KY 41094
Tel (859) 485-1212 *SIC* 4225 7389

LOUISIANA CRANE & CONSTRUCTION LLC p 880
1045 Highway 190, Eunice LA 70535
Tel (337) 550-6217 *SIC* 7389 7353 1623

■ TALENS MARINE & FUEL LLC p 1422
1707 Evangeline Hwy, Jennings LA 70546
Tel (800) 256-3835 *SIC* 5172 7389

AECO INTERIORS OF NEW ORLEANS p 28
1836 Iberville St, New Orleans LA 70112
Tel (504) 301-9600 *SIC* 7389

PAN-AMERICAN LIFE INSURANCE GROUP INC p 1110
601 Poydras St Ste 1000, New Orleans LA 70130
Tel (504) 566-1300 *SIC* 6311 7389

DIVERSIFIED BUSINESS COMMUNICATIONS p 444
121 Free St, Portland ME 04101
Tel (207) 842-5400
SIC 4833 4841 2721 7389

▲ WEX INC p 1603
97 Darling Ave, South Portland ME 04106
Tel (207) 773-8171 *SIC* 7389 7375

■ CITIFINANCIAL CREDIT CO p 310
300 Saint Paul St Fl 3, Baltimore MD 21202
Tel (410) 332-3000
SIC 6141 6162 7389 6331 6159 6022

▲ WALKER & DUNLOP INC p 1573
7501 Wisconsin Ave 1200e, Bethesda MD 20814
Tel (301) 215-5500 *SIC* 7389 8741

WELOCALIZE INC p 1591
241 E 4th St Ste 207, Frederick MD 21701
Tel (301) 668-0330 *SIC* 7389

■ LEIDOS ASPEN SYSTEMS CORP p 854
700 N Frederick Ave, Gaithersburg MD 20879
Tel (301) 240-7000 *SIC* 7374 7379 7389

ASBURY ATLANTIC INC p 115
20030 Century Blvd, Germantown MD 20874
Tel (301) 250-2100 *SIC* 7389

BFPE INTERNATIONAL INC p 179
7512 Connelley Dr, Hanover MD 21076
Tel (410) 768-2200 *SIC* 1731 7382 7389

GENGOTEX CORP p 603
12301 Old Columbia Pike, Silver Spring MD 20904
Tel (240) 753-5497 *SIC* 7389

E4E INC p 467
502 Washington Ave # 200, Towson MD 21204
Tel (443) 275-1632 *SIC* 7389

■ AMERICAN SCIENCE AND ENGINEERING INC p 79
829 Middlesex Tpke, Billerica MA 01821
Tel (978) 262-8700 *SIC* 7389 8734 7382

■ INDEPENDENT ADVERTISING INC p 736
53 State St, Boston MA 02109
Tel (617) 437-1600
SIC 7311 7331 7389 8732

INTERNATIONAL DATA GROUP INC p 755
1 Exeter Plz Fl 15, Boston MA 02116
Tel (617) 534-1200 *SIC* 2721 8732 7389

JOHN HANCOCK CORPORATE TAX CREDIT FUND I LP p 788
200 Clarendon St, Boston MA 02116
Tel (617) 572-6000 *SIC* 7389

LIBERTY MUTUAL GROUP INC p 862
175 Berkeley St, Boston MA 02116
Tel (617) 357-9500
SIC 6331 6321 6351 7389

LIBERTY MUTUAL HOLDING CO INC p 862
175 Berkeley St, Boston MA 02116
Tel (617) 357-9500 *SIC* 6331 6351 7389

LIBERTY MUTUAL INSURANCE CO p 862
175 Berkeley St, Boston MA 02116
Tel (617) 357-9500
SIC 6331 6321 6351 7389

LMHC MASSACHUSETTS HOLDINGS INC p 872
175 Berkeley St, Boston MA 02116
Tel (617) 357-9500
SIC 6331 6321 6351 7389

CONSUMER PRODUCT DISTRIBUTORS INC p 361
705 Meadow St, Chicopee MA 01013
Tel (413) 592-4141
SIC 5194 5141 7389 5145

■ NYPRO INC p 1069
101 Union St, Clinton MA 01510
Tel (978) 365-8100
SIC 3089 3559 7389 8711

BARTLETT NUCLEAR INC p 158
97 Libbey Industrial Pkwy # 400, East Weymouth MA 02189
Tel (508) 746-6464 *SIC* 7389 8734

HOME DIALYSIS OF MUHLENBERG COUNTY INC p 703
95 Hayden Ave, Lexington MA 02421
Tel (781) 402-9000 *SIC* 7389

GENERAL INSULATION CO p 601
278 Mystic Ave Ste 209, Medford MA 02155
Tel (781) 391-2070 *SIC* 5033 7389

CRANES PERSONAL DESIGN SERVICES p 389
1466 Curran Hwy, North Adams MA 01247
Tel (413) 664-4321 *SIC* 7389 2796 2759

CA COURTESY DEMOS INC p 234
85 Flagship Dr Ste C, North Andover MA 01845
Tel (978) 296-2600 *SIC* 7389

■ KEYW CORP p 816
250 Clark St, North Andover MA 01845
Tel (978) 682-7767 *SIC* 7371 8713 7389

SCHAFER GOVERNMENT SERVICES LLC p 1286
101 Billerica Ave, North Billerica MA 01862
Tel (978) 256-2070 *SIC* 7389

▲ LIONBRIDGE TECHNOLOGIES INC p 870
1050 Winter St Ste 2300, Waltham MA 02451
Tel (781) 434-6000 *SIC* 7389 7374 7371

■ MODUSLINK CORP p 981
1601 Trapelo Rd Ste 170, Waltham MA 02451
Tel (781) 663-5000 *SIC* 7379 7389 5045

OLAMETER CORP p 1080
4325 Concourse Dr, Ann Arbor MI 48108
Tel (734) 769-2600 *SIC* 7389

GEORGE P JOHNSON CO p 606
3600 Giddings Rd, Auburn Hills MI 48326
Tel (248) 475-2500 *SIC* 3993 7389

■ RGIS HOLDINGS LLC p 1231
2000 Taylor Rd, Auburn Hills MI 48326
Tel (248) 651-2511 *SIC* 7389

■ RGIS LLC p 1231
2000 Taylor Rd, Auburn Hills MI 48326
Tel (248) 651-2511 *SIC* 7389

ACRISURE LLC p 18
5664 Prairie Creek Dr Se, Caledonia MI 49316
Tel (800) 748-0351 *SIC* 7389

LOGISTICS HOLLINGSWORTH GROUP LLC p 874
14225 W Warren Ave, Dearborn MI 48126
Tel (313) 768-1400 *SIC* 7389

■ PERCEPTA LLC p 1134
290 Town Center Dr # 610, Dearborn MI 48126
Tel (866) 737-2378 *SIC* 7389

EXHIBIT WORKS INC p 519
27777 Inkster Rd Ste 200, Farmington Hills MI 48334
Tel (734) 525-9010 *SIC* 7389

MINACS GROUP USA INC p 972
34115 W 12 Mile Rd, Farmington Hills MI 48331
Tel (248) 553-8355 *SIC* 7389 8742

GARDEN CITY HOSPITAL FOUNDATION p 591
6245 Inkster Rd Ste 210, Garden City MI 48135
Tel (734) 458-4421 *SIC* 8741 7389

IRB MEDICAL EQUIPMENT LLC p 764
1000 Health Park Blvd B, Grand Blanc MI 48439
Tel (810) 953-0760 *SIC* 5047 7389

DISPLAY PACK INC p 443
1340 Monroe Ave Nw Ste 1, Grand Rapids MI 49505
Tel (616) 451-3061 *SIC* 3089 2759 7389

ROSKAM BAKING CO p 1251
4880 Corp Exch Blvd Se, Grand Rapids MI 49512
Tel (616) 574-5757 *SIC* 2051 2043 7389

KEY PLASTICS LLC p 814
19575 Victor Pkwy Ste 400, Livonia MI 48152
Tel (248) 449-6100 *SIC* 3089 7389

HPS LLC p 714
3275 N M 37 Hwy, Middleville MI 49333
Tel (269) 795-3308 *SIC* 7389

24/7 BAIL AGENCY INC p 2
Elizabeth Rd, Mount Clemens MI 48043
Tel (866) 322-2245 *SIC* 7389

HSS LLC p 715
5310 Hampton Pl Ste B, Saginaw MI 48604
Tel (989) 777-2983 *SIC* 8741 8742 7389

ASSOCIATED COMMUNITY SERVICES INC p 120
23800 W 10 Mile Rd # 200, Southfield MI 48033
Tel (248) 352-2600 *SIC* 7389

DIALOGUE MARKETING INC p 436
800 Tower Dr Ste 200, Troy MI 48098
Tel (800) 523-5867 *SIC* 7389

■ **NBD SERVICE CORP** p 1021
1235 E Big Beaver Rd, Troy MI 48083
Tel (248) 680-2600 *SIC* 7389

SET ENTERPRISES INC p 1308
30500 Van Dyke Ave # 701, Warren MI 48093
Tel (586) 573-3600
SIC 7389 3465 3544 3312

DATA LISTING SERVICES LLC p 413
11351 Rupp Dr, Burnsville MN 55337
Tel (952) 948-5488 *SIC* 7389

ADVANSTAR HOLDINGS CORP p 26
131 W 1st St, Duluth MN 55802
Tel (218) 740-7200 *SIC* 7389 2721 7331

■ **STREAM GLOBAL SERVICES INC** p 1393
3285 Northwood Cir # 120, Eagan MN 55121
Tel (651) 288-2979 *SIC* 7389

BLUESTEM GROUP INC p 193
7505 Flying Cloud Dr, Eden Prairie MN 55344
Tel (952) 656-3700 *SIC* 6799 7389

EXPRESSPOINT TECHNOLOGY SERVICES INC p 521
10900 Wayzata Blvd # 800, Hopkins MN 55305
Tel (763) 543-6000
SIC 5045 7379 7699 8741 7389 7378

RYT-WAY ACQUISITION CO LLC p 1261
21850 Grenada Ave, Lakeville MN 55044
Tel (952) 469-1417 *SIC* 7389 2023 3565

RYT-WAY INDUSTRIES LLC p 1261
21850 Grenada Ave, Lakeville MN 55044
Tel (952) 469-1417 *SIC* 7389 2023

RYT-WAY MIDCO LLC p 1261
21850 Grenada Ave, Lakeville MN 55044
Tel (952) 469-1417 *SIC* 7389 2023 3565

DUNGARVIN GROUP INC p 461
1444 Northland Dr Ste 200, Mendota Heights MN 55120
Tel (651) 699-6050 *SIC* 7389

▲ **AMERIPRISE FINANCIAL INC** p 83
55 Ameriprise Fincl Ctr, Minneapolis MN 55474
Tel (612) 671-3131
SIC 6282 7389 6411 6311

ATMOSPHERE COMMERCIAL INTERIORS LLC p 128
81 S 9th St Ste 350, Minneapolis MN 55402
Tel (612) 343-0868 *SIC* 5021 5023 7389

■ **MONEYGRAM PAYMENT SYSTEMS INC** p 984
1550 Utica Ave S Ste 100, Minneapolis MN 55416
Tel (952) 591-3000 *SIC* 6099 7389

■ **NORSTAN INC** p 1049
5050 Lincoln Dr Ste 300, Minneapolis MN 55436
Tel (952) 352-4000
SIC 7389 3661 8748 7379

CARLSON HOLDINGS INC p 257
701 Carlson Pkwy, Minnetonka MN 55305
Tel (763) 212-5000
SIC 7011 5812 6794 7389 4724

CARLSON INC p 258
701 Carlson Pkwy, Minnetonka MN 55305
Tel (763) 212-5000
SIC 7011 5812 6794 8742 8743 7389

CULLIGAN SOFT WATER SERVICE CO p 400
6030 Culligan Way, Minnetonka MN 55345
Tel (952) 933-7200 *SIC* 5999 7389

RADISSON HOTELS INTERNATIONAL INC p 1204
701 Carlson Pkwy, Minnetonka MN 55305
Tel (763) 212-5000
SIC 7011 6794 6552 6531 8742 7389

BEDIVERE INSURANCE CO p 168
605 Hwy 169th N Ste 800, Plymouth MN 55441
Tel (952) 852-2431
SIC 6331 6282 6159 7389

CERNX MN LLC p 284
2355 Highway 36 W Ste 400, Roseville MN 55113
Tel (320) 372-7400
SIC 4212 7389 4731 4222

HEALTHEAST CARE SYSTEM p 677
1700 University Ave W # 5, Saint Paul MN 55104
Tel (651) 232-5353 *SIC* 8741 8062 7389

MERRILL COMMUNICATIONS LLC p 950
1 Merrill Cir, Saint Paul MN 55108
Tel (651) 646-4501 *SIC* 7374 7389

MERRILL CORP p 950
1 Merrill Cir, Saint Paul MN 55108
Tel (651) 646-4501 *SIC* 7389 8111 8999

RATNER STEEL SUPPLY CO p 1209
2500 County Road B W 1a, Saint Paul MN 55113
Tel (219) 787-6700 *SIC* 5051 7389

SECURIAN FINANCIAL GROUP INC p 1298
400 Robert St N Ste A, Saint Paul MN 55101
Tel (651) 665-3500 *SIC* 7389 6399

SMYTH COMPANIES LLC p 1335
1085 Snelling Ave N, Saint Paul MN 55108
Tel (651) 646-4544
SIC 2679 2752 3993 7389 5084 7699

▲ **DELUXE CORP** p 427
3680 Victoria St N, Shoreview MN 55126
Tel (651) 483-7111 *SIC* 2782 2761 7389

■ **BROADRIDGE CUSTOMER COMMUNICATIONS LLC** p 215
2600 Southwest Blvd, Kansas City MO 64108
Tel (816) 221-1234
SIC 7389 2759 7374 7331 2752 7336

HALLMARK MARKETING CO LLC p 654
2501 Mcgee St, Kansas City MO 64108
Tel (816) 274-5111 *SIC* 5947 2542 7389

JACK COOPER TRANSPORT CO INC p 773
1100 Walnut St Ste 2400, Kansas City MO 64106
Tel (816) 983-4000 *SIC* 4213 7389

J D STREETT & CO INC p 771
144 Weldon Pkwy, Maryland Heights MO 63043
Tel (314) 432-6600
SIC 5171 5541 7389 5172

ANSIRA PARTNERS INC p 93
2300 Locust St, Saint Louis MO 63103
Tel (314) 783-2300 *SIC* 7389 7331

ARCTURIS INC p 106
720 Olive St Ste 200, Saint Louis MO 63101
Tel (314) 206-7100 *SIC* 8712 7389

▲ **CASS INFORMATION SYSTEMS INC** p 263
12444 Powerscort Dr # 550, Saint Louis MO 63131
Tel (314) 506-5500 *SIC* 7389 7374 6029

■ **CCO HOLDINGS LLC** p 270
12405 Powerscourt Dr, Saint Louis MO 63131
Tel (314) 965-0555 *SIC* 4841 4813 7389

FEDERAL INTERNATIONAL INC p 535
7935 Clayton Rd Ste A, Saint Louis MO 63117
Tel (314) 721-3377 *SIC* 3086 7389

KEEFE GROUP LLC p 807
10880 Linpage Pl, Saint Louis MO 63132
Tel (314) 963-8700 *SIC* 7389

■ **TALX CORP** p 1423
11432 Lackland Rd, Saint Louis MO 63146
Tel (314) 214-7000 *SIC* 7373 7379 7389

TIAA-CREF TRUST CO FSB p 1452
1 Metropolitan Sq, Saint Louis MO 63102
Tel (314) 588-9738 *SIC* 7389 6282

■ **UTILIMAP CORP** p 1537
10025 Office Center Ave, Saint Louis MO 63128
Tel (636) 533-0472 *SIC* 7389

■ **OZARK PURCHASING LLC** p 1101
233 S Patterson Ave, Springfield MO 65802
Tel (417) 862-6708 *SIC* 7389

▲ **NELNET INC** p 1025
121 S 13th St Ste 100, Lincoln NE 68508
Tel (402) 458-2370 *SIC* 6141 7389

RITCHIE BROS AUCTIONEERS (AMERICA) INC p 1236
4000 Pine Lake Rd, Lincoln NE 68516
Tel (402) 421-3631 *SIC* 7389

UNIVERSITY OF NEBRASKA FOUNDATION p 1523
1010 Lincoln Mall Ste 300, Lincoln NE 68508
Tel (402) 458-1100 *SIC* 7389

■ **FIRST DATA RESOURCES LLC** p 546
6855 Pacific St, Omaha NE 68106
Tel (303) 967-8000 *SIC* 7374 7389 7375

■ **PITNEY BOWES PRESORT SERVICES INC** p 1152
10110 I St, Omaha NE 68127
Tel (402) 339-6500 *SIC* 7389

SITEL CORP p 1327
5601 N 103rd St, Omaha NE 68134
Tel (402) 963-6810 *SIC* 7389

▲ **WEST CORP** p 1594
11808 Miracle Hills Dr, Omaha NE 68154
Tel (402) 963-1200
SIC 7389 7372 4813 7374

WEST CUSTOMER MANAGEMENT GROUP LLC p 1594
11808 Miracle Hills Dr, Omaha NE 68154
Tel (402) 571-7700 *SIC* 7389

■ **WEST INTERACTIVE CORP** p 1594
11650 Miracle Hills Dr, Omaha NE 68154
Tel (402) 963-1200 *SIC* 7389

■ **WEST REVENUE GENERATION SERVICES LLC** p 1595
11808 Miracle Hills Dr, Omaha NE 68154
Tel (800) 232-0900 *SIC* 7389

SUNSET STATION HOTEL AND CASINO p 1404
1301 W Sunset Rd, Henderson NV 89014
Tel (702) 547-7777 *SIC* 7011 5962 7389

BOULDER STATION INC p 204
4111 Boulder Hwy, Las Vegas NV 89121
Tel (702) 432-7777 *SIC* 7011 7389

BRAD HENRY FRIEDMUTTER & ASSOCIATES LTD p 206
4022 Dean Martin Dr, Las Vegas NV 89103
Tel (702) 736-7477 *SIC* 8712 7389

▲ **EVERI HOLDINGS INC** p 515
7250 S Tenaya Way Ste 100, Las Vegas NV 89113
Tel (800) 833-7110 *SIC* 7389

■ **EVERI PAYMENTS INC** p 515
7250 S Tenaya Way Ste 100, Las Vegas NV 89113
Tel (702) 855-3000 *SIC* 7389 6099

■ **GLOBAL EXPERIENCE SPECIALISTS INC** p 616
7000 Lindell Rd, Las Vegas NV 89118
Tel (702) 515-5500 *SIC* 7389

GPX CORP p 628
300 S 4th St Ste 1100, Las Vegas NV 89101
Tel (702) 386-4789 *SIC* 7389

LAS VEGAS CONVENTION & VISITORS AUTHORITY p 845
3150 Paradise Rd, Las Vegas NV 89109
Tel (702) 892-0711 *SIC* 7389

NATIONAL FIELD REPRESENTATIVES INC p 1012
136 Maple Ave, Claremont NH 03743
Tel (603) 543-5210 *SIC* 7389 1799

COLWEN MANAGEMENT INC p 343
230 Commerce Way Ste 200, Portsmouth NH 03801
Tel (603) 897-6100 *SIC* 8742 7389

■ **HEWLETT-PACKARD FINANCIAL SERVICES CO** p 688
200 Connell Dr Ste 5000, Berkeley Heights NJ 07922
Tel (908) 288-9315 *SIC* 6159 7389

IGATE CORP p 730
100 Somerset Corp Blvd # 5000, Bridgewater NJ 08807
Tel (908) 219-8050 *SIC* 7371 7374 7389

QUALITY PACKAGING SPECIALISTS INTERNATIONAL LLC p 1197
5 Cooper St, Burlington NJ 08016
Tel (609) 239-0503 *SIC* 7389 3565

AMERIQUEST BUSINESS SERVICES INC p 83
457 Haddonfield Rd # 220, Cherry Hill NJ 08002
Tel (800) 608-0809 *SIC* 7389

BOWLES CORPORATE SERVICES INC p 204
335 Broad St, Clifton NJ 07013
Tel (973) 773-0699 *SIC* 7381 7389 7361

AMSPEC LLC p 87
1249 S River Rd Ste 204, Cranbury NJ 08512
Tel (908) 925-7333 *SIC* 8734 7389

RAND DIRECT INC p 1207
112 Truman Dr, Edison NJ 08817
Tel (732) 985-0800 *SIC* 7389

BURRELLES INFORMATION SERVICES LLC p 228
30b Vreeland Rd, Florham Park NJ 07932
Tel (973) 992-6600 *SIC* 7389

CYBER CITY TELESERVICES MARKETING INC p 404
401 Hackensack Ave Fl 3, Hackensack NJ 07601
Tel (201) 487-1616 *SIC* 7389

TECHNOLOGY SUPPLIER LLC p 1432
81 Hobart St, Hackensack NJ 07601
Tel (201) 500-8050 *SIC* 7389

FOSTER WHEELER INC p 570
53 Frontage Rd, Hampton NJ 08827
Tel (908) 730-4000 *SIC* 7389

CHURCHILL CORPORATE SERVICES INC p 305
56 Utter Ave, Hawthorne NJ 07506
Tel (973) 636-9400 *SIC* 6513 7389

CEI HOLDINGS INC p 273
2182 State Route 35, Holmdel NJ 07733
Tel (732) 888-7788
SIC 2844 7389 4225 5122

COSMETIC ESSENCE LLC p 373
2182 Hwy 35, Holmdel NJ 07733
Tel (732) 888-7788 *SIC* 2844 7389 4225

ATLANTIC DETROIT DIESEL ALLISON LLC p 126
180 Route 17 South, Lodi NJ 07644
Tel (201) 489-5800 *SIC* 5084 7538 7389

■ **REALOGY GROUP LLC** p 1214
175 Park Ave, Madison NJ 07940
Tel (973) 407-2000
SIC 6531 6794 7389 6541

▲ **REALOGY HOLDINGS CORP** p 1214
175 Park Ave, Madison NJ 07940
Tel (973) 407-2000
SIC 6531 6794 7389 6541

■ **REALOGY INTERMEDIATE HOLDINGS LLC** p 1214
175 Park Ave, Madison NJ 07940
Tel (973) 407-0000
SIC 6531 6794 7389 6541

DIALAMERICA MARKETING INC p 436
960 Macarthur Blvd, Mahwah NJ 07430
Tel (201) 327-0200 *SIC* 7389

CANON FINANCIAL SERVICES INC p 247
158 Gaither Dr Ste 200, Mount Laurel NJ 08054
Tel (856) 813-1000 *SIC* 6159 7389

▲ **MARLIN BUSINESS SERVICES CORP** p 909
300 Fellowship Rd, Mount Laurel NJ 08054
Tel (888) 479-9111 *SIC* 7389 7359 6022

▲ **WYNDHAM WORLDWIDE CORP** p 1630
22 Sylvan Way, Parsippany NJ 07054
Tel (973) 753-6000
SIC 7011 8741 7389 6531

AUDIO AND VIDEO LABS INC p 130
7905 N Crescent Blvd, Pennsauken NJ 08110
Tel (856) 663-9030
SIC 3652 5099 7389 3651

BERLITZ LANGUAGES (UNITED STATES) INC p 175
7 Roszel Rd Fl 3, Princeton NJ 08540
Tel (609) 759-5371 *SIC* 8299 7389 2731

■ **HEARTLAND PAYMENT SYSTEMS LLC** p 679
300 Carnegie Ctr Ste 300, Princeton NJ 08540
Tel (609) 683-3831 *SIC* 7389 8721

■ **PA ACQUISITION CORP** p 1103
25 Green Pond Rd Ste 1, Rockaway NJ 07866
Tel (973) 453-8600 *SIC* 5947 7389

SGS NORTH AMERICA INC p 1310
301 Route 17, Rutherford NJ 07070
Tel (201) 508-3000
SIC 8734 7389 8071 4499 4785

SGS US HOLDING INC p 1310
201 Route 17, Rutherford NJ 07070
Tel (201) 508-3000 *SIC* 8734 6719 7389

CORPORATE TRADE INC p 372
51 John F Kennedy Pkwy, Short Hills NJ 07078
Tel (973) 218-2551 *SIC* 7389

A & E STORES INC p 4
1000 Huyler St, Teterboro NJ 07608
Tel (201) 393-0600
SIC 5621 8721 4226 7389

HIBBERT CO p 690
400 Pennington Ave, Trenton NJ 08618
Tel (609) 392-0478 *SIC* 7331 7389

HANOVER DIRECT INC p 658
1200 Harbor Blvd Fl 9, Weehawken NJ 07086
Tel (201) 863-7300
SIC 5712 5961 7389 2211 2221

NATIONAL EXCHANGE CARRIER ASSOCIATION p 1011
80 S Jefferson Rd Ste 1, Whippany NJ 07981
Tel (800) 228-8398 *SIC* 7389 8611

CROSSROADS ARENA LLC p 394
1 Seymour H Knox Iii Plz, Buffalo NY 14203
Tel (716) 855-4100 *SIC* 7389

CREATIVE MANAGEMENT SERVICES LLC p 390
3 Alpine Ct, Chestnut Ridge NY 10977
Tel (845) 578-1651 *SIC* 7389

UNIVERSAL PACKAGING SYSTEMS INC p 1517
6080 Jericho Tpke, Commack NY 11725
Tel (631) 543-2277
SIC 2844 7389 3565 2671

■ **PC INTERMEDIATE HOLDINGS INC** p 1123
80 Grasslands Rd, Elmsford NY 10523
Tel (914) 345-2020 *SIC* 7389

TRANSFIRST INC p 1471
1393 Veterans Hwy 307s, Hauppauge NY 11788
Tel (631) 840-6900 *SIC* 7389

Q INTERNATIONAL COURIER INC p 1194
17528 148th Ave, Jamaica NY 11434
Tel (718) 995-3616 *SIC* 7389

■ **CITICORP CREDIT SERVICES INC** p 310
One Court Square 25th Flr, Long Island City NY 11120
Tel (718) 248-3192 *SIC* 7389

CANON SOLUTIONS AMERICA INC p 247
1 Canon Park, Melville NY 11747
Tel (631) 330-5000 *SIC* 7389

EVO MERCHANT SERVICES LLC p 515
515 Broadhollow Rd # 100, Melville NY 11747
Tel (516) 479-9000 *SIC* 7389

PARKERJEWISH GERIATRIC INSTITUTE p 1116
27111 76th Ave, New Hyde Park NY 11040
Tel (718) 289-2100 *SIC* 7389

ADVANSTAR INC p 26
641 Lexington Ave Fl 8, New York NY 10022
Tel (212) 951-6600 *SIC* 2721 7389 8742

AEGIS LIFESTYLE INC p 29
32 Aveune Of The Americas, New York NY 10013
Tel (212) 366-3400 *SIC* 7311 7389 8743

ALM MEDIA HOLDINGS INC p 59
120 Broadway Fl 5, New York NY 10271
Tel (212) 457-9400
SIC 2721 2711 2741 2731 7389

ALM MEDIA LLC p 59
120 Broadway Fl 5, New York NY 10271
Tel (212) 457-9400
SIC 2721 2711 2741 2731 7389

▲ **AMERICAN EXPRESS CO** p 72
200 Vesey St, New York NY 10285
Tel (212) 640-2000
SIC 6141 7389 6282 6099 6311 6211

ANDREW W MELLON FOUNDATION p 90
140 E 62nd St, New York NY 10065
Tel (212) 838-8400 *SIC* 7389

■ **AXA ADVISORS LLC** p 139
1290 Ave Of Amrcs Fl Cnc1, New York NY 10104
Tel (212) 554-1234 *SIC* 7389

▲ **BANKRATE INC** p 152
1675 Broadway Fl 2, New York NY 10019
Tel (917) 368-8600 *SIC* 7389

BLUE STAR JETS LLC p 192
880 3rd Ave Fl 11, New York NY 10022
Tel (212) 446-9037 *SIC* 7389

BMO CAPITAL MARKETS CORP p 194
3 Times Sq, New York NY 10036
Tel (212) 885-4000 *SIC* 7389

BROADCAST MEDIA PARTNERS HOLDINGS INC p 215
605 3rd Ave Fl 12, New York NY 10158
Tel (212) 455-5200 *SIC* 4833 4813 7389

■ **CERBERUS LP LLC** p 283
875 3rd Ave Fl 11, New York NY 10022
Tel (212) 891-2100 *SIC* 7389 7374

CHRISTIES INC p 303
20 Rockefeller Plz, New York NY 10020
Tel (212) 636-2000 *SIC* 7389

▲ **CINEDIGM CORP** p 307
902 Broadway Fl 9, New York NY 10010
Tel (212) 206-8600 *SIC* 7384 7389 7371

CORPORATE RISK HOLDINGS LLC p 372
600 3rd Ave Fl 4, New York NY 10016
Tel (212) 896-2001
SIC 6719 8748 7375 7389

▲ **DEPOSITORY TRUST & CLEARING CORP** p 431
55 Water St Ste Conc3, New York NY 10041
Tel (212) 855-1000 *SIC* 6289 6211 7389

▲ **EXLSERVICE HOLDINGS INC** p 519
280 Park Ave Fl 38, New York NY 10017
Tel (212) 277-7100 *SIC* 7389

■ **EXLSERVICE.COM LLC** p 519
280 Park Ave, New York NY 10017
Tel (212) 277-7100 *SIC* 7389

FDG ASSOCIATES LLC p 533
605 3rd Ave Fl 15, New York NY 10158
Tel (212) 940-6864 *SIC* 7389

FGIC CORP p 539
125 Park Ave Fl 5, New York NY 10017
Tel (212) 312-3000 *SIC* 6411 7389

▲ **FIRST DATA CORP** p 546
225 Liberty St Fl 29, New York NY 10281
Tel (800) 735-3362 *SIC* 7389 6099 6153

■ **FOX BUSINESS NETWORK** p 572
1211 Avenue Of The, New York NY 10036
Tel (212) 601-7000 *SIC* 7389

FULLBEAUTY BRANDS INC p 584
1 New York Plz Fl 13, New York NY 10004
Tel (212) 613-9500 *SIC* 5961 7389 5611

■ **GSO CAPITAL PARTNERS LP** p 643
345 Park Ave Ste 1100, New York NY 10154
Tel (212) 583-5000 *SIC* 6722 7389

HAMMOND KENNEDY WHITNEY & CO INC p 656
420 Lexington Ave Rm 402, New York NY 10170
Tel (212) 867-1010 *SIC* 7389

INTERNATIONAL CENTRE FOR DISPUTE RESOLUTION p 754
120 Brdwy Fl 21, New York NY 10271
Tel (212) 484-4181 *SIC* 7389

KABLE MEDIA SERVICES INC p 800
14 Wall St Ste 4c, New York NY 10005
Tel (212) 705-4600 *SIC* 5192 7389

KING TELESERVICES LLC p 820
48 Wall St Fl 23, New York NY 10005
Tel (718) 238-7924 *SIC* 7389

KROLL LLC p 830
600 3rd Ave Fl 4, New York NY 10016
Tel (212) 593-1000
SIC 7381 8742 8748 7389

LINCOLNSHIRE MANAGEMENT INC p 868
780 3rd Ave Rm 4000, New York NY 10017
Tel (212) 319-3633 *SIC* 6211 7389 3599

MERCHANT CASH AND CAPITAL LLC p 944
460 Park Ave S Fl 10, New York NY 10016
Tel (212) 545-3180 *SIC* 6153 7389

MICHAEL J FOX FOUNDATION FOR PARKINSONS RESEARCH p 960
498 Fashion Ave, New York NY 10018
Tel (212) 509-0995 *SIC* 7389

MKTG INC p 979
32 Avenue Of The Americas # 20, New York NY 10013
Tel (212) 366-3400 *SIC* 7311 7389 8743

▲ **MSCI INC** p 996
250 Greenwich St Fl 49, New York NY 10007
Tel (212) 804-3900
SIC 7389 7371 6282 8742

MUTUAL OF AMERICA CORP p 1003
320 Park Ave Fl 5, New York NY 10022
Tel (212) 224-1147 SIC 6311 7389

NATIONAL CONVENTION SERVICES LLC p 1011
145 W 30th St Rm 200, New York NY 10001
Tel (212) 947-8255 SIC 7389

NEW YORK CONVENTION CENTER OPERATING CORP p 1035
655 W 34th St, New York NY 10001
Tel (212) 216-2000 SIC 7389

NFP CORP p 1041
340 Madison Ave Fl 21, New York NY 10173
Tel (212) 301-4000 SIC 6411 7389 6282

NIELSEN CO p 1043
85 Broad St Bsmt, New York NY 10004
Tel (646) 654-5000 SIC 7389

OCC NATIONAL BANK EXAMINERS p 1072
111 Wall St Bsmt 1, New York NY 10005
Tel (212) 527-1020 SIC 7389

PENTON MEDIA INC p 1132
1166 Avenue Of The Americ, New York NY 10036
Tel (212) 204-4200
SIC 2721 7389 7313 7375

PERKINS EASTMAN ARCHITECTS DPC p 1136
115 5th Ave Fl 3, New York NY 10003
Tel (212) 353-7200 SIC 8712 8742 7389

RELX INC p 1222
230 Park Ave, New York NY 10169
Tel (212) 309-8100
SIC 2721 2731 7389 7374 8748

RIPPLEWOOD HOLDINGS LLC p 1236
1 Rockefeller Plz Fl 10, New York NY 10020
Tel (212) 218-2705 SIC 7389 6211

ROCKEFELLER GROUP INC p 1244
1221 Ave Of The Am Flr 17, New York NY 10020
Tel (212) 282-2000 SIC 6531 7389

▲ **SEQUENTIAL BRANDS GROUP INC** p 1306
5 Bryant Park Fl 30, New York NY 10001
Tel (646) 564-2577 SIC 7389

SHACKLEFORDS CONSTRUCTION & CONTRACTING LTD p 1310
303 Lexington Ave, New York NY 10016
Tel (646) 771-4470
SIC 1522 1542 1541 7389

SHELLPOINT PARTNERS LLC p 1314
140 E 45th St Fl 37, New York NY 10017
Tel (212) 850-7700 SIC 6162 7389

▲ **SIGNATURE BANK** p 1322
565 5th Ave Fl 8r, New York NY 10017
Tel (646) 822-1500 SIC 6029 7389

■ **SMITH BARNEY CONSULTING CORP** p 1333
388 Greenwich St Ofc 1, New York NY 10013
Tel (212) 816-6000 SIC 7389

SOS INTERNATIONAL LLC p 1341
40 Fulton St Fl 26, New York NY 10038
Tel (212) 742-2410
SIC 3724 8711 7389 8732

SOS INTERNATIONAL LTD p 1341
40 Fulton St Fl 26, New York NY 10038
Tel (212) 742-2410 SIC 7389

STUART WEITZMAN RETAIL STORES LLC p 1394
625 Madison Ave Frnt 3, New York NY 10022
Tel (212) 582-6388 SIC 7389 3171 5999

SUGAR FOODS CORP p 1397
950 3rd Ave Fl 21, New York NY 10022
Tel (212) 753-6900
SIC 2869 2023 2099 2068 7389

SUMITOMO MITSUI FINANCE AND LEASING CO LTD p 1398
277 Park Ave Fl 15, New York NY 10172
Tel (212) 224-4000 SIC 7389

■ **TARGET SOURCING SERVICES CORP** p 1425
500 Fashion 7th Ave Fl 5a, New York NY 10018
Tel (800) 440-0680 SIC 7389

TRANSPERFECT GLOBAL INC p 1472
3 Park Ave Fl 39, New York NY 10016
Tel (212) 689-5555 SIC 7389 7371 8748

TRANSPERFECT TRANSLATIONS INTERNATIONAL INC p 1472
3 Park Ave Fl 39, New York NY 10016
Tel (212) 689-5555 SIC 7389 8748 8111

TRAXYS NORTH AMERICA LLC p 1475
825 3rd Ave Fl 9, New York NY 10022
Tel (212) 918-8000 SIC 6111 7389

UBM LLC p 1498
2 Penn Plz Fl 15, New York NY 10121
Tel (516) 562-5085
SIC 2721 2711 7319 7389

UNIVISION HOLDINGS INC p 1527
605 3rd Ave Fl 12, New York NY 10158
Tel (212) 455-5200 SIC 4833 4813 7389

VELO HOLDINGS INC p 1547
320 Park Ave Fl 18, New York NY 10022
Tel (212) 277-1500 SIC 7389

VIVENDI HOLDING I LLC p 1563
1755 Broadway Fl 2, New York NY 10019
Tel (212) 572-7000 SIC 7812 7389

▲ **VOYA FINANCIAL INC** p 1566
230 Park Ave Fl 14, New York NY 10169
Tel (212) 309-8200
SIC 6311 6411 6282 6211 7389

VSS-AHC CONSOLIDATED HOLDINGS CORP p 1567
350 Park Ave Fl 7, New York NY 10022
Tel (212) 935-4990 SIC 7389 2721 7331

■ **WARNER COMMUNICATIONS INC** p 1576
1 Time Warner Ctr, New York NY 10019
Tel (212) 484-8000 SIC 7812 4841 7389

WARNER-ELEKTRA-ATLANTIC CORP p 1576
1633 Broadway Lowr 2c01, New York NY 10019
Tel (212) 275-2000 SIC 7389

■ **WELLS FARGO CAPITAL FINANCE LLC** p 1590
100 Park Ave Fl 3, New York NY 10017
Tel (212) 840-2000 SIC 6162 7389

▲ **WISDOMTREE INVESTMENTS INC** p 1619
245 Park Ave Fl 35, New York NY 10167
Tel (212) 801-2080 SIC 7389

D & Y CHEESES INC p 406
20 N Broadway Ste 5, Nyack NY 10960
Tel (845) 353-4570 SIC 7389

NICE-PAK PRODUCTS INC p 1042
2 Nice Pak Park, Orangeburg NY 10962
Tel (845) 365-2772 SIC 2621 7389 2676

PROFESSIONAL DISPOSABLES INC p 1180
2 Nice Pak Park, Orangeburg NY 10962
Tel (845) 365-1700 SIC 2676 7389 2621

MARYHAVEN CENTER OF HOPE INC p 914
51 Terryville Rd, Port Jeff Sta NY 11776
Tel (631) 474-4120 SIC 8322 7389

KLG USA LLC p 823
20 W King St, Port Jervis NY 12771
Tel (845) 856-5311 SIC 2844 7389 2834

▲ **MASTERCARD INC** p 918
2000 Purchase St, Purchase NY 10577
Tel (914) 249-2000 SIC 7389

■ **MASTERCARD INTERNATIONAL INC** p 918
2000 Purchase St, Purchase NY 10577
Tel (914) 249-2000 SIC 7389 6099

5LINX ENTERPRISES INC p 3
1 S Clinton Ave Ste 800, Rochester NY 14604
Tel (585) 334-2600 SIC 7389

▲ **FINANCIAL INSTITUTIONS INC** p 542
220 Liberty St, Warsaw NY 14569
Tel (585) 786-1100 SIC 6021 7389

■ **ST CLAIRE FLORAL CO INC** p 1365
1600 Stewart Ave, Westbury NY 11590
Tel (516) 237-6000 SIC 7389

▲ **SPAR GROUP INC** p 1354
333 Westchester Ave S204, White Plains NY 10604
Tel (914) 332-4100 SIC 7389 8732

CARDWORKS INC p 254
101 Crossways Park Dr W, Woodbury NY 11797
Tel (516) 576-0404 SIC 7322 7389

CARDWORKS LP p 254
101 Crossways Park Dr W, Woodbury NY 11797
Tel (516) 576-0404 SIC 7389

■ **MAHARAM FABRIC CORP** p 897
74 Horseblock Rd, Yaphank NY 11980
Tel (631) 582-3434 SIC 5131 7389

CONSUMERS UNION OF UNITED STATES INC p 362
101 Truman Ave, Yonkers NY 10703
Tel (914) 378-2000 SIC 2741 2721 7389

DONNIE SHONOBI BRAND NAME TRADEMARK COLLECTION CORP p 451
160 Town Park Dr, Advance NC 27006
Tel (336) 940-5682 SIC 5699 7389

GUTHY-RENKER FULFILLMENT SERVICES LLC p 648
1845 Brevard Rd, Arden NC 28704
Tel (828) 684-4300 SIC 7389 7374

DAISY CHAIN DESIGNS p 409
2743 Goneaway Rd, Charlotte NC 28210
Tel (704) 517-8591 SIC 7389

OFFICE ENVIRONMENTS INC p 1075
11407 Granite St Ste B, Charlotte NC 28273
Tel (704) 714-7200 SIC 5021 7641 7389

REGULUS INTEGRATED SOLUTIONS LLC p 1220
9645-L Part Blvd, Charlotte NC 28216
Tel (704) 904-8759
SIC 2752 7389 3861 2759

▲ **TRIANGLE CAPITAL CORP** p 1478
3700 Glenwood Ave Ste 530, Raleigh NC 27612
Tel (919) 719-4770 SIC 7389

GLOBAL CONTACT SERVICES LLC p 616
118b S Main St B, Salisbury NC 28144
Tel (704) 647-9672 SIC 7319 7389

STATIC CONTROL IC-DISC INC p 1383
3010 Lee Ave, Sanford NC 27332
Tel (919) 774-3808 SIC 7389

ATLANTIC COAST MERCHANDISING LLC p 126
599 Wood Hollow Rd, Taylorsville NC 28681
Tel (910) 300-9231 SIC 8742 7389

■ **BLUE WATER FINANCE & INSURANCE** p 192
5041 New Cntre Dr Ste 212, Wilmington NC 28403
Tel (877) 934-9393 SIC 7389

INMAR INC p 744
635 Vine St, Winston Salem NC 27101
Tel (800) 765-1277 SIC 7389

STANTEC ARCHITECTURE INC p 1377
301 N Main St Ste 2452, Winston Salem NC 27101
Tel (336) 714-7413 SIC 8712 7389

INFOCISION MANAGEMENT CORP p 741
325 Springside Dr, Akron OH 44333
Tel (330) 668-1400 SIC 7389

OHIO UNIVERSITY FOUNDATION p 1078
Hdl Center Ste 218 Rm 168, Athens OH 45701
Tel (740) 593-1901 SIC 7389

WRIGHT-PATT FINANCIAL GROUP LTD p 1627
2455 Presidential Dr, Beavercreek OH 45324
Tel (937) 912-7000 SIC 7389

■ **SHRED-IT US JV LLC** p 1319
11311 Cornell Park Dr # 125, Blue Ash OH 45242
Tel (513) 245-8659 SIC 7389

■ **CONVERGYS CUSTOMER MANAGEMENT GROUP INC** p 365
201 E 4th St Bsmt, Cincinnati OH 45202
Tel (513) 723-6104 SIC 7389 8732

■ **GENERAL ELECTRIC INTERNATIONAL OPERATIONS CO INC** p 600
191 Rosa Parks St, Cincinnati OH 45202
Tel (513) 813-9133 SIC 7389

■ **NEIGHBORCARE INC** p 1024
201 E 4th St Ste 900, Cincinnati OH 45202
Tel (513) 719-2600
SIC 5122 5912 5047 7389

AMERICAN BREAD CO LLC p 69
8905 Lake Ave Fl 2, Cleveland OH 44102
Tel (216) 961-6767 SIC 7389

▲ **CBIZ INC** p 268
6050 Oak Tree Blvd # 500, Cleveland OH 44131
Tel (216) 447-9000 SIC 8742 7389 7363

FLIGHT SERVICES & SYSTEMS INC p 556
5005 Rockside Rd Ste 940, Cleveland OH 44131
Tel (216) 328-0090 SIC 7389

RESILIENCE CAPITAL PARTNERS LLC p 1226
25101 Chagrin Blvd # 350, Cleveland OH 44122
Tel (216) 292-0200 SIC 7389

AMERICAN SIGNATURE INC p 79
4300 E 5th Ave, Columbus OH 43219
Tel (614) 449-6107 SIC 7389

■ **BANC ONE SERVICES CORP** p 149
1111 Polaris Pkwy Ste B3, Columbus OH 43240
Tel (614) 248-5800 SIC 7389

CORPORATE FINANCE ASSOCIATES OF COLUMBUS INC p 372
671 Camden Yard Ct, Columbus OH 43235
Tel (614) 457-9219 SIC 8742 7389 6211

■ **JPMORGAN CHASE BANK NATIONAL ASSOCIATION** p 795
1111 Polaris Pkwy, Columbus OH 43240
Tel (614) 436-3055
SIC 6022 6099 6799 6211 6162 7389

SB CAPITAL GROUP LLC p 1285
4300 E 5th Ave, Columbus OH 43219
Tel (516) 829-2400 SIC 7389

PCCW TELESERVICES (US) INC p 1124
5200 Rings Rd, Dublin OH 43017
Tel (614) 652-6300 SIC 7389 7299

FALCON PACKAGING LLC p 526
1359 Sater St, Greenville OH 45331
Tel (937) 547-9800 SIC 7389 4225

THINGS REMEMBERED INC p 1448
5500 Avion Park Dr, Highland Heights OH 44143
Tel (440) 473-2000 SIC 7389 5947

MIDWEST TAPE LLC p 968
1417 Timber Wolf Dr, Holland OH 43528
Tel (419) 868-9370
SIC 7822 5099 8741 7389 5961 7374

■ **GRAPHIC COMMUNICATIONS HOLDINGS INC** p 631
5700 Darrow Rd Ste 110, Hudson OH 44236
Tel (330) 650-5522 SIC 5111 7389

■ **MACYS CREDIT AND CUSTOMER SERVICES INC** p 893
9111 Duke Blvd, Mason OH 45040
Tel (513) 398-5221 SIC 7389 7322 6141

■ **PRECISION STRIP INC** p 1169
86 S Ohio St, Minster OH 45865
Tel (419) 501-1347 SIC 7389

■ **ELDER-BEERMAN STORES CORP** p 484
3155 Elbee Rd Ste 201, Moraine OH 45439
Tel (937) 296-2700 SIC 5311 5661 7389

PROGRESSIVE QUALITY CARE INC p 1182
5553 Broadview Rd, Parma OH 44134
Tel (216) 661-6800 SIC 7389

CENTRAL FIRE PROTECTION CO INC p 278
583 Selma Rd, Springfield OH 45505
Tel (937) 322-0713 SIC 7389

P3 INFRASTRUCTURE INC p 1103
3105 Preakness Dr, Stow OH 44224
Tel (330) 686-1129 SIC 7389

▲ **VANTIV INC** p 1544
8500 Governors Hill Dr, Symmes Twp OH 45249
Tel (513) 900-5250 SIC 7389

SSOE INC p 1364
1001 Madison Ave Ste A, Toledo OH 43604
Tel (419) 255-3830
SIC 8711 8712 8742 1541 7389

SANESE SERVICES INC p 1279
2590 Elm Rd Ne, Warren OH 44483
Tel (614) 436-1234 SIC 5962 5812 7389

SHAMROCK COMPANIES INC p 1311
24090 Detroit Rd, Westlake OH 44145
Tel (440) 899-9510
SIC 5112 5199 7336 7389 2754 2395

CLEVELAND INTEGRITY SERVICES INC p 325
370669 E Old Highway 64, Cleveland OK 74020
Tel (918) 358-5735 SIC 7389

A&S ASSET RECOVERY INC p 7
608 Sw D Ave Ste 6, Lawton OK 73501
Tel (855) 692-2786 SIC 7389

PANHANDLE OILFIELD SERVICE COMPANIES INC p 1111
14000 Quail Springs Pkwy # 300, Oklahoma City OK 73134
Tel (405) 608-5330
SIC 1389 7389 3498 4212 5082 1794

WWSC HOLDINGS CORP p 1629
1730 W Reno Ave, Oklahoma City OK 73106
Tel (405) 235-3621 SIC 7389

AHS OKLAHOMA HEALTH SYSTEM LLP p 37
110 W 7th St Ste 2540, Tulsa OK 74119
Tel (918) 579-1000
SIC 8062 8069 7352 6512 7389 5999

▲ **CYPRESS ENERGY PARTNERS LP** p 405
5727 S Lewis Ave Ste 300, Tulsa OK 74105
Tel (918) 748-3900 SIC 1389 7389

PENNWELL CORP p 1131
1421 S Sheridan Rd, Tulsa OK 74112
Tel (918) 835-3161
SIC 2721 2731 2741 7389

PINNACLE PACKAGING CO INC p 1150
1203 E 33rd St Ste 200, Tulsa OK 74105
Tel (918) 744-5400 SIC 7389

ST JOHN HEALTH SYSTEM INC p 1367
1923 S Utica Ave, Tulsa OK 74104
Tel (918) 744-2180
SIC 7991 6512 7389 8361 8071 8062

T D WILLIAMSON INC p 1419
6120 S Yale Ave Ste 1700, Tulsa OK 74136
Tel (918) 493-9494 SIC 7389

HAMPTON LUMBER SALES CO p 656
9600 Sw Barnes Rd Ste 200, Portland OR 97225
Tel (503) 297-7691 SIC 5031 2421 7389

HARDER MECHANICAL CONTRACTORS INC p 660
2148 Ne Mlk Blvd, Portland OR 97212
Tel (503) 281-1112 SIC 1711 7389

OREGON METAL SLITTERS INC p 1093
7227 N Leadbetter Rd, Portland OR 97203
Tel (503) 286-0300 SIC 5051 7389

ZIMMER GUNSUL FRASCA ARCHITECTS LLP p 1643
1223 Sw Washington St # 200, Portland OR 97205
Tel (503) 224-3860 SIC 8712 8748 7389

CREDIT CARD PROCESSING USA INC p 390
2202 N Irving St, Allentown PA 18109
Tel (908) 790-1777 SIC 7389

ADVANCED CALL CENTER TECHNOLOGIES LLC p 25
1235 Westlakes Dr Ste 160, Berwyn PA 19312
Tel (610) 695-0500 SIC 7389

PREPAY NATION LLC p 1171
1055 Westlakes Dr Ste 300, Berwyn PA 19312
Tel (215) 987-3711 SIC 7389

GEO W KISTLER INC p 605
2210 City Line Rd, Bethlehem PA 18017
Tel (610) 266-7100
SIC 5063 7382 5087 7389

SDI INC p 1295
1414 Radcliffe St Ste 300, Bristol PA 19007
Tel (215) 633-1900
SIC 7374 7389 8711 8748

ANDRITZ INC p 91
500 Technology Dr, Canonsburg PA 15317
Tel (724) 597-7801 SIC 3554 8711 7389

FLAGSHIP CREDIT ACCEPTANCE LLC p 554
3 Christy Dr Ste 203, Chadds Ford PA 19317
Tel (610) 717-1916 SIC 7389

LA FRANCE CORP p 835
1 Lafrance Way, Concordville PA 19331
Tel (610) 361-4300
SIC 3089 3364 3993 5013 7389

SHARP CORP p 1312
22-23 Carland Rd, Conshohocken PA 19428
Tel (610) 395-5800 SIC 7389

SUPERIOR GROUP INC p 1406
100 Front St Ste 525, Conshohocken PA 19428
Tel (610) 397-2040
SIC 5051 3357 3317 3491 3469 7389

MUSICIANS LIVEORG p 1002
77 Brookfield Dr, Elizabethtown PA 17022
Tel (717) 413-3265 SIC 5736 5961 7389

UNITED CONCORDIA LIFE AND HEALTH INSURANCE CO p 1507
4401 Deer Path Rd, Harrisburg PA 17110
Tel (717) 260-7081 SIC 7389

■ **TELERX MARKETING INC** p 1435
723 Dresher Rd, Horsham PA 19044
Tel (215) 347-5700 SIC 7389 8742

NATIONAL PHILANTHROPIC TRUST p 1015
165 Township Line Rd # 1200, Jenkintown PA 19046
Tel (215) 277-3010 SIC 7389

■ **CARDCONNECT LLC** p 252
1000 Continental Dr # 300, King Of Prussia PA 19406
Tel (484) 581-2200 SIC 7389

PROCURIAN LLC p 1179
211 S Gulph Rd Ste 500, King Of Prussia PA 19406
Tel (484) 690-5000 SIC 7389 8748

JAY GROUP INC p 779
700 Indian Springs Dr, Lancaster PA 17601
Tel (717) 285-6200
SIC 5961 7389 7331 7319 5199

GOOD SAMARITAN HEALTH SERVICES FOUNDATION p 623
259 S 4th St Fl 2, Lebanon PA 17042
Tel (717) 270-7864 SIC 8741 7389 8721

ACCUPAC INC p 16
1501 Industrial Blvd, Mainland PA 19451
Tel (215) 256-7000 SIC 7389

VANGUARD CHARITABLE ENDOWMENT PROGRAM p 1543
100 Vanguard Blvd G19, Malvern PA 19355
Tel (888) 383-4483 SIC 7389

EDM AMERICAS INC p 478
10 Ed Preate Dr, Moosic PA 18507
Tel (800) 852-9809
SIC 4226 7389 7334 8741

MOZA LLC p 995
101 Church St Ofc 5, Moscow PA 18444
Tel (570) 848-7926 SIC 5141 7389

BERWIND INDUSTRIES INC p 176
3000 Ctr Sq W 1500 Mkt St, Philadelphia PA 19102
Tel (215) 563-2800 SIC 7389

■ **CARDINAL HEALTH 407 INC** p 253
3001 Red Lion Rd Ste Ag, Philadelphia PA 19114
Tel (215) 501-1210 SIC 7389 3086 3089

NELSON WORLDWIDE INC p 1025
222-230 Walnut St, Philadelphia PA 19106
Tel (215) 925-6562 SIC 7389

PACKAGING COORDINATORS LLC p 1106
3001 Red Lion Rd, Philadelphia PA 19114
Tel (215) 613-3600 SIC 7389

SPARKS MARKETING GROUP INC p 1354
2828 Charter Rd, Philadelphia PA 19154
Tel (800) 925-7727 SIC 7389

PITTSBURGH WATER & SEWER AUTHORITY p 1152
1200 Penn Ave Ste 100, Pittsburgh PA 15222
Tel (412) 255-8935 SIC 4941 7389

▲ **PNC FINANCIAL SERVICES GROUP INC** p 1158
300 5th Ave, Pittsburgh PA 15222
Tel (412) 762-2000
SIC 6021 6162 7389 6282 6211

■ **WESCO DISTRIBUTION INC** p 1593
225 W Station Square Dr # 700, Pittsburgh PA 15219
Tel (412) 454-2200
SIC 5063 5085 5065 7389

▲WESCO INTERNATIONAL INC p 1593
225 W Station Square Dr # 700, Pittsburgh PA 15219
Tel (412) 454-2200
SIC 5063 5084 5065 7389

▲ J G WENTWORTH CO p 771
201 King Of Prussia Rd # 501, Radnor PA 19087
Tel (484) 434-2300 SIC 7389 6798

ROARING SPRING BLANK BOOK CO p 1240
740 Spang St, Roaring Spring PA 16673
Tel (814) 224-2306
SIC 2678 5149 2653 7389

ALMAC CLINICAL SERVICES LLC p 59
25 Fretz Rd, Souderton PA 18964
Tel (215) 660-8500 SIC 7389

VELDOS LLC p 1547
435 Devon Park Dr Ste 500, Wayne PA 19087
Tel (610) 254-4121 SIC 7389

WILLIAMSPORT HOSPITAL p 1612
700 High St, Williamsport PA 17701
Tel (570) 321-1000 SIC 8062 7389

AUTORIDAD PARA EL FINANCIAMIENTO DE LA VIVIENDA p 135
Ave Barbosa 606pisos St Ave Barbo, Hato Rey PR 00917
Tel (787) 765-7577 SIC 7389

KRESS STORES OF PUERTO RICO INC p 829
598 Calle A, San Juan PR 00920
Tel (787) 783-5374 SIC 7389 8741

CORVIAS GROUP LLC p 373
1405 S County Trl, East Greenwich RI 02818
Tel (401) 228-2800 SIC 7389

CAROUSEL INDUSTRIES OF NORTH AMERICA INC p 260
659 South County Trl, Exeter RI 02822
Tel (401) 667-5400 SIC 7389

STATE OF RHODE ISLAND p 1382
114 Enfield Ave, Providence RI 02908
Tel (401) 351-8448 SIC 7389

■ STEVEN MARK SERVICE MERCHANDISERS INC p 1388
1 Cvs Dr, Woonsocket RI 02895
Tel (401) 765-1500 SIC 7389

PROVIDENCE HOSPITAL FOUNDATION p 1186
2601 Laurel St, Columbia SC 29204
Tel (803) 256-5300 SIC 7389

SPARTANBURG REGIONAL HEALTHCARE SYSTEM p 1355
411 Woodsberry Shoals Dr, Duncan SC 29334
Tel (864) 560-1406 SIC 7389

MUZAK LLC p 1003
3318 Lakemont Blvd, Fort Mill SC 29708
Tel (803) 396-3000 SIC 7389 6794

▲ REGIONAL MANAGEMENT CORP p 1219
509 W Butler Rd, Greenville SC 29607
Tel (864) 422-8011 SIC 7389 6141

FOREST SPARTANBURG PRODUCTS INC p 567
1431 Highway 101 S, Greer SC 29651
Tel (864) 699-3100 SIC 7389

GREENBAX ENTERPRISES INC p 637
884 Johnnie Dodds Blvd B, Mount Pleasant SC 29464
Tel (866) 891-1195 SIC 7389 6159 6512

INTELLIGENT INVESTMENTS LLC p 750
1010 Park Dr, Myrtle Beach SC 29577
Tel (980) 989-4016 SIC 6726 7389

USLC LLC p 1535
100 Dunbar St Ste 100, Spartanburg SC 29306
Tel (864) 577-0100 SIC 7389

AVERA MCKENNAN p 137
3900 W Avera Dr, Sioux Falls SD 57108
Tel (605) 322-7300 SIC 7389

MIDCO COMMUNICATIONS INC p 964
3901 N Louise Ave, Sioux Falls SD 57107
Tel (605) 334-1200
SIC 8748 5961 7389 4812

PREMIER BANKCARD LLC p 1170
3820 N Louise Ave, Sioux Falls SD 57107
Tel (605) 335-4000 SIC 7389

COMDATA HOLDINGS CORP p 344
5301 Maryland Way, Brentwood TN 37027
Tel (615) 370-7000 SIC 7374 7389 7375

HEALTHTRUST PURCHASING GROUP LP p 678
155 Franklin Rd Ste 400, Brentwood TN 37027
Tel (615) 377-1294 SIC 7389

FIVE STAR FOOD SERVICE INC p 553
6005 Century Oaks Dr # 100, Chattanooga TN 37416
Tel (423) 490-4428 SIC 5962 5812 7389

APHENA PHARMA SOLUTIONS HOLDINGS INC p 96
1920 Fisk Rd, Cookeville TN 38506
Tel (215) 953-5100 SIC 7389 2834

■ CONCORD EFS INC p 354
7000 Goodlett Farms Pkwy # 300, Cordova TN 38016
Tel (901) 371-8000
SIC 6099 7389 6091 5044

EDUCATIONAL SERVICES OF AMERICA INC p 479
12700 Kingston Pike, Farragut TN 37934
Tel (865) 824-3051 SIC 7389

■ CMH SERVICES INC p 329
5000 Clayton Rd, Maryville TN 37804
Tel (865) 380-3000 SIC 7389

EVERGREEN PACKAGING INC p 514
5350 Poplar Ave Ste 600, Memphis TN 38119
Tel (901) 821-5350 SIC 7389 2621

IDEAL CHEMICAL AND SUPPLY CO p 729
4025 Air Park St, Memphis TN 38118
Tel (901) 363-7720 SIC 5169 7389

INTERNATIONAL PAPER CORP p 756
6400 Poplar Ave, Memphis TN 38197
Tel (901) 818-5598 SIC 7389

■TERMINIX INTERNATIONAL CO LIMITED PARTNERSHIP p 1439
860 Ridge Lake Blvd, Memphis TN 38120
Tel (901) 766-1400 SIC 7342 7389

IPAYMENT INVESTORS INC p 763
40 Burton Hills Blvd, Nashville TN 37215
Tel (615) 665-1858 SIC 7389

MEDIFAX-EDI LLC p 938
26 Century Blvd, Nashville TN 37214
Tel (615) 932-3226 SIC 7374 7389

SITEL LLC p 1327
3102 West End Ave Ste 900, Nashville TN 37203
Tel (615) 301-7100 SIC 7389

SITEL OPERATING CORP p 1328
3102 West End Ave Ste 900, Nashville TN 37203
Tel (615) 301-7100 SIC 7389 7375

SITEL WORLDWIDE CORP p 1328
3102 West End Ave Ste 900, Nashville TN 37203
Tel (615) 301-7100 SIC 7389 7375

FHG CORP p 539
4637 Port Royal Rd, Spring Hill TN 37174
Tel (931) 499-7070 SIC 7389 5122

H Q GLOBAL HOLDINGS INC p 650
15305 Dallas Pkwy Ste 400, Addison TX 75001
Tel (972) 361-8100 SIC 6519 7389

HQ GLOBAL WORKPLACES INC p 714
15305 Dallas Pkwy Ste 400, Addison TX 75001
Tel (972) 361-8100 SIC 6519 7389

REGUS CORP p 1220
15305 Dallas Pkwy Ste 400, Addison TX 75001
Tel (972) 361-8100 SIC 7363 7389 6531

LIGHTNING FLUID SERVICES INC p 865
1310 Southwood St, Alice TX 78332
Tel (361) 396-0801 SIC 1389 7389

▲ PFSWEB INC p 1140
505 Millenium Dr, Allen TX 75013
Tel (972) 881-2900 SIC 8741 7389 8742

■ PRIORITY FULFILLMENT SERVICES INC p 1177
505 Millenium Dr, Allen TX 75013
Tel (972) 881-2900 SIC 7389

OLAMETER CORP p 1080
2261 Brookhollow Plaza Dr # 111, Arlington TX 76006
Tel (817) 385-0053 SIC 7389

HOMEAWAY INC p 703
1011 W 5th St Ste 300, Austin TX 78703
Tel (512) 684-1100 SIC 6531 7389 7375

MICHAEL & SUSAN DELL FOUNDATION p 959
4417 Westlake Dr, Austin TX 78746
Tel (512) 329-0799 SIC 7389

MOOD MEDIA CORP p 987
1703 W 5th St Ste 600, Austin TX 78703
Tel (800) 345-5000 SIC 7319 7389

MOOD MEDIA NORTH AMERICA LIMITED p 987
1703 W 5th St Ste 600, Austin TX 78703
Tel (512) 380-8500 SIC 6794 7389

ESCO MARINE INC p 509
16200 Jose Garza Rd, Brownsville TX 78521
Tel (956) 554-5300 SIC 4499 5093 7389

■WOOT INC p 1624
4121 International Pkwy, Carrollton TX 75007
Tel (972) 417-3959 SIC 7389

■WOOT SERVICES LLC p 1624
4121 Intl Pkwy Ste 900, Carrollton TX 75007
Tel (972) 417-3959 SIC 7389

TUBULAR MACHINED PRODUCTS p 1490
90 Campbell Acres Rd, Cleveland TX 77328
Tel (713) 504-8932 SIC 5051 3492 7389

12TH MAN STUDENT FOUNDATION INC p 1
12th Man Fndtion The Zone, College Station TX 77844
Tel (979) 846-8892 SIC 7389

■ HOMEWARD RESIDENTIAL HOLDINGS INC p 704
1525 S Belt Line Rd, Coppell TX 75019
Tel (877) 304-3100 SIC 7389

SHRED-IT DALLAS INC p 1319
825 W Sandy Lake Rd # 100, Coppell TX 75019
Tel (972) 556-0197 SIC 7389 5093 5087

■ACS IMAGE SOLUTIONS INC p 19
3988 N Central Expy, Dallas TX 75204
Tel (214) 818-3000
SIC 7389 5112 7374 7375

AEGIS COMMUNICATIONS GROUP LLC p 29
9999 Technology Blvd W, Dallas TX 75220
Tel (972) 830-1800 SIC 7389

ANTHELIO HEALTHCARE SOLUTIONS INC p 93
1 Lincoln Centre 5400 L, Dallas TX 75240
Tel (214) 257-7000 SIC 8741 8071 7389

APEX CLEARING CORP p 96
350 N Paul St Ste 1300, Dallas TX 75201
Tel (214) 765-1100
SIC 6099 7389 4813 6289

CENTERSTONE INSURANCE AND FINANCIAL SERVICES INC p 277
4851 Lyndon B Johnson Fwy, Dallas TX 75244
Tel (469) 791-3300 SIC 7389

■ CHASE PAYMENTECH SOLUTIONS LLC p 291
14221 Dallas Pkwy Bldg 2, Dallas TX 75254
Tel (214) 849-3000 SIC 6153 7389

CORGAN ASSOCIATES INC p 370
401 N Houston St, Dallas TX 75202
Tel (214) 748-2000 SIC 8712 7389

FORD FINANCIAL FUND II LP p 565
200 Crescent Ct, Dallas TX 75201
Tel (214) 871-5151 SIC 6282 6799 7389

FREEMAN DECORATING CO p 576
1600 Viceroy Dr Ste 100, Dallas TX 75235
Tel (214) 445-1000 SIC 7389

FREEMAN EXPOSITIONS INC p 577
1600 Viceroy Dr Ste 100, Dallas TX 75235
Tel (214) 445-1000 SIC 7389

HALLWOOD GROUP INC p 655
3710 Rawlins St Ste 1500, Dallas TX 75219
Tel (214) 528-5588 SIC 2221 7389

▲ HILLTOP HOLDINGS INC p 694
200 Crescent Ct Ste 1330, Dallas TX 75201
Tel (214) 855-2177 SIC 6022 7389

■ HOTELS.COM LP p 710
5400 Lyndon B Johnson Fwy # 500, Dallas TX 75240
Tel (214) 361-7311 SIC 7389 7375

MODEST BILLIONAIRES LLC p 981
3815 Martha Ln, Dallas TX 75229
Tel (972) 672-0755 SIC 7374 7371 7389

NATIONAL BANKRUPTCY SERVICES LLC p 1010
14841 Dallas Pkwy Ste 300, Dallas TX 75254
Tel (972) 643-6600 SIC 7389

■ PLAINSCAPITAL CORP p 1154
2323 Victory Ave Ste 1400, Dallas TX 75219
Tel (214) 252-4100 SIC 7389

RYAN LLC p 1260
13155 Noel Rd Ste 100, Dallas TX 75240
Tel (972) 934-0022 SIC 8721 7291 7389

■TRIAD FINANCIAL CORP p 1478
8585 N Stemmons Fwy, Dallas TX 75247
Tel (817) 521-8127 SIC 7389

■ XEROX BUSINESS SERVICES LLC p 1631
2828 N Haskell Ave Fl 1, Dallas TX 75204
Tel (214) 841-6111 SIC 7374 7375 7389

■ SALLY INVESTMENT HOLDINGS LLC p 1273
3001 Colorado Blvd, Denton TX 76210
Tel (940) 898-7500 SIC 7389

HUNT BUILDING CO LTD p 718
4401 N Mesa St Ste 201, El Paso TX 79902
Tel (915) 533-1122
SIC 1522 6531 1542 7389

TECMA GROUP L L C p 1432
2000 Wyoming Ave Ste A, El Paso TX 79903
Tel (915) 534-4252 SIC 7389

ALLIED ELECTRONICS INC p 56
7151 Jack Newell Blvd S, Fort Worth TX 76118
Tel (817) 595-3500 SIC 5065 7389 3999

■AMERICAN EAGLE HOLDING LLC p 71
14760 Trinity Blvd # 300, Fort Worth TX 76155
Tel (817) 963-1234 SIC 7389

FIRST COMMAND FINANCIAL SERVICES INC p 545
1 Firstcomm Plz, Fort Worth TX 76109
Tel (817) 731-8621 SIC 7389

NOVO 1 INC p 1063
4301 Cambridge Rd, Fort Worth TX 76155
Tel (817) 355-8909 SIC 7389

CONDUMEX INC p 355
900 Avenue S, Grand Prairie TX 75050
Tel (800) 925-9473 SIC 7389 5063

CAL DIVE INTERNATIONAL INC p 237
2500 Citywest Blvd # 2200, Houston TX 77042
Tel (713) 361-2600 SIC 7389 1623 1629

CARBER HOLDINGS INC p 252
12600 N Featherwood Dr # 450, Houston TX 77034
Tel (713) 797-2859 SIC 1389 7389

▲ CARDTRONICS INC p 253
3250 Briarpark Dr Ste 400, Houston TX 77042
Tel (832) 308-4000 SIC 7389 5049

ENRON NETWORKS LLC p 500
1400 Smith St, Houston TX 77002
Tel (713) 853-6161 SIC 7389

■ FURMANITE CORP p 585
10370 Richmond Ave # 600, Houston TX 77042
Tel (713) 634-7777 SIC 7699 7389

■ FURMANITE WORLDWIDE INC p 585
10370 Richmond Ave # 600, Houston TX 77042
Tel (972) 699-4000 SIC 7699 3599 7389

GC SERVICES LIMITED PARTNERSHIP p 595
6330 Gulfton St, Houston TX 77081
Tel (713) 777-4441 SIC 7322 7389

INSPECTORATE AMERICA CORP p 746
12000 Aerospace Ave # 200, Houston TX 77034
Tel (713) 944-2000 SIC 7389 8734 8731

INSPECTORATE AMERICA HOLDING INC p 746
12000 Aerospace Ave # 200, Houston TX 77034
Tel (713) 944-2000 SIC 7389 8734

■ IOS/PCI LLC p 762
652 N Sam Houston Pkwy E, Houston TX 77060
Tel (281) 310-5357 SIC 1389 7389

▲ NCI BUILDING SYSTEMS INC p 1022
10943 N Sam Huston Pkwy W, Houston TX 77064
Tel (281) 897-7788
SIC 3448 3444 3442 1542 1541 7389

PRINCE ENERGY LLC p 1176
7707 Wallisville Rd, Houston TX 77020
Tel (713) 673-5176 SIC 7389

▲ STEWART INFORMATION SERVICES CORP p 1389
1980 Post Oak Blvd, Houston TX 77056
Tel (713) 625-8100 SIC 6361 8742 7389

■ STEWART TITLE CO p 1389
1980 Post Oak Blvd Ste 80, Houston TX 77056
Tel (713) 625-8100
SIC 6361 7389 8713 8742 6541

■ SUSSER PETROLEUM CORP p 1409
555 E Airtex Dr, Houston TX 77073
Tel (832) 234-3746 SIC 5172 7389

■TELECHECK SERVICES INC p 1434
5251 Westheimr Rd B100, Houston TX 77056
Tel (713) 331-7600 SIC 7389 7374 6153

TRICON INTERNATIONAL LTD p 1479
777 Post Oak Blvd Ste 550, Houston TX 77056
Tel (713) 963-0066 SIC 5169 7389 4789

■ UNIVERSALPEGASUS INTERNATIONAL HOLDINGS INC p 1518
4848 Loop Central Dr # 600, Houston TX 77081
Tel (713) 425-6000 SIC 7389 8711 8713

■ UNIVERSALPEGASUS INTERNATIONAL INC p 1518
4848 Loop Central Dr # 600, Houston TX 77081
Tel (713) 425-6000 SIC 7389 8711 8713

WILLIAM STAMPS FARISH FUND p 1611
1100 La St Ste 1200, Houston TX 77002
Tel (713) 757-7313 SIC 7389

WOOD GROUP MUSTANG INC p 1622
17325 Park Row, Houston TX 77084
Tel (832) 809-8000
SIC 8711 8742 7389 1389

BANCTEC INC p 150
2701 E Grauwyler Rd, Irving TX 75061
Tel (972) 821-4000 SIC 7389

HOV SERVICES INC p 712
2701 E Grauwyler Rd, Irving TX 75061
Tel (248) 837-7100
SIC 7374 7334 7389 2752 7331 7379

PERIMETER INTERNATIONAL p 1136
2700 Story Rd W Ste 150, Irving TX 75038
Tel (877) 701-1919
SIC 7389 4412 4731 4581 4449

WERE READY TO ASSEMBLE INC p 1592
2201 W Royal Ln Ste 230, Irving TX 75063
Tel (972) 373-9484 SIC 7389 5399

DET NORSKE VERITAS HOLDING (USA) INC p 433
1400 Ravello Rd, Katy TX 77449
Tel (281) 396-1000
SIC 8711 7389 5734 8741

SCOT INDUSTRIES INC p 1293
3756 Fm 250 N, Lone Star TX 75668
Tel (903) 639-2551
SIC 7389 5051 3498 3471

APPLIED-CLEVELAND HOLDINGS INC p 100
2735 State Highway 322, Longview TX 75603
Tel (918) 358-5735 SIC 6719 7389

J & K EXPRESS INC p 770
5046 N Conway Ave, Mission TX 78573
Tel (956) 584-3130 SIC 7389

ETECH GLOBAL SERVICES LLC p 511
1903 Berry Dr, Nacogdoches TX 75964
Tel (936) 559-2200
SIC 7389 8742 7373 8741 8721 7374

TECHWELL SURVEYS CORP p 1432
610 W 83rd St, Odessa TX 79764
Tel (432) 362-3711 SIC 4911 7389

AEGON DIRECT MARKETING SERVICES INC p 29
2700 W Plano Pkwy, Plano TX 75075
Tel (972) 881-6000 SIC 7389

▲ALLIANCE DATA SYSTEMS CORP p 54
7500 Dallas Pkwy Ste 700, Plano TX 75024
Tel (214) 494-3000 SIC 7389

ANDERSON MERCHANDISERS LLC p 90
5601 Gran Pkwy Ste 1400, Plano TX 75024
Tel (972) 987-5516 SIC 7389

EGS CUSTOMER CARE INC p 481
5085 W Park Blvd Ste 300, Plano TX 75093
Tel (972) 943-7000 SIC 7389

WSOL INC p 1628
1820 Preston Park Blvd # 1150, Plano TX 75093
Tel (972) 964-4800 SIC 7389

■ SAFETY-KLEEN INC p 1266
2600 N Central Expy # 400, Richardson TX 75080
Tel (800) 669-5740
SIC 4953 3559 4212 5172 5085 7389

■ SAFETY-KLEEN SYSTEMS INC p 1266
2600 N Central Expy # 400, Richardson TX 75080
Tel (972) 265-2000
SIC 3559 7359 5172 4212 7389 5085

■ DELL FINANCIAL SERVICES LLC p 424
1 Dell Way, Round Rock TX 78682
Tel (800) 283-2210 SIC 7389

CHRISTUS SANTA ROSA HOME CARE p 304
4241 Woodcock Dr Ste A100, San Antonio TX 78228
Tel (210) 704-2011 SIC 7389

HARLAND CLARKE CORP p 661
15955 La Cantera Pkwy, San Antonio TX 78256
Tel (830) 609-5500 SIC 2782 2754 7389

HARLAND CLARKE HOLDINGS CORP p 661
15955 La Cantera Pkwy, San Antonio TX 78256
Tel (210) 697-8888 SIC 2782 2754 7389

GRAVICK GROUP LLC p 632
4985 Fm 1017, San Isidro TX 78588
Tel (956) 330-5676 SIC 8742 7371 7389

■ SABRE GLBL INC p 1264
3150 Sabre Dr, Southlake TX 76092
Tel (682) 605-1000
SIC 7375 7371 7374 7389 8748

SHOW SERVICES LLC p 1318
920 E Highway 199, Springtown TX 76082
Tel (800) 737-8757 SIC 7389

APPLUS RTD USA INC p 100
3 Sugar Creek Center Blvd # 600, Sugar Land TX 77478
Tel (832) 295-5000 SIC 7389

MONEY MANAGEMENT INTERNATIONAL INC p 984
14141 Southwest Fwy # 1000, Sugar Land TX 77478
Tel (713) 923-2227 SIC 7389

▲TEAM INC p 1430
13131 Dar Ashford Ste 600, Sugar Land TX 77478
Tel (281) 331-6154 SIC 7389 7699

HMT INC p 698
24 Waterway Ave Ste 400, The Woodlands TX 77380
Tel (281) 681-7000
SIC 7699 3443 7389 1791

■WOODLANDS OPERATING CO L P p 1623
24 Waterway Ave Ste 1100, The Woodlands TX 77380
Tel (281) 719-6100
SIC 6552 7997 7389 6513 6512

ALAN RITCHEY INC p 44
740 S Frontage Rd, Valley View TX 76272
Tel (940) 726-3276
SIC 7389 4213 2048 0291

KESTRA FINANCIAL INC p 814
1250 Capital Of Tex, West Lake Hills TX 78746
Tel (512) 697-6890 SIC 7389

TPUSA INC p 1468
6510 S Millrock Dr # 150, Holladay UT 84121
Tel (801) 257-5800 SIC 7389

DIRECT FINANCIAL SOLUTIONS LLC p 441
84 E 2400 N, Logan UT 84341
Tel (435) 774-8207 SIC 7389

CARE-A-LOT FUND p 254
1344 W 4675 S, Ogden UT 84405
Tel (801) 627-0900 SIC 7389

OPINIONOLOGY LLC p 1089
701 Timpanogos Pkwy Ste M, Orem UT 84097
Tel (801) 373-7735 SIC 7389 8732

FOCUS SERVICES LLC p 563
4102 S 1900 W, Roy UT 84067
Tel (801) 393-1635 SIC 7389

PACKSIZE LLC p 1107
6440 S Wasatch Blvd # 305, Salt Lake City UT 84121
Tel (801) 944-4814 SIC 7389

TPUSA INC p 1468
1991 S 4650 W, Salt Lake City UT 84104
Tel (801) 257-5800 SIC 7389

■ **ACS COMMERCIAL SOLUTIONS INC** p 18
510 W Parkland Dr, Sandy UT 84070
Tel (801) 567-5000 SIC 7374 7389

ARMED FORCES BENEFIT ASSOCIATION p 111
909 N Washington St # 767, Alexandria VA 22314
Tel (703) 549-4455 SIC 7389

AIRLINES REPORTING CORP p 40
3000 Wilson Blvd Ste 300, Arlington VA 22201
Tel (703) 816-8000 SIC 7389 6099 7374

HIGH SIERRA POOLS INC p 691
2704 Columbia Pike, Arlington VA 22204
Tel (703) 920-1750 SIC 8741 7389

INTERSTATE RESOURCES INC p 758
1300 Wilson Blvd Ste 1075, Arlington VA 22209
Tel (703) 243-3355 SIC 2631 2653 7389

PROMONTORY INTERFINANCIAL NETWORK LLC p 1183
1300 17th St N Ste 1800, Arlington VA 22209
Tel (703) 292-3400 SIC 7389

CREVENNA OAKS PRESERVATION LP p 392
11550 Oak Bluff Ct, Burke VA 22015
Tel (703) 323-7964 SIC 6513 7389

■ **GREENBRIER INTERNATIONAL INC** p 637
500 Volvo Pkwy, Chesapeake VA 23320
Tel (757) 321-5900 SIC 5199 7389

CGI FEDERAL INC p 285
12601 Fair Lakes Cir, Fairfax VA 22033
Tel (703) 227-6000 SIC 7379 7389 8999

CGI TECHNOLOGIES AND SOLUTIONS INC p 286
11325 Random Hills Rd, Fairfax VA 22030
Tel (703) 267-8000
SIC 7379 7373 7372 7389

UNIVERSITY OF MARY WASHINGTON p 1522
1301 College Ave, Fredericksburg VA 22401
Tel (540) 654-2060 SIC 8221 7389

■ **FANEUIL INC** p 527
2 Eaton St Ste 1002, Hampton VA 23669
Tel (757) 722-3235 SIC 7389

FUTRELL & HOLT INC p 585
2000 Enterprise Pkwy, Hampton VA 23666
Tel (757) 744-9552 SIC 7389

■ **NETWORK SOLUTIONS LLC** p 1028
13861 Sunrise Valley Dr # 300, Herndon VA 20171
Tel (703) 668-4600
SIC 7375 7389 4813 7374

COGNOSANTE HOLDINGS LLC p 334
8200 Greensboro Dr # 1200, Mc Lean VA 22102
Tel (703) 206-6000 SIC 7389

■ **CONTACT SOLUTIONS LLC** p 362
11950 Democracy Dr # 250, Reston VA 20190
Tel (703) 480-1620 SIC 7379 7371 7389

SES GOVERNMENT SOLUTIONS INC p 1308
11790 Sunrise Valley Dr # 300, Reston VA 20191
Tel (703) 610-1000 SIC 7389 3663

TRANSACTION NETWORK SERVICES INC p 1470
10740 Parkridge Blvd # 100, Reston VA 20191
Tel (703) 453-8300 SIC 4813 7389 7374

REYNOLDS PACKAGING GROUP LTD p 1231
6641 W Broad St Fl 5, Richmond VA 23230
Tel (804) 281-2000 SIC 7389

REYNOLDS PACKAGING INC p 1231
6641 W Broad St Fl 4, Richmond VA 23230
Tel (804) 281-2000 SIC 7389

LASERSHIP INC p 846
1912 Woodford Rd Ste Ll, Vienna VA 22182
Tel (703) 761-9030 SIC 7389

ADS TACTICAL INC p 24
621 Lynnhven Pkwy Ste 400, Virginia Beach VA 23452
Tel (757) 781-7758 SIC 7389

PROFESSIONAL HOSPITALITY RESOURCES INC p 1180
932 Laskin Rd, Virginia Beach VA 23451
Tel (757) 491-3000 SIC 7011 7389 5812

MAINVUE HOMES LLC p 898
1110 112th Ave Ne Ste 202, Bellevue WA 98004
Tel (425) 646-4022 SIC 7389 1521

AFF INC p 32
7400 45th Street Ct E, Fife WA 98424
Tel (253) 926-5000 SIC 4731 4213 7389

AMERICAN FAST FREIGHT INC p 72
7400 45th Street Ct E, Fife WA 98424
Tel (253) 926-5000
SIC 4731 4213 7389 4214

WAREHOUSE DEMO SERVICES INC p 1575
1301 4th Ave Nw Ste 202, Issaquah WA 98027
Tel (425) 889-0797 SIC 7389

■ **WYNDHAM RESORT DEVELOPMENT CORP** p 1630
9805 Willows Rd Ne, Redmond WA 98052
Tel (425) 498-2500 SIC 7389

ADAPTIS INC p 21
999 3rd Ave Ste 1700, Seattle WA 98104
Tel (206) 521-8833 SIC 7389

EVERGREEN PACIFIC PARTNERS MANAGEMENT CO INC p 514
1700 7th Ave Ste 2300, Seattle WA 98101
Tel (206) 262-4709 SIC 7389 6282

GLOBAL DIVING & SALVAGE INC p 616
3840 W Marginal Way Sw, Seattle WA 98106
Tel (206) 623-0621 SIC 4959 1629 7389

MILLIMAN INC p 971
1301 5th Ave Ste 3800, Seattle WA 98101
Tel (206) 624-7940 SIC 8742 8999 7389

■ **TOMMY BAHAMA GROUP INC** p 1459
400 Fairview Ave N # 488, Seattle WA 98109
Tel (206) 622-8688
SIC 7389 5651 5136 5137

SKYLINE EXHIBITS INLAND NW INC p 1330
10102 E Knox Ave Ste 450, Spokane Valley WA 99206
Tel (509) 892-5354 SIC 7389

ELECTRIC LIGHTWAVE COMMUNICATIONS INC p 484
18110 Se 34th St Bldg 1s, Vancouver WA 98683
Tel (360) 558-6900 SIC 7389 4813

PEACE HEALTH SOUTHWEST MEDICAL CENTER p 1125
602 Ne 92nd Ave Ste 120, Vancouver WA 98664
Tel (360) 514-2250 SIC 8062 7389

NOEL CORP p 1046
1001 S 1st St, Yakima WA 98901
Tel (509) 248-4545
SIC 2086 7389 4212 6512 4225 5962

■ **PARK MOUNTAINEER INC** p 1115
Hc 2, Chester WV 26034
Tel (304) 387-8300
SIC 7999 7011 7389 6512

VALLEY PACKAGING INDUSTRIES INC p 1541
110 N Kensington Dr, Appleton WI 54915
Tel (920) 749-5840 SIC 7389 8331

RPE INC p 1255
8550 Central Sands Rd, Bancroft WI 54921
Tel (715) 335-8050 SIC 7389

MEETINGS & INCENTIVES WORLDWIDE INC p 939
10520 7 Mile Rd, Caledonia WI 53108
Tel (262) 835-6710 SIC 4724 8742 7389

CHOICE PRODUCTS USA LLC p 302
3421 Truax Ct, Eau Claire WI 54703
Tel (715) 833-8761 SIC 5199 7389 2041

CYGNUS BUSINESS MEDIA INC p 405
1233 Janesville Ave, Fort Atkinson WI 53538
Tel (920) 563-6388 SIC 2721 7389 7319

PAYMENT SERVICE NETWORK INC p 1122
2901 International Ln # 100, Madison WI 53704
Tel (608) 442-5100 SIC 7389 6531 8721

GOODWILL INDUSTRIES OF NORTH CENTRAL WISCONSIN INC p 624
1800 Appleton Rd, Menasha WI 54952
Tel (920) 731-6601 SIC 5932 7389 8331

AA MANAGEMENT GROUP INC p 7
411 E Wisconsin Ave # 1900, Milwaukee WI 53202
Tel (414) 271-7240 SIC 6531 7389

AMERICAN APPRAISAL ASSOCIATES INC p 68
411 E Wisconsin Ave # 1900, Milwaukee WI 53202
Tel (630) 541-4650 SIC 8748 7389 6531

CHILDRENS HOSPITAL AND HEALTH SYSTEM INC p 299
8915 W Connell Ave, Milwaukee WI 53226
Tel (414) 266-2000
SIC 8069 8082 7389 7322

CHRYSALIS PACKAGING AND ASSEMBLY CORP p 304
130 W Edger Avenu Sut, Milwaukee WI 53207
Tel (414) 744-8550 SIC 7389

EXTENDICARE HEALTH SERVICES INC p 521
111 W Michigan St, Milwaukee WI 53203
Tel (414) 908-6720 SIC 8051 7389 5912

MERIDIAN INDUSTRIES INC p 949
735 N Water St Ste 630, Milwaukee WI 53202
Tel (414) 224-0610
SIC 3069 2843 2269 7389

NORTHWESTERN MUTUAL LIFE INSURANCE CO p 1060
720 E Wisconsin Ave, Milwaukee WI 53202
Tel (414) 271-1444 SIC 6311 6321 7389

XENTEL INC p 1631
720 W Virginia St, Milwaukee WI 53204
Tel (954) 522-5200 SIC 7389

ALTA RESOURCES CORP p 61
120 N Commercial St, Neenah WI 54956
Tel (877) 464-2582 SIC 7389 8742

KERLEY BIOKIMICA INC p 813
33707 Prairieview Ln, Oconomowoc WI 53066
Tel (262) 567-8840 SIC 7389

EMCO CHEMICAL DISTRIBUTORS INC p 491
8601 95th St, Pleasant Prairie WI 53158
Tel (262) 427-0400 SIC 5169 7389 2819

WARREN INDUSTRIES INC p 1577
3100 Mount Pleasant St, Racine WI 53404
Tel (262) 639-7800 SIC 7389

BOELTER COMPANIES INC p 197
N22 W23685 Rdgview Pkwy W, Waukesha WI 53188
Tel (262) 523-6200
SIC 5113 5046 7389 5087

CORIX UTILITIES (US) INC p 370
11020 W Plank Ct Ste 100, Wauwatosa WI 53226
Tel (414) 203-8700 SIC 1731 7389

M C HOLDINGS INC p 889
5709 Education Dr Apt 205, Cheyenne WY 82009
Tel (307) 514-1510 SIC 6719 7389

SIC 7513 Truck Rental & Leasing, Without Drivers

SOUTHLAND INTERNATIONAL TRUCKS INC p 1351
200 Oxmoor Blvd, Birmingham AL 35209
Tel (205) 942-6226
SIC 5511 5531 7538 7513

SWIFT LEASING CO INC p 1412
2200 S 75th Ave, Phoenix AZ 85043
Tel (602) 269-9700 SIC 7513

■ **U-HAUL CO OF DISTRICT OF COLUMBIA INC** p 1497
2727 N Central Ave, Phoenix AZ 85004
Tel (602) 263-6011 SIC 7513

■ **U-HAUL INTERNATIONAL INC** p 1498
2727 N Central Ave, Phoenix AZ 85004
Tel (602) 263-6011
SIC 7513 7519 7359 5531 4226 8741

DART TRANSPORTATION SERVICE A CORP p 413
1430 S Eastman Ave Ste 1, Commerce CA 90023
Tel (323) 981-8205 SIC 6798 7513

INLAND KENWORTH (US) INC p 743
9730 Cherry Ave, Fontana CA 92335
Tel (909) 823-9955
SIC 5012 7538 5013 7513

■ **U-HAUL CO OF CALIFORNIA** p 1497
44511 S Grimmer Blvd, Fremont CA 94538
Tel (800) 528-0463 SIC 7513 7519 4226

MIDWAY RENT A CAR INC p 967
4751 Wilshire Blvd # 120, Los Angeles CA 90010
Tel (323) 692-4000
SIC 5511 7515 5521 4119 7513

ENTERPRISE RENT-A-CAR CO OF LOS ANGELES LLC p 502
333 City Blvd W Ste 1000, Orange CA 92868
Tel (657) 221-4400
SIC 7515 7513 5511 7514

WESTRUX INTERNATIONAL INC p 1603
15555 Valley View Ave, Santa Fe Springs CA 90670
Tel (562) 404-1020
SIC 5511 5531 7513 7538

CENTER FOR TRANSPORTATION SAFETY LLC p 276
5700 E 56th Ave Unit I, Commerce City CO 80022
Tel (303) 227-0131 SIC 7513 7515

ROLLINS LEASING LLC p 1247
2200 Concord Pike, Wilmington DE 19803
Tel (302) 426-2700 SIC 7513

■ **HERTZ CORP** p 687
8501 Williams Rd, Estero FL 33928
Tel (239) 301-7000
SIC 7514 7515 7513 7359 5521 6794

UNIVERSAL TRAILER HOLDINGS CORP p 1518
12800 University Dr # 300, Fort Myers FL 33907
Tel (513) 671-3880 SIC 7513

■ **RYDER INTEGRATED LOGISTICS INC** p 1260
11690 Nw 105th St, Medley FL 33178
Tel (305) 500-3726 SIC 7513

▲ **RYDER SYSTEM INC** p 1260
11690 Nw 105th St, Medley FL 33178
Tel (305) 500-3726 SIC 7513 4212

■ **RYDER TRUCK RENTAL INC** p 1260
11690 Nw 105th St, Medley FL 33178
Tel (305) 500-3726 SIC 7513

FERMAN CHEVROLET OF TARPON SPRINGS p 538
43520 Us Highway 19 N, Tarpon Springs FL 34689
Tel (727) 942-4800
SIC 5511 7538 7515 7513 5521

PGA RESORT & SPA p 1140
1555 Palm Beach Lks, West Palm Beach FL 33401
Tel (561) 686-2000
SIC 8741 7377 7513 7515

■ **UPS LOGISTICS GROUP INC** p 1529
55 Glenlake Pkwy, Atlanta GA 30328
Tel (678) 746-4100
SIC 7389 7513 4731 4513

WHEELS INC p 1605
666 Garland Pl, Des Plaines IL 60016
Tel (847) 699-7000 SIC 7515 7513

▲ **CAMPING WORLD HOLDINGS INC** p 246
250 Parkway Dr Ste 270, Lincolnshire IL 60069
Tel (847) 808-3000 SIC 7513 6159 7539

SIRVA INC p 1327
1 Parkview Plz, Oakbrook Terrace IL 60181
Tel (630) 570-3047
SIC 4213 4214 4731 7513 6331

SIRVA WORLDWIDE INC p 1327
1 Parkview Plz Ste 300, Oakbrook Terrace IL 60181
Tel (630) 570-3047
SIC 4213 4214 4731 7513 6331

PALMER TRUCKS INC p 1109
2929 S Holt Rd, Indianapolis IN 46241
Tel (317) 243-1668
SIC 5511 5531 7538 7513 5012

SCHILLI LEASING INC p 1287
6358 W Us Highway 24, Remington IN 47977
Tel (888) 233-1919 SIC 7513 7359

RUAN TRANSPORTATION MANAGEMENT SYSTEMS INC p 1256
666 Grand Ave Ste 3100, Des Moines IA 50309
Tel (515) 245-2500 SIC 4213 7513

MURPHY-HOFFMAN CO p 1001
11120 Tomahawk Creek Pkwy, Leawood KS 66211
Tel (816) 483-6444
SIC 5012 7513 7538 6159 5511

WORLDWIDE EQUIPMENT INC p 1626
73 We Dr, Prestonsburg KY 41653
Tel (606) 874-2172
SIC 5012 5013 7538 7513

POHANKA OF SALISBURY INC p 1159
2015 N Salisbury Blvd, Salisbury MD 21801
Tel (410) 749-2301
SIC 5511 7513 7514 7538 7515

ELEMENT VEHICLE MANAGEMENT SERVICES LLC p 486
940 Ridgebrook Rd, Sparks MD 21152
Tel (410) 771-1900 SIC 7513 7515

■ **PHH VEHICLE SALES INC** p 1142
940 Ridgebrook Rd, Sparks MD 21152
Tel (800) 665-9744 SIC 7513

▲ **STAPLES INC** p 1377
500 Staples Dr, Framingham MA 01702
Tel (508) 253-5000
SIC 5943 5999 7513 5961 5712

■ **TOTAL LOGISTICS ONLINE LLC** p 1463
10717 Adams St Ste 200, Holland MI 49423
Tel (800) 333-5599 SIC 7513

LUTHER HOLDING CO p 886
3701 Alabama Ave S, Minneapolis MN 55416
Tel (763) 593-5755
SIC 5511 7515 7513 6512 6552 5611

UNIGROUP INC p 1503
1 Premier Dr, Fenton MO 63026
Tel (636) 305-5000 SIC 4213 7513 5087

KCR INTERNATIONAL TRUCKS INC p 806
7700 Ne 38th St, Kansas City MO 64161
Tel (816) 455-1833
SIC 5511 5531 7538 7513

■ **XTRA COMPANIES INC** p 1633
7911 Forsyth Blvd Ste 600, Saint Louis MO 63105
Tel (636) 207-6761 SIC 7513

■ **XTRA LEASE LLC** p 1633
7911 Forsyth Blvd Ste 600, Saint Louis MO 63105
Tel (800) 325-1453 SIC 7513

■ **XTRA LLC** p 1633
7911 Forsyth Blvd Ste 600, Saint Louis MO 63105
Tel (314) 719-0400 SIC 7513

TRANSPORT LEASING CO LLP p 1472
1901 Benefis Ct, Great Falls MT 59405
Tel (406) 727-7500 SIC 7513

TRANSWOOD CARRIERS INC p 1473
2565 Saint Marys Ave, Omaha NE 68105
Tel (402) 346-8092 SIC 4213 4212 7513

MALCO ENTERPRISES OF NEVADA INC p 899
7120 Haven St, Las Vegas NV 89119
Tel (702) 736-1212 SIC 5521 7514 7513

▲ **AMERCO** p 66
5555 Kietzke Ln Ste 100, Reno NV 89511
Tel (775) 688-6300 SIC 7513 7519 4226

■ **U-HAUL CO OF MAINE INC** p 1498
1325 Airmotive Way # 100, Reno NV 89502
Tel (775) 688-6300 SIC 7513

DANA TRANSPORT SYSTEM INC p 411
210 Essex Ave E, Avenel NJ 07001
Tel (732) 750-9100 SIC 4213 7513

NATIONAL FREIGHT INC p 1012
1515 Burnt Mill Rd, Cherry Hill NJ 08003
Tel (856) 691-7000 SIC 7513 4213

AUTOMOTIVE RENTALS INC p 134
4001 Leadenhall Rd, Mount Laurel NJ 08054
Tel (856) 778-1500 SIC 7513 7515 7549

■ **HERTZ INTERNATIONAL LTD** p 687
225 Brae Blvd, Park Ridge NJ 07656
Tel (201) 307-2000 SIC 7514 7515 7513

■ **HERTZ INVESTORS INC** p 687
225 Brae Blvd, Park Ridge NJ 07656
Tel (201) 307-2000
SIC 7514 7515 7513 7359 5521 6794

▲ **AVIS BUDGET GROUP INC** p 138
6 Sylvan Way Ste 1, Parsippany NJ 07054
Tel (973) 496-4700 SIC 7514 7513 6794

YOUNGS TRUCK CENTER INC p 1639
3880 Jeff Adams Dr, Charlotte NC 28206
Tel (704) 597-0551 SIC 5511 7513 7532

LEITH INC p 854
5607 Capital Blvd, Raleigh NC 27616
Tel (919) 876-5432
SIC 5511 7515 7513 5012

SALEM HOLDING CO p 1272
175 Charlois Blvd, Winston Salem NC 27103
Tel (336) 768-6800 SIC 7513 4213

SALEM LEASING CORP p 1272
175 Charlois Blvd, Winston Salem NC 27103
Tel (336) 768-6800 SIC 7513

WESTLIE MOTOR CO p 1601
500 S Broadway, Minot ND 58701
Tel (701) 852-1354 SIC 7513 5511

OHIO MACHINERY CO p 1077
3993 E Royalton Rd, Broadview Heights OH 44147
Tel (440) 526-6200
SIC 7513 6159 7699 5082 7353

FIRST GROUP INVESTMENT PARTNERSHIP p 547
600 Vine St Ste 1200, Cincinnati OH 45202
Tel (513) 241-2200
SIC 7513 4212 4213 4225 4151 4111

FIRSTGROUP USA INC p 550
600 Vine St Ste 1400, Cincinnati OH 45202
Tel (513) 241-2200
SIC 7513 4212 4213 4225 4151 4111

HY-TEK MATERIAL HANDLING INC p 722
2222 Rickenbacker Pkwy W, Columbus OH 43217
Tel (614) 497-2500
SIC 5084 5013 7538 7513 1796

VOSS AUTO NETWORK INC p 1566
766 Mmsburg Cnterville Rd, Dayton OH 45459
Tel (937) 428-2400
SIC 5511 7538 7515 7513 5521 5012

FORD MONTROSE INC p 565
3960 Medina Rd, Fairlawn OH 44333
Tel (330) 666-0711
SIC 5511 5521 7515 7513 7538 7532

AIM LEASING CO p 38
1500 Trumbull Ave, Girard OH 44420
Tel (330) 759-0438
SIC 7513 7538 4212 5983

■ **THRIFTY RENT-A-CAR SYSTEM INC** p 1451
14501 Hertz Quail Spgs, Oklahoma City OK 73134
Tel (918) 665-3930 SIC 7515 7514 7513

■ **THRIFTY INC** p 1451
5310 E 31st St Ste 100, Tulsa OK 74135
Tel (918) 665-3930
SIC 6794 7515 7514 7513

FRED BEANS FORD INC p 575
876 N Easton Rd, Doylestown PA 18902
Tel (888) 903-2085
SIC 5511 7513 5521 5012

DANELLA COMPANIES INC p 411
2290 Butler Pike, Plymouth Meeting PA 19462
Tel (610) 828-6200
SIC 7513 7353 8711 1623 8748

PENSKE DEDICATED LOGISTICS CORP p 1131
Green Hls Rr 10, Reading PA 19607
Tel (610) 775-6000 SIC 7513

PENSKE LOGISTICS LLC p 1131
Green Hls Rr 10, Reading PA 19603
Tel (800) 529-6531 SIC 7513 4213

PENSKE TRUCK LEASING CO LP p 1131
2675 Morgantown Rd, Reading PA 19607
Tel (610) 775-6000 SIC 7513

PENSKE TRUCK LEASING CORP p 1131
2675 Morgantown Rd, Reading PA 19607
Tel (610) 775-6000 SIC 7513

TRANSPORT INTERNATIONAL POOL INC p 1472
530 E Swedesford Rd, Wayne PA 19087
Tel (484) 254-0100
SIC 7519 7513 5511 5211

■ **FEDEX FREIGHT CORP** p 536
1715 Aaron Brenner Dr, Memphis TN 38120
Tel (901) 434-3100 SIC 4213 7513

TRI-STATE TRUCK CENTER INC p 1478
494 E Eh Crump Blvd, Memphis TN 38126
Tel (901) 947-5000 SIC 5511 7513 5012

TEXAS KENWORTH CO p 1444
4040 Irving Blvd, Dallas TX 75247
Tel (214) 920-7300
SIC 5012 5013 7513 7538

ROBERTS TRUCK CENTER HOLDING CO LLC p 1242
1825 Lakeway Dr Ste 700, Lewisville TX 75057
Tel (469) 645-7111 SIC 5012 7513 7538

■ **RUSH ADMINISTRATIVE SERVICES INC** p 1258
555 S Interstate 35 # 500, New Braunfels TX 78130
Tel (830) 626-5286
SIC 5012 7538 5531 5014 7513

▲ **RUSH ENTERPRISES INC** p 1258
555 S Ih 35 Ste 500, New Braunfels TX 78130
Tel (830) 302-5200
SIC 5012 7538 5531 5014 7513

GREATER RICHMOND BUSINESS INC p 636
1833 Commerce Rd, Richmond VA 23224
Tel (804) 232-3492
SIC 5511 5013 5531 7513

GWP HOLDINGS LLC p 648
3801 Airport Way S, Seattle WA 98108
Tel (206) 624-7383
SIC 5511 7513 7538 5012

BROADWAY FORD-HYUNDAI INC p 216
1010 S Military Ave, Green Bay WI 54304
Tel (920) 499-3131
SIC 7515 5511 7513 5521 5012

JX ENTERPRISES INC p 798
1320 Walnut Ridge Dr, Hartland WI 53029
Tel (800) 810-3410
SIC 5012 5511 7538 6159 7513

V & H INC p 1538
1505 S Central Ave, Marshfield WI 54449
Tel (715) 387-2545 SIC 5511 7513

LAKESIDE INTERNATIONAL LLC p 840
11000 W Silver Spring Dr, Milwaukee WI 53225
Tel (414) 353-4800
SIC 5511 5531 7538 7532 6159 7513

WILDE OF WEST ALLIS INC p 1609
3225 S 108th St, Milwaukee WI 53227
Tel (414) 329-6043
SIC 5511 5521 7538 7515 7513 5012

SIC 7514 Passenger Car Rental

FOX RENT A CAR INC p 572
5500 W Century Blvd, Los Angeles CA 90045
Tel (310) 342-5155 SIC 7514

GALPIN MOTORS INC p 590
15505 Roscoe Blvd, North Hills CA 91343
Tel (818) 787-3800
SIC 5511 5521 7538 7515 7514 5531

ENTERPRISE RENT-A-CAR CO OF LOS ANGELES LLC p 502
333 City Blvd W Ste 1000, Orange CA 92868
Tel (657) 221-4400
SIC 7515 7513 5511 7514

ENTERPRISE RENT-A-CAR CO OF SACRAMENTO LLC p 502
150 N Sunrise Ave, Roseville CA 95661
Tel (916) 787-4500 SIC 7515 7514 5511

ENTERPRISE RENT-A-CAR CO OF SAN FRANCISCO LLC p 502
2633 Camino Ramon Ste 400, San Ramon CA 94583
Tel (925) 464-5100 SIC 7514

PHIL LONG DEALERSHIPS INC p 1142
1114 Motor City Dr, Colorado Springs CO 80905
Tel (719) 575-7555 SIC 5511 7514 7515

REVOLUTION LLC p 1229
1717 Rhode Island Ave Nw # 1000, Washington DC 20036
Tel (202) 776-1400 SIC 6211 7514

■ **HERTZ CORP** p 687
8501 Williams Rd, Estero FL 33928
Tel (239) 301-7000
SIC 7514 7515 7513 7359 5521 6794

HERTZ GLOBAL HOLDINGS INC p 687
8501 Williams Rd Fl 3, Estero FL 33928
Tel (239) 301-7000 SIC 7515 7514

ENTERPRISE LEASING CO OF FLORIDA LLC p 502
3505 E Fontage Ste 200 Rd, Tampa FL 33607
Tel (813) 887-4299 SIC 7514 7515

ENTERPRISE LEASING CO OF GEORGIA LLC p 502
5909 Peachtree Ind, Atlanta GA 30341
Tel (770) 821-0399 SIC 7514 7515 5521

ILLINOIS AGRICULTURAL ASSOCIATION p 732
1701 Towanda Ave, Bloomington IL 61701
Tel (309) 557-2111
SIC 8611 6722 8742 6311 7514

▲ **SP PLUS CORP** p 1353
200 E Randolph St # 7700, Chicago IL 60601
Tel (312) 274-2000 SIC 7521 7514

ENTERPRISE LEASING CO OF CHICAGO LLC p 502
1050 N Lombard Rd, Lombard IL 60148
Tel (630) 693-2916 SIC 7515 7514

POHANKA OF SALISBURY INC p 1159
2015 N Salisbury Blvd, Salisbury MD 21801
Tel (410) 749-2301
SIC 5511 7513 7514 7538 7515

■ **ZIPCAR INC** p 1643
35 Thomson Pl, Boston MA 02210
Tel (617) 995-4231 SIC 7514

ALAMO RENTAL (US) INC p 44
600 Corporate Park Dr, Saint Louis MO 63105
Tel (314) 512-5000 SIC 7514

CRAWFORD GROUP INC p 389
600 Corporate Park Dr, Saint Louis MO 63105
Tel (314) 512-5000 SIC 7514 7515

EAN HOLDINGS LLC p 468
600 Corporate Park Dr, Saint Louis MO 63105
Tel (314) 512-5000 SIC 7514 7515

ENTERPRISE FLEET MANAGEMENT INC p 502
2600 S Hanley Rd Ste 460, Saint Louis MO 63144
Tel (314) 256-5100 SIC 7515 7514

ENTERPRISE HOLDINGS INC p 502
600 Corporate Park Dr, Saint Louis MO 63105
Tel (314) 512-5000 SIC 7514 7515

LOU FUSZ MOTOR CO p 879
10329 Old Olive Street Rd, Saint Louis MO 63141
Tel (314) 994-1500 SIC 5511 7514

MALCO ENTERPRISES OF NEVADA INC p 899
7120 Haven St, Las Vegas NV 89119
Tel (702) 736-1212 SIC 5521 7514 7513

TOWBIN AUTOMOTIVE ENTERPRISES INC p 1464
5550 W Sahara Ave, Las Vegas NV 89146
Tel (702) 253-7000 SIC 5511 7514

■ **HERTZ INTERNATIONAL LTD** p 687
225 Brae Blvd, Park Ridge NJ 07656
Tel (201) 307-2000 SIC 7514 7515 7513

■ **HERTZ INVESTORS INC** p 687
225 Brae Blvd, Park Ridge NJ 07656
Tel (201) 307-2000
SIC 7514 7515 7513 7359 5521 6794

■ **HERTZ LOCAL EDITION CORP** p 688
225 Brae Blvd, Park Ridge NJ 07656
Tel (201) 307-2000 SIC 7514

▲ **AVIS BUDGET GROUP INC** p 138
6 Sylvan Way Ste 1, Parsippany NJ 07054
Tel (973) 496-4700 SIC 7514 7513 6794

■ **AVIS GROUP HOLDINGS LLC** p 138
6 Sylvan Way Ste 1, Parsippany NJ 07054
Tel (973) 496-4328 SIC 7514

■ **AVIS RENT A CAR SYSTEM INC** p 138
6 Sylvan Way Ste 1, Parsippany NJ 07054
Tel (973) 496-3500 SIC 7514

AVIS RENTAL CAR SYSTEMS p 138
6 Sylvan Way Ste 1, Parsippany NJ 07054
Tel (973) 496-3000 SIC 7514

■ **BUDGET RENT A CAR SYSTEM INC** p 224
6 Sylvan Way Ste 1, Parsippany NJ 07054
Tel (973) 496-3500 SIC 7514

■ **BUDGET TRUCK RENTAL LLC** p 224
6 Sylvan Way Ste 1, Parsippany NJ 07054
Tel (973) 496-3500 SIC 7514

ELRAC LLC p 489
1550 Route 23, Wayne NJ 07470
Tel (973) 709-2499
SIC 7514 7515 5511 5521

■ **THRIFTY RENT-A-CAR SYSTEM INC** p 1451
14501 Hertz Quail Spgs, Oklahoma City OK 73134
Tel (918) 665-3930 SIC 7515 7514 7513

■ **DOLLAR RENT A CAR INC** p 448
5330 E 31st St Ste 100, Tulsa OK 74135
Tel (918) 669-3000 SIC 7514

■ **DOLLAR THRIFTY AUTOMOTIVE GROUP INC** p 448
5330 E 31st St, Tulsa OK 74135
Tel (918) 660-7700 SIC 6794 7514

NATIONAL RENTAL (US) INC p 1015
6929 N Lakewood Ave # 100, Tulsa OK 74117
Tel (918) 401-6000 SIC 7514

■ **THRIFTY INC** p 1451
5310 E 31st St Ste 100, Tulsa OK 74135
Tel (918) 665-3930
SIC 6794 7515 7514 7513

VANGUARD CAR RENTAL USA INC p 1543
6929 N Lakewood Ave # 100, Tulsa OK 74117
Tel (918) 401-6000 SIC 7514

■ **HERTZ TECHNOLOGIES INC** p 688
5601 Nw Expressway, Warr Acres OK 73132
Tel (405) 280-4983 SIC 7514

WEST ONE AUTOMOTIVE GROUP INC p 1595
2046 Nw Irving St, Portland OR 97209
Tel (503) 222-1335 SIC 7514

FORD MCCAFFERTY SALES INC p 565
1939 E Lincoln Hwy, Langhorne PA 19047
Tel (215) 945-8000
SIC 5511 5531 7538 7514 5521 5012

WALKER RESOURCES INC p 1573
1343 Hallmark Dr, San Antonio TX 78216
Tel (210) 341-6000 SIC 7514

OVERLAND WEST INC p 1099
2805 Washington Blvd, Ogden UT 84401
Tel (801) 621-5663 SIC 7514

BROADWAY ENTERPRISES INC p 216
1106 S Military Ave, Green Bay WI 54304
Tel (920) 429-6249 SIC 5511 7514

SIC 7515 Passenger Car Leasing

THREE-WAY CHEVROLET CO p 1450
4501 Wible Rd, Bakersfield CA 93313
Tel (661) 847-6400
SIC 5511 5531 7515 7538 7532

MIDWAY RENT A CAR INC p 967
4751 Wilshire Blvd # 120, Los Angeles CA 90010
Tel (323) 692-4000
SIC 5511 7515 5521 4119 7513

GALPIN MOTORS INC p 590
15505 Roscoe Blvd, North Hills CA 91343
Tel (818) 787-3800
SIC 5511 5521 7538 7515 7514 5531

ENTERPRISE RENT-A-CAR CO OF LOS ANGELES LLC p 502
333 City Blvd W Ste 1000, Orange CA 92868
Tel (657) 221-4400
SIC 7515 7513 5511 7514

ENTERPRISE RENT-A-CAR CO OF SACRAMENTO LLC p 502
150 N Sunrise Ave, Roseville CA 95661
Tel (916) 787-4500 SIC 7515 7514 5511

COUNTY FORD NORTH INC p 375
450 W Vista Way, Vista CA 92083
Tel (760) 945-9900
SIC 5511 5521 7538 7515 5531

PHIL LONG DEALERSHIPS INC p 1142
1114 Motor City Dr, Colorado Springs CO 80905
Tel (719) 575-7555 SIC 5511 7514 7515

PHIL LONG FORD LLC p 1142
1212 Motor City Dr, Colorado Springs CO 80905
Tel (719) 575-7100
SIC 5511 7515 7538 5531

CENTER FOR TRANSPORTATION SAFETY LLC p 276
5700 E 56th Ave Unit I, Commerce City CO 80022
Tel (303) 227-0131 SIC 7513 7515

■ **HERTZ CORP** p 687
8501 Williams Rd, Estero FL 33928
Tel (239) 301-7000
SIC 7514 7515 7513 7359 5521 6794

HERTZ GLOBAL HOLDINGS INC p 687
8501 Williams Rd Fl 3, Estero FL 33928
Tel (239) 301-7000 SIC 7515 7514

SCOTT-MCRAE AUTOMOTIVE GROUP INC p 1294
701 Riverside Park Pl # 120, Jacksonville FL 32204
Tel (904) 354-4000 SIC 5511 7515 6159

MUTZ MOTORS LTD PARTNERSHIP p 1003
1430 W Memorial Blvd, Lakeland FL 33815
Tel (863) 682-1100
SIC 5511 7538 7532 7515 5531 5521

ENTERPRISE LEASING CO OF FLORIDA LLC p 502
3505 E Fontage Ste 200 Rd, Tampa FL 33607
Tel (813) 887-4299 SIC 7514 7515

FERMAN CHEVROLET OF TARPON SPRINGS p 538
43520 Us Highway 19 N, Tarpon Springs FL 34689
Tel (727) 942-4800
SIC 5511 7538 7515 7513 5521

PGA RESORT & SPA p 1140
1555 Palm Beach Lks, West Palm Beach FL 33401
Tel (561) 686-2000
SIC 8741 7377 7513 7515

ROGER DEAN ENTERPRISES INC p 1246
2235 Okeechobee Blvd, West Palm Beach FL 33409
Tel (561) 683-8100
SIC 5511 5521 7538 7532 7515

LEASE PLAN USA INC p 850
1165 Sanctuary Pkwy, Alpharetta GA 30009
Tel (770) 933-9090 SIC 7515 8741

ENTERPRISE LEASING CO OF GEORGIA LLC p 502
5909 Peachtree Ind, Atlanta GA 30341
Tel (770) 821-0399 SIC 7514 7515 5521

■ **ASBURY AUTOMOTIVE ATLANTA LLC** p 115
3039 Premiere Pkwy # 900, Duluth GA 30097
Tel (404) 622-1921
SIC 5511 7515 5013 6159 5521

CUTTER MANAGEMENT CO p 403
1100 Alakea St Steth2, Honolulu HI 96814
Tel (808) 529-2000 SIC 5511 7515

MOTOR WERKS PARTNERS LP p 993
1475 S Barrington Rd, Barrington IL 60010
Tel (847) 842-1352 SIC 5511 7515

WHEELS INC p 1605
666 Garland Pl, Des Plaines IL 60016
Tel (847) 699-7000 SIC 7515 7513

ENTERPRISE LEASING CO OF CHICAGO LLC p 502
1050 N Lombard Rd, Lombard IL 60148
Tel (630) 693-2916 SIC 7515 7514

ARMON INC p 111
2265 Carlson Dr, Northbrook IL 60062
Tel (847) 498-4800 SIC 1711 7515 6552

JD BYRIDER SYSTEMS LLC p 780
12802 Hmlton Crssing Blvd, Carmel IN 46032
Tel (317) 249-3000
SIC 6794 5734 7538 7515 5521

CONKLIN FANGMAN INVESTMENT CO INC p 356
1400 E 11th Ave, Hutchinson KS 67501
Tel (620) 662-4467
SIC 7515 5511 7538 5521

POHANKA OF SALISBURY INC p 1159
2015 N Salisbury Blvd, Salisbury MD 21801
Tel (410) 749-2301
SIC 5511 7513 7514 7538 7515

ELEMENT VEHICLE MANAGEMENT SERVICES LLC p 486
940 Ridgebrook Rd, Sparks MD 21152
Tel (410) 771-1900 SIC 7513 7515

ATLANTIC AUTOMOTIVE CORP p 125
1 Olympic Pl Ste 1210, Towson MD 21204
Tel (410) 602-6177 SIC 5511 7538 7515

DANIEL J QUIRK INC p 411
372 Quincy Ave, Braintree MA 02184
Tel (781) 843-4800
SIC 5511 5013 5531 7538 5521 7515

▲ **FORD MOTOR CO** p 565
1 American Rd, Dearborn MI 48126
Tel (313) 322-3000
SIC 3711 3713 3714 6153 6141 7515

LUTHER HOLDING CO p 886
3701 Alabama Ave S, Minneapolis MN 55416
Tel (763) 593-5755
SIC 5511 7515 7513 6512 6552 5611

CRAWFORD GROUP INC p 389
600 Corporate Park Dr, Saint Louis MO 63105
Tel (314) 512-5000 SIC 7514 7515

EAN HOLDINGS LLC p 468
600 Corporate Park Dr, Saint Louis MO 63105
Tel (314) 512-5000 SIC 7514 7515

ENTERPRISE FLEET MANAGEMENT INC p 502
2600 S Hanley Rd Ste 460, Saint Louis MO 63144
Tel (314) 256-5100 SIC 7515 7514

ENTERPRISE HOLDINGS INC p 502
600 Corporate Park Dr, Saint Louis MO 63105
Tel (314) 512-5000 SIC 7514 7515

MERCHANTS AUTOMOTIVE GROUP INC p 944
1278 Hooksett Rd, Hooksett NH 03106
Tel (603) 669-4100 SIC 5521 7515

SUBARU OF AMERICA INC p 1395
2235 Rte 70 W, Cherry Hill NJ 08002
Tel (856) 488-8500
SIC 5012 5013 7515 8732

WARNOCK AUTOMOTIVE GROUP INC p 1576
175 State Route 10, East Hanover NJ 07936
Tel (973) 884-2100
SIC 5511 7515 5012 5013

AUTOMOTIVE RENTALS INC p 134
4001 Leadenhall Rd, Mount Laurel NJ 08054
Tel (856) 778-1500 SIC 7513 7515 7549

■ **HERTZ INTERNATIONAL LTD** p 687
225 Brae Blvd, Park Ridge NJ 07656
Tel (201) 307-2000 SIC 7514 7515 7513

■ **HERTZ INVESTORS INC** p 687
225 Brae Blvd, Park Ridge NJ 07656
Tel (201) 307-2000
SIC 7514 7515 7513 7359 5521 6794

VOLVO CARS OF NORTH AMERICA LLC p 1565
1 Volvo Dr, Rockleigh NJ 07647
Tel (201) 768-7300
SIC 5511 5013 6159 7515 3714

■ **DCH AUTO GROUP (USA) INC** p 418
955 Route 9 N, South Amboy NJ 08879
Tel (732) 727-9168
SIC 5511 7515 6512 6514

ELRAC LLC p 489
1550 Route 23, Wayne NJ 07470
Tel (973) 709-2499
SIC 7514 7515 5511 5521

MAJOR WORLD CHEVROLET LLC p 899
4340 Northern Blvd, Long Island City NY 11101
Tel (718) 937-3700
SIC 5511 7515 7538 5521

LEITH INC p 854
5607 Capital Blvd, Raleigh NC 27616
Tel (919) 876-5432
SIC 5511 7515 7513 5012

VAN DEVERE INC p 1542
300 W Market St, Akron OH 44303
Tel (330) 253-6137 SIC 5511 7515

VOSS AUTO NETWORK INC p 1566
766 Mmsburg Cnterville Rd, Dayton OH 45459
Tel (937) 428-2400
SIC 5511 7538 7515 7513 5521 5012

FORD MONTROSE INC p 565
3960 Medina Rd, Fairlawn OH 44333
Tel (330) 666-0711
SIC 5511 5521 7515 7513 7538 7532

YARK AUTOMOTIVE GROUP INC p 1635
6019 W Central Ave, Toledo OH 43615
Tel (419) 841-7771 SIC 5511 7515

■ **THRIFTY RENT-A-CAR SYSTEM INC** p 1451
14501 Hertz Quail Spgs, Oklahoma City OK 73134
Tel (918) 665-3930 SIC 7515 7514 7513

■ **THRIFTY INC** p 1451
5310 E 31st St Ste 100, Tulsa OK 74135
Tel (918) 665-3930
SIC 6794 7515 7514 7513

■ **ORIENTAL BANK** p 1094
254 Ave Munoz Rivera, San Juan PR 00918
Tel (787) 771-6800
SIC 6035 7359 7515 6733

DICK SMITH AUTOMOTIVE GROUP INC p 438
9940 Two Notch Rd, Columbia SC 29223
Tel (800) 944-8570 SIC 5511 7515

SOUTHEAST TEXAS CLASSIC AUTOMOTIVE INC p 1346
1000 Interstate 10 N, Beaumont TX 77702
Tel (409) 898-8001 SIC 5511 7515

KAHLIG MOTOR CO p 800
611 Lockhill Selma Rd, San Antonio TX 78216
Tel (210) 308-8900 SIC 5511 7515

PETERSBURG MOTOR CO INC p 1138
100 Myers Dr, Charlottesville VA 22901
Tel (434) 951-1000 SIC 5511 7515

BROADWAY FORD-HYUNDAI INC p 216
1010 S Military Ave, Green Bay WI 54304
Tel (920) 499-3131
SIC 7515 5511 7513 5521 5012

CUNA MUTUAL GROUP p 401
5910 Mineral Point Rd, Madison WI 53705
Tel (608) 238-5851
SIC 6331 6311 6351 6411 7515

FORD KAYSER INC p 565
2303 W Beltline Hwy, Madison WI 53713
Tel (608) 271-6000
SIC 5511 7538 7532 7515 5521

WILDE OF WEST ALLIS INC p 1609
3225 S 108th St, Milwaukee WI 53227
Tel (414) 329-6043
SIC 5511 5521 7538 7515 7513 5012

SIC 7519 Utility Trailers & Recreational Vehicle Rental

■ **U-HAUL INTERNATIONAL INC** p 1498
2727 N Central Ave, Phoenix AZ 85004
Tel (602) 263-6011
SIC 7513 7519 7359 5531 4226 8741

■ **U-HAUL CO OF CALIFORNIA** p 1497
44511 S Grimmer Blvd, Fremont CA 94538
Tel (800) 528-0463 SIC 7513 7519 4226

NATIONAL BUSINESS GROUP INC p 1010
15319 Chatsworth St, Mission Hills CA 91345
Tel (818) 221-6000
SIC 7353 5039 7359 3496 7519

COASTAL PACIFIC FOOD DISTRIBUTORS INC p 332
1015 Performance Dr, Stockton CA 95206
Tel (909) 947-2066
SIC 5141 4225 7519 4222

■ **WASHINGTON GAS LIGHT CO** p 1578
101 Constitution Ave Nw 200w, Washington DC 20001
Tel (703) 288-3614 SIC 7519

▲ **SPARTAN MOTORS INC** p 1355
1541 Reynolds Rd, Charlotte MI 48813
Tel (517) 543-6400 SIC 3711 3714 7519

▲AMERCO p 66
5555 Kietzke Ln Ste 100, Reno NV 89511
Tel (775) 688-6300 SIC 7513 7519 4226

NYK GROUP AMERICAS INC p 1069
300 Lighting Way Ste 500, Secaucus NJ 07094
Tel (201) 330-3000
SIC 4412 4731 4011 4491 7519

NYK LINE (NORTH AMERICA) INC p 1069
300 Lighting Way 4th, Secaucus NJ 07094
Tel (201) 330-3000
SIC 4412 4731 4213 4011 7519 4491

TRANSPORT INTERNATIONAL POOL INC p 1472
530 E Swedesford Rd, Wayne PA 19087
Tel (484) 254-0100
SIC 7519 7513 5511 5211

TRANSPORT INTERNATIONAL POOL INC p 1472
530 E Swedesford Rd, Wayne PA 19087
Tel (484) 254-0100 SIC 5511 7519

A DUIE PYLE INC p 5
650 Westtown Rd, West Chester PA 19382
Tel (610) 696-5800 SIC 4214 4225 7519

SIC 7521 Automobile Parking Lots & Garages

■ABM PARKING SERVICES INC p 12
1150 S Olive St Fl 19, Los Angeles CA 90015
Tel (213) 284-7600 SIC 7521 7349

VALET PARKING SERVICE A CALIFORNIA LTD PARTNERSHIP p 1540
6933 Hollywood Blvd, Los Angeles CA 90028
Tel (323) 465-5873 SIC 7521 7299

ACE PARKING MANAGEMENT INC p 16
645 Ash St, San Diego CA 92101
Tel (619) 233-6624 SIC 7521

LAZ PARKING LTD p 848
9333 Genesee Ave Ste 220, San Diego CA 92121
Tel (858) 587-8888 SIC 7521

LAZ KARP ASSOCIATES INC p 848
15 Lewis St Fl 5, Hartford CT 06103
Tel (860) 522-7641 SIC 7521 1799

LAZ PARKING LTD LLC p 848
15 Lewis St Fl 5, Hartford CT 06103
Tel (860) 713-2030 SIC 7521

COLONIAL PARKING INC p 337
1050 Thms Jfrsn St Nw 100, Washington DC 20007
Tel (202) 965-3096 SIC 7521

FORGE CO p 567
1050 Thmas Jfferson St Nw, Washington DC 20007
Tel (202) 295-8100 SIC 7521 7011

R G A INC p 1202
1001 G St Nw Ste 700w, Washington DC 20001
Tel (202) 393-1999 SIC 6552 7521 6531

METRO PARKING CORP p 955
8300 Nw 7th Ave, North Miami Beach FL 33160
Tel (305) 579-5300 SIC 7521 4119

SEVEN-ONE-SEVEN PARKING SERVICES INC p 1309
1410 N Florida Ave, Tampa FL 33602
Tel (813) 228-7722
SIC 7299 6519 7521 4119 8742

AMERIPARK LLC p 82
3200 Cobb Galleria Pkwy # 299, Atlanta GA 30339
Tel (404) 364-0342 SIC 7521 7299

LANIER PARKING HOLDINGS INC p 844
233 Peachtree St Ne # 2600, Atlanta GA 30303
Tel (404) 881-6076 SIC 7521

PARKING SERVICE INC p 1116
180 N La Salle St # 1700, Chicago IL 60601
Tel (312) 819-5050 SIC 7521

▲SP PLUS CORP p 1353
200 E Randolph St # 7700, Chicago IL 60601
Tel (312) 274-2000 SIC 7521 7514

SYSTEM PARKING INC p 1418
180 N La Salle St # 1700, Chicago IL 60601
Tel (312) 819-5050 SIC 7521

TPS PARKING MANAGEMENT LLC p 1467
200 W Monroe St Ste 1500, Chicago IL 60606
Tel (312) 781-9396 SIC 7521

TOWNE PARK LLC p 1466
1 Park Pl Ste 200, Annapolis MD 21401
Tel (410) 267-6111 SIC 7521 4119

BROADWAY SERVICES INC p 216
3709 E Monument St, Baltimore MD 21205
Tel (410) 563-6900
SIC 7349 7381 7521 6512 4119

VPNE PARKING SOLUTIONS LLC p 1566
343 Congress St Ste 3300, Boston MA 02210
Tel (617) 451-1393 SIC 7521

■PARBALL CORP p 1114
3655 Las Vegas Blvd S, Las Vegas NV 89109
Tel (702) 967-4111
SIC 7011 7999 6512 7521 7211

IMPERIAL PARKING (US) LLC p 734
900 Haddon Ave Ste 333, Collingswood NJ 08108
Tel (856) 854-7111 SIC 7521

IMPERIAL PARKING CORP p 734
900 Haddon Ave Ste 333, Collingswood NJ 08108
Tel (856) 854-7111 SIC 7521

▲ABM INDUSTRIES INC p 12
1 Liberty Plz Fl Con1, New York NY 10006
Tel (212) 297-0200
SIC 7349 7521 7381 8711

■ABM ONSITE SERVICES INC p 12
1 Liberty Plz Fl 7, New York NY 10006
Tel (212) 497-0600
SIC 7349 7381 7521 8711

JEWISH HOME LIFECARE MANHATTAN p 784
120 W 106th St, New York NY 10025
Tel (212) 870-5000 SIC 8361 7521

■KINNEY SYSTEM INC p 821
60 Madison Ave Fl 7, New York NY 10010
Tel (212) 889-2056 SIC 7521 8742

▲MACQUARIE INFRASTRUCTURE CORP p 893
125 W 55th St, New York NY 10019
Tel (212) 231-1000
SIC 5172 4581 4785 7521 4932

PARKING CO OF AMERICA INC p 1116
250 W Court St Ste 200e, Cincinnati OH 45202
Tel (513) 241-0415 SIC 7521

PHILADELPHIA PARKING AUTHORITY p 1143
701 Market St Ste 5400, Philadelphia PA 19106
Tel (215) 222-0224 SIC 7521

REPUBLIC PARKING SYSTEM LLC p 1225
633 Chestnut St Ste 2000, Chattanooga TN 37450
Tel (423) 756-2771 SIC 8742 7521

■CENTRAL PARKING CORP p 279
507 Mainstream Dr, Nashville TN 37228
Tel (615) 297-4255 SIC 7521

■CENTRAL PARKING SYSTEM INC p 279
507 Mainstream Dr, Nashville TN 37228
Tel (615) 297-4255 SIC 7521

■KCPC HOLDINGS INC p 806
2401 21st Ave S Ste 200, Nashville TN 37212
Tel (615) 297-4255 SIC 7521

■FOCUS POINT PARKING INC p 562
14141 W Hwy 290 Ste 700, Austin TX 78737
Tel (512) 894-3556 SIC 7521

DIAMOND PARKING SERVICES LLC p 437
605 1st Ave Ste 600, Seattle WA 98104
Tel (206) 284-2732 SIC 7521 6512

SIC 7532 Top, Body & Upholstery Repair & Paint Shops

REINHARDT MOTORS INC p 1221
720 Eastern Blvd, Montgomery AL 36117
Tel (334) 272-7147 SIC 5511 7532

THREE-WAY CHEVROLET CO p 1450
4501 Wible Rd, Bakersfield CA 93313
Tel (661) 847-6400
SIC 5511 5531 7515 7538 7532

FORNACA INC p 568
2400 National City Blvd, National City CA 91950
Tel (619) 474-5573 SIC 5511 7532 5531

QUALITY COLLISION CENTER p 1196
42480 Ritter Cir Ste 5, Palm Desert CA 92211
Tel (760) 779-5054 SIC 7532

QUALITY AUTO CRAFT INC p 1196
3295 Bernal Ave Ste B, Pleasanton CA 94566
Tel (925) 426-0120 SIC 7538 7532

GERMAN MOTORS CORP p 608
1140 Harrison St, San Francisco CA 94103
Tel (415) 590-3773 SIC 5511 7532

VOLKSWAGEN SANTA MONICA INC p 1564
2440 Santa Monica Blvd, Santa Monica CA 90404
Tel (310) 829-1888 SIC 5511 7532 7538

LOKEY AUTOMOTIVE GROUP INC p 875
27850 Us Highway 19 N, Clearwater FL 33761
Tel (888) 275-8388 SIC 5511 7532

TERRY TAYLOR FORD CO p 1440
1420 N Tomoka Farms Rd, Daytona Beach FL 32124
Tel (386) 274-6700 SIC 5511 7532

TRIANGLE AUTO CENTER INC p 1478
1841 N State Road 7, Hollywood FL 33021
Tel (855) 398-2449 SIC 5511 7532

MUTZ MOTORS LTD PARTNERSHIP p 1003
1430 W Memorial Blvd, Lakeland FL 33815
Tel (863) 682-1100
SIC 5511 7538 7532 7515 5531 5521

SEIDLE ENTERPRISES INC p 1301
2900 Nw 36th St, Miami FL 33142
Tel (305) 635-8000 SIC 5511 7538 7532

CHRISTENSEN ENTERPRISES INC p 302
333 Thorpe Rd, Orlando FL 32824
Tel (407) 830-6401 SIC 5531 7538 7532

ROGER DEAN ENTERPRISES INC p 1246
2235 Okeechobee Blvd, West Palm Beach FL 33409
Tel (561) 683-8100
SIC 5511 5521 7538 7532 7515

INTERNATIONAL AUTO PROCESSING INC p 754
1 Joe Frank Harris Blvd, Brunswick GA 31523
Tel (912) 554-8432
SIC 5012 7542 7538 7532

SINGLE SOURCE INC p 1326
601 W Crssvlle Rd Ste 100, Roswell GA 30075
Tel (770) 840-7877 SIC 5013 7532

ARLINGTON AUTOMOTIVE GROUP INC p 110
2095 N Rand Rd, Palatine IL 60074
Tel (847) 394-5100
SIC 7538 5521 5511 5531 7532

PATRICK SCHAUMBURG AUTOMOBILES INC p 1120
526 Mall Dr, Schaumburg IL 60173
Tel (847) 605-4000
SIC 5511 7539 7538 7532 5531 5013

■UTILIMASTER SERVICES LLC p 1537
603 Earthway Blvd, Bristol IN 46507
Tel (574) 848-2000 SIC 7532

SAM SWOPE AUTO GROUP LLC p 1274
10 Swope Autocenter Dr, Louisville KY 40299
Tel (502) 499-5000 SIC 5511 5012 7532

RUSSEL MOTOR CARS INC p 1259
6700 Baltimore Nat Pike, Baltimore MD 21228
Tel (410) 788-8400
SIC 5511 7538 7532 5521

ABRA AUTO BODY & GLASS LP p 12
7225 Northland Dr N # 210, Brooklyn Park MN 55428
Tel (651) 487-2470 SIC 6794 7532

■TOWN & COUNTRY FORD INC p 1464
5401 E Independence Blvd, Charlotte NC 28212
Tel (704) 536-5600
SIC 5511 7538 7532 5521

YOUNGS TRUCK CENTER INC p 1639
3880 Jeff Adams Dr, Charlotte NC 28206
Tel (704) 597-0551 SIC 5511 7513 7532

MICKEY TRUCK BODIES INC p 961
1305 Trinity Ave, High Point NC 27260
Tel (336) 882-6806
SIC 3713 7532 3711 3715

FORD MONTROSE INC p 565
3960 Medina Rd, Fairlawn OH 44333
Tel (330) 666-0711
SIC 5511 5521 7515 7513 7538 7532

COUGHLIN CHEVROLET INC p 374
9000 Broad St Sw, Pataskala OH 43062
Tel (740) 964-9191
SIC 5511 5012 7538 7532 5531

WMK LLC p 1620
4199 Kinross Lakes Pkwy # 300, Richfield OH 44286
Tel (234) 312-2000 SIC 5511 7532

AMERICAN BULK COMMODITIES INC p 69
8063 Southern Blvd, Youngstown OH 44512
Tel (330) 758-0841
SIC 4212 7532 6531 7363

READING EQUIPMENT & DISTRIBUTION LLC p 1213
1363 Bowmansville Rd, Bowmansville PA 17507
Tel (717) 445-6746 SIC 5531 7532

CEI GROUP INC p 272
4850 E Street Rd Ste 200, Feasterville Trevose PA 19053
Tel (215) 364-5600 SIC 6411 7532

MORGAN TRUCK BODY LLC p 989
111 Morgan Way, Morgantown PA 19543
Tel (610) 286-5025
SIC 3713 7532 5013 5084

TRG WIND DOWN LLC p 1476
201 Hancock Blvd, Reading PA 19611
Tel (610) 775-3301
SIC 3713 3792 3469 5531 7532

CSI HOLDINGS INC p 397
4850 E Street Rd Ste 230, Trevose PA 19053
Tel (215) 357-4400 SIC 6411 7532

DYER INC p 464
240 Killian Commons Pkwy, Columbia SC 29203
Tel (803) 691-5602 SIC 5511 7532

COVERT BUICK INC p 385
11750 Research Blvd Ste D, Austin TX 78759
Tel (512) 583-3000 SIC 5511 7532

▲GROUP 1 AUTOMOTIVE INC p 641
800 Gessner Rd Ste 500, Houston TX 77024
Tel (713) 647-5700
SIC 5511 6141 7538 7532 5531

MOSSY HOLDING CO INC p 992
12150 Old Katy Rd, Houston TX 77079
Tel (281) 558-9970 SIC 5511 6159 7532

CALIBER BODYWORKS OF TEXAS INC p 239
401 E Corp Dr Ste 150, Lewisville TX 75057
Tel (469) 948-9500 SIC 7532

CALIBER BODYWORKS PSA OF TEXAS INC p 239
401 E Corp Dr Ste 150, Lewisville TX 75057
Tel (469) 948-9500 SIC 7532

SERVICE KING HOLDINGS LLC p 1307
2600 N Central Expy # 400, Richardson TX 75080
Tel (972) 960-7595 SIC 7532

■SERVICE KING PAINT & BODY LLC p 1307
2600 N Central Expy, Richardson TX 75080
Tel (972) 960-7595 SIC 7532

CHECKERED FLAG MOTOR CAR CO INC p 292
5225 Virginia Beach Blvd, Virginia Beach VA 23462
Tel (757) 490-1111 SIC 5511 7532

FORD KAYSER INC p 565
2303 W Beltline Hwy, Madison WI 53713
Tel (608) 271-6000
SIC 5511 7538 7532 7515 5521

LAKESIDE INTERNATIONAL LLC p 840
11000 W Silver Spring Dr, Milwaukee WI 53225
Tel (414) 353-4800
SIC 5511 5531 7538 7532 6159 7513

SIC 7533 Automotive Exhaust System Repair Shops

MIDAS INC p 964
4300 Tbc Way, Palm Beach Gardens FL 33410
Tel (630) 438-3000 SIC 7533 6794

▲MONRO MUFFLER BRAKE INC p 985
200 Holleder Pkwy, Rochester NY 14615
Tel (585) 647-6400
SIC 7539 7533 7534 7549

DRIVEN BRANDS INC p 456
440 S Church St Ste 700, Charlotte NC 28202
Tel (704) 337-8855 SIC 7533

■PEP BOYS - MANNY MOE & JACK p 1133
3111 W Allegheny Ave, Philadelphia PA 19132
Tel (215) 430-9000 SIC 5531 7539 7533

■PEP BOYS MANNY MOE & JACK OF CALIFORNIA p 1133
3111 W Allegheny Ave, Philadelphia PA 19132
Tel (215) 430-9095 SIC 5531 7533 7539

SIC 7534 Tire Retreading & Repair Shops

MCGRIFF INDUSTRIES INC p 929
86 Walnut St Ne, Cullman AL 35055
Tel (256) 739-0780 SIC 5531 7534

REDBURN TIRE CO p 1216
3801 W Clarendon Ave, Phoenix AZ 85019
Tel (602) 272-7601 SIC 5014 7534

■WINGFOOT COMMERCIAL TIRE SYSTEMS LLC p 1616
1000 S 21st St, Fort Smith AR 72901
Tel (479) 788-6400 SIC 7534

TBC SHARED SERVICES INC p 1427
742 S Main St, Sebastopol CA 95472
Tel (707) 829-9864 SIC 5531 7534

A & E TIRE INC p 4
3855 E 52nd Ave, Denver CO 80216
Tel (303) 308-6900 SIC 5014 7534 5531

EARL W COLVARD INC p 468
816 S Woodland Blvd, Deland FL 32720
Tel (386) 734-6447 SIC 5531 7534

TBC RETAIL GROUP INC p 1427
4280 Prof Ctr Dr Ste 400, Palm Beach Gardens FL 33410
Tel (561) 383-3000 SIC 7538 5531 7534

BRIDGESTONE RETAIL OPERATIONS LLC p 211
333 E Lake St Ste 300, Bloomingdale IL 60108
Tel (630) 259-9000 SIC 5531 7534 5014

BEN TIRE DISTRIBUTORS LTD p 172
203 E Madison St, Toledo IL 62468
Tel (800) 252-8961
SIC 5014 5013 5531 7534

BRIDGESTONE BANDAG LLC p 211
2000 Bandag Dr, Muscatine IA 52761
Tel (563) 262-2511
SIC 7534 3559 5014 3011 7549 6794

C&M TIRE INC p 234
401 S 42nd St, Kansas City KS 66106
Tel (913) 321-3003
SIC 5531 7534 5014 3312

SULLIVAN INVESTMENT CO INC p 1397
41 Accord Park Dr, Norwell MA 02061
Tel (781) 982-1550 SIC 5531 7534

SOUTHERN TIRE MART LLC p 1350
800 Us 98, Columbia MS 39429
Tel (601) 424-3200 SIC 7534 5014

▲MONRO MUFFLER BRAKE INC p 985
200 Holleder Pkwy, Rochester NY 14615
Tel (585) 647-6400
SIC 7539 7533 7534 7549

SNIDER TIRE INC p 1335
200 E Meadowview Rd, Greensboro NC 27406
Tel (336) 691-5480 SIC 5531 7534

PARRISH TIRE CO p 1117
5130 Indiana Ave, Winston Salem NC 27106
Tel (336) 767-0202 SIC 5014 5531 7534

▲GOODYEAR TIRE & RUBBER CO p 625
200 E Innovation Way, Akron OH 44316
Tel (330) 796-2121
SIC 3011 3052 7534 7538 7539 5013

LES SCHWAB WAREHOUSE CENTER INC p 857
20900 Cooley Rd, Bend OR 97701
Tel (541) 447-4136 SIC 5014 7534 5531

SUPERIOR TIRE SERVICE INC p 1407
4230 27th Ct Se, Salem OR 97302
Tel (503) 585-1955 SIC 5014 7534 3011

SERVICE TIRE TRUCK CENTER INC p 1307
2255 Avenue A, Bethlehem PA 18017
Tel (610) 691-8473 SIC 7534 5531

VALLEY TIRE CO INC p 1541
15 Mckean Ave, Charleroi PA 15022
Tel (724) 489-4483
SIC 5531 7539 5014 7534

TIRE CENTERS LLC p 1455
310 Inglesby Pkwy, Duncan SC 29334
Tel (864) 329-2700 SIC 5014 5531 7534

APPALACHIAN TIRE PRODUCTS INC p 98
2907 4th Ave, Charleston WV 25387
Tel (304) 744-9473
SIC 5014 5531 5013 7534

BAUER BUILT INC p 160
1111 W Prospect St, Durand WI 54736
Tel (715) 672-8300
SIC 5531 5014 7534 5171

POMPS TIRE SERVICE INC p 1161
1122 Cedar St, Green Bay WI 54301
Tel (920) 435-8301 SIC 5531 5014 7534

SIC 7536 Automotive Glass Replacement Shops

SAFELITE GROUP INC p 1266
7400 Safelite Way, Columbus OH 43235
Tel (614) 210-9000 SIC 7536 3231 6411

FUYAO GLASS AMERICA INC p 586
2801 W Stroop Rd, Dayton OH 45439
Tel (937) 626-4092 SIC 7536

■PGW AUTO GLASS LLC p 1141
1 Ppg Pl Fl 6, Pittsburgh PA 15272
Tel (412) 434-4058 SIC 7536

SIC 7537 Automotive Transmission Repair Shops

JASPER ENGINE & TRANSMISSION EXCHANGE INC (KY) p 778
815 Wernsing Rd, Jasper IN 47546
Tel (812) 482-1041 SIC 5013 7537

PINE BELT ENTERPRISES INC p 1148
1088 Route 88, Lakewood NJ 08701
Tel (732) 363-2900 SIC 5511 7537 5531

RUMPKE TRANSPORTATION CO LLC p 1258
10795 Hughes Rd, Cincinnati OH 45251
Tel (513) 851-0122
SIC 3561 5084 7537 4953

TRI-W GROUP INC p 1478
835 Goodale Blvd, Columbus OH 43212
Tel (614) 228-5000 SIC 3694 7538 7537

■UNITED ENGINES LLC p 1508
5555 W Reno Ave, Oklahoma City OK 73127
Tel (800) 955-3321
SIC 5013 5084 7538 7537

■UNITED HOLDINGS LLC p 1509
5 N Mccormick St Ste 200, Oklahoma City OK 73127
Tel (405) 947-3321
SIC 5084 5013 7538 7537 3441

SIC 7538 General Automotive Repair Shop

SOUTHLAND INTERNATIONAL TRUCKS INC p 1351
200 Oxmoor Blvd, Birmingham AL 35209
Tel (205) 942-6226
SIC 5511 5531 7538 7513

EXPRESS OIL CHANGE LLC p 520
1880 Southpark Dr, Hoover AL 35244
Tel (205) 945-1771 SIC 7549 7538 6794

COURTESY CHEVROLET p 383
1233 E Camelback Rd, Phoenix AZ 85014
Tel (602) 279-3232 SIC 5511 5013 7538

HEAVY VEHICLE ELECTRONIC LICENSE PLATE INC p 680
101 N 1st Ave Ste 2275, Phoenix AZ 85003
Tel (602) 412-2240 SIC 7538

EARNHARDT FORD SALES CO INC p 469
7300 W Orchid Ln, Tempe AZ 85284
Tel (480) 893-0000
SIC 5511 5531 7538 5561

FREIGHTLINER STERLING WESTERN STAR OF ARIZONA LTD p 577
9899 W Roosevelt St, Tolleson AZ 85353
Tel (623) 907-9900 SIC 5013 5012 7538

THREE-WAY CHEVROLET CO p 1450
4501 Wible Rd, Bakersfield CA 93313
Tel (661) 847-6400
SIC 5511 5531 7515 7538 7532

GRIFFIN MOTORWERKE INC p 640
1146 6th St, Berkeley CA 94710
Tel (510) 524-7447 SIC 7538 5531

TRACY INDUSTRIES INC p 1468
3737 Capitol Ave, City Of Industry CA 90601
Tel (562) 692-9034 SIC 3519 7538

HARVEY & MADDING INC p 667
6300 Dublin Blvd, Dublin CA 94568
Tel (925) 828-8030
SIC 5511 7538 5015 5013

INLAND KENWORTH (US) INC p 743
9730 Cherry Ave, Fontana CA 92335
Tel (909) 823-9955
SIC 5012 7538 5013 7513

ROTOLO CHEVROLET INC p 1252
16666 S Highland Ave, Fontana CA 92336
Tel (866) 756-9776 SIC 5511 5521 7538

TOMS TRUCK CENTER INC p 1460
12221 Monarch St, Garden Grove CA 92841
Tel (714) 835-5070 SIC 5511 5012 7538

■ CUMMINS PACIFIC LLC p 401
1939 Deere Ave, Irvine CA 92606
Tel (949) 253-6000 SIC 3519 5063 7538

ATV INC p 129
14407 Alondra Blvd, La Mirada CA 90638
Tel (562) 977-8565 SIC 5531 7538

H W HUNTER INC p 651
1130 Auto Mall Dr, Lancaster CA 93534
Tel (661) 948-8411 SIC 5511 7538

JOHN L SULLIVAN INVESTMENTS INC p 789
6200 Northfront Rd, Livermore CA 94551
Tel (916) 969-5911 SIC 5511 7538

FOX HILLS AUTO INC p 572
5880 W Centinela Ave, Los Angeles CA 90045
Tel (310) 649-3673
SIC 5511 7538 5531 5521

TOPA EQUITIES LTD p 1460
1800 Ave Of The Ste 1400, Los Angeles CA 90067
Tel (310) 203-9199 SIC 6163 5181 7538

GIANT INLAND EMPIRE RV CENTER INC p 611
9150 Benson Ave, Montclair CA 91763
Tel (909) 981-0444 SIC 5561 7538

GALPIN MOTORS INC p 590
15505 Roscoe Blvd, North Hills CA 91343
Tel (818) 787-3800
SIC 5511 5521 7538 7515 7514 5531

GOLDEN GATE FREIGHTLINER INC p 621
8200 Baldwin St, Oakland CA 94621
Tel (559) 486-4310 SIC 5511 5531 7538

QUALITY AUTO CRAFT INC p 1196
3295 Bernal Ave Ste B, Pleasanton CA 94566
Tel (925) 426-0120 SIC 7538 7532

DAVID A CAMPBELL CORP p 415
3060 Adams St, Riverside CA 92504
Tel (951) 785-4444 SIC 5511 7538

LA MESA R V CENTER INC p 835
7430 Copley Park Pl, San Diego CA 92111
Tel (858) 874-8001 SIC 5561 7538

BUTLER SERVICE GROUP INC p 230
3820 State St Ste A, Santa Barbara CA 93105
Tel (201) 891-5312
SIC 7363 8711 8748 3661 7538

WESTRUX INTERNATIONAL INC p 1603
15555 Valley View Ave, Santa Fe Springs CA 90670
Tel (562) 404-1020
SIC 5511 5531 7513 7538

VOLKSWAGEN SANTA MONICA INC p 1564
2440 Santa Monica Blvd, Santa Monica CA 90404
Tel (310) 829-1888 SIC 5511 7532 7538

■ MILLER AUTOMOTIVE GROUP INC p 970
5425 Van Nuys Blvd, Sherman Oaks CA 91401
Tel (818) 787-8400 SIC 5511 7538 5521

COUNTY FORD NORTH INC p 375
450 W Vista Way, Vista CA 92083
Tel (760) 945-9900
SIC 5511 5521 7538 7515 5531

■ MCCANDLESS TRUCK CENTER LLC p 926
16704 E 32nd Ave, Aurora CO 80011
Tel (331) 332-5000 SIC 5013 7538 5012

PHIL LONG FORD LLC p 1142
1212 Motor City Dr, Colorado Springs CO 80905
Tel (719) 575-7100
SIC 5511 7515 7538 5531

IG BURTON & CO INC p 730
793 Bay Rd, Milford DE 19963
Tel (302) 422-3041 SIC 5511 7538

BILL USSERY MOTORS BODY SHOP INC p 182
300 Almeria Ave, Coral Gables FL 33134
Tel (305) 445-8593 SIC 5511 7538

■ WEBB AUTOMOTIVE GROUP INC p 1586
200 Sw 1st Ave, Fort Lauderdale FL 33301
Tel (954) 769-7000 SIC 7538

NEXTRAN CORP p 1041
1986 W Beaver St, Jacksonville FL 32209
Tel (904) 354-3721 SIC 5511 5531 7538

TOM NEHL TRUCK CO p 1459
417 Edgewood Ave S, Jacksonville FL 32254
Tel (904) 389-3653 SIC 5511 5531 7538

MCGEE TIRE STORES INC p 929
3939 Us Highway 98 S # 101, Lakeland FL 33812
Tel (863) 667-3347 SIC 5531 7538

MUTZ MOTORS LTD PARTNERSHIP p 1003
1430 W Memorial Blvd, Lakeland FL 33815
Tel (863) 682-1100
SIC 5511 7538 7532 7515 5531 5521

SEIDLE ENTERPRISES INC p 1301
2900 Nw 36th St, Miami FL 33142
Tel (305) 635-8000 SIC 5511 7538 7532

WARREN HENRY AUTOMOBILES INC p 1577
20800 Nw 2nd Ave, Miami FL 33169
Tel (305) 690-6010 SIC 5511 5531 7538

CHRISTENSEN ENTERPRISES INC p 302
333 Thorpe Rd, Orlando FL 32824
Tel (407) 830-6401 SIC 5531 7538 7532

TBC RETAIL GROUP INC p 1427
4280 Prof Ctr Dr Ste 400, Palm Beach Gardens FL 33410
Tel (561) 383-3000 SIC 7538 5531 7534

BILL CURRIE FORD INC p 182
5815 N Dale Mabry Hwy, Tampa FL 33614
Tel (813) 872-5555 SIC 5511 7538

FERMAN CHEVROLET OF TARPON SPRINGS p 538
43520 Us Highway 19 N, Tarpon Springs FL 34689
Tel (727) 942-4800
SIC 5511 7538 7515 7513 5521

ROGER DEAN ENTERPRISES INC p 1246
2235 Okeechobee Blvd, West Palm Beach FL 33409
Tel (561) 683-8100
SIC 5511 5521 7538 7532 7515

MERCEDES-BENZ USA LLC p 944
303 Perimeter Ctr N, Atlanta GA 30346
Tel (201) 573-0600
SIC 5012 5013 7538 5511

TOM GRADDY ENTERPRISES INC p 1459
3348 Peachtree Rd Ne, Atlanta GA 30326
Tel (404) 363-8390
SIC 5531 5511 7538 5012

INTERNATIONAL AUTO PROCESSING INC p 754
1 Joe Frank Harris Blvd, Brunswick GA 31523
Tel (912) 554-8432
SIC 5012 7542 7538 7532

M B FAYETTE SPECIALISTS INC p 889
1588 Highway 85 N, Fayetteville GA 30214
Tel (770) 461-3784 SIC 7538

BOYD GROUP U S INC p 205
500 W Lake St Ste 1, Elmhurst IL 60126
Tel (630) 832-0670 SIC 7549 7538

CENTRAL ILLINOIS TRUCKS INC p 278
200 W Northtown Rd, Normal IL 61761
Tel (800) 322-5017 SIC 5013 7538 5012

ARLINGTON AUTOMOTIVE GROUP INC p 110
2095 N Rand Rd, Palatine IL 60074
Tel (847) 394-5100
SIC 7538 5521 5511 5531 7532

PATRICK SCHAUMBURG AUTOMOBILES INC p 1120
526 Mall Dr, Schaumburg IL 60173
Tel (847) 605-4000
SIC 5511 7539 7538 7532 5531 5013

TRUCK CENTERS INC p 1485
2280 Formosa Rd, Troy IL 62294
Tel (618) 667-3454
SIC 5531 5511 7538 5012 4522 7699

JD BYRIDER SYSTEMS LLC p 780
12802 Hmlton Crssing Blvd, Carmel IN 46032
Tel (317) 249-3000
SIC 6794 5734 7538 7515 5521

■ CUMMINS CROSSPOINT LLC p 401
2601 Fortune Cir E 300c, Indianapolis IN 46241
Tel (317) 243-7979
SIC 5084 7538 5063 3519

■ CUMMINS CROSSPOINT LLC p 401
2601 Fortune Cir E Ste 30, Indianapolis IN 46241
Tel (317) 243-7979 SIC 5084 7538 3519

PALMER TRUCKS INC p 1109
2929 S Holt Rd, Indianapolis IN 46241
Tel (317) 243-1668
SIC 5511 5531 7538 7513 5012

TRUCK COUNTRY OF INDIANA INC p 1485
1851 W Thompson Rd, Indianapolis IN 46217
Tel (317) 788-1533
SIC 5511 5531 7538 7539

JASPER ENGINE EXCHANGE INC p 778
815 Wernsing Rd, Jasper IN 47546
Tel (812) 482-1041 SIC 3714 7538 6512

HARRISON TRUCK CENTERS INC p 664
3601 Adventureland Dr, Altoona IA 50009
Tel (515) 967-3500 SIC 5511 7538

MCCOY GROUP INC p 927
2099 Southpark Ct, Dubuque IA 52003
Tel (563) 556-3773 SIC 5012 7538 4213

TRUCK COUNTRY OF IOWA INC p 1485
2099 Southpark Ct Ste 2, Dubuque IA 52003
Tel (563) 556-3773 SIC 5012 5531 7538

CONKLIN FANGMAN INVESTMENT CO INC p 356
1400 E 11th Ave, Hutchinson KS 67501
Tel (620) 662-4467
SIC 7515 5511 7538 5521

MURPHY-HOFFMAN CO p 1001
11120 Tomahawk Creek Pkwy, Leawood KS 66211
Tel (816) 483-6444
SIC 5012 7513 7538 6159 5511

INLAND TRUCK PARTS CO INC p 744
4400 College Blvd Ste 145, Overland Park KS 66211
Tel (913) 345-9664 SIC 5013 7538

WATCO COMPANIES LLC p 1581
315 W 3rd St, Pittsburg KS 66762
Tel (620) 231-2230 SIC 4011 7538

WORLDWIDE EQUIPMENT INC p 1626
73 We Dr, Prestonsburg KY 41653
Tel (606) 874-2172
SIC 5012 5013 7538 7513

RUSSEL MOTOR CARS INC p 1259
6700 Baltimore Nat Pike, Baltimore MD 21228
Tel (410) 788-8400
SIC 5511 7538 7532 5521

R & H MOTOR CARS LTD p 1201
9727 Reisterstown Rd, Owings Mills MD 21117
Tel (410) 363-7793 SIC 5511 7538 5531

POHANKA OF SALISBURY INC p 1159
2015 N Salisbury Blvd, Salisbury MD 21801
Tel (410) 749-2301
SIC 5511 7513 7514 7538 7515

INTERNATIONAL MOTOR CARS INC p 756
5000 Auth Way, Suitland MD 20746
Tel (301) 423-8400 SIC 5511 7538 5521

ATLANTIC AUTOMOTIVE CORP p 125
1 Olympic Pl Ste 1210, Towson MD 21204
Tel (410) 602-6177 SIC 5511 7538 7515

DANIEL J QUIRK INC p 411
372 Quincy Ave, Braintree MA 02184
Tel (781) 843-4800
SIC 5511 5013 5531 7538 5521 7515

FOREIGN MOTORS WEST INC p 566
253 N Main St, Natick MA 01760
Tel (508) 655-5350 SIC 5511 7538

SULLIVAN TIRE CO INC p 1397
41 Accord Park Dr, Norwell MA 02061
Tel (781) 982-1550 SIC 5531 7538 5014

GALLERY AUTOMOTIVE GROUP LLC p 590
918 Providence Hwy, Norwood MA 02062
Tel (877) 201-8871 SIC 5511 5012 7538

TI AUTOMOTIVE INC p 1452
1272 Doris Rd Ste 100, Auburn Hills MI 48326
Tel (248) 276-4721 SIC 5013 7538

PENSKE CORP p 1131
2555 S Telegraph Rd, Bloomfield Hills MI 48302
Tel (248) 648-2000 SIC 5511 7538 7948

DETROIT DIESEL CORP p 433
13400 W Outer Dr, Detroit MI 48239
Tel (313) 592-5000 SIC 3519 3714 7538

JASPER WELLER LLC p 778
1500 Gezon Pkwy Sw, Grand Rapids MI 49509
Tel (616) 724-2000 SIC 7538 5013

■ CUMMINS BRIDGEWAY LLC p 401
21810 Clessie Ct, New Hudson MI 48165
Tel (248) 573-1600 SIC 5084 7538 3519

INTERSTATE COMPANIES INC p 758
2501 American Blvd E, Minneapolis MN 55425
Tel (952) 854-2044 SIC 7538 8711 5085

W D LARSON COMPANIES LTD INC p 1568
10700 Lyndale Ave S Ste A, Minneapolis MN 55420
Tel (952) 888-4934
SIC 5012 5013 7538 6159

GILLELAND CHEVROLET CADILLAC INC p 612
3019 W Division St, Saint Cloud MN 56301
Tel (320) 281-4290 SIC 5511 5531 7538

■ CUMMINS NPOWER LLC p 401
1600 Buerkle Rd, White Bear Lake MN 55110
Tel (800) 642-0085
SIC 5084 5063 7538 3519

PLAZA TIRE SERVICE INC p 1156
2075 Corporate Cir, Cape Girardeau MO 63703
Tel (573) 334-5036 SIC 5014 5531 7538

KCR INTERNATIONAL TRUCKS INC p 806
7700 Ne 38th St, Kansas City MO 64161
Tel (816) 455-1833
SIC 5511 5531 7538 7513

MIDWAY FORD TRUCK CENTER INC p 967
7601 Ne 38th St, Kansas City MO 64161
Tel (816) 455-3000 SIC 5511 7538

DAVE SINCLAIR FORD WEST p 415
7466 S Lindbergh Blvd, Saint Louis MO 63125
Tel (314) 892-2600
SIC 5511 7538 5521 5012

WESTERN DIESEL SERVICES INC p 1598
1100 Research Blvd, Saint Louis MO 63132
Tel (314) 868-8620 SIC 5084 7538

MERGENTHALER TRANSFER & STORAGE CO INC p 948
1414 N Montana Ave, Helena MT 59601
Tel (406) 442-9470 SIC 4213 4214 7538

■ CUMMINS CENTRAL POWER LLC p 401
10088 S 136th St, Omaha NE 68138
Tel (402) 551-7678
SIC 5084 7538 5999 3519

MCDEVITT TRUCKS INC p 927
1 Mack Ave, Manchester NH 03103
Tel (800) 370-6225 SIC 5012 5013 7538

INTER-CITY TIRE & AUTO CENTER INC p 751
777 Dowd Ave, Elizabeth NJ 07201
Tel (908) 354-5533 SIC 5531 5013 7538

ATLANTIC DETROIT DIESEL ALLISON LLC p 126
180 Route 17 South, Lodi NJ 07644
Tel (201) 489-5800 SIC 5084 7538 7389

JOHNSON & TOWERS INC p 790
2021 Briggs Rd, Mount Laurel NJ 08054
Tel (856) 234-6990
SIC 5084 5013 7699 7538 5085

FAPS INC p 528
371 Craneway St, Newark NJ 07114
Tel (973) 589-5656 SIC 3499 3711 7538

JMK AUTO SALES INC p 786
391-399 Rt 22 E, Springfield NJ 07081
Tel (973) 379-7744 SIC 7538 5511

KOST TIRE DISTRIBUTORS INC p 828
200 Holleder Pkwy, Binghamton NY 13904
Tel (607) 723-9471 SIC 5014 5531 7538

REGIONAL INTERNATIONAL CORP p 1219
1007 Lehigh Station Rd, Henrietta NY 14467
Tel (585) 359-2011
SIC 5013 5012 7539 7538 5531

GABRIELLI TRUCK SALES LTD p 588
15320 S Conduit Ave, Jamaica NY 11434
Tel (718) 977-7348 SIC 5511 5531 7538

MAJOR WORLD CHEVROLET LLC p 899
4340 Northern Blvd, Long Island City NY 11101
Tel (718) 937-3700
SIC 5511 7515 7538 5521

SOMERSET TIRE SERVICE INC p 1339
358 Saw Mill River Rd # 5, Millwood NY 10546
Tel (732) 356-8500
SIC 5531 5014 5013 7538

DORSCHEL REALTY CORP p 451
3817 W Henrietta Rd, Rochester NY 14623
Tel (585) 475-1700 SIC 5511 7538 7549

▲ SONIC AUTOMOTIVE INC p 1340
4401 Colwick Rd, Charlotte NC 28211
Tel (704) 566-2400 SIC 5511 7538

■ TOWN & COUNTRY FORD INC p 1464
5401 E Independence Blvd, Charlotte NC 28212
Tel (704) 536-5600
SIC 5511 7538 7532 5521

MACK TRUCKS INC p 892
7825 National Service Rd, Greensboro NC 27409
Tel (336) 291-9001
SIC 3711 3714 5012 6141 6153 7538

▲ GOODYEAR TIRE & RUBBER CO p 625
200 E Innovation Way, Akron OH 44316
Tel (330) 796-2121
SIC 3011 3052 7534 7538 7539 5013

HY-TEK MATERIAL HANDLING INC p 722
2222 Rickenbacker Pkwy W, Columbus OH 43217
Tel (614) 497-2500
SIC 5084 5013 7538 7513 1796

TRI-W GROUP INC p 1478
835 Goodale Blvd, Columbus OH 43212
Tel (614) 228-5000 SIC 3694 7538 7537

VOSS AUTO NETWORK INC p 1566
766 Mmsburg Cnterville Rd, Dayton OH 45459
Tel (937) 428-2400
SIC 5511 7538 7515 7513 5521 5012

K & M TIRE INC p 798
965 Spencerville Rd, Delphos OH 45833
Tel (419) 695-1061 SIC 5014 7538 5531

HILL INTERNATIONAL TRUCKS NA LLC p 693
47866 Y And O Rd, East Liverpool OH 43920
Tel (330) 386-6440 SIC 5511 5531 7538

FORD MONTROSE INC p 565
3960 Medina Rd, Fairlawn OH 44333
Tel (330) 666-0711
SIC 5511 5521 7515 7513 7538 7532

AIM LEASING CO p 38
1500 Trumbull Ave, Girard OH 44420
Tel (330) 759-0438
SIC 7513 7538 4212 5983

FORD LEBANON INC p 565
770 Columbus Ave, Lebanon OH 45036
Tel (513) 932-1010 SIC 5511 5521 7538

COUGHLIN CHEVROLET INC p 374
9000 Broad St Sw, Pataskala OH 43062
Tel (740) 964-9191
SIC 5511 5012 7538 7532 5531

■ TA OPERATING LLC p 1420
24601 Center Ridge Rd # 200, Westlake OH 44145
Tel (440) 808-9100
SIC 5541 7538 5812 5411 6794

■ TRAVELCENTERS OF AMERICA INC p 1474
24601 Center Ridge Rd # 200, Westlake OH 44145
Tel (440) 808-9100
SIC 5541 7538 5812 5411

▲ TRAVELCENTERS OF AMERICA LLC p 1474
24601 Center Ridge Rd # 200, Westlake OH 44145
Tel (440) 808-9100 SIC 5541 5812 7538

■ UNITED ENGINES LLC p 1508
5555 W Reno Ave, Oklahoma City OK 73127
Tel (800) 955-3321
SIC 5013 5084 7538 7537

■ UNITED HOLDINGS LLC p 1509
5 N Mccormick St Ste 200, Oklahoma City OK 73127
Tel (405) 947-3321
SIC 5084 5013 7538 7537 3441

TEC EQUIPMENT INC p 1430
750 Ne Columbia Blvd, Portland OR 97211
Tel (503) 285-7667 SIC 5511 7538 7549

■ CUMMINS POWER SYSTEMS LLC p 401
2727 Ford Rd, Bristol PA 19007
Tel (215) 785-6005
SIC 5084 5063 7538 7629 3519

HUNTER TRUCK SALES & SERVICE INC p 719
480 Pittsburgh Rd, Butler PA 16002
Tel (724) 586-5770 SIC 5511 5531 7538

FIVE STAR INTERNATIONAL LLC p 553
1810 S 19th St, Harrisburg PA 17104
Tel (717) 986-1500 SIC 5511 7538 5013

FORD MCCAFFERTY SALES INC p 565
1939 E Lincoln Hwy, Langhorne PA 19047
Tel (215) 945-8000
SIC 5511 5531 7538 7514 5521 5012

REEDMAN CHEVROLET INC p 1217
Rr 1, Langhorne PA 19047
Tel (215) 757-4961
SIC 5511 5531 7538 5521

HANUMAN BUSINESS INC p 659
5026 Wynnefield Ave, Philadelphia PA 19131
Tel (609) 929-5146 SIC 5541 7538

PENN DETROIT DIESEL ALLISON LLC p 1129
8330 State Rd, Philadelphia PA 19136
Tel (215) 335-5010 SIC 7699 7538

BERGEYS INC p 174
462 Harleysville Pike, Souderton PA 18964
Tel (215) 721-3430
SIC 5511 5531 7538 5013 5014

NORTH AMERICAN TRUCK & TRAILER INC p 1050
4500 N Cliff Ave, Sioux Falls SD 57104
Tel (605) 332-7112 SIC 5012 7538

PETERBILT OF KNOXVILLE INC p 1138
5218 Rutledge Pike, Knoxville TN 37924
Tel (800) 552-7779 SIC 5012 7538

T & W OF KNOXVILLE INC p 1419
10315 Parkside Dr, Knoxville TN 37922
Tel (865) 218-3300 SIC 5511 7538 5531

BEAMAN MOTOR CO p 165
1525 Broadway, Nashville TN 37203
Tel (615) 251-8430 SIC 5511 7538

TEXAS KENWORTH CO p 1444
4040 Irving Blvd, Dallas TX 75247
Tel (214) 920-7300
SIC 5012 5013 7513 7538

R V MCCLAINS INC p 1203
5601 S I 35 E, Denton TX 76210
Tel (940) 498-4398 SIC 5561 7538

TEXAS AERO ENGINE SERVICES LLC p 1442
2100 Eagle Pkwy, Fort Worth TX 76177
Tel (817) 224-0711 SIC 7538

LONESTAR FREIGHTLINER GROUP LLC p 876
2051 Hughes Rd, Grapevine TX 76051
Tel (817) 428-9736 SIC 5511 7538

▲ GROUP 1 AUTOMOTIVE INC p 641
800 Gessner Rd Ste 500, Houston TX 77024
Tel (713) 647-5700
SIC 5511 6141 7538 7532 5531

SELECTRANSPORTATION RESOURCES LLC p 1302
9550 North Loop E, Houston TX 77029
Tel (713) 672-4115
SIC 5012 5013 5511 7538

■ **SONIC AUTOMOTIVE OF TEXAS LP** p 1340
8477 North Fwy, Houston TX 77037
Tel (281) 931-3300 SIC 5511 7538

BENSON - SABIN INC p 173
2112 Gulf Fwy S, League City TX 77573
Tel (281) 338-9700 SIC 5511 7538

ROBERTS TRUCK CENTER HOLDING CO LLC p 1242
1825 Lakeway Dr Ste 700, Lewisville TX 75057
Tel (469) 645-7111 SIC 5012 7513 7538

■ **RUSH ADMINISTRATIVE SERVICES INC** p 1258
555 S Interstate 35 # 500, New Braunfels TX 78130
Tel (830) 626-5286
SIC 5012 7538 5531 5014 7513

▲ **RUSH ENTERPRISES INC** p 1258
555 S Ih 35 Ste 500, New Braunfels TX 78130
Tel (830) 302-5200
SIC 5012 7538 5531 5014 7513

FRENCH-ELLISON TRUCK CENTER LLC p 578
4300 N Cage Blvd, Pharr TX 78577
Tel (956) 781-2401
SIC 5013 5531 5511 5012 7538

■ **RUSH TRUCK CENTERS OF UTAH INC** p 1259
964 S 3800 W, Salt Lake City UT 84104
Tel (801) 972-5320 SIC 5012 7538 5531

SMITH POWER PRODUCTS INC p 1333
3065 W California Ave, Salt Lake City UT 84104
Tel (801) 262-2631
SIC 5084 7538 3714 5063

FREIGHTLINER OF UTAH A LIMITED LIABILITY CO p 577
2240 S 5370 W, West Valley City UT 84120
Tel (801) 978-8000
SIC 5012 5013 7539 7538 5511

KENWORTH SALES CO p 813
2125 S Constitution Blvd, West Valley City UT 84119
Tel (801) 487-4161
SIC 5012 5013 7538 3519

AMERICAN SERVICE CENTER ASSOCIATES OF ALEXANDRIA LLC p 79
200 S Pickett St, Alexandria VA 22304
Tel (703) 284-2490 SIC 5511 7538

TRUCK ENTERPRISES INC p 1485
3440 S Main St, Harrisonburg VA 22801
Tel (540) 564-6900
SIC 5511 5531 7538 7539

EXCEL TRUCK GROUP p 516
267 Lee Hwy, Roanoke VA 24019
Tel (540) 777-7700
SIC 5511 5013 7538 5012

GWP HOLDINGS LLC p 648
3801 Airport Way S, Seattle WA 98108
Tel (206) 624-7383
SIC 5511 7513 7538 5012

MOORES SERVICE CENTER LLC p 987
82 Winfield Rd, Saint Albans WV 25177
Tel (304) 722-1175 SIC 7538

TRUCK COUNTRY OF WISCONSIN INC p 1485
4195 Anderson Rd, Deforest WI 53532
Tel (608) 249-1090 SIC 5012 7538

JX ENTERPRISES INC p 798
1320 Walnut Ridge Dr, Hartland WI 53029
Tel (800) 810-3410
SIC 5012 5511 7538 6159 7513

FORD KAYSER INC p 565
2303 W Beltline Hwy, Madison WI 53713
Tel (608) 271-6000
SIC 5511 7538 7532 7515 5521

ZIMBRICK INC p 1643
1601 W Beltline Hwy, Madison WI 53713
Tel (608) 277-2277 SIC 5511 7538 5521

DARROW RUSS GROUP INC p 412
W133n8569 Executive Pkwy, Menomonee Falls WI 53051
Tel (262) 250-9600 SIC 5511 7538

LAKESIDE INTERNATIONAL LLC p 840
11000 W Silver Spring Dr, Milwaukee WI 53225
Tel (414) 353-4800
SIC 5511 5531 7538 7532 6159 7513

WILDE OF WEST ALLIS INC p 1609
3225 S 108th St, Milwaukee WI 53227
Tel (414) 329-6043
SIC 5511 5521 7538 7515 7513 5012

SIC 7539 Automotive Repair Shops, NEC

DENSO MANUFACTURING ARKANSAS INC p 428
100 Denso Rd, Osceola AR 72370
Tel (870) 622-9500 SIC 3089 7539

BI WAREHOUSING INC p 180
5404 Pacific St, Rocklin CA 95677
Tel (916) 624-0654 SIC 5531 5013 7539

EDF RENEWABLE SERVICES INC p 477
15445 Innovation Dr, San Diego CA 92128
Tel (858) 521-3575 SIC 7539

BONANDER PONTIAC INC p 199
231 S Center St, Turlock CA 95380
Tel (209) 632-8871 SIC 5511 7539 5012

MORGAN TIRE & AUTO LLC p 989
2021 Sunnydale Blvd, Clearwater FL 33765
Tel (727) 441-3727 SIC 7539 5531 5014

DINGMAN GROUP INC p 440
1051 W Webster Ave, Winter Park FL 32789
Tel (407) 644-6043 SIC 5511 5531 7539

▲ **CAMPING WORLD HOLDINGS INC** p 246
250 Parkway Dr Ste 270, Lincolnshire IL 60069
Tel (847) 808-3000 SIC 7513 6159 7539

CERTIFIED POWER INC p 284
970 Campus Dr, Mundelein IL 60060
Tel (847) 573-3800 SIC 3714 7539 5013

PATRICK SCHAUMBURG AUTOMOBILES INC p 1120
526 Mall Dr, Schaumburg IL 60173
Tel (847) 605-4000
SIC 5511 7539 7538 7532 5531 5013

TRUCK COUNTRY OF INDIANA INC p 1485
1851 W Thompson Rd, Indianapolis IN 46217
Tel (317) 788-1533
SIC 5511 5531 7538 7539

■ **WABASH NATIONAL TRAILER CENTERS INC** p 1570
1000 Sagamore Pkwy S, Lafayette IN 47905
Tel (765) 771-5300 SIC 5012 7539 5013

HAWK JIM GROUP INC p 669
3119 S 9th St, Council Bluffs IA 51501
Tel (712) 366-2241 SIC 5012 7539

BETHESDA INVESTMENT HOLDING CO INC p 178
10400 Auto Park Ave, Bethesda MD 20817
Tel (301) 469-6600
SIC 5511 7539 5013 5531

SCHLEGEL CORP p 1287
2750 High Meadow Cir, Auburn Hills MI 48326
Tel (248) 340-4100 SIC 5013 7539

QUALIS AUTOMOTIVE LLC p 1196
29380 John R Rd, Madison Heights MI 48071
Tel (248) 740-1668 SIC 5013 7539

PSC CUSTOM LP p 1188
1015 W Saint Germain St # 420, Saint Cloud MN 56301
Tel (320) 746-2255 SIC 7539 5012

TO HAAS TIRE CO INC p 1458
1415 W Commerce Way, Lincoln NE 68521
Tel (402) 434-3434 SIC 5014 5531 7539

AUTOMOTIVE SUPPLY ASSOCIATES INC p 134
129 Manchester St, Concord NH 03301
Tel (603) 225-4000
SIC 5013 7539 5531 5169 5015

HALE TRAILER BRAKE & WHEEL INC p 653
Cooper Rd Rr 73, Voorhees NJ 08043
Tel (800) 232-6535 SIC 5511 7539 5531

■ **PNMR SERVICES CO** p 1158
414 Silver Ave Sw Fl 4, Albuquerque NM 87102
Tel (505) 241-2700 SIC 7539

VAN BORTEL FORD INC p 1542
71 Marsh Rd, East Rochester NY 14445
Tel (585) 586-4415 SIC 5531 7539

REGIONAL INTERNATIONAL CORP p 1219
1007 Lehigh Station Rd, Henrietta NY 14467
Tel (585) 359-2011
SIC 5013 5012 7539 7538 5531

TRANSERVICE LEASE CORP p 1471
5 Dakota Dr, New Hyde Park NY 11042
Tel (800) 645-8018
SIC 7699 7539 4212 7353

▲ **MONRO MUFFLER BRAKE INC** p 985
200 Holleder Pkwy, Rochester NY 14615
Tel (585) 647-6400
SIC 7539 7533 7534 7549

▲ **GOODYEAR TIRE & RUBBER CO** p 625
200 E Innovation Way, Akron OH 44316
Tel (330) 796-2121
SIC 3011 3052 7534 7538 7539 5013

MAC TRAILER MANUFACTURING INC p 891
14599 Commerce St Ne, Alliance OH 44601
Tel (330) 823-9900
SIC 3715 5012 5013 5015 7539

FIRST SERVICES INC p 549
600 Vine St Ste 1200, Cincinnati OH 45202
Tel (513) 241-2200 SIC 8741 7539

FIRST TRANSIT INC p 550
600 Vine St Ste 1400, Cincinnati OH 45202
Tel (513) 241-2200 SIC 8741 7539 8742

▲ **LITHIA MOTORS INC** p 870
150 N Bartlett St, Medford OR 97501
Tel (541) 776-6401
SIC 5511 5531 5013 7539

VALLEY TIRE CO INC p 1541
15 Mckean Ave, Charleroi PA 15022
Tel (724) 489-4483
SIC 5531 7539 5014 7534

SMS TECHNICAL SERVICES LLC p 1334
210 W Kensinger Dr # 300, Cranberry Township PA 16066
Tel (724) 553-3420 SIC 3569 7539

■ **PEP BOYS - MANNY MOE & JACK** p 1133
3111 W Allegheny Ave, Philadelphia PA 19132
Tel (215) 430-9000 SIC 5531 7539 7533

■ **PEP BOYS MANNY MOE & JACK OF CALIFORNIA** p 1133
3111 W Allegheny Ave, Philadelphia PA 19132
Tel (215) 430-9095 SIC 5531 7533 7539

DIRECT AUCTION SERVICES LLC p 441
101 Jessica Lauren Ct, Hendersonville TN 37075
Tel (678) 570-3493
SIC 5012 7539 7549 7542 7361

TRUCKPRO HOLDING CORP p 1485
1610 Century Center Pkwy, Memphis TN 38134
Tel (901) 252-4200 SIC 5531 7539

TRUCKPRO LLC p 1485
1610 Century Center Pkwy, Memphis TN 38134
Tel (901) 252-4200 SIC 5531 7539

JBRE HOLDINGS LLC p 779
8150 N Central Expy, Dallas TX 75206
Tel (214) 276-5504 SIC 7539 6719

JBRE LLC p 779
8150 N Central Expy M1008, Dallas TX 75206
Tel (214) 276-5504 SIC 7539

■ **NORTH AMERICAN GALVANIZING & COATINGS INC** p 1050
3100 W 7th St Ste 500, Fort Worth TX 76107
Tel (817) 810-0095 SIC 7539 3312

▲ **INTEGRATED DRILLING EQUIPMENT HOLDINGS CORP** p 749
25311 I 45 N Bldg 6, Spring TX 77380
Tel (281) 465-9393 SIC 3533 7539 5084

UTILITY TRAILER SALES OF UTAH INC p 1537
4970 W 2100 S, Salt Lake City UT 84120
Tel (801) 973-4040 SIC 5511 5531 7539

FREIGHTLINER OF UTAH A LIMITED LIABILITY CO p 577
2240 S 5370 W, West Valley City UT 84120
Tel (801) 978-8000
SIC 5012 5013 7539 7538 5511

TRUCK ENTERPRISES INC p 1485
3440 S Main St, Harrisonburg VA 22801
Tel (540) 564-6900
SIC 5511 5531 7538 7539

MERCHANTS INC p 945
9073 Euclid Ave, Manassas VA 20110
Tel (703) 368-3171 SIC 5014 7539 5531

GREAT LAKES UTILITIES p 634
1323 S 7th St, Manitowoc WI 54221
Tel (920) 686-4342 SIC 7539

SIC 7542 Car Washes

AUTO WORLD CAR WASH LLC p 133
15951 Los Gatos Blvd, Los Gatos CA 95032
Tel (408) 345-6532 SIC 7542

CAR WASH PARTNERS INC p 252
1503 S Collins St, Plant City FL 33563
Tel (813) 754-0777 SIC 7542 7549

INTERNATIONAL AUTO PROCESSING INC p 754
1 Joe Frank Harris Blvd, Brunswick GA 31523
Tel (912) 554-8432
SIC 5012 7542 7538 7532

BUREAU SERVICE CO p 226
22069 Us Highway 34, Princeton IL 61356
Tel (815) 875-2800
SIC 5191 5172 5153 5411 7542

IOWA 80 GROUP INC p 762
515 Sterling Dr, Walcott IA 52773
Tel (563) 468-5500
SIC 5541 5399 7542 5812

IOWA 80 TRUCKSTOP INC p 762
755 W Iowa 80 Rd I-80, Walcott IA 52773
Tel (563) 284-6961
SIC 5541 5399 7542 5812

STAR FUEL CENTERS INC p 1378
11161 Overbrook Rd, Leawood KS 66211
Tel (913) 652-9400
SIC 5172 7542 5541 5411

BLUE BEACON USA LP II p 190
500 Graves Blvd, Salina KS 67401
Tel (785) 825-2221 SIC 7542

VERC ENTERPRISES INC p 1549
5 Chestnut St, Duxbury MA 02332
Tel (781) 934-7300 SIC 5541 7542

WASH DEPOT AUTO CENTERS LP p 1577
435 Eastern Ave, Malden MA 02148
Tel (781) 324-2000 SIC 7542 5541 5947

WASH DEPOT HOLDINGS INC p 1577
14 Summer St Ste 302, Malden MA 02148
Tel (781) 324-2000 SIC 7542 5541

WATERWAY GAS & WASH CO p 1582
727 Goddard Ave, Chesterfield MO 63005
Tel (636) 537-1111 SIC 5541 7542

WESTERN OIL INC p 1599
3553 Rider Trl S, Earth City MO 63045
Tel (314) 738-9900
SIC 5541 5411 7542 4225

DELTA-SONIC CARWASH SYSTEMS INC p 427
570 Delaware Ave, Buffalo NY 14202
Tel (716) 874-5668 SIC 5461 7542

SUPERIOR PETROLEUM CO p 1406
8199 Mcknight Rd, Pittsburgh PA 15237
Tel (412) 364-2200 SIC 7542

DIRECT AUCTION SERVICES LLC p 441
101 Jessica Lauren Ct, Hendersonville TN 37075
Tel (678) 570-3493
SIC 5012 7539 7549 7542 7361

SIC 7549 Automotive Svcs, Except Repair & Car Washes

EXPRESS OIL CHANGE LLC p 520
1880 Southpark Dr, Hoover AL 35244
Tel (205) 945-1771 SIC 7549 7538 6794

TK HOLDINGS INC p 1457
104 E 9th St, Douglas AZ 85607
Tel (520) 805-4000 SIC 7549

ATS NORTHEAST TOW INC p 129
2010 N Figueroa St, Los Angeles CA 90065
Tel (323) 342-0342 SIC 7549 5012

MOC PRODUCTS CO INC p 980
12306 Montague St, Pacoima CA 91331
Tel (818) 794-3500 SIC 5169 7549

AGFINITY INC p 34
260 Factory Rd, Eaton CO 80615
Tel (970) 454-4000
SIC 5172 2048 7549 5191

CLERMONT MOTOR SALES LLC p 325
16851 State Road 50, Clermont FL 34711
Tel (352) 404-7006 SIC 7549

HYUNDAI OF NEW PORT RICHEY LLC p 724
3936 Us Highway 19, New Port Richey FL 34652
Tel (727) 569-0999 SIC 5511 7549

CAR WASH PARTNERS INC p 252
1503 S Collins St, Plant City FL 33563
Tel (813) 754-0777 SIC 7542 7549

AMERICAN LUBEFAST LLC p 75
1550 N Brown Rd Ste 140, Lawrenceville GA 30043
Tel (770) 995-6312 SIC 6794 7549

BOYD GROUP U S INC p 205
500 W Lake St Ste 1, Elmhurst IL 60126
Tel (630) 832-0670 SIC 7549 7538

GERBER GLASS (DISTRICT 1) LLC p 608
500 W Lake St, Elmhurst IL 60126
Tel (800) 826-8682 SIC 7549

UNITED ROAD TOWING INC p 1511
9550 Bormet Dr Ste 304, Mokena IL 60448
Tel (708) 390-2200 SIC 7549

BRIDGESTONE BANDAG LLC p 211
2000 Bandag Dr, Muscatine IA 52761
Tel (563) 262-2511
SIC 7534 3559 5014 3011 7549 6794

■ **ASHLAND LLC** p 117
50 E Rivercenter Blvd # 1600, Covington KY 41011
Tel (859) 815-3333
SIC 2899 2851 2821 2911 5169 7549

■ **VALVOLINE INTERNATIONAL INC** p 1542
3499 Blazer Pkwy, Lexington KY 40509
Tel (800) 832-6825 SIC 7549 5172

ETX INC p 512
2000 Michigan Ave, Alma MI 48801
Tel (989) 463-1151 SIC 7549

KURABE AMERICA CORP p 832
37735 Interchange Dr, Farmington Hills MI 48335
Tel (248) 939-5803 SIC 7699 7549

■ **HHI GROUP HOLDINGS LLC** p 689
2727 W 14 Mile Rd, Royal Oak MI 48073
Tel (248) 284-2900 SIC 7549

POHLAD COMPANIES p 1159
60 S 6th St Ste 3700, Minneapolis MN 55402
Tel (612) 661-3700
SIC 8742 7929 6531 5013 7549 7379

POWER/MATION DIVISION INC p 1165
1310 Energy Ln, Saint Paul MN 55108
Tel (651) 605-3300
SIC 5085 5065 5084 5045 8742 7549

MFA OIL CO p 957
1 Ray Young Dr, Columbia MO 65201
Tel (573) 442-0171 SIC 7549 5541

AUTOMOTIVE RENTALS INC p 134
4001 Leadenhall Rd, Mount Laurel NJ 08054
Tel (856) 778-1500 SIC 7513 7515 7549

WWL VEHICLE SERVICES AMERICAS INC p 1629
188 Broadway Ste 1, Woodcliff Lake NJ 07677
Tel (201) 505-5100 SIC 4225 5531 7549

DORSCHEL REALTY CORP p 451
3817 W Henrietta Rd, Rochester NY 14623
Tel (585) 475-1700 SIC 5511 7538 7549

▲ **MONRO MUFFLER BRAKE INC** p 985
200 Holleder Pkwy, Rochester NY 14615
Tel (585) 647-6400
SIC 7539 7533 7534 7549

LUCOR INC p 884
790 Pershing Rd, Raleigh NC 27608
Tel (919) 828-9511 SIC 7549

FIRST VEHICLE SERVICES INC p 550
600 Vine St Ste 1400, Cincinnati OH 45202
Tel (513) 241-2200 SIC 7549

■ **CINTAS CORP NO 1** p 308
6800 Cintas Blvd, Mason OH 45040
Tel (513) 459-1200
SIC 7213 5136 5137 7549

TEC EQUIPMENT INC p 1430
750 Ne Columbia Blvd, Portland OR 97211
Tel (503) 285-7667 SIC 5511 7538 7549

DIRECT AUCTION SERVICES LLC p 441
101 Jessica Lauren Ct, Hendersonville TN 37075
Tel (678) 570-3493
SIC 5012 7539 7549 7542 7361

SPEEDCO INC p 1358
535 Marriott Dr, Nashville TN 37214
Tel (866) 773-3326 SIC 7549

TONY GULLO MOTORS I LP p 1460
500 Interstate 45 S, Conroe TX 77304
Tel (936) 539-9191 SIC 7549 5511 5531

ML INDUSTRIES INC p 979
605 W Austin St, Fredericksburg TX 78624
Tel (956) 279-8678 SIC 7549

ZXP TECHNOLOGIES LTD p 1645
409 Wallisville Rd, Highlands TX 77562
Tel (281) 426-8800 SIC 2992 2879 7549

JIFFY LUBE INTERNATIONAL INC p 785
700 Milam St, Houston TX 77002
Tel (713) 546-1400 SIC 7549

■ **BERKSHIRE HATHAWAY AUTOMOTIVE INC** p 175
8333 Royal Ridge Pkwy # 100, Irving TX 75063
Tel (972) 536-2900 SIC 7549 5511

PARKWAY CHEVROLET INC p 1117
25500 State Highway 249, Tomball TX 77375
Tel (281) 351-8211 SIC 5511 7549 5531

CARDWELL DISTRIBUTING INC p 253
8137 S State St Bldg 1, Midvale UT 84047
Tel (801) 561-4251
SIC 5171 7549 5172 5983

MILLER OIL CO INC p 970
1000 E City Hall Ave, Norfolk VA 23504
Tel (757) 623-6600
SIC 5411 5172 5983 7549

SIC 7622 Radio & TV Repair Shops

■ **QWEST BUSINESS & GOVERNMENT SERVICES INC** p 1201
1801 Calif St Ste 3800, Denver CO 80202
Tel (303) 391-8300
SIC 5999 1731 7629 7373 7371 7622

HISENSE USA CORP p 696
7310 Mcginnis Ferry Rd, Suwanee GA 30024
Tel (678) 318-9060 SIC 7622

AVI SYSTEMS INC p 137
9675 W 76th St Ste 200, Eden Prairie MN 55344
Tel (952) 949-3700
SIC 5065 7622 8748 1799

MORGENTHALER MANAGEMENT PARTNERS VI LLC p 989
50 Public Sq Ste 2700, Cleveland OH 44113
Tel (216) 416-7500
SIC 1731 5065 7622 7373 5999

INNOVATIVE IDM LLC p 745
1625 Wallace Dr Ste 110, Carrollton TX 75006
Tel (214) 574-9500 SIC 5063 7622 3699

■ **CC SCN FIBER LLC** p 269
1220 Augusta Dr Ste 600, Houston TX 77057
Tel (713) 570-3000 SIC 4899 7622 4812

CROWN CASTLE INTERNATIONAL CORP p 395
1220 Augusta Dr Ste 600, Houston TX 77057
Tel (713) 570-3000
SIC 4899 7622 4812 6798

▲ **CROWN CASTLE INTERNATIONAL CORP** p 395
1220 Augusta Dr Ste 600, Houston TX 77057
Tel (713) 570-3000
SIC 6798 4899 7622 4812

SIC 7623 Refrigeration & Air Conditioning Svc & Repair Shop

MATERIAL SUPPLY INC p 919
11700 Industry Ave, Fontana CA 92337
Tel (951) 727-2200
SIC 3444 5075 7623 1711

ACCO ENGINEERED SYSTEMS INC p 15
6265 San Fernando Rd, Glendale CA 91201
Tel (818) 244-6571 *SIC* 1711 7623

■ MESA ENERGY SYSTEMS INC p 951
2 Cromwell, Irvine CA 92618
Tel (949) 460-0460 *SIC* 1711 7623

AIR SYSTEMS INC p 39
940 Remillard Ct Frnt, San Jose CA 95122
Tel (408) 280-1666 *SIC* 1711 7623

PRIDE AIR CONDITIONING & APPLIANCE INC p 1174
2150 Nw 18th St, Pompano Beach FL 33069
Tel (954) 977-7433 *SIC* 6399 7623

CENTRAL STATES THERMO KING INC p 280
7200 W 132nd St Ste 270, Overland Park KS 66213
Tel (888) 566-5743 *SIC* 5078 7623 5084

AAF-MCQUAY GROUP INC p 8
9920 Corporate Campus Dr # 2200, Louisville KY 40223
Tel (502) 637-0111
SIC 5075 3585 3564 7623

EGAN CO p 481
7625 Boone Ave N, Brooklyn Park MN 55428
Tel (763) 595-4358
SIC 1711 1731 3444 7623 1793

PC RICHARD & SON INC p 1123
150 Price Pkwy, Farmingdale NY 11735
Tel (631) 843-4300
SIC 5722 5064 7629 7623

BRADY TRANE SERVICE INC p 207
1915 N Church St, Greensboro NC 27405
Tel (919) 781-0458 *SIC* 5075 1711 7623

GARDINER SERVICE CO p 592
31200 Bainbridge Rd Ste 1, Solon OH 44139
Tel (440) 349-5588 *SIC* 5075 1711 7623

CLARK ASSOCIATES INC p 322
2205 Old Philadelphia Pike, Lancaster PA 17602
Tel (717) 392-7550 *SIC* 5046 7623

BRANDT COMPANIES LLC p 208
1728 Briercroft Ct, Carrollton TX 75006
Tel (972) 241-9411 *SIC* 1711 1731 7623

ENTECH SALES AND SERVICE INC p 501
3404 Garden Brook Dr, Dallas TX 75234
Tel (972) 241-8188 *SIC* 1731 7623 1711

ENERFLEX ENERGY SYSTEMS INC p 497
10815 Telge Rd, Houston TX 77095
Tel (281) 345-9300
SIC 3585 7623 7699 3563

LETSOS CO p 857
8435 Westglen Dr, Houston TX 77063
Tel (713) 783-3200 *SIC* 1711 7623

■ COLONIALWEBB CONTRACTORS CO p 338
2820 Ackley Ave, Richmond VA 23228
Tel (804) 916-1400 *SIC* 1711 7623

SIC 7629 Electrical & Elex Repair Shop, NEC

ARCTIC OFFICE MACHINE INC p 106
100 W Fireweed Ln, Anchorage AK 99503
Tel (907) 276-2295
SIC 5112 5021 5044 7629

ASML US INC p 118
2650 W Geronimo Pl, Chandler AZ 85224
Tel (480) 696-2888 *SIC* 5065 7629

ROAD MACHINERY LLC p 1240
4710 E Elwood St Ste 6, Phoenix AZ 85040
Tel (602) 256-5128
SIC 5082 7359 7699 7353 7629

ARTESYN EMBEDDED TECHNOLOGIES INC p 114
2900 S Diablo Way Ste 190, Tempe AZ 85282
Tel (800) 759-1107
SIC 3679 3577 3571 7629 5045

ARKANSAS ELECTRIC COOPERATIVES INC p 109
1 Cooperative Way, Little Rock AR 72209
Tel (501) 570-2361
SIC 5063 1623 1629 7629

HAWAII BUSINESS EQUIPMENT INC p 668
2 Musick, Irvine CA 92618
Tel (949) 462-6000 *SIC* 5999 7629 5044

TOSHIBA BUSINESS SOLUTIONS (USA) INC p 1462
9740 Irvine Blvd, Irvine CA 92618
Tel (949) 462-6000 *SIC* 7629 5044 5999

▲ KLA-TENCOR CORP p 822
1 Technology Dr, Milpitas CA 95035
Tel (408) 875-3000
SIC 3827 3825 7699 7629

■ CUBIC GLOBAL DEFENSE INC p 399
9333 Balboa Ave, San Diego CA 92123
Tel (858) 277-6780 *SIC* 7629

KOKUSAI SEMICONDUCTOR EQUIPMENT CORP p 826
2460 N 1st St Ste 290, San Jose CA 95131
Tel (408) 456-2750 *SIC* 5065 7629

PETERSON MACHINERY CO p 1138
955 Marina Blvd, San Leandro CA 94577
Tel (541) 302-9199 *SIC* 7629

LIGHTS OF AMERICA INC p 865
611 Reyes Dr, Walnut CA 91789
Tel (909) 594-7883
SIC 3645 3846 7629 3641

■ QWEST BUSINESS & GOVERNMENT SERVICES INC p 1201
1801 Calif St Ste 3800, Denver CO 80202
Tel (303) 391-8300
SIC 5999 1731 7629 7373 7371 7622

NEOPOST USA INC p 1026
478 Wheelers Farms Rd, Milford CT 06461
Tel (203) 301-3400 *SIC* 3579 7359 7629

■ FRONTIER FLORIDA LLC p 581
401 Merritt 7, Norwalk CT 06851
Tel (813) 483-2011
SIC 4813 6519 8721 5065 7629

▲ XEROX CORP p 1631
45 Glover Ave Ste 700, Norwalk CT 06850
Tel (203) 968-3000
SIC 3861 3579 3577 7629 7378 7374

TLD AMERICA CORP p 1457
812 Bloomfield Ave, Windsor CT 06095
Tel (860) 602-3400 *SIC* 5088 3728 7629

■ B WILLIAMS HOLDING CORP p 142
1403 Foulk Rd Ste 200, Wilmington DE 19803
Tel (302) 656-8596
SIC 3579 3661 3861 7359 7629 6159

INTERBOND HOLDING CORP p 751
3200 Sw 42nd St, Fort Lauderdale FL 33312
Tel (954) 797-4000 *SIC* 7629 3699 5722

■ GLOBAL IMAGING SYSTEMS INC p 616
3903 Northdale Blvd 200w, Tampa FL 33624
Tel (813) 960-5508 *SIC* 5044 5045 7629

LANIER WORLDWIDE INC p 844
4667 N Royal Atlanta Dr, Tucker GA 30084
Tel (770) 493-2100
SIC 5044 5999 7359 7629

■ HAWAIIAN TELCOM INC p 669
1177 Bishop St, Honolulu HI 96813
Tel (808) 643-3456 *SIC* 4813 5065 7629

GENERAL BINDING CORP p 599
4 Corporate Dr, Lake Zurich IL 60047
Tel (847) 541-9500
SIC 5044 2782 3559 3589 7629 3579

ADVANCED TECHNOLOGY SERVICES INC p 26
8201 N University St # 1, Peoria IL 61615
Tel (309) 693-4000 *SIC* 7699 7629 7378

CDS OFFICE SYSTEMS INC p 271
612 S Dirksen Pkwy, Springfield IL 62703
Tel (800) 367-1508
SIC 5044 5999 7629 7378 3861 3577

■ AAR MANUFACTURING INC p 8
1100 N Wood Dale Rd, Wood Dale IL 60191
Tel (630) 227-2000 *SIC* 7629

ADAMS REMCO INC p 21
2612 Foundation Dr, South Bend IN 46628
Tel (574) 288-2113 *SIC* 5044 7629 8243

■ R K DIXON CO p 1202
5700 Utica Ridge Rd, Davenport IA 52807
Tel (563) 344-9100 *SIC* 5044 7629 7359

KENTUCKY ASSOCIATION OF ELECTRIC COOPERATIVES INC p 812
4515 Bishop Ln, Louisville KY 40218
Tel (502) 451-2430
SIC 3812 2721 7629 5063

CONTINENTAL RESOURCES INC p 363
175 Middlesex Tpke Ste 1, Bedford MA 01730
Tel (781) 275-0850
SIC 5045 5065 7377 7359 7378 7629

■ MICHIGAN OFFICE SOLUTIONS INC p 961
2859 Walkent Dr Nw, Grand Rapids MI 49544
Tel (616) 459-1161 *SIC* 5044 5045 7629

PHILLIPS SERVICE INDUSTRIES INC p 1144
11878 Hubbard St, Livonia MI 48150
Tel (734) 853-5000 *SIC* 7699 7694 7629

KENDALL ELECTRIC INC p 810
5101 S Sprinkle Rd, Portage MI 49002
Tel (800) 632-5422 *SIC* 5063 7629 5084

ARTESYN NORTH AMERICA LLC p 114
7575 Market Place Dr, Eden Prairie MN 55344
Tel (952) 392-6500 *SIC* 3679 7629

■ NEXTIRAONE LLC p 1040
5050 Lincoln Dr Ste 300, Minneapolis MN 55436
Tel (952) 352-4410
SIC 5065 7629 1731 5999 4813 4841

■ NORSTAN COMMUNICATIONS INC p 1049
5050 Lincoln Dr Ste 300, Minneapolis MN 55436
Tel (952) 935-9002 *SIC* 5065 1731 7629

CENTRAL POWER SYSTEMS & SERVICES LLC p 280
9200 Liberty Dr, Pleasant Valley MO 64068
Tel (816) 781-8070 *SIC* 5013 7629

KMM TELECOMMUNICATIONS INC p 824
9 Law Dr Ste 13, Fairfield NJ 07004
Tel (844) 566-8488 *SIC* 7629 4225

RADWELL INTERNATIONAL INC p 1205
1 Millenium Dr, Willingboro NJ 08046
Tel (609) 288-9393 *SIC* 5065 7629

PC RICHARD & SON INC p 1123
150 Price Pkwy, Farmingdale NY 11735
Tel (631) 843-4300
SIC 5722 5064 7629 7623

■ FRONTIER CALIFORNIA INC p 581
140 West St, New York NY 10007
Tel (212) 395-1000
SIC 4813 6519 8721 5065 1731 7629

CONTEC LLC p 362
1011 State St, Schenectady NY 12307
Tel (518) 382-8150 *SIC* 5065 7629

CAROLINA TRACTOR & EQUIPMENT CO INC p 259
9000 Statesville Rd, Charlotte NC 28269
Tel (704) 596-6700
SIC 5082 5084 5013 7353 7359 7629

LIEBERT CORP p 863
1050 Dearborn Dr, Columbus OH 43085
Tel (614) 888-0246 *SIC* 3585 3613 7629

EMERSON NETWORK POWER ENERGY SYSTEMS NORTH AMERICA INC p 492
1510 Kansas Ave, Lorain OH 44052
Tel (440) 288-1122 *SIC* 3661 3644 7629

MINUTE TRANSFER INC p 974
1055 Westlakes Dr Ste 300, Berwyn PA 19312
Tel (215) 987-3711 *SIC* 7629

■ CUMMINS POWER SYSTEMS LLC p 401
2727 Ford Rd, Bristol PA 19007
Tel (215) 785-6005
SIC 5084 5063 7538 7629 3519

RAM INDUSTRIAL SERVICES LLC p 1206
2850 Appleton St Ste D, Camp Hill PA 17011
Tel (717) 737-7810 *SIC* 5063 7629

CLEVELAND BROTHERS HOLDINGS INC p 325
5300 Paxton St, Harrisburg PA 17111
Tel (717) 564-2121
SIC 7353 5082 5084 7629

■ CATERPILLAR GLOBAL MINING AMERICA LLC p 265
2045 W Pike St, Houston PA 15342
Tel (724) 743-1200 *SIC* 3532 7629

BECKWITH MACHINERY CO INC p 167
4565 William Penn Hwy, Murrysville PA 15668
Tel (724) 327-1300
SIC 5082 5084 7629 7353

■ VERIZON PENNSYLVANIA INC p 1550
1717 Arch St Fl 15, Philadelphia PA 19103
Tel (215) 466-9900
SIC 4813 8721 1731 7629

COMMUNICATIONS TEST DESIGN INC p 347
1373 Enterprise Dr, West Chester PA 19380
Tel (610) 436-5203
SIC 7629 7378 5065 5999

NAUTIC PARTNERS LLC p 1019
100 Westminster St # 1220, Providence RI 02903
Tel (401) 278-6770 *SIC* 6799 7629

▲ SERVICEMASTER GLOBAL HOLDINGS INC p 1308
860 Ridge Lake Blvd, Memphis TN 38120
Tel (901) 597-1400 *SIC* 7342 7629 7641

ATRIUM WINDOWS AND DOORS INC p 129
3890 W Northwest Hwy # 500, Dallas TX 75220
Tel (214) 956-8031
SIC 3442 2431 3089 3354 7629

SOURCE INC p 1342
4550 Spring Valley Rd # 200, Dallas TX 75244
Tel (972) 371-2600 *SIC* 5065 7629

■ VERIZON NORTHWEST INC p 1550
600 Hidden Rdg, Irving TX 75038
Tel (972) 718-5600
SIC 4813 6519 8721 5065 7629

■ CONN APPLIANCES INC p 356
4055 Technology Frst, The Woodlands TX 77381
Tel (409) 832-1696
SIC 5722 5731 7629 6141 7359

■ FLUKE CORP p 561
6920 Seaway Blvd, Everett WA 98203
Tel (425) 446-5400 *SIC* 3823 5065 7629

SWANSON INDUSTRIES INC p 1411
2608 Smithtown Rd, Morgantown WV 26508
Tel (304) 292-0021
SIC 3593 3471 7629 5084

■ SPX TRANSFORMER SOLUTIONS INC p 1362
400 S Prairie Ave, Waukesha WI 53186
Tel (262) 547-0121 *SIC* 7629 3612

SIC 7631 Watch, Clock & Jewelry Repair

▲ MOVADO GROUP INC p 995
650 From Rd Ste 375, Paramus NJ 07652
Tel (201) 267-8000 *SIC* 3873 3915 7631

ROLEX INDUSTRIES INC p 1247
665 5th Ave Fl 6, New York NY 10022
Tel (212) 758-7700 *SIC* 5094 7631 6512

■ BEN BRIDGE - JEWELER INC p 172
2901 3rd Ave Ste 200, Seattle WA 98121
Tel (206) 448-8800 *SIC* 5944 7631

SIC 7641 Reupholstery & Furniture Repair

FSA NETWORK INC p 582
1545 N Park Dr Ste 101, Weston FL 33326
Tel (954) 745-2120 *SIC* 4212 7641

IRWIN SEATING HOLDING CO p 766
3251 Fruit Ridge Ave Nw, Grand Rapids MI 49544
Tel (616) 574-7400 *SIC* 2531 7641

OMNI WORKSPACE CO LLC p 1085
1300 Washington Ave N # 200, Minneapolis MN 55411
Tel (612) 627-1600 *SIC* 7641 4212 4226

COLOR ART INTEGRATED INTERIORS LLC p 338
1325 N Warson Rd, Saint Louis MO 63132
Tel (314) 432-3000
SIC 5021 7641 5999 5712 5099 2521

OFFICE ENVIRONMENTS INC p 1075
11407 Granite St Ste B, Charlotte NC 28273
Tel (704) 714-7200 *SIC* 5021 7641 7389

HUGHES FURNITURE INDUSTRIES INC p 717
952 S Stout Rd, Randleman NC 27317
Tel (336) 498-8700 *SIC* 2512 7641 2426

FURNITURE MART USA INC p 585
140 E Hinks Ln, Sioux Falls SD 57104
Tel (605) 336-5000 *SIC* 7641 5713

■ SERVICEMASTER CO LLC p 1307
860 Ridge Lake Blvd Fl 3, Memphis TN 38120
Tel (901) 597-1400
SIC 7349 7342 1711 1731 7641

▲ SERVICEMASTER GLOBAL HOLDINGS INC p 1308
860 Ridge Lake Blvd, Memphis TN 38120
Tel (901) 597-1400 *SIC* 7342 7629 7641

SERVICEMASTER HOLDING CORP p 1308
860 Ridge Lake Blvd, Memphis TN 38120
Tel (901) 597-1400
SIC 0782 7342 1711 1731 7349 7641

EASTERN SLEEP PRODUCTS CO p 472
4901 Fitzhugh Ave, Richmond VA 23230
Tel (804) 254-1711
SIC 2515 2512 7641 4213

SIC 7692 Welding Repair

SMITH COOPER/T CORP p 1333
118 N Royal St Ste 1000, Mobile AL 36602
Tel (251) 431-6100
SIC 4499 4492 2421 7692 4491

CENTRAL MAINTENANCE AND WELDING INC p 279
2620 E Keysville Rd, Lithia FL 33547
Tel (813) 229-0012 *SIC* 3443 1791 7692

TUBE PROCESSING CORP p 1490
604 E Legrande Ave, Indianapolis IN 46203
Tel (317) 787-1321
SIC 3498 3356 3469 7692 3444 3728

RIDGEVIEW INDUSTRIES INC p 1234
3093 Northridge Dr Nw, Grand Rapids MI 49544
Tel (616) 453-8636 *SIC* 3469 7692

CIC GROUP INC p 306
530 Maryville Centre Dr, Saint Louis MO 63141
Tel (314) 682-2900 *SIC* 7692 3542 8741

SMITHS TUBULAR SYSTEMS-LACONIA INC p 1334
93 Lexington Dr, Laconia NH 03246
Tel (603) 524-2064
SIC 3463 3498 8734 7692 3441 3398

ARC3 GASES INC p 103
1636 Us Highway 301 S, Dunn NC 28334
Tel (910) 892-4016
SIC 2813 5084 5169 7359 7692

KIRBY - SMITH MACHINERY INC p 821
6715 W Reno Ave, Oklahoma City OK 73127
Tel (888) 861-0219 *SIC* 7353 5082 7692

JV INDUSTRIAL COMPANIES LTD p 798
4040 Red Bluff Rd, Pasadena TX 77503
Tel (713) 568-2600 *SIC* 7692 3441 8711

PETERSEN INC p 1138
1527 N 2000 W, Ogden UT 84404
Tel (801) 731-1366
SIC 5084 3441 7692 3444

SIC 7694 Armature Rewinding Shops

ELECTRIC MOTOR SHOP p 484
253 Fulton St, Fresno CA 93721
Tel (559) 233-1153
SIC 5063 1731 7694 7922

■ TIMKEN MOTOR & CRANE SERVICES LLC p 1455
4850 Moline St, Denver CO 80239
Tel (303) 623-8658
SIC 5063 1731 7694 3813 3536

RATHJE ENTERPRISES INC p 1209
1845 N 22nd St, Decatur IL 62526
Tel (217) 423-2593 *SIC* 1731 7694 5063

YASKAWA AMERICA INC p 1635
2121 Norman Dr, Waukegan IL 60085
Tel (847) 887-7000
SIC 3621 7694 5063 3566 3823 3625

FLANDERS ELECTRIC MOTOR SERVICE INC p 554
8101 Baumgart Rd, Evansville IN 47725
Tel (812) 867-7421 *SIC* 7694 5063

KIRBY RISK CORP p 821
1815 Sagamore Pkwy N, Lafayette IN 47904
Tel (765) 448-4567
SIC 5063 7694 3599 3679 3629

PHILLIPS SERVICE INDUSTRIES INC p 1144
11878 Hubbard St, Livonia MI 48150
Tel (734) 853-5000 *SIC* 7699 7694 7629

ARROW MOTOR & PUMP INC p 113
629 Cent St, Wyandotte MI 48192
Tel (734) 285-7860
SIC 7694 5063 7699 5084

EC CO p 474
2121 Nw Thurman St, Portland OR 97210
Tel (503) 224-3511
SIC 1731 7694 5063 5084

INTEGRATED POWER SERVICES LLC p 749
3 Independence Pt Ste 100, Greenville SC 29615
Tel (864) 451-5600 *SIC* 7694

D M G INC p 407
809 W Russell St, Sioux Falls SD 57104
Tel (605) 336-3693
SIC 5063 7694 3599 1731

AMERIMEX MOTOR & CONTROLS LLC p 82
610 N Milby St, Houston TX 77003
Tel (713) 225-4300 *SIC* 5063 3625 7694

SHERMCO INDUSTRIES INC p 1316
2425 E Pioneer Dr, Irving TX 75061
Tel (972) 793-5523 *SIC* 8711 7694 5063

RAMSA ELECTROMECHANIC INC p 1207
207 W Ryan St, Laredo TX 78041
Tel (956) 568-5354 *SIC* 7694

L & S ELECTRIC INC p 833
5101 Mesker St, Schofield WI 54476
Tel (715) 359-3155
SIC 7694 5063 8711 3613

SIC 7699 Repair Shop & Related Svcs, NEC

INTEGRATED MEDICAL SYSTEMS INTERNATIONAL INC p 749
3316 2nd Ave N, Birmingham AL 35222
Tel (205) 879-3840 *SIC* 3841 7699

■ ARMY FLEET SUPPORT LLC p 112
1117 Dilly Branch Rd, Fort Rucker AL 36362
Tel (334) 598-0400 *SIC* 7699

G & R MINERAL SERVICES INC p 586
2355 Alton Rd, Irondale AL 35210
Tel (205) 956-7300 *SIC* 7349 7699

CAPITOL BUSINESS EQUIPMENT INC p 251
645 S Mcdonough St, Montgomery AL 36104
Tel (334) 265-8903
SIC 5045 5044 7699 5065

GO GREEN JANITORIAL SERVICES LLC p 619
8448 Crossland Loop, Montgomery AL 36117
Tel (334) 277-5880 *SIC* 7699

PEAK OILFIELD SERVICE CO LLC p 1126
5015 Business Park Blvd # 4000, Anchorage AK 99503
Tel (907) 263-7000 *SIC* 7699 1389

EMPIRE SOUTHWEST LLC p 493
1725 S Country Club Dr, Mesa AZ 85210
Tel (480) 633-4000 *SIC* 5082 7353 7699

WHITEMAN FAMILY CORP p 1606
1725 S Country Club Dr, Mesa AZ 85210
Tel (480) 633-4413
SIC 5082 5083 7353 7699 7359 5012

STANDARD AERO HOLDINGS INC p 1375
6710 N Scottsdale Rd # 250, Paradise Valley AZ 85253
Tel (480) 377-3100 *SIC* 7699

■ HONEYWELL AEROSPACE INC p 705
1944 E Sky Harbor Cir N, Phoenix AZ 85034
Tel (602) 365-3099 *SIC* 3812 7363 7699

ROAD MACHINERY LLC p 1240
4710 E Elwood St Ste 6, Phoenix AZ 85040
Tel (602) 256-5128
SIC 5082 7359 7699 7353 7629

■ **STRYKER SUSTAINABILITY SOLUTIONS INC** p 1394
1810 W Drake Dr Ste 101, Tempe AZ 85283
Tel (888) 888-3433
SIC 5084 5047 7699 3842 3841

PROPAK LOGISTICS INC p 1183
1100 Garrison Ave, Fort Smith AR 72901
Tel (479) 478-7800 SIC 7699 4731

HUGG AND HALL EQUIPMENT CO p 717
7201 Scott Hamilton Dr, Little Rock AR 72209
Tel (501) 562-1262
SIC 5084 5082 7353 7699 5083 3531

MP ENVIRONMENTAL SERVICES INC p 995
3400 Manor St, Bakersfield CA 93308
Tel (800) 458-3036
SIC 4953 4213 8748 7699

YALE/CHASE EQUIPMENT AND SERVICES INC p 1634
2615 Pellissier Pl, City Of Industry CA 90601
Tel (562) 463-8000 SIC 5084 7699 7359

GKN AEROSPACE CHEM-TRONICS INC p 613
1150 W Bradley Ave, El Cajon CA 92020
Tel (619) 448-2320 SIC 3724 7699

S & STOOL & SUPPLY INC p 1261
2700 Maxwell Way, Fairfield CA 94534
Tel (925) 335-4000
SIC 5085 7699 5072 7359

HEAT AND CONTROL INC p 679
21121 Cabot Blvd, Hayward CA 94545
Tel (510) 259-0500 SIC 3556 7699

R F MACDONALD CO p 1202
25920 Eden Landing Rd, Hayward CA 94545
Tel (510) 784-0110 SIC 5084 7699 5074

RJMS CORP p 1239
31010 San Antonio St, Hayward CA 94544
Tel (510) 675-0500 SIC 5084 5085 7699

KEOLIS TRANSIT AMERICA INC p 813
6053 W Century Blvd # 900, Los Angeles CA 90045
Tel (310) 981-9500 SIC 4119 7699

▲ **KLA-TENCOR CORP** p 822
1 Technology Dr, Milpitas CA 95035
Tel (408) 875-3000
SIC 3827 3825 7699 7629

HAWTHORNE MACHINERY CO p 670
16945 Camino San Bernardo, San Diego CA 92127
Tel (858) 674-7000
SIC 7353 7699 5082 7359

■ **CSE HOLDINGS INC** p 397
650 Brennan St, San Jose CA 95131
Tel (408) 436-1907
SIC 5087 5084 7699 5113 5199 5112

SSMB PACIFIC HOLDING CO INC p 1364
1755 Adams Ave, San Leandro CA 94577
Tel (510) 836-6100 SIC 5012 7699

MARBORG INDUSTRIES p 904
728 E Yanonali St, Santa Barbara CA 93103
Tel (805) 963-1852
SIC 4953 7359 7699 4212

RAYMOND HANDLING SOLUTIONS INC p 1210
9939 Norwalk Blvd, Santa Fe Springs CA 90670
Tel (562) 944-8067 SIC 5084 7699 7359

TURLOCK DAIRY & REFRIGERATION INC p 1492
1819 S Walnut Rd, Turlock CA 95380
Tel (209) 667-6455 SIC 5083 7699 1542

WAGNER EQUIPMENT CO p 1571
18000 Smith Rd, Aurora CO 80011
Tel (303) 739-3000 SIC 5082 7699 7353

TERUMO BCT INC p 1440
10811 W Collins Ave, Lakewood CO 80215
Tel (303) 232-6800
SIC 8733 3842 3845 5047 7352 7699

BLAKE GROUP HOLDINGS INC p 188
4 New Park Rd, East Windsor CT 06088
Tel (860) 243-1491
SIC 5074 5084 7699 8741

DONCASTERS INC p 450
36 Spring Ln, Farmington CT 06032
Tel (860) 677-1376
SIC 3511 3356 3728 7699

■ **OTIS ELEVATOR CO** p 1097
10 Farm Springs Rd, Farmington CT 06032
Tel (860) 676-6000 SIC 3534 1796 7699

GREENWICH AEROGROUP INC p 638
475 Steamboat Rd Fl 2, Greenwich CT 06830
Tel (203) 618-4861
SIC 4581 5088 7699 5085

■ **PETRO INC** p 1139
9 W Broad St Ste 3, Stamford CT 06902
Tel (203) 325-5400 SIC 5983 7699

■ **ANDERSON GROUP INC** p 90
3411 Silverside Rd # 103, Wilmington DE 19810
Tel (302) 478-6160
SIC 5047 5063 5099 7699 3443

BARLOWORLD USA INC p 155
1105 N Market St Ste 1300, Wilmington DE 19801
Tel (302) 427-2765 SIC 5084 7699 7359

■ **DELAWARE CAPITAL HOLDINGS INC** p 423
501 Silverside Rd Ste 5, Wilmington DE 19809
Tel (302) 793-4921 SIC 5084 3533 7699

KELLY TRACTOR CO p 809
8255 Nw 58th St, Doral FL 33166
Tel (305) 592-5360
SIC 5082 5083 7359 7353 5084 7699

EMBRAER AIRCRAFT HOLDING INC p 490
276 Sw 34th St, Fort Lauderdale FL 33315
Tel (954) 359-3700 SIC 7699

▲ **HEICO CORP** p 680
3000 Taft St, Hollywood FL 33021
Tel (954) 987-4000 SIC 3724 3728 7699

STEWART & STEVENSON FDDA LLC p 1389
5040 University Blvd W, Jacksonville FL 32216
Tel (904) 737-7330 SIC 5084 7699

HIG CAPITAL PARTNERS III LP p 690
1450 Brickell Ave # 3100, Miami FL 33131
Tel (305) 379-2322
SIC 6211 5084 7352 7699 8748 3842

PEARL PAINT CO INC p 1126
1033 E Oakland Park Blvd, Oakland Park FL 33334
Tel (954) 564-5700
SIC 5999 5199 7699 5112 5947 7311

■ **TEKTRONIX SERVICE SOLUTIONS INC** p 1433
6120 Hanging Moss Rd, Orlando FL 32807
Tel (407) 678-6900
SIC 3812 3674 8734 7699

■ **CHROMALLOY GAS TURBINE LLC** p 304
3999 Rca Blvd, Palm Beach Gardens FL 33410
Tel (561) 935-3571
SIC 3724 7699 4581 3764 3769 3533

HOERBIGER COMPRESSION TECHNOLOGY AMERICA HOLDING INC p 699
3350 Gateway Dr, Pompano Beach FL 33069
Tel (954) 974-5700 SIC 3494 7699

■ **ADVANCED DISPOSAL SERVICES SOLID WASTE MIDWEST LLC** p 25
90 Fort Wade Rd Ste 200, Ponte Vedra FL 32081
Tel (904) 737-7900 SIC 7699 4953 4959

WIGINTON CORP p 1608
699 Aero Ln, Sanford FL 32771
Tel (407) 585-3200 SIC 1711 7699 7389

FLORIDA LIFT SYSTEMS LLC p 559
115 S 78th St, Tampa FL 33619
Tel (904) 764-7662 SIC 5084 7359 7699

QUALAWASH HOLDINGS LLC p 1196
1302 N 19th St Ste 300, Tampa FL 33605
Tel (813) 321-6485 SIC 7699

QUALITY DISTRIBUTION LLC p 1197
4041 Park Oaks Blvd # 200, Tampa FL 33610
Tel (813) 630-5826 SIC 4213 7699 4212

YANMAR AMERICA CORP p 1635
101 International Pkwy, Adairsville GA 30103
Tel (770) 877-9894
SIC 5084 7699 5083 3519

THYSSENKRUPP ELEVATOR AMERICAS CORP p 1451
11605 Haynes Bridge Rd, Alpharetta GA 30009
Tel (678) 319-3240 SIC 7699 3534 1796

THYSSENKRUPP ELEVATOR CORP p 1451
11605 Haynes Bridge Rd # 650, Alpharetta GA 30009
Tel (678) 319-3240 SIC 3534 1796 7699

APTOS INC p 101
945 E Paces Ferry Rd Ne, Atlanta GA 30326
Tel (866) 493-7037
SIC 5044 5045 7378 7699

■ **MUELLER GROUP LLC** p 998
1200 Abernathy Rd, Atlanta GA 30328
Tel (770) 206-4200
SIC 3823 3321 3533 7699

YANCEY BROS CO p 1634
330 Lee Industrial Blvd # 1, Austell GA 30168
Tel (770) 941-2424
SIC 5082 5084 7699 7353

■ **LOCKHEED MARTIN AERONAUTICAL CO** p 873
86 S Cobb Dr Se, Marietta GA 30063
Tel (770) 494-4411
SIC 3721 3812 7699 3769

LANGDALE CO p 844
1202 Madison Hwy, Valdosta GA 31601
Tel (229) 242-7450
SIC 2421 2491 7011 7699 5031 5171

WESTERN STATES EQUIPMENT CO p 1600
500 E Overland Rd, Meridian ID 83642
Tel (208) 888-2287 SIC 5082 7699 5084

ASSOCIATED MATERIAL HANDLING INDUSTRIES INC p 120
133 N Swift Rd, Addison IL 60101
Tel (630) 588-8800 SIC 5084 7699 7353

PT HOLDINGS LLC p 1189
1150 N Swift Rd Ste A, Addison IL 60101
Tel (800) 438-8898
SIC 5084 5046 7699 6719

BEARD IMPLEMENT CO (INC) p 165
216 W Frederick St, Arenzville IL 62611
Tel (217) 997-5514 SIC 5083 7699

CENTRAL ILLINOIS AG INC p 278
200 E Sharon St, Atlanta IL 61723
Tel (217) 648-2307 SIC 5999 7699

ILLINOIS AUTO ELECTRIC CO p 732
700 Enterprise St, Aurora IL 60504
Tel (630) 862-3300
SIC 5084 5013 5083 5078 7699 3519

HELIGEAR ACQUISITION CO p 681
6006 W 73rd St, Bedford Park IL 60638
Tel (708) 728-2000 SIC 3724 7699

CARYLON CORP p 262
2500 W Arthington St, Chicago IL 60612
Tel (312) 666-7700
SIC 7699 1629 7349 8748 4959

NES RENTALS HOLDINGS INC p 1026
8420 W Bryn Mawr Ave # 310, Chicago IL 60631
Tel (773) 695-3999 SIC 7359 7699 5082

■ **DOVER PRINTING & IDENTIFICATION INC** p 453
3005 Highland Pkwy # 200, Downers Grove IL 60515
Tel (630) 541-1540
SIC 3556 3565 3593 7699

▲ **HERITAGE-CRYSTAL CLEAN INC** p 686
2175 Point Blvd Ste 375, Elgin IL 60123
Tel (847) 836-5670 SIC 7699 8734

EQUIPMENT DEPOT OF ILLINOIS INC p 506
751 Expressway Dr, Itasca IL 60143
Tel (847) 836-5005
SIC 5084 5087 5063 7699

KONE ELEVATOR p 827
1 Kone Ct, Moline IL 61265
Tel (309) 764-6771 SIC 7699 3534

KONE INC p 827
1 Kone Ct, Moline IL 61265
Tel (309) 764-6771 SIC 7699 3534 1796

DIVERSIFIED FOODSERVICE SUPPLY INC p 444
607 Dempster St, Mount Prospect IL 60056
Tel (847) 966-9700 SIC 5046 7699

ADVANCED TECHNOLOGY SERVICES INC p 26
8201 N University St # 1, Peoria IL 61615
Tel (309) 693-4000 SIC 7699 7629 7378

CONGLOBAL INDUSTRIES LLC p 356
8200 185th St Ste A, Tinley Park IL 60487
Tel (925) 543-0977
SIC 3743 4213 4231 1799 7699

TRUCK CENTERS INC p 1485
2280 Formosa Rd, Troy IL 62294
Tel (618) 667-3454
SIC 5531 5511 7538 5012 4522 7699

GLOBE UNION GROUP INC p 618
2500 Internationale Pkwy, Woodridge IL 60517
Tel (630) 679-1420 SIC 3261 3432 7699

TRADEBE GP p 1468
4343 Kennedy Ave, East Chicago IN 46312
Tel (800) 388-7242 SIC 4953 7699 1389

BASTIAN AUTOMATION ENGINEERING LLC p 159
2155 Fields Blvd, Greenfield IN 46140
Tel (317) 467-2583 SIC 3579 7699

MACALLISTER MACHINERY CO INC p 891
7515 E 30th St, Indianapolis IN 46219
Tel (317) 545-2151 SIC 5082 7699 5013

TRIMEDX INDIA LLC p 1480
5451 Lakeview Pkwy S Dr, Indianapolis IN 46268
Tel (877) 874-6339 SIC 7699

TRADEBE ENVIRONMENTAL SERVICES LLC p 1468
1433 E 83rd Ave Ste 200, Merrillville IN 46410
Tel (800) 388-7242 SIC 4953 7699 1389

SOMEBODY CARES INC p 1339
57 N Court St, Fairfield IA 52556
Tel (641) 472-5352 SIC 5947 7699 5999

RYKO SOLUTIONS INC p 1261
1500 Se 37th St, Grimes IA 50111
Tel (515) 986-3700 SIC 3589 1796 7699

■ **INSTRUMENT & VALVE SERVICES CO** p 747
205 S Center St, Marshalltown IA 50158
Tel (641) 754-3011 SIC 3494 3825 7699

G W VAN KEPPEL CO p 587
1801 N 9th St, Kansas City KS 66101
Tel (913) 281-4800
SIC 5082 7699 5084 7359

ROAD BUILDERS MACHINERY & SUPPLY CO INC p 1240
1001 S 7th St, Kansas City KS 66105
Tel (913) 371-3822 SIC 5082 7353 7699

INKCYCLE INC p 743
11100 W 82nd St, Lenexa KS 66214
Tel (913) 894-8387
SIC 3955 7699 7378 5045 8249 5734

D H PACE CO INC p 407
1901 E 119th St, Olathe KS 66061
Tel (816) 221-0543 SIC 5211 7699

EE NEWCOMER ENTERPRISES INC p 480
1901 E 119th St, Olathe KS 66061
Tel (816) 221-0543 SIC 5031 5211 7699

BERRY COMPANIES INC p 176
3223 N Hydraulic St, Wichita KS 67219
Tel (316) 838-3321
SIC 5082 7353 7699 5084

■ **HAWKER BEECHCRAFT GLOBAL CUSTOMER SUPPORT LLC** p 669
10511 E Central Ave, Wichita KS 67206
Tel (316) 676-7111 SIC 7699

ORICA GROUND SUPPORT INC p 1094
150 Summer Ct, Georgetown KY 40324
Tel (502) 863-6800
SIC 5082 3564 2439 7699

CARDINAL CARRYOR INC p 252
1055 Grade Ln, Louisville KY 40213
Tel (502) 363-6641
SIC 5084 7699 7359 5085 3535

TURNER INDUSTRIES GROUP LLC p 1493
8687 United Plaza Blvd, Baton Rouge LA 70809
Tel (225) 922-5050 SIC 7359 7699

TURNER SPECIALTY SERVICES LLC p 1493
8687 United Plaza Blvd, Baton Rouge LA 70809
Tel (225) 922-5050 SIC 1541 7699

ECOSERV LLC p 476
207 Towncenter Pkwy Fl 2, Lafayette LA 70506
Tel (337) 984-4445 SIC 4959 7699

LOUISIANA MACHINERY CO LLC p 880
3799 W Airline Hwy, Reserve LA 70084
Tel (985) 536-1121 SIC 5082 7699 7353

ALBAN TRACTOR CO INC p 45
8531 Pulaski Hwy, Baltimore MD 21237
Tel (410) 686-7777 SIC 5082 5084 7699

BHS CORRUGATED - NORTH AMERICA INC p 180
9103 Yellow Brick Rd N, Baltimore MD 21237
Tel (410) 574-1550 SIC 5084 7699 3316

C & T A CO INC p 231
11535 Hopewell Rd, Hagerstown MD 21740
Tel (800) 458-3835
SIC 5541 5172 7359 7699

■ **AAI CORP** p 8
124 Industry Ln, Hunt Valley MD 21030
Tel (410) 666-1400
SIC 3728 3769 7699 8711

▲ **BROOKS AUTOMATION INC** p 218
15 Elizabeth Dr, Chelmsford MA 01824
Tel (978) 262-2400
SIC 3559 3563 3823 7699

ABEL WOMACK INC p 11
1 International Way, Lawrence MA 01843
Tel (978) 989-9400 SIC 5084 7699

NORTHLAND INDUSTRIAL TRUCK CO INC p 1057
6 Jonspin Rd, Wilmington MA 01887
Tel (978) 658-5900 SIC 5084 7699 7359

KRAFT POWER CORP p 829
199 Wildwood Ave, Woburn MA 01801
Tel (781) 938-9100 SIC 5084 7699

KURABE AMERICA CORP p 832
37735 Interchange Dr, Farmington Hills MI 48335
Tel (248) 939-5803 SIC 7699 7549

MORRISON INDUSTRIES INC p 990
1825 Monroe Ave Nw, Grand Rapids MI 49505
Tel (616) 447-3838 SIC 5084 7699 7359

PHILLIPS SERVICE INDUSTRIES INC p 1144
11878 Hubbard St, Livonia MI 48150
Tel (734) 853-5000 SIC 7699 7694 7629

ARROW MOTOR & PUMP INC p 113
629 Cent St, Wyandotte MI 48192
Tel (734) 285-7860
SIC 7694 5063 7699 5084

PURITY CYLINDER GASES INC p 1192
2580 28th St Sw, Wyoming MI 49519
Tel (616) 532-2375
SIC 5085 7359 5999 7699

JAMAR CO p 776
4701 Mike Colalillo Dr, Duluth MN 55807
Tel (218) 628-1027
SIC 1711 1761 1742 5033 7699 3444

EXPRESSPOINT TECHNOLOGY SERVICES INC p 521
10900 Wayzata Blvd # 800, Hopkins MN 55305
Tel (763) 543-6000
SIC 5045 7379 7699 8741 7389 7378

POLAR CORP p 1159
1015 W St Germain St 42 Ste 420, Hopkins MN 55305
Tel (612) 430-6401 SIC 3443 5012 7699

API GROUP INC p 96
1100 Old Highway 8 Nw, Saint Paul MN 55112
Tel (651) 636-4320
SIC 1711 1742 7699 1799

■ **GCS SYSTEMS INC** p 595
370 Wabasha St N, Saint Paul MN 55102
Tel (651) 293-2134 SIC 5046 7699

▲ **PATTERSON COMPANIES INC** p 1121
1031 Mendota Heights Rd, Saint Paul MN 55120
Tel (651) 686-1600
SIC 5047 5112 7372 7699 2834

■ **Q3 CONTRACTING INC** p 1194
3066 Spruce St, Saint Paul MN 55117
Tel (651) 224-2424 SIC 1623 7699 3669

SMYTH COMPANIES LLC p 1335
1085 Snelling Ave N, Saint Paul MN 55108
Tel (651) 646-4544
SIC 2679 2752 3993 7389 5084 7699

ROSENBAUER MINNESOTA LLC p 1251
5181 260th St, Wyoming MN 55092
Tel (651) 462-1000 SIC 3713 7699 3711

PUCKETT MACHINERY CO p 1190
100 Caterpillar Dr, Flowood MS 39232
Tel (601) 969-6000
SIC 5082 5084 5063 7699

TAYLOR GROUP INC p 1427
650 N Church Ave, Louisville MS 39339
Tel (662) 773-3421 SIC 7699 5999

SIGNAL INTERNATIONAL LLC p 1322
601 Bayou Casotte Pkwy, Pascagoula MS 39581
Tel (228) 762-0010 SIC 7699 3731 3441

JOHN FABICK TRACTOR CO p 788
1 Fabick Dr, Fenton MO 63026
Tel (636) 343-5900 SIC 5082 7699

FANCOR INC p 527
821 Locust St, Kansas City MO 64106
Tel (816) 471-0231 SIC 3596 7699 5046

BAKER IMPLEMENT CO p 146
915 Homecrest St, Kennett MO 63857
Tel (573) 888-4646 SIC 5083 7699

CONTINENTAL DISC CORP p 363
3160 W Heartland Dr, Liberty MO 64068
Tel (816) 792-1500
SIC 3491 3498 7699 3494

PAS TECHNOLOGIES INC p 1119
1234 Atlantic Ave, North Kansas City MO 64116
Tel (816) 556-5113 SIC 7699 1389

NOOTER CORP p 1047
1500 S 2nd St, Saint Louis MO 63104
Tel (314) 421-7200
SIC 3443 3479 1796 8711 7699 1542

ROBERT FAMILY HOLDINGS INC p 1241
12430 Tesson Ferry Rd, Saint Louis MO 63128
Tel (314) 821-5665
SIC 2671 3572 3491 3498 7699 3494

SUMNER GROUP INC p 1399
6717 Waldemar Ave, Saint Louis MO 63139
Tel (314) 633-8000 SIC 5044 7699 5112

■ **TOTAL FILTRATION SERVICES INC** p 1463
2071 Congressional Dr, Saint Louis MO 63146
Tel (314) 202-3635 SIC 7699

DUNCAN AVIATION INC p 461
3701 Aviation Rd, Lincoln NE 68524
Tel (402) 479-1616
SIC 7699 5088 4522 4512

CASSLING DIAGNOSTIC IMAGING INC p 264
13808 F St, Omaha NE 68137
Tel (402) 334-5000 SIC 5047 7699

CASHMAN EQUIPMENT CO p 263
3300 Saint Rose Pkwy, Henderson NV 89052
Tel (702) 649-8777
SIC 5084 5063 7353 7699

GOSS INTERNATIONAL AMERICAS LLC p 626
121 Technology Dr, Durham NH 03824
Tel (603) 749-6600 SIC 7699 3555

■ **CONWAY TECHNOLOGY GROUP LLC** p 365
10 Capitol St, Nashua NH 03063
Tel (603) 889-1665
SIC 5044 5065 7699 7359

H BETTI INDUSTRIES INC p 649
303 Paterson Plank Rd, Carlstadt NJ 07072
Tel (201) 438-1300 SIC 5046 5091 7699

ISS TMC SERVICES INC p 767
81 Dorsa Ave, Livingston NJ 07039
Tel (973) 740-0032 SIC 6512 7349 7699

EASTERN LIFT TRUCK CO INC p 472
549 E Linwood Ave, Maple Shade NJ 08052
Tel (856) 779-8880 SIC 5084 7699 7359

SCHINDLER ELEVATOR CORP p 1287
20 Whippany Rd, Morristown NJ 07960
Tel (973) 397-6500 *SIC* 3534 7699 1796

SCHINDLER ENTERPRISES INC p 1287
20 Whippany Rd, Morristown NJ 07960
Tel (973) 397-6500 *SIC* 3534 7699 1796

JOHNSON & TOWERS INC p 790
2021 Briggs Rd, Mount Laurel NJ 08054
Tel (856) 234-6990
SIC 5084 5013 7699 7538 5085

GEA MECHANICAL EQUIPMENT US INC p 597
100 Fairway Ct, Northvale NJ 07647
Tel (201) 767-3900 *SIC* 5084 7699

ATLAS COPCO USA HOLDINGS INC p 128
7 Campus Dr Ste 200, Parsippany NJ 07054
Tel (973) 397-3432 *SIC* 6722 6159 7699

FOLEY INC p 563
855 Centennial Ave, Piscataway NJ 08854
Tel (732) 885-5555 *SIC* 5082 7699 7353

SAMSUNG OPTO-ELECTRONICS AMERICA INC p 1275
100 Challenger Rd Ste 700, Ridgefield Park NJ 07660
Tel (201) 325-2612 *SIC* 5043 7699 3861

BINDER MACHINERY CO INC p 183
2820 Hamilton Blvd, South Plainfield NJ 07080
Tel (908) 561-9000
SIC 5082 5084 7353 7699

PROCESS EQUIPMENT & SERVICE CO INC p 1179
5680 Us 64, Farmington NM 87401
Tel (505) 327-2222
SIC 3443 5084 7699 3533

MED SERVICES INC p 935
100 Knickerbocker Ave C, Bohemia NY 11716
Tel (631) 218-6450 *SIC* 3845 7699

■ CARR BUSINESS SYSTEMS INC p 260
500 Commack Rd Unit 110, Commack NY 11725
Tel (631) 249-9880 *SIC* 5044 7699

DUMAC BUSINESS SYSTEMS INC p 461
19 Corporate Cir Ste 1, East Syracuse NY 13057
Tel (315) 463-1010 *SIC* 5045 7699 3578

TRACEY ROAD EQUIPMENT INC p 1468
6803 Manlius Center Rd, East Syracuse NY 13057
Tel (315) 437-1471
SIC 5082 5012 7353 7699 5013

MULLER MARTINI CORP p 999
456 Wheeler Rd, Hauppauge NY 11788
Tel (631) 582-4343 *SIC* 5084 7699

ALSTOM USA INC p 61
1 Transit Dr, Hornell NY 14843
Tel (607) 324-4595 *SIC* 3321 7699

MECHANICAL DYNAMICS & ANALYSIS LTD p 934
19 British American Blvd, Latham NY 12110
Tel (518) 399-3616 *SIC* 8711 7699

NOUVEAU ELEVATOR INDUSTRIES INC p 1062
4755 37th St, Long Island City NY 11101
Tel (718) 349-4700 *SIC* 7699 1796

TRANSERVICE LEASE CORP p 1471
5 Dakota Dr, New Hyde Park NY 11042
Tel (800) 645-8018
SIC 7699 7539 4212 7353

DIAMOND CASTLE HOLDINGS LLC p 436
280 Pk Ave Fl 25 E Tower, New York NY 10017
Tel (212) 300-1900 *SIC* 7353 7699 5082

HMAN INTERMEDIATE HOLDINGS CORP p 697
245 Park Ave Fl 16, New York NY 10167
Tel (513) 851-4900 *SIC* 6719 5072 7699

MARUBENI AUTO & CONSTRUCTION MACHINERY (AMERICA) INC p 913
450 Lexington Ave, New York NY 10017
Tel (212) 450-0447 *SIC* 5082 7353 7699

▲ TRANSCAT INC p 1471
35 Vantage Point Dr, Rochester NY 14624
Tel (585) 352-7777 *SIC* 5049 7699

INDUSTRIAL DISTRIBUTION GROUP INC p 740
2100 The Oaks Pkwy, Belmont NC 28012
Tel (704) 398-5600 *SIC* 5084 7699

SHAMROCK ENVIRONMENTAL CORP p 1311
6106 Corporate Park Dr, Browns Summit NC 27214
Tel (336) 375-1989
SIC 4953 4212 8748 7699

■ BWXT INVESTMENT CO p 231
11525 N Community House, Charlotte NC 28277
Tel (704) 625-4900
SIC 3511 3443 3564 1629 1541 7699

E MASON ROBERT & ASSOCIATES INC p 466
1726 N Graham St, Charlotte NC 28206
Tel (704) 375-4465 *SIC* 5085 7699

▲ T AIR INC p 1419
3524 Airport Rd, Maiden NC 28650
Tel (828) 464-8741 *SIC* 4512 3728 7699

ELECTRICAL EQUIPMENT CO INC p 485
1440 Diggs Dr, Raleigh NC 27603
Tel (919) 828-5411 *SIC* 5063 7699

BUTLER MACHINERY CO p 230
3401 33rd St S, Fargo ND 58104
Tel (701) 298-1700 *SIC* 5082 7353 7699

RDO EQUIPMENT CO p 1212
700 7th St S, Fargo ND 58103
Tel (701) 239-8700
SIC 5083 5082 5084 7699 7359 7353

FAMOUS ENTERPRISES INC p 527
2620 Ridgewood Rd Ste 200, Akron OH 44313
Tel (330) 762-9621
SIC 5075 5031 5074 7699

■ BABCOCK & WILCOX CO p 143
20 S Van Buren Ave, Barberton OH 44203
Tel (330) 753-4511
SIC 1629 1711 3443 7699 8741 3822

GROB SYSTEMS INC p 641
1070 Navajo Dr, Bluffton OH 45817
Tel (419) 358-9015 *SIC* 3535 7699

OHIO MACHINERY CO p 1077
3993 E Royalton Rd, Broadview Heights OH 44147
Tel (440) 526-6200
SIC 7513 6159 7699 5082 7353

TOWLIFT INC p 1464
1395 Valley Belt Rd, Brooklyn Heights OH 44131
Tel (216) 749-6800 *SIC* 5084 7699 7359

▲ CHEMED CORP p 293
255 E 5th St Ste 2600, Cincinnati OH 45202
Tel (513) 762-6690 *SIC* 8082 1711 7699

■ GE AIRCRAFT ENGINES HOLDINGS INC p 595
1 Neumann Way, Cincinnati OH 45215
Tel (513) 243-8251 *SIC* 7699

■ GE ENGINE SERVICES LLC p 596
1 Neumann Way, Cincinnati OH 45215
Tel (513) 243-2000 *SIC* 7699

HILLMAN COMPANIES INC p 693
10590 Hamilton Ave, Cincinnati OH 45231
Tel (513) 851-4900 *SIC* 5072 7699

HMAN GROUP HOLDINGS INC p 697
10590 Hamilton Ave, Cincinnati OH 45231
Tel (513) 851-4900 *SIC* 6719 5072 7699

HMAN INTERMEDIATE II HOLDINGS CORP p 697
10590 Hamilton Ave, Cincinnati OH 45231
Tel (513) 851-4900 *SIC* 5072 7699

■ ROTO-ROOTER DEVELOPMENT CO p 1252
255 E 5th St Ste 2600, Cincinnati OH 45202
Tel (513) 762-6690 *SIC* 7699 1711

■ ROTO-ROOTER SERVICES CO p 1252
2500 Chemed Ctr 255e5th, Cincinnati OH 45202
Tel (513) 762-6690 *SIC* 7699 1711

▲ APPLIED INDUSTRIAL TECHNOLOGIES INC p 99
1 Applied Plz, Cleveland OH 44115
Tel (216) 426-4000 *SIC* 5085 5169 7699

■ METTLER-TOLEDO LLC p 957
1900 Polaris Pkwy Fl 6, Columbus OH 43240
Tel (614) 438-4511
SIC 3596 5049 7699 3821 3823 3826

ALL AMERICAN SPORTS CORP p 51
669 Sugar Ln, Elyria OH 44035
Tel (440) 366-8225 *SIC* 7699

MCNATIONAL INC p 932
502 2nd St E, South Point OH 45680
Tel (740) 377-4391 *SIC* 3731 7699 4491

MORRIS MATERIAL HANDLING INC p 990
4401 Gateway Blvd, Springfield OH 45502
Tel (937) 525-5520 *SIC* 3625 3443 7699

■ SCOTT FETZER CO p 1293
28800 Clemens Rd, Westlake OH 44145
Tel (440) 892-3000 *SIC* 7699

FORGE INDUSTRIES INC p 567
4450 Market St, Youngstown OH 44512
Tel (330) 782-8301
SIC 5085 3566 3599 3531 6411 7699

PENNSYLVANIA TOOL SALES & SERVICE INC p 1130
625 Bev Rd, Youngstown OH 44512
Tel (330) 758-0845 *SIC* 7699 5085 5084

LIVINGSTON MACHINERY CO p 871
5201 S Highway 81, Chickasha OK 73018
Tel (405) 224-5056
SIC 5083 5999 7699 5261

■ MATRIX SERVICE INC p 920
5100 E Skelly Dr Ste 700, Tulsa OK 74135
Tel (918) 838-8822
SIC 1623 1629 1799 7699

COLUMBIA HELICOPTERS INC p 340
14452 Arndt Rd Ne, Aurora OR 97002
Tel (503) 678-7510 *SIC* 7699 2411 4522

PAPE GROUP INC p 1112
355 Goodpasture Island Rd # 300, Eugene OR 97401
Tel (541) 334-3400
SIC 5084 5082 7699 6141 5599 4581

BLOUNT INC p 190
4909 Se International Way, Portland OR 97222
Tel (503) 653-8881
SIC 3546 3568 7699 3495

CH2M HILL INDUSTRIAL DESIGN & CONSTRUCTION INC p 286
2020 Sw 4th Ave Fl 3, Portland OR 97201
Tel (503) 224-6040
SIC 8711 8712 8741 7699

GIRARDS GARAGE DOOR SERVICES p 613
5962 Keystone Dr, Bath PA 18014
Tel (610) 837-4738 *SIC* 7699

ANDERSON EQUIPMENT CO p 90
1000 Washington Pike, Bridgeville PA 15017
Tel (412) 343-2300
SIC 5082 7699 7353 5531

MODERN GROUP LTD p 981
2501 Durham Rd, Bristol PA 19007
Tel (215) 943-9100 *SIC* 5084 7353 7699

GEISINGER HEALTH SYSTEM FOUNDATION p 597
100 N Academy Ave, Danville PA 17822
Tel (570) 271-6461 *SIC* 8741 6512 7699

HOOBER INC p 705
3452 Old Philadelphia Pike, Intercourse PA 17534
Tel (717) 768-8231 *SIC* 5999 7699 5083

▲ CALGON CARBON CORP p 238
3000 Gsk Dr, Moon Township PA 15108
Tel (412) 787-6700
SIC 2819 7699 3589 3564

HERMAN GOLDNER CO INC p 687
7777 Brewster Ave, Philadelphia PA 19153
Tel (215) 365-5400 *SIC* 1711 7699

J J WHITE INC p 771
5500 Bingham St, Philadelphia PA 19120
Tel (215) 722-1000 *SIC* 1711 1542 7699

PENN DETROIT DIESEL ALLISON LLC p 1129
8330 State Rd, Philadelphia PA 19136
Tel (215) 335-5010 *SIC* 7699 7538

S P INDUSTRIES INC p 1262
935 Mearns Rd, Warminster PA 18974
Tel (215) 672-7800
SIC 3826 3585 7699 3821

SFS INTEC INC p 1310
1045 Spring St, Wyomissing PA 19610
Tel (610) 376-5751 *SIC* 7699 5012 5085

ENGEL MACHINERY INC p 498
3740 Board Rd, York PA 17406
Tel (717) 764-6818 *SIC* 5084 7699

VOITH HYDRO INC p 1564
760 E Berlin Rd, York PA 17408
Tel (717) 792-7000 *SIC* 3511 7699

■ AMERICAN EQUIPMENT CO INC p 71
2106 Anderson Rd, Greenville SC 29611
Tel (864) 295-7800
SIC 7699 7359 5082 7353

SASKER REPAIR p 1283
27535 460th Ave, Chancellor SD 57015
Tel (605) 647-5766 *SIC* 7699

■ MUELLER CO LLC p 998
633 Chestnut St Ste 1200, Chattanooga TN 37450
Tel (423) 209-4800 *SIC* 3823 3533 7699

KELSAN INC p 809
5109 N National Dr, Knoxville TN 37914
Tel (865) 525-7132 *SIC* 5087 5169 7699

HEAVY MACHINES INC p 680
3926 E Raines Rd, Memphis TN 38118
Tel (901) 260-2200
SIC 5082 7699 7353 3531 5063

LILLY CO p 866
3613 Knight Arnold Rd, Memphis TN 38118
Tel (901) 363-6000
SIC 5084 7699 7359 5046

NEXAIR LLC p 1039
1385 Corporate Ave, Memphis TN 38132
Tel (901) 396-5050
SIC 5169 5084 7699 7359

■ TEAM INDUSTRIAL SERVICES INC p 1430
200 Hermann Dr, Alvin TX 77511
Tel (281) 388-5525 *SIC* 8748 8711 7699

COUFAL-PRATER EQUIPMENT LLC p 374
3110 W Highway 21, Bryan TX 77803
Tel (979) 822-7684 *SIC* 5999 7699 5082

CLEAVER-BROOKS SALES AND SERVICE INC p 325
1956 Singleton Blvd, Dallas TX 75212
Tel (214) 637-0020 *SIC* 5074 7699 1711

■ AVIALL SERVICES INC p 137
2750 Regent Blvd, Dfw Airport TX 75261
Tel (972) 586-1000 *SIC* 5088 7699

LANDMARK STRUCTURES I LP p 843
1665 Harmon Rd, Fort Worth TX 76177
Tel (817) 439-8888 *SIC* 1791 7699

AIRBUS HELICOPTERS INC p 40
2701 N Forum Dr, Grand Prairie TX 75052
Tel (972) 641-0000 *SIC* 5088 7699 3721

■ GE ON WING SUPPORT INC p 596
3010 Red Hawk Dr Ste B, Grand Prairie TX 75052
Tel (214) 960-3322 *SIC* 7699 8711

DALLAS AIRMOTIVE INC p 409
900 Nolen Dr Ste 100, Grapevine TX 76051
Tel (214) 956-3001 *SIC* 7699

INTERNATIONAL AIRMOTIVE HOLDING CO INC p 754
900 Nolen Dr Ste 100, Grapevine TX 76051
Tel (214) 956-3000 *SIC* 7699 3724

MASTER PUMPS & EQUIPMENT CORP p 918
805 Port America Pl # 100, Grapevine TX 76051
Tel (817) 251-6745 *SIC* 5084 7699

AXIP ENERGY SERVICES LP p 140
1301 Mckinney St Ste 900, Houston TX 77010
Tel (832) 294-6500 *SIC* 5084 7699

BAE SYSTEMS RESOLUTION INC p 144
1000 La St Ste 4950, Houston TX 77002
Tel (713) 868-7700
SIC 3713 5084 3711 7699 3351 3829

CARRUTH-DOGGETT INC p 261
7110 North Fwy, Houston TX 77076
Tel (713) 675-7000 *SIC* 5084 7359 7699

CGGVERITAS LAND (US) INC p 285
10300 Town Park Dr, Houston TX 77072
Tel (832) 351-8300 *SIC* 7699

ENERFLEX ENERGY SYSTEMS INC p 497
10815 Telge Rd, Houston TX 77095
Tel (281) 345-9300
SIC 3585 7623 7699 3563

EQUIPMENT DEPOT LTD p 506
840 Gessner Rd Ste 950, Houston TX 77024
Tel (713) 365-2547
SIC 5083 5084 7359 7699 7353

ETHOSENERGY GTS HOLDINGS (US) LLC p 511
2800 North Loop W # 1100, Houston TX 77092
Tel (281) 227-5600 *SIC* 1731 7699 4581

■ FURMANITE AMERICA INC p 585
10370 Richmond Ave # 600, Houston TX 77042
Tel (713) 634-7777 *SIC* 7699

■ FURMANITE CORP p 585
10370 Richmond Ave # 600, Houston TX 77042
Tel (713) 634-7777 *SIC* 7699 7389

■ FURMANITE WORLDWIDE INC p 585
10370 Richmond Ave # 600, Houston TX 77042
Tel (972) 699-4000 *SIC* 7699 3599 7389

▲ KIRBY CORP p 821
55 Waugh Dr Ste 1000, Houston TX 77007
Tel (713) 435-1000 *SIC* 4449 7699

MUNDY PLANT MAINTENANCE INC p 1000
11150 S Wilcrest Dr # 300, Houston TX 77099
Tel (281) 530-8711 *SIC* 7699

PVI HOLDINGS INC p 1193
840 Gessner Rd Ste 950, Houston TX 77024
Tel (713) 365-6805 *SIC* 5085 5084 7699

■ T-3 ENERGY SERVICES INC p 1420
140 Cypress Station Dr # 225, Houston TX 77090
Tel (713) 944-5950 *SIC* 5211 3491 7699

TOTAL SAFETY US INC p 1463
11111 Wilcrest Green Dr # 375, Houston TX 77042
Tel (713) 353-7100 *SIC* 8748 5084 7699

■ AARON BROTHERS INC p 8
8001 Ridgepoint Dr, Irving TX 75063
Tel (214) 492-6200 *SIC* 7699 5945

▲ GLOBAL POWER EQUIPMENT GROUP INC p 617
400 Las Colinas Blvd E, Irving TX 75039
Tel (214) 574-2000 *SIC* 3568 1796 7699

VERMEER EQUIPMENT OF TEXAS INC p 1551
3025 State Highway 161, Irving TX 75062
Tel (972) 255-3500 *SIC* 5082 7699 7353

■ COMPRESSOR SYSTEMS INC p 352
3809 S Fm 1788, Midland TX 79706
Tel (432) 563-1170 *SIC* 7359 7699 3563

PRODUCTION SPECIALTY SERVICES LLC p 1180
511 W Missouri Ave, Midland TX 79701
Tel (432) 620-0059 *SIC* 5082 7699

WARREN EQUIPMENT CO p 1577
10325 Younger Rd, Midland TX 79706
Tel (432) 571-8462
SIC 5082 5084 7699 3563 7359

WILHELMSEN SHIPS SERVICE INC p 1609
9400 New Century Dr, Pasadena TX 77507
Tel (281) 867-2000 *SIC* 5551 5088 7699

RAY LEE EQUIPMENT CO LTD p 1209
910 N Date St, Plainview TX 79072
Tel (806) 293-2538 *SIC* 5083 7699

■ FISHER-ROSEMOUNT SYSTEMS INC p 552
1100 W Louis Henna Blvd, Round Rock TX 78681
Tel (512) 835-2190 *SIC* 3625 3621 7699

■ CHROMALLOY COMPONENT SERVICES INC p 304
303 Industrial Park Rd, San Antonio TX 78226
Tel (210) 331-2300 *SIC* 7699 3724

HOLT TEXAS LTD p 702
5665 Se Loop 410, San Antonio TX 78222
Tel (210) 648-1111
SIC 3531 5082 7353 7699

ISS FACILITY SERVICES INC p 767
1019 Central Pkwy N # 100, San Antonio TX 78232
Tel (210) 495-6021 *SIC* 7699

STANDARD AERO INC p 1375
3523 General Hudnell Dr, San Antonio TX 78226
Tel (210) 704-1100 *SIC* 7699

VT SAN ANTONIO AEROSPACE INC p 1567
9800 John Saunders Rd, San Antonio TX 78216
Tel (210) 293-3200 *SIC* 7699

■ PLANT PERFORMANCE SERVICES LLC p 1154
4800 Sugar Grove Blvd # 450, Stafford TX 77477
Tel (832) 532-5600 *SIC* 1731 1799 7699

SULZER US HOLDING INC p 1397
2277 Plaza Dr Ste 600, Sugar Land TX 77479
Tel (832) 886-2299 *SIC* 7699 3594

▲ TEAM INC p 1430
13131 Dar Ashford Ste 600, Sugar Land TX 77478
Tel (281) 331-6154 *SIC* 7389 7699

HMT INC p 698
24 Waterway Ave Ste 400, The Woodlands TX 77380
Tel (281) 681-7000
SIC 7699 3443 7389 1791

■ MCC HOLDINGS INC p 926
4526 Res Frest Dr Ste 400, The Woodlands TX 77381
Tel (936) 271-6500 *SIC* 3491 7699

ALIMAK HEK INC p 50
12552 Galveston Rd Ste A 160, Webster TX 77598
Tel (713) 640-8500
SIC 5084 7699 3535 3534

GREAT BASIN INDUSTRIAL LLC p 633
1284 Flint Meadow Dr A, Kaysville UT 84037
Tel (801) 543-2100 *SIC* 3443 7699 1731

■ OEC MEDICAL SYSTEMS INC p 1075
384 N Wright Brothers Dr, Salt Lake City UT 84116
Tel (801) 328-9300 *SIC* 3844 7699

HUSKY INJECTION MOLDING SYSTEMS INC p 721
288 North Rd, Milton VT 05468
Tel (905) 951-5000 *SIC* 5084 7699

SAFRAN USA INC p 1267
700 S Washington St # 320, Alexandria VA 22314
Tel (703) 351-9898
SIC 3643 3621 7699 3724 5013 5088

FINCANTIERI MARINE SYSTEMS NORTH AMERICA INC p 543
800 Principal Ct Ste C, Chesapeake VA 23320
Tel (757) 548-6000 *SIC* 7699 5084

■ NORTHROP GRUMMAN TECHNICAL SERVICES INC p 1058
2340 Dulles Corner Blvd, Herndon VA 20171
Tel (703) 713-4096 *SIC* 4581 7699

BAE SYSTEMS NORFOLK SHIP REPAIR INC p 144
750 W Berkley Ave, Norfolk VA 23523
Tel (757) 494-4000 *SIC* 3731 3732 7699

WESTERN BRANCH DIESEL INC p 1597
3504 Shipwright St, Portsmouth VA 23703
Tel (757) 673-7000 *SIC* 5084 7699

ROLLS-ROYCE NORTH AMERICA HOLDINGS INC p 1248
1875 Explorer St Ste 200, Reston VA 20190
Tel (703) 834-1700 *SIC* 5088 8741 7699

NORTHWEST CASCADE INC p 1059
10412 John Bananola Way E, Puyallup WA 98374
Tel (253) 848-2371
SIC 1623 7359 7699 3272 1711

PHYSIO-CONTROL INC p 1146
11811 Willows Rd Ne, Redmond WA 98052
Tel (425) 867-4000
SIC 3841 3845 7699 7372

NORTH WEST HANDLING SYSTEMS INC p 1054
1100 Sw 7th St, Renton WA 98057
Tel (425) 255-0500 *SIC* 5084 7699

ENERGY NORTHWEST p 498
76 N Power Plant Loop, Richland WA 99354
Tel (509) 372-5000 *SIC* 4911 7699

EMERALD SERVICES INC p 491
7343 E Marginal Way S, Seattle WA 98108
Tel (206) 430-7795
SIC 4953 7699 2911 8748 7359

■ SPACELABS HEALTHCARE (WASHINGTON) INC p 1354
35301 Se Center St, Snoqualmie WA 98065
Tel (425) 396-3300
SIC 3845 3841 3575 7699 7378

■ SPACELABS HEALTHCARE INC p 1354
35301 Se Center St, Snoqualmie WA 98065
Tel (425) 396-3302
SIC 3841 3845 3575 7699 7378

WASHINGTON TRACTOR INC p 1579
2700 136th Avenue Ct E, Sumner WA 98390
Tel (253) 863-4436
SIC 3523 5083 5261 7699 7353

RISH EQUIPMENT CO p 1236
6384 Airport Rd, Bluefield WV 24701
Tel (304) 327-5124 *SIC* 5082 7699

■ **PRATT & WHITNEY ENGINE SERVICES INC** p 1167
1525 Midway Park Rd, Bridgeport WV 26330
Tel (860) 565-4321 *SIC* 7699 3724 4581

WISCONSIN LIFT TRUCK CORP p 1619
3125 Intertech Dr, Brookfield WI 53045
Tel (262) 790-6230 *SIC* 5084 5085 7699

ALLIED DIESEL INC p 56
13015 W Custer Ave, Butler WI 53007
Tel (262) 781-7100 *SIC* 5084 5531 7699

PNA HOLDINGS LLC p 1158
3150 Pleasant View Rd, Madison WI 53713
Tel (608) 203-1500
SIC 5044 5045 5112 7699

E O JOHNSON CO INC p 466
8400 Stewart Ave, Wausau WI 54401
Tel (715) 842-9999 *SIC* 5112 7699 5045

CKT SERVICES INC p 320
412 N Main St Ste 100, Buffalo WY 82834
Tel (713) 581-0819 *SIC* 5172 7699

SIC 7812 Motion Picture & Video Tape Production

METRO-GOLDWYN-MAYER INC p 955
245 N Beverly Dr, Beverly Hills CA 90210
Tel (310) 449-3000 *SIC* 7812

MGM HOLDINGS II INC p 958
245 N Beverly Dr, Beverly Hills CA 90210
Tel (310) 449-3000 *SIC* 7812

MGM HOLDINGS INC p 958
245 N Beverly Dr, Beverly Hills CA 90210
Tel (310) 449-3000 *SIC* 7812

REALD INC p 1214
100 N Crescent Dr, Beverly Hills CA 90210
Tel (424) 702-4327 *SIC* 7812

■ **ABC FAMILY WORLDWIDE INC** p 10
500 S Buena Vista St, Burbank CA 91521
Tel (818) 560-1000 *SIC* 7812 4841

■ **DISNEY ENTERPRISES INC** p 443
500 S Buena Vista St, Burbank CA 91521
Tel (818) 560-1000
SIC 7812 6794 5331 7996 7941

■ **DISNEY WORLDWIDE SERVICES INC** p 443
500 S Buena Vista St, Burbank CA 91521
Tel (877) 466-6669 *SIC* 7812 5736

▲ **WALT DISNEY CO** p 1574
500 S Buena Vista St, Burbank CA 91521
Tel (818) 560-1000
SIC 4833 4841 7011 7996 7812 2731

■ **WALT DISNEY RECORDS DIRECT** p 1574
500 S Buena Vista St, Burbank CA 91521
Tel (818) 560-1000 *SIC* 7812

■ **WARNER BROS ENTERTAINMENT INC** p 1576
4000 Warner Blvd, Burbank CA 91522
Tel (818) 954-6000 *SIC* 7812

COLUMBIA PICTURES INDUSTRIES INC p 341
10202 Washington Blvd, Culver City CA 90232
Tel (310) 244-4000 *SIC* 7812

SONY PICTURES ENTERTAINMENT INC p 1341
10202 Washington Blvd, Culver City CA 90232
Tel (310) 244-4000 *SIC* 7812 7822 7832

GUTHY-RENKER LLC p 648
100 N Sepulveda Blvd # 1600, El Segundo CA 90245
Tel (760) 773-9022
SIC 5099 7812 5999 7389

■ **PIXAR** p 1152
1200 Park Ave, Emeryville CA 94608
Tel (510) 922-3000 *SIC* 7812 7372 7371

■ **DWA HOLDINGS LLC** p 463
1000 Flower St, Glendale CA 91201
Tel (818) 695-5000 *SIC* 7812

AUDIO VISUAL SERVICES GROUP INC p 131
111 Ocean Beach Blvd Ste 1110, Long Beach CA 90802
Tel (562) 366-0620 *SIC* 7389 7812 7359

AUGE MEDIA CORP p 131
2029 Century Park E Fl 14, Los Angeles CA 90067
Tel (310) 739-8000 *SIC* 2741 7812

■ **FOX INC** p 572
2121 Ave Of The Ste 1100, Los Angeles CA 90067
Tel (310) 369-1000 *SIC* 4833 7812

METRO-GOLDWYN-MAYER STUDIOS INC p 955
10250 Constellation Blvd, Los Angeles CA 90067
Tel (310) 449-3590 *SIC* 7812

■ **PARAMOUNT PICTURES CORP** p 1114
5555 Melrose Ave, Los Angeles CA 90038
Tel (323) 956-5000
SIC 7812 5099 4833 7829

■ **PARAMOUNT TELEVISION SERVICE INC** p 1114
5555 Melrose Ave, Los Angeles CA 90038
Tel (323) 956-5000 *SIC* 7812

■ **TWENTIETH CENTURY FOX FILM CORP** p 1494
10201 W Pico Blvd, Los Angeles CA 90064
Tel (310) 369-1000 *SIC* 7812

■ **UNIVERSAL STUDIOS INC** p 1517
100 Universal City Plz, North Hollywood CA 91608
Tel (818) 777-1000
SIC 7812 3652 2741 5947 5944 5961

OOYALA HOLDINGS INC p 1089
4750 Patrick Henry Dr, Santa Clara CA 95054
Tel (650) 961-3400 *SIC* 7812 6719

LIONS GATE ENTERTAINMENT INC p 870
2700 Colorado Ave Ste 200, Santa Monica CA 90404
Tel (310) 449-9200 *SIC* 7812

DW STUDIOS LLC p 463
100 Universal City Plz, Universal City CA 91608
Tel (818) 695-5000 *SIC* 7812

■ **UNIVERSAL CITY STUDIOS INC** p 1516
100 Universal City Plz, Universal City CA 91608
Tel (818) 622-8477 *SIC* 7812 7996

■ **UNIVERSAL CITY STUDIOS PRODUCTIONS LLLP LP** p 1516
100 Universal City Plz, Universal City CA 91608
Tel (818) 777-1000
SIC 7812 3652 2741 5947 5944 5961

■ **STARZ ENTERTAINMENT LLC** p 1380
8900 Liberty Cir, Englewood CO 80112
Tel (720) 852-7700 *SIC* 7812

■ **STARZ LLC** p 1380
8900 Liberty Cir, Englewood CO 80112
Tel (720) 852-7700 *SIC* 7812

▲ **GAIA INC** p 589
833 W South Boulder Rd, Louisville CO 80027
Tel (303) 222-3600 *SIC* 7299 7812 7999

TAUNTON INC p 1426
63 S Main St, Newtown CT 06470
Tel (203) 426-8171
SIC 2721 2731 7812 5963

■ **TIME WARNER CABLE ENTERPRISES LLC** p 1454
400 Atlantic St Ste 6, Stamford CT 06901
Tel (877) 495-9201 *SIC* 7812 4841

▲ **WORLD WRESTLING ENTERTAINMENT INC** p 1625
1241 E Main St, Stamford CT 06902
Tel (203) 352-8600 *SIC* 7812 7929 2721

CORP FOR PUBLIC BROADCASTING p 371
401 9th St Nw Ste 200, Washington DC 20004
Tel (202) 879-9600 *SIC* 7812

■ **TURNER BROADCASTING SYSTEM INC** p 1492
1 Cnn Ctr Nw 14sw, Atlanta GA 30303
Tel (404) 575-7250
SIC 7822 4833 4841 7812

■ **TWCC HOLDING CORP** p 1494
300 Interstate N Pkwy Se, Atlanta GA 30339
Tel (770) 226-0000
SIC 4833 4813 7812 8999

WILTON BRANDS LLC p 1614
2240 75th St, Woodridge IL 60517
Tel (630) 963-7100
SIC 5023 2731 2721 7812 5199

WILTON HOLDINGS INC p 1614
2240 75th St, Woodridge IL 60517
Tel (630) 963-7100
SIC 5023 2731 2721 7812 5199

WILTON INDUSTRIES INC p 1614
2240 75th St, Woodridge IL 60517
Tel (630) 963-7100
SIC 5023 2731 2721 7812 5199

▲ **DISCOVERY COMMUNICATIONS INC** p 442
1 Discovery Pl, Silver Spring MD 20910
Tel (240) 662-2000 *SIC* 4841 7812 7922

WGBH EDUCATIONAL FOUNDATION p 1604
1 Guest St, Boston MA 02135
Tel (617) 300-2000 *SIC* 7812 4833 4832

LIFETOUCH INC p 865
11000 Viking Dr, Eden Prairie MN 55344
Tel (952) 826-4000 *SIC* 7221 7812 2741

MARCO TECHNOLOGIES LLC p 905
4510 Heatherwood Rd, Saint Cloud MN 56301
Tel (320) 259-3000
SIC 7371 4813 7313 7812

HUBBARD BROADCASTING INC p 716
3415 University Ave W, Saint Paul MN 55114
Tel (651) 642-4656 *SIC* 4833 7812 4832

VICE GROUP HOLDING INC p 1555
49 S 2nd St, Brooklyn NY 11249
Tel (718) 599-3101 *SIC* 8748 7812

■ **21ST CENTURY FOX AMERICA INC** p 1
1211 Ave Of The Americas, New York NY 10036
Tel (212) 852-7000
SIC 2752 2721 4833 7812

■ **ABC INC** p 10
77 W 66th St Rm 100, New York NY 10023
Tel (212) 456-7777
SIC 4833 4832 7812 6794 2711 2721

AMERICAN MANAGEMENT ASSOCIATION INTERNATIONAL p 75
1601 Broadway Fl 7, New York NY 10019
Tel (212) 586-8100
SIC 8299 2731 8621 7812 2721

■ **CBS BROADCASTING INC** p 269
51 W 52nd St, New York NY 10019
Tel (212) 975-4321 *SIC* 4833 4832 7812

■ **FOX ENTERTAINMENT GROUP INC** p 572
1211 Ave Of The Americas, New York NY 10036
Tel (212) 852-7000 *SIC* 7812 4841

■ **FOX NEWS NETWORK LLC** p 572
1211 Avenue Of The Americ, New York NY 10036
Tel (212) 301-3000 *SIC* 7812

■ **HISTORIC TW INC** p 696
75 Rockefeller Plz, New York NY 10019
Tel (212) 484-8000
SIC 3652 6794 2741 7812 4841 2721

■ **HOME BOX OFFICE INC** p 703
1100 Avenue Of The Americ, New York NY 10036
Tel (212) 512-1000 *SIC* 4841 7812

■ **MARTHA STEWART LIVING OMNIMEDIA INC** p 912
601 W 26th St Rm 900, New York NY 10001
Tel (212) 827-8000
SIC 2721 2731 4813 7812

■ **NBCUNIVERSAL MEDIA LLC** p 1021
30 Rockefeller Plz Fl 2, New York NY 10112
Tel (212) 664-4444
SIC 4841 4833 7812 7996

OGILVY & MATHER WORLDWIDE INC p 1076
636 11th Ave, New York NY 10036
Tel (212) 237-4000
SIC 7311 7812 7375 8742

▲ **SCHOLASTIC CORP** p 1288
557 Broadway Lbby 1, New York NY 10012
Tel (212) 343-6100
SIC 2731 2721 7372 7812 6794 7311

■ **SCHOLASTIC INC** p 1288
557 Broadway Lbby 1, New York NY 10012
Tel (800) 724-6527
SIC 2731 2721 7372 7812

SESAME WORKSHOP p 1308
1 Lincoln Plz Fl 2, New York NY 10023
Tel (212) 595-3456 *SIC* 7812 2731

SONY BROADBAND ENTERTAINMENT CORP p 1340
550 Madison Ave Fl 6, New York NY 10022
Tel (212) 833-6800
SIC 3652 7812 5734 7832 5735

▲ **TIME WARNER INC** p 1454
1 Time Warner Ctr Bsmt B, New York NY 10019
Tel (212) 484-8000
SIC 4841 7812 2731 2721

▲ **VIACOM INC** p 1554
1515 Broadway, New York NY 10036
Tel (212) 258-6000 *SIC* 4841 7812

■ **VIACOM SONGS INC** p 1554
1515 Broadway Lbby, New York NY 10036
Tel (212) 258-6000
SIC 6531 6519 7359 7941 7812 2731

VIVENDI HOLDING I LLC p 1563
1755 Broadway Fl 2, New York NY 10019
Tel (212) 572-7000 *SIC* 7812 7389

■ **VIVENDI UNIVERSAL ENTERTAINMENT LLLP** p 1563
30 Rockefeller Plz, New York NY 10112
Tel (212) 664-4444
SIC 7812 3652 2741 5947 5944 5961

■ **WARNER COMMUNICATIONS INC** p 1576
1 Time Warner Ctr, New York NY 10019
Tel (212) 484-8000 *SIC* 7812 4841 7389

▲ **COMCAST CORP** p 343
1701 Jfk Blvd, Philadelphia PA 19103
Tel (215) 286-1700
SIC 4841 4813 7812 7996

JOSH BIRT LLC p 794
2 Fordham Ave, Pittsburgh PA 15229
Tel (412) 719-7182 *SIC* 7812

PRODUCTION DESIGN ASSOCIATES INC p 1179
2799 Three Lakes Rd, North Charleston SC 29418
Tel (843) 554-3466 *SIC* 7812 1731

SONIFI SOLUTIONS INC p 1340
3900 W Innovation St, Sioux Falls SD 57107
Tel (605) 988-1000 *SIC* 7812 8082

■ **ALLBRITTON COMMUNICATIONS CO** p 52
1000 Wilson Blvd Ste 2700, Arlington VA 22209
Tel (703) 647-8700 *SIC* 4833 7812

INTERNATIONAL MISSION BOARD OF SOUTHERN BAPTIST CONVENTION p 756
3806 Monument Ave, Richmond VA 23230
Tel (804) 353-0151 *SIC* 8661 2731 7812

SIC 7819 Services Allied To Motion Picture Prdtn

ACADEMY OF MOTION PICTURE ARTS & SCIENCES p 13
8949 Wilshire Blvd, Beverly Hills CA 90211
Tel (310) 247-3000 *SIC* 8621 7819 8611

FOTO-KEM INDUSTRIES INC p 571
2801 W Alameda Ave, Burbank CA 91505
Tel (818) 846-3102 *SIC* 7819

TECHNICOLOR THOMSON GROUP INC p 1431
2233 N Ontario St Ste 300, Burbank CA 91504
Tel (818) 260-3600 *SIC* 7819 7384

■ **DTS INC** p 458
5220 Las Virgenes Rd, Calabasas CA 91302
Tel (818) 436-1000 *SIC* 7819 3651

TECHNICOLOR HOME ENTERTAINMENT SERVICES INC p 1431
3233 Mission Oaks Blvd, Camarillo CA 93012
Tel (805) 445-1122 *SIC* 7819

TECHNICOLOR VIDEOCASSETTE OF MICHIGAN INC p 1431
3233 Mission Oaks Blvd, Camarillo CA 93012
Tel (805) 445-1122 *SIC* 7819

■ **WALT DISNEY IMAGINEERING RESEARCH & DEVELOPMENT INC** p 1574
1401 Flower St, Glendale CA 91201
Tel (818) 544-6500
SIC 7819 8712 1542 8741 8711

ALLIANCE MEDICAL PRODUCTS INC p 54
9342 Jeronimo Rd, Irvine CA 92618
Tel (949) 768-4690 *SIC* 3841 7819

■ **BLIZZARD ENTERTAINMENT INC** p 189
16215 Alton Pkwy, Irvine CA 92618
Tel (949) 955-1380 *SIC* 7372 5734 7819

DELUXE ENTERTAINMENT SERVICES GROUP INC p 427
2400 W Empire Ave, Los Angeles CA 90027
Tel (323) 462-6171 *SIC* 7819 7313

■ **LIBERTY INTERACTIVE LLC** p 862
12300 Liberty Blvd, Englewood CO 80112
Tel (720) 875-5400
SIC 5961 4841 7819 4813

UNIVERSAL CITY FLORIDA PARTNERS p 1516
1000 Unversal Studios Plz, Orlando FL 32819
Tel (407) 363-8000 *SIC* 7996 7819

DELUXE MEDIA SERVICES INC p 427
568 Atrium Dr, Vernon Hills IL 60061
Tel (847) 990-4100 *SIC* 7819 7822

BERTELSMANN INC p 176
1745 Broadway Fl 20, New York NY 10019
Tel (212) 782-1000
SIC 2731 2721 7819 3652 6512

MACANDREWS & FORBES HOLDINGS INC p 891
35 E 62nd St, New York NY 10065
Tel (212) 572-8600 *SIC* 7819

MACANDREWS & FORBES INC p 891
38 E 63rd St, New York NY 10065
Tel (212) 688-9000
SIC 2844 2087 2121 7819 2721 2731

VI(Z)RT INC p 1554
352 7th Ave Fl 14, New York NY 10001
Tel (212) 560-0708 *SIC* 7819

VITAC CORP p 1562
101 Hillpointe Dr Ste 200, Canonsburg PA 15317
Tel (724) 514-4000 *SIC* 4899 7819

SIC 7822 Motion Picture & Video Tape Distribution

■ **WARNER BROS (TRANSATLANTIC) INC** p 1576
4000 Warner Blvd, Burbank CA 91522
Tel (818) 977-0018 *SIC* 7822

VOLCOM LLC p 1564
1740 Monrovia Ave, Costa Mesa CA 92627
Tel (949) 646-2175
SIC 7389 2253 7822 5136 5137

SONY PICTURES ENTERTAINMENT INC p 1341
10202 Washington Blvd, Culver City CA 90232
Tel (310) 244-4000 *SIC* 7812 7822 7832

ABS-CBN INTERNATIONAL p 12
150 Shoreline Dr, Redwood City CA 94065
Tel (800) 527-2820 *SIC* 4841 7822

VIACOM NETWORKS p 1554
2600 Colorado Ave, Santa Monica CA 90404
Tel (310) 453-4826 *SIC* 7822

■ **TURNER BROADCASTING SYSTEM INC** p 1492
1 Cnn Ctr Nw 14sw, Atlanta GA 30303
Tel (404) 575-7250
SIC 7822 4833 4841 7812

DELUXE MEDIA SERVICES INC p 427
568 Atrium Dr, Vernon Hills IL 60061
Tel (847) 990-4100 *SIC* 7819 7822

▲ **RLJ ENTERTAINMENT INC** p 1239
8515 Georgia Ave Ste 650, Silver Spring MD 20910
Tel (301) 608-2115 *SIC* 7822

▲ **SEACHANGE INTERNATIONAL INC** p 1296
50 Nagog Park, Acton MA 01720
Tel (978) 897-0100 *SIC* 3663 7822 7371

■ **HBO SERVICES INC** p 671
1100 Ave Of The Am Frnt 3, New York NY 10036
Tel (212) 512-1000 *SIC* 7822

■ **NBC INTERNATIONAL LTD** p 1021
30 Rockefeller Plz Fl 2, New York NY 10112
Tel (212) 664-4444 *SIC* 7822

BAKER & TAYLOR FULFILLMENT INC p 145
2550 W Tyvola Rd Ste 300, Charlotte NC 28217
Tel (704) 998-3154
SIC 5192 5045 7822 5065

BAKER & TAYLOR HOLDINGS LLC p 145
2550 W Tyvola Rd Ste 300, Charlotte NC 28217
Tel (704) 998-3100
SIC 5192 7822 5065 5045

BAKER & TAYLOR LLC p 145
2550 W Tyvola Rd Ste 300, Charlotte NC 28217
Tel (704) 998-3100
SIC 5192 7822 5065 5045 5099

BTAC ACQUISITION LLC p 222
2550 W Tyvola Rd Ste 300, Charlotte NC 28217
Tel (704) 998-3100
SIC 5192 7822 5065 5045

BTAC HOLDING CORP p 222
2550 W Tyvola Rd Ste 300, Charlotte NC 28217
Tel (704) 998-3100
SIC 5192 7822 5065 5045

MIDWEST TAPE LLC p 968
1417 Timber Wolf Dr, Holland OH 43528
Tel (419) 868-9370
SIC 7822 5099 8741 7389 5961 7374

SIC 7829 Services Allied To Motion Picture Distribution

■ **PARAMOUNT PICTURES CORP** p 1114
5555 Melrose Ave, Los Angeles CA 90038
Tel (323) 956-5000
SIC 7812 5099 4833 7829

SIC 7832 Motion Picture Theaters, Except Drive-In

THEATRES COBB III LLC p 1446
2000b Southbridge Pkwy # 100, Birmingham AL 35209
Tel (205) 802-7766 *SIC* 7832

SONY PICTURES ENTERTAINMENT INC p 1341
10202 Washington Blvd, Culver City CA 90232
Tel (310) 244-4000 *SIC* 7812 7822 7832

WESTSTAR CINEMAS INC p 1603
16530 Ventura Blvd # 500, Encino CA 91436
Tel (818) 784-6266 *SIC* 7832

DECURION CORP p 421
120 N Robertson Blvd Fl 3, Los Angeles CA 90048
Tel (310) 659-9432 *SIC* 7832 7833

NATIONWIDE THEATRES CORP p 1018
120 N Robertson Blvd Fl 3, Los Angeles CA 90048
Tel (310) 657-8420 *SIC* 7833 7832

▲ **READING INTERNATIONAL INC** p 1213
6100 Center Dr Ste 900, Los Angeles CA 90045
Tel (213) 235-2240
SIC 7832 7922 6512 6531

SILVER CINEMAS ACQUISITION CO p 1323
2222 S Barrington Ave, Los Angeles CA 90064
Tel (310) 473-6701 *SIC* 7832

■ **EDWARDS THEATRES CIRCUIT INC** p 480
300 Newport Center Dr, Newport Beach CA 92660
Tel (949) 640-4600 *SIC* 7832

■ **UNITED ARTISTS THEATRE CO** p 1506
9110 E Nichols Ave # 200, Centennial CO 80112
Tel (303) 792-3600 *SIC* 7832

GOODRICH QUALITY THEATERS INC p 624
31 Island Way Apt 606, Clearwater Beach FL 33767
Tel (616) 698-7733 *SIC* 7832

MUVICO THEATERS INC p 1003
2929 E Coml Blvd Ste 408, Fort Lauderdale FL 33308
Tel (954) 564-6550 *SIC* 7832 8741

▲ **CARMIKE CINEMAS INC** p 258
1301 1st Ave, Columbus GA 31901
Tel (706) 576-3400 *SIC* 7832

■ **GEORGE G KERASOTES CORP** p 606
1301 1st Ave, Columbus GA 31901
Tel (706) 576-3400 *SIC* 7832

■ **KERASOTES SHOWPLACE THEATRES LLC** p 813
224 N Des Plns Ste 200, Chicago IL 60661
Tel (312) 756-3360 SIC 7832

■ **AMC ENTERTAINMENT HOLDINGS INC** p 65
1 Amc Way 11500 Ash St, Leawood KS 66211
Tel (913) 213-2000 SIC 7832

■ **AMC ENTERTAINMENT INC** p 65
11500 Ash St, Leawood KS 66211
Tel (913) 213-2000 SIC 7832

■ **AMERICAN MULTI-CINEMA INC** p 76
1 Amc Way, Leawood KS 66211
Tel (913) 213-2000 SIC 7832 5812 8741

SOUTHERN THEATRES LLC p 1350
935 Gravier St Ste 1200, New Orleans LA 70112
Tel (504) 297-1133 SIC 7832

R/C THEATRES MANAGEMENT CORP p 1203
231 W Cherry Hill Ct, Reisterstown MD 21136
Tel (410) 526-4774 SIC 8741 7922 7832

■ **GENERAL CINEMA CORP OF TEXAS** p 599
1300 Boylston St, Chestnut Hill MA 02467
Tel (617) 738-3513 SIC 7832

▲ **NATIONAL AMUSEMENTS INC** p 1009
846 University Ave, Norwood MA 02062
Tel (781) 461-1600
SIC 7832 7833 4832 4833 4841

OLYMPIA ENTERTAINMENT INC p 1083
2211 Woodward Ave, Detroit MI 48201
Tel (313) 471-3200 SIC 7832

IMPERIAL PALACE OF MISSISSIPPI LLC p 734
850 Bayview Ave, Biloxi MS 39530
Tel (228) 432-3243
SIC 7011 5812 5813 7832

CLEARVIEW CINEMA GROUP INC p 324
97 Main St Ste A, Chatham NJ 07928
Tel (973) 377-4646 SIC 7832

CCG HOLDINGS LLC p 270
1111 Stewart Ave, Bethpage NY 11714
Tel (516) 803-2300 SIC 7832

▲ **PAR TECHNOLOGY CORP** p 1113
8383 Seneca Tpke Ste 2, New Hartford NY 13413
Tel (315) 738-0600 SIC 7372 7832

SONY BROADBAND ENTERTAINMENT CORP p 1340
550 Madison Ave Fl 6, New York NY 10022
Tel (212) 833-6800
SIC 3652 7812 5734 7832 5735

■ **CONSOLIDATED THEATRES INC** p 360
5970 Fairview Rd Ste 600, Charlotte NC 28210
Tel (704) 554-1695 SIC 7832 5441

■ **WALLACE THEATER HOLDINGS INC** p 1573
919 Sw Taylor St Ste 800, Portland OR 97205
Tel (503) 221-7090 SIC 7832

■ **REGAL CINEMAS CORP** p 1218
7132 Regal Ln, Knoxville TN 37918
Tel (865) 922-1123 SIC 7832 5812

■ **REGAL CINEMAS INC** p 1218
7132 Regal Ln, Knoxville TN 37918
Tel (865) 922-1123 SIC 7832

▲ **REGAL ENTERTAINMENT GROUP** p 1218
7132 Regal Ln, Knoxville TN 37918
Tel (865) 922-1123 SIC 7832

■ **REGAL ENTERTAINMENT HOLDINGS INC** p 1218
7132 Regal Ln, Knoxville TN 37918
Tel (865) 922-1123 SIC 7832

■ **UNITED ARTISTS THEATRE CIRCUIT INC** p 1506
7132 Regal Ln, Knoxville TN 37918
Tel (865) 922-1123 SIC 7832

RAVE CINEMAS LLC p 1209
3333 Welborn St Ste 100, Dallas TX 75219
Tel (214) 220-7600 SIC 7832

USA CINEMA INVESTMENT HOLDINGS INC p 1534
14951 Dallas Pkwy, Dallas TX 75254
Tel (972) 993-1553 SIC 7832

■ **CINEMARK INC** p 307
3900 Dallas Pkwy Ste 500, Plano TX 75093
Tel (800) 246-3627 SIC 7832

■ **CINEMARK USA INC** p 307
3900 Dallas Pkwy Ste 500, Plano TX 75093
Tel (972) 665-1000 SIC 7832

LARRY H MILLER THEATRES INC p 845
35 E 9270 S, Sandy UT 84070
Tel (801) 304-4500 SIC 7832

■ **MARCUS THEATRES CORP** p 905
100 E Wisconsin Ave, Milwaukee WI 53202
Tel (414) 905-1500 SIC 7832

SIC 7833 Drive-In Motion Picture Theaters

DECURION CORP p 421
120 N Robertson Blvd Fl 3, Los Angeles CA 90048
Tel (310) 659-9432 SIC 7832 7833

NATIONWIDE THEATRES CORP p 1018
120 N Robertson Blvd Fl 3, Los Angeles CA 90048
Tel (310) 657-8420 SIC 7833 7832

▲ **NATIONAL AMUSEMENTS INC** p 1009
846 University Ave, Norwood MA 02062
Tel (781) 461-1600
SIC 7832 7833 4832 4833 4841

■ **CENTURY THEATRES INC** p 282
3900 Dallas Pkwy Ste 500, Plano TX 75093
Tel (972) 665-1000 SIC 7833

▲ **MARCUS CORP** p 905
100 E Wisconsin Ave # 1, Milwaukee WI 53202
Tel (414) 905-1000 SIC 7011 7833

SIC 7841 Video Tape Rental

G A M INC p 586
900 W Main St, Dothan AL 36301
Tel (334) 677-2108 SIC 7841 5735

▲ **NETFLIX INC** p 1027
100 Winchester Cir, Los Gatos CA 95032
Tel (408) 540-3700 SIC 2741 7841

■ **BLOCKBUSTER LLC** p 189
9601 S Meridian Blvd, Englewood CO 80112
Tel (702) 262-0703 SIC 7841 5735

■ **REDBOX AUTOMATED RETAIL LLC** p 1216
1 Tower Ln Ste 1200, Oakbrook Terrace IL 60181
Tel (630) 756-8700 SIC 7841

MIDSTATES VIDEO CORP p 966
1022 E Adams St, Springfield IL 62703
Tel (217) 544-8433 SIC 7389 7841

SCHNUCK MARKETS INC p 1288
11420 Lackland Rd, Saint Louis MO 63146
Tel (314) 994-9900
SIC 5411 5912 5812 7841

▲ **TRANS WORLD ENTERTAINMENT CORP** p 1470
38 Corporate Cir, Albany NY 12203
Tel (518) 452-1242
SIC 5735 5731 5734 7841 5961

HOLLYWOOD ENTERTAINMENT CORP p 701
9275 Sw Peyton Ln, Wilsonville OR 97070
Tel (503) 214-4600 SIC 7841

MOVIE GALLERY INC p 995
9275 Sw Peyton Ln, Wilsonville OR 97070
Tel (503) 570-1700 SIC 7841 5735

HASTINGS ENTERTAINMENT INC p 667
3601 Plains Blvd, Amarillo TX 79102
Tel (806) 351-2300 SIC 5735 5942 7841

■ **COINSTAR LLC** p 335
1800 114th Ave Se, Bellevue WA 98004
Tel (425) 943-8000 SIC 7299 7841

SIC 7911 Dance Studios, Schools & Halls

JUILLIARD SCHOOL p 797
60 Lincoln Center Plz, New York NY 10023
Tel (212) 799-5000
SIC 8299 7911 5942 8221

SIC 7922 Theatrical Producers & Misc Theatrical Svcs

CABRILLO COMMUNITY COLLEGE DISTRICT FINANCING CORP p 235
6500 Soquel Dr, Aptos CA 95003
Tel (831) 479-6100 SIC 8222 7922 8221

▲ **LIVE NATION ENTERTAINMENT INC** p 871
9348 Civic Center Dr Lbby, Beverly Hills CA 90210
Tel (310) 867-7000 SIC 7922 7389 7941

SEGERSTROM CENTER FOR ARTS p 1300
600 Town Center Dr, Costa Mesa CA 92626
Tel (714) 556-2122 SIC 7922

ELECTRIC MOTOR SHOP p 484
253 Fulton St, Fresno CA 93721
Tel (559) 233-1153
SIC 5063 1731 7694 7922

CREATIVE ARTISTS AGENCY LLC p 390
2000 Avenue Of The Stars # 100, Los Angeles CA 90067
Tel (424) 288-2000 SIC 7922

▲ **READING INTERNATIONAL INC** p 1213
6100 Center Dr Ste 900, Los Angeles CA 90045
Tel (213) 235-2240
SIC 7832 7922 6512 6531

TICKETMASTER CORP p 1452
7060 Hollywood Blvd Ste 2, Los Angeles CA 90028
Tel (323) 769-4600 SIC 7999 7922

SAN FRANCISCO OPERA ASSOCIATION p 1276
301 Van Ness Ave, San Francisco CA 94102
Tel (415) 861-4008 SIC 7922

■ **STUBHUB INC** p 1394
199 Fremont St Fl 4, San Francisco CA 94105
Tel (415) 222-8400 SIC 7374 7999 7922

TRINITY CHRISTIAN CENTER OF SANTA ANA INC p 1481
2442 Michelle Dr, Tustin CA 92780
Tel (714) 665-3619 SIC 4833 7922

NBC STUDIOS INC p 1021
100 Universal City Plz, Universal City CA 91608
Tel (818) 777-1000 SIC 7922

ENDEMOL p 496
9255 W Sunset Blvd # 1100, West Hollywood CA 90069
Tel (310) 860-9914 SIC 7922

■ **TICKETMASTER ENTERTAINMENT LLC** p 1452
8800 W Sunset Blvd, West Hollywood CA 90069
Tel (800) 653-8000 SIC 7922

JOHN F KENNEDY CENTER FOR PERFORMING ARTS p 788
2700 F St Nw, Washington DC 20566
Tel (202) 416-8000 SIC 7922 7929

RFE/RL INC p 1231
1201 Conn Ave Nw Ste 400, Washington DC 20036
Tel (202) 457-6900 SIC 7922

■ **OVATIONS FOOD SERVICES LP** p 1099
18228 N Us Highway 41, Lutz FL 33549
Tel (813) 948-6900 SIC 8742 7922

COX MEDIA GROUP LLC p 386
6205 Pachtree Dunwoody Rd, Atlanta GA 30328
Tel (678) 645-0000
SIC 4833 4832 7922 7313

IN TOUCH MINISTRIES INC p 735
3836 Dekalb Tec Pkwy, Atlanta GA 30340
Tel (770) 451-1001 SIC 7922

LYRIC OPERA OF CHICAGO p 888
20 N Wacker Dr Ste 860, Chicago IL 60606
Tel (312) 332-2244 SIC 7922

▲ **TRIBUNE MEDIA CO** p 1479
435 N Michigan Ave Fl 2, Chicago IL 60611
Tel (212) 210-2786
SIC 4833 4832 7922 7941

WHITECO INDUSTRIES INC p 1606
1000 E 80th Pl Ste 700n, Merrillville IN 46410
Tel (219) 769-6601
SIC 7312 7011 7922 6552 7374 3993

R/C THEATRES MANAGEMENT CORP p 1203
231 W Cherry Hill Ct, Reisterstown MD 21136
Tel (410) 526-4774 SIC 8741 7922 7832

▲ **DISCOVERY COMMUNICATIONS INC** p 442
1 Discovery Pl, Silver Spring MD 20910
Tel (240) 662-2000 SIC 4841 7812 7922

WANG CENTER FOR PERFORMING ARTS INC p 1575
270 Tremont St, Boston MA 02116
Tel (617) 482-9393 SIC 7922

TAPPET BROTHERS ASSOCIATES p 1424
5 John F Kennedy St # 304, Cambridge MA 02138
Tel (617) 876-6632 SIC 7922

PALACE SPORTS & ENTERTAINMENT LLC p 1108
6 Championship Dr, Auburn Hills MI 48326
Tel (248) 377-0165 SIC 7941 7922

ILITCH HOLDINGS INC p 732
2211 Woodward Ave, Detroit MI 48201
Tel (313) 983-6000 SIC 7941 7922 5812

NEWPORT TELEVISION LLC p 1038
460 Nichols Rd Ste 250, Kansas City MO 64112
Tel (816) 751-0200 SIC 7922

PRODUCTION RESOURCE GROUP LLC p 1179
200 Business Park Dr # 109, Armonk NY 10504
Tel (212) 589-5400 SIC 3999 7922

VICE MEDIA LLC p 1555
49 S 2nd St, Brooklyn NY 11249
Tel (718) 732-8142 SIC 7922

CARNEGIE HALL CORP p 258
881 Sventh Ave At 57th St, New York NY 10019
Tel (212) 903-9600 SIC 7922 6531

JOHN GORE ORGANIZATION INC p 788
1619 Broadway Fl 9, New York NY 10019
Tel (917) 421-5400 SIC 7922

■ **LIVE NATION WORLDWIDE INC** p 871
220 W 42nd St, New York NY 10036
Tel (917) 421-5100 SIC 7922

METROPOLITAN OPERA ASSOCIATION INC p 956
Lincoln Ctr, New York NY 10023
Tel (212) 799-3100 SIC 7922

▲ **MSG NETWORKS INC** p 997
11 Penn Plz, New York NY 10001
Tel (212) 465-6400
SIC 4841 7922 7941 4832

■ **MSGN HOLDINGS LP** p 997
4 Penn Plz, New York NY 10121
Tel (212) 465-6000 SIC 4832 7922

SHUBERT ORGANIZATION INC p 1319
234 W 44th St Fl 6, New York NY 10036
Tel (212) 944-3700 SIC 6512 7922

TRUMP ORGANIZATION INC p 1487
725 5th Ave Bsmt A, New York NY 10022
Tel (212) 832-2000 SIC 6531 7922 6794

■ **WESTWOOD ONE INC** p 1603
220 W 42nd St Fl 4, New York NY 10036
Tel (212) 967-2888 SIC 4832 7922

INTERNATIONAL MANAGEMENT GROUP (OVERSEAS) LLC p 756
1360 E 9th St Ste 100, Cleveland OH 44114
Tel (216) 522-1200 SIC 7941 7999 7922

SMG HOLDINGS INC p 1332
300 Cnshohckn State Rd # 450, Conshohocken PA 19428
Tel (610) 729-7900 SIC 6512 8742 7922

■ **COMCAST CABLE HOLDINGS LLC** p 343
1500 Market St Ste Lmw 3, Philadelphia PA 19102
Tel (215) 665-1700 SIC 4841 7922 5961

LIVE NATION MUSIC GROUP TEXAS INC p 871
2000 West Loop S Ste 1300, Houston TX 77027
Tel (713) 693-8152 SIC 7922 6512

SIC 7929 Bands, Orchestras, Actors & Entertainers

BONANZA PRODUCTIONS INC p 199
4000 Warner Blvd, Burbank CA 91522
Tel (818) 954-4212 SIC 7929

■ **HOB ENTERTAINMENT LLC** p 698
7060 Hollywood Blvd, Los Angeles CA 90028
Tel (323) 769-4600 SIC 7929

LOS ANGELES PHILHARMONIC ASSOCIATION p 878
151 S Grand Ave, Los Angeles CA 90012
Tel (213) 972-7300 SIC 7929

▲ **TIVO CORP** p 1456
2 Circle Way, San Carlos CA 94070
Tel (408) 562-8400 SIC 7374 7929

SAN FRANCISCO SYMPHONY INC p 1276
201 Van Ness Ave, San Francisco CA 94102
Tel (415) 552-8000 SIC 7929

RED BULL NORTH AMERICA INC p 1215
1740 Stewart St, Santa Monica CA 90404
Tel (310) 460-5356 SIC 7929

PECHANGA DEVELOPMENT CORP p 1126
45000 Pechanga Pkwy, Temecula CA 92592
Tel (951) 695-4655 SIC 7011 7929 7999

▲ **CENTURY CASINOS INC** p 282
455 E Pikes Peak Ave # 210, Colorado Springs CO 80903
Tel (719) 527-8300 SIC 7011 7929 7999

WYOMING TRANSACTIONS INC p 1630
2373 Cntl Pk Blvd Ste 100, Denver CO 80238
Tel (303) 803-1397 SIC 8748 7929

▲ **WORLD WRESTLING ENTERTAINMENT INC** p 1625
1241 E Main St, Stamford CT 06902
Tel (203) 352-8600 SIC 7812 7929 2721

▲ **DOVER DOWNS GAMING & ENTERTAINMENT INC** p 453
1131 N Dupont Hwy, Dover DE 19901
Tel (302) 674-4600
SIC 7929 7999 7011 7948

JOHN F KENNEDY CENTER FOR PERFORMING ARTS p 788
2700 F St Nw, Washington DC 20566
Tel (202) 416-8000 SIC 7922 7929

FELD ENTERTAINMENT INC p 537
800 Feld Way, Palmetto FL 34221
Tel (941) 721-1200 SIC 7999 7929 5945

ROBERT W WOODRUFF ARTS CENTER INC p 1241
1280 Peachtree St Ne, Atlanta GA 30309
Tel (404) 733-4200
SIC 7929 8412 6512 8299

TROPICANA ENTERTAINMENT LLC p 1484
740 Centre View Blvd, Crestview Hills KY 41017
Tel (859) 669-1500 SIC 7929

BOSTON SYMPHONY ORCHESTRA INC p 203
301 Massachusetts Ave, Boston MA 02115
Tel (617) 266-1492 SIC 7929

POHLAD COMPANIES p 1159
60 S 6th St Ste 3700, Minneapolis MN 55402
Tel (612) 661-3700
SIC 8742 7929 6531 5013 7549 7379

CIRQUE DU SOLEIL AMERICA INC p 308
980 Kelly Johnson Dr 2nd, Las Vegas NV 89119
Tel (702) 352-0200 SIC 7929

LEGENDS HOSPITALITY LLC p 853
400 Bradacrest Dr Ste 200, Bloomfield NJ 07003
Tel (973) 707-2800 SIC 7929

ST REGIS MOHAWK EDUCATION AND COMMUNITY FUND INC p 1372
412 State Route 37, Hogansburg NY 13655
Tel (518) 358-2272 SIC 7929

NEPTUNE HOLDING US CORP p 1026
6 Corporate Center Dr, Melville NY 11747
Tel (516) 803-2265 SIC 7313 7929

■ **MARVEL ENTERTAINMENT LLC** p 913
135 W 50th St Fl 7, New York NY 10020
Tel (212) 576-4000
SIC 2721 6794 3944 7929

MLB ADVANCED MEDIA LP p 979
75 9th Ave Fl 5, New York NY 10011
Tel (212) 485-3444 SIC 4841 7313 7929

▲ **SFX ENTERTAINMENT INC** p 1310
902 Broadway Fl 8, New York NY 10010
Tel (646) 561-6400 SIC 7929

WMG ACQUISITION CORP p 1620
75 Rockefeller Plz, New York NY 10019
Tel (212) 275-2000 SIC 2782 2741 7929

WMG HOLDINGS CORP p 1620
75 Rockefeller Plz Fl 18, New York NY 10019
Tel (212) 275-2000 SIC 7929

MAIN EVENT ENTERTAINMENT LP p 897
6652 Pinecrest Dr Ste 100, Plano TX 75024
Tel (972) 406-2600 SIC 7929 5813 5812

AMERICAN MARITIME HOLDINGS INC p 75
813 Industrial Ave, Chesapeake VA 23324
Tel (757) 961-9311 SIC 3731 7929

TRUSTEES OF ROANOKE COLLEGE p 1488
221 College Ln, Salem VA 24153
Tel (540) 375-2500 SIC 8221 7929

SIC 7933 Bowling Centers

SANTA CRUZ SEASIDE CO INC p 1280
400 Beach St, Santa Cruz CA 95060
Tel (831) 423-5590
SIC 7996 7011 7933 6531

LUCKY STRIKE ENTERTAINMENT LLC p 884
15260 Ventura Blvd # 1110, Sherman Oaks CA 91403
Tel (323) 467-7776 SIC 7933

KINGPIN HOLDINGS LLC p 820
10 S Wacker Dr Ste 3175, Chicago IL 60606
Tel (312) 876-1275 SIC 7933

KINGPIN INTERMEDIATE CORP p 820
10 S Wacker Dr, Chicago IL 60606
Tel (312) 876-1275 SIC 7933

▲ **BRUNSWICK CORP** p 221
1 N Field Ct, Lake Forest IL 60045
Tel (847) 735-4700
SIC 3519 3732 3949 7933 5091

BOWLMOR AMF CORP p 204
222 W 44th St, New York NY 10036
Tel (212) 777-2214 SIC 7933

AMF BOWLING CENTERS HOLDINGS INC p 84
7313 Bell Creek Rd, Mechanicsville VA 23111
Tel (804) 417-2008 SIC 7933

AMF BOWLING CENTERS INC p 84
7313 Bell Creek Rd, Mechanicsville VA 23111
Tel (855) 263-7278 SIC 7933

AMF BOWLING WORLDWIDE INC p 84
7313 Bell Creek Rd, Mechanicsville VA 23111
Tel (804) 730-4000 SIC 3949 7933

QUBICAAMF WORLDWIDE LLC p 1198
8100 Amf Dr, Mechanicsville VA 23111
Tel (804) 569-1000 SIC 3949 7933

SIC 7941 Professional Sports Clubs & Promoters

■ **VIADS MARKETING & EVENTS GROUP** p 1554
1850 N Central Ave # 101, Phoenix AZ 85004
Tel (602) 207-4000 SIC 8742 7941

ANGELS BASEBALL LP p 91
2000 E Gene Autry Way, Anaheim CA 92806
Tel (714) 940-2000 SIC 7941

▲ **LIVE NATION ENTERTAINMENT INC** p 871
9348 Civic Center Dr Lbby, Beverly Hills CA 90210
Tel (310) 867-7000 SIC 7922 7389 7941

■ **DISNEY ENTERPRISES INC** p 443
500 S Buena Vista St, Burbank CA 91521
Tel (818) 560-1000
SIC 7812 6794 5331 7996 7941

FOX BSB HOLDCO INC p 572
1000 Vin Scully Ave, Los Angeles CA 90090
Tel (323) 224-1500 SIC 7941

COMPETITOR GROUP INC p 351
9477 Waples St Ste 150, San Diego CA 92121
Tel (858) 450-6510 SIC 2721 7941

PADRES LP p 1107
100 Pk Blvd Petco Park Petco Pk, San Diego CA 92101
Tel (619) 795-5000 SIC 7941

SAN FRANCISCO BASEBALL ASSOCIATES LLC p 1276
24 Willie Mays Plz, San Francisco CA 94107
Tel (415) 972-2000 SIC 7941 5947

SAN FRANCISCO FORTY NINERS p 1276
4949 Mrie P Debartolo Way, Santa Clara CA 95054
Tel (408) 562-4949 SIC 7941

ANSCHUTZ CORP p 93
555 17th St Ste 2400, Denver CO 80202
Tel (303) 298-1000 SIC 2711 1382 7941

COLORADO ROCKIES BASEBALL CLUB LTD p 339
2001 Blake St, Denver CO 80205
Tel (303) 292-0200 SIC 7941

KROENKE SPORTS HOLDINGS LLC p 830
1000 Chopper Cir, Denver CO 80204
Tel (303) 405-1100 SIC 7941

NATIONAL FOOTBALL LEAGUE PLAYERS ASSOCIATION p 1012
1133 20th St Nw Frnt 1, Washington DC 20036
Tel (202) 756-9100 SIC 7941

WASHINGTON SPORTS & ENTERTAINMENT LIMITED PARTNERSHIP p 1579
601 F St Nw, Washington DC 20004
Tel (202) 661-5000 SIC 7941

PROFESSIONAL GOLFERS ASSOCIATION OF AMERICA INC p 1180
100 Avenue Of Champions, Palm Beach Gardens FL 33418
Tel (561) 624-8400 SIC 7941 5961

LIGHTNING HOCKEY LP p 865
401 Channelside Dr, Tampa FL 33602
Tel (813) 301-6500 SIC 7941

■ **ATLANTA NATIONAL LEAGUE BASEBALL CLUB INC** p 125
755 Hank Aaron Dr Sw, Atlanta GA 30315
Tel (404) 522-7630 SIC 7941

▲ **TRIBUNE MEDIA CO** p 1479
435 N Michigan Ave Fl 2, Chicago IL 60611
Tel (212) 210-2786
SIC 4833 4832 7922 7941

UNITED CENTER JOINT VENTURE p 1507
1901 W Madison St, Chicago IL 60612
Tel (312) 455-4112 SIC 7941

KEMPER SPORTS INC p 810
500 Skokie Blvd Ste 444, Northbrook IL 60062
Tel (847) 850-1818 SIC 8743 7941 7992

PALACE SPORTS & ENTERTAINMENT LLC p 1108
6 Championship Dr, Auburn Hills MI 48326
Tel (248) 377-0165 SIC 7941 7922

ILITCH HOLDINGS INC p 732
2211 Woodward Ave, Detroit MI 48201
Tel (313) 983-6000 SIC 7941 7922 5812

AEG MANAGEMENT TWN LLC p 29
600 1st Ave N Ste Sky, Minneapolis MN 55403
Tel (612) 673-1300 SIC 7941

GREATER KANSAS CITY COMMUNITY FOUNDATION AND AFFILIATED TRUSTS p 635
1055 Broadway Blvd # 130, Kansas City MO 64105
Tel (816) 842-0944 SIC 6732 7941

BASELINEAGENT INC p 158
3960 Howard Hughes Pkwy # 500, Las Vegas NV 89169
Tel (813) 435-6244 SIC 7941

NEW JERSEY SPORTS & EXPOSITION AUTHORITY p 1031
1 Dekorte Park Plz, Lyndhurst NJ 07071
Tel (201) 460-1700 SIC 8641 7941 6512

NATIONAL BASKETBALL ASSOCIATION INC p 1010
100 Plaza Dr Fl 3, Secaucus NJ 07094
Tel (212) 407-8000 SIC 7941

NIAGARA FRONTIER HOCKEY LP p 1042
111 Eight Ave, Buffalo NY 14203
Tel (716) 855-4160 SIC 7941

MADISON SQUARE GARDEN CO p 894
2 Penn Plz Fl 15, New York NY 10121
Tel (212) 465-6000 SIC 7941

▲ **MSG NETWORKS INC** p 997
11 Penn Plz, New York NY 10001
Tel (212) 465-6400
SIC 4841 7922 7941 4832

MSG SPORTS & ENTERTAINMENT LLC p 997
2 Penn Plz Fl 15, New York NY 10121
Tel (212) 465-6000 SIC 7941

NATIONAL FOOTBALL LEAGUE INC p 1012
345 Park Ave Bsmt Lc1, New York NY 10154
Tel (212) 450-2000 SIC 7941

NHL ENTERPRISES INC p 1042
1185 Ave Of The Americas, New York NY 10036
Tel (212) 789-2000 SIC 7941

■ **VIACOM SONGS INC** p 1554
1515 Broadway Lbby, New York NY 10036
Tel (212) 258-6000
SIC 6531 6519 7359 7941 7812 2731

CAVALIERS HOLDINGS LLC p 267
1 Center Ct, Cleveland OH 44115
Tel (216) 420-2000 SIC 7941 6512

CAVALIERS OPERATING CO LLC p 267
1 Center Ct, Cleveland OH 44115
Tel (216) 420-2000 SIC 7941

INTERNATIONAL MANAGEMENT GROUP (OVERSEAS) LLC p 756
1360 E 9th St Ste 100, Cleveland OH 44114
Tel (216) 522-1200 SIC 7941 7999 7922

■ **NIKE USA INC** p 1043
1 Sw Bowerman Dr, Beaverton OR 97005
Tel (503) 671-6453 SIC 7941

PHILADELPHIA PHILLIES p 1143
1 Citizens Bank Way Ofc, Philadelphia PA 19148
Tel (215) 463-5000 SIC 7941

■ **SPECTRUM ARENA LIMITED PARTNERSHIP** p 1357
3601 S Broad St, Philadelphia PA 19148
Tel (215) 389-9524 SIC 6512 7941

AMERICAS POWERSPORTS INC p 81
825 Market St Bldg M, Allen TX 75013
Tel (214) 383-4835 SIC 5571 7941

CENTER OPERATING CO LP p 276
2500 Victory Ave, Dallas TX 75219
Tel (214) 222-3687 SIC 7941

BIG 12 CONFERENCE INC p 181
400 E John Carpenter Fwy, Irving TX 75062
Tel (469) 524-1000 SIC 7941 7997

LINCOLN HOLDINGS LLC p 867
627 N Glebe Rd Ste 850, Arlington VA 22203
Tel (202) 266-2200 SIC 7941

■ **ACKERLEY VENTURES INC** p 17
1301 5th Ave Ste 3525, Seattle WA 98101
Tel (206) 624-2888
SIC 7941 4833 4832 7319 7312

BASEBALL CLUB OF SEATTLE LLLP p 158
1250 1st Ave S, Seattle WA 98134
Tel (206) 346-4000 SIC 7941

FIRST & GOAL INC p 544
800 Occidental Ave S, Seattle WA 98134
Tel (206) 381-7940 SIC 1542 7941

VULCAN INC p 1567
505 5th Ave S Ste 900, Seattle WA 98104
Tel (206) 342-2000 SIC 6531 6722 7941

SIC 7948 Racing & Track Operations

NATIONAL HOT ROD ASSOCIATION p 1013
2035 E Financial Way, Glendora CA 91741
Tel (626) 914-4761 SIC 7948 2711 2741

WEMBLEY USA INC p 1591
10750 E Iliff Ave, Aurora CO 80014
Tel (303) 751-5918 SIC 7948

JACOBS ENTERTAINMENT INC p 775
17301 W Colfax Ave # 250, Golden CO 80401
Tel (303) 215-5196 SIC 7993 7948

▲ **DOVER DOWNS GAMING & ENTERTAINMENT INC** p 453
1131 N Dupont Hwy, Dover DE 19901
Tel (302) 674-4600
SIC 7929 7999 7011 7948

DELAWARE RACING ASSOCIATION p 424
777 Delaware Park Blvd, Wilmington DE 19804
Tel (302) 994-2521 SIC 7948 7993

▲ **INTERNATIONAL SPEEDWAY CORP** p 757
1 Daytona Blvd, Daytona Beach FL 32114
Tel (386) 254-2700 SIC 7948

HOOSIER PARK LLC p 706
4500 Dan Patch Cir Xxx, Anderson IN 46013
Tel (765) 642-7223 SIC 7948

CENTAUR ACQUISITION LLC p 275
111 Monument Cir Ste 777, Indianapolis IN 46204
Tel (317) 656-8787 SIC 7011 7948

CENTAUR INC p 275
111 Monument Cir, Indianapolis IN 46204
Tel (317) 656-8787 SIC 7948

CENTAUR LLC p 275
10 W Market St Ste 200, Indianapolis IN 46204
Tel (317) 656-8787 SIC 7948

PRAIRIE MEADOWS RACETRACK AND CASINO INC p 1167
1 Prairie Meadows Dr, Altoona IA 50009
Tel (515) 967-1000
SIC 7948 7993 7999 5947 5812 5813

KEENELAND ASSOCIATION INC p 807
4201 Versailles Rd, Lexington KY 40510
Tel (859) 288-4236 SIC 5154 7948 0751

▲ **CHURCHILL DOWNS INC** p 305
600 N Hurstbourne Pkwy, Louisville KY 40222
Tel (502) 636-4400 SIC 7948 7993 3578

PIMLICO RACING ASSOCIATION INC p 1148
5201 Park Heights Ave, Baltimore MD 21215
Tel (410) 542-9400 SIC 7948

PENSKE CORP p 1131
2555 S Telegraph Rd, Bloomfield Hills MI 48302
Tel (248) 648-2000 SIC 5511 7538 7948

ROUSH ENTERPRISES INC p 1253
12447 Levan Rd, Livonia MI 48150
Tel (734) 779-7006
SIC 8711 3714 7948 8734

▲ **ISLE OF CAPRI CASINOS INC** p 767
600 Emerson Rd Ste 300, Saint Louis MO 63141
Tel (314) 813-9200 SIC 7011 7948

DELAWARE NORTH COMPANIES GAMING & ENTERTAINMENT INC p 424
250 Delaware Ave Ste 3, Buffalo NY 14202
Tel (716) 858-5000 SIC 7948

NYRA INC p 1069
11000 Rockaway Blvd Ste 1, Jamaica NY 11420
Tel (718) 641-4700 SIC 7948

NEW YORK RACING ASSOCIATION INC p 1036
11000 Rockaway Blvd Ste 1, South Ozone Park NY 11420
Tel (718) 641-4700 SIC 7948

YONKERS RACING CORP p 1637
810 Yonkers Ave, Yonkers NY 10704
Tel (914) 968-4200 SIC 7948

▲ **SONIC FINANCIAL CORP** p 1340
5401 E Independence Blvd, Charlotte NC 28212
Tel (704) 536-5600 SIC 7948 6321 6311

■ **SPEEDWAY MOTORSPORTS INC** p 1358
5555 Concord Pkwy S, Concord NC 28027
Tel (704) 455-3239 SIC 7948

■ **SCIOTO DOWNS INC** p 1292
6000 S High St, Columbus OH 43207
Tel (614) 295-4700 SIC 7948

CHEROKEE NATION ENTERTAINMENT LLC p 294
777 W Cherokee St, Catoosa OK 74015
Tel (918) 458-1696
SIC 7999 7011 7948 5541 5993

INTERNATIONAL TURF INVESTMENT CO INC p 757
3001 Street Rd, Bensalem PA 19020
Tel (215) 639-9000 SIC 7948

▲ **PENN NATIONAL GAMING INC** p 1129
825 Berkshire Blvd # 200, Wyomissing PA 19610
Tel (610) 373-2400 SIC 7011 7948

MAXXAM INC p 923
1330 Post Oak Blvd # 2000, Houston TX 77056
Tel (832) 251-5960 SIC 6531 7948

■ **MTR GAMING GROUP INC** p 998
Hc 2 Box S, Chester WV 26034
Tel (304) 387-8000 SIC 7011 7948

WHEELING ISLAND GAMING INC p 1605
1 S Stone St, Wheeling WV 26003
Tel (304) 232-5050 SIC 7948 7011 5813

SIC 7991 Physical Fitness Facilities

YOUNG MENS CHRISTIAN ASSOCIATION OF BIRMINGHAM p 1638
2101 4th Ave N, Birmingham AL 35203
Tel (205) 801-9622
SIC 7991 8641 8351 7032

KSL ARIZONA HOLDINGS III INC p 831
2400 E Missouri Ave, Phoenix AZ 85016
Tel (602) 955-6600
SIC 7011 5812 7991 5813

JENNY CRAIG WEIGHT LOSS CENTERS INC p 782
5770 Fleet St, Carlsbad CA 92008
Tel (760) 696-4000 SIC 7299 7991

SPECTRUM CLUBS INC p 1357
840 Apollo St Ste 100, El Segundo CA 90245
Tel (310) 727-9300 SIC 7991

FITNESS INTERNATIONAL LLC p 553
3161 Michelson Dr Ste 600, Irvine CA 92612
Tel (949) 255-7200 SIC 7991 6794

JC RESORTS LLC p 780
533 Coast Blvd S, La Jolla CA 92037
Tel (858) 605-2700 SIC 8741 7992 7991

BALLY TOTAL FITNESS CORP p 149
12440 Imperial Hwy # 300, Norwalk CA 90650
Tel (562) 484-2000 SIC 7991

BALLY TOTAL FITNESS OF CALIFORNIA INC p 149
12440 Imperial Hwy # 300, Norwalk CA 90650
Tel (562) 484-2000 SIC 7991

PALA CASINO SPA & RESORT p 1108
35008 Pala Temecula Rd, Pala CA 92059
Tel (760) 510-5100 SIC 7991

PEBBLE BEACH RESORT CO DBA LONE CYPRESS SHOP p 1126
2700 17 Mile Dr, Pebble Beach CA 93953
Tel (831) 647-7500
SIC 7011 7992 5941 7991

CLUB ONE INC p 328
555 Market St Fl 13, San Francisco CA 94105
Tel (415) 477-3000 SIC 7991

YOUNG MENS CHRISTIAN ASSOCIATION OF SAN FRANCISCO p 1639
50 California St Ste 650, San Francisco CA 94111
Tel (415) 777-9622
SIC 8641 7991 8351 7032 8322

24 HOUR FITNESS USA INC p 2
12647 Alcosta Blvd # 500, San Ramon CA 94583
Tel (925) 543-3100 SIC 7991

24 HOUR FITNESS WORLDWIDE INC p 2
12647 Alcosta Blvd # 500, San Ramon CA 94583
Tel (925) 543-3100 SIC 7991

YMCA OF SILICON VALLEY p 1636
80 Saratoga Ave, Santa Clara CA 95051
Tel (408) 351-6400
SIC 8641 7991 8351 7032 8322

WELLBRIDGE CLUB MANAGEMENT LLC p 1589
6140 Greenwood Plaza Blvd, Greenwood Village CO 80111
Tel (303) 866-0800 SIC 7991

HEALTHTRAX INC p 678
2345 Main St, Glastonbury CT 06033
Tel (860) 633-5572 SIC 7991 7997

HEALTHTRAX INTERNATIONAL INC p 678
2345 Main St, Glastonbury CT 06033
Tel (860) 633-5572 SIC 7991

YOUNG MENS CHRISTIAN ASSOCIATION OF SUNCOAST p 1639
2469 Enterprise Rd, Clearwater FL 33763
Tel (312) 932-1200
SIC 8641 7991 8351 7032 8322

AMELIA ISLAND CO p 66
1423 Julia St, Fernandina Beach FL 32034
Tel (904) 261-6161
SIC 7011 6552 7992 7991 5812

FITNESS CENTRE AT CELEBRATION HEALTH p 552
400 Celebration Pl, Kissimmee FL 34747
Tel (407) 303-4400 SIC 7991

FONTAINEBLUEAU FLORIDA HOTEL LLC p 563
4441 Collins Ave, Miami FL 33140
Tel (305) 538-2000
SIC 6519 7011 5812 7991

HEALTH FIRST INC p 674
6450 Us Highway 1, Rockledge FL 32955
Tel (321) 434-4300
SIC 8062 8011 8082 8069 7991 6324

SARASOTA FAMILY YOUNG MENS CHRISTIAN ASSOCIATION INC p 1282
1 S School Ave Ste 301, Sarasota FL 34237
Tel (941) 951-2916
SIC 8641 8351 8322 7997 7991

YOUNG MENS CHRISTIAN ASSOCIATION OF METROPOLITAN ATLANTA INC p 1638
100 Edgewood Ave Ne, Atlanta GA 30303
Tel (404) 588-9622
SIC 8641 7991 8351 7032 8322

FOUNTAINHEAD DEVELOPMENT LLC p 571
100 Rue Charlemagne Dr, Braselton GA 30517
Tel (770) 867-0903
SIC 7992 7991 5921 5812 7011

BALLY TOTAL FITNESS HOLDING CORP p 149
8700 W Bryn Mawr Ave 620n, Chicago IL 60631
Tel (773) 380-3000 SIC 7991

LAKESHORE MANAGEMENT GROUP INC p 840
70 E Lake St Ste 1600, Chicago IL 60601
Tel (773) 981-1452 SIC 7991

OFC MANAGEMENT INC p 1075
446 E Ontario St 10-100, Chicago IL 60611
Tel (312) 642-0031 SIC 7991

TCA TOLEDO LLC p 1428
3611 N Kedzie Ave Fl 2, Chicago IL 60618
Tel (773) 463-1234 SIC 7991

TENNIS CORP OF AMERICA p 1438
3611 N Kedzie Ave Fl 2, Chicago IL 60618
Tel (773) 463-1234 SIC 7991

US HEALTH INC p 1532
8700 W Bryn Mawr Ave # 2, Chicago IL 60631
Tel (773) 399-7626 SIC 7991

TRUSTMARK MUTUAL HOLDING CO p 1488
400 N Field Dr, Lake Forest IL 60045
Tel (847) 615-1500 SIC 7991 8099

■ **AMERISTAR CASINO COUNCIL BLUFFS LLC** p 83
2200 River Rd, Council Bluffs IA 51501
Tel (712) 328-8888
SIC 7011 7991 5813 5812

YOUNG MENS CHRISTIAN ASSOCIATION OF WICHITA KANSAS p 1639
402 N Market St, Wichita KS 67202
Tel (316) 219-9622
SIC 8641 7991 8351 7032 8322

GLOBAL FITNESS HOLDINGS LLC p 616
1056 Wellington Way # 200, Lexington KY 40513
Tel (859) 252-5993 SIC 7991

YOUNG MENS CHRISTIAN ASSOCIATION OF GREATER LOUISVILLE p 1638
545 S 2nd St, Louisville KY 40202
Tel (502) 587-9622
SIC 8641 7991 8351 7032 8322

GENERAL HEALTH SYSTEM p 601
5757 Corp Blvd Ste 200, Baton Rouge LA 70808
Tel (225) 237-1500 SIC 8071 7991

ST CHARLES PARISH PUBLIC SCHOOLS p 1365
13855 River Rd, Luling LA 70070
Tel (985) 785-6289 SIC 7991

WTS INTERNATIONAL INC p 1628
3200 Tower Oaks Blvd # 400, Rockville MD 20852
Tel (301) 622-7800 SIC 7991 7992

MILLENNIUM PARTNERS SPORTS CLUB MANAGEMENT LLC p 970
7 Water St Ste 200, Boston MA 02109
Tel (617) 476-8910 SIC 7991

YMCA OF GREATER BOSTON INC p 1636
316 Huntington Ave Ste 1, Boston MA 02115
Tel (617) 536-6950
SIC 8641 7991 8351 7032 8322

OLD COLONY Y p 1080
320 Main St, Brockton MA 02301
Tel (508) 583-2155
SIC 8641 7991 8351 7032 8322

■ **MGM GRAND DETROIT LLC** p 958
1777 3rd St, Detroit MI 48226
Tel (313) 465-1777 SIC 7011 5812 7991

SPARROW HEALTH SYSTEM p 1354
1215 E Michigan Ave, Lansing MI 48912
Tel (517) 364-1000 SIC 8062 7991

HEALTH FITNESS CORP p 675
1700 W 82nd St Ste 200, Minneapolis MN 55431
Tel (800) 639-7913 SIC 8099 7991

YOUNG MENS CHRISTIAN ASSOCIATION OF GREATER KANSAS CITY p 1638
3100 Broadway Blvd # 1020, Kansas City MO 64111
Tel (816) 561-9622 SIC 8641 7993 7991

LV GAMING VENTURES LLC p 887
12300 Las Vegas Blvd S, Henderson NV 89044
Tel (702) 797-1000 SIC 7011 7991

■ **LVGV LLC** p 887
12300 Las Vegas Blvd S, Henderson NV 89044
Tel (702) 797-1000 SIC 7011 7991

▲ **PLANET FITNESS INC** p 1154
26 Fox Run Rd, Newington NH 03801
Tel (603) 750-0001 SIC 7991

AGT CRUNCH ACQUISITION LLC p 36
22 W 19th St Ste 3l, New York NY 10011
Tel (212) 993-0300 SIC 7991

BTF/CFI INC p 222
144 W 38th St, New York NY 10018
Tel (212) 993-0300
SIC 6794 7991 5621 5411

CRUNCH LLC p 396
220 W 19th St, New York NY 10011
Tel (212) 993-0300 SIC 7991 6794

EQUINOX HOLDINGS INC p 506
895 Broadway Fl 3, New York NY 10003
Tel (212) 677-0180 SIC 7991

EQUINOX-76TH STREET INC p 506
895 Broadway Fl 3, New York NY 10003
Tel (212) 677-0180 SIC 7991

EXHALE ENTERPRISES INC p 519
250 W 57th St Ste 1901, New York NY 10107
Tel (212) 300-2310 SIC 7991

FORSTMANN LITTLE & CO p 568
767 5th Ave Fl 4, New York NY 10153
Tel (212) 355-5656 SIC 7991 6211

SOULCYCLE INC p 1342
609 Greenwich St Fl Grnd, New York NY 10014
Tel (212) 787-7685 SIC 7991

▲ **TOWN SPORTS INTERNATIONAL HOLDINGS INC** p 1466
5 Penn Plz Fl 4, New York NY 10001
Tel (212) 246-6700 SIC 7991 7997

■ **TOWN SPORTS INTERNATIONAL INC** p 1466
5 Penn Plz Fl 4, New York NY 10001
Tel (212) 246-6700 SIC 7997 7991

▲ **WEIGHT WATCHERS INTERNATIONAL INC** p 1588
675 Ave Americas Fl 6, New York NY 10010
Tel (212) 589-2700 SIC 7299 7991

YOUNG MENS CHRISTIAN ASSOCIATION OF GREATER NEW YORK p 1638
5 W 63rd St Fl 6, New York NY 10023
Tel (212) 630-9600
SIC 8641 7991 8351 7032 8322

GROVE PARK INN RESORT INC p 642
290 Macon Ave, Asheville NC 28804
Tel (828) 252-2711
SIC 7011 5812 5813 7992 7991 7299

OMNI GROVE PARK LLC p 1084
290 Macon Ave, Asheville NC 28804
Tel (828) 252-2711
SIC 7299 5812 7011 5813 7992 7991

FIRSTHEALTH OF CAROLINAS INC p 550
155 Memorial Dr, Pinehurst NC 28374
Tel (910) 715-1000
SIC 8062 8093 8051 8021 7991 7219

YMCA OF NORTHWEST NORTH CAROLINA p 1636
301 N Main St Ste 1900, Winston Salem NC 27101
Tel (336) 777-8055
SIC 8641 7991 8351 7032 8322

YOUNG MENS CHRISTIAN ASSOCIATION OF GREATER DAYTON p 1638
118 W St Ste 300, Dayton OH 45402
Tel (937) 223-5201
SIC 8641 7991 8351 7032 8322

YOUNG MENS CHRISTIAN ASSOCIATION OF GREATER TOLEDO p 1638
1500 N Superior St Fl 2, Toledo OH 43604
Tel (419) 729-8135
SIC 8641 7991 8351 7032 8322

MATHIS BROS OKLAHOMA CITY LLC p 920
3434 W Reno Ave, Oklahoma City OK 73107
Tel (405) 943-3434 *SIC* 7991

ST JOHN HEALTH SYSTEM INC p 1367
1923 S Utica Ave, Tulsa OK 74104
Tel (918) 744-2180
SIC 7991 6512 7389 8361 8071 8062

YMCA GREATER BRANDYWINE p 1636
1 E Chestnut St, West Chester PA 19380
Tel (610) 643-9622
SIC 8641 7991 8351 7032 8322

GREATER PROVIDENCE YOUNG MENS CHRISTIAN ASSOCIATION p 636
371 Pine St, Providence RI 02903
Tel (401) 521-9622
SIC 8641 7991 8351 7032 8322

YMCA OF METROPOLITAN CHATTANOOGA p 1636
301 W 6th St, Chattanooga TN 37402
Tel (423) 266-3766
SIC 8641 7991 8351 7032 8322

RUSH FITNESS CORP p 1258
10708 Kingston Pike, Knoxville TN 37934
Tel (865) 671-6444 *SIC* 7991

YOUNG MENS CHRISTIAN ASSOCIATION OF MIDDLE TENNESSEE p 1638
1000 Church St, Nashville TN 37203
Tel (615) 259-9622
SIC 8641 7991 8351 7032 8322

■ **ARMC LP** p 111
6250 Highway 83 84, Abilene TX 79606
Tel (325) 428-1000
SIC 8062 8093 8011 7991

BAYLOR HEALTH ENTERPRISES LP p 162
411 N Washington Ave # 7200, Dallas TX 75246
Tel (214) 820-2492 *SIC* 5122 7011 7991

TRT HOLDINGS INC p 1485
4001 Maple Ave Ste 600, Dallas TX 75219
Tel (214) 283-8500 *SIC* 7011 7991 1382

YOUNG MENS CHRISTIAN ASSOCIATION OF METROPOLITAN p 1638
601 N Akard St, Dallas TX 75201
Tel (214) 880-9622
SIC 8641 7991 8351 7032 8322

YOUNG MENS CHRISTIAN ASSOCIATION OF GREATER HOUSTON AREA INC p 1638
2600 North Loop W Ste 300, Houston TX 77092
Tel (713) 659-5566
SIC 8641 7991 8351 7032 8322

GOLDS GYM INTERNATIONAL INC p 622
125 E J Carpentr Fwy 13, Irving TX 75062
Tel (972) 444-8527 *SIC* 7991 6794

BAY CLUB LOS ANGELES INC p 160
15759 San Pedro Ave, San Antonio TX 78232
Tel (210) 490-1980 *SIC* 7991

SPORT & HEALTH CLUBS LC p 1359
1760 Old Madow Rd Ste 300, Mc Lean VA 22102
Tel (703) 556-6556 *SIC* 7991

YOUNG MENS CHRISTIAN ASSOCIATION OF GREATER RICHMOND p 1638
2 W Franklin St, Richmond VA 23220
Tel (804) 644-9622
SIC 8641 7991 8351 7032 8322

YOUNG MENS CHRISTIAN ASSOCIATION OF PIERCE AND KITSAP COUNTY p 1639
4717 S 19th St Ste 201, Tacoma WA 98405
Tel (253) 534-7800
SIC 8699 7991 7032 8322

YOUNG MENS CHRISTIAN ASSOCIATION OF METROPOLITAN MILWAUKEE INC p 1638
161 W Wisconsin Ave, Milwaukee WI 53203
Tel (414) 291-9622
SIC 8641 7991 8351 7032 8322

SIC 7992 Public Golf Courses

■ **SHERATON PHOENICIAN CORP** p 1315
6000 E Camelback Rd, Scottsdale AZ 85251
Tel (480) 941-8200
SIC 7011 5812 5813 7999 7992

JC RESORTS LLC p 780
533 Coast Blvd S, La Jolla CA 92037
Tel (858) 605-2700 *SIC* 8741 7992 7991

KSL RECREATION MANAGEMENT OPERATIONS LLC p 831
50905 Avenida Bermudas, La Quinta CA 92253
Tel (760) 564-8000 *SIC* 7992 7011

AMERICAN GOLF CORP p 73
6080 Center Dr Ste 500, Los Angeles CA 90045
Tel (310) 664-4000
SIC 7997 7999 5812 5941 7992

SYAR INDUSTRIES INC p 1413
2301 Napa Vallejo Hwy, Napa CA 94558
Tel (707) 252-8711
SIC 5032 2951 0762 7992 5932

PEBBLE BEACH RESORT CO DBA LONE CYPRESS SHOP p 1126
2700 17 Mile Dr, Pebble Beach CA 93953
Tel (831) 647-7500
SIC 7011 7992 5941 7991

COURSECO INC p 383
1670 Corp Cir Ste 201, Petaluma CA 94954
Tel (707) 763-0335 *SIC* 7992

HERITAGE GOLF GROUP LLC p 686
12750 High Bluff Dr # 400, San Diego CA 92130
Tel (858) 720-0694 *SIC* 7992

BROADMOOR HOTEL INC p 215
1 Lake Ave, Colorado Springs CO 80906
Tel (719) 634-7711
SIC 7011 5812 5813 7992 7999 7389

AMELIA ISLAND CO p 66
1423 Julia St, Fernandina Beach FL 32034
Tel (904) 261-6161
SIC 7011 6552 7992 7991 5812

FAIRWAYS GOLF CORP p 525
5385 Gateway Blvd Ste 12, Lakeland FL 33811
Tel (407) 589-7200 *SIC* 7992

MEADOWBROOK GOLF GROUP INC p 934
5385 Gateway Blvd Ste 12, Lakeland FL 33811
Tel (407) 589-7200
SIC 8742 8741 7992 5941

ROSEN 9939 INC p 1251
9840 International Dr, Orlando FL 32819
Tel (407) 996-9939
SIC 7011 5812 5813 7992 7389

ROSEN HOTELS AND RESORTS INC p 1251
9840 International Dr, Orlando FL 32819
Tel (407) 996-1706
SIC 7011 5812 5813 7389 8011 7992

PGA TOUR HOLDINGS INC p 1140
112 Pga Tour Blvd, Ponte Vedra Beach FL 32082
Tel (904) 285-3700 *SIC* 7992 7997

ELAN CHATEAU RESORTS LLC p 483
100 Rue Charlemagne Dr, Braselton GA 30517
Tel (678) 425-0900
SIC 2084 5812 7992 7011

FOUNTAINHEAD DEVELOPMENT LLC p 571
100 Rue Charlemagne Dr, Braselton GA 30517
Tel (770) 867-0903
SIC 7992 7991 5921 5812 7011

SEA ISLAND ACQUISITION LP p 1295
100 Cloister Dr, Sea Island GA 31561
Tel (912) 638-3611 *SIC* 7011 0781 7992

SEA ISLAND CO p 1295
100 Cloister Dr, Sea Island GA 31561
Tel (888) 732-4752 *SIC* 7011 0781 7992

KAWAILOA DEVELOPMENT LLP p 805
1571 Poipu Rd Ste 3063, Koloa HI 96756
Tel (808) 742-1234 *SIC* 7011 7992

PARK GLENVIEW DISTRICT p 1115
1930 Prairie St, Glenview IL 60025
Tel (847) 657-3215 *SIC* 7997 7992

PARK NAPERVILLE DISTRICT p 1115
320 Jackson Ave, Naperville IL 60540
Tel (630) 848-5000
SIC 7992 7999 8322 8741

KEMPER SPORTS INC p 810
500 Skokie Blvd Ste 444, Northbrook IL 60062
Tel (847) 850-1818 *SIC* 8743 7941 7992

WTS INTERNATIONAL INC p 1628
3200 Tower Oaks Blvd # 400, Rockville MD 20852
Tel (301) 622-7800 *SIC* 7991 7992

BOYNE USA INC p 205
1 Boyne Mountain Rd, Boyne Falls MI 49713
Tel (231) 549-6000 *SIC* 7011 7992 7032

OAK LANE GOLF COURSE INC p 1070
800 N Main St, Webberville MI 48892
Tel (517) 521-3900 *SIC* 7992 5812

▲ **PEAK RESORTS INC** p 1126
17409 Hidden Valley Dr, Wildwood MO 63025
Tel (636) 938-7474 *SIC* 7992 7999 7011

GLOBAL INDUSTRIES INC p 617
1804 E 4th St, Grand Island NE 68801
Tel (800) 247-6621
SIC 7992 3589 3444 5084 5083 3535

SAGEBRUSH ENTERPRISES INC p 1267
4730 S Fort Apache Rd, Las Vegas NV 89147
Tel (702) 873-5338
SIC 1522 1542 7992 6799

GROVE PARK INN RESORT INC p 642
290 Macon Ave, Asheville NC 28804
Tel (828) 252-2711
SIC 7011 5812 5813 7992 7991 7299

OMNI GROVE PARK LLC p 1084
290 Macon Ave, Asheville NC 28804
Tel (828) 252-2711
SIC 7299 5812 7011 5813 7992 7991

PINEHURST LLC p 1149
80 Carolina Vista Dr, Pinehurst NC 28374
Tel (910) 295-6811
SIC 7011 7997 7992 5813 5812

CITIZEN POTAWATOMI NATION p 310
1601 Gordon Cooper Dr, Shawnee OK 74801
Tel (405) 275-3121
SIC 7992 5411 7011 8412

■ **TRACO DELAWARE INC** p 1468
71 Progress Ave, Cranberry Township PA 16066
Tel (724) 776-7000
SIC 3442 3211 3444 3448 3354 7992

■ **TRI CITY ALUMINUM CO** p 1476
71 Progress Ave, Cranberry Township PA 16066
Tel (724) 799-8917 *SIC* 3442 3354 7992

SCOTTS PEEK N PEAK LLC p 1294
2225 Downs Dr, Erie PA 16509
Tel (814) 868-9518 *SIC* 7011 7992

DOUBLE DIAMOND - DELAWARE INC p 452
5495 Belt Line Rd Ste 200, Dallas TX 75254
Tel (214) 706-9831 *SIC* 6552 7992

EVERGREEN ALLIANCE GOLF LIMITED LP p 514
4851 Lydon B Johnson Ste 600, Dallas TX 75244
Tel (214) 722-6000 *SIC* 7992 5091

■ **HOWARD HUGHES CORP** p 713
13355 Noel Rd Fl 22, Dallas TX 75240
Tel (702) 791-4000 *SIC* 6552 6512 7992

■ **STRATTON CORP** p 1393
5 Village Lodge Rd, South Londonderry VT 05155
Tel (802) 297-2200
SIC 7011 7992 1531 6512 5941

UNITED CO p 1507
1005 Glenway Ave, Bristol VA 24201
Tel (276) 466-3322 *SIC* 1382 7992

OGLEBAY RESORT CONFERENCE CENTER p 1076
Rr 88 Box N, Wheeling WV 26003
Tel (304) 243-4063 *SIC* 7011 7992 5812

■ **DELLONA ENTERPRISES INC** p 425
S944 Christmas Mtn Rd, Wisconsin Dells WI 53965
Tel (608) 253-1000 *SIC* 7011 7992 5812

SIC 7993 Coin-Operated Amusement Devices & Arcades

GILA RIVER GAMING ENTERPRISES p 611
5040 W Wldhorse Pass Blvd, Chandler AZ 85226
Tel (800) 946-4452 *SIC* 7993 5812

AK-CHIN INDIAN COMMUNITY DEVELOPMENT CORP p 41
42507 W Peters & Nall Rd, Maricopa AZ 85138
Tel (520) 568-1000
SIC 0131 0139 5251 7993

PETER PIPER INC p 1138
4745 N 7th St Ste 350, Phoenix AZ 85014
Tel (480) 609-6400 *SIC* 5812 7993 6794

BANDAI NAMCO HOLDINGS USA INC p 150
2120 Park Pl Ste 120, El Segundo CA 90245
Tel (714) 816-9500 *SIC* 3999 7993

SEGA ENTERTAINMENT USA INC p 1300
600 N Brand Blvd Fl 5, Glendale CA 91203
Tel (310) 217-9500 *SIC* 7993

RIOT GAMES INC p 1236
12333 W Olympic Blvd, Los Angeles CA 90064
Tel (310) 828-7953 *SIC* 7371 7993

FESTIVAL FUN PARKS LLC p 539
4590 Macarthur Blvd # 400, Newport Beach CA 92660
Tel (949) 261-0404 *SIC* 7999 7993

PALACE ENTERTAINMENT INC p 1108
4590 Macarthur Blvd # 400, Newport Beach CA 92660
Tel (949) 261-0404 *SIC* 7999 7993

JACOBS ENTERTAINMENT INC p 775
17301 W Colfax Ave # 250, Golden CO 80401
Tel (303) 215-5196 *SIC* 7993 7948

CENTERPLATE INC p 276
2187 Atlantic St, Stamford CT 06902
Tel (800) 698-6992
SIC 5812 7999 5947 7993

CENTERPLATE ULTIMATE HOLDINGS CORP p 276
2187 Atlantic St, Stamford CT 06902
Tel (800) 698-6992
SIC 5812 7999 5947 7993

VOLUME SERVICES INC p 1565
2187 Atlantic St Ste 6, Stamford CT 06902
Tel (203) 975-5900
SIC 5812 7999 5947 7993

DELAWARE RACING ASSOCIATION p 424
777 Delaware Park Blvd, Wilmington DE 19804
Tel (302) 994-2521 *SIC* 7948 7993

HIE HOLDINGS INC p 690
2839 Mokumoa St, Honolulu HI 96819
Tel (808) 833-2244 *SIC* 2095 7993

A H MANAGEMENT GROUP INC p 5
1151 Rohlwing Rd, Rolling Meadows IL 60008
Tel (847) 342-8065
SIC 5962 7993 5963 7389 5046

BUFFINGTON HARBOR RIVERBOAT LLC p 224
21 Buffington Harbor Dr, Gary IN 46406
Tel (219) 977-9999 *SIC* 5812 7993

PRAIRIE MEADOWS RACETRACK AND CASINO INC p 1167
1 Prairie Meadows Dr, Altoona IA 50009
Tel (515) 967-1000
SIC 7948 7993 7999 5947 5812 5813

▲ **CHURCHILL DOWNS INC** p 305
600 N Hurstbourne Pkwy, Louisville KY 40222
Tel (502) 636-4400 *SIC* 7948 7993 3578

GRAND TRAVERSE BAND ECONOMIC DEVELOPMENT CORP p 630
2331 N West Bay Shore Dr, Suttons Bay MI 49682
Tel (231) 534-8000 *SIC* 7011 7993 5812

YOUNG MENS CHRISTIAN ASSOCIATION OF GREATER KANSAS CITY p 1638
3100 Broadway Blvd # 1020, Kansas City MO 64111
Tel (816) 561-9622 *SIC* 8641 7993 7991

TOWN PUMP INC p 1465
600 S Main St, Butte MT 59701
Tel (406) 497-6700
SIC 5541 5411 7993 6512 5812

■ **BALLY TECHNOLOGIES INC** p 148
6601 Bermuda Rd, Las Vegas NV 89119
Tel (770) 420-2388
SIC 3999 7993 7372

E-T-T LLC p 467
3440 W Russell Rd, Las Vegas NV 89118
Tel (877) 736-5388 *SIC* 7993

▲ **FULL HOUSE RESORTS INC** p 584
4670 S Fort Apache Rd # 190, Las Vegas NV 89147
Tel (702) 221-7800 *SIC* 7011 7993

STATION CASINOS INC p 1383
1505 S Pavilion Center Dr, Las Vegas NV 89135
Tel (702) 495-3000 *SIC* 8741 7993 7011

DONALD J LAUGHLIN p 450
1650 S Casino Dr Pmb 500, Laughlin NV 89029
Tel (702) 298-2535 *SIC* 7993 5812

TEXAS STATION GAMBLING HALL & HOTEL INC p 1444
2101 Texas Star Ln, North Las Vegas NV 89032
Tel (702) 631-1000 *SIC* 7011 7993

DELAWARE NORTH COMPANIES INC p 424
250 Delaware Ave, Buffalo NY 14202
Tel (716) 858-5000
SIC 5461 7011 7993 7999

OAK HILL CAPITAL PARTNERS III LP p 1070
65 E 55th St Fl 32, New York NY 10022
Tel (212) 527-8400
SIC 5812 5813 7999 7993

WELLSPRING CAPITAL PARTNERS III LP p 1591
390 Park Ave Fl 5, New York NY 10022
Tel (212) 318-9800
SIC 5812 5813 7999 7993

WS MIDWAY HOLDINGS INC p 1628
390 Park Ave Fl 6, New York NY 10022
Tel (212) 318-9800
SIC 5812 5813 7999 7993

VIDEO GAMING TECHNOLOGIES INC p 1556
308 Mallory Station Rd, Franklin TN 37067
Tel (615) 372-1000 *SIC* 3999 7993

▲ **DAVE & BUSTERS ENTERTAINMENT INC** p 415
2481 Manana Dr, Dallas TX 75220
Tel (214) 357-9588 *SIC* 5812 7993

■ **DAVE & BUSTERS INC** p 415
2481 Manana Dr, Dallas TX 75220
Tel (214) 357-9588
SIC 5812 5813 7999 7993

CEC ENTERTAINMENT INC p 272
1707 Market Pl Ste 200, Irving TX 75063
Tel (972) 258-8507 *SIC* 5812 7993 6794

SNOQUALMIE ENTERTAINMENT p 1336
37500 Se North Bend Way, Snoqualmie WA 98065
Tel (425) 888-1234 *SIC* 7993 7011

SIC 7996 Amusement Parks

MEDIEVAL TIMES ENTERTAINMENT INC p 938
7662 Beach Blvd, Buena Park CA 90620
Tel (714) 523-1100 *SIC* 7041 7996

■ **DISNEY ENTERPRISES INC** p 443
500 S Buena Vista St, Burbank CA 91521
Tel (818) 560-1000
SIC 7812 6794 5331 7996 7941

■ **DISNEYLAND INTERNATIONAL INC** p 443
500 S Buena Vista St, Burbank CA 91521
Tel (818) 560-1000 *SIC* 7996

▲ **WALT DISNEY CO** p 1574
500 S Buena Vista St, Burbank CA 91521
Tel (818) 560-1000
SIC 4833 4841 7011 7996 7812 2731

SANTA CRUZ SEASIDE CO INC p 1280
400 Beach St, Santa Cruz CA 95060
Tel (831) 423-5590
SIC 7996 7011 7933 6531

■ **UNIVERSAL CITY STUDIOS INC** p 1516
100 Universal City Plz, Universal City CA 91608
Tel (818) 622-8477 *SIC* 7812 7996

ALFA SMARTPARKS INC p 49
1 W Adams St Ste 200, Jacksonville FL 32202
Tel (904) 358-1027 *SIC* 7996

PARC MANAGEMENT LLC p 1114
7892 Baymeadows Way, Jacksonville FL 32256
Tel (904) 732-7272 *SIC* 7996

■ **WALT DISNEY PARKS AND RESORTS US INC** p 1574
1375 E Buena Vista Dr, Lake Buena Vista FL 32830
Tel (407) 824-2222 *SIC* 7996 7011 5947

■ **SEA WORLD LLC** p 1295
9205 Southpark Ctr Loop, Orlando FL 32819
Tel (407) 226-5011 *SIC* 7996

■ **SEA WORLD OF FLORIDA LLC** p 1295
9205 Southpark Ctr Loop, Orlando FL 32819
Tel (407) 226-5011 *SIC* 7996

▲ **SEAWORLD ENTERTAINMENT INC** p 1298
9205 Southpark Center Loo, Orlando FL 32819
Tel (407) 226-5011 *SIC* 7996

■ **SEAWORLD PARKS & ENTERTAINMENT INC** p 1298
9205 Southpark Center Loo, Orlando FL 32819
Tel (407) 226-5011 *SIC* 7996

■ **UNIVERSAL CITY DEVELOPMENT PARTNERS LTD** p 1516
1000 Unversal Studios Plz, Orlando FL 32819
Tel (407) 363-8000 *SIC* 7996

UNIVERSAL CITY FLORIDA PARTNERS p 1516
1000 Unversal Studios Plz, Orlando FL 32819
Tel (407) 363-8000 *SIC* 7996 7819

■ **UNIVERSAL CITY TRAVEL PARTNERS** p 1516
1000 Unversal Studios Plz, Orlando FL 32819
Tel (407) 363-8000 *SIC* 7996

■ **UNIVERSAL ORLANDO ONLINE MERCHANDISE STORE** p 1517
1000 Unversal Studios Plz, Orlando FL 32819
Tel (407) 363-8000 *SIC* 7996

SUN VALLEY CO p 1401
1 Sun Valley Rd, Sun Valley ID 83353
Tel (208) 622-4111 *SIC* 7011 7996

ANHEUSER-BUSCH COMPANIES LLC p 91
1 Busch Pl, Saint Louis MO 63118
Tel (314) 632-6777 *SIC* 2082 3411 7996

■ **MANDALAY RESORT GROUP** p 901
3950 Las Vegas Blvd S, Las Vegas NV 89119
Tel (702) 693-7120 *SIC* 7011 7999 7996

■ **NEW YORK - NEW YORK HOTEL & CASINO LLC** p 1033
3790 Las Vegas Blvd S, Las Vegas NV 89109
Tel (702) 740-6969 *SIC* 7011 7996

MERLIN ENTERTAINMENTS GROUP US LLC p 950
234 W 42nd St Frnt 4, New York NY 10036
Tel (212) 512-9604 *SIC* 7996

■ **NBCUNIVERSAL MEDIA LLC** p 1021
30 Rockefeller Plz Fl 2, New York NY 10112
Tel (212) 664-4444
SIC 4841 4833 7812 7996

GREAT ESCAPE AMUSEMENT PARK p 633
1172 State Route 9, Queensbury NY 12804
Tel (518) 792-3500 *SIC* 7996

▲ **CEDAR FAIR LP** p 272
1 Cedar Point Dr, Sandusky OH 44870
Tel (419) 626-0830 *SIC* 7996

■ **KINGS DOMINION LLC** p 820
1 Cedar Point Dr, Sandusky OH 44870
Tel (419) 626-0830 *SIC* 7996

LMN DEVELOPMENT LLC p 872
7000 Kalahari Dr, Sandusky OH 44870
Tel (419) 433-7200 *SIC* 7011 7996 5091

■ **MAGNUM MANAGEMENT CORP** p 897
1 Cedar Point Dr, Sandusky OH 44870
Tel (419) 627-2334 *SIC* 4785 6552 7996

HERSHEY ENTERTAINMENT & RESORTS CO p 687
27 W Chocolate Ave # 100, Hershey PA 17033
Tel (717) 534-3131 *SIC* 7011 7996

▲ **COMCAST CORP** p 343
1701 Jfk Blvd, Philadelphia PA 19103
Tel (215) 286-1700
SIC 4841 4813 7812 7996

MYRTLE BEACH FARMS CO INC p 1005
8820 Marina Pkwy, Myrtle Beach SC 29572
Tel (843) 448-5123 *SIC* 6552 7996 6512

▲ **SIX FLAGS ENTERTAINMENT CORP** p 1328
924 E Avenue J, Grand Prairie TX 75050
Tel (972) 595-5000 *SIC* 7996

SIX FLAGS THEME PARKS INC p 1328
924 E Avenue J, Grand Prairie TX 75050
Tel (972) 595-5000 *SIC* 7996

FIESTA TEXAS INC p 541
17000 W Interstate 10, San Antonio TX 78257
Tel (210) 697-5000 *SIC* 7996

SIC 7997 Membership Sports & Recreation Clubs

RUSSELL LANDS INC p 1259
2544 Willow Point Rd, Alexander City AL 35010
Tel (256) 329-0835
SIC 5211 6514 4493 7997 7011

KARSTEN MANUFACTURING CORP p 804
2201 W Desert Cove Ave, Phoenix AZ 85029
Tel (602) 870-5000
SIC 3949 3398 3363 3325 8711 7997

DESERT MOUNTAIN PROPERTIES LIMITED PARTNERSHIP p 432
37700 N Desert Mtn Pkwy, Scottsdale AZ 85262
Tel (480) 595-4000 *SIC* 6552 7997

SYCUAN CASINO p 1413
5459 Casino Way, El Cajon CA 92019
Tel (619) 445-6002 *SIC* 7999 7997

AMERICAN GOLF CORP p 73
6080 Center Dr Ste 500, Los Angeles CA 90045
Tel (310) 664-4000
SIC 7997 7999 5812 5941 7992

AFFINITY GROUP HOLDING LLC p 32
2750 Park View Ct Ste 240, Oxnard CA 93036
Tel (805) 667-4100 *SIC* 7997 2721

AGI HOLDING CORP p 35
2575 Vista Del Mar Dr, Ventura CA 93001
Tel (805) 667-4100 *SIC* 7997 2741

FILLMORE CCA INVESTMENT LLC p 542
100 Fillmore St Ste 600, Denver CO 80206
Tel (720) 284-6400 *SIC* 7997

STARMARK MANAGEMENT HOLDINGS LLC p 1379
6140 Greenwood Plaza Blvd, Greenwood Village CO 80111
Tel (303) 866-0800 *SIC* 7997

TSG SKI & GOLF LLC p 1489
565 Mountain Village Blvd, Telluride CO 81435
Tel (970) 728-6900 *SIC* 7997

HEALTHTRAX INC p 678
2345 Main St, Glastonbury CT 06033
Tel (860) 633-5572 *SIC* 7991 7997

YMCA OF METROPOLITAN HARTFORD INC p 1636
50 State House Sq Fl 2, Hartford CT 06103
Tel (860) 522-9622 *SIC* 8641 7032 7997

YOUNG MENS CHRISTIAN ASSOCIATION OF WILMINGTON DELAWARE p 1639
100 W 10th St Ste 1100, Wilmington DE 19801
Tel (302) 221-9622 *SIC* 7997 7011

BRE/BATON OPERATING LESSEE LLC p 209
501 E Camino Real, Boca Raton FL 33432
Tel (561) 447-3000 *SIC* 7011 7997

■ **PANTHERS BRHC LLC** p 1111
501 E Camino Real, Boca Raton FL 33432
Tel (888) 543-1277 *SIC* 7011 5812 7997

DIPLOMAT p 441
501 Diplomat Pkwy, Hallandale Beach FL 33009
Tel (954) 883-4000 *SIC* 7997

DIPLOMAT PROPERTIES LIMITED PARTNERSHIP p 441
3555 S Ocean Dr, Hollywood FL 33019
Tel (954) 602-6000 *SIC* 7011 7997

GATE PETROLEUM CO p 593
9540 San Jose Blvd, Jacksonville FL 32257
Tel (904) 730-3470
SIC 5541 3272 5411 7997

ORANGE LAKE COUNTRY CLUB INC p 1092
8505 W Irlo Bronson Hwy, Kissimmee FL 34747
Tel (407) 239-0000
SIC 7011 6552 7997 5812 5813

VILLAGES OF LAKE-SUMTER INC p 1557
1000 Lake Sumter Lndg, Lady Lake FL 32162
Tel (352) 753-2270
SIC 6552 1521 7997 5812 7389

FLAGLER SYSTEM INC p 554
1 S County Rd, Palm Beach FL 33480
Tel (561) 655-6611 *SIC* 7041 7997

PGA TOUR HOLDINGS INC p 1140
112 Pga Tour Blvd, Ponte Vedra Beach FL 32082
Tel (904) 285-3700 *SIC* 7992 7997

PGA TOUR INC p 1140
112 Pga Tour Blvd, Ponte Vedra Beach FL 32082
Tel (904) 285-3700 *SIC* 7997

SARASOTA FAMILY YOUNG MENS CHRISTIAN ASSOCIATION INC p 1282
1 S School Ave Ste 301, Sarasota FL 34237
Tel (941) 951-2916
SIC 8641 8351 8322 7997 7991

■ **LINGER LONGER DEVELOPMENT CO** p 869
100 Linger Longer Rd, Greensboro GA 30642
Tel (888) 298-3119 *SIC* 6552 7997

NATIONAL COUNCIL OF YOUNG MENS CHRISTIAN ASSOCIATIONS OF UNITED STATES OF AMERICA p 1011
101 N Wacker Dr Ste 1600, Chicago IL 60606
Tel (312) 977-0031 *SIC* 7997 8399 8322

PARK GLENVIEW DISTRICT p 1115
1930 Prairie St, Glenview IL 60025
Tel (847) 657-3215 *SIC* 7997 7992

GOOD SAM ENTERPRISES LLC p 623
250 Parkway Dr Ste 270, Lincolnshire IL 60069
Tel (847) 229-6720 *SIC* 5561 7997 2721

LIFE TIME FITNESS INC p 864
2902 Corporate Pl, Chanhassen MN 55317
Tel (952) 229-7543 *SIC* 7997

■ **RIO HOTEL & CASINO INC** p 1236
3700 W Flamingo Rd, Las Vegas NV 89103
Tel (702) 777-7777 *SIC* 7011 7997

HIGHLAND LAKES COUNTRY CLUB & COMMUNITY ASSOCIATION p 691
2240 Lakeside Dr W, Highland Lakes NJ 07422
Tel (973) 764-4366 *SIC* 7997

WIN-SUM SKI CORP p 1614
6557 Holiday Valley Rd, Ellicottville NY 14731
Tel (716) 699-2345 *SIC* 7011 7997 6531

▲ **TOWN SPORTS INTERNATIONAL HOLDINGS INC** p 1466
5 Penn Plz Fl 4, New York NY 10001
Tel (212) 246-6700 *SIC* 7991 7997

■ **TOWN SPORTS INTERNATIONAL INC** p 1466
5 Penn Plz Fl 4, New York NY 10001
Tel (212) 246-6700 *SIC* 7997 7991

PINEHURST LLC p 1149
80 Carolina Vista Dr, Pinehurst NC 28374
Tel (910) 295-6811
SIC 7011 7997 7992 5813 5812

SALT FORK RESORT CLUB INC p 1273
74978 Broadhead Rd, Kimbolton OH 43749
Tel (740) 498-8116 *SIC* 7011 7997

■ **CCA CLUB OPERATIONS HOLDINGS LLC** p 269
3030 L B Johnson Fwy # 400, Dallas TX 75234
Tel (972) 243-6191 *SIC* 7997

■ **CLUBCORP CLUB OPERATIONS INC** p 328
3030 Lbj Fwy Ste 600, Dallas TX 75234
Tel (972) 243-6191 *SIC* 7997

▲ **CLUBCORP HOLDINGS INC** p 328
3030 Lbj Fwy Ste 600, Dallas TX 75234
Tel (972) 243-6191 *SIC* 7997

■ **CLUBCORP USA INC** p 328
3030 Lyndon B Johnson Fwy, Dallas TX 75234
Tel (972) 243-6191 *SIC* 7011 7997

BIG 12 CONFERENCE INC p 181
400 E John Carpenter Fwy, Irving TX 75062
Tel (469) 524-1000 *SIC* 7941 7997

US-LAS COLINAS LIMITED PARTNERSHIP p 1533
9830 Colonnade Blvd # 600, San Antonio TX 78230
Tel (210) 498-0626 *SIC* 7011 7997

■ **WOODLANDS OPERATING CO L P** p 1623
24 Waterway Ave Ste 1100, The Woodlands TX 77380
Tel (281) 719-6100
SIC 6552 7997 7389 6513 6512

STRATTON MOUNTAIN COUNTRY CLUB p 1393
Stratton Mtn Access Rd, South Londonderry VT 05155
Tel (802) 297-1005 *SIC* 7997

■ **BUSINESS AND SUPPORT SERVICES** p 229
3044 Catlin Ave, Quantico VA 22134
Tel (703) 432-0109 *SIC* 7997

SIC 7999 Amusement & Recreation Svcs, NEC

MADISON COUNTY COMMISSIONS p 894
783 Coleman Rd, New Market AL 35761
Tel (256) 379-2132 *SIC* 7999

TOHONO OODHAM GAMING ENTERPRISE p 1458
1100 W Pima Mine Rd, Green Valley AZ 85614
Tel (520) 342-3000 *SIC* 7999 7011

DREAMERS TRAVELS LLC p 455
830 E Sherman St, Phoenix AZ 85034
Tel (602) 305-6414 *SIC* 7999

■ **SHERATON PHOENICIAN CORP** p 1315
6000 E Camelback Rd, Scottsdale AZ 85251
Tel (480) 941-8200
SIC 7011 5812 5813 7999 7992

BELL GARDENS BICYCLE CLUB INC p 170
888 Bicycle Casino Dr, Bell Gardens CA 90201
Tel (562) 806-4646 *SIC* 7999 5812

■ **DISNEY REGIONAL ENTERTAINMENT INC** p 443
500 S Buena Vista St, Burbank CA 91521
Tel (818) 560-1000 *SIC* 7999 5812 5813

SYCUAN CASINO p 1413
5459 Casino Way, El Cajon CA 92019
Tel (619) 445-6002 *SIC* 7999 7997

TABLE MOUNTAIN CASINO p 1420
8184 Table Mountain Rd, Friant CA 93626
Tel (559) 822-2485 *SIC* 7999

HAWAIIAN GARDENS CASINO p 669
21520 Pioneer Blvd # 305, Hawaiian Gardens CA 90716
Tel (562) 860-5887 *SIC* 7999

SAN MANUEL INDIAN BINGO & CASINO p 1277
777 San Manuel Blvd, Highland CA 92346
Tel (909) 864-5050 *SIC* 7999

EAST VALLEY TOURIST DEVELOPMENT AUTHORITY p 471
84245 Indio Springs Dr, Indio CA 92203
Tel (760) 342-5000 *SIC* 7999

JACKSON RANCHERIA CASINO & HOTEL p 774
12222 New York Ranch Rd, Jackson CA 95642
Tel (209) 223-1677
SIC 7999 5812 7011 5813

AMERICAN GOLF CORP p 73
6080 Center Dr Ste 500, Los Angeles CA 90045
Tel (310) 664-4000
SIC 7997 7999 5812 5941 7992

TICKETMASTER CORP p 1452
7060 Hollywood Blvd Ste 2, Los Angeles CA 90028
Tel (323) 769-4600 *SIC* 7999 7922

TICKETMASTER GROUP INC p 1452
3701 Wilshire Blvd Fl 9, Los Angeles CA 90010
Tel (800) 745-3000 *SIC* 7999

FESTIVAL FUN PARKS LLC p 539
4590 Macarthur Blvd # 400, Newport Beach CA 92660
Tel (949) 261-0404 *SIC* 7999 7993

PALACE ENTERTAINMENT INC p 1108
4590 Macarthur Blvd # 400, Newport Beach CA 92660
Tel (949) 261-0404 *SIC* 7999 7993

EAST BAY REGIONAL PARK DISTRICT p 470
2950 Peralta Oaks Ct, Oakland CA 94605
Tel (888) 327-2757 *SIC* 7999

AGUA CALIENTE BAND OF CAHUILLA INDIANS p 36
5401 Dinah Shore Dr, Palm Springs CA 92264
Tel (760) 699-6800 *SIC* 8699 6552 7999

SHINGLE SPRINGS TRIBAL GAMING AUTHORITY p 1317
1 Red Hawk Pkwy, Placerville CA 95667
Tel (530) 677-7000 *SIC* 7999

■ **STUBHUB INC** p 1394
199 Fremont St Fl 4, San Francisco CA 94105
Tel (415) 222-8400 *SIC* 7374 7999 7922

BEACHBODY LLC p 164
3301 Exposition Blvd Fl 3, Santa Monica CA 90404
Tel (310) 883-9000 *SIC* 7313 7999

COLONY CAPITAL LLC p 338
2450 Broadway Ste 600, Santa Monica CA 90404
Tel (310) 282-8820
SIC 6799 7999 7011 5813 5812

CHUMASH CASINO RESORT p 305
3400 E Highway 246, Santa Ynez CA 93460
Tel (805) 686-0855 *SIC* 7999 7011

PECHANGA DEVELOPMENT CORP p 1126
45000 Pechanga Pkwy, Temecula CA 92592
Tel (951) 695-4655 *SIC* 7011 7929 7999

■ **PRINCESS CRUISES AND TOURS INC** p 1177
24305 Town Center Dr # 200, Valencia CA 91355
Tel (206) 336-6000 *SIC* 7999

BROADMOOR HOTEL INC p 215
1 Lake Ave, Colorado Springs CO 80906
Tel (719) 634-7711
SIC 7011 5812 5813 7992 7999 7389

▲ **CENTURY CASINOS INC** p 282
455 E Pikes Peak Ave # 210, Colorado Springs CO 80903
Tel (719) 527-8300 *SIC* 7011 7929 7999

HYLAND HILLS PARK & RECREATION DISTRICT p 724
8801 Pecos St, Denver CO 80260
Tel (303) 427-7873 *SIC* 7999

▲ **INTRAWEST RESORTS HOLDINGS INC** p 760
1621 18th St Ste 300, Denver CO 80202
Tel (303) 749-8200 *SIC* 7011 7999 6531

XANTERRA SOUTH RIM LLC p 1630
6312 S Fiddlers Green Cir, Greenwood Village CO 80111
Tel (303) 600-3400 *SIC* 7011 5813 7999

▲ **GAIA INC** p 589
833 W South Boulder Rd, Louisville CO 80027
Tel (303) 222-3600 *SIC* 7299 7812 7999

CENTERPLATE INC p 276
2187 Atlantic St, Stamford CT 06902
Tel (800) 698-6992
SIC 5812 7999 5947 7993

CENTERPLATE ULTIMATE HOLDINGS CORP p 276
2187 Atlantic St, Stamford CT 06902
Tel (800) 698-6992
SIC 5812 7999 5947 7993

VOLUME SERVICES INC p 1565
2187 Atlantic St Ste 6, Stamford CT 06902
Tel (203) 975-5900
SIC 5812 7999 5947 7993

▲ **DOVER DOWNS GAMING & ENTERTAINMENT INC** p 453
1131 N Dupont Hwy, Dover DE 19901
Tel (302) 674-4600
SIC 7929 7999 7011 7948

REED ELSEVIER US HOLDINGS INC p 1217
1105 N Market St Ste 501, Wilmington DE 19801
Tel (302) 427-2672
SIC 2721 7999 8748 6719

SEMINOLE TRIBE OF FLORIDA INC p 1302
6300 Stirling Rd, Hollywood FL 33024
Tel (954) 966-6300
SIC 7999 5194 2011 5182 2911

ELLER-ITO STEVEDORING CO LLC p 488
1007 N America Way # 501, Miami FL 33132
Tel (305) 379-3700 *SIC* 7999 4491

FELD ENTERTAINMENT INC p 537
800 Feld Way, Palmetto FL 34221
Tel (941) 721-1200 *SIC* 7999 7929 5945

■ **SCIENTIFIC GAMES INTERNATIONAL INC** p 1292
1500 Bluegrass Lakes Pkwy, Alpharetta GA 30004
Tel (770) 664-3700 *SIC* 7389 7999

HERSCHEND ENTERTAINMENT CO LLC p 687
5445 Triangle Pkwy # 200, Norcross GA 30092
Tel (770) 441-1940 *SIC* 7999 5947 5812

POLYNESIAN CULTURAL CENTER INC p 1160
55-370 Kamehameha Hwy, Laie HI 96762
Tel (808) 293-3000 *SIC* 7999 5812 5947

CHICAGO PARK DISTRICT p 297
541 N Fairbanks Ct # 300, Chicago IL 60611
Tel (312) 742-7529 *SIC* 7999

METROPOLITAN PIER AND EXPOSITION AUTHORITY p 956
301 Ecermak Rd Fl 5, Chicago IL 60616
Tel (312) 791-7000 *SIC* 7389 7999 7011

NAVY PIER INC p 1020
600 E Grand Ave Ste 134, Chicago IL 60611
Tel (312) 595-5333 *SIC* 6519 7999

■ **WMS INDUSTRIES INC** p 1620
3401 N California Ave, Chicago IL 60618
Tel (847) 785-3000 *SIC* 3999 7999

YOUNG MENS CHRISTIAN ASSOCIATION OF CHICAGO p 1638
1030 W Van Buren St, Chicago IL 60607
Tel (312) 932-1200
SIC 8641 7011 8351 8699 8322 7999

CASINO QUEEN INC p 263
200 Front St, East Saint Louis IL 62201
Tel (618) 874-5000 *SIC* 7999 7011

■ **EMPRESS CASINO JOLIET CORP** p 495
777 Hollywood Blvd, Joliet IL 60436
Tel (815) 744-9400 *SIC* 7999

PARK NAPERVILLE DISTRICT p 1115
320 Jackson Ave, Naperville IL 60540
Tel (630) 848-5000
SIC 7992 7999 8322 8741

KEMPER SPORTS MANAGEMENT INC p 810
500 Skokie Blvd Ste 444, Northbrook IL 60062
Tel (847) 850-1818 *SIC* 7999

PARK PALATINE DISTRICT p 1115
250 E Wood St, Palatine IL 60067
Tel (847) 991-0333 *SIC* 7999

ROCKFORD PARK DISTRICT p 1244
401 S Main St Ste 101, Rockford IL 61101
Tel (815) 987-8800 *SIC* 7999

■ **AMERISTAR EAST CHICAGO HOLDINGS LLC** p 83
777 Ameristar Blvd, East Chicago IN 46312
Tel (219) 378-3000 *SIC* 7999

■ **RIH ACQUISITIONS IN LLC** p 1235
777 Resorts Blvd, East Chicago IN 46312
Tel (219) 378-3000 *SIC* 7999

■ **HORSESHOE HAMMOND LLC** p 708
777 Casino Center Dr, Hammond IN 46320
Tel (866) 711-7463 *SIC* 7999 5947 5812

CELEBRATION STATION PROPERTIES INC p 273
1000 E 80th Pl Ste 420n, Merrillville IN 46410
Tel (219) 757-3500 *SIC* 7999

PRAIRIE MEADOWS RACETRACK AND CASINO INC p 1167
1 Prairie Meadows Dr, Altoona IA 50009
Tel (515) 967-1000
SIC 7948 7993 7999 5947 5812 5813

■ **PENINSULA GAMING LLC** p 1129
301 Bell St, Dubuque IA 52001
Tel (563) 690-4975 *SIC* 7999 7011

PENINSULA GAMING PARTNERS LLC p 1129
600 Star Brewery Dr # 110, Dubuque IA 52001
Tel (563) 690-4975 *SIC* 7999 7011

LOUISIANA RIVERBOAT GAMING PARTNERSHIP p 880
711 Diamondjacks Blvd, Bossier City LA 71111
Tel (318) 678-7633 *SIC* 7999

CYPRESS BAYOU CASINO p 405
832 Martin Luther King Rd, Charenton LA 70523
Tel (337) 923-7284 *SIC* 7999

LOUISIANA I GAMING LP p 880
4132 Peters Rd, Harvey LA 70058
Tel (504) 366-7711 *SIC* 7999

■ **TREASURE CHEST CASINO LLC** p 1475
5050 Williams Blvd, Kenner LA 70065
Tel (504) 443-8000 *SIC* 7999

TUNICA-BILOXI GAMING AUTHORITY p 1491
711 Paragon Pl, Marksville LA 71351
Tel (318) 253-1946 *SIC* 7011 7999 5999

■ **RED RIVER ENTERTAINMENT OF SHREVEPORT** p 1216
315 Clyde Fant Pkwy, Shreveport LA 71101
Tel (318) 424-7777 *SIC* 7999

MARYLAND-NATIONAL CAPITAL PARK AND PLANNING COMMISSION p 915
6611 Kenilworth Ave # 103, Riverdale MD 20737
Tel (301) 454-1540 *SIC* 7999

YMCA OF NORTH SHORE INC p 1636
245 Cabot St, Beverly MA 01915
Tel (978) 922-0990
SIC 7021 8322 8351 7999 7032

TOWN OF WALPOLE p 1465
135 School St, Walpole MA 02081
Tel (508) 660-7353 *SIC* 7999

DETROIT ENTERTAINMENT LLC p 433
2901 Grand River Ave, Detroit MI 48201
Tel (313) 237-7711 *SIC* 7999

YOUNG MENS CHRISTIAN ASSOCIATION OF METROPOLITAN DETROIT p 1638
1401 Broadway St Ste A, Detroit MI 48226
Tel (313) 267-5300 *SIC* 7999 8641

THREE RIVERS PARK DISTRICT p 1450
3000 Xenium Ln N, Plymouth MN 55441
Tel (763) 559-9000 *SIC* 7999

SHAKOPEE MDEWAKANTON SIOUX COMMUNITY p 1311
2330 Sioux Trl Nw, Prior Lake MN 55372
Tel (952) 445-8900 *SIC* 7999

SMSC GAMING ENTERPRISE p 1334
2400 Mystic Lake Blvd, Prior Lake MN 55372
Tel (952) 445-9000 *SIC* 7999 7011

PRAIRIE ISLAND INDIAN COMMUNITY p 1167
5636 Sturgeon Lake Rd, Welch MN 55089
Tel (800) 554-5473 *SIC* 7999 5812 7011

TREASURE ISLAND RESORT AND CASINO p 1475
5734 Sturgeon Lake Rd, Welch MN 55089
Tel (651) 388-6300 *SIC* 7999 7011 5812

■ **OLYMPIA BALLYS LIMITED PARTNERSHIP** p 1083
1450 Ballys Blvd, Robinsonville MS 38664
Tel (662) 357-1500
SIC 7999 7011 5813 5812

RIH ACQUISITIONS MS I LLC p 1235
1100 Casino Strip Resort, Robinsonville MS 38664
Tel (662) 363-7777 *SIC* 7999

RIH ACQUISITIONS MS II LLC p 1235
1450 Ballys Blvd, Robinsonville MS 38664
Tel (800) 382-2559 SIC 7999

■ **TUNICA ROADHOUSE CORP** p 1491
13615 Old Highway 61 N, Robinsonville MS 38664
Tel (662) 363-4900
SIC 7999 7011 5813 5812

■ **AMERISTAR CASINO VICKSBURG INC** p 83
4116 Washington St, Vicksburg MS 39180
Tel (601) 638-1000 SIC 7999 7011 5812

■ **AMERISTAR CASINO KANSAS CITY INC** p 83
3200 Ameristar Dr, Kansas City MO 64161
Tel (816) 414-7000 SIC 7011 7999

■ **ST LOUIS GAMING VENTURES LLC** p 1369
777 Casino Center Dr, Maryland Heights MO 63043
Tel (314) 770-7629 SIC 7999 7011

■ **HARRAHS NORTH KANSAS CITY LLC** p 663
1 Riverboat Dr, North Kansas City MO 64116
Tel (816) 472-7777 SIC 7999

■ **MISSOURI GAMING CO** p 976
777 Nw Argosy Pkwy, Riverside MO 64150
Tel (816) 746-3171 SIC 7999 7011

■ **AMERISTAR CASINO ST CHARLES INC** p 83
1 Ameristar Blvd, Saint Charles MO 63301
Tel (636) 949-7777 SIC 7999 7011

▲ **PEAK RESORTS INC** p 1126
17409 Hidden Valley Dr, Wildwood MO 63025
Tel (636) 938-7474 SIC 7992 7999 7011

AFFINITY GAMING FINANCE CORP p 32
3755 Breakthrough Way # 300, Las Vegas NV 89135
Tel (702) 341-2400 SIC 7011 7999

■ **BALLY TECHNOLOGIES INC** p 148
6601 Bermuda Rd, Las Vegas NV 89119
Tel (770) 420-2388
SIC 3999 7999 7993 7372

▲ **CAESARS ENTERTAINMENT CORP** p 237
1 Caesars Palace Dr, Las Vegas NV 89109
Tel (702) 407-6000 SIC 7011 7999

■ **CAESARS ENTERTAINMENT OPERATING CO INC** p 237
1 Caesars Palace Dr, Las Vegas NV 89109
Tel (702) 407-6000 SIC 7999

■ **CAESARS LICENSE CO LLC** p 237
3645 Las Vegas Blvd S, Las Vegas NV 89109
Tel (702) 739-4111 SIC 7999

■ **CAESARS WORLD INC** p 237
3570 Las Vegas Blvd S, Las Vegas NV 89109
Tel (702) 731-7110
SIC 7011 7999 5812 6552 5611 5621

▲ **GOLDEN ENTERTAINMENT INC** p 620
6595 S Jones Blvd, Las Vegas NV 89118
Tel (702) 893-7777 SIC 7999

HRHH GAMING SENIOR MEZZ LLC p 714
4455 Paradise Rd, Las Vegas NV 89169
Tel (702) 693-5026 SIC 7999

INTERNATIONAL GAME TECHNOLOGY INC p 755
7900 W Sunset Rd, Las Vegas NV 89113
Tel (702) 669-7777 SIC 7999

■ **MANDALAY RESORT GROUP** p 901
3950 Las Vegas Blvd S, Las Vegas NV 89119
Tel (702) 693-7120 SIC 7011 7999 7996

PA MEADOWS LLC p 1103
9107 W Russell Rd, Las Vegas NV 89148
Tel (702) 856-5158 SIC 7999

■ **PARBALL CORP** p 1114
3655 Las Vegas Blvd S, Las Vegas NV 89109
Tel (702) 967-4111
SIC 7011 7999 6512 7521 7211

PINNACLE ENTERTAINMENT INC p 1149
3980 Howard Hughes Pkwy, Las Vegas NV 89169
Tel (702) 541-7777 SIC 7999 7011

▲ **SCIENTIFIC GAMES CORP** p 1292
6650 El Camino Rd, Las Vegas NV 89118
Tel (702) 897-7150 SIC 7999 7373

STRATOSPHERE LLC p 1393
2000 Las Vegas Blvd S, Las Vegas NV 89104
Tel (702) 380-7777 SIC 7011 7999

■ **TROPICANA ENTERTAINMENT INC** p 1484
8345 W Sunset Rd Ste 300, Las Vegas NV 89113
Tel (702) 589-3900 SIC 7011 7999

MARNELL GAMING LLC p 909
2100 S Casino Dr, Laughlin NV 89029
Tel (702) 298-4000 SIC 7999

TEXAS GAMBLING HALL & HOTEL INC p 1443
2101 Texas Star Ln, North Las Vegas NV 89032
Tel (702) 631-1000 SIC 7011 7999 5812

PEPPERMILL CASINOS INC p 1134
90 W Grove St Ste 600, Reno NV 89509
Tel (775) 689-8900 SIC 7011 7999

RECREATIONAL ENTERPRISES INC p 1215
345 N Virginia St, Reno NV 89501
Tel (775) 786-5700
SIC 7011 7999 5813 5812

SIG SAUER INC p 1321
72 Pease Blvd, Newington NH 03801
Tel (603) 610-3000 SIC 3484 7999

TRUMP ENTERTAINMENT RESORTS INC p 1487
1000 Boardwalk, Atlantic City NJ 08401
Tel (609) 449-5534 SIC 7011 7999

INN OF MOUNTAIN GODS RESORT AND CASINO p 744
287 Carrizo Canyon Rd, Mescalero NM 88340
Tel (575) 464-7777 SIC 7999 7011

DELAWARE NORTH COMPANIES INC p 424
250 Delaware Ave, Buffalo NY 14202
Tel (716) 858-5000
SIC 5461 7011 7993 7999

FUN STATION ASSOCIATES INC p 585
40 Rockylyn Ave, Lynbrook NY 11563
Tel (516) 599-7757 SIC 7299 7999

▲ **ICAHN ENTERPRISES LP** p 726
767 5th Ave Ste 4700, New York NY 10153
Tel (212) 702-4300
SIC 6722 3714 7999 3743 5093 6531

OAK HILL CAPITAL PARTNERS III LP p 1070
65 E 55th St Fl 32, New York NY 10022
Tel (212) 527-8400
SIC 5812 5813 7999 7993

W2007/ACEP MANAGERS VOTECO LLC p 1569
85 Broad St, New York NY 10004
Tel (212) 902-1000 SIC 7011 7999

WELLSPRING CAPITAL PARTNERS III LP p 1591
390 Park Ave Fl 5, New York NY 10022
Tel (212) 318-9800
SIC 5812 5813 7999 7993

WS MIDWAY HOLDINGS INC p 1628
390 Park Ave Fl 6, New York NY 10022
Tel (212) 318-9800
SIC 5812 5813 7999 7993

HAMLET HOLDING LLC p 656
2 Manhattanville Rd, Purchase NY 10577
Tel (914) 694-8000 SIC 7011 7999

PAY-O-MATIC CORP p 1122
160 Oak Dr, Syosset NY 11791
Tel (516) 496-4900 SIC 6099 7381 7999

BILTMORE CO p 183
1 Lodge St, Asheville NC 28803
Tel (828) 225-6776 SIC 7999 5947 5812

MORALE WELFARE RECREATION ACTIVITY p 988
1401 West Rd, Camp Lejeune NC 28547
Tel (910) 451-2861
SIC 5311 5812 8322 7999 9711

DIVI HOTELS MARKETING INC p 444
6320 Quadrangle Dr # 210, Chapel Hill NC 27517
Tel (919) 419-3484 SIC 7011 7999 6531

LAKE SPIRIT TRIBE p 839
816 3rd Ave N, Fort Totten ND 58335
Tel (701) 766-1270
SIC 9131 0191 2394 2298 7999

INTERNATIONAL MANAGEMENT GROUP (OVERSEAS) LLC p 756
1360 E 9th St Ste 100, Cleveland OH 44114
Tel (216) 522-1200 SIC 7941 7999 7922

PARK CORP p 1115
6200 Riverside Dr, Cleveland OH 44135
Tel (216) 267-4870
SIC 3547 1711 3443 5084 6512 7999

JMAC INC p 786
200 W Nationwide Blvd # 1, Columbus OH 43215
Tel (614) 436-2418
SIC 3325 5198 7999 5511 8741

CHEROKEE NATION ENTERTAINMENT LLC p 294
777 W Cherokee St, Catoosa OK 74015
Tel (918) 458-1696
SIC 7999 7011 7948 5541 5993

OSAGE NATION GAMING ENTERPRISE p 1096
1121 W 36th St, Tulsa OK 74127
Tel (918) 699-7710 SIC 7999

STARPLEX CORP p 1379
12722 Ne Airport Way, Portland OR 97230
Tel (503) 222-5957 SIC 7381 7363 7999

COW CREEK BAND OF UMPQUA TRIBE OF INDIANS p 385
2371 Ne Stephens St, Roseburg OR 97470
Tel (541) 957-8945 SIC 9131 6321 7999

MOUNTAINVIEW THOROUGHBRED RACING ASSOCIATION LLC p 994
777 Hollywood Blvd, Grantville PA 17028
Tel (717) 469-2211 SIC 7999

■ **GOLD MERGER SUB LLC** p 620
845 Berkshire Blvd # 200, Wyomissing PA 19610
Tel (610) 401-2900 SIC 7999 7011

GTECH HOLDINGS CORP p 644
10 Memorial Blvd Ste 101, Providence RI 02903
Tel (401) 392-1000 SIC 7999 7371

IGT GLOBAL SOLUTIONS CORP p 730
10 Memorial Blvd, Providence RI 02903
Tel (401) 392-1000
SIC 7999 3575 7372 7378 2752 7374

CENTURY GOLF PARTNERS MANAGEMENT LP p 282
5430 L B Johnson Fwy 14 Ste 1400, Dallas TX 75240
Tel (972) 419-1400 SIC 7999

■ **DAVE & BUSTERS INC** p 415
2481 Manana Dr, Dallas TX 75220
Tel (214) 357-9588
SIC 5812 5813 7999 7993

▲ **MALIBU ENTERTAINMENT WORLDWIDE INC** p 899
717 N Harwood St Ste 1650, Dallas TX 75201
Tel (214) 210-8701 SIC 1629 7999

TOP GOLF USA INC p 1460
8750 N Cntl Expy Ste 1200, Dallas TX 75231
Tel (214) 377-5053 SIC 7999 5812 5941

MOODY GARDENS INC p 987
1 Hope Blvd, Galveston TX 77554
Tel (409) 744-4673
SIC 8412 8422 7999 7011

HOUSTON LIVESTOCK SHOW AND RODEO EDUCATIONAL FUND p 712
8334 Nrg Park Fl 2, Houston TX 77054
Tel (832) 667-1000 SIC 7999

■ **CLEAR CHANNEL OUTDOOR HOLDINGS INC** p 324
200 E Basse Rd Ste 100, San Antonio TX 78209
Tel (210) 832-3700 SIC 7312 7999

DEER VALLEY RESORT p 422
2250 Deer Valley Dr, Park City UT 84060
Tel (435) 649-1000 SIC 7999

RINK MANAGEMENT SERVICES CORP p 1235
9414 Charter Crossing Dr, Mechanicsville VA 23116
Tel (804) 550-7002 SIC 7999

RNGLNG BRS BRNM & BLY COMB SHO p 1240
8607 Westwood Center Dr # 500, Vienna VA 22182
Tel (703) 448-4000 SIC 7999

WASHINGTON GAMING INC p 1578
711 Powell Ave Sw, Renton WA 98057
Tel (425) 264-1050 SIC 7999

■ **PARK MOUNTAINEER INC** p 1115
Hc 2, Chester WV 26034
Tel (304) 387-8300
SIC 7999 7011 7389 6512

LAC DU FLAMBEAU BAND OF LAKE SUPERIOR CHIPPEWA INDIANS (INC) p 836
418 Little Pines Rd, Lac Du Flambeau WI 54538
Tel (715) 588-3303
SIC 8011 7999 5411 5541 8031

BINGO POTAWATOMI p 183
1721 W Canal St, Milwaukee WI 53233
Tel (414) 645-6888 SIC 7999 5812 5947

MILWAUKEE WORLD FESTIVAL INC p 972
114 N Jackson St, Milwaukee WI 53202
Tel (414) 273-2680 SIC 7999

JACKSON HOLE MOUNTAIN RESORT CORP p 774
3395 Cody Ln, Teton Village WY 83025
Tel (307) 733-2292 SIC 7999 6552

SIC 8011 Offices & Clinics Of Doctors Of Medicine

■ **AFFINITY HOSPITAL LLC** p 32
3690 Grandview Pkwy, Birmingham AL 35243
Tel (205) 592-1000 SIC 8062 8011

BAPTIST HEALTH SYSTEM INC p 153
1130 22nd St S Ste 1000, Birmingham AL 35205
Tel (205) 715-5000
SIC 8011 8741 8082 8059

■ **BROOKWOOD BAPTIST MEDICAL CENTER** p 218
2010 Brookwood Med Ctr Dr, Birmingham AL 35209
Tel (205) 877-1000 SIC 8011

EASTERN HEALTH SYSTEM INC p 472
Medical Park E Dr Bldg 1, Birmingham AL 35235
Tel (205) 838-3996
SIC 8062 8082 8051 8011 8322 8093

ST VINCENTS EAST p 1373
50 Medical Park Dr E, Birmingham AL 35235
Tel (205) 838-3000 SIC 8062 8011

MARSHALL MEDICAL CENTER SOUTH p 911
2505 Us Highway 431, Boaz AL 35957
Tel (256) 593-8310 SIC 8011

GULF HEALTH HOSPITALS INC p 646
750 Morphy Ave, Fairhope AL 36532
Tel (251) 928-2375 SIC 8062 8011

■ **GADSDEN REGIONAL MEDICAL CENTER LLC** p 589
1007 Goodyear Ave, Gadsden AL 35903
Tel (256) 494-4000
SIC 8062 8082 8011 7352

HEALTH CARE AUTHORITY OF CITY OF HUNTSVILLE p 674
101 Sivley Rd Sw, Huntsville AL 35801
Tel (256) 265-1000 SIC 8011 8062

RMC JACKSONVILLE p 1239
1701 Pelham Rd S, Jacksonville AL 36265
Tel (256) 782-4256 SIC 8011

PROVIDENCE HOSPITAL p 1186
6801 Airport Blvd, Mobile AL 36608
Tel (251) 633-1000 SIC 8062 8011

SOUTHERN MEDICAL HEALTH SYSTEMS INC p 1349
3632 Dauphin St Ste 101b, Mobile AL 36608
Tel (251) 460-5280
SIC 8741 8011 7374 7322

BRISTOL BAY AREA HEALTH CORP p 214
6000 Kanakanak Rd, Dillingham AK 99576
Tel (907) 842-5201 SIC 8062 8011

DENA NENA HENASH p 428
122 1st Ave Ste 600, Fairbanks AK 99701
Tel (907) 452-8251
SIC 8011 8331 8322 8093

SOUTHEAST ALASKA REGIONAL HEALTH CONSORTIUM p 1345
3100 Channel Dr Ste 300, Juneau AK 99801
Tel (907) 463-4000 SIC 8011 8062

MOUNTAIN VISTA SURGICAL SPECIALISTS p 994
10238 E Hampton Ave # 402, Mesa AZ 85209
Tel (480) 354-3200 SIC 8011

NEXTCARE HOLDINGS INC p 1040
1138 N Alma School Rd # 120, Mesa AZ 85201
Tel (480) 924-8382 SIC 8093 8741 8011

BANNER HEALTH p 153
2901 N Central Ave # 160, Phoenix AZ 85012
Tel (602) 747-4000
SIC 8062 8051 8082 7361 8011 8093

BANNER-UNIVERSITY MEDICAL GROUP p 153
2901 N Central Ave, Phoenix AZ 85012
Tel (602) 747-4000 SIC 8011

DISTRICT MEDICAL GROUP INC p 443
2929 E Thomas Rd, Phoenix AZ 85016
Tel (602) 274-8859 SIC 8011

ESTRELLA BANNER MEDICAL CENTER p 511
9201 W Thomas Rd, Phoenix AZ 85037
Tel (623) 327-4000 SIC 8011

SOUTHWEST CATHOLIC HEALTH NETWORK CORP p 1351
4350 E Cotton Center Blvd, Phoenix AZ 85040
Tel (602) 263-3000 SIC 8011

ST LUKES MEDICAL CENTER p 1370
1800 E Van Buren St, Phoenix AZ 85006
Tel (602) 251-8100 SIC 8011

YAVAPAI COMMUNITY HOSP ASSN p 1635
1003 Willow Creek Rd, Prescott AZ 86301
Tel (928) 445-2700 SIC 8062 8011

YAVAPAI REGIONAL MEDICAL CENTER FOUNDATION p 1635
1003 Willow Creek Rd, Prescott AZ 86301
Tel (928) 445-2700 SIC 8011 8082 2835

▲ **MAGELLAN HEALTH INC** p 895
4800 N Scottsdale Rd, Scottsdale AZ 85251
Tel (602) 572-6050 SIC 8063 8011 5122

MAYO CLINIC ARIZONA p 923
13400 E Shea Blvd, Scottsdale AZ 85259
Tel (480) 301-8000 SIC 8011

NAVAPACHE REGIONAL MEDICAL CENTER p 1019
2200 E Show Low Lake Rd, Show Low AZ 85901
Tel (928) 537-4375 SIC 8011

LABORATORY SCIENCES OF ARIZONA LLC p 836
1255 W Washington St, Tempe AZ 85281
Tel (602) 685-5000 SIC 8071 8011 8331

UNIVERSITY PHYSICIANS HEALTH CARE p 1527
1501 N Campbell Ave, Tucson AZ 85724
Tel (520) 626-6174 SIC 8011

WHITE RIVER MEDICAL CENTER p 1606
1710 Harrison St, Batesville AR 72501
Tel (870) 262-1200 SIC 8011

NORTH ARKANSAS REGIONAL MEDICA p 1050
620 N Main St, Harrison AR 72601
Tel (870) 365-2000 SIC 8011

SAINT JOSEPHS HOSPITAL INC p 1269
300 Werner St, Hot Springs AR 71913
Tel (501) 622-1000 SIC 8011

NEA BAPTIST CLINIC p 1022
3024 Red Wolf Blvd, Jonesboro AR 72401
Tel (870) 972-7000 SIC 8011

ARKANSAS HEART HOSPITAL LLC p 109
1701 S Shackleford Rd, Little Rock AR 72211
Tel (501) 219-7000 SIC 8062 8011

CENTRAL ARKANSAS RADIATION THERAPY INSTITUTE INC p 277
8901 Carti Way, Little Rock AR 72205
Tel (501) 906-3000 SIC 8011 8221

ST VINCENT INFIRMARY MEDICAL CENTER p 1373
2 Saint Vincent Cir, Little Rock AR 72205
Tel (501) 552-3000 SIC 8011

THOMAS RONALD HALL OD p 1449
3610 Pruetts Chapel Rd, Paragould AR 72450
Tel (870) 236-8500 SIC 8011

TELECARE CORP p 1434
1080 Marina Village Pkwy # 100, Alameda CA 94501
Tel (510) 337-7950 SIC 8063 8011

CLINICA SIERRA VISTA p 326
1430 Truxtun Ave Ste 400, Bakersfield CA 93301
Tel (661) 635-3050 SIC 8011

SAN JOAQUIN COMMUNITY HOSPITAL p 1277
2615 Chester Ave, Bakersfield CA 93301
Tel (661) 395-3000 SIC 8062 8011

EDEN TOWNSHIP HOSPITAL DISTRICT INC p 477
20400 Lake Chabot Rd # 303, Castro Valley CA 94546
Tel (510) 538-2031 SIC 8062 8011

ALTAMED HEALTH SERVICES CORP p 62
2040 Camfield Ave, Commerce CA 90040
Tel (323) 725-8751 SIC 8011 8099

■ **HEALTHCARE PARTNERS LLC** p 676
2175 Park Pl, El Segundo CA 90245
Tel (310) 354-4200 SIC 8011

COMMUNITY MEDICAL CENTER p 349
2823 Fresno St, Fresno CA 93721
Tel (559) 459-6000 SIC 8062 8011 8051

GARDENA HOSPITAL LP p 591
1145 W Redondo Beach Blvd, Gardena CA 90247
Tel (310) 532-4200 SIC 8062 8322 8011

GLENDALE ADVENTIST MEDICAL CENTER INC p 615
1509 Wilson Ter, Glendale CA 91206
Tel (818) 409-8000 SIC 8062 8093 8011

ADVENTIST MEDICAL CENTER-HANFORD p 27
115 Mall Dr, Hanford CA 93230
Tel (559) 582-9000 SIC 8011

▲ **CORVEL CORP** p 373
2010 Main St Ste 600, Irvine CA 92614
Tel (949) 851-1473 SIC 8741 8011

■ **EDWARDS LIFESCIENCES LLC** p 480
1 Edwards Way, Irvine CA 92614
Tel (949) 250-2500 SIC 8011

HOAG ORTHOPEDIC INSTITUTE LLC p 698
16250 Sand Canyon Ave, Irvine CA 92618
Tel (855) 999-4641 SIC 8011

■ **SUN HEALTHCARE GROUP INC** p 1400
18831 Von Karman Ave # 400, Irvine CA 92612
Tel (949) 255-7100 SIC 8011 8322

MARIN GENERAL HOSPITAL p 906
250 Bon Air Rd, Kentfield CA 94904
Tel (415) 925-7000 SIC 8062 8011

SADDLEBACK MEMORIAL MEDICAL CENTER p 1265
24451 Health Center Dr, Laguna Hills CA 92653
Tel (949) 837-4500
SIC 8062 8011 8093 8099 8071 8069

VALLEYCARE HOSPITAL CORP p 1541
1111 E Stanley Blvd, Livermore CA 94550
Tel (925) 447-7000 SIC 8011

LOMA LINDA UNIVERSITY HEALTH CARE p 875
11175 Campus St, Loma Linda CA 92350
Tel (909) 558-4729 SIC 8011

LOMA LINDA UNIVERSITY HEALTH CARE p 875
11370 Anderson St # 3900, Loma Linda CA 92350
Tel (909) 558-2806
SIC 8062 8011 8051 5999

LOMA LINDA UNIVERSITY MEDICAL CENTER p 875
11234 Anderson St, Loma Linda CA 92354
Tel (909) 558-4000
SIC 8062 8011 8051 5999

▲ **MOLINA HEALTHCARE INC** p 982
200 Oceangate Ste 100, Long Beach CA 90802
Tel (562) 435-3666 SIC 8011 6324

■ **MOLINA HEALTHCARE OF CALIFORNIA PARTNER PLAN INC** p 982
200 Oceangate Ste 100, Long Beach CA 90802
Tel (562) 435-3666 SIC 6321 8011

MOLINA INFORMATION SYSTEMS LLC p 982
200 Oceangate Ste 100, Long Beach CA 90802
Tel (562) 435-3666 SIC 8011

■ **MOLINA PATHWAYS LLC** p 983
200 Oceangate Ste 100, Long Beach CA 90802
Tel (562) 491-5773 SIC 8011

CHA HEALTH SYSTEMS INC p 286
3731 Wilshire Blvd # 850, Los Angeles CA 90010
Tel (213) 487-3211 SIC 8011

CHILDRENS HOSPITAL LOS ANGELES MEDICAL GROUP INC p 299
6430 W Sunset Blvd # 600, Los Angeles CA 90028
Tel (323) 361-2336 *SIC* 8011

GOOD SAMARITAN HOSPITAL AUXILIARY p 623
1225 Wilshire Blvd, Los Angeles CA 90017
Tel (213) 977-2121 *SIC* 8011

KECK HOSPITAL OF USC p 807
1500 San Pablo St, Los Angeles CA 90033
Tel (800) 872-2273 *SIC* 8011

PROSPECT MEDICAL HOLDINGS INC p 1184
3415 S Sepulveda Blvd # 9, Los Angeles CA 90034
Tel (310) 943-4500 *SIC* 8011

TRANSLATIONAL ONCOLOGY RESEARCH INTERNATIONAL INC p 1472
1033 Gayley Ave Ste 207, Los Angeles CA 90024
Tel (310) 824-1919 *SIC* 8011 8732 8742

ST FRANCIS MEDICAL CENTER p 1366
3630 E Imperial Hwy, Lynwood CA 90262
Tel (310) 900-8900 *SIC* 8011

VALLEY CHILDRENS HEALTHCARE p 1540
9300 Valley Childrens Pl, Madera CA 93636
Tel (559) 353-3000 *SIC* 8011 8069

■ **VANTAGE ONCOLOGY LLC** p 1544
1500 Rosecrans Ave # 400, Manhattan Beach CA 90266
Tel (310) 335-4000 *SIC* 8011

CFHS HOLDINGS INC p 285
4650 Lincoln Blvd, Marina Del Rey CA 90292
Tel (310) 823-8911 *SIC* 8062 8093 8011

MENLO HEALTH ALLIANCE p 943
1300 Crane St, Menlo Park CA 94025
Tel (650) 498-6640 *SIC* 8011

FUTTER GOLD MEDICAL FOUNDATION p 585
600 Coffee Rd, Modesto CA 95355
Tel (209) 550-4724 *SIC* 8011

SUTTER GOULD MEDICAL FOUNDATION p 1410
1700 Mchenry Ave Ste 60b, Modesto CA 95350
Tel (209) 526-4500 *SIC* 8011

COMMUNITY HOSPITAL OF MONTEREY PENINSULA p 349
23625 Holman Hwy, Monterey CA 93940
Tel (831) 624-5311 *SIC* 8069 8011

■ **INTREPID HEALTHCARE SERVICES INC** p 760
4605 Lankershim Blvd, North Hollywood CA 91602
Tel (888) 447-2362 *SIC* 8011

KAISER FOUNDATION HOSPITALS INC p 800
1 Kaiser Plz, Oakland CA 94612
Tel (510) 271-6611 *SIC* 8062 8011

PRIME HEALTHCARE FOUNDATION INC p 1175
3300 E Guasti Rd Fl 3, Ontario CA 91761
Tel (909) 235-4400 *SIC* 8011

ORANGE COUNTY HEALTH AUTHORITY A PUBLIC AGENCY p 1092
505 City Pkwy W, Orange CA 92868
Tel (714) 246-8500 *SIC* 8621 8011

■ **PALMDALE REGIONAL MEDICAL CENTER** p 1109
38600 Medical Center Dr, Palmdale CA 93551
Tel (661) 382-5000 *SIC* 8011

PALO ALTO MEDICAL FOUNDATION FOR HEALTH CARE RESEARCH AND EDUCATION (INC) p 1110
795 El Camino Real, Palo Alto CA 94301
Tel (650) 321-4121 *SIC* 8011

INTER-VALLEY HEALTH PLAN INC p 751
300 S Park Ave Ste 300, Pomona CA 91766
Tel (909) 623-6333 *SIC* 6324 8011

PAMONA VALLEY MEDICAL GROUP INC p 1110
9302 Pttsbrgh Ave Ste 220, Rancho Cucamonga CA 91730
Tel (909) 932-1045 *SIC* 8011 8741

PRIME HEALTHCARE SERVICES - SHASTA LLC p 1175
1100 Butte St, Redding CA 96001
Tel (530) 244-5400 *SIC* 8062 8011

PARKVIEW COMMUNITY HOSPITAL MEDICAL CENTER p 1117
3865 Jackson St, Riverside CA 92503
Tel (951) 354-7404 *SIC* 8062 8011

■ **RIVERSIDE COMMUNITY HEALTH SYSTEMS** p 1238
4445 Magnolia Ave Fl 6, Riverside CA 92501
Tel (951) 788-3000 *SIC* 8062 8011

RIVERSIDE MEDICAL CLINIC INC p 1238
3660 Arlington Ave, Riverside CA 92506
Tel (951) 683-6370 *SIC* 8011

RADIOLOGICAL ASSOCIATES OF SACRAMENTO MEDICAL GROUP INC p 1204
1500 Expo Pkwy, Sacramento CA 95815
Tel (916) 646-8300 *SIC* 8071 8011

SUTTER HEALTH p 1410
2200 River Plaza Dr, Sacramento CA 95833
Tel (916) 733-8800
SIC 8062 8051 8011 6513

NATIVIDAD HOSPITAL INC p 1018
1441 Constitution Blvd, Salinas CA 93906
Tel (831) 755-4111 *SIC* 8062 8011 8093

■ **AMN HEALTHCARE INC** p 85
12400 High Bluff Dr, San Diego CA 92130
Tel (858) 792-0711 *SIC* 8011

PROMETHEUS LABORATORIES INC p 1183
9410 Carroll Park Dr, San Diego CA 92121
Tel (858) 824-0895 *SIC* 2834 8011

CHINESE COMMUNITY HEALTH PLAN p 301
445 Grant Ave Ste 700, San Francisco CA 94108
Tel (415) 955-8800 *SIC* 8011

HEALTHRIGHT 360 p 677
1735 Mission St Ste 2050, San Francisco CA 94103
Tel (415) 762-3700 *SIC* 8093 8011

NORTH EAST MEDICAL SERVICES p 1052
1520 Stockton St, San Francisco CA 94133
Tel (415) 391-9686 *SIC* 8011

■ **MANAGED HEALTH NETWORK** p 900
2370 Kerner Blvd, San Rafael CA 94901
Tel (415) 460-8168
SIC 6324 8099 8093 8011

■ **MHN SERVICES** p 959
2370 Kerner Blvd, San Rafael CA 94901
Tel (415) 460-8300
SIC 6324 8011 8742 8322

CENTRO DE SALUD DE LA COMUNIDAD DE SAN YSIDRO INC p 281
4004 Beyer Blvd, San Ysidro CA 92173
Tel (619) 428-4463 *SIC* 8093 8011

WESTERN MEDICAL CENTER SANTA ANA p 1599
1001 N Tustin Ave, Santa Ana CA 92705
Tel (714) 953-3664 *SIC* 8011

SANSUM CLINIC p 1280
470 S Patterson Ave, Santa Barbara CA 93111
Tel (805) 681-7700 *SIC* 8011

PALO ALTO MEDICAL FOUNDATION STA CRUZ p 1110
2025 Soquel Ave, Santa Cruz CA 95062
Tel (831) 458-5670 *SIC* 8011

SONORA REGIONAL HOSPITAL p 1340
1000 Greenley Rd, Sonora CA 95370
Tel (209) 736-0249 *SIC* 8011

OLIVE VIEW-UCLA MEDICAL CENTER p 1082
14445 Olive View Dr, Sylmar CA 91342
Tel (818) 364-1555 *SIC* 8011

PROVIDENCE TARZANA MEDICAL CENTER p 1186
18321 Clark St, Tarzana CA 91356
Tel (818) 881-0800 *SIC* 8011

■ **BIOFUSION LLC** p 183
19110 Van Ness Ave, Torrance CA 90501
Tel (310) 803-8100 *SIC* 8011

SURGERY CENTER TORRANCE L P p 1408
23560 Crenshaw Blvd # 104, Torrance CA 90505
Tel (310) 784-5880 *SIC* 8011

HENRY MAYO NEWHALL MEMORIAL HOSPITAL p 684
23845 Mcbean Pkwy, Valencia CA 91355
Tel (661) 253-8112 *SIC* 8011

US HEALTHWORKS INC p 1532
25124 Springfield Ct, Valencia CA 91355
Tel (800) 720-2432 *SIC* 8011

VENTURA COUNTY MEDICAL CENTER p 1548
3291 Loma Vista Rd, Ventura CA 93003
Tel (805) 652-6000 *SIC* 8011

FAMILY HEALTHCARE NETWORK p 527
305 E Center Ave, Visalia CA 93291
Tel (559) 737-4700 *SIC* 8011

BRIGHT HEALTH PHYSICIANS p 212
15725 Whittier Blvd # 500, Whittier CA 90603
Tel (562) 947-8478 *SIC* 8011

INTERHEALTH CORP p 752
12401 Washington Blvd, Whittier CA 90602
Tel (562) 698-0811 *SIC* 8062 8011

■ **UNIVERSAL HEALTH SERVICES OF RANCHO SPRINGS INC** p 1517
36485 Inland Valley Dr, Wildomar CA 92595
Tel (951) 677-9712 *SIC* 8099 8062 8011

SISTERS OF CHARITY OF LEAVENWORTH HEALTH SYSTEM INC p 1327
500 Eldorado Blvd # 6300, Broomfield CO 80021
Tel (303) 813-5000 *SIC* 8062 8011 5912

CORRECTIONAL HEALTHCARE COMPANIES INC p 372
7388 S Revere Pkwy # 707, Centennial CO 80112
Tel (615) 312-7286 *SIC* 8011 8744

■ **INTEGRITY URGENT CARE CLINICS INC** p 750
4323 Integrity Center Pt, Colorado Springs CO 80917
Tel (719) 591-2558 *SIC* 8082 8011 8051

ACT FOR HEALTH INC p 19
500 E 8th Ave, Denver CO 80203
Tel (303) 253-7470 *SIC* 8011

■ **ROSE MEDICAL GROUP** p 1250
4900 S Monaco St Ste 204, Denver CO 80237
Tel (303) 320-2101 *SIC* 8062 8011 8099

SCHRYVER MEDICAL SALES AND MARKETING LLC p 1290
12075 E 45th Ave Ste 600, Denver CO 80239
Tel (303) 371-0073 *SIC* 8071 8011

NORTH COLORADO MEDICAL CENTER p 1052
1801 16th St, Greeley CO 80631
Tel (970) 352-4121 *SIC* 8011

MONTROSE MEMORIAL HOSPITAL INC p 987
800 S 3rd St, Montrose CO 81401
Tel (970) 249-2211 *SIC* 8062 8011

LUTHERAN MEDICAL CENTER p 886
8300 W 38th Ave, Wheat Ridge CO 80033
Tel (303) 425-4500
SIC 8011 7389 8082 8331

SCL HEALTH - FRONT RANGE INC p 1292
8300 W 38th Ave, Wheat Ridge CO 80033
Tel (303) 813-5000 *SIC* 8062 8011 8051

WESTERN CONNECTICUT MEDICAL GROUP p 1597
14 Research Dr, Bethel CT 06801
Tel (203) 794-5331 *SIC* 8011

FAIRFIELD COUNTRY RADIOLOGY A p 524
2800 Main St, Bridgeport CT 06606
Tel (203) 576-5033 *SIC* 8011

NORTHEAST MEDICAL GROUP INC p 1055
99 Hawley Ave Fl 3, Bridgeport CT 06606
Tel (203) 339-6499 *SIC* 8011

DANBURY OFFICE OF PHYSICIAN SERVICES PC p 411
25 Germantown Rd, Danbury CT 06810
Tel (203) 794-0090 *SIC* 8011

▲ **AETNA INC** p 31
151 Farmington Ave, Hartford CT 06156
Tel (860) 273-0123
SIC 6324 6321 6371 8011

■ **AETNA LIFE INSURANCE CO INC** p 31
151 Farmington Ave, Hartford CT 06156
Tel (860) 273-0123 *SIC* 6324 6321 8011

■ **AHP HOLDINGS INC** p 37
151 Farmington Ave, Hartford CT 06156
Tel (860) 273-0123 *SIC* 6321 6311 8011

SAINT FRANCIS HOSPITAL AND MEDICAL CENTER FOUNDATION INC p 1269
114 Woodland St, Hartford CT 06105
Tel (860) 714-4006 *SIC* 8062 8011 8069

HOSPITAL OF ST RAPHAEL PHYSICIANS IPA II INC p 709
1450 Chapel St, New Haven CT 06511
Tel (203) 789-3000 *SIC* 8062 8011

LAWRENCE & MEMORIAL HOSPITAL INC p 847
365 Montauk Ave, New London CT 06320
Tel (860) 442-0711 *SIC* 8011 8062

GREATER WATERBURY HEALTH NETWORK INC p 636
64 Robbins St, Waterbury CT 06708
Tel (203) 573-6000 *SIC* 8741 8093 8011

■ **MILFORD ANESTHESIA ASSOCIATES LLC** p 969
111 Continental Dr # 412, Newark DE 19713
Tel (203) 783-1831 *SIC* 8011

MEDICAL FACULTY ASSOCIATES INC p 937
2150 Pennsylvania Ave Nw, Washington DC 20037
Tel (202) 741-3000 *SIC* 8011

■ **METROPOLITAN HEALTH NETWORKS INC** p 956
2900 N Military Trl, Boca Raton FL 33431
Tel (561) 805-8500 *SIC* 8011

COMPREHENSIVE HEALTH HOLDINGS INC p 352
8810 Astronaut Blvd, Cape Canaveral FL 32920
Tel (321) 783-2720 *SIC* 8011

■ **ATLANTIC MEDICAL CENTER** p 127
303 N Clyde Morris Blvd, Daytona Beach FL 32114
Tel (386) 239-5001 *SIC* 8062 8011

HALIFAX HEALTH CARE SYSTEMS INC p 654
303 N Clyde Morris Blvd, Daytona Beach FL 32114
Tel (386) 254-4000 *SIC* 8062 8011 8063

AMERICAN HEALTH CHOICE INC p 73
8350 Nw 52nd Ter Ste 206, Doral FL 33166
Tel (305) 860-2333 *SIC* 8011

BROWARD GENERAL MEDICAL CENTER p 219
1600 S Andrews Ave, Fort Lauderdale FL 33316
Tel (954) 355-4400 *SIC* 8011

21ST CENTURY ONCOLOGY HOLDINGS INC p 2
2270 Colonial Blvd, Fort Myers FL 33907
Tel (239) 931-7254 *SIC* 8011

21ST CENTURY ONCOLOGY INC p 2
2270 Colonial Blvd, Fort Myers FL 33907
Tel (239) 931-7333 *SIC* 8011 7363

LEE MEMORIAL HEALTH SYSTEM p 851
2776 Cleveland Ave, Fort Myers FL 33901
Tel (239) 343-2000 *SIC* 8011

■ **NORTH FLORIDA REGIONAL MEDICAL CENTER INC** p 1052
6500 W Newberry Rd, Gainesville FL 32605
Tel (352) 333-4100
SIC 8062 8093 8011 8082 8069

SHANDS TEACHING HOSPITAL AND CLINICS INC p 1311
1600 Sw Archer Rd, Gainesville FL 32610
Tel (352) 265-0111 *SIC* 8011

GENESIS HEALTH INC p 603
3599 University Blvd S # 1, Jacksonville FL 32216
Tel (904) 858-7600 *SIC* 8069 8011 8741

UNIVERSITY OF FLORIDA JACKSONVILLE HEALTHCARE INC p 1521
3122 New Berlin Rd, Jacksonville FL 32226
Tel (904) 244-9500 *SIC* 8011

UNIVERSITY OF FLORIDA JACKSONVILLE PHYSICIANS INC p 1521
653 W 8th St, Jacksonville FL 32209
Tel (904) 244-9500 *SIC* 8011

WATSON CLINIC FOUNDATION INC p 1583
1600 Lakeland Hills Blvd, Lakeland FL 33805
Tel (863) 680-7000 *SIC* 8011

WATSON CLINIC LLP p 1583
1600 Lakeland Hills Blvd, Lakeland FL 33805
Tel (863) 680-7000 *SIC* 8011

ADCS CLINICS LLC p 21
151 Southhall Ln Ste 300, Maitland FL 32751
Tel (407) 875-2080 *SIC* 8011

FLORIDA HOSPITAL MEDICAL GROUP INC p 558
2600 Westhall Ln, Maitland FL 32751
Tel (407) 200-2700 *SIC* 8011

BEST DOCTORS INSURANCE HOLDINGS LLC p 177
5201 Blue Lagoon Dr # 300, Miami FL 33126
Tel (305) 269-2521 *SIC* 8011 6719

KENDALL REGIONAL MEDICAL CENTER INC p 810
11750 Sw 40th St, Miami FL 33175
Tel (305) 223-3000 *SIC* 8011

LEON FLAGLER HOLDINGS LLC p 856
7950 Nw 5th Ct, Miami FL 33150
Tel (305) 631-3900 *SIC* 8011

LEON MEDICAL CENTERS INC p 856
11501 Sw 40th St, Miami FL 33165
Tel (305) 559-2881 *SIC* 8011

■ **PHYSICIANS REGIONAL MEDICAL CENTER** p 1146
6101 Pine Ridge Rd, Naples FL 34119
Tel (239) 348-4400 *SIC* 8011 8062

JACKSON NORTH MEDICAL CENTER p 774
160 Nw 170th St, North Miami Beach FL 33169
Tel (305) 651-1100 *SIC* 8011 8062

MONROE REGIONAL HEALTH SYSTEM p 985
131 Sw 15th St, Ocala FL 34471
Tel (352) 351-7200 *SIC* 8011

FAMILY PHYSICIANS OF WINTER PARK PA p 527
6416 Old Winter Garden Rd, Orlando FL 32835
Tel (407) 293-2930 *SIC* 8011

PINELOCH FAMILY CARE p 1149
2898 S Osceola Ave, Orlando FL 32806
Tel (407) 812-8110 *SIC* 8011

ROSEN HOTELS AND RESORTS INC p 1251
9840 International Dr, Orlando FL 32819
Tel (407) 996-1706
SIC 7011 5812 5813 7389 8011 7992

BAY COUNTY HEALTH SYSTEM LLC p 160
615 N Bonita Ave, Panama City FL 32401
Tel (850) 769-1511 *SIC* 8011

BAY MEDICAL CENTER p 161
615 N Bonita Ave, Panama City FL 32401
Tel (850) 769-1511 *SIC* 8062 8011

SACRED HEART HEALTH SYSTEM INC p 1265
5151 N 9th Ave, Pensacola FL 32504
Tel (850) 416-1600 *SIC* 8062 8011

HEALTH FIRST INC p 674
6450 Us Highway 1, Rockledge FL 32955
Tel (321) 434-4300
SIC 8062 8011 8082 8069 7991 6324

BAYFRONT HMA MEDICAL CTR LLC p 161
701 6th St S, Saint Petersburg FL 33701
Tel (727) 823-1234 *SIC* 8011

■ **NORTHSIDE HOSPITAL** p 1058
6000 49th St N, Saint Petersburg FL 33709
Tel (727) 521-4411
SIC 8031 8011 8069 8062

BAPTIST HEALTH SOUTH FLORIDA INC p 153
6855 S Red Rd, South Miami FL 33143
Tel (305) 596-1960 *SIC* 8062 8011 8082

▲ **MEDNAX INC** p 938
1301 Concord Ter, Sunrise FL 33323
Tel (954) 384-0175 *SIC* 8011

■ **SHERIDAN HEALTHCARE INC** p 1315
1613 Harrison Pkwy # 200, Sunrise FL 33323
Tel (954) 838-2371 *SIC* 8011

CAPITAL HEALTH PLAN INC p 249
2140 Centerville Rd, Tallahassee FL 32308
Tel (850) 383-3333 *SIC* 8011

H LEE MOFFITT CANCER CENTER AND RESEARCH INSTITUTE INC p 650
12902 Usf Magnolia Dr, Tampa FL 33612
Tel (813) 745-4673 *SIC* 8011

UNIVERSITY OF SOUTH FLORIDA MEDICAL SERVICES SUPPORT CORP p 1525
12901 Brc Dwns Blvd Mdc62, Tampa FL 33612
Tel (813) 974-2201 *SIC* 8011 8741

NEWPORT RICHEY HOSPITAL INC p 1038
9330 State Road 54, Trinity FL 34655
Tel (727) 834-4000 *SIC* 8011

INDIAN RIVER MEMORIAL HOSPITAL INC p 737
1000 36th St, Vero Beach FL 32960
Tel (772) 567-4311 *SIC* 8062 8011

CENTER FOR PSYCHIATRY AT WINTER HAVEN INC p 276
200 Avenue F Ne, Winter Haven FL 33881
Tel (863) 297-1744 *SIC* 8011

WINTER PARK HEALTHCARE GROUP LTD p 1617
200 N Lakemont Ave, Winter Park FL 32792
Tel (407) 646-7000 *SIC* 8062 8011

FLORIDA MEDICAL CLINIC PA p 559
38135 Market Sq, Zephyrhills FL 33542
Tel (813) 780-8440 *SIC* 8011

PIEDMONT MEDICAL CENTER INC p 1147
1968 Peachtree Rd Nw, Atlanta GA 30309
Tel (404) 605-5000 *SIC* 8011

■ **UHS OF PEACHFORD LP** p 1500
2151 Peachford Rd, Atlanta GA 30338
Tel (770) 455-3200 *SIC* 8011

PHYSICIANS PRACTICE GROUP p 1146
1499 Walton Way Ste 1400, Augusta GA 30901
Tel (706) 724-6100 *SIC* 8011

GLYNN-BRUNSWICK MEMORIAL HOSPITAL AUTHORITY p 618
2415 Parkwood Dr, Brunswick GA 31520
Tel (912) 466-7000 *SIC* 8062 8011

LONGSTREET CLINIC P C p 877
725 Jesse Jewell Pkwy Se, Gainesville GA 30501
Tel (770) 718-1122 *SIC* 8011

COLQUITT REGIONAL MEDICAL CENTER p 339
3131 S Main St, Moultrie GA 31768
Tel (229) 985-3420 *SIC* 8011

SOUTHERN REGIONAL MEDICAL CENTER p 1350
11 Upper Riverdale Rd Sw, Riverdale GA 30274
Tel (770) 991-8520 *SIC* 8011

HARBIN CLINIC LLC p 659
221 Technology Pkwy Nw, Rome GA 30165
Tel (706) 295-5331 *SIC* 8011

■ **REDMOND PARK HOSPITAL LLC** p 1217
501 Redmond Rd Nw, Rome GA 30165
Tel (706) 291-0291 *SIC* 8062 8011

MEMORIAL HEALTH UNIVERSITY MEDICAL CENTER INC p 941
4700 Waters Ave, Savannah GA 31404
Tel (912) 350-8000 *SIC* 8062 8011

ORTHOPEDIC SURGERY CENTER L P p 1096
210 E Derenne Ave, Savannah GA 31405
Tel (912) 644-5300 *SIC* 8011

MOMI PALI MEDICAL CENTER p 983
98-1079 Moanalua Rd # 680, Aiea HI 96701
Tel (808) 486-6000 *SIC* 8011

HILO MEDICAL CENTER p 694
1190 Waianuenue Ave, Hilo HI 96720
Tel (808) 932-3000 *SIC* 8011

HAWAI I PACIFIC HEALTH p 668
55 Merchant St Ste 2500, Honolulu HI 96813
Tel (808) 535-7350 *SIC* 8062 8011

STRAUB CLINIC & HOSPITAL p 1393
888 S King St, Honolulu HI 96813
Tel (808) 522-4000 *SIC* 8011 8062

SUASIN CANCER CARE INC p 1395
1301 Punchbowl St, Honolulu HI 96813
Tel (512) 583-0205 *SIC* 8011

WILCOX HEALTH SYSTEM p 1609
3-3420 Kuhio Hwy, Lihue HI 96766
Tel (808) 245-1100 *SIC* 8741 8011

EUGENIA CHANG MD p 512
100 E Idaho St, Boise ID 83712
Tel (208) 381-2711 *SIC* 8011

ST LUKES REGIONAL MEDICAL CENTER LTD p 1370
190 E Bannock St, Boise ID 83712
Tel (208) 381-5500 *SIC* 8062 8011

EASTERN IDAHO REGIONAL MEDICAL CENTER AUXILIARY INC p 472
3100 Channing Way, Idaho Falls ID 83404
Tel (208) 529-6111 SIC 8011

SAINT ALPHONSUS MEDICAL CENTER - NAMPA HEALTH FOUNDATION INC p 1268
1512 12th Ave Rd, Nampa ID 83686
Tel (208) 467-1171 SIC 8062 8011

DRYER CANCER CENTER p 457
1221 N Highland Ave, Aurora IL 60506
Tel (630) 264-8656 SIC 5047 8011

WALGREENS INFUSION SERVICES INC p 1573
3000 Lakeside Dr Ste 300n, Bannockburn IL 60015
Tel (312) 940-2500
SIC 8082 8011 8059 5999 5122

OSF ST JOSEPH MEDICAL CENTER BLOOMINGTON p 1096
2200 E Washington St, Bloomington IL 61701
Tel (309) 662-3311 SIC 8011

CHRISTIE CLINIC LLC p 303
101 W University Ave, Champaign IL 61820
Tel (217) 366-1200 SIC 8011

ACCESS COMMUNITY HEALTH NETWORK p 14
600 W Fulton St Ste 200, Chicago IL 60661
Tel (312) 526-2200 SIC 8011

ADVOCATE HEALTH CENTERS INC p 28
2545 S Mrtn Lther King Dr, Chicago IL 60616
Tel (312) 842-7117 SIC 8011

ANN & ROBERT H LURIE CHILDRENS HOSPITAL OF CHICAGO p 92
225 E Chicago Ave, Chicago IL 60611
Tel (312) 227-7132 SIC 8011 8069

FAMILY HEALTH NETWORK INC p 527
322 S Green St Ste 400, Chicago IL 60607
Tel (312) 243-5235 SIC 8011

■ **HARMONY HEALTH SYSTEMS INC** p 662
200 W Adams St Ste 800, Chicago IL 60606
Tel (312) 372-3471 SIC 6324 8011

NORTHWESTERN MEDICAL FACULTY FOUNDATION INC p 1060
680 N Lake Shore Dr Ste 1, Chicago IL 60611
Tel (312) 926-2630 SIC 8011

PRESENCE HEALTH NETWORK p 1172
200 S Wacker Dr Fl 12, Chicago IL 60606
Tel (773) 774-8000
SIC 8082 8062 8011 8051

SINAI CHILDRENS HOSPITAL p 1326
1500 S Cal Ave K435 435 K, Chicago IL 60608
Tel (773) 542-2000 SIC 8011 8062

UNI CARE p 1502
233 S Wacker Dr, Chicago IL 60606
Tel (312) 234-7000 SIC 8011

ILLINOIS BONE AND JOINT INSTITUTE LLC p 732
900 Rand Rd Ste 200, Des Plaines IL 60016
Tel (847) 375-3000 SIC 8011

DU PAGE MEDICAL GROUP LTD p 458
1100 31st St Ste 300, Downers Grove IL 60515
Tel (630) 545-6000 SIC 8011

ELMHURST MEMORIAL HEALTHCARE p 489
155 E Brush Hill Rd, Elmhurst IL 60126
Tel (331) 221-1000 SIC 8011

NORTH SHORE UNIVERSITY HEALTH SYSTEM p 1053
2650 Ridge Ave, Evanston IL 60201
Tel (847) 570-2640 SIC 8011

FREEPORT REGIONAL HEALTH CARE FOUNDATION p 577
1045 W Stephenson St, Freeport IL 61032
Tel (815) 599-6000 SIC 8011

ILLINOIS BONE & JOINT INSTITUTE p 732
350 S Greenleaf St # 405, Gurnee IL 60031
Tel (847) 336-2344 SIC 8011

ADVENTIST MIDWEST HEALTH p 27
120 N Oak St, Hinsdale IL 60521
Tel (630) 856-9000 SIC 8062 5947 8011

FRANCISCAN SISTER OF CHICAGO p 573
11500 Theresa Dr, Lemont IL 60439
Tel (708) 647-6500 SIC 8661 8011

■ **MARION HOSPITAL CORP** p 907
3333 W Deyoung St, Marion IL 62959
Tel (618) 998-7800 SIC 8062 8011

SARAH BUSH LINCOLN HEALTH CENTER p 1282
1000 Health Center Dr, Mattoon IL 61938
Tel (217) 258-2525 SIC 8011 8062

LOYOLA UNIVERSITY MEDICAL CENTER p 882
2160 S 1st Ave, Maywood IL 60153
Tel (708) 216-9000 SIC 8011

MORRIS HOSPITAL p 990
150 W High St, Morris IL 60450
Tel (815) 942-2932 SIC 8011 8062

WEST SUBURBAN MEDICAL CENTER p 1595
3 Erie Ct, Oak Park IL 60302
Tel (708) 383-6200 SIC 8011

OSF SAINT FRANCIS MEDICAL CENTER p 1096
530 Ne Glen Oak Ave, Peoria IL 61637
Tel (309) 655-2000 SIC 8011

ROCKFORD HEALTH PHYSICIANS p 1244
2300 N Rockton Ave, Rockford IL 61103
Tel (815) 971-2000 SIC 8011

ROCKFORD MEMORIAL HOSPITAL p 1244
2400 N Rockton Ave, Rockford IL 61103
Tel (815) 971-5000
SIC 8062 8011 8071 8099

HSHS MEDICAL GROUP INC p 715
3051 Hollis Dr 200, Springfield IL 62704
Tel (217) 492-9696 SIC 8011

SIU PHYSICIANS & SURGEONS INC p 1328
801 N Rutledge St # 2050, Springfield IL 62702
Tel (217) 545-8065 SIC 8011

SPRINGFIELD CLINIC LLP p 1360
1025 S 6th St, Springfield IL 62703
Tel (217) 528-7541 SIC 8011

CARLE HOLDING CO INC p 257
602 W University Ave, Urbana IL 61801
Tel (217) 383-3311 SIC 8011

COMMUNITY HOSPITAL OF ANDERSON AND MADISON COUNTY INC p 349
1515 N Madison Ave, Anderson IN 46011
Tel (765) 298-4242 SIC 8062 8011

PHYSICIANS HEALTH PLAN OF NORTHERN INDIANA INC p 1145
8101 W Jefferson Blvd, Fort Wayne IN 46804
Tel (260) 432-6690 SIC 6321 8011 6411

AMERICAN HEALTH NETWORK INC p 73
10689 N Pennsylvna St # 200, Indianapolis IN 46280
Tel (317) 580-6309 SIC 8011

AMERICAN HEALTH NETWORK OF INDIANA INC p 73
10689 N Pennsylvna St # 200, Indianapolis IN 46280
Tel (317) 580-6314 SIC 6324 8011

AMERICAN HEALTH NETWORK OF INDIANA LLC p 73
10689 N Pennsylvna St # 200, Indianapolis IN 46280
Tel (317) 580-6309 SIC 8011

CARE GROUP LLC p 254
8333 Naab Rd Ste 340, Indianapolis IN 46260
Tel (317) 338-5050 SIC 8011 8093

COMMUNITY PHYSICIANS OF INDIANA INC p 350
7240 Shadeland Sta # 300, Indianapolis IN 46256
Tel (317) 621-7455 SIC 8011

ST VINCENT HEALTH INC p 1373
10330 N Meridian St, Indianapolis IN 46290
Tel (317) 338-2345 SIC 8011

ARNETT PHYSICIAN GROUP PC p 112
2600 Greenbush St, Lafayette IN 47904
Tel (765) 448-8000 SIC 8011

BETHANY CIRCLE OF KINGS DAUGHTERS OF MADISON INDIANA INC p 178
1373 E Sr 62, Madison IN 47250
Tel (812) 801-0800 SIC 8062 8011 8082

WORK RIGHT OCCUPATIONAL HEALTH p 1624
330 N Wabash Ave Ste 470, Marion IN 46952
Tel (765) 662-4198 SIC 8011

SAINT JOSEPH REGIONAL MEDICAL CENTER-SOUTH BEND CAMPUS INC p 1269
5215 Holy Cross Pkwy, Mishawaka IN 46545
Tel (574) 335-5000 SIC 8011

REID PHYSICIAN ASSOCIATES INC p 1221
1100 Reid Pkwy, Richmond IN 47374
Tel (765) 983-3000 SIC 8011

MAJOR HOSPITAL p 899
150 W Washington St, Shelbyville IN 46176
Tel (317) 392-3211 SIC 8062 8011

MCFARLAND CLINIC PC p 928
1215 Duff Ave, Ames IA 50010
Tel (515) 239-4400 SIC 8011

MERCY CARE MANAGEMENT INC p 945
701 10th St Se, Cedar Rapids IA 52403
Tel (319) 398-6011 SIC 8011 8741 8322

MERCYCARE SERVICE CORP p 948
701 10th St Se, Cedar Rapids IA 52403
Tel (319) 398-6011 SIC 8011

IOWA PHYSICIANS CLINIC MEDICAL FOUNDATION p 763
1221 Pleasant St Ste 200, Des Moines IA 50309
Tel (515) 241-6212 SIC 8011

FINLEY HOSPITAL p 543
350 N Grandview Ave, Dubuque IA 52001
Tel (563) 582-1881 SIC 8011

MERCY HOSPITAL IOWA CITY IOWA INC p 947
500 E Market St, Iowa City IA 52245
Tel (319) 339-0300
SIC 8062 8011 6512 8399

MERCY SERVICES IOWA CITY INC p 948
500 E Market St, Iowa City IA 52245
Tel (319) 339-3541 SIC 8011 8082

SPENCER MUNICIPAL HOSPITAL p 1358
1200 1st Ave E Ste 1, Spencer IA 51301
Tel (712) 264-6198 SIC 8062 8011

NEWMAN MEMORIAL HOSPITAL FOUNDATION p 1038
1201 W 12th Ave, Emporia KS 66801
Tel (620) 343-6800 SIC 8062 5047 8011

KANSAS UNIVERSITY PHYSICIANS INC p 803
3901 Rainbow Blvd, Kansas City KS 66160
Tel (913) 362-2128 SIC 8011

PROVIDENCE/SAINT JOHN FOUNDATION INC p 1186
8929 Parallel Pkwy, Kansas City KS 66112
Tel (913) 596-4000 SIC 8062 8741 8011

■ **COVENTRY HEALTH CARE OF KANSAS INC** p 385
9401 Indian Creek Pkwy # 1300, Overland Park KS 66210
Tel (800) 969-3343 SIC 6324 8011

MENORAH MEDICAL CENTER INC p 943
5721 W 119th St, Overland Park KS 66209
Tel (913) 498-6000 SIC 8011 8062

ST FRANCIS HEALTH CENTER INC p 1366
1700 Sw 7th St, Topeka KS 66606
Tel (785) 295-8000 SIC 8062 8011

■ **PREFERRED PLUS OF KANSAS INC** p 1169
8535 E 21st St N, Wichita KS 67206
Tel (316) 609-2345 SIC 8011

VIA CHRISTI CLINIC PA p 1554
3311 E Murdock St, Wichita KS 67208
Tel (316) 689-9111 SIC 8011

VIA CHRISTI HEALTH INC p 1554
2622 W Central Ave # 102, Wichita KS 67203
Tel (316) 858-4900 SIC 8011 8741

■ **WESLEY MEDICAL CENTER LLC** p 1593
550 N Hillside St, Wichita KS 67214
Tel (316) 962-2000 SIC 8011

OUR LADY OF BELLEFONTE HOSPITAL INC p 1098
1000 Saint Christopher Dr, Ashland KY 41101
Tel (606) 833-3333
SIC 8062 8082 8011 5999

GREENVIEW REGIONAL HOSPITAL p 638
1801 Ashley Cir, Bowling Green KY 42104
Tel (270) 793-1000 SIC 8011

ST ELIZABETH PHYSICIAN SERVICES LLC p 1366
334 Thomas More Pkwy, Crestview Hills KY 41017
Tel (859) 344-3737 SIC 8011

SUMMIT MEDICAL GROUP INC p 1399
334 Thomas More Pkwy, Crestview Hills KY 41017
Tel (859) 344-3737 SIC 8011

■ **FRANKFORT REGIONAL MEDICAL CENTER** p 574
299 Kings Daughters Dr, Frankfort KY 40601
Tel (502) 875-5240 SIC 8062 8011

■ **MARSHALL PHYSICIAN SERVICES LLC** p 911
1792 Alysheba Way Ste 150, Lexington KY 40509
Tel (877) 601-6372 SIC 8011

NEW LEXINGTON CLINIC PSC p 1032
1221 S Broadway, Lexington KY 40504
Tel (859) 258-4950 SIC 8011

SAINT JOSEPH HEALTH SYSTEM INC p 1269
1 Saint Joseph Dr, Lexington KY 40504
Tel (859) 313-1000 SIC 8062 8099 8011

UK HEALTHCARE GOODSAMARITAN HOSPITAL p 1500
310 S Limestone, Lexington KY 40508
Tel (859) 226-7000 SIC 8062 8011

BAPTIST HEALTHCARE SYSTEM INC p 154
2701 Eastpoint Pkwy, Louisville KY 40223
Tel (502) 896-5000 SIC 8062 8011 8741

COMMUNITY MEDICAL ASSOCIATES INC p 349
224 E Broadway Fl 5, Louisville KY 40202
Tel (502) 588-9490 SIC 8011

NORTON HOSPITALS INC p 1061
200 E Chestnut St, Louisville KY 40202
Tel (502) 629-8000
SIC 8062 8011 8093 8071

PHYSICIAN GROUP p 1145
6801 Dixie Hwy Ste 133, Louisville KY 40258
Tel (502) 937-3864 SIC 8011

SEVEN COUNTIES SERVICES INC p 1309
101 W Muhammad Ali Blvd, Louisville KY 40202
Tel (502) 589-8600
SIC 8399 8011 8093 8322 8031

UNIVERSITY HEALTH CARE INC p 1518
5100 Cmmerce Crossings Dr, Louisville KY 40229
Tel (502) 585-7900 SIC 8011 6411

BAPTIST HEALTH MADISONVILLE INC p 153
900 Hospital Dr, Madisonville KY 42431
Tel (270) 825-5100 SIC 8011 8062

ST CLAIRE MEDICAL CENTER INC p 1365
222 Medical Cir, Morehead KY 40351
Tel (606) 783-6500 SIC 8062 8011

OUR LADY OF LORDES REGIONAL MEDICAL CENTER INC p 1098
4801 Ambssdor Cffery Pkwy, Lafayette LA 70508
Tel (337) 289-2000 SIC 8011 8021

LAKE CHARLES MEMORIAL HOSPITAL p 838
1701 Oak Park Blvd, Lake Charles LA 70601
Tel (337) 494-2121 SIC 8011

OCHSNER CLINIC HEALTH SERVICES CORP p 1073
1514 Jefferson Hwy, New Orleans LA 70121
Tel (504) 842-4000 SIC 8011

TULANE UNIVERSITY HOSPITAL AND CLINIC p 1491
1415 Tulane Ave Fl 4, New Orleans LA 70112
Tel (504) 988-3516 SIC 8011

VA HOSPITAL p 1538
510 E Stoner Ave, Shreveport LA 71101
Tel (318) 221-8411 SIC 8011

IASIS GLENWOOD REGIONAL MEDICAL CENTER LP p 726
503 Mcmillan Rd, West Monroe LA 71291
Tel (318) 329-4200 SIC 8011

JEROME GROUP INC p 783
6 E Chestnut St, Augusta ME 04330
Tel (207) 626-1496 SIC 8011 8062

CENTRAL MAINE HEALTH VENTURES INC p 279
300 Main St, Lewiston ME 04240
Tel (207) 795-0111
SIC 8049 8052 7322 8011

SISTERS OF CHARITY HEALTH SYSTEMS p 1327
99 Campus Ave Ste 303, Lewiston ME 04240
Tel (207) 782-5424 SIC 8011

ST MARYS HEALTH SYSTEM p 1371
96 Campus Ave, Lewiston ME 04240
Tel (207) 777-8546
SIC 8062 8052 8051 8011 8361

ST MARYS REGIONAL MEDICAL CENTER p 1372
93 Campus Ave, Lewiston ME 04240
Tel (207) 777-8546
SIC 8062 8052 8051 8011 8361

AROOSTOOK MEDICAL CENTER INC p 112
140 Academy St, Presque Isle ME 04769
Tel (207) 768-4000 SIC 8062 8011 8052

NORTON SOUND HEALTH CORP p 1061
790 Lower St, Turner ME 04282
Tel (907) 443-3311
SIC 8062 8051 8069 8093 8011

MAINE GENERAL MEDICAL CENTER INC p 898
149 North St, Waterville ME 04901
Tel (207) 872-4190 SIC 8011

PHYSICIAN ENTERPRISE LLC p 1145
2001 Medical Pkwy, Annapolis MD 21401
Tel (443) 481-6554 SIC 8011

AEGON DIRECT MARKETING SERVICES INC p 29
100 Light St Fl B1, Baltimore MD 21202
Tel (410) 685-5500 SIC 6311 8011

FRANKLIN SQUARE HOSPITAL CENTER INC p 575
9000 Franklin Square Dr, Baltimore MD 21237
Tel (410) 933-2777 SIC 8062 8011

GREATER BALTIMORE MEDICAL CENTER INC p 635
6701 N Charles St, Baltimore MD 21204
Tel (410) 849-2000 SIC 8062 8011

HOPKINS JOHNS MEDICAL SERVICES CORP p 706
3100 Wyman Park Dr, Baltimore MD 21211
Tel (410) 338-3071 SIC 8011 8741

MEDSTAR GOOD SAMARITAN HOSPITAL p 939
5601 Loch Raven Blvd, Baltimore MD 21239
Tel (443) 444-4100 SIC 8062 8011

MERCY MEDICAL CENTER INC p 947
345 Saint Paul St, Baltimore MD 21202
Tel (410) 332-9000 SIC 8062 8011

UNIVERSITY OF MARYLAND MEDICAL SYSTEM CORP p 1522
22 S Greene St, Baltimore MD 21201
Tel (410) 328-8667 SIC 8011

PENNINSULA REGIONAL MEDICAL CENTER p 1130
10514 Racetrack Rd Ste C, Berlin MD 21811
Tel (410) 641-8585 SIC 8011

CENTERS FOR ADVANCED ORTHOPAEDICS LLC p 276
6707 Democracy Blvd # 504, Bethesda MD 20817
Tel (301) 637-8710 SIC 8011

MEDSTAR SOUTHERN MARYLAND HOSPITAL CENTER INC p 939
7503 Surratts Rd, Clinton MD 20735
Tel (301) 868-8000 SIC 8062 8011

MAXIM HEALTH SYSTEMS LLC p 922
7227 Lee Deforest Dr, Columbia MD 21046
Tel (410) 910-1500 SIC 8011 8099

MEDSTAR HEALTH INC p 939
5565 Sterrett Pl Ste 500, Columbia MD 21044
Tel (410) 772-6500
SIC 8741 8062 8082 8051 8011

CONMED INC p 356
7250 Parkway Dr Ste 400, Hanover MD 21076
Tel (410) 567-5520 SIC 8011

CAREFIRST BLUECHOICE INC p 254
10455 Mill Run Cir, Owings Mills MD 21117
Tel (202) 479-8000 SIC 6321 8011 6411

CENTER FOR PAIN MANAGEMENT LLC p 276
11921 Rockville Pike # 505, Rockville MD 20852
Tel (301) 881-7246 SIC 8011

OTSUKA AMERICA PHARMACEUTICAL INC p 1098
2440 Res Blvd Ste 500, Rockville MD 20850
Tel (301) 990-0030 SIC 8733 8011 8731

CAPITAL DIGESTIVE CARE LLC p 249
12510 Prosperity Dr # 200, Silver Spring MD 20904
Tel (240) 485-5203 SIC 8011

HOLY CROSS HOSPITAL p 702
2701 W 68th St, Silver Spring MD 20910
Tel (301) 754-7000 SIC 8062 8011

TRANS HEALTHCARE INC p 1470
930 Ridgebrook Rd, Sparks MD 21152
Tel (410) 773-1000 SIC 8011 8051

STURDY MEMORIAL HOSPITAL INC p 1395
211 Park St, Attleboro MA 02703
Tel (508) 222-5200 SIC 8062 8011

ATRIUS HEALTH INC p 129
275 Grove St Ste 3-300, Auburndale MA 02466
Tel (617) 559-8444 SIC 8011

CHILDRENS HOSPITAL PEDIATRIC ASSOCIATES INC p 300
20 Overland St Ste 2, Boston MA 02215
Tel (617) 919-2822 SIC 8011

COMMONWEALTH CARE ALLIANCE INC p 346
30 Winter St Fl 12, Boston MA 02108
Tel (617) 426-0600 SIC 8099 8011

FACULTY PRACTICE FOUNDATION INC AND AFFILIATES p 524
660 Harrison Ave, Boston MA 02118
Tel (617) 638-8923 SIC 8011

JOHN R GRAHAM HEADACHE CENTER INC p 789
1153 Centre St, Boston MA 02130
Tel (617) 983-7243 SIC 8011 8062

JOSLIN DIABETES CENTER INC p 794
1 Joslin Pl, Boston MA 02215
Tel (617) 732-2400 SIC 8011

LEILA A MANKARIOUS p 854
243 Charles St, Boston MA 02114
Tel (617) 573-3413 SIC 8011

MASSACHUSETTS EYE AND EAR ASSOCIATES INC p 916
243 Charles St, Boston MA 02114
Tel (617) 523-7900 SIC 8011

MASSACHUSETTS EYE AND EAR INFIRMARY & PHYSICIAN STAFF INC p 917
243 Charles St, Boston MA 02114
Tel (617) 573-3499 SIC 8069 8011

MASSACHUSETTS GENERAL HOSPITAL p 917
55 Fruit St, Boston MA 02114
Tel (617) 724-6454 SIC 8062 8011

MASSACHUSETTS GENERAL PHYSICIANS ORGANIZATION INC p 917
55 Fruit St 208, Boston MA 02114
Tel (617) 724-0578 SIC 8011

NEIGHBORHOOD HEALTH PLAN p 1024
253 Summer St Fl 5, Boston MA 02210
Tel (617) 772-5500 SIC 8011

SPAULDING REHABILITATION HOSPITAL (SRH) VOLUNTEER SERVICES p 1355
300 1st Ave, Charlestown MA 02129
Tel (617) 952-5000 SIC 8069 8011

DEDHAM MEDICAL ASSOCIATES INC p 421
1 Lyons St, Dedham MA 02026
Tel (781) 329-1400 SIC 8011 8021

SOUTHCOAST PHYSICIANS GROUP INC p 1345
200 Mill Rd Ste 180, Fairhaven MA 02719
Tel (508) 758-3781 SIC 8011

TAS-SAHC INC p 1426
795 Middle St, Fall River MA 02721
Tel (508) 674-5600 SIC 8062 8011

ACCOUNTS PAYABLE MERCY ME p 15
1221 Main St Ste 108, Holyoke MA 01040
Tel (413) 539-2692 SIC 8011

CAPE COD HOSPITAL p 248
27 Park St, Hyannis MA 02601
Tel (508) 862-7575 *SIC* 8062 8011 8063

CAMBRIDGE HEALTH ALLIANCE PHYSICIANS ORGANIZATION INC p 244
350 Main St Ste 16, Malden MA 02148
Tel (617) 498-1000 *SIC* 8011

MILFORD REGIONAL HEALTHCARE FOUNDATION INC p 969
14 Prospect St, Milford MA 01757
Tel (508) 473-1190 *SIC* 6733 8082 8011

BETH ISRAEL DEACONESS HOSPITAL - MILTON INC p 177
199 Reedsdale Rd, Milton MA 02186
Tel (617) 696-4600 *SIC* 8011

SOUTH SHORE MEDICAL CENTER INC p 1345
75 Washington St Ste 1, Norwell MA 02061
Tel (781) 878-5200 *SIC* 8011

HARBOR MEDICAL GROUP p 660
55 Highland Ave Ste 102, Salem MA 01970
Tel (978) 741-9500 *SIC* 8011

NORTH SHORE PHYSICIANS GROUP INC p 1053
81 Highland Ave, Salem MA 01970
Tel (617) 724-9841 *SIC* 8011

SOUTHBORO MEDICAL GROUP INC p 1345
24-28 Newton St, Southborough MA 01772
Tel (508) 481-5500 *SIC* 8011

MERCY HOSPITAL INC p 947
271 Carew St, Springfield MA 01104
Tel (413) 748-9000
SIC 8062 8071 8011 7219 8748

MERCY INPATIENT MEDICAL ASSOCIATES INC p 947
271 Carew St Ste 106, Springfield MA 01104
Tel (413) 748-9000 *SIC* 8011 8322

RELIANT MEDICAL GROUP INC p 1222
630 Plantation St, Worcester MA 01605
Tel (508) 368-5400 *SIC* 8011 7352 5912

UMASS MEMORIAL COMMUNITY MEDICAL GROUP INC p 1501
121 Lincoln St, Worcester MA 01605
Tel (508) 757-7745 *SIC* 8011

UMASS MEMORIAL HEALTH CARE INC p 1501
365 Plantation St Ste 300, Worcester MA 01605
Tel (508) 754-6026 *SIC* 8011

PROMEDICA NORTH REGION INC p 1183
818 Riverside Ave, Adrian MI 49221
Tel (517) 265-0390 *SIC* 8011

IHA HEALTH SERVICES CORP p 730
24 Frank Lloyd Wright Dr, Ann Arbor MI 48105
Tel (734) 747-6766 *SIC* 8011

INTEGRATED HEALTH ASSOCIATES INC p 749
24 Frank Lloyd Wright Dr, Ann Arbor MI 48105
Tel (734) 747-6766 *SIC* 8011

HEALTH ALLIANCE PLAN OF MICHIGAN p 674
2850 W Grand Blvd, Detroit MI 48202
Tel (313) 872-8100 *SIC* 6324 8011 8099

TOTAL HEALTH CARE INC p 1463
3011 W Grand Blvd # 1600, Detroit MI 48202
Tel (313) 871-2000 *SIC* 8011

SPECTRUM HEALTH PRIMARY CARE PARTNERS DBA p 1357
1840 Wealthy St Se, Grand Rapids MI 49506
Tel (616) 774-7322 *SIC* 8011

MIDMICHIGAN HEALTH SERVICES p 966
9249 W Lake City Rd, Houghton Lake MI 48629
Tel (989) 422-5148 *SIC* 8011

BRONSON PEDIATRIC NEUROLOGY SERVICE p 217
601 John St Ste M-460, Kalamazoo MI 49007
Tel (269) 341-8383 *SIC* 8011

BRONSON PHYSICIAN SERVICES INC p 217
601 John St Ste W002, Kalamazoo MI 49007
Tel (269) 341-6000 *SIC* 8011

PHYSICIANS HEALTH PLAN OF MID-MICHIGAN INC p 1145
1400 E Michigan Ave, Lansing MI 48912
Tel (517) 364-8400 *SIC* 8011 6321

MERCY HEALTH SERVICES-IOWA CORP p 946
20555 Victor Pkwy, Livonia MI 48152
Tel (734) 343-1000 *SIC* 8011

HENRY FORD MEDICAL CENTER p 684
39450 W 12 Mile Rd, Novi MI 48377
Tel (248) 661-7393 *SIC* 8011

CRITTENTON HOSPITAL MEDICAL CENTER p 393
1101 W University Dr, Rochester MI 48307
Tel (248) 652-5000 *SIC* 8062 8011

MAYO CLINIC HEALTH SYSTEM-ALBERT LEA AND AUSTIN p 924
404 W Fountain St, Albert Lea MN 56007
Tel (507) 373-2384
SIC 8062 8069 8051 8063 8011

REM CENTRAL LAKES INC p 1222
1802 Autumn Dr Nw, Alexandria MN 56308
Tel (320) 759-5650 *SIC* 8011

HEALTHPARTNERS INC p 677
8170 33rd Ave S, Bloomington MN 55425
Tel (952) 883-6000 *SIC* 8011

DULUTH CLINIC LTD p 460
400 E 3rd St, Duluth MN 55805
Tel (218) 786-3600 *SIC* 8011

ST LUKES HOSPITAL OF DULUTH p 1370
915 E 1st St, Duluth MN 55805
Tel (218) 726-5555 *SIC* 8062 8011

ST MARYS DULUTH CLINIC HEALTH SYSTEM p 1371
400 E 3rd St, Duluth MN 55805
Tel (218) 786-8364 *SIC* 8093 8011 8062

ALLINA HEALTH SYSTEM p 57
2925 Chicago Ave, Minneapolis MN 55407
Tel (612) 262-5000 *SIC* 8062 8741 8011

NORTH MEMORIAL HEALTH CARE p 1053
3300 Oakdale Ave N, Minneapolis MN 55422
Tel (763) 520-5200 *SIC* 8062 8011

PARK NICOLLET CLINIC p 1115
3800 Park Nicollet Blvd, Minneapolis MN 55416
Tel (952) 993-3123 *SIC* 8011 5912 5999

UNIVERSITY OF MINNESOTA PHYSICIANS p 1523
720 Washington Ave Se # 200, Minneapolis MN 55414
Tel (612) 884-0600 *SIC* 8011

MEDICA HEALTH PLANS p 936
401 Carlson Pkwy, Minnetonka MN 55305
Tel (952) 992-3056 *SIC* 8011

MAYO CLINIC HEALTH SYSTEM — OWATONNA p 923
2200 Nw 26th St, Owatonna MN 55060
Tel (507) 451-1120 *SIC* 8011

RED WING REGIONAL HOME HEALTH p 1216
1407 W 4th St, Red Wing MN 55066
Tel (651) 385-3410 *SIC* 8082 8011

MAYO CLINIC p 923
200 1st St Sw, Rochester MN 55905
Tel (507) 284-2511
SIC 8011 8062 8071 8733 8221

MAYO CLINIC p 923
200 1st St Sw, Rochester MN 55905
Tel (507) 284-2511
SIC 8062 8733 8071 8011

CENTRACARE CLINIC p 277
1200 6th Ave N, Saint Cloud MN 56303
Tel (320) 240-2829 *SIC* 8011

HEALTHEAST COMPANIES INC p 677
1700 University Ave W, Saint Paul MN 55104
Tel (651) 232-2300 *SIC* 8082 8051 8011

HMO MINNESOTA p 698
3535 Blue Cross Rd, Saint Paul MN 55122
Tel (952) 456-8434 *SIC* 8011

PEDIATRIC RHEUMATOLOGY p 1127
200 University Ave E, Saint Paul MN 55101
Tel (651) 229-3892 *SIC* 8011 8062

UNITED HOSPITAL INC p 1509
333 Smith Ave N, Saint Paul MN 55102
Tel (651) 241-8000 *SIC* 8011

PARK NICOLLET HEALTH SERVICES p 1115
3800 Park Nicollet Blvd, St Louis Park MN 55416
Tel (952) 993-3123 *SIC* 8011

STILLWATER MEDICAL GROUP p 1390
927 Churchill St W, Stillwater MN 55082
Tel (952) 883-6048 *SIC* 8011

AFFILIATED COMMUNITY MEDICAL CENTERS PA p 32
101 Willmar Ave Sw, Willmar MN 56201
Tel (320) 231-5000 *SIC* 8011

HATTIESBURG CLINIC PROFESSIONAL ASSOCIATION p 668
415 S 28th Ave 200, Hattiesburg MS 39401
Tel (601) 264-6000 *SIC* 8011

WESLEY HEALTH SYSTEM LLC p 1593
5001 Hardy St, Hattiesburg MS 39402
Tel (601) 268-8000
SIC 8051 8062 8082 8011

■ **JACKSON HMA LLC** p 774
1850 Chadwick Dr, Jackson MS 39204
Tel (601) 376-1000 *SIC* 8011

MCCLATCHY MEDICAL CENTER p 926
7235 Hacks Cross Rd, Olive Branch MS 38654
Tel (662) 893-7878 *SIC* 8011

CITIZENS MEMORIAL HOSPITAL DISTRICT p 311
1500 N Oakland Ave, Bolivar MO 65613
Tel (417) 326-6000 *SIC* 8011

CITIZENS MEMORIAL HOSPITAL DISTRICT OF POLK COUNTY p 311
1500 N Oakland Ave, Bolivar MO 65613
Tel (417) 326-6000 *SIC* 8062 8011 8082

SKAGGS COMMUNITY HOSPITAL ASSOCIATION p 1329
251 Skaggs Rd, Branson MO 65616
Tel (417) 335-7000
SIC 8062 8082 8011 7352 8051

TLC VISION (USA) CORP p 1457
16305 Swingley Ridge Rd # 300, Chesterfield MO 63017
Tel (636) 534-2300 *SIC* 8011

COMPASS HEALTH INC p 351
1800 Community, Clinton MO 64735
Tel (660) 885-8131
SIC 8011 8069 8093 8361

CARONDELET PHYSICIAN SERVICES INC p 260
1000 Carondelet Dr, Kansas City MO 64114
Tel (816) 943-2679 *SIC* 8011

SAINT LUKES HOSPITAL OF KANSAS CITY p 1270
4401 Wornall Rd, Kansas City MO 64111
Tel (816) 932-2000
SIC 8062 8742 8011 6512 8082 7322

BREECH REGIONAL MEDICAL CENTER p 209
100 Hospital Dr, Lebanon MO 65536
Tel (417) 533-6026 *SIC* 8011

▲ **CENTENE CORP** p 275
7700 Forsyth Blvd Ste 800, Saint Louis MO 63105
Tel (314) 725-4477 *SIC* 6324 8011 8099

CORIZON LLC p 370
12647 Olive Blvd Ste 400, Saint Louis MO 63141
Tel (314) 919-8501 *SIC* 8011

MERCY MEDICAL GROUP p 948
12800 Corporate Hill Dr, Saint Louis MO 63131
Tel (888) 700-7171 *SIC* 8011

SIGNATURE MEDICAL GROUP INC p 1322
12639 Old Tesson Rd # 115, Saint Louis MO 63128
Tel (314) 849-0311 *SIC* 8011

SSM HEALTH CARE CORP p 1364
10101 Woodfield Ln # 100, Saint Louis MO 63132
Tel (314) 994-7800
SIC 8062 8082 8011 8051

HEALTH SYSTEMS INC p 676
1220 N Main St, Sikeston MO 63801
Tel (573) 481-9625 *SIC* 6321 8011 8322

INTERNAL MEDICINE GROUP FREMONT p 754
1965 S Fremont Ave # 350, Springfield MO 65804
Tel (417) 820-3128 *SIC* 8011

LESTER E COX MEDICAL CENTER p 857
305 S National Ave # 500, Springfield MO 65802
Tel (417) 269-6000 *SIC* 8011

MERCY HOSPITAL SPRINGFIELD p 947
1235 E Cherokee St, Springfield MO 65804
Tel (417) 820-2000 *SIC* 8062 8011

KALISPELL REGIONAL HEALTHCARE SYSTEM p 801
310 Sunnyview Ln, Kalispell MT 59901
Tel (406) 752-8991
SIC 8051 8011 4522 7352

PHYSICIAN NETWORK p 1145
2000 Q St Fl 5th, Lincoln NE 68503
Tel (402) 421-0896 *SIC* 8011

TODD HLAVATY MD p 1458
601 W Leota St, North Platte NE 69101
Tel (308) 535-7405 *SIC* 8011

PHYSICIANS CLINIC INC p 1145
8601 W Dodge Rd Ste 216, Omaha NE 68114
Tel (402) 354-1700 *SIC* 8011 8031

UNIVERSITY OF NEBRASKA MEDICAL CENTER p 1523
42nd And Emile, Omaha NE 68105
Tel (402) 559-4000 *SIC* 8011

UNMC PHYSICIANS p 1528
988101 Nebraska Med Ctr, Omaha NE 68198
Tel (402) 559-9700 *SIC* 8011

■ **HEALTH PLAN OF NEVADA INC** p 675
2720 N Tenaya Way, Las Vegas NV 89128
Tel (702) 242-7300 *SIC* 8011

HEALTHCARE PARTNERS NEVADA LLC p 676
700 E Warm Springs Rd # 230, Las Vegas NV 89119
Tel (702) 932-8500 *SIC* 8011

MOUNTAINVIEW HOSPITAL INC p 994
3100 N Tenaya Way, Las Vegas NV 89128
Tel (702) 255-5000 *SIC* 8062 8011 4119

SPRING VALLEY HOSPITAL MEDICAL CENTER p 1360
5400 S Rainbow Blvd, Las Vegas NV 89118
Tel (702) 853-3000 *SIC* 8011

■ **SUMMERLIN HOSPITAL MEDICAL CENTER LLC** p 1398
657 N Town Center Dr, Las Vegas NV 89144
Tel (702) 233-7000 *SIC* 8062 8011

■ **VALLEY HEALTH SYSTEM LLC** p 1540
620 Shadow Ln, Las Vegas NV 89106
Tel (702) 388-4000 *SIC* 8062 8011

■ **NORTHERN NEVADA MEDICAL CENTER LP** p 1056
2375 E Prater Way, Sparks NV 89434
Tel (775) 331-7000
SIC 8062 8093 8071 8049 8011

■ **HEALTHSOURCE INC** p 677
2 College Park Dr, Hooksett NH 03106
Tel (603) 268-7000 *SIC* 6324 8741 8011

DARTMOUTH-HITCHCOCK MEDICAL CENTER p 413
1 Medical Center Dr, Lebanon NH 03756
Tel (603) 650-5000 *SIC* 8062 8011 8051

MAXIFACIAL DENTAL SURGERY p 922
1 Medical Center Dr, Lebanon NH 03756
Tel (603) 650-5000 *SIC* 8011

CATHOLIC MEDICAL CENTER PHYSICIAN PRACTICE ASSOCIATES p 267
100 Mcgregor St, Manchester NH 03102
Tel (603) 668-3545 *SIC* 8062 8011

SOUTHERN NEW HAMPSHIRE MEDICAL CENTER p 1349
8 Prospect St, Nashua NH 03060
Tel (603) 577-2000 *SIC* 8062 8011

SUMMIT MEDICAL GROUP PA p 1399
1 Diamond Hill Rd, Berkeley Heights NJ 07922
Tel (908) 277-8880 *SIC* 8099 8011

SANOFI-SYNTHELABO INC p 1280
55 Corporate Dr, Bridgewater NJ 08807
Tel (908) 981-5000 *SIC* 8011

TOTOWA PEDIATRICS p 1463
400 W Blackwell St, Dover NJ 07801
Tel (973) 989-3645 *SIC* 8011

ENGLEWOOD HOSPITAL AND MEDICAL CENTER FOUNDATION INC p 499
350 Engle St, Englewood NJ 07631
Tel (201) 894-3000 *SIC* 8062 8011

INNOVACARE SERVICES CO LLC p 744
173 Bridge Plz N, Fort Lee NJ 07024
Tel (201) 969-2300
SIC 6324 8011 8741 8742

LOVING CARE AGENCY INC p 881
611 Rte 46 W Ste 200, Hasbrouck Heights NJ 07604
Tel (201) 403-9300 *SIC* 8011 8082

ADVOCARE LLC p 28
25 Lindsley Dr Ste 205, Morristown NJ 07960
Tel (973) 993-8777 *SIC* 8011

ATLANTIC HEALTH p 126
200 South St, Morristown NJ 07960
Tel (973) 683-0104 *SIC* 8011

HORIZON HEALTHCARE PLAN HOLDING p 707
3 Penn Plz E Ste 15-D, Newark NJ 07105
Tel (973) 466-4000 *SIC* 8011

UNIVERSITY PHYSICIAN ASSOCIATES OF NEW JERSEY INC p 1527
30 Bergen St Ste 1, Newark NJ 07107
Tel (973) 972-5004 *SIC* 8221 8011

SOMERSET HEALTH CARE CORP p 1339
110 Rehill Ave, Somerville NJ 08876
Tel (908) 685-2200 *SIC* 8093 8011

TATEM BROWN FAMILY PRACTICE p 1426
2225 E Evesham Rd Ste 101, Voorhees NJ 08043
Tel (856) 795-7075 *SIC* 8011

ABQ HEALTH PARTNERS LLC p 12
5400 Gibson Blvd Se, Albuquerque NM 87108
Tel (505) 254-6500 *SIC* 8011

MEMORIAL MEDICAL CENTER INC p 942
2450 S Telshor Blvd, Las Cruces NM 88011
Tel (575) 522-8641 *SIC* 8011

PRESBYTERIAN MEDICAL SERVICES INC p 1171
1422 Paseo De Peralta # 1, Santa Fe NM 87501
Tel (505) 982-5565 *SIC* 8011

CAPITAL DISTRICT PHYSICIANS HEALTH PLAN INC p 249
500 Patroon Creek Blvd, Albany NY 12206
Tel (518) 641-3700 *SIC* 8011

LONG ISLAND HOME p 876
400 Sunrise Hwy, Amityville NY 11701
Tel (631) 264-4000
SIC 8063 8051 8099 8011

UNITED MEMORIAL MEDICAL CENTER p 1510
127 North St, Batavia NY 14020
Tel (585) 343-6030 *SIC* 8062 8049 8011

BROOKDALE HOSPITAL MEDICAL CENTER p 217
1 Brookdale Plz, Brooklyn NY 11212
Tel (718) 240-5000 *SIC* 8011 8062

BROOKDALE UNIVERSITY HOSPITAL & MEDICAL CENTER p 217
1 Brookdale Plz, Brooklyn NY 11212
Tel (718) 240-5000 *SIC* 8011 6324

LABOR MANAGEMENT HEALTHCARE FU p 836
3786 Broadway St, Buffalo NY 14227
Tel (716) 601-7980 *SIC* 8011

FREDERICK FERRIS THOMPSON HOSPITAL p 576
350 Parrish St, Canandaigua NY 14424
Tel (585) 396-6000 *SIC* 8062 8011

MARY IMOGENE BASSETT HOSPITAL p 914
1 Atwell Rd, Cooperstown NY 13326
Tel (607) 547-3456 *SIC* 8011 8062 5999

OGDEN ARNOT MEDICAL CENTER p 1076
600 Roe Ave, Elmira NY 14905
Tel (607) 737-4100 *SIC* 8011

QUEENS-LONG ISLAND MEDICAL GROUP PC p 1198
1000 Zeckendorf Blvd B, Garden City NY 11530
Tel (516) 542-5500 *SIC* 8011

GLENS FALLS HOSPITAL p 615
100 Park St, Glens Falls NY 12801
Tel (518) 926-1000 *SIC* 8011 8062 8221

NATHAN LITTAUER HOSPITAL ASSOCIATION p 1009
99 E State St, Gloversville NY 12078
Tel (518) 725-8621 *SIC* 8051 8062 8011

CORNELL UNIVERSITY p 370
308 Duffield Hall, Ithaca NY 14853
Tel (607) 254-4636 *SIC* 8221 8011

JAMAICA HOSPITAL MEDICAL CENTER p 776
8900 Van Wyck Expy, Jamaica NY 11418
Tel (718) 206-6000 *SIC* 8011

OCCUPATIONAL HEALTH SERVICE p 1072
207 Foote Ave, Jamestown NY 14701
Tel (716) 664-8165 *SIC* 8011 8062

KENMORE MERCY HOSPITAL p 810
2950 Elmwood Ave Fl 6, Kenmore NY 14217
Tel (716) 447-6100 *SIC* 8062 8059 8011

COMMUNITY CARE PHYSICIANS PC p 347
711 Troy Schenectady Rd # 201, Latham NY 12110
Tel (518) 783-3110 *SIC* 8011

NORTH SHORE UNIVERSITY HOSPITAL p 1053
300 Community Dr, Manhasset NY 11030
Tel (516) 562-0100 *SIC* 8062 8011

CAREMOUNT MEDICAL PC p 255
110 S Bedford Rd, Mount Kisco NY 10549
Tel (914) 241-1050 *SIC* 8011

FAXTON ST LUKES HEALTH CARE p 532
8411 Seneca Tpke Ste 1, New Hartford NY 13413
Tel (315) 724-0659 *SIC* 8011

ATC STAFFING SERVICES INC p 124
1983 Marcus Ave Ste E122, New Hyde Park NY 11042
Tel (516) 326-1396 *SIC* 7361 8093 8011

PROHEALTH CARE ASSOCIATES LLP p 1182
1 Dakota Dr, New Hyde Park NY 11042
Tel (516) 622-6000 *SIC* 8011

ADVANTAGECARE PHYSICIANS PC p 27
441 9th Ave Fl 8, New York NY 10001
Tel (646) 680-1563 *SIC* 8011

ASHER ALADJEM p 117
403 E 34th St Fl 3, New York NY 10016
Tel (212) 263-8360 *SIC* 8011

CATHOLIC MEDICAL MISSION BOARD INC p 267
100 Wall St Fl 9, New York NY 10005
Tel (212) 242-7757 *SIC* 8011

GUILDNET INC p 646
15 W 65th St, New York NY 10023
Tel (212) 769-6200 *SIC* 8011

HOSPITAL FOR SPECIALTY SURGERY p 709
535 E 70th St Fl 6, New York NY 10021
Tel (212) 606-1469 *SIC* 8011 8062

IATSE NATIONAL HEALTH AND WELFARE FUND p 726
55 W 39th St Fl 5, New York NY 10018
Tel (212) 580-9092 *SIC* 8011

INSTITUTE FOR FAMILY HEALTH p 747
2006 Madison Ave, New York NY 10035
Tel (212) 633-0800 *SIC* 8011

MOUNT SINAI HEALTH SYSTEM INC p 994
150 E 42nd St Bsmt 2, New York NY 10017
Tel (646) 605-4750 *SIC* 8011

NEW YORK AND PRESBYTERIAN HOSPITAL p 1034
525 E 68th St, New York NY 10065
Tel (212) 746-5454 *SIC* 8062 8011

NEW YORK HOTEL TRADES COUNCIL & HOTEL ASSOC OF NEW YORK p 1035
305 W 44th St, New York NY 10036
Tel (212) 586-6400 *SIC* 8011

NEW YORK PRESBYTERIAN HOSPITAL WEILL CORNELL UNIVERSITY MEDICAL CENTER p 1036
525 E 68th St, New York NY 10065
Tel (212) 746-1754 *SIC* 8011

NEW YORK UNIVERSITY MEDICAL CENTER p 1036
550 1st Ave, New York NY 10016
Tel (646) 929-7870 *SIC* 8011

NEW YORK-PRESBYTERIAN FUND INC p 1036
525 E 68th St, New York NY 10065
Tel (212) 297-4356 *SIC* 8011

PHYSICIAN AFFILIATE GROUP OF NEW YORK PC p 1145
55 W 125th St Rm 1002, New York NY 10027
Tel (646) 672-3651 *SIC* 8011

UNCN HOLDINGS INC p 1502
320 Park Ave Ste 2500, New York NY 10022
Tel (212) 893-9500 *SIC* 8011

YOUNG ADULT INSTITUTE INC p 1638
460 W 34th St Fl 11, New York NY 10001
Tel (212) 563-7474 *SIC* 8059 8361 8011

ZOCDOC INC p 1643
568 Broadway Fl 9, New York NY 10012
Tel (866) 962-3621 *SIC* 8011 8099

NYACK HOSPITAL FOUNDATION INC p 1068
160 N Midland Ave, Nyack NY 10960
Tel (845) 348-2000 *SIC* 8062 8011 8082

CLAXTON MEDICAL PC p 323
214 King St, Ogdensburg NY 13669
Tel (315) 393-1559 *SIC* 8011

HUDSON RIVER HEALTHCARE INC p 717
1200 Brown St Ste 12, Peekskill NY 10566
Tel (914) 734-8800 *SIC* 8011

DAVIS VISION INC p 416
159 Express St, Plainview NY 11803
Tel (210) 245-2200 *SIC* 8011

ST CHARLES HOSPITAL AND REHABILITATION CENTER p 1365
200 Belle Terre Rd, Port Jefferson NY 11777
Tel (631) 474-6000 *SIC* 8062 8011

ST FRANCIS HOSPITAL POUGHKEEPSIE NEW YORK p 1366
241 North Rd, Poughkeepsie NY 12601
Tel (845) 483-5000
SIC 8062 8069 8011 8351

WESTCHESTER MEDICAL GROUP PC p 1597
2700 Wstchstr Ave Ste 200, Purchase NY 10577
Tel (914) 682-0700 *SIC* 8011

NEW YORK STATE CATHOLIC HEALTH PLAN INC p 1036
9525 Queens Blvd Fl 8, Rego Park NY 11374
Tel (888) 343-3547 *SIC* 8011

PECONIC BAY PRIMARY MEDICAL CARE PC p 1127
1300 Roanoke Ave, Riverhead NY 11901
Tel (631) 288-6622 *SIC* 8011

CARESTREAM HEALTH INC p 255
150 Verona St, Rochester NY 14608
Tel (585) 627-1800 *SIC* 8011 7374

GENESEE VALLEY GROUP HEALTH ASSOCIATION p 602
800 Carter St, Rochester NY 14621
Tel (585) 338-1400 *SIC* 8011

GREATER ROCHESTER INDEPENDENT PRACTICE ASSOCIATION INC p 636
100 Kings Hwy S Ste 2500, Rochester NY 14617
Tel (585) 922-1500 *SIC* 8011

LEUKEMIA & LYMPHOMA SOCIETY INC p 858
3 International Dr # 200, Rye Brook NY 10573
Tel (914) 949-5213
SIC 8699 8399 8322 8011 8733 8621

MVP HEALTH PLAN INC p 1003
625 State St, Schenectady NY 12305
Tel (518) 370-4793 *SIC* 8011

STATE UNIVERSITY OF NEW YORK HEALTH SCIENCE CENTER AT SYRACUSE p 1383
750 E Adams St, Syracuse NY 13210
Tel (315) 464-5540 *SIC* 8011 8062

SUNY UPSTATE MEDICAL UNIVERSITY p 1405
750 E Adams St Ste Wh, Syracuse NY 13210
Tel (315) 464-5540 *SIC* 8011

SETON HEALTH SYSTEM INC p 1308
1300 Massachusetts Ave, Troy NY 12180
Tel (518) 268-5000 *SIC* 8062 8011

BOSTON CHILDRENS HEALTH PHYSICIANS LLP p 202
40 Sunshine Cottage Rd, Valhalla NY 10595
Tel (914) 594-2100 *SIC* 8011

UNLIMITED CARE INC p 1528
333 Westchester Ave G02, White Plains NY 10604
Tel (914) 428-4300 *SIC* 8059 8011

ST JOSEPHS HOSPITAL YONKERS p 1369
127 S Broadway, Yonkers NY 10701
Tel (914) 378-7000 *SIC* 8062 8011

BRUNSWICK NOVANT MEDICAL CENTER p 221
240 Hospital Dr Ne, Bolivia NC 28422
Tel (336) 277-1120 *SIC* 8011

WATAUGA MEDICAL CENTER INC p 1581
336 Deerfield Rd, Boone NC 28607
Tel (828) 262-4100 *SIC* 8062 8011

INTRAHEALTH INTERNATIONAL INC p 760
6340 Quadrangle Dr # 200, Chapel Hill NC 27517
Tel (919) 313-9100 *SIC* 8011

CHARLOTTE-MECKLENBURG HOSPITAL AUTHORITY p 290
1000 Blythe Blvd, Charlotte NC 28203
Tel (704) 355-2000
SIC 8062 8069 8063 8051 8011

MERCY MEDICAL SERVICE INC p 948
2001 Vail Ave, Charlotte NC 28207
Tel (704) 379-5000 *SIC* 8011

NOVANT MEDICAL GROUP INC p 1062
200 Hawthorne Ln, Charlotte NC 28204
Tel (704) 384-4966 *SIC* 8011

URGENT CARES OF AMERICA HOLDINGS LLC p 1530
935 Shotwell Rd Ste 108, Clayton NC 27520
Tel (919) 550-0821 *SIC* 6719 8011

CAPE FEAR VALLEY MEDICAL CENTER p 248
1638 Owen Dr, Fayetteville NC 28304
Tel (910) 615-4000 *SIC* 8011

SCOTLAND HEALTH CARE SYSTEM p 1293
500 Lauchwood Dr, Laurinburg NC 28352
Tel (910) 291-7000 *SIC* 8062 8011 8082

UNION MEMORIAL REGIONAL MEDICAL CENTER INC p 1504
600 Hospital Dr, Monroe NC 28112
Tel (980) 993-3100 *SIC* 8062 8011

UNION REGIONAL MEDICAL CENTER p 1505
600 Hospital Dr, Monroe NC 28112
Tel (704) 283-3100 *SIC* 8011

REX HEALTHCARE INC p 1230
4420 Lake Boone Trl, Raleigh NC 27607
Tel (919) 784-3100 *SIC* 8082 8011 8062

HALIFAX REGIONAL MEDICAL CENTER INC p 654
250 Smith Church Rd, Roanoke Rapids NC 27870
Tel (215) 994-4000 *SIC* 8062 8011

NASH HEALTH CARE SYSTEMS p 1008
2460 Curtis Ellis Dr, Rocky Mount NC 27804
Tel (252) 962-8000 *SIC* 8011 8741

WESTCARE HEALTH CORP p 1596
68 Hospital Rd, Sylva NC 28779
Tel (828) 586-7100 *SIC* 8011

SANDHILL CENTER LME/MCO p 1278
1120 7 Lakes Dr, West End NC 27376
Tel (910) 673-9111 *SIC* 8011

WILMINGTON HEALTH PLLC p 1613
1202 Medical Center Dr, Wilmington NC 28401
Tel (910) 341-3300 *SIC* 8011

SANFORD BISMARCK p 1279
300 N 7th St, Bismarck ND 58501
Tel (701) 323-6000 *SIC* 8011 8062

ESSENTIA HEALTH LLC p 510
1702 University Dr S, Fargo ND 58103
Tel (701) 364-8900 *SIC* 8011

SANFORD p 1279
801 Broadway N, Fargo ND 58102
Tel (701) 234-6000 *SIC* 8062 8011 8051

SANFORD NORTH p 1279
801 Broadway N, Fargo ND 58102
Tel (701) 234-2000 *SIC* 8011

ALTRU HEALTH SYSTEM p 63
1200 S Columbia Rd, Grand Forks ND 58201
Tel (701) 780-5000
SIC 7352 8011 8062 8063

TRINITY HEALTH p 1481
1 Burdick Expy W, Minot ND 58701
Tel (701) 857-5260 *SIC* 8011 8051 8062

AKRON GENERAL MEDICAL CENTER INC p 42
1 Akron General Ave, Akron OH 44307
Tel (330) 344-6000
SIC 8062 8011 8322 8221

CHRISTIAN HEALTHCARE MINISTRIES INC p 302
127 Hazelwood Ave, Barberton OH 44203
Tel (330) 848-1511 *SIC* 8011

SISTERS OF MERCY OF CLERMONT COUNTY OHIO INC p 1327
3000 Hospital Dr, Batavia OH 45103
Tel (513) 732-8200 *SIC* 8062 8011

AULTMAN HEALTH FOUNDATION p 131
2600 6th St Sw, Canton OH 44710
Tel (330) 452-9911 *SIC* 8011

CHILDRENS HOSPITAL MEDICAL CENTER p 299
3333 Burnet Ave, Cincinnati OH 45229
Tel (513) 636-4200
SIC 8733 8011 8069 8731

GOOD SAMARITAN HOSPITAL OF CINCINNATI p 623
375 Dixmyth Ave, Cincinnati OH 45220
Tel (513) 569-6251 *SIC* 8062 8082 8011

TRIHEALTH PHYSICIAN INSTITUTE p 1480
619 Oak St, Cincinnati OH 45206
Tel (513) 569-5126 *SIC* 8011

CLEVELAND CLINIC FOUNDATION p 325
9500 Euclid Ave, Cleveland OH 44195
Tel (216) 636-8335 *SIC* 8062 8011 8741

FAIRVIEW HOSPITAL p 525
18101 Lorain Ave, Cleveland OH 44111
Tel (216) 476-7000 *SIC* 8062 8011

HEALTHSPAN INTEGRATED CARE p 678
1001 Lakeside Ave E # 1200, Cleveland OH 44114
Tel (216) 621-5600 *SIC* 8011

LUTHERAN MEDICAL CENTER (INC) p 886
1730 W 25th St, Cleveland OH 44113
Tel (216) 696-4300 *SIC* 8062 8011 8069

AMERICAN HEALTH NETWORK INC p 73
2500 Corporate Exchange D, Columbus OH 43231
Tel (614) 794-4500 *SIC* 8011

DOCTORS OHIOHEALTH CORP p 447
5100 W Broad St, Columbus OH 43228
Tel (614) 544-5424 *SIC* 8062 8011

FAMILY MEDICINE NORTH INC p 527
1930 Crown Park Ct # 130, Columbus OH 43235
Tel (614) 457-1793 *SIC* 8011

UNION HOSPITAL ASSOCIATION p 1504
659 Boulevard St, Dover OH 44622
Tel (330) 343-3311 *SIC* 8062 8011

COMMUNITY HEALTH PARTNERS REGIONAL MEDICAL CENTER p 348
3700 Kolbe Rd, Lorain OH 44053
Tel (440) 960-4000 *SIC* 8011

ALLIANCE PHYSICIANS INC p 55
2110 Leiter Rd, Miamisburg OH 45342
Tel (937) 558-9070 *SIC* 8011

PORTSMOUTH HOSPITAL CORP p 1163
1901 Argonne Rd, Portsmouth OH 45662
Tel (740) 991-4000 *SIC* 8011

ROBINSON HEALTH SYSTEM INC p 1242
6847 N Chestnut St, Ravenna OH 44266
Tel (330) 297-0811 *SIC* 8062 8011

UNIVERSITY HOSPITALS HEALTH SYSTEM INC p 1519
3605 Warrensville Ctr Rd, Shaker Heights OH 44122
Tel (216) 767-8900 *SIC* 8062 8011 8741

TRINITY HEALTH SYSTEM p 1481
380 Summit Ave, Steubenville OH 43952
Tel (740) 283-7000 *SIC* 8062 8011

AFTER HOURS FAMILY CARE INC p 33
450 N Hyatt St Ste 204, Tipp City OH 45371
Tel (937) 667-2614 *SIC* 8011

FAMILY HEALTH PLAN INC p 527
2200 Jefferson Ave Fl 6, Toledo OH 43604
Tel (419) 241-6501 *SIC* 6324 8011

■ **HEARTLAND HEALTHCARE SERVICES LLC** p 679
4755 South Ave, Toledo OH 43615
Tel (419) 535-8435 *SIC* 8011

TOLEDO CLINIC INC p 1458
4235 Secor Rd, Toledo OH 43623
Tel (419) 473-3561 *SIC* 8011

TOLEDO HOSPITAL p 1458
2142 N Cove Blvd, Toledo OH 43606
Tel (419) 291-4000 *SIC* 8011 8062

UPPER VALLEY MEDICAL CENTER p 1529
3130 N County Road 25a, Troy OH 45373
Tel (937) 440-4000 *SIC* 8011 8062

■ **RGH ENTERPRISES INC** p 1231
1810 Summit Commerce Park, Twinsburg OH 44087
Tel (330) 963-6998 *SIC* 5999 5047 8011

FORUM HEALTH p 570
1350 E Market St 302, Warren OH 44483
Tel (330) 841-9011 *SIC* 8741 8011

TRUMBULL MEMORIAL HOSPITAL FOUNDATION p 1487
1350 E Market St, Warren OH 44483
Tel (330) 841-9376 *SIC* 8011

JANE PHILLIPS MEDICAL CENTER p 777
3450 E Frank Philips Blvd, Bartlesville OK 74006
Tel (918) 338-3730 *SIC* 8011

CHOCTAW MANAGEMENT SERVICES ENTERPRISE p 301
2101 W Arkansas St, Durant OK 74701
Tel (580) 924-8280 *SIC* 8099 8011 8031

■ **ST MARYS REGIONAL MEDICAL CENTER** p 1372
305 S 5th St, Enid OK 73701
Tel (580) 233-6100 *SIC* 8011

INOLA HEALTH CARE CENTER INC p 745
400 N Broadway, Inola OK 74036
Tel (918) 543-8800 *SIC* 8011

■ **MIDWEST REGIONAL MEDICAL CENTER LLC** p 967
2825 Parklawn Dr, Midwest City OK 73110
Tel (405) 610-4411 *SIC* 8011 8062

BOARD OF REGENTS OF UNIVERSITY OF OKLAHOMA-OU PHYSICIANS p 195
1122 Ne 13th St St236, Oklahoma City OK 73117
Tel (405) 271-1515 *SIC* 8011

■ **DEACONESS HEALTH SYSTEM LLC** p 419
5501 N Portland Ave, Oklahoma City OK 73112
Tel (405) 604-6000
SIC 8062 8051 8011 8361

▲ **FOUNDATION HEALTHCARE INC** p 571
13900 N Portland Ave # 200, Oklahoma City OK 73134
Tel (405) 608-1700 *SIC* 8062 8011 8093

MERCY CLINIC OKLAHOMA COMMUNITIES INC p 945
4300 W Memorial Rd, Oklahoma City OK 73120
Tel (405) 936-5213 *SIC* 8011

UAMS EYE CENTER p 1498
921 Ne 13th St, Oklahoma City OK 73104
Tel (405) 456-1000 *SIC* 8011

STILLWATER MEDICAL PHYSICIAN CLNIC p 1390
1815 W 6th Ave, Stillwater OK 74074
Tel (405) 743-7300 *SIC* 8011

TAHLEQUAH MEDICAL GROUP LLC p 1421
1400 E Downing St, Tahlequah OK 74464
Tel (918) 456-0641 *SIC* 8011 8062

SAINT FRANCIS HEALTH SYSTEM INC p 1269
6161 S Yale Ave, Tulsa OK 74136
Tel (918) 494-2200 *SIC* 8011

WARREN CLINIC INC p 1576
6161 S Yale Ave, Tulsa OK 74136
Tel (918) 488-6000 *SIC* 8011

ST CHARLES HEALTH SYSTEM INC p 1365
2500 Ne Neff Rd, Bend OR 97701
Tel (541) 382-4321 *SIC* 8062 8011

CORVALLIS CLINIC P C p 373
3680 Nw Samaritan Dr, Corvallis OR 97330
Tel (541) 754-1150 *SIC* 8011 5912

MID-VALLEY HEALTHCARE INC p 963
525 N Santiam Hwy, Lebanon OR 97355
Tel (541) 258-2101
SIC 8062 8051 8011 8082

YAMHILL COUNTY CARE ORGANIZATION INC p 1634
807 Ne 3rd St, Mcminnville OR 97128
Tel (503) 434-7339 *SIC* 8011

LEGACY HEALTH p 852
1919 Nw Lovejoy St, Portland OR 97209
Tel (503) 415-5600 *SIC* 8011

PORTLAND CLINIC LLP p 1163
800 Sw 13th Ave, Portland OR 97205
Tel (503) 221-0161 *SIC* 8011

SAINT CHARLES MEDICAL CENTER REDMOND p 1268
1253 Nw Canal Blvd, Redmond OR 97756
Tel (541) 548-8131 *SIC* 8011

MID VALLEY IPA INC p 963
2995 Ryan Dr Se Ste 200, Salem OR 97301
Tel (503) 371-7701 *SIC* 8011

MCKINSEY WILLIAMETTE p 930
1460 G St, Springfield OR 97477
Tel (541) 741-4600 *SIC* 8011 8062

MID-COLUMBIA MEDICAL CENTER p 963
1700 E 19th St, The Dalles OR 97058
Tel (541) 296-1111 *SIC* 8062 8011

■ **HEALTH NET HEALTH PLAN OF OREGON INC** p 675
13221 Sw 68th Pkwy Ste 20, Tigard OR 97223
Tel (503) 213-5000 *SIC* 6324 8011

LEGACY MERIDIAN PARK HOSPITAL p 852
19300 Sw 65th Ave, Tualatin OR 97062
Tel (503) 692-1212 *SIC* 8062 8011

LEHIGH VALLEY PHYSICIANS GROUP p 854
1605 N Cedar Crest Blvd # 110, Allentown PA 18104
Tel (610) 439-7500 *SIC* 8011

SACRED HEART HOSPITAL OF ALLENTOWN p 1265
421 Chew St, Allentown PA 18102
Tel (610) 776-4500 *SIC* 8062 8011

BLAIR MEDICAL ASSOCIATES p 188
1414 9th Ave, Altoona PA 16602
Tel (814) 944-0202 *SIC* 8011 8043

MAIN LINE SERVICES p 897
950 E Haverford Rd # 110, Bryn Mawr PA 19010
Tel (484) 337-8480 *SIC* 8011

CROZER-CHESTER MEDICAL CENTER p 396
1 Medical Center Blvd, Chester PA 19013
Tel (610) 447-2000 *SIC* 8011

GEISINGER CLINIC p 597
100 N Academy Ave, Danville PA 17822
Tel (570) 271-6211 *SIC* 8011 8733

GEISINGER HEALTH PLAN p 597
100 N Academy Ave, Danville PA 17822
Tel (570) 271-8778 *SIC* 8011

DUBOIS REGIONAL MEDICAL CENTER INC p 459
100 Hospital Ave, Du Bois PA 15801
Tel (814) 371-2200 *SIC* 8093 8011

EINSTEIN MEDICAL CENTER MONTGOMERY p 482
559 W Germantown Pike, East Norriton PA 19403
Tel (484) 622-1000 *SIC* 8011

BAYFRONT REGIONAL DEVELOPMENT CORP p 161
201 State St, Erie PA 16550
Tel (814) 877-7000 *SIC* 8011

SAINT VINCENT HEALTH SYSTEM p 1271
232 W 25th St, Erie PA 16544
Tel (814) 452-5000 *SIC* 8741 8011

HANOVER HEALTH CORP INC p 658
300 Highland Ave, Hanover PA 17331
Tel (717) 637-3711 *SIC* 8062 8011 5912

PINNACLE HEALTH MEDICAL SERVICES p 1150
409 S 2nd St Ste 2b, Harrisburg PA 17104
Tel (717) 231-8341 *SIC* 8011 8063

MILTON S HERSHEY MEDICAL CENTER p 972
500 University Dr, Hershey PA 17033
Tel (717) 531-8521 *SIC* 8011

INDIANA REGIONAL MEDICAL CENTER p 738
835 Hospital Rd, Indiana PA 15701
Tel (724) 357-7000 *SIC* 8062 8011

CLINICAL CARE ASSOCIATES OF UNIVERSITY OF PENNSYLVANIA HEALTH SYSTEM p 326
2200 Renaissance Blvd # 320, King Of Prussia PA 19406
Tel (800) 789-7366 *SIC* 8011

▲ **UNIVERSAL HEALTH SERVICES INC** p 1517
367 S Gulph Rd, King Of Prussia PA 19406
Tel (610) 768-3300
SIC 8062 8063 8093 8011 8741

ARMSTRONG COUNTY MEMORIAL HOSPITAL p 111
1 Nolte Dr, Kittanning PA 16201
Tel (724) 543-8500 *SIC* 8062 8011

PHILHAVEN HOSPITAL p 1143
283 Butler Rd, Lebanon PA 17042
Tel (717) 270-2414 *SIC* 8011 8063

EVANGELICAL MEDICAL SERVICES ORGANIZATION p 513
1 Hospital Dr, Lewisburg PA 17837
Tel (570) 522-2000 *SIC* 8011

FUJIREBIO DIAGNOSTICS INC p 583
201 Great Valley Pkwy, Malvern PA 19355
Tel (610) 240-3800 *SIC* 5047 8011

MEADVILLE MEDICAL CENTER p 934
751 Liberty St, Meadville PA 16335
Tel (814) 333-5000 *SIC* 8741 8062 8011

THREE RIVERS HOLDINGS INC p 1450
300 Oxford Dr, Monroeville PA 15146
Tel (412) 858-4000 *SIC* 8011

■ **PHYSICIAN SUPPORT SYSTEMS INC** p 1145
15 Eby Chiques Rd, Mount Joy PA 17552
Tel (717) 653-5340 *SIC* 8011

CATHOLIC HEALTH EAST p 266
3805 West Chester Pike # 100, Newtown Square PA 19073
Tel (610) 355-2000
SIC 8062 8051 8052 8059 8011

ST LUKES PHYSICIANS GROUP p 1370
7790 Easton Rd, Ottsville PA 18942
Tel (610) 847-2071 *SIC* 8011

MAIN LINE HEALTHCARE p 897
2 Industrial Blvd Ste 400, Paoli PA 19301
Tel (610) 648-1644 *SIC* 8099 8011

CHILDRENS SURGICAL ASSOCIATES LTD p 300
3400 Civic Center Blvd # 5, Philadelphia PA 19104
Tel (215) 590-2700 *SIC* 8011

EINSTEIN COMMUNITY HEALTH ASSOCIATES p 482
5501 Old York Rd, Philadelphia PA 19141
Tel (215) 456-7890 *SIC* 8011

HEALTH PARTNERS PLANS INC p 675
901 Market St Ste 500, Philadelphia PA 19107
Tel (215) 849-9606 *SIC* 8011

HEALTH SERVICES OF FOX CHASE CANCER CENTER p 676
333 Cottman Ave, Philadelphia PA 19111
Tel (215) 728-6900 *SIC* 8011 8062 8733

KEYSTONE HEALTH PLAN EAST INC p 815
1901 Market St Ste 1000, Philadelphia PA 19103
Tel (215) 241-2001 *SIC* 6324 8011

MCKEE SHEPARD & GRIASKA MEDICAL ASSOCIATES p 930
51 N 39th St Ste 1, Philadelphia PA 19104
Tel (215) 662-8978 *SIC* 8011

PHILADELPHIA HEALTH EDUCATION CORP p 1142
1601 Cherry St Ste 11511, Philadelphia PA 19102
Tel (215) 255-7755 *SIC* 8011

■ **PHOENIXVILLE HOSPITAL OF UNIVERSITY OF PENNSYLVANIA HEALTH SYSTEM** p 1145
140 Nutt Rd, Phoenixville PA 19460
Tel (610) 983-1000 *SIC* 8062 8011

PITTSBURGH p 1152
200 Lothrop St, Pittsburgh PA 15213
Tel (412) 648-8454 *SIC* 8011

READING HEALTH SYSTEM p 1213
6th Ave And Spruce St, Reading PA 19611
Tel (610) 988-8000
SIC 8062 6512 8093 8721 8011 7219

GUTHRIE CLINIC p 648
1 Guthrie Sq Ste B, Sayre PA 18840
Tel (570) 888-5858 *SIC* 8011 8062 8082

GUTHRIE HEALTHCARE SYSTEM p 648
1 Guthrie Sq Ste B, Sayre PA 18840
Tel (570) 888-6666 *SIC* 8011 7352 8741

GUTHRIE MEDICAL GROUP PC p 648
1 Guthrie Sq Ste B, Sayre PA 18840
Tel (570) 888-5858 *SIC* 8011

VALLEY MEDICAL FACILITIES INC p 1541
720 Blackburn Rd, Sewickley PA 15143
Tel (724) 728-7000 *SIC* 8011

LAUREL HEALTH SYSTEM INC p 847
22 Walnut St, Wellsboro PA 16901
Tel (570) 724-1010 *SIC* 8082 8741 8011

SUSQUEHANNA PHYSICIAN SERVICES p 1409
1100 Grampian Blvd, Williamsport PA 17701
Tel (570) 320-7444 *SIC* 8011

WILLIAMSPORT PATHOLOGY ASSOCS p 1612
700 High St, Williamsport PA 17701
Tel (570) 321-2321 *SIC* 8011

WELLSPAN MEDICAL GROUP (INC) p 1591
140 N Duke St, York PA 17401
Tel (717) 851-6515 *SIC* 8011

DORADO HEALTH INC p 451
Carrion Hernandez St Urb, Manati PR 00674
Tel (787) 621-3700 *SIC* 8011

AUXILIO MUTUO HOSPITAL p 135
735 Ave Ponce De Leon, San Juan PR 00917
Tel (787) 761-6600 *SIC* 8011 8062

■ **CAREMARK PHC LLC** p 255
695 George Washington Hwy, Lincoln RI 02865
Tel (401) 334-0069 *SIC* 8011 5912

LIFESPAN CORP p 864
167 Point St Ste 2b, Providence RI 02903
Tel (401) 444-3500 *SIC* 8011

ANMED HEALTH p 92
800 Nh Fant St, Anderson SC 29621
Tel (864) 261-1000 *SIC* 8062 8011

CARECORE NATIONAL LLC p 254
400 Buckwalter Place Blvd, Bluffton SC 29910
Tel (800) 918-8924 *SIC* 8011

ROPER ST FRANCIS PHYSICIANS NETWORK p 1250
125 Doughty St Ste 760, Charleston SC 29403
Tel (843) 724-2903 *SIC* 8011

■ **TRIDENT MEDICAL CENTER LLC** p 1479
9330 Medical Plaza Dr, Charleston SC 29406
Tel (843) 797-7000 *SIC* 8062 8011

MCLEOD PHYSICIAN ASSOCIATES INC p 931
555 E Cheves St, Florence SC 29506
Tel (843) 777-7000 *SIC* 8011

GEORGETOWN HEALTHCARE & REHAB INC p 606
2715 South Island Rd, Georgetown SC 29440
Tel (843) 546-4123 *SIC* 8011

HARTSVILLE LLC p 666
1304 W Bobo Newsom Hwy, Hartsville SC 29550
Tel (843) 339-2100 *SIC* 8011

MEDICAL SERVICES OF AMERICA INC p 937
171 Monroe Ln, Lexington SC 29072
Tel (803) 957-0500
SIC 8082 8741 8011 8071 7352 5999

■ **EAST COOPER COMMUNITY HOSPITAL INC** p 470
2000 Hospital Dr, Mount Pleasant SC 29464
Tel (843) 881-0100 *SIC* 8062 8011

ALLERGY CENTERS OF AMERICA LLC p 53
2430 Mall Dr Ste 210, North Charleston SC 29406
Tel (843) 747-4294 *SIC* 8011 8071

TUOMEY MEDICAL PROFESSIONALS p 1492
129 N Washington St, Sumter SC 29150
Tel (803) 774-9000 *SIC* 8011

LEXINGTON COUNTY HEALTH SERVICES DISTRICT INC p 859
2720 Sunset Blvd, West Columbia SC 29169
Tel (803) 791-2000
SIC 8062 8011 8299 8051

SANFORD HEALTH p 1279
1305 W 18th St, Sioux Falls SD 57105
Tel (605) 333-1720 *SIC* 8062 8011 8051

SANFORD HEALTH NETWORK p 1279
1305 W 18th St, Sioux Falls SD 57105
Tel (605) 328-2929 *SIC* 8741 8011

SACRED HEART HEALTH SERVICES p 1265
501 Summit St, Yankton SD 57078
Tel (605) 668-8000 *SIC* 8062 8011

CORIZON HEALTH INC p 370
103 Powell Ct, Brentwood TN 37027
Tel (800) 729-0069 *SIC* 8011

■ **CENTERRE HEALTHCARE CORP** p 276
113 Seaboard Ln Ste 201b, Franklin TN 37067
Tel (615) 846-9500 *SIC* 8011

■ **PSYCHIATRIC SOLUTIONS INC** p 1189
6640 Carothers Pkwy # 500, Franklin TN 37067
Tel (615) 312-5700 *SIC* 8011 8063

JACKSON CLINIC PROFESSIONAL ASSOCIATION p 773
828 N Parkway, Jackson TN 38305
Tel (731) 422-0200 *SIC* 5912 8011 8062

HOLSTON MEDICAL GROUP PC p 702
2323 N John B Dennis Hwy, Kingsport TN 37660
Tel (423) 857-2000 *SIC* 8011

METHODIST MEDICAL CENTER OF OAK RIDGE p 954
1420 Centerpoint Blvd C, Knoxville TN 37932
Tel (865) 374-6864 *SIC* 8011

PARKWEST MEDICAL CENTER p 1117
1420 Centerpoint Blvd, Knoxville TN 37932
Tel (865) 374-6872 *SIC* 8011

UNIVERSITY HEALTH SYSTEM INC p 1519
9000 Executive Park Dr D240, Knoxville TN 37923
Tel (865) 251-3700 *SIC* 6324 8011

BAPTIST MEMORIAL HEALTH CARE CORP p 154
350 N Humphreys Blvd, Memphis TN 38120
Tel (901) 227-2727
SIC 8062 8011 8741 5047

METHODIST HEALTHCARE MEMPHIS HOSPITALS p 953
848 Adams Ave, Memphis TN 38103
Tel (901) 287-5437 *SIC* 8069 8011

UT MEDICAL GROUP INC p 1536
1407 Union Ave Ste 700, Memphis TN 38104
Tel (901) 866-8864 *SIC* 8011

▲ **AMSURG CORP** p 87
1a Burton Hills Bvld, Nashville TN 37215
Tel (615) 665-1283 *SIC* 8011

CORRECT CARE SOLUTIONS LLC p 372
1283 Murfreesboro Pike # 500, Nashville TN 37217
Tel (800) 592-2974 *SIC* 8011

HAVEN BEHAVIORAL HEALTHCARE INC p 668
3102 West End Ave # 1000, Nashville TN 37203
Tel (615) 393-8800 *SIC* 8011

■ **HCA HEALTH SERVICES OF TENNESSEE INC** p 671
391 Wallace Rd, Nashville TN 37211
Tel (615) 781-4000 *SIC* 8011 8062

■ **HCA PSYCHIATRIC CO** p 672
1 Park Plz, Nashville TN 37203
Tel (615) 344-2390 *SIC* 8063 8011

■ **RESTON HOSPITAL CENTER LLC** p 1228
1 Park Plz, Nashville TN 37203
Tel (615) 344-9551 *SIC* 8011 8062

SYMBION HOLDINGS CORP p 1414
40 Burton Hills Blvd # 500, Nashville TN 37215
Tel (615) 234-5900 *SIC* 8011 8093 8062

SYMBION INC p 1414
40 Burton Hills Blvd # 500, Nashville TN 37215
Tel (615) 234-5900 *SIC* 8011 8093 8062

THOMAS SAINT MIDTOWN HOSPITAL p 1449
2000 Church St, Nashville TN 37236
Tel (615) 284-5555 *SIC* 8062 8011

■ **ARMC LP** p 111
6250 Highway 83 84, Abilene TX 79606
Tel (325) 428-1000
SIC 8062 8093 8011 7991

■ **CONCENTRA HEALTH SERVICES INC** p 354
5080 Spectrum Dr Ste 400w, Addison TX 75001
Tel (972) 364-8000 *SIC* 8093 8011

■ **CONCENTRA INC** p 354
5080 Spectrum Dr Ste 400w, Addison TX 75001
Tel (972) 364-8000 *SIC* 8011

UNITED SURGICAL PARTNERS INTERNATIONAL INC p 1514
15305 Dallas Pkwy # 1600, Addison TX 75001
Tel (972) 713-3500 *SIC* 8011

USPI GROUP HOLDINGS INC p 1535
15305 Dallas Pkwy # 1600, Addison TX 75001
Tel (972) 713-3500 *SIC* 8011

USPI HOLDINGS INC p 1535
15305 Dallas Pkwy # 1600, Addison TX 75001
Tel (972) 713-3500 *SIC* 8011

AUSTIN DIAGNOSTIC CLINIC ASSOCIATION p 132
12221 N Mo Pac Expy, Austin TX 78758
Tel (512) 901-1111 *SIC* 8011

COVENANT MANAGEMENT SYSTEMS LP p 384
4515 Seton Center Pkwy # 220, Austin TX 78759
Tel (512) 338-8388 *SIC* 8011

ST DAVIDS NORTH AUSTIN MEDICAL CENTER p 1366
12221 N Mo Pac Expy, Austin TX 78758
Tel (512) 901-1000
SIC 8062 8011 8069 8049

■ **ST DAVIDS SOUTH AUSTIN MEDICAL CENTER** p 1366
901 W Ben White Blvd, Austin TX 78704
Tel (512) 447-2211 *SIC* 8062 8011

CARTER BLOODCARE FDN p 261
2205 Highway 121, Bedford TX 76021
Tel (817) 412-5121 *SIC* 8011

TEXAS A&M UNIVERSITY SYSTEM p 1442
301 Tarrow St Fl 3, College Station TX 77840
Tel (979) 458-6100
SIC 8221 8731 8742 8011

DRISCOLL CHILDRENS HEALTH PLAN p 456
615 N Uppr Brdwy 1621, Corpus Christi TX 78401
Tel (361) 694-6432 *SIC* 8011 6399

BAYLOR REGIONAL MEDICAL CENTER AT PLANO p 162
2001 Bryan St Ste 2200, Dallas TX 75201
Tel (214) 820-4135 *SIC* 8011

FOREST PARK MEDICAL CENTER LLC p 567
11990 N Central Expy, Dallas TX 75243
Tel (972) 234-1900 *SIC* 8011

HEALTHTEXAS PROVIDER NETWORK p 678
8080 N Cntrl Expy Ste 600, Dallas TX 75206
Tel (972) 860-8600 *SIC* 8011

SUSAN G KOMEN BREAST CANCER FOUNDATION INC p 1409
5005 Lbj Fwy Ste 250, Dallas TX 75244
Tel (972) 855-1600
SIC 8699 8069 8011 8099

▲ **TENET HEALTHCARE CORP** p 1437
1445 Ross Ave Ste 1400, Dallas TX 75202
Tel (469) 893-2200
SIC 8062 8069 8741 8063 8082 8011

UNIVERSITY OF TEXAS SOUTHWESTERN MEDICAL CENTER p 1526
5323 Harry Hines Blvd, Dallas TX 75390
Tel (214) 648-3068 *SIC* 8733 8011

■ **DENTON REGIONAL MEDICAL CENTER INC** p 429
3535 S Interstate 35 E, Denton TX 76210
Tel (940) 384-3535 *SIC* 8062 8011

DAY EL PASO SURGERY LP p 417
1300 Murchison Dr Ste 200, El Paso TX 79902
Tel (915) 225-7600 *SIC* 8011

COOK CHILDRENS PHYSICIAN NETWORK p 365
801 7th Ave, Fort Worth TX 76104
Tel (682) 885-6800 *SIC* 8011

■ **PHYSASSIST SCRIBES INC** p 1145
6451 Brentwood Stair Rd # 100, Fort Worth TX 76112
Tel (817) 496-1009 *SIC* 8011

TRUE HEALTH DIAGNOSTICS LLC p 1486
6170 Research Rd Ste 211, Frisco TX 75033
Tel (844) 341-1491 *SIC* 8011 8069

BAYLOR MEDICAL CENTER AT GARLAND p 162
2300 Marie Curie Dr, Garland TX 75042
Tel (972) 487-5000
SIC 8062 8082 8011 8093

HARRIS HEALTH SYSTEM p 663
2525 Holly Hall St, Houston TX 77054
Tel (713) 566-6400 *SIC* 8062 8011

LEGACY COMMUNITY HEALTH SERVICES INC p 852
1415 California St, Houston TX 77006
Tel (713) 830-3000 *SIC* 8093 8011

METHODIST HEALTH CARE SYSTEM p 953
6565 Fannin St D200, Houston TX 77030
Tel (713) 793-1602 *SIC* 8011

▲ **NOBILIS HEALTH CORP** p 1046
11700 Katy Fwy Ste 300, Houston TX 77079
Tel (713) 355-8614 *SIC* 8011

REECE GREGORY MD p 1217
1515 Holcombe Blvd, Houston TX 77030
Tel (713) 794-1247 *SIC* 8011

SBMC HEALTHCARE LLC p 1285
1301 Mckinney St Ste 2025, Houston TX 77010
Tel (713) 953-1055 *SIC* 8011

TCH PEDIATRIC ASSOCIATES INC p 1428
8080 N Stadium Dr Ste 200, Houston TX 77054
Tel (832) 824-6626 *SIC* 8011

TEXAS CHILDRENS HOSPITAL p 1442
6621 Fannin St, Houston TX 77030
Tel (832) 824-1000 *SIC* 8011 8062

TEXAS CHILDRENS HOSPITAL FOUNDATION p 1442
6621 Fannin St Ste 210, Houston TX 77030
Tel (832) 824-6230 *SIC* 8011

TEXAS CHILDRENS PHYSICIAN GROUP INC p 1442
6621 Fannin St, Houston TX 77030
Tel (832) 824-2982 *SIC* 8011

UNIVERSITY TEXAS PHYSICIANS INF p 1527
6410 Fannin St Ste 600, Houston TX 77030
Tel (832) 325-7070 *SIC* 8011

UT PHYSICIANS p 1536
6410 Fannin St Ste 1500, Houston TX 77030
Tel (713) 500-5086 *SIC* 8011

CH WILKINSON PHYSICIAN NETWORK p 286
919 Hidden Rdg, Irving TX 75038
Tel (469) 282-2000 *SIC* 8011

KINGWOOD MEDICAL CENTER p 821
22999 Highway 59 N # 134, Kingwood TX 77339
Tel (281) 348-8000 *SIC* 8011

▲ **ADEPTUS HEALTH INC** p 22
2941 Lake Vista Dr # 200, Lewisville TX 75067
Tel (972) 899-6666 *SIC* 8741 8011

COVENANT MEDICAL GROUP p 384
3506 21st St Ste 506, Lubbock TX 79410
Tel (806) 725-4130 *SIC* 8011

COVENANT MEDICAL GROUP p 384
524 E 40th St Unit B, Lubbock TX 79404
Tel (806) 725-9800 *SIC* 8011

■ **COLUMBIA RIO GRANDE HEALTHCARE LP** p 341
101 E Ridge Rd, Mcallen TX 78503
Tel (956) 632-6000 *SIC* 8011 8062

BAYLOR MEDICAL CENTER AT MCKINNEY p 162
5252 W University Dr, Mckinney TX 75071
Tel (469) 764-4600 *SIC* 8011

PAMPA REGIONAL MEDICAL CENTER AUXILIARY p 1110
1 Medical Plz, Pampa TX 79065
Tel (806) 665-3721 *SIC* 8011

KELSEY-SEYBOLD MEDICAL GROUP PLLC p 809
11511 Shadow Creek Pkwy, Pearland TX 77584
Tel (713) 442-0000 *SIC* 8011 5912

FAMILY MEDICAL CENTER AT ROCKWALL p 527
1975 Alpha Dr 204, Rockwall TX 75087
Tel (972) 771-9155 *SIC* 8011

SETON MEDICAL CENTER WILLIAMSON p 1309
201 Seton Pkwy, Round Rock TX 78665
Tel (512) 324-4000 *SIC* 8011

■ **LAKE POINTE MEDICAL CENTER LTD** p 839
6800 Scenic Dr, Rowlett TX 75088
Tel (972) 412-2273 *SIC* 8011

SHANNON CLINIC p 1311
120 E Beauregard Ave, San Angelo TX 76903
Tel (325) 658-1511 *SIC* 8011

SHANNON HEALTH SYSTEM p 1311
120 E Harris Ave, San Angelo TX 76903
Tel (325) 653-6741 *SIC* 8011

BEXAR COUNTY HOSPITAL DISTRICT p 179
4502 Medical Dr Ms651, San Antonio TX 78229
Tel (210) 358-4000 *SIC* 8062 8011

■ **HUMANA HEALTH PLAN INC** p 718
8431 Fredericksburg Rd # 340, San Antonio TX 78229
Tel (210) 615-5100 *SIC* 6324 6321 8011

METHODIST HEALTHCARE MINISTRIES OF SOUTH TEXAS INC p 953
4507 Medical Dr, San Antonio TX 78229
Tel (210) 692-0234 *SIC* 8011 7363

■ **METHODIST HEALTHCARE SYSTEM OF SAN ANTONIO LTD LLP** p 953
8109 Fredericksburg Rd, San Antonio TX 78229
Tel (210) 575-8110 *SIC* 8062 8011

UNIVERSITY HEALTH SYSTEM p 1518
355 Spencer Ln Ste 2, San Antonio TX 78201
Tel (210) 358-9185 *SIC* 8011 6512

SHERMAN/GRAYSON HOSPITAL LLC p 1316
500 N Highland Ave, Sherman TX 75092
Tel (903) 870-4611 *SIC* 8011

PHYSICANS AT SUGAR CREEK p 1145
14023 Southwest Fwy, Sugar Land TX 77478
Tel (281) 325-4100 *SIC* 8011

ST LUKES COMMUNITY HEALTH SERVICES p 1370
17200 St Lukes Way, The Woodlands TX 77384
Tel (936) 266-2000 *SIC* 8011 8062

■ **US ONCOLOGY HOLDINGS INC** p 1532
10101 Woodloch Forest Dr, The Woodlands TX 77380
Tel (281) 863-1000 *SIC* 8093 8099 8011

■ **US ONCOLOGY INC** p 1532
10101 Woodloch Forest Dr, The Woodlands TX 77380
Tel (800) 381-2637 *SIC* 8093 8099 8011

EAST TEXAS MEDICAL CENTER p 471
1000 S Beckham Ave, Tyler TX 75701
Tel (903) 597-0351 *SIC* 8062 8011

TRINITY MOTHER FRANCIS HEALTH SYSTEM p 1481
910 E Houston St Ste 550, Tyler TX 75702
Tel (903) 526-2644 *SIC* 8011

KNAPP MEDICAL CENTER p 824
1401 E 8th St, Weslaco TX 78596
Tel (956) 968-8567 *SIC* 8011

MEYERTONS HOOD KIVLIN KOWERT & GOETZEL P C p 957
1120 S Capital Of Texas, West Lake Hills TX 78746
Tel (512) 853-8800 *SIC* 8011

CARDIOVASCULAR & THORACIC SURGICAL GROUP OF WICHITA FALLS P A p 253
912 Burnett St, Wichita Falls TX 76301
Tel (940) 764-8570 *SIC* 8011

INTERMOUNTAIN HEALTH CARE HEALTH SERVICES p 753
5121 S Cottonwood St, Murray UT 84107
Tel (801) 507-5358 *SIC* 8011

■ **NORTHERN UTAH HEALTHCARE CORP** p 1057
1200 E 3900 S, Salt Lake City UT 84124
Tel (801) 268-7111 *SIC* 8062 8082 8011

UNIVERSITY OF UTAH HOSPITALS AND CLINICS p 1526
50 N Medical Dr, Salt Lake City UT 84132
Tel (801) 581-2121 *SIC* 8062 8011

UNIVERSITY PATHOLOGY ASSOCIATES p 1527
50 N Medical Dr 5c124, Salt Lake City UT 84132
Tel (801) 581-5406 *SIC* 8071 8011

IHC HEALTH SERVICES INC p 730
1380 E Medical Center Dr, St George UT 84790
Tel (801) 442-5000
SIC 8062 8011 8322 8049 8093 8069

FLETCHER ALLEN HEALTH VENTURES INC p 555
111 Colchester Ave, Burlington VT 05401
Tel (802) 847-5669 *SIC* 8011

JOHNSTON MEMORIAL HOSPITAL INC p 791
16000 Johnston Memorial D, Abingdon VA 24211
Tel (276) 258-1000 *SIC* 8062 8011

INOVA WOODBURN SURGERY CENTER LLC p 745
3289 Woodburn Rd Ste 100, Annandale VA 22003
Tel (703) 226-2640 *SIC* 8011

DANVILLE REGIONAL HEALTH FOUNDATION p 412
142 S Main St, Danville VA 24541
Tel (434) 799-2100
SIC 8741 8062 8051 8011

■ **DANVILLE REGIONAL MEDICAL CENTER** p 412
142 S Main St, Danville VA 24541
Tel (434) 799-2100
SIC 8062 8011 8093 8069 8051

NORTHERN VIRGINIA SURGERY CENTER II LLC p 1057
3620 Joseph Siewick Dr # 406, Fairfax VA 22033
Tel (703) 766-6960 *SIC* 8011

RADIOLOGICAL CONSULTANTS FAIRFAX PC p 1204
2722 Merrilee Dr Ste 230, Fairfax VA 22031
Tel (703) 698-4444 *SIC* 8011

INOVA HEALTH SYSTEM p 745
8110 Gatehouse Rd 200e, Falls Church VA 22042
Tel (703) 289-2069
SIC 8741 8011 8062 8049 8059 8051

AUGUSTA HEALTH CARE FOR WOMEN p 131
70 Medical Center Cir, Fishersville VA 22939
Tel (540) 245-7007 *SIC* 8011

■ **SPOTSYLVANIA MEDICAL CENTER INC** p 1360
4600 Spotsylvania Pkwy, Fredericksburg VA 22408
Tel (540) 498-4000 *SIC* 8011

LOUDOUN MEDICAL GROUP PC p 879
224d Cornwall St Nw, Leesburg VA 20176
Tel (703) 737-6010 *SIC* 8011

PIEDMONT COMMUNITY HEALTHCARE INC p 1147
2316 Atherholt Rd, Lynchburg VA 24501
Tel (434) 947-4463 *SIC* 8011

CHILDRENS HOSPITAL OF KINGS DAUGHTERS INC p 300
601 Childrens Ln, Norfolk VA 23507
Tel (757) 668-7000 *SIC* 8069 8011

SENTARA ENTERPRISES p 1305
6015 Poplar Hall Dr, Norfolk VA 23502
Tel (757) 455-7000 *SIC* 8011

VIRGINIA PREMIER HEALTH PLAN INC p 1559
600 E Broad St Ste 400, Richmond VA 23219
Tel (804) 819-5164 *SIC* 8011

CARILION MEDICAL CENTER p 256
1906 Belleview Ave Se, Roanoke VA 24014
Tel (540) 981-7000 *SIC* 8011 8062

RIVERSIDE PHYSICIAN SVCS INC p 1238
608 Denbigh Blvd, Williamsburg VA 23185
Tel (757) 442-6600 *SIC* 8011

■ **MOLINA HEALTHCARE OF WASHINGTON INC** p 982
21540 30th Dr Se Ste 400, Bothell WA 98021
Tel (425) 424-1100 *SIC* 8011

HIGHLINE MEDICAL SERVICES INC p 692
16255 Sylvester Rd Sw # 202, Burien WA 98166
Tel (206) 431-5304 *SIC* 8011

■ EVERETT CLINIC PLLC p 514
3901 Hoyt Ave, Everett WA 98201
Tel (425) 339-5465 SIC 8011

EVERETT MSO INC p 514
3901 Hoyt Ave, Everett WA 98201
Tel (425) 339-5465 SIC 8011

NORTH PUGET SOUND CENTER FOR SLEEP DISORDERS LLC p 1053
1728 W Marine View Dr, Everett WA 98201
Tel (425) 339-5460 SIC 8011

CAPITAL MEDICAL CENTER p 250
3900 Capital Mall Dr Sw, Olympia WA 98502
Tel (360) 754-5858 SIC 8062 8011

FRANCISCAN HEALTH SYSTEMS p 573
451 Sw Sedgwick Rd, Port Orchard WA 98367
Tel (360) 874-5900 SIC 8011

A POLYCLINIC PROFESSIONAL CORP p 6
904 7th Ave, Seattle WA 98104
Tel (206) 292-2249 SIC 8011

GROUP HEALTH PERMANENTE p 641
320 Westlake Ave N # 100, Seattle WA 98109
Tel (206) 448-4491 SIC 8011

PACMED CLINICS p 1107
1200 12th Ave S, Seattle WA 98144
Tel (206) 326-2400 SIC 8011

SWEDISH HEALTH SERVICES p 1411
747 Broadway, Seattle WA 98122
Tel (206) 386-6000 SIC 8011

SWEDISH PHYSICIANS DIVISION p 1411
600 University St # 1200, Seattle WA 98101
Tel (206) 320-2700 SIC 8011 8741

TRUPANION INC p 1487
6100 4th Ave S Ste 200, Seattle WA 98108
Tel (855) 727-9079 SIC 6324 8011

VIRGINIA MASON MEDICAL CENTER p 1559
1100 9th Ave, Seattle WA 98101
Tel (206) 223-6600
SIC 8011 8051 6513 8062

VIRGINIA MASON SEATTLE MAIN CLINIC p 1559
1100 9th Ave, Seattle WA 98101
Tel (206) 223-6600 SIC 8011

ROCKWOOD CLINIC PS p 1245
400 E 5th Ave Frnt, Spokane WA 99202
Tel (509) 838-2531 SIC 8011

FRANCISCAN MEDICAL GROUP p 573
1717 S J St, Tacoma WA 98405
Tel (253) 792-4365 SIC 8011

SOUND INPATIENT PHYSICIANS HOLDINGS LLC p 1342
1498 Pacific Ave Ste 400, Tacoma WA 98402
Tel (253) 682-1710 SIC 8011 6719

SOUND INPATIENT PHYSICIANS INC p 1342
1498 Pacific Ave Ste 400, Tacoma WA 98402
Tel (253) 682-1710 SIC 8011

YAKIMA VALLEY FARM WORKERS CLINIC INC p 1634
518 W 1st Ave, Toppenish WA 98948
Tel (509) 865-5898
SIC 8011 8021 8093 1799

PEACEHEALTH p 1125
1115 Se 164th Ave, Vancouver WA 98683
Tel (360) 788-6841 SIC 8062 8011

SOUTHWEST WASHINGTON MEDICAL CENTER p 1352
400 Ne Mother Joseph Pl, Vancouver WA 98664
Tel (360) 514-1900 SIC 8011

VANCOUVER CLINICAL SERVICES PC p 1543
700 Ne 87th Ave, Vancouver WA 98664
Tel (360) 397-1500 SIC 8011

CONFLUENCE HEALTH p 356
820 N Chelan Ave, Wenatchee WA 98801
Tel (509) 663-8711 SIC 8011

WENATCHEE VALLEY MEDICAL GROUP PS p 1591
820 N Chelan Ave, Wenatchee WA 98801
Tel (509) 663-8711 SIC 8011

UNIVERSITY PHYSICIANS & SURGEONS INC p 1527
1600 Med Ctr Dr Ste 1400, Huntington WV 25701
Tel (304) 691-1630 SIC 8011

■ LOGAN GENERAL HOSPITAL LLC p 874
20 Hospital Dr, Logan WV 25601
Tel (304) 831-1101 SIC 8011

MONONGALIA HEALTH SYSTEM INC p 984
1200 J D Anderson Dr, Morgantown WV 26505
Tel (304) 598-1200 SIC 8062 8011

URGENT CARE HOLDINGS INC p 1530
1751 Earl L Core Rd, Morgantown WV 26505
Tel (304) 225-2500 SIC 8011

VIRGINIA WEST UNIVERSITY MEDICAL CORP p 1560
1 Stadium Dr, Morgantown WV 26506
Tel (304) 598-4200 SIC 8011

OHIO VALLEY HEALTH SERVICES AND EDUCATION CORP p 1078
2000 Eoff St, Wheeling WV 26003
Tel (304) 234-8174 SIC 8741 8062 8011

OHIO VALLEY MEDICAL CENTER INC p 1078
2000 Eoff St, Wheeling WV 26003
Tel (304) 234-0123 SIC 8062 8011

WHEELING HOSPITAL INC p 1605
1 Medical Park, Wheeling WV 26003
Tel (304) 243-3000 SIC 8062 8011

CLARK THEDA MEDICAL CENTER p 322
5320 W Michaels Dr, Appleton WI 54913
Tel (920) 735-7650 SIC 8011

BELOIT MEMORIAL HOSPITAL INC p 171
1969 W Hart Rd, Beloit WI 53511
Tel (608) 364-5011 SIC 8062 8011

THEDACARE MEDICAL CENTER - BERLIN INC p 1446
225 Memorial Dr, Berlin WI 54923
Tel (920) 361-1313 SIC 8062 8051 8011

LUTHER HOSPITAL p 886
733 W Clairemont Ave, Eau Claire WI 54701
Tel (715) 838-3060 SIC 8011

LUTHER MIDELFORT MAYO HEALTH SYSTEM p 886
733 W Clairemont Ave, Eau Claire WI 54701
Tel (715) 838-5353 SIC 6324 8011

MAYO CLINIC HEALTH SYSTEM p 923
733 W Clairemont Ave, Eau Claire WI 54701
Tel (715) 838-6968 SIC 8011

MAYO CLINIC HEALTH SYSTEM-NORTHWEST WISCONSIN REGION INC p 924
1221 Whipple St, Eau Claire WI 54703
Tel (715) 838-3311 SIC 8062 8011

FORT HEALTHCARE INC p 569
611 Sherman Ave E, Fort Atkinson WI 53538
Tel (920) 568-5401 SIC 8062 8011

AURORA BAYCARE MEDICAL CENTER p 131
2845 Greenbrier Rd, Green Bay WI 54311
Tel (920) 288-8000 SIC 8011

BAYCARE HEALTH SYSTEMS LLC p 161
164 N Broadway, Green Bay WI 54303
Tel (920) 490-9046 SIC 8011

PREVEA CLINIC INC p 1173
2710 Executive Dr, Green Bay WI 54304
Tel (920) 272-1100 SIC 8011

ST MARYS HOSPITAL p 1371
1726 Shawano Ave, Green Bay WI 54303
Tel (920) 498-4200 SIC 8011 8062

ST VINCENT HOSPITAL OF HOSPITAL SISTERS OF THIRD ORDER OF S p 1373
835 S Van Buren St, Green Bay WI 54301
Tel (920) 433-0111 SIC 8062 8011

GUNDERSEN CLINIC LTD p 647
1836 South Ave, La Crosse WI 54601
Tel (608) 782-7300 SIC 8011

GUNDERSON LUTHERAN INC p 647
1836 South Ave, La Crosse WI 54601
Tel (608) 782-7300 SIC 8011

■ LOGISTICS HEALTH INC p 874
328 Front St S, La Crosse WI 54601
Tel (866) 284-8788 SIC 8011

LAC DU FLAMBEAU BAND OF LAKE SUPERIOR CHIPPEWA INDIANS (INC) p 836
418 Little Pines Rd, Lac Du Flambeau WI 54538
Tel (715) 588-3303
SIC 8011 7999 5411 5541 8031

ST MARYS DEAN VENTURES INC p 1371
1808 W Beltline Hwy, Madison WI 53713
Tel (608) 250-1311 SIC 8011

MARSHFIELD CLINIC HEALTH SYSTEM INC p 911
1000 N Oak Ave, Marshfield WI 54449
Tel (715) 387-5511 SIC 8011

MARSHFIELD CLINIC INC p 911
1000 N Oak Ave, Marshfield WI 54449
Tel (715) 387-5511 SIC 8011

SECURITY HEALTH PLAN OF WISCONSIN INC p 1299
1515 N Saint Joseph Ave, Marshfield WI 54449
Tel (715) 221-9555 SIC 8011

NETWORK HEALTH SYSTEM INC p 1028
1165 Appleton Rd, Menasha WI 54952
Tel (920) 831-8920 SIC 8011

PROHEALTH CARE MEDICAL ASSOCIATES INC p 1182
W180n8000 Town Hall Rd, Menomonee Falls WI 53051
Tel (262) 255-2500 SIC 8011

UNIVERSITY OF WISCONSIN MEDICAL FOUNDATION INC p 1527
7974 Uw Health Ct, Middleton WI 53562
Tel (608) 821-4223
SIC 8221 8011 2834 8299 8042 8043

AURORA MEDICAL GROUP INC p 132
750 W Virginia St, Milwaukee WI 53204
Tel (414) 299-1781 SIC 8011

CHILDRENS SPECIALTY GROUP INC p 300
999 N 92nd St Ste C740, Milwaukee WI 53226
Tel (414) 292-7858 SIC 8011

COMMUNITY CARE ORGANIZATION p 347
3220 W Vliet St, Milwaukee WI 53208
Tel (414) 231-4000 SIC 8011

MINISTRY HEALTH CARE INC p 973
400 W River Woods Pkwy, Milwaukee WI 53212
Tel (414) 359-1060 SIC 8011 8051

MINISTRY MEDICAL GROUP INC p 973
11925 W Lake Park Dr, Milwaukee WI 53224
Tel (414) 359-1060 SIC 8011

ST MICHAEL HOSPITAL OF FRANCISCAN SISTERS MILWAUKEE INC p 1372
5000 W Chambers St, Milwaukee WI 53210
Tel (414) 447-2000 SIC 8062 8011

MONROE CLINIC INC p 985
515 22nd Ave, Monroe WI 53566
Tel (608) 324-2775 SIC 8062 8011

PROHEALTHCARE FOUNDATION p 1182
791 Summit Ave, Oconomowoc WI 53066
Tel (262) 569-9400 SIC 8062 8011

AURORA MEDICAL CENTER OSHKOSH p 132
855 N Westhaven Dr, Oshkosh WI 54904
Tel (920) 303-8730 SIC 8011

DIVINE SAVIOR HEALTHCARE INC p 444
2817 New Pinery Rd # 202, Portage WI 53901
Tel (608) 745-4598 SIC 8062 8011 8051

MINISTRY MEDICAL GROUP p 973
2251 N Shore Dr Ste 200, Rhinelander WI 54501
Tel (715) 361-4700 SIC 8011

GREATER WATERTOWN COMMUNITY HEALTH FOUNDATION INC p 636
125 Hospital Dr, Watertown WI 53098
Tel (920) 261-4210 SIC 8062 8011 8059

PROHEALTH CARE INC p 1182
725 American Ave, Waukesha WI 53188
Tel (262) 544-2011 SIC 8011 8062

ASPIRUS EMPLOYEE ASSISTANCE p 118
3000 Westhill Dr Ste 102, Wausau WI 54401
Tel (715) 847-2772 SIC 8011

SIC 8021 Offices & Clinics Of Dentists

SOUTHCENTRAL FOUNDATION p 1345
4501 Diplomacy Dr, Anchorage AK 99508
Tel (907) 729-4955 SIC 8093 8021 8042

YUKON-KUSKOKWIM HEALTH CORP p 1640
829 Hospin Hwy Ste 329, Bethel AK 99559
Tel (907) 543-6300
SIC 8062 7363 8069 8093 8042 8021

ONSITE DENTAL LLC p 1088
85 Argonaut Ste 220, Aliso Viejo CA 92656
Tel (888) 411-2290 SIC 8021

GENTLE DENTAL SERVICE CORP p 605
9800 S La Cienega Blvd # 800, Inglewood CA 90301
Tel (310) 765-2400 SIC 8021

INTERDENT INC p 752
9800 S La Cienega Blvd # 800, Inglewood CA 90301
Tel (310) 765-2400 SIC 8021

INTERDENT SERVICE CORP p 752
9800 S La Cienega Blvd # 800, Inglewood CA 90301
Tel (310) 765-2400 SIC 8021

PACIFIC DENTAL SERVICES INC p 1104
17000 Red Hill Ave, Irvine CA 92614
Tel (714) 845-8500 SIC 8021 6794

SMILE BRANDS GROUP INC p 1333
100 Spectrum Center Dr # 1500, Irvine CA 92618
Tel (714) 668-1300 SIC 8741 8021

WESTERN DENTAL SERVICES INC p 1598
530 S Main St Ste 600, Orange CA 92868
Tel (714) 480-3000 SIC 8021

HIG MIDDLE MARKET LLC p 690
1 Market Spear Tower 18f, San Francisco CA 94105
Tel (415) 439-5500 SIC 8021

FARAHMAND ARTA DDS p 528
23326 Hawthorne Blvd # 220, Torrance CA 90505
Tel (310) 373-3501 SIC 8021

DENTAL CARE ALLIANCE LLC p 429
6240 Lake Osprey Dr, Lakewood Ranch FL 34240
Tel (888) 876-4531 SIC 8021

COAST DENTAL SERVICES INC p 331
4010 W Boy Scout Blvd # 1100, Tampa FL 33607
Tel (813) 288-1999 SIC 8021

DELTA DENTAL PLAN OF IDAHO INC p 426
555 E Parkcenter Blvd, Boise ID 83706
Tel (208) 489-3580 SIC 6324 8021

OUR LADY OF LORDES REGIONAL MEDICAL CENTER INC p 1098
4801 Ambssdor Cffery Pkwy, Lafayette LA 70508
Tel (337) 289-2000 SIC 8011 8021

DEDHAM MEDICAL ASSOCIATES INC p 421
1 Lyons St, Dedham MA 02026
Tel (781) 329-1400 SIC 8011 8021

GREAT EXPRESSIONS DENTAL CENTERS PC p 633
28626 Telegraph Rd, Southfield MI 48034
Tel (248) 203-2330 SIC 8021 8741

DELTA DENTAL PLAN OF NEW HAMPSHIRE INC p 426
1 Delta Dr, Concord NH 03301
Tel (800) 537-1715 SIC 6324 8021

DARTMOUTH-HITCHCOCK MEDICAL CENTER p 413
1 Medical Center Dr, Lebanon NH 03756
Tel (603) 650-5150 SIC 8021

IVOCLAR VIVADENT INC p 769
175 Pineview Dr, Amherst NY 14228
Tel (716) 691-0010 SIC 5047 8021

ASPEN DENTAL MANAGEMENT INC p 118
281 Sanders Creek Pkwy, East Syracuse NY 13057
Tel (315) 454-6000 SIC 8021 8072 6794

■ SIRONA DENTAL SYSTEMS INC p 1327
3030 47th Ave Ste 500, Long Island City NY 11101
Tel (718) 482-2011
SIC 8021 3313 3843 3841

FIRSTHEALTH OF CAROLINAS INC p 550
155 Memorial Dr, Pinehurst NC 28374
Tel (910) 715-1000
SIC 8062 8093 8051 8021 7991 7219

DENTALCARE PARTNERS INC p 429
6200 Oak Tree Blvd # 200, Independence OH 44131
Tel (216) 584-1000 SIC 8021

WILLAMETTE DENTAL MANAGEMENT CORP p 1609
6950 Ne Campus Way, Hillsboro OR 97124
Tel (503) 952-2000 SIC 8021

PENNSYLVANIA DENTAL SERVICE CORP p 1130
1 Delta Dr, Mechanicsburg PA 17055
Tel (717) 766-8500 SIC 6324 8021

DELTA DENTAL OF RHODE ISLAND p 426
10 Charles St Ste 100, Providence RI 02904
Tel (401) 752-6246 SIC 6324 8021

MONARCH DENTAL CORP p 983
7989 Belt Line Rd Ste 90, Dallas TX 75248
Tel (972) 720-9017 SIC 8021

YAKIMA VALLEY FARM WORKERS CLINIC INC p 1634
518 W 1st Ave, Toppenish WA 98948
Tel (509) 865-5898
SIC 8011 8021 8093 1799

AMERICAN ORTHODONTICS CORP p 77
3524 Washington Ave, Sheboygan WI 53081
Tel (920) 457-5051 SIC 3843 8021

GREAT LAKES DENTAL LLC p 633
10101 W Innovation Dr # 700, Wauwatosa WI 53226
Tel (262) 966-2428 SIC 8021

SIC 8031 Offices & Clinics Of Doctors Of Osteopathy

DENT J GREGG & ASSOSICATES PLC p 429
400 Health Park Blvd, Saint Augustine FL 32086
Tel (904) 819-4565 SIC 8031

■ NORTHSIDE HOSPITAL p 1058
6000 49th St N, Saint Petersburg FL 33709
Tel (727) 521-4411
SIC 8031 8011 8069 8062

AMBULATORY SERVICES INC p 65
1301 Punchbowl St, Honolulu HI 96813
Tel (808) 538-9011 SIC 8031

SEVEN COUNTIES SERVICES INC p 1309
101 W Muhammad Ali Blvd, Louisville KY 40202
Tel (502) 589-8600
SIC 8399 8011 8093 8322 8031

■ LAKE CUMBERLAND REGIONAL HOSPITAL LLC p 839
305 Langdon St, Somerset KY 42503
Tel (606) 679-7441 SIC 8031

PHYSICIANS CLINIC INC p 1145
8601 W Dodge Rd Ste 216, Omaha NE 68114
Tel (402) 354-1700 SIC 8011 8031

JEWISH HOSPITAL CINCINNATI INC p 784
3200 Burnet Ave, Cincinnati OH 45229
Tel (513) 569-2367 SIC 8031

CHOCTAW MANAGEMENT SERVICES ENTERPRISE p 301
2101 W Arkansas St, Durant OK 74701
Tel (580) 924-8280 SIC 8099 8011 8031

UNT HEALTH SCIENCE CENTER p 1528
3500 Camp Bowie Blvd, Fort Worth TX 76107
Tel (817) 735-2000 SIC 8031

LAC DU FLAMBEAU BAND OF LAKE SUPERIOR CHIPPEWA INDIANS (INC) p 836
418 Little Pines Rd, Lac Du Flambeau WI 54538
Tel (715) 588-3303
SIC 8011 7999 5411 5541 8031

SIC 8042 Offices & Clinics Of Optometrists

SOUTHCENTRAL FOUNDATION p 1345
4501 Diplomacy Dr, Anchorage AK 99508
Tel (907) 729-4955 SIC 8093 8021 8042

YUKON-KUSKOKWIM HEALTH CORP p 1640
829 Hospin Hwy Ste 329, Bethel AK 99559
Tel (907) 543-6300
SIC 8062 7363 8069 8093 8042 8021

SCRIPPS HEALTH p 1294
4275 Campus Point Ct, San Diego CA 92121
Tel (858) 678-7000
SIC 8051 8082 8062 8049 8042 8043

■ VISION CARE INSTITUTE LLC p 1561
7500 Centurion Pkwy, Jacksonville FL 32256
Tel (904) 443-1086 SIC 8042

NATIONAL VISION INC p 1017
2435 Commerce Ave # 2200, Duluth GA 30096
Tel (770) 822-3600 SIC 5995 8042

LIGHTHOUSE GUILD INTERNATIONAL INC p 865
15 W 65th St, New York NY 10023
Tel (212) 769-6200 SIC 8322 8042

SHOPKO STORES OPERATING CO LLC p 1318
700 Pilgrim Way, Green Bay WI 54304
Tel (920) 429-2211 SIC 5311 5912 8042

UNIVERSITY OF WISCONSIN MEDICAL FOUNDATION INC p 1527
7974 Uw Health Ct, Middleton WI 53562
Tel (608) 821-4223
SIC 8221 8011 2834 8299 8042 8043

SIC 8043 Offices & Clinics Of Podiatrists

SCRIPPS HEALTH p 1294
4275 Campus Point Ct, San Diego CA 92121
Tel (858) 678-7000
SIC 8051 8082 8062 8049 8042 8043

STEVEN P KIM DPM p 1388
4761 Hoen Ave, Santa Rosa CA 95405
Tel (707) 545-0570 SIC 8043

BLAIR MEDICAL ASSOCIATES p 188
1414 9th Ave, Altoona PA 16602
Tel (814) 944-0202 SIC 8011 8043

UNIVERSITY OF WISCONSIN MEDICAL FOUNDATION INC p 1527
7974 Uw Health Ct, Middleton WI 53562
Tel (608) 821-4223
SIC 8221 8011 2834 8299 8042 8043

SIC 8049 Offices & Clinics Of Health Practitioners, NEC

ENDURACARE THERAPY MANAGEMENT INC p 496
3765a Government Blvd, Mobile AL 36693
Tel (251) 666-7867 SIC 8049 8741

ELITE ONE SOURCE NUTRISCIENCES INC p 487
13840 Magnolia Ave, Chino CA 91710
Tel (909) 902-5005 SIC 8049 8099 3999

■ ONYX PHARMACEUTICALS INC p 1088
1 Amgen Center Dr, Newbury Park CA 91320
Tel (650) 266-0000 SIC 2834 8049

TEXAS HOME HEALTH OF AMERICA LP p 1443
1455 Auto Center Dr # 200, Ontario CA 91761
Tel (972) 201-3800 SIC 8049

■ NURSEFINDERS LLC p 1067
12400 High Bluff Dr, San Diego CA 92130
Tel (858) 314-7427
SIC 7361 8082 7363 8049

SCRIPPS HEALTH p 1294
4275 Campus Point Ct, San Diego CA 92121
Tel (858) 678-7000
SIC 8051 8082 8062 8049 8042 8043

SIMI VALLEY HOSPITAL AND HEALTH CARE SERVICES p 1324
2975 Sycamore Dr, Simi Valley CA 93065
Tel (805) 955-6000 SIC 8049

CONNECTIONS COMMUNITY SUPPORT PROGRAMS INC p 357
3821 Lancaster Pike, Wilmington DE 19805
Tel (302) 984-2302 SIC 8322 8361 8049

■ DOCTORS HOSPITAL OF AUGUSTA LLC p 447
3651 Wheeler Rd, Augusta GA 30909
Tel (706) 651-3232 SIC 8062 8049

OPTION CARE ENTERPRISES INC p 1090
3000 Lakeside Dr Ste 300n, Bannockburn IL 60015
Tel (847) 964-4950
SIC 8082 5122 6794 5912 8049

ATI HOLDINGS LLC p 124
790 Remington Blvd, Bolingbrook IL 60440
Tel (630) 296-2222 SIC 8049

PRINOVA HOLDINGS LLC p 1177
285 Fullerton Ave, Carol Stream IL 60188
Tel (630) 868-0300 SIC 8049

SAINT LUKES METHODIST HOSPITAL INC p 1270
1026 A Ave Ne, Cedar Rapids IA 52402
Tel (319) 369-7209 SIC 8049

EVERGREEN REHABILITATION LLC p 515
136 Saint Matthews Ave # 300, Louisville KY 40207
Tel (502) 897-1700 SIC 8049

■ REHABCARE GROUP INC p 1220
680 S 4th St, Louisville KY 40202
Tel (502) 596-7300
SIC 8093 8099 8049 8051

▲ AMEDISYS INC p 66
3854 American Way Ste A, Baton Rouge LA 70816
Tel (225) 292-2031
SIC 8082 8051 8049 8361

CENTRAL MAINE HEALTH VENTURES INC p 279
300 Main St, Lewiston ME 04240
Tel (207) 795-0111
SIC 8049 8052 7322 8011

CENTRAL MAINE HEALTHCARE CORP p 279
300 Main St, Lewiston ME 04240
Tel (207) 795-0111 SIC 8062 8052 8049

WESTERN MARYLAND HEALTH SYSTEM REHAB p 1599
600 Memorial Ave, Cumberland MD 21502
Tel (301) 723-4200 SIC 8049 8093

SOUTH SHORE HOSPITAL INC p 1345
55 Fogg Rd, South Weymouth MA 02190
Tel (781) 624-8000 SIC 8062 8049

ENCORE REHABILITATION SERVICES LLC p 496
33533 W 12 Mile Rd # 290, Farmington Hills MI 48331
Tel (248) 865-1177 SIC 8093 8049

AGILITY HEALTH LLC p 35
607 Dewey Ave Nw Ste 300, Grand Rapids MI 49504
Tel (616) 356-5000 SIC 8049

ELLA E M BROWN CHARITABLE CIRCLE p 488
200 N Madison St, Marshall MI 49068
Tel (269) 781-4271 SIC 8062 8049

HERITAGE HOUSE NURSING CENTER p 686
3103 Wisconsin Ave, Vicksburg MS 39180
Tel (601) 883-9911 SIC 8049

CHRISTIAN HOSPITAL NORTHEAST SURGERY CENTER p 303
11133 Dunn Rd, Saint Louis MO 63136
Tel (314) 355-2300 SIC 8742 8049 5912

■ NORTHERN NEVADA MEDICAL CENTER LP p 1056
2375 E Prater Way, Sparks NV 89434
Tel (775) 331-7000
SIC 8062 8093 8071 8049 8011

▲ RCM TECHNOLOGIES INC p 1212
2500 Mcclellan Ave # 350, Pennsauken NJ 08109
Tel (856) 356-4500
SIC 8711 8748 7373 8049 7363

UNITED MEMORIAL MEDICAL CENTER p 1510
127 North St, Batavia NY 14020
Tel (585) 343-6030 SIC 8062 8049 8011

ALLIED HEALTHCARE INTERNATIONAL INC p 56
245 Park Ave Fl 39, New York NY 10167
Tel (212) 750-0064 SIC 8082 8049

MONARCH p 983
350 Pee Dee Ave Ste 101, Albemarle NC 28001
Tel (704) 986-1500
SIC 8322 8049 8331 8052

NCS HEALTHCARE INC p 1022
3201 Entp Pkwy Ste 220, Cleveland OH 44122
Tel (216) 514-3350
SIC 5122 8093 8049 8082 8742 5912

OHIOHEALTH CORP p 1078
180 E Broad St, Columbus OH 43215
Tel (614) 788-8860
SIC 8049 8062 8082 8051

TRUMBULL MEMORIAL HOSPITAL p 1487
1350 E Market St, Warren OH 44483
Tel (330) 841-9011 SIC 8062 8049

DRAKE REHAB WEST CHESTER p 455
7700 University Ct # 1600, West Chester OH 45069
Tel (513) 475-7454 SIC 8049

▲ HEALTHCARE SERVICES GROUP INC p 676
3220 Tillman Dr Ste 300, Bensalem PA 19020
Tel (215) 639-4274 SIC 8059 7349 8049

PHYSIOTHERAPY ASSOCIATES INC p 1146
855 Springdale Dr Ste 200, Exton PA 19341
Tel (610) 644-7824 SIC 8049 8093

PHYSIOTHERAPY CORP p 1146
855 Springdale Dr Ste 200, Exton PA 19341
Tel (610) 644-7824 SIC 8049

PHYSIOTHERAPY-BMI INC p 1146
855 Springdale Dr Ste 200, Exton PA 19341
Tel (610) 644-7824 SIC 8049

■ DRAYER PHYSICAL THERAPY INSTITUTE LLC p 455
8205 Presidents Dr Fl 2, Hummelstown PA 17036
Tel (717) 220-2100 SIC 8049

■ GENESIS ELDER CARE REHABILITATION SERVICES INC p 602
101 E State St, Kennett Square PA 19348
Tel (610) 925-4598 SIC 8049 8093

HILTON HEAD HOSPITAL REHAB p 695
35 Bill Fries Dr Bldg D, Hilton Head Island SC 29926
Tel (843) 681-4088 SIC 8049

SPRINGS MEMORIAL HOSPITAL p 1361
800 W Meeting St, Lancaster SC 29720
Tel (803) 286-1477 SIC 8062 8069 8049

AMERICAN HOMEPATIENT INC p 74
5200 Maryland Way Ste 400, Brentwood TN 37027
Tel (615) 221-8884 SIC 8049

PARAGON REHABILITATION INC p 1113
3100 West End Ave Ste 400, Nashville TN 37203
Tel (615) 345-2200 SIC 8049

■ NORTHWEST TEXAS HEALTHCARE SYSTEM INC p 1060
1501 S Coulter St, Amarillo TX 79106
Tel (806) 354-1000
SIC 8062 8063 8051 8049

ST DAVIDS NORTH AUSTIN MEDICAL CENTER p 1366
12221 N Mo Pac Expy, Austin TX 78758
Tel (512) 901-1000
SIC 8062 8011 8069 8049

■ TENET HEALTHCARE FOUNDATION p 1437
1445 Ross Ave Ste 1400, Dallas TX 75202
Tel (469) 893-2000 SIC 8049

▲ US PHYSICAL THERAPY INC p 1533
1300 W Sam Houston Pkwy S # 300, Houston TX 77042
Tel (713) 297-7000 SIC 8049

MIDLAND MEMORIAL HOSPITAL p 966
400 Rosalind Rdfrn Grovr, Midland TX 79701
Tel (432) 221-1111 SIC 8049

NURSES UNLIMITED INC p 1067
511 N Lincoln Ave, Odessa TX 79761
Tel (432) 580-2085 SIC 8049

OUTREACH HEALTH CARE INC p 1099
269 W Renner Rd, Richardson TX 75080
Tel (972) 840-7360 SIC 8093 8049 8082

ORTHOPAEDIC & NEUROLOGICAL REHABILITATION SPEECH PATHOLOGY INC p 1096
1101 S Cpitl Of Texas Hwy, West Lake Hills TX 78746
Tel (512) 327-4444 SIC 8049

VERNON HOME HEALTH CARE AGENCY INC p 1551
2733 Midwestern Pkwy # 120, Wichita Falls TX 76308
Tel (972) 840-3401 SIC 8093 8049 8082

IHC HEALTH SERVICES INC p 730
1380 E Medical Center Dr, St George UT 84790
Tel (801) 442-5000
SIC 8062 8011 8322 8049 8093 8069

INOVA HEALTH SYSTEM p 745
8110 Gatehouse Rd 200e, Falls Church VA 22042
Tel (703) 289-2069
SIC 8741 8011 8062 8049 8059 8051

AURORA MEDICAL CENTER GRAFTON LLC p 132
975 Port Washington Rd, Grafton WI 53024
Tel (262) 329-2723 SIC 8049

SIC 8051 Skilled Nursing Facilities

EASTERN HEALTH SYSTEM INC p 472
Medical Park E Dr Bldg 1, Birmingham AL 35235
Tel (205) 838-3996
SIC 8062 8082 8051 8011 8322 8093

▲ HEALTHSOUTH CORP p 677
3660 Grandview Pkwy # 200, Birmingham AL 35243
Tel (205) 967-7116 SIC 8069 8051

NOLAND HEALTH SERVICES INC p 1046
600 Corporate Pkwy # 100, Birmingham AL 35242
Tel (205) 321-5373 SIC 8051

USA HEALTHCARE INC p 1534
401 Arnold St Ne, Cullman AL 35055
Tel (256) 739-1239 SIC 8051

HEALTH CARE AUTHORITY OF LAUDERDALE COUNTY AND CITY OF FLORENCE p 674
205 Marengo St, Florence AL 35630
Tel (256) 768-9191 SIC 8051 8062

BALL HEALTHCARE SERVICES INC p 148
1 Southern Way, Mobile AL 36619
Tel (251) 432-5800 SIC 8051

CROWNE INVESTMENTS INC p 396
501 Whetstone St, Monroeville AL 36460
Tel (251) 743-3609 SIC 8051

ENGLEWOOD HEALTH CARE CENTER LLC p 499
2046 S Alabama Ave, Monroeville AL 36460
Tel (251) 575-3285 SIC 8051

DHS OF BLUNT COUNTY LLC p 435
212 Ellen St, Oneonta AL 35121
Tel (205) 625-3520 SIC 8051

PIEDMONT HEALTH CARE AUTHORITY p 1147
30 Roundtree Dr, Piedmont AL 36272
Tel (256) 447-8258 SIC 8051

RUSSELLVILLE HEALTH CARE INC p 1259
705 Gandy St Ne, Russellville AL 35653
Tel (256) 332-3773 SIC 8051

BANNER HEALTH p 153
2901 N Central Ave # 160, Phoenix AZ 85012
Tel (602) 747-4000
SIC 8062 8051 8082 7361 8011 8093

JOHN C LINCOLN HEALTH NETWORK p 788
250 E Dunlap Ave, Phoenix AZ 85020
Tel (602) 870-6060 SIC 8062 8051

ST LUKES MEDICAL CENTER LP p 1370
1800 E Van Buren St, Phoenix AZ 85006
Tel (602) 251-8535 SIC 8062 8063 8051

SUN HEALTH CORP p 1400
14719 W Grand Ave Ste 113, Surprise AZ 85374
Tel (623) 876-5350
SIC 8062 8051 8082 7361 8733 6531

TMC HEALTHCARE p 1457
5301 E Grant Rd, Tucson AZ 85712
Tel (520) 327-5461 SIC 8051 8062

TUCSON MEDICAL CENTER p 1490
5301 E Grant Rd, Tucson AZ 85712
Tel (520) 327-5461
SIC 8062 8051 6513 8741

BEVERLY ENTERPRISES - ALABAMA INC p 179
One Thousand Beverly Way, Fort Smith AR 72919
Tel (479) 201-2000 SIC 8082 8051

BEVERLY ENTERPRISES - ARKANSAS INC p 179
1000 Fianna Way, Fort Smith AR 72919
Tel (479) 636-6285 SIC 8051

BEVERLY ENTERPRISES - INDIANA INC p 179
1000 Fianna Way, Fort Smith AR 72919
Tel (479) 201-2000 SIC 8051

BEVERLY ENTERPRISES - MISSOURI INC p 179
1000 Fianna Way, Fort Smith AR 72919
Tel (479) 201-2000 SIC 8051 8059

BEVERLY ENTERPRISES - VIRGINIA INC p 179
1 1000 Beverly Way, Fort Smith AR 72919
Tel (479) 201-2000 SIC 8082 8051

BEVERLY ENTERPRISES - WISCONSIN INC p 179
1000 Fianna Way, Fort Smith AR 72919
Tel (479) 201-2000 SIC 8051

BEVERLY ENTERPRISES INC p 179
1000 Fianna Way, Fort Smith AR 72919
Tel (479) 201-2000 SIC 8741 8051 8082

BEVERLY ENTERPRISES-PENNSYLVANIA INC p 179
1000 Fianna Way, Fort Smith AR 72919
Tel (479) 201-2000 SIC 8051

GGNSC HOLDINGS LLC p 610
1000 Fianna Way, Fort Smith AR 72919
Tel (479) 201-2000
SIC 8059 8051 8082 8322

BAPTIST HEALTH p 153
11001 Executive Center Dr # 200, Little Rock AR 72211
Tel (501) 202-2000 SIC 8051

CONVACARE MANAGEMENT INC p 364
2908 Hawkins Dr, Searcy AR 72143
Tel (501) 305-3153 SIC 8051

COVENANT CARE CALIFORNIA LLC p 384
27071 Aliso Creek Rd # 100, Aliso Viejo CA 92656
Tel (949) 349-1200 SIC 8051

COVENANT CARE LLC p 384
27071 Aliso Creek Rd # 100, Aliso Viejo CA 92656
Tel (949) 349-1200 SIC 8051

OCADIAN CARE CENTERS LLC p 1072
104 Main St, Belvedere Tiburon CA 94920
Tel (415) 789-5427 SIC 8051

ESKATON p 509
5105 Manzanita Ave Ste D, Carmichael CA 95608
Tel (916) 334-0296 SIC 6512 8051

■ WILLOW CREEK HEALTHCARE CENTER LLC p 1613
650 W Alluvial Ave, Clovis CA 93611
Tel (559) 323-6200 SIC 8051

SETON MEDICAL CENTER p 1309
1900 Sullivan Ave, Daly City CA 94015
Tel (650) 992-4000 SIC 8062 8051

■ SKILLED HEALTHCARE LLC p 1330
27442 Portola Pkwy # 200, Foothill Ranch CA 92610
Tel (949) 282-5800 SIC 8051 6513 5122

COMMUNITY MEDICAL CENTER p 349
2823 Fresno St, Fresno CA 93721
Tel (559) 459-6000 SIC 8062 8011 8051

■ VALLEY HEALTHCARE CENTER LLC p 1541
4840 E Tulare Ave, Fresno CA 93727
Tel (559) 251-7161 SIC 8051

FRONT PORCH COMMUNITIES AND SERVICES - CASA DE MANANA LLC p 580
800 N Brand Blvd Fl 19, Glendale CA 91203
Tel (818) 729-8100 SIC 8059 8051

SOUTHERN CALIFORNIA PRESBYTERIAN HOMES p 1347
516 Burchett St, Glendale CA 91203
Tel (818) 247-0420 SIC 8051

SAN BENITO HEALTH CARE DISTRICT p 1275
911 Sunset Dr Ste A, Hollister CA 95023
Tel (831) 637-5711 SIC 8062 8051 8059

■ SUNBRIDGE CARE ENTERPRISES WEST LLC p 1401
1101 Stroud Ave, Kingsburg CA 93631
Tel (559) 897-5881 SIC 8051

LOMA LINDA UNIVERSITY HEALTH CARE p 875
11370 Anderson St # 3900, Loma Linda CA 92350
Tel (909) 558-2806
SIC 8062 8011 8051 5999

LOMA LINDA UNIVERSITY MEDICAL CENTER p 875
11234 Anderson St, Loma Linda CA 92354
Tel (909) 558-4000
SIC 8062 8011 8051 5999

SCAN LONG TERM CARE p 1286
3800 Kilroy Airport Way, Long Beach CA 90806
Tel (562) 989-5100 SIC 8051

CF MERCED LA SIERRA LLC p 285
2424 M St, Merced CA 95340
Tel (209) 723-4224 SIC 8051

▲ ENSIGN GROUP INC p 500
27101 Puerta Real Ste 450, Mission Viejo CA 92691
Tel (949) 487-9500 SIC 8051

AHMC GARFIELD MEDICAL CENTER LP p 37
525 N Garfield Ave, Monterey Park CA 91754
Tel (626) 573-2222 SIC 8051 8062

■ SOUTHWEST HEALTHCARE SYSTEM AUXILIARY p 1352
25500 Medical Center Dr, Murrieta CA 92562
Tel (951) 696-6000
SIC 8062 8051 8059 4119

SALEM CARE CENTER p 1272
2361 E 29th St, Oakland CA 94606
Tel (510) 534-3637 SIC 8051

FEATHER RIVER HOSPITAL p 533
5974 Pentz Rd, Paradise CA 95969
Tel (530) 877-9361 SIC 8062 8051

PASADENA HOSPITAL ASSOCIATION LTD p 1119
100 W California Blvd, Pasadena CA 91105
Tel (626) 397-5000 SIC 8062 8051 8063

HORIZON WEST HEALTHCARE INC p 707
4020 Sierra College Blvd # 190, Rocklin CA 95677
Tel (916) 624-6230 SIC 8051

HORIZON WEST INC p 708
4020 Sierra College Blvd, Rocklin CA 95677
Tel (916) 624-6230 SIC 8051

SUNRISE OAKS NURSING CENTER p 1404
600 Sunrise Ave, Roseville CA 95661
Tel (916) 782-3131 SIC 8051

SUTTER HEALTH p 1410
2200 River Plaza Dr, Sacramento CA 95833
Tel (916) 733-8800
SIC 8062 8051 8011 6513

SUTTERCARE CORP p 1410
2200 River Plaza Dr, Sacramento CA 95833
Tel (916) 733-8800 SIC 8051 8062

SCRIPPS HEALTH p 1294
4275 Campus Point Ct, San Diego CA 92121
Tel (858) 678-7000
SIC 8051 8082 8062 8049 8042 8043

SONORA REGIONAL MEDICAL CENTER p 1340
1000 Greenley Rd, Sonora CA 95370
Tel (209) 532-5000 SIC 8082 8051

BARTON MEMORIAL HOSPITAL p 158
2170 South Ave, South Lake Tahoe CA 96150
Tel (530) 541-3420 SIC 8062 8051

LITTLE CO OF MARY HOSPITAL p 871
4101 Torrance Blvd, Torrance CA 90503
Tel (310) 540-7676 SIC 8062 8051

■ ORCHARD - POST ACUTE CARE CENTER p 1093
12385 Washington Blvd, Whittier CA 90606
Tel (562) 693-7701 SIC 8051

SHADOW MOUNTAIN MANAGEMENT CORP p 1310
1401 Phay Ave, Canon City CO 81212
Tel (719) 275-8656 SIC 8051

■ INTEGRITY URGENT CARE CLINICS INC p 750
4323 Integrity Center Pt, Colorado Springs CO 80917
Tel (719) 591-2558 SIC 8082 8011 8051

CATHOLIC HEALTH INITIATIVES p 266
198 Inverness Dr W, Englewood CO 80112
Tel (303) 298-9100 SIC 8062 8051 8741

SCL HEALTH - FRONT RANGE INC p 1292
8300 W 38th Ave, Wheat Ridge CO 80033
Tel (303) 813-5000 SIC 8062 8011 8051

CHESTERFIELDS LTD p 295
132 Main St, Chester CT 06412
Tel (860) 526-5363 SIC 8051

PARADIGM HEALTHCARE DEVELOPMENT LLC p 1113
177 Whitewood Rd, Waterbury CT 06708
Tel (860) 748-4750 SIC 8051

■ CARLYLE PARTNERS IV LP p 258
1001 Pennsylvania Ave Nw, Washington DC 20004
Tel (202) 729-5626 SIC 8711 8069 8051

WASHINGTON HOSPITAL CENTER CORP p 1578
110 Irving St Nw, Washington DC 20010
Tel (202) 877-7000
SIC 8741 8082 8051 8062

ADVENTIST HEALTH SYSTEM/SUNBELT INC p 27
900 Hope Way, Altamonte Springs FL 32714
Tel (407) 357-1000 SIC 8062 8082 8051

SOLARIS FOUNDATION INC p 1338
9520 Bonita Beach Rd Se, Bonita Springs FL 34135
Tel (239) 919-1142 SIC 8051 8059

MORTON PLANT HOSPITAL ASSOCIATION INC p 991
300 Pinellas St, Clearwater FL 33756
Tel (727) 462-7000 SIC 8062 8051

HBA CORP p 671
5310 Nw 33rd Ave Ste 211, Fort Lauderdale FL 33309
Tel (954) 731-3350 SIC 8051

CHRISTIAN AND MISSIONARY ALLIANCE FOUNDATION INC p 302
15101 Shell Point Blvd, Fort Myers FL 33908
Tel (239) 466-1111 SIC 6513 8051 8059

LEE MEMORIAL HEALTH SYSTEM FOUNDATION INC p 851
2776 Cleveland Ave, Fort Myers FL 33901
Tel (239) 343-2000
SIC 8741 8062 8082 8051

AG HOLDINGS INC p 33
4601 Sheridan St Ste 500, Hollywood FL 33021
Tel (954) 987-7180 SIC 8051

SOUTH BROWARD HOSPITAL DISTRICT p 1343
3501 Johnson St, Hollywood FL 33021
Tel (954) 987-2000 SIC 8062 8051

COMMUNITY HOSPICE OF NORTHEAST FLORIDA INC p 349
4266 Sunbeam Rd Ste 100, Jacksonville FL 32257
Tel (904) 268-5200 SIC 8082 8051

GENESIS REHABILITATION HOSPITAL INC p 603
3599 University Blvd S # 1, Jacksonville FL 32216
Tel (904) 858-7600 SIC 8063 8069 8051

JUPITER MEDICAL CENTER INC p 797
1210 S Old Dixie Hwy, Jupiter FL 33458
Tel (561) 747-2234 SIC 8062 8051

CONCURRENT PARTNERS LLLP p 355
800 Cncrse Pkwy S Ste 200, Maitland FL 32751
Tel (407) 571-1560 SIC 8051

CONSULATE HEALTH CARE LLC p 361
800 Concourse Pkwy S, Maitland FL 32751
Tel (407) 571-1550 SIC 8051

CONSULATE MANAGEMENT CO LLC p 361
800 Concourse Pkwy S, Maitland FL 32751
Tel (407) 571-1550
SIC 8051 8059 8071 8093

MIAMI JEWISH HEALTH SYSTEMS INC p 959
5200 Ne 2nd Ave, Miami FL 33137
Tel (305) 751-8626 SIC 8051

■ VITAS HEALTHCARE CORP p 1563
100 S Biscayne Blvd # 1600, Miami FL 33131
Tel (305) 374-4143 SIC 8082 8051

EAST ORLANDO HEALTH & REHAB CENTER INC p 470
250 S Chickasaw Trl, Orlando FL 32825
Tel (407) 380-3466 SIC 8051

PRESBYTERIAN RETIREMENT COMMUNITIES INC p 1171
80 W Lucerne Cir, Orlando FL 32801
Tel (407) 839-5050 SIC 8361 8052 8051

GULF COAST HEALTH CARE LLC p 646
40 Palafox Pl Ste 400, Pensacola FL 32502
Tel (800) 881-9907 SIC 8051

■ WEST FLORIDA REGIONAL MEDICAL CENTER INC p 1594
8383 N Davis Hwy, Pensacola FL 32514
Tel (850) 494-4000
SIC 8062 8093 8063 8051

SENIOR CARE GROUP INC p 1304
1240 Marbella Plaza Dr, Tampa FL 33619
Tel (813) 341-2700 SIC 8051

TANDEM HEALTHCARE OF WEST PALM BEACH INC p 1424
1626 Davis Rd, West Palm Beach FL 33406
Tel (561) 439-8897 SIC 8059 8051

ST MARYS HEALTH CARE SYSTEM INC p 1371
1230 Baxter St, Athens GA 30606
Tel (706) 389-3000 SIC 8062 8051

CENTENNIAL HEALTHCARE CORP p 275
400 Perimeter Ctr Ter Ne, Atlanta GA 30346
Tel (770) 698-9040
SIC 8051 8069 8052 8741

GRANCARE LLC p 629
1 Ravinia Dr Ste 1400, Atlanta GA 30346
Tel (770) 393-0199
SIC 8051 8052 8093 8071

HEALTH CARE CAPITAL INC p 674
2 Ravinia Dr Ste 1350, Atlanta GA 30346
Tel (770) 393-3355 SIC 6162 8051 8741

HILLTOPPER HOLDING CORP p 694
303 Perimeter Ctr N # 500, Atlanta GA 30346
Tel (770) 698-9040 SIC 8051 8741

MARINER HEALTH CARE INC p 907
1 Ravinia Dr Ste 1500, Atlanta GA 30346
Tel (678) 443-7000
SIC 5912 8051 8093 8741 8062 3443

NATIONAL SENIOR CARE INC p 1016
1 Ravinia Dr Ste 1500, Atlanta GA 30346
Tel (678) 443-7000
SIC 5912 8051 8093 8741 8062 3443

SOVEREIGN HEALTHCARE LLC p 1353
5887 Glenridge Dr Ste 150, Atlanta GA 30328
Tel (404) 574-2033 SIC 8051

▲ **SUNLINK HEALTH SYSTEMS INC** p 1403
900 Cir 75 Pkwy Se # 650, Atlanta GA 30339
Tel (770) 933-7000 SIC 8062 8051 5912

■ **SUNLINK HEALTHCARE CORP** p 1403
900 Circle 75 Pkwy Se # 13, Atlanta GA 30339
Tel (770) 850-1109 SIC 8051 8062

TRANSITIONAL HEALTH PARTNERS p 1472
400 Perimeter Ctr Ter Ne, Atlanta GA 30346
Tel (770) 698-9040 SIC 8051

PAULDING MEDICAL CENTER INC p 1121
600 W Memorial Dr, Dallas GA 30132
Tel (770) 445-4411 SIC 8062 8051

ETHICA HEALTH & RETIREMENT COMMUNITIES p 511
1005 Boulder Dr, Gray GA 31032
Tel (478) 621-2100 SIC 8051

LA GRANGE TROUP COUNTY HOSPITAL AUTHORITY p 835
1514 Vernon Rd, Lagrange GA 30240
Tel (706) 882-1411 SIC 8062 8051

MEADOWS REGIONAL MEDICAL CENTER INC p 934
1703 Meadows Ln, Vidalia GA 30474
Tel (912) 537-8921 SIC 8062 8051

MAYO CLINIC HEALTH SYSTEM IN WAYCROSS INC p 923
1900 Tebeau St, Waycross GA 31501
Tel (912) 283-3030 SIC 8062 8051

ST FRANCIS HEALTHCARE SYSTEM OF HAWAII p 1366
2226 Liliha St Ste 227, Honolulu HI 96817
Tel (808) 547-6883 SIC 8051 8082

BMH INC p 194
98 Poplar St, Blackfoot ID 83221
Tel (208) 785-4100 SIC 8062 8051

PROTESTANT MEMORIAL MEDICAL CENTER INC p 1185
4500 Memorial Dr, Belleville IL 62226
Tel (618) 233-7750 SIC 8062 8051

HERITAGE ENTERPRISES INC p 686
115 W Jefferson St # 401, Bloomington IL 61701
Tel (309) 828-4361 SIC 8051

ALDEN MANAGEMENT SERVICES INC p 47
4200 W Peterson Ave # 142, Chicago IL 60646
Tel (773) 282-8183 SIC 8051 8741

ALDEN-WENTWORTH NURSING CENTER INC p 47
201 W 69th St, Chicago IL 60621
Tel (773) 487-1200 SIC 8051

ASSISTED LIVING CONCEPTS LLC p 119
330 N Wabash Ave Ste 3700, Chicago IL 60611
Tel (888) 252-5001
SIC 8052 8051 8059 8082

PRESENCE HEALTH NETWORK p 1172
200 S Wacker Dr Fl 12, Chicago IL 60606
Tel (773) 774-8000
SIC 8082 8062 8011 8051

FRANCISCAN COMMUNITIES INC p 573
11500 Theresa Dr, Lemont IL 60439
Tel (708) 647-6500 SIC 8051

CHRISTIAN HOMES INC p 302
200 N Postville Dr, Lincoln IL 62656
Tel (217) 732-9651 SIC 8052 8051

TRANSITIONAL CARE MANAGEMENT LLC p 1472
3333 Warrenville Rd # 200, Lisle IL 60532
Tel (847) 720-8700 SIC 8051

PRESENCE PRV HEALTH p 1172
19827 Hickory Crk Dr 30 Ste 300, Mokena IL 60448
Tel (815) 741-7137 SIC 8051 8062

RUSH OAK PARK HOSPITAL INC p 1258
520 S Maple Ave, Oak Park IL 60304
Tel (708) 383-9300 SIC 8051 8062

SYNERGON HEALTH SYSTEM INC p 1415
520 S Maple Ave, Oak Park IL 60304
Tel (708) 660-6661 SIC 8062 8051 8082

OSF HEALTHCARE SYSTEM p 1096
800 Ne Glen Oak Ave, Peoria IL 61603
Tel (309) 655-2850 SIC 8062 8051

GENESIS HEALTH SYSTEMS p 603
1455 Hospital Rd, Silvis IL 61282
Tel (309) 281-3270 SIC 8051 8059

REST HAVEN ILLIANA CHRISTIAN CONVALESCENT HOME p 1228
18601 North Creek Dr A, Tinley Park IL 60477
Tel (708) 342-8100 SIC 8051 8361

MEMORIAL MEDICAL CENTER-WOODSTOCK p 942
3701 Doty Rd, Woodstock IL 60098
Tel (815) 334-3880 SIC 8062 8051

WESLEYAN HOMES OF INDIANA INC p 1593
34 S Main St, Cloverdale IN 46120
Tel (765) 795-4260 SIC 8051

HENDRICKS COUNTY HOSPITAL p 683
1000 E Main St, Danville IN 46122
Tel (317) 745-4451 SIC 8062 8051

RENAISSANCE HEALTH CARE CORP p 1223
6050 S 800 E-92, Fort Wayne IN 46814
Tel (260) 625-3545 SIC 8052 8051

ST MARGARET MERCY HEALTHCARE CENTERS INC p 1370
5454 Hohman Ave, Hammond IN 46320
Tel (219) 932-2300 SIC 8062 8052 8051

FRANCISCAN ALLIANCE INC p 573
1515 W Dragoon Trl, Mishawaka IN 46544
Tel (574) 256-3935 SIC 8062 8051

APERION CARE PERU LLC p 96
1850 W Matador St, Peru IN 46970
Tel (765) 689-5000 SIC 8051

■ **KINDRED NURSING CENTERS LIMITED PARTNERSHIP** p 819
3500 Maple Ave, Terre Haute IN 47804
Tel (502) 596-7300 SIC 8051

MILLERS HEALTH SYSTEMS INC p 971
1690 S County Farm Rd, Warsaw IN 46580
Tel (574) 267-7211 SIC 8052 8051 8361

MERCY MEDICAL CENTER-CLINTON INC p 948
1410 N 4th St, Clinton IA 52732
Tel (563) 244-5555 SIC 8062 8051 5122

NORTHWEST IOWA HOSPITAL CORP p 1060
2800 Pierce St Ste 410, Sioux City IA 51104
Tel (712) 279-3500 SIC 8062 8051

CARE INITIATIVES p 254
1611 Westlakes Pkwy, West Des Moines IA 50266
Tel (515) 224-4442 SIC 8051 8052

ARKANSAS CITY PRESBYTERIAN MANOR INC p 109
1711 N 4th St, Arkansas City KS 67005
Tel (620) 442-8700 SIC 8051

MEDICALODGES INC p 937
201 W 8th St, Coffeyville KS 67337
Tel (620) 251-6700 SIC 8051

HAYS MEDICAL CENTER INC p 670
2220 Canterbury Dr, Hays KS 67601
Tel (785) 623-5000 SIC 8062 8051

LAWRENCE MEMORIAL HOSPITAL ENDOWMENT ASSOCIATION p 848
330 Arkansas St Ste 201, Lawrence KS 66044
Tel (785) 505-3318 SIC 8051 8062

■ **WATHENA HEALTHCARE AND REHABILITATION CENTER LLC** p 1582
2112 Highway 36, Wathena KS 66090
Tel (785) 989-3141 SIC 8051

CATHOLIC DIOCESE OF WICHITA INC p 266
424 N Broadway Ave, Wichita KS 67202
Tel (316) 269-3900 SIC 8661 8051

PRESBYTERIAN MANORS INC p 1171
2414 N Woodlawn Blvd, Wichita KS 67220
Tel (316) 685-1100 SIC 8051

ROSEWOOD HEALTH CARE CENTER p 1251
550 High St, Bowling Green KY 42101
Tel (270) 843-3296 SIC 8051 8093

LP HARRODSBURG LLC p 882
853 Lexington Rd, Harrodsburg KY 40330
Tel (859) 734-7791 SIC 8051

FIFTEENINONE OPCO GROUP LLC p 541
7400 New La Grange Rd, Louisville KY 40222
Tel (502) 429-8062 SIC 8051

▲ **KINDRED HEALTHCARE INC** p 819
680 S 4th St, Louisville KY 40202
Tel (502) 596-7300
SIC 8062 8051 8322 8082

■ **KINDRED HEALTHCARE OPERATING INC** p 819
680 S 4th St, Louisville KY 40202
Tel (502) 596-7300 SIC 8051

■ **KINDRED NURSING CENTERS EAST LLC** p 819
680 S 4th St, Louisville KY 40202
Tel (502) 596-7300 SIC 8051

■ **REHABCARE GROUP INC** p 1220
680 S 4th St, Louisville KY 40202
Tel (502) 596-7300
SIC 8093 8099 8049 8051

SIGNATURE HEALTHCARE LLC p 1322
12201 Bluegrass Pkwy, Louisville KY 40299
Tel (502) 568-7800 SIC 8051

TRILOGY REHAB SERVICES LLC p 1480
2701 Chestnut Station Ct, Louisville KY 40299
Tel (800) 335-1060
SIC 8059 1542 8741 8051

UNITED REHAB LLC p 1511
9510 Ormsby Station Rd # 101, Louisville KY 40223
Tel (502) 426-2242 SIC 8052 8051 8059

■ **VENCARE REHAB SERVICES INC** p 1547
600 S 4th St, Louisville KY 40202
Tel (502) 596-7300 SIC 8051

BRITTHAVEN OF KENTUCKY INC p 214
6301 Bass Rd, Prospect KY 40059
Tel (502) 228-9440 SIC 8051

▲ **AMEDISYS INC** p 66
3854 American Way Ste A, Baton Rouge LA 70816
Tel (225) 292-2031
SIC 8082 8051 8049 8361

PROVIDENT RESOURCES GROUP INC p 1186
5565 Bankers Ave, Baton Rouge LA 70808
Tel (225) 766-3977 SIC 8051

FOREST MANOR INC p 567
71338 Highway 21, Covington LA 70433
Tel (985) 892-6900 SIC 8051

PLANTATION MANAGEMENT CO LLC p 1154
301 Veterans Blvd, Denham Springs LA 70726
Tel (225) 664-6697 SIC 8051

COMMUNITY CARE CENTER OF WESTWOOD LLC p 347
1 Westwood Circel, Shreveport LA 71109
Tel (318) 635-4444 SIC 8051

HOLLY HILL HOUSE INC p 701
100 Kingston Rd, Sulphur LA 70663
Tel (337) 625-5843 SIC 8051

HOSPITAL SERVICE DISTRICT 3 LAFOURCHE PARISH p 709
602 N Acadia Rd, Thibodaux LA 70301
Tel (985) 493-4740 SIC 8062 8051 8082

MID COAST-PARKVIEW HEALTH p 963
123 Medical Center Dr G, Brunswick ME 04011
Tel (207) 729-0181 SIC 8062 8082 8051

HIBBARD NURSING HOME INC p 690
1037 W Main St, Dover Foxcroft ME 04426
Tel (207) 564-8129 SIC 8052 8051

ST MARYS HEALTH SYSTEM p 1371
96 Campus Ave, Lewiston ME 04240
Tel (207) 777-8546
SIC 8062 8052 8051 8011 8361

ST MARYS REGIONAL MEDICAL CENTER p 1372
93 Campus Ave, Lewiston ME 04240
Tel (207) 777-8546
SIC 8062 8052 8051 8011 8361

MARSHALL NURSING SERVICES INC p 911
9 Beal St, Machias ME 04654
Tel (207) 255-3387 SIC 8051

NORTON SOUND HEALTH CORP p 1061
790 Lower St, Turner ME 04282
Tel (907) 443-3311
SIC 8062 8051 8069 8093 8011

YORK HOSPITAL p 1637
15 Hospital Dr, York ME 03909
Tel (207) 351-2023
SIC 8062 8051 8069 7361

BON SECOURS BALTIMORE HEALTH SYTEM p 199
2000 W Baltimore St, Baltimore MD 21223
Tel (410) 362-3000 SIC 8051

CHARLESTOWN COMMUNITY INC p 290
719 Maiden Choice Ln, Baltimore MD 21228
Tel (410) 737-8830 SIC 6513 8051

FOREST HAVEN NURSING & CONVALE p 566
315 Ingleside Ave, Baltimore MD 21228
Tel (410) 747-7425 SIC 8051

JOHNS HOPKINS BAYVIEW MEDICAL CENTER INC p 790
4940 Eastern Ave, Baltimore MD 21224
Tel (410) 550-0100 SIC 8062 8051

OAK CREST VILLAGE INC p 1070
8800 Walther Blvd Ste 1, Baltimore MD 21234
Tel (410) 665-2222 SIC 8051 8052 8059

MEDSTAR HEALTH INC p 939
5565 Sterrett Pl Ste 500, Columbia MD 21044
Tel (410) 772-6500
SIC 8741 8062 8082 8051 8011

ALICE BYRD TAWES NURSING HOME INC p 50
201 Hall Hwy, Crisfield MD 21817
Tel (410) 968-1200 SIC 8051

ASBURY ATLANTIC INC p 115
201 Russell Ave, Gaithersburg MD 20877
Tel (301) 216-4100 SIC 8059 8051

KNOLLWOOD MANOR GENESIS ELDERCARE p 825
1221 Waugh Chapel Rd, Gambrills MD 21054
Tel (410) 987-1644 SIC 8051 8052

HEBREW HOME OF GREATER WASHINGTON p 680
6121 Montrose Rd, Rockville MD 20852
Tel (301) 881-0300 SIC 8051

TRANS HEALTHCARE INC p 1470
930 Ridgebrook Rd, Sparks MD 21152
Tel (410) 773-1000 SIC 8011 8051

NEXION HEALTH INC p 1040
6937 Warfield Ave, Sykesville MD 21784
Tel (410) 552-4800 SIC 8051

HOMEWOOD RETIREMENT CENTERS OF UNITED CHURCH OF CHRIST INC p 704
16107 Elliott Pkwy, Williamsport MD 21795
Tel (301) 582-1626 SIC 8051 8361

ALLIANCE HEALTH INC p 54
134 Rumford Ave Ste 306, Auburndale MA 02466
Tel (617) 332-3366 SIC 8051

LEDGEWOOD HEALTH CARE CORP p 851
87 Herrick St, Beverly MA 01915
Tel (978) 524-6100 SIC 8051

■ **BEACON HOSPICE INC** p 164
529 Main St Ste 126, Charlestown MA 02129
Tel (617) 242-4872 SIC 8051

POINT GROUP HEALTH CARE GROUP & SENIOR LIVING CENTER INC p 1159
3 Allied Dr Ste 106, Dedham MA 02026
Tel (781) 251-9001 SIC 8051 8741

DIOCESAN HEALTH FACILITIES OFFICE p 440
368 N Main St, Fall River MA 02720
Tel (508) 679-8154 SIC 8051

SAINTS MEDICAL CENTER INC p 1271
1 Hospital Dr, Lowell MA 01852
Tel (978) 458-1411 SIC 8051 8062

CONTINENTAL WINGATE CO INC p 364
1 Charles River Pl, Needham MA 02494
Tel (781) 707-9000 SIC 6513 8051

▲ **FIVE STAR QUALITY CARE INC** p 553
400 Centre St, Newton MA 02458
Tel (617) 796-8387 SIC 8051 8052

ELDER LIVING CONCEPTS INC p 484
51 Summer St, Rowley MA 01969
Tel (978) 948-7383 SIC 8051

EPOCH SL III INC p 505
51 Sawyer Rd Ste 500, Waltham MA 02453
Tel (781) 891-0777 SIC 8059 8051

ASCENTRIA CARE ALLIANCE p 116
14 E Worcester St Ste 300, Worcester MA 01604
Tel (774) 343-3900 SIC 8322 8051 8361

BRONSON BATTLE CREEK HOSPITAL p 217
300 North Ave, Battle Creek MI 49017
Tel (269) 966-8000 SIC 8062 8063 8051

LUTHERAN SOCIAL SERVICES OF MICHIGAN p 886
8131 E Jefferson Ave, Detroit MI 48214
Tel (313) 823-7700 SIC 8051 8322

HOLLAND HOME p 700
2100 Raybrook St Se # 300, Grand Rapids MI 49546
Tel (616) 235-5000 SIC 8361 8051

ST MARY HOSPITAL OF LIVONIA p 1371
36475 5 Mile Rd, Livonia MI 48154
Tel (734) 655-4800 SIC 8062 8051

TRINITY CONTINUING CARE SERVICES - INDIANA INC p 1481
17410 College Pkwy # 200, Livonia MI 48152
Tel (734) 542-8300 SIC 8051

MEBILODDE OF PLYMOUTH p 934
395 W Ann Arbor Trl, Plymouth MI 48170
Tel (734) 453-3983 SIC 8051

CHIPPEWA COUNTY WAR MEMORIAL HOSPITAL INC p 301
500 Osborn Blvd, Sault Sainte Marie MI 49783
Tel (906) 635-4460 SIC 8062 8051

MAYO CLINIC HEALTH SYSTEM-ALBERT LEA AND AUSTIN p 924
404 W Fountain St, Albert Lea MN 56007
Tel (507) 373-2384
SIC 8062 8069 8051 8063 8011

CUYUNA RANGE HOSPITAL INC p 403
320 E Main St, Crosby MN 56441
Tel (218) 546-7000 SIC 8062 8051

ST MARYS REGIONAL HEALTH CENTER p 1372
1027 Washington Ave, Detroit Lakes MN 56501
Tel (218) 847-5611 SIC 8062 8051

ESSENTIA HEALTH p 510
502 E 2nd St, Duluth MN 55805
Tel (218) 786-8376 SIC 8062 8051

AMERICAN BAPTIST HOMES OF MIDWEST p 68
14850 Scenic Heights Rd, Eden Prairie MN 55344
Tel (952) 941-3175 SIC 8051 8361 8052

ELIM CARE INC p 487
7485 Office Ridge Cir, Eden Prairie MN 55344
Tel (952) 259-4500 SIC 8051 8322

VOLUNTEERS OF AMERICA NATIONAL SERVICES p 1565
7530 Market Place Dr, Eden Prairie MN 55344
Tel (952) 941-0305 SIC 8051 8052

AUGUSTANA CARE p 131
1007 E 14th St, Minneapolis MN 55404
Tel (612) 238-5101 SIC 6513 8051

CATHOLIC ELDERCARE COMMUNITY FOUNDATION INC p 266
817 Main St Ne, Minneapolis MN 55413
Tel (612) 379-1370 SIC 8051

EBENEZER SOCIETY p 474
2722 Park Ave, Minneapolis MN 55407
Tel (612) 874-3460 SIC 8051 8741

NORTH RIDGE SKILLED LLC p 1053
5430 Boone Ave N, Minneapolis MN 55428
Tel (763) 592-3000 SIC 6513 8051

SENIOR TEALWOOD LIVING p 1304
7400 W 109th St, Minneapolis MN 55438
Tel (952) 888-2923 SIC 8051 8741

ST THERESE HOME INC p 1373
8000 Bass Lake Rd, Minneapolis MN 55428
Tel (763) 531-5000 SIC 8051

BEVERLY ENTERPRISES - MINNESOTA LLC p 179
650 Ramer Ave S, Rush City MN 55069
Tel (320) 358-4765 SIC 8051

ECUMEN p 476
3530 Lexington Ave N Fl 2, Saint Paul MN 55126
Tel (651) 766-4300 SIC 8051

HEALTHEAST COMPANIES INC p 677
1700 University Ave W, Saint Paul MN 55104
Tel (651) 232-2300 SIC 8082 8051 8011

LAKEWOOD HEALTH SYSTEM p 840
49725 County 83, Staples MN 56479
Tel (218) 894-1515 SIC 8062 8051

STERLING PARK HEALTH CARE CENTER p 1387
142 1st St N, Waite Park MN 56387
Tel (320) 252-9595 SIC 8051

WINONA HEALTH p 1617
855 Mankato Ave, Winona MN 55987
Tel (507) 454-3650 SIC 8062 8051

WINONA HEALTH SERVICES p 1617
859 Mankato Ave, Winona MN 55987
Tel (507) 454-3650 SIC 8062 8051

CLC OF BILOXI LLC p 323
2279 Atkinson Rd, Biloxi MS 39531
Tel (228) 388-1805 SIC 8051

LONGWOOD COMMUNITY LIVING CENTER p 877
200 Long St, Booneville MS 38829
Tel (662) 728-6234 SIC 8051

COPIAH COMMUNITY CARE CENTER LLC p 368
806 W Georgetown St, Crystal Springs MS 39059
Tel (601) 892-1880 SIC 8051

COMMUNITY CARE CENTER OF GRENADA LLC p 347
1950 Grandview Dr, Grenada MS 38901
Tel (662) 226-9554 SIC 8051

LAMAR COMMUNITY CARE CENTER LLC p 841
37 Hillcrest Dr Ofc, Hattiesburg MS 39402
Tel (601) 264-0058 SIC 8051

WESLEY HEALTH SYSTEM LLC p 1593
5001 Hardy St, Hattiesburg MS 39402
Tel (601) 268-8000
SIC 8051 8062 8082 8011

MISSISSIPPI BAPTST MEDICAL CENTER INC p 975
1225 N State St, Jackson MS 39202
Tel (601) 968-1000 SIC 8062 8069 8051

WAVERLEY GROUP INC p 1584
460 Briarwood Dr Ste 410, Jackson MS 39206
Tel (601) 956-1013 SIC 8051

CLC OF LAUREL LLC p 323
1036 West Dr, Laurel MS 39440
Tel (601) 425-3191 SIC 8051

LOUISIANA EXTENDED CARE CENTERS INC p 880
763 Avery Blvd N, Ridgeland MS 39157
Tel (601) 956-8884 SIC 8051 8052

MAGNOLIA MANAGEMENT CORP p 896
763 Avery Blvd N, Ridgeland MS 39157
Tel (601) 956-8884 SIC 8051

NORTH MISSISSIPPI MEDICAL CENTER INC p 1053
830 S Gloster St, Tupelo MS 38801
Tel (662) 377-3000 SIC 8062 8051 8082

COMMUNITY CARE CENTERS INC p 347
312 Solley Dr Rear, Ballwin MO 63021
Tel (636) 394-3000 SIC 8051

SKAGGS COMMUNITY HOSPITAL ASSOCIATION p 1329
251 Skaggs Rd, Branson MO 65616
Tel (417) 335-7000
SIC 8062 8082 8011 7352 8051

DAUGHTERS OF CHARITY SERVICES OF ST LOUIS p 414
12303 De Paul Dr, Bridgeton MO 63044
Tel (314) 344-6000
SIC 8062 8051 8063 8069

■ REHABILITATION CENTER OF INDEPENDENCE LLC p 1220
1800 S Swope Dr, Independence MO 64057
Tel (816) 257-2566 SIC 8051

MIDAMERICA CARE FOUNDATION INC p 964
7611 State Line Rd, Kansas City MO 64114
Tel (816) 444-0900 SIC 8051 8052

NEW LIBERTY HOSPITAL DISTRICT OF CLAY COUNTY MISSOURI p 1032
2525 Glenn Hendren Dr, Liberty MO 64068
Tel (816) 781-7200 SIC 8062 8051

CEDAR GATE PHASE II p 272
2350 Kanell Blvd, Poplar Bluff MO 63901
Tel (573) 785-3443 SIC 8051

PRO-AM INC p 1178
2350 Kanell Blvd, Poplar Bluff MO 63901
Tel (573) 785-0858 SIC 8051 8741

DEACONESS LONG TERM CARE OF MO INC p 419
8540 Blue Ridge Blvd, Raytown MO 64138
Tel (816) 380-3319 SIC 8051

SSM HEALTH CARE CORP p 1364
10101 Woodfield Ln # 100, Saint Louis MO 63132
Tel (314) 994-7800
SIC 8062 8082 8011 8051

SAINT LUKES NORTHLAND HOME CARE p 1270
601 S Us Highway 169, Smithville MO 64089
Tel (816) 532-3700
SIC 8062 8051 8069 8063

GALLATIN COUNTY REST HOME p 589
1221 Durston Rd, Bozeman MT 59715
Tel (406) 582-3300 SIC 8051

BENEFIS HOSPITALS INC p 173
1101 26th St S, Great Falls MT 59405
Tel (406) 455-5000 SIC 8062 8051

COONEY CONVALESCENT HOME p 366
2555 E Broadway St, Helena MT 59601
Tel (406) 447-1651 SIC 8059 8051

KALISPELL REGIONAL HEALTHCARE SYSTEM p 801
310 Sunnyview Ln, Kalispell MT 59901
Tel (406) 752-8991
SIC 8051 8011 4522 7352

TOBACCO ROOT MOUNTAINS CARE CENTER p 1458
326 Madison St, Sheridan MT 59749
Tel (406) 842-5418 SIC 8051

FREMONT HEALTH p 577
450 E 23rd St, Fremont NE 68025
Tel (402) 727-3795 SIC 8062 8051

MADONNA REHABILITATION HOSPITAL p 894
5401 South St, Lincoln NE 68506
Tel (402) 413-3000 SIC 8051

ROSE LANE HOME p 1250
1005 N 8th St, Loup City NE 68853
Tel (308) 745-0303 SIC 8051 6411

ALEGENT HEALTH - IMMANUEL MEDICAL CENTER p 48
6901 N 72nd St, Omaha NE 68122
Tel (402) 572-2121 SIC 8062 8051 8351

ARCHBISHOP BERGAN MERCY HOSPITAL p 104
7500 Mercy Rd, Omaha NE 68124
Tel (402) 398-6060 SIC 8062 8051

BROOKESTONE VILLAGE INC p 217
4330 S 144th St, Omaha NE 68137
Tel (402) 614-4000 SIC 8051

640 LAS VEGAS HEALTHCARE AND REHABIL p 3
2832 S Maryland Pkwy, Las Vegas NV 89109
Tel (702) 735-5848 SIC 8051

■ VA SOUTHERN NEVADA HEALTHCARE SYSTEM p 1538
6900 Pecos Rd, North Las Vegas NV 89086
Tel (702) 791-9000 SIC 8051 9451

■ 25 RIDGEWOOD ROAD OPERATIONS LLC p 2
25 Ridgewood Rd, Bedford NH 03110
Tel (603) 623-8805 SIC 8051

CAPITAL REGION HEALTH CARE CORP p 250
250 Pleasant St, Concord NH 03301
Tel (603) 225-2711
SIC 8741 8062 8051 8093 8082

DARTMOUTH-HITCHCOCK MEDICAL CENTER p 413
1 Medical Center Dr, Lebanon NH 03756
Tel (603) 650-5000 SIC 8062 8011 8051

TRYKO PARTNERS LLC p 1489
575 Route 70 Fl 2, Brick NJ 08723
Tel (732) 961-9991 SIC 6531 8051

CARE ONE LLC p 254
173 Bridge Plz N, Fort Lee NJ 07024
Tel (201) 242-4000 SIC 8051 8052

BRANDYWINE SENIOR LIVING MANAGEMENT LLC p 208
525 Fellowship Rd Ste 360, Mount Laurel NJ 08054
Tel (856) 778-6100 SIC 8361 8051

SENIOR BRANDYWINE CARE INC p 1303
525 Fellowship Rd Ste 360, Mount Laurel NJ 08054
Tel (856) 813-2000 SIC 8741 8322 8051

SENIOR PHS LIVING INC p 1304
13 Roszel Rd Ste C120, Princeton NJ 08540
Tel (609) 426-6802 SIC 8361 8052 8051

KENNEDY HEALTH CARE FOUNDATION INC p 811
18 E Laurel Rd, Stratford NJ 08084
Tel (856) 661-5100
SIC 6733 4119 8051 6531 7361 8721

■ BREYUT CONVALESCENT CENTER INC p 210
2240 Whthrse Mrcrville Rd, Trenton NJ 08619
Tel (609) 586-7500 SIC 8051 8069

KBWB OPERATIONS-RICE LLC p 806
1120 Alps Rd, Wayne NJ 07470
Tel (973) 339-8899 SIC 8051 8361

■ HARBORSIDE HEALTHCARE ADVISORS LIMITED PARTNERSHIP p 660
101 Sun Ave Ne, Albuquerque NM 87109
Tel (505) 821-1216 SIC 8051

■ HBR KENTUCKY LLC p 671
101 Sun Ave Ne, Albuquerque NM 87109
Tel (505) 821-3355 SIC 8051

SOUTH VALLEY CARE CENTER p 1345
1629 Bowe Ln Sw, Albuquerque NM 87105
Tel (505) 877-2200 SIC 8051 8059

■ SUNBRIDGE HEALTHCARE LLC p 1401
101 Sun Ave Ne, Albuquerque NM 87109
Tel (505) 821-3355 SIC 8052 8051

■ BELEN MEADOWS HEALTHCARE AND REHABILITATION CENTER LLC p 169
1831 Camino Del Llano, Belen NM 87002
Tel (505) 864-1600 SIC 8051

■ PEAK MEDICAL FARMINGTON LLC p 1126
806 W Maple St, Farmington NM 87401
Tel (505) 325-2910 SIC 8051

■ PEAK MEDICAL LAS CRUCES LLC p 1126
2905 Missouri Ave, Las Cruces NM 88011
Tel (575) 522-0404 SIC 8051

■ PEAK MEDICAL ROSWELL LLC p 1126
3200 Mission Arch Dr, Roswell NM 88201
Tel (575) 624-2583 SIC 8051

NEW MEXICO STATE VETERANS HOME p 1032
922 S Broadway St, T Or C NM 87901
Tel (575) 894-4200 SIC 8051

EDEN PARK MANAGEMENT INC p 477
22 Holland Ave, Albany NY 12209
Tel (518) 729-5230 SIC 8051

LONG ISLAND HOME p 876
400 Sunrise Hwy, Amityville NY 11701
Tel (631) 264-4000
SIC 8063 8051 8099 8011

AUBURN COMMUNITY HOSPITAL p 130
17 Lansing St, Auburn NY 13021
Tel (315) 255-7011 SIC 8062 8051

EPISCOPAL HEALTH SERVICES INC p 505
700 Hicksville Rd Ste 210, Bethpage NY 11714
Tel (516) 349-6100 SIC 8062 8051

UMH NY CORP p 1501
10 Acre Pl, Binghamton NY 13904
Tel (607) 775-6400 SIC 8059 8051 8741

UNITED HEALTH SERVICES INC p 1509
10-42 Mitchell Ave, Binghamton NY 13903
Tel (607) 762-3024 SIC 8062 8051

CENTERLIGHT HEALTHCARE INC p 276
1250 Waters Pl Ste 602, Bronx NY 10461
Tel (347) 640-6000 SIC 8051 8082 8322

RIVERDALE CENTER FOR NURSING AND REHABILITATION LLC p 1237
3220 Henry Hudson Pkwy, Bronx NY 10463
Tel (718) 514-2000 SIC 8051

BROOKLYN DEVELOPMENT CENTER p 218
888 Fountain Ave, Brooklyn NY 11239
Tel (718) 642-6002 SIC 8051

VICTORY MEMORIAL HOSPITAL p 1556
699 92nd St, Brooklyn NY 11228
Tel (718) 567-1234 SIC 8062 8051

CATHOLIC HEALTH SYSTEM INC p 266
144 Genesee St Fl 1, Buffalo NY 14203
Tel (716) 862-2400
SIC 8741 8062 5999 8051

PENINSULA GENERAL NURSING HOME CORP p 1129
5015 Beach Channel Dr, Far Rockaway NY 11691
Tel (718) 734-2000 SIC 8051

FINGER LAKES REGIONAL HEALTH SYSTEM INC p 543
196 North St, Geneva NY 14456
Tel (315) 787-4000 SIC 8051

NATHAN LITTAUER HOSPITAL ASSOCIATION p 1009
99 E State St, Gloversville NY 12078
Tel (518) 725-8621 SIC 8051 8062 8011

COLUMBIA MEMORIAL HOSPITAL p 341
71 Prospect Ave, Hudson NY 12534
Tel (518) 828-7601 SIC 8062 8051

HEALTHALLIANCE HOSPITAL MARYS AVENUE CAMPUS p 676
105 Marys Ave, Kingston NY 12401
Tel (845) 338-2500 SIC 8062 8051

PARKER JEWISH INSTITUTE FOR HEALTH CARE AND REHABILITATION FOUNDATION p 1116
27111 76th Ave, New Hyde Park NY 11040
Tel (516) 247-6500 SIC 8051 8082 8069

COLER GOLDWATER SPECIALTY HOSPITAL & NURSING FACILITY p 336
900 Main St, New York NY 10044
Tel (212) 848-6000 SIC 8069 8051

FIRST CHINESE PRESBYTERIAN COMMUNITY AFFAIRS HOME ATTENDANT CORP p 545
30 Broad St Ste 602, New York NY 10004
Tel (212) 226-4910 SIC 8051

ISABELLA GERIATRIC CENTER INC p 766
515 Audubon Ave, New York NY 10040
Tel (212) 342-9200 SIC 8051

JEWISH HOME LIFECARE HARRY AND JEANETTE WEINBERG CAMPUS BRONX p 784
120 W 106th St, New York NY 10025
Tel (212) 870-5000 SIC 8051

TERENCE CARDINAL COOKE HEALTH CARE CENTER p 1439
1249 5th Ave, New York NY 10029
Tel (212) 360-1000 SIC 8051

VILLAGE CENTER FOR CARE p 1557
120 Broadway Ste 2840, New York NY 10271
Tel (212) 367-3748 SIC 8051 8082 8322

ONEIDA HEALTH SYSTEMS INC p 1087
321 Genesee St, Oneida NY 13421
Tel (315) 363-6000 SIC 8062 8051

UNIVERSITY OF VERMONT CHAMPLAIN VALLEY PHYSICIANS HOSPITAL p 1526
75 Beekman St, Plattsburgh NY 12901
Tel (518) 561-2000 SIC 8062 8051

MONROE COMMUNITY HOSPITAL (INC) p 985
435 E Henrietta Rd, Rochester NY 14620
Tel (585) 760-6500 SIC 8051

PARK RIDGE NURSING HOME INC p 1115
1555 Long Pond Rd, Rochester NY 14626
Tel (585) 723-7205 SIC 8051

ST ANNS HOME FOR AGED p 1364
287 Flower City Park # 2, Rochester NY 14615
Tel (585) 697-6086 SIC 8051

ROME MEMORIAL HOSPITAL INC p 1249
1500 N James St, Rome NY 13440
Tel (315) 338-7000 SIC 8062 8051

SARATOGA HOSPITAL p 1282
211 Church St, Saratoga Springs NY 12866
Tel (518) 587-3222 SIC 8062 8051

DMN MANAGEMENT SERVICES LLC p 446
26 N Broadway, Schenectady NY 12305
Tel (518) 346-9640 SIC 8051

ELLIS HOSPITAL p 488
1101 Nott St, Schenectady NY 12308
Tel (518) 243-4000 SIC 8062 8051

FRANKLIN HOSPITAL p 575
900 Franklin Ave, Valley Stream NY 11580
Tel (516) 256-6000 SIC 8062 8051

GOOD SAMARITAN HOSPITAL MEDICAL CENTER p 623
1000 Montauk Hwy, West Islip NY 11795
Tel (631) 376-3000 SIC 8062 8051 8092

CAROLINA ADVENTIST RETIREMENT SYSTEMS INC p 259
95 Holcombe Cove Rd, Candler NC 28715
Tel (828) 667-9851 SIC 8052 8051 8082

PINELAKE HEALTH & REHAB p 1149
801 Pinehurst Ave, Carthage NC 28327
Tel (910) 947-5155 SIC 8051

CHARLOTTE-MECKLENBURG HOSPITAL AUTHORITY p 290
1000 Blythe Blvd, Charlotte NC 28203
Tel (704) 355-2000
SIC 8062 8069 8063 8051 8011

LIBERTY N & R CTR OF MECKLENBURG p 862
3700 Shamrock Dr, Charlotte NC 28215
Tel (704) 940-8367 SIC 8051

BRITTHAVEN OF EDENTON INC p 214
1341 Paradise Rd, Edenton NC 27932
Tel (252) 482-7481 SIC 8051 8052

HUGH CHATHAM MEMORIAL HOSPITAL INC p 717
180 Parkwood Dr, Elkin NC 28621
Tel (336) 835-3722 SIC 8062 8051 8361

CAROLINA HEALTHCARE CENTER OF CUMBERLAND LP p 259
4600 Cumberland Rd, Fayetteville NC 28306
Tel (910) 429-1690 SIC 8741 8051

BRITTHAVEN OF GOLDSBORO INC p 214
2401 Wayne Memorial Dr, Goldsboro NC 27534
Tel (919) 736-2121 SIC 8051 8052

SSC GOLDSBORO OPERATING CO LLC p 1363
1700 Wayne Memorial Dr, Goldsboro NC 27534
Tel (919) 731-2805 SIC 8051

GUILFORD HEALTH CARE CENTER INC p 646
2041 Willow Rd, Greensboro NC 27406
Tel (336) 272-9700 SIC 8051

GREENFIELD PLACE LLC p 638
2575 W 5th St, Greenville NC 27834
Tel (252) 830-9100 SIC 8051 8052 8059

HENDERSON COUNTY HOSPITAL CORP p 682
800 N Justice St, Hendersonville NC 28791
Tel (828) 698-7191 SIC 8062 8051 8082

HAMPTON WOODS HEALTH & REHABILITATION CENTER p 656
200 Hmpton Wods Cmplex Rd, Jackson NC 27845
Tel (252) 534-0131 SIC 8051 8052

BRITTHAVEN OF ONSLOW INC p 214
1839 Onslow Dr, Jacksonville NC 28540
Tel (910) 455-3610 SIC 8051 8052

BRITTHAVEN INC p 214
1435 Highway 258n, Kinston NC 28504
Tel (252) 939-4131 SIC 8051 8059

HILLCO LTD p 693
1435 Hwy 258 N, Kinston NC 28504
Tel (252) 523-9094
SIC 8051 8059 5047 5122

BRITTHAVEN OF MADISON INC p 214
1721 Bald Hill Loop, Madison NC 27025
Tel (336) 548-9658 SIC 8051 8052

BRITTHAVEN OF NEW BERN INC p 214
2600 Old Cherry Point Rd, New Bern NC 28560
Tel (252) 637-4730 SIC 8051

FIRSTHEALTH OF CAROLINAS INC p 550
155 Memorial Dr, Pinehurst NC 28374
Tel (910) 715-1000
SIC 8062 8093 8051 8021 7991 7219

MAYVIEW CONVALESCENT HOME INC p 924
513 E Whitaker Mill Rd, Raleigh NC 27608
Tel (919) 828-2348 SIC 8051

AUTUMN CORP p 135
451 N Winstead Ave, Rocky Mount NC 27804
Tel (252) 443-6265 SIC 8059 8051

LUTHERAN SERVICES FOR AGING INC p 886
1416 S Martin Luther, Salisbury NC 28144
Tel (704) 637-2870 SIC 8051 8052 8059

CLEVELAND COUNTY HEALTHCARE SYSTEM p 325
201 E Grover St, Shelby NC 28150
Tel (900) 487-3000 SIC 8062 8051

BRITTHAVEN OF SMITHFIELD INC p 214
515 Barbour Rd, Smithfield NC 27577
Tel (919) 934-6017 SIC 8051 8052

BRITTHAVEN OF SNOW HILL INC p 214
1304 Se 2nd St, Snow Hill NC 28580
Tel (252) 747-8126 SIC 8051 8052

IREDELL MEMORIAL HOSPITAL INC p 764
557 Brookdale Dr, Statesville NC 28677
Tel (704) 873-5661 SIC 8062 8051

■ STATESVILLE HMA LLC p 1383
218 Old Mocksville Rd, Statesville NC 28625
Tel (704) 873-0281 SIC 8051 8063 8062

TARBORO NURSING CARE p 1424
911 Western Blvd, Tarboro NC 27886
Tel (252) 823-2041 SIC 8051

BRITTHAVEN OF DAVIDSON INC p 214
706 Pineywood Rd, Thomasville NC 27360
Tel (336) 475-9116 SIC 8051 8052

RIDGEWOOD MANOR INC p 1234
1624 Highland Dr, Washington NC 27889
Tel (252) 946-9570 SIC 8051 8052

BRITTHAVEN OF WILKESBORO INC p 214
1016 Fletcher St, Wilkesboro NC 28697
Tel (336) 667-9261 SIC 8051

BRITTHAVEN OF WILSON INC p 214
403 Crestview Ave Sw, Wilson NC 27893
Tel (252) 237-0724 SIC 8051 8052

SSC WINSTON-SALEM OPERATING CO LLC p 1363
4911 Brian Center Ln, Winston Salem NC 27106
Tel (336) 744-5674 SIC 8051

TRIAD GROUP INC p 1478
623 W Main St, Yadkinville NC 27055
Tel (336) 679-8852 SIC 8051 5047 7374

YADKIN NURSING CARE CENTER INC p 1633
903 W Main St, Yadkinville NC 27055
Tel (336) 679-8863 SIC 8082 8051

SANFORD p 1279
801 Broadway N, Fargo ND 58102
Tel (701) 234-6000 SIC 8062 8011 8051

TRINITY HEALTH p 1481
1 Burdick Expy W, Minot ND 58701
Tel (701) 857-5260 SIC 8011 8051 8062

EZRA HEALTH CARE INC p 522
23258 Fernwood Dr, Beachwood OH 44122
Tel (440) 498-3000 SIC 8051

HEALTH CARE INDUSTRIES CORP p 674
4195 Sugarcreek Dr, Bellbrook OH 45305
Tel (937) 848-2973 SIC 8051 8052

OHIOGUIDESTONE p 1078
434 Eastland Rd, Berea OH 44017
Tel (440) 234-2006
SIC 8322 8361 8351 8051

APPALACHIAN RESPITE CARE LTD p 98
501 Pinecrest Dr, Beverly OH 45715
Tel (740) 984-4262 SIC 8051

NIGHTINGALE HOLDINGS LLC p 1043
4700 Ashwood Dr Ste 200, Blue Ash OH 45241
Tel (513) 489-7100 SIC 8051

■ BIORX LLC p 184
7167 E Kemper Rd, Cincinnati OH 45249
Tel (866) 442-4679
SIC 5122 8748 2834 5047 8051

CHILLICOTHE LONG TERM CARE INC p 300
7265 Kenwood Rd Ste 300, Cincinnati OH 45236
Tel (513) 793-8804 SIC 8051

DEACONESS LONG TERM CARE OF MISSOURI INC p 419
330 Straight St Ste 310, Cincinnati OH 45219
Tel (513) 487-3600
SIC 8059 8361 8052 8051

MARYMOUNT HOSPITAL INC p 915
9500 Euclid Ave, Cleveland OH 44195
Tel (216) 581-0500
SIC 8062 8063 8051 8082

MENORAH PARK CENTER FOR SENIOR LIVING BET MOSHAV ZEKENIM HADATI p 943
27100 Cedar Rd, Cleveland OH 44122
Tel (216) 831-6500 SIC 8051 6513 8322

NATIONAL CHURCH RESIDENCES p 1010
2333 N Bank Dr, Columbus OH 43220
Tel (614) 451-2151
SIC 6531 6513 8051 8059

OHIOHEALTH CORP p 1078
180 E Broad St, Columbus OH 43215
Tel (614) 788-8860
SIC 8049 8062 8082 8051

GALION COMMUNITY HOSPITAL p 589
269 Portland Way S, Galion OH 44833
Tel (419) 468-4841 SIC 8062 8051

OMNI MANOR INC p 1085
101 W Liberty St, Girard OH 44420
Tel (330) 545-1550 SIC 8051

CARINGTON HEALTH SYSTEMS p 256
8200 Beckett Park Dr, Hamilton OH 45011
Tel (513) 682-2700 SIC 8741 8051

HURON HEALTH CARE CENTER INC p 721
1920 Cleveland Rd W, Huron OH 44839
Tel (419) 433-4990 SIC 8051

HCF MANAGEMENT INC p 672
1100 Shawnee Rd, Lima OH 45805
Tel (419) 999-2010 SIC 8051 6513

UNITED CHURCH HOMES INC p 1507
170 E Center St, Marion OH 43302
Tel (740) 382-4885 SIC 8051

TWIN MAPLES NURSING HOME p 1495
31054 State Route 93, Mc Arthur OH 45651
Tel (740) 596-5955 SIC 8051 8052

RIVERSIDE CARE CENTER LLC p 1237
856 Riverside Dr S, Mc Connelsville OH 43756
Tel (740) 962-5303 SIC 8051

AMERICAN NURSING CARE INC p 77
1700 Edison Dr Ste 300, Milford OH 45150
Tel (513) 576-0262 SIC 8051

NORWALK AREA HEALTH SYSTEMS INC p 1061
272 Benedict Ave, Norwalk OH 44857
Tel (419) 668-8101 SIC 8062 8051

SALEM COMMUNITY HOSPITAL p 1272
1995 E State St, Salem OH 44460
Tel (330) 332-1551 SIC 8062 8051

■ HCR MANOR CARE INC p 672
333 N Summit St Ste 103, Toledo OH 43604
Tel (419) 252-5743 SIC 8051

■ HCR MANORCARE MEDICAL SERVICES OF FLORIDA LLC p 672
333 N Summit St Ste 100, Toledo OH 43604
Tel (419) 252-5500 SIC 8051

■ MANOR CARE INC p 902
333 N Summit St Ste 103, Toledo OH 43604
Tel (419) 252-5500 SIC 8051 8082 8062

■ MANOR CARE OF AMERICA INC p 902
333 N Summit St Ste 103, Toledo OH 43604
Tel (419) 252-5500 SIC 8051 8062 8082

WINCHESTER PLACE NURSING & REHABILITATION CENTER p 1614
36 Lehman Dr, Winchester OH 45697
Tel (614) 834-2273 SIC 8051

ZANDEX HEALTH CARE CORP p 1641
1122 Taylor St, Zanesville OH 43701
Tel (740) 454-1400 SIC 8052 8059 8051

ZANDEX INC p 1641
1122 Taylor St, Zanesville OH 43701
Tel (740) 454-1400 SIC 8052 8051

WCR ENTERPRISES INC p 1585
111 Sequoyah Ln Ste 7, Altus OK 73521
Tel (580) 482-4203 SIC 8052 8051

RAINBOW HEALTHCARE CENTER INC p 1205
111 E Washington Ave, Bristow OK 74010
Tel (918) 367-2246 SIC 8052 8051

FRANCES STREITEL - SOUTH p 573
2300 W Broadway St, Collinsville OK 74021
Tel (918) 371-2545 SIC 8051

GOLDEN AGE NURSING HOME OF GUTHRIE INC p 620
419 E Oklahoma Ave, Guthrie OK 73044
Tel (405) 282-6285 SIC 8051 8361

FOUNTAIN VIEW MANOR INC p 571
107 E Barclay St, Henryetta OK 74437
Tel (918) 652-7021 SIC 8051

MITCHELL MANOR CONVALESCENT HOME INC p 977
315 W Electric Ave, Mcalester OK 74501
Tel (918) 423-4661 SIC 8051 8059

BROADWAY MANOR NURSING HOME p 216
1622 E Broadway St, Muskogee OK 74403
Tel (918) 683-2851 SIC 8052 8051

EASTGATE VILLAGE RETIREMENT CENTER p 473
3500 Haskell Blvd, Muskogee OK 74403
Tel (918) 682-3191 SIC 8052 8051

■ DEACONESS HEALTH SYSTEM LLC p 419
5501 N Portland Ave, Oklahoma City OK 73112
Tel (405) 604-6000
SIC 8062 8051 8011 8361

PERRY GREEN VALLEY NURSING HOME INC p 1137
1103 Birch St, Perry OK 73077
Tel (580) 336-2285 SIC 8051

OKLAHOMA NURSING HOMES LTD p 1079
210 E Choctaw Ave, Sallisaw OK 74955
Tel (918) 775-4439 SIC 8051

WESTHAVEN NURSING HOME INC p 1601
1215 S Western Rd, Stillwater OK 74074
Tel (405) 743-1140 SIC 8051

TOUCHMARK LIVING CENTERS INC p 1463
5150 Sw Griffith Dr, Beaverton OR 97005
Tel (503) 646-5186 SIC 8051

COAST FORK NURSING CENTER INC p 331
515 Grant Ave, Cottage Grove OR 97424
Tel (541) 942-5528 SIC 8051

MID-VALLEY HEALTHCARE INC p 963
525 N Santiam Hwy, Lebanon OR 97355
Tel (541) 258-2101
SIC 8062 8051 8011 8082

PACIFIC RETIREMENT SERVICES INC p 1105
1 W Main St Ste 303, Medford OR 97501
Tel (541) 857-7777 SIC 8741 8051

AVAMERE HEALTH SERVICES LLC p 136
25115 Sw Parkway Ave A, Wilsonville OR 97070
Tel (503) 570-3405
SIC 8741 8051 8052 8093

GOOD SHEPHERD REHABILITATION HOSPITAL INC p 623
850 S 5th St, Allentown PA 18103
Tel (610) 776-3100
SIC 8361 8051 8093 8069

SHEPHERD GOOD REHABILITATION NETWORK p 1315
850 S 5th St, Allentown PA 18103
Tel (610) 776-3100 SIC 8051 8361 8322

QUALITY LIFE SERVICES p 1197
612 N Main St Ste A, Butler PA 16001
Tel (724) 431-0770 SIC 5912 8051

CONCORDIA LUTHERAN MINISTRIES p 355
134 Marwood Rd, Cabot PA 16023
Tel (724) 352-1571 SIC 8051

OSPREY RIDGE HEALTHCARE CENTER INC p 1097
45 N Scott St, Carbondale PA 18407
Tel (570) 282-1099 SIC 8051 8052

TANDEM HEALTH CARE OF CHESWICK INC p 1424
3876 Saxonburg Blvd, Cheswick PA 15024
Tel (412) 767-4998 SIC 8051

CHARLES COLE MEMORIAL HOSPITAL p 289
1001 E 2nd St, Coudersport PA 16915
Tel (814) 274-9300 SIC 7352 8069 8051

DOYLESTOWN HOSPITAL HEALTH AND WELLNESS CENTER INC p 454
595 W State St, Doylestown PA 18901
Tel (215) 345-2200 SIC 8051 8062

COUNTRY MEADOWS ASSOCIATES p 375
830 Cherry Dr, Hershey PA 17033
Tel (717) 533-2474 SIC 8051 8059 8741

GEORGE M LEADER FAMILY CORP p 606
830 Cherry Dr, Hershey PA 17033
Tel (800) 322-3441 SIC 8051

■ FC-GEN ACQUISITION INC p 532
101 E State St, Kennett Square PA 19348
Tel (610) 444-6350 SIC 8361 8051 8099

■ GENESIS ELDERCARE NATIONAL CENTERS INC p 602
101 E State St, Kennett Square PA 19348
Tel (610) 444-6350 SIC 8051 8361

■ GENESIS HEALTHCARE CORP p 603
101 E State St, Kennett Square PA 19348
Tel (610) 444-6350 SIC 8051 8361

▲ GENESIS HEALTHCARE INC p 603
101 E State St, Kennett Square PA 19348
Tel (610) 444-6350
SIC 8051 8052 8059 8361

■ GENESIS HEALTHCARE LLC p 603
101 E State St, Kennett Square PA 19348
Tel (610) 444-6350 SIC 8051 8099

PHILADELPHIA PRESBYTERY HOMES INC p 1143
2000 Joshua Rd, Lafayette Hill PA 19444
Tel (610) 834-1001 SIC 8361 8052 8051

■ CRESTVIEW NORTH INC p 392
262 Tollgate Rd, Langhorne PA 19047
Tel (215) 968-4650 SIC 8051

■ SELECT MEDICAL CORP p 1301
4714 Gettysburg Rd, Mechanicsburg PA 17055
Tel (717) 972-1100 SIC 8093 8051 8069

VIBRA HEALTHCARE LLC p 1555
4550 Lena Dr, Mechanicsburg PA 17055
Tel (717) 591-5700 SIC 8051

DIAKON LUTHERAN SOCIAL MINISTRIES p 436
1022 N Union St, Middletown PA 17057
Tel (610) 682-1262 SIC 8051 8322

DIAKON LUTHERAN SOCIAL MINISTRIES p 436
1022 N Union St, Middletown PA 17057
Tel (610) 682-1262 SIC 8322 8051

KRAMM HEALTHCARE CENTER INC p 829
743 Mahoning St, Milton PA 17847
Tel (570) 742-2681 SIC 8051

MORAVIAN SPRINGS HEALTH CENTER p 988
175 W North St, Nazareth PA 18064
Tel (610) 746-1000 SIC 8051

CATHOLIC HEALTH EAST p 266
3805 West Chester Pike # 100, Newtown Square PA 19073
Tel (610) 355-2000
SIC 8062 8051 8052 8059 8011

MADLYN AND LEONARD ABRAMSON CENTER FOR JEWISH LIFE p 894
1425 Horsham Rd, North Wales PA 19454
Tel (215) 371-3000 SIC 8051 8069 6513

PRESBYTERIAN SENIORCARE p 1171
1215 Hulton Rd, Oakmont PA 15139
Tel (412) 828-5600
SIC 8051 8052 6513 8741

ALBERT EINSTEIN MEDICAL ASSOCIATES INC p 46
5501 Old York Rd Ste 1, Philadelphia PA 19141
Tel (215) 456-7890 SIC 8062 8051

ALLEGHENY GENERAL HOSPITAL INC p 52
320 E North Ave, Pittsburgh PA 15212
Tel (412) 359-3131 SIC 8062 8051

CULWELL HEALTH INC p 400
4 Widgeon Dr, Pittsburgh PA 15238
Tel (412) 787-4103 SIC 8051

FOX NURSING HOME CORP p 572
251 Stenton Ave, Plymouth Meeting PA 19462
Tel (610) 828-2272 SIC 8051

ELK REGIONAL HEALTH SYSTEM p 487
763 Johnsonburg Rd, Saint Marys PA 15857
Tel (814) 788-8000
SIC 8062 8051 8361 8399

MERCY HOSPITAL SCRANTON PENNSYLVANIA p 947
746 Jefferson Ave, Scranton PA 18510
Tel (570) 348-7100 SIC 8062 8051

■ QUINCY SCRANTON HOSPITAL LLC p 1200
700 Quincy Ave, Scranton PA 18510
Tel (570) 340-2100 SIC 8062 8051

SIEMON NURSING HOME INC p 1320
228 Siemon Dr, Somerset PA 15501
Tel (814) 443-2811 SIC 8051

GREEN ACRES HEALTH SYSTEMS INC p 636
4 Ivybrook Blvd, Warminster PA 18974
Tel (215) 357-6055 SIC 8741 8051

KRAMM NURSING HOME INC p 829
245 E 8th St, Watsontown PA 17777
Tel (570) 538-2561 SIC 8051

ACTS RETIREMENT-LIFE COMMUNITIES INC p 20
375 Morris Rd, West Point PA 19486
Tel (215) 699-3204 SIC 8361 8051

RIVERSTREET MANOR p 1238
440 N River St, Wilkes Barre PA 18702
Tel (570) 825-5611 SIC 8361 8059 8051

■ CRESTVIEW CONVALESCENT HOME INC p 392
1245 Church Rd, Wyncote PA 19095
Tel (215) 884-9990 SIC 8051

MCWIL GROUP LTD p 925
209 N Beaver St, York PA 17401
Tel (717) 854-7857
SIC 8059 8051 8069 6513 8742 6552

WILMAC CORP p 1613
209 N Beaver St, York PA 17401
Tel (717) 854-7857
SIC 8059 8051 8069 6513 8742 6552

BROOKSIDE LIVING CENTER LLC p 218
208 James St, Anderson SC 29625
Tel (864) 226-3427 SIC 8051

BARNWELL COUNTY NURSING HOME p 156
31 Wren St, Barnwell SC 29812
Tel (803) 259-5547 SIC 8051 8052

KERSHAW HEALTH MEDICAL CENTER p 813
1315 Roberts St, Camden SC 29020
Tel (803) 432-4311 SIC 8062 8051 8082

UPSTATE AFFILIATE ORGANIZATION p 1529
701 Grove Rd, Greenville SC 29605
Tel (864) 455-7000 SIC 8069 8051

PIEDMONT LIVING CENTER LLC p 1147
401 Chandler Rd, Greer SC 29651
Tel (864) 879-1370 SIC 8051

ISLAND OAKS LIVING CENTER LLC p 766
3647 Maybank Hwy, Johns Island SC 29455
Tel (843) 559-5888 SIC 8051

LEXMED INC p 860
815 Old Cherokee Rd, Lexington SC 29072
Tel (803) 359-5181 SIC 8051

FALLS CREEK LIVING CENTER LLC p 526
2906 Geer Hwy, Marietta SC 29661
Tel (864) 836-6381 SIC 8051

LAUREL HILL INC p 847
716 E Cedar Rock St, Pickens SC 29671
Tel (864) 878-4739 SIC 8052 8051

ROSEMOND NURSING CENTER INC p 1250
138 Rosemond St, Pickens SC 29671
Tel (864) 878-9620 SIC 8051

SAINT STEPHEN NURSING FACILITY INC p 1270
1038 Mcgill Ln, Saint Stephen SC 29479
Tel (843) 567-2307 SIC 8051 8059

OCONEE MEDICAL CENTER p 1074
298 Memorial Dr, Seneca SC 29672
Tel (864) 482-3100 SIC 8062 8051

SUMMIT PLACE LIVING CENTER LLC p 1399
807 Se Main St, Simpsonville SC 29681
Tel (864) 963-6069 SIC 8051

OAK WHITE MANOR INC p 1070
130 E Main St, Spartanburg SC 29306
Tel (864) 582-7503 SIC 8051

LEXINGTON COUNTY HEALTH SERVICES DISTRICT INC p 859
2720 Sunset Blvd, West Columbia SC 29169
Tel (803) 791-2000
SIC 8062 8011 8299 8051

EVANGELICAL LUTHERAN GOOD SAMARITAN SOCIETY p 513
4800 W 57th St, Sioux Falls SD 57108
Tel (866) 928-1635 SIC 8051 8052 8059

SANFORD HEALTH p 1279
1305 W 18th St, Sioux Falls SD 57105
Tel (605) 333-1720 SIC 8062 8011 8051

DAVID M DORSETT HEALTH CARE p 415
1020 N 10th St, Spearfish SD 57783
Tel (605) 642-2716 SIC 8051

LANTIS ENTERPRISES INC p 844
4755 E Colorado Blvd, Spearfish SD 57783
Tel (605) 642-7736 SIC 8051 8052

ORIANNA HEALTH SYSTEMS p 1094
2723 Summer Oaks Dr, Bartlett TN 38134
Tel (901) 937-7994 SIC 6282 8051

■ AMERICAN RETIREMENT CORP p 78
111 Westwood Pl Ste 200, Brentwood TN 37027
Tel (615) 221-2250 SIC 8051

BOULEVARD TERRACE LLC p 204
6 Cadillac Dr Ste 310, Brentwood TN 37027
Tel (615) 896-4505 SIC 8051

▲ BROOKDALE SENIOR LIVING p 217
111 Westwood Pl Ste 400, Brentwood TN 37027
Tel (615) 221-2250 SIC 8059 8361 8051

CLP HEALTHCARE SERVICES INC p 328
10 Cadillac Dr Ste 400, Brentwood TN 37027
Tel (615) 224-8028 SIC 8051

▲ DIVERSICARE HEALTHCARE SERVICES INC p 443
1621 Galleria Blvd, Brentwood TN 37027
Tel (615) 771-7575 SIC 8051 8322

CLAY COUNTY MANOR INC p 323
120 Pitcock Ln, Celina TN 38551
Tel (931) 243-3139 SIC 8051

LIFE CARE CENTERS OF AMERICA INC p 863
3570 Keith St Nw, Cleveland TN 37312
Tel (423) 472-9585 SIC 8051 8052

LP COLUMBIA LLC p 882
1410 Trotwood Ave, Columbia TN 38401
Tel (931) 388-6443 SIC 8051

■ LIFETRUST AMERICA INC p 865
113 Seaboard Ln Ste 150a, Franklin TN 37067
Tel (615) 342-0601
SIC 8361 8051 8052 8059

WELLMONT HEALTH SYSTEM p 1589
1905 American Way, Kingsport TN 37660
Tel (423) 230-8200 SIC 8062 8051 8063

■ ACCREDO HEALTH GROUP INC p 15
1640 Century Center Pkwy # 110, Memphis TN 38134
Tel (877) 222-7336 SIC 8051 8052 8093

■ ST FRANCIS HOSPITAL INC p 1366
5959 Park Ave, Memphis TN 38119
Tel (901) 765-1000 SIC 8062 8051

N H C O P LP p 1005
100 E Vine St, Murfreesboro TN 37130
Tel (615) 890-2020 SIC 8051

▲ NATIONAL HEALTHCARE CORP p 1013
100 E Vine St, Murfreesboro TN 37130
Tel (615) 890-2020 SIC 8051 8082

AMERICAN HEALTH COMPANIES INC p 73
1971 Tennessee Ave N, Parsons TN 38363
Tel (731) 847-6343 SIC 8051 8052 8059

GRACE HEALTH CARE p 628
3425 Knight Dr, Whites Creek TN 37189
Tel (615) 876-2754 SIC 8051

HIGH PLAINS BAPTIST HOSPITAL INC p 690
1600 Wallace Blvd, Amarillo TX 79106
Tel (806) 358-5800 SIC 8062 6513 8051

■ NORTHWEST TEXAS HEALTHCARE SYSTEM INC p 1060
1501 S Coulter St, Amarillo TX 79106
Tel (806) 354-1000
SIC 8062 8063 8051 8049

SSC ATHENS OPERATING CO LLC p 1363
711 Lucas Dr, Athens TX 75751
Tel (903) 675-8538 SIC 8051

TRISUN HEALTHCARE LLC p 1483
1703 W 5th St, Austin TX 78703
Tel (512) 634-4900 SIC 8051

SAN JACINTO METHODIST HOSPITAL p 1277
4401 Garth Rd, Baytown TX 77521
Tel (281) 420-8600 SIC 8062 8063 8051

SENIOR LIVING PROPERTIES LLC p 1304
1316 S Florida St, Borger TX 79007
Tel (806) 273-3785 SIC 8051

EAST COKE COUNTY HOSPITAL DISTRICT p 470
900 S State St, Bronte TX 76933
Tel (325) 473-3621 SIC 8059 8051

CANTEX HEALTH CARE CENTERS LLC p 247
2537 Golden Bear Dr, Carrollton TX 75006
Tel (214) 954-4114 SIC 8051

▲ CAPITAL SENIOR LIVING CORP p 250
14160 Dallas Pkwy Ste 300, Dallas TX 75254
Tel (972) 770-5600 SIC 8051 8052

DAYBREAK VENTURE LLC p 417
401 N Elm St, Denton TX 76201
Tel (940) 387-4388 SIC 8051 8099

AMBROSIA GUILLEN TSVH p 65
9650 Kenworthy St, El Paso TX 79924
Tel (915) 751-0967 SIC 8051

PM MANAGEMENT - KILLEEN II NC LLC p 1157
415 Indian Oaks Dr, Harker Heights TX 76548
Tel (254) 699-5051 SIC 8051

CENTURY CARE OF AMERICA INC p 282
14800 Saint Marys Ln # 175, Houston TX 77079
Tel (832) 448-3700 SIC 8051

ST JOSEPH MEDICAL CENTER CORP p 1368
1401 St Joseph Pkwy, Houston TX 77002
Tel (713) 757-1000 SIC 8051

CHRISTUS HEALTH p 303
919 Hidden Rdg, Irving TX 75038
Tel (469) 282-2000 SIC 8062 8051

■ ODYSSEY HEALTHCARE INC p 1075
7801 Mesquite Bend Dr # 105, Irving TX 75063
Tel (888) 600-2411 SIC 8051

PETERSON SID MEMORIAL HOSPITAL p 1138
551 Hill Country Dr, Kerrville TX 78028
Tel (830) 896-4200 SIC 8051 8062

SSC LAREDO WEST OPERATING CO LLC p 1363
1200 E Lane St, Laredo TX 78040
Tel (956) 722-0031 SIC 8051

■ PINEY WOODS HEALTHCARE SYSTEM LP p 1149
505 S John Redditt Dr, Lufkin TX 75904
Tel (936) 634-8311
SIC 8062 8071 8099 8051

SSC MCALLEN RETAMA OPERATING CO LLC p 1363
900 S 12th St, Mcallen TX 78501
Tel (956) 682-4171 SIC 8051

GOLDEN LIVING LLC p 621
5220 Tennyson Pkwy # 400, Plano TX 75024
Tel (972) 372-6300
SIC 8051 8082 8731 8093

HOSPITAL ACQUISITION LLC p 709
5340 Legacy Dr Ste 150, Plano TX 75024
Tel (469) 241-2100 SIC 8069 8051

■ ICL HOLDING CO INC p 727
5340 Legacy Dr Bldg 4150, Plano TX 75024
Tel (469) 241-2100 SIC 8069 8051

LCI HOLDCO LLC p 849
5340 Legacy Dr Ste 150, Plano TX 75024
Tel (469) 241-2100 SIC 8069 8051

■ LCI INTERMEDIATE HOLDCO INC p 849
5340 Legacy Dr Bldg 4150, Plano TX 75024
Tel (469) 241-2100 SIC 8069 8051

LIFECARE HOLDINGS INC p 864
5340 Legacy Dr Ste 150, Plano TX 75024
Tel (469) 241-2100 SIC 8069 8051

PREFERRED CARE PARTNERS MANAGEMENT GROUP LP p 1169
5420 W Plano Pkwy, Plano TX 75093
Tel (972) 931-3800 SIC 8051 8052

OAKBEND MEDICAL CENTER p 1070
1705 Jackson St, Richmond TX 77469
Tel (713) 453-0446 SIC 8062 8051

ROCKDALE HOSPITAL AUTHORITY (INC) p 1244
1700 Brazos Ave, Rockdale TX 76567
Tel (512) 446-4500 SIC 8062 8051

SENIOR MANAGEMENT SERVICES OF NORMANDY AT SAN ANTONIO INC p 1304
841 Rice Rd, San Antonio TX 78220
Tel (210) 648-0101 SIC 8051

SSC SAN ANTONIO NORTHGATE OPERATING CO LLC p 1363
5757 N Knoll, San Antonio TX 78240
Tel (210) 694-7951 SIC 8051

WIND RIVER GROUP PT LLC p 1615
608 Sandau Rd, San Antonio TX 78216
Tel (210) 564-0100 SIC 8051

REGENCY INTEGRATED HEALTH SERVICES p 1219
101 W Goodwin Ave Ste 600, Victoria TX 77901
Tel (361) 576-0694 SIC 8051

MCHS - WEBSTER p 929
750 W Texas Ave, Webster TX 77598
Tel (281) 332-3496 SIC 8051

DESERET HEALTH GROUP LLC p 432
190 S Main St, Bountiful UT 84010
Tel (801) 296-5105 SIC 8051

AVALON HEALTH CARE INC p 136
206 N 2100 W Ste 300, Salt Lake City UT 84116
Tel (801) 596-8844 SIC 8741 8051

EDURO HEALTHCARE LLC p 479
1376 E 3300 S, Salt Lake City UT 84106
Tel (801) 601-1450 SIC 8051

SHAMIN HOTELS INC p 1311
2000 Ware Btm Spring Rd, Chester VA 23836
Tel (804) 777-9000
SIC 7011 8051 6512 6513

DANVILLE REGIONAL HEALTH FOUNDATION p 412
142 S Main St, Danville VA 24541
Tel (434) 799-2100
SIC 8741 8062 8051 8011

■ **DANVILLE REGIONAL MEDICAL CENTER** p 412
142 S Main St, Danville VA 24541
Tel (434) 799-2100
SIC 8062 8011 8093 8069 8051

INOVA HEALTH SYSTEM p 745
8110 Gatehouse Rd 200e, Falls Church VA 22042
Tel (703) 289-2069
SIC 8741 8011 8062 8049 8059 8051

PATRICK HENRY HOSPITAL INC p 1120
1000 Old Denbigh Blvd, Newport News VA 23602
Tel (757) 875-2000 SIC 8052 8059 8051

SENTARA LIFE CARE CORP p 1305
249 S Newtown Rd, Norfolk VA 23502
Tel (757) 892-5500 SIC 8051

AMERICAN HEALTHCARE LLC p 74
3131 Electric Rd, Roanoke VA 24018
Tel (540) 774-4263 SIC 8052 8051 8059

MEDICAL FACILITIES OF AMERICA VI AND XIII (LIMITED PARTNERSHIP) p 936
2917 Penn Forest Blvd, Roanoke VA 24018
Tel (540) 989-3618 SIC 8051

COMMUNITY MEMORIAL HEALTH CENTER PHYSICIAN-HOSPITAL ORGANIZATION LLC p 349
125 Buena Vista Cir, South Hill VA 23970
Tel (434) 447-3151 SIC 8062 8051

VALLEY HEALTH SYSTEM p 1540
1840 Amherst St, Winchester VA 22601
Tel (540) 536-8000
SIC 8062 8051 5047 8699

HIGHLINE MEDICAL CENTER p 692
16251 Sylvester Rd Sw, Burien WA 98166
Tel (206) 244-9970 SIC 8062 8051

AMERICAN BAPTIST HOMES OF WASHINGTON INC p 68
23600 Marine View Dr S, Des Moines WA 98198
Tel (206) 870-6641 SIC 8051 8059 8052

EAGLE HEALTHCARE INC p 468
12015 115th Ave Ne, Kirkland WA 98034
Tel (425) 285-3880 SIC 8051

PROVIDENCE HEALTH & SERVICES-WASHINGTON p 1186
1801 Lind Ave Sw 9016, Renton WA 98057
Tel (425) 525-3355
SIC 8062 8051 8052 6513 8069

SEA MAR COMMUNITY CARE CENTER p 1295
1040 S Henderson St, Seattle WA 98108
Tel (206) 763-5210 SIC 8051 8351

SEA-MAR COMMUNITY HEALTH CENTER p 1295
1040 S Henderson St, Seattle WA 98108
Tel (206) 763-5277
SIC 8322 8082 8093 8051

■ **SEQUOIA SPRINGS COTTAGES** p 1306
3131 Elliott Ave Ste 500, Seattle WA 98121
Tel (206) 298-2909 SIC 8051

VIRGINIA MASON MEDICAL CENTER p 1559
1100 9th Ave, Seattle WA 98101
Tel (206) 223-6600
SIC 8011 8051 6513 8062

CRISTA MINISTRIES p 392
19303 Fremont Ave N, Shoreline WA 98133
Tel (206) 546-7200 SIC 8322 8051 8211

EMPRES FINANCIAL SERVICES LLC p 494
4601 Ne 77th Ave Ste 300, Vancouver WA 98662
Tel (360) 892-6628 SIC 8051

EVERGREEN HEALTHCARE INC p 514
4601 Ne 77th Ave Ste 300, Vancouver WA 98662
Tel (360) 892-6472
SIC 8051 6513 8059 8741

PRESTIGE CARE INC p 1173
7700 Ne Parkway Dr # 300, Vancouver WA 98662
Tel (360) 735-7155 SIC 8051

■ **331 HOLT LANE OPERATIONS LLC** p 2
331 Holt Ln, Lewisburg WV 24901
Tel (304) 645-4453 SIC 8051

WEIRTON MEDICAL CENTER INC p 1588
601 Colliers Way, Weirton WV 26062
Tel (304) 797-6000 SIC 8062 8051

RICE HEALTH CARE FACILITIES OF WISCONSIN INC p 1232
1726 N Ballard Rd Ste 2, Appleton WI 54911
Tel (920) 991-9072 SIC 8051

BEAVER DAM COMMUNITY HOSPITALS INC p 166
707 S University Ave, Beaver Dam WI 53916
Tel (920) 887-7181 SIC 8062 8051

THEDACARE MEDICAL CENTER - BERLIN INC p 1446
225 Memorial Dr, Berlin WI 54923
Tel (920) 361-1313 SIC 8062 8051 8011

SANTA MARIA NURSING HOME INC p 1281
430 S Clay St, Green Bay WI 54301
Tel (920) 432-5231 SIC 8051

■ **HEARTLAND-WASHINGTON MANOR OF KENOSHA WI LLC** p 679
3100 Washington Rd, Kenosha WI 53144
Tel (262) 658-4622 SIC 8051

MAYO CLINIC HEALTH SYSTEM-FRANCISCAN HEALTHCARE INC p 924
700 West Ave S, La Crosse WI 54601
Tel (608) 785-0940 SIC 8062 8051

CAPITOL LAKES RETIREMENT COMMUNITY p 251
110 S Henry St, Madison WI 53703
Tel (608) 283-2000
SIC 6513 8051 8052 8361

AID HOLDINGS LLC p 37
W140n8981 Lilly Rd, Menomonee Falls WI 53051
Tel (262) 257-8888
SIC 8052 8051 8059 8082

EXTENDICARE FOUNDATION INC p 521
111 W Michigan St, Milwaukee WI 53203
Tel (414) 908-8000 SIC 8051

EXTENDICARE HEALTH SERVICES INC p 521
111 W Michigan St, Milwaukee WI 53203
Tel (414) 908-6720 SIC 8051 7389 5912

EXTENDICARE HOLDINGS LLC p 521
111 W Michigan St, Milwaukee WI 53203
Tel (414) 908-8000 SIC 8051

EXTENDICARE HOMES INC p 521
111 W Michigan St, Milwaukee WI 53203
Tel (414) 908-8000 SIC 8051

MINISTRY HEALTH CARE INC p 973
400 W River Woods Pkwy, Milwaukee WI 53212
Tel (414) 359-1060 SIC 8011 8051

■ **SENIOR BROOKDALE LIVING COMMUNITIES INC** p 1303
6737 W Wa St Ste 2300, Milwaukee WI 53214
Tel (414) 918-5000 SIC 8059 8051 8361

TENDERCARE (MICHIGAN) INC p 1437
111 W Michigan St, Milwaukee WI 53203
Tel (800) 395-5000 SIC 8051

LINDENGROVE MUKWONAGO p 868
837 County Road Nn E, Mukwonago WI 53149
Tel (262) 363-6830 SIC 8051

LINDENGROVE INC p 868
13700 W National Ave # 9, New Berlin WI 53151
Tel (262) 797-4600 SIC 8051 5912

DIVINE SAVIOR HEALTHCARE INC p 444
2817 New Pinery Rd # 202, Portage WI 53901
Tel (608) 745-4598 SIC 8062 8011 8051

TETON COUNTY HOSPITAL DISTRICT p 1441
625 E Broadway Ave, Jackson WY 83001
Tel (307) 733-3636 SIC 8062 8052 8051

SIC 8052 Intermediate Care Facilities

SUTTER HEALTH SACRAMENTO SIERRA REGION p 1410
2200 River Plaza Dr, Sacramento CA 95833
Tel (916) 733-8800 SIC 8062 8063 8052

SUNRISE COMMUNITY INC p 1403
9040 Sw 72nd St, Miami FL 33173
Tel (305) 275-3365 SIC 8052 8331 8322

PRESBYTERIAN RETIREMENT COMMUNITIES INC p 1171
80 W Lucerne Cir, Orlando FL 32801
Tel (407) 839-5050 SIC 8361 8052 8051

CENTENNIAL HEALTHCARE CORP p 275
400 Perimeter Ctr Ter Ne, Atlanta GA 30346
Tel (770) 698-9040
SIC 8051 8069 8052 8741

GRANCARE LLC p 629
1 Ravinia Dr Ste 1400, Atlanta GA 30346
Tel (770) 393-0199
SIC 8051 8052 8093 8071

LUTHERAN LIFE COMMUNITIES p 886
800 W Oakton St, Arlington Heights IL 60004
Tel (847) 368-7400 SIC 8052

ASSISTED LIVING CONCEPTS LLC p 119
330 N Wabash Ave Ste 3700, Chicago IL 60611
Tel (888) 252-5001
SIC 8052 8051 8059 8082

MISERICORDIA HOME p 975
6300 N Ridge Ave, Chicago IL 60660
Tel (773) 973-6300 SIC 8052

SENIOR LIFESTYLE CORP p 1304
303 E Wacker Dr Ste 2400, Chicago IL 60601
Tel (312) 673-4333 SIC 8052

CHRISTIAN HOMES INC p 302
200 N Postville Dr, Lincoln IL 62656
Tel (217) 732-9651 SIC 8052 8051

PRESENCE LIFE CONNECTIONS p 1172
18927 Hickory Creek Dr # 300, Mokena IL 60448
Tel (708) 478-7900 SIC 8052

RENAISSANCE HEALTH CARE CORP p 1223
6050 S 800 E-92, Fort Wayne IN 46814
Tel (260) 625-3545 SIC 8052 8051

ST MARGARET MERCY HEALTHCARE CENTERS INC p 1370
5454 Hohman Ave, Hammond IN 46320
Tel (219) 932-2300 SIC 8062 8052 8051

SANCTUARY AT HOLY CROSS p 1278
17475 Dugdale Dr, South Bend IN 46635
Tel (574) 247-7500 SIC 8322 8052

MILLERS HEALTH SYSTEMS INC p 971
1690 S County Farm Rd, Warsaw IN 46580
Tel (574) 267-7211 SIC 8052 8051 8361

CARE INITIATIVES p 254
1611 Westlakes Pkwy, West Des Moines IA 50266
Tel (515) 224-4442 SIC 8051 8052

CHEYENNE LODGE INC p 296
716 Cedar St, Jamestown KS 66948
Tel (785) 439-6211 SIC 8052

FOUR COURTS INC p 571
2100 Millvale Rd, Louisville KY 40205
Tel (502) 451-0990 SIC 8052

RES-CARE INC p 1226
9901 Linn Station Rd, Louisville KY 40223
Tel (502) 394-2100 SIC 8052 8331 7363

UNITED REHAB LLC p 1511
9510 Ormsby Station Rd # 101, Louisville KY 40223
Tel (502) 426-2242 SIC 8052 8051 8059

MAINE VETERANS HOMES p 898
460 Civic Center Dr, Augusta ME 04330
Tel (207) 622-0075 SIC 8052

HIBBARD NURSING HOME INC p 690
1037 W Main St, Dover Foxcroft ME 04426
Tel (207) 564-8129 SIC 8052 8051

CENTRAL MAINE HEALTH VENTURES INC p 279
300 Main St, Lewiston ME 04240
Tel (207) 795-0111
SIC 8049 8052 7322 8011

CENTRAL MAINE HEALTHCARE CORP p 279
300 Main St, Lewiston ME 04240
Tel (207) 795-0111 SIC 8062 8052 8049

ST MARYS HEALTH SYSTEM p 1371
96 Campus Ave, Lewiston ME 04240
Tel (207) 777-8546
SIC 8062 8052 8051 8011 8361

ST MARYS REGIONAL MEDICAL CENTER p 1372
93 Campus Ave, Lewiston ME 04240
Tel (207) 777-8546
SIC 8062 8052 8051 8011 8361

ROMAN CATHOLIC BISHOP OF PORTLAND p 1248
510 Ocean Ave, Portland ME 04103
Tel (207) 773-6471 SIC 8052 8661

AROOSTOOK MEDICAL CENTER INC p 112
140 Academy St, Presque Isle ME 04769
Tel (207) 768-4000 SIC 8062 8011 8052

OAK CREST VILLAGE INC p 1070
8800 Walther Blvd Ste 1, Baltimore MD 21234
Tel (410) 665-2222 SIC 8051 8052 8059

KNOLLWOOD MANOR GENESIS ELDERCARE p 825
1221 Waugh Chapel Rd, Gambrills MD 21054
Tel (410) 987-1644 SIC 8051 8052

BAY COVE HUMAN SERVICES INC p 160
66 Canal St, Boston MA 02114
Tel (617) 371-3000 SIC 8052 8093 8361

▲ **FIVE STAR QUALITY CARE INC** p 553
400 Centre St, Newton MA 02458
Tel (617) 796-8387 SIC 8051 8052

HOSPICE ADVANTAGE LLC p 708
401 Center Ave Ste 130, Bay City MI 48708
Tel (989) 891-2200 SIC 8052 8082

AMERICAN BAPTIST HOMES OF MIDWEST p 68
14850 Scenic Heights Rd, Eden Prairie MN 55344
Tel (952) 941-3175 SIC 8051 8361 8052

VOLUNTEERS OF AMERICA NATIONAL SERVICES p 1565
7530 Market Place Dr, Eden Prairie MN 55344
Tel (952) 941-0305 SIC 8051 8052

LOUISIANA EXTENDED CARE CENTERS INC p 880
763 Avery Blvd N, Ridgeland MS 39157
Tel (601) 956-8884 SIC 8051 8052

EASTER SEALS MIDWEST p 471
13545 Barrett Parkway Dr, Ballwin MO 63021
Tel (314) 394-7026
SIC 8361 8331 8322 8052

■ **GOOD SAMARITAN NURSING HOME** p 623
403 W Main St, Cole Camp MO 65325
Tel (660) 668-4515 SIC 8052

MIDAMERICA CARE FOUNDATION INC p 964
7611 State Line Rd, Kansas City MO 64114
Tel (816) 444-0900 SIC 8051 8052

BETHESDA HEALTH GROUP INC p 178
1630 Des Peres Rd Ste 290, Saint Louis MO 63131
Tel (314) 800-1900 SIC 8052

VETTER HEALTH SERVICES INC p 1553
20220 Harney St, Elkhorn NE 68022
Tel (402) 895-3932 SIC 8052

CARE ONE LLC p 254
173 Bridge Plz N, Fort Lee NJ 07024
Tel (201) 242-4000 SIC 8051 8052

SENIOR PHS LIVING INC p 1304
13 Roszel Rd Ste C120, Princeton NJ 08540
Tel (609) 426-6802 SIC 8361 8052 8051

■ **SUNBRIDGE HEALTHCARE LLC** p 1401
101 Sun Ave Ne, Albuquerque NM 87109
Tel (505) 821-3355 SIC 8052 8051

HAMISTER GROUP LLC p 655
10 Lafayette Sq Ste 1900, Buffalo NY 14203
Tel (716) 839-4000 SIC 7011 8052 8741

NATIONAL HEALTH CARE AFFILIATES INC p 1013
10 Lafayette Sq Ste 1900, Buffalo NY 14203
Tel (716) 839-4000 SIC 8082 8052

RESOURCE CENTER p 1227
200 Dunham Ave, Jamestown NY 14701
Tel (716) 661-4829
SIC 8093 6513 6512 8052

INSTITUTE FOR COMMUNITY LIVING INC p 747
125 Broad St, New York NY 10004
Tel (212) 385-3030 SIC 8052

DEVELOPMENTAL DISABILITIES INSTITUTE INC p 433
99 Hollywood Dr, Smithtown NY 11787
Tel (631) 366-2900 SIC 8211 8052

MONARCH p 983
350 Pee Dee Ave Ste 101, Albemarle NC 28001
Tel (704) 986-1500
SIC 8322 8049 8331 8052

CAROLINA ADVENTIST RETIREMENT SYSTEMS INC p 259
95 Holcombe Cove Rd, Candler NC 28715
Tel (828) 667-9851 SIC 8052 8051 8082

SENIOR LIVING COMMUNITES LLC p 1304
3530 Toringdon Way # 204, Charlotte NC 28277
Tel (704) 246-1620 SIC 8052

BRITTHAVEN OF EDENTON INC p 214
1341 Paradise Rd, Edenton NC 27932
Tel (252) 482-7481 SIC 8051 8052

BRITTHAVEN OF GOLDSBORO INC p 214
2401 Wayne Memorial Dr, Goldsboro NC 27534
Tel (919) 736-2121 SIC 8051 8052

GREENFIELD PLACE LLC p 638
2575 W 5th St, Greenville NC 27834
Tel (252) 830-9100 SIC 8051 8052 8059

HAMPTON WOODS HEALTH & REHABILITATION CENTER p 656
200 Hmpton Wods Cmplex Rd, Jackson NC 27845
Tel (252) 534-0131 SIC 8051 8052

BRITTHAVEN OF ONSLOW INC p 214
1839 Onslow Dr, Jacksonville NC 28540
Tel (910) 455-3610 SIC 8051 8052

HOWELL CHILD CARE CENTER INC p 713
3738 Howell Day Care Rd, La Grange NC 28551
Tel (252) 566-9011 SIC 8361 8052

RHA/HOWELL CARE CENTERS INC p 1231
3738 Howell Day Care Rd, La Grange NC 28551
Tel (252) 566-9011 SIC 8361 8052

BRITTHAVEN OF MADISON INC p 214
1721 Bald Hill Loop, Madison NC 27025
Tel (336) 548-9658 SIC 8051 8052

LUTHERAN SERVICES FOR AGING INC p 886
1416 S Martin Luther, Salisbury NC 28144
Tel (704) 637-2870 SIC 8051 8052 8059

BRITTHAVEN OF SMITHFIELD INC p 214
515 Barbour Rd, Smithfield NC 27577
Tel (919) 934-6017 SIC 8051 8052

BRITTHAVEN OF SNOW HILL INC p 214
1304 Se 2nd St, Snow Hill NC 28580
Tel (252) 747-8126 SIC 8051 8052

BRITTHAVEN OF DAVIDSON INC p 214
706 Pineywood Rd, Thomasville NC 27360
Tel (336) 475-9116 SIC 8051 8052

RIDGEWOOD MANOR INC p 1234
1624 Highland Dr, Washington NC 27889
Tel (252) 946-9570 SIC 8051 8052

BRITTHAVEN OF WILSON INC p 214
403 Crestview Ave Sw, Wilson NC 27893
Tel (252) 237-0724 SIC 8051 8052

HEALTH CARE INDUSTRIES CORP p 674
4195 Sugarcreek Dr, Bellbrook OH 45305
Tel (937) 848-2973 SIC 8051 8052

DEACONESS LONG TERM CARE OF MISSOURI INC p 419
330 Straight St Ste 310, Cincinnati OH 45219
Tel (513) 487-3600
SIC 8059 8361 8052 8051

OHIO DEPARTMENT OF MENTAL HEALTH p 1077
30 E Broad St Fl 8, Columbus OH 43215
Tel (614) 466-2337 SIC 8052

TWIN MAPLES NURSING HOME p 1495
31054 State Route 93, Mc Arthur OH 45651
Tel (740) 596-5955 SIC 8051 8052

FISHER-TITUS MEDICAL CENTER p 552
272 Benedict Ave, Norwalk OH 44857
Tel (419) 668-8101 SIC 8052 8062

ZANDEX HEALTH CARE CORP p 1641
1122 Taylor St, Zanesville OH 43701
Tel (740) 454-1400 SIC 8052 8059 8051

ZANDEX INC p 1641
1122 Taylor St, Zanesville OH 43701
Tel (740) 454-1400 SIC 8052 8051

WCR ENTERPRISES INC p 1585
111 Sequoyah Ln Ste 7, Altus OK 73521
Tel (580) 482-4203 SIC 8052 8051

RAINBOW HEALTHCARE CENTER INC p 1205
111 E Washington Ave, Bristow OK 74010
Tel (918) 367-2246 SIC 8052 8051

FORT GIBSON NURSING HOME p 568
205 E Poplar St, Fort Gibson OK 74434
Tel (918) 478-2456 SIC 8052

LEXINGTON NURSING HOME INC p 859
632 Se 3rd St, Lexington OK 73051
Tel (405) 527-6531 SIC 8052

BROADWAY MANOR NURSING HOME p 216
1622 E Broadway St, Muskogee OK 74403
Tel (918) 683-2851 SIC 8052 8051

EASTGATE VILLAGE RETIREMENT CENTER p 473
3500 Haskell Blvd, Muskogee OK 74403
Tel (918) 682-3191 SIC 8052 8051

POCOLA NURSING CENTER p 1158
200 Home St, Pocola OK 74902
Tel (918) 436-2228 SIC 8052

COUNTRYSIDE ESTATES INC p 375
Hwy 64 E, Warner OK 74469
Tel (918) 463-5143 SIC 8052

ALBERTINA KERR CENTERS p 46
424 Ne 22nd Ave, Portland OR 97232
Tel (503) 239-8101 SIC 8052 8361 8093

AVAMERE HEALTH SERVICES LLC p 136
25115 Sw Parkway Ave A, Wilsonville OR 97070
Tel (503) 570-3405
SIC 8741 8051 8052 8093

OSPREY RIDGE HEALTHCARE CENTER INC p 1097
45 N Scott St, Carbondale PA 18407
Tel (570) 282-1099 SIC 8051 8052

▲ **GENESIS HEALTHCARE INC** p 603
101 E State St, Kennett Square PA 19348
Tel (610) 444-6350
SIC 8051 8052 8059 8361

PHILADELPHIA PRESBYTERY HOMES INC p 1143
2000 Joshua Rd, Lafayette Hill PA 19444
Tel (610) 834-1001 SIC 8361 8052 8051

CATHOLIC HEALTH EAST p 266
3805 West Chester Pike # 100, Newtown Square PA 19073
Tel (610) 355-2000
SIC 8062 8051 8052 8059 8011

PRESBYTERIAN SENIORCARE p 1171
1215 Hulton Rd, Oakmont PA 15139
Tel (412) 828-5600
SIC 8051 8052 6513 8741

RESOURCES FOR HUMAN DEVELOPMENT INC p 1227
4700 Wphickon Ave Ste 126, Philadelphia PA 19144
Tel (215) 951-0300
SIC 8322 8093 8052 8331 8361

BARNWELL COUNTY NURSING HOME p 156
31 Wren St, Barnwell SC 29812
Tel (803) 259-5547 SIC 8051 8052

LAUREL HILL INC p 847
716 E Cedar Rock St, Pickens SC 29671
Tel (864) 878-4739 SIC 8052 8051

EVANGELICAL LUTHERAN GOOD SAMARITAN SOCIETY p 513
4800 W 57th St, Sioux Falls SD 57108
Tel (866) 928-1635 SIC 8051 8052 8059

LANTIS ENTERPRISES INC p 844
4755 E Colorado Blvd, Spearfish SD 57783
Tel (605) 642-7736 SIC 8051 8052

LIFE CARE CENTERS OF AMERICA INC p 863
3570 Keith St Nw, Cleveland TN 37312
Tel (423) 472-9585 SIC 8051 8052

■ LIFETRUST AMERICA INC p 865
113 Seaboard Ln Ste 150a, Franklin TN 37067
Tel (615) 342-0601
SIC 8361 8051 8052 8059

■ ACCREDO HEALTH GROUP INC p 15
1640 Century Center Pkwy # 110, Memphis TN 38134
Tel (877) 222-7336 SIC 8051 8052 8093

AMERICAN HEALTH COMPANIES INC p 73
1971 Tennessee Ave N, Parsons TN 38363
Tel (731) 847-6343 SIC 8051 8052 8059

▲ CAPITAL SENIOR LIVING CORP p 250
14160 Dallas Pkwy Ste 300, Dallas TX 75254
Tel (972) 770-5600 SIC 8051 8052

PREFERRED CARE PARTNERS MANAGEMENT GROUP LP p 1169
5420 W Plano Pkwy, Plano TX 75093
Tel (972) 931-3800 SIC 8051 8052

LIGHTHOUSE HOSPICE p 865
100 College St, Round Rock TX 78664
Tel (866) 678-0505 SIC 8052

CAPITAL HOSPICE p 249
2900 Telestar Ct, Falls Church VA 22042
Tel (703) 538-2065 SIC 8082 8052

■ SUNRISE SENIOR LIVING MANAGEMENT INC p 1404
7902 Westpark Dr, Mc Lean VA 22102
Tel (703) 273-7500 SIC 8361 8741 8052

PATRICK HENRY HOSPITAL INC p 1120
1000 Old Denbigh Blvd, Newport News VA 23602
Tel (757) 875-2000 SIC 8052 8059 8051

VIRGINIA SOUTHSIDE TRAINING CENTER INC p 1559
W Washington St, Petersburg VA 23803
Tel (804) 524-7333 SIC 8361 8052

AMERICAN HEALTHCARE LLC p 74
3131 Electric Rd, Roanoke VA 24018
Tel (540) 774-4263 SIC 8052 8051 8059

AMERICAN BAPTIST HOMES OF WASHINGTON INC p 68
23600 Marine View Dr S, Des Moines WA 98198
Tel (206) 870-6641 SIC 8051 8059 8052

PROVIDENCE HEALTH & SERVICES-WASHINGTON p 1186
1801 Lind Ave Sw 9016, Renton WA 98057
Tel (425) 525-3355
SIC 8062 8051 8052 6513 8069

CAPITOL LAKES RETIREMENT COMMUNITY p 251
110 S Henry St, Madison WI 53703
Tel (608) 283-2000
SIC 6513 8051 8052 8361

AID HOLDINGS LLC p 37
W140n8981 Lilly Rd, Menomonee Falls WI 53051
Tel (262) 257-8888
SIC 8052 8051 8059 8082

■ EMERITUS CORP p 492
3131 Elliott Ave Ste 500, Milwaukee WI 53214
Tel (206) 298-2909 SIC 8052

OCONOMOWOC RESIDENTIAL PROGRAMS INC p 1074
1746 Executive Dr, Oconomowoc WI 53066
Tel (262) 569-5515 SIC 8052 8361

TETON COUNTY HOSPITAL DISTRICT p 1441
625 E Broadway Ave, Jackson WY 83001
Tel (307) 733-3636 SIC 8062 8052 8051

SIC 8059 Nursing & Personal Care Facilities, NEC

BAPTIST HEALTH SYSTEM INC p 153
1130 22nd St S Ste 1000, Birmingham AL 35205
Tel (205) 715-5000
SIC 8011 8741 8082 8059

PRIME HEALTHCARE LLC p 1175
314 W Columbus St, Dadeville AL 36853
Tel (256) 825-9273 SIC 8059

GOODWATER HEALTH CENTER CARE LLC p 624
16 Jones Hill Rd, Goodwater AL 35072
Tel (256) 839-6711 SIC 8059

NHS MANAGEMENT LLC p 1042
931 Fairfax Park, Tuscaloosa AL 35406
Tel (205) 391-3600 SIC 8082 8059

WATERMARK RETIREMENT COMMUNITIES INC p 1582
2020 W Rudasill Rd, Tucson AZ 85704
Tel (520) 797-4000 SIC 8059

ALMA HEALTHCARE AND REHABILITATION CENTER LLC p 59
401 Heather Ln, Alma AR 72921
Tel (479) 632-4343 SIC 8059

RELIANCE HEALTH CARE MANAGEMENT p 1221
824 Salem Rd Ste 210, Conway AR 72034
Tel (501) 932-0050 SIC 8059

BEVERLY ENTERPRISES - MISSOURI INC p 179
1000 Fianna Way, Fort Smith AR 72919
Tel (479) 201-2000 SIC 8051 8059

BEVERLY ENTERPRISES-OHIO INC p 179
1 Thousand Beverly Way, Fort Smith AR 72919
Tel (479) 201-2000 SIC 8059

GGNSC HOLDINGS LLC p 610
1000 Fianna Way, Fort Smith AR 72919
Tel (479) 201-2000
SIC 8059 8051 8082 8322

CHRISTIAN HEALTHCARE OF MISSOURI INC p 302
5305 W Village Pkwy # 12, Rogers AR 72758
Tel (479) 464-0200 SIC 8059

PALOMAR HEALTH p 1110
456 E Grand Ave, Escondido CA 92025
Tel (442) 281-5000 SIC 8062 8059

FRONT PORCH COMMUNITIES AND SERVICES - CASA DE MANANA LLC p 580
800 N Brand Blvd Fl 19, Glendale CA 91203
Tel (818) 729-8100 SIC 8059 8051

COMPASS HEALTH INC p 351
200 S 13th St Ste 208, Grover Beach CA 93433
Tel (805) 474-7010 SIC 8059

SAN BENITO HEALTH CARE DISTRICT p 1275
911 Sunset Dr Ste A, Hollister CA 95023
Tel (831) 637-5711 SIC 8062 8051 8059

SENIOR SILVERADO LIVING INC p 1304
6400 Oak Cyn Ste 200, Irvine CA 92618
Tel (949) 240-7200 SIC 8059

VIENNA CONVALESCENT HOSPITAL INC p 1556
800 S Ham Ln, Lodi CA 95242
Tel (209) 368-7141 SIC 8059

AG FACILITIES OPERATIONS LLC p 33
6380 Wilshire Blvd # 800, Los Angeles CA 90048
Tel (323) 651-1808 SIC 8059

■ SOUTHWEST HEALTHCARE SYSTEM AUXILIARY p 1352
25500 Medical Center Dr, Murrieta CA 92562
Tel (951) 696-6000
SIC 8062 8051 8059 4119

SENIOR VINTAGE MANAGEMENT INC p 1304
23 Corporate Plaza Dr # 190, Newport Beach CA 92660
Tel (949) 719-4080 SIC 8059

SSC PITTSBURG OPERATING CO LP p 1363
2351 Loveridge Rd, Pittsburg CA 94565
Tel (925) 427-4444 SIC 8059

AMERICAN BAPTIST HOMES OF WEST p 68
6120 Stoneridge Mall Rd # 300, Pleasanton CA 94588
Tel (925) 924-7100 SIC 8059

▲ BIOSCRIP INC p 184
1600 Broadway Ste 700, Denver CO 80202
Tel (720) 697-5200 SIC 8059 6411

HARTFORD HEALTHCARE CORP p 665
1 State St Fl 19, Hartford CT 06103
Tel (860) 263-4100 SIC 8059

FLEET LANDING p 555
1 Fleet Landing Blvd, Atlantic Beach FL 32233
Tel (904) 246-9900 SIC 8059

SOLARIS FOUNDATION INC p 1338
9520 Bonita Beach Rd Se, Bonita Springs FL 34135
Tel (239) 919-1142 SIC 8051 8059

CHRISTIAN AND MISSIONARY ALLIANCE FOUNDATION INC p 302
15101 Shell Point Blvd, Fort Myers FL 33908
Tel (239) 466-1111 SIC 6513 8051 8059

AMERICAN HOSPICE HOLDINGS LLC p 74
50 N Laura St Ste 1800, Jacksonville FL 32202
Tel (904) 493-6745 SIC 8059

CONSULATE MANAGEMENT CO LLC p 361
800 Concourse Pkwy S, Maitland FL 32751
Tel (407) 571-1550
SIC 8051 8059 8071 8093

SEA CREST HEALTH CARE MANAGEMENT LLC p 1295
800 Concourse Pkwy S, Maitland FL 32751
Tel (813) 744-2800 SIC 8059

HOSPICE OF PALM BEACH COUNTY INC p 709
5300 East Ave, West Palm Beach FL 33407
Tel (561) 848-5200 SIC 8059

TANDEM HEALTHCARE OF WEST PALM BEACH INC p 1424
1626 Davis Rd, West Palm Beach FL 33406
Tel (561) 439-8897 SIC 8059 8051

PIEDMONT HEALTHCARE INC p 1147
1800 Hwll Mll Rd Nw 850, Atlanta GA 30318
Tel (770) 801-2550 SIC 8059

AGE GOLDEN PROPERTIES LTD p 34
19 Merritt St, Hawkinsville GA 31036
Tel (478) 783-1438 SIC 8059

ALTON MEMORIAL HOSPITAL FOUNDATION p 62
1 Memorial Dr, Alton IL 62002
Tel (618) 463-7311 SIC 8062 8059

WALGREENS INFUSION SERVICES INC p 1573
3000 Lakeside Dr Ste 300n, Bannockburn IL 60015
Tel (312) 940-2500
SIC 8082 8011 8059 5999 5122

ASSISTED LIVING CONCEPTS LLC p 119
330 N Wabash Ave Ste 3700, Chicago IL 60611
Tel (888) 252-5001
SIC 8052 8051 8059 8082

PRESENCE CHICAGO HOSPITALS NETWORK p 1172
7435 W Talcott Ave, Chicago IL 60631
Tel (773) 774-8000 SIC 8062 8059

SENIOR RESURRECTION SERVICES p 1304
7435 W Talcott Ave, Chicago IL 60631
Tel (773) 774-8000 SIC 8059

SWEDISH COVENANT HOSPITAL p 1411
5145 N California Ave, Chicago IL 60625
Tel (773) 878-8200 SIC 8062 8059

PRESENCE SAINT FRANCIS HOSPITAL p 1172
355 Ridge Ave, Evanston IL 60202
Tel (847) 316-4000 SIC 8062 8059

ROYAL MANAGEMENT CORP p 1254
665 W North Ave Ste 500, Lombard IL 60148
Tel (630) 495-1700 SIC 8059

SILVER CROSS HEALTH SYSTEM p 1323
1900 Silver Cross Blvd, New Lenox IL 60451
Tel (815) 300-1100 SIC 8059

PETERSEN HEALTH CARE INC p 1138
830 W Trailcreek Dr, Peoria IL 61614
Tel (309) 691-8113 SIC 8059

GENESIS HEALTH SYSTEMS p 603
1455 Hospital Rd, Silvis IL 61282
Tel (309) 281-3270 SIC 8051 8059

FRANCISCAN COMMUNITIES INC p 573
203 W Franciscan Dr, Crown Point IN 46307
Tel (219) 661-5100 SIC 8059

LIFESPACE COMMUNITIES INC p 864
100 E Grand Ave Ste 200, Des Moines IA 50309
Tel (515) 288-5805 SIC 8059

WESLEYLIFE p 1593
5508 Nw 88th St, Johnston IA 50131
Tel (515) 271-6789 SIC 8059

TRILOGY REHAB SERVICES LLC p 1480
2701 Chestnut Station Ct, Louisville KY 40299
Tel (800) 335-1060
SIC 8059 1542 8741 8051

UNITED REHAB LLC p 1511
9510 Ormsby Station Rd # 101, Louisville KY 40223
Tel (502) 426-2242 SIC 8052 8051 8059

COMMCARE CORP p 344
950 W Causeway Approach C, Mandeville LA 70471
Tel (504) 324-8950 SIC 8059

PENOBSCOT BAY MEDICAL CENTER p 1131
6 Glen Cove Dr, Rockport ME 04856
Tel (207) 230-6380 SIC 8062 8059

OAK CREST VILLAGE INC p 1070
8800 Walther Blvd Ste 1, Baltimore MD 21234
Tel (410) 665-2222 SIC 8051 8052 8059

DIMENSIONS HEALTH CORP p 440
3001 Hospital Dr, Cheverly MD 20785
Tel (301) 618-2000 SIC 8062 8059

LYRIC HEALTH CARE LLC p 888
7150 Columbia Gateway Dr J, Columbia MD 21046
Tel (443) 539-2369 SIC 8059

ADVENTIST HEALTHCARE INC p 27
820 W Diamond Ave Ste 600, Gaithersburg MD 20878
Tel (301) 315-3030 SIC 8082 8059 8062

ASBURY ATLANTIC INC p 115
201 Russell Ave, Gaithersburg MD 20877
Tel (301) 216-4100 SIC 8059 8051

M G H HEALTH SERVICES CORP p 889
55 Fruit St, Boston MA 02114
Tel (617) 724-0567
SIC 8082 8059 8071 8062

LAHEY CLINIC FOUNDATION INC p 838
41 Mall Rd, Burlington MA 01805
Tel (781) 273-5100 SIC 8059

LAHEY HEALTH SYSTEM INC p 838
41 Mall Rd, Burlington MA 01805
Tel (781) 744-5100 SIC 8059

EPOCH SL III INC p 505
51 Sawyer Rd Ste 500, Waltham MA 02453
Tel (781) 891-0777 SIC 8059 8051

BENEDICTINE HEALTH SYSTEM p 172
503 E 3rd St Ste 400, Duluth MN 55805
Tel (218) 786-2370 SIC 8059

SENIOR CARE COMMUNITIES INC p 1304
161 Saint Anthony Ave # 825, Saint Paul MN 55103
Tel (651) 287-6408 SIC 8059

CIRCLE B ENTERPRISES HOLDING CO INC p 308
731 N Main St Ste 106, Sikeston MO 63801
Tel (573) 471-1276 SIC 8059

BOZEMAN DEACONESS HEALTH SERVICES p 205
915 Highland Blvd, Bozeman MT 59715
Tel (406) 585-5000 SIC 8062 8059

COONEY CONVALESCENT HOME p 366
2555 E Broadway St, Helena MT 59601
Tel (406) 447-1651 SIC 8059 8051

NEW HAMPSHIRE CATHOLIC CHARITIES INC p 1030
215 Myrtle St, Manchester NH 03104
Tel (603) 669-3030
SIC 8322 8059 8331 8661 8361

ST JOSEPH RESIDENCE INC p 1368
495 Mammoth Rd, Manchester NH 03104
Tel (603) 668-6011 SIC 8059

SENIOR SPRINGPOINT LIVING INC p 1304
4814 Outlook Dr Ste 201, Wall Township NJ 07753
Tel (609) 987-8900 SIC 8059 8741

SOUTH VALLEY CARE CENTER p 1345
1629 Bowe Ln Sw, Albuquerque NM 87105
Tel (505) 877-2200 SIC 8051 8059

NORTHEAST HEALTH INC p 1054
315 S Manning Blvd, Albany NY 12208
Tel (518) 292-6200 SIC 8059 8322

UMH NY CORP p 1501
10 Acre Pl, Binghamton NY 13904
Tel (607) 775-6400 SIC 8059 8051 8741

BETH ABRAHAM HEALTH SERVICES p 177
2540 Barker Ave Ofc, Bronx NY 10467
Tel (718) 519-5831 SIC 8059 8351 8082

HEBREW HOME FOR AGED AT RIVERDALE p 680
5901 Palisade Ave, Bronx NY 10471
Tel (718) 581-1000 SIC 8059

CATHOLIC CHARITIES NEIGHBORHOOD SERVICES INC p 265
191 Joralemon St, Brooklyn NY 11201
Tel (718) 722-6000 SIC 8059 8322

PREFERRED HOME CARE INC p 1169
1267 57th St Ste 1p, Brooklyn NY 11219
Tel (718) 841-8000 SIC 8059

ROSALIND AND JOSEPH GURWIN JEWISH GERIATRIC CENTER OF LONG ISLAND INC p 1250
68 Hauppauge Rd, Commack NY 11725
Tel (631) 499-6500 SIC 8059

KENMORE MERCY HOSPITAL p 810
2950 Elmwood Ave Fl 6, Kenmore NY 14217
Tel (716) 447-6100 SIC 8062 8059 8011

NORTHERN SERVICES GROUP INC p 1056
2000 Fountainview Dr, Monsey NY 10952
Tel (845) 356-9880 SIC 8059

PROGRESSIVE HOME HEALTH SERVICES INC p 1181
225 W 34th St Fl 9, New York NY 10122
Tel (212) 273-5500 SIC 8059

PSILOS GROUP MANAGERS LLC p 1188
1 Liberty Plz Ste 2301, New York NY 10006
Tel (212) 242-8844 SIC 6799 8059

UNITED CEREBRAL PALSY ASSOCIATIONS OF NEW YORK STATE INC p 1507
330 W 34th St Fl 15, New York NY 10001
Tel (212) 947-5770 SIC 8059

YOUNG ADULT INSTITUTE INC p 1638
460 W 34th St Fl 11, New York NY 10001
Tel (212) 563-7474 SIC 8059 8361 8011

ROCHESTER GENERAL HEALTH SYSTEM p 1243
1425 Portland Ave, Rochester NY 14621
Tel (585) 922-4000 SIC 8741 8093 8059

UNLIMITED CARE INC p 1528
333 Westchester Ave G02, White Plains NY 10604
Tel (914) 428-4300 SIC 8059 8011

GREENFIELD PLACE LLC p 638
2575 W 5th St, Greenville NC 27834
Tel (252) 830-9100 SIC 8051 8052 8059

BRITTHAVEN INC p 214
1435 Highway 258n, Kinston NC 28504
Tel (252) 939-4131 SIC 8051 8059

HILLCO LTD p 693
1435 Hwy 258 N, Kinston NC 28504
Tel (252) 523-9094
SIC 8051 8059 5047 5122

AUTUMN CORP p 135
451 N Winstead Ave, Rocky Mount NC 27804
Tel (252) 443-6265 SIC 8059 8051

LUTHERAN SERVICES FOR AGING INC p 886
1416 S Martin Luther, Salisbury NC 28144
Tel (704) 637-2870 SIC 8051 8052 8059

BRIAN CENTER REHAB p 211
78 Weaver Blvd, Weaverville NC 28787
Tel (828) 645-4297 SIC 8059

DEACONESS LONG TERM CARE OF MISSOURI INC p 419
330 Straight St Ste 310, Cincinnati OH 45219
Tel (513) 487-3600
SIC 8059 8361 8052 8051

HOSPICE OF WESTERN RESERVE INC p 709
17876 Saint Clair Ave, Cleveland OH 44110
Tel (216) 383-2222 SIC 8059

NATIONAL CHURCH RESIDENCES p 1010
2333 N Bank Dr, Columbus OH 43220
Tel (614) 451-2151
SIC 6531 6513 8051 8059

KINGSTON HEALTHCARE CO p 821
1 Seagate Ste 1960, Toledo OH 43604
Tel (419) 247-2880 SIC 8059 8741

LAUREL HEALTH CARE CO OF NORTH WORTHTINGTON p 847
8181 Worthington Rd, Westerville OH 43082
Tel (614) 794-8800 SIC 8059 8741

ZANDEX HEALTH CARE CORP p 1641
1122 Taylor St, Zanesville OH 43701
Tel (740) 454-1400 SIC 8052 8059 8051

COUNTRY CLUB CARE p 375
1904 N Hwy 81, Duncan OK 73533
Tel (580) 255-4600 SIC 8059

K & C LLC p 798
204 W 1st St, Heavener OK 74937
Tel (918) 653-2464 SIC 8059

GRAND UNION HEALTHCARE LLC p 630
226 E Monore St, Jay OK 74346
Tel (918) 253-4500 SIC 8059

MITCHELL MANOR CONVALESCENT HOME INC p 977
315 W Electric Ave, Mcalester OK 74501
Tel (918) 423-4661 SIC 8051 8059

CALLAWAY NURSING HOME p 242
1300 W Lindsay Ave, Sulphur OK 73086
Tel (580) 622-2416 SIC 8059

▲ HEALTHCARE SERVICES GROUP INC p 676
3220 Tillman Dr Ste 300, Bensalem PA 19020
Tel (215) 639-4274 SIC 8059 7349 8049

CROZER-KEYSTONE HEALTH NETWORK p 396
2602 W 9th St, Chester PA 19013
Tel (610) 497-7400 SIC 8059

COUNTRY MEADOWS ASSOCIATES p 375
830 Cherry Dr, Hershey PA 17033
Tel (717) 533-2474 SIC 8051 8059 8741

▲ GENESIS HEALTHCARE INC p 603
101 E State St, Kennett Square PA 19348
Tel (610) 444-6350
SIC 8051 8052 8059 8361

NHS HUMAN SERVICES INC p 1042
620 Germantown Pike, Lafayette Hill PA 19444
Tel (610) 260-4600 SIC 8093 8059 8082

FAIR ACRES GERIATRIC CENTER p 524
340 N Middletown Rd, Media PA 19063
Tel (610) 891-5700 SIC 8059

COMMUNITY SERVICES GROUP INC p 350
320 Highland Dr, Mountville PA 17554
Tel (717) 285-7121 SIC 8093 8059

CATHOLIC HEALTH EAST p 266
3805 West Chester Pike # 100, Newtown Square PA 19073
Tel (610) 355-2000
SIC 8062 8051 8052 8059 8011

MAIN LINE HEALTH SYSTEM p 897
240 N Radnor Chester Rd, Radnor PA 19087
Tel (610) 225-6200
SIC 5999 8059 8361 8062

RIVERSTREET MANOR p 1238
440 N River St, Wilkes Barre PA 18702
Tel (570) 825-5611 SIC 8361 8059 8051

■ HEALTHCARE RESOURCES CORP p 676
1113 Easton Rd, Willow Grove PA 19090
Tel (215) 659-3060 SIC 8059 8361

WILLOW VALLEY COMMUNITIES p 1613
100 Willow Vly Lakes Dr, Willow Street PA 17584
Tel (717) 464-2741 SIC 8361 8059 8082

MCWIL GROUP LTD p 925
209 N Beaver St, York PA 17401
Tel (717) 854-7857
SIC 8059 8051 8069 6513 8742 6552

WILMAC CORP p 1613
209 N Beaver St, York PA 17401
Tel (717) 854-7857
SIC 8059 8051 8069 6513 8742 6552

SAINT STEPHEN NURSING FACILITY INC p 1270
1038 Mcgill Ln, Saint Stephen SC 29479
Tel (843) 567-2307 SIC 8051 8059

EVANGELICAL LUTHERAN GOOD SAMARITAN SOCIETY p 513
4800 W 57th St, Sioux Falls SD 57108
Tel (866) 928-1635 SIC 8051 8052 8059

▲ BROOKDALE SENIOR LIVING p 217
111 Westwood Pl Ste 400, Brentwood TN 37027
Tel (615) 221-2250 SIC 8059 8361 8051

■ LIFETRUST AMERICA INC p 865
113 Seaboard Ln Ste 150a, Franklin TN 37067
Tel (615) 342-0601
SIC 8361 8051 8052 8059

AMERICAN HEALTH COMPANIES INC p 73
1971 Tennessee Ave N, Parsons TN 38363
Tel (731) 847-6343 SIC 8051 8052 8059

AMERICAN HABILITATION SERVICES INC p 73
9050 N Capital Of Texa, Austin TX 78759
Tel (325) 676-8992 SIC 8059

D&S RESIDENTIAL SERVICES LP p 407
8911 N Capital Of Texas H, Austin TX 78759
Tel (512) 327-2325 SIC 8059

HARDEN HEALTHCARE TEXAS LP p 660
8701 N Mopac Expy, Austin TX 78759
Tel (512) 615-4965 SIC 8059

EAST COKE COUNTY HOSPITAL DISTRICT p 470
900 S State St, Bronte TX 76933
Tel (325) 473-3621 SIC 8059 8051

UT SOUTHWESTERN MEDICAL CENTER p 1536
5323 Harry Hines Blvd # 7200, Dallas TX 75390
Tel (214) 648-2508 SIC 8059

TEXOMA HEALTHCARE SYSTEM p 1445
1000 Memorial Dr, Denison TX 75020
Tel (903) 416-4000 SIC 8062 8059

MEMORIAL HERMANN HEALTHCARE SYSTEM p 941
929 Gessner Rd, Houston TX 77024
Tel (713) 338-5555 SIC 8059 8062

UNIVERSITY GENERAL HEALTH SYSTEM INC p 1518
7501 Fannin St, Houston TX 77054
Tel (713) 375-7100 SIC 8062 8059

GGNSC HOLDINGS LLC p 610
5220 Tennyson Pkwy # 400, Plano TX 75024
Tel (972) 372-6300 SIC 8059

RUTLAND REGIONAL HEALTH SERVICES p 1260
160 Allen St, Rutland VT 05701
Tel (802) 775-7111 SIC 8062 7352 8059

INOVA HEALTH SYSTEM p 745
8110 Gatehouse Rd 200e, Falls Church VA 22042
Tel (703) 289-2069
SIC 8741 8011 8062 8049 8059 8051

LOUDOUN HEALTHCARE INC p 879
44045 Riverside Pkwy, Leesburg VA 20176
Tel (703) 777-3300 SIC 8062 8059

PATRICK HENRY HOSPITAL INC p 1120
1000 Old Denbigh Blvd, Newport News VA 23602
Tel (757) 875-2000 SIC 8052 8059 8051

AMERICAN HEALTHCARE LLC p 74
3131 Electric Rd, Roanoke VA 24018
Tel (540) 774-4263 SIC 8052 8051 8059

GREENSPRING VILLAGE INC p 638
7440 Spring Village Dr, Springfield VA 22150
Tel (703) 313-7800 SIC 8059

WINCHESTER MEDICAL CENTER p 1614
1840 Amherst St, Winchester VA 22601
Tel (540) 536-8000 SIC 8059

AMERICAN BAPTIST HOMES OF WASHINGTON INC p 68
23600 Marine View Dr S, Des Moines WA 98198
Tel (206) 870-6641 SIC 8051 8059 8052

PAINTED POST PARTNERS p 1108
3131 Elliott Ave Ste 500, Seattle WA 98121
Tel (206) 298-2909 SIC 8059

EVERGREEN HEALTHCARE INC p 514
4601 Ne 77th Ave Ste 300, Vancouver WA 98662
Tel (360) 892-6472
SIC 8051 6513 8059 8741

AID HOLDINGS LLC p 37
W140n8981 Lilly Rd, Menomonee Falls WI 53051
Tel (262) 257-8888
SIC 8052 8051 8059 8082

■ SENIOR BROOKDALE LIVING COMMUNITIES INC p 1303
6737 W Wa St Ste 2300, Milwaukee WI 53214
Tel (414) 918-5000 SIC 8059 8051 8361

SENIOR BROOKDALE LIVING INC p 1303
6737 W Wa St Ste 2300, Milwaukee WI 53214
Tel (941) 625-1220 SIC 8059

GREATER WATERTOWN COMMUNITY HEALTH FOUNDATION INC p 636
125 Hospital Dr, Watertown WI 53098
Tel (920) 261-4210 SIC 8062 8011 8059

SIC 8062 General Medical & Surgical Hospitals

BAPTIST HEALTH SYSTEM INC p 153
1000 1st St N, Alabaster AL 35007
Tel (205) 620-8100 SIC 8062

REGIONAL MEDICAL CENTER BOARD p 1219
400 E 10th St, Anniston AL 36207
Tel (256) 235-5121 SIC 8062

GULF HEALTH HOSPITALS INC p 646
1815 Hand Ave, Bay Minette AL 36507
Tel (251) 937-5521 SIC 8062

UAB MEDICAL WEST p 1498
995 9th Ave Sw, Bessemer AL 35022
Tel (205) 481-7000 SIC 8062

■ AFFINITY HOSPITAL LLC p 32
3690 Grandview Pkwy, Birmingham AL 35243
Tel (205) 592-1000 SIC 8062 8011

CARRAWAY METHODIST HEALTH SYSTEMS p 260
1600 Carraway Blvd, Birmingham AL 35234
Tel (205) 502-4100 SIC 8069 8062

EASTERN HEALTH SYSTEM INC p 472
Medical Park E Dr Bldg 1, Birmingham AL 35235
Tel (205) 838-3996
SIC 8062 8082 8051 8011 8322 8093

ST VINCENTS BIRMINGHAM p 1373
810 Saint Vincents Dr, Birmingham AL 35205
Tel (205) 939-7000 SIC 8062

ST VINCENTS EAST p 1373
50 Medical Park Dr E, Birmingham AL 35235
Tel (205) 838-3000 SIC 8062 8011

ST VINCENTS HEALTH SYSTEM p 1373
810 Saint Vincents Dr, Birmingham AL 35205
Tel (205) 939-7000 SIC 8062

UNIVERSITY OF ALABAMA AT BIRMINGHAM p 1519
701 20th St S, Birmingham AL 35233
Tel (205) 934-5493 SIC 8221 8062

MARSHALL COUNTY HEALTH CARE AUTHORITY p 911
2505 Us Highway 431, Boaz AL 35957
Tel (256) 894-6600 SIC 8062

CULLMAN REGIONAL MEDICAL CENTER INC p 400
1912 Al Highway 157, Cullman AL 35058
Tel (256) 737-2000 SIC 8062

HEALTH CARE AUTHORITY OF CULLMAN COUNTY p 674
1912 Al Highway 157, Cullman AL 35058
Tel (256) 737-2000 SIC 8062

HEALTH CARE AUTHORITY OF MORGAN COUNTY - CITY OF DECATUR p 674
1201 7th St Se, Decatur AL 35601
Tel (256) 355-0370 SIC 8062

HOUSTON COUNTY HEALTHCARE AUTHORITY p 712
1108 Ross Clark Cir, Dothan AL 36301
Tel (334) 793-8111 SIC 8062

■ TRIAD OF ALABAMA LLC p 1478
4370 W Main St, Dothan AL 36305
Tel (334) 793-5000 SIC 8062 8082

GULF HEALTH HOSPITALS INC p 646
750 Morphy Ave, Fairhope AL 36532
Tel (251) 928-2375 SIC 8062 8011

ELIZA COFFEE MEMORIAL HOSPITAL p 487
205 Marengo St, Florence AL 35630
Tel (256) 768-9191 SIC 8062

HEALTH CARE AUTHORITY OF LAUDERDALE COUNTY AND CITY OF FLORENCE p 674
205 Marengo St, Florence AL 35630
Tel (256) 768-9191 SIC 8051 8062

■ FOLEY HOSPITAL CORP p 563
1613 N Mckenzie St, Foley AL 36535
Tel (251) 949-3400 SIC 8062

■ GADSDEN REGIONAL MEDICAL CENTER LLC p 589
1007 Goodyear Ave, Gadsden AL 35903
Tel (256) 494-4000
SIC 8062 8082 8011 7352

RIVERVIEW REGIONAL MEDICAL CENTER INC p 1239
600 S 3rd St, Gadsden AL 35901
Tel (256) 543-5200 SIC 8062

CRESTWOOD HEALTHCARE LP p 392
1 Hospital Dr Sw, Huntsville AL 35801
Tel (256) 429-4000 SIC 8062

HEALTH CARE AUTHORITY OF CITY OF HUNTSVILLE p 674
101 Sivley Rd Sw, Huntsville AL 35801
Tel (256) 265-1000 SIC 8011 8062

HUNTSVILLE HOSPITAL p 720
101 Sivley Rd Sw, Huntsville AL 35801
Tel (256) 265-1000 SIC 8062

WALKER REGIONAL MEDICAL CENTER INC p 1573
3400 Highway 78 E, Jasper AL 35501
Tel (205) 387-4000 SIC 8062

INFIRMARY HEALTH SYSTEM INC p 741
5 Mobile Infirmary Cir, Mobile AL 36607
Tel (251) 435-3030
SIC 8062 6512 1542 7322 5047 7389

MOBILE INFIRMARY ASSOCIATION p 980
5 Mobile Infirmary Cir, Mobile AL 36607
Tel (251) 435-2400 SIC 8062

PROVIDENCE HOSPITAL p 1186
6801 Airport Blvd, Mobile AL 36608
Tel (251) 633-1000 SIC 8062 8011

SPRINGHILL HOSPITALS INC p 1361
3719 Dauphin St Frnt, Mobile AL 36608
Tel (251) 344-9630 SIC 8062

UNIVERSITY OF SOUTH ALABAMA MEDICAL CENTER p 1525
2451 Fillingim St, Mobile AL 36617
Tel (251) 471-7110 SIC 8062

BAPTIST HEALTH p 153
301 Brown Springs Rd, Montgomery AL 36117
Tel (334) 273-4217 SIC 8062

HEALTHCARE AUTHORITY FOR BAPTIST HEALTH AND AFFILIATE OF UAB HEALTH SYSTEM p 676
2105 E South Blvd, Montgomery AL 36116
Tel (334) 286-2987 SIC 8062

JACKSON HOSPITAL & CLINIC INC p 774
1725 Pine St, Montgomery AL 36106
Tel (334) 293-8000 SIC 8062

EAST ALABAMA HEALTH CARE AUTHORITY p 469
2000 Pepperell Pkwy, Opelika AL 36801
Tel (334) 749-3411 SIC 8062

HH HEALTH SYSTEM - SHOALS LLC p 689
1300 S Mongomery Ave, Sheffield AL 35660
Tel (256) 386-4673 SIC 8062

CENTURY HEALTH ALLIANCE JOINT VENTURE p 282
809 University Blvd E, Tuscaloosa AL 35401
Tel (205) 759-7111 SIC 8062 8741

DCH HEALTH CARE AUTHORITY p 418
809 University Blvd E, Tuscaloosa AL 35401
Tel (205) 759-7111 SIC 8062 8093

HARDIN TAYLOR SECURE MEDICAL FACILITY p 661
1301 Jack Warner Pkwy Ne, Tuscaloosa AL 35404
Tel (205) 556-7060 SIC 8062 9431

CAPELLA HEALTH HOLDINGS LLC p 248
1000 Urban Center Dr # 501, Vestavia AL 35242
Tel (205) 969-3455 SIC 6798 8062

GALEN HOSPITAL ALASKA INC p 589
2801 Debarr Rd, Anchorage AK 99508
Tel (907) 276-1131 SIC 8062

USPHS AK NATIVE MEDICAL CENTER p 1535
4315 Diplomacy Dr, Anchorage AK 99508
Tel (907) 729-2544 SIC 8062

YUKON-KUSKOKWIM HEALTH CORP p 1640
829 Hospin Hwy Ste 329, Bethel AK 99559
Tel (907) 543-6300
SIC 8062 7363 8069 8093 8042 8021

BRISTOL BAY AREA HEALTH CORP p 214
6000 Kanakanak Rd, Dillingham AK 99576
Tel (907) 842-5201 SIC 8062 8011

SOUTHEAST ALASKA REGIONAL HEALTH CONSORTIUM p 1345
3100 Channel Dr Ste 300, Juneau AK 99801
Tel (907) 463-4000 SIC 8011 8062

MANIILAQ ASSOCIATION p 901
733 2nd Ave Ferguson Bldg, Kotzebue AK 99752
Tel (907) 442-3311 SIC 8062 8741

CENTRAL PENINSULA GENERAL HOSPITAL INC p 279
250 Hospital Pl, Soldotna AK 99669
Tel (907) 262-4404 SIC 8062

CASA GRANDE COMMUNITY HOSPITAL p 262
1800 E Florence Blvd, Casa Grande AZ 85122
Tel (520) 426-6300 SIC 8062

CHANDLER REGIONAL MEDICAL CENTER p 288
1955 W Frye Rd, Chandler AZ 85224
Tel (480) 728-3000 SIC 8062

VERDE VALLEY MEDICAL CENTER p 1549
269 S Candy Ln, Cottonwood AZ 86326
Tel (928) 634-2251 SIC 8062

FLAGSTAFF MEDICAL CENTER INC p 554
1200 N Beaver St, Flagstaff AZ 86001
Tel (928) 779-3366 SIC 8062

NORTHERN ARIZONA HEALTHCARE CORP p 1055
1200 N Beaver St, Flagstaff AZ 86001
Tel (928) 779-3366
SIC 8741 8062 8399 4119

GILBERT HOSPITAL LLC p 612
5656 S Power Rd Ste 133, Gilbert AZ 85295
Tel (480) 984-2000 SIC 8062

ACHMC INC p 17
18701 N 67th Ave, Glendale AZ 85308
Tel (623) 561-7170 SIC 8062

ABRAZO WEST CAMPUS p 12
13677 W Mcdowell Rd, Goodyear AZ 85395
Tel (623) 882-1500 SIC 8062

KINGMAN HOSPITAL INC p 820
3269 N Stockton Hill Rd, Kingman AZ 86409
Tel (928) 757-2101 SIC 8062

■ PHC-LAKE HAVASU INC p 1141
101 Civic Center Ln, Lake Havasu City AZ 86403
Tel (928) 855-8185 SIC 8062

BANNER HEALTH SYSTEM p 153
6644 E Baywood Ave, Mesa AZ 85206
Tel (480) 321-2000 SIC 8062

LUTHERAN HEART HOSPITAL p 886
6750 E Baywood Ave, Mesa AZ 85206
Tel (480) 854-5000 SIC 8062

MOUNTAIN VISTA MEDICAL CENTER LP p 994
1301 S Crismon Rd, Mesa AZ 85209
Tel (480) 358-6100 SIC 8062

ORO VALLEY HOSPITAL LLC p 1095
1551 E Tangerine Rd, Oro Valley AZ 85755
Tel (520) 901-3500 SIC 8062

■ ABRAZO CENTRAL CAMPUS p 12
2000 W Bethany Home Rd, Phoenix AZ 85015
Tel (602) 249-0212 SIC 8062

BANNER HEALTH p 153
2901 N Central Ave # 160, Phoenix AZ 85012
Tel (602) 747-4000
SIC 8062 8051 8082 7361 8011 8093

ESTRELLA BANNER SURGERY CENTER p 511
9301 W Thomas Rd, Phoenix AZ 85037
Tel (623) 388-5700 SIC 8062

JOHN C LINCOLN HEALTH NETWORK p 788
250 E Dunlap Ave, Phoenix AZ 85020
Tel (602) 870-6060 SIC 8062 8051

MARICOPA COUNTY SPECIAL HEALTH CARE DISTRICT p 906
2601 E Roosevelt St, Phoenix AZ 85008
Tel (602) 344-5726 SIC 8062

ST LUKES MEDICAL CENTER LP p 1370
1800 E Van Buren St, Phoenix AZ 85006
Tel (602) 251-8535 SIC 8062 8063 8051

TRIWEST HEALTHCARE ALLIANCE CORP p 1483
15810 N 28th Ave, Phoenix AZ 85053
Tel (602) 564-2000 SIC 8741 8062

YAVAPAI COMMUNITY HOSP ASSN p 1635
1003 Willow Creek Rd, Prescott AZ 86301
Tel (928) 445-2700 SIC 8062 8011

SCOTTSDALE HEALTHCARE CORP p 1294
8125 N Hayden Rd, Scottsdale AZ 85258
Tel (480) 882-4000 SIC 8062

SCOTTSDALE HEALTHCARE HOSPITALS p 1294
8125 N Hayden Rd, Scottsdale AZ 85258
Tel (480) 324-7215 SIC 8062

SUMMIT HEALTH CARE REGIONAL MEDICAL CENTER p 1399
2200 E Show Low Lake Rd, Show Low AZ 85901
Tel (928) 537-6338 SIC 8062

VISTA RCHP-SIERRA INC p 1562
5700 E Highway 90, Sierra Vista AZ 85635
Tel (520) 458-4641 SIC 8062

BANNER HEALTH p 153
14502 W Meeker Blvd, Sun City AZ 85375
Tel (623) 524-4000 SIC 8062

SUN HEALTH CORP p 1400
14719 W Grand Ave Ste 113, Surprise AZ 85374
Tel (623) 876-5350
SIC 8062 8051 8082 7361 8733 6531

TUBA CITY REGIONAL HEALTHCARE CORP p 1490
167 N Main St, Tuba City AZ 86045
Tel (928) 283-2501 SIC 8062

BANNER-UNIVERSITY MEDICAL CENTER SOUTH CAMPUS LLC p 153
2800 E Ajo Way, Tucson AZ 85713
Tel (520) 874-2000 SIC 8062

BANNER-UNIVERSITY MEDICAL CENTER TUCSON CAMPUS LLC p 153
1501 N Campbell Ave, Tucson AZ 85724
Tel (520) 694-0111 SIC 8062

CARONDELET HEALTH NETWORK p 260
2202 N Forbes Blvd, Tucson AZ 85745
Tel (520) 872-7542 SIC 8062

■ NORTHWEST MEDICAL CENTER p 1060
6200 N La Cholla Blvd, Tucson AZ 85741
Tel (520) 742-9000 SIC 8062

TMC HEALTHCARE p 1457
5301 E Grant Rd, Tucson AZ 85712
Tel (520) 327-5461 SIC 8051 8062

TUCSON MEDICAL CENTER p 1490
5301 E Grant Rd, Tucson AZ 85712
Tel (520) 327-5461
SIC 8062 8051 6513 8741

YUMA REGIONAL MEDICAL CENTER INC p 1640
2400 S Avenue A, Yuma AZ 85364
Tel (928) 344-2000 SIC 8062

WHITE RIVER HEALTH SYSTEM INC p 1606
1710 Harrison St, Batesville AR 72501
Tel (870) 262-1200 SIC 8062

SALINE COUNTY MEDICAL CENTER p 1272
1 Medical Park Dr, Benton AR 72015
Tel (501) 776-6000 SIC 8062

CONWAY REGIONAL MEDICAL CENTER INC p 365
2302 College Ave, Conway AR 72034
Tel (501) 329-3831 SIC 8062

WASHINGTON REGIONAL MEDICAL CENTER p 1579
3215 N Northhills Blvd, Fayetteville AR 72703
Tel (479) 463-6000 SIC 8062

WASHINGTON REGIONAL MEDICAL SYSTEM p 1579
3215 N Northhills Blvd, Fayetteville AR 72703
Tel (479) 463-1000 SIC 8062 8069

■ FORTH SMITH HMA LLC p 569
1001 Towson Ave, Fort Smith AR 72901
Tel (479) 441-4000 SIC 8062

MERCY HOSPITAL FORT SMITH p 947
7301 Rogers Ave, Fort Smith AR 72903
Tel (479) 314-6000 SIC 8062

■ SPARKS REGIONAL MEDICAL CENTER p 1354
1001 Towson Ave, Fort Smith AR 72901
Tel (479) 441-4000 SIC 8062

NORTH ARKANSAS REGIONAL MEDICAL CENTER p 1050
620 N Main St, Harrison AR 72601
Tel (870) 414-4000 SIC 8062

HOT SPRINGS NATIONAL PARK HOSPITAL HOLDINGS LLC p 710
1910 Malvern Ave, Hot Springs AR 71901
Tel (501) 321-1000 SIC 8062

ST JOSEPHS REGIONAL HEALTH CENTER (INC) p 1369
300 Werner St, Hot Springs AR 71913
Tel (501) 622-4500 SIC 8062

ST BERNARDS HOSPITAL INC p 1365
225 E Jackson Ave, Jonesboro AR 72401
Tel (870) 207-7300 SIC 8062

ARKANSAS CHILDRENS HOSPITAL p 109
1 Childrens Way, Little Rock AR 72202
Tel (501) 364-1100 SIC 8062 8069

ARKANSAS HEART HOSPITAL LLC p 109
1701 S Shackleford Rd, Little Rock AR 72211
Tel (501) 219-7000 SIC 8062 8011

BAPTIST HEALTH MEDICAL CENTER p 153
9601 Baptist Health Dr # 109, Little Rock AR 72205
Tel (501) 887-3000 SIC 8062

ST VINCENT HEALTH SERVICES INC p 1373
2 Saint Vincent Cir, Little Rock AR 72205
Tel (501) 552-2620 SIC 8062 8099

BAXTER COUNTY REGIONAL HOSPITAL INC p 160
624 Hospital Dr, Mountain Home AR 72653
Tel (870) 508-1000 SIC 8062

JEFFERSON HOSPITAL ASSOCIATION INC p 781
1600 W 40th Ave, Pine Bluff AR 71603
Tel (870) 541-7100 SIC 8062

MERCY HEALTH SYSTEM OF NORTHWEST ARKANSAS INC p 946
2710 S Rife Medical Ln, Rogers AR 72758
Tel (479) 338-8000 SIC 8062

MERCY HOSPITAL ROGERS p 947
2710 S Rife Medical Ln, Rogers AR 72758
Tel (479) 338-8000 SIC 8062

ST MARYS REGIONAL MEDICAL CENTER p 1372
1808 W Main St, Russellville AR 72801
Tel (479) 968-2841 SIC 8062

WHITE COUNTY MEDICAL CENTER p 1606
3214 E Race Ave, Searcy AR 72143
Tel (501) 268-6121 SIC 8082 8062

■ NORTHWEST HEALTH SYSTEM INC p 1059
609 W Maple Ave, Springdale AR 72764
Tel (479) 751-5711 SIC 8062

AHMC HEALTHCARE INC p 37
1000 S Fremont Ave Unit 6, Alhambra CA 91803
Tel (626) 943-7526 SIC 8062 8641

ANAHEIM REGIONAL MEDICAL CENTER p 88
1111 W La Palma Ave, Anaheim CA 92801
Tel (714) 774-1450 SIC 8069 8062

PRIME HEALTHCARE ANAHEIM LLC p 1175
3033 W Orange Ave, Anaheim CA 92804
Tel (714) 827-3000 SIC 8062

ST MARY MEDICAL CENTER p 1371
18300 Us Highway 18, Apple Valley CA 92307
Tel (760) 242-2311 SIC 8062

METHODIST HOSPITAL OF SOUTHERN CALIFORNIA p 954
300 W Huntington Dr, Arcadia CA 91007
Tel (626) 898-8000 SIC 8062

BAKERSFIELD MEMORIAL HOSPITAL p 146
420 34th St, Bakersfield CA 93301
Tel (661) 327-1792 *SIC* 8062

SAN JOAQUIN COMMUNITY HOSPITAL p 1277
2615 Chester Ave, Bakersfield CA 93301
Tel (661) 395-3000 *SIC* 8062 8011

SURGERY CENTER OF ALTA BATES SUMMIT MEDICAL CENTER LLC p 1408
2450 Ashby Ave, Berkeley CA 94705
Tel (510) 204-4444 *SIC* 8062

PIONEERS MEMORIAL HEALTHCARE DISTRICT p 1151
207 W Legion Rd, Brawley CA 92227
Tel (760) 351-3333 *SIC* 8062

MILLS-PENINSULA HEALTH SERVICES p 971
1501 Trousdale Dr, Burlingame CA 94010
Tel (650) 696-5400 *SIC* 8062

EDEN TOWNSHIP HOSPITAL DISTRICT INC p 477
20400 Lake Chabot Rd # 303, Castro Valley CA 94546
Tel (510) 538-2031 *SIC* 8062 8011

ENLOE MEDICAL CENTER p 500
1531 Esplanade, Chico CA 95926
Tel (530) 332-7300 *SIC* 8062

VERITAS HEALTH SERVICES INC p 1549
5451 Walnut Ave, Chino CA 91710
Tel (909) 464-8600 *SIC* 8062

SHARP CHULA VISTA AUXILIARY INC p 1312
751 Medical Center Ct, Chula Vista CA 91911
Tel (619) 421-6110 *SIC* 8062

SHARP CHULA VISTA MEDICAL CENTER p 1312
751 Medical Center Ct, Chula Vista CA 91911
Tel (619) 502-5800 *SIC* 8062

ARROWHEAD REGIONAL MEDICAL CENTER p 113
400 N Pepper Ave, Colton CA 92324
Tel (909) 580-1000 *SIC* 8062

■ **UHS-CORONA INC** p 1500
800 S Main St, Corona CA 92882
Tel (951) 737-4343 *SIC* 8062

SHARP CORONADO HOSPITAL & HEALTHCARE CENTER p 1312
250 Prospect Pl, Coronado CA 92118
Tel (619) 522-3600 *SIC* 8062

COLLEGE HOSPITAL COSTA MESA MSO INC p 336
301 Victoria St, Costa Mesa CA 92627
Tel (949) 642-2734 *SIC* 8062

SOUTHERN CALIFORNIA HOSPITAL AT CULVER CITY p 1347
3828 Delmas Ter, Culver City CA 90232
Tel (310) 836-7000 *SIC* 8062

SETON MEDICAL CENTER p 1309
1900 Sullivan Ave, Daly City CA 94015
Tel (650) 992-4000 *SIC* 8062 8051

DOWNEY REGIONAL MEDICAL CENTER-HOSPITAL INC p 453
11500 Brookshire Ave, Downey CA 90241
Tel (562) 698-0811 *SIC* 8062

CITY OF HOPE NATIONAL MEDICAL CENTER p 315
1500 Duarte Rd, Duarte CA 91010
Tel (626) 256-4673 *SIC* 8062

EL CENTRO REGIONAL MEDICAL CENTER INC p 482
1415 Ross Ave, El Centro CA 92243
Tel (760) 339-7100 *SIC* 8062

PALOMAR HEALTH p 1110
456 E Grand Ave, Escondido CA 92025
Tel (442) 281-5000 *SIC* 8062 8059

ST JOSEPH HOSPITAL p 1368
2700 Dolbeer St, Eureka CA 95501
Tel (707) 445-8121 *SIC* 8062

ST JOSEPH HOSPITAL OF EUREKA p 1368
2700 Dolbeer St, Eureka CA 95501
Tel (707) 445-8121 *SIC* 8062

NORTHBAY HEALTHCARE GROUP p 1054
1200 B Gale Wilson Blvd, Fairfield CA 94533
Tel (707) 646-5000 *SIC* 8062

■ **FOUNTAIN VALLEY REGIONAL HOSPITAL AND MEDICAL CENTER** p 571
17100 Euclid St, Fountain Valley CA 92708
Tel (714) 966-7200 *SIC* 8062

MEMORIAL HEALTH SERVICES p 941
17360 Brookhurst St # 160, Fountain Valley CA 92708
Tel (714) 377-6748 *SIC* 8062

ORANGE COAST MEMORIAL MEDICAL CENTER p 1091
9920 Talbert Ave, Fountain Valley CA 92708
Tel (714) 378-7000 *SIC* 8062

WASHINGTON HOSPITAL HEALTHCARE SYSTEM p 1578
2000 Mowry Ave, Fremont CA 94538
Tel (510) 797-3342 *SIC* 8062

SAN JOAQUIN HOSPITAL p 1277
500 W Hospital Rd, French Camp CA 95231
Tel (209) 468-6000 *SIC* 8062

COMMUNITY MEDICAL CENTER p 349
2823 Fresno St, Fresno CA 93721
Tel (559) 459-6000 *SIC* 8062 8011 8051

FRESNO COMMUNITY HOSPITAL AND MEDICAL CENTER p 579
2823 Fresno St, Fresno CA 93721
Tel (559) 459-6000 *SIC* 8062

SAINT AGNES MEDICAL CENTER p 1268
1303 E Herndon Ave, Fresno CA 93720
Tel (559) 450-3000 *SIC* 8062

ST JUDE HOSPITAL p 1369
101 E Valencia Mesa Dr, Fullerton CA 92835
Tel (714) 871-3280 *SIC* 8062

KENNETH CORP p 811
12601 Garden Grove Blvd, Garden Grove CA 92843
Tel (714) 537-5160 *SIC* 8062

GARDENA HOSPITAL LP p 591
1145 W Redondo Beach Blvd, Gardena CA 90247
Tel (310) 532-4200 *SIC* 8062 8322 8011

SAINT LOUISE HOSPITAL p 1270
9400 N Name Uno, Gilroy CA 95020
Tel (408) 848-2000 *SIC* 8062

GLENDALE ADVENTIST MEDICAL CENTER INC p 615
1509 Wilson Ter, Glendale CA 91206
Tel (818) 409-8000 *SIC* 8062 8093 8011

GLENDALE MEMORIAL HEALTH CORP p 615
1420 S Central Ave, Glendale CA 91204
Tel (818) 502-1900 *SIC* 8062

GLENOAKS CONVALESCENT HOSPITAL (LP) p 615
409 W Glenoaks Blvd, Glendale CA 91202
Tel (818) 240-4300 *SIC* 8062

FOOTHILL HOSPITAL-MORRIS L JOHNSTON MEMORIAL p 564
250 S Grand Ave, Glendora CA 91741
Tel (626) 857-3145 *SIC* 8062

SIERRA NEVADA MEMORIAL-MINERS HOSPITAL p 1321
155 Glasson Way, Grass Valley CA 95945
Tel (530) 274-6000 *SIC* 8062

MARIN HEALTHCARE DISTRICT p 906
100b Drakes Landing Rd, Greenbrae CA 94904
Tel (415) 464-2090 *SIC* 8062

CENTRAL VALLEY GENERAL HOSPITAL p 280
1025 N Douty St, Hanford CA 93230
Tel (559) 583-2100 *SIC* 8062

HANFORD COMMUNITY HOSPITAL p 657
450 Greenfield Ave, Hanford CA 93230
Tel (559) 582-9000 *SIC* 8062

HAYWARD SISTERS HOSPITAL p 670
27200 Calaroga Ave, Hayward CA 94545
Tel (510) 264-4000 *SIC* 8062

ST ROSE HOSPITAL p 1373
27200 Calaroga Ave, Hayward CA 94545
Tel (510) 264-4000 *SIC* 8062

HEMET VALLEY MEDICAL CENTER-EDUCATION p 682
1117 E Devonshire Ave, Hemet CA 92543
Tel (951) 652-2811 *SIC* 8062

PHYSICIANS FOR HEALTHY HOSPITALS INC p 1145
1117 E Devonshire Ave, Hemet CA 92543
Tel (951) 652-2811 *SIC* 8062

SAN BENITO HEALTH CARE DISTRICT p 1275
911 Sunset Dr Ste A, Hollister CA 95023
Tel (831) 637-5711 *SIC* 8062 8051 8059

PRIME HEALTHCARE CENTINELA LLC p 1175
555 E Hardy St, Inglewood CA 90301
Tel (310) 673-4660 *SIC* 8062

ALECTO HEALTHCARE SERVICES LLC p 48
16310 Bake Pkwy Ste 200, Irvine CA 92618
Tel (323) 938-3161 *SIC* 8062

MARIN GENERAL HOSPITAL p 906
250 Bon Air Rd, Kentfield CA 94904
Tel (415) 925-7000 *SIC* 8062 8011

SCHAETZEL CENTER-SCRIPPS MEMORIAL HOSPITAL p 1286
9890 Genesee Ave, La Jolla CA 92037
Tel (858) 626-7712 *SIC* 8062

GROSSMONT HOSPITAL CORP p 641
5555 Grossmont Center Dr, La Mesa CA 91942
Tel (619) 740-6000 *SIC* 8062

SADDLEBACK MEMORIAL MEDICAL CENTER p 1265
24451 Health Center Dr, Laguna Hills CA 92653
Tel (949) 837-4500
SIC 8062 8011 8093 8099 8071 8069

ANTELOPE VALLEY HOSPITAL AUXILIARY p 93
1600 W Avenue J, Lancaster CA 93534
Tel (661) 949-5000 *SIC* 8062

LODI MEMORIAL HOSPITAL ASSOCIATION INC p 874
975 S Fairmont Ave, Lodi CA 95240
Tel (209) 334-3411 *SIC* 8062

LOMA LINDA UNIVERSITY HEALTH CARE p 875
11370 Anderson St # 3900, Loma Linda CA 92350
Tel (909) 558-2806
SIC 8062 8011 8051 5999

LOMA LINDA UNIVERSITY MEDICAL CENTER p 875
11234 Anderson St, Loma Linda CA 92354
Tel (909) 558-4000
SIC 8062 8011 8051 5999

CATHOLIC HEALTHCARE WEST SOUTHERN CALIFORNIA p 267
1050 Linden Ave, Long Beach CA 90813
Tel (562) 491-9000 *SIC* 8062

LONG BEACH MEMORIAL MEDICAL CENTER p 876
2801 Atlantic Ave Fl 2, Long Beach CA 90806
Tel (562) 933-2000 *SIC* 8062

MEMORIAL HEALTH SERVICES - UNIVERSITY OF CALIFORNIA AT IRVINE CENTER FOR HEALTH EDUCATION p 941
2801 Atlantic Ave, Long Beach CA 90806
Tel (562) 933-2000 *SIC* 8062 8741

ST MARY MEDICAL CENTER p 1371
1050 Linden Ave, Long Beach CA 90813
Tel (562) 491-9000 *SIC* 8062

■ **LOS ALAMITOS MEDICAL CENTER INC** p 878
3751 Katella Ave, Los Alamitos CA 90720
Tel (714) 826-6400 *SIC* 8062

CALIFORNIA HOSPITAL MEDICAL CENTER FOUNDATION p 240
1401 S Grand Ave, Los Angeles CA 90015
Tel (213) 748-2411 *SIC* 8062

CHA HOLLYWOOD MEDICAL CENTER LP p 286
1300 N Vermont Ave, Los Angeles CA 90027
Tel (213) 413-3000 *SIC* 8062 8351

CHILDRENS HOSPITAL LOS ANGELES p 299
4650 W Sunset Blvd, Los Angeles CA 90027
Tel (323) 660-2450 *SIC* 8069 8062

GOOD SAMARITAN HOSPITAL p 623
1225 Wilshire Blvd, Los Angeles CA 90017
Tel (213) 977-2121 *SIC* 8062

GOOD SAMARITAN HOSPITAL p 623
600 Witmer St, Los Angeles CA 90017
Tel (213) 977-2121 *SIC* 8062

HOLLYWOOD MEDICAL CENTER LP p 701
1300 N Vermont Ave, Los Angeles CA 90027
Tel (213) 413-3000 *SIC* 8062

MEMORIAL HOSPITAL OF GARDENA p 942
4060 Woody Blvd, Los Angeles CA 90023
Tel (323) 268-5514 *SIC* 8062

PARACELSUS LOS ANGELES COMMUNITY HOSPITAL INC p 1113
4081 E Olympic Blvd, Los Angeles CA 90023
Tel (323) 267-0477 *SIC* 8062

QUEEN OF ANGELS HOLLYWOOD PRESBYTERIAN MEDICAL CENTER p 1198
1300 N Vermont Ave, Los Angeles CA 90027
Tel (213) 413-3000 *SIC* 8062

SOUTHERN CALIFORNIA HEALTHCARE SYSTEM INC p 1347
3415 S Sepulveda Blvd # 9, Los Angeles CA 90034
Tel (310) 943-4500 *SIC* 8062

ST VINCENT MEDICAL CENTER p 1373
2131 W 3rd St, Los Angeles CA 90057
Tel (213) 484-7111 *SIC* 8062

WHITE MEMORIAL MEDICAL CENTER INC p 1606
1720 E Cesar E Chavez Ave, Los Angeles CA 90033
Tel (323) 268-5000 *SIC* 8062

ST FRANCIS MEDICAL CENTER OF LYNWOOD FOUNDATION p 1367
3630 E Imperial Hwy, Lynwood CA 90262
Tel (310) 900-8900 *SIC* 8062

MADERA COMMUNITY HOSPITAL p 894
1250 E Almond Ave, Madera CA 93637
Tel (559) 675-5555 *SIC* 8062

CFHS HOLDINGS INC p 285
4650 Lincoln Blvd, Marina Del Rey CA 90292
Tel (310) 823-8911 *SIC* 8062 8093 8011

RIDEOUT MEMORIAL HOSPITAL p 1234
726 4th St, Marysville CA 95901
Tel (530) 749-4416 *SIC* 8062 8082

LELAND STANFORD JUNIOR UNIVERSITY p 854
2575 Sand Hill Rd, Menlo Park CA 94025
Tel (650) 723-2300 *SIC* 8221 8069 8062

MATER MISERICORDIAE HOSPITAL p 919
333 Mercy Ave, Merced CA 95340
Tel (209) 564-5000 *SIC* 8062

PROVIDENCE HOLY CROSS MEDICAL CENTER GUILD p 1186
15031 Rinaldi St, Mission Hills CA 91345
Tel (818) 365-8051 *SIC* 8062

MISSION HOSPITAL REGIONAL MEDICAL CENTER INC p 975
27700 Medical Center Rd, Mission Viejo CA 92691
Tel (949) 364-1400 *SIC* 8062

■ **DOCTORS MEDICAL CENTER OF MODESTO INC** p 447
1441 Florida Ave, Modesto CA 95350
Tel (209) 578-1211 *SIC* 8062

SUTTER CENTRAL VALLEY HOSPITALS p 1410
1700 Coffee Rd, Modesto CA 95355
Tel (209) 526-4500 *SIC* 8062

BEVERLY COMMUNITY HOSPITAL ASSOCIATION p 178
309 W Beverly Blvd, Montebello CA 90640
Tel (323) 726-1222 *SIC* 8062

AHMC GARFIELD MEDICAL CENTER LP p 37
525 N Garfield Ave, Monterey Park CA 91754
Tel (626) 573-2222 *SIC* 8051 8062

EL CAMINO HOSPITAL p 482
2500 Grant Rd, Mountain View CA 94040
Tel (408) 224-6660 *SIC* 8062

■ **SOUTHWEST HEALTHCARE SYSTEM AUXILIARY** p 1352
25500 Medical Center Dr, Murrieta CA 92562
Tel (951) 696-6000
SIC 8062 8051 8059 4119

QUEEN OF VALLEY MEDICAL CENTER p 1198
1000 Trancas St, Napa CA 94558
Tel (707) 252-4411 *SIC* 8062

PARADISE VALLEY HOSPITAL p 1113
2400 E 4th St, National City CA 91950
Tel (619) 470-4100 *SIC* 8062

HEALTHSMART PACIFIC INC p 677
20377 Sw Acacia St # 110, Newport Beach CA 92660
Tel (562) 595-1911 *SIC* 8062

HOAG MEMORIAL HOSPITAL PRESBYTERIAN p 698
1 Hoag Dr, Newport Beach CA 92663
Tel (949) 764-4624 *SIC* 8062

VALLEY HOSPITAL MEDICAL CENTER p 1541
18300 Roscoe Blvd, Northridge CA 91325
Tel (818) 885-8500 *SIC* 8062

CHILDRENS HOSPITAL & RESEARCH CENTER AT OAKLAND p 299
747 52nd St, Oakland CA 94609
Tel (510) 428-3000 *SIC* 8062

KAISER FOUNDATION HOSPITALS INC p 800
1 Kaiser Plz, Oakland CA 94612
Tel (510) 271-6611 *SIC* 8062 8011

KAISER PERMANENTE INTERNATIONAL p 800
1 Kaiser Plz, Oakland CA 94612
Tel (510) 271-5910 *SIC* 8062

REGENTS OF UNIVERSITY OF CALIFORNIA p 1219
1111 Franklin St, Oakland CA 94607
Tel (619) 543-3713 *SIC* 8062

SUMMIT MEDICAL CENTER p 1399
350 Hawthorne Ave, Oakland CA 94609
Tel (510) 655-4000 *SIC* 8062 8221 5947

TRI-CITY HOSPITAL DISTRICT INC p 1477
4002 Vista Way, Oceanside CA 92056
Tel (760) 724-8411 *SIC* 8062

PRIME HEALTHCARE SERVICES INC p 1175
3300 E Guasti Rd Ste 300, Ontario CA 91761
Tel (909) 235-4400 *SIC* 8062

ST JOSEPH HOSPITAL OF ORANGE p 1368
1100 W Stewart Dr, Orange CA 92868
Tel (714) 633-9111 *SIC* 8062

OROVILLE HOSPITAL p 1095
2767 Olive Hwy, Oroville CA 95966
Tel (530) 533-8500 *SIC* 8062

■ **DESERT REGIONAL MEDICAL CENTER INC** p 432
1150 N Indian Canyon Dr, Palm Springs CA 92262
Tel (760) 323-6374 *SIC* 8062

FEATHER RIVER HOSPITAL p 533
5974 Pentz Rd, Paradise CA 95969
Tel (530) 877-9361 *SIC* 8062 8051

HUNTINGTON HOSPITAL p 720
100 W California Blvd, Pasadena CA 91105
Tel (626) 397-5000 *SIC* 8062

PASADENA HOSPITAL ASSOCIATION LTD p 1119
100 W California Blvd, Pasadena CA 91105
Tel (626) 397-5000 *SIC* 8062 8051 8063

MARSHALL MEDICAL CENTER p 911
1100 Marshall Way, Placerville CA 95667
Tel (530) 622-1441 *SIC* 8062 8071 8082

HOSPITAL COMMITTEE FOR LIVERMORE-PLEASANTON AREAS p 709
5555 W Las Positas Blvd, Pleasanton CA 94588
Tel (925) 847-3000 *SIC* 8062 8741

POMONA VALLEY HOSPITAL MEDICAL CENTER p 1161
1798 N Garey Ave, Pomona CA 91767
Tel (909) 865-9500 *SIC* 8062

PALOMAR POMERADO HOSPITAL DISTRICT p 1110
15615 Pomerado Rd, Poway CA 92064
Tel (858) 613-4000 *SIC* 8062

MERCY HEALTHCARE SACRAMENTO p 947
3400 Data Dr, Rancho Cordova CA 95670
Tel (916) 379-2871 *SIC* 8062

EISENHOWER MEDICAL CENTER p 482
39000 Bob Hope Dr, Rancho Mirage CA 92270
Tel (760) 340-3911 *SIC* 8062 8082

ST ELIZABETH COMMUNITY HOSPITAL p 1366
2550 Sster Mary Clumba Dr, Red Bluff CA 96080
Tel (530) 529-7760 *SIC* 8062 6513

MERCY HOME SERVICES A CALIFORNIA LIMITED PARTNERSHIP p 947
2175 Rosaline Ave Ste A, Redding CA 96001
Tel (530) 225-6000 *SIC* 8062

PRIME HEALTHCARE SERVICES - SHASTA LLC p 1175
1100 Butte St, Redding CA 96001
Tel (530) 244-5400 *SIC* 8062 8011

SEQUOIA HEALTH SERVICES p 1306
170 Alameda De Las Pulgas, Redwood City CA 94062
Tel (650) 369-5811 *SIC* 8062

VERITY HEALTH SYSTEM OF CALIFORNIA INC p 1550
203 Redwood Shores Pkwy, Redwood City CA 94065
Tel (650) 551-6650 *SIC* 8062

RIDGECREST REGIONAL HOSPITAL p 1234
1081 N China Lake Blvd, Ridgecrest CA 93555
Tel (760) 446-3551 *SIC* 8062

PARKVIEW COMMUNITY HOSPITAL MEDICAL CENTER p 1117
3865 Jackson St, Riverside CA 92503
Tel (951) 354-7404 *SIC* 8062 8011

■ **RIVERSIDE COMMUNITY HEALTH SYSTEMS** p 1238
4445 Magnolia Ave Fl 6, Riverside CA 92501
Tel (951) 788-3000 *SIC* 8062 8011

■ **RIVERSIDE HEALTHCARE SYSTEM LP** p 1238
4445 Magnolia Ave, Riverside CA 92501
Tel (951) 788-3000 *SIC* 8062

ADVENTIST HEALTH SYSTEM/WEST p 27
2100 Douglas Blvd, Roseville CA 95661
Tel (916) 781-2000 *SIC* 8062

SUTTER ROSEVILLE MEDICAL CENTER p 1410
1 Medical Plaza Dr, Roseville CA 95661
Tel (916) 781-1000 *SIC* 8062

SUTTER ROSEVILLE MEDICAL CENTER FOUNDATION p 1410
1 Medical Plaza Dr, Roseville CA 95661
Tel (916) 781-1000 *SIC* 8062

MERCY METHODIST HOSPITAL p 948
7500 Hospital Dr, Sacramento CA 95823
Tel (916) 423-6063 *SIC* 8062

SUTTER HEALTH p 1410
2200 River Plaza Dr, Sacramento CA 95833
Tel (916) 733-8800
SIC 8062 8051 8011 6513

SUTTER HEALTH SACRAMENTO SIERRA REGION p 1410
2200 River Plaza Dr, Sacramento CA 95833
Tel (916) 733-8800 *SIC* 8062 8063 8052

SUTTERCARE CORP p 1410
2200 River Plaza Dr, Sacramento CA 95833
Tel (916) 733-8800 *SIC* 8051 8062

ST HELENA HOSPITAL p 1367
10 Woodland Rd, Saint Helena CA 94574
Tel (707) 963-1882 *SIC* 8062 8063

NATIVIDAD HOSPITAL INC p 1018
1441 Constitution Blvd, Salinas CA 93906
Tel (831) 755-4111 *SIC* 8062 8011 8093

SALINAS VALLEY MEMORIAL HEALTHCARE SYSTEMS p 1272
450 E Romie Ln, Salinas CA 93901
Tel (831) 757-4333 *SIC* 8062

COMMUNITY HOSPITAL OF SAN BERNARDINO p 349
1805 Medical Center Dr, San Bernardino CA 92411
Tel (909) 887-6333 *SIC* 8062

ALVARADO HOSPITAL LLC p 63
6655 Alvarado Rd, San Diego CA 92120
Tel (619) 287-3270 *SIC* 8062

MERCY SCRIPPS HOSPITAL p 948
4077 5th Ave Mer35, San Diego CA 92103
Tel (619) 294-8111 *SIC* 8062

SCRIPPS HEALTH p 1294
4275 Campus Point Ct, San Diego CA 92121
Tel (858) 678-7000
SIC 8051 8082 8062 8049 8042 8043

SHARP CHULA VISTA MEDICAL CENTER p 1312
8695 Spectrum Center Blvd, San Diego CA 92123
Tel (858) 499-5150 SIC 8062

SHARP HEALTHCARE p 1312
8695 Spectrum Center Blvd, San Diego CA 92123
Tel (858) 499-4000 SIC 8062 8741 6324

SHARP MEMORIAL HOSPITAL p 1312
7901 Frost St, San Diego CA 92123
Tel (858) 939-3636 SIC 8062

UNIVERSITY OF CALIFORNIA SAN DIEGO HEALTH SYSTEM p 1527
200 W Arbor Dr 8201, San Diego CA 92103
Tel (619) 543-3713 SIC 8062

CATHOLIC HEALTHCARE WEST p 266
450 Stanyan St, San Francisco CA 94117
Tel (415) 668-1000 SIC 8062

DIGNITY HEALTH p 439
185 Berry St Ste 300, San Francisco CA 94107
Tel (415) 438-5500 SIC 8062

SAINT FRANCIS MEMORIAL HOSPITAL p 1269
900 Hyde St, San Francisco CA 94109
Tel (415) 353-6000 SIC 8062

ST LUKES HOSPITAL p 1370
3555 Cesar Chavez, San Francisco CA 94110
Tel (415) 647-8600 SIC 8062

ST MARYS MEDICAL CENTER FOUNDATION p 1372
450 Stanyan St, San Francisco CA 94117
Tel (415) 668-1000 SIC 8062

SUTTER BAY HOSPITALS p 1410
633 Folsom St Fl 5, San Francisco CA 94107
Tel (415) 600-6000 SIC 8062 8733

■ GOOD SAMARITAN HOSPITAL LP p 623
2425 Samaritan Dr, San Jose CA 95124
Tel (408) 559-2011 SIC 8062

OCONNOR HOSPITAL p 1074
2105 Forest Ave, San Jose CA 95128
Tel (408) 947-2500 SIC 8062

SAN JOSE MEDICAL SYSTEMS LP p 1277
225 N Jackson Ave, San Jose CA 95116
Tel (408) 259-5000 SIC 8062

SANTA CLARA VALLEY MEDICAL CENTER p 1280
751 S Bascom Ave, San Jose CA 95128
Tel (408) 885-5000 SIC 8062 6324

FRENCH HOSPITAL MEDICAL CENTER FOUNDATION p 578
1911 Johnson Ave, San Luis Obispo CA 93401
Tel (805) 543-5353 SIC 8062

■ SIERRA VISTA HOSPITAL INC p 1321
1010 Murray Ave, San Luis Obispo CA 93405
Tel (805) 546-7600 SIC 8062

DOCTORS MEDICAL CENTER LLC p 447
2000 Vale Rd, San Pablo CA 94806
Tel (510) 970-5000 SIC 8062

■ SAN RAMON REGIONAL MEDICAL CENTER INC p 1277
6001 Norris Canyon Rd, San Ramon CA 94583
Tel (925) 275-0634 SIC 8062 8093

KPC HEALTHCARE INC p 828
1301 N Tustin Ave, Santa Ana CA 92705
Tel (714) 953-3652 SIC 8062 6719

WESTERN MEDICAL CENTER AUXILIARY p 1599
1301 N Tustin Ave, Santa Ana CA 92705
Tel (714) 835-3555 SIC 8062

COTTAGE HEALTH p 374
400 W Pueblo St, Santa Barbara CA 93105
Tel (805) 682-7111 SIC 8399 8062

SANTA BARBARA COTTAGE HOSPITAL p 1280
400 W Pueblo St, Santa Barbara CA 93105
Tel (805) 682-7111 SIC 8062

DOMINICAN HOSPITAL p 449
1555 Soquel Dr, Santa Cruz CA 95065
Tel (831) 462-7700 SIC 8062

MARIAN MEDICAL CENTER p 906
1400 E Church St, Santa Maria CA 93454
Tel (805) 739-3000 SIC 8062

SAINT JOHNS HEALTH CENTER FOUNDATION p 1269
2121 Santa Monica Blvd, Santa Monica CA 90404
Tel (310) 829-8424 SIC 8062

SANTA ROSA MEMORIAL HOSPITAL INC p 1281
1165 Montgomery Dr, Santa Rosa CA 95405
Tel (707) 546-3210 SIC 8062

SUTTER SANTA ROSA REGIONAL HOSPITAL p 1410
30 Mark West Springs Rd, Santa Rosa CA 95403
Tel (707) 576-4000 SIC 8062

SONORA REGIONAL MEDICAL CENTER p 1340
1000 Greenley Rd, Sonora CA 95370
Tel (209) 532-5000 SIC 8062 8051

BARTON HEALTHCARE SYSTEM p 158
2170 South Ave, South Lake Tahoe CA 96150
Tel (530) 541-3420 SIC 8062

BARTON HOSPITAL p 158
2170 South Ave, South Lake Tahoe CA 96150
Tel (530) 543-5685 SIC 8062

BARTON MEMORIAL HOSPITAL p 158
2170 South Ave, South Lake Tahoe CA 96150
Tel (530) 541-3420 SIC 8062 8051

STANFORD HEALTH CARE p 1376
300 Pasteur Dr, Stanford CA 94305
Tel (650) 723-4000 SIC 8062

ST JOSEPHS MEDICAL CENTER INC p 1369
1800 N California St, Stockton CA 95204
Tel (209) 943-2000 SIC 8062

ST JOSEPHS MEDICAL CENTER OF STOCKTON p 1369
1800 N California St, Stockton CA 95204
Tel (209) 943-2000 SIC 8062

AMI-HTI TARZANA ENCINO JOINT VENTURE p 85
18321 Clark St, Tarzana CA 91356
Tel (818) 881-0800 SIC 8062

■ AMISUB OF CALIFORNIA INC p 85
18321 Clark St, Tarzana CA 91356
Tel (818) 881-0800 SIC 8062

■ TEMECULA VALLEY HOSPITAL INC p 1436
31700 Temecula Pkwy, Temecula CA 92592
Tel (951) 331-2200 SIC 8062

■ LOS ROBLES HOSPITAL & MEDICAL CENTER p 879
215 W Janss Rd, Thousand Oaks CA 91360
Tel (805) 497-2727 SIC 8062

HARBOR-UCLA MEDICAL CENTER p 660
1000 W Carson St 2, Torrance CA 90502
Tel (310) 222-2345 SIC 8062

LITTLE CO OF MARY HOSPITAL p 871
4101 Torrance Blvd, Torrance CA 90503
Tel (310) 540-7676 SIC 8062 8051

TORRANCE HEALTH ASSOCIATION INC p 1462
23550 Hawthorne Blvd, Torrance CA 90505
Tel (310) 325-9110 SIC 8062

TORRANCE MEMORIAL MEDICAL CENTER p 1462
3330 Lomita Blvd, Torrance CA 90505
Tel (310) 325-9110 SIC 8062

TAHOE FOREST HOSPITAL DISTRICT p 1421
10121 Pine Ave, Truckee CA 96161
Tel (530) 587-6011 SIC 8062

TULARE LOCAL HEALTH CARE DISTRICT p 1491
869 N Cherry St, Tulare CA 93274
Tel (559) 685-3462 SIC 8062

■ EMANUEL MEDICAL CENTER INC p 490
825 Delbon Ave, Turlock CA 95382
Tel (209) 667-4200 SIC 8062

HEALTH INVESTMENT CORP p 675
14642 Newport Ave Ste 388, Tustin CA 92780
Tel (714) 669-2085 SIC 8062

PACIFIC HEALTH CORP p 1104
14642 Newport Ave, Tustin CA 92780
Tel (714) 838-9600 SIC 8062

UKIAH ADVENTIST HOSPITAL p 1500
275 Hospital Dr, Ukiah CA 95482
Tel (707) 463-7346 SIC 8062

SAN ANTONIO COMMUNITY HOSPITAL p 1275
999 San Bernardino Rd, Upland CA 91786
Tel (909) 985-2811 SIC 8062 5912

HENRY MAYO NEWHALL HOSPITAL p 684
23845 Mcbean Pkwy, Valencia CA 91355
Tel (661) 253-8000 SIC 8062

HENRY MAYO NEWHALL MEMORIAL HEALTH FOUNDATION INC p 684
23845 Mcbean Pkwy, Valencia CA 91355
Tel (661) 253-8000 SIC 8062

SUTTER SOLANO MEDICAL CENTER INC p 1410
300 Hospital Dr, Vallejo CA 94589
Tel (707) 554-4444 SIC 8062

VALLEY PRESBYTERIAN HOSPITAL p 1541
15107 Vanowen St, Van Nuys CA 91405
Tel (818) 782-6600 SIC 8062

COMMUNITY MEMORIAL HOSPITAL SAN BUENAVENTURA INC p 349
147 N Brent St, Ventura CA 93003
Tel (805) 652-5072 SIC 8062

KAWEAH DELTA HEALTH CARE DISTRICT GUILD p 805
400 W Mineral King Ave, Visalia CA 93291
Tel (559) 624-2000 SIC 8062

JOHN MUIR HEALTH p 789
1601 Ygnacio Valley Rd, Walnut Creek CA 94598
Tel (925) 947-4449 SIC 8062

JOHN MUIR PHYSICIAN NETWORK p 789
1450 Treat Blvd, Walnut Creek CA 94597
Tel (925) 296-9700
SIC 8062 8069 8093 7363

■ WATSONVILLE HEALTHCARE MANAGEMENT LLC p 1583
75 Neilson St, Watsonville CA 95076
Tel (831) 724-4741 SIC 8062

CITRUS VALLEY MEDICAL CENTER INC p 311
1115 S Sunset Ave, West Covina CA 91790
Tel (626) 962-4011 SIC 8062

CEDARS-SINAI MEDICAL CENTER p 272
8700 Beverly Blvd, West Hollywood CA 90048
Tel (310) 423-3277 SIC 8062

INTERHEALTH CORP p 752
12401 Washington Blvd, Whittier CA 90602
Tel (562) 698-0811 SIC 8062 8011

PRESBYTERIAN INTERCOMMUNITY HOSPITAL INC p 1171
12401 Washington Blvd, Whittier CA 90602
Tel (562) 698-0811 SIC 8062

■ UNIVERSAL HEALTH SERVICES OF RANCHO SPRINGS INC p 1517
36485 Inland Valley Dr, Wildomar CA 92595
Tel (951) 677-9712 SIC 8099 8062 8011

WOODLAND HEALTHCARE p 1623
1325 Cottonwood St, Woodland CA 95695
Tel (530) 662-3961 SIC 8062

■ HEALTH NET OF CALIFORNIA INC p 675
21281 Burbank Blvd Fl 4, Woodland Hills CA 91367
Tel (818) 676-6775
SIC 6324 8062 6311 6321 6331 5912

FREEMONT RIDEOUT HEALTH GROUP p 577
989 Plumas St, Yuba City CA 95991
Tel (530) 751-4010 SIC 8062

SAN LUIS VALLEY HEALTH REGIONAL MEDICAL CENTER p 1277
106 Blanca Ave, Alamosa CO 81101
Tel (719) 589-2511 SIC 8062

CHILDRENS HOSPITAL COLORADO p 299
3123 E 16th Ave, Aurora CO 80045
Tel (720) 777-1234 SIC 8062

HEALTHNOTES LLC p 677
1501 S Potomac St, Aurora CO 80012
Tel (303) 695-2600 SIC 8062

PLATTE VALLEY MEDICAL CENTER FOUNDATION p 1155
1600 Prairie Center Pkwy, Brighton CO 80601
Tel (303) 498-1600 SIC 8062

SISTERS OF CHARITY OF LEAVENWORTH HEALTH SYSTEM INC p 1327
500 Eldorado Blvd # 6300, Broomfield CO 80021
Tel (303) 813-5000 SIC 8062 8011 5912

MEMORIAL HOSPITAL CORP p 942
1400 E Boulder St, Colorado Springs CO 80909
Tel (719) 365-5000 SIC 8062

PENROSE HOSPITAL p 1131
2222 N Nevada Ave Ste 1, Colorado Springs CO 80907
Tel (719) 776-5000 SIC 8062

DENVER HEALTH AND HOSPITALS AUTHORITY INC p 429
777 Bannock St, Denver CO 80204
Tel (720) 956-2580 SIC 8062

■ HCA-HEALTHONE LLC p 672
4900 S Monaco St Ste 380, Denver CO 80237
Tel (303) 788-2500 SIC 8062

NATIONAL JEWISH HEALTH p 1014
1400 Jackson St, Denver CO 80206
Tel (303) 388-4461 SIC 8062

PACIFIC ALLIANCE MEDICAL CENTER INC p 1104
2525 S Downing St, Denver CO 80210
Tel (303) 778-1955 SIC 8062

PORTERCARE ADVENTIST HEALTH SYSTEM p 1162
2525 S Downing St, Denver CO 80210
Tel (303) 778-5736 SIC 8062

■ ROSE MEDICAL GROUP p 1250
4900 S Monaco St Ste 204, Denver CO 80237
Tel (303) 320-2101 SIC 8062 8011 8099

SAINT JOSEPH HOSPITAL INC p 1269
1375 E 19th Ave, Denver CO 80218
Tel (303) 812-2000 SIC 8062

ST JOSEPH HOSPITAL INC p 1368
1375 E 19th Ave, Denver CO 80218
Tel (303) 837-7111 SIC 8062

UNIVERSITY OF COLORADO HOSPITAL AUTHORITY p 1521
4200 E 9th Ave, Denver CO 80220
Tel (720) 848-0000 SIC 8062

CATHOLIC HEALTH INITIATIVES COLORADO FOUNDATION p 266
1010 Three Springs Blvd, Durango CO 81301
Tel (970) 247-4311 SIC 8062

CATHOLIC HEALTH INITIATIVES p 266
198 Inverness Dr W, Englewood CO 80112
Tel (303) 298-9100 SIC 8062 8051 8741

CATHOLIC HEALTH INITIATIVES COLORADO p 266
198 Inverness Dr W, Englewood CO 80112
Tel (303) 290-6500 SIC 8741 8062

POUDRE VALLEY HEALTH CARE INC p 1164
2315 E Harmony Rd Ste 200, Fort Collins CO 80528
Tel (970) 495-7000 SIC 8062

VALLEY VIEW HOSPITAL ASSOCIATION p 1541
1906 Blake Ave, Glenwood Springs CO 81601
Tel (970) 945-6535 SIC 8062

ST MARYS HOSPITAL & MEDICAL CENTER INC p 1371
2635 N 7th St, Grand Junction CO 81501
Tel (970) 298-2013 SIC 8062

NORTH COLORADO MEDICAL CENTER FOUNDATION INC p 1052
1801 16th St, Greeley CO 80631
Tel (970) 356-9020 SIC 8062

▲ ENVISION HEALTHCARE HOLDINGS INC p 504
6200 S Syracuse Way, Greenwood Village CO 80111
Tel (303) 495-1200 SIC 8062 4119

GOOD SAMARITAN MEDICAL CENTER FOUNDATION p 623
200 Exempla Cir, Lafayette CO 80026
Tel (303) 689-4000 SIC 8062

LONGMONT UNITED HOSPITAL p 877
1950 Mountain View Ave, Longmont CO 80501
Tel (303) 651-5111 SIC 8062

MEDICAL CENTER OF ROCKIES p 936
2500 Rocky Mountain Ave, Loveland CO 80538
Tel (970) 624-2500 SIC 8062

MONTROSE MEMORIAL HOSPITAL INC p 987
800 S 3rd St, Montrose CO 81401
Tel (970) 249-2211 SIC 8062 8011

PARKER ADVENTIST HOSPITAL p 1116
9395 Crown Crest Blvd, Parker CO 80138
Tel (303) 269-4000 SIC 8062

PARKVIEW HEALTH SYSTEM INC p 1117
400 W 16th St, Pueblo CO 81003
Tel (719) 584-4000 SIC 8062 7389

PARKVIEW MEDICAL CENTER INC p 1117
400 W 16th St, Pueblo CO 81003
Tel (719) 584-4000 SIC 8062 8063

ST MARY-CORWIN HOSPITAL OF PUEBLO CO (INC) p 1371
1008 Minnequa Ave, Pueblo CO 81004
Tel (719) 557-4000 SIC 8062

YAMPA VALLEY MEDICAL CENTER p 1634
1024 Central Park Dr, Steamboat Springs CO 80487
Tel (970) 879-1322 SIC 8062 8351

VAIL CLINIC INC p 1538
181 W Meadow Dr Ste 100, Vail CO 81657
Tel (970) 476-2451 SIC 8062

VAIL VALLEY SURGERY CENTER LLC p 1538
181 W Meadow Dr Ste 100, Vail CO 81657
Tel (970) 476-8872 SIC 8062

SCL HEALTH - FRONT RANGE INC p 1292
8300 W 38th Ave, Wheat Ridge CO 80033
Tel (303) 813-5000 SIC 8062 8011 8051

BRIDGEPORT HOSPITAL p 211
267 Grant St, Bridgeport CT 06610
Tel (203) 384-3000 SIC 8062

ST VINCENTS HEALTH SERVICES CORP p 1373
2800 Main St, Bridgeport CT 06606
Tel (203) 576-6000 SIC 8741 8062

ST VINCENTS MEDICAL CENTER FOUNDATION INC p 1373
2800 Main St, Bridgeport CT 06606
Tel (203) 576-6000 SIC 8062

BRISTOL HOSPITAL INC p 214
41 Brewster Rd, Bristol CT 06010
Tel (860) 585-3000 SIC 8062

HOSPITAL DANBURY INC p 709
24 Hospital Ave, Danbury CT 06810
Tel (203) 739-7000 SIC 8062

WESTERN CONNECTICUT HEALTH NETWORK INC p 1597
24 Hospital Ave, Danbury CT 06810
Tel (203) 739-7000 SIC 8062

GRIFFIN HOSPITAL INC p 640
130 Division St, Derby CT 06418
Tel (203) 735-7421 SIC 8062

GREENWICH HEALTH CARE SERVICES INC p 639
5 Perryridge Rd, Greenwich CT 06830
Tel (203) 661-5330 SIC 8062

GREENWICH HOSPITAL p 639
5 Perryridge Rd, Greenwich CT 06830
Tel (203) 863-3000 SIC 8062

HARTFORD HOSPITAL p 665
80 Seymour St, Hartford CT 06102
Tel (860) 545-5000 SIC 8062

SAINT FRANCIS HOSPITAL AND MEDICAL CENTER FOUNDATION INC p 1269
114 Woodland St, Hartford CT 06105
Tel (860) 714-4006 SIC 8062 8011 8069

EASTERN CONNECTICUT HEALTH NETWORK INC p 472
71 Haynes St, Manchester CT 06040
Tel (860) 533-6565 SIC 8062

MANCHESTER MEMORIAL HOSPITAL INC p 901
71 Haynes St, Manchester CT 06040
Tel (860) 646-1222 SIC 8062

MIDSTATE MEDICAL CENTER p 966
435 Lewis Ave, Meriden CT 06451
Tel (203) 694-8200 SIC 8062

MIDDLESEX HEALTH SYSTEM INC p 965
28 Crescent St, Middletown CT 06457
Tel (860) 358-6000 SIC 8062

MIDDLESEX HOSPITAL FOUNDATION INC p 965
28 Crescent St, Middletown CT 06457
Tel (860) 358-6000 SIC 8062

HOSPITAL OF CENTRAL CONNECTICUT p 709
100 Grand St, New Britain CT 06052
Tel (860) 224-5011 SIC 8062

HOSPITAL OF ST RAPHAEL PHYSICIANS IPA II INC p 709
1450 Chapel St, New Haven CT 06511
Tel (203) 789-3000 SIC 8062 8011

YALE-NEW HAVEN HOSPITAL INC p 1634
20 York St, New Haven CT 06510
Tel (203) 688-4242 SIC 8351 8062 8741

LAWRENCE & MEMORIAL HOSPITAL INC p 847
365 Montauk Ave, New London CT 06320
Tel (860) 442-0711 SIC 8011 8062

NORWALK HOSPITAL ASSOCIATION p 1061
34 Maple St, Norwalk CT 06850
Tel (203) 852-2000 SIC 8062

WILLIAM W BACKUS HOSPITAL p 1611
326 Washington St, Norwich CT 06360
Tel (860) 889-8331 SIC 8062

DAY KIMBALL HEALTHCARE INC p 417
320 Pomfret St, Putnam CT 06260
Tel (860) 928-6541 SIC 8062

STAMFORD HOSPITAL p 1375
1 Hospital Plz, Stamford CT 06902
Tel (203) 325-7000 SIC 8062

CHARLOTTE HUNGERFORD HOSPITAL p 290
540 Litchfield St, Torrington CT 06790
Tel (860) 496-6666 SIC 8062

SAINT MARYS HEALTH SYSTEM INC p 1270
56 Franklin St, Waterbury CT 06706
Tel (203) 709-6000 SIC 8062 7011

SAINT MARYS HOSPITAL INC p 1270
56 Franklin St Ste 1, Waterbury CT 06706
Tel (203) 709-6000 SIC 8062

WATERBURY HOSPITAL p 1581
64 Robbins St, Waterbury CT 06708
Tel (203) 573-6000 SIC 8062

WILTON SURGERY CENTER LLC p 1614
195 Danbury Rd Ste B100, Wilton CT 06897
Tel (203) 563-9470 SIC 8062

BAYHEALTH MEDICAL CENTER INC p 161
640 S State St, Dover DE 19901
Tel (302) 422-3311 SIC 8062

KENT GENERAL HOSPITAL p 812
640 S State St, Dover DE 19901
Tel (302) 674-4700 SIC 8062

BEEBE MEDICAL CENTER INC p 168
424 Savannah Rd, Lewes DE 19958
Tel (302) 645-3300 SIC 8062

NANTICOKE MEMORIAL HOSPITAL INC p 1007
801 Middleford Rd, Seaford DE 19973
Tel (302) 629-6611 SIC 8062

AI DUPONT HOSPITAL FOR CHILDREN p 37
1600 Rockland Rd, Wilmington DE 19803
Tel (302) 651-4620 SIC 8062

CHRISTIANA CARE HEALTH SERVICES INC p 303
501 W 14th St, Wilmington DE 19801
Tel (302) 733-1000 SIC 8062

ST FRANCIS HEALTH SERVICES CORP p 1366
7th N Clayton St, Wilmington DE 19805
Tel (302) 575-8301 SIC 8062

ST FRANCIS HOSPITAL INC p 1366
701 N Clayton St, Wilmington DE 19805
Tel (302) 421-4100 SIC 8062

BRIDGEPOINT HEALTHCARE LLC p 211
4601 Martin Luther Jr, Washington DC 20032
Tel (202) 741-4174 SIC 8062

CHILDRENS HOSPITAL p 299
111 Michigan Ave Nw, Washington DC 20010
Tel (202) 232-0521 SIC 8062

CHILDRENS HOSPITAL p 299
1917 C St Ne, Washington DC 20002
Tel (202) 476-5000 *SIC* 8062

CHILDRENS NATIONAL MEDICAL CENTER p 300
111 Michigan Ave Nw, Washington DC 20010
Tel (202) 476-5000 *SIC* 8062

GEORGE WASHINGTON UNIVERSITY HOSPITAL p 606
900 23rd St Nw, Washington DC 20037
Tel (202) 715-4000 *SIC* 8062

GEORGETOWN UNIVERSITY p 607
37th & O Sts Nw, Washington DC 20057
Tel (202) 687-0100 *SIC* 8221 8062

HOWARD UNIVERSITY HOSPITAL p 713
2041 Georgia Ave Nw, Washington DC 20060
Tel (202) 865-6100 *SIC* 8062

HOWARD UNIVERSITY HOSPITAL p 713
2041 Georgia Ave Nw, Washington DC 20060
Tel (202) 865-1441 *SIC* 8062

LUCY W HAYES TRAINING SCHOOL FOR DECONESSES & MISSIONARIES INC p 884
5255 Loughboro Rd Nw, Washington DC 20016
Tel (202) 537-4257 *SIC* 8062

MEDSTAR-GEORGETOWN MEDICAL CENTER INC p 939
3800 Reservoir Rd Nw, Washington DC 20007
Tel (202) 444-2000 *SIC* 8062 8221 8069

NOT-FOR-PROFIT HOSPITAL CORP p 1062
1310 Southern Ave Se, Washington DC 20032
Tel (202) 574-6000 *SIC* 8062

PROVIDENCE HOSPITAL p 1186
1150 Varnum St Ne, Washington DC 20017
Tel (202) 269-7000 *SIC* 8062

WASHINGTON HOSPITAL CENTER CORP p 1578
110 Irving St Nw, Washington DC 20010
Tel (202) 877-7000
SIC 8741 8082 8051 8062

ADVENTIST HEALTH SYSTEM/SUNBELT INC p 27
900 Hope Way, Altamonte Springs FL 32714
Tel (407) 357-1000 *SIC* 8062 8082 8051

AHS/CENTRAL TEXAS INC p 37
900 Hope Way, Altamonte Springs FL 32714
Tel (407) 357-1000 *SIC* 8062

BOCA RATON REGIONAL HOSPITAL INC p 196
800 Meadows Rd, Boca Raton FL 33486
Tel (561) 395-7100 *SIC* 8062

BRRH CORP p 220
800 Meadows Rd, Boca Raton FL 33486
Tel (561) 395-7100 *SIC* 8062 8082 8099

WEST BOCA MEDICAL CENTER INC p 1594
21644 State Road 7, Boca Raton FL 33428
Tel (561) 488-8000 *SIC* 8062

BETHESDA HOSPITAL INC p 178
2815 S Seacrest Blvd, Boynton Beach FL 33435
Tel (561) 737-7733 *SIC* 8062

■ **MANATEE MEMORIAL HOSPITAL** p 900
206 2nd St E, Bradenton FL 34208
Tel (941) 746-5111 *SIC* 8062

■ **GALENCARE INC** p 589
119 Oakfield Dr, Brandon FL 33511
Tel (813) 681-5551 *SIC* 8062

HCA HEALTH SERVICES OF FLORIDA INC p 671
11375 Cortez Blvd, Brooksville FL 34613
Tel (352) 597-3053 *SIC* 8062

■ **HERNANDO HEALTHCARE INC** p 687
17240 Cortez Blvd, Brooksville FL 34601
Tel (352) 796-5111 *SIC* 8062

■ **HERNANDO HMA INC** p 687
17240 Cortez Blvd, Brooksville FL 34601
Tel (352) 796-5111 *SIC* 8062

■ **OAK HILL HOSPITAL MEDICAL STAFF INC** p 1070
11375 Cortez Blvd, Brooksville FL 34613
Tel (352) 596-6632 *SIC* 8062

CAPE MEMORIAL HOSPITAL INC p 248
636 Del Prado Blvd S, Cape Coral FL 33990
Tel (239) 424-2000 *SIC* 8062

MORTON PLANT HOSPITAL ASSOCIATION INC p 991
300 Pinellas St, Clearwater FL 33756
Tel (727) 462-7000 *SIC* 8062 8051

SOUTH LAKE HOSPITAL INC p 1344
1900 Don Wickham Dr Lbby, Clermont FL 34711
Tel (352) 394-4071 *SIC* 8062

CAPE CANAVERAL HOSPITAL INC p 248
701 W Cocoa Beach Cswy, Cocoa Beach FL 32931
Tel (321) 799-7111 *SIC* 8062

DOCTORS HOSPITAL INC p 447
5000 University Dr, Coral Gables FL 33146
Tel (305) 666-2111 *SIC* 8062

■ **CRESTVIEW HOSPITAL CORP** p 392
151 E Redstone Ave, Crestview FL 32539
Tel (850) 423-1000 *SIC* 8062

■ **CITRUS HMA INC** p 311
6201 N Suncoast Blvd, Crystal River FL 34428
Tel (352) 563-5488 *SIC* 8062

■ **HAINES CITY HEALTH MANAGEMENT ASSOCIATION INC** p 653
40100 Highway 27, Davenport FL 33837
Tel (863) 422-4971 *SIC* 8062

■ **ATLANTIC MEDICAL CENTER** p 127
303 N Clyde Morris Blvd, Daytona Beach FL 32114
Tel (386) 239-5001 *SIC* 8062 8011

HALIFAX HEALTH CARE SYSTEMS INC p 654
303 N Clyde Morris Blvd, Daytona Beach FL 32114
Tel (386) 254-4000 *SIC* 8062 8011 8063

MEMORIAL HEALTH SYSTEMS INC p 941
301 Memorial Medical Pkwy, Daytona Beach FL 32117
Tel (386) 231-6000 *SIC* 8062

MEMORIAL HOSPITAL - WEST VOLUSIA INC p 942
701 W Plymouth Ave, Deland FL 32720
Tel (386) 943-4522 *SIC* 8062

■ **DELRAY MEDICAL CENTER INC** p 425
5352 Linton Blvd, Delray Beach FL 33484
Tel (561) 498-4440 *SIC* 8062

TRUSTEES OF MEASE HOSPITAL INC p 1488
601 Main St, Dunedin FL 34698
Tel (727) 733-1111 *SIC* 8062

HOLY CROSS HOSPITAL INC p 702
4725 N Federal Hwy, Fort Lauderdale FL 33308
Tel (954) 771-8000 *SIC* 8062

NORTH BROWARD HOSPITAL DISTRICT p 1051
1800 Nw 49th St, Fort Lauderdale FL 33309
Tel (954) 473-7010 *SIC* 8062

DOCTORS OSTEOPATHIC MEDICAL CENTER INC p 447
13681 Doctors Way, Fort Myers FL 33912
Tel (239) 768-5000 *SIC* 8062

GULF COAST MEDICAL CENTRE LTD p 646
13691 Metro Pkwy Ste 110, Fort Myers FL 33912
Tel (239) 343-1000 *SIC* 8062

LEE MEMORIAL HEALTH SYSTEM FOUNDATION INC p 851
2776 Cleveland Ave, Fort Myers FL 33901
Tel (239) 343-2000
SIC 8741 8062 8082 8051

LEE MEMORIAL HOSPITAL INC p 851
2776 Cleveland Ave, Fort Myers FL 33901
Tel (239) 343-2000 *SIC* 8062

■ **LAWNWOOD MEDICAL CENTER INC** p 847
1700 S 23rd St, Fort Pierce FL 34950
Tel (772) 461-4000 *SIC* 8062 8063 8069

■ **NORTH FLORIDA REGIONAL MEDICAL CENTER INC** p 1052
6500 W Newberry Rd, Gainesville FL 32605
Tel (352) 333-4100
SIC 8062 8093 8011 8082 8069

■ **LIFEMARK HOSPITALS OF FLORIDA INC** p 864
2001 W 68th St, Hialeah FL 33016
Tel (305) 823-5000 *SIC* 8062

PALM SPRINGS GENERAL HOSPITAL INC p 1109
1475 W 49th St, Hialeah FL 33012
Tel (305) 558-2500 *SIC* 8062

■ **TENET HIALEAH HEALTHSYSTEM INC** p 1437
651 E 25th St, Hialeah FL 33013
Tel (305) 693-6100 *SIC* 8062

SOUTH BROWARD HOSPITAL DISTRICT p 1343
3501 Johnson St, Hollywood FL 33021
Tel (954) 987-2000 *SIC* 8062 8051

HOMESTEAD HOSPITAL INC p 704
975 Baptist Way, Homestead FL 33033
Tel (786) 243-8000 *SIC* 8062

FOUNDATION RESOLUTION CORP p 571
502 W Highland Blvd, Inverness FL 34452
Tel (352) 726-1551 *SIC* 8062

BAPTIST MEDICAL CENTER OF BEACHES INC p 154
1350 13th Ave S, Jacksonville FL 32250
Tel (904) 247-2900 *SIC* 8062

BAPTIST MEDICAL CENTER OF BEACHES INC p 154
3563 Phillips Hwy, Jacksonville FL 32207
Tel (704) 202-1797 *SIC* 8062

MAYO CLINIC JACKSONVILLE (A NONPROFIT CORP) p 924
4500 San Pablo Rd S, Jacksonville FL 32224
Tel (904) 953-2000 *SIC* 8062

■ **MEMORIAL HOSPITAL JACKSONVILLE INC** p 942
3625 University Blvd S, Jacksonville FL 32216
Tel (904) 399-6111 *SIC* 8062

SHANDS JACKSONVILLE HEALTHCARE INC p 1311
655 W 8th St, Jacksonville FL 32209
Tel (904) 244-0411 *SIC* 8062

SHANDS JACKSONVILLE MEDICAL CENTER INC p 1311
655 W 8th St, Jacksonville FL 32209
Tel (904) 244-5576 *SIC* 8062

SOUTHERN BAPTIST HOSPITAL OF FLORIDA INC p 1347
800 Prudential Dr, Jacksonville FL 32207
Tel (904) 202-2000 *SIC* 8062

ST LUKES HOSPITAL ASSOCIATION p 1370
4201 Belfort Rd, Jacksonville FL 32216
Tel (904) 296-3700 *SIC* 8062

ST VINCENTS MEDICAL CENTER INC p 1373
4205 Belfort Rd Ste 4030, Jacksonville FL 32216
Tel (904) 308-7300 *SIC* 8062

JUPITER MEDICAL CENTER INC p 797
1210 S Old Dixie Hwy, Jupiter FL 33458
Tel (561) 747-2234 *SIC* 8062 8051

■ **LOWER KEYS MEDICAL CENTER** p 881
5900 College Rd, Key West FL 33040
Tel (305) 294-5531 *SIC* 8062

LAKELAND REGIONAL HEALTH SYSTEMS INC p 840
1324 Lakeland Hills Blvd, Lakeland FL 33805
Tel (863) 687-1100 *SIC* 8062

LAKELAND REGIONAL MEDICAL CENTER INC p 840
1324 Lakeland Hills Blvd, Lakeland FL 33805
Tel (863) 687-1100 *SIC* 8062

■ **LARGO MEDICAL CENTER INC** p 845
201 14th St Sw, Largo FL 33770
Tel (727) 588-5200 *SIC* 8062

LEESBURG REGIONAL MEDICAL CENTER INC p 852
600 E Dixie Ave, Leesburg FL 34748
Tel (352) 323-5762 *SIC* 8062

■ **PALMS WEST HOSPITAL LIMITED PARTNERSHIP** p 1109
13001 Southern Blvd, Loxahatchee FL 33470
Tel (561) 798-3300 *SIC* 8062

HOLMES REGIONAL MEDICAL CENTER INC p 702
1350 Hickory St, Melbourne FL 32901
Tel (321) 434-7000 *SIC* 8062

■ **KINDRED DEVELOPMENT 17 LLC** p 819
765 W Nasa Blvd, Melbourne FL 32901
Tel (321) 409-4044 *SIC* 8062

BAPTIST HOSPITAL OF MIAMI INC p 154
8900 N Kendall Dr, Miami FL 33176
Tel (786) 596-1960 *SIC* 8062

▲ **HIG SURGERY CENTERS LLC** p 690
1450 Brickell Ave Fl 31, Miami FL 33131
Tel (305) 379-2322 *SIC* 8062 3851

JACKSON MEMORIAL HOSPITAL p 774
1611 Nw 12th Ave, Miami FL 33136
Tel (305) 585-1111 *SIC* 8062

■ **KENDALL HEALTHCARE GROUP LTD** p 810
11750 Sw 40th St, Miami FL 33175
Tel (305) 227-5500 *SIC* 8062

KENDALL WEST BAPTIST HOSPITAL INC p 810
9555 Sw 162nd Ave, Miami FL 33196
Tel (786) 467-2000 *SIC* 8062

■ **MERCY HOSPITAL INC** p 947
3663 S Miami Ave, Miami FL 33133
Tel (305) 854-4400 *SIC* 8062

■ **MIAMI BEACH HEALTHCARE GROUP LTD** p 959
20900 Biscayne Blvd, Miami FL 33180
Tel (305) 682-7000 *SIC* 8062

■ **NORTH SHORE MEDICAL CENTER INC** p 1053
1100 Nw 95th St, Miami FL 33150
Tel (305) 835-6000 *SIC* 8062

PAN AMERICAN HOSPITAL CORP p 1110
5959 Nw 7th St, Miami FL 33126
Tel (305) 261-2273 *SIC* 8062

MOUNT SINAI MEDICAL CENTER OF FLORIDA INC p 994
4300 Alton Rd, Miami Beach FL 33140
Tel (305) 674-2121 *SIC* 8062 8741

■ **HEALTH MANAGEMENT ASSOCIATES INC** p 675
5811 Pelican Bay Blvd # 500, Naples FL 34108
Tel (239) 598-3131 *SIC* 8062

NAPLES COMMUNITY HOSPITAL INC p 1007
350 7th St N, Naples FL 34102
Tel (239) 436-5000 *SIC* 8062

NCH HEALTHCARE SYSTEM INC p 1022
350 7th St N, Naples FL 34102
Tel (239) 624-5000 *SIC* 8062

■ **PHYSICIANS REGIONAL MEDICAL CENTER** p 1146
6101 Pine Ridge Rd, Naples FL 34119
Tel (239) 348-4400 *SIC* 8011 8062

COMMUNITY HOSPITAL OF NEW PORT RICHEY p 349
5637 Marine Pkwy, New Port Richey FL 34652
Tel (727) 845-9127 *SIC* 8062

SOUTHEAST VOLUSIA HEALTHCARE CORP p 1346
401 Palmetto St, New Smyrna Beach FL 32168
Tel (386) 424-5000 *SIC* 8062

JACKSON NORTH MEDICAL CENTER p 774
160 Nw 170th St, North Miami Beach FL 33169
Tel (305) 651-1100 *SIC* 8011 8062

■ **MARION COMMUNITY HOSPITAL INC** p 907
1431 Sw 1st Ave, Ocala FL 34471
Tel (352) 401-1000 *SIC* 8062

■ **MARION WEST COMMUNITY HOSPITAL** p 907
4600 Sw 46th Ct, Ocala FL 34474
Tel (352) 291-3000 *SIC* 8062

MUNROE REGIONAL MEDICAL CENTER INC p 1000
1500 Sw 1st Ave, Ocala FL 34471
Tel (352) 351-7200 *SIC* 8062

ORLANDO HEALTH CENTRAL INC p 1095
10000 W Colonial Dr, Ocoee FL 34761
Tel (407) 296-1820 *SIC* 8062

WEST ORANGE HEALTHCARE DISTRICT INC p 1595
10000 W Colonial Dr Ofc, Ocoee FL 34761
Tel (407) 296-1000 *SIC* 8062

WEST ORANGE MEMORIAL HOSPITAL TAX DISTRICT p 1595
10000 W Colonial Dr Ofc, Ocoee FL 34761
Tel (407) 656-3555 *SIC* 8062

SOUTHWEST VOLUSIA HEALTHCARE CORP p 1352
1055 Saxon Blvd, Orange City FL 32763
Tel (386) 917-5000 *SIC* 8062

FLORIDA HOSPITAL MEDICAL CENTER INC p 558
601 E Rollins St, Orlando FL 32803
Tel (407) 303-5600 *SIC* 8062

LOYAL SOURCE GOVERNMENT SERVICES LLC p 882
12612 Challenger Pkwy # 365, Orlando FL 32826
Tel (407) 306-8441 *SIC* 8062

ORLANDO HEALTH INC p 1095
52 W Underwood St, Orlando FL 32806
Tel (321) 843-7000 *SIC* 8062 8741 8069

PALM BAY HOSPITAL INC p 1109
1425 Malabar Rd Ne, Palm Bay FL 32907
Tel (321) 434-8000 *SIC* 8062

MEMORIAL HOSPITAL FLAGLER INC p 942
60 Memorial Medical Pkwy, Palm Coast FL 32164
Tel (386) 586-2000 *SIC* 8062

BAY MEDICAL CENTER p 161
615 N Bonita Ave, Panama City FL 32401
Tel (850) 769-1511 *SIC* 8062 8011

BAPTIST HOSPITAL INC p 154
1000 W Moreno St, Pensacola FL 32501
Tel (850) 434-4011 *SIC* 8062

SACRED HEART HEALTH SYSTEM INC p 1265
5151 N 9th Ave, Pensacola FL 32504
Tel (850) 416-1600 *SIC* 8062 8011

WEST FLORIDA HOSPITAL p 1594
8383 N Davis Hwy, Pensacola FL 32514
Tel (850) 494-4000 *SIC* 8062

■ **WEST FLORIDA REGIONAL MEDICAL CENTER INC** p 1594
8383 N Davis Hwy, Pensacola FL 32514
Tel (850) 494-4000
SIC 8062 8093 8063 8051

SOUTH FLORIDA BAPTIST HOSPITAL INC p 1344
301 N Alexander St, Plant City FL 33563
Tel (813) 757-1200 *SIC* 8062

■ **COLUMBIA HOSPITAL CORP OF SOUTH BROWARD** p 341
8201 W Broward Blvd, Plantation FL 33324
Tel (954) 473-6600 *SIC* 8062

■ **PLANTATION GENERAL HOSPITAL LP** p 1154
401 Nw 42nd Ave, Plantation FL 33317
Tel (954) 587-5010 *SIC* 8062

■ **FAWCETT MEMORIAL HOSPITAL INC** p 532
21298 Olean Blvd, Port Charlotte FL 33952
Tel (941) 629-1181 *SIC* 8062

■ **PEACE RIVER REGIONAL MEDICAL CENTER** p 1125
2500 Harvard Blvd, Port Charlotte FL 33952
Tel (941) 766-4122 *SIC* 8062

HEALTH FIRST INC p 674
6450 Us Highway 1, Rockledge FL 32955
Tel (321) 434-4300
SIC 8062 8011 8082 8069 7991 6324

■ **ROCKLEDGE HMA LLC** p 1245
110 Longwood Ave, Rockledge FL 32955
Tel (321) 636-2211 *SIC* 8062

■ **SCHF NOT-FOR-PROFIT WIND-DOWN INC** p 1287
110 Longwood Ave, Rockledge FL 32955
Tel (321) 636-2211 *SIC* 8062

FLAGLER HEALTHCARE SYSTEMS INC p 554
400 Health Park Blvd, Saint Augustine FL 32086
Tel (904) 819-5155 *SIC* 8062

FLAGLER HOSPITAL INC p 554
400 Health Park Blvd, Saint Augustine FL 32086
Tel (904) 819-5155 *SIC* 8062

■ **BAYFRONT MEDICAL CENTER INC** p 161
701 6th St S, Saint Petersburg FL 33701
Tel (727) 893-6111 *SIC* 8062

■ **GALEN OF FLORIDA INC** p 589
6500 38th Ave N, Saint Petersburg FL 33710
Tel (727) 341-4055 *SIC* 8062

JOHNS HOPKINS ALL CHILDRENS HOSPITAL INC p 790
501 6th Ave S, Saint Petersburg FL 33701
Tel (727) 898-7451 *SIC* 8069 8062

■ **NORTHSIDE HOSPITAL** p 1058
6000 49th St N, Saint Petersburg FL 33709
Tel (727) 521-4411
SIC 8031 8011 8069 8062

ST ANTHONYS HOSPITAL INC p 1364
1200 7th Ave N, Saint Petersburg FL 33705
Tel (727) 825-1100 *SIC* 8062

■ **CENTRAL FLORIDA REGIONAL HOSPITAL INC** p 278
1401 W Seminole Blvd, Sanford FL 32771
Tel (407) 321-4500 *SIC* 8062

SARASOTA COUNTY PUBLIC HOSPITAL DISTRICT p 1282
1700 S Tamiami Trl, Sarasota FL 34239
Tel (941) 917-9000 *SIC* 8062 7372

■ **SARASOTA DOCTORS HOSPITAL INC** p 1282
5731 Bee Ridge Rd, Sarasota FL 34233
Tel (941) 342-1100 *SIC* 8062

■ **SEBASTIAN RIVER MEDICAL CENTER** p 1298
13695 Us Highway 1, Sebastian FL 32958
Tel (772) 589-3186 *SIC* 8062

FLORIDA HOSPITAL HEARTLAND MEDICAL CENTER p 558
4200 Sun N Lake Blvd, Sebring FL 33872
Tel (863) 314-4466 *SIC* 8062

BAPTIST HEALTH SOUTH FLORIDA INC p 153
6855 S Red Rd, South Miami FL 33143
Tel (305) 596-1960 *SIC* 8062 8011 8082

LARKIN COMMUNITY HOSPITAL INC p 845
7031 Sw 62nd Ave, South Miami FL 33143
Tel (305) 757-5707 *SIC* 8062

SOUTH MIAMI HOSPITAL INC p 1344
6200 Sw 73rd St, South Miami FL 33143
Tel (786) 662-4000 *SIC* 8062

MARTIN MEMORIAL HEALTH SYSTEMS INC p 912
200 Se Hospital Ave, Stuart FL 34994
Tel (772) 287-5200 *SIC* 8741 8062

MARTIN MEMORIAL MEDICAL CENTER INC p 912
200 Se Hospital Ave, Stuart FL 34994
Tel (772) 287-5200 *SIC* 8062

■ **TALLAHASSEE MEDICAL CENTER INC** p 1423
2626 Capital Medical Blvd, Tallahassee FL 32308
Tel (850) 325-5000 *SIC* 8062

TALLAHASSEE MEMORIAL HEALTHCARE INC p 1423
1300 Miccosukee Rd, Tallahassee FL 32308
Tel (850) 431-1155 *SIC* 8062

■ **UNIVERSITY HOSPITAL LTD** p 1519
7201 N University Dr, Tamarac FL 33321
Tel (954) 721-2200 *SIC* 8062

FLORIDA HEALTH SCIENCES CENTER INC p 558
1 Tampa General Cir, Tampa FL 33606
Tel (813) 844-7000 *SIC* 8062

H LEE MOFFITT CANCER CENTER & RESEARCH INSTITUTE p 650
12902 Usf Magnolia Dr, Tampa FL 33612
Tel (813) 745-4673 *SIC* 8062

ST JOSEPHS HOSPITAL INC p 1369
3001 W Dr Mrtn Lthr Kng B Martin Luther, Tampa FL 33607
Tel (813) 554-8500 *SIC* 8062

TAMPA GENERAL HOSPITAL p 1423
1 Tampa General Cir, Tampa FL 33606
Tel (813) 844-4527 *SIC* 8062

UNIVERSITY COMMUNITY HOSPITAL INC p 1518
3100 E Fletcher Ave, Tampa FL 33613
Tel (813) 615-7887 *SIC* 8062

TARPON SPRINGS HOSPITAL FOUNDATION INC p 1425
1395 S Pinellas Ave, Tarpon Springs FL 34689
Tel (727) 942-5000 *SIC* 8062

FLORIDA HOSPITAL WATERMAN INC p 559
1000 Waterman Way, Tavares FL 32778
Tel (352) 253-3333 SIC 8062

VILLAGES TRI-COUNTY MEDICAL CENTER INC p 1557
1451 El Camino Real, The Villages FL 32159
Tel (352) 751-8000 SIC 8062

BREVARD NORTH COUNTY HOSPITAL p 210
951 N Washington Ave, Titusville FL 32796
Tel (321) 268-6333 SIC 8062

VENICE REGIONAL HOSPITAL p 1547
540 The Rialto, Venice FL 34285
Tel (941) 485-7711 SIC 8062

INDIAN RIVER MEMORIAL HOSPITAL INC p 737
1000 36th St, Vero Beach FL 32960
Tel (772) 567-4311 SIC 8062 8011

FLORIDA HOSPITAL WESLEY CHAPEL INC p 559
2600 Bruce B Downs Blvd, Wesley Chapel FL 33544
Tel (813) 929-5000 SIC 8062

■ **ST MARYS MEDICAL CENTER** p 1371
901 45th St, West Palm Beach FL 33407
Tel (561) 844-6300 SIC 8062

■ **TENET GOOD SAMARITAN HOSPITAL INC** p 1437
1309 N Flagler Dr, West Palm Beach FL 33401
Tel (561) 655-5511 SIC 8062

■ **WELLINGTON REGIONAL MEDICAL CENTER INC** p 1589
10101 Forest Hill Blvd, West Palm Beach FL 33414
Tel (561) 798-8500 SIC 8062

CLEVELAND CLINIC FLORIDA FOUNDATION p 325
3100 Weston Rd, Weston FL 33331
Tel (954) 689-5000 SIC 8062

MID-FLORIDA MEDICAL SERVICES INC p 963
200 Avenue F Ne, Winter Haven FL 33881
Tel (863) 297-1895 SIC 8741 8062 8082

WINTER HAVEN HOSPITAL INC p 1617
200 Avenue F Ne, Winter Haven FL 33881
Tel (863) 293-1121 SIC 8062

WINTER PARK HEALTHCARE GROUP LTD p 1617
200 N Lakemont Ave, Winter Park FL 32792
Tel (407) 646-7000 SIC 8062 8011

FLORIDA HOSPITAL ZEPHYRHILLS p 559
37924 Medical Arts Ct, Zephyrhills FL 33541
Tel (813) 779-1900 SIC 8062

FLORIDA HOSPITAL ZEPHYRHILLS INC p 559
7050 Gall Blvd, Zephyrhills FL 33541
Tel (813) 788-0411 SIC 8062

PHOEBE PUTNEY MEMORIAL HOSPITAL INC p 1144
2000 Palmyra Rd, Albany GA 31701
Tel (229) 434-2000 SIC 8062

PHOEBE PUTNEY MEMORIAL HOSPITAL INC p 1144
417 W 3rd Ave, Albany GA 31701
Tel (229) 312-1000 SIC 8062

PIEDMONT ATHENS REGIONAL MEDICAL CENTER INC p 1146
1510 Prince Ave, Athens GA 30606
Tel (706) 475-7000 SIC 8062

ST MARYS HEALTH CARE SYSTEM INC p 1371
1230 Baxter St, Athens GA 30606
Tel (706) 389-3000 SIC 8062 8051

■ **ATLANTA MEDICAL CENTER** p 125
303 Parkway Dr Ne, Atlanta GA 30312
Tel (404) 265-4000 SIC 8062

EMORY CLINIC INC p 493
1365 Clifton Rd Ne, Atlanta GA 30322
Tel (404) 778-5000 SIC 8062

EMORY HEALTHCARE INC p 493
1440 Clifton Rd Ne, Atlanta GA 30322
Tel (404) 778-7777 SIC 8062

EMORY UNIVERSITY HOSPITAL MIDTOWN p 493
550 Peachtree St Ne, Atlanta GA 30308
Tel (404) 686-7100 SIC 8062

FULTON DEKALB HOSPITAL AUTHORITY p 584
191 Peachtree St Ne # 820, Atlanta GA 30303
Tel (404) 600-4097 SIC 8062

GRADY HEALTH SYSTEM p 628
80 Jesse Hill Jr Dr Se, Atlanta GA 30303
Tel (404) 616-4360 SIC 8062

MARINER HEALTH CARE INC p 907
1 Ravinia Dr Ste 1500, Atlanta GA 30346
Tel (678) 443-7000
SIC 5912 8051 8093 8741 8062 3443

NATIONAL SENIOR CARE INC p 1016
1 Ravinia Dr Ste 1500, Atlanta GA 30346
Tel (678) 443-7000
SIC 5912 8051 8093 8741 8062 3443

NORTHSIDE HOSPITAL INC p 1058
1000 Johnson Ferry Rd, Atlanta GA 30342
Tel (404) 851-8000 SIC 8062

PIEDMONT HOSPITAL INC p 1147
1968 Peachtree Rd Nw, Atlanta GA 30309
Tel (404) 605-5000 SIC 8062

PROMINA HEALTH SYSTEM INC p 1183
2727 Paces Ferry Rd Se, Atlanta GA 30339
Tel (404) 541-1111 SIC 8741 8062

SAINT JOSEPHS HOSPITAL OF ATLANTA INC p 1269
5665 Pchtr Dunwoody Rd Ne, Atlanta GA 30342
Tel (404) 851-7001 SIC 8062

SAINT JOSEPHS SERVICE CORP p 1270
5665 Pachtree Dunwoody Rd, Atlanta GA 30342
Tel (404) 851-7001 SIC 8062

▲ **SUNLINK HEALTH SYSTEMS INC** p 1403
900 Cir 75 Pkwy Se # 650, Atlanta GA 30339
Tel (770) 933-7000 SIC 8062 8051 5912

■ **SUNLINK HEALTHCARE CORP** p 1403
900 Circle 75 Pkwy Se # 13, Atlanta GA 30339
Tel (770) 850-1109 SIC 8051 8062

AU MEDICAL CENTER INC p 130
1120 15th St, Augusta GA 30912
Tel (706) 721-6569 SIC 8062

■ **DOCTORS HOSPITAL OF AUGUSTA LLC** p 447
3651 Wheeler Rd, Augusta GA 30909
Tel (706) 651-3232 SIC 8062 8049

EAST CENTRAL REGIONAL HOSPITAL p 470
3405 Mike Padgett Hwy, Augusta GA 30906
Tel (706) 792-7105 SIC 8062

GEORGIA HEALTH SCIENCES FOUNDATION INC p 607
1120 15th St, Augusta GA 30912
Tel (800) 869-1113 SIC 8062 8221

UNIVERSITY HEALTH INC p 1518
1350 Walton Way, Augusta GA 30901
Tel (706) 722-9011 SIC 8062

UNIVERSITY HEALTH SERVICES INC p 1518
1350 Walton Way, Augusta GA 30901
Tel (706) 722-9011 SIC 8062

COBB HOSPITAL INC p 332
3950 Austell Rd, Austell GA 30106
Tel (770) 792-7600 SIC 8062

GLYNN-BRUNSWICK MEMORIAL HOSPITAL AUTHORITY p 618
2415 Parkwood Dr, Brunswick GA 31520
Tel (912) 466-7000 SIC 8062 8011

ADVENTIST HEALTH SYSTEM GEORGIA INC p 27
1035 Red Bud Rd Ne, Calhoun GA 30701
Tel (706) 879-4714 SIC 8062

NORTHSIDE HOSPITAL - CHEROKEE INC p 1058
201 Hospital Rd, Canton GA 30114
Tel (770) 720-5100 SIC 8062

TANNER MEDICAL CENTER INC p 1424
705 Dixie St, Carrollton GA 30117
Tel (770) 836-9666 SIC 8062

COLUMBUS REGIONAL HEALTHCARE SYSTEM INC p 342
707 Center St Ste 300, Columbus GA 31901
Tel (706) 571-1495 SIC 8062

MEDICAL CENTER p 936
710 Center St, Columbus GA 31901
Tel (706) 660-6255 SIC 8062

■ **ST FRANCIS HOSPITAL INC** p 1366
2122 Manchester Expy, Columbus GA 31904
Tel (706) 596-4000 SIC 8062

■ **ROCKDALE HOSPITAL LLC** p 1244
1412 Milstead Ave Ne, Conyers GA 30012
Tel (770) 918-3101 SIC 8062

■ **ROCKDALE MEDICAL CENTER INC** p 1244
1412 Milstead Ave Ne, Conyers GA 30012
Tel (770) 918-3000 SIC 8062

PAULDING MEDICAL CENTER INC p 1121
600 W Memorial Dr, Dallas GA 30132
Tel (770) 445-4411 SIC 8062 8051

HAMILTON HEALTH CARE SYSTEM INC p 655
1200 Memorial Dr, Dalton GA 30720
Tel (706) 278-2105 SIC 8322 8062

HAMILTON MEDICAL CENTER INC p 655
1200 Memorial Dr, Dalton GA 30720
Tel (706) 272-6000 SIC 8062

DEKALB MEDICAL CENTER INC p 423
2701 N Decatur Rd, Decatur GA 30033
Tel (404) 501-1000 SIC 8062

COFFEE REGIONAL MEDICAL CENTER INC p 334
1101 Ocilla Rd, Douglas GA 31533
Tel (912) 384-1900 SIC 8062

DOUGLAS HOSPITAL INC p 452
8954 Hospital Dr Frnt, Douglasville GA 30134
Tel (770) 949-1500 SIC 8062

■ **FAIRVIEW PARK LIMITED PARTNERSHIP** p 525
200 Industrial Blvd, Dublin GA 31021
Tel (478) 274-3990 SIC 8062

FAYETTE COMMUNITY HOSPITAL INC p 532
1255 Highway 54 W, Fayetteville GA 30214
Tel (770) 719-7000 SIC 8062

NORTHEAST GEORGIA HEALTH SYSTEM INC p 1054
743 Spring St Ne, Gainesville GA 30501
Tel (770) 219-9000 SIC 8062

NORTHEAST GEORGIA MEDICAL CENTER INC p 1054
743 Spring St Ne, Gainesville GA 30501
Tel (770) 219-9000 SIC 8062

■ **TENET HEALTH SYSTEM SPALDING INC** p 1437
601 S 8th St, Griffin GA 30224
Tel (770) 228-2721 SIC 8062

EHCA JOHNS CREEK LLC p 481
6325 Hospital Pkwy, Johns Creek GA 30097
Tel (770) 813-0438 SIC 8062

LA GRANGE TROUP COUNTY HOSPITAL AUTHORITY p 835
1514 Vernon Rd, Lagrange GA 30240
Tel (706) 882-1411 SIC 8062 8051

WEST GEORGIA HEALTH SYSTEM INC p 1594
1514 Vernon Rd, Lagrange GA 30240
Tel (706) 882-1411 SIC 8062

GWINNETT HEALTH SYSTEM INC p 648
1000 Medical Center Blvd, Lawrenceville GA 30046
Tel (678) 312-1000 SIC 8062

GWINNETT HOSPITAL SYSTEM INC p 648
1000 Medical Center Blvd, Lawrenceville GA 30046
Tel (678) 343-3428 SIC 8062

■ **COLISEUM PARK HOSPITAL INC** p 336
350 Hospital Dr, Macon GA 31217
Tel (478) 765-7000 SIC 8062

MEDICAL CENTER OF CENTRAL GEORGIA INC p 936
777 Hemlock St, Macon GA 31201
Tel (478) 633-1000 SIC 8062

DOUGLAS HOSPITAL INC p 452
805 Sandy Plains Rd, Marietta GA 30066
Tel (770) 792-5023 SIC 8062

KENNESTONE HOSPITAL AT WINDY HILL INC p 811
677 Church St Ne, Marietta GA 30060
Tel (770) 793-5000 SIC 8062

KENNESTONE HOSPITAL INC p 811
805 Sandy Plains Rd, Marietta GA 30066
Tel (770) 792-5023 SIC 8062

WELLSTAR HEALTH SYSTEM INC p 1591
805 Sandy Plains Rd, Marietta GA 30066
Tel (770) 956-7827 SIC 8062

HOSPITAL AUTHORITY OF COLQUITT COUNTY p 709
3131 S Main St, Moultrie GA 31768
Tel (229) 985-3420 SIC 8062

PIEDMONT NEWNAN HOSPITAL INC p 1147
745 Poplar Rd, Newnan GA 30265
Tel (770) 253-2330 SIC 8062

BROOKS COUNTY HOSPITAL AUTHORITY p 218
903 N Court St, Quitman GA 31643
Tel (229) 263-4171 SIC 8062

PRIME HEALTHCARE FOUNDATION - SOUTHERN REGIONAL LLC p 1175
11 Upper Riverdale Rd Sw, Riverdale GA 30274
Tel (770) 991-8000 SIC 8062

SOUTHERN REGIONAL HEALTH SYSTEM INC p 1350
11 Upper Riverdale Rd Sw, Riverdale GA 30274
Tel (770) 991-8175 SIC 8062

FLOYD HEALTHCARE MANAGEMENT INC p 561
304 Turner Mccall Blvd Sw, Rome GA 30165
Tel (706) 509-5000 SIC 8062

■ **REDMOND PARK HOSPITAL LLC** p 1217
501 Redmond Rd Nw, Rome GA 30165
Tel (706) 291-0291 SIC 8062 8011

NORTH FULTON MEDICAL CENTER VOLUNTEER SERVICES ORGANIZATION INC p 1052
3000 Hospital Blvd, Roswell GA 30076
Tel (770) 751-2500 SIC 8062

CANDLER HOSPITAL INC p 247
5353 Reynolds St, Savannah GA 31405
Tel (912) 819-6000 SIC 8062

MEMORIAL HEALTH INC p 941
4700 Waters Ave, Savannah GA 31404
Tel (912) 350-8000 SIC 8062

MEMORIAL HEALTH UNIVERSITY MEDICAL CENTER INC p 941
4700 Waters Ave, Savannah GA 31404
Tel (912) 350-8000 SIC 8062 8011

SAINT JOSEPHS HOSPITAL INC p 1269
5353 Reynolds St, Savannah GA 31405
Tel (912) 355-9967 SIC 8062

SAINT JOSEPHS HOSPITAL INC p 1269
11705 Mercy Blvd, Savannah GA 31419
Tel (912) 819-4100 SIC 8062

ST JOSEPHS/CANDLER HEALTH SYSTEM INC p 1369
5353 Reynolds St Ste 101, Savannah GA 31405
Tel (912) 819-6000 SIC 8062

■ **EHCA EASTSIDE OCCUPATIONAL MEDICINE CENTER LLC** p 481
1700 Medical Way, Snellville GA 30078
Tel (770) 979-0200 SIC 8062

■ **STATESBORO HMA INC** p 1383
1499 Fair Rd, Statesboro GA 30458
Tel (912) 486-1000 SIC 8062

PIEDMONT HENRY HOSPITAL INC p 1147
1133 Eagles Landing Pkwy, Stockbridge GA 30281
Tel (678) 604-1001 SIC 8062

ARCHBOLD MEDICAL CENTER INC p 104
Gordon Ave At Mimosa Dr, Thomasville GA 31792
Tel (229) 228-2739 SIC 8741 8062

JOHN D ARCHBOLD MEMORIAL HOSPITAL p 788
915 Gordon Ave, Thomasville GA 31792
Tel (229) 228-2000 SIC 8062

TIFT COUNTY HOSPITAL AUTHORITY p 1453
901 18th St E, Tifton GA 31794
Tel (229) 382-7120 SIC 8062

TIFT REGIONAL MEDICAL CENTER p 1453
901 18th St E, Tifton GA 31794
Tel (229) 382-7120 SIC 8062

TIFT REGIONAL MEDICAL CENTER p 1453
901 18th St E, Tifton GA 31794
Tel (229) 382-7120 SIC 8062

HOSPITAL AUTHORITY OF VALDOSTA AND LOWNDES COUNTY GEORGIA p 709
2501 N Patterson St, Valdosta GA 31602
Tel (229) 333-1000 SIC 8062

SOUTH GEORGIA MEDICAL CENTER p 1344
2501 N Patterson St, Valdosta GA 31602
Tel (229) 333-1000 SIC 8062

MEADOWS HEALTHCARE ALLIANCE INC p 934
1 Meadows Pkwy, Vidalia GA 30474
Tel (912) 538-5866 SIC 8099 8062

MEADOWS REGIONAL MEDICAL CENTER INC p 934
1703 Meadows Ln, Vidalia GA 30474
Tel (912) 537-8921 SIC 8062 8051

HOUSTON HEALTHCARE SYSTEM INC p 712
1601 Watson Blvd, Warner Robins GA 31093
Tel (478) 922-4281 SIC 8062

HOUSTON HOSPITALS INC p 712
1601 Watson Blvd, Warner Robins GA 31093
Tel (478) 929-9544 SIC 8062

MAYO CLINIC HEALTH SYSTEM IN WAYCROSS INC p 923
1900 Tebeau St, Waycross GA 31501
Tel (912) 283-3030 SIC 8062 8051

HAWAII MEDICAL CENTER WEST LLC p 669
91-2141 Fort Weaver Rd, Ewa Beach HI 96706
Tel (808) 678-7000 SIC 8062

HAWAI I PACIFIC HEALTH p 668
55 Merchant St Ste 2500, Honolulu HI 96813
Tel (808) 535-7350 SIC 8062 8011

HAWAII MEDICAL CENTER p 669
2230 Liliha St Ste 227, Honolulu HI 96817
Tel (808) 547-6881 SIC 8062

KUAKINI HEALTH SYSTEM p 831
347 N Kuakini St, Honolulu HI 96817
Tel (808) 536-2236 SIC 8062

KUAKINI MEDICAL CENTER p 831
347 N Kuakini St, Honolulu HI 96817
Tel (808) 547-9231 SIC 8062

QUEENS HEALTH SYSTEMS p 1198
1301 Punchbowl St, Honolulu HI 96813
Tel (808) 691-5900 SIC 8062

QUEENS MEDICAL CENTER p 1198
1301 Punchbowl St, Honolulu HI 96813
Tel (808) 547-4329 SIC 8062 8621

STRAUB CLINIC & HOSPITAL p 1393
888 S King St, Honolulu HI 96813
Tel (808) 522-4000 SIC 8011 8062

CASTLE MEDICAL CENTER p 264
640 Ulukahiki St, Kailua HI 96734
Tel (808) 263-5500 SIC 8062

WILCOX MEMORIAL HOSPITAL p 1609
3-3420 Kuhio Hwy, Lihue HI 96766
Tel (808) 245-1100 SIC 8062

MAUI MEMORIAL MEDICAL CENTER p 921
221 Mahalani St, Wailuku HI 96793
Tel (808) 244-9056 SIC 8062

BMH INC p 194
98 Poplar St, Blackfoot ID 83221
Tel (208) 785-4100 SIC 8062 8051

SAINT ALPHONSUS REGIONAL MEDICAL CENTER INC p 1268
1055 N Curtis Rd, Boise ID 83706
Tel (208) 367-2121 SIC 8062

ST LUKES HEALTH SYSTEM LTD p 1370
190 E Bannock St, Boise ID 83712
Tel (208) 381-2222 SIC 8062

ST LUKES REGIONAL MEDICAL CENTER LTD p 1370
190 E Bannock St, Boise ID 83712
Tel (208) 381-5500 SIC 8062 8011

■ **WEST VALLEY MEDICAL CENTER INC** p 1596
1717 Arlington Ave, Caldwell ID 83605
Tel (208) 459-4641 SIC 8062

KOOTENAI HOSPITAL DISTRICT p 827
2003 Kootenai Health Way, Coeur D Alene ID 83814
Tel (208) 625-4000
SIC 8062 8063 8093 8734

MOUNTAIN VIEW HOSPITAL LLC p 994
2325 Coronado St, Idaho Falls ID 83404
Tel (208) 557-2700 SIC 8062

ST JOSEPH REGIONAL MEDICAL CENTER INC p 1368
415 6th St, Lewiston ID 83501
Tel (208) 743-2511 SIC 8062

SAINT ALPHONSUS MEDICAL CENTER - NAMPA HEALTH FOUNDATION INC p 1268
1512 12th Ave Rd, Nampa ID 83686
Tel (208) 467-1171 SIC 8062 8011

POCATELLO HEALTH SYSTEM LLC p 1158
777 Hospital Way, Pocatello ID 83201
Tel (208) 239-1000 SIC 8062

PORTNEUF MEDICAL CENTER INC p 1163
651 Memorial Dr, Pocatello ID 83201
Tel (208) 239-1000 SIC 8062

ST LUKES MAGIC VALLEY INC p 1370
801 Pole Line Rd W, Twin Falls ID 83301
Tel (208) 737-2000 SIC 8062 8063

ALTON MEMORIAL HOSPITAL FOUNDATION p 62
1 Memorial Dr, Alton IL 62002
Tel (618) 463-7311 SIC 8062 8059

ALEXIAN BROTHERS OF AMERICA INC p 49
3040 W Salt Creek Ln, Arlington Heights IL 60005
Tel (847) 640-7550 SIC 8742 8062 8361

NORTHWEST COMMUNITY HOSPITAL FOUNDATION p 1059
800 W Central Rd, Arlington Heights IL 60005
Tel (847) 618-1000 SIC 8062

NORTHWEST COMMUNITY HOSPITAL INC p 1059
800 W Central Rd, Arlington Heights IL 60005
Tel (847) 618-1000 SIC 8062

COPLEY MEMORIAL HOSPITAL INC p 368
2000 Ogden Ave, Aurora IL 60504
Tel (630) 978-6200 SIC 8062

RUSH-COPLEY MEDICAL CENTER INC p 1259
2000 Ogden Ave, Aurora IL 60504
Tel (630) 978-6200 SIC 8062

PROTESTANT MEMORIAL MEDICAL CENTER INC p 1185
4500 Memorial Dr, Belleville IL 62226
Tel (618) 233-7750 SIC 8062 8051

ST ELIZABETHS HOSPITAL OF BELLEVILLE INC p 1366
211 S 3rd St, Belleville IL 62220
Tel (618) 234-2120 SIC 8062

■ **MAC NEAL MEMORIAL HOSPITAL ASSOCIATION** p 891
3249 Oak Park Ave, Berwyn IL 60402
Tel (708) 783-9100 SIC 8062

■ **VHS OF ILLINOIS INC** p 1554
3249 Oak Park Ave, Berwyn IL 60402
Tel (708) 783-9100 SIC 8062

■ **BLUE ISLAND HOSPITAL CO LLC** p 192
12935 Gregory St, Blue Island IL 60406
Tel (708) 597-2000 SIC 8062

ADVENTIST BOLINGBROOK HOSPITAL p 27
500 Remington Blvd, Bolingbrook IL 60440
Tel (630) 312-5000 SIC 8062

PRESENCE HOSPITALS PRV p 1172
1000 Remington Blvd # 100, Bolingbrook IL 60440
Tel (877) 737-4636 SIC 8062

SOUTHERN ILLINOIS HEALTHCARE ENTERPRISES INC p 1348
1239 E Main St Ste C, Carbondale IL 62901
Tel (618) 457-5200 SIC 8062

SOUTHERN ILLINOIS HOSPITAL SERVICES p 1348
1239 E Main St Ste C, Carbondale IL 62901
Tel (618) 457-5200 SIC 8062

ST MARYS-GOOD SAMARITAN INC p 1372
400 N Pleasant Ave, Centralia IL 62801
Tel (618) 436-8000 SIC 8062

CHILDRENS HOSPITAL OF CHICAGO MEDICAL CENTER p 299
225 E Chicago Ave, Chicago IL 60611
Tel (312) 227-4000 SIC 8062 8733

COMMUNITY FIRST MEDICAL CENTER p 348
5645 W Addison St, Chicago IL 60634
Tel (773) 282-7000 SIC 8062

ILLINOIS MASONIC MEDICAL CENTER p 732
836 W Wellington Ave, Chicago IL 60657
Tel (773) 975-1600 SIC 8062

JACKSON PARK HOSPITAL FOUNDATION p 774
7531 S Stony Island Ave # 1, Chicago IL 60649
Tel (773) 947-7500 SIC 8062

MERCY HOSPITAL AND MEDICAL CENTER p 947
2525 S Michigan Ave, Chicago IL 60616
Tel (312) 567-2201 SIC 8062

MOUNT SINAI HOSPITAL MEDICAL CENTER OF CHICAGO p 994
1501 S California Ave, Chicago IL 60608
Tel (773) 542-2000 SIC 8062

NATIONAL SURGICAL HOSPITALS INC p 1016
250 S Wacker Dr Ste 500, Chicago IL 60606
Tel (312) 627-8400 SIC 8062 8093

NORTHWESTERN MEMORIAL HOSPITAL p 1060
251 E Huron St, Chicago IL 60611
Tel (312) 755-0604 SIC 8062

NORWEGIAN AMERICAN HOSPITAL INC p 1061
1044 N Francisco Ave, Chicago IL 60622
Tel (773) 278-8800 SIC 8062

PRESENCE CHICAGO HOSPITALS NETWORK p 1172
7435 W Talcott Ave, Chicago IL 60631
Tel (773) 737-4636 SIC 8062

PRESENCE CHICAGO HOSPITALS NETWORK p 1172
7435 W Talcott Ave, Chicago IL 60631
Tel (773) 774-8000 SIC 8062 8059

PRESENCE HEALTH NETWORK p 1172
200 S Wacker Dr Fl 12, Chicago IL 60606
Tel (773) 774-8000
SIC 8082 8062 8011 8051

PRESENCE SAINT JOSEPH HOSPITAL - CHICAGO p 1172
2900 N Lake Shore Dr, Chicago IL 60657
Tel (773) 665-3000 SIC 8062

PRESENCE SAINTS MARY AND ELIZABETH MEDICAL CENTER p 1172
2233 W Division St, Chicago IL 60622
Tel (312) 770-2000 SIC 8062

RUSH SYSTEM FOR HEALTH p 1258
1645 W Jackson Blvd Ste 5, Chicago IL 60612
Tel (312) 942-4061 SIC 8741 8062

RUSH UNIVERSITY MEDICAL CENTER p 1259
1653 W Congress Pkwy, Chicago IL 60612
Tel (312) 942-5000 SIC 8062

SAINT ANTHONY HOSPITAL p 1268
2875 W 19th St, Chicago IL 60623
Tel (773) 484-1000 SIC 8062

SINAI CHILDRENS HOSPITAL p 1326
1500 S Cal Ave K435 435 K, Chicago IL 60608
Tel (773) 542-2000 SIC 8011 8062

ST BERNARD HOSPITAL p 1365
326 W 64th St, Chicago IL 60621
Tel (773) 962-3900 SIC 8062

SWEDISH COVENANT HOSPITAL p 1411
5145 N California Ave, Chicago IL 60625
Tel (773) 878-8200 SIC 8062 8059

UNIVERSITY OF CHICAGO MEDICAL CENTER p 1520
5841 S Maryland Ave, Chicago IL 60637
Tel (773) 702-1000 SIC 8062

■ VHS ACQUISITION SUBSIDIARY NUMBER 3 INC p 1553
4646 N Marine Dr, Chicago IL 60640
Tel (773) 878-8700 SIC 8062

CENTEGRA HEALTH SYSTEM p 275
385 Millennium Dr Ste A, Crystal Lake IL 60012
Tel (815) 788-5800 SIC 8062

DECATUR MEMORIAL HOSPITAL p 421
2300 N Edward St, Decatur IL 62526
Tel (217) 877-8121 SIC 8062

DMH CORPORATE HEALTH SERVICES p 446
2300 N Edward St, Decatur IL 62526
Tel (217) 876-8121 SIC 8062

ST MARYS HOSPITAL p 1371
1800 E Lake Shore Dr, Decatur IL 62521
Tel (217) 464-2984 SIC 8062

ST MARYS HOSPITAL DECATUR OF HOSPITAL SISTERS OF THIRD ORDER OF ST FRANCIS p 1371
1800 E Lake Shore Dr, Decatur IL 62521
Tel (217) 464-2966 SIC 8062

KISHWAUKEE COMMUNITY HOSPITAL p 822
1 Kish Hospital Dr, Dekalb IL 60115
Tel (815) 756-1521 SIC 8062

PRESENCE HOLY FAMILY MEDICAL CENTER p 1172
100 N River Rd, Des Plaines IL 60016
Tel (847) 297-1800 SIC 8062

KATHERINE SHAW BETHEA HOSPITAL p 804
403 E 1st St, Dixon IL 61021
Tel (815) 288-5531 SIC 8062

ADVOCATE HEALTH AND HOSPITALS CORP p 28
3975 Highland Ave, Downers Grove IL 60515
Tel (630) 572-9393 SIC 8062

ST ANTHONYS MEMORIAL HOSPITAL OF HOSPITAL SISTERS OF THETHIRD ORDER OF ST FRANCIS p 1364
503 N Maple St, Effingham IL 62401
Tel (217) 342-2121 SIC 8062

SHERMAN ADVOCATE HOSPITAL p 1316
1425 N Randall Rd, Elgin IL 60123
Tel (847) 742-9800 SIC 8062

ALEXIAN BROTHERS HEALTH SYSTEM INC p 49
3040 Salt Creek Ln, Elk Grove Village IL 60007
Tel (847) 437-5500 SIC 8062

ALEXIAN BROTHERS MEDICAL CENTER INC p 49
800 Biesterfield Rd Fl 1, Elk Grove Village IL 60007
Tel (847) 437-5500 SIC 8062

ELMHURST MEMORIAL HOSPITAL INC p 489
133 E Brush Hill Rd, Elmhurst IL 60126
Tel (331) 221-9003 SIC 8062

PRESENCE SAINT FRANCIS HOSPITAL p 1172
355 Ridge Ave, Evanston IL 60202
Tel (847) 316-4000 SIC 8062 8059

LITTLE CO OF MARY HOSPITAL AND HEALTH CARE CENTERS p 871
2800 W 95th St, Evergreen Park IL 60805
Tel (708) 422-6200 SIC 8062

LITTLE CO OF MARY HOSPITAL AND HEALTH CARE CENTERS p 871
2800 W 95th St, Evergreen Park IL 60805
Tel (708) 422-6200 SIC 8062

PHYSICIAN MATCH p 1145
2800 W 95th St, Evergreen Park IL 60805
Tel (708) 423-3070 SIC 8062

PRESENCE CENTRAL AND SUBURBAN HOSPITALS NETWORK p 1172
9223 W Saint Francis Rd, Frankfort IL 60423
Tel (312) 308-3200 SIC 8062

FREEPORT MEMORIAL HOSPITAL INC p 577
1045 W Stephenson St, Freeport IL 61032
Tel (815) 599-0000 SIC 8062

DELNOR-COMMUNITY HOSPITAL p 425
300 Randall Rd, Geneva IL 60134
Tel (630) 208-3000 SIC 8062

ADVENTIST GLENOAKS HOSPITAL p 27
701 Winthrop Ave, Glendale Heights IL 60139
Tel (630) 545-8000 SIC 8062

■ GRANITE CITY HOSPITAL CORP p 631
2100 Madison Ave, Granite City IL 62040
Tel (618) 798-3000 SIC 8062

INGALLS HEALTH SYSTEM p 742
1 Ingalls Dr, Harvey IL 60426
Tel (708) 333-2333 SIC 8062

INGALLS MEMORIAL HOSPITAL p 742
1 Ingalls Dr, Harvey IL 60426
Tel (708) 333-2300 SIC 8062

ADVOCATE SOUTH SUBURBAN HOSPITAL p 28
17800 Kedzie Ave, Hazel Crest IL 60429
Tel (708) 799-8000 SIC 8062

ADVENTIST MIDWEST HEALTH p 27
120 N Oak St, Hinsdale IL 60521
Tel (630) 856-9000 SIC 8062 5947 8011

RML HEALTH PROVIDERS LIMITED PARTNERSHIP p 1239
5601 S County Line Rd, Hinsdale IL 60521
Tel (708) 783-5800 SIC 8062

ST ALEXIUS MEDICAL CENTER p 1364
1555 Barrington Rd Bldg 1, Hoffman Estates IL 60169
Tel (847) 884-9800 SIC 8062

PASSAVANT MEMORIAL AREA HOSPITAL ASSOCIATION p 1120
1600 W Walnut St, Jacksonville IL 62650
Tel (217) 245-4640 SIC 8062

RIVERSIDE HEALTH SYSTEM p 1238
350 N Wall St, Kankakee IL 60901
Tel (815) 933-1671
SIC 8082 8062 5912 5047

RIVERSIDE MEDICAL CENTER p 1238
350 N Wall St, Kankakee IL 60901
Tel (815) 933-1671 SIC 8062

LA GRANGE MEMORIAL HOSPITAL INC p 835
5101 Willow Springs Rd, La Grange IL 60525
Tel (708) 352-1200 SIC 8062

FOREST LAKE HOSPITAL p 567
660 N Westmoreland Rd, Lake Forest IL 60045
Tel (847) 234-5600 SIC 8062

LAKE FOREST HOSPITAL FOUNDATION p 839
660 N Westmoreland Rd, Lake Forest IL 60045
Tel (847) 234-5600 SIC 8062

NORTHWESTERN LAKE FOREST HOSPITAL p 1060
660 N Westmoreland Rd, Lake Forest IL 60045
Tel (847) 234-0945
SIC 8062 5947 5932 5812

ADVOCATE CONDELL MEDICAL CENTER p 28
801 S Milwaukee Ave, Libertyville IL 60048
Tel (847) 362-2900 SIC 8062

■ MARION HOSPITAL CORP p 907
3333 W Deyoung St, Marion IL 62959
Tel (618) 998-7800 SIC 8062 8011

MARION VA MEDICAL CENTER p 907
2401 W Main St, Marion IL 62959
Tel (618) 993-1122 SIC 8062

SOUTHWESTERN ILLINOIS HEALTH FACILITIES INC p 1353
6800 State Route 162, Maryville IL 62062
Tel (618) 288-5711 SIC 8062

SARAH BUSH LINCOLN HEALTH CENTER p 1282
1000 Health Center Dr, Mattoon IL 61938
Tel (217) 258-2525 SIC 8011 8062

NIMED CORP p 1043
4201 W Medical Center Dr, Mchenry IL 60050
Tel (815) 344-5555 SIC 8062

NORTHERN ILLINOIS MEDICAL CENTER p 1056
4201 W Medical Center Dr, Mchenry IL 60050
Tel (815) 344-5000 SIC 8062

GOTTLIEB MEMORIAL HOSPITAL p 626
701 W North Ave, Melrose Park IL 60160
Tel (708) 681-3200 SIC 8062

WESTLAKE HOSPITAL p 1601
1225 W Lake St, Melrose Park IL 60160
Tel (708) 681-3000 SIC 8062

PRESENCE PRV HEALTH p 1172
19827 Hickory Crk Dr 30 Ste 300, Mokena IL 60448
Tel (815) 741-7137 SIC 8051 8062

MORRIS HOSPITAL p 990
150 W High St, Morris IL 60450
Tel (815) 942-2932 SIC 8011 8062

GOOD SAMARITAN REGIONAL HEALTH CENTER p 623
1 Good Samaritan Way, Mount Vernon IL 62864
Tel (618) 242-4600 SIC 8062

EDWARD HOSPITAL p 480
801 S Washington St, Naperville IL 60540
Tel (630) 355-0450 SIC 8062

EDWARD-ELMHURST HEALTHCARE p 480
801 S Washington St, Naperville IL 60540
Tel (630) 355-0450 SIC 8062

SILVER CROSS HOSPITAL AND MEDICAL CENTERS p 1323
1900 Silver Cross Blvd, New Lenox IL 60451
Tel (815) 300-1100 SIC 8062

ADVOCATE NORTHSIDE HEALTH p 28
2025 Windsor Dr, Oak Brook IL 60523
Tel (630) 572-9393 SIC 8062

RUSH OAK PARK HOSPITAL INC p 1258
520 S Maple Ave, Oak Park IL 60304
Tel (708) 383-9300 SIC 8051 8062

SYNERGON HEALTH SYSTEM INC p 1415
520 S Maple Ave, Oak Park IL 60304
Tel (708) 660-6661 SIC 8062 8051 8082

ST JAMES HOSPITAL & HEALTH CENTERS INC p 1367
20201 Crawford Ave, Olympia Fields IL 60461
Tel (708) 747-4000 SIC 8062 5912

PALOS COMMMUNITY HOSPITAL p 1110
12251 S 80th Ave, Palos Heights IL 60463
Tel (708) 923-4000 SIC 8062

ADVOCATE HEALTH AND HOSPITALS CORP p 28
1775 Dempster St, Park Ridge IL 60068
Tel (847) 723-6610 SIC 8062

■ GREATER PEORIA SPECIALTY HOSPITAL LLC p 635
500 W Romeo B Garrett Ave, Peoria IL 61605
Tel (309) 680-1500 SIC 8062 8099

METHODIST HEALTH SERVICES CORP p 953
221 Ne Glen Oak Ave, Peoria IL 61636
Tel (309) 672-5522 SIC 8062

METHODIST MEDICAL CENTER OF ILLINOIS p 954
221 Ne Glen Oak Ave, Peoria IL 61636
Tel (309) 672-5522 SIC 8062

OSF HEALTHCARE SYSTEM p 1096
800 Ne Glen Oak Ave, Peoria IL 61603
Tel (309) 655-2850 SIC 8062 8051

PROCTOR HOSPITAL p 1179
5409 N Knoxville Ave # 1, Peoria IL 61614
Tel (309) 691-1000 SIC 8062

ILLINOIS VALLEY COMMUNITY HOSPITAL INC p 732
925 West St, Peru IL 61354
Tel (815) 223-3300 SIC 8062

IV HEALTHCORP INC p 769
925 West St, Peru IL 61354
Tel (815) 223-3300 SIC 8062 8741 5912

BLESSING HOSPITAL p 189
Broadway At 11th St, Quincy IL 62301
Tel (217) 223-1200 SIC 8062

TRINITY MEDICAL CENTER p 1481
2701 17th St, Rock Island IL 61201
Tel (309) 779-5000 SIC 8062

TRINITY REGIONAL HEALTH SYSTEM p 1481
2701 17th St, Rock Island IL 61201
Tel (309) 779-5000 SIC 8062 8741

MERCY HEALTH CORP p 946
2400 N Rockton Ave, Rockford IL 61103
Tel (815) 971-5000 SIC 8062

ROCKFORD MEMORIAL HOSPITAL p 1244
2400 N Rockton Ave, Rockford IL 61103
Tel (815) 971-5000
SIC 8062 8011 8071 8099

SWEDISHAMERICAN HEALTH SYSTEM CORP p 1411
1401 E State St, Rockford IL 61104
Tel (815) 968-4400
SIC 8743 6512 8742 8099 8082 8062

SWEDISHAMERICAN HOSPITAL p 1411
1401 E State St, Rockford IL 61104
Tel (815) 968-4400 SIC 8062

SKOKIE HOSPITAL p 1330
9600 Gross Point Rd, Skokie IL 60076
Tel (847) 677-9600 SIC 8062

MEMORIAL HEALTH SYSTEM p 941
701 N 1st St, Springfield IL 62781
Tel (217) 788-3000 SIC 8741 8062

MEMORIAL MEDICAL CENTER p 942
701 N 1st St, Springfield IL 62781
Tel (217) 788-3000 SIC 8062

ST JOHNS HOSPITAL SISTERS OF THIRD ORDER OF ST FRANCIS p 1367
800 E Carpenter St, Springfield IL 62769
Tel (217) 544-6464 SIC 8062

CGH MEDICAL CENTER p 285
100 E Le Fevre Rd, Sterling IL 61081
Tel (815) 625-0400 SIC 8062

CARLE FOUNDATION p 256
611 W Park St, Urbana IL 61801
Tel (217) 383-3311 SIC 8062

CARLE FOUNDATION HOSPITAL p 256
611 W Park St, Urbana IL 61801
Tel (217) 326-2900 SIC 8062

VICTORY HEALTH SERVICES p 1555
1324 N Sheridan Rd, Waukegan IL 60085
Tel (847) 360-3000 SIC 8062

VISTA HEALTH SYSTEM p 1562
1324 N Sheridan Rd, Waukegan IL 60085
Tel (847) 249-3505 SIC 8062

■ WAUKEGAN ILLINOIS HOSPITAL CO LLC p 1583
1324 N Sheridan Rd, Waukegan IL 60085
Tel (847) 360-3000 SIC 8062

CENTRAL DUPAGE HOSPITAL ASSOCIATION p 278
25 N Winfield Rd, Winfield IL 60190
Tel (630) 933-1600 SIC 8062

MEMORIAL MEDICAL CENTER-WOODSTOCK p 942
3701 Doty Rd, Woodstock IL 60098
Tel (815) 334-3880 SIC 8062 8051

COMMUNITY HOSPITAL OF ANDERSON AND MADISON COUNTY INC p 349
1515 N Madison Ave, Anderson IN 46011
Tel (765) 298-4242 SIC 8062 8011

ST VINCENT ANDERSON REGIONAL HOSPITAL INC p 1373
2015 Jackson St, Anderson IN 46016
Tel (765) 649-2511 SIC 8062 5047

IU HEALTH WEST HOSPITAL p 769
1111 Ronald Reagan Pkwy # 223, Avon IN 46123
Tel (317) 217-3000 SIC 8062

INDIANA UNIVERSITY HEALTH BLOOMINGTON INC p 739
601 W 2nd St, Bloomington IN 47403
Tel (812) 353-5252 SIC 8062

COLUMBUS REGIONAL HOSPITAL p 342
2400 17th St, Columbus IN 47201
Tel (812) 379-4441 SIC 8062

COLUMBUS REGIONAL HOSPITAL p 342
2400 17th St, Columbus IN 47201
Tel (812) 379-4441 SIC 8062

SAMC INC p 1274
1201 S Main St, Crown Point IN 46307
Tel (219) 738-2100 SIC 8062

HENDRICKS COUNTY HOSPITAL p 683
1000 E Main St, Danville IN 46122
Tel (317) 745-4451 SIC 8062 8051

HENDRICKS REGIONAL HEALTH GUILD INC p 683
1000 E Mn St, Danville IN 46122
Tel (317) 745-4451 SIC 8062

SAINT MARGARET MERCY HEALTHCARE CENTER p 1270
24 Joliet St, Dyer IN 46311
Tel (219) 865-2141 SIC 8062 8063

ST CATHERINE HOSPITAL INC p 1365
4321 Fir St, East Chicago IN 46312
Tel (219) 392-1700 SIC 8062

ELKHART GENERAL HOSPITAL INC p 488
600 East Blvd, Elkhart IN 46514
Tel (574) 294-2621 SIC 8062

DEACONESS HOSPITAL INC p 419
600 Mary St, Evansville IN 47710
Tel (812) 450-5000 SIC 8062

SAINT MARYS RIVERSIDE p 1270
37 Washington Ave, Evansville IN 47713
Tel (812) 485-8000 SIC 8062

ST MARYS HEALTH INC p 1371
3700 Washington Ave, Evansville IN 47714
Tel (812) 485-4000 SIC 8062

ST MARYS HEALTH INC p 1371
3700 Washington Ave, Evansville IN 47714
Tel (812) 485-7623 SIC 8062

IOM HEALTH SYSTEM LP p 762
7950 W Jefferson Blvd, Fort Wayne IN 46804
Tel (260) 435-7001 SIC 8062

■ LUTHERAN HOSPITAL OF INDIANA LP p 886
7950 W Jefferson Blvd, Fort Wayne IN 46804
Tel (260) 479-3434 SIC 8062

PARKVIEW FOUNDATION INC p 1117
2200 Randallia Dr, Fort Wayne IN 46805
Tel (260) 373-4000 SIC 8062

PARKVIEW HEALTH SYSTEM INC p 1117
10501 Corporate Dr, Fort Wayne IN 46845
Tel (260) 484-6636 SIC 8741 8062

PARKVIEW HOSPITAL INC p 1117
10501 Corporate Dr, Fort Wayne IN 46845
Tel (260) 373-4000 SIC 8062

METHODIST HOSPITALS INC p 954
600 Grant St, Gary IN 46402
Tel (219) 886-4000 SIC 8062

GOSHEN HOSPITAL ASSOCIATION INC p 626
200 High Park Ave, Goshen IN 46526
Tel (574) 533-2141 SIC 8062

HANCOCK REGIONAL HOSPITAL p 657
801 N State St, Greenfield IN 46140
Tel (317) 462-5544 SIC 8062

ST MARGARET MERCY HEALTHCARE CENTERS INC p 1370
5454 Hohman Ave, Hammond IN 46320
Tel (219) 932-2300 SIC 8062 8052 8051

ST MARY MEDICAL CENTER INC p 1371
1500 S Lake Park Ave, Hobart IN 46342
Tel (219) 942-0551 SIC 8062

COMMUNITY HEALTH NETWORK INC p 348
1500 N Ritter Ave, Indianapolis IN 46219
Tel (317) 355-1411 SIC 8062

ESKENAZI HEALTH CENTER INC p 509
720 Eskenazi Ave Fl 2, Indianapolis IN 46202
Tel (317) 880-0000 SIC 8062 8093 8099

HEALTH & HOSPITAL CORP OF MARION COUNTY p 674
3838 N Rural St Fl 8, Indianapolis IN 46205
Tel (317) 221-2000 SIC 8062

INDIANA UNIVERSITY HEALTH INC p 739
1701 Senate Blvd, Indianapolis IN 46202
Tel (317) 962-2000 SIC 8062 6324

METHODIST HEALTH GROUP INC p 953
1701 Senate Blvd, Indianapolis IN 46202
Tel (317) 962-2000 SIC 8062 6321

METHODIST HOSPITAL p 953
1900 N Capitol Ave Fl 3, Indianapolis IN 46202
Tel (317) 962-2000 SIC 8062

ST VINCENT HOSPITAL AND HEALTH CARE CENTER INC p 1373
2001 W 86th St Ste 200, Indianapolis IN 46260
Tel (317) 338-7000 SIC 8062

MEMORIAL HOSPITAL AND HEALTH CARE CENTER p 942
800 W 9th St, Jasper IN 47546
Tel (812) 482-2345 SIC 8062

CLARK MEMORIAL HOSPITAL p 322
1220 Missouri Ave, Jeffersonville IN 47130
Tel (812) 282-6631 SIC 8062 8063

■ **RHN CLARK MEMORIAL HOSPITAL LLC** p 1231
1220 Missouri Ave, Jeffersonville IN 47130
Tel (812) 282-6631 *SIC* 8062 8063

HOWARD COMMUNITY HOSPITAL p 713
3500 S Lafountain St, Kokomo IN 46902
Tel (765) 453-0702 *SIC* 8062 8063

ST JOSEPH MEMORIAL HOSPITAL p 1368
1907 W Sycamore St, Kokomo IN 46901
Tel (765) 456-5433 *SIC* 8062

IUHLP LIQUIDATION INC p 769
1007 Lincolnway, La Porte IN 46350
Tel (219) 326-1234 *SIC* 8062

■ **LA PORTE HOSPITAL CO LLC** p 835
1007 Lincolnway, La Porte IN 46350
Tel (219) 326-1234 *SIC* 8062

LAPORTE HOSPITAL INC p 845
Tunnel 7 Lincoln Way, La Porte IN 46350
Tel (219) 326-2305 *SIC* 8062

GREATER LAFAYETTE HEALTH SERVICES p 635
1501 Hartford St, Lafayette IN 47904
Tel (765) 423-6011 *SIC* 8062

GREATER LAFAYETTE HEALTH SERVICES INC p 635
1501 Hartford St, Lafayette IN 47904
Tel (765) 423-6011 *SIC* 8062

WITHAM MEMORIAL HOSPITAL p 1619
2605 N Lebanon St, Lebanon IN 46052
Tel (765) 485-8000 *SIC* 8062

BETHANY CIRCLE OF KINGS DAUGHTERS OF MADISON INDIANA INC p 178
1373 E Sr 62, Madison IN 47250
Tel (812) 801-0800 *SIC* 8062 8011 8082

MARION GENERAL HOSPITAL INC p 907
441 N Wabash Ave, Marion IN 46952
Tel (765) 660-6000 *SIC* 8062

FRANCISCAN ALLIANCE INC p 573
1515 W Dragoon Trl, Mishawaka IN 46544
Tel (574) 256-3935 *SIC* 8062 8051

SAINT JOSEPH MEDICAL CENTER INC p 1269
5215 Holy Cross Pkwy, Mishawaka IN 46545
Tel (574) 335-5000 *SIC* 8062

INDIANA UNIVERSITY HEALTH BALL MEMORIAL HOSPITAL INC p 739
2401 W University Ave, Muncie IN 47303
Tel (765) 751-1449 *SIC* 8062

COMMUNITY FOUNDATION OF NORTHWEST INDIANA INC p 348
905 Ridge Rd, Munster IN 46321
Tel (219) 836-0130 *SIC* 8741 8062

COMMUNITY HOSPITAL p 349
901 Macarthur Blvd, Munster IN 46321
Tel (219) 836-1600 *SIC* 8062

MUNSTER MEDICAL RESEARCH FOUNDATION INC p 1001
901 Macarthur Blvd, Munster IN 46321
Tel (219) 836-1600 *SIC* 8062

FLOYD MEMORIAL HOSPITAL AND HEALTH SERVICES p 561
1850 State St, New Albany IN 47150
Tel (812) 944-7701 *SIC* 8062

DEACONESS GATEWAY HOSPITAL p 419
4011 Gateway Blvd, Newburgh IN 47630
Tel (812) 842-2000 *SIC* 8062

DEACONESS WOMENS HOSPITAL OF SOUTHERN INDIANA LLC p 419
4199 Gateway Blvd, Newburgh IN 47630
Tel (812) 842-4200 *SIC* 8062

RIVERVIEW HOSPITAL p 1238
395 Westfield Rd, Noblesville IN 46060
Tel (317) 773-0760 *SIC* 8062

REID HOSPITAL & HEALTH CARE SERVICES FOUNDATION INC p 1220
1100 Reid Pkwy, Richmond IN 47374
Tel (765) 983-3102 *SIC* 8062

REID HOSPITAL & HEALTH CARE SERVICES INC p 1221
1100 Reid Pkwy, Richmond IN 47374
Tel (765) 983-3000 *SIC* 8062

JACKSON COUNTY SCHNECK MEMORIAL HOSPITAL p 773
411 W Tipton St, Seymour IN 47274
Tel (812) 522-2349 *SIC* 8062

MAJOR HOSPITAL p 899
150 W Washington St, Shelbyville IN 46176
Tel (317) 392-3211 *SIC* 8062 8011

MEMORIAL HOSPITAL OF SOUTH BEND INC p 942
615 N Michigan St, South Bend IN 46601
Tel (574) 647-7751 *SIC* 8062

UNION HOSPITAL INC p 1504
1606 N 7th St, Terre Haute IN 47804
Tel (812) 238-7000 *SIC* 8062

■ **PORTER FOUNDATION INC** p 1162
802 Laporte Ave, Valparaiso IN 46383
Tel (219) 465-4600 *SIC* 8062

PORTER REGIONAL HOSPITAL p 1162
85 E Us 6 Frontage Rd, Valparaiso IN 46383
Tel (219) 263-4600 *SIC* 8062

KNOX COUNTY HOSPITAL p 825
305 S 5th St, Vincennes IN 47591
Tel (812) 882-5220 *SIC* 8062

MARY GREELEY MEDICAL CENTER FOUNDATION p 914
1111 Duff Ave, Ames IA 50010
Tel (515) 239-2011 *SIC* 8062

TRINITY MEDICAL CENTER p 1481
4500 Utica Ridge Rd, Bettendorf IA 52722
Tel (563) 742-2000 *SIC* 8062

MERCY HOSPITAL CEDAR RAPIDS IOWA p 947
701 10th St Se, Cedar Rapids IA 52403
Tel (319) 398-6011 *SIC* 8062

ST LUKES METHODIST HOSPITAL INC p 1370
1026 A Ave Ne, Cedar Rapids IA 52402
Tel (319) 369-7211 *SIC* 8062

MERCY MEDICAL CENTER-CLINTON INC p 948
1410 N 4th St, Clinton IA 52732
Tel (563) 244-5555 *SIC* 8062 8051 5122

JENNIE EDMUNDSON MEMORIAL HOSPITAL p 782
933 E Pierce St, Council Bluffs IA 51503
Tel (712) 396-6000 *SIC* 8062

GENESIS MEDICAL CENTER p 603
1227 E Rusholme St, Davenport IA 52803
Tel (563) 421-6000 *SIC* 8062

BROADLAWNS MEDICAL CENTER GUILD p 215
1801 Hickman Rd, Des Moines IA 50314
Tel (515) 282-2200 *SIC* 8062

CATHOLIC HEALTH INITIATIVES - IOWA CORP p 266
1111 6th Ave, Des Moines IA 50314
Tel (515) 247-3121 *SIC* 8062

CENTRAL IOWA HOSPITAL CORP p 278
1200 Pleasant St, Des Moines IA 50309
Tel (515) 241-6212 *SIC* 8062

CHILDBIRTH EDUCATION p 298
350 N Grandview Ave, Dubuque IA 52001
Tel (563) 589-2406 *SIC* 8062

TRINITY REGIONAL MEDICAL CENTER p 1481
802 Kenyon Rd Ste 1, Fort Dodge IA 50501
Tel (515) 574-6800 *SIC* 8062 8093

MERCY HOSPITAL IOWA CITY IOWA INC p 947
500 E Market St, Iowa City IA 52245
Tel (319) 339-0300
SIC 8062 8011 6512 8399

UNIVERSITY OF IOWA HOSPITALS AND CLINICS p 1522
200 Hawkins Dr, Iowa City IA 52242
Tel (319) 356-1616 *SIC* 8062

MERCY MEDICAL CENTER FOUNDATION - NORTH IOWA p 947
1000 4th St Sw, Mason City IA 50401
Tel (641) 428-7000 *SIC* 8062

NORTHWEST IOWA HOSPITAL CORP p 1060
2800 Pierce St Ste 410, Sioux City IA 51104
Tel (712) 279-3500 *SIC* 8062 8051

SPENCER MUNICIPAL HOSPITAL p 1358
1200 1st Ave E Ste 1, Spencer IA 51301
Tel (712) 264-6198 *SIC* 8062 8011

ALLEN MEMORIAL HOSPITAL CORP p 53
1825 Logan Ave, Waterloo IA 50703
Tel (319) 235-3941 *SIC* 8062

COVENANT HEALTH SYSTEM INC p 384
3421 W 9th St, Waterloo IA 50702
Tel (319) 236-4111 *SIC* 8062

COVENANT MEDICAL CENTER INC p 384
3421 W 9th St, Waterloo IA 50702
Tel (319) 272-7296 *SIC* 8062

GREAT RIVER HEALTH SYSTEMS INC p 634
1221 S Gear Ave, West Burlington IA 52655
Tel (319) 768-1000 *SIC* 8062

GREAT RIVER MEDICAL CENTER p 634
1221 S Gear Ave, West Burlington IA 52655
Tel (319) 768-1000 *SIC* 8062

IOWA HEALTH SYSTEM p 762
1776 West Lakes Pkwy # 400, West Des Moines IA 50266
Tel (515) 241-6161 *SIC* 8062 8721 8741

NEWMAN MEMORIAL HOSPITAL FOUNDATION p 1038
1201 W 12th Ave, Emporia KS 66801
Tel (620) 343-6800 *SIC* 8062 5047 8011

ST CATHERINE HOSPITAL p 1365
401 E Spruce St, Garden City KS 67846
Tel (620) 272-2222 *SIC* 8062

HAYS MEDICAL CENTER INC p 670
2220 Canterbury Dr, Hays KS 67601
Tel (785) 623-5000 *SIC* 8062 8051

HEALTH CARE INC p 674
1701 E 23rd Ave, Hutchinson KS 67502
Tel (620) 665-2000 *SIC* 8062 7352 6512

HUTCHINSON REGIONAL MEDICAL CENTER INC p 722
1701 E 23rd Ave, Hutchinson KS 67502
Tel (620) 665-2000 *SIC* 8062

PROVIDENCE MEDICAL CENTER p 1186
8929 Parallel Pkwy, Kansas City KS 66112
Tel (913) 596-4870 *SIC* 8062

PROVIDENCE/SAINT JOHN FOUNDATION INC p 1186
8929 Parallel Pkwy, Kansas City KS 66112
Tel (913) 596-4000 *SIC* 8062 8741 8011

UNIVERSITY OF KANSAS HOSPITAL p 1522
3901 Rainbow Blvd, Kansas City KS 66160
Tel (913) 588-5000 *SIC* 8062

LAWRENCE MEMORIAL HOSPITAL p 848
325 Maine St, Lawrence KS 66044
Tel (785) 505-5000 *SIC* 8062

LAWRENCE MEMORIAL HOSPITAL ENDOWMENT ASSOCIATION p 848
330 Arkansas St Ste 201, Lawrence KS 66044
Tel (785) 505-3318 *SIC* 8051 8062

OLATHE MEDICAL CENTER INC p 1080
20333 W 151st St, Olathe KS 66061
Tel (913) 791-4200 *SIC* 8082 8062

MENORAH MEDICAL CENTER INC p 943
5721 W 119th St, Overland Park KS 66209
Tel (913) 498-6000 *SIC* 8011 8062

OVERLAND PARK REGIONAL MEDICAL CENTER INC p 1099
10500 Quivira Rd, Overland Park KS 66215
Tel (913) 541-0000 *SIC* 8062

VIA CHRISTI HOSPITAL PITTSBURG INC p 1554
1 Mt Carmel Way, Pittsburg KS 66762
Tel (620) 231-6100 *SIC* 8062

VIA CHRISTI HOSPITAL PITTSBURG INC p 1554
1 Mt Carmel Way, Pittsburg KS 66762
Tel (620) 232-9926 *SIC* 8062

SALINA REGIONAL HEALTH CENTER INC p 1272
400 S Santa Fe Ave, Salina KS 67401
Tel (785) 452-7000 *SIC* 8062

SAINT LUKES SOUTH HOSPITAL INC p 1270
12300 Metcalf Ave, Shawnee Mission KS 66213
Tel (913) 317-7000 *SIC* 8062

SHAWNEE MISSION MEDICAL CENTER INC p 1313
9100 W 74th St, Shawnee Mission KS 66204
Tel (913) 676-2000 *SIC* 8062

ST FRANCIS HEALTH CENTER INC p 1366
1700 Sw 7th St, Topeka KS 66606
Tel (785) 295-8000 *SIC* 8062 8011

STORMONT-VAIL HEALTHCARE INC p 1392
1500 Sw 10th Ave, Topeka KS 66604
Tel (785) 354-6000 *SIC* 8062

■ **HCA HOSPITAL SERVICES OF SAN DIEGO** p 672
550 N Hillside St, Wichita KS 67214
Tel (316) 962-2000 *SIC* 8062

VIA CHRISTI HOSPITALS WICHITA INC p 1554
929 N Saint Francis St, Wichita KS 67214
Tel (316) 268-5000 *SIC* 8062

ASHLAND HOSPITAL CORP p 117
2201 Lexington Ave, Ashland KY 41101
Tel (606) 408-4000 *SIC* 8062

KINGS DAUGHTERS HEALTH SYSTEM INC p 820
2201 Lexington Ave, Ashland KY 41101
Tel (606) 408-4000 *SIC* 8062

KINGS DAUGHTERS MEDICAL CENTER p 820
2201 Lexington Ave, Ashland KY 41101
Tel (606) 408-4000 *SIC* 8062

OUR LADY OF BELLEFONTE HOSPITAL INC p 1098
1000 Saint Christopher Dr, Ashland KY 41101
Tel (606) 833-3333
SIC 8062 8082 8011 5999

BOWLING GREEN-WARREN COUNTY COMMUNITY HOSPITAL CORP p 204
250 Park St, Bowling Green KY 42101
Tel (270) 745-1000 *SIC* 8062

COMMONWEALTH HEALTH CORP INC p 346
800 Park St, Bowling Green KY 42101
Tel (270) 745-1500 *SIC* 8062 6513

EPHRAIM MCDOWELL REGIONAL MEDICAL CENTER INC p 504
217 S 3rd St, Danville KY 40422
Tel (859) 239-1000 *SIC* 8062

SAINT ELIZABETH MEDICAL CENTER INC p 1269
1 Medical Village Dr, Edgewood KY 41017
Tel (859) 301-2000 *SIC* 8062 8069 8093

HARDIN MEMORIAL HOSPITAL FOUNDATION INC p 660
913 N Dixie Ave, Elizabethtown KY 42701
Tel (270) 737-1212 *SIC* 8062

■ **FRANKFORT REGIONAL MEDICAL CENTER** p 574
299 Kings Daughters Dr, Frankfort KY 40601
Tel (502) 875-5240 *SIC* 8062 8011

T J SAMPSON COMMUNITY HOSPITAL p 1419
1301 N Rise St, Glasgow KY 42141
Tel (270) 651-1305 *SIC* 8062

TJ SAMSON COMMUNITY HOSPITAL p 1457
1301 N Race St, Glasgow KY 42141
Tel (270) 651-4444 *SIC* 8062

COMMUNITY UNITED METHODIST HOSPITAL INC p 350
1305 N Elm St, Henderson KY 42420
Tel (270) 827-7700 *SIC* 8062

JENNIE STUART MEDICAL CENTER INC p 782
320 W 18th St, Hopkinsville KY 42240
Tel (270) 887-0100 *SIC* 8062

APPALACHIAN REGIONAL HEALTHCARE INC p 98
2260 Executive Dr, Lexington KY 40505
Tel (859) 226-2440 *SIC* 8062

SAINT JOSEPH HEALTH SYSTEM INC p 1269
1 Saint Joseph Dr, Lexington KY 40504
Tel (859) 313-1000 *SIC* 8062 8099 8011

UK HEALTHCARE GOODSAMARITAN HOSPITAL p 1500
310 S Limestone, Lexington KY 40508
Tel (859) 226-7000 *SIC* 8062 8011

UNIVERSITY OF KENTUCKY HOSPITAL AUXILIARY INC p 1522
800 Rose St, Lexington KY 40536
Tel (859) 323-5000 *SIC* 8062

BAPTIST HEALTHCARE AFFILIATES INC p 154
2701 Eastpoint Pkwy, Louisville KY 40223
Tel (502) 896-5008 *SIC* 8062

BAPTIST HEALTHCARE SYSTEM INC p 154
2701 Eastpoint Pkwy, Louisville KY 40223
Tel (502) 896-5000 *SIC* 8062 8011 8741

JEWISH HOSPITAL & ST MARYS HEALTHCARE INC p 784
200 Abraham Flexner Way # 1, Louisville KY 40202
Tel (502) 587-4011 *SIC* 8062 8082

JEWISH HOSPITAL HEALTHCARE SERVICES INC p 784
200 Abraham Flexner Way # 1, Louisville KY 40202
Tel (502) 587-4011 *SIC* 8062 8082

▲ **KINDRED HEALTHCARE INC** p 819
680 S 4th St, Louisville KY 40202
Tel (502) 596-7300
SIC 8062 8051 8322 8082

KOSAIR CHILDRENS HOSPITAL p 828
231 E Chestnut St Ste 100, Louisville KY 40202
Tel (502) 629-6000 *SIC* 8062

LOUISVILLE HOSPITAL p 881
217 E Chestnut St, Louisville KY 40202
Tel (502) 587-1100 *SIC* 8062

NORTON AUDUBON HOSPITAL p 1061
1 Audubon Plaza Dr, Louisville KY 40217
Tel (502) 636-7111 *SIC* 8062

NORTON HEALTHCARE INC p 1061
200 E Chestnut St, Louisville KY 40202
Tel (502) 629-8000 *SIC* 8741 8062

NORTON HOSPITAL p 1061
200 E Chestnut St Frnt, Louisville KY 40202
Tel (502) 629-8159 *SIC* 8062

NORTON HOSPITALS INC p 1061
200 E Chestnut St, Louisville KY 40202
Tel (502) 629-8000
SIC 8062 8011 8093 8071

UNIVERSITY MEDICAL CENTER INC p 1519
530 S Jackson St, Louisville KY 40202
Tel (502) 562-3000 *SIC* 8062

BAPTIST HEALTH MADISONVILLE INC p 153
900 Hospital Dr, Madisonville KY 42431
Tel (270) 825-5100 *SIC* 8011 8062

ST CLAIRE MEDICAL CENTER INC p 1365
222 Medical Cir, Morehead KY 40351
Tel (606) 783-6500 *SIC* 8062 8011

MURRAY-CALLOWAY COUNTY PUBLIC HOSPITAL CORP p 1002
803 Poplar St, Murray KY 42071
Tel (270) 762-1100 *SIC* 8062

OWENSBORO HEALTH INC p 1100
1201 Pleasant Valley Rd, Owensboro KY 42303
Tel (270) 688-2000 *SIC* 8062

MERCY HEALTH PARTNERS - LOURDES INC p 946
1530 Lone Oak Rd Int24, Paducah KY 42003
Tel (270) 444-2444 *SIC* 8062

PIKEVILLE MEDICAL CENTER INC p 1148
911 Bypass Rd, Pikeville KY 41501
Tel (606) 218-3500 *SIC* 8062

■ **LIFEPOINT OF LAKE CUMBERLAND LLC** p 864
305 Langdon St, Somerset KY 42503
Tel (606) 679-7441 *SIC* 8062 8082

CHRISTUS HEALTH CENTRAL LOUISIANA p 303
3330 Masonic Dr, Alexandria LA 71301
Tel (318) 487-1122 *SIC* 8062

■ **RAPIDES HEALTHCARE SYSTEM LLC** p 1208
211 4th St, Alexandria LA 71301
Tel (318) 473-3150 *SIC* 8062 5047

RAPIDES REGIONAL MEDICAL CENTER p 1208
211 4th St, Alexandria LA 71301
Tel (318) 473-3000 *SIC* 8062

BATON ROUGE GENERAL MEDICAL CENTER p 159
3600 Florida Blvd, Baton Rouge LA 70806
Tel (225) 387-7000 *SIC* 8062

EAST BATON ROUGE MEDICAL CENTER LLC p 469
17000 Medical Center Dr, Baton Rouge LA 70816
Tel (225) 752-2470 *SIC* 8062

MID CITY MEDICAL CENTER p 962
3600 Florida Blvd, Baton Rouge LA 70806
Tel (225) 387-7000 *SIC* 8062

OUR LADY OF LAKE HOSPITAL INC p 1098
5000 Hennessy Blvd, Baton Rouge LA 70808
Tel (225) 765-7709 *SIC* 8062

WOMANS HOSPITAL FOUNDATION INC p 1621
100 Womans Way, Baton Rouge LA 70817
Tel (225) 927-1300 *SIC* 8062

SAINT TAMMANY PARISH HOSPITAL SERVICE DISTRICT 1 p 1270
1202 S Tyler St, Covington LA 70433
Tel (985) 898-4000 *SIC* 8062

OUR LADY OF LAKE ASCENSION COMMUNITY HOSPITAL p 1098
1125 W Highway 30, Gonzales LA 70737
Tel (225) 647-5000 *SIC* 8062

HOSPITAL SERVICE DISTRICT NO 1 OF TANGIPAHOA PARISH p 710
15770 Paul Vega Md Dr, Hammond LA 70403
Tel (985) 230-6934 *SIC* 8062

HOSPITAL SERVICE DISTRICT NO 1 p 709
8166 Main St, Houma LA 70360
Tel (985) 873-4141 *SIC* 8062

OCHSNER MEDICAL CENTER - KENNER LLC p 1073
180 W Esplanade Ave, Kenner LA 70065
Tel (504) 468-8600 *SIC* 8062 8099

LAFAYETTE GENERAL HEALTH SYSTEM INC p 837
1214 Coolidge Blvd, Lafayette LA 70503
Tel (337) 289-8125 *SIC* 8062

LAFAYETTE GENERAL MEDICAL CENTER INC p 837
1214 Coolidge Blvd, Lafayette LA 70503
Tel (337) 289-7991 *SIC* 8062

LAFAYETTE GENERAL SURGICAL HOSPITAL LLC p 837
1000 W Pinhook Rd Ste 100, Lafayette LA 70503
Tel (337) 289-8095 *SIC* 8062

OUR LADY OF LOURDES REGIONAL MEDICAL CENTER INC p 1098
4801 Ambssdor Cffery Pkwy, Lafayette LA 70508
Tel (337) 470-2000 *SIC* 8062

CHRISTUS HEALTH SOUTHWESTERN LOUISIANA p 303
524 Dctor Mchael Dbkey Dr, Lake Charles LA 70601
Tel (337) 436-2511 *SIC* 8062

SOUTHWEST LOUISIANA HOSPITAL ASSOCIATION p 1352
1701 Oak Park Blvd, Lake Charles LA 70601
Tel (337) 494-2121 *SIC* 8062

SOUTHWEST LOUISIANA MEMORIAL FOUNDATION p 1352
1701 Oak Park Blvd, Lake Charles LA 70601
Tel (337) 494-3204 *SIC* 8062

HOSPITAL SERVICE DISTRICT 1 INC p 709
1101 Medical Center Blvd, Marrero LA 70072
Tel (504) 347-5511 *SIC* 8062

EAST JEFFERSON GENERAL HOSPITAL p 470
4200 Houma Blvd, Metairie LA 70006
Tel (504) 454-4000 *SIC* 8062

MONROE L BRFHH L C p 985
4864 Jackson St, Monroe LA 71202
Tel (318) 330-7000 *SIC* 8062

ST FRANCIS MEDICAL CENTER INC p 1367
309 Jackson St, Monroe LA 71201
Tel (318) 966-4000 *SIC* 8062

ST FRANCIS SPECIALTY HOSPITAL INC p 1367
309 Jackson St, Monroe LA 71201
Tel (318) 966-4196 *SIC* 8062

MEDICAL CENTER OF LOUISIANA AT NEW ORLEANS p 936
1532 Tulane Ave, New Orleans LA 70112
Tel (504) 903-3000 *SIC* 8062

OCHSNER CLINIC FOUNDATION p 1073
1514 Jefferson Hwy, New Orleans LA 70121
Tel (504) 842-3000 *SIC* 8062 5947

OCHSNER COMMUNITY HOSPITALS p 1073
1514 Jefferson Hwy, New Orleans LA 70121
Tel (504) 842-3400 *SIC* 8062

OCHSNER FOUNDATION HOSPITAL p 1073
1514 Jefferson Hwy, New Orleans LA 70121
Tel (504) 842-4000 *SIC* 8062

■ PENDLETON MEMORIAL METHODIST HOSPITAL p 1128
5620 Read Blvd, New Orleans LA 70127
Tel (504) 244-5100 *SIC* 8062

TOURO INFIRMARY p 1464
1401 Foucher St, New Orleans LA 70115
Tel (504) 897-7011 *SIC* 8062

■ UNIVERSITY HEALTHCARE SYSTEM LC p 1519
1415 Tulane Ave, New Orleans LA 70112
Tel (504) 988-5263 *SIC* 8062

UNIVERSITY MEDICAL CENTER MANAGEMENT CORP p 1519
2000 Canal St, New Orleans LA 70112
Tel (504) 903-3000 *SIC* 8062

OPELOUSAS GENERAL HEALTH SYSTEM p 1089
539 E Prudhomme St, Opelousas LA 70570
Tel (337) 948-3011 *SIC* 8062

BRFHH SHREVEPORT LLC p 211
1541 Kings Hwy, Shreveport LA 71103
Tel (318) 675-5000 *SIC* 8062

WILLIS-KNIGHTON MEDICAL CENTER p 1612
2600 Greenwood Rd, Shreveport LA 71103
Tel (318) 212-4000 *SIC* 8062

ST TAMMANY PARISH HOSPITAL SERVICE DISTRICT 2 p 1373
1001 Gause Blvd, Slidell LA 70458
Tel (985) 280-2200 *SIC* 8062

HOSPITAL SERVICE DISTRICT 3 LAFOURCHE PARISH p 709
602 N Acadia Rd, Thibodaux LA 70301
Tel (985) 493-4740 *SIC* 8062 8051 8082

GLENWOOD RESOLUTION AUTHORITY INC p 615
503 Mcmillan Rd, West Monroe LA 71291
Tel (318) 329-4200 *SIC* 8062

JEROME GROUP INC p 783
6 E Chestnut St, Augusta ME 04330
Tel (207) 626-1496 *SIC* 8011 8062

MAINEGENERAL HEALTH p 898
35 Medical Center Pkwy, Augusta ME 04330
Tel (207) 626-1000 *SIC* 8062

MAINEGENERAL MEDICAL CENTER p 898
35 Medical Center Pkwy, Augusta ME 04330
Tel (207) 626-1289 *SIC* 8062

EASTERN MAINE MEDICAL CENTER p 472
489 State St, Bangor ME 04401
Tel (207) 973-7000 *SIC* 8062

ST JOSEPH HOSPITAL p 1368
360 Broadway, Bangor ME 04401
Tel (207) 262-1000 *SIC* 8062

WALDO COUNTY GENERAL HOSPITAL p 1572
118 Northport Ave, Belfast ME 04915
Tel (207) 338-2500 *SIC* 8062

SOUTHERN MAINE HEALTH CARE p 1349
1 Medical Center Dr, Biddeford ME 04005
Tel (207) 283-7000 *SIC* 8062

EASTERN MAINE HEALTHCARE SYSTEMS p 472
43 Whiting Hill Rd # 500, Brewer ME 04412
Tel (207) 973-7050 *SIC* 8621 8062

MID COAST HOSPITAL p 962
123 Medical Center Dr, Brunswick ME 04011
Tel (207) 373-6000 *SIC* 8062

MID COAST-PARKVIEW HEALTH p 963
123 Medical Center Dr G, Brunswick ME 04011
Tel (207) 729-0181 *SIC* 8062 8082 8051

CENTRAL MAINE HEALTHCARE CORP p 279
300 Main St, Lewiston ME 04240
Tel (207) 795-0111 *SIC* 8062 8052 8049

CENTRAL MAINE MEDICAL CENTER INC p 279
300 Main St, Lewiston ME 04240
Tel (207) 795-0111 *SIC* 8062

ST MARYS HEALTH SYSTEM p 1371
96 Campus Ave, Lewiston ME 04240
Tel (207) 777-8546
SIC 8062 8052 8051 8011 8361

ST MARYS REGIONAL MEDICAL CENTER p 1372
93 Campus Ave, Lewiston ME 04240
Tel (207) 777-8546
SIC 8062 8052 8051 8011 8361

MAINE MEDICAL CENTER p 898
22 Bramhall St, Portland ME 04102
Tel (207) 662-0111 *SIC* 8062 8071 6513

MERCY HOSPITAL p 947
144 State St, Portland ME 04101
Tel (207) 879-3000 *SIC* 8062

AROOSTOOK MEDICAL CENTER INC p 112
140 Academy St, Presque Isle ME 04769
Tel (207) 768-4000 *SIC* 8062 8011 8052

PEN BAY MEDICAL CENTER p 1128
6 Glen Cove Dr, Rockport ME 04856
Tel (207) 921-8000 *SIC* 8062 8082

PENOBSCOT BAY MEDICAL CENTER p 1131
6 Glen Cove Dr, Rockport ME 04856
Tel (207) 230-6380 *SIC* 8062 8059

HENRIETTA D GOODALL HOSPITAL INC p 684
25 June St, Sanford ME 04073
Tel (207) 324-4310 *SIC* 8062

NORTON SOUND HEALTH CORP p 1061
790 Lower St, Turner ME 04282
Tel (907) 443-3311
SIC 8062 8051 8069 8093 8011

MAINE BEHAVIORAL HEALTHCARE p 898
123 Andover Rd, Westbrook ME 04092
Tel (207) 761-2200 *SIC* 8062

YORK HOSPITAL p 1637
15 Hospital Dr, York ME 03909
Tel (207) 351-2023
SIC 8062 8051 8069 7361

ANNE ARUNDEL MEDICAL CENTER INC p 92
2001 Medical Pkwy, Annapolis MD 21401
Tel (443) 481-1000 *SIC* 8062

ANNE ARUNDEL MEDICAL CENTER INC p 92
2001 Medical Pkwy, Annapolis MD 21401
Tel (443) 481-1000 *SIC* 8062 8093 6732

BON SECOURS BALTIMORE HEALTH CORP p 199
2000 W Baltimore St, Baltimore MD 21223
Tel (410) 362-3000 *SIC* 8062

BON SECOURS HOSPITAL BALTIMORE INC p 199
2000 W Baltimore St, Baltimore MD 21223
Tel (410) 362-3000 *SIC* 8062

FRANKLIN SQUARE HOSPITAL CENTER INC p 575
9000 Franklin Square Dr, Baltimore MD 21237
Tel (410) 933-2777 *SIC* 8062 8011

GOOD SAMARITAN HOSPITAL OF MD INC p 623
5601 Loch Raven Blvd, Baltimore MD 21239
Tel (443) 444-3780 *SIC* 8062 8741

GREATER BALTIMORE MEDICAL CENTER INC p 635
6701 N Charles St, Baltimore MD 21204
Tel (410) 849-2000 *SIC* 8062 8011

GREATER BALTIMORE MEDICAL CENTER LAND CORP p 635
6701 N Charles St, Baltimore MD 21204
Tel (443) 849-2000 *SIC* 8062

HARBOR HOSPITAL CENTER INC p 659
3001 S Hanover St, Baltimore MD 21225
Tel (410) 350-3200 *SIC* 8062

HARBOR HOSPITAL FOUNDATION INC p 659
3001 S Hanover St, Baltimore MD 21225
Tel (410) 350-2563 *SIC* 8062

JOHNS HOPKINS BAYVIEW MEDICAL CENTER INC p 790
4940 Eastern Ave, Baltimore MD 21224
Tel (410) 550-0100 *SIC* 8062 8051

JOHNS HOPKINS HEALTH SYS CORP p 790
600 N Wolfe St, Baltimore MD 21287
Tel (410) 955-5000 *SIC* 8062

JOHNS HOPKINS HOSPITAL p 790
1800 Orleans St, Baltimore MD 21287
Tel (410) 550-0730 *SIC* 8062

JOHNS HOPKINS MEDICINE INTERNATIONAL LLC p 790
600 N Wolfe St, Baltimore MD 21287
Tel (410) 955-1725 *SIC* 8062 8221

LIFEBRIDGE HEALTH INC p 864
2401 W Belvedere Ave, Baltimore MD 21215
Tel (410) 601-5653 *SIC* 8062

MARYLAND GENERAL HOSPITAL INC p 915
827 Linden Ave, Baltimore MD 21201
Tel (410) 225-8000 *SIC* 8062

MEDSTAR GOOD SAMARITAN HOSPITAL p 939
5601 Loch Raven Blvd, Baltimore MD 21239
Tel (443) 444-4100 *SIC* 8062 8011

MERCY MEDICAL CENTER INC p 947
345 Saint Paul St, Baltimore MD 21202
Tel (410) 332-9000 *SIC* 8062 8011

RUBIN INSTITUTE FOR ADVANCED ORTHOPEDICS p 1257
2401 W Belvedere Ave, Baltimore MD 21215
Tel (410) 601-9000 *SIC* 8062

SHEPPARD PRATT HEALTH SYSTEM INC p 1315
6501 N Charles St, Baltimore MD 21204
Tel (410) 938-3000 *SIC* 8741 8062

SINAI HOSPITAL OF BALTIMORE INC p 1326
2401 W Belvedere Ave, Baltimore MD 21215
Tel (410) 601-5678 *SIC* 8062

ST AGNES HEALTHCARE INC p 1364
900 S Caton Ave, Baltimore MD 21229
Tel (667) 234-6000 *SIC* 8062

UNION MEMORIAL HOSPITAL p 1504
201 E University Pkwy, Baltimore MD 21218
Tel (410) 554-2865 *SIC* 8062

UNIVERSITY OF MARYLAND MIDTOWN HEALTH INC p 1522
827 Linden Ave, Baltimore MD 21201
Tel (410) 225-8000 *SIC* 8062

UPPER CHESAPEAKE HEALTH FOUNDATION INC p 1529
520 Upper Chesapeake 40 Ste 405, Bel Air MD 21014
Tel (443) 643-1500 *SIC* 8062

UPPER CHESAPEAKE MEDICAL CENTER INC p 1529
500 Upper Chesapeake Dr, Bel Air MD 21014
Tel (443) 643-1000 *SIC* 8062

ATLANTIC GENERAL HOSPITAL CORP p 126
9733 Healthway Dr, Berlin MD 21811
Tel (410) 641-1100 *SIC* 8062

CHINDEX INTERNATIONAL INC p 301
4340 East West Hwy # 1100, Bethesda MD 20814
Tel (301) 215-7777 *SIC* 5047 8062

■ NATIONAL INSTITUTES OF HEALTH p 1013
9000 Rockville Pike # 1, Bethesda MD 20892
Tel (301) 496-4000 *SIC* 8062 9431

SUBURBAN HOSPITAL HEALTHCARE SYSTEM INC p 1396
8600 Old Georgetown Rd, Bethesda MD 20814
Tel (301) 896-3100 *SIC* 8062

SUBURBAN HOSPITAL INC p 1396
8600 Old Georgetown Rd, Bethesda MD 20814
Tel (301) 896-3100 *SIC* 8062

DIMENSIONS HEALTH CORP p 440
3001 Hospital Dr, Cheverly MD 20785
Tel (301) 618-2000 *SIC* 8062 8059

MEDSTAR SOUTHERN MARYLAND HOSPITAL CENTER INC p 939
7503 Surratts Rd, Clinton MD 20735
Tel (301) 868-8000 *SIC* 8062 8011

HOWARD COUNTY GENERAL HOSPITAL INC p 713
5755 Cedar Ln, Columbia MD 21044
Tel (410) 740-7935 *SIC* 8062

MEDSTAR HEALTH INC p 939
5565 Sterrett Pl Ste 500, Columbia MD 21044
Tel (410) 772-6500
SIC 8741 8062 8082 8051 8011

SACRED HEART HOSPITAL OF SISTERS OF CHARITY INC p 1265
12500 Willowbrook Rd, Cumberland MD 21502
Tel (240) 964-7000 *SIC* 8062

WESTERN MARYLAND HEALTH SYSTEM p 1599
12500 Willowbrook Rd, Cumberland MD 21502
Tel (240) 964-7000 *SIC* 8062

MEMORIAL HOSPITAL OF EASTON MD INC p 942
219 S Washington St, Easton MD 21601
Tel (410) 822-1000 *SIC* 8062

UNIVERSITY OF MARYLAND SHORE REGIONAL HEALTH INC p 1522
219 S Washington St, Easton MD 21601
Tel (410) 822-1000 *SIC* 8062

UNION HOSPITAL OF CECIL COUNTY HEALTH SERVICES INC p 1504
106 Bow St, Elkton MD 21921
Tel (410) 392-7009 *SIC* 6324 8062

UNION HOSPITAL OF CECIL COUNTY INC p 1504
106 Bow St, Elkton MD 21921
Tel (410) 620-3753 *SIC* 8062

FREDERICK MEMORIAL HOSPITAL INC p 576
400 W 7th St, Frederick MD 21701
Tel (240) 566-3300 *SIC* 8062

ADVENTIST HEALTHCARE INC p 27
820 W Diamond Ave Ste 600, Gaithersburg MD 20878
Tel (301) 315-3030 *SIC* 8082 8059 8062

BALTIMORE WASHINGTON MEDICAL SYSTEM INC p 149
301 Hospital Dr, Glen Burnie MD 21061
Tel (410) 787-4000 *SIC* 8062

MERITUS MEDICAL CENTER INC p 950
11116 Medical Campus Rd, Hagerstown MD 21742
Tel (301) 797-2000 *SIC* 8062

CONMED HEALTHCARE MANAGEMENT INC p 356
7250 Parkway Dr Ste 400, Hanover MD 21076
Tel (410) 712-4760 *SIC* 8062

HARFORD MEMORIAL HOSPITAL INC p 661
501 S Union Ave, Havre De Grace MD 21078
Tel (443) 843-5000 *SIC* 8062

HARFORD MEMORIAL HOSPITAL INC p 661
501 S Union Ave, Havre De Grace MD 21078
Tel (410) 939-2400 *SIC* 8062

CHARLES REGIONAL MEDICAL CENTER FOUNDATION INC p 289
5 Garrett Ave, La Plata MD 20646
Tel (301) 609-4000 *SIC* 8062

CIVISTA MEDICAL CENTER INC p 320
5 Garrett Ave, La Plata MD 20646
Tel (301) 609-4000 *SIC* 8062

DOCTORS HOSPITAL INC p 447
8118 Good Luck Rd, Lanham MD 20706
Tel (301) 552-8118 *SIC* 8062

ST MARYS HOSPITAL OF SAINT MARYS COUNTY INC p 1371
25500 Point Lookout Rd, Leonardtown MD 20650
Tel (301) 475-8981 *SIC* 8062

MID-ATLANTIC HEALTH CARE LLC p 963
1922 Greenspring Dr Ste 3, Lutherville Timonium MD 21093
Tel (410) 308-2300 *SIC* 8062

BON SECOURS HEALTH SYSTEM INC p 199
1505 Marriottsville Rd, Marriottsville MD 21104
Tel (410) 442-5511 *SIC* 8062 8099

MONTGOMERY GENERAL HOSPITAL INC p 986
18101 Prince Philip Dr, Olney MD 20832
Tel (301) 774-8882 *SIC* 8062

CALVERT MEMORIAL HOSPITAL OF CALVERT COUNTY p 243
100 Hospital Rd, Prince Frederick MD 20678
Tel (410) 535-4000 *SIC* 8062

NORTHWEST HOSPITAL CENTER INC p 1060
5401 Old Court Rd, Randallstown MD 21133
Tel (410) 521-2200 *SIC* 8062

GROVE SHADY ADVENTIST HOSPITAL p 642
9901 Medical Center Dr, Rockville MD 20850
Tel (240) 826-6000 *SIC* 8062

PENINSULA REGIONAL MEDICAL CENTER p 1129
100 E Carroll St, Salisbury MD 21801
Tel (410) 546-6400 *SIC* 8062

HOLY CROSS HEALTH INC p 702
1500 Forest Glen Rd, Silver Spring MD 20910
Tel (301) 754-7000 *SIC* 8062

HOLY CROSS HOSPITAL p 702
2701 W 68th St, Silver Spring MD 20910
Tel (301) 754-7000 *SIC* 8062 8011

LIVER AND PANCREAS CENTER UNIVERSITY OF MARYLAND ST JOSEPH MEDICAL CENTER p 871
7505 Osler Dr Ste 303, Towson MD 21204
Tel (410) 427-2024 *SIC* 8062

UNIVERSITY OF MARYLAND ST JOSEPH MEDICAL CENTER LLC p 1522
7601 Osler Dr, Towson MD 21204
Tel (410) 337-1000 *SIC* 8062

CARROLL HOSPITAL CENTER INC p 261
200 Memorial Ave, Westminster MD 21157
Tel (410) 848-3000 *SIC* 8062

STURDY MEMORIAL HOSPITAL INC p 1395
211 Park St, Attleboro MA 02703
Tel (508) 222-5200 *SIC* 8062 8011

ATRIUS HEALTH INC p 129
275 Grove St Ste 3-300, Auburndale MA 02466
Tel (617) 559-8000 *SIC* 8099 8062

NORTHEAST HOSPITAL CORP p 1055
85 Herrick St, Beverly MA 01915
Tel (978) 922-3000 *SIC* 8062

STEVEN LAVERTY p 1388
85 Herrick St, Beverly MA 01915
Tel (978) 927-7880 *SIC* 8062

BETH ISRAEL DEACONESS MEDICAL CENTER INC p 177
330 Brookline Ave, Boston MA 02215
Tel (617) 667-7000 *SIC* 8062

BOSTON MEDICAL CENTER CORP p 203
1 Boston Medical Ctr Pl # 1, Boston MA 02118
Tel (617) 414-5000 *SIC* 8062

BRIGHAM AND WOMENS FAULKNER HOSPITAL INC p 212
1153 Centre St, Boston MA 02130
Tel (617) 983-7000 *SIC* 8062

BRIGHAM AND WOMENS HOSPITAL INC p 212
75 Francis St, Boston MA 02115
Tel (617) 732-5500 *SIC* 8062

EAST BOSTON NEIGHBORHOOD HEALTH CENTER CORP p 470
10 Gove St, Boston MA 02128
Tel (617) 567-3600 *SIC* 8062

JOHN R GRAHAM HEADACHE CENTER INC p 789
1153 Centre St, Boston MA 02130
Tel (617) 983-7243 *SIC* 8011 8062

M G H HEALTH SERVICES CORP p 889
55 Fruit St, Boston MA 02114
Tel (617) 724-0567
SIC 8082 8059 8071 8062

MASSACHUSETTS GENERAL HOSPITAL p 917
55 Fruit St, Boston MA 02114
Tel (617) 724-6454 *SIC* 8062 8011

NEW ENGLAND BAPTIST HOSPITAL INC p 1030
125 Parker Hill Ave Ste 2, Boston MA 02120
Tel (617) 754-5000 *SIC* 8062

NEW ENGLAND DEACONESS HOSPITAL CORP p 1030
1 Deaconess Rd, Boston MA 02215
Tel (814) 777-4805 *SIC* 8062

STEWARD ST ELIZABETHS MEDICAL CENTER OF BOSTON INC p 1388
736 Cambridge St, Boston MA 02135
Tel (617) 789-3000 *SIC* 8062

TAS-CSEMCB INC p 1425
736 Cambridge St, Boston MA 02135
Tel (617) 789-3149 *SIC* 8062

TUFTS MEDICAL CENTER INC p 1491
800 Washington St, Boston MA 02111
Tel (617) 636-5000
SIC 8062 7371 8742 8741

TUFTS MEDICAL CENTER PARENT INC p 1491
800 Washington St, Boston MA 02111
Tel (617) 636-5000 *SIC* 8062 7371

UNIVERSITY OF MASSACHUSETTS INC p 1523
1 Beacon St Fl 31, Boston MA 02108
Tel (617) 287-7000 *SIC* 8221 8733 8062

BROCKTON HOSPITAL INC p 216
680 Centre St, Brockton MA 02302
Tel (508) 941-7000 *SIC* 8062

SIGNATURE HEALTHCARE CORP p 1322
680 Centre St, Brockton MA 02302
Tel (508) 941-7000 *SIC* 8062

TAS-CGSMC INC p 1425
235 N Pearl St, Brockton MA 02301
Tel (508) 427-3000 *SIC* 8062

LAHEY CLINIC HOSPITAL INC p 838
41 Mall Rd, Burlington MA 01805
Tel (781) 273-5100 *SIC* 8062

LAHEY CLINIC INC p 838
41 Mall Rd, Burlington MA 01805
Tel (781) 744-5100 *SIC* 8062

CAMBRIDGE HOSPITAL p 244
1493 Cambridge St, Cambridge MA 02139
Tel (617) 665-1000 *SIC* 8062

CAMBRIDGE PUBLIC HEALTH COMMISSION p 244
1493 Cambridge St, Cambridge MA 02139
Tel (617) 665-1000 *SIC* 8062

MOUNT AUBURN HOSPITAL p 993
330 Mount Auburn St, Cambridge MA 02138
Tel (617) 492-3500 *SIC* 8062

SPAULDING REHABILITATION HOSPITAL CORP p 1355
300 1st Ave, Charlestown MA 02129
Tel (617) 952-5000 *SIC* 8062

EMERSON HOSPITAL p 492
133 Old Rd To 9 Acre Cor, Concord MA 01742
Tel (978) 369-1400 *SIC* 8062

CHARLTON MEMORIAL HOSPITAL INC p 290
363 Highland Ave, Fall River MA 02720
Tel (508) 679-3131 *SIC* 8062

SOUTHCOAST HOSPITALS GROUP INC p 1345
363 Highland Ave, Fall River MA 02720
Tel (508) 679-3131 *SIC* 8062

STEWARD ST ANNES HOSPITAL CORP p 1388
795 Middle St, Fall River MA 02721
Tel (508) 674-5741 *SIC* 8062

TAS-SAHC INC p 1426
795 Middle St, Fall River MA 02721
Tel (508) 674-5600 *SIC* 8062 8011

FALMOUTH HOSPITAL ASSOCIATION INC p 526
100 Ter Heun Dr, Falmouth MA 02540
Tel (508) 548-5300 *SIC* 8062

■ VHS ACQUISITION SUBSIDIARY NUMBER 9 INC p 1553
115 Lincoln St, Framingham MA 01702
Tel (508) 383-1000 *SIC* 8062

HENRY HEYWOOD MEMORIAL HOSPITAL p 684
242 Green St, Gardner MA 01440
Tel (978) 632-3420 *SIC* 8062

FRANKLIN BAYSTATE MEDICAL CENTER p 575
164 High St, Greenfield MA 01301
Tel (413) 773-0211 *SIC* 8062

HOLYOKE MEDICAL CENTER INC p 702
575 Beech St, Holyoke MA 01040
Tel (413) 534-2554 *SIC* 8062

CAPE COD HEALTHCARE INC p 248
27 Park St, Hyannis MA 02601
Tel (508) 862-5030 *SIC* 8062

CAPE COD HOSPITAL p 248
27 Park St, Hyannis MA 02601
Tel (508) 862-7575 *SIC* 8062 8011 8063

LAWRENCE GENERAL HOSPITAL p 848
1 General St, Lawrence MA 01841
Tel (978) 683-4000 *SIC* 8062

HEALTHALLIANCE HOSPITALS INC p 676
60 Hospital Rd, Leominster MA 01453
Tel (978) 466-2000 *SIC* 8062

LOWELL GENERAL HOSPITAL p 881
295 Varnum Ave, Lowell MA 01854
Tel (978) 937-6000 *SIC* 8062

SAINTS MEDICAL CENTER INC p 1271
1 Hospital Dr, Lowell MA 01852
Tel (978) 458-1411 *SIC* 8051 8062

WHIDDEN MEMORIAL HOSPITAL INC p 1605
350 Main St Ste 16, Malden MA 02148
Tel (781) 306-8872 *SIC* 8062

TAS-CHFH p 1425
70 East St, Methuen MA 01844
Tel (978) 687-0156 *SIC* 8062

TAS-CVRHS INC p 1426
70 East St, Methuen MA 01844
Tel (978) 687-0151 *SIC* 8062

MILFORD REGIONAL MEDICAL CENTER INC p 969
14 Prospect St, Milford MA 01757
Tel (508) 473-1190 *SIC* 8062 8082

SAINT LUKES HOSPITAL OF NEW BEDFORD INC p 1270
101 Page St, New Bedford MA 02740
Tel (508) 997-1515 *SIC* 8062 8082 8093

SOUTHCOAST HEALTH SYSTEM INC p 1345
101 Page St, New Bedford MA 02740
Tel (508) 997-1515 *SIC* 8741 8062

ANNA JAQUES HOSPITAL p 92
25 Highland Ave, Newburyport MA 01950
Tel (978) 463-1000 *SIC* 8062

NEWTON WELLESLEY HOSPITAL CORP p 1039
2014 Washington St, Newton MA 02462
Tel (617) 243-6000 *SIC* 8062

COOLEY DICKINSON HEALTH CARE CORP p 366
30 Locust St, Northampton MA 01060
Tel (413) 582-2000 *SIC* 8062

COOLEY DICKINSON HOSPITAL INC p 366
30 Locust St, Northampton MA 01060
Tel (413) 582-2000 *SIC* 8062 8063 8069

COOLEY DICKINSON PHYSICIAN HOSPITAL ORGANIZATION INC p 366
30 Locust St, Northampton MA 01060
Tel (413) 582-2343 *SIC* 8062

STEWARD NORWOOD HOSPITAL INC p 1388
800 Washington St Ste 1, Norwood MA 02062
Tel (781) 769-4000 *SIC* 8062

TAS-CNH INC p 1425
800 Washington St Ste 1, Norwood MA 02062
Tel (781) 769-4000 *SIC* 8062

BERKSHIRE HEALTH SYSTEMS INC p 175
725 North St, Pittsfield MA 01201
Tel (413) 447-2000 *SIC* 8062

BERKSHIRE MEDICAL CENTER INC p 175
725 North St, Pittsfield MA 01201
Tel (413) 447-2000 *SIC* 8062

JORDAN HEALTH SYSTEMS INC p 793
275 Sandwich St, Plymouth MA 02360
Tel (508) 830-2388 *SIC* 8741 8062

JORDAN HOSPITAL CLUB INC p 793
275 Sandwich St, Plymouth MA 02360
Tel (508) 830-2391 *SIC* 8062

NORTH SHORE MEDICAL CENTER INC p 1053
81 Highland Ave, Salem MA 01970
Tel (978) 741-1200 *SIC* 8062

SALEM HOSPITAL p 1272
81 Highland Ave, Salem MA 01970
Tel (978) 741-1200 *SIC* 8062

SOUTH SHORE HEALTH AND EDUCATIONAL CORP p 1345
55 Fogg Rd, South Weymouth MA 02190
Tel (781) 340-8000 *SIC* 8062

SOUTH SHORE HOSPITAL INC p 1345
55 Fogg Rd, South Weymouth MA 02190
Tel (781) 624-8000 *SIC* 8062 8049

HARRINGTON MEMORIAL HOSPITAL INC p 663
100 South St Ste 1, Southbridge MA 01550
Tel (508) 765-9771 *SIC* 8062

BAYSTATE HEALTH INC p 162
759 Chestnut St, Springfield MA 01199
Tel (413) 784-0000 *SIC* 8062 8221 8249

BAYSTATE HEALTH SYSTEM HEALTH SERVICES INC p 162
280 Chestnut St, Springfield MA 01199
Tel (413) 794-9939
SIC 8741 8062 6324 6512

MERCY HOSPITAL INC p 947
271 Carew St, Springfield MA 01104
Tel (413) 748-9000
SIC 8062 8071 8011 7219 8748

MORTON HOSPITAL AND MEDICAL CENTER INC p 991
88 Washington St, Taunton MA 02780
Tel (508) 828-7000 *SIC* 6733 8062

WINCHESTER HOSPITAL p 1614
41 Highland Ave, Winchester MA 01890
Tel (781) 729-9000 *SIC* 8062

■ **SAINT VINCENT HOSPITAL LLC** p 1271
123 Summer St, Worcester MA 01608
Tel (508) 363-5000 *SIC* 8062

UMASS MEMORIAL COMMUNITY HOSPITALS INC p 1501
119 Belmont St, Worcester MA 01605
Tel (508) 334-1000 *SIC* 8062

UMASS MEMORIAL MEDICAL CENTER INC p 1501
55 Lake Ave N, Worcester MA 01655
Tel (508) 334-1000 *SIC* 8062

■ **UMASS MEMORIAL MEDICAL CENTER INC** p 1501
119 Belmont St, Worcester MA 01605
Tel (508) 334-1000 *SIC* 8062

MIDMICHIGAN MEDICAL CENTER-GRATIOT p 966
300 E Warwick Dr, Alma MI 48801
Tel (989) 463-1101 *SIC* 8062

ALPENA REGIONAL MEDICAL CENTER p 60
1501 W Chisholm St, Alpena MI 49707
Tel (989) 356-7390 *SIC* 8062

BRONSON BATTLE CREEK HOSPITAL p 217
300 North Ave, Battle Creek MI 49017
Tel (269) 966-8000 *SIC* 8062 8063 8051

BAY REGIONAL MEDICAL CENTER p 161
1900 Columbus Ave, Bay City MI 48708
Tel (989) 894-3000 *SIC* 8062

HENRY FORD MACOMB HOSPITAL CORP p 684
15855 19 Mile Rd, Clinton Township MI 48038
Tel (586) 263-2300 *SIC* 8062

■ **VHS HURON VALLEY-SINAI HOSPITAL INC** p 1554
1 William Carls Dr, Commerce Township MI 48382
Tel (248) 937-3300 *SIC* 8062

OAKWOOD HEALTHCARE INC p 1071
18101 Oakwood Blvd, Dearborn MI 48124
Tel (313) 593-7000 *SIC* 8062

GRACE SINAI HOSPITAL p 628
6701 W Outer Dr, Detroit MI 48235
Tel (313) 966-3333 *SIC* 8062

HENRY FORD HEALTH SYSTEM p 684
1 Ford Pl, Detroit MI 48202
Tel (313) 916-2600 *SIC* 8062

HUTZEL HOSPITAL p 722
3980 John R St, Detroit MI 48201
Tel (313) 745-7555 *SIC* 8062

■ **VHS DETROIT RECEIVING HOSPITAL INC** p 1553
4201 Saint Antoine St, Detroit MI 48201
Tel (313) 745-3000 *SIC* 8093 8069 8062

■ **VHS HARPER-HUTZEL HOSPITAL INC** p 1554
3980 John R St, Detroit MI 48201
Tel (313) 745-8040 *SIC* 8062

■ **VHS OF MICHIGAN INC** p 1554
3990 John R St, Detroit MI 48201
Tel (313) 745-1250 *SIC* 8062

■ **VHS SINAI-GRACE HOSPITAL INC** p 1554
6071 W Outer Dr, Detroit MI 48235
Tel (313) 966-3300 *SIC* 8062

BOTSFORD GENERAL HOSPITAL p 203
28050 Grand River Ave, Farmington Hills MI 48336
Tel (248) 471-8000 *SIC* 8062

ZIEGER HEALTH CARE CORP p 1643
28050 Grand River Ave, Farmington Hills MI 48336
Tel (248) 471-8000 *SIC* 8062

HURLEY MEDICAL CENTER p 721
1 Hurley Plz, Flint MI 48503
Tel (810) 257-9000 *SIC* 8062

MCLAREN HEALTH CARE CORP p 931
G3235 Beecher Rd Ste B, Flint MI 48532
Tel (810) 342-1100 *SIC* 8062

MCLAREN REGIONAL MEDICAL CENTER p 931
401 S Ballenger Hwy, Flint MI 48532
Tel (810) 342-2000 *SIC* 8062

GARDEN CITY HOSPITAL p 591
6245 Inkster Rd, Garden City MI 48135
Tel (734) 458-3300 *SIC* 8062

OTSEGO MEMORIAL HOSPITAL ASSOCIATION p 1097
825 N Center Ave, Gaylord MI 49735
Tel (989) 731-2100 *SIC* 8062

GENESYS HEALTH SYSTEM p 603
1 Genesys Pkwy, Grand Blanc MI 48439
Tel (810) 606-5710 *SIC* 8062

GENESYS REGIONAL MEDICAL CENTER p 603
1 Genesys Pkwy, Grand Blanc MI 48439
Tel (810) 606-5000 *SIC* 8062

SPECTRUM HEALTH HOSPITALS p 1357
100 Michigan St Ne Mc-498, Grand Rapids MI 49503
Tel (616) 391-1774
SIC 8062 6351 8082 6331

SPECTRUM HEALTH SYSTEM p 1357
100 Michigan St Ne, Grand Rapids MI 49503
Tel (616) 391-1774 *SIC* 8062

BON SECOURS COTTAGE HEALTH SERVICES p 199
159 Kercheval Ave, Grosse Pointe Farms MI 48236
Tel (313) 640-1000 *SIC* 8062

HOLLAND COMMUNITY HOSPITAL AUXILIARY INC p 700
602 Michigan Ave, Holland MI 49423
Tel (616) 748-9346 *SIC* 8062

LAKESHORE HEALTH PARTNERS p 840
3235 N Wellness Dr 120b, Holland MI 49424
Tel (616) 399-9522 *SIC* 8062

DICKINSON COUNTY HEALTHCARE SYSTEM p 438
1721 S Stephenson Ave, Iron Mountain MI 49801
Tel (906) 774-1313 *SIC* 8062

W A FOOTE MEMORIAL HOSPITAL p 1568
205 N East Ave, Jackson MI 49201
Tel (517) 788-4800 *SIC* 8062

BORGESS HEALTH ALLIANCE INC p 201
1521 Gull Rd, Kalamazoo MI 49048
Tel (269) 226-7000 *SIC* 8062

BORGESS MEDICAL CENTER p 201
1521 Gull Rd, Kalamazoo MI 49048
Tel (269) 226-7000 *SIC* 8062

BRONSON METHODIST HOSPITAL INC p 217
601 John St Ste E-012, Kalamazoo MI 49007
Tel (269) 341-7654 *SIC* 8062

EDWARD W SPARROW HOSPITAL ASSOCIATION p 480
1215 E Michigan Ave, Lansing MI 48912
Tel (517) 364-1000 *SIC* 8062

INGHAM REGIONAL MEDICAL CENTER p 743
401 W Greenlawn Ave, Lansing MI 48910
Tel (517) 975-7800 *SIC* 8062

SPARROW HEALTH SYSTEM p 1354
1215 E Michigan Ave, Lansing MI 48912
Tel (517) 364-1000 *SIC* 8062 7991

LAPEER REGIONAL MEDICAL CENTER p 845
1375 N Main St, Lapeer MI 48446
Tel (810) 667-5500 *SIC* 8062

ST MARY HOSPITAL OF LIVONIA p 1371
36475 5 Mile Rd, Livonia MI 48154
Tel (734) 655-4800 *SIC* 8062 8051

TRINITY HEALTH CORP p 1481
20555 Victor Pkwy, Livonia MI 48152
Tel (734) 343-1000 *SIC* 8741 8062

TRINITY HEALTH-MICHIGAN p 1481
20555 Victor Pkwy, Livonia MI 48152
Tel (810) 985-1500 *SIC* 8062

OAKLAND HOSPITAL p 1071
27351 Dequindre Rd, Madison Heights MI 48071
Tel (248) 967-7000 *SIC* 8062

MARQUETTE GENERAL HOSPITAL INC p 910
420 W Magnetic St, Marquette MI 49855
Tel (906) 228-9440 *SIC* 8062

ELLA E M BROWN CHARITABLE CIRCLE p 488
200 N Madison St, Marshall MI 49068
Tel (269) 781-4271 *SIC* 8062 8049

MIDMICHIGAN MEDICAL CENTER-MIDLAND p 966
4000 Wellness Dr, Midland MI 48670
Tel (989) 839-3000 *SIC* 8062

MERCY MEMORIAL HOSPITAL CORP p 948
718 N Macomb St, Monroe MI 48162
Tel (734) 240-8400 *SIC* 8062

HENRY FORD MACOMB HOSPITALS p 684
215 North Ave, Mount Clemens MI 48043
Tel (586) 466-9310 *SIC* 8062

MOUNT CLEMENS REGIONAL MEDICAL CENTER p 993
1000 Harrington St, Mount Clemens MI 48043
Tel (586) 493-8000 *SIC* 8062

HACKLEY HOSPITAL p 652
1700 Clinton St, Muskegon MI 49442
Tel (231) 728-4950 *SIC* 8062

MERCY GENERAL HEALTH PARTNERS p 946
1500 E Sherman Blvd, Muskegon MI 49444
Tel (231) 728-4032 *SIC* 8062

MEMORIAL HOSPITAL p 942
826 W King St, Owosso MI 48867
Tel (989) 723-5211 *SIC* 8062

HEALTHSHARE INC p 677
416 Connable Ave, Petoskey MI 49770
Tel (231) 487-4803 *SIC* 8741 8062

MCLAREN NORTHERN MICHIGAN p 931
416 Connable Ave, Petoskey MI 49770
Tel (800) 248-6777 *SIC* 8062

MCLAREN OAKLAND p 931
50 N Perry St, Pontiac MI 48342
Tel (248) 338-5000 *SIC* 8062

OAKLAND PHYSICIANS MEDICAL CENTER LLC p 1071
461 W Huron St, Pontiac MI 48341
Tel (248) 857-7200 *SIC* 8062

ST JOSEPH MERCY OAKLAND p 1368
44405 Woodward Ave, Pontiac MI 48341
Tel (248) 858-3000 *SIC* 8062

ST JOSEPH MERCY OAKLAND HOSPITAL p 1368
44405 Woodward Ave, Pontiac MI 48341
Tel (248) 858-6186 *SIC* 8062

CRITTENTON HOSPITAL MEDICAL CENTER p 393
1101 W University Dr, Rochester MI 48307
Tel (248) 652-5000 *SIC* 8062 8011

CRITTENTON HOSPITAL MEDICAL CENTER FOUNDATION p 393
1101 W University Dr, Rochester MI 48307
Tel (248) 652-5000 *SIC* 8741 8062

BEAUMONT HEALTH p 166
3601 W 13 Mile Rd, Royal Oak MI 48073
Tel (248) 898-5000 *SIC* 8062

WILLIAM BEAUMONT HOSPITAL p 1610
3601 W 13 Mile Rd, Royal Oak MI 48073
Tel (248) 898-5000 *SIC* 8062

COVENANT MEDICAL CENTER INC p 384
1447 N Harrison St, Saginaw MI 48602
Tel (989) 583-0000 *SIC* 8062

ST MARYS MEDICAL CENTER OF SAGINAW INC p 1372
800 S Washington Ave, Saginaw MI 48601
Tel (989) 907-8000 *SIC* 8062

LAKELAND HOSPITALS AT NILES AND ST JOSEPH INC p 840
1234 Napier Ave, Saint Joseph MI 49085
Tel (800) 968-0115 *SIC* 8062

CHIPPEWA COUNTY WAR MEMORIAL HOSPITAL INC p 301
500 Osborn Blvd, Sault Sainte Marie MI 49783
Tel (906) 635-4460 *SIC* 8062 8051

PROVIDENCE HOSPITAL p 1186
16001 W 9 Mile Rd, Southfield MI 48075
Tel (248) 849-3000 *SIC* 8062

MUNSON HEALTHCARE p 1000
1105 Sixth St, Traverse City MI 49684
Tel (800) 252-2065 *SIC* 8062

MUNSON MEDICAL CENTER p 1000
1105 Sixth St, Traverse City MI 49684
Tel (231) 935-6000 *SIC* 8062

DETROIT-MACOMB HOSPITAL CORP p 433
28000 Dequindre Rd, Warren MI 48092
Tel (313) 499-3000 *SIC* 8062

ST JOHN HOSPITAL AND MEDICAL CENTER p 1367
28000 Dequindre Rd, Warren MI 48092
Tel (313) 343-4000 *SIC* 8062

ST JOHN MACOMB-OAKLAND HOSPITAL p 1367
28000 Dequindre Rd, Warren MI 48092
Tel (586) 753-0094 *SIC* 8062

ST JOHN PROVIDENCE HEALTH SYSTEM p 1367
28000 Dequindre Rd, Warren MI 48092
Tel (586) 753-0500 *SIC* 8062

HENRY FORD WYANDOTTE HOSPITAL p 684
2333 Biddle Ave, Wyandotte MI 48192
Tel (734) 246-6000 *SIC* 8062

METROPOLITAN HOSPITAL p 956
5900 Byron Center Ave Sw, Wyoming MI 49519
Tel (616) 252-7200 *SIC* 8062 8069

MAYO CLINIC HEALTH SYSTEM-ALBERT LEA AND AUSTIN p 924
404 W Fountain St, Albert Lea MN 56007
Tel (507) 373-2384
SIC 8062 8069 8051 8063 8011

ST JOSEPHS MEDICAL CENTER p 1369
523 N 3rd St, Brainerd MN 56401
Tel (218) 829-2861 *SIC* 8062

CUYUNA RANGE HOSPITAL INC p 403
320 E Main St, Crosby MN 56441
Tel (218) 546-7000 *SIC* 8062 8051

ST MARYS REGIONAL HEALTH CENTER p 1372
1027 Washington Ave, Detroit Lakes MN 56501
Tel (218) 847-5611 *SIC* 8062 8051

ESSENTIA HEALTH p 510
502 E 2nd St, Duluth MN 55805
Tel (218) 786-8376 *SIC* 8062 8051

S M D C ST MARYS DULUTH CLINIC HEALTH SYSTEM HOSPICE & PALLIATIVE CARE p 1262
407 E 3rd St, Duluth MN 55805
Tel (218) 786-4020 *SIC* 8062

SMDC MEDICAL CENTER p 1332
502 E 2nd St, Duluth MN 55805
Tel (218) 726-4000 *SIC* 8062

ST LUKES HOSPITAL OF DULUTH p 1370
915 E 1st St, Duluth MN 55805
Tel (218) 726-5555 *SIC* 8062 8011

ST MARYS DULUTH CLINIC HEALTH SYSTEM p 1371
400 E 3rd St, Duluth MN 55805
Tel (218) 786-8364 *SIC* 8093 8011 8062

ST MARYS MEDICAL CENTER p 1371
407 E 3rd St, Duluth MN 55805
Tel (218) 786-4000 *SIC* 8062 8082 8351

LAKE REGION HEALTHCARE CORP p 839
712 S Cascade St, Fergus Falls MN 56537
Tel (218) 736-8000 *SIC* 8062

RANGE REGIONAL HEALTH SERVICES p 1208
750 E 34th St, Hibbing MN 55746
Tel (218) 262-4881 *SIC* 8062

UNITY FAMILY HEALTHCARE p 1515
815 2nd St Se, Little Falls MN 56345
Tel (320) 632-5441 *SIC* 8062

MAYO CLINIC HEALTH SYSTEM-MANKATO p 924
1025 Marsh St, Mankato MN 56001
Tel (507) 625-4031 *SIC* 8062

MAPLE GROVE HOSPITAL CORP p 903
9875 Hospital Dr, Maple Grove MN 55369
Tel (763) 581-1000 *SIC* 8062

ABBOTT NORTHWESTERN HOSPITAL p 9
800 E 28th St, Minneapolis MN 55407
Tel (612) 863-4000 *SIC* 8062

ALLINA HEALTH SYSTEM p 57
2925 Chicago Ave, Minneapolis MN 55407
Tel (612) 262-5000 *SIC* 8062 8741 8011

FAIRVIEW HEALTH SERVICES p 525
2450 Riverside Ave, Minneapolis MN 55454
Tel (612) 672-6300 *SIC* 8062

HEALTH PARTNERS INC p 675
8170 33rd Ave S, Minneapolis MN 55425
Tel (952) 883-6000 *SIC* 8062

HENNEPIN HEALTHCARE SYSTEM INC p 683
701 Park Ave, Minneapolis MN 55415
Tel (612) 873-3000 *SIC* 8062 5912

NORTH MEMORIAL HEALTH CARE p 1053
3300 Oakdale Ave N, Minneapolis MN 55422
Tel (763) 520-5200 *SIC* 8062 8011

REGIONS HOSPITAL p 1220
8170 33rd Ave S, Minneapolis MN 55425
Tel (952) 883-6280 *SIC* 8062

NORTHFIELD HOSPITAL & SKILLED NURSING p 1057
2000 North Ave, Northfield MN 55057
Tel (507) 646-1000 *SIC* 8062

MAYO CLINIC HEALTH SYSTEM - RED WING p 923
701 Hewitt Blvd, Red Wing MN 55066
Tel (651) 267-5000 *SIC* 8062

MAYO CLINIC p 923
200 1st St Sw, Rochester MN 55905
Tel (507) 284-2511
SIC 8062 8733 8071 8011

MAYO CLINIC p 923
200 1st St Sw, Rochester MN 55905
Tel (507) 284-2511
SIC 8011 8062 8071 8733 8221

OLMSTED MEDICAL CENTER p 1083
210 9th St Se Ste 1, Rochester MN 55904
Tel (507) 288-3443 *SIC* 8062

ROCHESTER METHODIST HOSPITAL AUXILIARY INC p 1243
1216 2nd St Sw, Rochester MN 55902
Tel (507) 255-5123 *SIC* 8062

SAINT MARYS HOSPITAL p 1270
1216 2nd St Sw, Rochester MN 55902
Tel (507) 255-5123 *SIC* 8062

CENTRACARE HEALTH SYSTEM p 277
1406 6th Ave N, Saint Cloud MN 56303
Tel (320) 656-7020 *SIC* 8062

ST CLOUD HOSPITAL p 1365
1406 6th Ave N, Saint Cloud MN 56303
Tel (320) 251-2700 *SIC* 8062

PARK NICOLLET METHODIST HOSPITAL p 1115
6500 Excelsior Blvd, Saint Louis Park MN 55426
Tel (952) 993-5000 *SIC* 8062

BETHESDA HEALTHEAST HOSPITAL p 178
559 Capitol Blvd Fl 6, Saint Paul MN 55103
Tel (651) 232-2000 *SIC* 8062 8741 8069

HEALTHEAST CARE SYSTEM p 677
1700 University Ave W # 5, Saint Paul MN 55104
Tel (651) 232-5353 *SIC* 8741 8062 7389

HEALTHEAST ST JOHNS HOSPITAL p 677
1575 Beam Ave, Saint Paul MN 55109
Tel (651) 232-7000 *SIC* 8062

HEALTHEAST ST JOSEPHS HOSPITAL p 677
45 10th St W, Saint Paul MN 55102
Tel (651) 232-3000 *SIC* 8062

PEDIATRIC RHEUMATOLOGY p 1127
200 University Ave E, Saint Paul MN 55101
Tel (651) 229-3892 *SIC* 8011 8062

REGIONS HOSPITAL p 1220
640 Jackson St, Saint Paul MN 55101
Tel (651) 254-3456 *SIC* 8062

REGIONS HOSPITAL FOUNDATION p 1220
640 Jackson St, Saint Paul MN 55101
Tel (651) 254-3456 *SIC* 8062

ST FRANCIS REGIONAL MEDICAL CENTER p 1367
1455 Saint Francis Ave, Shakopee MN 55379
Tel (952) 428-3000 *SIC* 8062

LAKEWOOD HEALTH SYSTEM p 840
49725 County 83, Staples MN 56479
Tel (218) 894-1515 *SIC* 8062 8051

SANFORD MEDICAL CENTER THIEF RIVER FALLS p 1279
120 Labree Ave S Ste A, Thief River Falls MN 56701
Tel (218) 681-4240 *SIC* 8062

RIDGEVIEW MEDICAL CENTER p 1234
500 S Maple St, Waconia MN 55387
Tel (952) 442-2191 *SIC* 8062

RICE MEMORIAL HOSPITAL p 1232
301 Becker Ave Sw, Willmar MN 56201
Tel (320) 235-4543 *SIC* 8062

WINONA HEALTH p 1617
855 Mankato Ave, Winona MN 55987
Tel (507) 454-3650 *SIC* 8062 8051

WINONA HEALTH SERVICES p 1617
859 Mankato Ave, Winona MN 55987
Tel (507) 454-3650 *SIC* 8062 8051

■ **BILOXI HMA LLC** p 182
150 Reynoir St, Biloxi MS 39530
Tel (228) 432-1571 *SIC* 8062

■ **BILOXI REGIONAL MEDICAL CENTER INC** p 183
150 Reynoir St, Biloxi MS 39530
Tel (228) 432-1571 *SIC* 8062

BAPTIST MEMORIAL HOSPITAL-GOLDEN TRIANGLE INC p 154
2520 5th St N, Columbus MS 39705
Tel (662) 244-1000 *SIC* 8062

MAGNOLIA REGIONAL HEALTH CENTER FOUNDATION INC p 896
611 Alcorn Dr, Corinth MS 38834
Tel (662) 293-1000 *SIC* 8062

■ **RIVER OAKS HOSPITAL LLC** p 1237
1030 River Oaks Dr, Flowood MS 39232
Tel (601) 932-1030 *SIC* 8062

SINGING RIVER HEALTH SYSTEM p 1326
2101 Highway 90, Gautier MS 39553
Tel (228) 497-7900 *SIC* 8062

DELTA REGIONAL MEDICAL CENTER p 427
1400 E Union St, Greenville MS 38703
Tel (662) 378-3783 *SIC* 8062

GREENWOOD LEFLORE HOSPITAL p 639
1401 River Rd, Greenwood MS 38930
Tel (662) 459-7000 *SIC* 8062

GULFPORT MEMORIAL HOSPITAL EMR p 647
4500 13th St, Gulfport MS 39501
Tel (228) 867-4000 *SIC* 8062

MEMORIAL HOSPITAL AUXILIARY INC p 942
4500 13th St, Gulfport MS 39501
Tel (228) 867-4000 *SIC* 8062

FORREST GENERAL HEALTH SERVICES INC p 568
6051 U S Highway 49, Hattiesburg MS 39401
Tel (601) 288-7000 *SIC* 8062 8063 8069

FORREST GENERAL HEALTH SERVICES INC p 568
6051 U S Highway 49, Hattiesburg MS 39401
Tel (601) 288-7000 *SIC* 8062

WESLEY HEALTH SYSTEM LLC p 1593
5001 Hardy St, Hattiesburg MS 39402
Tel (601) 268-8000
SIC 8051 8062 8082 8011

MISSISSIPPI BAPTST MEDICAL CENTER INC p 975
1225 N State St, Jackson MS 39202
Tel (601) 968-1000 *SIC* 8062 8069 8051

ST DOMINIC HEALTH SERVICES INC p 1366
969 Lakeland Dr, Jackson MS 39216
Tel (601) 200-2000
SIC 8741 8093 8069 8062

ST DOMINIC-JACKSON MEMORIAL HOSPITAL p 1366
969 Lakeland Dr, Jackson MS 39216
Tel (601) 200-6776 *SIC* 8062

UNIVERSITY NEUROSURGEONS PLLC p 1519
2500 N State St, Jackson MS 39216
Tel (601) 984-5700 *SIC* 8062

UNIVERSITY OF MISSISSIPPI MEDICAL CENTER RESEARCH DEVELOPMENT p 1523
2500 N State St, Jackson MS 39216
Tel (601) 984-1000 *SIC* 8062

SOUTH CENTRAL REGIONAL MEDICAL CENTER p 1343
1220 Jefferson St, Laurel MS 39440
Tel (601) 426-4000 *SIC* 8062

SOUTHWEST MISSISSIPPI REGIONAL MEDICAL CENTER p 1352
215 Marion Ave, Mccomb MS 39648
Tel (601) 249-5500 *SIC* 8062

ANDERSON REGIONAL MEDICAL CENTER p 90
2124 14th St, Meridian MS 39301
Tel (601) 553-6000 *SIC* 8062

RUSH MEDICAL FOUNDATION p 1258
1314 19th Ave, Meridian MS 39301
Tel (601) 483-0011 *SIC* 8062

BAPTIST MEMORIAL HOSPITAL - NORTH MISSISSIPPI INC p 154
2301 S Lamar Blvd, Oxford MS 38655
Tel (662) 232-8100 *SIC* 8062

BAPTIST MEMORIAL HOSPITAL-DESOTO INC p 154
7601 Southcrest Pkwy, Southaven MS 38671
Tel (662) 772-4000 *SIC* 8062

NORTH MISSISSIPPI MEDICAL CENTER INC p 1053
830 S Gloster St, Tupelo MS 38801
Tel (662) 377-3000 *SIC* 8062 8051 8082

■ **RIVER REGION BEHAVIORAL HEALTH** p 1237
1111 N Frontage Rd, Vicksburg MS 39180
Tel (601) 619-3838 *SIC* 8062

VICKSBURG HEALTHCARE LLC p 1555
2100 Highway 61 N, Vicksburg MS 39183
Tel (601) 883-4287 *SIC* 8062

CITIZENS MEMORIAL HOSPITAL DISTRICT OF POLK COUNTY p 311
1500 N Oakland Ave, Bolivar MO 65613
Tel (417) 326-6000 *SIC* 8062 8011 8082

SKAGGS COMMUNITY HOSPITAL ASSOCIATION p 1329
251 Skaggs Rd, Branson MO 65616
Tel (417) 335-7000
SIC 8062 8082 8011 7352 8051

DAUGHTERS OF CHARITY SERVICES OF ST LOUIS p 414
12303 De Paul Dr, Bridgeton MO 63044
Tel (314) 344-6000
SIC 8062 8051 8063 8069

FRANCIS SAINT MEDICAL CENTER p 573
211 Saint Francis Dr, Cape Girardeau MO 63703
Tel (573) 331-3000 *SIC* 8062

SOUTHEAST MISSOURI HOSPITAL ASSOCIATION p 1346
1701 Lacey St, Cape Girardeau MO 63701
Tel (573) 334-4822 *SIC* 8062

MERCY HEALTH p 946
14528 South Outer 40 Rd # 100, Chesterfield MO 63017
Tel (314) 579-6100 *SIC* 8062

MERCY HEALTH CENTER INC p 946
14528 South Outer 40 Rd # 100, Chesterfield MO 63017
Tel (405) 755-1515 *SIC* 8062

ST LUKES EPISCOPAL-PRESBYTERIAN HOSPITALS p 1370
232 S Woods Mill Rd, Chesterfield MO 63017
Tel (314) 434-1500 *SIC* 8062

BOONE HOSPITAL CENTER p 200
1600 E Broadway, Columbia MO 65201
Tel (573) 815-8000 *SIC* 8062

UNIVERSITY OF MISSOURI HEALTH CARE p 1523
1 Hospital Dr, Columbia MO 65201
Tel (573) 882-4141 *SIC* 8062

MERCY HOSPITAL JEFFERSON p 947
1400 Hwy 61 S, Crystal City MO 63019
Tel (636) 933-1000 *SIC* 8062

HANNIBAL REGIONAL HOSPITAL INC p 658
6000 Hospital Dr, Hannibal MO 63401
Tel (573) 248-1300 *SIC* 8062

CENTERPOINT MEDICAL CENTER OF INDEPENDENCE LLC p 276
19600 E 39th St S, Independence MO 64057
Tel (816) 698-8846 *SIC* 8062

CAPITAL REGION MEDICAL CENTER p 250
1125 Madison St, Jefferson City MO 65101
Tel (573) 632-5000 *SIC* 8062

FREEMAN HEALTH SYSTEM p 577
1102 W 32nd St, Joplin MO 64804
Tel (417) 347-1111 *SIC* 8062 8069

MERCY HOSPITAL JOPLIN p 947
100 Mercy Way, Joplin MO 64804
Tel (417) 781-2727 *SIC* 8062

■ **BAPTIST-LUTHERAN MEDICAL CENTER** p 154
6601 Rockhill Rd, Kansas City MO 64131
Tel (816) 276-7000 *SIC* 8062 8731

■ **MIDWEST DIVISION RMC LLC** p 967
2316 E Meyer Blvd, Kansas City MO 64132
Tel (816) 276-4000 *SIC* 8062

SAINT LUKES HEALTH SYSTEM INC p 1270
901 E 104th St, Kansas City MO 64131
Tel (816) 932-2000 *SIC* 8062

SAINT LUKES HOSPITAL OF KANSAS CITY p 1270
4401 Wornall Rd, Kansas City MO 64111
Tel (816) 932-2000
SIC 8062 8742 8011 6512 8082 7322

ST JOSEPH MEDICAL CENTER p 1368
1000 Carondelet Dr, Kansas City MO 64114
Tel (816) 942-4400 *SIC* 8062

ST LUKES HOSPITAL OF KANSAS CITY p 1370
4401 Wornall Rd, Kansas City MO 64111
Tel (816) 932-2000 *SIC* 8062

TRUMAN MEDICAL CENTER INC p 1486
2301 Holmes St, Kansas City MO 64108
Tel (816) 404-1000 *SIC* 8062

MERCY HOSPITAL LEBANON p 947
100 Hospital Dr, Lebanon MO 65536
Tel (417) 533-6100 *SIC* 8062

NEW LIBERTY HOSPITAL DISTRICT OF CLAY COUNTY MISSOURI p 1032
2525 Glenn Hendren Dr, Liberty MO 64068
Tel (816) 781-7200 *SIC* 8062 8051

NORTH KANSAS CITY HOSPITAL p 1052
2800 Clay Edwards Dr, North Kansas City MO 64116
Tel (816) 691-2000 *SIC* 8062

PROGRESS WEST HEALTHCARE CENTER p 1181
2 Progress Point Ct, O Fallon MO 63368
Tel (636) 344-1000 *SIC* 8062

LAKE REGIONAL HEALTH SYSTEM p 839
54 Hospital Dr, Osage Beach MO 65065
Tel (573) 348-8000 *SIC* 8062

■ **LUCY LEE HOSPITAL INC** p 884
2620 N Westwood Blvd, Poplar Bluff MO 63901
Tel (573) 785-7721 *SIC* 8062

POPLAR BLUFF REGIONAL MEDICAL CENTER INC p 1161
3100 Oak Grove Rd, Poplar Bluff MO 63901
Tel (573) 785-7721 *SIC* 8062

PHELPS COUNTY REGIONAL MEDICAL CENTER p 1141
1000 W 10th St, Rolla MO 65401
Tel (573) 364-8899 *SIC* 8062

SSM HEALTH ST JOSEPH HOSPITAL-ST CHARLES p 1364
300 1st Capitol Dr, Saint Charles MO 63301
Tel (636) 947-5000 *SIC* 8062

HEARTLAND HEALTH p 679
5325 Faraon St, Saint Joseph MO 64506
Tel (816) 271-6000 *SIC* 8062 7322 8721

HEARTLAND REGIONAL MEDICAL CENTER p 679
5325 Faraon St, Saint Joseph MO 64506
Tel (816) 271-6000 *SIC* 8062

BARNES HOSPITAL (INC) p 156
Barnes Hospital Plz, Saint Louis MO 63110
Tel (314) 362-5000 *SIC* 8062

BARNES-JEWISH HOSPITAL p 156
216 S Kingshwy Blvd 140, Saint Louis MO 63110
Tel (314) 747-3000 *SIC* 8062

BARNES-JEWISH HOSPITAL p 156
1 B J Hospital Plaza Dr, Saint Louis MO 63110
Tel (314) 747-3000 *SIC* 8062

BARNES-JEWISH WEST COUNTY HOSPITAL p 156
12634 Olive Blvd, Saint Louis MO 63141
Tel (314) 996-8000 *SIC* 8062

CHRISTIAN HOSPITAL NORTHEAST - NORTHWEST p 303
11133 Dunn Rd, Saint Louis MO 63136
Tel (314) 355-2300 *SIC* 8062 8322

■ **DES PERES HOSPITAL INC** p 431
2345 Dougherty Ferry Rd, Saint Louis MO 63122
Tel (314) 966-9100 *SIC* 8062

MERCY HOSPITALS EAST COMMUNITIES p 947
615 S New Ballas Rd, Saint Louis MO 63141
Tel (417) 820-2000 *SIC* 8062

MISSOURI BAPTIST MEDICAL CENTER p 976
3015 N Ballas Rd, Saint Louis MO 63131
Tel (314) 996-5000 *SIC* 8062

SSM HEALTH CARE CORP p 1364
10101 Woodfield Ln # 100, Saint Louis MO 63132
Tel (314) 994-7800
SIC 8062 8082 8011 8051

ST ANTHONYS MEDICAL CENTER p 1364
10010 Kennerly Rd, Saint Louis MO 63128
Tel (314) 525-1000 *SIC* 8062

BARNES-JEWISH ST PETERS HOSPITAL INC p 156
10 Hospital Dr, Saint Peters MO 63376
Tel (636) 916-9000 *SIC* 8062

MISSOURI DELTA MEDICAL CENTER p 976
1008 N Main St, Sikeston MO 63801
Tel (573) 471-1600 *SIC* 8062

SAINT LUKES NORTHLAND HOME CARE p 1270
601 S Us Highway 169, Smithville MO 64089
Tel (816) 532-3700
SIC 8062 8051 8069 8063

LESTER E COX MEDICAL CENTERS p 857
1423 N Jefferson Ave, Springfield MO 65802
Tel (417) 269-3000 *SIC* 8062 8069

MERCY HEALTH SPRINGFIELD COMMUNITIES p 946
1235 E Cherokee St, Springfield MO 65804
Tel (417) 885-2000 *SIC* 8062

MERCY HOSPITAL SPRINGFIELD p 947
1235 E Cherokee St, Springfield MO 65804
Tel (417) 820-2000 *SIC* 8062 8011

OZARKS COMMUNITY HOSPITAL INC p 1101
2828 N National Ave, Springfield MO 65803
Tel (417) 837-4000 *SIC* 8062

ST JOHNS CLINIC INC p 1367
1235 E Cherokee St, Springfield MO 65804
Tel (417) 820-2000 *SIC* 8062

MERCY HOSPITAL WASHINGTON p 947
901 E 5th St Ste 222, Washington MO 63090
Tel (636) 239-8000 *SIC* 8062

OZARKS MEDICAL CENTER p 1101
1100 N Kentucky Ave, West Plains MO 65775
Tel (417) 256-9111 *SIC* 8062

BILLINGS CLINIC p 182
2800 10th Ave N, Billings MT 59101
Tel (406) 657-4000 *SIC* 8062

ST VINCENT HEALTHCARE p 1373
1233 N 30th St, Billings MT 59101
Tel (406) 657-7000 *SIC* 8062

BOZEMAN DEACONESS HEALTH SERVICES p 205
915 Highland Blvd, Bozeman MT 59715
Tel (406) 585-5000 *SIC* 8062 8059

ST JAMES HEALTHCARE INC p 1367
400 S Clark St, Butte MT 59701
Tel (406) 723-2484 *SIC* 8062

BENEFIS HOSPITALS INC p 173
1101 26th St S, Great Falls MT 59405
Tel (406) 455-5000 *SIC* 8062 8051

ST PETERS HOSPITAL p 1372
2475 E Broadway St, Helena MT 59601
Tel (406) 442-2480 *SIC* 8062

KALISPELL REGIONAL MEDICAL CENTER INC p 801
310 Sunnyview Ln, Kalispell MT 59901
Tel (406) 752-5111 *SIC* 8062

CMC MISSOULA INC p 329
2827 Fort Missoula Rd, Missoula MT 59804
Tel (406) 728-4100 *SIC* 8062 8361

ST PATRICK HOSPITAL AND HEALTH SCIENCES CENTER p 1372
500 W Broadway St, Missoula MT 59802
Tel (406) 543-7271 *SIC* 8062

ST PATRICK HOSPITAL CORP p 1372
500 W Broadway St, Missoula MT 59802
Tel (406) 543-7271 *SIC* 8062

FREMONT HEALTH p 577
450 E 23rd St, Fremont NE 68025
Tel (402) 727-3795 *SIC* 8062 8051

SAINT FRANCIS MEDICAL CENTER INC p 1269
2620 W Faidley Ave, Grand Island NE 68803
Tel (308) 384-4600 *SIC* 8062 8069

MARY LANNING MEMORIAL HOSPITAL ASSOCIATION p 914
715 N Saint Joseph Ave, Hastings NE 68901
Tel (402) 463-4521 *SIC* 8062

GOOD SAMARITAN HOSPITAL p 623
4503 2nd Ave Ste 209, Kearney NE 68847
Tel (308) 865-2009 *SIC* 8062

GOOD SAMARITAN HOSPITAL KEARNEY NEBRASKA p 623
10 E 31st St, Kearney NE 68847
Tel (308) 865-7997 *SIC* 8062

BRYAN HEALTH p 221
1600 S 48th St, Lincoln NE 68506
Tel (402) 481-1111 *SIC* 8062

BRYAN HEALTH WEST CAMPUS p 221
2300 S 16th St, Lincoln NE 68502
Tel (402) 475-1011 *SIC* 8062

BRYAN MEDICAL CENTER p 221
1600 S 48th St, Lincoln NE 68506
Tel (402) 481-3190 *SIC* 8062

SAINT ELIZABETH REGIONAL MEDICAL CENTER p 1269
555 S 70th St, Lincoln NE 68510
Tel (402) 219-5200 *SIC* 8062 8082

NORTH PLATTE NEBRASKA HOSPITAL CORP p 1053
601 W Leota St, North Platte NE 69101
Tel (308) 534-9310 *SIC* 8062 8092

ALEGENT HEALTH - IMMANUEL MEDICAL CENTER p 48
6901 N 72nd St, Omaha NE 68122
Tel (402) 572-2121 *SIC* 8062 8051 8351

ALEGENT HEALTH- BERGAN MERCY HEALTH SYSTEM p 48
7500 Mercy Rd, Omaha NE 68124
Tel (402) 398-6060 *SIC* 8062

ARCHBISHOP BERGAN MERCY HOSPITAL p 104
7500 Mercy Rd, Omaha NE 68124
Tel (402) 398-6060 *SIC* 8062 8051

CREIGHTON ALEGENT CLINIC p 391
12809 W Dodge Rd, Omaha NE 68154
Tel (402) 343-4343 *SIC* 8062

■ **CREIGHTON ALEGENT HEALTH** p 391
601 N 30th St, Omaha NE 68131
Tel (402) 449-4000 *SIC* 8062

NEBRASKA MEDICAL CENTER p 1023
987400 Nebraska Med Ctr, Omaha NE 68198
Tel (402) 552-2000 *SIC* 8062

NEBRASKA METHODIST HEALTH SYSTEM INC p 1023
8511 W Dodge Rd, Omaha NE 68114
Tel (402) 354-2176 *SIC* 8062

NEBRASKA METHODIST HOSPITAL INC p 1023
8303 Dodge St, Omaha NE 68114
Tel (402) 354-4540 *SIC* 8062

ALEGENT HEALTH MEMORIAL HOSPITAL p 48
104 W 17th St, Schuyler NE 68661
Tel (402) 352-2441 *SIC* 8062

REGIONAL WEST MEDICAL CENTER p 1219
4021 Avenue B, Scottsbluff NE 69361
Tel (308) 635-3711 *SIC* 8062

CARSON TAHOE REGIONAL HEALTHCARE p 261
1600 Medical Pkwy, Carson City NV 89703
Tel (775) 445-8000 *SIC* 8062

■ **DESERT SPRINGS HOSPITAL MEDICAL CENTER** p 432
2075 E Flamingo Rd, Las Vegas NV 89119
Tel (702) 733-8800 *SIC* 8062

MOUNTAINVIEW HOSPITAL INC p 994
3100 N Tenaya Way, Las Vegas NV 89128
Tel (702) 255-5000 *SIC* 8062 8011 4119

■ **SPRING VALLEY MEDICAL CENTER INC** p 1360
5400 S Rainbow Blvd, Las Vegas NV 89118
Tel (702) 853-3000 *SIC* 8062

■ **SUMMERLIN HOSPITAL MEDICAL CENTER LLC** p 1398
657 N Town Center Dr, Las Vegas NV 89144
Tel (702) 233-7000 *SIC* 8062 8011

■ **SUNRISE HOSPITAL AND MEDICAL CENTER LLC** p 1404
3186 S Maryland Pkwy, Las Vegas NV 89109
Tel (702) 731-8080 *SIC* 8062

UNIVERSITY MEDICAL CENTER OF SOUTHERN NEVADA p 1519
1800 W Charleston Blvd, Las Vegas NV 89102
Tel (702) 383-2000 *SIC* 8062

■ **VALLEY HEALTH SYSTEM LLC** p 1540
620 Shadow Ln, Las Vegas NV 89106
Tel (702) 388-4000 *SIC* 8062 8011

VISTA NORTH HOSPITAL INC p 1562
1409 E Lake Mead Blvd, North Las Vegas NV 89030
Tel (702) 649-7711 *SIC* 8062

PRIME HEALTHCARE SERVICES - RENO LLC p 1175
235 W 6th St, Reno NV 89503
Tel (775) 770-3000 *SIC* 8062

RENOWN HEALTH p 1224
1155 Mill St, Reno NV 89502
Tel (775) 982-4100 SIC 8062

RENOWN REGIONAL MEDICAL CENTER p 1224
1155 Mill St, Reno NV 89502
Tel (775) 982-4100 SIC 8062

SAINT MARYS HEALTH CARE CORP p 1270
235 W 6th St, Reno NV 89503
Tel (775) 770-3000 SIC 8062

■ **NORTHERN NEVADA MEDICAL CENTER LP** p 1056
2375 E Prater Way, Sparks NV 89434
Tel (775) 331-7000
SIC 8062 8093 8071 8049 8011

CAPITAL REGION HEALTH CARE CORP p 250
250 Pleasant St, Concord NH 03301
Tel (603) 225-2711
SIC 8741 8062 8051 8093 8082

CONCORD HOSPITAL INC p 354
250 Pleasant St, Concord NH 03301
Tel (603) 227-7000 SIC 8062

■ **PARKLAND MEDICAL CENTER** p 1116
1 Parkland Dr, Derry NH 03038
Tel (603) 432-1500 SIC 8062

WENTWORTH-DOUGLASS HOSPITAL p 1592
789 Central Ave, Dover NH 03820
Tel (603) 742-5252 SIC 8062

CORE PHYSICIANS LLC p 369
7 Holland Way Fl 1, Exeter NH 03833
Tel (603) 580-7939 SIC 8062

EXETER HOSPITAL INC p 519
5 Alumni Dr, Exeter NH 03833
Tel (603) 778-7311 SIC 8062

CHESHIRE MEDICAL CENTER p 295
580 Court St, Keene NH 03431
Tel (603) 354-5400 SIC 8062

LRGHEALTHCARE p 882
80 Highland St, Laconia NH 03246
Tel (603) 524-3211 SIC 8062

DARTMOUTH-HITCHCOCK MEDICAL CENTER p 413
1 Medical Center Dr, Lebanon NH 03756
Tel (603) 650-5000 SIC 8062 8011 8051

MARY HITCHCOCK MEMORIAL HOSPITAL p 914
1 Medical Center Dr, Lebanon NH 03756
Tel (603) 650-5000 SIC 8062

LITTLETON HOSPITAL ASSOCIATION p 871
600 Saint Johnsbury Rd, Littleton NH 03561
Tel (603) 444-9000 SIC 8062

CATHOLIC MEDICAL CENTER p 267
100 Mcgregor St, Manchester NH 03102
Tel (603) 663-6888 SIC 8062

CATHOLIC MEDICAL CENTER PHYSICIAN PRACTICE ASSOCIATES p 267
100 Mcgregor St, Manchester NH 03102
Tel (603) 668-3545 SIC 8062 8011

ELLIOT HEALTH SYSTEM p 488
1 Elliot Way, Manchester NH 03103
Tel (603) 663-1600 SIC 8062

ELLIOT HOSPITAL OF CITY OF MANCHESTER p 488
1 Elliot Way, Manchester NH 03103
Tel (603) 669-5300 SIC 8062

SOUTHERN NEW HAMPSHIRE MEDICAL CENTER p 1349
8 Prospect St, Nashua NH 03060
Tel (603) 577-2000 SIC 8062 8011

ST JOSEPH HOSPITAL p 1368
172 Kinsley St, Nashua NH 03060
Tel (603) 882-3000 SIC 8062

■ **HCA HEALTH SERVICES OF NEW HAMPSHIRE INC** p 671
333 Borthwick Ave, Portsmouth NH 03801
Tel (603) 436-0600 SIC 8062 8063

SPECIALTY HOSPITAL OF AMERICA LLC p 1356
155 Fleet St, Portsmouth NH 03801
Tel (603) 570-4888 SIC 8062

FRISBIE MEMORIAL HOSPITAL p 580
11 Whitehall Rd, Rochester NH 03867
Tel (603) 332-5211 SIC 8062

ATLANTICARE REGIONAL MEDICAL CENTER INC p 127
1925 Pacific Ave, Atlantic City NJ 08401
Tel (609) 345-4000 SIC 8062

BAYONNE MEDICAL CENTER INC p 162
29th Street At Ave E, Bayonne NJ 07002
Tel (201) 858-5000 SIC 8062

CLARA MAASS MEDICAL CENTER (INC) p 321
1 Clara Maass Dr, Belleville NJ 07109
Tel (973) 450-2000 SIC 8062

INSPIRA MEDICAL CENTERS INC p 746
333 Irving Ave, Bridgeton NJ 08302
Tel (856) 575-4500 SIC 8062

DEBORAH HEART AND LUNG CENTER p 420
200 Trenton Rd, Browns Mills NJ 08015
Tel (609) 893-6611 SIC 8062

COOPER HEALTH SYSTEM p 366
1 Cooper Plz, Camden NJ 08103
Tel (856) 342-2000 SIC 8062

OUR LADY OF LOURDES MEDICAL CENTER INC p 1098
1600 Haddon Ave, Camden NJ 08103
Tel (856) 757-3500 SIC 8062

VIRTUA-WEST JERSEY HEALTH SYSTEM INC p 1560
1000 Atlantic Ave, Camden NJ 08104
Tel (856) 246-3000 SIC 8062

CAPE REGIONAL MEDICAL CENTER INC p 248
2 Stone Harbor Blvd, Cape May Court House NJ 08210
Tel (609) 463-2000 SIC 8062

PRIME HEALTHCARE SERVICES - SAINT CLARES LLC p 1175
25 Pocono Rd, Denville NJ 07834
Tel (973) 625-6000 SIC 8062

SAINT CLARES HOSPITAL INC p 1268
25 Pocono Rd, Denville NJ 07834
Tel (973) 625-6000 SIC 8062

DOVER GENERAL HOSPITAL & MEDICAL CENTER (INC) p 453
400 W Blackwell St, Dover NJ 07801
Tel (973) 989-3000 SIC 8062

EAST ORANGE GENERAL HOSPITAL (INC) p 470
300 Central Ave, East Orange NJ 07018
Tel (973) 672-8400 SIC 8062

COMMUNITY HOSPITAL GROUP INC p 349
98 James St Ste 400, Edison NJ 08820
Tel (732) 321-7000 SIC 8062 8069

HACKENSACK MERIDIAN HEALTH INC p 652
343 Thornall St, Edison NJ 08837
Tel (732) 751-7500 SIC 8062

JFK HEALTH SYSTEM INC p 785
80 James St, Edison NJ 08820
Tel (732) 321-7000 SIC 8062

TRINITAS REGIONAL MEDICAL CENTER p 1481
225 Williamson St, Elizabeth NJ 07202
Tel (908) 351-0714 SIC 8062

ENGLEWOOD HOSPITAL AND MEDICAL CENTER FOUNDATION INC p 499
350 Engle St, Englewood NJ 07631
Tel (201) 894-3000 SIC 8062 8011

HUNTERDON MEDICAL CENTER (INC) p 719
2100 Wescott Dr, Flemington NJ 08822
Tel (908) 788-6100 SIC 8062

CENTRASTATE MEDICAL CENTER INC p 281
901 W Main St, Freehold NJ 07728
Tel (732) 431-2000 SIC 8062

HACKENSACK UNIVERSITY HEALTH NETWORK INC p 652
30 Prospect Ave, Hackensack NJ 07601
Tel (551) 996-2000 SIC 8062

HACKENSACK UNIVERSITY MEDICAL CENTER p 652
30 Prospect Ave Ste 1, Hackensack NJ 07601
Tel (201) 996-2000 SIC 8062

HACKETTSTOWN COMMUNITY HOSPITAL (INC) p 652
651 Willow Grove St Ste A, Hackettstown NJ 07840
Tel (908) 852-5100 SIC 8062

ROBERT WOOD JOHNSON UNIVERSITY HOSPITAL AT HAMILTON p 1242
1 Hamilton Health Pl # 2, Hamilton NJ 08690
Tel (609) 586-7900 SIC 8062

HOBOKEN UNIVERSITY MEDICAL CENTER p 699
308 Willow Ave, Hoboken NJ 07030
Tel (201) 418-1000 SIC 8062

HUDSON HEALTHCARE INC p 716
308 Willow Ave, Hoboken NJ 07030
Tel (201) 418-1000 SIC 8062

HUMC OPCO LLC p 718
308 Willow Ave, Hoboken NJ 07030
Tel (201) 418-1000 SIC 8062

BAYSHORE COMMUNITY HEALTH SERVICES INC p 162
727 N Beers St, Holmdel NJ 07733
Tel (732) 739-5900 SIC 8062 8741

BAYSHORE COMMUNITY HOSPITAL p 162
727 N Beers St, Holmdel NJ 07733
Tel (732) 739-5900 SIC 8062

CAREPOINT HEALTH MANAGEMENT ASSOCIATES LLC p 255
10 Exchange Pl Fl 15, Jersey City NJ 07302
Tel (201) 795-8554 SIC 8062

CHRIST HOSPITAL p 302
176 Palisade Ave, Jersey City NJ 07306
Tel (201) 795-8200 SIC 8062

HUDSON HOSPITAL OPCO LLC p 716
176 Palisade Ave, Jersey City NJ 07306
Tel (201) 795-8200 SIC 8062

JERSEY CITY MEDICAL CENTER INC p 783
355 Grand St, Jersey City NJ 07302
Tel (201) 915-2000 SIC 8062

LIBERTY HEALTHCARE SYSTEM INC p 862
355 Grand St, Jersey City NJ 07302
Tel (318) 251-9458 SIC 8062

KIMBALL MEDICAL CENTER INC p 818
600 River Ave, Lakewood NJ 08701
Tel (732) 363-1900 SIC 8062

ST BARNABAS MEDICAL CTR p 1365
94 Old Short Hills Rd # 1, Livingston NJ 07039
Tel (973) 322-5000 SIC 8062

MONMOUTH MEDICAL CENTER INC p 984
300 2nd Ave, Long Branch NJ 07740
Tel (732) 222-5200 SIC 8062

SOUTHERN OCEAN COUNTY HEALTH SYSTEM INC p 1350
1140 Route 72 W, Manahawkin NJ 08050
Tel (609) 597-6011 SIC 8062

VIRTUA HEALTH INC p 1560
303 Lippincott Dr, Marlton NJ 08053
Tel (888) 847-8823 SIC 8062 8399

HACKENSACKUMC MOUNTAINSIDE p 652
1 Bay Ave, Montclair NJ 07042
Tel (973) 429-6000 SIC 8062

AHS HOSPITAL CORP p 37
465 South St, Morristown NJ 07960
Tel (973) 660-3100 SIC 8062 8249

ATLANTIC HEALTH SYSTEM INC p 126
475 South St, Morristown NJ 07960
Tel (973) 660-3100 SIC 8249 8062

VIRTUA MEMORIAL HOSPITAL BURLINGTON COUNTY INC p 1560
175 Madison Ave, Mount Holly NJ 08060
Tel (609) 267-0700 SIC 8062

MERIDIAN HOSPITALS CORP p 948
1945 Route 33, Neptune NJ 07753
Tel (732) 751-7500 SIC 8062

ROBERT WOOD JOHNSON UNIVERSITY HOSPITAL p 1241
1 Robert Wood Johnson Pl, New Brunswick NJ 08901
Tel (732) 828-3000 SIC 8062

SAINT PETERS UNIVERSITY HOSPITAL INC p 1270
254 Easton Ave, New Brunswick NJ 08901
Tel (732) 745-8600 SIC 8062

NEWARK BETH ISRAEL MEDICAL CENTER INC p 1036
201 Lyons Ave, Newark NJ 07112
Tel (973) 926-7000 SIC 8062

PRIME HEALTHCARE SERVICES - ST MICHAELS LLC p 1175
111 Central Ave, Newark NJ 07102
Tel (973) 877-5000 SIC 8062

SAINT MICHAELS MEDICAL CENTER INC p 1270
111 Center Ter, Newark NJ 07114
Tel (973) 877-5000 SIC 8062

UNIVERSITY HOSPITAL p 1519
150 Bergen St Ste 1, Newark NJ 07103
Tel (973) 972-4300 SIC 8062

NEWTON MEMORIAL HOSPITAL INC p 1039
175 High St, Newton NJ 07860
Tel (973) 383-2121 SIC 8062

PALISADES MEDICAL CENTER INC p 1108
7600 River Rd, North Bergen NJ 07047
Tel (201) 854-5000 SIC 8062

BERGEN REGIONAL MEDICAL CENTER LP p 174
230 E Ridgewood Ave, Paramus NJ 07652
Tel (201) 967-4000 SIC 8062

PRIME HEALTHCARE SERVICES - ST MARYS PASSAIC LLC p 1175
350 Boulevard, Passaic NJ 07055
Tel (973) 365-4300 SIC 8062

ST JOSEPHS HEALTHCARE SYSTEM INC p 1368
703 Main St, Paterson NJ 07503
Tel (973) 754-4500 SIC 8062

ST JOSEPHS HOSPITAL AND MEDICAL CENTER p 1368
703 Main St, Paterson NJ 07503
Tel (973) 754-2000 SIC 8062

RARITAN BAY MEDICAL CENTER A NEW JERSEY NONPROFIT CORP p 1209
530 New Brunswick Ave, Perth Amboy NJ 08861
Tel (732) 442-3700 SIC 8062

WARREN ST LUKES HOSPITAL INC p 1577
185 Roseberry St, Phillipsburg NJ 08865
Tel (908) 859-6700 SIC 8062 8093

MUHLENBERG REGIONAL MEDICAL CENTER INC p 999
Park Ave & Randolph Rd, Plainfield NJ 07060
Tel (908) 668-2000 SIC 8062

MEDICAL CENTER AT PRINCETON NEW JERSEY p 936
1 Plainsboro Rd, Plainsboro NJ 08536
Tel (609) 497-4000 SIC 8062

ATLANTICARE REGIONAL MEDICAL CENTER p 127
65 W Jimmie Leeds Rd, Pomona NJ 08240
Tel (609) 652-1000 SIC 8062

CHILTON HOSPITAL p 300
97 W Parkway, Pompton Plains NJ 07444
Tel (973) 831-5000 SIC 8062

ROBERT WOOD JOHNSON UNIVERSITY HOSPITAL AT RAHWAY p 1242
865 Stone St, Rahway NJ 07065
Tel (732) 381-4200 SIC 8062

VALLEY HEALTH SYSTEM INC p 1540
223 N Van Dien Ave, Ridgewood NJ 07450
Tel (201) 447-8000 SIC 8062 8099

VALLEY HOSPITAL INC p 1541
223 N Van Dien Ave, Ridgewood NJ 07450
Tel (201) 447-8000 SIC 8062

MHA LLC p 958
55 Meadowlands Pkwy, Secaucus NJ 07094
Tel (201) 392-3200 SIC 8062

SHORE MEMORIAL HEALTH FOUNDATION INC p 1318
100 Medical Center Way, Somers Point NJ 08244
Tel (609) 653-3500 SIC 8062

SHORE MEMORIAL HOSPITAL p 1318
100 Medical Center Way, Somers Point NJ 08244
Tel (609) 653-3500 SIC 8062

SOMERSET MEDICAL CENTER p 1339
110 Rehill Ave, Somerville NJ 08876
Tel (908) 685-2200 SIC 8062

UNION HOSPITAL p 1504
99 Beauvoir Ave, Summit NJ 07901
Tel (973) 740-0607 SIC 8062

HOLY NAME MEDICAL CENTER INC p 702
718 Teaneck Rd, Teaneck NJ 07666
Tel (201) 833-3000 SIC 8062

COMMUNITY MEDICAL CENTER INC p 349
99 Route 37 W, Toms River NJ 08755
Tel (732) 557-8000 SIC 8062

CAPITAL HEALTH SYSTEM INC p 249
750 Brunswick Ave, Trenton NJ 08638
Tel (609) 394-6000 SIC 8062

ST FRANCIS MEDICAL CENTER p 1366
601 Hamilton Ave, Trenton NJ 08629
Tel (609) 599-5000 SIC 8062

INSPIRA HEALTH NETWORK INC p 746
2950 College Dr Ste 2d, Vineland NJ 08360
Tel (856) 641-8680 SIC 8741 8062

KENNEDY HEALTH SYSTEM INC p 811
1099 White Horse Rd, Voorhees NJ 08043
Tel (856) 566-5200 SIC 8062

KENNEDY MEMORIAL HOSPITAL UNIVERSITY MEDICAL CENTER INC p 811
1099 White Horse Rd Fl 3, Voorhees NJ 08043
Tel (856) 566-2000 SIC 8062

ST JOSEPHS WAYNE HOSPITAL INC p 1369
224 Hamburg Tpke, Wayne NJ 07470
Tel (973) 942-6900 SIC 8062

■ **KESSLER REHABILITATION CORP** p 814
1199 Pleasant Valley Way, West Orange NJ 07052
Tel (973) 731-3600 SIC 8062

SAINT BARNABAS CORP p 1268
95 Old Short Hills Rd, West Orange NJ 07052
Tel (973) 322-5000 SIC 8062 8082

LOURDES MEDICAL CENTER OF BURLINGTON COUNTY p 881
218 Sunset Rd, Willingboro NJ 08046
Tel (609) 835-2900 SIC 8062

LOURDES MEDICAL CENTER OF BURLINGTON COUNTY A NEW JERSEY NONPROFIT CORP p 881
218 Sunset Rd, Willingboro NJ 08046
Tel (609) 835-2900 SIC 8062

INSPIRA MEDICAL CENTERS INC p 746
509 N Broad St, Woodbury NJ 08096
Tel (856) 845-0100 SIC 8062

UNDERWOOD MEMORIAL HOSPITAL INC p 1502
509 N Broad St, Woodbury NJ 08096
Tel (856) 845-0100 SIC 8062

OTERO COUNTY HOSPITAL ASSOCIATION INC p 1097
2669 Scenic Dr, Alamogordo NM 88310
Tel (575) 439-6100 SIC 8062

LOVELACE HEALTH SYSTEM INC p 881
4101 Indian School Rd Ne # 110, Albuquerque NM 87110
Tel (800) 808-7363 SIC 8062

PRESBYTERIAN HEALTHCARE SERVICES p 1171
9521 San Mateo Blvd Ne, Albuquerque NM 87113
Tel (505) 923-5700 SIC 8062

■ **CARLSBAD MEDICAL CENTER LLC** p 257
2430 W Pierce St, Carlsbad NM 88220
Tel (575) 887-4100 SIC 8062

SAN JUAN REGIONAL MEDICAL CENTER INC p 1277
801 W Maple St, Farmington NM 87401
Tel (505) 609-2000 SIC 8062

■ **LAS CRUCES MEDICAL CENTER LLC** p 845
4311 E Lohman Ave, Las Cruces NM 88011
Tel (575) 556-7600 SIC 8062

MEMORIAL MEDICAL CENTER INC p 942
2450 S Telshor Blvd, Las Cruces NM 88011
Tel (575) 522-8641 SIC 8062

■ **PHC-LAS CRUCES INC** p 1141
2450 S Telshor Blvd, Las Cruces NM 88011
Tel (575) 522-8641 SIC 8062

■ **ROSWELL HOSPITAL CORP** p 1252
405 W Country Club Rd, Roswell NM 88201
Tel (575) 622-8170 SIC 8062

ST VINCENT HOSPITAL p 1373
455 Saint Michaels Dr, Santa Fe NM 87505
Tel (505) 983-3361 SIC 8062

GILA REGIONAL MEDICAL CENTER p 611
1313 E 32nd St, Silver City NM 88061
Tel (575) 538-4000 SIC 8093 8062

ALBANY MEDICAL CENTER p 45
43 New Scotland Ave, Albany NY 12208
Tel (518) 262-3125 SIC 8062

ALBANY MEDICAL CENTER HOSPITAL p 45
43 New Scotland Ave, Albany NY 12208
Tel (518) 262-3125 SIC 8062 8249

MEMORIAL HOSPITAL p 942
600 Northern Blvd, Albany NY 12204
Tel (518) 471-3221 SIC 8062

ST PETERS HEALTH PARTNERS p 1372
315 S Manning Blvd, Albany NY 12208
Tel (518) 525-1550 SIC 8062

ST PETERS HEALTH PARTNERS p 1372
315 S Manning Blvd, Albany NY 12208
Tel (518) 525-1111 SIC 8062

ST MARYS HEALTHCARE p 1371
427 Guy Park Ave Ste 1, Amsterdam NY 12010
Tel (518) 842-1900 SIC 8062

AUBURN COMMUNITY HOSPITAL p 130
17 Lansing St, Auburn NY 13021
Tel (315) 255-7011 SIC 8062 8051

UNITED MEMORIAL MEDICAL CENTER p 1510
127 North St, Batavia NY 14020
Tel (585) 343-6030 SIC 8062 8049 8011

SOUTHSIDE HOSPITAL p 1351
301 E Main St, Bay Shore NY 11706
Tel (631) 968-3000 SIC 8062

BROOKHAVEN MEMORIAL HOSPITAL p 217
656 Bourdois Ave, Bellport NY 11713
Tel (631) 654-7770 SIC 8062

EPISCOPAL HEALTH SERVICES INC p 505
700 Hicksville Rd Ste 210, Bethpage NY 11714
Tel (516) 349-6100 SIC 8062 8051

WSNCHS NORTH INC p 1628
4295 Hempstead Tpke, Bethpage NY 11714
Tel (516) 579-6000 SIC 8062

LOURDES HOSPITAL p 881
169 Riverside Dr, Binghamton NY 13905
Tel (607) 798-5111 SIC 8062

OUR LADY OF LOURDES MEMORIAL HOSPITAL INC p 1098
169 Riverside Dr, Binghamton NY 13905
Tel (607) 798-5111 SIC 8062

UNITED HEALTH SERVICES HOSPITAL INC p 1509
10-42 Mitchell Ave, Binghamton NY 13903
Tel (607) 762-2200 SIC 8062

UNITED HEALTH SERVICES INC p 1509
10-42 Mitchell Ave, Binghamton NY 13903
Tel (607) 762-3024 SIC 8062 8051

BRONX LEBANON HOSPITAL CENTER (INC) p 217
1276 Fulton Ave, Bronx NY 10456
Tel (718) 590-1800 SIC 8062

LINCOLN MEDICAL AND MENTAL HEALTH CENTER p 867
234 E 149th St, Bronx NY 10451
Tel (718) 579-5000 SIC 8062

MONTEFIORE MEDICAL CENTER p 986
111 E 210th St, Bronx NY 10467
Tel (718) 920-4321 SIC 8062

ST BARNABAS COMMUNITY ENTERPRISES p 1365
4422 3rd Ave, Bronx NY 10457
Tel (718) 960-6100 SIC 8062

ST BARNABAS HOSPITAL p 1365
4422 3rd Ave, Bronx NY 10457
Tel (718) 960-9000 *SIC* 8062

LAWRENCE HOSPITAL CENTER p 848
55 Palmer Ave, Bronxville NY 10708
Tel (914) 787-1000 *SIC* 8062

BROOKDALE HOSPITAL CENTER HOUSING CO INC p 217
1 Brookdale Plz, Brooklyn NY 11212
Tel (718) 240-5000 *SIC* 8062

BROOKDALE HOSPITAL MEDICAL CENTER p 217
1 Brookdale Plz, Brooklyn NY 11212
Tel (718) 240-5000 *SIC* 8011 8062

BROOKLYN HOSPITAL CENTER p 218
121 Dekalb Ave, Brooklyn NY 11201
Tel (718) 250-8000 *SIC* 8062

INTERFAITH MEDICAL CENTER p 752
1545 Atlantic Ave, Brooklyn NY 11213
Tel (718) 613-4000 *SIC* 8062

KINGSBROOK JEWISH MEDICAL CENTER INC p 820
585 Schenectady Ave Ste 2, Brooklyn NY 11203
Tel (718) 604-5000 *SIC* 8062

L I C H CORP p 834
339 Hicks St, Brooklyn NY 11201
Tel (718) 780-1000 *SIC* 8062 8092 5912

LONG ISLAND COLLEGE HOSPITAL INC p 876
450 Clarkson Ave, Brooklyn NY 11203
Tel (718) 780-1000 *SIC* 8062 9431

MAIMONIDES MEDICAL CENTER p 897
4802 10th Ave, Brooklyn NY 11219
Tel (718) 581-0598 *SIC* 8062

NEW YORK COMMUNITY HOSPITAL p 1035
2525 Kings Hwy, Brooklyn NY 11229
Tel (718) 692-5300 *SIC* 8062

NEW YORK METHODIST HOSPITAL p 1035
506 6th St, Brooklyn NY 11215
Tel (718) 780-3000 *SIC* 8062

NYU LUTHERAN MEDICAL CENTER p 1069
150 55th St, Brooklyn NY 11220
Tel (718) 630-7000 *SIC* 8062 8621

VICTORY MEMORIAL HOSPITAL p 1556
699 92nd St, Brooklyn NY 11228
Tel (718) 567-1234 *SIC* 8062 8051

WOODHULL MEDICAL & MENTAL HEALTH CENTER AUXILIARY INC p 1623
760 Broadway Rm 3cc27, Brooklyn NY 11206
Tel (718) 963-8467 *SIC* 8062

WYCKOFF HEIGHTS MEDICAL CENTER p 1629
374 Stockholm St, Brooklyn NY 11237
Tel (718) 963-7272 *SIC* 8062

CATHOLIC HEALTH SYSTEM INC p 266
144 Genesee St Fl 1, Buffalo NY 14203
Tel (716) 862-2400
SIC 8741 8062 5999 8051

ERIE COUNTY MEDICAL CENTER CORP p 508
462 Grider St, Buffalo NY 14215
Tel (716) 898-3000 *SIC* 8062

KALEIDA HEALTH p 801
726 Exchange St, Buffalo NY 14210
Tel (716) 859-8000 *SIC* 8062

MERCY HOSPITAL OF BUFFALO p 947
565 Abbott Rd, Buffalo NY 14220
Tel (716) 826-7000 *SIC* 8062

MILLARD FILLMORE HOSPITALS p 969
100 High St D1-588, Buffalo NY 14203
Tel (716) 859-5960 *SIC* 8062

SISTERS OF CHARITY HOSPITAL OF BUFFALO NEW YORK p 1327
2157 Main St, Buffalo NY 14214
Tel (716) 862-1000 *SIC* 8062

FREDERICK FERRIS THOMPSON HOSPITAL p 576
350 Parrish St, Canandaigua NY 14424
Tel (585) 396-6000 *SIC* 8062 8011

PUTNAM HOSPITAL CENTER FOUNDATION INC p 1193
670 Stoneleigh Ave, Carmel NY 10512
Tel (845) 279-5711 *SIC* 8062

PUTNAM HOSPITAL CENTER HOME HEALTH AGENCY PRIVATE DUTY CARE SERVICE INC p 1193
670 Stoneleigh Ave, Carmel NY 10512
Tel (845) 279-5711 *SIC* 8062

MARY IMOGENE BASSETT HOSPITAL p 914
1 Atwell Rd, Cooperstown NY 13326
Tel (607) 547-3456 *SIC* 8011 8062 5999

CORNING HOSPITAL p 371
1 Guthrie Dr, Corning NY 14830
Tel (607) 937-7200 *SIC* 8062

HUDSON VALLEY HOSPITAL CENTER p 717
1980 Crompond Rd, Cortlandt Manor NY 10567
Tel (914) 737-9000 *SIC* 8062

ST JOHNS RIVERSIDE HOSPITAL DOBBS FERRY PAVILION p 1368
128 Ashford Ave, Dobbs Ferry NY 10522
Tel (914) 693-0700 *SIC* 8062

NASSAU HEALTH CARE CORP p 1008
2201 Hempstead Tpke, East Meadow NY 11554
Tel (516) 572-0123 *SIC* 8062

BROOKHAVEN MEMORIAL HOSPITAL MEDICAL CENTER INC p 217
101 Hospital Rd, East Patchogue NY 11772
Tel (631) 654-7100 *SIC* 8062

ELMHURST HOSPITAL CENTER p 489
7901 Broadway, Elmhurst NY 11373
Tel (718) 334-2424 *SIC* 8062

ARNOT HEALTH INC p 112
600 Roe Ave, Elmira NY 14905
Tel (607) 737-4231 *SIC* 8062

ST JOSEPHS HOSPITAL p 1368
555 Saint Josephs Blvd, Elmira NY 14901
Tel (607) 733-6541 *SIC* 8062

ST JOHNS EPISCOPAL HOSPITAL p 1367
327 Beach 19th St, Far Rockaway NY 11691
Tel (718) 869-7000 *SIC* 8062

FLUSHING HOSPITAL AND MEDICAL CENTER p 561
4500 Parsons Blvd, Flushing NY 11355
Tel (718) 670-5000 *SIC* 8062

NEWYORK-PRESBYTERIAN/QUEENS p 1039
5645 Main St, Flushing NY 11355
Tel (718) 670-2000 *SIC* 8062

FOREST HILLS HOSPITAL p 566
10201 66th Rd, Forest Hills NY 11375
Tel (718) 830-4000 *SIC* 8062

GENEVA GENERAL HOSPITAL p 603
196 North St, Geneva NY 14456
Tel (315) 787-4000 *SIC* 8062

GLEN COVE HOSPITAL p 614
101 Saint Andrews Ln, Glen Cove NY 11542
Tel (516) 674-7300 *SIC* 8062

GLENS FALLS HOSPITAL p 615
100 Park St, Glens Falls NY 12801
Tel (518) 926-1000 *SIC* 8011 8062 8221

NATHAN LITTAUER HOSPITAL ASSOCIATION p 1009
99 E State St, Gloversville NY 12078
Tel (518) 725-8621 *SIC* 8051 8062 8011

COLUMBIA MEMORIAL HOSPITAL p 341
71 Prospect Ave, Hudson NY 12534
Tel (518) 828-7601 *SIC* 8062 8051

HUNTINGTON HOSPITAL DOLAN FAMILY HEALTH CENTER INC p 720
270 Park Ave, Huntington NY 11743
Tel (631) 351-2000 *SIC* 8062

TLC HEALTH NETWORK p 1457
845 Route 5 And 20, Irving NY 14081
Tel (716) 951-7000 *SIC* 8062 8069

CAYUGA MEDICAL CENTER AT ITHACA INC p 268
101 Dates Dr, Ithaca NY 14850
Tel (607) 274-4011 *SIC* 8062

JAMAICA HOSPITAL p 776
8900 Van Wyck Expy Fl 4n, Jamaica NY 11418
Tel (718) 206-6290 *SIC* 8062

MEDISYS JAMAICA HOSPITAL & MEDICAL CENTER p 938
8900 Van Wyck Expy, Jamaica NY 11418
Tel (718) 206-6000 *SIC* 8062

OCCUPATIONAL HEALTH SERVICE p 1072
207 Foote Ave, Jamestown NY 14701
Tel (716) 664-8165 *SIC* 8011 8062

WCA GROUP INC p 1585
207 Foote Ave, Jamestown NY 14701
Tel (716) 487-0141 *SIC* 8062 4119

WOMANS CHRISTIAN ASSOCIATION OF JAMESTOWN N Y p 1621
207 Foote Ave, Jamestown NY 14701
Tel (716) 487-0141
SIC 8062 8063 8093 8069

KENMORE MERCY HOSPITAL p 810
2950 Elmwood Ave Fl 6, Kenmore NY 14217
Tel (716) 447-6100 *SIC* 8062 8059 8011

HEALTHALLIANCE HOSPITAL BROADWAY CAMPUS p 676
396 Broadway, Kingston NY 12401
Tel (845) 331-3131 *SIC* 8062

HEALTHALLIANCE HOSPITAL MARYS AVENUE CAMPUS p 676
105 Marys Ave, Kingston NY 12401
Tel (845) 338-2500 *SIC* 8062 8051

HEALTH ALLIANCE INC p 674
741 Grant Ave, Lake Katrine NY 12449
Tel (845) 334-3151 *SIC* 8062

MOUNT ST MARYS HOSPITAL OF NIAGARA FALLS p 994
5300 Military Rd, Lewiston NY 14092
Tel (716) 297-4800 *SIC* 8062

NORTH SHORE UNIVERSITY HOSPITAL p 1053
300 Community Dr, Manhasset NY 11030
Tel (516) 562-0100 *SIC* 8062 8011

ORANGE REGIONAL MEDICAL CENTER p 1092
707 E Main St, Middletown NY 10940
Tel (845) 343-2424 *SIC* 8062

WINTHROP-UNIVERSITY HOSPITAL (INC) p 1617
259 1st St, Mineola NY 11501
Tel (516) 663-0333 *SIC* 8062

NORTHERN WESTCHESTER HOSPITAL ASSOCIATION p 1057
400 E Main St, Mount Kisco NY 10549
Tel (914) 666-1200 *SIC* 8062

LONG ISLAND JEWISH MEDICAL CENTER p 876
27005 76th Ave, New Hyde Park NY 11040
Tel (516) 465-2600 *SIC* 8062 8063 8069

NORTHWELL HEALTH INC p 1059
2000 Marcus Ave, New Hyde Park NY 11042
Tel (516) 321-6000 *SIC* 8082 8062

MONTEFIORE NEW ROCHELLE HOSPITAL p 986
16 Guion Pl, New Rochelle NY 10801
Tel (914) 632-5000 *SIC* 8062

NRHMC INC p 1064
16 Guion Pl, New Rochelle NY 10801
Tel (914) 632-5000 *SIC* 8062 8721

SOUND SHORE HEALTH SYSTEM INC p 1342
16 Guion Pl, New Rochelle NY 10801
Tel (914) 632-5000 *SIC* 8062

SOUND SHORE MEDICAL CENTER OF WESTCHESTER p 1342
16 Guion Pl, New Rochelle NY 10801
Tel (914) 632-5000 *SIC* 8062

BETH ISRAEL MEDICAL CENTER p 177
First Ave 16th St, New York NY 10003
Tel (212) 420-2806 *SIC* 8062 8063

HARLEM HOSPITAL CENTER p 661
506 Malcolm X Blvd, New York NY 10037
Tel (212) 939-1000 *SIC* 8062

HOSPITAL FOR SPECIALTY SURGERY p 709
535 E 70th St Fl 6, New York NY 10021
Tel (212) 606-1469 *SIC* 8011 8062

LENOX HILL HOSPITAL p 856
210 E 64th St Fl 4, New York NY 10065
Tel (212) 472-8872 *SIC* 8062

LHH CORP p 860
100 E 77th St, New York NY 10075
Tel (212) 434-2000 *SIC* 8062

METROPOLITAN HOSPITAL CENTER ASSOCIATION INC p 956
1901 1st Ave, New York NY 10029
Tel (212) 423-6262 *SIC* 8062

MOUNT SINAI HOSPITAL p 994
1 Gustave L Levy Pl Fl 12, New York NY 10029
Tel (212) 241-6500 *SIC* 8062

NEW YORK AND PRESBYTERIAN HOSPITAL p 1034
525 E 68th St, New York NY 10065
Tel (212) 746-5454 *SIC* 8062 8011

NEW YORK CITY HEALTH AND HOSPITALS CORP p 1034
125 Worth St Rm 514, New York NY 10013
Tel (212) 788-3321 *SIC* 8062 8069 8093

NEW YORK DOWNTOWN HOSPITAL p 1035
170 William St, New York NY 10038
Tel (212) 312-5000 *SIC* 8062

NYU HOSPITALS CENTER p 1069
550 1st Ave, New York NY 10016
Tel (212) 263-7300 *SIC* 8062

ROCKEFELLER UNIVERSITY p 1244
1230 York Ave, New York NY 10065
Tel (212) 327-8078 *SIC* 8733 8221 8062

SAINT VINCENTS CATHOLIC MEDICAL CENTERS OF NEW YORK p 1271
5 Penn Plz Ste 900, New York NY 10001
Tel (212) 356-4792 *SIC* 8062

ST LUKES-ROOSEVELT HOSPITAL CENTER p 1370
1111 Amsterdam Ave, New York NY 10025
Tel (212) 523-4000 *SIC* 8062

TRUSTEES OF COLUMBIA UNIVERSITY IN CITY OF NEW YORK p 1487
116th And Bdwy Way, New York NY 10027
Tel (212) 854-9970 *SIC* 8221 8062

TRUSTEES OF COLUMBIA UNIVERSITY IN CITY OF NEW YORK p 1487
630 W 168th St Fl 4, New York NY 10032
Tel (212) 305-2862 *SIC* 8221 8733 8062

NEWARK-WAYNE COMMUNITY HOSPITAL p 1037
1200 Driving Park Ave, Newark NY 14513
Tel (315) 332-2022 *SIC* 8062

WAYNE NEWARK COMMUNITY HOSPITAL p 1584
1250 Driving Park Ave, Newark NY 14513
Tel (315) 332-2244 *SIC* 8062

ST LUKES CORNWALL HOSPITAL p 1370
70 Dubois St, Newburgh NY 12550
Tel (845) 561-4400 *SIC* 8062

NIAGARA FALLS MEMORIAL MEDICAL CENTER INC p 1042
621 10th St, Niagara Falls NY 14301
Tel (716) 278-4000 *SIC* 8062

NYACK HOSPITAL FOUNDATION INC p 1068
160 N Midland Ave, Nyack NY 10960
Tel (845) 348-2000 *SIC* 8062 8011 8082

SOUTH NASSAU COMMUNITIES HOSPITAL INC p 1344
1 Healthy Way, Oceanside NY 11572
Tel (516) 632-3000 *SIC* 8062

OLEAN GENERAL HOSPITAL p 1082
515 Main St, Olean NY 14760
Tel (716) 373-2600 *SIC* 8062

UPPER ALLEGHENY HEALTH SYSTEM INC p 1529
130 S Union St Ste 300, Olean NY 14760
Tel (716) 375-6975 *SIC* 8062

ONEIDA HEALTH CARE CENTER p 1087
321 Genesee St, Oneida NY 13421
Tel (315) 361-2342 *SIC* 8062

ONEIDA HEALTH SYSTEMS INC p 1087
321 Genesee St, Oneida NY 13421
Tel (315) 363-6000 *SIC* 8062 8051

OSWEGO HOSPITAL INC p 1097
110 W 6th St, Oswego NY 13126
Tel (315) 349-5511 *SIC* 8062 8063

PLAINVIEW HOSPITAL p 1154
888 Old Country Rd, Plainview NY 11803
Tel (516) 719-2200 *SIC* 8062

CHAMPLAIN VALLEY PHYSICIANS HOSPITAL p 287
75 Beekman St, Plattsburgh NY 12901
Tel (518) 561-2000 *SIC* 8062

COMMUNITY PROVIDERS INC p 350
75 Beekman St, Plattsburgh NY 12901
Tel (518) 561-2000 *SIC* 8062 8741 6512

UNIVERSITY OF VERMONT CHAMPLAIN VALLEY PHYSICIANS HOSPITAL p 1526
75 Beekman St, Plattsburgh NY 12901
Tel (518) 561-2000 *SIC* 8062 8051

JOHN T MATHER MEMORIAL HOSPITAL OF PORT JEFFERSON NEW YORK INC p 789
75 N Country Rd, Port Jefferson NY 11777
Tel (631) 476-2738 *SIC* 8062

ST CHARLES HOSPITAL AND REHABILITATION CENTER p 1365
200 Belle Terre Rd, Port Jefferson NY 11777
Tel (631) 474-6000 *SIC* 8062 8011

BON SECOURS COMMUNITY HOSPITAL p 199
160 E Main St, Port Jervis NY 12771
Tel (845) 858-7000 *SIC* 8062

CANTON-POTSDAM HOSPITAL p 248
50 Leroy St, Potsdam NY 13676
Tel (315) 265-3300 *SIC* 8062

HASTINGS HEALTH SYSTEMS INC p 667
241 North Rd, Poughkeepsie NY 12601
Tel (845) 471-2000 *SIC* 8741 8062

MIDHUDSON REGIONAL HOSPITAL OF WESTCHESTER MEDICAL CENTER p 965
241 North Rd, Poughkeepsie NY 12601
Tel (845) 483-5000 *SIC* 8062 8322

ST FRANCIS HOSPITAL POUGHKEEPSIE NEW YORK p 1366
241 North Rd, Poughkeepsie NY 12601
Tel (845) 483-5000
SIC 8062 8069 8011 8351

VASSAR BROTHERS HOSPITAL p 1545
45 Reade Pl, Poughkeepsie NY 12601
Tel (845) 454-8500 *SIC* 8062

VASSER BROTHERS MEDICAL CENTER p 1545
45 Reade Pl, Poughkeepsie NY 12601
Tel (845) 454-8500 *SIC* 8062

NORTHERN DUTCHESS HOSPITAL p 1056
6511 Spring Brook Ave, Rhinebeck NY 12572
Tel (845) 876-3001 *SIC* 8062

CENTRAL SUFFOLK HOSPITAL p 280
1300 Roanoke Ave, Riverhead NY 11901
Tel (631) 548-6000 *SIC* 8062

HIGHLAND HOSPITAL OF ROCHESTER p 691
1000 South Ave, Rochester NY 14620
Tel (585) 473-2200 *SIC* 8062

ROCHESTER GENERAL HOSPITAL INC p 1243
1425 Portland Ave, Rochester NY 14621
Tel (585) 922-4101 *SIC* 8062

RU SYSTEM INC p 1256
100 Kings Hwy S, Rochester NY 14617
Tel (585) 922-1053 *SIC* 8062

UNITY HEALTH SYSTEM p 1515
89 Genesee St, Rochester NY 14611
Tel (585) 723-7000 *SIC* 8062

UNITY HOSPITAL OF ROCHESTER p 1515
89 Genesee St, Rochester NY 14611
Tel (585) 723-7000 *SIC* 8062

CATHOLIC HEALTH SYSTEM OF LONG ISLAND INC p 266
992 N Village Ave, Rockville Centre NY 11570
Tel (516) 705-3700 *SIC* 8062

MERCY MEDICAL CENTER p 947
1000 N Village Ave, Rockville Centre NY 11570
Tel (516) 562-6907 *SIC* 8062

ROME MEMORIAL HOSPITAL INC p 1249
1500 N James St, Rome NY 13440
Tel (315) 338-7000 *SIC* 8062 8051

ADIRONDACK MEDICAL CENTER p 23
2233 State Route 86, Saranac Lake NY 12983
Tel (518) 891-4141 *SIC* 8062

SARATOGA CARE INC p 1282
211 Church St Ste 1, Saratoga Springs NY 12866
Tel (518) 587-3222 *SIC* 8062 8741

SARATOGA HOSPITAL p 1282
211 Church St, Saratoga Springs NY 12866
Tel (518) 587-3222 *SIC* 8062 8051

ELLIS HOSPITAL p 488
1101 Nott St, Schenectady NY 12308
Tel (518) 243-4000 *SIC* 8062 8051

PHELPS MEMORIAL HOSPITAL ASSOCIATION p 1141
701 N Broadway, Sleepy Hollow NY 10591
Tel (914) 366-3000 *SIC* 8062

ST CATHERINE OF SIENA MEDICAL CENTER p 1365
50 Route 25a, Smithtown NY 11787
Tel (631) 862-3000 *SIC* 8062

SOUTHAMPTON HOSPITAL ASSOCIATION p 1345
240 Meeting House Ln, Southampton NY 11968
Tel (631) 726-8200 *SIC* 8062

RICHMOND MEDICAL CENTER p 1233
355 Bard Ave, Staten Island NY 10310
Tel (718) 818-1234 *SIC* 8062

STATEN ISLAND UNIVERSITY HOSPITAL p 1383
475 Seaview Ave, Staten Island NY 10305
Tel (718) 226-9000 *SIC* 8062

GOOD SAMARITAN REGIONAL MEDICAL CENTER p 623
255 Lafayette Ave, Suffern NY 10901
Tel (845) 368-5000 *SIC* 8062

CROUSE HEALTH HOSPITAL INC p 394
736 Irving Ave, Syracuse NY 13210
Tel (315) 470-7111 *SIC* 8062

CROUSE HEALTH SYSTEM INC p 394
736 Irving Ave, Syracuse NY 13210
Tel (315) 470-7521 *SIC* 8062

CROUSE HOSPITAL AUXILIARY INC p 394
736 Irving Ave, Syracuse NY 13210
Tel (315) 470-7111 *SIC* 8062

ST JOSEPHS HOSPITAL HEALTH CENTER p 1369
301 Prospect Ave, Syracuse NY 13203
Tel (315) 448-5113 *SIC* 8062

STATE UNIVERSITY OF NEW YORK HEALTH SCIENCE CENTER AT SYRACUSE p 1383
750 E Adams St, Syracuse NY 13210
Tel (315) 464-5540 *SIC* 8011 8062

MONTEFIORE HEALTH SYSTEM INC p 986
555 S Broadway, Tarrytown NY 10591
Tel (718) 920-8239 *SIC* 8062

SAMARITAN HOSPITAL OF TROY NEW YORK p 1274
2215 Burdett Ave, Troy NY 12180
Tel (518) 271-3300 *SIC* 8062

SETON HEALTH SYSTEM INC p 1308
1300 Massachusetts Ave, Troy NY 12180
Tel (518) 268-5000 *SIC* 8062 8011

FAXTON-ST LUKES HEALTHCARE p 532
1656 Champlin Ave, Utica NY 13502
Tel (315) 624-6000 *SIC* 8062

MOHAWK VALLEY HEALTH SYSTEM p 982
1656 Champlin Ave, Utica NY 13502
Tel (315) 624-5116 *SIC* 8062

ST ELIZABETH MEDICAL CENTER p 1366
2209 Genesee St, Utica NY 13501
Tel (315) 798-8100 *SIC* 8062

WESTCHESTER COUNTY HEALTH CARE CORP p 1596
100 Woods Rd, Valhalla NY 10595
Tel (914) 493-7000 *SIC* 8062

FRANKLIN HOSPITAL p 575
900 Franklin Ave, Valley Stream NY 11580
Tel (516) 256-6000 *SIC* 8062 8051

SAMARITAN MEDICAL CENTER p 1274
830 Washington St, Watertown NY 13601
Tel (315) 785-4000 *SIC* 8062 5047

GOOD SAMARITAN HOSPITAL MEDICAL CENTER p 623
1000 Montauk Hwy, West Islip NY 11795
Tel (631) 376-3000 *SIC* 8062 8051 8092

WHITE PLAINS HOSPITAL MEDICAL CENTER p 1606
41 E Post Rd, White Plains NY 10601
Tel (914) 681-0600 *SIC* 8062

RIVERSIDE HEALTH CARE SYSTEM INC p 1238
967 N Broadway, Yonkers NY 10701
Tel (914) 964-4444 *SIC* 8062

ST JOSEPHS HOSPITAL YONKERS p 1369
127 S Broadway, Yonkers NY 10701
Tel (914) 378-7000 *SIC* 8062 8011

STANLY REGIONAL MEDICAL CENTER p 1377
301 Yadkin St, Albemarle NC 28001
Tel (704) 982-3888 *SIC* 8062

RANDOLPH HOSPITAL INC p 1207
364 White Oak St, Asheboro NC 27203
Tel (336) 625-5151 *SIC* 8062

MISSION HEALTH SYSTEM INC p 975
509 Biltm Ave Aka Hwy 25, Asheville NC 28801
Tel (828) 213-1111 *SIC* 8062

MISSION HEALTH SYSTEM INC p 975
400 Ridgefield Ct, Asheville NC 28806
Tel (828) 257-7004 *SIC* 8062

MISSION HOSPITAL INC p 975
509 Biltmore Ave, Asheville NC 28801
Tel (828) 213-1111 *SIC* 8062

APPALACHIAN REGIONAL HEALTHCARE SYSTEM INC p 98
336 Deerfield Rd, Boone NC 28607
Tel (828) 262-4100 *SIC* 8062

WATAUGA MEDICAL CENTER INC p 1581
336 Deerfield Rd, Boone NC 28607
Tel (828) 262-4100 *SIC* 8062 8011

ALAMANCE REGIONAL MEDICAL CENTER INC p 44
1240 Huffman Mill Rd, Burlington NC 27215
Tel (336) 538-7000 *SIC* 8062

CENTRAL REGIONAL HOSPITAL p 280
300 Veazey Dr, Butner NC 27509
Tel (919) 575-7211 *SIC* 8062 9431

UNIVERSITY OF NORTH CAROLINA HOSPITALS p 1524
101 Manning Dr Bldg 2, Chapel Hill NC 27514
Tel (919) 966-5111 *SIC* 8062

CAROLINAS MEDICAL CENTER AT HOME LLC p 259
1000 Blythe Blvd, Charlotte NC 28203
Tel (704) 355-3165 *SIC* 8062

CHARLOTTE-MECKLENBURG HOSPITAL AUTHORITY p 290
1000 Blythe Blvd, Charlotte NC 28203
Tel (704) 355-2000
SIC 8062 8069 8063 8051 8011

MEDCATH CORP p 935
10800 Sikes Pl Ste 200, Charlotte NC 28277
Tel (704) 815-7700 *SIC* 8099 8062

PRESBYTERIAN HEALTH SERVICES CORP p 1171
200 Hawthorne Ln, Charlotte NC 28204
Tel (704) 384-4000 *SIC* 8062

PRESBYTERIAN HOSPITAL p 1171
200 Hawthorne Ln, Charlotte NC 28204
Tel (704) 384-4000 *SIC* 8062

HAYWOOD REGIONAL MEDICAL CENTER p 671
262 Leroy George Dr, Clyde NC 28721
Tel (828) 456-7311 *SIC* 8062

CAROLINAS MEDICAL CENTER NORTHEAST p 259
920 Church St N, Concord NC 28025
Tel (704) 783-3000 *SIC* 8062 8221

HARNETT HEALTH SYSTEM INC p 662
800 Tilghman Dr, Dunn NC 28334
Tel (910) 892-1000 *SIC* 8062

DUKE UNIVERSITY HEALTH SYSTEM INC p 460
2301 Erwin Rd, Durham NC 27705
Tel (919) 684-8111 *SIC* 8062

DURHAM COUNTY HOSPITAL CORP p 462
3643 N Roxboro St, Durham NC 27704
Tel (919) 470-4000 *SIC* 8062

ALBEMARLE HOSPITAL AUTHORITY p 46
1144 N Road St, Elizabeth City NC 27909
Tel (252) 338-0101 *SIC* 8062

HUGH CHATHAM MEMORIAL HOSPITAL INC p 717
180 Parkwood Dr, Elkin NC 28621
Tel (336) 835-3722 *SIC* 8062 8051 8361

CUMBERLAND COUNTY HOSPITAL SYSTEM INC p 400
1638 Owen Dr, Fayetteville NC 28304
Tel (910) 609-4000 *SIC* 8062

CAROMONT REGIONAL MEDICAL CENTER p 260
2525 Court Dr, Gastonia NC 28054
Tel (704) 333-9033 *SIC* 8062

WAYNE MEMORIAL HOSPITAL INC p 1584
2700 Wayne Memorial Dr, Goldsboro NC 27534
Tel (919) 736-1110 *SIC* 8062

MOSES H CONE MEMORIAL HOSPITAL p 992
1200 N Elm St, Greensboro NC 27401
Tel (336) 832-7000 *SIC* 8062

MOSES H CONE MEMORIAL HOSPITAL OPERATING CORP p 992
1200 N Elm St, Greensboro NC 27401
Tel (336) 832-7000 *SIC* 8062

WESLEY LONG COMMUNITY HEALTH SERVICES INC p 1593
501 N Elam Ave, Greensboro NC 27403
Tel (336) 832-1000 *SIC* 8062

PITT COUNTY MEMORIAL HOSPITAL INC p 1152
2100 Stantonsburg Rd, Greenville NC 27834
Tel (252) 847-4100 *SIC* 8062

UNIVERSITY HEALTH SYSTEMS OF EASTERN CAROLINA INC p 1519
2100 Stantonsburg Rd, Greenville NC 27834
Tel (252) 847-4451 *SIC* 8062

FLETCHER HOSPITAL INC p 555
100 Hospital Dr, Hendersonville NC 28792
Tel (828) 684-8501 *SIC* 8062

HENDERSON COUNTY HOSPITAL CORP p 682
800 N Justice St, Hendersonville NC 28791
Tel (828) 698-7191 *SIC* 8062 8051 8082

CATAWBA VALLEY MEDICAL CENTER INC p 265
810 Fairgrove Church Rd, Hickory NC 28602
Tel (828) 326-3000 *SIC* 8062

■ **FRYE REGIONAL MEDICAL CENTER INC** p 582
420 N Center St Ste 20, Hickory NC 28601
Tel (828) 315-5000 *SIC* 8062

HIGH POINT REGIONAL HEALTH p 691
601 N Elm St, High Point NC 27262
Tel (336) 878-6000 *SIC* 8062

ONSLOW COUNTY HOSPITAL AUTHORITY p 1088
317 Western Blvd, Jacksonville NC 28546
Tel (910) 577-2345 *SIC* 8062

ONSLOW MEMORIAL HOSPITAL INC p 1088
241 New River Dr, Jacksonville NC 28540
Tel (910) 577-4703 *SIC* 8062

LENOIR MEMORIAL HOSPITAL INC p 856
100 Airport Rd, Kinston NC 28501
Tel (252) 522-7000 *SIC* 8062

SCOTLAND HEALTH CARE SYSTEM p 1293
500 Lauchwood Dr, Laurinburg NC 28352
Tel (910) 291-7000 *SIC* 8062 8011 8082

SCOTLAND MEMORIAL HOSPITAL INC p 1293
500 Lauchwood Dr, Laurinburg NC 28352
Tel (910) 291-7680 *SIC* 8062

CALDWELL MEMORIAL HOSPITAL INC p 238
321 Mulberry St Sw, Lenoir NC 28645
Tel (828) 757-5577 *SIC* 8062

DAVIDSON HEALTH CARE INC p 416
250 Hospital Dr, Lexington NC 27292
Tel (336) 248-5161 *SIC* 5912 8062

CAROLINAS MEDICAL CENTER-LINCOLN p 259
433 Mcalister Rd, Lincolnton NC 28092
Tel (980) 212-2000 *SIC* 8062

SOUTHEASTERN REGIONAL MEDICAL CENTER p 1347
300 W 27th St, Lumberton NC 28358
Tel (910) 671-5000 *SIC* 8062

PRESBYTERIAN MEDICAL CARE CORP p 1171
1500 Mtthews Twnship Pkwy, Matthews NC 28105
Tel (704) 384-6500 *SIC* 8062

CAROLINA MEDICAL CENTER UNION p 259
600 Hospital Dr, Monroe NC 28112
Tel (704) 283-3100 *SIC* 8062

UNION MEMORIAL REGIONAL MEDICAL CENTER INC p 1504
600 Hospital Dr, Monroe NC 28112
Tel (980) 993-3100 *SIC* 8062 8011

LAKE NORMAN REGIONAL MEDICAL CENTRE p 839
171 Fairview Rd, Mooresville NC 28117
Tel (704) 660-4000 *SIC* 8062

■ **MOORESVILLE HOSPITAL MANAGEMENT ASSOCIATES LLC** p 987
170 Medical Park Rd # 208, Mooresville NC 28117
Tel (704) 660-4000 *SIC* 8062

CARTERET COUNTY GENERAL HOSPITAL CORP p 262
3500 Arendell St, Morehead City NC 28557
Tel (252) 808-6000 *SIC* 8093 8062

BLUE RIDGE HEALTHCARE HOSPITALS INC p 192
2201 S Sterling St, Morganton NC 28655
Tel (828) 580-5000 *SIC* 8062

BLUE RIDGE HEALTHCARE SYSTEM INC p 192
2201 S Sterling St, Morganton NC 28655
Tel (828) 580-5580 *SIC* 8062

CAROLINAEAST MEDICAL CENTER p 259
2000 Neuse Blvd, New Bern NC 28560
Tel (252) 633-8111 *SIC* 8062

WRMC HOSPITAL OPERATING CORP p 1628
1370 W D St, North Wilkesboro NC 28659
Tel (336) 651-8100 *SIC* 8062

FIRSTHEALTH MOORE REGIONAL MEDICAL CENTER p 550
110 Page Rd, Pinehurst NC 28374
Tel (910) 715-1077 *SIC* 8062

FIRSTHEALTH OF CAROLINAS INC p 550
155 Memorial Dr, Pinehurst NC 28374
Tel (910) 715-1000
SIC 8062 8093 8051 8021 7991 7219

MOORE REGIONAL HOSPITAL p 987
20 Page Dr, Pinehurst NC 28374
Tel (910) 295-7888 *SIC* 8062

DUKE HEALTH RALEIGH HOSPITAL GUILD p 460
3400 Wake Forest Rd, Raleigh NC 27609
Tel (919) 954-3000 *SIC* 8062

REX HEALTHCARE INC p 1230
4420 Lake Boone Trl, Raleigh NC 27607
Tel (919) 784-3100 *SIC* 8082 8011 8062

REX HOSPITAL INC p 1230
4420 Lake Boone Trl, Raleigh NC 27607
Tel (919) 784-3100 *SIC* 8062

WAKEMED p 1572
3000 New Bern Ave G100, Raleigh NC 27610
Tel (919) 350-8000 *SIC* 8062

HALIFAX REGIONAL MEDICAL CENTER INC p 654
250 Smith Church Rd, Roanoke Rapids NC 27870
Tel (215) 994-4000 *SIC* 8062 8011

NHCS INC p 1041
2416 Professional Dr, Rocky Mount NC 27804
Tel (252) 962-8585 *SIC* 8062 8063

ROWAN HEALTH SERVICES CORP p 1253
612 Mocksville Ave, Salisbury NC 28144
Tel (704) 210-5000 *SIC* 8062

ROWAN REGIONAL MEDICAL CENTER INC p 1253
612 Mocksville Ave, Salisbury NC 28144
Tel (704) 210-5000 *SIC* 8062

CLEVELAND COUNTY HEALTHCARE SYSTEM p 325
201 E Grover St, Shelby NC 28150
Tel (900) 487-3000 *SIC* 8062 8051

JOHNSTON MEMORIAL HOSPITAL CORP p 791
509 N Brightleaf Blvd, Smithfield NC 27577
Tel (919) 934-8171 *SIC* 8062

IREDELL MEMORIAL HOSPITAL INC p 764
557 Brookdale Dr, Statesville NC 28677
Tel (704) 873-5661 *SIC* 8062 8051

■ **STATESVILLE HMA LLC** p 1383
218 Old Mocksville Rd, Statesville NC 28625
Tel (704) 873-0281 *SIC* 8051 8063 8062

■ **HRH OF NC INC** p 714
68 Hospital Rd, Sylva NC 28779
Tel (828) 586-7000 *SIC* 8062

COLUMBUS REGIONAL HEALTHCARE SYSTEM p 342
500 Jefferson St, Whiteville NC 28472
Tel (910) 642-8011 *SIC* 8062

NEW HANOVER REGIONAL MEDICAL CENTER INC p 1030
2131 S 17th St, Wilmington NC 28401
Tel (910) 343-7001 *SIC* 8062

HEALTH CARE FOUNDATION OF WILSON p 674
2505a Nash St Nw, Wilson NC 27896
Tel (252) 281-2105 *SIC* 8062

FORSYTH MEDICAL CENTER FOUNDATION p 568
3333 Silas Creek Pkwy, Winston Salem NC 27103
Tel (336) 277-1120 *SIC* 8062

FORSYTH MEMORIAL HOSPITAL INC p 568
3333 Silas Creek Pkwy, Winston Salem NC 27103
Tel (336) 277-1120 *SIC* 8062

NOVANT HEALTH INC p 1062
2085 Frontis Plaza Blvd, Winston Salem NC 27103
Tel (336) 277-1120 *SIC* 8062

WAKE FOREST BAPTIST MEDICAL CENTER p 1571
Medical Center Blvd, Winston Salem NC 27157
Tel (336) 716-2011 *SIC* 8062

WAKE FOREST BAPTIST MEDICAL CENTER p 1571
Medical Center Blvd, Winston Salem NC 27157
Tel (336) 748-8843 *SIC* 8062

SANFORD BISMARCK p 1279
300 N 7th St, Bismarck ND 58501
Tel (701) 323-6000 *SIC* 8011 8062

ST ALEXIUS MEDICAL CENTER p 1364
900 E Broadway Ave, Bismarck ND 58501
Tel (701) 530-7000 *SIC* 8062

SANFORD p 1279
801 Broadway N, Fargo ND 58102
Tel (701) 234-6000 *SIC* 8062 8011 8051

SANFORD MEDICAL CENTER FARGO p 1279
720 4th St N, Fargo ND 58122
Tel (701) 234-6000 *SIC* 8062

ALTRU HEALTH SYSTEM p 63
1200 S Columbia Rd, Grand Forks ND 58201
Tel (701) 780-5000
SIC 7352 8011 8062 8063

TRINITY HEALTH p 1481
1 Burdick Expy W, Minot ND 58701
Tel (701) 857-5260 *SIC* 8011 8051 8062

AKRON CITY HOSPITAL INC p 42
525 E Market St, Akron OH 44304
Tel (330) 253-5046 *SIC* 8062

AKRON GENERAL MEDICAL CENTER INC p 42
1 Akron General Ave, Akron OH 44307
Tel (330) 344-6000
SIC 8062 8011 8322 8221

SUMMA HEALTH SYSTEM p 1398
95 Arch St Ste G50, Akron OH 44304
Tel (330) 375-3000 *SIC* 8062

ALLIANCE CITIZENS HEALTH ASSOCIATION p 54
200 E State St, Alliance OH 44601
Tel (330) 596-6000 *SIC* 8062

ALLIANCE COMMUNITY HOSPITAL p 54
200 E State St, Alliance OH 44601
Tel (330) 596-6000 *SIC* 8062

ASHTABULA COUNTY MEDICAL CENTER p 117
2420 Lake Ave, Ashtabula OH 44004
Tel (440) 997-2262 *SIC* 8062

SHELTERING ARMS HOSPITAL FOUNDATION INC p 1315
55 Hospital Dr, Athens OH 45701
Tel (740) 592-9300 *SIC* 8062

SUMMA BARBERTON CITIZENS HOSPITAL p 1398
155 5th St Ne, Barberton OH 44203
Tel (330) 615-3000 *SIC* 8062

SISTERS OF MERCY OF CLERMONT COUNTY OHIO INC p 1327
3000 Hospital Dr, Batavia OH 45103
Tel (513) 732-8200 *SIC* 8062 8011

MARY RUTAN HOSPITAL p 914
205 E Palmer Rd, Bellefontaine OH 43311
Tel (937) 592-4015 *SIC* 8062

ST ELIZABETH BOARDMAN HEALTH CENTER p 1366
8401 Market St, Boardman OH 44512
Tel (330) 729-4580 *SIC* 8099 8062

WOOD COUNTY HOSPITAL ASSOC p 1622
960 W Wooster St, Bowling Green OH 43402
Tel (419) 354-8900 *SIC* 8062

SOUTHEASTERN OHIO REGIONAL MEDICAL CENTER p 1346
1341 Clark St, Cambridge OH 43725
Tel (740) 439-3561 *SIC* 8062

AULTMAN HOSPITAL p 131
2600 6th St Sw, Canton OH 44710
Tel (330) 452-9911 *SIC* 8062 8069 8221

COLUMBIA-CSA/HS GREATER CANTON AREA HEALTHCARE SYSTEMS LP p 342
1320 Mercy Dr Nw 30, Canton OH 44708
Tel (330) 489-1000 *SIC* 8062

MERCY MEDICAL CENTER INC p 947
1320 Mercy Dr Nw, Canton OH 44708
Tel (330) 489-1000 *SIC* 8062

UNIVERSITY HOSPITALS GEAUGA MEDICAL CENTER p 1519
13207 Ravenna Rd, Chardon OH 44024
Tel (440) 285-6000 *SIC* 8062

ADENA HEALTH SYSTEM p 22
272 Hospital Rd, Chillicothe OH 45601
Tel (740) 779-7360 *SIC* 8062

BETHESDA HOSPITAL INC p 178
619 Oak St, Cincinnati OH 45206
Tel (513) 569-6100 *SIC* 8062

BETHESDA INC p 178
619 Oak St 7n, Cincinnati OH 45206
Tel (513) 569-6400 *SIC* 8062

CHRIST HOSPITAL p 302
2139 Auburn Ave, Cincinnati OH 45219
Tel (513) 585-2000 *SIC* 8062

GAMBLE ELIZABETH DEACONESS HOME ASSOCIATION (INC) p 590
2139 Auburn Ave, Cincinnati OH 45219
Tel (513) 751-4224 *SIC* 8062 8082

GOOD SAMARITAN HOSPITAL OF CINCINNATI p 623
375 Dixmyth Ave, Cincinnati OH 45220
Tel (513) 569-6251 *SIC* 8062 8082 8011

JEWISH HOSPITAL LLC p 784
4777 E Galbraith Rd, Cincinnati OH 45236
Tel (513) 686-3000 *SIC* 8062

JEWISH HOSPITAL OF CINCINNATI INC p 785
4777 E Galbraith Rd, Cincinnati OH 45236
Tel (513) 686-3000 *SIC* 8062

MERCY FRANCISCAN HOSPITAL MT AIRY p 946
2446 Kipling Ave, Cincinnati OH 45239
Tel (513) 853-5101 *SIC* 8741 8062

MERCY HEALTH p 946
1701 Mercy Health Pl, Cincinnati OH 45237
Tel (513) 639-2800 *SIC* 8062

MERCY HEALTH ANDERSON HOSPITAL p 946
7500 State Rd, Cincinnati OH 45255
Tel (513) 624-4500 *SIC* 8062

MERCY HEALTH PARTNERS p 946
1701 Mercy Health Pl, Cincinnati OH 45237
Tel (513) 952-5000 *SIC* 8062

PROVIDENCE HOSPITAL p 1186
2446 Kipling Ave, Cincinnati OH 45239
Tel (513) 853-5000 *SIC* 8062

UNIVERSITY OF CINCINNATI MEDICAL CENTER LLC p 1521
234 Goodman St, Cincinnati OH 45219
Tel (513) 584-1000 *SIC* 8062

AUXILIARY BOARD OF FAIRVIEW GENERAL HOSPITAL p 135
18101 Lorain Ave, Cleveland OH 44111
Tel (216) 476-7000 *SIC* 8062

CLEVELAND CLINIC FOUNDATION p 325
9500 Euclid Ave, Cleveland OH 44195
Tel (216) 636-8335 *SIC* 8062 8011 8741

FAIRVIEW HOSPITAL p 525
18101 Lorain Ave, Cleveland OH 44111
Tel (216) 476-7000 *SIC* 8062 8011

LUTHERAN MEDICAL CENTER (INC) p 886
1730 W 25th St, Cleveland OH 44113
Tel (216) 696-4300 *SIC* 8062 8011 8069

MARYMOUNT HOSPITAL INC p 915
9500 Euclid Ave, Cleveland OH 44195
Tel (216) 581-0500
SIC 8062 8063 8051 8082

METROHEALTH MEDICAL CENTER p 955
2500 Metrohealth Dr, Cleveland OH 44109
Tel (216) 778-7800 *SIC* 8062

METROHEALTH SYSTEM p 955
2500 Metrohealth Dr, Cleveland OH 44109
Tel (216) 398-6000 *SIC* 8062

SOUTHWEST COMMUNITY HEALTH SYSTEMS (INC) p 1351
18697 Bagley Rd, Cleveland OH 44130
Tel (440) 816-8000 *SIC* 8062

SOUTHWEST GENERAL HEALTH CENTER p 1352
18697 Bagley Rd, Cleveland OH 44130
Tel (440) 816-8000 *SIC* 8062

ST VINCENT CHARITY MEDICAL CENTER p 1373
2351 E 22nd St, Cleveland OH 44115
Tel (216) 861-6200 *SIC* 8062

UNIVERSITY HOSPITALS HEALTH SY p 1519
11100 Euclid Ave, Cleveland OH 44106
Tel (216) 844-4663 *SIC* 8062

UNIVERSITY HOSPITALS OF CLEVELAND p 1519
11100 Euclid Ave, Cleveland OH 44106
Tel (216) 844-1000 *SIC* 8062 8069

DOCTORS OHIOHEALTH CORP p 447
5100 W Broad St, Columbus OH 43228
Tel (614) 544-5424 *SIC* 8062 8011

HOMETOWN URGENT CARE p 704
2400 Corp Exchange Dr # 102, Columbus OH 43231
Tel (614) 505-7633 *SIC* 8062

MOUNT CARMEL EAST HOSPITAL p 993
6001 E Broad St, Columbus OH 43213
Tel (614) 234-6000 *SIC* 8062

MOUNT CARMEL HEALTH p 993
793 W State St, Columbus OH 43222
Tel (614) 234-5000 *SIC* 8062

MOUNT CARMEL HEALTH SYSTEM p 993
793 W State St, Columbus OH 43222
Tel (614) 234-5000 *SIC* 8062

MOUNT CARMEL HEALTH SYSTEM p 993
6150 E Broad St, Columbus OH 43213
Tel (614) 234-6000 *SIC* 8062

NIAGARA HEALTH CORP p 1042
6150 E Broad St, Columbus OH 43213
Tel (614) 898-4000 SIC 8741 8062

OHIOHEALTH CORP p 1078
180 E Broad St, Columbus OH 43215
Tel (614) 788-8860
SIC 8049 8062 8082 8051

CUYAHOGA FALLS GENERAL HOSPITAL p 403
1900 23rd St, Cuyahoga Falls OH 44223
Tel (330) 971-7000 SIC 8062

DAYTON OSTEOPATHIC HOSPITAL p 418
405 W Grand Ave, Dayton OH 45405
Tel (937) 762-1629 SIC 8062

GOOD SAMARITAN HOSPITAL p 623
2222 Philadelphia Dr, Dayton OH 45406
Tel (937) 278-2612 SIC 8062

MED AMERICA HEALTH SYSTEMS CORP p 934
1 Wyoming St, Dayton OH 45409
Tel (937) 223-6192 SIC 8062 8741 8082

MIAMI VALLEY HOSPITAL p 959
1 Wyoming St, Dayton OH 45409
Tel (937) 208-8000 SIC 8062

SAMARITAN HEALTH PARTNERS p 1274
2222 Philadelphia Dr, Dayton OH 45406
Tel (937) 208-8400 SIC 8062

GRADY MEMORIAL HOSPITAL p 628
561 W Central Ave, Delaware OH 43015
Tel (740) 615-1000 SIC 8062

UNION HOSPITAL ASSOCIATION p 1504
659 Boulevard St, Dover OH 44622
Tel (330) 343-3311 SIC 8062 8011

EMH REGIONAL MEDICAL CENTER p 492
630 E River St, Elyria OH 44035
Tel (440) 329-7500 SIC 8062

EUCLID HOSPITAL p 512
18901 Lake Shore Blvd, Euclid OH 44119
Tel (216) 531-9000 SIC 8062

MERCY HAMILTON HOSPITAL p 946
3000 Mack Rd, Fairfield OH 45014
Tel (513) 603-8600 SIC 8062

BLANCHARD VALLEY REGIONAL HEALTH CENTER p 188
1900 S Main St, Findlay OH 45840
Tel (419) 423-4500 SIC 8062

GALION COMMUNITY HOSPITAL p 589
269 Portland Way S, Galion OH 44833
Tel (419) 468-4841 SIC 8062 8051

HOLZER CONSOLIDATED HEALTH SYSTEMS INC p 703
100 Jackson Pike, Gallipolis OH 45631
Tel (740) 446-5060 SIC 8062

HOLZER HEALTH SYSTEM p 703
100 Jackson Pike, Gallipolis OH 45631
Tel (740) 446-5000 SIC 8062

HOLZER HOSPITAL FOUNDATION INC p 703
100 Jackson Pike, Gallipolis OH 45631
Tel (740) 446-5000 SIC 8062

FORT HAMILTON HOSPITAL p 568
630 Eaton Ave, Hamilton OH 45013
Tel (513) 867-2000 SIC 8062

KETTERING MEDICAL CENTER p 814
3535 Southern Blvd, Kettering OH 45429
Tel (937) 298-4331 SIC 8062

LAKEWOOD HOSPITAL ASSOCIATION p 840
14519 Detroit Ave, Lakewood OH 44107
Tel (216) 529-7160 SIC 8062

FAIRFIELD MEDICAL CENTER p 525
401 N Ewing St, Lancaster OH 43130
Tel (740) 687-8000 SIC 8062 7352 5999

LIMA MEMORIAL HOSPITAL p 866
1001 Bellefontaine Ave, Lima OH 45804
Tel (419) 228-3335 SIC 8062

LIMA MEMORIAL JOINT OPERATING CO p 866
1001 Belelfontaine Ave, Lima OH 45804
Tel (419) 228-5165 SIC 8062

ST RITAS MEDICAL CENTER p 1373
730 W Market St, Lima OH 45801
Tel (419) 227-3361 SIC 8062 7352

COMMUNITY HEALTH PARTNERS REGIONAL FOUNDATION p 348
3700 Kolbe Rd, Lorain OH 44053
Tel (440) 960-4000 SIC 8062

COMMUNITY HEALTH PARTNERS REGIONAL HEALTH SYSTEM p 348
3700 Kolbe Rd, Lorain OH 44053
Tel (440) 960-4000 SIC 8062

MEDCENTRAL HEALTH SYSTEM p 935
335 Glessner Ave, Mansfield OH 44903
Tel (419) 526-8000 SIC 8062

MARIETTA MEMORIAL HOSPITAL INC p 906
401 Matthew St, Marietta OH 45750
Tel (740) 374-1400 SIC 8062 8069

MARION GENERAL HOSPITAL INC p 907
1000 Mckinley Park Dr, Marion OH 43302
Tel (740) 383-8400 SIC 8062

MEMORIAL HOSPITAL OF UNION COUNTY p 942
500 London Ave, Marysville OH 43040
Tel (937) 644-6115 SIC 8062

■ **DHSC LLC** p 435
875 8th St Ne, Massillon OH 44646
Tel (330) 832-8761 SIC 8062

■ **MASSILLON HEALTH SYSTEM LLC** p 917
400 Austin Ave Nw, Massillon OH 44646
Tel (330) 837-7200 SIC 8062

ST LUKES HOSPITAL p 1370
5901 Monclova Rd, Maumee OH 43537
Tel (419) 893-5911 SIC 8062 5912

SYLVANIA FRANCISCAN HEALTH p 1414
1715 Indian Wood Cir # 200, Maumee OH 43537
Tel (419) 882-8373 SIC 8062 8741

MEDINA HOSPITAL p 938
1000 E Washington St, Medina OH 44256
Tel (330) 725-1000 SIC 8062

LAKE HOSPITAL SYSTEMS p 839
7956 Tyler Blvd, Mentor OH 44060
Tel (440) 255-6400 SIC 8062

ATRIUM MEDICAL CENTER p 129
1 Medical Center Dr, Middletown OH 45005
Tel (513) 424-2111 SIC 8062

KNOX COMMUNITY HOSPITAL p 825
1330 Coshocton Ave, Mount Vernon OH 43050
Tel (740) 393-9000 SIC 8062

MOUNT CARMEL NEW ALBANY SURGICAL HOSPITAL p 993
7333 Smiths Mill Rd, New Albany OH 43054
Tel (614) 775-6600 SIC 8062

LICKING MEMORIAL HOSPITAL p 863
1320 W Main St, Newark OH 43055
Tel (740) 348-4137 SIC 8062

FISHER-TITUS MEDICAL CENTER p 552
272 Benedict Ave, Norwalk OH 44857
Tel (419) 668-8101 SIC 8052 8062

NORWALK AREA HEALTH SYSTEMS INC p 1061
272 Benedict Ave, Norwalk OH 44857
Tel (419) 668-8101 SIC 8062 8051

MERCY HEALTH - ST CHARLES HOSPITAL LLC p 946
2600 Navarre Ave, Oregon OH 43616
Tel (419) 696-7200 SIC 8062

LAKE HEALTH TRIPOINT MEDICAL CENTER p 839
7590 Auburn Rd, Painesville OH 44077
Tel (440) 375-8100 SIC 8062

PARMA COMMUNITY GENERAL HOSPITAL p 1117
7007 Powers Blvd, Parma OH 44129
Tel (440) 743-3000 SIC 8062

SOUTHERN OHIO MEDICAL CENTER p 1350
1805 27th St, Portsmouth OH 45662
Tel (740) 354-5000 SIC 8062

ROBINSON HEALTH SYSTEM INC p 1242
6847 N Chestnut St, Ravenna OH 44266
Tel (330) 297-0811 SIC 8062 8011

SALEM COMMUNITY HOSPITAL p 1272
1995 E State St, Salem OH 44460
Tel (330) 332-1551 SIC 8062 8051

FIRELANDS REGIONAL HEALTH SYSTEM p 543
1111 Hayes Ave, Sandusky OH 44870
Tel (419) 557-7400 SIC 8062

UNIVERSITY HOSPITALS HEALTH SYSTEM INC p 1519
3605 Warrensville Ctr Rd, Shaker Heights OH 44122
Tel (216) 767-8900 SIC 8062 8011 8741

SHELBY COUNTY MEMORIAL HOSPITAL ASSOCIATION p 1314
915 Michigan St, Sidney OH 45365
Tel (937) 498-2311 SIC 8062

WILSON MEMORIAL HOSPITAL p 1613
915 Michigan St, Sidney OH 45365
Tel (937) 498-2311 SIC 8062

COMMUNITY MERCY HEALTH PARTNERS p 349
100 Medical Center Dr, Springfield OH 45504
Tel (937) 523-6670 SIC 8062

TRINITY HEALTH SYSTEM p 1481
380 Summit Ave, Steubenville OH 43952
Tel (740) 283-7000 SIC 8062 8011

TRINITY HOSPITAL HOLDING CO p 1481
380 Summit Ave, Steubenville OH 43952
Tel (740) 264-8000 SIC 8062 8741

TRINITY MEDICAL CENTER WEST p 1481
4000 Johnson Rd, Steubenville OH 43952
Tel (740) 264-8000 SIC 8062

FLOWER HOSPITAL p 560
5200 Harroun Rd, Sylvania OH 43560
Tel (419) 824-1444 SIC 8062

■ **MANOR CARE INC** p 902
333 N Summit St Ste 103, Toledo OH 43604
Tel (419) 252-5500 SIC 8051 8082 8062

■ **MANOR CARE OF AMERICA INC** p 902
333 N Summit St Ste 103, Toledo OH 43604
Tel (419) 252-5500 SIC 8051 8062 8082

MEDICAL UNIVERSITY OF OHIO p 937
3000 Arlington Ave, Toledo OH 43614
Tel (419) 383-4000 SIC 8062 8221

MERCY HEALTH ST VINCENT MED LLC p 946
2213 Cherry St, Toledo OH 43608
Tel (419) 251-3232 SIC 8062

MERCY HEALTH SYSTEM - NORTHERN REGION p 946
2200 Jefferson Ave, Toledo OH 43604
Tel (419) 251-1359 SIC 8062

PROMEDICA HEALTH SYSTEMS INC p 1183
1801 Richards Rd, Toledo OH 43607
Tel (419) 469-3800
SIC 8062 6324 8351 8741

RIVERSIDE MERCY HOSPITAL p 1238
3404 W Sylvania Ave, Toledo OH 43623
Tel (419) 407-2663 SIC 8062

ST ANNE MERCY HOSPITAL p 1364
3404 W Sylvania Ave, Toledo OH 43623
Tel (419) 407-2663 SIC 8062

TOLEDO HOSPITAL p 1458
2142 N Cove Blvd, Toledo OH 43606
Tel (419) 291-4000 SIC 8011 8062

UPPER VALLEY MEDICAL CENTER p 1529
3130 N County Road 25a, Troy OH 45373
Tel (937) 440-4000 SIC 8011 8062

ST JOSEPH RIVERSIDE HOSPITAL p 1368
667 Eastland Ave Se, Warren OH 44484
Tel (330) 841-4000 SIC 8062

TRUMBULL MEMORIAL HOSPITAL p 1487
1350 E Market St, Warren OH 44483
Tel (330) 841-9011 SIC 8062 8049

CHESTER WEST MEDICAL CENTER p 295
7700 University Dr, West Chester OH 45069
Tel (513) 298-3000 SIC 8062

ST JOHN MEDICAL CENTER p 1367
29000 Center Ridge Rd, Westlake OH 44145
Tel (440) 835-8000 SIC 8062

RCHP - WILMINGTON LLC p 1212
610 W Main St, Wilmington OH 45177
Tel (937) 382-6611 SIC 8062 8361

MERCY HEALTH YOUNGSTOWN LLC p 946
1044 Belmont Ave, Youngstown OH 44504
Tel (330) 746-7211 SIC 8062 8071

BETHESDA HOSPITAL ASSOCIATION INC p 178
2951 Maple Ave, Zanesville OH 43701
Tel (740) 454-4000 SIC 8062 8063 8082

GENESIS HEALTHCARE SYSTEM p 603
2951 Maple Ave, Zanesville OH 43701
Tel (740) 454-4000 SIC 8062

MERCY HOSPITAL ARDMORE INC p 947
1011 14th Ave Nw, Ardmore OK 73401
Tel (580) 223-5400 SIC 8062

JANE PHILLIPS MEMORIAL MEDICAL CENTER INC p 777
3500 E Frank Phllips Blvd, Bartlesville OK 74006
Tel (918) 333-7200 SIC 8062

PHILLIPS JANE HEALTH CARE FOUNDATION INC p 1144
3500 E Frank Phllips Blvd, Bartlesville OK 74006
Tel (918) 333-7200 SIC 8062

AHS CLAREMORE REGIONAL HOSPITAL LLC p 37
1202 N Muskogee Pl, Claremore OK 74017
Tel (918) 341-2556 SIC 8062

DUNCAN REGIONAL HOSPITAL INC p 461
1407 N Whisenant Dr, Duncan OK 73533
Tel (580) 252-5300 SIC 8062

■ **DURANT HMA INC** p 462
1800 W University Blvd, Durant OK 74701
Tel (580) 924-3080 SIC 8062

COMANCHE COUNTY HOSPITAL AUTHORITY p 343
3401 W Gore Blvd, Lawton OK 73505
Tel (580) 355-8620 SIC 8062

■ **MIDWEST REGIONAL MEDICAL CENTER LLC** p 967
2825 Parklawn Dr, Midwest City OK 73110
Tel (405) 610-4411 SIC 8011 8062

MUSKOGEE REGIONAL MEDICAL CENTER LLC p 1002
300 Rockefeller Dr, Muskogee OK 74401
Tel (918) 682-5501 SIC 8062

NORMAN REGIONAL HOSPITAL AUTHORITY p 1049
901 N Porter Ave, Norman OK 73071
Tel (405) 307-1000 SIC 8062

COMMUNITY HOSPITAL LLC p 349
3100 Sw 89th St, Oklahoma City OK 73159
Tel (405) 602-8100 SIC 8062

■ **DEACONESS HEALTH SYSTEM LLC** p 419
5501 N Portland Ave, Oklahoma City OK 73112
Tel (405) 604-6000
SIC 8062 8051 8011 8361

EVERETT HOSPITAL p 514
1200 Everett Dr, Oklahoma City OK 73104
Tel (405) 271-4700 SIC 8062

▲ **FOUNDATION HEALTHCARE INC** p 571
13900 N Portland Ave # 200, Oklahoma City OK 73134
Tel (405) 608-1700 SIC 8062 8011 8093

■ **HCA HEALTH SERVICES OF OKLAHOMA INC** p 671
700 Ne 13th St, Oklahoma City OK 73104
Tel (405) 271-6035 SIC 8062

INTEGRIS AMBULATORY CARE CORP p 749
5300 N Independence Ave, Oklahoma City OK 73112
Tel (405) 949-6026 SIC 8062

INTEGRIS BAPTIST MEDICAL CENTER INC p 749
3300 Nw Expressway, Oklahoma City OK 73112
Tel (405) 949-3011 SIC 8062

INTEGRIS HEALTH INC p 749
3300 Nw Expwy Bldg C32, Oklahoma City OK 73112
Tel (405) 949-6066 SIC 8062

INTEGRIS RURAL HEALTHCARE OF OKLAHOMA INC p 749
3300 Nw Expwy, Oklahoma City OK 73112
Tel (405) 951-2277 SIC 8062 6513

OKLAHOMA HEART HOSPITAL SOUTH LLC p 1079
5200 E I 240 Service Rd, Oklahoma City OK 73135
Tel (405) 628-6000 SIC 8062

SOUTHWEST MEDICAL CENTER OF OKLAHOMA p 1352
4401 S Western Ave, Oklahoma City OK 73109
Tel (405) 636-7000 SIC 8062

SSM HEALTH CARE OF OKLAHOMA INC p 1364
1000 N Lee Ave, Oklahoma City OK 73102
Tel (405) 272-7000 SIC 8062

PAULS VALLEY HOSPITAL AUTHORITY p 1122
100 Valley Dr, Pauls Valley OK 73075
Tel (405) 238-5501 SIC 6324 8062

STILLWATER MEDICAL CENTER AUTHORITY p 1389
1323 W 6th Ave, Stillwater OK 74074
Tel (405) 372-1480 SIC 8062

TAHLEQUAH HOSPITAL AUTHORITY p 1421
1400 E Downing St, Tahlequah OK 74464
Tel (918) 456-0641 SIC 8062

TAHLEQUAH MEDICAL GROUP LLC p 1421
1400 E Downing St, Tahlequah OK 74464
Tel (918) 456-0641 SIC 8011 8062

AHS HILLCREST MEDICAL CENTER LLC p 37
1120 S Utica Ave, Tulsa OK 74104
Tel (918) 579-1000 SIC 8062

AHS OKLAHOMA HEALTH SYSTEM LLP p 37
110 W 7th St Ste 2540, Tulsa OK 74119
Tel (918) 579-1000
SIC 8062 8069 7352 6512 7389 5999

AHS SOUTHCREST HOSPITAL LLC p 37
8801 S 101st East Ave, Tulsa OK 74133
Tel (918) 294-4000 SIC 8062

AHS TULSA REGIONAL MEDICAL CENTER LLC p 37
744 W 9th St P252, Tulsa OK 74127
Tel (918) 587-2561 SIC 8062

JANEPHILLIPS HEALTH CROP p 777
1923 S Utica Ave, Tulsa OK 74104
Tel (918) 273-3102 SIC 8062

OKLAHOMA STATE UNIVERSITY MEDICAL TRUST p 1080
744 W 9th St, Tulsa OK 74127
Tel (918) 599-1000 SIC 8062

OKLAHOMA SURGICAL HOSPITAL LLC p 1080
2408 E 81st St Ste 900, Tulsa OK 74137
Tel (918) 477-5000 SIC 8062

SAINT FRANCIS HOSPITAL INC p 1269
6161 S Yale Ave, Tulsa OK 74136
Tel (918) 502-2050 SIC 8062 7352 5999

SAINT FRANCIS HOSPITAL SOUTH LLC p 1269
10501 E 91st St, Tulsa OK 74133
Tel (918) 307-6000 SIC 8062

ST JOHN HEALTH SYSTEM INC p 1367
1923 S Utica Ave, Tulsa OK 74104
Tel (918) 744-2180
SIC 7991 6512 7389 8361 8071 8062

ST JOHN MEDICAL CENTER INC p 1367
1923 S Utica Ave, Tulsa OK 74104
Tel (918) 744-2828 SIC 8062

■ **WOODWARD HEALTH SYSTEMS LLC** p 1623
900 17th St, Woodward OK 73801
Tel (580) 256-2820 SIC 8062

ALBANY GENERAL HOSPITAL p 45
1046 6th Ave Sw, Albany OR 97321
Tel (541) 812-4000 SIC 8062 8741

ALBANY GENERAL HOSPITAL LIFELINE p 45
1046 W 6th St, Albany OR 97321
Tel (541) 812-4000 SIC 8062

SAMARITAN ALBANY GENERAL HOSPITAL p 1274
1046 6th Ave Sw, Albany OR 97321
Tel (541) 812-4732 SIC 8062

COLUMBIA LUTHERAN CHARITIES p 341
2111 Exchange St, Astoria OR 97103
Tel (503) 325-4321 SIC 8062

ST CHARLES HEALTH SYSTEM INC p 1365
2500 Ne Neff Rd, Bend OR 97701
Tel (541) 382-4321 SIC 8062 8011

BAY AREA HEALTH DISTRICT p 160
1775 Thompson Rd, Coos Bay OR 97420
Tel (541) 269-8111 SIC 8062 8082

GOOD SAMARITAN HOSPITAL CORVALLIS p 623
3600 Nw Samaritan Dr, Corvallis OR 97330
Tel (541) 757-5111 SIC 8062

SAMARITAN HEALTH SERVICES INC p 1274
3600 Nw Samaritan Dr, Corvallis OR 97330
Tel (541) 757-5111 SIC 8741 8062

THREE RIVERS COMMUNITY HOSPITAL AND HEALTH CENTER p 1450
500 Sw Ramsey Ave, Grants Pass OR 97527
Tel (541) 472-7000 SIC 8062

LEGACY MOUNT HOOD MEDICAL CENTER p 852
24800 Se Stark St, Gresham OR 97030
Tel (503) 674-1122 SIC 8062 5912

TUALITY HEALTHCARE p 1490
335 Se 8th Ave, Hillsboro OR 97123
Tel (503) 681-1111 SIC 8062

TUALITY HOSPITAL INC p 1490
335 Se 8th Ave, Hillsboro OR 97123
Tel (503) 681-1111 SIC 8062

SKY LAKES MEDICAL CENTER FOUNDATION INC p 1330
2865 Daggett Ave, Klamath Falls OR 97601
Tel (541) 882-6311 SIC 8062

MID-VALLEY HEALTHCARE INC p 963
525 N Santiam Hwy, Lebanon OR 97355
Tel (541) 258-2101
SIC 8062 8051 8011 8082

WILLAMETTE VALLEY MEDICAL CENTER p 1610
2700 Se Stratus Ave, Mcminnville OR 97128
Tel (503) 472-6131 SIC 8062

ASANTE ROGUE REGIONAL MEDICAL CENTER p 115
2825 E Barnett Rd, Medford OR 97504
Tel (541) 608-4900 SIC 8062

PROVIDENCE MILWAUKIE HOSPITAL INC p 1186
10150 Se 32nd Ave, Milwaukie OR 97222
Tel (503) 513-8300 SIC 8062

WILLAMETT FALLS HOSPITAL p 1609
1500 Division St, Oregon City OR 97045
Tel (503) 650-6765 SIC 8062

LEGACY EMANUEL HOSPITAL & HEALTH CENTER p 852
2801 N Gantenbein Ave, Portland OR 97227
Tel (503) 413-2200 SIC 8062

PORTLAND ADVENTIST MEDICAL CENTER p 1163
10123 Se Market St, Portland OR 97216
Tel (503) 257-2500 SIC 8062

PROVIDENCE HEALTH SYSTEM-OREGON p 1186
4805 Ne Glisan St, Portland OR 97213
Tel (503) 215-6111 SIC 8062

ST VINCENT MEDICAL CENTER EAST PAVILION LOBBY GIFT SHOP p 1373
9205 Sw Barnes Rd, Portland OR 97225
Tel (503) 216-2100 SIC 8062

VA PORTLAND HEALTH CARE SYSTEM p 1538
3710 Sw Us Vtrans Hosp Rd, Portland OR 97239
Tel (503) 273-5048 SIC 8062 8742

MERCY MEDICAL CENTER INC p 947
2700 Nw Stewart Pkwy, Roseburg OR 97471
Tel (541) 673-0611 SIC 8062

SALEM HEALTH p 1272
890 Oak St Se, Salem OR 97301
Tel (503) 561-5200 SIC 8062

SILVERTON HEALTH p 1324
342 Fairview St, Silverton OR 97381
Tel (503) 873-1500 SIC 8062

SILVERTON HOSPITAL NETWORK p 1324
342 Fairview St, Silverton OR 97381
Tel (503) 873-1782 SIC 8062

■ **MCKENZIE-WILLAMETTE REGIONAL MEDICAL CENTER ASSOCIATES LLC** p 930
1460 G St, Springfield OR 97477
Tel (541) 726-4400 SIC 8062

MCKINSEY WILLIAMETTE p 930
1460 G St, Springfield OR 97477
Tel (541) 741-4600 SIC 8011 8062

MID-COLUMBIA MEDICAL CENTER p 963
1700 E 19th St, The Dalles OR 97058
Tel (541) 296-1111 SIC 8062 8011

LEGACY MERIDIAN PARK HOSPITAL p 852
19300 Sw 65th Ave, Tualatin OR 97062
Tel (503) 692-1212 SIC 8062 8011

ABINGTON MEMORIAL HOSPITAL INC p 11
1200 Old York Rd, Abington PA 19001
Tel (215) 481-2000 SIC 8062

LEHIGH VALLEY HEALTH NETWORK INC p 854
1247 S Cedar Crest Blvd, Allentown PA 18103
Tel (610) 402-8000 SIC 8062

LEHIGH VALLEY HOSPITAL INC p 854
1200 S Cedar Crest Blvd, Allentown PA 18103
Tel (610) 402-8000 SIC 8062

SACRED HEART HOSPITAL OF ALLENTOWN p 1265
421 Chew St, Allentown PA 18102
Tel (610) 776-4500 SIC 8062 8011

UPMC ALTOONA p 1528
620 Howard Ave, Altoona PA 16601
Tel (814) 889-2011 SIC 8062

HERITAGE VALLEY HEALTH SYSTEM INC p 686
2580 Constitution Blvd, Beaver Falls PA 15010
Tel (724) 728-7000 SIC 8741 8062

EIGHTH & EATON PROFESSIONAL BUILDING LP p 481
801 Ostrum St, Bethlehem PA 18015
Tel (610) 954-4000 SIC 8062

SAINT LUKES HOSPITAL OF BETHLEHEM PENNSYLVANIA p 1270
801 Ostrum St, Bethlehem PA 18015
Tel (484) 526-4000 SIC 8062 8249

ST LUKES HEALTH NETWORK INC p 1370
801 Ostrum St, Bethlehem PA 18015
Tel (610) 954-4000 SIC 8062

LOWER BUCKS HOSPITAL p 881
501 Bath Rd, Bristol PA 19007
Tel (215) 785-9200 SIC 8062

MAIN LINE HOSPITALS INC p 897
130 S Bryn Mawr Ave, Bryn Mawr PA 19010
Tel (610) 526-3000 SIC 8062

RIDDLE MEMORIAL HOSPITAL p 1234
950 E Haverford Rd, Bryn Mawr PA 19010
Tel (484) 337-8480 SIC 8062

BUTLER HEALTH SYSTEM INC p 230
1 Hospital Way, Butler PA 16001
Tel (724) 283-6666 SIC 8062

BUTLER HEALTHCARE PROVIDERS p 230
1 Hospital Way, Butler PA 16001
Tel (724) 283-6666 SIC 8062

HOLY SPIRIT HOSPITAL OF SISTERS OF CHRISTIAN CHARITY p 702
503 N 21st St, Camp Hill PA 17011
Tel (717) 763-2100 SIC 8062

■ **CARLISLE HMA INC** p 257
361 Alexander Spring Rd, Carlisle PA 17015
Tel (717) 249-1212 SIC 8062

■ **CARLISLE HMA LLC** p 257
361 Alexander Spring Rd, Carlisle PA 17015
Tel (717) 243-1900 SIC 8062

CHAMBERSBURG HOSPITAL p 287
112 N 7th St, Chambersburg PA 17201
Tel (717) 267-3000 SIC 8062

JEFFERSON HOSPITAL p 781
565 Coal Valley Rd, Clairton PA 15025
Tel (412) 267-6024 SIC 8062 8063 8069

■ **COATESVILLE HOSPITAL CORP** p 332
201 Reeceville Rd, Coatesville PA 19320
Tel (610) 383-8000 SIC 8062

MERCY CATHOLIC MEDICAL CENTER OF SOUTHEASTERN PENNSYLVANIA p 945
1 W Elm St, Conshohocken PA 19428
Tel (610) 567-6725 SIC 8062

MERCY HEALTH FOUNDATION OF SOUTHEASTERN PENNSYLVANIA p 946
1 W Elm St Ste 100, Conshohocken PA 19428
Tel (610) 567-6000 SIC 8062

MERCY HEALTH SYSTEM OF SOUTHEASTERN PENNSYLVANIA p 946
1 W Elm St Ste 100, Conshohocken PA 19428
Tel (610) 567-6000 SIC 8062

GEISINGER MEDICAL CENTER p 597
100 N Academy Ave, Danville PA 17822
Tel (570) 271-6211 SIC 8062

MERCY FITZGERALD HOSPITAL p 946
1500 Lansdowne Ave Ste 1, Darby PA 19023
Tel (610) 237-4000 SIC 8062

DOYLESTOWN HOSPITAL HEALTH AND WELLNESS CENTER INC p 454
595 W State St, Doylestown PA 18901
Tel (215) 345-2200 SIC 8051 8062

DELAWARE COUNTY MEMORIAL HOSPITAL p 423
501 N Lansdowne Ave, Drexel Hill PA 19026
Tel (610) 284-8100 SIC 8062

MERCY SUBURBAN HOSPITAL p 948
2701 Dekalb Pike, East Norriton PA 19401
Tel (215) 748-9000 SIC 8062

MONTGOMERY HOSPITAL p 986
559 W Germantown Pike, East Norriton PA 19403
Tel (215) 456-7890 SIC 8062

POCONO HEALTH SYSTEM p 1158
206 E Brown St, East Stroudsburg PA 18301
Tel (570) 421-4000 SIC 8062

POCONO MEDICAL CENTER p 1158
206 E Brown St, East Stroudsburg PA 18301
Tel (570) 421-4000 SIC 8062

■ **NORTHAMPTON HOSPITAL CORP** p 1054
250 S 21st St, Easton PA 18042
Tel (610) 250-4000 SIC 8062

ST LUKES HOSPITAL - ANDERSON CAMPUS p 1370
1872 St Lukes Blvd, Easton PA 18045
Tel (484) 503-3000 SIC 8062

EPHRATA COMMUNITY HOSPITAL INC p 504
169 Martin Ave, Ephrata PA 17522
Tel (717) 721-5883 SIC 8062

HAMOT HEALTH FOUNDATION p 656
201 State St, Erie PA 16550
Tel (814) 877-7020 SIC 8741 8062 6514

SAINT VINCENT HEALTH CENTER INC p 1271
232 W 25th St, Erie PA 16544
Tel (814) 452-5000 SIC 8062

UPMC HAMOT p 1528
201 State St, Erie PA 16550
Tel (814) 877-6000 SIC 8062

GETTYSBURG HOSPITAL p 609
147 Gettys St, Gettysburg PA 17325
Tel (717) 334-2121 SIC 8062

EXCELA HEALTH HOLDING CO INC p 516
532 W Pittsburgh St, Greensburg PA 15601
Tel (724) 832-4000
SIC 8062 8093 5999 7363 7322 8361

WESTMORELAND REGIONAL HOSPITAL p 1602
532 W Pittsburgh St, Greensburg PA 15601
Tel (724) 832-4000 SIC 8062

U P M C HORIZON p 1497
110 N Main St, Greenville PA 16125
Tel (724) 588-2100 SIC 8062

HANOVER HEALTH CORP INC p 658
300 Highland Ave, Hanover PA 17331
Tel (717) 637-3711 SIC 8062 8011 5912

HANOVER HOSPITAL INC p 658
300 Highland Ave, Hanover PA 17331
Tel (717) 637-3711 SIC 8062

PINNACLE HEALTH HOSPITAL p 1149
4300 Londonderry Rd, Harrisburg PA 17109
Tel (717) 782-3131 SIC 8062

PINNACLE HEALTH HOSPITALS p 1150
409 S 2nd St Ste 1c, Harrisburg PA 17104
Tel (717) 782-5678 SIC 8062

PINNACLE HEALTH SYSTEM p 1150
409 S 2nd St Ste 2b, Harrisburg PA 17104
Tel (717) 231-8010 SIC 8741 8062

NORTHEASTERN PENNSYLVANIA HEALTH CORP p 1055
700 E Broad St, Hazleton PA 18201
Tel (570) 501-4000 SIC 8062

PENN STATE MILTON S HERSHEY MEDICAL CENTER p 1129
500 University Dr, Hershey PA 17033
Tel (717) 531-5337 SIC 8062 8733 8211

WAYNE MEMORIAL HOSPITAL p 1584
601 Park St, Honesdale PA 18431
Tel (570) 253-8100 SIC 8062

INDIANA REGIONAL MEDICAL CENTER p 738
835 Hospital Rd, Indiana PA 15701
Tel (724) 357-7000 SIC 8062 8011

■ **CONEMAUGH HEALTH SYSTEM INC** p 355
1086 Franklin St, Johnstown PA 15905
Tel (814) 534-9000 SIC 8062 8741

■ **UHS OF DELAWARE INC** p 1500
367 S Gulph Rd, King Of Prussia PA 19406
Tel (610) 768-3300 SIC 8062

▲ **UNIVERSAL HEALTH SERVICES INC** p 1517
367 S Gulph Rd, King Of Prussia PA 19406
Tel (610) 768-3300
SIC 8062 8063 8093 8011 8741

ARMSTRONG COUNTY MEMORIAL HOSPITAL p 111
1 Nolte Dr, Kittanning PA 16201
Tel (724) 543-8500 SIC 8062 8011

LANCASTER GENERAL HEALTH p 841
555 N Duke St, Lancaster PA 17602
Tel (717) 290-5511 SIC 8062

LANCASTER GENERAL HOSPITAL p 841
555 N Duke St, Lancaster PA 17602
Tel (717) 544-5511 SIC 8062

■ **ROSE CITY HMA LLC** p 1250
250 College Ave, Lancaster PA 17603
Tel (717) 291-8211 SIC 8062

ST MARY MEDICAL CENTER p 1371
1201 Langhorne Newtown Rd, Langhorne PA 19047
Tel (215) 710-2000 SIC 8062

EXCELA HEALTH LATROBE AREA HOSPITAL p 516
1 Mellon Way, Latrobe PA 15650
Tel (877) 771-1234 SIC 8062

LATROBE AREA HOSPITAL INC p 846
1 Mellon Way, Latrobe PA 15650
Tel (724) 537-1000 SIC 8062

GOOD SAMARITAN HOSPITAL OF LEBANON PENNSYLVANIA p 623
252 S 4th St, Lebanon PA 17042
Tel (717) 270-7500 SIC 8062

GOOD SAMARITAN PHYSICIAN SERVICES p 623
259 S 4th St, Lebanon PA 17042
Tel (717) 270-7500 SIC 8062

EVANGELICAL COMMUNITY HOSPITAL p 513
1 Hospital Dr, Lewisburg PA 17837
Tel (570) 522-2000 SIC 8062

LEWISTOWN HOSPITAL p 859
400 Highland Ave, Lewistown PA 17044
Tel (717) 248-5411 SIC 8062 8221

UPMC BRADDOCK p 1528
1500 5th Ave, Mckeesport PA 15132
Tel (412) 636-5000 SIC 8062

UPMC MCKEESPORT p 1528
1500 5th Ave, Mckeesport PA 15132
Tel (412) 664-2000 SIC 8062

MEADVILLE MEDICAL CENTER p 934
751 Liberty St, Meadville PA 16335
Tel (814) 333-5000 SIC 8741 8062 8011

RIDDLE MEMORIAL HOSPITAL p 1234
1068 W Baltimore Pike, Media PA 19063
Tel (610) 566-9400 SIC 8062

MON-VALE HEALTH RESOURCES INC p 983
1163 Country Club Rd, Monongahela PA 15063
Tel (724) 258-1000 SIC 8062

MONONGAHELA VALLEY HOSPITAL INC p 984
1163 Country Club Rd, Monongahela PA 15063
Tel (724) 258-1000 SIC 8062 8063 8069

UPMC EAST p 1528
2775 Mosside Blvd, Monroeville PA 15146
Tel (412) 357-3000 SIC 8062

ALLE-KISKI MEDICAL CENTER p 52
1301 Carlisle St, Natrona Heights PA 15065
Tel (724) 224-5100 SIC 8062

JAMESON HEALTH SYSTEM INC p 777
1211 Wilmington Ave, New Castle PA 16105
Tel (724) 658-9001 SIC 8062

JAMESON MEMORIAL HOSPITAL p 777
1211 Wilmington Ave, New Castle PA 16105
Tel (724) 658-9001 SIC 8062

CATHOLIC HEALTH EAST p 266
3805 West Chester Pike # 100, Newtown Square PA 19073
Tel (610) 355-2000
SIC 8062 8051 8052 8059 8011

MAXIS HEALTH SYSTEM p 922
3805 West Chester Pike # 100, Newtown Square PA 19073
Tel (570) 281-1000 SIC 8062

ALBERT EINSTEIN HEALTHCARE NETWORK p 46
5501 Old York Rd, Philadelphia PA 19141
Tel (215) 456-7890 SIC 8062

ALBERT EINSTEIN MEDICAL ASSOCIATES INC p 46
5501 Old York Rd Ste 1, Philadelphia PA 19141
Tel (215) 456-7890 SIC 8062 8051

ALBERT EINSTEIN MEDICAL CENTER p 46
5501 Old York Rd Ste 1, Philadelphia PA 19141
Tel (215) 456-7890 SIC 8062

ALBERT M HOSPICE EINSTEIN p 46
5501 Old York Rd Ste 3, Philadelphia PA 19141
Tel (215) 456-7890 SIC 8062

ARIA HEALTH p 108
10800 Knights Rd, Philadelphia PA 19114
Tel (215) 612-4000 SIC 8062

CHH LIQUIDATING CO p 296
8835 Germantown Ave, Philadelphia PA 19118
Tel (215) 248-8200 SIC 8062

CHHC TRANSITION CO p 296
8835 Germantown Ave, Philadelphia PA 19118
Tel (215) 248-8200 SIC 8062

■ **CHHS HOSPITAL CO LLC** p 296
8835 Germantown Ave, Philadelphia PA 19118
Tel (215) 248-8200 SIC 8062

FOX CHASE CANCER CENTER FOUNDATION p 572
333 Cottman Ave, Philadelphia PA 19111
Tel (215) 728-6900 SIC 8069 8071 8062

HEALTH SERVICES OF FOX CHASE CANCER CENTER p 676
333 Cottman Ave, Philadelphia PA 19111
Tel (215) 728-6900 SIC 8011 8062 8733

HOSPITAL OF UNIVERSITY OF PENNSYLVANIA p 709
3400 Spruce St Ofc, Philadelphia PA 19104
Tel (215) 301-3776 SIC 8062

JEANES HOSPITAL p 781
7600 Central Ave, Philadelphia PA 19111
Tel (215) 728-2000 SIC 8062

JOSEPH STOKES INSTITUTE OF RESEARCH p 793
3615 Civic Center Blvd, Philadelphia PA 19104
Tel (215) 590-3800 SIC 8062 8733

NAZARETH HOSPITAL p 1020
2601 Holme Ave, Philadelphia PA 19152
Tel (215) 335-6000 SIC 8062

PENNSYLVANIA HOSPITAL OF UNIVERSITY OF PENNSYLVANIA HEALTH SYSTEM p 1130
800 Spruce St, Philadelphia PA 19107
Tel (215) 829-3000 SIC 8062 8063

PHILADELPHIA NORTH HEALTH SYSTEM p 1143
801 W Girard Ave, Philadelphia PA 19122
Tel (215) 787-9001 SIC 8062 8069 8063

PRESBYTERIAN MEDICAL CENTER OF UNIVERSITY OF PENNSYLVANIA HEALTH SYSTEM p 1171
51 N 39th St, Philadelphia PA 19104
Tel (215) 662-8000 SIC 8062

SOLIS HEALTHCARE LP p 1338
5800 Ridge Ave, Philadelphia PA 19128
Tel (215) 483-9900 SIC 8062

TEMPLE UNIVERSITY HOSPITAL INC p 1436
3401 N Broad St, Philadelphia PA 19140
Tel (215) 707-2000 SIC 8062

■ **TENET HEALTHSYSTEM HAHNEMANN LLC** p 1437
230 N Broad St, Philadelphia PA 19102
Tel (215) 762-7000 SIC 8062

THOMAS JEFFERSON UNIVERSITY p 1449
1020 Walnut St Ste 1, Philadelphia PA 19107
Tel (215) 955-6000 SIC 8062 8221

THOMAS JEFFERSON UNIVERSITY HOSPITALS INC p 1449
111 S 11th St, Philadelphia PA 19107
Tel (215) 955-5806 SIC 8062

■ **PHOENIXVILLE HOSPITAL CO LLC** p 1145
140 Nutt Rd, Phoenixville PA 19460
Tel (610) 983-1000 SIC 8062

■ **PHOENIXVILLE HOSPITAL OF UNIVERSITY OF PENNSYLVANIA HEALTH SYSTEM** p 1145
140 Nutt Rd, Phoenixville PA 19460
Tel (610) 983-1000 SIC 8062 8011

ALLEGHENY GENERAL HOSPITAL INC p 52
320 E North Ave, Pittsburgh PA 15212
Tel (412) 359-3131 SIC 8062 8051

CHILDRENS HOSPITAL OF PITTSBURGH p 300
1 Childrens Hospital Dr, Pittsburgh PA 15224
Tel (412) 692-5437 SIC 8062

MAGEE-WOMENS HOSPITAL OF UPMC p 895
300 Halket St, Pittsburgh PA 15213
Tel (412) 641-1000 SIC 8062

MERCY UPMC p 948
1400 Locust St, Pittsburgh PA 15219
Tel (412) 232-8111 SIC 8062

MONTEFIORE UNIVERSITY HOSPITAL p 986
3459 5th Ave, Pittsburgh PA 15213
Tel (412) 647-2345 SIC 8062

ST CLAIR HEALTH CORP p 1365
1000 Bower Hill Rd, Pittsburgh PA 15243
Tel (412) 561-4900 SIC 8062

ST CLAIR MEMORIAL HOSPITAL p 1365
1000 Bower Hill Rd, Pittsburgh PA 15243
Tel (412) 561-4900 SIC 8062

ST CLAIR MEMORIAL HOSPITAL FOUNDATION p 1365
1000 Bower Hill Rd, Pittsburgh PA 15243
Tel (412) 942-4000 SIC 8062

U P M C SHADYSIDE p 1497
5230 Centre Ave, Pittsburgh PA 15232
Tel (412) 623-2121 SIC 8062

UNIVERSITY OF PITTSBURGH MEDICAL CENTER p 1524
600 Grant St Fl 62, Pittsburgh PA 15219
Tel (412) 647-2345 SIC 8062

UNIVERSITY OF PITTSBURGH PHYSICIANS p 1524
200 Lothrop St, Pittsburgh PA 15213
Tel (412) 647-8762 SIC 8062

UPMC PASSAVANT p 1528
9100 Babcock Blvd, Pittsburgh PA 15237
Tel (412) 367-6700 SIC 8062

UPMC PRESBYTERIAN SHADYSIDE p 1529
200 Lothrop St, Pittsburgh PA 15213
Tel (412) 647-8762 SIC 8062

UPMC ST MARGARET p 1529
815 Freeport Rd, Pittsburgh PA 15215
Tel (412) 784-4000 SIC 8062

UPMC ST MARGARET TRANSITIONAL CARE UNIT p 1529
815 Freeport Rd, Pittsburgh PA 15215
Tel (412) 784-4000 SIC 8062

WEST PENN ALLEGHENY HEALTH SYSTEM INC p 1595
4800 Friendship Ave, Pittsburgh PA 15224
Tel (412) 578-5000 SIC 8062

WESTERN PENNSYLVANIA HOSPITAL p 1599
4800 Friendship Ave, Pittsburgh PA 15224
Tel (412) 578-5000 SIC 8062

POTTSTOWN HOSPITAL CO LLC p 1164
1600 E High St, Pottstown PA 19464
Tel (610) 327-7000 SIC 8062

■ **POTTSTOWN MEMORIAL MEDICAL CENTER** p 1164
1600 E High St, Pottstown PA 19464
Tel (610) 327-7000 SIC 8062

MAIN LINE HEALTH SYSTEM p 897
240 N Radnor Chester Rd, Radnor PA 19087
Tel (610) 225-6200
SIC 5999 8059 8361 8062

READING HEALTH SYSTEM p 1213
6th Ave And Spruce St, Reading PA 19611
Tel (610) 988-8000
SIC 8062 6512 8093 8721 8011 7219

READING HOSPITAL p 1213
6th And Spruce St, Reading PA 19611
Tel (484) 628-8000 SIC 8062 6512

ST JOSEPH REGIONAL HEALTH NETWORK p 1368
2500 Bernville Rd, Reading PA 19605
Tel (610) 378-2000 SIC 8062

TAYLOR HOSPITAL p 1427
175 E Chester Pike, Ridley Park PA 19078
Tel (610) 595-6000 SIC 8062

ELK REGIONAL HEALTH SYSTEM p 487
763 Johnsonburg Rd, Saint Marys PA 15857
Tel (814) 788-8000
SIC 8062 8051 8361 8399

GUTHRIE CLINIC p 648
1 Guthrie Sq Ste B, Sayre PA 18840
Tel (570) 888-5858 SIC 8011 8062 8082

ROBERT PACKER HOSPITAL p 1241
1 Guthrie Sq Ste B, Sayre PA 18840
Tel (570) 888-6666 SIC 8062

GEISINGER-COMMUNITY MEDICAL CENTER p 598
1822 Mulberry St, Scranton PA 18510
Tel (570) 969-8000 SIC 8062

■ **MERCY HEALTH PARTNERS** p 946
746 Jefferson Ave, Scranton PA 18510
Tel (570) 348-7100 SIC 8062

MERCY HOSPITAL SCRANTON PENNSYLVANIA p 947
746 Jefferson Ave, Scranton PA 18510
Tel (570) 348-7100 SIC 8062 8051

■ **QUINCY SCRANTON HOSPITAL LLC** p 1200
700 Quincy Ave, Scranton PA 18510
Tel (570) 340-2100 SIC 8062 8051

■ **SCRANTON HOSPITAL CO LLC** p 1294
746 Jefferson Ave, Scranton PA 18510
Tel (570) 348-7100 SIC 8062

GRAND VIEW HOSPITAL p 630
700 Lawn Ave, Sellersville PA 18960
Tel (215) 453-4000 SIC 8062

■ **SHARON REGIONAL HEALTH SYSTEM** p 1312
740 E State St, Sharon PA 16146
Tel (724) 983-3911 SIC 8062 8063 8069

MOUNT NITTANY HEALTH SYSTEM p 993
1800 E Park Ave, State College PA 16803
Tel (814) 231-7040 SIC 8062

MOUNT NITTANY MEDICAL CENTER p 993
1800 E Park Ave, State College PA 16803
Tel (814) 231-7000 SIC 8062

HOSPITAL UNIONTOWN INC p 710
500 W Berkeley St, Uniontown PA 15401
Tel (724) 430-5000 SIC 8062

WASHINGTON HOSPITAL p 1578
155 Wilson Ave, Washington PA 15301
Tel (724) 225-7000 SIC 8062

CHESTER COUNTY HOSPITAL *p* 295
701 E Marshall St, West Chester PA 19380
Tel (610) 431-5000 *SIC* 8062

CHESTER COUNTY HOSPITAL AND HEALTH SYSTEM *p* 295
701 E Marshall St, West Chester PA 19380
Tel (610) 431-5000 *SIC* 8062

GEISINGER WYOMING VALLEY MEDICAL CENTER *p* 597
1000 E Mountain Dr, Wilkes Barre PA 18711
Tel (570) 808-7300 *SIC* 8062

■ WILKES-BARRE HOSPITAL CO LLC *p* 1609
575 N River St, Wilkes Barre PA 18764
Tel (570) 829-8111 *SIC* 8062 8069

■ WYOMING VALLEY HEALTH & EDUCATION FOUNDATION *p* 1630
575 N River St, Wilkes Barre PA 18702
Tel (570) 829-8111 *SIC* 8062

DIVINE PROVIDENCE HOSPITAL OF SISTERS OF CHRISTIAN CHARITY *p* 444
1100 Grampian Blvd, Williamsport PA 17701
Tel (570) 321-1000 *SIC* 8062

SUSQUEHANNA VENTURES INC *p* 1409
1100 Grampian Blvd, Williamsport PA 17701
Tel (570) 326-8718 *SIC* 8062

WILLIAMSPORT HOSPITAL *p* 1612
700 High St, Williamsport PA 17701
Tel (570) 321-1000 *SIC* 8062 7389

YORK HOSPITAL *p* 1637
1001 S George St, York PA 17403
Tel (717) 851-2345 *SIC* 8062

YORK PENNSYLVANIA HOSPITAL CO LLC *p* 1637
325 S Belmont St, York PA 17403
Tel (717) 843-8623 *SIC* 8062 8082

GRUPO HIMA-SAN PABLO INC *p* 643
100 Calle Munoz Rivera, Caguas PR 00725
Tel (787) 653-3434 *SIC* 8062

HOSPITAL HIMA SAN PABLO CAGUAS *p* 709
100 Ave Luis Munoz Marin, Caguas PR 00725
Tel (787) 653-3434 *SIC* 8062

MENNONITE GENERAL HOSPITAL INC *p* 943
Carr 14 Km 131 Sctor Lmas St Ca, Cayey PR 00736
Tel (787) 535-1001 *SIC* 8062

HOSPITAL DAMAS INC *p* 709
2213 Ponce Byp, Ponce PR 00717
Tel (787) 840-8686 *SIC* 8062

METROPADIA HEALTH SYSTEM INC *p* 955
2445 Las America Ave, Ponce PR 00731
Tel (787) 848-5600 *SIC* 8062

AUXILIO MUTUO HOSPITAL *p* 135
735 Ave Ponce De Leon, San Juan PR 00917
Tel (787) 761-6600 *SIC* 8011 8062

SOCIEDAD ESPAOLA DE AUXILIO MUTUO Y BENEFICENCIA DE PUERTO RICO *p* 1336
Ponce De Leon Ave, San Juan PR 00917
Tel (787) 758-2000 *SIC* 8062

NEWPORT HEALTH CARE CORP *p* 1038
11 Friendship St, Newport RI 02840
Tel (401) 846-6400 *SIC* 8062 6531 6732

NEWPORT HOSPITAL *p* 1038
11 Friendship St Ste 1, Newport RI 02840
Tel (401) 846-6400 *SIC* 8062

PROSPECT CHARTERCARE SJHSRI LLC *p* 1184
200 High Service Ave, North Providence RI 02904
Tel (401) 456-3000 *SIC* 8062

MEMORIAL HOSPITAL *p* 942
111 Brewster St, Pawtucket RI 02860
Tel (401) 729-2000 *SIC* 8062 6513

CARE NEW ENGLAND HEALTH SYSTEM INC *p* 254
45 Willard Ave, Providence RI 02905
Tel (401) 453-7900
SIC 8063 8062 8069 8093 8082

MIRIAM HOSPITAL *p* 974
164 Summit Ave, Providence RI 02906
Tel (401) 793-2500 *SIC* 8062

RHODE ISLAND HOSPITAL *p* 1231
593 Eddy St, Providence RI 02903
Tel (401) 444-4000 *SIC* 8062

RHODE ISLAND HOSPITAL EMR *p* 1232
1 Hoppin St Ste 106, Providence RI 02903
Tel (401) 444-6237 *SIC* 8062

ROGER WILLIAMS MEDICAL CENTER *p* 1246
825 Chalkstone Ave, Providence RI 02908
Tel (401) 456-2000 *SIC* 8062

ROGER WILLIAMS MEDICAL CENTER *p* 1246
825 Chalkstone Ave, Providence RI 02908
Tel (401) 456-2000 *SIC* 8062

WOMEN & INFANTS HOSPITAL OF RHODE ISLAND *p* 1621
101 Dudley St, Providence RI 02905
Tel (401) 274-1100 *SIC* 8062

SOUTH COUNTY HOSPITAL HEALTHCARE SYSTEM *p* 1344
100 Kenyon Ave, Wakefield RI 02879
Tel (401) 782-8000 *SIC* 8062

SOUTH COUNTY HOSPITAL HEALTHCARE SYSTEM ENDOWMENT AND AFFILIATES *p* 1344
100 Kenyon Ave, Wakefield RI 02879
Tel (401) 782-8000 *SIC* 8062

KENT COUNTY MEMORIAL HOSPITAL *p* 812
455 Toll Gate Rd, Warwick RI 02886
Tel (401) 737-7000 *SIC* 8062

LANDMARK MEDICAL CENTER *p* 843
115 Cass Ave, Woonsocket RI 02895
Tel (401) 769-4100 *SIC* 8062

PRIME HEALTHCARE SERVICES-LANDMARK LLC *p* 1175
115 Cass Ave, Woonsocket RI 02895
Tel (401) 769-4100 *SIC* 8062

■ AIKEN REGIONAL MEDICAL CENTERS LLC *p* 38
302 University Pkwy, Aiken SC 29801
Tel (803) 641-5000 *SIC* 8062

ANMED HEALTH *p* 92
800 Nh Fant St, Anderson SC 29621
Tel (864) 261-1000 *SIC* 8062 8011

ANMED HEALTH RESOURCES INC *p* 92
800 N Fant St, Anderson SC 29621
Tel (864) 512-1000 *SIC* 8062

BEAUFORT COUNTY MEMORIAL HOSPITAL *p* 166
955 Ribaut Rd, Beaufort SC 29902
Tel (843) 522-5200 *SIC* 8062

KERSHAW HEALTH MEDICAL CENTER *p* 813
1315 Roberts St, Camden SC 29020
Tel (803) 432-4311 *SIC* 8062 8051 8082

CARE ALLIANCE HEALTH INC *p* 254
2095 Henry Tecklenburg Dr, Charleston SC 29414
Tel (843) 402-1000 *SIC* 8062

MEDICAL UNIVERSITY HOSPITAL AUTHORITY *p* 937
169 Ashley Ave, Charleston SC 29425
Tel (843) 792-1414 *SIC* 8062

MEDICAL UNIVERSITY OF SOUTH CAROLINA *p* 937
171 Ashley Ave, Charleston SC 29425
Tel (843) 792-2123 *SIC* 8062 8221 8069

ROPER HOSPITAL INC *p* 1250
316 Calhoun St, Charleston SC 29401
Tel (843) 724-2000 *SIC* 8062

■ TRIDENT MEDICAL CENTER LLC *p* 1479
9330 Medical Plaza Dr, Charleston SC 29406
Tel (843) 797-7000 *SIC* 8062 8011

PALMETTO HEALTH *p* 1109
1301 Taylor St Ste 8a, Columbia SC 29201
Tel (803) 296-2100 *SIC* 8062

PALMETTO HEALTH ALLIANCE INC *p* 1109
293 Greystone Blvd, Columbia SC 29210
Tel (803) 296-5220 *SIC* 8062

PALMETTO-RICHLAND MEMORIAL HOSPITAL *p* 1109
5 Richland Medical Pk Dr, Columbia SC 29203
Tel (803) 434-3460 *SIC* 8062

■ PROVIDENCE HOSPITAL LLC *p* 1186
2435 Forest Dr, Columbia SC 29204
Tel (803) 256-5300 *SIC* 8062

CONWAY HOSPITAL AUXILIARY *p* 365
300 Singleton Ridge Rd, Conway SC 29526
Tel (843) 347-7111 *SIC* 8062

CONWAY HOSPITAL INC *p* 365
300 Singleton Ridge Rd, Conway SC 29526
Tel (843) 347-7111 *SIC* 8062

SAINT EUGENE MEDICAL CENTER *p* 1269
301 E Jackson St, Dillon SC 29536
Tel (843) 774-4111 *SIC* 8062

BAPTIST EASLEY HOSPITAL *p* 153
200 Fleetwood Dr, Easley SC 29640
Tel (864) 442-7200 *SIC* 8062

MCLEOD HEALTH SERVICES INC *p* 931
555 E Cheves St, Florence SC 29506
Tel (843) 777-5146 *SIC* 8062

MCLEOD REGIONAL MEDICAL CENTER OF PEE DEE INC *p* 931
555 E Cheves St, Florence SC 29506
Tel (843) 777-2000 *SIC* 8062

■ QHG OF SOUTH CAROLINA INC *p* 1195
805 Pamplico Hwy, Florence SC 29505
Tel (843) 674-5000 *SIC* 8062

GEORGETOWN MEMORIAL HOSPITAL *p* 606
606 Black River Rd, Georgetown SC 29440
Tel (843) 626-9040 *SIC* 8062

BOB JONES UNIVERSITY INC OF GREENVILLE S C *p* 196
1700 Wade Hampton Blvd, Greenville SC 29614
Tel (864) 242-5100
SIC 8221 8211 8231 8062 5942 0191

PATEWOOD MEMORIAL HOSPITAL *p* 1120
175 Patewood Dr, Greenville SC 29615
Tel (864) 797-1000 *SIC* 8062

ST FRANCIS HOSPITAL INC *p* 1366
1 Saint Francis Dr, Greenville SC 29601
Tel (864) 255-1000 *SIC* 8062

SELF REGIONAL HEALTHCARE *p* 1302
1325 Spring St, Greenwood SC 29646
Tel (864) 725-4150 *SIC* 8062

■ HILTON HEAD HEALTH SYSTEM LP *p* 695
25 Hospital Cntr Blvrd, Hilton Head Island SC 29926
Tel (843) 681-6122 *SIC* 8062

SPRINGS MEMORIAL HOSPITAL *p* 1361
800 W Meeting St, Lancaster SC 29720
Tel (803) 286-1477 *SIC* 8062 8069 8049

■ EAST COOPER COMMUNITY HOSPITAL INC *p* 470
2000 Hospital Dr, Mount Pleasant SC 29464
Tel (843) 881-0100 *SIC* 8062 8011

WACCAMAW COMMUNITY HOSPITAL *p* 1570
4070 Highway 17 Business, Murrells Inlet SC 29576
Tel (843) 527-7000 *SIC* 8062

GRAND STRAND REGIONAL MEDICAL CENTER LLC *p* 630
809 82nd Pkwy, Myrtle Beach SC 29572
Tel (843) 449-4411 *SIC* 8062

REGIONAL MEDICAL CENTER *p* 1219
3000 Saint Matthews Rd, Orangeburg SC 29118
Tel (803) 395-2200 *SIC* 8062

REGIONAL MEDICAL CENTER OF ORANGEBURG & CALHOUN COUNTIES *p* 1219
3000 Saint Matthews Rd, Orangeburg SC 29118
Tel (803) 395-2200 *SIC* 8062

■ AMISUB OF SOUTH CAROLINA INC *p* 85
222 S Herlong Ave, Rock Hill SC 29732
Tel (803) 329-1234 *SIC* 8062

OCONEE MEDICAL CENTER *p* 1074
298 Memorial Dr, Seneca SC 29672
Tel (864) 482-3100 *SIC* 8062 8051

■ MARY BLACK HEALTH SYSTEMS INC *p* 914
1700 Skylyn Dr, Spartanburg SC 29307
Tel (864) 573-3000 *SIC* 8062

MARY BLACK MEMORIAL HOSPITAL INC *p* 914
1700 Skylyn Dr, Spartanburg SC 29307
Tel (864) 573-3004 *SIC* 8062

SPARTANBURG REGIONAL HEALTH SERVICES DISTRICT INC *p* 1355
101 E Wood St, Spartanburg SC 29303
Tel (864) 560-6000 *SIC* 8062

PALMETTO HEALTH TUOMEY *p* 1109
129 N Washington St, Sumter SC 29150
Tel (803) 774-9000 *SIC* 8062

LEXINGTON COUNTY HEALTH SERVICES DISTRICT INC *p* 859
2720 Sunset Blvd, West Columbia SC 29169
Tel (803) 791-2000
SIC 8062 8011 8299 8051

LEXINGTON MEDICAL CENTER *p* 859
2720 Sunset Blvd, West Columbia SC 29169
Tel (803) 791-2000 *SIC* 8062

AVERA ST LUKES *p* 137
305 S State St, Aberdeen SD 57401
Tel (605) 622-5000 *SIC* 8062 5912

ST BERNARDS PROVIDENCE HOSPITA *p* 1365
901 E Virgil Ave, Milbank SD 57252
Tel (605) 432-4538 *SIC* 8062

AVERA QUEEN OF PEACE *p* 137
525 N Foster St, Mitchell SD 57301
Tel (605) 995-2000 *SIC* 8062

AVERA QUEEN OF PEACE HOSPITAL *p* 137
525 N Foster St, Mitchell SD 57301
Tel (605) 995-2000 *SIC* 8062

RAPID CITY REGIONAL HOSPITAL INC *p* 1208
353 Fairmont Blvd, Rapid City SD 57701
Tel (605) 719-1000 *SIC* 8062

REGIONAL HEALTH INC *p* 1219
353 Fairmont Blvd, Rapid City SD 57701
Tel (605) 755-1000 *SIC* 8062

AVERA MCKENNAN HOSPITAL MEDICAL STAFF *p* 137
1325 S Cliff Ave, Sioux Falls SD 57105
Tel (605) 322-8000 *SIC* 8062

HEART HOSPITAL OF SOUTH DAKOTA LLC *p* 678
4500 W 69th St, Sioux Falls SD 57108
Tel (605) 977-7000 *SIC* 8062 3842

SANFORD HEALTH *p* 1279
1305 W 18th St, Sioux Falls SD 57105
Tel (605) 333-1720 *SIC* 8062 8011 8051

SIOUX FALLS SPECIALTY HOSPITAL LLP *p* 1326
910 E 20th St, Sioux Falls SD 57105
Tel (605) 334-6730 *SIC* 8062

PRAIRIE LAKES HEALTH CARE SYSTEM INC *p* 1167
401 9th Ave Nw, Watertown SD 57201
Tel (605) 882-7000 *SIC* 8062

SACRED HEART HEALTH SERVICES *p* 1265
501 Summit St, Yankton SD 57078
Tel (605) 668-8000 *SIC* 8062 8011

■ SAINT FRANCIS HOSPITAL - BARTLETT INC *p* 1269
2986 Kate Bond Rd, Bartlett TN 38133
Tel (901) 820-7000 *SIC* 8062

CAPELLA HEALTHCARE INC *p* 248
103 Continental Pl # 200, Brentwood TN 37027
Tel (615) 764-3000 *SIC* 8062

CAPELLA HOLDINGS INC *p* 248
103 Continental Pl # 200, Brentwood TN 37027
Tel (615) 844-9800 *SIC* 8062 6719

COGENT MEDICAL CARE PC *p* 334
5410 Maryland Way Ste 300, Brentwood TN 37027
Tel (615) 377-5600 *SIC* 8062

■ DLP HEALTHCARE LLC *p* 445
330 Seven Springs Way, Brentwood TN 37027
Tel (615) 372-8500 *SIC* 8062

■ HISTORIC LIFEPOINT HOSPITALS INC *p* 696
330 Seven Springs Way, Brentwood TN 37027
Tel (615) 372-8500 *SIC* 8062

▲ LIFEPOINT HEALTH INC *p* 864
330 Seven Springs Way, Brentwood TN 37027
Tel (615) 920-7000 *SIC* 8062 8742

■ PARKRIDGE MEDICAL CENTER INC *p* 1116
2333 Mccallie Ave, Chattanooga TN 37404
Tel (423) 698-6061 *SIC* 8062

CLARKSVILLE VOLUNTEER HEALTH INC *p* 322
651 Dunlop Ln, Clarksville TN 37040
Tel (931) 220-2532 *SIC* 8062 8621

■ CLEVELAND TENNESSEE HOSPITAL CO LLC *p* 326
2305 Chambliss Ave Nw, Cleveland TN 37311
Tel (423) 559-6000 *SIC* 8062

MAURY REGIONAL HOSPITAL *p* 921
1224 Trotwood Ave, Columbia TN 38401
Tel (931) 381-1111 *SIC* 8062

COOKEVILLE REGIONAL MEDICAL CENTER *p* 366
1 Medical Center Blvd, Cookeville TN 38501
Tel (931) 528-2541 *SIC* 8062

CUMBERLAND MEDICAL CENTER INC *p* 400
421 S Main St, Crossville TN 38555
Tel (931) 484-9511 *SIC* 8062

■ CHSPSC *p* 304
4000 Meridian Blvd, Franklin TN 37067
Tel (615) 465-7000 *SIC* 8062 6321

▲ COMMUNITY HEALTH SYSTEMS INC *p* 349
4000 Meridian Blvd, Franklin TN 37067
Tel (615) 465-7000 *SIC* 8062 8742

IASIS HEALTHCARE CORP *p* 726
117 Seaboard Ln Bldg E, Franklin TN 37067
Tel (615) 844-2747 *SIC* 8062

IASIS HEALTHCARE LLC *p* 726
117 Seaboard Ln Bldg E, Franklin TN 37067
Tel (615) 844-2747 *SIC* 8062

IASIS INVESTMENT LLC *p* 726
113 Seaboard Ln Ste 200a, Franklin TN 37067
Tel (615) 844-2747 *SIC* 8062

■ NATIONAL HEALTHCARE OF CLEVELAND INC *p* 1013
4000 Meridian Blvd, Franklin TN 37067
Tel (423) 339-4100 *SIC* 8062

WILLIAMSON COUNTY HOSPITAL INC *p* 1612
4321 Carothers Pkwy, Franklin TN 37067
Tel (615) 791-0500 *SIC* 8062

■ SRHS BANKRUPTCY INC *p* 1363
555 Hartsville Pike, Gallatin TN 37066
Tel (615) 452-4210 *SIC* 8062

■ HCA HEALTH SERVICES OF TENNESSEE INC *p* 671
5655 Frist Blvd, Hermitage TN 37076
Tel (615) 316-3000 *SIC* 8062

MEMORIAL NORTH PARK HOSPITAL *p* 942
2151 Hamill Rd, Hixson TN 37343
Tel (423) 495-7100 *SIC* 8062

JACKSON CLINIC PROFESSIONAL ASSOCIATION *p* 773
828 N Parkway, Jackson TN 38305
Tel (731) 422-0200 *SIC* 5912 8011 8062

■ JACKSON HOSPITAL CORP *p* 774
367 Hospital Blvd, Jackson TN 38305
Tel (731) 661-2000 *SIC* 8062

JACKSON-MADISON COUNTY GENERAL HOSPITAL DISTRICT *p* 774
620 Skyline Dr, Jackson TN 38301
Tel (731) 541-5000 *SIC* 8062

TENNESSEE WEST HEALTHCARE INC *p* 1438
620 Skyline Dr, Jackson TN 38301
Tel (731) 541-5000 *SIC* 8062

MOUNTAIN STATES HEALTH ALLIANCE *p* 994
400 N State Of Frnklin Rd, Johnson City TN 37604
Tel (423) 431-6111 *SIC* 8062

WELLMONT HEALTH SYSTEM *p* 1589
1905 American Way, Kingsport TN 37660
Tel (423) 230-8200 *SIC* 8062 8051 8063

■ BAPTIST HEALTH SYSTEM OF EAST TENNESSEE INC *p* 154
137 E Blount Ave Ste 1b, Knoxville TN 37920
Tel (865) 632-5011 *SIC* 8062

BAPTIST HOSPITAL OF EAST TENNESSEE INC *p* 154
137 E Blount Ave, Knoxville TN 37920
Tel (865) 632-5200 *SIC* 8062

■ BAPTIST HOSPITAL WEST INC *p* 154
10820 Parkside Dr, Knoxville TN 37934
Tel (865) 218-7011 *SIC* 8062

COVENANT HEALTH *p* 384
100 Fort Sanders W Blvd, Knoxville TN 37922
Tel (865) 531-5555 *SIC* 8062

FORT SANDERS REGIONAL MEDICAL CENTER *p* 569
1901 W Clinch Ave, Knoxville TN 37916
Tel (865) 541-1111 *SIC* 8062

■ MERCY HEALTH PARTNERS INC *p* 946
900 E Oak Hill Ave, Knoxville TN 37917
Tel (865) 545-8000 *SIC* 8062

PARKWEST MEDICAL CENTER *p* 1117
9352 Park West Blvd, Knoxville TN 37923
Tel (865) 373-1000 *SIC* 8062

UNIVERSITY HEALTH SYSTEM INC *p* 1519
1924 Alcoa Hwy, Knoxville TN 37920
Tel (865) 305-9000 *SIC* 8062

■ LEBANON HMA LLC *p* 850
1411 W Baddour Pkwy, Lebanon TN 37087
Tel (615) 444-8262 *SIC* 8062

BLOUNT MEMORIAL HOSPITAL INC *p* 190
907 Lamar Alexander Pkwy, Maryville TN 37804
Tel (865) 983-7211 *SIC* 8062

BAPTIST MEMORIAL HEALTH CARE CORP *p* 154
350 N Humphreys Blvd, Memphis TN 38120
Tel (901) 227-2727
SIC 8062 8011 8741 5047

BAPTIST MEMORIAL HOSPITAL *p* 154
6019 Walnut Grove Rd, Memphis TN 38120
Tel (901) 226-5000 *SIC* 8062

BOSTON BASKIN CANCER FOUNDATION INC *p* 202
80 Humphreys Center Dr # 330, Memphis TN 38120
Tel (901) 226-5000 *SIC* 8062

METHODIST HEALTHCARE MEMPHIS HOSPITALS *p* 953
1265 Union Ave, Memphis TN 38104
Tel (901) 516-7000 *SIC* 8062

METHODIST LE BONHEUR HEALTHCARE *p* 954
1211 Union Ave Ste 700, Memphis TN 38104
Tel (901) 516-7000 *SIC* 8062

SHELBY COUNTY HEALTH CARE CORP *p* 1314
877 Jefferson Ave, Memphis TN 38103
Tel (901) 545-7928 *SIC* 8062

■ ST FRANCIS HOSPITAL INC *p* 1366
5959 Park Ave, Memphis TN 38119
Tel (901) 765-1000 *SIC* 8062 8051

ST JUDE CHILDRENS RESEARCH HOSPITAL INC *p* 1369
262 Danny Thomas Pl, Memphis TN 38105
Tel (901) 595-3300 *SIC* 8733 8062

MIDDLE TENNESSEE MEDICAL CENTER *p* 964
1700 Medical Center Pkwy, Murfreesboro TN 37129
Tel (615) 396-4100 *SIC* 8062

SAINT THOMAS RUTHERFORD HOSPITAL *p* 1271
1700 Medical Center Pkwy, Murfreesboro TN 37129
Tel (615) 849-4100 *SIC* 8062

AHS HILLCREST HEALTHCARE SYSTEM LLC *p* 37
1 Burton Hills Blvd # 250, Nashville TN 37215
Tel (615) 296-3000 *SIC* 8062

ARDENT HEALTH PARTNERS LLC *p* 106
1 Burton Hills Blvd # 250, Nashville TN 37215
Tel (615) 296-3000 *SIC* 8069 8062

■ HCA HEALTH SERVICES OF FLORIDA INC *p* 671
1 Park Plz, Nashville TN 37203
Tel (615) 344-9551 *SIC* 8062 8093

■ HCA HEALTH SERVICES OF TENNESSEE INC *p* 671
1 Park Plz, Nashville TN 37203
Tel (615) 344-9551 *SIC* 8062

■ HCA HEALTH SERVICES OF TENNESSEE INC *p* 671
391 Wallace Rd, Nashville TN 37211
Tel (615) 781-4000 *SIC* 8011 8062

■ HCA HEALTH SERVICES OF TEXAS INC p 671
1 Park Plz, Nashville TN 37203
Tel (615) 344-9551 SIC 8062

▲ HCA HOLDINGS INC p 672
1 Park Plz, Nashville TN 37203
Tel (615) 344-9551 SIC 8062

■ HCA INC p 672
1 Park Plz, Nashville TN 37203
Tel (615) 344-9551
SIC 8063 8062 8069 8093

■ HCA-HOSPITAL CORP OF AMERICA p 672
1 Park Plz, Nashville TN 37203
Tel (615) 344-9551 SIC 8062 8063

HERCULES HOLDING II LLC p 685
1 Park Plz, Nashville TN 37203
Tel (615) 344-9551
SIC 8062 8063 8069 8093

■ HOSPITAL CORP OF AMERICA p 709
1 Park Plz, Nashville TN 37203
Tel (615) 344-9551 SIC 8062 8063

■ HTI MEMORIAL HOSPITAL CORP p 715
3441 Dickerson Pike, Nashville TN 37207
Tel (615) 769-2000 SIC 8062

■ NEW PORT RICHEY HOSPITAL INC p 1033
1 Park Plz, Nashville TN 37203
Tel (727) 848-1733 SIC 8062

■ RESTON HOSPITAL CENTER LLC p 1228
1 Park Plz, Nashville TN 37203
Tel (615) 344-9551 SIC 8011 8062

SAINT THOMAS HOSPITAL p 1271
4220 Harding Pike, Nashville TN 37205
Tel (615) 222-5976 SIC 8062

ST THOMAS HOSPITAL p 1373
4220 Harding Pike, Nashville TN 37205
Tel (615) 222-2111 SIC 8062

■ SURGERY PARTNERS INC p 1409
40 Burton Hills Blvd # 500, Nashville TN 37215
Tel (615) 234-5900 SIC 8062 3851

SYMBION HOLDINGS CORP p 1414
40 Burton Hills Blvd # 500, Nashville TN 37215
Tel (615) 234-5900 SIC 8011 8093 8062

SYMBION INC p 1414
40 Burton Hills Blvd # 500, Nashville TN 37215
Tel (615) 234-5900 SIC 8011 8093 8062

THOMAS SAINT MIDTOWN HOSPITAL p 1449
2000 Church St, Nashville TN 37236
Tel (615) 284-5555 SIC 8062 8011

VANDERBILT CHILDRENS HOSPITAL p 1543
2200 Chld Way Ste 2410, Nashville TN 37232
Tel (615) 322-7601 SIC 8062

VANDERBILT UNIVERSITY p 1543
211 Kirkland Hall, Nashville TN 37240
Tel (615) 322-5000 SIC 8221 8062

VANDERBILT UNIVERSITY MEDICAL CENTER p 1543
1211 Medical Center Dr, Nashville TN 37232
Tel (615) 875-9396 SIC 8062

■ VANGUARD HEALTH SYSTEMS INC p 1543
20 Burton Hills Blvd # 100, Nashville TN 37215
Tel (615) 665-6000 SIC 8062 6324

METHODIST MEDICAL CENTER OF OAK RIDGE p 954
990 Oak Ridge Tpke, Oak Ridge TN 37830
Tel (865) 835-1000 SIC 8062

■ HARTON JOHN W REGIONAL MEDICAL CENTER INC p 666
1801 N Jackson St, Tullahoma TN 37388
Tel (931) 393-3000 SIC 8062

■ TENNESSEE SOUTHERN REGIONAL HEALTH p 1438
185 Hospital Rd, Winchester TN 37398
Tel (931) 967-8200 SIC 8062

■ ARMC LP p 111
6250 Highway 83 84, Abilene TX 79606
Tel (325) 428-1000
SIC 8062 8093 8011 7991

HENDRICK MEDICAL CENTER p 683
1900 Pine St, Abilene TX 79601
Tel (325) 670-2000 SIC 8062

USP INTERNATIONAL HOLDINGS INC p 1535
15305 Dallas Pkwy, Addison TX 75001
Tel (972) 713-3500 SIC 8062

AHS AMARILLO HEALTH SYSTEM LLC p 37
1600 Wallace Blvd, Amarillo TX 79106
Tel (806) 212-2000 SIC 8062

BAPTIST ST ANTHONYS HOSPITAL CORP p 154
1600 Wallace Blvd, Amarillo TX 79106
Tel (806) 212-2000 SIC 8062

BAPTIST/ST ANTHONYS HEALTH SYSTEM p 154
1600 Wallace Blvd, Amarillo TX 79106
Tel (806) 212-2000 SIC 8062

BSA HEALTH SYSTEM OF AMARILLO LLC p 222
1600 Wallace Blvd, Amarillo TX 79106
Tel (806) 212-2000 SIC 8062

HIGH PLAINS BAPTIST HOSPITAL INC p 690
1600 Wallace Blvd, Amarillo TX 79106
Tel (806) 358-5800 SIC 8062 6513 8051

■ NORTHWEST TEXAS HEALTHCARE SYSTEM INC p 1060
1501 S Coulter St, Amarillo TX 79106
Tel (806) 354-1000
SIC 8062 8063 8051 8049

ARLINGTON MEMORIAL HOSPITAL ALLIANCE INC p 110
800 W Randol Mill Rd, Arlington TX 76012
Tel (817) 548-6100 SIC 8062

TEXAS HEALTH ARLINGTON MEMORIAL HOSPITAL p 1443
800 W Randol Mill Rd, Arlington TX 76012
Tel (682) 236-6695 SIC 8062

TEXAS HEALTH RESOURCES p 1443
612 E Lamar Blvd Ste 400, Arlington TX 76011
Tel (682) 236-7900 SIC 8062

USMD HOSPITAL AT ARLINGTON LP p 1535
801 W Interstate 20, Arlington TX 76017
Tel (817) 472-3400 SIC 8062

SETON HEALTHCARE FAMILY p 1308
1201 W 38th St, Austin TX 78705
Tel (512) 324-1000 SIC 8062

ST DAVIDS COMMUNITY HEALTH FOUNDATION INITIATIVE p 1365
1303 San Antonio St, Austin TX 78701
Tel (512) 879-6240 SIC 8062

ST DAVIDS FOUNDATION p 1365
1303 San Antonio St, Austin TX 78701
Tel (512) 879-6600 SIC 8062

ST DAVIDS HEALTHCARE PARTNERSHIP LP LLP p 1365
98 San Jacinto Blvd, Austin TX 78701
Tel (512) 708-9700 SIC 8062

ST DAVIDS HOSPITAL (INC) p 1366
919 E 32nd St, Austin TX 78705
Tel (512) 476-7111 SIC 8062

ST DAVIDS NORTH AUSTIN MEDICAL CENTER p 1366
12221 N Mo Pac Expy, Austin TX 78758
Tel (512) 901-1000
SIC 8062 8011 8069 8049

■ ST DAVIDS SOUTH AUSTIN MEDICAL CENTER p 1366
901 W Ben White Blvd, Austin TX 78704
Tel (512) 447-2211 SIC 8062 8011

SAN JACINTO METHODIST HOSPITAL p 1277
4401 Garth Rd, Baytown TX 77521
Tel (281) 420-8600 SIC 8062 8063 8051

■ TRIUMPH HOSPITAL BAYTOWN p 1483
1700 James Bowie Dr, Baytown TX 77520
Tel (281) 420-7800 SIC 8062

BAPTIST HOSPITALS OF SOUTHEAST TEXAS p 154
3080 College St, Beaumont TX 77701
Tel (409) 212-5000 SIC 8062

CHRISTUS HEALTH SOUTHEAST TEXAS p 303
2830 Calder St, Beaumont TX 77702
Tel (409) 892-7171 SIC 8062

MEMORIAL HERMANN BAPTIST HOSPITAL p 941
3080 College St, Beaumont TX 77701
Tel (409) 212-5000 SIC 8062

TEXAS HLTH HRS MTHDT HSPTL HEB p 1443
1615 Hospital Pkwy, Bedford TX 76022
Tel (817) 848-4000 SIC 8062 8063 8069

VALLEY BAPTIST MEDICAL CENTER - BROWNSVILLE p 1540
1040 W Jefferson St, Brownsville TX 78520
Tel (956) 389-1100 SIC 8062

BROWNWOOD HOSPITAL LP p 220
1501 Burnet Rd, Brownwood TX 76801
Tel (325) 646-8541 SIC 8062

ST JOSEPH REGIONAL HEALTH CENTER p 1368
2801 Franciscan Dr, Bryan TX 77802
Tel (979) 776-3777 SIC 8062 8322

ADVENTIST HEALTH SYSTEMS/ SUN BELT p 27
11801 South Fwy, Burleson TX 76028
Tel (817) 293-9110 SIC 8062

BAYLOR MEDICAL CENTER AT CARROLLTON p 162
4343 N Josey Ln, Carrollton TX 75010
Tel (972) 492-1010 SIC 8062

■ FIRST TEXAS HOSPITAL CARROLLTON LLC p 550
1401 E Trinity Mills Rd, Carrollton TX 75006
Tel (972) 810-0700 SIC 8062

■ CEDAR PARK HEALTH SYSTEM LP p 272
1401 Medical Pkwy, Cedar Park TX 78613
Tel (512) 528-7000 SIC 8062

■ COLLEGE STATION HOSPITAL LP p 337
1604 Rock Prairie Rd, College Station TX 77845
Tel (979) 764-5100 SIC 8062

■ CHCA CONROE LP p 292
504 Medical Center Blvd, Conroe TX 77304
Tel (936) 539-1111 SIC 8062

■ BAY AREA HEALTHCARE GROUP LTD p 160
3315 S Alameda St, Corpus Christi TX 78411
Tel (361) 761-1400
SIC 8062 8063 8069 8093

CHRISTUS SPOHN HEALTH SYSTEM CORP p 304
1702 Santa Fe St, Corpus Christi TX 78404
Tel (361) 881-3000 SIC 8062

■ COLUMBIA HOSPITAL CORP OF BAY AREA p 341
7101 S Padre Island Dr, Corpus Christi TX 78412
Tel (361) 761-1200 SIC 8062

NORTH CYPRESS MEDICAL CENTER OPERATING CO GP LLC p 1052
21214 Northwest Fwy, Cypress TX 77429
Tel (832) 912-3500 SIC 8062

BAYLOR HEALTH CARE SYSTEM p 162
3500 Gaston Ave, Dallas TX 75246
Tel (214) 820-0111 SIC 8062 8082 1542

BAYLOR SCOTT & WHITE HEALTH p 162
3500 Gaston Ave, Dallas TX 75246
Tel (214) 820-1075 SIC 8062 8082

BAYLOR SCOTT & WHITE HOLDINGS p 162
350 N Saint Paul St # 2900, Dallas TX 75201
Tel (214) 820-3151 SIC 8062

BAYLOR UNIVERSITY MEDICAL CENTER p 162
2001 Bryan St Ste 2200, Dallas TX 75201
Tel (214) 820-3151 SIC 8062

■ COLUMBIA HOSPITAL AT MEDICAL CITY DALLAS SUBSIDIARY LP p 340
7777 Forest Ln Ste C840, Dallas TX 75230
Tel (972) 566-7000 SIC 8062

■ COLUMBIA MEDICAL CENTER OF ARLINGTON SUBSIDIARY LP p 341
13455 Noel Rd, Dallas TX 75240
Tel (817) 465-3241 SIC 8062

DALLAS COUNTY HOSPITAL DISTRICT p 410
5200 Harry Hines Blvd, Dallas TX 75235
Tel (214) 590-8000 SIC 8062

DALLAS MEDICAL CENTER LLC p 410
7 Medical Pkwy, Dallas TX 75234
Tel (972) 888-7000 SIC 8062

MEDICAL CITY DALLAS IMAGING CENTER LLP p 936
7777 Forest Ln Ste C840, Dallas TX 75230
Tel (972) 566-7000 SIC 8062

METHODIST HOSPITALS OF DALLAS INC p 954
1441 N Beckley Ave, Dallas TX 75203
Tel (877) 637-4297 SIC 8062

▲ TENET HEALTHCARE CORP p 1437
1445 Ross Ave Ste 1400, Dallas TX 75202
Tel (469) 893-2200
SIC 8062 8069 8741 8063 8082 8011

■ TENET HEALTHSYSTEM HOSPITALS INC p 1437
13737 Noel Rd Ste 100, Dallas TX 75240
Tel (469) 893-2000 SIC 8062

■ TENET HEALTHSYSTEM MEDICAL INC p 1437
1445 Ross Ave Ste 1400, Dallas TX 75202
Tel (469) 893-2000 SIC 8062 8063 6512

TEXAS HEALTH PRESBYTERIAN HOSPITAL DALLAS p 1443
8200 Walnut Hill Ln, Dallas TX 75231
Tel (214) 345-6789 SIC 8062

WISE HEALTH FOUNDATION p 1619
609 Medical Center Dr, Decatur TX 76234
Tel (940) 627-5921 SIC 8062

TEXOMA HEALTHCARE SYSTEM p 1445
1000 Memorial Dr, Denison TX 75020
Tel (903) 416-4000 SIC 8062 8059

UHS OF TEXOMA INC p 1500
5016 S Us Highway 75, Denison TX 75020
Tel (903) 416-4000 SIC 8062

■ DENTON REGIONAL MEDICAL CENTER INC p 429
3535 S Interstate 35 E, Denton TX 76210
Tel (940) 384-3535 SIC 8062 8011

DENTON TRANSITIONAL LTCH LP p 429
2813 S Mayhill Rd, Denton TX 76208
Tel (940) 320-2300 SIC 8062

DOCTORS HOSPITAL AT RENAISSANCE LTD p 447
5501 S Mccoll Rd, Edinburg TX 78539
Tel (956) 362-8677 SIC 8062

EL PASO COUNTY HOSPITAL DISTRICT p 483
4815 Alameda Ave, El Paso TX 79905
Tel (915) 544-1200 SIC 8062

■ EL PASO HEALTHCARE SYSTEM LTD p 483
10301 Gateway Blvd W, El Paso TX 79925
Tel (915) 595-9000 SIC 8062

■ TENET HOSPITALS LIMITED p 1437
2001 N Oregon St, El Paso TX 79902
Tel (915) 577-6011 SIC 8062

BAYLOR ALL SAINTS MEDICAL CENTER p 162
1400 8th Ave, Fort Worth TX 76104
Tel (817) 926-2544 SIC 8062

■ COLUMBIA PLAZA MEDICAL CENTER OF FORT WORTH SUBSIDIARY LP p 341
900 8th Ave, Fort Worth TX 76104
Tel (817) 336-2100 SIC 8062

DECATUR HOSPITAL AUTHORITY p 420
900 W Leuda St, Fort Worth TX 76104
Tel (817) 332-7003 SIC 8062

TARRANT COUNTY HOSPITAL DISTRICT p 1425
1500 S Main St, Fort Worth TX 76104
Tel (817) 921-3431 SIC 8062

TEXAS HEALTH HARRIS METHODIST HOSPITAL FORT WORTH p 1443
1301 Pennsylvania Ave, Fort Worth TX 76104
Tel (817) 250-2000 SIC 8062

FRISCO MEDICAL CENTER LLP p 580
5601 Warren Pkwy, Frisco TX 75034
Tel (214) 618-2000 SIC 8062

UNIVERSITY OF TEXAS MEDICAL BRANCH AT GALVESTON p 1526
301 University Blvd, Galveston TX 77555
Tel (409) 772-1011 SIC 8062

BAYLOR MEDICAL CENTER AT GARLAND p 162
2300 Marie Curie Dr, Garland TX 75042
Tel (972) 487-5000
SIC 8062 8082 8011 8093

CORYELL COUNTY MEMORIAL HOSPITAL AUTHORITY p 373
1507 W Main St, Gatesville TX 76528
Tel (254) 248-6247 SIC 8062

■ GRANBURY HOSPITAL CORP p 629
1310 Paluxy Rd, Granbury TX 76048
Tel (817) 573-2273 SIC 8062

BAYLOR REGIONAL MEDICAL CENTER AT GRAPEVINE p 162
1650 W College St, Grapevine TX 76051
Tel (817) 481-1588 SIC 8062

HUNT MEMORIAL HOSPITAL DISTRICT p 719
4215 Joe Ramsey Blvd E, Greenville TX 75401
Tel (903) 408-5000 SIC 8062 8071 8082

HARLINGEN MEDICAL CENTER LIMITED PARTNERSHIP p 662
5501 S Expressway 77, Harlingen TX 78550
Tel (956) 365-3947 SIC 8062

■ CHCA WOMANS HOSPITAL LP p 292
7600 Fannin St, Houston TX 77054
Tel (713) 791-7534 SIC 8062

CHI ST LUKES HEALTH BAYLOR COLLEGE OF MEDICINE MEDICAL CENTER p 296
6624 Fannin St Ste 1100, Houston TX 77030
Tel (832) 355-1000 SIC 8062

CHRISTUS HEALTH GULF COAST p 303
18300 Saint John Dr, Houston TX 77058
Tel (281) 333-5503 SIC 8062

COMMUNITY HEALTH CHOICE INC p 348
2636 S Loop W Ste 700, Houston TX 77054
Tel (713) 295-2200 SIC 8062

■ CYPRESS FAIRBANKS MEDICAL CENTER INC p 405
10655 Steepletop Dr, Houston TX 77065
Tel (281) 890-4285 SIC 8062

HARRIS HEALTH SYSTEM p 663
2525 Holly Hall St, Houston TX 77054
Tel (713) 566-6400 SIC 8062 8011

■ HOUSTON NORTHWEST MEDICAL CENTER INC p 712
710 Cypress Creek Pkwy # 34, Houston TX 77090
Tel (281) 440-1000 SIC 8062

■ HOUSTON NORTHWEST MEDICAL CENTER EDUCATION FOUNDATION INC p 712
710 Cypress Station Dr # 340, Houston TX 77090
Tel (281) 440-1000 SIC 8062

INSTITUTE FOR REHABILITATION & RESEARCH p 747
1333 Moursund St, Houston TX 77030
Tel (713) 799-5000 SIC 8062

MEMORIAL HERMANN HEALTH SYSTEM p 941
909 Frostwood Dr Fl 2, Houston TX 77024
Tel (713) 242-3000 SIC 8062 8093

MEMORIAL HERMANN HEALTHCARE SYSTEM p 941
929 Gessner Rd, Houston TX 77024
Tel (713) 338-5555 SIC 8059 8062

MEMORIAL HERMANN TEXAS MEDICAL p 942
6411 Fannin St, Houston TX 77030
Tel (713) 704-4000 SIC 8062

METHODIST HOSPITAL p 953
6565 Fannin St, Houston TX 77030
Tel (713) 790-3311 SIC 8062

METHODIST WEST HOUSTON HOSPITAL p 954
18500 Katy Fwy, Houston TX 77094
Tel (832) 522-1000 SIC 8661 8062

■ SCCI HOSPITALS OF AMERICA INC p 1286
7333 North Fwy Ste 500, Houston TX 77076
Tel (713) 807-8686 SIC 8062

SIGNATURE HOSPITAL CORP p 1322
363 N Sam Houston Pkwy E, Houston TX 77060
Tel (281) 598-9800 SIC 8062

SJ MEDICAL CENTER LLC p 1328
1401 St Joseph Pkwy, Houston TX 77002
Tel (713) 757-1000 SIC 8062

SPRING BRANCH MEDICAL CENTER INC p 1360
6060 Richmond Ave Ste 315, Houston TX 77057
Tel (713) 722-3799 SIC 8062

ST LUKES EPISCOPAL HOSPITAL p 1370
6624 Fannin St, Houston TX 77030
Tel (713) 610-9326 SIC 8062

ST LUKES EPISCOPAL HOSPITAL INDEPENDENT PRACTICE ASSOCIATION INC p 1370
6720 Bertner Ave, Houston TX 77030
Tel (832) 355-1000 SIC 8062

ST LUKES HEALTH SYSTEM CORP p 1370
6624 Fannin St Ste 1100, Houston TX 77030
Tel (832) 355-1000 SIC 8062

TEXAS CHILDRENS HOSPITAL p 1442
6621 Fannin St, Houston TX 77030
Tel (832) 824-1000 SIC 8011 8062

UNIVERSITY GENERAL HEALTH SYSTEM INC p 1518
7501 Fannin St, Houston TX 77054
Tel (713) 375-7100 SIC 8062 8059

NORTHEAST HOSPITAL FOUNDATION p 1055
18951 N Memorial Dr, Humble TX 77338
Tel (281) 540-7817 SIC 8062

NORTHEAST MEDICAL CENTER HOSPITAL p 1055
9813 Memorial Blvd Ste H, Humble TX 77338
Tel (281) 540-7167 SIC 8062

HUNTSVILLE MEMORIAL HOSPITAL AUXILIARY p 721
110 Memorial Hospital Dr, Huntsville TX 77340
Tel (936) 291-3411 SIC 8062

BAYLOR MEDICAL CENTER AT IRVING p 162
1901 N Macarthur Blvd, Irving TX 75061
Tel (972) 579-8100 SIC 8062

CHRISTUS HEALTH p 303
919 Hidden Rdg, Irving TX 75038
Tel (469) 282-2000 SIC 8062 8051

CHRISTUS HEALTH p 303
919 Hidden Rdg, Irving TX 75038
Tel (281) 936-6000 SIC 8062

CHRISTUS HEALTH GULF COAST p 303
919 Hidden Rdg, Irving TX 75038
Tel (281) 599-5700 SIC 8062

USMD HOLDINGS INC p 1535
6333 N State Highway 161 # 200, Irving TX 75038
Tel (214) 493-4000 SIC 8062

MEMORIAL HERMANN KATY HOSPITAL p 942
23900 Katy Fwy, Katy TX 77494
Tel (281) 644-7000 SIC 8062

PETERSON SID MEMORIAL HOSPITAL p 1138
551 Hill Country Dr, Kerrville TX 78028
Tel (830) 896-4200 SIC 8051 8062

METROPLEX ADVENTIST HOSPITAL INC p 955
2201 S Clear Creek Rd, Killeen TX 76549
Tel (254) 526-7523 SIC 8062

BRAZOSPORT MEMORIAL HOSPITAL p 209
194 Abner Jackson Pkwy, Lake Jackson TX 77566
Tel (979) 299-2882 SIC 8062

■ LAREDO MEDICAL CENTER p 845
1700 E Saunders St, Laredo TX 78041
Tel (956) 796-5000 SIC 8062

■ LAREDO REGIONAL MEDICAL CENTER L P p 845
1700 E Saunders St, Laredo TX 78041
Tel (956) 796-5000 SIC 8062 8071

GOOD SHEPHERD HEALTH SYSTEM INC p 623
700 E Marshall Ave, Longview TX 75601
Tel (888) 784-4747 SIC 8062

■ LONGVIEW MEDICAL CENTER LP p 877
2901 4th St, Longview TX 75605
Tel (903) 758-1818 SIC 8062 8099

SHEPHERD GOOD HOSPITAL INC p 1315
700 E Marshall Ave, Longview TX 75601
Tel (903) 315-2000 SIC 8062

COVENANT HEALTH SYSTEM p 384
3615 19th St, Lubbock TX 79410
Tel (806) 725-1011 SIC 8062

LUBBOCK COUNTY HOSPITAL DISTRICT p 883
602 Indiana Ave, Lubbock TX 79415
Tel (806) 775-8200 SIC 8062

MEMORIAL HEALTH SYSTEM OF EAST TEXAS p 941
1201 W Frank Ave, Lufkin TX 75904
Tel (936) 634-8111 *SIC* 8062

■ **PINEY WOODS HEALTHCARE SYSTEM LP** p 1149
505 S John Redditt Dr, Lufkin TX 75904
Tel (936) 634-8311
SIC 8062 8071 8099 8051

HARRISON COUNTY HOSPITAL ASSOCIATION p 664
811 S Washington Ave, Marshall TX 75670
Tel (903) 927-6000 *SIC* 8062

■ **COLUMBIA RIO GRANDE HEALTHCARE LP** p 341
101 E Ridge Rd, Mcallen TX 78503
Tel (956) 632-6000 *SIC* 8011 8062

■ **MCALLEN MEDICAL CENTER LP** p 925
301 W Expressway 83, Mcallen TX 78503
Tel (956) 632-4000 *SIC* 8062

RIO GRANDE REGIONAL HOSPITAL p 1235
101 E Ridge Rd, Mcallen TX 78503
Tel (956) 632-6000 *SIC* 8062

MIDLAND COUNTY HOSPITAL DISTRICT p 965
400 R Redfern Grover Pkwy, Midland TX 79701
Tel (432) 685-1111 *SIC* 8062

MIDLAND MEMORIAL HOSPITAL & MEDICAL CENTER p 966
2200 W Illinois Ave, Midland TX 79701
Tel (432) 685-1111 *SIC* 8062

MISSION HOSPITAL INC p 975
900 S Bryan Rd, Mission TX 78572
Tel (956) 323-9000 *SIC* 8062

ECTOR COUNTY HOSPITAL DISTRICT p 476
500 W 4th St, Odessa TX 79761
Tel (432) 640-4000 *SIC* 8062

ODESSA REGIONAL HOSPITAL LP p 1074
520 E 6th St, Odessa TX 79761
Tel (432) 582-8000 *SIC* 8062

MEMORIAL HERMANN BAPTIST BELMONT p 941
608 Strickland Dr, Orange TX 77630
Tel (409) 883-9361 *SIC* 8062

ESSENT PRMC LP p 510
865 Deshong Dr, Paris TX 75460
Tel (903) 785-9082 *SIC* 8062

■ **PASADENA BAYSHORE HOSPITAL INC** p 1119
4000 Spencer Hwy, Pasadena TX 77504
Tel (713) 359-2000 *SIC* 8062

BAYLOR REGIONAL MEDICAL CENTER AT PLANO p 162
4700 Alliance Blvd, Plano TX 75093
Tel (469) 814-2000 *SIC* 8062

CHILDRENS AND PRESBYTERIAN HEALTH CARE CENTER OF NORTH TEXAS p 299
6200 W Parker Rd Ofc, Plano TX 75093
Tel (972) 981-8000 *SIC* 8062

■ **COLUMBIA MEDICAL CENTER OF PLANO SUBSIDIARY LP** p 341
3901 W 15th St, Plano TX 75075
Tel (972) 596-6800 *SIC* 8062

LHP HOSPITAL GROUP INC p 861
2400 Dallas Pkwy Ste 450, Plano TX 75093
Tel (972) 943-1700 *SIC* 8062

SMCL LLC p 1332
5340 Legacy Dr, Plano TX 75024
Tel (469) 241-2100 *SIC* 8062 8069

TEXAS HEART HOSPITAL OF SOUTHWEST LLP p 1443
1100 Allied Dr, Plano TX 75093
Tel (469) 241-8900 *SIC* 8062

CHRISTUS HEALTH SOUTHEAST TEXAS p 303
3600 Gates Blvd, Port Arthur TX 77642
Tel (409) 985-7431 *SIC* 8062

MEDICAL CENTER OF SOUTHEAST TEXAS L P p 936
2555 Jimmy Johnson Blvd, Port Arthur TX 77640
Tel (409) 724-7389 *SIC* 8062

OAKBEND MEDICAL CENTER p 1070
1705 Jackson St, Richmond TX 77469
Tel (713) 453-0446 *SIC* 8062 8051

ROCKDALE HOSPITAL AUTHORITY (INC) p 1244
1700 Brazos Ave, Rockdale TX 76567
Tel (512) 446-4500 *SIC* 8062 8051

PRESBYTERIAN HOSPITAL OF ROCKWALL p 1171
3150 Horizon Rd, Rockwall TX 75032
Tel (469) 698-1000 *SIC* 8062

ST DAVIDS HEALTHCARE PARTNERSHIP LLP p 1365
2400 Round Rock Ave, Round Rock TX 78681
Tel (512) 341-1000 *SIC* 8062

■ **SAN ANGELO HOSPITAL LP** p 1275
3501 Knickerbocker Rd, San Angelo TX 76904
Tel (325) 949-9511 *SIC* 8062

SHANNON MEDICAL CENTER p 1311
120 E Harris Ave, San Angelo TX 76903
Tel (325) 653-6741 *SIC* 8062

ACCORD MEDICAL MANAGEMENT LP p 15
414 Navarro St Ste 600, San Antonio TX 78205
Tel (210) 271-1800 *SIC* 8062

■ **BAPTIST HEALTH SYSTEM** p 153
215 E Quincy St Ste 200, San Antonio TX 78215
Tel (210) 297-1000 *SIC* 8062

BEXAR COUNTY HOSPITAL DISTRICT p 179
4502 Medical Dr Ms651, San Antonio TX 78229
Tel (210) 358-4000 *SIC* 8062 8011

■ **METHODIST HEALTHCARE SYSTEM OF SAN ANTONIO LTD LLP** p 953
8109 Fredericksburg Rd, San Antonio TX 78229
Tel (210) 575-8110 *SIC* 8062 8011

METHODIST HOSPITAL p 953
7700 Floyd Curl Dr, San Antonio TX 78229
Tel (210) 575-4000 *SIC* 8062

NIX HOSPITALS SYSTEM LLC p 1045
414 Navarro St Ste 600, San Antonio TX 78205
Tel (210) 271-1800 *SIC* 8062

S C SAN ANTONIO INC p 1262
7400 Barlite Blvd, San Antonio TX 78224
Tel (210) 921-2000 *SIC* 8062

ADVENTIST HEALTH SYSTEM/SUNBELT INC p 27
1301 Wonder World Dr, San Marcos TX 78666
Tel (512) 353-8979 *SIC* 8062

GUADALUPE REGIONAL MEDICAL CENTER p 644
1215 E Court St, Seguin TX 78155
Tel (830) 379-2411 *SIC* 8062

SCOTT & WHITE CLINIC p 1293
2401 S 31st St, Temple TX 76508
Tel (254) 724-2111 *SIC* 8062

SCOTT & WHITE MEMORIAL HOSPITAL p 1293
2401 S 31st St, Temple TX 76508
Tel (254) 724-2111
SIC 8062 6512 7352 7363

BRIM HEALTHCARE OF TEXAS LLC p 213
1000 Pine St, Texarkana TX 75501
Tel (903) 798-8000 *SIC* 8062

CHRISTUS HEALTH ARK-LA-TEX p 303
2600 Saint Michael Dr, Texarkana TX 75503
Tel (903) 614-1000 *SIC* 8062

WADLEY REGIONAL MEDICAL CENTER p 1571
1000 Pine St, Texarkana TX 75501
Tel (903) 798-8000 *SIC* 8062

ST LUKES COMMUNITY HEALTH SERVICES p 1370
17200 St Lukes Way, The Woodlands TX 77384
Tel (936) 266-2000 *SIC* 8011 8062

VICTORY HOSPITAL PROPERTIES LLC p 1556
2201 Timberloch Pl # 200, The Woodlands TX 77380
Tel (281) 863-2100 *SIC* 8062

VICTORY PARENT CO LLC p 1556
2201 Timberloch Pl # 200, The Woodlands TX 77380
Tel (281) 863-2100 *SIC* 8062

TOMBALL HOSPITAL AUTHORITY p 1459
605 Holderrieth Blvd, Tomball TX 77375
Tel (281) 351-1623 *SIC* 8062

TOMBALL TEXAS HOSPITAL CO LLC p 1459
605 Holderrieth Blvd, Tomball TX 77375
Tel (281) 401-7500 *SIC* 8062

CHRISTUS TRINITY MOTHER FRANCES HEALTH SYSTEM p 304
800 E Dawson St, Tyler TX 75701
Tel (903) 593-8441 *SIC* 8062

EAST TEXAS MEDICAL CENTER p 471
1000 S Beckham Ave, Tyler TX 75701
Tel (903) 597-0351 *SIC* 8062 8011

EAST TEXAS MEDICAL CENTER REGIONAL HEALTH SERVICES INC p 471
1000 S Beckham Ave, Tyler TX 75701
Tel (903) 597-0351 *SIC* 8062

EAST TEXAS MEDICAL CENTER REGIONAL HEALTHCARE SYST p 471
1000 S Beckham Ave, Tyler TX 75701
Tel (866) 333-3862 *SIC* 8062 8741

EAST TEXAS SPECIALTY HOSP p 471
1000 S Beckham Ave Fl 5, Tyler TX 75701
Tel (903) 596-3600 *SIC* 8062

MOTHER FRANCES HOSPITAL REGIONAL HEALTH CARE CENTER p 992
800 E Dawson St, Tyler TX 75701
Tel (903) 593-8441 *SIC* 8062

TRINITY MOTHER FRANCES HEALTH SYSTEM FOUNDATION p 1481
800 E Dawson St, Tyler TX 75701
Tel (903) 531-5057 *SIC* 8062

UNIVERSITY OF TEXAS HEALTH SCIENCE CENTER AT TYLER p 1526
11937 Us Highway 271, Tyler TX 75708
Tel (903) 877-7777 *SIC* 8062 8221

CITIZENS MEDICAL CENTER p 311
2701 Hospital Dr, Victoria TX 77901
Tel (361) 573-9181 *SIC* 8062

HILLCREST BAPTIST MEDICAL CENTER p 693
100 Hillcrest Med Blvd, Waco TX 76712
Tel (254) 202-8675 *SIC* 8062

PROVIDENCE HEALTH SERVICES OF WACO p 1186
6901 Medical Pkwy, Waco TX 76712
Tel (254) 751-4000 *SIC* 8062

BAYLOR MEDICAL CENTER AT WAXAHACHIE p 162
1405 W Jefferson St, Waxahachie TX 75165
Tel (972) 923-7000 *SIC* 8062

■ **WEATHERFORD REGIONAL MEDICAL CENTER** p 1586
713 E Anderson St, Weatherford TX 76086
Tel (682) 582-1000 *SIC* 8062

■ **CHCA CLEAR LAKE LP** p 292
500 W Medical Center Blvd, Webster TX 77598
Tel (281) 332-2511 *SIC* 8062

■ **CLEAR LAKE REGIONAL MEDICAL CENTER INC** p 324
500 W Medical Center Blvd, Webster TX 77598
Tel (713) 371-5000 *SIC* 8062

UNITED REGIONAL HEALTH CARE SYSTEM INC p 1511
1600 11th St, Wichita Falls TX 76301
Tel (940) 764-3211 *SIC* 8062

LAKEVIEW HOSPITAL p 840
630 Medical Dr, Bountiful UT 84010
Tel (801) 292-6231 *SIC* 8062

DAVIS HOSPITAL & MEDICAL CENTER INC p 416
1600 W Antelope Dr, Layton UT 84041
Tel (801) 807-1000 *SIC* 8062

■ **COLUMBIA OGDEN MEDICAL CENTER INC** p 341
5475 S 500 E, Ogden UT 84405
Tel (801) 479-2111 *SIC* 8062 8099

■ **TIMPANOGOS REGIONAL HOSPITAL** p 1455
750 W 800 N, Orem UT 84057
Tel (801) 714-6000 *SIC* 8062

TIMPANOGOS REGIONAL HOSPITAL p 1455
750 W 800 N, Orem UT 84057
Tel (801) 714-6000 *SIC* 8062

UTAH VALLEY REGIONAL MEDICAL CENTER p 1536
1034 N 500 W, Provo UT 84604
Tel (801) 357-7850 *SIC* 8062

UINTAH BASIN MEDICAL CENTER p 1500
250 W 300 N, Roosevelt UT 84066
Tel (435) 725-2008
SIC 8062 8082 7352 8092 8361

INTERMOUNTAIN HEALTH CARE INC p 753
36 S State St Ste 1600, Salt Lake City UT 84111
Tel (801) 442-2000 *SIC* 8062

LDS HOSPITAL p 849
8th Ave C St, Salt Lake City UT 84143
Tel (801) 408-1100 *SIC* 8062

■ **NORTHERN UTAH HEALTHCARE CORP** p 1057
1200 E 3900 S, Salt Lake City UT 84124
Tel (801) 268-7111 *SIC* 8062 8082 8011

SALT LAKE REGIONAL MEDICAL CENTER LP p 1273
1050 E South Temple, Salt Lake City UT 84102
Tel (801) 350-4631 *SIC* 8062

UNIVERSITY OF UTAH HOSPITALS AND CLINICS p 1526
50 N Medical Dr, Salt Lake City UT 84132
Tel (801) 581-2121 *SIC* 8062 8011

IHC HEALTH SERVICES INC p 730
1380 E Medical Center Dr, St George UT 84790
Tel (801) 442-5000
SIC 8062 8011 8322 8049 8093 8069

JORDAN VALLEY MEDICAL CENTER LP p 793
3580 W 9000 S, West Jordan UT 84088
Tel (801) 561-8888 *SIC* 8062

SOUTHWESTERN VERMONT MEDICAL CENTER INC p 1353
100 Hospital Dr, Bennington VT 05201
Tel (802) 442-6361 *SIC* 8062

CENTRAL VERMONT MEDICAL CENTER INC p 281
130 Fisher Rd Unit 1, Berlin VT 05602
Tel (802) 371-4100 *SIC* 8062

UNIVERSITY OF VERMONT MEDICAL CENTER INC p 1526
111 Colchester Ave, Burlington VT 05401
Tel (802) 847-0000 *SIC* 8062

RUTLAND HOSPITAL INC ACT 220 p 1260
160 Allen St, Rutland VT 05701
Tel (802) 775-7111 *SIC* 8062

RUTLAND REGIONAL HEALTH SERVICES p 1260
160 Allen St, Rutland VT 05701
Tel (802) 775-7111 *SIC* 8062 7352 8059

NORTHWESTERN MEDICAL CENTER INC p 1060
133 Fairfield St, Saint Albans VT 05478
Tel (802) 524-5911 *SIC* 8062

GOVERNOR JUAN F LUIS HOSPITAL & MEDICAL CENTER p 627
4007 Estate Diamond Ruby, Christiansted VI 00820
Tel (340) 778-6311 *SIC* 8062

JOHNSTON MEMORIAL HOSPITAL INC p 791
16000 Johnston Memorial D, Abingdon VA 24211
Tel (276) 258-1000 *SIC* 8062 8011

ALEXANDRIA INOVA HOSPITAL p 49
4320 Seminary Rd, Alexandria VA 22304
Tel (703) 504-3000 *SIC* 8062

VIRGINIA HOSPITAL CENTER ARLINGTON AUXILIARY INC p 1559
1701 N George Mason Dr, Arlington VA 22205
Tel (703) 558-5668 *SIC* 8062

■ **MONTGOMERY REGIONAL HOSPITAL INC** p 987
3700 S Main St, Blacksburg VA 24060
Tel (540) 951-1111 *SIC* 8062

MARTHA JEFFERSON HOSPITAL p 912
500 Martha Jefferson Dr, Charlottesville VA 22911
Tel (434) 982-7000 *SIC* 8062

CHESAPEAKE HOSPITAL AUTHORITY p 295
736 Battlefield Blvd N, Chesapeake VA 23320
Tel (757) 312-8121 *SIC* 8062

CARILION NEW RIVER VALLEY MEDICAL CENTER p 256
2900 Lamb Cir Ste 150, Christiansburg VA 24073
Tel (540) 731-2000 *SIC* 8062

DANVILLE REGIONAL HEALTH FOUNDATION p 412
142 S Main St, Danville VA 24541
Tel (434) 799-2100
SIC 8741 8062 8051 8011

■ **DANVILLE REGIONAL MEDICAL CENTER** p 412
142 S Main St, Danville VA 24541
Tel (434) 799-2100
SIC 8062 8011 8093 8069 8051

ALEXANDRIA INOVA HEALTH SERVICES CORP p 49
8110 Gatehouse Rd 200e, Falls Church VA 22042
Tel (703) 289-2000 *SIC* 8062

INOVA HEALTH CARE SERVICES p 745
8110 Gatehouse Rd 200e, Falls Church VA 22042
Tel (703) 289-2000 *SIC* 8062 8093

INOVA HEALTH SYSTEM p 745
8110 Gatehouse Rd 200e, Falls Church VA 22042
Tel (703) 289-2069
SIC 8741 8011 8062 8049 8059 8051

INOVA HEALTH SYSTEM SERVICES p 745
8110 Gatehouse Rd 200e, Falls Church VA 22042
Tel (703) 289-2000 *SIC* 8062

AUGUSTA HEALTH CARE INC p 131
78 Medical Center Dr, Fishersville VA 22939
Tel (540) 332-4000 *SIC* 8062

FORT BELVOIR COMMUNITY HOSPITAL p 568
9300 Dewitt Loop, Fort Belvoir VA 22060
Tel (703) 805-0510 *SIC* 8062

WASHINGTON HOSPITAL INC MARY p 1578
1001 Sam Perry Blvd, Fredericksburg VA 22401
Tel (540) 741-1100 *SIC* 8062 8069

RIVERSIDE MIDDLE PENINSULA HOSPITAL INC p 1238
7519 Hospital Dr, Gloucester VA 23061
Tel (757) 875-7545 *SIC* 8062

SENTARA CAREPLEX HOSPITAL p 1305
3000 Coliseum Dr, Hampton VA 23666
Tel (757) 736-1000 *SIC* 8062

LOUDOUN HEALTHCARE INC p 879
44045 Riverside Pkwy, Leesburg VA 20176
Tel (703) 777-3300 *SIC* 8062 8059

LOUDOUN HOSPITAL CENTER p 879
44045 Riverside Pkwy, Leesburg VA 20176
Tel (703) 858-6000 *SIC* 8062

CENTRA HEALTH INC p 277
1920 Atherholt Rd, Lynchburg VA 24501
Tel (434) 200-3204 *SIC* 8062

WILLIAM PRINCE HOSPITAL p 1611
8700 Sudley Rd, Manassas VA 20110
Tel (703) 369-8484 *SIC* 8062

BON SECOURS-MEMORIAL REGIONAL MEDICAL CENTER INC p 199
8260 Atlee Rd Ste 1203, Mechanicsville VA 23116
Tel (804) 764-1253 *SIC* 8082 8071

MARY IMMACULATE HOSPITAL INC p 914
2 Bernardine Dr, Newport News VA 23602
Tel (757) 886-6440 *SIC* 8062 8099

RIVERSIDE HOSPITAL INC p 1238
500 J Clyde Morris Blvd, Newport News VA 23601
Tel (757) 594-2000 *SIC* 8062

BON SECOURS - DEPAUL MEDICAL CENTER INC p 199
150 Kingsley Ln, Norfolk VA 23505
Tel (757) 889-5000 *SIC* 8062

SENTARA HEALTHCARE p 1305
6015 Poplar Hall Dr, Norfolk VA 23502
Tel (757) 455-7976 *SIC* 8062 6324

SENTARA HOSPITALS - NORFOLK p 1305
600 Gresham Dr, Norfolk VA 23507
Tel (757) 388-3000 *SIC* 8062

JOHNSTON-WILLIS HOSPITAL NURSES ALUMNAE ASSOCIATION p 791
1401 Johnston Willis Dr, North Chesterfield VA 23235
Tel (804) 560-5800 *SIC* 8062

■ **PETERSBURG HOSPITAL CO LLC** p 1138
200 Medical Park Blvd, Petersburg VA 23805
Tel (804) 765-5000 *SIC* 8062

MARYVIEW HOSPITAL p 915
3636 High St, Portsmouth VA 23707
Tel (757) 398-2200 *SIC* 8062

■ **CLINCH VALLEY MEDICAL CENTER INC** p 326
6801 Gov Gc Peery Hwy, Richlands VA 24641
Tel (276) 596-6000 *SIC* 8062

BON SECOURS - ST MARYS HOSPITAL OF RICHMOND INC p 199
5801 Bremo Rd, Richmond VA 23226
Tel (804) 288-5415 *SIC* 8062

■ **CHIPPENHAM & JOHNSTON-WILLIS HOSPITALS INC** p 301
7101 Jahnke Rd, Richmond VA 23225
Tel (804) 327-4046 *SIC* 8062

■ **CHIPPENHAM HOSPITAL INC** p 301
7101 Jahnke Rd, Richmond VA 23225
Tel (804) 320-3911 *SIC* 8062

■ **HCA HEALTH SERVICES OF VIRGINIA INC** p 672
1602 Skipwith Rd, Richmond VA 23229
Tel (804) 289-4500 *SIC* 8062 8093

VCU HEALTH SYSTEM AUTHORITY p 1546
1250 E Marshall St, Richmond VA 23298
Tel (804) 828-9000 *SIC* 8062

CARILION MEDICAL CENTER p 256
1906 Belleview Ave Se, Roanoke VA 24014
Tel (540) 981-7000 *SIC* 8011 8062

ROCKINGHAM HEALTH CARE INC p 1244
2010 Health Campus Dr, Rockingham VA 22801
Tel (540) 433-4100 *SIC* 8062

SENTARA RMH MEDICAL CENTER p 1305
2010 Health Campus Dr, Rockingham VA 22801
Tel (540) 433-4100 *SIC* 8062

■ **LEWIS-GALE HOSPITAL INC** p 859
1900 Electric Rd, Salem VA 24153
Tel (540) 776-4000 *SIC* 8062

COMMUNITY MEMORIAL HEALTH CENTER PHYSICIAN-HOSPITAL ORGANIZATION LLC p 349
125 Buena Vista Cir, South Hill VA 23970
Tel (434) 447-3151 *SIC* 8062 8051

LOUISE OBICI MEMORIAL HOSPITAL INC p 880
2800 Godwin Blvd, Suffolk VA 23434
Tel (757) 934-4000 *SIC* 8062

SENTARA LOUISE OBICI MEMORIAL HOSPITAL p 1305
2800 Godwin Blvd, Suffolk VA 23434
Tel (757) 934-4827 *SIC* 8062

SENTARA PRINCESS ANNE HOSPITAL p 1305
1925 Glenn Mitchell Dr, Virginia Beach VA 23456
Tel (757) 507-1660 *SIC* 8062

FAUQUIER HEALTH SYSTEM INC p 531
500 Hospital Dr, Warrenton VA 20186
Tel (540) 316-5000 *SIC* 8062

FHI SERVICES p 539
500 Hospital Dr, Warrenton VA 20186
Tel (540) 347-2550 *SIC* 8062

SENTARA WILLIAMSBURG REGIONAL MEDICAL CENTER p 1305
100 Sentara Cir, Williamsburg VA 23188
Tel (757) 984-6000 *SIC* 8062

VALLEY HEALTH SYSTEM p 1540
1840 Amherst St, Winchester VA 22601
Tel (540) 536-8000
SIC 8062 8051 5047 8699

VALLEY HEALTH SYSTEM GROUP RETURN p 1540
220 Campus Blvd Ste 310, Winchester VA 22601
Tel (540) 536-4302 *SIC* 8062

WINCHESTER MEDICAL CENTER AUXILIARY INC p 1614
1840 Amherst St, Winchester VA 22601
Tel (540) 536-8000 *SIC* 8062

POTOMAC HOSPITAL CORP OF PRINCE WILLIAM p 1164
2300 Opitz Blvd, Woodbridge VA 22191
Tel (703) 523-1000 *SIC* 8062

GRAYS HARBOR COMMUNITY HOSPITAL p 632
1006 N H St, Aberdeen WA 98520
Tel (360) 532-8330 *SIC* 8062

GRAYS HARBOR COMMUNITY HOSPITAL FOUNDATION p 632
915 Anderson Dr, Aberdeen WA 98520
Tel (360) 537-5000 *SIC* 8062

SKAGIT COUNTY PUBLIC HOSPITAL DISTRICT 2 p 1329
1211 24th St, Anacortes WA 98221
Tel (360) 299-1300 *SIC* 8062

■ **AUBURN REGIONAL MEDICAL CENTER INC** p 130
Plz 1 202 N Div St, Auburn WA 98001
Tel (253) 833-7711 *SIC* 8062

OVERLAKE HOSPITAL MEDICAL CENTER p 1099
1035 116th Ave Ne, Bellevue WA 98004
Tel (425) 688-5000 *SIC* 8062

HARRISON MEDICAL CENTER p 664
2520 Cherry Ave, Bremerton WA 98310
Tel (360) 744-6510 *SIC* 8062

HARRISON MEMORIAL HOSPITAL INC p 664
2520 Cherry Ave, Bremerton WA 98310
Tel (360) 377-3911 *SIC* 8062

HIGHLINE MEDICAL CENTER p 692
16251 Sylvester Rd Sw, Burien WA 98166
Tel (206) 244-9970 *SIC* 8062 8051

WHIDBEY ISLAND PUBLIC HOSPITAL DISTRICT p 1605
101 N Main St, Coupeville WA 98239
Tel (360) 678-5151 *SIC* 8062

SWEDISH EDMONDS p 1411
21601 76th Ave W, Edmonds WA 98026
Tel (425) 640-4000 *SIC* 8062

ST FRANCIS HOSPITAL p 1366
34515 9th Ave S, Federal Way WA 98003
Tel (253) 944-8100 *SIC* 8062

KENNEWICK PUBLIC HOSPITAL DISTRICT p 811
900 S Auburn St, Kennewick WA 99336
Tel (509) 586-6111 *SIC* 8062

KING COUNTY PUBLIC HOSPITAL DISTRICT 2 p 820
12040 Ne 128th St, Kirkland WA 98034
Tel (425) 899-2769 *SIC* 8062

PUBLIC HOSPITAL DISTRICT 1 SKAGIT COUNTY p 1189
1415 E Kincaid St, Mount Vernon WA 98274
Tel (360) 424-4111 *SIC* 8062

CAPITAL MEDICAL CENTER p 250
3900 Capital Mall Dr Sw, Olympia WA 98502
Tel (360) 754-5858 *SIC* 8062 8011

PROVIDENCE HEALTH AND SERVICES p 1186
413 Lilly Rd Ne, Olympia WA 98506
Tel (360) 491-9480 *SIC* 8062

OUR LADY OF LOURDES HOSPITAL AT PASCO p 1098
520 N 4th Ave, Pasco WA 99301
Tel (509) 547-7704 *SIC* 8062 8063

CLALLAM COUNTY PUBLIC HOSPITAL DISTRICT 2 p 321
939 Caroline St, Port Angeles WA 98362
Tel (360) 417-7000 *SIC* 8062

JEFFERSON COUNTY PUBLIC HOSPITAL DISTRICT 2 p 781
834 Sheridan St, Port Townsend WA 98368
Tel (360) 379-8031 *SIC* 8062

GOOD SAMARITAN COMMUNITY HEALTHCARE INC p 623
407 14th Ave Se, Puyallup WA 98372
Tel (253) 848-6661 *SIC* 8062

GOOD SAMARITAN HOSPITAL p 623
401 15th Ave Se, Puyallup WA 98372
Tel (253) 697-4000 *SIC* 8062 8069

PROVIDENCE HEALTH & SERVICES p 1185
1801 Lind Ave Sw, Renton WA 98057
Tel (425) 525-3355 *SIC* 8062

PROVIDENCE HEALTH & SERVICES - OREGON p 1185
1801 Lind Ave Sw, Renton WA 98057
Tel (425) 525-3355 *SIC* 8062

PROVIDENCE HEALTH & SERVICES AND SWEDISH HEALTH SERVICES p 1185
1801 Lind Ave Sw, Renton WA 98057
Tel (425) 525-3355 *SIC* 8062

PROVIDENCE HEALTH & SERVICES-WASHINGTON p 1186
1801 Lind Ave Sw 9016, Renton WA 98057
Tel (425) 525-3355
SIC 8062 8051 8052 6513 8069

PROVIDENCE HEALTH SYSTEM-SOUTHERN CALIFORNIA p 1186
1801 Lind Ave Sw, Renton WA 98057
Tel (425) 525-3355 *SIC* 8062

PUBLIC HOSPITAL DISTRICT 1 OF KING COUNTY p 1189
400 S 43rd St, Renton WA 98055
Tel (425) 228-3440 *SIC* 8062

KADLEC REGIONAL MEDICAL CENTER p 800
888 Swift Blvd, Richland WA 99352
Tel (509) 946-4611 *SIC* 8062

HARBORVIEW MEDICAL CENTER p 660
325 9th Ave, Seattle WA 98104
Tel (206) 731-3000 *SIC* 8062

NORTHWEST HOSPITAL & MEDICAL CENTER p 1060
1550 N 115th St, Seattle WA 98133
Tel (206) 364-0500 *SIC* 8741 8062

SEATTLE CHILDRENS HEALTHCARE SYSTEM p 1297
P.O. Box 5371, Seattle WA 98145
Tel (206) 987-4846 *SIC* 8062

SEATTLE CHILDRENS HOSPITAL p 1297
4800 Sand Point Way Ne, Seattle WA 98105
Tel (206) 987-2000 *SIC* 8062 8069

UW MEDICINE/NORTHWEST p 1538
1550 N 115th St, Seattle WA 98133
Tel (206) 364-0500 *SIC* 8062

UW MEDICINE/NORTHWEST p 1538
1550 N 115th St, Seattle WA 98133
Tel (206) 364-0500 *SIC* 8062

VIRGINIA MASON MEDICAL CENTER p 1559
1100 9th Ave, Seattle WA 98101
Tel (206) 223-6600
SIC 8011 8051 6513 8062

■ **DEACONESS MEDICAL CENTER** p 419
800 W 5th Ave, Spokane WA 99204
Tel (509) 458-5800 *SIC* 8062

DOMINICAN HEALTH SERVICES p 449
5633 N Lidgerwood St, Spokane WA 99208
Tel (509) 482-0111 *SIC* 8062

EMPIRE HEALTH CENTERS GROUP p 493
800 W 5th Ave, Spokane WA 99204
Tel (509) 473-5800 *SIC* 8062

PROVIDENCE HEALTH & SERVICES-WASHINGTON p 1186
5633 N Lidgerwood St, Spokane WA 99208
Tel (509) 482-0111 *SIC* 8062

SACRED HEART MEDICAL CENTER p 1265
101 W 8th Ave, Spokane WA 99204
Tel (509) 455-3131 *SIC* 8062 8071

■ **SPOKANE WASHINGTON HOSPITAL CO LLC** p 1359
800 W 5th Ave, Spokane WA 99204
Tel (509) 458-5800 *SIC* 8062

■ **SPOKANE VALLEY WASHINGTON HOSPITAL CO LLC** p 1359
12606 E Mission Ave, Spokane Valley WA 99216
Tel (509) 924-6650 *SIC* 8062

FRANCISCAN HEALTH SYSTEM p 573
1717 S J St, Tacoma WA 98405
Tel (253) 426-4101 *SIC* 8062

MULTICARE HEALTH SYSTEM p 999
316 M L King Jr Way # 314, Tacoma WA 98405
Tel (253) 403-1000 *SIC* 8062 8093 8069

ST JOSEPH MEDICAL CENTER p 1368
1717 S J St, Tacoma WA 98405
Tel (253) 627-4101 *SIC* 8062

PEACE HEALTH SOUTHWEST MEDICAL CENTER p 1125
602 Ne 92nd Ave Ste 120, Vancouver WA 98664
Tel (360) 514-2250 *SIC* 8062 7389

PEACEHEALTH p 1125
1115 Se 164th Ave, Vancouver WA 98683
Tel (360) 788-6841 *SIC* 8062 8011

SALMON LEGACY CREEK HOSPITAL p 1273
2211 Ne 139th St, Vancouver WA 98686
Tel (360) 487-1000 *SIC* 8062

SW WASHINGTON HOSPITAL INC p 1411
400 Ne Mother Joseph Pl, Vancouver WA 98664
Tel (360) 514-2000 *SIC* 8062

PROVIDENCE ST MARY MEDICAL CENTER p 1186
401 W Poplar St, Walla Walla WA 99362
Tel (509) 525-3320 *SIC* 8062

CENTRAL WASHINGTON HEALTH SERVICES ASSOCIATION p 281
1201 S Miller St, Wenatchee WA 98801
Tel (509) 662-1511 *SIC* 8062

WENATCHEE VALLEY HOSPITAL p 1591
820 N Chelan Ave, Wenatchee WA 98801
Tel (509) 663-8711 *SIC* 8062

■ **YAKIMA HMA LLC** p 1634
110 S 9th Ave, Yakima WA 98902
Tel (509) 575-5000 *SIC* 8062

YAKIMA VALLEY MEMORIAL HOSPITAL ASSOCIATION INC p 1634
2811 Tieton Dr, Yakima WA 98902
Tel (509) 249-5129 *SIC* 8062 8082

■ **RALEIGH GENERAL HOSPITAL** p 1206
1710 Harper Rd, Beckley WV 25801
Tel (304) 256-4100 *SIC* 8062

HEALTH SERVICES OF VIRGINIAS INC p 676
500 Cherry St, Bluefield WV 24701
Tel (304) 327-1100 *SIC* 8062

UNITED HOSPITAL CENTER INC p 1509
327 Medical Park Dr, Bridgeport WV 26330
Tel (681) 342-1000 *SIC* 8062

CAMC HEALTH SYSTEM INC p 244
501 Morris St, Charleston WV 25301
Tel (304) 388-5432 *SIC* 8062

CHARLESTON AREA MEDICAL CENTER INC p 289
501 Morris St, Charleston WV 25301
Tel (304) 348-5432 *SIC* 8062

CHARLESTON HOSPITAL INC p 290
333 Laidley St, Charleston WV 25301
Tel (304) 347-6500 *SIC* 8062

HERBERT J THOMAS MEMORIAL HOSPITAL ASSOCIATION p 685
4605 Maccorkle Ave Sw, Charleston WV 25309
Tel (304) 766-3600 *SIC* 8062

HUNTINGTON CABELL HOSPITAL INC p 720
1340 Hal Greer Blvd, Huntington WV 25701
Tel (304) 526-2000 *SIC* 8062

ST MARYS MEDICAL CENTER p 1371
2900 1st Ave, Huntington WV 25702
Tel (304) 526-1234 *SIC* 8062

CITY HOSPITAL INC p 312
2500 Hospital Dr, Martinsburg WV 25401
Tel (304) 264-1000 *SIC* 8062

CITY HOSPITAL INC p 312
2000 Foundation Way # 2310, Martinsburg WV 25401
Tel (304) 264-1244 *SIC* 8062

MONONGALIA COUNTY GENERAL HOSPITAL CO p 984
1200 J D Anderson Dr, Morgantown WV 26505
Tel (304) 598-1200 *SIC* 8062

MONONGALIA HEALTH SYSTEM INC p 984
1200 J D Anderson Dr, Morgantown WV 26505
Tel (304) 598-1200 *SIC* 8062 8011

VIRGINIA WEST UNIVERSITY HOSPITALS INC p 1560
1 Medical Center Dr, Morgantown WV 26506
Tel (304) 598-4000 *SIC* 8062

CAMDEN CLARK MEDICAL CENTER - ST JOSEPH CAMPUS p 244
800 Garfield Ave, Parkersburg WV 26101
Tel (304) 424-4111 *SIC* 8062

CAMDEN-CLARK MEMORIAL HOSPITAL CORP p 245
800 Garfield Ave, Parkersburg WV 26101
Tel (304) 424-2111 *SIC* 8062

PRINCETON COMMUNITY HOSPITAL ASSOCIATION INC p 1177
122 12th St, Princeton WV 24740
Tel (304) 487-7000 *SIC* 8062

THOMAS HJ MEMORIAL HOSPITAL INC p 1448
4605 Maccorkle Ave Sw, South Charleston WV 25309
Tel (304) 766-3697 *SIC* 8062

WEIRTON MEDICAL CENTER INC p 1588
601 Colliers Way, Weirton WV 26062
Tel (304) 797-6000 *SIC* 8062 8051

WEIRTON MEDICAL CORP p 1588
601 Colliers Way, Weirton WV 26062
Tel (304) 797-6000 *SIC* 8062

OHIO VALLEY HEALTH SERVICES AND EDUCATION CORP p 1078
2000 Eoff St, Wheeling WV 26003
Tel (304) 234-8174 *SIC* 8741 8062 8011

OHIO VALLEY MEDICAL CENTER INC p 1078
2000 Eoff St, Wheeling WV 26003
Tel (304) 234-0123 *SIC* 8062 8011

WHEELING HOSPITAL INC p 1605
1 Medical Park, Wheeling WV 26003
Tel (304) 243-3000 *SIC* 8062 8011

LANGLADE HOSPITAL - HOTEL DIEU OF ST JOSEPH OF ANTIGO WISCONSIN p 844
112 E 5th Ave, Antigo WI 54409
Tel (715) 623-2331 *SIC* 8062

APPLETON MEDICAL CENTER INC p 99
1818 N Meade St, Appleton WI 54911
Tel (920) 731-4101 *SIC* 8062

ST ELIZABETH HOSPITAL INC p 1366
1506 S Oneida St, Appleton WI 54915
Tel (920) 738-2000 *SIC* 8062

THEDACARE INC p 1446
122 E College Ave Ste 2a, Appleton WI 54911
Tel (920) 735-5560 *SIC* 8062

BEAVER DAM COMMUNITY HOSPITALS INC p 166
707 S University Ave, Beaver Dam WI 53916
Tel (920) 887-7181 *SIC* 8062 8051

BELOIT HEALTH SYSTEM INC p 171
1969 W Hart Rd, Beloit WI 53511
Tel (608) 364-5011 *SIC* 8062

BELOIT MEMORIAL HOSPITAL INC p 171
1969 W Hart Rd, Beloit WI 53511
Tel (608) 364-5011 *SIC* 8062 8011

THEDACARE MEDICAL CENTER - BERLIN INC p 1446
225 Memorial Dr, Berlin WI 54923
Tel (920) 361-1313 *SIC* 8062 8051 8011

FRIENDS OF ELMBROOK MEMORIAL HOSPITAL INC p 580
19333 W North Ave, Brookfield WI 53045
Tel (262) 785-2000 *SIC* 8062

MAYO CLINIC HEALTH SYSTEM-EAU CLAIRE CLINIC INC p 924
1400 Bellinger St, Eau Claire WI 54703
Tel (715) 838-5222 *SIC* 8062

MAYO CLINIC HEALTH SYSTEM-NORTHWEST WISCONSIN REGION INC p 924
1221 Whipple St, Eau Claire WI 54703
Tel (715) 838-3311 *SIC* 8062 8011

SACRED HEART HOSPITAL INC p 1265
900 W Clairemont Ave, Eau Claire WI 54701
Tel (715) 717-3926 *SIC* 8062

ST AGNES HOSPITAL OF FOND DU LAC WISC INC p 1364
430 E Division St, Fond Du Lac WI 54935
Tel (920) 929-2300 *SIC* 8062

FORT HEALTHCARE INC p 569
611 Sherman Ave E, Fort Atkinson WI 53538
Tel (920) 568-5401 *SIC* 8062 8011

COLUMBIA ST MARYS HOSPITAL OZAUKEE INC p 341
4425 N Port Washington Rd, Glendale WI 53212
Tel (414) 326-2230 *SIC* 8062

WHEATON FRANCISCAN HEALTHCARE - ALL SAINTS FOUNDATION INC p 1604
400 W River Woods Pkwy, Glendale WI 53212
Tel (414) 465-3000 *SIC* 8062

BELLIN HEALTH SYSTEMS INC p 170
744 S Webster Ave, Green Bay WI 54301
Tel (920) 433-3500 *SIC* 8062 8063 7352

BELLIN MEMORIAL HOSPITAL INC p 170
744 S Webster Ave, Green Bay WI 54301
Tel (920) 433-3500 *SIC* 8062

ST MARYS HOSPITAL p 1371
1726 Shawano Ave, Green Bay WI 54303
Tel (920) 498-4200 *SIC* 8011 8062

ST VINCENT HOSPITAL OF HOSPITAL SISTERS OF THIRD ORDER OF S p 1373
835 S Van Buren St, Green Bay WI 54301
Tel (920) 433-0111 *SIC* 8062 8011

MERCY HEALTH SYSTEM CORP p 946
1000 Mineral Point Ave, Janesville WI 53548
Tel (608) 741-6891 *SIC* 8062

UHS INC p 1500
6308 8th Ave, Kenosha WI 53143
Tel (262) 656-2273 *SIC* 8062

UNITED HOSPITAL SYSTEM INC p 1509
6308 8th Ave, Kenosha WI 53143
Tel (262) 656-2011 *SIC* 8062

GUNDERSEN LUTHERAN HEALTH SYSTEM INC p 647
1900 South Ave, La Crosse WI 54601
Tel (608) 782-7300 *SIC* 8062

GUNDERSEN LUTHERAN MEDICAL CENTER INC p 647
1900 South Ave, La Crosse WI 54601
Tel (608) 782-7300 *SIC* 8062 5912

MAYO CLINIC HEALTH SYSTEM-FRANCISCAN HEALTHCARE INC p 924
700 West Ave S, La Crosse WI 54601
Tel (608) 785-0940 *SIC* 8062 8051

MAYO CLINIC HEALTH SYSTEM-FRANCISCAN MEDICAL CENTER INC p 924
700 West Ave S, La Crosse WI 54601
Tel (608) 785-0940 *SIC* 8062

MERITER HOSPITAL INC p 949
202 S Park St, Madison WI 53715
Tel (608) 417-6000 *SIC* 8062

SSM HEALTH CARE OF WISCONSIN INC p 1364
1808 W Beltline Hwy, Madison WI 53713
Tel (608) 258-6551 *SIC* 8062

ST MARYS HOSPITAL p 1371
700 S Park St, Madison WI 53715
Tel (608) 251-6100 *SIC* 8062

UNIVERSITY OF WISCONSIN HOSPITAL AND CLINICS AUTHORITY p 1527
600 Highland Ave, Madison WI 53792
Tel (608) 263-6400 *SIC* 8062 8069

UNIVERSITY OF WISCONSIN HOSPITALS AND CLINICS p 1527
600 Highland Ave, Madison WI 53792
Tel (608) 263-8991 *SIC* 8062

FRANCISCAN SISTERS OF CHRISTIAN CHARITY SPONSORED MINISTRIES INC p 573
1415 S Rapids Rd, Manitowoc WI 54220
Tel (920) 684-7071 *SIC* 8741 8062

HOLY FAMILY MEMORIAL INC p 702
2300 Western Ave, Manitowoc WI 54220
Tel (920) 320-2011 *SIC* 8062

BAY AREA MEDICAL CENTER INC p 160
3100 Shore Dr, Marinette WI 54143
Tel (715) 735-4200 *SIC* 8062

SAINT JOSEPHS HOSPITAL OF MARSHFIELD INC p 1269
611 N Saint Joseph Ave, Marshfield WI 54449
Tel (715) 387-1713 *SIC* 8062

AFFINITY HEALTH SYSTEM p 32
1570 Midway Pl, Menasha WI 54952
Tel (920) 720-1700 *SIC* 8741 8062

COMMUNITY MEMORIAL HOSPITAL OF MENOMONEE FALLS INC p 349
W180n8085 Town Hall Rd, Menomonee Falls WI 53051
Tel (262) 251-1000 *SIC* 8062

FROEDTERT HEALTH INC p 580
400 Wood Prim Ste, Menomonee Falls WI 53051
Tel (262) 251-1000 *SIC* 8062

MAYO CLINIC HEALTH SYSTEM-RED CEDAR INC p 924
2415 Stout Rd, Menomonie WI 54751
Tel (715) 235-5531 *SIC* 8062

COLUMBIA ST MARYS HOSPITAL OZAUKEE INC p 341
13111 N Port Wash Rd, Mequon WI 53097
Tel (262) 243-7300 *SIC* 8062

AURORA HEALTH CARE INC p 132
750 W Virginia St, Milwaukee WI 53204
Tel (414) 647-3000 *SIC* 8741 8062

AURORA HEALTH CARE METRO INC p 132
2900 W Oklahoma Ave, Milwaukee WI 53215
Tel (414) 649-6000 *SIC* 8062

AURORA SINAI MEDICAL CENTER INC p 132
945 N 12th St, Milwaukee WI 53233
Tel (414) 219-2000 *SIC* 8062

AURORA WEST ALLIS MEDICAL CENTER p 132
8901 W Lincoln Ave, Milwaukee WI 53227
Tel (414) 328-6000 *SIC* 8062

COLUMBIA HOSPITAL INC p 341
4425 N Pt Wshngton Rd 1 1 Stop, Milwaukee WI 53212
Tel (414) 961-3300 *SIC* 8062

COLUMBIA ST MARYS HOSPITAL MILWAUKEE INC p 341
2301 N Lake Dr, Milwaukee WI 53211
Tel (414) 291-1000 *SIC* 8062

COLUMBIA ST MARYS INC p 342
4425 N Port Washington Rd, Milwaukee WI 53212
Tel (414) 326-2495 *SIC* 8062

COVENANT HEALTH CARE SYSTEM INC p 384
1126 S 70th St Ste S306, Milwaukee WI 53214
Tel (414) 456-3000 *SIC* 8062

FROEDTERT AND COMMUNITY HEALTH INC p 580
9200 W Wisconsin Ave, Milwaukee WI 53226
Tel (414) 777-0960 *SIC* 8062

FROEDTERT HEALTH HOSPITAL p 580
9200 W Wisconsin Ave, Milwaukee WI 53226
Tel (414) 805-3000 *SIC* 8062

ST FRANCIS HOSPITAL INC p 1366
3237 S 16th St, Milwaukee WI 53215
Tel (414) 647-5000 *SIC* 8062

ST MICHAEL HOSPITAL OF FRANCISCAN SISTERS MILWAUKEE INC p 1372
5000 W Chambers St, Milwaukee WI 53210
Tel (414) 447-2000 *SIC* 8062 8011

WHEATON FRANCISCAN p 1604
3070 N 51st St Ste 601, Milwaukee WI 53210
Tel (414) 447-2000 *SIC* 8062

WHEATON FRANCISCAN HEALTHCARE-FRANKLIN p 1604
3070 N 51st St Ste 210, Milwaukee WI 53210
Tel (414) 874-1171 *SIC* 8062

MONROE CLINIC INC p 985
515 22nd Ave, Monroe WI 53566
Tel (608) 324-2775 *SIC* 8062 8011

ALL SAINTS HEALTH CARE SYSTEM INC p 51
3801 Spring St, Mount Pleasant WI 53405
Tel (262) 687-4011 *SIC* 8062

THEDA CLARK MEMORIAL HOSPITAL (INC) p 1446
130 2nd St, Neenah WI 54956
Tel (920) 729-3100 *SIC* 8062

PROHEALTHCARE FOUNDATION p 1182
791 Summit Ave, Oconomowoc WI 53066
Tel (262) 569-9400 *SIC* 8062 8011

MERCY MEDICAL CENTER OF OSHKOSH INC p 948
2700 W 9th Ave Ste 100, Oshkosh WI 54904
Tel (920) 223-2000 *SIC* 8062

NEW LIFECARE HOSPITALS OF MILWAUKEE LLC p 1032
2400 Golf Rd, Pewaukee WI 53072
Tel (262) 524-2600 *SIC* 8062

DIVINE SAVIOR HEALTHCARE INC p 444
2817 New Pinery Rd # 202, Portage WI 53901
Tel (608) 745-4598 *SIC* 8062 8011 8051

LAKEVIEW MEDICAL CENTER INC OF RICE LAKE p 840
1700 W Stout St, Rice Lake WI 54868
Tel (715) 234-1515 *SIC* 8062

SAINT CLARES HOSPITAL OF WESTON INC p 1268
3400 Ministry Pkwy, Schofield WI 54476
Tel (715) 393-3000 *SIC* 8062

ST MICHAELS HOSPITAL INC p 1372
900 Illinois Ave, Stevens Point WI 54481
Tel (715) 346-5000 *SIC* 8062

GREATER WATERTOWN COMMUNITY HEALTH FOUNDATION INC p 636
125 Hospital Dr, Watertown WI 53098
Tel (920) 261-4210 *SIC* 8062 8011 8059

PROHEALTH CARE INC p 1182
725 American Ave, Waukesha WI 53188
Tel (262) 544-2011 *SIC* 8011 8062

WAUKESHA MEMORIAL HOSPITAL INC p 1583
725 American Ave, Waukesha WI 53188
Tel (262) 928-2292 *SIC* 8062

ASPIRUS INC p 118
425 Pine Ridge Blvd # 300, Wausau WI 54401
Tel (715) 847-2121 *SIC* 8062

ASPIRUS WAUSAU HOSPITAL INC p 119
425 Pine Ridge Blvd # 1, Wausau WI 54401
Tel (715) 847-2121 *SIC* 8062

SAINT JOSEPHS COMMUNITY HOSPITAL p 1269
3200 Pleasant Valley Rd, West Bend WI 53095
Tel (262) 334-5533 *SIC* 8062

RIVERVIEW HOSPITAL ASSOCIATION p 1238
410 Dewey St, Wisconsin Rapids WI 54494
Tel (715) 423-6060 *SIC* 8062

WYOMING MEDICAL CENTER p 1630
1233 E 2nd St, Casper WY 82601
Tel (307) 577-7201 *SIC* 8062

MEMORIAL HOSPITAL OF LARAMIE COUNTY p 942
214 E 23rd St, Cheyenne WY 82001
Tel (307) 633-7667 *SIC* 8062

WEST PARK HOSPITAL DISTRICT p 1595
707 Sheridan Ave, Cody WY 82414
Tel (307) 527-7501 *SIC* 8062

CAMPBELL COUNTY HOSPITAL DISTRICT p 245
501 S Burma Ave, Gillette WY 82716
Tel (307) 688-1551 *SIC* 8062

TETON COUNTY HOSPITAL DISTRICT p 1441
625 E Broadway Ave, Jackson WY 83001
Tel (307) 733-3636 *SIC* 8062 8052 8051

SIC 8063 Psychiatric Hospitals

ST LUKES MEDICAL CENTER LP p 1370
1800 E Van Buren St, Phoenix AZ 85006
Tel (602) 251-8535 *SIC* 8062 8063 8051

▲ MAGELLAN HEALTH INC p 895
4800 N Scottsdale Rd, Scottsdale AZ 85251
Tel (602) 572-6050 *SIC* 8063 8011 5122

TELECARE CORP p 1434
1080 Marina Village Pkwy # 100, Alameda CA 94501
Tel (510) 337-7950 *SIC* 8063 8011

CALIFORNIA DEPARTMENT OF STATE HOSPITALS-ATASCADERO FIRE DEPARTMENT p 240
10333 El Camino Real, Atascadero CA 93422
Tel (805) 468-2501 *SIC* 8063

DEANCO HEALTHCARE LLC p 420
14850 Roscoe Blvd, Panorama City CA 91402
Tel (818) 787-2222 *SIC* 8063

PASADENA HOSPITAL ASSOCIATION LTD p 1119
100 W California Blvd, Pasadena CA 91105
Tel (626) 397-5000 *SIC* 8062 8051 8063

CRESTWOOD BEHAVIORAL HEALTH INC p 392
520 Capitol Mall Ste 800, Sacramento CA 95814
Tel (510) 651-1244 *SIC* 8063

SUTTER HEALTH SACRAMENTO SIERRA REGION p 1410
2200 River Plaza Dr, Sacramento CA 95833
Tel (916) 733-8800 *SIC* 8062 8063 8052

ST HELENA HOSPITAL p 1367
10 Woodland Rd, Saint Helena CA 94574
Tel (707) 963-1882 *SIC* 8062 8063

PARKVIEW MEDICAL CENTER INC p 1117
400 W 16th St, Pueblo CO 81003
Tel (719) 584-4000 *SIC* 8062 8063

■ MAGELLAN PARTNERS RX INC p 895
55 Nod Rd, Avon CT 06001
Tel (860) 507-1900 *SIC* 8063

HALIFAX HEALTH CARE SYSTEMS INC p 654
303 N Clyde Morris Blvd, Daytona Beach FL 32114
Tel (386) 254-4000 *SIC* 8062 8011 8063

■ LAWNWOOD MEDICAL CENTER INC p 847
1700 S 23rd St, Fort Pierce FL 34950
Tel (772) 461-4000 *SIC* 8062 8063 8069

GENESIS REHABILITATION HOSPITAL INC p 603
3599 University Blvd S # 1, Jacksonville FL 32216
Tel (904) 858-7600 *SIC* 8063 8069 8051

■ WEST FLORIDA REGIONAL MEDICAL CENTER INC p 1594
8383 N Davis Hwy, Pensacola FL 32514
Tel (850) 494-4000
SIC 8062 8093 8063 8051

KOOTENAI HOSPITAL DISTRICT p 827
2003 Kootenai Health Way, Coeur D Alene ID 83814
Tel (208) 625-4000
SIC 8062 8063 8093 8734

ST LUKES MAGIC VALLEY INC p 1370
801 Pole Line Rd W, Twin Falls ID 83301
Tel (208) 737-2000 *SIC* 8062 8063

SAINT MARGARET MERCY HEALTHCARE CENTER p 1270
24 Joliet St, Dyer IN 46311
Tel (219) 865-2141 *SIC* 8062 8063

CLARK MEMORIAL HOSPITAL p 322
1220 Missouri Ave, Jeffersonville IN 47130
Tel (812) 282-6631 *SIC* 8062 8063

■ RHN CLARK MEMORIAL HOSPITAL LLC p 1231
1220 Missouri Ave, Jeffersonville IN 47130
Tel (812) 282-6631 *SIC* 8062 8063

HOWARD COMMUNITY HOSPITAL p 713
3500 S Lafountain St, Kokomo IN 46902
Tel (765) 453-0702 *SIC* 8062 8063

MCLEAN HOSPITAL CORP p 931
115 Mill St, Belmont MA 02478
Tel (617) 855-2000 *SIC* 8063

CAPE COD HOSPITAL p 248
27 Park St, Hyannis MA 02601
Tel (508) 862-7575 *SIC* 8062 8011 8063

COOLEY DICKINSON HOSPITAL INC p 366
30 Locust St, Northampton MA 01060
Tel (413) 582-2000 *SIC* 8062 8063 8069

BRONSON BATTLE CREEK HOSPITAL p 217
300 North Ave, Battle Creek MI 49017
Tel (269) 966-8000 *SIC* 8062 8063 8051

PINE REST CHRISTIAN MENTAL HEALTH SERVICES p 1149
300 68th St Se, Grand Rapids MI 49548
Tel (616) 455-5000 *SIC* 8063

MAYO CLINIC HEALTH SYSTEM-ALBERT LEA AND AUSTIN p 924
404 W Fountain St, Albert Lea MN 56007
Tel (507) 373-2384
SIC 8062 8069 8051 8063 8011

FORREST GENERAL HEALTH SERVICES INC p 568
6051 U S Highway 49, Hattiesburg MS 39401
Tel (601) 288-7000 *SIC* 8062 8063 8069

DAUGHTERS OF CHARITY SERVICES OF ST LOUIS p 414
12303 De Paul Dr, Bridgeton MO 63044
Tel (314) 344-6000
SIC 8062 8051 8063 8069

SAINT LUKES NORTHLAND HOME CARE p 1270
601 S Us Highway 169, Smithville MO 64089
Tel (816) 532-3700
SIC 8062 8051 8069 8063

■ HCA HEALTH SERVICES OF NEW HAMPSHIRE INC p 671
333 Borthwick Ave, Portsmouth NH 03801
Tel (603) 436-0600 *SIC* 8062 8063

LONG ISLAND HOME p 876
400 Sunrise Hwy, Amityville NY 11701
Tel (631) 264-4000
SIC 8063 8051 8099 8011

WOMANS CHRISTIAN ASSOCIATION OF JAMESTOWN N Y p 1621
207 Foote Ave, Jamestown NY 14701
Tel (716) 487-0141
SIC 8062 8063 8093 8069

LONG ISLAND JEWISH MEDICAL CENTER p 876
27005 76th Ave, New Hyde Park NY 11040
Tel (516) 465-2600 *SIC* 8062 8063 8069

BETH ISRAEL MEDICAL CENTER p 177
First Ave 16th St, New York NY 10003
Tel (212) 420-2806 *SIC* 8062 8063

MANHATTAN PSYCHIATRIC CENTER p 901
1 Wards Is Ofc 2, New York NY 10035
Tel (646) 672-6767 *SIC* 8063

OSWEGO HOSPITAL INC p 1097
110 W 6th St, Oswego NY 13126
Tel (315) 349-5511 *SIC* 8062 8063

CHARLOTTE-MECKLENBURG HOSPITAL AUTHORITY p 290
1000 Blythe Blvd, Charlotte NC 28203
Tel (704) 355-2000
SIC 8062 8069 8063 8051 8011

NHCS INC p 1041
2416 Professional Dr, Rocky Mount NC 27804
Tel (252) 962-8585 *SIC* 8062 8063

■ STATESVILLE HMA LLC p 1383
218 Old Mocksville Rd, Statesville NC 28625
Tel (704) 873-0281 *SIC* 8051 8063 8062

ALTRU HEALTH SYSTEM p 63
1200 S Columbia Rd, Grand Forks ND 58201
Tel (701) 780-5000
SIC 7352 8011 8062 8063

MARYMOUNT HOSPITAL INC p 915
9500 Euclid Ave, Cleveland OH 44195
Tel (216) 581-0500
SIC 8062 8063 8051 8082

BETHESDA HOSPITAL ASSOCIATION INC p 178
2951 Maple Ave, Zanesville OH 43701
Tel (740) 454-4000 *SIC* 8062 8063 8082

CASCADIA BEHAVIORAL HEALTHCARE INC p 263
847 Ne 19th Ave Ste 100, Portland OR 97232
Tel (503) 238-0769
SIC 8322 8093 8063 8361

JEFFERSON HOSPITAL p 781
565 Coal Valley Rd, Clairton PA 15025
Tel (412) 267-6024 *SIC* 8062 8063 8069

PINNACLE HEALTH MEDICAL SERVICES p 1150
409 S 2nd St Ste 2b, Harrisburg PA 17104
Tel (717) 231-8341 *SIC* 8011 8063

▲ UNIVERSAL HEALTH SERVICES INC p 1517
367 S Gulph Rd, King Of Prussia PA 19406
Tel (610) 768-3300
SIC 8062 8063 8093 8011 8741

PHILHAVEN HOSPITAL p 1143
283 Butler Rd, Lebanon PA 17042
Tel (717) 270-2414 *SIC* 8011 8063

MONONGAHELA VALLEY HOSPITAL INC p 984
1163 Country Club Rd, Monongahela PA 15063
Tel (724) 258-1000 *SIC* 8062 8063 8069

PENNSYLVANIA HOSPITAL OF UNIVERSITY OF PENNSYLVANIA HEALTH SYSTEM p 1130
800 Spruce St, Philadelphia PA 19107
Tel (215) 829-3000 *SIC* 8062 8063

PHILADELPHIA NORTH HEALTH SYSTEM p 1143
801 W Girard Ave, Philadelphia PA 19122
Tel (215) 787-9001 *SIC* 8062 8069 8063

■ SHARON REGIONAL HEALTH SYSTEM p 1312
740 E State St, Sharon PA 16146
Tel (724) 983-3911 *SIC* 8062 8063 8069

CARE NEW ENGLAND HEALTH SYSTEM INC p 254
45 Willard Ave, Providence RI 02905
Tel (401) 453-7900
SIC 8063 8062 8069 8093 8082

■ PSYCHIATRIC SOLUTIONS INC p 1189
6640 Carothers Pkwy # 500, Franklin TN 37067
Tel (615) 312-5700 *SIC* 8011 8063

WELLMONT HEALTH SYSTEM p 1589
1905 American Way, Kingsport TN 37660
Tel (423) 230-8200 *SIC* 8062 8051 8063

■ HCA INC p 672
1 Park Plz, Nashville TN 37203
Tel (615) 344-9551
SIC 8063 8062 8069 8093

■ HCA PSYCHIATRIC CO p 672
1 Park Plz, Nashville TN 37203
Tel (615) 344-2390 *SIC* 8063 8011

■ HCA-HOSPITAL CORP OF AMERICA p 672
1 Park Plz, Nashville TN 37203
Tel (615) 344-9551 *SIC* 8062 8063

HERCULES HOLDING II LLC p 685
1 Park Plz, Nashville TN 37203
Tel (615) 344-9551
SIC 8062 8063 8069 8093

■ HOSPITAL CORP OF AMERICA p 709
1 Park Plz, Nashville TN 37203
Tel (615) 344-9551 *SIC* 8062 8063

■ NORTHWEST TEXAS HEALTHCARE SYSTEM INC p 1060
1501 S Coulter St, Amarillo TX 79106
Tel (806) 354-1000
SIC 8062 8063 8051 8049

SAN JACINTO METHODIST HOSPITAL p 1277
4401 Garth Rd, Baytown TX 77521
Tel (281) 420-8600 *SIC* 8062 8063 8051

TEXAS HLTH HRS MTHDT HSPTL HEB p 1443
1615 Hospital Pkwy, Bedford TX 76022
Tel (817) 848-4000 *SIC* 8062 8063 8069

■ BAY AREA HEALTHCARE GROUP LTD p 160
3315 S Alameda St, Corpus Christi TX 78411
Tel (361) 761-1400
SIC 8062 8063 8069 8093

▲ TENET HEALTHCARE CORP p 1437
1445 Ross Ave Ste 1400, Dallas TX 75202
Tel (469) 893-2200
SIC 8062 8069 8741 8063 8082 8011

■ TENET HEALTHSYSTEM MEDICAL INC p 1437
1445 Ross Ave Ste 1400, Dallas TX 75202
Tel (469) 893-2000 *SIC* 8062 8063 6512

HARRIS CENTER FOR MENTAL HEALTH AND IDD p 663
9401 Southwest Fwy, Houston TX 77074
Tel (713) 970-7000 *SIC* 8063

OCEANS HEALTH CARE p 1073
5850 Granite Pkwy Ste 300, Plano TX 75024
Tel (972) 464-0022 *SIC* 8063

CHRISTUS SANTA ROSA HEALTH CARE CORP p 303
333 N Santa Rosa St, San Antonio TX 78207
Tel (210) 704-2011 *SIC* 8063 8069

SAN ANTONIO STATE HOSPITAL p 1275
6711 S New Braunfels Ave, San Antonio TX 78223
Tel (210) 532-8811 *SIC* 8063

■ BHC FAIRFAX HOSPITAL INC p 180
10200 Ne 132nd St, Kirkland WA 98034
Tel (425) 821-2000 *SIC* 8063

OUR LADY OF LOURDES HOSPITAL AT PASCO p 1098
520 N 4th Ave, Pasco WA 99301
Tel (509) 547-7704 *SIC* 8062 8063

BELLIN HEALTH SYSTEMS INC p 170
744 S Webster Ave, Green Bay WI 54301
Tel (920) 433-3500 *SIC* 8062 8063 7352

MILWAUKEE COUNTY BEHAVORIAL HEALTH DIVISION p 972
9455 W Watertown Plank Rd, Milwaukee WI 53226
Tel (414) 257-6995 *SIC* 8063

ROGERS MEMORIAL HOSPITAL INC p 1246
34700 Valley Rd, Oconomowoc WI 53066
Tel (800) 767-4411 *SIC* 8063

SIC 8069 Specialty Hospitals, Except Psychiatric

CARRAWAY METHODIST HEALTH SYSTEMS p 260
1600 Carraway Blvd, Birmingham AL 35234
Tel (205) 502-4100 *SIC* 8069 8062

CHILDRENS HOSPITAL OF ALABAMA p 299
1600 7th Ave S, Birmingham AL 35233
Tel (205) 939-9100 *SIC* 8069

▲ HEALTHSOUTH CORP p 677
3660 Grandview Pkwy # 200, Birmingham AL 35243
Tel (205) 967-7116 *SIC* 8069 8051

USA CHILDRENS AND WOMENS HOSPITAL p 1534
1700 Center St, Mobile AL 36604
Tel (251) 415-1000 *SIC* 8069

YUKON-KUSKOKWIM HEALTH CORP p 1640
829 Hospin Hwy Ste 329, Bethel AK 99559
Tel (907) 543-6300
SIC 8062 7363 8069 8093 8042 8021

PHOENIX CHILDRENS HOSPITAL INC p 1144
1919 E Thomas Rd, Phoenix AZ 85016
Tel (602) 546-1000 *SIC* 8069

WASHINGTON REGIONAL MEDICAL SYSTEM p 1579
3215 N Northhills Blvd, Fayetteville AR 72703
Tel (479) 463-1000 *SIC* 8062 8069

ARKANSAS CHILDRENS HOSPITAL p 109
1 Childrens Way, Little Rock AR 72202
Tel (501) 364-1100 *SIC* 8062 8069

ANAHEIM REGIONAL MEDICAL CENTER p 88
1111 W La Palma Ave, Anaheim CA 92801
Tel (714) 774-1450 *SIC* 8069 8062

■ CRC HEALTH CORP p 389
20400 Stevens Creek Blvd, Cupertino CA 95014
Tel (877) 272-8668
SIC 8069 8099 8322 8093

CITY OF HOPE p 315
1500 Duarte Rd Fl 4, Duarte CA 91010
Tel (626) 256-4673 *SIC* 8069

COMMUNITY HOSPITALS OF CENTRAL CALIFORNIA p 349
2823 Fresno St, Fresno CA 93721
Tel (559) 459-6000 *SIC* 8069

SADDLEBACK MEMORIAL MEDICAL CENTER p 1265
24451 Health Center Dr, Laguna Hills CA 92653
Tel (949) 837-4500
SIC 8062 8011 8093 8099 8071 8069

CHILDRENS HOSPITAL LOS ANGELES p 299
4650 W Sunset Blvd, Los Angeles CA 90027
Tel (323) 660-2450 *SIC* 8069 8062

TENET HEALTH SYSTEMS NORRIS INC p 1437
1441 Eastlake Ave, Los Angeles CA 90089
Tel (323) 865-3000 *SIC* 8069

CHILDRENS HOSPITAL CENTRAL CA p 299
9300 Valley Childrens Pl, Madera CA 93636
Tel (559) 353-6900 *SIC* 8069

VALLEY CHILDRENS HEALTHCARE p 1540
9300 Valley Childrens Pl, Madera CA 93636
Tel (559) 353-3000 *SIC* 8011 8069

VALLEY CHILDRENS HOSPITAL p 1540
9300 Valley Childrens Pl, Madera CA 93636
Tel (559) 353-3000 *SIC* 8069

■ DOCTORS HOSPITAL OF MANTECA INC p 447
1205 E North St, Manteca CA 95336
Tel (209) 823-3111 *SIC* 8069

LELAND STANFORD JUNIOR UNIVERSITY p 854
2575 Sand Hill Rd, Menlo Park CA 94025
Tel (650) 723-2300 *SIC* 8221 8069 8062

COMMUNITY HOSPITAL OF MONTEREY PENINSULA p 349
23625 Holman Hwy, Monterey CA 93940
Tel (831) 624-5311 *SIC* 8069 8011

CHILDRENS HEALTHCARE OF CALIFORNIA p 299
1201 W La Veta Ave, Orange CA 92868
Tel (714) 997-3000 *SIC* 8069

CHILDRENS HOSPITAL OF ORANGE COUNTY p 300
1201 W La Veta Ave, Orange CA 92868
Tel (714) 997-3000 *SIC* 8069

LUCILE SALTER PACKARD CHILDRENS HOSPITAL AT STANFORD p 884
725 Welch Rd, Palo Alto CA 94304
Tel (650) 497-8000 *SIC* 8069 8082 5912

REDLANDS COMMUNITY HOSPITAL p 1217
350 Terracina Blvd, Redlands CA 92373
Tel (909) 335-5500 *SIC* 8069

RADY CHILDRENS HOSPITAL AND HEALTH CENTER p 1205
3020 Childrens Way, San Diego CA 92123
Tel (858) 576-1700 *SIC* 8069

RADY CHILDRENS HOSPITAL-SAN DIEGO p 1205
3020 Childrens Way, San Diego CA 92123
Tel (858) 576-1700 *SIC* 8069

JOHN MUIR PHYSICIAN NETWORK p 789
1450 Treat Blvd, Walnut Creek CA 94597
Tel (925) 296-9700
SIC 8062 8069 8093 7363

CHILDRENS HOSPITAL COLORADO p 299
13123 E 16th Ave, Aurora CO 80045
Tel (720) 777-1234 *SIC* 8069

BOULDER COMMUNITY HEALTH p 204
1100 Balsam Ave, Boulder CO 80304
Tel (303) 440-2273 *SIC* 8069

CENTURA HEALTH CORP p 281
188 Inverness Dr W # 500, Englewood CO 80112
Tel (303) 290-6500 *SIC* 8069

CRAIG HOSPITAL p 388
3425 S Clarkson St, Englewood CO 80113
Tel (303) 789-8000 *SIC* 8069

LINNEA BASEY CANCER RESOURCE CENTER p 869
11600 W 2nd Pl, Lakewood CO 80228
Tel (773) 484-1000 SIC 8069

CCMC CORP p 270
282 Washington St, Hartford CT 06106
Tel (860) 545-9490 SIC 8069 7389 8299

CONNECTICUT CHILDRENS MEDICAL CENTER p 356
282 Washington St, Hartford CT 06106
Tel (860) 545-9000 SIC 8069

SAINT FRANCIS HOSPITAL AND MEDICAL CENTER FOUNDATION INC p 1269
114 Woodland St, Hartford CT 06105
Tel (860) 714-4006 SIC 8062 8011 8069

HOSPITAL FOR SPECIAL CARE p 709
2150 Corbin Ave, New Britain CT 06053
Tel (860) 827-4924 SIC 8069

MASONICARE CORP p 916
22 Masonic Ave, Wallingford CT 06492
Tel (203) 679-5900 SIC 8069 8082 8322

ALFRED IDUPONT HOSPITAL FOR CHILDREN p 50
1600 Rockland Rd, Wilmington DE 19803
Tel (302) 651-4000 SIC 8069

SIGHTSAVERS INTERNATIONAL INC p 1321
1000 N West St Ste 1200, Wilmington DE 19801
Tel (800) 707-9746 SIC 8069

■ CARLYLE PARTNERS IV LP p 258
1001 Pennsylvania Ave Nw, Washington DC 20004
Tel (202) 729-5626 SIC 8711 8069 8051

MEDSTAR-GEORGETOWN MEDICAL CENTER INC p 939
3800 Reservoir Rd Nw, Washington DC 20007
Tel (202) 444-2000 SIC 8062 8221 8069

NATIONAL REHABILITATION HOSPITAL INC p 1015
102 Irving St Nw, Washington DC 20010
Tel (202) 877-1000 SIC 8069

CANCER TREATMENT CENTERS OF AMERICA INC p 247
5900 Broken Sound Pkwy, Boca Raton FL 33487
Tel (800) 615-3055 SIC 8069

■ LAWNWOOD MEDICAL CENTER INC p 847
1700 S 23rd St, Fort Pierce FL 34950
Tel (772) 461-4000 SIC 8062 8063 8069

■ NORTH FLORIDA REGIONAL MEDICAL CENTER INC p 1052
6500 W Newberry Rd, Gainesville FL 32605
Tel (352) 333-4100
SIC 8062 8093 8011 8082 8069

GENESIS HEALTH INC p 603
3599 University Blvd S # 1, Jacksonville FL 32216
Tel (904) 858-7600 SIC 8069 8011 8741

GENESIS REHABILITATION HOSPITAL INC p 603
3599 University Blvd S # 1, Jacksonville FL 32216
Tel (904) 858-7600 SIC 8063 8069 8051

NEMOURS FOUNDATION p 1025
10140 Centurion Pkwy N, Jacksonville FL 32256
Tel (904) 697-4100 SIC 8069 8093

UNIVERSITY OF MIAMI MILLER SCHOOL OF MEDICINE p 1523
900 Nw 17th St Ste 1, Miami FL 33136
Tel (305) 326-6000 SIC 8069

VARIETY CHILDRENS HOSPITAL p 1544
3100 Sw 62nd Ave, Miami FL 33155
Tel (305) 666-6511 SIC 8069

ORANGE PARK MEDICAL CENTER p 1092
2001 Kingsley Ave, Orange Park FL 32073
Tel (904) 276-8500 SIC 8069

NEMOURS CHILDRENS HOSPITAL p 1025
13535 Nemours Pkwy, Orlando FL 32827
Tel (407) 567-4000 SIC 8069

ORLANDO HEALTH INC p 1095
52 W Underwood St, Orlando FL 32806
Tel (321) 843-7000 SIC 8062 8741 8069

LAKEVIEW CENTER INC p 840
1221 W Lakeview Ave, Pensacola FL 32501
Tel (850) 432-1222
SIC 8069 8093 7389 7371 7373

HEALTH FIRST INC p 674
6450 Us Highway 1, Rockledge FL 32955
Tel (321) 434-4300
SIC 8062 8011 8082 8069 7991 6324

JOHNS HOPKINS ALL CHILDRENS HOSPITAL INC p 790
501 6th Ave S, Saint Petersburg FL 33701
Tel (727) 898-7451 SIC 8069 8062

■ NORTHSIDE HOSPITAL p 1058
6000 49th St N, Saint Petersburg FL 33709
Tel (727) 521-4411
SIC 8031 8011 8069 8062

SHRINERS HOSPITALS FOR CHILDREN p 1319
12502 Usf Pine Dr, Tampa FL 33612
Tel (813) 972-2250 SIC 8069

INTERCOASTAL HEALTH SYSTEMS INC p 752
1309 N Flagler Dr, West Palm Beach FL 33401
Tel (561) 650-6272 SIC 8741 8069

CENTENNIAL HEALTHCARE CORP p 275
400 Perimeter Ctr Ter Ne, Atlanta GA 30346
Tel (770) 698-9040
SIC 8051 8069 8052 8741

CHILDRENS HEALTHCARE OF ATLANTA FOUNDATION INC p 299
1405 Clifton Rd Ne, Atlanta GA 30322
Tel (404) 785-7300 SIC 8069

CHILDRENS HEALTHCARE OF ATLANTA INC p 299
1600 Tullie Cir Ne, Atlanta GA 30329
Tel (404) 785-7000 SIC 8069

SHEPHERD CENTER INC p 1315
2020 Peachtree Rd Nw, Atlanta GA 30309
Tel (404) 352-2020 SIC 8069

KAPIOLANI MEDICAL CENTER FOR WOMEN AND CHILDREN p 803
1319 Punahou St, Honolulu HI 96826
Tel (808) 535-7401 SIC 8069

ANN & ROBERT H LURIE CHILDRENS HOSPITAL OF CHICAGO p 92
225 E Chicago Ave, Chicago IL 60611
Tel (312) 227-7132 SIC 8011 8069

REHABILITATION INSTITUTE OF CHICAGO p 1220
345 E Superior St, Chicago IL 60611
Tel (312) 238-1000 SIC 8069

MIDWESTERN REGIONAL MEDICAL CENTER INC p 968
2501 Emmaus Ave, Zion IL 60099
Tel (847) 731-1364 SIC 8069

INDIANA ORTHOPAEDIC HOSPITAL LLC p 738
8450 Northwest Blvd, Indianapolis IN 46278
Tel (317) 956-1000 SIC 8069

ST VINCENT HEART CENTER OF INDIANA LLC p 1373
10580 N Meridian St, Indianapolis IN 46290
Tel (317) 583-5000 SIC 8069

REID HOSPITAL & HEALTH CARE SERVICES INC p 1221
1100 Reid Pkwy, Richmond IN 47374
Tel (765) 983-3000 SIC 8069

SAINT ELIZABETH MEDICAL CENTER INC p 1269
1 Medical Village Dr, Edgewood KY 41017
Tel (859) 301-2000 SIC 8062 8069 8093

CENTRAL BAPTIST HOSPITAL p 277
1740 Nicholasville Rd, Lexington KY 40503
Tel (859) 260-6100 SIC 8069

■ KINDRED HOSPITALS LIMITED PARTNERSHIP p 819
1313 Saint Anthony Pl, Louisville KY 40204
Tel (502) 587-7001 SIC 8069

WOMENS HOSPITAL p 1622
100 Womans Way, Baton Rouge LA 70817
Tel (225) 927-1300 SIC 8069

LAKEVIEW REGIONAL MEDICAL CENTER p 840
95 Judge Tanner Blvd, Covington LA 70433
Tel (985) 867-3800 SIC 8069

CHILDRENS HOSPITAL p 299
200 Henry Clay Ave, New Orleans LA 70118
Tel (504) 899-9511 SIC 8069

LOUISIANA CHILDRENS MEDICAL CENTER INC p 880
200 Henry Clay Ave, New Orleans LA 70118
Tel (504) 896-9581 SIC 8069

CHRISTUS HEALTH NORTHERN LOUISIANA p 303
1 Saint Mary Pl, Shreveport LA 71101
Tel (318) 681-4500 SIC 8069

NORTON SOUND HEALTH CORP p 1061
790 Lower St, Turner ME 04282
Tel (907) 443-3311
SIC 8062 8051 8069 8093 8011

WATERVILLE OSTEOPATHIC HEALTH CARE (INC) p 1582
200 Kennedy Memorial Dr, Waterville ME 04901
Tel (207) 873-0731 SIC 8069

YORK HOSPITAL p 1637
15 Hospital Dr, York ME 03909
Tel (207) 351-2023
SIC 8062 8051 8069 7361

KENNEDY KRIEGER CHILDRENS HOSPITAL INC p 811
707 N Broadway, Baltimore MD 21205
Tel (443) 923-9400 SIC 8069

KENNEDY KRIEGER INSTITUTE INC p 811
707 N Broadway, Baltimore MD 21205
Tel (443) 923-9200 SIC 8069

UNIVERSITY OF MARYLAND REHABILITATION INSTITUTE OF SOUTHERN MARYLAND p 1522
2200 Kernan Dr, Gwynn Oak MD 21207
Tel (410) 448-2500 SIC 8069

CHILDRENS HOSPITAL CORP p 299
300 Longwood Ave, Boston MA 02115
Tel (617) 355-6000 SIC 8069

DANA-FARBER CANCER INSTITUTE INC p 411
450 Brookline Ave, Boston MA 02215
Tel (617) 632-3000 SIC 8733 8069

FOUNDATION OF MASSACHUSETTS EYE AND EAR INFIRMARY INC p 571
243 Charles St, Boston MA 02114
Tel (617) 523-7900 SIC 8069

HEBREW REHABILITATION CENTER p 680
1200 Centre St, Boston MA 02131
Tel (617) 363-8000 SIC 8069

MASSACHUSETTS EYE AND EAR INFIRMARY p 917
243 Charles St, Boston MA 02114
Tel (617) 573-3499 SIC 8069

MASSACHUSETTS EYE AND EAR INFIRMARY & PHYSICIAN STAFF INC p 917
243 Charles St, Boston MA 02114
Tel (617) 573-3499 SIC 8069 8011

■ FOUNDATION MEDICINE INC p 571
150 2nd St, Cambridge MA 02141
Tel (617) 418-2200 SIC 8069

SPAULDING REHABILITATION HOSPITAL (SRH) VOLUNTEER SERVICES p 1355
300 1st Ave, Charlestown MA 02129
Tel (617) 952-5000 SIC 8069 8011

COOLEY DICKINSON HOSPITAL INC p 366
30 Locust St, Northampton MA 01060
Tel (413) 582-2000 SIC 8062 8063 8069

■ SELECT SPECIALTY HOSPITAL-BATTLE CREEK INC p 1301
300 North Ave, Battle Creek MI 49017
Tel (269) 245-4675 SIC 8069

■ VHS CHILDRENS HOSPITAL OF MICHIGAN INC p 1553
3901 Beaubien St, Detroit MI 48201
Tel (313) 745-5437 SIC 8069

■ VHS DETROIT RECEIVING HOSPITAL INC p 1553
4201 Saint Antoine St, Detroit MI 48201
Tel (313) 745-3000 SIC 8093 8069 8062

KENT COUNTY CMH AUTHORITY p 812
790 Fuller Ave Ne, Grand Rapids MI 49503
Tel (616) 336-3765 SIC 8069

MARY FREE BED REHABILITATION HOSPITAL p 914
235 Wealthy St Se, Grand Rapids MI 49503
Tel (616) 242-0300 SIC 8069 8093

MCLAREN LAPEER REGION p 931
1375 N Main St, Lapeer MI 48446
Tel (810) 667-5580 SIC 8069

METROPOLITAN HOSPITAL p 956
5900 Byron Center Ave Sw, Wyoming MI 49519
Tel (616) 252-7200 SIC 8062 8069

MAYO CLINIC HEALTH SYSTEM-ALBERT LEA AND AUSTIN p 924
404 W Fountain St, Albert Lea MN 56007
Tel (507) 373-2384
SIC 8062 8069 8051 8063 8011

CHILDRENS HOSPITALS AND CLINICS OF MINNESOTA p 300
2525 Chicago Ave, Minneapolis MN 55404
Tel (612) 813-6000 SIC 8069

BETHESDA HEALTHEAST HOSPITAL p 178
559 Capitol Blvd Fl 6, Saint Paul MN 55103
Tel (651) 232-2000 SIC 8062 8741 8069

GILLETTE CHILDRENS SPECIALTY HEALTHCARE p 612
200 University Ave E, Saint Paul MN 55101
Tel (651) 291-2848 SIC 8069

WOODWINDS HEALTH CAMPUS p 1624
1925 Woodwinds Dr, Saint Paul MN 55125
Tel (651) 232-0100 SIC 8069

FORREST GENERAL HEALTH SERVICES INC p 568
6051 U S Highway 49, Hattiesburg MS 39401
Tel (601) 288-7000 SIC 8062 8063 8069

MISSISSIPPI BAPTIST HEALTH SYSTEMS INC p 975
1225 N State St Ofc, Jackson MS 39202
Tel (601) 968-1000 SIC 8741 8721 8069

MISSISSIPPI BAPTST MEDICAL CENTER INC p 975
1225 N State St, Jackson MS 39202
Tel (601) 968-1000 SIC 8062 8069 8051

ST DOMINIC HEALTH SERVICES INC p 1366
969 Lakeland Dr, Jackson MS 39216
Tel (601) 200-2000
SIC 8741 8093 8069 8062

DAUGHTERS OF CHARITY SERVICES OF ST LOUIS p 414
12303 De Paul Dr, Bridgeton MO 63044
Tel (314) 344-6000
SIC 8062 8051 8063 8069

COMPASS HEALTH INC p 351
1800 Community, Clinton MO 64735
Tel (660) 885-8131
SIC 8011 8069 8093 8361

FREEMAN HEALTH SYSTEM p 577
1102 W 32nd St, Joplin MO 64804
Tel (417) 347-1111 SIC 8062 8069

MERCY CHILDRENS HOSPITAL p 945
2401 Gillham Rd, Kansas City MO 64108
Tel (816) 234-3000 SIC 8069

SSM CARDINAL GLENNON CHILDRENS HOSPITAL p 1364
1465 S Grand Blvd, Saint Louis MO 63104
Tel (314) 577-5600 SIC 8069

ST LOUIS CHILDRENS HOSPITAL p 1369
1 Childrens Pl, Saint Louis MO 63110
Tel (314) 454-6000 SIC 8069

SAINT LUKES NORTHLAND HOME CARE p 1270
601 S Us Highway 169, Smithville MO 64089
Tel (816) 532-3700
SIC 8062 8051 8069 8063

LESTER E COX MEDICAL CENTERS p 857
1423 N Jefferson Ave, Springfield MO 65802
Tel (417) 269-3000 SIC 8062 8069

SAINT FRANCIS MEDICAL CENTER INC p 1269
2620 W Faidley Ave, Grand Island NE 68803
Tel (308) 384-4600 SIC 8062 8069

CHILDRENS FAMILY SUPPORT CENTER p 299
8200 Dodge St, Omaha NE 68114
Tel (402) 955-8117 SIC 8069

CHILDRENS HOSPITAL & MEDICAL CENTER p 299
8200 Dodge St, Omaha NE 68114
Tel (402) 955-5400 SIC 8069

NEBRASKA ORTHOPAEDIC HOSPITAL LLC p 1023
2808 S 143rd Plz, Omaha NE 68144
Tel (402) 637-0600 SIC 8069

COMMUNITY HOSPITAL GROUP INC p 349
98 James St Ste 400, Edison NJ 08820
Tel (732) 321-7000 SIC 8062 8069

CHILDRENS SPECIALIZED HOSPITAL INC p 300
150 New Providence Rd # 1, Mountainside NJ 07092
Tel (888) 244-5373 SIC 8069 8093

■ BREYUT CONVALESCENT CENTER INC p 210
2240 Whthrse Mrcrville Rd, Trenton NJ 08619
Tel (609) 586-7500 SIC 8051 8069

■ KESSLER INSTITUTE FOR REHABILITATION INC p 814
1199 Pleasant Valley Way, West Orange NJ 07052
Tel (973) 731-3600 SIC 8069 8093

ERNEST HEALTH INC p 508
7770 Jefferson St Ne # 320, Albuquerque NM 87109
Tel (505) 856-5300 SIC 8069

CALVARY HOSPITAL INC p 243
1740 Eastchester Rd, Bronx NY 10461
Tel (718) 518-2000 SIC 8069

FF THOMPSON HEALTH SYSTEM INC p 539
350 Parrish St, Canandaigua NY 14424
Tel (585) 396-6000 SIC 8741 8069

TLC HEALTH NETWORK p 1457
845 Route 5 And 20, Irving NY 14081
Tel (716) 951-7000 SIC 8062 8069

WOMANS CHRISTIAN ASSOCIATION OF JAMESTOWN N Y p 1621
207 Foote Ave, Jamestown NY 14701
Tel (716) 487-0141
SIC 8062 8063 8093 8069

LONG ISLAND JEWISH MEDICAL CENTER p 876
27005 76th Ave, New Hyde Park NY 11040
Tel (516) 465-2600 SIC 8062 8063 8069

PARKER JEWISH INSTITUTE FOR HEALTH CARE AND REHABILITATION FOUNDATION p 1116
27111 76th Ave, New Hyde Park NY 11040
Tel (516) 247-6500 SIC 8051 8082 8069

COLER GOLDWATER SPECIALTY HOSPITAL & NURSING FACILITY p 336
900 Main St, New York NY 10044
Tel (212) 848-6000 SIC 8069 8051

MEMORIAL HOSPITAL FOR CANCER AND ALLIED DISEASES p 942
1275 York Ave, New York NY 10065
Tel (212) 639-2000 SIC 8069

MEMORIAL SLOAN-KETTERING CANCER CENTER p 942
1275 York Ave, New York NY 10065
Tel (212) 639-2000 SIC 8069

NEW YORK CITY HEALTH AND HOSPITALS CORP p 1034
125 Worth St Rm 514, New York NY 10013
Tel (212) 788-3321 SIC 8062 8069 8093

NEW YORK EYE AND EAR INFIRMARY IPA INC p 1035
310 E 14th St, New York NY 10003
Tel (212) 979-4000 SIC 8069

NEW YORK SOCIETY FOR RELIEF OF RUPTURED AND CRIPPLED MAINTAINING HOSPITAL FOR p 1036
535 E 70th St, New York NY 10021
Tel (212) 606-1000 SIC 8069

NYU HOSPITAL FOR JOINT DISEASES p 1069
301 E 17th St Fl 14, New York NY 10003
Tel (212) 598-6000 SIC 8069

ST FRANCIS HOSPITAL POUGHKEEPSIE NEW YORK p 1366
241 North Rd, Poughkeepsie NY 12601
Tel (845) 483-5000
SIC 8062 8069 8011 8351

ST FRANCIS HOSPITAL ROSLYN NEW YORK p 1366
100 Port Washington Blvd, Roslyn NY 11576
Tel (516) 627-3813 SIC 8069

CHARLOTTE-MECKLENBURG HOSPITAL AUTHORITY p 290
1000 Blythe Blvd, Charlotte NC 28203
Tel (704) 355-2000
SIC 8062 8069 8063 8051 8011

MEDCATH INC p 935
10800 Sikes Pl Ste 200, Charlotte NC 28277
Tel (704) 815-7700 SIC 8069 8093 8742

PRESBYTERIAN-ORTHOPEDIC HOSPITAL p 1171
1901 Randolph Rd, Charlotte NC 28207
Tel (704) 316-2000 SIC 8069

WESTCARE HEALTH SYSTEM p 1596
68 Hospital Rd, Sylva NC 28779
Tel (828) 586-7000 SIC 8069

CHILDRENS HOSPITAL MEDICAL CENTER OF AKRON p 299
1 Perkins Sq, Akron OH 44308
Tel (330) 543-1000 SIC 8069

AULTMAN HOSPITAL p 131
2600 6th St Sw, Canton OH 44710
Tel (330) 452-9911 SIC 8062 8069 8221

CHILDRENS HOSPITAL MEDICAL CENTER p 299
3333 Burnet Ave, Cincinnati OH 45229
Tel (513) 636-4200
SIC 8733 8011 8069 8731

LUTHERAN MEDICAL CENTER (INC) p 886
1730 W 25th St, Cleveland OH 44113
Tel (216) 696-4300 SIC 8062 8011 8069

UNIVERSITY HOSPITALS OF CLEVELAND p 1519
11100 Euclid Ave, Cleveland OH 44106
Tel (216) 844-1000 SIC 8062 8069

NATIONWIDE CHILDRENS HOSPITAL p 1017
700 Childrens Dr, Columbus OH 43205
Tel (614) 722-3040 SIC 8069

CHILDRENS MEDICAL CENTER TOLEDO p 300
1 Childrens Plz, Dayton OH 45404
Tel (937) 641-3000 SIC 8069

DAYTON CHILDRENS HOSPITAL p 417
1 Childrens Plz, Dayton OH 45404
Tel (937) 641-3000 SIC 8069

STRESS CARE/BRIDGES p 1393
405 W Grand Ave, Dayton OH 45405
Tel (937) 723-3200 SIC 8069

MARIETTA MEMORIAL HOSPITAL INC p 906
401 Matthew St, Marietta OH 45750
Tel (740) 374-1400 SIC 8062 8069

MCBRIDE CLINIC ORTHOPEDIC HOSPITAL LLC p 926
9600 Broadway Ext, Oklahoma City OK 73114
Tel (405) 486-2515 SIC 8069

OKLAHOMA HEART HOSPITAL LLC p 1079
4050 W Memorial Rd, Oklahoma City OK 73120
Tel (405) 608-3200 SIC 8069

AHS OKLAHOMA HEALTH SYSTEM LLP p 37
110 W 7th St Ste 2540, Tulsa OK 74119
Tel (918) 579-1000
SIC 8062 8069 7352 6512 7389 5999

SOUTHWESTERN REGIONAL MEDICAL CENTER INC p 1353
10109 E 79th St, Tulsa OK 74133
Tel (918) 286-5000 SIC 8069

ASANTE p 115
2825 E Barnett Rd, Medford OR 97504
Tel (541) 789-7000 SIC 8069

LEGACY GOOD SAMARITAN HOSPITAL AND MEDICAL CENTER p 852
1015 Nw 22nd Ave, Portland OR 97210
Tel (503) 413-7711 SIC 8069

OREGON HEALTH & SCIENCE UNIVERSITY p 1093
3181 Sw Sam Jackson Pk Rd, Portland OR 97239
Tel (503) 494-8311 SIC 8221 8069

GOOD SHEPHERD REHABILITATION HOSPITAL INC p 623
850 S 5th St, Allentown PA 18103
Tel (610) 776-3100
SIC 8361 8051 8093 8069

JEFFERSON HOSPITAL p 781
565 Coal Valley Rd, Clairton PA 15025
Tel (412) 267-6024 SIC 8062 8063 8069

CHARLES COLE MEMORIAL HOSPITAL p 289
1001 E 2nd St, Coudersport PA 16915
Tel (814) 274-9300 SIC 7352 8069 8051

■ SELECT MEDICAL CORP p 1301
4714 Gettysburg Rd, Mechanicsburg PA 17055
Tel (717) 972-1100 SIC 8093 8051 8069

▲ SELECT MEDICAL HOLDINGS CORP p 1301
4714 Gettysburg Rd, Mechanicsburg PA 17055
Tel (717) 972-1100 SIC 8093 8069

MONONGAHELA VALLEY HOSPITAL INC p 984
1163 Country Club Rd, Monongahela PA 15063
Tel (724) 258-1000 SIC 8062 8063 8069

MADLYN AND LEONARD ABRAMSON CENTER FOR JEWISH LIFE p 894
1425 Horsham Rd, North Wales PA 19454
Tel (215) 371-3000 SIC 8051 8069 6513

AMERICAN ONCOLOGIC HOSPITAL INC p 77
333 Cottman Ave Frnt, Philadelphia PA 19111
Tel (215) 214-3264 SIC 8069

CHILDRENS HOSPITAL OF PHILADELPHIA p 300
3401 Civic Center Blvd, Philadelphia PA 19104
Tel (215) 590-1000 SIC 8069

EASTERN REGIONAL MEDICAL CENTER INC p 472
1331 E Wyoming Ave, Philadelphia PA 19124
Tel (215) 537-7400 SIC 8069

FOX CHASE CANCER CENTER FOUNDATION p 572
333 Cottman Ave, Philadelphia PA 19111
Tel (215) 728-6900 SIC 8069 8071 8062

PHILADELPHIA NORTH HEALTH SYSTEM p 1143
801 W Girard Ave, Philadelphia PA 19122
Tel (215) 787-9001 SIC 8062 8069 8063

■ TENET HEALTHSYSTEM ST CHRISTOPHERS HOSPITAL FOR CHILDREN LLC p 1437
160 E Erie Ave, Philadelphia PA 19134
Tel (215) 427-5000 SIC 8069

■ SHARON REGIONAL HEALTH SYSTEM p 1312
740 E State St, Sharon PA 16146
Tel (724) 983-3911 SIC 8062 8063 8069

■ WILKES-BARRE HOSPITAL CO LLC p 1609
575 N River St, Wilkes Barre PA 18764
Tel (570) 829-8111 SIC 8062 8069

MC WIL GROUP LTD p 925
209 N Beaver St, York PA 17401
Tel (717) 854-7857
SIC 8059 8051 8069 6513 8742 6552

WILMAC CORP p 1613
209 N Beaver St, York PA 17401
Tel (717) 854-7857
SIC 8059 8051 8069 6513 8742 6552

CARE NEW ENGLAND HEALTH SYSTEM INC p 254
45 Willard Ave, Providence RI 02905
Tel (401) 453-7900
SIC 8063 8062 8069 8093 8082

MEDICAL UNIVERSITY OF SOUTH CAROLINA p 937
171 Ashley Ave, Charleston SC 29425
Tel (843) 792-2123 SIC 8062 8221 8069

UPSTATE AFFILIATE ORGANIZATION p 1529
701 Grove Rd, Greenville SC 29605
Tel (864) 455-7000 SIC 8069 8051

SPRINGS MEMORIAL HOSPITAL p 1361
800 W Meeting St, Lancaster SC 29720
Tel (803) 286-1477 SIC 8062 8069 8049

CAMP RECOVERY CENTERS L P p 245
6100 Tower Cir Ste 1000, Franklin TN 37067
Tel (408) 998-7260 SIC 8069

EAST TENNESSEE CHILDRENS HOSPITAL ASSOCIATION INC p 471
2018 W Clinch Ave, Knoxville TN 37916
Tel (865) 541-8000 SIC 8069

METHODIST HEALTHCARE MEMPHIS HOSPITALS p 953
848 Adams Ave, Memphis TN 38103
Tel (901) 287-5437 SIC 8069 8011

AHS LEGACY OPERATIONS LLC p 37
1 Burton Hills Blvd, Nashville TN 37215
Tel (615) 296-3000 SIC 8069

ARDENT HEALTH PARTNERS LLC p 106
1 Burton Hills Blvd # 250, Nashville TN 37215
Tel (615) 296-3000 SIC 8069 8062

ARDENT LEGACY ACQUISITIONS INC p 106
1 Burton Hills Blvd, Nashville TN 37215
Tel (615) 296-3000 SIC 8069

ARDENT LEGACY HOLDINGS INC p 106
1 Burton Hills Blvd, Nashville TN 37215
Tel (615) 296-3000 SIC 8069

DSI HOLDING CO INC p 457
424 Church St Ste 1900, Nashville TN 37219
Tel (615) 777-8201 SIC 8092 8069 8742

DSI RENAL HOLDINGS LLC p 458
424 Church St Ste 1900, Nashville TN 37219
Tel (615) 777-8201 SIC 8092 8069 8742

■ HCA INC p 672
1 Park Plz, Nashville TN 37203
Tel (615) 344-9551
SIC 8063 8062 8069 8093

HERCULES HOLDING II LLC p 685
1 Park Plz, Nashville TN 37203
Tel (615) 344-9551
SIC 8062 8063 8069 8093

■ ISD RENAL INC p 766
424 Church St Ste 1900, Nashville TN 37219
Tel (615) 777-8200 SIC 8069 8092 8742

METDALSPI LLC p 953
17101 Dallas Pkwy, Addison TX 75001
Tel (469) 248-3900 SIC 8069

ST DAVIDS NORTH AUSTIN MEDICAL CENTER p 1366
12221 N Mo Pac Expy, Austin TX 78758
Tel (512) 901-1000
SIC 8062 8011 8069 8049

TEXAS HLTH HRS MTHDT HSPTL HEB p 1443
1615 Hospital Pkwy, Bedford TX 76022
Tel (817) 848-4000 SIC 8062 8063 8069

■ BAY AREA HEALTHCARE GROUP LTD p 160
3315 S Alameda St, Corpus Christi TX 78411
Tel (361) 761-1400
SIC 8062 8063 8069 8093

DRISCOLL CHILDRENS HOSPITAL p 456
3533 S Alameda St, Corpus Christi TX 78411
Tel (361) 694-5000 SIC 8069

CHILDRENS HEALTH SYSTEM OF TEXAS p 299
1935 Medical District Dr, Dallas TX 75235
Tel (844) 424-4537 SIC 8069

CHILDRENS MEDICAL CENTER OF DALLAS p 300
1935 Medical District Dr, Dallas TX 75235
Tel (214) 456-7000 SIC 8069

SUSAN G KOMEN BREAST CANCER FOUNDATION INC p 1409
5005 Lbj Fwy Ste 250, Dallas TX 75244
Tel (972) 855-1600
SIC 8699 8069 8011 8099

▲ TENET HEALTHCARE CORP p 1437
1445 Ross Ave Ste 1400, Dallas TX 75202
Tel (469) 893-2200
SIC 8062 8069 8741 8063 8082 8011

TEXAS SCOTTISH RITE HOSPITAL FOR CHILDREN p 1444
2222 Welborn St, Dallas TX 75219
Tel (214) 559-5000 SIC 8069

TEXAS SCOTTISH RITE HOSPITAL FOR CRIPPLED CHILDREN p 1444
2222 Welborn St, Dallas TX 75219
Tel (214) 559-5000 SIC 8069

COOK CHILDRENS HEALTH CARE SYSTEM p 365
801 7th Ave, Fort Worth TX 76104
Tel (682) 885-4555 SIC 8069

COOK CHILDRENS MEDICAL CENTER p 365
801 7th Ave, Fort Worth TX 76104
Tel (682) 885-4000 SIC 8069

■ CENTENNIAL MEDICAL CENTER p 275
12505 Lebanon Rd, Frisco TX 75035
Tel (972) 963-3333 SIC 8069

TRUE HEALTH DIAGNOSTICS LLC p 1486
6170 Research Rd Ste 211, Frisco TX 75033
Tel (844) 341-1491 SIC 8011 8069

LIGHTHOUSE HOSPICE p 865
305 Coke Ave Ste 140, Hillsboro TX 76645
Tel (254) 710-9800 SIC 8082 8069

DUBUIS HEALTH SYSTEM INC p 459
2707 North Loop W Ste 7, Houston TX 77008
Tel (713) 277-2300 SIC 8069

■ ORTHOPEDIC HOSPITAL LTD p 1096
7401 Main St, Houston TX 77030
Tel (713) 799-8600 SIC 8069

UNIVERSITY OF TEXAS MD ANDERSON CANCER CENTER p 1526
1515 Holcombe Blvd # 207, Houston TX 77030
Tel (713) 745-4428 SIC 8069

■ WHMC INC p 1607
12141 Richmond Ave, Houston TX 77082
Tel (281) 558-3444 SIC 8069

■ HORIZON HEALTH CORP p 707
1965 Lakepointe Dr # 100, Lewisville TX 75057
Tel (972) 420-8200 SIC 8093 8069

HOSPITAL ACQUISITION LLC p 709
5340 Legacy Dr Ste 150, Plano TX 75024
Tel (469) 241-2100 SIC 8069 8051

■ ICL HOLDING CO INC p 727
5340 Legacy Dr Bldg 4150, Plano TX 75024
Tel (469) 241-2100 SIC 8069 8051

LCI HOLDCO LLC p 849
5340 Legacy Dr Ste 150, Plano TX 75024
Tel (469) 241-2100 SIC 8069 8051

■ LCI INTERMEDIATE HOLDCO INC p 849
5340 Legacy Dr Bldg 4150, Plano TX 75024
Tel (469) 241-2100 SIC 8069 8051

LIFECARE HOLDINGS INC p 864
5340 Legacy Dr Ste 150, Plano TX 75024
Tel (469) 241-2100 SIC 8069 8051

SMCL LLC p 1332
5340 Legacy Dr, Plano TX 75024
Tel (469) 241-2100 SIC 8062 8069

CHRISTUS SANTA ROSA HEALTH CARE CORP p 303
333 N Santa Rosa St, San Antonio TX 78207
Tel (210) 704-2011 SIC 8063 8069

IHC HEALTH SERVICES INC p 730
1380 E Medical Center Dr, St George UT 84790
Tel (801) 442-5000
SIC 8062 8011 8322 8049 8093 8069

■ DANVILLE REGIONAL MEDICAL CENTER p 412
142 S Main St, Danville VA 24541
Tel (434) 799-2100
SIC 8062 8011 8093 8069 8051

WASHINGTON HOSPITAL INC MARY p 1578
1001 Sam Perry Blvd, Fredericksburg VA 22401
Tel (540) 741-1100 SIC 8062 8069

CHILDRENS HOSPITAL OF KINGS DAUGHTERS INC p 300
601 Childrens Ln, Norfolk VA 23507
Tel (757) 668-7000 SIC 8069 8011

HENRICO DOCTORS HOSPITAL p 683
1602 Skipwith Rd, Richmond VA 23229
Tel (804) 289-4500 SIC 8069

GOOD SAMARITAN HOSPITAL p 623
401 15th Ave Se, Puyallup WA 98372
Tel (253) 697-4000 SIC 8062 8069

PROVIDENCE HEALTH & SERVICES-WASHINGTON p 1186
1801 Lind Ave Sw 9016, Renton WA 98057
Tel (425) 525-3355
SIC 8062 8051 8052 6513 8069

SEATTLE CANCER CARE ALLIANCE p 1297
825 Eastlake Ave E, Seattle WA 98109
Tel (206) 288-7222 SIC 8069

SEATTLE CHILDRENS HEALTHCARE SYSTEM p 1297
4800 Sand Point Way Ne, Seattle WA 98105
Tel (206) 987-2000 SIC 8069

SEATTLE CHILDRENS HOSPITAL p 1297
4800 Sand Point Way Ne, Seattle WA 98105
Tel (206) 987-2000 SIC 8062 8069

MULTICARE HEALTH SYSTEM p 999
316 M L King Jr Way # 314, Tacoma WA 98405
Tel (253) 403-1000 SIC 8062 8093 8069

AGNESIAN HEALTHCARE INC p 35
430 E Division St, Fond Du Lac WI 54935
Tel (920) 929-2300 SIC 8069

UNIVERSITY OF WISCONSIN HOSPITAL AND CLINICS AUTHORITY p 1527
600 Highland Ave, Madison WI 53792
Tel (608) 263-6400 SIC 8062 8069

CHILDRENS HOSPITAL AND HEALTH SYSTEM INC p 299
8915 W Connell Ave, Milwaukee WI 53226
Tel (414) 266-2000
SIC 8069 8082 7389 7322

CHILDRENS HOSPITAL OF WISCONSIN INC p 300
9000 W Wscnsin Ave Stop 1, Milwaukee WI 53226
Tel (414) 266-2000 SIC 8069

SIC 8071 Medical Laboratories

LABORATORY SCIENCES OF ARIZONA LLC p 836
1255 W Washington St, Tempe AZ 85281
Tel (602) 685-5000 SIC 8071 8011 8331

SONORA QUEST LABORATORIES LLC p 1340
1255 W Washington St, Tempe AZ 85281
Tel (602) 685-5000 SIC 8071

CLARIENT DIAGNOSTIC SERVICES INC p 321
31 Columbia, Aliso Viejo CA 92656
Tel (949) 425-5700 SIC 3841 3826 8071

LAWRENCE BERKELEY NATIONAL LAB p 847
1 Cyclotron Rd, Berkeley CA 94720
Tel (510) 486-6792 SIC 8071

KAN-DI-KI LLC p 802
2820 N Ontario St, Burbank CA 91504
Tel (818) 549-1880 SIC 8071

PROOVE MEDICAL LABORATORIES INC p 1183
15326 Elton Pkwy, Irvine CA 92618
Tel (949) 427-5303 SIC 8071

SADDLEBACK MEMORIAL MEDICAL CENTER p 1265
24451 Health Center Dr, Laguna Hills CA 92653
Tel (949) 837-4500
SIC 8062 8011 8093 8099 8071 8069

INSIGHT HEALTH SERVICES HOLDINGS CORP p 746
26250 Entp Ct Ste 100, Lake Forest CA 92630
Tel (949) 282-6000 SIC 8071

▲ RADNET INC p 1204
1510 Cotner Ave, Los Angeles CA 90025
Tel (310) 445-2800 SIC 8071

UNIVERSITY OF SOUTHERN CALIFORNIA p 1525
3720 S Flower St Fl 3, Los Angeles CA 90007
Tel (213) 740-7762 SIC 8221 8071

SPECTRA LABORATORIES INC p 1357
525 Sycamore Dr, Milpitas CA 95035
Tel (408) 571-1290 SIC 8071

▲ ALLIANCE HEALTHCARE SERVICES INC p 54
100 Bayview Cir Ste 400, Newport Beach CA 92660
Tel (949) 242-5300 SIC 8071

MARSHALL MEDICAL CENTER p 911
1100 Marshall Way, Placerville CA 95667
Tel (530) 622-1441 SIC 8062 8071 8082

▲ GENOMIC HEALTH INC p 604
301 Penobscot Dr, Redwood City CA 94063
Tel (650) 556-9300 SIC 8071 8731

RADIOLOGICAL ASSOCIATES OF SACRAMENTO MEDICAL GROUP INC p 1204
1500 Expo Pkwy, Sacramento CA 95815
Tel (916) 646-8300 SIC 8071 8011

▲ NATERA INC p 1009
201 Industrial Rd Ste 410, San Carlos CA 94070
Tel (650) 249-9090 SIC 8071 2835

■ SEQUENOM CENTER FOR MOLECULAR MEDICINE LLC p 1306
3595 John Hopkins Ct, San Diego CA 92121
Tel (858) 202-9051 SIC 8071

■ NICHOLS INSTITUTE REFERENCE LABORATORIES p 1042
33608 Ortega Hwy, San Juan Capistrano CA 92675
Tel (949) 728-4000 SIC 8071

■ QUEST DIAGNOSTICS NICHOLS INSTITUTE p 1199
33608 Ortega Hwy, San Juan Capistrano CA 92675
Tel (949) 728-4000 SIC 3826 8071

■ UNILAB CORP p 1503
8401 Fallbrook Ave, West Hills CA 91304
Tel (818) 737-6000 SIC 8071

■ METWEST INC p 957
695 S Broadway, Denver CO 80209
Tel (303) 899-6000 SIC 8071

SCHRYVER MEDICAL SALES AND MARKETING LLC p 1290
12075 E 45th Ave Ste 600, Denver CO 80239
Tel (303) 371-0073 SIC 8071 8011

ACUREN INSPECTION INC p 20
30 Main St Ste 402, Danbury CT 06810
Tel (203) 702-8740 SIC 1389 8071

■ DIANON SYSTEMS INC p 437
1 Forest Pkwy, Shelton CT 06484
Tel (203) 926-7100 SIC 8071

GLAXOSMITHKLINE HOLDINGS (AMERICAS) INC p 614
1105 N Market St, Wilmington DE 19801
Tel (302) 656-5280
SIC 2834 2836 2833 2844 8071

US LABORATORIES INC p 1532
13773 Icot Blvd Ste 502, Clearwater FL 33760
Tel (954) 236-8100 SIC 8071

MEASE HOSPITALS p 934
601 Main St, Dunedin FL 34698
Tel (727) 734-6354 SIC 8071

▲ NEOGENOMICS INC p 1026
12701 Commwl Dr Ste 9, Fort Myers FL 33913
Tel (239) 768-0600 SIC 8734 8071

NEOGENOMICS LABORATORIES INC p 1026
12701 Commwl Dr Ste 9, Fort Myers FL 33913
Tel (239) 768-0600 SIC 8071

CONSULATE MANAGEMENT CO LLC p 361
800 Concourse Pkwy S, Maitland FL 32751
Tel (407) 571-1550
SIC 8051 8059 8071 8093

AMERICAN HEALTH ASSOCIATES INC p 73
2831 Corporate Way, Miramar FL 33025
Tel (954) 919-5005 SIC 8071

■ AMERIPATH HOLDINGS INC p 83
7111 Fairway Dr Ste 101, Palm Beach Gardens FL 33418
Tel (561) 845-1850 SIC 8071

■ AMERIPATH INC p 83
7111 Fairway Dr Ste 101, Palm Beach Gardens FL 33418
Tel (561) 712-6200 SIC 8071

AURORA DIAGNOSTICS HOLDINGS LLC p 132
11025 Rca Center Dr # 300, Palm Beach Gardens FL 33410
Tel (561) 626-5512 SIC 8071

WELLNEXT LLC p 1589
1301 Sawgrs Corp Pkwy, Sunrise FL 33323
Tel (954) 233-3301 SIC 8071

MEDQUEST INC p 938
3480 Preston Ridge Rd # 500, Alpharetta GA 30005
Tel (678) 992-7200 SIC 8071

GRANCARE LLC p 629
1 Ravinia Dr Ste 1400, Atlanta GA 30346
Tel (770) 393-0199
SIC 8051 8052 8093 8071

ROCKFORD MEMORIAL HOSPITAL p 1244
2400 N Rockton Ave, Rockford IL 61103
Tel (815) 971-5000
SIC 8062 8011 8071 8099

LIFEWATCH SERVICES INC p 865
10255 W Higgins Rd # 100, Rosemont IL 60018
Tel (847) 720-2100
SIC 5047 8099 3845 8071

CDH-DELNOR HEALTH SYSTEM p 271
25 N Winfield Rd, Winfield IL 60190
Tel (630) 933-1600 SIC 8071 8741

IMAGING CENTER OF N CENTRAL INDIANA p 733
2201 W Boulevard, Kokomo IN 46902
Tel (765) 452-0808 SIC 8071

SOUTH BEND MEDICAL FOUNDATION INC p 1343
530 N Lafayette Blvd, South Bend IN 46601
Tel (574) 234-4176 SIC 8071

■ LABONE INC p 836
10101 Renner Blvd, Lenexa KS 66219
Tel (913) 888-1770 SIC 8071 6411

NORTON HOSPITALS INC p 1061
200 E Chestnut St, Louisville KY 40202
Tel (502) 629-8000
SIC 8062 8011 8093 8071

COOPERATIVE HEALTH SERVICES INC p 367
811 E Parrish Ave, Owensboro KY 42303
Tel (270) 688-3075 SIC 8071

GENERAL HEALTH SYSTEM p 601
5757 Corp Blvd Ste 200, Baton Rouge LA 70808
Tel (225) 237-1500 SIC 8071 7991

AFFILIATED HEALTHCARE SYSTEMS p 32
931 Union St, Bangor ME 04401
Tel (207) 973-6720
SIC 5047 8071 8741 7322 6512

MAINE MEDICAL CENTER p 898
22 Bramhall St, Portland ME 04102
Tel (207) 662-0111 SIC 8062 8071 6513

M G H HEALTH SERVICES CORP p 889
55 Fruit St, Boston MA 02114
Tel (617) 724-0567
SIC 8082 8059 8071 8062

GENZYME CORP p 605
500 Kendall St, Cambridge MA 02142
Tel (617) 252-7500
SIC 2835 2834 8071 3842 2836 5122

MERCY HOSPITAL INC p 947
271 Carew St, Springfield MA 01104
Tel (413) 748-9000
SIC 8062 8071 8011 7219 8748

▲ ALERE INC p 48
51 Sawyer Rd Ste 200, Waltham MA 02453
Tel (781) 647-3900 SIC 2835 8071 8742

FRESENIUS MEDICAL CARE CARDIOVASCULAR RESOURCES INC p 578
920 Winter St Ste A, Waltham MA 02451
Tel (781) 402-9000 SIC 8092 5047 8071

■ ESOTERIX GENETIC LABORATORIES LLC p 509
3400 Computer Dr, Westborough MA 01581
Tel (508) 389-6650 SIC 8731 2835 8071

■ QUEST DIAGNOSTICS INC p 1199
1947 Technology Dr 100, Troy MI 48083
Tel (248) 364-1324 SIC 8071

MAYO CLINIC p 923
200 1st St Sw, Rochester MN 55905
Tel (507) 284-2511
SIC 8011 8062 8071 8733 8221

MAYO CLINIC p 923
200 1st St Sw, Rochester MN 55905
Tel (507) 284-2511
SIC 8062 8733 8071 8011

■ **QUEST DIAGNOSTICS INC** p 1199
4230 Burnham Ave, Las Vegas NV 89119
Tel (702) 733-7866 SIC 8071 8731

■ **NORTHERN NEVADA MEDICAL CENTER LP** p 1056
2375 E Prater Way, Sparks NV 89434
Tel (775) 331-7000
SIC 8062 8093 8071 8049 8011

ATLANTICARE HEALTH SYSTEM INC p 127
2500 English Creek Ave, Egg Harbor Township NJ 08234
Tel (609) 407-2300 SIC 8071 8082

■ **BIO-REFERENCE LABORATORIES INC** p 183
481 Edward H Ross Dr, Elmwood Park NJ 07407
Tel (201) 791-2600 SIC 8071 8734

▲ **QUEST DIAGNOSTICS INC** p 1199
3 Giralda Farms, Madison NJ 07940
Tel (973) 520-2700 SIC 8071 2835

■ **PRUCO SECURITIES LLC** p 1187
751 Broad St, Newark NJ 07102
Tel (800) 235-7637
SIC 6321 6331 6211 6282 8071

■ **ROCHE LABORATORIES INC** p 1243
340 Kingsland St, Nutley NJ 07110
Tel (973) 235-5000 SIC 8071

SGS NORTH AMERICA INC p 1310
301 Route 17, Rutherford NJ 07070
Tel (201) 508-3000
SIC 8734 7389 8071 4499 4785

TRICORE REFERENCE LABORATORIES p 1479
1001 Woodward Pl Ne, Albuquerque NM 87102
Tel (505) 938-8999 SIC 8071

■ **BRACOR INC** p 206
346 Delaware Ave, Buffalo NY 14202
Tel (716) 856-7500 SIC 8082 8071 7361

P C CORTLAND PATHOLOGY p 1102
134 Homer Ave, Cortland NY 13045
Tel (607) 756-3500 SIC 8071

ICON CENTRAL LABORATORIES INC p 727
123 Smith St, Farmingdale NY 11735
Tel (631) 777-8833 SIC 8071 8734

▲ **ENZO BIOCHEM INC** p 504
527 Madison Ave Rm 901, New York NY 10022
Tel (212) 583-0100 SIC 8071 8731

■ **LABORATORY CORP OF AMERICA** p 836
358 S Main St Ste 458, Burlington NC 27215
Tel (336) 229-1127 SIC 8071

▲ **LABORATORY CORP OF AMERICA HOLDINGS** p 836
358 S Main St, Burlington NC 27215
Tel (336) 229-1127 SIC 8071

BIOMERIEUX INC p 184
100 Rodolphe St, Durham NC 27712
Tel (919) 620-2000
SIC 3845 8071 3841 3826

■ **CONSTELLA GROUP LLC** p 360
2605 Meridian Pkwy # 200, Durham NC 27713
Tel (919) 544-8500
SIC 7371 8742 7375 8748 8731 8071

DUKE CLINICAL RESEARCH INSTITUTE p 460
2400 Pratt St, Durham NC 27705
Tel (919) 668-8725 SIC 8071

■ **SOLSTAS LAB PARTNERS GROUP LLC** p 1338
4380 Federal Dr Ste 100, Greensboro NC 27410
Tel (336) 664-6100 SIC 8071

MERCY HEALTH YOUNGSTOWN LLC p 946
1044 Belmont Ave, Youngstown OH 44504
Tel (330) 746-7211 SIC 8062 8071

ST JOHN HEALTH SYSTEM INC p 1367
1923 S Utica Ave, Tulsa OK 74104
Tel (918) 744-2180
SIC 7991 6512 7389 8361 8071 8062

■ **QUEST DIAGNOSTICS CLINICAL LABORATORIES INC** p 1199
1201 S Collegeville Rd, Collegeville PA 19426
Tel (610) 454-6000 SIC 8071

■ **QUEST DIAGNOSTICS INC** p 1199
900 Business Center Dr, Horsham PA 19044
Tel (866) 697-8378 SIC 8071

THEOREM CLINICAL RESEARCH INC p 1446
1016 W 9th Ave Ste 300, King Of Prussia PA 19406
Tel (484) 679-2400 SIC 8731 8071 2834

FOX CHASE CANCER CENTER FOUNDATION p 572
333 Cottman Ave, Philadelphia PA 19111
Tel (215) 728-6900 SIC 8069 8071 8062

■ **MED3000 INVESTMENTS INC** p 935
680 Andersen Dr Ste 10, Pittsburgh PA 15220
Tel (412) 937-8887 SIC 8071

MEDICAL SERVICES OF AMERICA INC p 937
171 Monroe Ln, Lexington SC 29072
Tel (803) 957-0500
SIC 8082 8741 8011 8071 7352 5999

ALLERGY CENTERS OF AMERICA LLC p 53
2430 Mall Dr Ste 210, North Charleston SC 29406
Tel (843) 747-4294 SIC 8011 8071

■ **DVA RENAL HEALTHCARE INC** p 463
5200 Virginia Way, Brentwood TN 37027
Tel (615) 320-4200 SIC 8092 8071

DIALYSIS CLINIC INC p 436
1633 Church St Ste 500, Nashville TN 37203
Tel (615) 327-3061 SIC 8092 5047 8071

SPECIALTY CARE SERVICES GROUP LLC p 1356
3100 West End Ave Ste 400, Nashville TN 37203
Tel (615) 345-5400 SIC 8071

BEXAR COUNTY CLINICAL SERVICES INC p 179
2801 Via Fortuna Ste 500, Austin TX 78746
Tel (512) 899-3995 SIC 8072 8071

CLINICAL PATHOLOGY LABORATORIES INC p 326
9200 Wall St, Austin TX 78754
Tel (512) 339-1275 SIC 8071

HARRIS COUNTY CLINICAL SERVICES INC p 663
2801 Via Fortuna, Austin TX 78746
Tel (512) 899-3995 SIC 8071

ANTHELIO HEALTHCARE SOLUTIONS INC p 93
1 Lincoln Centre 5400 L, Dallas TX 75240
Tel (214) 257-7000 SIC 8741 8071 7389

HUNT MEMORIAL HOSPITAL DISTRICT p 719
4215 Joe Ramsey Blvd E, Greenville TX 75401
Tel (903) 408-5000 SIC 8062 8071 8082

■ **PARK PLAZA HOSPITAL INC** p 1115
1313 Hermann Dr, Houston TX 77004
Tel (713) 527-5128 SIC 8071

TMH PHYSICIAN ORGANIZATION p 1457
6565 Fannin St Ste D200, Houston TX 77030
Tel (713) 441-4182 SIC 8071

■ **LAREDO REGIONAL MEDICAL CENTER L P** p 845
1700 E Saunders St, Laredo TX 78041
Tel (956) 796-5000 SIC 8062 8071

■ **PINEY WOODS HEALTHCARE SYSTEM LP** p 1149
505 S John Redditt Dr, Lufkin TX 75904
Tel (936) 634-8311
SIC 8062 8071 8099 8051

■ **HYCLONE LABORATORIES INC** p 723
925 W 1800 S, Logan UT 84321
Tel (435) 792-8000 SIC 2836 8071

ARUP LABORATORIES INC p 114
500 S Chipeta Way, Salt Lake City UT 84108
Tel (801) 583-2787 SIC 8071

UNIVERSITY PATHOLOGY ASSOCIATES p 1527
50 N Medical Dr 5c124, Salt Lake City UT 84132
Tel (801) 581-5406 SIC 8071 8011

BON SECOURS-MEMORIAL REGIONAL MEDICAL CENTER INC p 199
8260 Atlee Rd Ste 1203, Mechanicsville VA 23116
Tel (804) 764-1253 SIC 8062 8071

BLOODWORKS p 189
921 Terry Ave, Seattle WA 98104
Tel (206) 292-6500
SIC 8071 8099 8733 8732

PATHOLOGY ASSOCIATES MEDICAL LABORATORIES LLC p 1120
110 W Cliff Dr, Spokane WA 99204
Tel (800) 541-7891 SIC 8071

SACRED HEART MEDICAL CENTER p 1265
101 W 8th Ave, Spokane WA 99204
Tel (509) 455-3131 SIC 8062 8071

J V LABORATORIES INC p 772
1320 Wisconsin Ave # 101, Racine WI 53403
Tel (262) 687-2150 SIC 8071

SIC 8072 Dental Laboratories

JAMES R GLIDEWELL DENTAL CERAMICS INC p 777
4141 Macarthur Blvd, Newport Beach CA 92660
Tel (949) 440-2600 SIC 8072

NATIONAL DENTEX CORP p 1011
11601 Kew Gardens Ave, Palm Beach Gardens FL 33410
Tel (877) 942-5871 SIC 8072

SENTAGE CORP p 1305
801 12th Ave N, Minneapolis MN 55411
Tel (412) 431-3353 SIC 8072

ASPEN DENTAL MANAGEMENT INC p 118
281 Sanders Creek Pkwy, East Syracuse NY 13057
Tel (315) 454-6000 SIC 8021 8072 6794

BEXAR COUNTY CLINICAL SERVICES INC p 179
2801 Via Fortuna Ste 500, Austin TX 78746
Tel (512) 899-3995 SIC 8072 8071

SIC 8082 Home Health Care Svcs

BAPTIST HEALTH SYSTEM INC p 153
1130 22nd St S Ste 1000, Birmingham AL 35205
Tel (205) 715-5000
SIC 8011 8741 8082 8059

EASTERN HEALTH SYSTEM INC p 472
Medical Park E Dr Bldg 1, Birmingham AL 35235
Tel (205) 838-3996
SIC 8062 8082 8051 8011 8322 8093

■ **HEALTHSOUTH HOME HEALTH CORP** p 677
3660 Grandview Pkwy, Birmingham AL 35243
Tel (205) 967-7116 SIC 8082 8099

■ **HEALTHSOUTH HOME HEALTH HOLDINGS INC** p 677
3660 Grandview Pkwy, Birmingham AL 35243
Tel (205) 967-7116 SIC 8099 8082 6719

■ **TRIAD OF ALABAMA LLC** p 1478
4370 W Main St, Dothan AL 36305
Tel (334) 793-5000 SIC 8062 8082

■ **GADSDEN REGIONAL MEDICAL CENTER LLC** p 589
1007 Goodyear Ave, Gadsden AL 35903
Tel (256) 494-4000
SIC 8062 8082 8011 7352

SAAD ENTERPRISES INC p 1263
1515 S University Blvd, Mobile AL 36609
Tel (251) 343-9600
SIC 8082 5047 7352 5912 5621 8741

NHS MANAGEMENT LLC p 1042
931 Fairfax Park, Tuscaloosa AL 35406
Tel (205) 391-3600 SIC 8082 8059

SOUTHERN CARE INC p 1347
1000 Urban Center Dr # 115, Vestavia AL 35242
Tel (205) 868-4400 SIC 8082

BANNER HEALTH SYSTEM p 153
1650 Cowles St, Fairbanks AK 99701
Tel (907) 452-8181 SIC 8082

ARION CARE SOLUTIONS LLC p 108
1405 N Dobson Rd Ste 3, Chandler AZ 85224
Tel (480) 323-0468 SIC 8082

BANNER HEALTH p 153
2901 N Central Ave # 160, Phoenix AZ 85012
Tel (602) 747-4000
SIC 8062 8051 8082 7361 8011 8093

HOSPICE OF VALLEY p 709
1510 E Flower St, Phoenix AZ 85014
Tel (602) 530-6900 SIC 8082

YAVAPAI REGIONAL MEDICAL CENTER FOUNDATION p 1635
1003 Willow Creek Rd, Prescott AZ 86301
Tel (928) 445-2700 SIC 8011 8082 2835

SUN HEALTH CORP p 1400
14719 W Grand Ave Ste 113, Surprise AZ 85374
Tel (623) 876-5350
SIC 8062 8051 8082 7361 8733 6531

BEVERLY ENTERPRISES - ALABAMA INC p 179
One Thousand Beverly Way, Fort Smith AR 72919
Tel (479) 201-2000 SIC 8082 8051

BEVERLY ENTERPRISES - VIRGINIA INC p 179
1 1000 Beverly Way, Fort Smith AR 72919
Tel (479) 201-2000 SIC 8082 8051

BEVERLY ENTERPRISES INC p 179
1000 Fianna Way, Fort Smith AR 72919
Tel (479) 201-2000 SIC 8741 8051 8082

GGNSC HOLDINGS LLC p 610
1000 Fianna Way, Fort Smith AR 72919
Tel (479) 201-2000
SIC 8059 8051 8082 8322

HOMECARE PREFERRED CHOICE INC p 703
1000 Fianna Way, Fort Smith AR 72919
Tel (479) 201-2000 SIC 8082

WHITE COUNTY MEDICAL CENTER p 1606
3214 E Race Ave, Searcy AR 72143
Tel (501) 268-6121 SIC 8082 8062

PHFE p 1142
12801 Crossrds Pkwy S 2 200 S, City Of Industry CA 91746
Tel (562) 699-7320 SIC 8082

CENTRAL HEALTH PLAN OF CALIFORNIA INC p 278
1055 Park View Dr Ste 355, Covina CA 91724
Tel (626) 938-7120 SIC 8082

SUTTER VISITING NURSE ASSOCIATION & HOSPICE p 1410
1900 Powell St Ste 300, Emeryville CA 94608
Tel (866) 652-9178 SIC 8082

ACCENTCARE HOME HEALTH INC p 14
135 Technology Dr Ste 150, Irvine CA 92618
Tel (949) 623-1500 SIC 8082

ST JOSEPH HEALTH SYSTEM p 1368
3345 Michelson Dr Ste 100, Irvine CA 92612
Tel (949) 381-4000 SIC 8082 8741

APRIA HEALTHCARE GROUP INC p 100
26220 Enterprise Ct, Lake Forest CA 92630
Tel (949) 639-2000 SIC 8082

UCLA HEALTH SYSTEM AUXILIARY p 1499
10920 Wilshire Blvd # 1700, Los Angeles CA 90024
Tel (310) 794-0500 SIC 8082

RIDEOUT MEMORIAL HOSPITAL p 1234
726 4th St, Marysville CA 95901
Tel (530) 749-4416 SIC 8062 8082

■ **IMMEDIATE CLINIC HEALTHCARE INC** p 734
27101 Puerta Real Ste 450, Mission Viejo CA 92691
Tel (949) 487-9500 SIC 8082

UNIVERSITY HEALTHCARE ALLIANCE p 1519
7999 Gateway Blvd Ste 200, Newark CA 94560
Tel (510) 974-8281 SIC 8082

BRADEN PARTNERS LP A CALIFORNIA LIMITED PARTNERSHIP p 206
773 San Marin Dr Ste 2230, Novato CA 94945
Tel (415) 893-1518 SIC 8082

LUCILE SALTER PACKARD CHILDRENS HOSPITAL AT STANFORD p 884
725 Welch Rd, Palo Alto CA 94304
Tel (650) 497-8000 SIC 8069 8082 5912

MARSHALL MEDICAL CENTER p 911
1100 Marshall Way, Placerville CA 95667
Tel (530) 622-1441 SIC 8062 8071 8082

EISENHOWER MEDICAL CENTER p 482
39000 Bob Hope Dr, Rancho Mirage CA 92270
Tel (760) 340-3911 SIC 8062 8082

APEXCARE INC p 96
1418 Howe Ave Ste B, Sacramento CA 95825
Tel (916) 924-9111 SIC 8082

AMERICAN SPECIALTY HEALTH GROUP INC p 79
10221 Wateridge Cir # 201, San Diego CA 92121
Tel (858) 754-2000 SIC 8082

■ **NURSEFINDERS LLC** p 1067
12400 High Bluff Dr, San Diego CA 92130
Tel (858) 314-7427
SIC 7361 8082 7363 8049

SCRIPPS HEALTH p 1294
4275 Campus Point Ct, San Diego CA 92121
Tel (858) 678-7000
SIC 8051 8082 8062 8049 8042 8043

ON LOK SENIOR HEALTH SERVICES p 1086
1333 Bush St, San Francisco CA 94109
Tel (415) 292-8888 SIC 6324 8082

PEARL SENIOR CARE LLC p 1126
4 Embarcadero Ctr Ste 710, San Francisco CA 94111
Tel (415) 834-1477 SIC 8082

SENECA FAMILY OF AGENCIES p 1303
15942 Foothill Blvd, San Leandro CA 94578
Tel (510) 317-1444 SIC 8322 8299 8082

WEST CONTRA COSTA HEALTHCARE DISTRICT p 1594
2000 Vale Rd, San Pablo CA 94806
Tel (510) 970-5102 SIC 8082

UNIVERSITY OF COLORADO HEALTH p 1521
12401 E 17th Ave Ste F485, Aurora CO 80045
Tel (720) 848-1031 SIC 8082

■ **INTEGRITY URGENT CARE CLINICS INC** p 750
4323 Integrity Center Pt, Colorado Springs CO 80917
Tel (719) 591-2558 SIC 8082 8011 8051

ARGUS OF COLORADO INC p 108
720 S Colorado Blvd 600n, Denver CO 80246
Tel (303) 322-4100 SIC 8082 7361

■ **CORAM LLC** p 368
555 17th St Ste 1500, Denver CO 80202
Tel (303) 292-4973 SIC 8082

HSS INC p 715
900 S Broadway Ste 100, Denver CO 80209
Tel (303) 603-3000 SIC 8082 7381 7382

RENAL CARE GROUP INC p 1223
1 N Broadway Ste 100a, Denver CO 80203
Tel (303) 765-1699 SIC 8082

■ **T2 MEDICAL INC** p 1420
555 17th St Ste 1500, Denver CO 80202
Tel (303) 672-8631 SIC 8082

TOTAL LONGTERM CARE INC p 1463
8950 E Lowry Blvd, Denver CO 80230
Tel (303) 832-1001 SIC 8322 8082

LUTHERAN MEDICAL CENTER p 886
8300 W 38th Ave, Wheat Ridge CO 80033
Tel (303) 425-4500
SIC 8011 7389 8082 8331

ABILITY BEYOND DISABILITY INC p 11
4 Berkshire Blvd, Bethel CT 06801
Tel (203) 826-3025 SIC 8322 8082

CONNECTICUT VNA INC p 357
33 N Plains Industrial Rd, Wallingford CT 06492
Tel (203) 679-5300 SIC 8082 8741

MASONICARE CORP p 916
22 Masonic Ave, Wallingford CT 06492
Tel (203) 679-5900 SIC 8069 8082 8322

CAPITOL PARTNERS I LP p 251
1808 I St Nw Ste 200, Washington DC 20006
Tel (202) 955-7960 SIC 8082 6211

WASHINGTON HOSPITAL CENTER CORP p 1578
110 Irving St Nw, Washington DC 20010
Tel (202) 877-7000
SIC 8741 8082 8051 8062

ADVENTIST HEALTH SYSTEM/SUNBELT INC p 27
900 Hope Way, Altamonte Springs FL 32714
Tel (407) 357-1000 SIC 8062 8082 8051

BRRH CORP p 220
800 Meadows Rd, Boca Raton FL 33486
Tel (561) 395-7100 SIC 8062 8082 8099

LINCARE HOLDINGS INC p 866
19387 Us Highway 19 N, Clearwater FL 33764
Tel (727) 530-7700 SIC 8082 8093

LINCARE INC p 866
19387 Us Highway 19 N, Clearwater FL 33764
Tel (727) 530-7700 SIC 8082 5999

LIFE CARE HOME HEALTH SERVICES CORP p 863
4723 W Atl Ave Ste 21, Delray Beach FL 33445
Tel (561) 272-5866 SIC 8082 7361

LEE MEMORIAL HEALTH SYSTEM FOUNDATION INC p 851
2776 Cleveland Ave, Fort Myers FL 33901
Tel (239) 343-2000
SIC 8741 8062 8082 8051

■ **NORTH FLORIDA REGIONAL MEDICAL CENTER INC** p 1052
6500 W Newberry Rd, Gainesville FL 32605
Tel (352) 333-4100
SIC 8062 8093 8011 8082 8069

COMMUNITY HOSPICE OF NORTHEAST FLORIDA INC p 349
4266 Sunbeam Rd Ste 100, Jacksonville FL 32257
Tel (904) 268-5200 SIC 8082 8051

BAYCARE HOME CARE INC p 161
8452 118th Ave, Largo FL 33773
Tel (727) 394-6461 SIC 8082 7352

■ **VITAS HEALTHCARE CORP** p 1563
100 S Biscayne Blvd # 1600, Miami FL 33131
Tel (305) 374-4143 SIC 8082 8051

HALIFAX HOME HEALTH p 654
3800 Woodbriar Trl, Port Orange FL 32129
Tel (386) 322-4700 SIC 8082 7361

HEALTH FIRST INC p 674
6450 Us Highway 1, Rockledge FL 32955
Tel (321) 434-4300
SIC 8062 8011 8082 8069 7991 6324

SHRINERS INTERNATIONAL HEADQUARTERS INC p 1319
2900 N Rocky Point Dr, Rocky Point FL 33607
Tel (813) 281-0300 SIC 8082

TIDEWELL HOSPICE INC p 1452
5955 Rand Blvd, Sarasota FL 34238
Tel (941) 552-7500 SIC 8082

BAPTIST HEALTH SOUTH FLORIDA INC p 153
6855 S Red Rd, South Miami FL 33143
Tel (305) 596-1960 SIC 8062 8011 8082

INTERIM HEALTHCARE INC p 752
1601 Swgrs Corp Pkwy # 100, Sunrise FL 33323
Tel (800) 338-7786 SIC 6794 7363 8082

■ **PHARMERICA LONG-TERM CARE LLC** p 1141
3625 Queen Palm Dr, Tampa FL 33619
Tel (877) 975-2273
SIC 5912 5961 8082 5122

MID-FLORIDA MEDICAL SERVICES INC p 963
200 Avenue F Ne, Winter Haven FL 33881
Tel (863) 297-1895 SIC 8741 8062 8082

EMORY UNIVERSITY p 493
201 Dowman Dr Ne, Atlanta GA 30322
Tel (404) 727-6013 SIC 8221 8082

■ **GENTIVA HEALTH SERVICES INC** p 605
3350 Riverwood Pkwy Se # 1400, Atlanta GA 30339
Tel (770) 951-6450 SIC 8082

HARDEN HEALTHCARE SERVICES LLC p 660
3350 Riverwood Pkwy Se # 1, Atlanta GA 30339
Tel (512) 634-4965 SIC 8082

CARESOUTH HOME HEALTH SERVICES LLC p 255
1 10th St Ste 500, Augusta GA 30901
Tel (706) 855-5533 SIC 8082

CSLCS LLC p 398
1 10th St Ste 100, Augusta GA 30901
Tel (855) 458-5500 SIC 8082

PEDIATRIA HEALTHCARE LLC p 1127
5185 Peachtree Pkwy # 350, Norcross GA 30092
Tel (770) 840-1966 SIC 8082 8741

PEDIATRIC SERVICES HOLDING CORP p 1127
3720 Da Vinci Ct, Norcross GA 30092
Tel (770) 441-1580 SIC 8082 8719

PEDIATRIC SERVICES OF AMERICA INC p 1127
3720 Davinci Ct Ste 200, Norcross GA 30092
Tel (770) 441-1580 SIC 8082

PEDIATRIC SERVICES OF AMERICA INC (DE) p 1127
3720 Davinci Ct Ste 200, Norcross GA 30092
Tel (770) 441-1580 *SIC* 8082

PROVIDENT HEALTH SERVICES INC p 1186
4700 Waters Ave, Savannah GA 31404
Tel (912) 350-8000 *SIC* 8082 4119

HAWAII HEALTH SYSTEMS CORP p 669
3675 Kilauea Ave, Honolulu HI 96816
Tel (808) 733-4020 *SIC* 8082

ST FRANCIS HEALTHCARE SYSTEM OF HAWAII p 1366
2226 Liliha St Ste 227, Honolulu HI 96817
Tel (808) 547-6883 *SIC* 8051 8082

ADVANCED HEALTH CARE CORP p 25
215 N Whitley Dr Ste 1, Fruitland ID 83619
Tel (208) 452-6392 *SIC* 8082

OPTION CARE ENTERPRISES INC p 1090
3000 Lakeside Dr Ste 300n, Bannockburn IL 60015
Tel (847) 964-4950
SIC 8082 5122 6794 5912 8049

WALGREENS INFUSION SERVICES INC p 1573
3000 Lakeside Dr Ste 300n, Bannockburn IL 60015
Tel (312) 940-2500
SIC 8082 8011 8059 5999 5122

ASSISTED LIVING CONCEPTS LLC p 119
330 N Wabash Ave Ste 3700, Chicago IL 60611
Tel (888) 252-5001
SIC 8052 8051 8059 8082

HELP AT HOME LLC p 682
1 N State St Ste 800, Chicago IL 60602
Tel (312) 762-9999 *SIC* 8082

NORTHWESTERN MEMORIAL HEALTHCARE p 1060
251 E Huron St Ste 3-710, Chicago IL 60611
Tel (312) 926-2000
SIC 8082 6513 7389 8099

PRESENCE HEALTH NETWORK p 1172
200 S Wacker Dr Fl 12, Chicago IL 60606
Tel (773) 774-8000
SIC 8082 8062 8011 8051

CRITICAL CARE SYSTEMS INC p 393
108 Wilmot Rd, Deerfield IL 60015
Tel (847) 914-2500 *SIC* 8082

■ ADDUS HEALTHCARE INC p 22
2300 Warrenville Rd, Downers Grove IL 60515
Tel (630) 296-3400 *SIC* 8082

▲ ADDUS HOMECARE CORP p 22
2300 Warrenville Rd # 100, Downers Grove IL 60515
Tel (630) 296-3400 *SIC* 8082 8361

RIVERSIDE HEALTH SYSTEM p 1238
350 N Wall St, Kankakee IL 60901
Tel (815) 933-1671
SIC 8082 8062 5912 5047

RIVERSIDE MEDI-CENTER INC p 1238
350 N Wall St, Kankakee IL 60901
Tel (815) 933-1671 *SIC* 8082 5912 5999

SYNERGON HEALTH SYSTEM INC p 1415
520 S Maple Ave, Oak Park IL 60304
Tel (708) 660-6661 *SIC* 8062 8051 8082

METHODIST MEDICAL CENTER FOUNDATION p 954
221 Ne Glen Oak Ave, Peoria IL 61636
Tel (309) 672-4895 *SIC* 8082

SWEDISHAMERICAN HEALTH SYSTEM CORP p 1411
1401 E State St, Rockford IL 61104
Tel (815) 968-4400
SIC 8743 6512 8742 8099 8082 8062

COMMUNITY CARE SYSTEMS INC p 347
405 N Macarthur Blvd, Springfield IL 62702
Tel (217) 698-0200 *SIC* 8082

H D SMITH LLC p 650
3063 Fiat Ave, Springfield IL 62703
Tel (866) 232-1222 *SIC* 5122 8082

HOSPITAL SISTERS HEALTH SYSTEM p 710
4936 Laverna Rd, Springfield IL 62707
Tel (217) 523-4747 *SIC* 8082

BETHANY CIRCLE OF KINGS DAUGHTERS OF MADISON INDIANA INC p 178
1373 E Sr 62, Madison IN 47250
Tel (812) 801-0800 *SIC* 8062 8011 8082

BEACON HEALTH SYSTEM INC p 164
615 N Michigan St, South Bend IN 46601
Tel (574) 647-1000 *SIC* 8741 8399 8082

BEACON MEDICAL GROUP INC p 165
615 N Michigan St, South Bend IN 46601
Tel (574) 647-1000 *SIC* 8741 8399 8082

MARY GREELEY MEDICAL CENTER p 914
1111 Duff Ave, Ames IA 50010
Tel (515) 239-6730 *SIC* 8082

MERCY SERVICES IOWA CITY INC p 948
500 E Market St, Iowa City IA 52245
Tel (319) 339-3541 *SIC* 8011 8082

UNITYPOINT AT HOME p 1515
11333 Aurora Ave, Urbandale IA 50322
Tel (515) 557-3100 *SIC* 8082

AXELACARE HOLDINGS INC p 140
15529 College Blvd, Lenexa KS 66219
Tel (877) 342-9352 *SIC* 8082

OLATHE MEDICAL CENTER INC p 1080
20333 W 151st St, Olathe KS 66061
Tel (913) 791-4200 *SIC* 8082 8062

OUR LADY OF BELLEFONTE HOSPITAL INC p 1098
1000 Saint Christopher Dr, Ashland KY 41101
Tel (606) 833-3333
SIC 8062 8082 8011 5999

■ FAMILY HOME HEALTH CARE INC p 527
937 Campbellsville Rd R, Columbia KY 42728
Tel (270) 384-6411 *SIC* 8082

■ AFAM ACQUISITION LLC p 32
9510 Ormsby Station Rd, Louisville KY 40223
Tel (502) 640-9318 *SIC* 8082

▲ ALMOST FAMILY INC p 59
9510 Ormsby Station Rd # 103, Louisville KY 40223
Tel (502) 423-4336 *SIC* 8082

■ CAMBRIDGE HOME HEALTH CARE INC p 244
9510 Ormsby Station Rd # 300, Louisville KY 40223
Tel (330) 270-8661 *SIC* 8082

JEWISH HOSPITAL & ST MARYS HEALTHCARE INC p 784
200 Abraham Flexner Way # 1, Louisville KY 40202
Tel (502) 587-4011 *SIC* 8062 8082

JEWISH HOSPITAL HEALTHCARE SERVICES INC p 784
200 Abraham Flexner Way # 1, Louisville KY 40202
Tel (502) 587-4011 *SIC* 8062 8082

▲ KINDRED HEALTHCARE INC p 819
680 S 4th St, Louisville KY 40202
Tel (502) 596-7300
SIC 8062 8051 8322 8082

■ NATIONAL HEALTH INDUSTRIES INC p 1013
9510 Ormsby Station Rd # 300, Louisville KY 40223
Tel (502) 448-5862 *SIC* 8082

■ OMNI HOME HEALTH SERVICES LLC p 1084
9510 Ormsby Station Rd # 300, Louisville KY 40223
Tel (615) 712-2248 *SIC* 8082

SENIOR CARE INC p 1304
700 N Hurstbourne Pkwy # 200, Louisville KY 40222
Tel (502) 753-6000 *SIC* 8082

■ SENIOR HOME CARE INC p 1304
680 S 4th St, Louisville KY 40202
Tel (502) 596-7300 *SIC* 8082

SPECTRACARE INC p 1357
9000 Wessex Pl Ste 100, Louisville KY 40222
Tel (800) 467-5410 *SIC* 8082

■ SUNCREST HEALTHCARE INC p 1402
9510 Ormsby Station Rd # 300, Louisville KY 40223
Tel (615) 627-9267 *SIC* 8082

■ LIFEPOINT OF LAKE CUMBERLAND LLC p 864
305 Langdon St, Somerset KY 42503
Tel (606) 679-7441 *SIC* 8062 8082

ADVANCED HEALTH CONCEPTS p 25
134 Mcgehee Dr, Baton Rouge LA 70815
Tel (225) 275-1660 *SIC* 8082

■ AMEDISYS HOME HEALTH INC OF FLORIDA p 66
5959 S Shrwood Frest Blvd, Baton Rouge LA 70816
Tel (225) 292-2031 *SIC* 8082

■ AMEDISYS HOME HEALTH INC OF VIRGINIA p 66
5959 S Shrwood Frest Blvd, Baton Rouge LA 70816
Tel (225) 292-2031 *SIC* 8082

▲ AMEDISYS INC p 66
3854 American Way Ste A, Baton Rouge LA 70816
Tel (225) 292-2031
SIC 8082 8051 8049 8361

■ AMEDYSIS HOME HEALTH INC OF SOUTH CAROLINA p 66
5959 S Shrwood Frest Blvd, Baton Rouge LA 70816
Tel (225) 292-2031 *SIC* 8082

■ GEORGIA L AMEDISYS L C p 607
5959 S Shrwood Frest Blvd, Baton Rouge LA 70816
Tel (225) 292-2031 *SIC* 8082

▲ LHC GROUP INC p 860
901 Hugh Wallis Rd S, Lafayette LA 70508
Tel (337) 233-1307 *SIC* 8082 8322

ALTON OCHSNER MEDICAL FOUNDATION p 62
1516 Jefferson Hwy # 517, New Orleans LA 70121
Tel (504) 842-3700 *SIC* 8082

HOSPITAL SERVICE DISTRICT 3 LAFOURCHE PARISH p 709
602 N Acadia Rd, Thibodaux LA 70301
Tel (985) 493-4740 *SIC* 8062 8051 8082

MID COAST-PARKVIEW HEALTH p 963
123 Medical Center Dr G, Brunswick ME 04011
Tel (207) 729-0181 *SIC* 8062 8082 8051

PEN BAY MEDICAL CENTER p 1128
6 Glen Cove Dr, Rockport ME 04856
Tel (207) 921-8000 *SIC* 8062 8082

HH MEDSTAR HEALTH INC p 689
5565 Sterrett Pl Ste 500, Columbia MD 21044
Tel (410) 772-6500 *SIC* 8082

MAXIM HEALTHCARE SERVICES INC p 922
7227 Lee Deforest Dr, Columbia MD 21046
Tel (410) 910-1500 *SIC* 8082

MEDSTAR HEALTH INC p 939
5565 Sterrett Pl Ste 500, Columbia MD 21044
Tel (410) 772-6500
SIC 8741 8062 8082 8051 8011

ADVENTIST HEALTHCARE INC p 27
820 W Diamond Ave Ste 600, Gaithersburg MD 20878
Tel (301) 315-3030 *SIC* 8082 8059 8062

HEALTHWELL FOUNDATION p 678
9801 Washingtonian Blvd # 900, Gaithersburg MD 20878
Tel (800) 675-8416 *SIC* 8082

▲ CIVITAS SOLUTIONS INC p 320
313 Congress St Fl 6, Boston MA 02210
Tel (617) 790-4800 *SIC* 8082

M G H HEALTH SERVICES CORP p 889
55 Fruit St, Boston MA 02114
Tel (617) 724-0567
SIC 8082 8059 8071 8062

NATIONAL MENTOR HOLDINGS INC p 1014
313 Congress St Fl 5, Boston MA 02210
Tel (617) 790-4800 *SIC* 8082 8361

STEWARD HEALTH CARE SYSTEM LLC p 1388
500 Boylston St, Boston MA 02116
Tel (617) 419-4700 *SIC* 8082

STEWARD HOME CARE INC p 1388
500 Boylston St, Boston MA 02116
Tel (781) 551-5600 *SIC* 8082

VISITING NURSE ASSOCIATION OF BOSTON p 1561
500 Rutherford Ave # 200, Charlestown MA 02129
Tel (617) 886-6463 *SIC* 8082

VALLEY HEALTH SYSTEMS INC p 1540
575 Beech St, Holyoke MA 01040
Tel (413) 534-2500
SIC 8082 8093 8399 8741 8721

LGH CHARITABLE TRUST INC p 860
1 General St, Lawrence MA 01841
Tel (978) 683-4000 *SIC* 8082

KAZ INC p 805
400 Donald Lynch Blvd # 300, Marlborough MA 01752
Tel (508) 490-7000 *SIC* 8082 2834 5047

MILFORD REGIONAL HEALTHCARE FOUNDATION INC p 969
14 Prospect St, Milford MA 01757
Tel (508) 473-1190 *SIC* 6733 8082 8011

MILFORD REGIONAL MEDICAL CENTER INC p 969
14 Prospect St, Milford MA 01757
Tel (508) 473-1190 *SIC* 8062 8082

SAINT LUKES HOSPITAL OF NEW BEDFORD INC p 1270
101 Page St, New Bedford MA 02740
Tel (508) 997-1515 *SIC* 8062 8082 8093

■ ASSOCIATED HOME CARE LLC p 120
991 Osgood St, North Andover MA 01845
Tel (978) 682-0745 *SIC* 8082

BETH ISRAEL DEACONESS HOSPITAL - PLYMOUTH INC p 177
275 Sandwich St, Plymouth MA 02360
Tel (508) 746-2000 *SIC* 8082

VITALIZE CONSULTING SOLUTIONS INC p 1562
248 Main St Ste 101, Reading MA 01867
Tel (781) 670-1000 *SIC* 8082 7379

MARYLANE HOSPITAL p 915
759 Chestnut St, Springfield MA 01199
Tel (413) 794-5436 *SIC* 8082

VNA CARE NETWORK FOUNDATION INC p 1563
120 Thomas St, Worcester MA 01608
Tel (508) 786-0693 *SIC* 8082

HOSPICE ADVANTAGE LLC p 708
401 Center Ave Ste 130, Bay City MI 48708
Tel (989) 891-2200 *SIC* 8052 8082

SPECTRUM HEALTH HOSPITALS p 1357
100 Michigan St Ne Mc-498, Grand Rapids MI 49503
Tel (616) 391-1774
SIC 8062 6351 8082 6331

BRONSON MANAGEMENT SERVICES CORP p 217
1 Healthcare Plz, Kalamazoo MI 49007
Tel (269) 341-6000 *SIC* 8082

WILLOW ENTERPRISES INC p 1613
1221 Pine Grove Ave, Port Huron MI 48060
Tel (810) 987-2064 *SIC* 8082 5999

ARCADIA SERVICES INC p 103
20750 Civic Center Dr # 100, Southfield MI 48076
Tel (248) 352-7530 *SIC* 7363 8082

SANFORD HEALTH OF NORTHERN MINNESOTA p 1279
1300 Anne St Nw, Bemidji MN 56601
Tel (218) 751-5430 *SIC* 8082

ST MARYS MEDICAL CENTER p 1371
407 E 3rd St, Duluth MN 55805
Tel (218) 786-4000 *SIC* 8062 8082 8351

UNIVITA HEALTH HOLDINGS INC p 1528
11000 Prairie Lakes Dr # 600, Eden Prairie MN 55344
Tel (952) 516-6800 *SIC* 8082

HUTCHINSON HEALTH CARE p 722
1095 Highway 15 S, Hutchinson MN 55350
Tel (320) 234-5000 *SIC* 8082

MAYO CLINIC HEALTH SYSTEM -ST JAMES p 923
1025 Marsh St, Mankato MN 56001
Tel (507) 625-4031 *SIC* 8082

RED WING REGIONAL HOME HEALTH p 1216
1407 W 4th St, Red Wing MN 55066
Tel (651) 385-3410 *SIC* 8082 8011

ALLIANCE HEALTH CARE INC p 54
2260 Cliff Rd, Saint Paul MN 55122
Tel (651) 895-8030 *SIC* 8082

HEALTHEAST COMPANIES INC p 677
1700 University Ave W, Saint Paul MN 55104
Tel (651) 232-2300 *SIC* 8082 8051 8011

■ HOME HEALTH CARE AFFILIATES INC p 703
106 Riverview Dr, Flowood MS 39232
Tel (601) 362-7801 *SIC* 8082

FORREST GENERAL HOSPITAL p 568
1414 S 28th Ave, Hattiesburg MS 39402
Tel (601) 288-2500 *SIC* 8082 8093

WESLEY HEALTH SYSTEM LLC p 1593
5001 Hardy St, Hattiesburg MS 39402
Tel (601) 268-8000
SIC 8051 8062 8082 8011

STA-HOME HEALTH & HOSPICE INC p 1374
406 Briarwood Dr Ste 200, Jackson MS 39206
Tel (601) 956-5100 *SIC* 8082

NORTH MISSISSIPPI MEDICAL CENTER INC p 1053
830 S Gloster St, Tupelo MS 38801
Tel (662) 377-3000 *SIC* 8062 8051 8082

CITIZENS MEMORIAL HOSPITAL DISTRICT OF POLK COUNTY p 311
1500 N Oakland Ave, Bolivar MO 65613
Tel (417) 326-6000 *SIC* 8062 8011 8082

SKAGGS COMMUNITY HOSPITAL ASSOCIATION p 1329
251 Skaggs Rd, Branson MO 65616
Tel (417) 335-7000
SIC 8062 8082 8011 7352 8051

TRI-COUNTY GROUP XV INC p 1477
1912 Independence St, Cape Girardeau MO 63703
Tel (573) 339-1864 *SIC* 8082

CARONDELET HEALTH p 260
1000 Carondelet Dr, Kansas City MO 64114
Tel (816) 942-4400 *SIC* 8082

SAINT LUKES HOSPITAL OF KANSAS CITY p 1270
4401 Wornall Rd, Kansas City MO 64111
Tel (816) 932-2000
SIC 8062 8742 8011 6512 8082 7322

MEDICAL WEST RESPIRATORY SVCS LLC p 937
9301 Dielman Indus Dr, Saint Louis MO 63132
Tel (314) 993-8100 *SIC* 5047 8082

SSM HEALTH CARE CORP p 1364
10101 Woodfield Ln # 100, Saint Louis MO 63132
Tel (314) 994-7800
SIC 8062 8082 8011 8051

HEALTHCARE SERVICES OF OZARKS INC p 676
3660 S National Ave, Springfield MO 65807
Tel (417) 882-4170 *SIC* 7363 8082

NIGHTINGALE NURSING SERVICE INC p 1043
3301 Great Northrn Ave203 Ste 203, Missoula MT 59808
Tel (406) 541-1700 *SIC* 8082

SAINT ELIZABETH REGIONAL MEDICAL CENTER p 1269
555 S 70th St, Lincoln NE 68510
Tel (402) 219-5200 *SIC* 8062 8082

NORTH PLATTE NEBRASKA HOSPITAL CORP p 1053
601 W Leota St, North Platte NE 69101
Tel (308) 534-9310 *SIC* 8062 8082

■ SIERRA HEALTH SERVICES INC p 1320
2720 N Tenaya Way, Las Vegas NV 89128
Tel (702) 242-7000
SIC 6324 6311 8082 8741 8093

CAPITAL REGION HEALTH CARE CORP p 250
250 Pleasant St, Concord NH 03301
Tel (603) 225-2711
SIC 8741 8062 8051 8093 8082

COMPASSIONATE CARE HOSPICE OF CENTRAL NEW JERSEY LLC p 351
261 Connecticut Dr Ste 1, Burlington NJ 08016
Tel (609) 267-1178 *SIC* 8082

E WALSH MANAGEMENT CORP p 467
45 Main St, Eatontown NJ 07724
Tel (732) 443-8100 *SIC* 5999 8082

ATLANTICARE HEALTH SYSTEM INC p 127
2500 English Creek Ave, Egg Harbor Township NJ 08234
Tel (609) 407-2300 *SIC* 8071 8082

CARE FINDERS TOTAL CARE LLC p 254
171 Main St Ste 2, Hackensack NJ 07601
Tel (201) 342-5122 *SIC* 8082

LOVING CARE AGENCY INC p 881
611 Rte 46 W Ste 200, Hasbrouck Heights NJ 07604
Tel (201) 403-9300 *SIC* 8011 8082

VIRTUA MEDICAL GROUP PA p 1560
301 Lippincott Dr, Marlton NJ 08053
Tel (856) 355-0340 *SIC* 8099 8082

BAYADA HOME HEALTH CARE INC p 161
290 Chester Ave, Moorestown NJ 08057
Tel (856) 231-1000 *SIC* 8082

LOVING HANDS LTD p 881
676 Winters Ave Ste 1, Paramus NJ 07652
Tel (201) 265-3523 *SIC* 7363 8082

VISITING NURSE ASSOCIATION OF CENTRAL JERSEY INC p 1561
176 Riverside Ave, Red Bank NJ 07701
Tel (732) 747-1204 *SIC* 8082

BARNABAS HEALTH INC p 155
95 Old Short Hills Rd, West Orange NJ 07052
Tel (973) 322-4018 *SIC* 8082 8099

■ PATIENT CARE INC p 1120
300 Executive Dr Ste 175, West Orange NJ 07052
Tel (973) 243-6299 *SIC* 8082

SAINT BARNABAS CORP p 1268
95 Old Short Hills Rd, West Orange NJ 07052
Tel (973) 322-5000 *SIC* 8062 8082

AMBERCARE CORP p 65
420 N Main St, Belen NM 87002
Tel (505) 861-0060
SIC 8082 8361 5047 7352

NEXT PHASE INC p 1040
1410 S Main St, Roswell NM 88203
Tel (575) 624-9999 *SIC* 8082

PERSONAL TOUCH HOME CARE p 1137
22215 Northern Blvd Fl 3, Bayside NY 11361
Tel (718) 468-4747 *SIC* 8082

BETH ABRAHAM HEALTH SERVICES p 177
2540 Barker Ave Ofc, Bronx NY 10467
Tel (718) 519-5831 *SIC* 8059 8351 8082

CENTERLIGHT HEALTHCARE INC p 276
1250 Waters Pl Ste 602, Bronx NY 10461
Tel (347) 640-6000 *SIC* 8051 8082 8322

ATTENTIVE HOME CARE AGENCY INC p 129
3131 Coney Island Ave, Brooklyn NY 11235
Tel (718) 843-8430 *SIC* 8082

BROOKDALE HOSPITAL CENTER HOUSING CO INC p 217
10101 Avenue D, Brooklyn NY 11236
Tel (718) 240-5000 *SIC* 8082

CABS HOME ATTENDANTS SERVICE INC p 235
44 Varet St, Brooklyn NY 11206
Tel (718) 388-0220 *SIC* 8082

METROPOLITAN JEWISH HOME CARE INC p 956
6323 7th Ave Ste 2, Brooklyn NY 11220
Tel (718) 921-7742 *SIC* 8082

SPECIAL TOUCH HOME HEALTH CARE SERVICES INC p 1356
2091 Coney Island Ave, Brooklyn NY 11223
Tel (718) 627-1122 *SIC* 8082

■ BRACOR INC p 206
346 Delaware Ave, Buffalo NY 14202
Tel (716) 856-7500 *SIC* 8082 8071 7361

NATIONAL HEALTH CARE AFFILIATES INC p 1013
10 Lafayette Sq Ste 1900, Buffalo NY 14203
Tel (716) 839-4000 *SIC* 8082 8052

ROCKAWAY HOME ATTENDANT SERVICES INC p 1243
1603 Central Ave 100, Far Rockaway NY 11691
Tel (718) 327-1850 *SIC* 8082 8361

HEALTH ACQUISITION CORP p 674
7000 Austin St Ste 2, Forest Hills NY 11375
Tel (718) 657-2966 *SIC* 8082

FAMILY AIDES INC p 526
120 W John St B, Hicksville NY 11801
Tel (516) 681-2300 *SIC* 8082

UTOPIA HOME CARE INC p 1537
60 E Main St, Kings Park NY 11754
Tel (631) 544-6005 *SIC* 8082 8093

BESTCARE INC p 177
3000 Hempstead Tpke # 205, Levittown NY 11756
Tel (516) 731-3535 *SIC* 8082

RECCO HOME CARE SERVICE INC p 1214
524 Hicksville Rd, Massapequa NY 11758
Tel (516) 798-6688 *SIC* 8082

STAR MULTI CARE SERVICES INC p 1378
115 Broadhollow Rd # 275, Melville NY 11747
Tel (631) 423-6689 *SIC* 8082 7361

NORTHWELL HEALTH INC p 1059
2000 Marcus Ave, New Hyde Park NY 11042
Tel (516) 321-6000 *SIC* 8082 8062

PARKER JEWISH INSTITUTE FOR HEALTH CARE AND REHABILITATION FOUNDATION p 1116
27111 76th Ave, New Hyde Park NY 11040
Tel (516) 247-6500 *SIC* 8051 8082 8069

ALLIED HEALTHCARE INTERNATIONAL INC p 56
245 Park Ave Fl 39, New York NY 10167
Tel (212) 750-0064 *SIC* 8082 8049

NEW PARTNERS INC p 1032
1250 Broadway Fl 10, New York NY 10001
Tel (212) 609-7700 *SIC* 8082

PEOPLE CARE HOLDINGS INC p 1132
116 W 32nd St Fl 15, New York NY 10001
Tel (212) 631-7300 *SIC* 8082

PEOPLE CARE INC p 1132
116 W 32nd St Fl 15, New York NY 10001
Tel (212) 631-7300 *SIC* 8082

■TIPTREE OPERATING CO LLC p 1455
780 3rd Ave Rm 2103, New York NY 10017
Tel (212) 446-1410 *SIC* 8082

VILLAGE CENTER FOR CARE p 1557
120 Broadway Ste 2840, New York NY 10271
Tel (212) 367-3748 *SIC* 8051 8082 8322

VISITING NURSE SERVICE OF NEW YORK p 1561
5 Penn Plz Ste 1201, New York NY 10001
Tel (212) 609-6100 *SIC* 8082

VISITING NURSE SERVICE OF NEW YORK HOME CARE p 1561
107 E 70th St, New York NY 10021
Tel (212) 484-3950 *SIC* 8082

VISITING NURSE SERVICE OF NEW YORK HOME CARE II p 1561
5 Penn Plz Fl 12, New York NY 10001
Tel (212) 609-5716 *SIC* 8082

VISITING NURSE SERVICE OF NEW YORK HOSPICE CARE p 1561
5 Penn Plz Ste 1201, New York NY 10001
Tel (212) 609-5716 *SIC* 8082

VNS CHOICE p 1563
5 Penn Plz Ste 1201, New York NY 10001
Tel (212) 609-5600 *SIC* 8082

NYACK HOSPITAL FOUNDATION INC p 1068
160 N Midland Ave, Nyack NY 10960
Tel (845) 348-2000 *SIC* 8062 8011 8082

VIP HEALTH CARE SERVICES INC p 1558
11612 Myrtle Ave, Richmond Hill NY 11418
Tel (718) 849-2300 *SIC* 8082

GENESEE REGION HOME CARE ASSOCIATION INC p 602
3111 Winton Rd S, Rochester NY 14623
Tel (585) 214-1000 *SIC* 8082

NATIONAL HOME HEALTH CARE CORP p 1013
700 White Plains Rd Ste 2, Scarsdale NY 10583
Tel (914) 722-9000 *SIC* 8082 7361

STELLA ORTON HOME CARE AGENCY INC p 1385
3155 Amboy Rd Ste 1, Staten Island NY 10306
Tel (718) 987-4300 *SIC* 8082

▲NEW YORK HEALTH CARE INC p 1035
20 E Sunrise Hwy Ste 201, Valley Stream NY 11581
Tel (718) 375-6700 *SIC* 2834 8082

CAROLINA ADVENTIST RETIREMENT SYSTEMS INC p 259
95 Holcombe Cove Rd, Candler NC 28715
Tel (828) 667-9851 *SIC* 8052 8051 8082

HENDERSON COUNTY HOSPITAL CORP p 682
800 N Justice St, Hendersonville NC 28791
Tel (828) 698-7191 *SIC* 8062 8051 8082

ADVANCED HOME CARE INC p 25
4001 Piedmont Pkwy, High Point NC 27265
Tel (336) 878-8950 *SIC* 8082 5999

HOME CARE OF CENTRAL CAROLINA INC p 703
4001 Piedmont Pkwy, High Point NC 27265
Tel (336) 878-8822 *SIC* 8082

SCOTLAND HEALTH CARE SYSTEM p 1293
500 Lauchwood Dr, Laurinburg NC 28352
Tel (910) 291-7000 *SIC* 8062 8011 8082

REX HEALTHCARE INC p 1230
4420 Lake Boone Trl, Raleigh NC 27607
Tel (919) 784-3100 *SIC* 8062 8011 8062

LIBERTY HOMECARE GROUP LLC p 862
2334 S 41st St, Wilmington NC 28403
Tel (910) 815-3122 *SIC* 8082

INTERIM HOME HEALTHCARE CO p 752
2526 Ward Blvd, Wilson NC 27893
Tel (252) 243-7808 *SIC* 8082

TRIAD MEDICAL SERVICES INC p 1478
623 W Main St, Yadkinville NC 27055
Tel (336) 679-8852 *SIC* 8082

YADKIN NURSING CARE CENTER INC p 1633
903 W Main St, Yadkinville NC 27055
Tel (336) 679-8863 *SIC* 8082 8051

HASCO MEDICAL INC p 667
810 Moe Dr, Akron OH 44310
Tel (214) 302-0930 *SIC* 5999 8082

▲CHEMED CORP p 293
255 E 5th St Ste 2600, Cincinnati OH 45202
Tel (513) 762-6690 *SIC* 8082 1711 7699

GAMBLE ELIZABETH DEACONESS HOME ASSOCIATION (INC) p 590
2139 Auburn Ave, Cincinnati OH 45219
Tel (513) 751-4224 *SIC* 8062 8082

GOOD SAMARITAN HOSPITAL OF CINCINNATI p 623
375 Dixmyth Ave, Cincinnati OH 45220
Tel (513) 569-6251 *SIC* 8062 8082 8011

■OMNICARE INC p 1085
900 Omnicare Ctr, Cincinnati OH 45202
Tel (513) 719-2600
SIC 5122 5047 8082 8741

MARYMOUNT HOSPITAL INC p 915
9500 Euclid Ave, Cleveland OH 44195
Tel (216) 581-0500
SIC 8062 8063 8051 8082

NCS HEALTHCARE INC p 1022
3201 Entp Pkwy Ste 220, Cleveland OH 44122
Tel (216) 514-3350
SIC 5122 8093 8049 8082 8742 5912

OHIOHEALTH CORP p 1078
180 E Broad St, Columbus OH 43215
Tel (614) 788-8860
SIC 8049 8062 8082 8051

SALO INC p 1273
960 Checkrein Ave Ste A, Columbus OH 43229
Tel (614) 436-9404 *SIC* 8082

MED AMERICA HEALTH SYSTEMS CORP p 934
1 Wyoming St, Dayton OH 45409
Tel (937) 223-6192 *SIC* 8062 8741 8082

PREMIER HEALTH PARTNERS p 1170
110 N Main St, Dayton OH 45402
Tel (937) 499-9596 *SIC* 8082

B H C SERVICES INC p 142
26250 Euclid Ave Ste 901, Euclid OH 44132
Tel (216) 289-5300 *SIC* 8082

DISCOUNT DRUG MART INC p 442
211 Commerce Dr, Medina OH 44256
Tel (330) 725-2340
SIC 5912 5331 5411 5451 5122 8082

HEALTH PLAN OF UPPER OHIO VALLEY INC p 675
52160 National Rd E, Saint Clairsville OH 43950
Tel (740) 695-3585 *SIC* 6324 8082

■IN HOME HEALTH LLC p 735
333 N Summit St, Toledo OH 43604
Tel (419) 252-5500 *SIC* 8082

■MANOR CARE INC p 902
333 N Summit St Ste 103, Toledo OH 43604
Tel (419) 252-5500 *SIC* 8051 8082 8062

■MANOR CARE OF AMERICA INC p 902
333 N Summit St Ste 103, Toledo OH 43604
Tel (419) 252-5500 *SIC* 8051 8062 8082

BETHESDA HOSPITAL ASSOCIATION INC p 178
2951 Maple Ave, Zanesville OH 43701
Tel (740) 454-4000 *SIC* 8062 8063 8082

GENESIS HEALTHCARE SYSTEM p 603
2951 Maple Ave, Zanesville OH 43701
Tel (740) 454-5000 *SIC* 8082

BAY AREA HEALTH DISTRICT p 160
1775 Thompson Rd, Coos Bay OR 97420
Tel (541) 269-8111 *SIC* 8062 8082

TUALITY HOME HEALTH INC p 1490
1809 Maple St, Forest Grove OR 97116
Tel (503) 357-2737 *SIC* 8082

TUALITY HEALTHCARE FOUNDATION INC p 1490
335 Se 8th Ave, Hillsboro OR 97123
Tel (503) 681-1850
SIC 8082 7374 6512 5999 7359

MID-VALLEY HEALTHCARE INC p 963
525 N Santiam Hwy, Lebanon OR 97355
Tel (541) 258-2101
SIC 8062 8051 8011 8082

FAMILYCARE INC p 527
825 Ne Multnomah St # 300, Portland OR 97232
Tel (503) 222-2880 *SIC* 8082

LEGACY VISITING NURSE ASSOCIATION p 852
815 Ne Davis St, Portland OR 97232
Tel (503) 220-1000 *SIC* 8399 5999 8082

P C NORTHWEST PERMANENTE p 1102
500 Ne Multnomah St # 100, Portland OR 97232
Tel (877) 313-3424 *SIC* 8082

■CRITICAL HOMECARE SOLUTIONS HOLDINGS INC p 393
2 Tower Brg 2 Tower Bridge, Conshohocken PA 19428
Tel (610) 825-2061 *SIC* 8082

■CRITICAL HOMECARE SOLUTIONS INC p 393
1 Fayette St, Conshohocken PA 19428
Tel (720) 697-5200 *SIC* 8082

GEISINGER SYSTEM SERVICES p 597
100 N Academy Ave, Danville PA 17822
Tel (570) 271-6211 *SIC* 8741 8082

HOLY REDEEMER HEALTH SYSTEM INC p 702
667 Welsh Rd Ste 300, Huntingdon Valley PA 19006
Tel (215) 938-0180 *SIC* 8082

ARSENS HOME CARE INC p 113
101 Washington Ln Ste G6, Jenkintown PA 19046
Tel (215) 663-8090 *SIC* 8082

NHS HUMAN SERVICES INC p 1042
620 Germantown Pike, Lafayette Hill PA 19444
Tel (610) 260-4600 *SIC* 8093 8059 8082

NORTHEAST BEHAVIORAL HEALTH CARE CONSORTIUM p 1054
72 Glenmaura Nat Blvd, Moosic PA 18507
Tel (570) 344-9618 *SIC* 8082

GENERAL HEALTHCARE RESOURCES INC p 601
2250 Hickory Rd Ste 240, Plymouth Meeting PA 19462
Tel (610) 834-1122 *SIC* 8082

GUTHRIE CLINIC p 648
1 Guthrie Sq Ste B, Sayre PA 18840
Tel (570) 888-5858 *SIC* 8011 8062 8082

PENTEC HEALTH INC p 1132
4 Creek Pkwy Ste A, Upper Chichester PA 19061
Tel (610) 494-8700 *SIC* 2834 8082

LAUREL HEALTH SYSTEM INC p 847
22 Walnut St, Wellsboro PA 16901
Tel (570) 724-1010 *SIC* 8082 8741 8011

WILLOW VALLEY COMMUNITIES p 1613
100 Willow Vly Lakes Dr, Willow Street PA 17584
Tel (717) 464-2741 *SIC* 8361 8059 8082

YORK PENNSYLVANIA HOSPITAL CO LLC p 1637
325 S Belmont St, York PA 17403
Tel (717) 843-8623 *SIC* 8062 8082

SPECIAL CARE PHARMACY SERVICES INC p 1355
1221 Ave Americo Miranda, San Juan PR 00921
Tel (787) 783-8579 *SIC* 5912 8082

CARE NEW ENGLAND HEALTH SYSTEM INC p 254
45 Willard Ave, Providence RI 02905
Tel (401) 453-7900
SIC 8063 8062 8069 8093 8082

PROSPECT CHARTERCARE LLC p 1184
825 Chalkstone Ave, Providence RI 02908
Tel (401) 456-2001 *SIC* 8082

KERSHAW HEALTH MEDICAL CENTER p 813
1315 Roberts St, Camden SC 29020
Tel (803) 432-4311 *SIC* 8062 8051 8082

MEDICAL SERVICES OF AMERICA INC p 937
171 Monroe Ln, Lexington SC 29072
Tel (803) 957-0500
SIC 8082 8741 8011 8071 7352 5999

SONIFI SOLUTIONS INC p 1340
3900 W Innovation St, Sioux Falls SD 57107
Tel (605) 988-1000 *SIC* 7812 8082

AHOM HOLDINGS INC (DE) p 37
5200 Maryland Way Ste 400, Brentwood TN 37027
Tel (615) 221-8884 *SIC* 8082

■QUORUM HEALTH RESOURCES LLC p 1201
1573 Mallory Ln 200, Brentwood TN 37027
Tel (615) 371-7979
SIC 8742 8741 8082 8231 6324

MEMORIAL HEALTH CARE SYSTEM INC p 941
2525 Desales Ave, Chattanooga TN 37404
Tel (423) 495-2525 *SIC* 8082

▲HEALTHWAYS INC p 678
701 Cool Springs Blvd, Franklin TN 37067
Tel (615) 614-4929 *SIC* 8082 8099

■PARALLON BUSINESS SOLUTIONS LLC p 1114
6640 Carothers Pkwy, Franklin TN 37067
Tel (615) 344-3000 *SIC* 8082

■HHC INC p 689
6501 Deane Hill Dr, Knoxville TN 37919
Tel (865) 292-6000 *SIC* 8082

■HOUSECALL MEDICAL RESOURCES INC p 711
1400 Cntrpint Blvd St 100, Knoxville TN 37932
Tel (865) 689-7123 *SIC* 8082 8741 5999

▲NATIONAL HEALTHCARE CORP p 1013
100 E Vine St, Murfreesboro TN 37130
Tel (615) 890-2020 *SIC* 8051 8082

CHARTWELL COMMUNITY SERVICES INC p 291
14295 Midway Rd Ste 400, Addison TX 75001
Tel (972) 713-3400 *SIC* 8082

NURSECORE MANAGEMENT SERVICES LLC p 1067
2201 Brookhollow Plaza Dr # 450, Arlington TX 76006
Tel (817) 649-1166 *SIC* 8742 8082

GIRLING HEALTH CARE INC p 613
1703 W 5th St Fl 7, Austin TX 78703
Tel (512) 452-5781 *SIC* 8082

HARDEN HOME HEALTH LLC p 660
8701 N Mopac Expy, Austin TX 78759
Tel (512) 634-4909 *SIC* 8082

ABUNDANT LIFE HOME HEALTH INC p 13
1900 Pecan, Brownsville TX 78520
Tel (956) 544-7714 *SIC* 8082

LOPEZ HEALTH SYSTEMS INC p 877
2209 N Highway 83, Crystal City TX 78839
Tel (830) 374-3525 *SIC* 8082

ACCENTCARE INC p 14
17855 Dallas Pkwy, Dallas TX 75287
Tel (800) 834-3059 *SIC* 8082

■ADVANCED HOMECARE MANAGEMENT INC p 25
6688 N Cntrl Expy # 1300, Dallas TX 75206
Tel (214) 239-6500 *SIC* 8082

BAYLOR HEALTH CARE SYSTEM p 162
3500 Gaston Ave, Dallas TX 75246
Tel (214) 820-0111 *SIC* 8062 8082 1542

BAYLOR SCOTT & WHITE HEALTH p 162
3500 Gaston Ave, Dallas TX 75246
Tel (214) 820-1075 *SIC* 8082 8062

CARECYCLE SOLUTIONS LLC p 254
3406 Main St, Dallas TX 75226
Tel (214) 698-0600 *SIC* 8082

■EHHI HOLDINGS INC p 481
6688 N Cntrl Expy # 1300, Dallas TX 75206
Tel (877) 330-7657 *SIC* 8082

EPIC HEALTH SERVICES INC p 505
5220 Spring Valley Rd, Dallas TX 75254
Tel (214) 466-1340 *SIC* 8082

INTREPID USA INC p 760
4055 Valley View Ln # 500, Dallas TX 75244
Tel (214) 445-3750 *SIC* 7363 8082

▲TENET HEALTHCARE CORP p 1437
1445 Ross Ave Ste 1400, Dallas TX 75202
Tel (469) 893-2200
SIC 8062 8069 8741 8063 8082 8011

■VISTACARE INC p 1562
717 N Harwood St Ste 1500, Dallas TX 75201
Tel (480) 648-4545 *SIC* 8082

COOK CHILDRENS HEALTH PLAN p 365
801 7th Ave, Fort Worth TX 76104
Tel (817) 334-2247 *SIC* 8082

■CONIFER HEALTH SOLUTIONS LLC p 356
3560 Dallas Pkwy, Frisco TX 75034
Tel (469) 803-3000 *SIC* 8082

BAYLOR MEDICAL CENTER AT GARLAND p 162
2300 Marie Curie Dr, Garland TX 75042
Tel (972) 487-5000
SIC 8062 8082 8011 8093

HUNT MEMORIAL HOSPITAL DISTRICT p 719
4215 Joe Ramsey Blvd E, Greenville TX 75401
Tel (903) 408-5000 *SIC* 8062 8071 8082

LIGHTHOUSE HOSPICE p 865
305 Coke Ave Ste 140, Hillsboro TX 76645
Tel (254) 710-9800 *SIC* 8082 8069

EVEROSE HEALTHCARE INC p 515
11200 Westheimer Rd # 100, Houston TX 77042
Tel (919) 482-9036 *SIC* 8082

HEALTH CARE TEMPORARIES INC p 674
8926 Sherbourne St Ste D, Houston TX 77016
Tel (713) 631-7106
SIC 8082 1542 1522 1081 5082

CAPROCK HOME HEALTH SERVICES INC p 251
8806 University Ave, Lubbock TX 79423
Tel (806) 748-7722 *SIC* 8082

HEALTH CARE UNLIMITED INC p 674
1100 E Laurel Ave, Mcallen TX 78501
Tel (956) 994-9911 *SIC* 5047 8082

JORDAN HEALTH CARE INC p 793
412 Texas Highway 37 S, Mount Vernon TX 75457
Tel (903) 537-3600 *SIC* 8082

JORDAN HEALTHCARE HOLDINGS INC p 793
412 Texas Highway 37 S, Mount Vernon TX 75457
Tel (903) 537-2445 *SIC* 6719 8082

GOLDEN LIVING LLC p 621
5220 Tennyson Pkwy # 400, Plano TX 75024
Tel (972) 372-6300
SIC 8051 8082 8731 8093

CHILDRENS HOME HEALTHCARE INC p 299
901 Waterfall Way Ste 105, Richardson TX 75080
Tel (972) 661-3737 *SIC* 8082

OUTREACH HEALTH CARE INC p 1099
269 W Renner Rd, Richardson TX 75080
Tel (972) 840-7360 *SIC* 8093 8049 8082

VNA AND HOSPICE OF SOUTH TEXAS p 1563
4241 Woodcock Dr Ste A100, San Antonio TX 78228
Tel (210) 785-5800 *SIC* 8082

■WELLMED MEDICAL MANAGEMENT INC p 1589
8637 Fredericksburg Rd # 360, San Antonio TX 78240
Tel (210) 615-9355 *SIC* 8082

GIRLING HEALTH CENTER p 613
1920 Birdcreek Dr, Temple TX 76502
Tel (254) 778-4210 *SIC* 8082

VERNON HOME HEALTH CARE AGENCY INC p 1551
2733 Midwestern Pkwy # 120, Wichita Falls TX 76308
Tel (972) 840-3401 *SIC* 8093 8049 8082

UINTAH BASIN MEDICAL CENTER p 1500
250 W 300 N, Roosevelt UT 84066
Tel (435) 725-2008
SIC 8062 8082 7352 8092 8361

■NORTHERN UTAH HEALTHCARE CORP p 1057
1200 E 3900 S, Salt Lake City UT 84124
Tel (801) 268-7111 *SIC* 8062 8082 8011

MARTHA JEFFERSON HOSPITAL p 912
459 Locust Ave, Charlottesville VA 22902
Tel (434) 982-7000 *SIC* 8082

CAPITAL HOSPICE p 249
2900 Telestar Ct, Falls Church VA 22042
Tel (703) 538-2065 *SIC* 8082 8052

SENTARA MEDICAL GROUP p 1305
835 Glenrock Rd, Norfolk VA 23502
Tel (757) 252-3070 *SIC* 8093 8082

MEDICAL TEAM INC p 937
1902 Campus Commons Dr # 650, Reston VA 20191
Tel (703) 390-2300 *SIC* 8082

MID-ATLANTIC HOME HEALTH NETWORK INC p 963
25 Winchester St, Warrenton VA 20186
Tel (540) 347-4901 *SIC* 8082

SENIOR AEGIS COMMUNITIES LLC p 1303
17602 Ne Union Hill Rd, Redmond WA 98052
Tel (866) 688-5829 *SIC* 8082

SEA-MAR COMMUNITY HEALTH CENTER p 1295
1040 S Henderson St, Seattle WA 98108
Tel (206) 763-5277
SIC 8322 8082 8093 8051

YAKIMA VALLEY MEMORIAL HOSPITAL ASSOCIATION INC p 1634
2811 Tieton Dr, Yakima WA 98902
Tel (509) 249-5129 *SIC* 8062 8082

LOVED ONES IN HOME CARE LLC p 881
144 7th Ave, South Charleston WV 25303
Tel (304) 744-4081 *SIC* 8082

AID HOLDINGS LLC p 37
W140n8981 Lilly Rd, Menomonee Falls WI 53051
Tel (262) 257-8888
SIC 8052 8051 8059 8082

CHILDRENS HOSPITAL AND HEALTH SYSTEM INC p 299
8915 W Connell Ave, Milwaukee WI 53226
Tel (414) 266-2000
SIC 8069 8082 7389 7322

LUTHERAN SOCIAL SERVICES OF WISCONSIN AND UPPER MICHIGAN INC p 886
647 W Virginia St Ste 200, Milwaukee WI 53204
Tel (262) 896-3446 *SIC* 8322 8082

SIC 8092 Kidney Dialysis Centers

■RENAL TREATMENT CENTERS-SOUTHEAST LP p 1223
3947 Gulf Shores Pkwy, Gulf Shores AL 36542
Tel (251) 967-2205 *SIC* 8092

SATELLITE HEALTHCARE INC p 1283
300 Santana Row Ste 300, San Jose CA 95128
Tel (650) 404-3600 *SIC* 8092

▲DAVITA INC p 416
2000 16th St, Denver CO 80202
Tel (303) 405-2100 *SIC* 8092 8093

■ DVA HEALTHCARE RENAL CARE INC p 463
2000 16th St, Denver CO 80202
Tel (253) 280-9501 *SIC* 8092

■ TOTAL RENAL CARE INC p 1463
2000 16th St, Denver CO 80202
Tel (253) 280-9501 *SIC* 8092

IHS DIALYSIS INC p 731
6001 Broken Sound Pkwy Nw, Boca Raton FL 33487
Tel (561) 443-0743 *SIC* 8092

RENEX CORP p 1224
201 Alhambra Cir Ste 800, Coral Gables FL 33134
Tel (305) 448-2044 *SIC* 8092

■ DAVITA ARLINGTON HEIGHTS RENAL CENTER p 416
17 W Golf Rd, Arlington Heights IL 60005
Tel (847) 437-2188 *SIC* 8092

■ CAREMARK INTERNATIONAL LLC p 255
2211 Sanders Rd, Northbrook IL 60062
Tel (847) 559-4700
SIC 5961 6411 8099 8092 8093

■ CAREMARK LLC p 255
2211 Sanders Rd, Northbrook IL 60062
Tel (847) 559-4700
SIC 5961 6411 8099 8092 8093 8742

TOTAL RENAL CARE INC p 1463
13155 S La Grange Rd, Orland Park IL 60462
Tel (800) 424-6589 *SIC* 8092

■ ISD PLAINFIELD LLC p 766
8110 Network Dr, Plainfield IN 46168
Tel (317) 838-8089 *SIC* 8092

■ RENAL TREATMENT CENTERS-ILLINOIS INC p 1223
1930 E Parrish Ave, Owensboro KY 42303
Tel (270) 926-0120 *SIC* 8092

▲ AMERICAN RENAL ASSOCIATES HOLDINGS INC p 78
500 Cummings Ctr Ste 6550, Beverly MA 01915
Tel (978) 922-3080 *SIC* 8092

■ AMERICAN RENAL ASSOCIATES LLC p 78
500 Cummings Ctr Ste 6550, Beverly MA 01915
Tel (978) 922-3080 *SIC* 8092

■ AMERICAN RENAL HOLDINGS INC p 78
500 Cummings Ctr Ste 6550, Beverly MA 01915
Tel (978) 922-3080 *SIC* 8092

BIO-MEDICAL APPLICATIONS MANAGEMENT CO INC p 183
95 Hayden Ave, Lexington MA 02421
Tel (781) 402-9000 *SIC* 8092

BIO MEDICAL APPLICATIONS OF FLORIDA INC p 183
920 Winter St Ste A, Waltham MA 02451
Tel (781) 699-9000 *SIC* 8092

BIO-MEDICAL APPLICATIONS OF CALIFORNIA INC p 183
920 Winter St, Waltham MA 02451
Tel (781) 699-4404 *SIC* 8092

BIO-MEDICAL APPLICATIONS OF NORTH CAROLINA INC p 183
920 Winter St, Waltham MA 02451
Tel (781) 699-4404 *SIC* 8092

FRESENIUS MEDICAL CARE CARDIOVASCULAR RESOURCES INC p 578
920 Winter St Ste A, Waltham MA 02451
Tel (781) 402-9000 *SIC* 8092 5047 8071

FRESENIUS MEDICAL CARE HOLDINGS INC p 578
920 Winter St, Waltham MA 02451
Tel (781) 699-9000 *SIC* 3841 8092

FRESENIUS MEDICAL CARE NORTH AMERICA p 578
920 Winter St, Waltham MA 02451
Tel (781) 699-4404 *SIC* 8092

NATIONAL MEDICAL CARE INC p 1014
920 Winter St Ste A, Waltham MA 02451
Tel (781) 699-9000 *SIC* 8092

L I C H CORP p 834
339 Hicks St, Brooklyn NY 11201
Tel (718) 780-1000 *SIC* 8062 8092 5912

RENAL RESEARCH INSTITUTE LLC p 1223
315 E 62nd St Fl 4, New York NY 10065
Tel (212) 360-6579 *SIC* 8092

GOOD SAMARITAN HOSPITAL MEDICAL CENTER p 623
1000 Montauk Hwy, West Islip NY 11795
Tel (631) 376-3000 *SIC* 8062 8051 8092

■ DVA RENAL HEALTHCARE INC p 463
5200 Virginia Way, Brentwood TN 37027
Tel (615) 320-4200 *SIC* 8092 8071

■ ACCREDO HEALTH INC p 15
1640 Century Center Pkwy # 110, Memphis TN 38134
Tel (901) 373-8958 *SIC* 2835 8092

DIALYSIS CLINIC INC p 436
1633 Church St Ste 500, Nashville TN 37203
Tel (615) 327-3061 *SIC* 8092 5047 8071

DIALYSIS NEWCO INC p 436
424 Church St Ste 1900, Nashville TN 37219
Tel (615) 777-8200 *SIC* 8092

DSI HOLDING CO INC p 457
424 Church St Ste 1900, Nashville TN 37219
Tel (615) 777-8201 *SIC* 8092 8069 8742

DSI RENAL HOLDINGS LLC p 458
424 Church St Ste 1900, Nashville TN 37219
Tel (615) 777-8201 *SIC* 8092 8069 8742

■ ISD RENAL INC p 766
424 Church St Ste 1900, Nashville TN 37219
Tel (615) 777-8200 *SIC* 8069 8092 8742

RENAL CARE GROUP INC p 1223
2525 West End Ave Ste 600, Nashville TN 37203
Tel (615) 345-5500 *SIC* 8092

US RENAL CARE INC p 1533
5851 Legacy Cir Ste 900, Plano TX 75024
Tel (214) 736-2700 *SIC* 8092

UINTAH BASIN MEDICAL CENTER p 1500
250 W 300 N, Roosevelt UT 84066
Tel (435) 725-2008
SIC 8062 8082 7352 8092 8361

NORTHWEST KIDNEY CENTERS p 1060
700 Broadway, Seattle WA 98122
Tel (206) 292-2771 *SIC* 8092

SIC 8093 Specialty Outpatient Facilities, NEC

EASTERN HEALTH SYSTEM INC p 472
Medical Park E Dr Bldg 1, Birmingham AL 35235
Tel (205) 838-3996
SIC 8062 8082 8051 8011 8322 8093

■ HEALTHSOUTH REHABILITATION HOSPITAL OF CYPRESS LLC p 678
3660 Grandview Pkwy, Birmingham AL 35243
Tel (205) 967-7116 *SIC* 8093

UNIVERSITY OF ALABAMA HEALTH SERVICES FOUNDATION PC p 1519
500 22nd St S Ste 100, Birmingham AL 35233
Tel (205) 731-9600 *SIC* 8093

THREE SPRINGS INC p 1450
1131 Eagletree Ln Sw, Huntsville AL 35801
Tel (256) 880-3339 *SIC* 8322 8093

DCH HEALTH CARE AUTHORITY p 418
809 University Blvd E, Tuscaloosa AL 35401
Tel (205) 759-7111 *SIC* 8062 8093

SOUTHCENTRAL FOUNDATION p 1345
4501 Diplomacy Dr, Anchorage AK 99508
Tel (907) 729-4955 *SIC* 8093 8021 8042

YUKON-KUSKOKWIM HEALTH CORP p 1640
829 Hospin Hwy Ste 329, Bethel AK 99559
Tel (907) 543-6300
SIC 8062 7363 8069 8093 8042 8021

DENA NENA HENASH p 428
122 1st Ave Ste 600, Fairbanks AK 99701
Tel (907) 452-8251
SIC 8011 8331 8322 8093

NEXTCARE HOLDINGS INC p 1040
1138 N Alma School Rd # 120, Mesa AZ 85201
Tel (480) 924-8382 *SIC* 8093 8741 8011

NEXTCARE INC p 1040
2550 N Thunderbird Cir # 303, Mesa AZ 85215
Tel (480) 924-8382 *SIC* 8093 8741

BANNER HEALTH p 153
2901 N Central Ave # 160, Phoenix AZ 85012
Tel (602) 747-4000
SIC 8062 8051 8082 7361 8011 8093

EL RIO SANTA CRUZ NEIGHBORHOOD HEALTH CENTER INC p 483
839 W Congress St, Tucson AZ 85745
Tel (520) 792-9890 *SIC* 8093

DAYSPRING SERVICES OF ARKANSAS LLC p 417
1610 W 3rd St, Little Rock AR 72201
Tel (501) 372-4440 *SIC* 8093

PACIFIC CLINICS p 1104
800 S Santa Anita Ave, Arcadia CA 91006
Tel (626) 254-5000 *SIC* 8093

■ CRC HEALTH CORP p 389
20400 Stevens Creek Blvd, Cupertino CA 95014
Tel (877) 272-8668
SIC 8069 8099 8322 8093

■ CRC HEALTH CORPORATE p 389
20400 Stevens, Cupertino CA 95014
Tel (408) 367-0044 *SIC* 8093

GLENDALE ADVENTIST MEDICAL CENTER INC p 615
1509 Wilson Ter, Glendale CA 91206
Tel (818) 409-8000 *SIC* 8062 8093 8011

SADDLEBACK MEMORIAL MEDICAL CENTER p 1265
24451 Health Center Dr, Laguna Hills CA 92653
Tel (949) 837-4500
SIC 8062 8011 8093 8099 8071 8069

AIDS HEALTHCARE FOUNDATION p 37
6255 W Sunset Blvd Fl 21, Los Angeles CA 90028
Tel (323) 860-5200 *SIC* 5932 8093 5912

LOS ANGELES COUNTY DEVELOPMENTAL SERVICES FOUNDATION p 878
3303 Wilshire Blvd # 700, Los Angeles CA 90010
Tel (213) 383-1300 *SIC* 8099 8322 8093

CFHS HOLDINGS INC p 285
4650 Lincoln Blvd, Marina Del Rey CA 90292
Tel (310) 823-8911 *SIC* 8062 8093 8011

GOLDEN VALLEY HEALTH CENTERS p 621
737 W Childs Ave, Merced CA 95341
Tel (209) 383-1848 *SIC* 8093

NATIVIDAD HOSPITAL INC p 1018
1441 Constitution Blvd, Salinas CA 93906
Tel (831) 755-4111 *SIC* 8062 8011 8093

FAMILY HEALTH CENTERS OF SAN DIEGO INC p 527
823 Gateway Center Way, San Diego CA 92102
Tel (619) 515-2303 *SIC* 8093

HEALTHRIGHT 360 p 677
1735 Mission St Ste 2050, San Francisco CA 94103
Tel (415) 762-3700 *SIC* 8093 8011

PLANNED PARENTHOOD MAR MONTE INC p 1154
1691 The Alameda, San Jose CA 95126
Tel (408) 287-7532 *SIC* 8093

■ MANAGED HEALTH NETWORK p 900
2370 Kerner Blvd, San Rafael CA 94901
Tel (415) 460-8168
SIC 6324 8099 8093 8011

■ SAN RAMON REGIONAL MEDICAL CENTER INC p 1277
6001 Norris Canyon Rd, San Ramon CA 94583
Tel (925) 275-0634 *SIC* 8062 8093

CENTRO DE SALUD DE LA COMUNIDAD DE SAN YSIDRO INC p 281
4004 Beyer Blvd, San Ysidro CA 92173
Tel (619) 428-4463 *SIC* 8093 8011

CLINICAS DEL CAMINO REAL INC p 326
200 S Wells Rd Ste 200, Ventura CA 93004
Tel (805) 647-6322 *SIC* 8093

JOHN MUIR PHYSICIAN NETWORK p 789
1450 Treat Blvd, Walnut Creek CA 94597
Tel (925) 296-9700
SIC 8062 8069 8093 7363

▲ DAVITA INC p 416
2000 16th St, Denver CO 80202
Tel (303) 405-2100 *SIC* 8092 8093

MENTAL HEALTH CENTER OF DENVER p 943
4141 E Dickenson Pl, Denver CO 80222
Tel (303) 504-6501 *SIC* 8093

APPLE HEALTH CARE INC p 98
21 Waterville Rd, Avon CT 06001
Tel (860) 678-9755 *SIC* 8093

GREATER WATERBURY HEALTH NETWORK INC p 636
64 Robbins St, Waterbury CT 06708
Tel (203) 573-6000 *SIC* 8741 8093 8011

BACO RATON COMMUNITY HOSPITAL INC p 143
800 Meadows Rd, Boca Raton FL 33486
Tel (561) 955-5966 *SIC* 8093

LINCARE HOLDINGS INC p 866
19387 Us Highway 19 N, Clearwater FL 33764
Tel (727) 530-7700 *SIC* 8082 8093

■ NORTH FLORIDA REGIONAL MEDICAL CENTER INC p 1052
6500 W Newberry Rd, Gainesville FL 32605
Tel (352) 333-4100
SIC 8062 8093 8011 8082 8069

HEALOGICS INC p 673
5220 Belfort Rd Ste 130, Jacksonville FL 32256
Tel (904) 296-6526 *SIC* 8093

NEMOURS FOUNDATION p 1025
10140 Centurion Pkwy N, Jacksonville FL 32256
Tel (904) 697-4100 *SIC* 8069 8093

CONSULATE MANAGEMENT CO LLC p 361
800 Concourse Pkwy S, Maitland FL 32751
Tel (407) 571-1550
SIC 8051 8059 8071 8093

LAKEVIEW CENTER INC p 840
1221 W Lakeview Ave, Pensacola FL 32501
Tel (850) 432-1222
SIC 8069 8093 7389 7371 7373

■ WEST FLORIDA REGIONAL MEDICAL CENTER INC p 1594
8383 N Davis Hwy, Pensacola FL 32514
Tel (850) 494-4000
SIC 8062 8093 8063 8051

GOODWILL INDUSTRIES-SUNCOAST INC p 625
10596 Gandy Blvd N, Saint Petersburg FL 33702
Tel (727) 523-1512 *SIC* 5932 8093

ACCOMPLISH THERAPY LLC p 15
1665 Palm Beach Lks, West Palm Beach FL 33401
Tel (561) 223-4332 *SIC* 8093

ATLANTA OUTPATIENT PEACHTREE DUNWOODY CENTER p 125
5730 Glenridge Dr Ste 400, Atlanta GA 30328
Tel (404) 847-0893 *SIC* 8093

GRANCARE LLC p 629
1 Ravinia Dr Ste 1400, Atlanta GA 30346
Tel (770) 393-0199
SIC 8051 8052 8093 8071

MARINER HEALTH CARE INC p 907
1 Ravinia Dr Ste 1500, Atlanta GA 30346
Tel (678) 443-7000
SIC 5912 8051 8093 8741 8062 3443

NATIONAL SENIOR CARE INC p 1016
1 Ravinia Dr Ste 1500, Atlanta GA 30346
Tel (678) 443-7000
SIC 5912 8051 8093 8741 8062 3443

MOUNTAIN STATES TUMOR INSTITUTE INC p 994
190 E Bannock St, Boise ID 83712
Tel (208) 381-2222 *SIC* 8093

KOOTENAI HOSPITAL DISTRICT p 827
2003 Kootenai Health Way, Coeur D Alene ID 83814
Tel (208) 625-4000
SIC 8062 8063 8093 8734

GATEWAY FOUNDATION INC p 593
55 E Jackson Blvd # 1500, Chicago IL 60604
Tel (312) 663-1130 *SIC* 8093

NATIONAL SURGICAL HOSPITALS INC p 1016
250 S Wacker Dr Ste 500, Chicago IL 60606
Tel (312) 627-8400 *SIC* 8062 8093

▲ SURGICAL CARE AFFILIATES INC p 1409
510 Lake Cook Rd Ste 400, Deerfield IL 60015
Tel (847) 236-0921 *SIC* 8093

BROMENN REGIONAL MEDICAL CENTER p 217
1304 Franklin Ave, Normal IL 61761
Tel (309) 454-1400 *SIC* 8093

■ CAREMARK INTERNATIONAL LLC p 255
2211 Sanders Rd, Northbrook IL 60062
Tel (847) 559-4700
SIC 5961 6411 8099 8092 8093

■ CAREMARK LLC p 255
2211 Sanders Rd, Northbrook IL 60062
Tel (847) 559-4700
SIC 5961 6411 8099 8092 8093 8742

SELECT REHABILITATION-MIDWEST LLC p 1301
550 W Frontage Rd # 2415, Northfield IL 60093
Tel (847) 441-5593 *SIC* 8093

LUTHERAN GENERAL MEDICAL GROUP S C p 886
1775 Dempster St Ste 10, Park Ridge IL 60068
Tel (847) 795-2800 *SIC* 8093

ST VINCENT CARMEL HOSPITAL p 1373
13500 N Meridian St, Carmel IN 46032
Tel (317) 582-7000 *SIC* 8093

ADVANCED PHYSICAL THERAPY PC p 26
5949 W Raymond St, Indianapolis IN 46241
Tel (317) 486-2186 *SIC* 8093

CARE GROUP LLC p 254
8333 Naab Rd Ste 340, Indianapolis IN 46260
Tel (317) 338-5050 *SIC* 8011 8093

ESKENAZI HEALTH CENTER INC p 509
720 Eskenazi Ave Fl 2, Indianapolis IN 46202
Tel (317) 880-0000 *SIC* 8062 8093 8099

VISIONARY ENTERPRISES INC p 1561
6626 E 75th St Ste 100, Indianapolis IN 46250
Tel (317) 621-4000 *SIC* 6531 8742 8093

SAINT ANTHONY MEMORIAL HEALTH CENTERS p 1268
301 W Homer St, Michigan City IN 46360
Tel (219) 877-1710 *SIC* 8093

TRINITY REGIONAL MEDICAL CENTER p 1481
802 Kenyon Rd Ste 1, Fort Dodge IA 50501
Tel (515) 574-6800 *SIC* 8062 8093

ROSEWOOD HEALTH CARE CENTER p 1251
550 High St, Bowling Green KY 42101
Tel (270) 843-3296 *SIC* 8051 8093

SAINT ELIZABETH MEDICAL CENTER INC p 1269
1 Medical Village Dr, Edgewood KY 41017
Tel (859) 301-2000 *SIC* 8062 8069 8093

NORTON HOSPITALS INC p 1061
200 E Chestnut St, Louisville KY 40202
Tel (502) 629-8000
SIC 8062 8011 8093 8071

■ REHABCARE GROUP INC p 1220
680 S 4th St, Louisville KY 40202
Tel (502) 596-7300
SIC 8093 8099 8049 8051

SEVEN COUNTIES SERVICES INC p 1309
101 W Muhammad Ali Blvd, Louisville KY 40202
Tel (502) 589-8600
SIC 8399 8011 8093 8322 8031

TROVER CLINIC FOUNDATION p 1484
200 Clinic Dr, Madisonville KY 42431
Tel (270) 825-7200 *SIC* 8093

COMMCARE CORP p 344
2755 Pan American Lf Ctr, New Orleans LA 70130
Tel (504) 324-8950 *SIC* 8093

COMMCARE LOUISIANA p 344
601 Poydras St, New Orleans LA 70130
Tel (504) 324-8950 *SIC* 8093

MARTINS POINT HEALTH CARE INC p 913
331 Veranda St Ste 1, Portland ME 04103
Tel (207) 774-5801 *SIC* 8093

NORTON SOUND HEALTH CORP p 1061
790 Lower St, Turner ME 04282
Tel (907) 443-3311
SIC 8062 8051 8069 8093 8011

ANNE ARUNDEL MEDICAL CENTER INC p 92
2001 Medical Pkwy, Annapolis MD 21401
Tel (443) 481-1000 *SIC* 8062 8093 6732

WESTERN MARYLAND HEALTH SYSTEM REHAB p 1599
600 Memorial Ave, Cumberland MD 21502
Tel (301) 723-4200 *SIC* 8049 8093

MOSAIC COMMUNITY SERVICES INC p 991
1925 Greenspring Dr, Lutherville Timonium MD 21093
Tel (410) 453-9553 *SIC* 8322 8093

▲ MEDIFAST INC p 938
3600 Crondall Ln, Owings Mills MD 21117
Tel (410) 581-8042 *SIC* 2099 2023 8093

BAY COVE HUMAN SERVICES INC p 160
66 Canal St, Boston MA 02114
Tel (617) 371-3000 *SIC* 8052 8093 8361

HEALTH & EDUCATION SERVICES INC p 673
199 Rosewood Dr Ste 250, Danvers MA 01923
Tel (978) 921-1293 *SIC* 8093

VALLEY HEALTH SYSTEMS INC p 1540
575 Beech St, Holyoke MA 01040
Tel (413) 534-2500
SIC 8082 8093 8399 8741 8721

LYNN COMMUNITY HEALTH INC p 888
269 Union St, Lynn MA 01901
Tel (781) 581-3900 *SIC* 8093

BRIDGEWELL INC p 212
471 Broadway, Lynnfield MA 01940
Tel (781) 599-4240 *SIC* 8361 8093

SAINT LUKES HOSPITAL OF NEW BEDFORD INC p 1270
101 Page St, New Bedford MA 02740
Tel (508) 997-1515 *SIC* 8062 8082 8093

BEHAVIORAL HEALTH NETWORK INC p 168
417 Liberty St Ste 1, Springfield MA 01104
Tel (413) 747-0705 *SIC* 8093 8322

CEREBRAL PALSY OF MASSACHUSETTS INC p 283
600 Technology Center Dr, Stoughton MA 02072
Tel (800) 924-7570 *SIC* 8093

SPECTRUM HEALTH SYSTEMS INC p 1357
10 Mechanic St Ste 302, Worcester MA 01608
Tel (508) 792-1508 *SIC* 8361 8093

MACOMB OAKLAND REGIONAL CENTER INC p 893
16200 19 Mile Rd, Clinton Township MI 48038
Tel (586) 263-8700 *SIC* 8093

BARBARA ANN KARMANOS CANCER INSTITUTE p 154
4100 John R St, Detroit MI 48201
Tel (800) 527-6266 *SIC* 8733 8093

■ VHS DETROIT RECEIVING HOSPITAL INC p 1553
4201 Saint Antoine St, Detroit MI 48201
Tel (313) 745-3000 *SIC* 8093 8069 8062

ENCORE REHABILITATION SERVICES LLC p 496
33533 W 12 Mile Rd # 290, Farmington Hills MI 48331
Tel (248) 865-1177 *SIC* 8093 8049

MARY FREE BED REHABILITATION HOSPITAL p 914
235 Wealthy St Se, Grand Rapids MI 49503
Tel (616) 242-0300 *SIC* 8069 8093

ST MARYS DULUTH CLINIC HEALTH SYSTEM p 1371
400 E 3rd St, Duluth MN 55805
Tel (218) 786-8364 *SIC* 8093 8011 8062

FORREST GENERAL HOSPITAL p 568
1414 S 28th Ave, Hattiesburg MS 39402
Tel (601) 288-2500 *SIC* 8082 8093

ST DOMINIC HEALTH SERVICES INC p 1366
969 Lakeland Dr, Jackson MS 39216
Tel (601) 200-2000
SIC 8741 8093 8069 8062

ST MARYS REGIONAL REHAB CENTER p 1372
201 Nw R D Mize Rd, Blue Springs MO 64014
Tel (816) 228-5900 SIC 8093

COMPASS HEALTH INC p 351
1800 Community, Clinton MO 64735
Tel (660) 885-8131
SIC 8011 8069 8093 8361

■ POPLAR BLUFF REGIONAL MEDICAL CENTER p 1161
3100 Oak Grove Rd, Poplar Bluff MO 63901
Tel (573) 686-4111 SIC 8093

■ REHABCARE HOSPITAL HOLDINGS LLC p 1220
7733 Forsyth Blvd # 2300, Saint Louis MO 63105
Tel (800) 677-1238 SIC 8093

REHABILITATION THERAPIST p 1220
1500 Koenigstein Ave, Norfolk NE 68701
Tel (402) 644-7396 SIC 8093

■ SIERRA HEALTH SERVICES INC p 1320
2720 N Tenaya Way, Las Vegas NV 89128
Tel (702) 242-7000
SIC 6324 6311 8082 8741 8093

■ NORTHERN NEVADA MEDICAL CENTER LP p 1056
2375 E Prater Way, Sparks NV 89434
Tel (775) 331-7000
SIC 8062 8093 8071 8049 8011

CAPITAL REGION HEALTH CARE CORP p 250
250 Pleasant St, Concord NH 03301
Tel (603) 225-2711
SIC 8741 8062 8051 8093 8082

J F K JOHNSON REHABILITION INSTITUTE p 771
65 James St, Edison NJ 08820
Tel (732) 321-7070 SIC 8093

CHILDRENS SPECIALIZED HOSPITAL INC p 300
150 New Providence Rd # 1, Mountainside NJ 07092
Tel (888) 244-5373 SIC 8069 8093

YOUTH CONSULTATION SERVICE (INC) p 1639
284 Broadway, Newark NJ 07104
Tel (973) 482-2774 SIC 8093 8361 8211

WARREN ST LUKES HOSPITAL INC p 1577
185 Roseberry St, Phillipsburg NJ 08865
Tel (908) 859-6700 SIC 8062 8093

RIVERVIEW MEDICAL HOSPITAL p 1238
1 Riverview Plz, Red Bank NJ 07701
Tel (732) 741-2700 SIC 8093

SOMERSET HEALTH CARE CORP p 1339
110 Rehill Ave, Somerville NJ 08876
Tel (908) 685-2200 SIC 8093 8011

■ KESSLER INSTITUTE FOR REHABILITATION INC p 814
1199 Pleasant Valley Way, West Orange NJ 07052
Tel (973) 731-3600 SIC 8069 8093

GILA REGIONAL MEDICAL CENTER p 611
1313 E 32nd St, Silver City NM 88061
Tel (575) 538-4000 SIC 8093 8062

CENTER FOR DISABILITY SERVICES INC p 275
314 S Manning Blvd, Albany NY 12208
Tel (518) 437-5506
SIC 8351 8093 8361 8099

SAMARITAN DAYTOP VILLAGE INC p 1274
13802 Queens Blvd Fl 1, Briarwood NY 11435
Tel (718) 206-2000 SIC 8322 8093

PSCH INC p 1188
14202 20th Ave Rm 301, Flushing NY 11351
Tel (718) 559-0516 SIC 8361 8331 8093

NASSAU ASSOCIATION FOR HELP OF RETARDED CHILDREN INC p 1008
189 Wheatley Rd, Glen Head NY 11545
Tel (516) 626-1000 SIC 8093 8322

RESOURCE CENTER p 1227
200 Dunham Ave, Jamestown NY 14701
Tel (716) 661-4829
SIC 8093 6513 6512 8052

WOMANS CHRISTIAN ASSOCIATION OF JAMESTOWN N Y p 1621
207 Foote Ave, Jamestown NY 14701
Tel (716) 487-0141
SIC 8062 8063 8093 8069

■ WEIGHT WATCHERS NORTH AMERICA INC p 1588
300 Jericho Quadrangle # 350, Jericho NY 11753
Tel (516) 390-1400 SIC 8093

UTOPIA HOME CARE INC p 1537
60 E Main St, Kings Park NY 11754
Tel (631) 544-6005 SIC 8082 8093

NYSARC INC p 1069
29 British American Blvd # 2, Latham NY 12110
Tel (518) 439-8311
SIC 8361 8322 8093 8331

ATC STAFFING SERVICES INC p 124
1983 Marcus Ave Ste E122, New Hyde Park NY 11042
Tel (516) 326-1396 SIC 7361 8093 8011

FEDCAP REHABILITATION SERVICES INC p 533
633 3rd Ave Fl 6, New York NY 10017
Tel (212) 727-4200 SIC 8093

NEW YORK CITY HEALTH AND HOSPITALS CORP p 1034
125 Worth St Rm 514, New York NY 10013
Tel (212) 788-3321 SIC 8062 8069 8093

PLANNED PARENTHOOD FEDERATION OF AMERICA INC p 1154
123 William St Fl 10, New York NY 10038
Tel (212) 541-7800 SIC 8093

THERACARE OF NEW YORK INC p 1447
116 W 32nd St Fl 8, New York NY 10001
Tel (212) 564-2350 SIC 8093 7361

INTEGRAMED AMERICA INC p 749
2 Manhattanville Rd, Purchase NY 10577
Tel (914) 253-8000 SIC 8093

HILLSIDE FAMILY OF AGENCIES p 694
1183 Monroe Ave, Rochester NY 14620
Tel (585) 256-7500 SIC 8361 8322 8093

ROCHESTER GENERAL HEALTH SYSTEM p 1243
1425 Portland Ave, Rochester NY 14621
Tel (585) 922-4000 SIC 8741 8093 8059

COMMUNITY CAREPARTNERS INC p 347
68 Sweeten Creek Rd, Asheville NC 28803
Tel (828) 274-2400 SIC 8322 8093

MEDCATH INC p 935
10800 Sikes Pl Ste 200, Charlotte NC 28277
Tel (704) 815-7700 SIC 8069 8093 8742

CAROMONT HEALTH INC p 259
2525 Court Dr, Gastonia NC 28054
Tel (704) 834-2000 SIC 8741 8093

CARTERET COUNTY GENERAL HOSPITAL CORP p 262
3500 Arendell St, Morehead City NC 28557
Tel (252) 808-6000 SIC 8093 8062

FIRSTHEALTH OF CAROLINAS INC p 550
155 Memorial Dr, Pinehurst NC 28374
Tel (910) 715-1000
SIC 8062 8093 8051 8021 7991 7219

COASTAL REHABILITATION HOSPITAL p 332
2131 S 17th St, Wilmington NC 28401
Tel (910) 343-7845 SIC 8093

INNOVIS HEALTH LLC p 745
1702 University Dr S, Fargo ND 58103
Tel (701) 364-8000 SIC 8093

NCS HEALTHCARE INC p 1022
3201 Entp Pkwy Ste 220, Cleveland OH 44122
Tel (216) 514-3350
SIC 5122 8093 8049 8082 8742 5912

CHI HEALTH AT HOME p 296
1700 Edison Dr Ste 300, Milford OH 45150
Tel (513) 576-0262 SIC 7363 8093

▲ FOUNDATION HEALTHCARE INC p 571
13900 N Portland Ave # 200, Oklahoma City OK 73134
Tel (405) 608-1700 SIC 8062 8011 8093

HEALTHCARE PARTNERS INVESTMENTS LLC p 676
14024 Quail Pointe Dr, Oklahoma City OK 73134
Tel (405) 424-6677 SIC 8093

ALBERTINA KERR CENTERS p 46
424 Ne 22nd Ave, Portland OR 97232
Tel (503) 239-8101 SIC 8052 8361 8093

CASCADIA BEHAVIORAL HEALTHCARE INC p 263
847 Ne 19th Ave Ste 100, Portland OR 97232
Tel (503) 238-0769
SIC 8322 8093 8063 8361

AVAMERE HEALTH SERVICES LLC p 136
25115 Sw Parkway Ave A, Wilsonville OR 97070
Tel (503) 570-3405
SIC 8741 8051 8052 8093

GOOD SHEPHERD REHABILITATION HOSPITAL INC p 623
850 S 5th St, Allentown PA 18103
Tel (610) 776-3100
SIC 8361 8051 8093 8069

ALLIED SERVICES FOUNDATION INC p 57
100 Abington Executive Pa, Clarks Summit PA 18411
Tel (570) 348-1407 SIC 8093 8361

DUBOIS REGIONAL MEDICAL CENTER INC p 459
100 Hospital Ave, Du Bois PA 15801
Tel (814) 371-2200 SIC 8093 8011

PHYSIOTHERAPY ASSOCIATES INC p 1146
855 Springdale Dr Ste 200, Exton PA 19341
Tel (610) 644-7824 SIC 8049 8093

EXCELA HEALTH HOLDING CO INC p 516
532 W Pittsburgh St, Greensburg PA 15601
Tel (724) 832-4000
SIC 8062 8093 5999 7363 7322 8361

■ GENESIS ELDER CARE REHABILITATION SERVICES INC p 602
101 E State St, Kennett Square PA 19348
Tel (610) 925-4598 SIC 8049 8093

PROMPTCARE COMPANIES INC p 1183
741 3rd Ave, King Of Prussia PA 19406
Tel (610) 278-1623 SIC 8093

▲ UNIVERSAL HEALTH SERVICES INC p 1517
367 S Gulph Rd, King Of Prussia PA 19406
Tel (610) 768-3300
SIC 8062 8063 8093 8011 8741

NHS HUMAN SERVICES INC p 1042
620 Germantown Pike, Lafayette Hill PA 19444
Tel (610) 260-4600 SIC 8093 8059 8082

▲ BIOTELEMETRY INC p 184
1000 Cedar Hollow Rd, Malvern PA 19355
Tel (610) 729-7000 SIC 3845 8093

■ SELECT MEDICAL CORP p 1301
4714 Gettysburg Rd, Mechanicsburg PA 17055
Tel (717) 972-1100 SIC 8093 8051 8069

▲ SELECT MEDICAL HOLDINGS CORP p 1301
4714 Gettysburg Rd, Mechanicsburg PA 17055
Tel (717) 972-1100 SIC 8093 8069

COMMUNITY SERVICES GROUP INC p 350
320 Highland Dr, Mountville PA 17554
Tel (717) 285-7121 SIC 8093 8059

GAUDENZIA INC p 594
106 W Main St, Norristown PA 19401
Tel (610) 239-9600 SIC 8361 8093

HORIZON HOUSE INC p 707
120 S 30th St, Philadelphia PA 19104
Tel (215) 386-3838
SIC 8361 6512 8322 8093

RESOURCES FOR HUMAN DEVELOPMENT INC p 1227
4700 Wphickon Ave Ste 126, Philadelphia PA 19144
Tel (215) 951-0300
SIC 8322 8093 8052 8331 8361

MERCY LIFE CENTER CORP p 947
1200 Reedsdale St Ste 1, Pittsburgh PA 15233
Tel (412) 323-8026 SIC 8093

READING HEALTH SYSTEM p 1213
6th Ave And Spruce St, Reading PA 19611
Tel (610) 988-8000
SIC 8062 6512 8093 8721 8011 7219

CARE NEW ENGLAND HEALTH SYSTEM INC p 254
45 Willard Ave, Providence RI 02905
Tel (401) 453-7900
SIC 8063 8062 8069 8093 8082

UCI MEDICAL AFFILIATES INC p 1499
1818 Henderson St, Columbia SC 29201
Tel (803) 782-4278 SIC 8093 8741

▲ AAC HOLDINGS INC p 8
200 Powell Pl, Brentwood TN 37027
Tel (615) 732-1231 SIC 8093

▲ ACADIA HEALTHCARE CO INC p 13
6100 Tower Cir Ste 1000, Franklin TN 37067
Tel (615) 861-6000 SIC 8093

FRONTIER HEALTH p 581
1167 Spratlin Park Dr, Gray TN 37615
Tel (423) 467-3600 SIC 8093 8322

COVENANT HEALTHCARE INC p 384
1451 Bowell Springs Blvd, Knoxville TN 37909
Tel (865) 970-9800 SIC 8093

■ ACCREDO HEALTH GROUP INC p 15
1640 Century Center Pkwy # 110, Memphis TN 38134
Tel (877) 222-7336 SIC 8051 8052 8093

■ BASIC AMERICAN MEDICAL INC p 158
1 Park Plz, Nashville TN 37203
Tel (615) 344-9551 SIC 5912 2599 8093

CENTERSTONE OF TENNESSEE INC p 277
44 Vantage Way, Nashville TN 37228
Tel (615) 463-6610 SIC 8093

■ HCA HEALTH SERVICES OF FLORIDA INC p 671
1 Park Plz, Nashville TN 37203
Tel (615) 344-9551 SIC 8062 8093

■ HCA INC p 672
1 Park Plz, Nashville TN 37203
Tel (615) 344-9551
SIC 8063 8062 8069 8093

HERCULES HOLDING II LLC p 685
1 Park Plz, Nashville TN 37203
Tel (615) 344-9551
SIC 8062 8063 8069 8093

SYMBION HOLDINGS CORP p 1414
40 Burton Hills Blvd # 500, Nashville TN 37215
Tel (615) 234-5900 SIC 8011 8093 8062

SYMBION INC p 1414
40 Burton Hills Blvd # 500, Nashville TN 37215
Tel (615) 234-5900 SIC 8011 8093 8062

■ ARMC LP p 111
6250 Highway 83 84, Abilene TX 79606
Tel (325) 428-1000
SIC 8062 8093 8011 7991

■ CONCENTRA HEALTH SERVICES INC p 354
5080 Spectrum Dr Ste 400w, Addison TX 75001
Tel (972) 364-8000 SIC 8093 8011

■ CONCENTRA OPERATING CORP p 354
5080 Spectrum Dr Ste 400w, Addison TX 75001
Tel (972) 364-8000 SIC 8093

HANGER INC p 657
10910 Domain Dr Ste 300, Austin TX 78758
Tel (512) 777-3800 SIC 8093 5047 3842

■ BAY AREA HEALTHCARE GROUP LTD p 160
3315 S Alameda St, Corpus Christi TX 78411
Tel (361) 761-1400
SIC 8062 8063 8069 8093

BHG HOLDINGS LLC p 180
5001 Spring Valley Rd 600e, Dallas TX 75244
Tel (214) 365-6100 SIC 8093

MENTAL HEALTH MENTAL RETARDATION OF TARRANT COUNTY p 943
3840 Hulen St, Fort Worth TX 76107
Tel (817) 569-4300 SIC 8093 8322 8361

BAYLOR MEDICAL CENTER AT GARLAND p 162
2300 Marie Curie Dr, Garland TX 75042
Tel (972) 487-5000
SIC 8062 8082 8011 8093

LEGACY COMMUNITY HEALTH SERVICES INC p 852
1415 California St, Houston TX 77006
Tel (713) 830-3000 SIC 8093 8011

MEMORIAL HERMANN HEALTH SYSTEM p 941
909 Frostwood Dr Fl 2, Houston TX 77024
Tel (713) 242-3000 SIC 8062 8093

■ HORIZON HEALTH CORP p 707
1965 Lakepointe Dr # 100, Lewisville TX 75057
Tel (972) 420-8200 SIC 8093 8069

GOLDEN LIVING LLC p 621
5220 Tennyson Pkwy # 400, Plano TX 75024
Tel (972) 372-6300
SIC 8051 8082 8731 8093

OUTREACH HEALTH CARE INC p 1099
269 W Renner Rd, Richardson TX 75080
Tel (972) 840-7360 SIC 8093 8049 8082

BEXAR COUNTY BOARD OF TRUSTEES FOR MENTAL HEALTH MENTAL RETARDATION p 179
3031 W Interstate 10, San Antonio TX 78201
Tel (210) 261-1000 SIC 8361 8093

DISABILITY SERVICES OF SOUTHWEST INC p 442
6243 W Interstate 10 # 395, San Antonio TX 78201
Tel (210) 798-0123 SIC 8093

■ US ONCOLOGY HOLDINGS INC p 1532
10101 Woodloch Forest Dr, The Woodlands TX 77380
Tel (281) 863-1000 SIC 8093 8099 8011

■ US ONCOLOGY INC p 1532
10101 Woodloch Forest Dr, The Woodlands TX 77380
Tel (800) 381-2637 SIC 8093 8099 8011

VERNON HOME HEALTH CARE AGENCY INC p 1551
2733 Midwestern Pkwy # 120, Wichita Falls TX 76308
Tel (972) 840-3401 SIC 8093 8049 8082

VALLEY MENTAL HEALTH INC p 1541
5965 S 900 E, Salt Lake City UT 84121
Tel (801) 263-7100 SIC 8093

IHC HEALTH SERVICES INC p 730
1380 E Medical Center Dr, St George UT 84790
Tel (801) 442-5000
SIC 8062 8011 8322 8049 8093 8069

VIRGINIA HOSPITAL CENTER ARLINGTON HEALTH SYSTEM p 1559
1701 N George Mason Dr, Arlington VA 22205
Tel (703) 558-5000 SIC 8093

■ DANVILLE REGIONAL MEDICAL CENTER p 412
142 S Main St, Danville VA 24541
Tel (434) 799-2100
SIC 8062 8011 8093 8069 8051

INOVA HEALTH CARE SERVICES p 745
8110 Gatehouse Rd 200e, Falls Church VA 22042
Tel (703) 289-2000 SIC 8062 8093

■ PATHWAYS HEALTH AND COMMUNITY SUPPORT LLC p 1120
10304 Spotsylvania Ave, Fredericksburg VA 22408
Tel (540) 710-6085 SIC 8093

■ MAGELLAN MEDICAID ADMINISTRATION INC p 895
11013 W Broad St Ste 500, Glen Allen VA 23060
Tel (804) 548-0100
SIC 7374 8093 6411 8741

SENTARA MEDICAL GROUP p 1305
835 Glenrock Rd, Norfolk VA 23502
Tel (757) 252-3070 SIC 8093 8082

■ HCA HEALTH SERVICES OF VIRGINIA INC p 672
1602 Skipwith Rd, Richmond VA 23229
Tel (804) 289-4500 SIC 8062 8093

MHM SERVICES INC p 959
1593 Spring Hill Rd # 600, Vienna VA 22182
Tel (703) 749-4600 SIC 8093 8361

GROUP HEALTH COOPERATIVE p 641
320 Westlake Ave N # 100, Seattle WA 98109
Tel (206) 448-4141
SIC 6324 5999 8093 6321

SEA-MAR COMMUNITY HEALTH CENTER p 1295
1040 S Henderson St, Seattle WA 98108
Tel (206) 763-5277
SIC 8322 8082 8093 8051

MULTICARE HEALTH SYSTEM p 999
316 M L King Jr Way # 314, Tacoma WA 98405
Tel (253) 403-1000 SIC 8062 8093 8069

YAKIMA VALLEY FARM WORKERS CLINIC INC p 1634
518 W 1st Ave, Toppenish WA 98948
Tel (509) 865-5898
SIC 8011 8021 8093 1799

SIC 8099 Health & Allied Svcs, NEC

■ HEALTHSOUTH HOME HEALTH CORP p 677
3660 Grandview Pkwy, Birmingham AL 35243
Tel (205) 967-7116 SIC 8082 8099

■ HEALTHSOUTH HOME HEALTH HOLDINGS INC p 677
3660 Grandview Pkwy, Birmingham AL 35243
Tel (205) 967-7116 SIC 8099 8082 6719

NEA - ALASKA HEALTH PLAN TRUST FUND p 1022
4003 Iowa Dr, Anchorage AK 99517
Tel (907) 274-7526 SIC 8099

SHELL MEDICAL PLAN p 1314
P.O. Box 53456, Phoenix AZ 85072
Tel (800) 352-3705 SIC 8099

BLOOD SYSTEMS INC p 189
6210 E Oak St, Scottsdale AZ 85257
Tel (480) 946-4201 SIC 8099

CREATIVE TESTING SOLUTIONS p 390
2424 W Erie Dr, Tempe AZ 85282
Tel (602) 343-7000 SIC 8099

AAH MEDICAL LLC p 8
2051 W 25th St, Yuma AZ 85364
Tel (928) 344-1411 SIC 8099

ST VINCENT HEALTH SERVICES INC p 1373
2 Saint Vincent Cir, Little Rock AR 72205
Tel (501) 552-2620 SIC 8062 8099

MILLS PENINSULA HOSPITAL INC p 971
1635 Rollins Rd, Burlingame CA 94010
Tel (650) 652-3807 SIC 8099

GLANBIA NUTRITIONALS (NA) INC p 614
2840 Loker Ave E Ste 100, Carlsbad CA 92010
Tel (760) 438-0089 SIC 5169 2833 8099

ELITE ONE SOURCE NUTRISCIENCES INC p 487
13840 Magnolia Ave, Chino CA 91710
Tel (909) 902-5005 SIC 8049 8099 3999

ALTAMED HEALTH SERVICES CORP p 62
2040 Camfield Ave, Commerce CA 90040
Tel (323) 725-8751 SIC 8011 8099

■ CRC HEALTH CORP p 389
20400 Stevens Creek Blvd, Cupertino CA 95014
Tel (877) 272-8668
SIC 8069 8099 8322 8093

■ CRC HEALTH GROUP INC p 389
20400 Stev Creek Blvd 6, Cupertino CA 95014
Tel (877) 272-8668 SIC 8099

CHIRON CORP p 301
4560 Horton St, Emeryville CA 94608
Tel (510) 655-8730 SIC 8099

LABOR HEALTH & WEL TR FNDNE CA p 836
220 Campus Ln, Fairfield CA 94534
Tel (707) 864-2800 SIC 8099

INNOVATION INSTITUTE LLC p 744
1 Centerpointe Dr Ste 200, La Palma CA 90623
Tel (714) 735-3750 SIC 8099

SADDLEBACK MEMORIAL MEDICAL CENTER p 1265
24451 Health Center Dr, Laguna Hills CA 92653
Tel (949) 837-4500
SIC 8062 8011 8093 8099 8071 8069

SCAN HEALTH PLAN ARIZONA p 1286
3800 Kilroy Airport Way # 100, Long Beach CA 90806
Tel (602) 778-3300 SIC 8099

BIOMAT USA INC p 184
2410 Lillyvale Ave, Los Angeles CA 90032
Tel (323) 225-2221 SIC 8099

LOS ANGELES COUNTY DEVELOPMENTAL SERVICES FOUNDATION p 878
3303 Wilshire Blvd # 700, Los Angeles CA 90010
Tel (213) 383-1300 SIC 8099 8322 8093

BLOODSOURCE INC p 189
10536 Peter A Mccuen Blvd, Mather CA 95655
Tel (916) 456-1500 SIC 8099

FACEY MEDICAL FOUNDATION p 523
15451 San Fernando Msn, Mission Hills CA 91345
Tel (818) 365-9531 SIC 8099

KAISER FDN HEALTH PLAN OF COLORADO p 800
1 Kaiser Plz Ste 15l, Oakland CA 94612
Tel (510) 271-6611 SIC 8099

LA CLINICA DE LA RAZA INC p 835
1450 Fruitvale Ave Fl 3, Oakland CA 94601
Tel (510) 535-4000 SIC 8099

PERMANENTE MEDICAL GROUP INC p 1136
1950 Franklin St Fl 18th, Oakland CA 94612
Tel (866) 858-2226 SIC 8099

DIGNITY HEALTH MEDICAL FOUNDATION p 439
3400 Data Dr, Rancho Cordova CA 95670
Tel (916) 379-2840 SIC 8099

SR MARY PHILIPPA HEALTH CENTER p 1362
2235 Hayes St Fl 5, San Francisco CA 94117
Tel (415) 750-5500 SIC 8099

■ **MANAGED HEALTH NETWORK** p 900
2370 Kerner Blvd, San Rafael CA 94901
Tel (415) 460-8168
SIC 6324 8099 8093 8011

PRIME HEALTHCARE SERVICESFOUNDATION p 1175
16716 Bear Valley Rd, Victorville CA 92395
Tel (760) 241-1200 SIC 8099

■ **UNIVERSAL HEALTH SERVICES OF RANCHO SPRINGS INC** p 1517
36485 Inland Valley Dr, Wildomar CA 92595
Tel (951) 677-9712 SIC 8099 8062 8011

BRIGHTON COMMUNITY HOSPITAL ASSOCIATION p 213
1600 Prairie Center Pkwy, Brighton CO 80601
Tel (303) 498-1600 SIC 8099

SAINT JOHNS HEALTH CTR D6 p 1269
500 Eldorado Blvd # 6300, Broomfield CO 80021
Tel (913) 895-2800 SIC 8099

■ **ROSE MEDICAL GROUP** p 1250
4900 S Monaco St Ste 204, Denver CO 80237
Tel (303) 320-2101 SIC 8062 8011 8099

BEHAVORIAL HEALTHCARE INC p 168
155 Inverness Dr W, Englewood CO 80112
Tel (720) 490-4400 SIC 8099

WELLDYNE INC p 1589
7472 S Tucson Way Ste 100, Englewood CO 80112
Tel (888) 479-2000 SIC 8099

EAGLE GROUP INC p 468
100 Industrial Blvd, Clayton DE 19938
Tel (302) 653-3000 SIC 3589 8099

NANTICOKE HEALTH SERVICES INC p 1007
801 Middleford Rd, Seaford DE 19973
Tel (302) 629-6611 SIC 8099

ELIZABETH GLASER PEDIATRIC AIDS FOUNDATION p 487
1140 Conn Ave Nw Ste 200, Washington DC 20036
Tel (310) 314-1459 SIC 8099 8733

UNITY HEALTH CARE INC p 1515
1220 12th St Se Ste 120, Washington DC 20003
Tel (202) 715-7901 SIC 8099

BRRH CORP p 220
800 Meadows Rd, Boca Raton FL 33486
Tel (561) 395-7100 SIC 8062 8082 8099

SCRIBEAMERICA LLC p 1294
1200 E Las Olas Blvd # 201, Fort Lauderdale FL 33301
Tel (786) 279-1057 SIC 8099

LEE MEMORIAL WOMENS HEALTH PRO p 851
4761 S Cleveland Ave, Fort Myers FL 33907
Tel (239) 343-9734 SIC 8099

ST JOSEPHS HOSPITAL-NORTH p 1369
4211 Van Dyke Rd, Lutz FL 33558
Tel (813) 443-7000 SIC 8099

PSA HEALTHCARE p 1188
760 North Dr Ste D, Melbourne FL 32934
Tel (321) 254-4254 SIC 8099

ARMOR CORRECTIONAL HEALTH SERVICES INC p 111
4960 Sw 72nd Ave Ste 400, Miami FL 33155
Tel (305) 662-8522 SIC 8099

FLORIDAS BLOOD CENTERS INC p 560
8669 Commodity Cir Lbby, Orlando FL 32819
Tel (407) 226-3800 SIC 8099

ONEBLOOD FOUNDATION INC p 1087
8669 Commodity Cir, Orlando FL 32819
Tel (407) 248-5480 SIC 8099

ONEBLOOD INC p 1087
8669 Commodity Cir, Orlando FL 32819
Tel (407) 455-7551 SIC 8099

BROADSPIRE SERVICES INC p 215
1391 Nw 136th Ave, Sunrise FL 33323
Tel (954) 452-4000 SIC 8099 6331

INTEGRAL HEALTH PLAN INC p 748
4631 Woodland Corp Blvd, Tampa FL 33614
Tel (866) 258-4326 SIC 8099

LIFELINK FOUNDATION INC p 864
9661 Delaney Creek Blvd, Tampa FL 33619
Tel (813) 253-2640 SIC 8099

WATERMARK MEDICAL HOLDINGS INC p 1582
1641 Worthington Rd # 320, West Palm Beach FL 33409
Tel (561) 283-1191 SIC 8099

JACKSON HEALTHCARE STAFFING HOLDINGS LLC p 774
2655 Northwinds Pkwy, Alpharetta GA 30009
Tel (770) 643-5500 SIC 8099

MQ ASSOCIATES INC p 996
3480 Preston Ridge Rd # 600, Alpharetta GA 30005
Tel (770) 300-0101 SIC 8099

■ **ALERE HEALTH LLC** p 48
3200 Windy Hill Rd Se 100b, Atlanta GA 30339
Tel (770) 767-4500 SIC 8099

EXAMWORKS GROUP INC p 516
3280 Peachtree Rd Ne # 2625, Atlanta GA 30305
Tel (404) 952-2400 SIC 8099

MORRISON MANAGEMENT SPECIALISTS INC p 990
5801 Pachtree Dunwoody Rd, Atlanta GA 30342
Tel (404) 845-3330 SIC 8099

CARESOUTH HEALTH SYSTEM INC p 255
1 10th St Ste 500, Augusta GA 30901
Tel (706) 855-5533 SIC 8099

CRAWFORD & CO p 389
1001 Summit Blvd Ste 500, Brookhaven GA 30319
Tel (404) 300-1000
SIC 6411 8111 8099 6331

GLOBAL HEALTH SOLUTIONS INC p 616
325 Swanton Way, Decatur GA 30030
Tel (404) 592-1430 SIC 8099

MEDICAL CEN p 936
691 Cherry St Fl 5, Macon GA 31201
Tel (478) 633-6831 SIC 8099

MEADOWS HEALTHCARE ALLIANCE INC p 934
1 Meadows Pkwy, Vidalia GA 30474
Tel (912) 538-5866 SIC 8099 8062

SOUTHERN ILLINOIS HEALTHCARE E p 1348
2370 N Mcroy Dr, Carbondale IL 62901
Tel (618) 457-5200 SIC 8099

AMERICAN HOSPITAL ASSOCIATION p 74
155 N Wacker Dr Ste 400, Chicago IL 60606
Tel (312) 422-3000 SIC 2721 2731 8099

AVIV HEALTHCARE PROPERTIES LIMITED PARTNERSHIP p 138
303 W Madison St, Chicago IL 60606
Tel (312) 855-0930 SIC 8099

HEALTHCARE INFORMATION AND MANAGEMENT SYSTEMS SOCIETY p 676
33 W Monroe St Ste 1700, Chicago IL 60603
Tel (312) 664-4467 SIC 8099

NORTHWESTERN MEMORIAL HEALTHCARE p 1060
251 E Huron St Ste 3-710, Chicago IL 60611
Tel (312) 926-2000
SIC 8082 6513 7389 8099

EDWARD MEDICAL GROUP p 480
16151 Weber Rd Ste 201, Crest Hill IL 60403
Tel (815) 773-7827 SIC 8099

TRUSTMARK MUTUAL HOLDING CO p 1488
400 N Field Dr, Lake Forest IL 60045
Tel (847) 615-1500 SIC 7991 8099

MEDCOR INC p 935
4805 Prime Pkwy, Mchenry IL 60050
Tel (815) 363-9500 SIC 8099

■ **CAREMARK INTERNATIONAL LLC** p 255
2211 Sanders Rd, Northbrook IL 60062
Tel (847) 559-4700
SIC 5961 6411 8099 8092 8093

■ **CAREMARK LLC** p 255
2211 Sanders Rd, Northbrook IL 60062
Tel (847) 559-4700
SIC 5961 6411 8099 8092 8093 8742

■ **GREATER PEORIA SPECIALTY HOSPITAL LLC** p 635
500 W Romeo B Garrett Ave, Peoria IL 61605
Tel (309) 680-1500 SIC 8062 8099

ROCKFORD MEMORIAL HOSPITAL p 1244
2400 N Rockton Ave, Rockford IL 61103
Tel (815) 971-5000
SIC 8062 8011 8071 8099

SWEDISHAMERICAN HEALTH SYSTEM CORP p 1411
1401 E State St, Rockford IL 61104
Tel (815) 968-4400
SIC 8743 6512 8742 8099 8082 8062

LIFEWATCH CORP p 865
10255 W Higgins Rd # 100, Rosemont IL 60018
Tel (847) 720-2100 SIC 8099 5047 3845

LIFEWATCH SERVICES INC p 865
10255 W Higgins Rd # 100, Rosemont IL 60018
Tel (847) 720-2100
SIC 5047 8099 3845 8071

INTERACTIVE HEALTH HOLDINGS CORP p 751
1700 E Golf Rd Ste 900, Schaumburg IL 60173
Tel (847) 590-0200 SIC 8099

INTERACTIVE HEALTH SOLUTIONS INC p 751
1700 E Golf Rd Ste 900, Schaumburg IL 60173
Tel (866) 279-1636 SIC 8099

CARLE HEALTH CARE INC p 257
611 W Park St, Urbana IL 61801
Tel (217) 383-3206 SIC 8099

■ **ST JOSEPH HEALTH SYSTEM LLC** p 1368
700 Broadway, Fort Wayne IN 46802
Tel (260) 425-3000 SIC 8099

ESKENAZI HEALTH CENTER INC p 509
720 Eskenazi Ave Fl 2, Indianapolis IN 46202
Tel (317) 880-0000 SIC 8062 8093 8099

MAGNOLIA HEALTH SYSTEMS INC p 896
9480 Prority W Dr, Indianapolis IN 46240
Tel (317) 818-1240 SIC 8099

■ **NATIONAL GOVERNMENT SERVICES INC** p 1012
8115 Knue Rd, Indianapolis IN 46250
Tel (317) 841-4400 SIC 8099

SAINT JOSEPH HEALTH SYSTEM INC p 1269
1 Saint Joseph Dr, Lexington KY 40504
Tel (859) 313-1000 SIC 8062 8099 8011

KENTUCKYONE HEALTH INC p 813
200 Abraham Flexner Way, Louisville KY 40202
Tel (502) 587-4011 SIC 8099

KENTUCKYONE HEALTH MEDICAL GRO p 813
100 E Liberty St Ste 100, Louisville KY 40202
Tel (502) 315-1458 SIC 8099

RECOVERCARE LLC p 1215
1920 Stanley Gault Pkwy # 100, Louisville KY 40223
Tel (502) 489-9449 SIC 5047 8099

■ **REHABCARE GROUP INC** p 1220
680 S 4th St, Louisville KY 40202
Tel (502) 596-7300
SIC 8093 8099 8049 8051

OCHSNER MEDICAL CENTER - KENNER LLC p 1073
180 W Esplanade Ave, Kenner LA 70065
Tel (504) 468-8600 SIC 8062 8099

OCHSNER HEALTH SYSTEM p 1073
1516 Jefferson Hwy, New Orleans LA 70121
Tel (504) 842-3483 SIC 8099

ST JOSEPH HEALTHCARE FOUNDATION INC p 1368
360 Broadway, Bangor ME 04401
Tel (207) 907-1000 SIC 8099

HENRY M JACKSON FOUNDATION FOR ADVANCEMENT OF MILITARY MEDICINE INC p 684
6720a Rockledge Dr # 100, Bethesda MD 20817
Tel (240) 694-2000 SIC 8099

MAXIM HEALTH SYSTEMS LLC p 922
7227 Lee Deforest Dr, Columbia MD 21046
Tel (410) 910-1500 SIC 8011 8099

TRANSIT EMPLOYEE HEALTH & WELFARE PLAN p 1472
2701 Whitney Pl Ste B, Forestville MD 20747
Tel (301) 568-2294 SIC 8099

BON SECOURS HEALTH SYSTEM INC p 199
1505 Marriottsville Rd, Marriottsville MD 21104
Tel (410) 442-5511 SIC 8062 8099

ATRIUS HEALTH INC p 129
275 Grove St Ste 3-300, Auburndale MA 02466
Tel (617) 559-8000 SIC 8099 8062

COMMONWEALTH CARE ALLIANCE INC p 346
30 Winter St Fl 12, Boston MA 02108
Tel (617) 426-0600 SIC 8099 8011

NSMC HEALTHCARE INC p 1065
81 Highland Ave, Salem MA 01970
Tel (978) 354-2575 SIC 8099

BAYSTATE MEDICAL PRACTICES INC p 162
759 Chestnut St, Springfield MA 01199
Tel (413) 794-0000 SIC 8099

CARELINK NETWORK INC p 255
1333 Brewery Park Blvd, Detroit MI 48207
Tel (313) 656-0000 SIC 8099

HEALTH ALLIANCE PLAN OF MICHIGAN p 674
2850 W Grand Blvd, Detroit MI 48202
Tel (313) 872-8100 SIC 6324 8011 8099

MICHIGAN HEALTH ENDOWMENT FUND p 961
330 Marshall St Ste 200, Lansing MI 48912
Tel (517) 374-0031 SIC 8099

■ **SUMMIT HEALTH INC** p 1399
27175 Haggerty Rd, Novi MI 48377
Tel (248) 799-8303 SIC 8099 8741

LAKELAND MEDICAL HEALTH CENTER p 840
1234 Napier Ave, Saint Joseph MI 49085
Tel (269) 982-4935 SIC 8099

HEALTH FITNESS CORP p 675
1700 W 82nd St Ste 200, Minneapolis MN 55431
Tel (800) 639-7913 SIC 8099 7991

NATIONAL MARROW DONOR PROGRAM INC p 1014
500 N 5th St, Minneapolis MN 55401
Tel (612) 627-5800 SIC 8099 8742

HEALTH MISSISSIPPI ORGANIZATION INC p 675
570 E Woodrow Wilson Ave, Jackson MS 39216
Tel (601) 576-7400 SIC 8099

MISSISSIPPI ACTION FOR PROGRESS INC p 975
1751 Morson Rd, Jackson MS 39209
Tel (601) 923-4100 SIC 8099 8211

ASCENSION HEALTH p 116
4600 Edmundson Rd, Saint Louis MO 63134
Tel (314) 733-8000 SIC 8099

▲ **CENTENE CORP** p 275
7700 Forsyth Blvd Ste 800, Saint Louis MO 63105
Tel (314) 725-4477 SIC 6324 8011 8099

SIGMA-ALDRICH CORP p 1321
3050 Spruce St, Saint Louis MO 63103
Tel (314) 771-5765 SIC 2899 5169 8099

ST MARYS HEALTH CENTER p 1371
6420 Clayton Rd, Saint Louis MO 63117
Tel (228) 233-4998 SIC 8099

RENOWN SOUTH MEADOWS MEDICAL CENTER p 1224
1155 Mill St, Reno NV 89502
Tel (775) 982-4404 SIC 8099

FOUNDATION MEDICAL PARTNERS IN p 571
8 Prospect St, Nashua NH 03060
Tel (603) 577-2000 SIC 8099

SUMMIT MEDICAL GROUP PA p 1399
1 Diamond Hill Rd, Berkeley Heights NJ 07922
Tel (908) 277-8880 SIC 8099 8011

MUSCULOSKELETAL TRANSPLANT FOUNDATION INC p 1002
125 May St, Edison NJ 08837
Tel (732) 661-0202 SIC 8099

KEDRION BIOPHARMA INC p 807
400 Kelby St Ste 11, Fort Lee NJ 07024
Tel (201) 242-8900 SIC 8099

CENTRASTATE HEALTHCARE SYSTEM INC p 281
901 W Main St, Freehold NJ 07728
Tel (732) 431-2000 SIC 8099 8741

INTERNATIONAL VITAMIN CORP p 757
500 Halls Mill Rd, Freehold NJ 07728
Tel (951) 361-1120 SIC 2834 5149 8099

UM HOLDING CO p 1501
56 N Haddon Ave Ste 300, Haddonfield NJ 08033
Tel (856) 354-2200 SIC 8099

VIRTUA MEDICAL GROUP PA p 1560
301 Lippincott Dr, Marlton NJ 08053
Tel (856) 355-0340 SIC 8099 8082

UFCW LOCAL 152 HEALTH & WELFARE FUND p 1499
27 Roland Ave Ste 100, Mount Laurel NJ 08054
Tel (856) 793-2500 SIC 8099

VALLEY HEALTH SYSTEM INC p 1540
223 N Van Dien Ave, Ridgewood NJ 07450
Tel (201) 447-8000 SIC 8062 8099

BARNABAS HEALTH INC p 155
95 Old Short Hills Rd, West Orange NJ 07052
Tel (973) 322-4018 SIC 8082 8099

CENTER FOR DISABILITY SERVICES INC p 275
314 S Manning Blvd, Albany NY 12208
Tel (518) 437-5506
SIC 8351 8093 8361 8099

LONG ISLAND HOME p 876
400 Sunrise Hwy, Amityville NY 11701
Tel (631) 264-4000
SIC 8063 8051 8099 8011

SUNSET PARK HEALTH COUNCIL INC p 1404
150 55th St Ste 1, Brooklyn NY 11220
Tel (718) 630-7000 SIC 8099

DOROTHEA HOPFER SCHOOL OF NURSING p 451
53 Valentine St, Mount Vernon NY 10550
Tel (914) 361-6221 SIC 8099

AFTRA HEALTH FUND p 33
261 Madison Ave Fl 8, New York NY 10016
Tel (212) 499-4800 SIC 8099

BRIGHTPOINT HEALTH p 213
71 W 23rd St Fl 8, New York NY 10010
Tel (718) 681-8700 SIC 8099

▲ **EVERYDAY HEALTH INC** p 515
345 Hudson St Rm 1600, New York NY 10014
Tel (646) 728-9500 SIC 8099 7319

NEW YORK BLOOD CENTER INC p 1034
310 E 67th St, New York NY 10065
Tel (212) 570-3010 SIC 8099 2836

NYSARC INC p 1069
83 Maiden Ln, New York NY 10038
Tel (212) 780-2635 SIC 8099

ZOCDOC INC p 1643
568 Broadway Fl 9, New York NY 10012
Tel (866) 962-3621 SIC 8011 8099

HEALTH QUEST p 675
45 Reade Pl, Poughkeepsie NY 12601
Tel (845) 454-8500 SIC 8099

BON SECOURS CHARITY HEALTH SYSTEM INC p 199
255 Lafayette Ave, Suffern NY 10901
Tel (845) 368-5000 SIC 8099

NORTH SHORE-LONG ISLAND JEWISH HEALTH CARE p 1053
972 Brush Hollow Rd 5th, Westbury NY 11590
Tel (516) 876-6611 SIC 8099

APS HEALTHCARE BETHESDA INC p 100
44 S Broadway Ste 1200, White Plains NY 10601
Tel (800) 305-3720 SIC 8099

APS HEALTHCARE INC p 100
44 S Broadway Ste 1200, White Plains NY 10601
Tel (914) 288-4700 SIC 8099

APS HEALTHCARE NORTHWEST INC p 100
44 S Broadway Ste 1200, White Plains NY 10601
Tel (800) 305-3720 SIC 8099

INNOVATIVE RESOURCE GROUP LLC p 745
44 S Broadway Ste 1200, White Plains NY 10601
Tel (800) 305-3720 SIC 8099

ASHEVILLE NURSING AND REHAB CENTER p 117
91 Victoria Rd, Asheville NC 28801
Tel (828) 255-0076 SIC 8099

MEDCATH CORP p 935
10800 Sikes Pl Ste 200, Charlotte NC 28277
Tel (704) 815-7700 SIC 8099 8062

TALECRIS PLASMA RESOURCES INC p 1422
79 Tw Alexander Dr 4101, Durham NC 27709
Tel (817) 921-1886 SIC 8099

VIDANT MEDICAL GROUP LLC p 1556
104 Mark Dr, Edenton NC 27932
Tel (252) 482-5171 SIC 8099

CAROMONT OCCUPATIONAL MEDICINE LLC p 260
2525 Court Dr, Gastonia NC 28054
Tel (704) 834-2000 SIC 8099

EAST CAROLINA HEALTH INC p 470
2100 Stantonsburg Rd, Greenville NC 27834
Tel (252) 847-6156 SIC 8099

CORNERSTONE HEALTH CARE PA p 371
1701 Westchester Dr # 850, High Point NC 27262
Tel (336) 802-2700 SIC 8741 8099

NATIONAL CANCER COALITION LLC p 1010
225 Hillsborough St # 280, Raleigh NC 27603
Tel (919) 821-2182 SIC 8099

ST ELIZABETH BOARDMAN HEALTH CENTER p 1366
8401 Market St, Boardman OH 44512
Tel (330) 729-4580 SIC 8099 8062

MOUNT CARMEL HEALTH PLAN MEDIG p 993
6150 E Broad St, Columbus OH 43213
Tel (614) 546-3138 SIC 8099

FOUNDATION FOR COMMUNITY BLOOD CENTER/COMMUNITY TISSUE SERVICES p 571
349 S Main St, Dayton OH 45402
Tel (937) 461-3450 SIC 8099

ATRIUM MEDICAL CENTER p 129
1 Medical Center Dr, Middletown OH 45005
Tel (937) 499-9596 SIC 8099

CHOCTAW MANAGEMENT SERVICES ENTERPRISE p 301
2101 W Arkansas St, Durant OK 74701
Tel (580) 924-8280 SIC 8099 8011 8031

INTEGRIS HEALTH INC p 749
5300 N Independence Ave # 280, Oklahoma City OK 73112
Tel (405) 949-6026 SIC 8099

INTERCOMMUNITY HEALTH PLANS INC p 752
3600 Nw Samaritan Dr, Corvallis OR 97330
Tel (541) 757-5111 SIC 8099

SAMARITAN HEALTH SERVICES p 1274
990 Nw Circle Blvd # 201, Corvallis OR 97330
Tel (541) 768-4773 SIC 8099

CHEHALEM HEALTH & REHAB CENTER p 293
1900 Fulton St, Newberg OR 97132
Tel (503) 538-2108 SIC 8099

HEALTH SHARE OF OREGON p 676
2121 Sw Broadway Ste 200, Portland OR 97201
Tel (503) 416-2172 SIC 8099

MEDICAL TEAMS INTERNATIONAL p 937
14150 Sw Milton Ct, Tigard OR 97224
Tel (503) 624-1000 SIC 8099 8399

SUMMIT HEALTH p 1398
112 N 7th St, Chambersburg PA 17201
Tel (717) 267-3000 SIC 8099

RESEARCH PHARMACEUTICAL SERVICES INC p 1226
520 Virginia Dr, Fort Washington PA 19034
Tel (215) 540-0700 SIC 8099

KEYSTONE PEER REVIEW ORGANIZATION INC p 816
777 E Park Dr, Harrisburg PA 17111
Tel (717) 564-8288 SIC 8099

HOLY REDEEMER HEALTHCARE SYSTEM p 702
667 Welsh Rd Ste 300, Huntingdon Valley PA 19006
Tel (215) 938-0180 SIC 8099

■ FC-GEN ACQUISITION INC p 532
101 E State St, Kennett Square PA 19348
Tel (610) 444-6350 SIC 8361 8051 8099

■ GENESIS HEALTHCARE LLC p 603
101 E State St, Kennett Square PA 19348
Tel (610) 444-6350 SIC 8051 8099

CONEMAUGH HEALTH SYSTEM p 355
4186 Cortland Dr, New Paris PA 15554
Tel (814) 839-4108 SIC 8099

MAIN LINE HEALTHCARE p 897
2 Industrial Blvd Ste 400, Paoli PA 19301
Tel (610) 648-1644 SIC 8099 8011

BIOLIFE PLASMA SERVICES LP p 184
1435 Lake Cook Rd, Philadelphia PA 19182
Tel (847) 940-5559 SIC 5122 8099

ALLEGHENY HEALTH NETWORK p 52
30 Isabella St Ste 320, Pittsburgh PA 15212
Tel (412) 330-2400 SIC 8099

HM HEALTH SOLUTIONS INC p 697
120 5th Ave, Pittsburgh PA 15222
Tel (412) 544-7226 SIC 8099 6321

INSTITUTE FOR TRANSFUSION MEDICINE p 747
5 Parkway Ctr 875, Pittsburgh PA 15220
Tel (412) 209-7316 SIC 8099

UPMC HEALTH SYSTEM p 1528
600 Grant St, Pittsburgh PA 15219
Tel (412) 281-6646 SIC 8099

NTHRIVE SOLUTIONS INC p 1065
1275 Drummers Ln Ste 200, Wayne PA 19087
Tel (800) 555-2311 SIC 8099

▲ CVS HEALTH CORP p 404
1 Cvs Dr, Woonsocket RI 02895
Tel (401) 765-1500 SIC 5912 5961 8099

ADVANTAGE HEALTH SYSTEMS INC p 26
106 Doctor Cir Ste A, Columbia SC 29203
Tel (803) 376-4190 SIC 8099

MCLEOD HEALTH p 931
555 E Cheves St, Florence SC 29506
Tel (843) 777-2256 SIC 8099

PREMISE HEALTH HOLDING CORP p 1171
5500 Maryland Way Ste 200, Brentwood TN 37027
Tel (615) 468-6295 SIC 8099

CONTINUCARE HEALTHSERVICES INC p 364
1501 Riverside Dr Ste 350, Chattanooga TN 37406
Tel (423) 386-1000 SIC 8099

▲ HEALTHWAYS INC p 678
701 Cool Springs Blvd, Franklin TN 37067
Tel (615) 614-4929 SIC 8082 8099

■ TEAM HEALTH INC p 1430
265 Brookview Centre Way, Knoxville TN 37919
Tel (865) 693-1000 SIC 8099

INTERSTATE BLOOD BANK INC p 758
5700 Pleasant View Rd, Memphis TN 38134
Tel (901) 384-6200 SIC 8099

MEDTRONIC SOFAMOR DANEK USA INC p 939
1800 Pyramid Pl, Memphis TN 38132
Tel (901) 396-3133 SIC 3842 8099

CHANGE HEALTHCARE OPERATIONS LLC p 288
3055 Lebanon Pike # 1000, Nashville TN 37214
Tel (615) 932-3000 SIC 7374 8741 8099

SPECIALTYCARE INC p 1356
3100 West End Ave Ste 800, Nashville TN 37203
Tel (615) 345-5405 SIC 8099

SONIC HEALTHCARE USA INC p 1340
9737 Great Hills Trl # 100, Austin TX 78759
Tel (512) 439-1600 SIC 8099

LORIS GIFTS INC p 878
2125 Chenault Dr Ste 100, Carrollton TX 75006
Tel (972) 759-5000 SIC 5947 8099 5999

PARKLAND COMMUNITY HEALTH PLAN p 1116
2777 N Stemmons Fwy, Dallas TX 75207
Tel (214) 266-2100 SIC 8099

SUSAN G KOMEN BREAST CANCER FOUNDATION INC p 1409
5005 Lbj Fwy Ste 250, Dallas TX 75244
Tel (972) 855-1600
SIC 8699 8069 8011 8099

TEXAS-HEALTH-PHYSICIANS-GROUP p 1445
9229 Lbj Fwy Ste 250, Dallas TX 75243
Tel (214) 860-6390 SIC 8099

DAYBREAK VENTURE LLC p 417
401 N Elm St, Denton TX 76201
Tel (940) 387-4388 SIC 8051 8099

GULF COAST REGIONAL BLOOD CENTER p 646
1400 La Concha Ln, Houston TX 77054
Tel (713) 790-1200 SIC 8099 7371 7363

MEMORIAL HERMANN MEDICAL GROUP p 942
909 Frostwood Dr Fl 2, Houston TX 77024
Tel (713) 448-5555 SIC 8099

TEXAS HEART INSTITUTE p 1443
2450 Holcombe Blvd # 341, Houston TX 77021
Tel (832) 828-1000 SIC 8099

EMSI HOLDING CO p 495
3050 Regent Blvd Ste 400, Irving TX 75063
Tel (602) 288-4488 SIC 8099

EXAMINATION MANAGEMENT SERVICES INC p 516
3050 Regent Blvd Ste 100, Irving TX 75063
Tel (214) 689-3600 SIC 8099

■ LONGVIEW MEDICAL CENTER LP p 877
2901 4th St, Longview TX 75605
Tel (903) 758-1818 SIC 8062 8099

■ PINEY WOODS HEALTHCARE SYSTEM LP p 1149
505 S John Redditt Dr, Lufkin TX 75904
Tel (936) 634-8311
SIC 8062 8071 8099 8051

DALLAS REGIONAL MEDICAL CENTER p 410
1011 N Galloway Ave, Mesquite TX 75149
Tel (214) 320-7000 SIC 8099

UNIVERSITY HEALTH SYSTEM p 1519
4502 Medical Dr, San Antonio TX 78229
Tel (210) 358-4000 SIC 8099

UT MEDICINE SAN ANTONIO p 1536
6126 Wurzbach Rd, San Antonio TX 78238
Tel (210) 450-9000 SIC 8099

■ US ONCOLOGY HOLDINGS INC p 1532
10101 Woodloch Forest Dr, The Woodlands TX 77380
Tel (281) 863-1000 SIC 8093 8099 8011

■ US ONCOLOGY INC p 1532
10101 Woodloch Forest Dr, The Woodlands TX 77380
Tel (800) 381-2637 SIC 8093 8099 8011

MORINDA HOLDINGS INC p 989
737 E 1180 S, American Fork UT 84003
Tel (801) 234-1000 SIC 5149 8099 3999

■ COLUMBIA OGDEN MEDICAL CENTER INC p 341
5475 S 500 E, Ogden UT 84405
Tel (801) 479-2111 SIC 8062 8099

▲ EVOLENT HEALTH INC p 515
800 N Glebe Rd Ste 500, Arlington VA 22203
Tel (571) 389-6000 SIC 8099

■ SIX3 ADVANCED SYSTEMS INC p 1328
45200 Business Ct Ste 100, Dulles VA 20166
Tel (703) 742-7660
SIC 3825 4899 8099 4789

WASHINGTON HEALTHCARE PHYSICIANS MARY p 1578
2300 Fall Hill Ave # 314, Fredericksburg VA 22401
Tel (540) 741-1100 SIC 8099

MARY IMMACULATE HOSPITAL INC p 914
2 Bernardine Dr, Newport News VA 23602
Tel (757) 886-6440 SIC 8062 8099

EASTERN VIRGINIA MEDICAL SCHOOL p 472
714 Woodis Ave, Norfolk VA 23510
Tel (757) 446-6052 SIC 8221 8099

LIFENET HEALTH p 864
1864 Concert Dr, Virginia Beach VA 23453
Tel (757) 464-4761 SIC 8099

ONSITE HEALTH INC p 1088
1308 Devils Reach Rd # 302, Woodbridge VA 22192
Tel (949) 441-9530 SIC 8099

PROVIDENCE EVERETT MEDICAL CENTER p 1185
900 Pacific Ave Ste 501, Everett WA 98201
Tel (425) 258-7311 SIC 8099

BLOODWORKS p 189
921 Terry Ave, Seattle WA 98104
Tel (206) 292-6500
SIC 8071 8099 8733 8732

PEACEHEALTH SOUTHWEST MEDICAL CENTER p 1125
400 Ne Mother Joseph Pl, Vancouver WA 98664
Tel (360) 514-2097 SIC 8099

SACRED HEART HOSPITAL OF HOSPITAL SISTERS-3RD ORDER OF ST FRANCIS p 1265
1110 Oak Ridge Dr, Eau Claire WI 54701
Tel (715) 717-4131 SIC 8099

AURORA HEALTH CARE SOUTHERN LAKES INC p 132
36500 Aurora Dr, Gleason WI 54435
Tel (262) 434-1000 SIC 8099

DEAN HEALTH SYSTEMS INC p 420
1808 W Beltline Hwy, Madison WI 53713
Tel (608) 250-1435 SIC 8099

GROUP HEALTH COOPERATIVE ADMINISTRATION p 641
1265 John Q Hammons Dr # 200, Madison WI 53717
Tel (608) 251-4156 SIC 8099

MIDVALE INDEMNITY CO p 966
6000 American Pkwy, Madison WI 53783
Tel (847) 320-2000 SIC 6331 8099

UW HEALTH p 1537
7974 Uw Health Ct, Middleton WI 53562
Tel (608) 829-5217 SIC 8099

AURORA HEALTH CARE CENTRAL INC p 132
3031 W Montana St, Milwaukee WI 53215
Tel (414) 647-3211 SIC 8099

BLOODCENTER OF WISCONSIN INC p 189
638 N 18th St, Milwaukee WI 53233
Tel (414) 933-5000 SIC 8099

SIC 8111 Legal Svcs

BRADLEY ARANT BOULT CUMMINGS LLP p 206
1819 5th Ave N Ste 200, Birmingham AL 35203
Tel (205) 521-8000 SIC 8111

SNELL & WILMER LLP p 1335
400 E Van Buren St Fl 10, Phoenix AZ 85004
Tel (602) 382-6000 SIC 8111

CALIBER CAPITAL GROUP LLC p 239
5900 Katella Ave Ste A101, Cypress CA 90630
Tel (714) 507-1998 SIC 6282 8111

KNOBBE MARTENS OLSON & BEAR LLP p 824
2040 Main St Fl 14, Irvine CA 92614
Tel (949) 760-0404 SIC 8111

COX CASTLE & NICHOLSON LLP p 386
2029 Cntury Nicholson Llp, Los Angeles CA 90067
Tel (310) 284-2200 SIC 8111

GIBSON DUNN & CRUTCHER LLP p 611
333 S Grand Ave Ste 4600, Los Angeles CA 90071
Tel (213) 229-7000 SIC 8111

LATHAM & WATKINS LLP p 846
355 S Grand Ave Ste 1000, Los Angeles CA 90071
Tel (213) 485-1234 SIC 8111

LEWIS BRISBOIS BISGAARD & SMITH LLP p 858
633 W 5th St Ste 4000, Los Angeles CA 90071
Tel (213) 250-1800 SIC 8111

MANATT PHELPS & PHILLIPS LLP p 900
11355 W Olympic Blvd Fl 2, Los Angeles CA 90064
Tel (310) 312-4000 SIC 8111

OMELVENY & MYERS LLP p 1084
400 S Hope St Fl 19, Los Angeles CA 90071
Tel (213) 430-6000 SIC 8111

PAUL HASTINGS LLP p 1121
515 S Flower St Fl 25, Los Angeles CA 90071
Tel (213) 683-6000 SIC 8111

QUINN EMANUEL URQUHART & SULLIVAN LLP p 1200
865 S Figueroa St Fl 10, Los Angeles CA 90017
Tel (213) 443-3000 SIC 8111

SHEPPARD MULLIN RICHTER & HAMPTON LLP p 1315
333 S Hope St Fl 43, Los Angeles CA 90071
Tel (213) 620-1780 SIC 8111

FENWICK & WEST LLP p 537
801 California St, Mountain View CA 94041
Tel (650) 988-8500 SIC 8111

PACIFIC LIFECORP p 1105
700 Newport Center Dr, Newport Beach CA 92660
Tel (949) 219-3011
SIC 6371 6311 6321 6035 8111

COOLEY LLP p 366
3175 Hanover St, Palo Alto CA 94304
Tel (650) 843-5000 SIC 8111

WILSON SONSINI GOODRICH & ROSATI PROFESSIONAL CORP p 1614
650 Page Mill Rd, Palo Alto CA 94304
Tel (650) 493-9300 SIC 8111

LITTLER MENDELSON PC p 871
333 Bush St Fl 34, San Francisco CA 94104
Tel (415) 433-1940 SIC 8111

MORGAN LEWIS & BOCKIUS LLP p 988
1 Market St Ste 500, San Francisco CA 94105
Tel (415) 393-2000 SIC 8111

MORRISON & FOERSTER LLP p 990
425 Market St Fl 30, San Francisco CA 94105
Tel (415) 268-7000 SIC 8111

ORRICK HERRINGTON & SUTCLIFFE LLP p 1095
405 Howard St, San Francisco CA 94105
Tel (415) 773-5700 SIC 8111

REES GORDON SCULLY MANSUKHANI LLP p 1217
275 Battery St Ste 2000, San Francisco CA 94111
Tel (415) 986-5900 SIC 8111

SEDGWICK LLP p 1300
333 Bush St Fl 30, San Francisco CA 94104
Tel (415) 781-7900 SIC 8111

NATIONAL GOLF PROPERTIES LLC p 1012
2951 28th St Ste 3000, Santa Monica CA 90405
Tel (310) 664-4000 SIC 6519 8111

COMPEX LEGAL SERVICES INC p 351
325 Maple Ave, Torrance CA 90503
Tel (310) 782-1801 SIC 8111 7338 7334

BROWNSTEIN HYATT FARBER SCHRECK LLP p 220
410 17th St Ste 2200, Denver CO 80202
Tel (303) 223-1100 SIC 8111

CENTURION DISCOVERY INC p 281
518 17th St Ste 925, Denver CO 80202
Tel (303) 645-4555 SIC 8111

HOLLAND & HART LLP p 700
555 17th St Ste 3200, Denver CO 80202
Tel (303) 295-8000 SIC 8111

DAY PITNEY LLP p 417
242 Trumbull St Fl 5, Hartford CT 06103
Tel (617) 345-4600 SIC 8111

ROBINSON & COLE LLP p 1242
280 Trumbull St Fl 28, Hartford CT 06103
Tel (860) 275-8200 SIC 8111

WITHERS BERGMAN LLP p 1619
157 Church St Fl 19, New Haven CT 06510
Tel (203) 789-1320 SIC 8111

THOMSON REUTERS (GRC) INC p 1449
2711 Centerville Rd # 400, Wilmington DE 19808
Tel (212) 227-7357
SIC 7291 8111 8721 8733 8741

AKIN GUMP STRAUSS HAUER & FELD LLP p 42
1333 New Hampshire Ave Nw # 400, Washington DC 20036
Tel (202) 887-4000 SIC 8111

ARENT FOX LLP p 107
1717 K St Nw Ste B1, Washington DC 20006
Tel (202) 857-6000 SIC 8111

ARNOLD & PORTER LLP p 112
601 Massachusetts Ave Nw, Washington DC 20001
Tel (202) 942-5000 SIC 8111

COVINGTON & BURLING LLP p 385
1 Citycenter 850 Tenth, Washington DC 20001
Tel (202) 662-6000 SIC 8111

CROWELL & MORING LLP p 394
1001 Penn Ave Nw Fl 10, Washington DC 20004
Tel (202) 624-2500 SIC 8111

DICKSTEIN SHAPIRO LLP p 438
1825 Eye St Nw Fl 1200, Washington DC 20006
Tel (202) 420-2200 SIC 8111

FINNEGAN HENDERSON FARABOW GARRETT & DUNNER LLP p 543
901 New York Ave Nw # 1150, Washington DC 20001
Tel (202) 408-4000 SIC 8111

HOGAN LOVELLS US LLP p 699
555 13th St Nw, Washington DC 20004
Tel (202) 637-5600 SIC 8111

HOWREY LLP p 714
1299 Pennsylvania Ave Nw, Washington DC 20004
Tel (202) 783-0800 SIC 8111

MCKENNA LONG & ALDRIDGE LLP p 930
1900 K St Nw Ste Ll100, Washington DC 20006
Tel (202) 496-7145 SIC 8111

PATTON BOGGS LLP p 1121
2550 M St Nw Ste 200, Washington DC 20037
Tel (202) 457-6000 SIC 8111

SPECIAL COUNSEL p 1355
1400 I St Nw Ste 325, Washington DC 20005
Tel (202) 737-3436 SIC 7363 8111 7361

STEPTOE & JOHNSON LLP p 1386
1330 Connecticut Ave Nw, Washington DC 20036
Tel (202) 429-3000 SIC 8111

SUTHERLAND ASBILL & BRENNAN LLP p 1409
700 6th St Nw Ste 700, Washington DC 20001
Tel (202) 383-0100 SIC 8111

VENABLE LLP p 1547
575 7th St Nw Ste 1, Washington DC 20004
Tel (202) 344-4000 SIC 8111

WILEY REIN LLP p 1609
1776 K St Nw, Washington DC 20006
Tel (202) 719-7000 SIC 8111

WILLIAMS & CONNOLLY LLP p 1611
725 12th St Nw, Washington DC 20005
Tel (202) 434-5800 SIC 8111

WILMER CUTLER PICKERING HALE AND DORR LLP p 1613
1875 Pennsylvania Ave Nw, Washington DC 20006
Tel (202) 663-6000 SIC 8111

HOLLAND & KNIGHT LLP p 700
524 Grand Regency Blvd, Brandon FL 33510
Tel (813) 901-4200 SIC 8111

AKERMAN LLP p 42
98 Se 7th St Ste 1100, Miami FL 33131
Tel (305) 374-5600 SIC 8111

GREENBERG TRAURIG PA p 637
333 Se 2nd Ave Ste 4100, Miami FL 33131
Tel (305) 579-0500 SIC 8111

DANIEL J NEWLIN PA p 411
7335 W Sand Lake Rd # 200, Orlando FL 32819
Tel (407) 888-8000 SIC 8111

MORGAN & MORGAN PA p 988
20 N Orange Ave Ste 1607, Orlando FL 32801
Tel (407) 420-1414 SIC 8111

FLORIDA DEPARTMENT OF LEGAL AFFAIRS p 558
107 W Gaines St, Tallahassee FL 32399
Tel (850) 414-3300 SIC 8111 9222

ALDRIDGE PITE LLP p 48
3575 Piedmont Rd Ne # 500, Atlanta GA 30305
Tel (404) 994-7400 SIC 8111

ALSTON & BIRD LLP p 61
1201 W Peachtree St Ne # 4000, Atlanta GA 30309
Tel (404) 881-7654 SIC 8111

FISHER & PHILLIPS LLP p 552
1075 Peachtree St Ne # 3500, Atlanta GA 30309
Tel (404) 231-1400 SIC 8111

KILPATRICK TOWNSEND & STOCKTON LLP p 818
1100 Peachtree St Ne, Atlanta GA 30309
Tel (404) 815-6500 SIC 8111

KING & SPALDING LLP p 820
1180 Peachtree St, Atlanta GA 30309
Tel (404) 572-4600 SIC 8111

TROUTMAN SANDERS LLP p 1484
600 Peachtree St Ne # 5200, Atlanta GA 30308
Tel (404) 885-3000 SIC 8111

CRAWFORD & CO p 389
1001 Summit Blvd Ste 500, Brookhaven GA 30319
Tel (404) 300-1000
SIC 6411 8111 8099 6331

AON RISK SERVICES COMPANIES INC p 95
200 E Randolph St Fl 14, Chicago IL 60601
Tel (312) 381-1000 SIC 6411 8111

BAKER & MCKENZIE LLP p 145
300 E Randolph St # 5000, Chicago IL 60601
Tel (312) 861-8000 SIC 8111

CHAPMAN AND CUTLER LLP p 288
111 W Monroe St Ste 1700, Chicago IL 60603
Tel (312) 845-3000 SIC 8111

DENTONS US LLP p 429
233 S Wacker Dr Ste 5900, Chicago IL 60606
Tel (312) 876-8000 SIC 8111

HARDIN SCHIFF LLP p 660
233 S Wacker Dr Ste 6600, Chicago IL 60606
Tel (312) 258-5500 SIC 8111

HINSHAW & CULBERTSON LLP p 695
222 N La Salle St Ste 300, Chicago IL 60601
Tel (312) 704-3000 SIC 8111

JEFFREY L LONDON p 782
70 W Madison St Ste 4200, Chicago IL 60602
Tel (312) 583-2339 SIC 8111

JENNER & BLOCK LLP p 782
353 N Clark St Ste 3200, Chicago IL 60654
Tel (312) 222-9350 SIC 8111

KATTEN MUCHIN ROSENMAN LLP p 804
525 W Monroe St Ste 1900, Chicago IL 60661
Tel (312) 902-5200 SIC 8111

KIRKLAND & ELLIS LLP p 822
300 N La Salle Dr # 2400, Chicago IL 60654
Tel (312) 862-2000 SIC 8111

MAYER BROWN LLP p 923
71 S Wacker Dr Ste 1000, Chicago IL 60606
Tel (312) 782-0600 SIC 8111

MCDERMOTT WILL & EMERY LLP INC p 927
227 W Monroe St Ste 4400, Chicago IL 60606
Tel (312) 372-2000 SIC 8111

PRITZKER GROUP- CHICAGO LLC p 1178
111 S Wacker Dr Ste 4000, Chicago IL 60606
Tel (312) 447-6000 SIC 8111

SEYFARTH SHAW LLP p 1309
131 S Dearborn St # 2400, Chicago IL 60603
Tel (312) 460-5000 SIC 8111

SIDLEY AUSTIN LLP p 1319
1 S Dearborn St Ste 900, Chicago IL 60603
Tel (312) 853-7000 SIC 8111

WINSTON & STRAWN LLP p 1617
35 W Wacker Dr Ste 4200, Chicago IL 60601
Tel (312) 558-5600 SIC 8111

BARNES & THORNBURG LLP p 156
11 S Meridian St Ste 1313, Indianapolis IN 46204
Tel (317) 236-1313 SIC 8111

FAEGRE BAKER DANIELS LLP p 524
300 N Meridian St # 2700, Indianapolis IN 46204
Tel (317) 237-0300 SIC 8111

ICE MILLER LLP p 727
1 American Sq Ste 2900, Indianapolis IN 46282
Tel (317) 236-2100 SIC 8111

RAWLINGS CO LLC p 1209
1 Eden Pkwy, La Grange KY 40031
Tel (502) 587-1279 SIC 8748 8111

ADAMS AND REESE LLP p 21
701 Poydras St Ste 4500, New Orleans LA 70139
Tel (504) 581-3234 SIC 8111

JONES WALKER LLP p 792
201 Saint Charles Ave # 5200, New Orleans LA 70170
Tel (504) 582-8000 SIC 8111

PHELPS DUNBAR LLP p 1141
365 Canal St Ste 2000, New Orleans LA 70130
Tel (504) 566-1311 SIC 8111

DLA PIPER LLP (US) p 445
6225 Smith Ave Ste 200, Baltimore MD 21209
Tel (410) 580-3000 SIC 8111

MILES & STOCKBRIDGE PC p 969
100 Light St Fl 5, Baltimore MD 21202
Tel (410) 385-3671 SIC 8111

VENABLE LLP p 1547
750 E Pratt St Ste 900, Baltimore MD 21202
Tel (410) 244-7400 SIC 8111

BMC PARTNERS LLP p 193
1 Federal St, Boston MA 02110
Tel (617) 951-8000 SIC 8111

EDWARDS WILDMAN PALMER LLP p 480
111 Huntington Ave, Boston MA 02199
Tel (617) 239-0100 SIC 8111

FISH & RICHARDSON PC p 551
1 Marina Park Dr Ste 1700, Boston MA 02210
Tel (617) 542-5070 SIC 8111

GOODWIN PROCTER LLP p 625
100 Northern Ave, Boston MA 02210
Tel (617) 570-1000 SIC 8111

MINTZ LEVIN COHN FERRIS GLOVSKY AND POPEO PC p 974
1 Financial Ctr Fl 39, Boston MA 02111
Tel (617) 348-4951 SIC 8111

ROPES & GRAY LLP p 1250
800 Prudential Tower # 3600, Boston MA 02199
Tel (617) 951-7000 SIC 8111

DYKEMA GOSSETT PLLC p 464
400 Renaissance Ctr, Detroit MI 48243
Tel (313) 568-6800 SIC 8111 8742

HONIGMAN MILLER SCHWARTZ AND COHN LLP p 705
660 Woodward Ave Ste 2290, Detroit MI 48226
Tel (313) 465-7000 SIC 8111

MILLER CANFIELD PADDOCK AND STONE PLC p 970
150 W Jefferson Ave # 2500, Detroit MI 48226
Tel (313) 963-6420 SIC 8111

DORSEY & WHITNEY LLP p 451
50 S 6th St Ste 1500, Minneapolis MN 55402
Tel (612) 340-2600 SIC 8111

LLP ROBINS KAPLAN p 872
800 Lasalle Ave Ste 2800, Minneapolis MN 55402
Tel (612) 349-8500 SIC 8111

RUST CONSULTING INC p 1260
625 Marquette Ave Ste 900, Minneapolis MN 55402
Tel (612) 359-2000 SIC 8741 8111

■ **3M INNOVATIVE PROPERTIES CO** p 2
3m Center Bldg 2253s06, Saint Paul MN 55144
Tel (651) 733-8904 SIC 8111

MERRILL CORP p 950
1 Merrill Cir, Saint Paul MN 55108
Tel (651) 646-4501 SIC 7389 8111 8999

P C YOUNGWILLIAMS p 1102
141 Township Ave Ste 200, Ridgeland MS 39157
Tel (601) 990-3100 SIC 8111

HUSCH BLACKWELL LLP p 721
4801 Main St Ste 1000, Kansas City MO 64112
Tel (816) 983-8000 SIC 8111

LATHROP & GAGE LLP p 846
2345 Grand Blvd Ste 2200, Kansas City MO 64108
Tel (816) 292-2000 SIC 8111

POLSINELLI PC p 1160
900 W 48th Pl Ste 900, Kansas City MO 64112
Tel (816) 753-1000 SIC 8111

SHOOK HARDY & BACON LLP p 1318
2555 Grand Blvd, Kansas City MO 64108
Tel (816) 474-6550 SIC 8111

STINSON LEONARD STREET LLP p 1390
1201 Walnut St Ste 2900, Kansas City MO 64106
Tel (816) 842-8600 SIC 8111

BRYAN CAVE LLP p 221
1 Metropolitan Sq, Saint Louis MO 63102
Tel (314) 259-2000 SIC 8111

THOMPSON COBURN LLP p 1449
505 N 7th St Ste 2700, Saint Louis MO 63101
Tel (314) 552-6000 SIC 8111

KUTAK ROCK LLP p 832
1650 Farnam St Fl 2, Omaha NE 68102
Tel (402) 346-6000 SIC 8111

■ **AIG CLAIM SERVICES INC** p 37
100 Connell Dr Ste 2100, Berkeley Heights NJ 07922
Tel (973) 402-2800 SIC 6411 8111

MCCARTER & ENGLISH LLP p 926
2 Tower Center Blvd Fl 11, East Brunswick NJ 08816
Tel (732) 393-1900 SIC 8111

MC ELROY DEUTSCH MULVANEY & CARPERNTER LLP p 925
1300 Mount Kemble Ave, Morristown NJ 07960
Tel (973) 993-8100 SIC 8111

LOWENSTEIN SANDLER LLP p 881
65 Livingston Ave Ste 2, Roseland NJ 07068
Tel (973) 597-2500 SIC 8111

ROSE L BRAND & ASSOCIATES PC p 1250
7301 Jefferson St Ne, Albuquerque NM 87109
Tel (505) 833-3036 SIC 8111

AFTRA HEALTH & RETIREMENT FUND (INC) p 33
261 Madison Ave Fl 7, New York NY 10016
Tel (212) 499-4800 SIC 6371 8111

C T CORP SYSTEM p 233
111 8th Ave Fl 13, New York NY 10011
Tel (212) 894-8940 SIC 8111

CADWALADER WICKERSHAM & TAFT LLP p 236
200 Liberty St, New York NY 10281
Tel (212) 504-6000 SIC 8111

CHADBOURNE & PARKE LLP p 286
1301 Ave Of The Americas, New York NY 10019
Tel (212) 408-5100 SIC 8111

CLEARY GOTTLIEB STEEN & HAMILTON LLP p 325
1 Liberty Plz Fl 43, New York NY 10006
Tel (212) 225-2000 SIC 8111

CLIFFORD CHANCE US LLP p 326
31 W 52nd St Fl 3, New York NY 10019
Tel (212) 878-8000 SIC 8111

CRAVATH SWAINE & MOORE LLP p 389
825 8th Ave Lbby L, New York NY 10019
Tel (212) 474-1000 SIC 8111

DAVIS POLK & WARDWELL LLP p 416
450 Lexington Ave Fl 10, New York NY 10017
Tel (212) 450-4000 SIC 8111

DEBEVOISE & PLIMPTON LLP p 420
919 3rd Ave Lbby 2, New York NY 10022
Tel (212) 909-6000 SIC 8111

FRAGOMEN DEL REY BERNSEN & LOEWY LLP p 573
7 Hanover Sq Ste 800, New York NY 10004
Tel (732) 862-5000 SIC 8111

FRIED FRANK HARRIS SHRIVER & JACOBSON LLP p 579
1 New York Plz Fl 27, New York NY 10004
Tel (212) 859-8000 SIC 8111

GREENBERG TRAURIG LLP p 637
200 Park Ave Fl 39, New York NY 10166
Tel (212) 801-9200 SIC 8111

HUGHES HUBBARD & REED LLP p 717
1 Battery Park, New York NY 10004
Tel (212) 837-6000 SIC 8111

KAYE SCHOLER LLP p 805
250 W 55th St Fl 4, New York NY 10019
Tel (212) 836-8000 SIC 8111

KELLEY DRYE & WARREN LLP p 808
101 Park Ave Fl 30, New York NY 10178
Tel (212) 808-7800 SIC 8111

KRAMER LEVIN NAFTALIS & FRANKEL LLP p 829
1177 Ave Of The Americas, New York NY 10036
Tel (212) 715-9236 SIC 8111

LEGAL AID SOCIETY p 853
199 Water St Frnt 3, New York NY 10038
Tel (212) 577-3346 SIC 8111

MILBANK TWEED HADLEY & MCCLOY LLP p 969
28 Liberty St Fl 47, New York NY 10005
Tel (212) 530-5000 SIC 8111

■ **NBC UNIVERSAL LLC** p 1021
1221 Avenue Of The Americ, New York NY 10020
Tel (212) 664-4444 SIC 4833 8111

PAUL WEISS RIFKIND WHARTON & GARRISON LLP p 1121
1285 Ave Of The Americas, New York NY 10019
Tel (212) 373-3000 SIC 8111 8748

PILLSBURY WINTHROP SHAW PITTMAN LLP p 1148
1540 Broadway Fl 9, New York NY 10036
Tel (212) 858-1000 SIC 8111

PROSKAUER ROSE LLP p 1184
11 Times Sq Fl 17, New York NY 10036
Tel (212) 969-3000 SIC 8111

SCHULTE ROTH & ZABEL LLP p 1290
919 3rd Ave Frnt 2, New York NY 10022
Tel (212) 756-2000 SIC 8111

SHEARMAN & STERLING LLP p 1313
599 Lexington Ave Fl 16, New York NY 10022
Tel (212) 848-4000 SIC 8111

SIMPSON THACHER & BARTLETT LLP p 1325
425 Lexington Ave Fl 15, New York NY 10017
Tel (212) 455-2000 SIC 8111 6531

SKADDEN ARPS SLATE MEAGHER & FLOM LLP p 1329
4 Times Sq Fl 24, New York NY 10036
Tel (212) 735-3000 SIC 8111

STROOCK & STROOCK & LAVAN LLP p 1394
180 Maiden Ln Fl 17, New York NY 10038
Tel (212) 806-5400 SIC 8111

SULLIVAN & CROMWELL LLP p 1397
125 Broad St Fl 35, New York NY 10004
Tel (212) 558-4000 SIC 8111

■ **THOMSON REUTERS CORP** p 1450
3 Times Sq Lbby Mailroom, New York NY 10036
Tel (646) 223-4000
SIC 2741 8111 7372 7383

TRANSPERFECT TRANSLATIONS INTERNATIONAL INC p 1472
3 Park Ave Fl 39, New York NY 10016
Tel (212) 689-5555 SIC 7389 8748 8111

WACHTELL LIPTON ROSEN & KATZ p 1570
51 W 52nd St Fl 29, New York NY 10019
Tel (212) 403-1000 SIC 8111

WEIL GOTSHAL & MANGES LLP p 1588
767 5th Ave Fl Conc1, New York NY 10153
Tel (212) 310-8000 SIC 8111

WHITE & CASE LLP p 1605
1155 Avenue Of The Americ, New York NY 10036
Tel (212) 819-8200 SIC 8111

WILLKIE FARR & GALLAGHER LLP p 1612
787 7th Ave Fl 2, New York NY 10019
Tel (212) 728-8000 SIC 8111

WILSON ELSER MOSKOWITZ EDELMAN & DICKER LLP p 1613
150 E 42nd St Fl 23, New York NY 10017
Tel (212) 490-3000 SIC 8111

NIXON PEABODY LLP p 1045
1300 Clinton Sq, Rochester NY 14604
Tel (585) 263-1000 SIC 8111

LEWIS P C JACKSON p 859
1133 Weschester Ave, White Plains NY 10604
Tel (914) 872-8060 SIC 8111

MOORE & VAN ALLEN PLLC p 987
100 N Tryon St Ste 4700, Charlotte NC 28202
Tel (704) 331-1000 SIC 8111

WOMBLE CARLYLE SANDRIDGE & RICE LLP p 1621
1 W 4th St, Winston Salem NC 27101
Tel (336) 721-3600 SIC 8111

DINSMORE & SHOHL LLP p 440
255 E 5th St Ste 1900, Cincinnati OH 45202
Tel (513) 977-8200 SIC 8111

FROST BROWN TODD LLC p 581
3300 Grt Amrcn Towe 301e, Cincinnati OH 45202
Tel (513) 651-6800 SIC 8111

BAKER & HOSTETLER LLP p 145
127 Public Sq Ste 2000, Cleveland OH 44114
Tel (216) 621-0200 SIC 8111

JONES DAY LIMITED PARTNERSHIP p 792
901 Lakeside Ave E Ste 2, Cleveland OH 44114
Tel (216) 586-3939 SIC 8111

SQUIRE PATTON BOGGS (US) LLP p 1362
4900 Key Tower 127 Pub Sq, Cleveland OH 44114
Tel (216) 479-8500 SIC 8111

THOMPSON HINE LLP p 1449
127 Public Sq, Cleveland OH 44114
Tel (216) 566-5500 SIC 8111

WELTMAN WEINBERG & REIS CO LPA p 1591
323 W Lkeside Ave Ste 200, Cleveland OH 44113
Tel (216) 685-1000 SIC 8111

VORYS SATER SEYMOUR AND PEASE LLP p 1566
52 E Gay St, Columbus OH 43215
Tel (614) 464-6400 SIC 8111

LEGALSHIELD p 853
1 Prepaid Way, Ada OK 74820
Tel (323) 325-3198 SIC 8111

STOEL RIVES LLP p 1390
760 Sw 9th Ave Ste 3000, Portland OR 97205
Tel (503) 224-3380 SIC 8111

CITY COUNTY INSURANCE SERVICES p 312
1212 Court St Ne, Salem OR 97301
Tel (503) 763-3800 SIC 6411 8111

SAIF CORP p 1268
400 High St Se, Salem OR 97312
Tel (503) 373-8000 SIC 6321 8111 6331

BALLARD SPAHR LLP p 148
1735 Market St Fl 51, Philadelphia PA 19103
Tel (215) 665-8500 SIC 8111

BLANK ROME LLP p 189
1 Logan Sq, Philadelphia PA 19103
Tel (215) 569-5500 SIC 8111

COZEN OCONNOR p 387
1650 Market St Ste 2800, Philadelphia PA 19103
Tel (215) 665-2053 SIC 8111

DECHERT LLP p 421
2929 Arch St Ste 400, Philadelphia PA 19104
Tel (202) 261-3300 SIC 8111

DRINKER BIDDLE & REATH LLP p 456
1 Logan Sq Ste 2000, Philadelphia PA 19103
Tel (215) 988-2700 SIC 8111

DUANE MORRIS LLP p 459
30 S 17th St Fl 5, Philadelphia PA 19103
Tel (215) 979-1000 SIC 8111

FOX ROTHSCHILD LLP p 572
2000 Market St Fl 20, Philadelphia PA 19103
Tel (215) 299-2000 SIC 8111

MARSHALL DENNEHEY WARNER COLEMAN & GOGGIN PC p 911
2000 Market St Fl 23, Philadelphia PA 19103
Tel (215) 575-2600 SIC 8111

MORGAN LEWIS & BOCKIUS LLP p 988
1701 Market St Ste Con, Philadelphia PA 19103
Tel (215) 963-5000 SIC 8111

PEPPER HAMILTON LLP p 1133
3000 Two Logan Sq, Philadelphia PA 19103
Tel (215) 981-4000 SIC 8111

SAUL EWING LLP p 1283
1500 Market St Fl 38, Philadelphia PA 19102
Tel (215) 972-7777 SIC 8111

BUCHANAN INGERSOLL & ROONEY PC p 222
301 Grant St Fl 20, Pittsburgh PA 15219
Tel (412) 562-8800 SIC 8111

ECKERT SEAMANS CHERIN & MELLOTT LLC p 475
600 Grant St Fl 44, Pittsburgh PA 15219
Tel (412) 566-6000 SIC 8111

K&L GATES LLP p 799
210 6th Ave Ste 1100, Pittsburgh PA 15222
Tel (412) 355-6500 SIC 8111

REED SMITH LLP p 1217
225 5th Ave Ste 1200, Pittsburgh PA 15222
Tel (412) 288-3131 SIC 8111

FOX MANAGEMENT INC p 572
251 Stenton Ave, Plymouth Meeting PA 19462
Tel (610) 283-7561 SIC 8111

SOUTH CAROLINA STATE PORTS AUTHORITY p 1343
176 Concord St, Charleston SC 29401
Tel (843) 723-8651 SIC 4491 8111 2721

NELSON MULLINS RILEY & SCARBOROUGH LLP p 1025
1320 Main St Ste 1700, Columbia SC 29201
Tel (803) 799-2000 SIC 8111

OGLETREE DEAKINS NASH SMOAK & STEWART PC p 1077
300 N Main St Ste 500, Greenville SC 29601
Tel (864) 271-1300 SIC 8111

BAKER DONELSON BEARMAN CALDWELL & BERKOWITZ p 146
165 Madison Ave Ste 2000, Memphis TN 38103
Tel (901) 526-2000 SIC 8111

LINEBARGER GOGGAN BLAIR & SAMPSON LLP p 869
2700 Via Fortuna Ste 400, Austin TX 78746
Tel (512) 447-6675 SIC 8111

TEXAS A&M ENGINEERING EXTENSION SERVICE p 1442
301 Tarrow St, College Station TX 77840
Tel (979) 845-7641
SIC 8331 8711 8748 8111

GARDERE WYNNE SEWELL LLP p 591
1601 Elm St Ste 3000, Dallas TX 75201
Tel (214) 999-3000 SIC 8111

HAYNES AND BOONE LLP p 670
2323 Victory Ave Ste 700, Dallas TX 75219
Tel (214) 651-5000 SIC 8111

JACKSON WALKER LLP p 774
2323 Ross Ave Ste 600, Dallas TX 75201
Tel (214) 953-6000 SIC 8111

LOCKE LORD LLP p 873
2200 Ross Ave Ste 2800, Dallas TX 75201
Tel (214) 740-8000 SIC 8111

THOMPSON & KNIGHT LLP p 1449
1 Arts Plz 1722, Dallas TX 75201
Tel (214) 969-1700 SIC 8111

ANDREWS KURTH LLP p 90
600 Travis St Ste 4200, Houston TX 77002
Tel (713) 220-4200 SIC 8111

BAKER BOTTS LLP p 145
910 Louisiana St Ste 3200, Houston TX 77002
Tel (713) 229-1234 SIC 8111

BRACEWELL LLP p 206
711 Louisiana St Ste 2300, Houston TX 77002
Tel (713) 223-2300 SIC 8111

LAW OFFICES OF ETHERIDGE & OUGRAH LLP p 847
340 N Sam Houston Pkwy E, Houston TX 77060
Tel (832) 563-3620 SIC 8111

NORTON ROSE FULBRIGHT US LLP p 1061
1301 Mckinney St Ste 5100, Houston TX 77010
Tel (713) 651-5151 SIC 8111

TEXAS AMERICAN TITLE CO p 1442
2000 Bering Dr Ste 900, Houston TX 77057
Tel (713) 988-9999 SIC 6361 8111

US LEGAL SUPPORT INC p 1532
363 N Sam Houston Pkwy E # 1200, Houston TX 77060
Tel (713) 653-7100 SIC 8111

VINSON & ELKINS LLP p 1558
1001 Fannin St Ste 2500, Houston TX 77002
Tel (713) 758-2222 SIC 8111

INTEGREON MANAGED SOLUTIONS INC p 749
2011 Crystal Dr Ste 200, Arlington VA 22202
Tel (201) 213-6107 SIC 8111

■ **FORFEITURE SUPPORT ASSOCIATES LLC** p 567
20110 Ashbrook Pl Ste 220, Ashburn VA 20147
Tel (571) 291-8900 SIC 8111 8742

HUNTON & WILLIAMS LLP p 720
Riverfront Plz E Towe 951, Richmond VA 23219
Tel (804) 788-8200 SIC 8111

LECLAIRRYAN A PROFESSNL CORP p 851
951 E Byrd St Fl 8, Richmond VA 23219
Tel (804) 783-2003 SIC 8111

MCGUIREWOODS LLP p 929
800 E Canal St, Richmond VA 23219
Tel (804) 775-1000 SIC 8111

DAVIS WRIGHT TREMAINE LLP p 416
1201 3rd Ave Ste 2200, Seattle WA 98101
Tel (206) 622-3150 SIC 8111

LANE POWELL PC p 843
1420 5th Ave Ste 4200, Seattle WA 98101
Tel (206) 223-7000 SIC 8111

PERKINS COIE LLP p 1136
1201 3rd Ave Ste 4900, Seattle WA 98101
Tel (206) 359-8000 SIC 8111

NORDIC GROUP OF COMPANIES LTD p 1048
715 Lynn Ave Ste 100, Baraboo WI 53913
Tel (608) 356-7303 SIC 8742 8111 5561

FOLEY & LARDNER LLP p 563
777 E Wisconsin Ave # 3800, Milwaukee WI 53202
Tel (414) 271-2400 SIC 8111

MICHAEL BEST & FRIEDRICH LLP p 960
100 E Wisconsin Ave # 3300, Milwaukee WI 53202
Tel (414) 271-6560 SIC 8111

OGLETREE DEAKINS NASH SMOAK & STEWART PC p 1077
1243 N 10th St Ste 210, Milwaukee WI 53205
Tel (414) 239-6400 SIC 8111

QUARLES & BRADY LLP p 1198
411 E Wisconsin Ave # 2040, Milwaukee WI 53202
Tel (414) 277-5000 SIC 8111

SIC 8211 Elementary & Secondary Schools

CALHOUN COUNTY SCHOOL DISTRICT p 238
4400 Mcclellan Blvd, Anniston AL 36206
Tel (256) 741-7400 SIC 8211

LIMESTONE COUNTY BOARD OF EDUCATION p 866
300 S Jefferson St, Athens AL 35611
Tel (256) 232-5353 SIC 8211

LIMESTONE COUNTY SCHOOL DISTRICT p 866
300 S Jefferson St, Athens AL 35611
Tel (256) 232-5353 SIC 8211

AUBURN CITY SCHOOL DISTRICT p 130
855 E Samford Ave, Auburn AL 36830
Tel (334) 887-2100 SIC 8211

BALDWIN COUNTY BOARD OF EDUCATION p 147
2600a Hand Ave, Bay Minette AL 36507
Tel (251) 937-0306 SIC 8211

BALDWIN COUNTY PUBLIC SCHOOLS p 147
2600a Hand Ave, Bay Minette AL 36507
Tel (251) 937-0306 SIC 8211

BIRMINGHAM CITY SCHOOLS p 185
2015 Park Pl, Birmingham AL 35203
Tel (205) 231-4600 SIC 8211

JEFFERSON COUNTY BOARD OF EDUCATION p 781
2100 Richard Arrington Jr, Birmingham AL 35209
Tel (205) 379-2000 *SIC* 8211 9111

JEFFERSON COUNTY SCHOOLS p 781
2100 Richard Arrington Jr, Birmingham AL 35209
Tel (205) 379-2000 *SIC* 8211

SHELBY CO SCHOOL DISTRICT p 1314
410 E College St, Columbiana AL 35051
Tel (205) 682-7000 *SIC* 8211

SHELBY COUNTY BOARD OF EDUCATION p 1314
410 E College St, Columbiana AL 35051
Tel (205) 682-7000 *SIC* 8211

CULLMAN COUNTY BOARD OF EDUCATION p 400
402 Arnold St Ne, Cullman AL 35055
Tel (256) 734-2933 *SIC* 8211

CULLMAN COUNTY SCHOOL DISTRICT p 400
402 Arnold St Ne, Cullman AL 35055
Tel (256) 734-2933 *SIC* 8211

DECATUR CITY BOARD OF EDUCATION p 420
302 4th Ave Ne, Decatur AL 35601
Tel (256) 552-3000 *SIC* 8211

DECATUR CITY SCHOOLS p 420
302 4th Ave Ne, Decatur AL 35601
Tel (256) 552-3000 *SIC* 8211

MORGAN COUNTY BOARD OF EDUCATION (INC) p 988
302 Fourth Ave, Decatur AL 35601
Tel (256) 309-2100 *SIC* 8211

MORGAN COUNTY SCHOOLS FOUNDATION p 988
235 Highway 67 S, Decatur AL 35603
Tel (256) 309-2100 *SIC* 8211

ARCHDIOCESE OF MOBILE ED OFF p 105
2700 W Main St, Dothan AL 36301
Tel (334) 793-6742 *SIC* 8211

DOTHAN CITY BOARD OF EDUCATION p 452
500 Dusy St, Dothan AL 36301
Tel (334) 793-1397 *SIC* 8211

DOTHAN CITY SCHOOLS p 452
500 Dusy St, Dothan AL 36301
Tel (334) 793-1397 *SIC* 8211

LAUDERDALE COUNTY BOARD OF EDUCATION p 847
355 County Road 61, Florence AL 35634
Tel (256) 760-1300 *SIC* 8211

LAUDERDALE COUNTY SCHOOL SYSTEM p 847
355 County Road 61, Florence AL 35634
Tel (256) 760-1300 *SIC* 8211

ETOWAH COUNTY BOARD OF EDUCATION p 512
3200 W Meighan Blvd, Gadsden AL 35904
Tel (256) 549-7560 *SIC* 8211

ETOWAH COUNTY SCHOOLS p 512
3200 W Meighan Blvd, Gadsden AL 35904
Tel (256) 549-7560 *SIC* 8211

HOOVER CITY SCHOOL DISTRICT p 706
2810 Metropolitan Way, Hoover AL 35216
Tel (205) 439-1000 *SIC* 8211

HUNTSVILLE CITY BOARD OF EDUCATION p 720
200 White St Se, Huntsville AL 35801
Tel (256) 428-6800 *SIC* 8211

HUNTSVILLE CITY SCHOOLS p 720
200 White St Se, Huntsville AL 35801
Tel (256) 428-6800 *SIC* 8211

MADISON COUNTY BOARD OF EDUCATION p 894
1275 Jordan Rd, Huntsville AL 35811
Tel (256) 852-2557 *SIC* 8211

MADISON COUNTY SCHOOLS p 894
1275 Jordan Rd, Huntsville AL 35811
Tel (256) 852-2557 *SIC* 8211

WALKER COUNTY BOARD OF EDUCATION p 1573
1710 Alabama Ave Ste 106, Jasper AL 35501
Tel (205) 387-2156 *SIC* 8211

BOARD OF SCHOOL COMMISSIONERS OF MOBILE COUNTY p 195
1 Magnum Pass, Mobile AL 36618
Tel (251) 221-3084 *SIC* 8211

MOBILE COUNTY PUBLIC SCHOOLS p 980
1 Magnum Pass, Mobile AL 36618
Tel (251) 221-4394 *SIC* 8211

MONTGOMERY PUBLIC SCHOOLS p 987
307 S Decatur St, Montgomery AL 36104
Tel (334) 223-6873 *SIC* 8211

LEE COUNTY SCHOOL DISTRICT p 851
2410 Society Hill Rd, Opelika AL 36804
Tel (334) 705-6000 *SIC* 8211

AUTAUGA COUNTY SCHOOL BOARD OF EDUCATION p 133
153 W 4th St, Prattville AL 36067
Tel (334) 365-5706 *SIC* 8211

AUTAUGA COUNTY SCHOOL SYSTEM p 133
153 W 4th St, Prattville AL 36067
Tel (334) 365-5706 *SIC* 8211

SARALAND CITY SCHOOLS p 1282
943 Highway 43 S, Saraland AL 36571
Tel (251) 375-5420 *SIC* 8211

SELMA PUBLIC SCHOOLS p 1302
2194 Broad St, Selma AL 36701
Tel (334) 874-1600 *SIC* 8211

ALABAMA INSTITUTE FOR DEAF AND BLIND p 43
205 South St E, Talladega AL 35160
Tel (256) 761-3200 *SIC* 8249 8211

TALLADEGA COUNTY BOARD OF EDUCATION p 1423
106 South St W Ste A, Talladega AL 35160
Tel (256) 362-1401 *SIC* 8211

PIKE COUNTY BOARD OF EDUCATION p 1148
101 W Love St, Troy AL 36081
Tel (334) 566-1850 *SIC* 8211

TUSCALOOSA CITY BOARD OF EDUCATION p 1493
1210 21st Ave, Tuscaloosa AL 35401
Tel (205) 759-3700 *SIC* 8211

TUSCALOOSA CITY SCHOOLS p 1493
1210 21st Ave, Tuscaloosa AL 35401
Tel (205) 759-3560 *SIC* 8211

TUSCALOOSA COUNTY BOARD OF EDUCATION p 1493
1118 Greensboro Ave, Tuscaloosa AL 35401
Tel (205) 758-0411 *SIC* 8211

ELMORE COUNTY SCHOOL DISTRICT p 489
100 H H Robinson Dr, Wetumpka AL 36092
Tel (334) 567-1200 *SIC* 8211

ANCHORAGE SCHOOL DISTRICT p 89
5530 E Nthrn Lights Blvd, Anchorage AK 99504
Tel (907) 742-4000 *SIC* 8211

FAIRBANKS NORTH STAR BOROUGH SCHOOL DISTRICT p 524
520 5th Ave, Fairbanks AK 99701
Tel (907) 452-2000 *SIC* 8211

MATANUSKA SUSITNA BOROUGH SCHOOL DISTRICT p 919
501 N Gulkana St, Palmer AK 99645
Tel (907) 746-9255 *SIC* 8211

KENAI PENINSULA BOROUGH SCHOOL DISTRICT p 810
148 N Binkley St, Soldotna AK 99669
Tel (907) 714-8888 *SIC* 8211

CHANDLER UNIFIED SCHOOL DISTRICT p 288
1525 W Frye Rd, Chandler AZ 85224
Tel (480) 812-7000 *SIC* 8211

CHANDLER UNIFIED SCHOOL DISTRICT 80-HHS AFJROTC p 288
3700 S Arizona Ave, Chandler AZ 85248
Tel (480) 883-5000 *SIC* 8211

FLAGSTAFF UNIFIED SCHOOL DISTRICT p 554
3285 E Sparrow Ave, Flagstaff AZ 86004
Tel (928) 527-6000 *SIC* 8211

GILBERT UNIFIED SCHOOL DISTRICT 41 p 612
140 S Gilbert Rd, Gilbert AZ 85296
Tel (480) 497-3452 *SIC* 8211

GLENDALE ELEMENTARY SCHOOL DISTRICT p 615
7301 N 58th Ave, Glendale AZ 85301
Tel (623) 237-4000 *SIC* 8211

GLENDALE UNION HIGH SCHOOL DISTRICT p 615
7650 N 43rd Ave, Glendale AZ 85301
Tel (623) 435-0152 *SIC* 8211

PEORIA UNIFIED SCHOOL DISTRICT NO11 p 1133
6330 W Thunderbird Rd, Glendale AZ 85306
Tel (623) 486-6000 *SIC* 8211

WASHINGTON ELEMENTARY SCHOOL DISTRICT 6 p 1578
4650 W Sweetwater Ave, Glendale AZ 85304
Tel (602) 347-2600 *SIC* 8211

LITCHFIELD ELEMENTARY SCHOOL DISTRICT 79 p 870
272 E Sagebrush St, Litchfield Park AZ 85340
Tel (623) 535-6000 *SIC* 8211

MARANA UNIFIED SCHOOL DISTRICT p 904
11279 W Grier Rd, Marana AZ 85653
Tel (520) 682-4749 *SIC* 8211

MARANA UNIFIED SCHOOL DISTRICT PARENT/CITIZEN ORGANIZATION p 904
11279 W Grier Rd, Marana AZ 85653
Tel (520) 682-3243 *SIC* 8211

MESA UNIFIED SCHOOL DISTRICT 4 p 951
63 E Main St Ste 101, Mesa AZ 85201
Tel (480) 472-0000 *SIC* 8211

ALHAMBRA SCHOOL DISTRICT 68 p 50
4510 N 37th Ave, Phoenix AZ 85019
Tel (602) 336-2920 *SIC* 8211

CARTWRIGHT SCHOOL DISTRICT NO83 p 262
5220 W Indian School Rd, Phoenix AZ 85031
Tel (623) 691-4000 *SIC* 8211

CREIGHTON SCHOOL DISTRICT p 391
2702 E Flower St, Phoenix AZ 85016
Tel (602) 381-6000 *SIC* 8211

DEER VALLEY SCHOOL DISTRICT 97 p 422
20402 N 15th Ave, Phoenix AZ 85027
Tel (623) 445-5000 *SIC* 8211

GREAT HEARTS ACADEMIES p 633
3102 N 56th St Ste 300, Phoenix AZ 85018
Tel (602) 438-7045 *SIC* 8211

LEONA GROUP L L C p 856
7878 N 16th St Ste 150, Phoenix AZ 85020
Tel (602) 953-2933 *SIC* 8211

PARADISE VALLEY UNIFIED SCHOOL DISTRICT p 1113
15002 N 32nd St, Phoenix AZ 85032
Tel (602) 867-5100 *SIC* 8211

PENDERGAST ELEMENTARY SCHOOL DISTRICT 92 p 1128
3802 N 91st Ave, Phoenix AZ 85037
Tel (623) 772-2200 *SIC* 8211

PHOENIX ELEMENTARY SCHOOL DISTRICT 1 p 1145
1817 N 7th St, Phoenix AZ 85006
Tel (602) 257-3755 *SIC* 8211

PHOENIX UNION HIGH SCHOOL DISTRICT NO 210 p 1145
4502 N Central Ave, Phoenix AZ 85012
Tel (602) 271-3302 *SIC* 8211

ROOSEVELT SCHOOL DISTRICT NO 66 p 1249
6000 S 7th St, Phoenix AZ 85042
Tel (602) 243-2624 *SIC* 8211

SCOTTSDALE UNIFIED SCHOOL DISTRICT p 1294
7575 E Main St, Scottsdale AZ 85251
Tel (480) 484-6100 *SIC* 8211

DYSART UNIFIED SCHOOL DISTRICT p 465
15802 N Parkview Pl, Surprise AZ 85374
Tel (623) 876-7000 *SIC* 8211

KYRENE ELEMENTARY DISTRICT p 833
8700 S Kyrene Rd, Tempe AZ 85284
Tel (480) 541-1000 *SIC* 8211

KYRENE SCHOOL DISTRICT p 833
8700 S Kyrene Rd, Tempe AZ 85284
Tel (480) 541-1000 *SIC* 8211

TEMPE ELEMENTARY SCHOOL DISTRICT p 1436
3205 S Rural Rd, Tempe AZ 85282
Tel (480) 730-7359 *SIC* 8211

TEMPE UNION HIGH SCHOOL DISTRICT 213 (INC) p 1436
500 W Guadalupe Rd, Tempe AZ 85283
Tel (480) 839-0292 *SIC* 8211

PIMA COUNTY AMPHITHEATER SCHOOLS p 1148
701 W Wetmore Rd, Tucson AZ 85705
Tel (520) 696-5000 *SIC* 8211

SUNNYSIDE UNIFIED SCHOOL DISTRICT 12 p 1403
2238 E Ginter Rd, Tucson AZ 85706
Tel (520) 545-2024 *SIC* 8211

TUCSON UNIFIED SCHOOL DISTRICT p 1490
1010 E 10th St, Tucson AZ 85719
Tel (520) 225-6000 *SIC* 8211

VISIONQUEST NONPROFIT CORP p 1561
600 N Swan Rd, Tucson AZ 85711
Tel (520) 881-3950 *SIC* 8361 8211 8322

VAIL SCHOOL DISTRICT p 1538
13801 E Benson Hwy Unit B, Vail AZ 85641
Tel (520) 879-2000 *SIC* 8211

YUMA SCHOOL DISTRICT ONE p 1640
450 W 6th St, Yuma AZ 85364
Tel (928) 782-6581 *SIC* 8211

BENTONVILLE SCHOOL DISTRICT 6 p 173
500 Tiger Blvd, Bentonville AR 72712
Tel (479) 254-5000 *SIC* 8211

BRYANT SCHOOL DISTRICT 25 p 221
200 Nw 4th St, Bryant AR 72022
Tel (501) 847-5600 *SIC* 8211

CABOT SCHOOL DISTRICT 4 (INC) p 235
602 N Lincoln St, Cabot AR 72023
Tel (501) 843-3363 *SIC* 8211

FAYETTEVILLE SCHOOL DISTRICT 1 p 532
1000 W Bulldog Blvd, Fayetteville AR 72701
Tel (479) 444-3000 *SIC* 8211

SPECIAL SCHOOL DISTRICT OF FORT SMITH p 1356
3205 Jenny Lind Rd, Fort Smith AR 72901
Tel (479) 785-2501 *SIC* 8211

PATHFINDER INC p 1120
2520 W Main St, Jacksonville AR 72076
Tel (501) 982-0528 *SIC* 8211

LITTLE ROCK SCHOOL DISTRICT p 871
810 W Markham St, Little Rock AR 72201
Tel (501) 447-1000 *SIC* 8211

PULASKI COUNTY SPECIAL SCHOOL DISTRICT p 1191
925 E Dixon Rd, Little Rock AR 72206
Tel (501) 490-2000 *SIC* 8211

NORTH LITTLE ROCK SCHOOL DISTRICT p 1053
2700 N Poplar St, North Little Rock AR 72114
Tel (501) 771-8000 *SIC* 8211

ROGERS SCHOOL DISTRICT 30 p 1246
500 W Walnut St, Rogers AR 72756
Tel (479) 636-3910 *SIC* 8211

FRIENDSHIP COMMUNITY CARE INC p 580
920 University Dr, Russellville AR 72801
Tel (479) 967-2316 *SIC* 8211

SPRINGDALE PUBLIC SCHOOL DISTRICT 50 p 1360
804 W Johnson Ave, Springdale AR 72764
Tel (479) 750-8800 *SIC* 8211

ADELANTO ELEMENTARY SCHOOL DISTRICT p 22
11824 Air Expy, Adelanto CA 92301
Tel (760) 246-8691 *SIC* 8211

ALAMEDA UNIFIED SCHOOL DISTRICT p 44
2060 Challenger Dr, Alameda CA 94501
Tel (510) 337-7060 *SIC* 8211 8299

ALHAMBRA UNIFIED SCHOOL DISTRICT p 50
1515 W Mission Rd, Alhambra CA 91803
Tel (626) 943-3000 *SIC* 8211

ANAHEIM CITY SCHOOL DISTRICT p 88
1001 S East St, Anaheim CA 92805
Tel (714) 517-7500 *SIC* 8211

ANAHEIM UNION HIGH SCHOOL DIST p 88
501 N Crescent Way, Anaheim CA 92801
Tel (714) 999-3511 *SIC* 8211

ANTIOCH UNIFIED SCHOOL DISTRICT p 94
510 G St, Antioch CA 94509
Tel (925) 779-7500 *SIC* 8211

APPLE VALLEY UNIFIED SCHOOL DISTRICT PUBLIC FACILITIES CORP p 99
12555 Navajo Rd, Apple Valley CA 92308
Tel (760) 247-7267 *SIC* 8211

LUCIA MAR UNIFIED SCHOOL DISTRICT p 884
602 Orchard Ave, Arroyo Grande CA 93420
Tel (805) 474-3000 *SIC* 8211

MERCED UNION HIGH SCHOOL DISTRICT CAPITAL FACILITIES CORP p 944
3430 A St, Atwater CA 95301
Tel (209) 385-6400 *SIC* 8211

AZUSA UNIFIED SCHOOL DISTRICT p 141
546 S Citrus Ave, Azusa CA 91702
Tel (626) 967-6211 *SIC* 8211

AZUSA UNIFIED SCHOOL DISTRICT FACILITIES CORP p 141
546 S Citrus Ave, Azusa CA 91702
Tel (626) 858-6159 *SIC* 8211

BAKERSFIELD CITY SCHOOL DISTRICT EDUCATIONAL FOUNDATION p 146
1300 Baker St, Bakersfield CA 93305
Tel (661) 631-4600 *SIC* 8211

GREENFIELD UNION SCHOOL DISTRICT p 638
1624 Fairview Rd, Bakersfield CA 93307
Tel (661) 837-6000 *SIC* 8211 9411

KERN COUNTY SUPERINTENDENT OF SCHOOLS EDUCATIONAL SERVICES FOUNDATION p 813
1300 17th St, Bakersfield CA 93301
Tel (661) 636-4000 *SIC* 8211

KERN HIGH SCHOOL DST p 813
5801 Sundale Ave, Bakersfield CA 93309
Tel (661) 827-3100 *SIC* 8211

PANAMA-BUENA VISTA UNION SCHOOL DISTRICT p 1111
4200 Ashe Rd, Bakersfield CA 93313
Tel (661) 831-8331 *SIC* 8211

BALDWIN PARK UNIFIED SCHOOL DISTRICT p 147
3699 Holly Ave, Baldwin Park CA 91706
Tel (626) 939-4000 *SIC* 8211

BELLFLOWER UNIFIED SCHOOL DISTRICT p 170
16703 Clark Ave, Bellflower CA 90706
Tel (562) 866-9011 *SIC* 8211

BERKELEY UNIFIED SCHOOL DISTRICT p 175
2020 Bonar St Rm 202, Berkeley CA 94702
Tel (510) 644-4500 *SIC* 8211

BURBANK UNIFIED SCHOOL DISTRICT p 226
1900 W Olive Ave, Burbank CA 91506
Tel (818) 729-4400 *SIC* 8211

PLEASANT VALLEY SCHOOL DISTRICT p 1156
600 Temple Ave, Camarillo CA 93010
Tel (805) 445-8637 *SIC* 8211

CARLSBAD UNIFIED SCHOOL DISTRICT p 257
6225 El Camino Real, Carlsbad CA 92009
Tel (760) 331-5000 *SIC* 8211

SAN JUAN UNIFIED SCHOOL DISTRICT p 1277
3738 Walnut Ave, Carmichael CA 95608
Tel (916) 971-7700 *SIC* 8211

CERES UNIFIED SCHOOL DISTRICT p 283
2503 Lawrence St, Ceres CA 95307
Tel (209) 556-1500 *SIC* 8211

A B C UNIFIED SCHOOL DISTRICT p 5
16700 Norwalk Blvd, Cerritos CA 90703
Tel (562) 926-5567 *SIC* 8211

BEAUMONT UNIFIED SCHOOL DISTRICT p 166
350 W Brookside Ave, Cherry Valley CA 92223
Tel (951) 845-1631 *SIC* 8211

CHICO UNIFIED SCHOOL DISTRICT p 298
1163 E 7th St, Chico CA 95928
Tel (530) 891-3000 *SIC* 8211

CHINO VALLEY UNIFIED SCHOOL DISTRICT p 301
5130 Riverside Dr, Chino CA 91710
Tel (909) 628-1201 *SIC* 8211

CHULA VISTA ELEM SCHOOL DISTRICT p 305
84 E J St, Chula Vista CA 91910
Tel (619) 425-9600 *SIC* 8211

SWEETWATER UNION HIGH SCHOOL DISTRICT p 1412
1130 Fifth Ave, Chula Vista CA 91911
Tel (619) 691-5500 *SIC* 8211

HACIENDA-LA PUENTE UNIFIED SCHOOL DISTRICT p 652
15959 Gale Ave, City Of Industry CA 91745
Tel (626) 933-1000 *SIC* 8211

CLOVIS UNIFIED SCHOOL DISTRICT p 328
1450 Herndon Ave, Clovis CA 93611
Tel (559) 327-9000 *SIC* 8211

COLTON JOINT UNIFIED SCHOOL DISTRICT p 340
1212 Valencia Dr, Colton CA 92324
Tel (909) 580-5000 *SIC* 8211

COMPTON UNIFIED SCHOOL DISTRICT p 352
501 S Santa Fe Ave, Compton CA 90221
Tel (310) 604-6508 *SIC* 8211

MT DIABLO UNIFIED SCHOOL DISTRICT p 997
1936 Carlotta Dr, Concord CA 94519
Tel (925) 682-8000 *SIC* 8211

ALVORD UNIFIED SCHOOL DISTRICT p 63
9 Kpc Pkwy, Corona CA 92879
Tel (951) 509-5000 *SIC* 8211

NEWPORT MESA UNIFIED SCHOOL DISTRICT p 1038
2985 Bear St Ste A, Costa Mesa CA 92626
Tel (714) 424-5000 *SIC* 8211

ORANGE COUNTY SUPERINTENDENT OF SCHOOLS p 1092
200 Kalmus Dr, Costa Mesa CA 92626
Tel (714) 966-4000 *SIC* 8211

COVINA-VALLEY UNIFIED SCHOOL DISTRICT FACILITIES FINANCE CORP p 385
519 E Badillo St, Covina CA 91723
Tel (626) 974-7000 *SIC* 8211

CUPERTINO UNION SCHOOL DISTRICT p 401
10301 Vista Dr, Cupertino CA 95014
Tel (408) 252-3000 *SIC* 8211

SAN RAMON VALLEY UNIFIED SCHOOL DISTRICT p 1277
699 Old Orchard Dr, Danville CA 94526
Tel (925) 552-5500 *SIC* 8211

DOWNEY UNIFIED SCHOOL DISTRICT p 453
11627 Brookshire Ave, Downey CA 90241
Tel (562) 904-3500 *SIC* 8211

LOS ANGELES COUNTY OFFICE OF EDUCATION p 878
9300 Imperial Hwy, Downey CA 90242
Tel (562) 922-6111 *SIC* 8211

DUBLIN UNIFIED SCHOOL DISTRICT p 459
7471 Larkdale Ave, Dublin CA 94568
Tel (925) 828-2551 *SIC* 8211

CAJON VALLEY UNION SCHOOL DISTRICT p 237
750 E Main St, El Cajon CA 92020
Tel (619) 588-3000 *SIC* 8211

GROSSMONT UNION HIGH SCHOOL DISTRICT SCHOOL FACILITIES CORP p 641
1100 Murray Dr, El Cajon CA 92020
Tel (619) 644-8000 *SIC* 8211

EL MONTE CITY SCHOOL DISTRICT p 483
3540 Lexington Ave, El Monte CA 91731
Tel (626) 453-3700 *SIC* 8211

EL MONTE UNION HIGH SCHOOL DISTRICT p 483
3537 Johnson Ave, El Monte CA 91731
Tel (626) 258-4905 *SIC* 8211

MOUNTAIN VIEW ELEMENTARY SCHOOL DISTRICT p 994
3320 Gilman Rd, El Monte CA 91732
Tel (626) 652-4000 *SIC* 8211

GROVE ELK UNIFIED SCHOOL DISTRICT p 642
9510 Elk Grove Florin Rd, Elk Grove CA 95624
Tel (916) 686-5085 *SIC* 8211

ESCONDIDO UNION SCHOOL DISTRICT p 509
2310 Aldergrove Ave, Escondido CA 92029
Tel (760) 432-2400 *SIC* 8211

ETIWANDA SCHOOL DISTRICT p 511
6061 East Ave, Etiwanda CA 91739
Tel (909) 899-2451 *SIC* 8211

FAIRFIELD-SUISUN UNIFIED SCHOOL DISTRICT p 525
2490 Hilborn Rd, Fairfield CA 94534
Tel (707) 399-5000 *SIC* 8211

FONTANA UNIFIED SCHOOL DISTRICT p 563
9680 Citrus Ave, Fontana CA 92335
Tel (909) 357-7600 *SIC* 8211

SAN MATEO-FOSTER CITY SCHOOL DISTRICT p 1277
1170 Chess Dr, Foster City CA 94404
Tel (650) 312-7700 *SIC* 8211

FREMONT UNIFIED SCHOOL DISTRICT p 578
4210 Technology Dr, Fremont CA 94538
Tel (510) 657-2350 *SIC* 8211

CENTRAL UNIFIED SCHOOL DISTRICT p 280
4605 N Polk Ave, Fresno CA 93722
Tel (559) 274-4700 *SIC* 8211

DIOCESE OF FRESNO EDUCATION CORP p 440
1550 N Fresno St, Fresno CA 93703
Tel (559) 488-7400 *SIC* 8211 8661

FRESNO COUNTY SUPERINTENDENT OF SCHOOLS p 579
1111 Van Ness Ave, Fresno CA 93721
Tel (559) 265-3000 *SIC* 8211

FRESNO UNIFIED SCHOOL DISTRICT p 579
2309 Tulare St, Fresno CA 93721
Tel (559) 457-3000 *SIC* 8211

FULLERTON JOINT UNION HIGH SCHOOL DISTRICT EDUCATIONAL FOUNDATION p 584
1051 W Bastanchury Rd, Fullerton CA 92833
Tel (714) 870-2800 *SIC* 8211

GARDEN GROVE UNIFIED SCHOOL DISTRICT p 591
10331 Stanford Ave, Garden Grove CA 92840
Tel (714) 663-6000 *SIC* 8211

GLENDALE UNIFIED SCHOOL DISTRICT p 615
223 N Jackson St, Glendale CA 91206
Tel (818) 241-3111 *SIC* 8211

HAYWARD UNIFIED SCHOOL DISTRICT p 670
24411 Amador St, Hayward CA 94544
Tel (510) 784-2600 *SIC* 8211

HEMET UNIFIED SCHOOL DISTRICT p 682
1791 W Acacia Ave, Hemet CA 92545
Tel (951) 765-5100 *SIC* 8211

HESPERIA UNIFIED SCHOOL DISTRICT p 688
15576 Main St, Hesperia CA 92345
Tel (760) 244-4411 *SIC* 8211

HUNTINGTON BEACH UNION HIGH SCHOOL DISTRICT p 720
5832 Bolsa Ave, Huntington Beach CA 92649
Tel (714) 903-7000 *SIC* 8211

OCEAN VIEW SCHOOL DISTRICT (INC) p 1073
17200 Pinehurst Ln, Huntington Beach CA 92647
Tel (714) 847-2551 *SIC* 8211

SOUTH BAY UNION SCHOOL DISTRICT p 1342
601 Elm Ave, Imperial Beach CA 91932
Tel (619) 628-1600 *SIC* 8211

INGLEWOOD UNIFIED SCHOOL DISTRICT p 743
401 S Inglewood Ave, Inglewood CA 90301
Tel (310) 419-2500 *SIC* 8211

IRVINE UNIFIED SCHOOL DISTICT p 765
5050 Barranca Pkwy, Irvine CA 92604
Tel (949) 936-5000 *SIC* 8211

JURUPA UNIFIED SCHOOL DISTRICT p 797
4850 Pedley Rd, Jurupa Valley CA 92509
Tel (951) 360-4100 *SIC* 8211

LA MESA-SPRING VALLEY SCHOOL DISTRICT p 835
4750 Date Ave, La Mesa CA 91942
Tel (619) 668-5700 *SIC* 8211

DESERT SANDS UNIFIED SCHOOL DISTRICT SCHOOL BUILDING CORP p 432
47950 Dune Palms Rd, La Quinta CA 92253
Tel (760) 771-8567 *SIC* 8211

LAKE ELSINORE UNIFIED SCHOOL DISTRICT p 839
545 Chaney St, Lake Elsinore CA 92530
Tel (951) 253-7000 *SIC* 8211

ANTELOPE VALLEY UNION HIGH SCHOOL DISTRICT p 93
44811 Sierra Hwy, Lancaster CA 93534
Tel (661) 948-7655 *SIC* 8211

LANCASTER SCHOOL DISTRICT p 841
44711 Cedar Ave, Lancaster CA 93534
Tel (661) 948-4661 *SIC* 8211

LINDEN UNIFIED SCHOOL DISTRICT p 868
18527 E Highway 26, Linden CA 95236
Tel (209) 887-3894 *SIC* 8211

LIVERMORE VALLEY JOINT UNIFIED SCHOOL DISTRICT p 871
685 E Jack London Blvd, Livermore CA 94551
Tel (925) 606-3200 *SIC* 8211

LODI UNIFIED SCHOOL DISTRICT p 874
1305 E Vine St, Lodi CA 95240
Tel (209) 331-7000 *SIC* 8211

LOMPOC UNIFIED SCHOOL DISTRICT p 875
1301 N A St, Lompoc CA 93436
Tel (805) 742-3300 *SIC* 8211

LONG BEACH UNIFIED SCHOOL DISTRICT p 876
1515 Hughes Way, Long Beach CA 90810
Tel (562) 997-8000 *SIC* 8211

GREEN DOT PUBLIC SCHOOLS CALIFORNIA p 637
1149 S Hill St Ste 600, Los Angeles CA 90015
Tel (323) 565-1600 *SIC* 8211

GREEN DOT PUBLIC SCHOOLS NATIONAL p 637
1149 S Hill St Fl 6, Los Angeles CA 90015
Tel (323) 565-1600 *SIC* 8211

INTERNATIONAL CHURCH OF FOURSQUARE GOSPEL p 754
1910 W Sunset Blvd # 200, Los Angeles CA 90026
Tel (213) 989-4234
SIC 8661 6512 7032 8211 8221

LOS ANGELES UNIFIED SCHOOL DISTRICT p 879
333 S Beaudry Ave Ste 209, Los Angeles CA 90017
Tel (213) 241-1000 *SIC* 8211

LOYOLA MARYMOUNT UNIVERSITY INC p 882
1 Lmu Dr Ste 100, Los Angeles CA 90045
Tel (310) 338-2700 *SIC* 8211

LYNWOOD UNIFIED SCHOOL DISTRICT p 888
11321 Bullis Rd, Lynwood CA 90262
Tel (310) 639-5627 *SIC* 8211

MADERA UNIFIED SCHOOL DISTRICT p 894
1902 Howard Rd, Madera CA 93637
Tel (559) 675-4500 *SIC* 8211

MANTECA UNIFIED SCHOOL DISTRICT p 903
2271 W Louise Ave, Manteca CA 95337
Tel (209) 825-3200 *SIC* 8211

MARYSVILLE JOINT UNIFIED SCHOOL DISTRICT p 915
1919 B St, Marysville CA 95901
Tel (530) 741-6000 *SIC* 8211

TWIN RIVERS UNIFIED SCHOOL DISTRICT p 1495
5115 Dudley Blvd, Mcclellan CA 95652
Tel (916) 566-1600 *SIC* 8211

MERCED CITY SCHOOL DISTRICT p 944
444 W 23rd St, Merced CA 95340
Tel (209) 385-6600 *SIC* 8211

MERCED COUNTY OFFICE OF EDUCATION p 944
632 W 13th St, Merced CA 95341
Tel (209) 381-6600 *SIC* 8211

MILPITAS UNIFIED SCHOOL DISTRICT p 972
1331 E Calaveras Blvd, Milpitas CA 95035
Tel (408) 635-2600 *SIC* 8211

SADDLEBACK VALLEY UNIFIED SCHOOL DISTRICT p 1265
25631 Peter Hartman Way, Mission Viejo CA 92691
Tel (949) 586-1234 *SIC* 8211

MODESTO CITY SCHOOL DISTRICT p 981
426 Locust St, Modesto CA 95351
Tel (209) 576-4011 *SIC* 8211

SYLVAN UNION SCHOOL DISTRICT p 1413
605 Sylvan Ave, Modesto CA 95350
Tel (209) 574-5000 *SIC* 8211

MONTEBELLO UNIFIED SCHOOL DISTRICT PROTECTIVE LEAGUE p 986
123 S Montebello Blvd, Montebello CA 90640
Tel (323) 887-7900 *SIC* 8211

MONTEREY PENINSULA UNIFIED SCHOOL DISTRICT p 986
700 Pacific St, Monterey CA 93940
Tel (831) 392-3915 *SIC* 8211

MORENO VALLEY UNIFIED SCHOOL DISTRICT p 988
25634 Alessandro Blvd, Moreno Valley CA 92553
Tel (951) 571-7500 *SIC* 8211

MURRIETA VALLEY UNIFIED SCHOOL DISTRICT p 1002
41870 Mcalby Ct, Murrieta CA 92562
Tel (951) 696-1600 *SIC* 8211

NAPA VALLEY UNIFIED SCHOOL DISTRICT p 1007
2425 Jefferson St, Napa CA 94558
Tel (707) 253-3715 *SIC* 8211

NATIONAL SCHOOL DISTRICT p 1016
1500 N Ave, National City CA 91950
Tel (619) 336-7500 *SIC* 8211

NORWALK LA MIRADA UNIFIED SCHOOL DISTRICT p 1061
12820 Pioneer Blvd, Norwalk CA 90650
Tel (562) 868-0431 *SIC* 8211

ASPIRE PUBLIC SCHOOLS p 118
1001 22nd Ave Ste 100, Oakland CA 94606
Tel (510) 251-1660 *SIC* 8211

OAKLAND UNIFIED SCHOOL DISTRICT p 1071
1000 Broadway Fl 4, Oakland CA 94607
Tel (510) 434-7790 *SIC* 8211

ROMAN CATHOLIC WELFARE CORP OF OAKLAND p 1249
3014 Lakeshore Ave, Oakland CA 94610
Tel (510) 893-4711 *SIC* 8211

OCEANSIDE UNIFIED SCHOOL DISTRICT p 1073
2111 Mission Ave, Oceanside CA 92058
Tel (760) 966-4000 *SIC* 8211

CHAFFEY JOINT UNION HIGH SCHOOL DISTRICT p 286
211 W 5th St, Ontario CA 91762
Tel (909) 988-8511 *SIC* 8211

ONTARIO-MONTCLAIR SCHOOL DISTRICT p 1088
950 W D St, Ontario CA 91762
Tel (909) 459-2500 *SIC* 8211

ORANGE UNIFIED SCHOOL DISTRICT p 1092
1401 N Handy St, Orange CA 92867
Tel (714) 628-4000 *SIC* 8211

BUTTE COUNTY OFFICE OF EDUCATION p 230
1859 Bird St, Oroville CA 95965
Tel (530) 532-5650 *SIC* 8211

OXNARD SCHOOL DISTRICT p 1101
1051 S A St, Oxnard CA 93030
Tel (805) 487-3918 *SIC* 8211

OXNARD UNION HIGH SCHOOL DIST p 1101
309 S K St, Oxnard CA 93030
Tel (805) 385-2500 *SIC* 8211

PALM SPRINGS UNIFIED SCHOOL DIST p 1109
980 E Tahquitz Canyon Way, Palm Springs CA 92262
Tel (760) 416-6177 *SIC* 8211

PALMDALE SCHOOL DISTRICT p 1109
39139 10th St E, Palmdale CA 93550
Tel (661) 947-7191 *SIC* 8211

PALO ALTO UNIFIED SCHOOL DISTRICT p 1110
25 Churchill Ave, Palo Alto CA 94306
Tel (650) 329-3804 *SIC* 8211

PALOMAR MOUNTAIN OUTDOOR SCHOOL CAMP p 1110
19452 State Park Rd, Palomar Mountain CA 92060
Tel (760) 742-2128 *SIC* 8211

PARAMOUNT UNIFIED SCHOOL DISTRICT p 1114
15110 California Ave, Paramount CA 90723
Tel (562) 602-6000 *SIC* 8211

PASADENA UNIFIED SCHOOL DISTRICT p 1119
351 S Hudson Ave, Pasadena CA 91101
Tel (626) 396-3600 *SIC* 8211

VAL VERDE UNIFIED SCH DIS p 1539
975 Morgan St, Perris CA 92571
Tel (951) 940-6100 *SIC* 8211

PITTSBURG UNIFIED SCHOOL DISTRICT FINANCING CORP p 1152
2000 Railroad Ave, Pittsburg CA 94565
Tel (925) 473-2300 *SIC* 8211

PLACENTIA-YORBA LINDA UNIFIED SCHOOL DISTRICT p 1153
1301 E Orangethorpe Ave, Placentia CA 92870
Tel (714) 986-7000 *SIC* 8211

NORTHERN CALIFORNIA CONFERENCE OF SEVENTH-DAY ADVENTISTS p 1055
401 Taylor Blvd, Pleasant Hill CA 94523
Tel (925) 685-4300 *SIC* 8211 8661

PLEASANTON UNIFIED SCHOOL DISTRICT p 1156
4665 Bernal Ave, Pleasanton CA 94566
Tel (925) 462-5500 *SIC* 8211

POMONA UNIFIED SCHOOL DISTRICT p 1161
800 S Garey Ave, Pomona CA 91766
Tel (909) 397-4700 *SIC* 8211

CORDOVA FOLSOM UNIFIED SCHOOL DISTRICT p 369
1965 Birkmont Dr, Rancho Cordova CA 95742
Tel (916) 294-9000 *SIC* 8211

REDLANDS UNIFIED SCHOOL DISTRICT p 1217
20 W Lugonia Ave, Redlands CA 92374
Tel (909) 307-5300 *SIC* 8211

SEQUOIA UNION HIGH SCHOOL DISTRICT p 1306
480 James Ave, Redwood City CA 94062
Tel (650) 369-1411 *SIC* 8211

RIALTO UNIFIED SCHOOL DISTRICT p 1232
182 E Walnut Ave, Rialto CA 92376
Tel (909) 820-7700 *SIC* 8211

WEST CONTRA COSTA UNIFIED SCHOOL DISTRICT p 1594
1108 Bissell Ave, Richmond CA 94801
Tel (510) 231-1100 *SIC* 8211

RIVERSIDE COUNTY OFFICE OF EDUCATION p 1238
3939 13th St, Riverside CA 92501
Tel (951) 826-6530 *SIC* 8211 8249

RIVERSIDE COUNTY SCHOOLS p 1238
11840 Magnolia Ave Ste G, Riverside CA 92503
Tel (951) 788-7274 *SIC* 8211

RIVERSIDE UNIFIED SCHOOL DISTRICT p 1238
3380 14th St, Riverside CA 92501
Tel (951) 788-7135 *SIC* 8211

SOUTHEASTERN CALIFORNIA CONFERENCE OF SEVENTH-DAY ADVENTISTS p 1346
11330 Pierce St, Riverside CA 92505
Tel (951) 509-2200 *SIC* 8211 8661

ROCKLIN UNIFIED SCHOOL DISTRICT p 1245
2615 Sierra Meadows Dr, Rocklin CA 95677
Tel (916) 624-2428 *SIC* 8211

ROWLAND UNIFIED SCHOOL DISTRICT p 1253
1830 Nogales St, Rowland Heights CA 91748
Tel (626) 854-8317 *SIC* 8211

NATOMAS UNIFIED SCHOOL DISTRICT p 1018
1901 Arena Blvd, Sacramento CA 95834
Tel (916) 567-5400 *SIC* 8211

SALINAS UNION HIGH SCHOOL DISTRICT SCHOOL BUILDING CORP p 1272
431 W Alisal St, Salinas CA 93901
Tel (831) 796-7000 *SIC* 8211

SAN BERNARDINO CITY UNIFIED SCHOOL DISTRICT p 1275
777 N F St, San Bernardino CA 92410
Tel (909) 381-1100 *SIC* 8211

SAN BERNARDINO COUNTY SCHOOL DISTRICT p 1275
601 N E St, San Bernardino CA 92415
Tel (909) 386-2417 *SIC* 8211

UNIVERSITY ENTERPRISES CORP AT CSUSB p 1518
5500 University Pkwy, San Bernardino CA 92407
Tel (909) 537-5929 *SIC* 5812 5942 8211

POWAY UNIFIED SCHOOL DISTRICT p 1164
15250 Ave Of Science, San Diego CA 92128
Tel (858) 748-0010 *SIC* 8211

SAN DIEGO COUNTY OFFICE OF EDUCATION p 1276
6401 Linda Vista Rd, San Diego CA 92111
Tel (858) 292-3500 *SIC* 8211

SAN DIEGO UNIFIED SCHOOL DISTRICT p 1276
4100 Normal St, San Diego CA 92103
Tel (619) 725-8000 *SIC* 8211

SOUTHERN CAL SCHOOLS VOL EMP BENEFITS ASSOC p 1347
8885 Rio San Diego Dr # 327, San Diego CA 92108
Tel (619) 278-0021 *SIC* 8211

BONITA UNIFIED SCHOOL DISTRICT p 200
115 W Allen Ave, San Dimas CA 91773
Tel (909) 971-8200 *SIC* 8211

SAN FRANCISCO UNIFIED SCHOOL DISTRICT p 1277
555 Franklin St, San Francisco CA 94102
Tel (415) 241-6000 *SIC* 8211 8741

SAN FRANCISCO UNIFIED SCHOOL DISTRICT BOARD OF EDUCATION p 1277
555 Franklin St, San Francisco CA 94102
Tel (415) 241-6000 *SIC* 8211

ALUM ROCK UNION ELEMENTARY SCHOOL DISTRICT p 63
2930 Gay Ave, San Jose CA 95127
Tel (408) 928-6800 *SIC* 8211

CAMPBELL UNION HIGH SCHOOL DIST p 246
3235 Union Ave, San Jose CA 95124
Tel (408) 371-0960 *SIC* 8211

EASTSIDE UNION HIGH SCHOOL DISTRICT p 473
830 N Capitol Ave, San Jose CA 95133
Tel (408) 347-5000 *SIC* 8211

EVERGREEN SCHOOL DISTRICT p 515
3188 Quimby Rd, San Jose CA 95148
Tel (408) 270-6800 *SIC* 8211

GROVE OAK SCHOOL DISTRICT p 642
6578 Santa Teresa Blvd, San Jose CA 95119
Tel (408) 227-8300 *SIC* 8211

SAN JOSE UNIFIED SCHOOL DISTRICT p 1277
855 Lenzen Ave, San Jose CA 95126
Tel (408) 535-6000 *SIC* 8211

SANTA CLARA COUNTY OFFICE OF EDUCATION p 1280
1290 Ridder Park Dr, San Jose CA 95131
Tel (408) 453-6500 *SIC* 8211

CAPISTRANO UNIFIED SCHOOL DISTRICT p 249
33122 Valle Rd, San Juan Capistrano CA 92675
Tel (949) 234-9200 *SIC* 8211

SAN LORENZO UNIFIED SCHOOL DISTRICT p 1277
15510 Usher St, San Lorenzo CA 94580
Tel (510) 317-4600 *SIC* 8211

SAN MARCOS UNIFIED SCHOOL DISTRICT p 1277
255 Pico Ave Ste 250, San Marcos CA 92069
Tel (760) 744-4776 *SIC* 8211

SANGER UNIFIED SCHOOL DISTRICT p 1279
1905 7th St, Sanger CA 93657
Tel (559) 237-3171 *SIC* 8211

SANTA ANA UNIFIED SCHOOL DISTRICT PUBLIC FACILITIES CORP p 1280
1601 E Chestnut Ave, Santa Ana CA 92701
Tel (714) 558-5501 *SIC* 8211

SANTA BARBARA UNIFIED SCHOOL DISTRICT p 1280
720 Santa Barbara St, Santa Barbara CA 93101
Tel (805) 963-4338 *SIC* 8211

SANTA CLARA UNIFIED SCHOOL DISTRICT p 1280
1889 Lawrence Rd, Santa Clara CA 95051
Tel (408) 423-2000 *SIC* 8211

SAUGUS UNION SCHOOL DISTRICT p 1283
24930 Avenue Stanford, Santa Clarita CA 91355
Tel (661) 294-5300 *SIC* 8211

WILLIAM S HART UNION HIGH SCHOOL DISTRICT p 1611
21380 Centre Pointe Pkwy, Santa Clarita CA 91350
Tel (661) 259-0033 *SIC* 8211

SANTA MARIA-BONITA SCHOOL DIST p 1281
708 S Miller St, Santa Maria CA 93454
Tel (805) 928-1783 *SIC* 8211

LUTHER BURBANK CORP p 886
520 3rd St Fl 4, Santa Rosa CA 95401
Tel (707) 523-9898 *SIC* 8211

SANTA ROSA CITY SCHOOL DIST p 1281
211 Ridgway Ave, Santa Rosa CA 95401
Tel (707) 528-5409 *SIC* 8211

SANTEE SCHOOL DISTRICT p 1281
9625 Cuyamaca St, Santee CA 92071
Tel (619) 258-2300 *SIC* 8211

SIMI VALLEY UNIFIED SCHOOL DISTRICT p 1324
875 Cochran St, Simi Valley CA 93065
Tel (805) 306-4500 *SIC* 8211

SOUTH SAN FRANCISCO UNIFIED SCHOOL DISTRICT p 1345
398 B St, South San Francisco CA 94080
Tel (650) 877-8700 *SIC* 8211

DIOCESE OF STOCKTON EDUCATIONAL OFFICE p 441
212 N San Joaquin St, Stockton CA 95202
Tel (209) 466-0636 *SIC* 8211

STOCKTON UNIFIED SCHOOL DISTRICT p 1390
701 N Madison St, Stockton CA 95202
Tel (209) 933-7000 *SIC* 8211

TEMECULA VALLEY UNIFIED SCHOOL DISTRICT p 1436
31350 Rancho Vista Rd, Temecula CA 92592
Tel (951) 676-2661 *SIC* 8211

COACHELLA VALLEY UNIFIED SCHDIST p 331
87225 Church St, Thermal CA 92274
Tel (760) 399-5137 *SIC* 8211

CONEJO VALLEY UNIFIED SCHOOL DISTRICT p 355
1400 E Janss Rd, Thousand Oaks CA 91362
Tel (805) 497-9511 *SIC* 8211

TORRANCE UNIFIED SCHOOL DISTRICT p 1462
2335 Plaza Del Amo, Torrance CA 90501
Tel (310) 972-6500 *SIC* 8211

TRACY UNIFIED SCHOOL DISTRICT p 1468
1875 W Lowell Ave, Tracy CA 95376
Tel (209) 830-3200 *SIC* 8211

TUSTIN UNIFIED SCHOOL DISTRICT p 1493
300 S C St, Tustin CA 92780
Tel (714) 730-7515 *SIC* 8211

MORONGO UNIFIED SCHOOL DISTRICT p 989
5715 Utah Trl, Twentynine Palms CA 92277
Tel (760) 367-9191 *SIC* 8211

NEW HAVEN UNIFIED SCHOOL DISTRICT p 1030
34200 Alvarado Niles Rd, Union City CA 94587
Tel (510) 471-1100 *SIC* 8211

UPLAND UNIFIED SCHOOL DISTRICT p 1528
390 N Euclid Ave Ste 100, Upland CA 91786
Tel (909) 985-1864 *SIC* 8211

VACAVILLE UNIFIED SCHOOL DISTRICT p 1538
401 NutTree Rd Ste 100, Vacaville CA 95687
Tel (707) 453-6121 *SIC* 8211

VALLEJO CITY UNIFIED SCHOOL DISTRICT p 1540
665 Walnut Ave, Vallejo CA 94592
Tel (707) 556-8921 *SIC* 8211

VENTURA UNIFIED SCHOOL DISTRICT p 1548
255 W Stanley Ave Ste 100, Ventura CA 93001
Tel (805) 641-5000 *SIC* 8211

VICTOR ELEMENTARY SCHOOL DISTRICT p 1555
12219 Second Ave, Victorville CA 92395
Tel (760) 245-1691 *SIC* 8211

VISALIA UNIFIED SCHOOL DISTRICT p 1560
5000 W Cypress Ave, Visalia CA 93277
Tel (559) 730-7529 *SIC* 8211 8299

VISTA UNIFIED SCHOOL DISTRICT INC p 1562
1234 Arcadia Ave, Vista CA 92084
Tel (760) 726-2170 *SIC* 8211

WALNUT VALLEY UNIFIED SCHOOL DISTRICT p 1574
880 S Lemon Ave, Walnut CA 91789
Tel (909) 595-1261 *SIC* 8211

PAJARO VALLEY UNIFIED SCHOOL DISTRICT p 1108
294 Green Valley Rd Fl 1, Watsonville CA 95076
Tel (831) 786-2100 *SIC* 8211

WESTMINSTER SCHOOL DISTRICT p 1601
14121 Cedarwood St, Westminster CA 92683
Tel (714) 892-8946 *SIC* 8211

WHITTIER UNION HIGH SCHOOL DIST p 1607
9401 Painter Ave, Whittier CA 90605
Tel (562) 698-8121 *SIC* 8211

WOODLAND JOINT UNIFIED SCHOOL DISTRICT p 1623
435 6th St, Woodland CA 95695
Tel (530) 662-0201 *SIC* 8211

AURORA PUBLIC SCHOOLS p 132
15701 E 1st Ave Ste 106, Aurora CO 80011
Tel (303) 365-5810 *SIC* 8211

BOULDER VALLEY SCHOOL DISTRICT RE-2 p 204
6500 Arapahoe Rd, Boulder CO 80303
Tel (303) 447-1010 *SIC* 8211

SCHOOL DISTRICT 27J CAPITAL FACILITY FEE FOUNDATION p 1289
18551 E 160th Ave, Brighton CO 80601
Tel (303) 655-2900 *SIC* 8211

ACADEMY SCHOOL DISTRICT 20 p 13
1110 Chapel Hills Dr, Colorado Springs CO 80920
Tel (719) 234-1200 *SIC* 8211

COLORADO SPRINGS SCHOOL DISTRICT 11 p 339
1115 N El Paso St, Colorado Springs CO 80903
Tel (719) 520-2000 *SIC* 8211

HARRISON SCHOOL DISTRICT TWO p 664
1060 Harrison Rd, Colorado Springs CO 80905
Tel (719) 579-2000 *SIC* 8211

WIDEFIELD SCHOOL DISTRICT 3 p 1608
1820 Main St, Colorado Springs CO 80911
Tel (719) 391-3000 *SIC* 8211

DENVER PUBLIC SCHOOLS p 429
1860 N Lincoln St, Denver CO 80203
Tel (720) 423-3200 *SIC* 8211

POUDRE SCHOOL DISTRICT p 1164
2407 Laporte Ave, Fort Collins CO 80521
Tel (970) 482-7420 *SIC* 8211

EL PASO COUNTY SCHOOL DISTRICT 8 p 483
10665 Jimmy Camp Rd, Fountain CO 80817
Tel (719) 382-1300 *SIC* 8211

JEFFERSON COUNTY SCHOOL DISTRICT NO R-1 p 781
1829 Denver West Dr # 27, Golden CO 80401
Tel (303) 982-6500 *SIC* 8211

MESA COUNTY VALLEY SCHOOL DISTRICT 51 (INC) p 951
2115 Grand Ave, Grand Junction CO 81501
Tel (970) 254-5100 *SIC* 8211

WELD COUNTY SCHOOL DISTRICT 6 p 1589
1025 9th Ave Ste Main, Greeley CO 80631
Tel (970) 348-6000 *SIC* 8211

CHERRY CREEK SCHOOL DISTRICT 5 p 294
4700 S Yosemite St # 223, Greenwood Village CO 80111
Tel (303) 773-1184 *SIC* 8211

ST VRAIN VALLEY SCHOOL DISTRICT RE-1J p 1373
395 S Pratt Pkwy, Longmont CO 80501
Tel (303) 776-6200 *SIC* 8211

THOMPSON SCHOOL DISTRICT R2J p 1449
800 S Taft Ave, Loveland CO 80537
Tel (970) 613-5000 *SIC* 8211

FALCON SCHOOL DISTRICT 49 (INC) p 526
10850 E Woodmen Rd, Peyton CO 80831
Tel (719) 495-3601 *SIC* 8211

PUEBLO SCHOOL DISTRICT 70 p 1191
24951 E Us Highway 50, Pueblo CO 81006
Tel (719) 542-0220 *SIC* 8211

PUEBLO SCHOOL DISTRICT NO 60 p 1191
315 W 11th St, Pueblo CO 81003
Tel (719) 549-7100 *SIC* 8211

ADAMS 12 FIVE STAR SCHOOLS p 21
1500 E 128th Ave, Thornton CO 80241
Tel (720) 972-4000 *SIC* 8211

WESTMINSTER PUBLIC SCHOOLS p 1601
7002 Raleigh St, Westminster CO 80030
Tel (303) 428-3511 *SIC* 8211

BRIDGEPORT CITY SCHOOL DISTRICT p 211
45 Lyon Ter, Bridgeport CT 06604
Tel (203) 576-7291 *SIC* 8211

DANBURY SCHOOL DISTRICT p 411
63 Beaver Brook Rd, Danbury CT 06810
Tel (203) 797-4701 *SIC* 8211

FAIRFIELD PUBLIC SCHOOLS p 525
501 Kings Hwy E Ste 210, Fairfield CT 06825
Tel (203) 255-7201 *SIC* 8211

FAIRFIELD UNIVERSITY p 525
1073 N Benson Rd, Fairfield CT 06824
Tel (203) 254-4000 *SIC* 8221 8211

GREENWICH SCHOOL DISTRICT p 639
290 Greenwich Ave, Greenwich CT 06830
Tel (203) 625-7400 *SIC* 8211

SECURITY CAPITAL CORP p 1299
8 Greenwich Office Park # 2, Greenwich CT 06831
Tel (203) 625-0770 *SIC* 6411 8211

CONNECTICUT INSTITUTE FOR BLIND INC p 357
120 Holcomb St, Hartford CT 06112
Tel (860) 242-2274 *SIC* 8211 8361

HARTFORD SCHOOL DISTRICT p 665
960 Main St Fl 9, Hartford CT 06103
Tel (860) 695-8400 *SIC* 8211

MANCHESTER BOARD OF EDUCATION p 901
45 N School St, Manchester CT 06042
Tel (860) 647-3442 *SIC* 8211

MANCHESTER SCHOOL DISTRICT p 901
45 N School St, Manchester CT 06042
Tel (860) 647-3442 *SIC* 8211

MERIDEN PUBLIC SCHOOLS p 948
22 Liberty St, Meriden CT 06450
Tel (203) 630-4171 *SIC* 8211 9411

CONSOLIDATED SCHOOL DISTRICT OF NEW BRITAIN p 360
272 Main St, New Britain CT 06051
Tel (860) 827-2200 *SIC* 8211

NEW HAVEN PUBLIC SCHOOLS p 1030
54 Meadow St Fl 1, New Haven CT 06519
Tel (203) 946-8501 *SIC* 8211

NORWALK PUBLIC SCHOOL DISTRICT p 1061
125 East Ave, Norwalk CT 06851
Tel (203) 852-9874 *SIC* 8211 9111

WATERBURY PUBLIC SCHOOL DISTRICT p 1581
236 Grand St Ste 1, Waterbury CT 06702
Tel (203) 574-8004 *SIC* 8211

WATERBURY SCHOOL DISTRICT p 1582
236 Grand St Ste 1, Waterbury CT 06702
Tel (203) 574-8000 *SIC* 8211

CAPITAL SCHOOL DISTRICT p 250
198 Commerce Way, Dover DE 19904
Tel (302) 672-1500 *SIC* 8211

COLONIAL SCHOOL DISTRICT p 338
318 E Basin Rd, New Castle DE 19720
Tel (302) 323-2700 *SIC* 8211

APPOQUINIMINK SCHOOL DISTRICT INC p 100
118 S 6th St, Odessa DE 19730
Tel (302) 376-4128 *SIC* 8211

INDIAN RIVER SCHOOL DISTRICT p 737
31 Hosier St, Selbyville DE 19975
Tel (302) 436-1000 *SIC* 8211

BRANDYWINE SCHOOL DISTRICT p 208
1311 Brandywine Blvd, Wilmington DE 19809
Tel (302) 793-5000 *SIC* 8211

CHRISTINA SCHOOL DISTRICT p 303
600 N Lombard St, Wilmington DE 19801
Tel (302) 552-2600 *SIC* 8211

DISTRICT OF COLUMBIA PUBLIC SCHOOLS p 443
1200 1st St Ne Fl 9, Washington DC 20002
Tel (202) 442-5885 *SIC* 8211

FRIENDSHIP PUBLIC CHARTER SCHOOL INC p 580
120 Q St Ne Ste 200, Washington DC 20002
Tel (202) 281-1700 *SIC* 8211

KIPP DC p 821
2600 Virginia Ave Nw # 900, Washington DC 20037
Tel (202) 223-4505 *SIC* 8211

POLK COUNTY SCHOOL DISTRICT p 1159
1915 S Floral Ave, Bartow FL 33830
Tel (863) 534-0500 *SIC* 8211

SCHOOL BOARD OF POLK COUNTY p 1289
1915 S Floral Ave, Bartow FL 33830
Tel (863) 534-0500 *SIC* 8211

SCHOOL DISTRICT OF MANATEE COUNTY FLORIDA p 1289
215 Manatee Ave W, Bradenton FL 34205
Tel (941) 708-8770 *SIC* 8211

SCHOOL DISTRICT OF HERNANDO COUNTY FLORIDA p 1289
919 N Broad St, Brooksville FL 34601
Tel (352) 797-7000 *SIC* 8211

SCHOOL BOARD OF FLAGLER COUNTY p 1289
1769 E Moody Blvd Bldg 2f, Bunnell FL 32110
Tel (386) 437-7526 *SIC* 8211 8222

ECKERD YOUTH ALTERNATIVES INC p 475
100 Starcrest Dr, Clearwater FL 33765
Tel (727) 461-2990 *SIC* 8211

NOVA SOUTHEASTERN UNIVERSITY INC p 1062
3301 College Ave, Davie FL 33314
Tel (954) 262-7300 *SIC* 8221 8211

VOLUSIA COUNTY SCHOOL DISTRICT p 1565
200 N Clara Ave, Deland FL 32720
Tel (386) 734-7190 *SIC* 8211

IMAGINE SCHOOLS OF DELAWARE INC p 733
8071 Nw 54th St, Doral FL 33166
Tel (305) 648-5962 *SIC* 8211

NASSAU COUNTY SCHOOL DISTRICT p 1008
1201 Atlantic Ave, Fernandina Beach FL 32034
Tel (904) 491-9900 *SIC* 8211

BROWARD COUNTY PUBLIC SCHOOLS p 219
600 Se 3rd Ave, Fort Lauderdale FL 33301
Tel (754) 321-0000 *SIC* 8211

CHARTER SCHOOLS USA INC p 291
800 Corporate Dr Ste 124, Fort Lauderdale FL 33334
Tel (954) 202-3500 *SIC* 8211

RENAISSANCE CHARTER SCHOOL INC p 1223
6245 N Federal Hwy # 500, Fort Lauderdale FL 33308
Tel (954) 202-3500 *SIC* 8211

SCHOOL BOARD OF BROWARD COUNTY p 1289
600 Se 3rd Ave, Fort Lauderdale FL 33301
Tel (754) 321-0000 *SIC* 8211

SCHOOL BOARD OF BROWARD COUNTY (INC) p 1289
600 Se 3rd Ave, Fort Lauderdale FL 33301
Tel (754) 321-0000 *SIC* 8211 8222

LEE COUNTY PUBLIC SCHOOLS p 851
2855 Colonial Blvd, Fort Myers FL 33966
Tel (239) 337-8523 *SIC* 8211

ST LUCIE COUNTY SCHOOL BOARD p 1370
4204 Okeechobee Rd, Fort Pierce FL 34947
Tel (772) 429-3600 *SIC* 8211

ST LUCIE PUBLIC SCHOOLS p 1370
4204 Okeechobee Rd, Fort Pierce FL 34947
Tel (772) 429-3600 *SIC* 8211

OKALOOSA COUNTY SCHOOL DISTRICT p 1079
120 Lowery Pl Se, Fort Walton Beach FL 32548
Tel (850) 689-7300 *SIC* 8211

ALACHUA COUNTY PUBLIC SCHOOLS p 43
620 E University Ave, Gainesville FL 32601
Tel (352) 955-7300 *SIC* 8211

SCHOOL DISTRICT OF CLAY COUNTY p 1289
900 Walnut St, Green Cove Springs FL 32043
Tel (904) 284-6500 *SIC* 8211

CITRUS COUNTY SCHOOL BOARD LEASING CORP p 311
1007 W Main St, Inverness FL 34450
Tel (352) 726-1931 *SIC* 8211

CITRUS COUNTY SCHOOLS p 311
1007 W Main St, Inverness FL 34450
Tel (352) 726-1931 *SIC* 8211

DUVAL COUNTY PUBLIC SCHOOLS p 463
1701 Prudential Dr, Jacksonville FL 32207
Tel (904) 390-2000 *SIC* 8211

FLORIDA SCHOOL CHOICE p 559
4655 Salisbury Rd Ste 400, Jacksonville FL 32256
Tel (800) 447-1636 *SIC* 8211

MONROE COUNTY SCHOOL DISTRICT p 985
241 Trumbo Rd, Key West FL 33040
Tel (305) 293-1400 *SIC* 8211

OSCEOLA COUNTY SCHOOL BOARD p 1096
817 Bill Beck Blvd, Kissimmee FL 34744
Tel (407) 870-4600 *SIC* 8211

OSCEOLAK12FL p 1096
817 Bill Beck Blvd, Kissimmee FL 34744
Tel (407) 870-4630 *SIC* 8211

SCHOOL DISTRICT OF OSCEOLA COUNTY FL p 1289
817 Bill Beck Blvd, Kissimmee FL 34744
Tel (407) 870-4600 *SIC* 8211

HENDRY COUNTY SCHOOL DISTRICT p 683
25 E Hickpochee Ave, Labelle FL 33935
Tel (863) 674-4642 *SIC* 8211

COLUMBIA COUNTY SCHOOL BOARD p 340
372 W Duval St, Lake City FL 32055
Tel (386) 755-8010 *SIC* 8211

COLUMBIA COUNTY SCHOOL DISTRICT p 340
372 W Duval St, Lake City FL 32055
Tel (386) 755-8000 *SIC* 8211 9411

DISTRICT SCHOOL BOARD OF PASCO COUNTY p 443
7227 Land O Lakes Blvd, Land O Lakes FL 34638
Tel (813) 794-2000 *SIC* 8211

PASCO COUNTY SCHOOLS p 1119
7227 Land O Lakes Blvd, Land O Lakes FL 34638
Tel (813) 794-2651 *SIC* 8211

PINELLAS COUNTY PUBLIC SCHOOLS p 1149
301 4th St Sw, Largo FL 33770
Tel (727) 588-6000 *SIC* 8211

PINELLAS COUNTY SCHOOL BOARD p 1149
301 4th St Sw, Largo FL 33770
Tel (727) 588-6000 *SIC* 8211 4832

JACKSON COUNTY PUBLIC SCHOOLS p 773
2903 Jefferson St, Marianna FL 32446
Tel (850) 482-1200 *SIC* 8211

MIAMI-DADE COUNTY PUBLIC SCHOOLS-158 p 959
1450 Ne 2nd Ave, Miami FL 33132
Tel (305) 995-1000 *SIC* 8211

SCHOOL BOARD OF MIAMI-DADE COUNTY p 1289
1450 Ne 2nd Ave, Miami FL 33132
Tel (305) 995-1000 *SIC* 8211

COUNTY OF SANTA ROSA BOARD OF PUBLIC INSTRUCTION p 381
5086 Canal St, Milton FL 32570
Tel (850) 983-5000 *SIC* 8211

SOMERSET NEIGHBORHOOD SCHOOL INC p 1339
12425 Sw 53rd St, Miramar FL 33027
Tel (305) 829-2406 *SIC* 8211

COLLIER COUNTY PUBLIC SCHOOLS p 337
5775 Osceola Trl, Naples FL 34109
Tel (239) 377-0001 *SIC* 8211

MARION COUNTY PUBLIC SCHOOLS p 907
512 Se 3rd St, Ocala FL 34471
Tel (352) 671-7700 *SIC* 8211

MARION COUNTY SCHOOL BOARD p 907
512 Se 3rd St, Ocala FL 34471
Tel (352) 671-7700 *SIC* 8211

ARR INVESTMENTS INC p 112
2600 E Jackson St, Orlando FL 32803
Tel (407) 894-8401 *SIC* 8351 8211

FLORIDA VIRTUAL SCHOOL p 559
5401 S Kirkman Rd Ste 550, Orlando FL 32819
Tel (407) 857-6588 *SIC* 8211

ORANGE COUNTY PUBLIC SCHOOLS p 1092
445 W Amelia St, Orlando FL 32801
Tel (407) 317-3200 *SIC* 8211

SCHOOL BOARD OF ORANGE COUNTY FLORIDA p 1289
445 W Amelia St Lbby, Orlando FL 32801
Tel (407) 317-3200 *SIC* 8211

SCHOOL DISTRICT OF PUTNAM COUNTY FLORIDA p 1290
200 Reid St Ste 1, Palatka FL 32177
Tel (386) 329-0653 *SIC* 8211

BAY DISTRICT SCHOOL BOARD p 160
1311 Balboa Ave, Panama City FL 32401
Tel (850) 767-4100 *SIC* 8211

BAY DISTRICT SCHOOLS p 161
1311 Balboa Ave, Panama City FL 32401
Tel (850) 767-4101 *SIC* 8211

ESCAMBIA COUNTY SCHOOL BOARD p 509
75 N Pace Blvd, Pensacola FL 32505
Tel (850) 432-6121 *SIC* 8211

ESCAMBIA COUNTY SCHOOL DISTRICT p 509
75 N Pace Blvd, Pensacola FL 32505
Tel (850) 432-6121 *SIC* 8211

CHARLOTTE COUNTY PUBLIC SCHOOLS p 290
1445 Education Way, Port Charlotte FL 33948
Tel (941) 255-0808 *SIC* 8211

SCHOOL BOARD OF CHARLOTTE COUNTY FLORIDA p 1289
1445 Education Way, Port Charlotte FL 33948
Tel (941) 255-0808 *SIC* 8211

GADSDEN COUNTY SCHOOLS p 588
35 Martin Luther King, Quincy FL 32351
Tel (850) 627-9651 *SIC* 8211

ST JOHNS COUNTY SCHOOL BOARD p 1367
40 Orange St, Saint Augustine FL 32084
Tel (904) 547-7500 *SIC* 8211

ST JOHNS COUNTY SCHOOL BOARD OF PUBLIC INSTRUCTION p 1367
2980 Collins Ave, Saint Augustine FL 32084
Tel (904) 824-4401 *SIC* 8211

ST JOHNS COUNTY SCHOOL DISTRICT p 1367
40 Orange St, Saint Augustine FL 32084
Tel (904) 547-7500 *SIC* 8211

SEMINOLE COUNTY PUBLIC SCHOOLS p 1302
400 E Lake Mary Blvd, Sanford FL 32773
Tel (407) 320-0000 *SIC* 8211

SARASOTA COUNTY SCHOOLS p 1282
1960 Landings Blvd, Sarasota FL 34231
Tel (941) 927-9000 *SIC* 8211

SCHOOL BOARD OF SARASOTA COUNTY p 1289
1960 Landings Blvd, Sarasota FL 34231
Tel (941) 927-9000 *SIC* 8211

HIGHLANDS COUNTY SCHOOLS p 691
426 School St, Sebring FL 33870
Tel (863) 471-5564 *SIC* 8211

SCHOOL BOARD OF HIGHLANDS COUNTY p 1289
426 School St, Sebring FL 33870
Tel (863) 471-5555 *SIC* 8211

MARTIN COUNTY SCHOOL DISTRICT p 912
500 Se Ocean Blvd, Stuart FL 34994
Tel (772) 219-1200 *SIC* 8211

LEON COUNTY SCHOOL BOARD p 856
2757 W Pensacola St, Tallahassee FL 32304
Tel (850) 487-7100 *SIC* 8211

LEON COUNTY SCHOOL DISTRICT p 856
2757 W Pensacola St, Tallahassee FL 32304
Tel (850) 487-7100 *SIC* 8211

HILLSBOROUGH COUNTY PUBLIC SCHOOLS p 694
901 E Kennedy Blvd, Tampa FL 33602
Tel (813) 272-4050 *SIC* 8211

HILLSBOROUGH COUNTY SCHOOL DISTRICT p 694
901 E Kennedy Blvd, Tampa FL 33602
Tel (813) 272-4000 *SIC* 8211

LAKE COUNTY SCHOOLS p 838
201 W Burleigh Blvd, Tavares FL 32778
Tel (352) 253-6500 *SIC* 8211

SCHOOL BOARD OF LAKE COUNTY (INC) p 1289
201 W Burleigh Blvd, Tavares FL 32778
Tel (352) 253-6500 *SIC* 8211

SCHOOL DISTRICT OF HILLSBOROUGH COUNTY p 1289
129 Glen Ridge Ave, Temple Terrace FL 33617
Tel (813) 817-4507 *SIC* 8211

SCHOOL DISTRICT OF INDIAN RIVER COUNTY p 1289
6500 57th St, Vero Beach FL 32967
Tel (772) 564-3000 *SIC* 8211

BREVARD COUNTY SCHOOLS p 210
2700 Jdge Fran Jmeson Way, Viera FL 32940
Tel (321) 633-1000 *SIC* 8211

SCHOOL BOARD OF BREVARD COUNTY p 1289
2700 Jdge Fran Jmeson Way, Viera FL 32940
Tel (321) 633-1000 *SIC* 8211

SCHOOL BOARD OF PALM BEACH COUNTY p 1289
3300 Forest Hill Blvd C316, West Palm Beach FL 33406
Tel (561) 434-8000 *SIC* 8211

SCHOOL DISTRICT OF WEST PALM BEACH COUNTY p 1290
3300 Forest Hill Blvd, West Palm Beach FL 33406
Tel (561) 434-8747 *SIC* 8211

FLORIDA CONFERENCE ASSOCIATION OF SEVENTH-DAY ADVENTISTS p 557
655 N Wymore Rd, Winter Park FL 32789
Tel (407) 644-5000
SIC 8661 8211 5942 6513

DOUGHERTY COUNTY SCHOOL SYSTEM p 452
200 Pine Ave, Albany GA 31701
Tel (229) 431-1264 *SIC* 8211

CLARKE COUNTY SCHOOL DISTRICT p 322
240 Mitchell Bridge Rd, Athens GA 30606
Tel (706) 546-7721 *SIC* 8211

ATLANTA BOARD OF EDUCATION p 125
130 Trinity Ave Sw, Atlanta GA 30303
Tel (404) 802-3500 *SIC* 8211

ATLANTA PUBLIC SCHOOLS p 125
130 Trinity Ave Sw, Atlanta GA 30303
Tel (404) 802-3500 *SIC* 8211

FULTON COUNTY BOARD OF EDUCATION p 584
6201 Powers Ferry Rd, Atlanta GA 30339
Tel (404) 768-3600 *SIC* 8211

FULTON COUNTY SCHOOL SYSTEM p 584
6201 Powers Ferry Rd, Atlanta GA 30339
Tel (470) 254-3600 *SIC* 8211

GEORGIA DEPARTMENT OF EDUCATION p 607
205 Jesse Hill Jr Dr Se, Atlanta GA 30334
Tel (404) 656-2497 *SIC* 8211 9411

TECHNICAL COLLEGE SYSTEM OF GEORGIA FOUNDATION INC p 1431
1800 Century Pl Ne # 550, Atlanta GA 30345
Tel (404) 679-1600 *SIC* 8211 9199

RICHMOND COUNTY BOARD OF EDUCATION p 1233
864 Broad St, Augusta GA 30901
Tel (706) 826-1000 *SIC* 8211

RICHMOND COUNTY SCHOOL SYSTEM p 1233
864 Broad St, Augusta GA 30901
Tel (706) 826-1000 *SIC* 8211

DECATUR COUNTY SCHOOL DISTRICT p 420
100 S West St, Bainbridge GA 39817
Tel (229) 248-2200 *SIC* 8211

BRYAN COUNTY SCHOOLS p 221
8810 Us Highway 280 E, Black Creek GA 31308
Tel (912) 851-4000 *SIC* 8211

GLYNN COUNTY BOARD OF EDUCATION p 618
1313 Egmont St, Brunswick GA 31520
Tel (912) 267-4100 *SIC* 8211

GLYNN COUNTY SCHOOL SYSTEM p 618
1313 Egmont St, Brunswick GA 31520
Tel (912) 267-4100 *SIC* 8211

CHEROKEE COUNTY BOARD OF EDUCATION p 294
110 Academy St, Canton GA 30114
Tel (770) 479-1871 *SIC* 8211

CHEROKEE COUNTY SCHOOL DISTRICT p 294
110 Academy St, Canton GA 30114
Tel (770) 479-1871 *SIC* 8211

CARROLL COUNTY BOARD OF EDUCATION p 261
164 Independence Dr, Carrollton GA 30116
Tel (770) 834-3348 *SIC* 8211

CARROLL COUNTY SCHOOLS p 261
164 Independence Dr, Carrollton GA 30116
Tel (770) 832-3568 *SIC* 8211

BARTOW COUNTY BOARD OF EDUCATION p 158
65 Gilreath Rd Nw, Cartersville GA 30121
Tel (770) 606-5800 *SIC* 8211

BARTOW COUNTY SCHOOL SYSTEM p 158
65 Gilreath Rd Nw, Cartersville GA 30121
Tel (770) 606-5800 *SIC* 8211

POLK SCHOOL DISTRICT p 1159
612 S College St, Cedartown GA 30125
Tel (770) 748-3821 *SIC* 8211

MURRAY COUNTY SCHOOLS p 1001
1006 Green Rd, Chatsworth GA 30705
Tel (706) 695-4531 *SIC* 8211

HABERSHAM COUNTY BOARD OF EDUCATION p 651
132 Stanford Mill Rd, Clarkesville GA 30523
Tel (706) 754-2110 *SIC* 8211

MUSCOGEE COUNTY SCHOOL DISTRICT p 1002
2960 Macon Rd, Columbus GA 31906
Tel (706) 748-2000 *SIC* 8211

ROCKDALE COUNTY BOARD OF EDUCATION p 1243
954 N Main St Nw, Conyers GA 30012
Tel (770) 483-4713 *SIC* 8211

ROCKDALE COUNTY PUBLIC SCHOOLS p 1243
954 N Main St Nw, Conyers GA 30012
Tel (770) 483-4713 *SIC* 8211

NEWTON COUNTY BOARD OF EDUCATION p 1039
2109 Newton Dr Ne, Covington GA 30014
Tel (770) 787-1330 *SIC* 8211

NEWTON COUNTY SCHOOLS p 1039
2109 Newton Dr Ne, Covington GA 30014
Tel (770) 787-1330 *SIC* 8211

FORSYTH COUNTY BOARD OF EDUCATION p 568
1120 Dahlonega Hwy, Cumming GA 30040
Tel (770) 887-2461 *SIC* 8211

FORSYTH COUNTY SCHOOLS p 568
1120 Dahlonega Hwy, Cumming GA 30040
Tel (770) 887-2461 *SIC* 8211

PAULDING COUNTY BOARD OF EDUCATION p 1121
3236 Atlanta Hwy, Dallas GA 30132
Tel (770) 443-8000 *SIC* 8211

PAULDING COUNTY SCHOOL DISTRICT p 1121
3236 Atlanta Hwy, Dallas GA 30132
Tel (770) 443-8000 *SIC* 8211

DALTON PUBLIC SCHOOLS p 410
300 W Waugh St, Dalton GA 30720
Tel (706) 876-4000 *SIC* 8211

WHITFIELD COUNTY SCHOOLS p 1606
1306 S Thornton Ave, Dalton GA 30720
Tel (706) 217-6780 *SIC* 8211

WHITFIELD EDUCATION FOUNDATION INC p 1606
1306 S Thornton Ave, Dalton GA 30720
Tel (706) 226-3710 *SIC* 8211

COFFEE COUNTY SCHOOL DISTRICT p 334
1311 Peterson Ave S, Douglas GA 31533
Tel (912) 384-2086 *SIC* 8211

DOUGLAS COUNTY BOARD OF EDUCATION p 452
9030 Highway 5, Douglasville GA 30134
Tel (770) 651-2000 *SIC* 8211

DOUGLAS COUNTY SCHOOL SYSTEM p 452
9030 Highway 5, Douglasville GA 30134
Tel (770) 651-2000 *SIC* 8211

COLUMBIA COUNTY SCHOOL DISTRICT p 340
4781 Hereford Farm Rd, Evans GA 30809
Tel (706) 541-0650 *SIC* 8211

FAYETTE COUNTY BOARD OF EDUCATION p 532
210 Stonewall Ave W, Fayetteville GA 30214
Tel (770) 460-3520 *SIC* 8211

FAYETTE COUNTY PUBLIC SCHOOLS p 532
210 Stonewall Ave W, Fayetteville GA 30214
Tel (770) 460-3535 *SIC* 8211

HALL COUNTY BOARD OF EDUCATION p 654
711 Green St Nw Ste 100, Gainesville GA 30501
Tel (770) 534-1080 *SIC* 8211

HALL COUNTY SCHOOL DISTRICT p 654
711 Green St Nw Ste 100, Gainesville GA 30501
Tel (770) 534-1080 *SIC* 8211

GRIFFIN-SPALDING COUNTY SCHOOLS SYSTEM p 640
216 S 6th St, Griffin GA 30224
Tel (770) 229-3700 *SIC* 8211

LIBERTY COUNTY BOARD OF EDUCATION p 861
200 Bradwell St, Hinesville GA 31313
Tel (912) 876-2162 *SIC* 8211

LIBERTY COUNTY SCHOOL SYSTEM p 861
200 Bradwell St, Hinesville GA 31313
Tel (912) 876-2161 *SIC* 8211

JACKSON COUNTY SCHOOL DISTRICT p 773
1660 Winder Hwy, Jefferson GA 30549
Tel (706) 367-5151 *SIC* 8211

CLAYTON COUNTY BOARD OF EDUCATION p 323
1058 5th Ave, Jonesboro GA 30236
Tel (770) 473-2700 *SIC* 8211

CLAYTON COUNTY PUBLIC SCHOOLS p 323
1058 5th Ave, Jonesboro GA 30236
Tel (678) 817-3076 *SIC* 8211

CLAYTON COUNTY SCHOOL DISTRICT p 323
1058 5th Ave, Jonesboro GA 30236
Tel (770) 473-2700 *SIC* 8211

CAMDEN COUNTY BOARD OF EDUCATION p 244
311 S East St, Kingsland GA 31548
Tel (912) 729-5687 *SIC* 8211

CAMDEN COUNTY SCHOOL DISTRICT p 244
311 S East St, Kingsland GA 31548
Tel (912) 729-5687 *SIC* 8211

WALKER COUNTY BOARD OF EDUCATION p 1573
201 S Duke St, La Fayette GA 30728
Tel (706) 638-1240 *SIC* 8211

WALKER COUNTY SCHOOL DISTRICT p 1573
201 S Duke St, La Fayette GA 30728
Tel (706) 638-1240 *SIC* 8211

TROUP COUNTY BOARD OF EDUCATION p 1484
100 N Davis Rd Ste C, Lagrange GA 30241
Tel (706) 812-7900 *SIC* 8211

TROUP COUNTY SCHOOL SYSTEM p 1484
100 N Davis Rd, Lagrange GA 30241
Tel (706) 812-7900 *SIC* 8211

BIBB COUNTY BOARD OF EDUCATION p 181
484 Mulberry St Ste 300, Macon GA 31201
Tel (478) 765-8711 *SIC* 8211

BIBB COUNTY SCHOOL DISTRICT p 181
484 Mulberry St Ste 300, Macon GA 31201
Tel (478) 765-8711 *SIC* 8211

COBB COUNTY BOARD OF EDUCATION p 332
514 Glover St Se, Marietta GA 30060
Tel (770) 426-3300 *SIC* 8211

COBB COUNTY PUBLIC SCHOOLS p 332
514 Glover St Se, Marietta GA 30060
Tel (770) 426-3300 *SIC* 8211

MARIETTA CITY SCHOOLS (INC) p 906
250 Howard St Ne, Marietta GA 30060
Tel (770) 422-3500 *SIC* 8211

HENRY COUNTY BOARD OF EDUCATION p 684
33 N Zack Hinton Pkwy, Mcdonough GA 30253
Tel (770) 957-6601 *SIC* 8211

HENRY COUNTY SCHOOLS p 684
33 N Zack Hinton Pkwy, Mcdonough GA 30253
Tel (770) 957-6601 *SIC* 8211

WALTON COUNTY SCHOOL DISTRICT p 1575
200 Double Sprng Ch Rd Sw, Monroe GA 30656
Tel (770) 266-4520 *SIC* 8211

COLQUITT COUNTY BOARD OF EDUCATION p 339
710 28th Ave Se, Moultrie GA 31768
Tel (229) 985-1550 *SIC* 8211

COLQUITT COUNTY SCHOOLS p 339
710 28th Ave Se, Moultrie GA 31768
Tel (229) 890-6200 *SIC* 8211

COWETA COUNTY SCHOOL SYSTEM p 385
237 Jackson St, Newnan GA 30263
Tel (770) 254-2800 *SIC* 8211

COWETA COUNTY SCHOOL SYSTEM BOARD OF EDUCATION p 385
237 Jackson St, Newnan GA 30263
Tel (770) 254-2801 *SIC* 8211

HOUSTON COUNTY BOARD OF EDUCATION p 712
1100 Main St, Perry GA 31069
Tel (478) 988-6200 *SIC* 8211

HOUSTON COUNTY SCHOOL SYSTEM p 712
1100 Main St, Perry GA 31069
Tel (478) 988-6200 *SIC* 8211

CATOOSA COUNTY PUBLIC SCHOOLS p 267
307 Cleveland St, Ringgold GA 30736
Tel (706) 965-3977 *SIC* 8211 9411

FLOYD COUNTY BOARD OF EDUCATION p 560
600 Riverside Pkwy Ne, Rome GA 30161
Tel (706) 234-1031 *SIC* 8211

FLOYD COUNTY SCHOOLS p 560
600 Riverside Pkwy Ne, Rome GA 30161
Tel (706) 234-1031 *SIC* 8211

BOARD OF EDUCATION FOR CITY OF SAVANNAH AND COUNTY OF CHATHAM (INC) p 195
208 Bull St, Savannah GA 31401
Tel (912) 395-1000 *SIC* 8211

CATHOLIC DIOCESE OF SAVANNAH p 266
2170 E Victory Dr, Savannah GA 31404
Tel (912) 201-4100 *SIC* 8661 8211

CHATHAM COUNTY BOARD OF EDUCATION p 291
208 Bull St, Savannah GA 31401
Tel (912) 395-1000 *SIC* 8211

SAVANNAH-CHATHAM COUNTY PUBLIC SCHOOL SYSTEM p 1284
208 Bull St, Savannah GA 31401
Tel (912) 395-5600 *SIC* 8211

EFFINGHAM COUNTY BOARD OF EDUCATION p 480
405 N Ash St, Springfield GA 31329
Tel (912) 754-6491 *SIC* 8211

EFFINGHAM COUNTY SCHOOLS p 480
405 N Ash St, Springfield GA 31329
Tel (912) 754-6491 *SIC* 8211

BULLOCH COUNTY BOARD OF EDUCATION p 225
150 Williams Rd Ste A, Statesboro GA 30458
Tel (912) 764-6201 *SIC* 8211

BULLOCH COUNTY SCHOOLS p 225
150 Williams Rd Ste A, Statesboro GA 30458
Tel (912) 212-8500 *SIC* 8211

DEKALB COUNTY BOARD OF EDUCATION p 423
1701 Mountain Indus Blvd, Stone Mountain GA 30083
Tel (678) 676-1200 *SIC* 8211

DEKALB COUNTY SCHOOLS p 423
1701 Mountain Indus Blvd, Stone Mountain GA 30083
Tel (678) 676-1200 *SIC* 8211

GWINNETT COUNTY PUBLIC SCHOOLS p 648
437 Old Peachtree Rd Nw, Suwanee GA 30024
Tel (678) 301-6000 *SIC* 8211

TIFT COUNTY BOARD OF EDUCATION p 1453
207 Ridge Ave N, Tifton GA 31794
Tel (229) 387-2400 *SIC* 8211

TIFT COUNTY SCHOOLS p 1453
207 Ridge Ave N, Tifton GA 31794
Tel (229) 387-2400 *SIC* 8211

LOWNDES COUNTY BOARD OF EDUCATION INC p 882
1592 Norman Dr, Valdosta GA 31601
Tel (229) 245-2250 *SIC* 8211

LOWNDES COUNTY SCHOOLS p 882
1592 Norman Dr, Valdosta GA 31601
Tel (229) 245-2250 *SIC* 8211

VALDOSTA CITY SCHOOL DISTRICT p 1539
1204 Williams St, Valdosta GA 31601
Tel (229) 333-8500 *SIC* 8211

BARROW COUNTY BOARD OF EDUCATION p 157
179 W Athens St, Winder GA 30680
Tel (770) 867-4527 *SIC* 8211

BARROW COUNTY SCHOOL SYSTEM p 157
179 W Athens St, Winder GA 30680
Tel (770) 867-4527 *SIC* 8211

HAWAII SCHOOL DISTRICT p 669
75 Aupuni St Rm 203, Hilo HI 96720
Tel (808) 974-6600 *SIC* 8211 9411

HONOLULU SCHOOL DISTRICT p 705
4967 Kilauea Ave, Honolulu HI 96816
Tel (808) 733-4950 *SIC* 8211

PUNAHOU SCHOOL p 1192
1601 Punahou St, Honolulu HI 96822
Tel (808) 944-5711 *SIC* 8211

TRUSTEES OF ESTATE OF BERNICE PAUAHI BISHOP p 1487
567 S King St Ste 200, Honolulu HI 96813
Tel (808) 523-6200 *SIC* 8211

LEEWARD OAHU SCHOOL DISTRICT p 852
601 Kamokila Blvd Ste 418, Kapolei HI 96707
Tel (808) 564-6066 *SIC* 8211 9411

KAUAI SCHOOL DISTRICT p 805
3060 Eiwa St Ste 305, Lihue HI 96766
Tel (808) 274-3502 *SIC* 8211 9411

MAUI SCHOOL DISTRICT p 921
54 S High St Fl 4, Wailuku HI 96793
Tel (808) 984-8001 *SIC* 8211 9411

BZ INTERMEDIATE HOLDINGS LLC p 231
1111 W Jefferson St, Boise ID 83702
Tel (208) 384-7000 *SIC* 8211

INDEPENDENT SCHOOL DISTRICT OF BOISE CITY p 737
8169 W Victory Rd, Boise ID 83709
Tel (208) 854-4000 *SIC* 8211

COEUR D ALENE SCHOOL DISTRICT 271 p 333
1400 N Northwood Ctr Ct, Coeur D Alene ID 83814
Tel (208) 664-8241 *SIC* 8211

BONNEVILLE JOINT SCHOOL DISTRICT NO 93 p 200
3497 N Ammon Rd, Idaho Falls ID 83401
Tel (208) 525-4400 *SIC* 8211

IDAHO FALLS SCHOOL DISTRICT NO 91 EDUCATION FOUNDATION INC p 728
690 John Adams Pkwy, Idaho Falls ID 83401
Tel (208) 525-7500 *SIC* 8211

MACKAY JOINT SCHOOL DIST 182 p 892
411 Rose Ave, Mackay ID 83251
Tel (208) 588-2896 *SIC* 8211

JOINT SCHOOL DISTRICT p 792
1303 E Central Dr, Meridian ID 83642
Tel (208) 350-5093 *SIC* 8211

JOINT SCHOOL DISTRICT 2 p 792
1303 E Central Dr, Meridian ID 83642
Tel (208) 855-4500 *SIC* 8211

NAMPA SCHOOL DISTRICT 131 p 1007
619 S Canyon St, Nampa ID 83686
Tel (208) 468-4600 *SIC* 8211

POCATELLO/CHUBBUCK SCHOOL DISTRICT 25 p 1158
3115 Pole Line Rd, Pocatello ID 83201
Tel (208) 235-3295 *SIC* 8211

TWIN FALLS SCHOOL DISTRICT 411 p 1495
201 Main Ave W, Twin Falls ID 83301
Tel (208) 733-0134 *SIC* 8211

DUPAGE HIGH SCHOOL DISTRICT 88 p 462
2 Friendship Plz, Addison IL 60101
Tel (630) 530-3990 *SIC* 8211

CONSOLIDATED SCHOOL DISTRICT 158 p 360
650 Academic Dr, Algonquin IL 60102
Tel (847) 659-6158 *SIC* 8211 8741

COMMUNITY CONSOLIDATED SCHOOL DISTRICT 59 p 348
2123 S Arlington Hts Rd, Arlington Heights IL 60005
Tel (847) 593-4300 *SIC* 8211

TOWNSHIP HIGH SCHOOL DISTRICT 214 p 1466
2121 S Goebbert Rd, Arlington Heights IL 60005
Tel (847) 718-7600 *SIC* 8211

AURORA WEST SCHOOL DISTRICT 129 p 132
1877 W Downer Pl Ste 100, Aurora IL 60506
Tel (630) 301-5000 *SIC* 8211

EAST AURORA SCHOOL DISTRICT 131 p 469
417 5th St, Aurora IL 60505
Tel (630) 299-8355 *SIC* 8211

INDIAN PRAIRIE COMMUNITY UNIT SCHOOL DISTRICT p 737
780 Shoreline Dr, Aurora IL 60504
Tel (630) 375-3000 *SIC* 8211

BARRINGTON 220 COMMUNITY UNIT SCHOOL DISTRICT p 157
310 James St, Barrington IL 60010
Tel (847) 381-6300 *SIC* 8211

EGYPTIAN AREA SCHOOLS EMPLOYEE BENEFIT TRUST p 481
1109 Hartman Ln, Belleville IL 62221
Tel (618) 973-8221 *SIC* 8211

COMMUNITY UNIT SCHOOL DISTRICT 300 p 350
2550 Harnish Dr, Carpentersville IL 60110
Tel (847) 426-1300 *SIC* 8211

CHAMPAIGN COMMUNITY UNIT SCHOOL DISTRICT 4 (INC) p 287
703 S New St, Champaign IL 61820
Tel (217) 351-3800 *SIC* 8211 8351

BOARD OF EDUCATION OF CITY OF CHICAGO p 195
125 S Clark St Fl 14, Chicago IL 60603
Tel (773) 553-2760 *SIC* 8211

BOARD OF EDUCATION OF CITY OF CHICAGO p 195
42 W Madison St Fl 2, Chicago IL 60602
Tel (773) 553-1000 *SIC* 8211

CHICAGO PUBLIC SCHOOLS p 297
42 W Madison St, Chicago IL 60602
Tel (773) 553-1000 *SIC* 8211

NATIONAL LOUIS UNIVERSITY p 1014
122 S Michigan Ave # 600, Chicago IL 60603
Tel (312) 261-3599 *SIC* 8221 8211

NOBLE NETWORK OF CHARTER SCHOOLS p 1046
1 N State St Fl 7, Chicago IL 60602
Tel (773) 278-6895 *SIC* 8211

UNO CHARTER SCHOOL NETWORK INC p 1528
209 W Jackson Blvd # 500, Chicago IL 60606
Tel (312) 637-3900 *SIC* 8211

CICERO PUBLIC SCHOOL DISTRICT 99 p 306
5110 W 24th St, Cicero IL 60804
Tel (708) 863-4856 *SIC* 8211

CRETE-MONEE SCHOOL DISTRICT NO 201-U p 392
1500 S Sangamon St, Crete IL 60417
Tel (708) 367-8300 *SIC* 8211

CRYSTAL LAKE COMMUNITY CONSOLIDATED SCHOOL DISTRICT 47 p 397
300 Commerce Dr, Crystal Lake IL 60014
Tel (815) 459-6070 *SIC* 8211 8741

DECATUR SCHOOL DISTRICT 61 INC p 421
101 W Cerro Gordo St, Decatur IL 62523
Tel (217) 362-3000 *SIC* 8211

COMMUNITY HIGH SCHOOL DISTRICT 99 p 349
6301 Springside Ave, Downers Grove IL 60516
Tel (630) 795-7100 *SIC* 8211

EAST ST LOUIS SCHOOL DISTRICT 189 p 470
1005 State St, East Saint Louis IL 62201
Tel (618) 646-3000 *SIC* 8211

EDWARDSVILLE COMMUNITY SCHOOL DISTRICT 7 p 480
708 Saint Louis St, Edwardsville IL 62025
Tel (618) 659-3672 *SIC* 8211

SCHOOL DISTRICT U-46 p 1290
355 E Chicago St, Elgin IL 60120
Tel (847) 888-5000 *SIC* 8211

EVANSTON CONSOLIDATED COMMUNITY SCHOOL DISTRICT 65 p 513
1500 Mcdaniel Ave, Evanston IL 60201
Tel (847) 859-8000 *SIC* 8211

EVANSTON TOWNSHIP HIGH SCHOOL DISTRICT 202 p 513
1600 Dodge Ave, Evanston IL 60201
Tel (847) 424-7000 *SIC* 8211

COMMUNITY UNIT SCHOOL DISTRICT 205 p 350
932 Harrison St, Galesburg IL 61401
Tel (309) 343-3623 *SIC* 8211 8741

GENEVA COMMUNITY UNIT SCHOOL DISTRICT 304 p 603
227 N 4th St, Geneva IL 60134
Tel (630) 463-3000 *SIC* 8211

GLENBARD TOWNSHIP HIGH SCHOOL DISTRICT 87 p 615
596 Crescent Blvd, Glen Ellyn IL 60137
Tel (630) 469-9100 *SIC* 8211

THORTON TOWNSHIP HIGH SCHOOL DISTRICT 205 p 1450
15001 Broadway Ave, Harvey IL 60426
Tel (708) 225-4036 *SIC* 8211

HERSCHER SCHOOL DISTRICT 2 p 687
501 N Main St, Herscher IL 60941
Tel (815) 426-2162 *SIC* 8211

NORTHSHORE SCHOOL DST 112 p 1058
1936 Green Bay Rd, Highland Park IL 60035
Tel (224) 765-3000 *SIC* 8211

JOLIET PUBLIC SCHOOLS DISTRICT 86 p 792
420 N Raynor Ave, Joliet IL 60435
Tel (815) 740-3196 *SIC* 8211

COMMUNITY UNIT SCHOOL DISTRICT 95 p 350
400 S Old Rand Rd, Lake Zurich IL 60047
Tel (847) 438-2831 *SIC* 8211

ADLAI E STEVENSON HIGH SCHOOL DISTRICT 125 p 23
1 Stevenson Dr, Lincolnshire IL 60069
Tel (847) 415-4000 SIC 8211

HARLEM SCHOOL DISTRICT 122 p 661
8605 N 2nd St, Machesney Park IL 61115
Tel (815) 654-4500 SIC 8211 8741

MOLINE-COAL VALLEY COMMUNITY UNIT SCHOOL DISTRICT 40 p 983
1619 11th Ave, Moline IL 61265
Tel (309) 743-1600 SIC 8211

NAPERVILLE COMMUNITY UNIT SCHOOL DISTRICT 203 p 1007
203 W Hillside Rd, Naperville IL 60540
Tel (630) 420-6300 SIC 8211

TRINITY SERVICES INC p 1482
301 Veterans Pkwy, New Lenox IL 60451
Tel (815) 485-6197 SIC 8211 8322

MCLEAN COUNTY UNIT DISTRICT NO 5 p 931
1809 Hovey Ave, Normal IL 61761
Tel (309) 557-4000 SIC 8211

OAK PARK & RIVER FOREST HIGH SCHOOL DIST 200 p 1070
201 N Scoville Ave, Oak Park IL 60302
Tel (708) 383-0700 SIC 8211

CONSOLIDATED HIGH SCHOOL DISTRICT NO 230 NOT FOR PRO p 360
15100 S 94th Ave Uppr, Orland Park IL 60462
Tel (708) 349-5759 SIC 8211

COMMUNITY CONSOLIDATED SCHOOL DISTRICT 15 COOK COUNTY p 348
580 N 1st Bank Dr, Palatine IL 60067
Tel (847) 963-3000 SIC 8211

TOWNSHIP HIGH SCHOOL DISTRICT 211 FOUNDATION p 1466
1750 S Roselle Rd Ste 100, Palatine IL 60067
Tel (708) 359-3300 SIC 8211

MAINE TOWNSHIP HIGH SCHOOL DISTRICT 207 p 898
1177 S Dee Rd, Park Ridge IL 60068
Tel (847) 696-3600 SIC 8211

PEORIA BOARD OF EDUCATION (INC) p 1133
3202 N Wisconsin Ave, Peoria IL 61603
Tel (309) 672-6512 SIC 8211

PLAINFIELD COMMUNITY CONSOLIDATED SCHOOL DISTRICT 202 p 1153
15732 S Howard St, Plainfield IL 60544
Tel (815) 439-5482 SIC 8211

ROCK ISLAND/MILAN SCHOOL DISTRICT 41 p 1243
2101 6th Ave, Rock Island IL 61201
Tel (309) 793-5900 SIC 8211

CATHOLIC DIOCESE OF ROCKFORD p 266
555 Colman Center Dr, Rockford IL 61108
Tel (815) 399-4300
SIC 8661 8322 8361 8211 6553

ROCKFORD BOARD OF EDUCATION p 1244
501 7th St, Rockford IL 61104
Tel (815) 966-3000 SIC 8211

VALLEY VIEW COMMUNITY UNIT SCHOOL DISTRICT 365U p 1541
755 Dalhart Ave, Romeoville IL 60446
Tel (815) 886-2700 SIC 8211

COMMUNITY UNIT SCHOOL DISTRICT 303 p 350
201 S 7th St, Saint Charles IL 60174
Tel (630) 513-3030 SIC 8211

ST CHARLES COMMUNITY UNIT SCHOOL DISTRICT 303 p 1365
201 S 7th St, Saint Charles IL 60174
Tel (331) 228-2000 SIC 8211

SCHAUMBURG COMMUNITY CONSOLIDATED SCHOOL DISTRICT 54 p 1286
524 E Schaumburg Rd, Schaumburg IL 60194
Tel (847) 357-5000 SIC 8211

SPRINGFIELD SCHOOL DISTRICT 186 p 1361
1900 W Monroe St, Springfield IL 62704
Tel (217) 525-3000 SIC 8211

WAUKEGAN COMMUNITY UNIT SCHOOL DISTRICT 60 p 1583
1201 N Sheridan Rd, Waukegan IL 60085
Tel (847) 360-7028 SIC 8211

COMMUNITY UNIT SCHOOL DISTRICT 200 p 350
130 W Park Ave, Wheaton IL 60189
Tel (630) 682-2000 SIC 8211

COMMUNITY CONSOLIDATED SCHOOL DISTRICT 21 p 348
999 W Dundee Rd, Wheeling IL 60090
Tel (847) 520-2700 SIC 8211

WOODSTOCK COMMUNITY UNIT SCHOOL DISTRICT 200 p 1623
227 W Judd St, Woodstock IL 60098
Tel (815) 338-8200 SIC 8211

AVON COMMUNITY SCHOOL CORP p 139
7203 E Us Highway 36, Avon IN 46123
Tel (317) 272-2920 SIC 8211

MONROE COUNTY COMMUNITY SCHOOL CORP p 985
315 E North Dr, Bloomington IN 47401
Tel (812) 330-7700 SIC 8211

CARMEL CLAY SCHOOLS p 258
5201 E Main St, Carmel IN 46033
Tel (317) 844-9961 SIC 8211

SCHOOL CITY OF EAST CHICAGO p 1289
1401 E 144th St, East Chicago IN 46312
Tel (219) 391-4100 SIC 8211

ELKHART COMMUNITY SCHOOLS p 488
2720 California Rd, Elkhart IN 46514
Tel (574) 262-5500 SIC 8211

EVANSVILLE-VANDERBURGH SCHOOL DISTRICT p 513
951 Walnut St, Evansville IN 47713
Tel (812) 435-8477 SIC 8211

FORT WAYNE COMMUNITY SCHOOLS p 569
1200 S Clinton St, Fort Wayne IN 46802
Tel (260) 467-2160 SIC 8211

SMITH ACADEMY FOR EXCELLENCE INC p 1333
2625 Belvedere Dr Ste 108, Fort Wayne IN 46802
Tel (260) 749-5832 SIC 8211

GARY COMMUNITY SCHOOLS CORP p 593
1988 Polk St, Gary IN 46407
Tel (219) 886-6400 SIC 8211

GOSHEN COMMUNITY SCHOOLS p 626
613 E Purl St, Goshen IN 46526
Tel (574) 533-8631 SIC 8211

HAMMOND PUBLIC SCHOOLS p 656
41 Williams St, Hammond IN 46320
Tel (219) 933-2400 SIC 8211

HUNTINGTON COUNTY COMMUNITY SCHOOL CORP p 720
2485 Waterworks Rd, Huntington IN 46750
Tel (260) 356-8312 SIC 8211

INDIANAPOLIS PUBLIC SCHOOLS p 739
120 E Walnut St, Indianapolis IN 46204
Tel (317) 226-4000 SIC 8211

METROPOLITAN SCHOOL DISTRICT OF LAWRENCE TOWNSHIP p 956
6501 Sunnyside Rd, Indianapolis IN 46236
Tel (317) 423-8200 SIC 8211

METROPOLITAN SCHOOL DISTRICT OF WARREN TOWNSHIP p 956
975 N Post Rd, Indianapolis IN 46219
Tel (317) 869-4300 SIC 8211

METROPOLITAN SCHOOL DISTRICT OF WAYNE TOWNSHIP p 956
1220 S High School Rd, Indianapolis IN 46241
Tel (317) 988-8600 SIC 8211

METROPOLITAN SCHOOL DISTRICT WASHINGTON TOWNSHIP p 956
8550 Wdfld Xing Blvd, Indianapolis IN 46240
Tel (317) 845-9400 SIC 8211

PERRY TOWNSHIP SCHOOLS p 1137
6548 Orinoco Ave, Indianapolis IN 46227
Tel (317) 789-3700 SIC 8211

ROMAN CATHOLIC ARCHDIOCESE OF INDIANAPOLIS INC p 1248
1400 N Meridian St, Indianapolis IN 46202
Tel (317) 236-1400 SIC 8661 8211

ST BARNABAS SCHOOL p 1365
8300 Rahke Rd, Indianapolis IN 46217
Tel (317) 881-7422 SIC 8211

GREATER CLARK COUNTY SCHOOLS p 635
2112 Utica Sellersburg Rd, Jeffersonville IN 47130
Tel (812) 283-0701 SIC 8211

KOKOMO SCHOOL CORP p 826
1500 S Washington St, Kokomo IN 46902
Tel (765) 455-8000 SIC 8211

LAFAYETTE SCHOOL CORP p 838
2300 Cason St, Lafayette IN 47904
Tel (765) 771-6000 SIC 8211

TIPPECANOE SCHOOL CORP p 1455
21 Elston Rd, Lafayette IN 47909
Tel (765) 474-2481 SIC 8211

MARION COMMUNITY SCHOOLS p 907
750 W 26th St, Marion IN 46953
Tel (765) 662-2546 SIC 8211

MICHIGAN CITY AREA SCHOOLS p 960
408 S Carroll Ave, Michigan City IN 46360
Tel (219) 873-2000 SIC 8211

MUNCIE COMMUNITY SCHOOLS p 1000
2501 N Oakwood Ave, Muncie IN 47304
Tel (765) 747-5205 SIC 8211

NEW ALBANY FLOYD COUNTY CONSOLIDATED SCHOOL CORP p 1029
2813 Grant Line Rd, New Albany IN 47150
Tel (812) 949-4200 SIC 8211

EAST ALLEN COUNTY SCHOOLS p 469
1240 State Road 930 E, New Haven IN 46774
Tel (260) 446-0100 SIC 8211

PORTAGE TOWNSHIP SCHOOLS p 1162
6240 Us Highway 6, Portage IN 46368
Tel (219) 762-6511 SIC 8211

LAKE CENTRAL SCHOOL CORP p 838
8260 Wicker Ave, Saint John IN 46373
Tel (219) 365-8507 SIC 8211

SOUTH BEND COMMUNITY SCHOOL CORP RILEY SCHOOL BUILDING p 1343
215 S Saint Joseph St, South Bend IN 46601
Tel (574) 283-8000 SIC 8211

VIGO COUNTY SCHOOL CORP p 1556
686 Wabash Ave, Terre Haute IN 47807
Tel (812) 462-4011 SIC 8211

WASHINGTON WESTFIELD SCHOOLS p 1579
1143 E 181st St, Westfield IN 46074
Tel (317) 867-8000 SIC 8211

ANKENY COMMUNITY SCHOOLS INC p 92
306 Sw School St, Ankeny IA 50023
Tel (515) 965-9600 SIC 8211

CEDAR RAPIDS COMMUNITY SCHOOL DISTRICT p 272
2500 Edgewood Rd Nw, Cedar Rapids IA 52405
Tel (319) 558-2000 SIC 8211

AREA EDUCATION AGENCY 267 p 106
9184b 265th St Ste B, Clear Lake IA 50428
Tel (641) 357-6125 SIC 8211

COUNCIL BLUFFS COMMUNITY SCHOOL DISTRICT p 374
300 W Broadway Ste 1600, Council Bluffs IA 51503
Tel (712) 328-6419 SIC 8211

DAVENPORT COMMUNITY SCHOOL DISTRICT p 415
1606 Brady St Ste 100, Davenport IA 52803
Tel (563) 336-5000 SIC 8211

DES MOINES INDEPENDENT COMMUNITY SCHOOL DISTRICT p 431
2323 Grand Ave, Des Moines IA 50312
Tel (515) 242-7911 SIC 8211

DUBUQUE COMMUNITY SCHOOL DISTRICT p 459
2300 Chaney Rd, Dubuque IA 52001
Tel (563) 552-3000 SIC 8211

IOWA CITY COMMUNITY SCHOOL DISTRICT p 762
1725 N Dodge St, Iowa City IA 52245
Tel (319) 688-1000 SIC 8211

MUSCATINE COMMUNITY SCHOOL DISTRICT p 1002
2900 Mulberry Ave, Muscatine IA 52761
Tel (563) 263-7223 SIC 8211

SIOUX CITY COMMUNITY SCHOOL DISTRICT INC p 1326
627 4th St Ofc, Sioux City IA 51101
Tel (712) 279-6667 SIC 8211

WEST DES MOINES COMMUNITY SCHOOL DISTRICT p 1594
3550 Mills Civic Pkwy, West Des Moines IA 50265
Tel (515) 633-5078 SIC 8211

DERBY PUBLIC SCHOOLS p 431
120 E Washington St, Derby KS 67037
Tel (316) 788-8400 SIC 8211

EMPORIA UNIFIED SCHOOL DISTRICT 253 p 494
1700 W 7th Ave, Emporia KS 66801
Tel (620) 341-2200 SIC 8211

GARDEN CITY PUBLIC SCHOOLS p 591
1205 Fleming St, Garden City KS 67846
Tel (620) 805-7000 SIC 8211

GARDNER EDGERTON UNIFIED SCHOOL DISTRICT 231 p 592
231 E Madison St, Gardner KS 66030
Tel (913) 856-7102 SIC 8211

GEARY COUNTY UNIFIED SCHOOL DISTRICT 475 p 597
123 N Eisenhower Dr, Junction City KS 66441
Tel (785) 717-4000 SIC 8211

ARCHDIOCESE OF KANSAS CITY IN KANSAS p 105
12615 Parallel Pkwy, Kansas City KS 66109
Tel (913) 721-1570
SIC 8661 8211 8222 2711

BOARD OF EDUCATION OF KANSAS CITY KS (INC) p 195
2010 N 59th St, Kansas City KS 66104
Tel (913) 551-3200 SIC 8211

LAWRENCE PUBLIC SCHOOLS p 848
110 Mcdonald Dr, Lawrence KS 66044
Tel (785) 832-5000 SIC 8211

LIBERAL SCHOOL DISTRICT p 861
401 N Kansas Ave, Liberal KS 67901
Tel (620) 604-1010 SIC 8211

UNIFIED SCHOOL DISTRICT 383 p 1503
2031 Poyntz Ave, Manhattan KS 66502
Tel (785) 587-2000 SIC 8211 8249

OLATHE UNIFIED SCHOOL DISTRICT 233 p 1080
14160 S Blackbob Rd, Olathe KS 66062
Tel (913) 780-7000 SIC 8211

SHAWNEE MISSION UNIFIED SCHOOL DISTRICT p 1313
7235 Antioch Rd, Overland Park KS 66204
Tel (913) 993-6200 SIC 8211

SALINA PUBLIC SCHOOLS p 1272
1511 Gypsum Ave, Salina KS 67401
Tel (785) 309-4700 SIC 8211

SHAWNEE MISSION BOARD OF EDUCATION p 1313
7235 Antioch Rd, Shawnee Mission KS 66204
Tel (913) 993-6200 SIC 8211

SHAWNEE MISSION SCHOOL DISTRICT p 1313
7235 Antioch Rd, Shawnee Mission KS 66204
Tel (913) 993-6200 SIC 8211

TOPEKA UNIFIED SCHOOL DISTRICT 501 p 1461
624 Sw 24th St, Topeka KS 66611
Tel (785) 295-3000 SIC 8211

UNIFIED SCHOOL DISTRICT 259 p 1503
201 N Water St, Wichita KS 67202
Tel (316) 973-4000 SIC 8211 8249 8331

WICHITA PUBLIC SCHOOLS p 1608
201 N Water St, Wichita KS 67202
Tel (316) 973-4000 SIC 8211

WARREN COUNTY PUBLIC SCHOOLS p 1576
303 Lovers Ln, Bowling Green KY 42103
Tel (270) 781-2392 SIC 8211

COVINGTON BOARD OF EDUCATION p 385
25 E 7th St, Covington KY 41011
Tel (859) 292-5800 SIC 8211

DIOCESE OF COVINGTON p 440
1125 Madison Ave, Covington KY 41011
Tel (859) 392-1500 SIC 8211 8661

OLDHAM COUNTY SCHOOL DISTRICT p 1082
6165 W Highway 146, Crestwood KY 40014
Tel (502) 241-3500 SIC 8211

HARDIN COUNTY BOARD OF EDUCATION p 660
65 W A Jenkins Rd, Elizabethtown KY 42701
Tel (270) 369-7370 SIC 8211

BOONE COUNTY BOARD OF EDUCATION p 200
8330 Us Highway 42, Florence KY 41042
Tel (859) 283-1003 SIC 8211

BOONE COUNTY SCHOOLS p 200
8330 Us Highway 42, Florence KY 41042
Tel (859) 283-1003 SIC 8211

FRANKLIN COUNTY BOARD OF EDUCATION p 575
190 Kings Daughters Dr B-300, Frankfort KY 40601
Tel (502) 695-6700 SIC 8211

KENTON COUNTY SCHOOL DISTRICT p 812
1055 Eaton Dr, Ft Wright KY 41017
Tel (859) 344-8888 SIC 8211

SCOTT COUNTY BOARD OF EDUCATION p 1293
2168 Frankfort Rd, Georgetown KY 40324
Tel (502) 863-3663 SIC 8211

SCOTT COUNTY SCHOOLS p 1293
2168 Frankfort Rd, Georgetown KY 40324
Tel (502) 863-3663 SIC 8211

HENDERSON COUNTY SCHOOL DISTRICT p 682
1805 2nd St, Henderson KY 42420
Tel (270) 831-5000 SIC 8211

CHRISTIAN COUNTY SCHOOL DISTRICT FINANCE CORP p 302
200 Glass Ave, Hopkinsville KY 42240
Tel (270) 887-7000 SIC 8211

BOARD OF EDUCATION FAYETTE COUNTY KY p 195
701 E Main St Ste 107, Lexington KY 40502
Tel (859) 381-4141 SIC 8211

FAYETTE COUNTY PUBLIC SCHOOLS p 532
701 E Main St Rm 219, Lexington KY 40502
Tel (859) 381-4159 SIC 8211

FAYETTE COUNTY PUBLIC SCHOOLS p 532
1126 Russell Cave Rd, Lexington KY 40505
Tel (859) 381-4000 SIC 8211

LAUREL COUNTY BOARD OF EDUCATION p 847
718 N Main St, London KY 40741
Tel (606) 862-4608 SIC 8211

JEFFERSON COUNTY BOARD OF EDUCATION p 781
3332 Newburg Rd, Louisville KY 40218
Tel (502) 485-3011 SIC 8211 8741

JEFFERSON COUNTY PUBLIC SCHOOL DISTRICT p 781
3332 Newburg Rd, Louisville KY 40218
Tel (502) 485-3011 SIC 8211

HOPKINS COUNTY SCHOOL DISTRICT p 706
320 S Seminary St, Madisonville KY 42431
Tel (270) 825-6000 SIC 8211

HART COUNTY SCHOOLS p 664
25 Quality St, Munfordville KY 42765
Tel (270) 524-2631 SIC 8211

JESSAMINE COUNTY BOARD OF EDUCATION (INC) p 783
871 Wilmore Rd, Nicholasville KY 40356
Tel (859) 885-4179 SIC 8211

DAVIESS COUNTY BOARD OF EDUCATION p 416
1622 Southeastern Pkwy, Owensboro KY 42303
Tel (270) 852-7000 SIC 8211

MCCRACKEN COUNTY PUBLIC SCHOOLS p 927
5347 Benton Rd, Paducah KY 42003
Tel (270) 538-4000 SIC 8211

PIKE COUNTY SCHOOLS p 1148
316 S Mayo Trl, Pikeville KY 41501
Tel (606) 432-7700 SIC 8211

FLOYD COUNTY SCHOOLS p 560
106 N Front Ave, Prestonsburg KY 41653
Tel (606) 886-2354 SIC 8211

MADISON COUNTY SCHOOL DISTRICT p 894
550 S Keeneland Dr, Richmond KY 40475
Tel (859) 624-4500 SIC 8211

BULLITT COUNTY PUBLIC SCHOOLS p 225
1040 Highway 44 E, Shepherdsville KY 40165
Tel (502) 869-8000 SIC 8211

BULLITT COUNTY PUBLIC SCHOOLS p 225
1040 Highway 44 E, Shepherdsville KY 40165
Tel (502) 869-8000 SIC 8211

PULASKI COUNTY SCHOOL DISTRICT FINANCE CORP p 1191
501 E University Dr, Somerset KY 42503
Tel (606) 679-1123 SIC 8211 8741

PULASKI COUNTY SCHOOLS p 1191
501 E University Dr, Somerset KY 42503
Tel (606) 679-1123 SIC 8211

VERMILION PARISH SCHOOL BOARD p 1551
220 S Jefferson St, Abbeville LA 70510
Tel (337) 893-3973 SIC 8211

RAPIDES PARISH SCHOOL DISTRICT p 1208
619 6th St, Alexandria LA 71301
Tel (318) 487-0888 SIC 8211

TANGIPAHOA PARISH SCHOOL BOARD INC p 1424
59656 Puleston Rd, Amite LA 70422
Tel (985) 748-2433 SIC 8211

TANGIPAHOA PARISH SCHOOL SYSTEM p 1424
59656 Puleston Rd, Amite LA 70422
Tel (985) 748-2416 SIC 8211

EAST BATON ROUGE PARISH SCHOOL DISTRICT p 469
1050 S Foster Dr, Baton Rouge LA 70806
Tel (225) 922-5400 SIC 8211

BOSSIER PARISH SCHOOL BOARD INC p 202
410 N Sibley St, Benton LA 71006
Tel (318) 549-5000 SIC 8211

BOSSIER PARISH SCHOOLS p 202
410 N Sibley St, Benton LA 71006
Tel (318) 549-5000 SIC 8211

ST MARTIN PARISH SCHOOL BOARD p 1370
625 Corporate Blvd, Breaux Bridge LA 70517
Tel (337) 394-6261 SIC 8211

ST MARTIN PARISH SCHOOL DISTRICT p 1370
P.O. Box 1000, Breaux Bridge LA 70517
Tel (337) 394-6261 SIC 8211

ST MARY PARISH SCHOOL BOARD p 1371
474 Hwy 317, Centerville LA 70522
Tel (337) 836-9661 SIC 8211

ST MARY PARISH SCHOOLS p 1371
474 Hwy 317, Centerville LA 70522
Tel (337) 836-9661 SIC 8211

SAINT TAMMANY PARISH SCHOOL BOARD p 1270
321 N Theard St, Covington LA 70433
Tel (985) 892-2276 SIC 8211

ST TAMMANY PARISH PUBLIC SCHOOL SYSTEM p 1373
321 N Theard St, Covington LA 70433
Tel (985) 892-2276 SIC 8211

ACADIA PARISH SCHOOL DISTRICT p 13
2402 N Parkerson Ave, Crowley LA 70526
Tel (337) 783-3664 SIC 8211

ASCENSION PARISH SCHOOLS p 116
1100 Webster St, Donaldsonville LA 70346
Tel (225) 257-2000 SIC 8211

JEFFERSON PARISH PUBLIC SCHOOL SYSTEM p 782
501 Manhattan Blvd, Harvey LA 70058
Tel (504) 349-7600 SIC 8211

JEFFERSON PARISH SCHOOL BOARD INC p 782
501 Manhattan Blvd, Harvey LA 70058
Tel (504) 349-7803 SIC 8211

TERREBONNE PARISH SCHOOL BOARD INC p 1439
201 Stadium Dr, Houma LA 70360
Tel (985) 876-7400 *SIC* 8211

TERREBONNE PARISH SCHOOLS p 1440
201 Stadium Dr, Houma LA 70360
Tel (985) 876-7400 *SIC* 8211

LAFAYETTE PARISH SCHOOL BOARD p 837
113 Chaplin Dr, Lafayette LA 70508
Tel (337) 521-7000 *SIC* 8211

LAFAYETTE PARISH SCHOOL SYSTEM p 838
113 Chaplin Dr, Lafayette LA 70508
Tel (337) 521-7000 *SIC* 8211

CALCASIEU PARISH PUBLIC SCHOOLS p 238
3310 Broad St, Lake Charles LA 70615
Tel (337) 217-4000 *SIC* 8211

CALCASIEU PARISH SCHOOL BOARD p 238
3310 Broad St, Lake Charles LA 70615
Tel (337) 217-4000 *SIC* 8211

VERNON PARISH SCHOOL BOARD p 1551
201 Belview Rd, Leesville LA 71446
Tel (337) 239-3401 *SIC* 8211

VERNON PARISH SCHOOL DISTRICT p 1551
201 Belview Rd, Leesville LA 71446
Tel (337) 239-3401 *SIC* 8211

LIVINGSTON PARISH SCHOOL DISTRICT p 872
13909 Florida Blvd, Livingston LA 70754
Tel (225) 686-7044 *SIC* 8211

MONROE CITY SCHOOLS INC p 985
2006 Tower Dr, Monroe LA 71201
Tel (318) 325-0601 *SIC* 8211

OUACHITA PARISH SCHOOL SYSTEM p 1098
100 Bry St, Monroe LA 71201
Tel (318) 432-5000 *SIC* 8211

IBERIA PARISH SCHOOL DISTRICT p 726
1500 Jane St, New Iberia LA 70563
Tel (337) 685-4395 *SIC* 8211

ARCHDIOCESE OF NEW ORLEANS INC p 105
7887 Walmsley Ave, New Orleans LA 70125
Tel (504) 861-9521 *SIC* 8211 8661

ORLEANS PARISH SCHOOL DISTRICT p 1095
3520 Gen Degaulle Dr # 5055, New Orleans LA 70114
Tel (504) 304-3520 *SIC* 8211

ST LANDRY PARISH SCHOOLS p 1369
1013 Creswell Ln, Opelousas LA 70570
Tel (337) 948-3657 *SIC* 8211

ST JOHN BAPTIST PARISH PUBLIC SCHOOLS p 1367
118 W 10th St, Reserve LA 70084
Tel (985) 536-1106 *SIC* 8211

LINCOLN PARISH WILDLIFE FEDERATION p 867
410 S Farmerville St, Ruston LA 71270
Tel (318) 255-1430 *SIC* 8211

CADDO PARISH PUBLIC SCHOOLS p 236
1961 Midway St, Shreveport LA 71108
Tel (318) 603-6300 *SIC* 8211

CADDO PARISH SCHOOL BOARD p 236
1961 Midway St, Shreveport LA 71108
Tel (318) 636-0210 *SIC* 8211

LAFOURCHE PARISH SCHOOL BOARD INC p 838
805 E 7th St, Thibodaux LA 70301
Tel (985) 446-5631 *SIC* 8211

LAFOURCHE PARISH SCHOOL DISTRICT p 838
805 E 7th St, Thibodaux LA 70301
Tel (985) 446-5631 *SIC* 8211

AUBURN SCHOOL DEPARTMENT p 130
60 Court St Fl 4, Auburn ME 04210
Tel (207) 784-6431 *SIC* 8211

COUNCIL INTERNATIONAL STUDY PROGRAMS INC (ISP) p 374
300 Fore St Fl 2, Portland ME 04101
Tel (207) 553-4000 *SIC* 8211

DIOCESE OF PORTLAND SCHOOL OFFICE p 440
510 Ocean Ave, Portland ME 04103
Tel (207) 773-6471 *SIC* 8211

PORTLAND PUBLIC SCHOOL DISTRICT p 1163
353 Cumberland Ave, Portland ME 04101
Tel (207) 874-8100 *SIC* 8211

SCHOOL UNION 42 CSD 10 p 1290
45 Millard Harrison Dr, Readfield ME 04355
Tel (207) 685-3336 *SIC* 8211

ANNE ARUNDEL COUNTY BOARD OF EDUCATION p 92
2644 Riva Rd, Annapolis MD 21401
Tel (410) 222-5000 *SIC* 8211

ANNE ARUNDEL COUNTY PUBLIC SCHOOLS p 92
2644 Riva Rd, Annapolis MD 21401
Tel (410) 222-5000 *SIC* 8211

ARCHDIOCESES OF BALTIMORE p 105
320 Cathedral St Ste 1, Baltimore MD 21201
Tel (410) 547-5442 *SIC* 8211

BALTIMORE CITY PUBLIC SCHOOL SYSTEMS (INC) p 149
200 E North Ave, Baltimore MD 21202
Tel (410) 222-5000 *SIC* 8211

HARFORD COUNTY BOARD OF EDUCATION (INC) p 661
102 S Hickory Ave, Bel Air MD 21014
Tel (410) 838-7300 *SIC* 8211

HARFORD COUNTY PUBLIC SCHOOL DISTRICT p 661
102 S Hickory Ave, Bel Air MD 21014
Tel (410) 838-7300 *SIC* 8211

QUEEN ANNES COUNTY PUBLIC SCHOOLS p 1198
202 Chesterfield Ave, Centreville MD 21617
Tel (410) 758-2403 *SIC* 8211

ALLEGANY COUNTY PUBLIC SCHOOLS p 52
108 Washington St, Cumberland MD 21502
Tel (301) 759-2000 *SIC* 8211

BOARD OF EDUCATION OF ALLEGANY COUNTY MD INC p 195
108 Washington St, Cumberland MD 21502
Tel (301) 722-6013 *SIC* 8211

CECIL COUNTY PUBLIC SCHOOLS p 272
201 Booth St, Elkton MD 21921
Tel (410) 996-5400 *SIC* 8211

HOWARD COUNTY PUBLIC SCHOOL SYSTEM p 713
10910 State Route 108, Ellicott City MD 21042
Tel (410) 313-6600 *SIC* 8211

BOARD OF EDUCATION OF FREDERICK COUNTY MD (INC) p 195
191 S East St, Frederick MD 21701
Tel (301) 696-6850 *SIC* 8211

FREDERICK COUNTY PUBLIC SCHOOLS p 576
191 S East St, Frederick MD 21701
Tel (301) 644-5000 *SIC* 8211

WASHINGTON COUNTY BOARD OF EDUCATION p 1578
10435 Downsville Pike, Hagerstown MD 21740
Tel (301) 766-2800 *SIC* 8211

WASHINGTON COUNTY PUBLIC SCHOOLS p 1578
10435 Downsville Pike, Hagerstown MD 21740
Tel (301) 766-2800 *SIC* 8211

CHARLES COUNTY BOARD OF EDUCATION p 289
5980 Radio Station Rd, La Plata MD 20646
Tel (301) 934-7224 *SIC* 8211

FOUNDATION FOR PUBLIC SCHOOL CHILDREN OF CHARLES COUNTY INC p 571
5980 Radio Station Rd, La Plata MD 20646
Tel (301) 932-6610 *SIC* 8211

BOARD OF EDUCATION OF ST MARYS COUNTY p 195
23160 Moakley St Ste 101, Leonardtown MD 20650
Tel (301) 475-5511 *SIC* 8211

LEONARDTOWN SCHOOL DISTRICT p 856
P.O. Box 641, Leonardtown MD 20650
Tel (301) 475-4250 *SIC* 8211

ST MARYS COUNTY PUBLIC SCHOOLS p 1371
23160 Moakley St Ste 101, Leonardtown MD 20650
Tel (301) 475-5511 *SIC* 8211

WORCESTER COUNTY PUBLIC SCHOOLS p 1624
6270 Worcester Hwy, Newark MD 21841
Tel (410) 632-5020 *SIC* 8211

CALVERT COUNTY PUBLIC SCHOOLS p 243
1305 Dares Beach Rd, Prince Frederick MD 20678
Tel (410) 535-1700 *SIC* 8211

MONTGOMERY COUNTY PUBLIC SCHOOLS p 986
850 Hungerford Dr Rm 149, Rockville MD 20850
Tel (301) 279-3617 *SIC* 8211

WICOMICO COUNTY PUBLIC SCHOOLS p 1608
2424 Northgate Dr Ste 100, Salisbury MD 21801
Tel (410) 677-4400 *SIC* 8211

BALTIMORE COUNTY PUBLIC SCHOOLS p 149
6901 N Charles St, Towson MD 21204
Tel (410) 887-4554 *SIC* 8211

PRINCE GEORGES COUNTY PUBLIC SCHOOLS p 1176
14201 School Ln, Upper Marlboro MD 20772
Tel (301) 952-6000 *SIC* 8211

BOARD OF EDUCATION OF CARROLL COUNTY p 195
125 N Court St, Westminster MD 21157
Tel (410) 751-3000 *SIC* 8211

CARROLL COUNTY PUBLIC SCHOOLS p 261
125 N Court St Ste 101, Westminster MD 21157
Tel (410) 751-3128 *SIC* 8211

ANDOVER PUBLIC SCHOOLS p 90
50 Bartlet St, Andover MA 01810
Tel (978) 623-8519 *SIC* 8211

TRUSTEES OF PHILLIPS ACADEMY p 1488
180 Main St, Andover MA 01810
Tel (978) 749-4000 *SIC* 8211 8412

BILLERICA PUBLIC SCHOOLS p 182
365 Boston Rd, Billerica MA 01821
Tel (978) 528-7900 *SIC* 8211

BROOKLINE SCHOOL DISTRICT p 218
333 Washington St, Brookline MA 02445
Tel (617) 730-2401 *SIC* 8211

CAMBRIDGE PUBLIC SCHOOLS p 244
159 Thorndike St, Cambridge MA 02141
Tel (617) 349-6400 *SIC* 8211

TRUSTEES OF DEERFIELD ACADEMY p 1487
7 Boyden Ln, Deerfield MA 01342
Tel (413) 772-0241 *SIC* 8211

WEYMOUTH PUBLIC SCHOOLS p 1603
111 Middle St, East Weymouth MA 02189
Tel (781) 337-7500 *SIC* 8211

EVERETT PUBLIC SCHOOLS p 514
121 Vine St, Everett MA 02149
Tel (617) 394-2400 *SIC* 8211

FALL RIVER PUBLIC SCHOOLS p 526
417 Rock St, Fall River MA 02720
Tel (508) 675-8420 *SIC* 8211

ROMAN CATHOLIC DIOCESE OF FALL RIVER OFFICE OF AIDS MINISTR p 1248
47 Underwood St, Fall River MA 02720
Tel (508) 235-1184 *SIC* 6661 8211

HOLYOKE PUBLIC SCHOOLS p 702
57 Suffolk St Ste 101, Holyoke MA 01040
Tel (413) 534-2000 *SIC* 8211

LAWRENCE SCHOOL DISTRICT p 848
233 Haverhill St, Lawrence MA 01840
Tel (978) 975-5905 *SIC* 8211

LYNN PUBLIC SCHOOLS p 888
100 Bennett St, Lynn MA 01905
Tel (781) 593-1680 *SIC* 8211

NEWTON PUBLIC SCHOOL DISTRICT p 1039
100 Walnut St, Newton MA 02460
Tel (617) 559-6000 *SIC* 8211

PITTSFIELD PUBLIC SCHOOLS p 1152
269 1st St, Pittsfield MA 01201
Tel (413) 395-0101 *SIC* 8211

PLYMOUTH PUBLIC SCHOOLS p 1157
253 S Meadow Rd, Plymouth MA 02360
Tel (508) 830-4348 *SIC* 8211

QUINCY PUBLIC SCHOOLS p 1200
34 Coddington St, Quincy MA 02169
Tel (617) 984-8700 *SIC* 8211

BOSTON PUBLIC SCHOOLS p 203
2300 Washington St, Roxbury MA 02119
Tel (617) 635-9000 *SIC* 8211

SPRINGFIELD PUBLIC SCHOOLS p 1361
1550 Main St Fl 2, Springfield MA 01103
Tel (413) 787-7100 *SIC* 8211

WELLESLEY PUBLIC SCHOOLS p 1589
40 Kingsbury St, Wellesley MA 02481
Tel (781) 446-6200 *SIC* 8211

WESTFIELD PUBLIC SCHOOLS p 1601
94 N Elm St Ste 101, Westfield MA 01085
Tel (413) 572-6403 *SIC* 8211

SEVEN HILLS FOUNDATION INC p 1309
81 Hope Ave, Worcester MA 01603
Tel (508) 755-2340 *SIC* 8211 8361

WORCESTER PUBLIC SCHOOLS p 1624
20 Irving St, Worcester MA 01609
Tel (508) 799-3116 *SIC* 8211

PUBLIC SCHOOLS OF CITY ANN ARBOR p 1189
2555 S State St, Ann Arbor MI 48104
Tel (734) 994-2200 *SIC* 8211

WASHTENAW INTERMEDIATE SCHOOL DISTRICT p 1580
1819 S Wagner Rd, Ann Arbor MI 48103
Tel (734) 994-8100 *SIC* 8211

SCHOOL DISTRICT OF CITY OF BIRMINGHAM p 1289
31301 Evergreen Rd, Beverly Hills MI 48025
Tel (248) 203-3000 *SIC* 8211

ARCHDIOCESE OF DETROIT ED OFF p 105
3691 Lincoln Rd, Bloomfield MI 48301
Tel (248) 646-2612 *SIC* 8211

BLOOMFIELD HILLS SCHOOL DISTRICT p 190
7273 Wing Lake Rd Ste A, Bloomfield Hills MI 48301
Tel (248) 341-5400 *SIC* 8211

BRIGHTON AREA SCHOOL DISTRICT p 213
125 S Church St, Brighton MI 48116
Tel (810) 299-4000 *SIC* 8211

CLARKSTON COMMUNITY SCHOOLS p 322
6389 Clarkston Rd, Clarkston MI 48346
Tel (248) 623-5400 *SIC* 8211

CHIPPEWA VALLEY SCHOOLS (INC) p 301
19120 Cass Ave, Clinton Township MI 48038
Tel (586) 723-2000 *SIC* 8211

LANSE CREUSE PUBLIC SCHOOLS p 844
24076 Frdrick Pankow Blvd, Clinton Township MI 48036
Tel (586) 783-6300 *SIC* 8211

MACOMB INTERMEDIATE SCHOOL DISTRICT p 893
44001 Garfield Rd, Clinton Township MI 48038
Tel (586) 228-3479 *SIC* 8211

DEARBORN PUBLIC SCHOOLS p 420
18700 Audette St, Dearborn MI 48124
Tel (313) 827-3000 *SIC* 8211 8222

BOARD OF EDUCATION OF CITY OF DETROIT p 195
3011 W Grand Blvd Fl 6, Detroit MI 48202
Tel (313) 873-7860 *SIC* 8211

DETROIT CITY SCHOOL DISTRICT p 433
3011 W Grand Blvd Fl 14, Detroit MI 48202
Tel (313) 873-7553 *SIC* 8211

EAST DETROIT PUBLIC SCHOOLS p 470
24685 Kelly Rd, Eastpointe MI 48021
Tel (586) 445-4400 *SIC* 8211

FARMINGTON PUBLIC SCHOOL DISTRICT p 530
32500 Shiawassee Rd, Farmington MI 48336
Tel (248) 489-3300 *SIC* 8211

GENESEE INTERMEDIATE SCHOOL DISTRICT p 602
2413 W Maple Ave, Flint MI 48507
Tel (810) 591-4400 *SIC* 8211

SCHOOL DISTRICT OF CITY OF FLINT p 1289
923 E Kearsley St, Flint MI 48503
Tel (810) 760-1000 *SIC* 8211

GRAND BLANC COMMUNITY SCHOOLS p 629
11920 S Saginaw St, Grand Blanc MI 48439
Tel (810) 591-6000 *SIC* 8211

FOREST HILLS PUBLIC SCHOOLS p 566
6590 Cascade Rd Se, Grand Rapids MI 49546
Tel (616) 493-8800 *SIC* 8211

GRAND RAPIDS PUBLIC SCHOOLS p 630
1331 Franklin St Se, Grand Rapids MI 49506
Tel (616) 819-2000 *SIC* 8211

KENT INTERMEDIATE SCHOOL DISTRICT p 812
2930 Knapp St Ne, Grand Rapids MI 49525
Tel (616) 364-1333 *SIC* 8211

KENTWOOD PUBLIC SCHOOLS p 813
5820 Eastern Ave Se, Grand Rapids MI 49508
Tel (616) 455-4400 *SIC* 8211

NATIONAL HERITAGE ACADEMIES INC p 1013
3850 Broadmoor Ave Se # 201, Grand Rapids MI 49512
Tel (877) 223-6402 *SIC* 8211 8741

GROSSE POINTE PUBLIC SCHOOL SYSTEM p 641
389 Saint Clair St, Grosse Pointe MI 48230
Tel (313) 432-3000 *SIC* 8211

HAZEL PARK PUBLIC SCHOOL DISTRICT p 671
1620 E Elza Ave, Hazel Park MI 48030
Tel (248) 658-5217 *SIC* 8211

HURON VALLEY BOARD OF EDUCATION p 721
2390 S Milford Rd, Highland MI 48357
Tel (248) 684-8000 *SIC* 8211

HURON VALLEY SCHOOLS p 721
2390 S Milford Rd, Highland MI 48357
Tel (248) 684-8000 *SIC* 8211

HILLSDALE COLLEGE p 694
33 E College St, Hillsdale MI 49242
Tel (517) 437-7341 *SIC* 8221 8211

WEST OTTAWA PUBLIC SCHOOLS p 1595
1138 136th Ave, Holland MI 49424
Tel (616) 738-5700 *SIC* 8211

WEST OTTAWA SCHOOLS p 1595
1138 136th Ave, Holland MI 49424
Tel (616) 738-5710 *SIC* 8211

HOWELL PUBLIC SCHOOLS p 713
411 N Highlander Way, Howell MI 48843
Tel (517) 548-6200 *SIC* 8211

JACKSON PUBLIC SCHOOLS p 774
522 Wildwood Ave, Jackson MI 49201
Tel (517) 841-2200 *SIC* 8211

KALAMAZOO PUBLIC SCHOOL DISTRICT p 801
1220 Howard St, Kalamazoo MI 49008
Tel (269) 337-0113 *SIC* 8211

LAKE ORION COMMUNITY SCHOOLS p 839
315 N Lapeer St, Lake Orion MI 48362
Tel (248) 693-5400 *SIC* 8211

LANSING SCHOOL DISTRICT p 844
519 W Kalamazoo St, Lansing MI 48933
Tel (517) 755-1000 *SIC* 8211

LIVONIA PUBLIC SCHOOL DISTRICT p 872
15125 Farmington Rd, Livonia MI 48154
Tel (734) 744-2500 *SIC* 8211

MIDLAND PUBLIC SCHOOL DISTRICT p 966
600 E Carpenter St, Midland MI 48640
Tel (989) 923-5001 *SIC* 8211

NORTHVILLE PUBLIC SCHOOL DISTRICT p 1059
501 W Main St, Northville MI 48167
Tel (248) 349-3400 *SIC* 8211

PLYMOUTH-CANTON COMMUNITY SCHOOLS p 1157
454 S Harvey St, Plymouth MI 48170
Tel (734) 416-2700 *SIC* 8211

SCHOOL DISTRICT OF CITY OF PONTIAC p 1289
47200 Woodward Ave, Pontiac MI 48342
Tel (248) 451-6800 *SIC* 8211

PORT HURON AREA SCHOOL DISTRICT p 1162
2720 Riverside Dr, Port Huron MI 48060
Tel (810) 984-3101 *SIC* 8211

PORTAGE PUBLIC SCHOOLS p 1162
8107 Mustang Dr, Portage MI 49002
Tel (269) 323-6800 *SIC* 8211

ROCHESTER COMMUNITY SCHOOLS p 1243
501 W University Dr, Rochester MI 48307
Tel (248) 726-3000 *SIC* 8211

ARCHDIOCESE OF DETROIT ED OFF p 105
2633 John R Rd, Rochester Hills MI 48307
Tel (248) 299-3798 *SIC* 8211

ROCKFORD PUBLIC SCHOOLS p 1244
350 N Main St, Rockford MI 49341
Tel (616) 863-6320 *SIC* 8211

SOUTH LYON COMMUNITY SCHOOLS p 1344
345 S Warren St, South Lyon MI 48178
Tel (248) 573-8127 *SIC* 8211

SOUTHFIELD PUBLIC SCHOOL DISTRICT p 1351
24661 Lahser Rd, Southfield MI 48033
Tel (248) 746-8500 *SIC* 8211

UTICA COMMUNITY SCHOOLS p 1537
11303 Greendale Dr, Sterling Heights MI 48312
Tel (586) 797-1000 *SIC* 8211

TAYLOR SCHOOL DISTRICT p 1427
23033 Northline Rd, Taylor MI 48180
Tel (734) 374-1200 *SIC* 8211

TRAVERSE CITY AREA PUBLIC SCHOOLS p 1475
412 Webster St, Traverse City MI 49686
Tel (231) 933-1700 *SIC* 8211

TROY SCHOOL DISTRICT p 1485
475 First St, Troy MI 48098
Tel (248) 823-4000 *SIC* 8211

LAKE WALLED CONSOLIDATED SCHOOL DISTRICT p 839
850 Ladd Rd Bldg D, Walled Lake MI 48390
Tel (248) 956-2000 *SIC* 8211

WARREN CONSOLIDATED SCHOOLS p 1576
31300 Anita Dr, Warren MI 48093
Tel (586) 825-2400 *SIC* 8211

OAKLAND SCHOOLS INC p 1071
2111 Pontiac Lake Rd, Waterford MI 48328
Tel (248) 209-2000 *SIC* 8211

WATERFORD SCHOOL DISTRICT p 1582
501 N Cass Lake Rd, Waterford MI 48328
Tel (248) 682-7800 *SIC* 8211

WEST BLOOMFIELD SCHOOL DISTRICT p 1594
5810 Commerce Rd, West Bloomfield MI 48324
Tel (248) 865-6420 *SIC* 8211

WAYNE-WESTLAND COMMUNITY SCHOOLS p 1584
36745 Marquette St, Westland MI 48185
Tel (734) 419-2000 *SIC* 8211

ANOKA-HENNEPIN SCHOOL DIST NO 11 p 92
2727 N Ferry St, Anoka MN 55303
Tel (763) 506-1000 *SIC* 8211

INDEPENDENT SCHOOL DISTRICT 271 p 737
1350 W 106th St, Bloomington MN 55431
Tel (952) 681-6400 *SIC* 8211

BRAINERD PUBLIC SCHOOLS p 207
804 Oak St, Brainerd MN 56401
Tel (218) 454-6900 *SIC* 8211

INDEPENDENT SCHOOL DISTRICT 181 p 737
804 Oak St, Brainerd MN 56401
Tel (218) 454-6900 *SIC* 8211

BURNSVILLE EAGAN SAVAGE INDEPENDENT SCHOOL DISTRICT 191 p 228
100 River Ridge Ct, Burnsville MN 55337
Tel (952) 707-2000 *SIC* 8211

BURNSVILLE-EAGAN-SAVAGE BOARD OF EDUCATION p 228
100 River Ridge Ct, Burnsville MN 55337
Tel (952) 707-2000 *SIC* 8211

SOUTH WASHINGTON COUNTY SCHOOLS ISD 833 p 1345
7362 E Point Douglas Rd S, Cottage Grove MN 55016
Tel (651) 458-6300 *SIC* 8211

INDEPENDENT SCHOOL DISTRICT 709 p 737
215 N 1st Ave E, Duluth MN 55802
Tel (218) 336-8700 *SIC* 8211

EDEN PRAIRIE SCHOOLS p 477
8100 School Rd, Eden Prairie MN 55344
Tel (952) 975-7000 *SIC* 8211

ELK RIVER AREA SCHOOL DISTRICT 728 p 487
815 Highway 10, Elk River MN 55330
Tel (763) 241-3400 SIC 8211

FARMINGTON AREA PUBLIC SCHOOLS p 530
20655 Flagstaff Ave, Farmington MN 55024
Tel (651) 463-5001 SIC 8211

INDEPENDENT SCHOOL DISTRICT 831 p 737
6100 210th St N, Forest Lake MN 55025
Tel (651) 982-8100 SIC 8211

INDEPENDENT SCHOOL DISTRICT 270 p 737
1001 Highway 7, Hopkins MN 55305
Tel (952) 988-4000 SIC 8211

LAKEVILLE AREA PUBLIC SCHOOLS p 840
8670 210th St W, Lakeville MN 55044
Tel (952) 232-2000 SIC 8211

INDEPENDENT SCHOOL DISTRICT NO 77 p 737
10 Civic Center Plz, Mankato MN 56001
Tel (507) 387-3167 SIC 8211

INDEPENDENT SCHOOL DISTRICT 279 p 737
11200 93rd Ave N, Maple Grove MN 55369
Tel (763) 391-7000 SIC 8211

INDEPENDENT SCHOOL DISTRICT 273 p 737
5701 Normandale Rd, Minneapolis MN 55424
Tel (952) 848-3900 SIC 8211

INDEPENDENT SCHOOL DISTRICT 281 p 737
4148 Winnetka Ave N, Minneapolis MN 55427
Tel (763) 504-8000 SIC 8211

INDEPENDENT SCHOOL DISTRICT NO 271 p 737
1350 W 106th St, Minneapolis MN 55431
Tel (952) 681-6400 SIC 8211

MINNEAPOLIS PUBLIC SCHOOL DISTRICT p 973
1250 W Broadway Ave, Minneapolis MN 55411
Tel (612) 668-0200 SIC 8211

MINNETONKA INDEPENDENT SCHOOL DISTRICT 276 p 974
5621 County Road 101, Minnetonka MN 55345
Tel (952) 401-5000 SIC 8211

INDEPENDENT SCHOOL DISTRICT #535 p 737
615 7th St Sw, Rochester MN 55902
Tel (507) 328-3000 SIC 8211

ROSEMOUNT-APPLE VALLEY-EAGAN SCHOOL BOARD p 1251
3455 153rd St W, Rosemount MN 55068
Tel (651) 423-7700 SIC 8211

ROSEMOUNT-APPLE VALLEY-EAGAN SCHOOL DISTRICT p 1251
3455 153rd St W, Rosemount MN 55068
Tel (651) 423-7700 SIC 8211

ST CLOUD AREA SCHOOL DISTRICT p 1365
1000 44th Ave N Ste 100, Saint Cloud MN 56303
Tel (320) 253-9333 SIC 8211

IND SCHOOL DIST 621 p 735
350 Highway 96 W, Saint Paul MN 55126
Tel (651) 621-6000 SIC 8211 8742

INDEPENDENT SCHOOL DISTRICT 622 p 737
2520 12th Ave E, Saint Paul MN 55109
Tel (651) 748-7622 SIC 8211

INDEPENDENT SCHOOL DISTRICT 623 (INC) p 737
1251 County Road B2 W, Saint Paul MN 55113
Tel (651) 635-1600 SIC 8211

NORTH SAINT PAUL MAPLEWOOD & OAKDALE SCHOOL DISTRICT 622 p 1053
2520 12th Ave E, Saint Paul MN 55109
Tel (651) 748-7420 SIC 8211

ST PETER PUBLIC SCHOOL DISTRICT p 1372
100 Lincoln Dr Ste 229, Saint Peter MN 56082
Tel (507) 934-5703 SIC 8211

MOUNDS VIEW PUBLIC SCHOOL DISTRICT p 993
350 Highway 96 W, Shoreview MN 55126
Tel (651) 621-6017 SIC 8211

INDEPENDENT SCHOOL DISTRICT 834 p 737
1875 Greeley St S, Stillwater MN 55082
Tel (651) 351-8340 SIC 8211

WAYZATA INDEPENDENT SCHOOL DISTRICT 284 p 1584
210 County Road 101 N, Wayzata MN 55391
Tel (763) 745-5000 SIC 8211

INDEPENDENT SCHOOL DISTRICT 624 (INC) p 737
4855 Bloom Ave, White Bear Lake MN 55110
Tel (651) 407-7500 SIC 8211

RANKIN COUNTY SCHOOL DISTRICT ASSOCIATION OF EDUCATIONAL OFFICE PERSONNEL INC p 1208
1220 Apple Park Pl, Brandon MS 39042
Tel (601) 825-5590 SIC 8211

JONES COUNTY SCHOOL DISTRICT p 792
5204 Highway 11 N, Ellisville MS 39437
Tel (601) 649-5201 SIC 8211 9411

GREENVILLE PUBLIC SCHOOLS INC p 638
412 S Main St, Greenville MS 38701
Tel (662) 334-7000 SIC 8211 9411

HARRISON COUNTY SCHOOL DISTRICT p 664
11072 Highway 49, Gulfport MS 39503
Tel (228) 539-5956 SIC 8211

JACKSON PUBLIC SCHOOL DISTRICT LEASE CORP INC p 774
662 S President St, Jackson MS 39201
Tel (601) 960-8921 SIC 8211

MISSISSIPPI ACTION FOR PROGRESS INC p 975
1751 Morson Rd, Jackson MS 39209
Tel (601) 923-4100 SIC 8099 8211

LAUDERDALE COUNTY SCHOOL DISTRICT p 847
410 Constitution Ave Fl 3, Meridian MS 39301
Tel (601) 482-9746 SIC 8211

MERIDIAN PUBLIC SCHOOL DISTRICT p 949
1019 25th Ave, Meridian MS 39301
Tel (601) 483-6271 SIC 8211

JACKSON COUNTY BOARD OF EDUCATION p 773
4700 Col Vickery Rd, Ocean Springs MS 39565
Tel (228) 826-1757 SIC 8211

PASCAGOULA SCHOOL DISTRICT p 1119
1006 Communy Ave, Pascagoula MS 39567
Tel (228) 938-6491 SIC 8211

CALHOUN COUNTY SCHOOL DISTRICT p 238
119 W Main St, Pittsboro MS 38951
Tel (662) 412-3152 SIC 8211

LAMAR CO SCHOOL SYSTEM p 841
424 Martin Luther King Dr, Purvis MS 39475
Tel (601) 794-1030 SIC 8211

MADISON COUNTY SCHOOL DISTRICT p 894
476 Highland Colony Pkwy, Ridgeland MS 39157
Tel (601) 879-3000 SIC 8211

STARKVILLE OKTIBBEHA CONSOLIDATED SCHOOL DISTRICT p 1379
401 Greensboro St, Starkville MS 39759
Tel (662) 324-4050 SIC 8211

TUPELO PUBLIC SCHOOL DISTRICT p 1492
72 S Green St, Tupelo MS 38804
Tel (662) 841-8850 SIC 8211

JACKSON COUNTY SCHOOL DISTRICT p 773
4700 Colonel Vickrey Rd, Vancleave MS 39565
Tel (228) 826-1757 SIC 8211

FOX C-6 SCHOOL DISTRICT p 572
745 Jeffco Blvd, Arnold MO 63010
Tel (636) 296-8000 SIC 8211

BLUE SPRINGS R-IV SCHOOL DISTRICT p 192
1801 Nw Vesper St, Blue Springs MO 64015
Tel (816) 224-1300 SIC 8211

PARKWAY SCHOOL DISTRICT p 1117
455 N Woods Mill Rd, Chesterfield MO 63017
Tel (314) 415-8100 SIC 8211

COLUMBIA PUBLIC SCHOOLS p 341
1818 W Worley St, Columbia MO 65203
Tel (573) 214-3400 SIC 8211

ROCKWOOD SCHOOL DISTRICT R-6 (INC) p 1245
111 E North St, Eureka MO 63025
Tel (636) 733-2000 SIC 8211

FERGUSON REORGANIZED SCHOOL DISTRICT R-2 p 538
1005 Waterford Dr, Florissant MO 63033
Tel (314) 506-9000 SIC 8211

HAZELWOOD SCHOOL DISTRICT p 671
15955 New Halls Ferry Rd, Florissant MO 63031
Tel (314) 953-5000 SIC 8211

INDEPENDENCE SCHOOL BOARD OF EDUCATION p 736
201 N Forest Ave, Independence MO 64050
Tel (816) 521-5300 SIC 8211

INDEPENDENCE SCHOOL DISTRICT p 736
201 N Forest Ave Ste 30, Independence MO 64050
Tel (816) 521-5300 SIC 8211

JEFFERSON CITY PUBLIC SCHOOLS p 781
315 E Dunklin St, Jefferson City MO 65101
Tel (573) 659-3000 SIC 8211

JOPLIN SCHOOL p 793
310 W 8th St, Joplin MO 64801
Tel (417) 625-5200 SIC 8211

CATHOLIC DIOCESE OF KANSAS CITY-ST JOSEPH p 266
850 Main St, Kansas City MO 64105
Tel (816) 756-1850
SIC 8661 8211 8351 8361 6553

HICKMAN MILLS C-1 SCHOOL DISTRICT p 690
9000 Old Santa Fe Rd, Kansas City MO 64138
Tel (816) 316-7000 SIC 8211

KANSAS CITY PUBLIC SCHOOLS p 802
2901 Troost Ave, Kansas City MO 64109
Tel (816) 418-7000 SIC 8211

NORTH KANSAS CITY SCHOOL DISTRICT NO 74 p 1053
2000 Ne 46th St, Kansas City MO 64116
Tel (816) 413-5000 SIC 8211

PARK HILL SCHOOL DISTRICT p 1115
7703 Nw Barry Rd, Kansas City MO 64153
Tel (816) 359-4040 SIC 8211

LEES SUMMIT R-7 SCHOOL DISTRICT p 852
301 Ne Tudor Rd, Lees Summit MO 64086
Tel (816) 986-1000 SIC 8211

LIBERTY 53 SCHOOL DISTRICT p 861
8 Victory Ln Ste 100, Liberty MO 64068
Tel (816) 736-5300 SIC 8211

FT ZUMWALT R-II SCHOOL DISTRICT p 582
555 E Terra Ln, O Fallon MO 63366
Tel (636) 240-2072 SIC 8211

CONSOLIDATED SCHOOL DISTRICT 2 (INC) p 360
6608 Raytown Rd, Raytown MO 64133
Tel (816) 268-7000 SIC 8211

PATTONVILLE SCHOOL DISTRICT p 1121
11097 St Charles Rock Rd, Saint Ann MO 63074
Tel (314) 213-8500 SIC 8211

FRANCIS HOWELL SCHOOL DISTRICT p 573
4545 Central School Rd, Saint Charles MO 63304
Tel (636) 851-4000 SIC 8211

ST JOSEPH SCHOOL DISTRICT p 1368
925 Felix St, Saint Joseph MO 64501
Tel (816) 671-4000 SIC 8211

KIRKWOOD R-VII SCHOOL DISTRICT p 822
11289 Manchester Rd, Saint Louis MO 63122
Tel (314) 213-6100 SIC 8211

MEHLVILLE R-IX SCHOOL DISTRICT p 940
3120 Lemay Ferry Rd, Saint Louis MO 63125
Tel (314) 892-5000 SIC 8211

PRINCIPIA CORP p 1177
13201 Clayton Rd, Saint Louis MO 63131
Tel (314) 434-2100 SIC 8211 8221

SPECIAL SCHOOL DISTRICT OF ST LOUIS COUNTY p 1356
12110 Clayton Rd, Saint Louis MO 63131
Tel (314) 989-8100 SIC 8211

ST LOUIS PUBLIC SCHOOLS p 1370
801 N 11th St, Saint Louis MO 63101
Tel (314) 231-3720 SIC 8211

MISSOURI STATE UNIVERSITY p 976
901 S National Ave, Springfield MO 65897
Tel (417) 836-5000 SIC 8221 8211

SPRINGFIELD SCHOOL DISTRICT R12 p 1361
1359 E Saint Louis St, Springfield MO 65802
Tel (417) 523-0000 SIC 8211

TROY R-III SCHOOL DISTRICT p 1485
951 W College St, Troy MO 63379
Tel (636) 462-6098 SIC 8211

WENTZVILLE R-IV SCHOOL DISTRICT p 1592
1 Campus Dr, Wentzville MO 63385
Tel (636) 327-3800 SIC 8211

BILLINGS SCHOOL DISTRICT 2 p 182
415 N 30th St, Billings MT 59101
Tel (406) 281-5000 SIC 8211

GREAT FALLS PUBLIC SCHOOLS DIST1 p 633
1100 4th St S, Great Falls MT 59405
Tel (406) 268-6052 SIC 8211

HAVRE SCHOOL DISTRICT 16-A p 668
425 6th St, Havre MT 59501
Tel (406) 265-4356 SIC 8211

ROMAN CATHOLIC BISHOP OF HELENA MONTANA p 1248
515 N Ewing St, Helena MT 59601
Tel (406) 442-5820
SIC 8661 8211 8221 2741

MISSOULA COUNTY PUBLIC SCHOOLS p 976
215 S 6th St W, Missoula MT 59801
Tel (406) 728-2400 SIC 8299 8211

BELLEVUE PUBLIC SCHOOLS p 170
2600 Arboretum Dr, Bellevue NE 68005
Tel (402) 293-4000 SIC 8299 8748 8211

ELKHORN SCHOOL DISTRICT 010 p 488
20650 Glenn St, Elkhorn NE 68022
Tel (402) 289-2579 SIC 8211

HALL COUNTY SCHOOL DISTRICT 2 p 654
123 S Webb Rd, Grand Island NE 68803
Tel (308) 385-5886 SIC 8211 9411

LINCOLN PUBLIC SCHOOLS INC p 868
5905 O St, Lincoln NE 68510
Tel (402) 436-1000 SIC 8211

MILLARD PUBLIC SCHOOLS p 970
5606 S 147th St, Omaha NE 68137
Tel (402) 715-8200 SIC 8211

OMAHA PUBLIC SCHOOLS p 1083
3215 Cuming St, Omaha NE 68131
Tel (402) 557-2120 SIC 8211

WESTSIDE COMMUNITY SCHOOL DISTRICT 66 p 1603
909 S 76th St, Omaha NE 68114
Tel (402) 390-2100 SIC 8211

PAPILLION-LAVISTA PUBLIC SCHOOLS p 1112
420 S Washington St, Papillion NE 68046
Tel (402) 537-6244 SIC 8211

ELKO COUNTY SCHOOL DISTRICT p 488
850 Elm St, Elko NV 89801
Tel (775) 738-5196 SIC 8211

CLARK COUNTY SCHOOL DIST p 322
5101 Obannon Dr Apt 233, Las Vegas NV 89146
Tel (702) 799-1042 SIC 8211

CLARK COUNTY SCHOOL DISTRICT p 322
5100 W Sahara Ave, Las Vegas NV 89146
Tel (702) 799-5000 SIC 8211

UHS SUMMERLIN RECEIVING p 1500
657 N Town Center Dr, Las Vegas NV 89144
Tel (702) 233-7000 SIC 8211

WASHOE COUNTY SCHOOL DISTRICT p 1580
425 E 9th St, Reno NV 89512
Tel (775) 348-0200 SIC 8211

LYON COUNTY SCHOOL DISTRICT p 888
25 Joe Parr Way, Yerington NV 89447
Tel (775) 463-3006 SIC 8211

EXETER SCHOOL DISTRICT p 519
24 Front St Ste 111, Exeter NH 03833
Tel (603) 778-7772 SIC 8211

PHILLIPS EXETER ACADEMY p 1144
20 Main St, Exeter NH 03833
Tel (603) 772-4311 SIC 8211

SCHOOL ADMINISTRATIVE UNIT 16 p 1288
30 Linden St, Exeter NH 03833
Tel (603) 775-8400 SIC 8211

NASHUA SCHOOL DISTRICT p 1008
141 Ledge St, Nashua NH 03060
Tel (603) 966-1000 SIC 8211

SCHOOL ADMINISTRATIVE UNIT 42 p 1289
141 Ledge St, Nashua NH 03060
Tel (603) 966-1000 SIC 8211

TIMBERLANE REGIONAL SAU p 1454
30 Greenough Rd, Plaistow NH 03865
Tel (603) 382-6119 SIC 8211

ATLANTIC CITY BOARD OF EDUCATION p 126
1300 Atlantic Ave Ste 500, Atlantic City NJ 08401
Tel (609) 343-7200 SIC 8211

ATLANTIC CITY PUBLIC SCHOOL p 126
1300 Atlantic Ave, Atlantic City NJ 08401
Tel (609) 343-0086 SIC 8211

BAYONNE SCHOOL DISTRICT p 162
669 Avenue A, Bayonne NJ 07002
Tel (201) 858-5814 SIC 8211

GLOUCESTER TOWNSHIP BOARD OF EDUCATION p 618
17 Erial Rd, Blackwood NJ 08012
Tel (856) 227-1400 SIC 8211

GLOUCESTER TOWNSHIP PUBLIC SCHOOLS p 618
17 Erial Rd, Blackwood NJ 08012
Tel (856) 227-1400 SIC 8211

BRICK TOWNSHIP BOARD OF EDUCATION p 211
101 Hendrickson Ave, Brick NJ 08724
Tel (732) 785-3000 SIC 8211

BRICK TOWNSHIP PUBLIC SCHOOL BOARD p 211
101 Hendrickson Ave, Brick NJ 08724
Tel (732) 785-3000 SIC 8211

BRIDGEWATER-RARITAN REGIONAL SCHOOL DISTRICT p 212
836 Newmans Ln, Bridgewater NJ 08807
Tel (908) 685-2777 SIC 8211

BRIDGEWATER-RARITAN REGIONAL SCHOOL DISTRICT p 212
836 Newmans Ln, Bridgewater NJ 08807
Tel (908) 685-2777 SIC 8211

CAMDEN CITY BOARD OF EDUCATION FOUNDATION INC p 244
201 N Front St, Camden NJ 08102
Tel (856) 966-2000 SIC 8211

CAMDEN CITY PUBLIC SCHOOLS p 244
201 N Front St, Camden NJ 08102
Tel (856) 966-2000 SIC 8211

BANCROFT NEUROHEALTH A NEW JERSEY NONPROFIT CORP p 150
1255 Caldwell Rd, Cherry Hill NJ 08034
Tel (856) 348-1183 SIC 8361 8299 8211

CHERRY HILL PUBLIC SCHOOL DISTRICT p 294
315 Roosevelt Dr, Cherry Hill NJ 08002
Tel (856) 667-1220 SIC 8211

CLIFTON BOARD OF EDUCATION INC p 326
745 Clifton Ave, Clifton NJ 07013
Tel (973) 470-2300 SIC 8211 8741

ROMAN CATHOLIC DIOCESE OF PATERSON (INC) p 1249
777 Valley Rd, Clifton NJ 07013
Tel (973) 777-8818 SIC 8211 8661

EAST BRUNSWICK BOARD OF EDUCATION (INC) p 470
760 State Route 18, East Brunswick NJ 08816
Tel (732) 613-6700 SIC 8211

EAST BRUNSWICK PUBLIC SCHOOLS p 470
760 Highway 18, East Brunswick NJ 08816
Tel (732) 613-6700 SIC 8211

EAST ORANGE SCHOOL DISTRICT p 470
199 4th Ave, East Orange NJ 07017
Tel (862) 233-7300 SIC 8211 9111

EDISON TOWNSHIP PUBLIC SCHOOLS p 478
312 Pierson Ave, Edison NJ 08837
Tel (732) 452-4900 SIC 8211

MIDDLESEX COUNTY COLLEGE p 965
2600 Woodbridge Ave, Edison NJ 08837
Tel (732) 548-6000
SIC 8222 9111 8221 8211

EGG HARBOR TOWNSHIP BOARD OF EDUCATION INC p 481
13 Swift Ave, Egg Harbor Township NJ 08234
Tel (609) 646-7911 SIC 8211

ELIZABETH PUBLIC SCHOOLS p 487
500 N Broad St, Elizabeth NJ 07208
Tel (908) 436-5010 SIC 8211

FREEHOLD REGIONAL HIGH SCHOOL DISTRICT p 576
11 Pine St, Englishtown NJ 07726
Tel (732) 792-7300 SIC 8211

MANALAPAN-ENGLISHTOWN REGIONAL SCHOOL DISTRICT p 900
54 Main St, Englishtown NJ 07726
Tel (732) 786-2500 SIC 8211

HACKENSACK CITY SCHOOL DISTRICT p 652
191 2nd St, Hackensack NJ 07601
Tel (201) 646-8000 SIC 8211

HILLSBOROUGH TOWNSHIP BOARD OF EDUCATION p 694
379 S Branch Rd, Hillsborough NJ 08844
Tel (908) 431-6600 SIC 8211

HILLSBOROUGH TOWNSHIP SCHOOL DISTRICT p 694
379 S Branch Rd, Hillsborough NJ 08844
Tel (908) 431-6600 SIC 8211

HOWELL TOWNSHIP BOARD OF EDUCATION p 713
200 Sqnkum Yellowbrook Rd, Howell NJ 07731
Tel (732) 751-2480 SIC 8211

IRVINGTON PUBLIC SCHOOLS p 765
1 University Pl Fl 4, Irvington NJ 07111
Tel (973) 399-6800 SIC 8211

JACKSON TOWNSHIP SCHOOL DISTRICT p 774
151 Don Connor Blvd, Jackson NJ 08527
Tel (732) 833-4600 SIC 8211

EDISONLEARNING INC p 478
Harborside Financial Center 2910, Jersey City NJ 07311
Tel (201) 630-2600 SIC 8211

JERSEY CITY BOARD OF EDUCATION (INC) p 783
346 Claremont Ave, Jersey City NJ 07305
Tel (201) 915-6202 SIC 8211

JERSEY CITY PUBLIC SCHOOLS p 783
346 Claremont Ave, Jersey City NJ 07305
Tel (201) 915-6202 SIC 8211

KEARNY PUBLIC SCHOOLS p 807
100 Davis Ave, Kearny NJ 07032
Tel (201) 955-5000 SIC 8211

LAKEWOOD BOARD OF EDUCATION (INC) p 840
200 Ramsey Ave, Lakewood NJ 08701
Tel (732) 730-1606 SIC 8211

LAWRENCEVILLE SCHOOL p 848
2500 Main St, Lawrenceville NJ 08648
Tel (609) 896-0400 SIC 8211

MIDDLETOWN TOWNSHIP BOARD OF EDUCATION p 965
834 Leonardville Rd Fl 2, Leonardo NJ 07737
Tel (732) 671-3850 SIC 8211

BOARD OF EDUCATION OF SOUTH ORANGE-MAPLEWOOD p 195
525 Academy St, Maplewood NJ 07040
Tel (973) 378-9613 SIC 8211

MARLBORO TOWNSHIP BOARD OF EDUCATION p 909
1980 Township Dr, Marlboro NJ 07746
Tel (732) 972-2000 SIC 8211

OLD BRIDGE TOWNSHIP BOARD OF EDUCATION p 1080
4207 Hwy 516, Matawan NJ 07747
Tel (732) 566-1000 SIC 8211

HAMILTON TOWNSHIP SCHOOL DISTRICT p 655
1876 Dr Dennis Foreman Dr, Mays Landing NJ 08330
Tel (609) 476-6300 SIC 8211

MIDDLETOWN TOWNSHIP SCHOOL DISTRICT p 965
834 Leonardville Rd, Middletown NJ 07748
Tel (732) 671-3850 SIC 8211

MILLVILLE BOARD OF EDUCATION p 971
110 N 3rd St, Millville NJ 08332
Tel (856) 293-2000 *SIC* 8211

MILLVILLE PUBLIC SCHOOLS p 971
110 N 3rd St, Millville NJ 08332
Tel (856) 293-2000 *SIC* 8211

SOUTH BRUNSWICK TOWNSHIP BOARD OF EDUCATION p 1343
4 Executive Dr, Monmouth Junction NJ 08852
Tel (732) 297-7800 *SIC* 8211

MONROE TOWNSHIP BOARD OF EDUCATION p 985
423 Buckelew Ave, Monroe Township NJ 08831
Tel (732) 521-2111 *SIC* 8211

MONTCLAIR BOARD OF EDUCATION (INC) p 986
22 Valley Rd, Montclair NJ 07042
Tel (973) 509-4000 *SIC* 8211

MONTCLAIR PUBLIC SCHOOLS p 986
22 Valley Rd, Montclair NJ 07042
Tel (973) 509-4000 *SIC* 8211

NEW BRUNSWICK PUBLIC SCHOOLS p 1029
268 Baldwin St, New Brunswick NJ 08901
Tel (732) 745-5300 *SIC* 8211

NEWARK PUBLIC SCHOOLS p 1037
2 Cedar St Ste 1, Newark NJ 07102
Tel (973) 733-7333 *SIC* 8211

YOUTH CONSULTATION SERVICE (INC) p 1639
284 Broadway, Newark NJ 07104
Tel (973) 482-2774 *SIC* 8093 8361 8211

NORTH BRUNSWICK TOWNSHIP BOARD OF EDUCATION p 1051
300 Old Georges Rd, North Brunswick NJ 08902
Tel (732) 289-3000 *SIC* 8211

PARAMUS BOARD OF EDUCATION INC p 1114
145 Spring Valley Rd, Paramus NJ 07652
Tel (201) 261-7800 *SIC* 8211

PARSIPPANY-TROY HILLS TOWNSHIP SCHOOL DISTRICT p 1117
292 Parsippany Rd, Parsippany NJ 07054
Tel (973) 263-7200 *SIC* 8211 9111

BOARD OF EDUCATION OF CITY OF PASSAIC INC p 195
101 Passaic Ave, Passaic NJ 07055
Tel (973) 470-5244 *SIC* 8211

PASSAIC CITY PUBLIC SCHOOLS p 1119
101 Passaic Ave, Passaic NJ 07055
Tel (973) 470-5500 *SIC* 8211

PATERSON PUBLIC SCHOOL DISTRICT p 1120
90 Delaware Ave, Paterson NJ 07503
Tel (973) 321-0980 *SIC* 8211

PEMBERTON TOWNSHIP SCHOOL DISTRICT p 1128
1 Egbert St, Pemberton NJ 08068
Tel (609) 893-8141 *SIC* 8211

PERTH AMBOY PUBLIC SCHOOLS p 1137
178 Barracks St, Perth Amboy NJ 08861
Tel (732) 376-6200 *SIC* 8211

PLAINFIELD PUBLIC SCHOOL DISTRICT p 1153
1200 Myrtle Ave, Plainfield NJ 07063
Tel (908) 731-4200 *SIC* 8211

PRINCETON PUBLIC SCHOOLS INC p 1177
25 Valley Rd, Princeton NJ 08540
Tel (609) 806-4204 *SIC* 8211

WEST WINDSOR-PLAINSBORO REGIONAL BOARD OF EDUCATION p 1596
321 Village Rd E, Princeton Junction NJ 08550
Tel (609) 716-5000 *SIC* 8211

WASHINGTON TOWNSHIP BOARD OF EDUCATION p 1579
206 E Holly Ave, Sewell NJ 08080
Tel (856) 589-6644 *SIC* 8211

WASHINGTON TOWNSHIP PUBLIC SCHOOL DISTRICT p 1579
206 E Holly Ave, Sewell NJ 08080
Tel (856) 589-6644 *SIC* 8211

LENAPE REGIONAL HIGH SCHOOL DISTRICT p 855
93 Willow Grove Rd, Shamong NJ 08088
Tel (609) 268-2588 *SIC* 8211

FRANKLIN TOWNSHIP BOARD OF EDUCATION p 575
1755 Amwell Rd, Somerset NJ 08873
Tel (732) 873-2400 *SIC* 8211

FRANKLIN TOWNSHIP PUBLIC SCHOOL DISTRICT OF SOMERSET p 575
1755 Amwell Rd, Somerset NJ 08873
Tel (732) 873-2400 *SIC* 8211

BOARD OF EDUCATION OF TOMS RIVER SCHOOLS (INC) p 195
1144 Hooper Ave Ste 304, Toms River NJ 08753
Tel (732) 505-5500 *SIC* 8211

TOMS RIVER REGIONAL SCHOOLS p 1460
1144 Hooper Ave Ste 304, Toms River NJ 08753
Tel (732) 505-5500 *SIC* 8211 8741

BOARD OF EDUCATION OF CITY OF TRENTON (INC) p 195
108 N Clinton Ave, Trenton NJ 08609
Tel (609) 656-4900 *SIC* 8211

HAMILTON TOWNSHIP BOARD OF EDUCATION p 655
90 Park Ave, Trenton NJ 08690
Tel (609) 631-4100 *SIC* 8211

HAMILTON TOWNSHIP SCHOOL DISTRICT p 655
90 Park Ave, Trenton NJ 08690
Tel (609) 631-4100 *SIC* 8211

TRENTON PUBLIC SCHOOL DISTRICT p 1476
108 N Clinton Ave, Trenton NJ 08609
Tel (609) 656-4900 *SIC* 8211

BOARD OF EDUCATION OF TOWNSHIP OF UNION p 195
2369 Morris Ave, Union NJ 07083
Tel (908) 810-0492 *SIC* 8211

VINELAND BOARD OF EDUCATION p 1557
625 E Plum St, Vineland NJ 08360
Tel (856) 207-6229 *SIC* 8211

VINELAND PUBLIC SCHOOLS p 1558
625 E Plum St, Vineland NJ 08360
Tel (856) 794-6700 *SIC* 8211

WAYNE TOWNSHIP BOARD OF EDUCATION p 1584
50 Nellis Dr, Wayne NJ 07470
Tel (973) 633-3000 *SIC* 8211

WAYNE TOWNSHIP PUBLIC SCHOOLS p 1584
50 Nellis Dr, Wayne NJ 07470
Tel (973) 633-3000 *SIC* 8211

WEST NEW YORK SCHOOL DISTRICT p 1595
6028 Broadway, West New York NJ 07093
Tel (201) 553-4000 *SIC* 8211

WEST WINDSOR-PLAINSBORO REGIONAL SCHOOL DISTRICT p 1596
321 Village Rd E, West Windsor NJ 08550
Tel (609) 716-5000 *SIC* 8211

WOODBRIDGE TOWNSHIP BOARD OF EDUCATION (INC) p 1622
428 School St, Woodbridge NJ 07095
Tel (732) 750-3200 *SIC* 8211

WOODBRIDGE TOWNSHIP SCHOOL DISTRICT p 1622
428 School St, Woodbridge NJ 07095
Tel (732) 750-3200 *SIC* 8211

ALBUQUERQUE PUBLIC SCHOOL DISTRICT p 47
6400 Uptown Blvd Ne, Albuquerque NM 87110
Tel (505) 880-3700 *SIC* 8211

CITY OF CLOVIS BOARD OF EDUCATION SCHOOL DISTRICT 1 p 314
1009 N Main St, Clovis NM 88101
Tel (575) 769-4300 *SIC* 8211

CLOVIS MUNICIPAL SCHOOL DISTRICT p 328
1009 N Main St, Clovis NM 88101
Tel (575) 769-4300 *SIC* 8211

FARMINGTON MUNICIPAL SCHOOLS p 530
2001 N Dustin Ave, Farmington NM 87401
Tel (505) 324-9840 *SIC* 8211

GALLUP-MC KINLEY COUNTY PUBLIC SCHOOL DISTRICT 1 (INC) p 590
700 Boardman Dr, Gallup NM 87301
Tel (505) 722-7711 *SIC* 8211

HOBBS MUNICIPAL SCHOOLS p 699
1515 E Sanger St, Hobbs NM 88240
Tel (575) 433-0100 *SIC* 8211

LAS CRUCES PUBLIC SCHOOLS p 845
505 S Main St Ste 249, Las Cruces NM 88001
Tel (575) 527-5893 *SIC* 8211

RIO RANCHO PUBLIC SCHOOLS p 1236
500 Laser Rd Ne, Rio Rancho NM 87124
Tel (505) 896-0667 *SIC* 8211

ROSWELL INDEPENDENT SCHOOL DISTRICT (INC) p 1252
300 N Kentucky Ave, Roswell NM 88201
Tel (575) 627-2500 *SIC* 8211

BOARD OF EDUCATION OF CITY OF SANTA FE (INC) p 195
610 Alta Vista St, Santa Fe NM 87505
Tel (505) 467-2000 *SIC* 8211

SANTA FE PUBLIC SCHOOLS p 1280
610 Alta Vista St, Santa Fe NM 87505
Tel (505) 467-2000 *SIC* 8211

CENTRAL CONSOLIDATED SCHOOL DIST 22 p 278
U S Hwy 64, Shiprock NM 87420
Tel (505) 368-4984 *SIC* 8211

GADSDEN INDEPENDENT SCHOOL DISTRICT p 589
4950 Mcnutt Rd, Sunland Park NM 88063
Tel (575) 882-6200 *SIC* 8211

ALBANY CITY SCHOOL DISTRICT p 45
1 Academy Park, Albany NY 12207
Tel (518) 475-6000 *SIC* 8211

CAPITAL REGION BOCES p 250
900 Watervliet Shaker Rd # 102, Albany NY 12205
Tel (518) 862-4924 *SIC* 8211

SOUTH COLONIE CENTRAL SCHOOLS DISTRICT p 1344
102 Loralee Dr, Albany NY 12205
Tel (518) 869-6481 *SIC* 8211

NORTH BABYLON UNION FREE SCHOOL DISTRICT p 1051
5 Jardine Pl, Babylon NY 11703
Tel (631) 321-3209 *SIC* 8211 8741

BALDWIN UNION FREE SCHOOL DISTRICT p 147
960 Hastings St, Baldwin NY 11510
Tel (516) 377-9312 *SIC* 8211

BALLSTON SPA CENTRAL SCHOOL DISTRICT p 148
70 Malta Ave, Ballston Spa NY 12020
Tel (518) 884-7195 *SIC* 8211

BAY SHORE UNION FREE SCHOOL DISTRICT p 161
75 Perkal St, Bay Shore NY 11706
Tel (631) 968-1100 *SIC* 8211

NEW YORK CITY GEOGRAPHIC DISTRICT 26 p 1034
6115 Oceania St, Bayside NY 11364
Tel (718) 631-6982 *SIC* 8211

BETHPAGE UNION FREE SCHOOL DISTRICT p 178
10 Cherry Ave, Bethpage NY 11714
Tel (516) 644-4100 *SIC* 8211

CONNETQUOT CENTRAL SCHOOL DISTRICT OF ISLIP p 358
780 Ocean Ave, Bohemia NY 11716
Tel (631) 244-2203 *SIC* 8211

BRENTWOOD UNION FREE SCHOOL DISTRICT p 210
52 3rd Ave, Brentwood NY 11717
Tel (631) 434-2335 *SIC* 8211

NEW YORK CITY GEOGRAPHIC DISTRICT 10 p 1034
1 Fordham Plz Rm 835, Bronx NY 10458
Tel (718) 741-5852 *SIC* 8211

NEW YORK CITY GEOGRAPHIC DISTRICT 12 p 1034
1970 W Farms Rd, Bronx NY 10460
Tel (718) 328-2310 *SIC* 8211

NEW YORK CITY GEOGRAPHIC DISTRICT 7 p 1034
501 Courtland Ave, Bronx NY 10451
Tel (718) 742-6500 *SIC* 8211

NEW YORK CITY GEOGRAPHIC DISTRICT 8 p 1034
601 Stickball Blvd, Bronx NY 10473
Tel (718) 828-6653 *SIC* 8211

NEW YORK CITY GEOGRAPHIC DISTRICT 9 p 1034
250 E 164th St, Bronx NY 10456
Tel (718) 741-3157 *SIC* 8211

NEW YORK GEOGRAPHIC DISTRICT 11 p 1035
2750 Throop Ave, Bronx NY 10469
Tel (718) 519-2620 *SIC* 8211

NEW YORK CITY GEOGRAPHIC DISTRICT 13 p 1034
355 Park Pl, Brooklyn NY 11238
Tel (718) 636-3204 *SIC* 8211

NEW YORK CITY GEOGRAPHIC DISTRICT 14 p 1034
215 Heyward St, Brooklyn NY 11206
Tel (718) 302-7600 *SIC* 8211

NEW YORK CITY GEOGRAPHIC DISTRICT 15 p 1034
131 Livingston St Rm 301, Brooklyn NY 11201
Tel (718) 935-4317 *SIC* 8211

NEW YORK CITY GEOGRAPHIC DISTRICT 17 p 1034
1224 Park Pl, Brooklyn NY 11213
Tel (718) 221-4372 *SIC* 8211

NEW YORK CITY GEOGRAPHIC DISTRICT 19 p 1034
335 Adams St, Brooklyn NY 11201
Tel (718) 923-5124 *SIC* 8211

NEW YORK CITY GEOGRAPHIC DISTRICT 20 p 1034
415 89th St, Brooklyn NY 11209
Tel (718) 759-3942 *SIC* 8211

NEW YORK CITY GEOGRAPHIC DISTRICT 21 p 1034
501 West Ave, Brooklyn NY 11224
Tel (718) 714-2502 *SIC* 8211

NEW YORK CITY GEOGRAPHIC DISTRICT 22 p 1034
5619 Flatlands Ave, Brooklyn NY 11234
Tel (718) 968-6117 *SIC* 8211

NEW YORK CITY GEOGRAPHIC DISTRICT 23 p 1034
1665 Saint Marks Ave, Brooklyn NY 11233
Tel (718) 922-4794 *SIC* 8211

NEW YORK GEOGRAPHIC DISTRICT 18 p 1035
1106 E 95th St, Brooklyn NY 11236
Tel (718) 566-6008 *SIC* 8211

BUFFALO CITY SCHOOL DISTRICT p 224
65 Niagara Sq Rm 712, Buffalo NY 14202
Tel (716) 816-3500 *SIC* 8211

KENMORE-TONAWANDA UNION FREE SCHOOL DISTRICT p 810
1500 Colvin Blvd, Buffalo NY 14223
Tel (716) 874-8400 *SIC* 8211

MIDDLE COUNTRY CENTRAL SCHOOL DISTRICT p 964
8 43rd St, Centereach NY 11720
Tel (631) 285-8000 *SIC* 8211

CENTRAL ISLIP UNION FREE SCHOOL DISTRICT p 279
50 Wheeler Rd, Central Islip NY 11722
Tel (631) 348-5112 *SIC* 8211

MONROE-WOODBURY CENTRAL SCHOOL DISTRICT p 985
278 Route 32, Central Valley NY 10917
Tel (845) 460-6200 *SIC* 8211

CHAPPAQUA CENTRAL SCHOOL DISTRICT INC p 288
70 Roaring Brook Rd, Chappaqua NY 10514
Tel (914) 238-7200 *SIC* 8211

SHENENDEHOWA CENTRAL SCHOOL DISTRICT p 1315
5 Chelsea Pl, Clifton Park NY 12065
Tel (518) 881-0600 *SIC* 8211

WESTERN SUFFOLK BOCES SECOND SUPERVISORY DISTRICT SUFFOLK COUNTY p 1600
507 Deer Park Rd, Dix Hills NY 11746
Tel (631) 549-4900 *SIC* 8211

WILLIAMSVILLE CENTRAL SCHOOL DISTRICT p 1612
Administratiion Center 10 Er Stratiion Cent, East Amherst NY 14051
Tel (716) 626-8050 *SIC* 8211

COMMACK UNION FREE SCHOOL DISTRICT 10 p 344
480 Clay Pitts Rd, East Northport NY 11731
Tel (631) 912-2000 *SIC* 8211

CITY SCHOOL DISTRICT OF CITY OF ELMIRA NY p 319
951 Hoffman St, Elmira NY 14905
Tel (607) 735-3000 *SIC* 8211

BOARD OF COOPERATIVE EDUCATIONAL SERVICES FIRST SUPERVISORY DISTRICT OF MONROE COUNTY p 195
41 Oconnor Rd, Fairport NY 14450
Tel (585) 377-4660 *SIC* 8211

SEWANHAKA CENTRAL HIGH SCHOOL DISTRICT p 1309
77 Landau Ave, Floral Park NY 11001
Tel (516) 488-9810 *SIC* 8211

FREEPORT UNION FREE SCHOOL DISTRICT p 577
235 N Ocean Ave, Freeport NY 11520
Tel (516) 867-5200 *SIC* 8211

NASSAU BOCES SCHOOL DISTRICT p 1008
71 Clinton Rd Ste 100, Garden City NY 11530
Tel (516) 396-2500 *SIC* 8211

HAVERSTRAW STONY POINT CENTRAL SCHOOL DISTRICT INC p 668
65 Chapel St, Garnerville NY 10923
Tel (845) 942-3053 *SIC* 8211

ORANGE-ULSTER BOCES INC p 1092
53 Gibson Rd, Goshen NY 10924
Tel (845) 291-0100 *SIC* 8211

GREAT NECK PUBLIC SCHOOLS p 634
345 Lakeville Rd, Great Neck NY 11020
Tel (516) 441-4001 *SIC* 8211

GUILDERLAND CENTRAL SCHOOL DISTRICT p 646
8 School Rd, Guilderland Center NY 12085
Tel (518) 456-6200 *SIC* 8211

FRONTIER CENTRAL SCHOOL DISTRICT p 581
5120 Orchard Ave, Hamburg NY 14075
Tel (716) 926-1710 *SIC* 8211

HAUPPAUGE UNION FREE SCHOOL DISTRICT p 668
495 Hoffman Ln Ste 1, Hauppauge NY 11788
Tel (631) 265-3630 *SIC* 8211

HEMPSTEAD UNION FREE SCHOOL DISTRICT p 682
185 Peninsula Blvd, Hempstead NY 11550
Tel (516) 292-7001 *SIC* 8211

RUSH-HENRIETTA CENTRAL SCHOOL DISTRICT p 1259
2034 Lehigh Station Rd, Henrietta NY 14467
Tel (585) 359-5000 *SIC* 8211

HICKSVILLE UNION FREE SCHOOL DISTRICT (INC) p 690
200 Division Ave, Hicksville NY 11801
Tel (516) 733-6600 *SIC* 8211

RAMAPO CENTRAL SCHOOL DISTRICT p 1206
45 Mountain Ave, Hillburn NY 10931
Tel (845) 357-7783 *SIC* 8211

NEW YORK CITY GEOGRAPHIC DISTRICT 29 p 1034
22214 Jamaica Ave, Hollis NY 11423
Tel (718) 217-7740 *SIC* 8211

WAPPINGERS CENTRAL SCHOOL DISTRICT p 1575
25 Corporate Park Rd, Hopewell Junction NY 12533
Tel (845) 298-5000 *SIC* 8211

SOUTH HUNTINGTON UNION FREE SCHOOL DISTRICT p 1344
60 Weston St, Huntington Station NY 11746
Tel (631) 425-5300 *SIC* 8211

EAST ISLIP UNION FREE SCHOOL DISTRICT 3 p 470
1 Craig B Gariepy Ave, Islip Terrace NY 11752
Tel (631) 224-2000 *SIC* 8211

ITHACA CITY SCHOOL DISTRICT p 768
400 Lake St, Ithaca NY 14850
Tel (607) 274-2201 *SIC* 8211

NEW YORK CITY GEOGRAPHIC DISTRICT 28 p 1034
9027 Sutphin Blvd Rm 24, Jamaica NY 11435
Tel (718) 557-2618 *SIC* 8211

CITY SCHOOL DISTRICT KINGSTON NY p 319
61 Crown St, Kingston NY 12401
Tel (845) 339-3000 *SIC* 8211

BAKER HALL p 146
780 Ridge Rd, Lackawanna NY 14218
Tel (716) 828-9515 *SIC* 8361 8211 8322

ARLINGTON CENTRAL SCHOOL DISTRICT p 110
144 Todd Hill Rd, Lagrangeville NY 12540
Tel (845) 486-4460 *SIC* 8211

SACHEM CENTRAL SCHOOL DISTRICT AT HOLBROOK p 1264
51 School St, Lake Ronkonkoma NY 11779
Tel (631) 471-1336 *SIC* 8211

LANCASTER CENTRAL SCHOOLS DISTRICT p 841
177 Central Ave, Lancaster NY 14086
Tel (716) 686-3200 *SIC* 8211 9411

NORTH COLONIE CENTRAL SCHOOL DISTRICT p 1052
91 Fiddlers Ln, Latham NY 12110
Tel (518) 785-8591 *SIC* 8211

LAWRENCE UNION FREE SCHOOL DISTRICT p 848
195 Broadway, Lawrence NY 11559
Tel (516) 295-7000 *SIC* 8211

LINDENHURST UNION FREE SCHOOL DISTRICT p 868
350 Daniel St, Lindenhurst NY 11757
Tel (631) 226-6441 *SIC* 8211

LIVERPOOL CENTRAL SCHOOL DISTRICT p 871
195 Blackberry Rd, Liverpool NY 13090
Tel (315) 622-7148 *SIC* 8211

NEW YORK CITY GEOGRAPHIC DISTRICT 30 p 1034
2811 Queens Plz N, Long Island City NY 11101
Tel (718) 391-8323 *SIC* 8211

MAMARONECK UNION FREE SCHOOL DISTRICT p 900
1000 W Boston Post Rd, Mamaroneck NY 10543
Tel (914) 220-3000 *SIC* 8211

MASSAPEQUA UNION FREE SCHOOL DISTRICT p 917
4925 Merrick Rd, Massapequa NY 11758
Tel (516) 308-5900 *SIC* 8211

MT VERNON CITY SCHOOL DISTRICT p 997
165 N Columbus Ave, Mount Vernon NY 10553
Tel (914) 665-5000 *SIC* 8211

HERRICKS UNION FREE SCHOOL DISTRICT p 687
999 Herricks Rd Ste B, New Hyde Park NY 11040
Tel (516) 305-8903 *SIC* 8211

CITY SCHOOL DISTRICT OF NEW ROCHELLE (INC) p 320
515 North Ave, New Rochelle NY 10801
Tel (914) 576-4243 *SIC* 8211

CHAPIN SCHOOL p 288
100 E End Ave, New York NY 10028
Tel (212) 744-2335 SIC 8211

ETHICAL CULTURE FIELDSTON SCHOOL p 511
33 Central Park W, New York NY 10023
Tel (212) 712-6220 SIC 8211

NEW YORK CITY BOARD OF EDUCATION p 1034
52 Chambers St Ste 320, New York NY 10007
Tel (212) 374-5141 SIC 8211

NEW YORK CITY GEOGRAPHIC DISTRICT 1 p 1034
166 Essex St, New York NY 10002
Tel (212) 353-2948 SIC 8211

NEW YORK CITY GEOGRAPHIC DISTRICT 2 p 1034
333 7th Ave Fl 7, New York NY 10001
Tel (212) 356-3815 SIC 8211

NEW YORK CITY GEOGRAPHIC DISTRICT 3 p 1034
501 W 165th St, New York NY 10032
Tel (212) 678-5857 SIC 8211

NEW YORK CITY GEOGRAPHIC DISTRICT 4 p 1034
319 E 117th St, New York NY 10035
Tel (212) 831-4981 SIC 8211

NEW YORK CITY GEOGRAPHIC DISTRICT 5 p 1034
425 W 123rd St, New York NY 10027
Tel (212) 769-7500 SIC 8211

NEW YORK CITY GEOGRAPHIC DISTRICT 6 p 1034
4360 Broadway Rm 527, New York NY 10033
Tel (212) 521-3757 SIC 8211

TRINITY EPISCOPAL SCHOOL CORP p 1481
139 W 91st St, New York NY 10024
Tel (212) 873-1650 SIC 8211

NEWBURGH CITY SCHOOL DISTRICT p 1037
124 Grand St, Newburgh NY 12550
Tel (845) 563-3400 SIC 8211

CITY SCHOOL DISTRICT OF CITY OF NIAGARA FALLS p 320
630 66th St, Niagara Falls NY 14304
Tel (716) 286-4211 SIC 8211

NORTH SYRACUSE CENTRAL SCHOOL DISTRICT p 1054
5355 W Taft Rd, North Syracuse NY 13212
Tel (315) 218-2100 SIC 8211

SPRINGBROOK NY INC p 1360
105 Campus Dr, Oneonta NY 13820
Tel (607) 286-7171 SIC 8211

OSSINING UNION FREE SCHOOL DISTRICT p 1097
400 Executive Blvd, Ossining NY 10562
Tel (914) 941-7700 SIC 8211

NEW YORK CITY GEOGRAPHIC DISTRICT 27 p 1034
8201 Rockaway Blvd, Ozone Park NY 11416
Tel (718) 642-5861 SIC 8211

CARMEL CENTRAL SCHOOL DISTRICT p 258
81 South St, Patterson NY 12563
Tel (845) 878-2094 SIC 8211

PITTSFORD CENTRAL SCHOOL DISTRICT p 1152
75 Barker Rd, Pittsford NY 14534
Tel (585) 267-1800 SIC 8211

PLAINVIEW-OLD BETHPAGE CENTRAL SCHOOL DISTRICT p 1154
106 Washington Ave, Plainview NY 11803
Tel (516) 937-6300 SIC 8211

DUTCHESS EDUCATIONAL HEALTH INSURAN p 463
5 Boces Rd, Poughkeepsie NY 12601
Tel (845) 486-4800 SIC 8211

GREECE CENTRAL SCHOOL DISTRICT p 636
750 Maiden Ln, Rochester NY 14615
Tel (585) 966-2000 SIC 8211

PENFIELD CENTRAL SCHOOL DISTRICT INC p 1128
2590 Atlantic Ave, Rochester NY 14625
Tel (585) 249-5700 SIC 8211

ROCHESTER CITY SCHOOL DISTRICT p 1243
131 W Broad St, Rochester NY 14614
Tel (585) 262-8100 SIC 8211

ROME CITY SCHOOL DISTRICT p 1249
409 Bell Rd S, Rome NY 13440
Tel (315) 338-6500 SIC 8211

ROSLYN UNION FREE SCHOOL DISTRICT p 1251
300 Harbor Hill Rd, Roslyn NY 11576
Tel (516) 801-5000 SIC 8211

PORT CHESTER-RYE UNION FREE SCHOOL DISTRICT p 1162
113 Bowman Ave, Rye Brook NY 10573
Tel (914) 934-7900 SIC 8211

WESTCHESTER BOCES SCHOOL DISTRICT p 1596
17 Berkley Dr, Rye Brook NY 10573
Tel (914) 937-6107 SIC 8211

SARATOGA SPRINGS CITY SCHOOL DISTRICT p 1282
3 Blue Streak Blvd, Saratoga Springs NY 12866
Tel (518) 583-4708 SIC 8211

LAKELAND CENTRAL SCHOOL DISTRICT OF SHRUB OAK INC p 839
1086 E Main St, Shrub Oak NY 10588
Tel (914) 245-1700 SIC 8211

DEVELOPMENTAL DISABILITIES INSTITUTE INC p 433
99 Hollywood Dr, Smithtown NY 11787
Tel (631) 366-2900 SIC 8211 8052

SMITHTOWN CENTRAL SCHOOL DISTRICT p 1334
26 New York Ave Unit 1, Smithtown NY 11787
Tel (631) 382-2000 SIC 8211

BOARD OF COOP EDUC SERVICES OF 2ND SUPERVISORY DISTRICT OF MONROE & ORLEANS COUNTIES p 194
3599 Big Ridge Rd, Spencerport NY 14559
Tel (585) 352-2412 SIC 8211

EAST RAMAPO CENTRAL SCHOOL DISTRICT p 470
105 S Madison Ave, Spring Valley NY 10977
Tel (845) 577-6000 SIC 8211

NEW YORK CITY GEOGRAPHIC DISTRICT 31 p 1034
715 Ocean Ter Rm 129, Staten Island NY 10301
Tel (718) 420-5667 SIC 8211

THREE VILLAGE CENTRAL SCHOOL DISTRICT p 1450
100 Suffolk Ave, Stony Brook NY 11790
Tel (631) 730-4000 SIC 8211

SYOSSET CENTRAL SCHOOL DISTRICT p 1416
99 Pell Ln, Syosset NY 11791
Tel (516) 364-5600 SIC 8211

ONONDAGA-CORTLAND-MADISON BOCES p 1088
6820 Thompson Rd, Syracuse NY 13211
Tel (315) 433-8300 SIC 8211

SYRACUSE CITY SCHOOL DISTRICT p 1416
725 Harrison St, Syracuse NY 13210
Tel (315) 435-4499 SIC 8211

ENLARGED CITY SCHOOL DISTRICT OF TROY p 500
2920 5th Ave, Troy NY 12180
Tel (518) 328-5005 SIC 8211

UNIONDALE UNION FREE SCHOOL DISTRICT p 1505
933 Goodrich St, Uniondale NY 11553
Tel (516) 560-8957 SIC 8211

UTICA CITY SCHOOL DISTRICT p 1537
106 Memorial Pkwy, Utica NY 13501
Tel (315) 792-2222 SIC 8211

MADISON-ONEIDA COUNTY BOCES (INC) p 894
4937 Spring Rd, Verona NY 13478
Tel (315) 361-5500 SIC 8211

WEBSTER CENTRAL SCHOOL DISTRICT p 1587
119 South Ave, Webster NY 14580
Tel (585) 265-6500 SIC 8211

WEST BABYLON UNION FREE SCHOOL DISTRICT p 1593
10 Farmingdale Rd, West Babylon NY 11704
Tel (631) 321-3143 SIC 8211

ERIE 1 BOARD OF COOPERATIVE EDUCATIONAL SERVICES p 508
355 Harlem Rd, West Seneca NY 14224
Tel (716) 821-7000 SIC 8211

WEST SENECA CENTRAL SCHOOL DISTRICT p 1595
1397 Orchard Park Rd # 1, West Seneca NY 14224
Tel (716) 677-3100 SIC 8211

EAST MEADOW UFSD (INC) p 470
718 The Plain Rd Ste 1, Westbury NY 11590
Tel (516) 478-5730 SIC 8211

WESTBURY UNION FREE SCHOOL DISTRICT p 1596
2 Hitchcock Ln, Westbury NY 11568
Tel (516) 876-5000 SIC 8211

WHITE PLAINS PUBLIC SCHOOLS p 1606
5 Homeside Ln, White Plains NY 10605
Tel (914) 422-2000 SIC 8211

YONKERS CITY SCHOOL DISTRICT p 1637
1 Larkin Ctr Fl 3, Yonkers NY 10701
Tel (914) 376-8000 SIC 8211 9111

STANLY COUNTY SCHOOLS p 1377
1000 N 1st St Ste 4, Albemarle NC 28001
Tel (704) 961-3000 SIC 8211

RANDOLPH COUNTY BOARD OF EDUCATION p 1207
2222 S Fayetteville St C, Asheboro NC 27205
Tel (336) 318-6100 SIC 8211

BUNCOMBE COUNTY SCHOOL DISTRICT p 225
175 Bingham Rd, Asheville NC 28806
Tel (828) 251-0499 SIC 8211

CARTERET COUNTY BOARD OF EDUCATION (INC) p 262
107 Safrit Dr, Beaufort NC 28516
Tel (252) 728-4583 SIC 8211

BRUNSWICK COUNTY BOARD OF EDUCATION p 221
35 Referendum Dr Ne, Bolivia NC 28422
Tel (910) 253-2900 SIC 8211

BRUNSWICK COUNTY SCHOOLS p 221
35 Referendum Dr Ne, Bolivia NC 28422
Tel (910) 253-2900 SIC 8211

PENDER COUNTY SCHOOLS p 1128
925 Penderlea Hwy, Burgaw NC 28425
Tel (910) 259-2187 SIC 8211

ALAMANCE-BURLINGTON SCHOOL DISTRICT p 44
1712 Vaughn Rd, Burlington NC 27217
Tel (336) 570-6060 SIC 8211

MOORE COUNTY BOARD OF EDUCATION p 987
5227 Us 15 501 Hwy, Carthage NC 28327
Tel (910) 947-2976 SIC 8211

MOORE COUNTY SCHOOLS p 987
5277 Hwy 15 501 S, Carthage NC 28327
Tel (910) 947-2976 SIC 8211

WAKE COUNTY PUBLIC SCHOOL SYSTEM p 1571
5625 Dillard Dr, Cary NC 27518
Tel (919) 431-7343 SIC 8211

CHAPEL HILL-CARRBORO CITY SCHOOL SYSTEM p 288
750 S Merritt Mill Rd, Chapel Hill NC 27516
Tel (919) 967-8211 SIC 8211

CHARLOTTE CATH HIGH p 290
7702 Pneville Matthews Rd, Charlotte NC 28226
Tel (704) 543-1127 SIC 8211

CHARLOTTE-MECKLENBURG SCHOOL DISTRICT p 290
600 E 4th St, Charlotte NC 28202
Tel (980) 343-6372 SIC 8211

CABARRUS COUNTY SCHOOL p 234
4401 Old Airport Rd, Concord NC 28025
Tel (704) 786-6191 SIC 8211

SURRY COUNTY SCHOOL DISTRICT p 1409
209 N Crutchfield St, Dobson NC 27017
Tel (336) 386-8211 SIC 8211

DURHAM PUBLIC SCHOOLS p 463
511 Cleveland St, Durham NC 27701
Tel (919) 560-2000 SIC 8211

ROCKINGHAM COUNTY SCHOOLS p 1244
511 Harrington Hwy, Eden NC 27288
Tel (336) 627-2600 SIC 8211

CUMBERLAND COUNTY SCHOOLS p 400
2465 Gillespie St, Fayetteville NC 28306
Tel (910) 678-2300 SIC 8211

RUTHERFORD COUNTY SCHOOLS p 1260
382 W Main St, Forest City NC 28043
Tel (828) 288-2200 SIC 8211

GASTON COUNTY SCHOOL DISTRICT p 593
943 Osceola St, Gastonia NC 28054
Tel (704) 866-6100 SIC 8211

WAYNE COUNTY PUBLIC SCHOOLS FOUNDATION INC p 1584
2001 Royall Ave, Goldsboro NC 27534
Tel (919) 705-6117 SIC 8211

GUILFORD COUNTY SCHOOL SYSTEM p 646
712 N Eugene St, Greensboro NC 27401
Tel (336) 370-8100 SIC 8211

PITT COUNTY SCHOOLS p 1152
1717 W 5th St, Greenville NC 27834
Tel (252) 830-4200 SIC 8211

UHS PHYSICIANS LLC p 1500
2100 Stantonsburg Rd, Greenville NC 27834
Tel (252) 847-6809 SIC 8211

RICHMOND COUNTY SCHOOL DISTRICT p 1233
118 Vance St, Hamlet NC 28345
Tel (910) 582-5860 SIC 8211

VANCE COUNTY BOARD OF EDUCATION p 1543
1724 Graham Ave, Henderson NC 27536
Tel (252) 492-2127 SIC 8211

HENDERSON COUNTY BOARD OF PUBLIC EDUCATION p 682
414 4th Ave W, Hendersonville NC 28739
Tel (828) 697-4510 SIC 8211

HENDERSON COUNTY SCHOOLS p 682
414 4th Ave W, Hendersonville NC 28739
Tel (828) 697-4733 SIC 8211

ORANGE COUNTY SCHOOLS p 1092
200 E King St, Hillsborough NC 27278
Tel (919) 732-8126 SIC 8211

ONSLOW COUNTY SCHOOLS INC p 1088
200 Broadhurst Rd, Jacksonville NC 28540
Tel (910) 455-2211 SIC 8211

DUPLIN COUNTY BOARD OF EDUCATION p 462
315 N Main St, Kenansville NC 28349
Tel (910) 293-4218 SIC 8211

LENOIR COUNTY BOARD OF EDUCATION INC p 855
2017 W Vernon Ave, Kinston NC 28504
Tel (252) 527-1109 SIC 8211

LENOIR COUNTY PUBLIC SCHOOLS p 855
2017 W Vernon Ave, Kinston NC 28504
Tel (252) 527-1109 SIC 8211

SCOTLAND COUNTY SCHOOL SYSTEM p 1293
322 S Main St, Laurinburg NC 28352
Tel (910) 276-1138 SIC 8211

CALDWELL COUNTY SCHOOLS p 238
1914 Hickory Blvd Sw, Lenoir NC 28645
Tel (828) 728-8407 SIC 8211

DAVIDSON COUNTY BOARD OF EDUCATION p 416
250 County School Rd, Lexington NC 27292
Tel (336) 249-6704 SIC 8211

DAVIDSON COUNTY SCHOOLS p 416
250 County School Rd, Lexington NC 27292
Tel (336) 249-8181 SIC 8211

HARNETT COUNTY BOARD OF EDUCATION p 662
1008 S 11th St, Lillington NC 27546
Tel (910) 893-8151 SIC 8211

HARNETT COUNTY SCHOOLS p 662
1008 11th St, Lillington NC 27546
Tel (910) 893-8151 SIC 8211

LINCOLN COUNTY SCHOOL DISTRICT p 866
353 N Generals Blvd, Lincolnton NC 28092
Tel (704) 732-2261 SIC 8211

PUBLIC SCHOOLS OF ROBESON COUNTY p 1189
410 Caton Rd, Lumberton NC 28360
Tel (910) 671-6000 SIC 8211

MC DOWELL COUNTY BOARD OF EDUCATION (INC) p 925
334 S Main St, Marion NC 28752
Tel (828) 652-4535 SIC 8211

UNION COUNTY BOARD OF EDUCATION p 1504
400 N Church St, Monroe NC 28112
Tel (704) 296-9898 SIC 8211

UNION COUNTY PUBLIC SCHOOLS p 1504
400 N Church St, Monroe NC 28112
Tel (704) 296-9898 SIC 8211

BURKE COUNTY PUBLIC SCHOOLS p 227
700 E Parker Rd, Morganton NC 28655
Tel (828) 437-4770 SIC 8211

J IVERSON RIDDLE DEVELOPMENT CENTER p 771
300 Enola Rd, Morganton NC 28655
Tel (828) 433-2800 SIC 8211

NASH-ROCKY MOUNT SCHOOLS p 1008
930 Eastern Ave, Nashville NC 27856
Tel (252) 459-5220 SIC 8211

CRAVEN COUNTY SCHOOL DISTRICT p 389
3600 Trent Rd, New Bern NC 28562
Tel (252) 514-6300 SIC 8211

CATAWBA COUNTY SCHOOLS p 265
10 E 25th St, Newton NC 28658
Tel (828) 464-8333 SIC 8211

WILKES COUNTY BOARD OF EDUCATION p 1609
613 Cherry St, North Wilkesboro NC 28659
Tel (336) 667-1121 SIC 8211

WILKES COUNTY SCHOOLS p 1609
613 Cherry St, North Wilkesboro NC 28659
Tel (336) 667-1121 SIC 8211

NC HEALTH AND HUMAN SERVICES p 1021
3006 Mail Service Ctr, Raleigh NC 27699
Tel (252) 208-4000 SIC 8211

SALISBURY SCHOOL ROWAN SYSTEM p 1272
500 N Main St, Salisbury NC 28144
Tel (704) 630-6026 SIC 8211

LEE COUNTY SCHOOLS p 851
106 Gordon St, Sanford NC 27330
Tel (919) 774-6226 SIC 8211

CLEVELAND COUNTY SCHOOLS p 325
400 W Marion St, Shelby NC 28150
Tel (704) 476-8000 SIC 8211

JOHNSTON COUNTY SCHOOLS p 791
2320 Us Highway 70 Bus E, Smithfield NC 27577
Tel (919) 934-6031 SIC 8211

IREDELL-STATESVILLE SCHOOLS p 764
549 N Race St, Statesville NC 28677
Tel (704) 872-8931 SIC 8211

EDGECOMBE COUNTY SCHOOLS p 477
2311 N Main St, Tarboro NC 27886
Tel (252) 641-2600 SIC 8211

BEAUFORT COUNTY BOARD OF EDUCATION p 166
321 Smaw Rd, Washington NC 27889
Tel (252) 946-6593 SIC 8211

BEAUFORT COUNTY SCHOOLS p 166
321 Smaw Rd, Washington NC 27889
Tel (252) 946-6593 SIC 8211

HAYWOOD COUNTY PUBLIC SCHOOLS INC p 671
1230 N Main St, Waynesville NC 28786
Tel (828) 456-2400 SIC 8211

COLUMBUS COUNTY BOARD OF EDUCATION p 342
817 Washington St, Whiteville NC 28472
Tel (910) 642-5168 SIC 8211

MARTIN COUNTY BOARD OF EDUCATION p 912
300 N Watts St, Williamston NC 27892
Tel (252) 792-1575 SIC 8211

NEW HANOVER COUNTY BLACK LEADERSHIP CONFERENCE p 1030
6410 Carolina Beach Rd, Wilmington NC 28412
Tel (910) 763-5431 SIC 8211

NEW HANOVER COUNTY SCHOOLS p 1030
6410 Carolina Beach Rd, Wilmington NC 28412
Tel (910) 254-4206 SIC 8211

WILSON COUNTY SCHOOLS p 1613
117 Tarboro St Ne, Wilson NC 27893
Tel (252) 399-7700 SIC 8211

SALEM WINSTON FORSYTH COUNTY SCHOOLS p 1272
475 Corporate Square Dr, Winston Salem NC 27105
Tel (336) 748-4000 SIC 8211

WINSTON-SALEM/FORSYTH COUNTY SCHOOLS p 1617
4801 Bethania Station Rd, Winston Salem NC 27105
Tel (336) 727-2635 SIC 8211 9111

FARGO SCHOOL DISTRICT NO 1 p 528
415 4th St N, Fargo ND 58102
Tel (701) 446-1000 SIC 8211

GRAND FORKS PUBLIC SCHOOLS p 629
2400 47th Ave S, Grand Forks ND 58201
Tel (701) 746-2200 SIC 8211

MINOT PUBLIC SCHOOLS p 974
215 2nd St Se, Minot ND 58701
Tel (701) 420-7503 SIC 8211

WEST FARGO SCHOOL DISTRICT 6 p 1594
207 Main Ave W, West Fargo ND 58078
Tel (701) 356-2000 SIC 8211

AKRON PUBLIC SCHOOLS p 42
70 N Broadway St, Akron OH 44308
Tel (330) 761-1661 SIC 8211

EDUCATION UNLIMITED OF OHIO INC p 479
8216 Kennedy Rd, Blacklick OH 43004
Tel (614) 451-1309 SIC 8211

CANTON CITY SCHOOL DISTRICT p 247
305 Mckinley Ave Nw, Canton OH 44702
Tel (330) 438-2500 SIC 8211

ARCHDIOCESE OF CINCINNATI p 105
100 E 8th St Fl 8, Cincinnati OH 45202
Tel (513) 421-3131 SIC 8661 8211

CINCINNATI PUBLIC SCHOOLS p 307
2651 Burnet Ave, Cincinnati OH 45219
Tel (513) 363-0000 SIC 8211

FOREST HILLS SCHOOL DISTRICT p 566
7550 Forest Rd, Cincinnati OH 45255
Tel (513) 231-3335 SIC 8211

NORTHWEST LOCAL SCHOOL DISTRICT p 1060
3240 Banning Rd, Cincinnati OH 45239
Tel (513) 923-1000 SIC 8211

PRINCETON CITY SCHOOL DISTRICT p 1177
3900 Cottingham Dr, Cincinnati OH 45241
Tel (513) 864-1000 SIC 8211

WEST CLERMONT LOCAL SCHOOL DISTRICT p 1594
4350 Aicholtz Rd Ste 220, Cincinnati OH 45245
Tel (513) 943-5000 SIC 8211

CLEVELAND MUNICIPAL SCHOOL DISTRICT p 325
1111 Superior Ave E # 1800, Cleveland OH 44114
Tel (216) 838-0000 SIC 8211 8399

MAYFIELD CITY SCHOOL DISTRICT p 923
1101 Som Center Rd, Cleveland OH 44124
Tel (440) 995-6800 SIC 8211

MENTOR REM p 943
9775 Rockside Rd Ste 200, Cleveland OH 44125
Tel (216) 642-5339 SIC 8211

COLUMBUS PUBLIC SCHOOL DISTRICT p 342
270 E State St Fl 3, Columbus OH 43215
Tel (614) 365-5000 SIC 8211 8299

ELECTRONIC CLASSROOM OF TOMORROW p 485
3700 S High St Ste 95, Columbus OH 43207
Tel (888) 326-8395 SIC 8211

HILLIARD CITY SCHOOL DISTRICT p 693
2140 Atlas St, Columbus OH 43228
Tel (614) 921-7000 *SIC* 8211

CUYAHOGA VALLEY CHRISTIAN ACADEMY ENDOWMENT FUND p 403
4687 Wyoga Lake Rd, Cuyahoga Falls OH 44224
Tel (330) 929-0575 *SIC* 8211

DAYTON BOARD OF EDUCATION p 417
156 Grant St, Dayton OH 45404
Tel (937) 226-1084 *SIC* 8211

KETTERING CITY SCHOOL DISTRICT p 814
3750 Far Hills Ave, Dayton OH 45429
Tel (937) 499-1400 *SIC* 8211

DUBLIN CITY SCHOOLS p 459
7030 Coffman Rd, Dublin OH 43017
Tel (614) 764-5913 *SIC* 8211

ELYRIA CITY SCHOOL DISTRICT p 490
42101 Griswold Rd, Elyria OH 44035
Tel (440) 284-8000 *SIC* 8211

FAIRFIELD CITY SCHOOL DISTRICT (INC) p 524
4641 Bach Ln, Fairfield OH 45014
Tel (513) 829-6300 *SIC* 8211

SOUTH- WESTERN CITY SCHOOL DISTRICT p 1345
3805 Marlane Dr, Grove City OH 43123
Tel (614) 801-3000 *SIC* 8211

BUTLER TECHNOLOGY & CAREER DEVELOPMENT SCHOOLS p 230
3603 Hmlton Middletown Rd, Hamilton OH 45011
Tel (513) 868-1911 *SIC* 8211

HAMILTON CITY SCHOOL DISTRICT p 655
533 Dayton St, Hamilton OH 45011
Tel (513) 887-5000 *SIC* 8211

OLENTANGY LOCAL SCHOOL DISTRICT p 1082
814 Shanahan Rd Ste 100, Lewis Center OH 43035
Tel (740) 657-4050 *SIC* 8211

LAKOTA LOCAL SCHOOL DISTRICT p 840
5572 Princeton Rd, Liberty Twp OH 45011
Tel (513) 874-5505 *SIC* 8211

LORAIN CITY SCHOOL DISTRICT p 878
2350 Pole Ave, Lorain OH 44052
Tel (440) 233-2232 *SIC* 8211

OHIO VIRTUAL ACADEMY p 1078
1690 Woodlands Dr Ste 200, Maumee OH 43537
Tel (419) 482-0948 *SIC* 8211

MEDINA CITY SCHOOL DISTRICT p 938
739 Weymouth Rd, Medina OH 44256
Tel (330) 725-8831 *SIC* 8211

MENTOR EXEMPTED VILLAGE SCHOOL DISTRICT p 943
6451 Center St, Mentor OH 44060
Tel (440) 255-4444 *SIC* 8211

MILFORD EXEMPTED VILLAGE SCHOOL DISTRICT p 969
777 Garfield Ave, Milford OH 45150
Tel (513) 576-4175 *SIC* 8211

NEWARK CITY SCHOOLS p 1036
621 Mount Vernon Rd, Newark OH 43055
Tel (740) 670-7000 *SIC* 8211

PARMA CITY SCHOOL DISTRICT p 1117
5311 Longwood Ave, Parma OH 44134
Tel (440) 842-5300 *SIC* 8211

PICKERINGTON LOCAL SCHOOL DISTRICT p 1146
90 N East St, Pickerington OH 43147
Tel (614) 833-2110 *SIC* 8211

SPRINGFIELD BOARD OF EDUCATION p 1360
1500 W Jefferson St, Springfield OH 45506
Tel (937) 505-2800 *SIC* 8211

SPRINGFIELD CITY SCHOOL DISTRICT p 1360
1500 W Jefferson St, Springfield OH 45506
Tel (937) 505-2800 *SIC* 8211

SYLVANIA CITY SCHOOL DISTRICT p 1413
4747 N Hlland Sylvania Rd, Sylvania OH 43560
Tel (419) 824-8500 *SIC* 8211

TOLEDO PUBLIC SCHOOLS p 1459
1609 N Summit St, Toledo OH 43604
Tel (419) 729-8200 *SIC* 8211

CLEVELAND HEIGHTS UNIVERSITY HEIGHTS CITY SCHOOLS p 325
2155 Miramar Blvd, University Heights OH 44118
Tel (216) 371-7171 *SIC* 8211

WESTERVILLE CITY SCHOOL DISTRICT p 1600
936 Eastwind Dr Ste 200, Westerville OH 43081
Tel (614) 797-5700 *SIC* 8211

WILLOUGHBY-EASTLAKE CITY SCHOOLS p 1613
37047 Ridge Rd, Willoughby OH 44094
Tel (440) 946-5000 *SIC* 8211

WORTHINGTON CITY SCHOOLS p 1626
200 E Wilson Bridge Rd # 200, Worthington OH 43085
Tel (614) 450-6000 *SIC* 8211

YOUNGSTOWN CITY SCHOOLS p 1639
20 W Wood St, Youngstown OH 44503
Tel (330) 744-6900 *SIC* 8211

ANTLERS PUBLIC SCHOOLS p 94
219 Ne A St, Antlers OK 74523
Tel (580) 298-5504 *SIC* 8211

BROKEN ARROW INDEPENDENT SCHOOL p 217
701 S Main St, Broken Arrow OK 74012
Tel (918) 259-5700 *SIC* 8211

EDMOND PUBLIC SCHOOLS p 478
1001 W Danforth Rd, Edmond OK 73003
Tel (405) 340-2800 *SIC* 8211

JENKS PUBLIC SCHOOLS p 782
205 E B St, Jenks OK 74037
Tel (918) 299-4415 *SIC* 8211

LAWTON PUBLIC SCHOOL DISTRICT I-008 p 848
753 Nw Fort Sill Blvd, Lawton OK 73507
Tel (580) 357-6900 *SIC* 8211

MOORE INDEPENDENT SCHOOL DISTRICT NO 2 p 987
1500 Se 4th St, Moore OK 73160
Tel (405) 735-4200 *SIC* 8211

MUSTANG PUBLIC SCHOOLS p 1003
906 S Heights Dr, Mustang OK 73064
Tel (405) 376-2461 *SIC* 8211

INDEPENDENT SCHOOL DISTRICT I-29 p 737
131 S Flood Ave, Norman OK 73069
Tel (405) 364-1339 *SIC* 8211

INDEPENDENT SCHOOL DISTRICT 52 p 737
7217 Se 15th St, Oklahoma City OK 73110
Tel (405) 737-4461 *SIC* 8211

MIDWEST CITY PUBLIC SCHOOLS I-52 p 967
7217 Se 15th St, Oklahoma City OK 73110
Tel (405) 737-4461 *SIC* 8211

OKLAHOMA CITY PUBLIC SCHOOLS p 1079
900 N Klein Ave, Oklahoma City OK 73106
Tel (405) 587-0000 *SIC* 8211

SEMINOLE SCHOOL DISTRICT I01 p 1302
617 Timmons St, Seminole OK 74868
Tel (405) 382-5085 *SIC* 8211

INDEPENDENT SCHOOL DISTRICT 1 OF TULSA COUNTY p 737
3027 S New Haven Ave, Tulsa OK 74114
Tel (918) 746-6800 *SIC* 8211

INDEPENDENT SCHOOL DISTRICT 9 TULSA COUNTY OK p 737
8506 E 61st St, Tulsa OK 74133
Tel (918) 357-4321 *SIC* 8211

PUTNAM CITY SCHOOL DISTRICT I-001 OKLAHOMA COUNTY p 1193
5401 Nw 40th St, Warr Acres OK 73122
Tel (405) 495-5200 *SIC* 8211

PUTNAM CITY SCHOOLS p 1193
5401 Nw 40th St, Warr Acres OK 73122
Tel (405) 495-5200 *SIC* 8211

GREATER ALBANY PUBLIC SCHOOL DISTRICT 8 J p 635
718 7th Ave Sw, Albany OR 97321
Tel (541) 967-4501 *SIC* 8211

BEAVERTON SCHOOL DISTRICT p 166
16550 Sw Merlo Rd, Beaverton OR 97003
Tel (503) 591-8000 *SIC* 8211

BEND-LAPINE SCHOOLS p 172
520 Nw Wall St, Bend OR 97703
Tel (541) 383-6000 *SIC* 8211

EUGENE SCHOOL DISTRICT 4J p 512
200 N Monroe St, Eugene OR 97402
Tel (541) 790-7600 *SIC* 8211

REYNOLDS SCHOOL DISTRICT 7 (INC) p 1231
1204 Ne 201st Ave, Fairview OR 97024
Tel (503) 492-4921 *SIC* 8211

GRESHAM-BARLOW SCHOOL DISTRICT p 639
1331 Nw Eastman Pkwy, Gresham OR 97030
Tel (503) 618-2470 *SIC* 8211

HILLSBORO SCHOOL DISTRICT 1J p 694
3083 Ne 49th Pl, Hillsboro OR 97124
Tel (503) 640-8403 *SIC* 8211

MEDFORD SCHOOL DISTRICT 549C p 935
815 S Oakdale Ave, Medford OR 97501
Tel (541) 842-3621 *SIC* 8211

NORTH CLACKAMAS SCHOOLS p 1052
12400 Se Freeman Way # 100, Milwaukie OR 97222
Tel (503) 353-6001 *SIC* 8211

OREGON CITY SCHOOL DISTRICT 62 p 1093
1417 12th St, Oregon City OR 97045
Tel (503) 785-8000 *SIC* 8211

DAVID DOUGLAS SCHOOOL DISTRICT p 415
11300 Ne Halsey St # 100, Portland OR 97220
Tel (503) 252-2900 *SIC* 8211

PORTLAND PUBLIC SCHOOLS p 1163
501 N Dixon St, Portland OR 97227
Tel (503) 916-2000 *SIC* 8211

SALEM-KEIZER SCHOOL DISTRICT 24J p 1272
2450 Lancaster Dr Ne # 100, Salem OR 97305
Tel (503) 399-3000 *SIC* 8211

SPRINGFIELD SCHOOL DISTRICT 19 p 1361
525 Mill St, Springfield OR 97477
Tel (541) 726-3331 *SIC* 8211

TIGARD-TUALATIN SCHOOL DISTRICT p 1453
6960 Sw Sandburg St, Tigard OR 97223
Tel (503) 431-4000 *SIC* 8211

WEST LINN-WILSONVILLE SCHOOL DISTRICT 3JT p 1595
22210 Sw Stafford Rd, Tualatin OR 97062
Tel (503) 673-7000 *SIC* 8211

ABINGTON SCHOOL DISTRICT p 11
970 Highland Ave, Abington PA 19001
Tel (215) 884-4700 *SIC* 8211

PARKLAND SCHOOL DISTRICT AUTHORITY p 1116
1210 Springhouse Rd, Allentown PA 18104
Tel (610) 351-5503 *SIC* 8211

SCHOOL DISTRICT OF CITY OF ALLENTOWN p 1289
31 S Penn St, Allentown PA 18102
Tel (484) 765-4001 *SIC* 8211

ALTOONA AREA SCHOOL DISTRICT INC p 62
1415 6th Ave, Altoona PA 16602
Tel (814) 946-8211 *SIC* 8211

WISSAHICKON SCHOOL DISTRICT p 1619
601 Knight Rd, Ambler PA 19002
Tel (215) 619-8000 *SIC* 8211

MERION LOWER SCHOOL DISTRICT INC p 949
301 E Montgomery Ave, Ardmore PA 19003
Tel (610) 645-1983 *SIC* 8211

MELMARK INC p 941
2600 Wayland Rd, Berwyn PA 19312
Tel (610) 353-1726 *SIC* 8211 8361

BETHLEHEM AREA SCHOOL DISTRICT p 178
1516 Sycamore St, Bethlehem PA 18017
Tel (610) 807-5571 *SIC* 8211

BOYERTOWN AREA SCHOOL DISTRICT p 205
911 Montgomery Ave, Boyertown PA 19512
Tel (610) 367-6031 *SIC* 8211

PLEASANT VALLEY SCHOOL DISTRICT p 1156
2233 Route 115 Ste 100, Brodheadsville PA 18322
Tel (570) 402-1000 *SIC* 8211

CHESTER COUNTY INTERMEDIATE UNIT 24 (INC) p 295
1525 E Lincoln Hwy, Coatesville PA 19320
Tel (610) 383-7400 *SIC* 8211

DALLASTOWN AREA SCHOOL DISTRICT p 410
700 New School Ln, Dallastown PA 17313
Tel (717) 244-4021 *SIC* 8211

DOWNINGTOWN AREA SCHOOL DISTRICT p 453
540 Trestle Pl, Downingtown PA 19335
Tel (610) 269-8460 *SIC* 8211

UPPER DARBY SCHOOL DISTRICT (INC) p 1529
4611 Bond Ave, Drexel Hill PA 19026
Tel (610) 789-7200 *SIC* 8211

EAST STROUDSBURG AREA SCHOOL DISTRICT p 471
50 Vine St, East Stroudsburg PA 18301
Tel (570) 424-8500 *SIC* 8211

COLONIAL INTERMEDIATE UNIT 20 p 337
6 Danforth Dr, Easton PA 18045
Tel (610) 252-5550 *SIC* 8211

EAST PENN SCHOOL DISTRICT p 470
800 Pine St, Emmaus PA 18049
Tel (610) 966-8300 *SIC* 8211

DR GERTRUDE A BARBER CENTER INC p 454
100 Barber Pl, Erie PA 16507
Tel (814) 453-7661 *SIC* 8361 8211

MILLCREEK TOWNSHIP SCHOOL DISTRICT p 970
3740 W 26th St, Erie PA 16506
Tel (814) 835-5300 *SIC* 8211 9111

SCHOOL DISTRICT OF CITY OF ERIE p 1289
148 W 21st St, Erie PA 16502
Tel (814) 874-6000 *SIC* 8211

FARRELL AREA SCHOOL DISTRICT p 530
1600 Roemer Blvd, Farrell PA 16121
Tel (724) 346-6585 *SIC* 8211

FLEETWOOD AREA SCHOOL DISTRICT p 555
801 N Richmond St, Fleetwood PA 19522
Tel (610) 944-8111 *SIC* 8211

RIDLEY SCHOOL DISTRICT AUTHORITY p 1234
901 Morton Ave Unit A, Folsom PA 19033
Tel (610) 534-1900 *SIC* 8211

HEMPFIELD AREA SCHOOL DISTRICT p 682
4347 State Route 136, Greensburg PA 15601
Tel (724) 834-2590 *SIC* 8211

CENTRAL DAUPHIN SCHOOL DISTRICT AUTHORITY p 278
600 Rutherford Rd, Harrisburg PA 17109
Tel (717) 540-4606 *SIC* 8211

COMMONWEALTH CHARTER ACADEMY p 346
4050 Crums Mill Rd # 303, Harrisburg PA 17112
Tel (717) 651-7200 *SIC* 8211

HARRISBURG SCHOOL DISTRICT INC p 664
1601 State St, Harrisburg PA 17103
Tel (717) 703-4000 *SIC* 8211

ROMAN CATHOLIC DIOCESE OF HARRISBURG p 1249
4800 Union Deposit Rd, Harrisburg PA 17111
Tel (717) 657-4804 *SIC* 8661 8211

HAVERFORD TOWNSHIP SCHOOL DISTRICT p 668
50 E Eagle Rd, Havertown PA 19083
Tel (610) 853-5900 *SIC* 8211

HAZLETON AREA SCHOOL DISTRICT p 671
1515 W 23rd St, Hazle Township PA 18202
Tel (570) 459-3111 *SIC* 8211

MILTON HERSHEY SCHOOL p 972
1201 Homestead Ln, Hershey PA 17033
Tel (717) 520-2000 *SIC* 8211

MILTON HERSHEY SCHOOL & SCHOOL TRUST p 972
711 Crest Ln, Hershey PA 17033
Tel (717) 520-1100 *SIC* 8211

PENN STATE MILTON S HERSHEY MEDICAL CENTER p 1129
500 University Dr, Hershey PA 17033
Tel (717) 531-5337 *SIC* 8062 8733 8211

ALLEGHENY INTERMEDIATE UNIT 3 FOUNDATION p 52
475 E Waterfront Dr, Homestead PA 15120
Tel (412) 394-5700 *SIC* 8211

AGORA CYBER CHARTER SCHOOL p 35
590 N Gulph Rd, King Of Prussia PA 19406
Tel (610) 230-0775 *SIC* 8211

SCHOOL DISTRICT OF LANCASTER p 1289
251 S Prince St, Lancaster PA 17603
Tel (717) 299-2700 *SIC* 8211

NESHAMINY SCHOOL DISTRICT p 1026
2001 Old Lincoln Hwy, Langhorne PA 19047
Tel (215) 809-6562 *SIC* 8211

WOODS SERVICES INC p 1623
40 Martin Gross Dr, Langhorne PA 19047
Tel (215) 750-4000 *SIC* 8322 8211

PENN NORTH SCHOOL DISTRICT p 1129
401 E Hancock St, Lansdale PA 19446
Tel (215) 368-0400 *SIC* 8211

PENN WILLIAM SCHOOL DISTRICT p 1129
100 Green Ave, Lansdowne PA 19050
Tel (610) 284-8080 *SIC* 8211

BRISTOL TOWNSHIP SCHOOL DISTRICT AUTHORITY p 214
6401 Mill Creek Rd, Levittown PA 19057
Tel (215) 943-3200 *SIC* 8211

PENNSBURY SCHOOL DISTRICT p 1130
19058-0338 Yardley Ave, Levittown PA 19058
Tel (215) 428-4100 *SIC* 8211

MCKEESPORT AREA SCHOOL DISTRICT p 930
3590 Oneil Blvd, Mckeesport PA 15132
Tel (412) 664-3610 *SIC* 8211

CUMBERLAND VALLEY SCHOOL DISTRICT p 400
6746 Carlisle Pike, Mechanicsburg PA 17050
Tel (717) 697-1167 *SIC* 8211

ELWYN p 490
111 Elwyn Rd, Media PA 19063
Tel (610) 891-2000 *SIC* 8211

DELAWARE COUNTY INTERMEDIATE UNIT EDUCATION FOUNDATION p 423
200 Yale Ave, Morton PA 19070
Tel (610) 938-9000 *SIC* 8211

WEST SHORE SCHOOL BOARD p 1595
507 Fishing Creek Rd, New Cumberland PA 17070
Tel (717) 938-9577 *SIC* 8211

WEST SHORE SCHOOL DISTRICT p 1595
507 Fishing Creek Rd, New Cumberland PA 17070
Tel (717) 938-9577 *SIC* 8211

COUNCIL ROCK SCHOOL DISTRICT p 374
30 N Chancellor St, Newtown PA 18940
Tel (215) 944-1000 *SIC* 8211

METHACTON SCHOOL DISTRICT p 953
1001 Kriebel Mill Rd, Norristown PA 19403
Tel (610) 489-5000 *SIC* 8211

PENNRIDGE SCHOOL DISTRICT p 1130
1200 N 5th St, Perkasie PA 18944
Tel (215) 257-5011 *SIC* 8211

SCHOOL DISTRICT OF PHILADELPHIA p 1289
440 N Broad St, Philadelphia PA 19130
Tel (215) 400-4000 *SIC* 8211

TEMPLE UNIVERSITY HEALTH SYSTEM FOUNDATION p 1436
3509 N Broad St Fl 9, Philadelphia PA 19140
Tel (215) 707-2000 *SIC* 8211 8221

BOARD OF PUBLIC EDUCATION SCHOOL DISTRICT OF PITTSBURGH (INC) p 195
341 S Bellefield Ave, Pittsburgh PA 15213
Tel (412) 622-3500 *SIC* 8211

MT LEBANON SCHOOL DISTRICT p 997
7 Horsman Dr, Pittsburgh PA 15228
Tel (412) 344-2077 *SIC* 8211

NORTH ALLEGHENY SCHOOL DISTRICT p 1049
200 Hillvue Ln Ste 1, Pittsburgh PA 15237
Tel (412) 369-5484 *SIC* 8211

PITTSBURGH SCHOOL DISTRICT p 1152
341 S Bellefield Ave, Pittsburgh PA 15213
Tel (412) 622-3500 *SIC* 8211

READING SCHOOL DISTRICT p 1213
800 Washington St, Reading PA 19601
Tel (484) 258-7000 *SIC* 8211

SPRING-FORD AREA SCHOOL DISTRICT p 1360
857 S Lewis Rd, Royersford PA 19468
Tel (610) 705-6000 *SIC* 8211

SPRING-FORD AREA SCHOOL DISTRICT OFFICE p 1360
857 S Lewis Rd, Royersford PA 19468
Tel (610) 705-6000 *SIC* 8211

CARBON-LEHIGH INTERMEDIATE UNIT 21 p 252
4210 Independence Dr, Schnecksville PA 18078
Tel (610) 799-4111 *SIC* 8211

CATHOLIC SOCIAL SERVICES OF DIOCESE OF SCRANTON INC p 267
516 Fig St, Scranton PA 18505
Tel (570) 207-2283
SIC 8661 2711 8211 8322 6553

SCRANTON SCHOOL DISTRICT p 1294
425 N Washington Ave, Scranton PA 18503
Tel (570) 348-3474 *SIC* 8211

STATE COLLEGE AREA SCHOOL DISTRICT p 1380
131 W Nittany Ave, State College PA 16801
Tel (814) 231-1016 *SIC* 8211

POCONO MOUNTAIN SCHOOL DISTRICT p 1158
134 Pocono Mtn Schl Rd, Swiftwater PA 18370
Tel (570) 839-7121 *SIC* 8211

CENTENNIAL SCHOOL DISTRICT p 275
433 Centennial Rd, Warminster PA 18974
Tel (215) 441-6000 *SIC* 8211

TREDYFFRIN-EASTTOWN SCHOOL DISTRICT (INC) p 1475
940 W Valley Rd Ste 1700, Wayne PA 19087
Tel (610) 240-1900 *SIC* 8211

ACADEMIC ACQUISITION CORP p 13
1615 W Chester Pike, West Chester PA 19382
Tel (484) 947-2000 *SIC* 8211 8299

NOBEL LEARNING COMMUNITIES INC p 1046
1615 W Chester Pike # 200, West Chester PA 19382
Tel (484) 947-2000 *SIC* 8211 8299

WEST CHESTER AREA SCHOOL DISTRICT p 1594
829 Paoli Pike, West Chester PA 19380
Tel (484) 266-1000 *SIC* 8211

WILKES-BARRE AREA SCHOOL DISTRICT p 1609
730 S Main St, Wilkes Barre PA 18702
Tel (570) 826-7127 *SIC* 8211

CRANSTON PUBLIC SCHOOLS p 389
845 Park Ave, Cranston RI 02910
Tel (401) 270-8000 *SIC* 8211

PAWTUCKET SCHOOL DEPARTMENT p 1122
286 Main St, Pawtucket RI 02860
Tel (401) 729-6300 *SIC* 8211 9411

PROVIDENCE PUBLIC SCHOOLS p 1186
797 Westminster St, Providence RI 02903
Tel (401) 456-9100 *SIC* 8211 8742

WARWICK PUBLIC SCHOOLS p 1577
34 Warwick Lake Ave, Warwick RI 02889
Tel (401) 734-3000 *SIC* 8211

WOONSOCKET CITY SCHOOL DISTRICT p 1624
108 High St, Woonsocket RI 02895
Tel (401) 767-4600 *SIC* 8211

AIKEN COUNTY SCHOOL DISTRICT p 38
1000 Brookhaven Dr, Aiken SC 29803
Tel (803) 641-2428 *SIC* 8211

ANDERSON COUNTY SCHOOL DISTRICT FIVE INC p 89
400 Pearman Dairy Rd, Anderson SC 29625
Tel (864) 260-5000 *SIC* 8211

LEXINGTON SCHOOL DISTRICT 5 p 859
1020 Dutchfork Rd, Ballentine SC 29002
Tel (803) 732-8011 *SIC* 8211

BEAUFORT COUNTY SCHOOL DISTRICT p 166
2900 Mink Point Blvd, Beaufort SC 29902
Tel (843) 322-2300 *SIC* 8211

KERSHAW COUNTY SCHOOL DISTRICT p 813
2029 W Dekalb St, Camden SC 29020
Tel (803) 432-8416 *SIC* 8211

CHARLESTON COUNTY SCHOOL DISTRICT DEVELOPMENT CORP p 290
75 Calhoun St, Charleston SC 29401
Tel (843) 937-6300 *SIC* 8211

RICHLAND COUNTY SCHOOL DISTRICT 1 p 1233
1616 Richland St, Columbia SC 29201
Tel (803) 231-7000 *SIC* 8211

RICHLAND SCHOOL DISTRICT TWO FOUNDATION p 1233
6831 Brookfield Rd, Columbia SC 29206
Tel (803) 787-1910 *SIC* 8211

SC PUBLIC CHARTER SCHOOL DISTRICT p 1285
3700 Forest Dr Ste 406, Columbia SC 29204
Tel (803) 734-8322 *SIC* 8211

SOUTH CAROLINA PUBLIC CHARTER SCHOOL DISTRICT p 1343
3710 Landmark Dr Ste 203, Columbia SC 29204
Tel (803) 734-8322 *SIC* 8211

HORRY COUNTY SCHOOL DISTRICT p 708
335 Four Mile Rd, Conway SC 29526
Tel (843) 488-6700 *SIC* 8211

DARLINGTON COUNTY SCHOOL DISTRICT p 412
120 E Smith Ave, Darlington SC 29532
Tel (843) 398-5100 *SIC* 8211

SCHOOL DISTRICT OF PICKENS COUNTY p 1289
1348 Griffin Mill Rd, Easley SC 29640
Tel (864) 397-1000 *SIC* 8211

FLORENCE SCHOOL DISTRICT ONE p 557
319 S Dargan St, Florence SC 29506
Tel (843) 669-4141 *SIC* 8211

FORT MILL SCHOOL DISTRICT 4 p 569
2233 Deerfield Dr, Fort Mill SC 29715
Tel (803) 548-2527 *SIC* 8211

CHEROKEE COUNTY SCHOOL DISTRICT 1 p 294
141 Twin Lake Rd, Gaffney SC 29341
Tel (864) 902-3500 *SIC* 8211

GEORGETOWN COUNTY SCHOOL DISTRICT p 606
2018 Church St, Georgetown SC 29440
Tel (843) 436-7000 *SIC* 8211

BOB JONES UNIVERSITY INC OF GREENVILLE S C p 196
1700 Wade Hampton Blvd, Greenville SC 29614
Tel (864) 242-5100
SIC 8221 8211 8231 8062 5942 0191

GREENVILLE COUNTY SCHOOL DISTRICT p 638
301 E Camperdown Way, Greenville SC 29601
Tel (864) 355-3100 *SIC* 8211

GREENVILLE TECHNICAL COLLEGE PUBLIC FACILITIES CORP p 638
506 S Pleasantburg Dr, Greenville SC 29607
Tel (864) 250-8000 *SIC* 8222 8211 8221

GREENWOOD SCHOOL DISTRICT 50 p 639
1855 Calhoun Rd, Greenwood SC 29649
Tel (864) 941-5400 *SIC* 8211

SCHOOL DISTRICT FIVE OF LEXINGTON AND RICHLAND COUNTIES p 1289
1020 Dutch Fork Rd, Irmo SC 29063
Tel (803) 476-8000 *SIC* 8211

LANCASTER COUNTY SCHOOL DISTRICT p 841
300 S Catawba St, Lancaster SC 29720
Tel (803) 286-6972 *SIC* 8211

LEXINGTON COUNTY SCHOOL DISTRICT NO 1 p 859
100 Tarrar Springs Rd, Lexington SC 29072
Tel (803) 821-1000 *SIC* 8211

LEXINGTON SCHOOL DISTRICT 01 p 859
100 Tarrar Springs Rd, Lexington SC 29072
Tel (803) 321-1002 *SIC* 8211

BERKELEY COUNTY SCHOOL DISTRICT p 175
229 E Main St, Moncks Corner SC 29461
Tel (843) 899-8600 *SIC* 8211

NEWBERRY COUNTY SCHOOL DISTRICT p 1037
3419 Main St, Newberry SC 29108
Tel (803) 321-2600 *SIC* 8211

ORANGEBURG CONSOLIDATED SCHOOL DISTRICT 5 p 1092
578 Ellis Ave, Orangeburg SC 29115
Tel (803) 534-5454 *SIC* 8211

ROCK HILL SCHOOL DISTRICT 3 p 1243
660 Anderson Rd N, Rock Hill SC 29730
Tel (803) 981-1000 *SIC* 8211

SPARTANBURG SCHOOL DISTRICT 6 p 1355
1390 Cavalier Way, Roebuck SC 29376
Tel (864) 576-4212 *SIC* 8211

SPARTANBURG COUNTY SCHOOL DISTRICT NO 7 p 1355
610 Dupre Dr, Spartanburg SC 29307
Tel (864) 594-4400 *SIC* 8211

DORCHESTER SCHOOL DISTRICT TWO p 451
102 Greenwave Blvd, Summerville SC 29483
Tel (843) 873-2901 *SIC* 8211

SUMTER SCHOOL DISTRICT p 1399
1345 Wilson Hall Rd, Sumter SC 29150
Tel (803) 469-6900 *SIC* 8211

SCHOOL DISTRICT OF OCONEE COUNTY p 1289
414 S Pine St, Walhalla SC 29691
Tel (864) 886-4400 *SIC* 8211

COLLETON COUNTY SCHOOL DISTRICT p 337
213 N Jefferies Blvd, Walterboro SC 29488
Tel (843) 549-5715 *SIC* 8211

BOOKLAND CAYCE SCHOOL DISTRICT NO 2 p 200
715 9th St, West Columbia SC 29169
Tel (803) 739-4057 *SIC* 8211

FAIRFIELD COUNTY SCHOOL DISTRICT p 524
1226 Us Highway 321 Byp S, Winnsboro SC 29180
Tel (803) 635-4607 *SIC* 8211

RAPID CITY AREA SCHOOL DISTRICT 51 4 p 1208
300 6th St Ste 2, Rapid City SD 57701
Tel (605) 394-4031 *SIC* 8211

SIOUX FALLS SCHOOL DISTRICT NO 49-5 p 1326
201 E 38th St, Sioux Falls SD 57105
Tel (605) 367-7900 *SIC* 8211

CHEATHAM COUNTY SCHOOL DISTRICT (INC) p 292
102 Elizabeth St, Ashland City TN 37015
Tel (615) 792-5664 *SIC* 8211

SULLIVAN COUNTY SCHOOLS p 1397
154 Blountville Byp, Blountville TN 37617
Tel (423) 354-1000 *SIC* 8211

CLARKSVILLE-MONTGOMERY COUNTY SCHOOL SYS p 322
621 Gracey Ave, Clarksville TN 37040
Tel (931) 648-5600 *SIC* 8211

ANDERSON COUNTY SCHOOLS p 90
101 S Main St Ste 500, Clinton TN 37716
Tel (865) 463-8631 *SIC* 8211

MAURY COUNTY PUBLIC SCHOOLS p 921
501 W 8th St, Columbia TN 38401
Tel (931) 388-8403 *SIC* 8211

TIPTON COUNTY SCHOOL DISTRICT INC p 1455
1580 Highway 51 S, Covington TN 38019
Tel (901) 476-7148 *SIC* 8211

JEFFERSON COUNTY SCHOOL DISTRICT p 781
1221 Gay St, Dandridge TN 37725
Tel (865) 397-3138 *SIC* 8211

WILLIAMSON COUNTY SCHOOL DISTRICT p 1612
1320 W Main St Ste 202, Franklin TN 37064
Tel (615) 472-4000 *SIC* 8211

SUMNER COUNTY BOARD OF EDUCATION p 1399
695 E Main St, Gallatin TN 37066
Tel (615) 451-5200 *SIC* 8211

SUMNER COUNTY SCHOOL DISTRICT p 1399
695 E Main St, Gallatin TN 37066
Tel (615) 451-5200 *SIC* 8211

JACKSON-MADISON COUNTY SCHOOL SYSTEM p 774
310 N Parkway, Jackson TN 38305
Tel (731) 664-2500 *SIC* 8211

WASHINGTON COUNTY BOARD OF EDUCATION p 1578
405 W College St, Jonesborough TN 37659
Tel (423) 753-1100 *SIC* 8211

ROANE COUNTY SCHOOLS p 1240
105 Bluff Rd, Kingston TN 37763
Tel (865) 376-5592 *SIC* 8211

WILSON COUNTY BOARD OF EDUCATION p 1613
351 Stumpy Ln, Lebanon TN 37090
Tel (615) 444-3282 *SIC* 8211

WILSON COUNTY SCHOOLS p 1613
351 Stumpy Ln, Lebanon TN 37090
Tel (615) 444-3282 *SIC* 8211

BLOUNT COUNTY SCHOOLS p 190
831 Grandview Dr, Maryville TN 37803
Tel (865) 984-1212 *SIC* 8211

BOARD OF EDUCATION-MEMPHIS CITY SCHOOLS p 195
160 S Hollywood St, Memphis TN 38112
Tel (901) 416-5300 *SIC* 8211

SHELBY COUNTY BOARD OF EDUCATION p 1314
160 S Hollywood St, Memphis TN 38112
Tel (901) 321-2500 *SIC* 8211

SHELBY COUNTY SCHOOLS p 1314
160 S Hollywood St, Memphis TN 38112
Tel (901) 321-2500 *SIC* 8211

HAMBLEN COUNTY BOARD OF EDUCATION p 655
210 E Morris Blvd, Morristown TN 37813
Tel (423) 586-7700 *SIC* 8211

HAMBLEN COUNTY SCHOOL DISTRICT p 655
210 E Morris Blvd, Morristown TN 37813
Tel (423) 586-7700 *SIC* 8211

MURFREESBORO CITY SCHOOLS p 1001
2552 S Church St Ste 100, Murfreesboro TN 37127
Tel (615) 893-2313 *SIC* 8211

LIPSCOMB UNIVERSITY p 870
1 University Park Dr, Nashville TN 37204
Tel (615) 966-1000 *SIC* 8221 8211

METROPOLITAN NASHVILLE PUBLIC SCHOOLS p 956
2601 Bransford Ave, Nashville TN 37204
Tel (615) 259-4636 *SIC* 8211

TENNESSEE BOARD OF REGENTS p 1438
1 Bridgestone Park, Nashville TN 37214
Tel (615) 366-4400 *SIC* 8211

SEVIER COUNTY BOARD OF EDUCATION p 1309
226 Cedar St, Sevierville TN 37862
Tel (865) 453-4671 *SIC* 8211

SEVIER COUNTY SCHOOL SYSTEM p 1309
226 Cedar St, Sevierville TN 37862
Tel (865) 453-4671 *SIC* 8211

FAYETTE COUNTY SCHOOLS p 532
126 W Market St, Somerville TN 38068
Tel (901) 465-5260 *SIC* 8211

ROBERTSON COUNTY SCHOOL DISTRICT p 1242
800 Ms Couts Blvd Ste 2, Springfield TN 37172
Tel (615) 384-5588 *SIC* 8211

ABILENE INDEPENDENT SCHOOL DISTRICT p 11
241 Pine St, Abilene TX 79601
Tel (325) 677-1444 *SIC* 8211

ALICE INDEPENDENT SCHOOL DISTRICT p 50
2 Coyote Trl, Alice TX 78332
Tel (361) 664-0981 *SIC* 8211

ALLEN INDEPENDENT SCHOOL DISTRICT p 53
612 E Bethany Dr, Allen TX 75002
Tel (972) 727-0511 *SIC* 8211

ALVIN INDEPENDENT SCHOOL DISTRICT p 63
301 E House St, Alvin TX 77511
Tel (281) 388-1130 *SIC* 8211

AMARILLO INDEPENDENT SCHOOL DISTRICT p 64
7200 W Interstate 40, Amarillo TX 79106
Tel (806) 326-1000 *SIC* 8211

ARLINGTON INDEPENDENT SCHOOL DISTRICT p 110
1203 W Pioneer Pkwy, Arlington TX 76013
Tel (682) 867-4611 *SIC* 8211

AUSTIN INDEPENDENT SCHOOL DISTRICT (INC) p 133
1111 W 6th St, Austin TX 78703
Tel (512) 414-1700 *SIC* 8211

EDUCATION AGENCY TEXAS p 479
1701 Congress Ave, Austin TX 78701
Tel (512) 463-9734 *SIC* 8211 9411

BASTROP INDEPENDENT SCHOOL DISTRICT p 159
906 Farm St, Bastrop TX 78602
Tel (512) 321-2292 *SIC* 8211

GOOSE CREEK CONSOLIDATED INDEPENDENT SCHOOL DISTRICT p 625
4544 Interstate 10 E, Baytown TX 77521
Tel (281) 420-4800 *SIC* 8211

BEAUMONT INDEPENDENT SCHOOL DISTRICT p 166
3395 Harrison Ave, Beaumont TX 77706
Tel (409) 617-5000 *SIC* 8211

HURST-EULESS-BEDFORD INDEPENDENT SCHOOL DISTRICT p 721
1849 Central Dr, Bedford TX 76022
Tel (817) 267-3311 *SIC* 8211

BELTON INDEPENDENT SCHOOL DISTRICT p 171
400 N Wall St, Belton TX 76513
Tel (254) 215-2000 *SIC* 8211

BROWNSVILLE INDEPENDENT SCHOOL DISTRICT p 220
1900 E Price Rd, Brownsville TX 78521
Tel (956) 548-8000 *SIC* 8211

BRYAN INDEPENDENT SCHOOL DISTRICT p 221
101 N Texas Ave, Bryan TX 77803
Tel (979) 209-1000 *SIC* 8211

BURLESON INDEPENDENT SCHOOL DISTRICT p 227
1160 Sw Wilshire Blvd, Burleson TX 76028
Tel (817) 245-1000 *SIC* 8211

CANYON INDEPENDENT SCHOOL DISTRICT p 248
3301 N 23rd St, Canyon TX 79015
Tel (806) 677-2600 *SIC* 8211

CARROLLTON-FARMERS BRANCH INDEPENDENT SCHOOL DISTRICT p 261
1445 N Perry Rd, Carrollton TX 75006
Tel (972) 968-6100 *SIC* 8211

BRAZOSPORT INDEPENDENT SCHOOL DISTRICT (INC) p 209
301 W Brazoswood Dr, Clute TX 77531
Tel (979) 730-7000 *SIC* 8211

COLLEGE STATION INDEPENDENT SCHOOL DISTRICT p 337
1812 Welsh Ave, College Station TX 77840
Tel (979) 764-5400 *SIC* 8211

CONROE INDEPENDENT SCHOOL DISTRICT p 358
3205 W Davis St, Conroe TX 77304
Tel (936) 709-7751 *SIC* 8211

COPPELL INDEPENDENT SCHOOL DISTRICT p 368
200 S Denton Tap Rd, Coppell TX 75019
Tel (214) 496-6000 *SIC* 8211

COPPERAS COVE INDEPENDENT SCHOOL DISTRICT p 368
703 W Avenue D, Copperas Cove TX 76522
Tel (254) 547-1227 *SIC* 8211

CORPUS CHRISTI INDEPENDENT SCHOOL DISTRICT p 372
801 Leopard St, Corpus Christi TX 78401
Tel (361) 886-9200 *SIC* 8211

CROWLEY INDEPENDENT SCHOOL DISTRICT 912 p 395
512 Peach St, Crowley TX 76036
Tel (817) 297-5800 *SIC* 8211

■ **CAMBIUM LEARNING GROUP INC** p 244
17855 Dallas Pkwy Ste 400, Dallas TX 75287
Tel (214) 932-9500 *SIC* 8299 8211 7372

DALLAS COUNTY SCHOOLS p 410
5151 Samuell Blvd, Dallas TX 75228
Tel (214) 944-4545 *SIC* 8211

DALLAS INDEPENDENT SCHOOL DISTRICT p 410
3700 Ross Ave, Dallas TX 75204
Tel (972) 925-3700 *SIC* 8211

ED HIGHER HOLDINGS LLC p 476
600 N Pearl St Ste 900, Dallas TX 75201
Tel (214) 210-7300 *SIC* 8211

HIGHLAND PARK INDEPENDENT SCHOOL DISTRICT p 691
7015 Westchester Dr, Dallas TX 75205
Tel (214) 780-3000 *SIC* 8211

UPLIFT EDUCATION p 1528
1825 Market Center Blvd # 500, Dallas TX 75207
Tel (469) 621-8500 *SIC* 8211

DEER PARK INDEPENDENT SCHOOL DISTRICT (INC) p 421
2800 Texas Ave, Deer Park TX 77536
Tel (832) 668-7080 *SIC* 8211

SAN FELIPE DEL RIO CONSOLIDATED INDEPENDENT SCHOOL DISTRICT p 1276
315 Griner St, Del Rio TX 78840
Tel (830) 778-4000 *SIC* 8211

DENTON INDEPENDENT SCHOOL DISTRICT p 429
1307 N Locust St, Denton TX 76201
Tel (940) 369-0000 *SIC* 8211

DESOTO INDEPENDENT SCHOOL DISTRICT p 432
200 E Belt Line Rd, Desoto TX 75115
Tel (972) 223-6666 *SIC* 8211

DICKINSON INDEPENDENT SCHOOL DISTRICT p 438
2218 Fm 517 Rd E, Dickinson TX 77539
Tel (281) 229-6000 *SIC* 8211

DONNA INDEPENDENT SCHOOL DISTRICT p 450
116 N 10th St, Donna TX 78537
Tel (956) 464-1600 *SIC* 8211

DUNCANVILLE INDEPENDENT SCHOOL DISTRICT p 461
710 S Cedar Ridge Dr, Duncanville TX 75137
Tel (972) 708-2000 *SIC* 8211

EAGLE PASS INDEPENDENT SCHOOL DISTRICT p 468
1420 Eidson Rd, Eagle Pass TX 78852
Tel (830) 773-5181 *SIC* 8211

EDGEWOOD INDEPENDENT SCHOOL DISTRICT 903 p 478
804 E Pine St, Edgewood TX 75117
Tel (903) 896-4332 *SIC* 8211 9411

EDINBURG CONSOLIDATED INDEPENDENT SCHOOL DISTRICT p 478
411 N 8th Ave, Edinburg TX 78541
Tel (956) 289-2300 *SIC* 8211

CLINT INDEPENDENT SCHOOL DISTRICT p 326
14521 Horizon Blvd, El Paso TX 79928
Tel (915) 926-4000 *SIC* 8211 9411

EL PASO INDEPENDENT SCHOOL DISTRICT p 483
6531 Boeing Dr, El Paso TX 79925
Tel (915) 230-2000 *SIC* 8211

SOCORRO INDEPENDENT SCHOOL DISTRICT p 1336
12440 Rojas Dr, El Paso TX 79928
Tel (915) 937-0100 *SIC* 8211

YSLETA INDEPENDENT SCHOOL DISTRICT p 1640
9600 Sims Dr, El Paso TX 79925
Tel (915) 434-0240 *SIC* 8211

LEWISVILLE INDEPENDENT SCHOOL DISTRICT p 859
1800 Timber Creek Rd, Flower Mound TX 75028
Tel (469) 713-5200 *SIC* 8211

EAGLE MOUNTAIN-SAGINAW INDEPENDENT SCHOOL DISTRICT p 468
1200 Old Decatur Rd, Fort Worth TX 76179
Tel (817) 232-0123 *SIC* 8211

FORT WORTH INDEPENDENT SCHOOL DISTRICT p 569
100 N University Dr, Fort Worth TX 76107
Tel (817) 871-2000 *SIC* 8211

FRISCO INDEPENDENT SCHOOL DISTRICT p 580
5515 Ohio Dr, Frisco TX 75035
Tel (469) 633-6000 *SIC* 8211

GALVESTON INDEPENDENT SCHOOL DISTRICT p 590
3904 Avenue T, Galveston TX 77550
Tel (409) 765-2101 *SIC* 8211

GARLAND INDEPENDENT SCHOOL DISTRICT p 592
501 S Jupiter Rd, Garland TX 75042
Tel (972) 494-8201 *SIC* 8211

GEORGETOWN INDEPENDENT SCHOOL DISTRICT p 606
603 Lakeway Dr, Georgetown TX 78628
Tel (512) 943-5000 *SIC* 8211

GRAND PRAIRIE INDEPENDENT SCHOOL DISTRICT p 630
2602 S Belt Line Rd, Grand Prairie TX 75052
Tel (972) 264-6141 *SIC* 8211

CARROLL INDEPENDENT SCHOOL DISTRICT p 261
3051 Dove Rd, Grapevine TX 76051
Tel (817) 949-8230 *SIC* 8211

GRAPEVINE - COLLYVILLE INDEPENDENT SCHOOL DIST p 631
3051 Ira E Woods Ave, Grapevine TX 76051
Tel (817) 251-5466 *SIC* 8211

GRAPEVINE/COLLEYVILLE INDEPENDENT SCHOOL DISTRICT p 631
3051 Ira E Woods Ave, Grapevine TX 76051
Tel (817) 251-5200 *SIC* 8211

BIRDVILLE INDEPENDENT SCHOOL DISTRICT p 185
6125 E Belknap St, Haltom City TX 76117
Tel (817) 547-5700 *SIC* 8211

HARLINGEN CONSOLIDATED INDEPENDENT SCHOOL DISTRICT p 662
407 N 77 Sunshinestrip, Harlingen TX 78550
Tel (956) 430-9500 *SIC* 8211

ALDINE INDEPENDENT SCHOOL DISTRICT p 48
2520 Ww Thorne Blvd, Houston TX 77073
Tel (281) 449-1011 *SIC* 8211

ALIEF INDEPENDENT SCHOOL DISTRICT p 50
4250 Cook Rd, Houston TX 77072
Tel (281) 498-8110 *SIC* 8211

CYPRESS-FAIRBANKS INDEPENDENT SCHOOL DISTRICT p 405
10300 Jones Rd, Houston TX 77065
Tel (281) 897-4000 *SIC* 8211

HARMONY PUBLIC SCHOOLS p 662
9321 W Sam Houston Pkwy S, Houston TX 77099
Tel (281) 888-9764 *SIC* 8211

HOUSTON INDEPENDENT SCHOOL DISTRICT p 712
4400 W 18th St, Houston TX 77092
Tel (713) 556-6005 *SIC* 8211

KIPP INC p 821
10711 Kipp Way Dr, Houston TX 77099
Tel (832) 328-1051 *SIC* 8211

NORTH FOREST INDEPENDENT SCHOOL DISTRICT p 1052
4400 W 18th St, Houston TX 77092
Tel (713) 633-1600 *SIC* 8211

NORTH FOREST ISD p 1052
4400 W 18th St, Houston TX 77092
Tel (713) 633-1600 *SIC* 8211

PARK GALENA INDEPENDENT SCHOOL DISTRICT p 1115
14705 Woodforest Blvd A, Houston TX 77015
Tel (832) 386-1000 *SIC* 8211

SPRING BRANCH INDEPENDENT SCHOOL DISTRICT (INC) p 1360
955 Campbell Rd, Houston TX 77024
Tel (713) 464-1511 *SIC* 8211

SPRING INDEPENDENT SCHOOL DISTRICT p 1360
16717 Ella Blvd, Houston TX 77090
Tel (281) 891-6000 *SIC* 8211

YES PREP PUBLIC SCHOOLS INC p 1636
6201 Bonhomme Rd Ste 168n, Houston TX 77036
Tel (713) 967-9001 *SIC* 8211

HUMBLE INDEPENDENT SCHOOL DISTRICT p 718
20200 Eastway Village Dr, Humble TX 77338
Tel (281) 641-1000 *SIC* 8211

HUNTSVILLE INDEPENDENT SCHOOL DISTRICT p 720
441 Fm 2821 Rd E, Huntsville TX 77320
Tel (936) 435-6300 *SIC* 8211

IRVING INDEPENDENT SCHOOL DISTRICT INC p 765
2621 W Airport Fwy, Irving TX 75062
Tel (972) 600-5000 *SIC* 8211

NORTHWEST INDEPENDENT SCHOOL DISTRICT p 1060
2001 Texan Dr, Justin TX 76247
Tel (817) 215-0000 *SIC* 8211

KATY INDEPENDENT SCHOOL DISTRICT p 805
6301 S Stadium Ln, Katy TX 77494
Tel (281) 396-6000 *SIC* 8211

KATY INDEPENDENT SCHOOL DISTRICT DARE ADVISORY BOARD INC p 805
20380 Franz Rd, Katy TX 77449
Tel (281) 396-2500 *SIC* 8211

KELLER INDEPENDENT SCHOOL DISTRICT p 808
350 Keller Pkwy, Keller TX 76248
Tel (817) 744-1000 *SIC* 8211

KILLEEN INDEPENDENT SCHOOL DISTRICT p 818
200 N W S Young Dr, Killeen TX 76543
Tel (254) 336-0000 *SIC* 8211

HAYS CONSOLIDATED I S D p 670
21003 Interstate 35, Kyle TX 78640
Tel (512) 268-8442 *SIC* 8211

LA JOYA INDEPENDENT SCHOOL DISTRICT p 835
200 W Expressway 83, La Joya TX 78560
Tel (956) 580-2000 *SIC* 8211

LA PORTE INDEPENDENT SCHOOL DISTRICT p 835
1002 San Jacinto St, La Porte TX 77571
Tel (281) 604-7000 *SIC* 8211

LAREDO INDEPENDENT SCHOOL DISTRICT EDUCATIONAL FOUNDATION p 845
1702 Houston St, Laredo TX 78040
Tel (956) 795-3200 *SIC* 8211

UNITED INDEPENDENT SCHOOL DISTRICT p 1509
201 Lindenwood Dr, Laredo TX 78045
Tel (956) 473-6201 *SIC* 8211

CLEAR CREEK INDEPENDENT SCHOOL DISTRICT p 324
2425 E Main St, League City TX 77573
Tel (281) 284-0000 *SIC* 8211

LEANDER INDEPENDENT SCHOOL DISTRICT p 850
204 W South St, Leander TX 78641
Tel (512) 570-0000 *SIC* 8211

LEWISVILLE INDEPENDENT SCHOOL DISTRICT p 859
1565 W Main St Ste 101, Lewisville TX 75067
Tel (469) 713-5200 *SIC* 8211

RESPONSIVE EDUCATION SOLUTIONS p 1228
1301 Waters Ridge Dr, Lewisville TX 75057
Tel (972) 420-7050 *SIC* 8211

JUDSON INDEPENDENT SCHOOL DISTRICT p 797
8012 Shin Oak Dr, Live Oak TX 78233
Tel (210) 945-5100 *SIC* 8211

LONGVIEW INDEPENDENT SCHOOL DISTRICT p 877
1301 E Young St, Longview TX 75602
Tel (903) 753-0206 *SIC* 8211

LOS FRESNOS CONSOLIDATED INDEPENDENT SCHOOL DISTRICT p 879
600 N Mesquite St, Los Fresnos TX 78566
Tel (956) 233-4407 *SIC* 8211

LUBBOCK INDEPENDENT SCHOOL DISTRICT p 883
1628 19th St, Lubbock TX 79401
Tel (806) 766-1000 *SIC* 8211

MABANK INDEPENDENT SCHOOL DISTRICT p 891
310 E Market St, Mabank TX 75147
Tel (903) 880-1300 *SIC* 8211

MAGNOLIA INDEPENDENT SCHOOL DISTRICT p 896
31141 Nichols Sawmill Rd, Magnolia TX 77355
Tel (281) 356-3571 *SIC* 8211

MANOR INDEPENDENT SCHOOL DISTRICT p 902
10335 Us Highway 290 E, Manor TX 78653
Tel (512) 278-4000 *SIC* 8211

MANSFIELD INDEPENDENT SCHOOL DISTRICT p 903
605 E Broad St, Mansfield TX 76063
Tel (817) 299-6300 *SIC* 8211

MCALLEN INDEPENDENT SCHOOL DISTRICT p 925
2000 N 23rd St, Mcallen TX 78501
Tel (956) 618-6000 *SIC* 8211

MCKINNEY INDEPENDENT SCHOOL DISTRICT p 930
1 Duvall St, Mckinney TX 75069
Tel (469) 302-4000 *SIC* 8211

MESQUITE INDEPENDENT SCHOOL DISTRICT p 951
405 E Davis St, Mesquite TX 75149
Tel (972) 288-6411 *SIC* 8211

MIDLAND INDEPENDENT SCHOOL DISTRICT p 965
615 W Missouri Ave, Midland TX 79701
Tel (432) 689-1000 *SIC* 8211

MIDLOTHIAN INDEPENDENT SCHOOL DISTRICT p 966
100 Walter Stephenson Rd, Midlothian TX 76065
Tel (972) 723-6290 *SIC* 8211

MISSION CONSOLIDATED INDEPENDENT SCHOOL DISTRICT p 975
1201 Bryce Dr, Mission TX 78572
Tel (956) 323-5500 *SIC* 8211

BARBERS HILL INDEPENDENT SCHOOL DISTRICT EDUCATION FOUNDATION p 154
9600 Eagle Dr, Mont Belvieu TX 77580
Tel (281) 576-2221 *SIC* 8211

MOUNT PLEASANT INDEPENDENT SCHOOL DISTRICT p 994
2230 N Edwards Ave, Mount Pleasant TX 75455
Tel (903) 575-2000 *SIC* 8211

COMAL INDEPENDENT SCHOOL DISTRICT p 343
1404 N Interstate 35, New Braunfels TX 78130
Tel (830) 221-2000 *SIC* 8611 8211

NEW CANEY INDEPENDENT SCHOOL DISTRICT p 1029
21580 Loop 494, New Caney TX 77357
Tel (281) 577-8600 *SIC* 8211

ECTOR COUNTY INDEPENDENT SCHOOL DISTRICT p 476
802 N Sam Houston Ave, Odessa TX 79761
Tel (432) 456-0002 *SIC* 8211

PASADENA INDEPENDENT SCHOOL DISTRICT p 1119
1515 Cherrybrook Ln, Pasadena TX 77502
Tel (713) 740-0000 *SIC* 8211

PEARLAND INDEPENDENT SCHOOL DISTRICT p 1126
1928 N Main St, Pearland TX 77581
Tel (281) 485-3203 *SIC* 8211

PFLUGERVILLE INDEPENDENT SCHOOL DISTRICT p 1140
1401 W Pecan St, Pflugerville TX 78660
Tel (512) 594-0000 *SIC* 8211

PHARR SAN JUAN-ALAMO INDEPENDENT SCHOOL DISTRICT p 1141
601 E Kelly Ave, Pharr TX 78577
Tel (956) 354-2000 *SIC* 8211

PLANO INDEPENDENT SCHOOL DISTRICT p 1154
2700 W 15th St, Plano TX 75075
Tel (469) 752-8100 *SIC* 8211

PORT ARTHUR INDEPENDENT SCHOOL DISTRICT p 1162
4801 9th Ave, Port Arthur TX 77642
Tel (409) 989-6100 *SIC* 8211

RICHARDSON INDEPENDENT SCHOOL DISTRICT p 1232
400 S Greenville Ave # 205, Richardson TX 75081
Tel (469) 593-0000 *SIC* 8211

RIO GRANDE CITY CONSOLIDATED INDEPEDENT SCHOOL DISTRICT p 1235
1 S Fort Ringgold St, Rio Grande City TX 78582
Tel (956) 716-6700 *SIC* 8211

ROCKWALL INDEPENDENT SCHOOL DISTRICT PUBLIC FACILITY CORP p 1245
1050 Williams St, Rockwall TX 75087
Tel (972) 771-0605 *SIC* 8211

ROMA INDEPENDENT SCHOOL DISTRICT p 1248
608 N Garcia St, Roma TX 78584
Tel (956) 849-1377 *SIC* 8211

LAMAR CONSOLIDATED INDEPENDENT SCHOOL DISTRICT (INC) p 841
3911 Avenue I, Rosenberg TX 77471
Tel (832) 223-0000 *SIC* 8211

ROUND ROCK INDEPENDENT SCHOOL DISTRICT (INC) p 1252
1311 Round Rock Ave, Round Rock TX 78681
Tel (512) 464-5000 *SIC* 8211 8748

SAN ANGELO INDEPENDENT SCHOOL DISTRICT p 1275
1621 University Ave, San Angelo TX 76904
Tel (325) 947-3700 *SIC* 8211

EAST CENTRAL INDEPENDENT SCHOOL DISTRICT p 470
6634 New Sulphur Sprng Rd, San Antonio TX 78263
Tel (210) 648-7861 *SIC* 8211

EDGEWOOD INDEPENDENT SCHOOL DISTRICT p 478
5358 W Comm St, San Antonio TX 78237
Tel (210) 444-4500 *SIC* 8211

HARLANDALE INDEPENDENT SCHOOL DISTRICT PUBLIC FACILITIES CORP p 661
102 Genevieve Dr, San Antonio TX 78214
Tel (210) 989-4340 *SIC* 8211

NORTH EAST INDEPENDENT SCHOOL DISTRICT p 1052
8961 Tesoro Dr, San Antonio TX 78217
Tel (210) 407-0359 *SIC* 8211

NORTHSIDE INDEPENDENT SCHOOL DISTRICT p 1058
5900 Evers Rd, San Antonio TX 78238
Tel (210) 397-8770 *SIC* 8211

SAN ANTONIO INDEPENDENT SCHOOL DISTRICT FAC p 1275
141 Lavaca St, San Antonio TX 78210
Tel (210) 554-2200 *SIC* 8211

SOUTH SAN ANTONIO INDEPENDENT SCHOOL DISTRICT p 1345
5622 Ray Ellison Blvd, San Antonio TX 78242
Tel (210) 977-7000 *SIC* 8211

SOUTHWEST INDEPENDENT SCHOOL DISTRICT p 1352
11914 Dragon Ln, San Antonio TX 78252
Tel (210) 622-4300 *SIC* 8211

SAN BENITO CONSOLIDATED INDEPENDENT SCHOOL DISTRICT PUBLIC FACILITIES p 1275
240 N Crockett St, San Benito TX 78586
Tel (956) 361-6100 *SIC* 8211

SAN MARCOS CONSOLIDATED INDEPENDENT SCHOOL DISTRICT p 1277
501 S Lbj Dr, San Marcos TX 78666
Tel (512) 393-6700 *SIC* 8211

SCHERTZ-CIBOLO-UNIVERSAL CITY INDEPENDENT SCHOOL DISTRICT p 1286
1060 Elbel Rd, Schertz TX 78154
Tel (210) 945-6200 *SIC* 8211

SEGUIN INDEPENDENT SCHOOL DISTRICT p 1300
1221 E Kingsbury St, Seguin TX 78155
Tel (830) 372-5771 *SIC* 8211

SHERMAN INDEPENDENT SCHOOL DISTRICT p 1316
2701 N Loy Lake Rd, Sherman TX 75090
Tel (903) 891-6400 *SIC* 8211

KLEIN INDEPENDENT SCHOOL DISTRICT p 823
7200 Spring Cypress Rd, Spring TX 77379
Tel (832) 249-4000 *SIC* 8211

FORT BEND INDEPENDENT SCHOOL DISTRICT p 568
16431 Lexington Blvd, Sugar Land TX 77479
Tel (281) 634-1000 *SIC* 8211

TEMPLE INDEPENDENT SCHOOL DISTRICT p 1436
200 N 23rd St, Temple TX 76504
Tel (254) 215-7513 *SIC* 8211 8299

LIBERTY-EYLAU INDEPENDENT SCHOOL DISTRICT p 863
2901 Leopard Dr, Texarkana TX 75501
Tel (903) 832-1535 *SIC* 8211

TOMBALL INDEPENDENT SCHOOL DISTRICT p 1459
310 S Cherry St, Tomball TX 77375
Tel (281) 357-3100 *SIC* 8211

TYLER INDEPENDENT SCHOOL DISTRICT p 1496
1319 Earl Campbell Pkwy, Tyler TX 75701
Tel (903) 262-1000 *SIC* 8211

INDUSTRIAL INDEPENDENT SCHOOL DISTRICT p 740
511 5th St, Vanderbilt TX 77991
Tel (361) 284-3226 *SIC* 8211

VICTORIA INDEPENDENT SCHOOL DISTRICT p 1555
102 Profit Dr, Victoria TX 77901
Tel (361) 576-3131 *SIC* 8211

WACO INDEPENDENT SCHOOL DISTRICT p 1570
501 Franklin Ave Ofc, Waco TX 76701
Tel (254) 755-9473 *SIC* 8211

IDEA PUBLIC SCHOOLS p 729
505 Angelita Dr Ste 9, Weslaco TX 78599
Tel (956) 377-8000 *SIC* 8211

WESLACO INDEPENDENT SCHOOL DISTRICT p 1593
319 W 4th St, Weslaco TX 78596
Tel (956) 969-6500 *SIC* 8211

EANES INDEPENDENT SCHOOL DISTRICT p 468
601 Camp Craft Rd, West Lake Hills TX 78746
Tel (512) 732-9000 *SIC* 8211

WICHITA FALLS INDEPENDENT SCHOOL DISTRICT p 1607
1104 Broad St, Wichita Falls TX 76301
Tel (940) 235-1000 *SIC* 8211

MIDWAY INDEPENDENT SCHOOL DISTRICT p 967
13885 Woodway Dr, Woodway TX 76712
Tel (254) 761-5610 *SIC* 8211

WYLIE INDEPENDENT SCHOOL DISTRICT p 1629
951 S Ballard Ave, Wylie TX 75098
Tel (972) 442-5444 *SIC* 8211

ALPINE SCHOOL DISTRICT p 60
575 N 100 E, American Fork UT 84003
Tel (801) 610-8400 *SIC* 8211

BOX ELDER COUNTY SCHOOL DISTRICT p 204
960 S Main St Ste 1, Brigham City UT 84302
Tel (435) 734-4800 *SIC* 8211

DAVIS SCHOOL DISTRICT p 416
45 E St St, Farmington UT 84025
Tel (801) 402-5261 *SIC* 8211

CACHE COUNTY SCHOOL DISTRICT p 235
2063 N 1200 E, North Logan UT 84341
Tel (435) 752-3925 *SIC* 8211

BOARD OF EDUC OF OGDEN CITY SD p 195
1950 Monroe Blvd, Ogden UT 84401
Tel (801) 737-8000 *SIC* 8211

OGDEN CITY SCHOOL DISTRICT p 1076
1950 Monroe Blvd, Ogden UT 84401
Tel (801) 737-8000 *SIC* 8211

WEBER SCHOOL DISTRICT p 1586
5320 Adams Ave Pkwy, Ogden UT 84405
Tel (801) 476-7800 *SIC* 8211

PROVO CITY SCHOOL DISTRICT p 1187
280 W 940 N, Provo UT 84604
Tel (801) 374-4800 *SIC* 8211

GRANITE SCHOOL DISTRICT p 631
2500 S State St, Salt Lake City UT 84115
Tel (385) 646-5000 *SIC* 8211

SALT LAKE CITY SCHOOL DISTRICT p 1273
440 E 100 S, Salt Lake City UT 84111
Tel (801) 578-8307 *SIC* 8211

CANYONS SCHOOL DISTRICT p 248
9361 S 300 E, Sandy UT 84070
Tel (801) 826-5340 *SIC* 8211

CHALLENGER SCHOOLS p 287
9424 S 300 W, Sandy UT 84070
Tel (801) 569-2700 *SIC* 8351 8211

NEBO SCHOOL DISTRICT p 1023
350 S Main St, Spanish Fork UT 84660
Tel (801) 354-7400 *SIC* 8211

WASHINGTON COUNTY SCHOOL DISTRICT p 1578
121 W Tabernacle St, St George UT 84770
Tel (435) 673-3553 *SIC* 8211

TOOELE COUNTY SCHOOL DISTRICT p 1460
92 Lodestone Way, Tooele UT 84074
Tel (435) 833-1900 *SIC* 8211

BOX ELDER SCHOOL DISTRICT p 205
515 N 800 W, Tremonton UT 84337
Tel (435) 257-2560 *SIC* 8211 8742

JORDAN SCHOOL DISTRICT p 793
7387 S Campus View Dr, West Jordan UT 84084
Tel (801) 280-3689 *SIC* 8211

ALEXANDRIA CITY PUBLIC SCHOOLS p 49
1340 Braddock Pl Ste 100, Alexandria VA 22314
Tel (703) 619-8000 *SIC* 8211

ARLINGTON PUBLIC SCHOOLS p 110
1426 N Quincy St, Arlington VA 22207
Tel (703) 228-6000 *SIC* 8211

IMAGINE SCHOOLS ON BROADWAY p 733
1005 N Glebe Rd Ste 610, Arlington VA 22201
Tel (703) 527-2600 *SIC* 8211

HANOVER COUNTY PUBLIC SCHOOLS p 658
200 Berkley St, Ashland VA 23005
Tel (804) 365-4500 *SIC* 8211

BEDFORD COUNTY SCHOOL DISTRICT p 168
310 S Bridge St, Bedford VA 24523
Tel (540) 586-1045 *SIC* 8211

LOUDOUN COUNTY PUBLIC SCHOOL DISTRICT p 879
21000 Education Ct, Broadlands VA 20148
Tel (571) 252-1000 *SIC* 8211

ALBEMARLE COUNTY PUBLIC SCHOOLS p 46
401 Mcintire Rd, Charlottesville VA 22902
Tel (434) 296-5820 *SIC* 8211

PITTSYLVANIA COUNTY SCHOOL BOARD p 1152
39 Bank St, Chatham VA 24531
Tel (434) 432-2761 *SIC* 8211

CHESAPEAKE SCHOOL DISTRICT p 295
312 Cedar Rd, Chesapeake VA 23322
Tel (757) 547-0153 *SIC* 8211

CHESTERFIELD COUNTY PUBLIC SCHOOLS p 295
9900 Krause Rd, Chesterfield VA 23832
Tel (804) 748-1405 *SIC* 8211

MONTGOMERY COUNTY PUBLIC SCHOOLS p 986
750 Imperial St, Christiansburg VA 24073
Tel (540) 382-5100 *SIC* 8211

HENRY COUNTY SCHOOL DISTRICT p 684
3300 Kings Mountain Rd, Collinsville VA 24078
Tel (276) 634-4700 *SIC* 8211

CULPEPER COUNTY PUBLIC SCHOOLS p 400
450 Radio Ln, Culpeper VA 22701
Tel (540) 825-3677 *SIC* 8211

FAIRFAX COUNTY PUBLIC SCHOOLS p 524
8115 Gatehouse Rd, Falls Church VA 22042
Tel (571) 423-1010 *SIC* 8211

SPOTSYLVANIA COUNTY PUBLIC SCHOOLS p 1360
8020 River Stone Dr, Fredericksburg VA 22407
Tel (540) 834-2500 *SIC* 8211

SPOTSYLVANIA COUNTY SCHOOL BOARD p 1360
8020 River Stone Dr, Fredericksburg VA 22407
Tel (540) 898-6032 *SIC* 8211

GLOUCESTER COUNTY SCHOOLS p 618
6099 T C Walker Rd, Gloucester VA 23061
Tel (804) 693-5300 *SIC* 8211

HALIFAX COUNTY PUBLIC SCHOOLS p 654
1030 Mary Bethune St, Halifax VA 24558
Tel (434) 476-2171 *SIC* 8211

HAMPTON CITY SCHOOL DISTRICT p 656
1 Franklin St Fl 2, Hampton VA 23669
Tel (757) 727-2000 *SIC* 8211

ROCKINGHAM COUNTY SCHOOL DISTRICT p 1244
100 Mount Clinton Pike, Harrisonburg VA 22802
Tel (540) 564-3200 *SIC* 8211

▲ K12 INC p 799
2300 Corporate Park Dr, Herndon VA 20171
Tel (703) 483-7000 *SIC* 8211 8299

PRINCE WILLIAM COUNTY SCHOOL BOARD p 1176
14800 Joplin Rd, Manassas VA 20112
Tel (703) 791-8308 *SIC* 8211

NEWPORT NEWS PUBLIC SCHOOL DISTRICT p 1038
12465 Warwick Blvd, Newport News VA 23606
Tel (757) 591-4500 *SIC* 8211

NORFOLK PUBLIC SCHOOLS p 1048
800 E City Hall Ave # 1201, Norfolk VA 23510
Tel (757) 628-3830 *SIC* 8211

SCHOOL BOARD OF CITY OF NORFOLK p 1289
800 E City Hall Ave # 1201, Norfolk VA 23510
Tel (757) 628-3830 *SIC* 8211

PORTSMOUTH CITY PUBLIC SCHOOLS p 1163
801 Crawford St, Portsmouth VA 23704
Tel (757) 393-8751 *SIC* 8211

PORTSMOUTH CITY SCHOOL BOARD p 1163
801 Crawford St Fl 3, Portsmouth VA 23704
Tel (757) 393-8751 *SIC* 8211

PRINCE GEORGE COUNTY SCHOOL BOARD p 1176
6410 Courts Dr, Prince George VA 23875
Tel (804) 733-2700 *SIC* 8211

CHURCH SCHOOLS IN DIOCESE OF VIRGINIA p 305
8727 River Rd, Richmond VA 23229
Tel (804) 288-6045 *SIC* 8211

HENRICO COUNTY PUBLIC SCHOOLS p 683
3820 Nine Mile Rd Ste A, Richmond VA 23223
Tel (804) 652-3717 *SIC* 8211

RICHMOND CITY PUBLIC SCHOOLS p 1233
301 N 9th St Fl 17, Richmond VA 23219
Tel (804) 780-7775 *SIC* 8211

ROANOKE CITY PUBLIC SCHOOL DISTRICT p 1240
40 Douglas Ave Nw, Roanoke VA 24012
Tel (540) 853-2502 *SIC* 8211

ROANOKE CITY PUBLIC SCHOOLS p 1240
40 Douglas Ave Nw, Roanoke VA 24012
Tel (540) 853-2381 *SIC* 8211

FRANKLIN COUNTY PUBLIC SCHOOLS p 575
25 Bernard Rd, Rocky Mount VA 24151
Tel (540) 483-5138 *SIC* 8211

FRANKLIN COUNTY SCHOOL BOARD p 575
25 Bernard Rd, Rocky Mount VA 24151
Tel (540) 483-5138 *SIC* 8211

STAFFORD COUNTY PUBLIC SCHOOL BOARD p 1374
31 Stafford Ave, Stafford VA 22554
Tel (540) 658-6000 *SIC* 8211

STAFFORD COUNTY PUBLIC SCHOOLS p 1374
31 Stafford Ave, Stafford VA 22554
Tel (540) 658-6000 *SIC* 8211

SUFFOLK CITY OF PUBLIC SCHOOLS p 1396
100 N Main St Ste 1, Suffolk VA 23434
Tel (757) 925-6754 *SIC* 8211

TAZEWELL COUNTY BOARD OF EDUCATION p 1427
209 W Fincastle Tpke, Tazewell VA 24651
Tel (276) 988-5511 *SIC* 8211

AUGUSTA COUNTY SCHOOL BOARD p 131
18 Government Center Ln, Verona VA 24482
Tel (540) 245-5100 *SIC* 8211

SCHOOL BOARD OF CITY OF VIRGINIA BEACH p 1289
2512 George Mason Dr, Virginia Beach VA 23456
Tel (757) 263-1033 *SIC* 8211

FAUQUIER COUNTY PUBLIC SCHOOLS p 531
320 Hospital Dr Ste 40, Warrenton VA 20186
Tel (540) 422-7000 *SIC* 8211

WILLIAMSBURG-JAMES CITY COUNTY PUBLIC SCHOOLS p 1612
117 Ironbound Rd, Williamsburg VA 23185
Tel (757) 603-6400 *SIC* 8211

FREDERICK COUNTY SCHOOL DISTRICT p 576
1415 Amherst St, Winchester VA 22601
Tel (540) 662-3888 *SIC* 8211

WISE COUNTY PUBLIC SCHOOLS p 1619
628 Lake St Ne, Wise VA 24293
Tel (276) 328-8017 *SIC* 8211

MINNIELAND PRIVATE DAY SCHOOL INC p 974
4300 Prince William Pkwy, Woodbridge VA 22192
Tel (703) 680-2548 *SIC* 8351 8211

YORK COUNTY SCHOOL DIVISION p 1637
302 Dare Rd, Yorktown VA 23692
Tel (757) 898-0300 *SIC* 8211

AUBURN SCHOOL DISTRICT p 130
915 4th St Ne, Auburn WA 98002
Tel (253) 931-4900 *SIC* 8211

BELLEVUE SCHOOL DISTRICT p 170
12111 Ne 1st St, Bellevue WA 98005
Tel (425) 456-4000 *SIC* 8211

BELLINGHAM PUBLIC SCHOOLS p 171
1306 Dupont St, Bellingham WA 98225
Tel (360) 676-6400 *SIC* 8211

BELLINGHAM SCHOOL BOARD p 171
1306 Dupont St, Bellingham WA 98225
Tel (360) 676-6400 *SIC* 8211

NORTHSHORE SCHOOL DISTRICT p 1058
3330 Monte Villa Pkwy, Bothell WA 98021
Tel (425) 408-6000 *SIC* 8211

BATTLE GROUND SCHOOL DISTRICT p 160
11104 Ne 149th St, Brush Prairie WA 98606
Tel (360) 885-5300 *SIC* 8211

HIGHLINE PUBLIC SCHOOLS p 692
15675 Ambaum Blvd Sw, Burien WA 98166
Tel (206) 631-3000 *SIC* 8211

EVERETT PUBLIC SCHOOLS p 514
3900 Broadway, Everett WA 98201
Tel (425) 385-4000 *SIC* 8211

MUKILTEO SCHOOL DISTRICT p 999
9401 Sharon Dr, Everett WA 98204
Tel (425) 356-1274 *SIC* 8211

FEDERAL WAY PUBLIC SCHOOLS p 536
33330 8th Ave S, Federal Way WA 98003
Tel (253) 830-6246 *SIC* 8211

ISSAQUAH SCHOOL DISTRICT 411 p 767
565 Nw Holly St, Issaquah WA 98027
Tel (425) 837-7000 *SIC* 8211 9411

KENNEWICK SCHOOL DISTRICT 17 p 811
1000 W 4th Ave, Kennewick WA 99336
Tel (509) 222-5000 *SIC* 8211 9411

KENT SCHOOL DISTRICT p 812
12033 Se 256th St, Kent WA 98030
Tel (253) 373-7000 *SIC* 8211

THURSTON NORTH PUBLIC SCHOOLS p 1451
305 College St Ne, Lacey WA 98516
Tel (360) 412-4400 *SIC* 8211

LAKE STEVENS SCHOOL DISTRICT p 839
12309 22nd St Ne, Lake Stevens WA 98258
Tel (425) 335-1500 *SIC* 8211

PARK CLOVER SCHOOL DISTRICT p 1115
10903 Gravelly Lake Dr Sw, Lakewood WA 98499
Tel (253) 583-5494 *SIC* 8211

EDMONDS SCHOOL DISTRICT 15 p 478
20420 68th Ave W, Lynnwood WA 98036
Tel (425) 431-7000 *SIC* 8211

MEAD SCHOOL DISTRICT #354 p 933
2323 E Farwell Rd, Mead WA 99021
Tel (509) 465-7480 *SIC* 8211

MOSES LAKE SCHOOL DIST 161 p 992
920 W Ivy Ave, Moses Lake WA 98837
Tel (509) 766-2650 *SIC* 8211

OLYMPIA SCHOOL DISTRICT p 1083
1113 Legion Way Se, Olympia WA 98501
Tel (360) 596-6100 *SIC* 8211

PASCO SCHOOL DISTRICT 1 p 1119
1215 W Lewis St, Pasco WA 99301
Tel (509) 546-2691 *SIC* 8211

SOUTH KITSAP SCHOOL DISTRICT 402 p 1344
2689 Hoover Ave Se, Port Orchard WA 98366
Tel (360) 874-7000 *SIC* 8211

PUYALLUP SCHOOL DISTRICT p 1193
302 2nd St Se, Puyallup WA 98372
Tel (253) 840-8971 *SIC* 8211

LAKE WASHINGTON SCHOOL DISTRICT p 839
16250 Ne 74th St, Redmond WA 98052
Tel (425) 936-1200 *SIC* 8211

RENTON SCHOOL DISTRICT p 1224
300 Sw 7th St, Renton WA 98057
Tel (425) 204-2300 *SIC* 8211

RICHLAND SCHOOL DISTRICT p 1233
615 Snow Ave, Richland WA 99352
Tel (509) 967-6000 *SIC* 8211

SEATTLE PUBLIC SCHOOLS p 1298
2445 3rd Ave S, Seattle WA 98134
Tel (206) 252-0000 *SIC* 8211

CRISTA MINISTRIES p 392
19303 Fremont Ave N, Shoreline WA 98133
Tel (206) 546-7200 *SIC* 8322 8051 8211

SHORELINE SCHOOL DISTRICT p 1318
18560 1st Ave Ne, Shoreline WA 98155
Tel (206) 367-6111 *SIC* 8211

SHORELINE SCHOOL DISTRICT p 1318
18560 1st Ave Ne, Shoreline WA 98155
Tel (206) 361-4208 *SIC* 8211

CENTRAL KITSAP SCHOOL DISTRICT p 279
9210 Silverdale Way Nw, Silverdale WA 98383
Tel (360) 662-1610 *SIC* 8211

SNOHOMISH SCHOOL DISTRICT 201 p 1335
1601 Avenue D, Snohomish WA 98290
Tel (360) 563-7263 *SIC* 8211

BETHEL SCHOOL DISTRICT p 178
516 176th St E, Spanaway WA 98387
Tel (253) 683-6000 *SIC* 8211

SPOKANE PUBLIC SCHOOLS p 1359
200 N Bernard St, Spokane WA 99201
Tel (509) 354-5900 *SIC* 8211

CENTRAL VALLEY SCHOOL DISTRICT p 280
19307 E Cataldo Ave, Spokane Valley WA 99016
Tel (509) 228-5404 *SIC* 8211

FRANKLIN-PIERCE SCHOOL DISTRICT p 575
315 129th St S, Tacoma WA 98444
Tel (253) 298-3000 *SIC* 8211

TACOMA PUBLIC SCHOOLS p 1421
601 S 8th St, Tacoma WA 98405
Tel (253) 571-1000 *SIC* 8211

TOLEDO SCHOOL DISTRICT 237 p 1459
130 N 5th St, Toledo WA 98591
Tel (360) 864-6325 *SIC* 8211

EVERGREEN PUBLIC SCHOOLS p 514
13501 Ne 28th St, Vancouver WA 98682
Tel (360) 604-4000 *SIC* 8211

VANCOUVER PUBLIC SCHOOLS p 1543
2901 Falk Rd, Vancouver WA 98661
Tel (360) 313-1000 *SIC* 8211

WENATCHEE PUBLIC SCHOOLS p 1591
235 Sunset Ave, Wenatchee WA 98801
Tel (509) 663-8161 *SIC* 8211

YAKIMA SCHOOL DISTRICT p 1634
104 N 4th Ave, Yakima WA 98902
Tel (509) 573-7000 *SIC* 8211

RALEIGH COUNTY BOARD OF EDUCATION p 1206
105 Adair St, Beckley WV 25801
Tel (304) 256-4500 *SIC* 8211 9111

RALEIGH COUNTY SCHOOL DISTRICT p 1206
105 Adair St, Beckley WV 25801
Tel (304) 256-4500 *SIC* 8211

KANAWHA COUNTY BOARD OF EDUCATION p 802
200 Elizabeth St, Charleston WV 25311
Tel (304) 348-7770 *SIC* 8211

KANAWHA COUNTY SCHOOLS p 802
200 Elizabeth St, Charleston WV 25311
Tel (304) 348-7770 *SIC* 8211

HARRISON COUNTY SCHOOL DISTRICT p 664
408 E B Saunders Way, Clarksburg WV 26301
Tel (304) 326-7300 *SIC* 8211 9111

MARION COUNTY BOARD OF EDUCATION INC p 907
200 Gaston Ave, Fairmont WV 26554
Tel (304) 367-2100 *SIC* 8211

MARION COUNTY SCHOOLS p 907
200 Gaston Ave, Fairmont WV 26554
Tel (304) 367-2100 *SIC* 8211

FAYETTE COUNTY SCHOOLS p 532
111 Fayette Ave, Fayetteville WV 25840
Tel (304) 574-1176 *SIC* 9111 8211

LINCOLN COUNTY SCHOOLS p 866
10 Marland Ave, Hamlin WV 25523
Tel (304) 824-3033 *SIC* 8211

CABELL COUNTY BOARD-EDUCATION p 235
2850 5th Ave, Huntington WV 25702
Tel (304) 528-5000 *SIC* 8211

CABELL COUNTY SCHOOL DIST INC p 235
2850 5th Ave, Huntington WV 25702
Tel (304) 528-5000 *SIC* 8211

LOGAN COUNTY SCHOOLS p 874
506 Holly Ave, Logan WV 25601
Tel (304) 792-2060 *SIC* 8211

BERKELEY COUNTY SCHOOLS p 175
401 S Queen St, Martinsburg WV 25401
Tel (304) 267-3500 *SIC* 8211

MONONGALIA COUNTY BOARD OF EDUCATION p 984
13 S High St, Morgantown WV 26501
Tel (304) 291-9210 *SIC* 8211

WOOD COUNTY SCHOOLS p 1622
1210 13th St, Parkersburg WV 26101
Tel (304) 420-9663 *SIC* 8211

MERCER COUNTY BOARD OF EDUCATION p 944
1403 Honaker Ave, Princeton WV 24740
Tel (304) 487-1551 *SIC* 8211

MERCER COUNTY PUBLIC SCHOOLS p 944
1403 Honaker Ave, Princeton WV 24740
Tel (304) 487-1551 *SIC* 8211

JACKSON COUNTY SCHOOLS p 773
1 School St, Ripley WV 25271
Tel (304) 372-7300 *SIC* 8211

WAYNE COUNTY SCHOOLS p 1584
212 N Court St, Wayne WV 25570
Tel (304) 272-5116 *SIC* 8211

APPLETON AREA SCHOOL DISTRICT p 99
122 E College Ave Ste 1a, Appleton WI 54911
Tel (920) 832-6161 *SIC* 8211

EAU CLAIRE AREA SCHOOL DISTRICT p 474
500 Main St, Eau Claire WI 54701
Tel (715) 852-3000 *SIC* 8211

FOND DU LAC SCHOOL DISTRICT p 563
72 W 9th St, Fond Du Lac WI 54935
Tel (920) 929-2900 *SIC* 8211

GREEN BAY AREA PUBLIC SCHOOL DISTRICT p 636
200 S Broadway, Green Bay WI 54303
Tel (920) 448-2101 *SIC* 8211

JANESVILLE SCHOOL DISTRICT p 777
527 S Franklin St, Janesville WI 53548
Tel (608) 743-5000 *SIC* 8211

KENOSHA UNIFIED SCHOOL DISTRICT 1 p 811
3600 52nd St, Kenosha WI 53144
Tel (262) 359-6300 *SIC* 8211

SCHOOL DISTRICT OF LACROSSE p 1289
807 East Ave S, La Crosse WI 54601
Tel (608) 789-7600 *SIC* 8211

MADISON METROPOLITAN SCHOOL DISTRICT p 894
545 W Dayton St, Madison WI 53703
Tel (608) 663-1879 *SIC* 8211

MIDDLETON-CROSS PLAINS-AREA SCHOOL DISTRICT p 965
7106 South Ave, Middleton WI 53562
Tel (608) 829-9000 *SIC* 8211

MILWAUKEE PUBLIC SCHOOLS (INC) p 972
5225 W Vliet St, Milwaukee WI 53208
Tel (414) 475-8393 *SIC* 8211

WEST ALLIS-WEST MILWAUKEE p 1593
1205 S 70th St, Milwaukee WI 53214
Tel (414) 604-3033 *SIC* 8211

OSHKOSH AREA SCHOOL DISTRICT p 1096
215 S Eagle St, Oshkosh WI 54902
Tel (920) 424-0160 *SIC* 8211

RACINE UNIFIED SCHOOL DISTRICT p 1203
3109 Mount Pleasant St, Racine WI 53404
Tel (262) 635-5600 *SIC* 8211

SHEBOYGAN AREA SCHOOL DISTRICT p 1313
830 Virginia Ave, Sheboygan WI 53081
Tel (920) 459-3500 *SIC* 8211 8741

STEVENS POINT AREA PUBLIC SCHOOL DISTRICT p 1388
1900 Polk St, Stevens Point WI 54481
Tel (715) 345-5444 *SIC* 8211

WAUKESHA SCHOOL DISTRICT p 1583
222 Maple Ave, Waukesha WI 53186
Tel (262) 970-1038 *SIC* 8211

WAUWATOSA SCHOOL DISTRICT p 1583
12121 W North Ave, Wauwatosa WI 53226
Tel (414) 773-1000 *SIC* 8211

SCHOOL DISTRICT OF WEST ALLIS-WEST MILWAUKEE ET AL p 1290
1205 S 70th St Ste 440, West Allis WI 53214
Tel (414) 604-3000 *SIC* 8211

WEST BEND JOINT SCHOOL DISTRICT NO 1 p 1593
735 S Main St Stop 2, West Bend WI 53095
Tel (262) 335-5435 *SIC* 8211

NATRONA COUNTY SCHOOL DISTRICT p 1018
970 N Glenn Rd, Casper WY 82601
Tel (307) 253-5200 *SIC* 8211

LARAMIE COUNTY SCHOOL DISTRICT 1 p 845
2810 House Ave, Cheyenne WY 82001
Tel (307) 771-2100 *SIC* 8211

CAMPBELL COUNTY SCHOOL DISTRICT 1 p 245
1000 W 8th St, Gillette WY 82716
Tel (307) 682-5171 *SIC* 8211

ALBANY COUNTY SCHOOL DISTRICT ONE p 45
1948 E Grand Ave, Laramie WY 82070
Tel (307) 721-4400 *SIC* 8211

SWEETWATER COUNTY SCHOOL DISTRICT 1 p 1411
3550 Foothill Blvd, Rock Springs WY 82901
Tel (307) 352-3400 *SIC* 8211

SIC 8221 Colleges, Universities & Professional Schools

AUBURN UNIVERSITY p 130
107 Samford Hall, Auburn AL 36849
Tel (334) 844-4539 *SIC* 8221

SAMFORD UNIVERSITY p 1274
800 Lakeshore Dr, Birmingham AL 35229
Tel (205) 726-2011 *SIC* 8221

UNIVERSITY OF ALABAMA AT BIRMINGHAM p 1519
701 20th St S, Birmingham AL 35233
Tel (205) 934-5493 *SIC* 8221 8062

VIRGINIA COLLEGE LLC p 1558
3660 Grandview Pkwy # 300, Birmingham AL 35243
Tel (205) 329-7900 *SIC* 8221

ALABAMA A & M UNIVERSITY p 43
4900 Meridian St N, Huntsville AL 35810
Tel (256) 372-5200 *SIC* 8221

UNIVERSITY OF ALABAMA IN HUNTSVILLE p 1519
301 Sparkman Dr Nw, Huntsville AL 35805
Tel (256) 824-6340 *SIC* 8221

UNIVERSITY OF SOUTH ALABAMA p 1525
307 N University Blvd # 380, Mobile AL 36608
Tel (251) 460-6101 *SIC* 8221

ALABAMA STATE UNIVERSITY (INC) p 43
915 S Jackson St, Montgomery AL 36104
Tel (334) 229-4100 *SIC* 8221

TROY UNIVERSITY p 1485
600 University Ave, Troy AL 36082
Tel (334) 670-3179 *SIC* 8221

UNIVERSITY OF ALABAMA FOUNDATION INC p 1519
301 Rose Adm Bldg, Tuscaloosa AL 35487
Tel (205) 348-6010 *SIC* 8221

TUSKEGEE UNIVERSITY p 1493
1200 W Montgomery Rd, Tuskegee Institute AL 36088
Tel (334) 727-8011 *SIC* 8221

UNIVERSITY OF ALASKA ANCHORAGE p 1519
3211 Providence Dr, Anchorage AK 99508
Tel (907) 786-1800 *SIC* 8221

UNIVERSITY OF ALASKA FAIRBANKS p 1520
910 Yukon Dr 202, Fairbanks AK 99775
Tel (907) 474-7211 *SIC* 8221

UNIVERSITY OF ALASKA SYSTEM p 1520
3295 College Rd, Fairbanks AK 99709
Tel (907) 450-8079 *SIC* 8221

NORTHERN ARIZONA UNIVERSITY p 1055
601 S Knoles Dr Rm 220, Flagstaff AZ 86011
Tel (928) 523-9011 *SIC* 8221

▲APOLLO EDUCATION GROUP INC p 97
4025 S Riverpoint Pkwy, Phoenix AZ 85040
Tel (480) 966-5394 *SIC* 8221 8299 8748

ARIZONA BOARD OF REGENTS p 108
2020 N Central Ave # 230, Phoenix AZ 85004
Tel (602) 229-2500 *SIC* 8221 9411

▲GRAND CANYON EDUCATION INC p 629
3300 W Camelback Rd, Phoenix AZ 85017
Tel (602) 639-7500 *SIC* 8221

■GRAND CANYON UNIVERSITY INC p 629
3300 W Camelback Rd, Phoenix AZ 85017
Tel (602) 639-7500 *SIC* 8221

HIGH-TECH INSTITUTE INC p 691
2250 W Peoria Ave A100, Phoenix AZ 85029
Tel (602) 274-4300 *SIC* 8221

■UNIVERSITY OF PHOENIX INC p 1524
4025 S Riverpoint Pkwy, Phoenix AZ 85040
Tel (480) 966-5394 *SIC* 8221

ARIZONA STATE UNIVERSITY p 109
300 E University Dr # 410, Tempe AZ 85281
Tel (480) 965-2100 *SIC* 8221

UNIVERSITY OF ARIZONA p 1520
888 N Euclid Ave Rm 510, Tucson AZ 85719
Tel (520) 626-6000 *SIC* 8221

HENDRIX COLLEGE p 683
1600 Washington Ave, Conway AR 72032
Tel (501) 329-6811 *SIC* 8221

UNIVERSITY OF CENTRAL ARKANSAS p 1520
201 Donaghey Ave, Conway AR 72035
Tel (501) 450-5000 *SIC* 8221

CENTRAL ARKANSAS RADIATION THERAPY INSTITUTE INC p 277
8901 Carti Way, Little Rock AR 72205
Tel (501) 906-3000 *SIC* 8011 8221

UNIVERSITY OF ARKANSAS FOR MEDICAL SCIENCES p 1520
4301 W Markham St, Little Rock AR 72205
Tel (501) 686-6606 *SIC* 8221

UNIVERSITY OF ARKANSAS SYSTEM p 1520
2404 N University Ave, Little Rock AR 72207
Tel (501) 686-2500 *SIC* 8221

UNIVERSITY OF ARKANSAS AT PINE BLUFF p 1520
1200 University Dr, Pine Bluff AR 71601
Tel (870) 575-8000 *SIC* 8221

ARKANSAS TECH UNIVERSITY p 110
1605 Coliseum Dr, Russellville AR 72801
Tel (479) 968-0300 *SIC* 8221

HARDING UNIVERSITY INC p 661
915 E Market Ave, Searcy AR 72149
Tel (501) 279-4000 *SIC* 8221

CABRILLO COMMUNITY COLLEGE DISTRICT FINANCING CORP p 235
6500 Soquel Dr, Aptos CA 95003
Tel (831) 479-6100 *SIC* 8222 7922 8221

AZUSA PACIFIC UNIVERSITY p 141
901 E Alosta Ave, Azusa CA 91702
Tel (626) 969-3434 *SIC* 8221

UNIVERSITY CALIFORNIA BERKELEY p 1518
200 Clfrnia Hall Spc 1500, Berkeley CA 94720
Tel (510) 642-6000 *SIC* 8221

CALIFORNIA STATE UNIVERSITY CHICO p 241
400 W 1st St, Chico CA 95929
Tel (530) 898-4636 *SIC* 8221 9411

CLAREMONT GRADUATE UNIVERSITY p 321
150 E 10th St, Claremont CA 91711
Tel (909) 607-8632 *SIC* 8221

CLAREMONT MCKENNA COLLEGE FOUNDATION p 321
500 E 9th St, Claremont CA 91711
Tel (909) 621-8088 *SIC* 8221

HARVEY MUDD COLLEGE p 667
301 Platt Blvd, Claremont CA 91711
Tel (909) 621-8000 *SIC* 8221

POMONA COLLEGE p 1161
550 N College Ave, Claremont CA 91711
Tel (909) 621-8135 *SIC* 8221

COAST COMMUNITY COLLEGE DISTRICT ENTERPRISE INC p 331
1370 Adams Ave, Costa Mesa CA 92626
Tel (714) 438-4600 *SIC* 8222 8221

ORANGE COAST COLLEGE p 1091
2701 Fairview Rd, Costa Mesa CA 92626
Tel (714) 432-5772 *SIC* 8221 8299

UNIVERSITY OF CALIFORNIA DAVIS p 1520
1 Shields Ave, Davis CA 95616
Tel (530) 752-1011 *SIC* 8221 9411

GROSSMONT-CUYAMACA COMMUNITY COLLEGE DISTRICT p 641
8800 Grossmont College Dr, El Cajon CA 92020
Tel (619) 644-7010 *SIC* 8221

CALIFORNIA STATE UNIVERSITY EAST BAY p 241
25800 Carlos Bee Blvd Sa, Hayward CA 94542
Tel (510) 885-3500 *SIC* 8221 9411

BRANDMAN UNIVERSITY p 208
16355 Laguna Canyon Rd, Irvine CA 92618
Tel (949) 341-9800 *SIC* 8221

CONCORDIA UNIVERSITY p 355
1530 Concordia, Irvine CA 92612
Tel (949) 854-8002 *SIC* 8221

UNIVERSITY OF CALIFORNIA IRVINE p 1520
510 Aldrich Hall, Irvine CA 92697
Tel (949) 824-8343 *SIC* 8221 9411

MARIN COMMUNITY COLLEGE DISTRICT p 906
835 College Ave, Kentfield CA 94904
Tel (415) 457-8811 *SIC* 8222 8221

NATIONAL UNIVERSITY p 1016
11355 N Torrey Pines Rd, La Jolla CA 92037
Tel (858) 642-8000 *SIC* 8221

UNIVERSITY OF CALIFORNIA SAN DIEGO p 1520
9500 Gilman Dr, La Jolla CA 92093
Tel (858) 534-2230 *SIC* 8221 9411

BIOLA UNIVERSITY INC p 184
13800 Biola Ave, La Mirada CA 90639
Tel (562) 903-6000 *SIC* 8221

UNIVERSITY OF LA VERNE p 1522
1950 3rd St, La Verne CA 91750
Tel (909) 593-3511 *SIC* 8221

ANTELOPE VALLEY COMMUNITY COLLEGE DISTRICT p 93
3041 W Avenue K, Lancaster CA 93536
Tel (661) 722-6300 *SIC* 8222 8221

LOMA LINDA UNIVERSITY p 875
11060 Anderson St, Loma Linda CA 92350
Tel (909) 558-4540 *SIC* 8221

CALIFORNIA STATE UNIVERSITY LONG BEACH p 241
1250 N Bellflower Blvd, Long Beach CA 90840
Tel (562) 985-4111 *SIC* 8221 9411

CALIFORNIA STATE UNIVERSITY SYSTEM p 241
401 Golden Shore, Long Beach CA 90802
Tel (562) 951-4000 *SIC* 8221 9411

FOOTHILL-DE ANZA COMMUNITY COLLEGE DISTRICT FINANCING CORP p 564
12345 S El Monte Rd, Los Altos Hills CA 94022
Tel (650) 949-6100 *SIC* 8222 8221

CALIFORNIA STATE UNIVERSITY LOS ANGELES p 241
5151 State University Dr, Los Angeles CA 90032
Tel (323) 343-3000 *SIC* 8221 9411

CHARLES DREW UNIVERSITY OF MEDICINE AND SCIENCE p 289
1731 E 120th St, Los Angeles CA 90059
Tel (323) 563-4800 *SIC* 8221

INTERNATIONAL CHURCH OF FOURSQUARE GOSPEL p 754
1910 W Sunset Blvd # 200, Los Angeles CA 90026
Tel (213) 989-4234
SIC 8661 6512 7032 8211 8221

OCCIDENTAL COLLEGE p 1072
1600 Campus Rd, Los Angeles CA 90041
Tel (323) 259-2500 *SIC* 8221

UNIVERSITY OF CALIFORNIA LOS ANGELES p 1520
405 Hilgard Ave, Los Angeles CA 90095
Tel (310) 825-4321 *SIC* 8221 9411

UNIVERSITY OF SOUTHERN CALIFORNIA p 1525
3720 S Flower St Fl 3, Los Angeles CA 90007
Tel (213) 740-7762 *SIC* 8221 8071

PEPPERDINE UNIVERSITY p 1133
24255 Pacific Coast Hwy # 5000, Malibu CA 90263
Tel (310) 506-4000 *SIC* 8221

LELAND STANFORD JUNIOR UNIVERSITY p 854
2575 Sand Hill Rd, Menlo Park CA 94025
Tel (650) 723-2300 *SIC* 8221 8069 8062

SOUTH ORANGE COUNTY COMMUNITY COLLEGE DISTRICT p 1344
28000 Marguerite Pkwy, Mission Viejo CA 92692
Tel (949) 582-4500 *SIC* 8222 8221

■ **NAVAL POSTGRADUATE SCHOOL** p 1019
1 University Cir Rm M10, Monterey CA 93943
Tel (831) 656-7893 *SIC* 8221 9711

SAINT MARYS COLLEGE OF CALIFORNIA p 1270
1928 Saint Marys Rd, Moraga CA 94575
Tel (925) 631-4000 *SIC* 8221

CERRITOS COMMUNITY COLLEGE DISTRICT p 284
11110 Alondra Blvd, Norwalk CA 90650
Tel (562) 860-2451 *SIC* 8221 8222

MILLS COLLEGE p 971
5000 Macarthur Blvd, Oakland CA 94613
Tel (510) 430-2255 *SIC* 8221

REGENTS OF UNIVERSITY OF CALIFORNIA p 1219
1111 Franklin St Fl 12, Oakland CA 94607
Tel (510) 987-0700 *SIC* 8221 8733

SUMMIT MEDICAL CENTER p 1399
350 Hawthorne Ave, Oakland CA 94609
Tel (510) 655-4000 *SIC* 8062 8221 5947

CHAPMAN UNIVERSITY p 288
1 University Dr, Orange CA 92866
Tel (714) 997-6815 *SIC* 8221

CHAPMAN UNIVERSITY p 288
283 N Cypress St, Orange CA 92866
Tel (714) 997-6765 *SIC* 8221

ART CENTER COLLEGE OF DESIGN INC p 113
1700 Lida St, Pasadena CA 91103
Tel (626) 396-2200 *SIC* 8221

FULLER THEOLOGICAL SEMINARY p 584
135 N Oakland Ave, Pasadena CA 91182
Tel (626) 584-5200 *SIC* 8221

DIABLO VALLEY COLLEGE FOUNDATION p 436
321 Golf Club Rd, Pleasant Hill CA 94523
Tel (925) 685-1230 *SIC* 7389 8221

WESTERN UNIVERSITY OF HEALTH SCIENCES p 1600
309 E 2nd St, Pomona CA 91766
Tel (909) 623-6116 *SIC* 8221

FOLSOM-CORDOVA UNIF SCH DIST p 563
1965 Birkmont Dr, Rancho Cordova CA 95742
Tel (916) 294-9000 *SIC* 8221

CHAFFEY COMMUNITY COLLEGE DISTRICT (INC) p 286
5885 Haven Ave, Rancho Cucamonga CA 91737
Tel (909) 652-6560 *SIC* 8222 8221

UNIVERSITY OF REDLANDS p 1524
1200 E Colton Ave, Redlands CA 92374
Tel (909) 793-2121 *SIC* 8221

CALIFORNIA BAPTIST UNIVERSITY p 239
8432 Magnolia Ave, Riverside CA 92504
Tel (951) 689-5771 *SIC* 8221

LA SIERRA UNIVERSITY p 836
4500 Riverwalk Pkwy, Riverside CA 92505
Tel (951) 785-2000 *SIC* 8221

UNIVERSITY OF CALIFORNIA RIVERSIDE ALUMNI ASSOCIATION p 1520
900 University Ave, Riverside CA 92521
Tel (951) 827-1012 *SIC* 8221 9411

SIERRA JOINT COMMUNITY COLLEGE DISTRICT p 1320
5000 Rocklin Rd, Rocklin CA 95677
Tel (916) 624-3333 *SIC* 8222 8221

CALIFORNIA COMMUNITY COLLEGES SYSTEM p 239
1102 Q St Fl 4, Sacramento CA 95811
Tel (916) 445-8752 *SIC* 8221

CALIFORNIA STATE UNIVERSITY SAN BERNARDINO p 241
5500 University Pkwy, San Bernardino CA 92407
Tel (909) 537-5000 *SIC* 8221 9411

LOMA LINDA UNIVERSITY HEALTHCARE p 875
350 Commercial Rd Ste 101, San Bernardino CA 92408
Tel (909) 558-7132 *SIC* 8221

■ **ASHFORD UNIVERSITY LLC** p 117
8620 Spectrum Center Blvd # 100, San Diego CA 92123
Tel (800) 798-0584 *SIC* 8221

▲ **BRIDGEPOINT EDUCATION INC** p 211
13500 Evening Creek Dr N, San Diego CA 92128
Tel (858) 668-2586 *SIC* 8221

POINT LOMA NAZARENE UNIVERSITY p 1159
3900 Lomaland Dr, San Diego CA 92106
Tel (619) 221-2200 *SIC* 8221

SAN DIEGO COMMUNITY COLLEGE DISTRICT p 1276
3375 Camino Del Rio S, San Diego CA 92108
Tel (619) 388-6500 *SIC* 8222 8249 8221

SAN DIEGO STATE UNIVERSITY p 1276
5500 Campanile Dr, San Diego CA 92182
Tel (619) 594-7985 *SIC* 8221 9411

SAN DIEGO STATE UNIVERSITY FOUNDATION p 1276
5250 Campanile Dr Mc1947, San Diego CA 92182
Tel (619) 594-1900 *SIC* 8221 9411

UNIVERSITY OF SAN DIEGO p 1525
5998 Alcala Park Frnt, San Diego CA 92110
Tel (619) 260-4600 *SIC* 8221

CITY COLLEGE OF SAN FRANCISCO p 312
50 Phelan Ave, San Francisco CA 94112
Tel (415) 239-3000 *SIC* 8221 8222

SAN FRANCISCO STATE UNIVERSITY p 1276
1600 Holloway Ave, San Francisco CA 94132
Tel (415) 338-1111 *SIC* 8221 9411

STEPHENS INSTITUTE p 1386
79 New Montgomery St, San Francisco CA 94105
Tel (415) 274-2200 *SIC* 8299 8221

UNIVERSITY OF CALIFORNIA SAN FRANCISCO p 1520
505 Parnassus Ave, San Francisco CA 94143
Tel (415) 476-9000 *SIC* 8221

UNIVERSITY OF SAN FRANCISCO INC p 1525
2130 Fulton St, San Francisco CA 94117
Tel (415) 422-5555 *SIC* 8221

SAN JOSE STATE UNIVERSITY p 1277
1 Washington Sq, San Jose CA 95192
Tel (408) 924-1000 *SIC* 8221 9411

CALIFORNIA POLYTECHNIC STATE UNIVERSITY p 241
1 Grand Ave, San Luis Obispo CA 93407
Tel (805) 756-7414 *SIC* 8221 9411

UNIVERSITY OF LAVERNE CENTRAL CAMPUS p 1522
4119 Broad St Ste 200, San Luis Obispo CA 93401
Tel (805) 788-6200 *SIC* 8221

CALIFORNIA STATE UNIVERSITY SAN MARCOS p 241
333 S Twin Oaks Valley Rd, San Marcos CA 92096
Tel (760) 750-4000 *SIC* 8221 9411

DOMINICAN UNIVERSITY OF CALIFORNIA p 449
50 Acacia Ave, San Rafael CA 94901
Tel (415) 457-4440 *SIC* 8221

RANCHO SANTIAGO COMMUNITY COLLEGE DISTRICT INC p 1207
2323 N Broadway Fl 4, Santa Ana CA 92706
Tel (714) 480-7300 *SIC* 8222 8221

UNIVERSITY OF CALIFORNIA SANTA BARBARA p 1520
Uc Santa Barbara Mosher A, Santa Barbara CA 93106
Tel (805) 893-8000 *SIC* 8221 9411

PRESIDENT AND BOARD OF TRUSTEES OF SANTA CLARA COLLEGE p 1172
500 El Camino Real, Santa Clara CA 95050
Tel (408) 554-4000 *SIC* 8221

SANTA CLARITA COMMUNITY COLLEGE DISTRICT p 1280
26455 Rockwell Canyon Rd, Santa Clarita CA 91355
Tel (661) 259-7800 *SIC* 8222 8221

UNIVERSITY OF CALIFORNIA SANTA CRUZ p 1520
1156 High St, Santa Cruz CA 95064
Tel (831) 459-0111 *SIC* 8221

SONOMA COUNTY JUNIOR COLLEGE DISTRICT p 1340
1501 Mendocino Ave, Santa Rosa CA 95401
Tel (707) 527-4011 *SIC* 8222 8221

WEST VALLEY-MISSION COMMUNITY COLLEGE DISTRICT p 1596
14000 Fruitvale Ave, Saratoga CA 95070
Tel (408) 867-2200 *SIC* 8222 8221

STANFORD UNIVERSITY p 1376
295 Galvez St, Stanford CA 94305
Tel (650) 723-2300 *SIC* 8221

UNIVERSITY OF PACIFIC p 1524
3601 Pacific Ave, Stockton CA 95211
Tel (209) 946-2401 *SIC* 8221

CALIFORNIA LUTHERAN UNIVERSITY p 240
60 W Olsen Rd, Thousand Oaks CA 91360
Tel (805) 493-3135 *SIC* 8221

CALIFORNIA INSTITUTE OF ARTS p 240
24700 Mcbean Pkwy, Valencia CA 91355
Tel (661) 255-1050 *SIC* 8221 8231 8249

VENTURA COUNTY COMMUNITY COLLEGE DISTRICT p 1548
255 W Stanley Ave Ste 150, Ventura CA 93001
Tel (805) 652-5500 *SIC* 8222 8221

REGENTS OF UNIVERSITY OF COLORADO p 1219
3100 Marine St Ste 48157, Boulder CO 80303
Tel (303) 735-6624 *SIC* 8221 8621

COLORADO COLLEGE p 338
14 E Cache La Poudre St, Colorado Springs CO 80903
Tel (719) 389-6000 *SIC* 8221

RHODES COLLEGES INC p 1232
1815 Jet Wing Dr, Colorado Springs CO 80916
Tel (719) 638-6580 *SIC* 8221 8222

COLORADO SEMINARY p 339
2199 S Univ Blvd, Denver CO 80210
Tel (303) 871-2000 *SIC* 8221

COLORADO STATE UNIVERSITY SYSTEM p 339
475 17th St Ste 1550, Denver CO 80202
Tel (303) 534-6290 *SIC* 8221

METROPOLITAN STATE UNIVERSITY OF DENVER p 956
890 Auraria Pkwy, Denver CO 80204
Tel (303) 556-3030 *SIC* 8221

REGIS UNIVERSITY p 1220
3333 Regis Blvd, Denver CO 80221
Tel (303) 458-4100 *SIC* 8221

COLORADO STATE UNIVERSITY p 339
6003 Campus Delivery, Fort Collins CO 80523
Tel (970) 491-1372 *SIC* 8221

TRUSTEES OF COLORADO SCHOOL OF MINES p 1487
1500 Illinois St, Golden CO 80401
Tel (303) 273-3000 *SIC* 8221

COLORADO MESA UNIVERSITY p 339
1100 North Ave, Grand Junction CO 81501
Tel (970) 248-1020 *SIC* 8221

UNIVERSITY OF NORTHERN COLORADO p 1524
501 20th St, Greeley CO 80639
Tel (970) 351-1890 *SIC* 8221

COLORADO CHRISTIAN UNIVERSITY INC p 338
8787 W Alameda Ave, Lakewood CO 80226
Tel (303) 963-3000 *SIC* 8221

COLORADO STATE UNIVERSITY-PUEBLO p 339
2200 Bonforte Blvd, Pueblo CO 81001
Tel (719) 549-2100 *SIC* 8221

UNIVERSITY OF BRIDGEPORT p 1520
126 Park Ave, Bridgeport CT 06604
Tel (203) 576-4000 *SIC* 8221

GOODWIN COLLEGE INC p 625
1 Riverside Dr, East Hartford CT 06118
Tel (860) 895-8000 *SIC* 8221

FAIRFIELD UNIVERSITY p 525
1073 N Benson Rd, Fairfield CT 06824
Tel (203) 254-4000 *SIC* 8221 8211

SACRED HEART UNIVERSITY INC p 1265
5151 Park Ave, Fairfield CT 06825
Tel (203) 371-7999 *SIC* 8221

QUINNIPIAC UNIVERSITY p 1200
275 Mount Carmel Ave, Hamden CT 06518
Tel (203) 582-8200 *SIC* 8221

BOARD OF TRUSTEES OF COMMUNITY-TECHNICAL COLLEGE p 196
61 Woodland St Ste 2, Hartford CT 06105
Tel (860) 723-0011 *SIC* 8221

CONNECTICUT STATE COLLEGES & UNIVERSITIES BOARD OF REGENTS FOR HIGHER EDUCATION p 357
61 Woodland St, Hartford CT 06105
Tel (860) 723-0000 *SIC* 8221

CONNECTICUT STATE UNIVERSITY SYSTEM p 357
61 Woodland St, Hartford CT 06105
Tel (860) 493-0000 *SIC* 8221

TRINITY COLLEGE p 1481
300 Summit St Ste 1, Hartford CT 06106
Tel (860) 297-2000 *SIC* 8221

WESLEYAN UNIVERSITY p 1593
45 Wyllys Ave, Middletown CT 06459
Tel (860) 685-2000 *SIC* 8221 6552

YALE UNIVERSITY p 1634
105 Wall St, New Haven CT 06511
Tel (203) 432-2550
SIC 8221 2731 2721 2741

CONNECTICUT COLLEGE p 356
270 Mohegan Ave, New London CT 06320
Tel (860) 447-1911 *SIC* 8221

UNIVERSITY OF CONNECTICUT p 1521
343 Mansfield Rd U-1130, Storrs CT 06269
Tel (860) 486-2000 *SIC* 8221 9199

UNIVERSITY OF HARTFORD p 1521
200 Bloomfield Ave, West Hartford CT 06117
Tel (860) 768-4393 *SIC* 8221

UNIVERSITY OF NEW HAVEN INC p 1523
300 Boston Post Rd, West Haven CT 06516
Tel (203) 932-7000 *SIC* 8221

WILMINGTON UNIVERSITY INC p 1613
320 N Dupont Hwy, New Castle DE 19720
Tel (302) 356-6824 *SIC* 8221

UNIVERSITY OF DELAWARE p 1521
220 Hullihen Hall, Newark DE 19716
Tel (302) 831-2107 *SIC* 8221

AMERICAN UNIVERSITY p 81
4400 Massachusetts Ave Nw, Washington DC 20016
Tel (202) 885-1000 *SIC* 8221

CATHOLIC UNIVERSITY OF AMERICA p 267
620 Michigan Ave Ne, Washington DC 20064
Tel (202) 319-5000 *SIC* 8221

GALLAUDET UNIVERSITY p 589
800 Florida Ave Ne, Washington DC 20002
Tel (202) 651-5000 *SIC* 8221

GEORGE WASHINGTON UNIVERSITY p 606
2121 I St Nw Ste 601, Washington DC 20052
Tel (202) 242-6600 *SIC* 8221

GEORGETOWN UNIVERSITY p 607
37th & O Sts Nw, Washington DC 20057
Tel (202) 687-0100 *SIC* 8221 8062

HOWARD UNIVERSITY p 713
2400 6th St Nw, Washington DC 20059
Tel (202) 806-6100 *SIC* 8221

MEDSTAR-GEORGETOWN MEDICAL CENTER INC p 939
3800 Reservoir Rd Nw, Washington DC 20007
Tel (202) 444-2000 *SIC* 8062 8221 8069

UNIVERSITY OF DISTRICT OF COLUMBIA p 1521
4200 Conn Ave Nw Ste 200, Washington DC 20008
Tel (202) 274-5000 *SIC* 8221

FLORIDA ATLANTIC UNIVERSITY p 557
777 Glades Rd, Boca Raton FL 33431
Tel (561) 297-3000 *SIC* 8221

LYNN UNIVERSITY INC p 888
3601 N Military Trl, Boca Raton FL 33431
Tel (561) 237-7000 *SIC* 8221

BOARD OF TRUSTEES ST PETERSBURG COLLEGE p 196
6021 142nd Ave N, Clearwater FL 33760
Tel (727) 341-3329 *SIC* 8221

EASTERN FLORIDA STATE COLLEGE p 472
1519 Clearlake Rd, Cocoa FL 32922
Tel (321) 433-7345 *SIC* 8221

UNIVERSITY OF MIAMI p 1523
1320 S Dixie Hwy Ste 150, Coral Gables FL 33146
Tel (305) 284-5155 *SIC* 8221

NOVA SOUTHEASTERN UNIVERSITY INC p 1062
3301 College Ave, Davie FL 33314
Tel (954) 262-7300 *SIC* 8221 8211

BETHUNE-COOKMAN UNIVERSITY INC p 178
640 Dr Mary Mcleod Bethun, Daytona Beach FL 32114
Tel (386) 481-2000 *SIC* 8221

EMBRY-RIDDLE AERONAUTICAL UNIVERSITY INC p 490
600 S Clyde Morris Blvd, Daytona Beach FL 32114
Tel (386) 226-6000 *SIC* 8221

STETSON UNIVERSITY INC p 1388
421 N Woodland Blvd, Deland FL 32723
Tel (386) 822-7000 *SIC* 8221

EVERGLADES COLLEGE INC p 514
1900 W Coml Blvd Ste 180, Fort Lauderdale FL 33309
Tel (954) 776-4476 *SIC* 8221

FLORIDA GULF COAST UNIVERSITY p 558
10501 Fgcu Blvd S, Fort Myers FL 33965
Tel (239) 590-1000 *SIC* 8221

SANTA FE COLLEGE p 1280
3000 Nw 83rd St, Gainesville FL 32606
Tel (352) 395-5000 *SIC* 8222 8221

UNIVERSITY OF FLORIDA p 1521
300 Sw 13th St, Gainesville FL 32611
Tel (352) 392-3261 *SIC* 8221

UNIVERSITY OF FLORIDA FOUNDATION INC p 1521
2012 W University Ave, Gainesville FL 32603
Tel (352) 392-1691 *SIC* 8399 8641 8221

FLORIDA STATE COLLEGE AT JACKSONVILLE p 559
501 W State St Ste 307, Jacksonville FL 32202
Tel (904) 632-3251 *SIC* 8221

JACKSONVILLE UNIVERSITY p 774
2800 University Blvd N, Jacksonville FL 32211
Tel (904) 256-8000 *SIC* 8221

UNIVERSITY OF NORTH FLORIDA p 1524
1 U N F Dr, Jacksonville FL 32224
Tel (904) 620-1000 *SIC* 8221

REMINGTON COLLEGES INC p 1222
7131 Bus Pk Ln Ste 300, Lake Mary FL 32746
Tel (407) 562-5500 *SIC* 8221 8222

PALM BEACH STATE COLLEGE p 1109
4200 S Congress Ave, Lake Worth FL 33461
Tel (561) 868-3350 *SIC* 8222 8351 8221

FLORIDA SOUTHERN COLLEGE p 559
111 Lake Hollingsworth Dr, Lakeland FL 33801
Tel (863) 680-4111 *SIC* 8221

FLORIDA INSTITUTE OF TECHNOLOGY INC p 559
150 W University Blvd Ofc, Melbourne FL 32901
Tel (321) 674-8000 *SIC* 8221 4581 8299

FLORIDA INTERNATIONAL UNIVERSITY p 559
11200 Sw 8th St, Miami FL 33199
Tel (305) 348-2494 *SIC* 8221

MIAMI DADE COLLEGE p 959
300 Ne 2nd Ave Rm 3116, Miami FL 33132
Tel (305) 237-3000 *SIC* 8222 9411 8221

BARRY UNIVERSITY INC p 157
11300 Ne 2nd Ave, Miami Shores FL 33161
Tel (305) 899-3050 *SIC* 8221

UNIVERSITY OF CENTRAL FLORIDA BOARD OF TRUSTEES p 1520
4000 Central Florida Blvd, Orlando FL 32816
Tel (407) 823-2000 *SIC* 8221

PENSACOLA CHRISTIAN COLLEGE INC p 1131
250 Brent Ln, Pensacola FL 32503
Tel (850) 478-8496 *SIC* 8221

UNIVERSITY OF WEST FLORIDA p 1526
11000 University Pkwy # 10, Pensacola FL 32514
Tel (850) 474-2000 *SIC* 8221

SAINT LEO UNIVERSITY INC p 1270
33701 State Road 52, Saint Leo FL 33574
Tel (352) 588-8200 *SIC* 8221

SEMINOLE STATE COLLEGE OF FLORIDA p 1302
100 Weldon Blvd, Sanford FL 32773
Tel (407) 708-4722 *SIC* 8221

BOARD OF GOVERNORS STATE UNIVERSITY SYSTEM OF FLORIDA p 195
325 W Gaines St Ste 1625, Tallahassee FL 32399
Tel (850) 245-0466 *SIC* 8221

FLORIDA A & M UNIVERSITY p 557
1601 S M L King Jr Blvd, Tallahassee FL 32307
Tel (850) 599-3000 *SIC* 8221

FLORIDA STATE UNIVERSITY p 559
600 W College Ave, Tallahassee FL 32306
Tel (850) 644-5482 *SIC* 8221

UNIVERSITY OF SOUTH FLORIDA BOARD OF TRUSTESS p 1525
4202 E Fowler Ave, Tampa FL 33620
Tel (813) 974-2011 *SIC* 8221

UNIVERSITY OF TAMPA INC p 1525
401 W Kennedy Blvd, Tampa FL 33606
Tel (813) 253-3333 *SIC* 8221

PALM BEACH ATLANTIC UNIVERSITY INC p 1109
901 S Flagler Dr, West Palm Beach FL 33401
Tel (561) 803-2000 *SIC* 8221

ROLLINS COLLEGE p 1247
1000 Holt Ave 2718, Winter Park FL 32789
Tel (407) 646-2000 *SIC* 8221

■ KAPLAN HIGHER EDUCATION LLC p 803
900 North Point Pkwy # 250, Alpharetta GA 30005
Tel (770) 360-6100 *SIC* 8221 8244

UNIVERSITY OF GEORGIA p 1521
424 E Broad St, Athens GA 30602
Tel (706) 542-2786 *SIC* 8221

ATLANTA CLARK UNIVERSITY INC p 125
223 James P Brawley Dr Sw, Atlanta GA 30314
Tel (404) 880-8000 *SIC* 8221

BOARD OF REGENTS OF UNIVERSITY SYSTEM OF GEORGIA p 195
270 Washington St Sw Fl 7, Atlanta GA 30334
Tel (404) 962-3050 *SIC* 8221

CARTER CENTER COLABORATIVE INC p 261
453 Freedom Pkwy Ne, Atlanta GA 30307
Tel (404) 420-5100 *SIC* 8221

EMORY UNIVERSITY p 493
201 Dowman Dr Ne, Atlanta GA 30322
Tel (404) 727-6013 *SIC* 8221 8082

GEORGIA INSTITUTE OF TECHNOLOGY p 607
225 North Ave Nw, Atlanta GA 30332
Tel (404) 894-2000 *SIC* 8221

GEORGIA STATE UNIVERSITY p 607
30 Courtland St Se, Atlanta GA 30303
Tel (404) 413-2000 *SIC* 8221

MOREHOUSE COLLEGE (INC) p 988
830 Westview Dr Sw, Atlanta GA 30314
Tel (404) 681-2800 *SIC* 8221

MOREHOUSE SCHOOL OF MEDICINE INC p 988
720 Westview Dr Sw, Atlanta GA 30310
Tel (404) 752-1500 *SIC* 8322 8221

SPELMAN COLLEGE p 1358
350 Spelman Ln Sw 589, Atlanta GA 30314
Tel (404) 681-3643 *SIC* 8221

AUGUSTA UNIVERSITY p 131
1120 15th St, Augusta GA 30912
Tel (706) 721-0011 *SIC* 8221

GEORGIA HEALTH SCIENCES FOUNDATION INC p 607
1120 15th St, Augusta GA 30912
Tel (800) 869-1113 *SIC* 8062 8221

UNIVERSITY OF WEST GEORGIA p 1526
1601 Maple St, Carrollton GA 30118
Tel (678) 839-4780 *SIC* 8221

UNIVERSITY OF NORTH GEORGIA p 1524
82 College Ln, Dahlonega GA 30533
Tel (706) 864-1400 *SIC* 8221

KENNESAW STATE UNIVERSITY p 811
1000 Chastain Rd Nw, Kennesaw GA 30144
Tel (770) 423-6000 *SIC* 8221

CORP OF MERCER UNIVERSITY p 371
1400 Coleman Ave, Macon GA 31207
Tel (478) 301-2700 *SIC* 8221

MIDDLE GEORGIA STATE UNIVERSITY p 964
100 University Pkwy, Macon GA 31206
Tel (478) 471-2700 *SIC* 8221

SOUTHERN POLYTECHNIC STATE UNIVERSITY FOUNDATION INC p 1350
1100 S Marietta Pkwy Se, Marietta GA 30060
Tel (678) 915-7778 *SIC* 8221

BERRY COLLEGE INC p 176
2277 Martha Berry Hwy Nw, Rome GA 30161
Tel (706) 232-5374 *SIC* 8221

SAVANNAH COLLEGE OF ART AND DESIGN INC p 1284
126 E Gaston St, Savannah GA 31401
Tel (912) 525-5000 *SIC* 8221

GEORGIA SOUTHERN UNIVERSITY p 607
1582 Southern Dr, Statesboro GA 30458
Tel (912) 681-5224 *SIC* 8221

VALDOSTA STATE UNIVERSITY p 1539
1500 N Patterson St, Valdosta GA 31698
Tel (229) 333-5800 *SIC* 8221

HAWAII PACIFIC UNIVERSITY p 669
1164 Bishop St Ste 800, Honolulu HI 96813
Tel (808) 544-0200 *SIC* 8221

UNIVERSITY OF HAWAII SYSTEMS p 1521
2444 Dole St, Honolulu HI 96822
Tel (808) 956-8278 *SIC* 8221 8222

BRIGHAM YOUNG UNIVERSITY-HAWAII p 212
55-220 Kulanui St, Laie HI 96762
Tel (808) 293-3211 *SIC* 8221

BOISE STATE UNIVERSITY p 198
1910 University Dr, Boise ID 83725
Tel (208) 426-1011 *SIC* 8221

REGENTS OF UNIVERSITY OF IDAHO p 1219
875 Perimeter Dr Ms3020, Moscow ID 83844
Tel (208) 885-6174 *SIC* 8221

IDAHO STATE UNIVERSITY p 728
921 S 8th Ave, Pocatello ID 83209
Tel (208) 282-0211 *SIC* 8221

BRIGHAM YOUNG UNIVERSITY-IDAHO p 212
525 S Center St, Rexburg ID 83460
Tel (208) 496-1901 *SIC* 8221

SOUTHWESTERN ILLINOIS COLLEGE COMMUNITY COLLEGE DISTRICT NO 522 p 1353
2500 Carlyle Ave, Belleville IL 62221
Tel (618) 235-2700 *SIC* 8222 8221

OLIVET NAZARENE UNIVERSITY p 1082
1 University Ave, Bourbonnais IL 60914
Tel (815) 939-5247 *SIC* 8221

SOUTHERN ILLINOIS UNIVERSITY INC p 1349
1400 Douglas Dr, Carbondale IL 62901
Tel (618) 536-3475 *SIC* 8221

SOUTHERN ILLINOIS UNIVERSITY SYSTEM p 1349
1400 Douglas Dr, Carbondale IL 62901
Tel (618) 536-3331 *SIC* 8221

EASTERN ILLINOIS UNIVERSITY p 472
600 Lincoln Ave, Charleston IL 61920
Tel (217) 581-5000 *SIC* 8221 5812

BOARD OF TRUSTEES OF COMMUNITY COLLEGE DISTRICT 508 (INC) p 196
226 W Jackson Blvd # 103, Chicago IL 60606
Tel (312) 553-2752 *SIC* 8221 8222

CHICAGO SCHOOL OF PROFESSIONAL PSYCHOLOGY p 297
325 N Wells St Fl 4, Chicago IL 60654
Tel (312) 379-1699 *SIC* 8221

CHICAGO STATE UNIVERSITY p 297
9501 S King Dr, Chicago IL 60628
Tel (773) 995-2000 *SIC* 8221

COLUMBIA COLLEGE CHICAGO p 340
600 S Michigan Ave Fl 5, Chicago IL 60605
Tel (312) 663-1600 *SIC* 8221

DE PAUL UNIVERSITY p 419
1 E Jackson Blvd, Chicago IL 60604
Tel (312) 362-6714 *SIC* 8221

ILLINOIS INSTITUTE OF TECHNOLOGY p 732
10 W 35th St, Chicago IL 60616
Tel (312) 567-3000 *SIC* 8221

LOYOLA UNIVERSITY OF CHICAGO INC p 882
1032 W Sheridan Rd, Chicago IL 60660
Tel (773) 274-3000 *SIC* 8221

MOODY BIBLE INSTITUTE OF CHICAGO p 987
820 N La Salle Dr, Chicago IL 60610
Tel (312) 329-4000
SIC 8661 8299 8221 4832 2731

NATIONAL LOUIS UNIVERSITY p 1014
122 S Michigan Ave # 600, Chicago IL 60603
Tel (312) 261-3599 *SIC* 8221 8211

NORTH PARK UNIVERSITY p 1053
2543 W Cullom Ave, Chicago IL 60618
Tel (773) 244-6200 *SIC* 8221

NORTHEASTERN ILLINOIS UNIVERSITY p 1055
5500 N Saint Louis Ave, Chicago IL 60625
Tel (773) 442-4000 *SIC* 8221

ROOSEVELT UNIVERSITY p 1249
430 S Michigan Ave, Chicago IL 60605
Tel (312) 341-3500 *SIC* 8221

SAINT XAVIER UNIVERSITY p 1271
3700 W 103rd St, Chicago IL 60655
Tel (773) 298-3000 *SIC* 8221

TOYOTA TECHNOLOGICAL INSTITUTE AT CHICAGO p 1467
6045 S Kenwood Ave, Chicago IL 60637
Tel (773) 834-2500 *SIC* 8221

UNIVERSITY OF CHICAGO p 1520
5801 S Ellis Ave Ste 1, Chicago IL 60637
Tel (773) 702-1234 *SIC* 8221

MCHENRY COUNTY COLLEGE p 929
8900 Us Highway 14, Crystal Lake IL 60012
Tel (815) 455-3700 *SIC* 8222 8221 9411

NORTHERN ILLINOIS UNIVERSITY ALUMNI ASSOCIATION p 1056
1425 W Lincoln Hwy, Dekalb IL 60115
Tel (815) 753-9500 *SIC* 8221

OAKTON COMMUNITY COLLEGE p 1071
1600 E Golf Rd Rm 1505, Des Plaines IL 60016
Tel (847) 635-1600 *SIC* 8221 8222

▲ DEVRY EDUCATION GROUP INC p 434
3005 Highland Pkwy # 700, Downers Grove IL 60515
Tel (630) 515-7700
SIC 8221 8299 8249 8243

■ DEVRY UNIVERSITY INC p 434
3005 Highland Pkwy # 700, Downers Grove IL 60515
Tel (630) 515-7700 *SIC* 8221

MIDWESTERN UNIVERSITY p 968
555 31st St, Downers Grove IL 60515
Tel (630) 515-7300 *SIC* 8221

ELGIN COMMUNITY COLLEGE p 486
1700 Spartan Dr, Elgin IL 60123
Tel (847) 697-1000 *SIC* 8222 8221 9411

ELMHURST COLLEGE p 489
190 S Prospect Ave, Elmhurst IL 60126
Tel (630) 279-4100 *SIC* 8221

NORTHWESTERN UNIVERSITY p 1061
633 Clark St, Evanston IL 60208
Tel (847) 491-3741 *SIC* 8221

LAKE FOREST COLLEGE p 839
555 N Sheridan Rd, Lake Forest IL 60045
Tel (847) 234-3100 *SIC* 8221

BENEDICTINE UNIVERSITY p 172
5700 College Rd, Lisle IL 60532
Tel (630) 829-6000 *SIC* 8221

WESTERN ILLINOIS UNIVERSITY INC p 1598
1 University Cir, Macomb IL 61455
Tel (309) 298-1800 *SIC* 8221

LAKE LAND COLLEGE p 839
5001 Lake Land Blvd, Mattoon IL 61938
Tel (217) 234-5253 *SIC* 8222 8221

NORTH CENTRAL COLLEGE p 1051
30 N Brainard St, Naperville IL 60540
Tel (630) 637-5100 *SIC* 8221

BOARD OF TRUSTEES OF ILLINOIS STATE UNIVERSITY p 196
302 Hovey Hall, Normal IL 61790
Tel (309) 438-2111 *SIC* 8221

ROSALIND FRANKLIN UNIVERSITY OF MEDICINE AND SCIENCE p 1250
3333 Green Bay Rd, North Chicago IL 60064
Tel (847) 578-3000 *SIC* 8221

HARPER COLLEGE p 663
1200 W Algonquin Rd, Palatine IL 60067
Tel (847) 925-6707 *SIC* 8221

BRADLEY UNIVERSITY p 206
1501 W Bradley Ave, Peoria IL 61625
Tel (309) 677-3150 *SIC* 8221

DOMINICAN UNIVERSITY p 449
7900 Division St, River Forest IL 60305
Tel (708) 366-2490 *SIC* 8221

LEWIS UNIVERSITY p 859
1 University Pkwy, Romeoville IL 60446
Tel (815) 838-0500 *SIC* 8221

▲ CAREER EDUCATION CORP p 254
231 N Martingale Rd # 100, Schaumburg IL 60173
Tel (847) 781-3600 *SIC* 8221 8244 8299

ILLINOIS COMMUNITY COLLEGE SYSTEM p 732
401 E Capitol Ave, Springfield IL 62701
Tel (217) 528-2858 *SIC* 8221 9411

GOVERNORS STATE UNIVERSITY p 627
1 University Pkwy, University Park IL 60484
Tel (708) 534-5000 *SIC* 8221

UNIVERSITY OF ILLINOIS p 1521
506 S Wright St Rm 364, Urbana IL 61801
Tel (217) 333-1000 *SIC* 8221

TRUSTEES OF WHEATON COLLEGE p 1488
501 College Ave, Wheaton IL 60187
Tel (630) 752-5000 *SIC* 8221

TRUSTEES OF INDIANA UNIVERSITY p 1488
509 E 3rd St, Bloomington IN 47401
Tel (812) 855-0516 *SIC* 8221

ITT EDUCATIONAL SERVICES INC p 768
13000 N Meridian St, Carmel IN 46032
Tel (317) 706-9200 *SIC* 8221

UNIVERSITY OF SOUTHERN INDIANA p 1525
8600 University Blvd, Evansville IN 47712
Tel (812) 464-8600 *SIC* 8221

INDIANA INSTITUTE OF TECHNOLOGY INC p 738
1600 E Washington Blvd, Fort Wayne IN 46803
Tel (260) 422-5561 *SIC* 8221

DEPAUW UNIVERSITY p 430
313 S Locust St, Greencastle IN 46135
Tel (765) 658-4800 *SIC* 8221

BUTLER UNIVERSITY p 230
4600 Sunset Ave, Indianapolis IN 46208
Tel (317) 940-8000 *SIC* 8221

EDUCATIONAL MANAGEMENT CORP p 479
550 E Washington St, Indianapolis IN 46204
Tel (317) 264-5656 *SIC* 8221

IVY TECH COMMUNITY COLLEGE OF INDIANA p 769
50 W Fall Creek Pkwy N Dr, Indianapolis IN 46208
Tel (317) 921-4882 *SIC* 8221

UNIVERSITY OF INDIANAPOLIS p 1521
1400 E Hanna Ave, Indianapolis IN 46227
Tel (317) 788-3368 *SIC* 8221

INDIANA WESLEYAN UNIVERSITY p 739
4201 S Washington St, Marion IN 46953
Tel (765) 674-6901 *SIC* 8221

BALL STATE UNIVERSITY p 148
2000 W University Ave, Muncie IN 47306
Tel (765) 289-1241 *SIC* 8221

UNIVERSITY OF NOTRE DAME DU LAC p 1524
805 Grace Hall, Notre Dame IN 46556
Tel (574) 631-6401 *SIC* 8221

EARLHAM COLLEGE p 469
801 National Rd W, Richmond IN 47374
Tel (765) 983-1200 *SIC* 8221

INDIANA STATE UNIVERSITY p 738
200 N 7th St, Terre Haute IN 47809
Tel (800) 468-6478 *SIC* 8221

ROSE-HULMAN INSTITUTE OF TECHNOLOGY INC p 1250
5500 Wabash Ave, Terre Haute IN 47803
Tel (812) 877-1511 *SIC* 8221

LUTHERAN UNIVERSITY ASSOCIATION INC p 886
1700 Chapel Dr, Valparaiso IN 46383
Tel (219) 464-5000 *SIC* 8221

VINCENNES UNIVERSITY p 1557
1002 N 1st St, Vincennes IN 47591
Tel (812) 888-8888 *SIC* 8221 5942

PURDUE UNIVERSITY p 1192
401 S Grant St, West Lafayette IN 47907
Tel (765) 494-8000 *SIC* 8221

IOWA STATE UNIVERSITY OF SCIENCE AND TECHNOLOGY p 763
1350 Beardshear Hall, Ames IA 50011
Tel (515) 294-6162 *SIC* 8221

DES MOINES AREA COMMUNITY COLLEGE p 431
2006 S Ankeny Blvd, Ankeny IA 50023
Tel (515) 964-6214 *SIC* 8221

UNIVERSITY OF NORTHERN IOWA p 1524
1227 W 27th St, Cedar Falls IA 50614
Tel (319) 242-7325 *SIC* 8221

ST AMBROSE UNIVERSITY p 1364
518 W Locust St, Davenport IA 52803
Tel (563) 333-6000 *SIC* 8221

DRAKE UNIVERSITY p 455
2507 University Ave, Des Moines IA 50311
Tel (515) 271-2011 *SIC* 8221

MERCY COLLEGE OF HEALTH SCIENCES p 946
928 6th Ave, Des Moines IA 50309
Tel (515) 643-3180 *SIC* 8221

TRUSTEES OF GRINNELL COLLEGE p 1488
733 Broad St, Grinnell IA 50112
Tel (641) 269-3500 *SIC* 8221

UNIVERSITY OF IOWA p 1521
101 Jessup Hall, Iowa City IA 52242
Tel (319) 335-3500 *SIC* 8221

GRACELAND UNIVERSITY p 628
1 University Pl, Lamoni IA 50140
Tel (641) 784-5000 *SIC* 8221

EASTERN IOWA COMMUNITY COLLEGE DISTRICT p 472
152 Colorado St, Muscatine IA 52761
Tel (563) 264-2088 *SIC* 8222 8221

WARTBURG COLLEGE p 1577
100 Wartburg Blvd, Waverly IA 50677
Tel (319) 352-8200 *SIC* 8221

EMPORIA STATE UNIVERSITY p 494
1 Kellogg Cir, Emporia KS 66801
Tel (620) 341-1200 *SIC* 8221

FORT HAYS STATE UNIVERSITY p 568
600 Park St, Hays KS 67601
Tel (785) 628-4000 *SIC* 8221

UNIVERSITY OF KANSAS MEDICAL CENTER RESEARCH INSTITUTE INC p 1522
3901 Rainbow Blvd, Kansas City KS 66160
Tel (913) 588-5000 *SIC* 8221

UNIVERSITY OF KANSAS p 1522
1450 Jayhawk Blvd Rm 225, Lawrence KS 66045
Tel (785) 864-4868 *SIC* 8221

KANSAS STATE UNIVERSITY p 803
110 Anderson Hall, Manhattan KS 66506
Tel (785) 532-6210 *SIC* 8221

JOHNSON COUNTY COMMUNITY COLLEGE p 791
12345 College Blvd, Overland Park KS 66210
Tel (913) 469-8500 *SIC* 8222 8221

WASHBURN UNIVERSITY OF TOPEKA p 1577
1700 Sw College Ave, Topeka KS 66621
Tel (785) 670-1010 *SIC* 8221

BEREA COLLEGE p 174
101 Chestnut St, Berea KY 40403
Tel (859) 985-3000 *SIC* 8221

WESTERN KENTUCKY UNIVERSITY p 1598
1906 College Heights Blvd # 11026, Bowling Green KY 42101
Tel (270) 745-0111 *SIC* 8221

CENTRE COLLEGE OF KENTUCKY p 281
600 W Walnut St, Danville KY 40422
Tel (859) 238-5200 *SIC* 8221

EASTERN KENTUCKY UNIVERSITY p 472
91 Lilley Cornett Br, Hallie KY 41821
Tel (606) 633-5828 *SIC* 8221

UNIVERSITY OF KENTUCKY p 1522
411 S Limestone, Lexington KY 40508
Tel (859) 257-4759 *SIC* 8221

UNIVERSITY OF LOUISVILLE p 1522
2301 S 3rd St, Louisville KY 40292
Tel (502) 852-5555 *SIC* 8221

MOREHEAD STATE UNIVERSITY p 988
207 Hal Mcdowell, Morehead KY 40351
Tel (606) 783-2053 *SIC* 8221

MURRAY STATE UNIVERSITY p 1002
102 Curris Ctr, Murray KY 42071
Tel (270) 809-3774 *SIC* 8221

NORTHERN KENTUCKY UNIVERSITY p 1056
Nunn Dr, Newport KY 41099
Tel (859) 572-5100 *SIC* 8221

EASTERN KENTUCKY UNIVERSITY p 472
521 Lancaster Ave, Richmond KY 40475
Tel (859) 622-1791 *SIC* 8221

LOUISIANA STATE UNIVERSITY p 880
202 Himes Hall, Baton Rouge LA 70803
Tel (225) 578-2760 *SIC* 8221

LOUISIANA STATE UNIVERSITY p 880
3810 W Lkshore Dr Ste 111, Baton Rouge LA 70808
Tel (225) 578-2760 *SIC* 8221

SOUTHERN UNIVERSITY AGRICULTURAL & MECHANICAL COLLEGE p 1350
G Leon Netherville Dr, Baton Rouge LA 70813
Tel (225) 771-5021 *SIC* 8221 9411

SOUTHERN UNIVERSITY AND A&M COLLEGE SYSTEM p 1350
J S Clark Adm Bldg 3rd Fl, Baton Rouge LA 70813
Tel (225) 771-4680 *SIC* 8221

GRAMBLING STATE UNIVERSITY p 629
403 Main St, Grambling LA 71245
Tel (318) 274-2558 *SIC* 8221 9411

SOUTHEASTERN LOUISIANA UNIVERSITY p 1346
500 Ned Mcgehee Dr, Hammond LA 70402
Tel (985) 549-2068 *SIC* 8221

UNIVERSITY OF LOUISIANA AT LAFAYETTE p 1522
104 E University Ave, Lafayette LA 70503
Tel (337) 482-1000 *SIC* 8221

ADMINISTRATORS OF TULANE EDUCATIONAL FUND p 23
6823 Saint Charles Ave, New Orleans LA 70118
Tel (504) 865-5000 *SIC* 8221 8733

LOYOLA UNIVERSITY NEW ORLEANS INC p 882
6363 Saint Charles Ave, New Orleans LA 70118
Tel (504) 865-2011 *SIC* 8221

UNIVERSITY OF NEW ORLEANS p 1523
2000 Lakeshore Dr, New Orleans LA 70122
Tel (888) 514-4275 *SIC* 8221

XAVIER UNIVERSITY OF LOUISIANA p 1631
1 Drexel Dr, New Orleans LA 70125
Tel (504) 520-7411 *SIC* 8221

LOUISIANA TECH UNIVERSITY p 880
1100 Hull Ave, Ruston LA 71270
Tel (318) 257-3267 *SIC* 8221

UNIVERSITY OF MAINE SYSTEM p 1522
16 Central St, Bangor ME 04401
Tel (207) 973-3300 *SIC* 8221

UNIVERSITY OF NEW ENGLAND p 1523
11 Hills Beach Rd, Biddeford ME 04005
Tel (207) 282-3025 *SIC* 8221 5942

BOWDOIN COLLEGE p 204
5600 College Sta, Brunswick ME 04011
Tel (207) 725-3000 *SIC* 8221

PRESIDENT & TRUSTEES OF BATES COLLEGE p 1172
2 Andrews Rd, Lewiston ME 04240
Tel (207) 786-6255 *SIC* 8221

UNIVERSITY OF MAINE AT ORONO p 1522
168 College Ave, Orono ME 04469
Tel (207) 581-1865 *SIC* 8221

TRUSTEES OF ST JOSEPHS COLLEGE p 1488
278 Whites Bridge Rd, Standish ME 04084
Tel (207) 892-6766 *SIC* 8221

COLBY COLLEGE p 335
4000 Mayflower Hl, Waterville ME 04901
Tel (207) 859-4000 *SIC* 8221

UNIVERSITY OF MARYLAND UNIVERSITY COLLEGE ALUMNI ASSOCIATION INC p 1522
3501 University Blvd E # 105, Adelphi MD 20783
Tel (301) 985-7122 *SIC* 8221

UNIVERSITY SYSTEM OF MARYLAND p 1527
3300 Metzerott Rd, Adelphi MD 20783
Tel (301) 445-2740 *SIC* 8221

EDUCATION AFFILIATES INC p 479
5026 Campbell Blvd, Baltimore MD 21236
Tel (410) 633-2929 *SIC* 8221

GOUCHER COLLEGE p 626
1021 Dulaney Valley Rd, Baltimore MD 21204
Tel (410) 337-6000 *SIC* 8221

JOHNS HOPKINS MEDICINE INTERNATIONAL LLC p 790
600 N Wolfe St, Baltimore MD 21287
Tel (410) 955-1725 *SIC* 8062 8221

JOHNS HOPKINS UNIVERSITY p 790
3400 N Charles St, Baltimore MD 21218
Tel (410) 516-8000 *SIC* 8221

LOYOLA UNIVERSITY MARYLAND INC p 882
5000 York Rd Ste 200, Baltimore MD 21212
Tel (410) 617-2000 *SIC* 8221

MARYLAND INSTITUTE p 915
1300 W Mount Royal Ave, Baltimore MD 21217
Tel (410) 383-2063 *SIC* 8221

MORGAN STATE UNIVERSITY p 989
1700 E Cold Spring Ln, Baltimore MD 21251
Tel (443) 885-3015 *SIC* 8221

TOWSON UNIVERSITY p 1466
8000 York Rd, Baltimore MD 21252
Tel (410) 704-2000 *SIC* 8221

UNIVERSITY OF MARYLAND p 1522
220 Arch St Fl 14, Baltimore MD 21201
Tel (410) 706-2929 *SIC* 8221 8299

UNIVERSITY OF MARYLAND BALTIMORE COUNTY p 1522
1000 Hilltop Cir, Baltimore MD 21250
Tel (410) 455-2695 *SIC* 8221

WASHINGTON COLLEGE p 1577
300 Washington Ave, Chestertown MD 21620
Tel (410) 778-2800 *SIC* 8221

UNIVERSITY OF MARYLAND COLLEGE PARK p 1522
Patuxent Bldg 010, College Park MD 20742
Tel (301) 405-1000 *SIC* 8221

MOUNT SAINT MARYS UNIVERSITY INC p 994
16300 Old Emmitsburg Rd, Emmitsburg MD 21727
Tel (301) 447-3723 *SIC* 8221

UNIVERSITY OF MARYLAND EASTERN SHORE p 1522
11868 Academic Oval, Princess Anne MD 21853
Tel (410) 651-2200 *SIC* 8221

JULIE VILLA COLLEGE p 797
1525 Greenspring Vly Rd, Stevenson MD 21153
Tel (410) 486-7000 *SIC* 8221

STEVENSON UNIVERSITY INC p 1388
1525 Greenspring Vly Rd, Stevenson MD 21153
Tel (410) 486-7000 *SIC* 8221

PRINCE GEORGES COMMUNITY COLLEGE p 1176
301 Largo Rd, Upper Marlboro MD 20774
Tel (301) 336-6000 *SIC* 8221 8222

TRUSTEES OF AMHERST COLLEGE p 1487
103 Converse Hl, Amherst MA 01002
Tel (413) 542-2000 *SIC* 8221

TRUSTEES OF HAMPSHIRE COLLEGE p 1488
893 West St, Amherst MA 01002
Tel (413) 549-4600 *SIC* 8221

BABSON COLLEGE p 143
231 Forest St, Babson Park MA 02457
Tel (781) 235-1200 *SIC* 8221

ENDICOTT COLLEGE p 496
376 Hale St, Beverly MA 01915
Tel (978) 927-0585 *SIC* 8221

ENDICOTT COLLEGE p 496
376 Hale St, Beverly MA 01915
Tel (978) 927-0585 *SIC* 8221

BERKLEE COLLEGE OF MUSIC INC p 175
1140 Boylston St, Boston MA 02215
Tel (617) 266-1400 *SIC* 8221

BOSTON UNIVERSITY p 203
590 Commonwealth Ave # 255, Boston MA 02215
Tel (617) 353-2000 *SIC* 8221

EMERSON COLLEGE p 492
120 Boylston St Ste 414, Boston MA 02116
Tel (617) 824-8500 *SIC* 8221

EMMANUEL COLLEGE (INC) p 493
400 Fenway, Boston MA 02115
Tel (617) 277-9340 *SIC* 8221

HARVARD BUSINESS SCHOOL STUDENT ASSOCIATION INC p 666
Soldiers Fld, Boston MA 02163
Tel (617) 495-6000 *SIC* 8221

MCPHS UNIVERSITY p 932
179 Longwood Ave, Boston MA 02115
Tel (617) 732-2132 *SIC* 8221

NORTHEASTERN UNIVERSITY p 1055
360 Huntington Ave, Boston MA 02115
Tel (617) 373-2000 *SIC* 8221

SIMMONS COLLEGE p 1324
300 Fenway, Boston MA 02115
Tel (617) 521-2000 *SIC* 8221

SUFFOLK UNIVERSITY p 1396
120 Tremont St, Boston MA 02108
Tel (617) 573-8000 *SIC* 8221 8244

SUFFOLK UNIVERSITY p 1397
8 Ashburton Pl, Boston MA 02108
Tel (617) 573-8000 *SIC* 8221

TRUSTEES OF BOSTON UNIVERSITY p 1487
1 Silber Way, Boston MA 02215
Tel (617) 353-9550 *SIC* 8221

UNIVERSITY OF MASSACHUSETTS INC p 1523
1 Beacon St Fl 31, Boston MA 02108
Tel (617) 287-7000 *SIC* 8221 8733 8062

WENTWORTH INSTITUTE OF TECHNOLOGY INC p 1592
550 Huntington Ave, Boston MA 02115
Tel (617) 989-4590 *SIC* 8221

BRIDGEWATER STATE UNIVERSITY p 212
131 Summer St Rm 109, Bridgewater MA 02325
Tel (508) 531-1000 *SIC* 8221 9199

LESLEY UNIVERSITY p 857
29 Everett St, Cambridge MA 02138
Tel (617) 868-9600 *SIC* 8221

MASSACHUSETTS INSTITUTE OF TECHNOLOGY p 917
77 Massachusetts Ave, Cambridge MA 02139
Tel (617) 253-1000 *SIC* 8221

PRESIDENT AND FELLOWS OF HARVARD COLLEGE p 1172
1350 Massachusetts Ave, Cambridge MA 02138
Tel (617) 496-4873 *SIC* 8221 8732 2721

TRUSTEES OF BOSTON COLLEGE p 1487
140 Commonwealth Ave, Chestnut Hill MA 02467
Tel (617) 552-8000 *SIC* 8221

CURRY COLLEGE p 402
1071 Blue Hill Ave, Milton MA 02186
Tel (617) 333-0500 *SIC* 8221

MERRIMACK COLLEGE p 950
315 Turnpike St, North Andover MA 01845
Tel (978) 837-5000 *SIC* 8221

STONEHILL COLLEGE INC p 1391
320 Washington St, North Easton MA 02357
Tel (508) 565-1000 *SIC* 8221

TRUSTEES OF SMITH COLLEGE p 1488
10 Elm St College Hall, Northampton MA 01063
Tel (413) 585-2550 *SIC* 8221

SALEM STATE UNIVERSITY p 1272
352 Lafayette St, Salem MA 01970
Tel (978) 542-6000 *SIC* 8221

TRUSTEES OF TUFTS COLLEGE p 1488
169 Holland St Ste 318, Somerville MA 02144
Tel (617) 628-5000 *SIC* 8221 2791 2752

TRUSTEES OF MOUNT HOLYOKE COLLEGE p 1488
50 College St, South Hadley MA 01075
Tel (413) 538-2000 *SIC* 8221

BAYSTATE HEALTH INC p 162
759 Chestnut St, Springfield MA 01199
Tel (413) 784-0000 *SIC* 8062 8221 8249

SPRINGFIELD COLLEGE p 1360
263 Alden St, Springfield MA 01109
Tel (413) 748-3000 *SIC* 8221

WESTERN NEW ENGLAND UNIVERSITY p 1599
1215 Wilbraham Rd, Springfield MA 01119
Tel (413) 782-1243 *SIC* 8221

BENTLEY UNIVERSITY p 173
175 Forest St, Waltham MA 02452
Tel (781) 891-2000 *SIC* 8221

BRANDEIS UNIVERSITY p 208
415 South St Ms110, Waltham MA 02453
Tel (781) 736-8318 *SIC* 8221

WELLESLEY COLLEGE p 1589
106 Central St, Wellesley MA 02481
Tel (781) 283-1000 *SIC* 8221

PRESIDENT & TRUSTEES OF WILLIAMS COLLEGE p 1172
880 Main St Fl 1, Williamstown MA 01267
Tel (413) 597-4412 *SIC* 8221

WOOD HOLE OCEANAL GRAPHICS INSTITUTION INC p 1622
38 Water St, Woods Hole MA 02543
Tel (508) 457-2620 *SIC* 8731 8733 8221

ASSUMPTION COLLEGE p 121
500 Salisbury St, Worcester MA 01609
Tel (508) 767-7000 *SIC* 8221

COLLEGE OF HOLY CROSS p 336
1 College St, Worcester MA 01610
Tel (508) 793-2011 *SIC* 8221

TRUSTEES OF CLARK UNIVERSITY p 1487
950 Main St, Worcester MA 01610
Tel (508) 793-7711 *SIC* 8221

WORCESTER POLYTECHNIC INSTITUTE p 1624
100 Institute Rd, Worcester MA 01609
Tel (508) 831-5000 *SIC* 8221

GRAND VALLEY STATE UNIVERSITY p 630
1 Campus Dr, Allendale MI 49401
Tel (616) 331-5000 *SIC* 8221

REGENTS OF UNIVERSITY OF MICHIGAN p 1219
503 Thompson St, Ann Arbor MI 48109
Tel (734) 764-1817 *SIC* 8221

WASHTENAW COMMUNITY COLLEGE p 1580
4800 E Huron River Dr, Ann Arbor MI 48105
Tel (734) 973-3300 *SIC* 8222 8221

ANDREWS UNIVERSITY p 90
4150 Aministration Dr, Berrien Springs MI 49104
Tel (269) 471-7771 *SIC* 8221

FERRIS STATE UNIVERSITY p 538
1201 S State St, Big Rapids MI 49307
Tel (231) 591-2000 *SIC* 8221

UNIVERSITY OF DETROIT MERCY p 1521
4001 W Mcnichols Rd, Detroit MI 48221
Tel (313) 993-6000 *SIC* 8221

WAYNE STATE UNIVERSITY p 1584
656 W Kirby 4200 Faculty, Detroit MI 48202
Tel (313) 577-2230 *SIC* 8221

MICHIGAN STATE UNIVERSITY p 961
426 Auditorium Rd Rm 301, East Lansing MI 48824
Tel (517) 355-5029 *SIC* 8221

BAKER COLLEGE p 145
1050 W Bristol Rd, Flint MI 48507
Tel (810) 767-7600 *SIC* 8222 8221

DAVENPORT EDUCATIONAL SYSTEMS INC p 415
6191 Kraft Ave Se, Grand Rapids MI 49512
Tel (616) 698-7111 *SIC* 8221

DAVENPORT UNIVERSITY p 415
6191 Kraft Ave Se, Grand Rapids MI 49512
Tel (616) 698-7111 *SIC* 8221

HILLSDALE COLLEGE p 694
33 E College St, Hillsdale MI 49242
Tel (517) 437-7341 *SIC* 8221 8211

HOPE COLLEGE p 706
141 E 12th St, Holland MI 49423
Tel (616) 395-7000 *SIC* 8221

MICHIGAN TECHNOLOGICAL UNIVERSITY p 961
1400 Townsend Dr, Houghton MI 49931
Tel (906) 487-1885 *SIC* 8221

KALAMAZOO COLLEGE p 801
1200 Academy St, Kalamazoo MI 49006
Tel (269) 337-7000 *SIC* 8221

WESTERN MICHIGAN UNIVERSITY p 1599
1903 W Michigan Ave, Kalamazoo MI 49008
Tel (269) 387-1000 *SIC* 8221

NORTHERN MICHIGAN UNIVERSITY p 1056
1401 Presque Isle Ave, Marquette MI 49855
Tel (906) 227-1000 *SIC* 8221

NORTHWOOD UNIVERSITY p 1061
4000 Whiting Dr, Midland MI 48640
Tel (800) 622-9000 *SIC* 8221

CENTRAL MICHIGAN UNIVERSITY p 279
1200 S Franklin St, Mount Pleasant MI 48859
Tel (989) 774-4000
SIC 8221 5942 4833 4832 5812

OAKLAND UNIVERSITY p 1071
2200 N Squirrel Rd, Rochester MI 48309
Tel (248) 370-2100 *SIC* 8221

MACOMB COMMUNITY COLLEGE p 893
14500 E 12 Mile Rd, Warren MI 48088
Tel (586) 445-7306 *SIC* 8221

EASTERN MICHIGAN UNIVERSITY p 472
202 Welch Hall, Ypsilanti MI 48197
Tel (734) 487-2031 *SIC* 8221

UNIVERSITY OF MINNESOTA DULUTH p 1523
1049 University Dr, Duluth MN 55812
Tel (218) 726-8000 *SIC* 8221

MINNESOTA STATE UNIVERSITY MANKATO p 974
620 South Rd, Mankato MN 56001
Tel (507) 389-1866 *SIC* 8221 9199

AUGSBURG COLLEGE p 131
2211 Riverside Ave, Minneapolis MN 55454
Tel (612) 330-1000 *SIC* 8221

▲ **CAPELLA EDUCATION CO** p 248
225 S 6th St Fl 9, Minneapolis MN 55402
Tel (888) 227-3552 *SIC* 8221

■ **CAPELLA UNIVERSITY INC** p 248
225 S 6th St Fl 9, Minneapolis MN 55402
Tel (612) 339-8650 *SIC* 8221

REGENTS OF UNIVERSITY OF MINNESOTA p 1219
600 Mcnamara Alumni # 200, Minneapolis MN 55455
Tel (612) 625-5000 *SIC* 8221

CARLETON COLLEGE p 257
1 N College St, Northfield MN 55057
Tel (507) 222-4000 *SIC* 8221

ST OLAF COLLEGE p 1372
1520 Saint Olaf Ave, Northfield MN 55057
Tel (507) 786-2222 *SIC* 8221

MAYO CLINIC p 923
200 1st St Sw, Rochester MN 55905
Tel (507) 284-2511
SIC 8011 8062 8071 8733 8221

MINNESOTA STATE COLLEGES AND UNIVERSITIES p 974
720 4th Ave S, Saint Cloud MN 56301
Tel (320) 308-0121 *SIC* 8221 9199

BETHEL UNIVERSITY p 178
3900 Bethel Dr, Saint Paul MN 55112
Tel (651) 638-6400 *SIC* 8221

HAMLINE UNIVERSITY p 656
1536 Hewitt Ave, Saint Paul MN 55104
Tel (651) 523-2015 *SIC* 8221

MACALESTER COLLEGE p 891
1600 Grand Ave, Saint Paul MN 55105
Tel (651) 696-6000 *SIC* 8221

MINNESOTA STATE COLLEGES AND UNIVERSITIES p 974
30 7th St E Ste 350, Saint Paul MN 55101
Tel (651) 296-8012 *SIC* 8221 9411

ST CATHERINE UNIVERSITY p 1365
2004 Randolph Ave, Saint Paul MN 55105
Tel (651) 690-6000 *SIC* 8221

TRUSTEES OF HAMLINE UNIVERSITY OF MINNESOTA p 1488
1536 Hewitt Ave Ms-Ai775, Saint Paul MN 55104
Tel (651) 523-2800 *SIC* 8221

UNIVERSITY OF NORTHWESTERN - ST PAUL p 1524
3003 Snelling Ave N, Saint Paul MN 55113
Tel (651) 631-5100 *SIC* 8221

UNIVERSITY OF ST THOMAS p 1525
2115 Summit Ave, Saint Paul MN 55105
Tel (651) 962-5000 *SIC* 8221 2741 2721

GUSTAVUS ADOLPHUS COLLEGE p 648
800 W College Ave, Saint Peter MN 56082
Tel (507) 933-7508 *SIC* 8221

SAINT MARYS UNIVERSITY OF MINNESOTA p 1270
700 Terrace Hts 8, Winona MN 55987
Tel (507) 457-1436 *SIC* 8221

WINONA STATE UNIVERSITY FOUNDATION p 1617
175 W Mark St, Winona MN 55987
Tel (507) 457-5000 *SIC* 8221 9199

UNIVERSITY OF SOUTHERN MISSISSIPPI p 1525
118 College Dr, Hattiesburg MS 39406
Tel (601) 266-1000 *SIC* 8221

JACKSON STATE UNIVERSITY p 774
1400 J R Lynch St Ste 206, Jackson MS 39217
Tel (601) 979-2121 *SIC* 8221

MISSISSIPPI STATE UNIVERSITY p 976
245 Barr Ave Mcrthur Hl Mcarthur Hall, Mississippi State MS 39762
Tel (662) 325-2302 *SIC* 8221

HINDS COMMUNITY COLLEGE DISTRICT PUBLIC IMPROVEMENT CORP p 695
501 E Main St, Raymond MS 39154
Tel (601) 857-5261 *SIC* 8222 8221

UNIVERSITY OF MISSISSIPPI p 1523
113 Falkner, University MS 38677
Tel (662) 915-6538 *SIC* 8221

SOUTHEAST MISSOURI STATE UNIVERSITY p 1346
1 University Plz, Cape Girardeau MO 63701
Tel (573) 651-2000 *SIC* 8221

COLUMBIA COLLEGE p 340
1001 Rogers St, Columbia MO 65216
Tel (573) 875-8700 *SIC* 8221

UNIVERSITY OF MISSOURI SYSTEM p 1523
321 University Hall, Columbia MO 65211
Tel (573) 882-2712 *SIC* 8221

A T STILL UNIVERSITY OF HEALTH SCIENCES p 6
800 W Jefferson St, Kirksville MO 63501
Tel (660) 626-2121 *SIC* 8221

PARK UNIVERSITY p 1116
8700 Nw River Park Dr, Parkville MO 64152
Tel (816) 741-2000 *SIC* 8221

SCHOOL OF OZARKS p 1290
100 Opportunity Ave, Point Lookout MO 65726
Tel (417) 239-1900 *SIC* 8221

LINDENWOOD UNIVERSITY p 868
209 S Kingshighway St, Saint Charles MO 63301
Tel (636) 949-2000 *SIC* 8221

MISSOURI WESTERN STATE UNIVERSITY p 976
4525 Downs Dr, Saint Joseph MO 64507
Tel (816) 271-4464 *SIC* 8221

PRINCIPIA CORP p 1177
13201 Clayton Rd, Saint Louis MO 63131
Tel (314) 434-2100 *SIC* 8211 8221

SAINT LOUIS UNIVERSITY p 1270
1 N Grand Blvd, Saint Louis MO 63103
Tel (314) 977-2500 *SIC* 8221

UNIVERSITY OF MISSOURI AT SAINT LOUIS p 1523
1 University Blvd, Saint Louis MO 63121
Tel (314) 516-5000 *SIC* 8221

WASHINGTON UNIVERSITY p 1579
1 Brookings Dr, Saint Louis MO 63130
Tel (314) 935-8566 *SIC* 8221

WEBSTER UNIVERSITY p 1587
470 E Lockwood Ave, Saint Louis MO 63119
Tel (314) 968-6900 *SIC* 8221

COMMUNITY COLLEGE DISTRICT OF CENTRAL SW MO p 348
1001 E Chestnut Expy, Springfield MO 65802
Tel (417) 447-7500 *SIC* 8222 8221

MISSOURI STATE UNIVERSITY p 976
901 S National Ave, Springfield MO 65897
Tel (417) 836-5000 *SIC* 8221 8211

UNIVERSITY OF CENTRAL MISSOURI p 1520
415 E Clark St 213, Warrensburg MO 64093
Tel (660) 543-4233 *SIC* 8221

MONTANA STATE UNIVERSITY-BILLINGS p 986
1500 University Dr, Billings MT 59101
Tel (406) 657-2011 *SIC* 4832 5942 8221

MONTANA STATE UNIVERSITY INC p 986
901 W Garfield St, Bozeman MT 59717
Tel (406) 994-4361 *SIC* 8221

MONTANA UNIVERSITY SYSTEM p 986
2500 E Broadway St, Helena MT 59601
Tel (406) 444-6570 *SIC* 8221

ROMAN CATHOLIC BISHOP OF HELENA MONTANA p 1248
515 N Ewing St, Helena MT 59601
Tel (406) 442-5820
SIC 8661 8211 8221 2741

UNIVERSITY OF MONTANA p 1523
32 Campus Dr Main Hall, Missoula MT 59812
Tel (406) 243-6670 *SIC* 8221

BOARD OF REGENTS OF UNIVERSITY OF NEBRASKA p 195
3835 Holdrege St, Lincoln NE 68503
Tel (402) 472-2111 *SIC* 8221

CREIGHTON UNIVERSITY p 391
2500 California Plz, Omaha NE 68178
Tel (402) 280-2900 *SIC* 8221

BOARD OF REGENTS NEVADA SYSTEM OF HIGHER EDUCATION p 195
4505 S Maryland Pkwy, Las Vegas NV 89154
Tel (702) 895-4727 *SIC* 8221 9411

UNIVERSITY OF NEVADA LAS VEGAS p 1523
4505 S Maryland Pkwy, Las Vegas NV 89154
Tel (702) 895-3011 *SIC* 8221

UNIVERSITY OF NEVADA LAS VEGAS p 1523
4505 S Maryland Pkwy, Las Vegas NV 89154
Tel (702) 895-3354 *SIC* 8221 9411

NEVADA SYSTEM OF HIGHER EDUCATION p 1028
2601 Enterprise Rd, Reno NV 89512
Tel (775) 784-4901 *SIC* 8221 9411

UNIVERSITY OF NEVADA RENO p 1523
1664 N Virginia St, Reno NV 89557
Tel (775) 784-1110 *SIC* 8221 9411

UNIVERSITY SYSTEM OF NEW HAMPSHIRE p 1527
5 Chenell Dr Ste 301, Concord NH 03301
Tel (603) 862-1800 *SIC* 8221

TRUSTEES OF DARTMOUTH COLLEGE p 1487
20 Lebanon St, Hanover NH 03755
Tel (603) 646-1110 *SIC* 8221

SAINT ANSELM COLLEGE p 1268
100 Saint Anselm Dr, Manchester NH 03102
Tel (603) 641-7000 *SIC* 8221

SOUTHERN NEW HAMPSHIRE UNIVERSITY p 1349
2500 N River Rd, Manchester NH 03106
Tel (603) 668-2211 *SIC* 8221

MIDDLESEX COUNTY COLLEGE p 965
2600 Woodbridge Ave, Edison NJ 08837
Tel (732) 548-6000
SIC 8222 9111 8221 8211

COLLEGE OF NEW JERSEY p 337
2000 Pennington Rd, Ewing NJ 08618
Tel (609) 771-2495 *SIC* 8221

STOCKTON UNIVERSITY p 1390
101 Vera King Farris Dr, Galloway NJ 08205
Tel (609) 652-1776 *SIC* 8221

ROWAN UNIVERSITY p 1253
201 Mullica Hill Rd, Glassboro NJ 08028
Tel (856) 256-4000 *SIC* 8221

ROWAN UNIVERSITY/RUTGERS-CAMDEN BOARD OF GOVERNORS p 1253
201 Mullica Hill Rd, Glassboro NJ 08028
Tel (856) 256-4121 *SIC* 8221

STEVENS INSTITUTE OF TECHNOLOGY (INC) p 1388
1 Castle Point Ter, Hoboken NJ 07030
Tel (201) 216-5000 *SIC* 8221

NEW JERSEY CITY UNIVERSITY p 1031
2039 Kennedy Blvd, Jersey City NJ 07305
Tel (201) 200-2000 *SIC* 8221

ST PETERS UNIVERSITY p 1372
2641 John F Kennedy Blvd, Jersey City NJ 07306
Tel (201) 761-6000 *SIC* 8221

RIDER UNIVERSITY A NEW JERSEY NON-PROFIT CORP p 1234
2083 Lawrenceville Rd, Lawrenceville NJ 08648
Tel (609) 896-5000 *SIC* 8221

DREW UNIVERSITY p 455
36 Madison Ave, Madison NJ 07940
Tel (973) 408-3000 *SIC* 8221

RAMAPO COLLEGE OF NEW JERSEY p 1206
505 Ramapo Valley Rd, Mahwah NJ 07430
Tel (201) 684-7500 *SIC* 8221

RUTGER STATE UNIVERSITY p 1260
Asb 3 Rutgers Pl, New Brunswick NJ 08901
Tel (732) 932-4370 *SIC* 8221

NEW JERSEY INSTITUTE OF TECHNOLOGY (INC) p 1031
323 Dr Martin Luth, Newark NJ 07102
Tel (973) 596-3000 *SIC* 8221

UNIVERSITY OF MEDICINE AND DENTISTRY OF NJ (INC) p 1523
150 Bergen St, Newark NJ 07103
Tel (973) 972-4400 *SIC* 8221 9411

UNIVERSITY PHYSICIAN ASSOCIATES OF NEW JERSEY INC p 1527
30 Bergen St Ste 1, Newark NJ 07107
Tel (973) 972-5004 *SIC* 8221 8011

PASSAIC COUNTY COMMUNITY COLLEGE (INC) p 1119
1 College Blvd, Paterson NJ 07505
Tel (973) 684-6868 *SIC* 8222 8221

RUTGERS STATE UNIVERSITY p 1260
96 Davidson Rd, Piscataway NJ 08854
Tel (732) 932-4636 *SIC* 8221

TRUSTEES OF PRINCETON UNIVERSITY p 1488
1 Nassau Hall, Princeton NJ 08544
Tel (609) 258-3000 *SIC* 8221

SETON HALL UNIVERSITY p 1308
400 S Orange Ave, South Orange NJ 07079
Tel (973) 761-9000 *SIC* 8221

FAIRLEIGH DICKINSON UNIVERSITY p 525
1000 River Rd, Teaneck NJ 07666
Tel (800) 338-8803 *SIC* 8221

KENNEDY UNIVERSITY HOSPITAL INC p 811
435 Hurffvl Cross Keys Rd, Turnersville NJ 08012
Tel (856) 582-2500 *SIC* 8221

KEAN UNIVERSITY REALTY FOUNDATION INC p 807
1000 Morris Ave Ste 1, Union NJ 07083
Tel (908) 527-2000 *SIC* 8221

WILLIAM PATERSON UNIVERSITY p 1610
300 Pompton Rd, Wayne NJ 07470
Tel (973) 720-2000 *SIC* 8221

MONMOUTH UNIVERSITY p 984
400 Cedar Ave, West Long Branch NJ 07764
Tel (732) 571-3400 *SIC* 8221

UNIVERSITY OF NEW MEXICO p 1523
1800 Roma Blvd Ne, Albuquerque NM 87131
Tel (505) 277-0732 *SIC* 8221

NEW MEXICO STATE UNIVERSITY p 1032
2850 Weddell St Rm 210, Las Cruces NM 88003
Tel (575) 646-0111 *SIC* 8221

SANTA FE COMMUNITY COLLEGE p 1280
6401 S Richards Ave, Santa Fe NM 87508
Tel (505) 428-1000 *SIC* 8222 8221

NEW MEXICO INSTITUTE OF MINING AND TECHNOLOGY p 1032
801 Leroy Pl, Socorro NM 87801
Tel (575) 835-5312 *SIC* 8221

COLLEGE OF SAINT ROSE p 337
432 Western Ave, Albany NY 12203
Tel (518) 454-5111 *SIC* 8221

EXCELSIOR COLLEGE p 517
7 Columbia Cir, Albany NY 12203
Tel (518) 464-8500 *SIC* 8221

STATE UNIVERSITY OF NEW YORK p 1383
353 Broadway, Albany NY 12246
Tel (518) 320-1100 *SIC* 8221 9411

UNIVERSITY AT ALBANY p 1518
1400 Washington Ave, Albany NY 12222
Tel (518) 442-3300 *SIC* 8221 9411

BARD COLLEGE p 155
30 Campus Rd, Annandale On Hudson NY 12504
Tel (845) 758-7518 *SIC* 8221

BINGHAMTON UNIVERSITY p 183
4400 Vestal Pkwy, Binghamton NY 13902
Tel (607) 777-2000 *SIC* 8221 9411

ALBERT EINSTEIN COLLEGE OF MEDICINE p 46
1300 Morris Park Ave, Bronx NY 10461
Tel (718) 430-2000 *SIC* 8221

FORDHAM UNIVERSITY p 566
441 E Fordham Rd, Bronx NY 10458
Tel (718) 817-1000 *SIC* 8221

HERBERT H LEHMAN COLLEGE p 685
250 Bedford Park Blvd W, Bronx NY 10468
Tel (718) 960-8261 *SIC* 8221

MANHATTAN COLLEGE CORP p 901
4513 Mnhttan College Pkwy, Bronx NY 10471
Tel (718) 862-8000 *SIC* 8221

BROOKLYN LAW SCHOOL p 218
250 Joralemon St, Brooklyn NY 11201
Tel (718) 625-2200 *SIC* 8221

POLYTECHNIC INSTITUTE OF NEW YORK UNIVERSITY p 1160
6 Metrotech Ctr, Brooklyn NY 11201
Tel (718) 260-3600 *SIC* 8221

PRATT INSTITUTE p 1167
200 Willoughby Ave, Brooklyn NY 11205
Tel (718) 636-3600 *SIC* 8221

ST JOSEPHS COLLEGE NEW YORK p 1368
245 Clinton Ave, Brooklyn NY 11205
Tel (718) 940-5300 *SIC* 8221

SUNY DOWNSTATE MEDICAL CENTER p 1405
450 Clarkson Ave, Brooklyn NY 11203
Tel (718) 270-1000 *SIC* 8221 9411

CANISIUS COLLEGE p 247
2001 Main St, Buffalo NY 14208
Tel (716) 883-7000 *SIC* 8221

SUNY UNIVERSITY AT BUFFALO p 1405
501 Capen Hall, Buffalo NY 14260
Tel (716) 645-2901 *SIC* 8221 9411

UNIVERSITY AT BUFFALO p 1518
501 Capen Hall, Buffalo NY 14260
Tel (716) 645-2000 *SIC* 8221

ST LAWRENCE UNIVERSITY p 1369
23 Romoda Dr, Canton NY 13617
Tel (315) 229-5011 *SIC* 8221 7011

HAMILTON COLLEGE p 655
198 College Hill Rd, Clinton NY 13323
Tel (315) 859-4727 *SIC* 8221

SUNY COLLEGE AT CORTLAND p 1405
38 Cheney Hall, Cortland NY 13045
Tel (607) 753-2011 *SIC* 8221 9411

MERCY COLLEGE p 946
555 Broadway Frnt, Dobbs Ferry NY 10522
Tel (914) 455-2650 *SIC* 8221

SUNY COLLEGE AT FREDONIA p 1405
280 Central Ave, Fredonia NY 14063
Tel (716) 673-3111 *SIC* 8221 9411

ADELPHI UNIVERSITY p 22
1 S Ave Lvh 310 310 Lvh, Garden City NY 11530
Tel (516) 877-3000 *SIC* 8221

HOBART AND WILLIAM SMITH COLLEGES p 698
300 Pulteney St, Geneva NY 14456
Tel (315) 781-3337 *SIC* 8221

HOBART AND WILLIAM SMITH COLLEGES p 698
327 Pulteney St, Geneva NY 14456
Tel (315) 781-3337 *SIC* 8221

GLENS FALLS HOSPITAL p 615
100 Park St, Glens Falls NY 12801
Tel (518) 926-1000 *SIC* 8011 8062 8221

LONG ISLAND UNIVERSITY p 876
700 Northern Blvd, Greenvale NY 11548
Tel (516) 299-2535 *SIC* 8221

COLGATE UNIVERSITY p 336
13 Oak Dr, Hamilton NY 13346
Tel (315) 228-1000 *SIC* 8221

HOFSTRA UNIVERSITY p 699
100 Hofstra University, Hempstead NY 11549
Tel (516) 463-6600 *SIC* 8221

CULINARY INSTITUTE OF AMERICA p 400
1946 Campus Dr, Hyde Park NY 12538
Tel (845) 452-9600 *SIC* 8221

CORNELL UNIVERSITY p 370
308 Duffield Hall, Ithaca NY 14853
Tel (607) 254-4636 *SIC* 8221 8011

ITHACA COLLEGE p 768
953 Danby Rd, Ithaca NY 14850
Tel (607) 274-3011 *SIC* 8221

ST JOHNS UNIVERSITY NEW YORK p 1368
8000 Utopia Pkwy, Jamaica NY 11439
Tel (718) 990-6161 *SIC* 8221

RESEARCH FOUNDATION OF CITY UNIVERSITY OF NEW YORK p 1226
2 Court Sq, Long Island City NY 11101
Tel (212) 417-8557 *SIC* 8221

SIENA COLLEGE p 1320
515 Loudon Rd, Loudonville NY 12211
Tel (518) 783-2300 *SIC* 8221

IONA COLLEGE (INC) p 762
715 North Ave, New Rochelle NY 10801
Tel (914) 633-2000 *SIC* 8221

AMERICAN MUSEUM OF NATURAL HISTORY p 76
Central Park W At 79th St, New York NY 10024
Tel (212) 769-5000 *SIC* 8412 8221

AMERICAN UNIVERSITY IN CAIRO p 81
420 5th Ave Fl 3, New York NY 10018
Tel (212) 730-8800 *SIC* 8221

AMERICAN UNIVERSITY OF BEIRUT INC p 81
3 Dag Hammarskjold Plz # 8, New York NY 10017
Tel (212) 583-7600 *SIC* 8221

BARNARD COLLEGE p 155
3009 Broadway Frnt 1, New York NY 10027
Tel (212) 854-7732 *SIC* 8221

CITY UNIVERSITY OF NEW YORK p 320
230 W 41st St Fl 10, New York NY 10036
Tel (212) 397-5600 *SIC* 8221

COLLEGE ENTRANCE EXAMINATION BOARD p 336
250 Vesey St, New York NY 10281
Tel (212) 713-8000 *SIC* 8299 8221 2732

JUILLIARD SCHOOL p 797
60 Lincoln Center Plz, New York NY 10023
Tel (212) 799-5000
SIC 8299 7911 5942 8221

LEBANESE AMERICAN UNIVERSITY p 850
211 E 46th St Fl 3, New York NY 10017
Tel (212) 203-4333 *SIC* 8221

MONTCLAIR STATE UNIVERSITY p 986
825 8th Ave Fl 14, New York NY 10019
Tel (973) 655-4000 *SIC* 8221

NEW SCHOOL p 1033
66 W 12th St, New York NY 10011
Tel (212) 229-5600 *SIC* 8221

NEW YORK UNIVERSITY p 1036
70 Washington Sq S, New York NY 10012
Tel (212) 998-1212 *SIC* 8221

NYU p 1069
120 Sullivan St Apt 1b, New York NY 10012
Tel (212) 998-1212 *SIC* 8221

PACE UNIVERSITY p 1103
1 Pace Plz, New York NY 10038
Tel (212) 346-1956 *SIC* 8221

RESEARCH FOUNDATION OF CITY UNIVERSITY OF NEW YORK p 1226
50 W 40th St, New York NY 10018
Tel (212) 417-8557 *SIC* 8221

ROCKEFELLER UNIVERSITY p 1244
1230 York Ave, New York NY 10065
Tel (212) 327-8078 *SIC* 8733 8221 8062

SCHOOL OF VISUAL ARTS INC p 1290
209 E 23rd St Frnt 1, New York NY 10010
Tel (212) 592-2000 *SIC* 8221 5734 5999

TEACHERS COLLEGE COLUMBIA UNIVERSITY p 1429
525 W 120th St, New York NY 10027
Tel (212) 678-3000 *SIC* 8221

TOURO COLLEGE p 1464
500 7th Ave Fl 5, New York NY 10018
Tel (646) 565-6000 *SIC* 8221

TRUSTEES OF COLUMBIA UNIVERSITY IN CITY OF NEW YORK p 1487
116th And Bdwy Way, New York NY 10027
Tel (212) 854-9970 *SIC* 8221 8062

TRUSTEES OF COLUMBIA UNIVERSITY IN CITY OF NEW YORK p 1487
630 W 168th St Fl 4, New York NY 10032
Tel (212) 305-2862 *SIC* 8221 8733 8062

YESHIVA UNIVERSITY p 1636
500 W 185th St, New York NY 10033
Tel (212) 960-5400 *SIC* 8221

NIAGARA UNIVERSITY p 1042
5795 Lewiston Rd, Niagara University NY 14109
Tel (716) 285-1212 *SIC* 8221

DOWLING COLLEGE INC p 453
150 Idle Hour Blvd, Oakdale NY 11769
Tel (631) 244-3000 *SIC* 8221

NEW YORK INSTITUTE OF TECHNOLOGY INC p 1035
Northern Blvd, Old Westbury NY 11568
Tel (516) 686-7530 *SIC* 8221

SUNY COLLEGE AT ONEONTA p 1405
108 Ravine Pkwy, Oneonta NY 13820
Tel (607) 436-3500 *SIC* 8221 9411

SUNY COLLEGE AT OSWEGO p 1405
702 Culkin Hall, Oswego NY 13126
Tel (315) 312-2222 *SIC* 8221 9411

MARIST COLLEGE p 907
3399 North Rd, Poughkeepsie NY 12601
Tel (845) 575-3000 *SIC* 8221

VASSAR COLLEGE p 1545
124 Raymond Ave Box 12, Poughkeepsie NY 12604
Tel (845) 437-7000 *SIC* 8221

ROCHESTER INSTITUTE OF TECHNOLOGY (INC) p 1243
1 Lomb Memorial Dr, Rochester NY 14623
Tel (585) 475-2411 *SIC* 8221

ST JOHN FISHER COLLEGE p 1367
3690 East Ave Ofc, Rochester NY 14618
Tel (585) 385-8000 *SIC* 8221

UNIVERSITY OF ROCHESTER p 1525
601 Elmwood Ave, Rochester NY 14642
Tel (585) 275-5000 *SIC* 8221

MOLLOY COLLEGE p 983
1000 Hempstead Ave Unit 1, Rockville Centre NY 11570
Tel (516) 678-5733 *SIC* 8221

SKIDMORE COLLEGE p 1329
815 N Broadway, Saratoga Springs NY 12866
Tel (518) 580-5000 *SIC* 8221

TRUSTEES OF UNION COLLEGE IN TOWN OF SCHENECTADY IN STATE OF NEW YORK p 1488
807 Union St, Schenectady NY 12308
Tel (518) 388-6630 *SIC* 8221

WAGNER COLLEGE p 1571
1 Campus Rd, Staten Island NY 10301
Tel (718) 390-3100 *SIC* 8221

STONY BROOK UNIVERSITY p 1391
100 Nicolls Rd, Stony Brook NY 11794
Tel (631) 632-6000 *SIC* 8221 9411

LE MOYNE COLLEGE p 849
1419 Salt Springs Rd, Syracuse NY 13214
Tel (315) 445-4100 *SIC* 8221

SYRACUSE UNIVERSITY p 1416
900 S Crouse Ave Ste 620, Syracuse NY 13244
Tel (315) 443-1870 *SIC* 8221

UPSTATE UNIVERSITY MEDICAL ASSOCIATES AT SYRACUSE INC p 1530
750 E Adams St, Syracuse NY 13210
Tel (315) 464-7087 *SIC* 8221 9411 8231

RENSSELAER POLYTECHNIC INSTITUTE p 1224
110 8th St, Troy NY 12180
Tel (518) 276-6000 *SIC* 8221

NEW YORK MEDICAL COLLEGE (INC) p 1035
40 Sunshine Cottage Rd, Valhalla NY 10595
Tel (914) 594-4100 *SIC* 8221

UNIVERSITY OF NORTH CAROLINA AT ASHEVILLE p 1523
1 University Hts, Asheville NC 28804
Tel (828) 232-5009 *SIC* 8221

APPALACHIAN STATE UNIVERSITY INC p 98
438 Academy St Rm 340, Boone NC 28608
Tel (828) 262-2000 *SIC* 8221

CAMPBELL UNIVERSITY INC p 246
148 Main St, Buies Creek NC 27506
Tel (910) 893-1240 *SIC* 8221

UNIVERSITY OF NORTH CAROLINA p 1523
910 Raleigh Rd, Chapel Hill NC 27514
Tel (919) 962-1000 *SIC* 8221

UNIVERSITY OF NORTH CAROLINA AT CHAPEL HILL p 1523
104 Airport Dr, Chapel Hill NC 27599
Tel (919) 962-1370 *SIC* 8221

UNIVERSITY OF NORTH CAROLINA AT CHARLOTTE p 1523
9201 University City Blvd, Charlotte NC 28223
Tel (704) 687-5727 *SIC* 8221

CAROLINAS MEDICAL CENTER NORTHEAST p 259
920 Church St N, Concord NC 28025
Tel (704) 783-3000 *SIC* 8062 8221

WESTERN CAROLINA UNIVERSITY p 1597
565 H F Robinson, Cullowhee NC 28723
Tel (828) 227-7211 *SIC* 8221

TRUSTEES OF DAVIDSON COLLEGE p 1487
209 Ridge Rd, Davidson NC 28035
Tel (704) 894-2000 *SIC* 8221

DUKE UNIVERSITY p 460
2200 W Main St Ste 710, Durham NC 27705
Tel (919) 684-3030 *SIC* 8221

NORTH CAROLINA CENTRAL UNIVERSITY p 1051
1801 Fayetteville St, Durham NC 27707
Tel (919) 530-6100 *SIC* 8221

ELON UNIVERSITY p 489
100 Campus Dr, Elon NC 27244
Tel (336) 278-2000 *SIC* 8221

FAYETTEVILLE STATE UNIVERSITY p 532
1200 Murchison Rd, Fayetteville NC 28301
Tel (910) 672-1111 *SIC* 8221

NORTH CAROLINA AGRICULTURAL AND TECHNICAL STATE UNIVERSITY p 1051
1601 E Marke St Dowdy Bld, Greensboro NC 27411
Tel (336) 334-7684 *SIC* 8221

UNIVERSITY OF NORTH CAROLINA AT GREENSBORO INVESTMENT FUND INC p 1523
1202 Spring Garden St, Greensboro NC 27412
Tel (336) 334-5000 *SIC* 8221

EAST CAROLINA UNIVERSITY p 470
E Fifth St, Greenville NC 27858
Tel (252) 328-6131 *SIC* 8221

HIGH POINT UNIVERSITY p 691
1 University Pkwy, High Point NC 27268
Tel (336) 841-9000 *SIC* 8221

NORTH CAROLINA STATE UNIVERSITY p 1051
2701 Sullivan Dr Ste 240, Raleigh NC 27695
Tel (919) 515-2011 *SIC* 8221

UNIVERSITY OF NORTH CAROLINA WILMINGTON p 1524
601 S College Rd, Wilmington NC 28403
Tel (910) 962-7209 *SIC* 8221

WINGATE UNIVERSITY p 1616
220 N Camden Rd, Wingate NC 28174
Tel (704) 233-8000 *SIC* 8221

WAKE FOREST UNIVERSITY p 1571
1834 Wake Forest Rd, Winston Salem NC 27109
Tel (336) 758-5000 *SIC* 8221

WINSTON-SALEM STATE UNIVERSITY FOUNDATION INC p 1617
601 S Martin Lut, Winston Salem NC 27110
Tel (336) 750-2000 *SIC* 8221

NORTH DAKOTA UNIVERSITY SYSTEM FOUNDATION p 1052
600 E Boulevard Ave # 215, Bismarck ND 58505
Tel (701) 328-2960 *SIC* 8221

NORTH DAKOTA STATE UNIVERSITY p 1052
1919 University Dr N # 102, Fargo ND 58102
Tel (701) 231-7015 *SIC* 8221

NORTH DAKOTA UNIVERSITY SYSTEM p 1052
2000 44th St S Ste 301, Fargo ND 58103
Tel (701) 231-6326 *SIC* 8221

UNIVERSITY OF NORTH DAKOTA p 1524
264 Centennial Dr, Grand Forks ND 58202
Tel (701) 777-2015 *SIC* 8221

OHIO NORTHERN UNIVERSITY p 1078
525 S Main St Unit 1, Ada OH 45810
Tel (419) 772-2000 *SIC* 8221

AKRON GENERAL MEDICAL CENTER INC p 42
1 Akron General Ave, Akron OH 44307
Tel (330) 344-6000
SIC 8062 8011 8322 8221

UNIVERSITY OF AKRON p 1519
302 Buchtel Mall, Akron OH 44325
Tel (330) 972-7111 *SIC* 8221

ZANESVILLE COMMUNITY SCHOOL p 1641
401 College Ave, Ashland OH 44805
Tel (419) 289-5125 *SIC* 8221

OHIO UNIVERSITY p 1078
1 Ohio University, Athens OH 45701
Tel (740) 593-1000 *SIC* 8221

BALDWIN WALLACE UNIVERSITY p 147
275 Eastland Rd, Berea OH 44017
Tel (440) 826-2900 *SIC* 8221

BOWLING GREEN STATE UNIVERSITY p 204
110 Mcfall Ctr, Bowling Green OH 43403
Tel (419) 372-2311 *SIC* 8221

AULTMAN HOSPITAL p 131
2600 6th St Sw, Canton OH 44710
Tel (330) 452-9911 *SIC* 8062 8069 8221

CEDARVILLE UNIVERSITY p 272
251 N Main St, Cedarville OH 45314
Tel (937) 766-7700 *SIC* 8221

UNIVERSITY OF CINCINNATI p 1520
2600 Clifton Ave, Cincinnati OH 45220
Tel (513) 556-6000 *SIC* 8221

XAVIER UNIVERSITY p 1630
3800 Victory Pkwy Unit 1, Cincinnati OH 45207
Tel (513) 961-0133 *SIC* 8221

CASE WESTERN RESERVE UNIVERSITY p 263
10900 Euclid Ave, Cleveland OH 44106
Tel (216) 368-2000 *SIC* 8221

CLEVELAND STATE UNIVERSITY p 325
2121 Euclid Ave, Cleveland OH 44115
Tel (216) 687-2000 *SIC* 8221

COLUMBUS STATE COMMUNITY COLLEGE p 342
550 E Spring St, Columbus OH 43215
Tel (614) 287-2400 *SIC* 8222 8221

OHIO STATE UNIVERSITY p 1078
Student Acade Servi Bldg, Columbus OH 43210
Tel (614) 292-6446 *SIC* 8221 5812

SINCLAIR COMMUNITY COLLEGE p 1326
444 W 3rd St, Dayton OH 45402
Tel (937) 512-2525 *SIC* 8222 8221

UNIVERSITY OF DAYTON p 1521
300 College Park Ave, Dayton OH 45469
Tel (937) 229-2919 *SIC* 8221 8733

WRIGHT STATE UNIVERSITY p 1627
3640 Colonel Glenn Hwy, Dayton OH 45435
Tel (937) 775-3333 *SIC* 8221

OHIO WESLEYAN UNIVERSITY p 1078
61 S Sandusky St, Delaware OH 43015
Tel (800) 922-8953 *SIC* 8221

UNIVERSITY OF FINDLAY p 1521
1000 N Main St, Findlay OH 45840
Tel (419) 422-8313 *SIC* 8221

DENISON UNIVERSITY p 428
100 W College St, Granville OH 43023
Tel (740) 587-0810 *SIC* 8221

KENT STATE UNIVERSITY p 812
1500 Horning Rd, Kent OH 44242
Tel (330) 672-3000 *SIC* 8221

HOCKING TECHNICAL COLLEGE p 699
3301 Hocking Pkwy, Nelsonville OH 45764
Tel (740) 753-3591 *SIC* 8222 8249 8221

OBERLIN COLLEGE p 1072
173 W Lorain St, Oberlin OH 44074
Tel (440) 775-8121 *SIC* 8221

MIAMI UNIVERSITY p 959
501 E High St, Oxford OH 45056
Tel (513) 529-1809 *SIC* 8221

BOARD OF DIRECTORS OF WITTENBERG COLLEGE p 195
200 W Ward St, Springfield OH 45504
Tel (937) 327-6231 *SIC* 8221

FRANCISCAN UNIVERSITY OF STEUBENVILLE p 574
1235 University Blvd, Steubenville OH 43952
Tel (740) 283-3771 *SIC* 8221

MEDICAL UNIVERSITY OF OHIO p 937
3000 Arlington Ave, Toledo OH 43614
Tel (419) 383-4000 *SIC* 8062 8221

UNIVERSITY OF TOLEDO p 1526
2801 W Bancroft St, Toledo OH 43606
Tel (419) 530-4636 *SIC* 8221

JOHN CARROLL UNIVERSITY p 788
1 John Carroll Blvd, University Heights OH 44118
Tel (216) 397-1886 *SIC* 8221

ANTIOCH UNIVERSITY p 94
900 Dayton St, Yellow Springs OH 45387
Tel (937) 769-1370 *SIC* 8221

YOUNGSTOWN STATE UNIVERSITY INC p 1639
1 University Plz, Youngstown OH 44555
Tel (330) 941-3000 *SIC* 8221

UNIVERSITY OF CENTRAL OKLAHOMA p 1520
100 N University Dr, Edmond OK 73034
Tel (405) 974-2000 *SIC* 8221

UNIVERSITY OF OKLAHOMA p 1524
2800 Venture Dr, Norman OK 73069
Tel (405) 325-2000 *SIC* 8221

OKLAHOMA CITY UNIVERSITY p 1079
2501 N Blackwelder Ave, Oklahoma City OK 73106
Tel (405) 208-5000 *SIC* 8221

OKLAHOMA STATE UNIVERSITY p 1080
401 Whitehurst Hall, Stillwater OK 74078
Tel (405) 744-5892 *SIC* 8221

NORTHEASTERN STATE UNIVERSITY p 1055
600 N Grand Ave, Tahlequah OK 74464
Tel (918) 456-5511 *SIC* 8221

ORAL ROBERTS UNIVERSITY p 1091
7777 S Lewis Ave, Tulsa OK 74171
Tel (918) 495-6161 *SIC* 8221

UNIVERSITY OF TULSA p 1526
800 S Tucker Dr, Tulsa OK 74104
Tel (918) 631-2000 *SIC* 8221

OREGON STATE UNIVERSITY p 1094
308 Kerr Adm Bldg, Corvallis OR 97331
Tel (541) 737-1000 *SIC* 8221

OREGON UNIVERSITY SYSTEM p 1094
P.O. Box 488, Corvallis OR 97339
Tel (541) 737-0827 *SIC* 8221

UNIVERSITY OF OREGON p 1524
1585 E 13th Ave, Eugene OR 97403
Tel (541) 346-1000 *SIC* 8221

PACIFIC UNIVERSITY p 1106
2043 College Way, Forest Grove OR 97116
Tel (503) 357-6151 *SIC* 8221

MT HOOD COMMUNITY COLLEGE DISTRICT FOUNDATION INC p 997
26000 Se Stark St, Gresham OR 97030
Tel (503) 491-6422 *SIC* 8222 8221

GEORGE FOX UNIVERSITY p 606
414 N Meridian St, Newberg OR 97132
Tel (503) 538-8383 *SIC* 8221

LEWIS & CLARK COLLEGE p 858
0615 Sw Palatine Hill Rd, Portland OR 97219
Tel (503) 768-7000 *SIC* 8221

OREGON HEALTH & SCIENCE UNIVERSITY p 1093
3181 Sw Sam Jackson Pk Rd, Portland OR 97239
Tel (503) 494-8311 *SIC* 8221 8069

PORTLAND STATE UNIVERSITY p 1163
1600 Sw 4th Ave Ste 730, Portland OR 97201
Tel (503) 725-4444 *SIC* 8221

UNIVERSITY OF PORTLAND p 1524
5000 N Willamette Blvd, Portland OR 97203
Tel (503) 943-7337 *SIC* 8221

WILLAMETTE UNIVERSITY p 1609
900 State St, Salem OR 97301
Tel (503) 370-6728 *SIC* 8221

MUHLENBERG COLLEGE p 999
2400 Chew St, Allentown PA 18104
Tel (484) 664-3100 *SIC* 8221

LEHIGH UNIVERSITY p 854
27 Memorial Dr W Unit 8, Bethlehem PA 18015
Tel (610) 758-3000 *SIC* 8221

BLOOMSBURG UNIVERSITY FOUNDATION INC p 190
400 E 2nd St, Bloomsburg PA 17815
Tel (570) 389-4000 *SIC* 8221 9411

BRYN MAWR COLLEGE p 221
101 N Merion Ave, Bryn Mawr PA 19010
Tel (610) 526-5000 *SIC* 8221

DICKINSON COLLEGE p 438
College & Louther St, Carlisle PA 17013
Tel (717) 245-1010 *SIC* 8221

DESALES UNIVERSITY p 431
2755 Station Ave, Center Valley PA 18034
Tel (610) 282-1100 *SIC* 8221

WIDENER UNIVERSITY p 1608
1 University Pl, Chester PA 19013
Tel (610) 499-4000 *SIC* 8221

MISERICORDIA UNIVERSITY p 975
301 Lake St, Dallas PA 18612
Tel (570) 674-6400 *SIC* 8221

EAST STROUDSBURG UNIVERSITY p 471
200 Prospect St Ste 1, East Stroudsburg PA 18301
Tel (570) 422-3211 *SIC* 8221 9411

LAFAYETTE COLLEGE p 837
730 High St, Easton PA 18042
Tel (610) 330-5000 *SIC* 8221

ELIZABETHTOWN COLLEGE p 487
1 Alpha Dr, Elizabethtown PA 17022
Tel (717) 361-1000 *SIC* 8221

GANNON UNIVERSITY p 591
109 University Sq, Erie PA 16541
Tel (814) 871-7000 *SIC* 8221

LAKE ERIE COLLEGE OF OSTEOPATHIC MEDICINE INC p 839
1858 W Grandview Blvd, Erie PA 16509
Tel (814) 866-3986 *SIC* 8221

MERCYHURST UNIVERSITY p 948
501 E 38th St, Erie PA 16546
Tel (814) 824-2000
SIC 8221 8243 8742 8299

GETTYSBURG COLLEGE p 609
300 N Washington St, Gettysburg PA 17325
Tel (717) 337-6000 *SIC* 8221

ARCADIA UNIVERSITY p 103
450 S Easton Rd, Glenside PA 19038
Tel (215) 572-2900 *SIC* 8221

CORP OF HAVERFORD COLLEGE p 371
370 Lancaster Ave, Haverford PA 19041
Tel (610) 896-1000 *SIC* 8221

INDIANA UNIVERSITY OF PENNSYLVANIA p 739
1011 S Dr Room 201 Sutton, Indiana PA 15705
Tel (724) 357-2200 *SIC* 8221 9411

FRANKLIN AND MARSHALL COLLEGE p 574
415 Harrisburg Ave, Lancaster PA 17603
Tel (717) 291-3911 *SIC* 8221

BUCKNELL UNIVERSITY p 223
1 Dent Dr, Lewisburg PA 17837
Tel (570) 577-2000 *SIC* 8221

LEWISTOWN HOSPITAL p 859
400 Highland Ave, Lewistown PA 17044
Tel (717) 248-5411 *SIC* 8062 8221

SAINT FRANCIS UNIVERSITY p 1269
117 Evergreen Dr, Loretto PA 15940
Tel (814) 472-3000 *SIC* 8221

ALLEGHENY COLLEGE p 52
520 N Main St, Meadville PA 16335
Tel (814) 332-3100 *SIC* 8221

MESSIAH COLLEGE p 951
1 College Ave Ste 3000, Mechanicsburg PA 17055
Tel (717) 766-2511 *SIC* 8221

MILLERSVILLE UNIVERSITY OF PENNSYLVANIA p 971
1 S George St, Millersville PA 17551
Tel (717) 872-3011 *SIC* 8221 9411

COMMUNITY COLLEGE OF PHILADELPHIA FOUNDATION p 348
1700 Spring Garden St, Philadelphia PA 19130
Tel (215) 751-8010 *SIC* 8221

DREXEL UNIVERSITY p 456
3141 Chestnut St, Philadelphia PA 19104
Tel (215) 895-2000 *SIC* 8221

LASALLE UNIVERSITY p 846
1900 W Olney Ave, Philadelphia PA 19141
Tel (215) 951-1000 *SIC* 8221

PHILADELPHIA COLLEGE OF OSTEOPATHIC MEDICINE p 1142
4190 City Ave, Philadelphia PA 19131
Tel (215) 871-6100 *SIC* 8221

PHILADELPHIA HEALTH AND EDUCATION CORP p 1142
245 N 15th St, Philadelphia PA 19102
Tel (215) 762-8288 *SIC* 8221

SAINT JOSEPHS UNIVERSITY p 1270
5600 City Ave, Philadelphia PA 19131
Tel (610) 660-1000 *SIC* 8221

TEMPLE UNIVERSITY HEALTH SYSTEM FOUNDATION p 1436
3509 N Broad St Fl 9, Philadelphia PA 19140
Tel (215) 707-2000 *SIC* 8211 8221

TEMPLE UNIVERSITY-OF COMMONWEALTH SYSTEM OF HIGHER EDUCATION p 1436
1801 N Broad St, Philadelphia PA 19122
Tel (215) 204-1380 *SIC* 8221

THOMAS JEFFERSON UNIVERSITY p 1449
1020 Walnut St Ste 1, Philadelphia PA 19107
Tel (215) 955-6000 *SIC* 8062 8221

TRUSTEES OF UNIVERSITY OF PENNSYLVANIA p 1488
3451 Walnut St, Philadelphia PA 19104
Tel (215) 898-6301 *SIC* 8221 9411

UNIVERSITY OF ARTS p 1520
320 S Broad St, Philadelphia PA 19102
Tel (215) 717-6000 *SIC* 8221

UNIVERSITY OF PENNSYLVANIA p 1524
3451 Walnut St, Philadelphia PA 19104
Tel (215) 898-6636 *SIC* 8221

UNIVERSITY OF SCIENCES IN PHILADELPHIA p 1525
600 S 43rd St, Philadelphia PA 19104
Tel (215) 596-8800 *SIC* 8221

CARNEGIE MELLON UNIVERSITY p 258
5000 Forbes Ave, Pittsburgh PA 15213
Tel (412) 268-2000 *SIC* 8221

DUQUESNE UNIVERSITY OF HOLY SPIRIT p 462
600 Forbes Ave, Pittsburgh PA 15219
Tel (412) 396-6000 *SIC* 8221

■ **EDUCATION MANAGEMENT CORP** p 479
210 6th Ave Ste 3300, Pittsburgh PA 15222
Tel (412) 562-0900 *SIC* 8221

POINT PARK UNIVERSITY p 1159
201 Wood St, Pittsburgh PA 15222
Tel (412) 391-4100 *SIC* 8221

SOUTH UNIVERSITY ONLINE p 1345
1400 Penn Ave Ste 201, Pittsburgh PA 15222
Tel (412) 995-7424 *SIC* 8221

UNIVERSITY OF PITTSBURGH p 1524
4200 5th Ave, Pittsburgh PA 15260
Tel (412) 624-4141 *SIC* 8221

UNIVERSITY OF SCRANTON p 1525
800 Linden St, Scranton PA 18510
Tel (888) 727-2686 *SIC* 8221

SLIPPERY ROCK UNIVERSITY p 1331
1 Morrow Way, Slippery Rock PA 16057
Tel (724) 738-9000 *SIC* 8221 9411

SWARTHMORE COLLEGE p 1411
500 College Ave Ste 2, Swarthmore PA 19081
Tel (610) 328-8000 *SIC* 8221

PENNSYLVANIA STATE UNIVERSITY p 1130
201 Old Main, University Park PA 16802
Tel (814) 865-4700 *SIC* 8221

VILLANOVA UNIVERSITY IN STATE OF PENNSYLVANIA p 1557
800 E Lancaster Ave, Villanova PA 19085
Tel (610) 519-4500 *SIC* 8221

WASHINGTON & JEFFERSON COLLEGE p 1577
60 S Lincoln St, Washington PA 15301
Tel (724) 222-4400 *SIC* 8221

EASTERN UNIVERSITY p 472
1300 Eagle Rd, Wayne PA 19087
Tel (610) 341-5800 *SIC* 8221

WEST CHESTER UNIVERSITY OF PENNSYLVANIA p 1594
700 S High St, West Chester PA 19383
Tel (610) 436-1000 *SIC* 8221 9411

WILKES UNIVERSITY p 1609
84 W South St, Wilkes Barre PA 18766
Tel (570) 408-4200 *SIC* 8221

PENNSYLVANIA COLLEGE OF TECHNOLOGY p 1130
1 College Ave, Williamsport PA 17701
Tel (570) 320-2400 *SIC* 8221

YORK COLLEGE OF PENNSYLVANIA INC p 1637
441 Country Club Rd, York PA 17403
Tel (717) 815-1780 *SIC* 8221

UNIVERSIDAD INTERAMERICANA DE PUERTO RICO INC p 1518
Recinto De Aguadil, Aguadilla PR 00605
Tel (787) 891-0925 *SIC* 8221

PONTIFICAL CATHOLIC UNIVERSITY OF PUERTO RICO p 1161
2250 Blvd Luis Ferre, Ponce PR 00717
Tel (787) 841-2000 *SIC* 8221

SISTEMA UNIVERSITARIO ANA G MENDEZ INC p 1327
Carr 176 Km 0 3 Cpey Lowr St Ca, San Juan PR 00928
Tel (787) 751-0178 *SIC* 8221 4833

UNIVERSIDAD INTERAMERICANA DE PUERTO RICO INC p 1518
399 Calle Galileo, San Juan PR 00927
Tel (787) 766-1912 *SIC* 8221

UNIVERSITY OF PUERTO RICO p 1524
Jardin Botanico Sur 1187, San Juan PR 00926
Tel (787) 250-0000 *SIC* 8221

ROGER WILLIAMS UNIVERSITY p 1246
1 Old Ferry Rd, Bristol RI 02809
Tel (401) 253-1040 *SIC* 8221

UNIVERSITY OF RHODE ISLAND p 1524
75 Lower College Rd Ste 0, Kingston RI 02881
Tel (401) 874-1000 *SIC* 8221

BROWN UNIVERSITY IN PROVIDENCE IN STATE OF RHODE ISLAND AND PROVIDENCE PLANTATIONS p 220
1 Prospect St, Providence RI 02912
Tel (401) 863-1000 *SIC* 8221

PROVIDENCE COLLEGE p 1185
1 Cunningham Sq, Providence RI 02918
Tel (401) 865-1000 *SIC* 8221

RHODE ISLAND SCHOOL OF DESIGN INC p 1232
2 College St, Providence RI 02903
Tel (401) 454-6100 *SIC* 8221

BRYANT UNIVERSITY p 221
1150 Douglas Pike, Smithfield RI 02917
Tel (401) 232-6000 *SIC* 8221

COLLEGE OF CHARLESTON p 336
66 George St, Charleston SC 29424
Tel (843) 953-5570 *SIC* 8221

MEDICAL UNIVERSITY OF SOUTH CAROLINA p 937
171 Ashley Ave, Charleston SC 29425
Tel (843) 792-2123 *SIC* 8062 8221 8069

CLEMSON UNIVERSITY p 325
201 Sikes Ave, Clemson SC 29631
Tel (864) 656-6182 *SIC* 8221

MIDLANDS TECHNICAL COLLEGE FOUNDATION p 966
316 Beltline Blvd, Columbia SC 29205
Tel (803) 738-8324 *SIC* 8222 8221

U S C EDUCATIONAL FOUNDATION p 1497
1600 Hampton St Ste 814, Columbia SC 29208
Tel (803) 777-1466 *SIC* 8221

UNIVERSITY OF SOUTH CAROLINA p 1525
1400 Wheat St, Columbia SC 29208
Tel (803) 777-2001 *SIC* 8221

COASTAL CAROLINA UNIVERSITY p 331
103 Tom Trout Dr, Conway SC 29526
Tel (843) 347-3161 *SIC* 8221

COASTAL CAROLINA UNIVERSITY p 331
642 Century Cir, Conway SC 29526
Tel (843) 347-3161 *SIC* 8221

BOB JONES UNIVERSITY INC OF GREENVILLE S C p 196
1700 Wade Hampton Blvd, Greenville SC 29614
Tel (864) 242-5100
SIC 8221 8211 8231 8062 5942 0191

GREENVILLE TECHNICAL COLLEGE PUBLIC FACILITIES CORP p 638
506 S Pleasantburg Dr, Greenville SC 29607
Tel (864) 250-8000 *SIC* 8222 8211 8221

CHARLESTON SOUTHERN UNIVERSITY p 290
9200 University Blvd, North Charleston SC 29406
Tel (843) 863-7000 *SIC* 8221

SOUTH CAROLINA STATE UNIVERSITY p 1343
300 College Ave, Orangeburg SC 29115
Tel (803) 536-7000 *SIC* 8221 9411

WINTHROP UNIVERSITY p 1617
701 Oakland Ave, Rock Hill SC 29733
Tel (803) 323-2211 *SIC* 8221

SOUTH DAKOTA STATE UNIVERSITY p 1344
2201 Administration Lane, Brookings SD 57007
Tel (605) 688-6101 *SIC* 8221

SOUTH DAKOTA BOARD OF REGENTS p 1344
306 E Capitol Ave Ste 200, Pierre SD 57501
Tel (605) 773-3455 *SIC* 8221

▲ **NATIONAL AMERICAN UNIVERSITY HOLDINGS INC** p 1009
5301 S Highway 16 Ste 200, Rapid City SD 57701
Tel (605) 721-5220 *SIC* 8221 6531 1531

UNIVERSITY OF SOUTH DAKOTA p 1525
414 E Clark St, Vermillion SD 57069
Tel (605) 677-5011 *SIC* 8221 9411

LEE UNIVERSITY p 852
1120 N Ocoee St Ste 102, Cleveland TN 37311
Tel (423) 614-8000 *SIC* 8221 8661

TENNESSEE TECHNOLOGICAL UNIVERSITY p 1438
1 William L Jones Dr, Cookeville TN 38505
Tel (931) 372-3101 *SIC* 8221

LINCOLN MEMORIAL UNIVERSITY p 867
6965 Cumberland Gap Pkwy, Harrogate TN 37752
Tel (423) 869-3611 *SIC* 8221

UNION UNIVERSITY p 1505
1050 Union University Dr, Jackson TN 38305
Tel (731) 668-1818 *SIC* 8221

EAST TENNESSEE STATE UNIVERSITY p 471
1276 Gilbreath Dr, Johnson City TN 37614
Tel (423) 439-1000 *SIC* 8221

UNIVERSITY OF TENNESSEE p 1525
1331 Circle Park Dr, Knoxville TN 37916
Tel (865) 974-2303 *SIC* 8221

BETHEL UNIVERSITY p 178
325 Cherry Ave, Mc Kenzie TN 38201
Tel (731) 352-4000 *SIC* 8221 5942

UNIVERSITY OF MEMPHIS p 1523
101 Wilder Tower, Memphis TN 38152
Tel (901) 678-2111 *SIC* 8221

MIDDLE TENNESSEE STATE UNIVERSITY p 964
1301 E Main St, Murfreesboro TN 37132
Tel (615) 898-2300 *SIC* 8221

BELMONT UNIVERSITY p 171
1900 Belmont Blvd, Nashville TN 37212
Tel (615) 460-6000 *SIC* 8221

LIPSCOMB UNIVERSITY p 870
1 University Park Dr, Nashville TN 37204
Tel (615) 966-1000 *SIC* 8221 8211

MEHARRY MEDICAL COLLEGE p 940
1005 Dr Db Todd Jr Blvd, Nashville TN 37208
Tel (615) 327-6111 *SIC* 8221

TENNESSEE STATE UNIVERSITY p 1438
3500 John A Merritt Blvd, Nashville TN 37209
Tel (615) 963-5000 *SIC* 8221

VANDERBILT UNIVERSITY p 1543
211 Kirkland Hall, Nashville TN 37240
Tel (615) 322-5000 *SIC* 8221 8062

UNIVERSITY OF SOUTH p 1525
735 University Ave, Sewanee TN 37383
Tel (931) 598-1000 *SIC* 8221

ABILENE CHRISTIAN UNIVERSITY INC p 11
1600 Campus Ct, Abilene TX 79601
Tel (325) 674-2000 SIC 8221

AMARILLO JUNIOR COLLEGE DISTRICT p 64
2201 S Washington St, Amarillo TX 79109
Tel (806) 371-5000 SIC 8222 8221

UNIVERSITY OF TEXAS AT ARLINGTON p 1525
701 S Nedderman Dr, Arlington TX 76019
Tel (817) 272-2011 SIC 8221 8731

SAINT EDWARDS UNIVERSITY INC p 1268
3001 S Congress Ave, Austin TX 78704
Tel (512) 448-8400 SIC 8221

TEXAS STATE UNIVERSITY SYSTEM p 1444
208 E 10th St Ste 600, Austin TX 78701
Tel (512) 463-1808 SIC 8221

UNIVERSITY OF TEXAS AT AUSTIN p 1525
110 Inner Campus Dr G3400, Austin TX 78712
Tel (512) 471-3434 SIC 8221

UNIVERSITY OF TEXAS SYSTEM p 1526
210 W 6th St, Austin TX 78701
Tel (512) 499-4587 SIC 8221

LAMAR UNIVERSITY p 841
4400 S M L King Jr Pkwy, Beaumont TX 77705
Tel (409) 880-8932 SIC 8221

UNIVERSITY OF MARY HARDIN-BAYLOR p 1522
900 College St, Belton TX 76513
Tel (254) 295-8642 SIC 8221

BLINN COLLEGE p 189
902 College Ave, Brenham TX 77833
Tel (979) 830-4000 SIC 8221 8222

UNIVERSITY OF TEXAS AT BROWNSVILLE p 1525
1 W University Blvd, Brownsville TX 78520
Tel (956) 882-8200 SIC 8221

TEXAS A & M UNIVERSITY p 1441
301 Tarrow St Fl 6, College Station TX 77840
Tel (979) 862-3003 SIC 8221

TEXAS A&M AGRILIFE EXTENSION SERVICE p 1442
2147 Tamu, College Station TX 77843
Tel (979) 458-4383 SIC 8731 8221

TEXAS A&M AGRILIFE RESEARCH p 1442
2147 Tamu, College Station TX 77843
Tel (979) 458-4383 SIC 8731 8221

TEXAS A&M HEALTH SCIENCE CENTER p 1442
200 Technology Way, College Station TX 77845
Tel (979) 436-9200 SIC 8299 8221

TEXAS A&M UNIVERSITY SYSTEM p 1442
301 Tarrow St Fl 3, College Station TX 77840
Tel (979) 458-6100
SIC 8221 8731 8742 8011

TEXAS A&M UNIVERSITY-COMMERCE p 1442
2600 W Neal St, Commerce TX 75428
Tel (903) 886-5041 SIC 8221

TEXAS A&M UNIVERSITY-CORPUS CHRISTI p 1442
6300 Ocean Dr Unit 5756, Corpus Christi TX 78412
Tel (361) 825-5700 SIC 8221

DALLAS BAPTIST UNIVERSITY p 410
3000 Mountain Creek Pkwy, Dallas TX 75211
Tel (214) 333-5360 SIC 8221

SOUTHERN METHODIST UNIVERSITY INC p 1349
6425 Boaz Ln, Dallas TX 75205
Tel (214) 768-2000 SIC 8221

TEXAS WOMANS UNIVERSITY FOUNDATION p 1445
304 Administration Dr, Denton TX 76204
Tel (940) 898-3525 SIC 8221

UNIVERSITY OF NORTH TEXAS SYSTEM p 1524
1302 Teasley Ln, Denton TX 76205
Tel (940) 565-2281 SIC 8221

UNIVERSITY OF TEXAS RIO GRANDE VALLEY p 1526
1201 W University Dr, Edinburg TX 78539
Tel (956) 665-2110 SIC 8221

UNIVERSITY OF TEXAS AT EL PASO p 1525
500 W University Ave, El Paso TX 79968
Tel (915) 747-5000 SIC 8221

SOUTHWESTERN BAPTIST THEOLOGICAL SEMINARY p 1353
2001 W Seminary Dr, Fort Worth TX 76115
Tel (817) 923-1921 SIC 8221

TARRANT COUNTY COLLEGE DISTRICT p 1425
1500 Houston St, Fort Worth TX 76102
Tel (817) 515-5220 SIC 5942 8221

TEXAS CHRISTIAN UNIVERSITY INC p 1442
2800 S University Dr, Fort Worth TX 76129
Tel (817) 257-7000 SIC 8221

TEXAS WESLEYAN UNIVERSITY p 1444
1204 Nicole St Apt 1603, Fort Worth TX 76120
Tel (817) 531-4444 SIC 8221

UNIVERSITY OF NORTH TEXAS HEALTH SCIENCE CENTER AT FORT WORTH TEXAS p 1524
3500 Camp Bowie Blvd, Fort Worth TX 76107
Tel (817) 735-2000 SIC 8221

SOUTHWESTERN UNIVERSITY p 1353
1001 E University Ave, Georgetown TX 78626
Tel (512) 863-6511 SIC 8221

UNIVERSITY OF TEXAS RIO GRANDE VALLEY FOUNDATION UTRGV FOUNDATION p 1526
2102 Treasure Hills Blvd, Harlingen TX 78550
Tel (956) 365-8740 SIC 8221

BAYLOR COLLEGE OF MEDICINE p 162
1 Baylor Plz, Houston TX 77030
Tel (713) 798-4951 SIC 8221

HOUSTON BAPTIST UNIVERSITY p 712
7502 Fondren Rd, Houston TX 77074
Tel (281) 649-3000 SIC 8221 8661

TEXAS SOUTHERN UNIVERSITY p 1444
3100 Cleburne St, Houston TX 77004
Tel (713) 313-7011 SIC 8221

UNIVERSITY OF HOUSTON SYSTEM p 1521
4302 University Dr, Houston TX 77204
Tel (713) 743-0945 SIC 8221

UNIVERSITY OF TEXAS HEALTH SCIENCE CENTER AT HOUSTON p 1526
7000 Fannin St Ste 700a, Houston TX 77030
Tel (713) 500-4472 SIC 8221

WILLIAM MARSH RICE UNIVERSITY INC p 1610
6100 Main St, Houston TX 77005
Tel (713) 348-4055 SIC 8221

HOUSTON SAM STATE UNIVERSITY p 712
1806 Ave J, Huntsville TX 77340
Tel (936) 294-1111 SIC 8221

TEXAS A & M UNIVERSITY KINGSVILLE p 1441
700 University Blvd, Kingsville TX 78363
Tel (361) 593-3344 SIC 8221

TEXAS TECH UNIVERSITY HEALTH SCIENCES CENTER p 1444
4004 82nd St C, Lubbock TX 79423
Tel (806) 743-1842 SIC 8221

TEXAS TECH UNIVERSITY SYSTEM p 1444
2500 Broadway, Lubbock TX 79409
Tel (806) 742-2011 SIC 8221

TTU HSC RESEARCH & GRADUATE SCHOOL p 1490
3601 4th St Rm 2b106, Lubbock TX 79430
Tel (806) 743-2556 SIC 8221

STEPHEN F AUSTIN STATE UNIVERSITY p 1386
1936 North St, Nacogdoches TX 75965
Tel (936) 468-3401 SIC 8221

STEPHEN F AUSTIN STATE UNIVERSITY FOUNDATION INC p 1386
Vista At Alumni Dr 303, Nacogdoches TX 75962
Tel (936) 468-5406 SIC 8221

PRAIRIE VIEW A&M UNIVERSITY p 1167
100 University Dr, Prairie View TX 77445
Tel (936) 261-3311 SIC 8221

UNIVERSITY OF TEXAS AT DALLAS p 1525
800 W Campbell Rd, Richardson TX 75080
Tel (972) 883-6325 SIC 8221

NORTHWEST VISTA COLLEGE p 1060
3535 N Ellison Dr, San Antonio TX 78251
Tel (210) 706-9291 SIC 8222 8221

ST MARYS UNIVERSITY OF SAN ANTONIO TEXAS p 1372
1 Camino Santa Maria St, San Antonio TX 78228
Tel (210) 436-3506 SIC 8221

TRINITY UNIVERSITY p 1482
1 Trinity Pl, San Antonio TX 78212
Tel (210) 999-7011 SIC 8221

UNIVERSITY OF INCARNATE WORD p 1521
4301 Broadway St, San Antonio TX 78209
Tel (210) 829-6000 SIC 8221

UNIVERSITY OF TEXAS AT SAN ANTONIO p 1525
1 Utsa Cir, San Antonio TX 78249
Tel (210) 458-4011 SIC 8221

UNIVERSITY OF TEXAS HEALTH SCIENCE CENTER AT SAN ANTONIO p 1526
7703 Floyd Curl Dr, San Antonio TX 78229
Tel (210) 567-7000 SIC 8221

TEXAS STATE UNIVERSITY-SAN MARCOS p 1444
601 University Dr, San Marcos TX 78666
Tel (512) 245-2111 SIC 8221

TARLETON STATE UNIVERSITY p 1425
1333 W Washington St, Stephenville TX 76401
Tel (254) 968-9107 SIC 8221

UNIVERSITY OF TEXAS AT TYLER p 1526
3900 University Blvd, Tyler TX 75799
Tel (903) 566-7000 SIC 8221

UNIVERSITY OF TEXAS HEALTH SCIENCE CENTER AT TYLER p 1526
11937 Us Highway 271, Tyler TX 75708
Tel (903) 877-7777 SIC 8062 8221

BAYLOR UNIVERSITY p 162
700 S University Parks Dr, Waco TX 76706
Tel (254) 710-1561 SIC 8221

TEXAS STATE TECHNICAL COLLEGE p 1444
3801 Campus Dr Bldg 3210, Waco TX 76705
Tel (254) 799-3611 SIC 8221 8222

SOUTHERN UTAH UNIVERSITY FOUNDATION p 1351
351 W University Blvd, Cedar City UT 84720
Tel (435) 586-7700 SIC 8221

UTAH STATE UNIVERSITY p 1536
1000 Old Main Hl, Logan UT 84322
Tel (435) 797-1057 SIC 8221

WEBER STATE UNIVERSITY p 1586
3848 Harrison Blvd, Ogden UT 84408
Tel (801) 626-6606 SIC 8221

UTAH VALLEY UNIVERSITY p 1536
800 W University Pkwy, Orem UT 84058
Tel (801) 863-8000 SIC 8221

BRIGHAM YOUNG UNIVERSITY p 212
A 41 Asb Brgham Yung Univ, Provo UT 84602
Tel (801) 422-1211 SIC 8221

CORP OF PRESIDENT OF CHURCH OF JESUS CHRIST OF LATTER-DAY SAINTS p 371
50 W North Temple, Salt Lake City UT 84150
Tel (801) 240-1000 SIC 8661 8221

SALT LAKE COMMUNITY COLLEGE (INC) p 1273
4600 S Redwood Rd, Salt Lake City UT 84123
Tel (801) 957-4111 SIC 8222 8221

UNIVERSITY OF UTAH p 1526
201 Presidents Cir Rm 203, Salt Lake City UT 84112
Tel (801) 581-7200 SIC 8221

WESTERN GOVERNORS UNIVERSITY p 1598
4001 S 700 E Ste 700, Salt Lake City UT 84107
Tel (801) 274-3280 SIC 8299 8221

WESTMINSTER COLLEGE p 1601
1840 S 1300 E, Salt Lake City UT 84105
Tel (801) 484-7651 SIC 8221

WORLD LEARNING INC p 1625
1 Kipling Rd, Brattleboro VT 05301
Tel (802) 257-7751 SIC 8221 8299

UNIVERSITY OF VERMONT & STATE AGRICULTURAL COLLEGE p 1526
85 S Prospect St, Burlington VT 05405
Tel (802) 656-3131 SIC 8221

SAINT MICHAELS COLLEGE INC p 1270
1 Winooski Park, Colchester VT 05439
Tel (802) 654-2000 SIC 8221

LYNDON STATE COLLEGE p 888
1001 College Rd, Lyndonville VT 05851
Tel (802) 626-6200 SIC 8221

PRESIDENT AND FELLOWS OF MIDDLEBURY COLLEGE p 1172
38 College St, Middlebury VT 05753
Tel (802) 443-5000 SIC 8221

VERMONT STATE COLLEGES p 1551
660 Elm St, Montpelier VT 05602
Tel (802) 828-2800 SIC 8221

NORWICH UNIVERSITY p 1061
158 Harmon Dr, Northfield VT 05663
Tel (802) 485-2000 SIC 8221

MARYMOUNT UNIVERSITY p 915
2807 N Glebe Rd, Arlington VA 22207
Tel (703) 284-1500 SIC 8221

RANDOLPH-MACON COLLEGE p 1208
204 Henry St, Ashland VA 23005
Tel (804) 752-7200 SIC 8221

VIRGINIA POLYTECHNIC INSTITUTE & STATE UNIVERSITY p 1559
300 Turner St Nw Ste 4200, Blacksburg VA 24061
Tel (540) 231-6000 SIC 8221

CFA INSTITUTE p 285
915 E High St, Charlottesville VA 22902
Tel (434) 951-5499 SIC 8621 6282 8221

RECTOR & VISITORS OF UNIVERSITY OF VIRGINIA p 1215
1001 Emmet St N, Charlottesville VA 22903
Tel (434) 924-0311 SIC 8221

UNIVERSITY OF VIRGINIA p 1526
1215 Lee St, Charlottesville VA 22908
Tel (434) 924-0000 SIC 8221

UNIVERSITY OF VIRGINIA MEDICAL CENTER p 1526
1215 Lee St, Charlottesville VA 22908
Tel (434) 924-0211 SIC 8221

GEORGE MASON UNIVERSITY p 606
4400 University Dr, Fairfax VA 22030
Tel (703) 993-1000 SIC 8221

UNIVERSITY OF MARY WASHINGTON p 1522
1301 College Ave, Fredericksburg VA 22401
Tel (540) 654-2060 SIC 8221 7389

HAMPTON UNIVERSITY p 656
100 E Queen St, Hampton VA 23668
Tel (757) 727-5000 SIC 8221

JAMES MADISON UNIVERSITY INC p 776
800 S Main St, Harrisonburg VA 22807
Tel (540) 568-6211 SIC 8221

▲ STRAYER EDUCATION INC p 1393
2303 Dulles Station Blvd, Herndon VA 20171
Tel (703) 561-1600 SIC 8221

STRAYER UNIVERSITY INC p 1393
2303 Dulles Station Blvd # 100, Herndon VA 20171
Tel (703) 561-1710 SIC 8221

WASHINGTON AND LEE UNIVERSITY p 1577
204 W Washington St, Lexington VA 24450
Tel (540) 458-8400 SIC 8221

LIBERTY UNIVERSITY INC p 862
1971 University Blvd, Lynchburg VA 24515
Tel (434) 582-2000 SIC 8221

LYNCHBURG COLLEGE p 887
1501 Lakeside Dr, Lynchburg VA 24501
Tel (434) 544-8100 SIC 8221

CHRISTOPHER NEWPORT UNIVERSITY p 303
1 Avenue Of The Arts, Newport News VA 23606
Tel (757) 594-7000 SIC 8221

EASTERN VIRGINIA MEDICAL SCHOOL p 472
714 Woodis Ave, Norfolk VA 23510
Tel (757) 446-6052 SIC 8221 8099

NORFOLK STATE UNIVERSITY p 1048
700 Park Ave, Norfolk VA 23504
Tel (757) 823-8600 SIC 8221 9411

OLD DOMINION UNIVERSITY p 1080
5115 Hampton Blvd, Norfolk VA 23529
Tel (757) 683-3000 SIC 8221 9411

VIRGINIA WESLEYAN COLLEGE p 1560
1584 Wesleyan Dr, Norfolk VA 23502
Tel (757) 455-3200 SIC 8221

VIRGINIA STATE UNIVERSITY p 1559
1 Hayden Dr, Petersburg VA 23803
Tel (804) 524-5000 SIC 8221 9411

RADFORD UNIVERSITY p 1204
801 E Main St, Radford VA 24142
Tel (540) 831-5000 SIC 8221

UNIVERSITY OF RICHMOND p 1524
28 Westhampton Way, Richmond VA 23173
Tel (804) 289-8133 SIC 8221

VIRGINIA COMMONWEALTH UNIVERSITY p 1558
912 W Franklin St, Richmond VA 23284
Tel (804) 828-0100 SIC 8221

TRUSTEES OF ROANOKE COLLEGE p 1488
221 College Ln, Salem VA 24153
Tel (540) 375-2500 SIC 8221 7929

COLLEGE OF WILLIAM & MARY p 337
261 Richmond Rd, Williamsburg VA 23185
Tel (757) 221-3966 SIC 8221 9411

SHENANDOAH UNIVERSITY p 1315
1460 University Dr, Winchester VA 22601
Tel (540) 665-4500 SIC 8221

GREEN RIVER COLLEGE p 637
12401 Se 320th St, Auburn WA 98092
Tel (253) 833-9111 SIC 8222 8299 8221

BELLEVUE COLLEGE FOUNDATION p 170
3000 Landerholm Cir Se, Bellevue WA 98007
Tel (425) 564-1000 SIC 8222 8221

WESTERN WASHINGTON UNIVERSITY p 1600
516 High St, Bellingham WA 98225
Tel (360) 650-3720 SIC 8221

WA STATE COMMUNITY COLLEGE DIST 3 p 1569
1600 Chester Ave, Bremerton WA 98337
Tel (360) 792-6050 SIC 8221

EASTERN WASHINGTON UNIVERSITY INC p 472
307 Showalter Hall, Cheney WA 99004
Tel (509) 359-6200 SIC 8221

CENTRAL WASHINGTON UNIVERSITY INC p 281
400 E University Way, Ellensburg WA 98926
Tel (509) 963-1111 SIC 8221

WASHINGTON STATE UNIVERSITY INC p 1579
240 French Adm Bldg, Pullman WA 99164
Tel (509) 335-2022 SIC 8221

SEATTLE PACIFIC UNIVERSITY INC p 1298
3307 3rd Ave W, Seattle WA 98119
Tel (206) 281-2000 SIC 8221 8661

SEATTLE UNIVERSITY p 1298
901 12th Ave, Seattle WA 98122
Tel (206) 296-6150 SIC 8221

UNIVERSITY OF WASHINGTON INC p 1526
4311 11th Ave Ne Ste 600, Seattle WA 98105
Tel (206) 543-2100 SIC 8221

CORP OF GONZAGA UNIVERSITY p 371
502 E Boone Ave, Spokane WA 99258
Tel (509) 328-4220 SIC 8221

PACIFIC LUTHERAN UNIVERSITY INC p 1105
12180 Park Ave S, Tacoma WA 98447
Tel (253) 531-6900 SIC 8221

UNIVERSITY OF PUGET SOUND p 1524
1500 N Warner St, Tacoma WA 98416
Tel (253) 879-3100 SIC 8221

WHITMAN COLLEGE p 1607
345 Boyer Ave, Walla Walla WA 99362
Tel (509) 527-5111 SIC 8221

▲ AMERICAN PUBLIC EDUCATION INC p 78
111 W Congress St, Charles Town WV 25414
Tel (304) 724-3700 SIC 8221

MARSHALL UNIVERSITY p 911
1 John Marshall Dr, Huntington WV 25755
Tel (304) 696-2385 SIC 8221

WEST VIRGINIA UNIVERSITY p 1596
103 Stewart Hl, Morgantown WV 26506
Tel (304) 293-2545 SIC 8221

NORTHEAST WISCONSIN TECHNICAL COLLEGE DISTRICT p 1055
2740 W Mason St, Green Bay WI 54303
Tel (920) 498-5400 SIC 8221 8222

CARTHAGE COLLEGE p 262
2001 Alford Park Dr, Kenosha WI 53140
Tel (262) 551-8500 SIC 8221

VITERBO UNIVERSITY INC p 1563
900 Viterbo Dr, La Crosse WI 54601
Tel (608) 796-3000 SIC 8221

WESTERN TECHNICAL COLLEGE p 1600
400 7th St N, La Crosse WI 54601
Tel (608) 785-9200 SIC 8222 8221

UNIVERSITY OF WISCONSIN SYSTEM p 1527
1700 Van Hise Ave, Madison WI 53726
Tel (608) 262-2321 SIC 8221 8741

UNIVERSITY OF WISCONSIN-MADISON p 1527
500 Lincoln Dr, Madison WI 53706
Tel (608) 262-9946 SIC 8221

UNIVERSITY OF WISCONSIN- SYSTEM p 1527
712s Brdwy 125m Admn Bld, Menomonie WI 54751
Tel (715) 232-2441 SIC 8221

CONCORDIA UNIVERSITY WISCONSIN INC p 355
12800 N Lake Shore Dr, Mequon WI 53097
Tel (262) 243-5700 SIC 8221

UNIVERSITY OF WISCONSIN MEDICAL FOUNDATION INC p 1527
7974 Uw Health Ct, Middleton WI 53562
Tel (608) 821-4223
SIC 8221 8011 2834 8299 8042 8043

ALVERNO COLLEGE p 63
3400 S 43rd St, Milwaukee WI 53219
Tel (414) 382-6000 SIC 8221

CARDINAL STRITCH UNIVERSITY INC p 253
6801 N Yates Rd, Milwaukee WI 53217
Tel (414) 410-4000 SIC 8221

MARQUETTE UNIVERSITY p 910
1250 W Wisconsin Ave, Milwaukee WI 53233
Tel (414) 288-7223 SIC 8221

MEDICAL COLLEGE OF WISCONSIN INC p 936
8701 W Watertown Plank Rd, Milwaukee WI 53226
Tel (414) 456-8296 SIC 8221

MILWAUKEE AREA TECHNICAL COLLEGE FOUNDATION INC p 972
700 W State St, Milwaukee WI 53233
Tel (414) 297-6792 SIC 8222 8221

MILWAUKEE SCHOOL OF ENGIINEERING p 972
1025 N Broadway, Milwaukee WI 53202
Tel (414) 277-6763 SIC 8221

MILWAUKEE SCHOOL OF ENGINEERING p 972
1025 N Broadway, Milwaukee WI 53202
Tel (414) 277-7300 SIC 8221

LAKELAND COLLEGE p 840
W3718 South Dr, Plymouth WI 53073
Tel (920) 565-2111 SIC 8221

UNIVERSITY OF WISCONSIN STEVENS POINT p 1527
1015 Reserve St, Stevens Point WI 54481
Tel (715) 346-0123 SIC 8221

UNIVERSITY OF WYOMING p 1527
1000 E University Ave # 3434, Laramie WY 82071
Tel (307) 766-5766 SIC 8221

SIC 8222 Junior Colleges & Technical Institutes

YAVAPAI COUNTY COMMUNITY COLLEGE DISTRICT p 1635
1100 E Sheldon St, Prescott AZ 86301
Tel (928) 445-7300 SIC 8222

MARICOPA COUNTY COMMUNITY COLLEGE DISTRICT p 906
2411 W 14th St, Tempe AZ 85281
Tel (480) 731-8000 SIC 8222

PIMA COUNTY COMMUNITY COLLEGE DISTRICT INC p 1148
4905 E Broadway Blvd, Tucson AZ 85709
Tel (520) 206-4500 SIC 8222

NORTH ORANGE COUNTY COMMUNITY COLLEGE DISTRICT p 1053
1830 W Romneya Dr, Anaheim CA 92801
Tel (714) 808-4500 SIC 8222

CABRILLO COMMUNITY COLLEGE DISTRICT FINANCING CORP p 235
6500 Soquel Dr, Aptos CA 95003
Tel (831) 479-6100 SIC 8222 7922 8221

KERN COMMUNITY COLLEGE DISTRICT p 813
2100 Chester Ave, Bakersfield CA 93301
Tel (661) 336-5100 SIC 8222

WEST HILLS COMMUNITY COLLEGE DISTRICT FINANCING CORP p 1594
9900 Cody Ave, Coalinga CA 93210
Tel (559) 934-2000 SIC 8222

COAST COMMUNITY COLLEGE DISTRICT ENTERPRISE INC p 331
1370 Adams Ave, Costa Mesa CA 92626
Tel (714) 438-4600 SIC 8222 8221

CHABOT-LAS POSITAS COMMUNITY COLLEGE DISTRICT FINANCING CORP p 286
7600 Dublin Blvd Ste 102, Dublin CA 94568
Tel (925) 485-5201 SIC 8222

STATE CENTER COMMUNITY COLLEGE DISTRICT p 1380
1525 E Weldon Ave, Fresno CA 93704
Tel (559) 226-0720 SIC 8222

GLENDALE COMMUNITY COLLEGE DIST p 615
1500 N Verdugo Rd, Glendale CA 91208
Tel (818) 240-1000 SIC 8222

CITRUS COMMUNITY COLLEGE DISTRICT p 311
1000 W Foothill Blvd, Glendora CA 91741
Tel (626) 963-0323 SIC 8222

MARIN COMMUNITY COLLEGE DISTRICT p 906
835 College Ave, Kentfield CA 94904
Tel (415) 457-8811 SIC 8222 8221

ANTELOPE VALLEY COMMUNITY COLLEGE DISTRICT p 93
3041 W Avenue K, Lancaster CA 93536
Tel (661) 722-6300 SIC 8222 8221

LONG BEACH COMMUNITY COLLEGE DISTRICT p 876
4901 E Carson St, Long Beach CA 90808
Tel (562) 938-5020 SIC 8222

FOOTHILL-DE ANZA COMMUNITY COLLEGE DISTRICT FINANCING CORP p 564
12345 S El Monte Rd, Los Altos Hills CA 94022
Tel (650) 949-6100 SIC 8222 8221

LOS ANGELES CITY COLLEGE p 878
855 N Vermont Ave, Los Angeles CA 90029
Tel (323) 953-4000 SIC 8222

LOS ANGELES COMMUNITY COLLEGE DISTRICT p 878
770 Wilshire Blvd, Los Angeles CA 90017
Tel (213) 891-2000 SIC 8222

CONTRA COSTA COMMUNITY COLLEGE DISTRICT p 364
500 Court St Fl 1, Martinez CA 94553
Tel (925) 229-1000 SIC 8222

SOUTH ORANGE COUNTY COMMUNITY COLLEGE DISTRICT p 1344
28000 Marguerite Pkwy, Mission Viejo CA 92692
Tel (949) 582-4500 SIC 8222 8221

YOSEMITE COMMUNITY COLLEGE DISTRICT p 1637
2201 Blue Gum Ave, Modesto CA 95358
Tel (209) 575-7800 SIC 8222

CERRITOS COMMUNITY COLLEGE DISTRICT p 284
11110 Alondra Blvd, Norwalk CA 90650
Tel (562) 860-2451 SIC 8221 8222

PERALTA COMMUNITY COLLEGE DISTRICT p 1134
333 E 8th St, Oakland CA 94606
Tel (510) 466-7200 SIC 8222

PASADENA AREA COMMUNITY COLLEGE DISTRICT p 1119
1570 E Colorado Blvd, Pasadena CA 91106
Tel (626) 585-7123 SIC 8222

CHAFFEY COMMUNITY COLLEGE DISTRICT (INC) p 286
5885 Haven Ave, Rancho Cucamonga CA 91737
Tel (909) 652-6560 SIC 8222 8221

RIVERSIDE COMMUNITY COLLEGE DISTRICT p 1238
3801 Market St, Riverside CA 92501
Tel (951) 328-3663 SIC 8222

SIERRA JOINT COMMUNITY COLLEGE DISTRICT p 1320
5000 Rocklin Rd, Rocklin CA 95677
Tel (916) 624-3333 SIC 8222 8221

LOS RIOS COMMUNITY COLLEGE DISTRICT p 879
1919 Spanos Ct, Sacramento CA 95825
Tel (916) 568-3041 SIC 8222

SAN BERNARDINO COMMUNITY COLLEGE DISTRICT p 1275
114 S Del Rosa Dr, San Bernardino CA 92408
Tel (909) 382-4000 SIC 8222 4832 4833

SAN DIEGO COMMUNITY COLLEGE DISTRICT p 1276
3375 Camino Del Rio S, San Diego CA 92108
Tel (619) 388-6500 SIC 8222 8249 8221

CITY COLLEGE OF SAN FRANCISCO p 312
50 Phelan Ave, San Francisco CA 94112
Tel (415) 239-3000 SIC 8221 8222

SAN JOSE/EVERGREEN COMMUNITY COLLEGE DISTRICT FOUNDATION p 1277
40 S Market St, San Jose CA 95113
Tel (408) 918-6131 SIC 8222

PALOMAR COMMUNITY COLLEGE DISTRICT FINANCING CORP p 1110
1140 W Mission Rd, San Marcos CA 92069
Tel (760) 744-1150 SIC 8222

SAN MATEO COUNTY COMMUNITY COLLEGE DISTRICT p 1277
3401 Csm Dr, San Mateo CA 94402
Tel (650) 358-6742 SIC 8222

RANCHO SANTIAGO COMMUNITY COLLEGE DISTRICT INC p 1207
2323 N Broadway Fl 4, Santa Ana CA 92706
Tel (714) 480-7300 SIC 8222 8221

SANTA BARBARA COMMUNITY COLLEGE DISTRICT p 1280
721 Cliff Dr, Santa Barbara CA 93109
Tel (805) 965-0581 SIC 8222

SANTA CLARITA COMMUNITY COLLEGE DISTRICT p 1280
26455 Rockwell Canyon Rd, Santa Clarita CA 91355
Tel (661) 259-7800 SIC 8222 8221

SANTA MONICA COMMUNITY COLLEGE DISTRICT p 1281
1900 Pico Blvd, Santa Monica CA 90405
Tel (310) 434-4000 SIC 8222

SONOMA COUNTY JUNIOR COLLEGE DISTRICT p 1340
1501 Mendocino Ave, Santa Rosa CA 95401
Tel (707) 527-4011 SIC 8222 8221

WEST VALLEY-MISSION COMMUNITY COLLEGE DISTRICT p 1596
14000 Fruitvale Ave, Saratoga CA 95070
Tel (408) 867-2200 SIC 8222 8221

EL CAMINO COMMUNITY COLLEGE DISTRICT p 482
16007 Crenshaw Blvd, Torrance CA 90506
Tel (310) 532-3670 SIC 8222

VENTURA COUNTY COMMUNITY COLLEGE DISTRICT p 1548
255 W Stanley Ave Ste 150, Ventura CA 93001
Tel (805) 652-5500 SIC 8222 8221

VICTOR VALLEY COMITY COLGE DIST p 1555
18422 Bear Valley Rd, Victorville CA 92395
Tel (760) 245-4271 SIC 8222

MT SAN ANTONIO COMMUNITY COLLEGE DISTRICT p 997
1100 N Grand Ave, Walnut CA 91789
Tel (909) 594-5611 SIC 8222

RHODES COLLEGES INC p 1232
1815 Jet Wing Dr, Colorado Springs CO 80916
Tel (719) 638-6580 SIC 8221 8222

STATE BOARD FOR COMMUNITY COLLEGES AND OCCUPATIONAL EDUCATIONAL SYSTEM p 1380
9101 E Lowry Pl, Denver CO 80230
Tel (303) 595-1552 SIC 8222

ARAPAHOE COMMUNITY COLLEGE FOUNDATION INC p 102
5900 S Santa Fe Dr, Littleton CO 80120
Tel (303) 797-4222 SIC 8222

DELAWARE TECHNICAL & COMMUNITY COLLEGE p 424
100 Campus Dr, Dover DE 19904
Tel (302) 857-1000 SIC 8222

SCHOOL BOARD OF FLAGLER COUNTY p 1289
1769 E Moody Blvd Bldg 2f, Bunnell FL 32110
Tel (386) 437-7526 SIC 8211 8222

BROWARD COLLEGE p 219
111 E Las Olas Blvd, Fort Lauderdale FL 33301
Tel (954) 201-7400 SIC 8222

SCHOOL BOARD OF BROWARD COUNTY (INC) p 1289
600 Se 3rd Ave, Fort Lauderdale FL 33301
Tel (754) 321-0000 SIC 8211 8222

INDIAN RIVER STATE COLLEGE FOUNDATION INC p 737
3209 Virginia Ave, Fort Pierce FL 34981
Tel (772) 462-7340 SIC 8222

SANTA FE COLLEGE p 1280
3000 Nw 83rd St, Gainesville FL 32606
Tel (352) 395-5000 SIC 8222 8221

EDUCATION AMERICA INC p 479
7131 Bus Pk Ln Ste 300, Lake Mary FL 32746
Tel (407) 562-5500 SIC 8222

REMINGTON COLLEGES INC p 1222
7131 Bus Pk Ln Ste 300, Lake Mary FL 32746
Tel (407) 562-5500 SIC 8221 8222

PALM BEACH STATE COLLEGE p 1109
4200 S Congress Ave, Lake Worth FL 33461
Tel (561) 868-3350 SIC 8222 8351 8221

MIAMI DADE COLLEGE p 959
300 Ne 2nd Ave Rm 3116, Miami FL 33132
Tel (305) 237-3000 SIC 8222 9411 8221

VALENCIA COLLEGE p 1539
1800 S Kirkman Rd, Orlando FL 32811
Tel (407) 299-5000 SIC 8222

HILLSBOROUGH COMMUNITY COLLEGE INC p 694
39 Columbia Dr, Tampa FL 33606
Tel (813) 253-7000 SIC 8222

FULL SAIL LLC p 584
3300 University Blvd, Winter Park FL 32792
Tel (407) 679-0100 SIC 8222 7389

GEORGIA PERIMETER COLLEGE p 607
3251 Panthersville Rd, Decatur GA 30034
Tel (678) 891-2300 SIC 8222

UNIVERSITY OF HAWAII SYSTEMS p 1521
2444 Dole St, Honolulu HI 96822
Tel (808) 956-8278 SIC 8221 8222

SOUTHWESTERN ILLINOIS COLLEGE COMMUNITY COLLEGE DISTRICT NO 522 p 1353
2500 Carlyle Ave, Belleville IL 62221
Tel (618) 235-2700 SIC 8222 8221

BOARD OF TRUSTEES OF COMMUNITY COLLEGE DISTRICT 508 (INC) p 196
226 W Jackson Blvd # 103, Chicago IL 60606
Tel (312) 553-2752 SIC 8221 8222

MCHENRY COUNTY COLLEGE p 929
8900 Us Highway 14, Crystal Lake IL 60012
Tel (815) 455-3700 SIC 8222 8221 9411

OAKTON COMMUNITY COLLEGE p 1071
1600 E Golf Rd Rm 1505, Des Plaines IL 60016
Tel (847) 635-1600 SIC 8221 8222

ELGIN COMMUNITY COLLEGE p 486
1700 Spartan Dr, Elgin IL 60123
Tel (847) 697-1000 SIC 8222 8221 9411

COMMUNITY COLLEGE DISTRICT 502 p 348
425 Fawell Blvd, Glen Ellyn IL 60137
Tel (630) 942-2800 SIC 8222

COLLEGE OF LAKE COUNTY p 337
19351 W Washington St, Grayslake IL 60030
Tel (847) 543-2000 SIC 8222

JOLIET JUNIOR COLLEGE DISTRICT 525 p 792
1215 Houbolt Rd, Joliet IL 60431
Tel (815) 280-6767 SIC 8222

LAKE LAND COLLEGE p 839
5001 Lake Land Blvd, Mattoon IL 61938
Tel (217) 234-5253 SIC 8222 8221

MORAINE VALLEY COMMUNITY COLLEGE p 988
9000 W College Pkwy, Palos Hills IL 60465
Tel (708) 974-4300 SIC 8222

ILLINOIS CENTRAL COLLEGE p 732
1 College Dr, Peoria IL 61635
Tel (309) 694-5011 SIC 8222

WAUBONSEE COMMUNITY COLLEGE FOUNDATION p 1583
At Waubonsee Dr Rr 47, Sugar Grove IL 60554
Tel (630) 466-7900 SIC 8222

NORTHEAST IOWA COMMUNITY COLLEGE FOUNDATION p 1055
1625 Highway 150, Calmar IA 52132
Tel (563) 562-3263 SIC 8222

KIRKWOOD COMMUNITY COLLEGE FOUNDATION p 822
6301 Kirkwood Blvd Sw, Cedar Rapids IA 52404
Tel (319) 398-5411 SIC 8222

EASTERN IOWA COMMUNITY COLLEGE DISTRICT p 472
152 Colorado St, Muscatine IA 52761
Tel (563) 264-2088 SIC 8222 8221

HAWKEYE COMMUNITY COLLEGE p 669
1501 E Orange Rd, Waterloo IA 50701
Tel (319) 296-4201 SIC 8222

ARCHDIOCESE OF KANSAS CITY IN KANSAS p 105
12615 Parallel Pkwy, Kansas City KS 66109
Tel (913) 721-1570
SIC 8661 8211 8222 2711

JOHNSON COUNTY COMMUNITY COLLEGE p 791
12345 College Blvd, Overland Park KS 66210
Tel (913) 469-8500 SIC 8222 8221

KENTUCKY COMMUNITY AND TECHNICAL COLLEGE SYSTEM p 812
300 N Main St, Versailles KY 40383
Tel (859) 256-3100 SIC 8222

MAINE COMMUNITY COLLEGE SYSTEM p 898
323 State St, Augusta ME 04330
Tel (207) 629-4000 SIC 8222

ANNE ARUNDEL COMMUNITY COLLEGE p 92
101 College Pkwy, Arnold MD 21012
Tel (410) 777-2222 SIC 8222

COMMUNITY COLLEGE OF BALTIMORE COUNTY p 348
7200 Sollers Point Rd, Baltimore MD 21222
Tel (443) 840-3620 SIC 8222

EDUCATION AFFILIATES LLC p 479
5204 Campbell Blvd Ste A, Baltimore MD 21236
Tel (410) 633-2929 SIC 8222 6211

STATE OF MARYLAND p 1381
2901 Liberty Heights Ave, Baltimore MD 21215
Tel (410) 462-8300 SIC 8222

FREDERICK COMMUNITY COLLEGE p 576
7932 Opossumtown Pike, Frederick MD 21702
Tel (301) 846-2400 SIC 8222

MONTGOMERY COLLEGE p 986
900 Hungerford Dr, Rockville MD 20850
Tel (240) 567-5000 SIC 8222

PRINCE GEORGES COMMUNITY COLLEGE p 1176
301 Largo Rd, Upper Marlboro MD 20774
Tel (301) 336-6000 SIC 8221 8222

MASSACHUSETTS COMMUNITY COLLEGES p 916
15 Court Sq Ste 1100, Boston MA 02108
Tel (617) 542-2911 SIC 8222 9199

MASSASOIT COMMUNITY COLLEGE p 917
1 Massasoit Blvd, Brockton MA 02302
Tel (508) 588-9100 SIC 8222

MATHWORKS INC p 920
3 Apple Hill Dr, Natick MA 01760
Tel (508) 647-7000 SIC 7371 3823 8222

WASHTENAW COMMUNITY COLLEGE p 1580
4800 E Huron River Dr, Ann Arbor MI 48105
Tel (734) 973-3300 SIC 8222 8221

KELLOGG COMMUNITY COLLEGE FOUNDATION p 808
450 North Ave, Battle Creek MI 49017
Tel (269) 965-4142 SIC 8222

OAKLAND COMMUNITY COLLEGE FOUNDATION p 1071
2480 Opdyke Rd, Bloomfield Hills MI 48304
Tel (248) 341-2000 SIC 8222

DEARBORN PUBLIC SCHOOLS p 420
18700 Audette St, Dearborn MI 48124
Tel (313) 827-3000 SIC 8211 8222

BAKER COLLEGE p 145
1050 W Bristol Rd, Flint MI 48507
Tel (810) 767-7600 SIC 8222 8221

KALAMAZOO VALLEY COMMUNITY COLLEGE p 801
6767 W O Ave, Kalamazoo MI 49009
Tel (269) 488-4400 SIC 8222

LANSING COMMUNITY COLLEGE p 844
610 N Capitol Ave, Lansing MI 48933
Tel (517) 483-1957 SIC 8222

SCHOOLCRAFT COLLEGE p 1290
18600 Haggerty Rd, Livonia MI 48152
Tel (734) 462-4400 SIC 8222

CENTURY COLLEGE p 282
3300 Century Ave N, Saint Paul MN 55110
Tel (651) 779-3300 SIC 8222 9199

MISSISSIPPI GULF COAST COMMUNITY COLLEGE p 975
51 Main St, Perkinston MS 39573
Tel (601) 928-5211 SIC 8222

HINDS COMMUNITY COLLEGE DISTRICT PUBLIC IMPROVEMENT CORP p 695
501 E Main St, Raymond MS 39154
Tel (601) 857-5261 SIC 8222 8221

JUNIOR COLLEGE DISTRICT OF METROPOLITAN KANSAS CITY MISSOURI p 797
3200 Broadway Blvd, Kansas City MO 64111
Tel (816) 604-1000 SIC 8222

JUNIOR COLLEGE DISTRICT OF ST LOUIS p 797
300 S Broadway, Saint Louis MO 63102
Tel (314) 206-2150 SIC 8222

ST LOUIS COMMUNITY COLLEGE p 1369
5600 Oakland Ave, Saint Louis MO 63110
Tel (314) 644-9100 SIC 8222

COMMUNITY COLLEGE DISTRICT OF CENTRAL SW MO p 348
1001 E Chestnut Expy, Springfield MO 65802
Tel (417) 447-7500 SIC 8222 8221

SOUTHEAST COMMUNITY COLLEGE AREA p 1345
301 S 68th Street Pl, Lincoln NE 68510
Tel (402) 323-3400 SIC 8222

METROPOLITAN COMMUNITY COLLEGE p 955
5300 N 30th St, Omaha NE 68111
Tel (402) 457-2400 SIC 8222

COLLEGE OF SOUTHERN NEVADA FOUNDATION INC p 337
3200 E Cheyenne Ave, North Las Vegas NV 89030
Tel (702) 651-4000 SIC 8222

COMMUNITY COLLEGE SYSTEM OF NEW HAMPSHIRE p 348
26 College Dr, Concord NH 03301
Tel (603) 230-3500 SIC 8222

CAMDEN COUNTY COLLEGE p 244
200 College Dr, Blackwood NJ 08012
Tel (856) 227-7200 SIC 8222

MIDDLESEX COUNTY COLLEGE p 965
2600 Woodbridge Ave, Edison NJ 08837
Tel (732) 548-6000
SIC 8222 9111 8221 8211

BROOKDALE COMMUNITY COLLEGE INC p 217
765 Newman Springs Rd, Lincroft NJ 07738
Tel (732) 842-1900 SIC 8222

BERGEN COMMUNITY COLLEGE p 174
400 Paramus Rd Ste A330-C, Paramus NJ 07652
Tel (201) 447-7100 SIC 8222

PASSAIC COUNTY COMMUNITY COLLEGE (INC) p 1119
1 College Blvd, Paterson NJ 07505
Tel (973) 684-6868 SIC 8222 8221

COUNTY COLLEGE OF MORRIS p 375
214 Center Grove Rd, Randolph NJ 07869
Tel (973) 328-5000 SIC 8222

MERCER COUNTY COMMUNITY COLLEGE p 944
1200 Old Trenton Rd, Trenton NJ 08690
Tel (609) 586-4800 SIC 8222

▲ LINCOLN EDUCATIONAL SERVICES CORP p 866
200 Executive Dr Ste 340, West Orange NJ 07052
Tel (973) 736-9340 SIC 8222

■ LINCOLN TECHNICAL INSTITUTE INC p 868
200 Executive Dr Ste 340, West Orange NJ 07052
Tel (718) 246-4001 SIC 8222

CENTRAL NEW MEXICO COMMUNITY COLLEGE p 279
525 Buena Vista Dr Se, Albuquerque NM 87106
Tel (505) 224-4511 SIC 8249 8222

SANTA FE COMMUNITY COLLEGE p 1280
6401 S Richards Ave, Santa Fe NM 87508
Tel (505) 428-1000 SIC 8222 8221

EUGENIO MARIA DEHOSTOS COMMUNITY COLLEGE p 512
500 Grand Concourse, Bronx NY 10451
Tel (718) 518-4444 SIC 8222

ERIE COMMUNITY COLLEGE p 508
121 Ellicott St, Buffalo NY 14203
Tel (716) 842-2770 SIC 5942 8222

NASSAU COMMUNITY COLLEGE p 1008
1 Education Dr, Garden City NY 11530
Tel (516) 572-7501 SIC 8222 9411

BACK TO SCHOOL ACQUISITION LLC p 143
540 Madison Ave Fl 25, New York NY 10022
Tel (212) 339-8500 SIC 8222

FASHION INSTITUTE OF TECHNOLOGY p 531
7th Ave 27th St Rm C908, New York NY 10001
Tel (212) 217-7999 SIC 8222 9411

DUTCHESS COMMUNITY COLLEGE p 463
53 Pendell Rd, Poughkeepsie NY 12601
Tel (845) 431-8000 SIC 8222 9411

MONROE COMMUNITY COLLEGE p 985
1000 E Henrietta Rd, Rochester NY 14623
Tel (585) 292-2000 SIC 8222 9411

AMERICAN UNIVERSITY OF GREECE p 81
53 N Park Ave Ste 50, Rockville Centre NY 11570
Tel (516) 766-2718 SIC 8222

SUFFOLK COUNTY COMMUNITY COLLEGE p 1396
533 College Rd, Selden NY 11784
Tel (631) 451-4110 SIC 8222 9411

ONONDAGA COMMUNITY COLLEGE p 1088
4585 W Seneca Tpke, Syracuse NY 13215
Tel (315) 498-2622 SIC 8222 9411

HUDSON VALLEY COMMUNITY COLLEGE p 717
80 Vandenburgh Ave Ste 1, Troy NY 12180
Tel (518) 629-4822 SIC 8222 9411

WESTCHESTER COMMUNITY COLLEGE p 1596
75 Grasslands Rd, Valhalla NY 10595
Tel (914) 606-6600 SIC 8222 9411

CENTRAL PIEDMONT COMMUNITY COLLEGE p 279
1201 Elizabeth Ave, Charlotte NC 28204
Tel (704) 330-2722 SIC 8222 9411

FAYETTEVILLE TECHNICAL COMMUNITY COLLEGE FOUNDATION INC p 532
2201 Hull Rd, Fayetteville NC 28303
Tel (910) 678-8400 SIC 8222 9411

NORTH CAROLINA COMMUNITY COLLEGE SYSTEM p 1051
200 W Jones St, Raleigh NC 27603
Tel (919) 807-7100 SIC 8222 9411

WAKE TECHNICAL COMMUNITY COLLEGE FOUNDATION INC p 1572
9101 Fayetteville Rd, Raleigh NC 27603
Tel (919) 866-5000 SIC 8222 9411

CAPE FEAR COMMUNITY COLLEGE p 248
411 N Front St, Wilmington NC 28401
Tel (910) 362-7000 SIC 8222 9411

FORSYTH TECHNICAL COMMUNITY COLLEGE INC p 568
2100 Silas Creek Pkwy, Winston Salem NC 27103
Tel (336) 723-0371 SIC 8222 9411

PITT COMMUNITY COLLEGE p 1152
1986 Pitt Tech Dr, Winterville NC 28590
Tel (252) 321-4200 SIC 8222

CINCINNATI STATE TECHNICAL AND COMMUNITY COLLEGE p 307
3520 Central Pkwy, Cincinnati OH 45223
Tel (513) 569-1500 SIC 8222

CUYAHOGA COMMUNITY COLLEGE p 403
700 Carnegie Ave, Cleveland OH 44115
Tel (216) 987-6000 SIC 8222

COLUMBUS STATE COMMUNITY COLLEGE p 342
550 E Spring St, Columbus OH 43215
Tel (614) 287-2400 SIC 8222 8221

SINCLAIR COMMUNITY COLLEGE p 1326
444 W 3rd St, Dayton OH 45402
Tel (937) 512-2525 SIC 8222 8221

LORAIN COUNTY COMMUNITY COLLEGE DISTRICT p 878
1005 Abbe Rd N, Elyria OH 44035
Tel (440) 365-5222 SIC 8222

HOCKING TECHNICAL COLLEGE p 699
3301 Hocking Pkwy, Nelsonville OH 45764
Tel (740) 753-3591 SIC 8222 8249 8221

STARK STATE COLLEGE p 1379
6200 Frank Ave Nw, North Canton OH 44720
Tel (330) 494-6170 SIC 8222

OWENS COMMUNITY COLLEGE p 1100
30335 Oregon Rd, Perrysburg OH 43551
Tel (567) 661-7000 SIC 8222

LAKE COUNTY COMMUNITY COLLEGE DISTRICT p 838
7700 Clocktower Dr, Willoughby OH 44094
Tel (440) 525-7000 SIC 8222

ROSE STATE COLLEGE p 1250
6420 Se 15th St, Oklahoma City OK 73110
Tel (405) 733-7673 SIC 8222

TULSA COMMUNITY COLLEGE FOUNDATION p 1491
6111 E Skelly Dr Ste 200, Tulsa OK 74135
Tel (918) 595-7000 SIC 8222

LANE COMMUNITY COLLEGE p 843
4000 E 30th Ave, Eugene OR 97405
Tel (541) 463-3000 SIC 8222

MT HOOD COMMUNITY COLLEGE DISTRICT FOUNDATION INC p 997
26000 Se Stark St, Gresham OR 97030
Tel (503) 491-6422 SIC 8222 8221

CLACKAMAS COMMUNITY COLLEGE FOUNDATION p 321
19600 Molalla Ave, Oregon City OR 97045
Tel (503) 594-6100 SIC 8222

PORTLAND COMMUNITY COLLEGE FOUNDATION INC p 1163
12000 Sw 49th Ave, Portland OR 97219
Tel (971) 722-6111 SIC 8222

REED INSTITUTE p 1217
3203 Se Woodstock Blvd, Portland OR 97202
Tel (503) 771-1112 SIC 8222

NORTHAMPTON COMMUNITY COLLEGE p 1054
3835 Green Pond Rd, Bethlehem PA 18020
Tel (610) 861-5300 SIC 8222

MONTGOMERY COUNTY COMMUNITY COLLEGE p 986
340 Dekalb Pike, Blue Bell PA 19422
Tel (215) 641-6300 SIC 8222

HARRISBURG AREA COMMUNITY COLLEGE FOUNDATION p 664
1 Hacc Dr, Harrisburg PA 17110
Tel (717) 780-2300 SIC 8222

COMMUNITY COLLEGE OF ALLEGHENY COUNTY p 348
808 Ridge Ave, Pittsburgh PA 15212
Tel (412) 323-2323 SIC 8222

WESTMORELAND COUNTY COMMUNITY COLLEGE EDUCATIONAL FOUNDATION INC p 1602
145 Pavilion Ln, Youngwood PA 15697
Tel (724) 925-4000 SIC 8222

GRUPO EDUK INC p 643
Marginal Rd 20 Km 2 3, Guaynabo PR 00966
Tel (787) 982-3000
SIC 8249 8244 8243 8222 7231

INSTITUTO DE BANCA Y COMERCIO INC p 747
56 Carr 20, Guaynabo PR 00966
Tel (787) 982-3000
SIC 8249 8244 8243 8222 7231

MIDLANDS TECHNICAL COLLEGE FOUNDATION p 966
316 Beltline Blvd, Columbia SC 29205
Tel (803) 738-8324 SIC 8222 8221

GREENVILLE TECHNICAL COLLEGE PUBLIC FACILITIES CORP p 638
506 S Pleasantburg Dr, Greenville SC 29607
Tel (864) 250-8000 SIC 8222 8211 8221

UNIVERSITY AND COMMUNITY COLLEGE SYSTEM TENNESSEE STATE p 1518
1415 Murfreesboro Pike, Nashville TN 37217
Tel (615) 366-4400 SIC 8222

AMARILLO JUNIOR COLLEGE DISTRICT p 64
2201 S Washington St, Amarillo TX 79109
Tel (806) 371-5000 SIC 8222 8221

AUSTIN COMMUNITY COLLEGE p 132
5930 Middle Fiskville Rd, Austin TX 78752
Tel (512) 223-7000 SIC 8222

BLINN COLLEGE p 189
902 College Ave, Brenham TX 77833
Tel (979) 830-4000 SIC 8221 8222

DEL MAR COLLEGE DISTRICT p 423
101 Baldwin Blvd, Corpus Christi TX 78404
Tel (361) 698-1259 SIC 8222

EL PASO COUNTY COMMUNITY COLLEGE DISTRICT p 483
9050 Viscount Blvd, El Paso TX 79925
Tel (915) 831-3722 SIC 8222

HOUSTON COMMUNITY COLLEGE INC p 712
3100 Main St Ste Mc1148, Houston TX 77002
Tel (713) 718-5001 SIC 8222

SOUTH TEXAS COLLEGE p 1345
3201 Pecan Blvd, Mcallen TX 78501
Tel (956) 872-8311 SIC 8222

COLLIN COUNTY COMMUNITY COLLEGE DISTRICT p 337
3452 Spur 399, Mckinney TX 75069
Tel (972) 758-3100 SIC 8222

DALLAS COUNTY COMMUNITY COLLEGE DISTRICT p 410
4343 Interstate 30, Mesquite TX 75150
Tel (972) 860-7700 SIC 8222

SAN JACINTO COMMUNITY COLLEGE DISTRICT p 1277
4624 Fairmont Pkwy # 106, Pasadena TX 77504
Tel (281) 998-6306 SIC 8222

ALAMO COMMUNITY COLLEGE DISTRICT p 44
201 W Sheridan, San Antonio TX 78204
Tel (210) 485-0000 SIC 8222

NORTHWEST VISTA COLLEGE p 1060
3535 N Ellison Dr, San Antonio TX 78251
Tel (210) 706-9291 SIC 8222 8221

NHM COMMUNITY COLLEGE DISTRICT p 1042
5000 Research Forest Dr, Spring TX 77381
Tel (832) 813-6500 SIC 8222

LONE STAR COLLEGE SYSTEM p 875
5000 Research Forest Dr, The Woodlands TX 77381
Tel (832) 813-6500 SIC 8222

TEXAS STATE TECHNICAL COLLEGE p 1444
3801 Campus Dr Bldg 3210, Waco TX 76705
Tel (254) 799-3611 SIC 8221 8222

SALT LAKE COMMUNITY COLLEGE (INC) p 1273
4600 S Redwood Rd, Salt Lake City UT 84123
Tel (801) 957-4111 SIC 8222 8221

CHAMPLAIN COLLEGE INC p 287
246 S Willard St, Burlington VT 05401
Tel (802) 860-2700 SIC 8222

VIRGINIA PALACE NEWSPAPERS INC p 1559
150 W Brambleton Ave, Norfolk VA 23510
Tel (757) 446-2000 SIC 8222

VIRGINIA COMMUNITY COLLEGE SYSTEM OFFICE p 1558
300 Arboretum Pl Ste 200, North Chesterfield VA 23236
Tel (804) 819-4901 SIC 8222

GREEN RIVER COLLEGE p 637
12401 Se 320th St, Auburn WA 98092
Tel (253) 833-9111 SIC 8222 8299 8221

BELLEVUE COLLEGE FOUNDATION p 170
3000 Landerholm Cir Se, Bellevue WA 98007
Tel (425) 564-1000 SIC 8222 8221

EDMONDS COMMUNITY COLLEGE FOUNDATION p 478
20000 68th Ave W, Lynnwood WA 98036
Tel (425) 640-1459 SIC 8222

SEATTLE COLLEGES p 1297
1500 Harvard Ave, Seattle WA 98122
Tel (206) 934-4100 SIC 8222

TACOMA COMMUNITY COLLEGE p 1421
6501 S 19th St Bldg 14, Tacoma WA 98466
Tel (253) 566-5058 SIC 8222 8351

CHIPPEWA VALLEY TECHNICAL COLLEGE FOUNDATION INC p 301
620 W Clairemont Ave, Eau Claire WI 54701
Tel (715) 833-6200 SIC 8222

NORTHEAST WISCONSIN TECHNICAL COLLEGE DISTRICT p 1055
2740 W Mason St, Green Bay WI 54303
Tel (920) 498-5400 SIC 8221 8222

WESTERN TECHNICAL COLLEGE p 1600
400 7th St N, La Crosse WI 54601
Tel (608) 785-9200 SIC 8222 8221

MADISON AREA TECHNICAL COLLEGE DISTRICT p 894
1701 Wright St, Madison WI 53704
Tel (608) 246-6100 SIC 8222

WISCONSIN TECHNICAL COLLEGE SYSTEM BOARD p 1619
4622 University Ave, Madison WI 53705
Tel (608) 266-1207 SIC 8222

MILWAUKEE AREA TECHNICAL COLLEGE FOUNDATION INC p 972
700 W State St, Milwaukee WI 53233
Tel (414) 297-6792 SIC 8222 8221

WAUKESHA COUNTY AREA TECHNICAL COLLEGE DISTRICT p 1583
800 Main St, Pewaukee WI 53072
Tel (262) 691-5566 SIC 8222

WISCONSIN INDIANHEAD TECHNICAL COLLEGE FOUNDATION INC p 1618
505 Pine Ridge Dr, Shell Lake WI 54871
Tel (715) 468-2815 SIC 8222

SIC 8231 Libraries & Information Centers

HENRY E HUNTINGTON LIBRARY AND ART GALLERY p 684
1151 Oxford Rd, San Marino CA 91108
Tel (626) 405-2100 SIC 8231

CALIFORNIA INSTITUTE OF ARTS p 240
24700 Mcbean Pkwy, Valencia CA 91355
Tel (661) 255-1050 SIC 8221 8231 8249

■ LIBRARY OF CONGRESS p 863
101 Independence Ave Se, Washington DC 20540
Tel (202) 707-5000 SIC 8231 9121

FRIENDS OF LIBRARY FLAGLER COUNTY INC p 580
2500 Palm Coast Pkwy Nw, Palm Coast FL 32137
Tel (386) 445-1389 SIC 8231

CONSOLIDATED LIBRARY DISTRICT NO 3 p 360
15616 E Us Highway 24, Independence MO 64050
Tel (816) 836-8175 SIC 8231

DARTMOUTH COLLEGE p 413
6193 Hinman, Hanover NH 03755
Tel (603) 646-2191 SIC 8231

WAYNE PUBLIC LIBRARY INC p 1584
461 Valley Rd, Wayne NJ 07470
Tel (973) 694-4272 SIC 8231

BROOKLYN PUBLIC LIBRARY p 218
280 Cadman Plz W, Brooklyn NY 11201
Tel (718) 230-2100 SIC 8231

QUEENS BOROUGH PUBLIC LIBRARY p 1198
8911 Merrick Blvd, Jamaica NY 11432
Tel (718) 990-0700 SIC 8231

BORO OF MANHATTAN COMMUNITY CO p 201
199 Chambers St, New York NY 10007
Tel (212) 220-8000 SIC 8231

NEW YORK PUBLIC LIBRARY p 1036
5th Ave & 42nd St, New York NY 10018
Tel (212) 592-7400 SIC 8231

NEW YORK PUBLIC LIBRARY ASTOR LENOX AND TILDEN FOUNDATIONS p 1036
188 Madison Ave, New York NY 10016
Tel (212) 592-7403 SIC 8231

UPSTATE UNIVERSITY MEDICAL ASSOCIATES AT SYRACUSE INC p 1530
750 E Adams St, Syracuse NY 13210
Tel (315) 464-7087 SIC 8221 9411 8231

BOB JONES UNIVERSITY INC OF GREENVILLE S C p 196
1700 Wade Hampton Blvd, Greenville SC 29614
Tel (864) 242-5100
SIC 8221 8211 8231 8062 5942 0191

■ QUORUM HEALTH RESOURCES LLC p 1201
1573 Mallory Ln 200, Brentwood TN 37027
Tel (615) 371-7979
SIC 8742 8741 8082 8231 6324

GEORGE W BUSH PRESIDENTIAL LIBRARY FOUNDATION p 606
6166 N Rental Expy, Dallas TX 75206
Tel (214) 890-9943 SIC 8231

DYNIX CORP p 465
400 W 5050 N, Provo UT 84604
Tel (800) 288-8820 SIC 8231

KING COUNTY LIBRARY SYSTEM p 820
960 Newport Way Nw, Issaquah WA 98027
Tel (425) 369-3200 SIC 8231

SIC 8243 Data Processing Schools

▲ ORACLE CORP p 1091
500 Oracle Pkwy, Redwood City CA 94065
Tel (650) 506-7000
SIC 7372 7379 8243 3571 3674

■ ORACLE SYSTEMS CORP p 1091
500 Oracle Pkwy, Redwood City CA 94065
Tel (650) 506-7000 SIC 7372 7379 8243

EDUCATION TRAINING CORP p 479
3383 N State Road 7, Lauderdale Lakes FL 33319
Tel (954) 400-2000 SIC 8243

FCC HOLDINGS INC p 533
3383 N State Road 7, Lauderdale Lakes FL 33319
Tel (954) 535-8700 SIC 8243

EXECUTRAIN CORP p 518
2500 Northwinds Pkwy # 460, Alpharetta GA 30009
Tel (770) 667-7700 SIC 6794 8243

CDC SOFTWARE HOLDINGS INC p 270
Two Cncourse Pkwy Ste 800, Atlanta GA 39901
Tel (770) 351-9600 SIC 7372 7379 8243

▲ DEVRY EDUCATION GROUP INC p 434
3005 Highland Pkwy # 700, Downers Grove IL 60515
Tel (630) 515-7700
SIC 8221 8299 8249 8243

IFS NORTH AMERICA INC p 730
300 Park Blvd Ste 555, Itasca IL 60143
Tel (888) 437-4968 SIC 7372 7379 8243

ADAMS REMCO INC p 21
2612 Foundation Dr, South Bend IN 46628
Tel (574) 288-2113 SIC 5044 7629 8243

COMPUTER GENERATED SOLUTIONS INC p 352
200 Vesey St Fl 27, New York NY 10281
Tel (212) 408-3800
SIC 7373 7379 7371 8243

GLOBAL KNOWLEDGE TRAINING LLC p 617
9000 Regency Pkwy Ste 400, Cary NC 27518
Tel (919) 388-1064 SIC 8243

SAS INSTITUTE INC p 1282
100 Sas Campus Dr, Cary NC 27513
Tel (919) 677-8000 SIC 8243 7372

NEW HORIZONS WORLDWIDE INC p 1031
100 4 Falls Corporate Ctr # 408, Conshohocken PA 19428
Tel (888) 236-3625 SIC 6794 8243

MERCYHURST UNIVERSITY p 948
501 E 38th St, Erie PA 16546
Tel (814) 824-2000
SIC 8221 8243 8742 8299

■ EPLUS TECHNOLOGY OF PENNSYLVANIA INC p 505
130 Futura Dr, Pottstown PA 19464
Tel (610) 495-7800 SIC 5734 7378 8243

GRUPO EDUK INC p 643
Marginal Rd 20 Km 2 3, Guaynabo PR 00966
Tel (787) 982-3000
SIC 8249 8244 8243 8222 7231

INSTITUTO DE BANCA Y COMERCIO INC p 747
56 Carr 20, Guaynabo PR 00966
Tel (787) 982-3000
SIC 8249 8244 8243 8222 7231

BURNETT COMPANIES CONSOLIDATED INC p 228
9800 Richmond Ave Ste 800, Houston TX 77042
Tel (713) 977-4777 SIC 7361 8243

SOFTWARE FORENSICS INC p 1337
384 S 400 W Ste 200, Lindon UT 84042
Tel (801) 377-5410 SIC 7371 8243

SYMQUEST GROUP INC p 1414
30 Community Dr Ste 5, South Burlington VT 05403
Tel (802) 658-9890 SIC 5044 8243

▲ LEARNING TREE INTERNATIONAL INC p 850
13650 Dulles Tech Dr # 400, Herndon VA 20171
Tel (703) 709-9119 SIC 8243

SIC 8244 Business & Secretarial Schools

■ KAPLAN HIGHER EDUCATION LLC p 803
900 North Point Pkwy # 250, Alpharetta GA 30005
Tel (770) 360-6100 SIC 8221 8244

▲ CAREER EDUCATION CORP p 254
231 N Martingale Rd # 100, Schaumburg IL 60173
Tel (847) 781-3600 SIC 8221 8244 8299

SUFFOLK UNIVERSITY p 1396
120 Tremont St, Boston MA 02108
Tel (617) 573-8000 SIC 8221 8244

BRYANT & STRATTON COLLEGE INC p 221
2410 N Forest Rd Ste 101, Getzville NY 14068
Tel (716) 250-7500 SIC 8244

GRUPO EDUK INC p 643
Marginal Rd 20 Km 2 3, Guaynabo PR 00966
Tel (787) 982-3000
SIC 8249 8244 8243 8222 7231

INSTITUTO DE BANCA Y COMERCIO INC p 747
56 Carr 20, Guaynabo PR 00966
Tel (787) 982-3000
SIC 8249 8244 8243 8222 7231

SIC 8249 Vocational Schools Except High Schools

ALABAMA INSTITUTE FOR DEAF AND BLIND p 43
205 South St E, Talladega AL 35160
Tel (256) 761-3200 SIC 8249 8211

▲ UNIVERSAL TECHNICAL INSTITUTE INC p 1517
16220 N Scottsdale Rd # 100, Scottsdale AZ 85254
Tel (623) 445-9500 SIC 8249

GEMOLOGICAL INSTITUTE OF AMERICA INC p 598
5345 Armada Dr, Carlsbad CA 92008
Tel (760) 603-4000 SIC 8249 8733

INTERNATIONAL EDUCATION CORP p 755
16485 Laguna Canyon Rd # 300, Irvine CA 92618
Tel (949) 272-7200 SIC 8249

UNITED EDUCATION INSTITUTE p 1508
16485 Laguna Canyon Rd # 300, Irvine CA 92618
Tel (949) 272-7200 SIC 8249

RIVERSIDE COUNTY OFFICE OF EDUCATION p 1238
3939 13th St, Riverside CA 92501
Tel (951) 826-6530 SIC 8211 8249

■ KAPLAN HIGHER EDUCATION LLC p 803
9055 Balboa Ave, San Diego CA 92123
Tel (858) 279-4500 SIC 8249

SAN DIEGO COMMUNITY COLLEGE DISTRICT p 1276
3375 Camino Del Rio S, San Diego CA 92108
Tel (619) 388-6500 SIC 8222 8249 8221

■ URS HOLDINGS INC p 1530
600 Montgomery St Fl 25, San Francisco CA 94111
Tel (415) 774-2700
SIC 8711 7389 6531 8249 4581

CALIFORNIA INSTITUTE OF ARTS p 240
24700 Mcbean Pkwy, Valencia CA 91355
Tel (661) 255-1050 SIC 8221 8231 8249

ALTA COLLEGES INC p 61
10249 Church Ranch Way # 100, Westminster CO 80021
Tel (303) 846-1700 SIC 8249

PREMIER EDUCATION GROUP LIMITED PARTNERSHIP p 1170
545 Long Wharf Dr Fl 5, New Haven CT 06511
Tel (203) 672-2300 SIC 8249

■ TIGRENT ENTERPRISES INC p 1453
1612 Cape Coral Pkwy E, Cape Coral FL 33904
Tel (239) 542-0643 SIC 8249

▲ TIGRENT INC p 1453
1612 Cape Coral Pkwy E, Cape Coral FL 33904
Tel (239) 542-0643 SIC 8249

ADVENTIST UNIVERSITY OF HEALTH SCIENCES INC p 27
671 Winyah Dr, Orlando FL 32803
Tel (407) 303-7742 SIC 8249

SUNCOAST TECHNICAL COLLEGE p 1402
4748 Beneva Rd, Sarasota FL 34233
Tel (941) 361-6590 SIC 8249

CAE USA INC p 236
4908 Tampa West Blvd, Tampa FL 33634
Tel (813) 885-7481
SIC 3699 7373 8299 8249 8711

IDAHO STATE UNIVERSITY p 728
1455 Flightline, Pocatello ID 83204
Tel (208) 232-8485 SIC 8249

▲ DEVRY EDUCATION GROUP INC p 434
3005 Highland Pkwy # 700, Downers Grove IL 60515
Tel (630) 515-7700
SIC 8221 8299 8249 8243

ASCEND LEARNING LLC p 115
11161 Overbrook Rd, Leawood KS 66211
Tel (800) 667-7531 SIC 8249

INKCYCLE INC p 743
11100 W 82nd St, Lenexa KS 66214
Tel (913) 894-8387
SIC 3955 7699 7378 5045 8249 5734

UNIFIED SCHOOL DISTRICT 383 p 1503
2031 Poyntz Ave, Manhattan KS 66502
Tel (785) 587-2000 *SIC* 8211 8249

UNIFIED SCHOOL DISTRICT 259 p 1503
201 N Water St, Wichita KS 67202
Tel (316) 973-4000 *SIC* 8211 8249 8331

ATC GROUP HOLDINGS LLC p 124
221 Rue De Jean Ste 300, Lafayette LA 70508
Tel (337) 324-8777
SIC 8711 8732 8731 8249 8748

ATC GROUP SERVICES LLC p 124
221 Rue De Jean Ste 200, Lafayette LA 70508
Tel (337) 234-8777
SIC 8711 8734 8731 8249 8748

URS FEDERAL SUPPORT SERVICES INC p 1530
20501 Seneca Meadows Pkwy # 300, Germantown MD 20876
Tel (301) 944-3100 *SIC* 8249 4581

CORINTHIAN SCHOOLS INC p 370
124 Washington St Ste 101, Foxboro MA 02035
Tel (714) 427-3001 *SIC* 8249

BAYSTATE HEALTH INC p 162
759 Chestnut St, Springfield MA 01199
Tel (413) 784-0000 *SIC* 8062 8221 8249

MICHIGAN DEPARTMENT OF HUMAN SERVICES p 961
235 S Grand Ave, Lansing MI 48933
Tel (517) 373-2000 *SIC* 9441 8249

BUREAU OF ENGRAVING INC p 226
6465 Wayzata Blvd Ste 240, Minneapolis MN 55426
Tel (612) 788-1000 *SIC* 2752 8249

VATTEROTT EDUCATIONAL CENTERS INC p 1545
7730 Carondelet Ave # 400, Saint Louis MO 63105
Tel (314) 264-1500 *SIC* 8249

AHS HOSPITAL CORP p 37
465 South St, Morristown NJ 07960
Tel (973) 660-3100 *SIC* 8062 8249

ATLANTIC HEALTH SYSTEM INC p 126
475 South St, Morristown NJ 07960
Tel (973) 660-3100 *SIC* 8249 8062

CENTRAL NEW MEXICO COMMUNITY COLLEGE p 279
525 Buena Vista Dr Se, Albuquerque NM 87106
Tel (505) 224-4511 *SIC* 8249 8222

ALBANY MEDICAL CENTER HOSPITAL p 45
43 New Scotland Ave, Albany NY 12208
Tel (518) 262-3125 *SIC* 8062 8249

ALBANY MEDICAL COLLEGE p 45
47 New Scotland Ave, Albany NY 12208
Tel (518) 262-6008 *SIC* 8249

ALBERT EINSTEIN COLLEGE OF MEDICINE INC p 46
1300 Morris Park Ave, Bronx NY 10461
Tel (718) 920-6758 *SIC* 8249

COLD SPRING HARBOR LABORATORY ASSOCIATION INC p 335
1 Bungtown Rd, Cold Spring Harbor NY 11724
Tel (516) 367-8446
SIC 8733 2731 2741 8249

ICAHN SCHOOL OF MEDICINE AT MOUNT SINAI p 726
1 Gustave L Levy Pl, New York NY 10029
Tel (212) 241-6500 *SIC* 8249

BOARD OF COOPERATIVE EDUCATIONAL SERVICES p 195
201 Sunrise Hwy W, Patchogue NY 11772
Tel (631) 289-2200 *SIC* 8249

HOCKING TECHNICAL COLLEGE p 699
3301 Hocking Pkwy, Nelsonville OH 45764
Tel (740) 753-3591 *SIC* 8222 8249 8221

■ **BOEING AEROSPACE OPERATIONS INC** p 197
6001 S Air Depot Blvd, Oklahoma City OK 73135
Tel (405) 622-6000 *SIC* 8711 8249

SAINT LUKES HOSPITAL OF BETHLEHEM PENNSYLVANIA p 1270
801 Ostrum St, Bethlehem PA 18015
Tel (484) 526-4000 *SIC* 8062 8249

HAY GROUP HOLDINGS INC p 670
1650 Arch St Ste 2300, Philadelphia PA 19103
Tel (215) 861-2000 *SIC* 8742 8249 8733

EMPIRE BEAUTY SCHOOL INC p 493
396 Pttsvlle St Clair Hwy, Pottsville PA 17901
Tel (570) 429-4321 *SIC* 8249

GRUPO EDUK INC p 643
Marginal Rd 20 Km 2 3, Guaynabo PR 00966
Tel (787) 982-3000
SIC 8249 8244 8243 8222 7231

INSTITUTO DE BANCA Y COMERCIO INC p 747
56 Carr 20, Guaynabo PR 00966
Tel (787) 982-3000
SIC 8249 8244 8243 8222 7231

MANAGEMENT & TRAINING CORP p 900
500 N Market Place Dr # 100, Centerville UT 84014
Tel (801) 693-2600
SIC 8744 8331 7349 8741 8249

SIC 8299 Schools & Educational Svcs, NEC

EDUCATION CORP OF AMERICA p 479
3660 Grandview Pkwy # 300, Birmingham AL 35243
Tel (205) 329-7900 *SIC* 8299

DEPARTMENT OF CORRECTIONS ALASKA p 430
802 3rd St, Douglas AK 99824
Tel (907) 465-4652
SIC 9223 8322 9441 8299

▲ **APOLLO EDUCATION GROUP INC** p 97
4025 S Riverpoint Pkwy, Phoenix AZ 85040
Tel (480) 966-5394 *SIC* 8221 8299 8748

ROGERS PUBLIC SCHOOLS p 1246
220 S 5th St, Rogers AR 72756
Tel (479) 631-3696 *SIC* 8299

ALAMEDA UNIFIED SCHOOL DISTRICT p 44
2060 Challenger Dr, Alameda CA 94501
Tel (510) 337-7060 *SIC* 8211 8299

CARLSBAD SD MICHELLE WHS p 257
6225 El Camino Real Ste P, Carlsbad CA 92009
Tel (760) 331-5000 *SIC* 8299

ORANGE COAST COLLEGE p 1091
2701 Fairview Rd, Costa Mesa CA 92626
Tel (714) 432-5772 *SIC* 8221 8299

ELI AND EDYTHE BROAD FOUNDATION p 486
2121 Avenue Of The Stars 30t, Los Angeles CA 90067
Tel (310) 954-5050 *SIC* 8299

COMMUNITY COLLEGE FOUNDATION p 348
1901 Royal Oaks Dr # 100, Sacramento CA 95815
Tel (916) 418-5100 *SIC* 8299 8748

UNIVERSITY ENTERPRISES INC p 1518
6000 J St, Sacramento CA 95819
Tel (916) 278-6672 *SIC* 8299 8741

ROMAN CATHOLIC ARCHDIOCESE OF SAN FRANCISCO p 1248
1 Peter Yorke Way 1, San Francisco CA 94109
Tel (415) 614-5500 *SIC* 8299

STEPHENS INSTITUTE p 1386
79 New Montgomery St, San Francisco CA 94105
Tel (415) 274-2200 *SIC* 8299 8221

SENECA FAMILY OF AGENCIES p 1303
15942 Foothill Blvd, San Leandro CA 94578
Tel (510) 317-1444 *SIC* 8322 8299 8082

THINK TOGETHER p 1448
2101 E 4th St Ste 200b, Santa Ana CA 92705
Tel (714) 543-3807 *SIC* 8299

ITUTOR GROUP INC p 769
3945 Freedom Cir Ste 500, Santa Clara CA 95054
Tel (408) 982-9401 *SIC* 8299

VISALIA UNIFIED SCHOOL DISTRICT p 1560
5000 W Cypress Ave, Visalia CA 93277
Tel (559) 730-7529 *SIC* 8211 8299

CAPITOL REGION EDUCATION COUNCIL FOUNDATION INC p 251
111 Charter Oak Ave, Hartford CT 06106
Tel (860) 524-4068 *SIC* 8299

CCMC CORP p 270
282 Washington St, Hartford CT 06106
Tel (860) 545-9490 *SIC* 8069 7389 8299

LEARN p 850
44 Hatchetts Hill Rd, Old Lyme CT 06371
Tel (860) 434-4800 *SIC* 8299

AMERICANS FOR PROSPERITY p 81
1728 M St Nw, Washington DC 20036
Tel (866) 730-0150 *SIC* 8299

ASPEN INSTITUTE p 118
1 Dupont Cir Nw Ste 700, Washington DC 20036
Tel (202) 736-5800 *SIC* 8299

■ **LEGACY EDUCATION ALLIANCE INC** p 852
1612 Cape Coral Pkwy E, Cape Coral FL 33904
Tel (239) 542-0643 *SIC* 8299

EARLY LEARNING COALITION OF BROWARD COUNTY INC p 469
6301 Nw 5th Way Ste 3400, Fort Lauderdale FL 33309
Tel (954) 377-2188 *SIC* 8299

■ **KAPLAN INC** p 803
6301 Kaplan Univ Ave, Fort Lauderdale FL 33309
Tel (212) 492-5800
SIC 8299 7361 7372 2731

STEP UP FOR STUDENTS INC p 1386
4655 Salisbury Rd Ste 400, Jacksonville FL 32256
Tel (877) 735-7837 *SIC* 8299

FLORIDA INSTITUTE OF TECHNOLOGY INC p 559
150 W University Blvd Ofc, Melbourne FL 32901
Tel (321) 674-8000 *SIC* 8221 4581 8299

CAE USA INC p 236
4908 Tampa West Blvd, Tampa FL 33634
Tel (813) 885-7481
SIC 3699 7373 8299 8249 8711

ROBERT W WOODRUFF ARTS CENTER INC p 1241
1280 Peachtree St Ne, Atlanta GA 30309
Tel (404) 733-4200
SIC 7929 8412 6512 8299

COLLEGE OF WESTERN IDAHO p 337
6056 Birch Ln, Nampa ID 83687
Tel (208) 562-3200 *SIC* 8299

ART INSTITUTE OF CHICAGO p 113
111 S Michigan Ave, Chicago IL 60603
Tel (312) 443-3600 *SIC* 8412 8299

BRAIN HURRICANE LLC p 207
2510 S Christiana Ave, Chicago IL 60623
Tel (312) 577-0066 *SIC* 8299

INSTITUTE FOR INTERNATIONAL EDUCATION OF STUDENTS p 747
33 W Monroe St Ste 2300, Chicago IL 60603
Tel (312) 944-1750 *SIC* 8299

MID-CITY TRUCK DRIVING ACADEMY INC p 963
6740 W Belmont Ave, Chicago IL 60634
Tel (773) 725-3000 *SIC* 8299 5511

MOODY BIBLE INSTITUTE OF CHICAGO p 987
820 N La Salle Dr, Chicago IL 60610
Tel (312) 329-4000
SIC 8661 8299 8221 4832 2731

NATIONAL ASSOCIATION OF REALTORS p 1010
430 N Michigan Ave Lowr 2, Chicago IL 60611
Tel (800) 874-6500 *SIC* 8611 2721 8299

■ **BECKER PROFESSIONAL DEVELOPMENT CORP** p 167
3005 Highland Pkwy # 700, Downers Grove IL 60515
Tel (630) 515-7700 *SIC* 8299

▲ **DEVRY EDUCATION GROUP INC** p 434
3005 Highland Pkwy # 700, Downers Grove IL 60515
Tel (630) 515-7700
SIC 8221 8299 8249 8243

RASMUSSEN INC p 1209
1415 W 22nd St Ste 400, Oak Brook IL 60523
Tel (630) 366-2800 *SIC* 8299

▲ **CAREER EDUCATION CORP** p 254
231 N Martingale Rd # 100, Schaumburg IL 60173
Tel (847) 781-3600 *SIC* 8221 8244 8299

INDIANA UNIVERSITY FOUNDATION INC p 739
1500 N State Road 46 Byp, Bloomington IN 47408
Tel (812) 855-8311 *SIC* 8299

WATERLOO COMMUNITY SCHOOL DISTRICT INC p 1582
1516 Washington St, Waterloo IA 50702
Tel (319) 433-1800 *SIC* 8299

CONNECTIONS EDUCATION LLC p 357
1001 Fleet St Fl 5, Baltimore MD 21202
Tel (443) 529-1000 *SIC* 8299

EDGE ACQUISITION LLC p 477
1001 Fleet St, Baltimore MD 21202
Tel (410) 843-8000 *SIC* 8299 8748

JHPIEGO CORP p 785
1615 Thames St Ste 310, Baltimore MD 21231
Tel (410) 537-1800 *SIC* 8299

LAUREATE EDUCATION INC p 847
650 S Exeter St Fl 7, Baltimore MD 21202
Tel (410) 843-6100 *SIC* 8299

UNIVERSITY OF MARYLAND p 1522
220 Arch St Fl 14, Baltimore MD 21201
Tel (410) 706-2929 *SIC* 8221 8299

INTERNATIONAL BACCALAUREATE ORGANIZATION INC p 754
7501 Wisconsin Ave # 200, Bethesda MD 20814
Tel (301) 202-3000 *SIC* 8299

EDUCATE INC p 479
4 North Park Dr Ste 500, Hunt Valley MD 21030
Tel (410) 843-8000 *SIC* 8299

▲ **2U INC** p 2
8201 Corporate Dr Ste 900, Landover MD 20785
Tel (301) 892-4350 *SIC* 7372 8748 8299

CITY YEAR INC p 320
287 Columbus Ave Ste 1, Boston MA 02116
Tel (617) 927-2500 *SIC* 8299

MUSEUM OF FINE ARTS p 1002
465 Huntington Ave, Boston MA 02115
Tel (617) 369-3861 *SIC* 8412 5961 8299

PR EDUCATION LLC p 1166
111 Speen St, Framingham MA 01701
Tel (508) 663-5050 *SIC* 8748 8299

PRINCETON REVIEW INC p 1177
24 Prime Park Way Ste 201, Natick MA 01760
Tel (800) 273-8439 *SIC* 8748 8299

LEARNING CARE GROUP INC p 850
21333 Haggerty Rd Ste 300, Novi MI 48375
Tel (248) 697-9000 *SIC* 8351 8299

CONCORDIA COLLEGE CORP p 355
901 8th St S, Moorhead MN 56562
Tel (218) 299-4000 *SIC* 8299

INDEPENDENT SCHOOL DIST 625 p 737
360 Colborne St, Saint Paul MN 55102
Tel (651) 767-8100 *SIC* 8299

MACALESTER COLLEGE p 891
200 Amherst St, Saint Paul MN 55105
Tel (651) 698-8650 *SIC* 8299

MISSOULA COUNTY PUBLIC SCHOOLS p 976
215 S 6th St W, Missoula MT 59801
Tel (406) 728-2400 *SIC* 8299 8211

WATKINS AND SHEPARD TRUCKING INC p 1582
N6400 Hwy 10 W, Missoula MT 59801
Tel (406) 532-6121 *SIC* 4213 8299

BELLEVUE PUBLIC SCHOOLS p 170
2600 Arboretum Dr, Bellevue NE 68005
Tel (402) 293-4000 *SIC* 8299 8748 8211

CATAPULT LEARNING LLC p 265
2 Aquarium Dr Ste 100, Camden NJ 08103
Tel (856) 831-7909 *SIC* 8299

BANCROFT NEUROHEALTH A NEW JERSEY NONPROFIT CORP p 150
1255 Caldwell Rd, Cherry Hill NJ 08034
Tel (856) 348-1183 *SIC* 8361 8299 8211

HUNTINGTON LEARNING CORP p 720
496 Kinderkamack Rd G01, Oradell NJ 07649
Tel (201) 261-8400 *SIC* 8299

BERLITZ CORP p 175
7 Roszel Rd Fl 3, Princeton NJ 08540
Tel (207) 828-3768 *SIC* 8299 8748

BERLITZ LANGUAGES (UNITED STATES) INC p 175
7 Roszel Rd Fl 3, Princeton NJ 08540
Tel (609) 759-5371 *SIC* 8299 7389 2731

KUMON NORTH AMERICA INC p 832
300 Frank W Burr Blvd # 6, Teaneck NJ 07666
Tel (201) 928-0444 *SIC* 8299

EDUCATION DEPARTMENT NEW YORK STATE p 479
89 Washington Ave, Albany NY 12234
Tel (518) 474-3852 *SIC* 8299 9411

BROOME-TIOGA BOARD OF COOPERATIVE EDUCATIONAL SERVICES p 218
435 Glenwood Rd, Binghamton NY 13905
Tel (607) 763-3618 *SIC* 8299

NEW YORK BOTANICAL GARDEN p 1034
2900 Southern Blvd, Bronx NY 10458
Tel (718) 817-8779 *SIC* 8422 8299

AMPLIFY EDUCATION INC p 86
55 Washington St Ste 900, Brooklyn NY 11201
Tel (212) 213-8177 *SIC* 7371 8299

MONROE 1 BOCES EDUCATIONAL FOUNDATION INC p 985
41 Oconnor Rd, Fairport NY 14450
Tel (585) 377-4660 *SIC* 8299

AMERICAN MANAGEMENT ASSOCIATION INTERNATIONAL p 75
1601 Broadway Fl 7, New York NY 10019
Tel (212) 586-8100
SIC 8299 2731 8621 7812 2721

COLLEGE ENTRANCE EXAMINATION BOARD p 336
250 Vesey St, New York NY 10281
Tel (212) 713-8000 *SIC* 8299 8211 2732

GEORGE WASHINGTON CARVER ACADEMY p 606
45 Broadway Fl 17, New York NY 10006
Tel (404) 841-2305 *SIC* 8299

HARLEM CHILDRENS ZONE INC p 661
35 E 125th St, New York NY 10035
Tel (212) 534-0700 *SIC* 8299

INSTITUTE OF INTERNATIONAL EDUCATION INC p 747
809 United Nations Plz, New York NY 10017
Tel (212) 883-8200 *SIC* 8299

JUILLIARD SCHOOL p 797
60 Lincoln Center Plz, New York NY 10023
Tel (212) 799-5000
SIC 8299 7911 5942 8221

■ **KAPLAN K12 LEARNING SERVICES LLC** p 803
395 Hudson St Fl 4, New York NY 10014
Tel (888) 527-5268 *SIC* 8299

MCGRAW-HILL GLOBAL EDUCATION LLC p 929
2 Penn Plz Fl 20, New York NY 10121
Tel (646) 766-2000 *SIC* 8299

SCOPE INC p 1293
100 Lawrence Ave Ste 105, Smithtown NY 11787
Tel (631) 360-0800 *SIC* 8299

AMERICAN INSTITUTE OF CERTIFIED PUBLIC ACCOUNTANTS p 75
220 Leigh Farm Rd, Durham NC 27707
Tel (919) 402-0682 *SIC* 8299 8621 2721

CENTER FOR CREATIVE LEADERSHIP INC p 275
1 Leadership Pl, Greensboro NC 27410
Tel (336) 288-7210 *SIC* 8299 2731

COLUMBUS PUBLIC SCHOOL DISTRICT p 342
270 E State St Fl 3, Columbus OH 43215
Tel (614) 365-5000 *SIC* 8211 8299

CLEVELAND HEIGHTS BOARD OF EDUCATION p 325
2155 Miramar Blvd, University Heights OH 44118
Tel (216) 371-7171 *SIC* 8299

■ **ABX AIR INC** p 13
145 Hunter Dr, Wilmington OH 45177
Tel (937) 382-5591
SIC 4513 5088 4581 8299

■ **KC DISTANCE LEARNING INC** p 806
830 Ne Holladay St # 100, Portland OR 97232
Tel (503) 731-5427 *SIC* 8299

KINDERCARE EDUCATION LLC p 819
650 Ne Holladay St # 1400, Portland OR 97232
Tel (503) 872-1300 *SIC* 8299

NORTHWEST EVALUATION ASSOCIATION p 1059
121 Nw Everett St, Portland OR 97209
Tel (503) 624-1951 *SIC* 8299 8748

MERCYHURST UNIVERSITY p 948
501 E 38th St, Erie PA 16546
Tel (814) 824-2000
SIC 8221 8243 8742 8299

NHS PENNYLVANIA p 1042
620 Germantown Pike, Lafayette Hill PA 19444
Tel (610) 238-4403 *SIC* 8699 8299

LANCASTER-LEBANON INTERMEDIATE UNIT 13 (INC) p 841
1020 New Holland Ave, Lancaster PA 17601
Tel (717) 606-1600 *SIC* 8299

REGENTS OF MERCERSBURG COLLEGE p 1219
300 E Seminary St, Mercersburg PA 17236
Tel (717) 328-6110 *SIC* 8299

LINCOLN INTERMEDIATE UNIT 12 p 867
65 Billerbeck St, New Oxford PA 17350
Tel (717) 624-4616 *SIC* 8299

▲ **EDUCATION MANAGEMENT CORP** p 479
210 6th Ave Fl 33, Pittsburgh PA 15222
Tel (412) 562-0900 *SIC* 8299

■ **EEG INC** p 480
396 Pttsvle St Clair Hwy, Pottsville PA 17901
Tel (570) 429-4321 *SIC* 8299

ACADEMIC ACQUISITION CORP p 13
1615 W Chester Pike, West Chester PA 19382
Tel (484) 947-2000 *SIC* 8211 8299

NOBEL LEARNING COMMUNITIES INC p 1046
1615 W Chester Pike # 200, West Chester PA 19382
Tel (484) 947-2000 *SIC* 8211 8299

YORK NAMI PA COUNTY p 1637
140 Roosevelt Ave Ste 200, York PA 17401
Tel (717) 848-3784 *SIC* 8299

INSTITUCION EDUCATIVA NETS INC p 747
Urb Sierra Bayamn, Bayamon PR 00961
Tel (787) 785-5511 *SIC* 8299 8322

LEXINGTON COUNTY HEALTH SERVICES DISTRICT INC p 859
2720 Sunset Blvd, West Columbia SC 29169
Tel (803) 791-2000
SIC 8062 8011 8299 8051

MEMPHIS CITY BOARD OF EDUCATIO p 942
2597 Avery Ave, Memphis TN 38112
Tel (901) 416-5444 *SIC* 8299

CHANCELIGHT INC p 287
1321 Murfreesboro Pike, Nashville TN 37217
Tel (615) 361-4000 *SIC* 8299

▲ **CORECIVIC INC** p 369
10 Burton Hills Blvd, Nashville TN 37215
Tel (615) 263-3000
SIC 6798 8744 8361 8299

■ **KEYSTONE EDUCATION AND YOUTH SERVICES LLC** p 815
3401 West End Ave Ste 400, Nashville TN 37203
Tel (615) 250-0000 *SIC* 8299 8322

TEXAS A&M HEALTH SCIENCE CENTER p 1442
200 Technology Way, College Station TX 77845
Tel (979) 436-9200 *SIC* 8299 8221

■ **CAMBIUM LEARNING GROUP INC** p 244
17855 Dallas Pkwy Ste 400, Dallas TX 75287
Tel (214) 932-9500 *SIC* 8299 8211 7372

HARRIS COUNTY DEPARTMENT OF EDUCATION PUBLIC FACILITY CORP p 663
6300 Irvington Blvd, Houston TX 77022
Tel (713) 694-6300 *SIC* 8299

SHUNA & CAM p 1319
805 Van Zandt Ave Apt G, Marshall TX 75670
Tel (903) 578-5478 *SIC* 8299

TEMPLE INDEPENDENT SCHOOL DISTRICT p 1436
200 N 23rd St, Temple TX 76504
Tel (254) 215-7513 *SIC* 8211 8299

WESTERN GOVERNORS UNIVERSITY p 1598
4001 S 700 E Ste 700, Salt Lake City UT 84107
Tel (801) 274-3280 *SIC* 8299 8221

WORLD LEARNING INC p 1625
1 Kipling Rd, Brattleboro VT 05301
Tel (802) 257-7751 *SIC* 8221 8299

KING ARTHUR FLOUR CO INC p 820
135 Us Route 5 S, Norwich VT 05055
Tel (802) 649-3881
SIC 5149 5961 5461 8299

▲ GRAHAM HOLDINGS CO p 629
1300 17th St N Ste 1700, Arlington VA 22209
Tel (703) 345-6300
SIC 8299 4833 4841 2721

IMAGINE SCHOOLS NON-PROFIT INC p 733
1005 N Glebe Rd Ste 610, Arlington VA 22201
Tel (703) 527-2600 *SIC* 8299

▲ K12 INC p 799
2300 Corporate Park Dr, Herndon VA 20171
Tel (703) 483-7000 *SIC* 8211 8299

CENTRAL VIRGINIA TRAINING CENTER p 281
521 Colony Rd, Madison Heights VA 24572
Tel (804) 947-6313 *SIC* 8299

WILLIAMSBURG JAMES CITY COUNTY PUBLIC SCHOOLS p 1612
117 Ironbound Rd, Williamsburg VA 23185
Tel (757) 603-6400 *SIC* 8299

GREEN RIVER COLLEGE p 637
12401 Se 320th St, Auburn WA 98092
Tel (253) 833-9111 *SIC* 8222 8299 8221

PENINSULA SCHOOL DISTRICT p 1129
14015 62nd Ave Nw, Gig Harbor WA 98332
Tel (253) 530-1000 *SIC* 8299

UNIVERSITY OF WISCONSIN MEDICAL FOUNDATION INC p 1527
7974 Uw Health Ct, Middleton WI 53562
Tel (608) 821-4223
SIC 8221 8011 2834 8299 8042 8043

CARE p 254
2000 Polk St, Stevens Point WI 54481
Tel (715) 345-5620 *SIC* 8299

NATIONAL OUTDOOR LEADERSHIP SCHOOL p 1014
284 Lincoln St, Lander WY 82520
Tel (800) 710-6657 *SIC* 8299 5941

SIC 8322 Individual & Family Social Svcs

EASTERN HEALTH SYSTEM INC p 472
Medical Park E Dr Bldg 1, Birmingham AL 35235
Tel (205) 838-3996
SIC 8062 8082 8051 8011 8322 8093

SEQUEL TSI HOLDINGS LLC p 1306
1131 Eagletree Ln Sw # 300, Huntsville AL 35801
Tel (256) 880-3339 *SIC* 8361 8322

SEQUEL YOUTH AND FAMILY SERVICES LLC p 1306
1131 Eagletree Ln Sw, Huntsville AL 35801
Tel (256) 880-3339 *SIC* 8322 8361

THREE SPRINGS INC p 1450
1131 Eagletree Ln Sw, Huntsville AL 35801
Tel (256) 880-3339 *SIC* 8322 8093

DEPARTMENT OF CORRECTIONS ALASKA p 430
802 3rd St, Douglas AK 99824
Tel (907) 465-4652
SIC 9223 8322 9441 8299

DENA NENA HENASH p 428
122 1st Ave Ste 600, Fairbanks AK 99701
Tel (907) 452-8251
SIC 8011 8331 8322 8093

RISE INC p 1236
4554 E Inverness Ave # 134, Mesa AZ 85206
Tel (480) 497-1889 *SIC* 8322

MAKE-A-WISH FOUNDATION OF AMERICA p 899
4742 N 24th St Ste 400, Phoenix AZ 85016
Tel (602) 279-9474 *SIC* 8322

ST MARYS FOOD BANK ALLIANCE p 1371
2831 N 31st Ave, Phoenix AZ 85009
Tel (602) 242-3663 *SIC* 8322

VALLEY OF SUN YOUNG MENS CHRISTIAN ASSOCIATION p 1541
350 N 1st Ave, Phoenix AZ 85003
Tel (602) 257-5120 *SIC* 8641 8322

COMMUNITY PROVIDER OF ENRICHMENT SERVICES INC p 350
4825 N Sabino Canyon Rd, Tucson AZ 85750
Tel (480) 516-0298 *SIC* 8322

VISIONQUEST NONPROFIT CORP p 1561
600 N Swan Rd, Tucson AZ 85711
Tel (520) 881-3950 *SIC* 8361 8211 8322

GGNSC HOLDINGS LLC p 610
1000 Fianna Way, Fort Smith AR 72919
Tel (479) 201-2000
SIC 8059 8051 8082 8322

ARKANSAS ELDER OUTREACH OF LITTLE ROCK p 109
12111 Hinson Rd, Little Rock AR 72212
Tel (225) 906-2274 *SIC* 8322

EASTERN LOS ANGELES REGIONAL CENTER FOR DEVELOPMENTALLY DISABLED INC p 472
1000 S Fremont Ave # 23, Alhambra CA 91803
Tel (626) 299-4700 *SIC* 8322

KERN REGIONAL CENTER p 813
3200 N Sillect Ave, Bakersfield CA 93308
Tel (661) 327-8531 *SIC* 8322

SAN ANDREAS REGIONAL CENTER p 1275
300 Orchard Cy Dr Ste 170, Campbell CA 95008
Tel (408) 374-9960 *SIC* 8322

SENIOR KISCO LIVING LLC p 1304
5790 Fleet St Ste 300, Carlsbad CA 92008
Tel (760) 804-5900 *SIC* 8322 8741

■ ASPEN EDUCATION GROUP INC p 118
17777 Center Court Dr N # 300, Cerritos CA 90703
Tel (562) 467-5500 *SIC* 8741 8322

CHILD CARE RESOURCE CENTER INC p 298
20001 Prairie St, Chatsworth CA 91311
Tel (818) 717-1000 *SIC* 8322

COASTAL DEVELOPMENTAL SERVICES FOUNDATION p 331
5901 Green Valley Cir # 320, Culver City CA 90230
Tel (310) 258-4000 *SIC* 8322

■ CRC HEALTH CORP p 389
20400 Stevens Creek Blvd, Cupertino CA 95014
Tel (877) 272-8668
SIC 8069 8099 8322 8093

RANCHO LOS AMIGOS NATIONAL REHABILIATATION CENTER p 1207
7601 Imperial Hwy, Downey CA 90242
Tel (562) 401-7111 *SIC* 8322

HALLMARK REHABILITATION GP LLC p 655
27442 Portola Pkwy # 200, El Toro CA 92610
Tel (949) 282-5900 *SIC* 8322

FRESNO COUNTY ECONOMIC OPPORTUNITIES COMMISSION p 579
1920 Mariposa Mall # 300, Fresno CA 93721
Tel (559) 263-1010 *SIC* 8322 8399

GARDENA HOSPITAL LP p 591
1145 W Redondo Beach Blvd, Gardena CA 90247
Tel (310) 532-4200 *SIC* 8062 8322 8011

DIRECT RELIEF p 441
27 S La Patera Ln, Goleta CA 93117
Tel (805) 964-4767 *SIC* 8322

SENIOR MBK LIVING LLC p 1304
4 Park Plz Ste 400, Irvine CA 92614
Tel (949) 242-1400 *SIC* 8322

■ SUN HEALTHCARE GROUP INC p 1400
18831 Von Karman Ave # 400, Irvine CA 92612
Tel (949) 255-7100 *SIC* 8011 8322

CRYSTAL STAIRS INC p 397
5110 W Goldleaf Cir # 150, Los Angeles CA 90056
Tel (323) 299-8998 *SIC* 8322

INTERNATIONAL MEDICAL CORPS p 756
12400 Wilshire Blvd # 1500, Los Angeles CA 90025
Tel (310) 826-7800 *SIC* 8322

LIVHOME INC p 871
5670 Wilshire Blvd # 500, Los Angeles CA 90036
Tel (800) 807-5854 *SIC* 8322

LOS ANGELES COUNTY DEVELOPMENTAL SERVICES FOUNDATION p 878
3303 Wilshire Blvd # 700, Los Angeles CA 90010
Tel (213) 383-1300 *SIC* 8099 8322 8093

LOS ANGELES FIREMAN RELIEF ASSOCIATION INC p 878
2900 W Temple St, Los Angeles CA 90026
Tel (800) 244-3439 *SIC* 8322

VOLUNTEERS OF AMERICA OF LOS ANGELES p 1565
3600 Wilshire Blvd # 1500, Los Angeles CA 90010
Tel (213) 389-1500 *SIC* 8322 6531

NORTH BAY DEVELOPMENTAL DISABILITIES SERVICES INC p 1051
10 Executive Ct Ste A, Napa CA 94558
Tel (707) 256-1224 *SIC* 8331 8322

REGIONAL CENTER OF EAST BAY INC p 1219
7677 Oakport St Ste 300, Oakland CA 94621
Tel (510) 383-1200 *SIC* 8322

LA ASOCIACION NACIONAL PRO PERSONAS MAYORES p 835
234 E Colo Blvd Ste 300, Pasadena CA 91101
Tel (626) 564-1988 *SIC* 8322

CORNERSTONE AFFILIATES INC p 370
6120 Stoneridge, Pleasanton CA 94588
Tel (925) 924-7100 *SIC* 8322

SAN GABRIEL/POMONA VALLEYS DEVELOPMENTAL SERVICES INC p 1277
75 Rancho Camino Dr, Pomona CA 91766
Tel (909) 620-7722 *SIC* 8322

FAR NORTHERN COORDINATING COUNCIL ON DEVELOPMENTAL DISABILITIES p 528
1900 Churn Creek Rd # 31, Redding CA 96002
Tel (530) 222-4791 *SIC* 8322

ALTA CALIFORNIA REGIONAL CENTER INC p 61
2241 Harvard St Ste 100, Sacramento CA 95815
Tel (916) 978-6400 *SIC* 8322

ARC OF SAN DIEGO p 103
3030 Market St, San Diego CA 92102
Tel (619) 685-1175
SIC 8399 8351 8361 8322

NEIGHBORHOOD HOUSE ASSOCIATION p 1024
5660 Copley Dr, San Diego CA 92111
Tel (858) 715-2642 *SIC* 8322

NEW ALTERNATIVES INC p 1029
3589 4th Ave, San Diego CA 92103
Tel (619) 543-0293 *SIC* 8322

SAN DIEGO FOUNDATION p 1276
2508 Historic Decatur Rd # 200, San Diego CA 92106
Tel (619) 235-2300 *SIC* 8322

SAN DIEGO-IMPERIAL COUNTIES DEVELOPMENTAL SERVICES INC p 1276
4355 Ruffin Rd Ste 220, San Diego CA 92123
Tel (858) 576-2996 *SIC* 8322

DELANCEY STREET FOUNDATION p 423
600 The Embarcadero, San Francisco CA 94107
Tel (415) 957-9800
SIC 8361 5199 8322 4212 5812

GOLDEN GATE REGIONAL CENTER INC p 621
1355 Market St Ste 220, San Francisco CA 94103
Tel (415) 546-9222 *SIC* 8322

SAN FRANCISCO FOOD BANK p 1276
900 Pennsylvania Ave, San Francisco CA 94107
Tel (415) 282-1900 *SIC* 8322

YOUNG MENS CHRISTIAN ASSOCIATION OF SAN FRANCISCO p 1639
50 California St Ste 650, San Francisco CA 94111
Tel (415) 777-9622
SIC 8641 7991 8351 7032 8322

SECOND HARVEST FOOD BANK OF SANTA CLARA & SAN MATEO COUNTIES p 1298
750 Curtner Ave, San Jose CA 95125
Tel (408) 266-8866 *SIC* 8322

SENECA FAMILY OF AGENCIES p 1303
15942 Foothill Blvd, San Leandro CA 94578
Tel (510) 317-1444 *SIC* 8322 8299 8082

■ MHN SERVICES p 959
2370 Kerner Blvd, San Rafael CA 94901
Tel (415) 460-8300
SIC 6324 8011 8742 8322

VOLUNTEERS OF AMERICA p 1565
2100 N Broadway Ste 300, Santa Ana CA 92706
Tel (714) 426-9834 *SIC* 8322 7361 9531

TRI-COUNTIES ASSOCIATION FOR DEVELOPMENTALLY DISABLED INC p 1477
520 E Montecito St, Santa Barbara CA 93103
Tel (805) 962-7881 *SIC* 8322

YMCA OF SILICON VALLEY p 1636
80 Saratoga Ave, Santa Clara CA 95051
Tel (408) 351-6400
SIC 8641 7991 8351 7032 8322

VALLEY MOUNTAIN REGIONAL CENTER INC p 1541
702 N Aurora St, Stockton CA 95202
Tel (209) 473-0951 *SIC* 8322

FOCUS ON FAMILY p 562
8605 Explorer Dr, Colorado Springs CO 80920
Tel (719) 531-3300 *SIC* 8322

FOOD BANK OF ROCKIES INC p 564
10700 E 45th Ave, Denver CO 80239
Tel (303) 371-9250 *SIC* 8322

TOTAL LONGTERM CARE INC p 1463
8950 E Lowry Blvd, Denver CO 80230
Tel (303) 832-1001 *SIC* 8322 8082

■ MAGELLAN BEHAVIORAL HEALTH SERVICE LLC p 895
55 Nod Rd, Avon CT 06001
Tel (860) 507-1900 *SIC* 8322

ABILITY BEYOND DISABILITY INC p 11
4 Berkshire Blvd, Bethel CT 06801
Tel (203) 826-3025 *SIC* 8322 8082

SAVE CHILDREN FEDERATION INC p 1284
501 Kings Hwy E Ste 400, Fairfield CT 06825
Tel (203) 221-4000 *SIC* 8322 5947

■ AETNA FINANCIAL HOLDINGS LLC p 31
151 Farmington Ave, Hartford CT 06156
Tel (860) 273-0123 *SIC* 8322

VISTAR/VSA OF HARTFORD INC p 1562
175 Sullivan Ave, South Windsor CT 06074
Tel (860) 688-7702 *SIC* 5141 5812 8322

AMERICARES FOUNDATION INC p 81
88 Hamilton Ave, Stamford CT 06902
Tel (203) 658-9500 *SIC* 8322

▲ PROVIDENCE SERVICE CORP p 1186
700 Canal St Ste 3, Stamford CT 06902
Tel (203) 307-2800 *SIC* 8322 8742 7389

MASONICARE CORP p 916
22 Masonic Ave, Wallingford CT 06492
Tel (203) 679-5900 *SIC* 8069 8082 8322

CONNECTIONS COMMUNITY SUPPORT PROGRAMS INC p 357
3821 Lancaster Pike, Wilmington DE 19805
Tel (302) 984-2302 *SIC* 8322 8361 8049

AMERICAN RED CROSS p 78
431 18th St Nw, Washington DC 20006
Tel (202) 737-8300 *SIC* 8322

COMMUNITY PARTNERSHIP FOR PREVENTION OF HOMELESSNESS INC p 349
801 Pennsylvania Ave Se # 31, Washington DC 20003
Tel (202) 543-5298 *SIC* 8322

DKT INTERNATIONAL INC p 445
1701 K St Nw Ste 900, Washington DC 20006
Tel (202) 223-8780 *SIC* 8322

FIRST BOOK p 545
1319 F St Nw Ste 1000, Washington DC 20004
Tel (202) 393-1222 *SIC* 8322

HEALTH SERVICES FOR CHILDREN WITH SPECIAL NEEDS INC p 676
1101 Vermont Ave Nw # 1002, Washington DC 20005
Tel (202) 467-2737 *SIC* 8322

NATIONAL CAUCUS AND CENTER ON BLACK AGING INC p 1010
1220 L St Nw Ste 800, Washington DC 20005
Tel (202) 637-8400 *SIC* 8322 8641

PATIENT-CENTERED OUTCOMES RESEARCH INSTITUTE p 1120
1828 L St Nw Ste 900, Washington DC 20036
Tel (202) 827-7700 *SIC* 8322

SPECIAL OLYMPICS INC p 1356
1133 19th St Nw Ste 1200, Washington DC 20036
Tel (202) 628-3630 *SIC* 8322

UNITED STATES ASSOCIATION FOR UNHCR p 1512
1775 K St Nw Ste 580, Washington DC 20006
Tel (855) 808-6427 *SIC* 8322

WITT OBRIENS LLC p 1619
1201 15th St Nw Ste 600, Washington DC 20005
Tel (202) 585-0780 *SIC* 4959 8748 8322

YOUNG MENS CHRISTIAN ASSOCIATION OF SUNCOAST p 1639
2469 Enterprise Rd, Clearwater FL 33763
Tel (312) 932-1200
SIC 8641 7991 8351 7032 8322

AMADEUS NORTH AMERICA INC p 64
3470 Nw 82nd Ave Ste 1000, Doral FL 33122
Tel (305) 499-6613 *SIC* 7371 8322

CHILDNET INC p 298
1100 W Mcnab Rd, Fort Lauderdale FL 33309
Tel (954) 414-6000 *SIC* 8322

BAPTIST HEALTH SYSTEM FOUNDATION INC p 153
841 Prudential Dr # 1300, Jacksonville FL 32207
Tel (904) 202-2919 *SIC* 8322

OUR KIDS OF MIAMI-DADE/MONROE INC p 1098
401 Nw 2nd Ave Ste S212, Miami FL 33128
Tel (305) 455-6000 *SIC* 8322

SUNRISE COMMUNITY INC p 1403
9040 Sw 72nd St, Miami FL 33173
Tel (305) 275-3365 *SIC* 8052 8331 8322

FAMILY CENTRAL INC p 526
840 N Lauderdale Ave, North Lauderdale FL 33068
Tel (954) 720-1000 *SIC* 8322

COMMUNITY COORDINATED CARE FOR CHILDREN INC p 348
3500 W Colonial Dr, Orlando FL 32808
Tel (407) 522-2252 *SIC* 8322

CROSS INTERNATIONAL INC p 393
600 Sw 3rd St Ste 2201, Pompano Beach FL 33060
Tel (954) 657-9000 *SIC* 8322

SARASOTA FAMILY YOUNG MENS CHRISTIAN ASSOCIATION INC p 1282
1 S School Ave Ste 301, Sarasota FL 34237
Tel (941) 951-2916
SIC 8641 8351 8322 7997 7991

CENTRAL FLORIDA BEHAVIORAL HEALTH NETWORK INC p 278
719 S Us Highway 301, Tampa FL 33619
Tel (813) 740-4811 *SIC* 8322

G4S YOUTH SERVICES LLC p 588
6302 Benjamin Rd Ste 400, Tampa FL 33634
Tel (813) 514-6275 *SIC* 8322

LUTHERAN SERVICES FLORIDA INC p 886
3627a W Waters Ave, Tampa FL 33614
Tel (813) 868-4438 *SIC* 8322

CHILDRENS HOME SOCIETY OF FLORIDA p 299
1485 S Semoran Blvd, Winter Park FL 32792
Tel (407) 657-2197 *SIC* 8322 8361

HABITAT FOR HUMANITY INTERNATIONAL INC p 651
121 Habitat St, Americus GA 31709
Tel (800) 422-4828
SIC 8399 8661 8322 1521 1531

ATLANTA COMMUNITY FOOD BANK INC p 125
732 Jseph E Lwery Blvd Nw, Atlanta GA 30318
Tel (404) 892-9822 *SIC* 8322 4783

BOYS & GIRLS CLUBS OF AMERICA p 205
1275 Peachtree St Ne # 500, Atlanta GA 30309
Tel (404) 527-7100 *SIC* 8322

COOPERATIVE FOR ASSISTANCE AND RELIEF EVERYWHERE INC p 367
151 Ellis St Ne, Atlanta GA 30303
Tel (404) 681-2552 *SIC* 8641 8322

MOREHOUSE SCHOOL OF MEDICINE INC p 988
720 Westview Dr Sw, Atlanta GA 30310
Tel (404) 752-1500 *SIC* 8322 8221

YOUNG MENS CHRISTIAN ASSOCIATION OF METROPOLITAN ATLANTA INC p 1638
100 Edgewood Ave Ne, Atlanta GA 30303
Tel (404) 588-9622
SIC 8641 7991 8351 7032 8322

SALVATION ARMY p 1273
1424 Northeast Expy Ne, Brookhaven GA 30329
Tel (404) 728-1300 *SIC* 8661 8322

HAMILTON HEALTH CARE SYSTEM INC p 655
1200 Memorial Dr, Dalton GA 30720
Tel (706) 278-2105 *SIC* 8322 8062

KAPIOLANI MEDICAL CENTER AT PALI MOMI p 803
55 Merchant St, Honolulu HI 96813
Tel (808) 486-6000 *SIC* 8322

MIDWEST FOOD BANK NFP p 967
1703 S Veterans Pkwy, Bloomington IL 61701
Tel (309) 663-5350 *SIC* 8322

FEEDING AMERICA p 537
35 E Wacker Dr Ste 2000, Chicago IL 60601
Tel (312) 263-2303 *SIC* 8322

GREATER CHICAGO FOOD DEPOSITORY p 635
4100 W 42nd Pl, Chicago IL 60632
Tel (773) 247-3663 *SIC* 8322

NATIONAL COUNCIL OF YOUNG MENS CHRISTIAN ASSOCIATIONS OF UNITED STATES OF AMERICA p 1011
101 N Wacker Dr Ste 1600, Chicago IL 60606
Tel (312) 977-0031 *SIC* 7997 8399 8322

YOUNG MENS CHRISTIAN ASSOCIATION OF CHICAGO p 1638
1030 W Van Buren St, Chicago IL 60607
Tel (312) 932-1200
SIC 8641 7011 8351 8699 8322 7999

LUTHERAN SOCIAL SERVICES OF ILLINOIS p 886
1001 E Touhy Ave Ste 50, Des Plaines IL 60018
Tel (847) 635-4600 *SIC* 8322 6514 6513

NORTHERN ILLINOIS FOOD BANK p 1056
273 Dearborn Ct, Geneva IL 60134
Tel (630) 443-6910 *SIC* 8322

CENTRAL TERRITORIAL OF SALVATION ARMY p 280
5550 Prairie Stone Pkwy # 130, Hoffman Estates IL 60192
Tel (847) 294-2000 *SIC* 8661 8322

PARK NAPERVILLE DISTRICT p 1115
320 Jackson Ave, Naperville IL 60540
Tel (630) 848-5000
SIC 7992 7999 8322 8741

TRINITY SERVICES INC p 1482
301 Veterans Pkwy, New Lenox IL 60451
Tel (815) 485-6197 *SIC* 8211 8322

CATHOLIC DIOCESE OF ROCKFORD p 266
555 Colman Center Dr, Rockford IL 61108
Tel (815) 399-4300
SIC 8661 8322 8361 8211 6553

ILLINOIS MASONIC CHARITIES FUND p 732
2866 Via Verde St, Springfield IL 62703
Tel (217) 529-8900 *SIC* 8322

■ ZEE MEDICAL INC p 1641
8021 Knue Rd Ste 100, Indianapolis IN 46250
Tel (949) 252-9500 *SIC* 8748 8322

SANCTUARY AT HOLY CROSS p 1278
17475 Dugdale Dr, South Bend IN 46635
Tel (574) 247-7500 *SIC* 8322 8052

MERCY CARE MANAGEMENT INC p 945
701 10th St Se, Cedar Rapids IA 52403
Tel (319) 398-6011 *SIC* 8011 8741 8322

YOUNG MENS CHRISTIAN ASSOCIATION OF CEDAR RAPIDS METROPOLITAN AREA p 1638
207 7th Ave Se, Cedar Rapids IA 52401
Tel (319) 366-6421 SIC 8641 8322

YOUNG MENS CHRISTIAN ASSOCIATION OF WICHITA KANSAS p 1639
402 N Market St, Wichita KS 67202
Tel (316) 219-9622
SIC 8641 7991 8351 7032 8322

CHRISTIAN APPALACHIAN PROJECT INC p 302
6550 S Ky Route 321, Hagerhill KY 41222
Tel (606) 789-9791 SIC 8322

BLUEGRASSORG p 193
1351 Newtown Pike, Lexington KY 40511
Tel (859) 253-1686 SIC 8322

▲ **KINDRED HEALTHCARE INC** p 819
680 S 4th St, Louisville KY 40202
Tel (502) 596-7300
SIC 8062 8051 8322 8082

SEVEN COUNTIES SERVICES INC p 1309
101 W Muhammad Ali Blvd, Louisville KY 40202
Tel (502) 589-8600
SIC 8399 8011 8093 8322 8031

YOUNG MENS CHRISTIAN ASSOCIATION OF GREATER LOUISVILLE p 1638
545 S 2nd St, Louisville KY 40202
Tel (502) 587-9622
SIC 8641 7991 8351 7032 8322

▲ **LHC GROUP INC** p 860
901 Hugh Wallis Rd S, Lafayette LA 70508
Tel (337) 233-1307 SIC 8082 8322

GULF COAST TEACHING FAMILY SERVICES INC p 646
2400 Edenborn Ave Ste 299, Metairie LA 70001
Tel (504) 831-6561 SIC 8322

ANNIE E CASEY FOUNDATION INC p 92
701 Saint Paul St, Baltimore MD 21202
Tel (410) 547-6600 SIC 8322 8361

ASSOCIATED CATHOLIC CHARITIES INC p 120
320 Cathedral St, Baltimore MD 21201
Tel (410) 561-6363 SIC 8322

CATHOLIC RELIEF SERVICES - UNITED STATES CONFERENCE OF CATHOLIC BISHOPS p 267
228 W Lexington St, Baltimore MD 21201
Tel (410) 625-2220 SIC 8322

MOSAIC COMMUNITY SERVICES INC p 991
1925 Greenspring Dr, Lutherville Timonium MD 21093
Tel (410) 453-9553 SIC 8322 8093

MELWOOD HORTICULTURAL TRAINING CENTER INC p 941
5606 Dower House Rd, Upper Marlboro MD 20772
Tel (301) 599-8000 SIC 8331 8322

STAVROS CENTER FOR INDEPENDENT LIVING INC p 1383
210 Old Farm Rd, Amherst MA 01002
Tel (413) 256-0473 SIC 8322

YMCA OF NORTH SHORE INC p 1636
245 Cabot St, Beverly MA 01915
Tel (978) 922-0990
SIC 7021 8322 8351 7999 7032

ACTION FOR BOSTON COMMUNITY DEVELOPMENT INC p 19
178 Tremont St, Boston MA 02111
Tel (617) 357-6000 SIC 8399 8322

YMCA OF GREATER BOSTON INC p 1636
316 Huntington Ave Ste 1, Boston MA 02115
Tel (617) 536-6950
SIC 8641 7991 8351 7032 8322

OLD COLONY Y p 1080
320 Main St, Brockton MA 02301
Tel (508) 583-2155
SIC 8641 7991 8351 7032 8322

NORTH AMERICAN FAMILY INSTITUTE INC p 1050
300 Rosewood Dr Ste 101, Danvers MA 01923
Tel (978) 538-0286 SIC 8322

NORTHEAST ARC INC p 1054
64 Holten St, Danvers MA 01923
Tel (978) 762-4878 SIC 8361 8322 8331

RIVERSIDE COMMUNITY CARE INC p 1237
270 Bridge St Ste 301, Dedham MA 02026
Tel (617) 969-4925 SIC 8322

ELIOT COMMUNITY HUMAN SERVICES INC p 487
186 Bedford St, Lexington MA 02420
Tel (781) 861-0890 SIC 8361 8322

BEHAVIORAL HEALTH NETWORK INC p 168
417 Liberty St Ste 1, Springfield MA 01104
Tel (413) 747-0705 SIC 8093 8322

CENTER FOR HUMAN DEVELOPMENT INC p 276
332 Birnie Ave, Springfield MA 01107
Tel (413) 733-6624 SIC 8322

MERCY INPATIENT MEDICAL ASSOCIATES INC p 947
271 Carew St Ste 106, Springfield MA 01104
Tel (413) 748-9000 SIC 8011 8322

PATHFINDER INTERNATIONAL p 1120
9 Galen St Ste 217, Watertown MA 02472
Tel (617) 924-7200 SIC 8322

ASCENTRIA CARE ALLIANCE p 116
14 E Worcester St Ste 300, Worcester MA 01604
Tel (774) 343-3900 SIC 8322 8051 8361

MORC REHABILITATION SERVICES p 988
16200 19 Mile Rd, Clinton Township MI 48038
Tel (586) 739-5792 SIC 8322

LUTHERAN SOCIAL SERVICES OF MICHIGAN p 886
8131 E Jefferson Ave, Detroit MI 48214
Tel (313) 823-7700 SIC 8051 8322

BETHANY CHRISTIAN SERVICES p 178
901 Eastern Ave Ne, Grand Rapids MI 49503
Tel (616) 224-7550 SIC 8322

BETHANY CHRISTIAN SERVICES USA LLC p 178
901 Eastern Ave Ne, Grand Rapids MI 49503
Tel (616) 224-7610 SIC 8322

■ **AMGRAM CASSELL-EAST LLC** p 85
40020 Grand River Ave, Novi MI 48375
Tel (248) 615-6025 SIC 8322

COMMUNITY LIVING SERVICES INC p 349
35425 W Michigan Ave # 1, Wayne MI 48184
Tel (734) 467-7600 SIC 8322

ELIM CARE INC p 487
7485 Office Ridge Cir, Eden Prairie MN 55344
Tel (952) 259-4500 SIC 8051 8322

VOLUNTEERS OF AMERICA CARE FACILITIES p 1565
7530 Market Place Dr, Eden Prairie MN 55344
Tel (952) 941-0305 SIC 8322

GREATER TWIN CITIES UNITED WAY p 636
404 S 8th St Ste 100, Minneapolis MN 55404
Tel (612) 340-7400 SIC 8322

NEXUS p 1041
505 Highway 169 N Ste 500, Plymouth MN 55441
Tel (763) 551-8640 SIC 8322 8361

GOODWILL INDUSTRIES INC p 624
553 Fairview Ave N, Saint Paul MN 55104
Tel (651) 379-5800
SIC 4953 8331 8322 5932 4226

LUTHERAN SOCIAL SERVICE OF MINNESOTA p 886
2485 Como Ave, Saint Paul MN 55108
Tel (651) 642-5990 SIC 8322

SECOND HARVEST HEARTLAND p 1298
1140 Gervais Ave, Saint Paul MN 55109
Tel (651) 484-5117 SIC 8322

TL WALLACE CONSTRUCTION INC p 1457
4025 Highway 35 N, Columbia MS 39429
Tel (601) 736-4525 SIC 1611 4212 8322

EASTER SEALS MIDWEST p 471
13545 Barrett Parkway Dr, Ballwin MO 63021
Tel (314) 394-7026
SIC 8361 8331 8322 8052

MISSOURI DEPARTMENT OF SOCIAL SERVICES p 976
221 W High St Ste 240, Jefferson City MO 65101
Tel (573) 751-4815 SIC 9441 8322

CHILDREN INTERNATIONAL p 298
2000 E Red Bridge Rd, Kansas City MO 64131
Tel (816) 943-3722 SIC 8322

HARVESTERS - COMMUNITY FOOD NETWORK p 667
3801 Topping Ave, Kansas City MO 64129
Tel (816) 231-3173 SIC 8322

CATHOLIC CHARITIES OF ST LOUIS p 266
4445 Lindell Blvd, Saint Louis MO 63108
Tel (314) 367-5500 SIC 8699 8322

CHRISTIAN HOSPITAL NORTHEAST - NORTHWEST p 303
11133 Dunn Rd, Saint Louis MO 63136
Tel (314) 355-2300 SIC 8062 8322

GATEWAY REGION YOUNG MENS CHRISTIAN ASSOCIATION p 594
326 S 21st St Ste 400, Saint Louis MO 63103
Tel (314) 436-1177 SIC 8641 8741 8322

HEALTH SYSTEMS INC p 676
1220 N Main St, Sikeston MO 63801
Tel (573) 481-9625 SIC 6321 8011 8322

ALTERNATIVE OPPORTUNITIES INC p 62
1111 S Glenstone Ave 3-100, Springfield MO 65804
Tel (417) 869-8911 SIC 8322

CONVOY OF HOPE p 365
330 S Patterson Ave # 100, Springfield MO 65802
Tel (417) 823-8998 SIC 8322

DREAM MARRIAGE GROUP INC p 455
2533 N Carson St Ste 3988, Carson City NV 89706
Tel (310) 200-8875 SIC 8322

WESTCARE FOUNDATION INC p 1596
1711 Whitney Mesa Dr # 100, Henderson NV 89014
Tel (702) 385-3330 SIC 8322 8611

EASTER SEAL NEW HAMPSHIRE INC p 471
555 Auburn St, Manchester NH 03103
Tel (603) 623-8863
SIC 8331 8399 4119 8322

NEW HAMPSHIRE CATHOLIC CHARITIES INC p 1030
215 Myrtle St, Manchester NH 03104
Tel (603) 669-3030
SIC 8322 8059 8331 8661 8361

BANCROFT REHABILITATION SERVICES A NEW JERSEY NONPROFIT CORP p 150
1255 Caldwell Rd, Cherry Hill NJ 08034
Tel (856) 348-1183 SIC 8322

EASTER SEALS NEW JERSEY p 471
25 Kennedy Blvd Ste 600, East Brunswick NJ 08816
Tel (732) 257-6662 SIC 8322

COMMUNITY FOOD BANK OF NEW JERSEY INC p 348
31 Evans Terminal, Hillside NJ 07205
Tel (908) 355-3663 SIC 8322

CARE ONE AT HOLMDEL LLC p 254
188 State Route 34, Holmdel NJ 07733
Tel (732) 946-4200 SIC 8322

SENIOR BRANDYWINE CARE INC p 1303
525 Fellowship Rd Ste 360, Mount Laurel NJ 08054
Tel (856) 813-2000 SIC 8741 8322 8051

ESSEX COUNTY WELFARE BOARD INC p 510
18 Rector St Ste 9, Newark NJ 07102
Tel (973) 733-3326 SIC 8322 8399

COMMUNITY OPTIONS INC p 349
16 Farber Rd, Princeton NJ 08540
Tel (609) 951-9900 SIC 8322

OAKS INTEGRATED CARE INC p 1071
770 Woodlane Rd Ste 23, Westampton NJ 08060
Tel (609) 267-5928 SIC 8322

CATHOLIC CHARITIES OF DIOCESE OF ALBANY p 266
40 N Main Ave Ste 1, Albany NY 12203
Tel (518) 453-6650 SIC 8322

CENTER RESIDENCE CORP p 276
314 S Manning Blvd, Albany NY 12208
Tel (518) 437-5700 SIC 8322

NEW YORK DEPARTMENT OF CORRECTIONS AND COMMUNITY SUPERVISION p 1035
1220 Washngtn Ave Bldg 2, Albany NY 12226
Tel (518) 457-8126 SIC 8322 9223

NEW YORK STATE INDUSTRIES FOR DISABLED INC p 1036
11 Columbia Cir, Albany NY 12203
Tel (518) 463-9706 SIC 8322

NORTHEAST HEALTH INC p 1054
315 S Manning Blvd, Albany NY 12208
Tel (518) 292-6200 SIC 8059 8322

HILLSIDES CHILDRENS CENTER p 694
24 Liberty St, Bath NY 14810
Tel (607) 776-7480 SIC 8322

ADULTS AND CHILDREN WITH LEARNING AND DEVELOPMENTAL DISABILITIES INC p 24
807 S Oyster Bay Rd, Bethpage NY 11714
Tel (516) 681-4500 SIC 8322 8331

SAMARITAN DAYTOP VILLAGE INC p 1274
13802 Queens Blvd Fl 1, Briarwood NY 11435
Tel (718) 206-2000 SIC 8322 8093

CENTERLIGHT HEALTHCARE INC p 276
1250 Waters Pl Ste 602, Bronx NY 10461
Tel (347) 640-6000 SIC 8051 8082 8322

REGIONAL AID FOR INTERIM NEEDS INC p 1219
811 Morris Park Ave, Bronx NY 10462
Tel (718) 892-5520 SIC 8322

CATHOLIC CHARITIES DIOCESE OF BROOKLYN & QUEENS p 265
191 Joralemon St, Brooklyn NY 11201
Tel (718) 722-6000 SIC 8322 8361

CATHOLIC CHARITIES NEIGHBORHOOD SERVICES INC p 265
191 Joralemon St, Brooklyn NY 11201
Tel (718) 722-6000 SIC 8059 8322

HEARTSHARE HUMAN SERVICES OF NY ROMAN CATHOLIC DIOCESE OF BROOKLYN p 679
12 Metrotech Ctr Fl 29, Brooklyn NY 11201
Tel (718) 422-4200 SIC 8322

MARAMONT CORP p 904
5600 1st Ave, Brooklyn NY 11220
Tel (718) 439-8900 SIC 2099 8322

METROPOLITAN JEWISH HEALTH SYSTEM INC p 956
6323 7th Ave Ste 2, Brooklyn NY 11220
Tel (718) 621-3600 SIC 8322

ST NICHOLAS LOCAL DEVELOPMENT CORP p 1372
11 Catherine St, Brooklyn NY 11211
Tel (718) 388-2233 SIC 8322

ASPIRE OF WESTERN NEW YORK INC p 118
2356 N Forest Rd, Getzville NY 14068
Tel (716) 505-5500 SIC 8322

SCO FAMILY OF SERVICES p 1292
1 Alexander Pl, Glen Cove NY 11542
Tel (516) 671-1253 SIC 8322

NASSAU ASSOCIATION FOR HELP OF RETARDED CHILDREN INC p 1008
189 Wheatley Rd, Glen Head NY 11545
Tel (516) 626-1000 SIC 8093 8322

NASSAU COUNTY A H R C p 1008
189 Wheatley Rd, Glen Head NY 11545
Tel (516) 626-1000 SIC 8331 8322

HUNTINGTON HOSPITAL AUXILIARY p 720
270 Park Ave, Huntington NY 11743
Tel (631) 351-2257 SIC 5947 5499 8322

BAKER HALL p 146
780 Ridge Rd, Lackawanna NY 14218
Tel (716) 828-9515 SIC 8361 8211 8322

NYSARC INC p 1069
29 British American Blvd # 2, Latham NY 12110
Tel (518) 439-8311
SIC 8361 8322 8093 8331

CITIHOPE INTERNATIONAL INC p 310
629 Main St Ste 2, Margaretville NY 12455
Tel (845) 586-6202 SIC 8322

CATHOLIC GUARDIAN SERVICES p 266
1011 1st Ave Fl 10, New York NY 10022
Tel (212) 371-1011 SIC 8322 8361

CHILDRENS AID SOCIETY p 298
711 3rd Ave Rm 700, New York NY 10017
Tel (212) 949-4800 SIC 8322

CHINESE AMERICAN PLANNING p 301
1 York St Fl 2, New York NY 10013
Tel (212) 219-8100 SIC 8322

CITY HARVEST INC p 312
6 E 32nd St Fl 5, New York NY 10016
Tel (646) 412-0600 SIC 8322

COVENANT HOUSE p 384
5 Penn Plz Ste 201, New York NY 10001
Tel (212) 727-4000 SIC 8322 8361

GOOD SHEPHERD SERVICES p 623
305 7th Ave Fl 9, New York NY 10001
Tel (212) 243-7070 SIC 8322

HADASSAH MEDICAL RELIEF ASSOCIATION INC p 652
40 Wall St, New York NY 10005
Tel (212) 355-7900 SIC 8322

HELP USA INC p 682
115 E 13th St, New York NY 10003
Tel (212) 400-7000 SIC 6513 8322

HELP USA INC AND AFFILIATES p 682
115 E 13th St, New York NY 10003
Tel (212) 400-7000 SIC 8322

INDEPENDENCE CARE SYSTEMS INC p 736
257 Park Ave S Fl 2, New York NY 10010
Tel (212) 584-2500 SIC 8322 6324

INTERNATIONAL RESCUE COMMITTEE INC p 756
122 E 42nd St Fl 12, New York NY 10168
Tel (212) 551-3000 SIC 8322

JEWISH BOARD OF FAMILY AND CHILDRENS SERVICES INC p 784
135 W 50th St Fl 6, New York NY 10020
Tel (212) 582-9100 SIC 8361 8322

LIFESPIRE INC p 864
1 Whitehall St Fl 9, New York NY 10004
Tel (212) 741-0100 SIC 8322

LIGHTHOUSE GUILD INTERNATIONAL INC p 865
15 W 65th St, New York NY 10023
Tel (212) 769-6200 SIC 8322 8042

NATIONAL MULTIPLE SCLEROSIS SOCIETY p 1014
733 3rd Ave Fl 3, New York NY 10017
Tel (212) 463-9791 SIC 8322

NYSARC p 1069
252 W 29th St Rm 700, New York NY 10001
Tel (212) 780-2500 SIC 8322

PROJECT OHR INC p 1182
80 Maiden Ln Fl 10, New York NY 10038
Tel (718) 853-2700 SIC 8322 8742

ROBIN HOOD FOUNDATION p 1242
826 Broadway Fl 9, New York NY 10003
Tel (212) 227-6601 SIC 8699 8322

SERVICES FOR UNDERSERVED INC p 1308
305 7th Ave Fl 10, New York NY 10001
Tel (212) 633-6900 SIC 8322

UNITED CEREBRAL PALSY OF NEW YORK CITY INC p 1507
80 Maiden Ln Fl 8, New York NY 10038
Tel (212) 683-6700 SIC 8322

VILLAGE CARE OF NEW YORK INC p 1557
120 Broadway Ste 2840, New York NY 10271
Tel (212) 337-5816 SIC 8741 8322

VILLAGE CENTER FOR CARE p 1557
120 Broadway Ste 2840, New York NY 10271
Tel (212) 367-3748 SIC 8051 8082 8322

YOUNG MENS CHRISTIAN ASSOCIATION OF GREATER NEW YORK p 1638
5 W 63rd St Fl 6, New York NY 10023
Tel (212) 630-9600
SIC 8641 7991 8351 7032 8322

MARYHAVEN CENTER OF HOPE INC p 914
51 Terryville Rd, Port Jeff Sta NY 11776
Tel (631) 474-4120 SIC 8322 7389

MIDHUDSON REGIONAL HOSPITAL OF WESTCHESTER MEDICAL CENTER p 965
241 North Rd, Poughkeepsie NY 12601
Tel (845) 483-5000 SIC 8062 8322

HILLSIDE FAMILY OF AGENCIES p 694
1183 Monroe Ave, Rochester NY 14620
Tel (585) 256-7500 SIC 8322

HILLSIDE FAMILY OF AGENCIES p 694
1183 Monroe Ave, Rochester NY 14620
Tel (585) 256-7500 SIC 8361 8322 8093

LIFETIME ASSISTANCE INC p 864
425 Paul Rd, Rochester NY 14624
Tel (585) 247-2255 SIC 8322 6512

LEUKEMIA & LYMPHOMA SOCIETY INC p 858
3 International Dr # 200, Rye Brook NY 10573
Tel (914) 949-5213
SIC 8699 8399 8322 8011 8733 8621

SUNNYSIDE HOME CARE PROJECT INC p 1403
4331 39th St Ste A, Sunnyside NY 11104
Tel (718) 784-6173 SIC 8361 8322

LORETTO HEALTH AND REHABILITATION CENTER p 878
700 E Brighton Ave, Syracuse NY 13205
Tel (315) 469-1991 SIC 8322

UPSTATE CEREBRAL PALSY INC p 1529
1020 Mary St, Utica NY 13501
Tel (315) 724-6907 SIC 8322

AMERICAN CANCER SOCIETY EASTERN DIVISION INC p 69
2 Lyon Pl, White Plains NY 10601
Tel (914) 949-4800 SIC 8322

MONARCH p 983
350 Pee Dee Ave Ste 101, Albemarle NC 28001
Tel (704) 986-1500
SIC 8322 8049 8331 8052

COMMUNITY CAREPARTNERS INC p 347
68 Sweeten Creek Rd, Asheville NC 28803
Tel (828) 274-2400 SIC 8322 8093

SAMARITANS PURSE p 1274
801 Bamboo Rd, Boone NC 28607
Tel (828) 262-1980 SIC 8322 6732

MORALE WELFARE RECREATION ACTIVITY p 988
1401 West Rd, Camp Lejeune NC 28547
Tel (910) 451-2861
SIC 5311 5812 8322 7999 9711

EASTER SEALS UCP NORTH CAROLINA & VIRGINIA INC p 471
5171 Glenwood Ave Ste 400, Raleigh NC 27612
Tel (919) 832-3787 SIC 8322

FOOD BANK OF CENTRAL & EASTERN NORTH CAROLINA INC p 564
1924 Capital Blvd, Raleigh NC 27604
Tel (919) 875-0707 SIC 8322

YMCA OF NORTHWEST NORTH CAROLINA p 1636
301 N Main St Ste 1900, Winston Salem NC 27101
Tel (336) 777-8055
SIC 8641 7991 8351 7032 8322

AKRON GENERAL MEDICAL CENTER INC p 42
1 Akron General Ave, Akron OH 44307
Tel (330) 344-6000
SIC 8062 8011 8322 8221

MATURE SERVICES INC p 921
415 S Portage Path, Akron OH 44320
Tel (330) 253-4597 SIC 8322

ORIANA HOUSE INC p 1094
885 E Buchtel Ave, Akron OH 44305
Tel (330) 535-8116 SIC 8322 9111

OHIOGUIDESTONE p 1078
434 Eastland Rd, Berea OH 44017
Tel (440) 234-2006
SIC 8322 8361 8351 8051

AVALON FOODSERVICE INC p 135
1 Avalon Dr, Canal Fulton OH 44614
Tel (330) 854-4551
SIC 5142 5149 5169 5113 8322 5812

MENORAH PARK CENTER FOR SENIOR LIVING BET MOSHAV ZEKENIM HADATI p 943
27100 Cedar Rd, Cleveland OH 44122
Tel (216) 831-6500 *SIC* 8051 6513 8322

YOUNG MENS CHRISTIAN ASSOCIATION OF GREATER DAYTON p 1638
118 W St Ste 300, Dayton OH 45402
Tel (937) 223-5201
SIC 8641 7991 8351 7032 8322

MID-OHIO FOODBANK p 963
3960 Brookham Dr, Grove City OH 43123
Tel (614) 317-9400 *SIC* 8322

HIGHLAND COUNTY COMMUNITY ACTION ORGANIZATION INC p 691
1487 N High St Ste 500, Hillsboro OH 45133
Tel (937) 393-3060 *SIC* 8322

CHRISTIAN AID MINISTRIES p 302
4464 State Route 39, Millersburg OH 44654
Tel (330) 893-2428 *SIC* 8322 5999

YOUNG MENS CHRISTIAN ASSOCIATION OF GREATER TOLEDO p 1638
1500 N Superior St Fl 2, Toledo OH 43604
Tel (419) 729-8135
SIC 8641 7991 8351 7032 8322

PROVIDENCE MEDFORD MEDICAL CENTER p 1186
1111 Crater Lake Ave, Medford OR 97504
Tel (541) 732-5000 *SIC* 8322

CASCADIA BEHAVIORAL HEALTHCARE INC p 263
847 Ne 19th Ave Ste 100, Portland OR 97232
Tel (503) 238-0769
SIC 8322 8093 8063 8361

MERCY CORPS p 946
45 Sw Ankeny St, Portland OR 97204
Tel (503) 796-6800 *SIC* 8322

DIAKON p 436
798 Hausman Rd Ste 300, Allentown PA 18104
Tel (610) 682-1262 *SIC* 8322

SHEPHERD GOOD REHABILITATION NETWORK p 1315
850 S 5th St, Allentown PA 18103
Tel (610) 776-3100 *SIC* 8051 8361 8322

KENCREST SERVICES p 810
960 Harvest Dr Ste 100a, Blue Bell PA 19422
Tel (610) 825-9360 *SIC* 8361 8322 8351

ARCHDIOCESE OF PHILADELPHIA p 105
222 N 17th St, Bryn Mawr PA 19010
Tel (215) 587-3500 *SIC* 8322

MONTGOMERY CAPITAL INC p 986
7111 Valley Green Rd, Fort Washington PA 19034
Tel (877) 836-8300 *SIC* 8322

KEYSTONE HUMAN SERVICES p 815
124 Pine St, Harrisburg PA 17101
Tel (717) 232-7509 *SIC* 8322

YOUTH ADVOCATE PROGRAMS INC p 1639
2007 N 3rd St, Harrisburg PA 17102
Tel (717) 232-7580 *SIC* 8322

WOODS SERVICES INC p 1623
40 Martin Gross Dr, Langhorne PA 19047
Tel (215) 750-4000 *SIC* 8322 8211

DIAKON LUTHERAN SOCIAL MINISTRIES p 436
1022 N Union St, Middletown PA 17057
Tel (610) 682-1262 *SIC* 8322 8051

DIAKON LUTHERAN SOCIAL MINISTRIES p 436
1022 N Union St, Middletown PA 17057
Tel (610) 682-1262 *SIC* 8051 8322

KIDSPEACE NATIONAL CENTERS OF NEW YORK INC p 817
5300 Kidspeace Dr, Orefield PA 18069
Tel (800) 992-9543 *SIC* 8322

COMMUNITY BEHAVIORAL HEALTH p 347
801 Market St Ste 7000, Philadelphia PA 19107
Tel (215) 413-3100 *SIC* 8322

HORIZON HOUSE INC p 707
120 S 30th St, Philadelphia PA 19104
Tel (215) 386-3838
SIC 8361 6512 8322 8093

JEVS HUMAN SERVICES p 784
1845 Walnut St Ste 700, Philadelphia PA 19103
Tel (215) 875-7387 *SIC* 8322 8331

PHILADELPHIA CORP FOR AGING INC p 1142
642 N Broad St Fl 5, Philadelphia PA 19130
Tel (215) 765-9040 *SIC* 8322

RESOURCES FOR HUMAN DEVELOPMENT INC p 1227
4700 Wphickon Ave Ste 126, Philadelphia PA 19144
Tel (215) 951-0300
SIC 8322 8093 8052 8331 8361

MERCY LIFE CENTER CORP p 947
1200 Reedsdale St Ste 1, Pittsburgh PA 15233
Tel (412) 578-6675 *SIC* 8322

UPMC COMMUNITY PROVIDER SERVIES p 1528
200 Lthrpst Frbtwr 1005 Ste Forbes Tower, Pittsburgh PA 15213
Tel (412) 647-0548 *SIC* 8322

KIDSPEACE NATIONAL CENTERS OF NORTH AMERICA INC p 817
4085 Independence Dr, Schnecksville PA 18078
Tel (610) 799-8353 *SIC* 8322

ALLIED HEALTH CARE SERVICES p 56
475 Morgan Hwy, Scranton PA 18508
Tel (570) 348-1300 *SIC* 8322

CATHOLIC SOCIAL SERVICES OF DIOCESE OF SCRANTON INC p 267
516 Fig St, Scranton PA 18505
Tel (570) 207-2283
SIC 8661 2711 8211 8322 6553

NORTHEASTERN PENNSYLVANIA CENTER FOR INDEPENDENT LIVING INC p 1055
1142 Sanderson Ave, Scranton PA 18509
Tel (570) 344-7211 *SIC* 8322

ACTIVE DAY INC p 20
6 Neshaminy Interplex Dr # 401, Trevose PA 19053
Tel (215) 642-6600 *SIC* 8322

YMCA GREATER BRANDYWINE p 1636
1 E Chestnut St, West Chester PA 19380
Tel (610) 643-9622
SIC 8641 7991 8351 7032 8322

STEP-BY-STEP INC p 1386
744 Kidder St Frnt, Wilkes Barre PA 18702
Tel (570) 829-3477 *SIC* 8322 8361

INSTITUCION EDUCATIVA NETS INC p 747
Urb Sierra Bayamn, Bayamon PR 00961
Tel (787) 785-5511 *SIC* 8299 8322

GREATER PROVIDENCE YOUNG MENS CHRISTIAN ASSOCIATION p 636
371 Pine St, Providence RI 02903
Tel (401) 521-9622
SIC 8641 7991 8351 7032 8322

PLAN INTERNATIONAL USA INC p 1154
155 Plan Way Ste A, Warwick RI 02886
Tel (401) 562-8400 *SIC* 8322

PGBA LLC p 1140
I-20 Alpine Rd, Columbia SC 29219
Tel (803) 788-3860 *SIC* 8322

SC DJJ PIEDMONT REGIONAL OFFICE p 1285
300 E Courthouse Pub Sq, Laurens SC 29360
Tel (864) 681-1035 *SIC* 8322

▲ **DIVERSICARE HEALTHCARE SERVICES INC** p 443
1621 Galleria Blvd, Brentwood TN 37027
Tel (615) 771-7575 *SIC* 8051 8322

YMCA OF METROPOLITAN CHATTANOOGA p 1636
301 W 6th St, Chattanooga TN 37402
Tel (423) 266-3766
SIC 8641 7991 8351 7032 8322

MEDSOLUTIONS INC p 938
730 Cool Springs Blvd # 250, Franklin TN 37067
Tel (615) 468-0600 *SIC* 6324 8322

FRONTIER HEALTH p 581
1167 Spratlin Park Dr, Gray TN 37615
Tel (423) 467-3600 *SIC* 8093 8322

MARYVILLE HEALTHCARE & REHABILITATION p 915
1012 Jamestown Way, Maryville TN 37803
Tel (865) 984-7400 *SIC* 8322

YOUTH VILLAGES INC p 1639
3320 Brother Blvd, Memphis TN 38133
Tel (901) 251-5000 *SIC* 8361 8322

■ **CHILDRENS COMPREHENSIVE SERVICES INC** p 299
3401 West End Ave Ste 400, Nashville TN 37203
Tel (615) 250-0000 *SIC* 8322

■ **KEYSTONE EDUCATION AND YOUTH SERVICES LLC** p 815
3401 West End Ave Ste 400, Nashville TN 37203
Tel (615) 250-0000 *SIC* 8299 8322

TENNESSEE DEPARTMENT OF CHILDRENS SERVICES p 1438
Cordell Hull Bldg 7th Fl, Nashville TN 37243
Tel (615) 741-9699 *SIC* 8322 9441

YOUNG MENS CHRISTIAN ASSOCIATION OF MIDDLE TENNESSEE p 1638
1000 Church St, Nashville TN 37203
Tel (615) 259-9622
SIC 8641 7991 8351 7032 8322

NEIGHBORHOOD CENTERS INC p 1024
4500 Bissonnet St Ste 200, Bellaire TX 77401
Tel (713) 667-9400 *SIC* 8351 8322

ST JOSEPH REGIONAL HEALTH CENTER p 1368
2801 Franciscan Dr, Bryan TX 77802
Tel (979) 776-3777 *SIC* 8062 8322

ED RACHAL FOUNDATION INC p 476
500 N Shoreline Blvd # 606, Corpus Christi TX 78401
Tel (361) 881-9040 *SIC* 8322

NORTH TEXAS FOOD BANK p 1054
4500 S Cockrell Hill Rd, Dallas TX 75236
Tel (214) 330-1396 *SIC* 8322

YOUNG MENS CHRISTIAN ASSOCIATION OF METROPOLITAN p 1638
601 N Akard St, Dallas TX 75201
Tel (214) 880-9622
SIC 8641 7991 8351 7032 8322

KICKAPOO TRADITIONAL TRIBE OF TEXAS p 817
2212 Rosita Valley Rd, Eagle Pass TX 78852
Tel (830) 773-2105 *SIC* 8322

MENTAL HEALTH MENTAL RETARDATION OF TARRANT COUNTY p 943
3840 Hulen St, Fort Worth TX 76107
Tel (817) 569-4300 *SIC* 8093 8322 8361

YOUNG MENS CHRISTIAN ASSOCIATION OF GREATER HOUSTON AREA p 1638
2600 North Loop W Ste 300, Houston TX 77092
Tel (713) 659-5566 *SIC* 8322

YOUNG MENS CHRISTIAN ASSOCIATION OF GREATER HOUSTON AREA INC p 1638
2600 North Loop W Ste 300, Houston TX 77092
Tel (713) 659-5566
SIC 8641 7991 8351 7032 8322

BCFS HEALTH AND HUMAN SERVICES p 164
1506 Bexar Crossing St, San Antonio TX 78232
Tel (210) 832-5000 *SIC* 8322

SAN ANTONIO FOOD BANK p 1275
5200 Enrique M Barrera Pa, San Antonio TX 78227
Tel (210) 337-3663 *SIC* 4225 8322

HEIGHTS OF TYLER p 681
2650 Elkton Trl, Tyler TX 75703
Tel (903) 266-7200 *SIC* 8322

UTAH DEPARTMENT OF HUMAN SERVICES p 1536
195 N 1950 W, Salt Lake City UT 84116
Tel (801) 538-4001 *SIC* 8322 9441

IHC HEALTH SERVICES INC p 730
1380 E Medical Center Dr, St George UT 84790
Tel (801) 442-5000
SIC 8062 8011 8322 8049 8093 8069

EASTER SEALS VERMONT INC p 471
641 Comstock Rd Ste 1, Berlin VT 05602
Tel (802) 223-4744 *SIC* 8322

HOWARDCENTER INC p 713
208 Flynn Ave Ste 3j, Burlington VT 05401
Tel (802) 488-6900 *SIC* 8322

VOLUNTEERS OF AMERICA INC p 1565
1660 Duke St Ste 100, Alexandria VA 22314
Tel (703) 341-5000 *SIC* 8322 6531

EXPERIENCE WORKS INC p 520
4401 Wilson Blvd Ste 1100, Arlington VA 22203
Tel (703) 522-7272 *SIC* 8322 8331

INTERNATIONAL RELIEF AND DEVELOPMENT INC p 756
1621 N Kent St Ste 400, Arlington VA 22209
Tel (703) 247-3068 *SIC* 8322

BEACON HEALTH OPTIONS INC p 164
240 Corporate Blvd # 100, Norfolk VA 23502
Tel (757) 459-5100 *SIC* 6324 8322 6411

YOUNG MENS CHRISTIAN ASSOCIATION OF GREATER RICHMOND p 1638
2 W Franklin St, Richmond VA 23220
Tel (804) 644-9622
SIC 8641 7991 8351 7032 8322

COUNTY OF FAUQUIER p 378
70 Culpeper St, Warrenton VA 20186
Tel (540) 422-8080 *SIC* 8322

CATHOLIC COMMUNITY SERVICES OF WESTERN WASHINGTON p 266
100 23rd Ave S, Seattle WA 98144
Tel (206) 328-5696 *SIC* 8322

SEA-MAR COMMUNITY HEALTH CENTER p 1295
1040 S Henderson St, Seattle WA 98108
Tel (206) 763-5277
SIC 8322 8082 8093 8051

YOUNG MENS CHRISTIAN ASSOCIATION OF GREATER SEATTLE p 1638
909 4th Ave, Seattle WA 98104
Tel (206) 382-5342 *SIC* 8641 8322

CRISTA MINISTRIES p 392
19303 Fremont Ave N, Shoreline WA 98133
Tel (206) 546-7200 *SIC* 8322 8051 8211

ST ANDREWS ACQUISITION INC p 1364
9720 South Tacoma Way, Tacoma WA 98499
Tel (253) 584-2170 *SIC* 8322 8361

YOUNG MENS CHRISTIAN ASSOCIATION OF PIERCE AND KITSAP COUNTY p 1639
4717 S 19th St Ste 201, Tacoma WA 98405
Tel (253) 534-7800
SIC 8699 7991 7032 8322

COMMUNITY CARE INC p 347
205 Bishops Way Ofc, Brookfield WI 53005
Tel (414) 385-6600 *SIC* 8322

■ **UNITEDHEALTHCARE LIFE INSURANCE CO** p 1515
3100 Ams Blvd, Green Bay WI 54313
Tel (800) 232-5432
SIC 6411 6324 6311 8322

CARE WISCONSIN FIRST INC p 254
1617 Sherman Ave, Madison WI 53704
Tel (608) 240-0020 *SIC* 8322

COMMUNITY LIVING ALLIANCE INC p 349
1414 Macarthur Rd, Madison WI 53714
Tel (608) 242-8335 *SIC* 8322

LUTHERAN SOCIAL SERVICES OF WISCONSIN AND UPPER MICHIGAN INC p 886
647 W Virginia St Ste 200, Milwaukee WI 53204
Tel (262) 896-3446 *SIC* 8322 8082

YOUNG MENS CHRISTIAN ASSOCIATION OF METROPOLITAN MILWAUKEE INC p 1638
161 W Wisconsin Ave, Milwaukee WI 53203
Tel (414) 291-9622
SIC 8641 7991 8351 7032 8322

SIC 8331 Job Training & Vocational Rehabilitation Svcs

DENA NENA HENASH p 428
122 1st Ave Ste 600, Fairbanks AK 99701
Tel (907) 452-8251
SIC 8011 8331 8322 8093

GOODWILL INDUSTRIES OF CENTRAL ARIZONA FOUNDATION INC p 624
2626 W Beryl Ave, Phoenix AZ 85021
Tel (602) 535-4000 *SIC* 8331

LABORATORY SCIENCES OF ARIZONA LLC p 836
1255 W Washington St, Tempe AZ 85281
Tel (602) 685-5000 *SIC* 8071 8011 8331

BOST INC p 202
7701 S Zero St, Fort Smith AR 72903
Tel (479) 478-5600 *SIC* 8331 8351

OWL EDUCATION AND TRAINING INC p 1100
2465 Campus Dr, Irvine CA 92612
Tel (949) 797-2000 *SIC* 8331

GOODWILL INDUSTRIES OF SOUTHERN CALIFORNIA p 625
342 N San Fernando Rd, Los Angeles CA 90031
Tel (323) 223-1211 *SIC* 5331 8331

NORTH BAY DEVELOPMENTAL DISABILITIES SERVICES INC p 1051
10 Executive Ct Ste A, Napa CA 94558
Tel (707) 256-1224 *SIC* 8331 8322

OWL COMPANIES p 1100
4695 Macarthur Ct Ste 950, Newport Beach CA 92660
Tel (949) 797-2000 *SIC* 8331 6519 4911

CLOUDERA INC p 327
1001 Page Mill Rd Bldg 3, Palo Alto CA 94304
Tel (650) 644-3900 *SIC* 7371 5734 8331

GOODWILL SOUTHERN CALIFORNIA p 625
8120 Palm Ln, San Bernardino CA 92410
Tel (909) 885-3831 *SIC* 5932 8331

GOODWILL INDUSTRIES OF SAN DIEGO COUNTY p 625
3663 Rosecrans St, San Diego CA 92110
Tel (619) 225-2200 *SIC* 8331

DISCOVER GOODWILL OF SOUTHERN & WESTERN COLORADO p 442
1460 Grdn Of The Gods Rd, Colorado Springs CO 80907
Tel (719) 635-4483 *SIC* 5932 8331

LUTHERAN MEDICAL CENTER p 886
8300 W 38th Ave, Wheat Ridge CO 80033
Tel (303) 425-4500
SIC 8011 7389 8082 8331

AARP FOUNDATION p 8
601 E St Nw, Washington DC 20049
Tel (202) 434-2020 *SIC* 8331 8399

GOODWILL INDUSTRIES-MANASOTA INC p 625
2705 51st Ave E, Bradenton FL 34203
Tel (941) 355-2721 *SIC* 8331

GOODWILL INDUSTRIES OF SOUTH FLORIDA INC p 625
2121 Nw 21st St, Miami FL 33142
Tel (305) 325-9114 *SIC* 8331

SUNRISE COMMUNITY INC p 1403
9040 Sw 72nd St, Miami FL 33173
Tel (305) 275-3365 *SIC* 8052 8331 8322

GOODWILL INDUSTRIES OF CENTRAL FLORIDA INC p 624
7531 S Orange Blossom Trl, Orlando FL 32809
Tel (407) 857-0659 *SIC* 8331 8741

■ **DAL GLOBAL SERVICES LLC** p 409
980 Virginia Ave 4th, Atlanta GA 30354
Tel (404) 715-4300
SIC 7361 8331 7382 5088

GOODWILL INDUSTRIES OF NORTH GEORGIA INC p 624
2201 Lawrenceville Hwy, Decatur GA 30033
Tel (404) 420-9914 *SIC* 8331

GOODWILL OF NORTH GEORGIA INC p 625
2201 Lawrenceville Hwy, Decatur GA 30033
Tel (404) 420-9900 *SIC* 5932 8331

ANTHONY WAYNE REHABILITATION CENTER FOR HANDICAPPED AND BLIND INC p 94
8515 Bluffton Rd, Fort Wayne IN 46809
Tel (260) 744-6145
SIC 8331 7331 3441 3412 2449 2448

AW HOLDINGS LLC p 139
8515 Bluffton Rd, Fort Wayne IN 46809
Tel (260) 744-6145 *SIC* 8331

GOODWILL INDUSTRIES OF CENTRAL INDIANA INC p 624
1635 W Michigan St, Indianapolis IN 46222
Tel (317) 564-4313
SIC 5932 4783 8331 4953

UNIFIED SCHOOL DISTRICT 259 p 1503
201 N Water St, Wichita KS 67202
Tel (316) 973-4000 *SIC* 8211 8249 8331

RES-CARE INC p 1226
9901 Linn Station Rd, Louisville KY 40223
Tel (502) 394-2100 *SIC* 8052 8331 7363

EVERGREEN PRESBYTERIAN MINISTRIES INC p 514
2101 Highway 80, Haughton LA 71037
Tel (318) 949-5500 *SIC* 8331 8361

GOODWILL INDUSTRIES OF NORTHERN NEW ENGLAND p 625
75 Washington Ave Ste 300, Portland ME 04101
Tel (207) 774-6323 *SIC* 8331 2392

CHIMES DISTRICT OF COLUMBIA INC p 300
4815 Seton Dr, Baltimore MD 21215
Tel (410) 358-5193 *SIC* 8331

MELWOOD HORTICULTURAL TRAINING CENTER INC p 941
5606 Dower House Rd, Upper Marlboro MD 20772
Tel (301) 599-8000 *SIC* 8331 8322

VINFEN CORP p 1558
950 Cambridge St, Cambridge MA 02141
Tel (617) 441-1800 *SIC* 8361 8331

NORTHEAST ARC INC p 1054
64 Holten St, Danvers MA 01923
Tel (978) 762-4878 *SIC* 8361 8322 8331

HOPE NETWORK p 706
3075 Orchard Vista Dr Se # 100, Grand Rapids MI 49546
Tel (616) 301-8000 *SIC* 8331

MIDWEST CASE MANAGEMENT INC p 967
2905 Lucerne Dr Se # 102, Grand Rapids MI 49546
Tel (616) 957-7796 *SIC* 8331

PECKHAM VOCATIONAL INDUSTRIES INC p 1126
3510 Capitol City Blvd, Lansing MI 48906
Tel (517) 316-4000
SIC 8331 2396 2311 2331 2339 2326

GOODWILL INDUSTRIES INC p 624
553 Fairview Ave N, Saint Paul MN 55104
Tel (651) 379-5800
SIC 4953 8331 8322 5932 4226

MINACT INC p 972
5220 Keele St, Jackson MS 39206
Tel (601) 362-1631 *SIC* 8331 8742

EASTER SEALS MIDWEST p 471
13545 Barrett Parkway Dr, Ballwin MO 63021
Tel (314) 394-7026
SIC 8361 8331 8322 8052

MERS/MISSOURI GOODWILL INDUSTRIES p 951
1727 Locust St, Saint Louis MO 63103
Tel (314) 241-3464 *SIC* 8331

AWARE INC p 139
205 E Park Ave, Anaconda MT 59711
Tel (406) 563-5229 *SIC* 8361 8331

EASTER SEAL NEW HAMPSHIRE INC p 471
555 Auburn St, Manchester NH 03103
Tel (603) 623-8863
SIC 8331 8399 4119 8322

NEW HAMPSHIRE CATHOLIC CHARITIES INC p 1030
215 Myrtle St, Manchester NH 03104
Tel (603) 669-3030
SIC 8322 8059 8331 8661 8361

GOODWILL INDUSTRIES OF GREATER NEW YORK INC p 624
421 27th Ave, Astoria NY 11102
Tel (718) 728-5400 SIC 8331

ADULTS AND CHILDREN WITH LEARNING AND DEVELOPMENTAL DISABILITIES INC p 24
807 S Oyster Bay Rd, Bethpage NY 11714
Tel (516) 681-4500 SIC 8322 8331

PSCH INC p 1188
14202 20th Ave Rm 301, Flushing NY 11351
Tel (718) 559-0516 SIC 8361 8331 8093

NASSAU COUNTY A H R C p 1008
189 Wheatley Rd, Glen Head NY 11545
Tel (516) 626-1000 SIC 8331 8322

FULTON COUNTY A R C p 584
465 N Perry St, Johnstown NY 12095
Tel (518) 762-0024 SIC 8331 8361

NYSARC INC p 1069
29 British American Blvd # 2, Latham NY 12110
Tel (518) 439-8311
SIC 8361 8322 8093 8331

CAREER SYSTEMS DEVELOPMENT CORP p 254
75 Thruway Park Dr # 100, West Henrietta NY 14586
Tel (585) 334-8080 SIC 8741 8331

MONARCH p 983
350 Pee Dee Ave Ste 101, Albemarle NC 28001
Tel (704) 986-1500
SIC 8322 8049 8331 8052

GOODWILL INDUSTRIES OF NORTHWEST NORTH CAROLINA INC p 625
2701 University Pkwy, Winston Salem NC 27105
Tel (336) 724-3621 SIC 5932 8331

A W S INC p 7
1275 Lakeside Ave E, Cleveland OH 44114
Tel (216) 861-0250
SIC 8331 7374 7334 7331

VOCATIONAL GUIDANCE SERVICES INC p 1564
2239 E 55th St, Cleveland OH 44103
Tel (216) 431-7800 SIC 8331

ARC INDUSTRIES INC OF FRANKLIN COUNTY OHIO p 103
2879 Johnstown Rd, Columbus OH 43219
Tel (614) 475-6440 SIC 8331

HUNTER DEFENSE TECHNOLOGIES INC p 719
30500 Aurora Rd Ste 100, Solon OH 44139
Tel (216) 438-6111
SIC 3433 3569 3822 8331 8711 3549

LOTT INDUSTRIES INC p 879
3350 Hill Ave, Toledo OH 43607
Tel (419) 534-4980 SIC 8331 8741

DEPAUL INDUSTRIES p 430
4950 Ne Martin Luther Ki, Portland OR 97211
Tel (503) 281-1289 SIC 7361 8331

GOODWILL INDUSTRIES OF COLUMBIA WILLAMETTE p 624
1943 Se 6th Ave, Portland OR 97214
Tel (503) 238-6100 SIC 8331

GOODWILL KEYSTONE AREA p 625
1150 Goodwill Dr, Harrisburg PA 17101
Tel (610) 777-7875 SIC 8331

JEVS HUMAN SERVICES p 784
1845 Walnut St Ste 700, Philadelphia PA 19103
Tel (215) 875-7387 SIC 8322 8331

RESOURCES FOR HUMAN DEVELOPMENT INC p 1227
4700 Wphickon Ave Ste 126, Philadelphia PA 19144
Tel (215) 951-0300
SIC 8322 8093 8052 8331 8361

GOODWILL OF SOUTHWESTERN PENNSYLVANIA p 625
118 52nd St, Pittsburgh PA 15201
Tel (412) 481-9005 SIC 8331

DEPARTMENT OF FAMILY p 430
Sevilla Plz Bldg Se, San Juan PR 00919
Tel (787) 643-1855 SIC 9441 8331

ARC OF NORTHERN RHODE ISLAND INC p 103
80 Siaban St 1 Sox Ri, Woonsocket RI 02895
Tel (401) 765-3700 SIC 8331 8361

GOODWILL INDUSTRIES OF CENTRAL TEXAS p 624
1015 Norwood Park Blvd, Austin TX 78753
Tel (512) 637-7100 SIC 8331

TEXAS A&M ENGINEERING EXTENSION SERVICE p 1442
301 Tarrow St, College Station TX 77840
Tel (979) 845-7641
SIC 8331 8711 8748 8111

GOODWILL INDUSTRIES OF SAN ANTONIO p 625
406 W Commerce St, San Antonio TX 78207
Tel (210) 924-8581 SIC 8331

MANAGEMENT & TRAINING CORP p 900
500 N Market Place Dr # 100, Centerville UT 84014
Tel (801) 693-2600
SIC 8744 8331 7349 8741 8249

▲ FRANKLIN COVEY CO p 575
2200 W Parkway Blvd, Salt Lake City UT 84119
Tel (801) 817-1776 SIC 8742 8331 2741

EXPERIENCE WORKS INC p 520
4401 Wilson Blvd Ste 1100, Arlington VA 22203
Tel (703) 522-7272 SIC 8322 8331

CHENEGA INTEGRATED SYSTEMS LLC p 294
14295 Pk Madow Dr Ste 400, Chantilly VA 20151
Tel (571) 291-8500 SIC 7381 7382 8331

RAYTHEON TECHNICAL SERVICES CO LLC p 1211
22270 Pacific Blvd, Dulles VA 20166
Tel (571) 250-2100 SIC 8331 8711

■ NORTHROP GRUMMAN ENTERPRISE MANAGEMENT SERVICES CORP p 1058
2340 Dulles Corner Blvd, Herndon VA 20171
Tel (703) 713-4000
SIC 8741 8744 4731 8331 7349

DIDLAKE INC p 438
8641 Breeden Ave Ste 101, Manassas VA 20110
Tel (703) 361-4195
SIC 8331 7331 7349 7334

SERVICESOURCE INC p 1308
10467 White Granite Dr # 100, Oakton VA 22124
Tel (703) 461-6000 SIC 8331 7331

GOODWILL OF CENTRAL AND COASTAL VIRGINIA INC p 625
6301 Midlothian Tpke, Richmond VA 23225
Tel (804) 745-6300 SIC 8331

MALLORY SAFETY AND SUPPLY LLC p 900
1040 Industrial Way, Longview WA 98632
Tel (360) 636-5750 SIC 5099 8331

VALLEY PACKAGING INDUSTRIES INC p 1541
110 N Kensington Dr, Appleton WI 54915
Tel (920) 749-5840 SIC 7389 8331

GOODWILL INDUSTRIES OF SOUTHEASTERN WISCONSIN INC p 625
5400 S 60th St, Greendale WI 53129
Tel (414) 847-4200 SIC 8331 7349

GOODWILL INDUSTRIES OF NORTH CENTRAL WISCONSIN INC p 624
1800 Appleton Rd, Menasha WI 54952
Tel (920) 731-6601 SIC 5932 7389 8331

SIC 8351 Child Day Care Svcs

YOUNG MENS CHRISTIAN ASSOCIATION OF BIRMINGHAM p 1638
2101 4th Ave N, Birmingham AL 35203
Tel (205) 801-9622
SIC 7991 8641 8351 7032

BOST INC p 202
7701 S Zero St, Fort Smith AR 72903
Tel (479) 478-5600 SIC 8331 8351

CHA HOLLYWOOD MEDICAL CENTER LP p 286
1300 N Vermont Ave, Los Angeles CA 90027
Tel (213) 413-3000 SIC 8062 8351

ARC OF SAN DIEGO p 103
3030 Market St, San Diego CA 92102
Tel (619) 685-1175
SIC 8399 8351 8361 8322

YOUNG MENS CHRISTIAN ASSOCIATION OF SAN FRANCISCO p 1639
50 California St Ste 650, San Francisco CA 94111
Tel (415) 777-9622
SIC 8641 7991 8351 7032 8322

CHILD DEVELOPMENT INC p 298
20 Great Oaks Blvd # 200, San Jose CA 95119
Tel (408) 556-7300 SIC 8351

YMCA OF SILICON VALLEY p 1636
80 Saratoga Ave, Santa Clara CA 95051
Tel (408) 351-6400
SIC 8641 7991 8351 7032 8322

CHILDRENS CREATIVE LEARNING CENTER INC p 299
794 E Duane Ave, Sunnyvale CA 94085
Tel (408) 732-2500 SIC 8351

COMMUNITY DEVELOPMENT INSTITUTE HEAD START p 348
10065 E Harvard Ave # 700, Denver CO 80231
Tel (720) 747-5100 SIC 8351

YAMPA VALLEY MEDICAL CENTER p 1634
1024 Central Park Dr, Steamboat Springs CO 80487
Tel (970) 879-1322 SIC 8062 8351

YALE-NEW HAVEN HOSPITAL INC p 1634
20 York St, New Haven CT 06510
Tel (203) 688-4242 SIC 8351 8062 8741

EARLY LEARNING COALITION OF PALM BEACH COUNTY INC p 469
2300 High Ridge Rd # 115, Boynton Beach FL 33426
Tel (561) 214-8000 SIC 8351

HEALTHY START COALITION OF PALM BEACH COUNTY IN p 678
2300 High Ridge Rd, Boynton Beach FL 33426
Tel (561) 374-7613 SIC 8351

YOUNG MENS CHRISTIAN ASSOCIATION OF SUNCOAST p 1639
2469 Enterprise Rd, Clearwater FL 33763
Tel (312) 932-1200
SIC 8641 7991 8351 7032 8322

EARLY LEARNING COALITION OF MIAMI-DADE MONROE INC p 469
2555 Ponce De Leon Blvd # 5, Coral Gables FL 33134
Tel (305) 646-7220 SIC 8351

CHILDREN OF AMERICA INC p 298
5300 W Atl Ave Ste 700, Delray Beach FL 33484
Tel (561) 999-0710 SIC 8351

PALM BEACH STATE COLLEGE p 1109
4200 S Congress Ave, Lake Worth FL 33461
Tel (561) 868-3350 SIC 8222 8351 8221

ARR INVESTMENTS INC p 112
2600 E Jackson St, Orlando FL 32803
Tel (407) 894-8401 SIC 8351 8211

SARASOTA FAMILY YOUNG MENS CHRISTIAN ASSOCIATION INC p 1282
1 S School Ave Ste 301, Sarasota FL 34237
Tel (941) 951-2916
SIC 8641 8351 8322 7997 7991

YOUNG MENS CHRISTIAN ASSOCIATION OF METROPOLITAN ATLANTA INC p 1638
100 Edgewood Ave Ne, Atlanta GA 30303
Tel (404) 588-9622
SIC 8641 7991 8351 7032 8322

CHILD DEVELOPMENT SCHOOLS INC p 298
6053 Veterans Pkwy # 300, Columbus GA 31909
Tel (706) 562-8600 SIC 8351

CHAMPAIGN COMMUNITY UNIT SCHOOL DISTRICT 4 (INC) p 287
703 S New St, Champaign IL 61820
Tel (217) 351-3800 SIC 8211 8351

LEARNING CARE GROUP INC p 850
130 S Jefferson St # 300, Chicago IL 60661
Tel (312) 469-5656 SIC 8351

YOUNG MENS CHRISTIAN ASSOCIATION OF CHICAGO p 1638
1030 W Van Buren St, Chicago IL 60607
Tel (312) 932-1200
SIC 8641 7011 8351 8699 8322 7999

YOUNG MENS CHRISTIAN ASSOCIATION OF WICHITA KANSAS p 1639
402 N Market St, Wichita KS 67202
Tel (316) 219-9622
SIC 8641 7991 8351 7032 8322

YOUNG MENS CHRISTIAN ASSOCIATION OF GREATER LOUISVILLE p 1638
545 S 2nd St, Louisville KY 40202
Tel (502) 587-9622
SIC 8641 7991 8351 7032 8322

YMCA OF CENTRAL MARYLAND INC p 1636
303 W Chesapeake Ave, Baltimore MD 21204
Tel (443) 322-9622 SIC 8641 8351

COLLEGE OF SOUTHERN MARYLAND FOUNDATION INC p 337
8730 Mitchell Rd, La Plata MD 20646
Tel (301) 934-2251 SIC 8351

YMCA OF NORTH SHORE INC p 1636
245 Cabot St, Beverly MA 01915
Tel (978) 922-0990
SIC 7021 8322 8351 7999 7032

YMCA OF GREATER BOSTON INC p 1636
316 Huntington Ave Ste 1, Boston MA 02115
Tel (617) 536-6950
SIC 8641 7991 8351 7032 8322

OLD COLONY Y p 1080
320 Main St, Brockton MA 02301
Tel (508) 583-2155
SIC 8641 7991 8351 7032 8322

MULBERRY CHILD CARE CENTERS INC p 999
990 Washington St Ste 104, Dedham MA 02026
Tel (781) 320-9222 SIC 8351

COMMUNITY DAY CARE CENTER OF LAWRENCE INC p 348
190 Hampshire St Ste 2, Lawrence MA 01840
Tel (978) 682-6628 SIC 8351

■ BRIGHT HORIZONS CHILDRENS CENTERS LLC p 212
200 Talcott Ave, Watertown MA 02472
Tel (617) 673-8000 SIC 8351

▲ BRIGHT HORIZONS FAMILY SOLUTIONS INC p 212
200 Talcott Ave, Watertown MA 02472
Tel (617) 673-8000 SIC 8351

■ BRIGHT HORIZONS FAMILY SOLUTIONS LLC p 212
200 Talcott Ave, Watertown MA 02472
Tel (617) 673-8000 SIC 8351

CHILDRENS COURTYARD INC p 299
21333 Haggerty Rd Ste 300, Novi MI 48375
Tel (248) 697-9000 SIC 8351

CHILDTIME CHILDCARE INC p 300
21333 Haggerty Rd Ste 300, Novi MI 48375
Tel (248) 697-9000 SIC 8351

LA PETITE ACADEMY INC p 835
21333 Haggerty Rd Ste 300, Novi MI 48375
Tel (877) 861-5078 SIC 8351

LA PETITE HOLDINGS CORP p 835
21333 Haggerty Rd Ste 300, Novi MI 48375
Tel (248) 697-9000 SIC 8351

LEARNING CARE GROUP (US) INC p 850
21333 Haggerty Rd Ste 300, Novi MI 48375
Tel (248) 697-9000 SIC 8351

LEARNING CARE GROUP INC p 850
21333 Haggerty Rd Ste 300, Novi MI 48375
Tel (248) 697-9000 SIC 8351 8299

LPA INVESTMENT LLC p 882
21333 Haggerty Rd Ste 300, Novi MI 48375
Tel (866) 244-5384 SIC 8351

TUTOR TIME LEARNING CENTERS LLC p 1493
21333 Haggerty Rd Ste 300, Novi MI 48375
Tel (248) 697-9000 SIC 8351

ST MARYS MEDICAL CENTER p 1371
407 E 3rd St, Duluth MN 55805
Tel (218) 786-4000 SIC 8062 8082 8351

EARLY BLOOM LEARNING p 469
17805 County Road 6, Minneapolis MN 55447
Tel (763) 449-0600 SIC 8351

NEW HORIZON ENTERPRISES INC p 1031
3405 Annapolis Ln N # 100, Minneapolis MN 55447
Tel (763) 557-1111 SIC 8351

SOUTHEAST MISSOURI STATE UNIVERSITY p 1346
1 University Plz, Cape Girardeau MO 63701
Tel (573) 651-2000 SIC 8351

CATHOLIC DIOCESE OF KANSAS CITY-ST JOSEPH p 266
850 Main St, Kansas City MO 64105
Tel (816) 756-1850
SIC 8661 8211 8351 8361 6553

ALEGENT HEALTH - IMMANUEL MEDICAL CENTER p 48
6901 N 72nd St, Omaha NE 68122
Tel (402) 572-2121 SIC 8062 8051 8351

CENTER FOR DISABILITY SERVICES INC p 275
314 S Manning Blvd, Albany NY 12208
Tel (518) 437-5506
SIC 8351 8093 8361 8099

BETH ABRAHAM HEALTH SERVICES p 177
2540 Barker Ave Ofc, Bronx NY 10467
Tel (718) 519-5831 SIC 8059 8351 8082

YELED V YALDA EARLY CHILDHOOD CENTER INC p 1635
1312 38th St, Brooklyn NY 11218
Tel (718) 686-3700 SIC 8351

YOUNG MENS CHRISTIAN ASSOCIATION OF GREATER NEW YORK p 1638
5 W 63rd St Fl 6, New York NY 10023
Tel (212) 630-9600
SIC 8641 7991 8351 7032 8322

ST FRANCIS HOSPITAL POUGHKEEPSIE NEW YORK p 1366
241 North Rd, Poughkeepsie NY 12601
Tel (845) 483-5000
SIC 8062 8069 8011 8351

YMCA OF NORTHWEST NORTH CAROLINA p 1636
301 N Main St Ste 1900, Winston Salem NC 27101
Tel (336) 777-8055
SIC 8641 7991 8351 7032 8322

OHIOGUIDESTONE p 1078
434 Eastland Rd, Berea OH 44017
Tel (440) 234-2006
SIC 8322 8361 8351 8051

YOUNG MENS CHRISTIAN ASSOCIATION OF GREATER DAYTON p 1638
118 W St Ste 300, Dayton OH 45402
Tel (937) 223-5201
SIC 8641 7991 8351 7032 8322

PROMEDICA HEALTH SYSTEMS INC p 1183
1801 Richards Rd, Toledo OH 43607
Tel (419) 469-3800
SIC 8062 6324 8351 8741

YOUNG MENS CHRISTIAN ASSOCIATION OF GREATER TOLEDO p 1638
1500 N Superior St Fl 2, Toledo OH 43604
Tel (419) 729-8135
SIC 8641 7991 8351 7032 8322

CHILDRENS CREATIVE LEARNING CENTERS LLC p 299
650 Ne Holladay St # 1400, Portland OR 97232
Tel (503) 872-1300 SIC 8351

KINDERCARE LEARNING CENTERS LLC p 819
650 Ne Holladay St # 1400, Portland OR 97232
Tel (503) 872-1300 SIC 8351

MULBERRY CHILDCARE CENTERS INC p 999
650 Ne Holladay St # 1400, Portland OR 97232
Tel (503) 872-1300 SIC 8351

KENCREST SERVICES p 810
960 Harvest Dr Ste 100a, Blue Bell PA 19422
Tel (610) 825-9360 SIC 8361 8322 8351

CENTRAL BUCKS SCHOOL DISTRICT p 277
20 Weldon Dr, Doylestown PA 18901
Tel (267) 893-2000 SIC 8351

RESPIRONICS INC p 1227
1010 Murry Ridge Ln, Murrysville PA 15668
Tel (724) 387-5200
SIC 3641 3845 3841 3564 8351

CARING PEOPLE ALLIANCE p 256
8 Penn Ctr, Philadelphia PA 19103
Tel (215) 545-5230 SIC 8351

YMCA GREATER BRANDYWINE p 1636
1 E Chestnut St, West Chester PA 19380
Tel (610) 643-9622
SIC 8641 7991 8351 7032 8322

GREATER PROVIDENCE YOUNG MENS CHRISTIAN ASSOCIATION p 636
371 Pine St, Providence RI 02903
Tel (401) 521-9622
SIC 8641 7991 8351 7032 8322

SUNSHINE HOUSE INC p 1404
12 Interchange Blvd, Greenville SC 29607
Tel (864) 990-1820 SIC 8351

TEKAKWITHA LIVING CENTER INC p 1433
622 Veterans Ave, Sisseton SD 57262
Tel (605) 698-7693 SIC 8351

YMCA OF METROPOLITAN CHATTANOOGA p 1636
301 W 6th St, Chattanooga TN 37402
Tel (423) 266-3766
SIC 8641 7991 8351 7032 8322

YOUNG MENS CHRISTIAN ASSOCIATION OF MIDDLE TENNESSEE p 1638
1000 Church St, Nashville TN 37203
Tel (615) 259-9622
SIC 8641 7991 8351 7032 8322

NEIGHBORHOOD CENTERS INC p 1024
4500 Bissonnet St Ste 200, Bellaire TX 77401
Tel (713) 667-9400 SIC 8351 8322

YOUNG MENS CHRISTIAN ASSOCIATION OF METROPOLITAN p 1638
601 N Akard St, Dallas TX 75201
Tel (214) 880-9622
SIC 8641 7991 8351 7032 8322

YOUNG MENS CHRISTIAN ASSOCIATION OF GREATER HOUSTON AREA INC p 1638
2600 North Loop W Ste 300, Houston TX 77092
Tel (713) 659-5566
SIC 8641 7991 8351 7032 8322

CHALLENGER SCHOOLS p 287
9424 S 300 W, Sandy UT 84070
Tel (801) 569-2700 SIC 8351 8211

YOUNG MENS CHRISTIAN ASSOCIATION OF GREATER RICHMOND p 1638
2 W Franklin St, Richmond VA 23220
Tel (804) 644-9622
SIC 8641 7991 8351 7032 8322

MINNIELAND PRIVATE DAY SCHOOL INC p 974
4300 Prince William Pkwy, Woodbridge VA 22192
Tel (703) 680-2548 SIC 8351 8211

SEA MAR COMMUNITY CARE CENTER p 1295
1040 S Henderson St, Seattle WA 98108
Tel (206) 763-5210 SIC 8051 8351

TACOMA COMMUNITY COLLEGE p 1421
6501 S 19th St Bldg 14, Tacoma WA 98466
Tel (253) 566-5058 SIC 8222 8351

YOUNG MENS CHRISTIAN ASSOCIATION OF METROPOLITAN MILWAUKEE INC p 1638
161 W Wisconsin Ave, Milwaukee WI 53203
Tel (414) 291-9622
SIC 8641 7991 8351 7032 8322

SIC 8361 Residential Care

SEQUEL TSI HOLDINGS LLC p 1306
1131 Eagletree Ln Sw # 300, Huntsville AL 35801
Tel (256) 880-3339 SIC 8361 8322

SEQUEL YOUTH AND FAMILY SERVICES LLC p 1306
1131 Eagletree Ln Sw, Huntsville AL 35801
Tel (256) 880-3339 SIC 8322 8361

SUMMIT MEDICAL PLAZA LLC p 1399
2200 E Show Low Lake Rd, Show Low AZ 85901
Tel (928) 537-4375 SIC 8361

VISIONQUEST NONPROFIT CORP p 1561
600 N Swan Rd, Tucson AZ 85711
Tel (520) 881-3950 SIC 8361 8211 8322

ASERACARE HOSPICE - NEW HORIZONS LLC p 116
1 1000 Beverly Way, Fort Smith AR 72919
Tel (479) 201-2000 SIC 8361

ESKATON PROPERTIES INC p 509
5105 Manzanita Ave Ste A, Carmichael CA 95608
Tel (916) 334-0810 SIC 8361

■ **SUMMERVILLE AT HAZEL CREEK LLC** p 1398
6125 Hazel Ave, Orangevale CA 95662
Tel (916) 988-7901 SIC 8361

GOOD SHEPHERD LUTHERAN HOME OF WEST p 623
119 N Main St, Porterville CA 93257
Tel (559) 791-2000 SIC 8361

ARC OF SAN DIEGO p 103
3030 Market St, San Diego CA 92102
Tel (619) 685-1175
SIC 8399 8351 8361 8322

DELANCEY STREET FOUNDATION p 423
600 The Embarcadero, San Francisco CA 94107
Tel (415) 957-9800
SIC 8361 5199 8322 4212 5812

SOCIAL VOCATIONAL SERVICES INC p 1336
3555 Torrance Blvd, Torrance CA 90503
Tel (310) 944-3303 SIC 8361

EPISCOPAL SENIOR COMMUNITIES p 505
2185 N Calif Blvd Ste 575, Walnut Creek CA 94596
Tel (925) 956-7400 SIC 8361

CONNECTICUT INSTITUTE FOR BLIND INC p 357
120 Holcomb St, Hartford CT 06112
Tel (860) 242-2274 SIC 8211 8361

PENINSULA UNITED METHODIST HOMES INC p 1129
726 Loveville Rd Ste 3000, Hockessin DE 19707
Tel (302) 235-6800 SIC 8361

CONNECTIONS COMMUNITY SUPPORT PROGRAMS INC p 357
3821 Lancaster Pike, Wilmington DE 19805
Tel (302) 984-2302 SIC 8322 8361 8049

PHINEAS CORP p 1144
9040 Sw 72nd St, Miami FL 33173
Tel (305) 596-9040 SIC 8361 8399 6531

PRESBYTERIAN RETIREMENT COMMUNITIES INC p 1171
80 W Lucerne Cir, Orlando FL 32801
Tel (407) 839-5050 SIC 8361 8052 8051

CHILDRENS HOME SOCIETY OF FLORIDA p 299
1485 S Semoran Blvd, Winter Park FL 32792
Tel (407) 657-2197 SIC 8322 8361

■ **CARTERSVILLE MEDICAL CENTER LLC** p 262
960 Joe Frank Harris, Cartersville GA 30120
Tel (770) 382-1530 SIC 8361

ALEXIAN BROTHERS OF AMERICA INC p 49
3040 W Salt Creek Ln, Arlington Heights IL 60005
Tel (847) 640-7550 SIC 8742 8062 8361

▲ **ADDUS HOMECARE CORP** p 22
2300 Warrenville Rd # 100, Downers Grove IL 60515
Tel (630) 296-3400 SIC 8082 8361

PRESBYTERIAN HOMES p 1171
3200 Grant St, Evanston IL 60201
Tel (847) 492-4800 SIC 8361

CATHOLIC DIOCESE OF ROCKFORD p 266
555 Colman Center Dr, Rockford IL 61108
Tel (815) 399-4300
SIC 8661 8322 8361 8211 6553

REST HAVEN ILLIANA CHRISTIAN CONVALESCENT HOME p 1228
18601 North Creek Dr A, Tinley Park IL 60477
Tel (708) 342-8100 SIC 8051 8361

MILLERS HEALTH SYSTEMS INC p 971
1690 S County Farm Rd, Warsaw IN 46580
Tel (574) 267-7211 SIC 8052 8051 8361

HOPE HAVEN AREA DEVELOPMENT CENTER CORP p 706
828 N 7th St Ste 1, Burlington IA 52601
Tel (319) 752-0110 SIC 8361

ST JOHNS REST HOME INC p 1368
2225 Canterbury Dr, Hays KS 67601
Tel (785) 735-2208 SIC 8361

SAINT FRANCIS COMMUNITY SERVICES INC p 1269
509 E Elm St, Salina KS 67401
Tel (785) 825-0541 SIC 8741 8361

▲ **AMEDISYS INC** p 66
3854 American Way Ste A, Baton Rouge LA 70816
Tel (225) 292-2031
SIC 8082 8051 8049 8361

EVERGREEN PRESBYTERIAN MINISTRIES INC p 514
2101 Highway 80, Haughton LA 71037
Tel (318) 949-5500 SIC 8331 8361

NORTH COUNTRY ASSOCIATES INC p 1052
179 Lisbon St Ste 3, Lewiston ME 04240
Tel (207) 786-3554 SIC 8361

ST MARYS HEALTH SYSTEM p 1371
96 Campus Ave, Lewiston ME 04240
Tel (207) 777-8546
SIC 8062 8052 8051 8011 8361

ST MARYS REGIONAL MEDICAL CENTER p 1372
93 Campus Ave, Lewiston ME 04240
Tel (207) 777-8546
SIC 8062 8052 8051 8011 8361

ANNIE E CASEY FOUNDATION INC p 92
701 Saint Paul St, Baltimore MD 21202
Tel (410) 547-6600 SIC 8322 8361

ASBURY COMMUNITIES INC p 115
20030 Century Blvd # 300, Germantown MD 20874
Tel (301) 250-2100 SIC 8361

RIDERWOOD VILLAGE INC p 1234
3150 Gracefield Rd, Silver Spring MD 20904
Tel (301) 572-1300 SIC 8361

HOMEWOOD RETIREMENT CENTERS OF UNITED CHURCH OF CHRIST INC p 704
16107 Elliott Pkwy, Williamsport MD 21795
Tel (301) 582-1626 SIC 8051 8361

BAY COVE HUMAN SERVICES INC p 160
66 Canal St, Boston MA 02114
Tel (617) 371-3000 SIC 8052 8093 8361

NATIONAL MENTOR HOLDINGS INC p 1014
313 Congress St Fl 5, Boston MA 02210
Tel (617) 790-4800 SIC 8082 8361

NATIONAL MENTOR INC p 1014
313 Congress St Fl 5, Boston MA 02210
Tel (617) 790-4800 SIC 8361

NMH INVESTMENT LLC p 1045
313 Congress St Fl 5, Boston MA 02210
Tel (617) 790-4800 SIC 8361

VINFEN CORP p 1558
950 Cambridge St, Cambridge MA 02141
Tel (617) 441-1800 SIC 8361 8331

NORTHEAST ARC INC p 1054
64 Holten St, Danvers MA 01923
Tel (978) 762-4878 SIC 8361 8322 8331

ELIOT COMMUNITY HUMAN SERVICES INC p 487
186 Bedford St, Lexington MA 02420
Tel (781) 861-0890 SIC 8361 8322

BRIDGEWELL INC p 212
471 Broadway, Lynnfield MA 01940
Tel (781) 599-4240 SIC 8361 8093

CRESSON SECURE TREATMENT UNIT p 391
160 Gould St Ste 300, Needham MA 02494
Tel (781) 559-4900 SIC 8361

MAY INSTITUTE INC p 923
41 Pacella Park Dr, Randolph MA 02368
Tel (781) 440-0400 SIC 8361

CUMMINGS FOUNDATION INC p 401
200 W Cummings Park, Woburn MA 01801
Tel (781) 935-8000 SIC 8361 6512

ASCENTRIA CARE ALLIANCE p 116
14 E Worcester St Ste 300, Worcester MA 01604
Tel (774) 343-3900 SIC 8322 8051 8361

SEVEN HILLS FOUNDATION INC p 1309
81 Hope Ave, Worcester MA 01603
Tel (508) 755-2340 SIC 8211 8361

SPECTRUM HEALTH SYSTEMS INC p 1357
10 Mechanic St Ste 302, Worcester MA 01608
Tel (508) 792-1508 SIC 8361 8093

HOLLAND HOME p 700
2100 Raybrook St Se # 300, Grand Rapids MI 49546
Tel (616) 235-5000 SIC 8361 8051

TRINITY SENIOR LIVING COMMUNITIES p 1482
17410 College Pkwy # 200, Livonia MI 48152
Tel (734) 542-8300 SIC 8361

SPECTRUM COMMUNITY SERVICES p 1357
28303 Joy Rd, Westland MI 48185
Tel (734) 453-8804 SIC 8361

SPECTRUM HUMAN SERVICES INC p 1357
28303 Joy Rd, Westland MI 48185
Tel (734) 458-8736 SIC 8361

HAZELDEN BETTY FORD FOUNDATION p 671
15251 Pleasant Valley Rd, Center City MN 55012
Tel (651) 213-4000 SIC 8361 2731

AMERICAN BAPTIST HOMES OF MIDWEST p 68
14850 Scenic Heights Rd, Eden Prairie MN 55344
Tel (952) 941-3175 SIC 8051 8361 8052

WALKER METHODIST p 1573
3737 Bryant Ave S, Minneapolis MN 55409
Tel (612) 827-5931 SIC 8361

NEXUS p 1041
505 Highway 169 N Ste 500, Plymouth MN 55441
Tel (763) 551-8640 SIC 8322 8361

PRESBYTERIAN HOMES AND SERVICES p 1171
2845 Hamline Ave N # 200, Roseville MN 55113
Tel (651) 631-6100 SIC 8361

EASTER SEALS MIDWEST p 471
13545 Barrett Parkway Dr, Ballwin MO 63021
Tel (314) 394-7026
SIC 8361 8331 8322 8052

COMPASS HEALTH INC p 351
1800 Community, Clinton MO 64735
Tel (660) 885-8131
SIC 8011 8069 8093 8361

CATHOLIC DIOCESE OF KANSAS CITY-ST JOSEPH p 266
850 Main St, Kansas City MO 64105
Tel (816) 756-1850
SIC 8661 8211 8351 8361 6553

LUTHERAN SENIOR SERVICES p 886
1150 Hanley Industrial Ct, Saint Louis MO 63144
Tel (314) 968-9313 SIC 8361

AWARE INC p 139
205 E Park Ave, Anaconda MT 59711
Tel (406) 563-5229 SIC 8361 8331

CMC MISSOULA INC p 329
2827 Fort Missoula Rd, Missoula MT 59804
Tel (406) 728-4100 SIC 8062 8361

FATHER FLANAGANS BOYS HOME p 531
14086 Mother Theresa Ln, Boys Town NE 68010
Tel (402) 498-1111 SIC 8361

MOSAIC p 991
4980 S 118th St, Omaha NE 68137
Tel (402) 896-3884 SIC 8361 8741

NEW HAMPSHIRE CATHOLIC CHARITIES INC p 1030
215 Myrtle St, Manchester NH 03104
Tel (603) 669-3030
SIC 8322 8059 8331 8661 8361

BANCROFT NEUROHEALTH A NEW JERSEY NONPROFIT CORP p 150
1255 Caldwell Rd, Cherry Hill NJ 08034
Tel (856) 348-1183 SIC 8361 8299 8211

CLONDALKIN PHARMA & HEALTHCARE LLC p 327
1224 N Church St, Moorestown NJ 08057
Tel (856) 439-1700 SIC 5122 8361

BRANDYWINE SENIOR LIVING MANAGEMENT LLC p 208
525 Fellowship Rd Ste 360, Mount Laurel NJ 08054
Tel (856) 778-6100 SIC 8361 8051

YOUTH CONSULTATION SERVICE (INC) p 1639
284 Broadway, Newark NJ 07104
Tel (973) 482-2774 SIC 8093 8361 8211

SENIOR PHS LIVING INC p 1304
13 Roszel Rd Ste C120, Princeton NJ 08540
Tel (609) 426-6802 SIC 8361 8052 8051

KBWB OPERATIONS-RICE LLC p 806
1120 Alps Rd, Wayne NJ 07470
Tel (973) 339-8899 SIC 8051 8361

AMBERCARE CORP p 65
420 N Main St, Belen NM 87002
Tel (505) 861-0060
SIC 8082 8361 5047 7352

CENTER FOR DISABILITY SERVICES INC p 275
314 S Manning Blvd, Albany NY 12208
Tel (518) 437-5506
SIC 8351 8093 8361 8099

CATHOLIC CHARITIES DIOCESE OF BROOKLYN & QUEENS p 265
191 Joralemon St, Brooklyn NY 11201
Tel (718) 722-6000 SIC 8322 8361

JEWISH CHILD CARE ASSOCIATION OF NEW YORK p 784
858 E 29th St, Brooklyn NY 11210
Tel (917) 808-4800 SIC 8361 8399

PHOENIX HOUSE FOUNDATION INC p 1145
50 Jay St, Brooklyn NY 11201
Tel (646) 505-2000 SIC 8361

ROCKAWAY HOME ATTENDANT SERVICES INC p 1243
1603 Central Ave 100, Far Rockaway NY 11691
Tel (718) 327-1850 SIC 8082 8361

PSCH INC p 1188
14202 20th Ave Rm 301, Flushing NY 11351
Tel (718) 559-0516 SIC 8361 8331 8093

CENTER FOR DISCOVERY INC p 275
641 Old Route 17, Harris NY 12742
Tel (845) 794-1400 SIC 8361

FULTON COUNTY A R C p 584
465 N Perry St, Johnstown NY 12095
Tel (518) 762-0024 SIC 8331 8361

BAKER HALL p 146
780 Ridge Rd, Lackawanna NY 14218
Tel (716) 828-9515 SIC 8361 8211 8322

NYSARC INC p 1069
29 British American Blvd # 2, Latham NY 12110
Tel (518) 439-8311
SIC 8361 8322 8093 8331

INDEPENDENT TRANSPORTERS OF HANDICAPPED INC p 737
221 N Sunrise Service Rd, Manorville NY 11949
Tel (631) 878-9270 SIC 8361 4729

CATHOLIC GUARDIAN SERVICES p 266
1011 1st Ave Fl 10, New York NY 10022
Tel (212) 371-1011 SIC 8322 8361

COVENANT HOUSE p 384
5 Penn Plz Ste 201, New York NY 10001
Tel (212) 727-4000 SIC 8322 8361

JEWISH BOARD OF FAMILY AND CHILDRENS SERVICES INC p 784
135 W 50th St Fl 6, New York NY 10020
Tel (212) 582-9100 SIC 8361 8322

JEWISH HOME LIFECARE MANHATTAN p 784
120 W 106th St, New York NY 10025
Tel (212) 870-5000 SIC 8361 7521

NEW YORK FOUNDLING HOSPITAL p 1035
590 Ave Of The Americas # 1, New York NY 10011
Tel (212) 633-9300 SIC 8361 8399

YOUNG ADULT INSTITUTE INC p 1638
460 W 34th St Fl 11, New York NY 10001
Tel (212) 563-7474 SIC 8059 8361 8011

HILLSIDE FAMILY OF AGENCIES p 694
1183 Monroe Ave, Rochester NY 14620
Tel (585) 256-7500 SIC 8361 8322 8093

SUNNYSIDE HOME CARE PROJECT INC p 1403
4331 39th St Ste A, Sunnyside NY 11104
Tel (718) 784-6173 SIC 8361 8322

PEOPLE INC p 1132
1219 N Forest Rd, Williamsville NY 14221
Tel (716) 817-7400 SIC 8361

HUGH CHATHAM MEMORIAL HOSPITAL INC p 717
180 Parkwood Dr, Elkin NC 28621
Tel (336) 835-3722 SIC 8062 8051 8361

HOWELL CHILD CARE CENTER INC p 713
3738 Howell Day Care Rd, La Grange NC 28551
Tel (252) 566-9011 SIC 8361 8052

RHA/HOWELL CARE CENTERS INC p 1231
3738 Howell Day Care Rd, La Grange NC 28551
Tel (252) 566-9011 SIC 8361 8052

OHIOGUIDESTONE p 1078
434 Eastland Rd, Berea OH 44017
Tel (440) 234-2006
SIC 8322 8361 8351 8051

J & R ASSOCIATES p 770
14803 Holland Rd, Brookpark OH 44142
Tel (440) 250-4080 SIC 1542 8361 6514

DEACONESS LONG TERM CARE OF MISSOURI INC p 419
330 Straight St Ste 310, Cincinnati OH 45219
Tel (513) 487-3600
SIC 8059 8361 8052 8051

OHIO PRESBYTERIAN RETIREMENT SERVICES (INC) p 1078
1001 Kingsmill Pkwy, Columbus OH 43229
Tel (614) 888-7800 SIC 8361

CHAMPAIGN RESIDENTIAL SERVICES INC p 287
1150 Scioto St Ste 201, Urbana OH 43078
Tel (937) 653-1320 SIC 8361

RCHP - WILMINGTON LLC p 1212
610 W Main St, Wilmington OH 45177
Tel (937) 382-6611 SIC 8062 8361

GOLDEN AGE NURSING HOME OF GUTHRIE INC p 620
419 E Oklahoma Ave, Guthrie OK 73044
Tel (405) 282-6285 SIC 8051 8361

■ **DEACONESS HEALTH SYSTEM LLC** p 419
5501 N Portland Ave, Oklahoma City OK 73112
Tel (405) 604-6000
SIC 8062 8051 8011 8361

ST JOHN HEALTH SYSTEM INC p 1367
1923 S Utica Ave, Tulsa OK 74104
Tel (918) 744-2180
SIC 7991 6512 7389 8361 8071 8062

HARVEST MANAGEMENT SUB LLC p 666
5885 Meadows Rd Ste 500, Lake Oswego OR 97035
Tel (503) 370-7070 SIC 8361

ALBERTINA KERR CENTERS p 46
424 Ne 22nd Ave, Portland OR 97232
Tel (503) 239-8101 SIC 8052 8361 8093

CASCADIA BEHAVIORAL HEALTHCARE INC p 263
847 Ne 19th Ave Ste 100, Portland OR 97232
Tel (503) 238-0769
SIC 8322 8093 8063 8361

GOOD SHEPHERD REHABILITATION HOSPITAL INC p 623
850 S 5th St, Allentown PA 18103
Tel (610) 776-3100
SIC 8361 8051 8093 8069

SHEPHERD GOOD REHABILITATION NETWORK p 1315
850 S 5th St, Allentown PA 18103
Tel (610) 776-3100 SIC 8051 8361 8322

MELMARK INC p 941
2600 Wayland Rd, Berwyn PA 19312
Tel (610) 353-1726 SIC 8211 8361

KENCREST SERVICES p 810
960 Harvest Dr Ste 100a, Blue Bell PA 19422
Tel (610) 825-9360 SIC 8361 8322 8351

ALLIED SERVICES FOUNDATION INC p 57
100 Abington Executive Pa, Clarks Summit PA 18411
Tel (570) 348-1407 SIC 8093 8361

ALLEGHENY VALLEY SCHOOL p 52
1996 Ewings Mill Rd, Coraopolis PA 15108
Tel (412) 299-7777 SIC 8361

PRESBYTERIAN HOMES INC p 1171
1 Trinity Dr E Ste 201, Dillsburg PA 17019
Tel (717) 697-2255 SIC 8361

MASONIC VILLAGES OF GRAND LODGE OF PENNSYLVANIA p 916
1 Masonic Dr, Elizabethtown PA 17022
Tel (717) 367-1121 SIC 8361

DR GERTRUDE A BARBER CENTER INC p 454
100 Barber Pl, Erie PA 16507
Tel (814) 453-7661 SIC 8361 8211

EXCELA HEALTH HOLDING CO INC p 516
532 W Pittsburgh St, Greensburg PA 15601
Tel (724) 832-4000
SIC 8062 8093 5999 7363 7322 8361

KEYSTONE SERVICE SYSTEMS INC p 816
124 Pine St, Harrisburg PA 17101
Tel (717) 232-7509 SIC 8361

■ **FC-GEN ACQUISITION INC** p 532
101 E State St, Kennett Square PA 19348
Tel (610) 444-6350 SIC 8361 8051 8099

■ **GENESIS ELDERCARE NATIONAL CENTERS INC** p 602
101 E State St, Kennett Square PA 19348
Tel (610) 444-6350 SIC 8051 8361

■ **GENESIS HEALTHCARE CORP** p 603
101 E State St, Kennett Square PA 19348
Tel (610) 444-6350 SIC 8051 8361

▲ **GENESIS HEALTHCARE INC** p 603
101 E State St, Kennett Square PA 19348
Tel (610) 444-6350
SIC 8051 8052 8059 8361

PHILADELPHIA PRESBYTERY HOMES INC p 1143
2000 Joshua Rd, Lafayette Hill PA 19444
Tel (610) 834-1001 SIC 8361 8052 8051

FAIR ACRES GERIATRIC CENTER p 524
340 N Middletown Rd, Media PA 19063
Tel (610) 891-5600 SIC 8361

GAUDENZIA INC p 594
106 W Main St, Norristown PA 19401
Tel (610) 239-9600 SIC 8361 8093

HORIZON HOUSE INC p 707
120 S 30th St, Philadelphia PA 19104
Tel (215) 386-3838
SIC 8361 6512 8322 8093

RESOURCES FOR HUMAN DEVELOPMENT INC p 1227
4700 Wphickon Ave Ste 126, Philadelphia PA 19144
Tel (215) 951-0300
SIC 8322 8093 8052 8331 8361

MAIN LINE HEALTH SYSTEM p 897
240 N Radnor Chester Rd, Radnor PA 19087
Tel (610) 225-6200
SIC 5999 8059 8361 8062

ELK REGIONAL HEALTH SYSTEM p 487
763 Johnsonburg Rd, Saint Marys PA 15857
Tel (814) 788-8000
SIC 8062 8051 8361 8399

OAK HEALTH AND REHABILITATION CENTERS INC p 1070
5 Morgan Hwy, Scranton PA 18508
Tel (215) 346-6454 SIC 8361

DEVEREUX FOUNDATION p 434
444 Devereux Dr, Villanova PA 19085
Tel (610) 520-3000 SIC 8361

ACTS RETIREMENT-LIFE COMMUNITIES INC p 20
375 Morris Rd, West Point PA 19486
Tel (215) 699-3204 SIC 8361 8051

RIVERSTREET MANOR p 1238
440 N River St, Wilkes Barre PA 18702
Tel (570) 825-5611 SIC 8361 8059 8051

STEP-BY-STEP INC p 1386
744 Kidder St Frnt, Wilkes Barre PA 18702
Tel (570) 829-3477 SIC 8322 8361

■ **HEALTHCARE RESOURCES CORP** p 676
1113 Easton Rd, Willow Grove PA 19090
Tel (215) 659-3060 SIC 8059 8361

WILLOW VALLEY COMMUNITIES p 1613
100 Willow Vly Lakes Dr, Willow Street PA 17584
Tel (717) 464-2741 SIC 8361 8059 8082

ARC OF NORTHERN RHODE ISLAND INC p 103
80 Siaban St 1 Sox Ri, Woonsocket RI 02895
Tel (401) 765-3700 SIC 8331 8361

▲ BROOKDALE SENIOR LIVING p 217
111 Westwood Pl Ste 400, Brentwood TN 37027
Tel (615) 221-2250 SIC 8059 8361 8051

■ LIFETRUST AMERICA INC p 865
113 Seaboard Ln Ste 150a, Franklin TN 37067
Tel (615) 342-0601
SIC 8361 8051 8052 8059

SUPPORT SOLUTIONS OF MID-SOUTH LLC p 1408
5909 Shelby Oaks Dr # 100, Memphis TN 38134
Tel (901) 383-9193 SIC 8361

YOUTH VILLAGES INC p 1639
3320 Brother Blvd, Memphis TN 38133
Tel (901) 251-5000 SIC 8361 8322

▲ CORECIVIC INC p 369
10 Burton Hills Blvd, Nashville TN 37215
Tel (615) 263-3000
SIC 6798 8744 8361 8299

OMNI VISION INC p 1085
301 S Perimeter Park Dr # 210, Nashville TN 37211
Tel (615) 726-3603 SIC 8361

SEARS METHODIST RETIREMENT SYSTEM INC p 1297
1 Village Dr Ste 400, Abilene TX 79606
Tel (325) 691-5519 SIC 8361

SOUTHWEST KEY PROGRAMS INC p 1352
6002 Jain Ln, Austin TX 78721
Tel (512) 462-2181 SIC 8361

DALLAS COUNTY MENTAL HEALTH & MENTAL RETARDATION CENTER (INC) p 410
1345 River Bend Dr # 200, Dallas TX 75247
Tel (214) 743-1200 SIC 8361

MENTAL HEALTH MENTAL RETARDATION OF TARRANT COUNTY p 943
3840 Hulen St, Fort Worth TX 76107
Tel (817) 569-4300 SIC 8093 8322 8361

BEXAR COUNTY BOARD OF TRUSTEES FOR MENTAL HEALTH MENTAL RETARDATION p 179
3031 W Interstate 10, San Antonio TX 78201
Tel (210) 261-1000 SIC 8361 8093

UINTAH BASIN MEDICAL CENTER p 1500
250 W 300 N, Roosevelt UT 84066
Tel (435) 725-2008
SIC 8062 8082 7352 8092 8361

VIRGINIA UNITED METHODIST HOMES INC p 1560
5101 Cox Rd Ste 225, Glen Allen VA 23060
Tel (804) 474-8700 SIC 8361

■ SUNRISE SENIOR LIVING MANAGEMENT INC p 1404
7902 Westpark Dr, Mc Lean VA 22102
Tel (703) 273-7500 SIC 8361 8741 8052

VIRGINIA SOUTHSIDE TRAINING CENTER INC p 1559
W Washington St, Petersburg VA 23803
Tel (804) 524-7333 SIC 8361 8052

MHM SERVICES INC p 959
1593 Spring Hill Rd # 600, Vienna VA 22182
Tel (703) 749-4600 SIC 8093 8361

LEISURE CARE LLC p 854
999 3rd Ave Ste 4500, Seattle WA 98104
Tel (800) 327-3490 SIC 8361

ST ANDREWS ACQUISITION INC p 1364
9720 South Tacoma Way, Tacoma WA 98499
Tel (253) 584-2170 SIC 8322 8361

CAPITOL LAKES RETIREMENT COMMUNITY p 251
110 S Henry St, Madison WI 53703
Tel (608) 283-2000
SIC 6513 8051 8052 8361

PHOENIX CARE SYSTEMS INC p 1144
1744 N Farwell Ave, Milwaukee WI 53202
Tel (414) 225-4460 SIC 8361

■ SENIOR BROOKDALE LIVING COMMUNITIES INC p 1303
6737 W Wa St Ste 2300, Milwaukee WI 53214
Tel (414) 918-5000 SIC 8059 8051 8361

WILLOWGLEN ACADEMY-WISCONSIN INC p 1613
1744 N Farwell Ave, Milwaukee WI 53202
Tel (414) 225-4460 SIC 8361

OCONOMOWOC RESIDENTIAL PROGRAMS INC p 1074
1746 Executive Dr, Oconomowoc WI 53066
Tel (262) 569-5515 SIC 8052 8361

BETHESDA LUTHERAN COMMUNITIES INC p 178
600 Hoffmann Dr, Watertown WI 53094
Tel (920) 261-3050 SIC 8361

SIC 8399 Social Services, NEC

ALASKA NATIVE TRIBAL HEALTH CONSORTIUM p 45
4000 Ambassador Dr, Anchorage AK 99508
Tel (907) 729-1900 SIC 8399 8741

RURAL ALASKA COMMUNITY ACTION PROGRAM INC p 1258
731 E 8th Ave, Anchorage AK 99501
Tel (907) 279-2511 SIC 8399

NORTHERN ARIZONA HEALTHCARE CORP p 1055
1200 N Beaver St, Flagstaff AZ 86001
Tel (928) 779-3366
SIC 8741 8062 8399 4119

UNVRSTY OF AR FONDTIN INC p 1528
535 W Research Ctr Blvd, Fayetteville AR 72701
Tel (479) 575-5581 SIC 8399

BILL HILLARY & CHELSEA CLINTON FOUNDATION p 182
1200 Prsident Clinton Ave, Little Rock AR 72201
Tel (501) 748-0471 SIC 8399

HEIFER PROJECT INTERNATIONAL INC p 681
1 World Ave, Little Rock AR 72202
Tel (501) 907-2600 SIC 8399 6732 9532

PROVIDENCE HEALTH & SERVICES FOUNDATION/SAN FERNANDO AND SANTA p 1185
501 S Buena Vista St, Burbank CA 91505
Tel (818) 843-5111 SIC 8399

CITY OF HOPE p 315
1500 E Duarte Blvd, Duarte CA 91010
Tel (626) 256-4673 SIC 8741 8399

FRESNO COUNTY ECONOMIC OPPORTUNITIES COMMISSION p 579
1920 Mariposa Mall # 300, Fresno CA 93721
Tel (559) 263-1010 SIC 8322 8399

GROSSMONT HOSPITAL FOUNDATION p 641
5555 Grossmont Center Dr, La Mesa CA 91942
Tel (619) 740-4200 SIC 8399

PIERPASS INC p 1147
444 W Ocean Blvd Ste 700, Long Beach CA 90802
Tel (562) 437-9112 SIC 8399 7322

ASSOCIATED STUDENTS UCLA p 121
308 Westwood Plz, Los Angeles CA 90095
Tel (310) 825-4321 SIC 8399 5942

CALIFORNIA ENDOWMENT p 240
1000 N Alameda St, Los Angeles CA 90012
Tel (800) 449-4149 SIC 8399

SOUTH CENTRAL LOS ANGELES REGIONAL CENTER FOR DEVELOPMENTALLY DISABLED PERSONS INC p 1343
2500 S Western Ave, Los Angeles CA 90018
Tel (213) 744-7000 SIC 8399

SIERRA CLUB p 1320
2101 Webster St Ste 1300, Oakland CA 94612
Tel (415) 977-5500 SIC 8641 8399

ARC OF SAN DIEGO p 103
3030 Market St, San Diego CA 92102
Tel (619) 685-1175
SIC 8399 8351 8361 8322

JEWISH COMMUNITY FEDERATION OF SAN FRANCISCO PENINSULA MARIN & SONOMA COUNTIES p 784
121 Steuart St Fl 7, San Francisco CA 94105
Tel (415) 777-0411 SIC 8399

TIDES CENTER p 1452
The Prsdio 1014 Trney Ave, San Francisco CA 94129
Tel (415) 561-6400 SIC 8399

TIDES FOUNDATION p 1452
Presidio Bldg 1014, San Francisco CA 94129
Tel (415) 561-6400 SIC 8399

SILICON VALLEY EDUCATION FOUNDATION p 1323
1400 Parkmoor Ave Ste 200, San Jose CA 95126
Tel (408) 790-9400 SIC 8399

EASTER SEALS SOUTHERN CALIFORNIA INC p 471
1570 E 17th St, Santa Ana CA 92705
Tel (714) 834-1111 SIC 8399

COTTAGE HEALTH p 374
400 W Pueblo St, Santa Barbara CA 93105
Tel (805) 682-7111 SIC 8399 8062

HARBOR DEVELOPMENTAL DISABILITIES FOUNDATION INC p 659
21231 Hawthorne Blvd, Torrance CA 90503
Tel (310) 540-1711 SIC 8399

COMPASSION INTERNATIONAL INC p 351
12290 Voyager Pkwy, Colorado Springs CO 80921
Tel (719) 487-7000 SIC 8399

GOODWILL INDUSTRIES OF DENVER p 624
6850 Federal Blvd, Denver CO 80221
Tel (303) 650-7700 SIC 8399

UNIVERSITY OF COLORADO FOUNDATION p 1521
1800 N Grant St Ste 725, Denver CO 80203
Tel (303) 813-7935 SIC 8399

ST VINCENTS DEVELOPMENT INC p 1373
2800 Main St, Bridgeport CT 06606
Tel (203) 576-6000 SIC 8399 6531

AARP p 8
601 E St Nw, Washington DC 20049
Tel (202) 434-2277 SIC 5192 8399

AARP FOUNDATION p 8
601 E St Nw, Washington DC 20049
Tel (202) 434-2020 SIC 8331 8399

AFRICARE p 33
440 R St Nw, Washington DC 20001
Tel (202) 328-5320 SIC 8399

NATIONAL ENDOWMENT FOR DEMOCRACY INC p 1011
1025 F St Nw Ste 800, Washington DC 20004
Tel (202) 378-9700 SIC 8399

PACT INC p 1107
1828 L St Nw Ste 300, Washington DC 20036
Tel (202) 466-5666 SIC 8399 8699

PAN AMERICAN DEVELOPMENT FOUNDATION INC p 1110
1889 F St Nw Fl 2, Washington DC 20006
Tel (202) 458-3969 SIC 8399

PAN AMERICAN HEALTH ORGANIZATION INC p 1110
525 23rd St Nw, Washington DC 20037
Tel (202) 974-3000 SIC 8399

PARALYZED VETERANS OF AMERICA p 1114
801 18th St Nw Frnt 1, Washington DC 20006
Tel (202) 872-1300 SIC 8399 7389 8641

UNITED NEGRO COLLEGE FUND INC p 1510
1805 7th St Nw Ste 100, Washington DC 20001
Tel (800) 331-2244 SIC 8399

HOSPICE OF FLORIDA SUNCOAST p 709
5771 Roosevelt Blvd # 400, Clearwater FL 33760
Tel (727) 527-4483 SIC 8399

FOOD FOR POOR INC p 564
6401 Lyons Rd, Coconut Creek FL 33073
Tel (954) 427-2222 SIC 8399

UNIVERSITY OF FLORIDA FOUNDATION INC p 1521
2012 W University Ave, Gainesville FL 32603
Tel (352) 392-1691 SIC 8399 8641 8221

■ SPACE COAST HEALTH FOUNDATION INC p 1354
6905 N Wickham Rd Ste 301, Melbourne FL 32940
Tel (321) 241-6600 SIC 8399

AMERICAN NICARAGUAN FOUNDATION INC p 77
1000 Nw 57th Ct Ste 770, Miami FL 33126
Tel (305) 374-3391 SIC 8399 8641

JOHN S AND JAMES L KNIGHT FOUNDATION INC p 789
200 S Biscayne Blvd # 3300, Miami FL 33131
Tel (305) 358-1061 SIC 8399

PHINEAS CORP p 1144
9040 Sw 72nd St, Miami FL 33173
Tel (305) 596-9040 SIC 8361 8399 6531

FLORIDA DEPARTMENT OF HEALTH p 558
4052 Bald Cypress Way, Tallahassee FL 32399
Tel (850) 245-4500 SIC 9431 8399

GULFSTREAM GOODWILL INDUSTRIES INC p 647
1715 E Tiffany Dr, West Palm Beach FL 33407
Tel (561) 848-7200 SIC 8399

HABITAT FOR HUMANITY INTERNATIONAL INC p 651
121 Habitat St, Americus GA 31709
Tel (800) 422-4828
SIC 8399 8661 8322 1521 1531

MAP INTERNATIONAL (INC) p 903
4700 Glynco Pkwy, Brunswick GA 31525
Tel (912) 265-6010 SIC 8399

PEACE OFFICERS ANNUITY & BENEFITS FUND OF GEORGIA INC p 1125
1208 Greenbelt Dr, Griffin GA 30224
Tel (770) 228-8461 SIC 8399

CATHOLIC CHARITIES OF ARCHDIOCESE OF CHICAGO p 266
721 N La Salle Dr, Chicago IL 60654
Tel (312) 655-7000 SIC 8399

DESTINY HEALTH INC p 432
200 W Monroe St Ste 1900, Chicago IL 60606
Tel (312) 224-7100 SIC 6321 8399

JEWISH FEDERATION OF METROPOLITAN CHICAGO p 784
30 S Wells St, Chicago IL 60606
Tel (312) 357-4790 SIC 8399

JEWISH UNITED FUND OF METROPOLITAN CHICAGO p 785
30 S Wells St, Chicago IL 60606
Tel (312) 357-4805 SIC 8399

NATIONAL COUNCIL OF YOUNG MENS CHRISTIAN ASSOCIATIONS OF UNITED STATES OF AMERICA p 1011
101 N Wacker Dr Ste 1600, Chicago IL 60606
Tel (312) 977-0031 SIC 7997 8399 8322

OPPORTUNITY INTERNATIONAL INC p 1090
550 W Van Buren St # 200, Chicago IL 60607
Tel (630) 242-4100 SIC 8399

WILLIAM RAINEY HARPER COLLEGE EDUCATIONAL FOUNDATION p 1611
1200 W Algonquin Rd, Palatine IL 60067
Tel (847) 925-6490 SIC 8399

BARTHOLOMEW CONSOLIDATED SCHOOL FOUNDATION INC p 157
1200 Central Ave, Columbus IN 47201
Tel (812) 376-4234 SIC 8399

BEACON HEALTH SYSTEM INC p 164
615 N Michigan St, South Bend IN 46601
Tel (574) 647-1000 SIC 8741 8399 8082

BEACON MEDICAL GROUP INC p 165
615 N Michigan St, South Bend IN 46601
Tel (574) 647-1000 SIC 8741 8399 8082

IOWA STATE UNIVERSITY FOUNDATION p 763
2505 University Blvd, Ames IA 50010
Tel (515) 294-4607 SIC 8399

CEDAR RAPIDS COMMUNITY SCHOOL DISTRICT FOUNDATION p 272
2500 Edgewood Rd Nw, Cedar Rapids IA 52405
Tel (319) 558-2000 SIC 8399

GENESIS HEALTH SYSTEM p 603
1227 E Rusholme St, Davenport IA 52803
Tel (563) 421-1000 SIC 8741 8399 7218

MERCY HOSPITAL IOWA CITY IOWA INC p 947
500 E Market St, Iowa City IA 52245
Tel (319) 339-0300
SIC 8062 8011 6512 8399

STATE UNIVERSITY OF IOWA FOUNDATION p 1383
1 W Park Rd, Iowa City IA 52242
Tel (319) 335-3305 SIC 8399 7371 7359

UNBOUND p 1502
1 Elmwood Ave, Kansas City KS 66103
Tel (913) 384-6500 SIC 8399

HEART TO HEART INTERNATIONAL INC p 678
13250 W 98th St, Lenexa KS 66215
Tel (913) 764-5200 SIC 8399

KENTON COUNTY SCHOOL DISTRICT EDUCATIONAL FOUNDATION INC p 812
1055 Eaton Dr, Ft Wright KY 41017
Tel (859) 344-8888 SIC 8399

SEVEN COUNTIES SERVICES INC p 1309
101 W Muhammad Ali Blvd, Louisville KY 40202
Tel (502) 589-8600
SIC 8399 8011 8093 8322 8031

CYSTIC FIBROSIS FOUNDATION p 406
6931 Arlington Rd Fl 2, Bethesda MD 20814
Tel (301) 951-4422 SIC 8733 8399

AMERICAN KIDNEY FUND INC p 75
11921 Rockville Pike # 300, Rockville MD 20852
Tel (301) 881-3690 SIC 8399

ACTION FOR BOSTON COMMUNITY DEVELOPMENT INC p 19
178 Tremont St, Boston MA 02111
Tel (617) 357-6000 SIC 8399 8322

COMBINED JEWISH PHILANTHROPIES OF GREATER BOSTON INC p 343
126 High St Fl 2, Boston MA 02110
Tel (617) 457-8500 SIC 8399

GREATER BOSTON FOOD BANK INC p 635
70 S Bay Ave, Boston MA 02118
Tel (617) 427-5200 SIC 8399

OXFAM AMERICA INC p 1100
226 Causeway St Fl 5, Boston MA 02114
Tel (617) 482-1211 SIC 8399

VALLEY HEALTH SYSTEMS INC p 1540
575 Beech St, Holyoke MA 01040
Tel (413) 534-2500
SIC 8082 8093 8399 8741 8721

ELEMENT CARE INC p 486
37 Friend St, Lynn MA 01902
Tel (781) 715-6608 SIC 8399

W K KELLOGG FOUNDATION p 1568
1 Michigan Ave E, Battle Creek MI 49017
Tel (269) 968-1611 SIC 8399

UNIVERSITY PHYSICIAN GROUP p 1527
540 E Cnfield St Ste 1241, Troy MI 48083
Tel (877) 978-3627 SIC 8399

MAYO CLINIC HEALTH SYSTEM-AUSTIN p 924
1000 1st Dr Nw, Austin MN 55912
Tel (507) 433-7351 SIC 8399

SCHOLARSHIP AMERICA INC p 1288
7900 Intl Dr Ste 500, Minneapolis MN 55425
Tel (800) 537-4180 SIC 8399

UNITED WAY OF MINN AREA p 1515
404 S 8th St Ste 100, Minneapolis MN 55404
Tel (612) 340-7400 SIC 8399

SAINT PAUL FOUNDATION INC p 1270
101 5th St E Ste 2400, Saint Paul MN 55101
Tel (651) 224-5463 SIC 8641 8399

GREATER HORIZONS p 635
1055 Broadway Blvd # 130, Kansas City MO 64105
Tel (816) 842-0944 SIC 8399

MISSOURI FOUNDATION FOR HEALTH p 976
415 S 18th St Ste 400, Saint Louis MO 63103
Tel (314) 345-5500 SIC 8399

OMAHA COMMUNITY FOUNDATION p 1083
302 S 36th St Ste 100, Omaha NE 68131
Tel (402) 342-3458 SIC 8399 8733

EASTER SEAL NEW HAMPSHIRE INC p 471
555 Auburn St, Manchester NH 03103
Tel (603) 623-8863
SIC 8331 8399 4119 8322

AMERICAN INSTITUTE OF CERTIFIED PUBLIC ACCOUNTANTS FOUNDATION p 75
201 Plaza Three Harborsid, Jersey City NJ 07311
Tel (903) 823-2727 SIC 8399

VIRTUA HEALTH INC p 1560
303 Lippincott Dr, Marlton NJ 08053
Tel (888) 847-8823 SIC 8062 8399

ESSEX COUNTY WELFARE BOARD INC p 510
18 Rector St Ste 9, Newark NJ 07102
Tel (973) 733-3326 SIC 8322 8399

NEW COMMUNITY CORP p 1029
233 W Market St, Newark NJ 07103
Tel (973) 623-2800 SIC 8399

BARNABAS RWJ HEALTH INC p 155
95 Old Short Hills Rd, West Orange NJ 07052
Tel (973) 322-4000 SIC 8399

ACACIA NETWORK INC p 13
300 E 175th St, Bronx NY 10457
Tel (718) 299-1100 SIC 8399

CAMBA INC p 243
1720 Church Ave Ste 2, Brooklyn NY 11226
Tel (718) 287-2600 SIC 8399

JEWISH CHILD CARE ASSOCIATION OF NEW YORK p 784
858 E 29th St, Brooklyn NY 11210
Tel (917) 808-4800 SIC 8361 8399

FEDERATION EMPLOYMENT AND GUIDANCE SERVICE INC p 536
445 Oak St, Copiague NY 11726
Tel (212) 366-8040 SIC 8399

AMERICAN SOCIETY FOR TECHNION-ISRAEL INSTITUTE OF TECHNOLOGY INC p 79
55 E 59th St Fl 14, New York NY 10022
Tel (212) 407-6300 SIC 8399

BAR-ILAN UNIVERSITY IN ISRAEL p 154
160 E 56th St Fl 5, New York NY 10022
Tel (212) 906-3900 SIC 8399

EDUCATIONAL ALLIANCE INC p 479
197 E Brdwy, New York NY 10002
Tel (646) 654-1297 SIC 8399

JDRF INTERNATIONAL p 781
26 Broadway, New York NY 10004
Tel (212) 785-9500 SIC 8399 8733

JEWISH AGENCY FOR ISRAEL INC p 784
111 8th Ave Fl 11, New York NY 10011
Tel (212) 284-6900 SIC 8399

JEWISH FEDERATIONS OF NORTH AMERICA INC p 784
25 Broadway Fl 17, New York NY 10004
Tel (212) 284-6500 SIC 8399

MEDECINS SANS FRONTIERES USA INC p 935
333 7th Ave Fl 2, New York NY 10001
Tel (212) 679-6800 SIC 8399 7363

NEW YORK FOUNDLING HOSPITAL p 1035
590 Ave Of The Americas # 1, New York NY 10011
Tel (212) 633-9300 SIC 8361 8399

OPEN SOCIETY INSTITUTE p 1089
224 W 57th St Frnt 1, New York NY 10019
Tel (212) 548-0600 SIC 8399

ROGOSIN INSTITUTE INC p 1246
505 E 70th St Fl 2, New York NY 10021
Tel (212) 746-1551 SIC 8733 8399

SIMONS FOUNDATION INC p 1325
160 5th Ave Fl 7, New York NY 10010
Tel (646) 654-0066 SIC 8399

UNITED JEWISH APPEAL-FEDERATION OF JEWISH PHILANTHROPIES OF NEW YORK CHARITABLE FUND LLC p 1509
130 E 59th St Fl 3, New York NY 10022
Tel (212) 980-1000 SIC 8399

UNITED STATES FUND FOR UNICEF p 1513
125 Maiden Ln Fl 11, New York NY 10038
Tel (800) 367-5437 SIC 8399

UNITED STATES FUND FOR UNICEF IN KIND ASSISTANCE CORP p 1513
125 Maiden Ln Fl 10, New York NY 10038
Tel (212) 686-5522 SIC 8399

VOLUNTEERS OF AMERICA - GREATER NEW YORK INC p 1565
340 W 85th St, New York NY 10024
Tel (212) 873-2600 SIC 8399

WORLD CULTURAL ORGANIZATION INC p 1625
1330 Avenue Ste 23, New York NY 10019
Tel (212) 653-0657 SIC 8399

FAMILY RESIDENCES & ESSENTIAL ENTERPRISES INC p 527
191 Bethpage Sweet Holw, Old Bethpage NY 11804
Tel (516) 870-1600 SIC 8399

LEUKEMIA & LYMPHOMA SOCIETY INC p 858
3 International Dr # 200, Rye Brook NY 10573
Tel (914) 949-5213
SIC 8699 8399 8322 8011 8733 8621

RESOURCE CENTER FOR INDEPENDENT LIVING (INC) p 1227
401 Columbia St, Utica NY 13502
Tel (315) 797-4642 SIC 8399

MARCH OF DIMES FOUNDATION p 905
1275 Mamaroneck Ave, White Plains NY 10605
Tel (914) 428-7100 SIC 8399

STANLY COUNTY SCHOOLS EDUCATIONAL FOUNDATION INC p 1377
1000 N 1st St Ste 4, Albemarle NC 28001
Tel (704) 983-5151 SIC 8399

FOUNDATION FOR CAROLINAS p 571
220 N Tryon St, Charlotte NC 28202
Tel (704) 973-4500 SIC 8399

NORTH CAROLINA PARTNERSHIP FOR CHILDREN INC p 1051
1100 Wake Forest Rd, Raleigh NC 27604
Tel (919) 821-7999 SIC 8399

NORIDIAN MUTUAL INSURANCE CO p 1048
4510 13th Ave S, Fargo ND 58121
Tel (701) 282-1100 SIC 8399 6321 6324

MATTHEW 25 MINISTRIES INC p 920
11060 Kenwood Rd, Blue Ash OH 45242
Tel (513) 793-6256 SIC 8399

CLEVELAND MUNICIPAL SCHOOL DISTRICT p 325
1111 Superior Ave E # 1800, Cleveland OH 44114
Tel (216) 838-0000 SIC 8211 8399

JEWISH FEDERATION OF CLEVELAND p 784
25701 Science Park Dr, Cleveland OH 44122
Tel (216) 593-2900 SIC 8399

OKLAHOMA DEPARTMENT OF MENTAL HEALTH AND SUBSTANCE ABUSE SERVICES p 1079
1200 Ne 13th St, Oklahoma City OK 73117
Tel (405) 522-3878 SIC 8399 9431

LEGACY VISITING NURSE ASSOCIATION p 852
815 Ne Davis St, Portland OR 97232
Tel (503) 220-1000 SIC 8399 5999 8082

OREGON COMMUNITY FOUNDATION p 1093
1221 Sw Yamhill St Ste 100, Portland OR 97205
Tel (503) 227-6846 SIC 8399 2741

OREGON HEALTH & SCIENCE UNIVERSITY FOUNDATION INC p 1093
1121 Sw Salmon St Ste 100, Portland OR 97205
Tel (503) 228-1730
SIC 8399 6091 8733 6732

MEDICAL TEAMS INTERNATIONAL p 937
14150 Sw Milton Ct, Tigard OR 97224
Tel (503) 624-1000 SIC 8099 8399

LEE REGIONAL HEALTH SYSTEM INC p 851
132 Walnut St Ste 3, Johnstown PA 15901
Tel (814) 533-0751 SIC 8399

CHILDRENS HOSPITAL OF PHILADELPHIA FOUNDATION p 300
3401 Civic Center Blvd, Philadelphia PA 19104
Tel (215) 590-1000 SIC 8741 8399

BROTHERS BROTHER FOUNDATION p 219
1200 Galveston Ave, Pittsburgh PA 15233
Tel (412) 321-3160 SIC 8399

CORNELL ABRAXAS GROUP INC p 370
2840 Liberty Ave Ste 300, Pittsburgh PA 15222
Tel (412) 361-0695 SIC 8399

PRESSLEY RIDGE FOUNDATION p 1173
5500 Corporate Dr Ste 400, Pittsburgh PA 15237
Tel (412) 872-9400 SIC 8399

ELK REGIONAL HEALTH SYSTEM p 487
763 Johnsonburg Rd, Saint Marys PA 15857
Tel (814) 788-8000
SIC 8062 8051 8361 8399

PLAN INTERNATIONAL INC p 1154
155 Plan Way Ste A, Warwick RI 02886
Tel (401) 294-3693 SIC 8399

OPERATION COMPASSION p 1089
114 Stuart Rd Ne Ste 370, Cleveland TN 37312
Tel (423) 479-3770 SIC 8399

EXPERIAN HEALTH INC p 519
720 Cool Springs Blvd, Franklin TN 37067
Tel (615) 661-5657 SIC 7372 8399

AMERICAN LEBANESE SYRIAN ASSOCIATED CHARITIES INC p 75
501 Saint Jude Pl, Memphis TN 38105
Tel (901) 578-2150 SIC 8399

COMMUNITY FOUNDATION OF GREATER MEMPHIS INC p 348
1900 Union Ave, Memphis TN 38104
Tel (901) 728-4600 SIC 8399

TEXAS A&M FOUNDATION p 1442
401 George Bush Dr, College Station TX 77840
Tel (979) 845-8161 SIC 6732 8399

AMERICAN HEART ASSOCIATION INC p 74
7272 Greenville Ave, Dallas TX 75231
Tel (214) 373-6300 SIC 8399 2721

COMMUNITIES FOUNDATION OF TEXAS p 347
5500 Caruth Haven Ln, Dallas TX 75225
Tel (214) 378-4500 SIC 8399

HOUSTON FOOD BANK p 712
535 Portwall St, Houston TX 77029
Tel (713) 223-3700 SIC 8399

UNITED WAY OF GREATER HOUSTON p 1515
50 Waugh Dr, Houston TX 77007
Tel (713) 685-2300 SIC 8399

▲ HEALTHEQUITY INC p 677
15 W Scenic Pointe Dr # 100, Draper UT 84020
Tel (801) 727-1000
SIC 8399 6371 6036 6321 6282

CHILDRENS MIRACLE NETWORK p 300
205 W 700 S, Salt Lake City UT 84101
Tel (801) 214-7400 SIC 8399

CHARITIES AID FOUNDATION AMERICA p 288
1800 Diagonal Rd Ste 150, Alexandria VA 22314
Tel (703) 549-8931 SIC 8399

GOOD360 p 624
675 N Washington St # 330, Alexandria VA 22314
Tel (703) 836-2121 SIC 8399

PARTNERSHIP FOR SUPPLY CHAIN MANAGEMENT INC p 1118
1616 Fort Myer Dr Fl 12, Arlington VA 22209
Tel (571) 227-8600 SIC 8399

UNITED SERVICE ORGANIZATIONS INC p 1511
2111 Wilson Blvd Ste 1200, Arlington VA 22201
Tel (703) 908-6400 SIC 8399

PROJECT HOPE-PEOPLE-TO-PEOPLE HEALTH FOUNDATION INC p 1182
255 Carter Hall Ln, Millwood VA 22646
Tel (540) 837-2100 SIC 8399

CHILDFUND INTERNATIONAL USA p 298
2821 Emerywood Pkwy, Richmond VA 23294
Tel (804) 756-2700 SIC 8399

SOURCEAMERICA p 1342
8401 Old Courthouse Rd, Vienna VA 22182
Tel (888) 411-8424 SIC 8399

PATH p 1120
2201 Westlake Ave Ste 200, Seattle WA 98121
Tel (206) 285-3500 SIC 8399

SEATTLE FOUNDATION p 1297
1200 5th Ave Ste 1300, Seattle WA 98101
Tel (206) 622-2294 SIC 8399

UNITED WAY OF KING COUNTY p 1515
720 2nd Ave, Seattle WA 98104
Tel (206) 461-3700 SIC 8399

AVANTI HEALTH SYSTEMS INC p 136
300 Villa Dr, Hurley WI 54534
Tel (715) 561-3200 SIC 8399

INDIANHEAD COMMUNITY ACTION AGENCY INC p 739
1000 College Ave W, Ladysmith WI 54848
Tel (715) 532-4222 SIC 8399

WHEATON FRANCISCAN HEALTHCARE- ST FRANCIS INC p 1604
3237 S 16th St Ste 1005, Milwaukee WI 53215
Tel (414) 647-5000 SIC 8399

SIC 8412 Museums & Art Galleries

J PAUL GETTY TRUST p 772
1200 Getty Center Dr # 500, Los Angeles CA 90049
Tel (310) 440-7300 SIC 8412

MUSEUM ASSOCIATES p 1002
5905 Wilshire Blvd, Los Angeles CA 90036
Tel (323) 857-6172 SIC 8412

CALIFORNIA ACADEMY OF SCIENCES p 239
55 Music Concourse Dr, San Francisco CA 94118
Tel (415) 379-8000 SIC 8422 2721 8412

SAN FRANCISCO MUSEUM OF MODERN ART p 1276
151 3rd St, San Francisco CA 94103
Tel (415) 357-4035 SIC 8412 5942

■ NATIONAL GALLERY OF ART p 1012
6th And Cnsttution Ave Nw, Washington DC 20565
Tel (202) 737-4215 SIC 5942 8412

■ SMITHSONIAN INSTITUTION p 1334
1000 Jefferson Dr Sw, Washington DC 20560
Tel (202) 633-1000 SIC 8412 8422

■ UNITED STATES HOLOCAUST MEMORIAL MUSEUM p 1513
100 Roul Wallenberg Pl Sw, Washington DC 20024
Tel (202) 488-0400 SIC 8412 9411

MICCOSUKEE TRIBE OF INDIANS OF FLORIDA p 959
Sw 8th St & Us Hwy 41, Miami FL 33194
Tel (305) 223-8380
SIC 5812 5331 8412 5947 4489

CARTER CENTER INC p 261
453 Freedom Pkwy Ne, Atlanta GA 30307
Tel (404) 420-5100 SIC 8651 8412

ROBERT W WOODRUFF ARTS CENTER INC p 1241
1280 Peachtree St Ne, Atlanta GA 30309
Tel (404) 733-4200 SIC 8412

ROBERT W WOODRUFF ARTS CENTER INC p 1241
1280 Peachtree St Ne, Atlanta GA 30309
Tel (404) 733-4200
SIC 7929 8412 6512 8299

ART INSTITUTE OF CHICAGO p 113
111 S Michigan Ave, Chicago IL 60603
Tel (312) 443-3600 SIC 8412 8299

FIELD MUSEUM OF NATURAL HISTORY p 541
1400 S Lake Shore Dr, Chicago IL 60605
Tel (312) 922-9410 SIC 8412

EMILY DICKINSON MUSEUM p 493
280 Main St, Amherst MA 01002
Tel (413) 542-8161 SIC 8412

TRUSTEES OF PHILLIPS ACADEMY p 1488
180 Main St, Andover MA 01810
Tel (978) 749-4000 SIC 8211 8412

MUSEUM OF FINE ARTS p 1002
465 Huntington Ave, Boston MA 02115
Tel (617) 369-3861 SIC 8412 5961 8299

EDSEL & ELEANOR FORD HOUSE p 479
1100 Lake Shore Rd, Grosse Pointe Shores MI 48236
Tel (313) 884-4222 SIC 8412

AMERICAN MUSEUM OF NATURAL HISTORY p 76
Central Park W At 79th St, New York NY 10024
Tel (212) 769-5000 SIC 8412 8221

METROPOLITAN MUSEUM OF ART p 956
1000 5th Ave, New York NY 10028
Tel (212) 535-7710 SIC 8412 5999

MUSEUM OF MODERN ART p 1002
11 W 53rd St, New York NY 10019
Tel (212) 708-9400 SIC 8412 5942

SOLOMON R GUGGENHEIM FOUNDATION p 1338
1071 5th Ave, New York NY 10128
Tel (212) 423-3500 SIC 8412

WHITNEY MUSEUM OF AMERICAN ART p 1607
99 Gansevoort St, New York NY 10014
Tel (212) 570-3600 SIC 8412

MUSEUM OF BIBLE INC p 1002
7507 Sw 44th St, Oklahoma City OK 73179
Tel (405) 996-4900 SIC 8412

CITIZEN POTAWATOMI NATION p 310
1601 Gordon Cooper Dr, Shawnee OK 74801
Tel (405) 275-3121
SIC 7992 5411 7011 8412

PHILADELPHIA MUSEUM OF ART INC p 1143
2600 Bnjmin Frnklin Pkwy, Philadelphia PA 19130
Tel (215) 763-8100 SIC 8412

CARNEGIE INSTITUTE p 258
4400 Forbes Ave, Pittsburgh PA 15213
Tel (412) 622-3131 SIC 8412

MOODY GARDENS INC p 987
1 Hope Blvd, Galveston TX 77554
Tel (409) 744-4673
SIC 8412 8422 7999 7011

MUSEUM OF FINE ARTS OF HOUSTON p 1002
1001 Bissonnet St, Houston TX 77005
Tel (713) 639-7300 SIC 8412 5999

COLONIAL WILLIAMSBURG FOUNDATION p 338
427 Franklin St Rm 212, Williamsburg VA 23185
Tel (757) 229-1000
SIC 5947 8412 5812 7011

MUSEUM OF FLIGHT FOUNDATION p 1002
9404 E Marginal Way S, Tukwila WA 98108
Tel (206) 764-5720 SIC 8412

SIC 8422 Arboreta, Botanical & Zoological Gardens

ZOOLOGICAL SOCIETY OF SAN DIEGO p 1644
2920 Zoo Dr, San Diego CA 92101
Tel (619) 231-1515 SIC 8422 5812 5947

CALIFORNIA ACADEMY OF SCIENCES p 239
55 Music Concourse Dr, San Francisco CA 94118
Tel (415) 379-8000 SIC 8422 2721 8412

■ SMITHSONIAN INSTITUTION p 1334
1000 Jefferson Dr Sw, Washington DC 20560
Tel (202) 633-1000 SIC 8412 8422

NEW YORK BOTANICAL GARDEN p 1034
2900 Southern Blvd, Bronx NY 10458
Tel (718) 817-8779 SIC 8422 8299

WILDLIFE CONSERVATION SOCIETY p 1609
2300 Southern Blvd, Bronx NY 10460
Tel (718) 220-5144 SIC 8422 8641

MOODY GARDENS INC p 987
1 Hope Blvd, Galveston TX 77554
Tel (409) 744-4673
SIC 8412 8422 7999 7011

CONSERVATION FUND A NONPROFIT CORP p 358
1655 Fort Myer Dr # 1300, Arlington VA 22209
Tel (703) 525-6300 SIC 8422

SIC 8611 Business Associations

MARINE PRESERVATION ASSOCIATION INC p 906
20645 N Pima Rd Ste 100, Scottsdale AZ 85255
Tel (480) 991-5500 SIC 8611

ACADEMY OF MOTION PICTURE ARTS & SCIENCES p 13
8949 Wilshire Blvd, Beverly Hills CA 90211
Tel (310) 247-3000 SIC 8621 7819 8611

CARECRAFT INC p 254
880 Carlsbad Village Dr # 202, Carlsbad CA 92008
Tel (949) 373-3333 SIC 8611

ALL STATE ASSOCIATION INC p 51
11487 San Fernando Rd, San Fernando CA 91340
Tel (877) 425-2558 SIC 8611

AFFINION GROUP HOLDINGS INC p 32
6 High Ridge Park Bldg A, Stamford CT 06905
Tel (203) 956-1000 SIC 8611 6282 8748

AMERICAN BEVERAGE ASSOCIATION p 68
1101 16th St Nw Ste 700, Washington DC 20036
Tel (202) 223-4832 SIC 8611

AMERICAN CHEMISTRY COUNCIL INC p 70
700 2nd St Ne Fl 8-10, Washington DC 20002
Tel (202) 249-7000
SIC 8611 8748 8621 8699

AMYOTROPHIC LATERAL SCLEROSIS ASSOCIATION p 88
1275 K St Nw Ste 250, Washington DC 20005
Tel (202) 407-8580 SIC 8611

ASSOCIATION OF UNIVERSITIES FOR RESEARCH IN ASTRONOMY INC p 121
1212 New York Ave Nw # 450, Washington DC 20005
Tel (202) 483-2101 SIC 8611

EDISON ELECTRIC INSTITUTE INC p 478
701 Pennsylv Ave Nw Fl 3, Washington DC 20004
Tel (202) 508-5000 SIC 8611

FINANCIAL INDUSTRY REGULATORY AUTHORITY INC p 542
1735 K St Nw, Washington DC 20006
Tel (301) 590-6500 SIC 8611

NATIONAL PUBLIC RADIO INC p 1015
1111 N Capitol St Ne, Washington DC 20002
Tel (202) 513-2000 SIC 8611

NEIGHBORHOOD REINVESTMENT CORP p 1024
999 N Capitol St Ne # 900, Washington DC 20002
Tel (202) 760-4000 SIC 8611

PHARMACEUTICAL RESEARCH AND MANUFACTURERS OF AMERICA p 1141
950 F St Nw Ste 300, Washington DC 20004
Tel (202) 835-3400 SIC 8611

US CHAMBER OF COMMERCE p 1531
1615 H St Nw, Washington DC 20062
Tel (202) 659-6000 SIC 8611

DAYTONA BEACH AREA ASSOCIATION OF REALTORS FOUNDATION INC p 418
1716 Ridgewood Ave, Holly Hill FL 32117
Tel (386) 677-7131 SIC 8611

■ HORIZON BAY MANAGEMENT LLC p 707
5426 Bay Center Dr # 600, Tampa FL 33609
Tel (813) 287-3900 SIC 8611 6531 1522

ATHLETIC DEALERS LLC p 124
5423 Village Dr, Viera FL 32955
Tel (321) 254-0091 SIC 8611

GEORGIA MUNICIPAL ASSOCIATION INC p 607
201 Pryor St Sw, Atlanta GA 30303
Tel (404) 688-0472 SIC 2711 2741 8611

CHEM-NUT INC p 293
800 Business Park Dr, Leesburg GA 31763
Tel (229) 883-7050 SIC 5191 8611

SNAKE RIVER SUGAR CO p 1335
1951 S Saturn Way Ste 100, Boise ID 83709
Tel (208) 383-6500 SIC 8611 2063

KUNA GOOD NEIGHBORS INC p 832
12689 S Five Mile Rd, Kuna ID 83634
Tel (208) 362-1907 SIC 8611

ILLINOIS AGRICULTURAL ASSOCIATION p 732
1701 Towanda Ave, Bloomington IL 61701
Tel (309) 557-2111
SIC 8611 6722 8742 6311 7514

NATIONAL ASSOCIATION OF REALTORS p 1010
430 N Michigan Ave Lowr 2, Chicago IL 60611
Tel (800) 874-6500 SIC 8611 2721 8299

NATIONAL FUTURES ASSOCIATION (INC) p 1012
300 S Riverside Plz # 1800, Chicago IL 60606
Tel (312) 781-1300 SIC 8611

PROFESSIONAL CONVENTION MANAGEMENT ASSOCIATION p 1180
35 E Wacker Dr Ste 500, Chicago IL 60601
Tel (312) 423-7262 SIC 8611

DAIRY MANAGEMENT INC p 409
10255 W Higgins Rd # 900, Rosemont IL 60018
Tel (847) 803-2000 SIC 8611

NATIONAL DAIRY PROMOTION AND RESEARCH BOARD p 1011
10255 W Higgins Rd # 900, Rosemont IL 60018
Tel (847) 803-2000 SIC 8611

RACING ASSOCIATION OF CENTRAL p 1203
1 Prairie Meadows Dr, Altoona IA 50009
Tel (515) 967-1000 SIC 8611

MIDWEST ENERGY INC p 967
1330 Canterbury Dr, Hays KS 67601
Tel (785) 625-3437 SIC 4911 8611

MAINE MUNICIPAL ASSOCIATION p 898
60 Community Dr, Augusta ME 04330
Tel (207) 621-2645 SIC 8611

ISO NEW ENGLAND INC p 767
1 Sullivan Rd, Holyoke MA 01040
Tel (413) 535-4000 SIC 8611

TCML BUSINESS TRUST p 1428
95 Longwater Cir, Norwell MA 02061
Tel (781) 878-1070 SIC 8611

MICHIGAN MILK PRODUCERS ASSOCIATION p 961
41310 Bridge St, Novi MI 48375
Tel (248) 474-6672
SIC 5143 2023 2021 8611 2026

DAKOTA ELECTRIC ASSOCIATION p 409
4300 220th St W, Farmington MN 55024
Tel (651) 463-6212 SIC 8611

H ENTERPRISES INTERNATIONAL INC p 650
120 S 6th St Ste 2300, Minneapolis MN 55402
Tel (612) 343-8293 SIC 5032 8611 5211

BOARD OF TRUSTEES OF STATE INSTITUTIONS OF HIGHER LEARNING p 196
3825 Ridgewood Rd, Jackson MS 39211
Tel (601) 432-6198 SIC 8611

ARIZON COMPANIES INC p 108
11880 Dorsett Rd, Maryland Heights MO 63043
Tel (314) 739-0037
SIC 3585 1711 2394 1541 1542 8611

WESTCARE FOUNDATION INC p 1596
1711 Whitney Mesa Dr # 100, Henderson NV 89014
Tel (702) 385-3330 SIC 8322 8611

NEW YORK SHIPPING ASSOCIATION INC p 1036
333 Thornall St Ste 3a, Edison NJ 08837
Tel (732) 452-7800 SIC 8611

NEW JERSEY TRANSPORTATION TRUST FUND AUTHORITY p 1032
1035 Parkway Ave, Ewing NJ 08618
Tel (609) 530-2035 SIC 8611

■ PSEG SERVICES CORP p 1188
80 Park Plz Ste 3, Newark NJ 07102
Tel (973) 430-7000 SIC 8611

NATIONAL EXCHANGE CARRIER ASSOCIATION p 1011
80 S Jefferson Rd Ste 1, Whippany NJ 07981
Tel (800) 228-8398 SIC 7389 8611

DORMITORY AUTHORITY - STATE OF NEW YORK p 451
515 Broadway Ste 100, Albany NY 12207
Tel (518) 257-3000 SIC 8611

MAGAZINE PUBLISHERS OF AMERICA p 895
810 7th Ave Fl 24, New York NY 10019
Tel (212) 872-3700 SIC 8611

■ M&T BANK NATIONAL ASSOCIATION p 890
48 Main St, Oakfield NY 14125
Tel (800) 528-6532 SIC 8611

AFFINION GROUP HOLDINGS LLC p 32
1 Manhattanville Rd # 201, Purchase NY 10577
Tel (203) 956-1000 SIC 8611

BUCKEYE POWER INC p 223
6677 Busch Blvd, Columbus OH 43229
Tel (614) 781-0573 SIC 8611 4911

OHIO BUSINESS DEVELOPMENT COALITION p 1077
41 S High St Ste 3625, Columbus OH 43215
Tel (614) 469-1044 SIC 8611

OKLAHOMA CITY ENVIRONMENTAL ASSISTANCE TRUST p 1079
200 N Walker Ave Ste 302, Oklahoma City OK 73102
Tel (405) 297-2424 *SIC* 8611

OKLAHOMA STATE UNIVERSITY FOUNDATION p 1080
400 S Monroe St, Stillwater OK 74074
Tel (405) 385-5100 *SIC* 8611

PUBLIC BUILDING AUTHORITY p 1189
Cond Centro Plz, San Juan PR 00909
Tel (787) 722-0101 *SIC* 8611

DEE PEE ELECTRIC COOPERATIVE INC p 421
1355 E Mciver Rd, Darlington SC 29532
Tel (843) 665-4070 *SIC* 4911 8611

PALMETTO ELECTRIC COOPERATIVE INC p 1109
4063 Grays Hwy, Ridgeland SC 29936
Tel (843) 726-5551 *SIC* 8611 4911

NATIONAL FEDERATION OF INDEPENDENT BUSINESS p 1011
53 Century Blvd Ste 250, Nashville TN 37214
Tel (615) 872-5800 *SIC* 8611

TML MULTISTATE INTERGOVERNMENTAL EMPLOYEE BENEFITS POOL p 1457
1821 Rutherford Ln 300, Austin TX 78754
Tel (512) 719-6500 *SIC* 8611

TAMU COMMERCE p 1423
P.O. Box 3011, Commerce TX 75429
Tel (903) 886-5060 *SIC* 8611

COMAL INDEPENDENT SCHOOL DISTRICT p 343
1404 N Interstate 35, New Braunfels TX 78130
Tel (830) 221-2000 *SIC* 8611 8211

CONSUMER TECHNOLOGY ASSOCIATION p 361
1919 S Eads St Ste Ll, Arlington VA 22202
Tel (703) 907-7600 *SIC* 8611

NATIONAL ASSOCIATION OF STATE DEPARTMENTS OF AGRICULTURE INC p 1010
4350 Fairfax Dr Ste 910, Arlington VA 22203
Tel (202) 296-9680 *SIC* 8611

NATIONAL RURAL ELECTRIC COOPERATIVE ASSOCIATION p 1016
4301 Wilson Blvd Ste 1, Arlington VA 22203
Tel (703) 907-5500 *SIC* 8611

NATIONAL TELECOMMUNICATIONS COOPERATIVE ASSOCIATION p 1016
4121 Wilson Blvd Ste 1000, Arlington VA 22203
Tel (703) 351-2000 *SIC* 8611 8741

NORTHERN VIRGINIA ELECTRIC COOPERATIVE p 1057
10323 Lomond Dr, Manassas VA 20109
Tel (703) 335-0500
SIC 4911 8611 8741 4939

GRANGE INSURANCE ASSOCIATION INC p 630
200 Cedar St, Seattle WA 98121
Tel (206) 448-4911 *SIC* 8611

NORTHWEST DAIRY ASSOCIATION p 1059
1130 Rainier Ave S, Seattle WA 98144
Tel (206) 284-7220 *SIC* 8611

FARMFIRST DAIRY COOPERATIVE p 530
4001 Nakoosa Trl Ste 100, Madison WI 53714
Tel (608) 244-3373 *SIC* 5143 8611

SIC 8621 Professional Membership Organizations

SUMMIT HEALTHCARE ASSOCIATION p 1399
2200 E Show Low Lake Rd, Show Low AZ 85901
Tel (928) 537-4375 *SIC* 8621

ACADEMY OF MOTION PICTURE ARTS & SCIENCES p 13
8949 Wilshire Blvd, Beverly Hills CA 90211
Tel (310) 247-3000 *SIC* 8621 7819 8611

CALIFORNIA TEACHERS ASSOCIATION p 241
1705 Murchison Dr, Burlingame CA 94010
Tel (650) 697-1400 *SIC* 8621 8631

CALIFORNIA EMERGENCY PHYSICIANS FOUNDATION p 240
2100 Powell St Ste 900, Emeryville CA 94608
Tel (510) 350-2700 *SIC* 8621

OPENGATE CAPITAL LLC p 1089
10250 Constellation Blvd, Los Angeles CA 90067
Tel (310) 432-7000 *SIC* 2721 6799 8621

TRUCK UNDERWRITERS ASSOCIATION p 1485
4680 Wilshire Blvd, Los Angeles CA 90010
Tel (323) 932-3200 *SIC* 8621

ORANGE COUNTY HEALTH AUTHORITY A PUBLIC AGENCY p 1092
505 City Pkwy W, Orange CA 92868
Tel (714) 246-8500 *SIC* 8621 8011

MEDIMPACT HEALTHCARE SYSTEMS INC p 938
10181 Scripps Gateway Ct, San Diego CA 92131
Tel (858) 566-2727 *SIC* 8621

CHINESE COMMUNITY HEALTH CARE ASSOCIATION p 301
445 Grant Ave Ste 700, San Francisco CA 94108
Tel (415) 955-8800 *SIC* 8621

CHINESE HOSPITAL ASSOCIATION p 301
845 Jackson St, San Francisco CA 94133
Tel (415) 982-2400 *SIC* 8621

DAMERON HOSPITAL ASSOCIATION INC p 410
525 W Acacia St, Stockton CA 95203
Tel (209) 944-5550 *SIC* 8621

REGENTS OF UNIVERSITY OF COLORADO p 1219
3100 Marine St Ste 48157, Boulder CO 80303
Tel (303) 735-6624 *SIC* 8221 8621

AMERICAN ASSOCIATION FOR ADVANCEMENT OF SCIENCE p 68
1200 New York Ave Nw, Washington DC 20005
Tel (202) 898-0873 *SIC* 8621 2721

AMERICAN CHEMICAL SOCIETY p 70
1155 16th St Nw, Washington DC 20036
Tel (202) 872-4600 *SIC* 8621 7319

AMERICAN CHEMISTRY COUNCIL INC p 70
700 2nd St Ne Fl 8-10, Washington DC 20002
Tel (202) 249-7000
SIC 8611 8748 8621 8699

AMERICAN COLLEGE OF CARDIOLOGY FOUNDATION p 70
2400 N St Nw, Washington DC 20037
Tel (202) 375-6000 *SIC* 8621

AMERICAN FOREIGN SERVICE PROTECTIVE ASSOCIATION p 72
1620 L St Nw Ste 800, Washington DC 20036
Tel (202) 833-4910 *SIC* 8621

AMERICAN PSYCHOLOGICAL ASSOCIATION INC p 78
750 1st St Ne Ste 605, Washington DC 20002
Tel (202) 336-5500 *SIC* 8621

ASSOCIATION OF AMERICAN MEDICAL COLLEGES p 121
655 K St Nw Ste 100, Washington DC 20001
Tel (202) 828-0400 *SIC* 8621

BROOKINGS INSTITUTION p 218
1775 Massachusetts Ave Nw, Washington DC 20036
Tel (202) 797-6000 *SIC* 8733 2741 8621

UNITED NATIONS FOUNDATION INC p 1510
1750 Penn Ave Nw Ste 300, Washington DC 20006
Tel (202) 887-9040 *SIC* 8621

ATP TOUR INC p 128
201 Atp Tour Blvd, Ponte Vedra Beach FL 32082
Tel (904) 285-9886 *SIC* 8621

UNIVERSITY MEDICAL SERVICE ASSOCIATION INC p 1519
12901 Brc Dwns Blvd Mdc62, Tampa FL 33612
Tel (813) 974-2124 *SIC* 8621

AMERICAN CANCER SOCIETY INC p 69
250 Williams St Nw # 6000, Atlanta GA 30303
Tel (404) 320-3333 *SIC* 8621

PRUITT CORP p 1187
1626 Jeurgens Ct, Norcross GA 30093
Tel (706) 552-1699 *SIC* 8621

QUEENS MEDICAL CENTER p 1198
1301 Punchbowl St, Honolulu HI 96813
Tel (808) 547-4329 *SIC* 8062 8621

AMERICAN BAR ASSOCIATION p 68
321 N Clark St Ste Ll2, Chicago IL 60654
Tel (312) 988-5000 *SIC* 8621 2721 2731

AMERICAN COLLEGE OF SURGEONS INC p 70
633 N Saint Clair St # 2600, Chicago IL 60611
Tel (312) 202-5000 *SIC* 8621

AMERICAN DENTAL ASSOCIATION p 71
211 E Chicago Ave, Chicago IL 60611
Tel (312) 440-2500 *SIC* 8621

AMERICAN MEDICAL ASSOCIATION INC p 76
330 N Wabash Ave # 39300, Chicago IL 60611
Tel (312) 464-5000
SIC 8621 2721 6321 6282

BLUE CROSS & BLUE SHIELD ASSOCIATION p 191
225 N Michigan Ave Fl 5, Chicago IL 60601
Tel (312) 297-6000 *SIC* 8621 6324

ILLINOIS STATE MEDICAL SOCIETY p 732
20 N Michigan Ave Ste 700, Chicago IL 60602
Tel (312) 782-2749 *SIC* 8621

ADVOCATE HEALTH CARE NETWORK p 28
3075 Highland Pkwy Fl 6, Downers Grove IL 60515
Tel (630) 572-9393 *SIC* 8621

AMERICAN ACADEMY OF PEDIATRICS p 67
141 Northwest Point Blvd, Elk Grove Village IL 60007
Tel (847) 228-5005 *SIC* 8621

ONE ROTARY CENTER p 1086
1560 Sherman Ave Ste Ll1, Evanston IL 60201
Tel (847) 869-5417 *SIC* 8621

COLLEGE OF AMERICAN PATHOLOGISTS p 336
325 Waukegan Rd, Northfield IL 60093
Tel (800) 323-4040 *SIC* 8621

JOINT COMMISSION ON ACCREDITATION OF HEALTHCARE ORGANIZATIONS p 792
1 Renaissance Blvd, Oakbrook Terrace IL 60181
Tel (630) 792-5000 *SIC* 8621

M D WISE INC p 889
1200 Madison Ave Ste 400, Indianapolis IN 46225
Tel (317) 822-7300 *SIC* 8621

AMERICAN ACADEMY OF FAMILY PHYSICIANS p 67
11400 Tomahawk Creek Pkwy, Leawood KS 66211
Tel (913) 906-6000 *SIC* 8621

EASTERN MAINE HEALTHCARE SYSTEMS p 472
43 Whiting Hill Rd # 500, Brewer ME 04412
Tel (207) 973-7050 *SIC* 8621 8062

■ **FTI LLC** p 583
909 Commerce Rd, Annapolis MD 21401
Tel (410) 224-8770 *SIC* 8621

MONTGOMERY COUNTY PUBLIC SCHOOLS p 986
850 Hungerford Dr, Rockville MD 20850
Tel (301) 517-5099 *SIC* 8621 8741

HARVARD MEDICAL FACULTY PHYSICIANS AT BETH ISRAEL DEACONESS MEDICAL CENTER INC p 666
375 Longwood Ave Ste 3, Boston MA 02215
Tel (617) 632-9755 *SIC* 8621

AMERICAN DENTAL PARTNERS INC p 71
401 Edgewater Pl Ste 430, Wakefield MA 01880
Tel (781) 224-0880 *SIC* 8621 8742

MASSACHUSETTS MEDICAL SOCIETY INC p 917
860 Winter St, Waltham MA 02451
Tel (781) 893-4610 *SIC* 2721 8621

■ **DECARE DENTAL LLC** p 420
3560 Delta Dental Dr, Saint Paul MN 55122
Tel (800) 371-6561 *SIC* 6324 8621

NATIONAL ASSOCIATION OF INSURANCE COMMISSIONERS p 1009
1100 Walnut St Ste 1500, Kansas City MO 64106
Tel (816) 842-3600 *SIC* 8621

OVERLOOK HOSPITAL ASSOCIATION p 1099
99 Beauvoir Ave, Summit NJ 07901
Tel (908) 522-2000 *SIC* 8621

NEW JERSEY EDUCATION ASSOCIATION INC p 1031
180 W State St, Trenton NJ 08608
Tel (609) 599-4561 *SIC* 8621

NYU LUTHERAN MEDICAL CENTER p 1069
150 55th St, Brooklyn NY 11220
Tel (718) 630-7000 *SIC* 8062 8621

AMERICAN MANAGEMENT ASSOCIATION INTERNATIONAL p 75
1601 Broadway Fl 7, New York NY 10019
Tel (212) 586-8100
SIC 8299 2731 8621 7812 2721

AMERICAN SOCIETY OF COMPOSERS AUTHORS AND PUBLISHERS p 79
1 Lincoln Plz Fl 6, New York NY 10023
Tel (212) 621-6000 *SIC* 8621

INSTITUTE OF ELECTRICAL AND ELECTRONICS ENGINEERS INC p 747
3 Park Ave Fl 17, New York NY 10016
Tel (212) 419-7900 *SIC* 8621

NEW YORK UNIVERSITY p 1036
250 Park Ave S Fl 6, New York NY 10003
Tel (212) 998-5813 *SIC* 8621

LEUKEMIA & LYMPHOMA SOCIETY INC p 858
3 International Dr # 200, Rye Brook NY 10573
Tel (914) 949-5213
SIC 8699 8399 8322 8011 8733 8621

AMERICAN INSTITUTE OF CERTIFIED PUBLIC ACCOUNTANTS p 75
220 Leigh Farm Rd, Durham NC 27707
Tel (919) 402-0682 *SIC* 8299 8621 2721

NC MEDICAL SOCIETY HEALTH p 1021
700 Spring Forest Rd # 400, Raleigh NC 27609
Tel (919) 878-7513 *SIC* 8621

PEDIATRIC ACADEMIC ASSOCIATION p 1127
700 Childrens Dr, Columbus OH 43205
Tel (614) 722-2459 *SIC* 8621

PHYSICIANS OF OHIO STATE UNIVERSITY p 1146
700 Ackerman Rd Ste 360, Columbus OH 43202
Tel (614) 263-2450 *SIC* 8621

CAREOREGON INC p 255
315 Sw 5th Ave Ste 900, Portland OR 97204
Tel (503) 416-4100 *SIC* 8621

CHILDRENS HEALTH CARE ASSOCIATES INC p 299
100 N 20th St Ste 301, Philadelphia PA 19103
Tel (215) 567-2422 *SIC* 8621

LAW ENFORCEMENT HEALTH BENEFITS INC p 847
2233 Spring Garden St, Philadelphia PA 19130
Tel (215) 763-8290 *SIC* 8621

CLARKSVILLE VOLUNTEER HEALTH INC p 322
651 Dunlop Ln, Clarksville TN 37040
Tel (931) 220-2532 *SIC* 8062 8621

ST DAVIDS HEALTH CARE FOUNDATION p 1365
811 Barton Springs Rd # 600, Austin TX 78704
Tel (512) 879-6600 *SIC* 8621

TEXAS ELECTRIC COOPERATIVES INC p 1443
1122 Colorado St Ste 2400, Austin TX 78701
Tel (512) 454-0311 *SIC* 2491 3612 8621

YOUNG PRESIDENTS ORGANIZATION p 1639
600 Las Colinas Blvd E # 10, Irving TX 75039
Tel (972) 587-1500 *SIC* 8621

DENTALONE PARTNERS INC p 429
7160 Dallas Pkwy Ste 400, Plano TX 75024
Tel (972) 755-0800 *SIC* 8621

AMERICAN SOCIETY OF CLINICAL ONCOLOGY INC p 79
2318 Mill Rd Ste 800, Alexandria VA 22314
Tel (571) 483-1300 *SIC* 8621

SOCIETY FOR HUMAN RESOURCE MANAGEMENT p 1336
1800 Duke St, Alexandria VA 22314
Tel (703) 548-3440 *SIC* 8621

CFA INSTITUTE p 285
915 E High St, Charlottesville VA 22902
Tel (434) 951-5499 *SIC* 8621 6282 8221

OVERLAKE HOSPITAL ASSOCIATION p 1099
1035 116th Ave Ne, Bellevue WA 98004
Tel (425) 688-5000 *SIC* 8621

ASSOCIATION OF WASHINGTON CITIES p 121
1076 Franklin St Se, Olympia WA 98501
Tel (360) 753-4137 *SIC* 8621

ASSOCIATION OF UNIVERSITY PHYSICIANS p 121
701 5th Ave Ste 700, Seattle WA 98104
Tel (206) 520-5388 *SIC* 8621

GUNDERSEN LUTHERAN ADMINISTRATIVE SERVICES INC p 647
1900 South Ave, La Crosse WI 54601
Tel (608) 782-7300 *SIC* 8621

FAMILY HEALTH CENTER OF A MARSHFIELD INC p 527
1000 N Oak Ave, Marshfield WI 54449
Tel (715) 387-9137 *SIC* 8621

SIC 8631 Labor Unions & Similar Organizations

UFCW AND EMPLOYERS AZ H AND W TRUST p 1499
2400 W Dunlap Ave Ste 250, Phoenix AZ 85021
Tel (602) 249-3582 *SIC* 8631

CALIFORNIA TEACHERS ASSOCIATION p 241
1705 Murchison Dr, Burlingame CA 94010
Tel (650) 697-1400 *SIC* 8621 8631

UNITED FOOD AND COMMERCIAL WORKERS UNIONS AND FOOD EMPLOYERS BEN FUND p 1508
6425 Katella Ave, Cypress CA 90630
Tel (714) 220-2297 *SIC* 8631

LABORERS HEALTH & WELFARE TRUST FUND FOR SOUTHERN p 836
4399 Santa Anita Ave # 200, El Monte CA 91731
Tel (626) 279-3000 *SIC* 8631

TEAMSTER BENEFIT TRUST p 1430
39420 Liberty St Ste 260, Fremont CA 94538
Tel (510) 796-4676 *SIC* 8631 6411

IBEW LOCAL 18 p 726
4189 W 2nd St, Los Angeles CA 90004
Tel (213) 387-8274 *SIC* 8631

SEIU UNITED HEALTHCARE WORKERS-WEST LOCAL 2005 p 1301
560 Thomas L Berkley Way, Oakland CA 94612
Tel (510) 251-1250 *SIC* 8631

CALIFORNIA IRONWORKERS FIELD WELFARE PLAN p 240
131 N El Molino Ave # 330, Pasadena CA 91101
Tel (626) 792-7337 *SIC* 8631

INTERNATIONAL UNION OF OPERATING ENGINEERS p 757
1121 L St Ste 401, Sacramento CA 95814
Tel (916) 444-6880 *SIC* 8631

PACIFIC MARITIME ASSOCIATION INC p 1105
555 Market St Fl 3, San Francisco CA 94105
Tel (415) 576-3200 *SIC* 8631

SHEET METAL WORKERS LOCAL 104 HEALTH CARE PLAN p 1313
2610 Crow Canyon Rd, San Ramon CA 94583
Tel (925) 208-9999 *SIC* 8631

AMERICAN FEDERATION OF LABOR & CONGRESS OF INDUSTRIAL ORGANZATION p 72
815 16th St Nw, Washington DC 20006
Tel (202) 637-5000 *SIC* 8631

AMERICAN FEDERATION OF STATE COUNTY & MUNICIPAL EMPLOYEES p 72
1625 L St Nw, Washington DC 20036
Tel (202) 429-1000 *SIC* 8631

AMERICAN POSTAL WORKERS UNION p 77
1300 L St Nw Ste 200, Washington DC 20005
Tel (202) 842-4200 *SIC* 8631

ASSOCIATION OF FLIGHT ATTENDANTS p 121
501 3rd St Nw Fl 10, Washington DC 20001
Tel (202) 387-1968 *SIC* 8631

COMMUNICATIONS WORKERS OF AMERICA AFL-CIO CLC p 347
501 3rd St Nw, Washington DC 20001
Tel (202) 434-1100 *SIC* 8631

INTERNATIONAL BROTHERHOOD OF ELECTRICAL WORKERS p 754
900 7th St Nw Bsmt 1, Washington DC 20001
Tel (202) 833-7000 *SIC* 8631

INTERNATIONAL BROTHERHOOD OF ELECTRICAL WORKERS - PENSION BENEFIT FUND p 754
900 7th St Nw, Washington DC 20001
Tel (202) 728-6200 *SIC* 8631

INTERNATIONAL BROTHERHOOD OF TEAMSTERS p 754
25 Louisiana Ave Nw, Washington DC 20001
Tel (202) 624-6800 *SIC* 8631

LABORERS INTERNATIONAL UNION OF NORTH AMERICA p 836
905 16th St Nw, Washington DC 20006
Tel (202) 737-8320 *SIC* 8631

NATIONAL ASSOCIATION OF LETTER CARRIERS p 1010
100 Indana Ave Nw Ste 709, Washington DC 20001
Tel (202) 393-4695 *SIC* 8631

NATIONAL EDUCATION ASSOCIATION OF UNITED STATES p 1011
1201 16th St Nw, Washington DC 20036
Tel (202) 833-4000 *SIC* 8631

NATIONAL POSTAL MAIL HANDLERS UNION p 1015
1101 Conn Ave Nw Ste 500, Washington DC 20036
Tel (202) 833-9095 *SIC* 8631

SERVICE EMPLOYEES INTERNATIONAL UNION p 1307
1800 Massachusetts Ave Nw, Washington DC 20036
Tel (202) 730-7000 *SIC* 8631

UNITED FOOD AND COMMERCIAL WORKERS INTERNATIONAL UNION p 1508
1775 K St Nw, Washington DC 20006
Tel (202) 223-3111 *SIC* 8631

IUPAT DISTRICT COUNCIL 78 p 769
1300 Sw 12th Ave, Pompano Beach FL 33069
Tel (954) 946-9311 *SIC* 8631

FIREFIGHTERS PENSION FUND GEORGIA p 543
2171 Eastview Pkwy, Conyers GA 30013
Tel (770) 388-5757 *SIC* 8631 9651

PROGRESSIVE LOGISTICS SERVICES LLC p 1181
6525 The Corners Pkwy # 520, Norcross GA 30092
Tel (404) 564-1222 *SIC* 8631

SERVICE EMPLOYEES INTERNATIONAL UNION LOCAL 1 p 1307
111 E Wacker Dr Ste 2500, Chicago IL 60601
Tel (312) 240-1600 *SIC* 8631

NECA IBEW WELFARE TRUST FUND p 1023
2120 Hubbard Ave, Decatur IL 62526
Tel (800) 765-4239 *SIC* 8631

NATIONAL FARMERS ORGANIZATION p 1011
528 Billy Sunday Rd # 100, Ames IA 50010
Tel (515) 292-2000 *SIC* 8631

NFO INC p 1041
528 Billy Sunday Rd # 100, Ames IA 50010
Tel (515) 292-2000 *SIC* 8631

UNITED ASSOCIATION OF JOURNEYMEN & APPRENTICES OF PLUMBING & PIPEFITTERS p 1506
3 Park Pl, Annapolis MD 21401
Tel (410) 269-2000 *SIC* 8631

NORTHERN NEW ENGLAND DISTRICT COUNCIL OF CARPENTERS INC p 1056
350 Fordham Rd, Wilmington MA 01887
Tel (800) 383-2759 *SIC* 8631

INTERNATIONAL UNION UNITED AUTOMOBILE AEROSPACE AND AGRICULTURAL IMPLEMENT WORKERS OF AM p 757
8000 E Jefferson Ave, Detroit MI 48214
Tel (313) 926-5000 *SIC* 8631

INTERNATIONAL OPERATING ENGINEERS UNION 49 HEALTH AND WELFARE FUND p 756
3001 Metro Dr Ste 500, Bloomington MN 55425
Tel (952) 854-0795 *SIC* 8631

TEACHERS RETIREMENT FUND p 1429
625 E Central Entrance, Duluth MN 55811
Tel (218) 722-2894 *SIC* 8631

OPERATING ENGINEERS LOCAL 49 p 1089
308 Lundin Blvd, Mankato MN 56001
Tel (507) 625-3670 *SIC* 8631

MISSOURI VALLEY LINE CONTRACTORS p 976
7505 Nw Tffany Sprng Pkwy, Kansas City MO 64153
Tel (816) 891-9066 *SIC* 8742 8631

CARPENTERS HEALTH & WELFARE TRUST FUND OF ST LOUIS p 260
1419 Hampton Ave, Saint Louis MO 63139
Tel (314) 644-4802 *SIC* 8631

NJ CARPENTERS CATASTROPHIC HEALTH FUND p 1045
P.O. Box 7818, Edison NJ 08818
Tel (732) 417-3900 *SIC* 8631

HEAVY & GENERAL CONSTRUCTION LABORERS UNION LOCAL NO 472 p 679
700 Raymond Blvd, Newark NJ 07105
Tel (973) 589-5050 *SIC* 8631

TEAMSTERS HEALTH AND WELFARE FUND OF PHILADELPHIA AND VICINITY p 1430
6981 N Park Dr Ste 400, Pennsauken NJ 08109
Tel (856) 382-2400 *SIC* 8631

HEAVY & GENERAL LABORERS LOCAL 472 & 172 FUNDS OF NJ p 679
604 Us Highway 206, Trenton NJ 08610
Tel (609) 291-9197 *SIC* 8631

CIVIL SERVICE EMPLOYEES ASSOCIATION INC p 320
143 Washington Ave, Albany NY 12210
Tel (518) 257-1000 *SIC* 8631

NYS POLICE INVESTIGATORS ASSOCIATION EMERGENCY ASSISTANCE FUND INC p 1069
11 N Pearl St Ste 1202, Albany NY 12207
Tel (518) 436-0120 *SIC* 8631

NEW YORK STATE UNITED TEACHERS p 1036
800 Troy Schenectady Rd, Latham NY 12110
Tel (518) 213-6000 *SIC* 8631

1199SEIU UNITED HEALTH CARE WORKERS EAST p 1
310 W 43rd St, New York NY 10036
Tel (212) 582-1890 *SIC* 8631

LOCAL 94 94A 94B HEALTH & BENEFIT TRUST FUND IUOE AFL-CIO p 872
331 W 44th St 337, New York NY 10036
Tel (212) 541-9880 *SIC* 8631

MASON TENDERS DISTRICT COUNCIL GREATER NEW YORK p 916
520 8th Ave Rm 650, New York NY 10018
Tel (212) 452-9400 *SIC* 8631

NEW YORK HOTEL TRADES COUNCIL AND HOTEL ASSOC OF NYC INC HEALTH BENEFITS FUND p 1035
305 W 44th St, New York NY 10036
Tel (212) 586-6400 *SIC* 8631

UNITED BROTHERHOOD OF CARPENTERS AND RESILIENT FLOOR COVERERS LOCAL 2287 p 1506
395 Hudson St Fl 8, New York NY 10014
Tel (212) 929-2940 *SIC* 8631

INTERNATIONAL UNION OF OPERATING ENGINEERS LOCAL 30 p 757
11506 Myrtle Ave, Richmond Hill NY 11418
Tel (718) 847-8484 *SIC* 8631 6512

UA (UNITED ASSOCIATION) LOCAL 13 OF JOURNEY MAN AND A PREMISES OF PLUMBING p 1498
1850 Mount Read Blvd, Rochester NY 14615
Tel (585) 338-2360 *SIC* 8631

N Y S TEAMSTER HEALTH PENSION & RETIREMENT FUND p 1006
151 Northern Concourse, Syracuse NY 13212
Tel (315) 455-9790 *SIC* 8631

AMALGAMATED NATIONAL HEALTH FUND p 64
333 Westchester Ave N101, White Plains NY 10604
Tel (914) 367-5000 *SIC* 8631

UNITED STEEL PAPER AND FORESTRY RUBBER MANUFACTURING ENERGY ALLIED p 1514
5 Gateway Ctr, Pittsburgh PA 15222
Tel (412) 562-2400 *SIC* 8631

UNITED STEELWORKERS p 1514
60 Bolevard Of The Allies, Pittsburgh PA 15222
Tel (412) 562-2400 *SIC* 8631

CENTRAL PENNSYLVANIA TEAMSTERS p 279
1055 Spring St, Reading PA 19610
Tel (610) 320-5500 *SIC* 8631

AIR LIQUIDE ELECTRONICS US LP p 39
9101 Lyndon B Johnson Fwy # 800, Dallas TX 75243
Tel (972) 301-5200
SIC 2813 3564 8631 2819

AIRLINE PILOTS ASSOCIATION INTERNATIONAL p 40
1625 Massachusetts Ave Nw, Herndon VA 20172
Tel (703) 689-2270 *SIC* 8631 6512

WASHINGTON TEAMSTERS WELFARE TRUST p 1579
2323 Eastlake Ave E, Seattle WA 98102
Tel (206) 329-4900 *SIC* 8631

WESTERN TEAMSTERS WELFARE TRUST p 1600
2323 Eastlake Ave E, Seattle WA 98102
Tel (206) 329-4900 *SIC* 8631

ASEA AFSCME LOCAL 52 HEALTH BENEFITS TRUST p 116
111 W Cataldo Ave, Spokane WA 99201
Tel (509) 328-0300 *SIC* 8631

SIC 8641 Civic, Social & Fraternal Associations

AUBURN UNIVERSITY FOUNDATION p 130
317 S College St, Auburn AL 36849
Tel (334) 844-1124 *SIC* 7389 8641

YOUNG MENS CHRISTIAN ASSOCIATION OF BIRMINGHAM p 1638
2101 4th Ave N, Birmingham AL 35203
Tel (205) 801-9622
SIC 7991 8641 8351 7032

UNIVERSITY OF ALABAMA p 1519
1202 Coliseum Cir, Tuscaloosa AL 35487
Tel (205) 348-0628 *SIC* 8641

VALLEY OF SUN YOUNG MENS CHRISTIAN ASSOCIATION p 1541
350 N 1st Ave, Phoenix AZ 85003
Tel (602) 257-5120 *SIC* 8641 8322

AHMC HEALTHCARE INC p 37
1000 S Fremont Ave Unit 6, Alhambra CA 91803
Tel (626) 943-7526 *SIC* 8062 8641

SUTTER EAST BAY MEDFNDTN p 1410
3687 Mt Diablo Blvd # 200, Lafayette CA 94549
Tel (510) 204-6622 *SIC* 8641

LOS ANGELES POLICE RELIEF ASSOCIATION INC p 878
600 N Grand Ave, Los Angeles CA 90012
Tel (213) 674-3701 *SIC* 8641

YOUNG MENS CHRISTIAN ASSOCIATION OF METROPOLITAN LOS ANGELES p 1638
625 S New Hampshire Ave, Los Angeles CA 90005
Tel (213) 351-2256 *SIC* 8641

SIERRA CLUB p 1320
2101 Webster St Ste 1300, Oakland CA 94612
Tel (415) 977-5500 *SIC* 8641 8399

PASADENA TOURNAMENT OF ROSES ASSOCIATION p 1119
391 S Orange Grove Blvd, Pasadena CA 91184
Tel (626) 449-4100 *SIC* 8641

TOSA FOUNDATION p 1462
3130 Alpine Rd, Portola Vally CA 94028
Tel (650) 851-6922 *SIC* 8641

SACRAMENTO CITY UNIFIED SCHOOL DISTRICT p 1264
5735 47th Ave, Sacramento CA 95824
Tel (916) 643-7400 *SIC* 8641

YMCA OF SAN DIEGO COUNTY p 1636
3708 Ruffin Rd, San Diego CA 92123
Tel (858) 292-9622 *SIC* 8641

YOUNG MENS CHRISTIAN ASSOCIATION OF SAN FRANCISCO p 1639
50 California St Ste 650, San Francisco CA 94111
Tel (415) 777-9622
SIC 8641 7991 8351 7032 8322

DCHS MEDICAL FOUNDATION p 418
625 Lincoln Ave, San Jose CA 95126
Tel (408) 278-3000 *SIC* 8641

YMCA OF SILICON VALLEY p 1636
80 Saratoga Ave, Santa Clara CA 95051
Tel (408) 351-6400
SIC 8641 7991 8351 7032 8322

UNIVERSITY CORP FOR ATMOSPHERIC RESEARCH FOUNDATION p 1518
P.O. Box 3000, Boulder CO 80307
Tel (303) 497-8575 *SIC* 8641

INDEPENDENT ORDER OF ODD FELLOWS p 736
575 S Union Blvd, Colorado Springs CO 80910
Tel (719) 633-2002 *SIC* 8641

YMCA OF METROPOLITAN HARTFORD INC p 1636
50 State House Sq Fl 2, Hartford CT 06103
Tel (860) 522-9622 *SIC* 8641 7032 7997

KNIGHTS OF COLUMBUS p 824
1 Columbus Plz Ste 1700, New Haven CT 06510
Tel (203) 752-4000 *SIC* 6411 8641

ACDI/VOCA p 16
50 F St Nw Ste 1000, Washington DC 20001
Tel (202) 469-6000 *SIC* 8748 8641

CONSERVATION INTERNATIONAL FOUNDATION p 358
1003 K St Nw Ste 404, Washington DC 20001
Tel (703) 341-2400 *SIC* 8641

NATIONAL CAUCUS AND CENTER ON BLACK AGING INC p 1010
1220 L St Nw Ste 800, Washington DC 20005
Tel (202) 637-8400 *SIC* 8322 8641

NATIONAL FISH & WILDLIFE FOUNDATION p 1012
1133 15th St Nw Fl 11, Washington DC 20005
Tel (202) 857-0166 *SIC* 8641

PARALYZED VETERANS OF AMERICA p 1114
801 18th St Nw Frnt 1, Washington DC 20006
Tel (202) 872-1300 *SIC* 8399 7389 8641

WORLD WILDLIFE FUND INC p 1625
1250 24th St Nw Fl 2, Washington DC 20037
Tel (202) 293-4800 *SIC* 8641

WYSS FOUNDATION p 1630
1601 Conn Ave Nw Ste 800, Washington DC 20009
Tel (202) 232-4418 *SIC* 8641

YMCA OF METROPOLITAN WASHINGTON p 1636
1112 16th St Nw Ste 720, Washington DC 20036
Tel (202) 232-6700 *SIC* 8641

YOUNG MENS CHRISTIAN ASSOCIATION OF SUNCOAST p 1639
2469 Enterprise Rd, Clearwater FL 33763
Tel (312) 932-1200
SIC 8641 7991 8351 7032 8322

YOUNG MENS CHRISTIAN ASSOCIATION OF BROWARD COUNTY FLORIDA INC p 1638
900 Se 3rd Ave, Fort Lauderdale FL 33316
Tel (954) 334-9622 *SIC* 8641

UNIVERSITY OF FLORIDA FOUNDATION INC p 1521
2012 W University Ave, Gainesville FL 32603
Tel (352) 392-1691 *SIC* 8399 8641 8221

WOUNDED WARRIOR PROJECT INC p 1627
4899 Belfort Rd Ste 300, Jacksonville FL 32256
Tel (904) 296-7350 *SIC* 8641

YMCA OF FLORIDAS FIRST COAST p 1636
40 E Adams St Ste 210, Jacksonville FL 32202
Tel (904) 296-3220 *SIC* 8741 8641

AMERICAN NICARAGUAN FOUNDATION INC p 77
1000 Nw 57th Ct Ste 770, Miami FL 33126
Tel (305) 374-3391 *SIC* 8399 8641

CENTRAL FLORIDA YOUNG MENS CHRISTIAN ASSOCIATION INC p 278
433 N Mills Ave, Orlando FL 32803
Tel (407) 896-9220 *SIC* 8641

SARASOTA FAMILY YOUNG MENS CHRISTIAN ASSOCIATION INC p 1282
1 S School Ave Ste 301, Sarasota FL 34237
Tel (941) 951-2916
SIC 8641 8351 8322 7997 7991

TAMPA METROPOLITAN AREA YOUNG MENS CHRISTIAN ASSOCIATION INC p 1423
110 E Oak Ave, Tampa FL 33602
Tel (813) 224-9622 *SIC* 8641

PALM BEACH ATLANTIC UNIVERSITY ALUMNI ASSOCIATION p 1109
901 S Flagler Dr, West Palm Beach FL 33401
Tel (561) 803-2000 *SIC* 8641

COOPERATIVE FOR ASSISTANCE AND RELIEF EVERYWHERE INC p 367
151 Ellis St Ne, Atlanta GA 30303
Tel (404) 681-2552 *SIC* 8641 8322

YOUNG MENS CHRISTIAN ASSOCIATION OF METROPOLITAN ATLANTA INC p 1638
100 Edgewood Ave Ne, Atlanta GA 30303
Tel (404) 588-9622
SIC 8641 7991 8351 7032 8322

ST ELIZABETHS HOSPITAL OF THIRD ORDER OF ST FRANCIS p 1366
211 S 3rd St, Belleville IL 62220
Tel (618) 234-2120 *SIC* 8641

CHICAGO COMMUNITY TRUST p 297
225 N Michigan Ave # 2200, Chicago IL 60601
Tel (312) 616-8000 *SIC* 8641

NATIONAL YMCA EMPLOYEE BENEFITS TRUST p 1017
101 N Wacker Dr Ste 1500, Chicago IL 60606
Tel (312) 977-0031 *SIC* 8641

ROBERT R MCCORMICK FOUNDATION p 1241
205 N Michigan Ave # 4300, Chicago IL 60601
Tel (312) 445-5000 *SIC* 8641 8699

YOUNG MENS CHRISTIAN ASSOCIATION OF CHICAGO p 1638
1030 W Van Buren St, Chicago IL 60607
Tel (312) 932-1200
SIC 8641 7011 8351 8699 8322 7999

ROTARY INTERNATIONAL p 1252
1 Rotary Ctr, Evanston IL 60201
Tel (847) 866-3000 *SIC* 8641

YOUNG MENS CHRISTIAN ASSOCIATION OF CEDAR RAPIDS METROPOLITAN AREA p 1638
207 7th Ave Se, Cedar Rapids IA 52401
Tel (319) 366-6421 *SIC* 8641 8322

YOUNG MENS CHRISTIAN ASSOCIATION OF WICHITA KANSAS p 1639
402 N Market St, Wichita KS 67202
Tel (316) 219-9622
SIC 8641 7991 8351 7032 8322

DISABLED AMERICAN VETERANS p 442
3725 Alexandria Pike, Cold Spring KY 41076
Tel (859) 441-7300 *SIC* 8641

ENERGY AND ENVIRONMENT CABINET p 497
500 Mero St Ste 4, Frankfort KY 40601
Tel (502) 564-3350 *SIC* 8641 9611

YOUNG MENS CHRISTIAN ASSOCIATION OF GREATER LOUISVILLE p 1638
545 S 2nd St, Louisville KY 40202
Tel (502) 587-9622
SIC 8641 7991 8351 7032 8322

UNITED ASSOCIATION p 1506
3 Park Pl Ste 300, Annapolis MD 21401
Tel (410) 269-2000 *SIC* 8641

NATIONAL ASSOCIATION FOR ADVANCEMENT OF COLORED PEOPLE p 1009
4805 Mount Hope Dr, Baltimore MD 21215
Tel (410) 358-8900 *SIC* 8641

YMCA OF CENTRAL MARYLAND INC p 1636
303 W Chesapeake Ave, Baltimore MD 21204
Tel (443) 322-9622 *SIC* 8641 8351

COLUMBIA ASSOCIATION INC p 340
6310 Hillside Ct Ste 100, Columbia MD 21046
Tel (410) 715-3000 *SIC* 8641

BETHESDA-CHEVY CHASE CHAPTER IZAAK WALTON LEAGUE OF AMERICA p 178
20601 Izaak Walton Way, Poolesville MD 20837
Tel (301) 972-8913 *SIC* 8641

YMCA OF GREATER BOSTON INC p 1636
316 Huntington Ave Ste 1, Boston MA 02115
Tel (617) 536-6950
SIC 8641 7991 8351 7032 8322

OLD COLONY Y p 1080
320 Main St, Brockton MA 02301
Tel (508) 583-2155
SIC 8641 7991 8351 7032 8322

YOUNG MENS CHRISTIAN ASSOCIATION OF METROPOLITAN DETROIT p 1638
1401 Broadway St Ste A, Detroit MI 48226
Tel (313) 267-5300 *SIC* 7999 8641

MEMORIAL HEALTH CARE INC p 941
826 W King St, Owosso MI 48867
Tel (989) 725-8101 *SIC* 8641 5947

FOUNDATION HOLDINGS INC p 571
3311 E Old Shakopee Rd, Minneapolis MN 55425
Tel (952) 853-8100 *SIC* 8641 8721

YOUNG MENS CHRISTIAN ASSOCIATION OF GREATER TWIN CITIES p 1638
2125 E Hennepin Ave, Minneapolis MN 55413
Tel (612) 465-0450 *SIC* 8641

CATHOLIC UNITED FINANCIAL p 267
3499 Lexington Ave N, Saint Paul MN 55126
Tel (651) 490-0170 *SIC* 8641 6411

SAINT PAUL FOUNDATION INC p 1270
101 5th St E Ste 2400, Saint Paul MN 55101
Tel (651) 224-5463 *SIC* 8641 8399

SCOTTISH RITE TEMPLE p 1294
200 Plato Blvd E, Saint Paul MN 55107
Tel (651) 222-2676 *SIC* 8641

PEARL RIVER RESORT p 1126
13541 Highway 16 W, Philadelphia MS 39350
Tel (601) 663-4438 *SIC* 5812 8641

PARKWAY SCHOOL DISTRICT PARENT-TEACHERS ORGANIZATION COUNCIL p 1117
455 N Woods Mill Rd, Chesterfield MO 63017
Tel (314) 415-8100 *SIC* 8641

JEFFERSON MEMORIAL COMMUNITY FOUNDATION 145 p 782
1450 Parkway W, Festus MO 63028
Tel (636) 638-1400 *SIC* 8641

CHILDRENS MERCY HOSPITAL FOUNDATION p 300
2401 Gillham Rd, Kansas City MO 64108
Tel (816) 234-3000 *SIC* 8641

VETERANS OF FOREIGN WARS OF UNITED STATES p 1553
406 W 34th St Fl 11, Kansas City MO 64111
Tel (816) 756-3390 *SIC* 8641

YOUNG MENS CHRISTIAN ASSOCIATION OF GREATER KANSAS CITY p 1638
3100 Broadway Blvd # 1020, Kansas City MO 64111
Tel (816) 561-9622 *SIC* 8641 7993 7991

GATEWAY REGION YOUNG MENS CHRISTIAN ASSOCIATION p 594
326 S 21st St Ste 400, Saint Louis MO 63103
Tel (314) 436-1177 *SIC* 8641 8741 8322

ROBERT B DAUGHERTY FOUNDATION INC p 1241
1 Valmont Plz, Omaha NE 68154
Tel (402) 933-4663 *SIC* 8641

SHERWOOD FOUNDATION p 1316
3555 Farnam St, Omaha NE 68131
Tel (402) 341-1717 *SIC* 8641

SUSAN THOMPSON BUFFETT FOUNDATION p 1409
222 Kiewit Plz, Omaha NE 68131
Tel (402) 943-1300 *SIC* 8641

NORTHPOINT PROPERTY MANAGEMENT LLC p 1058
55 Lake St Ste 4, Nashua NH 03060
Tel (603) 594-2300 *SIC* 8641 6531

NEW JERSEY SPORTS & EXPOSITION AUTHORITY p 1031
1 Dekorte Park Plz, Lyndhurst NJ 07071
Tel (201) 460-1700 *SIC* 8641 7941 6512

■ A D P FOUNDATION p 5
1 Adp Blvd Ste 1, Roseland NJ 07068
Tel (973) 994-5000 *SIC* 8641

WILDLIFE CONSERVATION SOCIETY p 1609
2300 Southern Blvd, Bronx NY 10460
Tel (718) 220-5144 *SIC* 8422 8641

NYSARC INC FULTON COUNTY CHAPTER p 1069
465 N Perry St, Johnstown NY 12095
Tel (518) 773-7931 *SIC* 8641

OHI PARENT INC p 1077
111 Radio Circle Dr, Mount Kisco NY 10549
Tel (914) 241-7430 *SIC* 8641

ENVIRONMENTAL DEFENSE FUND INC p 503
257 Park Ave S Fl 17, New York NY 10010
Tel (212) 505-2100 *SIC* 8641 8748

GIRL SCOUTS OF UNITED STATES OF AMERICA p 613
420 5th Ave Fl 13, New York NY 10018
Tel (212) 852-8000
SIC 8641 5137 6794 2721

ISRAEL BIRTHRIGHT FOUNDATION p 767
33 E 33rd St Fl 7, New York NY 10016
Tel (212) 457-0036 *SIC* 8641

JPB FOUNDATION p 795
9 W 57th St Ste 3800, New York NY 10019
Tel (212) 364-6266 *SIC* 8641

MDRC p 933
16 E 34th St Fl 19, New York NY 10016
Tel (212) 532-3200 *SIC* 8641 8733

NATIONAL AUDUBON SOCIETY INC p 1010
225 Varick St Fl 7, New York NY 10014
Tel (212) 979-3000 *SIC* 8641 2721

NATURAL RESOURCES DEFENSE COUNCIL INC p 1018
40 W 20th St, New York NY 10011
Tel (212) 727-2700 *SIC* 8641

NOVO FOUNDATION p 1063
535 5th Ave Fl 33, New York NY 10017
Tel (212) 808-5400 *SIC* 8641

YOUNG MENS CHRISTIAN ASSOCIATION OF GREATER NEW YORK p 1638
5 W 63rd St Fl 6, New York NY 10023
Tel (212) 630-9600
SIC 8641 7991 8351 7032 8322

YOUNG MEN S CHRISTIAN ASSOCIATION OF GREATER CHARLOTTE p 1638
400 E Morehead St, Charlotte NC 28202
Tel (704) 716-6200 *SIC* 7032 8641

YMCA OF NORTHWEST NORTH CAROLINA p 1636
301 N Main St Ste 1900, Winston Salem NC 27101
Tel (336) 777-8055
SIC 8641 7991 8351 7032 8322

YOUNG MENS CHRISTIAN ASSOCIATION OF GREATER CINCINNATI p 1638
1105 Elm St, Cincinnati OH 45202
Tel (513) 651-2100 *SIC* 8641

KAPPA KAPPA GAMMA FOUNDATION p 803
530 E Town St, Columbus OH 43215
Tel (614) 228-6515 *SIC* 8641

OHIO STATE UNIVERSITY FOUNDATION p 1078
364 W Lane Ave Ste B, Columbus OH 43201
Tel (614) 292-6261 *SIC* 8641

YOUNG MENS CHRISTIAN ASSOCIATION OF CENTRAL OHIO p 1638
40 W Long St, Columbus OH 43215
Tel (614) 224-1142 *SIC* 8641

YOUNG MENS CHRISTIAN ASSOCIATION OF GREATER DAYTON p 1638
118 W St Ste 300, Dayton OH 45402
Tel (937) 223-5201
SIC 8641 7991 8351 7032 8322

GRAND AERIE OF FRATERNAL ORDER OF EAGLES p 629
1623 Gateway Cir, Grove City OH 43123
Tel (614) 883-2200 SIC 8641

KIDS IN NEED FOUNDATION p 817
3055 Kettering Blvd # 119, Moraine OH 45439
Tel (937) 296-1230 SIC 8641

COMMUNITY MERCY FOUNDATION p 349
1 S Limestone St Ste 700, Springfield OH 45502
Tel (937) 328-7000 SIC 8641

YOUNG MENS CHRISTIAN ASSOCIATION OF GREATER TOLEDO p 1638
1500 N Superior St Fl 2, Toledo OH 43604
Tel (419) 729-8135
SIC 8641 7991 8351 7032 8322

CITY OF MUSKOGEE FOUNDATION p 316
120 N 3rd St, Muskogee OK 74401
Tel (918) 577-6562 SIC 8641

GEORGE KAISER FAMILY FOUNDATION p 606
7030 S Yale Ave Ste 600, Tulsa OK 74136
Tel (918) 392-1612 SIC 8641

ALLEGHENY FOUNDATION p 52
301 Grant St Ste 1, Pittsburgh PA 15219
Tel (412) 392-2900 SIC 8641

YMCA GREATER BRANDYWINE p 1636
1 E Chestnut St, West Chester PA 19380
Tel (610) 643-9622
SIC 8641 7991 8351 7032 8322

GREATER PROVIDENCE YOUNG MENS CHRISTIAN ASSOCIATION p 636
371 Pine St, Providence RI 02903
Tel (401) 521-9622
SIC 8641 7991 8351 7032 8322

YMCA OF METROPOLITAN CHATTANOOGA p 1636
301 W 6th St, Chattanooga TN 37402
Tel (423) 266-3766
SIC 8641 7991 8351 7032 8322

CENTRAL BAND OF CHEROKEE p 277
870 Lawrence Ave, Lawrenceburg TN 38464
Tel (931) 242-6398 SIC 8641

FOOTHILLS LAND CONSERVANCY INC p 564
373 Ellis Ave, Maryville TN 37804
Tel (865) 681-8326 SIC 8641

GOODWILL INDUSTRIES OF MIDDLE TENNESSEE INC p 624
1015 Herman St, Nashville TN 37208
Tel (615) 742-4151 SIC 8641

YOUNG MENS CHRISTIAN ASSOCIATION OF MIDDLE TENNESSEE p 1638
1000 Church St, Nashville TN 37203
Tel (615) 259-9622
SIC 8641 7991 8351 7032 8322

YOUNG MENS CHRISTIAN ASSOCIATION OF METROPOLITAN p 1638
601 N Akard St, Dallas TX 75201
Tel (214) 880-9622
SIC 8641 7991 8351 7032 8322

TERRY FOUNDATION p 1440
600 Jefferson St Ste 1600, Houston TX 77002
Tel (713) 552-0002 SIC 8641

YOUNG MENS CHRISTIAN ASSOCIATION OF GREATER HOUSTON AREA INC p 1638
2600 North Loop W Ste 300, Houston TX 77092
Tel (713) 659-5566
SIC 8641 7991 8351 7032 8322

BOY SCOUTS OF AMERICA p 205
1325 W Walnut Hill Ln, Irving TX 75038
Tel (972) 580-2000
SIC 8641 5136 5091 2721

NATURE CONSERVANCY p 1018
4245 Fairfax Dr Ste 100, Arlington VA 22203
Tel (703) 841-5300 SIC 8641

NAVY MUTUAL AID ASSOCIATION p 1020
Henderson Hall, 29, Arlington VA 22212
Tel (703) 945-1440 SIC 8641 6411

CFA INSTITUTE RESEARCH FOUNDATION p 285
915 E High St, Charlottesville VA 22902
Tel (434) 951-5499 SIC 8641

YOUNG MENS CHRISTIAN ASSOCIATION OF SOUTH HAMPTON ROADS p 1639
920 Corporate Ln, Chesapeake VA 23320
Tel (757) 624-9622 SIC 8641

YOUNG MENS CHRISTIAN ASSOCIATION OF GREATER RICHMOND p 1638
2 W Franklin St, Richmond VA 23220
Tel (804) 644-9622
SIC 8641 7991 8351 7032 8322

CHIEF SEATTLE COUNCIL BOY SCOUTS OF AMERICA p 298
3120 Rainier Ave S, Seattle WA 98144
Tel (206) 725-5200 SIC 8641

SATTERBERG FOUNDATION p 1283
1904 3rd Ave Ste 825, Seattle WA 98101
Tel (206) 441-3045 SIC 8641

YOUNG MENS CHRISTIAN ASSOCIATION OF GREATER SEATTLE p 1638
909 4th Ave, Seattle WA 98104
Tel (206) 382-5342 SIC 8641 8322

YOUNG MENS CHRISTIAN ASSOCIATION OF METROPOLITAN MILWAUKEE INC p 1638
161 W Wisconsin Ave, Milwaukee WI 53203
Tel (414) 291-9622
SIC 8641 7991 8351 7032 8322

SIC 8651 Political Organizations

CONSORTIUM FOR ELECTIONS & POLITICAL PROCESS STRENGTHENING p 360
1225 I St Nw Ste 700, Washington DC 20005
Tel (202) 408-9450 SIC 8651

NATIONAL DEMOCRATIC INSTITUTE FOR INTERNATIONAL AFFAIRS p 1011
455 Mdcchstts Ave Nw Fl 8, Washington DC 20001
Tel (202) 728-5500 SIC 8651

CARTER CENTER INC p 261
453 Freedom Pkwy Ne, Atlanta GA 30307
Tel (404) 420-5100 SIC 8651 8412

TROUTMAN SANDERS LLP POLITICAL ACTION COMMITTEE INC p 1484
600 Peachtree St Ne Ste 5, Atlanta GA 30308
Tel (404) 885-3000 SIC 8651

BUCKS COUNTY INTERMEDIATE UNIT 22 p 223
705 N Shady Retreat Rd, Doylestown PA 18901
Tel (215) 348-2940 SIC 8651

SIC 8661 Religious Organizations

CATHOLIC DIOCESE OF BIRMINGHAM IN ALABAMA p 266
2121 3rd Ave N, Birmingham AL 35203
Tel (205) 838-8307 SIC 8661

ARCHDIOCESE OF MOBILE p 105
400 Government St, Mobile AL 36602
Tel (251) 434-1530 SIC 8661

CATHOLIC ARCHDIOCESE OF MOBILE p 265
356 Government St, Mobile AL 36602
Tel (251) 434-1585 SIC 8661

ROMAN CATHOLIC CHURCH OF DIOCESE OF PHOENIX p 1248
400 E Monroe St, Phoenix AZ 85004
Tel (602) 257-0030 SIC 8661

ROMAN CATHOLIC CHURCH OF DIOCESE OF TUCSON p 1248
64 E Broadway Blvd, Tucson AZ 85701
Tel (520) 792-3410 SIC 8661

DIOCESE OF FRESNO EDUCATION CORP p 440
1550 N Fresno St, Fresno CA 93703
Tel (559) 488-7400 SIC 8211 8661

ROMAN CATHOLIC DIOCESE OF ORANGE p 1249
13280 Chapman Ave, Garden Grove CA 92840
Tel (714) 282-3000 SIC 8661

SALVATION ARMY p 1273
180 E Ocean Blvd Fl 2, Long Beach CA 90802
Tel (562) 491-8464 SIC 8661

CHURCH OF SCIENTOLOGY INTERNATIONAL p 305
6331 Hollywood Blvd # 801, Los Angeles CA 90028
Tel (323) 960-3500 SIC 8661

INTERNATIONAL CHURCH OF FOURSQUARE GOSPEL p 754
1910 W Sunset Blvd # 200, Los Angeles CA 90026
Tel (213) 989-4234
SIC 8661 6512 7032 8211 8221

ROMAN CATHOLIC ARCHBISHOP OF LOS ANGELES p 1248
3424 Wilshire Blvd, Los Angeles CA 90010
Tel (213) 637-7000 SIC 8661

ROMAN CATHOLIC BISHOP MONTEREY p 1248
485 Church St, Monterey CA 93940
Tel (831) 373-4666 SIC 8661

ROMAN CATHOLIC BISHOP OF OAKLAND p 1248
2121 Harrison St Ste 100, Oakland CA 94612
Tel (510) 893-4711 SIC 8661

SISTERS OF ST JOSEPH OF ORANGE p 1327
480 S Batavia St, Orange CA 92868
Tel (714) 633-8121 SIC 8661

NORTHERN CALIFORNIA CONFERENCE OF SEVENTH-DAY ADVENTISTS p 1055
401 Taylor Blvd, Pleasant Hill CA 94523
Tel (925) 685-4300 SIC 8211 8661

SOUTHEASTERN CALIFORNIA CONFERENCE OF SEVENTH-DAY ADVENTISTS p 1346
11330 Pierce St, Riverside CA 92505
Tel (951) 509-2200 SIC 8211 8661

ROMAN CATHOLIC BISHOP OF SACRAMENTO p 1248
2110 Broadway, Sacramento CA 95818
Tel (916) 733-0100 SIC 8661

ROMAN CATHOLIC BISHOP OF SAN BERNARDINO p 1248
1201 E Highland Ave, San Bernardino CA 92404
Tel (909) 475-5300 SIC 8661

ROMAN CATHOLIC BISHOP OF SAN DIEGO p 1248
3888 Paducah Dr, San Diego CA 92117
Tel (858) 490-8200 SIC 8661

ROMAN CATHOLIC BISHOP OF SAN JOSE p 1248
1150 N 1st St Ste 100, San Jose CA 95112
Tel (408) 983-0100 SIC 8661

PACIFIC UNION ASSOCIATION OF SEVENTH-DAY ADVENTISTS p 1106
2686 Townsgate Rd, Thousand Oaks CA 91361
Tel (805) 497-9457 SIC 8661

JOURNEY CHURCH COLORADO p 794
8237 S Holly St Ste C, Centennial CO 80122
Tel (303) 921-5595 SIC 8661

NAVIGATORS p 1020
3820 N 30th St, Colorado Springs CO 80904
Tel (719) 598-1212 SIC 8661 7032 5942

YOUNG LIFE p 1638
420 N Cascade Ave, Colorado Springs CO 80903
Tel (719) 381-1800 SIC 8661 7032

ARCHDIOCESE OF DENVER p 105
1300 S Steele St, Denver CO 80210
Tel (303) 722-4687 SIC 8661

YOUTH FOR CHRIST/USA INC p 1639
7670 S Vaughn Ct Ste 100, Englewood CO 80112
Tel (303) 843-9000 SIC 8661

HARTFORD CATHOLIC DEVELOPMENT CORP p 665
134 Farmington Ave, Hartford CT 06105
Tel (860) 541-6491 SIC 8661

CATHOLIC DIOCESE OF WILMINGTON INC p 266
1925 Delaware Ave, Wilmington DE 19806
Tel (302) 573-3100 SIC 8661

INTERCHURCH MEDICAL ASSISTANCE INC p 752
1730 M St Nw Ste 1100, Washington DC 20036
Tel (202) 888-6200 SIC 8661

UNITED STATES CONFERENCE OF CATHOLIC BISHOPS p 1512
3211 4th St Ne, Washington DC 20017
Tel (202) 541-3000 SIC 8661 4832 4833

CHURCH OF SCIENTOLOGY FLAG SERVICE ORGANIZATION INC p 305
210 S Fort Harrison Ave, Clearwater FL 33756
Tel (727) 461-1282 SIC 8661

DIOCESE OF ST AUGUSTINE INC p 440
11625 Old St Augustine Rd, Jacksonville FL 32258
Tel (904) 824-2806 SIC 8661 6531

ARCHDIOCESE OF MIAMI INC p 105
9401 Biscayne Blvd, Miami Shores FL 33138
Tel (305) 757-6241 SIC 8661

CAMPUS CRUSADE FOR CHRIST INC p 246
100 Lake Hart Dr, Orlando FL 32832
Tel (407) 826-2000 SIC 8661

DIOCESE OF ORLANDO HUMAN CONCERNS FOUNDATION INC p 440
50 E Robinson St, Orlando FL 32801
Tel (407) 246-4800 SIC 8661

WYCLIFFE BIBLE TRANSLATORS INC p 1629
11221 John Wycliffe Blvd, Orlando FL 32832
Tel (407) 852-3600 SIC 8661

CON EL OF DIOCESE OF PALM BEACH INC p 354
9995 N Military Trl, Palm Beach Gardens FL 33410
Tel (561) 775-9500 SIC 8661

DIOCESE OF ST PETERSBURG INC p 441
6363 9th Ave N, Saint Petersburg FL 33710
Tel (727) 345-3338 SIC 8661

NEW TRIBES MISSION INC p 1033
1000 E 1st St, Sanford FL 32771
Tel (407) 323-3430 SIC 8661

FLORIDA CONFERENCE ASSOCIATION OF SEVENTH-DAY ADVENTISTS p 557
655 N Wymore Rd, Winter Park FL 32789
Tel (407) 644-5000
SIC 8661 8211 5942 6513

HABITAT FOR HUMANITY INTERNATIONAL INC p 651
121 Habitat St, Americus GA 31709
Tel (800) 422-4828
SIC 8399 8661 8322 1521 1531

NORTH GEORGIA CONFERENCE OF METHODIST CHURCH INC p 1052
159 Ralph Mcgill Blvd Ne, Atlanta GA 30308
Tel (706) 548-6616 SIC 8661

SALVATION ARMY p 1273
1424 Northeast Expy Ne, Brookhaven GA 30329
Tel (404) 728-1300 SIC 8661 8322

SOUTHERN UNION CONFERENCE ASSOCIATION OF SEVENTH-DAY ADVENTISTS p 1350
302 Research Dr, Norcross GA 30092
Tel (404) 299-1832 SIC 8661

CATHOLIC DIOCESE OF SAVANNAH p 266
2170 E Victory Dr, Savannah GA 31404
Tel (912) 201-4100 SIC 8661 8211

CATHOLIC FOUNDATION OF NORTH GEORGIA INC p 266
2401 Lake Park Dr Se # 100, Smyrna GA 30080
Tel (404) 920-7300 SIC 8661

HONPA HONGWANJI HAWAII BETSUIN p 705
1727 Pali Hwy, Honolulu HI 96813
Tel (808) 536-7044 SIC 8661

ROMAN CATHOLIC CHURCH IN STATE OF HAWAII p 1248
1184 Bishop St, Honolulu HI 96813
Tel (808) 536-7036 SIC 8661

CATHOLIC BISHOP OF CHICAGO p 265
835 N Rush St, Chicago IL 60611
Tel (312) 534-8200 SIC 8661

CATHOLIC CHURCH EXTENSION SOCIETY OF UNITED STATES OF AMERICA p 266
150 S Wacker Dr Ste 2000, Chicago IL 60606
Tel (312) 236-7240 SIC 8661

EVANGELICAL COVENANT CHURCH p 513
8303 W Higgins Rd Fl 1, Chicago IL 60631
Tel (773) 907-3303 SIC 8661

INTERNATIONAL FELLOWSHIP OF CHRISTIANS & JEWS INC p 755
30 N La Salle St Ste 2600, Chicago IL 60602
Tel (312) 641-7200 SIC 8661

MOODY BIBLE INSTITUTE OF CHICAGO p 987
820 N La Salle Dr, Chicago IL 60610
Tel (312) 329-4000
SIC 8661 8299 8221 4832 2731

SISTERS OF THIRD ORDER OF ST FRANCIS p 1327
1175 Saint Francis Ln, East Peoria IL 61611
Tel (309) 699-7215 SIC 8661

CENTRAL TERRITORIAL OF SALVATION ARMY p 280
5550 Prairie Stone Pkwy # 130, Hoffman Estates IL 60192
Tel (847) 294-2000 SIC 8661 8322

ROMAN CATHOLIC DIOCESE OF JOLIET p 1249
425 Summit St, Joliet IL 60435
Tel (815) 722-6606 SIC 8661

FRANCISCAN SISTER OF CHICAGO p 573
11500 Theresa Dr, Lemont IL 60439
Tel (708) 647-6500 SIC 8661 8011

CATHOLIC DIOCESE OF ROCKFORD p 266
555 Colman Center Dr, Rockford IL 61108
Tel (815) 399-4300
SIC 8661 8322 8361 8211 6553

DIOCESE OF FORT WAYNE-SOUTH BEND INVESTMENT TRUST INC p 440
915 S Clinton St, Fort Wayne IN 46802
Tel (260) 422-4611 SIC 8661

INDIANA ANNUAL UNITED METHODIST CHURCH p 738
301 Pennsylvania Pkwy, Indianapolis IN 46280
Tel (317) 924-1321 SIC 8661

ROMAN CATHOLIC ARCHDIOCESE OF INDIANAPOLIS INC p 1248
1400 N Meridian St, Indianapolis IN 46202
Tel (317) 236-1400 SIC 8661 8211

DIOCESE OF SIOUX CITY p 440
1821 Jackson St, Sioux City IA 51105
Tel (712) 255-7933 SIC 8661

ARCHDIOCESE OF KANSAS CITY IN KANSAS p 105
12615 Parallel Pkwy, Kansas City KS 66109
Tel (913) 721-1570
SIC 8661 8211 8222 2711

SISTERS OF CHARITY OF LEAVENWORTH p 1327
4200 S 4th St Traffic Way, Leavenworth KS 66048
Tel (913) 682-5151 SIC 8661

CATHOLIC DIOCESE OF WICHITA INC p 266
424 N Broadway Ave, Wichita KS 67202
Tel (316) 269-3900 SIC 8661 8051

■ **UNION UNDERWEAR CO INC** p 1505
1 Fruit Of The Loom Dr, Bowling Green KY 42103
Tel (270) 781-6400 SIC 8661

DIOCESE OF COVINGTON p 440
1125 Madison Ave, Covington KY 41011
Tel (859) 392-1500 SIC 8211 8661

PRESBYTERIAN CHURCH (USA) A CORP p 1171
100 Witherspoon St, Louisville KY 40202
Tel (800) 728-7228 SIC 8661

ROMAN CATHOLIC BISHOP OF LOUISVILLE p 1248
212 E College St, Louisville KY 40203
Tel (502) 585-3291 SIC 8661

ROMAN CATHOLIC CHURCH OF DIOCESE OF BATON ROUGE p 1248
1800 S Acadian Thruway, Baton Rouge LA 70808
Tel (225) 387-0561 SIC 8661

DIOCESE OF LAFAYETTE p 440
1408 Carmel Dr, Lafayette LA 70501
Tel (337) 261-5652 SIC 8661

ARCHDIOCESE OF NEW ORLEANS INC p 105
7887 Walmsley Ave, New Orleans LA 70125
Tel (504) 861-9521 SIC 8211 8661

ROMAN CATHOLIC CHURCH OF DIOCESE OF HOUMA THIBODAUX p 1248
2779 Highway 311, Schriever LA 70395
Tel (985) 868-7720 SIC 8661

ROMAN CATHOLIC BISHOP OF PORTLAND p 1248
510 Ocean Ave, Portland ME 04103
Tel (207) 773-6471 SIC 8052 8661

CENTRAL SERVICES OF ROMAN CATHOLIC ARCHBISHOP OF BALTIMORE (INC) p 280
320 Cathedral St, Baltimore MD 21201
Tel (410) 547-5555 SIC 8661

GENERAL CONFERENCE OF SEVENTH-DAY ADVENTISTS p 599
12501 Old Columbia Pike, Silver Spring MD 20904
Tel (301) 680-6000 SIC 8661

ROMAN CATHOLIC ARCHBISHOP OF BOSTON p 1248
66 Brooks Dr, Braintree MA 02184
Tel (617) 254-0100 SIC 8661

ROMAN CATHOLIC DIOCESE OF FALL RIVER OFFICE OF AIDS MINISTR p 1248
47 Underwood St, Fall River MA 02720
Tel (508) 235-1184 SIC 8661 8211

ROMAN CATHOLIC BISHOP OF SPRINGFIELD p 1248
65 Elliot St, Springfield MA 01105
Tel (413) 732-3175 SIC 8661

ROMAN CATHOLIC BISHOP OF WORCESTER p 1248
49 Elm St, Worcester MA 01609
Tel (508) 791-7171 SIC 8661

ROMAN CATHOLIC ARCHDIOCESE OF DETROIT p 1248
12 State St, Detroit MI 48226
Tel (313) 237-5800 SIC 8661

CALVIN COLLEGE p 243
3201 Burton St Se, Grand Rapids MI 49546
Tel (616) 526-6000 SIC 8661

ROMAN CATHOLIC DIOCESE OF GRAND RAPIDS p 1248
360 Division Ave S, Grand Rapids MI 49503
Tel (616) 243-0491 SIC 8661

DIOCESE OF LANSING p 440
228 N Walnut St, Lansing MI 48933
Tel (517) 342-2440 SIC 8661

ACADEMY OF OUR LADY OF LOURDES INC p 13
1001 14th St Nw Ste 100, Rochester MN 55901
Tel (507) 282-7441 SIC 8661

ARCHDIOCESE OF SAINT PAUL AND MINNEAPOLIS p 105
226 Summit Ave, Saint Paul MN 55102
Tel (651) 291-4400 SIC 8661

DIOCESE OF WINONA FOUNDATION p 441
55 W Sanborn St, Winona MN 55987
Tel (507) 454-4643 SIC 8661

JOYCE MEYER MINISTRIES INC p 794
700 Grace Pkwy, Fenton MO 63026
Tel (636) 349-0303 SIC 8661

CATHOLIC DIOCESE OF KANSAS CITY-ST JOSEPH p 266
850 Main St, Kansas City MO 64105
Tel (816) 756-1850
SIC 8661 8211 8351 8361 6553

FELLOWSHIP OF CHRISTIAN ATHLETES p 537
8701 Leeds Rd, Kansas City MO 64129
Tel (816) 921-0909 SIC 8661

FELLOWSHIP OF CHRISTIAN ATHLETES p 537
8701 Leeds Rd, Kansas City MO 64129
Tel (816) 921-0909 SIC 8661

ARCHDIOCESE OF ST LOUIS p 105
20 Archbishop May Dr, Saint Louis MO 63119
Tel (314) 633-2222 *SIC* 8661

DAUGHTERS OF CHARITY PROVINCE OF ST LOUISE p 414
4330 Olive St, Saint Louis MO 63108
Tel (314) 533-4770 *SIC* 8661 5912

LUTHERAN CHURCH - MISSOURI SYNOD p 886
1333 S Kirkwood Rd, Saint Louis MO 63122
Tel (314) 965-9000 *SIC* 8661

ROMAN CATHOLIC BISHOP OF HELENA MONTANA p 1248
515 N Ewing St, Helena MT 59601
Tel (406) 442-5820
SIC 8661 8211 8221 2741

NEW HAMPSHIRE CATHOLIC CHARITIES INC p 1030
215 Myrtle St, Manchester NH 03104
Tel (603) 669-3030
SIC 8322 8059 8331 8661 8361

ROMAN CATHOLIC BISHOP OF MANCHESTER p 1248
153 Ash St, Manchester NH 03104
Tel (603) 669-3100 *SIC* 8661

DIOCESE OF CAMDEN NEW JERSEY p 440
631 Market St, Camden NJ 08102
Tel (856) 756-7900 *SIC* 2711 8661

ROMAN CATHOLIC DIOCESE OF PATERSON (INC) p 1249
777 Valley Rd, Clifton NJ 07013
Tel (973) 777-8818 *SIC* 8211 8661

ROMAN CATHOLIC ARCHDIOCESE OF NEWARK p 1248
171 Clifton Ave, Newark NJ 07104
Tel (973) 497-4000 *SIC* 8661

DIOCESE OF METUCHEN INC p 440
146 Metlars Ln, Piscataway NJ 08854
Tel (732) 562-1990 *SIC* 8661

DIOCESE OF TRENTON p 441
701 Lawrenceville Rd, Trenton NJ 08648
Tel (609) 406-7400 *SIC* 8661

ROMAN CATHOLIC DIOCESE OF ALBANY INC p 1248
40 N Main Ave Ste 4, Albany NY 12203
Tel (518) 453-6600 *SIC* 8661

ROMAN CATHOLIC DIOCESE OF BROOKLYN p 1248
310 Prospect Park W, Brooklyn NY 11215
Tel (718) 399-5900 *SIC* 8661

SISTERS OF CHARITY HOSPITAL OF BUFFALO p 1327
144 Genesee St, Buffalo NY 14203
Tel (716) 828-3723 *SIC* 8661

ARCHDIOCESE OF NEW YORK p 105
1011 1st Ave, New York NY 10022
Tel (212) 371-1000 *SIC* 8661

PEACE OF CHRIST ROMAN CATHOLIC PARISH p 1125
25 Empire Blvd, Rochester NY 14609
Tel (585) 288-5000 *SIC* 8661

CATHOLIC CHARITIES OF ROMAN CATHOLIC DIOCESE OF SYRACUSE NY p 266
240 E Onondaga St, Syracuse NY 13202
Tel (315) 470-1450 *SIC* 8661

SALVATION ARMY p 1273
440 W Nyack Rd Ofc, West Nyack NY 10994
Tel (845) 620-7200 *SIC* 8661

BILLY GRAHAM EVANGELISTIC ASSN p 182
1 Billy Graham Pkwy, Charlotte NC 28201
Tel (704) 401-2432 *SIC* 8661

ROMAN CATHOLIC DIOCESE OF CHARLOTTE p 1248
1123 S Church St, Charlotte NC 28203
Tel (704) 370-6299 *SIC* 8661

CHRISTIAN HEALTHCARE MINISTRIES INC p 302
127 Hazelwood Ave, Barberton OH 44203
Tel (800) 791-6225 *SIC* 8661

CHRISTIAN AID MINISTRIES p 302
4464 State Rte 39 E, Berlin OH 44610
Tel (330) 893-2428 *SIC* 8661 5999 5947

ARCHDIOCESE OF CINCINNATI p 105
100 E 8th St Fl 8, Cincinnati OH 45202
Tel (513) 421-3131 *SIC* 8661 8211

CATHOLIC DIOCESE OF CLEVELAND p 266
1404 E 9th St Ste 201, Cleveland OH 44114
Tel (216) 696-6525 *SIC* 8661

SISTERS OF CHARITY OF ST AUGUSTINE HEALTH SYSTEM INC p 1327
2475 E 22nd St, Cleveland OH 44115
Tel (216) 696-5560 *SIC* 8661 8733

DIOCESE OF STEUBENVILLE CATHOLIC CHARITIES p 441
422 Washington St Ste 1, Steubenville OH 43952
Tel (740) 282-3631 *SIC* 8661

DIOCESE OF TOLEDO p 441
1933 Spielbusch Ave, Toledo OH 43604
Tel (419) 244-6711 *SIC* 8661

ROMAN CATHOLIC DIOCESE OF YOUNGSTOWN p 1249
144 W Wood St, Youngstown OH 44503
Tel (330) 744-8451 *SIC* 8661

INTERNATIONAL PENTECOSTAL HOLINESS CHURCH p 756
7300 Nw 39th Expy, Bethany OK 73008
Tel (405) 787-7110 *SIC* 8661

LIFE COVENANT CHURCH INC p 863
4600 E 2nd St, Edmond OK 73034
Tel (405) 680-5433 *SIC* 8661

FEED CHILDREN INC p 537
333 N Meridian Ave, Oklahoma City OK 73107
Tel (800) 627-4556 *SIC* 8661 8699 4832

ROMAN CATHOLIC ARCHBISHOP OF PORTLAND IN OREGON AND SUCCESSORS A CORP SOLE p 1248
2838 E Burnside St, Portland OR 97214
Tel (503) 234-5334 *SIC* 8661

DIOCESE OF ALLENTOWN p 440
4029 W Tilghman St Ste 3, Allentown PA 18104
Tel (610) 437-0755 *SIC* 8661

CATHOLIC DIOCESE OF ERIE p 266
429 E Grandview Blvd, Erie PA 16504
Tel (814) 824-1111 *SIC* 8661

ROMAN CATHOLIC DIOCESE OF GREENSBURG p 1248
723 E Pittsburgh St, Greensburg PA 15601
Tel (724) 837-0901 *SIC* 8661

ROMAN CATHOLIC DIOCESE OF HARRISBURG p 1249
4800 Union Deposit Rd, Harrisburg PA 17111
Tel (717) 657-4804 *SIC* 8661 8211

CLEMENS FAMILY CORP p 325
2700 Clemens Rd, Hatfield PA 19440
Tel (800) 523-5291
SIC 0213 2011 4222 8661

DIOCESE OF ALTOONA-JOHNSTOWN p 440
927 S Logan Blvd, Hollidaysburg PA 16648
Tel (814) 695-5579 *SIC* 8661

SISTERS SERVANTS OF IMMACULATE HEART OF MARY INC p 1327
1140 King Rd, Immaculata PA 19345
Tel (610) 647-2160 *SIC* 8661

SISTERS OF MERCY OF AMERICAS MID-ATLANTIC COMMUNITY INC p 1327
515 Montgomery Ave, Merion Station PA 19066
Tel (610) 664-6650 *SIC* 8661

SOCIETY OF CATHOLIC MEDICAL MISSIONARIES INC p 1336
8400 Pine Rd Ste A, Philadelphia PA 19111
Tel (215) 742-6100 *SIC* 8661

TEMPLE PHYSICIANS INC p 1436
3509 N Broad St, Philadelphia PA 19140
Tel (215) 926-9050 *SIC* 8661

DIOCESE OF PITTSBURGH p 440
111 Blvd Of The Allies, Pittsburgh PA 15222
Tel (412) 456-3000 *SIC* 8661

CATHOLIC SOCIAL SERVICES OF DIOCESE OF SCRANTON INC p 267
516 Fig St, Scranton PA 18505
Tel (570) 207-2283
SIC 8661 2711 8211 8322 6553

IGLESIA EPISCOPAL PUERTORRIQUENA INC p 730
Carr 848 Km 1 1 Bo Sait J St Ca, Trujillo Alto PR 00978
Tel (787) 761-9800 *SIC* 8661

ROMAN CATHOLIC BISHOP OF PROVIDENCE (INC) p 1248
1 Cathedral Sq, Providence RI 02903
Tel (401) 278-4616 *SIC* 8661

CHRISTIAN BLIND MISSION INTERNATIONAL INC p 302
228 Adley Way, Greenville SC 29607
Tel (864) 239-0065 *SIC* 8661

CHURCH OF GOD p 305
2490 Keith St Nw, Cleveland TN 37311
Tel (423) 472-3361 *SIC* 8661

LEE UNIVERSITY p 852
1120 N Ocoee St Ste 102, Cleveland TN 37311
Tel (423) 614-8000 *SIC* 8221 8661

CATHOLIC DIOCESE OF MEMPHIS p 266
5825 Shelby Oaks Dr, Memphis TN 38134
Tel (901) 373-1200 *SIC* 8661

HOPE CHRISTIAN COMMUNITY FOUNDATION p 706
4515 Poplar Ave Ste 324, Memphis TN 38117
Tel (901) 682-6201 *SIC* 8661

GIDEONS INTERNATIONAL p 611
50 Century Blvd, Nashville TN 37214
Tel (615) 564-5000 *SIC* 8661 5942

MARKETPLACE MINISTRIES INC p 908
2001 W Plano Pkwy, Dallas TX 75201
Tel (972) 941-4400 *SIC* 8661

ROMAN CATHOLIC DIOCESE OF DALLAS p 1248
3725 Blackburn St, Dallas TX 75219
Tel (214) 528-2240 *SIC* 8661

CATHOLIC DIOCESE OF FORT WORTH p 266
800 W Loop 820 S, Fort Worth TX 76108
Tel (817) 560-3300 *SIC* 8661

DIOCESE OF GALVESTON-HOUSTON EDUCATION FOUNDATION p 440
1700 San Jacinto St, Houston TX 77002
Tel (713) 652-8248 *SIC* 8661

HOUSTON BAPTIST UNIVERSITY p 712
7502 Fondren Rd, Houston TX 77074
Tel (281) 649-3000 *SIC* 8221 8661

METHODIST WEST HOUSTON HOSPITAL p 954
18500 Katy Fwy, Houston TX 77094
Tel (832) 522-1000 *SIC* 8661 8062

SECOND BAPTIST CHURCH p 1298
6400 Woodway Dr, Houston TX 77057
Tel (713) 465-3408 *SIC* 8661

JOSH MCDOWELL MINISTRY p 794
2001 W Plano Pkwy # 2400, Plano TX 75075
Tel (972) 907-1000 *SIC* 8661

ARCHDIOCESE OF SAN ANTONIO p 105
2718 W Woodlawn Ave, San Antonio TX 78228
Tel (210) 433-0411 *SIC* 8661

GATEWAY CHURCH p 593
500 S Nolen Dr Ste 300, Southlake TX 76092
Tel (817) 328-1000 *SIC* 8661

CORP OF PRESIDENT OF CHURCH OF JESUS CHRIST OF LATTER-DAY SAINTS p 371
50 W North Temple, Salt Lake City UT 84150
Tel (801) 240-1000 *SIC* 8661 8221

CORP OF PRESIDING BISHOP OF CHURCH OF JESUS CHRIST OF LATTER-DAY SAINTS p 371
50 E North Temple, Salt Lake City UT 84150
Tel (801) 240-1000 *SIC* 8661

SALVATION ARMY NATIONAL CORP p 1273
615 Slaters Ln, Alexandria VA 22314
Tel (703) 684-5500 *SIC* 8661 8699

CATHOLIC DIOCESE OF ARLINGTON p 266
200 N Glebe Rd Ste 901, Arlington VA 22203
Tel (703) 841-2500 *SIC* 8661

INTERNATIONAL MISSION BOARD OF SOUTHERN BAPTIST CONVENTION p 756
3806 Monument Ave, Richmond VA 23230
Tel (804) 353-0151 *SIC* 8661 2731 7812

ROMAN CATHOLIC DIOCESE OF RICHMOND p 1249
7800 Carousel Ln, Richmond VA 23294
Tel (804) 359-5661 *SIC* 8661

CHRISTIAN BROADCASTING NETWORK INC p 302
977 Centerville Tpke, Virginia Beach VA 23463
Tel (757) 226-3030
SIC 8661 4833 4832 5999 4724

CORP OF CATHOLIC ARCHBISHOP OF SEATTLE p 371
910 Marion St, Seattle WA 98104
Tel (206) 382-4884 *SIC* 8661

SEATTLE PACIFIC UNIVERSITY INC p 1298
3307 3rd Ave W, Seattle WA 98119
Tel (206) 281-2000 *SIC* 8221 8661

INTERVARSITY CHRISTIAN FELLOWSHIP/USA p 759
635 Science Dr, Madison WI 53711
Tel (608) 274-9001 *SIC* 8661 2731 7032

ROMAN CATHOLIC DIOCESE OF MADISON INC p 1249
702 S High Point Rd, Madison WI 53719
Tel (608) 821-3000 *SIC* 8661

SIC 8699 Membership Organizations, NEC

JEFFERSON COUNTY SCHOOLS PUBLIC EDUCATION FOUNDATION p 781
2100 Rich Arrington Jr Bl, Birmingham AL 35203
Tel (205) 379-2216 *SIC* 8699

SOUTHEASTERN CONFERENCE p 1346
2201 Richard Arringtn Jr, Birmingham AL 35203
Tel (205) 949-8960 *SIC* 8699

TANANA CHIEFS CONFERENCE p 1424
122 1st Ave Ste 600, Fairbanks AK 99701
Tel (907) 452-8251 *SIC* 8699

VALLEY OF SUN UNITED WAY p 1541
3200 E Camelback Rd # 375, Phoenix AZ 85018
Tel (602) 631-4800 *SIC* 8699

UNIVERSITY OF ARIZONA FOUNDATION p 1520
1111 N Cherry Ave, Tucson AZ 85721
Tel (520) 621-5494 *SIC* 8699

WALTON FAMILY FOUNDATION INC p 1575
125 W Central Ave Rm 218, Bentonville AR 72712
Tel (479) 273-5605 *SIC* 8699

ARKANSAS CHILDRENS HOSPITAL FOUNDATION INC p 109
1 Childrens Way, Little Rock AR 72202
Tel (501) 320-1100 *SIC* 8699

CEDARS-SINAI MEDICAL CARE FOUNDATION p 272
200 N Robertson Blvd # 101, Beverly Hills CA 90211
Tel (310) 385-3200 *SIC* 8699

CHG FOUNDATION p 296
740 Bay Blvd, Chula Vista CA 91910
Tel (619) 422-0422 *SIC* 8699

AAA NORTHERN CALIFORNIA NEVADA AND UTAH p 7
1900 Powell St Ste 1200, Emeryville CA 94608
Tel (510) 596-3669 *SIC* 6331 8699

AMERICAN AUTOMOBILE ASSOCIATION OF NORTHERN CALIFORNIA NEVADA & UTAH p 68
1900 Powell St Ste 1200, Emeryville CA 94608
Tel (800) 922-8228 *SIC* 8699

UNITED AGRICULTURAL ASSOCIATION EMP WELFARE BENE PLTR p 1506
54 Corporate Park, Irvine CA 92606
Tel (949) 975-1424 *SIC* 8699

PRICE FAMILY CHARITABLE FUND p 1174
7979 Ivanhoe Ave Ste 520, La Jolla CA 92037
Tel (858) 551-2327 *SIC* 8699

U C SAN DIEGO FOUNDATION p 1497
9500 Gilman Dr, La Jolla CA 92093
Tel (858) 534-1032 *SIC* 8699

DAVID AND LUCILE PACKARD FOUNDATION p 415
300 2nd St, Los Altos CA 94022
Tel (650) 917-7167 *SIC* 8699

AUTOMOBILE CLUB OF SOUTHERN CALIFORNIA p 134
2601 S Figueroa St, Los Angeles CA 90007
Tel (213) 741-3686 *SIC* 6411 8699

JEWISH COMMUNITY FOUNDATION p 784
6505 Wilshire Blvd # 1200, Los Angeles CA 90048
Tel (323) 761-8700 *SIC* 8699

MIKE KELLY FOUNDATION FOR ARTS p 968
7019 N Figueroa St, Los Angeles CA 90042
Tel (323) 257-7853 *SIC* 8699

HEWLETT WILLIAM AND FLORA FOUNDATION (INC) p 688
2121 Sand Hill Rd, Menlo Park CA 94025
Tel (650) 234-4500 *SIC* 8699

AGUA CALIENTE BAND OF CAHUILLA INDIANS p 36
5401 Dinah Shore Dr, Palm Springs CA 92264
Tel (760) 699-6800 *SIC* 8699 6552 7999

CAL POLY POMONA FOUNDATION INC p 237
3801 W Temple Ave Bldg 55, Pomona CA 91768
Tel (909) 869-2950 *SIC* 8699

ASSOCIATED STUDENTS OF SAN DIEGO STATE UNIVERSITY p 121
5500 Campanile Dr, San Diego CA 92182
Tel (619) 594-0234 *SIC* 8699

COMMUNITY FUND OF UNITED JEWISH p 348
4950 Murphy Canyon Rd # 100, San Diego CA 92123
Tel (858) 279-2740 *SIC* 8699 8733

CHRISTENSEN FUND p 302
487 Bryant St, San Francisco CA 94107
Tel (415) 644-0135 *SIC* 8699

ILWU-PMA WELFARE TRUST p 733
1188 Franklin St Ste 101, San Francisco CA 94109
Tel (415) 673-8500 *SIC* 8699

SCHWAB CHARITABLE FUND p 1291
211 Main St, San Francisco CA 94105
Tel (415) 667-9131 *SIC* 8699

UNIVERSITY OF CALIFORNIA SAN FRANCISCO FOUNDATION p 1520
44 Montgomery St Ste 2200, San Francisco CA 94104
Tel (415) 476-6922 *SIC* 8699

RCEB p 1212
500 Davis St Ste 100, San Leandro CA 94577
Tel (510) 432-7123 *SIC* 8699

EMANUEL MEDICAL CENTER AUXILLARY p 490
825 Delbon Ave, Turlock CA 95382
Tel (209) 667-4200 *SIC* 5932 5947 8699

VICTOR ELEMENTARY SCHOOL DISTRICT FINANCING CORP p 1555
15579 Eighth St, Victorville CA 92395
Tel (760) 245-1691 *SIC* 8699 7389

CATHOLIC HEALTH INITIATIVES COLORADO p 266
2222 N Nevada Ave, Colorado Springs CO 80907
Tel (719) 776-5911 *SIC* 8699

UNITED STATES OLYMPIC COMMITTEE INC p 1513
1 Olympic Plz, Colorado Springs CO 80903
Tel (719) 632-5551 *SIC* 8699

AFFINION GROUP LLC p 32
6 High Ridge Park Bldg A, Stamford CT 06905
Tel (203) 956-1000
SIC 8699 8748 7319 7331

DALIO FOUNDATION INC p 409
1 Glendinning Pl, Westport CT 06880
Tel (203) 291-5130 *SIC* 8699

AAA CLUB ALLIANCE INC p 7
1 River Pl, Wilmington DE 19801
Tel (302) 299-4700
SIC 8699 6331 6351 6512 4724

AMERICAN CHEMISTRY COUNCIL INC p 70
700 2nd St Ne Fl 8-10, Washington DC 20002
Tel (202) 249-7000
SIC 8611 8748 8621 8699

COMMUNITY FOUNDATION FOR NATIONAL CAPITAL REGION p 348
1201 15th St Nw Ste 420, Washington DC 20005
Tel (202) 263-4799 *SIC* 8699

HUMANE SOCIETY OF UNITED STATES p 718
1255 23rd St Nw Ste 800, Washington DC 20037
Tel (202) 452-1100 *SIC* 8699

PACT INC p 1107
1828 L St Nw Ste 300, Washington DC 20036
Tel (202) 466-5666 *SIC* 8399 8699

LADIES PROFESSIONAL GOLF ASSOCIATION p 837
100 International Golf Dr, Daytona Beach FL 32124
Tel (386) 274-6200 *SIC* 8699

UNIVERSITY ATHLETIC ASSOCIATION INC p 1518
157 Gale Lemerand Dr, Gainesville FL 32611
Tel (352) 375-4683 *SIC* 8699

AMERICAN AUTOMOBILE ASSOCIATION INC p 68
1000 Aaa Dr Ms28, Heathrow FL 32746
Tel (407) 444-7000 *SIC* 8699

SECOND HARVEST FOOD BANK OF CENTRAL FLORIDA INC p 1298
411 Mercy Dr, Orlando FL 32805
Tel (407) 295-1066 *SIC* 8699

ASSOCIATED GROCERS OF FLORIDA INC p 120
1141 Sw 12th Ave, Pompano Beach FL 33069
Tel (954) 876-3000 *SIC* 8699

▲ **ILG** p 731
6262 Sunset Dr, South Miami FL 33143
Tel (305) 666-1861 *SIC* 8699

■ **INTERVAL HOLDING CO INC** p 759
6262 Sunset Dr Fl 6, South Miami FL 33143
Tel (305) 666-1861 *SIC* 8699 8721 6531

■ **INTERVAL INTERNATIONAL INC** p 759
6262 Sunset Dr Ste 400, South Miami FL 33143
Tel (305) 666-1861 *SIC* 8699

AAA AUTO CLUB SOUTH INC p 7
1515 N West Shore Blvd, Tampa FL 33607
Tel (813) 289-5000
SIC 4724 6331 8699 6311

UNIVERSITY OF SOUTH FLORIDA FOUNDATION INC p 1525
3802 Spectrum Blvd # 100, Tampa FL 33612
Tel (813) 974-5095 *SIC* 8699

NATIONAL CHRISTIAN CHARITABLE p 1010
11625 Rainwater Dr # 500, Alpharetta GA 30009
Tel (404) 252-0100 *SIC* 8699

UNIVERSITY OF GEORGIA ATHLETIC ASSOCIATION INC p 1521
1 Selig Cir B, Athens GA 30602
Tel (706) 542-1306 *SIC* 8699

UNIVERSITY OF GEORGIA FOUNDATION p 1521
394 S Milledge Ave # 100, Athens GA 30605
Tel (706) 542-6677 *SIC* 8699

GEORGIA FARM BUREAU FEDERATION INC p 607
1620 Bass Rd, Macon GA 31210
Tel (478) 474-8411
SIC 6111 5154 8699 5191

HAWAIIAN NATIVE CORP p 669
900 Fort Street Mall # 1850, Honolulu HI 96813
Tel (808) 536-5500 *SIC* 8699

AMOCO OIL HOLDING CO p 86
200 E Randolph St, Chicago IL 60601
Tel (312) 856-4650 *SIC* 8699 4953

ROBERT R MCCORMICK FOUNDATION p 1241
205 N Michigan Ave # 4300, Chicago IL 60601
Tel (312) 445-5000 *SIC* 8641 8699

UNITED STATES SOCCER FEDERATION INC p 1514
1801 S Prairie Ave, Chicago IL 60616
Tel (312) 808-1300 *SIC* 8699

YOUNG MENS CHRISTIAN ASSOCIATION OF CHICAGO p 1638
1030 W Van Buren St, Chicago IL 60607
Tel (312) 932-1200
SIC 8641 7011 8351 8699 8322 7999

CHARLES AND MARGERY BARANCIK FOUNDATION p 289
520 Lake Cook Rd, Deerfield IL 60015
Tel (847) 948-9340 SIC 8699

BIG TEN CONFERENCE INC p 182
5440 Park Pl, Des Plaines IL 60018
Tel (847) 696-1010 SIC 8699

TOPCO HOLDINGS INC (COOPERATIVE) p 1461
150 Northwest Point Blvd, Elk Grove Village IL 60007
Tel (847) 676-3030 SIC 5141 8699

ROTARY FOUNDATION OF ROTARY INTERNATIONAL p 1252
1560 Sherman Ave Ste 1111, Evanston IL 60201
Tel (847) 866-3000 SIC 8699

UNIVERSITY OF ILLINOIS FOUNDATION p 1521
1305 W Green St, Urbana IL 61801
Tel (217) 333-0810 SIC 8699

CULVER EDUCATIONAL FOUNDATION p 400
1300 Academy Rd, Culver IN 46511
Tel (574) 842-8222 SIC 8699

LILY CARES FOUNDATION INC p 866
Lilly Corporate Center, Indianapolis IN 46285
Tel (317) 277-9109 SIC 8699

NATIONAL COLLEGIATE ATHLETIC ASSOCIATION p 1011
700 W Washington St, Indianapolis IN 46204
Tel (317) 917-6222 SIC 8699

RENAISSANCE CHARITABLE FOUNDATION INC p 1223
8910 Purdue Rd Ste 550, Indianapolis IN 46268
Tel (317) 843-5400 SIC 8699

IOWA FARM BUREAU FEDERATION p 762
5400 University Ave, West Des Moines IA 50266
Tel (515) 225-5400
SIC 8699 5154 6311 6321 6411

KANSAS ATHLETICS INC p 802
1651 Naismith Dr, Lawrence KS 66045
Tel (785) 864-7050 SIC 8699

WEINBERG HARRY & JEANETTE FOUNDATION INC p 1588
7 Park Center Ct, Owings Mills MD 21117
Tel (410) 654-8500 SIC 8699

NEW BALANCE ATHLETICS INC p 1029
100 Guest St Fl 5, Boston MA 02135
Tel (617) 783-4000 SIC 8699

AGERO - CHECK p 34
1 Cabot Rd, Medford MA 02155
Tel (781) 393-9300 SIC 8699

AGERO INC p 34
1 Cabot Rd Ste 4, Medford MA 02155
Tel (781) 393-9300 SIC 8699

AUTO CLUB GROUP p 133
1 Auto Club Dr, Dearborn MI 48126
Tel (313) 336-1234 SIC 8699

HENRY FORD HEALTH SYSTEM p 684
1 Ford Pl 5f, Detroit MI 48202
Tel (313) 876-1031 SIC 8699

WEGE FOUNDATION p 1587
99 Monroe Ave Nw Ste 902, Grand Rapids MI 49503
Tel (616) 957-0480 SIC 8699

COMMUNITY FOUNDATION OF WYANDOTTE COUNTY p 348
1055 Broadway Blvd # 150, Kansas City MO 64105
Tel (816) 842-0944 SIC 8699

EWING MARION KAUFFMAN FOUNDATION p 516
4801 Rockhill Rd, Kansas City MO 64110
Tel (816) 932-1000 SIC 8699

FRANCIS HOWELL SCHOOL DISTRICT EDUCATIONAL FACILITIES AUTHORITY p 573
4545 Central School Rd, Saint Charles MO 63304
Tel (636) 851-4000 SIC 8699

AUTOMOBILE CLUB OF MISSOURI p 134
12901 N 40 Dr, Saint Louis MO 63141
Tel (314) 523-7350 SIC 8699 4724

CATHOLIC CHARITIES OF ST LOUIS p 266
4445 Lindell Blvd, Saint Louis MO 63108
Tel (314) 367-5500 SIC 8699 8322

UNITED STATES GOLF ASSOCIATION p 1513
77 Liberty Corner Rd, Far Hills NJ 07931
Tel (908) 234-2300 SIC 8699

MERCK PATIENT ASSISTANCE PROGRAM INC p 945
2 Clerico Ln Apt 201, Hillsborough NJ 08844
Tel (908) 423-1000 SIC 8699

JOHNSON & JOHNSON PATIENT ASSISTANCE FOUNDATION INC p 790
1 Johnson And Johnson Plz, New Brunswick NJ 08933
Tel (732) 524-1394 SIC 8699

H & GL FUNDS OF NJ p 649
700 Raymond Blvd, Newark NJ 07105
Tel (973) 589-5056 SIC 8699

MATAN B SETER FOUNDATION INC p 919
65 Livingston Ave, Roseland NJ 07068
Tel (973) 597-2510 SIC 8699

LOS ALAMOS NATIONAL LABORATORY FOUNDATION p 878
1112 Plaza Del Norte, Espanola NM 87532
Tel (505) 753-8890 SIC 8699

HSCB FOUNDATION INC p 715
450 Clarkson Ave, Brooklyn NY 11203
Tel (718) 270-3041 SIC 8699

ROBERT W WILSON CHARITABLE TRUST p 1241
520 83rd St, Brooklyn NY 11209
Tel (718) 748-6113 SIC 8699

AMERICAN CIVIL LIBERTIES UNION FOUNDATION INC p 70
125 Broad St Fl 18, New York NY 10004
Tel (212) 549-2500 SIC 8699

AMERICAN JEWISH JOINT DISTRIBUTION COMMITTEE INC p 75
711 3rd Ave Rm 901, New York NY 10017
Tel (212) 687-6200 SIC 8699

AMERICAN SOCIETY FOR PREVENTION OF CRUELTY TO ANIMALS (INC) p 79
424 E 92nd St, New York NY 10128
Tel (212) 876-7700 SIC 8699

BLOOMBERG FAMILY FOUNDATION INC p 189
909 3rd Ave, New York NY 10022
Tel (212) 205-0100 SIC 8699

CONFERENCE ON JEWISH MATERIAL CLAIMS AGAINST GERMANY INC p 356
1359 Broadway Rm 2000, New York NY 10018
Tel (646) 536-9100 SIC 8699

DISTRICT COUNCIL 37 HEALTH & SECURITY PLAN TRUST p 443
125 Barclay St, New York NY 10007
Tel (212) 815-1305 SIC 8699

HKI SUPPORT INC p 697
352 Park Ave S, New York NY 10010
Tel (212) 532-0544 SIC 8699

J P MORGAN CHASE FOUNDATION p 772
270 Park Ave Fl 6, New York NY 10017
Tel (212) 270-6000 SIC 8699

MAJOR LEAGUE BASEBALL ENTERPRISES INC p 899
245 Park Ave, New York NY 10167
Tel (212) 931-7500 SIC 4833 8699

PROJECT ORBIS INTERNATIONAL INC p 1182
520 8th Ave Rm 1101, New York NY 10018
Tel (646) 674-5500 SIC 8699

ROBERTSON FOUNDATION p 1242
101 Park Ave Fl 48, New York NY 10178
Tel (212) 984-5714 SIC 8699

ROBIN HOOD FOUNDATION p 1242
826 Broadway Fl 9, New York NY 10003
Tel (212) 227-6601 SIC 8699 8322

ROCKEFELLER FOUNDATION p 1244
420 5th Ave Fl 22, New York NY 10018
Tel (212) 869-8500 SIC 8699

SHUBERT FOUNDATION INC p 1319
234 W 44th St Fl 6, New York NY 10036
Tel (212) 944-3777 SIC 8699 6512

SMILE TRAIN INC p 1333
41 Madison Ave Ste 2801, New York NY 10010
Tel (212) 689-9199 SIC 8699

SUS - MENTAL HEALTH PROGRAMS INC p 1409
305 7th Ave Fl 7, New York NY 10001
Tel (212) 633-6900 SIC 8699

UNITED NATIONS MINE ACTION SERVICE p 1510
1 United Nations Plz Fl 6, New York NY 10017
Tel (212) 963-3768 SIC 8699

VNS CHOICE COMMUNITY CARE p 1563
5 Penn Plz Fl 12, New York NY 10001
Tel (212) 609-5716 SIC 8699

GENESEE REGION HOME CARE ASSOCIATION INC p 602
165 Court St, Rochester NY 14647
Tel (585) 238-4399 SIC 8699

LEUKEMIA & LYMPHOMA SOCIETY INC p 858
3 International Dr # 200, Rye Brook NY 10573
Tel (914) 949-5213
SIC 8699 8399 8322 8011 8733 8621

UNITED STATES TENNIS ASSOCIATION INC p 1514
70 W Red Oak Ln Fl 1, White Plains NY 10604
Tel (914) 696-7000 SIC 8699

MURDOCH CENTER FOUNDATION INC p 1001
1600 E C St, Butner NC 27509
Tel (919) 575-1000 SIC 8699

CAROLINA MOTOR CLUB INC p 259
6600 Aaa Dr, Charlotte NC 28212
Tel (704) 377-3600 SIC 8699 4724

JOHN M BELK EDUCATIONL ENDOWMENT p 789
4201 Congress St Ste 470, Charlotte NC 28209
Tel (704) 357-1000 SIC 8699

SECOND HARVEST FOOD BANK OF METROLINA INC p 1298
500 Spratt St Ste B, Charlotte NC 28206
Tel (704) 376-1785 SIC 8699

MOSES CONE-WESLEY LONG COMMUNITY HEALTH FOUNDATION INC p 992
1200 N Elm St, Greensboro NC 27401
Tel (336) 832-9555 SIC 8699

WILLIAM PRINCE HOSPITAL p 1611
2085 Frontis Plaza Blvd, Winston Salem NC 27103
Tel (336) 718-2803 SIC 8699

AAA ALLIED GROUP INC p 7
15 W Central Pkwy, Cincinnati OH 45202
Tel (513) 762-3100 SIC 4724 8699

AMERICAN ENDOWMENT FOUNDATION p 71
1521 Georgetown Rd # 104, Hudson OH 44236
Tel (330) 655-7552 SIC 8699 8733

FEED CHILDREN INC p 537
333 N Meridian Ave, Oklahoma City OK 73107
Tel (800) 627-4556 SIC 8661 8699 4832

KNIGHT FOUNDATION p 824
1 Sw Bowerman Dr, Beaverton OR 97005
Tel (503) 671-3500 SIC 8699

UNIVERSITY OF OREGON FOUNDATION p 1524
1720 E 13th Ave Ste 410, Eugene OR 97403
Tel (541) 302-0300 SIC 8699

ENERGY TRUST OF OREGON INC p 498
421 Sw Oak St Ste 300, Portland OR 97204
Tel (866) 368-7878 SIC 8699

JOHN TEMPLETON FOUNDATION p 789
300 Conshohocken State Rd # 500, Conshohocken PA 19428
Tel (610) 941-2828 SIC 8699

EMPLOYEE BENEFIT TR OF EASTERN PA p 494
6 Danforth Dr, Easton PA 18045
Tel (610) 515-6412 SIC 6351 8699 6321

NHS PENNYLVANIA p 1042
620 Germantown Pike, Lafayette Hill PA 19444
Tel (610) 238-4403 SIC 8699 8299

APPLE LEISURE GROUP p 98
7 Campus Blvd Ste 100, Newtown Square PA 19073
Tel (610) 359-6500 SIC 8699

PROJECT MANAGEMENT INSTITUTE INC p 1182
14 Campus Blvd, Newtown Square PA 19073
Tel (610) 356-4600 SIC 8699

LINCOLN NATIONAL CORP VOLUNTARY EMPLOYEE BENEFICIARY ASSN p 867
150 N Radnor Chester Rd, Radnor PA 19087
Tel (484) 583-1669 SIC 8699

AAA NORTHEAST p 7
110 Royal Little Dr, Providence RI 02904
Tel (401) 868-2000 SIC 8699 6411 4724

UT FOUNDATION INC p 1536
600 Henley St Ste 100, Knoxville TN 37996
Tel (865) 974-1558 SIC 8699

HIGH PLAINS CHRISTIAN MINISTRIES FDN p 690
701 Park Place Ave Fl 2, Amarillo TX 79101
Tel (806) 337-5292 SIC 8699

ODONNELL FOUNDATION p 1074
100 Crescent Ct Ste 1660, Dallas TX 75201
Tel (214) 871-5800 SIC 8699

SUSAN G KOMEN BREAST CANCER FOUNDATION INC p 1409
5005 Lbj Fwy Ste 250, Dallas TX 75244
Tel (972) 855-1600
SIC 8699 8069 8011 8099

LAURA AND JOHN ARNOLD FOUNDATION p 847
2800 Post Oak Blvd # 225, Houston TX 77056
Tel (713) 554-1349 SIC 8699

SALVATION ARMY NATIONAL CORP p 1273
615 Slaters Ln, Alexandria VA 22314
Tel (703) 684-5500 SIC 8661 8699

CHARLES G KOCH CHARITABLE FOUNDATION p 289
1515 N Courthouse Rd # 200, Arlington VA 22201
Tel (703) 875-1600 SIC 8699

KINGSWAY CHARITIES INC p 821
1119 Commonwealth Ave, Bristol VA 24201
Tel (276) 466-3014 SIC 8699

NATIONAL RIFLE ASSOCIATION OF AMERICA p 1016
11250 Waples Mill Rd # 1, Fairfax VA 22030
Tel (703) 267-1000 SIC 8699

PATIENT SERVICES INC p 1120
3104 E Boundary Ct, Midlothian VA 23112
Tel (804) 744-3813 SIC 8699

OPERATION BLESSING INTERNATIONAL RELIEF AND DEVELOPMENT CORP p 1089
977 Centerville Tpke, Virginia Beach VA 23463
Tel (757) 226-3401 SIC 8699

VALLEY HEALTH SYSTEM p 1540
1840 Amherst St, Winchester VA 22601
Tel (540) 536-8000
SIC 8062 8051 5047 8699

AAA WASHINGTON p 8
3605 132nd Ave Se, Bellevue WA 98006
Tel (425) 646-2015 SIC 8699

BILL & MELINDA GATES FOUNDATION p 182
440 5th Ave N, Seattle WA 98109
Tel (206) 709-3100 SIC 8699

PAUL G ALLEN FAMILY FOUNDATION p 1121
505 5th Ave S Ste 900, Seattle WA 98104
Tel (206) 342-2000 SIC 8699

YOUNG MENS CHRISTIAN ASSOCIATION OF PIERCE AND KITSAP COUNTY p 1639
4717 S 19th St Ste 201, Tacoma WA 98405
Tel (253) 534-7800
SIC 8699 7991 7032 8322

UNIVERSITY OF WISCONSIN FOUNDATION p 1527
1848 University Ave, Madison WI 53726
Tel (608) 263-4545 SIC 8699

GREATER MILWAUKEE FOUNDATION INC p 635
101 W Pleasant St Ste 210, Milwaukee WI 53212
Tel (414) 272-5805 SIC 8699 8733

SIC 8711 Engineering Services

■ B E & K ENGINEERING CO (INC) p 141
2000 International Pk Dr, Birmingham AL 35243
Tel (205) 972-6000 SIC 8711

■ B E & K INC p 141
2000 International Pk Dr, Birmingham AL 35243
Tel (205) 972-6000
SIC 1541 8711 1796 1711

■ TECHNICAL STAFFING RESOURCES LLC p 1431
10 Inverness Center Pkwy, Birmingham AL 35242
Tel (205) 437-7100 SIC 8711 7363

■ CAS INC p 262
100 Quality Cir Nw, Huntsville AL 35806
Tel (256) 922-4200 SIC 8711 7371

COLSA CORP p 339
6728 Odyssey Dr Nw, Huntsville AL 35806
Tel (256) 964-5361
SIC 8731 7373 8744 8711

ENGINEERING RESEARCH AND CONSULTING INC p 499
308 Voyager Way Nw # 200, Huntsville AL 35806
Tel (256) 430-3080 SIC 8731 8711

INTUITIVE RESEARCH AND TECHNOLOGY CORP p 760
5030 Bradford Dr Nw # 205, Huntsville AL 35805
Tel (256) 922-9300 SIC 8711 8748

RADIANCE TECHNOLOGIES INC p 1204
350 Wynn Dr Nw, Huntsville AL 35805
Tel (256) 704-3400
SIC 3721 8711 3429 3812

■ SCITECHNOLOGY INC p 1292
13000 Memorial Pkwy Sw, Huntsville AL 35803
Tel (256) 882-4800
SIC 3672 3829 8711 3663

SYSTEM STUDIES & SIMULATION INC p 1418
615 Discovery Dr Nw, Huntsville AL 35806
Tel (256) 539-1700 SIC 3761 7379 8711

TORCH TECHNOLOGIES INC p 1461
4035 Chris Dr Sw Ste C, Huntsville AL 35802
Tel (256) 319-6000 SIC 8711

DAVID VOLKERT & ASSOCIATES INC p 415
3809 Moffett Rd, Mobile AL 36618
Tel (251) 342-1070 SIC 8711

HARGROVE AND ASSOCIATES INC p 661
20 S Royal St, Mobile AL 36602
Tel (251) 476-0605 SIC 8711

VOLKERT INC p 1564
3809 Moffett Rd, Mobile AL 36618
Tel (251) 342-1070 SIC 8711

UDELHOVEN OILFIELD SYSTEMS SERVICES INC p 1499
184 E 53rd Ave, Anchorage AK 99518
Tel (907) 344-1577 SIC 1541 1542 8711

■ AVIATION COMMUNICATION & SURVEILLANCE SYSTEMS LLC p 138
19810 N 7th Ave, Phoenix AZ 85027
Tel (623) 445-7030 SIC 8711

EXODYNE INC p 519
8433 N Black Canyon Hwy # 100, Phoenix AZ 85021
Tel (602) 995-3700
SIC 8711 8731 8741 8744 8748

KARSTEN MANUFACTURING CORP p 804
2201 W Desert Cove Ave, Phoenix AZ 85029
Tel (602) 870-5000
SIC 3949 3398 3363 3325 8711 7997

KITCHELL CORP p 822
1707 E Highland Ave # 100, Phoenix AZ 85016
Tel (602) 264-4411
SIC 1542 1541 1521 8711 5078 6552

PULICE CONSTRUCTION INC p 1191
2033 W Mountain View Rd, Phoenix AZ 85021
Tel (602) 944-2241 SIC 1611 8711

STANTEC TECHNOLOGY INTERNATIONAL INC p 1377
8211 S 48th St, Phoenix AZ 85044
Tel (602) 438-2200 SIC 8711

SWCA INC p 1411
3033 N Central Ave # 145, Phoenix AZ 85012
Tel (602) 274-3831
SIC 8748 8711 8731 8733

TELGIAN CORP p 1435
10230 S 50th Pl, Phoenix AZ 85044
Tel (480) 753-5444
SIC 1711 8711 1731 8748

GENERAL DYNAMICS C4 SYSTEMS INC p 600
8201 E Mcdowell Rd, Scottsdale AZ 85257
Tel (480) 441-3033 SIC 8711

M3 ENGINEERING & TECHNOLOGY CORP p 890
2051 W Sunset Rd Ste 101, Tucson AZ 85704
Tel (520) 293-1488 SIC 8741 8712 8711

GARVER LLC p 592
4701 Northshore Dr, North Little Rock AR 72118
Tel (501) 376-3633 SIC 8711

▲ WILLDAN GROUP INC p 1610
2401 E Katella Ave # 300, Anaheim CA 92806
Tel (800) 424-9144 SIC 8711 8748

ARES CORP p 107
1440 Chapin Ave Ste 390, Burlingame CA 94010
Tel (505) 661-6390 SIC 8711

ARES HOLDING CORP p 107
1440 Chapin Ave Ste 390, Burlingame CA 94010
Tel (650) 401-7100 SIC 8711

ENVIRONMENTAL CHEMICAL CORP p 503
1240 Bayshore Hwy, Burlingame CA 94010
Tel (650) 347-1555 SIC 8711 1542 8744

NATIONAL TECHNICAL SYSTEMS INC p 1016
24007 Ventura Blvd # 200, Calabasas CA 91302
Tel (818) 591-0776 SIC 8711

■ TETRA TECH EMC INC p 1441
100 Camino Ruiz, Camarillo CA 93012
Tel (805) 484-9082 SIC 8711 7371

■ ALPHATEC SPINE INC p 60
5818 El Camino Real, Carlsbad CA 92008
Tel (760) 494-6610 SIC 3842 8711 5047

ONCORE MANUFACTURING LLC p 1086
9340 Owensmouth Ave, Chatsworth CA 91311
Tel (818) 734-6500 SIC 3672 8711

GILBANE FEDERAL p 611
1655 Grant St Fl 12, Concord CA 94520
Tel (925) 946-3100 SIC 8711 8748

AEROSPACE CORP p 30
2310 E El Segundo Blvd, El Segundo CA 90245
Tel (310) 336-5000 SIC 8733 8731 8711

■ WYLE INC p 1629
1960 E Grand Ave Ste 900, El Segundo CA 90245
Tel (310) 563-6800 SIC 8711 7371 8731

■ WYLE SERVICES CORP p 1629
1960 E Grand Ave Ste 900, El Segundo CA 90245
Tel (310) 563-6800 SIC 8711 7371

BAKER ELECTRIC INC p 146
1298 Pacific Oaks Pl, Escondido CA 92029
Tel (760) 745-2001 SIC 1731 8711

BI TECHNOLOGIES CORP p 180
4200 Bonita Pl, Fullerton CA 92835
Tel (714) 447-2300 SIC 3679 5065 8711

■ WALT DISNEY IMAGINEERING RESEARCH & DEVELOPMENT INC p 1574
1401 Flower St, Glendale CA 91201
Tel (818) 544-6500
SIC 7819 8712 1542 8741 8711

■ ABM FACILITY SERVICES LLC p 11
152 Technology Dr, Irvine CA 92618
Tel (949) 330-1555 SIC 8711

■ BRINDERSON LP p 213
19000 Macarthur Blvd # 800, Irvine CA 92612
Tel (714) 466-7100 SIC 8711 1629

GKK CORP p 613
2355 Main St Ste 220, Irvine CA 92614
Tel (949) 250-1500 SIC 8712 8711

■ EARTH TECH (INFRASTRUCTURE) INC p 469
300 Oceangate Ste 700, Long Beach CA 90802
Tel (562) 951-2000 SIC 8711 8712

MOFFATT & NICHOL p 982
3780 Kilroy Arprt Way, Long Beach CA 90806
Tel (562) 590-6500 SIC 8711

STEARNS CONRAD AND SCHMIDT CONSULTING ENGINEERS INC p 1384
3900 Kilroy Arprt Way # 100, Long Beach CA 90806
Tel (562) 426-9544 *SIC* 8711 1541 8748

▲AECOM p 28
1999 Avenue Of The Stars # 2600, Los Angeles CA 90067
Tel (213) 593-8000 *SIC* 8711 8712

■AECOM E&C HOLDINGS INC p 28
1999 Avenue Of Ste 2600, Los Angeles CA 90067
Tel (213) 593-8000
SIC 8711 1611 1629 1623 1541 1622

■AECOM GLOBAL II LLC p 28
1999 Avenue Of The Stars, Los Angeles CA 90067
Tel (213) 593-8100 *SIC* 8711 8712 8741

■AECOM SERVICES INC p 28
555 S Flower St Ste 3700, Los Angeles CA 90071
Tel (213) 593-8000 *SIC* 8712 8741 8711

■AECOM TECHNICAL SERVICES INC p 28
300 S Grand Ave Ste 1100, Los Angeles CA 90071
Tel (213) 593-8000
SIC 4953 8748 8742 8711

■EARTH TECHNOLOGY CORP USA p 469
1999 Avenue Of Ste 2600, Los Angeles CA 90067
Tel (213) 593-8000
SIC 4953 8748 8742 8711

LINQUEST CORP p 869
5140 W Goldleaf Cir # 400, Los Angeles CA 90056
Tel (323) 924-1600 *SIC* 8711

PSOMAS p 1188
555 S Flower St Ste 4300, Los Angeles CA 90071
Tel (310) 954-3700 *SIC* 8713 8711

■URS GROUP INC p 1530
300 S Grand Ave Ste 1100, Los Angeles CA 90071
Tel (213) 593-8000 *SIC* 8711 8712 8741

▲EXPONENT INC p 520
149 Commonwealth Dr, Menlo Park CA 94025
Tel (650) 326-9400 *SIC* 8711 8742 8999

CREATIVE HOLDINGS INC p 390
1901 Mccarthy Blvd, Milpitas CA 95035
Tel (408) 428-6600
SIC 5045 3577 3931 3674 8711 3651

BOYD LTI p 205
600 S Mcclure Rd, Modesto CA 95357
Tel (800) 554-0200 *SIC* 3549 3053 8711

■SCALED COMPOSITES LLC p 1285
1624 Flight Line, Mojave CA 93501
Tel (661) 824-4541 *SIC* 3721 3999 8711

▲AEROVIRONMENT INC p 31
800 Royal Oaks Dr Ste 210, Monrovia CA 91016
Tel (626) 357-9983 *SIC* 3721 8711 3694

NOVA MANAGEMENT INC p 1062
660 Camino Aguajito # 300, Monterey CA 93940
Tel (831) 373-4544 *SIC* 8711 7361

JACOBS ENGINEERING GROUP MEDICAL PLAN TRUST p 775
300 Frank H Ogawa Plz # 10, Oakland CA 94612
Tel (510) 457-0027 *SIC* 8711

■HOLMES & NARVER INC p 701
999 W Town And Country Rd, Orange CA 92868
Tel (714) 567-2400
SIC 8711 8742 8741 1542

ORANGE COUNTY TRANSPORTATION AUTHORITY p 1092
550 S Main St, Orange CA 92868
Tel (714) 636-7433 *SIC* 4111 8711

■JACOBS ENGINEERING CO p 775
1111 S Arroyo Pkwy, Pasadena CA 91105
Tel (626) 449-2171 *SIC* 8711 1629

■JACOBS ENGINEERING INC p 775
155 N Lake Ave, Pasadena CA 91101
Tel (626) 578-3500 *SIC* 8711

■JACOBS INTERNATIONAL LTD INC p 775
155 N Lake Ave, Pasadena CA 91101
Tel (626) 578-3500 *SIC* 8711

PARSONS CONSTRUCTORS INC p 1118
100 W Walnut St, Pasadena CA 91124
Tel (626) 440-2000 *SIC* 8741 8711

PARSONS CORP p 1118
100 W Walnut St, Pasadena CA 91124
Tel (626) 440-2000
SIC 1629 1611 8711 8741

PARSONS ENGINEERING SCIENCE INC p 1118
100 W Walnut St, Pasadena CA 91124
Tel (626) 440-2000 *SIC* 8711

PARSONS GOVERNMENT SERVICES INC p 1118
100 W Walnut St, Pasadena CA 91124
Tel (626) 440-2000 *SIC* 8711

PARSONS WATER & INFRASTRUCTURE INC p 1118
100 W Walnut St, Pasadena CA 91124
Tel (626) 440-7000 *SIC* 8711

▲TETRA TECH INC p 1441
3475 E Foothill Blvd, Pasadena CA 91107
Tel (626) 351-4664 *SIC* 8711

■PERFORMANCE MECHANICAL INC p 1135
701 Willow Pass Rd Ste 2, Pittsburg CA 94565
Tel (925) 432-4080 *SIC* 1541 1711 8711

J T THORPE & SON INC p 772
1060 Hensley St, Richmond CA 94801
Tel (510) 233-2500 *SIC* 1741 8711

TERRA MILLENNIUM CORP p 1439
1060 Hensley St, Richmond CA 94801
Tel (510) 233-2500 *SIC* 1741 8711

HERMAN WEISSKER INC p 687
1645 Brown Ave, Riverside CA 92509
Tel (951) 826-8800 *SIC* 1623 8711 1731

SKANSKA USA CIVIL WEST CALIFORNIA DISTRICT INC p 1329
1995 Agua Mansa Rd, Riverside CA 92509
Tel (951) 684-5360
SIC 1611 1622 1629 8711 2951

AIRCO MECHANICAL INC p 40
8210 Demetre Ave, Sacramento CA 95828
Tel (916) 381-4523 *SIC* 1711 8711

REX MOORE GROUP INC p 1230
6001 Outfall Cir, Sacramento CA 95828
Tel (916) 372-1300 *SIC* 1731 8711

SHAW ENVIRONMENTAL & INFRASTRUCTURE INC p 1312
1326 N Market Blvd, Sacramento CA 95834
Tel (916) 928-3300 *SIC* 8711

EPSILON SYSTEMS SOLUTIONS INC p 506
9242 Lightwave Ave # 100, San Diego CA 92123
Tel (619) 702-1700 *SIC* 8711

KLEINFELDER GROUP INC p 823
550 W C St Ste 1200, San Diego CA 92101
Tel (619) 831-4600 *SIC* 8711

KLEINFELDER INC p 823
550 W C St Ste 1200, San Diego CA 92101
Tel (619) 831-4600 *SIC* 8711 8712

■KRATOS DEFENSE & ROCKET SUPPORT SERVICES INC p 829
4820 Estgate Mall Ste 200, San Diego CA 92121
Tel (858) 812-7300 *SIC* 8711

▲KRATOS DEFENSE & SECURITY SOLUTIONS INC p 829
4820 Estgate Mall Ste 200, San Diego CA 92121
Tel (858) 812-7300
SIC 3761 8711 8744 7382

WEST CONSULTANTS-GANNETT FLEMING JOINT VENTURE p 1594
11440 W Bernardo Ct # 360, San Diego CA 92127
Tel (858) 487-9378 *SIC* 8711

AMERICAN BECHTEL INC p 68
50 Beale St, San Francisco CA 94105
Tel (415) 768-1234 *SIC* 8711

ARUP NORTH AMERICA LIMITED p 114
560 Mission St Fl 7, San Francisco CA 94105
Tel (415) 957-9445 *SIC* 8711

BABCOCK & BROWN RENEWABLE HOLDINGS INC p 143
1 Letterman Dr Ste 216, San Francisco CA 94129
Tel (415) 512-1515 *SIC* 8711

BECHTEL CORP p 167
50 Beale St, San Francisco CA 94105
Tel (415) 768-1234 *SIC* 8711 1629 8742

BECHTEL ENERGY CORP p 167
50 Beale St Bsmt 1, San Francisco CA 94105
Tel (415) 768-1234 *SIC* 8711 8741

BECHTEL GROUP INC p 167
50 Beale St Bsmt 1, San Francisco CA 94105
Tel (415) 768-1234 *SIC* 8711 1629 8742

BECHTEL POWER CORP p 167
50 Beale St Bsmt 2, San Francisco CA 94105
Tel (415) 768-1234 *SIC* 8711 8742 1629

CROWN BUILDING MAINTENANCE CO p 395
868 Folsom St, San Francisco CA 94107
Tel (415) 981-8070 *SIC* 7349 8711

CROWN ENERGY SERVICES INC p 395
868 Folsom St, San Francisco CA 94107
Tel (415) 546-6534 *SIC* 8711

HELLMUTH OBATA & KASSABAUM INC p 682
1 Bush St Ste 200, San Francisco CA 94104
Tel (415) 243-0555
SIC 8712 8711 8742 7389 0781

KENNEDY/JENKS CONSULTANTS INC p 811
303 2nd St Ste 300s, San Francisco CA 94107
Tel (415) 243-2150 *SIC* 8711

T Y LIN INTERNATIONAL p 1420
345 California St Fl 23, San Francisco CA 94104
Tel (415) 291-3700 *SIC* 8711

T Y LIN INTERNATIONAL GROUP p 1496
345 California St Fl 23, San Francisco CA 94104
Tel (415) 291-3700 *SIC* 8711

■URS HOLDINGS INC p 1530
600 Montgomery St Fl 25, San Francisco CA 94111
Tel (415) 774-2700
SIC 8711 7389 6531 8249 4581

▲MONOLITHIC POWER SYSTEMS INC p 984
79 Great Oaks Blvd, San Jose CA 95119
Tel (408) 826-0600 *SIC* 3674 8711

STRUCTURAL INTEGRITY ASSOCIATES INC p 1394
5215 Hellyer Ave Ste 210, San Jose CA 95138
Tel (408) 978-8200 *SIC* 8711

■VERIFONE INC p 1549
88 W Plumeria Dr, San Jose CA 95134
Tel (408) 232-7800
SIC 3578 7372 3577 3575 8711 3643

DUTRA GROUP p 463
2350 Kerner Blvd Ste 200, San Rafael CA 94901
Tel (415) 258-6876 *SIC* 1629 8711 1429

BUTLER AMERICA LLC p 230
3820 State St Ste B, Santa Barbara CA 93105
Tel (203) 926-2700 *SIC* 8711 8748 7361

BUTLER SERVICE GROUP INC p 230
3820 State St Ste A, Santa Barbara CA 93105
Tel (201) 891-5312
SIC 7363 8711 8748 3661 7538

MACAULAY BROWN INC p 891
2933 Bunker Hill Ln # 220, Santa Clara CA 95054
Tel (937) 426-3421 *SIC* 8711

RENESAS ELECTRONICS AMERICA INC p 1223
2801 Scott Blvd, Santa Clara CA 95050
Tel (408) 588-6000
SIC 5065 8731 5731 5045 8711

THERMAL ENGINEERING INTERNATIONAL (USA) INC p 1447
10375 Slusher Dr, Santa Fe Springs CA 90670
Tel (323) 726-0641 *SIC* 3443 8711

DMS FACILITY SERVICES LLC p 446
1040 Arroyo Dr, South Pasadena CA 91030
Tel (626) 305-8500 *SIC* 8711 7349 0781

▲TUTOR PERINI CORP p 1493
15901 Olden St, Sylmar CA 91342
Tel (818) 362-8391
SIC 1542 8741 1611 1791 8711

BROWN AND CALDWELL p 219
201 N Civic Dr Ste 115, Walnut Creek CA 94596
Tel (925) 937-9010 *SIC* 8711

CAROLLO ENGINEERS PC p 259
2700 Ygnacio Valley Rd # 300, Walnut Creek CA 94598
Tel (925) 932-1710 *SIC* 8711

ERM-WEST INC p 508
1277 Treat Blvd Ste 500, Walnut Creek CA 94597
Tel (925) 946-0455 *SIC* 8711 8742

MWH AMERICAS INC p 1004
370 Interlocken Blvd, Broomfield CO 80021
Tel (303) 410-4000 *SIC* 8711

MWH CONSTRUCTORS INC p 1004
370 Interlocken Blvd # 300, Broomfield CO 80021
Tel (303) 439-2800 *SIC* 8711 1629

MWH GLOBAL INC p 1004
370 Interlocken Blvd # 300, Broomfield CO 80021
Tel (303) 533-1900 *SIC* 8711 8741

SEAKR ENGINEERING INC p 1296
6221 S Racine Cir, Centennial CO 80111
Tel (303) 662-1449 *SIC* 3674 8711

CH2M HILL COMPANIES LTD p 286
9191 S Jamaica St, Englewood CO 80112
Tel (303) 771-0900 *SIC* 8711

CH2M HILL CONSTRUCTORS INC p 286
9189 S Jamaica St, Englewood CO 80112
Tel (720) 286-2000 *SIC* 8711

CH2M HILL INC p 286
9191 S Jamaica St, Englewood CO 80112
Tel (303) 771-0900 *SIC* 8711

CLARK-NEXSEN/CH2M HILL p 322
9191 S Jamaica St, Englewood CO 80112
Tel (303) 771-0900 *SIC* 8711

ARCADIS US INC p 103
630 Plaza Dr Ste 200, Highlands Ranch CO 80129
Tel (720) 344-3500 *SIC* 8748 8711 8741

CARDNO INC p 253
10004 Park Meadows Dr # 300, Lone Tree CO 80124
Tel (720) 257-5800
SIC 8711 8748 8742 8741

CARDNO USA INC p 253
10004 Park Meadows Dr # 300, Lone Tree CO 80124
Tel (720) 257-5800 *SIC* 8711 5045 8748

CYIENT INC p 405
330 Roberts St Ste 400, East Hartford CT 06108
Tel (860) 528-5430 *SIC* 8711

■ELECTRIC BOAT CORP p 484
75 Eastern Point Rd, Groton CT 06340
Tel (860) 433-3000 *SIC* 3731 8711

■HARTFORD STEAM BOILER INSPECTION AND INSURANCE CO p 665
1 State St Fl 5-12, Hartford CT 06103
Tel (860) 722-1866
SIC 6331 8711 7373 8742

■HSB GROUP INC p 714
1 State St, Hartford CT 06102
Tel (860) 722-1866
SIC 6331 6411 6799 8711 8742

EMHART TEKNOLOGIES LLC p 492
480 Myrtle St, New Britain CT 06053
Tel (800) 783-6427 *SIC* 8711 3541

ASEA BROWN BOVERI INC p 116
501 Merritt 7, Norwalk CT 06851
Tel (203) 750-2200
SIC 3612 3613 5063 3511 3625 8711

GARDNER DENVER NASH LLC p 592
2 Trefoil Dr, Trumbull CT 06611
Tel (203) 459-3923
SIC 5084 3563 8711 3561

SONALYSTS INC p 1339
215 Parkway N, Waterford CT 06385
Tel (860) 442-4355
SIC 8711 7373 8748 8732 3993

LEGRAND NORTH AMERICA LLC p 853
60 Woodlawn St, West Hartford CT 06110
Tel (860) 233-6251 *SIC* 8711

■ALSTOM POWER INC p 61
200 Great Pond Dr, Windsor CT 06095
Tel (866) 257-8664
SIC 3443 3564 3621 3823 8711

ALSTOM USA INC p 61
2000 Day Hill Rd, Windsor CT 06095
Tel (860) 285-3790 *SIC* 8711

■TRC ENVIRONMENTAL CORP p 1475
21 Griffin Rd N Ste 1, Windsor CT 06095
Tel (860) 289-8631 *SIC* 8748 8711

A JBEK JOINT VENTURE CO p 6
242 Chapman Rd, Newark DE 19702
Tel (302) 452-9000 *SIC* 8711 8741

DUPONT PERFORMANCE COATINGS INC p 462
4417 Lncaster Pike Barley, Wilmington DE 19805
Tel (302) 892-1064 *SIC* 8711

■CARLYLE PARTNERS IV LP p 258
1001 Pennsylvania Ave Nw, Washington DC 20004
Tel (202) 729-5626 *SIC* 8711 8069 8051

FACILITY LEADERS IN ARCHITECTURAL/ENGINEERING DESIGN PC p 523
1201 Conn Ave Nw Fl 10, Washington DC 20036
Tel (608) 238-2661 *SIC* 8712 8711

FUTUREGEN INDUSTRIAL ALLIANCE INC p 586
1101 Penn Ave Nw Fl 6, Washington DC 20004
Tel (202) 756-4520 *SIC* 8711

GRYPHON TECHNOLOGIES LC p 643
80 M St Se Ste 600, Washington DC 20003
Tel (202) 617-2004
SIC 8741 8711 8731 7371

PAGE SOUTHERLAND PAGE INC p 1107
1615 M St Nw Ste 700, Washington DC 20036
Tel (202) 909-4900 *SIC* 8712 8711

PARSONS BRINCKERHOFF INTERNATIONAL INC p 1118
1401 K St Nw Ste 701, Washington DC 20005
Tel (202) 783-0241 *SIC* 8711

PARSONS TRANSPORTATION GROUP INC p 1118
100 M St Se Ste 1200, Washington DC 20003
Tel (202) 775-3300 *SIC* 8711

PARSONS TRANSPORTATION GROUP INC OF VIRGINIA p 1118
1133 15th St Nw Ste 800, Washington DC 20005
Tel (202) 775-3300 *SIC* 8711

ATKINS NORTH AMERICA INC p 125
2001 Nw 107th Ave, Doral FL 33172
Tel (813) 282-7275 *SIC* 8711

CSI INTERNATIONAL INC p 398
6700 N Andrews Ave # 400, Fort Lauderdale FL 33309
Tel (954) 308-4300 *SIC* 8744 8711

▲NV5 GLOBAL INC p 1068
200 S Park Rd Ste 350, Hollywood FL 33021
Tel (954) 495-2112 *SIC* 8711 8748

■NV5 INC p 1068
200 S Park Rd Ste 350, Hollywood FL 33021
Tel (954) 495-2112 *SIC* 8711

RS&H INC p 1255
10748 Deerwood Park Blvd, Jacksonville FL 32256
Tel (904) 256-2500 *SIC* 8711 8712

STELLAR COMPANIES INC p 1385
2900 Hartley Rd, Jacksonville FL 32257
Tel (904) 899-9393 *SIC* 1542 8711 1541

HOLTEC INTERNATIONAL p 702
1001 N Us Highway 1, Jupiter FL 33477
Tel (561) 745-7772 *SIC* 2819 8711

DOWNRITE HOLDINGS INC p 453
14241 Sw 143rd Ct, Miami FL 33186
Tel (305) 232-2340
SIC 1611 1623 8711 1794

KEYSTONE HOLDINGS LLC p 815
10 Nw 42nd Ave Ste 700, Miami FL 33126
Tel (305) 567-1577
SIC 8711 3053 3081 3082 3545

POINT BLANK ENTERPRISES INC p 1159
2102 Sw 2nd St, Pompano Beach FL 33069
Tel (954) 630-0900
SIC 3842 3462 3728 8711

BUREAU VERITAS HOLDINGS INC p 226
1601 Sawgrass Corporate S Ste 400, Sunrise FL 33323
Tel (954) 835-9309
SIC 7389 8748 8711 8742

BUREAU VERITAS NORTH AMERICA INC p 227
1601 Sawgrs Corp Pkwy, Sunrise FL 33323
Tel (954) 236-8100
SIC 7389 8748 8734 8711 8742

ATKINS NORTH AMERICA HOLDINGS CORP p 125
4030 W Boy Scout Blvd, Tampa FL 33607
Tel (813) 282-7275 *SIC* 8712 6519 8711

CAE USA INC p 236
4908 Tampa West Blvd, Tampa FL 33634
Tel (813) 885-7481
SIC 3699 7373 8299 8249 8711

AMEC E&I HOLDINGS INC p 66
1105 Lakewood Pkwy # 300, Alpharetta GA 30009
Tel (770) 360-0600 *SIC* 8744 8711

AMEC E&I INC p 66
1105 Lakewood Pkwy # 300, Alpharetta GA 30009
Tel (770) 360-0600 *SIC* 8711

AMEC FOSTER WHEELER ENVIRONMENT & INFRASTRUCTURE INC p 66
1105 Lakewood Pkwy # 300, Alpharetta GA 30009
Tel (770) 360-0600 *SIC* 8748 8711

■AUTOTOTE SYSTEMS INC p 135
1500 Bluegrass Lakes Pkwy, Alpharetta GA 30004
Tel (770) 664-3700
SIC 3578 7373 7359 8711

TENSAR CORP GEORGIA p 1438
2500 Northwinds Pkwy # 50, Alpharetta GA 30009
Tel (770) 344-2090 *SIC* 3089 8711

TENSAR INTERNATIONAL CORP p 1438
2500 Northwinds Pkwy # 500, Alpharetta GA 30009
Tel (770) 344-2090 *SIC* 8711 3089

BYERS ENGINEERING CO p 231
6285 Barfield Rd Fl 4, Atlanta GA 30328
Tel (404) 843-1000 *SIC* 8711 7371

GOLDER ASSOCIATES INC p 622
3730 Chamblee Tucker Rd, Atlanta GA 30341
Tel (770) 496-1893 *SIC* 8711

HEERY INTERNATIONAL INC p 680
999 Peachtree St Ne # 300, Atlanta GA 30309
Tel (404) 881-9880 *SIC* 8712 8711 8742

MCKENNEYS INC p 930
1056 Moreland Indus Blvd, Atlanta GA 30316
Tel (404) 622-5000 *SIC* 1711 8711

SCIENTIFIC RESEARCH CORP p 1292
2300 Windy Ridge Pkwy Se 400s, Atlanta GA 30339
Tel (770) 859-9161 *SIC* 8732 8711

■SOUTHERN CO SERVICES INC p 1347
30 Ivan Allen Jr Blvd Nw, Atlanta GA 30308
Tel (404) 506-5000 *SIC* 8711

ENERCON SERVICES INC p 497
500 Townpark Ln Nw # 275, Kennesaw GA 30144
Tel (770) 919-1930 *SIC* 8711

APPLIED TECHNICAL SERVICES INC p 100
1049 Triad Ct, Marietta GA 30062
Tel (770) 423-1400 *SIC* 8734 8711 8731

VANDERLANDE INDUSTRIES INC p 1543
1975 W Oak Cir, Marietta GA 30062
Tel (770) 250-2800 *SIC* 8711 3535

OSMOSE UTILITIES SERVICES INC p 1097
635 Highway 74 S, Peachtree City GA 30269
Tel (770) 632-6700 *SIC* 8741 8711 1623

AMEC FOSTER WHEELER E&C SERVICES INC p 66
1979 Lkeside Pkwy Ste 400, Tucker GA 30084
Tel (770) 688-2500 *SIC* 8711

AMEC FOSTER WHEELER VENTURES INC p 66
1979 Lkeside Pkwy Ste 400, Tucker GA 30084
Tel (770) 688-2500 *SIC* 8748 8711

DAEHAN SOLUTION GEORGIA LLC p 408
791 S Progress Pkwy, West Point GA 31833
Tel (706) 902-5200 *SIC* 5013 8711 3714

DAWSON TECHNICAL LLC p 417
900 Fort Street Mall # 1850, Honolulu HI 96813
Tel (808) 536-5500 *SIC* 8711 1542

■WASHINGTON DMILITARIZATION LLC p 1578
720 E Park Blvd, Boise ID 83712
Tel (208) 386-5000 *SIC* 8711

POWER ENGINEERS INC p 1165
3940 Glenbrook Dr, Hailey ID 83333
Tel (208) 788-3456 *SIC* 8711

AMI SEMICONDUCTOR INC p 85
2300 W Buckskin Rd, Pocatello ID 83201
Tel (208) 233-4690 *SIC* 3674 8711

A EPSTEIN AND SONS INTERNATIONAL INC p 5
600 W Fulton St Ste 800, Chicago IL 60661
Tel (312) 454-9100
SIC 8711 8712 7389 1542 1541 8742

ALFRED BENESCH & CO p 49
205 N Michigan Ave # 2400, Chicago IL 60601
Tel (312) 565-2497 *SIC* 8711

EXP US SERVICES INC p 519
205 N Mich Aveste 3600, Chicago IL 60601
Tel (312) 616-0000 *SIC* 8711 8712

GREELEY AND HANSEN LLC p 636
100 S Wacker Dr Ste 1400, Chicago IL 60606
Tel (312) 558-9000 *SIC* 8711

H W LOCHNER INC p 651
225 W Washington St # 1200, Chicago IL 60606
Tel (312) 372-7346 *SIC* 8711 8742

INVENERGY LLC p 760
1 S Wacker Dr Ste 1800, Chicago IL 60606
Tel (312) 224-1400 *SIC* 8711

S & C ELECTRIC CO p 1261
6601 N Ridge Blvd, Chicago IL 60626
Tel (773) 338-1000
SIC 3613 3643 3625 8711

SARGENT & LUNDY LLC p 1282
55 E Monroe St Ste 2700, Chicago IL 60603
Tel (312) 269-2000 *SIC* 8711

THOMA CRESSEY BRAVO INC p 1448
300 N La Salle Dr # 4350, Chicago IL 60654
Tel (312) 254-3300
SIC 6799 8711 6311 6321 6531 7373

■ MAVERICK TECHNOLOGIES HOLDINGS LLC p 921
265 Admiral Trost Rd, Columbia IL 62236
Tel (618) 281-9100 *SIC* 8711 8748 1731

■ MAVERICK TECHNOLOGIES LLC p 921
265 Admiral Trost Rd, Columbia IL 62236
Tel (618) 281-9100 *SIC* 8711 8748 1731

IMS COMPANIES LLC p 735
1 Innovation Dr, Des Plaines IL 60016
Tel (847) 391-8100
SIC 3469 8711 3679 3714 3444

■ UOP LLC p 1528
25 E Algonquin Rd, Des Plaines IL 60016
Tel (847) 391-2000
SIC 2819 8711 8731 8999 3823 3479

AMBITECH ENGINEERING CORP p 65
1411 Opus Pl Ste 200, Downers Grove IL 60515
Tel (630) 963-5800 *SIC* 8711

ELGIN NATIONAL INDUSTRIES INC p 486
2001 Bttrfeld Rd Ste 1020, Downers Grove IL 60515
Tel (630) 434-7200 *SIC* 3532 8711

WYNRIGHT CORP p 1630
2500 Elmhurst Rd, Elk Grove Village IL 60007
Tel (847) 595-9400 *SIC* 5084 3535 8711

LANCO INTERNATIONAL INC p 842
3111 167th St, Hazel Crest IL 60429
Tel (708) 596-5200
SIC 3531 8711 5084 3536 7353 3537

MI-JACK PRODUCTS INC p 959
3111 167th St, Hazel Crest IL 60429
Tel (708) 596-5200 *SIC* 3531 8711

ONYX ENVIRONMENTAL SERVICES LLC p 1088
700 E Bttrfeld Rd Ste 201, Lombard IL 60148
Tel (630) 218-1500
SIC 8711 4953 2869 1799 1629

WISS JANNEY ELSTNER ASSOCIATES INC p 1619
330 Pfingsten Rd, Northbrook IL 60062
Tel (847) 272-2186 *SIC* 8711 8712 8734

PROFESSIONAL SERVICE INDUSTRIES HOLDING INC p 1180
1901 S Meyers Rd Ste 400, Oakbrook Terrace IL 60181
Tel (630) 691-1490 *SIC* 8711 8734

PROFESSIONAL SERVICE INDUSTRIES INC p 1180
1901 S Meyers Rd Ste 400, Oakbrook Terrace IL 60181
Tel (630) 691-1490 *SIC* 8711 8734

COULTER COMPANIES INC p 374
4700 N Sterling Ave Ste 2, Peoria IL 61615
Tel (309) 686-8033 *SIC* 4953 8711

EN ENGINEERING LLC p 495
28100 Torch Pkwy Ste 400, Warrenville IL 60555
Tel (630) 353-4000 *SIC* 8711

UCC HOLDINGS CORP p 1499
2100 Norman Dr, Waukegan IL 60085
Tel (847) 473-5900 *SIC* 3443 8711

JOHNSON SERVICE GROUP INC p 791
1 E Oakhill Dr Ste 200, Westmont IL 60559
Tel (630) 655-3500 *SIC* 7363 8711

TELAMON CORP p 1433
1000 E 116th St, Carmel IN 46032
Tel (317) 818-6888 *SIC* 4813 8711 3357

■ VECTREN ENERGY MARKETING AND SERVICES INC p 1546
1 Vectren Sq, Evansville IN 47708
Tel (812) 491-4000 *SIC* 8748 8711 8742

SHAMBAUGH & SON LP p 1311
7614 Opportunity Dr, Fort Wayne IN 46825
Tel (260) 487-7814 *SIC* 8711 3556 5122

KYB AMERICAS CORP p 833
2625 N Morton St, Franklin IN 46131
Tel (317) 736-7774 *SIC* 3714 8711

ENDRESS + HAUSER INC p 496
2350 Endress Pl, Greenwood IN 46143
Tel (317) 535-7138 *SIC* 8711

BASTIAN SOLUTIONS LLC p 159
10585 N Meridian St Fl 3, Indianapolis IN 46290
Tel (317) 575-9992 *SIC* 8711

HALO LLC p 655
10585 N Meridian St Fl 3, Indianapolis IN 46290
Tel (317) 575-9992 *SIC* 8711 3535

HERITAGE ENVIRONMENTAL SERVICES INC p 686
7901 W Morris St, Indianapolis IN 46231
Tel (317) 243-0811
SIC 5093 4213 8731 7389 1799 8711

HERITAGE ENVIRONMENTAL SERVICES LLC p 686
7901 W Morris St, Indianapolis IN 46231
Tel (317) 243-0811
SIC 5093 4213 8731 7389 1799 8711

HIRATA CORP OF AMERICA p 695
5625 Decatur Blvd, Indianapolis IN 46241
Tel (317) 856-8600 *SIC* 3535 3537 8711

IEA RENEWABLE ENERGY INC p 729
2647 Wtrfrnt Pw E Dr # 100, Indianapolis IN 46214
Tel (765) 832-8526 *SIC* 8711 8748

■ ENERGY SYSTEMS GROUP LLC p 498
4655 Rosebud Ln, Newburgh IN 47630
Tel (812) 492-3734 *SIC* 8711 1711 1629

■ VECTREN ENERGY SERVICES CORP p 1546
4655 Rosebud Ln, Newburgh IN 47630
Tel (812) 492-3723
SIC 8711 8742 8748 6719

AM GENERAL HOLDINGS LLC p 63
105 N Niles Ave, South Bend IN 46617
Tel (574) 237-6222 *SIC* 3714 3711 8711

AM GENERAL LLC p 63
105 N Niles Ave, South Bend IN 46617
Tel (574) 237-6222 *SIC* 3711 3714 8711

ROYAL ADHESIVES AND SEALANTS LLC p 1254
2001 W Washington St, South Bend IN 46628
Tel (574) 246-5000 *SIC* 2891 7389 8711

GREEN COMPANIES INC p 636
8710 Earhart Ln Sw, Cedar Rapids IA 52404
Tel (319) 841-4000
SIC 8711 8748 8713 4911 1623

SC COMPANIES INC p 1285
225 Iowa Ave, Muscatine IA 52761
Tel (563) 264-6600 *SIC* 8711

STANLEY CONSULTANTS INC p 1377
225 Iowa Ave, Muscatine IA 52761
Tel (563) 264-6600 *SIC* 8711

ELECTRICAL ENGINEERING AND EQUIPMENT CO p 485
953 73rd St, Windsor Heights IA 50324
Tel (515) 273-0100 *SIC* 5063 8711

ICM INC p 727
310 N 1st St, Colwich KS 67030
Tel (316) 796-0900 *SIC* 8748 8711

PERFORMANCE CONTRACTING INC p 1135
11145 Thompson Ave, Lenexa KS 66219
Tel (913) 888-8600 *SIC* 1742 8711

TERRACON CONSULTANTS INC p 1439
18001 W 106th St Ste 300, Olathe KS 66061
Tel (913) 599-6886
SIC 8742 8711 8748 8741

B&V - GENSLER JV p 142
6800 W 115th St Ste 2200, Overland Park KS 66211
Tel (913) 458-6650 *SIC* 8711

B&V-BAKER GUAM JV p 142
6601 College Blvd, Overland Park KS 66211
Tel (913) 458-4300 *SIC* 8711

BLACK & VEATCH CORP p 186
11401 Lamar Ave, Overland Park KS 66211
Tel (913) 458-2000 *SIC* 8711

BLACK & VEATCH HOLDING CO p 186
11401 Lamar Ave, Overland Park KS 66211
Tel (913) 458-2000 *SIC* 8711 8741

BVH INC p 230
11401 Lamar Ave, Overland Park KS 66211
Tel (913) 458-2000 *SIC* 8711 8741

ABMB-HNTB JOINT VENTURE LLC p 12
500 Main St, Baton Rouge LA 70801
Tel (225) 765-7400 *SIC* 8711

CB&I GOVERNMENT SOLUTIONS INC p 268
4171 Essen Ln, Baton Rouge LA 70809
Tel (225) 932-2500
SIC 8711 8734 8748 1541 1542 1611

FORD BACON & DAVIS LLC p 565
12021 Lakeland Park Blvd # 212, Baton Rouge LA 70809
Tel (225) 297-3431 *SIC* 8711 1541 1623

PALA INTERSTATE LLC p 1108
16347 Old Hammond Hwy, Baton Rouge LA 70816
Tel (225) 272-5194 *SIC* 1541 8711

SHAW GROUP INC p 1312
4171 Essen Ln, Baton Rouge LA 70809
Tel (225) 932-2500
SIC 8711 8734 1629 3498

ATC GROUP HOLDINGS LLC p 124
221 Rue De Jean Ste 300, Lafayette LA 70508
Tel (337) 324-8777
SIC 8711 8732 8731 8249 8748

ATC GROUP SERVICES LLC p 124
221 Rue De Jean Ste 200, Lafayette LA 70508
Tel (337) 234-8777
SIC 8711 8734 8731 8249 8748

■ ENTERGY SERVICES INC p 501
639 Loyola Ave Ste 300, New Orleans LA 70113
Tel (504) 576-4000 *SIC* 8741 8711

HUNT GUILLOT & ASSOCIATES LLC p 719
603 E Reynolds Dr, Ruston LA 71270
Tel (318) 255-6825 *SIC* 8711

■ BATH IRON WORKS CORP p 159
700 Washington St Stop 1, Bath ME 04530
Tel (207) 443-3311 *SIC* 3731 8711

WAHLCOMETROFLEX INC p 1571
29 Lexington St, Lewiston ME 04240
Tel (207) 784-2338 *SIC* 3441 3822 8711

NICHOLS PORTLAND LLC p 1042
2400 Congress St, Portland ME 04102
Tel (207) 774-6121 *SIC* 3714 8711

WOODARD & CURRAN INC p 1622
41 Hutchins Dr, Portland ME 04102
Tel (800) 426-4262 *SIC* 8711 8748

■ ARINC INC p 108
2551 Riva Rd, Annapolis MD 21401
Tel (410) 266-4000 *SIC* 8711 4899

■ ARINC RESEARCH CORP p 108
2551 Riva Rd, Annapolis MD 21401
Tel (410) 266-4000 *SIC* 8711

CCE/DFS INC p 270
201 Defense Hwy Ste 202, Annapolis MD 21401
Tel (410) 263-6422 *SIC* 1542 8711 8744

■ RADIO HOLDINGS INC p 1204
2551 Riva Rd, Annapolis MD 21401
Tel (410) 266-4000 *SIC* 8711 4899

BERGER GROUP HOLDINGS INC p 174
111 Market Pl, Baltimore MD 21202
Tel (410) 468-4054 *SIC* 8711 8732 8712

JENSEN HUGHES INC p 782
3610 Commerce Dr Ste 817, Baltimore MD 21227
Tel (410) 737-8677 *SIC* 8748 8711 8734

RUMMEL KLEPPER & KAHL LLP p 1257
81 Mosher St, Baltimore MD 21217
Tel (410) 728-2900
SIC 8711 8741 1623 8999 8713 1611

■ ATK SPACE SYSTEMS INC p 125
11310 Frederick Ave, Beltsville MD 20705
Tel (301) 595-5500 *SIC* 8711

MIL CORP p 968
4000 Mitchellville Rd R, Bowie MD 20716
Tel (301) 805-8500
SIC 7371 7373 7374 7375 7376 8711

GEA PROCESS ENGINEERING INC p 597
9165 Rumsey Rd, Columbia MD 21045
Tel (410) 772-5792 *SIC* 8711

▲ GP STRATEGIES CORP p 627
11000 Broken Land Pkwy # 200, Columbia MD 21044
Tel (443) 367-9600 *SIC* 8742 8711 8748

■ KBRWYLE TECHNOLOGY SOLUTIONS LLC p 806
7000 Columbia Gateway Dr # 100, Columbia MD 21046
Tel (410) 964-7000 *SIC* 4899 8711

SCIENCE AND ENGINEERING SERVICES LLC p 1292
6992 Columbia Gateway Dr # 200, Columbia MD 21046
Tel (443) 539-0139 *SIC* 8711 8731 3826

STRUCTURAL TECHNOLOGIES LLC p 1394
10150 Old Columbia Rd, Columbia MD 21046
Tel (410) 850-7000 *SIC* 1622 8711

MACAULAY-BROWN INC p 891
1951 Polaris Rd, Finksburg MD 21048
Tel (937) 426-3421 *SIC* 8711

BECHTEL NATIONAL INC p 167
5275 Westview Dr, Frederick MD 21703
Tel (415) 768-1234 *SIC* 8711 1629 8742

■ LOCKHEED MARTIN SERVICES INC p 873
700 N Frederick Ave, Gaithersburg MD 20879
Tel (301) 240-7669 *SIC* 8711 8741 8742

■ OAO CORP p 1071
700 N Frederick Ave, Gaithersburg MD 20879
Tel (301) 240-7000
SIC 7371 8711 3823 3559

■ URS FEDERAL SERVICES INC p 1530
20501 Seneca Meadows Pkwy # 300, Germantown MD 20876
Tel (301) 944-3100 *SIC* 8711

URS FEDERAL SERVICES INTERNATIONAL INC p 1530
20501 Seneca Meadows Pkwy # 300, Germantown MD 20876
Tel (301) 944-3100 *SIC* 8711

URS FEDERAL TECHINCAL SERVICES INC p 1530
20501 Seneca Meadows Pkwy # 300, Germantown MD 20876
Tel (301) 944-3100 *SIC* 8711

AEROTEK INC p 31
7301 Parkway Dr, Hanover MD 21076
Tel (410) 694-5100 *SIC* 7363 8748 8711

KELLER FOUNDATIONS LLC p 808
7550 Teague Rd Ste 300, Hanover MD 21076
Tel (410) 551-8200 *SIC* 1799 8711

■ KEYW CORP p 816
7740 Milestone Pkwy # 400, Hanover MD 21076
Tel (443) 733-1600 *SIC* 8711 8748

■ AAI CORP p 8
124 Industry Ln, Hunt Valley MD 21030
Tel (410) 666-1400
SIC 3728 3769 7699 8711

■ UNITED INDUSTRIAL CORP p 1509
124 Industry Ln, Hunt Valley MD 21030
Tel (410) 628-3500 *SIC* 8711

J F TAYLOR INC p 771
21610 S Essex Dr, Lexington Park MD 20653
Tel (301) 862-4744 *SIC* 8711

■ BOOZ ALLEN HAMILTON ENGINEERING SERVICES LLC p 200
900 Elkridge Landing Rd # 100, Linthicum MD 21090
Tel (703) 902-5000 *SIC* 8711

BAE SYSTEMS TECHNOLOGY SOLUTIONS & SERVICES INC p 144
520 Gaither Rd, Rockville MD 20850
Tel (301) 738-4880 *SIC* 8711

TECHNOLOGY SERVICE CORP p 1432
962 Wayne Ave, Silver Spring MD 20910
Tel (301) 576-2300 *SIC* 8711

FIDELITY ENGINEERING CORP p 540
25 Loveton Cir, Sparks MD 21152
Tel (410) 771-9400
SIC 1711 5063 1799 8711

JOHNSON MIRMIRAN & THOMPSON INC p 791
72 Loveton Cir, Sparks MD 21152
Tel (410) 329-3100 *SIC* 8711

KCI TECHNOLOGIES INC p 806
936 Ridgebrook Rd, Sparks MD 21152
Tel (410) 316-7800 *SIC* 8711

KCI HOLDINGS INC p 806
936 Ridgebrook Rd, Sparks Glencoe MD 21152
Tel (410) 316-7800 *SIC* 8711 1799

■ DYNAMICS RESEARCH CORP p 464
2 Tech Dr, Andover MA 01810
Tel (978) 289-1500 *SIC* 7373 7379 8711

■ ENGILITY CORP p 499
35 New Engld Busctr Dr200, Andover MA 01810
Tel (978) 749-2100 *SIC* 8711

MITRE CORP p 977
202 Burlington Rd, Bedford MA 01730
Tel (781) 271-2000 *SIC* 8733 8711

MORPHOTRUST USA LLC p 990
296 Concord Rd Ste 300, Billerica MA 01821
Tel (978) 215-2400 *SIC* 7374 8711

CDM SMITH INC p 271
75 State St Ste 701, Boston MA 02109
Tel (617) 452-6000 *SIC* 8711

■ METCALF & EDDY INC p 953
1 Federal St Ste 800, Boston MA 02110
Tel (781) 246-5200 *SIC* 8711

STONE & WEBSTER OVERSEAS GROUP INC p 1391
45 Milk St Bsmt, Boston MA 02109
Tel (617) 778-7500 *SIC* 8742 8711

VEOLIA NORTH AMERICA LLC p 1548
53 State St Ste 14, Boston MA 02109
Tel (312) 552-2800 *SIC* 8711

HALEY & ALDRICH INC p 653
70 Blanchard Rd Ste 204, Burlington MA 01803
Tel (617) 886-7400 *SIC* 8748 8711

■ RANGE SYSTEMS ENGINEERING SUPPORT CO p 1208
2 Wayside Rd, Burlington MA 01803
Tel (781) 983-1396 *SIC* 8711

ASSURANCE TECHNOLOGY CORP p 121
84 South St, Carlisle MA 01741
Tel (978) 369-8848 *SIC* 8711 3629

■ AECOM C&E INC p 28
250 Apollo Dr, Chelmsford MA 01824
Tel (978) 905-2100 *SIC* 8711

ENSR INTL CORP p 501
250 Apollo Dr, Chelmsford MA 01824
Tel (978) 589-3000 *SIC* 8748 8711

■ NYPRO INC p 1069
101 Union St, Clinton MA 01510
Tel (978) 365-8100
SIC 3089 3559 7389 8711

SECURE ENERGY SOLUTIONS LLC p 1298
12 Somers Rd 14, East Longmeadow MA 01028
Tel (413) 733-2571 *SIC* 8711

▲ AMERESCO INC p 66
111 Speen St Ste 410, Framingham MA 01701
Tel (508) 661-2200 *SIC* 8711 1731

GZA GEOENVIRONMENTAL INC p 649
249 Vanderbilt Ave, Norwood MA 02062
Tel (781) 278-3700 *SIC* 8711 8734

GZA GEOENVIRONMENTAL TECHNOLOGIES INC p 649
249 Vanderbilt Ave Unit 2, Norwood MA 02062
Tel (781) 278-3700
SIC 8711 8999 1799 8744

WESTON & SAMPSON INC p 1602
5 Centennial Dr Ste 1, Peabody MA 01960
Tel (978) 532-1900 *SIC* 8711 8748 4953

DENNIS GROUP INC p 428
1537 Main St Fl 2, Springfield MA 01103
Tel (413) 787-1785 *SIC* 8711

SIMPSON GUMPERTZ & HEGER INC p 1325
41 Seyon St Ste 500, Waltham MA 02453
Tel (781) 907-9000 *SIC* 8711

VANASSE HANGEN BRUSTLIN INC p 1543
101 Walnut St, Watertown MA 02472
Tel (617) 924-1770 *SIC* 8711

■ NORESCO INC p 1048
1 Research Dr Ste 400c, Westborough MA 01581
Tel (508) 614-1000
SIC 8711 8741 8748 4911 4924

■ NORESCO LLC p 1048
1 Research Dr Ste 400c, Westborough MA 01581
Tel (508) 614-1000
SIC 8711 8741 8744 8748 4911 4924

■ GENERAL DYNAMICS NETWORK SYSTEMS INC p 600
101 Station Dr Apt 200, Westwood MA 02090
Tel (781) 400-7669 *SIC* 8711

■ ACCELLENT LLC p 14
100 Fordham Rd Bldg C, Wilmington MA 01887
Tel (978) 570-6900 *SIC* 3841 8711

■ MEDSOURCE TECHNOLOGIES HOLDINGS LLC p 939
100 Fordham Rd Bldg C, Wilmington MA 01887
Tel (978) 570-6900 *SIC* 3841 8711

GEI CONSULTANTS INC p 597
400 Unicorn Park Dr Ste 8, Woburn MA 01801
Tel (781) 721-4000 *SIC* 8711

AUTOMOTIVE LIGHTING LLC p 134
3900 Automation Ave, Auburn Hills MI 48326
Tel (248) 418-3000 *SIC* 8711 3647

FAURECIA AUTOMOTIVE SEATING LLC p 531
2800 High Meadow Cir, Auburn Hills MI 48326
Tel (248) 288-1000 *SIC* 8711

GRUPO ANTOLIN NORTH AMERICA INC p 643
1700 Atlantic Blvd, Auburn Hills MI 48326
Tel (248) 373-1437 *SIC* 8741 8711

LOTUS INTERNATIONAL CO p 879
6880 Commerce Blvd, Canton MI 48187
Tel (734) 245-0140 *SIC* 8711 3651 1221

SERVICE SOLUTIONS US LLC p 1307
7121 N Haggerty Rd, Canton MI 48187
Tel (734) 582-2382 *SIC* 8711

BURTEK HOLDINGS INC p 229
50325 Patricia St, Chesterfield MI 48051
Tel (586) 421-8000 *SIC* 7371 3812 8711

GHAFARI ASSOCIATES LLC p 610
17101 Michigan Ave, Dearborn MI 48126
Tel (313) 271-6280 *SIC* 8711

MSX INTERNATIONAL INC p 997
500 Woodward Ave Ste 2150, Detroit MI 48226
Tel (248) 829-6300
SIC 8748 7363 8742 8711

SMITHGROUP COMPANIES INC p 1334
500 Griswold St Fl 1700, Detroit MI 48226
Tel (313) 442-8351 SIC 8712 8711

HIRAIN TECHNOLOGIES USA INC p 695
37632 Hills Tech Dr, Farmington Hills MI 48331
Tel (248) 839-1309 SIC 5013 8711

TACHI-S ENGINEERING USA INC p 1421
23227 Commerce Dr, Farmington Hills MI 48335
Tel (248) 478-5050 SIC 2531 8711

DEMATIC CORP p 428
507 Plymouth Ave Ne, Grand Rapids MI 49505
Tel (678) 695-4500 SIC 3535 1796 8711

ROUSH ENTERPRISES INC p 1253
12447 Levan Rd, Livonia MI 48150
Tel (734) 779-7006
SIC 8711 3714 7948 8734

ROUSH INDUSTRIES INC p 1253
12447 Levan Rd, Livonia MI 48150
Tel (734) 779-7006 SIC 8734 8711

NEWKIRK ELECTRIC ASSOCIATES INC p 1037
1875 Roberts St, Muskegon MI 49442
Tel (231) 722-1691 SIC 1731 1629 8711

NHK INTERNATIONAL CORP p 1041
46855 Magellan Dr Ste 200, Novi MI 48377
Tel (248) 926-0111 SIC 8711

TATA TECHNOLOGIES INC p 1426
41050 W 11 Mile Rd, Novi MI 48375
Tel (248) 426-1482 SIC 8711

JOHNSON ELECTRIC NORTH AMERICA INC p 791
47660 Halyard Dr, Plymouth MI 48170
Tel (734) 392-5300
SIC 5063 3625 3674 8711

■ MEARS GROUP INC p 934
4500 N Mission Rd, Rosebush MI 48878
Tel (989) 433-2929 SIC 1623 8711

MERRILL TOOL HOLDING CO p 950
400 Florence St, Saginaw MI 48602
Tel (989) 791-6676
SIC 3443 3599 8734 8711 3724

ATWELL LLC p 130
2 Towne Sq Ste 700, Southfield MI 48076
Tel (248) 447-2000
SIC 8999 8713 8748 8711

EPITEC INC p 505
24800 Denso Dr Ste 150, Southfield MI 48033
Tel (248) 353-6800
SIC 7371 7379 7373 8748 8711

■ GENERAL DYNAMICS LAND SYSTEMS INC p 600
38500 Mound Rd, Sterling Heights MI 48310
Tel (586) 825-4000 SIC 5088 8711

IWKA HOLDING CORP p 769
6600 Center Dr, Sterling Heights MI 48312
Tel (586) 795-2000
SIC 3549 5084 7371 8711

RONCELLI INC p 1249
6471 Metropolitan Pkwy, Sterling Heights MI 48312
Tel (586) 264-2060 SIC 1541 8711

■ JOHNSON KADANT INC p 791
805 Wood St, Three Rivers MI 49093
Tel (269) 278-1715
SIC 3494 8711 1389 3052 1099

ALTAIR ENGINEERING INC p 61
1820 E Big Beaver Rd, Troy MI 48083
Tel (248) 614-2400 SIC 8711

MAGNA EXTERIORS OF AMERICA INC p 896
750 Tower Dr, Troy MI 48098
Tel (248) 631-1100 SIC 3714 3544 8711

RAPID GLOBAL BUSINESS SOLUTIONS INC p 1208
1200 Stephenson Hwy, Troy MI 48083
Tel (248) 589-1135 SIC 8711 7371 7361

UTICA ENTERPRISES INC p 1537
5750 New King Dr Ste 200, Troy MI 48098
Tel (586) 726-4300
SIC 3548 3549 3545 8711 3541 3544

COLD HEADING CO p 335
21777 Hoover Rd, Warren MI 48089
Tel (586) 497-7000 SIC 3452 8711

GT TECHNOLOGIES INC p 644
5859 E Executive Dr, Westland MI 48185
Tel (734) 467-8371
SIC 8711 3714 3545 3089

TEAM INDUSTRIES BAGLEY-AUDUBON INC p 1430
105 Park Ave Nw, Bagley MN 56621
Tel (218) 694-3550 SIC 3599 8711 3714

TEAM INDUSTRIES INC p 1430
105 Park Ave Nw, Bagley MN 56621
Tel (218) 694-3550 SIC 3599 8711 3714

LOGIC PD INC p 874
6201 Bury Dr, Eden Prairie MN 55346
Tel (952) 646-1191 SIC 3672 8711

METROPOLITAN MECHANICAL CONTRACTORS INC p 956
7450 Flying Cloud Dr, Eden Prairie MN 55344
Tel (952) 941-7010 SIC 1711 8711

WUNDERLICH-MALEC ENGINEERING INC p 1628
6101 Blue Circle Dr, Eden Prairie MN 55343
Tel (952) 933-3222 SIC 8711

BARR ENGINEERING CO p 156
4300 Marketpointe Dr # 200, Minneapolis MN 55435
Tel (952) 832-2600 SIC 8711

BRAUN INTERTEC CORP p 209
11001 Hampshire Ave S, Minneapolis MN 55438
Tel (952) 995-2000 SIC 8711 8734

EBERSEN INC p 474
7401 Central Ave Ne Ste 2, Minneapolis MN 55432
Tel (763) 572-2661
SIC 4911 1521 6211 1382 4731 8711

■ ELLERBE BECKET INC p 488
800 Lasalle Ave Fl 5, Minneapolis MN 55402
Tel (612) 376-2000 SIC 8712 8711

HAMMEL GREEN AND ABRAHAMSON INC p 656
420 N 5th St Ste 100, Minneapolis MN 55401
Tel (612) 758-4000 SIC 8712 8711

INTERSTATE COMPANIES INC p 758
2501 American Blvd E, Minneapolis MN 55425
Tel (952) 854-2044 SIC 7538 8711 5085

OPEN ACCESS TECHNOLOGY INTERNATIONAL INC p 1089
3660 Technology Dr, Minneapolis MN 55418
Tel (763) 201-2000 SIC 7371 8711

PARSONS ELECTRIC LLC p 1118
5960 Main St Ne, Minneapolis MN 55432
Tel (763) 571-8000 SIC 1731 7382 8711

ATRENNE INTEGRATED SOLUTIONS INC p 129
9210 Science Center Dr, New Hope MN 55428
Tel (763) 533-3533 SIC 8711 5065

■ SEBESTA INC p 1298
1450 Energy Park Dr # 300, Saint Paul MN 55108
Tel (651) 634-0775 SIC 8711

SHORT-ELLIOTT-HENDRICKSON INC p 1318
3535 Vadnais Center Dr # 200, Saint Paul MN 55110
Tel (651) 490-2000 SIC 8711 8712

NEEL-SCHAFFER INC p 1024
125 S Congress St # 1100, Jackson MS 39201
Tel (601) 948-3071 SIC 8711

BILFINGER INDUSTRIAL SERVICES INC p 182
15933 Clayton Rd Ste 305, Ballwin MO 63011
Tel (636) 391-4500
SIC 1541 1731 1796 8711 8744

■ MITEK INDUSTRIES INC p 977
16023 Swinly Rdg, Chesterfield MO 63017
Tel (314) 434-1200 SIC 8711 8748

■ MITEK USA INC p 977
16023 Swingley Ridge Rd, Chesterfield MO 63017
Tel (314) 434-1200
SIC 3443 3429 3542 8711 5051 5085

BURNS & MCDONNELL ENGINEERING CO INC p 228
9400 Ward Pkwy, Kansas City MO 64114
Tel (816) 333-9400 SIC 1382 8711

BURNS & MCDONNELL INC p 228
9400 Ward Pkwy, Kansas City MO 64114
Tel (816) 333-9400 SIC 8711 8741

CLARK RICHARDSON AND BISKUP CONSULTING ENGINEERS INC p 322
1251 Nw Briarcliff Pkwy # 500, Kansas City MO 64116
Tel (816) 880-9800 SIC 8711

HNTB CORP p 698
715 Kirk Dr, Kansas City MO 64105
Tel (816) 472-1201 SIC 8711 8712

HNTB HOLDINGS LTD p 698
715 Kirk Dr, Kansas City MO 64105
Tel (816) 472-1201 SIC 8712 8711

TRANSYSTEMS CORP p 1473
2400 Pershing Rd Ste 400, Kansas City MO 64108
Tel (816) 329-8700 SIC 8711

BARRY-WEHMILLER COMPANIES INC p 157
8020 Forsyth Blvd, Saint Louis MO 63105
Tel (314) 862-8000
SIC 3565 3535 3554 8711

BARRY-WEHMILLER GROUP INC p 157
8020 Forsyth Blvd, Saint Louis MO 63105
Tel (314) 862-8000
SIC 3565 3535 3554 8711

■ BOEING SERVICE CO p 197
6200 J S Mcdonnell Blvd, Saint Louis MO 63134
Tel (972) 705-8000 SIC 8741 8711

HOK GROUP INC p 699
10 S Broadway Ste 200, Saint Louis MO 63102
Tel (314) 421-2000 SIC 8711 8712 8742

HOK INC p 699
10 S Broadway Ste 200, Saint Louis MO 63102
Tel (314) 421-2000 SIC 0781 8712 8711

■ JACOBS FACILITIES INC p 775
501 N Broadway, Saint Louis MO 63102
Tel (314) 335-4000
SIC 8712 8711 8713 8741 1542 1541

NOOTER CORP p 1047
1500 S 2nd St, Saint Louis MO 63104
Tel (314) 421-7200
SIC 3443 3479 1796 8711 7699 1542

CTA INC p 399
13 N 23rd St, Billings MT 59101
Tel (406) 248-7455 SIC 8711 8712

ELECTRICAL CONSULTANTS INC p 485
3521 Gabel Rd Ste A, Billings MT 59102
Tel (406) 259-9933 SIC 8711

EPC SERVICES CO p 504
3521 Gabel Rd Ste B, Billings MT 59102
Tel (406) 294-8544 SIC 1731 8711

OLSSON ASSOCIATES INC p 1083
601 P St, Lincoln NE 68508
Tel (402) 474-6311 SIC 8711

HDR ARCHITECTURE INC p 673
8404 Indian Hills Dr, Omaha NE 68114
Tel (402) 399-1000 SIC 8711

HDR ENGINEERING INC p 673
8404 Indian Hills Dr, Omaha NE 68114
Tel (402) 399-1000 SIC 8742 8711

HDR INC p 673
8404 Indian Hills Dr, Omaha NE 68114
Tel (402) 399-1000
SIC 8712 8711 8742 8748 4789

LEO A DALY/BURNS & MCCONNELL JOINT VENTURE p 856
8600 Indian Hills Dr, Omaha NE 68114
Tel (402) 391-8111 SIC 8712 8711

ARCATA ASSOCIATES INC p 104
2588 Fire Mesa St Ste 110, Las Vegas NV 89128
Tel (702) 642-9500 SIC 8711

JT3 LLC p 796
821 Grier Dr, Las Vegas NV 89119
Tel (702) 492-2100 SIC 8711

LAS VEGAS PAVING CORP p 845
4420 S Decatur Blvd, Las Vegas NV 89103
Tel (702) 251-5800 SIC 1611 1629 8711

TRAX INTERNATIONAL CORP p 1475
8337 W Sunset Rd Ste 250, Las Vegas NV 89113
Tel (702) 216-4455
SIC 7373 8711 7376 8742 8744

BECHTEL NEVADA CORP p 167
2621 Losee Rd, North Las Vegas NV 89030
Tel (702) 295-1000 SIC 8711 1629

NATIONAL SECURITY TECHNOLOGIES LLC p 1016
2621 Losee Rd, North Las Vegas NV 89030
Tel (702) 295-1000 SIC 8711 1629

MITSUBISHI HITACHI POWER SYSTEMS AMERICA-ENERGY AND ENVIRONMENT LTD p 977
645 Martinsville Rd, Basking Ridge NJ 07920
Tel (908) 542-9101 SIC 8711

DEWBERRY ENGINEERS INC p 434
200 Broadacres Dr Ste 410, Bloomfield NJ 07003
Tel (973) 338-9100 SIC 8711

LUMMUS OVERSEAS CORP p 885
1515 Broad St, Bloomfield NJ 07003
Tel (973) 893-1515 SIC 8711 1629 8741

D & S CONSULTANTS INC p 406
40 Christopher Way, Eatontown NJ 07724
Tel (732) 389-2140 SIC 8711

FOSTER WHEELER ZACK INC p 571
53 Frontage Rd, Hampton NJ 08827
Tel (908) 730-4000
SIC 8711 1629 3569 4931

MACDONALD MOTT GROUP INC p 892
111 Wood Ave S Ste 5, Iselin NJ 08830
Tel (973) 379-3400 SIC 8711

ONE DIVERSIFIED LLC p 1086
37 Market St, Kenilworth NJ 07033
Tel (908) 245-4833
SIC 5099 7373 4899 8711

LOUIS BERGER AND ASSOCIATES INC p 879
412 Mount Kemble Ave, Morristown NJ 07960
Tel (973) 407-1000 SIC 8711

LOUIS BERGER GROUP INC p 879
412 Mount Kemble Ave, Morristown NJ 07960
Tel (973) 407-1000 SIC 8748 8712 8711

LIME ENERGY CO p 866
4 Gateway Ctr Fl 4, Newark NJ 07102
Tel (201) 416-2575 SIC 1711 8711

BURNS & ROE GROUP INC p 228
800 Kinderkamack Rd Ste 1, Oradell NJ 07649
Tel (201) 265-2000 SIC 8711

URS CORP p 1530
Mack Ctr Ii Mack Ctr Dr, Paramus NJ 07652
Tel (201) 262-7000 SIC 8711 8748

LANGAN ENGINEERING AND ENVIRONMENTAL SERVICES INC p 844
300 Kimball Dr, Parsippany NJ 07054
Tel (201) 794-6900 SIC 8711

LANGAN ENGINEERING ENVIRONMENTAL SURVEYING AND LANDSCAPE ARCHITECTURE DPC p 844
300 Kimball Dr Ste 4, Parsippany NJ 07054
Tel (973) 560-4900
SIC 8711 8748 1389 0781

■ RCM TECHNOLOGIES (USA) INC p 1212
2500 Mcclellan Ave # 350, Pennsauken NJ 08109
Tel (856) 356-4500 SIC 8742 7379 8711

▲ RCM TECHNOLOGIES INC p 1212
2500 Mcclellan Ave # 350, Pennsauken NJ 08109
Tel (856) 356-4500
SIC 8711 8748 7373 8049 7363

BINSKY & SNYDER LLC p 183
281 Centennial Ave Ste 1, Piscataway NJ 08854
Tel (732) 885-0700 SIC 1711 8711

▲ MISTRAS GROUP INC p 976
195 Clarksville Rd Ste 2, Princeton Junction NJ 08550
Tel (609) 716-4000
SIC 8711 7372 3829 3825

MASER CONSULTING PA p 915
331 Newman Springs Rd # 203, Red Bank NJ 07701
Tel (732) 383-1950 SIC 8711 8742 8713

ENERGY CAPITAL PARTNERS II LLC p 497
51 John F Kennedy Pkwy # 200, Short Hills NJ 07078
Tel (973) 671-6100 SIC 6799 4953 8711

OPERATING ENGINEERS LOCAL NO 825 WELFARE FUND p 1089
65 Springfield Ave Ste 2, Springfield NJ 07081
Tel (973) 921-1661 SIC 8711

AASKI TECHNOLOGY INC p 8
1 Radar Way, Tinton Falls NJ 07724
Tel (732) 493-1700 SIC 8711

MEADOWGATE TECHNOLOGIES LLC p 934
171 Jersey St Ste 1, Trenton NJ 08611
Tel (609) 393-3618 SIC 5045 8711

P C BOHLER ENGINEERING p 1102
35 Technology Dr Ste 5, Warren NJ 07059
Tel (908) 222-0023 SIC 8711

PAULUS SOKOLOWSKI & SARTOR ENGINEERING A PROFESSIONAL CORP p 1122
67b Mountain Blvd Ext, Warren NJ 07059
Tel (732) 560-9700 SIC 8711 8748 8712

CHA CONSULTING INC p 286
3 Winners Cir Ste 301, Albany NY 12205
Tel (518) 453-4500 SIC 8711

CHA HOLDINGS INC p 286
3 Winners Cir, Albany NY 12205
Tel (518) 453-4500 SIC 8711

CLOUGH HARBOUR & ASSOCIATES LLP p 327
3 Winners Cir Ste 100, Albany NY 12205
Tel (518) 453-4500 SIC 8711

M+W US INC p 890
201 Fuller Rd Ste 400, Albany NY 12203
Tel (518) 266-3400 SIC 1542 8711

GREENMAN-PEDERSEN INC p 638
325 W Main St Bldg 1, Babylon NY 11702
Tel (631) 587-5060 SIC 8711

OHL USA INC p 1078
2615 Ulmer St, Flushing NY 11354
Tel (718) 554-2320 SIC 8711

▲ ECOLOGY AND ENVIRONMENT INC p 476
368 Pleasant View Dr, Lancaster NY 14086
Tel (716) 684-8060 SIC 8748 8734 8711

CG POWER USA INC p 285
7 Century Hill Dr, Latham NY 12110
Tel (518) 452-7718 SIC 8711

MECHANICAL DYNAMICS & ANALYSIS LTD p 934
19 British American Blvd, Latham NY 12110
Tel (518) 399-3616 SIC 8711 7699

▲ ABM INDUSTRIES INC p 12
1 Liberty Plz Fl Con1, New York NY 10006
Tel (212) 297-0200
SIC 7349 7521 7381 8711

■ ABM ONSITE SERVICES INC p 12
1 Liberty Plz Fl 7, New York NY 10006
Tel (212) 497-0600
SIC 7349 7381 7521 8711

ARUP AMERICAS INC p 114
77 Water St, New York NY 10005
Tel (212) 896-3000 SIC 8711

ENER-G GROUP INC p 497
1261 Broadway Fl 6, New York NY 10001
Tel (917) 281-0020 SIC 8711

GOLDBERG LINDSAY & CO LLC p 620
630 5th Ave Fl 30, New York NY 10111
Tel (212) 651-1100 SIC 6799 8711 8712

HAKS ENGINEERS ARCHITECTS AND LAND SURVEYORS PC p 653
40 Wall St Fl 11, New York NY 10005
Tel (212) 747-1997 SIC 8712 8711 8713

HAZEN AND SAWYER DPC p 671
498 Fashion Ave Fl 11, New York NY 10018
Tel (212) 539-7000 SIC 8711

IHI INC p 731
150 E 52nd St Fl 24, New York NY 10022
Tel (212) 599-8100
SIC 5099 8732 8711 5084

MARUBENI POWER SERVICES INC p 913
375 Lexington Ave, New York NY 10017
Tel (212) 450-0640 SIC 1629 4911 8711

PARSONS BRINCKERHOFF GROUP LLC p 1117
1 Penn Plz 2nd, New York NY 10119
Tel (212) 465-5000 SIC 8742 8711 8741

PARSONS BRINCKERHOFF INC p 1117
1 Penn Plz Ste 200, New York NY 10119
Tel (212) 465-5000 SIC 8711 8748

SH GROUP INC p 1310
1515 Broadway, New York NY 10036
Tel (212) 921-2300 SIC 8748 8711 1542

SOS INTERNATIONAL LLC p 1341
40 Fulton St Fl 26, New York NY 10038
Tel (212) 742-2410
SIC 3724 8711 7389 8732

STANTEC CONSULTING SERVICES INC p 1377
50 W 23rd St Fl 8, New York NY 10010
Tel (212) 366-5600 SIC 8731 8711 1541

STEMCOR USA INC p 1385
2 Park Ave Rm 1600, New York NY 10016
Tel (212) 563-0262 SIC 5051 8711

STV INC p 1395
225 Park Ave S Fl 5, New York NY 10003
Tel (212) 529-2722 SIC 8711 8712 8741

SYSKA HENNESSY GROUP INC p 1418
1515 Broadway Fl 14, New York NY 10036
Tel (212) 921-2300 SIC 8711

THORNTON TOMASETTI INC p 1450
51 Madison Ave Fl 19, New York NY 10010
Tel (917) 661-7800 SIC 8711 8712

TOSHIBA NUCLEAR ENERGY HOLDINGS (US) INC p 1462
1251 Ave Of Amrcs 400 Ste 4100, New York NY 10020
Tel (212) 596-0600
SIC 8711 3829 3823 2819

WSP USA CORP p 1628
1 Penn Plz 250w, New York NY 10119
Tel (914) 747-1120 SIC 8711 8732

WSP USA HOLDINGS INC p 1628
512 7th Ave Fl 13, New York NY 10018
Tel (212) 532-9600 SIC 8711 8732

OPTIMATION TECHNOLOGY INC p 1090
50 High Tech Dr, Rush NY 14543
Tel (585) 321-2300 SIC 8711

OBRIEN & GERE LIMITED p 1072
333 W Washington St # 400, Syracuse NY 13202
Tel (315) 437-6100 SIC 8711 8741

ARCADIS CE INC p 103
44 S Broadway Ste 1500, White Plains NY 10601
Tel (914) 694-2100 SIC 8711 8731

ABB INC p 9
12040 Regency Pkwy # 200, Cary NC 27518
Tel (919) 856-2360
SIC 8711 3612 3511 5063 3613 3625

ALLIED STAFF AUGMENTATION PARTNERS INC p 57
7421 Carmel Executive Par, Charlotte NC 28226
Tel (980) 219-8477 SIC 8711

AREVA INC p 107
7207 Ibm Dr, Charlotte NC 28262
Tel (704) 805-2000
SIC 3823 3829 8711 5085 3561 2819

MIDREX TECHNOLOGIES INC p 966
2725 Water Ridge Pkwy # 100, Charlotte NC 28217
Tel (704) 373-1600 SIC 8711

PARSONS ENVIRONMENT & INFRASTRUCTURE GROUP INC p 1118
4701 Hedgemore Dr, Charlotte NC 28209
Tel (704) 529-6246 SIC 8711

■ BAHNSON HOLDINGS INC p 145
4731 Commercial Park Ct, Clemmons NC 27012
Tel (336) 760-3111
SIC 8711 1711 3585 3564

■ BAHNSON INC p 145
4731 Commercial Park Ct, Clemmons NC 27012
Tel (336) 760-3111 SIC 8711 1711

▲ MAXPOINT INTERACTIVE INC p 923
3020 Carrington Mill Blvd, Morrisville NC 27560
Tel (800) 916-9960 SIC 7311 8711

NNE PHARMAPLAN INC p 1045
3005 Carrington Mill Blvd, Morrisville NC 27560
Tel (919) 481-3765 SIC 8711

PIKE CORP p 1147
100 Pike Way, Mount Airy NC 27030
Tel (336) 789-2171 SIC 1731 8711

PIKE ELECTRIC LLC p 1148
100 Pike Way, Mount Airy NC 27030
Tel (336) 789-2171 SIC 1731 8711

PIONEER PARENT INC p 1151
100 Pike Way, Mount Airy NC 27030
Tel (336) 789-2171 SIC 1731 8711

APPLIED RESEARCH ASSOCIATES INC p 100
11 Villiage Club Ct, Pinehurst NC 28374
Tel (910) 246-2030 SIC 8711 8731

APHC INC p 96
421 Fayetteville St # 600, Raleigh NC 27601
Tel (919) 677-2000 SIC 8711

KIMLEY-HORN AND ASSOCIATES INC p 818
421 Fayetteville St # 600, Raleigh NC 27601
Tel (919) 677-2000 SIC 8711

MCKIM & CREED PA p 930
1730 Varsity Dr Ste 500, Raleigh NC 27606
Tel (919) 233-8091 SIC 8711 8713

S&ME INC p 1263
3201 Spring Forest Rd, Raleigh NC 27616
Tel (919) 872-2660 SIC 8711

WALKER AND ASSOCIATES INC p 1573
7129 Old Hwy 52, Welcome NC 27374
Tel (336) 731-6391
SIC 4813 5065 8731 8711 3572 3571

WALKER GROUP INC p 1573
7129 Old Hwy 52, Welcome NC 27374
Tel (336) 731-6391
SIC 4813 8748 5065 8711

CHEMTEX INTERNATIONAL INC p 293
1979 Eastwood Rd, Wilmington NC 28403
Tel (910) 509-4400 SIC 8711 8731

KLJ SOLUTIONS CO p 823
4585 Coleman St, Bismarck ND 58503
Tel (701) 355-8400 SIC 8711 8713

KADRMAS LEE & JACKSON INC p 800
1463 I94 Business Loop E, Dickinson ND 58601
Tel (701) 355-8400 SIC 8711 8713

GLAUS PYLE SCHOMER BURNS & DEHAVEN INC p 614
520 S Main St Ste 2531, Akron OH 44311
Tel (330) 572-2100 SIC 8711 8712

ROVISYS CO p 1253
1455 Danner Dr, Aurora OH 44202
Tel (330) 562-8600 SIC 8711

MACAULAY-BROWN INC p 891
4021 Executive Dr, Beavercreek OH 45430
Tel (937) 426-3421 SIC 8711 8733

WOOLPERT INC p 1624
4454 Idea Center Blvd, Beavercreek OH 45430
Tel (937) 461-5660 SIC 8711

BELCAN ENGINEERING GROUP LLC p 169
10200 Anderson Way, Blue Ash OH 45242
Tel (513) 891-0972 SIC 8711

BELCAN LLC p 169
10200 Anderson Way, Blue Ash OH 45242
Tel (513) 891-0972 SIC 7363 8711

DLHBOWLES INC p 445
2422 Leo Ave Sw, Canton OH 44706
Tel (330) 478-2503 SIC 8711 3089 3082

■ CECO GROUP INC p 272
4625 Red Bank Rd Ste 200, Cincinnati OH 45227
Tel (513) 458-2600
SIC 8711 3564 8734 3443 3444 1761

■ GENERAL ELECTRIC INTERNATIONAL INC p 600
191 Rosa Parks St, Cincinnati OH 45202
Tel (513) 813-9133 SIC 8711

QUEST GLOBAL SERVICES-NA INC p 1199
11499 Chester Rd Ste 600, Cincinnati OH 45246
Tel (513) 648-4900 SIC 8731 8711

AUSTIN BUILDING AND DESIGN INC p 132
6095 Parkland Blvd # 100, Cleveland OH 44124
Tel (440) 544-2600
SIC 1541 1542 8742 8711 8712

CROWNE GROUP LLC p 396
127 Public Sq Ste 5110, Cleveland OH 44114
Tel (216) 589-0198 SIC 3559 8711

MIDDOUGH INC p 965
1901 E 13th St Ste 400, Cleveland OH 44114
Tel (216) 367-6000 SIC 8711 8712

NESCO INC p 1026
6140 Parkland Blvd # 110, Cleveland OH 44124
Tel (440) 461-6000
SIC 3535 3541 3544 8711 6531

STEVENS ENGINEERS & CONSTRUCTORS INC p 1388
7850 Freeway Cir Ste 100, Cleveland OH 44130
Tel (440) 234-7888 SIC 1541 1711 8711

■ URS FEDERAL SERVICES INTERNATIONAL INC p 1530
1300 E 9th St Ste 500, Cleveland OH 44114
Tel (301) 944-3100 SIC 8711

■ AMERICAN ELECTRIC POWER SERVICE CORP p 71
1 Riverside Plz Fl 1, Columbus OH 43215
Tel (614) 716-1000
SIC 4911 8711 8713 8721

BURGESS & NIPLE INC p 227
5085 Reed Rd, Columbus OH 43220
Tel (502) 254-2344 SIC 8711 8712

FISHEL CO p 551
1366 Dublin Rd, Columbus OH 43215
Tel (614) 274-8100 SIC 1623 1731 8711

BENDIX COMMERCIAL VEHICLE SYSTEMS LLC p 172
901 Cleveland St, Elyria OH 44035
Tel (440) 329-9000 SIC 5013 8711

SIERRA LOBO INC p 1320
102 Pinnacle Dr, Fremont OH 43420
Tel (419) 332-7101 SIC 8711

■ CORRPRO COMPANIES INC p 373
1055 W Smith Rd, Medina OH 44256
Tel (330) 723-5082 SIC 3699 8711

ROLLS-ROYCE ENERGY SYSTEMS INC p 1247
105 N Sandusky St, Mount Vernon OH 43050
Tel (740) 393-8888 SIC 3511 5084 8711

WASTREN ADVANTAGE INC p 1581
1571 Shyville Rd, Piketon OH 45661
Tel (970) 254-1277 SIC 4959 8744 8711

HDT GLOBAL INC p 673
30500 Aurora Rd Ste 100, Solon OH 44139
Tel (216) 438-6111 SIC 8711

HUNTER DEFENSE TECHNOLOGIES INC p 719
30500 Aurora Rd Ste 100, Solon OH 44139
Tel (216) 438-6111
SIC 3433 3569 3822 8331 8711 3549

SSOE INC p 1364
1001 Madison Ave Ste A, Toledo OH 43604
Tel (419) 255-3830
SIC 8711 8712 8742 1541 7389

CLARKWESTERN DIETRICH BUILDING SYSTEMS LLC p 322
9100 Centre Pointe Dr # 210, West Chester OH 45069
Tel (513) 870-1100 SIC 3444 8711 3081

TSS TECHNOLOGIES INC p 1489
8800 Global Way, West Chester OH 45069
Tel (513) 772-7000 SIC 3599 8711

CHOCTAW ARCHIVING ENTERPRISE p 301
2101 W Arkansas St, Durant OK 74701
Tel (580) 920-1501 SIC 8711 4226

■ BOEING AEROSPACE OPERATIONS INC p 197
6001 S Air Depot Blvd, Oklahoma City OK 73135
Tel (405) 622-6000 SIC 8711 8249

FORD AUDIO-VIDEO SYSTEMS LLC p 565
4800 W Interstate 40, Oklahoma City OK 73128
Tel (405) 946-9966 SIC 1731 8711

ENOVATION CONTROLS LLC p 500
5311 S 122nd East Ave, Tulsa OK 74146
Tel (918) 317-4100
SIC 3625 3714 3694 8711

LINDE ENGINEERING NORTH AMERICA INC p 868
6100 S Yale Ave Ste 1200, Tulsa OK 74136
Tel (918) 477-1200 SIC 3567 8711

LINDE HOLDINGS LLC p 868
6100 S Yale Ave Ste 1200, Tulsa OK 74136
Tel (918) 477-1200 SIC 8711

LINDE PROCESS PLANTS INC p 868
6100 S Yale Ave Ste 1200, Tulsa OK 74136
Tel (918) 477-1200 SIC 3444 8711 1629

■ MATRIX PDM ENGINEERING INC p 920
5100 E Skelly Dr Ste 800, Tulsa OK 74135
Tel (918) 624-6300 SIC 1542 1623 8711

▲ MATRIX SERVICE CO p 920
5100 E Skelly Dr Ste 700, Tulsa OK 74135
Tel (918) 838-8822
SIC 1542 1623 7349 8711

WILLBROS DOWNSTREAM LLC p 1610
4300 E 36th St N, Tulsa OK 74115
Tel (918) 556-3600 SIC 8711

CH2M HILL INDUSTRIAL DESIGN & CONSTRUCTION INC p 286
2020 Sw 4th Ave Fl 3, Portland OR 97201
Tel (503) 224-6040
SIC 8711 8712 8741 7699

DAVID EVANS AND ASSOCIATES INC p 415
2100 Sw River Pkwy, Portland OR 97201
Tel (503) 223-6663 SIC 8711 8713 8741

OTAK INC p 1097
808 Sw 3rd Ave Ste 220, Portland OR 97204
Tel (503) 274-5445
SIC 0781 8712 8711 8713 8742 8999

▲ CUI GLOBAL INC p 400
20050 Sw 112th Ave, Tualatin OR 97062
Tel (503) 612-2300 SIC 3824 8711

UHDE CORP OF AMERICA p 1500
1370 Wash Pike Ste 510, Bridgeville PA 15017
Tel (412) 257-8277 SIC 8711 7299

SDI INC p 1295
1414 Radcliffe St Ste 300, Bristol PA 19007
Tel (215) 633-1900
SIC 7374 7389 8711 8748

FLEMING GANNETT INC p 555
207 Senate Ave, Camp Hill PA 17011
Tel (717) 763-7211 SIC 8711

GANNETT FLEMING AFFILIATES INC p 590
207 Senate Ave, Camp Hill PA 17011
Tel (717) 763-7211 SIC 8711 7374 6512

ANDRITZ INC p 91
500 Technology Dr, Canonsburg PA 15317
Tel (724) 597-7801 SIC 3554 8711 7389

AMERICAN BRIDGE CO p 69
1000 American Bridge Way, Coraopolis PA 15108
Tel (412) 631-1000 SIC 1791 8711 1622

WESTINGHOUSE ELECTRIC CO LLC p 1601
1000 Westinghouse Dr, Cranberry Township PA 16066
Tel (412) 374-2020
SIC 3829 8711 3823 2819

PENN ENGINEERING & MANUFACTURING CORP p 1129
5190 Old Easton Rd, Danboro PA 18916
Tel (215) 766-8853 SIC 3429 3549 8711

STV ARCHITECTS INC p 1395
205 W Welsh Dr, Douglassville PA 19518
Tel (610) 385-8200 SIC 8711

STV GROUP INC p 1395
205 W Welsh Dr, Douglassville PA 19518
Tel (610) 385-8200 SIC 8712 8711

DELPHINUS ENGINEERING INC p 425
1510 Chester Pike Ste 380, Eddystone PA 19022
Tel (610) 874-9160 SIC 8711

GAI CONSULTANTS INC p 589
385 E Waterfront Dr Fl 1, Homestead PA 15120
Tel (412) 476-2000 SIC 8711

CONCURRENT TECHNOLOGIES CORP p 355
100 Ctc Dr, Johnstown PA 15904
Tel (814) 266-2874 SIC 8711

UNITEK GLOBAL SERVICES INC p 1515
2010 Renaissance Blvd, King Of Prussia PA 19406
Tel (267) 464-1700
SIC 1731 8741 8742 8711

ERM-NA HOLDINGS CORP p 508
75 Valley Stream Pkwy # 200, Malvern PA 19355
Tel (484) 913-0300 SIC 8711 8748 8742

HENRY F TEICHMANN INC p 684
3009 Washington Rd, Mc Murray PA 15317
Tel (724) 941-9550 SIC 1541 8711 8742

BECHTEL PLANT MACHINERY INC p 167
3500 Technology Dr, Monroeville PA 15146
Tel (412) 829-8626 SIC 8711

EMCON INC p 491
2790 Mosside Blvd, Monroeville PA 15146
Tel (412) 372-7701 SIC 8711 8999

MICHAEL BAKER INTERNATIONAL HOLDCO CORP p 960
100 Airside Dr, Moon Township PA 15108
Tel (412) 269-6300 SIC 8711

VEOLIA WATER TECHNOLOGIES p 1549
250 Airside Dr, Moon Township PA 15108
Tel (412) 809-6000 SIC 8711

PKF-MARK III INC p 1153
17 Blacksmith Rd Ste 101, Newtown PA 18940
Tel (215) 968-5031
SIC 1611 1629 1711 1731 1771 8711

▲ CDI CORP p 271
1735 Market St Ste 200, Philadelphia PA 19103
Tel (215) 569-2200
SIC 8711 7371 7373 7376 7361 7363

■ CDI CORP p 271
1735 Market St Ste 200, Philadelphia PA 19103
Tel (215) 569-2200
SIC 7363 8711 7361 6794

DAY & ZIMMERMANN GROUP INC p 417
1500 Spring Garden St # 900, Philadelphia PA 19130
Tel (215) 299-8000
SIC 8711 8712 8741 7381 7382 3489

DAY & ZIMMERMANN INTERNATIONAL INC p 417
1500 Spring Garden St # 900, Philadelphia PA 19130
Tel (215) 299-8000 SIC 8711 1541 8741

DAY AND ZIMMERMANN INC p 417
1500 Spring Garden St # 900, Philadelphia PA 19130
Tel (215) 299-8000
SIC 8744 8712 8711 3559 3483

MCKEAN DEFENSE GROUP LLC p 930
1 Crescent Dr Ste 400, Philadelphia PA 19112
Tel (215) 271-6108 SIC 8711

PENNONI ASSOCIATES INC p 1130
3001 Market St Ste 200, Philadelphia PA 19104
Tel (215) 222-3000 SIC 8711

TAYLOR MCCORMICK INC p 1427
2001 Market St Fl 10, Philadelphia PA 19103
Tel (215) 592-4200 SIC 8711

BAKER MICHAEL INTERNATIONAL INC p 146
500 Grant St Ste 5400, Pittsburgh PA 15219
Tel (412) 269-6300 SIC 8711 8741

CIVIL & ENVIRONMENTAL CONSULTANTS INC p 320
333 Baldwin Rd Ste 1, Pittsburgh PA 15205
Tel (412) 429-2324 SIC 8711 0781

MICHAEL BAKER INTERNATIONAL LLC p 960
500 Grant St Ste 5400, Pittsburgh PA 15219
Tel (412) 918-4000 SIC 8711

DANELLA COMPANIES INC p 411
2290 Butler Pike, Plymouth Meeting PA 19462
Tel (610) 828-6200
SIC 7513 7353 8711 1623 8748

GENESIS ENGINEERS INC p 602
1850 Gravers Rd Ste 300, Plymouth Meeting PA 19462
Tel (610) 592-0280 SIC 8711 8741

NAVMAR APPLIED SCIENCES CORP p 1020
65 W Street Rd Ste C, Warminster PA 18974
Tel (215) 675-4900 SIC 8731 8711

CARIBBEAN ARCHITECTS & ENGINEERS p 256
D14 Calle 6 Apt 1101, Guaynabo PR 00966
Tel (787) 783-5500 SIC 8711 8712

FACTORY MUTUAL INSURANCE CO p 524
270 Central Ave, Johnston RI 02919
Tel (401) 275-3000 SIC 6331 8711 6512

WILBUR SMITH ASSOCIATES GROUP INC p 1608
1301 Gervais St Ste 1600, Columbia SC 29201
Tel (803) 758-4500 SIC 8711

WILBUR SMITH ASSOCIATES INC p 1608
1301 Gervais St Ste 1600, Columbia SC 29201
Tel (803) 758-4500 SIC 8711

AFL NETWORK SERVICES INC p 33
170 Ridgeview Cnt Dr, Duncan SC 29334
Tel (864) 433-0333 SIC 8711

CONTINENTAL AUTOMOTIVE INC p 362
1830 Macmillan Park Dr, Fort Mill SC 29707
Tel (704) 583-3900 SIC 3011 8711

■ JACOBS APPLIED TECHNOLOGY INC p 775
2040 Bushy Park Rd, Goose Creek SC 29445
Tel (843) 824-1100
SIC 3559 3443 8711 1629

■ FLUOR FEDERAL SERVICES INC p 561
100 Fluor Daniel Dr, Greenville SC 29607
Tel (864) 281-4400 SIC 8711

ONEAL INC p 1087
10 Falcon Crest Dr, Greenville SC 29607
Tel (864) 298-2000 SIC 8711 8712

LIFE CYCLE ENGINEERING INC p 863
4360 Corporate Rd Ste 100, North Charleston SC 29405
Tel (843) 744-7110
SIC 7371 7373 7376 7379 8711

CH2M HILL ENGINEERS INC p 286
1500 International Dr, Spartanburg SC 29303
Tel (864) 578-2000 SIC 8711 8742 1629

INFRASTRUCTURE CORP OF AMERICA p 742
750 Old Hickory Blvd # 200, Brentwood TN 37027
Tel (615) 377-4730 SIC 8742 8711 8741

NISSAN NORTH AMERICA INC p 1044
1 Nissan Way, Franklin TN 37067
Tel (615) 725-1000
SIC 5012 8711 8734 6141 8741 3711

DIVERSIFIED CONVEYORS INC p 444
2163 Airways Blvd Ste 300, Memphis TN 38114
Tel (901) 333-8346 SIC 8711

YOROZU NORTH AMERICA INC p 1637
395 Mt View Industrial Dr, Morrison TN 37357
Tel (931) 668-7700 SIC 8711 8742

BARGE WAGGONER SUMNER AND CANNON INC p 155
211 Commerce St Ste 600, Nashville TN 37201
Tel (615) 254-1500 SIC 8711

BRIDGESTONE INDUSTRIAL PRODUCTS AMERICA INC p 211
402 Bna Dr Ste 212, Nashville TN 37217
Tel (615) 365-0600 SIC 5085 8711

AEROSPACE TESTING ALLIANCE p 31
600 William Northern Blvd, Tullahoma TN 37388
Tel (931) 454-3000 SIC 8711

■ JACOBS TECHNOLOGY INC p 775
600 William Northern Blvd, Tullahoma TN 37388
Tel (931) 455-6400 SIC 8711

FESCO LTD p 539
1000 Fesco Dr, Alice TX 78332
Tel (361) 664-3479 SIC 8711 5082

■ TEAM INDUSTRIAL SERVICES INC p 1430
200 Hermann Dr, Alvin TX 77511
Tel (281) 388-5525 SIC 8748 8711 7699

FERROVIAL AGROMAN TEXAS LLC p 538
9600 Great Hills Trl 200e, Austin TX 78759
Tel (512) 637-8587 SIC 8711

TOKYO ELECTRON AMERICA INC p 1458
2400 Grove Blvd, Austin TX 78741
Tel (512) 424-1000 SIC 3559 8711

JONES & CARTER INC p 792
6330 West Loop S Ste 150, Bellaire TX 77401
Tel (713) 777-5337 SIC 8711

WORLEYPARSONS GROUP INC p 1626
6330 West Loop S, Bellaire TX 77401
Tel (713) 407-5000 SIC 8711 8742

TEXAS A&M ENGINEERING EXPERIMENT STATION p 1442
7607 Eastmark Dr Ste 101, College Station TX 77840
Tel (979) 458-7643 SIC 8711

TEXAS A&M ENGINEERING EXTENSION SERVICE p 1442
301 Tarrow St, College Station TX 77840
Tel (979) 845-7641
SIC 8331 8711 8748 8111

■ QUALSPEC INC p 1198
5602 Ih 37, Corpus Christi TX 78407
Tel (281) 479-3300 SIC 8711

BRANDT ENGINEERING CO INC p 208
1728 Briercrest Dr, Dallas TX 75229
Tel (972) 395-6000 SIC 1711 8711

▲ JACOBS ENGINEERING GROUP INC p 775
1999 Bryan St Ste 1200, Dallas TX 75201
Tel (214) 583-8500
SIC 8711 1629 1541 8748

▲ PRIMORIS SERVICES CORP p 1176
2100 Mckinney Ave # 1500, Dallas TX 75201
Tel (214) 740-5600 SIC 1623 8711

TD SERVICES INC p 1429
13850 Diplomat Dr, Dallas TX 75234
Tel (972) 888-9500 SIC 8711

■ CARTER & BURGESS INC p 261
777 Main St Ste 2500, Fort Worth TX 76102
Tel (817) 735-6000 SIC 8711 8712 8713

FREESE AND NICHOLS INC p 577
4055 Intl Plz Ste 200, Fort Worth TX 76109
Tel (817) 735-7491 SIC 8711

FTS INTERNATIONAL SERVICES LLC p 583
777 Main St Ste 2900, Fort Worth TX 76102
Tel (817) 850-1008
SIC 3561 8711 7353 4225

■ NUCLEAR LOGISTICS INC p 1066
7410 Pebble Dr, Fort Worth TX 76118
Tel (817) 284-0077 SIC 5065 8711

PAE APPLIED TECHNOLOGIES LLC p 1107
6500 West Fwy Ste 600, Fort Worth TX 76116
Tel (817) 737-1500
SIC 8741 8711 8744 4581 7381

WEIR GROUP INC p 1588
7601 Wyatt Dr, Fort Worth TX 76108
Tel (817) 246-2461 SIC 3561 8711

■ WILLBROS UTILITY T&D HOLDINGS LLC p 1610
115 W 7th St Ste 1420, Fort Worth TX 76102
Tel (682) 233-9010 SIC 8711

■ GE ON WING SUPPORT INC p 596
3010 Red Hawk Dr Ste B, Grand Prairie TX 75052
Tel (214) 960-3322 SIC 7699 8711

■ SABINE MINING CO p 1264
6501 Fm 968 W, Hallsville TX 75650
Tel (903) 660-4200 SIC 1241 8711 1221

AKER SUBSEA INC p 42
3010 Briarpark Dr, Houston TX 77042
Tel (713) 685-5700 SIC 3533 1389 8711

AMEC FOSTER WHEELER OIL & GAS INC p 66
585 N Dairy Ashford Rd, Houston TX 77079
Tel (713) 929-5000 SIC 8711 8742 8741

AMEC FOSTER WHEELER USA CORP p 66
585 N Dairy Ashford Rd, Houston TX 77079
Tel (713) 929-5000 SIC 8711 3443 1629

ARAMCO SERVICES CO p 102
9009 West Loop S, Houston TX 77096
Tel (713) 432-4000 SIC 8711 8742

AZKU INC p 140
1616 S Voss Rd Ste 550, Houston TX 77057
Tel (713) 782-1080 SIC 5082 8711

BECHTEL-JACOBS JOINT VENTURE p 167
3000 Post Oak Blvd, Houston TX 77056
Tel (713) 235-2000 SIC 8711

BURROW GLOBAL SERVICES LLC p 228
6200 Savoy Dr Ste 800, Houston TX 77036
Tel (713) 963-0930 SIC 1542 1541 8711

CAMAC INTERNATIONAL CORP p 243
1330 Post Oak Blvd Ste 22, Houston TX 77056
Tel (713) 965-5100
SIC 8711 6552 1382 8741 1389

FABCO LLC p 523
13835 Beaumont Hwy, Houston TX 77049
Tel (713) 633-6500 SIC 3441 8741 8711

FUGRO (USA) INC p 583
6100 Hillcroft St Ste 700, Houston TX 77081
Tel (713) 772-3700 SIC 1389 8711 8999

FUGRO CONSULTANTS INC p 583
6100 Hillcroft St Ste 100, Houston TX 77081
Tel (713) 369-5400 SIC 8711

GIBSON APPLIED TECHNOLOGY & ENGINEERING (TEXAS) INC p 611
16360 Park Ten Pl Ste 206, Houston TX 77084
Tel (281) 398-5781 SIC 8711

GULF INTERNATIONAL CORP p 646
16010 Barkers Point Ln, Houston TX 77079
Tel (713) 850-3400 SIC 8711

GULF INTERSTATE ENGINEERING CO p 646
16010 Barkers Point Ln # 600, Houston TX 77079
Tel (713) 850-3400 SIC 8711

▲ HALLIBURTON CO p 654
3000 N Sam Houston Pkwy E, Houston TX 77032
Tel (281) 871-2699
SIC 1389 1382 1381 8711

■ HALLIBURTON DELAWARE INC p 654
3000 Houston Ave, Houston TX 77009
Tel (713) 759-2600
SIC 1629 1611 1622 8711 1389

HEATH CONSULTANTS INC p 679
9030 W Monroe Rd, Houston TX 77061
Tel (713) 844-1300 SIC 8711 3826 3812

HUNTING INNOVA INC p 719
8383 N Sam Houston Pkwy W, Houston TX 77064
Tel (281) 653-5500 SIC 3672 3613 8711

IHI E&C INTERNATIONAL CORP p 731
1080 Eldridge Pkwy, Houston TX 77077
Tel (713) 270-3100 SIC 8711

INVENSYS SYSTEMS INC p 761
10900 Equity Dr, Houston TX 77041
Tel (713) 329-1600 SIC 3823 8711 8741

■ JACOBS FIELD SERVICES NORTH AMERICA INC p 775
5995 Rogerdale Rd, Houston TX 77072
Tel (832) 351-6000 SIC 8711

■ KBR HOLDINGS LLC p 806
601 Jefferson St Ste 7911, Houston TX 77002
Tel (713) 753-4176 SIC 1629 8711 8741

▲ KBR INC p 806
601 Jefferson St Ste 3400, Houston TX 77002
Tel (713) 753-3011 SIC 1629 8711 8741

■ KELLOGG BROWN & ROOT LLC p 808
601 Jefferson St Ste 100, Houston TX 77002
Tel (713) 753-2000 SIC 8711 1629

M-I LLC p 890
5950 N Course Dr, Houston TX 77072
Tel (281) 561-1300
SIC 1389 2865 2869 8711 8741

MEITECHNOLOGIES INC p 940
18050 Saturn Ln Ste 300, Houston TX 77058
Tel (281) 283-6200 SIC 8711 8733

MODEC INTERNATIONAL INC p 980
15011 Katy Fwy Ste 500, Houston TX 77094
Tel (281) 529-8100 SIC 8711 2499 3731

▲ OCEANEERING INTERNATIONAL INC p 1073
11911 Fm 529 Rd, Houston TX 77041
Tel (713) 329-4500 SIC 1389 3731 8711

PB ENERGY STORAGE SERVICES INC p 1123
16200 Park Row Ste 200, Houston TX 77084
Tel (281) 496-5590 SIC 8711

PIPING TECHNOLOGY & PRODUCTS INC p 1151
3701 Holmes Rd, Houston TX 77051
Tel (800) 787-5914 SIC 3494 8711 3441

PRIDE INTERNATIONAL INC p 1174
5847 San Felipe St # 3400, Houston TX 77057
Tel (713) 789-1400 SIC 1381 1389 8711

R & B FALCON DRILLING INTERNATIONAL DEEPWATER INC p 1201
2000 W Sam Houston Pkwy S, Houston TX 77042
Tel (713) 278-6000 SIC 1381 8711

RIMKUS CONSULTING GROUP INC p 1235
8 Greenway Plz Ste 500, Houston TX 77046
Tel (713) 621-3550 SIC 8711

S & B HOLDINGS LTD p 1261
7809 Park Place Blvd, Houston TX 77087
Tel (713) 645-4141 SIC 1629 8711

S AND B ENGINEERS AND CONSTRUCTORS LTD p 1261
7825 Park Place Blvd, Houston TX 77087
Tel (713) 645-4141 SIC 1629 8711

SAIPEM AMERICA INC p 1271
15950 Park Row, Houston TX 77084
Tel (281) 552-5600 SIC 8711 1389

STRESS ENGINEERING SERVICES INC p 1393
13800 Westfair East Dr, Houston TX 77041
Tel (281) 955-2900 SIC 8711

TAS COMMERCIAL CONCRETE LLC p 1425
19319 Oil Center Blvd, Houston TX 77073
Tel (281) 230-7500 SIC 8711

TECHNIP STONE & WEBSTER PROCESS TECHNOLOGY INC p 1431
11740 Katy Fwy Ste 100, Houston TX 77079
Tel (281) 870-1111 SIC 8711

TECHNIP USA HOLDINGS INC p 1431
11740 Katy Fwy Ste 100, Houston TX 77079
Tel (281) 870-1111 SIC 8711

TECHNIP USA INC p 1431
11740 Katy Fwy Ste 100, Houston TX 77079
Tel (281) 870-1111 SIC 8711 8741

TROY CONSTRUCTION LLC p 1485
8521 Mchard Rd, Houston TX 77053
Tel (281) 437-8214 SIC 1623 8711

UNITED SPACE ALLIANCE LLC p 1512
3700 Bay Area Blvd # 100, Houston TX 77058
Tel (281) 212-6200 SIC 8711

■ UNIVERSALPEGASUS INTERNATIONAL HOLDINGS INC p 1518
4848 Loop Central Dr # 600, Houston TX 77081
Tel (713) 425-6000 SIC 7389 8711 8713

■ UNIVERSALPEGASUS INTERNATIONAL INC p 1518
4848 Loop Central Dr # 600, Houston TX 77081
Tel (713) 425-6000 SIC 7389 8711 8713

▲ WILLBROS GROUP INC p 1610
4400 Post Oak Pkwy, Houston TX 77027
Tel (713) 403-8000 SIC 8711 1542

WILLBROS INTERNATIONAL INC p 1610
4400 Post Oak Pkwy # 1000, Houston TX 77027
Tel (713) 403-8000 SIC 8711

■ WILLBROS UNITED STATES HOLDINGS INC p 1610
4400 Post Oak Pkwy # 1000, Houston TX 77027
Tel (713) 403-8000 SIC 8711 1623

WOOD GROUP MUSTANG INC p 1622
17325 Park Row, Houston TX 77084
Tel (832) 809-8000
SIC 8711 8742 7389 1389

WOOD GROUP PSN INC p 1622
17325 Park Row, Houston TX 77084
Tel (281) 647-1041 SIC 1629 1542 8711

WORLEYPARSONS CORP p 1626
575 N Gary Ashford, Houston TX 77079
Tel (713) 407-5000 SIC 8711 8742

▲ FLUOR CORP p 561
6700 Las Colinas Blvd, Irving TX 75039
Tel (469) 398-7000 SIC 8711 1629 1541

■ FLUOR ENTERPRISES INC p 561
6700 Las Colinas Blvd, Irving TX 75039
Tel (469) 398-7000 SIC 1799 8711

SHERMCO INDUSTRIES INC p 1316
2425 E Pioneer Dr, Irving TX 75061
Tel (972) 793-5523 SIC 8711 7694 5063

VCC LLC p 1545
600 Las Colinas Blvd E # 1525, Irving TX 75039
Tel (214) 574-4500 SIC 1542 8711 8742

DET NORSKE VERITAS HOLDING (USA) INC p 433
1400 Ravello Rd, Katy TX 77449
Tel (281) 396-1000
SIC 8711 7389 5734 8741

JV INDUSTRIAL COMPANIES LTD p 798
4040 Red Bluff Rd, Pasadena TX 77503
Tel (713) 568-2600 SIC 7692 3441 8711

VENTECH ENGINEERS INTERNATIONAL CORP p 1548
1149 Ellsworth Dr Ofc, Pasadena TX 77506
Tel (713) 477-0201
SIC 8711 8711 3559 5084

VENTECH INC p 1548
1149 Ellsworth Dr Ofc, Pasadena TX 77506
Tel (713) 477-0201
SIC 8711 3491 5084 6512

M+W AMERICAS INC p 890
1001 Klein Rd Ste 400, Plano TX 75074
Tel (972) 535-7300
SIC 3433 8712 8711 8741

HALFF ASSOCIATES INC p 654
1201 N Bowser Rd, Richardson TX 75081
Tel (214) 346-6200 SIC 8711 8713

INFOVISION INC p 742
800 E Campbell Rd Ste 388, Richardson TX 75081
Tel (972) 234-0058 SIC 8711 7371

BAKER MICHAEL JR INC p 146
810 Hesters Crossing Rd # 163, Round Rock TX 78681
Tel (512) 248-8651 SIC 8711

RABA KISTNER INC p 1203
12821 W Golden Ln, San Antonio TX 78249
Tel (210) 699-9090 SIC 8711

SOUTHWEST RESEARCH INSTITUTE INC p 1352
6220 Culebra Rd, San Antonio TX 78238
Tel (210) 684-5111 SIC 8731 8711

ZACHRY HOLDINGS INC p 1640
527 Logwood Ave, San Antonio TX 78221
Tel (210) 588-5000
SIC 1541 8711 1629 1623

▲ THERMON GROUP HOLDINGS INC p 1447
100 Thermon Dr, San Marcos TX 78666
Tel (512) 396-5801 SIC 8711

■ THERMON HEAT TRACING SERVICES INC p 1447
100 Thermon Dr, San Marcos TX 78666
Tel (512) 396-5801 SIC 8711

NOBLE DRILLING CORP p 1046
13135 Dairy Ashford Rd # 700, Sugar Land TX 77478
Tel (281) 276-6100 SIC 1381 8711

AIM GROUP INC p 38
9450 Grogans Mill Rd # 120, The Woodlands TX 77380
Tel (281) 847-2000 SIC 8711

CHICAGO BRIDGE & IRON CO p 297
2103 Research Forest Dr, The Woodlands TX 77380
Tel (832) 513-1000 SIC 8711

CHICAGO BRIDGE & IRON CO (DELAWARE) p 297
2103 Research Forest Dr, The Woodlands TX 77380
Tel (832) 513-1000 SIC 8711 3325 3462

UTAH STATE UNIVERSITY RESEARCH FOUNDATION p 1536
1695 N Research Pkwy, North Logan UT 84341
Tel (435) 713-3400
SIC 8711 8734 8733 7371

APX GROUP INC p 101
4931 N 300 W, Provo UT 84604
Tel (801) 377-9111
SIC 8711 3822 1711 5065

APX PARENT HOLDCO INC p 101
4931 N 300 W, Provo UT 84604
Tel (801) 377-9111
SIC 6719 3822 1711 8711 5065 5074

ENERGYSOLUTIONS INC p 498
299 S Main St Ste 1700, Salt Lake City UT 84111
Tel (801) 649-2000 SIC 4953 8711

ENERGYSOLUTIONS LLC p 498
299 Suth Main St Ste 1700, Salt Lake City UT 84111
Tel (801) 649-2000 SIC 4953 8711

JOB INDUSTRIAL SERVICES INC p 787
1805 S Redwood Rd # 150, Salt Lake City UT 84104
Tel (801) 433-0901 SIC 8711

■ HEADWATERS RESOURCES INC p 673
10701 S River Front Pkwy # 300, South Jordan UT 84095
Tel (801) 984-9400 SIC 5032 4953 8711

■ FLUOR-LANE LLC p 561
6315 Bren Mar Dr Ste 250, Alexandria VA 22312
Tel (571) 480-4641 SIC 8711

MODERN TECHNOLOGY SOLUTIONS INC p 981
5285 Shawnee Rd Ste 400, Alexandria VA 22312
Tel (703) 564-3800
SIC 8711 8742 8731 7379

R&R ENTERPRISES INC p 1203
1101 King St Ste 550, Alexandria VA 22314
Tel (703) 739-0084 SIC 8711

SENTEL CORP p 1305
2800 Eisenhower Ave # 300, Alexandria VA 22314
Tel (571) 481-2000 SIC 8711 8742 8741

VISION TECHNOLOGIES ELECTRONICS INC p 1561
99 Canal Center Plz # 210, Alexandria VA 22314
Tel (703) 739-2610 SIC 8711

▲ VSE CORP p 1566
6348 Walker Ln, Alexandria VA 22310
Tel (703) 960-4600 SIC 8711 8742 8741

ALENIA AERMACCHI NORTH AMERICA INC p 48
1235 S Clark St Ste 700, Arlington VA 22202
Tel (703) 413-2125 SIC 8711

BNG AMERICA LLC p 194
1235 S Clark St Ste 700a, Arlington VA 22202
Tel (703) 412-2500
SIC 8711 8741 4953 2819

■ CACI INC - FEDERAL p 235
1100 N Glebe Rd Ste 200, Arlington VA 22201
Tel (703) 841-7800
SIC 7373 7372 7371 8711

■ CACI TECHNOLOGIES INC p 236
1100 N Glebe Rd Ste 200, Arlington VA 22201
Tel (703) 841-7800 SIC 7373 8711

■ EMCOR GOVERNMENT SERVICES INC p 491
2800 Crystal Dr Ste 600, Arlington VA 22202
Tel (571) 403-8900 SIC 8741 8711 1731

MILLENNIUM ENGINEERING AND INTEGRATION CO p 970
1400 Crystal Dr Ste 800, Arlington VA 22202
Tel (703) 413-7750 SIC 8711 8731

PACIFIC ARCHITECTS AND ENGINEERS INC p 1104
1320 N Courthouse Rd # 800, Arlington VA 22201
Tel (888) 526-5416 SIC 8711 8712

PAE HOLDING CORP p 1107
1320 N Courthouse Rd # 800, Arlington VA 22201
Tel (703) 717-6000 SIC 6719 8742 8711

SIEMENS GOVERNMENT TECHNOLOGIES INC p 1320
2231 Crystal Dr Ste 700, Arlington VA 22202
Tel (703) 860-1574
SIC 8711 7373 7376 7379 8712 7378

THALES USA INC p 1446
2733 Crystal Dr, Arlington VA 22202
Tel (703) 413-6029
SIC 5065 3699 3679 3841 8711 7371

AMERICAN SYSTEMS CORP p 80
14151 Pk Madow Dr Ste 500, Chantilly VA 20151
Tel (703) 968-6300
SIC 8711 1731 8742 7373

BOWMAN CONSULTING GROUP LTD p 204
3863 Centerview Dr # 300, Chantilly VA 20151
Tel (703) 464-1000 SIC 8711 8713

▲ ENGILITY HOLDINGS INC p 499
3750 Centerview Dr, Chantilly VA 20151
Tel (703) 708-1400 SIC 8711 8741

■ ENGILITY LLC p 499
4803 Stonecroft Blvd, Chantilly VA 20151
Tel (703) 708-1400 SIC 8711

ENGINEERING CONSULTING SERVICES LTD p 499
14026 Thunderbolt Pl, Chantilly VA 20151
Tel (703) 471-8400 SIC 8711

ENGINEERING SOLUTIONS & PRODUCTS LLC p 499
14566 Lee Rd, Chantilly VA 20151
Tel (571) 375-1400
SIC 8711 7379 4813 8742 8748

VENCORE HOLDING CORP p 1547
15052 Conference Ctr Dr, Chantilly VA 20151
Tel (571) 313-6000
SIC 6719 8711 8733 3812 7372

VENCORE INC p 1547
15052 Conference Ctr Dr, Chantilly VA 20151
Tel (571) 313-6000
SIC 8711 8733 3812 7372

JO-KELL INC p 787
1716 Lambert Ct, Chesapeake VA 23320
Tel (757) 523-2900 SIC 5063 8711

HARRIS TECHNICAL SERVICES CORP p 664
21000 Atl Blvd Ste 300, Dulles VA 20166
Tel (703) 610-4200
SIC 7371 7379 8711 3577

RAYTHEON TECHNICAL SERVICES CO LLC p 1211
22270 Pacific Blvd, Dulles VA 20166
Tel (571) 250-2100 SIC 8331 8711

CDM FEDERAL PROGRAMS CORP p 271
3201 Jermantown Rd # 400, Fairfax VA 22030
Tel (703) 691-6500
SIC 8711 8742 8744 8748 8999

CDM-AECOM MULTIMEDIA JOINT VENTURE p 271
3201 Jermantown Rd # 400, Fairfax VA 22030
Tel (703) 691-6500 SIC 8711

DEWBERRY COMPANIES LC p 434
8401 Arlington Blvd Ste 1, Fairfax VA 22031
Tel (703) 849-0100 SIC 8711

DEWBERRY CONSULTANTS LLC p 434
8401 Arlington Blvd Ste 1, Fairfax VA 22031
Tel (703) 849-0311 SIC 8711 8712 8731

■ GENERAL DYNAMICS INFORMATION TECHNOLOGY INC p 600
3211 Jermantown Rd, Fairfax VA 22030
Tel (703) 995-8700 SIC 7379 8711 7373

▲ MANTECH INTERNATIONAL CORP p 903
12015 Lee Jackson Hwy, Fairfax VA 22033
Tel (703) 218-6000 SIC 7373 8711 7379

■ MANTECH SYSTEMS ENGINEERING CORP p 903
12015 Lee Jackson Hwy, Fairfax VA 22033
Tel (703) 218-6000 SIC 7373 8711

■ QSS GROUP INC p 1195
8270 Willow Oaks Corp Dr, Fairfax VA 22031
Tel (703) 289-8000 SIC 8711

■ SIGNAL SOLUTIONS LLC p 1322
3211 Jermantown Rd # 700, Fairfax VA 22030
Tel (703) 205-0500
SIC 8711 7379 7374 4813 7373 8731

EOIR TECHNOLOGIES INC p 504
10300 Spotsylvania Ave, Fredericksburg VA 22408
Tel (540) 834-4888
SIC 8711 7371 8731 8742

■ CUBIC GLOBAL DEFENSE INC p 399
205 Van Buren St Ste 310, Herndon VA 20170
Tel (703) 821-8930
SIC 7379 7371 7373 8711

■ HARRIS IT SERVICES CORP p 663
2235 Monroe St, Herndon VA 20171
Tel (703) 673-1400 SIC 8711 3663 3674

■ NTT DATA SERVICES FEDERAL GOVERNMENT INC p 1066
13880 Dulles Corner Ln, Herndon VA 20171
Tel (703) 289-8000 SIC 8711 7373 7374

■ BWXT TECHNICAL SERVICES GROUP INC p 231
2016 Mount Athos Rd, Lynchburg VA 24504
Tel (434) 522-6000 SIC 8711 8731

ALION SCIENCE AND TECHNOLOGY CORP p 50
1750 Tysons Blvd Ste 1300, Mc Lean VA 22102
Tel (703) 918-4480 SIC 8711 8731

SALIENT FEDERAL-SGIS INC p 1272
8255 Greensboro Dr # 400, Mc Lean VA 22102
Tel (703) 891-8200 SIC 7373 8711 7382

■ CDI MARINE CO LLC p 271
4600 Village Ave, Norfolk VA 23502
Tel (757) 763-6666
SIC 8711 8712 3732 3731

TIMMONS GROUP INC p 1455
1001 Boulders Pkwy # 300, North Chesterfield VA 23225
Tel (804) 200-6500 SIC 8711 8713

BECHTEL NUCLEAR SECURITY & ENVIRONMENTAL INC p 167
12021 Sunset Hills Rd, Reston VA 20190
Tel (415) 768-1234 SIC 8711 1629 8742

■ CACI NSS INC p 236
11955 Freedom Dr Fl 2, Reston VA 20190
Tel (703) 434-4000 SIC 7373 8711

■ LEIDOS ENGINEERING LLC p 854
11951 Freedom Dr, Reston VA 20190
Tel (571) 526-6000 SIC 8711 1541

▲ NCI INC p 1022
11730 Plaza America Dr # 700, Reston VA 20190
Tel (703) 707-6900 SIC 7373 8711

■ SCITOR CORP p 1292
12010 Sunset Hills Rd, Reston VA 20190
Tel (703) 961-4000 SIC 8711

FROEHLING & ROBERTSON INC p 580
3015 Dumbarton Rd, Richmond VA 23228
Tel (804) 264-2701 SIC 8711 8734

VIRGINIA DEPARTMENT OF TRANSPORTATION p 1559
1401 E Broad St, Richmond VA 23219
Tel (804) 786-2836 SIC 8711

■ HAYES SEAY MATTERN & MATTERN INC p 670
10 S Jefferson St # 1600, Roanoke VA 24011
Tel (540) 857-3100 SIC 8711 8712

TMEIC CORP p 1457
1325 Electric Rd, Salem VA 24153
Tel (540) 283-2000 SIC 8711

▲ VERSAR INC p 1551
6850 Versar Ctr Ste 201, Springfield VA 22151
Tel (703) 750-3000
SIC 8711 8748 8712 8731

■ RAYTHEON TECHNICAL SERVICES INTERNATIONAL CO LLC p 1211
22265 Pacific Blvd, Sterling VA 20166
Tel (310) 647-9438 SIC 8711

■ AMSEC CORP p 87
5701 Cleveland St, Virginia Beach VA 23462
Tel (757) 463-6666 SIC 8711

■ AMSEC LLC p 87
5701 Cleveland St, Virginia Beach VA 23462
Tel (757) 463-6666 SIC 8711

QED SYSTEMS INC p 1194
4646 N Witchduck Rd, Virginia Beach VA 23455
Tel (757) 490-5000 SIC 8711 3731

VT SERVICES INC p 1567
529 Viking Dr, Virginia Beach VA 23452
Tel (912) 573-3671 SIC 8744 8711

▲ BSQUARE CORP p 222
110 110th Ave Ne Ste 300, Bellevue WA 98004
Tel (425) 519-5900 SIC 7371 8711

ALPHA TECHNOLOGIES INC p 60
3767 Alpha Way, Bellingham WA 98226
Tel (360) 647-2360 SIC 8742 8711

■ INSITU INC p 746
118 Columbia River Way, Bingen WA 98605
Tel (509) 493-8600 SIC 8711 3999

PANASONIC AVIONICS CORP p 1111
3303 Monte Villa Pkwy, Bothell WA 98021
Tel (425) 415-9000 SIC 8711

AVIATION TECHNICAL SERVICES INC p 138
3121 109th St Sw, Everett WA 98204
Tel (425) 347-3030 SIC 4581 8711

WASHINGTON ENERGY SERVICES CO p 1578
3909 196th St Sw, Lynnwood WA 98036
Tel (800) 398-4663 SIC 5074 1711 8711

CUBIC GLOBAL DEFENSE INC p 399
400 Union Ave Se Ste 300, Olympia WA 98501
Tel (360) 493-6275
SIC 7373 8744 8711 7376 8748 8741

PARAMETRIX INC p 1114
1019 39th Ave Se Ste 100, Puyallup WA 98374
Tel (206) 394-3700
SIC 8748 8711 8742 1389 4789

■ **WASHINGTON RIVER PROTECTION SOLUTIONS LLC** p 1579
2425 Stevens Center Pl, Richland WA 99354
Tel (509) 376-8103 SIC 8711

KPFF INC p 828
1601 5th Ave Ste 1600, Seattle WA 98101
Tel (206) 622-5822 SIC 8711

RAYTHEON PIKEWERKS CORP p 1211
321 3rd Ave S Ste 203, Seattle WA 98104
Tel (310) 647-9438 SIC 8711

PSF MECHANICAL INC p 1188
11621 E Marginal Way S, Tukwila WA 98168
Tel (206) 764-9663 SIC 1711 8711

■ **LUNDA CONSTRUCTION CO** p 886
620 Gebhardt Rd, Black River Falls WI 54615
Tel (715) 284-2322 SIC 1622 8711

SEAGRAVE FIRE APPARATUS LLC p 1296
105 E 12th St, Clintonville WI 54929
Tel (715) 823-2141 SIC 5012 3713 8711

AFFILIATED ENGINEERS INC p 32
5802 Research Park Blvd, Madison WI 53719
Tel (608) 238-2616 SIC 8711

MEAD AND HUNT INC p 933
2440 Deming Way, Middleton WI 53562
Tel (608) 273-6380 SIC 8712 8711

CORPORATE GROUP INC p 372
7123 W Calumet Rd, Milwaukee WI 53223
Tel (414) 355-7740 SIC 8711 1731

■ **EMTEQ LLC** p 495
5349 S Emmer Dr, New Berlin WI 53151
Tel (262) 679-6170 SIC 8711

FRANKLIN ENERGY SERVICES LLC p 575
102 N Franklin St, Port Washington WI 53074
Tel (800) 598-4376 SIC 8711

L & S ELECTRIC INC p 833
5101 Mesker St, Schofield WI 54476
Tel (715) 359-3155
SIC 7694 5063 8711 3613

FRENCH HOLDINGS LLC p 578
3101 S Taylor Dr, Sheboygan WI 53081
Tel (920) 458-7724 SIC 3363 3341 8711

NEMAK AUTOMOTIVE CASTINGS INC p 1025
3101 S Taylor Dr, Sheboygan WI 53081
Tel (920) 458-7724 SIC 3341 3363 8711

■ **A & B PROCESS SYSTEMS CORP** p 4
201 S Wisconsin Ave, Stratford WI 54484
Tel (715) 687-4332 SIC 3443 1799 8711

SIC 8712 Architectural Services

M3 ENGINEERING & TECHNOLOGY CORP p 890
2051 W Sunset Rd Ste 101, Tucson AZ 85704
Tel (520) 293-1488 SIC 8741 8712 8711

■ **WALT DISNEY IMAGINEERING RESEARCH & DEVELOPMENT INC** p 1574
1401 Flower St, Glendale CA 91201
Tel (818) 544-6500
SIC 7819 8712 1542 8741 8711

GKK CORP p 613
2355 Main St Ste 220, Irvine CA 92614
Tel (949) 250-1500 SIC 8712 8711

■ **EARTH TECH (INFRASTRUCTURE) INC** p 469
300 Oceangate Ste 700, Long Beach CA 90802
Tel (562) 951-2000 SIC 8711 8712

▲ **AECOM** p 28
1999 Avenue Of The Stars # 2600, Los Angeles CA 90067
Tel (213) 593-8000 SIC 8711 8712

■ **AECOM GLOBAL II LLC** p 28
1999 Avenue Of The Stars, Los Angeles CA 90067
Tel (213) 593-8100 SIC 8711 8712 8741

■ **AECOM SERVICES INC** p 28
555 S Flower St Ste 3700, Los Angeles CA 90071
Tel (213) 593-8000 SIC 8712 8741 8711

■ **URS GROUP INC** p 1530
300 S Grand Ave Ste 1100, Los Angeles CA 90071
Tel (213) 593-8000 SIC 8711 8712 8741

KLEINFELDER INC p 823
550 W C St Ste 1200, San Diego CA 92101
Tel (619) 831-4600 SIC 8711 8712

HELLMUTH OBATA & KASSABAUM INC p 682
1 Bush St Ste 200, San Francisco CA 94104
Tel (415) 243-0555
SIC 8712 8711 8742 7389 0781

INTERIOR ARCHITECTS INC p 752
500 Sansome St Ste 8th, San Francisco CA 94111
Tel (415) 434-3305 SIC 8712

M ARTHUR GENSLER JR & ASSOCIATES INC p 889
2 Harrison St Fl 4, San Francisco CA 94105
Tel (415) 433-3700 SIC 8712

M&C HOTEL INTERESTS INC p 890
6560 Greenwood Plaza Blvd # 300, Greenwood Village CO 80111
Tel (303) 779-2000
SIC 8741 8712 6321 6331 7389

RICHFIELD HOLDINGS INC p 1233
5775 Dtc Blvd Ste 300, Greenwood Village CO 80111
Tel (303) 220-2000
SIC 6321 8712 7389 6331 7011

BALFOUR BEATTY LLC p 148
1011 Centre Rd Ste 322, Wilmington DE 19805
Tel (302) 573-3873 SIC 1542 8712 8741

FACILITY LEADERS IN ARCHITECTURAL/ENGINEERING DESIGN PC p 523
1201 Conn Ave Nw Fl 10, Washington DC 20036
Tel (608) 238-2661 SIC 8712 8711

PAGE SOUTHERLAND PAGE INC p 1107
1615 M St Nw Ste 700, Washington DC 20036
Tel (202) 909-4900 SIC 8712 8711

SMITHGROUPJJR INC p 1334
1700 New York Ave Nw # 100, Washington DC 20006
Tel (602) 265-2200 SIC 8712

WILL PERKINS INC p 1609
1250 24th St Nw Ste 800, Washington DC 20037
Tel (312) 755-0770 SIC 8712 7389

HASKELL CO p 667
111 Riverside Ave, Jacksonville FL 32202
Tel (904) 791-4500
SIC 1541 1542 1522 1623 8712 3272

HASKELL CO INC p 667
111 Riverside Ave, Jacksonville FL 32202
Tel (904) 791-4500
SIC 1541 1542 1522 1623 8712 3272

RS&H INC p 1255
10748 Deerwood Park Blvd, Jacksonville FL 32256
Tel (904) 256-2500 SIC 8711 8712

MANHATTAN CONSTRUCTION (FLORIDA) INC p 901
3705 Westview Dr Ste 1, Naples FL 34104
Tel (239) 643-6000
SIC 1542 8712 1531 1521 8741

SCOTT + CORMIA ARCHITECTURE AND INTERIORS LLC p 1293
429 S Keller Rd Ste 200, Orlando FL 32810
Tel (407) 660-2766 SIC 8712

ATKINS NORTH AMERICA HOLDINGS CORP p 125
4030 W Boy Scout Blvd, Tampa FL 33607
Tel (813) 282-7275 SIC 8712 6519 8711

HEERY INTERNATIONAL INC p 680
999 Peachtree St Ne # 300, Atlanta GA 30309
Tel (404) 881-9880 SIC 8712 8711 8742

A EPSTEIN AND SONS INTERNATIONAL INC p 5
600 W Fulton St Ste 800, Chicago IL 60661
Tel (312) 454-9100
SIC 8711 8712 7389 1542 1541 8742

EXP US SERVICES INC p 519
205 N Mich Aveste 3600, Chicago IL 60601
Tel (312) 616-0000 SIC 8711 8712

PERKINS & WILL GROUP LTD p 1136
410 N Michigan Ave # 1600, Chicago IL 60611
Tel (312) 755-0770 SIC 8712 7389

SKIDMORE OWINGS & MERRILL LLP p 1329
224 S Michigan Ave # 1000, Chicago IL 60604
Tel (312) 554-9090 SIC 8712

VELOCITEL INC p 1547
1033 Skokie Blvd Ste 320, Northbrook IL 60062
Tel (224) 757-0001 SIC 7373 8712

WISS JANNEY ELSTNER ASSOCIATES INC p 1619
330 Pfingsten Rd, Northbrook IL 60062
Tel (847) 272-2186 SIC 8711 8712 8734

GRAY CONSTRUCTION INC p 632
10 Quality St, Lexington KY 40507
Tel (859) 281-5000 SIC 1541 1542 8712

BERGER GROUP HOLDINGS INC p 174
111 Market Pl, Baltimore MD 21202
Tel (410) 468-4054 SIC 8711 8732 8712

CALLISONRTKL INC p 242
901 S Bond St, Baltimore MD 21231
Tel (410) 537-6000 SIC 8712

■ **RED THREAD SPACES LLC** p 1216
101 Seaport Blvd Ste 600, Boston MA 02210
Tel (617) 439-4900
SIC 5999 5021 8712 5198

STANTEC ARCHITECTURE AND ENGINEERING PC p 1377
311 Summer St, Boston MA 02210
Tel (617) 234-3100 SIC 8712

SMITHGROUP COMPANIES INC p 1334
500 Griswold St Fl 1700, Detroit MI 48226
Tel (313) 442-8351 SIC 8712 8711

■ **ELLERBE BECKET INC** p 488
800 Lasalle Ave Fl 5, Minneapolis MN 55402
Tel (612) 376-2000 SIC 8712 8711

HAMMEL GREEN AND ABRAHAMSON INC p 656
420 N 5th St Ste 100, Minneapolis MN 55401
Tel (612) 758-4000 SIC 8712 8711

SHORT-ELLIOTT-HENDRICKSON INC p 1318
3535 Vadnais Center Dr # 200, Saint Paul MN 55110
Tel (651) 490-2000 SIC 8711 8712

HNTB CORP p 698
715 Kirk Dr, Kansas City MO 64105
Tel (816) 472-1201 SIC 8711 8712

HNTB HOLDINGS LTD p 698
715 Kirk Dr, Kansas City MO 64105
Tel (816) 472-1201 SIC 8712 8711

ARCTURIS INC p 106
720 Olive St Ste 200, Saint Louis MO 63101
Tel (314) 206-7100 SIC 8712 7389

HOK GROUP INC p 699
10 S Broadway Ste 200, Saint Louis MO 63102
Tel (314) 421-2000 SIC 8711 8712 8742

HOK INC p 699
10 S Broadway Ste 200, Saint Louis MO 63102
Tel (314) 421-2000 SIC 0781 8712 8711

■ **JACOBS FACILITIES INC** p 775
501 N Broadway, Saint Louis MO 63102
Tel (314) 335-4000
SIC 8712 8711 8713 8741 1542 1541

CTA INC p 399
13 N 23rd St, Billings MT 59101
Tel (406) 248-7455 SIC 8711 8712

HDR INC p 673
8404 Indian Hills Dr, Omaha NE 68114
Tel (402) 399-1000
SIC 8712 8711 8742 8748 4789

LEO A DALY CO p 856
8600 Indian Hills Dr, Omaha NE 68114
Tel (808) 521-8889 SIC 8712

LEO A DALY/BURNS & MCCONNELL JOINT VENTURE p 856
8600 Indian Hills Dr, Omaha NE 68114
Tel (402) 391-8111 SIC 8712 8711

BRAD HENRY FRIEDMUTTER & ASSOCIATES LTD p 206
4022 Dean Martin Dr, Las Vegas NV 89103
Tel (702) 736-7477 SIC 8712 7389

LOUIS BERGER GROUP INC p 879
412 Mount Kemble Ave, Morristown NJ 07960
Tel (973) 407-1000 SIC 8748 8712 8711

PAULUS SOKOLOWSKI & SARTOR ENGINEERING A PROFESSIONAL CORP p 1122
67b Mountain Blvd Ext, Warren NJ 07059
Tel (732) 560-9700 SIC 8711 8748 8712

CANNON CORP p 247
2170 Whitehaven Rd, Grand Island NY 14072
Tel (716) 773-6800 SIC 8712

GEORGE G SHARP INC p 606
160 Broadway, New York NY 10038
Tel (212) 732-2800 SIC 3731 4225 8712

GOLDBERG LINDSAY & CO LLC p 620
630 5th Ave Fl 30, New York NY 10111
Tel (212) 651-1100 SIC 6799 8711 8712

HAKS ENGINEERS ARCHITECTS AND LAND SURVEYORS PC p 653
40 Wall St Fl 11, New York NY 10005
Tel (212) 747-1997 SIC 8712 8711 8713

HANRAHANMEYERS ARCHITECTS LLP p 658
6 Maiden Ln Rm 510, New York NY 10038
Tel (212) 989-6026 SIC 8712

PERKINS EASTMAN ARCHITECTS DPC p 1136
115 5th Ave Fl 3, New York NY 10003
Tel (212) 353-7200 SIC 8712 8742 7389

STV INC p 1395
225 Park Ave S Fl 5, New York NY 10003
Tel (212) 529-2722 SIC 8711 8712 8741

THORNTON TOMASETTI INC p 1450
51 Madison Ave Fl 19, New York NY 10010
Tel (917) 661-7800 SIC 8711 8712

TURNER INTERNATIONAL INDUSTRIES INC p 1493
375 Hudson St Fl 6, New York NY 10014
Tel (212) 229-6000 SIC 8741 8712 1542

7MOD2 LLC p 4
6565 Wetherole St Apt 3j, Rego Park NY 11374
Tel (347) 581-3742 SIC 8712

WECTEC GLOBAL PROJECT SERVICES INC p 1587
128 S Tryon St Ste 1000, Charlotte NC 28202
Tel (980) 859-6837 SIC 1731 8712

STANTEC ARCHITECTURE INC p 1377
301 N Main St Ste 2452, Winston Salem NC 27101
Tel (336) 714-7413 SIC 8712 7389

GLAUS PYLE SCHOMER BURNS & DEHAVEN INC p 614
520 S Main St Ste 2531, Akron OH 44311
Tel (330) 572-2100 SIC 8711 8712

AUSTIN BUILDING AND DESIGN INC p 132
6095 Parkland Blvd # 100, Cleveland OH 44124
Tel (440) 544-2600
SIC 1541 1542 8742 8711 8712

GARLAND INDUSTRIES INC p 592
3800 E 91st St, Cleveland OH 44105
Tel (216) 641-7500 SIC 2952 6512 8712

MIDDOUGH INC p 965
1901 E 13th St Ste 400, Cleveland OH 44114
Tel (216) 367-6000 SIC 8711 8712

BURGESS & NIPLE INC p 227
5085 Reed Rd, Columbus OH 43220
Tel (502) 254-2344 SIC 8711 8712

DLZ CORP p 445
6121 Huntley Rd, Columbus OH 43229
Tel (614) 888-0040 SIC 1623 8713 8712

SSOE INC p 1364
1001 Madison Ave Ste A, Toledo OH 43604
Tel (419) 255-3830
SIC 8711 8712 8742 1541 7389

CH2M HILL INDUSTRIAL DESIGN & CONSTRUCTION INC p 286
2020 Sw 4th Ave Fl 3, Portland OR 97201
Tel (503) 224-6040
SIC 8711 8712 8741 7699

OTAK INC p 1097
808 Sw 3rd Ave Ste 220, Portland OR 97204
Tel (503) 274-5445
SIC 0781 8712 8711 8713 8742 8999

ZIMMER GUNSUL FRASCA ARCHITECTS LLP p 1643
1223 Sw Washington St # 200, Portland OR 97205
Tel (503) 224-3860 SIC 8712 8748 7389

STV GROUP INC p 1395
205 W Welsh Dr, Douglassville PA 19518
Tel (610) 385-8200 SIC 8712 8711

DAY & ZIMMERMANN GROUP INC p 417
1500 Spring Garden St # 900, Philadelphia PA 19130
Tel (215) 299-8000
SIC 8711 8712 8741 7381 7382 3489

DAY AND ZIMMERMANN INC p 417
1500 Spring Garden St # 900, Philadelphia PA 19130
Tel (215) 299-8000
SIC 8744 8712 8711 3559 3483

WORLEYPARSONS OF VIRGINIA INC p 1626
2675 Morgantown Rd, Reading PA 19607
Tel (610) 855-2000 SIC 8712

CARIBBEAN ARCHITECTS & ENGINEERS p 256
D14 Calle 6 Apt 1101, Guaynabo PR 00966
Tel (787) 783-5500 SIC 8711 8712

ONEAL INC p 1087
10 Falcon Crest Dr, Greenville SC 29607
Tel (864) 298-2000 SIC 8711 8712

GRESHAM SMITH AND PARTNERS p 639
511 Union St 1400 Nashvle, Nashville TN 37219
Tel (615) 770-8100 SIC 8712

BECK INTERNATIONAL LLC p 167
1807 Ross Ave Ste 500, Dallas TX 75201
Tel (214) 303-6200 SIC 1542 8712

CORGAN ASSOCIATES INC p 370
401 N Houston St, Dallas TX 75202
Tel (214) 748-2000 SIC 8712 7389

HKS INC p 697
350 N Saint Paul St # 100, Dallas TX 75201
Tel (214) 969-5599 SIC 8712

■ **CARTER & BURGESS INC** p 261
777 Main St Ste 2500, Fort Worth TX 76102
Tel (817) 735-6000 SIC 8711 8712 8713

M+W AMERICAS INC p 890
1001 Klein Rd Ste 400, Plano TX 75074
Tel (972) 535-7300
SIC 3433 8712 8711 8741

PACIFIC ARCHITECTS AND ENGINEERS INC p 1104
1320 N Courthouse Rd # 800, Arlington VA 22201
Tel (888) 526-5416 SIC 8711 8712

SIEMENS GOVERNMENT TECHNOLOGIES INC p 1320
2231 Crystal Dr Ste 700, Arlington VA 22202
Tel (703) 860-1574
SIC 8711 7373 7376 7379 8712 7378

DEWBERRY CONSULTANTS LLC p 434
8401 Arlington Blvd Ste 1, Fairfax VA 22031
Tel (703) 849-0311 SIC 8711 8712 8731

■ **CDI MARINE CO LLC** p 271
4600 Village Ave, Norfolk VA 23502
Tel (757) 763-6666
SIC 8711 8712 3732 3731

■ **HAYES SEAY MATTERN & MATTERN INC** p 670
10 S Jefferson St # 1600, Roanoke VA 24011
Tel (540) 857-3100 SIC 8711 8712

▲ **VERSAR INC** p 1551
6850 Versar Ctr Ste 201, Springfield VA 22151
Tel (703) 750-3000
SIC 8711 8748 8712 8731

NBBJ LP p 1021
223 Yale Ave N, Seattle WA 98109
Tel (206) 223-5555 SIC 8712

MEAD AND HUNT INC p 933
2440 Deming Way, Middleton WI 53562
Tel (608) 273-6380 SIC 8712 8711

SIC 8713 Surveying Services

TOPCON POSITIONING SYSTEMS INC p 1461
7400 National Dr, Livermore CA 94550
Tel (925) 245-8300
SIC 3829 3625 3823 3699 8713 1794

PSOMAS p 1188
555 S Flower St Ste 4300, Los Angeles CA 90071
Tel (310) 954-3700 SIC 8713 8711

SUNGEVITY INC p 1402
66 Franklin St Ste 310, Oakland CA 94607
Tel (510) 496-5500 SIC 1711 8713

DRS TRAINING & CONTROL SYSTEMS LLC p 457
645 Anchors St Nw, Fort Walton Beach FL 32548
Tel (850) 302-3000 SIC 3812 8713

QUANTUM SPATIAL INC p 1198
10033 Mlk St N Ste 200, Saint Petersburg FL 33716
Tel (920) 457-3631 SIC 2741 8713

ELM ENTERPRISES LLC p 489
60 State St Ste 201, Peoria IL 61602
Tel (309) 671-4300 SIC 8748 8713

USIC LLC p 1535
9045 River Rd Ste 300, Indianapolis IN 46240
Tel (317) 575-7800 SIC 1623 8713

GREEN COMPANIES INC p 636
8710 Earhart Ln Sw, Cedar Rapids IA 52404
Tel (319) 841-4000
SIC 8711 8748 8713 4911 1623

GARMIN INTERNATIONAL INC p 592
1200 E 151st St, Olathe KS 66062
Tel (913) 397-8200 SIC 3812 3669 8713

C & C TECHNOLOGIES INC p 231
730 E Kaliste Saloom Rd, Lafayette LA 70508
Tel (337) 210-0000 SIC 8713

FUGRO CHANCE INC p 583
200 Dulles Dr, Lafayette LA 70506
Tel (337) 237-1300 SIC 8713

RUMMEL KLEPPER & KAHL LLP p 1257
81 Mosher St, Baltimore MD 21217
Tel (410) 728-2900
SIC 8711 8741 1623 8999 8713 1611

■ **KEYW CORP** p 816
250 Clark St, North Andover MA 01845
Tel (978) 682-7767 SIC 7371 8713 7389

ATWELL LLC p 130
2 Towne Sq Ste 700, Southfield MI 48076
Tel (248) 447-2000
SIC 8999 8713 8748 8711

■ **JACOBS FACILITIES INC** p 775
501 N Broadway, Saint Louis MO 63102
Tel (314) 335-4000
SIC 8712 8711 8713 8741 1542 1541

MASER CONSULTING PA p 915
331 Newman Springs Rd # 203, Red Bank NJ 07701
Tel (732) 383-1950 SIC 8711 8742 8713

HAKS ENGINEERS ARCHITECTS AND LAND SURVEYORS PC p 653
40 Wall St Fl 11, New York NY 10005
Tel (212) 747-1997 SIC 8712 8711 8713

MCKIM & CREED PA p 930
1730 Varsity Dr Ste 500, Raleigh NC 27606
Tel (919) 233-8091 SIC 8711 8713

KLJ SOLUTIONS CO p 823
4585 Coleman St, Bismarck ND 58503
Tel (701) 355-8400 SIC 8711 8713

KADRMAS LEE & JACKSON INC p 800
1463 I94 Business Loop E, Dickinson ND 58601
Tel (701) 355-8400 SIC 8711 8713

■**AMERICAN ELECTRIC POWER SERVICE CORP** p 71
1 Riverside Plz Fl 1, Columbus OH 43215
Tel (614) 716-1000
SIC 4911 8711 8713 8721

DLZ CORP p 445
6121 Huntley Rd, Columbus OH 43229
Tel (614) 888-0040 SIC 1623 8713 8712

DAVID EVANS AND ASSOCIATES INC p 415
2100 Sw River Pkwy, Portland OR 97201
Tel (503) 223-6663 SIC 8711 8713 8741

OTAK INC p 1097
808 Sw 3rd Ave Ste 220, Portland OR 97204
Tel (503) 274-5445
SIC 0781 8712 8711 8713 8742 8999

SURVEYING AND MAPPING LLC p 1409
4801 Sw Pkwy Ste 100, Austin TX 78735
Tel (512) 447-0575 SIC 8713

■**CARTER & BURGESS INC** p 261
777 Main St Ste 2500, Fort Worth TX 76102
Tel (817) 735-6000 SIC 8711 8712 8713

GYRODATA INC p 649
23000 Nw Lake Dr, Houston TX 77095
Tel (713) 461-3146 SIC 1389 8713

PETROLEUM GEO-SERVICES INC p 1139
15375 Memorial Dr Ste 100, Houston TX 77079
Tel (281) 509-8000 SIC 3827 8713 1382

■**STEWART TITLE CO** p 1389
1980 Post Oak Blvd Ste 80, Houston TX 77056
Tel (713) 625-8100
SIC 6361 7389 8713 8742 6541

■**UNIVERSALPEGASUS INTERNATIONAL HOLDINGS INC** p 1518
4848 Loop Central Dr # 600, Houston TX 77081
Tel (713) 425-6000 SIC 7389 8711 8713

■**UNIVERSALPEGASUS INTERNATIONAL INC** p 1518
4848 Loop Central Dr # 600, Houston TX 77081
Tel (713) 425-6000 SIC 7389 8711 8713

▲**DAWSON GEOPHYSICAL CO** p 417
508 W Wall St Ste 800, Midland TX 79701
Tel (432) 684-3000 SIC 1382 8713

HALFF ASSOCIATES INC p 654
1201 N Bowser Rd, Richardson TX 75081
Tel (214) 346-6200 SIC 8711 8713

QUALTRICS LABS INC p 1198
400 W Qualtrics Dr # 100, Provo UT 84604
Tel (800) 340-9194 SIC 8713

BOWMAN CONSULTING GROUP LTD p 204
3863 Centerview Dr # 300, Chantilly VA 20151
Tel (703) 464-1000 SIC 8711 8713

TIMMONS GROUP INC p 1455
1001 Boulders Pkwy # 300, North Chesterfield VA 23225
Tel (804) 200-6500 SIC 8711 8713

SIC 8721 Accounting, Auditing & Bookkeeping Svcs

CARR RIGGS & INGRAM LLC p 260
901 Boll Weevil Cir # 200, Enterprise AL 36330
Tel (334) 347-0088 SIC 8721

WARREN AVERETT COMPANIES LLC p 1576
2500 Acton Rd Ste 200, Vestavia AL 35243
Tel (205) 979-4100
SIC 8721 8741 7363 8742

SWAN EMPLOYER SERVICES p 1411
1306 E 74th Ave Ste 200, Anchorage AK 99518
Tel (907) 344-7926 SIC 7363 8721

ACUMEN FISCAL AGENT LLC p 20
4542 E Inverness Ave # 210, Mesa AZ 85206
Tel (480) 497-1889 SIC 8721

SIMPLIFIED BUSINESS SOLUTIONS INC p 1325
10201 S 51st St Ste 100, Phoenix AZ 85044
Tel (602) 414-0062 SIC 8721

TEAM BENEFITS CORP p 1429
901 W Alameda Ave 100, Burbank CA 91506
Tel (818) 558-3261 SIC 8721

TEAM COMPANIES INC p 1429
901 W Alameda Ave Ste 100, Burbank CA 91506
Tel (818) 558-3261 SIC 8721

▲**TRUCEPT INC** p 1485
500 La Terraza Blvd, Escondido CA 92025
Tel (866) 961-5763 SIC 8721 8748 8742

IC COMPLIANCE LLC p 726
1065 E Hillsdale Blvd # 300, Foster City CA 94404
Tel (650) 378-4150 SIC 7371 8721

▲**RESOURCES CONNECTION INC** p 1227
17101 Armstrong Ave, Irvine CA 92614
Tel (714) 430-6400 SIC 8742 7389 8721

CALIFORNIA CARTAGE CO LLC p 239
2931 Redondo Ave, Long Beach CA 90806
Tel (562) 427-1143 SIC 4226 8741 8721

MEDICAL MANAGEMENT CONSULTANTS INC p 937
8150 Beverly Blvd, Los Angeles CA 90048
Tel (310) 659-3835
SIC 7363 8742 8748 8721

■**PROTIVITI INC** p 1185
2884 Sand Hill Rd Ste 200, Menlo Park CA 94025
Tel (650) 234-6000 SIC 8742 8721

▲**ROBERT HALF INTERNATIONAL INC** p 1241
2884 Sand Hill Rd Ste 200, Menlo Park CA 94025
Tel (650) 234-6000
SIC 7363 7361 8748 8721

SUTTER CONNECT LLC p 1410
10470 Old Placrvl Rd # 100, Sacramento CA 95827
Tel (916) 854-6600 SIC 8742 8741 8721

GO-STAFF INC p 619
8798 Complex Dr, San Diego CA 92123
Tel (858) 292-8562 SIC 7363 8721

INNOVATIVE EMPLOYEE SOLUTIONS INC p 744
9665 Gran Rdge Dr Ste 420, San Diego CA 92123
Tel (858) 715-5100 SIC 8721

INTERPACIFIC GROUP INC p 757
576 Beale St, San Francisco CA 94105
Tel (415) 442-0711 SIC 8721

▲**TRINET GROUP INC** p 1480
1100 San Leandro Blvd # 300, San Leandro CA 94577
Tel (510) 352-5000 SIC 7361 8721

ARMANINO LLP p 111
12657 Alcosta Blvd # 500, San Ramon CA 94583
Tel (925) 790-2600 SIC 8721 8742

TREFZ CORP p 1475
10 Middle St Ste 1701, Bridgeport CT 06604
Tel (203) 367-3621 SIC 5812 6531 8721

YALE-NEW HAVEN HEALTH SERVICES CORP p 1634
789 Howard Ave, New Haven CT 06519
Tel (888) 461-0106 SIC 5912 8721

■**FRONTIER FLORIDA LLC** p 581
401 Merritt 7, Norwalk CT 06851
Tel (813) 483-2011
SIC 4813 6519 8721 5065 7629

COTIVITI CORP p 374
50 Danbury Rd, Wilton CT 06897
Tel (203) 642-0727 SIC 8721

COTIVITI LLC p 374
50 Danbury Rd, Wilton CT 06897
Tel (203) 529-2000 SIC 8721

LEXISNEXIS RISK ASSETS INC p 859
1105 N Market St Ste 501, Wilmington DE 19801
Tel (770) 752-6000
SIC 6411 7375 8721 7323

THOMSON REUTERS (GRC) INC p 1449
2711 Centerville Rd # 400, Wilmington DE 19808
Tel (212) 227-7357
SIC 7291 8111 8721 8733 8741

■**VERIZON WASHINGTON DC INC** p 1551
1300 I St Nw, Washington DC 20005
Tel (202) 392-9900 SIC 4813 8721

MORTON PLANT MEASE HEALTH CARE INC p 991
300 Pinellas St, Clearwater FL 33756
Tel (727) 462-7777 SIC 8741 8721

S2 HR SOLUTIONS 1A LLC p 1263
3001 Executive Dr Ste 340, Clearwater FL 33762
Tel (727) 565-2950 SIC 8721

MERCANTIL COMMERCEBANK HOLDING CORP p 943
220 Alhambra Cir, Coral Gables FL 33134
Tel (305) 441-5555 SIC 6021 7389 8721

PAYROLL MADE EASY INC p 1123
11691 Gateway Blvd # 104, Fort Myers FL 33913
Tel (239) 592-9700 SIC 8721

CHECKS IN MOTION p 292
11071 Minneapolis Dr, Hollywood FL 33026
Tel (954) 433-8080 SIC 8721

STERLING HOSPITALITY INC p 1387
2950 Reedy Creek Blvd, Kissimmee FL 34747
Tel (407) 997-3481 SIC 8741 8721

ZEROCHAOS LLC p 1642
420 S Orange Ave Ste 600, Orlando FL 32801
Tel (407) 770-6161 SIC 8721

■**INTERVAL HOLDING CO INC** p 759
6262 Sunset Dr Fl 6, South Miami FL 33143
Tel (305) 666-1861 SIC 8699 8721 6531

OASIS OUTSOURCING INC p 1071
2054 Vista Pkwy Ste 300, West Palm Beach FL 33411
Tel (561) 227-6500 SIC 8721 8742 7363

■**MCKESSON TECHNOLOGIES INC** p 930
11475 Great Oaks Way # 400, Alpharetta GA 30022
Tel (404) 338-6000
SIC 7374 8741 8721 7322 7373

■**AGL RESOURCES SERVICE CO** p 35
10 Peachtree Pl Ne # 1000, Atlanta GA 30309
Tel (404) 584-9470
SIC 8742 8721 8744 4924

▲**COTIVITI HOLDINGS INC** p 374
115 Prmter Ctr Pl Ste 700, Atlanta GA 30346
Tel (770) 379-2800 SIC 8721

▲**PRGX GLOBAL INC** p 1173
600 Galleria Pkwy Se # 100, Atlanta GA 30339
Tel (770) 779-3900 SIC 8721

WRD INC p 1627
1641 Sigman Rd Nw, Conyers GA 30012
Tel (770) 922-8000 SIC 8721

■**GOLDLEAF FINANCIAL SOLUTIONS INC** p 622
350 Technology Pkwy # 200, Norcross GA 30092
Tel (678) 966-0844 SIC 8721 8741

ACCRETIVE SOLUTIONS INC p 16
1 S Wacker Dr Ste 950, Chicago IL 60606
Tel (312) 994-4600 SIC 8721

ACCRETIVE SOLUTIONS OPERATING CORP p 16
1 S Wacker Dr Ste 950, Chicago IL 60606
Tel (312) 994-4600 SIC 8721 7363 7361

■**AMERITECH SERVICES INC** p 84
208 S Lasalle St Ste 814, Chicago IL 60604
Tel (847) 248-2000
SIC 7389 4225 8742 8721

BAKERTILLY VIRCHOW KRAUSE LLP p 146
205 N Michigan Ave # 2800, Chicago IL 60601
Tel (312) 729-8000 SIC 8721

BDO USA LLP p 164
130 E Randolph St # 2800, Chicago IL 60601
Tel (312) 240-1236 SIC 8721

CROWE HORWATH LLP p 394
225 W Wacker Dr Ste 2600, Chicago IL 60606
Tel (312) 899-7000 SIC 8721

GRANT THORNTON LLP p 631
171 N Clark St Ste 200, Chicago IL 60601
Tel (312) 856-0200 SIC 8721 8742

■**ILLINOIS BELL TELEPHONE CO** p 732
225 W Randolph St Fl Ll, Chicago IL 60606
Tel (618) 344-9077 SIC 4813 8721 6512

NLFH ACCT PAYABLE BILL CH p 1045
541 N Fairbanks Ct Fl 16, Chicago IL 60611
Tel (312) 926-2094 SIC 8721

NORTH ADVOCATE SIDE HEALTH NETWORK p 1049
836 W Wellington Ave, Chicago IL 60657
Tel (773) 296-5699 SIC 8741 8721

RSM US LLP p 1256
1 S Wacker Dr Ste 800, Chicago IL 60606
Tel (312) 634-3400 SIC 8721 8742 7291

TWG HOLDINGS INC p 1494
175 W Jackson Blvd Fl 11, Chicago IL 60604
Tel (312) 356-3000 SIC 6399 8721 6411

TWG WARRANTY GROUP INC p 1494
175 W Jackson Blvd Fl 11, Chicago IL 60604
Tel (312) 356-3000 SIC 6399 8721 6411

UHY ADVISORS INC p 1500
30 S Wacker Dr Ste 1330, Chicago IL 60606
Tel (312) 578-9600 SIC 8721

■**WEC BUSINESS SERVICES LLC** p 1587
200 E Randolph St # 2200, Chicago IL 60601
Tel (312) 240-3877 SIC 8742 8721

NORTHERN ILLINOIS HEALTH PLAN p 1056
773 W Lincoln St Ste 402, Freeport IL 61032
Tel (815) 599-7050 SIC 8741 8721

■**SUREPAYROLL INC** p 1408
2350 Ravine Way Ste 100, Glenview IL 60025
Tel (847) 676-8420 SIC 8721

■**DEERE PAYROLL SERVICES INC** p 422
1 John Deere Pl, Moline IL 61265
Tel (309) 765-8000 SIC 8721

SIKICH LLP p 1322
1415 W Diehl Rd Ste 400, Naperville IL 60563
Tel (630) 566-8400 SIC 8721

WILLIS STEIN & PARTNERS MANAGEMENT III LLC p 1612
1033 Skokie Blvd Ste 360, Northbrook IL 60062
Tel (312) 422-2400
SIC 6799 3479 2721 8721

VILLA FINANCIAL SERVICES LLC p 1557
3755 Chase Ave, Skokie IL 60076
Tel (847) 440-2660 SIC 8721

■**AMERITECH** p 84
240 N Meridian St, Indianapolis IN 46204
Tel (317) 265-2266 SIC 4813 8721

IOWA HEALTH SYSTEM p 762
1776 West Lakes Pkwy # 400, West Des Moines IA 50266
Tel (515) 241-6161 SIC 8062 8721 8741

KENTUCKY MEDICAL SERVICES FOUNDATION INC p 812
2333 Alumni Park Plz # 200, Lexington KY 40517
Tel (859) 257-7910 SIC 8721

SOURCECORP HEALTHSERVE RADIOLOGY INC p 1342
602 N English Station Rd, Louisville KY 40223
Tel (502) 244-0035 SIC 7334 8748 8721

■**CAROLINA TELEPHONE AND TELEGRAPH CO LLC** p 259
100 Centurylink Dr, Monroe LA 71203
Tel (318) 388-9000 SIC 4813 8721 5065

■**CENTURYTEL SERVICE GROUP LLC** p 283
100 Centurylink Dr, Monroe LA 71203
Tel (318) 388-9500 SIC 8721

■**VERIZON MARYLAND LLC** p 1550
1710 Undrpamd Way Ste 401, Hagerstown MD 21740
Tel (301) 790-7135 SIC 4813 8721

PAY STAFF p 1122
700 King Farm Blvd # 300, Rockville MD 20850
Tel (301) 527-0655 SIC 7363 8721

JANJER ENTERPRISES INC p 777
12150 Tech Rd, Silver Spring MD 20904
Tel (301) 625-5920 SIC 5812 8721 8741

■**VERIZON NEW ENGLAND INC** p 1550
185 Franklin St 4th, Boston MA 02110
Tel (617) 743-9800 SIC 4813 8721

VALLEY HEALTH SYSTEMS INC p 1540
575 Beech St, Holyoke MA 01040
Tel (413) 534-2500
SIC 8082 8093 8399 8741 8721

■**EAGLE INVESTMENT SYSTEMS LLC** p 468
45 William St Ste 200, Wellesley MA 02481
Tel (781) 943-2200
SIC 6722 6282 8721 7372

■**MICHIGAN BELL TELEPHONE CO** p 960
444 Michigan Ave, Detroit MI 48226
Tel (313) 223-9900 SIC 4813 8721

HENRY FORD ALLEGIANCE HEALTH GROUP p 684
205 N East Ave, Jackson MI 49201
Tel (517) 788-4800 SIC 8741 8721

REHMANN LLC p 1220
1500 W Big Beaver Rd, Macomb MI 48044
Tel (866) 799-9580 SIC 8748 8721

PLANTE & MORAN PLLC p 1154
27400 Northwestern Hwy # 300, Southfield MI 48034
Tel (248) 223-3247 SIC 8721 8742

PLANTE MORAN PC p 1154
27400 Northwestern Hwy # 300, Southfield MI 48034
Tel (248) 352-2500 SIC 8721

CERIDIAN LLC p 283
3311 E Old Shakopee Rd, Minneapolis MN 55425
Tel (952) 853-8100 SIC 8721

CLIFTONLARSONALLEN LLP p 326
220 S 6th St Ste 300, Minneapolis MN 55402
Tel (612) 376-4620 SIC 8742 7371 8721

FOUNDATION HOLDINGS INC p 571
3311 E Old Shakopee Rd, Minneapolis MN 55425
Tel (952) 853-8100 SIC 8641 8721

CONSUMER DIRECTIONS INC p 361
425 E Saint Germain St # 200, Saint Cloud MN 56304
Tel (320) 420-3423 SIC 7361 8721

HEALTHEAST CARE INC p 676
559 Capitol Blvd, Saint Paul MN 55103
Tel (651) 232-2300 SIC 8741 8721

MISSISSIPPI BAPTIST HEALTH SYSTEMS INC p 975
1225 N State St Ofc, Jackson MS 39202
Tel (601) 968-1000 SIC 8741 8721 8069

HORNE LLP p 708
1020 Highland Colony Pkwy # 400, Ridgeland MS 39157
Tel (601) 948-0940 SIC 8721 8742

■**H&R BLOCK GROUP INC** p 651
4400 Main St, Kansas City MO 64111
Tel (816) 854-3000 SIC 6211 8721 8742

MYERS AND STAUFFER LC p 1004
700 W 47th St Ste 1100, Kansas City MO 64112
Tel (816) 945-5300 SIC 8721

HEARTLAND HEALTH p 679
5325 Faraon St, Saint Joseph MO 64506
Tel (816) 271-6000 SIC 8062 7322 8721

BKD LLP p 186
910 E Saint Louis St # 400, Springfield MO 65806
Tel (417) 865-8701 SIC 8721

■**APPLIED UNDERWRITERS INC** p 100
10805 Old Mill Rd, Omaha NE 68154
Tel (402) 342-4900
SIC 6331 8721 8741 8742

WHITTLESEA-BELL p 1607
100 Sunshine Ln, Reno NV 89502
Tel (775) 785-3533 SIC 8721

WHITE ROSE INC p 1606
380 Middlesex Ave, Carteret NJ 07008
Tel (732) 541-5555
SIC 5141 5143 5142 5122 7311 8721

■**VERIZON NEW JERSEY INC** p 1550
540 Broad St, Newark NJ 07102
Tel (973) 649-9900 SIC 4813 8721

■**HEARTLAND PAYMENT SYSTEMS LLC** p 679
300 Carnegie Ctr Ste 300, Princeton NJ 08540
Tel (609) 683-3831 SIC 7389 8721

WITHUMSMITH+BROWN PC p 1619
506 Carnegie Ctr Ste 400, Princeton NJ 08540
Tel (609) 520-1188 SIC 8721

■**ADP ATLANTIC LLC** p 24
1 Adp Blvd Ms420, Roseland NJ 07068
Tel (605) 809-4388 SIC 8721

EYEA LLLP p 522
200 Plaza Dr Ste 2222, Secaucus NJ 07094
Tel (201) 872-2200 SIC 8721

KENNEDY HEALTH CARE FOUNDATION INC p 811
18 E Laurel Rd, Stratford NJ 08084
Tel (856) 661-5100
SIC 6733 4119 8051 6531 7361 8721

A & E STORES INC p 4
1000 Huyler St, Teterboro NJ 07608
Tel (201) 393-0600
SIC 5621 8721 4226 7389

COWORX STAFFING SERVICES LLC p 386
1375 Plainfield Ave Ste 1, Watchung NJ 07069
Tel (908) 757-5300 SIC 7361 8721

EMPLOYER SERVICES CORP p 494
20 Pineview Dr Ste 3, Amherst NY 14228
Tel (716) 691-4455 SIC 7363 8721

EVO PAYMENTS INTERNATIONAL LLC p 515
515 Broadhollow Rd # 100, Melville NY 11747
Tel (800) 227-3794 SIC 8721

NRHMC INC p 1064
16 Guion Pl, New Rochelle NY 10801
Tel (914) 632-5000 SIC 8062 8721

COHNREZNICK LLP p 335
1301 Ave Of The Americas, New York NY 10019
Tel (212) 297-0400 SIC 8721

DELOITTE & TOUCHE LLP p 425
30 Rockefeller Plz # 4350, New York NY 10112
Tel (212) 492-4000 SIC 8721

DELOITTE FINANCIAL ADVISORY SERVICES LLP p 425
30 Rockefeller Plz, New York NY 10112
Tel (212) 492-4000 SIC 8721

DELOITTE LLP p 425
30 Rockefeller Plz, New York NY 10112
Tel (212) 492-4000 SIC 8742 8721

DELOITTE SERVICES LP p 425
1633 Broadway Fl 35, New York NY 10019
Tel (212) 492-2000 SIC 8721

EISNERAMPER LLP p 482
750 3rd Ave, New York NY 10017
Tel (212) 949-8700 SIC 8742 8721

ERNST & YOUNG LLP p 508
5 Times Sq Fl Conlv1, New York NY 10036
Tel (212) 773-3000 SIC 8721

■**FRONTIER CALIFORNIA INC** p 581
140 West St, New York NY 10007
Tel (212) 395-1000
SIC 4813 6519 8721 5065 1731 7629

GELLER & CO LLC p 598
909 3rd Ave Fl 15, New York NY 10022
Tel (212) 583-6000 SIC 8742 8721

KPMG LLP p 828
345 Park Ave Lowr Ll4, New York NY 10154
Tel (212) 758-9700 SIC 8721

MARCUM LLP p 905
750 3rd Ave Fl 11, New York NY 10017
Tel (212) 485-5500 SIC 8721

MARKS PANETH LLP p 909
685 3rd Ave Fl 4, New York NY 10017
Tel (212) 503-8800 SIC 8721

■**OUTSOURCE PARTNERS INTERNATIONAL INC** p 1099
280 Park Ave Rm 3801w, New York NY 10017
Tel (212) 752-2439 SIC 8721 8748

PRICEWATERHOUSECOOPERS LLP p 1174
300 Madison Ave Fl 24, New York NY 10017
Tel (646) 471-4000 SIC 8721 8742

WEISERMAZARS LLP p 1588
135 W 50th St, New York NY 10020
Tel (212) 812-7000 SIC 8721

▲**PAYCHEX INC** p 1122
911 Panorama Trl S, Rochester NY 14625
Tel (585) 385-6666 SIC 8721 7363

STAFF LEASING OF CENTRAL NEW YORK INC p 1374
149 Northern Concourse # 3, Syracuse NY 13212
Tel (315) 641-3600 SIC 7363 8721

DIXON HUGHES GOODMAN LLP p 445
4350 Congress St Ste 900, Charlotte NC 28209
Tel (704) 367-7760 SIC 8721

STERITECH GROUP INC p 1386
6701 Carmel Rd Ste 300, Charlotte NC 28226
Tel (704) 544-1900 *SIC* 7342 8721

APPAREL BRANDS INC p 98
434 Carolina Way, Highlands NC 28741
Tel (828) 526-0167 *SIC* 2325 2337 8721

EIDE BAILLY LLP p 481
4310 17th Ave S, Fargo ND 58103
Tel (701) 239-8500 *SIC* 8721

SANFORD CLINIC NORTH p 1279
801 Broadway N, Fargo ND 58102
Tel (701) 234-2000 *SIC* 8741 8721

PAYCOR INC p 1122
4811 Montgomery Rd, Cincinnati OH 45212
Tel (513) 381-0505 *SIC* 8721

■ OHIO BELL TELEPHONE CO p 1077
45 Erieview Plz, Cleveland OH 44114
Tel (216) 822-3439 *SIC* 4813 8721

■ AMERICAN ELECTRIC POWER SERVICE CORP p 71
1 Riverside Plz Fl 1, Columbus OH 43215
Tel (614) 716-1000
SIC 4911 8711 8713 8721

PUBLIC EMPLOYEE DEFERRED COMPENSATION OHIO p 1189
257 E Town St Ste 457, Columbus OH 43215
Tel (614) 466-7245 *SIC* 8721 9311

▲ PAYCOM SOFTWARE INC p 1122
7501 W Memorial Rd, Oklahoma City OK 73142
Tel (405) 722-6900 *SIC* 8721 7371 7372

■ XPO ENTERPRISE SERVICES INC p 1632
1717 Nw 21st Ave, Portland OR 97209
Tel (503) 450-2000 *SIC* 8721

LEHIGH VALLEY HEALTH SERVICES INC p 854
2166 S 12th St, Allentown PA 18103
Tel (610) 791-3682 *SIC* 4813 8741 8721

■ AMERISOURCEBERGEN SERVICES CORP p 83
1300 Morris Dr Ste 100, Chesterbrook PA 19087
Tel (610) 727-7000
SIC 5122 5047 5199 8721

■ CONEMAUGH HEALTH INITIATIVES INC p 355
1020 Franklin St, Johnstown PA 15905
Tel (814) 534-9000 *SIC* 8741 8721

GOOD SAMARITAN HEALTH SERVICES FOUNDATION p 623
259 S 4th St Fl 2, Lebanon PA 17042
Tel (717) 270-7864 *SIC* 8741 7389 8721

DOLLAR FINANCIAL GROUP INC p 448
74 E Swedesford Rd, Malvern PA 19355
Tel (610) 296-3400 *SIC* 6099 8721

■ VERIZON PENNSYLVANIA INC p 1550
1717 Arch St Fl 15, Philadelphia PA 19103
Tel (215) 466-9900
SIC 4813 8721 1731 7629

■ MED3000 GROUP INC p 935
680 Andersen Dr Foster Pl, Pittsburgh PA 15220
Tel (412) 937-8887 *SIC* 8742 8721

READING HEALTH SYSTEM p 1213
6th Ave And Spruce St, Reading PA 19611
Tel (610) 988-8000
SIC 8062 6512 8093 8721 8011 7219

▲ EVERTEC INC p 515
Km 1/3 Rr 176, San Juan PR 00926
Tel (787) 759-9999
SIC 8741 8748 7379 8721

A & M SPECIAL PURCHASING INC p 4
375 Commerce Park Rd, North Kingstown RI 02852
Tel (401) 295-2672 *SIC* 8721

AVERA HEALTH p 137
3900 W Avera Dr, Sioux Falls SD 57108
Tel (605) 322-4700 *SIC* 8741 8721

ADMINISTRATIVE RESOURCES INC p 23
801 Sunset Dr F1, Johnson City TN 37604
Tel (423) 283-0296
SIC 8721 8741 8742 6794

ATWORK FRANCHISE INC p 130
3215 W Gov J Sevier Hwy, Knoxville TN 37920
Tel (865) 609-6911 *SIC* 6794 8742 8721

COUNTRYWIDE HR p 375
135 Fox Rd Ste F, Knoxville TN 37922
Tel (877) 257-6662 *SIC* 8721 7361

BELZ HOTEL GROUP LLC p 171
5118 Park Ave Ste 245, Memphis TN 38117
Tel (901) 762-5466 *SIC* 8741 8721

BODYCOTE USA INC p 197
12700 Park Central Dr # 700, Dallas TX 75251
Tel (214) 904-2420 *SIC* 8721

RYAN LLC p 1260
13155 Noel Rd Ste 100, Dallas TX 75240
Tel (972) 934-0022 *SIC* 8721 7291 7389

MEDSYNERGIES INC p 939
909 Hidden Rdg Ste 300, Irving TX 75038
Tel (972) 791-1224 *SIC* 8741 8742 8721

■ VERIZON NORTHWEST INC p 1550
600 Hidden Rdg, Irving TX 75038
Tel (972) 718-5600
SIC 4813 6519 8721 5065 7629

■ VERIZON SOUTH INC p 1550
600 Hidden Rdg, Irving TX 75038
Tel (972) 718-5600 *SIC* 4813 5065 8721

ETECH GLOBAL SERVICES LLC p 511
1903 Berry Dr, Nacogdoches TX 75964
Tel (936) 559-2200
SIC 7389 8742 7373 8741 8721 7374

RESOURCING EDGE INC p 1227
1309 Ridge Rd Ste 200, Rockwall TX 75087
Tel (214) 771-4411 *SIC* 8721 8742

■ RIO TINTO SERVICES INC p 1236
4700 W Daybreak Pkwy, South Jordan UT 84009
Tel (801) 204-2000 *SIC* 8721 8741

■ VERIZON BUSINESS GLOBAL LLC p 1550
22001 Loudoun County Pkwy, Ashburn VA 20147
Tel (703) 886-5600 *SIC* 4813 8721 4822

UNIVERSITY OF VIRGINIA PHYSICIANS GROUP p 1526
4105 Lewis And Clark Dr, Charlottesville VA 22911
Tel (434) 980-6110 *SIC* 8721

LTD MANAGEMENT CO LLC p 883
1564 Crossways Blvd, Chesapeake VA 23320
Tel (757) 420-0900 *SIC* 8741 8721

■ DATATRAC INFORMATION SERVICES INC p 414
3170 Fairview Park Dr, Falls Church VA 22042
Tel (703) 876-1000 *SIC* 8742 0781 8721

WINTERGREEN RESORTS INC p 1617
11 Grassy Ridge Dr, Nellysford VA 22958
Tel (434) 325-8237 *SIC* 8721 7011 5812

CHERRY BEKAERT LLP p 294
200 S 10th St Ste 900, Richmond VA 23219
Tel (804) 673-5700 *SIC* 8721

MCV ASSOCIATED PHYSICIANS p 933
830 E Main St Ste 1900, Richmond VA 23219
Tel (804) 358-6100 *SIC* 8741 8721

MOSS ADAMS LLP p 992
999 3rd Ave Ste 2800, Seattle WA 98104
Tel (206) 302-6500 *SIC* 8721

HEALTHCARE RESOURCE GROUP INC p 676
12610 E Mirabeau Pkwy # 900, Spokane Valley WA 99216
Tel (509) 209-2000
SIC 6411 7322 8742 8721

■ FRONTIER WEST VIRGINIA INC p 581
1500 Maccorkle Ave Se, Charleston WV 25396
Tel (304) 344-6409 *SIC* 4813 8721

PAYMENT SERVICE NETWORK INC p 1122
2901 International Ln # 100, Madison WI 53704
Tel (608) 442-5100 *SIC* 7389 6531 8721

■ EXPERIS FINANCE US LLC p 520
100 W Manpower Pl, Milwaukee WI 53212
Tel (414) 319-3400 *SIC* 8721

WIPFLI LLP p 1618
10000 W Innovation Dr 250-260, Milwaukee WI 53226
Tel (414) 431-9300 *SIC* 8748 8721

■ WISCONSIN BELL INC p 1618
722 N Broadway, Milwaukee WI 53202
Tel (414) 271-9619 *SIC* 4813 8721

SIC 8731 Commercial Physical & Biological Research

CAMBER CORP p 243
670 Discovery Dr Nw, Huntsville AL 35806
Tel (256) 922-0200 *SIC* 8731 7371

COLSA CORP p 339
6728 Odyssey Dr Nw, Huntsville AL 35806
Tel (256) 964-5361
SIC 8731 7373 8744 8711

DYNETICS INC p 465
1002 Explorer Blvd Nw, Huntsville AL 35806
Tel (256) 964-4000 *SIC* 8731

ENGINEERING RESEARCH AND CONSULTING INC p 499
308 Voyager Way Nw # 200, Huntsville AL 35806
Tel (256) 430-3080 *SIC* 8731 8711

■ TELEDYNE BROWN ENGINEERING INC p 1434
300 Sparkman Dr Nw, Huntsville AL 35805
Tel (256) 726-1000 *SIC* 8731

EXODYNE INC p 519
8433 N Black Canyon Hwy # 100, Phoenix AZ 85021
Tel (602) 995-3700
SIC 8711 8731 8741 8744 8748

SWCA INC p 1411
3033 N Central Ave # 145, Phoenix AZ 85012
Tel (602) 274-3831
SIC 8748 8711 8731 8733

TRANSLATIONAL GENOMICS RESEARCH INSTITUTE p 1472
445 N 5th St, Phoenix AZ 85004
Tel (602) 343-8400 *SIC* 8731

CLINICAL RESEARCH ADVANTAGE INC p 326
2141 E Broadway Rd # 120, Tempe AZ 85282
Tel (480) 820-5656 *SIC* 8731

▲ IONIS PHARMACEUTICALS INC p 762
2855 Gazelle Ct, Carlsbad CA 92010
Tel (760) 931-9200 *SIC* 2834 8731 3845

SYNTERACTHCR CORP p 1416
5759 Fleet St Ste 100, Carlsbad CA 92008
Tel (760) 268-8200 *SIC* 8731

SYNTERACTHCR HOLDINGS CORP p 1416
5759 Fleet St Ste 100, Carlsbad CA 92008
Tel (760) 268-8200 *SIC* 8731

SYNTERACTHCR INC p 1416
5759 Fleet St Ste 100, Carlsbad CA 92008
Tel (760) 268-8200 *SIC* 8731

▲ AEMETIS INC p 29
20400 Stevens, Cupertino CA 95014
Tel (408) 213-0940 *SIC* 8731 2911

AEROSPACE CORP p 30
2310 E El Segundo Blvd, El Segundo CA 90245
Tel (310) 336-5000 *SIC* 8733 8731 8711

■ WYLE INC p 1629
1960 E Grand Ave Ste 900, El Segundo CA 90245
Tel (310) 563-6800 *SIC* 8711 7371 8731

■ WYLE LABORATORIES INC p 1629
1960 E Grand Ave Ste 900, El Segundo CA 90245
Tel (310) 563-6800 *SIC* 8734 8731

DELTA AMERICA LTD p 426
46101 Fremont Blvd, Fremont CA 94538
Tel (510) 668-5100 *SIC* 5065 3679 8731

TECOLOTE RESEARCH INC p 1432
420 S Fairview Ave # 201, Goleta CA 93117
Tel (805) 571-6366 *SIC* 8742 8731

GENSIA SICOR INC p 604
19 Hughes, Irvine CA 92618
Tel (949) 455-4700 *SIC* 2834 8731

■ TALON THERAPEUTICS INC p 1423
157 Technology Dr, Irvine CA 92618
Tel (949) 788-6700 *SIC* 2834 8731

SALK INSTITUTE FOR BIOLOGICAL STUDIES SAN DIEGO CALIFORNIA p 1273
10010 N Torrey Pines Rd, La Jolla CA 92037
Tel (858) 453-4100 *SIC* 8731

PARSONS GOVERNMENT SERVICES INC p 1118
25531 Commercentre Dr, Lake Forest CA 92630
Tel (949) 768-8161 *SIC* 8731

CALIFORNIA NATURAL PRODUCTS p 240
15789 Mckinley Ave, Lathrop CA 95330
Tel (209) 249-1616 *SIC* 2099 8731 3612

UNITED STATES DEPARTMENT OF ENERGY LIVERMORE OFFICE p 1512
7000 East Ave, Livermore CA 94550
Tel (925) 422-1100 *SIC* 9611 8731

■ SEMINIS INC p 1302
2700 Camino Del Sol, Oxnard CA 93030
Tel (805) 485-7317 *SIC* 8731 8742 2099

■ DANISCO US INC p 412
925 Page Mill Rd, Palo Alto CA 94304
Tel (650) 846-7500
SIC 2835 8731 2899 2869

ELECTRIC POWER RESEARCH INSTITUTE INC p 484
3420 Hillview Ave, Palo Alto CA 94304
Tel (650) 855-2000 *SIC* 8731

■ ROCHE MOLECULAR SYSTEMS INC p 1243
4300 Hacienda Dr, Pleasanton CA 94588
Tel (925) 730-8000 *SIC* 8731

▲ GENOMIC HEALTH INC p 604
301 Penobscot Dr, Redwood City CA 94063
Tel (650) 556-9300 *SIC* 8071 8731

■ AGOURON PHARMACEUTICALS INC p 35
10777 Science Center Dr, San Diego CA 92121
Tel (858) 622-3000 *SIC* 2834 5122 8731

■ GEN-PROBE INC p 598
10210 Genetic Center Dr, San Diego CA 92121
Tel (858) 410-8000 *SIC* 8731

GENERAL ATOMIC TECHNOLOGIES CORP p 599
3550 General Atomics Ct, San Diego CA 92121
Tel (858) 455-3000
SIC 8731 3829 3443 7374 3499 2819

GENERAL ATOMICS p 599
3550 General Atomics Ct, San Diego CA 92121
Tel (858) 455-2810 *SIC* 8731

INOVA DIAGNOSTICS INC p 745
9900 Old Grove Rd, San Diego CA 92131
Tel (858) 586-9900 *SIC* 2835 8731

▲ RETROPHIN INC p 1229
12255 El Camino Real # 250, San Diego CA 92130
Tel (760) 260-8600 *SIC* 2834 8731

■ SEQUENOM INC p 1306
3595 John Hopkins Ct, San Diego CA 92121
Tel (858) 202-9000 *SIC* 8731

IXONOS USA LIMITED p 769
85 2nd St, San Francisco CA 94105
Tel (949) 278-1354 *SIC* 7373 8731

▲ QUANTUM CORP p 1198
224 Airport Pkwy Ste 300, San Jose CA 95110
Tel (408) 944-4000 *SIC* 3572 8731

RENESAS ELECTRONICS AMERICA INC p 1223
2801 Scott Blvd, Santa Clara CA 95050
Tel (408) 588-6000
SIC 5065 8731 5731 5045 8711

■ SPECTRA-PHYSICS INC p 1357
3635 Peterson Way, Santa Clara CA 95054
Tel (650) 961-2550 *SIC* 3699 8731

TOSHIBA AMERICA MRI INC p 1462
280 Utah Ave Ste 200, South San Francisco CA 94080
Tel (650) 737-6686 *SIC* 3845 8731

■ AMAZON LAB126 p 64
1100 Enterprise Way, Sunnyvale CA 94089
Tel (650) 426-1100 *SIC* 8731

FUJITSU LABORATORIES OF AMERICA INC p 584
1240 E Arques Ave 345, Sunnyvale CA 94085
Tel (408) 530-4500 *SIC* 8731

■ TELEDYNE SCIENTIFIC & IMAGING LLC p 1434
1049 Camino Dos Rios, Thousand Oaks CA 91360
Tel (805) 373-4545 *SIC* 8731 8732 8733

QIAGEN INC p 1195
27220 Turnberry Ln # 200, Valencia CA 91355
Tel (661) 702-3598
SIC 3826 5047 8731 2835

PLANT SCIENCES INC p 1154
342 Green Valley Rd, Watsonville CA 95076
Tel (831) 728-3323 *SIC* 5122 8748 8731

RENEWABLE ENERGY SYSTEMS p 1224
11101 W 120th Ave Ste 400, Broomfield CO 80021
Tel (303) 439-4200 *SIC* 8731

NEXUS BIOENERGY INC p 1041
3026 Castle Peak Ave, Superior CO 80027
Tel (720) 318-2339 *SIC* 4939 7389 8731

APTUIT LLC p 101
2 Greenwich Office Park, Greenwich CT 06831
Tel (203) 422-6600 *SIC* 8731

FRC FOUNDERS CORP p 575
1 Lafayette Pl Ste 3, Greenwich CT 06830
Tel (203) 661-6601
SIC 8741 1311 1389 8731 5084

AMYLIN PHARMACEUTICALS LLC p 88
1800 Concord Pike, Wilmington DE 19897
Tel (858) 552-2200 *SIC* 2834 8731

GRYPHON TECHNOLOGIES LC p 643
80 M St Se Ste 600, Washington DC 20003
Tel (202) 617-2004
SIC 8741 8711 8731 7371

INTERNATIONAL FOOD POLICY RESEARCH INSTITUTE p 755
2033 K St Nw Ste 400, Washington DC 20006
Tel (202) 862-5600 *SIC* 8731 8733

▲ VANDA PHARMACEUTICALS INC p 1543
2200 Penn Ave Nw Ste 300e, Washington DC 20037
Tel (202) 734-3400 *SIC* 2834 8731

BIOTEST PHARMACEUTICALS CORP p 184
5800 Pk Of Commerce Blvd, Boca Raton FL 33487
Tel (561) 989-5800 *SIC* 8731 2834

INTERNATIONAL CONSORTIUM FOR ADVANCED MANUFACTURING RESEARCH INC p 755
3 Courthouse Sq Fl 2, Kissimmee FL 34741
Tel (407) 742-4252 *SIC* 8731

CENTRO INTERNACIONAL DE AGRICULTURA TROPICAL p 281
7343 Nw 79th Ter, Medley FL 33166
Tel (305) 863-9127 *SIC* 8731

LATAMSCIENCE LLC p 846
2151 S Le Jeune Rd # 307, Miami FL 33134
Tel (305) 871-0701 *SIC* 8731 8999

▲ OPKO HEALTH INC p 1089
4400 Biscayne Blvd, Miami FL 33137
Tel (305) 575-4100 *SIC* 2834 2835 8731

OXBOW CORP p 1100
1601 Forum Pl Ste 1400, West Palm Beach FL 33401
Tel (561) 907-5422 *SIC* 8731

GEORGIA TECH APPLIED RESEARCH CORP p 607
505 10th St Nw, Atlanta GA 30318
Tel (404) 894-4819 *SIC* 8731

APPLIED TECHNICAL SERVICES INC p 100
1049 Triad Ct, Marietta GA 30062
Tel (770) 423-1400 *SIC* 8734 8711 8731

ATLANTIX GLOBAL SYSTEMS LLC p 127
1 Sun Ct, Norcross GA 30092
Tel (770) 248-7700 *SIC* 8731

DYNAMIX GROUP INC p 464
1905 Woodstock Rd # 4150, Roswell GA 30075
Tel (770) 643-8877 *SIC* 7373 8731

UCB INC p 1498
1950 Lake Park Dr Se, Smyrna GA 30080
Tel (770) 970-7500 *SIC* 5122 8731 8732

BATTELLE ENERGY ALLIANCE LLC p 159
2525 Fremont Ave, Idaho Falls ID 83402
Tel (208) 533-7606 *SIC* 8731 7382

FERMI RESEARCH ALLIANCE LLC p 538
Ms 105 Wilson & Kirk Rds, Batavia IL 60510
Tel (630) 406-7901 *SIC* 8731

FERMILAB p 538
Wilson Str And Kirk Rd, Batavia IL 60510
Tel (630) 840-3000 *SIC* 8731

IPSOS PUBLIC AFFAIRS INC p 764
222 S Rverside Plz Fl 4, Chicago IL 60606
Tel (312) 526-4000 *SIC* 8732 8731

■ UOP LLC p 1528
25 E Algonquin Rd, Des Plaines IL 60016
Tel (847) 391-2000
SIC 2819 8711 8731 8999 3823 3479

■ KNOWLES ELECTRONICS HOLDINGS INC p 825
1151 Maplewood Dr, Itasca IL 60143
Tel (630) 250-5100
SIC 3679 3625 3651 8731 6159

ANGIOTECH PHARMACEUTICALS (US) INC p 91
241 W Palatine Rd, Wheeling IL 60090
Tel (847) 637-3333
SIC 3841 3541 3842 8731

INFRASTRUCTURE AND ENERGY ALTERNATIVES LLC p 742
3900 White Ave, Clinton IN 47842
Tel (708) 397-4200 *SIC* 8731 1731

■ DOW AGROSCIENCES LLC p 453
9330 Zionsville Rd, Indianapolis IN 46268
Tel (317) 337-3000
SIC 2879 5191 0721 8731

■ ELI LILLY INTERNATIONAL CORP p 487
893 S Delaware St, Indianapolis IN 46225
Tel (317) 276-2000
SIC 8742 2834 8731 3841 2879

HERITAGE ENVIRONMENTAL SERVICES INC p 686
7901 W Morris St, Indianapolis IN 46231
Tel (317) 243-0811
SIC 5093 4213 8731 7389 1799 8711

HERITAGE ENVIRONMENTAL SERVICES LLC p 686
7901 W Morris St, Indianapolis IN 46231
Tel (317) 243-0811
SIC 5093 4213 8731 7389 1799 8711

■ MYCOGEN CORP p 1004
9330 Zionsville Rd, Indianapolis IN 46268
Tel (317) 337-3000
SIC 5191 2879 0721 8731

CENTRAL IOWA RENEWABLE ENERGY LLC p 278
415 Locust St, Goldfield IA 50542
Tel (515) 825-3161 *SIC* 8731

CFPB HOLDINGS LLC p 285
604 Goff Industrial Pk Rd, Arkansas City KS 67005
Tel (620) 741-3100 *SIC* 8731

UNIVERSITY OF KANSAS CENTER FOR RESEARCH INC p 1522
2385 Irving Hill Rd, Lawrence KS 66045
Tel (785) 864-3441
SIC 8733 8732 8741 8731

ATC GROUP HOLDINGS LLC p 124
221 Rue De Jean Ste 300, Lafayette LA 70508
Tel (337) 324-8777
SIC 8711 8732 8731 8249 8748

ATC GROUP SERVICES LLC p 124
221 Rue De Jean Ste 200, Lafayette LA 70508
Tel (337) 234-8777
SIC 8711 8734 8731 8249 8748

■ PRODUCTION MANAGEMENT INDUSTRIES LLC p 1179
1204 Youngs Rd, Morgan City LA 70380
Tel (985) 631-3837 *SIC* 1389 8731 4789

AMERITOX LIMITED PARTNERSHIP p 84
300 E Lombard St Ste 1610, Baltimore MD 21202
Tel (443) 220-0115 *SIC* 7374 8734 8731

SCIENCE AND ENGINEERING SERVICES LLC p 1292
6992 Columbia Gateway Dr # 200, Columbia MD 21046
Tel (443) 539-0139 *SIC* 8711 8731 3826

SMITHS DETECTION INC p 1334
2202 Lakeside Blvd, Edgewood MD 21040
Tel (410) 510-9100
SIC 3824 3823 3829 8731

■ LEIDOS TECHNICAL SERVICES INC p 854
700 N Frederick Ave, Gaithersburg MD 20879
Tel (301) 240-7000 *SIC* 8731

MEDIMMUNE BIOLOGICS INC p 938
1 Medimmune Way, Gaithersburg MD 20878
Tel (301) 398-0000 *SIC* 8731

OCIMUM BIOSOLUTIONS INC p 1074
50 W Watkins Mill Rd, Gaithersburg MD 20878
Tel (317) 228-0600 SIC 8731

▲ INTREXON CORP p 760
20374 Seneca Meadows Pkwy, Germantown MD 20876
Tel (301) 556-9900 SIC 8731

▲ KEYW HOLDING CORP p 816
7740 Milestone Pkwy # 400, Hanover MD 21076
Tel (443) 733-1600
SIC 7373 7372 8731 7375

SMARTRONIX INC p 1332
44150 Smartronix Way, Hollywood MD 20636
Tel (301) 373-6000 SIC 7371 8731 7373

JOHNS HOPKINS UNIVERSITY APPLIED PHYSICS LABORATORY LLC p 790
11100 Johns Hopkins Rd, Laurel MD 20723
Tel (240) 228-5000 SIC 8731

BIORELIANCE CORP p 184
14920 Broschart Rd, Rockville MD 20850
Tel (301) 738-1000 SIC 8734 8731

HUMAN GENOME SCIENCES INC p 718
14200 Shady Grove Rd, Rockville MD 20850
Tel (301) 309-8504 SIC 8731 2834

OTSUKA AMERICA PHARMACEUTICAL INC p 1098
2440 Res Blvd Ste 500, Rockville MD 20850
Tel (301) 990-0030 SIC 8733 8011 8731

UNITED STATES PHARMACOPOEIAL CONVENTION p 1514
12601 Twinbrook Pkwy, Rockville MD 20852
Tel (301) 881-0666 SIC 8731 8734

INSTRUMENTATION LABORATORY CO p 747
180 Hartwell Rd, Bedford MA 01730
Tel (800) 955-9525
SIC 3841 2819 8731 2835

▲ VERTEX PHARMACEUTICALS INC p 1552
50 Northern Ave, Boston MA 02210
Tel (617) 341-6100 SIC 2834 8731

INVENTIV GROUP HOLDINGS INC p 761
1 Van De Graaff Dr, Burlington MA 01803
Tel (609) 951-6800 SIC 8742 8731

INVENTIV HEALTH INC p 761
1 Van De Graaff Dr, Burlington MA 01803
Tel (800) 416-0555 SIC 8731

▲ ARIAD PHARMACEUTICALS INC p 108
26 Landsdowne St Ste 175, Cambridge MA 02139
Tel (617) 494-0400 SIC 2836 8731

▲ BIOGEN INC p 184
225 Binney St, Cambridge MA 02142
Tel (617) 679-2000 SIC 2834 2836 8731

▲ INFINITY PHARMACEUTICALS INC p 741
784 Memorial Dr, Cambridge MA 02139
Tel (617) 453-1000 SIC 2834 8731

▲ IRONWOOD PHARMACEUTICALS INC p 765
301 Binney St, Cambridge MA 02142
Tel (617) 621-7722 SIC 2834 8731

MILLENNIUM PHARMACEUTICALS INC p 970
40 Landsdowne St, Cambridge MA 02139
Tel (617) 679-7000 SIC 8731

SHIRE HUMAN GENETIC THERAPIES INC p 1317
300 Shire Way, Lexington MA 02421
Tel (617) 349-0200 SIC 8731

PRESS GANEY HOLDINGS INC p 1172
401 Edgewater Pl Ste 500, Wakefield MA 01880
Tel (781) 295-5000 SIC 8731

ALKERMES INC p 50
852 Winter St, Waltham MA 02451
Tel (781) 609-6000 SIC 2834 8731

▲ PAREXEL INTERNATIONAL CORP p 1114
195 West St, Waltham MA 02451
Tel (781) 487-9900 SIC 8731

■ PAREXEL INTERNATIONAL LLC p 1114
195 West St, Waltham MA 02451
Tel (781) 487-9900 SIC 8731

QINETIQ NORTH AMERICA INC p 1195
350 2nd Ave Bldg 1, Waltham MA 02451
Tel (781) 684-4000 SIC 3812 8731

ENANTA PHARMACEUTICALS INC p 495
500 Arsenal St, Watertown MA 02472
Tel (617) 607-0800 SIC 2834 8731

■ ESOTERIX GENETIC LABORATORIES LLC p 509
3400 Computer Dr, Westborough MA 01581
Tel (508) 389-6650 SIC 8731 2835 8071

■ BIOGEN MA INC p 184
133 Boston Post Rd, Weston MA 02493
Tel (617) 679-2000 SIC 2836 8731

■ CHARLES RIVER LABORATORIES INC p 289
251 Ballardvale St, Wilmington MA 01887
Tel (978) 658-6000
SIC 8742 8734 8731 0279

▲ CHARLES RIVER LABORATORIES INTERNATIONAL INC p 289
251 Ballardvale St, Wilmington MA 01887
Tel (781) 222-6000 SIC 8731

WOOD HOLE OCEANAL GRAPHICS INSTITUTION INC p 1622
38 Water St, Woods Hole MA 02543
Tel (508) 457-2620 SIC 8731 8733 8221

NSF INTERNATIONAL p 1065
789 N Dixboro Rd, Ann Arbor MI 48105
Tel (734) 769-8010 SIC 8731 8734

EFTEC NORTH AMERICA LLC p 481
31601 Research Park Dr, Madison Heights MI 48071
Tel (248) 526-4565
SIC 2891 8731 3296 2899 2851

MPI RESEARCH INC p 995
54943 N Main St, Mattawan MI 49071
Tel (269) 668-3336 SIC 8731

JOHNSON ELECTRIC AUTOMOTIVE INC p 791
47660 Halyard Dr, Plymouth MI 48170
Tel (734) 392-1022 SIC 5013 8731 8742

MOBIS NORTH AMERICA LLC p 980
46501 Commerce Dr, Plymouth MI 48170
Tel (248) 426-5577 SIC 5013 8731

TRICO PRODUCTS CORP p 1479
3255 W Hamlin Rd, Rochester Hills MI 48309
Tel (248) 371-1700
SIC 3714 3069 3082 8734 8731

HUTCHINSON TECHNOLOGY INC p 722
40 W Highland Park Dr Ne, Hutchinson MN 55350
Tel (320) 587-3797 SIC 3679 8731

▲ BIO-TECHNE CORP p 183
614 Mckinley Pl Ne, Minneapolis MN 55413
Tel (612) 379-8854 SIC 2835 8731

LAB HOLDINGS INC p 836
8500 Normandale Lake Blvd # 1750, Minneapolis MN 55437
Tel (612) 607-1700 SIC 8734 8731

PACE ANALYTICAL SERVICES LLC p 1103
1800 Elm St Se, Minneapolis MN 55414
Tel (612) 607-6369 SIC 8734 8748 8731

■ RESEARCH AND DIAGNOSTIC SYSTEMS INC p 1226
614 Mckinley Pl Ne, Minneapolis MN 55413
Tel (612) 379-2956
SIC 8731 2833 8731 3829 3625

GEODIGM CORP p 605
1740 Prior Ave N, Saint Paul MN 55113
Tel (952) 556-5657 SIC 8731

■ BAPTIST-LUTHERAN MEDICAL CENTER p 154
6601 Rockhill Rd, Kansas City MO 64131
Tel (816) 276-7000 SIC 8062 8731

MRIGLOBAL p 996
425 Volker Blvd, Kansas City MO 64110
Tel (816) 753-7600 SIC 8731 6794

CELERION HOLDINGS INC p 273
621 Rose St, Lincoln NE 68502
Tel (402) 476-2811 SIC 8731

CELERION INC p 273
621 Rose St, Lincoln NE 68502
Tel (402) 476-2811 SIC 8731

■ QUEST DIAGNOSTICS INC p 1199
4230 Burnham Ave, Las Vegas NV 89119
Tel (702) 733-7866 SIC 8071 8731

LONZA AMERICA INC p 877
90 Boroline Rd Ste 1, Allendale NJ 07401
Tel (201) 316-9200 SIC 8731

LIFE SCIENCES RESEARCH INC p 864
Mettlers Rd, East Millstone NJ 08875
Tel (732) 649-9961 SIC 8731

LION HOLDINGS INC p 869
Mettlers Rd, East Millstone NJ 08875
Tel (732) 649-9961 SIC 8731

ELEMENTIS SPECIALTIES INC p 486
469 Old Trenton Rd, East Windsor NJ 08512
Tel (609) 443-2000
SIC 2851 8731 2899 2865 2816

BIOCON INC p 183
125 May St, Edison NJ 08837
Tel (732) 661-0202 SIC 8731

■ CHARLES RIVER LABORATORIES SA USA INC p 289
30 Two Bridges Rd Ste 200, Fairfield NJ 07004
Tel (919) 245-3114 SIC 8731

RADWARE INC p 1205
575 Corporate Dr Ste 205, Mahwah NJ 07430
Tel (201) 512-9771 SIC 8731

TRIS PHARMA INC p 1482
2033 Rte 130 Ste D, Monmouth Junction NJ 08852
Tel (732) 940-2800 SIC 8731

DAIICHI SANKYO INC p 408
2 Hilton Ct Ste 1, Parsippany NJ 07054
Tel (973) 359-2600 SIC 5122 8731

■ COVANCE INC p 383
210 Carnegie Ctr Ste 106, Princeton NJ 08540
Tel (609) 452-4440
SIC 8731 8734 8733 8732

INVENTIV HEALTH CLINICAL INC p 761
504 Carnegie Ctr, Princeton NJ 08540
Tel (609) 514-9400 SIC 8731

SIEMENS CORPORATE RESEARCH INC p 1320
755 College Rd E, Princeton NJ 08540
Tel (609) 734-6500 SIC 8731 7373

■ JANSSEN RESEARCH & DEVELOPMENT LLC p 777
920 Us Highway 202, Raritan NJ 08869
Tel (908) 704-4000 SIC 2834 8731

BAYER HEALTHCARE LLC p 161
100 Bayer Blvd, Whippany NJ 07981
Tel (862) 404-3000
SIC 2834 8731 3845 3841

EISAI CORP OF NORTH AMERICA p 482
100 Tice Blvd, Woodcliff Lake NJ 07677
Tel (201) 692-1100 SIC 5169 8731

APPLIED RESEARCH ASSOCIATES INC p 100
4300 San Mateo Blvd Ne A220, Albuquerque NM 87110
Tel (505) 883-3636 SIC 8731 8748

▲ ALBANY MOLECULAR RESEARCH INC p 45
26 Corporate Cir, Albany NY 12203
Tel (518) 512-2000 SIC 2836 8731

▲ ACORDA THERAPEUTICS INC p 18
420 Saw Mill River Rd, Ardsley NY 10502
Tel (914) 347-4300 SIC 2834 8731 2836

■ CORNING RESEARCH & DEVELOPMENT CORP p 371
1 Riverfront Plz, Corning NY 14831
Tel (607) 974-9000 SIC 8731

▲ ENZO BIOCHEM INC p 504
527 Madison Ave Rm 901, New York NY 10022
Tel (212) 583-0100 SIC 8071 8731

▲ HC2 HOLDINGS INC p 671
450 Park Ave Fl 30, New York NY 10022
Tel (212) 235-2690 SIC 4813 3325 8731

STANTEC CONSULTING SERVICES INC p 1377
50 W 23rd St Fl 8, New York NY 10010
Tel (212) 366-5600 SIC 8731 8711 1541

MITSUI CHEMICALS AMERICA INC p 978
800 Westchester Ave N607, Rye Brook NY 10573
Tel (914) 253-0777
SIC 2821 2865 3082 8731 5169 6159

KAPL INC p 803
2401 River Rd, Schenectady NY 12309
Tel (877) 527-5522 SIC 8731

ARCADIS CE INC p 103
44 S Broadway Ste 1500, White Plains NY 10601
Tel (914) 694-2100 SIC 8711 8731

CHICAGO BRIDGE & IRON CO p 297
128 S Tryon St Ste 400, Charlotte NC 28202
Tel (704) 331-6200 SIC 8731

■ CONSTELLA GROUP LLC p 360
2605 Meridian Pkwy # 200, Durham NC 27713
Tel (919) 544-8500
SIC 7371 8742 7375 8748 8731 8071

■ KENDLE INTERNATIONAL LLC p 810
3201 Beechleaf Ct, Durham NC 27703
Tel (919) 876-9300 SIC 8731

▲ QUINTILES IMS HOLDINGS INC p 1200
4820 Emperor Blvd, Durham NC 27703
Tel (919) 998-2000 SIC 8731

■ QUINTILES INC p 1200
4820 Emperor Blvd, Durham NC 27703
Tel (919) 998-2000 SIC 8731

■ QUINTILES TRANSNATIONAL CORP p 1200
4820 Emperor Blvd, Durham NC 27703
Tel (919) 998-2000 SIC 8732 8731 8999

RESEARCH TRIANGLE INSTITUTE INC p 1226
3040 Cornwallis Rd, Durham NC 27709
Tel (919) 541-6000 SIC 8732 8731

■ NOVELLA CLINICAL INC p 1063
1700 Perimeter Park Dr, Morrisville NC 27560
Tel (919) 484-1921 SIC 8731

APPLIED RESEARCH ASSOCIATES INC p 100
11 Villiage Club Ct, Pinehurst NC 28374
Tel (910) 246-2030 SIC 8711 8731

▲ INC RESEARCH HOLDINGS INC p 735
3201 Beechleaf Ct Ste 600, Raleigh NC 27604
Tel (919) 876-9300 SIC 8731

■ INC RESEARCH LLC p 735
3201 Beechleaf Ct Ste 600, Raleigh NC 27604
Tel (919) 876-9300 SIC 8731

■ PRA HEALTH SCIENCES INC p 1167
4130 Parklake Ave Ste 400, Raleigh NC 27612
Tel (919) 786-8200 SIC 8731

■ PRA INTERNATIONAL OPERATIONS INC p 1167
4130 Parklake Ave Ste 400, Raleigh NC 27612
Tel (919) 786-8200 SIC 8731

CASE FARMS LLC p 263
385 Pilch Rd, Troutman NC 28166
Tel (704) 528-4501 SIC 2015 8731

WALKER AND ASSOCIATES INC p 1573
7129 Old Hwy 52, Welcome NC 27374
Tel (336) 731-6391
SIC 4813 5065 8731 8711 3572 3571

ALCAMI CAROLINAS CORP p 47
2320 Scientific Park Dr, Wilmington NC 28405
Tel (910) 254-7000 SIC 2834 8734 8731

ALCAMI HOLDINGS LLC p 47
2320 Scientific Park Dr, Wilmington NC 28405
Tel (910) 254-7000 SIC 2834 8731 8734

APPLIED BIOSCIENCE INTERNATIONAL LLC p 99
3151 S 17th St, Wilmington NC 28412
Tel (910) 251-0081 SIC 8731

CHEMTEX INTERNATIONAL INC p 293
1979 Eastwood Rd, Wilmington NC 28403
Tel (910) 509-4400 SIC 8711 8731

PHARMACEUTICAL PRODUCT DEVELOPMENT LLC p 1141
929 N Front St, Wilmington NC 28401
Tel (910) 251-0081 SIC 8731

PPD DEVELOPMENT LP p 1166
929 N Front St, Wilmington NC 28401
Tel (910) 251-0081 SIC 8731

PPD DEVELOPMENT LP p 1166
929 N Front St, Wilmington NC 28401
Tel (910) 251-0081 SIC 8731

BRIDGESTONE RESEARCH LLC p 211
1655 S Main St, Akron OH 44301
Tel (330) 379-7570 SIC 8731

CHILDRENS HOSPITAL MEDICAL CENTER p 299
3333 Burnet Ave, Cincinnati OH 45229
Tel (513) 636-4200
SIC 8733 8011 8069 8731

▲ MEDPACE HOLDINGS INC p 938
5375 Medpace Way, Cincinnati OH 45227
Tel (513) 579-9911 SIC 2834 8731

■ MEDPACE INC p 938
5375 Medpace Way, Cincinnati OH 45227
Tel (513) 579-9911 SIC 8731 5122 5047

QUEST GLOBAL SERVICES-NA INC p 1199
11499 Chester Rd Ste 600, Cincinnati OH 45246
Tel (513) 648-4900 SIC 8731 8711

BATTELLE MEMORIAL INSTITUTE INC p 159
505 King Ave, Columbus OH 43201
Tel (614) 424-6424 SIC 8731

ADVICS NORTH AMERICA INC p 28
1650 Kingsview Dr, Lebanon OH 45036
Tel (513) 696-5450
SIC 8731 8742 5013 5531

NORTH AMERICAN SCIENCE ASSOCIATES INC p 1050
6750 Wales Rd, Northwood OH 43619
Tel (419) 666-9455 SIC 8731 8734

RICERCA BIOSCIENCES LLC p 1232
7528 Auburn Rd, Painesville OH 44077
Tel (440) 357-3300 SIC 8731

GUTTMAN ENERGY INC p 648
200 Speers Rd, Belle Vernon PA 15012
Tel (724) 489-5199 SIC 8731 5172

■ UNITED BIOSOURCE LLC p 1506
920 Harvest Dr Ste 200, Blue Bell PA 19422
Tel (215) 591-2880 SIC 8731

■ WYETH PHARMACEUTICALS INC p 1629
500 Arcola Rd, Collegeville PA 19426
Tel (484) 865-5000 SIC 5122 8731

THEOREM CLINICAL RESEARCH INC p 1446
1016 W 9th Ave Ste 300, King Of Prussia PA 19406
Tel (484) 679-2400 SIC 8731 8071 2834

EUROFINS LANCASTER LABORATORIES INC p 512
2425 New Holland Pike, Lancaster PA 17601
Tel (717) 656-2300 SIC 8731 8734

ICON CLINICAL RESEARCH LLC p 727
2100 Pennbrook Pkwy, North Wales PA 19454
Tel (215) 616-3000 SIC 8731

ECOG-ACRIN MEDICAL RESEARCH FOUNDATION INC p 476
1818 Market St, Philadelphia PA 19103
Tel (215) 789-3600 SIC 8731

THOMSON REUTERS (SCIENTIFIC) INC p 1450
1500 Spring Garden St # 400, Philadelphia PA 19130
Tel (215) 386-0100 SIC 8731

GENTEX CORP p 604
324 Main St, Simpson PA 18407
Tel (570) 282-3550 SIC 3842 8731 2295

NAVMAR APPLIED SCIENCES CORP p 1020
65 W Street Rd Ste C, Warminster PA 18974
Tel (215) 675-4900 SIC 8731 8711

SAVANNAH RIVER NUCLEAR SOLUTIONS LLC p 1284
203 Laurens St Sw Frnt, Aiken SC 29801
Tel (803) 643-4570 SIC 8731

HEALTH SCIENCES SOUTH CAROLINA p 675
1320 Main St Ste 625, Columbia SC 29201
Tel (803) 544-4772 SIC 8731

3V SIGMA USA INC p 3
888 Woodstock St, Georgetown SC 29440
Tel (843) 546-8556 SIC 2869 2899 8731

PRECISION SOUTHEAST INC p 1169
4900 Highway 501, Myrtle Beach SC 29579
Tel (843) 347-4218 SIC 3089 8731 3083

SIGNAL ENERGY LLC p 1322
2034 Hamilton Place Blvd # 400, Chattanooga TN 37421
Tel (423) 443-4190 SIC 1542 8731

UT-BATTELLE LLC p 1536
1 Bethel Valley Rd, Oak Ridge TN 37830
Tel (865) 574-2227 SIC 8731

UNIVERSITY OF TEXAS AT ARLINGTON p 1525
701 S Nedderman Dr, Arlington TX 76019
Tel (817) 272-2011 SIC 8221 8731

▲ LUMINEX CORP p 885
12212 Technology Blvd, Austin TX 78727
Tel (512) 219-8020 SIC 3841 8731

TEXAS A&M AGRILIFE EXTENSION SERVICE p 1442
2147 Tamu, College Station TX 77843
Tel (979) 458-4383 SIC 8731 8221

TEXAS A&M AGRILIFE RESEARCH p 1442
2147 Tamu, College Station TX 77843
Tel (979) 458-4383 SIC 8731 8221

TEXAS A&M UNIVERSITY SYSTEM p 1442
301 Tarrow St Fl 3, College Station TX 77840
Tel (979) 458-6100
SIC 8221 8731 8742 8011

INSPECTORATE AMERICA CORP p 746
12000 Aerospace Ave # 200, Houston TX 77034
Tel (713) 944-2000 SIC 7389 8734 8731

ROCKWATER ENERGY SOLUTIONS INC p 1245
515 Post Oak Blvd Ste 200, Houston TX 77027
Tel (713) 235-9500 SIC 8731 8748

STOLLER USA INC p 1390
9090 Katy Fwy Ste 400, Houston TX 77024
Tel (713) 461-1493 SIC 5191 8731

■ CNA HOLDINGS LLC p 330
222 Las Colinas Blvd W, Irving TX 75039
Tel (972) 443-4000
SIC 2823 2821 2819 5169 8731

KEL-TECH INC p 808
3408 E State Highway 158, Midland TX 79706
Tel (432) 684-4700 SIC 1389 8731

GOLDEN LIVING LLC p 621
5220 Tennyson Pkwy # 400, Plano TX 75024
Tel (972) 372-6300
SIC 8051 8082 8731 8093

▲ DELL TECHNOLOGIES INC p 425
1 Dell Way, Round Rock TX 78682
Tel (800) 289-3355 SIC 8731 5734

SOUTHWEST RESEARCH INSTITUTE INC p 1352
6220 Culebra Rd, San Antonio TX 78238
Tel (210) 684-5111 SIC 8731 8711

▲ MYRIAD GENETICS INC p 1005
320 S Wakara Way, Salt Lake City UT 84108
Tel (801) 584-3600 SIC 2835 8731

MODERN TECHNOLOGY SOLUTIONS INC p 981
5285 Shawnee Rd Ste 400, Alexandria VA 22312
Tel (703) 564-3800
SIC 8711 8742 8731 7379

MILLENNIUM ENGINEERING AND INTEGRATION CO p 970
1400 Crystal Dr Ste 800, Arlington VA 22202
Tel (703) 413-7750 SIC 8711 8731

NATIONAL RADIO ASTRONOMY OBSERVATORY p 1015
520 Edgemont Rd, Charlottesville VA 22903
Tel (434) 296-0211 SIC 8731

ASM RESEARCH LLC p 118
4050 Legato Rd Ste 1100, Fairfax VA 22033
Tel (703) 645-0420 SIC 7371 8731

DEWBERRY CONSULTANTS LLC p 434
8401 Arlington Blvd Ste 1, Fairfax VA 22031
Tel (703) 849-0311 SIC 8711 8712 8731

■ SIGNAL SOLUTIONS LLC p 1322
3211 Jermantown Rd # 700, Fairfax VA 22030
Tel (703) 205-0500
SIC 8711 7379 7374 4813 7373 8731

ENSCO INC p 500
3110 Frview Pk Dr Ste 300, Falls Church VA 22042
Tel (703) 321-4713 SIC 8731

EOIR TECHNOLOGIES INC p 504
10300 Spotsylvania Ave, Fredericksburg VA 22408
Tel (540) 834-4888
SIC 8711 7371 8731 8742

DRS GLOBAL ENTERPRISE SOLUTIONS INC p 457
12930 Worldgate Dr, Herndon VA 20170
Tel (703) 896-7100 SIC 7371 8731

■ **BWXT TECHNICAL SERVICES GROUP INC** p 231
2016 Mount Athos Rd, Lynchburg VA 24504
Tel (434) 522-6000 SIC 8711 8731

ALION SCIENCE AND TECHNOLOGY CORP p 50
1750 Tysons Blvd Ste 1300, Mc Lean VA 22102
Tel (703) 918-4480 SIC 8711 8731

THOMAS JEFFERSON NATIONAL ACCELERATOR FACILITY p 1449
12000 Jefferson Ave # 12, Newport News VA 23606
Tel (757) 269-7100 SIC 8731

BECHTEL MARINE PROPULSION CORP p 167
12011 Sunset Hills Rd, Reston VA 20190
Tel (301) 228-6000 SIC 8731

▲ **LEIDOS HOLDINGS INC** p 854
11951 Freedom Dr Ste 500, Reston VA 20190
Tel (571) 526-6000
SIC 8731 7371 7373 8742 3674

■ **LEIDOS INC** p 854
11951 Freedom Dr Ste 500, Reston VA 20190
Tel (571) 526-6000 SIC 8731 7373

▲ **VERSAR INC** p 1551
6850 Versar Ctr Ste 201, Springfield VA 22151
Tel (703) 750-3000
SIC 8711 8748 8712 8731

■ **IMMUNEX CORP** p 734
51 University St, Seattle WA 98101
Tel (206) 551-5169 SIC 2834 8731 2836

MYLAN SPECIALTY LP p 1004
781 Chestnut Ridge Rd, Morgantown WV 26505
Tel (304) 554-4519 SIC 2834 8731

ALCAMI WISCONSIN CORP p 47
W130n10497 Washington Dr, Germantown WI 53022
Tel (262) 251-5044 SIC 8731 8734

MORTARA INSTRUMENT INC p 991
7865 N 86th St, Milwaukee WI 53224
Tel (414) 354-1600 SIC 8731 3845

COOPERATIVE RESOURCES INTERNATIONAL INC p 367
117 E Green Bay St, Shawano WI 54166
Tel (715) 526-2141
SIC 0751 5159 0762 8731

SIC 8732 Commercial Economic, Sociological & Educational Research

JD POWER AND ASSOCIATES p 780
3200 Park Center Dr Fl 13, Costa Mesa CA 92626
Tel (714) 621-6200 SIC 8732

■ **UHC OF CALIFORNIA** p 1500
5995 Plaza Dr, Cypress CA 90630
Tel (714) 952-1121 SIC 6324 8732

ADVANTAGE SALES & MARKETING LLC p 26
18100 Von Karman Ave # 900, Irvine CA 92612
Tel (949) 797-2900 SIC 5141 8732

BDS MARKETING INC p 164
10 Holland, Irvine CA 92618
Tel (949) 472-6700 SIC 7311 8743 8732

▲ **CORELOGIC INC** p 369
40 Pacifica Ste 900, Irvine CA 92618
Tel (949) 214-1000
SIC 7323 7299 8742 8732

TRANSLATIONAL ONCOLOGY RESEARCH INTERNATIONAL INC p 1472
1033 Gayley Ave Ste 207, Los Angeles CA 90024
Tel (310) 824-1919 SIC 8011 8732 8742

UNICOM GLOBAL INC p 1502
15535 San Fernando Mssion, Mission Hills CA 91345
Tel (818) 838-0606
SIC 8732 6552 7389 7371

MEDALLIA INC p 935
395 Page Mill Rd Ste 100, Palo Alto CA 94306
Tel (650) 321-3000 SIC 7372 8732

RAND CORP p 1207
1776 Main St, Santa Monica CA 90401
Tel (310) 393-0411 SIC 8733 8742 8732

■ **TELEDYNE SCIENTIFIC & IMAGING LLC** p 1434
1049 Camino Dos Rios, Thousand Oaks CA 91360
Tel (805) 373-4545 SIC 8731 8732 8733

AUSTEN GROUP LLC p 132
679 Founders Ave, Eagle CO 81631
Tel (970) 331-2965 SIC 8732

IHS GLOBAL INC p 731
15 Inverness Way E, Englewood CO 80112
Tel (303) 790-0600
SIC 7299 8732 8748 7375 7373

IHS HOLDING INC p 731
15 Inverness Way E, Englewood CO 80112
Tel (303) 790-0600
SIC 7299 8732 8748 7375

IHS INC p 731
15 Inverness Way E, Englewood CO 80112
Tel (303) 790-0600
SIC 7299 8732 8748 7375

■ **HEALTHCARE TECHNOLOGY INTERMEDIATE INC** p 676
83 Wooster Hts, Danbury CT 06810
Tel (203) 448-4600 SIC 8742 8732

■ **IBG LLC** p 726
1 Pickwick Plz, Greenwich CT 06830
Tel (203) 618-5800 SIC 6211 8732

SMARTREVENUE.COM INC p 1332
60 Twin Ridge Rd, Ridgefield CT 06877
Tel (203) 733-9156 SIC 8732

SURVEY SAMPLING INTERNATIONAL LLC p 1409
6 Research Dr Ste 200, Shelton CT 06484
Tel (203) 225-6191 SIC 8732

▲ **GARTNER INC** p 592
56 Top Gallant Rd, Stamford CT 06902
Tel (203) 316-1111 SIC 8732 8742 8741

SONALYSTS INC p 1339
215 Parkway N, Waterford CT 06385
Tel (860) 442-4355
SIC 8711 7373 8748 8732 3993

ACADEMY FOR EDUCATIONAL DEVELOPMENT INC p 13
1825 Conn Ave Nw Ste 800, Washington DC 20009
Tel (202) 884-8976 SIC 8742 8732

▲ **ADVISORY BOARD CO** p 28
2445 M St Nw Ste 500, Washington DC 20037
Tel (202) 266-5600 SIC 8732 8741 7372

AMERICAN ENTERPRISE INSTITUTE FOR PUBLIC POLICY RESEARCH p 71
1150 17th St Nw Ste 1100, Washington DC 20036
Tel (202) 862-5800 SIC 8733 8732

APCO WORLDWIDE INC p 96
1299 Penn Ave Nw Ste 300, Washington DC 20004
Tel (202) 638-4082 SIC 8748 8742 8732

POPULATION SERVICES INTERNATIONAL p 1161
1120 19th St Nw Ste 600, Washington DC 20036
Tel (202) 785-0072 SIC 8733 8732

HART JEFFREY GROUP INC p 665
4400 N Federal Hwy, Boca Raton FL 33431
Tel (561) 997-2238 SIC 8732 6799

▲ **EQUIFAX INC** p 506
1550 Peachtree St Nw, Atlanta GA 30309
Tel (404) 885-8000
SIC 7323 7389 8732 8741

GEORGIA TECH RESEARCH CORP p 607
505 10th St Nw, Atlanta GA 30318
Tel (404) 894-4819 SIC 8732

SCIENTIFIC RESEARCH CORP p 1292
2300 Windy Ridge Pkwy Se 400s, Atlanta GA 30339
Tel (770) 859-9161 SIC 8732 8711

UCB INC p 1498
1950 Lake Park Dr Se, Smyrna GA 30080
Tel (770) 970-7500 SIC 5122 8731 8732

CUSHMAN & WAKEFIELD INC p 402
77 W Wacker Dr Ste 1800, Chicago IL 60601
Tel (312) 424-8000 SIC 6531 8742 8732

IPSOS PUBLIC AFFAIRS INC p 764
222 S Rverside Plz Fl 4, Chicago IL 60606
Tel (312) 526-4000 SIC 8732 8731

NATIONAL OPINION RESEARCH CENTER p 1014
1155 E 60th St, Chicago IL 60637
Tel (773) 753-7500 SIC 8732

RESEARCH INTERNATIONAL USA p 1226
222 Merchandise Mart Plz # 250, Chicago IL 60654
Tel (312) 787-4060 SIC 8732

OMRON MANAGEMENT CENTER OF AMERICA INC p 1085
2895 Greenspoint Pkwy # 100, Hoffman Estates IL 60169
Tel (224) 520-7650
SIC 5044 5046 5065 5047 5045 8732

KANTAR OPERATIONS p 803
3333 Warrenville Rd # 400, Lisle IL 60532
Tel (630) 505-0066 SIC 8732

CCH INC p 270
2700 Lake Cook Rd, Riverwoods IL 60015
Tel (847) 267-7000
SIC 2721 2731 7389 7338 8732 7371

PER MAR SECURITY AND RESEARCH CORP p 1134
1910 E Kimberly Rd, Davenport IA 52807
Tel (563) 359-3200
SIC 8732 7381 5099 7389 7382

UNIVERSITY OF KANSAS CENTER FOR RESEARCH INC p 1522
2385 Irving Hill Rd, Lawrence KS 66045
Tel (785) 864-3441
SIC 8733 8732 8741 8731

ATC GROUP HOLDINGS LLC p 124
221 Rue De Jean Ste 300, Lafayette LA 70508
Tel (337) 324-8777
SIC 8711 8732 8731 8249 8748

BIOMEDICAL RESEARCH FOUNDATION OF NORTHWEST LOUISIANA p 184
2031 Kings Hwy, Shreveport LA 71103
Tel (318) 716-4100 SIC 8733 8732

BERGER GROUP HOLDINGS INC p 174
111 Market Pl, Baltimore MD 21202
Tel (410) 468-4054 SIC 8711 8732 8712

ESCAL INSTITUTE OF ADVANCED TECHNOLOGIES INC p 509
8120 Woodmont Ave Ste 310, Bethesda MD 20814
Tel (301) 951-0102 SIC 8732

NIELSEN AUDIO INC p 1043
7000 Columbia Gateway Dr # 200, Columbia MD 21046
Tel (410) 312-8000 SIC 8732 7372

WESTAT INC p 1596
1600 Research Blvd, Rockville MD 20850
Tel (301) 251-1500
SIC 8732 7371 7373 8741 8742 8999

COOPERATIVE HOUSING FOUNDATION CORP p 367
8601 Georgia Ave Ste 300, Silver Spring MD 20910
Tel (301) 587-4700 SIC 8732

ANALYSIS GROUP INC p 88
111 Huntington Ave Fl 10, Boston MA 02199
Tel (617) 425-8000 SIC 8732

■ **INDEPENDENT ADVERTISING INC** p 736
53 State St, Boston MA 02109
Tel (617) 437-1600
SIC 7311 7331 7389 8732

INTERNATIONAL DATA GROUP INC p 755
1 Exeter Plz Fl 15, Boston MA 02116
Tel (617) 534-1200 SIC 2721 8732 7389

DECISION RESOURCES INC p 421
800 District Ave Ste 600, Burlington MA 01803
Tel (781) 993-2500 SIC 8732 2721

■ **ENDURANCE INTERNATIONAL GROUP INC** p 497
10 Corporate Dr Ste 300, Burlington MA 01803
Tel (866) 897-5421 SIC 8732

ABT ASSOCIATES INC p 13
55 Wheeler St Ste 1a, Cambridge MA 02138
Tel (617) 492-7100 SIC 8732

▲ **FORRESTER RESEARCH INC** p 568
60 Acorn Park Dr, Cambridge MA 02140
Tel (617) 613-6000 SIC 8732

PRESIDENT AND FELLOWS OF HARVARD COLLEGE p 1172
1350 Massachusetts Ave, Cambridge MA 02138
Tel (617) 496-4873 SIC 8221 8732 2721

IDC RESEARCH INC p 728
5 Speen St, Framingham MA 01701
Tel (508) 872-8200 SIC 8732

FIRST MARKET RESEARCH CORP p 547
99 Needham St Apt 1305, Newton MA 02461
Tel (617) 734-7080 SIC 8732

EDUCATION DEVELOPMENT CENTER INC p 479
43 Foundry Ave, Waltham MA 02453
Tel (617) 969-7100 SIC 8732 2741

MARKET STRATEGIES INC p 908
17430 College Pkwy, Livonia MI 48152
Tel (734) 542-7600 SIC 8742 8732

UNITED MAILING INC p 1510
1001 Park Rd, Chanhassen MN 55317
Tel (952) 474-0961 SIC 7331 2759 8732

DATA RECOGNITION CORP p 413
13490 Bass Lake Rd, Maple Grove MN 55311
Tel (763) 268-2000 SIC 8732 2752

MARITZ HOLDINGS INC p 907
1375 N Highway Dr, Fenton MO 63099
Tel (636) 827-4000
SIC 4725 8748 8732 4899

MARITZ LLC p 907
1375 N Highway Dr, Fenton MO 63099
Tel (636) 827-4000
SIC 4725 8748 8732 4899

MARITZCX RESEARCH LLC p 907
1355 N Highway Dr, Fenton MO 63026
Tel (636) 827-4000 SIC 8732

▲ **NATIONAL RESEARCH CORP** p 1015
1245 Q St Ste 100, Lincoln NE 68508
Tel (402) 475-2525 SIC 8732

RUFFIN ACQUISITION LLC p 1257
3300 Las Vegas Blvd S, Las Vegas NV 89109
Tel (800) 944-7444 SIC 8732

MEASURED PROGRESS INC p 934
100 Education Way, Dover NH 03820
Tel (603) 749-9102 SIC 8732

SUBARU OF AMERICA INC p 1395
2235 Rte 70 W, Cherry Hill NJ 08002
Tel (856) 488-8500
SIC 5012 5013 7515 8732

CREDIT-BASED ASSET SERVICING AND SECURITIZATION LLC p 391
333 Thornall St Ste 602, Edison NJ 08837
Tel (212) 850-7700 SIC 8732

■ **COVANCE INC** p 383
210 Carnegie Ctr Ste 106, Princeton NJ 08540
Tel (609) 452-4440
SIC 8731 8734 8733 8732

EDUCATIONAL TESTING SERVICE INC p 479
660 Rosedale Rd, Princeton NJ 08540
Tel (609) 921-9000 SIC 8748 8732

MATHEMATICA INC p 919
600 Alexander Park # 100, Princeton NJ 08540
Tel (609) 799-3535 SIC 8732

MATHEMATICA POLICY RESEARCH INC p 919
600 Alexander Park, Princeton NJ 08540
Tel (609) 799-3535 SIC 8732

ORC INTERNATIONAL INC p 1093
902 Carnegie Ctr Ste 220, Princeton NJ 08540
Tel (609) 452-5400 SIC 8732

HEALTH PRODUCTS RESEARCH INC p 675
500 Atrium Dr Ste 100, Somerset NJ 08873
Tel (908) 534-4148 SIC 8742 8732

ACN HOLDINGS INC p 18
85 Broad St, New York NY 10004
Tel (646) 654-5000 SIC 8732

ACNIELSEN CORP p 18
85 Broad St, New York NY 10004
Tel (646) 654-5000 SIC 8732

ADVENTITY INC p 27
444 Park Ave S Ste 1202, New York NY 10016
Tel (212) 404-2468 SIC 7375 8742 8732

CASTLE HARLAN PARTNERS III LP p 264
150 E 58th St Fl 38, New York NY 10155
Tel (212) 644-8600
SIC 5812 6282 6211 8732

CUSHMAN & WAKEFIELD HOLDINGS INC p 402
1290 Ave Of The Americas, New York NY 10104
Tel (212) 841-7500 SIC 6531 8742 8732

GFK CUSTOM RESEARCH LLC p 610
200 Liberty St Fl 4, New York NY 10281
Tel (212) 240-5300 SIC 8732

GLOBAL DATA PUBLICATIONS INC p 616
441 Lexington Ave Fl 3, New York NY 10017
Tel (646) 395-5460 SIC 7379 8732 8748

■ **GUY CARPENTER & CO LLC** p 648
1166 Ave Of The Americas, New York NY 10036
Tel (917) 937-3000 SIC 6411 8742 8732

IHI INC p 731
150 E 52nd St Fl 24, New York NY 10022
Tel (212) 599-8100
SIC 5099 8732 8711 5084

■ **MCCANN-ERICKSON USA INC** p 926
622 3rd Ave Fl 16, New York NY 10017
Tel (646) 865-2000 SIC 8732 7311

MILLWARD BROWN LLC p 971
11 Madison Ave Ste 1200, New York NY 10010
Tel (212) 548-7200 SIC 8732

■ **MOMENTUM-NA INC** p 983
250 Hudson St Fl 2, New York NY 10013
Tel (646) 638-5400 SIC 8743 7311 8732

NEW YORK CITY DEPT OF EDUCATION p 1034
52 Chambrs St Twd Crthse Tweed Courthouse, New York NY 10007
Tel (212) 374-6000 SIC 8732

NIELSEN CO US LLC p 1043
85 Broad St, New York NY 10004
Tel (646) 654-5000 SIC 8732

■ **NYNEX INFORMATION SOLUTIONS GROUP INC** p 1069
1095 Ave Of The Amer Fl 7, New York NY 10036
Tel (212) 395-1000 SIC 8732 7371 7379

OGILVY GROUP LLC p 1076
636 11th Ave, New York NY 10036
Tel (212) 237-4000
SIC 7311 8743 8748 7336 7361 8732

■ **SIMON & SCHUSTER INC** p 1324
1230 Ave Of The Americas, New York NY 10020
Tel (212) 698-7000
SIC 2731 2741 7372 8732

SOS INTERNATIONAL LLC p 1341
40 Fulton St Fl 26, New York NY 10038
Tel (212) 742-2410
SIC 3724 8711 7389 8732

TNC (US) HOLDINGS INC p 1458
770 Broadway Fl 8, New York NY 10003
Tel (646) 654-5500
SIC 8732 2721 2732 2741

UBM INC p 1498
2 Penn Plz, New York NY 10121
Tel (212) 600-3000
SIC 2721 2711 8732 2741

VNU MARKETING INFORMATION INC p 1564
770 Broadway Fl 15, New York NY 10003
Tel (646) 654-5011
SIC 8732 6282 7374 5045

WSP USA CORP p 1628
1 Penn Plz 250w, New York NY 10119
Tel (914) 747-1120 SIC 8711 8732

WSP USA HOLDINGS INC p 1628
512 7th Ave Fl 13, New York NY 10018
Tel (212) 532-9600 SIC 8711 8732

NPD GROUP INC p 1064
900 W Shore Rd, Port Washington NY 11050
Tel (516) 625-0700 SIC 8732

▲ **SPAR GROUP INC** p 1354
333 Westchester Ave S204, White Plains NY 10604
Tel (914) 332-4100 SIC 7389 8732

DEX ONE CORP p 434
1001 Winstead Dr Ste 100, Cary NC 27513
Tel (919) 297-1600 SIC 2741 8732

■ **QUINTILES TRANSNATIONAL CORP** p 1200
4820 Emperor Blvd, Durham NC 27703
Tel (919) 998-2000 SIC 8732 8731 8999

RESEARCH TRIANGLE INSTITUTE INC p 1226
3040 Cornwallis Rd, Durham NC 27709
Tel (919) 541-6000 SIC 8732 8731

CAPITOL BROADCASTING CO INC p 250
2619 Western Blvd, Raleigh NC 27606
Tel (919) 890-6000
SIC 4833 4832 4841 8732

■ **CONVERGYS CUSTOMER MANAGEMENT GROUP INC** p 365
201 E 4th St Bsmt, Cincinnati OH 45202
Tel (513) 723-6104 SIC 7389 8732

NECTAR ACQUISITION CORP p 1023
410 Horsham Rd Frnt, Horsham PA 19044
Tel (215) 442-9000 SIC 8732

PEW CHARITABLE TRUSTS p 1140
2005 Market St Fl 28, Philadelphia PA 19103
Tel (215) 575-9050 SIC 8732 6732

MM USA HOLDINGS LLC p 979
780 Township Line Rd, Yardley PA 19067
Tel (267) 685-2300 SIC 2741 8732

ESSEX TECHNOLOGY GROUP INC p 510
455 Industrial Blvd Ste C, La Vergne TN 37086
Tel (615) 620-5444 SIC 5045 8732 5261

HEALTHCARE TECHNOLOGY INTERMEDIATE HOLDINGS INC p 676
301 Commerce St Ste 3300, Fort Worth TX 76102
Tel (817) 871-4000 SIC 8732

RESEARCH NOW GROUP INC p 1226
5800 Tennyson Pkwy # 600, Plano TX 75024
Tel (214) 365-5000 SIC 8732

FROST & SULLIVAN p 581
7550 W Ih 10 Ste 400, San Antonio TX 78229
Tel (210) 348-1000 SIC 8732 8742

OPINIONOLOGY LLC p 1089
701 Timpanogos Pkwy Ste M, Orem UT 84097
Tel (801) 373-7735 SIC 7389 8732

CNA CORP p 329
3003 Washington Blvd, Arlington VA 22201
Tel (703) 824-2000 SIC 8732

ACG SEATTLE INC p 17
24 Roy St 442, Seattle WA 98109
Tel (206) 524-5300 SIC 8732

BLOODWORKS p 189
921 Terry Ave, Seattle WA 98104
Tel (206) 292-6500
SIC 8071 8099 8733 8732

SIC 8733 Noncommercial Research Organizations

AMERICAN CANCER SOCIETY MID-SOUTH DIVISION INC p 69
1100 Ireland Way Ste 300, Birmingham AL 35205
Tel (205) 879-2242 SIC 8733

WESTAR AEROSPACE & DEFENSE GROUP INC p 1596
890 Explorer Blvd Nw, Huntsville AL 35806
Tel (256) 922-6800 SIC 8733

SWCA INC p 1411
3033 N Central Ave # 145, Phoenix AZ 85012
Tel (602) 274-3831
SIC 8748 8711 8731 8733

SUN HEALTH CORP p 1400
14719 W Grand Ave Ste 113, Surprise AZ 85374
Tel (623) 876-5350
SIC 8062 8051 8082 7361 8733 6531

WINROCK INTERNATIONAL INSTITUTE FOR AGRICULTURAL DEVELOPMENT p 1617
2101 Riverfront Dr, Little Rock AR 72202
Tel (501) 280-3000 SIC 8733

WINDGATE FOUNDATION p 1615
115 E University St, Siloam Springs AR 72761
Tel (479) 524-9829 SIC 8733

GEMOLOGICAL INSTITUTE OF AMERICA INC p 598
5345 Armada Dr, Carlsbad CA 92008
Tel (760) 603-4000 SIC 8249 8733

HISAMITSU PHARMACEUTICAL CO INC p 696
2730 Loker Ave W, Carlsbad CA 92010
Tel (760) 931-1756 SIC 8733

WHEELCHAIR FOUNDATION p 1605
3820 Blackhawk Rd, Danville CA 94506
Tel (925) 736-8234 SIC 8733

BECKMAN RESEARCH INSTITUTE OF CITY OF HOPE p 167
1500 Duarte Rd, Duarte CA 91010
Tel (626) 359-8111 SIC 8733

CITY OF HOPE MEDICAL FOUNDATION p 315
1500 Duarte Rd, Duarte CA 91010
Tel (626) 256-4673 SIC 8733

AEROSPACE CORP p 30
2310 E El Segundo Blvd, El Segundo CA 90245
Tel (310) 336-5000 SIC 8733 8731 8711

■ RENAL TREATMENT CENTERS INC p 1223
601 Hawaii St, El Segundo CA 90245
Tel (310) 536-2400 SIC 8733

SANFORD BURNHAM PREBYS MEDICAL DISCOVERY INSTITUTE p 1279
10901 N Torrey Pines Rd, La Jolla CA 92037
Tel (858) 795-5000 SIC 8733

SRI INTERNATIONAL p 1363
333 Ravenswood Ave, Menlo Park CA 94025
Tel (650) 859-2000 SIC 8733 8748

RAPTOR PHARMACEUTICAL CORP p 1209
7 Hamilton Landing # 100, Novato CA 94949
Tel (415) 408-6200 SIC 8733 2834

PUBLIC HEALTH INSTITUTE p 1189
555 12th St Ste 1050, Oakland CA 94607
Tel (510) 285-5500 SIC 8733

REGENTS OF UNIVERSITY OF CALIFORNIA p 1219
1111 Franklin St Fl 12, Oakland CA 94607
Tel (510) 987-0700 SIC 8221 8733

CALIFORNIA INSTITUTE OF TECHNOLOGY p 240
1200 E California Blvd, Pasadena CA 91125
Tel (626) 395-6811 SIC 8733

COMMUNITY FUND OF UNITED JEWISH p 348
4950 Murphy Canyon Rd # 100, San Diego CA 92123
Tel (858) 279-2740 SIC 8699 8733

J DAVID GLADSTONE INSTITUTES p 771
1650 Owens St, San Francisco CA 94158
Tel (415) 734-2000 SIC 8733

SUTTER BAY HOSPITALS p 1410
633 Folsom St Fl 5, San Francisco CA 94107
Tel (415) 600-6000 SIC 8062 8733

WESTED p 1597
730 Harrison St Ste 500, San Francisco CA 94107
Tel (415) 565-3000 SIC 8733

RAND CORP p 1207
1776 Main St, Santa Monica CA 90401
Tel (310) 393-0411 SIC 8733 8742 8732

FIVE PRIME THERAPEUTICS INC p 553
2 Corporate Dr, South San Francisco CA 94080
Tel (415) 365-5600 SIC 2834 8733

AEDAN INC p 29
27447, Sun City CA 92586
Tel (888) 272-5505
SIC 7371 7381 8733 3812 7382

■ AMGEN PHARMACEUTICALS INC p 85
1 Amgen Center Dr, Thousand Oaks CA 91320
Tel (805) 447-1000 SIC 8733

■ TELEDYNE SCIENTIFIC & IMAGING LLC p 1434
1049 Camino Dos Rios, Thousand Oaks CA 91360
Tel (805) 373-4545 SIC 8731 8732 8733

NATIONAL ECOLOGICAL OBSERVATORY NETWORK INC p 1011
1685 38th St Ste 100, Boulder CO 80301
Tel (720) 746-4844 SIC 8733

UNIVERSITY CORP FOR ATMOSPHERIC RESEARCH p 1518
3090 Center Green Dr, Boulder CO 80301
Tel (303) 497-1000 SIC 8733

ALLIANCE FOR SUSTAINABLE ENERGY LLC p 54
15013 Denver West Pkwy, Lakewood CO 80401
Tel (303) 275-3000 SIC 8733

TERUMO BCT INC p 1440
10811 W Collins Ave, Lakewood CO 80215
Tel (303) 232-6800
SIC 8733 3842 3845 5047 7352 7699

HARTFORD FOUNDATION FOR PUBLIC GIVING p 665
10 Columbus Blvd Fl 8, Hartford CT 06106
Tel (860) 548-1888 SIC 6732 8733

▲ ALEXION PHARMACEUTICALS INC p 49
100 College St, New Haven CT 06510
Tel (203) 272-2596 SIC 2834 8733

THOMSON REUTERS (GRC) INC p 1449
2711 Centerville Rd # 400, Wilmington DE 19808
Tel (212) 227-7357
SIC 7291 8111 8721 8733 8741

AMERICAN ENTERPRISE INSTITUTE FOR PUBLIC POLICY RESEARCH p 71
1150 17th St Nw Ste 1100, Washington DC 20036
Tel (202) 862-5800 SIC 8733 8742

AMERICAN INSTITUTES FOR RESEARCH IN BEHAVIORAL SCIENCES p 75
1000 Thmas Jfferson St Nw, Washington DC 20007
Tel (202) 403-5000 SIC 8733

BROOKINGS INSTITUTION p 218
1775 Massachusetts Ave Nw, Washington DC 20036
Tel (202) 797-6000 SIC 8733 2741 8621

CARNEGIE INSTITUTION OF WASHINGTON p 258
1530 P St Nw, Washington DC 20005
Tel (202) 387-6400 SIC 8733

CORE INC p 369
1201 New York Ave Nw # 420, Washington DC 20005
Tel (202) 332-0063 SIC 8733

ELIZABETH GLASER PEDIATRIC AIDS FOUNDATION p 487
1140 Conn Ave Nw Ste 200, Washington DC 20036
Tel (310) 314-1459 SIC 8099 8733

HERITAGE FOUNDATION p 686
214 Msschstts Ave Ne Bsmt, Washington DC 20002
Tel (202) 546-4400 SIC 8733

INTERNATIONAL FOOD POLICY RESEARCH INSTITUTE p 755
2033 K St Nw Ste 400, Washington DC 20006
Tel (202) 862-5600 SIC 8731 8733

NATIONAL ACADEMY OF SCIENCES OF UNITED STATES OF AMERICA p 1009
2101 Constitution Ave Nw, Washington DC 20418
Tel (202) 334-2000 SIC 8733 8999 8748

POPULATION SERVICES INTERNATIONAL p 1161
1120 19th St Nw Ste 600, Washington DC 20036
Tel (202) 785-0072 SIC 8733 8732

URBAN INSTITUTE p 1530
2100 M St Nw Fl 5, Washington DC 20037
Tel (202) 833-7200 SIC 8733

LIFE EXTENSION FOUNDATION INC p 863
3600 W Coml Blvd Ste 100, Fort Lauderdale FL 33309
Tel (954) 766-8433 SIC 8733

H LEE MOFFITT CANCER CENTER & RESEARCH INSTITUTE HOSPITAL INC p 650
12902 Usf Magnolia Dr, Tampa FL 33612
Tel (813) 745-4673 SIC 8733

RESEARCH CORP OF UNIVERSITY OF HAWAII p 1226
2800 Woodlawn Dr Ste 200, Honolulu HI 96822
Tel (808) 988-8311 SIC 8733

CHILDRENS HOSPITAL OF CHICAGO MEDICAL CENTER p 299
225 E Chicago Ave, Chicago IL 60611
Tel (312) 227-4000 SIC 8062 8733

MUSCULAR DYSTROPHY ASSOCIATION INC p 1002
222 S Riverside Plz # 1500, Chicago IL 60606
Tel (520) 529-2000 SIC 8733

UCHICAGO ARGONNE LLC p 1499
5801 S Ellis Ave Ste 601, Chicago IL 60637
Tel (773) 702-9476 SIC 8733

PURDUE RESEARCH FOUNDATION p 1192
1281 Win Hentschel Blvd, West Lafayette IN 47906
Tel (765) 588-3470 SIC 8733

CROSS OVER LLC p 393
621 Alta Vista Dr, Carroll IA 51401
Tel (712) 790-4549 SIC 8733 7389

INTEGRATED DNA TECHNOLOGIES INC p 749
1710 Commercial Park, Coralville IA 52241
Tel (319) 626-8400 SIC 8733 5047

UNIVERSITY OF KANSAS MEDICAL CENTER p 1522
3901 Rainbow Blvd, Kansas City KS 66160
Tel (913) 588-1443 SIC 8733

UNIVERSITY OF KANSAS CENTER FOR RESEARCH INC p 1522
2385 Irving Hill Rd, Lawrence KS 66045
Tel (785) 864-3441
SIC 8733 8732 8741 8731

UNIVERSITY OF KENTUCKY RESEARCH FOUNDATION p 1522
102 Kinkead Hall, Lexington KY 40506
Tel (859) 257-4758 SIC 8733

ADMINISTRATORS OF TULANE EDUCATIONAL FUND p 23
6823 Saint Charles Ave, New Orleans LA 70118
Tel (504) 865-5000 SIC 8221 8733

BIOMEDICAL RESEARCH FOUNDATION OF NORTHWEST LOUISIANA p 184
2031 Kings Hwy, Shreveport LA 71103
Tel (318) 716-4100 SIC 8733 8732

JACKSON LABORATORY p 774
600 Main St, Bar Harbor ME 04609
Tel (207) 288-6000 SIC 8733

CYSTIC FIBROSIS FOUNDATION p 406
6931 Arlington Rd Fl 2, Bethesda MD 20814
Tel (301) 951-4422 SIC 8733 8399

INOVALON INC p 745
4321 Collington Rd # 100, Bowie MD 20716
Tel (301) 262-3848 SIC 8733

HOWARD HUGHES MEDICAL INSTITUTE INC p 713
4000 Jones Bridge Rd, Chevy Chase MD 20815
Tel (301) 215-8500 SIC 8733

UNIVERSITIES SPACE RESEARCH ASSOCIATION p 1518
7178 Columbia Gateway Dr, Columbia MD 21046
Tel (410) 730-2656 SIC 8733

■ LEIDOS BIOMEDICAL RESEARCH INC p 854
1050 Boyles St, Frederick MD 21702
Tel (301) 846-5031 SIC 8733

ICON DEVELOPMENT SOLUTIONS LLC p 727
820 W Diamond Ave Ste 100, Gaithersburg MD 20878
Tel (301) 944-6810 SIC 8733

OTSUKA AMERICA PHARMACEUTICAL INC p 1098
2440 Res Blvd Ste 500, Rockville MD 20850
Tel (301) 990-0030 SIC 8733 8011 8731

MITRE CORP p 977
202 Burlington Rd, Bedford MA 01730
Tel (781) 271-2000 SIC 8733 8711

DANA-FARBER CANCER INSTITUTE INC p 411
450 Brookline Ave, Boston MA 02215
Tel (617) 632-3000 SIC 8733 8069

UNIVERSITY OF MASSACHUSETTS INC p 1523
1 Beacon St Fl 31, Boston MA 02108
Tel (617) 287-7000 SIC 8221 8733 8062

BROAD INSTITUTE INC p 215
415 Main St, Cambridge MA 02142
Tel (617) 714-7000 SIC 8733

TOYOTA RESEARCH INSTITUTE INC p 1467
1 Kendall Sq Bldg 100, Cambridge MA 02139
Tel (857) 285-6160 SIC 8733

WOOD HOLE OCEANAL GRAPHICS INSTITUTION INC p 1622
38 Water St, Woods Hole MA 02543
Tel (508) 457-2620 SIC 8731 8733 8221

WOODS HOLE OCEANOGRAPHIC INSTITUTION p 1623
266 Woods Hole Rd, Woods Hole MA 02543
Tel (508) 457-2000 SIC 8733

BARBARA ANN KARMANOS CANCER INSTITUTE p 154
4100 John R St, Detroit MI 48201
Tel (800) 527-6266 SIC 8733 8093

VAN ANDEL INSTITUTE p 1542
333 Bostwick Ave Ne, Grand Rapids MI 49503
Tel (616) 234-5000 SIC 8733

VAN ANDEL RESEARCH INSTITUTE p 1542
333 Bostwick Ave Ne, Grand Rapids MI 49503
Tel (616) 234-5000 SIC 8733

L GARY HART ASSOCIATED p 834
13381 440th Ave Sw, East Grand Forks MN 56721
Tel (520) 297-3237 SIC 8733

■ RESEARCH AND DIAGNOSTIC SYSTEMS INC p 1226
614 Mckinley Pl Ne, Minneapolis MN 55413
Tel (612) 379-2956
SIC 8733 2833 8731 3829 3625

MAYO CLINIC p 923
200 1st St Sw, Rochester MN 55905
Tel (507) 284-2511
SIC 8062 8733 8071 8011

MAYO CLINIC p 923
200 1st St Sw, Rochester MN 55905
Tel (507) 284-2511
SIC 8011 8062 8071 8733 8221

■ GUIDANT SALES LLC p 645
4100 Hamline Ave N, Saint Paul MN 55112
Tel (800) 949-9459
SIC 3841 3845 5047 8733

STOWERS INSTITUTE FOR MEDICAL RESEARCH p 1392
1000 E 50th St, Kansas City MO 64110
Tel (816) 926-4000 SIC 8733

OMAHA COMMUNITY FOUNDATION p 1083
302 S 36th St Ste 100, Omaha NE 68131
Tel (402) 342-3458 SIC 8399 8733

■ HOFFMANN-LA ROCHE INC p 699
340 Kingsland St, Nutley NJ 07110
Tel (973) 235-5000 SIC 2834 8733

NOVO-NORDISK OF NORTH AMERICA INC p 1063
800 Scudders Mill Rd, Plainsboro NJ 08536
Tel (609) 987-5800
SIC 8741 8733 5122 2833 2834

■ COVANCE INC p 383
210 Carnegie Ctr Ste 106, Princeton NJ 08540
Tel (609) 452-4440
SIC 8731 8734 8733 8732

LOVELACE BIOMEDICAL & ENVIRONMENTAL RESEARCH INSTITUTE p 881
2425 Ridgecrest Dr Se, Albuquerque NM 87108
Tel (505) 348-9400 SIC 8733

■ SANDIA CORP p 1278
1515 Eubank Blvd Se, Albuquerque NM 87123
Tel (505) 284-4784 SIC 8733

■ ALO ACQUISITION LLC p 59
26 Corporate Cir, Albany NY 12203
Tel (518) 464-0279 SIC 2833 5122 8733

RESEARCH FOUNDATION FOR STATE UNIVERSITY OF NEW YORK p 1226
35 State St, Albany NY 12207
Tel (518) 434-7000 SIC 8733

TOM CHEITORAH INSTITUTE p 1459
1372 47th St, Brooklyn NY 11219
Tel (718) 438-3061 SIC 8733

ROSWELL PARK CANCER INSTITUTE p 1252
Elm And Carlton St, Buffalo NY 14263
Tel (716) 845-2300 SIC 8733

COLD SPRING HARBOR LABORATORY ASSOCIATION INC p 335
1 Bungtown Rd, Cold Spring Harbor NY 11724
Tel (516) 367-8446
SIC 8733 2731 2741 8249

HEALTH RESEARCH INC p 675
150 Broadway Ste 560, Menands NY 12204
Tel (518) 431-1200 SIC 8733

RESEARCH FOD FOR MTAL HY INC p 1226
150 Broadway Ste 301, Menands NY 12204
Tel (518) 474-5661 SIC 8733

JDRF INTERNATIONAL p 781
26 Broadway, New York NY 10004
Tel (212) 785-9500 SIC 8399 8733

LUDWIG INSTITUTE FOR CANCER RESEARCH p 884
666 3rd Ave Fl 28, New York NY 10017
Tel (212) 450-1500 SIC 8733

MDRC p 933
16 E 34th St Fl 19, New York NY 10016
Tel (212) 532-3200 SIC 8641 8733

PUBLIC HEALTH SOLUTIONS p 1189
40 Worth St Fl 5, New York NY 10013
Tel (646) 619-6400 SIC 8733

RESEARCH FOUNDATION OF CITY UNIVERSITY OF NEW YORK p 1226
230 W 41st St Fl 7, New York NY 10036
Tel (212) 417-8300 SIC 8733

RIVERSIDE RESEARCH INSTITUTE p 1238
156 William St Fl 9, New York NY 10038
Tel (212) 563-4545 SIC 8733

ROCKEFELLER UNIVERSITY p 1244
1230 York Ave, New York NY 10065
Tel (212) 327-8078 SIC 8733 8221 8062

ROGOSIN INSTITUTE INC p 1246
505 E 70th St Fl 2, New York NY 10021
Tel (212) 746-1551 SIC 8733 8399

SLOAN-KETTERING INSTITUTE FOR CANCER RESEARCH p 1331
1275 York Ave, New York NY 10065
Tel (212) 639-2000 SIC 8733

TRUSTEES OF COLUMBIA UNIVERSITY IN CITY OF NEW YORK p 1487
630 W 168th St Fl 4, New York NY 10032
Tel (212) 305-2862 SIC 8221 8733 8062

SRC INC p 1363
7502 Round Pond Rd, North Syracuse NY 13212
Tel (315) 452-8000 SIC 8733

CLARKSON UNIVERSITY p 322
8 Clarkson Ave, Potsdam NY 13676
Tel (315) 268-6400 SIC 8733

LEUKEMIA & LYMPHOMA SOCIETY INC p 858
3 International Dr # 200, Rye Brook NY 10573
Tel (914) 949-5213
SIC 8699 8399 8322 8011 8733 8621

BROOKHAVEN SCIENCE ASSOCIATES LLC p 217
2 Center St, Upton NY 11973
Tel (631) 344-8000 SIC 8733

FAMILY HEALTH INTERNATIONAL INC p 527
359 Blackwell St Ste 200, Durham NC 27701
Tel (919) 544-7040 SIC 8733

PARATA SYSTEMS LLC p 1114
2600 Meridian Pkwy, Durham NC 27713
Tel (919) 433-4400 SIC 3826 8733

■ CHARLES RIVER LABORATORIES ASHLAND LLC p 289
1407 George Rd, Ashland OH 44805
Tel (419) 282-8700 SIC 8733

MACAULAY-BROWN INC p 891
4021 Executive Dr, Beavercreek OH 45430
Tel (937) 426-3421 SIC 8711 8733

CHILDRENS HOSPITAL MEDICAL CENTER p 299
3333 Burnet Ave, Cincinnati OH 45229
Tel (513) 636-4200
SIC 8733 8011 8069 8731

SISTERS OF CHARITY OF ST AUGUSTINE HEALTH SYSTEM INC p 1327
2475 E 22nd St, Cleveland OH 44115
Tel (216) 696-5560 SIC 8661 8733

BATTELLE LIBRARY p 159
505 King Ave, Columbus OH 43201
Tel (614) 424-6302 SIC 8733

UNIVERSITY OF DAYTON p 1521
300 College Park Ave, Dayton OH 45469
Tel (937) 229-2919 SIC 8221 8733

AMERICAN ENDOWMENT FOUNDATION p 71
1521 Georgetown Rd # 104, Hudson OH 44236
Tel (330) 655-7552 SIC 8699 8733

SAMUEL ROBERTS NOBLE FOUNDATION INC p 1275
2510 Sam Noble Pkwy, Ardmore OK 73401
Tel (580) 226-2178 SIC 8733

TULSA COMMUNITY FOUNDATION p 1491
7030 S Yale Ave Ste 600, Tulsa OK 74136
Tel (918) 494-8823 SIC 8733

OREGON HEALTH & SCIENCE UNIVERSITY FOUNDATION INC p 1093
1121 Sw Salmon St Ste 100, Portland OR 97205
Tel (503) 228-1730
SIC 8399 6091 8733 6732

GEISINGER CLINIC p 597
100 N Academy Ave, Danville PA 17822
Tel (570) 271-6211 SIC 8011 8733

AMERICAN CANCER SOCIETY EAST CENTRAL DIVISION INC p 69
Sipe Ave Rr 422, Hershey PA 17033
Tel (717) 533-6144 SIC 8733

PENN STATE MILTON S HERSHEY MEDICAL CENTER p 1129
500 University Dr, Hershey PA 17033
Tel (717) 531-5337 SIC 8062 8733 8211

HAY GROUP HOLDINGS INC p 670
1650 Arch St Ste 2300, Philadelphia PA 19103
Tel (215) 861-2000 SIC 8742 8249 8733

HEALTH SERVICES OF FOX CHASE CANCER CENTER p 676
333 Cottman Ave, Philadelphia PA 19111
Tel (215) 728-6900 SIC 8011 8062 8733

JOSEPH STOKES INSTITUTE OF RESEARCH p 793
3615 Civic Center Blvd, Philadelphia PA 19104
Tel (215) 590-3800 SIC 8062 8733

SUBSIDIARIES OF INSTITUTE FOR TRANSFUSION MEDICINE p 1396
5 Parkway Ctr, Pittsburgh PA 15220
Tel (412) 209-7300 SIC 8733

SOUTH CAROLINA RESEARCH AUTHORITY INC p 1343
1000 Catawba St Ste 100, Columbia SC 29201
Tel (803) 799-4070 SIC 8733

ST JUDE CHILDRENS RESEARCH HOSPITAL INC p 1369
262 Danny Thomas Pl, Memphis TN 38105
Tel (901) 595-3300 SIC 8733 8062

■ LOCKHEED MARTIN ENERGY RESEARCH CORP p 873
1 Bethel Valley Rd, Oak Ridge TN 37830
Tel (865) 574-1000 SIC 8733

OAK RIDGE ASSOCIATED UNIVERSITIES INC p 1070
100 Orau Way, Oak Ridge TN 37830
Tel (865) 576-3000 SIC 8733

UNIVERSITY OF TEXAS SOUTHWESTERN MEDICAL CENTER p 1526
5323 Harry Hines Blvd, Dallas TX 75390
Tel (214) 648-3068 SIC 8733 8011

ALCON RESEARCH LTD p 47
6201 South Fwy, Fort Worth TX 76134
Tel (817) 551-4555 SIC 8733 3841 2834

GREATER HOUSTON COMMUNITY FOUNDATION p 635
5120 Woodway Dr Ste 6000, Houston TX 77056
Tel (713) 333-2200 *SIC* 8733

MEI TECHNOLOGIES INC p 940
18050 Saturn Ln Ste 300, Houston TX 77058
Tel (281) 283-6200 *SIC* 8711 8733

WANG JING p 1575
1400 Herrmann Pressler Dr, Houston TX 77030
Tel (713) 794-4190 *SIC* 8733

UTAH STATE UNIVERSITY RESEARCH FOUNDATION p 1536
1695 N Research Pkwy, North Logan UT 84341
Tel (435) 713-3400
SIC 8711 8734 8733 7371

DONORS TRUST INC p 451
1800 Diagonal Rd Ste 280, Alexandria VA 22314
Tel (703) 535-3563 *SIC* 6732 8733

INSTITUTE FOR DEFENSE ANALYSES INC p 747
4850 Mark Center Dr, Alexandria VA 22311
Tel (703) 845-2000 *SIC* 8733

IFES INC p 730
2011 Crystal Dr Fl 10, Arlington VA 22202
Tel (202) 350-6750 *SIC* 8733

EDWARD VIA VIRGINIA COLLEGE OF OSTEOPATHIC MEDICINE p 480
2265 Kraft Dr, Blacksburg VA 24060
Tel (540) 231-4000 *SIC* 8733

VIRGINIA TECH CORPORATE RESEARCH CENTER INC p 1560
1715 Pratt Dr Ste 1000, Blacksburg VA 24060
Tel (540) 961-3600 *SIC* 8733

VENCORE HOLDING CORP p 1547
15052 Conference Ctr Dr, Chantilly VA 20151
Tel (571) 313-6000
SIC 6719 8711 8733 3812 7372

VENCORE INC p 1547
15052 Conference Ctr Dr, Chantilly VA 20151
Tel (571) 313-6000
SIC 8711 8733 3812 7372

■ XEROX FEDERAL SOLUTIONS LLC p 1631
8260 Willow Oaks Corp Dr, Fairfax VA 22031
Tel (703) 891-8774 *SIC* 8733

■ CSRA LLC p 398
3170 Fairview Park Dr, Falls Church VA 22042
Tel (703) 876-1000
SIC 7371 8733 7376 7374 7379

NOBLIS INC p 1046
3150 Fairview Park Dr, Falls Church VA 22042
Tel (703) 610-2000 *SIC* 8733 8748

■ NORTHROP GRUMMAN INFORMATION TECHNOLOGY GLOBAL CORP p 1058
7575 Colshire Dr, Mc Lean VA 22102
Tel (703) 556-3187 *SIC* 8733

■ NORTHROP GRUMMAN INFORMATION TECHNOLOGY INC p 1058
7575 Colshire Dr, Mc Lean VA 22102
Tel (703) 556-1000 *SIC* 7373 7372 8733

BATTELLE MEMORIAL INSTITUTE p 159
900 Battelle Blvd, Richland WA 99354
Tel (509) 371-7608 *SIC* 8733

ALLEN INSTITUTE FOR BRAIN SCIENCE p 53
1441 N 34th St, Seattle WA 98103
Tel (206) 548-7000 *SIC* 8733

BLOODWORKS p 189
921 Terry Ave, Seattle WA 98104
Tel (206) 292-6500
SIC 8071 8099 8733 8732

CASCADE DESIGNS INC p 262
4000 1st Ave S, Seattle WA 98134
Tel (206) 583-0583
SIC 2515 3089 3949 8733

FRED HUTCHINSON CANCER RESEARCH CENTER p 575
1100 Fairview Ave N, Seattle WA 98109
Tel (206) 667-4877 *SIC* 8733

WEST VIRGINIA UNIVERSITY RESEARCH CORP p 1596
886 Chestnut Ridge Rd, Morgantown WV 26505
Tel (304) 293-7398 *SIC* 8733

GREATER MILWAUKEE FOUNDATION INC p 635
101 W Pleasant St Ste 210, Milwaukee WI 53212
Tel (414) 272-5805 *SIC* 8699 8733

SIC 8734 Testing Laboratories

■ TELEDYNE ISOTOPES (INC) p 1434
300 Sparkman Dr Nw, Huntsville AL 35805
Tel (256) 726-1000 *SIC* 8734

■ WYLE LABORATORIES INC p 1629
1960 E Grand Ave Ste 900, El Segundo CA 90245
Tel (310) 563-6800 *SIC* 8734 8731

MILLENNIUM HEALTH LLC p 970
16981 Via Tazon Ste F, San Diego CA 92127
Tel (877) 451-3534 *SIC* 8734

EAG INC p 467
2710 Walsh Ave, Santa Clara CA 95051
Tel (408) 454-4600 *SIC* 8734

SIEGEL OIL CO p 1320
1380 Zuni St, Denver CO 80204
Tel (303) 893-5273 *SIC* 5172 8734

▲ NEOGENOMICS INC p 1026
12701 Commwl Dr Ste 9, Fort Myers FL 33913
Tel (239) 768-0600 *SIC* 8734 8071

M C TEST SERVICE INC p 889
425 North Dr, Melbourne FL 32934
Tel (321) 956-3052 *SIC* 3672 8734

MC ASSEMBLY HOLDINGS INC p 925
425 North Dr, Melbourne FL 32934
Tel (321) 253-0541 *SIC* 8734 3672

■ TEKTRONIX SERVICE SOLUTIONS INC p 1433
6120 Hanging Moss Rd, Orlando FL 32807
Tel (407) 678-6900
SIC 3812 3674 8734 7699

BUREAU VERITAS NORTH AMERICA INC p 227
1601 Sawgrs Corp Pkwy, Sunrise FL 33323
Tel (954) 236-8100
SIC 7389 8748 8734 8711 8742

TIMBER PRODUCTS INSPECTION INC p 1454
1641 Sigman Rd Nw, Conyers GA 30012
Tel (770) 922-8000 *SIC* 0851 8734

APPLIED TECHNICAL SERVICES INC p 100
1049 Triad Ct, Marietta GA 30062
Tel (770) 423-1400 *SIC* 8734 8711 8731

KOOTENAI HOSPITAL DISTRICT p 827
2003 Kootenai Health Way, Coeur D Alene ID 83814
Tel (208) 625-4000
SIC 8062 8063 8093 8734

▲ HERITAGE-CRYSTAL CLEAN INC p 686
2175 Point Blvd Ste 375, Elgin IL 60123
Tel (847) 836-5670 *SIC* 7699 8734

EXOVA INC p 519
194 Internationale Blvd, Glendale Heights IL 60139
Tel (630) 221-0385 *SIC* 8734

▲ LANDAUER INC p 842
2 Science Rd, Glenwood IL 60425
Tel (708) 755-7000 *SIC* 8734 5047 3829

■ ATLAS MATERIAL TESTING TECHNOLOGY LLC p 128
1500 Bishop Ct, Mount Prospect IL 60056
Tel (773) 327-4520
SIC 3823 3569 3599 8734 3825 3821

UL LLC p 1500
333 Pfingsten Rd, Northbrook IL 60062
Tel (847) 272-8800 *SIC* 8734

UNDERWRITERS LABORATORIES INC p 1502
333 Pfingsten Rd, Northbrook IL 60062
Tel (847) 272-8800 *SIC* 8734

WISS JANNEY ELSTNER ASSOCIATES INC p 1619
330 Pfingsten Rd, Northbrook IL 60062
Tel (847) 272-2186 *SIC* 8711 8712 8734

PROFESSIONAL SERVICE INDUSTRIES HOLDING INC p 1180
1901 S Meyers Rd Ste 400, Oakbrook Terrace IL 60181
Tel (630) 691-1490 *SIC* 8711 8734

PROFESSIONAL SERVICE INDUSTRIES INC p 1180
1901 S Meyers Rd Ste 400, Oakbrook Terrace IL 60181
Tel (630) 691-1490 *SIC* 8711 8734

CB&I GOVERNMENT SOLUTIONS INC p 268
4171 Essen Ln, Baton Rouge LA 70809
Tel (225) 932-2500
SIC 8711 8734 8748 1541 1542 1611

SHAW GROUP INC p 1312
4171 Essen Ln, Baton Rouge LA 70809
Tel (225) 932-2500
SIC 8711 8734 1629 3498

ATC GROUP SERVICES LLC p 124
221 Rue De Jean Ste 200, Lafayette LA 70508
Tel (337) 234-8777
SIC 8711 8734 8731 8249 8748

AMERITOX LIMITED PARTNERSHIP p 84
300 E Lombard St Ste 1610, Baltimore MD 21202
Tel (443) 220-0115 *SIC* 7374 8734 8731

JENSEN HUGHES INC p 782
3610 Commerce Dr Ste 817, Baltimore MD 21227
Tel (410) 737-8677 *SIC* 8748 8711 8734

■ ACTERNA LLC p 19
20250 Century Blvd # 100, Germantown MD 20874
Tel (301) 353-1550
SIC 3669 7379 3825 5065 3679 8734

BIORELIANCE CORP p 184
14920 Broschart Rd, Rockville MD 20850
Tel (301) 738-1000 *SIC* 8734 8731

UNITED STATES PHARMACOPEIAL CONVENTION p 1514
12601 Twinbrook Pkwy, Rockville MD 20852
Tel (301) 881-0666 *SIC* 8731 8734

TRIDENT USA HEALTH SERVICES LLC p 1480
930 Ridgebrook Rd Fl 3, Sparks MD 21152
Tel (800) 786-8015 *SIC* 8734

■ AMERICAN SCIENCE AND ENGINEERING INC p 79
829 Middlesex Tpke, Billerica MA 01821
Tel (978) 262-8700 *SIC* 7389 8734 7382

EMPIRIX INC p 494
600 Technology Park Dr # 1, Billerica MA 01821
Tel (978) 313-7000 *SIC* 7371 8734

CHARLES STARK DRAPER LABORATORY INC p 289
555 Technology Sq, Cambridge MA 02139
Tel (617) 258-1000 *SIC* 8734

BARTLETT NUCLEAR INC p 158
97 Libbey Industrial Pkwy # 400, East Weymouth MA 02189
Tel (508) 746-6464 *SIC* 7389 8734

▲ TRC COMPANIES INC p 1475
650 Suffolk St, Lowell MA 01854
Tel (978) 970-5600
SIC 7363 8734 7382 8748

GZA GEOENVIRONMENTAL INC p 649
249 Vanderbilt Ave, Norwood MA 02062
Tel (781) 278-3700 *SIC* 8711 8734

TUV SUD AMERICA INC p 1493
10 Centennial Dr Fl 2a, Peabody MA 01960
Tel (978) 573-2500 *SIC* 8734

■ CHARLES RIVER LABORATORIES INC p 289
251 Ballardvale St, Wilmington MA 01887
Tel (978) 658-6000
SIC 8742 8734 8731 0279

NSF INTERNATIONAL p 1065
789 N Dixboro Rd, Ann Arbor MI 48105
Tel (734) 769-8010 *SIC* 8731 8734

GENERIC DRUG HOLDINGS INC p 602
31778 Enterprise Dr, Livonia MI 48150
Tel (734) 743-6000 *SIC* 8734 5122 5047

■ HARVARD DRUG GROUP L L C p 666
17177 N Laurel Park Dr # 233, Livonia MI 48152
Tel (734) 525-8700 *SIC* 5122 5047 8734

ROUSH ENTERPRISES INC p 1253
12447 Levan Rd, Livonia MI 48150
Tel (734) 779-7006
SIC 8711 3714 7948 8734

ROUSH INDUSTRIES INC p 1253
12447 Levan Rd, Livonia MI 48150
Tel (734) 779-7006 *SIC* 8734 8711

TRICO PRODUCTS CORP p 1479
3255 W Hamlin Rd, Rochester Hills MI 48309
Tel (248) 371-1700
SIC 3714 3069 3082 8734 8731

MERRILL TOOL HOLDING CO p 950
400 Florence St, Saginaw MI 48602
Tel (989) 791-6676
SIC 3443 3599 8734 8711 3724

BRAUN INTERTEC CORP p 209
11001 Hampshire Ave S, Minneapolis MN 55438
Tel (952) 995-2000 *SIC* 8711 8734

LAB HOLDINGS INC p 836
8500 Normandale Lake Blvd # 1750, Minneapolis MN 55437
Tel (612) 607-1700 *SIC* 8734 8731

PACE ANALYTICAL SERVICES LLC p 1103
1800 Elm St Se, Minneapolis MN 55414
Tel (612) 607-6369 *SIC* 8734 8748 8731

PAULO PRODUCTS CO p 1121
5711 W Park Ave, Saint Louis MO 63110
Tel (314) 647-7500
SIC 3471 3398 8734 3567

SMITHS TUBULAR SYSTEMS-LACONIA INC p 1334
93 Lexington Dr, Laconia NH 03246
Tel (603) 524-2064
SIC 3463 3498 8734 7692 3441 3398

EMSL ANALYTICAL INC p 495
200 Route 130 N, Cinnaminson NJ 08077
Tel (856) 858-4800 *SIC* 8734

AMSPEC LLC p 87
1249 S River Rd Ste 204, Cranbury NJ 08512
Tel (908) 925-7333 *SIC* 8734 7389

■ BIO-REFERENCE LABORATORIES INC p 183
481 Edward H Ross Dr, Elmwood Park NJ 07407
Tel (201) 791-2600 *SIC* 8071 8734

■ ZOETIS P&U LLC p 1644
100 Campus Dr, Florham Park NJ 07932
Tel (973) 822-7000 *SIC* 5159 0742 8734

■ INNOVEX INC p 745
10 Waterview Blvd Ste 100, Parsippany NJ 07054
Tel (973) 257-4500 *SIC* 8734 8999 7374

■ COVANCE INC p 383
210 Carnegie Ctr Ste 106, Princeton NJ 08540
Tel (609) 452-4440
SIC 8731 8734 8733 8732

SGS NORTH AMERICA INC p 1310
301 Route 17, Rutherford NJ 07070
Tel (201) 508-3000
SIC 8734 7389 8071 4499 4785

SGS US HOLDING INC p 1310
201 Route 17, Rutherford NJ 07070
Tel (201) 508-3000 *SIC* 8734 6719 7389

DIVAL SAFETY EQUIPMENT INC p 443
1721 Niagara St, Buffalo NY 14207
Tel (716) 874-9060
SIC 5099 8748 8734 5047 5136 5661

INTERTEK TESTING SERVICES NA INC p 759
3933 Us Route 11, Cortland NY 13045
Tel (607) 753-6711 *SIC* 8734

ICON CENTRAL LABORATORIES INC p 727
123 Smith St, Farmingdale NY 11735
Tel (631) 777-8833 *SIC* 8071 8734

▲ ECOLOGY AND ENVIRONMENT INC p 476
368 Pleasant View Dr, Lancaster NY 14086
Tel (716) 684-8060 *SIC* 8748 8734 8711

NORTH SHORE-LONG ISLAND JEWISH HEALTH SYSTEM LABORATORIES p 1054
10 Nevada Dr, New Hyde Park NY 11042
Tel (516) 719-1000 *SIC* 8734

ALCAMI CAROLINAS CORP p 47
2320 Scientific Park Dr, Wilmington NC 28405
Tel (910) 254-7000 *SIC* 2834 8734 8731

ALCAMI HOLDINGS LLC p 47
2320 Scientific Park Dr, Wilmington NC 28405
Tel (910) 254-7000 *SIC* 2834 8731 8734

■ CRL SAFETY ASSESSMENT INC p 393
1407 George Rd, Ashland OH 44805
Tel (419) 952-0553 *SIC* 8734

■ CECO GROUP INC p 272
4625 Red Bank Rd Ste 200, Cincinnati OH 45227
Tel (513) 458-2600
SIC 8711 3564 8734 3443 3444 1761

STERIS ISOMEDIX OPERATIONS INC p 1386
5960 Heisley Rd, Mentor OH 44060
Tel (440) 354-2600 *SIC* 8734

TESTAMERICA ENVIRONMENTAL SERVICES LLC p 1441
4101 Shuffel St Nw, North Canton OH 44720
Tel (330) 497-9396 *SIC* 8734

TESTAMERICA HOLDINGS INC p 1441
4101 Shuffel St Nw, North Canton OH 44720
Tel (330) 497-9396 *SIC* 8734

TESTAMERICA LABORATORIES INC p 1441
4101 Shuffel St Nw, North Canton OH 44720
Tel (800) 456-9396 *SIC* 8734

NORTH AMERICAN SCIENCE ASSOCIATES INC p 1050
6750 Wales Rd, Northwood OH 43619
Tel (419) 666-9455 *SIC* 8731 8734

BIOCLINICA INC p 183
2005 S Easton Rd Ste 304, Doylestown PA 18901
Tel (267) 757-3000 *SIC* 8734

MDS PHARMA SERVICES (US) INC p 933
2200 Rnpance Blvd Ste 400, King Of Prussia PA 19406
Tel (610) 239-7900 *SIC* 8734

EUROFINS LANCASTER LABORATORIES INC p 512
2425 New Holland Pike, Lancaster PA 17601
Tel (717) 656-2300 *SIC* 8731 8734

ERESEARCHTECHNOLOGY INC p 507
1818 Market St Ste 1000, Philadelphia PA 19103
Tel (215) 972-0420 *SIC* 8734

MICROBAC LABORATORIES INC p 961
101 Bellevue Rd Ste 301, Pittsburgh PA 15229
Tel (412) 459-1060 *SIC* 8734

AMERICAN ESOTERIC LABORATORIES p 72
2763 Summer Oaks Dr, Bartlett TN 38134
Tel (901) 937-1910 *SIC* 8734

NISSAN NORTH AMERICA INC p 1044
1 Nissan Way, Franklin TN 37067
Tel (615) 725-1000
SIC 5012 8711 8734 6141 8741 3711

ALS GROUP USA CORP p 61
10450 Stncliff Rd Ste 210, Houston TX 77099
Tel (281) 530-5656 *SIC* 8734

INSPECTORATE AMERICA CORP p 746
12000 Aerospace Ave # 200, Houston TX 77034
Tel (713) 944-2000 *SIC* 7389 8734 8731

INSPECTORATE AMERICA HOLDING INC p 746
12000 Aerospace Ave # 200, Houston TX 77034
Tel (713) 944-2000 *SIC* 7389 8734

INTERTEK USA INC p 759
2 Riverway Ste 500, Houston TX 77056
Tel (713) 543-3600 *SIC* 4785 8734

SHAWCOR INC p 1313
3838 N Sam Houston Pkwy E # 300, Houston TX 77032
Tel (281) 886-2350 *SIC* 8734

SOUTHERN PETROLEUM LABORATORIES INC p 1350
8850 Interchange Dr, Houston TX 77054
Tel (713) 660-0901 *SIC* 5172 8999 8734

EXFO AMERICA INC p 519
3400 Waterview Pkwy # 100, Richardson TX 75080
Tel (972) 761-9271 *SIC* 3825 8734

UTAH STATE UNIVERSITY RESEARCH FOUNDATION p 1536
1695 N Research Pkwy, North Logan UT 84341
Tel (435) 713-3400
SIC 8711 8734 8733 7371

NELSON LABORATORIES INC p 1025
6280 S Redwood Rd, Salt Lake City UT 84123
Tel (801) 290-7500 *SIC* 8734

HEALTH DIAGNOSTIC LABORATORY INC p 674
4401 Dominion Blvd, Glen Allen VA 23060
Tel (804) 343-2718 *SIC* 8734

FROEHLING & ROBERTSON INC p 580
3015 Dumbarton Rd, Richmond VA 23228
Tel (804) 264-2701 *SIC* 8711 8734

ALCAMI WISCONSIN CORP p 47
W130n10497 Washington Dr, Germantown WI 53022
Tel (262) 251-5044 *SIC* 8731 8734

NATIONAL COALITION OF CERTIFICATION CENTERS p 1010
4940 88th Ave, Kenosha WI 53144
Tel (262) 914-1515 *SIC* 8734

■ COVANCE LABORATORIES INC p 384
3301 Kinsman Blvd, Madison WI 53704
Tel (608) 241-4471 *SIC* 8734

SIC 8741 Management Services

BAPTIST HEALTH SYSTEM INC p 153
1130 22nd St S Ste 1000, Birmingham AL 35205
Tel (205) 715-5000
SIC 8011 8741 8082 8059

■ SOUTHERN NUCLEAR OPERATING CO INC p 1350
42 Inverness Center Pkwy, Birmingham AL 35242
Tel (205) 992-5000 *SIC* 8741

■ SURGICAL CARE AFFILIATES LLC p 1409
569 Brookwood Vlg Ste 901, Birmingham AL 35209
Tel (205) 545-2572 *SIC* 8741

YULISTA HOLDING LLC p 1640
631 Discovery Dr Nw, Huntsville AL 35806
Tel (907) 275-2917 *SIC* 8741

ENDURACARE THERAPY MANAGEMENT INC p 496
3765a Government Blvd, Mobile AL 36693
Tel (251) 666-7867 *SIC* 8049 8741

SAAD ENTERPRISES INC p 1263
1515 S University Blvd, Mobile AL 36609
Tel (251) 343-9600
SIC 8082 5047 7352 5912 5621 8741

SOUTHERN MEDICAL HEALTH SYSTEMS INC p 1349
3632 Dauphin St Ste 101b, Mobile AL 36608
Tel (251) 460-5280
SIC 8741 8011 7374 7322

CENTURY HEALTH ALLIANCE JOINT VENTURE p 282
809 University Blvd E, Tuscaloosa AL 35401
Tel (205) 759-7111 *SIC* 8062 8741

WARREN AVERETT COMPANIES LLC p 1576
2500 Acton Rd Ste 200, Vestavia AL 35243
Tel (205) 979-4100
SIC 8721 8741 7363 8742

ALASKA NATIVE TRIBAL HEALTH CONSORTIUM p 45
4000 Ambassador Dr, Anchorage AK 99508
Tel (907) 729-1900 *SIC* 8399 8741

KONIAG DEVELOPMENT CO LLC p 827
3800 Centerpoint Dr # 502, Anchorage AK 99503
Tel (907) 561-2668 *SIC* 8741 6719

MANIILAQ ASSOCIATION p 901
733 2nd Ave Ferguson Bldg, Kotzebue AK 99752
Tel (907) 442-3311 *SIC* 8062 8741

NORTHERN ARIZONA HEALTHCARE CORP p 1055
1200 N Beaver St, Flagstaff AZ 86001
Tel (928) 779-3366
SIC 8741 8082 8399 4119

NEXTCARE HOLDINGS INC p 1040
1138 N Alma School Rd # 120, Mesa AZ 85201
Tel (480) 924-8382 *SIC* 8093 8741 8011

NEXTCARE INC p 1040
2550 N Thunderbird Cir # 303, Mesa AZ 85215
Tel (480) 924-8382 *SIC* 8093 8741

EXODYNE INC p 519
8433 N Black Canyon Hwy # 100, Phoenix AZ 85021
Tel (602) 995-3700
SIC 8711 8731 8741 8744 8748

FARMERS INSURANCE CO OF ARIZONA p 529
16001 N 28th Ave, Phoenix AZ 85053
Tel (602) 863-8100 SIC 6411 8741

■ HUNT CONSTRUCTION GROUP INC p 719
7720 N 16th St Ste 100, Phoenix AZ 85020
Tel (480) 368-4700 SIC 8741

LONDEN INSURANCE GROUP INC p 875
4343 E Camelback Rd # 400, Phoenix AZ 85018
Tel (602) 957-1650 SIC 6311 6321 8741

SOUTHWEST NETWORK p 1352
2700 N Central Ave # 1050, Phoenix AZ 85004
Tel (602) 266-8402 SIC 8741

TRIWEST HEALTHCARE ALLIANCE CORP p 1483
15810 N 28th Ave, Phoenix AZ 85053
Tel (602) 564-2000 SIC 8741 8062

■ TUTOR PERINI BUILDING CORP p 1493
5055 E Washington St # 210, Phoenix AZ 85034
Tel (602) 256-6777 SIC 1541 1542 8741

■ U-HAUL INTERNATIONAL INC p 1498
2727 N Central Ave, Phoenix AZ 85004
Tel (602) 263-6011
SIC 7513 7519 7359 5531 4226 8741

TROON GOLF LLC p 1484
15044 N Scottsdale Rd # 300, Scottsdale AZ 85254
Tel (480) 606-1000 SIC 8741 6552

SUNDT CONSTRUCTION INC p 1402
2620 S 55th St, Tempe AZ 85282
Tel (480) 293-3000
SIC 1542 1611 1629 1541 8741

LEONI WIRING SYSTEMS INC p 856
3100 N Campbell Ave # 101, Tucson AZ 85719
Tel (520) 741-0895 SIC 3643 8741 5063

M3 ENGINEERING & TECHNOLOGY CORP p 890
2051 W Sunset Rd Ste 101, Tucson AZ 85704
Tel (520) 293-1488 SIC 8741 8712 8711

TUCSON MEDICAL CENTER p 1490
5301 E Grant Rd, Tucson AZ 85712
Tel (520) 327-5461
SIC 8062 8051 6513 8741

▲ DELTIC TIMBER CORP p 427
210 E Elm St, El Dorado AR 71730
Tel (870) 881-9400
SIC 0811 2411 6531 8741

BEVERLY ENTERPRISES INC p 179
1000 Fianna Way, Fort Smith AR 72919
Tel (479) 201-2000 SIC 8741 8051 8082

SPECTRA HEALTHCARE ALLIANCE INC p 1357
1000 Fianna Way, Fort Smith AR 72919
Tel (479) 201-2000 SIC 8741

VANTAGE HEALTHCARE CORP p 1544
1000 Fianna Way, Fort Smith AR 72919
Tel (479) 201-2000 SIC 8741

COUNTRY VILLA SERVICE CORP p 375
2400 E Katella Ave # 800, Anaheim CA 92806
Tel (310) 574-3733 SIC 8741

CBM 2012 A CALIFORNIA LIMITED PARTNERSHIP p 268
1010 Racquet Club Dr # 108, Auburn CA 95603
Tel (530) 823-2477
SIC 1531 1522 6513 6531 8741

■ CAMARILLO HEALTHCARE CENTER p 243
205 Granada St, Camarillo CA 93010
Tel (805) 482-9805 SIC 8741

CAMERON DICKINSON CONSTRUCTION CO INC p 245
6184 Innovation Way, Carlsbad CA 92009
Tel (760) 438-9114 SIC 1542 8741

SENIOR KISCO LIVING LLC p 1304
5790 Fleet St Ste 300, Carlsbad CA 92008
Tel (760) 804-5900 SIC 8322 8741

■ ASPEN EDUCATION GROUP INC p 118
17777 Center Court Dr N # 300, Cerritos CA 90703
Tel (562) 467-5500 SIC 8741 8322

PUBLIC HEALTH FOUNDATION ENTERPRISES INC p 1189
12801 Crossrds Pkwy S 200, City Of Industry CA 91746
Tel (562) 692-4643 SIC 8741

EXPERIAN HOLDINGS INC p 520
475 Anton Blvd, Costa Mesa CA 92626
Tel (714) 830-7000 SIC 8741

CITRUS VALLEY HEALTH PARTNERS INC p 311
210 W San Bernardino Rd, Covina CA 91723
Tel (626) 331-7331 SIC 8741

CITY OF HOPE p 315
1500 E Duarte Blvd, Duarte CA 91010
Tel (626) 256-4673 SIC 8741 8399

■ UNIVERSITY MECHANICAL & ENGINEERING CONTRACTORS INC p 1519
1168 Fesler St, El Cajon CA 92020
Tel (619) 956-2500 SIC 1711 1623 8741

ROEBBELEN CONTRACTING INC p 1246
1241 Hawks Flight Ct, El Dorado Hills CA 95762
Tel (916) 939-4000 SIC 1542 1541 8741

FILM MUSICIANS SECONDARY MARKETS FUND p 542
15910 Ventura Blvd # 900, Encino CA 91436
Tel (818) 755-7777 SIC 8741 6722

LEGACY PARTNERS RESIDENTIAL INC p 852
4000 E 3rd Ave Ste 600, Foster City CA 94404
Tel (650) 571-2250 SIC 8741

STEELWAVE INC p 1385
4000 E 3rd Ave Ste 600, Foster City CA 94404
Tel (650) 571-2200 SIC 6552 8741 6531

STEELWAVE LLC p 1385
4000 E 3rd Ave Ste 500, Foster City CA 94404
Tel (650) 571-2200 SIC 6552 8741 6531

DELTA PRODUCTS CORP p 427
46101 Fremont Blvd, Fremont CA 94538
Tel (510) 668-5100
SIC 5065 5045 8741 5063 3577

■ WALT DISNEY IMAGINEERING RESEARCH & DEVELOPMENT INC p 1574
1401 Flower St, Glendale CA 91201
Tel (818) 544-6500
SIC 7819 8712 1542 8741 8711

EUREKA RESTAURANT GROUP LLC p 512
12101 Crenshaw Blvd, Hawthorne CA 90250
Tel (310) 331-8233 SIC 5812 8741

GOLD STANDARD ASSET MANAGEMENT LLC p 620
5155 W Rosecrans Ave # 238, Hawthorne CA 90250
Tel (310) 644-3600 SIC 8741

STAFF PRO INC p 1374
15272 Jason Cir, Huntington Beach CA 92649
Tel (714) 230-7200 SIC 7382 8741

▲ CORVEL CORP p 373
2010 Main St Ste 600, Irvine CA 92614
Tel (949) 851-1473 SIC 8741 8011

■ FIDELITY NATIONAL TITLE INSURANCE CO p 541
3220 El Camino Real, Irvine CA 92602
Tel (949) 622-4600
SIC 6361 8741 6541 6531

KIA MOTORS AMERICA INC p 816
111 Peters Canyon Rd, Irvine CA 92606
Tel (949) 468-4800 SIC 5511 5013 8741

ROLAND DGA CORP p 1247
15363 Barranca Pkwy, Irvine CA 92618
Tel (949) 727-2100 SIC 5045 8741

SMILE BRANDS GROUP INC p 1333
100 Spectrum Center Dr # 1500, Irvine CA 92618
Tel (714) 668-1300 SIC 8741 8021

ST JOSEPH HEALTH SYSTEM p 1368
3345 Michelson Dr Ste 100, Irvine CA 92612
Tel (949) 381-4000 SIC 8082 8741

HALL MANAGEMENT CORP p 654
759 S Madera Ave, Kerman CA 93630
Tel (559) 846-7382 SIC 8741

JC RESORTS LLC p 780
533 Coast Blvd S, La Jolla CA 92037
Tel (858) 605-2700 SIC 8741 7992 7991

LADEKI RESTAURANT GROUP p 837
7596 Eads Ave Ste 200, La Jolla CA 92037
Tel (858) 454-2222 SIC 8741

HOSPITAL COMMITTEE FOR LIVERMORE-PLEASANTON AREAS p 709
1111 E Stanley Blvd, Livermore CA 94550
Tel (925) 447-7000 SIC 8741

KNOX & ASSOCIATES LLC p 825
615 Candlewood Ct, Lodi CA 95242
Tel (209) 365-1567 SIC 8741 5812

CALIFORNIA CARTAGE CO LLC p 239
2931 Redondo Ave, Long Beach CA 90806
Tel (562) 427-1143 SIC 4226 8741 8721

MEMORIAL HEALTH SERVICES - UNIVERSITY OF CALIFORNIA AT IRVINE CENTER FOR HEALTH EDUCATION p 941
2801 Atlantic Ave, Long Beach CA 90806
Tel (562) 933-2000 SIC 8062 8741

TRISTAR INSURANCE GROUP INC p 1482
100 Oceangate Ste 700, Long Beach CA 90802
Tel (562) 495-6600 SIC 6331 8741

US SKILLSERVE INC p 1533
4115 E Broadway Ste A, Long Beach CA 90803
Tel (562) 930-0777 SIC 8741

HARMAN MANAGEMENT CORP p 662
199 1st St Ste 212, Los Altos CA 94022
Tel (650) 941-5681 SIC 8741 5812 5046

■ AECOM GLOBAL II LLC p 28
1999 Avenue Of The Stars, Los Angeles CA 90067
Tel (213) 593-8100 SIC 8711 8712 8741

■ AECOM SERVICES INC p 28
555 S Flower St Ste 3700, Los Angeles CA 90071
Tel (213) 593-8000 SIC 8712 8741 8711

CAPITAL GROUP COMPANIES INC p 249
333 S Hope St Fl 55, Los Angeles CA 90071
Tel (213) 486-9200
SIC 6282 6091 6722 8741

GRIFFIN HOLDINGS LLC p 640
2121 Avenue Of The Stars, Los Angeles CA 90067
Tel (424) 245-4423 SIC 8741

INTERNATIONAL LEASE FINANCE CORP p 755
10250 Constellation Blvd, Los Angeles CA 90067
Tel (310) 788-1999 SIC 7359 8741 5599

■ RADNET MANAGEMENT INC p 1205
1510 Cotner Ave, Los Angeles CA 90025
Tel (310) 445-2800 SIC 8741

■ SUNAMERICA INVESTMENTS INC p 1401
1 Sun America Ctr Fl 37, Los Angeles CA 90067
Tel (310) 772-6000
SIC 8741 6211 6282 7311

TICKETMOB LLC p 1452
11833 Mississippi Ave, Los Angeles CA 90025
Tel (800) 927-0939 SIC 8741

■ URS GROUP INC p 1530
300 S Grand Ave Ste 1100, Los Angeles CA 90071
Tel (213) 593-8000 SIC 8711 8712 8741

RIM CORP p 1235
915 17th St, Modesto CA 95354
Tel (209) 523-8331 SIC 8741

COMMUNITY HOSPITAL FOUNDATION INC p 349
23625 Holman Hwy, Monterey CA 93940
Tel (831) 625-4830 SIC 8741

KOLL MANAGEMENT SERVICES INC p 826
4343 Von Karman Ave # 150, Newport Beach CA 92660
Tel (949) 833-3030 SIC 6531 8741

■ HOLMES & NARVER INC p 701
999 W Town And Country Rd, Orange CA 92868
Tel (714) 567-2400
SIC 8711 8742 8741 1542

OROHEALTH CORP p 1095
2767 Olive Hwy, Oroville CA 95966
Tel (530) 533-8500 SIC 8741

ALFATECH CAMBRIDGE GROUP GP p 49
345 S California Ave # 3, Palo Alto CA 94306
Tel (650) 543-3030 SIC 8741 8742

BON APPETIT MANAGEMENT CO p 199
100 Hamilton Ave Ste 400, Palo Alto CA 94301
Tel (650) 798-8000 SIC 8741

PARSONS CONSTRUCTORS INC p 1118
100 W Walnut St, Pasadena CA 91124
Tel (626) 440-2000 SIC 8741 8711

PARSONS CORP p 1118
100 W Walnut St, Pasadena CA 91124
Tel (626) 440-2000
SIC 1629 1611 8711 8741

HOSPITAL COMMITTEE FOR LIVERMORE-PLEASANTON AREAS p 709
5555 W Las Positas Blvd, Pleasanton CA 94588
Tel (925) 847-3000 SIC 8062 8741

PAMONA VALLEY MEDICAL GROUP INC p 1110
9302 Pttsbrgh Ave Ste 220, Rancho Cucamonga CA 91730
Tel (909) 932-1045 SIC 8011 8741

JIPC MANAGEMENT INC p 786
22342 Avenida Empresa # 220, Rcho Sta Marg CA 92688
Tel (949) 916-2000 SIC 8741

RHS CORP p 1232
350 Terracina Blvd, Redlands CA 92373
Tel (909) 335-5500 SIC 8741

BOB FRINK MANAGEMENT INC p 196
5112 Madison Ave Ste 201, Sacramento CA 95841
Tel (916) 338-7333 SIC 8741 5511

L LYON WILLIAM & ASSOCIATES INC p 834
3640 American River Dr, Sacramento CA 95864
Tel (916) 978-4200 SIC 8741

SUTTER CONNECT LLC p 1410
10470 Old Placrvl Rd # 100, Sacramento CA 95827
Tel (916) 854-6600 SIC 8742 8741 8721

SUTTER MEDICAL FOUNDATION p 1410
2700 Gateway Oaks Dr, Sacramento CA 95833
Tel (916) 887-7122 SIC 8741

UNIVERSITY ENTERPRISES INC p 1518
6000 J St, Sacramento CA 95819
Tel (916) 278-6672 SIC 8299 8741

INLAND COUNTIES REGIONAL CENTER INC p 743
1365 S Waterman Ave, San Bernardino CA 92408
Tel (909) 890-3000 SIC 8741

EVOLUTION HOSPITALITY LLC p 515
1211 Puerta Del Sol # 170, San Clemente CA 92673
Tel (949) 325-1350 SIC 8741 7011

■ ARROWHEAD MANAGEMENT CO p 113
701 B St Ste 2100, San Diego CA 92101
Tel (800) 669-1889 SIC 6411 8741

BARNHART INC p 156
10620 Treena St Ste 300, San Diego CA 92131
Tel (858) 635-7400 SIC 1542 8741

ROEL CONSTRUCTION CO INC p 1246
1615 Murray Canyon Rd # 1000, San Diego CA 92108
Tel (619) 297-4156 SIC 1541 8741

SCRIPPS CLINIC FOUNDATION p 1294
12395 El Camino Real, San Diego CA 92130
Tel (858) 554-9000 SIC 8741

SHARP HEALTHCARE p 1312
8695 Spectrum Center Blvd, San Diego CA 92123
Tel (858) 499-4000 SIC 8062 8741 6324

SOLPAC CONSTRUCTION INC p 1338
2424 Congress St, San Diego CA 92110
Tel (619) 296-6247 SIC 8741 1542 1611

BECHTEL CAPITAL MANAGEMENT CORP p 167
50 Beale St, San Francisco CA 94105
Tel (415) 768-1234 SIC 8741

BECHTEL CONSTRUCTION OPERATIONS INC p 167
50 Beale St Bsmt 1, San Francisco CA 94105
Tel (415) 768-1234
SIC 1541 1629 1623 8741 7353

BECHTEL ENERGY CORP p 167
50 Beale St Bsmt 1, San Francisco CA 94105
Tel (415) 768-1234 SIC 8711 8741

FAIRMONT HOTEL PARTNERS LLC p 525
950 Mason St, San Francisco CA 94108
Tel (415) 772-5000 SIC 8741

GOLDEN GATE PRIVATE EQUITY INC p 621
1 Embarcadero Ctr Fl 39, San Francisco CA 94111
Tel (415) 983-2706 SIC 8741 5621

HARBOR VIEW HOLDINGS INC p 660
433 California St Fl 7, San Francisco CA 94104
Tel (415) 982-7777
SIC 1522 1521 6512 8741

JOIE DE VIVRE HOSPITALITY LLC p 792
530 Bush St Ste 501, San Francisco CA 94108
Tel (415) 835-0300 SIC 8741

KIMPTON HOTEL & RESTAURANT GROUP LLC p 819
222 Kearny St Ste 200, San Francisco CA 94108
Tel (415) 397-5572 SIC 8741

MERITAGE GROUP LP p 949
The Embarcad Pier 5 St Pier, San Francisco CA 94111
Tel (415) 399-5330 SIC 8741

PARTHENON DCS HOLDINGS LLC p 1118
4 Embarcadero Ctr, San Francisco CA 94111
Tel (925) 960-4800 SIC 8741

▲ RPX CORP p 1255
1 Market Plz Ste 800, San Francisco CA 94105
Tel (866) 779-7641 SIC 6794 8741

SAN FRANCISCO UNIFIED SCHOOL DISTRICT p 1277
555 Franklin St, San Francisco CA 94102
Tel (415) 241-6000 SIC 8211 8741

■ XPO LOGISTICS WORLDWIDE INC p 1633
560 Mission St Ste 2950, San Francisco CA 94105
Tel (415) 486-2660
SIC 4731 4225 4213 8741

POLYCOM INC p 1160
6001 America Center Dr, San Jose CA 95002
Tel (408) 586-6000 SIC 8741

▲ MINDBODY INC p 972
4051 Broad St Ste 220, San Luis Obispo CA 93401
Tel (877) 755-4279 SIC 7372 8741

CALIFORNIA CASUALTY MANAGEMENT CO p 239
1900 Almeda De Las Pulgas, San Mateo CA 94403
Tel (650) 574-4000 SIC 6331 8741

SANTA CLARITA HEALTH CARE ASSOCIATION INC p 1280
23845 Mcbean Pkwy, Santa Clarita CA 91355
Tel (661) 253-8000 SIC 8741

EXCHANGE BANK p 517
440 Aviation Blvd, Santa Rosa CA 95403
Tel (707) 524-3000 SIC 6036 8741 6022

ACTIVE WELLNESS LLC p 20
4000 Bridgeway Ste 101, Sausalito CA 94965
Tel (415) 331-1600 SIC 8741

TRAFFIC MANAGEMENT INC p 1469
2435 Lemon Ave, Signal Hill CA 90755
Tel (562) 595-4278 SIC 7389 8741

HCL AMERICA INC p 672
330 Potrero Ave, Sunnyvale CA 94085
Tel (408) 733-0480 SIC 7376 7371 8741

▲ TUTOR PERINI CORP p 1493
15901 Olden St, Sylmar CA 91342
Tel (818) 362-8391
SIC 1542 8741 1611 1791 8711

ACT 1 GROUP INC p 19
1999 W 190th St, Torrance CA 90504
Tel (310) 532-1529 SIC 7361 8741

PROVIDENCE LITTLE CO OF MARY MEDICAL CENTER-TORRANCE p 1186
4101 Torrance Blvd, Torrance CA 90503
Tel (310) 540-7676 SIC 8741

FALCON AEROSPACE HOLDINGS LLC p 526
27727 Avenue Scott, Valencia CA 91355
Tel (661) 775-7200 SIC 8741

▲ WESCO AIRCRAFT HOLDINGS INC p 1593
24911 Avenue Stanford, Valencia CA 91355
Tel (661) 775-7200 SIC 8741 5072

KELLEYAMERIT HOLDINGS INC p 808
1331 N Calif Blvd Ste 150, Walnut Creek CA 94596
Tel (877) 512-6374 SIC 8741

SAGE CLIENT 283 LLC p 1267
3155 S Vaughn Way, Aurora CO 80014
Tel (303) 595-7200 SIC 7011 8741

MWH GLOBAL INC p 1004
370 Interlocken Blvd # 300, Broomfield CO 80021
Tel (303) 533-1900 SIC 8711 8741

ALEUT MANAGEMENT SERVICES LLC p 48
5540 Tech Center Dr # 100, Colorado Springs CO 80919
Tel (719) 531-9090 SIC 8741

ARDENT MILLS LLC p 106
1875 Lawrence St Ste 1400, Denver CO 80202
Tel (800) 851-9618 SIC 2041 4789 8741

COREPOWER YOGA MANAGEMENT LLC p 369
3001 Brighton Blvd # 269, Denver CO 80216
Tel (303) 813-9020 SIC 8741

▲ JANUS CAPITAL GROUP INC p 778
151 Detroit St, Denver CO 80206
Tel (303) 333-3863 SIC 6282 8741

MSHC INC p 997
12005 E 45th Ave, Denver CO 80239
Tel (303) 455-2825 SIC 8741

■ POLICY STUDIES INC p 1159
1515 Wynkoop St Ste 400, Denver CO 80202
Tel (303) 863-0900 SIC 8741 8742 7371

■ PSI SERVICES HOLDING INC p 1188
1515 Wynkoop St Ste 400, Denver CO 80202
Tel (303) 863-0900
SIC 8741 8742 7371 8748

ADVANTEDGE BUSINESS GROUP LLC p 27
9777 Pyramid Ct Ste 220, Englewood CO 80112
Tel (303) 734-9424 SIC 8741 7291 7363

CATHOLIC HEALTH INITIATIVES p 266
198 Inverness Dr W, Englewood CO 80112
Tel (303) 298-9100 SIC 8062 8051 8741

CATHOLIC HEALTH INITIATIVES COLORADO p 266
198 Inverness Dr W, Englewood CO 80112
Tel (303) 290-6500 SIC 8741 8062

DESTINATION RESIDENCES LLC p 432
10333 E Dry Creek Rd, Englewood CO 80112
Tel (303) 799-3830 SIC 7011 8741

FASCORE LLC p 530
8515 E Orchard Rd, Greenwood Village CO 80111
Tel (303) 737-3600 SIC 8741

M&C HOTEL INTERESTS INC p 890
6560 Greenwood Plaza Blvd # 300, Greenwood Village CO 80111
Tel (303) 779-2000
SIC 8741 8712 6321 6331 7389

RICHFIELD HOSPITALITY INC p 1233
7600 E Orchard Rd 230s, Greenwood Village CO 80111
Tel (303) 220-2000 SIC 8741

ARCADIS US INC p 103
630 Plaza Dr Ste 200, Highlands Ranch CO 80129
Tel (720) 344-3500 SIC 8748 8711 8741

CARDNO INC p 253
10004 Park Meadows Dr # 300, Lone Tree CO 80124
Tel (720) 257-5800
SIC 8711 8748 8742 8741

PARK VIEW HOSPITAL p 1116
400 W 16th St, Pueblo CO 81003
Tel (719) 584-4556 SIC 8741

CASEY INDUSTRIAL INC p 263
1400 W 122nd Ave Ste 200, Westminster CO 80234
Tel (541) 926-8641 SIC 1541 8741

ST VINCENTS HEALTH SERVICES CORP p 1373
2800 Main St, Bridgeport CT 06606
Tel (203) 576-6000 SIC 8741 8062

BLAKE GROUP HOLDINGS INC p 188
4 New Park Rd, East Windsor CT 06088
Tel (860) 243-1491
SIC 5074 5084 7699 8741

PROHEALTH PHYSICIANS INC p 1182
3 Farm Glen Blvd Ste 202, Farmington CT 06032
Tel (860) 409-7700 SIC 8741

AMERICAN INDUSTRIAL ACQUISITION CORP p 74
1465 E Putnam Ave Ste 229, Greenwich CT 06830
Tel (203) 698-9595 SIC 8741

FRC FOUNDERS CORP p 575
1 Lafayette Pl Ste 3, Greenwich CT 06830
Tel (203) 661-6601
SIC 8741 1311 1389 8731 5084

SILVER POINT CAPITAL LIMITED PARTNERSHIP p 1324
2 Greenwich Plz, Greenwich CT 06830
Tel (203) 542-4200 SIC 8741 6726

WEXFORD CAPITAL LP p 1603
411 W Putnam Ave Ste 125, Greenwich CT 06830
Tel (203) 862-7000
SIC 8741 6282 1221 1222

ECHN ENTERPRISES INC p 475
71 Haynes St, Manchester CT 06040
Tel (860) 646-1222 SIC 8741

CENTRAL CONNECTICUT HEALTH ALLIANCE INC p 278
100 Grand St, New Britain CT 06052
Tel (860) 224-5757 SIC 8741

YALE-NEW HAVEN HOSPITAL INC p 1634
20 York St, New Haven CT 06510
Tel (203) 688-4242 SIC 8351 8062 8741

LAWRENCE + MEMORIAL CORP p 847
365 Montauk Ave, New London CT 06320
Tel (860) 442-0711 SIC 8741

HOMESERVE USA CORP p 704
601 Merritt 7 Fl 6, Norwalk CT 06851
Tel (203) 351-4924 SIC 8741 1521

MERRITT HOSPITALITY LLC p 950
101 Merritt 7 Ste 14, Norwalk CT 06851
Tel (203) 849-8844 SIC 8741

BACKUS CORP p 143
326 Washington St, Norwich CT 06360
Tel (860) 823-6330 SIC 8741

■ CLAYTON HOLDINGS LLC p 323
100 Beard Sawmill Rd # 200, Shelton CT 06484
Tel (203) 926-5600 SIC 8741 7389 6531

NEW CASTLE HOTELS LLC p 1029
2 Corporate Dr Ste 154, Shelton CT 06484
Tel (203) 925-8370 SIC 7011 8741 8742

■ PRUDENTIAL ANNUITIES INC p 1187
1 Corporate Dr Ste 800, Shelton CT 06484
Tel (203) 926-1888 SIC 6411 8741

▲ GARTNER INC p 592
56 Top Gallant Rd, Stamford CT 06902
Tel (203) 316-1111 SIC 8732 8742 8741

NOVITEX ENTERPRISE SOLUTIONS INC p 1063
300 First Stamford Pl # 2, Stamford CT 06902
Tel (844) 668-4839 SIC 7334 8741

PAVARINI NORTH EAST CONSTRUCTION CO INC p 1122
30 Oak St Fl 3, Stamford CT 06905
Tel (203) 327-0100 SIC 1542 8741

STAMFORD HEALTH SYSTEM INC p 1375
30 Shelburne Rd, Stamford CT 06902
Tel (203) 325-7000 SIC 8741

■ STARWOOD HOTELS & RESORTS WORLDWIDE LLC p 1379
1 Star Pt, Stamford CT 06902
Tel (203) 964-6000 SIC 7011 8741

CONNECTICUT VNA INC p 357
33 N Plains Industrial Rd, Wallingford CT 06492
Tel (203) 679-5300 SIC 8082 8741

GREATER WATERBURY HEALTH NETWORK INC p 636
64 Robbins St, Waterbury CT 06708
Tel (203) 573-6000 SIC 8741 8093 8011

■ OAKLEAF WASTE MANAGEMENT LLC p 1071
415 Day Hill Rd, Windsor CT 06095
Tel (860) 290-1250 SIC 8741 4953

SPECIALTY RISK SERVICES INC p 1356
100 Corporate Dr Ste 211, Windsor CT 06095
Tel (860) 520-2500 SIC 8741

■ SS&C TECHNOLOGIES INC p 1363
80 Lamberton Rd, Windsor CT 06095
Tel (860) 298-4500 SIC 7372 7371 8741

A JBEK JOINT VENTURE CO p 6
242 Chapman Rd, Newark DE 19702
Tel (302) 452-9000 SIC 8711 8741

CHRISTIANA CARE HEALTH SYSTEM INC p 303
200 Hygeia Dr, Newark DE 19713
Tel (302) 733-1000 SIC 8741

■ J P MORGAN SERVICES INC p 772
500 Stanton Christiana Rd, Newark DE 19713
Tel (302) 634-1000 SIC 7374 8741

BALFOUR BEATTY LLC p 148
1011 Centre Rd Ste 322, Wilmington DE 19805
Tel (302) 573-3873 SIC 1542 8712 8741

CONSTRUCTION MANAGEMENT SERVICES INC p 361
3600 Silverside Rd, Wilmington DE 19810
Tel (302) 478-4200 SIC 1731 8741

SEVERN TRENT (DEL) INC p 1309
1011 Centre Rd Ste 320, Wilmington DE 19805
Tel (302) 427-5990 SIC 3589 7371 8741

SYNGENTA CORP p 1415
3411 Silverside Rd # 100, Wilmington DE 19810
Tel (302) 425-2000 SIC 2879 5191 8741

THOMSON REUTERS (GRC) INC p 1449
2711 Centerville Rd # 400, Wilmington DE 19808
Tel (212) 227-7357
SIC 7291 8111 8721 8733 8741

▲ ADVISORY BOARD CO p 28
2445 M St Nw Ste 500, Washington DC 20037
Tel (202) 266-5600 SIC 8732 8741 7372

GRYPHON TECHNOLOGIES LC p 643
80 M St Se Ste 600, Washington DC 20003
Tel (202) 617-2004
SIC 8741 8711 8731 7371

PORTFOLIO LOGIC LLC p 1163
600 New Hampshire Ave Nw 9f, Washington DC 20037
Tel (202) 266-6519 SIC 6726 8741

SOUTHEASTERN UNIVERSITIES RESEARCH ASSOCIATION INC p 1347
1201 New York Ave Nw # 430, Washington DC 20005
Tel (202) 408-7872 SIC 8741

WASHINGTON HOSPITAL CENTER CORP p 1578
110 Irving St Nw, Washington DC 20010
Tel (202) 877-7000
SIC 8741 8082 8051 8062

CAMPUS MANAGEMENT CORP p 246
5201 Congress Ave C220, Boca Raton FL 33487
Tel (561) 923-2500 SIC 7373 8741

ECONOMOS PROPERTIES INC p 476
4000 N Federal Hwy # 206, Boca Raton FL 33431
Tel (561) 361-2504 SIC 8741

PRO UNLIMITED INC p 1178
7777 Glades Rd Ste 208, Boca Raton FL 33434
Tel (800) 291-1099 SIC 8741

PRO UNLIMITED INC p 1178
7777 Glades Rd Ste 208, Boca Raton FL 33434
Tel (561) 994-9500 SIC 8741 7372

PROMISE HEALTHCARE INC p 1183
999 Yamato Rd Ste 300, Boca Raton FL 33431
Tel (561) 869-3100 SIC 8741

SUNTECK TRANSPORT CO INC p 1405
6413 Congress Ave Ste 260, Boca Raton FL 33487
Tel (561) 988-9456 SIC 8741 4731

BAYCARE HEALTH SYSTEM INC p 161
2985 Drew St, Clearwater FL 33759
Tel (727) 519-1200 SIC 8741

MORTON PLANT MEASE HEALTH CARE INC p 991
300 Pinellas St, Clearwater FL 33756
Tel (727) 462-7777 SIC 8741 8721

▲ MASTEC INC p 917
800 S Douglas Rd Ste 1200, Coral Gables FL 33134
Tel (305) 599-1800 SIC 1623 8741

ABB/CON-CISE OPTICAL GROUP LLC p 9
12301 Nw 39th St, Coral Springs FL 33065
Tel (800) 852-8089 SIC 5048 3851 8741

■ RESORTQUEST REAL ESTATE OF FLORIDA INC p 1227
35000 Emerald Coast Pkwy, Destin FL 32541
Tel (850) 837-3700 SIC 7011 8741

ANSA MCAL TRADING INC p 93
11403 Nw 39th St, Doral FL 33178
Tel (305) 599-8766
SIC 8741 5084 5085 4731

TRI-STARR MANAGEMENT SERVICES INC p 1477
1941 Citrona Dr, Fernandina Beach FL 32034
Tel (909) 321-0507 SIC 8741

MUVICO THEATERS INC p 1003
2929 E Coml Blvd Ste 408, Fort Lauderdale FL 33308
Tel (954) 564-6550 SIC 7832 8741

LEE MEMORIAL HEALTH SYSTEM FOUNDATION INC p 851
2776 Cleveland Ave, Fort Myers FL 33901
Tel (239) 343-2000
SIC 8741 8062 8082 8051

BERNARD EGAN & CO p 176
1900 N Old Dixie Hwy, Fort Pierce FL 34946
Tel (772) 465-7555 SIC 0723 8741 0174

SANTAFE HEALTHCARE INC p 1281
4300 Nw 89th Blvd, Gainesville FL 32606
Tel (352) 372-8400 SIC 8741

BAPTIST HEALTH SYSTEM INC p 153
800 Prudential Dr, Jacksonville FL 32207
Tel (904) 202-2000 SIC 8741

■ BLACK KNIGHT FINANCIAL SERVICES LLC p 187
601 Riverside Ave, Jacksonville FL 32204
Tel (904) 854-8100
SIC 6361 6331 6531 8741

■ BLACK KNIGHT HOLDINGS INC p 187
601 Riverside Ave, Jacksonville FL 32204
Tel (904) 854-8100
SIC 6361 6331 6531 8741

▲ FIDELITY NATIONAL FINANCIAL INC p 540
601 Riverside Ave Fl 4, Jacksonville FL 32204
Tel (904) 854-8100
SIC 6361 6331 6531 8741 3699

GENESIS HEALTH INC p 603
3599 University Blvd S # 1, Jacksonville FL 32216
Tel (904) 858-7600 SIC 8069 8011 8741

■ SERVICELINK HOLDINGS LLC p 1307
601 Riverside Ave Bldg 5, Jacksonville FL 32204
Tel (904) 854-8100
SIC 6361 6331 6531 8741 3699

ST VINCENTS HEALTH SYSTEM INC p 1373
4203 Belfort Rd Ste 155, Jacksonville FL 32216
Tel (904) 308-7300 SIC 8741

YMCA OF FLORIDAS FIRST COAST p 1636
40 E Adams St Ste 210, Jacksonville FL 32202
Tel (904) 296-3220 SIC 8741 8641

STERLING HOSPITALITY INC p 1387
2950 Reedy Creek Blvd, Kissimmee FL 34747
Tel (407) 997-3481 SIC 8741 8721

WW LBV INC p 1629
2000 Hotel Plaza Blvd, Lake Buena Vista FL 32830
Tel (407) 828-2424 SIC 8741

MEADOWBROOK GOLF GROUP INC p 934
5385 Gateway Blvd Ste 12, Lakeland FL 33811
Tel (407) 589-7200
SIC 8742 8741 7992 5941

CENTRAL FLORIDA HEALTH ALLIANCE INC p 278
600 E Dixie Ave, Leesburg FL 34748
Tel (352) 323-5000 SIC 8741

SPECIALTY RESTAURANT DEVELOPMENT LLC p 1356
2600 Westhall Ln Ste 100, Maitland FL 32751
Tel (407) 661-3151 SIC 8741

AMERIJET HOLDINGS INC p 82
3401 Nw 72nd Ave Ste A, Miami FL 33122
Tel (800) 927-6059
SIC 4512 8741 4581 4213

CLUB MED SALES INC p 328
6505 Blue Lagoon Dr # 225, Miami FL 33126
Tel (305) 925-9000
SIC 4724 4725 7011 8741

LEON MANAGEMENT INTERNATIONAL INC p 856
11501 Sw 40th St Fl 2, Miami FL 33165
Tel (305) 642-5366 SIC 8741

MOUNT SINAI MEDICAL CENTER OF FLORIDA INC p 994
4300 Alton Rd, Miami Beach FL 33140
Tel (305) 674-2121 SIC 8062 8741

CC-NAPLES INC p 269
704 Village Cir, Naples FL 34110
Tel (239) 596-4702 SIC 8741

MANHATTAN CONSTRUCTION (FLORIDA) INC p 901
3705 Westview Dr Ste 1, Naples FL 34104
Tel (239) 643-6000
SIC 1542 8712 1531 1521 8741

ORIX USA CORP p 1095
676 W Prospect Rd, Oakland Park FL 33309
Tel (214) 237-2000 SIC 8741

ALE HOUSE MANAGEMENT INC p 48
5750 Major Blvd Ste 400, Orlando FL 32819
Tel (407) 547-1120 SIC 8741

CFI RESORTS MANAGEMENT INC p 285
5601 Windhover Dr, Orlando FL 32819
Tel (407) 351-3350 SIC 8741

GOODWILL INDUSTRIES OF CENTRAL FLORIDA INC p 624
7531 S Orange Blossom Trl, Orlando FL 32809
Tel (407) 857-0659 SIC 8331 8741

KESSLER ENTERPRISE INC p 813
4901 Vineland Rd Ste 650, Orlando FL 32811
Tel (407) 996-9999 SIC 8741 7011

ORLANDO HEALTH INC p 1095
52 W Underwood St, Orlando FL 32806
Tel (321) 843-7000 SIC 8062 8741 8069

RESORT HOSPITALITY ENTERPRISES LTD p 1227
1002 W 23rd St Ste 400, Panama City FL 32405
Tel (321) 953-7272 SIC 8741

BAPTIST HEALTH CARE CORP p 153
1000 W Moreno St, Pensacola FL 32501
Tel (850) 434-4080 SIC 8741

PRC LLC p 1168
8151 Peters Rd Ste 4000, Plantation FL 33324
Tel (954) 693-3700 SIC 8741

ST JOSEPH PREFERRED HEALTHCARE INC p 1368
2500 Harbor Blvd, Port Charlotte FL 33952
Tel (941) 625-4122 SIC 8741

PINNACLE HOTEL MANAGEMENT CO LLC p 1150
1480 Royal Palm Bch Blvd, Royal Palm Beach FL 33411
Tel (561) 242-9066 SIC 8741

COX TARGET MEDIA INC p 386
1 Valpak Ave N, Saint Petersburg FL 33716
Tel (727) 399-3000
SIC 7331 8741 8742 2759

■ RAYMOND JAMES & ASSOCIATES INC p 1210
880 Carillon Pkwy, Saint Petersburg FL 33716
Tel (727) 567-1000 SIC 6211 6722 8741

MARTIN MEMORIAL HEALTH SYSTEMS INC p 912
200 Se Hospital Ave, Stuart FL 34994
Tel (772) 287-5200 SIC 8741 8062

SHERIDAN HEALTHCORP INC p 1316
1613 Nw 136th Ave, Sunrise FL 33323
Tel (954) 838-2371 SIC 8741

AQUA VENTURE HOLDINGS LLC p 101
14400 Carlson Cir, Tampa FL 33626
Tel (813) 855-8636 SIC 8741

■ COMPREHENSIVE HEALTH MANAGEMENT INC p 352
8735 Henderson Rd, Tampa FL 33634
Tel (813) 206-1033 SIC 8741

GREYSTONE HEALTHCARE MANAGEMENT CORP p 640
4042 Park Oaks Blvd # 300, Tampa FL 33610
Tel (813) 635-9500 SIC 8741

HEALTHPLAN SERVICES INC p 677
3501 E Frontage Rd # 125, Tampa FL 33607
Tel (813) 289-1000 SIC 8741

HI DEVELOPMENT CORP p 689
111 W Fortune St, Tampa FL 33602
Tel (813) 229-6686 SIC 8741

UNIVERSITY OF SOUTH FLORIDA MEDICAL SERVICES SUPPORT CORP p 1525
12901 Brc Dwns Blvd Mdc62, Tampa FL 33612
Tel (813) 974-2201 SIC 8011 8741

VALENTI FLORIDA MANAGEMENT INC p 1539
3930 Premier North Dr, Tampa FL 33618
Tel (813) 935-8777 SIC 8741

INTERCOASTAL HEALTH SYSTEMS INC p 752
1309 N Flagler Dr, West Palm Beach FL 33401
Tel (561) 650-6272 SIC 8741 8069

ISLAND HOSPITALITY MANAGEMENT LLC p 766
222 Lakeview Ave Ste 200, West Palm Beach FL 33401
Tel (561) 832-6132 SIC 8741

PGA RESORT & SPA p 1140
1555 Palm Beach Lks, West Palm Beach FL 33401
Tel (561) 686-2000
SIC 8741 7377 7513 7515

TOOJAYS MANAGEMENT LLC p 1460
3654 Georgia Ave, West Palm Beach FL 33405
Tel (561) 659-9011 SIC 8741

MID-FLORIDA MEDICAL SERVICES INC p 963
200 Avenue F Ne, Winter Haven FL 33881
Tel (863) 297-1895 SIC 8741 8062 8082

CONVERGENT RESOURCES HOLDINGS LLC p 365
555 N Point Ctr E Ste 175, Alpharetta GA 30022
Tel (866) 867-0179 SIC 8741

LEASE PLAN USA INC p 850
1165 Sanctuary Pkwy, Alpharetta GA 30009
Tel (770) 933-9090 SIC 7515 8741

■ MCKESSON TECHNOLOGIES INC p 930
11475 Great Oaks Way # 400, Alpharetta GA 30022
Tel (404) 338-6000
SIC 7374 8741 8721 7322 7373

SELECT MANAGEMENT RESOURCES LLC p 1301
3440 Preston Ridge Rd # 500, Alpharetta GA 30005
Tel (678) 823-4700 SIC 8741

BRISTOL HOTEL & RESORTS INC p 214
3 Ravinia Dr Ste 100, Atlanta GA 30346
Tel (770) 604-2000 SIC 8741

CENTENNIAL HEALTHCARE CORP p 275
400 Perimeter Ctr Ter Ne, Atlanta GA 30346
Tel (770) 698-9040
SIC 8051 8069 8052 8741

CHICK-FIL-A INC p 298
5200 Buffington Rd, Atlanta GA 30349
Tel (404) 765-8038 SIC 5812 8741

CLEVELAND GROUP INC p 325
1281 Fulton Indus Blvd Nw, Atlanta GA 30336
Tel (404) 696-4550 SIC 1731 8741 1711

COMMUNITY LOANS OF AMERICA INC p 349
8601 Dunwoody Pl Ste 406, Atlanta GA 30350
Tel (770) 587-1901 SIC 8741

DAVIDSON HOTEL CO p 416
1 Ravinia Dr Ste 1600, Atlanta GA 30346
Tel (678) 349-0909 SIC 8741 7011

EMPLOYMENT SOLUTIONS MANAGEMENT INC p 494
1040 Crown Pointe Pkwy, Atlanta GA 30338
Tel (770) 671-1900 SIC 8741

▲ EQUIFAX INC p 506
1550 Peachtree St Nw, Atlanta GA 30309
Tel (404) 885-8000
SIC 7323 7389 8732 8741

GEORGIA BAPTIST HEALTH CARE SYSTEM INC p 607
100 10th St Nw Ste 700, Atlanta GA 30309
Tel (404) 814-4477 SIC 8741

H J RUSSELL & CO p 650
171 17th St Nw Ste 1600, Atlanta GA 30363
Tel (404) 330-1000
SIC 1542 8741 7389 8742

HEALTH CARE CAPITAL INC p 674
2 Ravinia Dr Ste 1350, Atlanta GA 30346
Tel (770) 393-3355 SIC 6162 8051 8741

HILLTOPPER HOLDING CORP p 694
303 Perimeter Ctr N # 500, Atlanta GA 30346
Tel (770) 698-9040 SIC 8051 8741

HOTEL EQUITIES INC p 710
41 Perimeter Ctr E # 510, Atlanta GA 30346
Tel (770) 934-2170 SIC 6799 8741

INTERCONTINENTAL HOTELS GROUP RESOURCES INC p 752
3 Ravinia Dr Ste 100, Atlanta GA 30346
Tel (770) 604-5000 SIC 7011 8741 6794

MARINER HEALTH CARE INC p 907
1 Ravinia Dr Ste 1500, Atlanta GA 30346
Tel (678) 443-7000
SIC 5912 8051 8093 8741 8062 3443

NATIONAL SENIOR CARE INC p 1016
1 Ravinia Dr Ste 1500, Atlanta GA 30346
Tel (678) 443-7000
SIC 5912 8051 8093 8741 8062 3443

NEW SOUTH CONSTRUCTION CO INC p 1033
1180 W Peachtree St Nw # 70, Atlanta GA 30309
Tel (404) 443-4000 SIC 1541 8741

PROMINA HEALTH SYSTEM INC p 1183
2727 Paces Ferry Rd Se, Atlanta GA 30339
Tel (404) 541-1111 SIC 8741 8082

RAM PARTNERS LLC p 1206
3284 Northside Pkwy Nw # 300, Atlanta GA 30327
Tel (770) 437-5200 SIC 8741 8742

ROYAL HOSPITALITY CORP p 1254
255 E Paces Ferry Rd Ne # 300, Atlanta GA 30305
Tel (404) 239-0329 SIC 6794 8741 5812

SAINT JOSEPHS PRIMARY CARE NETWORK INC p 1269
5673 Peachtree Dunwdy, Atlanta GA 30342
Tel (404) 778-6100 SIC 8741

SIX CONTINENTS HOTELS INC p 1328
3 Ravinia Dr Ste 100, Atlanta GA 30346
Tel (770) 604-2000 SIC 7011 6794 8741

■ THD AT-HOME SERVICES INC p 1446
2690 Cumberland Pkwy Se # 300, Atlanta GA 30339
Tel (770) 779-1423 SIC 8741

UNIVERSITY HEALTH RESOURCES INC p 1518
1350 Walton Way, Augusta GA 30901
Tel (706) 722-9011 SIC 8741

FLOURNOY DEVELOPMENT CO p 560
900 Brookstone Ctr Pkwy, Columbus GA 31904
Tel (706) 324-4000 SIC 6552 1522 8741

DEKALB REGIONAL HEALTH SYSTEM INC p 423
2701 N Decatur Rd, Decatur GA 30033
Tel (404) 501-1000 SIC 8741

LAY MANAGEMENT CORP OF GEORIGA p 848
790 Dixon Rd Apt J7, Jonesboro GA 30238
Tel (678) 558-5631 SIC 8741

ENCOMPASS SUPPLY CHAIN SOLUTIONS INC p 496
775 Tipton Industrial Dr, Lawrenceville GA 30046
Tel (800) 432-8542 SIC 8741

NAVICENT HEALTH INC p 1020
777 Hemlock St, Macon GA 31201
Tel (478) 633-1000 SIC 8741

BENEVIS LLC p 173
1090 Northchase Pkwy Se, Marietta GA 30067
Tel (770) 916-9000 SIC 8741 7389

ASSET MANAGEMENT OUTSOURCING RECOVERIES INC p 119
5655 Peachtree Pkwy # 213, Norcross GA 30092
Tel (678) 259-9600 SIC 8741

BRAMBLES USA INC (DEL) p 207
180 Technology Pkwy # 600, Norcross GA 30092
Tel (770) 776-1900
SIC 4953 4212 7353 8741 7359

■ **GOLDLEAF FINANCIAL SOLUTIONS INC** p 622
350 Technology Pkwy # 200, Norcross GA 30092
Tel (678) 966-0844 SIC 8721 8741

PEDIATRIA HEALTHCARE LLC p 1127
5185 Peachtree Pkwy # 350, Norcross GA 30092
Tel (770) 840-1966 SIC 8082 8741

RECALL CORP p 1214
180 Technology Pkwy # 100, Norcross GA 30092
Tel (770) 776-1000 SIC 8741

SBS SERVICES CORP p 1285
3091 Holcomb Bridge Rd, Norcross GA 30071
Tel (678) 534-4861 SIC 8741

■ **WESTROCK SHARED SERVICES LLC** p 1603
504 Thrasher St, Norcross GA 30071
Tel (770) 448-2193 SIC 8741

OSMOSE UTILITIES SERVICES INC p 1097
635 Highway 74 S, Peachtree City GA 30269
Tel (770) 632-6700 SIC 8741 8711 1623

ARCHBOLD MEDICAL CENTER INC p 104
Gordon Ave At Mimosa Dr, Thomasville GA 31792
Tel (229) 228-2739 SIC 8741 8062

PRUITTHEALTH CORP p 1187
209 E Doyle St, Toccoa GA 30577
Tel (706) 886-8493 SIC 8741

WILCOX HEALTH SYSTEM p 1609
3-3420 Kuhio Hwy, Lihue HI 96766
Tel (808) 245-1100 SIC 8741 8011

CONSOLIDATED SCHOOL DISTRICT 158 p 360
650 Academic Dr, Algonquin IL 60102
Tel (847) 659-6158 SIC 8211 8741

SYNERGY55 INC p 1415
85 W Algonquin Rd Ste 600, Arlington Heights IL 60005
Tel (847) 437-0200 SIC 8741

ACCRETIVE HEALTH INC p 15
401 N Michigan Ave # 2700, Chicago IL 60611
Tel (312) 324-7820 SIC 8741

ALDEN MANAGEMENT SERVICES INC p 47
4200 W Peterson Ave # 142, Chicago IL 60646
Tel (773) 282-8183 SIC 8051 8741

AON US HOLDINGS INC p 95
200 E Randolph St, Chicago IL 60601
Tel (312) 381-1000 SIC 6411 6799 8741

BAGCRAFTPAPERCON LLC p 144
3900 W 43rd St, Chicago IL 60632
Tel (773) 843-8000 SIC 8741

BARRY CALLEBAUT USA LLC p 157
600 W Chicago Ave Ste 860, Chicago IL 60654
Tel (312) 496-7491 SIC 2066 8741

FLAT OUT CRAZY LLC p 554
303 W Erie St Ste 600, Chicago IL 60654
Tel (312) 284-6500 SIC 8741 5812

LETTUCE ENTERTAIN YOU ENTERPRISES INC p 857
5419 N Sheridan Rd, Chicago IL 60640
Tel (773) 878-7340 SIC 5812 8741

MADISON CAPITAL PARTNERS CORP p 894
500 W Madison St Ste 3890, Chicago IL 60661
Tel (312) 277-0323 SIC 3542 8741

NORTH ADVOCATE SIDE HEALTH NETWORK p 1049
836 W Wellington Ave, Chicago IL 60657
Tel (773) 296-5699 SIC 8741 8721

RUSH SYSTEM FOR HEALTH p 1258
1645 W Jackson Blvd Ste 5, Chicago IL 60612
Tel (312) 942-4061 SIC 8741 8062

SAC WIRELESS LLC p 1264
540 W Madison St Ste 1600, Chicago IL 60661
Tel (847) 944-1600 SIC 8741 8742

SINAI HEALTH SYSTEM p 1326
1500 S Fairfield Ave, Chicago IL 60608
Tel (773) 542-2000 SIC 6512 8741

■ **STAFF MANAGEMENT SOLUTIONS LLC** p 1374
860 W Evergreen Ave, Chicago IL 60642
Tel (312) 915-0900 SIC 7363 8741

THOUGHTWORKS INC p 1450
200 E Randolph St # 2500, Chicago IL 60601
Tel (312) 373-1000 SIC 8741

■ **TRANSUNION LLC** p 1473
555 W Adams St Fl 1, Chicago IL 60661
Tel (312) 985-2000 SIC 8741

ULTIMA HOSPITALITY LLC p 1500
30 S Wacker Dr Ste 3600, Chicago IL 60606
Tel (312) 948-4500 SIC 8741

COOPERS HAWK INTERMEDIATE HOLDING LLC p 367
5325 9th Ave, Countryside IL 60525
Tel (708) 839-2920
SIC 8741 2084 5182 5812

CRYSTAL LAKE COMMUNITY CONSOLIDATED SCHOOL DISTRICT 47 p 397
300 Commerce Dr, Crystal Lake IL 60014
Tel (815) 459-6070 SIC 8211 8741

SPIRE HOSPITALITY LLC p 1359
111 S Pfingsten Rd # 425, Deerfield IL 60015
Tel (847) 498-6650 SIC 8741

HEARTLAND HOME FOODS INC p 679
1400 Opus Pl Ste 900, Downers Grove IL 60515
Tel (800) 492-5592 SIC 5812 8741

▲ **UNIVAR INC** p 1516
3075 Highland Pkwy # 200, Downers Grove IL 60515
Tel (331) 777-6000 SIC 5169 5191 8741

PROCTOR HEALTH CARE INC p 1179
12529 N Fillyside Dr, Dunlap IL 61525
Tel (309) 691-1000 SIC 8741

NORTHERN ILLINOIS HEALTH PLAN p 1056
773 W Lincoln St Ste 402, Freeport IL 61032
Tel (815) 599-7050 SIC 8741 8721

COMMUNITY UNIT SCHOOL DISTRICT 205 p 350
932 Harrison St, Galesburg IL 61401
Tel (309) 343-3623 SIC 8211 8741

UNLIMITED DEVELOPMENT INC p 1528
285 S Farnham St, Galesburg IL 61401
Tel (309) 343-1550 SIC 8741

SPRENGER ENTERPRISES INC p 1360
2198 Gladstone Ct, Glendale Heights IL 60139
Tel (630) 529-0700 SIC 8741

RDG CHICAGO INC p 1212
1840 Pickwick Ln, Glenview IL 60026
Tel (847) 510-2037 SIC 8741

■ **INNOVEL SOLUTIONS INC** p 745
3333 Beverly Rd, Hoffman Estates IL 60179
Tel (847) 286-2500 SIC 4731 8741 8742

LEOPARDO COMPANIES INC p 856
5200 Prairie Stone Pkwy, Hoffman Estates IL 60192
Tel (847) 783-3000 SIC 1542 8741

▲ **ARTHUR J GALLAGHER & CO** p 114
2 Pierce Pl, Itasca IL 60143
Tel (630) 773-3800 SIC 6411 6282 8741

■ **GALLAGHER BASSETT SERVICES INC** p 589
2 Pierce Pl Ste 100, Itasca IL 60143
Tel (630) 773-3800 SIC 6411 8741

HARLEM SCHOOL DISTRICT 122 p 661
8605 N 2nd St, Machesney Park IL 61115
Tel (815) 654-4500 SIC 8211 8741

GOTTLIEB HEALTH RESOURCES INC p 626
701 W North Ave, Melrose Park IL 60160
Tel (708) 681-3200 SIC 8741

HEART OF AMERICA MANAGEMENT LLC p 678
1501 River Dr, Moline IL 61265
Tel (309) 797-9300 SIC 8741 5812 7011

CORE CONSTRUCTION GROUP LTD p 369
866 N Main St, Morton IL 61550
Tel (309) 263-0808 SIC 8741

PARK NAPERVILLE DISTRICT p 1115
320 Jackson Ave, Naperville IL 60540
Tel (630) 848-5000
SIC 7992 7999 8322 8741

MERIT HEALTH SYSTEMS LLC p 949
1033 Skokie Blvd Ste 360, Northbrook IL 60062
Tel (502) 753-0890 SIC 8741

EVANGELICAL SERVICES CORP p 513
2025 Windsor Dr, Oak Brook IL 60523
Tel (630) 572-9393 SIC 8741

■ **MCDONALDS RESTAURANT OPERATIONS INC** p 928
2111 Mcdonalds Dr, Oak Brook IL 60523
Tel (630) 623-3000 SIC 5812 8741

■ **MCDONALDS RESTAURANTS OF WASHINGTON INC** p 928
1 Mcdonalds Dr, Oak Brook IL 60523
Tel (630) 623-3000 SIC 5812 8741

UNION PARTNERS I LLC p 1505
1400 16th St Ste 250, Oak Brook IL 60523
Tel (630) 822-7000 SIC 8741 7389

VONACHEN SERVICES INC p 1565
8900 N Pioneer Rd, Peoria IL 61615
Tel (309) 691-6202
SIC 7349 4731 8741 7361

IV HEALTHCORP INC p 769
925 West St, Peru IL 61354
Tel (815) 223-3300 SIC 8062 8741 5912

CBI SERVICES INC p 268
14107 S Route 59, Plainfield IL 60544
Tel (815) 439-6668 SIC 1629 8741

BLESSING CORPORATE SERVICES INC p 189
Broadway At 11th, Quincy IL 62305
Tel (217) 223-1200 SIC 8741

TRINITY REGIONAL HEALTH SYSTEM p 1481
2701 17th St, Rock Island IL 61201
Tel (309) 779-5000 SIC 8062 8741

ROCKFORD HEALTH SYSTEM p 1244
2400 N Rockton Ave, Rockford IL 61103
Tel (815) 971-5000 SIC 8741

HOSTMARK INVESTORS LIMITED PARTNERSHIP p 710
1300 E Wdfield Rd Ste 400, Schaumburg IL 60173
Tel (847) 517-9100 SIC 8741

COVENANT RETIREMENT COMMUNITIES INC p 384
5700 Old Orchard Rd, Skokie IL 60077
Tel (773) 878-2294 SIC 8741

MEMORIAL HEALTH SYSTEM p 941
701 N 1st St, Springfield IL 62781
Tel (217) 788-3000 SIC 8741 8062

WHEATON FRANCISCAN SERVICES INC p 1604
26w 171 Roosevelt Rd, Wheaton IL 60189
Tel (414) 465-3000 SIC 8741 5999

CDH-DELNOR HEALTH SYSTEM p 271
25 N Winfield Rd, Winfield IL 60190
Tel (630) 933-1600 SIC 8071 8741

BEAVERS HOLDINGS LLC p 166
3550 Hobson Rd Fl 3, Woodridge IL 60517
Tel (630) 963-2736 SIC 8741 6531

CARDON & ASSOCIATES INC p 253
2749 E Covenanter Dr, Bloomington IN 47401
Tel (812) 332-2265 SIC 8741 6513 8742

DEACONESS HEALTH SYSTEM INC p 419
600 Mary St, Evansville IN 47710
Tel (812) 450-5000 SIC 8741

PARKVIEW HEALTH SYSTEM INC p 1117
10501 Corporate Dr, Fort Wayne IN 46845
Tel (260) 484-6636 SIC 8741 8062

TIPPMANN PROPERTIES INC p 1455
9009 Coldwater Rd Ste 300, Fort Wayne IN 46825
Tel (260) 490-3000 SIC 8741

STRACK AND VAN TIL SUPER MARKET INC p 1392
9632 Cline Ave, Highland IN 46322
Tel (219) 924-6932 SIC 5411 8741 4226

NEW CENTAUR LLC p 1029
10 W Market St Ste 2700, Indianapolis IN 46204
Tel (317) 656-8787 SIC 8741

TLC MANAGEMENT INC p 1457
1800 N Wabash Rd Ste 300, Marion IN 46952
Tel (765) 671-2282 SIC 8741

■ **NISOURCE CORPORATE SERVICES CO** p 1044
801 E 86th Ave, Merrillville IN 46410
Tel (219) 647-4222 SIC 8741

WHITE LODGING SERVICES CORP p 1606
701 E 83rd Ave Ste 17, Merrillville IN 46410
Tel (219) 472-2900 SIC 8741 6552

COMMUNITY FOUNDATION OF NORTHWEST INDIANA INC p 348
905 Ridge Rd, Munster IN 46321
Tel (219) 836-0130 SIC 8741 8062

BEACON HEALTH SYSTEM INC p 164
615 N Michigan St, South Bend IN 46601
Tel (574) 647-1000 SIC 8741 8399 8082

BEACON MEDICAL GROUP INC p 165
615 N Michigan St, South Bend IN 46601
Tel (574) 647-1000 SIC 8741 8399 8082

MERCY CARE MANAGEMENT INC p 945
701 10th St Se, Cedar Rapids IA 52403
Tel (319) 398-6011 SIC 8011 8741 8322

GENESIS HEALTH SYSTEM p 603
1227 E Rusholme St, Davenport IA 52803
Tel (563) 421-1000 SIC 8741 8399 7218

JACOBSON WAREHOUSE CO INC p 775
3811 Dixon St, Des Moines IA 50313
Tel (515) 265-6171
SIC 4226 4221 4225 8741 6552 4783

CONLON CONSTRUCTION CO OF IOWA p 356
1100 Rockdale Rd, Dubuque IA 52003
Tel (563) 583-1724 SIC 1542 8741 1541

ABCM CORP p 10
1320 4th St Ne, Hampton IA 50441
Tel (641) 456-5636 SIC 8741 6519 7011

VOGEL PAINT INC p 1564
1110 Albany Pl Se, Orange City IA 51041
Tel (712) 737-8880 SIC 2851 8741

UNITY POINT HEALTH ST LUKE p 1515
2720 Stone Park Blvd, Sioux City IA 51104
Tel (712) 279-3500 SIC 8741

ALLEN HEALTH SYSTEMS INC p 53
1825 Logan Ave, Waterloo IA 50703
Tel (319) 235-3941 SIC 8741

IOWA HEALTH SYSTEM p 762
1776 West Lakes Pkwy # 400, West Des Moines IA 50266
Tel (515) 241-6161 SIC 8062 8721 8741

MERCY HEALTH NETWORK INC p 946
1755 59th Pl, West Des Moines IA 50266
Tel (515) 247-3121 SIC 8741

PROVIDENCE/SAINT JOHN FOUNDATION INC p 1186
8929 Parallel Pkwy, Kansas City KS 66112
Tel (913) 596-4000 SIC 8062 8741 8011

UNIVERSITY OF KANSAS CENTER FOR RESEARCH INC p 1522
2385 Irving Hill Rd, Lawrence KS 66045
Tel (785) 864-3441
SIC 8733 8732 8741 8731

■ **AMERICAN MULTI-CINEMA INC** p 76
1 Amc Way, Leawood KS 66211
Tel (913) 213-2000 SIC 7832 5812 8741

TERRACON CONSULTANTS INC p 1439
18001 W 106th St Ste 300, Olathe KS 66061
Tel (913) 599-6886
SIC 8742 8711 8748 8741

BLACK & VEATCH HOLDING CO p 186
11401 Lamar Ave, Overland Park KS 66211
Tel (913) 458-2000 SIC 8711 8741

BVH INC p 230
11401 Lamar Ave, Overland Park KS 66211
Tel (913) 458-2000 SIC 8711 8741

MIQ HOLDINGS INC p 974
11501 Outlook St Ste 500, Overland Park KS 66211
Tel (913) 696-7363 SIC 4225 4731 8741

MIQ LOGISTICS LLC p 974
11501 Outlook St Ste 500, Overland Park KS 66211
Tel (913) 696-7100 SIC 4731 8741

QUALITY TECHNOLOGY SERVICES LLC p 1197
12851 Foster St, Overland Park KS 66213
Tel (913) 814-9988 SIC 7376 8741

■ **SPRINT/UNITED MANAGEMENT CO** p 1361
6200 Sprint Pkwy, Overland Park KS 66251
Tel (800) 697-6000 SIC 8741

SAINT FRANCIS COMMUNITY SERVICES INC p 1269
509 E Elm St, Salina KS 67401
Tel (785) 825-0541 SIC 8741 8361

LODGING ENTERPRISES LLC p 874
8080 E Central Ave # 180, Wichita KS 67206
Tel (316) 630-6300 SIC 7011 8741 6552

UNIVERSAL COMPANIES INC p 1516
2824 N Ohio St, Wichita KS 67219
Tel (316) 832-0151
SIC 5171 5541 6512 8741 6099 2992

VIA CHRISTI HEALTH INC p 1554
2622 W Central Ave # 102, Wichita KS 67203
Tel (316) 858-4900 SIC 8011 8741

COMMONWEALTH HOTELS LLC p 346
100 E Rivercenter Blvd # 1050, Covington KY 41011
Tel (859) 392-2264 SIC 7011 8741

CORPOREX REALTY & INVESTMENT LLC p 372
100 E Riverctr Ste 1100, Covington KY 41011
Tel (859) 292-5500
SIC 1542 6531 6552 8741 6512

TOYOTA MOTOR ENGINEERING & MANUFACTURING NORTH AMERICA INC p 1466
25 Atlantic Ave, Erlanger KY 41018
Tel (469) 292-1074 SIC 3711 3713 8741

■ **ADP BENEFIT SERVICES KY INC** p 24
11405 Bluegrass Pkwy, Louisville KY 40299
Tel (888) 421-7477 SIC 8741

BAPTIST HEALTHCARE SYSTEM INC p 154
2701 Eastpoint Pkwy, Louisville KY 40223
Tel (502) 896-5000 SIC 8062 8011 8741

■ **HUMANA INSURANCE CO OF KENTUCKY** p 718
500 W Main St Ste 300, Louisville KY 40202
Tel (502) 580-1000 SIC 6321 8741

JEFFERSON COUNTY BOARD OF EDUCATION p 781
3332 Newburg Rd, Louisville KY 40218
Tel (502) 485-3011 SIC 8211 8741

NORTON HEALTHCARE INC p 1061
200 E Chestnut St, Louisville KY 40202
Tel (502) 629-8000 SIC 8741 8062

■ **SPECIALTY HEALTHCARE SERVICES INC** p 1356
680 S 4th St, Louisville KY 40202
Tel (502) 596-7300 SIC 8741

TRILOGY REHAB SERVICES LLC p 1480
2701 Chestnut Station Ct, Louisville KY 40299
Tel (800) 335-1060
SIC 8059 1542 8741 8051

VALIANT CONSTRUCTION LLC p 1540
4229 Bardstown Rd Ste 206, Louisville KY 40218
Tel (502) 562-0037 SIC 8741

BRANSCUM CONSTRUCTION CO/ROBINS & MORTON A JOINT VENTURE p 208
90 Key Village Rd, Russell Springs KY 42642
Tel (270) 866-5107 SIC 1541 8741 1542

PULASKI COUNTY SCHOOL DISTRICT FINANCE CORP p 1191
501 E University Dr, Somerset KY 42503
Tel (606) 679-1123 SIC 8211 8741

CB&I ENVIRONMENTAL & INFRASTRUCTURE INC p 268
3867 Plaza Tower Dr, Baton Rouge LA 70816
Tel (225) 932-2500
SIC 8748 1794 1795 8744 8741

FRANCISCAN MISSIONARIES OF OUR LADY HEALTH SYSTEM INC p 573
4200 Essen Ln, Baton Rouge LA 70809
Tel (225) 526-4500 SIC 8741

GENERAL HEALTH SYSTEM p 601
8585 Picardy Ave, Baton Rouge LA 70809
Tel (225) 387-7000 SIC 8741 6324

SCHUMACHER GROUP OF LOUISIANA INC p 1291
200 Corporate Blvd # 201, Lafayette LA 70508
Tel (337) 237-1915 SIC 8741

■ **ENTERGY SERVICES INC** p 501
639 Loyola Ave Ste 300, New Orleans LA 70113
Tel (504) 576-4000 SIC 8741 8711

ALLEGIANCE HEALTH MANAGEMENT INC p 53
504 Texas St Ste 200, Shreveport LA 71101
Tel (318) 226-8202 SIC 8741

KISATCHIE CORP p 822
9258 Highway 84, Winnfield LA 71483
Tel (318) 628-4116 SIC 8741

AFFILIATED HEALTHCARE SYSTEMS p 32
931 Union St, Bangor ME 04401
Tel (207) 973-6720
SIC 5047 8071 8741 7322 6512

MILES HEALTH CARE INC p 969
35 Miles St, Damariscotta ME 04543
Tel (207) 563-1234 SIC 8741

MAINEHEALTH p 898
110 Free St, Portland ME 04101
Tel (207) 661-7001 SIC 8741

PORTLAND WATER DISTRICT p 1163
225 Douglass St, Portland ME 04102
Tel (207) 761-8310 SIC 4941 4952 8741

FIRST ATLANTIC CORP p 545
100 Waterman Dr Ste 401, South Portland ME 04106
Tel (207) 874-2700 SIC 8741

HOTEL ACQUISITION CO LLC p 710
1997 Annapolis Exch Pkwy, Annapolis MD 21401
Tel (410) 268-0515 SIC 8741 7011

1132 TRUST LLC p 1
1 E Chase St Ste 1132a, Baltimore MD 21202
Tel (410) 601-3042 SIC 8741

DOME CORP p 448
1101 E 33rd St Ste E100, Baltimore MD 21218
Tel (443) 997-3737 SIC 8741

GOOD SAMARITAN HOSPITAL OF MD INC p 623
5601 Loch Raven Blvd, Baltimore MD 21239
Tel (443) 444-3780 SIC 8062 8741

HOPKINS JOHNS MEDICAL SERVICES CORP p 706
3100 Wyman Park Dr, Baltimore MD 21211
Tel (410) 338-3071 SIC 8011 8741

PROMETRIC INC p 1183
1501 S Clinton St # 1200, Baltimore MD 21224
Tel (443) 455-8000 SIC 8748 8741

RUMMEL KLEPPER & KAHL LLP p 1257
81 Mosher St, Baltimore MD 21217
Tel (410) 728-2900
SIC 8711 8741 1623 8999 8713 1611

SHEPPARD PRATT HEALTH SYSTEM INC p 1315
6501 N Charles St, Baltimore MD 21204
Tel (410) 938-3000 SIC 8741 8062

WHITING-TURNER CONTRACTING CO p 1607
300 E Joppa Rd Ste 800, Baltimore MD 21286
Tel (410) 821-1100
SIC 1542 1541 1629 8741

LASALLE HOTEL OPERATING PARTNERSHIP LP p 846
7550 Wisconsin Ave Fl 10, Bethesda MD 20814
Tel (301) 941-1500 SIC 8741

■ **MARRIOTT WORLDWIDE SALES AND MARKETING INC** p 910
10400 Fernwood Rd, Bethesda MD 20817
Tel (301) 634-5100 SIC 8741

RENAISSANCE HOTEL OPERATING CO INC p 1223
10400 Fernwood Rd, Bethesda MD 20817
Tel (301) 380-3000 SIC 7011 8741 6794

▲ **WALKER & DUNLOP INC** p 1573
7501 Wisconsin Ave 1200e, Bethesda MD 20814
Tel (301) 215-5500 SIC 7389 8741

ERICKSON LIVING MANAGEMENT LLC p 507
701 Maiden Choice Ln, Catonsville MD 21228
Tel (410) 402-2097 SIC 8741

MEDSTAR HEALTH INC p 939
5565 Sterrett Pl Ste 500, Columbia MD 21044
Tel (410) 772-6500
SIC 8741 8062 8082 8051 8011

SHORE HEALTH SYSTEM INC p 1318
219 S Washington St, Easton MD 21601
Tel (410) 822-1000 SIC 8741

ROMMEL HOLDINGS INC p 1249
103 E Main St, Fruitland MD 21826
Tel (410) 749-3600 *SIC* 5211 8741

CORPORATE FOOD SERVICES INC p 372
9801 Washington Blvd, Gaithersburg MD 20878
Tel (301) 987-4000 *SIC* 8741

■ **LEIDOS INTEGRATED TECHNOLOGY LLC** p 854
700 N Frederick Ave, Gaithersburg MD 20879
Tel (301) 240-7000 *SIC* 8741

■ **LOCKHEED MARTIN SERVICES INC** p 873
700 N Frederick Ave, Gaithersburg MD 20879
Tel (301) 240-7669 *SIC* 8711 8741 8742

SDH EDUCATION WEST LLC p 1295
9801 Washington Blvd, Gaithersburg MD 20878
Tel (301) 987-4000 *SIC* 8741

SMO FINANCE CORP p 1334
9801 Washington Blvd, Gaithersburg MD 20878
Tel (301) 987-4000 *SIC* 8741

SODEXO AMERICA LLC p 1336
9801 Washington Blvd, Gaithersburg MD 20878
Tel (301) 987-4000 *SIC* 8741

SODEXO LAUNDRY SERVICES INC p 1337
9801 Washington Blvd, Gaithersburg MD 20878
Tel (301) 987-4000 *SIC* 8741

SODEXO MANAGEMENT INC p 1337
9801 Washingtonian Blvd, Gaithersburg MD 20878
Tel (301) 987-4000 *SIC* 8741 6552

SODEXO OPERATIONS LLC p 1337
9801 Washingtonian Blvd, Gaithersburg MD 20878
Tel (301) 987-4000 *SIC* 8741 5812 7349

SODEXO SERVICES OF TX LTD PARTNERSHIP p 1337
9801 Washington Blvd, Gaithersburg MD 20878
Tel (301) 987-4000 *SIC* 8741

MARYLAND HOSPITALITY INC p 915
6411 Ivy Ln Ste 510, Greenbelt MD 20770
Tel (301) 474-3307 *SIC* 7011 8741 8742

WASHINGTON COUNTY ENDOWMENT FUND (INC) p 1578
251 E Antietam St, Hagerstown MD 21740
Tel (301) 790-8102 *SIC* 8741

NATIONAL AUTOMATIC SPRINKLER INDUSTRY WELFARE FUND p 1010
8000 Corporate Dr, Landover MD 20785
Tel (301) 577-1700 *SIC* 8741 6371

REAL HOSPITALITY GROUP LLC p 1213
12800 Hospitality Ln, Ocean City MD 21842
Tel (410) 213-1971 *SIC* 8741

FUTURE CARE HEALTH AND MANAGEMENT OF HOMEWOOD INC p 585
8028 Ritchie Hwy Ste 210b, Pasadena MD 21122
Tel (410) 766-1995 *SIC* 8741

R/C THEATRES MANAGEMENT CORP p 1203
231 W Cherry Hill Ct, Reisterstown MD 21136
Tel (410) 526-4774 *SIC* 8741 7922 7832

AVENDRA LLC p 136
702 King Farm Blvd # 600, Rockville MD 20850
Tel (301) 825-0500 *SIC* 8741

MONTGOMERY COUNTY PUBLIC SCHOOLS p 986
850 Hungerford Dr, Rockville MD 20850
Tel (301) 517-5099 *SIC* 8621 8741

WESTAT INC p 1596
1600 Research Blvd, Rockville MD 20850
Tel (301) 251-1500
SIC 8732 7371 7373 8741 8742 8999

JANJER ENTERPRISES INC p 777
12150 Tech Rd, Silver Spring MD 20904
Tel (301) 625-5920 *SIC* 5812 8721 8741

SUNBURST HOSPITALITY CORP p 1401
10750 Columbia Pike # 300, Silver Spring MD 20901
Tel (301) 592-3800 *SIC* 8741 7011

NORTHEAST HEALTH SYSTEMS INC p 1055
85 Herrick St, Beverly MA 01915
Tel (978) 922-3000 *SIC* 8741

BERKSHIRE PARTNERS LLC p 175
200 Clarendon St Ste 3500, Boston MA 02116
Tel (617) 227-0050 *SIC* 6211 6726 8741

BLUE CROSS AND BLUE SHIELD OF MASSACHUSETTS INC p 191
101 Huntington Ave # 1300, Boston MA 02199
Tel (617) 246-5000 *SIC* 6321 8741 6324

■ **BOSTON BREWING CO INC** p 202
1 Design Center Pl # 850, Boston MA 02210
Tel (617) 368-5250 *SIC* 8741

BRIGHAM AND WOMENS HEALTH CARE INC p 212
75 Francis St, Boston MA 02115
Tel (617) 732-5500 *SIC* 8741

CAREGROUP INC p 255
375 Longwood Ave Fl 7, Boston MA 02215
Tel (617) 667-1715 *SIC* 8741

HARVARD MANAGEMENT CO INC p 666
600 Atlantic Ave Ste 15, Boston MA 02210
Tel (617) 720-6526 *SIC* 8741 6722

▲ **IRON MOUNTAIN INC** p 764
1 Federal St Fl 7, Boston MA 02110
Tel (617) 535-4766
SIC 4226 8741 7375 6798

LYONS GROUP LTD p 888
334 Boylston St Ste 501, Boston MA 02116
Tel (617) 262-2605 *SIC* 8741

PARTNERS HEALTHCARE SYSTEM INC p 1118
800 Boylston St Ste 1150, Boston MA 02199
Tel (617) 278-1000 *SIC* 8741

PARTNERS MEDICAL INTERNATIONAL INC p 1118
100 Cambridge St Fl 20, Boston MA 02114
Tel (617) 535-6400 *SIC* 8741

TUFTS MEDICAL CENTER INC p 1491
800 Washington St, Boston MA 02111
Tel (617) 636-5000
SIC 8062 7371 8742 8741

UNIDINE CORP p 1503
1000 Washington St # 510, Boston MA 02118
Tel (617) 467-3700 *SIC* 8741

WINNRESIDENTIAL LLC p 1617
6 Faneuil Hall Market Pl, Boston MA 02109
Tel (617) 742-4500 *SIC* 8741

EGENERA INC p 481
80 Central St Ste 300, Boxborough MA 01719
Tel (978) 206-6300 *SIC* 7373 1731 8741

ASSOCIATED INSURANCE MANAGEMENT LLC p 120
54 3rd Ave, Burlington MA 01803
Tel (781) 221-1600 *SIC* 8741

CONSTRUCTION MANAGEMENT & BUILDERS INC p 361
75 Sylvan St Ste C103, Danvers MA 01923
Tel (781) 246-9400 *SIC* 8741

POINT GROUP HEALTH CARE GROUP & SENIOR LIVING CENTER INC p 1159
3 Allied Dr Ste 106, Dedham MA 02026
Tel (781) 251-9001 *SIC* 8051 8741

BOSTON COACH CORP p 202
69 Norman St Ste 13, Everett MA 02149
Tel (800) 672-7676 *SIC* 4119 8741

ST ANNES HEALTH CARE SYSTEM INC p 1364
795 Middle St, Fall River MA 02721
Tel (508) 674-5741 *SIC* 8741

HEYWOOD HEALTHCARE INC p 688
242 Green St, Gardner MA 01440
Tel (978) 632-3420 *SIC* 8741

VALLEY HEALTH SYSTEMS INC p 1540
575 Beech St, Holyoke MA 01040
Tel (413) 534-2500
SIC 8082 8093 8399 8741 8721

CENTRAL NEW ENGLAND HEALTHALLIANCE INC p 279
60 Hospital Rd, Leominster MA 01453
Tel (978) 343-5000 *SIC* 8741

EAST COAST TILE IMPORTS INC p 470
8 Stony Brook St Ste 1, Ludlow MA 01056
Tel (518) 344-7000 *SIC* 5032 8741

CIVIGENICS INC p 320
290 Donald Lynch Blvd # 301, Marlborough MA 01752
Tel (508) 486-9300 *SIC* 8741

HALLMARK HEALTH CORP p 654
170 Governors Ave, Medford MA 02155
Tel (781) 979-3000 *SIC* 8741

HALLMARK HEALTH SYSTEM INC p 654
585 Lebanon St, Melrose MA 02176
Tel (781) 979-3000 *SIC* 8741

WINGATE HEALTH CARE HOLDINGS INC p 1616
63 Kendrick St, Needham MA 02494
Tel (781) 707-9000 *SIC* 8741

WINGATE HEALTH CARE INC p 1616
589 Highland Ave, Needham MA 02494
Tel (781) 707-9500 *SIC* 8741

SOUTHCOAST HEALTH SYSTEM INC p 1345
101 Page St, New Bedford MA 02740
Tel (508) 997-1515 *SIC* 8741 8062

SOUTHCOAST PHYSICIAN SERVICES INC p 1345
101 Page St, New Bedford MA 02740
Tel (508) 961-5555 *SIC* 8741

NEWTON-WELLESLEY HEALTH CARE SYSTEM INC p 1039
2014 Washington St, Newton MA 02462
Tel (617) 243-6000 *SIC* 8741 7374 6512

■ **SOFTBANK HOLDINGS INC** p 1337
1188 Centre St Ste 2, Newton MA 02459
Tel (617) 928-9300 *SIC* 8741

JORDAN HEALTH SYSTEMS INC p 793
275 Sandwich St, Plymouth MA 02360
Tel (508) 830-2388 *SIC* 8741 8062

J CALNAN & ASSOCIATES INC p 770
3 Batterymarch Park # 500, Quincy MA 02169
Tel (617) 801-0200 *SIC* 8741 1542

BAYSTATE HEALTH SYSTEM HEALTH SERVICES INC p 162
280 Chestnut St, Springfield MA 01199
Tel (413) 794-9939
SIC 8741 8062 6324 6512

SPHS CORP p 1358
271 Carew St, Springfield MA 01104
Tel (413) 748-9000 *SIC* 8741

HMG HOLDING CORP p 698
920 Winter St, Waltham MA 02451
Tel (781) 699-9000 *SIC* 8741 6719

■ **NORESCO INC** p 1048
1 Research Dr Ste 400c, Westborough MA 01581
Tel (508) 614-1000
SIC 8711 8741 8748 4911 4924

■ **NORESCO LLC** p 1048
1 Research Dr Ste 400c, Westborough MA 01581
Tel (508) 614-1000
SIC 8711 8741 8744 8748 4911 4924

PUMA NORTH AMERICA INC p 1192
10 Lyberty Way, Westford MA 01886
Tel (978) 698-1000
SIC 5136 5139 8741 5137

WINCHESTER HEALTHCARE MANAGEMENT INC p 1614
41 Highland Ave, Winchester MA 01890
Tel (781) 756-2126 *SIC* 8741

DEVERE CONSTRUCTION CO INC p 433
1030 Devere Dr, Alpena MI 49707
Tel (989) 356-4411
SIC 1542 1541 1629 8741

■ **DOMINOS PIZZA LLC** p 449
30 Frank Lloyd Wright Dr, Ann Arbor MI 48105
Tel (734) 930-3030
SIC 5812 6794 5046 5149 8741 2045

GRUPO ANTOLIN NORTH AMERICA INC p 643
1700 Atlantic Blvd, Auburn Hills MI 48326
Tel (248) 373-1437 *SIC* 8741 8711

GEMINI GROUP INC p 598
175 Thompson Rd Ste A, Bad Axe MI 48413
Tel (989) 269-6272 *SIC* 8741 3089

SANCTUS LLC p 1278
348 E Maple Rd, Birmingham MI 48009
Tel (248) 594-2396 *SIC* 8741 7319 8742

LITTLE CAESAR ENTERPRISES INC p 870
2211 Woodward Ave, Detroit MI 48201
Tel (313) 983-6000
SIC 5812 6794 5141 5046 8741

WALBRIDGE ALDINGER LLC p 1572
777 Woodward Ave Ste 300, Detroit MI 48226
Tel (313) 963-8000 *SIC* 1541 1542 8741

WALBRIDGE INTERNATIONAL LLC p 1572
777 Woodward Ave Fl 3, Detroit MI 48226
Tel (313) 963-8000 *SIC* 8741

GARDEN CITY HOSPITAL FOUNDATION p 591
6245 Inkster Rd Ste 210, Garden City MI 48135
Tel (734) 458-4421 *SIC* 8741 7389

FAMILY CHRISTIAN STORES LLC p 526
5300 Patterson Ave Se, Grand Rapids MI 49530
Tel (616) 554-8700
SIC 5942 5735 5947 5699 8741

NATIONAL HERITAGE ACADEMIES INC p 1013
3850 Broadmoor Ave Se # 201, Grand Rapids MI 49512
Tel (877) 223-6402 *SIC* 8211 8741

CHAMPION INC p 287
180 Traders Mine Rd, Iron Mountain MI 49801
Tel (906) 779-2300
SIC 8741 1542 5063 5082 3273 3272

HENRY FORD ALLEGIANCE HEALTH GROUP p 684
205 N East Ave, Jackson MI 49201
Tel (517) 788-4800 *SIC* 8741 8721

BRONSON HEALTH CARE GROUP INC p 217
301 John St, Kalamazoo MI 49007
Tel (269) 341-6000 *SIC* 8741

CHRISTMAN CO p 303
208 N Capitol Ave Fl 4, Lansing MI 48933
Tel (517) 482-1488
SIC 8741 1542 1541 1629

TRINITY HEALTH CORP p 1481
20555 Victor Pkwy, Livonia MI 48152
Tel (734) 343-1000 *SIC* 8741 8062

MIDMICHIGAN HEALTH p 966
4000 Wellness Dr, Midland MI 48670
Tel (989) 839-3000 *SIC* 8741

MIDWAY PRODUCTS GROUP INC p 967
1 Lyman E Hoyt Dr, Monroe MI 48161
Tel (734) 241-7242 *SIC* 8741 3469

■ **SUMMIT HEALTH INC** p 1399
27175 Haggerty Rd, Novi MI 48377
Tel (248) 799-8303 *SIC* 8099 8741

HEALTHSHARE INC p 677
416 Connable Ave, Petoskey MI 49770
Tel (231) 487-4803 *SIC* 8741 8062

CRITTENTON HOSPITAL MEDICAL CENTER FOUNDATION p 393
1101 W University Dr, Rochester MI 48307
Tel (248) 652-5000 *SIC* 8741 8062

HSS LLC p 715
5310 Hampton Pl Ste B, Saginaw MI 48604
Tel (989) 777-2983 *SIC* 8741 8742 7389

NGS AMERICAN INC p 1041
27575 Harper Ave, Saint Clair Shores MI 48081
Tel (586) 552-4656 *SIC* 6411 8741

LAKELAND REGIONAL HEALTH SYSTEM p 840
1234 Napier Ave, Saint Joseph MI 49085
Tel (269) 983-8300 *SIC* 8741

JK & T WINGS INC p 786
13405 W Star Dr Ste 2, Shelby Township MI 48315
Tel (586) 781-0591 *SIC* 8741

BARTON MALOW CO p 158
26500 American Dr, Southfield MI 48034
Tel (248) 436-5000 *SIC* 8741

BARTON MALOW ENTERPRISES INC p 158
26500 American Dr, Southfield MI 48034
Tel (248) 436-5000 *SIC* 8741 1542 1541

GREAT EXPRESSIONS DENTAL CENTERS PC p 633
28626 Telegraph Rd, Southfield MI 48034
Tel (248) 203-2330 *SIC* 8021 8741

THYSSENKRUPP MATERIALS NA INC p 1451
22355 W 11 Mile Rd, Southfield MI 48033
Tel (248) 233-5600
SIC 5051 5162 3444 8741

SELECTCARE INC p 1301
2401 W Big Beaver Rd, Troy MI 48084
Tel (248) 358-2560 *SIC* 6324 8741

NATIONAL CONSTRUCTION ENTERPRISES INC p 1011
5075 Carpenter Rd, Ypsilanti MI 48197
Tel (734) 434-1600 *SIC* 8741

PRIME THERAPEUTICS LLC p 1175
1305 Corporate Center Dr, Eagan MN 55121
Tel (612) 777-4000 *SIC* 8741 6411 2834

■ **OPTUMHEALTH HOLDINGS LLC** p 1090
13625 Technology Dr, Eden Prairie MN 55344
Tel (763) 595-3200 *SIC* 6324 8741 6411

■ **OPTUMINSIGHT INC** p 1091
11000 Optum Cir, Eden Prairie MN 55344
Tel (952) 833-7100
SIC 7371 7375 8742 8741

EXPRESSPOINT TECHNOLOGY SERVICES INC p 521
10900 Wayzata Blvd # 800, Hopkins MN 55305
Tel (763) 543-6000
SIC 5045 7379 7699 8741 7389 7378

■ **3M INTERAMERICA INC** p 2
2501 Old Hudson Rd, Maplewood MN 55144
Tel (651) 733-1110
SIC 5113 5085 5065 5084 5122 8741

AIMIA PROPRIETARY LOYALTY US INC p 38
100 N 6th St Ste 700b, Minneapolis MN 55403
Tel (763) 445-3000 *SIC* 8741

ALLINA HEALTH SYSTEM p 57
2925 Chicago Ave, Minneapolis MN 55407
Tel (612) 262-5000 *SIC* 8062 8741 8011

DAMICO & PARTNERS INC p 410
211 N 1st St Ste 175, Minneapolis MN 55401
Tel (612) 317-4223 *SIC* 8741

EBENEZER SOCIETY p 474
2722 Park Ave, Minneapolis MN 55407
Tel (612) 874-3460 *SIC* 8051 8741

NATH MINNESOTA FRANCHISE GROUP INC p 1009
900 E 79th St Ste 300, Minneapolis MN 55420
Tel (952) 853-1400 *SIC* 5812 8741

■ **NUCLEAR MANAGEMENT CO LLC** p 1066
414 Nicollet Mall, Minneapolis MN 55401
Tel (612) 330-5500 *SIC* 8741 8999

RUST CONSULTING INC p 1260
625 Marquette Ave Ste 900, Minneapolis MN 55402
Tel (612) 359-2000 *SIC* 8741 8111

SENIOR TEALWOOD LIVING p 1304
7400 W 109th St, Minneapolis MN 55438
Tel (952) 888-2923 *SIC* 8051 8741

ST FRANCIS HEALTH SERVICES OF MORRIS INC p 1366
801 Nevada Ave, Morris MN 56267
Tel (320) 589-2004 *SIC* 8741

MAYO FOUNDATION FOR MEDICAL EDUCATION AND RESEARCH p 924
200 1st St Sw, Rochester MN 55905
Tel (507) 284-2511 *SIC* 8741

BETHESDA HEALTHEAST HOSPITAL p 178
559 Capitol Blvd Fl 6, Saint Paul MN 55103
Tel (651) 232-2000 *SIC* 8062 8741 8069

HEALTHEAST CARE INC p 676
559 Capitol Blvd, Saint Paul MN 55103
Tel (651) 232-2300 *SIC* 8741 8721

HEALTHEAST CARE SYSTEM p 677
1700 University Ave W # 5, Saint Paul MN 55104
Tel (651) 232-5353 *SIC* 8741 8062 7389

HOOD DISTRIBUTION INC p 705
15 Professional Pkwy # 8, Hattiesburg MS 39402
Tel (601) 264-2962 *SIC* 8741

MISSISSIPPI BAPTIST HEALTH SYSTEMS INC p 975
1225 N State St Ofc, Jackson MS 39202
Tel (601) 968-1000 *SIC* 8741 8721 8069

ST DOMINIC HEALTH SERVICES INC p 1366
969 Lakeland Dr, Jackson MS 39216
Tel (601) 200-2000
SIC 8741 8093 8069 8062

RUSH HEALTH SYSTEMS INC p 1258
1314 19th Ave, Meridian MS 39301
Tel (601) 703-9607 *SIC* 8741

RUSH SERVICE CO INC p 1258
1314 19th Ave, Meridian MS 39301
Tel (601) 483-0011 *SIC* 8741 7371

COMMUNITY ELDERCARE SERVICES LLC p 348
2844 Traceland Dr, Tupelo MS 38801
Tel (662) 680-7300 *SIC* 8741

NORTH MISSISSIPPI HEALTH SERVICES INC p 1053
830 S Gloster St, Tupelo MS 38801
Tel (662) 377-3000 *SIC* 8741

DELMAR GARDENS ENTERPRISES INC p 425
14805 North Outer 40 Rd # 300, Chesterfield MO 63017
Tel (636) 733-7000 *SIC* 8741

ST LUKES HEALTH CORP p 1370
232 S Woods Mill Rd, Chesterfield MO 63017
Tel (314) 434-1500 *SIC* 8741

AMERICAN CENTURY SERVICES CORP p 70
4500 Main St, Kansas City MO 64111
Tel (816) 531-5575 *SIC* 7374 8741

■ **BLOCK FINANCIAL CORP** p 189
4400 Main St, Kansas City MO 64111
Tel (816) 753-6900 *SIC* 8741

BURNS & MCDONNELL INC p 228
9400 Ward Pkwy, Kansas City MO 64114
Tel (816) 333-9400 *SIC* 8711 8741

MIDAMERICA DIVISION INC p 964
903 E 104th St Ste 500, Kansas City MO 64131
Tel (816) 508-4000 *SIC* 8741

STOWERS RESOURCE MANAGEMENT INC p 1392
1000 E 50th St, Kansas City MO 64110
Tel (816) 926-4000 *SIC* 8741

■ **UNITED HEALTHCARE OF MIDWEST INC** p 1509
13655 Riverport Dr, Maryland Heights MO 63043
Tel (314) 592-7000 *SIC* 8741 6324

WORLD WIDE TECHNOLOGY INC p 1625
60 Weldon Pkwy, Maryland Heights MO 63043
Tel (314) 569-7000 *SIC* 5045 5065 8741

PRO-AM INC p 1178
2350 Kanell Blvd, Poplar Bluff MO 63901
Tel (573) 785-0858 *SIC* 8051 8741

■ **AMEREN SERVICES CO** p 66
1901 Chouteau Ave, Saint Louis MO 63103
Tel (314) 621-3222 *SIC* 8741

BJC HEALTH SYSTEM p 186
4901 Forest Park Ave, Saint Louis MO 63108
Tel (314) 286-2000 *SIC* 8741

■ **BOEING SERVICE CO** p 197
6200 J S Mcdonnell Blvd, Saint Louis MO 63134
Tel (972) 705-8000 *SIC* 8741 8711

CIC GROUP INC p 306
530 Maryville Centre Dr, Saint Louis MO 63141
Tel (314) 682-2900 *SIC* 7692 3542 8741

GATEWAY REGION YOUNG MENS CHRISTIAN ASSOCIATION p 594
326 S 21st St Ste 400, Saint Louis MO 63103
Tel (314) 436-1177 *SIC* 8641 8741 8322

HIMAGINE SOLUTIONS INC p 695
600 Emerson Rd Ste 225, Saint Louis MO 63141
Tel (314) 627-5135 *SIC* 8741 7361

■ **JACOBS FACILITIES INC** p 775
501 N Broadway, Saint Louis MO 63102
Tel (314) 335-4000
SIC 8712 8711 8713 8741 1542 1541

MIDWEST GERIATRIC MANAGEMENT LLC p 967
477 N Lindbergh Blvd # 310, Saint Louis MO 63141
Tel (314) 631-3000 *SIC* 8741

ST JOHNS MERCY HEALTH CARE p 1367
645 Maryville Centre Dr # 100, Saint Louis MO 63141
Tel (314) 364-2400 *SIC* 8741

■ CENTRAL PLAINS CEMENT CO LLC p 279
15100 E Crtney Athrton Rd, Sugar Creek MO 64058
Tel (816) 257-4028 SIC 8741

DA DAVIDSON COMPANIES p 407
8 3rd St N, Great Falls MT 59401
Tel (406) 727-4200 SIC 6211 6733 8741

STERLING GROUP INC p 1387
3010 Santa Fe Ct, Missoula MT 59808
Tel (406) 251-5788 SIC 8741

WASHINGTON CORPS p 1577
101 International Dr, Missoula MT 59808
Tel (406) 523-1300
SIC 5082 7353 4213 8741

CHI NEBRASKA p 296
555 S 70th St, Lincoln NE 68510
Tel (402) 219-8000 SIC 8741

■ APPLIED UNDERWRITERS INC p 100
10805 Old Mill Rd, Omaha NE 68154
Tel (402) 342-4900
SIC 6331 8721 8741 8742

MOSAIC p 991
4980 S 118th St, Omaha NE 68137
Tel (402) 896-3884 SIC 8361 8741

OMAHA STEAKS INTERNATIONAL INC p 1083
11030 O St, Omaha NE 68137
Tel (402) 597-3000 SIC 5142 8741

REGIONAL WEST HEALTH SERVICES INC p 1219
4021 Avenue B, Scottsbluff NE 69361
Tel (308) 635-3711 SIC 8741

DIAMOND RESORTS CORP p 437
10600 W Charleston Blvd, Las Vegas NV 89135
Tel (702) 684-8000 SIC 7041 6141 8741

DIAMOND RESORTS HOLDINGS LLC p 437
10600 W Charleston Blvd, Las Vegas NV 89135
Tel (877) 787-0906 SIC 7011 6141 8741

■ EG&G SPECIAL PROJECTS INC p 481
811 Grier Dr Ste A, Las Vegas NV 89119
Tel (702) 492-7800 SIC 8741

HAKKASAN HOLDINGS LLC p 653
6385 S Rainbow Blvd # 800, Las Vegas NV 89118
Tel (702) 212-8804 SIC 8741

INTERNATIONAL MARKET CENTERS LP p 756
495 S Grand Central Pkwy, Las Vegas NV 89106
Tel (702) 599-9621 SIC 8741

NORTH AMERICAN KIOSK LLC p 1050
3930 Howard Hughes Pkwy # 500, Las Vegas NV 89169
Tel (702) 691-2948 SIC 8741

■ SIERRA HEALTH SERVICES INC p 1320
2720 N Tenaya Way, Las Vegas NV 89128
Tel (702) 242-7000
SIC 6324 6311 8082 8741 8093

STATION CASINOS INC p 1383
1505 S Pavilion Center Dr, Las Vegas NV 89135
Tel (702) 495-3000 SIC 8741 7993 7011

CAPITAL REGION HEALTH CARE CORP p 250
250 Pleasant St, Concord NH 03301
Tel (603) 225-2711
SIC 8741 8062 8051 8093 8082

CHUBB AMERICA SERVICE CORP p 304
1 Granite Pl, Concord NH 03301
Tel (603) 224-7741 SIC 8741

SHIPSTON GROUP US INC p 1317
363 Exeter Rd, Hampton NH 03842
Tel (603) 929-6811 SIC 8741

■ HEALTHSOURCE INC p 677
2 College Park Dr, Hooksett NH 03106
Tel (603) 268-7000 SIC 6324 8741 8011

LUMMUS OVERSEAS CORP p 885
1515 Broad St, Bloomfield NJ 07003
Tel (973) 893-1515 SIC 8711 1629 8741

COOPER HEALTH CARE p 366
1 Cooper Plz Ste 504, Camden NJ 08103
Tel (856) 342-2000 SIC 8741

OUR LADY OF LOURDES HEALTH CARE SERVICES INC p 1098
1600 Haddon Ave, Camden NJ 08103
Tel (856) 757-3500 SIC 8741

CAPE HEALTH SYSTEM INC p 248
2 Stone Harbor Blvd, Cape May Court House NJ 08210
Tel (609) 463-2000 SIC 8741

TOLL GLOBAL FORWARDING SCS (USA) INC p 1459
800 Federal Blvd Ste 2, Carteret NJ 07008
Tel (732) 750-9000 SIC 4731 8741

NFI INDUSTRIES INC p 1041
1515 Burnt Mill Rd, Cherry Hill NJ 08003
Tel (856) 691-7000
SIC 4213 4212 8741 4225 4214 4783

CLIFTON BOARD OF EDUCATION INC p 326
745 Clifton Ave, Clifton NJ 07013
Tel (973) 470-2300 SIC 8211 8741

ESSEX VALLEY HEALTHCARE INC p 510
300 Central Ave, East Orange NJ 07018
Tel (973) 672-8400 SIC 8741

DAICEL AMERICA HOLDINGS INC p 408
1 Parker Plz, Fort Lee NJ 07024
Tel (201) 461-4466 SIC 8741

INNOVACARE SERVICES CO LLC p 744
173 Bridge Plz N, Fort Lee NJ 07024
Tel (201) 969-2300
SIC 6324 8011 8741 8742

CENTRASTATE HEALTHCARE SYSTEM INC p 281
901 W Main St, Freehold NJ 07728
Tel (732) 431-2000 SIC 8099 8741

FRANCISCAN HEALTH SYSTEMS OF NEW JERSEY INC p 573
308 Willow Ave, Hoboken NJ 07030
Tel (201) 418-1000 SIC 8741

BAYSHORE COMMUNITY HEALTH SERVICES INC p 162
727 N Beers St, Holmdel NJ 07733
Tel (732) 739-5900 SIC 8062 8741

H & M INTERNATIONAL TRANSPORTATION INC p 649
485b Us Highway 1 S # 110, Iselin NJ 08830
Tel (732) 510-4640 SIC 4731 8741 4225

IJKG LLC p 731
714 Bergen Ave, Jersey City NJ 07306
Tel (201) 858-5000 SIC 8741

IJKG OPCO LLC p 731
714 Bergen Ave, Jersey City NJ 07306
Tel (201) 858-5000 SIC 8741

■ MERCK SHARP & DOHME CORP p 945
2000 Galloping Hill Rd, Kenilworth NJ 07033
Tel (908) 740-4000 SIC 2834 8741

■ CIT GROUP (NJ) LLC p 309
1 Cit Dr, Livingston NJ 07039
Tel (973) 740-5000 SIC 8741

■ SYSCO GUEST SUPPLY LLC p 1417
4301 Us Highway 1 Ste 300, Monmouth Junction NJ 08852
Tel (609) 514-9696
SIC 5122 2844 5131 5139 7011 8741

▲ PHH CORP p 1142
1 Mortgage Way, Mount Laurel NJ 08054
Tel (856) 917-1744 SIC 6531 8741

SENIOR BRANDYWINE CARE INC p 1303
525 Fellowship Rd Ste 360, Mount Laurel NJ 08054
Tel (856) 813-2000 SIC 8741 8322 8051

NORTH JERSEY HEALTH CARE CORP p 1052
175 High St, Newton NJ 07860
Tel (973) 383-2121 SIC 8741

NICE SYSTEMS INC p 1042
461 From Rd Ste 103, Paramus NJ 07652
Tel (201) 964-2600
SIC 7372 7382 1731 8741

■ DOLCE INTERNATIONAL HOLDINGS INC p 448
22 Sylvan Way, Parsippany NJ 07054
Tel (201) 307-8700 SIC 7011 8741

SKANSKA USA BUILDING INC p 1329
389 Interpace Pkwy Ste 5, Parsippany NJ 07054
Tel (973) 753-3500 SIC 1541 1542 8741

WYNDHAM INTERNATIONAL INC p 1630
22 Sylvan Way, Parsippany NJ 07054
Tel (973) 753-6000 SIC 7011 8741

▲ WYNDHAM WORLDWIDE CORP p 1630
22 Sylvan Way, Parsippany NJ 07054
Tel (973) 753-6000
SIC 7011 8741 7389 6531

ST MARY HEALTH CORP p 1370
211 Pennington Ave, Passaic NJ 07055
Tel (973) 470-3000 SIC 8741

FRANCIS E PARKER MEMORIAL HOME INC p 573
1421 River Rd, Piscataway NJ 08854
Tel (732) 545-8330 SIC 8741

NOVO-NORDISK OF NORTH AMERICA INC p 1063
800 Scudders Mill Rd, Plainsboro NJ 08536
Tel (609) 987-5800
SIC 8741 8733 5122 2833 2834

PRINCETON HEALTHCARE SYSTEM A NEW JERSEY NONPROFIT CORP p 1177
1 Plainsboro Rd, Plainsboro NJ 08536
Tel (609) 497-4000 SIC 8741

RANBAXY INC p 1207
600 College Rd E Ste 2100, Princeton NJ 08540
Tel (609) 720-9200 SIC 8741

VATAMERICA LP p 1545
344 Nassau St, Princeton NJ 08540
Tel (609) 430-4960 SIC 8741

RAY ANGELINI INC p 1209
105 Blckwood Barnsboro Rd, Sewell NJ 08080
Tel (856) 228-5566 SIC 1731 1711 8741

■ DUN & BRADSTREET INTERNATIONAL LTD p 461
103 Jfk Pkwy, Short Hills NJ 07078
Tel (973) 921-5500 SIC 7323 8741

OLAM HOLDINGS PARTNERSHIP p 1080
25 Union Pl Fl 2, Summit NJ 07901
Tel (908) 988-1960 SIC 8741

TOMS RIVER REGIONAL SCHOOLS p 1460
1144 Hooper Ave Ste 304, Toms River NJ 08753
Tel (732) 505-5500 SIC 8211 8741

CONGOLEUM CORP p 356
3500 Quakerbridge Rd, Trenton NJ 08619
Tel (609) 584-3000 SIC 3081 5713 8741

INSPIRA HEALTH NETWORK INC p 746
2950 College Dr Ste 2d, Vineland NJ 08360
Tel (856) 641-8680 SIC 8741 8062

SENIOR SPRINGPOINT LIVING INC p 1304
4814 Outlook Dr Ste 201, Wall Township NJ 07753
Tel (609) 987-8900 SIC 8059 8741

LEE HECHT HARRISON LLC p 851
50 Tice Blvd Ste 115, Woodcliff Lake NJ 07677
Tel (201) 930-9333 SIC 8742 8741

BBL LLC p 163
302 Washington Ave, Albany NY 12203
Tel (518) 452-8200
SIC 1542 1541 1521 1622 8741

NORTHEAST HEALTH p 1054
600 Northern Blvd, Albany NY 12204
Tel (518) 471-3229 SIC 8741

■ MERITAIN HEALTH INC p 949
300 Corporate Pkwy 100s, Amherst NY 14226
Tel (716) 319-5500 SIC 8741

NORTH BABYLON UNION FREE SCHOOL DISTRICT p 1051
5 Jardine Pl, Babylon NY 11703
Tel (631) 321-3209 SIC 8211 8741

UMH NY CORP p 1501
10 Acre Pl, Binghamton NY 13904
Tel (607) 775-6400 SIC 8059 8051 8741

LINROC COMMUNITY SERVICES CORP p 869
Linden Blvd At Brookdale, Brooklyn NY 11212
Tel (718) 240-5656 SIC 8741

BUFFALO ORLANDO I LLC p 224
570 Delaware Ave, Buffalo NY 14202
Tel (716) 886-0211 SIC 8741

CATHOLIC HEALTH SYSTEM INC p 266
144 Genesee St Fl 1, Buffalo NY 14203
Tel (716) 862-2400
SIC 8741 8062 5999 8051

FIRSTSOURCE SOLUTIONS USA INC p 551
205 Bryant Woods S, Buffalo NY 14228
Tel (716) 564-4400 SIC 8741

HAMISTER GROUP LLC p 655
10 Lafayette Sq Ste 1900, Buffalo NY 14203
Tel (716) 839-4000 SIC 7011 8052 8741

FF THOMPSON HEALTH SYSTEM INC p 539
350 Parrish St, Canandaigua NY 14424
Tel (585) 396-6000 SIC 8741 8069

BAST HATFIELD INC p 159
1399 Vischers Ferry Rd, Clifton Park NY 12065
Tel (518) 373-2000 SIC 1542 1541 8741

■ CENTRAL COCA-COLA BOTTLING CO INC p 277
555 Taxter Rd Ste 550, Elmsford NY 10523
Tel (914) 789-1100 SIC 5149 2086 8741

SAM ASH MUSIC CORP p 1273
278 Duffy Ave Unit A, Hicksville NY 11801
Tel (516) 932-6400
SIC 5736 5731 5734 5961 7359 8741

ONGWEOWEH CORP p 1088
767 Warren Rd, Ithaca NY 14850
Tel (607) 266-7070 SIC 8741 4953

MEDISYS HEALTH NETWORK INC p 938
8900 Van Wyck Expy, Jamaica NY 11418
Tel (718) 206-6000 SIC 8741

HEALTH QUEST SYSTEMS INC p 675
1351 Route 55 Ste 200, Lagrangeville NY 12540
Tel (845) 475-9500 SIC 8741

AP CARIB HOLDING LTD p 95
9 W 57th St Fl 43, New York NY 10019
Tel (212) 515-3202 SIC 8741 8748 7379

■ APOLLO MANAGEMENT HOLDINGS LP p 97
9 W 57th St Fl 43, New York NY 10019
Tel (212) 515-3200 SIC 8741

BLACKSTONE REAL ESTATE PARTNERS VI LP p 188
345 Park Ave, New York NY 10154
Tel (212) 583-5000 SIC 8741 6531

BROADSTONE GROUP INC p 215
156 W 56th St Ste 1604, New York NY 10019
Tel (212) 333-2100 SIC 6552 7011 8741

BROOKFIELD ASSET MANAGEMENT (US) INC p 217
Brookfield Pl 250 Vesey S, New York NY 10281
Tel (212) 417-7000 SIC 8741

BROOKFIELD ASSET MANAGEMENT INC p 217
3 World Financial Ctr, New York NY 10281
Tel (212) 417-7000 SIC 8741

CANON BUSINESS PROCESS SERVICES INC p 247
460 W 34th St Fl 6, New York NY 10001
Tel (212) 502-2100 SIC 8741

CHARTERHOUSE GROUP INC p 291
535 Madison Ave Fl 28, New York NY 10022
Tel (212) 584-3200 SIC 8741 6799 6282

■ CONTINENTAL CORP p 363
111 8th Ave, New York NY 10011
Tel (212) 440-3000
SIC 6331 6351 6321 6159 8741 6411

DHG MANAGEMENT CO LLC p 435
551 5th Ave Fl 10, New York NY 10176
Tel (212) 465-3700 SIC 8741

ENSEMBLE PARENT LLC p 500
345 Park Ave, New York NY 10154
Tel (212) 583-5000 SIC 7363 8741

FAIRFIELD-MAXWELL LTD p 525
60 E 42nd St Fl 55, New York NY 10165
Tel (212) 297-9030
SIC 8741 4731 5172 4412

FIAT USA INC p 539
375 Park Ave Ste 2703, New York NY 10152
Tel (212) 355-2600
SIC 3714 8741 3535 5012 5013 5082

FOJP SERVICE CORP p 563
28 E 28th St Fl 14, New York NY 10016
Tel (212) 891-0700 SIC 8741

GENPACT LIMITED p 604
1155 Avenue Of The Americ, New York NY 10036
Tel (212) 896-6600 SIC 8741 7372

GILBERT GLOBAL EQUITY CAPITAL LLC p 612
767 5th Ave Fl 15, New York NY 10153
Tel (212) 584-6200 SIC 8741

■ HEALTH PLUS PREPAID HEALTH SERVICES PLAN INC p 675
9 Pine St Fl 14, New York NY 10005
Tel (718) 532-1011 SIC 6321 6324 8741

HF MANAGEMENT SERVICES LLC p 688
100 Church St Fl 18, New York NY 10007
Tel (212) 801-6000 SIC 8741

HOCHTIEF USA INC p 699
375 Hudson St Fl 6, New York NY 10014
Tel (212) 229-6000
SIC 1542 1541 1522 8741 8742 6799

■ IHP I OWNER JV LLC p 731
399 Park Ave, New York NY 10022
Tel (212) 547-2640 SIC 8741

LEGENDS HOSPITALITY MANAGEMENT LIMITED LIABILITY CO p 853
61 Broadway Ste 2400, New York NY 10006
Tel (646) 977-8521 SIC 8741 8744 8742

LENDLEASE (US) CONSTRUCTION INC p 855
200 Park Ave Fl 9, New York NY 10166
Tel (212) 592-6700
SIC 1541 1542 1522 8741 8742

LENDLEASE (US) CONSTRUCTION LMB INC p 855
200 Park Ave Fl 9, New York NY 10166
Tel (212) 592-6700
SIC 1522 1541 1542 8741 8742

M & F WORLDWIDE CORP p 888
35 E 62nd St, New York NY 10065
Tel (212) 572-8600 SIC 5149 8741 2782

M/L BOVIS HOLDINGS LTD p 890
200 Park Ave Fl 9, New York NY 10166
Tel (212) 592-6700
SIC 1522 1541 1542 8741 8742

MANAGEMENT-ILA MANAGED HEALTH CARE TRUST FUND p 900
111 Broadway Fl 5, New York NY 10006
Tel (212) 766-5700 SIC 8741

MSIG HOLDINGS (AMERICAS) INC p 997
560 Lexington Ave Fl 20, New York NY 10022
Tel (212) 446-3600 SIC 8741 6331

NEXTSOURCE INC p 1041
1040 Avenue Of The Americ, New York NY 10018
Tel (212) 736-5870 SIC 7363 8741

▲ NORTHSTAR ASSET MANAGEMENT GROUP INC p 1058
399 Park Ave Fl 18, New York NY 10022
Tel (212) 547-2600 SIC 8741 6531 6282

PARSONS BRINCKERHOFF GROUP LLC p 1117
1 Penn Plz 2nd, New York NY 10119
Tel (212) 465-5000 SIC 8742 8711 8741

PATRIARCH PARTNERS LLC p 1120
1 Broadway Fl 5, New York NY 10004
Tel (212) 825-0550 SIC 8741

PINEBRIDGE INVESTMENTS LLC p 1149
399 Park Ave Fl 4, New York NY 10022
Tel (646) 857-8000 SIC 8741

PLAZA CONSTRUCTION LLC p 1155
1065 Avenue Of The Americ, New York NY 10018
Tel (212) 849-4800 SIC 1542 8741

PRADA USA CORP p 1167
609 W 51st St, New York NY 10019
Tel (212) 307-9300
SIC 5136 5137 5139 5661 5632 8741

ROOSEVELT MANAGEMENT CO LLC p 1249
1540 Broadway Ste 1500, New York NY 10036
Tel (212) 704-4106 SIC 8741

ROTHSCHILD NORTH AMERICA INC p 1252
1251 Ave Of The Ave Fl 51, New York NY 10020
Tel (212) 403-3500
SIC 6211 6159 8742 6221 6282 8741

RUDER FINN GROUP INC p 1257
301 E 57th St, New York NY 10022
Tel (212) 593-5838 SIC 8743 6799 8741

SKANSKA INC p 1329
350 5th Ave Fl 32, New York NY 10118
Tel (917) 438-4500 SIC 8741 1542

SKANSKA USA INC p 1329
350 5th Ave Fl 32, New York NY 10118
Tel (917) 438-4500 SIC 8741 1542

STRUCTURE TONE INC p 1394
330 W 34th St Fl 11, New York NY 10001
Tel (212) 481-6100 SIC 8741

STV INC p 1395
225 Park Ave S Fl 5, New York NY 10003
Tel (212) 529-2722 SIC 8711 8712 8741

SUCCESS ACADEMY CHARTER SCHOOLS INC p 1396
95 Pine St Fl 6, New York NY 10005
Tel (646) 597-4641 SIC 8741

■ TISHMAN CONSTRUCTION CORP p 1455
100 Park Ave Fl 5, New York NY 10017
Tel (212) 708-6800 SIC 8741 1611

■ TISHMAN REALTY & CONSTRUCTION CO INC p 1456
100 Park Ave Fl 5, New York NY 10017
Tel (212) 708-6800 SIC 8741 6552

TURNER CONSTRUCTION CO INC p 1492
375 Hudson St Fl 6, New York NY 10014
Tel (212) 229-6000
SIC 1542 1541 1522 8741 8742

TURNER INTERNATIONAL INDUSTRIES INC p 1493
375 Hudson St Fl 6, New York NY 10014
Tel (212) 229-6000 SIC 8741 8712 1542

VILLAGE CARE OF NEW YORK INC p 1557
120 Broadway Ste 2840, New York NY 10271
Tel (212) 337-5816 SIC 8741 8322

WILLIAMS LEA INC p 1611
381 Park Ave S Fl 5, New York NY 10016
Tel (212) 351-9000 SIC 8741

WIND HOTELS HOLDINGS INC p 1615
345 Park Ave, New York NY 10154
Tel (212) 583-5000 SIC 7011 8741

COINMACH CORP p 335
303 Sunnyside Blvd # 70, Plainview NY 11803
Tel (516) 349-8555
SIC 7215 7359 5087 5064 7211 8741

COMMUNITY PROVIDERS INC p 350
75 Beekman St, Plattsburgh NY 12901
Tel (518) 561-2000 SIC 8062 8741 6512

ST CHARLES CORP p 1365
200 Belle Terre Rd, Port Jefferson NY 11777
Tel (631) 474-6260 SIC 8741

HASTINGS HEALTH SYSTEMS INC p 667
241 North Rd, Poughkeepsie NY 12601
Tel (845) 471-2000 SIC 8741 8062

EJ DEL MONTE CORP p 482
909 Linden Ave Ste 1, Rochester NY 14625
Tel (585) 586-3121
SIC 6552 8741 6512 6799 7011

HUDSON HOTELS CORP p 716
400 Linden Oaks Ste 120, Rochester NY 14625
Tel (585) 419-4000 SIC 7011 8741

RESOURCES MANAGEMENT INC p 1227
1931 Buffalo Rd, Rochester NY 14624
Tel (585) 426-8000 SIC 8741

ROCHESTER GENERAL HEALTH SYSTEM p 1243
1425 Portland Ave, Rochester NY 14621
Tel (585) 922-4000 SIC 8741 8093 8059

CHS SERVICES INC p 304
992 N Village Ave, Rockville Centre NY 11570
Tel (516) 705-1935 SIC 8741

FRAMACO INTERNATIONAL INC p 573
800 Westchester Ave S430, Rye Brook NY 10573
Tel (914) 633-6600 SIC 8741

NEW COUNTRY MOTOR CAR GROUP INC p 1029
358 Broadway Ste 403, Saratoga Springs NY 12866
Tel (518) 583-4896 SIC 8741 5511

SARATOGA CARE INC p 1282
211 Church St Ste 1, Saratoga Springs NY 12866
Tel (518) 587-3222 SIC 8062 8741

CLINICAL PRACTICE MANAGEMENT PLAN p 326
Suny At Stony Brk Hsc, Stony Brook NY 11790
Tel (631) 444-2055 SIC 8741

OBRIEN & GERE LIMITED p 1072
333 W Washington St # 400, Syracuse NY 13202
Tel (315) 437-6100 SIC 8711 8741

TDK USA CORP p 1429
455 Rxr Plz, Uniondale NY 11556
Tel (516) 535-2600 SIC 3679 8741

NATIONAL HEALTH CARE ASSOCIATES INC p 1013
20 E Sunrise Hwy Unit 1, Valley Stream NY 11581
Tel (516) 705-4800 SIC 8741

CAREER SYSTEMS DEVELOPMENT CORP p 254
75 Thruway Park Dr # 100, West Henrietta NY 14586
Tel (585) 334-8080 SIC 8741 8331

■ **SHERATON CORP** p 1315
1111 Westchester Ave, White Plains NY 10604
Tel (800) 328-6242 SIC 7011 8741 6794

STANLY HEALTH SERVICES INC p 1377
301 Yadkin St, Albemarle NC 28001
Tel (704) 982-3888 SIC 8741

RHA HEALTH SERVICES INC p 1231
17 Church St, Asheville NC 28801
Tel (828) 232-6844 SIC 8741

BELK FINANCE CO INC p 169
2801 W Tyvola Rd, Charlotte NC 28217
Tel (704) 357-1000 SIC 8741

■ **ESA MANAGEMENT LLC** p 509
11525 N Community House R, Charlotte NC 28277
Tel (980) 345-1600 SIC 8741

PREMIER HEALTHCARE ALLIANCE LP p 1170
13034 Balntyn Corp Pl, Charlotte NC 28277
Tel (704) 357-0022 SIC 8741

■ **PREMIER HEALTHCARE SOLUTIONS INC** p 1170
13034 Balntyn Corp Pl, Charlotte NC 28277
Tel (704) 357-0022 SIC 8741

WINN-DIXIE CHARLOTTE INC p 1616
2401 Nevada Blvd, Charlotte NC 28273
Tel (704) 587-4000
SIC 5411 8741 5141 4226 4222

BKRY PHYSICIAN GROUP INC p 186
1000 Park Forty Plz # 500, Durham NC 27713
Tel (919) 383-0355 SIC 8741 8742

STERLING GROUP PHYSICIAN SERVICES LLC p 1387
1000 Park Forty Plz # 500, Durham NC 27713
Tel (919) 383-0355 SIC 8741 8742

CAROLINA HEALTHCARE CENTER OF CUMBERLAND LP p 259
4600 Cumberland Rd, Fayetteville NC 28306
Tel (910) 429-1690 SIC 8741 8051

CAROMONT HEALTH INC p 259
2525 Court Dr, Gastonia NC 28054
Tel (704) 834-2000 SIC 8741 8093

WAYNE HEALTH CORP p 1584
2700 Wayne Memorial Dr, Goldsboro NC 27534
Tel (919) 736-1110 SIC 8741

KAYSER-ROTH CORP p 805
102 Corporate Center Blvd, Greensboro NC 27408
Tel (336) 852-2030
SIC 2252 2251 5961 8741 3842

WORTH BON INC p 1626
40 Francis Rd, Hendersonville NC 28792
Tel (828) 697-2216
SIC 2331 5621 2339 2335 2337 8741

CORNERSTONE HEALTH CARE PA p 371
1701 Westchester Dr # 850, High Point NC 27262
Tel (336) 802-2700 SIC 8741 8099

■ **XPO LOGISTICS WORLDWIDE GOVERNMENT SERVICES LLC** p 1633
4035 Piedmont Pkwy, High Point NC 27265
Tel (844) 742-5976
SIC 4731 4225 4213 8741

AFFORDABLE CARE INC p 32
1400 Industrial Dr, Kinston NC 28504
Tel (252) 527-6121 SIC 8741

PIKE ENTERPRISES LLC p 1148
100 Pike Way, Mount Airy NC 27030
Tel (336) 789-2171 SIC 8741

■ **GENWORTH MORTGAGE INSURANCE CORP** p 605
8325 Six Forks Rd, Raleigh NC 27615
Tel (919) 846-4100 SIC 6351 8741

INVESTORS MANAGEMENT CORP p 761
801 N West St, Raleigh NC 27603
Tel (919) 653-7499 SIC 5812 8741

NASH HEALTH CARE SYSTEMS p 1008
2460 Curtis Ellis Dr, Rocky Mount NC 27804
Tel (252) 962-8000 SIC 8011 8741

■ **SEALY INC** p 1296
1 Office Parkway Rd, Trinity NC 27370
Tel (336) 861-3500 SIC 8741

WESTCON INC p 1597
7401 Yukon Dr, Bismarck ND 58503
Tel (701) 222-0076 SIC 1541 3498 8741

SANFORD CLINIC NORTH p 1279
801 Broadway N, Fargo ND 58102
Tel (701) 234-2000 SIC 8741 8721

AKRON GENERAL HEALTH SYSTEM p 42
1 Akron General Ave, Akron OH 44307
Tel (330) 344-6000 SIC 8741

■ **BABCOCK & WILCOX CO** p 143
20 S Van Buren Ave, Barberton OH 44203
Tel (330) 753-4511
SIC 1629 1711 3443 7699 8741 3822

REQ/JQH HOLDINGS INC p 1226
4243 Hunt Rd Ste 2, Blue Ash OH 45242
Tel (513) 891-1066 SIC 8741 6552

TRUSTAFF MANAGEMENT INC p 1487
4675 Cornell Rd, Blue Ash OH 45241
Tel (513) 272-3999 SIC 8741

VIUS SERVICES CORP p 1563
9395 Kenwood Rd Ste 200, Blue Ash OH 45242
Tel (513) 731-3590 SIC 7349 8741 3714

FISHER FOODS MARKETING INC p 552
4855 Frank Ave Nw, Canton OH 44720
Tel (330) 433-1180 SIC 5411 8741

HOSPITALISTS MANAGEMENT GROUP LLC p 710
4535 Dressler Rd Nw, Canton OH 44718
Tel (866) 464-7497 SIC 8741

DE FOXX & ASSOCIATES INC p 419
324 W 9th St Fl 5, Cincinnati OH 45202
Tel (513) 621-5522 SIC 8742 8741

FIRST SERVICES INC p 549
600 Vine St Ste 1200, Cincinnati OH 45202
Tel (513) 241-2200 SIC 8741 7539

FIRST TRANSIT INC p 550
600 Vine St Ste 1400, Cincinnati OH 45202
Tel (513) 241-2200 SIC 8741 7539 8742

HOBSONS INC p 699
50 E Business Way Ste 300, Cincinnati OH 45241
Tel (513) 891-5444 SIC 8741

■ **MEDPACE ACQUISITION INC** p 938
5375 Medpace Way, Cincinnati OH 45227
Tel (513) 579-9911 SIC 8741

■ **MEDPACE INTERMEDIATECO INC** p 938
5375 Medpace Way, Cincinnati OH 45227
Tel (513) 579-9911 SIC 8741

MERCY FRANCISCAN HOSPITAL MT AIRY p 946
2446 Kipling Ave, Cincinnati OH 45239
Tel (513) 853-5101 SIC 8741 8062

■ **MILACRON INTERMEDIATE HOLDINGS INC** p 968
3010 Disney St, Cincinnati OH 45209
Tel (513) 536-2000 SIC 5962 8741

■ **NEIGHBORCARE HOLDINGS INC** p 1024
201 E 4th St Ste 900, Cincinnati OH 45202
Tel (513) 719-2600 SIC 8741

■ **OMNICARE INC** p 1085
900 Omnicare Ctr, Cincinnati OH 45202
Tel (513) 719-2600
SIC 5122 5047 8082 8741

■ **OMNICARE MANAGEMENT CO** p 1085
201 E 4th St Ste 900, Cincinnati OH 45202
Tel (513) 719-1535 SIC 8741

STERLING MEDICAL CORP p 1387
411 Oak St, Cincinnati OH 45219
Tel (513) 984-1800 SIC 8741

TRIHEALTH INC p 1480
619 Oak St, Cincinnati OH 45206
Tel (513) 569-6111 SIC 8741

UC HEALTH LLC p 1498
3200 Burnet Ave, Cincinnati OH 45229
Tel (513) 585-6000 SIC 8741

CLEVELAND CLINIC FOUNDATION p 325
9500 Euclid Ave, Cleveland OH 44195
Tel (216) 636-8335 SIC 8062 8011 8741

CLEVELAND CLINIC HEALTH SYSTEM-WESTERN REGION p 325
18101 Lorain Ave, Cleveland OH 44111
Tel (216) 476-7000 SIC 8741

DMD MANAGEMENT INC p 446
12380 Plaza Dr, Cleveland OH 44130
Tel (216) 898-8399 SIC 8741

SAFEGUARD PROPERTIES LLC p 1266
7887 Safeguard Cir, Cleveland OH 44125
Tel (216) 739-2900 SIC 8741 7382 7381

CAMERON MITCHELL RESTAURANTS LLC p 245
515 Park St, Columbus OH 43215
Tel (614) 621-3663 SIC 8741 5812

CRANE GROUP CO p 389
330 W Spring St Ste 200, Columbus OH 43215
Tel (614) 754-3000 SIC 8741

DAMONS INTERNATIONAL INC p 410
4645 Executive Dr, Columbus OH 43220
Tel (614) 442-7900 SIC 6794 8741 5812

ELFORD INC p 486
1220 Dublin Rd, Columbus OH 43215
Tel (614) 488-4000 SIC 1542 1541 8741

JMAC INC p 786
200 W Nationwide Blvd # 1, Columbus OH 43215
Tel (614) 436-2418
SIC 3325 5198 7999 5511 8741

NIAGARA HEALTH CORP p 1042
6150 E Broad St, Columbus OH 43213
Tel (614) 898-4000 SIC 8741 8062

OHIO STATE UNIVERSITY WEXNER MEDICAL CENTER p 1078
1492 E Broad St, Columbus OH 43205
Tel (614) 293-8000 SIC 8741

CORBUS LLC p 368
1129 Miamisbrg Cntrvle Rd Ste, Dayton OH 45449
Tel (937) 226-7724 SIC 8741 7373

KETTERING ADVENTIST HEALTHCARE p 814
3535 Southern Blvd, Dayton OH 45429
Tel (937) 298-4331 SIC 8741

MED AMERICA HEALTH SYSTEMS CORP p 934
1 Wyoming St, Dayton OH 45409
Tel (937) 223-6192 SIC 8062 8741 8082

SHOOK CONSTRUCTION CO p 1318
4977 Northcutt Pl, Dayton OH 45414
Tel (937) 276-6666 SIC 1629 1542 8741

SHOOK NATIONAL CORP p 1318
4977 Northcutt Pl, Dayton OH 45414
Tel (937) 276-6666
SIC 8741 1542 1629 1541

SOIN INTERNATIONAL LLC p 1337
1129 Miamsbg Ctrvl Rd 1 Ste, Dayton OH 45449
Tel (937) 427-7646 SIC 8741

AMERICAN HEALTH FOUNDATION INC p 73
5920 Venture Dr Ste 100, Dublin OH 43017
Tel (614) 798-5110 SIC 8741

▲ **CARDINAL HEALTH INC** p 253
7000 Cardinal Pl, Dublin OH 43017
Tel (614) 757-5000
SIC 5122 5047 8741 3842

COMPREHENSIVE HEALTH CARE OF OHIO INC p 352
630 E River St, Elyria OH 44035
Tel (440) 329-7500 SIC 8741

RESERVE GROUP MANAGEMENT CO p 1226
3560 W Market St Ste 300, Fairlawn OH 44333
Tel (330) 665-6706 SIC 8741

BLANCHARD VALLEY HEALTH SYSTEM p 188
1900 S Main St, Findlay OH 45840
Tel (419) 423-4500 SIC 8741 7349

CARINGTON HEALTH SYSTEMS p 256
8200 Beckett Park Dr, Hamilton OH 45011
Tel (513) 682-2700 SIC 8741 8051

FORT HAMILTON-HUGHES HEALTHCARE CORP p 568
630 Eaton Ave, Hamilton OH 45013
Tel (513) 867-2000 SIC 8741

MIDWEST TAPE LLC p 968
1417 Timber Wolf Dr, Holland OH 43528
Tel (419) 868-9370
SIC 7822 5099 8741 7389 5961 7374

■ **FEDEX SUPPLY CHAIN SERVICES INC** p 537
5455 Darrow Rd, Hudson OH 44236
Tel (800) 588-3020
SIC 8742 4213 8741 4731

SYLVANIA FRANCISCAN HEALTH p 1414
1715 Indian Wood Cir # 200, Maumee OH 43537
Tel (419) 882-8373 SIC 8062 8741

LICKING MEMORIAL HEALTH SYSTEMS p 863
1320 W Main St, Newark OH 43055
Tel (740) 348-4000 SIC 8741 6411

JTD HEALTH SYSTEMS INC p 796
200 Saint Clair Ave, Saint Marys OH 45885
Tel (419) 394-3335 SIC 8741

UNIVERSITY HOSPITALS HEALTH SYSTEM INC p 1519
3605 Warrensville Ctr Rd, Shaker Heights OH 44122
Tel (216) 767-8900 SIC 8062 8011 8741

TRINITY HOSPITAL HOLDING CO p 1481
380 Summit Ave, Steubenville OH 43952
Tel (740) 264-8000 SIC 8062 8741

KINGSTON HEALTHCARE CO p 821
1 Seagate Ste 1960, Toledo OH 43604
Tel (419) 247-2880 SIC 8059 8741

LOTT INDUSTRIES INC p 879
3350 Hill Ave, Toledo OH 43607
Tel (419) 534-4980 SIC 8331 8741

PROMEDICA HEALTH SYSTEMS INC p 1183
1801 Richards Rd, Toledo OH 43607
Tel (419) 469-3800
SIC 8062 6324 8351 8741

FORUM HEALTH p 570
1350 E Market St 302, Warren OH 44483
Tel (330) 841-9011 SIC 8741 8011

CORNA KOKOSING CONSTRUCTION CO p 370
6235 Westerville Rd, Westerville OH 43081
Tel (614) 901-8844 SIC 1541 1542 8741

LAUREL HEALTH CARE CO p 847
8181 Worthington Rd Uppr, Westerville OH 43082
Tel (614) 794-8800 SIC 8741

LAUREL HEALTH CARE CO OF NORTH WORTHINGTON p 847
8181 Worthington Rd, Westerville OH 43082
Tel (614) 794-8800 SIC 8059 8741

KLINGBEIL CAPITAL MANAGEMENT LLC p 823
500 W Wilson Bridge Rd, Worthington OH 43085
Tel (614) 396-4919 SIC 6799 8741

CONSTELLATIONS ENTERPRISE LLC p 361
1775 Logan Ave, Youngstown OH 44505
Tel (330) 740-8208 SIC 8741

AMITY CARE LLC p 85
4350 Will Rogers Pkwy, Oklahoma City OK 73108
Tel (405) 943-1144 SIC 8741

SOUTH OKLAHOMA CITY HOSPITAL CORP p 1344
4401 S Western Ave, Oklahoma City OK 73109
Tel (405) 636-7000 SIC 8741

ALBANY GENERAL HOSPITAL p 45
1046 6th Ave Sw, Albany OR 97321
Tel (541) 812-4000 SIC 8062 8741

SAMARITAN HEALTH SERVICES INC p 1274
3600 Nw Samaritan Dr, Corvallis OR 97330
Tel (541) 757-5111 SIC 8741 8062

PACIFIC RETIREMENT SERVICES INC p 1105
1 W Main St Ste 303, Medford OR 97501
Tel (541) 857-7777 SIC 8741 8051

CH2M HILL INDUSTRIAL DESIGN & CONSTRUCTION INC p 286
2020 Sw 4th Ave Fl 3, Portland OR 97201
Tel (503) 224-6040
SIC 8711 8712 8741 7699

DAVID EVANS AND ASSOCIATES INC p 415
2100 Sw River Pkwy, Portland OR 97201
Tel (503) 223-6663 SIC 8711 8713 8741

FRONTIER MANAGEMENT LLC p 581
7420 Sw Bridgeprt Rd 10 Ste 105, Portland OR 97224
Tel (503) 443-1818 SIC 8741

HOFFMAN CORP p 699
805 Sw Broadway Ste 2100, Portland OR 97205
Tel (503) 221-8811
SIC 8741 1541 1542 1623 1629

IDC CONSTRUCTION MANAGEMENT INC p 728
2020 Sw 4th Ave Ste 300, Portland OR 97201
Tel (503) 224-6040 SIC 8741

MARQUIS COMPANIES I INC p 910
725 Se 202nd Ave, Portland OR 97233
Tel (503) 665-3118 SIC 8741

SHILO MANAGEMENT CORP p 1316
11600 Sw Shilo Ln, Portland OR 97225
Tel (503) 641-6565 SIC 8741

YOSHIDAS INC p 1637
8440 Ne Alderwood Rd A, Portland OR 97220
Tel (503) 731-3702 SIC 5149 8741

AVAMERE HEALTH SERVICES LLC p 136
25115 Sw Parkway Ave A, Wilsonville OR 97070
Tel (503) 570-3405
SIC 8741 8051 8052 8093

BUTZ ENTERPRISES INC p 230
840 Hamilton St, Allentown PA 18101
Tel (610) 395-6871 SIC 8741

HOSPITAL CENTRAL SERVICES INC p 709
2171 28th St Sw, Allentown PA 18103
Tel (610) 791-2222 SIC 8741

LEHIGH VALLEY HEALTH SERVICES INC p 854
2166 S 12th St, Allentown PA 18103
Tel (610) 791-3682 SIC 4813 8741 8721

SACRED HEART HEALTH CARE SYSTEM INC p 1265
421 Chew St, Allentown PA 18102
Tel (610) 776-4900 SIC 8741 5912

LEXINGTON HOLDINGS INC p 859
620 Howard Ave, Altoona PA 16601
Tel (814) 946-2204 SIC 8741

L F DRISCOLL CO LLC p 834
401 E City Ave Ste 500, Bala Cynwyd PA 19004
Tel (610) 668-0950 SIC 8741

HERITAGE VALLEY HEALTH SYSTEM INC p 686
2580 Constitution Blvd, Beaver Falls PA 15010
Tel (724) 728-7000 SIC 8741 8062

■ **CHARMING SHOPPES OF DELAWARE INC** p 290
3750 State Rd, Bensalem PA 19020
Tel (215) 245-9100 SIC 5621 8741

ST LUKES HOSPITAL & HEALTH NETWORK INC p 1370
801 Ostrum St, Bethlehem PA 18015
Tel (484) 526-4000 SIC 8741

ST LUKES PHYSICIAN GROUP INC p 1370
801 Ostrum St Ste 1, Bethlehem PA 18015
Tel (610) 954-4990 SIC 8741

UNITEK USA LLC p 1515
1777 Sentry Pkwy W # 302, Blue Bell PA 19422
Tel (267) 464-1700 SIC 8742 8741

■ **AQUA PENNSYLVANIA INC** p 101
762 W Lancaster Ave, Bryn Mawr PA 19010
Tel (610) 525-1400
SIC 4941 8741 4971 1623

KVAERNER NORTH AMERICAN CONSTRUCTION INC p 832
701 Technology Dr, Canonsburg PA 15317
Tel (724) 416-6900 SIC 1542 8741

KYNETIC LLC p 833
225 Washington St, Conshohocken PA 19428
Tel (484) 534-8100 SIC 8741 5961

■ **EXCO RESOURCES (PA) LLC** p 517
260 Executive Dr Ste 100, Cranberry Township PA 16066
Tel (724) 720-2500
SIC 1382 1381 1311 8741 6211

GEISINGER HEALTH SYSTEM FOUNDATION p 597
100 N Academy Ave, Danville PA 17822
Tel (570) 271-6461 SIC 8741 6512 7699

GEISINGER SYSTEM SERVICES p 597
100 N Academy Ave, Danville PA 17822
Tel (570) 271-6211 SIC 8741 8082

LOBAR INC p 872
1 Old Mill Rd, Dillsburg PA 17019
Tel (717) 432-9728
SIC 1541 1542 8741 1629 1731 7371

STV CONSTRUCTION INC p 1395
205 W Welsh Dr, Douglassville PA 19518
Tel (610) 385-8200 SIC 8741

MARTIN LIMESTONE INC p 912
3580 Division Hwy, East Earl PA 17519
Tel (717) 335-4500
SIC 3273 3271 1611 1422 8741 5211

AMERICAS BUSINESS SOLUTION LLC p 81
1070 Coolbaugh Rd, East Stroudsburg PA 18302
Tel (718) 308-1331 SIC 8741 8742

▲ **ERIE INSURANCE GROUP EMPLOYEES** p 508
100 Erie Insurance Pl, Erie PA 16530
Tel (814) 870-2000 SIC 6411 8741

HAMOT HEALTH FOUNDATION p 656
201 State St, Erie PA 16550
Tel (814) 877-7020 SIC 8741 8062 6514

SAINT VINCENT HEALTH SYSTEM p 1271
232 W 25th St, Erie PA 16544
Tel (814) 452-5000 SIC 8741 8011

SCOTT ENTERPRISES INC p 1293
1000 S Main St, Greensburg PA 15601
Tel (814) 868-9500 SIC 8741

ALLEGHENY ELECTRIC COOP INC p 52
212 Locust St Ste 500, Harrisburg PA 17101
Tel (717) 233-5704 SIC 4911 8741

CLARK RESOURCES INC p 322
321 N Front St, Harrisburg PA 17101
Tel (717) 230-8861 SIC 8741

PINNACLE HEALTH SYSTEM p 1150
409 S 2nd St Ste 2b, Harrisburg PA 17104
Tel (717) 231-8010 SIC 8741 8062

QUANDEL CONSTRUCTION GROUP INC p 1198
3003 N Front St Ste 203, Harrisburg PA 17110
Tel (717) 657-0909
SIC 1542 1541 1629 8741

QUANDEL ENTERPRISES INC p 1198
3003 N Front St Ste 203, Harrisburg PA 17110
Tel (717) 657-0909 SIC 1542 1629 8741

VALENTI MID-ATLANTIC MANAGEMENT LLC p 1539
1 Rutherford Rd Ste 100, Harrisburg PA 17109
Tel (717) 652-7822 SIC 8741

BENJAMIN FOODS LLC p 173
1001 S York Rd, Hatboro PA 19040
Tel (215) 437-5000 SIC 5141 8741

COUNTRY MEADOWS ASSOCIATES p 375
830 Cherry Dr, Hershey PA 17033
Tel (717) 533-2474 SIC 8051 8059 8741

EATN PARK HOSPITALITY GROUP INC p 473
285 E Waterfront Dr # 200, Homestead PA 15120
Tel (412) 461-2000 SIC 8741

APAC CUSTOMER SERVICES INC p 95
507 Prudential Rd, Horsham PA 19044
Tel (215) 441-3000 SIC 8741

INDIANA HEALTHCARE CORP p 738
835 Hospital Rd, Indiana PA 15701
Tel (724) 357-7000 SIC 8741

INDIANA HOSPITAL p 738
823 Hospital Rd, Indiana PA 15701
Tel (724) 357-7125 SIC 8741

■ CONEMAUGH HEALTH INITIATIVES INC p 355
1020 Franklin St, Johnstown PA 15905
Tel (814) 534-9000 SIC 8741 8721

■ CONEMAUGH HEALTH SYSTEM INC p 355
1086 Franklin St, Johnstown PA 15905
Tel (814) 534-9000 SIC 8062 8741

QUALTEK USA LLC p 1198
1150 1st Ave Ste 600, King Of Prussia PA 19406
Tel (484) 804-4540 SIC 8741

UNITEK GLOBAL SERVICES INC p 1515
2010 Renaissance Blvd, King Of Prussia PA 19406
Tel (267) 464-1700
SIC 1731 8741 8742 8711

▲ UNIVERSAL HEALTH SERVICES INC p 1517
367 S Gulph Rd, King Of Prussia PA 19406
Tel (610) 768-3300
SIC 8062 8063 8093 8011 8741

WOHLSEN CONSTRUCTION CO INC p 1620
548 Steel Way, Lancaster PA 17601
Tel (717) 299-2500 SIC 1542 1541 8741

GOOD SAMARITAN HEALTH SERVICES FOUNDATION p 623
259 S 4th St Fl 2, Lebanon PA 17042
Tel (717) 270-7864 SIC 8741 7389 8721

BALFOUR BEATTY INVESTMENTS INC p 148
1 Country View Rd Ste 100, Malvern PA 19355
Tel (610) 355-8100
SIC 6531 8748 1731 8999 8741

ELLUCIAN CO LP p 489
4 Country View Rd, Malvern PA 19355
Tel (610) 647-5930 SIC 7373 8741

NORWOOD CO p 1061
375 Technology Dr, Malvern PA 19355
Tel (610) 240-4400 SIC 1541 1542 8741

■ SUSQUEHANNA COMMERCIAL FINANCE INC p 1409
2 Country View Rd Ste 300, Malvern PA 19355
Tel (610) 705-4999 SIC 8741

MEADVILLE MEDICAL CENTER p 934
751 Liberty St, Meadville PA 16335
Tel (814) 333-5000 SIC 8741 8062 8011

BALANCED CARE CORP p 147
5000 Ritter Rd Ste 202, Mechanicsburg PA 17055
Tel (412) 487-6925 SIC 8741

EDM AMERICAS INC p 478
10 Ed Preate Dr, Moosic PA 18507
Tel (800) 852-9809
SIC 4226 7389 7334 8741

MAIN LINE HEALTH INC p 897
3803 West Chester Pike # 250, Newtown Square PA 19073
Tel (484) 565-1644 SIC 8741

PRESBYTERIAN SENIORCARE p 1171
1215 Hulton Rd, Oakmont PA 15139
Tel (412) 828-5600
SIC 8051 8052 6513 8741

CHILDRENS HOSPITAL OF PHILADELPHIA FOUNDATION p 300
3401 Civic Center Blvd, Philadelphia PA 19104
Tel (215) 590-1000 SIC 8741 8399

CLONDALKIN HOLDINGS INC p 327
Crtis Centre Ste, Philadelphia PA 19106
Tel (215) 440-0570
SIC 2673 2621 2752 8741

DAY & ZIMMERMANN GROUP INC p 417
1500 Spring Garden St # 900, Philadelphia PA 19130
Tel (215) 299-8000
SIC 8711 8712 8741 7381 7382 3489

DAY & ZIMMERMANN INTERNATIONAL INC p 417
1500 Spring Garden St # 900, Philadelphia PA 19130
Tel (215) 299-8000 SIC 8711 1541 8741

EINSTEIN PRACTICE PLAN INC p 482
5501 Old York Rd Ste 2, Philadelphia PA 19141
Tel (215) 456-6070 SIC 8741

GEODIS USA INC p 605
5101 S Broad St, Philadelphia PA 19112
Tel (215) 238-8600 SIC 4731 8741

▲ HILL INTERNATIONAL INC p 693
2005 Market St Fl 17, Philadelphia PA 19103
Tel (215) 309-7700 SIC 8742 8741

INTECH CONSTRUCTION LLC p 748
3020 Market St Fl 2, Philadelphia PA 19104
Tel (215) 243-2000 SIC 8741

PUBLIC HEALTH MANAGEMENT CORP p 1189
Centre Sq E 1500 Market, Philadelphia PA 19102
Tel (215) 985-2500 SIC 8741

TEMPLE UNIVERSITY HEALTH SYSTEM INC p 1436
2450 W Hunting Park Ave, Philadelphia PA 19129
Tel (215) 926-9050 SIC 8741

BAKER MICHAEL INTERNATIONAL INC p 146
500 Grant St Ste 5400, Pittsburgh PA 15219
Tel (412) 269-6300 SIC 8711 8741

■ HEINZ FROZEN FOOD CO p 681
357 6th Ave, Pittsburgh PA 15222
Tel (412) 237-5700 SIC 2038 2037 8741

■ LIMBACH FACILITY SERVICES LLC p 866
31 35th St, Pittsburgh PA 15201
Tel (412) 359-2100 SIC 1711 8741

PJ DICK INC p 1153
225 N Shore Dr, Pittsburgh PA 15212
Tel (412) 462-9300 SIC 1542 8741

WEXFORD HEALTH SOURCES INC p 1603
501 Hlday Dr Foster Plz 4, Pittsburgh PA 15220
Tel (888) 633-6468 SIC 8741

GENESIS ENGINEERS INC p 602
1850 Gravers Rd Ste 300, Plymouth Meeting PA 19462
Tel (610) 592-0280 SIC 8711 8741

SYNOVOS INC p 1415
100 Matsonford Rd Ste 400, Radnor PA 19087
Tel (610) 293-5940 SIC 5085 8741

BOSCOVS DEPARTMENT STORE LLC p 202
4500 Perkiomen Ave, Reading PA 19606
Tel (610) 779-2000 SIC 8741 5311

BOSCOVS INC p 202
4500 Perkiomen Ave, Reading PA 19606
Tel (610) 779-2000 SIC 8741 5311

■ HOLLYWOOD CASINO CORP p 701
825 Berkshire Blvd # 200, Reading PA 19610
Tel (610) 373-2400 SIC 7011 8741

GUTHRIE HEALTHCARE SYSTEM p 648
1 Guthrie Sq Ste B, Sayre PA 18840
Tel (570) 888-6666 SIC 8011 7352 8741

TWIN TIER MANAGEMENT CORP p 1495
Guthrie Sq, Sayre PA 18840
Tel (570) 888-6666 SIC 8741 5912

COMMUNITY PHARMACY SERVICES p 349
1822 Mulberry St, Scranton PA 18510
Tel (570) 969-8000 SIC 8741

UPMC NORTHWEST p 1528
100 Fairfield Dr, Seneca PA 16346
Tel (814) 676-7600 SIC 8741

PROSPECT CROZER LLC p 1184
100 W Sproul Rd, Springfield PA 19064
Tel (610) 338-8200 SIC 8741

SHANER OPERATING CORP p 1311
1965 Waddle Rd, State College PA 16803
Tel (814) 234-4460 SIC 8741

GREEN ACRES HEALTH SYSTEMS INC p 636
4 Ivybrook Blvd, Warminster PA 18974
Tel (215) 357-6055 SIC 8741 8051

LAUREL HEALTH SYSTEM INC p 847
22 Walnut St, Wellsboro PA 16901
Tel (570) 724-1010 SIC 8082 8741 8011

■ HAAS GROUP p 651
1475 Phoenixville Pike, West Chester PA 19380
Tel (484) 564-4500 SIC 8741 3369

SUSQUEHANNA HEALTH SYSTEM p 1409
700 High St, Williamsport PA 17701
Tel (570) 321-1000 SIC 8741

CENTRO MEDICO DEL TURABO INC p 281
100 Ave Luis Munoz Marin, Caguas PR 00725
Tel (787) 653-3434 SIC 8741

ADMINISTRACION DE SERVICIOS MEDICOS DE PR p 23
Intersection Monacillos W, San Juan PR 00921
Tel (787) 777-3535 SIC 8741

▲ EVERTEC INC p 515
Km 1/3 Rr 176, San Juan PR 00926
Tel (787) 759-9999
SIC 8741 8748 7379 8721

KRESS STORES OF PUERTO RICO INC p 829
598 Calle A, San Juan PR 00920
Tel (787) 783-5374 SIC 7389 8741

■ HASBRO MANAGERIAL SERVICES INC p 667
1027 Newport Ave, Pawtucket RI 02861
Tel (401) 431-8697 SIC 8741

GILBANE INC p 611
7 Jackson Walkway, Providence RI 02903
Tel (401) 456-5800
SIC 1541 1542 8741 6513 6512

CB&I AREVA MOX SERVICES LLC p 268
Savannah River Site, Aiken SC 29801
Tel (803) 819-2000 SIC 8741

■ SCANA SERVICES INC p 1286
220 Operation Way, Cayce SC 29033
Tel (803) 217-9000 SIC 8741

BEACH CO p 164
211 King St Ste 300, Charleston SC 29401
Tel (843) 722-2615 SIC 6552 8741 1542

CAREALLIANCE HEALTH SERVICES p 254
316 Calhoun St, Charleston SC 29401
Tel (843) 724-2000 SIC 8741

UCI MEDICAL AFFILIATES INC p 1499
1818 Henderson St, Columbia SC 29201
Tel (803) 782-4278 SIC 8093 8741

HMR ADVANTAGE HEALTH SYSTEMS INC p 698
101 Grace Dr, Easley SC 29640
Tel (864) 269-3725 SIC 8741

MUSTANG PROCESS AND INDUSTRIAL INC p 1003
30 Patewood Dr Ste 200, Greenville SC 29615
Tel (864) 288-3009 SIC 8741

GBP MANAGEMENT INC p 594
979 Batesville Rd, Greer SC 29651
Tel (864) 297-6101 SIC 8741

GUARDIAN BUILDING PRODUCTS INC p 645
979 Batesville Rd Ste A, Greer SC 29651
Tel (864) 297-6101 SIC 3296 2452 8741

MEDICAL SERVICES OF AMERICA INC p 937
171 Monroe Ln, Lexington SC 29072
Tel (803) 957-0500
SIC 8082 8741 8071 7352 5999

ADVANCED TECHNOLOGY INTERNATIONAL p 26
315 Sigma Dr, Summerville SC 29486
Tel (843) 760-3200 SIC 8741

BIG D OIL CO p 181
3685 Sturgis Rd, Rapid City SD 57702
Tel (605) 342-6777 SIC 5541 5172 8741

AVERA HEALTH p 137
3900 W Avera Dr, Sioux Falls SD 57108
Tel (605) 322-4700 SIC 8741 8721

SANFORD HEALTH NETWORK p 1279
1305 W 18th St, Sioux Falls SD 57105
Tel (605) 328-2929 SIC 8741 8011

BRIM HOLDINGS INC p 213
105 Westwood Pl Ste 300, Brentwood TN 37027
Tel (615) 309-6053 SIC 8741

INFRASTRUCTURE CORP OF AMERICA p 742
750 Old Hickory Blvd # 200, Brentwood TN 37027
Tel (615) 377-4730 SIC 8742 8711 8741

■ PROVINCE HEALTHCARE CO p 1187
103 Powell Ct Ste 200, Brentwood TN 37027
Tel (205) 487-7900 SIC 8741

▲ QUORUM HEALTH CORP p 1201
1573 Mallory Ln, Brentwood TN 37027
Tel (615) 465-7189 SIC 8741

■ QUORUM HEALTH RESOURCES LLC p 1201
1573 Mallory Ln 200, Brentwood TN 37027
Tel (615) 371-7979
SIC 8742 8741 8082 8231 6324

REGIONAL CARE HOSPITAL PARTNERS INC p 1219
103 Continental Pl # 400, Brentwood TN 37027
Tel (615) 844-9800 SIC 8741

LAMBERTI SYNTHESIS USA INC p 841
4001 N Hawthorne St, Chattanooga TN 37406
Tel (423) 697-0526 SIC 8741

■ DIVERSICARE MANAGEMENT SERVICES CO p 444
277 Mallory Station Rd # 130, Franklin TN 37067
Tel (615) 771-7575 SIC 8741

HCTEC PARTNERS LLC p 672
7105 S Springs Dr Ste 208, Franklin TN 37067
Tel (615) 577-4030 SIC 8741

NISSAN NORTH AMERICA INC p 1044
1 Nissan Way, Franklin TN 37067
Tel (615) 725-1000
SIC 5012 8711 8734 6141 8741 3711

SERVPRO INTELLECTUAL PROPERTY INC p 1308
801 Industrial Blvd, Gallatin TN 37066
Tel (615) 451-0200 SIC 7349 8741 5087

ADMINISTRATIVE RESOURCES INC p 23
801 Sunset Dr F1, Johnson City TN 37604
Tel (423) 283-0296
SIC 8721 8741 8742 6794

MOUNTAIN STATES HEALTH ALLIANCE p 994
400 N State Of Frnklin Rd, Johnson City TN 37604
Tel (423) 431-6111 SIC 8741

■ HOUSECALL MEDICAL RESOURCES INC p 711
1400 Cntrpint Blvd St 100, Knoxville TN 37932
Tel (865) 689-7123 SIC 8082 8741 5999

▲ TEAM HEALTH HOLDINGS INC p 1430
265 Brookview Centre Way, Knoxville TN 37919
Tel (865) 693-1000 SIC 7363 8741

BAPTIST AND PHYSICIANS LOCAL SERVICES BUREAU INC p 153
350 N Humphreys Blvd, Memphis TN 38120
Tel (901) 227-5117 SIC 8741

BAPTIST MEMORIAL HEALTH CARE CORP p 154
350 N Humphreys Blvd, Memphis TN 38120
Tel (901) 227-2727
SIC 8062 8011 8741 5047

BELZ HOTEL GROUP LLC p 171
5118 Park Ave Ste 245, Memphis TN 38117
Tel (901) 762-5466 SIC 8741 8721

CARLISLE LLC p 257
263 Wagner Pl, Memphis TN 38103
Tel (901) 526-5000 SIC 5812 8741 6531

COMPREHENSIVE PHARMACY SERVICES LLC p 352
6409 N Quail Hollow Rd, Memphis TN 38120
Tel (901) 748-0470 SIC 8742 8741

MARTIN MONTGOMERY CONTRACTORS LLC p 913
8245 Tournament Dr # 300, Memphis TN 38125
Tel (901) 374-9400 SIC 1542 1541 8741

PPS HOLDINGS INC p 1166
6409 N Quail Hollow Rd, Memphis TN 38120
Tel (901) 748-0470 SIC 8741

PROMUS HOTEL CORP p 1183
755 Crossover Ln, Memphis TN 38117
Tel (901) 374-5000 SIC 7011 8741 6794

■ PROMUS HOTELS LLC p 1183
755 Crossover Ln, Memphis TN 38117
Tel (719) 265-6600 SIC 7011 8741 6794

■ PROMUS OPERATING CO INC p 1183
755 Crossover Ln, Memphis TN 38117
Tel (901) 374-5000 SIC 7011 8741 6794

HEALTH SERVICES MANAGEMENT INC p 676
206 Fortress Blvd, Murfreesboro TN 37128
Tel (615) 896-1191 SIC 8741

CHANGE HEALTHCARE OPERATIONS LLC p 288
3055 Lebanon Pike # 1000, Nashville TN 37214
Tel (615) 932-3000 SIC 7374 8741 8099

GRAND OLE OPRY LLC p 629
1 Gaylord Dr, Nashville TN 37214
Tel (615) 316-6180 SIC 8741

SHONEYS NORTH AMERICA LLC p 1317
1717 Elm Hill Pike Ste B1, Nashville TN 37210
Tel (615) 231-2333 SIC 6794 8741 5812

■ VHS HOLDINGS LLC p 1554
20 Burton Hills Blvd, Nashville TN 37215
Tel (615) 665-6000 SIC 8741

■ VHS SAN ANTONIO PARTNERS LLC p 1554
20 Burton Hills Blvd # 1, Nashville TN 37215
Tel (615) 665-6036 SIC 8741

▲ PFSWEB INC p 1140
505 Millenium Dr, Allen TX 75013
Tel (972) 881-2900 SIC 8741 7389 8742

■ AMERICAN PHYSICIANS SERVICE GROUP INC p 77
1221 S Mo Pac Expy # 200, Austin TX 78746
Tel (512) 328-0888
SIC 6282 8741 6411 6211

BLACKHAWK HEALTHCARE LLC p 187
6836 Fm 2244 Rd Ste 202, Austin TX 78746
Tel (512) 617-6363 SIC 8741

HID GLOBAL CORP p 690
611 Center Ridge Dr, Austin TX 78753
Tel (800) 237-7769 SIC 3825 1731 8741

SUCCESS FOODS MANAGEMENT GROUP LLC p 1396
4501 Springdale Rd, Austin TX 78723
Tel (512) 441-8900 SIC 8741 5812

■ TEXAS EZPAWN MANAGEMENT INC p 1443
1901 Capital Pkwy, Austin TX 78746
Tel (512) 314-3400 SIC 8741

EBCO GENERAL CONTRACTOR LTD p 474
305 W Gillis Ave, Cameron TX 76520
Tel (254) 697-8516 SIC 1542 8741

G6 HOSPITALITY LLC p 588
4001 International Pkwy, Carrollton TX 75007
Tel (972) 360-9000 SIC 8741

TEXAS A & M RESEARCH FOUNDATION INC p 1441
400 Harvey Mtchl Pkwy 3, College Station TX 77845
Tel (979) 845-8600 SIC 8741

GARRY BRADFORD MANAGEMENT CO LTD p 592
4646 Corona Dr Ste 105, Corpus Christi TX 78411
Tel (361) 852-6392 SIC 8741

■ ALON USA DELAWARE LLC p 59
12700 Park Central Dr # 1600, Dallas TX 75251
Tel (972) 367-3600 SIC 8741

ANTHELIO HEALTHCARE SOLUTIONS INC p 93
1 Lincoln Centre 5400 L, Dallas TX 75240
Tel (214) 257-7000 SIC 8741 8071 7389

BURCH MANAGEMENT CO INC p 226
10723 Composite Dr, Dallas TX 75220
Tel (214) 358-0055 SIC 8741 5813 5812

CULINAIRE INTERNATIONAL INC p 400
8303 Elmbrook Dr, Dallas TX 75247
Tel (214) 754-1645 SIC 8742 5812 8741

EIGHT-O MANAGEMENT INC p 481
1722 S Harwood St, Dallas TX 75215
Tel (214) 969-9321 SIC 8741

FIRSTSERVICE RESIDENTIAL TEXAS INC p 551
3102 Oak Lawn Ave Ste 202, Dallas TX 75219
Tel (214) 871-9700 SIC 8741

GREYSTAR RS GROUP LLC p 639
1201 Elm St Ste 1600, Dallas TX 75270
Tel (214) 290-7300 SIC 8741

OMNITRACS LLC p 1085
717 N Harwood St Ste 1300, Dallas TX 75201
Tel (888) 627-2716 SIC 8741 4214

REMINGTON HOTEL CORP p 1222
14185 Dallas Pkwy # 1150, Dallas TX 75254
Tel (972) 980-2700 SIC 8741

SENIOR CARE CENTERS LLC p 1304
600 N Pearl St Ste 1100, Dallas TX 75201
Tel (214) 252-7600 SIC 8741

■ SHOOTING STAR p 1318
8144 Walnut Hill Ln Fl 16, Dallas TX 75231
Tel (972) 770-1600 SIC 6411 8741

▲ TENET HEALTHCARE CORP p 1437
1445 Ross Ave Ste 1400, Dallas TX 75202
Tel (469) 893-2200
SIC 8062 8069 8741 8063 8082 8011

TF COURIER INC p 1445
5429 Lyndon B Johnson Fwy, Dallas TX 75240
Tel (214) 560-9000 SIC 4513 4215 8741

TFI HOLDINGS USA INC p 1445
5429 L B Johnson Fwy 10 Ste 1000, Dallas TX 75240
Tel (877) 396-2639 SIC 4215 8741 4513

EL PASO FIRST HEALTH PLANS INC p 483
1145 Westmoreland Dr, El Paso TX 79925
Tel (915) 298-7198 SIC 8741

PAE APPLIED TECHNOLOGIES LLC p 1107
6500 West Fwy Ste 600, Fort Worth TX 76116
Tel (817) 737-1500
SIC 8741 8711 8744 4581 7381

GAL-TEX HOTEL CORP p 589
2302 Pstoffice St Ste 500, Galveston TX 77550
Tel (409) 763-8536 SIC 7011 8741

REGENT MANAGEMENT SERVICES LIMITED PARTNERSHIP p 1219
2302 Post Office St # 402, Galveston TX 77550
Tel (409) 763-6000 SIC 8741

BUFFETS LLC p 224
120 Chula Vis, Hollywood Park TX 78232
Tel (651) 994-8608 SIC 5812 8741

ABS GROUP OF COMPANIES INC p 12
16855 Northchase Dr, Houston TX 77060
Tel (281) 673-2800 SIC 4785 8741

AMEC FOSTER WHEELER OIL & GAS INC p 66
585 N Dairy Ashford Rd, Houston TX 77079
Tel (713) 929-5000 SIC 8711 8742 8741

CAMAC INTERNATIONAL CORP p 243
1330 Post Oak Blvd Ste 22, Houston TX 77056
Tel (713) 965-5100
SIC 8711 6552 1382 8741 1389

■ CARDINAL HEALTH 109 INC p 253
1330 Enclave Pkwy, Houston TX 77077
Tel (281) 749-4000 SIC 8741

EQUIVA SERVICES LLC p 507
1100 La St Ste 3030, Houston TX 77002
Tel (713) 241-6161 SIC 8741

FABCO LLC p 523
13835 Beaumont Hwy, Houston TX 77049
Tel (713) 633-6500 SIC 3441 8741 8711

GDF SUEZ ENERGY NORTH AMERICA INC p 595
1990 Post Oak Blvd # 1900, Houston TX 77056
Tel (713) 636-0000 SIC 1311 8741 1629

■ HERCULES DRILLING CO LLC p 685
9 Greenway Plz Ste 2200, Houston TX 77046
Tel (713) 350-5100 SIC 8741

HOWCO METALS MANAGEMENT LLC p 713
9611 Telge Rd, Houston TX 77095
Tel (281) 649-8800 SIC 5051 3999 8741

HUNTING ENERGY SERVICES INC p 719
2 Northpoint Dr Ste 400, Houston TX 77060
Tel (281) 820-3838 SIC 1389 8741

INVENSYS SYSTEMS INC p 761
10900 Equity Dr, Houston TX 77041
Tel (713) 329-1600 SIC 3823 8711 8741

■ KBR HOLDINGS LLC p 806
601 Jefferson St Ste 7911, Houston TX 77002
Tel (713) 753-4176 SIC 1629 8711 8741

▲ KBR INC p 806
601 Jefferson St Ste 3400, Houston TX 77002
Tel (713) 753-3011 SIC 1629 8711 8741

KS MANAGEMENT SERVICES LLC p 831
2727 W Holcombe Blvd, Houston TX 77025
Tel (713) 442-0000 SIC 8741

M-I LLC p 890
5950 N Course Dr, Houston TX 77072
Tel (281) 561-1300
SIC 1389 2865 2869 8711 8741

■ NATURAL GAS PIPELINE CO OF AMERICA LLC p 1018
1001 Louisiana St, Houston TX 77002
Tel (713) 369-9000 *SIC* 4922 1311 8741

PINNACLE SUMMER INVESTMENTS INC p 1150
600 Travis St Ste 5800, Houston TX 77002
Tel (781) 749-7409 *SIC* 6282 8741

ROCTX LAKESIDE LLC p 1242
1455 Lakeside Estates Dr, Houston TX 77042
Tel (801) 284-5960 *SIC* 8741

■ SCI VIRGINIA FUNERAL SERVICES INC p 1292
1929 Allen Pkwy, Houston TX 77019
Tel (713) 522-5141 *SIC* 8741

SINGER EQUITIES INC p 1326
125 Mccarty St, Houston TX 77029
Tel (713) 714-3610 *SIC* 8741

TECHNIP USA INC p 1431
11740 Katy Fwy Ste 100, Houston TX 77079
Tel (281) 870-1111 *SIC* 8711 8741

TORCH ENERGY ADVISORS INC p 1461
1331 Lamar St Ste 1450, Houston TX 77010
Tel (713) 650-1246
SIC 1311 1382 8741 8742

■ GOLDMAN SACHS REALTY MANAGEMENT LP p 622
6011 Connection Dr, Irving TX 75039
Tel (972) 368-2200 *SIC* 8741

HIGHGATE HOTELS INC p 691
545 E J Carpentr Fwy 14, Irving TX 75062
Tel (972) 444-9700 *SIC* 8741

JPI MANAGEMENT LLC p 795
600 Las Colinas Blvd E, Irving TX 75039
Tel (972) 556-1700 *SIC* 8741

■ LA QUINTA LLC p 836
909 Hidden Rdg Ste 600, Irving TX 75038
Tel (214) 492-6600 *SIC* 7011 6794 8741

MEDIEVAL TIMES ENTERTAINMENT INC p 938
6363 N State Highway 161 # 400, Irving TX 75038
Tel (214) 596-7600 *SIC* 8741

MEDSYNERGIES INC p 939
909 Hidden Rdg Ste 300, Irving TX 75038
Tel (972) 791-1224 *SIC* 8741 8742 8721

MEDSYNERGIES NORTH TEXAS INC p 939
909 Hidden Rdg Ste 300, Irving TX 75038
Tel (972) 791-1224 *SIC* 8741

DET NORSKE VERITAS HOLDING (USA) INC p 433
1400 Ravello Rd, Katy TX 77449
Tel (281) 396-1000
SIC 8711 7389 5734 8741

TRENT SEVERN ENVIRONMENTAL SERVICES INC p 1476
2002 W Grand Pkwy N, Katy TX 77449
Tel (281) 578-4200 *SIC* 8741 3589

BUC-EES LTD p 222
327 Fm 2004 Rd, Lake Jackson TX 77566
Tel (979) 230-2930 *SIC* 8741

▲ ADEPTUS HEALTH INC p 22
2941 Lake Vista Dr # 200, Lewisville TX 75067
Tel (972) 899-6666 *SIC* 8741 8011

BAKER DRYWALL LTD p 146
401 Hwy 80 E, Mesquite TX 75150
Tel (972) 285-8878 *SIC* 8741

BAKER DRYWALL MANAGEMENT LLC p 146
401 Us Highway 80 E, Mesquite TX 75150
Tel (972) 285-8878 *SIC* 8741

ETECH GLOBAL SERVICES LLC p 511
1903 Berry Dr, Nacogdoches TX 75964
Tel (936) 559-2200
SIC 7389 8742 7373 8741 8721 7374

SEI HOLDING I CORP p 1300
11233 Shadow Creek Pkwy # 235, Pearland TX 77584
Tel (410) 553-9192 *SIC* 8741

AIMBRIDGE HOSPITALITY LLC p 38
5851 Legacy Cir Ste 400, Plano TX 75024
Tel (972) 952-0200 *SIC* 8741

■ B27 LLC p 143
1417 Gables Ct Ste 201, Plano TX 75075
Tel (972) 244-4350 *SIC* 8741 5084

CHANNEL POINT HOSPITALITY LLC p 288
5851 Legacy Cir Ste 400, Plano TX 75024
Tel (972) 952-0200 *SIC* 8741

M+W AMERICAS INC p 890
1001 Klein Rd Ste 400, Plano TX 75074
Tel (972) 535-7300
SIC 3433 8712 8711 8741

■ DELL USA CORP p 425
1 Dell Way, Round Rock TX 78682
Tel (512) 338-4400 *SIC* 8741 5045

LGD MANAGEMENT LP p 860
608 Sandau Rd, San Antonio TX 78216
Tel (210) 564-0100 *SIC* 8741

■ TESORO COMPANIES INC p 1440
19100 Ridgewood Pkwy, San Antonio TX 78259
Tel (210) 626-7390 *SIC* 8741

TOUCHSTONE COMMUNITIES INC p 1464
250 W Nottingham Dr # 200, San Antonio TX 78209
Tel (210) 828-5686 *SIC* 8741

ANCOR HOLDINGS LP p 89
100 Throckmorton St St Ste 1600, Southlake TX 76092
Tel (817) 877-4458 *SIC* 8741 8742

■ PHYSICIAN RELIANCE NETWORK INC p 1145
10101 Woodloch Forest Dr, Spring TX 77380
Tel (281) 863-1000 *SIC* 8741

JST ENTERPRISES p 796
5120 Summerhill Rd, Texarkana TX 75503
Tel (903) 794-3743 *SIC* 8741

BENCHMARK HOSPITALITY INC p 172
4 Waterway Square Pl # 300, The Woodlands TX 77380
Tel (281) 367-5757 *SIC* 8741 5046

EAST TEXAS MEDICAL CENTER REGIONAL HEALTHCARE SYST p 471
1000 S Beckham Ave, Tyler TX 75701
Tel (866) 333-3862 *SIC* 8062 8741

LEAVITT GROUP ENTERPRISES INC p 850
216 S 200 W, Cedar City UT 84720
Tel (435) 586-1555 *SIC* 6153 8741 6411

MANAGEMENT & TRAINING CORP p 900
500 N Market Place Dr # 100, Centerville UT 84014
Tel (801) 693-2600
SIC 8744 8331 7349 8741 8249

MTA DEVELOPMENT INC p 997
3222 E Autumn Ln, Eagle Mountain UT 84005
Tel (801) 647-3247 *SIC* 8741

AVALON HEALTH CARE INC p 136
206 N 2100 W Ste 300, Salt Lake City UT 84116
Tel (801) 596-8844 *SIC* 8741 8051

BARRICK GOLD OF NORTH AMERICA INC p 157
460 W 50 N Ste 500, Salt Lake City UT 84101
Tel (416) 861-9911 *SIC* 8741 1041

ZIONS MOUNTAIN VIEW HOME AND ASSOCIATES LTD p 1643
2730 E 3300 S, Salt Lake City UT 84109
Tel (801) 487-0896 *SIC* 8741

LARRY H MILLER GROUP OF COMPANIES p 845
9350 S 150 E Ste 1000, Sandy UT 84070
Tel (801) 563-4100 *SIC* 8741

■ RIO TINTO SERVICES INC p 1236
4700 W Daybreak Pkwy, South Jordan UT 84009
Tel (801) 204-2000 *SIC* 8721 8741

SOUTHWESTERN VERMONT HEALTH CARE CORP p 1353
100 Hospital Dr, Bennington VT 05201
Tel (802) 442-6361 *SIC* 8741

SENTEL CORP p 1305
2800 Eisenhower Ave # 300, Alexandria VA 22314
Tel (571) 481-2000 *SIC* 8711 8742 8741

▲ VSE CORP p 1566
6348 Walker Ln, Alexandria VA 22310
Tel (703) 960-4600 *SIC* 8711 8742 8741

BNG AMERICA LLC p 194
1235 S Clark St Ste 700a, Arlington VA 22202
Tel (703) 412-2500
SIC 8711 8741 4953 2819

DRS TECHNOLOGIES INC p 457
2345 Crystal Dr Ste 1000, Arlington VA 22202
Tel (973) 898-1500
SIC 3812 3699 3572 3669 3679 8741

■ EMCOR GOVERNMENT SERVICES INC p 491
2800 Crystal Dr Ste 600, Arlington VA 22202
Tel (571) 403-8900 *SIC* 8741 8711 1731

HIGH SIERRA POOLS INC p 691
2704 Columbia Pike, Arlington VA 22204
Tel (703) 920-1750 *SIC* 8741 7389

INTERSTATE MANAGEMENT CO LLC p 758
4501 Fairfax Dr Ste 500, Arlington VA 22203
Tel (703) 387-3100 *SIC* 8741

■ KELLOGG BROWN & ROOT SERVICES INC p 808
200 12th St S Ste 300, Arlington VA 22202
Tel (703) 526-7500 *SIC* 8741

NATIONAL TELECOMMUNICATIONS COOPERATIVE ASSOCIATION p 1016
4121 Wilson Blvd Ste 1000, Arlington VA 22203
Tel (703) 351-2000 *SIC* 8611 8741

SERVICES MANAGEMENT CORP p 1308
4121 Wilson Blvd Fl 10, Arlington VA 22203
Tel (703) 351-2074 *SIC* 8741

M V M INC p 890
44620 Guilford Dr Ste 150, Ashburn VA 20147
Tel (571) 223-4500 *SIC* 7381 8741

▲ ENGILITY HOLDINGS INC p 499
3750 Centerview Dr, Chantilly VA 20151
Tel (703) 708-1400 *SIC* 8711 8741

COMMONWEALTH ASSISTED LIVING LLC p 345
534 E Main St Ste B, Charlottesville VA 22902
Tel (434) 220-1055 *SIC* 8741

MARTHA JEFFERSON HEALTH SERVICES CORP p 912
500 Martha Jefferson Dr, Charlottesville VA 22911
Tel (434) 654-7000 *SIC* 8741

LTD MANAGEMENT CO LLC p 883
1564 Crossways Blvd, Chesapeake VA 23320
Tel (757) 420-0900 *SIC* 8741 8721

DALY SEVEN INC p 410
4829 Riverside Dr, Danville VA 24541
Tel (434) 822-2161 *SIC* 8741 1522 6531

DANVILLE REGIONAL HEALTH FOUNDATION p 412
142 S Main St, Danville VA 24541
Tel (434) 799-2100
SIC 8741 8062 8051 8011

CHG GROUP INC p 296
23031 Ladbrook Dr, Dulles VA 20166
Tel (703) 661-0283 *SIC* 8741

GUEST SERVICES INC p 645
3055 Prosperity Ave, Fairfax VA 22031
Tel (703) 849-9300 *SIC* 5148 8741

INOVA HEALTH SYSTEM p 745
8110 Gatehouse Rd 200e, Falls Church VA 22042
Tel (703) 289-2069
SIC 8741 8011 8062 8049 8059 8051

WASHINGTON HEALTHCARE MARY p 1578
2300 Fall Hill Ave # 314, Fredericksburg VA 22401
Tel (540) 741-2507 *SIC* 8741

ATLANTIC COAST DINING INC p 126
4701 Cox Rd Ste 345, Glen Allen VA 23060
Tel (804) 747-5050 *SIC* 8741

■ MAGELLAN MEDICAID ADMINISTRATION INC p 895
11013 W Broad St Ste 500, Glen Allen VA 23060
Tel (804) 548-0100
SIC 7374 8093 6411 8741

■ MARKEL VENTURES INC p 908
4521 Highwoods Pkwy, Glen Allen VA 23060
Tel (804) 747-0136 *SIC* 8741

PATIENT FIRST CORP p 1120
5000 Cox Rd Ste 100, Glen Allen VA 23060
Tel (804) 968-5700 *SIC* 8741

AKIMA LLC p 42
13873 Park Center Rd 400n, Herndon VA 20171
Tel (571) 323-5200 *SIC* 8741

■ NORTHROP GRUMMAN ENTERPRISE MANAGEMENT SERVICES CORP p 1058
2340 Dulles Corner Blvd, Herndon VA 20171
Tel (703) 713-4000
SIC 8741 8744 4731 8331 7349

PARSONS BRINCKERHOFF CONSTRUCTION SERVICES INC p 1117
13530 Dulles Tech Dr # 100, Herndon VA 20171
Tel (703) 742-5700 *SIC* 8741

LUCK STONE CORP p 884
515 Stone Mill Dr, Manakin Sabot VA 23103
Tel (804) 784-3383
SIC 1423 2899 3281 5211 8741

NORTHERN VIRGINIA ELECTRIC COOPERATIVE p 1057
10323 Lomond Dr, Manassas VA 20109
Tel (703) 335-0500
SIC 4911 8611 8741 4939

WILLIAM PRINCE HEALTH SYSTEM p 1611
8650 Sudley Rd Ste 411, Manassas VA 20110
Tel (703) 369-8270 *SIC* 8741

ACTIVEOPS USA INC p 20
8300 Greensboro Dr # 800, Mc Lean VA 22102
Tel (703) 918-4918 *SIC* 8741

▲ CARDINAL FINANCIAL CORP p 253
8270 Greensboro Dr # 500, Mc Lean VA 22102
Tel (703) 584-3400 *SIC* 6021 6211 8741

■ DYNCORP INTERNATIONAL INC p 465
1700 Old Meadow Rd, Mc Lean VA 22102
Tel (571) 722-0210
SIC 8741 7371 7381 7361 7363

■ SUNRISE SENIOR LIVING MANAGEMENT INC p 1404
7902 Westpark Dr, Mc Lean VA 22102
Tel (703) 273-7500 *SIC* 8361 8741 8052

RIVERSIDE HEALTHCARE ASSOCIATION INC p 1238
701 Town Center Dr # 1000, Newport News VA 23606
Tel (757) 534-7000 *SIC* 8741

RIVERSIDE HEALTHCARE SERVICES INC p 1238
608 Denbigh Blvd Ste 800, Newport News VA 23608
Tel (757) 856-7038 *SIC* 8741

ALTERNATIVE BEHAVIORAL SERVICES INC p 62
240 Corporate Blvd, Norfolk VA 23502
Tel (757) 459-5200 *SIC* 8741

CHILDRENS HEALTH SYSTEM INC p 299
601 Childrens Ln, Norfolk VA 23507
Tel (757) 622-2134 *SIC* 8741

OHL GLOBAL FREIGHT MANAGEMENT p 1078
223 E Cy Hall Ave Ste 208, Norfolk VA 23510
Tel (757) 314-4300 *SIC* 8741

▲ MAXIMUS INC p 922
1891 Metro Center Dr, Reston VA 20190
Tel (703) 251-8500 *SIC* 8742 8741

ROLLS-ROYCE NORTH AMERICA (USA) HOLDINGS CO p 1247
1875 Explorer St Ste 200, Reston VA 20190
Tel (703) 834-1700
SIC 5088 8741 6159 3724

ROLLS-ROYCE NORTH AMERICA HOLDINGS INC p 1248
1875 Explorer St Ste 200, Reston VA 20190
Tel (703) 834-1700 *SIC* 5088 8741 7699

ROLLS-ROYCE NORTH AMERICA INC p 1248
1875 Explorer St Ste 200, Reston VA 20190
Tel (703) 834-1700 *SIC* 5088 8741 1731

APPLE EIGHT HOSPITALITY MANAGEMENT INC p 98
814 E Main St, Richmond VA 23219
Tel (804) 727-6337 *SIC* 8741

CORNETT HOSPITALITY LLC p 371
2120 Staples Mill Rd, Richmond VA 23230
Tel (804) 678-9000 *SIC* 8741

LANDOR INTERNATIONAL INC p 843
2120 Staples Mill Rd # 300, Richmond VA 23230
Tel (804) 346-8200 *SIC* 6552 8741 4724

MCV ASSOCIATED PHYSICIANS p 933
830 E Main St Ste 1900, Richmond VA 23219
Tel (804) 358-6100 *SIC* 8741 8721

CARILION CLINIC p 256
1906 Belleview Ave Se, Roanoke VA 24014
Tel (540) 981-7900 *SIC* 8741

COORDINATED SERVICES MANAGEMENT INC p 367
3333 Peters Creek Rd Nw, Roanoke VA 24019
Tel (540) 366-0622 *SIC* 8741

ALVAREZ LLC p 63
8251 Greensboro Dr # 230, Tysons Corner VA 22102
Tel (301) 830-4020
SIC 8742 8741 7379 5044

JIM KOONS MANAGEMENT CO p 785
2000 Chain Bridge Rd, Vienna VA 22182
Tel (703) 448-7000 *SIC* 8741

COLONIAL WILLIAMSBURG CO p 338
101 Visitor Center Dr, Williamsburg VA 23185
Tel (888) 965-7254 *SIC* 8741

SUMITOMO FORESTRY AMERICA INC p 1398
1110 112th Ave Ne Ste 202, Bellevue WA 98004
Tel (425) 454-2355 *SIC* 8741 5099

EAGLE GROUP SYSTEMS INC p 468
230 Grant Rd, East Wenatchee WA 98802
Tel (509) 665-0319
SIC 4214 4119 4522 7373 7374 8741

KING COUNTY PUBLIC HOSPITAL DISTRICT NO 2 p 820
12040 Ne 128th St, Kirkland WA 98034
Tel (425) 899-1000 *SIC* 8741

CUBIC GLOBAL DEFENSE INC p 399
400 Union Ave Se Ste 300, Olympia WA 98501
Tel (360) 493-6275
SIC 7373 8744 8711 7376 8748 8741

■ UNIVAR USA INC p 1516
17411 Ne Union Hill Rd, Redmond WA 98052
Tel (331) 777-6000 *SIC* 5169 5191 8741

MISSION SUPPORT ALLIANCE LLC p 975
2490 Garlick Blvd, Richland WA 99354
Tel (509) 376-6770 *SIC* 8741

DOUBLE E FOODS LLC p 452
801 S Fidalgo St Ste 100, Seattle WA 98108
Tel (206) 768-8979 *SIC* 8741

NORTHWEST HOSPITAL & MEDICAL CENTER p 1060
1550 N 115th St, Seattle WA 98133
Tel (206) 364-0500 *SIC* 8741 8062

PINNACLE REALTY MANAGEMENT CO p 1150
2801 Alaskan Way Ste 200, Seattle WA 98121
Tel (206) 215-9700
SIC 6531 8741 6513 6512 1522

SELLEN CONSTRUCTION CO INC p 1302
227 Westlake Ave N, Seattle WA 98109
Tel (206) 682-7770 *SIC* 1542 8741

SWEDISH PHYSICIANS DIVISION p 1411
600 University St # 1200, Seattle WA 98101
Tel (206) 320-2700 *SIC* 8011 8741

VIRGINIA MASON HEALTH SYSTEM p 1559
1100 9th Ave, Seattle WA 98101
Tel (206) 233-6600 *SIC* 8741

EMBASSY MANAGEMENT LLC p 490
5709 W Sunset Hwy Ste 100, Spokane WA 99224
Tel (509) 328-2740 *SIC* 8741

EVERGREEN HEALTHCARE INC p 514
4601 Ne 77th Ave Ste 300, Vancouver WA 98662
Tel (360) 892-6472
SIC 8051 6513 8059 8741

HOLLAND INC p 700
109 W 17th St, Vancouver WA 98660
Tel (360) 694-1521 *SIC* 8741

HOLLAND RESIDENTIAL LLC p 700
1111 Main St Ste 700, Vancouver WA 98660
Tel (360) 694-7888 *SIC* 6513 8741

SOUTHWEST WASHINGTON HEALTH SYSTEM p 1352
400 Ne Mother Joseph Pl, Vancouver WA 98664
Tel (360) 514-2000 *SIC* 8741

AMFM INC p 85
240 Capitol St Ste 500, Charleston WV 25301
Tel (304) 344-1623 *SIC* 8741 8742

WEST VIRGINIA UNITED HEALTH SYSTEM INC p 1596
1 Medical Center Dr, Morgantown WV 26506
Tel (304) 598-4000 *SIC* 8741

SNOWSHOE MOUNTAIN INC p 1336
10 Snowshoe Dr, Slatyfork WV 26291
Tel (304) 572-5601
SIC 8741 7011 5813 5812

THOMAS HEALTH SYSTEM INC p 1448
4605 Maccorkle Ave Sw, South Charleston WV 25309
Tel (304) 347-6500 *SIC* 8741

OHIO VALLEY HEALTH SERVICES AND EDUCATION CORP p 1078
2000 Eoff St, Wheeling WV 26003
Tel (304) 234-8174 *SIC* 8741 8062 8011

JUSTICE FAMILY GROUP LLC p 797
101 Main St W, Wht Sphr Spgs WV 24986
Tel (304) 252-1074 *SIC* 8741

INNOVATIVE MATTRESS SOLUTIONS LLC p 745
11060 Winfield Rd, Winfield WV 25213
Tel (304) 586-2863 *SIC* 8741

J H FINDORFF & SON INC p 771
300 S Bedford St, Madison WI 53703
Tel (608) 257-5321
SIC 1542 1541 8741 1522

MERITER HEALTH SERVICES INC p 949
202 S Park St, Madison WI 53715
Tel (608) 417-5800 *SIC* 8741

REGIONAL DIVISION INC p 1219
600 Highland Ave, Madison WI 53792
Tel (608) 263-7923 *SIC* 8741

UNIVERSITY OF WISCONSIN SYSTEM p 1527
1700 Van Hise Ave, Madison WI 53726
Tel (608) 262-2321 *SIC* 8221 8741

FRANCISCAN SISTERS OF CHRISTIAN CHARITY SPONSORED MINISTRIES INC p 573
1415 S Rapids Rd, Manitowoc WI 54220
Tel (920) 684-7071 *SIC* 8741 8082

AFFINITY HEALTH SYSTEM p 32
1570 Midway Pl, Menasha WI 54952
Tel (920) 720-1700 *SIC* 8741 8062

RAYMOND MANAGEMENT CO INC p 1210
8333 Greenway Blvd # 200, Middleton WI 53562
Tel (608) 833-4100 *SIC* 6552 8741 7011

AURORA HEALTH CARE INC p 132
750 W Virginia St, Milwaukee WI 53204
Tel (414) 647-3000 *SIC* 8741 8062

C G SCHMIDT INC p 232
11777 W Lake Park Dr, Milwaukee WI 53224
Tel (414) 577-1177 *SIC* 1542 8741

SHEBOYGAN AREA SCHOOL DISTRICT p 1313
830 Virginia Ave, Sheboygan WI 53081
Tel (920) 459-3500 *SIC* 8211 8741

SIC 8742 Management Consulting Services

DIAGNOSTIC HEALTH CORP p 436
22 Inverness Pkwy Ste 425, Birmingham AL 35242
Tel (205) 980-2500 *SIC* 8742

■ DST HEALTH SOLUTIONS INC p 458
2500 Corporate Dr, Birmingham AL 35242
Tel (205) 437-6204 *SIC* 8742

ALLIANCE HR INC p 54
9076 Madison Blvd Ste G, Madison AL 35758
Tel (256) 203-6432 *SIC* 8742

WARREN AVERETT COMPANIES LLC p 1576
2500 Acton Rd Ste 200, Vestavia AL 35243
Tel (205) 979-4100
SIC 8721 8741 7363 8742

ALEUT CORP p 48
4000 Old Seward Hwy # 300, Anchorage AK 99503
Tel (907) 561-4300 *SIC* 6799 1542 8742

ALUTIIQ PACIFIC LLC p 63
3909 Arctic Blvd Ste 500, Anchorage AK 99503
Tel (907) 222-9500 *SIC* 8742 7379

CHENEGA CORP p 294
3000 C St Ste 301, Anchorage AK 99503
Tel (907) 277-5706
SIC 8744 7379 7376 3629 8742

BURNS CONSULTING INC p 228
15414 N 7th St Ste 8122, Phoenix AZ 85022
Tel (602) 993-3070 SIC 8742 7389

■ INFORMEDRX INC p 742
4805 E Thistle Landing Dr # 100, Phoenix AZ 85044
Tel (800) 282-3232 SIC 8742

SWIFT LOGISTICS CO INC p 1412
2200 S 75th Ave, Phoenix AZ 85043
Tel (602) 269-9700 SIC 8742

■ VIADS MARKETING & EVENTS GROUP p 1554
1850 N Central Ave # 101, Phoenix AZ 85004
Tel (602) 207-4000 SIC 8742 7941

CRA LLC p 388
8901 E Pima Center Pkwy # 230, Scottsdale AZ 85258
Tel (480) 889-9900 SIC 8742

■ MURPHY OIL USA INC p 1001
200 E Peach St, El Dorado AR 71730
Tel (870) 862-6411
SIC 8742 2911 1311 4213

AON CONSULTING INC p 94
315 W 3rd St, Little Rock AR 72201
Tel (501) 374-9300 SIC 8742

VESTCOM INTERNATIONAL INC p 1552
2800 Cantrell Rd Ste 400, Little Rock AR 72202
Tel (501) 663-0100 SIC 8742 7389

WRITERS GUILD INDUSTRY HEALTH FUND p 1627
1015 N Hollywood Way # 200, Burbank CA 91505
Tel (818) 846-1015 SIC 8742

PRESCRIPTION SOLUTIONS p 1171
2858 Loker Ave E Ste 100, Carlsbad CA 92010
Tel (760) 804-2370 SIC 8742

AVANTI HEALTH SYSTEM LLC p 136
222 N Sepulveda Blvd # 950, El Segundo CA 90245
Tel (310) 356-0550 SIC 8742

▲ TRUCEPT INC p 1485
500 La Terraza Blvd, Escondido CA 92025
Tel (866) 961-5763 SIC 8721 8748 8742

VISIONARY INTEGRATION PROFESSIONALS LLC p 1561
80 Iron Point Cir Ste 100, Folsom CA 95630
Tel (916) 608-8320 SIC 8742 7379

TECOLOTE RESEARCH INC p 1432
420 S Fairview Ave # 201, Goleta CA 93117
Tel (805) 571-6366 SIC 8742 8731

MAYERLING GROUP INC p 923
12065 Creekview Rd, Granada Hills CA 91344
Tel (323) 707-4748 SIC 8742

AGILITY LOGISTICS CORP p 35
240 Commerce, Irvine CA 92602
Tel (714) 617-6300
SIC 4731 8742 7372 1381

▲ CORELOGIC INC p 369
40 Pacifica Ste 900, Irvine CA 92618
Tel (949) 214-1000
SIC 7323 7299 8742 8732

EXULT INC p 521
121 Innovation Dr Ste 200, Irvine CA 92617
Tel (949) 856-8800 SIC 8742

▲ RESOURCES CONNECTION INC p 1227
17101 Armstrong Ave, Irvine CA 92614
Tel (714) 430-6400 SIC 8742 7389 8721

TRACE3 INC p 1468
7565 Irvine Center Dr # 200, Irvine CA 92618
Tel (949) 333-1801 SIC 8742

■ PERFORMANT RECOVERY INC p 1135
333 N Canyons Pkwy # 100, Livermore CA 94551
Tel (209) 858-3994 SIC 7322 8742 7371

WENTE BROS p 1592
5565 Tesla Rd, Livermore CA 94550
Tel (925) 456-2300 SIC 2084 8742

FOUNDATION PROPERTY MANAGEMENT INC p 571
911 N Studebaker Rd # 100, Long Beach CA 90815
Tel (562) 257-5100 SIC 8742

■ AECOM TECHNICAL SERVICES INC p 28
300 S Grand Ave Ste 1100, Los Angeles CA 90071
Tel (213) 593-8000
SIC 4953 8748 8742 8711

BLACKSTONE CONSULTING INC p 188
11726 San Vicente Blvd # 550, Los Angeles CA 90049
Tel (310) 826-4389 SIC 8742

■ CBRE GLOBAL INVESTORS LLC p 269
515 S Flower St Ste 3100, Los Angeles CA 90071
Tel (213) 683-4200 SIC 8742

▲ CBRE GROUP INC p 269
400 S Hope St Ste 25, Los Angeles CA 90071
Tel (213) 613-3333 SIC 6531 6162 8742

■ EARTH TECHNOLOGY CORP USA p 469
1999 Avenue Of Ste 2600, Los Angeles CA 90067
Tel (213) 593-8000
SIC 4953 8748 8742 8711

JACK NADEL INC p 773
8701 Bellanca Ave, Los Angeles CA 90045
Tel (310) 815-2600 SIC 8742 5199

▲ KORN/FERRY INTERNATIONAL p 828
1900 Avenue Stars, Los Angeles CA 90067
Tel (310) 552-1834 SIC 8742 7361

LONGWOOD MANAGEMENT CORP p 877
4032 Wilshire Blvd Fl 6, Los Angeles CA 90010
Tel (213) 389-6900 SIC 8742 6513

MEDICAL MANAGEMENT CONSULTANTS INC p 937
8150 Beverly Blvd, Los Angeles CA 90048
Tel (310) 659-3835
SIC 7363 8742 8748 8721

TRANSLATIONAL ONCOLOGY RESEARCH INTERNATIONAL INC p 1472
1033 Gayley Ave Ste 207, Los Angeles CA 90024
Tel (310) 824-1919 SIC 8011 8732 8742

INFOGAIN CORP p 741
485 Alberto Way Ste 100, Los Gatos CA 95032
Tel (408) 355-6000
SIC 7379 7373 8742 8748 7374 1731

▲ EXPONENT INC p 520
149 Commonwealth Dr, Menlo Park CA 94025
Tel (650) 326-9400 SIC 8711 8742 8999

■ PROTIVITI INC p 1185
2884 Sand Hill Rd Ste 200, Menlo Park CA 94025
Tel (650) 234-6000 SIC 8742 8721

ZENSHO AMERICA CORP p 1642
27261 Las Ramblas Ste 240, Mission Viejo CA 92691
Tel (760) 585-8455 SIC 8742

SUMMIT REALTY GROUP INC p 1399
177 Riverside Ave Ste F, Newport Beach CA 92663
Tel (619) 987-1630 SIC 8742

■ HOLMES & NARVER INC p 701
999 W Town And Country Rd, Orange CA 92868
Tel (714) 567-2400
SIC 8711 8742 8741 1542

■ SEMINIS INC p 1302
2700 Camino Del Sol, Oxnard CA 93030
Tel (805) 485-7317 SIC 8731 8742 2099

CFO CONSULTANTS INC p 285
829 E Francis Dr, Palm Springs CA 92262
Tel (760) 899-1919 SIC 8742

ALFATECH CAMBRIDGE GROUP GP p 49
345 S California Ave # 3, Palo Alto CA 94306
Tel (650) 543-3030 SIC 8741 8742

INTEGRATED ARCHIVE SYSTEMS INC p 749
1121 San Antonio Rd D100, Palo Alto CA 94303
Tel (650) 390-9995 SIC 8742 5045

CAMEO GLOBAL INC p 245
4695 Chabot Dr Ste 101, Pleasanton CA 94588
Tel (925) 479-7800
SIC 7373 7371 7379 7363 4813 8742

OMIDYAR NETWORK SERVICES LLC p 1084
1991 Broadway St Ste 200, Redwood City CA 94063
Tel (650) 482-2500 SIC 8742

■ YODLEE INC p 1636
3600 Bridge Pkwy Ste 200, Redwood City CA 94065
Tel (650) 980-3600 SIC 8742

SUTTER CONNECT LLC p 1410
10470 Old Placrvl Rd # 100, Sacramento CA 95827
Tel (916) 854-6600 SIC 8742 8741 8721

■ CAREFUSION CORP p 255
3750 Torrey View Ct, San Diego CA 92130
Tel (858) 617-2000 SIC 3841 3845 8742

GARICH INC p 592
6336 Greenwich Dr Ste A, San Diego CA 92122
Tel (858) 453-1331 SIC 7361 8742

■ UPS STORE INC p 1529
6060 Cornerstone Ct W, San Diego CA 92121
Tel (858) 455-8800 SIC 7389 8742 4783

■ ACHIEVERS LLC p 17
660 3rd St Ste 302, San Francisco CA 94107
Tel (888) 622-3343 SIC 8742

AKQA INC p 42
360 3rd St Ste 500, San Francisco CA 94107
Tel (415) 645-9400 SIC 8742

■ AMTECH SERVICES INC p 87
420 Taylor St 200, San Francisco CA 94102
Tel (415) 733-4000 SIC 7349 8742

BECHTEL CORP p 167
50 Beale St, San Francisco CA 94105
Tel (415) 768-1234 SIC 8711 1629 8742

BECHTEL GROUP INC p 167
50 Beale St Bsmt 1, San Francisco CA 94105
Tel (415) 768-1234 SIC 8711 1629 8742

BECHTEL POWER CORP p 167
50 Beale St Bsmt 2, San Francisco CA 94105
Tel (415) 768-1234 SIC 8711 8742 1629

HELLMUTH OBATA & KASSABAUM INC p 682
1 Bush St Ste 200, San Francisco CA 94104
Tel (415) 243-0555
SIC 8712 8711 8742 7389 0781

PROPHET BRAND STRATEGY p 1184
1 Bush St Fl 7, San Francisco CA 94104
Tel (415) 677-0909 SIC 8742

▲ SERVICESOURCE INTERNATIONAL INC p 1308
760 Market St Fl 4, San Francisco CA 94102
Tel (415) 901-6030 SIC 8742

STEELE INTERNATIONAL INC p 1384
1 Sansome St Ste 3500, San Francisco CA 94104
Tel (415) 781-4300 SIC 7381 8742 8748

TRIAGE CONSULTING GROUP p 1478
221 Main St Ste 1100, San Francisco CA 94105
Tel (415) 512-9400 SIC 8742 8748

BRIDGE BANK NATIONAL ASSOCIATION p 211
55 Almaden Blvd Ste 200, San Jose CA 95113
Tel (408) 423-8500 SIC 6022 8742

BRISTLECONE INC p 213
10 Almaden Blvd Ste 600, San Jose CA 95113
Tel (650) 386-4000 SIC 7371 8742

KP LLC p 828
13951 Washington Ave, San Leandro CA 94578
Tel (510) 346-0729
SIC 2752 7334 7331 7374 7389 8742

▲ WAGEWORKS INC p 1571
1100 Park Pl Fl 4, San Mateo CA 94403
Tel (650) 577-5200 SIC 8742

■ MHN SERVICES p 959
2370 Kerner Blvd, San Rafael CA 94901
Tel (415) 460-8300
SIC 6324 8011 8742 8322

ARMANINO LLP p 111
12657 Alcosta Blvd # 500, San Ramon CA 94583
Tel (925) 790-2600 SIC 8721 8742

GRUBB & ELLIS CO p 642
1551 N Tustin Ave Ste 300, Santa Ana CA 92705
Tel (714) 667-8252 SIC 6531 8742 6162

GUARDSMARK LLC p 645
1551 N Tustin Ave Ste 650, Santa Ana CA 92705
Tel (714) 619-9700 SIC 7381 8742 2721

BUTLER INTERNATIONAL INC p 230
3820 State St Ste A, Santa Barbara CA 93105
Tel (805) 882-2200 SIC 7363 8742

RAND CORP p 1207
1776 Main St, Santa Monica CA 90401
Tel (310) 393-0411 SIC 8733 8742 8732

SAN JOAQUIN COUNCIL OF GOVERNMENTS p 1277
555 E Weber Ave, Stockton CA 95202
Tel (209) 235-0600 SIC 8742

▲ FINANCIAL ENGINES INC p 542
1050 Enterprise Way Fl 3, Sunnyvale CA 94089
Tel (408) 498-6000 SIC 8742 6282 6411

BROKER SOLUTIONS INC p 217
14511 Myford Rd Ste 100, Tustin CA 92780
Tel (800) 450-2010 SIC 8742 6162

FENCES4LESS INC p 537
31290 Manzanita Crest Rd, Valley Center CA 92082
Tel (760) 749-2069 SIC 8742

OFFDUTYOFFICERS.COM p 1075
2365 La Mirada Dr, Vista CA 92081
Tel (888) 408-5900 SIC 7381 8742

ERM-WEST INC p 508
1277 Treat Blvd Ste 500, Walnut Creek CA 94597
Tel (925) 946-0455 SIC 8711 8742

GRAEBEL COMPANIES INC p 628
16346 Airport Cir, Aurora CO 80011
Tel (303) 214-6683 SIC 8742

■ ALPINE ACCESS INC p 60
1290 N Broadway Ste 1400, Denver CO 80203
Tel (303) 850-3700 SIC 7361 8742 8748

INTELLISOURCE LLC p 750
1899 Wynkoop St Ste 900, Denver CO 80202
Tel (303) 692-1100 SIC 8742

■ INTERMOUNTAIN ELECTRIC INC p 753
5050 Osage St Ste 500, Denver CO 80221
Tel (303) 733-7248 SIC 1542 8742 3671

KRG CAPITAL PARTNERS LLC p 830
1800 Larimer St Ste 2200, Denver CO 80202
Tel (303) 390-5001 SIC 6726 8742 6411

■ POLICY STUDIES INC p 1159
1515 Wynkoop St Ste 400, Denver CO 80202
Tel (303) 863-0900 SIC 8741 8742 7371

■ PSI SERVICES HOLDING INC p 1188
1515 Wynkoop St Ste 400, Denver CO 80202
Tel (303) 863-0900
SIC 8741 8742 7371 8748

■ TRIZETTO CORP p 1483
9655 Maroon Cir, Englewood CO 80112
Tel (303) 495-7000 SIC 7373 8742

CENTER PARTNERS INC p 276
4401 Innovation Dr, Fort Collins CO 80525
Tel (970) 206-9000 SIC 7379 8742 7363

■ STRANDED OIL RESOURCES CORP p 1392
110 N Rubey Dr Unit 120, Golden CO 80403
Tel (512) 279-7870 SIC 8742

▲ STARTEK INC p 1379
8200 E Maplewood Ave # 100, Greenwood Village CO 80111
Tel (303) 262-4500 SIC 7374 7379 8742

■ INTEGER GROUP L L C p 748
7245 W Alaska Dr, Lakewood CO 80226
Tel (303) 393-3000 SIC 7311 8742 8743

CARDNO INC p 253
10004 Park Meadows Dr # 300, Lone Tree CO 80124
Tel (720) 257-5800
SIC 8711 8748 8742 8741

ITP RAIL ASSOCIATES INC p 768
35 E Main St Ste 415, Avon CT 06001
Tel (860) 693-6120 SIC 8742

■ CIGNA HEALTH MANAGEMENT INC p 306
900 Cottage Grove Rd, Bloomfield CT 06002
Tel (860) 226-0533 SIC 8742

GENPACT LLC p 604
42 Old Ridgebury Rd Ste 1, Danbury CT 06810
Tel (203) 730-5110 SIC 8742

■ HEALTHCARE TECHNOLOGY INTERMEDIATE INC p 676
83 Wooster Hts, Danbury CT 06810
Tel (203) 448-4600 SIC 8742 8732

A&M CAPITAL-GP LP p 7
289 Greenwich Ave Ste 2, Greenwich CT 06830
Tel (212) 759-4433 SIC 8742

■ HARTFORD STEAM BOILER INSPECTION AND INSURANCE CO p 665
1 State St Fl 5-12, Hartford CT 06103
Tel (860) 722-1866
SIC 6331 8711 7373 8742

■ HSB GROUP INC p 714
1 State St, Hartford CT 06102
Tel (860) 722-1866
SIC 6331 6411 6799 8711 8742

GENERAL SUPPLY & SERVICES INC p 602
1000 Bridgeport Ave 5-1, Shelton CT 06484
Tel (203) 925-2400 SIC 5063 8742

NEW CASTLE HOTELS LLC p 1029
2 Corporate Dr Ste 154, Shelton CT 06484
Tel (203) 925-8370 SIC 7011 8741 8742

DAYMON WORLDWIDE INC p 417
700 Fairfield Ave Ste 1, Stamford CT 06902
Tel (203) 352-7500 SIC 8742

ENCOMPASS DIGITAL MEDIA INC p 495
250 Harbor Dr, Stamford CT 06902
Tel (203) 965-6000 SIC 4841 8742

▲ GARTNER INC p 592
56 Top Gallant Rd, Stamford CT 06902
Tel (203) 316-1111 SIC 8732 8742 8741

■ GE CONSUMER FINANCE INC p 595
777 Long Ridge Rd, Stamford CT 06902
Tel (203) 921-1443 SIC 8742

▲ INFORMATION SERVICES GROUP INC p 742
281 Tresser Blvd Ste 901, Stamford CT 06901
Tel (203) 517-3100 SIC 8742 7379

PRA HOLDINGS INC p 1167
1 Stamford Forum, Stamford CT 06901
Tel (203) 853-0123 SIC 2834 5122 8742

▲ PROVIDENCE SERVICE CORP p 1186
700 Canal St Ste 3, Stamford CT 06902
Tel (203) 307-2800 SIC 8322 8742 7389

■ SECURITY CAPITAL GROUP INC p 1299
292 Long Ridge Rd, Stamford CT 06902
Tel (203) 373-2211 SIC 6799 8742

TOWERS WATSON PENNSYLVANIA INC p 1464
263 Tresser Blvd Ste 700, Stamford CT 06901
Tel (203) 326-5400 SIC 8742 7371

BRIDGEWATER ASSOCIATES LP p 212
1 Glendinning Pl, Westport CT 06880
Tel (203) 226-3030 SIC 6282 8742

CHANNEL 1 CORP p 288
15 River Rd Ste 210, Wilton CT 06897
Tel (203) 523-5500 SIC 8742

SIRIUSDECISIONS INC p 1327
187 Danbury Rd, Wilton CT 06897
Tel (203) 665-4000 SIC 6282 8742

■ PHILLIPS PETROLEUM INTERNATIONAL INVESTMENT CO LLC p 1144
2711 Centerville Rd # 400, Wilmington DE 19808
Tel (918) 661-6600 SIC 8742

ACADEMY FOR EDUCATIONAL DEVELOPMENT INC p 13
1825 Conn Ave Nw Ste 800, Washington DC 20009
Tel (202) 884-8976 SIC 8742 8732

APCO WORLDWIDE INC p 96
1299 Penn Ave Nw Ste 300, Washington DC 20004
Tel (202) 638-4082 SIC 8748 8742 8732

CHEMONICS INTERNATIONAL INC p 293
1717 H St Nw, Washington DC 20006
Tel (202) 955-3300 SIC 8742 8748

▲ FTI CONSULTING INC p 583
1101 K St Nw Ste B100, Washington DC 20005
Tel (202) 312-9100 SIC 8742

GALLUP INC p 590
901 F St Nw Ste 400, Washington DC 20004
Tel (202) 715-3030 SIC 8742

■ PROMONTORY FINANCIAL GROUP LLC p 1183
801 17th St Nw Ste 1100, Washington DC 20006
Tel (202) 384-1200 SIC 8742

QUIVUS SYSTEMS LLC p 1200
3803 T St Nw, Washington DC 20007
Tel (202) 587-5756 SIC 8742

DCR WORKFORCE INC p 418
7795 Nw Beacon Sq 201, Boca Raton FL 33487
Tel (561) 998-3737 SIC 7379 7363 8742

CODINA PARTNERS LLC p 333
135 San Lorenzo Ave # 750, Coral Gables FL 33146
Tel (305) 529-1300
SIC 6552 6531 1521 8742

■ PHELPS DODGE INTERNATIONAL CORP p 1141
9850 Nw 41st St Ste 200, Doral FL 33178
Tel (305) 648-7888 SIC 8742 3357 3315

SEITLIN & CO p 1301
1000 Corp Dr Ste 400, Fort Lauderdale FL 33334
Tel (305) 591-0090 SIC 6411 8742

SIGNATURE CONSULTANTS LLC p 1322
200 W Cypress Creek Rd # 400, Fort Lauderdale FL 33309
Tel (954) 677-1020 SIC 7379 8742

SOLID RESOURCES INC p 1338
2200 Eller Dr, Fort Lauderdale FL 33316
Tel (941) 928-0958 SIC 8742

■ TEMPLETON WORLDWIDE INC p 1436
500 E Broward Blvd # 900, Fort Lauderdale FL 33394
Tel (954) 527-7500
SIC 6211 6282 8742 8748

CAMBRIDGE INTEGRATED SERVICES GROUP INC p 244
7369 Sheridan St Ste 301, Hollywood FL 33024
Tel (954) 966-4772 SIC 8742 7389

ADECCO USA INC p 22
10151 Deerwood Bldg 200, Jacksonville FL 32256
Tel (904) 359-4710
SIC 7363 7361 8742 6794

FIRST COAST SERVICE OPTIONS INC p 545
532 Riverside Ave, Jacksonville FL 32202
Tel (904) 791-8000 SIC 8742

MPS GROUP INC p 995
10151 Deerwood Park Blvd 200-400, Jacksonville FL 32256
Tel (904) 360-2000 SIC 7363 8742 7361

ONE CALL MEDICAL INC p 1086
841 Prudential Dr Ste 900, Jacksonville FL 32207
Tel (904) 646-0199 SIC 8742 7389

G4S HOLDING ONE INC p 588
1395 University Blvd, Jupiter FL 33458
Tel (561) 622-5656
SIC 7381 7382 8744 8748 8742

G4S SECURE SOLUTIONS (USA) INC p 588
1395 University Blvd, Jupiter FL 33458
Tel (561) 622-5656
SIC 7381 8744 8748 8742

MEADOWBROOK GOLF GROUP INC p 934
5385 Gateway Blvd Ste 12, Lakeland FL 33811
Tel (407) 589-7200
SIC 8742 8741 7992 5941

■ OVATIONS FOOD SERVICES LP p 1099
18228 N Us Highway 41, Lutz FL 33549
Tel (813) 948-6900 SIC 8742 7922

■ ADP TOTALSOURCE GROUP INC p 24
10200 Sw 72nd St, Miami FL 33173
Tel (305) 630-1000 SIC 8742

▲ HACKETT GROUP INC p 652
1001 Brickell Bay Dr # 3000, Miami FL 33131
Tel (305) 375-8005 SIC 8742

HIG CAPITAL INC p 690
1450 Brickell Ave # 3100, Miami FL 33131
Tel (305) 379-2322 SIC 8742 6211

HIG TRANSPORT HOLDINGS INC p 690
1450 Brickell Ave Fl 31, Miami FL 33131
Tel (305) 379-2322 SIC 8742

■ TERREMARK WORLDWIDE INC p 1440
2 S Biscayne Blvd # 2800, Miami FL 33131
Tel (305) 961-3200 SIC 4813 8742

ARMA GLOBAL CORP p 110
2701 N Rocky Point Dr # 1150, Rocky Point FL 33607
Tel (866) 554-9333 SIC 5045 8748 8742

CERIDIAN BENEFITS SERVICES p 283
3201 34th St S, Saint Petersburg FL 33711
Tel (800) 689-7893 SIC 8742

COXTARGET MEDIA INC p 386
1 Valpak Ave N, Saint Petersburg FL 33716
Tel (727) 399-3000
SIC 7331 8741 8742 2759

FINANCIAL INSURANCE MANAGEMENT CORP p 542
1440 Main St, Sarasota FL 34236
Tel (941) 952-5522 SIC 6411 8742

BUREAU VERITAS HOLDINGS INC p 226
1601 Sawgrass Corporate S Ste 400, Sunrise FL 33323
Tel (954) 835-9309
SIC 7389 8748 8711 8742

BUREAU VERITAS NORTH AMERICA INC p 227
1601 Sawgrs Corp Pkwy, Sunrise FL 33323
Tel (954) 236-8100
SIC 7389 8748 8734 8711 8742

FLORIDA TOURISM INDUSTRY MARKETING CORP p 559
2450 W Exec Ctr Cir 200, Tallahassee FL 32301
Tel (850) 488-5607 SIC 4724 8743 8742

SEVEN-ONE-SEVEN PARKING SERVICES INC p 1309
1410 N Florida Ave, Tampa FL 33602
Tel (813) 228-7722
SIC 7299 6519 7521 4119 8742

COMVEST INVESTMENT PARTNERS III LP p 353
525 Okeechobee Blvd # 1050, West Palm Beach FL 33401
Tel (561) 727-2000
SIC 4731 5912 5999 3652 8742 1731

OASIS OUTSOURCING INC p 1071
2054 Vista Pkwy Ste 300, West Palm Beach FL 33411
Tel (561) 227-6500 SIC 8721 8742 7363

MARKETSOURCE INC p 908
11700 Great Oaks Way, Alpharetta GA 30022
Tel (770) 674-5000 SIC 8742

MEDASSETS INC p 935
200 N Point Ctr E Ste 200, Alpharetta GA 30022
Tel (678) 323-2500 SIC 8742

MEDASSETS NET REVENUE SYSTEMS LLC p 935
200 N Point Ctr E Ste 400, Alpharetta GA 30022
Tel (678) 248-8200 SIC 8742 7371

■ **UPS SUPPLY CHAIN SOLUTIONS INC** p 1529
12380 Morris Rd, Alpharetta GA 30005
Tel (800) 742-5727 SIC 8742

■ **AGL RESOURCES SERVICE CO** p 35
10 Peachtree Pl Ne # 1000, Atlanta GA 30309
Tel (404) 584-9470
SIC 8742 8721 8744 4924

AMERICOLD LOGISTICS LLC p 82
10 Glenlake Pkwy Ste 324, Atlanta GA 30328
Tel (678) 441-1400
SIC 4222 4899 8742 7389

▲ **DLH HOLDINGS CORP** p 445
3565 Piedmont Rd Ne, Atlanta GA 30305
Tel (770) 554-3545 SIC 7363 8742

■ **FINANCIAL SERVICE CORP** p 543
2300 Windy Ridge Pkwy Se 1100s, Atlanta GA 30339
Tel (770) 916-6500
SIC 6722 6411 8742 6211

FIRST ADVANTAGE CORP p 544
1 Concourse Pkwy Ste 200, Atlanta GA 30328
Tel (800) 888-5773
SIC 7323 8742 7372 7389 7381

FORMATION CAPITAL LLC p 567
3500 Lenox Rd Ne Ste 510, Atlanta GA 30326
Tel (770) 754-9660 SIC 6211 8742

■ **FSC CORP** p 582
2300 Windy Ridge Pkwy Se # 1100, Atlanta GA 30339
Tel (770) 916-6500
SIC 6722 6411 8742 6211

H J RUSSELL & CO p 650
171 17th St Nw Ste 1600, Atlanta GA 30363
Tel (404) 330-1000
SIC 1542 8741 7389 8742

HEERY INTERNATIONAL INC p 680
999 Peachtree St Ne # 300, Atlanta GA 30309
Tel (404) 881-9880 SIC 8712 8711 8742

KURT SALMON US LLC p 832
1355 Peachtree St Ne # 900, Atlanta GA 30309
Tel (404) 892-0321 SIC 8742

MATRIX RESOURCES INC p 920
1000 Abernathy Rd Ste 500, Atlanta GA 30328
Tel (770) 677-2400 SIC 8742

NEXXLINX CORP INC p 1041
3565 Piedmont Rd Ne 2-104, Atlanta GA 30305
Tel (877) 747-0658 SIC 7389 8742

NORTH HIGHLAND CO LLC p 1052
3333 Piedmont Rd Ne # 1000, Atlanta GA 30305
Tel (404) 233-1015 SIC 8742 7379

NORTH HIGHLAND HOLDING CO INC p 1052
3333 Piedmont Rd Ne # 1000, Atlanta GA 30305
Tel (404) 233-1015 SIC 8742

RAM PARTNERS LLC p 1206
3284 Northside Pkwy Nw # 300, Atlanta GA 30327
Tel (770) 437-5200 SIC 8741 8742

SAVASENIORCARE LLC p 1284
1 Ravinia Dr Ste 1500, Atlanta GA 30346
Tel (770) 829-5100 SIC 8742

SOUTHEASTRANS INC p 1347
4751 Best Rd Ste 140, Atlanta GA 30337
Tel (404) 209-4000 SIC 8742

US MOTIVATION INC p 1532
7840 Roswe Rd Usm Bldg 10, Atlanta GA 30350
Tel (770) 290-4700 SIC 8742

INTERNATIONAL MANAGEMENT SERVICES CO INC p 756
3633 Wheeler Rd Ste 350, Augusta GA 30909
Tel (706) 855-1014 SIC 8742

■ **NDCHEALTH CORP** p 1022
1564 Northeast Expy Ne, Brookhaven GA 30329
Tel (404) 728-2000 SIC 7374 8742

■ **BB &T FINANCIAL FSB A FEDERAL SAVINGS BANK** p 163
4 Bradley Park Ct Ste 1c, Columbus GA 31904
Tel (706) 653-7885 SIC 8742

■ **HEALTHCARE SOLUTIONS INC** p 676
2736 Meadow Church Rd # 300, Duluth GA 30097
Tel (866) 810-4332 SIC 8742

PS ENERGY GROUP INC p 1187
4480 N Shallowford Rd # 100, Dunwoody GA 30338
Tel (770) 350-3000 SIC 8742 5172 4924

BLUE EAGLE HOLDINGS LP p 192
6465 E Johns Xing, Johns Creek GA 30097
Tel (678) 584-4000 SIC 7389 7374 8742

RADIAL SOUTH LP p 1204
6465 E Johns Xing, Johns Creek GA 30097
Tel (678) 584-4000 SIC 7389 7374 8742

ASAP SOLUTIONS GROUP LLC p 115
3885 Holcomb Bridge Rd, Norcross GA 30092
Tel (770) 246-1718 SIC 7379 8742

■ **GYPSUM MANAGEMENT AND SUPPLY INC** p 649
100 Crescent Center Pkwy # 800, Tucker GA 30084
Tel (770) 939-1711 SIC 5032 8742

■ **COFFEE PARTNERS HAWAII** p 334
210 Ward Ave Ste 105, Honolulu HI 96814
Tel (808) 545-1149 SIC 8742

ALEXIAN BROTHERS OF AMERICA INC p 49
3040 W Salt Creek Ln, Arlington Heights IL 60005
Tel (847) 640-7550 SIC 8742 8062 8361

■ **LEHIGH CONSUMER PRODUCTS LLC** p 853
3901 Liberty St, Aurora IL 60504
Tel (630) 851-7330
SIC 3965 2298 3462 3452 8742

AFNI INC p 33
404 Brock Dr, Bloomington IL 61701
Tel (309) 828-5226 SIC 8742 7322

CC SERVICES INC p 269
1701 Towanda Ave, Bloomington IL 61701
Tel (309) 821-3372 SIC 8742 6411

ILLINOIS AGRICULTURAL ASSOCIATION p 732
1701 Towanda Ave, Bloomington IL 61701
Tel (309) 557-2111
SIC 8611 6722 8742 6311 7514

QUANTUM FOODS LLC p 1198
750 S Schmidt Rd, Bolingbrook IL 60440
Tel (319) 627-6000 SIC 8742

INTERNATIONAL SERVICES INC p 756
1250 Barclay Blvd, Buffalo Grove IL 60089
Tel (847) 808-5590 SIC 8742

A EPSTEIN AND SONS INTERNATIONAL INC p 5
600 W Fulton St Ste 800, Chicago IL 60661
Tel (312) 454-9100
SIC 8711 8712 7389 1542 1541 8742

A T KEARNEY INC p 6
227 W Monroe St, Chicago IL 60606
Tel (312) 648-0111 SIC 8742

ACCENTURE INC p 14
161 N Clark St Ste 1100, Chicago IL 60601
Tel (312) 737-8842 SIC 7379 7389 8742

ACCENTURE LLC p 14
161 N Clark St Ste 1100, Chicago IL 60601
Tel (312) 693-0161 SIC 7379 7389 8742

ACCENTURE LLP p 14
161 N Clark St Ste 1100, Chicago IL 60601
Tel (312) 693-0161 SIC 8742

ACCENTURE SUB INC p 14
161 N Clark St Ste 1100, Chicago IL 60601
Tel (312) 693-0161 SIC 8742

■ **AMERITECH SERVICES INC** p 84
208 S Lasalle St Ste 814, Chicago IL 60604
Tel (847) 248-2000
SIC 7389 4225 8742 8721

AON CORP p 95
200 E Randolph St, Chicago IL 60601
Tel (312) 381-1000 SIC 6411 8742

AON GROUP INC p 95
200 E Randolph St Fl 5, Chicago IL 60601
Tel (312) 381-2738 SIC 6311 8742 6411

AON HEWITT LLC p 95
200 E Randolph St Ll3, Chicago IL 60601
Tel (312) 381-1000 SIC 8742 8999

CIVC PARTNERS LP p 320
191 N Wacker Dr Ste 1100, Chicago IL 60606
Tel (312) 521-2000 SIC 8742 6799

COMPSYCH EMPLOYEE ASSISTANCE PROGRAMS INC p 352
455 N Ctyfrnt Plz Dr # 1300, Chicago IL 60611
Tel (312) 595-4000 SIC 8742

CROWN GOLF PROPERTIES LP p 395
222 N La Salle St # 2000, Chicago IL 60601
Tel (312) 395-7701 SIC 8742 1629

CUSHMAN & WAKEFIELD INC p 402
77 W Wacker Dr Ste 1800, Chicago IL 60601
Tel (312) 424-8000 SIC 6531 8742 8732

FLS TRANSPORTATION SERVICES INC p 561
180 N La Salle St # 2950, Chicago IL 60601
Tel (877) 744-7357 SIC 8742 4731

GRANT THORNTON LLP p 631
171 N Clark St Ste 200, Chicago IL 60601
Tel (312) 856-0200 SIC 8721 8742

H W LOCHNER INC p 651
225 W Washington St # 1200, Chicago IL 60606
Tel (312) 372-7346 SIC 8711 8742

▲ **HURON CONSULTING GROUP INC** p 721
550 W Van Buren St # 1600, Chicago IL 60607
Tel (312) 583-8700 SIC 8742 8748

MARKET TRACK LLC p 908
233 S Wacker Dr, Chicago IL 60606
Tel (312) 529-5102 SIC 8742

MARKETING STORE WORLDWIDE L L C p 908
55 W Monroe St Fl 14, Chicago IL 60603
Tel (312) 614-4600 SIC 7311 8742

MMS USA HOLDINGS INC p 979
35 W Wacker Dr, Chicago IL 60601
Tel (800) 933-3622 SIC 8742

MONTERREY SECURITY CONSULTANTS INC p 986
2232 S Blue Island Ave, Chicago IL 60608
Tel (773) 843-0434 SIC 8742

▲ **NAVIGANT CONSULTING INC** p 1020
30 S Wacker Dr Ste 3550, Chicago IL 60606
Tel (312) 573-5600 SIC 8742

NUVEEN JOHN & CO INC (DEL) p 1068
333 W Wacker Dr Fl 33, Chicago IL 60606
Tel (312) 917-7700 SIC 6211 8742

RSM US LLP p 1256
1 S Wacker Dr Ste 800, Chicago IL 60606
Tel (312) 634-3400 SIC 8721 8742 7291

SAC WIRELESS LLC p 1264
540 W Madison St Ste 1600, Chicago IL 60661
Tel (847) 944-1600 SIC 8741 8742

■ **SIMPLER NORTH AMERICA LLC** p 1325
1 N Dearborn St Ste 1400, Chicago IL 60602
Tel (312) 533-3500 SIC 8742 7379

SMITHBUCKLIN CORP p 1333
330 N Wabash Ave, Chicago IL 60611
Tel (312) 644-6610 SIC 8742 8743 4724

■ **WEC BUSINESS SERVICES LLC** p 1587
200 E Randolph St # 2200, Chicago IL 60601
Tel (312) 240-3877 SIC 8742 8721

GCG FINANCIAL INC p 595
3 Parkway N Ste 500, Deerfield IL 60015
Tel (847) 457-3000 SIC 6411 8742 6211

MERIDIAN GROUP INTERNATIONAL INC p 948
9 Parkway N Ste 500, Deerfield IL 60015
Tel (847) 940-1200 SIC 8742 6159

FRANK CONSOLIDATED ENTERPRISES INC p 574
666 Garland Pl, Des Plaines IL 60016
Tel (847) 699-7000 SIC 8742

■ **FIRST HEALTH GROUP CORP** p 547
3200 Highland Ave, Downers Grove IL 60515
Tel (630) 737-7900
SIC 8742 6324 6321 6411

ZS ASSOCIATES INC p 1644
1800 Sherman Ave Ste 37, Evanston IL 60201
Tel (858) 677-2200 SIC 8742

DEERE PARK ASSOCIATES INC p 422
240 N Deere Park Dr W, Highland Park IL 60035
Tel (847) 509-1000 SIC 8742

■ **INNOVEL SOLUTIONS INC** p 745
3333 Beverly Rd, Hoffman Estates IL 60179
Tel (847) 286-2500 SIC 4731 8741 8742

PRISM COMPANIES INC p 1178
248 Spring Lake Dr, Itasca IL 60143
Tel (630) 216-5788 SIC 8742

AON CONSULTING WORLDWIDE INC p 95
100 Half Day Rd 2, Lincolnshire IL 60069
Tel (312) 381-4800
SIC 6311 6321 6331 8742 6411 6351

ITEX DEVELOPMENT CORP p 768
6633 N Lincoln Ave, Lincolnwood IL 60712
Tel (847) 674-2383 SIC 8742

MENNIES MACHINE CO p 943
Mennie Dr Rr 71, Mark IL 61340
Tel (815) 339-2226 SIC 3544 8742

GROUP O INC p 642
4905 77th Ave E, Milan IL 61264
Tel (309) 736-8100
SIC 8742 7389 4226 5085

■ **CAREMARK LLC** p 255
2211 Sanders Rd, Northbrook IL 60062
Tel (847) 559-4700
SIC 5961 6411 8099 8092 8093 8742

CITIZENS RX LLC p 311
1144 Lake St Ste 401, Oak Park IL 60301
Tel (888) 545-1120 SIC 8742

PROBIDDER LLC p 1178
945 E Kenilworth Ave, Palatine IL 60074
Tel (847) 962-3140 SIC 8742 7371

SWEDISHAMERICAN HEALTH SYSTEM CORP p 1411
1401 E State St, Rockford IL 61104
Tel (815) 968-4400
SIC 8743 6512 8742 8099 8082 8062

NISSHIN HOLDING INC p 1044
1701 Golf Rd, Rolling Meadows IL 60008
Tel (847) 290-5100 SIC 8742

LESAINT LOGISTICS LLC p 857
868 W Crossroads Pkwy, Romeoville IL 60446
Tel (630) 243-5950 SIC 4731 4225 8742

IPC INTERNATIONAL CORP p 763
10255 W Hggi, Rosemont IL 60018
Tel (847) 444-2000
SIC 7381 8742 2389 3199

OMRON AUTOMOTIVE ELECTRONICS INC p 1085
3709 Ohio Ave, Saint Charles IL 60174
Tel (630) 443-6800
SIC 5065 3625 3714 8742

■ **CATAMARAN CORP** p 264
1600 Mcconnor Pkwy Fl 1, Schaumburg IL 60173
Tel (800) 282-3232 SIC 8742

NETWORK ASSOCIATES INC p 1028
1100 E Wdfield Rd Ste 200, Schaumburg IL 60173
Tel (847) 803-4888 SIC 8742 5113

UNITED CONTRACTORS MIDWEST INC p 1507
3151 Robbins Rd Ste A, Springfield IL 62704
Tel (217) 546-6192 SIC 8742 1622 5082

DRIVELINE RETAIL MERCHANDISING INC p 456
1141 E 1500 North Rd, Taylorville IL 62568
Tel (704) 663-7741 SIC 8742

HH GLOBAL USA INC p 689
175 E Hawthorn Pkwy # 325, Vernon Hills IL 60061
Tel (847) 816-6303 SIC 8742

SEGERDAHL GRAPHICS INC p 1300
1351 Wheeling Rd, Wheeling IL 60090
Tel (847) 541-1080 SIC 2752 8742

CARDON & ASSOCIATES INC p 253
2749 E Covenanter Dr, Bloomington IN 47401
Tel (812) 332-2265 SIC 8741 6513 8742

■ **VECTREN ENERGY MARKETING AND SERVICES INC** p 1546
1 Vectren Sq, Evansville IN 47708
Tel (812) 491-4000 SIC 8748 8711 8742

ALPHA RAE PERSONNEL INC p 60
347 W Berry St Ste 700, Fort Wayne IN 46802
Tel (260) 426-8227 SIC 8742

■ **LINCOLN FINANCIAL ADVISORS CORP** p 867
1300 S Clinton St, Fort Wayne IN 46802
Tel (800) 237-3813
SIC 6311 6282 8748 8742

PHOENIX GROUP INC p 1145
164 S Park Blvd, Greenwood IN 46143
Tel (317) 884-3600 SIC 8742 6719

■ **ELI LILLY INTERNATIONAL CORP** p 487
893 S Delaware St, Indianapolis IN 46225
Tel (317) 276-2000
SIC 8742 2834 8731 3841 2879

HIGHPOINT GLOBAL LLC p 692
300 N Meridian St Ste 190, Indianapolis IN 46204
Tel (317) 576-4500 SIC 8742

PINNACLE OIL HOLDINGS LLC p 1150
5009 W 81st St, Indianapolis IN 46268
Tel (317) 875-9465 SIC 2992 5172 8742

VISIONARY ENTERPRISES INC p 1561
6626 E 75th St Ste 100, Indianapolis IN 46250
Tel (317) 621-4000 SIC 6531 8742 8093

■ **VECTREN ENERGY SERVICES CORP** p 1546
4655 Rosebud Ln, Newburgh IN 47630
Tel (812) 492-3723
SIC 8711 8742 8748 6719

PRESS GANEY ASSOCIATES INC p 1172
404 Columbia St, South Bend IN 46601
Tel (574) 232-3387 SIC 8742

CBE COMPANIES INC p 268
1309 Technology Pkwy, Cedar Falls IA 50613
Tel (319) 226-5161 SIC 8742

CBE GROUP INC p 268
1309 Technology Pkwy, Cedar Falls IA 50613
Tel (319) 234-6686 SIC 7322 8742

RUAN LOGISTICS CORP p 1256
666 Grand Ave Ste 3100, Des Moines IA 50309
Tel (515) 245-2500 SIC 8742

CUNA MUTUAL LIFE INSURANCE CO p 401
2000 Heritage Way, Waverly IA 50677
Tel (319) 352-4090 SIC 6411 6321 8742

HMA INC p 697
3001 Westown Pkwy Stop 1, West Des Moines IA 50266
Tel (515) 223-6800 SIC 6411 6321 8742

ITA GROUP INC p 767
4600 Westown Pkwy Ste 100, West Des Moines IA 50266
Tel (515) 326-3400 SIC 8742 4724

TERRACON CONSULTANTS INC p 1439
18001 W 106th St Ste 300, Olathe KS 66061
Tel (913) 599-6886
SIC 8742 8711 8748 8741

INTOUCH SOLUTIONS INC p 759
7045 College Blvd Ste 300, Overland Park KS 66211
Tel (913) 317-9700 SIC 8742

SHAMROCK TRADING CORP p 1311
9300 Metcalf Ave, Overland Park KS 66212
Tel (913) 310-2200
SIC 4731 6153 8742 7323

GREAT PLAINS HEALTH ALLIANCE INC p 634
625 3rd St, Phillipsburg KS 67661
Tel (785) 543-2111 SIC 8742

TRANSFREIGHT LLC p 1471
3940 Olympic Blvd Ste 500, Erlanger KY 41018
Tel (859) 372-5930 SIC 4213 8742

CORKEN STEEL PRODUCTS CO p 370
7920 Kentucky Dr, Florence KY 41042
Tel (859) 291-4664
SIC 5075 3444 5051 8742 6411

VASCOR LTD p 1545
100 Farmers Bank Sq # 310, Georgetown KY 40324
Tel (502) 868-0277 SIC 8742

MEDICAL REHABILITATION CENTERS LLC p 937
1050 Chinoe Rd Ste 300, Lexington KY 40502
Tel (859) 255-0075 SIC 8742

SENTURE LLC p 1305
460 Industrial Blvd, London KY 40741
Tel (606) 878-4205
SIC 7379 7389 7374 7373 8742

A&R LOGISTICS INC p 7
600 N Hurstbourne Pkwy # 110, Louisville KY 40222
Tel (815) 941-5200 SIC 8742 4731

PAYMENT ALLIANCE PROCESSING CORP p 1122
6060 Dutchmans Ln Ste 320, Louisville KY 40205
Tel (502) 212-4000 SIC 8742

SHPS HOLDINGS INC p 1319
9200 Shelbyville Rd # 100, Louisville KY 40222
Tel (502) 267-4900 SIC 6411 8742

HAMMERMAN & GAINER INTERNATIONAL INC p 656
1010 Common St Ste 2600, New Orleans LA 70112
Tel (504) 681-6135 SIC 8742

CIANBRO COMPANIES p 305
1 Hunnewell Ave, Pittsfield ME 04967
Tel (207) 487-3311
SIC 1629 1622 1542 1541 8742

CIANBRO CORP p 305
101 Cianbro Sq, Pittsfield ME 04967
Tel (207) 487-3311
SIC 1622 1629 1542 1541 8742

MSTC INC p 997
10900 Pump House Rd Ste B, Annapolis Junction MD 20701
Tel (240) 280-8064 SIC 8742 8748

MARYLAND ECONOMIC DEVELOPMENT CORP p 914
300 E Lombard St Ste 1000, Baltimore MD 21202
Tel (410) 727-8049 SIC 8742

UNIVERSITY RESEARCH CO LLC p 1527
7200 Wisconsin Ave # 600, Bethesda MD 20814
Tel (301) 654-8338 SIC 8742 8748

ABACUS TECHNOLOGY CORP p 9
5404 Wscnsin Ave Ste 1100, Chevy Chase MD 20815
Tel (301) 907-8500 SIC 8742

▲ **GP STRATEGIES CORP** p 627
11000 Broken Land Pkwy # 200, Columbia MD 21044
Tel (443) 367-9600 SIC 8742 8711 8748

L B & B ASSOCIATES INC p 833
9891 Broken Land Pkwy # 400, Columbia MD 21046
Tel (301) 621-3944
SIC 8744 7338 4225 8742 8748 4581

MERKLE INC p 950
7001 Columbia Gateway Dr, Columbia MD 21046
Tel (443) 542-4000 *SIC* 8742

PLANNED SYSTEMS INTERNATIONAL INC p 1154
10632 Little Patuxent Pkw, Columbia MD 21044
Tel (410) 964-8000 *SIC* 8742

BECHTEL NATIONAL INC p 167
5275 Westview Dr, Frederick MD 21703
Tel (415) 768-1234 *SIC* 8711 1629 8742

■ **LOCKHEED MARTIN SERVICES INC** p 873
700 N Frederick Ave, Gaithersburg MD 20879
Tel (301) 240-7669 *SIC* 8711 8741 8742

SODEXOMAGIC LLC p 1337
9801 Washingtonian Blvd, Gaithersburg MD 20878
Tel (301) 987-4433 *SIC* 8742

MARYLAND HOSPITALITY INC p 915
6411 Ivy Ln Ste 510, Greenbelt MD 20770
Tel (301) 474-3307 *SIC* 7011 8741 8742

TRIVERGENT HEALTH ALLIANCE MSO LLC p 1483
1800 Dual Hwy Ste 304, Hagerstown MD 21740
Tel (301) 790-9130 *SIC* 8742

CONVERGENCE MARKETING INC p 364
7361 Coca Cola Dr Ste A, Hanover MD 21076
Tel (443) 688-5100 *SIC* 8742

TECH USA INC p 1431
8334 Veterans Hwy, Millersville MD 21108
Tel (410) 584-9003 *SIC* 8742

KEY IMPACT SALES & SYSTEMS INC p 814
1701 Crossroads Dr, Odenton MD 21113
Tel (410) 381-1239 *SIC* 8742

APEX COMPANIES LLC p 96
15850 Crabbs Branch Way # 200, Rockville MD 20855
Tel (301) 417-0200 *SIC* 8744 8748 8742

INFOSYS PUBLIC SERVICES INC p 742
800 King Farm Blvd # 505, Rockville MD 20850
Tel (301) 354-8600 *SIC* 7371 7374 8742

WESTAT INC p 1596
1600 Research Blvd, Rockville MD 20850
Tel (301) 251-1500
SIC 8732 7371 7373 8741 8742 8999

BAIN & CO INC p 145
131 Dartmouth St Ste 901, Boston MA 02116
Tel (617) 572-2000 *SIC* 8742

BOSTON CONSULTING GROUP INC p 202
1 Beacon St Fl 10, Boston MA 02108
Tel (617) 850-3700 *SIC* 8742

CAREER PARTNERS INTERNATIONAL LLC p 254
125 Summer St Ste 1020, Boston MA 02110
Tel (919) 401-4260 *SIC* 8742

▲ **CRA INTERNATIONAL INC** p 388
200 Clarendon St, Boston MA 02116
Tel (617) 425-3000 *SIC* 8742

CRESA PARTNERS LLC p 391
200 State St Ste 13a, Boston MA 02109
Tel (617) 758-6000 *SIC* 8742 6531

DIGITAS INC p 439
33 Arch St Fl 8, Boston MA 02110
Tel (617) 369-8000 *SIC* 8742

FIDESSA BUY-SIDE INC p 541
160 Federal St, Boston MA 02110
Tel (617) 235-1000 *SIC* 6726 8742

FULD & CO INC p 584
131 Oliver St Fl 3, Boston MA 02110
Tel (617) 492-5900 *SIC* 8742

IPROSPECT.COM INC p 763
1 South Sta Ste 300, Boston MA 02110
Tel (617) 449-4300 *SIC* 8742

■ **JACK MORTON WORLDWIDE INC** p 773
142 Berkeley St Ste 6, Boston MA 02116
Tel (617) 585-7000 *SIC* 8748 8742

JOHN SNOW INC p 789
44 Farnsworth St Fl 7, Boston MA 02210
Tel (617) 482-9485 *SIC* 8742

JSI RESEARCH AND TRAINING INSTITUTE INC p 796
44 Farnsworth St Fl 7, Boston MA 02210
Tel (617) 482-9485 *SIC* 8742

■ **MERCER HUMAN RESOURCE CONSULTING OF MASSACHUSETTS INC** p 944
99 High St, Boston MA 02110
Tel (617) 450-6000 *SIC* 8742

NATIXIS GLOBAL ASSET MANAGEMENT LP p 1018
399 Boylston St, Boston MA 02116
Tel (617) 449-2100 *SIC* 6282 8742

PROMUTUAL GROUP INC p 1183
1 Financial Ctr Fl 13, Boston MA 02111
Tel (617) 330-1755 *SIC* 6321 8742

PUBLIC CONSULTING GROUP INC p 1189
148 State St Fl 10, Boston MA 02109
Tel (617) 426-2026 *SIC* 8742

RENAISSANCE WORLDWIDE INC p 1223
711 Boylston St, Boston MA 02116
Tel (617) 535-5000
SIC 7363 8742 7379 7361 8748 7371

SAPIENT CORP p 1281
131 Dartmouth St Ste 301, Boston MA 02116
Tel (617) 621-0200
SIC 7373 7374 7371 8742

STONE & WEBSTER OVERSEAS GROUP INC p 1391
45 Milk St Bsmt, Boston MA 02109
Tel (617) 778-7500 *SIC* 8742 8711

TUFTS MEDICAL CENTER INC p 1491
800 Washington St, Boston MA 02111
Tel (617) 636-5000
SIC 8062 7371 8742 8741

■ **WILLIAM GALLAGHER ASSOCIATES INSURANCE BROKERS INC** p 1610
470 Atlantic Ave Fl 13, Boston MA 02210
Tel (617) 261-6700 *SIC* 6411 8742

INVENTIV GROUP HOLDINGS INC p 761
1 Van De Graaff Dr, Burlington MA 01803
Tel (609) 951-6800 *SIC* 8742 8731

PSE HOLDING CORP p 1188
115 Constitution Blvd, Franklin MA 02038
Tel (508) 553-3800 *SIC* 8742

WINTERGREEN RESEARCH INC p 1617
6 Raymond St, Lexington MA 02421
Tel (781) 863-5078 *SIC* 8748 8742

MANAGEMENT SCIENCES FOR HEALTH INC p 900
200 Rivers Edge Dr, Medford MA 02155
Tel (617) 250-9500 *SIC* 8742

▲ **RMR GROUP INC** p 1239
255 Washington St Ste 300, Newton MA 02458
Tel (617) 928-1300 *SIC* 8742

IRC INC p 764
1 Corporation Way Ste 230, Peabody MA 01960
Tel (781) 581-9800 *SIC* 8742

ARBELLA SERVICE CO INC p 102
1100 Crown Colony Dr, Quincy MA 02169
Tel (617) 328-2800 *SIC* 8742

MCMC LLC p 932
300 Crown Colony Dr # 203, Quincy MA 02169
Tel (617) 375-7700 *SIC* 8742

AMERICAN DENTAL PARTNERS INC p 71
401 Edgewater Pl Ste 430, Wakefield MA 01880
Tel (781) 224-0880 *SIC* 8621 8742

▲ **EDGEWATER TECHNOLOGY INC** p 477
200 Harvard Mill Sq # 210, Wakefield MA 01880
Tel (781) 246-3343 *SIC* 7379 8742

▲ **ALERE INC** p 48
51 Sawyer Rd Ste 200, Waltham MA 02453
Tel (781) 647-3900 *SIC* 2835 8071 8742

■ **CSC CONSULTING INC** p 397
404 Wyman St Ste 355, Waltham MA 02451
Tel (781) 890-7446 *SIC* 7373 7371 8742

■ **CHARLES RIVER LABORATORIES INC** p 289
251 Ballardvale St, Wilmington MA 01887
Tel (978) 658-6000
SIC 8742 8734 8731 0279

■ **TRUVEN HEALTH ANALYTICS INC** p 1489
100 Phoenix Dr, Ann Arbor MI 48108
Tel (734) 913-3000 *SIC* 8742

■ **TRUVEN HOLDING CORP** p 1489
100 Phoenix Dr Ste 100, Ann Arbor MI 48108
Tel (734) 913-3000 *SIC* 8742

MC DONALDS OF CALHOUN INC p 925
806 Columbia Ave W, Battle Creek MI 49015
Tel (269) 965-1402 *SIC* 5812 8742 6794

QUESTOR MANAGEMENT CO LLC p 1199
101 Southfield Rd Fl 2, Birmingham MI 48009
Tel (248) 593-1930 *SIC* 8742

QUESTOR PARTNERS FUND II LP p 1199
101 Southfield Rd 2, Birmingham MI 48009
Tel (248) 593-1930 *SIC* 8742 2099

SANCTUS LLC p 1278
348 E Maple Rd, Birmingham MI 48009
Tel (248) 594-2396 *SIC* 8741 7319 8742

FIRST INTERNATIONAL EXCHANGE GROUP (INC) p 547
6632 Telegraph Rd Ste 231, Bloomfield Hills MI 48301
Tel (248) 737-9300 *SIC* 8742

LOWRY HOLDING CO INC p 882
9420 Maltby Rd, Brighton MI 48116
Tel (810) 229-7200
SIC 5045 2672 8742 7373 5044 5734

DYKEMA GOSSETT PLLC p 464
400 Renaissance Ctr, Detroit MI 48243
Tel (313) 568-6800 *SIC* 8111 8742

MSX INTERNATIONAL INC p 997
500 Woodward Ave Ste 2150, Detroit MI 48226
Tel (248) 829-6300
SIC 8748 7363 8742 8711

STRATEGIC STAFFING SOLUTIONS LC p 1392
645 Griswold St Ste 2900, Detroit MI 48226
Tel (888) 738-3261 *SIC* 8742

URBAN SCIENCE APPLICATIONS INC p 1530
400 Renaissance Ctr # 2900, Detroit MI 48243
Tel (313) 259-9900 *SIC* 8742

ACCESSPOINT LLC p 15
28800 Orchard Lake Rd # 200, Farmington Hills MI 48334
Tel (248) 504-6539 *SIC* 8742

MINACS GROUP USA INC p 972
34115 W 12 Mile Rd, Farmington Hills MI 48331
Tel (248) 553-8355 *SIC* 7389 8742

SERRA AUTOMOTIVE INC p 1306
3118 E Hill Rd, Grand Blanc MI 48439
Tel (810) 695-1451 *SIC* 5511 8742

DIALOGDIRECT INC p 436
13700 Oakland St, Highland Park MI 48203
Tel (313) 957-5100 *SIC* 8742

DIALOGDIRECT LLC p 436
13700 Oakland St, Highland Park MI 48203
Tel (313) 957-5100 *SIC* 6799 8742

PICO ENTERPRISES INC p 1146
4150 Grange Hall Rd, Holly MI 48442
Tel (248) 328-5000 *SIC* 8742

MIRAMED GLOBAL SERVICES INC p 974
255 W Michigan Ave, Jackson MI 49201
Tel (866) 544-6647 *SIC* 8742

MARKET STRATEGIES INC p 908
17430 College Pkwy, Livonia MI 48152
Tel (734) 542-7600 *SIC* 8742 8732

LEONA GROUP L L C p 856
2125 University Park Dr # 250, Okemos MI 48864
Tel (517) 333-9030 *SIC* 8742

RSI LOGISTICS INC p 1256
2419 Science Pkwy, Okemos MI 48864
Tel (517) 349-7713 *SIC* 8742 4231

JOHNSON ELECTRIC AUTOMOTIVE INC p 791
47660 Halyard Dr, Plymouth MI 48170
Tel (734) 392-1022 *SIC* 5013 8731 8742

TECHNICAL TRAINING INC p 1431
3903 W Hamlin Rd, Rochester Hills MI 48309
Tel (248) 853-5550 *SIC* 8742 8999

HSS LLC p 715
5310 Hampton Pl Ste B, Saginaw MI 48604
Tel (989) 777-2983 *SIC* 8741 8742 7389

MORLEY COMPANIES INC p 989
1 Morley Plz, Saginaw MI 48603
Tel (989) 791-2550 *SIC* 8742 4724

PLANTE & MORAN PLLC p 1154
27400 Northwestern Hwy # 300, Southfield MI 48034
Tel (248) 223-3247 *SIC* 8721 8742

R L POLK & CO p 1202
26933 Northwestern Hwy, Southfield MI 48033
Tel (248) 728-7000 *SIC* 8742

TIBA LLC p 1452
29600 Southfield Rd 200, Southfield MI 48076
Tel (248) 633-6067 *SIC* 8742

ADMINISTRATIVE EMPLOYER SERVICES INC p 23
13900 Lakeside Cir 200, Sterling Heights MI 48313
Tel (586) 997-3377 *SIC* 8742

VCST INC p 1545
13854 Lakeside Cir 201, Sterling Heights MI 48313
Tel (586) 685-1747 *SIC* 8742

LINC LOGISTICS CO p 866
12755 E 9 Mile Rd, Warren MI 48089
Tel (586) 467-1500 *SIC* 8742

■ **LOGISTICS INSIGHT CORP** p 874
12755 E 9 Mile Rd, Warren MI 48089
Tel (586) 467-1500 *SIC* 8742

WIMSATT BUILDING MATERIALS CORP p 1614
36340 Van Born Rd, Wayne MI 48184
Tel (734) 722-3460 *SIC* 5033 8742

SINGH MANAGEMENT CO INC p 1326
7125 Orchard Lake Rd # 200, West Bloomfield MI 48322
Tel (248) 865-1600 *SIC* 6531 6513 8742

UPONOR NORTH AMERICA INC p 1529
5925 148th St W, Apple Valley MN 55124
Tel (952) 891-2000 *SIC* 8742 3312

CAPITOL SALES CO INC p 251
1245 Trapp Rd Ste 130, Eagan MN 55121
Tel (651) 688-6830 *SIC* 5064 5065 8742

■ **OPTUMINSIGHT INC** p 1091
11000 Optum Cir, Eden Prairie MN 55344
Tel (952) 833-7100
SIC 7371 7375 8742 8741

SCHOENECKERS INC p 1288
7630 Bush Lake Rd, Edina MN 55439
Tel (952) 835-4800 *SIC* 8742 7361

■ **AMERICAN ENTERPRISE INVESTMENT SERVICES INC** p 71
70400 Axp Financial Ctr, Minneapolis MN 55474
Tel (612) 671-3131 *SIC* 8742

■ **BEST BUY ENTERPRISE SERVICES INC** p 177
7601 Penn Ave S, Minneapolis MN 55423
Tel (612) 291-1000 *SIC* 8742

C&N ETHANOL MARKETING LLC p 234
8011 34th Ave S Ste 350, Minneapolis MN 55425
Tel (888) 263-8357 *SIC* 8742

CLIFTONLARSONALLEN LLP p 326
220 S 6th St Ste 300, Minneapolis MN 55402
Tel (612) 376-4620 *SIC* 8742 7371 8721

■ **KORN FERRY HAY GROUP INC** p 828
33 S 6th St Ste 4900, Minneapolis MN 55402
Tel (612) 339-0927 *SIC* 8742

NATIONAL MARROW DONOR PROGRAM INC p 1014
500 N 5th St, Minneapolis MN 55401
Tel (612) 627-5800 *SIC* 8099 8742

POHLAD COMPANIES p 1159
60 S 6th St Ste 3700, Minneapolis MN 55402
Tel (612) 661-3700
SIC 8742 7929 6531 5013 7549 7379

THRIVENT FINANCIAL FOR LUTHERANS FOUNDATION p 1451
625 4th Ave S, Minneapolis MN 55415
Tel (920) 734-5721
SIC 6311 6321 8742 6411 6211

CARLSON INC p 258
701 Carlson Pkwy, Minnetonka MN 55305
Tel (763) 212-5000
SIC 7011 5812 6794 8742 8743 7389

RADISSON HOTELS INTERNATIONAL INC p 1204
701 Carlson Pkwy, Minnetonka MN 55305
Tel (763) 212-5000
SIC 7011 6794 6552 6531 8742 7389

FRANDSEN CORP p 574
5481 Saint Croix Trl # 200, North Branch MN 55056
Tel (651) 407-5700 *SIC* 8742

TAYLOR CORP p 1427
1725 Roe Crest Dr, North Mankato MN 56003
Tel (507) 625-2828
SIC 8742 2752 2677 2759

SKYBRIDGE AMERICAS INC p 1330
7600 69th Ave, Rockford MN 55373
Tel (763) 477-7600 *SIC* 8742

ARCHWAY MARKETING HOLDINGS INC p 105
19850 S Diamond Lake Rd, Rogers MN 55374
Tel (763) 428-3300 *SIC* 8742

ARCHWAY MARKETING SERVICES INC p 105
19850 S Diamond Lake Rd, Rogers MN 55374
Tel (763) 428-3300 *SIC* 8742 4225

AVIANDS LLC p 137
1751 County Road B W # 300, Roseville MN 55113
Tel (651) 631-0940 *SIC* 8742

CORVAL GROUP INC p 373
1633 Eustis St, Saint Paul MN 55108
Tel (651) 645-0451 *SIC* 8742

IND SCHOOL DIST 621 p 735
350 Highway 96 W, Saint Paul MN 55126
Tel (651) 621-6000 *SIC* 8211 8742

POWER/MATION DIVISION INC p 1165
1310 Energy Ln, Saint Paul MN 55108
Tel (651) 605-3300
SIC 5085 5065 5084 5045 8742 7549

PAR SYSTEMS INC p 1113
707 County Road E W, Shoreview MN 55126
Tel (651) 484-7261 *SIC* 8742

MINACT INC p 972
5220 Keele St, Jackson MS 39206
Tel (601) 362-1631 *SIC* 8331 8742

HORNE LLP p 708
1020 Highland Colony Pkwy # 400, Ridgeland MS 39157
Tel (601) 948-0940 *SIC* 8721 8742

PREMIUM RETAIL SERVICES INC p 1171
618 Spirit Dr Ste 200, Chesterfield MO 63005
Tel (636) 728-0592 *SIC* 8742

■ **VANLINER GROUP INC** p 1544
1 Premier Dr, Fenton MO 63026
Tel (636) 343-9889 *SIC* 6411 8742

■ **CERNER DHT INC** p 284
2800 Rock Creek Pkwy, Kansas City MO 64117
Tel (816) 221-1024 *SIC* 8742 7372 7371

■ **H&R BLOCK GROUP INC** p 651
4400 Main St, Kansas City MO 64111
Tel (816) 854-3000 *SIC* 6211 8721 8742

MISSOURI VALLEY LINE CONTRUCTORS p 976
7505 Nw Tffany Sprng Pkwy, Kansas City MO 64153
Tel (816) 891-9066 *SIC* 8742 8631

SAINT LUKES HOSPITAL OF KANSAS CITY p 1270
4401 Wornall Rd, Kansas City MO 64111
Tel (816) 932-2000
SIC 8062 8742 8011 6512 8082 7322

VML INC p 1563
250 Nw Richards Rd # 255, Kansas City MO 64116
Tel (816) 283-0700 *SIC* 7311 7373 8742

▲ **AMERICAN RAILCAR INDUSTRIES INC** p 78
100 Clark St, Saint Charles MO 63301
Tel (636) 940-6000 *SIC* 3743 8742

CHRISTIAN HOSPITAL NORTHEAST SURGERY CENTER p 303
11133 Dunn Rd, Saint Louis MO 63136
Tel (314) 355-2300 *SIC* 8742 8049 5912

DAUGHERTY SYSTEMS INC p 414
3 Cityplace Dr Ste 400, Saint Louis MO 63141
Tel (314) 432-8200
SIC 7379 7371 8742 7373 7372

FUSION PERFORMANCE MARKETING LLC p 585
1928 Locust St, Saint Louis MO 63103
Tel (314) 576-7500 *SIC* 8742

HBE CORP p 671
11330 Olive Blvd, Saint Louis MO 63141
Tel (314) 567-9000 *SIC* 1542 8742

HOK GROUP INC p 699
10 S Broadway Ste 200, Saint Louis MO 63102
Tel (314) 421-2000 *SIC* 8711 8712 8742

■ **APPLIED UNDERWRITERS INC** p 100
10805 Old Mill Rd, Omaha NE 68154
Tel (402) 342-4900
SIC 6331 8721 8741 8742

HDR ENGINEERING INC p 673
8404 Indian Hills Dr, Omaha NE 68114
Tel (402) 399-1000 *SIC* 8742 8711

HDR INC p 673
8404 Indian Hills Dr, Omaha NE 68114
Tel (402) 399-1000
SIC 8712 8711 8742 8748 4789

SILVERSTONE GROUP INC p 1324
11516 Miracle Hills Dr # 100, Omaha NE 68154
Tel (402) 964-5400
SIC 6371 6311 8742 6411

TENASKA CAPITAL MANAGEMENT LLC p 1437
14302 Fnb Pkwy, Omaha NE 68154
Tel (402) 691-9571 *SIC* 8742

TENASKA ENERGY INC p 1437
14302 Fnb Pkwy, Omaha NE 68154
Tel (402) 691-9500
SIC 4911 4924 4939 8742

TENASKA INC p 1437
14302 Fnb Pkwy, Omaha NE 68154
Tel (402) 691-9500
SIC 4924 4911 4939 8742

HUSKER AG MARKETING INC p 721
54048 Highway 20, Plainview NE 68769
Tel (402) 582-4446 *SIC* 8742

TRAX INTERNATIONAL CORP p 1475
8337 W Sunset Rd Ste 250, Las Vegas NV 89113
Tel (702) 216-4455
SIC 7373 8711 7376 8742 8744

IT CONVERGENCE p 767
5370 Kietzke Ln Ste 200, Reno NV 89511
Tel (415) 675-7935 *SIC* 8742

NEW ENGLAND ALLIANCE FOR HEALTH LLC p 1029
1 Medical Center Dr, Lebanon NH 03756
Tel (603) 653-1223 *SIC* 8742

SURGE RESOURCES INC p 1408
920 Candia Rd, Manchester NH 03109
Tel (603) 623-0007 *SIC* 8742 7361 7363

COLWEN MANAGEMENT INC p 343
230 Commerce Way Ste 200, Portsmouth NH 03801
Tel (603) 897-6100 *SIC* 8742 7389

NFI INTERACTIVE LOGISTICS LLC p 1041
1515 Burnt Mill Rd, Cherry Hill NJ 08003
Tel (856) 857-1324 *SIC* 4731 8742

NB VENTURES INC p 1021
100 Walnut Ave Ste 304, Clark NJ 07066
Tel (732) 382-6565 *SIC* 8742

C & A MARKETING INC p 231
114 Tived Ln E, Edison NJ 08837
Tel (201) 881-1900
SIC 5065 8742 7384 5946 7359 7221

PWC STRATEGY& (US) LLC p 1193
300 Campus Dr Ste 100, Florham Park NJ 07932
Tel (973) 630-6791 *SIC* 8742

INNOVACARE SERVICES CO LLC p 744
173 Bridge Plz N, Fort Lee NJ 07024
Tel (201) 969-2300
SIC 6324 8011 8741 8742

ROSETTA LLC p 1251
100 American Metro Blvd # 201, Hamilton NJ 08619
Tel (609) 689-6100 *SIC* 8742

SHIPCO TRANSPORT INC p 1317
80 Washington St, Hoboken NJ 07030
Tel (973) 457-3300 *SIC* 8742 4731

DIRECT ENERGY BUSINESS MARKETING LLC p 441
194 Wood Ave S Fl 2, Iselin NJ 08830
Tel (732) 516-7500 *SIC* 8742

AXON SOLUTIONS INC p 140
1 Evertrust Plz Ste 501, Jersey City NJ 07302
Tel (201) 680-7000 *SIC* 8742

C SCEC-USA INC p 233
525 Washington Blvd Fl 31, Jersey City NJ 07310
Tel (201) 876-2788 *SIC* 8742

J KNIPPER AND CO INC p 771
1 Healthcare Way, Lakewood NJ 08701
Tel (732) 905-7878 *SIC* 8742

■ AIG TECHNOLOGIES INC p 38
2 Peach Tree Hill Rd, Livingston NJ 07039
Tel (973) 597-0285 *SIC* 8742 6411 7374

■ RCM TECHNOLOGIES (USA) INC p 1212
2500 Mcclellan Ave # 350, Pennsauken NJ 08109
Tel (856) 356-4500 *SIC* 8742 7379 8711

TELCORDIA TECHNOLOGIES INC p 1433
444 Hoes Ln, Piscataway NJ 08854
Tel (732) 699-6800 *SIC* 7371 7373 8742

MASER CONSULTING PA p 915
331 Newman Springs Rd # 203, Red Bank NJ 07701
Tel (732) 383-1950 *SIC* 8711 8742 8713

SAMSUNG C&T AMERICA INC p 1275
105 Challenger Rd Fl 3, Ridgefield Park NJ 07660
Tel (201) 229-4000 *SIC* 5169 6799 8742

■ XEROX HR SOLUTIONS LLC p 1631
200 Plaza Dr Nj, Secaucus NJ 07094
Tel (201) 902-2300 *SIC* 8742

HEALTH PRODUCTS RESEARCH INC p 675
500 Atrium Dr Ste 100, Somerset NJ 08873
Tel (908) 534-4148 *SIC* 8742 8732

VENTIV HEALTH INC p 1548
200 Cottontail Ln Ste J, Somerset NJ 08873
Tel (732) 537-4800 *SIC* 8742

MINDLANCE INC p 972
1095 Morris Ave Unit 101a, Union NJ 07083
Tel (201) 386-5400 *SIC* 8742

ADVANTEDGE HEALTHCARE SOLUTIONS INC p 27
30 Technology Dr Ste 1n, Warren NJ 07059
Tel (908) 279-8111 *SIC* 8742

VITAQUEST INTERNATIONAL LLC p 1563
8 Henderson Dr, West Caldwell NJ 07006
Tel (973) 575-9200
SIC 2834 5149 5122 8742

LEE HECHT HARRISON LLC p 851
50 Tice Blvd Ste 115, Woodcliff Lake NJ 07677
Tel (201) 930-9333 *SIC* 8742 8741

NEW YORK STATE ENVIRONMENTAL FACILITIES CORP p 1036
625 Broadway, Albany NY 12207
Tel (518) 486-9267 *SIC* 8742

TRITEC BUILDING CO INC p 1483
45 Research Way Ste 100, East Setauket NY 11733
Tel (631) 751-0300 *SIC* 6552 8742

MANNING & NAPIER ADVISORS LLC p 902
290 Woodcliff Dr Ste 300, Fairport NY 14450
Tel (800) 551-0224 *SIC* 6282 8742 7375

▲ MANNING & NAPIER INC p 902
290 Woodcliff Dr Ste 300, Fairport NY 14450
Tel (585) 325-6880 *SIC* 6282 8742 6722

■ SPX FLOWTECHNOLOGY SYSTEMS INC p 1362
105 Crosspoint Pkwy, Getzville NY 14068
Tel (716) 692-3000 *SIC* 3556 8742

AJILON LLC p 41
175 Broadhollow Rd, Melville NY 11747
Tel (631) 844-7800 *SIC* 7379 8742 7374

EXPANSION STRATEGIES INC p 519
17 Rollingwood Dr, New Hartford NY 13413
Tel (315) 793-3137 *SIC* 8742

488 PERFORMANCE GROUP INC p 3
18 E 41st St Fl 13, New York NY 10017
Tel (212) 758-4385 *SIC* 8742

■ A C S HUMAN RESOURCES SOLUTIONS INC p 5
112 W 34th St Ste 605, New York NY 10120
Tel (212) 685-7981 *SIC* 8742 6282

ADVANSTAR INC p 26
641 Lexington Ave Fl 8, New York NY 10022
Tel (212) 951-6600 *SIC* 2721 7389 8742

ADVENTITY INC p 27
444 Park Ave S Ste 1202, New York NY 10016
Tel (212) 404-2468 *SIC* 7375 8742 8732

ALLOY INC p 58
151 W 26th St Fl 11, New York NY 10001
Tel (609) 655-8878
SIC 8743 8742 7331 7312

ALVAREZ & MARSAL CORPORATE PERFORMANCE IMPROVEMENT LLC p 63
600 Madison Ave Fl 8, New York NY 10022
Tel (212) 759-4433 *SIC* 8748 8742

ALVAREZ & MARSAL INC p 63
600 Madison Ave Fl 8, New York NY 10022
Tel (212) 759-4433 *SIC* 8742

■ BORDERFREE INC p 201
292 Madison Ave, New York NY 10017
Tel (212) 299-3500 *SIC* 8742 4731 7312

■ BUCK CONSULTANTS LLC p 222
485 Lexington Ave Fl 10, New York NY 10017
Tel (212) 330-1000 *SIC* 8742 6282 2741

▲ CA INC p 234
520 Madison Ave Fl 22, New York NY 10022
Tel (800) 225-5224 *SIC* 7372 8742

■ CAPITAL IQ INC p 249
55 Water St Fl 49, New York NY 10041
Tel (212) 438-8736 *SIC* 8742

■ CMGRP INC p 329
909 3rd Ave, New York NY 10022
Tel (212) 445-8000
SIC 8743 7311 7319 8742

COGR INC p 334
200 Park Ave Fl 20, New York NY 10166
Tel (212) 370-5600 *SIC* 8742

CORPORATE RESOURCE SERVICES INC p 372
160 Broadway Rm 1300, New York NY 10038
Tel (646) 443-2380 *SIC* 7363 8742

CPA 17 LIMITED PARTNERSHIP p 387
50 Rockefeller Plz, New York NY 10020
Tel (212) 492-1100 *SIC* 8742

CUSHMAN & WAKEFIELD HOLDINGS INC p 402
1290 Ave Of The Americas, New York NY 10104
Tel (212) 841-7500 *SIC* 6531 8742 8732

DELOITTE CONSULTING LLP p 425
30 Rockefeller Plz, New York NY 10112
Tel (212) 492-4000 *SIC* 8742

DELOITTE LLP p 425
30 Rockefeller Plz, New York NY 10112
Tel (212) 492-4000 *SIC* 8742 8721

DUFF & PHELPS LLC p 459
55 E 52nd St Fl 31, New York NY 10055
Tel (212) 871-2000 *SIC* 8742

EISNERAMPER LLP p 482
750 3rd Ave, New York NY 10017
Tel (212) 949-8700 *SIC* 8742 8721

FORESTERS FINANCIAL SERVICES p 567
40 Wall St Fl 10, New York NY 10005
Tel (212) 858-8000
SIC 6036 6211 6282 6311 8742 6153

GELLER & CO LLC p 598
909 3rd Ave Fl 15, New York NY 10022
Tel (212) 583-6000 *SIC* 8742 8721

GENERAL ATLANTIC SERVICE CO LLC p 599
55 E 52nd St Fl 32, New York NY 10055
Tel (203) 629-8600 *SIC* 8742

GENESIS CORP p 602
950 3rd Ave Ste 2702, New York NY 10022
Tel (212) 688-5522 *SIC* 7379 8742

GUGGENHEIM PARTNERS LLC p 645
330 Madison Ave Rm 201, New York NY 10017
Tel (212) 739-0700 *SIC* 8742

■ GUY CARPENTER & CO LLC p 648
1166 Ave Of The Americas, New York NY 10036
Tel (917) 937-3000 *SIC* 6411 8742 8732

HELMSLEY ENTERPRISES INC p 682
230 Park Ave Rm 659, New York NY 10169
Tel (212) 679-3600 *SIC* 6513 8742 1522

HOCHTIEF USA INC p 699
375 Hudson St Fl 6, New York NY 10014
Tel (212) 229-6000
SIC 1542 1541 1522 8741 8742 6799

HUNTER ROBERTS CONSTRUCTION GROUP LLC p 719
55 Water St Fl 51, New York NY 10041
Tel (212) 321-6800 *SIC* 8742 1542

ICROSSING INC p 728
300 W 57th St Fl 20f, New York NY 10019
Tel (212) 649-3900 *SIC* 8742 7311

■ INTERBRAND CORP p 751
130 5th Ave Fl 4, New York NY 10011
Tel (212) 798-7500 *SIC* 8742 7336

▲ INTERPUBLIC GROUP OF COMPANIES INC p 757
909 3rd Ave Fl 7, New York NY 10022
Tel (212) 704-1200 *SIC* 7311 8742

IPSOFT INC p 764
17 State St Fl 14, New York NY 10004
Tel (888) 477-6388
SIC 7376 7363 7374 8742

IPSOS AMERICA INC p 764
1271 Ave Of The, New York NY 10020
Tel (212) 265-3200 *SIC* 8742

KERING AMERICAS INC p 813
3 E 57th St, New York NY 10022
Tel (212) 238-3010 *SIC* 8742

■ KINNEY SYSTEM INC p 821
60 Madison Ave Fl 7, New York NY 10010
Tel (212) 889-2056 *SIC* 7521 8742

KROLL LLC p 830
600 3rd Ave Fl 4, New York NY 10016
Tel (212) 593-1000
SIC 7381 8742 8748 7389

LEGENDS HOSPITALITY MANAGEMENT LIMITED LIABILITY CO p 853
61 Broadway Ste 2400, New York NY 10006
Tel (646) 977-8521 *SIC* 8741 8744 8742

LENDLEASE (US) CONSTRUCTION HOLDINGS INC p 855
200 Park Ave Fl 9, New York NY 10166
Tel (212) 592-6700 *SIC* 1542 1541 8742

LENDLEASE (US) CONSTRUCTION INC p 855
200 Park Ave Fl 9, New York NY 10166
Tel (212) 592-6700
SIC 1541 1542 1522 8741 8742

LENDLEASE (US) CONSTRUCTION LMB INC p 855
200 Park Ave Fl 9, New York NY 10166
Tel (212) 592-6700
SIC 1522 1541 1542 8741 8742

M/L BOVIS HOLDINGS LTD p 890
200 Park Ave Fl 9, New York NY 10166
Tel (212) 592-6700
SIC 1522 1541 1542 8741 8742

▲ MARSH & MCLENNAN COMPANIES INC p 910
1166 Avenue Of The Americ, New York NY 10036
Tel (212) 345-5000 *SIC* 6411 6282 8742

■ MARSH LLC p 911
1166 Avenue Of The Americ, New York NY 10036
Tel (212) 345-5000 *SIC* 6411 6282 8742

MCKINSEY & CO INC p 930
55 E 52nd St Fl 21, New York NY 10055
Tel (212) 446-7000 *SIC* 8742

■ MERCER (US) INC p 944
1166 Ave Of The Americ, New York NY 10036
Tel (212) 345-7000 *SIC* 8742

■ MERCER HEALTH & BENEFITS LLC p 944
1166 Ave Of The Americas, New York NY 10036
Tel (212) 345-7000 *SIC* 8742

MIDOCEAN US ADVISOR LP p 966
320 Park Ave Fl 16, New York NY 10022
Tel (212) 497-1400 *SIC* 8742

MITSUBISHI GAS CHEMICAL AMERICA INC p 977
655 3rd Ave Fl 24, New York NY 10017
Tel (212) 687-9030 *SIC* 5169 8742

MKTG INC p 979
32 Avenue Of The Americas # 20, New York NY 10013
Tel (212) 366-3481 *SIC* 8742

▲ MSCI INC p 996
250 Greenwich St Fl 49, New York NY 10007
Tel (212) 804-3900
SIC 7389 7371 6282 8742

MULTIPLAN INC p 999
115 5th Ave Fl 7, New York NY 10003
Tel (212) 780-2000 *SIC* 8742

▲ NASDAQ INC p 1008
1 Liberty Plz Ste 4900, New York NY 10006
Tel (212) 401-8700 *SIC* 6231 8742

OGILVY & MATHER WORLDWIDE INC p 1076
636 11th Ave, New York NY 10036
Tel (212) 237-4000
SIC 7311 7812 7375 8742

■ PARIBAS PROPERTIES INC p 1114
787 7th Ave Fl 33, New York NY 10019
Tel (212) 841-3000
SIC 6211 6221 6799 8742

PARSONS BRINCKERHOFF GROUP LLC p 1117
1 Penn Plz 2nd, New York NY 10119
Tel (212) 465-5000 *SIC* 8742 8711 8741

PERKINS EASTMAN ARCHITECTS DPC p 1136
115 5th Ave Fl 3, New York NY 10003
Tel (212) 353-7200 *SIC* 8712 8742 7389

PMX AGENCY INC p 1158
5 Hanover Sq Fl 6, New York NY 10004
Tel (212) 387-0300 *SIC* 8742

PRICEWATERHOUSECOOPERS LLP p 1174
300 Madison Ave Fl 24, New York NY 10017
Tel (646) 471-4000 *SIC* 8721 8742

PROJECT OHR INC p 1182
80 Maiden Ln Fl 10, New York NY 10038
Tel (718) 853-2700 *SIC* 8322 8742

PWC STRATEGY& (US) LLC p 1193
101 Park Ave Fl 18, New York NY 10178
Tel (212) 697-1900 *SIC* 8742

RAKUTEN MARKETING LLC p 1206
215 Park Ave S Fl 9, New York NY 10003
Tel (646) 943-8200 *SIC* 8742 7375

■ RISKMETRICS GROUP INC p 1236
1 Chase Manhattan Plz F, New York NY 10005
Tel (212) 981-7475 *SIC* 8742

ROTHSCHILD NORTH AMERICA INC p 1252
1251 Ave Of The Ave Fl 51, New York NY 10020
Tel (212) 403-3500
SIC 6211 6159 8742 6221 6282 8741

SEGAL GROUP INC p 1300
333 W 34th St, New York NY 10001
Tel (212) 251-5000 *SIC* 8742

SPRINKLR INC p 1361
29 W 35th St Fl 7, New York NY 10001
Tel (917) 933-7800 *SIC* 8742 7372

SURDNA FOUNDATION INC p 1408
330 Madison Ave Fl 30, New York NY 10017
Tel (212) 557-0010 *SIC* 6732 8742

■ TELESECTOR RESOURCES GROUP INC p 1435
140 West St, New York NY 10007
Tel (212) 395-1000 *SIC* 8742

TOWERS WATSON DELAWARE HOLDINGS INC p 1464
335 Madison Ave Fl 20, New York NY 10017
Tel (212) 309-3400 *SIC* 8742 8999

TURNER CONSTRUCTION CO INC p 1492
375 Hudson St Fl 6, New York NY 10014
Tel (212) 229-6000
SIC 1542 1541 1522 8741 8742

TURNER CORP p 1492
375 Hudson St Rm 700, New York NY 10014
Tel (212) 229-6000
SIC 1542 1541 1522 8742

VERITAS CAPITAL FUND II L P p 1549
590 Madison Ave Ste 3501, New York NY 10022
Tel (212) 415-6700 *SIC* 8742 7374

WILLIS NORTH AMERICA INC p 1612
200 Liberty St Fl 7, New York NY 10281
Tel (212) 915-8888
SIC 6411 8742 8999 8748

YOUNG & RUBICAM INC p 1637
3 Columbus Cir Fl 8, New York NY 10019
Tel (212) 210-3000 *SIC* 8742

ZETA INTERACTIVE CORP p 1642
185 Madison Ave, New York NY 10016
Tel (212) 967-5055 *SIC* 8742

HOLT CONSTRUCTION CORP p 702
50 E Washington Ave, Pearl River NY 10965
Tel (845) 735-4054 *SIC* 1541 8742

SUTHERLAND GLOBAL SERVICES INC p 1409
1160 Pittsford Victor Rd A, Pittsford NY 14534
Tel (585) 586-5757 *SIC* 8742

PUBLISHERS CLEARING HOUSE LLC p 1190
382 Channel Dr, Port Washington NY 11050
Tel (516) 883-5432 *SIC* 5961 8742

MARKIT INC p 909
250 Mill St Ste 303, Rochester NY 14614
Tel (585) 777-4018 *SIC* 8742

FLIK INTERNATIONAL CORP p 557
2 International Dr Fl 2, Rye Brook NY 10573
Tel (914) 935-5300 *SIC* 8742 5812

■ AYCO CO L P p 140
321 Broadway, Saratoga Springs NY 12866
Tel (518) 886-4000
SIC 6411 6282 8742 7291

■ SYSTEMS MADE SIMPLE INC p 1419
149 Northern Concourse # 1, Syracuse NY 13212
Tel (315) 455-3200 *SIC* 7371 8742

OPENLINK FINANCIAL LLC p 1089
1502 Rxr Plz Fl 15w, Uniondale NY 11556
Tel (516) 227-6600 *SIC* 7371 7372 8742

■ SPAR MARAKETING FORCE INC p 1354
333 Westc Ave South Build, White Plains NY 10604
Tel (914) 332-4100 *SIC* 8742

EXECUSOURCE INC p 517
5925 Carnegie Blvd # 350, Charlotte NC 28209
Tel (704) 483-9800 *SIC* 8742

MEDCATH INC p 935
10800 Sikes Pl Ste 200, Charlotte NC 28277
Tel (704) 815-7700 *SIC* 8069 8093 8742

▲ PREMIER INC p 1170
13034 Balntyn Corp Pl, Charlotte NC 28277
Tel (704) 357-0022 *SIC* 8742 7375

BKRY PHYSICIAN GROUP INC p 186
1000 Park Forty Plz # 500, Durham NC 27713
Tel (919) 383-0355 *SIC* 8741 8742

■ CONSTELLA GROUP LLC p 360
2605 Meridian Pkwy # 200, Durham NC 27713
Tel (919) 544-8500
SIC 7371 8742 7375 8748 8731 8071

STERLING GROUP PHYSICIAN SERVICES LLC p 1387
1000 Park Forty Plz # 500, Durham NC 27713
Tel (919) 383-0355 *SIC* 8741 8742

TOSHIBA GLOBAL COMMERCE SOLUTIONS INC p 1462
3901 S Miami Blvd, Durham NC 27703
Tel (984) 444-7153 *SIC* 8742 7375

GET YOU FOUND ONLINE MARKETING INC p 609
301 S Elm St Ste 401, Greensboro NC 27401
Tel (336) 790-6735 *SIC* 8742

TRANSPORTATION INSIGHT LLC p 1472
310 Main Avenue Way Se, Hickory NC 28602
Tel (828) 485-5000 *SIC* 8742

ZEN HRO INC p 1642
110 Hepler St Ste E, Kernersville NC 27284
Tel (877) 569-8660 *SIC* 7363 8742

■ HANESBRANDS DIRECT LLC p 657
450 W Hanes Mill Rd, Morganton NC 28655
Tel (336) 519-8080 *SIC* 8742

ATLANTIC COAST MERCHANDISING LLC p 126
599 Wood Hollow Rd, Taylorsville NC 28681
Tel (910) 300-9231 *SIC* 8742 7389

RIGHT HUMAN RESOURCE CONSULTANTS INC p 1234
4445 Lake Forest Dr # 470, Blue Ash OH 45242
Tel (513) 733-1313 *SIC* 8742 7361

DE FOXX & ASSOCIATES INC p 419
324 W 9th St Fl 5, Cincinnati OH 45202
Tel (513) 621-5522 *SIC* 8742 8741

FIRST TRANSIT INC p 550
600 Vine St Ste 1400, Cincinnati OH 45202
Tel (513) 241-2200 *SIC* 8741 7539 8742

AUSTIN BUILDING AND DESIGN INC p 132
6095 Parkland Blvd # 100, Cleveland OH 44124
Tel (440) 544-2600
SIC 1541 1542 8742 8711 8712

▲ CBIZ INC p 268
6050 Oak Tree Blvd # 500, Cleveland OH 44131
Tel (216) 447-9000 *SIC* 8742 7389 7363

■ COMEX NORTH AMERICA INC p 344
101 W Prospect Ave # 1020, Cleveland OH 44115
Tel (303) 307-2100
SIC 2851 8742 5198 5231

NCS HEALTHCARE INC p 1022
3201 Entp Pkwy Ste 220, Cleveland OH 44122
Tel (216) 514-3350
SIC 5122 8093 8049 8082 8742 5912

CORPORATE FINANCE ASSOCIATES OF COLUMBUS INC p 372
671 Camden Yard Ct, Columbus OH 43235
Tel (614) 457-9219 *SIC* 8742 7389 6211

MIDWEST MOTOR SUPPLY CO p 967
4800 Roberts Rd, Columbus OH 43228
Tel (800) 233-1294 *SIC* 3965 3399 8742

NATIONWIDE FINANCIAL SERVICES INC p 1017
1 Nationwide Plz, Columbus OH 43215
Tel (614) 249-7111 *SIC* 6311 6411 8742

SAFELITE SOLUTIONS LLC p 1266
7400 Safelite Way, Columbus OH 43235
Tel (614) 210-9000 *SIC* 8742

STANDARD REGISTER INC p 1376
600 Albany St, Dayton OH 45417
Tel (937) 221-1000 *SIC* 8742

FRANK GATES COMPANIES INC p 574
5000 Bradenton Ave, Dublin OH 43017
Tel (614) 793-8000 *SIC* 8742 6411

FRANK GATES SERVICE CO p 574
5000 Bradenton Ave # 100, Dublin OH 43017
Tel (614) 793-8000 *SIC* 8742

TRILOGY FULFILLMENT LLC p 1480
6600 Alum Creek Dr, Groveport OH 43125
Tel (614) 491-0553 *SIC* 8742

■ FEDEX SUPPLY CHAIN SERVICES INC p 537
5455 Darrow Rd, Hudson OH 44236
Tel (800) 588-3020
SIC 8742 4213 8741 4731

ADVICS NORTH AMERICA INC p 28
1650 Kingsview Dr, Lebanon OH 45036
Tel (513) 696-5450
SIC 8731 8742 5013 5531

TSG RESOURCES INC p 1489
339 E Maple St Ste 110, North Canton OH 44720
Tel (330) 498-8107 *SIC* 8742

JARRETT LOGISTICS SYSTEMS INC p 778
1347 N Main St, Orrville OH 44667
Tel (330) 682-0099 *SIC* 8742 4731

SSOE INC p 1364
1001 Madison Ave Ste A, Toledo OH 43604
Tel (419) 255-3830
SIC 8711 8712 8742 1541 7389

EXPERIENT INC p 520
2500 E Enterprise Pkwy, Twinsburg OH 44087
Tel (330) 425-8333 *SIC* 8742

AVI FOOD SYSTEMS INC p 137
2590 Elm Rd Ne, Warren OH 44483
Tel (330) 372-6000 *SIC* 5962 5812 8742

PROGRESSIVE ENTERPRISES HOLDINGS INC p 1181
250 Progressive Way, Westerville OH 43082
Tel (614) 794-3300 *SIC* 8742

ACCORD HUMAN RESOURCES INC p 15
210 Park Ave Ste 1200, Oklahoma City OK 73102
Tel (405) 232-9888 SIC 8742

ADDISON GROUP L L C p 22
901 N Lincoln Blvd # 305, Oklahoma City OK 73104
Tel (405) 235-6700 SIC 7361 8742

INTEGRIS PHYSICIANS SERVICES INC p 749
5300 N Independence Ave # 260, Oklahoma City OK 73112
Tel (405) 951-2529 SIC 8742

OTAK INC p 1097
808 Sw 3rd Ave Ste 220, Portland OR 97204
Tel (503) 274-5445
SIC 0781 8712 8711 8713 8742 8999

VA PORTLAND HEALTH CARE SYSTEM p 1538
3710 Sw Us Vtrans Hosp Rd, Portland OR 97239
Tel (503) 273-5048 SIC 8062 8742

IDEAL CONCEPTS INC p 729
667 Union Blvd, Allentown PA 18109
Tel (610) 740-0000 SIC 8742

CORRECTIONAL MEDICAL CARE INC p 372
980 Harvest Dr Ste 202, Blue Bell PA 19422
Tel (215) 542-5800 SIC 6324 8742

UNITEK USA LLC p 1515
1777 Sentry Pkwy W # 302, Blue Bell PA 19422
Tel (267) 464-1700 SIC 8742 8741

DEVELOPMENT DIMENSIONS INTERNATIONAL INC p 433
1225 Washington Pike, Bridgeville PA 15017
Tel (412) 257-0600 SIC 8742

BRYN MAWR HOSPITAL p 221
130 S Bryn Mawr Ave, Bryn Mawr PA 19010
Tel (610) 526-3620 SIC 8742

CROTHALL HEALTHCARE INC p 394
1500 Liberty Ridge Dr # 210, Chesterbrook PA 19087
Tel (610) 576-5100 SIC 8742

SMG HOLDINGS INC p 1332
300 Cnshohckn State Rd # 450, Conshohocken PA 19428
Tel (610) 729-7900 SIC 6512 8742 7922

KM2 SOLUTIONS LLC p 824
112 Christine Dr, Downingtown PA 19335
Tel (610) 213-1408 SIC 8742

AMERICAS BUSINESS SOLUTION LLC p 81
1070 Coolbaugh Rd, East Stroudsburg PA 18302
Tel (718) 308-1331 SIC 8741 8742

MERCYHURST UNIVERSITY p 948
501 E 38th St, Erie PA 16546
Tel (814) 824-2000
SIC 8221 8243 8742 8299

MILL SERVICES CORP p 969
12 Monongahela Ave, Glassport PA 15045
Tel (412) 678-6141
SIC 3295 1422 8742 3341

PSECU SERVICES INC p 1188
1 Credit Union Pl Ste 1, Harrisburg PA 17110
Tel (800) 237-7238 SIC 8742

INTERNATIONAL MILL SERVICE INC p 756
1155 Bus Ctr Dr Ste 200, Horsham PA 19044
Tel (215) 956-5500
SIC 3295 3341 1422 8742

■ TELERX MARKETING INC p 1435
723 Dresher Rd, Horsham PA 19044
Tel (215) 347-5700 SIC 7389 8742

ASHFIELD HEALTHCARE LLC p 117
1 Ivybrook Blvd Ste 110, Ivyland PA 18974
Tel (215) 347-6400 SIC 8742

RAF INDUSTRIES INC p 1205
165 Township Line Rd # 2100, Jenkintown PA 19046
Tel (215) 572-0738 SIC 8742 3564

CHATHAM FINANCIAL CORP p 291
235 Whitehorse Ln Frnt, Kennett Square PA 19348
Tel (610) 925-3120 SIC 8742

UNITEK GLOBAL SERVICES INC p 1515
2010 Renaissance Blvd, King Of Prussia PA 19406
Tel (267) 464-1700
SIC 1731 8741 8742 8711

AMERICAN FUTURE SYSTEMS INC p 73
370 Technology Dr, Malvern PA 19355
Tel (610) 695-8600 SIC 2741 8742

ERM-NA HOLDINGS CORP p 508
75 Valley Stream Pkwy # 200, Malvern PA 19355
Tel (484) 913-0300 SIC 8711 8748 8742

HENRY F TEICHMANN INC p 684
3009 Washington Rd, Mc Murray PA 15317
Tel (724) 941-9550 SIC 1541 8711 8742

ESSINTIAL ENTERPRISE SOLUTIONS LLC p 510
100 Sterling Pkwy Ste 307, Mechanicsburg PA 17050
Tel (717) 610-3200 SIC 8742

■ REGENCY HOSPITAL CO LLC p 1219
4714 Gettysburg Rd, Mechanicsburg PA 17055
Tel (717) 972-1100 SIC 8742

PUBLICIS HEALTHCARE SOLUTIONS INC p 1190
1000 Floral Vale Blvd # 400, Morrisville PA 19067
Tel (866) 616-4777 SIC 8742

■ ALLIANCE GLOBAL SERVICES LLC p 54
41 University Dr Ste 202, Newtown PA 18940
Tel (610) 234-4301 SIC 8742

▲ EPAM SYSTEMS INC p 504
41 University Dr Ste 202, Newtown PA 18940
Tel (267) 759-9000 SIC 7371 8742

■ GMH COMMUNITIES TRUST p 619
10 Campus Blvd, Newtown Square PA 19073
Tel (610) 355-8000 SIC 6798 6513 8742

GRAHAM PARTNERS INC p 629
3811 West Chester Pike # 200, Newtown Square PA 19073
Tel (610) 408-0500 SIC 8742 6799

▲ SEI INVESTMENTS CO p 1300
1 Freedom Valley Dr, Oaks PA 19456
Tel (610) 676-1000 SIC 6722 8742

■ COMCAST SPECTACOR INC p 343
3601 S Broad St Ste 2, Philadelphia PA 19148
Tel (215) 875-5202 SIC 8742

HAY GROUP HOLDINGS INC p 670
1650 Arch St Ste 2300, Philadelphia PA 19103
Tel (215) 861-2000 SIC 8742 8249 8733

■ HAY GROUP INC p 670
1650 Arch St Ste 2300, Philadelphia PA 19103
Tel (215) 861-2000 SIC 8742

▲ HILL INTERNATIONAL INC p 693
2005 Market St Fl 17, Philadelphia PA 19103
Tel (215) 309-7700 SIC 8742 8741

ASSOCIATED CLEANING CONSULTANTS AND SERVICES INC p 120
431 Davidson Rd, Pittsburgh PA 15239
Tel (412) 795-9200 SIC 7349 8742

BAYER BUSINESS AND TECHNOLOGY SERVICES LLC p 161
100 Bayer Rd, Pittsburgh PA 15205
Tel (412) 777-2000 SIC 8742

MANAGEMENT SCIENCE ASSOCIATES INC p 900
6565 Penn Ave, Pittsburgh PA 15206
Tel (412) 362-2000 SIC 8742 7371

■ MED3000 GROUP INC p 935
680 Andersen Dr Foster Pl, Pittsburgh PA 15220
Tel (412) 937-8887 SIC 8742 8721

NTHRIVE SOLUTIONS p 1065
1275 Drummers Ln Ste 200, Wayne PA 19087
Tel (610) 688-2464 SIC 8742

WESTON SOLUTIONS INC p 1602
1400 Weston Way, West Chester PA 19380
Tel (610) 701-3000 SIC 8742 8748

LOOMIS CO p 877
850 N Park Rd, Wyomissing PA 19610
Tel (610) 374-4040 SIC 6411 8742

ARTHUR J GLATFELTER AGENCY INC p 114
183 Leaders Heights Rd, York PA 17402
Tel (717) 741-0911 SIC 6411 8742

MC WIL GROUP LTD p 925
209 N Beaver St, York PA 17401
Tel (717) 854-7857
SIC 8059 8051 8069 6513 8742 6552

WILMAC CORP p 1613
209 N Beaver St, York PA 17401
Tel (717) 854-7857
SIC 8059 8051 8069 6513 8742 6552

MANAGEMENT SSS INC p 900
Roosevlt Av 145a Fl 3, San Juan PR 00918
Tel (787) 758-7700 SIC 8742

MANAGEMENT TEMPORARY & CONTRACT EMPLOYMENT SERVICES INC p 900
145 A Roosevelt Ave, San Juan PR 00919
Tel (787) 758-7700 SIC 8742

PROVIDENCE PUBLIC SCHOOLS p 1186
797 Westminster St, Providence RI 02903
Tel (401) 456-9100 SIC 8211 8742

WDS INC p 1585
1632 Village Harbor Dr, Clover SC 29710
Tel (803) 619-0301 SIC 5085 1541 8742

M B KAHN CONSTRUCTION CO INC p 889
101 Flintlake Rd, Columbia SC 29223
Tel (803) 736-2950 SIC 1542 8742

RED VENTURES LLC p 1216
1101 Red Ventures Dr, Fort Mill SC 29707
Tel (704) 971-2300 SIC 8742

■ LOCKHEED MARTIN LOGISTICS MANAGEMENT INC p 873
244 Terminal Rd, Greenville SC 29605
Tel (864) 277-7230 SIC 8742

ONEAL CONSTRUCTORS LLC p 1087
10 Falcon Crest Dr # 300, Greenville SC 29607
Tel (864) 298-6510 SIC 8742

CH2M HILL ENGINEERS INC p 286
1500 International Dr, Spartanburg SC 29303
Tel (864) 578-2000 SIC 8711 8742 1629

GEODIS LOGISTICS LLC p 605
7101 Executive Center Dr # 333, Brentwood TN 37027
Tel (615) 401-6400
SIC 4225 8742 4226 4731

INFRASTRUCTURE CORP OF AMERICA p 742
750 Old Hickory Blvd # 200, Brentwood TN 37027
Tel (615) 377-4730 SIC 8742 8711 8741

▲ LIFEPOINT HEALTH INC p 864
330 Seven Springs Way, Brentwood TN 37027
Tel (615) 920-7000 SIC 8062 8742

OZBURN-HESSEY HOLDING CO LLC p 1101
7101 Executive Center Dr # 333, Brentwood TN 37027
Tel (615) 401-6400 SIC 4225 8742

■ QUORUM HEALTH RESOURCES LLC p 1201
1573 Mallory Ln 200, Brentwood TN 37027
Tel (615) 371-7979
SIC 8742 8741 8082 8231 6324

MEMORIAL HEALTH CARE SYSTEM FOUNDATION INC p 941
2525 De Sales Ave, Chattanooga TN 37404
Tel (423) 495-2525 SIC 8742

REPUBLIC PARKING SYSTEM LLC p 1225
633 Chestnut St Ste 2000, Chattanooga TN 37450
Tel (423) 756-2771 SIC 8742 7521

▲ COMMUNITY HEALTH SYSTEMS INC p 349
4000 Meridian Blvd, Franklin TN 37067
Tel (615) 465-7000 SIC 8062 8742

ADMINISTRATIVE RESOURCES INC p 23
801 Sunset Dr F1, Johnson City TN 37604
Tel (423) 283-0296
SIC 8721 8741 8742 6794

■ EASTMAN CHEMICAL LTD CORP p 473
200 S Wilcox Dr, Kingsport TN 37660
Tel (423) 229-2000 SIC 5169 8742

ATWORK FRANCHISE INC p 130
3215 W Gov J Sevier Hwy, Knoxville TN 37920
Tel (865) 609-6911 SIC 6794 8742 8721

JANUS GLOBAL HOLDINGS LLC p 778
2229 Old Highway 95, Lenoir City TN 37771
Tel (865) 988-6063 SIC 8742

JANUS GLOBAL OPERATIONS LLC p 778
2229 Old Highway 95, Lenoir City TN 37771
Tel (865) 988-6063
SIC 4959 7381 7373 7379 8742

■ CB RICHARD ELLIS MEMPHIS LLC p 268
2620 Thousand Oaks Blvd # 4000, Memphis TN 38118
Tel (901) 528-1000 SIC 6531 8742

COMPREHENSIVE PHARMACY SERVICES LLC p 352
6409 N Quail Hollow Rd, Memphis TN 38120
Tel (901) 748-0470 SIC 8742 8741

YOROZU NORTH AMERICA INC p 1637
395 Mt View Industrial Dr, Morrison TN 37357
Tel (931) 668-7700 SIC 8711 8742

SETECH INC p 1308
410 New Salem Hwy Ste 106, Murfreesboro TN 37129
Tel (615) 890-1758 SIC 8742 8748 5085

■ CAREMARKPCS HEALTH LLC p 255
211 Commerce St Ste 800, Nashville TN 37201
Tel (615) 743-6600 SIC 8742

DSI HOLDING CO INC p 457
424 Church St Ste 1900, Nashville TN 37219
Tel (615) 777-8201 SIC 8092 8069 8742

DSI RENAL HOLDINGS LLC p 458
424 Church St Ste 1900, Nashville TN 37219
Tel (615) 777-8201 SIC 8092 8069 8742

■ ISD RENAL INC p 766
424 Church St Ste 1900, Nashville TN 37219
Tel (615) 777-8200 SIC 8069 8092 8742

▲ PFSWEB INC p 1140
505 Millenium Dr, Allen TX 75013
Tel (972) 881-2900 SIC 8741 7389 8742

NURSECORE MANAGEMENT SERVICES LLC p 1067
2201 Brookhollow Plaza Dr # 450, Arlington TX 76006
Tel (817) 649-1166 SIC 8742 8082

ABRAMS INTERNATIONAL INC p 12
111 Congress Ave Ste 2400, Austin TX 78701
Tel (512) 322-4000
SIC 1611 1622 1629 6799 7359 8742

PLANVIEW INC p 1154
12301 Research Blvd 5-100, Austin TX 78759
Tel (512) 346-8600 SIC 7371 8748 8742

SELL-THRU SERVICES INC p 1302
4807 Spicewd Spgs Rd # 3120, Austin TX 78759
Tel (512) 346-5075 SIC 5141 8742

STATE NATIONAL COMPANIES INC p 1381
1900 L Don Dodson Dr, Bedford TX 76021
Tel (817) 265-2000 SIC 8742

WORLEYPARSONS GROUP INC p 1626
6330 West Loop S, Bellaire TX 77401
Tel (713) 407-5000 SIC 8711 8742

WORLEYPARSONS INTERNATIONAL INC p 1626
6330 West Loop S Ste 200, Bellaire TX 77401
Tel (713) 407-5000 SIC 8742

■ MCLANE FOODSERVICE INC p 931
2085 Midway Rd, Carrollton TX 75006
Tel (972) 364-2000
SIC 8742 5141 5311 5113

TEXAS A&M UNIVERSITY SYSTEM p 1442
301 Tarrow St Fl 3, College Station TX 77840
Tel (979) 458-6100
SIC 8221 8731 8742 8011

■ ACS HEALTH CARE INC p 19
2828 N Haskell Ave, Dallas TX 75204
Tel (214) 841-6111 SIC 7376 8742

ACTIVE NETWORK LLC p 20
717 N Harwood St Ste 2500, Dallas TX 75201
Tel (888) 543-7223 SIC 8742

BENEFITMALL INC p 173
4851 Freeway Ste 100, Dallas TX 75244
Tel (469) 791-3300 SIC 6411 8742 7375

CULINAIRE INTERNATIONAL INC p 400
8303 Elmbrook Dr, Dallas TX 75247
Tel (214) 754-1645 SIC 8742 5812 8741

■ EMPLOYERS GENERAL INSURANCE GROUP INC p 494
1700 Pacific Ave Ste 1600, Dallas TX 75201
Tel (214) 665-6100 SIC 6331 8742

■ MARKETING ARM INC p 908
1999 Bryan St Fl 18, Dallas TX 75201
Tel (214) 259-3200 SIC 8742

MAYA MANAGEMENT GROUP LLC p 923
11411 Hillguard Rd, Dallas TX 75243
Tel (214) 751-2290 SIC 8742

RYAN GOVERNMENT SERVICES LLC p 1260
13155 Noel Rd Ste 100, Dallas TX 75240
Tel (972) 934-0022 SIC 8742

WILLIAM HERBERT HUNT TRUST ESTATE p 1610
1601 Elm St Ste 3900, Dallas TX 75201
Tel (214) 880-8400 SIC 8742 6799

DEX MEDIA HOLDINGS INC p 434
2200 W Airfield Dr, Dfw Airport TX 75261
Tel (972) 453-7000 SIC 8742

MCDONALD TRANSIT ASSOCIATES INC p 927
3800 Sandshell Dr Ste 185, Fort Worth TX 76137
Tel (817) 232-9551 SIC 8742

POINT 180 LLC p 1159
3575 Lone Star Cir, Fort Worth TX 76177
Tel (817) 490-0100 SIC 8742

VALLEY BAPTIST MEDICAL CENTER HARLINGEN AUXILIARY INC p 1540
2101 Pease St, Harlingen TX 78550
Tel (956) 389-1100 SIC 8742

FOOD MANAGEMENT PARTNERS INC p 564
120 Chula Vis, Hollywood Park TX 78232
Tel (210) 248-9340 SIC 8742

AMEC FOSTER WHEELER OIL & GAS INC p 66
585 N Dairy Ashford Rd, Houston TX 77079
Tel (713) 929-5000 SIC 8711 8742 8741

ARAMCO SERVICES CO p 102
9009 West Loop S, Houston TX 77096
Tel (713) 432-4000 SIC 8711 8742

▲ CARBO CERAMICS INC p 252
575 N Dairy Ashford Rd # 30, Houston TX 77079
Tel (281) 921-6400
SIC 3291 5945 8742 7371

COMPLETERX LTD p 351
3100 S Gessner Rd Ste 640, Houston TX 77063
Tel (713) 355-1196 SIC 8742

■ EC SOURCE SERVICES LLC p 474
16055 Space Center Blvd # 700, Houston TX 77062
Tel (281) 480-4600 SIC 1623 8742

HOUSTON TRIBOLOGY SALES & MARKETING OFFICE p 712
10450 Stncliff Rd Ste 210, Houston TX 77099
Tel (281) 599-1242 SIC 8742

INTEGRA US MARKETING LLC p 748
5075 Westheimer Rd # 790, Houston TX 77056
Tel (713) 224-2044 SIC 8742

PLAZA GROUP INC p 1156
10375 Richmond Ave # 1620, Houston TX 77042
Tel (713) 266-0707 SIC 8742

PRODUCTION SERVICES NETWORK US INC p 1180
9821 Katy Fwy Ste 400, Houston TX 77024
Tel (713) 984-1000 SIC 8742

■ QUANTA FIBER NETWORKS INC p 1198
1360 Post Oak Blvd # 2100, Houston TX 77056
Tel (713) 629-7600 SIC 1731 8742

SHELL INFORMATION TECHNOLOGY INTERNATIONAL INC p 1314
910 Louisiana St, Houston TX 77002
Tel (855) 697-4355 SIC 8742 7371

SOFEC INC p 1337
15011 Katy Fwy Ste 500, Houston TX 77094
Tel (713) 510-6600 SIC 3533 8742

▲ STEWART INFORMATION SERVICES CORP p 1389
1980 Post Oak Blvd, Houston TX 77056
Tel (713) 625-8100 SIC 6361 8742 7389

■ STEWART TITLE CO p 1389
1980 Post Oak Blvd Ste 80, Houston TX 77056
Tel (713) 625-8100
SIC 6361 7389 8713 8742 6541

TORCH ENERGY ADVISORS INC p 1461
1331 Lamar St Ste 1450, Houston TX 77010
Tel (713) 650-1246
SIC 1311 1382 8741 8742

WOOD GROUP MUSTANG INC p 1622
17325 Park Row, Houston TX 77084
Tel (832) 809-8000
SIC 8711 8742 7389 1389

WORLEYPARSONS CORP p 1626
575 N Gary Ashford, Houston TX 77079
Tel (713) 407-5000 SIC 8711 8742

MEDSYNERGIES INC p 939
909 Hidden Rdg Ste 300, Irving TX 75038
Tel (972) 791-1224 SIC 8741 8742 8721

MOSAIC SALES SOLUTIONS US OPERATING CO LLC p 992
220 Las Colinas Blvd E, Irving TX 75039
Tel (972) 870-4800 SIC 8742 8743 7374

ONE SOURCE VIRTUAL HR INC p 1086
5601 N Macarthur Blvd, Irving TX 75038
Tel (972) 916-9847 SIC 8742

VCC LLC p 1545
600 Las Colinas Blvd E # 1525, Irving TX 75039
Tel (214) 574-4500 SIC 1542 8711 8742

VIZIENT INC p 1563
290 E John Carpenter Fwy # 1500, Irving TX 75062
Tel (972) 830-0000 SIC 8742

▲ INSPERITY INC p 746
19001 Crescent Springs Dr, Kingwood TX 77339
Tel (281) 358-8986
SIC 8742 7363 7361 6311

MESQUITE SPECIALTY HOSPITAL p 951
1024 N Galloway Ave, Mesquite TX 75149
Tel (972) 216-2300 SIC 8742

ETECH GLOBAL SERVICES LLC p 511
1903 Berry Dr, Nacogdoches TX 75964
Tel (936) 559-2200
SIC 7389 8742 7373 8741 8721 7374

■ VICEROY INC p 1555
3225 Pasadena Blvd, Pasadena TX 77503
Tel (713) 475-4518
SIC 1629 3443 1796 8742 8748 7363

CROSSMARK CONSUMER ENGAGEMENTS LLC p 394
5100 Legacy Dr, Plano TX 75024
Tel (469) 814-1000 SIC 8742

■ HP ENTERPRISE SERVICES LLC p 714
5400 Legacy Dr, Plano TX 75024
Tel (972) 604-6000 SIC 7374 7371 8742

SERVICE EXPERTS LLC p 1307
3820 American Dr Ste 200, Plano TX 75075
Tel (972) 231-5468
SIC 1711 5074 5075 8742

SERVICE EXPERTS HEATING & AIR CONDITIONING LLC p 1307
2140 Lake Park Blvd, Richardson TX 75080
Tel (972) 535-3800
SIC 1711 5074 5075 8742

RESOURCING EDGE INC p 1227
1309 Ridge Rd Ste 200, Rockwall TX 75087
Tel (214) 771-4411 SIC 8721 8742

■ EMERSON PROCESS MANAGEMENT LLLP p 492
1100 W Louis Henna Blvd, Round Rock TX 78681
Tel (512) 835-2190 SIC 8742

EEMPLOYERS SOLUTIONS INC p 480
12211 Huebner Rd, San Antonio TX 78230
Tel (210) 495-1171 SIC 8742 6411

FROST & SULLIVAN p 581
7550 W Ih 10 Ste 400, San Antonio TX 78229
Tel (210) 348-1000 SIC 8732 8742

LABATT FOOD SERVICE LLC p 836
4500 Industry Park Dr, San Antonio TX 78218
Tel (210) 661-4216 SIC 8742

USAA INSURANCE AGENCY INC p 1534
9800 Fredericksburg Rd B-2e, San Antonio TX 78288
Tel (210) 498-2211 SIC 6331 6321 8742

GRAVICK GROUP LLC p 632
4985 Fm 1017, San Isidro TX 78588
Tel (956) 330-5676 SIC 8742 7371 7389

ANCOR HOLDINGS LP p 89
100 Throckmorton St St Ste 1600, Southlake TX 76092
Tel (817) 877-4458 SIC 8741 8742

PLURALSIGHT LLC p 1157
182 N Union Ave, Farmington UT 84025
Tel (801) 784-9007 SIC 8742

MARITZCX HOLDINGS LLC p 907
3451 N Triumph Blvd, Lehi UT 84043
Tel (385) 695-2800 SIC 8742 6719

■ **MARKETSTAR CORP** p 908
2475 Washington Blvd, Ogden UT 84401
Tel (801) 393-1155 SIC 8742

ENGLAND LOGISTICS INC p 499
1325 S 4700 W, Salt Lake City UT 84104
Tel (801) 656-4500 SIC 8742

▲ **FRANKLIN COVEY CO** p 575
2200 W Parkway Blvd, Salt Lake City UT 84119
Tel (801) 817-1776 SIC 8742 8331 2741

BOX ELDER SCHOOL DISTRICT p 205
515 N 800 W, Tremonton UT 84337
Tel (435) 257-2560 SIC 8211 8742

AHL SERVICES INC p 36
102 S Union St, Alexandria VA 22314
Tel (703) 682-0729 SIC 8742

CATAPULT TECHNOLOGY LTD p 265
11 Canal Center Plz Fl 2, Alexandria VA 22314
Tel (240) 482-2100 SIC 7373 8742

MODERN TECHNOLOGY SOLUTIONS INC p 981
5285 Shawnee Rd Ste 400, Alexandria VA 22312
Tel (703) 564-3800
SIC 8711 8742 8731 7379

SENTEL CORP p 1305
2800 Eisenhower Ave # 300, Alexandria VA 22314
Tel (571) 481-2000 SIC 8711 8742 8741

▲ **VSE CORP** p 1566
6348 Walker Ln, Alexandria VA 22310
Tel (703) 960-4600 SIC 8711 8742 8741

ACCENTURE FEDERAL SERVICES LLC p 14
800 N Glebe Rd Ste 300, Arlington VA 22203
Tel (703) 947-2000 SIC 8742 7379

■ **ARMED FORCES SERVICES CORP** p 111
2800 S Shirlington Rd # 350, Arlington VA 22206
Tel (571) 312-7670 SIC 8742

▲ **CEB INC** p 272
1919 N Lynn St, Arlington VA 22209
Tel (571) 303-3000 SIC 8742

CHANGEIS INC p 288
1530 Wilson Blvd Ste 340, Arlington VA 22209
Tel (301) 237-1622 SIC 8742

MANAGEMENT SYSTEMS INTERNATIONAL INC p 900
200 12th St S, Arlington VA 22202
Tel (703) 979-7100 SIC 8742

PAE AVIATION AND TECHNICAL SERVICES LLC p 1107
1320 N Courthouse Rd # 800, Arlington VA 22201
Tel (856) 866-2200 SIC 4581 3728 8742

PAE HOLDING CORP p 1107
1320 N Courthouse Rd # 800, Arlington VA 22201
Tel (703) 717-6000 SIC 6719 8742 8711

THALES INC p 1446
2733 Crystal Dr Ste 1200, Arlington VA 22202
Tel (703) 838-9685 SIC 8742

TOWERS WATSON DELAWARE INC p 1464
901 N Glebe Rd, Arlington VA 22203
Tel (703) 258-8000 SIC 8742

WTW DELAWARE HOLDINGS LLC p 1628
901 N Glebe Rd, Arlington VA 22203
Tel (703) 258-8000 SIC 8742

FCI FEDERAL INC p 533
20135 Lakeview Center Plz # 300, Ashburn VA 20147
Tel (703) 443-1888 SIC 8742 8748

■ **FORFEITURE SUPPORT ASSOCIATES LLC** p 567
20110 Ashbrook Pl Ste 220, Ashburn VA 20147
Tel (571) 291-8900 SIC 8111 8742

AMERICAN SYSTEMS CORP p 80
14151 Pk Madow Dr Ste 500, Chantilly VA 20151
Tel (703) 968-6300
SIC 8711 1731 8742 7373

ENGINEERING SOLUTIONS & PRODUCTS LLC p 499
14566 Lee Rd, Chantilly VA 20151
Tel (571) 375-1400
SIC 8711 7379 4813 8742 8748

SRA COMPANIES INC p 1362
15036 Conference Ctr Dr, Chantilly VA 20151
Tel (703) 803-1500 SIC 7372 8742

CDM FEDERAL PROGRAMS CORP p 271
3201 Jermantown Rd # 400, Fairfax VA 22030
Tel (703) 691-6500
SIC 8711 8742 8744 8748 8999

■ **EAGLE GROUP INTERNATIONAL LLC** p 468
10530 Rosehaven St # 500, Fairfax VA 22030
Tel (703) 272-6161 SIC 8742

ECS FEDERAL LLC p 476
2750 Prosperity Ave # 600, Fairfax VA 22031
Tel (703) 270-1540 SIC 7371 7379 8742

■ **ICF CONSULTING GROUP INC** p 727
9300 Lee Hwy, Fairfax VA 22031
Tel (703) 934-3000 SIC 8742

■ **ICF INC LLC** p 727
9300 Lee Hwy Ste 200, Fairfax VA 22031
Tel (703) 934-3000 SIC 8742 8748

▲ **ICF INTERNATIONAL INC** p 727
9300 Lee Hwy Ste 200, Fairfax VA 22031
Tel (703) 934-3000 SIC 8742 8748

■ **DATATRAC INFORMATION SERVICES INC** p 414
3170 Fairview Park Dr, Falls Church VA 22042
Tel (703) 876-1000 SIC 8742 0781 8721

EOIR TECHNOLOGIES INC p 504
10300 Spotsylvania Ave, Fredericksburg VA 22408
Tel (540) 834-4888
SIC 8711 7371 8731 8742

THREE SAINTS BAY LLC p 1450
10440 Balls Ford Rd, Manassas VA 20109
Tel (703) 365-0450 SIC 8742

BAE SYSTEMS INFORMATION SOLUTIONS INC p 144
8201 Greensboro Dr # 1200, Mc Lean VA 22102
Tel (703) 847-5820 SIC 8742

▲ **BOOZ ALLEN HAMILTON HOLDING CORP** p 201
8283 Greensboro Dr, Mc Lean VA 22102
Tel (703) 902-5000 SIC 8742

■ **BOOZ ALLEN HAMILTON INC** p 201
8283 Greensboro Dr # 700, Mc Lean VA 22102
Tel (703) 902-5000 SIC 8742

LOGISTICS MANAGEMENT INSTITUTE p 874
7940 Jones Branch Dr, Mc Lean VA 22102
Tel (703) 917-9800 SIC 8742

SOURCE HOME ENTERTAINMENT LLC p 1342
8251 Greensboro Dr # 400, Mc Lean VA 22102
Tel (239) 949-4450
SIC 5192 5099 8742 2541

STRATEGIC RESOURCES INC p 1392
7927 Jones Branch Dr 600w, Mc Lean VA 22102
Tel (703) 749-3040 SIC 8742 8748 7373

ACADEMI LLC p 13
12018 Sunrise Valley Dr # 140, Reston VA 20191
Tel (252) 435-2488 SIC 7382 8742

BECHTEL NUCLEAR SECURITY & ENVIRONMENTAL INC p 167
12021 Sunset Hills Rd, Reston VA 20190
Tel (415) 768-1234 SIC 8711 1629 8742

GATE GOURMET US INC p 593
1880 Campus Commons Dr # 200, Reston VA 20191
Tel (703) 964-2300 SIC 5812 8742

GATEGROUP US HOLDING INC p 593
11710 Plaza America Dr # 800, Reston VA 20190
Tel (703) 964-2300 SIC 5812 8742

▲ **LEIDOS HOLDINGS INC** p 854
11951 Freedom Dr Ste 500, Reston VA 20190
Tel (571) 526-6000
SIC 8731 7371 7373 8742 3674

■ **MAXIMUS FEDERAL SERVICES INC** p 922
1891 Metro Center Dr, Reston VA 20190
Tel (703) 251-8500 SIC 8742

▲ **MAXIMUS INC** p 922
1891 Metro Center Dr, Reston VA 20190
Tel (703) 251-8500 SIC 8742 8741

HR SOLUTIONS LLC p 714
47632 Loweland Ter, Sterling VA 20165
Tel (703) 493-0084 SIC 8742

ALVAREZ LLC p 63
8251 Greensboro Dr # 230, Tysons Corner VA 22102
Tel (301) 830-4020
SIC 8742 8741 7379 5044

■ **AT&T GOVERNMENT SOLUTIONS INC** p 123
1900 Gallows Rd Ste 105, Vienna VA 22182
Tel (703) 506-5000
SIC 5999 8742 7373 7371

MANAGEMENT CONSULTING INC p 900
1961 Diamond Springs Rd, Virginia Beach VA 23455
Tel (757) 460-0879 SIC 8742

ZEIDERS ENTERPRISES INC p 1641
2750 Killarney Dr Ste 100, Woodbridge VA 22192
Tel (703) 496-9000 SIC 8742

ALPHA TECHNOLOGIES INC p 60
3767 Alpha Way, Bellingham WA 98226
Tel (360) 647-2360 SIC 8742 8711

PARAMETRIX INC p 1114
1019 39th Ave Se Ste 100, Puyallup WA 98374
Tel (206) 394-3700
SIC 8748 8711 8742 1389 4789

3MD INC p 3
17735 Ne 65th St Ste 130, Redmond WA 98052
Tel (425) 467-8000 SIC 5045 8742

PACTERA TECHNOLOGIES NA INC p 1107
14980 Ne 31st Way Ste 120, Redmond WA 98052
Tel (425) 233-8578 SIC 7371 8742

AMERICAN MANAGEMENT SERVICES LLC p 75
2801 Alaskan Way Ste 200, Seattle WA 98121
Tel (206) 215-9700 SIC 8742

AVANADE INC p 136
818 Stewart St Ste 400, Seattle WA 98101
Tel (206) 239-5600 SIC 7379 8742

FRAZIER HEALTHCARE II LP p 575
601 Union St Ste 3200, Seattle WA 98101
Tel (206) 621-7200 SIC 8742

MILLIMAN INC p 971
1301 5th Ave Ste 3800, Seattle WA 98101
Tel (206) 624-7940 SIC 8742 8999 7389

SLALOM LLC p 1331
821 2nd Ave Ste 1900, Seattle WA 98104
Tel (206) 374-4200 SIC 8742 7373

■ **ZILLOW INC** p 1643
1301 2nd Ave Fl 31, Seattle WA 98101
Tel (206) 470-7000 SIC 7371 8742

ECOVA INC p 476
1313 N Atl St Ste 5000, Spokane WA 99201
Tel (509) 747-5069 SIC 8742

ENGIE HOLDINGS INC p 498
1313 N Atl St Ste 5000, Spokane WA 99201
Tel (509) 329-7600 SIC 8742

HEALTHCARE RESOURCE GROUP INC p 676
12610 E Mirabeau Pkwy # 900, Spokane Valley WA 99216
Tel (509) 209-2000
SIC 6411 7322 8742 8721

CATHOLIC HEALTH INITIATIVES WESTERN REGION p 266
1149 Market St, Tacoma WA 98402
Tel (253) 552-4100 SIC 8742

■ **CLP RESOURCES INC** p 328
1015 A St, Tacoma WA 98402
Tel (775) 321-8000 SIC 8742

▲ **BARRETT BUSINESS SERVICES INC** p 157
8100 Ne Parkway Dr # 200, Vancouver WA 98662
Tel (360) 828-0700 SIC 7361 8742

AMFM INC p 85
240 Capitol St Ste 500, Charleston WV 25301
Tel (304) 344-1623 SIC 8741 8742

ST FRANCIS HOSPITAL p 1366
333 Laidley St, Charleston WV 25301
Tel (304) 347-6860 SIC 8742

FITZ VOGT & ASSOCIATES LTD p 553
21 Armory Dr Ste L-1, Wheeling WV 26003
Tel (603) 644-0117 SIC 5812 8742 7349

NORDIC GROUP OF COMPANIES LTD p 1048
715 Lynn Ave Ste 100, Baraboo WI 53913
Tel (608) 356-7303 SIC 8742 8111 5561

MEETINGS & INCENTIVES WORLDWIDE INC p 939
10520 7 Mile Rd, Caledonia WI 53108
Tel (262) 835-6710 SIC 4724 8742 7389

SCHNEIDER NATIONAL INC p 1288
3101 Packerland Dr, Green Bay WI 54313
Tel (920) 592-2000 SIC 8742 4213

■ **AMERIPRISE FINANCIAL SERVICES INC** p 83
500 2nd St S Ste 101, La Crosse WI 54601
Tel (608) 783-2639
SIC 6282 6411 6211 8742

GREAT LAKES FINANCIAL MANAGEMENT GROUP INC p 633
2033 Marinette Ave, Marinette WI 54143
Tel (715) 732-9955
SIC 6211 8742 6282 6411

■ **BANTA CORP** p 153
1457 Earl St, Menasha WI 54952
Tel (312) 326-8000 SIC 2759 8742

■ **METAVANTE CORP** p 953
4900 W Brown Deer Rd, Milwaukee WI 53223
Tel (904) 438-6000 SIC 7374 8742 6153

ALTA RESOURCES CORP p 61
120 N Commercial St, Neenah WI 54956
Tel (877) 464-2582 SIC 7389 8742

J J KELLER & ASSOCIATES INC p 771
3003 Breezewood Ln, Neenah WI 54956
Tel (920) 722-2848 SIC 2741 8742

SIC 8743 Public Relations Svcs

BEST WESTERN INTERNATIONAL INC p 177
6201 N 24th Pkwy, Phoenix AZ 85016
Tel (602) 957-4200
SIC 7389 7311 5046 8743

MAGIC JOHNSON ENTERPRISES INC p 895
9100 Wilshire Blvd 700e, Beverly Hills CA 90212
Tel (310) 247-2033 SIC 8743 7389

MAGIC WORKFORCE SOLUTIONS LLC p 895
9100 Wilsh Blvd Ste 700e, Beverly Hills CA 90212
Tel (310) 246-6153 SIC 8743

BDS MARKETING INC p 164
10 Holland, Irvine CA 92618
Tel (949) 472-6700 SIC 7311 8743 8732

■ **INTEGER GROUP L L C** p 748
7245 W Alaska Dr, Lakewood CO 80226
Tel (303) 393-3000 SIC 7311 8742 8743

FLORIDA TOURISM INDUSTRY MARKETING CORP p 559
2450 W Exec Ctr Cir 200, Tallahassee FL 32301
Tel (850) 488-5607 SIC 4724 8743 8742

BURNS GROUP UNLIMITED LLC p 228
833 Piedmont Ave Ne Ste B, Atlanta GA 30308
Tel (404) 873-0772 SIC 8743

DANIEL J EDELMAN HOLDINGS INC p 411
200 E Randolph St Fl 63, Chicago IL 60601
Tel (312) 240-3000 SIC 7313 8743

DANIEL J EDELMAN INC p 411
200 E Randolph St Fl 63, Chicago IL 60601
Tel (312) 240-3000 SIC 7313 8743

■ **GOLIN/HARRIS INTERNATIONAL INC** p 622
875 N Michigan Ave # 2600, Chicago IL 60611
Tel (312) 729-4000 SIC 8743

SMITHBUCKLIN CORP p 1333
330 N Wabash Ave, Chicago IL 60611
Tel (312) 644-6610 SIC 8742 8743 4724

TERLATO WINE GROUP LTD p 1439
900 Armour Dr, Lake Bluff IL 60044
Tel (847) 604-8900 SIC 5182 2084 8743

FREEDOMROADS HOLDING CO LLC p 576
250 Parkway Dr Ste 270, Lincolnshire IL 60069
Tel (847) 808-3000 SIC 8743

KEMPER SPORTS INC p 810
500 Skokie Blvd Ste 444, Northbrook IL 60062
Tel (847) 850-1818 SIC 8743 7941 7992

SWEDISHAMERICAN HEALTH SYSTEM CORP p 1411
1401 E State St, Rockford IL 61104
Tel (815) 968-4400
SIC 8743 6512 8742 8099 8082 8062

■ **ASPEN MARKETING SERVICES LLC** p 118
1240 W North Ave, West Chicago IL 60185
Tel (630) 293-9600 SIC 8743 8748 5199

ARNOLD WORLDWIDE LLC p 112
10 Summer St Ste 600, Boston MA 02110
Tel (617) 587-8000 SIC 7311 8743

FEV NORTH AMERICA INC p 539
4554 Glenmeade Ln, Auburn Hills MI 48326
Tel (248) 475-4761 SIC 8748 8743

UAW PUBLIC RELATIONS p 1498
8000 E Jefferson Ave, Detroit MI 48214
Tel (313) 926-5291 SIC 8743

VALASSIS INTERNATIONAL INC p 1539
19975 Victor Pkwy, Livonia MI 48152
Tel (734) 591-3000
SIC 8743 3993 2759 2752

CARLSON INC p 258
701 Carlson Pkwy, Minnetonka MN 55305
Tel (763) 212-5000
SIC 7011 5812 6794 8742 8743 7389

■ **FLEISHMAN-HILLARD INC** p 555
200 N Broadway, Saint Louis MO 63102
Tel (314) 982-1700 SIC 8743

■ **CAMPBELL SALES CO** p 245
1 Campbell Pl, Camden NJ 08103
Tel (856) 342-4800 SIC 8743

MWW GROUP LLC p 1004
1 Meadowlands Plz Ste 600, East Rutherford NJ 07073
Tel (201) 507-9500 SIC 8743

AEGIS LIFESTYLE INC p 29
32 Aveune Of The Americas, New York NY 10013
Tel (212) 366-3400 SIC 7311 7389 8743

ALLOY INC p 58
151 W 26th St Fl 11, New York NY 10001
Tel (609) 655-8878
SIC 8743 8742 7331 7312

ALLOY MEDIA HOLDINGS LLC p 58
19 W 44th St Fl 18, New York NY 10036
Tel (212) 784-2010 SIC 8743

■ **CMGRP INC** p 329
909 3rd Ave, New York NY 10022
Tel (212) 445-8000
SIC 8743 7311 7319 8742

COURT SQUARE CAPITAL LIMITED p 383
55 E 52nd St Rm 3400, New York NY 10055
Tel (212) 752-6110 SIC 8743 6162

■ **FCB WORLDWIDE INC** p 532
100 W 33rd St Fl 5, New York NY 10001
Tel (212) 885-3000 SIC 7311 8743

HILL AND KNOWLTON STRATEGIES LLC p 693
466 Lexington Ave Frnt 4, New York NY 10017
Tel (212) 885-0300 SIC 8743 8748

KDDI AMERICA INC p 806
825 3rd Ave Fl 3, New York NY 10022
Tel (212) 295-1200
SIC 4813 7375 7374 8743

■ **KETCHUM INC** p 814
1285 Avenue Of The Americ, New York NY 10019
Tel (646) 935-3900 SIC 8743

MKTG INC p 979
32 Avenue Of The Americas # 20, New York NY 10013
Tel (212) 366-3400 SIC 7311 7389 8743

■ **MOMENTUM-NA INC** p 983
250 Hudson St Fl 2, New York NY 10013
Tel (646) 638-5400 SIC 8743 7311 8732

OGILVY GROUP LLC p 1076
636 11th Ave, New York NY 10036
Tel (212) 237-4000
SIC 7311 8743 8748 7336 7361 8732

OGILVY PUBLIC RELATIONS WORLDWIDE INC p 1076
636 11th Ave, New York NY 10036
Tel (212) 880-5200 SIC 8743 8999

RUDER FINN GROUP INC p 1257
301 E 57th St, New York NY 10022
Tel (212) 593-5838 SIC 8743 6799 8741

RUDER FINN INC p 1257
425 E 53rd St, New York NY 10022
Tel (212) 593-6400 SIC 8743 7311 2752

STRIVECTIN OPERATING CO INC p 1394
601 W 26th St Rm 1505, New York NY 10001
Tel (212) 220-3400 SIC 8743

■ **TBWA CHIAT/DAY INC** p 1427
488 Madison Ave Fl 7, New York NY 10022
Tel (212) 804-1000 SIC 7311 8743

MOSAIC SALES SOLUTIONS US OPERATING CO LLC p 992
220 Las Colinas Blvd E, Irving TX 75039
Tel (972) 870-4800 SIC 8742 8743 7374

■ **JCP MEDIA INC** p 780
6501 Legacy Dr, Plano TX 75024
Tel (972) 431-1000 SIC 8743

■ **MARTIN AGENCY INC** p 912
1 Shockoe Plz, Richmond VA 23219
Tel (804) 649-1496
SIC 7331 7311 8743 7313

SMITHFIELD FARMLAND SALES CORP p 1333
111 Commerce St, Smithfield VA 23430
Tel (757) 357-3131 SIC 5147 8743 5963

WAGGENER EDSTROM WORLDWIDE INC p 1571
225 108th Ave Ne Ste 700, Bellevue WA 98004
Tel (425) 638-7000 SIC 8743

SMITH JOHNSON LAVEY AND BELL INC p 1333
2025 1st Ave Ste 11150, Seattle WA 98121
Tel (206) 443-8846 SIC 8743

■ **GMR MARKETING LLC** p 619
5000 S Towne Dr, New Berlin WI 53151
Tel (262) 786-5600 SIC 8743

SIC 8744 Facilities Support Mgmt Svcs

COLSA CORP p 339
6728 Odyssey Dr Nw, Huntsville AL 35806
Tel (256) 964-5361
SIC 8731 7373 8744 8711

KWAJALEIN RANGE SERVICES LLC p 832
4975 Bradford Dr Nw # 600, Huntsville AL 35805
Tel (256) 890-8536 SIC 8744

CHENEGA CORP p 294
3000 C St Ste 301, Anchorage AK 99503
Tel (907) 277-5706
SIC 8744 7379 7376 3629 8742

CHUGACH ALASKA CORP p 304
3800 Cntrpint Dr Ste 1200, Anchorage AK 99503
Tel (907) 563-8866
SIC 8744 4959 7361 0851 7373

KOYITLOTSINA LIMITED p 828
1603 College Rd Ste 2, Fairbanks AK 99709
Tel (907) 452-8119 SIC 6798 8744 7349

SEALASKA CORP p 1296
1 Sealaska Plz Ste 400, Juneau AK 99801
Tel (907) 586-1512
SIC 5099 8744 7371 8748 1542

EXODYNE INC p 519
8433 N Black Canyon Hwy # 100, Phoenix AZ 85021
Tel (602) 995-3700
SIC 8711 8731 8741 8744 8748

NORTHSTAR DEMOLITION AND REMEDIATION LP p 1058
404 N Berry St, Brea CA 92821
Tel (714) 672-3500 SIC 1795 1799 8744

ENVIRONMENTAL CHEMICAL CORP p 503
1240 Bayshore Hwy, Burlingame CA 94010
Tel (650) 347-1555 SIC 8711 1542 8744

KW INTERNATIONAL INC p 832
18655 Bishop Ave, Carson CA 90746
Tel (310) 747-1380 SIC 4731 4226 8744

SERVICON SYSTEMS INC p 1308
3965 Landmark St, Culver City CA 90232
Tel (310) 204-5040 SIC 8744 7349 1771

OCCIDENTAL PETROLEUM INVESTMENT CO INC p 1072
10889 Wilshire Blvd Fl 10, Los Angeles CA 90024
Tel (310) 208-8800 SIC 1382 8744

▲ KRATOS DEFENSE & SECURITY SOLUTIONS INC p 829
4820 Estgate Mall Ste 200, San Diego CA 92121
Tel (858) 812-7300
SIC 3761 8711 8744 7382

ONE WORKPLACE L FERRARI LLC p 1086
2500 De La Cruz Blvd, Santa Clara CA 95050
Tel (669) 800-2500 SIC 5021 8744

■ AMERICAN REPROGRAPHICS CO LLC p 78
1981 N Broadway Ste 385, Walnut Creek CA 94596
Tel (925) 949-5100 SIC 8744 7334

■ STOLLER NEWPORT NEWS NUCLEAR INC p 1390
105 Technology Dr Ste 190, Broomfield CO 80021
Tel (303) 546-4300 SIC 8744

CORRECTIONAL HEALTHCARE COMPANIES INC p 372
7388 S Revere Pkwy # 707, Centennial CO 80112
Tel (615) 312-7286 SIC 8011 8744

▲ VECTRUS INC p 1546
655 Space Center Dr, Colorado Springs CO 80915
Tel (719) 591-3600 SIC 8744

■ VECTRUS SYSTEMS CORP p 1546
655 Space Center Dr, Colorado Springs CO 80915
Tel (719) 591-3600 SIC 8744 7376

▲ PITNEY BOWES INC p 1152
3001 Summer St Ste 3, Stamford CT 06905
Tel (203) 356-5000
SIC 3579 7359 3661 8744 7372

CORRECTIONAL SERVICES CORP LLC p 373
621 Nw 53rd St Ste 700, Boca Raton FL 33487
Tel (561) 893-0101 SIC 8744

GEO CORRECTIONS AND DETENTION LLC p 605
621 Nw 53rd St Ste 700, Boca Raton FL 33487
Tel (561) 999-7490 SIC 8744

GEO REENTRY INC p 605
621 Nw 53rd St Ste 700, Boca Raton FL 33487
Tel (561) 893-0101 SIC 8744

IAP WORLD SERVICES INC p 725
7315 N Atlantic Ave, Cape Canaveral FL 32920
Tel (321) 784-7100
SIC 4731 4581 8744 4911 1541 4813

IAP WORLDWIDE SERVICES INC p 725
7315 N Atlantic Ave, Cape Canaveral FL 32920
Tel (973) 633-5115
SIC 4731 4581 8744 4911

CSI INTERNATIONAL INC p 398
6700 N Andrews Ave # 400, Fort Lauderdale FL 33309
Tel (954) 308-4300 SIC 8744 8711

G4S HOLDING ONE INC p 588
1395 University Blvd, Jupiter FL 33458
Tel (561) 622-5656
SIC 7381 7382 8744 8748 8742

G4S SECURE SOLUTIONS (USA) INC p 588
1395 University Blvd, Jupiter FL 33458
Tel (561) 622-5656
SIC 7381 8744 8748 8742

TRINITY SERVICES GROUP INC p 1482
477 Commerce Blvd, Oldsmar FL 34677
Tel (813) 854-4264 SIC 8744

CENTERRA GROUP LLC p 276
7121 Fairway Dr Ste 301, Palm Beach Gardens FL 33418
Tel (561) 472-0600 SIC 7381 8744

EAGLE CONSTRUCTION & ENVIRONMENTAL SERVICES LLC p 468
600 Grand Panama Blvd, Panama City Beach FL 32407
Tel (254) 442-1553 SIC 8744

AMEC E&I HOLDINGS INC p 66
1105 Lakewood Pkwy # 300, Alpharetta GA 30009
Tel (770) 360-0600 SIC 8744 8711

■ AGL RESOURCES SERVICE CO p 35
10 Peachtree Pl Ne # 1000, Atlanta GA 30309
Tel (404) 584-9470
SIC 8742 8721 8744 4924

INNOVATIVE SERVICE TECHNOLOGY MANAGEMENT SERVICES INC p 745
934 Glenwood Ave Se # 250, Atlanta GA 30316
Tel (404) 582-8850 SIC 8744

ONEPATH SYSTEMS LLC p 1088
2053 Franklin Way Se, Marietta GA 30067
Tel (678) 695-5500
SIC 7389 8744 7378 7376 7382

■ WILLIAMS PLANT SERVICES LLC p 1611
100 Crescent Center Pkwy # 1240, Tucker GA 30084
Tel (770) 879-4500 SIC 1629 8744

BOISE CASCADE HOLDINGS LLC p 198
1111 W Jefferson St # 300, Boise ID 83702
Tel (208) 384-6161 SIC 5031 8744

FOREST PRODUCTS HOLDINGS LLC p 567
1111 W Jefferson St # 300, Boise ID 83702
Tel (208) 384-6161 SIC 5031 8744

MADISON DEARBORN PARTNERS IV LP p 894
70 W Madison St Ste 3800, Chicago IL 60602
Tel (312) 895-1000 SIC 5031 8744

■ ROCKWELL COLLINS SIMULATION & TRAINING SOLUTIONS LLC p 1245
400 Collins Rd Ne, Cedar Rapids IA 52498
Tel (319) 295-1000 SIC 3699 8744

CB&I ENVIRONMENTAL & INFRASTRUCTURE INC p 268
3867 Plaza Tower Dr, Baton Rouge LA 70816
Tel (225) 932-2500
SIC 8748 1794 1795 8744 8741

UNITED STATES ENVIRONMENTAL SERVICES LLC p 1513
2809 E Judge Perez Dr, Meraux LA 70075
Tel (504) 279-9930 SIC 8744

CH2M HILL - DYNETICS SYNERGY ALLIANCE LLC p 286
1515 Poydras St Ste 1550, New Orleans LA 70112
Tel (504) 593-9421 SIC 8744

CCE/DFS INC p 270
201 Defense Hwy Ste 202, Annapolis MD 21401
Tel (410) 263-6422 SIC 1542 8711 8744

L B & B ASSOCIATES INC p 833
9891 Broken Land Pkwy # 400, Columbia MD 21046
Tel (301) 621-3944
SIC 8744 7338 4225 8742 8748 4581

AC FIRST LLC p 13
20501 Seneca Meadows Pkwy, Germantown MD 20876
Tel (817) 698-6860 SIC 8744

■ AECOM SPECIAL MISSIONS SERVICES INC p 28
20501 Seneca Meadows Pkwy, Germantown MD 20876
Tel (412) 367-6060 SIC 8744

NOVITEX GOVERNMENT SOLUTIONS LLC p 1063
8401 Corporate Dr Ste 420, Landover MD 20785
Tel (301) 731-4595 SIC 8744

APEX COMPANIES LLC p 96
15850 Crabbs Branch Way # 200, Rockville MD 20855
Tel (301) 417-0200 SIC 8744 8748 8742

■ SALESLINK CORP p 1272
425 Medford St, Charlestown MA 02129
Tel (617) 886-4800 SIC 7379 8744 7331

GZA GEOENVIRONMENTAL TECHNOLOGIES INC p 649
249 Vanderbilt Ave Unit 2, Norwood MA 02062
Tel (781) 278-3700
SIC 8711 8999 1799 8744

■ NORESCO LLC p 1048
1 Research Dr Ste 400c, Westborough MA 01581
Tel (508) 614-1000
SIC 8711 8741 8744 8748 4911 4924

BILFINGER INDUSTRIAL SERVICES INC p 182
15933 Clayton Rd Ste 305, Ballwin MO 63011
Tel (636) 391-4500
SIC 1541 1731 1796 8711 8744

ENVIRONMENTAL RESTORATION LLC p 503
1666 Fabick Dr, Fenton MO 63026
Tel (636) 227-7477 SIC 8744

TRAX INTERNATIONAL CORP p 1475
8337 W Sunset Rd Ste 250, Las Vegas NV 89113
Tel (702) 216-4455
SIC 7373 8711 7376 8742 8744

DB SERVICES NEW JERSEY INC p 418
100 Plaza One, Jersey City NJ 07311
Tel (201) 593-4183 SIC 8744

COMMUNITY EDUCATION CENTERS INC p 348
35 Fairfield Pl, West Caldwell NJ 07006
Tel (973) 226-2900 SIC 8744

GLOBAL FACILITY MANAGEMENT & CONSTRUCTION INC p 616
525 Broadhollow Rd # 100, Melville NY 11747
Tel (866) 213-2337 SIC 8744

LEGENDS HOSPITALITY MANAGEMENT LIMITED LIABILITY CO p 853
61 Broadway Ste 2400, New York NY 10006
Tel (646) 977-8521 SIC 8741 8744 8742

SWISS POST SOLUTIONS INC p 1412
10 E 40th St Fl 9, New York NY 10016
Tel (212) 204-0900 SIC 8744

CB&I FEDERAL SERVICES LLC p 268
2401 River Rd, Schenectady NY 12309
Tel (518) 557-2518 SIC 8744

CAROLINA RHA/NORTH MR INC p 259
1200 Rdgfeld Blvd Ste 270, Asheville NC 28806
Tel (828) 322-4200 SIC 8744

AKIMA CORP p 42
11405 N Community House R, Charlotte NC 28277
Tel (704) 552-0082 SIC 8744

■ EMCOR FACILITIES SERVICES INC p 491
15 W Voorhees St, Cincinnati OH 45215
Tel (888) 846-9462 SIC 8744

FIRSTGROUP AMERICA INC p 550
600 Vine St Ste 1400, Cincinnati OH 45202
Tel (513) 241-2200
SIC 4151 4111 4119 4131 4141 8744

MPW INDUSTRIAL SERVICES GROUP INC p 996
9711 Lancaster Rd, Hebron OH 43025
Tel (740) 927-8790 SIC 7349 8744 3589

WASTREN ADVANTAGE INC p 1581
1571 Shyville Rd, Piketon OH 45661
Tel (970) 254-1277 SIC 4959 8744 8711

DAY AND ZIMMERMANN INC p 417
1500 Spring Garden St # 900, Philadelphia PA 19130
Tel (215) 299-8000
SIC 8744 8712 8711 3559 3483

PHILADELPHIA FACILITIES MANAGEMENT CORP p 1142
800 W Montgomery Ave, Philadelphia PA 19122
Tel (215) 684-3000 SIC 8744

LIBERTY TIRE RECYCLING LLC p 862
1251 Waterfront Pl # 400, Pittsburgh PA 15222
Tel (412) 562-1700 SIC 5093 4953 8744

DEL-JEN INC p 423
4465 Guthrie Hwy, Clarksville TN 37040
Tel (931) 552-0232 SIC 8744

■ SAFETY & ECOLOGY HOLDINGS CORP p 1266
2800 Solway Rd, Knoxville TN 37931
Tel (865) 690-0501 SIC 8744 8748

▲ CORECIVIC INC p 369
10 Burton Hills Blvd, Nashville TN 37215
Tel (615) 263-3000
SIC 6798 8744 8361 8299

BECHTEL JACOBS CO LLC p 167
E Tennessee Techn 58, Oak Ridge TN 37831
Tel (865) 241-1151 SIC 8744

AEROSPACE CENTER SUPPORT p 30
100 Kindel Dr Ste A211, Tullahoma TN 37389
Tel (931) 454-3000 SIC 8744

AMERICAN EAGLE PROTECTIVE SERVICES CORP p 71
7700 Chevy Chase Dr, Austin TX 78752
Tel (512) 380-9700 SIC 8744

DG21 LLC p 435
14900 Landmark Blvd # 400, Dallas TX 75254
Tel (972) 774-8850 SIC 8744

PAE APPLIED TECHNOLOGIES LLC p 1107
6500 West Fwy Ste 600, Fort Worth TX 76116
Tel (817) 737-1500
SIC 8741 8711 8744 4581 7381

■ ABM FACILITY SOLUTIONS GROUP LLC p 11
1201 Louisiana St, Houston TX 77002
Tel (832) 214-5500 SIC 8744

REMEDIAL CONSTRUCTION SVCS LP p 1222
9977 W Sam Houston Pkwy N, Houston TX 77064
Tel (281) 955-2442 SIC 8744 1629

PARSONS GOVERNMENT SUPPORT SERVICES INC p 1118
1301 W President George B, Richardson TX 75080
Tel (972) 991-0800 SIC 8744

■ STREAM INTERNATIONAL INC p 1393
3010 Waterview Pkwy, Richardson TX 75080
Tel (469) 624-5000 SIC 8744

MANAGEMENT & TRAINING CORP p 900
500 N Market Place Dr # 100, Centerville UT 84014
Tel (801) 693-2600
SIC 8744 8331 7349 8741 8249

HENSEL PHELPS SERVICES LLC p 685
4437 Brookfield Corp 20 Ste 207, Chantilly VA 20151
Tel (703) 828-3200
SIC 1522 8744 1521 1541 1623 1611

CDM FEDERAL PROGRAMS CORP p 271
3201 Jermantown Rd # 400, Fairfax VA 22030
Tel (703) 691-6500
SIC 8711 8742 8744 8748 8999

■ NORTHROP GRUMMAN ENTERPRISE MANAGEMENT SERVICES CORP p 1058
2340 Dulles Corner Blvd, Herndon VA 20171
Tel (703) 713-4000
SIC 8741 8744 4731 8331 7349

■ DYNCORP p 465
1700 Old Meadow Rd, Mc Lean VA 22102
Tel (571) 722-0210
SIC 7373 7371 7374 7375 8744 4581

SECURIGUARD INC p 1298
6858 Old Dominion Dr # 307, Mc Lean VA 22101
Tel (703) 821-6777 SIC 7381 8744

INDYNE INC p 740
11800 Sunrise Valley Dr # 250, Reston VA 20191
Tel (703) 903-6900 SIC 8744 8748 7382

SERCO GROUP INC p 1306
1818 Library St Ste 1000, Reston VA 20190
Tel (703) 939-6000 SIC 8744

SERCO NORTH AMERICA (HOLDINGS) INC p 1306
1818 Library St Ste 1000, Reston VA 20190
Tel (703) 939-6000 SIC 8744

VT SERVICES INC p 1567
529 Viking Dr, Virginia Beach VA 23452
Tel (912) 573-3671 SIC 8744 8711

SKOOKUM EDUCATIONAL PROGRAMS INC p 1330
4525 Auto Center Way, Bremerton WA 98312
Tel (360) 475-0756 SIC 8744

CUBIC GLOBAL DEFENSE INC p 399
400 Union Ave Se Ste 300, Olympia WA 98501
Tel (360) 493-6275
SIC 7373 8744 8711 7376 8748 8741

JOHNSON CONTROLS INC p 791
5757 N Green Bay Ave, Milwaukee WI 53209
Tel (414) 524-1200
SIC 2531 3714 3691 3822 8744

SIC 8748 Business Consulting Svcs, NEC

INTUITIVE RESEARCH AND TECHNOLOGY CORP p 760
5030 Bradford Dr Nw # 205, Huntsville AL 35805
Tel (256) 922-9300 SIC 8711 8748

ALUTIIQ LLC p 63
3909 Arctic Blvd Ste 500, Anchorage AK 99503
Tel (907) 222-9500 SIC 8748

OLD HARBOR NATIVE CORP p 1080
2702 Denali St Ste 100, Anchorage AK 99503
Tel (907) 278-6100 SIC 8748

SEALASKA CORP p 1296
1 Sealaska Plz Ste 400, Juneau AK 99801
Tel (907) 586-1512
SIC 5099 8744 7371 8748 1542

EXCEPTIONAL EDUCATIONAL SERVICES LLC p 517
5960 S Cooper Rd Ste 1, Chandler AZ 85249
Tel (480) 398-1994 SIC 8748

REDFLEX TRAFFIC SYSTEMS INC p 1216
5651 W Talavi Blvd # 200, Glendale AZ 85306
Tel (623) 207-2000 SIC 8748

▲ APOLLO EDUCATION GROUP INC p 97
4025 S Riverpoint Pkwy, Phoenix AZ 85040
Tel (480) 966-5394 SIC 8221 8299 8748

EXODYNE INC p 519
8433 N Black Canyon Hwy # 100, Phoenix AZ 85021
Tel (602) 995-3700
SIC 8711 8731 8741 8744 8748

SWCA INC p 1411
3033 N Central Ave # 145, Phoenix AZ 85012
Tel (602) 274-3831
SIC 8748 8711 8731 8733

TELGIAN CORP p 1435
10230 S 50th Pl, Phoenix AZ 85044
Tel (480) 753-5444
SIC 1711 8711 1731 8748

■ ENSYNCH INC p 501
6820 S Harl Ave, Tempe AZ 85283
Tel (480) 894-3500 SIC 8748

POLLYS INC p 1160
173 E Freedom Ave, Anaheim CA 92801
Tel (714) 459-0041 SIC 8748

▲ WILLDAN GROUP INC p 1610
2401 E Katella Ave # 300, Anaheim CA 92806
Tel (800) 424-9144 SIC 8711 8748

MP ENVIRONMENTAL SERVICES INC p 995
3400 Manor St, Bakersfield CA 93308
Tel (800) 458-3036
SIC 4953 4213 8748 7699

PSI SERVICES LLC p 1188
2950 N Hollywood Way # 200, Burbank CA 91505
Tel (818) 847-6180 SIC 8748

1105 MEDIA INC p 1
9201 Oakdale Ave Ste 101, Chatsworth CA 91311
Tel (818) 814-5200
SIC 7313 7389 2721 2741 8748

GILBANE FEDERAL p 611
1655 Grant St Fl 12, Concord CA 94520
Tel (925) 946-3100 SIC 8711 8748

BERKELEY RESEARCH GROUP LLC p 175
2200 Powell St Ste 1200, Emeryville CA 94608
Tel (510) 285-3300 SIC 8748

▲ TRUCEPT INC p 1485
500 La Terraza Blvd, Escondido CA 92025
Tel (866) 961-5763 SIC 8721 8748 8742

RICHARD HEATH & ASSOCIATES INC p 1232
590 W Locust Ave Ste 103, Fresno CA 93650
Tel (559) 447-7000 SIC 8748

RISK MANAGEMENT STRATEGIES INC p 1236
8530 La Mesa Blvd Ste 200, La Mesa CA 91942
Tel (619) 281-1100 SIC 8748

STEARNS CONRAD AND SCHMIDT CONSULTING ENGINEERS INC p 1384
3900 Kilroy Arprt Way # 100, Long Beach CA 90806
Tel (562) 426-9544 SIC 8711 1541 8748

■ AECOM TECHNICAL SERVICES INC p 28
300 S Grand Ave Ste 1100, Los Angeles CA 90071
Tel (213) 593-8000
SIC 4953 8748 8742 8711

■ EARTH TECHNOLOGY CORP USA p 469
1999 Avenue Of Ste 2600, Los Angeles CA 90067
Tel (213) 593-8000
SIC 4953 8748 8742 8711

MEDICAL MANAGEMENT CONSULTANTS INC p 937
8150 Beverly Blvd, Los Angeles CA 90048
Tel (310) 659-3835
SIC 7363 8742 8748 8721

YUCAIPA COMPANIES LLC p 1640
9130 W Sunset Blvd, Los Angeles CA 90069
Tel (310) 789-7200 SIC 8748 6719 6726

INFOGAIN CORP p 741
485 Alberto Way Ste 100, Los Gatos CA 95032
Tel (408) 355-6000
SIC 7379 7373 8742 8748 7374 1731

CORNERSTONE RESEARCH INC p 371
1000 El Camino Real # 250, Menlo Park CA 94025
Tel (650) 853-1660 SIC 8748 7389

▲ ROBERT HALF INTERNATIONAL INC p 1241
2884 Sand Hill Rd Ste 200, Menlo Park CA 94025
Tel (650) 234-6000
SIC 7363 7361 8748 8721

SRI INTERNATIONAL p 1363
333 Ravenswood Ave, Menlo Park CA 94025
Tel (650) 859-2000 SIC 8733 8748

ALLIANT INSURANCE SERVICES INC p 55
1301 Dove St Ste 200, Newport Beach CA 92660
Tel (949) 756-0271 SIC 6411 8748

GORDON E AND BETTY I MOORE FOUNDATION p 626
1661 Page Mill Rd, Palo Alto CA 94304
Tel (650) 213-3000 SIC 8748

SYMPHONY TECHNOLOGY GROUP LLC p 1414
2475 Hanover St, Palo Alto CA 94304
Tel (650) 935-9500 SIC 8748 6719

COMMUNITY COLLEGE FOUNDATION p 348
1901 Royal Oaks Dr # 100, Sacramento CA 95815
Tel (916) 418-5100 SIC 8299 8748

CENTER FOR SUSTAINABLE ENERGY p 276
9325 Sky Park Ct Ste 100, San Diego CA 92123
Tel (858) 244-1177 SIC 8748

KLEINFELDER ASSOCIATES p 823
550 W C St Ste 1200, San Diego CA 92101
Tel (619) 831-4600 SIC 8748

CLIMATEWORKS FOUNDATION p 326
235 Montgomery St # 1300, San Francisco CA 94104
Tel (415) 433-0500 SIC 8748

NEXANT INC p 1039
101 2nd St Ste 1000, San Francisco CA 94105
Tel (415) 369-1000 SIC 8748

STEELE INTERNATIONAL INC p 1384
1 Sansome St Ste 3500, San Francisco CA 94104
Tel (415) 781-4300 SIC 7381 8742 8748

TRIAGE CONSULTING GROUP p 1478
221 Main St Ste 1100, San Francisco CA 94105
Tel (415) 512-9400 SIC 8742 8748

WEISSCOMM GROUP LTD p 1588
50 Francisco St Ste 400, San Francisco CA 94133
Tel (415) 362-5018 SIC 8748

▲ FAIR ISAAC CORP p 524
181 Metro Dr Ste 700, San Jose CA 95110
Tel (408) 535-1500 SIC 7372 8748 7389

BUTLER AMERICA LLC p 230
3820 State St Ste B, Santa Barbara CA 93105
Tel (203) 926-2700 SIC 8711 8748 7361

BUTLER SERVICE GROUP INC p 230
3820 State St Ste A, Santa Barbara CA 93105
Tel (201) 891-5312
SIC 7363 8711 8748 3661 7538

ALL-CITY MANAGEMENT SERVICES INC p 51
10440 Pioneer Blvd Ste 5, Santa Fe Springs CA 90670
Tel (310) 202-8284 SIC 8748

SILICON VALLEY EXECUTIVE NETWORK p 1323
1336 Nelson Way, Sunnyvale CA 94087
Tel (408) 746-5803 SIC 8748

HONDA NORTH AMERICA INC p 704
700 Van Ness Ave, Torrance CA 90501
Tel (310) 781-4961 SIC 3711 8748

NORTH LA COUNTY REGIONAL CENTER INC p 1053
15400 Sherman Way Ste 170, Van Nuys CA 91406
Tel (818) 778-1900 *SIC* 8748

PLANT SCIENCES INC p 1154
342 Green Valley Rd, Watsonville CA 95076
Tel (831) 728-3323 *SIC* 5122 8748 8731

CORDEN PHARMA COLORADO INC p 369
2075 55th St, Boulder CO 80301
Tel (303) 442-1926 *SIC* 2833 8748 2834

■ ALPINE ACCESS INC p 60
1290 N Broadway Ste 1400, Denver CO 80203
Tel (303) 850-3700 *SIC* 7361 8742 8748

CRITIGEN LLC p 393
7604 Tech Way Ste 300, Denver CO 80237
Tel (303) 706-0990 *SIC* 8748

■ PSI SERVICES HOLDING INC p 1188
1515 Wynkoop St Ste 400, Denver CO 80202
Tel (303) 863-0900
SIC 8741 8742 7371 8748

WYOMING TRANSACTIONS INC p 1630
2373 Cntl Pk Blvd Ste 100, Denver CO 80238
Tel (303) 803-1397 *SIC* 8748 7929

IHS GLOBAL INC p 731
15 Inverness Way E, Englewood CO 80112
Tel (303) 790-0600
SIC 7299 8732 8748 7375 7373

IHS HOLDING INC p 731
15 Inverness Way E, Englewood CO 80112
Tel (303) 790-0600
SIC 7299 8732 8748 7375

IHS INC p 731
15 Inverness Way E, Englewood CO 80112
Tel (303) 790-0600
SIC 7299 8732 8748 7375

■ JEPPESEN SANDERSON INC p 783
55 Inverness Dr E, Englewood CO 80112
Tel (303) 799-9090 *SIC* 2741 2731 8748

ANATOLIA MINERALS DEVELOPMENT LTD p 88
3721 Hwy 74 Ste 14, Evergreen CO 80439
Tel (303) 670-9945 *SIC* 1382 8748

ARCADIS US INC p 103
630 Plaza Dr Ste 200, Highlands Ranch CO 80129
Tel (720) 344-3500 *SIC* 8748 8711 8741

CARDNO INC p 253
10004 Park Meadows Dr # 300, Lone Tree CO 80124
Tel (720) 257-5800
SIC 8711 8748 8742 8741

CARDNO USA INC p 253
10004 Park Meadows Dr # 300, Lone Tree CO 80124
Tel (720) 257-5800 *SIC* 8711 5045 8748

AFFINION GROUP HOLDINGS INC p 32
6 High Ridge Park Bldg A, Stamford CT 06905
Tel (203) 956-1000 *SIC* 8611 6282 8748

AFFINION GROUP LLC p 32
6 High Ridge Park Bldg A, Stamford CT 06905
Tel (203) 956-1000
SIC 8699 8748 7319 7331

DMG INFORMATION INC p 446
46 Southfield Ave Ste 400, Stamford CT 06902
Tel (203) 973-2940 *SIC* 6719 1731 8748

SONALYSTS INC p 1339
215 Parkway N, Waterford CT 06385
Tel (860) 442-4355
SIC 8711 7373 8748 8732 3993

■ TRC ENVIRONMENTAL CORP p 1475
21 Griffin Rd N Ste 1, Windsor CT 06095
Tel (860) 289-8631 *SIC* 8711 8748

REED ELSEVIER US HOLDINGS INC p 1217
1105 N Market St Ste 501, Wilmington DE 19801
Tel (302) 427-2672
SIC 2721 7999 8748 6719

ACDI/VOCA p 16
50 F St Nw Ste 1000, Washington DC 20001
Tel (202) 469-6000 *SIC* 8748 8641

AMERICAN CHEMISTRY COUNCIL INC p 70
700 2nd St Ne Fl 8-10, Washington DC 20002
Tel (202) 249-7000
SIC 8611 8748 8621 8699

APCO WORLDWIDE INC p 96
1299 Penn Ave Nw Ste 300, Washington DC 20004
Tel (202) 638-4082 *SIC* 8748 8742 8732

CHEMONICS INTERNATIONAL INC p 293
1717 H St Nw, Washington DC 20006
Tel (202) 955-3300 *SIC* 8742 8748

NATIONAL ACADEMY OF SCIENCES OF UNITED STATES OF AMERICA p 1009
2101 Constitution Ave Nw, Washington DC 20418
Tel (202) 334-2000 *SIC* 8733 8999 8748

WITT OBRIENS LLC p 1619
1201 15th St Nw Ste 600, Washington DC 20005
Tel (202) 585-0780 *SIC* 4959 8748 8322

▲ SEACOR HOLDINGS INC p 1296
2200 Eller Dr, Fort Lauderdale FL 33316
Tel (954) 523-2200
SIC 4412 4424 4449 4959 8748

■ TEMPLETON WORLDWIDE INC p 1436
500 E Broward Blvd # 900, Fort Lauderdale FL 33394
Tel (954) 527-7500
SIC 6211 6282 8742 8748

▲ NV5 GLOBAL INC p 1068
200 S Park Rd Ste 350, Hollywood FL 33021
Tel (954) 495-2112 *SIC* 8711 8748

PHYSICIANS PARTNERS PLUS LLC p 1146
1131 Nw 74th Ter, Hollywood FL 33024
Tel (352) 622-7000 *SIC* 8748

G4S HOLDING ONE INC p 588
1395 University Blvd, Jupiter FL 33458
Tel (561) 622-5656
SIC 7381 7382 8744 8748 8742

G4S SECURE SOLUTIONS (USA) INC p 588
1395 University Blvd, Jupiter FL 33458
Tel (561) 622-5656
SIC 7381 8744 8748 8742

DIGITAL RISK LLC p 439
2301 Maitland Center Pkwy # 165, Maitland FL 32751
Tel (407) 215-2900 *SIC* 8748

BUSINESS TELECOMMUNICATIONS SERVICES INC p 230
2620 Sw 27th Ave, Miami FL 33133
Tel (305) 358-5850 *SIC* 4813 5999 8748

HIG CAPITAL PARTNERS III LP p 690
1450 Brickell Ave # 3100, Miami FL 33131
Tel (305) 379-2322
SIC 6211 5084 7352 7699 8748 3842

ANSWER GROUP INC p 93
7562 Southgate Blvd, North Lauderdale FL 33068
Tel (954) 720-4002 *SIC* 7371 8748

ARMA GLOBAL CORP p 110
2701 N Rocky Point Dr # 1150, Rocky Point FL 33607
Tel (866) 554-9333 *SIC* 5045 8748 8742

IQOR GLOBAL SERVICES LLC p 764
1 Progress Plz Ste 7, Saint Petersburg FL 33701
Tel (727) 369-0878 *SIC* 8748 4731

BUREAU VERITAS HOLDINGS INC p 226
1601 Sawgrafl Corporate S Ste 400, Sunrise FL 33323
Tel (954) 835-9309
SIC 7389 8748 8711 8742

BUREAU VERITAS NORTH AMERICA INC p 227
1601 Sawgrs Corp Pkwy, Sunrise FL 33323
Tel (954) 236-8100
SIC 7389 8748 8734 8711 8742

AMEC FOSTER WHEELER ENVIRONMENT & INFRASTRUCTURE INC p 66
1105 Lakewood Pkwy # 300, Alpharetta GA 30009
Tel (770) 360-0600 *SIC* 8748 8711

LEXISNEXIS RISK SOLUTIONS INC p 860
1000 Alderman Dr, Alpharetta GA 30005
Tel (678) 694-6000 *SIC* 8748

INTEGRAL GROUP LLC p 748
191 Peachtree St Ne # 4100, Atlanta GA 30303
Tel (404) 224-1860
SIC 6552 8748 6798 6799 6722

ENERGY CONSULTING GROUP p 497
1000 Emc Pkwy Ne, Marietta GA 30060
Tel (678) 355-3190 *SIC* 8748

■ REVENUEMED INC p 1229
3740 Davinci Ct Ste 300, Norcross GA 30092
Tel (770) 246-9797 *SIC* 8748

SAVANNAH COLLEGE OF ART AND DESIGN INC p 1284
115 E York St, Savannah GA 31401
Tel (912) 525-5800 *SIC* 8748

EAST GEORGIA REGIONAL MEDICAL CENTER p 470
1499 Fair Rd, Statesboro GA 30458
Tel (912) 486-1000 *SIC* 8748

AMEC FOSTER WHEELER VENTURES INC p 66
1979 Lkeside Pkwy Ste 400, Tucker GA 30084
Tel (770) 688-2500 *SIC* 8748 8711

PHOENIX V LLC p 1145
311 Pacific St, Honolulu HI 96817
Tel (808) 532-7400 *SIC* 5169 8748

INTERTEK p 759
545 E Algonquin Rd Ste F, Arlington Heights IL 60005
Tel (847) 871-1020 *SIC* 8748

HUMAN FACTORS APPLICATIONS INC p 718
1000 Burr Ridge Pkwy, Burr Ridge IL 60527
Tel (630) 850-6900 *SIC* 7363 8748

CARYLON CORP p 262
2500 W Arthington St, Chicago IL 60612
Tel (312) 666-7700
SIC 7699 1629 7349 8748 4959

COLSON ASSOCIATES INC p 339
1 N Franklin St Ste 2420, Chicago IL 60606
Tel (312) 980-1100 *SIC* 8748

COMMUNITY AND ECONOMIC DEVELOPMENT ASSOCIATION OF COOK COUNTY INC p 347
567 W Lake St Ste 1200, Chicago IL 60661
Tel (312) 795-8844 *SIC* 8748

▲ HURON CONSULTING GROUP INC p 721
550 W Van Buren St # 1600, Chicago IL 60607
Tel (312) 583-8700 *SIC* 8742 8748

■ HURON CONSULTING SERVICES LLC p 721
550 W Van Buren St # 1600, Chicago IL 60607
Tel (312) 583-8700 *SIC* 8748

■ JPMORGAN CAPITAL CORP p 795
55 W Monroe St, Chicago IL 60603
Tel (614) 248-5800 *SIC* 8748 6726

■ MARMON GROUP LLC p 909
181 W Madison St Ste 2600, Chicago IL 60602
Tel (312) 372-9500 *SIC* 8748

■ POWER CO USA LLC p 1165
1165 N Clark St Ste 400, Chicago IL 60610
Tel (312) 496-3729 *SIC* 8748

SMT TELECOM INC p 1335
5219 N Harlem Ave, Chicago IL 60656
Tel (773) 842-4412 *SIC* 8748

■ MAVERICK TECHNOLOGIES HOLDINGS LLC p 921
265 Admiral Trost Rd, Columbia IL 62236
Tel (618) 281-9100 *SIC* 8711 8748 1731

■ MAVERICK TECHNOLOGIES LLC p 921
265 Admiral Trost Rd, Columbia IL 62236
Tel (618) 281-9100 *SIC* 8711 8748 1731

CCMSI HOLDINGS INC p 270
2 E Main St Ste 208, Danville IL 61832
Tel (217) 446-1089 *SIC* 8748

■ SGK LLC p 1310
1600 Sherwin Ave, Des Plaines IL 60018
Tel (847) 827-9494 *SIC* 8748

HAVI GLOBAL SOLUTIONS LLC p 668
3500 Lacey Rd Ste 600, Downers Grove IL 60515
Tel (630) 493-7400 *SIC* 8748

■ T-SYSTEMS NORTH AMERICA INC p 1420
1901 Butterfield Rd # 700, Downers Grove IL 60515
Tel (630) 493-6100 *SIC* 7379 8748

TELVENT USA LLC p 1435
1415 S Roselle Rd, Palatine IL 60067
Tel (717) 944-5460 *SIC* 7379 8748

ELM ENTERPRISES LLC p 489
60 State St Ste 201, Peoria IL 61602
Tel (309) 671-4300 *SIC* 8748 8713

ENVIRONMENTAL RESOURCES MANAGEMENT - NORTH CENTRAL INC p 503
1701 Golf Rd Ste 1-700, Rolling Meadows IL 60008
Tel (610) 524-3500 *SIC* 8748

ACS AUXILIARIES GROUP INC p 18
1100 E Woodfield Rd # 550, Schaumburg IL 60173
Tel (847) 273-7700 *SIC* 8748

■ ASPEN MARKETING SERVICES LLC p 118
1240 W North Ave, West Chicago IL 60185
Tel (630) 293-9600 *SIC* 8743 8748 5199

■ VECTREN ENERGY MARKETING AND SERVICES INC p 1546
1 Vectren Sq, Evansville IN 47708
Tel (812) 491-4000 *SIC* 8748 8711 8742

VIGO COAL OPERATING CO INC p 1556
250 N Cross Pointe Blvd, Evansville IN 47715
Tel (812) 759-8446 *SIC* 1221 8748

■ LINCOLN FINANCIAL ADVISORS CORP p 867
1300 S Clinton St, Fort Wayne IN 46802
Tel (800) 237-3813
SIC 6311 6282 8748 8742

IEA RENEWABLE ENERGY INC p 729
2647 Wtrfrnt Pw E Dr # 100, Indianapolis IN 46214
Tel (765) 832-8526 *SIC* 8711 8748

JUBILEE CENTER p 796
10330 N Meridian St, Indianapolis IN 46290
Tel (317) 415-5300 *SIC* 8748

■ ZEE MEDICAL INC p 1641
8021 Knue Rd Ste 100, Indianapolis IN 46250
Tel (949) 252-9500 *SIC* 8748 8322

■ ACCENT MARKETING SERVICES LLC p 14
4550 Town Center Blvd, Jeffersonville IN 47130
Tel (812) 941-1112 *SIC* 7331 7389 8748

■ VECTREN ENERGY SERVICES CORP p 1546
4655 Rosebud Ln, Newburgh IN 47630
Tel (812) 492-3723
SIC 8711 8742 8748 6719

GREEN COMPANIES INC p 636
8710 Earhart Ln Sw, Cedar Rapids IA 52404
Tel (319) 841-4000
SIC 8711 8748 8713 4911 1623

ACT INC p 19
500 Act Dr, Iowa City IA 52243
Tel (319) 337-1000 *SIC* 8748

VGM GROUP INC p 1553
1111 W San Marnan Dr, Waterloo IA 50701
Tel (319) 235-7100 *SIC* 8748 5047

ICM INC p 727
310 N 1st St, Colwich KS 67030
Tel (316) 796-0900 *SIC* 8748 8711

EPIQ SYSTEMS INC p 505
501 Kansas Ave, Kansas City KS 66105
Tel (913) 621-9500 *SIC* 7371 8748

AGSPRING LLC p 36
5250 W 116th Pl Ste 200, Leawood KS 66211
Tel (913) 333-3035 *SIC* 0191 8748

TERRACON CONSULTANTS INC p 1439
18001 W 106th St Ste 300, Olathe KS 66061
Tel (913) 599-6886
SIC 8742 8711 8748 8741

ALEXANDER OPEN SYSTEMS INC p 49
12980 Foster St Ste 300, Overland Park KS 66213
Tel (913) 307-2300
SIC 5045 7373 8748 7376 3577 1731

SECURITY BENEFIT LIFE INSURANCE CO p 1299
1 Sw Security Benefit Pl, Topeka KS 66636
Tel (785) 438-3000
SIC 6311 6722 6091 6211 8748

KOCH BUSINESS SOLUTIONS LP p 825
4111 E 37th St N, Wichita KS 67220
Tel (316) 828-5500 *SIC* 8748

AMERICAN FUJI SEAL INC p 73
1051 Bloomfield Rd, Bardstown KY 40004
Tel (502) 348-9211 *SIC* 8748 2671

BARREN RIVER DEVELOPMENT COUNCIL INC p 157
177 Graham Ave, Bowling Green KY 42101
Tel (270) 781-2381 *SIC* 8748

■ ABM GOVERNMENT SERVICES LLC p 12
101 Walton Way, Hopkinsville KY 42240
Tel (270) 885-4642 *SIC* 8748

RAWLINGS CO LLC p 1209
1 Eden Pkwy, La Grange KY 40031
Tel (502) 587-1279 *SIC* 8748 8111

SOURCECORP HEALTHSERVE RADIOLOGY INC p 1342
602 N English Station Rd, Louisville KY 40223
Tel (502) 244-0035 *SIC* 7334 8748 8721

CB&I ENVIRONMENTAL & INFRASTRUCTURE INC p 268
3867 Plaza Tower Dr, Baton Rouge LA 70816
Tel (225) 932-2500
SIC 8748 1794 1795 8744 8741

CB&I GOVERNMENT SOLUTIONS INC p 268
4171 Essen Ln, Baton Rouge LA 70809
Tel (225) 932-2500
SIC 8711 8734 8748 1541 1542 1611

ATC GROUP HOLDINGS LLC p 124
221 Rue De Jean Ste 300, Lafayette LA 70508
Tel (337) 324-8777
SIC 8711 8732 8731 8249 8748

ATC GROUP SERVICES LLC p 124
221 Rue De Jean Ste 200, Lafayette LA 70508
Tel (337) 234-8777
SIC 8711 8734 8731 8249 8748

WOODARD & CURRAN INC p 1622
41 Hutchins Dr, Portland ME 04102
Tel (800) 426-4262 *SIC* 8711 8748

MSTC INC p 997
10900 Pump House Rd Ste B, Annapolis Junction MD 20701
Tel (240) 280-8064 *SIC* 8742 8748

■ CONSTELLATION NEWENERGY INC p 361
1310 Point St Fl 9, Baltimore MD 21231
Tel (410) 783-2800 *SIC* 4911 8748

EDGE ACQUISITION LLC p 477
1001 Fleet St, Baltimore MD 21202
Tel (410) 843-8000 *SIC* 8299 8748

JENSEN HUGHES INC p 782
3610 Commerce Dr Ste 817, Baltimore MD 21227
Tel (410) 737-8677 *SIC* 8748 8711 8734

PROMETRIC INC p 1183
1501 S Clinton St # 1200, Baltimore MD 21224
Tel (443) 455-8000 *SIC* 8748 8741

DAI GLOBAL LLC p 408
7600 Wisconsin Ave # 200, Bethesda MD 20814
Tel (301) 771-7600 *SIC* 8748

TRIBALCO LLC p 1479
4915 Saint Elmo Ave # 501, Bethesda MD 20814
Tel (301) 652-8450 *SIC* 8748

UNIVERSITY RESEARCH CO LLC p 1527
7200 Wisconsin Ave # 600, Bethesda MD 20814
Tel (301) 654-8338 *SIC* 8742 8748

GEA PT NORTH AMERICA INC p 597
9165 Rumsey Rd, Columbia MD 21045
Tel (410) 997-8700 *SIC* 8748

▲ GP STRATEGIES CORP p 627
11000 Broken Land Pkwy # 200, Columbia MD 21044
Tel (443) 367-9600 *SIC* 8742 8711 8748

L B & B ASSOCIATES INC p 833
9891 Broken Land Pkwy # 400, Columbia MD 21046
Tel (301) 621-3944
SIC 8744 7338 4225 8742 8748 4581

▲ BROADSOFT INC p 215
9737 Washingtonian Blvd # 350, Gaithersburg MD 20878
Tel (301) 977-9440 *SIC* 7372 7371 8748

AEROTEK INC p 31
7301 Parkway Dr, Hanover MD 21076
Tel (410) 694-5100 *SIC* 7363 8748 8711

■ KEYW CORP p 816
7740 Milestone Pkwy # 400, Hanover MD 21076
Tel (443) 733-1600 *SIC* 8711 8748

MARYLAND DEPARTMENT OF TRANSPORTATION p 914
7201 Corporate Center Dr, Hanover MD 21076
Tel (410) 865-1037 *SIC* 8748 9621

▲ 2U INC p 2
8201 Corporate Dr Ste 900, Landover MD 20785
Tel (301) 892-4350 *SIC* 7372 8748 8299

CLAMPETT INDUSTRIES LLC p 321
10461 Mill Run Cir # 1100, Owings Mills MD 21117
Tel (410) 785-6200 *SIC* 8748 6531

APEX COMPANIES LLC p 96
15850 Crabbs Branch Way # 200, Rockville MD 20855
Tel (301) 417-0200 *SIC* 8744 8748 8742

▲ ARGAN INC p 107
1 Church St Ste 201, Rockville MD 20850
Tel (301) 315-0027 *SIC* 4813 1623 8748

FCN INC p 533
12315 Wilkins Ave, Rockville MD 20852
Tel (301) 770-2925 *SIC* 8748

DB CONSULTING GROUP INC p 418
8401 Colesville Rd # 300, Silver Spring MD 20910
Tel (301) 589-4020 *SIC* 8748

■ OXFORD GLOBAL RESOURCES LLC p 1101
100 Cummings Ctr Ste 206c, Beverly MA 01915
Tel (978) 236-1182 *SIC* 7363 8748

■ JACK MORTON WORLDWIDE INC p 773
142 Berkeley St Ste 6, Boston MA 02116
Tel (617) 585-7000 *SIC* 8748 8742

RENAISSANCE WORLDWIDE INC p 1223
711 Boylston St, Boston MA 02116
Tel (617) 535-5000
SIC 7363 8742 7379 7361 8748 7371

CENTRA TECHNOLOGY INC p 277
25 Burlington Mall Rd # 504, Burlington MA 01803
Tel (781) 272-7887 *SIC* 8748

ENVIROBUSINESS INC p 503
21 B St, Burlington MA 01803
Tel (781) 273-2500 *SIC* 8748

HALEY & ALDRICH INC p 653
70 Blanchard Rd Ste 204, Burlington MA 01803
Tel (617) 886-7400 *SIC* 8748 8711

ENSR INTL CORP p 501
250 Apollo Dr, Chelmsford MA 01824
Tel (978) 589-3000 *SIC* 8748 8711

PR EDUCATION LLC p 1166
111 Speen St, Framingham MA 01701
Tel (508) 663-5050 *SIC* 8748 8299

WINTERGREEN RESEARCH INC p 1617
6 Raymond St, Lexington MA 02421
Tel (781) 863-5078 *SIC* 8748 8742

▲ TRC COMPANIES INC p 1475
650 Suffolk St, Lowell MA 01854
Tel (978) 970-5600
SIC 7363 8734 7382 8748

PRINCETON REVIEW INC p 1177
24 Prime Park Way Ste 201, Natick MA 01760
Tel (800) 273-8439 *SIC* 8748 8299

WESTON & SAMPSON INC p 1602
5 Centennial Dr Ste 1, Peabody MA 01960
Tel (978) 532-1900 *SIC* 8711 8748 4953

MERCY HOSPITAL INC p 947
271 Carew St, Springfield MA 01104
Tel (413) 748-9000
SIC 8062 8071 8011 7219 8748

TRI-WIRE ENGINEERING SOLUTIONS INC p 1478
890 East St, Tewksbury MA 01876
Tel (978) 640-6899 *SIC* 1623 8748

APOLLO SECURITY INTERNATIONAL INC p 97
2150 Bston Providence Hwy, Walpole MA 02081
Tel (508) 660-1197 *SIC* 7381 8748

CONSERVATION SERVICES GROUP INC p 358
50 Washington St Ste 3000, Westborough MA 01581
Tel (508) 836-9500 *SIC* 8748

■ NORESCO INC p 1048
1 Research Dr Ste 400c, Westborough MA 01581
Tel (508) 614-1000
SIC 8711 8741 8748 4911 4924

■ **NORESCO LLC** p 1048
1 Research Dr Ste 400c, Westborough MA 01581
Tel (508) 614-1000
SIC 8711 8741 8744 8748 4911 4924

UMASS MEMORIAL HEALTH CARE INC AND AFFILIATES GROUP RETURN p 1501
306 Belmont St 120, Worcester MA 01604
Tel (508) 334-5106 SIC 8748

FEV NORTH AMERICA INC p 539
4554 Glenmeade Ln, Auburn Hills MI 48326
Tel (248) 475-4761 SIC 8748 8743

CW PROFESSIONAL SERVICES LLC p 404
150 W Jefferson Ave # 1200, Detroit MI 48226
Tel (313) 416-1011 SIC 8748

FUTURENET GROUP INC p 586
12801 Auburn St, Detroit MI 48223
Tel (313) 544-7117 SIC 1542 8748

MSX INTERNATIONAL INC p 997
500 Woodward Ave Ste 2150, Detroit MI 48226
Tel (248) 829-6300
SIC 8748 7363 8742 8711

HEALTHPLUS PARTNERS INC p 677
2050 S Linden Rd, Flint MI 48532
Tel (810) 230-2192 SIC 8748

▲ **STEELCASE INC** p 1384
901 44th St Se, Grand Rapids MI 49508
Tel (616) 247-2710
SIC 2522 2521 3648 8748

REHMANN LLC p 1220
1500 W Big Beaver Rd, Macomb MI 48044
Tel (866) 799-9580 SIC 8748 8721

■ **DOW HOLDINGS LLC** p 453
2030 Dow Ctr, Midland MI 48674
Tel (989) 636-1000 SIC 8748

WESTON SOLUTIONS OF MICHIGAN INC p 1602
2501 Jolly Rd Ste 100, Okemos MI 48864
Tel (517) 381-5920 SIC 8748

ATWELL LLC p 130
2 Towne Sq Ste 700, Southfield MI 48076
Tel (248) 447-2000
SIC 8999 8713 8748 8711

EPITEC INC p 505
24800 Denso Dr Ste 150, Southfield MI 48033
Tel (248) 353-6800
SIC 7371 7379 7373 8748 8711

▲ **SYNTEL INC** p 1416
525 E Big Beaver Rd # 300, Troy MI 48083
Tel (248) 619-2800 SIC 7371 7372 8748

AVI SYSTEMS INC p 137
9675 W 76th St Ste 200, Eden Prairie MN 55344
Tel (952) 949-3700
SIC 5065 7622 8748 1799

ROSENS DIVERSIFIED INC p 1251
1120 Lake Ave, Fairmont MN 56031
Tel (507) 238-4201
SIC 2011 8748 5149 2879

NCS PEARSON INC p 1022
5601 Green Valley Dr # 220, Minneapolis MN 55437
Tel (952) 681-3000
SIC 3577 7372 7374 8748 7379

■ **NORSTAN INC** p 1049
5050 Lincoln Dr Ste 300, Minneapolis MN 55436
Tel (952) 352-4000
SIC 7389 3661 8748 7379

PACE ANALYTICAL SERVICES LLC p 1103
1800 Elm St Se, Minneapolis MN 55414
Tel (612) 607-6369 SIC 8734 8748 8731

SOURCECORP LEGAL INC p 1342
625 Marquette Ave Ste 880, Minneapolis MN 55402
Tel (612) 359-2822 SIC 8748

▲ **COMMUNICATIONS SYSTEMS INC** p 347
10900 Red Circle Dr, Minnetonka MN 55343
Tel (952) 996-1674
SIC 3661 3577 3663 8748

ANTEA USA INC p 93
5910 Rice Creek Pkwy, Saint Paul MN 55126
Tel (651) 639-9449 SIC 8748

TENIX HOLDINGS INC p 1437
925 Tommy Munro Dr Ste J, Biloxi MS 39532
Tel (228) 594-6800 SIC 8748

■ **MITEK INDUSTRIES INC** p 977
16023 Swinly Rdg, Chesterfield MO 63017
Tel (314) 434-1200 SIC 8711 8748

ROSE INTERNATIONAL INC p 1250
16401 Swingley Ridge Rd, Chesterfield MO 63017
Tel (636) 812-4000 SIC 7371 8748

MARITZ HOLDINGS INC p 907
1375 N Highway Dr, Fenton MO 63099
Tel (636) 827-4000
SIC 4725 8748 8732 4899

MARITZ LLC p 907
1375 N Highway Dr, Fenton MO 63099
Tel (636) 827-4000
SIC 4725 8748 8732 4899

INTEGRITY SOLUTION SERVICES INC p 750
20 Corporate Hills Dr, Saint Charles MO 63301
Tel (636) 530-7985 SIC 8748 7322

■ **CHARTER COMMUNICATIONS LLC** p 291
12405 Powerscourt Dr, Saint Louis MO 63131
Tel (314) 288-3478 SIC 8748

WORLD WIDE TECHNOLOGY HOLDING CO INC p 1625
60 Weldon Pkwy, Saint Louis MO 63101
Tel (314) 919-1400 SIC 5045 5065 8748

BELLEVUE PUBLIC SCHOOLS p 170
2600 Arboretum Dr, Bellevue NE 68005
Tel (402) 293-4000 SIC 8299 8748 8211

HDR INC p 673
8404 Indian Hills Dr, Omaha NE 68114
Tel (402) 399-1000
SIC 8712 8711 8742 8748 4789

MUTUAL OF OMAHA INSURANCE CO p 1003
Mutual Of Omaha Plaza, Omaha NE 68175
Tel (402) 342-7600 SIC 6311 6211 8748

COLEEN M MCCORMICK p 336
415 Center St Dakota Pl, Ulysses NE 68669
Tel (402) 549-2778 SIC 8748 6799

NOS COMMUNICATIONS INC p 1062
250 Pilot Rd Ste 300, Las Vegas NV 89119
Tel (702) 547-8000 SIC 8748 4813

ADAMS AND ASSOCIATES INC p 21
10395 Double R Blvd, Reno NV 89521
Tel (775) 348-0900 SIC 8748

■ **WASTE MANAGEMENT OF MASSACHUSETTS INC** p 1580
4 Liberty Ln W, Hampton NH 03842
Tel (603) 929-3000 SIC 4953 8748

RCG GLOBAL SERVICES INC p 1212
379 Thornall St Ste 14, Edison NJ 08837
Tel (732) 744-3500 SIC 8748

CLEAN VENTURE INC p 324
201 S 1st St, Elizabeth NJ 07206
Tel (908) 355-5800
SIC 4225 4212 4953 8748

LOUIS BERGER GROUP INC p 879
412 Mount Kemble Ave, Morristown NJ 07960
Tel (973) 407-1000 SIC 8748 8712 8711

URS CORP p 1530
Mack Ctr Ii Mack Ctr Dr, Paramus NJ 07652
Tel (201) 262-7000 SIC 8711 8748

LANGAN ENGINEERING ENVIRONMENTAL SURVEYING AND LANDSCAPE ARCHITECTURE DPC p 844
300 Kimball Dr Ste 4, Parsippany NJ 07054
Tel (973) 560-4900
SIC 8711 8748 1389 0781

■ **TETRA TECH EC INC** p 1441
6 Century Dr Ste 3, Parsippany NJ 07054
Tel (973) 630-8000 SIC 8748

▲ **RCM TECHNOLOGIES INC** p 1212
2500 Mcclellan Ave # 350, Pennsauken NJ 08109
Tel (856) 356-4500
SIC 8711 8748 7373 8049 7363

SYNECHRON INC p 1415
1 Corporate Pl S Ste 200, Piscataway NJ 08854
Tel (732) 562-0088 SIC 8748

BERLITZ CORP p 175
7 Roszel Rd Fl 3, Princeton NJ 08540
Tel (207) 828-3768 SIC 8299 8748

EDUCATIONAL TESTING SERVICE INC p 479
660 Rosedale Rd, Princeton NJ 08540
Tel (609) 921-9000 SIC 8748 8732

ERASE INC p 507
107 Myrtle Ave 27, Ramsey NJ 07446
Tel (201) 760-0189 SIC 8748

▲ **ORBCOMM INC** p 1092
395 W Passaic St Ste 3, Rochelle Park NJ 07662
Tel (703) 433-6361 SIC 4899 8748

CGI AMS p 285
75 Livingston Ave Ste 202, Roseland NJ 07068
Tel (972) 788-0400
SIC 7379 8748 7374 7371

GROUNDWATER AND ENVIRONMENTAL SERVICES INC p 641
1599 Rte 34 Ste 1, Wall Township NJ 07727
Tel (800) 220-3068 SIC 8748

PAULUS SOKOLOWSKI & SARTOR ENGINEERING A PROFESSIONAL CORP p 1122
67b Mountain Blvd Ext, Warren NJ 07059
Tel (732) 560-9700 SIC 8711 8748 8712

APPLIED RESEARCH ASSOCIATES INC p 100
4300 San Mateo Blvd Ne A220, Albuquerque NM 87110
Tel (505) 883-3636 SIC 8731 8748

NAVAJO NATION GAMING ENTERPRISE p 1019
249 E Nm State Hwy 118, Church Rock NM 87311
Tel (505) 905-7100 SIC 8748

LOS ALAMOS NATIONAL SECURITY LLC p 878
105 Central Park Sq, Los Alamos NM 87544
Tel (877) 723-4101 SIC 8748

NATIONAL GRID ENERGY CORP p 1013
1 Metrotech Ctr Fl 1, Brooklyn NY 11201
Tel (718) 403-2000 SIC 8748

VICE GROUP HOLDING INC p 1555
49 S 2nd St, Brooklyn NY 11249
Tel (718) 599-3101 SIC 8748 7812

DIVAL SAFETY EQUIPMENT INC p 443
1721 Niagara St, Buffalo NY 14207
Tel (716) 874-9060
SIC 5099 8748 8734 5047 5136 5661

■ **PPC BROADBAND INC** p 1166
6176 E Molloy Rd, East Syracuse NY 13057
Tel (315) 431-7200 SIC 8748

▲ **ECOLOGY AND ENVIRONMENT INC** p 476
368 Pleasant View Dr, Lancaster NY 14086
Tel (716) 684-8060 SIC 8748 8734 8711

■ **AECOM USA INC** p 29
605 3rd Ave, New York NY 10158
Tel (212) 973-2900 SIC 8748

ALVAREZ & MARSAL CORPORATE PERFORMANCE IMPROVEMENT LLC p 63
600 Madison Ave Fl 8, New York NY 10022
Tel (212) 759-4433 SIC 8748 8742

AP CARIB HOLDING LTD p 95
9 W 57th St Fl 43, New York NY 10019
Tel (212) 515-3202 SIC 8741 8748 7379

BAHA INDUSTRIES CORP p 145
462 7th Ave Fl 15, New York NY 10018
Tel (212) 273-1921 SIC 8748

BUSINESS DEVELOPMENT CORP OF AMERICA p 229
405 Park Ave Fl 15, New York NY 10022
Tel (212) 415-6500 SIC 8748

CAPGEMINI US LLC p 249
623 5th Ave Fl 33, New York NY 10022
Tel (917) 934-8000 SIC 8748

CORPORATE RISK HOLDINGS LLC p 372
600 3rd Ave Fl 4, New York NY 10016
Tel (212) 896-2001
SIC 6719 8748 7375 7389

ENVIRONMENTAL DEFENSE FUND INC p 503
257 Park Ave S Fl 17, New York NY 10010
Tel (212) 505-2100 SIC 8641 8748

EWT HOLDINGS I CORP p 516
666 5th Ave Fl 36, New York NY 10103
Tel (212) 644-5900 SIC 8748

GLOBAL DATA PUBLICATIONS INC p 616
441 Lexington Ave Fl 3, New York NY 10017
Tel (646) 395-5460 SIC 7379 8732 8748

GOLDMAN SACHS FOUNDATION p 622
375 Park Ave Ste 1002, New York NY 10152
Tel (212) 902-6875 SIC 8748

HILL AND KNOWLTON STRATEGIES LLC p 693
466 Lexington Ave Frnt 4, New York NY 10017
Tel (212) 885-0300 SIC 8743 8748

INFOR LUX BOND CO p 741
641 Ave Of The Americas, New York NY 10011
Tel (646) 336-1700 SIC 7371 7372 8748

IPREO HOLDINGS LLC p 763
1359 Broadway Fl 2, New York NY 10018
Tel (212) 849-5000 SIC 8748

IPREO LLC p 763
1359 Broadway Fl 2, New York NY 10018
Tel (212) 849-5000 SIC 8748

KROLL LLC p 830
600 3rd Ave Fl 4, New York NY 10016
Tel (212) 593-1000
SIC 7381 8742 8748 7389

MAJOR LEAGUE BASEBALL PROPERTIES INC p 899
245 Park Ave Fl 34, New York NY 10167
Tel (212) 931-7800 SIC 6794 4833 8748

■ **MANAGEMENT SHIP LLC GENCO** p 900
299 Park Ave Fl 12, New York NY 10171
Tel (646) 443-8550 SIC 8748

▲ **MDC PARTNERS INC** p 933
745 5th Ave Fl 19, New York NY 10151
Tel (646) 429-1800 SIC 7311 8748

■ **MERCER INC** p 944
1166 Avenue Of The Americ, New York NY 10036
Tel (212) 345-7000 SIC 8748

OGILVY GROUP LLC p 1076
636 11th Ave, New York NY 10036
Tel (212) 237-4000
SIC 7311 8743 8748 7336 7361 8732

ONE EQUITY PARTNERS LLC p 1086
320 Park Ave Fl 18, New York NY 10022
Tel (212) 794-3434 SIC 6726 8748

■ **OUTSOURCE PARTNERS INTERNATIONAL INC** p 1099
280 Park Ave Rm 3801w, New York NY 10017
Tel (212) 752-2439 SIC 8721 8748

PARSONS BRINCKERHOFF INC p 1117
1 Penn Plz Ste 200, New York NY 10119
Tel (212) 465-5000 SIC 8711 8748

PAUL WEISS RIFKIND WHARTON & GARRISON LLP p 1121
1285 Ave Of The Americas, New York NY 10019
Tel (212) 373-3000 SIC 8111 8748

RELX INC p 1222
230 Park Ave, New York NY 10169
Tel (212) 309-8100
SIC 2721 2731 7389 7374 8748

SH GROUP INC p 1310
1515 Broadway, New York NY 10036
Tel (212) 921-2300 SIC 8748 8711 1542

TRANSPERFECT GLOBAL INC p 1472
3 Park Ave Fl 39, New York NY 10016
Tel (212) 689-5555 SIC 7389 7371 8748

TRANSPERFECT TRANSLATIONS INTERNATIONAL INC p 1472
3 Park Ave Fl 39, New York NY 10016
Tel (212) 689-5555 SIC 7389 8748 8111

WILLIS NORTH AMERICA INC p 1612
200 Liberty St Fl 7, New York NY 10281
Tel (212) 915-8888
SIC 6411 8742 8999 8748

GHD SERVICES INC p 610
2055 Niagara Falls Blvd, Niagara Falls NY 14304
Tel (716) 297-6150 SIC 8748

NOVA CORP INC p 1062
1 Main St, Nyack NY 10960
Tel (201) 567-4404 SIC 1541 8748

RIGHT LIGHT ENERGY SERVICES LLC p 1234
811 Court St Ste 214, Utica NY 13502
Tel (315) 723-2329 SIC 8748

■ **CONSOLIDATED EDISON SOLUTIONS INC** p 359
100 Summit Lake Dr # 410, Valhalla NY 10595
Tel (914) 286-7000 SIC 4924 4911 8748

SHAMROCK ENVIRONMENTAL CORP p 1311
6106 Corporate Park Dr, Browns Summit NC 27214
Tel (336) 375-1989
SIC 4953 4212 8748 7699

■ **SPECTRASITE COMMUNICATIONS LLC** p 1357
400 Regency Forest Dr # 300, Cary NC 27518
Tel (919) 468-0112
SIC 4812 8748 1623 3661 4813 4899

AMWINS GROUP INC p 87
4725 Piedmont Row Dr # 600, Charlotte NC 28210
Tel (704) 749-2700 SIC 6411 8748

MERCHANDISING CORP OF AMERICA INC p 944
11121 Carmel Commons Blvd # 455, Charlotte NC 28226
Tel (704) 944-4600 SIC 8748

■ **CONSTELLA GROUP LLC** p 360
2605 Meridian Pkwy # 200, Durham NC 27713
Tel (919) 544-8500
SIC 7371 8742 7375 8748 8731 8071

MEASUREMENT INC p 934
423 Morris St, Durham NC 27701
Tel (919) 683-2413
SIC 2752 8748 2791 2789 2759

TRIEST AG GROUP INC p 1480
1101 Industrial Blvd, Greenville NC 27834
Tel (252) 758-4263 SIC 8748

WALKER GROUP INC p 1573
7129 Old Hwy 52, Welcome NC 27374
Tel (336) 731-6391
SIC 4813 8748 5065 8711

■ **CENTENNIAL ENERGY HOLDINGS INC** p 275
Schuchart Bldg 918e, Bismarck ND 58501
Tel (701) 222-7900 SIC 1382 8748 1221

ACTIONLINK LLC p 19
2279 Romig Rd, Akron OH 44320
Tel (888) 737-8757 SIC 8748

■ **BIORX LLC** p 184
7167 E Kemper Rd, Cincinnati OH 45249
Tel (866) 442-4679
SIC 5122 8748 2834 5047 8051

INTERNATIONAL COMMUNICATIONS EXCHANGE CORP p 755
4033 Ellery Ave, Moraine OH 45439
Tel (937) 296-9605 SIC 8748 7379

NAVEX GLOBAL INC p 1020
5500 Meadows Rd Ste 500, Lake Oswego OR 97035
Tel (971) 250-4100 SIC 8748

NORTHWEST EVALUATION ASSOCIATION p 1059
121 Nw Everett St, Portland OR 97209
Tel (503) 624-1951 SIC 8299 8748

ZIMMER GUNSUL FRASCA ARCHITECTS LLP p 1643
1223 Sw Washington St # 200, Portland OR 97205
Tel (503) 224-3860 SIC 8712 8748 7389

SDI INC p 1295
1414 Radcliffe St Ste 300, Bristol PA 19007
Tel (215) 633-1900
SIC 7374 7389 8711 8748

XL ENVIRONMENTAL INC p 1632
505 Eagleview Blvd # 100, Exton PA 19341
Tel (800) 327-1414 SIC 6411 8748

SEVERN TRENT SERVICES INC p 1309
220 Gibraltar Rd Ste 200, Fort Washington PA 19034
Tel (215) 646-9201 SIC 8748 3589

AMERICAN MANUFACTURING CORP p 75
555 Croton Rd Ste 200, King Of Prussia PA 19406
Tel (610) 962-3770 SIC 8748

PROCURIAN LLC p 1179
211 S Gulph Rd Ste 500, King Of Prussia PA 19406
Tel (484) 690-5000 SIC 7389 8748

BALFOUR BEATTY INVESTMENTS INC p 148
1 Country View Rd Ste 100, Malvern PA 19355
Tel (610) 355-8100
SIC 6531 8748 1731 8999 8741

ENVIRONMENTAL RESOURCES MANAGEMENT INC p 503
75 Valley Stream Pkwy # 200, Malvern PA 19355
Tel (484) 913-0300 SIC 8748

ERM NORTH AMERICA INC p 508
75 Valley Stream Pkwy, Malvern PA 19355
Tel (484) 913-0300 SIC 8748

ERM-NA HOLDINGS CORP p 508
75 Valley Stream Pkwy # 200, Malvern PA 19355
Tel (484) 913-0300 SIC 8711 8748 8742

HARRON COMMUNICATIONS LP p 664
70 E Lancaster Ave, Malvern PA 19355
Tel (610) 644-7500 SIC 8748

AMERIHEALTH INC p 82
1901 Market St Fl 32, Philadelphia PA 19103
Tel (215) 241-3019 SIC 6411 6324 8748

INDEPENDENCE BLUE CROSS LLC p 736
1901 Market St Fl 32, Philadelphia PA 19103
Tel (215) 241-2400 SIC 6324 6411 8748

NATIONAL BOARD OF MEDICAL EXAMINERS OF UNITED STATES OF AMERICA p 1010
3750 Market St, Philadelphia PA 19104
Tel (215) 590-9500 SIC 8748

WOLTERS KLUWER HEALTH INC p 1621
2001 Market St Lbby 1, Philadelphia PA 19103
Tel (215) 521-8300
SIC 2721 2731 2741 7372 8748

PACEC LLC p 1103
333 Baldwin Rd, Pittsburgh PA 15205
Tel (412) 429-2324 SIC 8748

DANELLA COMPANIES INC p 411
2290 Butler Pike, Plymouth Meeting PA 19462
Tel (610) 828-6200
SIC 7513 7353 8711 1623 8748

LIQUIDHUB INC p 870
500 E Swedesford Rd # 300, Wayne PA 19087
Tel (610) 688-6531 SIC 8748

PRECYSE ADVANCED TECHNOLOGIES LLC p 1169
1275 Drummers Ln Ste 200, Wayne PA 19087
Tel (800) 555-2311 SIC 8748

PRECYSE HOLDINGS LLC p 1169
1275 Drummers Ln Ste 200, Wayne PA 19087
Tel (800) 555-2311 SIC 8748

WESTON SOLUTIONS HOLDINGS INC p 1602
1400 Weston Way, West Chester PA 19380
Tel (610) 692-7533 SIC 8748

WESTON SOLUTIONS INC p 1602
1400 Weston Way, West Chester PA 19380
Tel (610) 701-3000 SIC 8742 8748

RICO CLARO PUERTO p 1233
1515 Frnklin D Rsvelt Ave, Guaynabo PR 00968
Tel (787) 766-2355 SIC 4812 8748

RICO PUERTO TELEPHONE CO INC p 1233
1515 Ave Fd Roosevelt, Guaynabo PR 00968
Tel (787) 781-1314 SIC 8748

▲ **EVERTEC INC** p 515
Km 1/3 Rr 176, San Juan PR 00926
Tel (787) 759-9999
SIC 8741 8748 7379 8721

SOUTHEASTERN HEALTHCARE SYSTEM INC p 1346
111 Brewster St, Pawtucket RI 02860
Tel (401) 729-2000 SIC 8748

▲ **BLACKBAUD INC** p 187
2000 Daniel Island Dr, Daniel Island SC 29492
Tel (843) 216-6200 SIC 7372 8748

CONTRACT ENVIRONMENTAL SERVICES INC p 364
636 Powdersville Rd, Easley SC 29642
Tel (864) 306-7785 SIC 8748

TOLT SOLUTIONS INC p 1459
3550 Rutherford Rd, Taylors SC 29687
Tel (864) 322-4200
SIC 8748 7379 7374 7373

SOUTH DAKOTA HOUSING DEVELOPMENT AUTHORITY p 1344
3060 E Elizabeth St, Pierre SD 57501
Tel (605) 773-3181 *SIC* 8748

MIDCO COMMUNICATIONS INC p 964
3901 N Louise Ave, Sioux Falls SD 57107
Tel (605) 334-1200
SIC 8748 5961 7389 4812

■ SAFETY & ECOLOGY HOLDINGS CORP p 1266
2800 Solway Rd, Knoxville TN 37931
Tel (865) 690-0501 *SIC* 8744 8748

SETECH INC p 1308
410 New Salem Hwy Ste 106, Murfreesboro TN 37129
Tel (615) 890-1758 *SIC* 8742 8748 5085

■ TEAM INDUSTRIAL SERVICES INC p 1430
200 Hermann Dr, Alvin TX 77511
Tel (281) 388-5525 *SIC* 8748 8711 7699

■ AT&T LABS INC p 123
9505 Arboretum Blvd, Austin TX 78759
Tel (512) 372-5000 *SIC* 8748

CLEARESULT CONSULTING INC p 324
4301 Westbank Dr Ste A250, Austin TX 78746
Tel (512) 327-9200 *SIC* 8748

PLANVIEW INC p 1154
12301 Research Blvd 5-100, Austin TX 78759
Tel (512) 346-8600 *SIC* 7371 8748 8742

TEXAS A&M ENGINEERING EXTENSION SERVICE p 1442
301 Tarrow St, College Station TX 77840
Tel (979) 845-7641
SIC 8331 8711 8748 8111

BT AMERICAS INC p 222
8951 Cypress Waters Blvd # 200, Coppell TX 75019
Tel (877) 272-0832 *SIC* 8748

BEARINGPOINT INC p 166
100 Crescent Ct Ste 700, Dallas TX 75201
Tel (214) 459-2770 *SIC* 8748

COMPUCOM SYSTEMS HOLDING LLC p 352
7171 Forest Ln, Dallas TX 75230
Tel (972) 856-3600
SIC 7373 5045 7378 8748

D&M HOLDING INC p 407
5001 Spring Valley Rd 800e, Dallas TX 75244
Tel (214) 368-6391 *SIC* 8748

■ ENERGY TRANSFER PARTNERS LLC p 498
8111 Westchester Dr # 600, Dallas TX 75225
Tel (214) 981-0700 *SIC* 8748

▲ JACOBS ENGINEERING GROUP INC p 775
1999 Bryan St Ste 1200, Dallas TX 75201
Tel (214) 583-8500
SIC 8711 1629 1541 8748

PARIVEDA SOLUTIONS INC p 1115
2811 Mckinney Ave Ste 220, Dallas TX 75204
Tel (214) 777-4600 *SIC* 8748

TRINITY CONSULTANTS INC p 1481
12700 Park Central Dr # 2100, Dallas TX 75251
Tel (972) 661-8100 *SIC* 8748

USA ENVIRONMENT LP p 1534
316 Georgia Ave, Deer Park TX 77536
Tel (713) 425-6900 *SIC* 8748

SOURCEHOV TAX INC p 1342
4150 International Plz, Fort Worth TX 76109
Tel (817) 732-5494 *SIC* 8748

ABSG CONSULTING INC p 12
16855 Northchase Dr, Houston TX 77060
Tel (281) 673-2800 *SIC* 8748

BRACE INDUSTRIAL GROUP INC p 206
14950 Heathrow Fore, Houston TX 77032
Tel (281) 749-1020 *SIC* 8748

BRACE INTEGRATED SERVICES INC p 206
14950 Heathrow Frst, Houston TX 77032
Tel (281) 749-1020 *SIC* 8748

■ BUCKEYE ENERGY SERVICES LLC p 223
1 Greenway Plz Ste 600, Houston TX 77046
Tel (832) 615-8600 *SIC* 8748

ENTRIX HOLDING CO p 502
5252 Westchester St # 250, Houston TX 77005
Tel (713) 666-6223 *SIC* 8748

■ EP ENERGY GLOBAL LLC p 504
1001 Louisiana St, Houston TX 77002
Tel (713) 420-2600 *SIC* 8748

NORTHSTAR MEMORIAL GROUP LLC p 1059
1900 Saint James Pl # 300, Houston TX 77056
Tel (713) 979-9690 *SIC* 8748

PSC HOLDINGS II LP p 1188
5151 San Felipe St # 1600, Houston TX 77056
Tel (713) 623-8777 *SIC* 4953 8748

ROCKWATER ENERGY SOLUTIONS INC p 1245
515 Post Oak Blvd Ste 200, Houston TX 77027
Tel (713) 235-9500 *SIC* 8731 8748

TOTAL SAFETY US INC p 1463
11111 Wilcrest Green Dr # 375, Houston TX 77042
Tel (713) 353-7100 *SIC* 8748 5084 7699

SOURCEHOV LLC p 1342
2701 E Grauwyler Rd, Irving TX 75061
Tel (866) 321-5854 *SIC* 8748

ENDEAVOR ENERGY RESOURCES LP p 496
110 N Marienfeld St # 200, Midland TX 79701
Tel (432) 687-1575 *SIC* 1311 8748

■ VICEROY INC p 1555
3225 Pasadena Blvd, Pasadena TX 77503
Tel (713) 475-4518
SIC 1629 3443 1796 8742 8748 7363

COMPUCOM SYSTEMS INC p 352
8383 Dominion Pkwy, Plano TX 75024
Tel (972) 856-3600
SIC 7373 5045 7378 8748

HUAWEI TECHNOLOGIES USA INC p 715
5700 Tennyson Pkwy # 500, Plano TX 75024
Tel (214) 545-3700 *SIC* 8748

ROUND ROCK INDEPENDENT SCHOOL DISTRICT (INC) p 1252
1311 Round Rock Ave, Round Rock TX 78681
Tel (512) 464-5000 *SIC* 8211 8748

LINK AMERICA LLC p 869
3002 Century Dr, Rowlett TX 75088
Tel (972) 463-0050 *SIC* 8748

HARCOURT ASSESSMENT INC p 660
19500 Bulverde Rd, San Antonio TX 78259
Tel (210) 339-5000 *SIC* 8748 2741

■ SABRE GLBL INC p 1264
3150 Sabre Dr, Southlake TX 76092
Tel (682) 605-1000
SIC 7375 7371 7374 7389 8748

▲ LAYNE CHRISTENSEN CO p 848
1800 Hughes Landing Blvd, The Woodlands TX 77380
Tel (281) 475-2600
SIC 1781 1623 5084 1481 8748

VERMONT ENERGY INVESTMENT CORP p 1551
128 Lakeside Ave Ste 401, Burlington VT 05401
Tel (802) 860-4095 *SIC* 8748

CALIBRE SYSTEMS INC p 239
6354 Walker Ln Ste 300, Alexandria VA 22310
Tel (703) 797-8500 *SIC* 7379 8748

CONSERVATION INTERNATIONAL FOUNDATION p 358
2011 Crystal Dr Ste 500, Arlington VA 22202
Tel (703) 341-2400 *SIC* 8748

PAE GOVERNMENT SERVICES INC p 1107
1320 N Courthouse Rd # 800, Arlington VA 22201
Tel (703) 717-6000 *SIC* 8748

RAMBOLL ENVIRON INC p 1206
4350 Fairfax Dr Ste 300, Arlington VA 22203
Tel (703) 516-2300 *SIC* 8748 8999

RAMBOLL ENVIRON US CORP p 1207
4350 Fairfax Dr Ste 300, Arlington VA 22203
Tel (703) 516-2300 *SIC* 8748 8999

FCI FEDERAL INC p 533
20135 Lakeview Center Plz # 300, Ashburn VA 20147
Tel (703) 443-1888 *SIC* 8742 8748

ENGINEERING SOLUTIONS & PRODUCTS LLC p 499
14566 Lee Rd, Chantilly VA 20151
Tel (571) 375-1400
SIC 8711 7379 4813 8742 8748

■ SRA INTERNATIONAL INC p 1362
15036 Conference Ctr Dr, Chantilly VA 20151
Tel (703) 803-1500 *SIC* 7373 8748

CDM FEDERAL PROGRAMS CORP p 271
3201 Jermantown Rd # 400, Fairfax VA 22030
Tel (703) 691-6500
SIC 8711 8742 8744 8748 8999

■ ICF INC LLC p 727
9300 Lee Hwy Ste 200, Fairfax VA 22031
Tel (703) 934-3000 *SIC* 8742 8748

▲ ICF INTERNATIONAL INC p 727
9300 Lee Hwy Ste 200, Fairfax VA 22031
Tel (703) 934-3000 *SIC* 8742 8748

SALIENT CRGT HOLDINGS INC p 1272
4000 Legato Rd Ste 600, Fairfax VA 22033
Tel (703) 891-8200 *SIC* 7371 8748

SALIENT CRGT INC p 1272
4000 Legato Rd Ste 600, Fairfax VA 22033
Tel (703) 891-8200 *SIC* 7373 8748

■ VANGENT INC p 1543
3211 Jermantown Rd, Fairfax VA 22030
Tel (703) 995-2666
SIC 8748 7371 7372 7373 7374 7376

NOBLIS INC p 1046
3150 Fairview Park Dr, Falls Church VA 22042
Tel (703) 610-2000 *SIC* 8733 8748

PACEM SOLUTION INTERNATIONAL LLC p 1103
2941 Frview Pk Dr Ste 550, Falls Church VA 22042
Tel (703) 309-1891 *SIC* 8748

■ STAR SECOND MERGER SUB LLC p 1378
3170 Fairview Park Dr, Falls Church VA 22042
Tel (703) 876-1000 *SIC* 7373 8748

ORANGE BUSINESS SERVICES US INC p 1091
13775 Mclearen Rd, Herndon VA 20171
Tel (866) 849-4185 *SIC* 4813 8748

ENVIROSOLUTIONS HOLDINGS INC p 503
9650 Hawkins Dr, Manassas VA 20109
Tel (703) 633-3000 *SIC* 8748

COGNOSANTE LLC p 334
8200 Greensboro Dr # 1200, Mc Lean VA 22102
Tel (703) 206-6000 *SIC* 7379 8748

STRATEGIC RESOURCES INC p 1392
7927 Jones Branch Dr 600w, Mc Lean VA 22102
Tel (703) 749-3040 *SIC* 8742 8748 7373

ACUMEN SOLUTIONS INC p 20
1660 Intl Dr Ste 500, Mclean VA 22102
Tel (703) 600-4000 *SIC* 8748

■ FEDERAL NETWORK SYSTEMS LLC p 535
11710 Plaza America Dr, Reston VA 20190
Tel (703) 694-7200 *SIC* 8748

GRADUATE MANAGEMENT ADMISSION COUNCIL INC p 628
11921 Freedom Dr Ste 300, Reston VA 20190
Tel (703) 668-9600 *SIC* 8748

INDYNE INC p 740
11800 Sunrise Valley Dr # 250, Reston VA 20191
Tel (703) 903-6900 *SIC* 8744 8748 7382

TRIPLE CANOPY INC p 1482
12018 Sunrise Valley Dr # 140, Reston VA 20191
Tel (703) 673-5000 *SIC* 7381 8748

▲ VERSAR INC p 1551
6850 Versar Ctr Ste 201, Springfield VA 22151
Tel (703) 750-3000
SIC 8711 8748 8712 8731

NEW CUSTOMER SERVICE COMPANIES INC p 1029
22894 Pacific Blvd, Sterling VA 20166
Tel (703) 318-7700 *SIC* 8748

SLAIT PARTNERS INC p 1331
100 Landmark Sq, Virginia Beach VA 23452
Tel (757) 313-6500
SIC 5045 3571 8748 7373

PARKER SMITH & FEEK INC p 1116
2233 112th Ave Ne, Bellevue WA 98004
Tel (425) 709-3600 *SIC* 6411 6351 8748

HAGGEN ACQUISITION LLC p 653
2211 Rimland Dr Ste 300, Bellingham WA 98226
Tel (360) 733-8720 *SIC* 8748

HAGGEN OPERATIONS HOLDINGS LLC p 653
2211 Rimland Dr Ste 300, Bellingham WA 98226
Tel (360) 733-8720 *SIC* 8748

JACO ENVIRONMENTAL INC p 775
18323 Bothell Everett Hwy # 110, Bothell WA 98012
Tel (425) 398-6200 *SIC* 8748

RILEY GROUP INC p 1235
17522 Bthell Way Ne Ste A, Bothell WA 98011
Tel (425) 415-0551 *SIC* 8748

CUBIC GLOBAL DEFENSE INC p 399
400 Union Ave Se Ste 300, Olympia WA 98501
Tel (360) 493-6275
SIC 7373 8744 8711 7376 8748 8741

PARAMETRIX INC p 1114
1019 39th Ave Se Ste 100, Puyallup WA 98374
Tel (206) 394-3700
SIC 8748 8711 8742 1389 4789

EMERALD SERVICES INC p 491
7343 E Marginal Way S, Seattle WA 98108
Tel (206) 430-7795
SIC 4953 7699 2911 8748 7359

HARTUNG BROTHERS INC p 666
708 Heartland Trl # 2000, Madison WI 53717
Tel (608) 829-6000 *SIC* 0161 0115 8748

AMERICAN APPRAISAL ASSOCIATES INC p 68
411 E Wisconsin Ave # 1900, Milwaukee WI 53202
Tel (630) 541-4650 *SIC* 8748 7389 6531

WIPFLI LLP p 1618
10000 W Innovation Dr 250-260, Milwaukee WI 53226
Tel (414) 431-9300 *SIC* 8748 8721

■ UMR INC p 1502
11 Scott St, Wausau WI 54403
Tel (800) 826-9781 *SIC* 6324 8748

SIC 8999 Services Not Elsewhere Classified

CAPITOL RECORDS LLC p 251
1750 Vine St, Los Angeles CA 90028
Tel (213) 462-6252 *SIC* 7389 8999

▲ EXPONENT INC p 520
149 Commonwealth Dr, Menlo Park CA 94025
Tel (650) 326-9400 *SIC* 8711 8742 8999

KENNETH RAININ FOUNDATION p 811
155 Grand Ave Ste 1000, Oakland CA 94612
Tel (510) 625-5200 *SIC* 8999

MCCLATCHY CO p 926
2100 Q St, Sacramento CA 95816
Tel (916) 321-1941 *SIC* 8999

LEDCOR CMI INC p 851
6405 Mira Mesa Blvd # 100, San Diego CA 92121
Tel (602) 595-3017
SIC 1541 1611 1629 1623 1522 8999

CLEARWIRE INC p 324
1490 Holly Dr, Tracy CA 95376
Tel (408) 794-8220 *SIC* 8999

TIMS AIRBRUSH LLC p 1455
10490 Vaughn Way, Commerce City CO 80022
Tel (303) 944-9497 *SIC* 8999 7389

UNITEDGLOBALCOM INC p 1515
12300 Liberty Blvd, Englewood CO 80112
Tel (303) 220-6676 *SIC* 8999 4813

■ COGENT COMMUNICATIONS GROUP INC p 334
2450 N St Nw, Washington DC 20037
Tel (202) 295-4200 *SIC* 8999

NATIONAL ACADEMY OF SCIENCES OF UNITED STATES OF AMERICA p 1009
2101 Constitution Ave Nw, Washington DC 20418
Tel (202) 334-2000 *SIC* 8733 8999 8748

SALLYPORT GLOBAL LLC p 1273
27200 Riverview Ste 309, Bonita Springs FL 34134
Tel (239) 390-1900 *SIC* 8999

LANGFORD SERVICES INC p 844
6480 State Road 60 E, Lake Wales FL 33898
Tel (863) 528-2242 *SIC* 8999

LATAMSCIENCE LLC p 846
2151 S Le Jeune Rd # 307, Miami FL 33134
Tel (305) 871-0701 *SIC* 8731 8999

■ GREATER MEDIA INC p 635
3033 Riviera Dr Ste 200, Naples FL 34103
Tel (239) 263-5000 *SIC* 2711 8999 4832

BURKS COMPANIES p 227
191 Peachtree St Ne # 800, Atlanta GA 30303
Tel (404) 589-4600
SIC 1752 5085 7349 4953 8999

INSTITUTE OF NUCLEAR POWER OPERATIONS p 747
700 Galleria Pkwy Se # 100, Atlanta GA 30339
Tel (770) 644-8000 *SIC* 8999

■ TWCC HOLDING CORP p 1494
300 Interstate N Pkwy Se, Atlanta GA 30339
Tel (770) 226-0000
SIC 4833 4813 7812 8999

AON HEWITT LLC p 95
200 E Randolph St Ll3, Chicago IL 60601
Tel (312) 381-1000 *SIC* 8742 8999

■ UOP LLC p 1528
25 E Algonquin Rd, Des Plaines IL 60016
Tel (847) 391-2000
SIC 2819 8711 8731 8999 3823 3479

RUMMEL KLEPPER & KAHL LLP p 1257
81 Mosher St, Baltimore MD 21217
Tel (410) 728-2900
SIC 8711 8741 1623 8999 8713 1611

WESTAT INC p 1596
1600 Research Blvd, Rockville MD 20850
Tel (301) 251-1500
SIC 8732 7371 7373 8741 8742 8999

▲ ACACIA COMMUNICATIONS INC p 13
3 Mill And Main Pl # 400, Maynard MA 01754
Tel (978) 938-4896 *SIC* 3674 8999

GZA GEOENVIRONMENTAL TECHNOLOGIES INC p 649
249 Vanderbilt Ave Unit 2, Norwood MA 02062
Tel (781) 278-3700
SIC 8711 8999 1799 8744

TECHNICAL TRAINING INC p 1431
3903 W Hamlin Rd, Rochester Hills MI 48309
Tel (248) 853-5550 *SIC* 8742 8999

ATWELL LLC p 130
2 Towne Sq Ste 700, Southfield MI 48076
Tel (248) 447-2000
SIC 8999 8713 8748 8711

■ OPTUMHEALTH CARE SOLUTIONS INC p 1090
6300 Olson Memorial Hwy, Golden Valley MN 55427
Tel (877) 801-3507 *SIC* 6324 7374 8999

■ NUCLEAR MANAGEMENT CO LLC p 1066
414 Nicollet Mall, Minneapolis MN 55401
Tel (612) 330-5500 *SIC* 8741 8999

MERRILL CORP p 950
1 Merrill Cir, Saint Paul MN 55108
Tel (651) 646-4501 *SIC* 7389 8111 8999

TYCO ELECTRONICS SUBSEA COMMUNICATIONS LLC p 1496
250 Industrial Way W, Eatontown NJ 07724
Tel (732) 578-7000
SIC 3661 5063 7373 1731 8999

ROUND-THE-WORLD LOGISTICS (USA) CORP p 1253
333 Cantor Ave Unit C, Linden NJ 07036
Tel (908) 862-3535 *SIC* 8999

■ INNOVEX INC p 745
10 Waterview Blvd Ste 100, Parsippany NJ 07054
Tel (973) 257-4500 *SIC* 8734 8999 7374

DREW MARINE GROUP INC p 455
100 S Jefferson Rd # 204, Whippany NJ 07981
Tel (973) 526-5700 *SIC* 8999 5169

BARD COLLEGE PUBLICATIONS p 155
Annandale Rd, Annandale On Hudson NY 12504
Tel (845) 758-7417 *SIC* 8999 2759 5311

NATIONAL RESPONSE CORP p 1015
3500 Sunrise Hwy, Great River NY 11739
Tel (631) 224-9141 *SIC* 4959 8999

C P C HOME ATTENDANT PROGRAM p 233
40 Worth St Fl 13, New York NY 10013
Tel (212) 219-8100 *SIC* 8999

MAXUS COMMUNICATIONS LLC p 923
498 Fashion Ave, New York NY 10018
Tel (212) 297-8300 *SIC* 8999

MOSBY HOLDINGS CORP p 992
125 Park Ave, New York NY 10017
Tel (212) 309-8100 *SIC* 2741 8999

OGILVY PUBLIC RELATIONS WORLDWIDE INC p 1076
636 11th Ave, New York NY 10036
Tel (212) 880-5200 *SIC* 8743 8999

TOWERS WATSON DELAWARE HOLDINGS INC p 1464
335 Madison Ave Fl 20, New York NY 10017
Tel (212) 309-3400 *SIC* 8742 8999

WILLIS NORTH AMERICA INC p 1612
200 Liberty St Fl 7, New York NY 10281
Tel (212) 915-8888
SIC 6411 8742 8999 8748

■ QUINTILES TRANSNATIONAL CORP p 1200
4820 Emperor Blvd, Durham NC 27703
Tel (919) 998-2000 *SIC* 8732 8731 8999

■ COMMSCOPE CONNECTIVITY SOLUTIONS LLC p 346
1100 Commscope Pl Se, Hickory NC 28602
Tel (828) 324-2200
SIC 3661 3357 3643 8999

OTAK INC p 1097
808 Sw 3rd Ave Ste 220, Portland OR 97204
Tel (503) 274-5445
SIC 0781 8712 8711 8713 8742 8999

BALFOUR BEATTY INVESTMENTS INC p 148
1 Country View Rd Ste 100, Malvern PA 19355
Tel (610) 355-8100
SIC 6531 8748 1731 8999 8741

EMCON INC p 491
2790 Mosside Blvd, Monroeville PA 15146
Tel (412) 372-7701 *SIC* 8711 8999

COMMUNITY SERVICE OFFICE p 350
84 W South St, Wilkes Barre PA 18766
Tel (570) 408-5905 *SIC* 8999

MMODAL SERVICES LTD INC p 979
5000 Meridian Blvd # 200, Franklin TN 37067
Tel (800) 233-3030 *SIC* 8999

TRANSPLANT SERVICES DALLAS p 1472
3410 Worth St Ste 950, Dallas TX 75246
Tel (214) 820-2050 *SIC* 8999

FUGRO (USA) INC p 583
6100 Hillcroft St Ste 700, Houston TX 77081
Tel (713) 772-3700 *SIC* 1389 8711 8999

NETVERSANT SOLUTIONS LLC p 1028
9750 W Sam Houston Pkwy N # 100, Houston TX 77064
Tel (800) 540-2739 *SIC* 7373 8999 7381

SOUTHERN PETROLEUM LABORATORIES INC p 1350
8850 Interchange Dr, Houston TX 77054
Tel (713) 660-0901 *SIC* 5172 8999 8734

STALLION OILFIELD HOLDINGS LTD p 1375
950 Corbindale Rd Ste 300, Houston TX 77024
Tel (713) 528-5544 *SIC* 8999

RAMBOLL ENVIRON INC p 1206
4350 Fairfax Dr Ste 300, Arlington VA 22203
Tel (703) 516-2300 *SIC* 8748 8999

RAMBOLL ENVIRON US CORP p 1207
4350 Fairfax Dr Ste 300, Arlington VA 22203
Tel (703) 516-2300 *SIC* 8748 8999

CDM FEDERAL PROGRAMS CORP p 271
3201 Jermantown Rd # 400, Fairfax VA 22030
Tel (703) 691-6500
SIC 8711 8742 8744 8748 8999

CGI FEDERAL INC p 285
12601 Fair Lakes Cir, Fairfax VA 22033
Tel (703) 227-6000 *SIC* 7379 7389 8999

HEADSTRONG CORP p 673
11921 Freedom Dr Ste 550, Reston VA 20190
Tel (703) 272-6761 *SIC* 7379 8999

SERCO INC p 1306
1818 Library St Ste 1000, Reston VA 20190
Tel (703) 939-6000 *SIC* 8999

MILLIMAN INC p 971
1301 5th Ave Ste 3800, Seattle WA 98101
Tel (206) 624-7940 *SIC* 8742 8999 7389

DIRECTOR OF V0LUNTEERS SERVICE p 442
2900 1st Ave, Huntington WV 25702
Tel (304) 526-1400 *SIC* 8999

SIC 9111 Executive Offices

CITY OF BIRMINGHAM p 313
710 20th St N Ste 600, Birmingham AL 35203
Tel (205) 254-2000 *SIC* 9111

JEFFERSON COUNTY ALABAMA p 781
716 Richard Arrington Jr, Birmingham AL 35203
Tel (205) 731-2880 *SIC* 9111

JEFFERSON COUNTY BOARD OF EDUCATION p 781
2100 Richard Arrington Jr, Birmingham AL 35209
Tel (205) 379-2000 *SIC* 8211 9111

CITY OF HUNTSVILLE p 315
308 Fountain Cir Sw Fl 8, Huntsville AL 35801
Tel (256) 427-5080 *SIC* 9111

COUNTY OF MADISON p 379
100 Northside Sq, Huntsville AL 35801
Tel (256) 532-3492 *SIC* 9111

CITY OF MOBILE p 316
205 Government St, Mobile AL 36602
Tel (251) 208-7395 *SIC* 9111

COUNTY OF MOBILE p 380
205 Government St, Mobile AL 36644
Tel (251) 574-5077 *SIC* 9111

ALABAMA JUDICIAL BUILDING AUTHORITY p 43
100 N Union St Rm 224, Montgomery AL 36104
Tel (334) 353-3328 *SIC* 9111

CITY OF MONTGOMERY p 316
103 N Perry St, Montgomery AL 36104
Tel (334) 625-2025 *SIC* 9111

EXECUTIVE OFFICE OF STATE OF ALABAMA p 517
600 Dexter Ave Ste S105, Montgomery AL 36130
Tel (334) 242-7205 *SIC* 9111

STATE OF ALABAMA p 1381
300 Dexter Ave, Montgomery AL 36104
Tel (334) 242-7100 *SIC* 9111

CITY OF TUSCALOOSA p 319
2201 University Blvd, Tuscaloosa AL 35401
Tel (205) 349-2010 *SIC* 9111

ANCHORAGE MUNICIPALITY OF (INC) p 89
632 W 6th Ave Ste 810, Anchorage AK 99501
Tel (907) 343-6610 *SIC* 9111

NORTH SLOPE BOROUGH p 1054
1274 Agvik St, Barrow AK 99723
Tel (907) 852-2611 *SIC* 9111

CITY & BOROUGH OF JUNEAU p 312
155 S Seward St, Juneau AK 99801
Tel (907) 789-0819 *SIC* 9111

EXECUTIVE OFFICE OF STATE OF ALASKA p 517
Capitol Bldg Fl 3, Juneau AK 99811
Tel (907) 465-3500 *SIC* 9111

STATE OF ALASKA p 1381
120 4th St, Juneau AK 99801
Tel (907) 465-3500 *SIC* 9111

COUNTY OF COCHISE p 377
1415 W Melody Ln Bldg G, Bisbee AZ 85603
Tel (520) 432-9200 *SIC* 9111

CITY OF CHANDLER p 313
175 S Arizona Ave, Chandler AZ 85225
Tel (480) 782-2000 *SIC* 9111

COUNTY OF COCONINO p 377
219 E Cherry Ave, Flagstaff AZ 86001
Tel (928) 679-7120 *SIC* 9111

COUNTY OF PINAL p 381
31 N Pinal St, Florence AZ 85132
Tel (520) 866-6000 *SIC* 9111

TOWN OF GILBERT p 1465
50 E Civic Center Dr, Gilbert AZ 85296
Tel (480) 503-6000 *SIC* 9111

TOWN OF GILBERT ARIZONA p 1465
50 E Civic Center Dr, Gilbert AZ 85296
Tel (480) 503-6400 *SIC* 9111

CITY OF GLENDALE p 315
5850 W Glendale Ave Fl 4, Glendale AZ 85301
Tel (623) 930-2000 *SIC* 9111

COUNTY OF MOHAVE p 380
700 W Beale St, Kingman AZ 86401
Tel (928) 753-0729 *SIC* 9111

CITY OF MESA p 316
20 E Main St, Mesa AZ 85201
Tel (480) 644-2011 *SIC* 9111

CITY OF PEORIA p 317
8401 W Monroe St, Peoria AZ 85345
Tel (623) 773-7148 *SIC* 9111

CITY OF PHOENIX p 317
200 W Washington St Fl 11, Phoenix AZ 85003
Tel (602) 262-7111 *SIC* 9111

COUNTY OF MARICOPA p 379
301 W Jefferson St # 960, Phoenix AZ 85003
Tel (602) 506-3011 *SIC* 9111

EXECUTIVE OFFICE OF STATE OF ARIZONA p 517
1700 W Washington St # 602, Phoenix AZ 85007
Tel (602) 542-4331 *SIC* 9111

STATE OF ARIZONA p 1381
1700 W Washington St Fl 7, Phoenix AZ 85007
Tel (602) 542-4331 *SIC* 9111

COUNTY OF YAVAPAI p 383
1015 Fair St, Prescott AZ 86305
Tel (928) 771-3200 *SIC* 9111

CITY OF SCOTTSDALE MUNICIPAL PROPERTY CORP p 318
7447 E Indian School Rd R, Scottsdale AZ 85251
Tel (480) 312-7859 *SIC* 9111

CITY OF TEMPE p 319
31 E 5th St, Tempe AZ 85281
Tel (480) 350-8355 *SIC* 9111

CITY OF TUCSON p 319
255 W Alameda St, Tucson AZ 85701
Tel (520) 791-4561 *SIC* 9111

PIMA COUNTY p 1148
97 E Congress St Fl 3, Tucson AZ 85701
Tel (520) 243-1800 *SIC* 9111 1623

CITY OF YUMA p 319
1 City Plz, Yuma AZ 85364
Tel (928) 373-5187 *SIC* 9111

COUNTY OF YUMA p 383
198 S Main St, Yuma AZ 85364
Tel (928) 373-1010 *SIC* 9111

EXECUTIVE OFFICE OF STATE OF ARKANSAS p 517
State Capitol Ste 250, Little Rock AR 72201
Tel (501) 682-2345 *SIC* 9111

STATE OF ARKANSAS p 1381
4 Capitol Mall Rm 403a, Little Rock AR 72201
Tel (501) 682-2345 *SIC* 9111

CITY OF ALAMEDA p 312
2263 Santa Clara Ave, Alameda CA 94501
Tel (510) 747-7400 *SIC* 9111

COUNTY OF PLACER p 381
2968 Richardson Dr, Auburn CA 95603
Tel (530) 889-4200 *SIC* 9111

CITY OF BAKERSFIELD p 313
1600 Truxtun Ave Fl 5th, Bakersfield CA 93301
Tel (661) 326-3000 *SIC* 9111

COUNTY OF KERN p 379
1115 Truxtun Ave Rm 505, Bakersfield CA 93301
Tel (661) 868-3690 *SIC* 9111

CITY OF BURBANK p 313
275 E Olive Ave, Burbank CA 91502
Tel (818) 238-5800 *SIC* 9111

COUNTY OF HUMBOLDT p 378
825 5th St, Eureka CA 95501
Tel (707) 268-2543 *SIC* 9111

CITY OF FAIRFIELD p 314
1000 Webster St, Fairfield CA 94533
Tel (707) 428-7569 *SIC* 9111

COUNTY OF SOLANO p 382
675 Texas St Ste 2600, Fairfield CA 94533
Tel (707) 784-6706 *SIC* 9111

CITY OF FOLSOM p 314
50 Natoma St, Folsom CA 95630
Tel (916) 355-7200 *SIC* 9111

CITY OF FONTANA p 314
8353 Sierra Ave, Fontana CA 92335
Tel (909) 350-7605 *SIC* 9111

CITY OF FREMONT p 315
3300 Capitol Ave, Fremont CA 94538
Tel (510) 284-4000 *SIC* 9111

CITY OF FRESNO p 315
2600 Fresno St, Fresno CA 93721
Tel (559) 621-7001 *SIC* 9111

CITY OF GLENDALE p 315
141 N Glendale Ave Fl 2, Glendale CA 91206
Tel (818) 548-2085 *SIC* 9111

COUNTY OF KINGS p 379
1400 W Lacey Blvd, Hanford CA 93230
Tel (559) 582-0326 *SIC* 9111

CITY OF INGLEWOOD p 315
1 W Manchester Blvd, Inglewood CA 90301
Tel (310) 412-5301 *SIC* 9111

CITY OF IRVINE p 315
1 Civic Center Plz, Irvine CA 92606
Tel (949) 724-6000 *SIC* 9121 9111

CITY OF LONG BEACH p 316
333 W Ocean Blvd Fl 10, Long Beach CA 90802
Tel (562) 570-6450 *SIC* 9111

CITY OF LOS ANGELES p 316
200 N Spring St Ste 303, Los Angeles CA 90012
Tel (213) 978-0600 *SIC* 9111

COUNTY OF LOS ANGELES p 379
500 W Temple St Ste 375, Los Angeles CA 90012
Tel (213) 974-1101 *SIC* 9111

COUNTY OF MADERA p 379
209 W Yosemite Ave, Madera CA 93637
Tel (559) 675-7726 *SIC* 9111

COUNTY OF CONTRA COSTA p 377
625 Court St Ste 100, Martinez CA 94553
Tel (925) 957-5280 *SIC* 9111

COUNTY OF YUBA p 383
915 8th St Ste 109, Marysville CA 95901
Tel (530) 749-7575 *SIC* 9111

COUNTY OF MERCED p 379
2222 M St, Merced CA 95340
Tel (209) 385-7511 *SIC* 9111

COUNTY OF STANISLAUS p 382
1010 10th St Ste 5100, Modesto CA 95354
Tel (209) 525-6398 *SIC* 9111

MODESTO CITY OF (INC) p 981
1010 10th St Ste 2100, Modesto CA 95354
Tel (209) 577-5200 *SIC* 9111

COUNTY OF NAPA p 380
1195 Third St Ste 310, Napa CA 94559
Tel (707) 253-4421 *SIC* 9111

COUNTY OF NEVADA p 380
950 Maidu Ave, Nevada City CA 95959
Tel (530) 265-1480 *SIC* 9111

CITY OF OAKLAND p 317
150 Frank H Ogawa Plz # 3332, Oakland CA 94612
Tel (510) 238-3280 *SIC* 9111

COUNTY OF ALAMEDA p 376
1221 Oak St Ste 555, Oakland CA 94612
Tel (510) 272-6691 *SIC* 9111

CITY OF OCEANSIDE p 317
300 N Coast Hwy, Oceanside CA 92054
Tel (760) 435-3830 *SIC* 9111

CITY OF ONTARIO p 317
303 E B St, Ontario CA 91764
Tel (909) 395-2012 *SIC* 9111

CITY OF OXNARD p 317
300 W 3rd St Uppr Fl4, Oxnard CA 93030
Tel (805) 385-7803 *SIC* 9111

CITY OF PALO ALTO p 317
250 Hamilton Ave, Palo Alto CA 94301
Tel (650) 329-2571 *SIC* 9111

CITY OF PASADENA p 317
100 N Garfield Ave, Pasadena CA 91101
Tel (626) 744-4386 *SIC* 9111

COUNTY OF EL DORADO p 377
330 Fair Ln, Placerville CA 95667
Tel (530) 621-5830 *SIC* 9111

COUNTY OF SAN MATEO p 381
400 County Ctr, Redwood City CA 94063
Tel (650) 363-4123 *SIC* 9111

CITY OF RICHMOND p 318
450 Civic Center Plaza, Richmond CA 94804
Tel (510) 620-6727 *SIC* 9111

CITY OF RIVERSIDE p 318
3900 Main St Fl 7, Riverside CA 92522
Tel (951) 826-5311 *SIC* 9111

COUNTY OF RIVERSIDE p 381
4080 Lemon St Fl 11, Riverside CA 92501
Tel (951) 955-1110 *SIC* 9111

CITY OF ROSEVILLE p 318
311 Vernon St, Roseville CA 95678
Tel (916) 774-5200 *SIC* 9111

CITY OF SACRAMENTO p 318
915 I St Fl 5, Sacramento CA 95814
Tel (916) 808-5300 *SIC* 9111

COUNTY OF SACRAMENTO p 381
700 H St Ste 7650, Sacramento CA 95814
Tel (916) 874-5544 *SIC* 9111

EXECUTIVE OFFICE OF STATE OF CALIFORNIA p 517
Governors Ofc, Sacramento CA 95814
Tel (916) 445-2841 *SIC* 9111

STATE OF CALIFORNIA p 1381
State Capital, Sacramento CA 95814
Tel (916) 445-2864 *SIC* 9111

COUNTY OF MONTEREY p 380
168 W Alisal St Fl 3, Salinas CA 93901
Tel (831) 755-5040 *SIC* 9111

CALIFORNIA CITY OF SAN BERNARDINO p 239
300 N D St, San Bernardino CA 92418
Tel (909) 384-5128 *SIC* 9111

COUNTY OF SAN BERNARDINO p 381
385 N Arrowhead Ave, San Bernardino CA 92415
Tel (909) 387-3841 *SIC* 9111

CITY OF SAN DIEGO p 318
202 C St, San Diego CA 92101
Tel (619) 236-6330 *SIC* 9111

COUNTY OF SAN DIEGO p 381
1600 Pacific Hwy Ste 209, San Diego CA 92101
Tel (619) 531-5880 *SIC* 9111

CITY & COUNTY OF SAN FRANCISCO p 312
1 Dr Carlton B Goodlett P, San Francisco CA 94102
Tel (415) 554-7500 *SIC* 9111

CITY OF SAN JOSE p 318
200 E Santa Clara St, San Jose CA 95113
Tel (408) 535-3500 *SIC* 9111

COUNTY OF SAN LUIS OBISPO p 381
Government Center Rm. 300, San Luis Obispo CA 93408
Tel (805) 781-5040 *SIC* 9111

COUNTY OF MARIN p 379
1600 Los Gamos Dr Ste 200, San Rafael CA 94903
Tel (415) 473-6358 *SIC* 9111

CITY OF SANTA ANA p 318
20 Civic Center Plz Fl 8, Santa Ana CA 92701
Tel (714) 647-5400 *SIC* 9111

CITY OF SANTA BARBARA p 318
735 Anacapa St, Santa Barbara CA 93101
Tel (805) 564-5334 *SIC* 9111

COUNTY OF SANTA BARBARA p 381
105 E Anapamu St Rm 406, Santa Barbara CA 93101
Tel (805) 568-3400 *SIC* 9111

CITY OF SANTA CLARA p 318
1500 Warburton Ave, Santa Clara CA 95050
Tel (408) 615-2200 *SIC* 9111

COUNTY OF SANTA CRUZ p 381
701 Ocean St Rm 520, Santa Cruz CA 95060
Tel (831) 454-2100 *SIC* 9111

CITY OF SANTA MONICA p 318
1685 Main St, Santa Monica CA 90401
Tel (310) 458-8411 *SIC* 9111

COUNTY OF SONOMA p 382
585 Fiscal Dr 100, Santa Rosa CA 95403
Tel (707) 565-2431 *SIC* 9111

COUNTY OF TUOLUMNE p 382
2 S Green St, Sonora CA 95370
Tel (209) 533-5521 *SIC* 9111

CITY OF STOCKTON p 318
425 N El Dorado St, Stockton CA 95202
Tel (209) 937-8212 *SIC* 9111

COUNTY OF SAN JOAQUIN p 381
44 N San Joaquin St # 640, Stockton CA 95202
Tel (209) 468-3203 *SIC* 9111

CITY OF TORRANCE p 319
3031 Torrance Blvd, Torrance CA 90503
Tel (310) 328-5310 *SIC* 9111

COUNTY OF MENDOCINO p 379
501 Low Gap Rd Rm 1010, Ukiah CA 95482
Tel (707) 463-4441 *SIC* 9111

COUNTY OF VENTURA p 382
800 S Victoria Ave, Ventura CA 93009
Tel (805) 654-2551 *SIC* 9111

COUNTY OF TULARE p 382
2800 W Burrel Ave, Visalia CA 93291
Tel (559) 636-5005 *SIC* 9111

COUNTY OF YOLO p 383
625 Court St Ste 102, Woodland CA 95695
Tel (530) 666-8114 *SIC* 9111

CITY OF AURORA p 313
15151 E Alameda Pkwy, Aurora CO 80012
Tel (303) 739-7056 *SIC* 9111 9511

BOULDER CITY OF (INC) p 204
1777 Broadway, Boulder CO 80302
Tel (303) 441-3090
SIC 9111 9224 9221 9511

COUNTY OF BOULDER p 376
2020 13th St, Boulder CO 80302
Tel (303) 441-3500 *SIC* 9111

COUNTY OF EL PASO p 377
200 S Cascade Ave Ste 100, Colorado Springs CO 80903
Tel (719) 520-7276 *SIC* 9111

CITY & COUNTY OF DENVER p 312
1437 Bannock St Rm 350, Denver CO 80202
Tel (720) 865-9000 *SIC* 9111

EXECUTIVE OFFICE OF STATE OF COLORADO p 517
136 State Capitol Bldg, Denver CO 80203
Tel (303) 866-2471 *SIC* 9111 9223

STATE OF COLORADO p 1381
200 E Colfax Ave Ste 91, Denver CO 80203
Tel (303) 866-5000 *SIC* 9111

CITY OF FORT COLLINS p 314
215 N Mason St, Fort Collins CO 80524
Tel (970) 221-6770 *SIC* 9111

COUNTY OF LARIMER p 379
200 W Oak St Ste 4000, Fort Collins CO 80521
Tel (970) 498-5930 *SIC* 9111

COUNTY OF JEFFERSON p 378
100 Jefferson County Pkwy, Golden CO 80401
Tel (303) 271-8585 *SIC* 9111

COUNTY OF WELD p 383
1150 O St, Greeley CO 80631
Tel (970) 356-4000 *SIC* 9111

COUNTY OF ARAPAHOE p 376
5334 S Prince St, Littleton CO 80120
Tel (303) 795-4620 *SIC* 9111

PUEBLO COUNTY GOVERNMENT p 1190
215 W 10th St, Pueblo CO 81003
Tel (719) 583-6000 *SIC* 9111

CITY OF BRIDGEPORT p 313
999 Broad St Ste 2, Bridgeport CT 06604
Tel (203) 576-3964 *SIC* 9111

CITY OF BRISTOL p 313
111 N Main St Ste 17, Bristol CT 06010
Tel (860) 584-6100 *SIC* 9111

TOWN OF GREENWICH p 1465
101 Field Point Rd Ste 1, Greenwich CT 06830
Tel (203) 622-7700 *SIC* 9111

HAMDEN TOWN OF (INC) p 655
2750 Dixwell Ave Fl 2, Hamden CT 06518
Tel (203) 287-7100 *SIC* 9111

CITY OF HARTFORD p 315
550 Main St Ste 1, Hartford CT 06103
Tel (860) 757-9311 *SIC* 9111

GOVERNORS OFFICE STATE OF CONNECTICUT p 627
210 Capitol Ave Ste 202, Hartford CT 06106
Tel (860) 566-4840 *SIC* 9111

STATE OF CONNECTICUT p 1381
210 Capitol Ave Ste 1, Hartford CT 06106
Tel (860) 566-4840 *SIC* 9111

CITY OF MERIDEN p 316
142 E Main St Rm 218, Meriden CT 06450
Tel (203) 630-4124 *SIC* 9111

CITY OF NEW BRITAIN p 316
27 W Main St, New Britain CT 06051
Tel (860) 826-3415 *SIC* 9111

CITY OF NEW HAVEN p 316
165 Church St Fl 2, New Haven CT 06510
Tel (203) 946-8200 *SIC* 9111

CITY OF NORWALK p 317
125 East Ave, Norwalk CT 06851
Tel (203) 854-7900 *SIC* 9111

NORWALK PUBLIC SCHOOL DISTRICT p 1061
125 East Ave, Norwalk CT 06851
Tel (203) 852-9874 *SIC* 8211 9111

CITY OF SHELTON p 318
54 Hill St, Shelton CT 06484
Tel (203) 924-1555 *SIC* 9111

CITY OF STAMFORD p 318
888 Washington Blvd, Stamford CT 06901
Tel (203) 977-4150 *SIC* 9111

TOWN OF STRATFORD p 1465
2725 Main St, Stratford CT 06615
Tel (203) 385-4001 *SIC* 9111

TOWN OF TRUMBULL p 1465
5866 Main St, Trumbull CT 06611
Tel (203) 452-5080 *SIC* 9111

TOWN OF VERNON p 1465
14 Park Pl, Vernon CT 06066
Tel (860) 870-3690 *SIC* 9111

CITY OF WATERBURY p 319
236 Grand St, Waterbury CT 06702
Tel (203) 574-6712 *SIC* 9111

TOWN OF WEST HARTFORD p 1465
50 S Main St Ste 2, West Hartford CT 06107
Tel (860) 561-7500 *SIC* 9111

TOWN OF WESTPORT p 1465
110 Myrtle Ave, Westport CT 06880
Tel (203) 226-8311 *SIC* 9111

WINDHAM TOWN OF (INC) p 1615
979 Main St, Willimantic CT 06226
Tel (860) 465-3000 *SIC* 9111

EXECUTIVE OFFICE OF GOVERNOR OF DELAWARE p 517
150 Mlk Jr Blvd S Fl 2, Dover DE 19901
Tel (302) 744-4101 *SIC* 9111

COUNTY OF NEW CASTLE p 380
87 Reads Way, New Castle DE 19720
Tel (302) 395-5555 *SIC* 9111

CITY OF WILMINGTON p 319
800 N French St Fl 5, Wilmington DE 19801
Tel (302) 576-2415 *SIC* 9111

■ **EXECUTIVE OFFICE OF UNITED STATES GOVERNMENT** p 518
1600 Pennsylvania Ave Nw, Washington DC 20006
Tel (202) 456-1414 *SIC* 9111

GOVERNMENT OF DISTRICT OF COLUMBIA p 627
441 4th St Nw, Washington DC 20001
Tel (202) 727-2277 *SIC* 9111

▲ **GOVERNMENT OF UNITED STATES** p 627
1600 Pennsylvania Ave Nw, Washington DC 20500
Tel (202) 456-1414 *SIC* 9111

POLK COUNTY FLORIDA p 1159
330 W Church St, Bartow FL 33830
Tel (863) 534-6000 *SIC* 9111

CITY OF BOCA RATON p 313
201 W Palmetto Park Rd, Boca Raton FL 33432
Tel (561) 393-7896 *SIC* 9111

COUNTY OF HERNANDO p 378
20 N Main St, Brooksville FL 34601
Tel (352) 754-4201 SIC 9111

CITY OF CAPE CORAL p 313
1015 Cultural Park Blvd, Cape Coral FL 33990
Tel (239) 242-3410 SIC 9111

CITY OF CAPE CORAL p 313
1015 Cultural Park Blvd, Cape Coral FL 33990
Tel (239) 574-0401 SIC 9111

CITY OF CLEARWATER p 314
Clearwater Cy Hl Fl 3, Clearwater FL 33756
Tel (727) 562-4567 SIC 9111

COUNTY OF WALTON p 382
571 E Nelson Ave Ste 301, Defuniak Springs FL 32433
Tel (850) 892-8115 SIC 9111

COUNTY OF VOLUSIA p 382
123 W Indiana Ave Ste A, Deland FL 32720
Tel (386) 736-2700 SIC 9111

CITY OF FORT LAUDERDALE p 314
100 N Andrews Ave, Fort Lauderdale FL 33301
Tel (954) 828-5013 SIC 9111

COUNTY OF BROWARD p 376
115 S Andrews Ave Ste 409, Fort Lauderdale FL 33301
Tel (954) 357-7050 SIC 9111

COUNTY OF LEE p 379
2115 2nd St, Fort Myers FL 33901
Tel (239) 533-2737 SIC 9111

CITY OF GAINESVILLE p 315
200 E University Ave, Gainesville FL 32601
Tel (352) 334-5010 SIC 9111

COUNTY OF ALACHUA p 375
12 Se 1st St 2, Gainesville FL 32601
Tel (352) 374-3605 SIC 9111

COUNTY OF CLAY p 377
477 Houston St, Green Cove Springs FL 32043
Tel (904) 269-6376 SIC 9111

CITY OF HIALEAH p 315
501 Palm Ave, Hialeah FL 33010
Tel (305) 883-8075 SIC 9111

HOLLYWOOD CITY OF (INC) p 701
2600 Hollywood Blvd Ste B, Hollywood FL 33020
Tel (954) 921-3231 SIC 9111

CITY OF JACKSONVILLE p 315
117 W Duval St Fl Mess, Jacksonville FL 32202
Tel (904) 630-1776 SIC 9111

COUNTY OF OSCEOLA p 380
1 Courthouse Sq, Kissimmee FL 34741
Tel (407) 742-2000 SIC 9111

CITY OF LAKELAND p 316
228 S Massachusetts Ave, Lakeland FL 33801
Tel (863) 834-6000 SIC 9111

CITY OF LARGO p 316
201 Highland Ave N, Largo FL 33770
Tel (727) 587-6700 SIC 9111

FLORIDA DEPARTMENT OF VETERANS AFFAIRS p 558
11351 Ulmerton Rd Rm 311k, Largo FL 33778
Tel (727) 319-7427 SIC 9451 9111

CITY OF MIAMI p 316
3500 Pan American Dr Fl 2, Miami FL 33133
Tel (305) 250-5300 SIC 9111

COUNTY OF MIAMI-DADE p 380
111 Nw 1st St Ste 2550, Miami FL 33128
Tel (305) 375-5147 SIC 9111

CITY OF MIAMI BEACH p 316
1700 Convention Center Dr # 3, Miami Beach FL 33139
Tel (305) 673-7000 SIC 9111

COUNTY OF COLLIER p 377
3299 Tamiami Trl E # 700, Naples FL 34112
Tel (239) 252-8999 SIC 9111

COUNTY OF PASCO p 380
8731 Citizens Dr, New Port Richey FL 34654
Tel (727) 847-2411 SIC 9111

CITY OF OCALA p 317
110 Se Watula Ave, Ocala FL 34471
Tel (352) 401-3914 SIC 9111

MARION COUNTY BOARD OF COUNTY COMMISSIONERS p 907
601 Se 25th Ave, Ocala FL 34471
Tel (352) 438-2323 SIC 9111

CITY OF ORLANDO p 317
1 City Cmmns 400 S Orange, Orlando FL 32801
Tel (407) 246-2121 SIC 9111

COUNTY OF ORANGE p 380
201 S Rosalind Ave Fl 5, Orlando FL 32801
Tel (407) 836-7390 SIC 9111

COUNTY OF PUTNAM p 381
2509 Crill Ave Ste 900, Palatka FL 32177
Tel (386) 329-0205 SIC 9111

CITY OF PEMBROKE PINES p 317
10100 Pines Blvd Fl 5, Pembroke Pines FL 33026
Tel (954) 431-4330 SIC 9111

COUNTY OF ESCAMBIA p 378
221 Palafox Pl Ste 200, Pensacola FL 32502
Tel (850) 595-3000 SIC 9111

COUNTY OF CHARLOTTE p 377
18500 Murdock Cir Ste 423, Port Charlotte FL 33948
Tel (941) 637-2199 SIC 9111

COUNTY OF ST JOHNS p 382
500 San Sebastian Vw, Saint Augustine FL 32084
Tel (904) 209-0300 SIC 9111

CITY OF SAINT PETERSBURG p 318
175 5th St N, Saint Petersburg FL 33701
Tel (727) 893-7111 SIC 9111

COUNTY OF SEMINOLE p 381
1101 E 1st St, Sanford FL 32771
Tel (407) 665-7664 SIC 9111

COUNTY OF SARASOTA p 381
1660 Ringling Blvd, Sarasota FL 34236
Tel (941) 861-5165 SIC 9111

CITY OF SUNRISE p 318
10770 W Oakland Park Blvd, Sunrise FL 33351
Tel (954) 746-3297 SIC 9111

EXECUTIVE OFFICE OF GOVERNOR OF FLORIDA p 517
400 S Monroe St, Tallahassee FL 32399
Tel (850) 488-4505 SIC 9111

FLORIDA DEPARTMENT OF AGRICULTURE AND CONSUMER SERVICES p 558
10 The Capitol, Tallahassee FL 32399
Tel (850) 617-7700 SIC 9641 9611 9111

FLORIDA DEPARTMENT OF LABOR AND EMPLOYMENT SECURITY p 558
2012 Capital Cir Se, Tallahassee FL 32399
Tel (850) 942-8341 SIC 9651 9111

FLORIDA DEPARTMENT OF REVENUE p 558
2450 Oak Blvd, Tallahassee FL 32399
Tel (850) 617-8600 SIC 9311 9111

STATE OF FLORIDA p 1381
400 S Monroe St, Tallahassee FL 32399
Tel (850) 488-7146 SIC 9111

TALLAHASSEE CITY OF (INC) p 1423
300 S Adams St, Tallahassee FL 32301
Tel (850) 891-8441 SIC 9111

CITY OF TAMPA p 319
306 E Jackson St Fl 7, Tampa FL 33602
Tel (813) 274-8211 SIC 9111

COUNTY OF HILLSBOROUGH p 378
601 E Kennedy Blvd Fl 23, Tampa FL 33602
Tel (813) 276-2720 SIC 9111

COUNTY OF LAKE p 379
315 W Main St, Tavares FL 32778
Tel (352) 343-9808 SIC 9111

INDIAN RIVER COUNTY p 737
1800 27th St Bldg B, Vero Beach FL 32960
Tel (772) 567-8000 SIC 9111

BREVARD COUNTY CO p 210
2725 Jdge Fran Jmeson Way, Viera FL 32940
Tel (321) 633-2046 SIC 9111

CITY OF WEST PALM BEACH p 319
401 Clematis St, West Palm Beach FL 33401
Tel (561) 822-1200 SIC 9111

COUNTY OF PALM BEACH p 380
301 N Olive Ave Frnt, West Palm Beach FL 33401
Tel (561) 355-2959 SIC 9111

UNIFIED GOVERNMENT OF ATHENS-CLARKE COUNTY p 1503
301 College Ave Ste 300, Athens GA 30601
Tel (706) 613-3010 SIC 9111

CITY OF ATLANTA p 313
55 Trinity Ave Sw # 3900, Atlanta GA 30303
Tel (404) 330-6100 SIC 9111

COUNTY OF FULTON p 378
141 Pryor St Sw, Atlanta GA 30303
Tel (404) 612-4000 SIC 9111

EXECUTIVE OFFICE OF STATE OF GEORGIA p 517
203 State Capitol Sw, Atlanta GA 30334
Tel (404) 656-1776 SIC 9111

STATE OF GEORGIA p 1381
206 Washington St Sw # 111, Atlanta GA 30334
Tel (404) 656-1776 SIC 9111

COUNTY OF AUGUSTA-RICHMOND p 376
535 Telfair St, Augusta GA 30901
Tel (706) 821-2429 SIC 9111

COUNTY OF CHEROKEE p 377
1130 Bluffs Pkwy, Canton GA 30114
Tel (678) 493-6000 SIC 9111

COLUMBUS GEORGIA CONSOLIDATED GOVERNMENT p 342
100 10th St, Columbus GA 31901
Tel (706) 653-4000 SIC 9111

COUNTY OF FORSYTH p 378
110 E Main St Ste 210, Cumming GA 30040
Tel (770) 781-2101 SIC 9111

HALL COUNTY OF GEORGIA p 654
2875 Browns Bridge Rd, Gainesville GA 30504
Tel (770) 535-8288 SIC 9111

COUNTY OF CLAYTON p 377
112 Smith St, Jonesboro GA 30236
Tel (770) 477-3208 SIC 9111

GWINNETT COUNTY GOVERNMENT p 648
75 Langley Dr, Lawrenceville GA 30046
Tel (770) 822-8000 SIC 9111

CITY OF MACON p 316
700 Poplar St, Macon GA 31201
Tel (478) 751-7258 SIC 9111

CITY OF MARIETTA p 316
205 Lawrence St Ne, Marietta GA 30060
Tel (770) 794-5507 SIC 9111

COUNTY OF HENRY p 378
140 Henry Pkwy, Mcdonough GA 30253
Tel (770) 288-6000 SIC 9111

CITY OF SAVANNAH p 318
2 E Bay St, Savannah GA 31401
Tel (912) 651-6415 SIC 9111

UNION CITY CITY OF INC p 1504
5047 Union St, Union City GA 30291
Tel (770) 964-2288 SIC 9111 9221

COUNTY OF HAWAII p 378
25 Aupuni St Ste 107, Hilo HI 96720
Tel (808) 961-8211 SIC 9111

CITY & COUNTY OF HONOLULU p 312
530 S King St Rm 208, Honolulu HI 96813
Tel (808) 523-4141 SIC 9111

EXECUTIVE OFFICE OF STATE OF HAWAII p 517
415 S Beretania St Fl 5, Honolulu HI 96813
Tel (808) 586-0034 SIC 9111

STATE OF HAWAII p 1381
201 Merchant St Ste 1805, Honolulu HI 96813
Tel (808) 586-1735 SIC 9111

COUNTY OF KAUAI p 379
4444 Rice St Ste 150, Lihue HI 96766
Tel (808) 241-4200 SIC 9111

COUNTY OF MAUI p 379
200 S High St, Wailuku HI 96793
Tel (808) 270-7855 SIC 9111

CITY OF BOISE p 313
150 N Capitol Blvd, Boise ID 83702
Tel (208) 384-4422 SIC 9111

EXECUTIVE OFFICE OF STATE OF IDAHO p 517
700 W Jefferson St, Boise ID 83720
Tel (208) 334-2100 SIC 9111

CITY OF AURORA p 313
44 E Downer Pl, Aurora IL 60505
Tel (630) 892-8811 SIC 9111

CITY OF CHICAGO p 314
121 N La Salle St, Chicago IL 60602
Tel (312) 744-5000 SIC 9111

COUNTY OF COOK p 377
118 N Clark St, Chicago IL 60602
Tel (312) 603-5500 SIC 9111

COUNTY OF MADISON p 379
157 N Main St Rm 382, Edwardsville IL 62025
Tel (618) 692-7040 SIC 9111

COUNTY OF KANE p 379
719 S Batavia Ave, Geneva IL 60134
Tel (630) 232-3400 SIC 9111

WILL COUNTY p 1609
302 N Chicago St, Joliet IL 60432
Tel (815) 740-4602 SIC 9111

CITY OF NAPERVILLE p 316
400 S Eagle St, Naperville IL 60540
Tel (630) 420-6111 SIC 9111

COUNTY OF PEORIA p 381
324 Main St, Peoria IL 61602
Tel (309) 672-6056 SIC 9111

CITY OF ROCKFORD p 318
425 E State St, Rockford IL 61104
Tel (779) 348-7300 SIC 9111

COUNTY OF WINNEBAGO p 383
404 Elm St Ste 104, Rockford IL 61101
Tel (815) 319-4444 SIC 9111

CITY OF SPRINGFIELD p 318
800 E Monroe St Ste 300, Springfield IL 62701
Tel (217) 789-2200 SIC 9111

DEPARTMENT OF CORRECTIONS ILLINOIS p 430
1301 Concordia Ct, Springfield IL 62702
Tel (217) 557-1030 SIC 9223 9111

EXECUTIVE OFFICE OF GOVERNOR p 517
207 S State St, Springfield IL 62704
Tel (217) 782-6832 SIC 9111

ILLINOIS DEPARTMENT OF NATURAL RESOURCES p 732
1 Natural Resources Way # 100, Springfield IL 62702
Tel (217) 782-6302 SIC 9512 9111

JUDICIAL COURTS OF STATE OF ILLINOIS p 796
Clerk Supreme Court Bldg, Springfield IL 62704
Tel (217) 782-2035 SIC 9111 9211

STATE OF ILLINOIS p 1381
207 State House, Springfield IL 62706
Tel (217) 782-6830 SIC 9111

COUNTY OF LAKE p 379
18 N County St Fl 8, Waukegan IL 60085
Tel (847) 377-2373 SIC 9111

COUNTY OF DU PAGE p 377
421 N County Farm Rd, Wheaton IL 60187
Tel (630) 407-6000 SIC 9111

LAKE COUNTY OF INDIANA p 838
2293 N Main St, Crown Point IN 46307
Tel (219) 755-3465 SIC 9111

CITY OF FORT WAYNE p 314
200 E Berry St, Fort Wayne IN 46802
Tel (260) 427-1111 SIC 9111

COUNTY OF ALLEN p 376
Courthouse Rm 201, Fort Wayne IN 46802
Tel (260) 449-7245 SIC 9111

CITY OF HAMMOND p 315
5925 Calumet Ave, Hammond IN 46320
Tel (219) 853-6301 SIC 9111

CITY OF INDIANAPOLIS p 315
200 E Washington St # 2501, Indianapolis IN 46204
Tel (317) 327-3601 SIC 9111

COUNTY OF MARION p 379
200 E Washington St # 801, Indianapolis IN 46204
Tel (317) 327-3001 SIC 9111

EXECUTIVE OFFICE OF STATE OF INDIANA p 517
200 W Washington St # 206, Indianapolis IN 46204
Tel (317) 232-4567 SIC 9111

INDIANA DEPT OF WORKFORCE DEVELOPMENT p 738
10 N Senate Ave, Indianapolis IN 46204
Tel (317) 233-5661 SIC 9111

M S D WAYNE TOWNSHIP p 889
1220 S High School Rd, Indianapolis IN 46241
Tel (317) 243-8251 SIC 9111

STATE OF INDIANA p 1381
200 W Washington St # 201, Indianapolis IN 46204
Tel (317) 232-4567 SIC 9111

CITY OF SOUTH BEND p 318
227 W Jefferson Blvd, South Bend IN 46601
Tel (574) 235-9216 SIC 9111

CITY OF AMES p 313
515 Clark Ave, Ames IA 50010
Tel (515) 239-5140 SIC 9111

CITY OF CEDAR RAPIDS p 313
101 1st St Se, Cedar Rapids IA 52401
Tel (319) 286-5080 SIC 9111

CITY OF DES MOINES p 314
400 Robert D Ray Dr Ste B, Des Moines IA 50309
Tel (515) 283-4500 SIC 9111

COUNTY OF POLK p 381
111 Court Ave Ste 390, Des Moines IA 50309
Tel (515) 286-3200 SIC 9111

IOWA DEPARTMENT OF EXECUTIVE OFFICE p 762
State Capital, Des Moines IA 50319
Tel (515) 281-5211 SIC 9111

STATE OF IOWA p 1381
1007 E Grand Ave Rm 105, Des Moines IA 50319
Tel (515) 281-5211 SIC 9111

UNIFIED GOVERNMENT OF WYANDOTTE COUNTY p 1503
701 N 7th St, Kansas City KS 66101
Tel (913) 573-5000 SIC 9111

COUNTY OF JOHNSON p 378
111 S Cherry St Ste 1200, Olathe KS 66061
Tel (913) 715-0435 SIC 9111

COUNTY OF SHAWNEE p 381
200 Se 7th St, Topeka KS 66603
Tel (785) 233-8200 SIC 9111

EXECUTIVE OFFICE OF STATE OF KANSAS p 517
300 Sw 10th Ave, Topeka KS 66612
Tel (785) 296-6240 SIC 9111

STATE OF KANSAS p 1381
300 Sw 10th Ave Ste 222s, Topeka KS 66612
Tel (785) 354-1388 SIC 9111

COUNTY OF SEDGWICK p 381
525 N Main St Ste 823, Wichita KS 67203
Tel (316) 660-9000 SIC 9111

WICHITA CITY OF (INC) p 1607
455 N Main St Fl 5, Wichita KS 67202
Tel (316) 268-4351 SIC 9111

COMMONWEALTH OF KENTUCKY p 346
700 Capital Ave Ste 100, Frankfort KY 40601
Tel (502) 564-2611 SIC 9111

EXECUTIVE OFFICE OF COMMONWEALTH OF KENTUCKY p 517
State Cptl 700 Cpitol Ave State Capitol, Frankfort KY 40601
Tel (502) 564-2611 SIC 9111

KENTUCKY EDUCATION AND WORK FORCE DEVELOPMENT CABINET p 812
500 Mero St Ste 3, Frankfort KY 40601
Tel (502) 564-6606 SIC 9441 9111

LEXINGTON-FAYETTE URBAN COUNTY GOVERNMENT p 859
200 E Main St, Lexington KY 40507
Tel (859) 258-3100 SIC 9121 9111

LOUISVILLE-JEFFERSON COUNTY METRO GOVERNMENT p 881
527 W Jefferson St, Louisville KY 40202
Tel (502) 574-2003 SIC 9111

CITY OF BATON ROUGE p 313
222 Saint Louis St Rm 301, Baton Rouge LA 70802
Tel (225) 389-3061 SIC 9111

EXECUTIVE OFFICE OF STATE OF LOUISIANA p 517
900 N 3rd St Fl 4, Baton Rouge LA 70802
Tel (225) 342-7015 SIC 9111

LOUISIANA DEPARTMENT OF TRANSPORTATION AND DEVELOPMENT p 880
1201 Capitol Access Rd, Baton Rouge LA 70802
Tel (225) 379-1232 SIC 9111

STATE OF LOUISIANA p 1381
900 N 3rd St Fl 4, Baton Rouge LA 70802
Tel (225) 342-0991 SIC 9111

PARISH OF JEFFERSON p 1115
200 Derbigny St, Gretna LA 70053
Tel (504) 364-2600 SIC 9111

TERREBONNE PARISH CONSOLIDATED GOVERNMENT p 1439
8026 Main St Ste 300, Houma LA 70360
Tel (985) 873-6454 SIC 9111

LAFAYETTE CITY PARISH CONSOLIDATED GOVERNMENT p 837
705 W University Ave, Lafayette LA 70506
Tel (337) 291-8353 SIC 9111

LAFAYETTE CONSOLIDATED GOVERNMENT p 837
705 W University Ave, Lafayette LA 70506
Tel (337) 291-8200 SIC 9111

CITY OF LAKE CHARLES p 316
326 Pujo St, Lake Charles LA 70601
Tel (337) 491-1201 SIC 9111

CITY OF MONROE p 316
700 Washington St, Monroe LA 71201
Tel (318) 329-2310 SIC 9111

CITY OF NEW ORLEANS p 317
1300 Perdido St Bsmt Fl2, New Orleans LA 70112
Tel (504) 658-4900 SIC 9111

CITY OF SHREVEPORT p 318
505 Travis St Ste 600, Shreveport LA 71101
Tel (318) 673-7900 SIC 9111

EXECUTIVE OFFICE OF STATE OF MAINE p 518
1 Stathuse Stn 2nd Fl 236, Augusta ME 04333
Tel (207) 287-3531 SIC 9111

STATE OF MAINE p 1381
1 State House Sta, Augusta ME 04333
Tel (207) 549-7182 SIC 9111

CITY OF PORTLAND p 317
389 Congress St Rm 110, Portland ME 04101
Tel (207) 874-8665 SIC 9111

COUNTY OF ANNE ARUNDEL p 376
44 Calvert St Ste 1, Annapolis MD 21401
Tel (410) 222-1166 SIC 9111

EXECUTIVE OFFICE OF STATE OF MARYLAND p 518
100 State Cir, Annapolis MD 21401
Tel (410) 974-3901 SIC 9111

STATE OF MARYLAND p 1381
45 Calvert St Ste 1, Annapolis MD 21401
Tel (410) 974-3901 SIC 9111

CITY OF BALTIMORE p 313
100 Holliday St Ste 250, Baltimore MD 21202
Tel (410) 396-3835 SIC 9111

COUNTY OF BALTIMORE p 376
400 Washington Ave Rm 100, Baltimore MD 21204
Tel (410) 887-2008 SIC 9111

COUNTY OF HARFORD p 378
220 S Main St, Bel Air MD 21014
Tel (410) 638-3314 SIC 9111

HOWARD COUNTY OF MARYLAND (INC) p 713
3430 Court House Dr # 100, Ellicott City MD 21043
Tel (410) 313-2195 SIC 9111

COUNTY OF FREDERICK p 378
355 Montevue Ln 101, Frederick MD 21702
Tel (301) 600-9000 SIC 9111

CHARLES COUNTY GOVERNMENT p 289
200 Baltimore St, La Plata MD 20646
Tel (301) 645-0550 SIC 9111

COUNTY OF CALVERT p 376
175 Main St, Prince Frederick MD 20678
Tel (410) 535-1600 *SIC* 9111

COUNTY OF MONTGOMERY p 380
101 Monroe St Fl 15, Rockville MD 20850
Tel (240) 777-8220 *SIC* 9111

COUNTY OF PRINCE GEORGES p 381
14741 Gvrnor Oden Bwie Dr, Upper Marlboro MD 20772
Tel (301) 952-6000 *SIC* 9111

COMMISSIONERS OF CARROLL COUNTY p 345
225 N Center St, Westminster MD 21157
Tel (410) 386-2400 *SIC* 9111

TOWN OF AGAWAM p 1465
36 Main St, Agawam MA 01001
Tel (413) 786-0400 *SIC* 9111

TOWN OF ANDOVER p 1465
36 Bartlet St, Andover MA 01810
Tel (978) 623-8225 *SIC* 9111

TOWN OF ARLINGTON p 1465
730 Massachusetts Ave, Arlington MA 02476
Tel (781) 316-3000 *SIC* 9111

CITY OF ATTLEBORO p 313
77 Park St Ste 1, Attleboro MA 02703
Tel (508) 223-2222 *SIC* 9111

TOWN OF BILLERICA p 1465
365 Boston Rd Ste 207, Billerica MA 01821
Tel (978) 671-0928 *SIC* 9111

CITY OF BOSTON p 313
1 City Hall Sq Ste 242, Boston MA 02201
Tel (617) 635-4545 *SIC* 9111

COMMONWEALTH OF MASSACHUSETTS p 346
1 Ashburton Pl Fl 9, Boston MA 02108
Tel (617) 727-5000 *SIC* 9111

COUNTY OF SUFFOLK p 382
1 City Hall Sq Ste 550, Boston MA 02201
Tel (617) 635-4000 *SIC* 9111

EXECUTIVE OFFICE OF COMMONWEALTH OF MASSACHUSETTS p 517
24 Beacon St Rm 360, Boston MA 02133
Tel (617) 727-3600 *SIC* 9111

MASSACHUSETTS DEPARTMENT OF CHILDREN AND FAMILIES p 916
600 Washington St, Boston MA 02111
Tel (617) 748-2000 *SIC* 9111

CITY OF BROCKTON p 313
45 School St, Brockton MA 02301
Tel (508) 580-7123 *SIC* 9111

BROOKLINE TOWN OF (INC) p 218
333 Washington St, Brookline MA 02445
Tel (617) 730-2000 *SIC* 9111

CITY OF CAMBRIDGE p 313
795 Massachusetts Ave, Cambridge MA 02139
Tel (617) 349-4260 *SIC* 9111

COUNTY OF MIDDLESEX p 380
40 Thorndike St, Cambridge MA 02141
Tel (617) 494-4113 *SIC* 9111

TOWN OF CHELMSFORD p 1465
50 Billerica Rd, Chelmsford MA 01824
Tel (978) 250-5201 *SIC* 9111

CITY OF CHELSEA p 314
500 Broadway Ste 1, Chelsea MA 02150
Tel (617) 466-4240 *SIC* 9111

CITY OF CHICOPEE p 314
274 Front St, Chicopee MA 01013
Tel (413) 594-1490 *SIC* 9111

CITY OF EVERETT p 314
484 Broadway Rm 14, Everett MA 02149
Tel (617) 394-2270 *SIC* 9111

CITY OF FALL RIVER p 314
1 Government Ctr, Fall River MA 02722
Tel (508) 324-2000 *SIC* 9111

CITY OF FITCHBURG p 314
166 Boulder Dr Ste 108, Fitchburg MA 01420
Tel (978) 345-9567 *SIC* 9111

TOWN OF FRAMINGHAM p 1465
150 Concord St, Framingham MA 01702
Tel (508) 532-5400 *SIC* 9111

TOWN OF FRANKLIN p 1465
355 E Central St Ste 1, Franklin MA 02038
Tel (508) 528-7900 *SIC* 9111

CITY OF HAVERHILL p 315
City Hl Rm 100, Haverhill MA 01830
Tel (978) 374-2300 *SIC* 9111

CITY OF HOLYOKE p 315
536 Dwight St, Holyoke MA 01040
Tel (413) 322-5510 *SIC* 9111

TOWN OF BARNSTABLE p 1465
230 South St, Hyannis MA 02601
Tel (508) 862-4661 *SIC* 9111

CITY OF LAWRENCE p 316
200 Common St, Lawrence MA 01840
Tel (978) 620-3010 *SIC* 9111

CITY OF LEOMINSTER p 316
25 West St Ste 5, Leominster MA 01453
Tel (978) 534-7500 *SIC* 9111

TOWN OF LEXINGTON p 1465
1625 Massachusetts Ave, Lexington MA 02420
Tel (781) 862-0500 *SIC* 9111

CITY OF MARLBOROUGH p 316
140 Main St Ofc 4, Marlborough MA 01752
Tel (508) 460-3775 *SIC* 9111

CITY OF MEDFORD p 316
85 George P Hassett Dr, Medford MA 02155
Tel (781) 396-5500 *SIC* 9111

CITY OF METHUEN p 316
41 Pleasant St, Methuen MA 01844
Tel (978) 983-8505 *SIC* 9111

TOWN OF NATICK p 1465
13 E Central St Ste 1, Natick MA 01760
Tel (508) 647-6410 *SIC* 9111

TOWN OF NEEDHAM p 1465
1471 Highland Ave, Needham MA 02492
Tel (781) 455-7500 *SIC* 9111

NEW BEDFORD CITY OF (INC) p 1029
133 William St Unit 208, New Bedford MA 02740
Tel (508) 979-1400 *SIC* 9111

CITY OF NEWTON p 317
1000 Cmmwl Ave Newton Ctr, Newton MA 02459
Tel (617) 796-1200 *SIC* 9111

TOWN OF DARTMOUTH p 1465
400 Slocum Rd, North Dartmouth MA 02747
Tel (508) 910-1800 *SIC* 9111

CITY OF NORTHAMPTON p 317
210 Main St Rm 4, Northampton MA 01060
Tel (413) 587-1249 *SIC* 9111

CITY OF PEABODY p 317
24 Lowell St, Peabody MA 01960
Tel (978) 532-3000 *SIC* 9111

CITY OF QUINCY p 317
1305 Hancock St, Quincy MA 02169
Tel (617) 376-1000 *SIC* 9111

CITY OF SALEM p 318
93 Washington St, Salem MA 01970
Tel (978) 745-9595 *SIC* 9111

CITY OF SOMERVILLE p 318
93 Highland Ave, Somerville MA 02143
Tel (617) 666-3311 *SIC* 9111

CITY OF SOMERVILLE p 318
42 Cross St, Somerville MA 02145
Tel (617) 625-6600 *SIC* 9111

SPRINGFIELD CITY OF (INC) p 1360
36 Court St, Springfield MA 01103
Tel (413) 736-3111 *SIC* 9111

TOWN OF SUDBURY p 1465
322 Concord Rd, Sudbury MA 01776
Tel (978) 443-8891 *SIC* 9111

CITY OF TAUNTON p 319
141 Oak St, Taunton MA 02780
Tel (508) 821-1000 *SIC* 9111

TOWN OF WALPOLE p 1465
135 School St, Walpole MA 02081
Tel (508) 660-7289 *SIC* 9111

CITY OF WALTHAM p 319
610 Main St Fl 2, Waltham MA 02452
Tel (781) 314-3000 *SIC* 9111

TOWN OF WELLESLEY p 1465
525 Washington St, Wellesley MA 02482
Tel (781) 431-1019 *SIC* 9111

CITY OF WESTFIELD p 319
59 Court St Ste 1, Westfield MA 01085
Tel (413) 572-6200 *SIC* 9111

TOWN OF WESTFORD p 1465
55 Main St, Westford MA 01886
Tel (978) 692-5500 *SIC* 9111

TOWN OF WESTON p 1465
11 Townhouse Rd, Weston MA 02493
Tel (781) 786-5070 *SIC* 9111

TOWN OF WESTWOOD p 1465
580 High St, Westwood MA 02090
Tel (781) 326-6450 *SIC* 9111

TOWN OF WEYMOUTH p 1465
75 Middle St, Weymouth MA 02189
Tel (781) 335-2000 *SIC* 9111

CITY OF WOBURN p 319
10 Common St Ste 12, Woburn MA 01801
Tel (781) 932-4400 *SIC* 9111

CITY OF WORCESTER p 319
455 Main St Rm 112, Worcester MA 01608
Tel (508) 799-1049 *SIC* 9111

COUNTY OF WASHTENAW p 382
220 N Main St, Ann Arbor MI 48104
Tel (734) 222-4357 *SIC* 9111

COUNTY OF BAY p 376
515 Center Ave Ste 401, Bay City MI 48708
Tel (989) 895-4130 *SIC* 9111

CITY OF DETROIT p 314
2 Woodward Ave Rm 1126, Detroit MI 48226
Tel (313) 224-3400 *SIC* 9111

COUNTY OF WAYNE p 382
500 Griswold St Fl 31, Detroit MI 48226
Tel (313) 224-5952 *SIC* 9111

COUNTY OF GENESEE p 378
1101 Beach St Fl 3, Flint MI 48502
Tel (810) 257-3040 *SIC* 9111

CITY OF GRAND RAPIDS p 315
300 Monroe Ave Nw Unit 1, Grand Rapids MI 49503
Tel (616) 456-3000 *SIC* 9111

KENT COUNTY OF (INC) p 812
300 Monroe Ave Nw Unit 1, Grand Rapids MI 49503
Tel (616) 632-7580 *SIC* 9111

CITY OF KALAMAZOO p 315
241 W South St, Kalamazoo MI 49007
Tel (269) 337-8047 *SIC* 9111

COUNTY OF KALAMAZOO p 379
201 W Kalamazoo Ave # 101, Kalamazoo MI 49007
Tel (269) 384-8305 *SIC* 9111

CITY OF LANSING p 316
124 W Michigan Ave Fl 5, Lansing MI 48933
Tel (517) 483-4433 *SIC* 9111

EXECUTIVE OFFICE OF STATE OF MICHIGAN p 518
Romne Bldg 111 S Cap, Lansing MI 48933
Tel (517) 373-3400 *SIC* 9111

MICHIGAN DEPARTMENT OF INFORMATION TECHNOLOGY p 961
111 S Capitol Ave, Lansing MI 48933
Tel (517) 241-2000 *SIC* 9111

STATE OF MICHIGAN p 1382
111 S Capitol Ave, Lansing MI 48933
Tel (517) 373-3400 *SIC* 9111

COUNTY OF INGHAM p 378
Ingham County Court House, Mason MI 48854
Tel (517) 676-7206 *SIC* 9111

COUNTY OF MACOMB p 379
120 N Main St, Mount Clemens MI 48043
Tel (586) 469-5260 *SIC* 9111

COUNTY OF MUSKEGON p 380
990 Terrace St, Muskegon MI 49442
Tel (231) 724-6520 *SIC* 9111

COUNTY OF OAKLAND p 380
1200 N Telegraph Rd Ste 1, Pontiac MI 48341
Tel (248) 858-1000 *SIC* 9111

CITY OF WARREN p 319
1 City Sq Ste 215, Warren MI 48093
Tel (586) 574-4500 *SIC* 9111

HANNAHVILLE INDIAN COMMUNITY p 658
N14911 Hannahville Rd B 1, Wilson MI 49896
Tel (906) 466-2932 *SIC* 9111

COUNTY OF ANOKA p 376
2100 3rd Ave, Anoka MN 55303
Tel (763) 421-4760 *SIC* 9111

COUNTY OF DAKOTA p 377
1590 Highway 55, Hastings MN 55033
Tel (651) 437-3191 *SIC* 9111

CITY OF MINNEAPOLIS p 316
350 S 5th St Ste 325m, Minneapolis MN 55415
Tel (612) 673-3000 *SIC* 9111

HENNEPIN COUNTY p 683
300 S 6th St, Minneapolis MN 55487
Tel (612) 348-3000 *SIC* 9111

COUNTY OF OLMSTED p 380
151 4th St Se Ste 11, Rochester MN 55904
Tel (507) 328-6001 *SIC* 9111

CITY OF SAINT PAUL p 318
15 Kellogg Blvd W Ste 390, Saint Paul MN 55102
Tel (651) 266-8500 *SIC* 9111

COUNTY OF RAMSEY p 381
15 Kellogg Blvd W Ste 270, Saint Paul MN 55102
Tel (651) 266-8044 *SIC* 9111

EXECUTIVE OFFICE OF STATE OF MINNESOTA p 518
75 Rev Doc Martin Luther, Saint Paul MN 55155
Tel (651) 201-3400 *SIC* 9111

STATE OF MINNESOTA p 1382
116 Veteran Service Bld, Saint Paul MN 55155
Tel (218) 828-2400 *SIC* 9111

CITY OF JACKSON p 315
219 S President St, Jackson MS 39201
Tel (601) 960-1111 *SIC* 9111

EXECUTIVE OFFICE OF STATE OF MISSISSIPPI p 518
550 High St, Jackson MS 39201
Tel (601) 359-3100 *SIC* 9111

STATE OF MISSISSIPPI p 1382
501 N West St, Jackson MS 39201
Tel (601) 359-3100 *SIC* 9111

COUNTY OF JACKSON p 378
2902c Shortcut Rd, Pascagoula MS 39567
Tel (228) 769-3258 *SIC* 9111

COLUMBIA CITY OF (INC) p 340
701 E Broadway, Columbia MO 65201
Tel (573) 874-7457 *SIC* 9111

CITY OF INDEPENDENCE p 315
111 E Maple Ave, Independence MO 64050
Tel (816) 325-7000 *SIC* 9111

EXECUTIVE OFFICE OF STATE OF MISSOURI p 518
201 W Capitol Ave Rm 216, Jefferson City MO 65101
Tel (573) 751-1851 *SIC* 9111

STATE OF MISSOURI p 1382
201 W Capitol Ave Rm 216, Jefferson City MO 65101
Tel (573) 751-3222 *SIC* 9111

JACKSON COUNTY p 773
415 E 12th St, Kansas City MO 64106
Tel (816) 881-3333 *SIC* 9111

MISSOURI CITY OF KANSAS CITY p 976
414 E 12th St Ste 105, Kansas City MO 64106
Tel (816) 513-1313 *SIC* 9111

COUNTY OF ST LOUIS p 382
41 S Central Ave, Saint Louis MO 63105
Tel (314) 615-7016 *SIC* 9111

CITY OF SPRINGFIELD p 318
840 N Boonville Ave, Springfield MO 65802
Tel (417) 864-1000 *SIC* 9111

EXECUTIVE OFFICE OF STATE OF MONTANA p 518
State Capitol Rm 204, Helena MT 59620
Tel (406) 444-3111 *SIC* 9111

CITY OF LINCOLN p 316
555 S 10th St Rm B115, Lincoln NE 68508
Tel (402) 441-7511 *SIC* 9111

COUNTY OF LANCASTER p 379
555 S 10th St Rm 110, Lincoln NE 68508
Tel (402) 441-4944 *SIC* 9111

STATE OF NEBRASKA p 1382
1445 K St Oom 2316, Lincoln NE 68509
Tel (402) 471-2311 *SIC* 9111

CITY OF OMAHA p 317
1819 Farnam St Rm 300, Omaha NE 68183
Tel (402) 444-5000 *SIC* 9111

DOUGLAS COUNTY NEBRASKA p 452
Omaha Douglas Civic Cente, Omaha NE 68183
Tel (402) 444-7025 *SIC* 9111

EXECUTIVE OFFICE OF STATE OF NEVADA p 518
101 N Carson St, Carson City NV 89701
Tel (775) 684-5670 *SIC* 9111

STATE OF NEVADA p 1382
101 N Carson St Ste 1, Carson City NV 89701
Tel (775) 684-5000 *SIC* 9111

CITY OF HENDERSON p 315
240 S Water St, Henderson NV 89015
Tel (702) 267-2323 *SIC* 9111

CITY OF LAS VEGAS p 316
495 S Main St, Las Vegas NV 89101
Tel (702) 229-6321 *SIC* 9111

COUNTY OF CLARK p 377
500 S Grand Central Pkwy # 6, Las Vegas NV 89155
Tel (702) 455-3530 *SIC* 9111

CITY OF NORTH LAS VEGAS p 317
2250 Las Vegas Blvd N # 100, North Las Vegas NV 89030
Tel (702) 633-1007 *SIC* 9111

CITY OF RENO p 317
1 E 1st St Fl 1, Reno NV 89501
Tel (775) 334-2020 *SIC* 9111

EXECUTIVE OFFICE OF STATE OF NEW HAMPSHIRE p 518
107 N Main St Rm 208, Concord NH 03301
Tel (603) 271-2121 *SIC* 9111

STATE OF NEW HAMPSHIRE p 1382
64 South St, Concord NH 03301
Tel (603) 271-1110 *SIC* 9111

CITY OF MANCHESTER p 316
1 City Hall Plz, Manchester NH 03101
Tel (603) 624-6460 *SIC* 9111

CITY OF ATLANTIC CITY (INC) p 313
1301 Bacharach Blvd, Atlantic City NJ 08401
Tel (609) 347-5300 *SIC* 9111

COUNTY OF ATLANTIC p 376
1333 Atlantic Ave, Atlantic City NJ 08401
Tel (609) 345-6700 *SIC* 9111

CITY OF BAYONNE p 313
630 Avenue C, Bayonne NJ 07002
Tel (201) 858-6046 *SIC* 9111

COUNTY OF WARREN p 382
165 County Road 519 Ste 1, Belvidere NJ 07823
Tel (908) 475-6500 *SIC* 9111

CITY OF CAMDEN p 313
520 Marke St City Hall 4t, Camden NJ 08101
Tel (856) 757-7200 *SIC* 9111

COUNTY OF CAMDEN p 376
520 Market St Fl 11, Camden NJ 08102
Tel (856) 225-5000 *SIC* 9111

COUNTY OF CAPE MAY p 376
4 Moore Rd, Cape May Court House NJ 08210
Tel (609) 465-1125 *SIC* 9111

CITY OF EAST ORANGE p 314
44 City Hall Plz, East Orange NJ 07018
Tel (973) 266-5140 *SIC* 9111

EAST ORANGE SCHOOL DISTRICT p 470
199 4th Ave, East Orange NJ 07017
Tel (862) 233-7300 *SIC* 8211 9111

MIDDLESEX COUNTY COLLEGE p 965
2600 Woodbridge Ave, Edison NJ 08837
Tel (732) 548-6000
SIC 8222 9111 8221 8211

CITY OF ELIZABETH p 314
50 Winfield Scott Plz, Elizabeth NJ 07201
Tel (908) 820-4111 *SIC* 9111

COUNTY OF UNION p 382
10 Elizabeth Ave, Elizabeth NJ 07206
Tel (908) 659-7407 *SIC* 9111

COUNTY OF MONMOUTH p 380
1 E Main St, Freehold NJ 07728
Tel (732) 431-7000 *SIC* 9111

COUNTY OF BERGEN p 376
1 Bergen County Plz Ste 1, Hackensack NJ 07601
Tel (201) 336-6000 *SIC* 9111

CITY OF JERSEY CITY p 315
280 Grove St, Jersey City NJ 07302
Tel (201) 547-5000 *SIC* 9111

COUNTY OF HUDSON p 378
567 Pavonia Ave Fl 4, Jersey City NJ 07306
Tel (201) 795-6000 *SIC* 9111 9223

COUNTY OF MORRIS p 380
Court St, Morristown NJ 07960
Tel (973) 285-6010 *SIC* 9111

MIDDLESEX COUNTY OF (INC) p 965
75 Bayard St, New Brunswick NJ 08901
Tel (732) 745-3000 *SIC* 9111

CITY OF NEWARK NEW JERSEY p 317
920 Broad St, Newark NJ 07102
Tel (973) 733-3934 *SIC* 9111

COUNTY OF ESSEX p 378
465 Martn L King Jr Blvd, Newark NJ 07102
Tel (973) 621-4454 *SIC* 9111

CITY OF ORANGE TOWNSHIP p 317
29 N Day St, Orange NJ 07050
Tel (973) 266-4000 *SIC* 9111

PARSIPPANY-TROY HILLS TOWNSHIP SCHOOL DISTRICT p 1117
292 Parsippany Rd, Parsippany NJ 07054
Tel (973) 263-7200 *SIC* 8211 9111

COUNTY OF PASSAIC p 380
401 Grand St Ste 1, Paterson NJ 07505
Tel (973) 881-4405 *SIC* 9111

PATERSON CITY OF (INC) p 1120
155 Market St Fl 2, Paterson NJ 07505
Tel (973) 321-1350 *SIC* 9111

COUNTY OF SOMERSET p 382
20 Grove St, Somerville NJ 08876
Tel (908) 231-7000 *SIC* 9111

COUNTY OF OCEAN p 380
101 Hooper Ave, Toms River NJ 08753
Tel (732) 929-2101 *SIC* 9111

CITY OF TRENTON p 319
319 E State St, Trenton NJ 08608
Tel (609) 989-3030 *SIC* 9111

COUNTY OF MERCER p 379
640 S Broad St, Trenton NJ 08611
Tel (609) 989-6502 *SIC* 9111

EXECUTIVE OFFICE OF STATE OF NEW JERSEY p 518
125 W State St, Trenton NJ 08608
Tel (609) 292-6000 *SIC* 9111

STATE OF NEW JERSEY p 1382
125 W State St, Trenton NJ 08608
Tel (609) 396-4657 *SIC* 9111

GLOUCESTER COUNTY NEW JERSEY (INC) p 618
2 S Broad St, Woodbury NJ 08096
Tel (856) 853-3200 *SIC* 9111

CITY OF ALBUQUERQUE p 312
400 Marquette Ave Nw, Albuquerque NM 87102
Tel (505) 768-3000 *SIC* 9111

COUNTY OF BERNALILLO p 376
1 Civic Plz Nw Fl 10, Albuquerque NM 87102
Tel (505) 468-7240 *SIC* 9111

PUEBLO OF ISLETA p 1190
Tribal Rd 40 Bldg 117-A, Isleta NM 87022
Tel (505) 869-3111 *SIC* 9111

CITY OF LAS CRUCES p 316
700 N Main St, Las Cruces NM 88001
Tel (575) 541-2000 *SIC* 9111

CITY OF SANTA FE p 318
200 Lincoln Ave, Santa Fe NM 87501
Tel (505) 955-6532 SIC 9111

GOVERNORS OFFICE NEW MEXICO p 627
490 Old Santa Fe Trl # 400, Santa Fe NM 87501
Tel (505) 476-2200 SIC 9111

STATE OF NEW MEXICO p 1382
237 Don Gaspar Ave, Santa Fe NM 87501
Tel (505) 827-3000 SIC 9111

CITY OF ALBANY p 312
24 Eagle St Rm 102, Albany NY 12207
Tel (518) 434-5100 SIC 9111

COUNTY OF ALBANY p 376
112 State St Rm 900, Albany NY 12207
Tel (518) 447-7130 SIC 9111

EXECUTIVE OFFICE OF STATE OF NEW YORK p 518
Executive Chamber Capitol, Albany NY 12224
Tel (518) 474-8390 SIC 9111

COUNTY OF SARATOGA p 381
25 W High St, Ballston Spa NY 12020
Tel (518) 884-4742 SIC 9111

GENESEE COUNTY OF (INC) p 602
15 Main St, Batavia NY 14020
Tel (585) 344-2550 SIC 9111

BROOME COUNTY p 218
60 Hawley St, Binghamton NY 13901
Tel (607) 778-2452 SIC 9111

CITY OF BUFFALO p 313
65 Niagara Sq Rm 201, Buffalo NY 14202
Tel (716) 851-4200 SIC 9111

COUNTY OF ERIE p 378
95 Franklin St Rm 1603, Buffalo NY 14202
Tel (716) 858-8500 SIC 9111

COUNTY OF ONTARIO p 380
20 Ontario St, Canandaigua NY 14424
Tel (585) 396-4400 SIC 9111

ST LAWRENCE COUNTY p 1369
48 Court St, Canton NY 13617
Tel (315) 379-2276 SIC 9111

TOWN OF CHEEKTOWAGA p 1465
3301 Broadway St, Cheektowaga NY 14227
Tel (716) 686-3400 SIC 9111

TOWN OF EDMESTON p 1465
607965 6th W St, Edmeston NY 13335
Tel (607) 965-9823 SIC 9111

COUNTY OF CHEMUNG p 377
320 E Market St, Elmira NY 14901
Tel (607) 737-2925 SIC 9111

TOWN OF BROOKHAVEN p 1465
1 Independence Hl Frnt, Farmingville NY 11738
Tel (631) 451-6680 SIC 9111

COUNTY OF SUFFOLK p 382
100 Veterans Hwy, Hauppauge NY 11788
Tel (631) 853-4000 SIC 9111

TOWN OF HEMPSTEAD p 1465
1 Washington St, Hempstead NY 11550
Tel (516) 489-5000 SIC 9111

TOWN OF HUNTINGTON p 1465
100 Main St, Huntington NY 11743
Tel (631) 351-3177 SIC 9111

COUNTY OF ULSTER p 382
244 Fair St, Kingston NY 12401
Tel (845) 340-3000 SIC 9111

COUNTY OF CATTARAUGUS p 376
303 Court St, Little Valley NY 14755
Tel (716) 938-9111 SIC 9111

COUNTY OF NIAGARA p 380
175 Hawley St, Lockport NY 14094
Tel (716) 439-7085 SIC 9111

TOWN OF LORRAINE p 1465
20876 County Route 189, Lorraine NY 13659
Tel (315) 232-4676 SIC 9111

COUNTY OF WAYNE p 383
9 Pearl St Rm 1, Lyons NY 14489
Tel (315) 946-5400 SIC 9111

STATE OF NEW YORK p 1382
800 N Pearl St, Menands NY 12204
Tel (518) 473-6790 SIC 9111

COUNTY OF NASSAU p 380
1550 Franklin Ave, Mineola NY 11501
Tel (516) 571-3131 SIC 9111

SULLIVAN COUNTY p 1397
100 North St, Monticello NY 12701
Tel (845) 794-3000 SIC 9111

COUNTY OF ROCKLAND p 381
11 New Hempstead Rd # 100, New City NY 10956
Tel (845) 638-5122 SIC 9111

ADMINISTRATIVE TRIALS & HEARINGS OFFICE OF (OATH) p 23
100 Church St Fl 12, New York NY 10007
Tel (844) 628-4692 SIC 9111

CITY OF NEW YORK p 317
City Hl, New York NY 10007
Tel (212) 788-3000 SIC 9111

CITY OF NIAGARA FALLS p 317
745 Main St, Niagara Falls NY 14301
Tel (716) 286-4310 SIC 9111

COUNTY OF OSWEGO p 380
46 E Bridge St, Oswego NY 13126
Tel (315) 349-8393 SIC 9111

DUTCHESS COUNTY OF (INC) p 463
626 Dutchess Tpke, Poughkeepsie NY 12603
Tel (845) 486-2000 SIC 9111

CITY OF ROCHESTER p 318
400 Dewey Ave, Rochester NY 14613
Tel (585) 428-6755 SIC 9111

COUNTY OF MONROE p 380
39 W Main St Ste 110, Rochester NY 14614
Tel (585) 428-5301 SIC 9111

COUNTY OF SCHENECTADY p 381
620 State St, Schenectady NY 12305
Tel (518) 285-8435 SIC 9111

CITY OF SYRACUSE p 319
233 E Wshngtn St Ste 231, Syracuse NY 13202
Tel (315) 448-8005 SIC 9111

COUNTY OF ONONDAGA p 380
1000 Erie Blvd W, Syracuse NY 13204
Tel (315) 435-8683 SIC 9111

RENSSELAER COUNTY p 1224
1600 7th Ave Ste 3, Troy NY 12180
Tel (518) 270-2626 SIC 9111

COUNTY OF ONEIDA p 380
800 Park Ave Ste 5, Utica NY 13501
Tel (315) 798-5780 SIC 9111

COUNTY OF JEFFERSON p 378
175 Arsenal St Rm 2, Watertown NY 13601
Tel (315) 785-3055 SIC 9111

COUNTY OF WESTCHESTER p 383
148 Martine Ave, White Plains NY 10601
Tel (914) 995-2000 SIC 9111

CITY OF YONKERS p 319
40 S Broadway Ste 1, Yonkers NY 10701
Tel (914) 377-6000 SIC 9111

YONKERS CITY SCHOOL DISTRICT p 1637
1 Larkin Ctr Fl 3, Yonkers NY 10701
Tel (914) 376-8000 SIC 8211 9111

COUNTY OF BUNCOMBE p 376
200 College St Ste 300, Asheville NC 28801
Tel (828) 250-4100 SIC 9111

CITY OF BURLINGTON p 313
425 S Lexington Ave, Burlington NC 27215
Tel (336) 222-5060 SIC 9111

TOWN OF CARY p 1465
316 N Academy St, Cary NC 27513
Tel (919) 469-4048 SIC 9111

CITY OF CHARLOTTE p 313
600 E 4th St, Charlotte NC 28202
Tel (704) 336-7600 SIC 9111

COUNTY OF MECKLENBURG p 379
600 E 4th St, Charlotte NC 28202
Tel (704) 336-2108 SIC 9111

COUNTY OF CABARRUS p 376
65 Church St S, Concord NC 28025
Tel (704) 920-2107 SIC 9111

CITY OF DURHAM p 314
101 City Hall Plz, Durham NC 27701
Tel (919) 560-4333 SIC 9111

COUNTY OF DURHAM p 377
200 E Main St Ste 235, Durham NC 27701
Tel (919) 560-0035 SIC 9111

CITY OF FAYETTEVILLE p 314
433 Hay St, Fayetteville NC 28301
Tel (910) 433-1990 SIC 9111

COUNTY OF CUMBERLAND p 377
117 Dick St, Fayetteville NC 28301
Tel (910) 678-7740 SIC 9111

GASTON COUNTY p 593
128 W Main Ave, Gastonia NC 28052
Tel (704) 866-3100 SIC 9111

COUNTY OF ALAMANCE p 376
124 W Elm St, Graham NC 27253
Tel (336) 228-1312 SIC 9111

CITY OF GREENSBORO p 315
300 W Washington St, Greensboro NC 27401
Tel (336) 373-2002 SIC 9111

COUNTY OF GUILFORD p 378
301 W Market St, Greensboro NC 27401
Tel (336) 641-3836 SIC 9111

CITY OF HIGH POINT p 315
211 S Hamilton St, High Point NC 27260
Tel (336) 883-3289 SIC 9111

COUNTY OF ONSLOW p 380
4024 Richlands Hwy, Jacksonville NC 28540
Tel (910) 455-1750 SIC 9111

COUNTY OF CATAWBA p 376
100 Southwest Blvd Bldg A, Newton NC 28658
Tel (828) 465-8200 SIC 9111

CITY OF RALEIGH p 317
222 W Hargett St, Raleigh NC 27601
Tel (919) 996-3000 SIC 9111

COUNTY OF WAKE p 382
300 S Salisbury St # 4800, Raleigh NC 27601
Tel (919) 856-6160 SIC 9111

EXECUTIVE OFFICE OF STATE OF NORTH CAROLINA p 518
20301 Mail Svc Ctr, Raleigh NC 27699
Tel (919) 814-2000 SIC 9111

STATE OF NORTH CAROLINA p 1382
20301 Mail Service Ctr, Raleigh NC 27699
Tel (919) 715-1411 SIC 9111

COUNTY OF ROWAN p 381
130 W Innes St Ste 120, Salisbury NC 28144
Tel (704) 636-0361 SIC 9111

LEE COUNTY OF (INC) p 851
106 Hillcrest Dr, Sanford NC 27330
Tel (919) 718-4600 SIC 9111

COUNTY OF JOHNSTON p 379
207 E Johnston St, Smithfield NC 27577
Tel (919) 989-5100 SIC 9111

CITY OF WILMINGTON p 319
305 Chestnut St, Wilmington NC 28401
Tel (910) 341-7800 SIC 9111

COUNTY OF NEW HANOVER p 380
230 Govt Ctr Dr 125, Wilmington NC 28403
Tel (910) 798-7187 SIC 9111

CITY OF WINSTON-SALEM p 319
101 N Main St, Winston Salem NC 27101
Tel (336) 727-8000 SIC 9111

COUNTY OF FORSYTH p 378
201 N Chestnut St, Winston Salem NC 27101
Tel (336) 703-2050 SIC 9111

WINSTON-SALEM/FORSYTH COUNTY SCHOOLS p 1617
4801 Bethania Station Rd, Winston Salem NC 27105
Tel (336) 727-2635 SIC 8211 9111

EXECUTIVE OFFICE OF STATE OF NORTH DAKOTA p 518
600 E Boulevard Ave, Bismarck ND 58505
Tel (701) 328-2680 SIC 9111

STATE OF NORTH DAKOTA p 1382
600 E Boulevard Ave # 101, Bismarck ND 58505
Tel (701) 328-4905 SIC 9111

CITY OF AKRON p 312
166 S High St Rm 502, Akron OH 44308
Tel (330) 375-2720 SIC 9111

COUNTY OF SUMMIT p 382
650 Dan St, Akron OH 44310
Tel (330) 643-2500 SIC 9111

ORIANA HOUSE INC p 1094
885 E Buchtel Ave, Akron OH 44305
Tel (330) 535-8116 SIC 8322 9111

COUNTY OF CLERMONT p 377
177 E Main St, Batavia OH 45103
Tel (513) 732-7980 SIC 9111

WOOD COUNTY OHIO p 1622
1 Court House Sq, Bowling Green OH 43402
Tel (419) 354-9100 SIC 9111

CITY OF CANTON p 313
218 Cleveland Ave Sw, Canton OH 44702
Tel (330) 438-4300 SIC 9111

COUNTY OF STARK p 382
110 Central Plz S Ste 240, Canton OH 44702
Tel (330) 451-7371 SIC 9111

CITY OF CINCINNATI p 314
801 Plum St Rm 246, Cincinnati OH 45202
Tel (513) 352-3221 SIC 9111

COUNTY OF HAMILTON p 378
138 E Court St Rm 607, Cincinnati OH 45202
Tel (513) 946-4400 SIC 9111

CITY OF CLEVELAND p 314
601 Lakeside Ave E Rm 210, Cleveland OH 44114
Tel (216) 664-2000 SIC 9111

CITY OF COLUMBUS p 314
90 W Broad St Rm B33, Columbus OH 43215
Tel (614) 645-7671 SIC 9111

EXECUTIVE OFFICE STATE OF OHIO p 518
30 E Broad St, Columbus OH 43215
Tel (614) 466-3555 SIC 9111

FRANKLIN COUNTY BOARD OF COMMISSIONERS p 575
373 S High St Fl 26, Columbus OH 43215
Tel (614) 525-3322 SIC 9111

SECRETARY OF STATE OHIO p 1298
180 E Broad St Fl 16, Columbus OH 43215
Tel (614) 466-2655 SIC 9111 9611

STATE OF OHIO p 1382
30 E Broad St Fl 40, Columbus OH 43215
Tel (614) 466-3455 SIC 9111

CITY OF CUYAHOGA FALLS p 314
2310 2nd St, Cuyahoga Falls OH 44221
Tel (330) 971-8230 SIC 9111

CITY OF DAYTON p 314
101 W 3rd St, Dayton OH 45402
Tel (937) 333-3333 SIC 9111

COUNTY OF MONTGOMERY p 380
451 W 3rd St Fl 4, Dayton OH 45422
Tel (937) 225-4000 SIC 9111

COUNTY OF DELAWARE p 377
101 N Sandusky St, Delaware OH 43015
Tel (740) 368-1800 SIC 9111

COUNTY OF LORAIN p 379
226 Middle Ave, Elyria OH 44035
Tel (440) 329-5201 SIC 9111

COUNTY OF ASHTABULA p 376
25 W Jefferson St, Jefferson OH 44047
Tel (440) 576-3783 SIC 9111

COUNTY OF WARREN p 382
406 Justice Dr Rm 323, Lebanon OH 45036
Tel (513) 695-1242 SIC 9111

COUNTY OF ALLEN p 376
301 N Main St, Lima OH 45801
Tel (419) 228-3700 SIC 9111

COUNTY OF RICHLAND p 381
50 Park Ave E Ste 3, Mansfield OH 44902
Tel (419) 774-5501 SIC 9111

COUNTY OF MEDINA p 379
144 N Brdwy St Rm 201, Medina OH 44256
Tel (330) 722-9208 SIC 9111

COUNTY OF LICKING p 379
20 S 2nd St, Newark OH 43055
Tel (740) 670-5040 SIC 9111

COUNTY OF LAKE p 379
8 N State St Ste 215, Painesville OH 44077
Tel (440) 350-2500 SIC 9111

COUNTY OF PORTAGE p 381
449 S Meridian St Fl 7, Ravenna OH 44266
Tel (330) 297-3561 SIC 9111

COUNTY OF CLARK p 377
50 E Columbia St Fl 5, Springfield OH 45502
Tel (937) 521-2005 SIC 9111

CITY OF TOLEDO p 319
1 Government Ctr Ste 2050, Toledo OH 43604
Tel (419) 245-1050 SIC 9111

COUNTY OF LUCAS p 379
1 Government Ctr Ste 600, Toledo OH 43604
Tel (419) 213-4406 SIC 9111

COUNTY OF MIAMI p 379
201 W Main St, Troy OH 45373
Tel (937) 440-5900 SIC 9111

COUNTY OF TRUMBULL p 382
160 High St Nw, Warren OH 44481
Tel (330) 675-2420 SIC 9111

CITY OF WOOSTER p 319
538 N Market St, Wooster OH 44691
Tel (330) 263-5200 SIC 9111

GREENE COUNTY p 638
35 Greene St, Xenia OH 45385
Tel (937) 562-5006 SIC 9111

CITY OF OKLAHOMA CITY p 317
100 N Walker Ave, Oklahoma City OK 73102
Tel (405) 297-2506 SIC 9111

COUNTY OF OKLAHOMA p 380
320 Robert S Kerr Ave # 505, Oklahoma City OK 73102
Tel (405) 270-0082 SIC 9111

EXECUTIVE OFFICE OF STATE OF OKLAHOMA p 518
2300 N Lincoln Blvd, Oklahoma City OK 73105
Tel (405) 521-2342 SIC 9111

OKLAHOMA DEPT OF MILITARY p 1079
3501 Ne Military Cir, Oklahoma City OK 73111
Tel (405) 228-5000 SIC 9111

CITY OF TULSA p 319
175 E 2nd St Ste 15129, Tulsa OK 74103
Tel (918) 596-2100 SIC 9111

COUNTY OF TULSA p 382
500 S Denver Ave, Tulsa OK 74103
Tel (918) 596-5000 SIC 9111

CITY OF EUGENE p 314
99 W 10th Ave Ste 310, Eugene OR 97401
Tel (541) 682-5010 SIC 9111

COUNTY OF LANE p 379
125 E 8th Ave, Eugene OR 97401
Tel (541) 682-4203 SIC 9111

COUNTY OF WASHINGTON p 382
155 N 1st Ave Ste 300, Hillsboro OR 97124
Tel (503) 846-8685 SIC 9111

COUNTY OF JACKSON p 378
10 S Oakdale Ave, Medford OR 97501
Tel (541) 774-6001 SIC 9111

CITY OF PORTLAND p 317
1221 Sw 4th Ave Rm 340, Portland OR 97204
Tel (503) 823-4120 SIC 9111

COUNTY OF MULTNOMAH p 380
501 Se Hawthorne Blvd # 100, Portland OR 97214
Tel (503) 988-3511 SIC 9111

CITY OF SALEM p 318
555 Liberty St Se Rm 230, Salem OR 97301
Tel (503) 588-6255 SIC 9111 9224 9221

EXECUTIVE OFFICE OF STATE OF OREGON p 518
900 Court St Ne, Salem OR 97301
Tel (503) 378-3111 SIC 9111

STATE OF OREGON p 1382
900 Court St Ne Ste 160, Salem OR 97301
Tel (503) 378-3111 SIC 9111

CITY OF ALLENTOWN p 313
435 Hamilton St, Allentown PA 18101
Tel (610) 437-7546 SIC 9111

COUNTY OF LEHIGH p 379
17 S 7th St, Allentown PA 18101
Tel (610) 782-3000 SIC 9111

COUNTY OF BEAVER p 376
810 3rd St, Beaver PA 15009
Tel (724) 728-5700 SIC 9111

BUCKS COUNTY OF p 223
55 E Court St Fl 5, Doylestown PA 18901
Tel (215) 348-6424 SIC 9111

COUNTY OF NORTHAMPTON p 380
669 Washington St, Easton PA 18042
Tel (610) 559-3000 SIC 9111

COUNTY OF ERIE p 378
140 W 6th St Erie, Erie PA 16501
Tel (814) 451-6000 SIC 9111

MILLCREEK TOWNSHIP SCHOOL DISTRICT p 970
3740 W 26th St, Erie PA 16506
Tel (814) 835-5300 SIC 8211 9111

COMMONWEALTH OF PENNSYLVANIA p 346
238 Main Capitol Building, Harrisburg PA 17120
Tel (717) 787-5962 SIC 9111

COUNTY OF DAUPHIN p 377
Market & Front Sts, Harrisburg PA 17101
Tel (717) 780-6300 SIC 9111

EXECUTIVE OFFICE OF COMMONWEALTH OF PENNSYLVANIA p 517
225 Capitol Bldg, Harrisburg PA 17120
Tel (717) 787-5962 SIC 9111

COUNTY OF LANCASTER p 379
150 N Queen St Ste 712, Lancaster PA 17603
Tel (717) 299-8262 SIC 9111

LEBANON COUNTY p 850
400 S 8th St Ste 1, Lebanon PA 17042
Tel (717) 274-2801 SIC 9111

DELAWARE COUNTY PENNSYLVANIA p 423
201 W Front St, Media PA 19063
Tel (610) 891-4000 SIC 9111

COUNTY OF MONTGOMERY p 380
530 Port Indian Rd, Norristown PA 19403
Tel (610) 278-3072 SIC 9111

CITY OF PHILADELPHIA p 317
215 City Hall, Philadelphia PA 19107
Tel (215) 686-2181 SIC 9111

CITY OF PITTSBURGH p 317
414 Grant St, Pittsburgh PA 15219
Tel (412) 255-2640 SIC 9111

COUNTY OF ALLEGHENY p 376
436 Grant St Ste 104, Pittsburgh PA 15219
Tel (412) 350-5300 SIC 9111

COUNTY OF BERKS p 376
633 Court St, Reading PA 19601
Tel (610) 478-6640 SIC 9111

WASHINGTON COUNTY p 1577
100 W Beau St Ste 403, Washington PA 15301
Tel (724) 228-6700 SIC 9111

COUNTY OF CHESTER p 377
313 W Market St, West Chester PA 19382
Tel (610) 344-6000 SIC 9111

LUZERNE COUNTY p 887
200 N River St, Wilkes Barre PA 18711
Tel (570) 825-1500 SIC 9111

COUNTY OF YORK p 383
28 E Market St Rm 216, York PA 17401
Tel (717) 771-9964 SIC 9111

MUNICIPIO DE BAYAMON p 1000
Road 2 Km 11 Hm 3 St Ro, Bayamon PR 00959
Tel (787) 780-5552 SIC 9111

CAGUAS MUNICIPALITY p 237
Calle Padial Final Esq, Caguas PR 00725
Tel (787) 743-2476 SIC 9111

CAROLINA MUNICIPALITY p 259
Ignacio Arzuaga St, Carolina PR 00985
Tel (787) 757-2626 SIC 9111

MUNICPALITY OF GUAYNABO p 1000
Jose De Diego St Final, Guaynabo PR 00969
Tel (787) 720-4040 SIC 9111

MUNICIPIO DE MAYAGUEZ p 1000
Betances St Crnr Mckinley Corner Mckinley, Mayaguez PR 00680
Tel (787) 834-8585 SIC 9111

MUNICIPIO DE PONCE p 1000
Calle Comercio Frente, Ponce PR 00731
Tel (787) 284-4141 SIC 9111
COMMONWEALTH OF PUERTO RICO p 346
63 Calle De La Fortaleza, San Juan PR 00901
Tel (787) 721-7000 SIC 9111
EXECUTIVE OFFICE OF COMMONWEALTH OF PUERTO RICO p 517
San Jose St Crn San, San Juan PR 00901
Tel (787) 722-2121 SIC 9111
MUNICIPIO DE SAN JUAN p 1000
1306 Ave Fernandez Juncos, San Juan PR 00909
Tel (787) 724-7171 SIC 9111
CITY OF EAST PROVIDENCE p 314
145 Taunton Ave, East Providence RI 02914
Tel (401) 435-7521 SIC 9111
CITY OF PROVIDENCE p 317
25 Dorrance St Unit 1, Providence RI 02903
Tel (401) 421-7740 SIC 9111
EXECUTIVE OFFICE OF STATE OF RHODE ISLAND p 518
82 Smith St Ste 217, Providence RI 02903
Tel (401) 574-8423 SIC 9111
STATE OF RHODE ISLAND AND PROVIDENCE PLANTATIONS p 1382
82 Smith St Ste 102, Providence RI 02903
Tel (401) 222-2080 SIC 9111
CITY OF WOONSOCKET p 319
169 Main St, Woonsocket RI 02895
Tel (401) 762-6400 SIC 9111
COUNTY OF BEAUFORT p 376
100 Ribaut Rd, Beaufort SC 29902
Tel (843) 255-7151 SIC 9111
CITY OF CHARLESTON p 313
116 Meeting St, Charleston SC 29401
Tel (843) 795-7543 SIC 9111
COUNTY OF CHARLESTON p 377
4045 Bridge View Dr, Charleston SC 29405
Tel (843) 958-4000 SIC 9111
CITY OF COLUMBIA p 314
1737 Main St, Columbia SC 29201
Tel (803) 545-3075 SIC 9111
COUNTY OF RICHLAND p 381
2020 Hampton St, Columbia SC 29204
Tel (803) 576-2600 SIC 9111
EXECUTIVE OFFICE OF STATE OF SOUTH CAROLINA p 518
Wade Hampton Bldg Fl 6, Columbia SC 29211
Tel (803) 734-2320 SIC 9111
STATE OF SOUTH CAROLINA p 1382
1205 Pendleton St, Columbia SC 29201
Tel (803) 734-2100 SIC 9111
COUNTY OF HORRY p 378
1301 2nd Ave, Conway SC 29526
Tel (843) 915-5000 SIC 9111
COUNTY OF GREENVILLE p 378
301 University Rdg # 2400, Greenville SC 29601
Tel (864) 467-7105 SIC 9111
COUNTY OF LEXINGTON p 379
212 S Lake Dr, Lexington SC 29072
Tel (803) 785-8100 SIC 9111
COUNTY OF YORK p 383
6 S Congress St, York SC 29745
Tel (803) 684-8511 SIC 9111
EXECUTIVE OFFICE OF STATE OF SOUTH DAKOTA p 518
500 E Capitol Ave, Pierre SD 57501
Tel (605) 773-3411 SIC 9111
STATE OF SOUTH DAKOTA p 1382
500 E Capitol Ave, Pierre SD 57501
Tel (605) 773-3378 SIC 9111
COUNTY OF SULLIVAN p 382
3411 Highway 126 Ste 201, Blountville TN 37617
Tel (423) 323-6400 SIC 9111
COUNTY OF DICKSON p 377
Court House Sq, Charlotte TN 37036
Tel (615) 789-5093 SIC 9111
CITY OF CHATTANOOGA p 313
101 E 11th St Ste G13, Chattanooga TN 37402
Tel (423) 425-3700 SIC 9111
COUNTY OF HAMILTON p 378
208 Courths 625 Ga Av 201, Chattanooga TN 37402
Tel (423) 209-6100 SIC 9111
CITY OF CLARKSVILLE p 314
1 Public Sq Ste 4, Clarksville TN 37040
Tel (931) 648-6106 SIC 9111
COUNTY OF BRADLEY p 376
155 Broad St Nw Ste H, Cleveland TN 37311
Tel (423) 728-7141 SIC 9111
COUNTY OF ANDERSON p 376
100 N Main St Rm 115, Clinton TN 37716
Tel (865) 457-6200 SIC 9111
COUNTY OF MAURY p 379
5 Public Sq, Columbia TN 38401
Tel (931) 381-3690 SIC 9111
COUNTY OF TIPTON p 382
100 Court Sq E, Covington TN 38019
Tel (901) 476-0219 SIC 9111
COUNTY OF CUMBERLAND p 377
2 N Main St Ste 303, Crossville TN 38555
Tel (931) 484-5730 SIC 9111
COUNTY OF WEAKLEY p 383
8319 Highway 22 Ste B, Dresden TN 38225
Tel (731) 364-5413 SIC 9111
COUNTY OF SUMNER p 382
355 N Belvedere Dr Rm 302, Gallatin TN 37066
Tel (615) 452-3604 SIC 9111
COUNTY OF GREENE p 378
204 N Cutler St Ste 206, Greeneville TN 37745
Tel (423) 798-1703 SIC 9111
CITY OF JOHNSON CITY p 315
601 E Main St, Johnson City TN 37601
Tel (423) 434-6000 SIC 9111
ROANE COUNTY p 1240
200 E Race St Ste 1, Kingston TN 37763
Tel (865) 376-3184 SIC 9111
CITY OF KNOXVILLE p 316
400 W Main St Rm L108, Knoxville TN 37902
Tel (865) 215-2040 SIC 9111
COUNTY OF KNOX p 379
400 W Main St Rm 615, Knoxville TN 37902
Tel (865) 215-2005 SIC 9111
COUNTY OF BLOUNT p 376
341 Court St, Maryville TN 37804
Tel (865) 273-5700 SIC 9111
CITY OF MEMPHIS p 316
125 N Main St Ste 468, Memphis TN 38103
Tel (901) 576-6657 SIC 9111
CITY OF MURFREESBORO p 316
111 W Vine St, Murfreesboro TN 37130
Tel (615) 849-2629 SIC 9111
COUNTY OF RUTHERFORD p 381
1 Public Sq Ste 101, Murfreesboro TN 37130
Tel (615) 898-7745 SIC 9199 9111
EXECUTIVE OFFICE OF STATE OF TENNESSEE p 518
600 Charlotte Ave, Nashville TN 37243
Tel (615) 741-2001 SIC 9111
METROPOLITAN GOVERNMENT OF NASHVILLE & DAVIDSON COUNTY p 955
100 Metro Courthouse, Nashville TN 37201
Tel (615) 862-5000 SIC 9111
STATE OF TENNESSEE p 1382
312 Rosa L Prks Ave Fl 21, Nashville TN 37243
Tel (615) 741-2001 SIC 9111
COUNTY OF GILES p 378
222 W Madison St, Pulaski TN 38478
Tel (931) 424-4001 SIC 9111
COUNTY OF ROBERTSON p 381
108 Crthuse 501 S Main St, Springfield TN 37172
Tel (615) 384-2476 SIC 9111
CITY OF ABILENE p 312
555 Walnut St, Abilene TX 79601
Tel (325) 676-6200 SIC 9111
CITY OF AMARILLO p 313
509 Se 7th Ave Rm 303, Amarillo TX 79101
Tel (806) 378-3000 SIC 9111
COUNTY OF BRAZORIA p 376
111 E Locust St Ste 303, Angleton TX 77515
Tel (979) 864-1275 SIC 9111
CITY OF ARLINGTON p 313
101 W Abram St, Arlington TX 76010
Tel (817) 275-3271 SIC 9111
CITY OF AUSTIN p 313
301 W 2nd St, Austin TX 78701
Tel (512) 974-2000 SIC 9111
COUNTY OF TRAVIS p 382
700 Lavaca St Fl 11, Austin TX 78701
Tel (512) 854-9125 SIC 9111
EXECUTIVE OFFICE OF STATE OF TEXAS p 518
1100 San Jacinto Blvd, Austin TX 78701
Tel (512) 463-2000 SIC 9111
STATE OF TEXAS p 1382
1100 San Jacinto Blvd, Austin TX 78701
Tel (512) 463-2000 SIC 9111
CITY OF BEAUMONT p 313
801 Main St, Beaumont TX 77701
Tel (409) 880-3716 SIC 9111
COUNTY OF JEFFERSON p 378
1149 Pearl St Ste 301, Beaumont TX 77701
Tel (409) 835-8466 SIC 9111
BELL COUNTY TEXAS p 170
101 E Central Ave, Belton TX 76513
Tel (254) 933-5115 SIC 9111
CITY OF BROWNSVILLE p 313
1001 E Elizabeth St # 234, Brownsville TX 78520
Tel (956) 542-2064 SIC 9111
COUNTY OF CAMERON p 376
1100 E Monroe St, Brownsville TX 78520
Tel (956) 544-0823 SIC 9111
COUNTY OF MONTGOMERY p 380
501 N Thompson St, Conroe TX 77301
Tel (936) 539-7885 SIC 9111
CITY OF CORPUS CHRISTI p 314
1201 Leopard St, Corpus Christi TX 78401
Tel (361) 880-3000 SIC 9111
COUNTY OF NUECES p 380
901 Leopard St Rm 304, Corpus Christi TX 78401
Tel (361) 888-0556 SIC 9111
CITY OF DALLAS p 314
1500 Marilla St, Dallas TX 75201
Tel (214) 670-3146 SIC 9111
COUNTY OF DALLAS p 377
509 Main St Fl 6, Dallas TX 75202
Tel (214) 653-6472 SIC 9111
CITY OF DENTON p 314
215 E Mckinney St, Denton TX 76201
Tel (940) 349-8200 SIC 9111
COUNTY OF DENTON p 377
110 W Hickory St, Denton TX 76201
Tel (940) 349-3100 SIC 9111
COUNTY OF HIDALGO p 378
100 N Closner Blvd # 303, Edinburg TX 78539
Tel (956) 289-7850 SIC 9111
CITY OF EL PASO p 314
1 Civic Center Plz, El Paso TX 79901
Tel (915) 541-4000 SIC 9111
COUNTY OF EL PASO p 377
500 E San Antonio Ave # 314, El Paso TX 79901
Tel (915) 546-2000 SIC 9111
CITY OF FORT WORTH p 314
1000 Throckmorton St, Fort Worth TX 76102
Tel (817) 392-6118 SIC 9111
TARRANT COUNTY TEXAS (INC) p 1425
100 E Weatherford St, Fort Worth TX 76196
Tel (817) 884-1111 SIC 9111
TEXAS CITY OF FRISCO p 1442
6101 Frisco Square Blvd # 1000, Frisco TX 75034
Tel (972) 335-5555 SIC 9111
COUNTY OF GALVESTON p 378
722 21st St Fl 1, Galveston TX 77550
Tel (409) 795-2100 SIC 9111
CITY OF GARLAND p 315
200 N 5th St, Garland TX 75040
Tel (972) 205-2000 SIC 9111
COUNTY OF WILLIAMSON p 383
710 S Main St Ste 303, Georgetown TX 78626
Tel (512) 943-1550 SIC 9111
GRAND PRAIRIE CITY OF (INC) p 630
317 College St, Grand Prairie TX 75050
Tel (972) 237-8000 SIC 9111
CITY OF HOUSTON p 315
901 Bagby St, Houston TX 77002
Tel (713) 837-0311 SIC 9111
COUNTY OF HARRIS p 378
201 Caroline St Ste 800, Houston TX 77002
Tel (713) 755-6411 SIC 9111
CITY OF IRVING p 315
825 W Irving Blvd, Irving TX 75060
Tel (972) 721-2600 SIC 9111
CITY OF KILLEEN p 315
101 College St, Killeen TX 76541
Tel (254) 501-7895 SIC 9111
CITY OF LAREDO p 316
1110 Houston St, Laredo TX 78040
Tel (956) 791-7308 SIC 9111
COUNTY OF WEBB p 383
1000 Houston St, Laredo TX 78040
Tel (956) 523-4600 SIC 9111
CITY OF LUBBOCK p 316
1625 13th St, Lubbock TX 79401
Tel (806) 775-2016 SIC 9111
CITY OF MC ALLEN p 316
1300 W Houston Ave, Mcallen TX 78501
Tel (956) 681-1000 SIC 9111
COUNTY OF COLLIN p 377
2300 Bloomdale Rd, Mckinney TX 75071
Tel (972) 424-1460 SIC 9111
CITY OF MESQUITE p 316
1515 N Galloway Ave, Mesquite TX 75149
Tel (972) 216-6218 SIC 9111
CITY OF PLANO p 317
1520 Ave K, Plano TX 75074
Tel (972) 941-7121 SIC 9111
COUNTY OF FORT BEND p 378
301 Jackson St Ste 719, Richmond TX 77469
Tel (281) 342-3411 SIC 9111
COUNTY OF BEXAR p 376
101 W Nueva Ste 1019, San Antonio TX 78205
Tel (210) 335-2626 SIC 9111
CITY OF WACO p 319
300 Austin Ave, Waco TX 76701
Tel (254) 750-5600 SIC 9111
CITY OF WICHITA FALLS p 319
1300 7th St, Wichita Falls TX 76301
Tel (940) 761-7462 SIC 9111
CITY OF SALT LAKE CITY p 318
451 S State St Rm 145, Salt Lake City UT 84111
Tel (801) 535-7704 SIC 9111
COUNTY OF SALT LAKE p 381
2001 S State St S2-200, Salt Lake City UT 84190
Tel (801) 468-3225 SIC 9111
EXECUTIVE OFFICE OF STATE OF UTAH p 518
2110 State Ofc Bldg, Salt Lake City UT 84114
Tel (801) 538-3020 SIC 9111
SALT LAKE CITY CORP p 1273
4380 W 2100 S, Salt Lake City UT 84120
Tel (801) 535-7704 SIC 9111
STATE OF UTAH p 1382
350 N State St Ste 200, Salt Lake City UT 84114
Tel (801) 538-1000 SIC 9111
EXECUTIVE OFFICE OF STATE OF VERMONT p 518
109 State St Ste 5, Montpelier VT 05609
Tel (802) 828-3333 SIC 9111
STATE OF VERMONT p 1382
109 State St Ste 4, Montpelier VT 05609
Tel (802) 828-1452 SIC 9111
GOVERNMENT OF US VIRGIN ISLANDS p 627
21-22 Kongens Gade, Charlotte Amalie VI 00802
Tel (340) 774-0001 SIC 9111
CITY OF ALEXANDRIA p 312
301 King St, Alexandria VA 22314
Tel (703) 746-4000 SIC 9111
COUNTY OF ARLINGTON p 376
2100 Clarendon Blvd # 500, Arlington VA 22201
Tel (703) 228-3130 SIC 9111
■ **NATIONAL SCIENCE FOUNDATION** p 1016
4201 Wilson Blvd Ste 1205, Arlington VA 22230
Tel (703) 292-5050 SIC 9199 9111
COUNTY OF ALBEMARLE p 376
401 Mcintire Rd Rm 149, Charlottesville VA 22902
Tel (434) 296-5855 SIC 9111
CITY OF CHESAPEAKE p 314
306 Cedar Rd, Chesapeake VA 23322
Tel (757) 382-6586 SIC 9111
COUNTY OF CHESTERFIELD p 377
9901 Lori Rd, Chesterfield VA 23832
Tel (804) 748-1000 SIC 9111
COUNTY OF MONTGOMERY p 380
755 Roanoke St Ste 2e, Christiansburg VA 24073
Tel (540) 382-5700 SIC 9111
COUNTY OF CULPEPER p 377
302 N Main St, Culpeper VA 22701
Tel (540) 727-3427 SIC 9111
CITY OF DANVILLE p 314
427 Patton St, Danville VA 24541
Tel (434) 799-5100 SIC 9111
CITY OF HAMPTON p 315
22 Lincoln St, Hampton VA 23669
Tel (757) 728-5177 SIC 9111
COUNTY OF HANOVER p 378
7497 County Complex Rd, Hanover VA 23069
Tel (804) 365-6000 SIC 9111
COUNTY OF HENRICO p 378
4301 E Parham Rd, Henrico VA 23228
Tel (804) 501-4000 SIC 9111 9511
CITY OF LYNCHBURG p 316
900 Church St Ste 102, Lynchburg VA 24504
Tel (434) 455-3990 SIC 9111
CITY OF NEWPORT NEWS p 317
2400 Washington Ave Main, Newport News VA 23607
Tel (757) 926-8411 SIC 9111
VIRGINIA PORT AUTHORITY p 1559
600 World Trade Ctr, Norfolk VA 23510
Tel (757) 683-8000 SIC 9621 9111
CITY OF PORTSMOUTH p 317
801 Crawford St Fl 5, Portsmouth VA 23704
Tel (757) 393-8000 SIC 9111
CITY OF RICHMOND p 318
900 E Broad St Ste 201, Richmond VA 23219
Tel (804) 646-7970 SIC 9111
COMMONWEALTH OF VIRGINIA p 346
101 N 14st James Monroe St, Richmond VA 23219
Tel (804) 225-3131 SIC 9111
EXECUTIVE OFFICE OF VIRGINIA p 518
1111 E Broad St Fl 3, Richmond VA 23219
Tel (804) 225-4534 SIC 9111
VIRGINIA SECRETARY OF PUBLIC SAFETY AND HOMELAND SECURITY p 1559
1111 E Broad St, Richmond VA 23219
Tel (804) 786-5351 SIC 9111
CITY OF ROANOKE p 318
215 Church Ave Sw Ste 461, Roanoke VA 24011
Tel (540) 853-2333 SIC 9111
COUNTY OF ROANOKE p 381
5204 Bernard Dr, Roanoke VA 24018
Tel (540) 772-2004 SIC 9111
COUNTY OF FRANKLIN p 378
1255 Franklin St Ste 106, Rocky Mount VA 24151
Tel (540) 483-3030 SIC 9111
COUNTY OF CAMPBELL p 376
47 Court House Ln, Rustburg VA 24588
Tel (434) 332-9667 SIC 9111
CITY OF SALEM p 318
114 N Broad St, Salem VA 24153
Tel (540) 375-4112 SIC 9111
CITY OF VIRGINIA BEACH p 319
2401 Courthouse Dr, Virginia Beach VA 23456
Tel (757) 385-4508 SIC 9111
COUNTY OF PRINCE WILLIAM p 381
1 County Complex Ct, Woodbridge VA 22192
Tel (703) 792-4640 SIC 9111
CITY OF BELLEVUE p 313
450 110th Ave Ne, Bellevue WA 98004
Tel (425) 452-6800 SIC 9111
CITY OF EVERETT p 314
2930 Wetmore Ave Ste 100, Everett WA 98201
Tel (425) 257-8700 SIC 9111
COUNTY OF SNOHOMISH p 382
3000 Rockefeller Ave Ms508, Everett WA 98201
Tel (425) 388-3460 SIC 9111
COUNTY OF THURSTON p 382
2000 Lakeridge Dr Sw, Olympia WA 98502
Tel (360) 754-3800 SIC 9111
EXECUTIVE OFFICE OF STATE OF WASHINGTON p 518
1115 Washington St Se, Olympia WA 98501
Tel (360) 753-6780 SIC 9111
STATE OF WASHINGTON p 1382
106 Legislative Building, Olympia WA 98504
Tel (360) 902-4111 SIC 9111
WASHINGTON STATE DEPARTMENT OF ENTERPRISE SERVICES p 1579
1500 Jefferson St Se, Olympia WA 98501
Tel (360) 407-2200 SIC 9111
WASHINGTON STATE DEPARTMENT OF LICENSING p 1579
1125 Washington St Se, Olympia WA 98501
Tel (360) 920-3600 SIC 9111
COUNTY OF KITSAP p 379
619 Division St, Port Orchard WA 98366
Tel (360) 337-7164 SIC 9111
CITY OF SEATTLE p 318
700 5th Ave Ste 4350, Seattle WA 98104
Tel (206) 684-0702 SIC 9111
COUNTY OF KING p 379
401 5th Ave Ste 3, Seattle WA 98104
Tel (206) 296-4040 SIC 9111
CITY OF SPOKANE p 318
808 W Spokane Falls Blvd, Spokane WA 99201
Tel (509) 625-6200 SIC 9111
CITY OF TACOMA p 319
747 Market St, Tacoma WA 98402
Tel (253) 591-5088 SIC 9111
COUNTY OF PIERCE p 381
615 S 9th St Ste 100, Tacoma WA 98405
Tel (253) 798-7285 SIC 9111
COUNTY OF CLARK p 377
1300 Franklin St, Vancouver WA 98660
Tel (360) 397-2232 SIC 9111
COUNTY OF YAKIMA p 383
128 N 2nd St Rm 408, Yakima WA 98901
Tel (509) 574-1500 SIC 9111
RALEIGH COUNTY BOARD OF EDUCATION p 1206
105 Adair St, Beckley WV 25801
Tel (304) 256-4500 SIC 8211 9111
EXECUTIVE OFFICE STATE OF WEST VIRGINIA p 518
1900 Kanawha Blvd E, Charleston WV 25305
Tel (304) 558-2000 SIC 9111
STATE OF WEST VIRGINIA p 1382
1900 Kanawha Blvd E # 714, Charleston WV 25305
Tel (304) 558-2000 SIC 9111
HARRISON COUNTY SCHOOL DISTRICT p 664
408 E B Saunders Way, Clarksburg WV 26301
Tel (304) 326-7300 SIC 8211 9111
FAYETTE COUNTY SCHOOLS p 532
111 Fayette Ave, Fayetteville WV 25840
Tel (304) 574-1176 SIC 9111 8211
COUNTY OF OUTAGAMIE p 380
410 S Walnut St, Appleton WI 54911
Tel (920) 832-1684 SIC 9111
COUNTY OF WALWORTH p 382
100 W Walworth St Ste 116, Elkhorn WI 53121
Tel (262) 741-4241 SIC 9111
COUNTY OF BROWN p 376
2077 Airport Dr Ste 18, Green Bay WI 54313
Tel (920) 448-4035 SIC 9111
COUNTY OF ROCK p 381
51 S Main St, Janesville WI 53545
Tel (608) 757-5660 SIC 9111

COUNTY OF KENOSHA p 379
1010 56th St, Kenosha WI 53140
Tel (262) 653-2552 SIC 9111

CITY OF LA CROSSE p 316
400 La Crosse St, La Crosse WI 54601
Tel (608) 784-8477 SIC 9111

COUNTY OF LA CROSSE p 379
400 4th St N, La Crosse WI 54601
Tel (608) 785-9581 SIC 9111

CITY OF MADISON p 316
210 Martin Luther, Madison WI 53703
Tel (608) 266-4671 SIC 9111

EXECUTIVE OFFICE OF STATE OF WISCONSIN p 518
115 E State Capitol, Madison WI 53702
Tel (608) 266-1212 SIC 9111

STATE OF WISCONSIN p 1382
115 E Capitol, Madison WI 53702
Tel (608) 266-1212 SIC 9111

CITY OF MILWAUKEE p 316
200 E Wells St, Milwaukee WI 53202
Tel (414) 286-3321 SIC 9111

WISCONSIN MILWAUKEE COUNTY p 1619
901 N 9th St Ste 306, Milwaukee WI 53233
Tel (414) 278-4211 SIC 9111

CITY OF RACINE p 317
730 Washington Ave, Racine WI 53403
Tel (262) 636-9101 SIC 9111

COUNTY OF SHEBOYGAN p 381
508 New York Ave, Sheboygan WI 53081
Tel (920) 459-3000 SIC 9111

COUNTY OF WAUKESHA p 382
515 W Mrland Blvd Ste G72, Waukesha WI 53188
Tel (262) 548-7902 SIC 9111

EXECUTIVE OFFICE OF STATE OF WYOMING p 518
200 W 24th St Rm 124, Cheyenne WY 82001
Tel (307) 777-7434 SIC 9111

STATE OF WYOMING p 1382
122 W 25th St Fl 4, Cheyenne WY 82001
Tel (307) 777-7758 SIC 9111

SIC 9121 Legislative Bodies

CITY OF ANAHEIM p 313
200 S Anaheim Blvd, Anaheim CA 92805
Tel (714) 765-5162 SIC 9121

CITY OF BERKELEY p 313
2120 Milvia St, Berkeley CA 94704
Tel (510) 981-7300 SIC 9121

COUNTY OF IMPERIAL p 378
940 W Main St Ste 208, El Centro CA 92243
Tel (760) 482-4556 SIC 9121

CITY OF FREMONT p 315
3300 Capitol Ave, Fremont CA 94538
Tel (510) 574-2050 SIC 9121

CITY OF IRVINE p 315
1 Civic Center Plz, Irvine CA 92606
Tel (949) 724-6000 SIC 9121 9111

OFFICE OF LEGISLATIVE COUNSEL p 1075
State Cpitol Bldg Rm 3021, Sacramento CA 95814
Tel (916) 341-8000 SIC 9121

SANTA ROSA CITY OF p 1281
100 Santa Rosa Ave, Santa Rosa CA 95404
Tel (707) 543-3010 SIC 9121

TOWN OF FAIRFIELD p 1465
725 Old Post Rd, Fairfield CT 06824
Tel (203) 256-3000 SIC 9121

LEGISLATIVE OFFICE OF STATE OF CONNECTICUT p 853
300 Capitol Ave, Hartford CT 06106
Tel (860) 240-0100 SIC 9121

■ ARCHITECT OF CAPITOL p 105
Us Capitol Bldg Rm Sb-16, Washington DC 20515
Tel (202) 228-1793 SIC 9121

■ CONGRESS UNITED STATES p 356
U S Capitol Senate Office, Washington DC 20510
Tel (202) 225-3121 SIC 9121

■ HOUSE OF REPRESENTATIVES UNITED STATES p 711
The Capitol, Washington DC 20515
Tel (202) 224-3121 SIC 9121

■ LIBRARY OF CONGRESS p 863
101 Independence Ave Se, Washington DC 20540
Tel (202) 707-5000 SIC 8231 9121

■ SENATE UNITED STATES p 1303
111 Russell Senate Bldg, Washington DC 20510
Tel (202) 224-3121 SIC 9121

COUNTY OF MANATEE p 379
1112 Manatee Ave W, Bradenton FL 34205
Tel (941) 748-4501 SIC 9121

COUNTY OF PINELLAS p 381
315 Court St Rm 300, Clearwater FL 33756
Tel (727) 464-3485 SIC 9121

LEGISLATIVE OFFICE OF FLORIDA p 853
400 S Monroe St, Tallahassee FL 32399
Tel (850) 488-4505 SIC 9121

CITY OF ALBANY p 312
222 Pine Ave Ste 560, Albany GA 31701
Tel (229) 883-6955 SIC 9121

COUNTY OF ADA p 375
200 W Front St, Boise ID 83702
Tel (208) 287-7080 SIC 9121

CITY OF EVANSVILLE p 314
1 Nw Martin Luther, Evansville IN 47708
Tel (812) 436-4994 SIC 9121

CITY OF GARY p 315
401 Broadway Ste 100, Gary IN 46402
Tel (219) 881-1301 SIC 9121

LEXINGTON-FAYETTE URBAN COUNTY GOVERNMENT p 859
200 E Main St, Lexington KY 40507
Tel (859) 258-3100 SIC 9121 9111

MAYOR AND CITY COUNCIL OF OCEAN CITY p 924
301 N Baltimore Ave, Ocean City MD 21842
Tel (410) 289-8221 SIC 9121

CITY OF BEVERLY p 313
191 Cabot St Rm 1, Beverly MA 01915
Tel (978) 922-2500 SIC 9121

TOWN OF MARSHFIELD p 1465
870 Moraine St, Marshfield MA 02050
Tel (781) 834-5552 SIC 9121

COMMONWEALTH OF MASSACHUSETTS DEPARTMENT OF CORRECTION p 346
50 Maple St Ste 3, Milford MA 01757
Tel (508) 233-6530 SIC 9121

TOWN OF NORTH ATTLEBOROUGH p 1465
43 S Washington St, North Attleboro MA 02760
Tel (508) 699-0100 SIC 9121

TOWN OF NORWOOD p 1465
566 Washington St, Norwood MA 02062
Tel (781) 762-1240 SIC 9121

TOWN OF RANDOLPH p 1465
41 S Main St, Randolph MA 02368
Tel (781) 961-0911 SIC 9121

TOWN OF SCITUATE p 1465
600 Chief Just Cshng Hghy, Scituate MA 02066
Tel (781) 545-8700 SIC 9121

LEGISLATIVE OFFICE OF MICHIGAN p 853
George Romney Building, Lansing MI 48933
Tel (517) 373-3400 SIC 9121

LEGISLATIVE OFFICE OF STATE OF MINNESOTA p 853
100 Rev Dr M L King Jr Bl, Saint Paul MN 55155
Tel (651) 296-2146 SIC 9121

LEGISLATIVE OFFICE OF STATE OF MISSOURI p 853
201 W Capitol Ave, Jefferson City MO 65101
Tel (573) 751-3829 SIC 9121

CITY OF ST LOUIS p 318
1200 Market St Rm 212, Saint Louis MO 63103
Tel (314) 622-3201 SIC 9121

LEGISLATIVE OFFICE STATE OF NY p 853
State Capital Bldg, Albany NY 12248
Tel (518) 455-4100 SIC 9121

STATE ASSEMBLY NEW YORK p 1380
1 Enterprise Dr, Albany NY 12204
Tel (518) 455-4100 SIC 9121

COUNTY OF ORANGE p 380
265 Main St, Goshen NY 10924
Tel (845) 291-2480 SIC 9121

COUNTY OF CHAUTAUQUA p 377
3 N Erie St, Mayville NY 14757
Tel (716) 753-7111 SIC 9121

COUNTY OF CUYAHOGA p 377
1215 W 3rd St, Cleveland OH 44113
Tel (216) 443-7022 SIC 9121

BUTLER COUNTY OF OHIO p 230
315 High St Fl 6, Hamilton OH 45011
Tel (513) 887-3278 SIC 9121

ASHTABULA COUNTY COMMISSIONERS p 117
25 W Jefferson St, Jefferson OH 44047
Tel (440) 576-3649 SIC 9121

MAHONING COUNTY p 897
21 W Boardman St Ste 200, Youngstown OH 44503
Tel (330) 740-2130 SIC 9121

COUNTY OF MARION p 379
451 Division St Ne Ste 1, Salem OR 97301
Tel (503) 588-5212 SIC 9121

WESTMORELAND COUNTY COURTHOUSE p 1602
2 N Main St Ste 101, Greensburg PA 15601
Tel (724) 830-3752 SIC 9121

HOUSE OF REPRESENTATIVES PENNSYLVANIA p 711
Main Capitol Bldg Rm 132, Harrisburg PA 17120
Tel (717) 787-3607 SIC 9121

LEGISLATIVE OFFICE OF COMMONWEALTH OF PENNSYLVANIA p 853
Main Capitol Bldg Rm 225, Harrisburg PA 17120
Tel (717) 787-5962 SIC 9121

CITY OF NORTH CHARLESTON p 317
2500 City Hall Ln, North Charleston SC 29406
Tel (843) 554-5700 SIC 9121

COUNTY OF SPARTANBURG p 382
Main Level Ste 1000 366 N, Spartanburg SC 29303
Tel (864) 596-2509 SIC 9121

CITY OF SIOUX FALLS p 318
224 W 9th St, Sioux Falls SD 57104
Tel (605) 367-8000 SIC 9121

CITY OF MARYVILLE p 316
404 W Broadway Ave, Maryville TN 37801
Tel (865) 273-3401 SIC 9121

HOUSE OF REPRESENTATIVES TEXAS p 711
105 W 15th St, Austin TX 78701
Tel (512) 463-0865 SIC 9121

LEGISLATIVE OFFICE TEXAS p 853
1200 N Congress Ave Ste 2, Austin TX 78701
Tel (512) 463-0001 SIC 9121

FAIRFAX COUNTY VIRGINIA p 524
12000 Government Ste 214, Fairfax VA 22035
Tel (703) 324-3126 SIC 9121

COUNTY OF SPOKANE p 382
1116 W Broadway Ave, Spokane WA 99260
Tel (509) 477-2265 SIC 9121

CITY OF VANCOUVER p 319
415 W 6th St, Vancouver WA 98660
Tel (360) 619-1068 SIC 9121

COUNTY OF DANE p 377
210 M Lthr Kng Jr Blv 425, Madison WI 53703
Tel (608) 266-4114 SIC 9121

SIC 9131 Executive & Legislative Offices Combined

POARCH BAND OF CREEK INDIANS p 1158
303 Poarch Rd, Atmore AL 36502
Tel (251) 368-9136 SIC 9131

SALT RIVER PIMA-MARICOPA INDIAN COMMUNITY EDUCATIONAL SE p 1273
10005 E Osborn Rd, Scottsdale AZ 85256
Tel (480) 362-7400 SIC 9131

TOHONO OODHAM NATION p 1458
Hc 86, Sells AZ 85634
Tel (520) 383-6540 SIC 9131

WHITE MOUNTAIN APACHE TRIBE p 1606
201 E Walnut St, Whiteriver AZ 85941
Tel (928) 338-4346 SIC 9131

NAVAJO NATION TRIBAL GOVERNMENT p 1019
2 Miles N Of Hwy 264, Window Rock AZ 86515
Tel (928) 871-6352 SIC 9131

UNITED AUBURN INDIAN COMMUNITY p 1506
10720 Indian Hill Rd, Auburn CA 95603
Tel (530) 883-2390 SIC 9131

YOCHA DEHE WINTUN NATION p 1636
18960 County Rd 75 A, Brooks CA 95606
Tel (530) 796-2109 SIC 9131

COLUSA INDIAN COMMUNITY COUNCIL p 343
3730 State Highway 45 B, Colusa CA 95932
Tel (530) 458-8231 SIC 9131

SYCUAN BAND OF KUMEYAAY NATION p 1413
3007 Dehesa Rd, El Cajon CA 92019
Tel (619) 445-6002 SIC 9131

CABAZON BAND OF MISSION INDIANS p 234
84245 Indio Springs Dr, Indio CA 92203
Tel (760) 342-2593 SIC 9131

SANTA ROSA INDIAN COMMUNITY OF SANTA ROSA RANCHERIA p 1281
16835 Alkali Dr, Lemoore CA 93245
Tel (559) 924-1278 SIC 9131

FORT MOJAVE TRIBAL COUNCIL p 569
500 Merriman St, Needles CA 92363
Tel (760) 629-4591 SIC 9131

SHINGLE SPRINGS RANCHERIA p 1317
5168 Honpie Rd, Placerville CA 95667
Tel (530) 672-8059 SIC 9131

FEDERATED INDIANS OF GRATON RANCHERIA p 536
6400 Redwood Dr Ste 300, Rohnert Park CA 94928
Tel (619) 917-9566 SIC 9131

SOBOBA BAND OF LUISENO INDIANS p 1336
23906 Soboba Rd, San Jacinto CA 92583
Tel (951) 654-2765 SIC 9131

SOUTHERN UTE INDIAN TRIBE p 1351
356 Ouray Dr, Ignacio CO 81137
Tel (970) 563-0100 SIC 9131

MASHANTUCKET PEQUOT TRIBAL NATION p 915
2 Matts Path, Mashantucket CT 06338
Tel (860) 396-6500 SIC 9131

■ BUREAU OF INDIAN AFFAIRS p 226
1849 C St Nw, Washington DC 20240
Tel (202) 208-6123 SIC 9131

COEUR DALENE TRIBE p 333
850 A St, Plummer ID 83851
Tel (208) 686-1800 SIC 9131

PRAIRIE BAND POTAWATOMI NATION p 1167
16281 Q Rd, Mayetta KS 66509
Tel (785) 966-2255 SIC 9131

CHITIMACHA TRIBE OF LOUISIANA p 301
155 Chitimacha Loop, Charenton LA 70523
Tel (337) 923-4973 SIC 9131

COUSHATTA ALLIANCE p 383
1940 C C Bel Rd, Elton LA 70532
Tel (337) 584-1401 SIC 9131

SAULT SAINTE MARIE TRIBE OF CHIPPEWA INDIANS p 1283
523 Ashmun St, Sault Sainte Marie MI 49783
Tel (906) 635-6050 SIC 9131

GRAND TRAVERSE BAND LLC p 630
2605 N West Bay Shore Dr, Suttons Bay MI 49682
Tel (231) 534-7750 SIC 9131

FOND DU LAC RESERVATION p 563
1785 Highway 210, Carlton MN 55718
Tel (218) 879-4593 SIC 9131

ST LOUIS COUNTY OF (INC) p 1369
100 N 5th Ave W Rm 320, Duluth MN 55802
Tel (218) 726-2340 SIC 9131

WHITE EARTH BAND OF CHIPPEWA INDIANS p 1606
35500 Eagleview Rd, Ogema MN 56569
Tel (800) 950-3248 SIC 9131

MISSISSIPPI BAND OF CHOCTAW INDIANS p 975
101 Industrial Rd, Choctaw MS 39350
Tel (601) 650-1845 SIC 9131

CROW TRIBE OF INDIANS p 394
Hwy 212 & 87, Crow Agency MT 59022
Tel (406) 638-3700 SIC 9131

MESCALERO APACHE TRIBE p 951
108 Old Mescalero Blvd, Mescalero NM 88340
Tel (575) 464-4494 SIC 9131

SENECA NATION OF INDIANS p 1303
90 Ohiyo Way, Salamanca NY 14779
Tel (716) 945-1790 SIC 9131

EASTERN BAND OF CHEROKEE INDIANS p 471
88 Council House Loop, Cherokee NC 28719
Tel (828) 497-2771 SIC 9131

LAKE SPIRIT TRIBE p 839
816 3rd Ave N, Fort Totten ND 58335
Tel (701) 766-1270
SIC 9131 0191 2394 2298 7999

CHICKASAW NATION p 298
520 Arlington St, Ada OK 74820
Tel (580) 436-2603 SIC 9131

CHICKASAW NATION HEADQUARTERS ADMINISTRATION p 298
520 Arlington St, Ada OK 74820
Tel (580) 310-6403 SIC 9131

CHOCTAW NATION OF OKLAHOMA p 302
529 N 16th Ave, Durant OK 74701
Tel (580) 924-8280 SIC 9131

MUSCOGEE CREEK NATION p 1002
1008 E Eufaula St, Okmulgee OK 74447
Tel (918) 756-8700 SIC 9131

CHEROKEE NATION p 294
17675 S Muskogee Ave, Tahlequah OK 74464
Tel (918) 453-5000 SIC 9131

COW CREEK BAND OF UMPQUA TRIBE OF INDIANS p 385
2371 Ne Stephens St, Roseburg OR 97470
Tel (541) 957-8945 SIC 9131 6321 7999

MUCKLESHOOT INDIAN TRIBE p 998
39015 172nd Ave Se, Auburn WA 98092
Tel (253) 333-8741 SIC 9131

CONFEDERATED TRIBES OF COLVILLE RESERVATION p 355
1 Colville St, Nespelem WA 99155
Tel (509) 634-2857 SIC 9131

HO-CHUNK NATION p 698
W9814 Airport Rd, Black River Falls WI 54615
Tel (800) 280-2843 SIC 9131

ONEIDA TRIBE OF INDIANS OF WISCONSIN p 1087
N7210 Seminary Rd, Oneida WI 54155
Tel (920) 869-2214 SIC 9131

COUNTY OF WINNEBAGO p 383
112 Otter Ave, Oshkosh WI 54901
Tel (920) 236-4800 SIC 9131

ST CROIX CHIPPEWA INDIANS OF WISCONSIN p 1365
24663 Angeline Ave, Webster WI 54893
Tel (715) 349-2195 SIC 9131

SIC 9199 General Government, NEC

ALABAMA DEPT OF MENTAL HEALTH p 43
100 N Union St Ste 520, Montgomery AL 36104
Tel (334) 242-3107 SIC 9199

GEOLOGICAL SURVEY OF ALABAMA p 606
420 Hackberry Ln, Tuscaloosa AL 35487
Tel (205) 247-3592 SIC 9199

ALASKA DEPARTMENT OF ADMINISTRATION p 44
333 Willoughby Ave, Juneau AK 99801
Tel (907) 465-2200 SIC 9199

ARIZONA DEPARTMENT OF ADMINISTRATION p 108
100 N 15th Ave Ste 401, Phoenix AZ 85007
Tel (602) 542-1500 SIC 9199

CITY OF LITTLE ROCK p 316
500 W Markham St, Little Rock AR 72201
Tel (501) 371-4510 SIC 9199

CITY OF HUNTINGTON BEACH p 315
2000 Main St, Huntington Beach CA 92648
Tel (714) 536-5202 SIC 9199

COUNTY OF SHASTA p 381
1450 Court St Ste 308a, Redding CA 96001
Tel (530) 225-5561 SIC 9199

■ GSA PACIFIC RIM REGION OFFICE OF REGIONAL ADMINISTRATOR p 643
450 Golden Gate Ave Fl 5, San Francisco CA 94102
Tel (415) 522-3001 SIC 9199

COUNTY OF SANTA CLARA p 381
3180 Newberry Dr Ste 150, San Jose CA 95118
Tel (408) 299-5105 SIC 9199

CALIFORNIA DEPARTMENT OF GENERAL SERVICES p 240
707 3rd St, West Sacramento CA 95605
Tel (916) 376-5000 SIC 9199

COLORADO SPRINGS CITY GOVERNMENT p 339
107 N Nevada Ave, Colorado Springs CO 80903
Tel (719) 385-5900 SIC 9199

CONNECTICUT DEPARTMENT OF ADMINISTRATIVE SERVICES p 356
165 Capitol Ave Ste 7, Hartford CT 06106
Tel (860) 713-5100 SIC 9199

UNIVERSITY OF CONNECTICUT p 1521
343 Mansfield Rd U-1130, Storrs CT 06269
Tel (860) 486-2000 SIC 8221 9199

■ COUNCIL OF INSPECTORS GENERAL ON INTEGRITY AND EFFICIENCY p 374
1717 H St Nw Ste 825, Washington DC 20006
Tel (202) 292-2604 SIC 9199

■ GENERAL SERVICES ADMINISTRATION US p 602
1800 F St Nw Rm 6100, Washington DC 20405
Tel (202) 501-8880 SIC 9199

■ GSA NATIONAL CAPITAL AREA REGION OF REGIONAL ADMINISTRATOR (11A) p 643
7 & D St Sw Ste 7022th, Washington DC 20407
Tel (202) 708-9100 SIC 9199

■ GSA NATIONAL CAPITAL REGION p 643
7 & D St Sw Rm 1065th, Washington DC 20407
Tel (202) 708-5891 SIC 9199

■ GSA OFFICE OF CHIEF FINANCIAL OFFICER p 643
1800 F St Nw Rm 2140, Washington DC 20405
Tel (202) 501-1721 SIC 9199

■ LEGAL SERVICES CORP p 853
3333 K St Nw Ste 1, Washington DC 20007
Tel (202) 295-1500 SIC 6732 9199

■ U S OFFICE OF PERSONNEL MANAGEMENT p 1497
1900 E St Nw Ste 7114, Washington DC 20415
Tel (202) 606-1800 SIC 9199

■ US GOVERNMENT PUBLISHING OFFICE p 1532
732 N Capitol St Nw, Washington DC 20401
Tel (202) 512-0000 SIC 9199

ORANGE COUNTY GOVERNMENT p 1092
21 S Roseland Ave, Orlando FL 32801
Tel (407) 836-7370 SIC 9199

FLORIDA DEPARTMENT OF ECONOMIC OPPORTUNITY p 558
107 E Madison St St120, Tallahassee FL 32399
Tel (850) 245-7362 SIC 9199

GEORGIA TECHNOLOGY AUTHORITY p 607
47 Trinity Ave Sw, Atlanta GA 30334
Tel (404) 463-2300 SIC 4899 9199

TECHNICAL COLLEGE SYSTEM OF GEORGIA FOUNDATION INC p 1431
1800 Century Pl Ne # 550, Atlanta GA 30345
Tel (404) 679-1600 SIC 8211 9199

HAWAII DEPARTMENT OF HUMAN RESOURCES DEVELOPMENT p 668
235 S Beretania St # 1400, Honolulu HI 96813
Tel (808) 587-1100 SIC 9199

TEACHERS RETIREMENT SYSTEM OF STATE OF ILLINOIS p 1429
2815 W Washington St # 200, Springfield IL 62702
Tel (217) 753-0370 *SIC* 6371 9199

COUNTY OF CHAMPAIGN p 376
1776 E Washington St Ofc, Urbana IL 61802
Tel (217) 384-3772 *SIC* 9199

CITY OF TOPEKA EMPLOYEES FRIENDSHIP FUND p 319
620 Se Madison St Ste 203, Topeka KS 66607
Tel (785) 368-3749 *SIC* 9199

KENTUCKY OFFICE OF ATTORNEY GENERAL p 812
Capitol Building Rm 100, Frankfort KY 40601
Tel (502) 696-5615 *SIC* 9199

LOUISIANA DIVISION OF ADMINISTRATION p 880
1201 N 3rd St Ste 7-20, Baton Rouge LA 70802
Tel (225) 342-7000 *SIC* 9199

■ **NATIONAL ARCHIVES AND RECORDS ADMINISTRATION** p 1009
8601 Adelphi Rd Ste 4200, College Park MD 20740
Tel (301) 837-2000 *SIC* 9199

ADMINISTRATION AND FINANCE MASSACHUSETTS EXECUTIVE OFFICE FOR p 23
24 Beacon St Ste 373, Boston MA 02133
Tel (617) 727-2040 *SIC* 9199 9311

MASSACHUSETTS COMMUNITY COLLEGES p 916
15 Court Sq Ste 1100, Boston MA 02108
Tel (617) 542-2911 *SIC* 8222 9199

MASSACHUSETTS TURNPIKE AUTHORITY p 917
10 Park Plz Ste 5170, Boston MA 02116
Tel (617) 248-2800 *SIC* 4785 9199

BRIDGEWATER STATE UNIVERSITY p 212
131 Summer St Rm 109, Bridgewater MA 02325
Tel (508) 531-1000 *SIC* 8221 9199

DEPARTMENT OF STATE MICHIGAN p 430
430 W Allegan St, Lansing MI 48933
Tel (517) 373-2510 *SIC* 9199

MINNESOTA STATE UNIVERSITY MANKATO p 974
620 South Rd, Mankato MN 56001
Tel (507) 389-1866 *SIC* 8221 9199

MINNESOTA STATE COLLEGES AND UNIVERSITIES p 974
720 4th Ave S, Saint Cloud MN 56301
Tel (320) 308-0121 *SIC* 8221 9199

CENTURY COLLEGE p 282
3300 Century Ave N, Saint Paul MN 55110
Tel (651) 779-3300 *SIC* 8222 9199

WINONA STATE UNIVERSITY FOUNDATION p 1617
175 W Mark St, Winona MN 55987
Tel (507) 457-5000 *SIC* 8221 9199

MISSOURI OFFICE OF ADMINISTRATION p 976
201 W Capitol Ave Rm125, Jefferson City MO 65101
Tel (573) 751-1851 *SIC* 9199

NEBRASKA DEPARTMENT OF ADMINISTRATIVE SERVICES p 1023
1526 K St Ste 250, Lincoln NE 68508
Tel (402) 471-2331 *SIC* 9199

NEBRASKA INDUSTRAIL COMPETITIVENESS SERVICE p 1023
8800 O St, Lincoln NE 68520
Tel (402) 437-2535 *SIC* 9199

COUNTY OF BURLINGTON p 376
49 Rancocas Rd, Mount Holly NJ 08060
Tel (609) 265-5000 *SIC* 9199

NEW JERSEY HOUSING AND MORTGAGE FINANCE AGENCY CJ p 1031
637 S Clinton Ave, Trenton NJ 08611
Tel (609) 278-7400 *SIC* 6162 9199

INSURANCE FUND NEW YORK STATE p 748
199 Church St Fl 13, New York NY 10007
Tel (212) 587-7390 *SIC* 9199

TOWN OF OYSTER BAY p 1465
54 Audrey Ave, Oyster Bay NY 11771
Tel (516) 624-6498 *SIC* 9199

■ **INTERNATIONAL BROADCASTING BUREAU** p 754
3919 Voa Site B Rd, Grimesland NC 27837
Tel (252) 758-2171 *SIC* 9199

COUNTY OF STARK p 382
110 Central Plz S Ste 240, Canton OH 44702
Tel (330) 451-7999 *SIC* 9199

OHIO BUREAU OF WORKERS COMPENSATION p 1077
30 W Spring St Fl 2-29, Columbus OH 43215
Tel (614) 644-6292 *SIC* 6331 9199

OHIO DEPARTMENT OF ADMINISTRATIVE SERVICES p 1077
30 E Broad St Fl 39, Columbus OH 43215
Tel (614) 466-6511 *SIC* 9199

GOVERNMENT SERVICE CENTER p 627
315 High St Fl 10, Hamilton OH 45011
Tel (513) 887-3000 *SIC* 9199

COUNTY OF CLACKAMAS p 377
2051 Kaen Rd, Oregon City OR 97045
Tel (503) 655-8459 *SIC* 9199

OREGON DEPARTMENT OF ADMINISTRATIVE SERVICES p 1093
155 Cottage St Ne Ste U50, Salem OR 97301
Tel (503) 378-8344 *SIC* 9199

PENNSYLVANIA STATE EMPLOYEES CREDIT UNION p 1130
1500 Elmerton Ave, Harrisburg PA 17110
Tel (800) 237-7328 *SIC* 6062 9199

■ **GSA MID-ATLANTIC REGION OFC OF REGIONAL ADMINISTRATOR (3A)** p 643
20 N 8th St, Philadelphia PA 19107
Tel (215) 446-4900 *SIC* 9199

LACKAWANNA COUNTY GOVERNMENT p 837
200 Adams Ave, Scranton PA 18503
Tel (570) 963-6800 *SIC* 9611 9199

MUNICIPIO DE ARECIBO p 1000
Jose De Diego St, Arecibo PR 00612
Tel (787) 879-1561 *SIC* 9199

PUERTO RICO DEPARTMENT OF LABOR AND HUMAN RESOURCES p 1191
505 Ave Munoz Rivera, San Juan PR 00918
Tel (787) 754-2119 *SIC* 9199

STATE OF RHODE ISLAND DEPARTMENT OF ADMINISTRATION p 1382
1 Capitol Hl Ste 1, Providence RI 02908
Tel (401) 222-2280 *SIC* 9199

COUNTY OF RUTHERFORD p 381
1 Public Sq Ste 101, Murfreesboro TN 37130
Tel (615) 898-7745 *SIC* 9199 9111

■ **GSA GREATER SOUTHWEST REGION OFC OF REGIONAL ADMINISTRATOR** p 643
819 Taylor St Rm 11a00, Fort Worth TX 76102
Tel (817) 978-2321 *SIC* 9199

CITY OF SAN ANTONIO p 318
City Hall 100 Military Plz, San Antonio TX 78205
Tel (210) 207-6000 *SIC* 9199

■ **GSA FEDERAL ACQUISITION SERVICE (Q)** p 643
2200 Crystal Dr Rm 1100, Arlington VA 22202
Tel (703) 605-5400 *SIC* 9199

■ **NATIONAL SCIENCE FOUNDATION** p 1016
4201 Wilson Blvd Ste 1205, Arlington VA 22230
Tel (703) 292-5050 *SIC* 9199 9111

LOUDOUN COUNTY p 879
1 Harrison St Se Fl 1, Leesburg VA 20175
Tel (703) 777-0100 *SIC* 9199

COLVILLE CONFEDERATED TRIBES INC p 343
44 School Loop Rd, Nespelem WA 99155
Tel (509) 634-2200 *SIC* 9199

SIC 9211 Courts

ALABAMA UNIFIED JUDICIAL SYSTEM p 43
300 Dexter Ave, Montgomery AL 36104
Tel (334) 954-5000 *SIC* 9211

JUDICIARY COURTS OF STATE OF ARIZONA p 796
1501 W Washington St, Phoenix AZ 85007
Tel (602) 452-3300 *SIC* 9211

JUDICIARY COURTS OF STATE OF ARKANSAS p 796
625 Marshall St Ste 1100, Little Rock AR 72201
Tel (501) 682-6849 *SIC* 9211

PULASKI COUNTY p 1191
201 Broadway St Ste 440, Little Rock AR 72201
Tel (501) 340-8381 *SIC* 9211

SUPERIOR COURT OF CALIFORNIA p 1406
247 W 3rd St, San Bernardino CA 92415
Tel (909) 708-8678 *SIC* 9211

JUDICIAL COUNCIL OF CALIFORNIA p 796
455 Golden Gate Ave # 1521, San Francisco CA 94102
Tel (415) 865-4200 *SIC* 9211

JUDICIARY COURTS OF STATE OF COLORADO p 796
1300 N Broadway Ste 1200, Denver CO 80203
Tel (303) 837-3741 *SIC* 9211

JUDICIAL BRANCH STATE OF CONNECTICUT p 796
231 Capitol Ave, Hartford CT 06106
Tel (860) 706-5146 *SIC* 9211

SUPREME COURT OF STATE OF DELAWARE p 1408
55 The Grn, Dover DE 19901
Tel (302) 739-4155 *SIC* 9211

COURT OF APPEALS OF DISTRICT OF COLUMBIA p 383
500 Indiana Ave Nw, Washington DC 20001
Tel (202) 879-2700 *SIC* 9211

■ **COURT OF APPEALS UNITED STATES** p 383
1 Columbus Cir Ne, Washington DC 20544
Tel (202) 879-1010 *SIC* 9211

■ **SUPREME COURT UNITED STATES** p 1408
1 1st St Ne, Washington DC 20543
Tel (202) 479-3000 *SIC* 9211

FLORIDA DIVISION OF ADMINISTRATIVE HEARINGS p 558
1230 Apalachee Pkwy, Tallahassee FL 32301
Tel (850) 488-9675 *SIC* 9211

STATE OF FLORIDA OF JUDICIARY COURTS p 1381
500 S Duval St, Tallahassee FL 32399
Tel (850) 922-5081 *SIC* 9211

JUDICIARY COURTS OF STATE OF HAWAII p 796
417 S King St, Honolulu HI 96813
Tel (808) 539-4700 *SIC* 9211

JUDICIAL COURTS OF STATE OF ILLINOIS p 796
Clerk Supreme Court Bldg, Springfield IL 62704
Tel (217) 782-2035 *SIC* 9111 9211

JUDICIARY COURTS OF STATE OF INDIANA p 796
200 W Washington St # 217, Indianapolis IN 46204
Tel (317) 232-1930 *SIC* 9211

JUDICIARY COURTS OF STATE OF IOWA p 796
1111 E Court Ave, Des Moines IA 50319
Tel (515) 281-5241 *SIC* 9211

JUDICIARY COURTS OF STATE OF KANSAS p 796
301 Sw 10th Ave, Topeka KS 66612
Tel (785) 296-4873 *SIC* 9211

JUDICIARY COURTS OF COMMONWEALTH OF KENTUCKY p 796
700 Capital Ave Rm 231, Frankfort KY 40601
Tel (502) 564-6753 *SIC* 9211

JUDICIARY COURTS OF STATE OF LOUISIANA p 796
400 Royal St Ste 4200, New Orleans LA 70130
Tel (504) 310-2300 *SIC* 9211

COURT OF APPEALS MARYLAND STATE p 383
580 Taylor Ave, Annapolis MD 21401
Tel (410) 260-1500 *SIC* 9211

MASSACHUSETTS SUPREME JUDICIAL COURT p 917
1 Pemberton Sq Ste 2500, Boston MA 02108
Tel (617) 557-1020 *SIC* 9211

JUDICIARY COURTS OF STATE OF MICHIGAN p 797
925 W Ottawa St, Lansing MI 48915
Tel (517) 373-0120 *SIC* 9211

JUDICIARY COURTS OF STATE OF MINNESOTA p 797
25 Rev Dr Mlk Jr Blvd, Saint Paul MN 55155
Tel (651) 297-7650 *SIC* 9211

MS SUPREME COURT p 996
450 High St Ste 300, Jackson MS 39201
Tel (601) 359-3694 *SIC* 9211

JUDICIARY COURTS OF STATE OF MISSOURI p 797
207 High St, Jefferson City MO 65101
Tel (573) 751-4144 *SIC* 9211

JUDICIARY COURTS OF STATE OF NEVADA p 797
201 S Carson St Ste 201, Carson City NV 89701
Tel (775) 684-1700 *SIC* 9211

JUDICIARY COURTS OF STATE OF NEW JERSEY p 797
25 Market St, Trenton NJ 08611
Tel (609) 984-0627 *SIC* 9211

NEW YORK STATE DIVISION OF CRIMINAL JUSTICE SERVICES p 1036
80 S Swan St, Albany NY 12210
Tel (518) 457-9896 *SIC* 9211

UNIFIED COURT SYSTEM OF NEW YORK STATE p 1503
20 Eagle St, Albany NY 12207
Tel (518) 455-7700 *SIC* 9211

JUDICIARY COURTS OF STATE OF NORTH CAROLINA p 797
2 E Morgan St, Raleigh NC 27601
Tel (919) 733-3723 *SIC* 9211

JUDICIARY COURTS OF STATE OF OREGON p 797
1163 State St, Salem OR 97301
Tel (503) 986-5555 *SIC* 9211

ADMINISTRATIVE OFFICE OF PENNSYLVANIA COURTS p 23
601 Commonwealth Ave # 1500, Harrisburg PA 17120
Tel (717) 231-3300 *SIC* 9211

SUPREME COURT OF COMMONWEALTH OF PUERTO RICO p 1408
286 Munoz Rrivera Ave We Western, San Juan PR 00919
Tel (787) 641-6600 *SIC* 9211

SUPREME COURT OF STATE OF TENNESSEE p 1408
511 Union St Ste 600, Nashville TN 37219
Tel (615) 253-2868 *SIC* 9211

JUDICIARY COURTS OF STATE OF TEXAS p 797
205 W 14th St Ste 600, Austin TX 78701
Tel (512) 463-1312 *SIC* 9211

JUDICIARY COURTS OF COMMONWEALTH OF VIRGINIA p 796
100 N 9th St, Richmond VA 23219
Tel (804) 786-6455 *SIC* 9211

JUDICIARY COURTS OF STATE OF WASHINGTON p 797
Temple Of Justice, Olympia WA 98504
Tel (360) 357-2077 *SIC* 9211

JUDICIARY COURTS OF STATE OF WEST VIRGINIA p 797
State Capital Bldg E100, Charleston WV 25305
Tel (304) 558-0145 *SIC* 9211

SIC 9221 Police Protection

HIGHWAY PATROL CALIFORNIA p 692
601 N 7th St, Sacramento CA 95811
Tel (916) 376-3256 *SIC* 9221

BOULDER CITY OF (INC) p 204
1777 Broadway, Boulder CO 80302
Tel (303) 441-3090
SIC 9111 9224 9221 9511

CONNECTICUT DEPARTMENT OF EMERGENCY SERVICES & PUBLIC PROTECTION p 357
1111 Country Club Rd, Middletown CT 06457
Tel (860) 685-8000 *SIC* 9221

CONNECTICUT DEPARTMENT OF PUBLIC SAFETY p 357
1111 Country Club Rd, Middletown CT 06457
Tel (860) 685-8000 *SIC* 9221 9229

DEPARTMENT OF SAFETY AND HOMELAND SECURITY (DSHS) p 430
303 Transportation Cir, Dover DE 19901
Tel (302) 744-2672 *SIC* 9221 9229

■ **CAPITOL POLICE US** p 251
119 D St Ne, Washington DC 20510
Tel (202) 593-3647 *SIC* 9221

■ **FEDERAL BUREAU OF INVESTIGATION** p 533
935 Pennsylvania Ave Nw, Washington DC 20535
Tel (202) 324-3000 *SIC* 9221

LEE COUNTY SHERIFF DEPARTMENT p 851
14750 6 Mile Cypress Pkwy, Fort Myers FL 33912
Tel (239) 477-1000 *SIC* 9221

CITY OF JACKSONVILLE p 315
501 E Bay St, Jacksonville FL 32202
Tel (904) 630-0500 *SIC* 9221

PASCO SHERIFFS OFFICE p 1119
8700 Citizens Dr, New Port Richey FL 34654
Tel (727) 847-5878 *SIC* 9221

FLORIDA DEPARTMENT OF LAW ENFORCEMENT p 558
2331 Phillips Rd, Tallahassee FL 32308
Tel (850) 410-7000 *SIC* 9221

UNION CITY CITY OF INC p 1504
5047 Union St, Union City GA 30291
Tel (770) 964-2288 *SIC* 9111 9221

HAWAII DEPARTMENT OF PUBLIC SAFETY p 668
919 Ala Moana Blvd # 407, Honolulu HI 96814
Tel (808) 587-1288 *SIC* 9221 9229

ILLINOIS STATE OF STATE POLICE p 732
801 S 7th St, Springfield IL 62703
Tel (217) 782-7263 *SIC* 9221

INDIANA POLICE STATE p 738
100 N Senate Ave Rm N340, Indianapolis IN 46204
Tel (317) 232-8241 *SIC* 9221

LOUISIANA DEPARTMENT OF PUBLIC SAFETY & CORRECTIONS p 880
7919 Independence Blvd, Baton Rouge LA 70806
Tel (225) 925-6006 *SIC* 9221

JEFFERSON PARISH SHERIFFS OFFICE p 782
1233 Westbank Expy, Harvey LA 70058
Tel (504) 363-5500 *SIC* 9221 9223

■ **MARSHALS SERVICE UNITED STATES** p 911
3601 Pennsy Dr, Landover MD 20785
Tel (202) 307-9001 *SIC* 9221

STATE POLICE MARYLAND p 1382
1201 Reisterstown Rd, Pikesville MD 21208
Tel (410) 653-4219 *SIC* 9221

MASSACHUSETTS DEPARTMENT OF PUBLIC SAFETY p 916
1 Ashburton Pl Rm 2133, Boston MA 02108
Tel (617) 727-7775 *SIC* 9221 9229 9223

MASSACHUSETTS DEPARTMENT OF STATE POLICE p 916
470 Worcester Rd, Framingham MA 01702
Tel (508) 820-2350 *SIC* 9221

MICHIGAN DEPARTMENT OF STATE POLICE p 961
7150 Harris Dr, Dimondale MI 48821
Tel (517) 241-1075 *SIC* 9221

MISSISSIPPI DEPARTMENT OF PUBLIC SAFETY p 975
1900 E Woodrow Wilson Ave, Jackson MS 39216
Tel (601) 987-1212 *SIC* 9229 9221

NEW HAMPSHIRE STATE POLICE p 1030
33 Hazen Dr, Concord NH 03305
Tel (603) 223-8500 *SIC* 9221 9229

NEW JERSEY DEPT OF LAW & PUBLIC SAFETY p 1031
25 Market St Fl 8, Trenton NJ 08611
Tel (609) 292-4925 *SIC* 9222 9221

STATE POLICE NEW YORK p 1382
1220 Washngtn Ave Bldg 22, Albany NY 12226
Tel (518) 457-6721 *SIC* 9221

NORTH CAROLINA DEPARTMENT OF CRIME CONTROL AND PUBLIC SAFETY p 1051
512 N Salisbury St, Raleigh NC 27604
Tel (919) 825-2720 *SIC* 9221

CITY OF SALEM p 318
555 Liberty St Se Rm 230, Salem OR 97301
Tel (503) 588-6255 *SIC* 9111 9224 9221

OREGON DEPARTMENT OF STATE POLICE p 1093
255 Capitol St Ne Fl 4, Salem OR 97310
Tel (503) 378-3720 *SIC* 9221

PENNSYLVANIA DEPT OF STATE POLICE p 1130
1800 Elmerton Ave, Harrisburg PA 17110
Tel (717) 783-5599 *SIC* 9221

SOUTH CAROLINA DEPARTMENT OF LAW ENFORCEMENT p 1343
4400 Broad River Rd, Columbia SC 29210
Tel (803) 737-9000 *SIC* 9221

TEXAS DEPARTMENT OF PUBLIC SAFETY p 1443
5805 N Lamar Blvd, Austin TX 78752
Tel (512) 424-2000 *SIC* 9229 9221

VIRGINIA DEPARTMENT OF STATE POLICE p 1559
7700 Midlothian Tpke, North Chesterfield VA 23235
Tel (804) 674-2000 *SIC* 9221

WASHINGTON STATE PATROL p 1579
210 11th Ave Sw Rm 116, Olympia WA 98501
Tel (360) 753-6540 *SIC* 9221

WEST VIRGINIA DEPARTMENT OF MILITARY AFFAIRS AND PUBLIC SAFETY p 1596
1900 Kanawha Blvd E Rm 1, Charleston WV 25305
Tel (304) 558-8045 *SIC* 9711 9221 9229

SIC 9222 Legal Counsel & Prosecution

DEPARTMENT OF CORRECTIONS ALABAMA p 430
301 S Ripley St, Montgomery AL 36104
Tel (334) 353-3844 *SIC* 9222

ATTORNEY GENERAL CALIFORNIA OFFICE OF p 129
1300 I St Ste 1101, Sacramento CA 95814
Tel (916) 445-9555 *SIC* 9222

CALIFORNIA DEPARTMENT OF JUSTICE p 240
1300 I St Ste 1142, Sacramento CA 95814
Tel (916) 324-5437 *SIC* 9222

■ **CONSOLIDATED EXECUTIVE OFFICE** p 359
950 Pennsylvania Ave Nw, Washington DC 20530
Tel (202) 616-6788 *SIC* 9222

■ **TRUSTEE PROGRAM UNITED STATES** p 1487
20 Massachusetts, Washington DC 20530
Tel (202) 307-1399 *SIC* 9222

■ **UNITED STATES DEPARTMENT OF JUSTICE** p 1512
950 Pennsylvania Ave Nw, Washington DC 20530
Tel (202) 514-2201 *SIC* 9222 9223

CITY OF HOLLYWOOD p 315
2600 Hollywood Blvd Ste B, Hollywood FL 33020
Tel (954) 921-3435 *SIC* 9222

FLORIDA DEPARTMENT OF LEGAL AFFAIRS p 558
107 W Gaines St, Tallahassee FL 32399
Tel (850) 414-3300 *SIC* 8111 9222

FLORIDA OFFICE OF ATTORNEY GENERAL p 559
Pl-01 The Capitol, Tallahassee FL 32399
Tel (850) 414-3300 *SIC* 9222

GEORGIA DEPARTMENT OF JUVENILE JUSTICE p 607
3408 Covington Hwy, Decatur GA 30032
Tel (404) 508-6500 SIC 9222

MONTANA DEPT OF JUSTICE p 986
215 N Sanders St, Helena MT 59601
Tel (406) 444-2026 SIC 9222

NEW JERSEY DEPT OF LAW & PUBLIC SAFETY p 1031
25 Market St Fl 8, Trenton NJ 08611
Tel (609) 292-4925 SIC 9222 9221

ATTORNEY GENERAL NEW YORK STATE p 129
The Capitol, Albany NY 12224
Tel (518) 776-2000 SIC 9222

NORTH CAROLINA DEPARTMENT OF JUSTICE p 1051
114 W Edenton St, Raleigh NC 27603
Tel (919) 779-8213 SIC 9222

ATTORNEY GENERAL OF OHIO p 129
30 E Broad St Fl 17, Columbus OH 43215
Tel (614) 466-6963 SIC 9222

OREGON DEPARTMENT OF JUSTICE p 1093
1162 Court St Ne, Salem OR 97301
Tel (503) 378-4320 SIC 9222

DISTRICT ATTORNEYS GENERAL CONFERENCE TENNESSEE p 443
226 Capitol Blvd Ste 800, Nashville TN 37219
Tel (615) 741-1696 SIC 9222

DISTRICT PUBLIC DEFENDERS CONFERENCE TENNESSEE p 443
211 7th Ave N Ste 320, Nashville TN 37219
Tel (615) 741-5562 SIC 9222

ATTORNEY GENERAL TEXAS p 129
300 W 15th St, Austin TX 78701
Tel (512) 475-4375 SIC 9222

ATTORNEY GENERAL OFFICE OF p 129
1125 Washington St Se, Olympia WA 98501
Tel (360) 753-6200 SIC 9222

SIC 9223 Correctional Institutions

DEPARTMENT OF CORRECTIONS ALASKA p 430
802 3rd St, Douglas AK 99824
Tel (907) 465-4652
SIC 9223 8322 9441 8299

DEPT OF CORRECTIONS ARIZONA p 431
1601 W Jefferson St, Phoenix AZ 85007
Tel (602) 542-5225 SIC 9223

DEPARTMENT OF CORRECTION ARKANSAS p 429
6814 Princeton Pike, White Hall AR 71602
Tel (870) 267-6999 SIC 9223

CALIFORNIA DEPARTMENT OF CORRECTIONS & REHABILITATION p 239
1515 S St, Sacramento CA 95811
Tel (916) 341-7066 SIC 9223

JUVENILE JUSTICE DIVISION CALIFORNIA p 798
1515 S St Ste 502s, Sacramento CA 95811
Tel (916) 323-2848 SIC 9223

COLORADO DEPARTMENT OF CORRECTIONS p 338
2862 S Circle Dr, Colorado Springs CO 80906
Tel (719) 579-9580 SIC 9223

EXECUTIVE OFFICE OF STATE OF COLORADO p 517
136 State Capitol Bldg, Denver CO 80203
Tel (303) 866-2471 SIC 9111 9223

CONNECTICUT DEPARTMENT OF CORRECTION p 356
24 Wolcott Hill Rd, Wethersfield CT 06109
Tel (860) 692-7481 SIC 9223

DELAWARE DEPARTMENT OF CORRECTION p 424
245 Mckee Rd, Dover DE 19904
Tel (302) 857-5317 SIC 9223

■ **FEDERAL BUREAU OF PRISONS** p 533
320 1st St Nw Ste 654, Washington DC 20534
Tel (202) 307-3198 SIC 9223

■ **FEDERAL PRISON INDUSTRIES INC** p 535
320 1st St Nw, Washington DC 20534
Tel (202) 305-3500 SIC 9223

■ **UNITED STATES DEPARTMENT OF JUSTICE** p 1512
950 Pennsylvania Ave Nw, Washington DC 20530
Tel (202) 514-2201 SIC 9222 9223

FLORIDA DEPARTMENT OF CORRECTIONS p 558
501 S Calhoun St, Tallahassee FL 32399
Tel (850) 488-7480 SIC 9223

FLORIDA DEPARTMENT OF JUVENILE JUSTICE p 558
2737 Centerview Dr # 1225, Tallahassee FL 32399
Tel (850) 921-3048 SIC 9223

GEORGIA DEPARTMENT OF CORRECTIONS p 607
300 Patrol Rd, Forsyth GA 31029
Tel (404) 656-4593 SIC 9223

DEPARTMENT OF CORRECTION IDAHO p 429
1299 N Orchard St Ste 110, Boise ID 83706
Tel (208) 658-2000 SIC 9223

DEPARTMENT OF CORRECTIONS ILLINOIS p 430
1301 Concordia Ct, Springfield IL 62702
Tel (217) 557-1030 SIC 9223 9111

INDIANA DEPT OF CORRECTION p 738
302 W Washington St E334, Indianapolis IN 46204
Tel (317) 232-2430 SIC 9223

IOWA DEPARTMENT OF CORRECTIONS p 762
510 E 12th St Rm 4, Des Moines IA 50319
Tel (515) 725-5701 SIC 9223

KANSAS DEPARTMENT OF CORRECTIONS p 803
714 Sw Jackson St Fl 3, Topeka KS 66603
Tel (785) 296-3317 SIC 9223

DEPARTMENT OF CORRECTIONS KENTUCKY p 430
275 E Main St Rm 36, Frankfort KY 40601
Tel (502) 564-4726 SIC 9223

LOUISIANA DEPARTMENT OF PUBLIC SAFETY AND CORRECTIONS p 880
504 Mayflower St, Baton Rouge LA 70802
Tel (225) 342-6740 SIC 9229 9223

JEFFERSON PARISH SHERIFFS OFFICE p 782
1233 Westbank Expy, Harvey LA 70058
Tel (504) 363-5500 SIC 9221 9223

DEPARTMENT OF CORRECTIONS MAINE p 430
25 Tyson Dr 3rd Flr, Augusta ME 04333
Tel (207) 287-2711 SIC 9223

MARYLAND DEPARTMENT OF JUVENILE SERVICES p 914
120 W Fayette St, Baltimore MD 21201
Tel (410) 230-3333 SIC 9223

MARYLAND DEPT OF PUBLIC SAFETY & CORRECTIONAL SERVICES p 914
300 E Joppa Rd Ste 1000, Towson MD 21286
Tel (410) 339-5000 SIC 9223

MASSACHUSETTS DEPARTMENT OF PUBLIC SAFETY p 916
1 Ashburton Pl Rm 2133, Boston MA 02108
Tel (617) 727-7775 SIC 9221 9229 9223

DEPARTMENT OF CORRECTIONS MICHIGAN p 430
206 E Michigan Ave, Lansing MI 48933
Tel (517) 373-0720 SIC 9223

DEPARTMENT OF CORRECTIONS MINNESOTA p 430
1450 Energy Park Dr # 200, Saint Paul MN 55108
Tel (651) 361-7200 SIC 9223

DEPARTMENT OF CORRECTIONS MISSISSIPPI p 430
633 N State St Ste 208, Jackson MS 39202
Tel (601) 359-5600 SIC 9223

DEPARTMENT OF CORRECTIONS MISSOURI p 430
2729 Plaza Dr, Jefferson City MO 65109
Tel (573) 751-2389 SIC 9223

DEPARTMENT OF CORRECTIONS MONTANA p 430
5 S Last Chance Gulch, Helena MT 59601
Tel (406) 444-3930 SIC 9223

NEVADA DEPARTMENT OF CORRECTIONS p 1028
5500 Snyder Ave Bldg 89, Carson City NV 89701
Tel (775) 887-3285 SIC 9223

NEW HAMPSHIRE DEPT OF CORRECTIONS p 1030
105 Pleasant St Fl 4, Concord NH 03301
Tel (603) 271-4053 SIC 9223

COUNTY OF HUDSON p 378
567 Pavonia Ave Fl 4, Jersey City NJ 07306
Tel (201) 795-6000 SIC 9111 9223

NJ DEPARTMENT OF CORRECTIONS p 1045
Stuyvesant Av Whttlesey Rd Whittlesey, Trenton NJ 08618
Tel (609) 292-2162 SIC 9223

CORRECTIONS DEPARTMENT NEW MEXICO p 373
4337 State Highway 14, Santa Fe NM 87508
Tel (505) 827-8793 SIC 9223

NEW YORK DEPARTMENT OF CORRECTIONS AND COMMUNITY SUPERVISION p 1035
1220 Washngtn Ave Bldg 2, Albany NY 12226
Tel (518) 457-8126 SIC 8322 9223

NORTH CAROLINA DEPARTMENT OF PUBLIC SAFETY p 1051
512 N Salisbury St, Raleigh NC 27604
Tel (919) 733-2126 SIC 9223

NORTH CAROLINA DIVISION OF ADULT PROBATION AND PAROLE p 1051
4000 Wake Forest Rd, Raleigh NC 27609
Tel (919) 850-2900 SIC 9223

NORTH CAROLINA DIVISION OF PRISONS p 1051
831 W Morgan St, Raleigh NC 27603
Tel (919) 838-4000 SIC 9223

OHIO DEPARTMENT OF REHABILITATION AND CORRECTION p 1077
770 W Broad St, Columbus OH 43222
Tel (614) 752-1233 SIC 9223

DEPT OF CORRECTIONS OKLAHOMA p 431
3400 N Mtn Lthr Kng Ave, Oklahoma City OK 73111
Tel (405) 425-2500 SIC 9223

OREGON DEPARTMENT OF CORRECTIONS p 1093
2575 Center St Ne, Salem OR 97301
Tel (503) 945-9090 SIC 9223

COMMONWEALTH OF PENNSYLVANIA DEPARTMENT OF CORRECTIONS p 346
1920 Technology Pkwy, Mechanicsburg PA 17050
Tel (717) 728-2573 SIC 9223

RHODE ISLAND AND PROVIDENCE PLANTATIONS DEPARTMENT OF CORRECTIONS p 1231
40 Howard Ave, Cranston RI 02920
Tel (401) 462-2611 SIC 9223

SOUTH CAROLINA DEPARTMENT OF CORRECTIONS (INC) p 1343
4444 Broad River Rd, Columbia SC 29210
Tel (803) 896-8500 SIC 9223

TENNESSEE DEPARTMENT OF CORRECTION p 1438
320 6th Ave N Fl 6, Nashville TN 37243
Tel (615) 741-1000 SIC 9223

PAROLE DIVISION TEXAS p 1117
209 W 14th St Ste 500, Austin TX 78701
Tel (512) 926-7570 SIC 9223

TEXAS DEPARTMENT OF CRIMINAL JUSTICE p 1443
861 Interstate 45 N 227b, Huntsville TX 77320
Tel (936) 295-6371 SIC 9223 9229

DEPARTMENT OF CORRECTIONS UTAH p 430
14717 S Minuteman Dr, Draper UT 84020
Tel (801) 545-5500 SIC 9223

VIRGINIA DEPARTMENT OF CORRECTIONS p 1559
6900 Atmore Dr, Richmond VA 23225
Tel (804) 674-3000 SIC 9223

VIRGINIA DEPARTMENT OF JUVENILE JUSTICE p 1559
7th & Franklin Sts, Richmond VA 23219
Tel (804) 371-0700 SIC 9223

DEPARTMENT OF CORRECTIONS WASHINGTON STATE p 430
7345 Linderson Way Sw, Tumwater WA 98501
Tel (360) 725-8213 SIC 9223

WISCONSIN DEPARTMENT OF CORRECTIONS p 1618
3099 E Washington Ave, Madison WI 53704
Tel (608) 240-5000 SIC 9223

DEPARTMENT OF CORRECTIONS WYOMING p 430
1934 Wyott Dr Ste 100, Cheyenne WY 82007
Tel (307) 777-7208 SIC 9223

SIC 9224 Fire Protection

ORANGE COUNTY FIRE AUTHORITY p 1092
1 Fire Authority Rd, Irvine CA 92602
Tel (714) 573-6000 SIC 9224

BOULDER CITY OF (INC) p 204
1777 Broadway, Boulder CO 80302
Tel (303) 441-3090
SIC 9111 9224 9221 9511

ORANGE COUNTY FIRE & RESCUE p 1092
6590 Amory Ct, Winter Park FL 32792
Tel (407) 836-9112 SIC 9224

CITY OF SALEM p 318
555 Liberty St Se Rm 230, Salem OR 97301
Tel (503) 588-6255 SIC 9111 9224 9221

PUERTO RICO FIREFIGHTERS CORPS p 1191
2432 Calle Loiza, San Juan PR 00913
Tel (787) 725-3444 SIC 9224

ORANGE COUNTY EMERGENCY SERVICES DISTRICT p 1092
2351 Highway 12, Vidor TX 77662
Tel (409) 769-6241 SIC 9224

SIC 9229 Public Order & Safety, NEC

ALABAMA DEPT OF PUBLIC SAFETY p 43
301 S Ripley St, Montgomery AL 36104
Tel (334) 242-4394 SIC 9229

PUBLIC SAFETY ARIZONA p 1189
2102 W Encanto Blvd, Phoenix AZ 85009
Tel (602) 223-2000 SIC 9229

COLORADO DEPARTMENT OF PUBLIC SAFETY p 339
700 Kipling St Ste 1000, Lakewood CO 80215
Tel (303) 239-4400 SIC 9229

CONNECTICUT DEPARTMENT OF PUBLIC SAFETY p 357
1111 Country Club Rd, Middletown CT 06457
Tel (860) 685-8000 SIC 9221 9229

DEPARTMENT OF SAFETY AND HOMELAND SECURITY (DSHS) p 430
303 Transportation Cir, Dover DE 19901
Tel (302) 744-2672 SIC 9221 9229

■ **FEDERAL EMERGENCY MANAGEMENT AGENCY** p 534
500 C St Sw Ocfo, Washington DC 20472
Tel (202) 646-2500 SIC 9229

■ **UNITED STATES SECRET SERVICE** p 1514
950 H St Nw, Washington DC 20223
Tel (202) 406-5708 SIC 9229

GEORGIA DEPARTMENT OF PUBLIC SAFETY p 607
959 E Confederate Ave Se, Atlanta GA 30316
Tel (404) 624-7739 SIC 9229

HAWAII DEPARTMENT OF PUBLIC SAFETY p 668
919 Ala Moana Blvd # 407, Honolulu HI 96814
Tel (808) 587-1288 SIC 9221 9229

JUSTICE AND PUBLIC SAFETY CABINET OF KENTUCKY p 797
125 Holmes St Fl 2, Frankfort KY 40601
Tel (502) 564-7554 SIC 9229

LOUISIANA DEPARTMENT OF PUBLIC SAFETY AND CORRECTIONS p 880
504 Mayflower St, Baton Rouge LA 70802
Tel (225) 342-6740 SIC 9229 9223

MASSACHUSETTS DEPARTMENT OF PUBLIC SAFETY p 916
1 Ashburton Pl Rm 2133, Boston MA 02108
Tel (617) 727-7775 SIC 9221 9229 9223

MINNESOTA DEPARTMENT OF PUBLIC SAFETY p 973
445 Minnesota St, Saint Paul MN 55101
Tel (651) 201-7000 SIC 9229

MISSISSIPPI DEPARTMENT OF PUBLIC SAFETY p 975
1900 E Woodrow Wilson Ave, Jackson MS 39216
Tel (601) 987-1212 SIC 9229 9221

MISSOURI DEPARTMENT OF PUBLIC SAFETY p 976
1101 Riverside Dr 4w, Jefferson City MO 65101
Tel (573) 751-4905 SIC 9229

NEVADA DEPARTMENT OF PUBLIC SAFETY p 1028
555 Wright Way, Carson City NV 89701
Tel (775) 684-4556 SIC 9229

NEW HAMPSHIRE STATE POLICE p 1030
33 Hazen Dr, Concord NH 03305
Tel (603) 223-8500 SIC 9221 9229

NEW MEXICO DEPARTMENT OF PUBLIC SAFETY p 1032
4491 Cerrillos Rd, Santa Fe NM 87507
Tel (505) 827-9000 SIC 9229

HAMILTON COURT JUSTICE OFFICE p 655
1000 Sycamore St Ste 110, Cincinnati OH 45202
Tel (513) 946-6400 SIC 9229

OHIO DEPARTMENT OF PUBLIC SAFETY p 1077
1970 W Broad St Fl 5, Columbus OH 43223
Tel (614) 466-3383 SIC 9229

OKLAHOMA DEPT OF PUBLIC SAFETY p 1079
3600 N Martin Luther Knl, Oklahoma City OK 73111
Tel (405) 425-2424 SIC 9229

SOUTH CAROLINA DEPARTMENT OF PUBLIC SAFETY p 1343
10311 Wilson Blvd, Blythewood SC 29016
Tel (803) 896-9000 SIC 9229

TENNESSEE DEPARTMENT OF SAFETY p 1438
1150 Foster Ave Fl 2, Nashville TN 37243
Tel (615) 251-5166 SIC 9229

CONSOLIDATED NUCLEAR SECURITY LLC p 360
301 Bear Creek Rd, Oak Ridge TN 37830
Tel (865) 576-3456 SIC 9229

TEXAS DEPARTMENT OF PUBLIC SAFETY p 1443
5805 N Lamar Blvd, Austin TX 78752
Tel (512) 424-2000 SIC 9229 9221

TEXAS DEPARTMENT OF CRIMINAL JUSTICE p 1443
861 Interstate 45 N 227b, Huntsville TX 77320
Tel (936) 295-6371 SIC 9223 9229

UTAH DEPARTMENT OF PUBLIC SAFETY p 1536
4501 S Constitution Blvd, Taylorsville UT 84129
Tel (801) 965-4461 SIC 9229

■ **DRUG ENFORCEMENT ADMINISTRATION** p 457
8701 Morrissette Dr, Springfield VA 22152
Tel (202) 307-1000 SIC 9229

WEST VIRGINIA DEPARTMENT OF MILITARY AFFAIRS AND PUBLIC SAFETY p 1596
1900 Kanawha Blvd E Rm 1, Charleston WV 25305
Tel (304) 558-8045 SIC 9711 9221 9229

SIC 9311 Public Finance, Taxation & Monetary Policy

DEPT OF REVENUE ALABAMA p 431
50 N Ripley St Fl 4, Montgomery AL 36130
Tel (334) 242-1170 SIC 9311

DEPT OF REVENUE ARIZONA p 431
1600 W Monroe St, Phoenix AZ 85007
Tel (602) 542-2054 SIC 9311

ARKANSAS DEPT OF FINANCE AND ADMINISTRATION p 109
1509 W 7th St, Little Rock AR 72201
Tel (501) 682-2242 SIC 9311

COUNTY OF BUTTE p 376
25 County Center Dr # 110, Oroville CA 95965
Tel (530) 538-7701 SIC 9311

GRATON ECONOMIC DEVELOPMENT AUTHORITY p 632
915 Golf Course Dr, Rohnert Park CA 94928
Tel (707) 800-7616 SIC 9311

CALIFORNIA STATE BOARD OF EQUALIZATION p 241
450 N St, Sacramento CA 95814
Tel (916) 445-6464 SIC 9311

CONTROLLER CALIFORNIA STATE p 364
300 Capitol Mall Ste 1850, Sacramento CA 95814
Tel (916) 445-2636 SIC 9311

FRANCHISE TAX BOARD CALIFORNIA p 573
9646 Butterfield Way, Sacramento CA 95827
Tel (916) 845-3650 SIC 9311

CONNECTICUT DEPARTMENT OF REVENUE SERVICES p 357
450 Columbus Blvd Ste 1, Hartford CT 06103
Tel (860) 297-5962 SIC 9311

■ **BUREAU OF ENGRAVING AND PRINTING** p 226
14th And C St Sw, Washington DC 20228
Tel (202) 874-2361 SIC 9311

■ **BUREAU OF IMMIGRATION & CUSTOMS ENFORCEMENT** p 226
500 12th St Sw, Washington DC 20536
Tel (202) 732-2427 SIC 9721 9311

FEDERAL DEPOSIT INSURANCE CORP p 534
550 17th St Nw, Washington DC 20429
Tel (877) 275-3342 SIC 6399 9311

■ **FISCAL SERVICE BUREAU OF** p 551
401 14th St Sw Rm 548, Washington DC 20227
Tel (202) 622-7000 SIC 9311

■ **GOVERNMENT ACCOUNTABILITY OFFICE** p 627
441 G St Nw, Washington DC 20548
Tel (202) 512-3000 SIC 9311

■ **INTERNAL REVENUE SERVICE** p 754
1111 Constitution Ave Nw, Washington DC 20224
Tel (202) 803-9000 SIC 9311

■ **UNITED STATES DEPT OF TREASURY** p 1513
1500 Pennsylvania Ave Nw, Washington DC 20220
Tel (202) 622-1100 SIC 9311

■ **UNITED STATES MINT** p 1513
801 9th St Nw, Washington DC 20220
Tel (202) 756-6468 SIC 9311

FLORIDA DEPARTMENT OF REVENUE p 558
2450 Oak Blvd, Tallahassee FL 32399
Tel (850) 617-8600 SIC 9311 9111

GEORGIA DEPARTMENT OF REVENUE p 607
1800 Century Blvd Ne # 1200, Atlanta GA 30345
Tel (877) 423-6711 SIC 9311

DEPARTMENT OF REVENUE ILLINOIS p 430
101 W Jefferson St, Springfield IL 62702
Tel (217) 782-3336 SIC 9311

■ **DEFENSE FINANCE & ACCOUNTING SERVICE** p 422
8899 E 56th St, Indianapolis IN 46249
Tel (317) 212-0585 SIC 9311

COMPTROLLER OF MARYLAND OFFICE OF p 352
80 Calvert St L1, Annapolis MD 21401
Tel (410) 260-7801 SIC 9311

STATE OF MARYLAND TREASURERS OFFICE p 1382
80 Calvert St, Annapolis MD 21401
Tel (800) 974-0468 SIC 9311

ADMINISTRATION AND FINANCE MASSACHUSETTS EXECUTIVE OFFICE FOR p 23
24 Beacon St Ste 373, Boston MA 02133
Tel (617) 727-2040 SIC 9199 9311

MASSACHUSETTS DEPARTMENT OF REVENUE p 916
100 Cambridge St, Boston MA 02114
Tel (617) 626-2201 SIC 9311

LOWELL CITY OF (INC) p 881
375 Merrimack St Rm 27, Lowell MA 01852
Tel (978) 970-4200 SIC 9311

MICHIGAN DEPARTMENT OF TREASURY p 961
430 W Allegan St, Lansing MI 48933
Tel (517) 373-3223 SIC 9311

DEPARTMENT OF REVENUE MINNESOTA p 430
600 Robert St N, Saint Paul MN 55101
Tel (651) 556-3000 SIC 9311

DEPARTMENT OF REVENUE MISSOURI p 430
301 W High St, Jefferson City MO 65101
Tel (573) 751-4450 SIC 9311

DEPARTMENT OF REVENUE MONTANA p 430
125 N Roberts St Fl 34, Helena MT 59601
Tel (406) 444-2460 SIC 9311

COUNTY OF WASHOE p 382
1001 E 9th St Bldg A, Reno NV 89512
Tel (775) 328-2552 SIC 9311

NEW JERSEY DEPARTMENT OF TREASURY p 1031
125 W State St, Trenton NJ 08608
Tel (609) 292-6748 SIC 9311

NEW MEXICO DEPARTMENT OF FINANCE & ADMINISTRATION p 1032
Bataan Memorial Bldg 180, Santa Fe NM 87501
Tel (505) 827-4985 SIC 9311

NEW MEXICO DEPARTMENT OF TAXATION AND REVENUE p 1032
1100 S Saint Francis Dr, Santa Fe NM 87505
Tel (505) 827-0700 SIC 9311

NEW YORK STATE OFFICE OF STATE COMPTROLLER p 1036
110 State St, Albany NY 12207
Tel (518) 474-4044 SIC 9311

TAXATION AND FINANCE DEPARTMENT NEW YORK STATE p 1426
W A Harriman Campus Bldg, Albany NY 12227
Tel (518) 457-2244 SIC 9311

NORTH CAROLINA DEPARTMENT OF REVENUE p 1051
501 N Wilmington St, Raleigh NC 27604
Tel (877) 252-3052 SIC 9311

OHIO DEPARTMENT OF TAXATION p 1077
30 E Broad St Fl 22, Columbus OH 43215
Tel (614) 466-3020 SIC 9311

PUBLIC EMPLOYEE DEFERRED COMPENSATION OHIO p 1189
257 E Town St Ste 457, Columbus OH 43215
Tel (614) 466-7245 SIC 8721 9311

STATE OF OHIO OFFICE OF BUDGET AND MANAGEMENT STATE ACCOUNTING p 1382
30 E Broad St, Columbus OH 43215
Tel (614) 466-4034 SIC 9311

OKLAHOMA OFFICE OF MANAGEMENT AND ENTERPRISE SERVICES p 1080
2300 N Lincoln Blvd # 122, Oklahoma City OK 73105
Tel (405) 521-2141 SIC 9311

OREGON DEPARTMENT OF CONSUMER AND BUSINESS SERVICES p 1093
350 Winter St Ne, Salem OR 97301
Tel (503) 378-4100 SIC 9651 9311

PENNSYLVANIA DEPARTMENT OF REVENUE p 1130
1147 Strawberry Sq, Harrisburg PA 17128
Tel (717) 787-6300 SIC 9311

PUERTO RICO DEPARTMENT OF TREASURY p 1191
10 Paseo Covadonga, San Juan PR 00901
Tel (787) 721-2020 SIC 9311

COMPTROLLER OF PUBLIC ACCOUNTS TEXAS p 352
111 E 17th St Rm 138, Austin TX 78701
Tel (512) 763-8550 SIC 9311

TAX COMMISSION UTAH STATE p 1426
210 N 1950 W, Salt Lake City UT 84134
Tel (801) 297-2200 SIC 9311

VIRGINIA SECRETARY OF FINANCE p 1559
1111 E Broad St Ste 5035, Richmond VA 23219
Tel (804) 786-1148 SIC 9311

WASHINGTON STATE DEPARTMENT OF REVENUE p 1579
1025 Union Ave Se Ste 500, Olympia WA 98501
Tel (360) 570-5900 SIC 9311

WASHINGTON STATE DEPARTMENT OF LABOR AND INDUSTRIES p 1579
7273 Linderson Way Sw, Tumwater WA 98501
Tel (360) 902-5743 SIC 9311

BUREAU OF THE PUBLIC DEBT p 226
200 3rd St 5f, Parkersburg WV 26106
Tel (304) 480-6514 SIC 9311

STATE OF WISCONSIN p 1382
2135 Rimrock Rd, Madison WI 53713
Tel (608) 266-6466 SIC 9311

SIC 9411 Administration Of Educational Programs

ALABAMA COMMUNITY COLLEGE SYSTEM p 43
135 S Union St, Montgomery AL 36130
Tel (334) 262-8734 SIC 9411

DEKALB COUNTY BOARD OF EDUCATION p 423
306 Main St W, Rainsville AL 35986
Tel (256) 638-7265 SIC 9411

ARIZONA BOARD OF REGENTS p 108
2020 N Central Ave # 230, Phoenix AZ 85004
Tel (602) 229-2500 SIC 8221 9411

ARKANSAS DEPARTMENT OF EDUCATION p 109
4 Capitol Mall, Little Rock AR 72201
Tel (501) 682-4475 SIC 9411

GREENFIELD UNION SCHOOL DISTRICT p 638
1624 Fairview Rd, Bakersfield CA 93307
Tel (661) 837-6000 SIC 8211 9411

CALIFORNIA STATE UNIVERSITY CHICO p 241
400 W 1st St, Chico CA 95929
Tel (530) 898-4636 SIC 8221 9411

UNIVERSITY OF CALIFORNIA DAVIS p 1520
1 Shields Ave, Davis CA 95616
Tel (530) 752-1011 SIC 8221 9411

KINGS COUNTY OFFICE OF EDUCATION p 820
1144 W Lacey Blvd, Hanford CA 93230
Tel (559) 589-7026 SIC 9411

CALIFORNIA STATE UNIVERSITY EAST BAY p 241
25800 Carlos Bee Blvd Sa, Hayward CA 94542
Tel (510) 885-3500 SIC 8221 9411

UNIVERSITY OF CALIFORNIA IRVINE p 1520
510 Aldrich Hall, Irvine CA 92697
Tel (949) 824-8343 SIC 8221 9411

UNIVERSITY OF CALIFORNIA SAN DIEGO p 1520
9500 Gilman Dr, La Jolla CA 92093
Tel (858) 534-2230 SIC 8221 9411

CALIFORNIA STATE UNIVERSITY LONG BEACH p 241
1250 N Bellflower Blvd, Long Beach CA 90840
Tel (562) 985-4111 SIC 8221 9411

CALIFORNIA STATE UNIVERSITY SYSTEM p 241
401 Golden Shore, Long Beach CA 90802
Tel (562) 951-4000 SIC 8221 9411

CALIFORNIA STATE UNIVERSITY LOS ANGELES p 241
5151 State University Dr, Los Angeles CA 90032
Tel (323) 343-3000 SIC 8221 9411

UNIVERSITY OF CALIFORNIA LOS ANGELES p 1520
405 Hilgard Ave, Los Angeles CA 90095
Tel (310) 825-4321 SIC 8221 9411

UNIVERSITY OF CALIFORNIA RIVERSIDE ALUMNI ASSOCIATION p 1520
900 University Ave, Riverside CA 92521
Tel (951) 827-1012 SIC 8221 9411

CALIFORNIA DEPARTMENT OF EDUCATION p 240
1430 N St Ste 5602, Sacramento CA 95814
Tel (916) 319-0815 SIC 9411

CALIFORNIA STATE UNIVERSITY SAN BERNARDINO p 241
5500 University Pkwy, San Bernardino CA 92407
Tel (909) 537-5000 SIC 8221 9411

SAN DIEGO STATE UNIVERSITY p 1276
5500 Campanile Dr, San Diego CA 92182
Tel (619) 594-7985 SIC 8221 9411

SAN DIEGO STATE UNIVERSITY FOUNDATION p 1276
5250 Campanile Dr Mc1947, San Diego CA 92182
Tel (619) 594-1900 SIC 8221 9411

SAN FRANCISCO STATE UNIVERSITY p 1276
1600 Holloway Ave, San Francisco CA 94132
Tel (415) 338-1111 SIC 8221 9411

SAN JOSE STATE UNIVERSITY p 1277
1 Washington Sq, San Jose CA 95192
Tel (408) 924-1000 SIC 8221 9411

CALIFORNIA POLYTECHNIC STATE UNIVERSITY p 241
1 Grand Ave, San Luis Obispo CA 93407
Tel (805) 756-7414 SIC 8221 9411

CALIFORNIA STATE UNIVERSITY SAN MARCOS p 241
333 S Twin Oaks Valley Rd, San Marcos CA 92096
Tel (760) 750-4000 SIC 8221 9411

UNIVERSITY OF CALIFORNIA SANTA BARBARA p 1520
Uc Santa Barbara Mosher A, Santa Barbara CA 93106
Tel (805) 893-8000 SIC 8221 9411

YUBA CITY UNIFIED SCHOOL DISTRICT FINANCING CORP p 1640
750 N Palora Ave, Yuba City CA 95991
Tel (530) 822-7601 SIC 9411

DOUGLAS COUNTY SCHOOL DISTRICT p 452
620 Wilcox St, Castle Rock CO 80104
Tel (303) 387-0100 SIC 9411

COLORADO DEPARTMENT OF HIGHER EDUCATION p 338
1560 Broadway Ste 1600, Denver CO 80202
Tel (303) 866-2723 SIC 9411

MERIDEN PUBLIC SCHOOLS p 948
22 Liberty St, Meriden CT 06450
Tel (203) 630-4171 SIC 8211 9411

STRATFORD SCHOOL DISTRICT p 1392
1000 E Broadway, Stratford CT 06615
Tel (203) 381-2012 SIC 9411

RED CLAY CONSOLIDATED SCHOOL DISTRICT p 1215
1502 Spruce Ave, Wilmington DE 19805
Tel (302) 552-3700 SIC 9411

■ **UNITED STATES DEPT OF EDUCATION** p 1513
400 Maryland Ave Sw, Washington DC 20202
Tel (202) 245-7468 SIC 9411

■ **UNITED STATES HOLOCAUST MEMORIAL MUSEUM** p 1513
100 Raoul Wallenberg Pl Sw, Washington DC 20024
Tel (202) 488-0400 SIC 8412 9411

COLUMBIA COUNTY SCHOOL DISTRICT p 340
372 W Duval St, Lake City FL 32055
Tel (386) 755-8000 SIC 8211 9411

MIAMI DADE COLLEGE p 959
300 Ne 2nd Ave Rm 3116, Miami FL 33132
Tel (305) 237-3000 SIC 8222 9411 8221

FLORIDA DEPARTMENT OF CHILDREN & FAMILIES p 558
1317 Winewood Blvd Rm 306, Tallahassee FL 32399
Tel (850) 488-2840 SIC 9441 9411

FLORIDA DEPARTMENT OF EDUCATION p 558
325 W Gaines St Ste 101, Tallahassee FL 32399
Tel (850) 245-0505 SIC 9411

GEORGIA DEPARTMENT OF EDUCATION p 607
205 Jesse Hill Jr Dr Se, Atlanta GA 30334
Tel (404) 656-2497 SIC 8211 9411

CATOOSA COUNTY PUBLIC SCHOOLS p 267
307 Cleveland St, Ringgold GA 30736
Tel (706) 965-3977 SIC 8211 9411

HAWAII SCHOOL DISTRICT p 669
75 Aupuni St Rm 203, Hilo HI 96720
Tel (808) 974-6600 SIC 8211 9411

HAWAII STATE DEPARTMENT OF EDUCATION p 669
1390 Miller St Rm 305309, Honolulu HI 96813
Tel (808) 586-3310 SIC 9411

LEEWARD OAHU SCHOOL DISTRICT p 852
601 Kamokila Blvd Ste 418, Kapolei HI 96707
Tel (808) 564-6066 SIC 8211 9411

KAUAI SCHOOL DISTRICT p 805
3060 Eiwa St Ste 305, Lihue HI 96766
Tel (808) 274-3502 SIC 8211 9411

MAUI SCHOOL DISTRICT p 921
54 S High St Fl 4, Wailuku HI 96793
Tel (808) 984-8001 SIC 8211 9411

MCHENRY COUNTY COLLEGE p 929
8900 Us Highway 14, Crystal Lake IL 60012
Tel (815) 455-3700 SIC 8222 8221 9411

ELGIN COMMUNITY COLLEGE p 486
1700 Spartan Dr, Elgin IL 60123
Tel (847) 697-1000 SIC 8222 8221 9411

ILLINOIS COMMUNITY COLLEGE SYSTEM p 732
401 E Capitol Ave, Springfield IL 62701
Tel (217) 528-2858 SIC 8221 9411

ILLINOIS STATE BOARD OF EDUCATION p 732
100 N 1st St Ste 1, Springfield IL 62702
Tel (217) 782-4321 SIC 9411

KENTUCKY DEPT OF TECHNICAL EDUCATION p 812
500 Mero St Ste 2, Frankfort KY 40601
Tel (502) 564-4286 SIC 9411 9441

KENTUCKY EDUCATION AND WORKFORCE DEVELOPMENT CABINET p 812
500 Mero St Ste 3, Frankfort KY 40601
Tel (502) 564-0372 SIC 9411

LOUISIANA BOARD OF REGENTS p 880
1201 N 3rd St Ste 6-200, Baton Rouge LA 70802
Tel (225) 342-4253 SIC 9411

LOUISIANA DEPARTMENT OF PUBLIC EDUCATION p 880
1201 N 3rd St, Baton Rouge LA 70802
Tel (225) 342-3836 SIC 9411

SOUTHERN UNIVERSITY AGRICULTURAL & MECHANICAL COLLEGE p 1350
G Leon Netherville Dr, Baton Rouge LA 70813
Tel (225) 771-5021 SIC 8221 9411

UNIVERSITIES OF LOUISIANA SYSTEM p 1518
1201 N 3rd St Ste 7300, Baton Rouge LA 70802
Tel (225) 342-6950 SIC 9411

GRAMBLING STATE UNIVERSITY p 629
403 Main St, Grambling LA 71245
Tel (318) 274-2558 SIC 8221 9411

RECOVERY SCHOOL DISTRICT p 1215
1615 Poydras St Ste 400, New Orleans LA 70112
Tel (504) 373-6200 SIC 9411

MARYLAND STATE DEPARTMENT OF EDUCATION p 915
200 W Baltimore St, Baltimore MD 21201
Tel (410) 767-0462 SIC 9411

MASSACHUSETTS BOARD OF HIGHER EDUCATION SYSTEM p 916
1 Ashburton Pl Rm 1401, Boston MA 02108
Tel (617) 727-7785 SIC 9411

MINNESOTA STATE COLLEGES AND UNIVERSITIES p 974
30 7th St E Ste 350, Saint Paul MN 55101
Tel (651) 296-8012 SIC 8221 9411

JONES COUNTY SCHOOL DISTRICT p 792
5204 Highway 11 N, Ellisville MS 39437
Tel (601) 649-5201 SIC 8211 9411

GREENVILLE PUBLIC SCHOOLS INC p 638
412 S Main St, Greenville MS 38701
Tel (662) 334-7000 SIC 8211 9411

MISSOURI DEPARTMENT OF ELEMENTARY AND SECONDARY EDUCATION p 976
205 Jefferson St, Jefferson City MO 65101
Tel (573) 751-4212 SIC 9411

HALL COUNTY SCHOOL DISTRICT 2 p 654
123 S Webb Rd, Grand Island NE 68803
Tel (308) 385-5886 SIC 8211 9411

BOARD OF REGENTS NEVADA SYSTEM OF HIGHER EDUCATION p 195
4505 S Maryland Pkwy, Las Vegas NV 89154
Tel (702) 895-4727 SIC 8221 9411

UNIVERSITY OF NEVADA LAS VEGAS p 1523
4505 S Maryland Pkwy, Las Vegas NV 89154
Tel (702) 895-3354 SIC 8221 9411

NEVADA SYSTEM OF HIGHER EDUCATION p 1028
2601 Enterprise Rd, Reno NV 89512
Tel (775) 784-4901 SIC 8221 9411

UNIVERSITY OF NEVADA RENO p 1523
1664 N Virginia St, Reno NV 89557
Tel (775) 784-1110 SIC 8221 9411

UNIVERSITY OF MEDICINE AND DENTISTRY OF NJ (INC) p 1523
150 Bergen St, Newark NJ 07103
Tel (973) 972-4400 SIC 8221 9411

EDUCATIONAL SERVICES COMMISSION OF NEW JERSEY p 479
1660 Stelton Rd, Piscataway NJ 08854
Tel (732) 777-9848 SIC 9411

NEW JERSEY COMMISSION ON HIGHER EDUCATION p 1031
20 W State St Fl 7, Trenton NJ 08608
Tel (609) 292-4310 SIC 9411

EDUCATION DEPARTMENT NEW YORK STATE p 479
89 Washington Ave, Albany NY 12234
Tel (518) 474-3852 SIC 8299 9411

STATE UNIVERSITY OF NEW YORK p 1383
353 Broadway, Albany NY 12246
Tel (518) 320-1100 SIC 8221 9411

UNIVERSITY AT ALBANY p 1518
1400 Washington Ave, Albany NY 12222
Tel (518) 442-3300 SIC 8221 9411

BINGHAMTON UNIVERSITY p 183
4400 Vestal Pkwy, Binghamton NY 13902
Tel (607) 777-2000 SIC 8221 9411

SUNY DOWNSTATE MEDICAL CENTER p 1405
450 Clarkson Ave, Brooklyn NY 11203
Tel (718) 270-1000 SIC 8221 9411

SUNY UNIVERSITY AT BUFFALO p 1405
501 Capen Hall, Buffalo NY 14260
Tel (716) 645-2901 SIC 8221 9411

SUNY COLLEGE AT CORTLAND p 1405
38 Cheney Hall, Cortland NY 13045
Tel (607) 753-2011 SIC 8221 9411

SUNY COLLEGE AT FREDONIA p 1405
280 Central Ave, Fredonia NY 14063
Tel (716) 673-3111 SIC 8221 9411

NASSAU COMMUNITY COLLEGE p 1008
1 Education Dr, Garden City NY 11530
Tel (516) 572-7501 SIC 8222 9411

LANCASTER CENTRAL SCHOOLS DISTRICT p 841
177 Central Ave, Lancaster NY 14086
Tel (716) 686-3200 SIC 8211 9411

FASHION INSTITUTE OF TECHNOLOGY p 531
7th Ave 27th St Rm C908, New York NY 10001
Tel (212) 217-7999 SIC 8222 9411

SUNY COLLEGE AT ONEONTA p 1405
108 Ravine Pkwy, Oneonta NY 13820
Tel (607) 436-3500 SIC 8221 9411

SUNY COLLEGE AT OSWEGO p 1405
702 Culkin Hall, Oswego NY 13126
Tel (315) 312-2222 SIC 8221 9411

DUTCHESS COMMUNITY COLLEGE p 463
53 Pendell Rd, Poughkeepsie NY 12601
Tel (845) 431-8000 SIC 8222 9411

MONROE COMMUNITY COLLEGE p 985
1000 E Henrietta Rd, Rochester NY 14623
Tel (585) 292-2000 SIC 8222 9411

SUFFOLK COUNTY COMMUNITY COLLEGE p 1396
533 College Rd, Selden NY 11784
Tel (631) 451-4110 SIC 8222 9411

STONY BROOK UNIVERSITY p 1391
100 Nicolls Rd, Stony Brook NY 11794
Tel (631) 632-6000 SIC 8221 9411

ONONDAGA COMMUNITY COLLEGE p 1088
4585 W Seneca Tpke, Syracuse NY 13215
Tel (315) 498-2622 SIC 8222 9411

UPSTATE UNIVERSITY MEDICAL ASSOCIATES AT SYRACUSE INC p 1530
750 E Adams St, Syracuse NY 13210
Tel (315) 464-7087 SIC 8221 9411 8231

HUDSON VALLEY COMMUNITY COLLEGE p 717
80 Vandenburgh Ave Ste 1, Troy NY 12180
Tel (518) 629-4822 SIC 8222 9411

WESTCHESTER COMMUNITY COLLEGE p 1596
75 Grasslands Rd, Valhalla NY 10595
Tel (914) 606-6600 SIC 8222 9411

CENTRAL PIEDMONT COMMUNITY COLLEGE p 279
1201 Elizabeth Ave, Charlotte NC 28204
Tel (704) 330-2722 SIC 8222 9411

FAYETTEVILLE TECHNICAL COMMUNITY COLLEGE FOUNDATION INC p 532
2201 Hull Rd, Fayetteville NC 28303
Tel (910) 678-8400 SIC 8222 9411

NORTH CAROLINA COMMUNITY COLLEGE SYSTEM p 1051
200 W Jones St, Raleigh NC 27603
Tel (919) 807-7100 SIC 8222 9411

WAKE TECHNICAL COMMUNITY COLLEGE FOUNDATION INC p 1572
9101 Fayetteville Rd, Raleigh NC 27603
Tel (919) 866-5000 SIC 8222 9411

CAPE FEAR COMMUNITY COLLEGE p 248
411 N Front St, Wilmington NC 28401
Tel (910) 362-7000 SIC 8222 9411

FORSYTH TECHNICAL COMMUNITY COLLEGE INC p 568
2100 Silas Creek Pkwy, Winston Salem NC 27103
Tel (336) 723-0371 SIC 8222 9411

BLOOMSBURG UNIVERSITY FOUNDATION INC p 190
400 E 2nd St, Bloomsburg PA 17815
Tel (570) 389-4000 SIC 8221 9411

EAST STROUDSBURG UNIVERSITY p 471
200 Prospect St Ste 1, East Stroudsburg PA 18301
Tel (570) 422-3211 SIC 8221 9411

DEPT OF EDUCATION PENNSYLVANIA p 431
333 Market St, Harrisburg PA 17101
Tel (717) 787-5820 SIC 9411

PENNSYLVANIA HIGHER EDUCATION ASSISTANCE AGENCY p 1130
1200 N 7th St, Harrisburg PA 17102
Tel (717) 720-2700 SIC 9411

STATE SYSTEM OF HIGHER EDUCATION OF COMMONWEALTH OF PENNSYLVANIA p 1383
2986 N 2nd St, Harrisburg PA 17110
Tel (717) 720-4000 SIC 9411

INDIANA UNIVERSITY OF PENNSYLVANIA p 739
1011 S Dr Room 201 Sutton, Indiana PA 15705
Tel (724) 357-2200 SIC 8221 9411

MILLERSVILLE UNIVERSITY OF PENNSYLVANIA p 971
1 S George St, Millersville PA 17551
Tel (717) 872-3011 SIC 8221 9411

TRUSTEES OF UNIVERSITY OF PENNSYLVANIA p 1488
3451 Walnut St, Philadelphia PA 19104
Tel (215) 898-6301 *SIC* 8221 9411

BERKS COUNTY INTERMEDIATE UNIT p 175
1111 Commons Blvd, Reading PA 19605
Tel (610) 987-2248 *SIC* 9411

SLIPPERY ROCK UNIVERSITY p 1331
1 Morrow Way, Slippery Rock PA 16057
Tel (724) 738-9000 *SIC* 8221 9411

WEST CHESTER UNIVERSITY OF PENNSYLVANIA p 1594
700 S High St, West Chester PA 19383
Tel (610) 436-1000 *SIC* 8221 9411

DEPARTMENT OF EDUCATION OF PUERTO RICO p 430
150 Calle Federico Costa, San Juan PR 00918
Tel (787) 759-2000 *SIC* 9411

PAWTUCKET SCHOOL DEPARTMENT p 1122
286 Main St, Pawtucket RI 02860
Tel (401) 729-6300 *SIC* 8211 9411

SC STATE BOARD FOR TECHNICAL AND COMPREHENSIVE EDUCATION p 1285
111 Executive Center Dr # 1, Columbia SC 29210
Tel (803) 896-5280 *SIC* 9411

SOUTH CAROLINA DEPARTMENT OF EDUCATION p 1343
1429 Senate St, Columbia SC 29201
Tel (803) 734-8500 *SIC* 9411

SOUTH CAROLINA STATE UNIVERSITY p 1343
300 College Ave, Orangeburg SC 29115
Tel (803) 536-7000 *SIC* 8221 9411

UNIVERSITY OF SOUTH DAKOTA p 1525
414 E Clark St, Vermillion SD 57069
Tel (605) 677-5011 *SIC* 8221 9411

HAMILTON COUNTY ECONOMIC DEVELOPMENT FOUNDATION INC p 655
3074 Hickory Valley Rd, Chattanooga TN 37421
Tel (423) 209-8400 *SIC* 9411

TENNESSEE DEPARTMENT OF EDUCATION p 1438
710 James Robertson Pkwy, Nashville TN 37243
Tel (615) 741-5158 *SIC* 9411

EDUCATION AGENCY TEXAS p 479
1701 Congress Ave, Austin TX 78701
Tel (512) 463-9734 *SIC* 8211 9411

EDGEWOOD INDEPENDENT SCHOOL DISTRICT 903 p 478
804 E Pine St, Edgewood TX 75117
Tel (903) 896-4332 *SIC* 8211 9411

CLINT INDEPENDENT SCHOOL DISTRICT p 326
14521 Horizon Blvd, El Paso TX 79928
Tel (915) 926-4000 *SIC* 8211 9411

■ DEPARTMENT OF DEFENSE EDUCATION ACTIVITY p 430
4800 Mark Center Dr, Alexandria VA 22350
Tel (571) 372-1337 *SIC* 9711 9411

NORFOLK STATE UNIVERSITY p 1048
700 Park Ave, Norfolk VA 23504
Tel (757) 823-8600 *SIC* 8221 9411

OLD DOMINION UNIVERSITY p 1080
5115 Hampton Blvd, Norfolk VA 23529
Tel (757) 683-3000 *SIC* 8221 9411

VIRGINIA STATE UNIVERSITY p 1559
1 Hayden Dr, Petersburg VA 23803
Tel (804) 524-5000 *SIC* 8221 9411

STATE COUNCIL OF HIGHER EDUCATION FOR VIRGINIA p 1380
101 N 14th St Fl 9, Richmond VA 23219
Tel (804) 225-2627 *SIC* 9411

VIRGINIA SECRETARY OF EDUCATION p 1559
1111 E Broad St Fl 5, Richmond VA 23219
Tel (804) 786-1151 *SIC* 9411

COLLEGE OF WILLIAM & MARY p 337
261 Richmond Rd, Williamsburg VA 23185
Tel (757) 221-3966 *SIC* 8221 9411

ISSAQUAH SCHOOL DISTRICT 411 p 767
565 Nw Holly St, Issaquah WA 98027
Tel (425) 837-7000 *SIC* 8211 9411

KENNEWICK SCHOOL DISTRICT 17 p 811
1000 W 4th Ave, Kennewick WA 99336
Tel (509) 222-5000 *SIC* 8211 9411

WEST VIRGINIA DEPARTMENT OF EDUCATION AND ARTS p 1596
1900 Kanawha Blvd E # 358, Charleston WV 25305
Tel (304) 558-2440 *SIC* 9411

SIC 9431 Administration Of Public Health Programs

ALABAMA DEPARTMENT OF PUBLIC HEALTH p 43
201 Monroe St Ste 1050, Montgomery AL 36104
Tel (334) 206-5300 *SIC* 9431

HARDIN TAYLOR SECURE MEDICAL FACILITY p 661
1301 Jack Warner Pkwy Ne, Tuscaloosa AL 35404
Tel (205) 556-7060 *SIC* 8062 9431

ALASKA DEPARTMENT OF HEALTH AND SOCIAL SERVICES p 45
350 Main St Rm 427, Juneau AK 99801
Tel (907) 465-3030 *SIC* 9431 9441

HEALTH SERVICES DEPARTMENT p 676
150 N 18th Ave Ste 163, Phoenix AZ 85007
Tel (602) 542-1025 *SIC* 9431

ARKANSAS DEPARTMENT OF HEALTH p 109
4815 W Markham St, Little Rock AR 72205
Tel (501) 661-2000 *SIC* 9431

CALIFORNIA DEPARTMENT OF DEVELOPMENTAL SERVICES p 239
1600 9th St, Sacramento CA 95814
Tel (916) 654-1690 *SIC* 9431

CALIFORNIA DEPARTMENT OF PUBLIC HEALTH p 240
1615 Capitol Ave, Sacramento CA 95814
Tel (916) 558-1700 *SIC* 9431

CALIFORNIA DEPARTMENT OF REHABILITATION p 240
721 Capitol Mall Fl 6, Sacramento CA 95814
Tel (916) 558-5683 *SIC* 9431

CALIFORNIA DEPARTMENT OF STATE HOSPITALS p 240
1600 9th St Ste 120, Sacramento CA 95814
Tel (916) 654-3890 *SIC* 9431

CALIFORNIA HEALTH & HUMAN SERVCS AGENCY p 240
1600 9th St Ste 460, Sacramento CA 95814
Tel (916) 654-3454 *SIC* 9431 9441

DEPARTMENT OF HEALTH CARE SERVICES p 430
1501 Capitol Ave, Sacramento CA 95814
Tel (916) 445-4171 *SIC* 9431

COUNTY OF ORANGE p 380
333 W Santa Ana Blvd 3f, Santa Ana CA 92701
Tel (714) 834-6200 *SIC* 9431

COLORADO DEPARTMENT OF PUBLIC HEALTH AND ENVIRONMENT p 339
4300 E Cherry Creek S Dr, Denver CO 80246
Tel (303) 692-2000 *SIC* 9431 9511

CONNECTICUT DEPARTMENT OF DEVELOPMENTAL SERVICES p 356
460 Capitol Ave, Hartford CT 06106
Tel (860) 424-3000 *SIC* 9431

CONNECTICUT DEPARTMENT OF MENTAL HEALTH AND ADDICTION SERVICES p 357
410 Capitol Ave Fl 4, Hartford CT 06106
Tel (860) 418-7000 *SIC* 9431

DELAWARE DEPT OF HEALTH AND SOCIAL SERVICES p 424
1901 N Dupont Hwy, New Castle DE 19720
Tel (302) 255-9040 *SIC* 9431 9441

■ UNITED STATES DEPARTMENT OF HEALTH & HUMAN SERVICES p 1512
200 Independence Ave Sw, Washington DC 20201
Tel (202) 401-2281 *SIC* 9431

FLORIDA DEPARTMENT OF HEALTH p 558
4052 Bald Cypress Way, Tallahassee FL 32399
Tel (850) 245-4500 *SIC* 9431 8399

■ CENTERS FOR DISEASE CONTROL AND PREVENTION p 276
1600 Clifton Rd Ne, Atlanta GA 30329
Tel (404) 639-3311 *SIC* 9431

DEPARTMENT OF BEHAVIORAL HEALTH AND DEVELOPMENTAL DISABILITIES p 429
2 Peachtree St Nw, Atlanta GA 30303
Tel (404) 657-1650 *SIC* 9431

GEORGIA DEPARTMENT OF PUBLIC HEALTH p 607
2 Peachtree St Nw Fl 15, Atlanta GA 30303
Tel (404) 657-2700 *SIC* 9431

STATE HAWAII DEPARTMENT OF HEALTH p 1381
1250 Punchbowl St, Honolulu HI 96813
Tel (808) 586-4400 *SIC* 9431

IDAHO DEPARTMENT OF HEALTH AND WELFARE p 728
450 W State St Fl 9, Boise ID 83702
Tel (208) 334-5500 *SIC* 9431

COOK COUNTY BUREAU OF HEALTH SERVICES p 365
1900 W Polk St Ste 220, Chicago IL 60612
Tel (312) 864-7571 *SIC* 9431

ILLINOIS DEPARTMENT OF HUMAN SERVICES p 732
401 S Clinton St, Chicago IL 60607
Tel (312) 793-1547 *SIC* 9431

ILLINOIS DEPARTMENT OF PUBLIC HEALTH p 732
535 W Jefferson St Lbby, Springfield IL 62702
Tel (217) 785-4302 *SIC* 9431

INDIANA STATE DEPARTMENT OF HEALTH p 738
2 N Meridian St Ste 1, Indianapolis IN 46204
Tel (317) 233-1325 *SIC* 9431

KANSAS DEPARTMENT FOR CHILDREN AND FAMILIES p 803
915 Sw Harrison St, Topeka KS 66612
Tel (785) 368-6358 *SIC* 9441 9431

DEPARTMENT OF COMMUNITY BASED SERVICES p 429
275 E Main St Ste 3wa, Frankfort KY 40601
Tel (502) 564-3703 *SIC* 9431 9441

HEALTH & FAMILY SERVICES KENTUCKY CABINET FOR p 673
275 E Main St B, Frankfort KY 40601
Tel (502) 564-5497 *SIC* 9431

LOUISIANA DEPARTMENT OF HEALTH AND HOSPITALS p 880
628 N 4th St, Baton Rouge LA 70802
Tel (225) 342-9500 *SIC* 9431

MAINE DEPARTMENT OF HEALTH AND HUMAN SERVICES p 898
221 State St, Augusta ME 04330
Tel (207) 287-1716 *SIC* 9441 9431

ME DEPT OF BEHAVIORAL AND DEVELOPMENTAL SERVICES p 933
40 State House Sta, Augusta ME 04333
Tel (207) 287-4200 *SIC* 9431

■ CENTERS FOR MEDICARE AND MEDICAID SERVICES p 276
7500 Sec Blvd Ms C31103, Baltimore MD 21244
Tel (410) 786-3000 *SIC* 9431

MARYLAND DEPARTMENT OF HEALTH & MENTAL HYGIENE p 914
201 W Preston St Fl 5, Baltimore MD 21201
Tel (410) 767-6500 *SIC* 9431

■ NATIONAL INSTITUTES OF HEALTH p 1013
9000 Rockville Pike # 1, Bethesda MD 20892
Tel (301) 496-4000 *SIC* 8062 9431

■ HEALTH RESOURCES & SERVICES ADMINISTRATION p 675
5600 Fishers Ln, Rockville MD 20852
Tel (301) 443-5460 *SIC* 9431

■ FOOD & DRUG ADMINISTRATION p 563
10903 Nh Ave Ste 2217, Silver Spring MD 20903
Tel (301) 796-5000 *SIC* 9431

■ OFFICE OF REGULATORY AFFAIRS p 1075
10903 Nh Ave Wo31 Rm 3528, Silver Spring MD 20993
Tel (301) 796-8800 *SIC* 9431

MASSACHUSETTS DEPT OF MENTAL HEALTH p 916
25 Staniford St, Boston MA 02114
Tel (617) 626-8000 *SIC* 9431

MASSACHUSETTS DEPT OF MENTAL RETARDATION p 916
500 Harrison Ave Ste 1r, Boston MA 02118
Tel (617) 727-5608 *SIC* 9431

MASSACHUSETTS DEPT OF PUBLIC HEALTH p 916
250 Washington St, Boston MA 02108
Tel (617) 624-6000 *SIC* 9431

MASSACHUSETTS EXECUTIVE OFFICE OF HEALTH AND HUMAN SERVICES p 916
1 Ashburton Pl Rm 1111, Boston MA 02108
Tel (617) 573-1600 *SIC* 9431 9441

MICHIGAN DEPARTMENT OF COMMUNITY HEALTH p 960
201 Townsend St Fl 7, Lansing MI 48933
Tel (517) 241-1193 *SIC* 9431

MICHIGAN DEPARTMENT OF HEALTH & HUMAN SERVICES p 961
201 Townsend St, Lansing MI 48933
Tel (517) 373-3740 *SIC* 9431 9441

DEPARTMENT OF HEALTH MINNESOTA p 430
625 Robert St N, Saint Paul MN 55155
Tel (651) 201-5000 *SIC* 9431

MISSISSIPPI DEPARTMENT OF MENTAL HEALTH p 975
239 N Lamar St Ste 1101, Jackson MS 39201
Tel (601) 359-1288 *SIC* 9431

MISSOURI DEPARTMENT OF HEALTH AND SENIOR SERVICES p 976
920 Wildwood Dr, Jefferson City MO 65109
Tel (573) 751-6014 *SIC* 9431

MISSOURI DEPARTMENT OF MENTAL HEALTH p 976
1706 E Elm St, Jefferson City MO 65101
Tel (573) 751-4122 *SIC* 9431

MONTANA DEPARTMENT OF PUBLIC HEALTH AND HUMAN SERVICES p 986
111 N Sanders St Rm 6, Helena MT 59601
Tel (406) 444-4228 *SIC* 9431

NEVADA DEPARTMENT OF HEALTH AND HUMAN SERVICES p 1028
4126 Tech Way Ste 100, Carson City NV 89706
Tel (775) 684-4000 *SIC* 9431

NEW HAMPSHIRE DEPT OF HEALTH AND HUMAN SERVICES p 1030
129 Pleasant St, Concord NH 03301
Tel (603) 271-4688 *SIC* 9431 9441

NEW JERSEY DEPARTMENT OF HEALTH p 1031
369 S Warren St, Trenton NJ 08608
Tel (609) 292-6915 *SIC* 9431

NEW MEXICO DEPARTMENT OF HEALTH p 1032
1190 S Saint Francis Dr, Santa Fe NM 87505
Tel (505) 827-2613 *SIC* 9431

NEW YORK DEPARTMENT OF HEALTH p 1035
Empire State Plaza, Albany NY 12237
Tel (518) 474-2011 *SIC* 9431

NEW YORK OFFICE OF ALCOHOLISM & SUBSTANCE ABUSE SERVICES p 1035
1450 Western Ave, Albany NY 12203
Tel (518) 457-2061 *SIC* 9431

NEW YORK STATE OFFICE OF MENTAL HEALTH p 1036
44 Holland Ave, Albany NY 12208
Tel (518) 474-4403 *SIC* 9431

PEOPLE WITH DEVELOPMENTAL DISABILITIES NEW YORK STATE OFFICE FOR p 1132
44 Holland Ave, Albany NY 12208
Tel (518) 473-1997 *SIC* 9431

LONG ISLAND COLLEGE HOSPITAL INC p 876
450 Clarkson Ave, Brooklyn NY 11203
Tel (718) 780-1000 *SIC* 8062 9431

WESTERN NEW YORK DEVELOPMENTAL DISABILITIES SERVICES OFFICE p 1599
1200 East And West Rd, West Seneca NY 14224
Tel (716) 517-2000 *SIC* 9431

CENTRAL REGIONAL HOSPITAL p 280
300 Veazey Dr, Butner NC 27509
Tel (919) 575-7211 *SIC* 8062 9431

DEPARTMENT OF HEALTH OHIO p 430
246 N High St, Columbus OH 43215
Tel (614) 466-3543 *SIC* 9431

OHIO DEPARTMENT OF MENTAL HEALTH AND ADDICTION SERVICES p 1077
30 E Broad St Fl 11, Columbus OH 43215
Tel (614) 466-2337 *SIC* 9431

HEALTH DEPARTMENT OKLAHOMA STATE p 674
1000 Ne 10th St, Oklahoma City OK 73117
Tel (405) 271-5600 *SIC* 9431

OKLAHOMA DEPARTMENT OF MENTAL HEALTH AND SUBSTANCE ABUSE SERVICES p 1079
1200 Ne 13th St, Oklahoma City OK 73117
Tel (405) 522-3878 *SIC* 8399 9431

OKLAHOMA DEPT OF HUMAN SERVICES p 1079
2400 N Lincoln Blvd, Oklahoma City OK 73105
Tel (405) 521-3646 *SIC* 9431 9441

OREGON DEPARTMENT OF HUMAN SERVICES p 1093
500 Summer St Ne Dept 4, Salem OR 97301
Tel (503) 945-5944 *SIC* 9431 9441

DEPARTMENT OF HEALTH PENNSYLVANIA p 430
625 Forster St, Harrisburg PA 17120
Tel (717) 787-6325 *SIC* 9431

ADMINISTRACION DE FAMILIAS Y NINOS p 23
Ave Ponce De Leon Stp2, San Juan PR 00907
Tel (787) 625-4900 *SIC* 9431

DEPARTMENT OF BEHAVIORAL HEALTHCARE DEVELOPMENTAL DISABILITIES AND HOSPITALS p 429
14 Harrington Rd, Cranston RI 02920
Tel (401) 462-3201 *SIC* 9431

SOUTH CAROLINA DEPARTMENT OF DISABILITIES AND SPECIAL NEEDS p 1343
3440 Harden Street Ext, Columbia SC 29203
Tel (803) 898-9600 *SIC* 9431

SOUTH CAROLINA DEPARTMENT OF HEALTH AND ENVIRONMENTAL CONTROL p 1343
2600 Bull St, Columbia SC 29201
Tel (803) 898-3510 *SIC* 9431

SOUTH CAROLINA DEPARTMENT OF MENTAL HEALTH p 1343
2414 Bull St, Columbia SC 29201
Tel (803) 898-8581 *SIC* 9431

TENNESSEE DEPARTMENT OF MENTAL HEALTH & SUBSTANCE ABUSE SERVICES p 1438
500 Deaderick St, Nashville TN 37243
Tel (615) 770-0464 *SIC* 9431

TENNESSEE DEPT OF HEALTH p 1438
710 James Robertson Pkwy, Nashville TN 37243
Tel (615) 741-3111 *SIC* 9431

HEALTH AND HUMAN SERVICES COMMISSION TEXAS p 674
4900 N Lamar Blvd, Austin TX 78751
Tel (512) 424-6500 *SIC* 9441 9431

TEXAS DEPARTMENT OF STATE HEALTH SERVICES p 1443
1100 W 49th St, Austin TX 78756
Tel (512) 776-6946 *SIC* 9431

PARKLAND HEALTH AND HOSPITAL SYSTEM AUXILIARY p 1116
5200 Harry Hines Blvd, Dallas TX 75235
Tel (214) 590-4123 *SIC* 9431

DEPARTMENT OF HEALTH AND HUMAN SERVICES p 430
8000 N Stadium Dr Fl 8, Houston TX 77054
Tel (713) 794-9370 *SIC* 9431

DEPARTMENT OF HEALTH UTAH p 430
288 N 1460 W, Salt Lake City UT 84116
Tel (801) 538-6111 *SIC* 9431

■ DEFENSE HEALTH AGENCY p 422
7700 Arlington Blvd # 5101, Falls Church VA 22042
Tel (703) 681-1730 *SIC* 9431 9711

VIRGINIA DEPARTMENT OF HEALTH p 1559
109 Governor St Ste 1221, Richmond VA 23219
Tel (804) 864-7045 *SIC* 9431

VIRGINIA SECRETARY OF HEALTH AND HUMAN RESOURCES p 1559
202 E 9th St, Richmond VA 23224
Tel (804) 786-7765 *SIC* 9431 9441

WASHINGTON STATE DEPARTMENT OF HEALTH p 1579
101 Israel Rd Se, Tumwater WA 98501
Tel (360) 236-4300 *SIC* 9431

WEST VIRGINIA DEPARTMENT OF HEALTH AND HUMAN RESOURCES p 1596
1 Davis Sq Ste 100e, Charleston WV 25301
Tel (304) 558-0684 *SIC* 9431 9441

WISCONSIN DEPARTMENT OF HEALTH SERVICES p 1618
1 W Wilson St Rm 650, Madison WI 53703
Tel (608) 266-1865 *SIC* 9431 9441

WYOMING DEPARTMENT OF HEALTH p 1630
2300 Capitol Ave Ste 1, Cheyenne WY 82001
Tel (307) 777-6780 *SIC* 9431

SIC 9441 Administration Of Social, Human Resource & Income Programs

ALABAMA DEPARTMENT OF LABOR p 43
649 Monroe St, Montgomery AL 36131
Tel (334) 242-8055 *SIC* 9441

ALABAMA DEPT OF HUMAN RESOURCES p 43
50 N Ripley St, Montgomery AL 36130
Tel (334) 242-1310 *SIC* 9441

PUBLIC EMPLOYEES INDIVIDUAL RETIREMENT ACCOUNT FUND/DEFERRED COMPENSATION PLAN p 1189
201 S Union St, Montgomery AL 36104
Tel (334) 517-7000 *SIC* 9441

DEPARTMENT OF CORRECTIONS ALASKA p 430
802 3rd St, Douglas AK 99824
Tel (907) 465-4652
SIC 9223 8322 9441 8299

ALASKA DEPARTMENT OF HEALTH AND SOCIAL SERVICES p 45
350 Main St Rm 427, Juneau AK 99801
Tel (907) 465-3030 *SIC* 9431 9441

ARIZONA DEPT OF ECONOMIC SECURITY p 109
1717 W Jefferson St, Phoenix AZ 85007
Tel (602) 542-7166 *SIC* 9441

ARKANSAS DEPARTMENT OF HUMAN SERVICES p 109
700 Main St, Little Rock AR 72201
Tel (501) 682-1001 *SIC* 9441

CALIFORNIA DEPARTMENT OF EMPLOYMENT DEVELOPMENT p 240
800 Capitol Mall 83, Sacramento CA 95814
Tel (916) 654-8210 *SIC* 9441

CALIFORNIA DEPT OF SOCIAL SERVICES p 240
744 P St, Sacramento CA 95814
Tel (916) 657-2598 *SIC* 9441

CALIFORNIA HEALTH & HUMAN SERVCS AGENCY p 240
1600 9th St Ste 460, Sacramento CA 95814
Tel (916) 654-3454 *SIC* 9431 9441

CALIFORNIA PUBLIC EMPLOYEES RETIREMENT SYSTEM p 241
400 Q St, Sacramento CA 95811
Tel (916) 795-3000 *SIC* 6371 9441

CALIFORNIA STATE TEACHERS RETIREMENT SYSTEM p 241
100 Waterfront Pl, West Sacramento CA 95605
Tel (800) 228-5453 SIC 6371 9441

COLORADO DEPARTMENT OF HUMAN SERVICE p 338
1575 N Sherman St, Denver CO 80203
Tel (303) 866-5948 SIC 9441

COLORADO DEPARTMENT OF HUMAN SERVICES p 338
1575 N Sherman St Fl 8, Denver CO 80203
Tel (303) 866-5700 SIC 9441

COLORADO DEPARTMENT OF LABOR & EMPLOYMENT p 338
633 17th St Ste 1100, Denver CO 80202
Tel (303) 620-4700 SIC 9651 9441

CONNECTICUT DEPARTMENT OF CHILDREN AND FAMILIES p 356
505 Hudson St, Hartford CT 06106
Tel (860) 566-2700 SIC 9441

CONNECTICUT DEPARTMENT OF SOCIAL SERVICES p 357
55 Farmington Ave Fl 1, Hartford CT 06105
Tel (860) 424-4908 SIC 9441

DELAWARE DEPT OF HEALTH AND SOCIAL SERVICES p 424
1901 N Dupont Hwy, New Castle DE 19720
Tel (302) 255-9040 SIC 9431 9441

■ **CHILDREN AND FAMILIES ADMINISTRATION FOR** p 298
330 C St Sw, Washington DC 20201
Tel (202) 401-1822 SIC 9441

■ **EMPLOYMENT AND TRAINING ADMINISTRATION** p 494
200 Constitution Ave Nw S2307, Washington DC 20210
Tel (202) 693-3500 SIC 9441

■ **EQUAL EMPLOYMENT OPPORTUNITY COMMISSION** p 506
131 M St Ne, Washington DC 20507
Tel (202) 663-4519 SIC 9441

FLORIDA DEPARTMENT OF CHILDREN & FAMILIES p 558
1317 Winewood Blvd Rm 306, Tallahassee FL 32399
Tel (850) 488-2840 SIC 9441 9411

GEORGIA DEPARTMENT OF HUMAN SERVICES p 607
2 Peachtree St Nw, Atlanta GA 30303
Tel (404) 651-9361 SIC 9441

HAWAII DEPARTMENT OF HUMAN SERVICES p 668
1390 Miller St Ste 209, Honolulu HI 96813
Tel (808) 586-4997 SIC 9441

■ **RAILROAD RETIREMENT BOARD UNITED STATES** p 1205
844 N Rush St, Chicago IL 60611
Tel (877) 772-5772 SIC 9441

IYPAD INTERNATIONAL INC NFP p 769
419 S East Ave, Oak Park IL 60302
Tel (773) 654-7141 SIC 9441

INDIANA FAMILY AND SOCIAL SERVICES ADMINISTRATION p 738
402 W Washington St W461, Indianapolis IN 46204
Tel (317) 233-4454 SIC 9441

IOWA DEPARTMENT OF HUMAN SERVICES p 762
1305 E Walnut St Rm 114, Des Moines IA 50319
Tel (515) 281-5454 SIC 9441

KANSAS DEPARTMENT FOR CHILDREN AND FAMILIES p 803
915 Sw Harrison St, Topeka KS 66612
Tel (785) 368-6358 SIC 9441 9431

DEPARTMENT OF COMMUNITY BASED SERVICES p 429
275 E Main St Ste 3wa, Frankfort KY 40601
Tel (502) 564-3703 SIC 9431 9441

KENTUCKY DEPT OF TECHNICAL EDUCATION p 812
500 Mero St Ste 2, Frankfort KY 40601
Tel (502) 564-4286 SIC 9411 9441

KENTUCKY EDUCATION AND WORK FORCE DEVELOPMENT CABINET p 812
500 Mero St Ste 3, Frankfort KY 40601
Tel (502) 564-6606 SIC 9441 9111

LOUISIANA DEPARTMENT OF CHILDREN AND FAMILY SERVICES p 880
627 N 4th St, Baton Rouge LA 70802
Tel (225) 342-4220 SIC 9441

MAINE DEPARTMENT OF HEALTH AND HUMAN SERVICES p 898
221 State St, Augusta ME 04330
Tel (207) 287-1716 SIC 9441 9431

MARYLAND DEPARTMENT OF HUMAN RESOURCES p 914
311 W Saratoga St, Baltimore MD 21201
Tel (410) 767-7109 SIC 9441

■ **SOCIAL SECURITY ADMINISTRATION** p 1336
6401 Security Blvd, Baltimore MD 21235
Tel (410) 965-8882 SIC 9441

EXECUTIVE OFFICE OF LABOR AND WORKFORCE DEVELOPMENT p 517
19 Staniford St, Boston MA 02114
Tel (617) 626-5680 SIC 9441

MASSACHUSETTS DEPT OF TRANSITIONAL ASSISTANCE p 916
600 Washington St Fl 5, Boston MA 02111
Tel (617) 348-8500 SIC 9441

MASSACHUSETTS EXECUTIVE OFFICE OF HEALTH AND HUMAN SERVICES p 916
1 Ashburton Pl Rm 1111, Boston MA 02108
Tel (617) 573-1600 SIC 9431 9441

MICHIGAN DEPARTMENT OF HEALTH & HUMAN SERVICES p 961
201 Townsend St, Lansing MI 48933
Tel (517) 373-3740 SIC 9431 9441

MICHIGAN DEPARTMENT OF HUMAN SERVICES p 961
235 S Grand Ave, Lansing MI 48933
Tel (517) 373-2000 SIC 9441 8249

MINNESOTA DEPARTMENT OF EMPLOYMENT AND ECONOMIC DEVELOPMENT p 973
332 Minnesota St Ste E200, Saint Paul MN 55101
Tel (651) 259-7114 SIC 9441

MINNESOTA DEPARTMENT OF HUMAN SERVICES p 973
540 Cedar St, Saint Paul MN 55164
Tel (651) 431-2000 SIC 9441

MISSISSIPPI DEPARTMENT OF HUMAN SERVICES p 975
750 N State St, Jackson MS 39202
Tel (601) 359-5131 SIC 9441

MISSOURI DEPARTMENT OF SOCIAL SERVICES p 976
221 W High St Ste 240, Jefferson City MO 65101
Tel (573) 751-4815 SIC 9441 8322

NEW HAMPSHIRE DEPT OF HEALTH AND HUMAN SERVICES p 1030
129 Pleasant St, Concord NH 03301
Tel (603) 271-4688 SIC 9431 9441

NEW JERSEY DEPARTMENT OF HUMAN SERVICES p 1031
222 S Warren St, Trenton NJ 08608
Tel (609) 292-3717 SIC 9441

NEW JERSEY DEPT OF COMMUNITY AFFAIRS p 1031
101 S Broad St, Trenton NJ 08608
Tel (609) 292-6420 SIC 9441

STATE DEPARTMENT OF COMMUNITY AFFAIRS p 1380
101 S Broad St, Trenton NJ 08608
Tel (609) 292-6420 SIC 9441

NEW MEXICO DEPARTMENT OF CHILDREN YOUTH AND FAMILIES p 1032
1120 Paseo De Peralta, Santa Fe NM 87501
Tel (505) 827-7602 SIC 9441

NEW MEXICO DEPARTMENT OF HUMAN SERVICES p 1032
2009 S Pacheco St, Santa Fe NM 87505
Tel (505) 827-7750 SIC 9441

NEW YORK OFFICE OF TEMPORARY & DISABILITY ASSISTANCE p 1035
40 N Pearl St Ste 100, Albany NY 12207
Tel (518) 426-2950 SIC 9441

PUBLIC SERVICE COMMISSION NEW YORK STATE p 1190
3 Empire State Plz 20th, Albany NY 12223
Tel (518) 474-7080 SIC 9441

NORTH CAROLINA DEPARTMENT OF HEALTH & HUMAN SERVICES p 1051
2025 Mail Service Ctr, Raleigh NC 27699
Tel (919) 733-4534 SIC 9441

NORTH DAKOTA DEPARTMENT OF HUMAN SERVICES p 1052
600 E Boulevard Ave # 325, Bismarck ND 58505
Tel (701) 872-2081 SIC 9441

WORKERS SAFETY INSURANCE p 1624
1600 E Century Ave Ste 1, Bismarck ND 58503
Tel (701) 328-3800 SIC 9441

OHIO DEPARTMENT OF DEVELOPMENTAL DISABILITIES p 1077
30 E Broad St Fl 13, Columbus OH 43215
Tel (614) 728-5544 SIC 9441

OHIO DEPARTMENT OF JOB AND FAMILY SERVICES p 1077
30 E Broad St Fl 32, Columbus OH 43215
Tel (614) 466-6282 SIC 9441

OHIO PUBLIC EMPLOYEES RETIREMENT SYSTEM p 1078
277 E Town St, Columbus OH 43215
Tel (614) 228-8471 SIC 6371 9441

SCHOOL EMPLOYEES RETIREMENT SYSTEM OF OHIO p 1290
300 E Broad St Ste 100, Columbus OH 43215
Tel (614) 222-5853 SIC 6371 9441

STATE OF OHIO p 1382
30 W Spring St Fl 5, Columbus OH 43215
Tel (614) 466-8660 SIC 9441

OKLAHOMA DEPT OF HUMAN SERVICES p 1079
2400 N Lincoln Blvd, Oklahoma City OK 73105
Tel (405) 521-3646 SIC 9431 9441

DEPARTMENT OF EMPLOYMENT OREGON p 430
875 Union St Ne, Salem OR 97311
Tel (503) 947-1470 SIC 9441

OREGON DEPARTMENT OF HUMAN SERVICES p 1093
500 Summer St Ne Dept 4, Salem OR 97301
Tel (503) 945-5944 SIC 9431 9441

OREGON DIVISION OF ADULT & FAMILY SERVICES p 1093
500 Summer St Ne, Salem OR 97301
Tel (503) 945-5601 SIC 9441

PENNSYLVANIA DEPARTMENT OF HUMAN SERVICES p 1130
625 Forster St, Harrisburg PA 17120
Tel (717) 787-2600 SIC 9441

PUBLIC SCHOOL EMPLOYEES RETIREMENT SYSTEM p 1189
5 N 5th St, Harrisburg PA 17101
Tel (717) 720-4734 SIC 6371 9441

CORPORACION DEL FONDO DEL SEGURO DEL ESTADO p 372
Urb La Riviera Se 1024, Rio Piedras PR 00921
Tel (787) 793-5959 SIC 9441

DEPARTMENT OF FAMILY p 430
Sevilla Plz Bldg Se, San Juan PR 00919
Tel (787) 643-1855 SIC 9441 8331

RHODE ISLAND DEPT OF HUMAN SERVICES p 1231
57 Howard Ave Fl 2, Cranston RI 02920
Tel (401) 462-1000 SIC 9441

SOCIAL SERVICES SOUTH CAROLINA DEPARTMENT p 1336
1535 Confederate Ave, Columbia SC 29201
Tel (803) 898-7601 SIC 9441

SOUTH CAROLINA DEPARTMENT OF EMPLOYMENT AND WORKFORCE p 1343
1550 Gadsden St, Columbia SC 29201
Tel (803) 737-2400 SIC 9441

SOUTH DAKOTA DEPARTMENT OF HUMAN SERVICES p 1344
500 E Capitol Ave, Pierre SD 57501
Tel (605) 773-5990 SIC 9441

SOUTH DAKOTA DEPARTMENT OF SOCIAL SERVICES p 1344
700 Governors Dr, Pierre SD 57501
Tel (605) 773-3165 SIC 9441

TENNESSEE DEPARTMENT OF CHILDRENS SERVICES p 1438
Cordell Hull Bldg 7th Fl, Nashville TN 37243
Tel (615) 741-9699 SIC 8322 9441

TENNESSEE DEPARTMENT OF HUMAN SERVICES p 1438
400 Deaderick St Fl 15, Nashville TN 37243
Tel (615) 313-4700 SIC 9441

EMPLOYEES RETIREMENT SYSTEM OF TEXAS p 494
200 E 18th St, Austin TX 78701
Tel (512) 867-7199 SIC 6371 9441

HEALTH AND HUMAN SERVICES COMMISSION TEXAS p 674
4900 N Lamar Blvd, Austin TX 78751
Tel (512) 424-6500 SIC 9441 9431

TEXAS DEPARTMENT OF AGING AND DISABILITY SERVICES p 1442
701 W 51st St, Austin TX 78751
Tel (512) 438-3011 SIC 9441

TEXAS DEPARTMENT OF ASSISTIVE AND REHABILITATIVE SERVICES p 1442
4900 N Lamar Blvd, Austin TX 78751
Tel (512) 424-4601 SIC 9441

TEXAS DEPT OF FAMILY AND PROTECTIVE SERVICES p 1443
701 W 51st St, Austin TX 78751
Tel (512) 438-3240 SIC 9441

UTAH DEPARTMENT OF HUMAN SERVICES p 1536
195 N 1950 W, Salt Lake City UT 84116
Tel (801) 538-4001 SIC 8322 9441

UTAH DEPT OF WORKFORCE SERVICES p 1536
140 E Broadway, Salt Lake City UT 84111
Tel (801) 526-9432 SIC 9441

VERMONT AGENCY OF HUMAN SERVICES p 1551
280 State Dr, Waterbury VT 05671
Tel (802) 871-3007 SIC 9441

EMPLOYMENT COMMISSION VIRGINIA p 494
703 E Main St, Richmond VA 23219
Tel (804) 786-3021 SIC 9441

VIRGINIA DEPARTMENT OF SOCIAL SERVICES p 1559
801 E Main St Fl 3, Richmond VA 23219
Tel (804) 726-7000 SIC 9441

VIRGINIA SECRETARY OF HEALTH AND HUMAN RESOURCES p 1559
202 E 9th St, Richmond VA 23224
Tel (804) 786-7765 SIC 9431 9441

WASHINGTON STATE DEPARTMENT OF EMPLOYMENT SECURITY p 1579
212 Maple Park Ave Se, Olympia WA 98501
Tel (360) 902-9500 SIC 9441

WASHINGTON STATE DEPARTMENT OF SOCIAL AND HEALTH SERVICES p 1579
14th And Jefferson, Olympia WA 98504
Tel (360) 902-8400 SIC 9441

WEST VIRGINIA DEPARTMENT OF HEALTH AND HUMAN RESOURCES p 1596
1 Davis Sq Ste 100e, Charleston WV 25301
Tel (304) 558-0684 SIC 9431 9441

WISCONSIN DEPARTMENT OF HEALTH SERVICES p 1618
1 W Wilson St Rm 650, Madison WI 53703
Tel (608) 266-1865 SIC 9431 9441

SIC 9451 Administration Of Veterans Affairs, except Health Insurance

ALASKA DEPARTMENT OF MILITARY AND VETERANS AFFAIRS p 45
49000 Army Guard Rd Ste 6, Jber AK 99505
Tel (907) 428-6008 SIC 9711 9451

CALIFORNIA DEPARTMENT OF VETERANS AFFAIRS p 240
1227 O St Ste 105, Sacramento CA 95814
Tel (800) 952-5626 SIC 9451

CONNECTICUT DEPARTMENT OF VETERANS AFFAIRS p 357
287 West St, Rocky Hill CT 06067
Tel (860) 721-5891 SIC 9451

■ **NATIONAL CEMETERY ADMINISTRATION** p 1010
810 Vrmont Ave Nw Ste 427, Washington DC 20420
Tel (800) 827-1000 SIC 6553 9451

■ **UNITED STATES DEPT OF VETERANS AFFAIRS** p 1513
810 Vermont Ave Nw, Washington DC 20420
Tel (202) 273-5400 SIC 9451

■ **VETERANS BENEFITS ADMINISTRATION** p 1552
810 Vermont Ave Nw, Washington DC 20420
Tel (202) 273-5674 SIC 9451

■ **VETERANS HEALTH ADMINISTRATION** p 1553
810 Vermont Ave Nw, Washington DC 20420
Tel (202) 461-4800 SIC 9451

FLORIDA DEPARTMENT OF VETERANS AFFAIRS p 558
11351 Ulmerton Rd Rm 311k, Largo FL 33778
Tel (727) 319-7427 SIC 9451 9111

ILLINOIS DEPARTMENT OF VETERANS AFFAIRS p 732
833 S Spring St, Springfield IL 62704
Tel (217) 782-6641 SIC 9451

LOUISIANA DEPARTMENT OF MILITARY AFFAIRS p 880
6400 Saint Claude Ave, New Orleans LA 70117
Tel (504) 278-8071 SIC 9711 9451

MICHIGAN DEPARTMENT OF MILITARY AND VETERANS AFFAIRS p 961
3411 N Martin Luther King, Lansing MI 48906
Tel (517) 481-8083 SIC 9711 9451

VETERANS COMMISSION MISSOURI p 1553
205 Jefferson St Fl 12, Jefferson City MO 65101
Tel (573) 751-3779 SIC 9451

■ **VA SOUTHERN NEVADA HEALTHCARE SYSTEM** p 1538
6900 Pecos Rd, North Las Vegas NV 89086
Tel (702) 791-9000 SIC 8051 9451

PA DEPARTMENT OF MILITARY AND VETERANS AFFAIRS p 1103
47 Bldg S-O, Annville PA 17003
Tel (717) 861-8500 SIC 9711 9451

VETERANS AFFAIRS PENNSYLVANIA BUREAU FOR p 1552
0 47 Ftig Bldg S, Annville PA 17003
Tel (717) 861-8901 SIC 9451

MILITARY PERSONNEL SERVICES CORP p 969
6066 Leesburg Pike # 900, Falls Church VA 22041
Tel (571) 481-4000 SIC 9451

SIC 9511 Air, Water Resource & Solid Waste Management

AIR RESOURCES BOARD p 39
1001 I St, Sacramento CA 95814
Tel (916) 322-2990 SIC 9511

CALIFORNIA DEPARTMENT OF PESTICIDE REGULATION p 240
1001 I St, Sacramento CA 95814
Tel (916) 445-4000 SIC 9511

CALIFORNIA DEPARTMENT OF WATER RESOURCES p 240
1416 9th St, Sacramento CA 95814
Tel (916) 653-9394 SIC 9511

CALIFORNIA ENVIRONMENTAL PROTECTION AGENCY p 240
1001 I St, Sacramento CA 95814
Tel (916) 323-2514 SIC 9511

WATER RESOURCES CONTROL BOARD CALIFORNIA p 1581
1001 I St, Sacramento CA 95814
Tel (916) 341-5250 SIC 9511

SANITATION DISTRICT OF LOS ANGELES COUNTY DISTRICT 2 p 1279
1955 Workman Mill Rd, Whittier CA 90601
Tel (562) 699-7411 SIC 9511

CITY OF AURORA p 313
15151 E Alameda Pkwy, Aurora CO 80012
Tel (303) 739-7056 SIC 9111 9511

BOULDER CITY OF (INC) p 204
1777 Broadway, Boulder CO 80302
Tel (303) 441-3090
SIC 9111 9224 9221 9511

COLORADO DEPARTMENT OF PUBLIC HEALTH AND ENVIRONMENT p 339
4300 E Cherry Creek S Dr, Denver CO 80246
Tel (303) 692-2000 SIC 9431 9511

CONNECTICUT DEPARTMENT OF ENERGY & ENVIRONMENTAL PROTECTION p 357
79 Elm St Fl 3, Hartford CT 06106
Tel (860) 424-4100 SIC 9511

CONNECTICUT DEPARTMENT OF PUBLIC WORKS p 357
165 Capitol Ave Ste 6, Hartford CT 06106
Tel (860) 713-5790 SIC 9511

STATE OF DELAWARE DNREC p 1381
89 Kings Hwy, Dover DE 19901
Tel (302) 739-9101 SIC 9511 9512

■ **BUREAU OF RECLAMATION** p 226
1849 C St Nw, Washington DC 20240
Tel (202) 513-0501 SIC 9511

DISTRICT OF COLUMBIA WATER & SEWER AUTHORITY p 443
5000 Overlook Ave Sw, Washington DC 20032
Tel (202) 787-2000 SIC 9511

■ **ENVIRONMENTAL PROTECTION AGENCY** p 503
1200 Pennsylvania Ave Nw, Washington DC 20460
Tel (202) 272-0167 SIC 9511

METROPOLITAN WATER RECLAIMATION DISTRICT OF GREATER CHICAGO p 957
100 E Erie St, Chicago IL 60611
Tel (312) 751-5600 SIC 9511

ILLINOIS ENVIRONMENTAL PROTECTION AGENCY p 732
1021 North Grand Ave E, Springfield IL 62702
Tel (217) 782-3397 SIC 9511

LOUISIANA DEPARTMENT OF ENVIRONMENTAL QUALITY p 880
602 N 5th St, Baton Rouge LA 70802
Tel (225) 219-3953 SIC 9511

ENVIRONMENT MARYLAND DEPARTMENT OF p 503
1800 Washington Blvd A, Baltimore MD 21230
Tel (410) 537-3000 SIC 9511

■ **NATIONAL OCEAN SERVICE** p 1014
1305 E West Hwy, Silver Spring MD 20910
Tel (301) 713-3074 SIC 9511

■ **OFFICE OF OCEANIC AND ATMOSPHERIC RESEARCH** p 1075
1315 E West Hwy Fl 11, Silver Spring MD 20910
Tel (301) 713-2458 SIC 9511

MASSACHUSETTS DEPARTMENT OF ENVIRONMENTAL PROTECTION p 916
1 Winter St, Boston MA 02108
Tel (617) 292-5500 SIC 9511

MASSACHUSETTS EXECUTIVE OFFICE OF ENERGY & ENVIRONMENTAL AFFAIRS p 916
100 Cambridge St Ste 900, Boston MA 02114
Tel (617) 626-1000 SIC 9511 9512 9641

MASSACHUSETTS WATER RESOURCES AUTHORITY p 917
100 1st Ave, Boston MA 02129
Tel (617) 242-6000 SIC 9511

MICHIGAN DEPARTMENT OF ENVIRONMENTAL QUALITY p 961
525 W Allegan St, Lansing MI 48933
Tel (517) 284-6700 SIC 9511

NEW JERSEY DEPARTMENT OF ENVIRONMENTAL PROTECTION p 1031
401 E State St, Trenton NJ 08608
Tel (609) 292-2885 SIC 9512 9511

OHIO ENVIRONMENTAL PROTECTION AGENCY p 1077
50 W Town St Ste 700, Columbus OH 43215
Tel (614) 644-3020 SIC 9511

STATE OF OHIO OFFICE OF BUDGET AND MANAGEMENT STATE ACCOUNTING p 1382
30 E Broad St Fl 34, Columbus OH 43215
Tel (614) 466-4034 SIC 9511

OKLAHOMA SECRETARY OF ENERGY & ENVIRONMENT p 1080
204 N Robinson Ave # 1010, Oklahoma City OK 73102
Tel (405) 522-7099 SIC 9511

PENNSYLVANIA DEPT OF ENVIRONMENTAL PROTECTION p 1130
400 Market St, Harrisburg PA 17101
Tel (717) 787-1319 SIC 9511

AUTORIDAD DE ACUEDUCTOS Y ALCANTARILLADOS DE PR p 135
604 Ave Barbosa, San Juan PR 00917
Tel (787) 620-2482 SIC 9511

TENNESSEE DEPARTMENT OF ENVIRONMENT AND CONSERVATION p 1438
312 Rosa L Parks Ave, Nashville TN 37243
Tel (615) 532-0109 SIC 9511

ENVIRONMENTAL QUALITY TEXAS COMMISSION ON p 503
12100 Pk Thirty Five Cir, Austin TX 78753
Tel (512) 239-5500 SIC 9511

COUNTY OF HENRICO p 378
4301 E Parham Rd, Henrico VA 23228
Tel (804) 501-4000 SIC 9111 9511

■ **UNITED STATES DEPT OF GEOLOGICAL SURVEY** p 1513
12201 Sunrise Valley Dr, Reston VA 20192
Tel (703) 648-4000 SIC 9511

NATURAL RESOURCES VIRGINIA p 1018
1111 E Broad St, Richmond VA 23219
Tel (804) 786-0044 SIC 9511 9512

WASHINGTON STATE DEPARTMENT OF ECOLOGY p 1579
300 Desmond Dr Se, Olympia WA 98503
Tel (360) 407-6000 SIC 9511

SIC 9512 Land, Mineral, Wildlife & Forest Conservation

ALABAMA DEPT OF CONSERVATION & NATURAL RESOURCES p 43
64 N Union St Rm 458, Montgomery AL 36130
Tel (334) 242-3468 SIC 9512

ALASKA DEPARTMENT OF FISH AND GAME p 45
1255 W 8th St, Juneau AK 99801
Tel (907) 465-4210 SIC 9512

ARKANSAS DEPARTMENT OF PARKS AND TOURISM p 109
1 Capitol Mall Ste 900, Little Rock AR 72201
Tel (501) 682-7777 SIC 9512 9611

CALIFORNIA DEPARTMENT OF FISH AND WILDLIFE p 240
1416 9th St Fl 12, Sacramento CA 95814
Tel (916) 445-0411 SIC 9512

CALIFORNIA DEPARTMENT OF PARKS AND RECREATION p 240
1416 9th St Ste 1041, Sacramento CA 95814
Tel (800) 777-0369 SIC 9512

CALIFORNIA NATURAL RESOURCES AGENCY p 240
1416 9th St Ste 1311, Sacramento CA 95814
Tel (916) 653-5656 SIC 9512

FORESTRY AND FIRE PROTECTION CALIFORNIA DEPARTMENT OF p 567
1416 9th St Ste 1535, Sacramento CA 95814
Tel (916) 653-7772 SIC 9512

COLORADO DEPARTMENT OF NATURAL RESOURCES p 339
1313 N Sherman St Ste 718, Denver CO 80203
Tel (303) 866-3311 SIC 9512

STATE OF DELAWARE DNREC p 1381
89 Kings Hwy, Dover DE 19901
Tel (302) 739-9903 SIC 9512

STATE OF DELAWARE DNREC p 1381
89 Kings Hwy, Dover DE 19901
Tel (302) 739-9101 SIC 9511 9512

■ **BUREAU OF LAND MANAGEMENT** p 226
1849 C St Nw Rm 5665, Washington DC 20240
Tel (202) 208-3801 SIC 9512

■ **NATIONAL PARK SERVICE** p 1015
1849 C St Nw, Washington DC 20240
Tel (202) 208-6843 SIC 9512

■ **NATURAL RESOURCES CONSERVATION SERVICE** p 1018
1400 Independence Ave Sw, Washington DC 20250
Tel (202) 720-7246 SIC 9512

■ **UNITED STATES DEPARTMENT OF INTERIOR** p 1512
1849 C St Nw, Washington DC 20240
Tel (202) 208-7351 SIC 9512

■ **USDA FOREST SERVICE** p 1534
201 14th St Sw, Washington DC 20024
Tel (202) 205-1680 SIC 9512

FISH & WILDLIFE CONSERVATION COMMISSION FLORIDA p 551
620 S Meridian St, Tallahassee FL 32399
Tel (850) 487-3796 SIC 9512

FLORIDA DEPARTMENT OF ENVIRONMENTAL PROTECTION p 558
3900 Commwl Blvd, Tallahassee FL 32399
Tel (850) 245-2112 SIC 9512

GEORGIA DEPARTMENT OF NATURAL RESOURCES p 607
2 Martin Luther King Jr, Atlanta GA 30334
Tel (404) 656-3500 SIC 9512

COUNTY OF COBB p 377
100 Cherokee St Ste 400, Marietta GA 30090
Tel (770) 528-3300 SIC 9512

ILLINOIS DEPARTMENT OF NATURAL RESOURCES p 732
1 Natural Resources Way # 100, Springfield IL 62702
Tel (217) 782-6302 SIC 9512 9111

INDIANA DEPARTMENT OF NATURAL RESOURCES p 738
402 W Washington St W299, Indianapolis IN 46204
Tel (317) 232-4020 SIC 9512

KENTUCKY DEPARTMENT OF PARKS p 812
Capital Plaza Tower 10th, Frankfort KY 40601
Tel (502) 564-2172 SIC 9512

TOURISM ARTS AND HERITAGE CABINET p 1464
500 Mero St Fl 24, Frankfort KY 40601
Tel (502) 564-4270 SIC 9512

MARYLAND DEPARTMENT OF NATURAL RESOURCES p 914
580 Taylor Ave Bldg E3, Annapolis MD 21401
Tel (410) 260-8100 SIC 9512

MASSACHUSETTS EXECUTIVE OFFICE OF ENERGY & ENVIRONMENTAL AFFAIRS p 916
100 Cambridge St Ste 900, Boston MA 02114
Tel (617) 626-1000 SIC 9511 9512 9641

HURON-CLINTON METROPOLITAN AUTHORITY p 721
13000 Highridge Dr, Brighton MI 48114
Tel (810) 227-2757 SIC 9512

MICHIGAN DEPARTMENT OF NATURAL RESOURCES p 961
525 W Allegan St, Lansing MI 48933
Tel (517) 284-5936 SIC 9512

MINNESOTA DEPARTMENT OF NATURAL RESOURCES p 973
500 Lafayette Rd N, Saint Paul MN 55155
Tel (651) 296-6157 SIC 9512

MISSOURI DEPARTMENT OF CONSERVATION p 976
2901 W Truman Blvd, Jefferson City MO 65109
Tel (573) 751-4115 SIC 9512

MISSOURI DEPARTMENT OF NATURAL RESOURCES p 976
1101 Riverside Dr, Jefferson City MO 65101
Tel (573) 751-3443 SIC 9512

NEW JERSEY DEPARTMENT OF ENVIRONMENTAL PROTECTION p 1031
401 E State St, Trenton NJ 08608
Tel (609) 292-2885 SIC 9512 9511

NEW YORK DEPARTMENT OF ENVIRONMENTAL CONSERVATION p 1035
625 Broadway, Albany NY 12207
Tel (518) 402-8545 SIC 9512

NORTH CAROLINA DEPARTMENT OF ENVIRONMENTAL QUALITY p 1051
217 W Jones St Ste 5103, Raleigh NC 27603
Tel (877) 623-6748 SIC 9512

OHIO DEPARTMENT OF NATURAL RESOURCES p 1077
2045 Morse Rd Bldg D-3, Columbus OH 43229
Tel (614) 265-6875 SIC 9512

OREGON DEPARTMENT OF FISH AND WILDLIFE p 1093
4034 Fairview Indus Dr Se, Salem OR 97302
Tel (503) 947-6000 SIC 9512

PENNSYLVANIA DEPARTMENT OF CONSERVATION & NATURAL RESOURCES p 1130
400 Market St Fl 7, Harrisburg PA 17101
Tel (717) 787-2869 SIC 9512

UTAH DEPARTMENT OF NATURAL RESOURCES p 1536
1594 W North Temple, Salt Lake City UT 84116
Tel (801) 538-7200 SIC 9512

■ **FISH & WILDLIFE SERVICE UNITED STATES** p 551
4401 Fairfax Dr Ste 325, Arlington VA 22203
Tel (703) 358-1742 SIC 9512

NATURAL RESOURCES VIRGINIA p 1018
1111 E Broad St, Richmond VA 23219
Tel (804) 786-0044 SIC 9511 9512

VIRGINIA DEPARTMENT OF CONSERVATION AND RECREATION p 1559
600 E Main St Fl 24, Richmond VA 23219
Tel (804) 371-0099 SIC 9512

WASHINGTON STATE DEPARTMENT OF FISH & WILDLIFE p 1579
600 Capitol Way N, Olympia WA 98501
Tel (360) 902-2200 SIC 9512

WASHINGTON STATE DEPARTMENT OF NATURAL RESOURCES p 1579
1111 Washington St Se, Olympia WA 98501
Tel (360) 902-1000 SIC 9512

WISCONSIN DEPT OF NATURAL RESOURCES p 1618
101 S Webster St, Madison WI 53703
Tel (608) 266-2621 SIC 9512

SIC 9531 Administration Of Housing Programs

CHUKCHANSI INDIAN HOUSING AUTHORITY p 305
8080 N Palm Ave Ste 207, Fresno CA 93711
Tel (559) 370-4141 SIC 9531

HOUSING AUTHORITY OF CITY OF LOS ANGELES p 711
2600 Wilshire Blvd Fl 2, Los Angeles CA 90057
Tel (213) 252-2500 SIC 9531

BUSINESS TRANSPORTATION & HOUSING AGENCY STATE OF CALIFORNIA p 230
915 Capitol Mall, Sacramento CA 95814
Tel (916) 323-5400
SIC 9611 9621 9531 9532

CALIFORNIA DEPARTMENT OF HOUSING & COMMUNITY DEVELOPMENT p 240
1800 3rd St Fl 1, Sacramento CA 95811
Tel (916) 445-4782 SIC 9531 9532

VOLUNTEERS OF AMERICA p 1565
2100 N Broadway Ste 300, Santa Ana CA 92706
Tel (714) 426-9834 SIC 8322 7361 9531

■ **CFO ACCOUNTING CENTER** p 285
451 7th St Sw, Washington DC 20410
Tel (202) 708-0950 SIC 9531

■ **UNITED STATES DEPT OF HOUSING AND URBAN DEVELOPMENT** p 1513
451 7th St Sw Rm 5256, Washington DC 20410
Tel (202) 708-0417 SIC 9531

CHICAGO HOUSING AUTHORITY p 297
60 E Van Buren St Fl 10, Chicago IL 60605
Tel (312) 791-8500 SIC 9531

HOUSING AUTHORITY OF CITY OF NEWARK p 711
500 Broad St, Newark NJ 07102
Tel (973) 273-6000 SIC 9531

MESCALERO APACHE HOUSING AUTHORITY p 951
101 Central Ave, Mescalero NM 88340
Tel (575) 464-9245 SIC 9531

NEW YORK STATE DIVISION OF HOUSING AND COMMUNITY RENEWAL p 1036
38-40 State St, Albany NY 12207
Tel (518) 473-2517 SIC 9531

NEW YORK CITY HOUSING AUTHORITY p 1034
250 Broadway, New York NY 10007
Tel (212) 306-3000 SIC 9531

PHILADELPHIA HOUSING AUTHORITY p 1142
12 S 23rd St, Philadelphia PA 19103
Tel (215) 684-4000 SIC 9531

SIC 9532 Administration Of Urban Planning & Community & Rural Dvlpt

HEIFER PROJECT INTERNATIONAL INC p 681
1 World Ave, Little Rock AR 72202
Tel (501) 907-2600 SIC 8399 6732 9532

BUSINESS TRANSPORTATION & HOUSING AGENCY STATE OF CALIFORNIA p 230
915 Capitol Mall, Sacramento CA 95814
Tel (916) 323-5400
SIC 9611 9621 9531 9532

CALIFORNIA DEPARTMENT OF HOUSING & COMMUNITY DEVELOPMENT p 240
1800 3rd St Fl 1, Sacramento CA 95811
Tel (916) 445-4782 SIC 9531 9532

SACRAMENTO HOUSING AND REDEVELOPMENT AGENCY p 1265
801 12th St, Sacramento CA 95814
Tel (916) 440-1390 SIC 9532

COUNTY OF ADAMS p 375
4430 S Adams County Pkwy W5000a, Brighton CO 80601
Tel (720) 523-6100 SIC 9532

WESTPORT SENIOR LIVING INVESTMENT FUND LP p 1602
11360 N Jog Rd Ste 102, Palm Beach Gardens FL 33418
Tel (561) 624-1225 SIC 9532

COUNTY OF DEKALB p 377
1300 Commerce Dr, Decatur GA 30030
Tel (404) 371-2881 SIC 9532

SAC & FOX TRIBAL OFFICES p 1264
349 Meskwaki Rd, Tama IA 52339
Tel (641) 484-4678 SIC 9532

METROPOLITAN COUNCIL MINNESOTA p 955
390 Robert St N, Saint Paul MN 55101
Tel (651) 602-1629 SIC 9532

CUYAHOGA METROPOLITAN HOUSING AUTHORITY p 403
8120 Kinsman Rd, Cleveland OH 44104
Tel (216) 348-5000 SIC 9532

ST GEORGE CITY GOVERNMENT (INC) p 1367
175 E 200 N, St George UT 84770
Tel (435) 627-4000 SIC 9532

SIC 9611 Administration Of General Economic Programs

ARKANSAS DEPARTMENT OF PARKS AND TOURISM p 109
1 Capitol Mall Ste 900, Little Rock AR 72201
Tel (501) 682-7777 SIC 9512 9611

UNITED STATES DEPARTMENT OF ENERGY BERKELEY OFFICE p 1512
1 Cyclotron Rd, Berkeley CA 94720
Tel (510) 486-4000 SIC 9611

UNITED STATES DEPARTMENT OF ENERGY LIVERMORE OFFICE p 1512
7000 East Ave, Livermore CA 94550
Tel (925) 422-1100 SIC 9611 8731

BUSINESS TRANSPORTATION & HOUSING AGENCY STATE OF CALIFORNIA p 230
915 Capitol Mall, Sacramento CA 95814
Tel (916) 323-5400
SIC 9611 9621 9531 9532

CALIFORNIA DEPARTMENT OF CONSUMER AFFAIRS p 239
1625 N Market Blvd # 103, Sacramento CA 95834
Tel (916) 574-7130 SIC 9611

CALIFORNIA GOVERNMENT OPERATIONS AGENCY p 240
915 Capitol Mall Ste 200, Sacramento CA 95814
Tel (916) 651-9011 SIC 9611

■ **WESTERN AREA POWER ADMINISTRATION** p 1597
12155 W Alameda Pkwy, Lakewood CO 80228
Tel (720) 962-7000 SIC 9611

■ **FEDERAL ENERGY REGULATORY COMMISSION** p 534
888 1st St Ne, Washington DC 20426
Tel (202) 502-6629 SIC 9611

■ **INTERNATIONAL DEVELOPMENT UNITED STATES AGENCY FOR** p 755
1300 Penn Ave Nw 848, Washington DC 20004
Tel (202) 712-0000 SIC 9611

■ **INTERNATIONAL TRADE ADMINISTRATION** p 757
14th /Constitution Ave Nw, Washington DC 20230
Tel (202) 482-2000 SIC 9611

■ **SMALL BUSINESS ADMINISTRATION US** p 1332
409 3rd St Sw Ste 5000, Washington DC 20416
Tel (202) 205-6770 SIC 9611

■ **UNITED STATES DEPARTMENT OF COMMERCE** p 1512
1401 Constitution Ave Nw, Washington DC 20230
Tel (202) 482-0267 SIC 9611

■ **UNITED STATES DEPT OF ENERGY** p 1513
1000 Independence Ave Sw, Washington DC 20585
Tel (202) 586-5000 SIC 9611

■ **US DEPARTMENT OF COMMERCE** p 1531
1401 Constitution Ave Nw, Washington DC 20230
Tel (202) 482-4661 SIC 9611

■ **USAID/ASIA & NEAR EAST BUREAU** p 1534
1300 Pa Ave Rnld Raegn, Washington DC 20523
Tel (202) 712-0200 SIC 9611

FLORIDA DEPARTMENT OF AGRICULTURE AND CONSUMER SERVICES p 558
10 The Capitol, Tallahassee FL 32399
Tel (850) 617-7700 SIC 9641 9611 9111

■ **US DEPT OF ENERGY CHICAGO OFFICE** p 1531
9800 S Cass Ave Ste 1, Lemont IL 60439
Tel (630) 252-2442 SIC 9611

DEPARTMENT OF CHILD SERVICES p 429
302 W Washington St E306, Indianapolis IN 46204
Tel (317) 234-5739 SIC 9611

UNITED STATES DEPARTMENT OF ENERGY AMES OFFICE p 1512
111 Tasf Iowa State Univ, Ames IA 50011
Tel (515) 294-5643 SIC 9611

ENERGY AND ENVIRONMENT CABINET p 497
500 Mero St Ste 4, Frankfort KY 40601
Tel (502) 564-3350 SIC 8641 9611

■ **NATIONAL INSTITUTE OF STANDARDS & TECHNOLOGY** p 1013
100 Bureau Dr Stop 1070, Gaithersburg MD 20899
Tel (301) 975-6478 SIC 9611

■ **NATIONAL OCEANIC AND ATMOSPHERIC ADMINISTRATION** p 1014
1305 Ew Hwy Fl 10, Silver Spring MD 20910
Tel (301) 713-3155 SIC 9611

■ **NATIONAL WEATHER SERVICE** p 1017
1325 E West Hwy, Silver Spring MD 20910
Tel (609) 261-6600 SIC 9611

■ **WESTERN PACIFIC REGIONAL FISHERY MANAGEMENT COUNCIL** p 1599
1315 E West Hwy, Silver Spring MD 20910
Tel (301) 713-2239 SIC 9611

■ **CENSUS BUREAU UNITED STATES** p 275
4600 Silver Hill Rd, Suitland MD 20746
Tel (301) 763-2135 SIC 9611

MISSOURI DEPARTMENT OF ECONOMIC DEVELOPMENT p 976
301 W High St, Jefferson City MO 65101
Tel (573) 751-4962 SIC 9611

COMMERCE & ECONOMIC GROWTH COMMISSION NEW JERSEY p 344
20 W State St, Trenton NJ 08608
Tel (609) 292-1800 SIC 9611

UNITED STATES DEPARTMENT OF ENERGY ALBUQUERQUE OFFICE p 1512
1515 Eubank Blvd Se, Albuquerque NM 87123
Tel (505) 845-0011 SIC 9611

UNITED NATIONS POPULATION FUND p 1510
605 3rd Ave, New York NY 10158
Tel (212) 297-5000 SIC 9611

■ **UNITED STATES DEPT OF ENERGY OHIO FIELD OFFICE** p 1513
250 E 5th St Ste 500, Cincinnati OH 45202
Tel (513) 246-0500 SIC 9611

SECRETARY OF STATE OHIO p 1298
180 E Broad St Fl 16, Columbus OH 43215
Tel (614) 466-2655 SIC 9111 9611

DEPARTMENT OF COMMERCE OHIO p 429
6606 Tussing Rd, Reynoldsburg OH 43068
Tel (614) 644-2223 SIC 9611

OKLAHOMA DEPARTMENT OF COMMERCE p 1079
900 N Stiles Ave, Oklahoma City OK 73104
Tel (405) 815-6552 SIC 9611

OKLAHOMA DEPT OF TOURISM AND RECREATION p 1079
120 N Robinson Ave # 600, Oklahoma City OK 73102
Tel (405) 230-8300 SIC 9611

LACKAWANNA COUNTY GOVERNMENT p 837
200 Adams Ave, Scranton PA 18503
Tel (570) 963-6800 SIC 9611 9199

MUNICIPIO DE SAN JUAN p 1000
1205 Ave Ponce De Leon, San Juan PR 00907
Tel (787) 289-0310 SIC 9611

SOUTH CAROLINA DEPARTMENT OF COMMERCE p 1343
1201 Main St Ste 1600, Columbia SC 29201
Tel (803) 737-0400 SIC 9611

■ UNITED STATES DEPT OF ENERGY OAKRIDGE FIELD OFFICE p 1513
200 Administration Rd Fm-73, Oak Ridge TN 37830
Tel (865) 576-0770 SIC 9611

VIRGINIA SECRETARY OF COMMERCE AND TRADE p 1559
Ninth St Off Bldg Ste 723, Richmond VA 23219
Tel (804) 786-7831 SIC 9611

■ UNITED STATES DEPT OF ENERGY RICHLAND OPERATIONS OFFICE p 1513
825 Jadwin Ave Ste 700, Richland WA 99352
Tel (509) 376-7395 SIC 9611

WISCONSIN DEPARTMENT OF ADMINISTRATION p 1618
101 E Wilson St Fl 10, Madison WI 53703
Tel (608) 266-1741 SIC 9611

SIC 9621 Regulation & Administration Of Transportation Programs

ALABAMA DEPT OF TRANSPORTATION p 43
1409 Coliseum Blvd, Montgomery AL 36110
Tel (334) 242-6258 SIC 9621

ALASKA DEPARTMENT OF TRANSPORTATION AND PUBLIC FACILITIES p 45
3132 Channel Dr Ste 300, Juneau AK 99801
Tel (907) 465-3900 SIC 9621

ARIZONA DEPT OF TRANSPORTATION p 109
206 S 17th Ave, Phoenix AZ 85007
Tel (602) 712-7227 SIC 9621

ARKANSAS DEPARTMENT OF HIGHWAY AND TRANSPORTATION p 109
10324 Interstate 30, Little Rock AR 72209
Tel (501) 569-2000 SIC 9621

BUSINESS TRANSPORTATION & HOUSING AGENCY STATE OF CALIFORNIA p 230
915 Capitol Mall, Sacramento CA 95814
Tel (916) 323-5400
SIC 9611 9621 9531 9532

CALIFORNIA DEPARTMENT OF MOTOR VEHICLES p 240
2415 1st Ave, Sacramento CA 95818
Tel (916) 657-6847 SIC 9621

CALIFORNIA DEPT OF TRANSPORTATION p 240
1120 N St, Sacramento CA 95814
Tel (916) 654-5266 SIC 9621

SANTA CLARA VALLEY TRANSPORTATION AUTHORITY p 1280
3331 N 1st St, San Jose CA 95134
Tel (408) 321-2300 SIC 9621

COLORADO DEPARTMENT OF TRANSPORTATION p 339
4201 E Arkansas Ave, Denver CO 80222
Tel (303) 757-9557 SIC 9621

CONNECTICUT DEPARTMENT OF TRANSPORTATION p 357
2800 Berlin Tpke, Newington CT 06111
Tel (860) 594-3000 SIC 9621

DELAWARE DEPARTMENT OF TRANSPORTATION p 424
800 S Bay Rd Ste 1, Dover DE 19901
Tel (302) 760-2080 SIC 9621

■ FEDERAL AVIATION ADMINISTRATION p 533
800 Independence Ave Sw, Washington DC 20591
Tel (866) 835-5322 SIC 9621

■ FEDERAL HIGHWAY ADMINISTRATION p 534
1200 New Jersey Ave Se, Washington DC 20590
Tel (202) 366-0650 SIC 9621

■ UNITED STATES COAST GUARD p 1512
2100 2nd St Sw Stop 7238, Washington DC 20593
Tel (202) 372-4411 SIC 9621

■ UNITED STATES DEPARTMENT OF TRANSPORTATION p 1512
1200 New Jersey Ave Se, Washington DC 20590
Tel (202) 366-4000 SIC 9621

FLORIDA DEPARTMENT OF HIGHWAY SAFETY AND MOTOR VEHICLES p 558
2900 Apalachee Pkwy, Tallahassee FL 32399
Tel (850) 617-3100 SIC 9621

FLORIDA DEPARTMENT OF TRANSPORTATION p 558
605 Suwannee St, Tallahassee FL 32399
Tel (850) 414-4500 SIC 9621

GEORGIA DEPARTMENT OF TRANSPORTATION p 607
600 W Peachtree St Nw, Atlanta GA 30308
Tel (404) 631-1014 SIC 9621

HAWAII DEPARTMENT OF TRANSPORTATION p 668
869 Punchbowl St Rm 509, Honolulu HI 96813
Tel (808) 587-1830 SIC 9621

IDAHO DEPARTMENT OF TRANSPORTATION p 728
3311 W State St, Boise ID 83703
Tel (208) 334-8000 SIC 9621

ILLINOIS STATE OF TOLL HIGHWAY AUTHORITY p 732
2700 Ogden Ave, Downers Grove IL 60515
Tel (630) 241-6800 SIC 9621

ILLINOIS DEPARTMENT OF TRANSPORTATION p 732
2300 S Dirksen Pkwy, Springfield IL 62764
Tel (217) 782-7820 SIC 9621

INDIANA DEPARTMENT OF TRANSPORTATION p 738
100 N Senate Ave Rm N758, Indianapolis IN 46204
Tel (317) 232-3166 SIC 9621

IOWA DEPARTMENT OF TRANSPORTATION p 762
800 Lincoln Way, Ames IA 50010
Tel (515) 239-1111 SIC 9621

KANSAS DEPARTMENT OF TRANSPORTATION p 803
700 Sw Harrison St # 500, Topeka KS 66603
Tel (785) 296-3501 SIC 9621

DEPARTMENT OF HIGHWAYS KENTUCKY p 430
200 Mero St, Frankfort KY 40601
Tel (502) 564-4890 SIC 9621

TRANSPORTATION CABINET KENTUCKY p 1472
200 Mero St, Frankfort KY 40601
Tel (502) 564-3020 SIC 9621

MAINE DEPARTMENT OF TRANSPORTATION p 898
16 State House Sta, Augusta ME 04333
Tel (207) 624-3000 SIC 9621

MARYLAND DEPARTMENT OF TRANSPORTATION p 914
7201 Corporate Center Dr, Hanover MD 21076
Tel (410) 865-1037 SIC 8748 9621

MASSACHUSETTS BAY TRANSPORTATION AUTHORITY p 916
Mbta 10 Park Plz Ste 3910, Boston MA 02116
Tel (617) 222-3106 SIC 9621

MASSACHUSETTS DEPARTMENT OF TRANSPORTATION p 916
10 Park Plz Ste 4160, Boston MA 02116
Tel (857) 368-4636 SIC 9621

MINNESOTA DEPARTMENT OF TRANSPORTATION p 973
395 John Ireland Blvd, Saint Paul MN 55155
Tel (651) 296-3000 SIC 9621

MISSISSIPPI DEPARTMENT OF TRANSPORTATION p 975
401 N West St, Jackson MS 39201
Tel (601) 359-7001 SIC 9621

MISSOURI DEPARTMENT OF TRANSPORTATION p 976
105 W Capitol Ave, Jefferson City MO 65101
Tel (573) 751-2551 SIC 9621

MONTANA DEPARTMENT OF TRANSPORTATION p 986
2701 Prospect Ave, Helena MT 59601
Tel (406) 444-6201 SIC 9621

NEVADA DEPARTMENT OF MOTOR VEHICLES p 1028
555 Wright Way, Carson City NV 89711
Tel (775) 684-4549 SIC 9621

NEVADA DEPARTMENT OF TRANSPORTATION p 1028
1263 S Stewart St, Carson City NV 89712
Tel (775) 888-7440 SIC 9621

NEW HAMPSHIRE DEPARTMENT OF TRANSPORTATION p 1030
7 Hazen Dr, Concord NH 03301
Tel (603) 271-3734 SIC 9621

NEW JERSEY DEPT OF TRANSPORTATION p 1031
1035 Parkway Ave Fl 2, Ewing NJ 08618
Tel (609) 530-3855 SIC 9621

NEW MEXICO DEPARTMENT OF TRANSPORTATION p 1032
1120 Cerrillos Rd, Santa Fe NM 87505
Tel (505) 827-5100 SIC 9621

NEW YORK DEPARTMENT OF TRANSPORTATION p 1035
50 Wolf Rd Ste 5, Albany NY 12205
Tel (518) 457-4445 SIC 9621

NEW YORK STATE DEPARTMENT OF MOTOR VEHICLES p 1036
6 Empire State Plz Rm 321, Albany NY 12223
Tel (518) 474-0835 SIC 9621

NORTH CAROLINA DEPARTMENT OF TRANSPORTATION p 1051
1 S Wilmington St, Raleigh NC 27601
Tel (919) 707-2500 SIC 9621

NORTH CAROLINA DIVISION OF HIGHWAYS p 1051
1 S Wilmington St, Raleigh NC 27601
Tel (919) 733-7384 SIC 9621

NORTH DAKOTA DEPT OF TRANSPORTATION p 1052
608 E Boulevard Ave, Bismarck ND 58505
Tel (701) 328-2500 SIC 9621

OHIO DEPARTMENT OF TRANSPORTATION p 1077
1980 W Broad St, Columbus OH 43223
Tel (614) 466-7170 SIC 9621

OKLAHOMA DEPARTMENT OF TRANSPORTATION p 1079
200 Ne 21st St, Oklahoma City OK 73105
Tel (405) 521-2631 SIC 9621

DRIVER & MOTOR VEHICLE SERVICES OREGON p 456
1905 Lana Ave Ne, Salem OR 97314
Tel (503) 945-5000 SIC 9621

OREGON DEPARTMENT OF TRANSPORTATION p 1093
355 Capitol St Ne Ms21, Salem OR 97301
Tel (503) 378-5849 SIC 9621

PENNSYLVANIA DEPT OF TRANSPORTATION p 1130
400 North St Fl 8, Harrisburg PA 17120
Tel (717) 787-6875 SIC 9621

TURNPIKE COMMISSION PA p 1493
700 S Eisenhower Blvd, Middletown PA 17057
Tel (717) 939-9551 SIC 9621

AUTORIDAD DE CARRETERAS p 135
Calle De Diego C, San Juan PR 00923
Tel (787) 723-1390 SIC 9621

PUERTO RICO PORTS AUTHORITY p 1191
Lindbergh St 64antigu, San Juan PR 00907
Tel (787) 723-2260 SIC 9621

SOUTH CAROLINA DEPARTMENT OF MOTOR VEHICLES p 1343
10311 Wilson Blvd, Blythewood SC 29016
Tel (803) 896-5000 SIC 9621

SOUTH CAROLINA DEPARTMENT OF TRANSPORTATION p 1343
955 Park St, Columbia SC 29201
Tel (803) 737-1243 SIC 9621

SOUTH DAKOTA DEPARTMENT OF TRANSPORTATION p 1344
700 E Broadway Ave, Pierre SD 57501
Tel (605) 773-3265 SIC 9621

TENNESSEE DEPARTMENT OF TRANSPORTATION p 1438
505 Deaderick St Ste 700, Nashville TN 37243
Tel (615) 741-2848 SIC 9621

TEXAS DEPARTMENT OF TRANSPORTATION p 1443
150 E Riverside Dr, Austin TX 78704
Tel (512) 463-8588 SIC 9621

UTAH DEPARTMENT OF TRANSPORTATION p 1536
4501 S Constitution Blvd, Taylorsville UT 84129
Tel (801) 965-4000 SIC 9621

VERMONT AGENCY OF TRANSPORTATION p 1551
1 National Life Dr # 20, Montpelier VT 05602
Tel (802) 828-2657 SIC 9621

■ TRANSPORTATION SECURITY ADMINISTRATION p 1472
601 S 12th St, Arlington VA 20598
Tel (877) 872-7990 SIC 9621

VIRGINIA PORT AUTHORITY p 1559
600 World Trade Ctr, Norfolk VA 23510
Tel (757) 683-8000 SIC 9621 9111

VIRGINIA DEPARTMENT OF MOTOR VEHICLES p 1559
2300 W Broad St, Richmond VA 23220
Tel (804) 367-0538 SIC 9621

VIRGINIA DEPARTMENT OF TRANSPORTATION p 1559
1401 E Broad St, Richmond VA 23219
Tel (804) 786-2701 SIC 9621

VIRGINIA SECRETARY OF TRANSPORTATION p 1559
1111 E Broad St Fl 3, Richmond VA 23219
Tel (804) 786-8032 SIC 9621

WASHINGTON STATE DEPARTMENT OF LICENSING p 1579
1125 Washington St Se, Olympia WA 98501
Tel (360) 902-3600 SIC 9651 9621

WASHINGTON STATE DEPARTMENT OF TRANSPORTATION p 1579
310 Maple Park Ave Se, Olympia WA 98501
Tel (360) 705-7000 SIC 9621

WEST VIRGINIA DEPARTMENT OF TRANSPORTATION p 1596
1900 Kanawha Blvd E # 109, Charleston WV 25305
Tel (304) 558-0330 SIC 9621

WISCONSIN DEPARTMENT OF TRANSPORTATION p 1618
4802 Sheboygan Ave, Madison WI 53705
Tel (608) 266-2878 SIC 9621

WYOMING DEPARTMENT OF TRANSPORTATION p 1630
5300 Bishop Blvd, Cheyenne WY 82009
Tel (307) 777-4375 SIC 9621

SIC 9631 Regulation & Administration Of Communications & Utilities

■ FEDERAL COMMUNICATIONS COMMISSION p 533
445 12th St Sw, Washington DC 20554
Tel (202) 418-1925 SIC 9631

■ NUCLEAR REGULATORY COMMISSION UNITED STATES p 1066
11555 Rockville Pike, Rockville MD 20852
Tel (800) 368-5642 SIC 9631

US NUCLEAR REGULATORY COMMISSION p 1532
21 Church St, Rockville MD 20850
Tel (301) 415-7000 SIC 9631

■ BONNEVILLE POWER ADMINISTRATION p 200
905 Ne 11th Ave, Portland OR 97232
Tel (503) 230-3000 SIC 9631

■ TENNESSEE VALLEY AUTHORITY p 1438
400 W Summit Hill Dr, Knoxville TN 37902
Tel (865) 632-2101 SIC 4911 9631

WASHINGTON STATE DEPARTMENT OF LICENSING p 1579
421 Black Lake Blvd Sw, Olympia WA 98502
Tel (360) 902-3900 SIC 9631

SIC 9641 Regulation Of Agricultural Marketing & Commodities

FOOD & AGRICULTURE CALIFORNIA DEPT p 563
1220 N St Ste 365, Sacramento CA 95814
Tel (916) 654-0462 SIC 9641

■ AGRICULTURAL MARKETING SERVICE p 36
1400 Independence Ave Sw, Washington DC 20250
Tel (202) 720-8998 SIC 9641

■ FARM SERVICE AGENCY p 529
1400 Independence Ave Sw # 3086, Washington DC 20250
Tel (202) 720-6215 SIC 9641

■ GRAIN INSPECTION PACKERS & STOCKYARDS ADMINISTRATION p 629
1400 Independence Ave Sw, Washington DC 20250
Tel (202) 720-0219 SIC 9641

■ NATIONAL AGRICULTURAL STATISTICS SERVICE p 1009
1400 Independence Ave Sw, Washington DC 20250
Tel (202) 720-2707 SIC 9641

■ NATIONAL INSTITUTE OF FOOD AND AGRICULTURE p 1013
1400 Independence Ave Sw, Washington DC 20250
Tel (202) 720-4276 SIC 9641

■ UNITED STATES DEPARTMENT OF AGRICULTURE p 1512
1400 Independence Ave Sw, Washington DC 20250
Tel (202) 720-3631 SIC 9641

■ USDA RURAL DEVELOPMENT p 1534
1400 Independence Ave Sw, Washington DC 20250
Tel (202) 720-9540 SIC 9641

FLORIDA DEPARTMENT OF AGRICULTURE AND CONSUMER SERVICES p 558
10 The Capitol, Tallahassee FL 32399
Tel (850) 617-7700 SIC 9641 9611 9111

■ AGRICULTURAL RESEARCH SERVICE p 36
5601 Sunnyside Ave, Beltsville MD 20705
Tel (301) 504-1147 SIC 9641

■ USDA APHIS VETERINARY p 1534
4700 River Rd Unit 54, Riverdale MD 20737
Tel (301) 851-2873 SIC 9641

MASSACHUSETTS EXECUTIVE OFFICE OF ENERGY & ENVIRONMENTAL AFFAIRS p 916
100 Cambridge St Ste 900, Boston MA 02114
Tel (617) 626-1000 SIC 9511 9512 9641

NORTH CAROLINA DEPARTMENT OF AGRICULTURE & CONSUMER SERVICES p 1051
2 W Edenton St, Raleigh NC 27601
Tel (919) 707-3000 SIC 9641

EUGENE WATER & ELECTRIC BOARD p 512
500 E 4th Ave, Eugene OR 97401
Tel (541) 685-7000 SIC 4931 9641

■ FOOD & NUTRITION SERVICE p 563
3101 Park Center Dr # 200, Alexandria VA 22302
Tel (703) 305-2060 SIC 9641

SIC 9651 Regulation, Licensing, Inspection Of Misc Commercial Sectors

CALIFORNIA DEPARTMENT OF INSURANCE p 240
300 Capitol Mall Ste 1700, Sacramento CA 95814
Tel (916) 492-3500 SIC 9651

CALIFORNIA DEPARTMENT OF INDUSTRIAL RELATIONS p 240
455 Golden Gate Ave Fl 8, San Francisco CA 94102
Tel (415) 557-0100 SIC 9651

COLORADO DEPARTMENT OF LABOR & EMPLOYMENT p 338
633 17th St Ste 1100, Denver CO 80202
Tel (303) 620-4700 SIC 9651 9441

■ BUREAU OF ALCOHOL TOBACCO FIREARMS & EXPLOSIVES p 226
99 New York Ave Ne # 5514, Washington DC 20002
Tel (202) 648-8500 SIC 9651

■ BUREAU OF LABOR STATISTICS p 226
2 Massachusetts Ave Ne, Washington DC 20212
Tel (202) 691-5200 SIC 9651

■ EMPLOYMENT STANDARDS ADMINISTRATION p 494
200 Constitution Ave Nw, Washington DC 20210
Tel (202) 541-3610 SIC 9651

■ NATIONAL LABOR RELATIONS BOARD p 1014
1015 Half St Se, Washington DC 20003
Tel (202) 273-3884 SIC 9651

■ OCCUPATIONAL SAFETY AND HEALTH ADMINISTRATION p 1072
200 Constitution Ave Nw N3626, Washington DC 20210
Tel (202) 693-2000 SIC 9651

■ OFFICE OF ASSISTANT SECRETARY FOR ADMINISTRATION AND MANAGEMENT p 1075
200 Constitution Ave Nw S-2203, Washington DC 20210
Tel (202) 693-4040 SIC 9651

■ OFFICE OF THE COMPTROLLER OF THE CURRENCY p 1076
400 7th St Sw Ste 3e218, Washington DC 20219
Tel (202) 649-6800 SIC 9651

■ OFFICE OF THRIFT SUPERVISION p 1076
1700 G St Nw, Washington DC 20552
Tel (202) 906-6900 SIC 9651

■ SECURITIES AND EXCHANGE COMMISSION US p 1299
100 F St Ne, Washington DC 20549
Tel (202) 942-8088 SIC 9651

■ UNITED STATES DEPARTMENT OF LABOR p 1512
200 Constitution Ave Nw, Washington DC 20210
Tel (202) 693-6002 SIC 9651

FLORIDA DEPARTMENT OF FINANCIAL SERVICES p 558
200 E Gaines St, Tallahassee FL 32399
Tel (850) 413-3100 SIC 9651

FLORIDA DEPARTMENT OF LABOR AND EMPLOYMENT SECURITY p 558
2012 Capital Cir Se, Tallahassee FL 32399
Tel (850) 942-8341 SIC 9651 9111

GEORGIA DEPARTMENT OF LABOR p 607
148 Andrew Yng Intl Blvd # 100, Atlanta GA 30303
Tel (404) 232-3540 SIC 9651

FIREFIGHTERS PENSION FUND GEORGIA p 543
2171 Eastview Pkwy, Conyers GA 30013
Tel (770) 388-5757 SIC 8631 9651

WORKFORCE COMMISSION LOUISIANA p 1624
1001 N 23rd St, Baton Rouge LA 70802
Tel (225) 342-3103 SIC 9651

MASSACHUSETTS DEPT OF WORKFORCE DEVELOPMENT p 916
1 Ashburton Pl Rm 2112, Boston MA 02108
Tel (617) 626-7122 SIC 9651

NEW JERSEY DEPARTMENT OF LABOR AND WORKFORCE DEVELOPMENT p 1031
1 John Fitch Plz Fl 13, Trenton NJ 08611
Tel (609) 292-2323 SIC 9651

OREGON DEPARTMENT OF CONSUMER AND BUSINESS SERVICES p 1093
350 Winter St Ne, Salem OR 97301
Tel (503) 378-4100 SIC 9651 9311

LIQUOR CONTROL BOARD PENNSYLVANIA p 870
Nw Office Bldg 910, Harrisburg PA 17124
Tel (717) 787-7963 *SIC* 9651

PENNSYLVANIA DEPARTMENT OF LABOR & INDUSTRY p 1130
Labor/Industry Bldg Fl 17, Harrisburg PA 17120
Tel (717) 787-5279 *SIC* 9651

TENNESSEE DEPARTMENT OF LABOR AND WORKFORCE DEVELOPMENT p 1438
220 French Landing Dr, Nashville TN 37243
Tel (615) 741-3002 *SIC* 9651

TEXAS DEPARTMENT OF INSURANCE p 1443
333 Guadalupe St Ste 2, Austin TX 78701
Tel (512) 463-6169 *SIC* 6411 9651

WORKFORCE COMMISSION TEXAS p 1624
101 E 15th St, Austin TX 78778
Tel (512) 463-2222 *SIC* 9651

■ **UNITED STATES PATENT AND TRADEMARK OFFICE** p 1513
600 Dulany St Ste 1, Alexandria VA 22314
Tel (571) 272-4100 *SIC* 9651

■ **MINE SAFETY AND HEALTH ADMINISTRATION** p 973
201 12th St S Ste 401, Arlington VA 22202
Tel (202) 693-9899 *SIC* 9651

VIRGINIA DEPARTMENT OF ALCOHOLIC BEVERAGE CONTROL p 1559
2901 Hermitage Rd, Richmond VA 23220
Tel (804) 213-4400 *SIC* 9651

WASHINGTON STATE DEPARTMENT OF LICENSING p 1579
1125 Washington St Se, Olympia WA 98501
Tel (360) 902-3600 *SIC* 9651 9621

WASHINGTON STATE LIQUOR CONTROL BOARD p 1579
3000 Pacific Ave Se, Olympia WA 98501
Tel (360) 664-1600 *SIC* 9651

WISCONSIN DEPARTMENT OF WORKFORCE DEVELOPMENT p 1618
201 E Wa Ave Rm 400x, Madison WI 53703
Tel (608) 266-3131 *SIC* 9651

SIC 9661 Space Research & Technology

■ **NASA/GEORGE C MARSHALL SPACE FLIGHT CENTER** p 1007
George C Marsha, Huntsville AL 35812
Tel (256) 544-8620 *SIC* 9661

■ **NASA/JET PROPULSION LABORATORY INC** p 1008
4800 Oak Grove Dr, La Canada Flintridge CA 91011
Tel (818) 354-4321 *SIC* 9661

■ **NATIONAL AERONAUTICS AND SPACE ADMINISTRATION** p 1009
300 E St Sw Ste 5r30, Washington DC 20546
Tel (202) 358-0000 *SIC* 9661

■ **NAVAL RESEARCH LABORATORY** p 1019
4555 Overlook Ave Sw, Washington DC 20375
Tel (202) 767-2370 *SIC* 9661

■ **JOHN F KENNEDY SPACE CENTER** p 788
6225 Vectorspace Blvd, Titusville FL 32780
Tel (321) 867-5000 *SIC* 9661

■ **NASA/GODDARD SPACE FLIGHT CENTER** p 1008
8800 Greenbelt Rd, Greenbelt MD 20771
Tel (301) 286-2000 *SIC* 9661

■ **NASA GLENN RESEARCH CENTER** p 1007
21000 Brookpark Rd, Cleveland OH 44135
Tel (216) 433-4000 *SIC* 9661

■ **B JOHNSON NASA/LYNDON SPACE CENTER** p 142
2101 Nasa Pkwy, Houston TX 77058
Tel (281) 483-0123 *SIC* 9661

■ **NASA LANGLEY RESEARCH CENTER** p 1007
11 Langley Blvd, Hampton VA 23681
Tel (757) 864-1000 *SIC* 9661

SIC 9711 National Security

CIVIL AIR PATROL INC p 320
105 S Hansell St Bldg 714, Maxwell Afb AL 36112
Tel (334) 953-7748 *SIC* 9711

DEPARTMENT OF MILITARY ALABAMA p 430
1720 Congsman Wl Dksn Dr, Montgomery AL 36109
Tel (334) 271-7435 *SIC* 9711

ALASKA DEPARTMENT OF MILITARY AND VETERANS AFFAIRS p 45
49000 Army Guard Rd Ste 6, Jber AK 99505
Tel (907) 428-6008 *SIC* 9711 9451

ARIZONA DEPARTMENT OF EMERGENCY AND MILITARY AFFAIRS p 109
5636 E Mcdowell Rd, Phoenix AZ 85008
Tel (602) 267-2700 *SIC* 9711

ARKANSAS DEPARTMENT OF NATIONAL GUARD p 109
Camp Robinson Bldg 6000, North Little Rock AR 72199
Tel (501) 212-5100 *SIC* 9711

■ **NAVAL POSTGRADUATE SCHOOL** p 1019
1 University Cir Rm M10, Monterey CA 93943
Tel (831) 656-7893 *SIC* 8221 9711

DEPARTMENT OF MILITARY CALIFORNIA p 430
9800 Goethe Rd 10, Sacramento CA 95827
Tel (916) 854-3500 *SIC* 9711

COLORADO DEPARTMENT OF MILITARY AND VETERANS AFFAIRS p 339
6848 S Revere Pkwy, Centennial CO 80112
Tel (720) 250-1530 *SIC* 9711

MILITARY DEPARTMENT CONNECTICUT p 969
360 Broad St, Hartford CT 06105
Tel (860) 524-4953 *SIC* 9711

NATIONAL GUARD DELAWARE p 1013
250 Airport Rd, New Castle DE 19720
Tel (302) 326-7160 *SIC* 9711

■ **BUREAU OF CUSTOMS AND BORDER PROTECTION** p 226
1300 Pennsylvania Ave Nw, Washington DC 20229
Tel (202) 927-0529 *SIC* 9711

■ **DEFENSE TECHNOLOGY SECURITY ADMINISTRATION** p 422
2000 Defense Pentagon 4b661, Washington DC 20301
Tel (703) 697-3249 *SIC* 9711

■ **DOD TEST RESOURCE MANGEMENT CENTER** p 447
3000 Defense Pentagon, Washington DC 20301
Tel (571) 372-2700 *SIC* 9711

■ **OFFICE OF THE SECRETARY OF DEFENSE** p 1076
1400 Defense Pentagon, Washington DC 20301
Tel (703) 545-6700 *SIC* 9711

■ **PENTAGON FORCE PROTECTION AGENCY** p 1131
The Pentagon 2e165b, Washington DC 20301
Tel (703) 697-1001 *SIC* 9711

■ **U S ARMY CORPS OF ENGINEERS** p 1497
441 G Street Nw, Washington DC 20314
Tel (804) 435-9362 *SIC* 9711

■ **UNITED STATES DEPARTMENT OF DEFENSE** p 1512
1000 Defense Pentagon # 3, Washington DC 20301
Tel (703) 692-7100 *SIC* 9711

■ **UNITED STATES DEPARTMENT OF HOMELAND SECURITY** p 1512
245 Murray Ln Sw, Washington DC 20528
Tel (202) 282-8000 *SIC* 9711

■ **UNITED STATES DEPARTMENT OF THE AIR FORCE** p 1512
1000 Air Force Pentagon, Washington DC 20330
Tel (703) 545-6700 *SIC* 9711

■ **UNITED STATES DEPARTMENT OF THE ARMY** p 1512
1400 Defense Pentagon, Washington DC 20310
Tel (703) 695-1717 *SIC* 9711

■ **UNITED STATES DEPARTMENT OF THE NAVY** p 1512
1200 Navy Pentagon, Washington DC 20350
Tel (703) 545-6700 *SIC* 9711

■ **UNITED STATES MARINE CORPS** p 1513
Pentagon Rm 4b544, Washington DC 20380
Tel (816) 394-7628 *SIC* 9711

FLORIDA DEPARTMENT OF MILITARY p 558
190 San Marco Ave, Saint Augustine FL 32084
Tel (904) 823-4748 *SIC* 9711

MILITARY DIVISION OF STATE OF IDAHO p 969
4040 W Guard St Bldg 600, Boise ID 83705
Tel (208) 422-5507 *SIC* 9711

ILLINOIS DEPARTMENT OF MILITARY AFFAIRS p 732
1301 N Macarthur Blvd, Springfield IL 62702
Tel (217) 761-3910 *SIC* 9711

INDIANA OFFICE OF ADJUTANT GENERAL p 738
2002 S Holt Rd, Indianapolis IN 46241
Tel (317) 247-3559 *SIC* 9711

IOWA DEPARTMENT OF PUBLIC DEFENSE p 762
7105 Nw 70th Ave, Johnston IA 50131
Tel (515) 252-4211 *SIC* 9711

ADJUTANT GENERALS DEPARTMENT KANSAS p 23
2800 Sw Topeka Blvd, Topeka KS 66611
Tel (785) 274-1000 *SIC* 9711

LOUISIANA DEPARTMENT OF MILITARY AFFAIRS p 880
6400 Saint Claude Ave, New Orleans LA 70117
Tel (504) 278-8071 *SIC* 9711 9451

TWENTIETH SUPPORT COMMAND p 1494
2400 21st St Bush Rver Rd, Aberdeen Proving Gro MD 21010
Tel (410) 436-0330 *SIC* 9711

■ **NATIONAL GEOSPATIAL-INTELLIGENCE AGENCY** p 1012
4600 Sangamore Rd, Bethesda MD 20816
Tel (703) 262-4316 *SIC* 9711

■ **DEFENSE INFORMATION SYSTEMS AGENCY** p 422
6910 Cooper Rd, Fort Meade MD 20755
Tel (301) 225-1474 *SIC* 9711

■ **DEFENSE MEDIA ACTIVITY** p 422
6700 Taylor Ave, Fort Meade MD 20755
Tel (301) 222-6000 *SIC* 9711

MASSACHUSETTS NATIONAL GUARD p 917
2 Randolph Rd, Hanscom Afb MA 01731
Tel (339) 202-3832 *SIC* 9711

MICHIGAN DEPARTMENT OF MILITARY AND VETERANS AFFAIRS p 961
3411 N Martin Luther King, Lansing MI 48906
Tel (517) 481-8083 *SIC* 9711 9451

MILITARY DEPARTMENT MISSISSIPPI p 969
1410 Riverside Dr, Jackson MS 39202
Tel (601) 313-6209 *SIC* 9711

NEW MEXICO DEPT OF MILITARY AFFAIRS p 1032
47 Bataan Blvd, Santa Fe NM 87508
Tel (505) 474-1200 *SIC* 9711

NEW YORK DIVISION OF MILITARY AND NAVAL AFFAIRS p 1035
330 Old Niskayuna Rd, Latham NY 12110
Tel (518) 786-4500 *SIC* 9711

■ **UNITED STATES MILITARY ACADEMY** p 1513
646 Swift Rd, West Point NY 10996
Tel (845) 938-2523 *SIC* 9711

MORALE WELFARE RECREATION ACTIVITY p 988
1401 West Rd, Camp Lejeune NC 28547
Tel (910) 451-2861
SIC 5311 5812 8322 7999 9711

■ **ARMY FORCES COMMAND UNITED STATES** p 112
4700 Knox St, Fort Bragg NC 28310
Tel (910) 570-7200 *SIC* 9711

■ **ARMY RESERVE COMMAND UNITED STATES** p 112
4710 Knox St, Fort Bragg NC 28310
Tel (910) 570-8472 *SIC* 9711

NATIONAL GUARD NORTH CAROLINA p 1013
1636 Gold Star Dr, Raleigh NC 27607
Tel (919) 664-6000 *SIC* 9711

NORTH DAKOTA DEPARTMENT OF MILITARY AFFAIRS p 1052
30 Fraine Barracks Ln, Bismarck ND 58504
Tel (701) 333-2079 *SIC* 9711

OHIO NATIONAL GUARD p 1077
2825 W Dblin Granville Rd, Columbus OH 43235
Tel (614) 336-7000 *SIC* 9711

DEPARTMENT OF MILITARY OREGON p 430
1776 Militia Way Se, Salem OR 97301
Tel (503) 584-3910 *SIC* 9711

AIR NATIONAL GUARD PENNSYLVANIA p 39
215 S O 47 Bldg, Annville PA 17003
Tel (717) 861-8667 *SIC* 9711

PA DEPARTMENT OF MILITARY AND VETERANS AFFAIRS p 1103
47 Bldg S-O, Annville PA 17003
Tel (717) 861-8500 *SIC* 9711 9451

ARMY NATIONAL GUARD PENNSYLVANIA p 112
14th & Calder St, Harrisburg PA 17103
Tel (717) 787-5113 *SIC* 9711

■ **DLA DOCUMENT SERVICES** p 445
5450 Carlisle Pike Bldg 9, Mechanicsburg PA 17050
Tel (717) 605-2362 *SIC* 9711

ADJUTANT GENERAL SOUTH CAROLINA p 23
1 National Guard Rd, Columbia SC 29201
Tel (803) 299-4308 *SIC* 9711

TENNESSEE MILITARY DEPARTMENT p 1438
3041 Sidco Dr Ste 401, Nashville TN 37204
Tel (615) 313-3001 *SIC* 9711

TEXAS DEPARTMENT OF MILITARY p 1443
2200 W 35th St Bldg 11, Austin TX 78703
Tel (512) 782-5001 *SIC* 9711

■ **ARMY & AIR FORCE EXCHANGE SERVICE** p 112
3911 S Walton Walker Blvd, Dallas TX 75236
Tel (214) 312-2011 *SIC* 5399 9711

NATIONAL GUARD UTAH p 1013
12953 S Minuteman Dr, Draper UT 84020
Tel (801) 432-4439 *SIC* 9711

DEPARTMENT OF MILITARY VERMONT p 430
789 National Guard Rd, Colchester VT 05446
Tel (802) 338-3310 *SIC* 9711

■ **DEFENSE HUMAN RESOURCES ACTIVITY** p 422
4800 Mark Center Dr D, Alexandria VA 22350
Tel (571) 372-1949 *SIC* 9711

■ **DEPARTMENT OF DEFENSE EDUCATION ACTIVITY** p 430
4800 Mark Center Dr, Alexandria VA 22350
Tel (571) 372-1337 *SIC* 9711 9411

■ **MILITARY SURFACE DEPLOYMENT & DISTRIBUTION COMMAND** p 969
200 Stovall St Fl 18, Alexandria VA 22332
Tel (703) 428-2753 *SIC* 9711

■ **OFFICE OF THE INSPECTOR GENERAL** p 1076
4800 Mark Center Dr, Alexandria VA 22350
Tel (703) 604-8669 *SIC* 9711

■ **DEFENSE HEALTH AGENCY** p 422
7700 Arlington Blvd # 5101, Falls Church VA 22042
Tel (703) 681-1730 *SIC* 9431 9711

■ **DOD PATIENT SAFETY PROGRAM** p 447
5111 Leesburg Pike # 810, Falls Church VA 22041
Tel (703) 681-0064 *SIC* 9711

■ **DEFENSE LOGISTICS AGENCY** p 422
Andrew T Mcnamara Bld, Fort Belvoir VA 22060
Tel (703) 767-4012 *SIC* 9711

■ **DEFENSE COMMISSARY AGENCY** p 422
1300 E Ave, Fort Lee VA 23801
Tel (804) 734-8000 *SIC* 9711

192D COMMUNICATIONS FLIGHT p 1
165 Sweeney Blvd Ste 214, Langley Afb VA 23665
Tel (757) 764-1607 *SIC* 9711

■ **DEFENSE SECURITY SERVICE** p 422
27130 Telegraph Rd, Quantico VA 22134
Tel (571) 305-6751 *SIC* 9711

■ **NAVY EXCHANGE SERVICE COMMAND** p 1020
3280 Virginia Beach Blvd, Virginia Beach VA 23452
Tel (757) 631-3696 *SIC* 5399 9711

WEST VIRGINIA DEPARTMENT OF MILITARY AFFAIRS AND PUBLIC SAFETY p 1596
1900 Kanawha Blvd E Rm 1, Charleston WV 25305
Tel (304) 558-8045 *SIC* 9711 9221 9229

■ **BIOMETRICS IDENTITY MANAGEMENT AGENCY** p 184
340 Washington Ave, Clarksburg WV 26301
Tel (304) 326-3000 *SIC* 9711

DEPARTMENT OF MILITARY WYOMING p 430
5500 Bishop Blvd, Cheyenne WY 82009
Tel (307) 772-6201 *SIC* 9711

SIC 9721 International Affairs

■ **BROADCASTING BOARD OF GOVERNORS** p 215
330 Independence Ave Sw # 3360, Washington DC 20237
Tel (202) 203-4000 *SIC* 9721

■ **BUREAU OF CONSULAR AFFAIRS** p 226
2201 C St Nw Ste 6811, Washington DC 20520
Tel (202) 647-9576 *SIC* 9721

■ **BUREAU OF IMMIGRATION & CUSTOMS ENFORCEMENT** p 226
500 12th St Sw, Washington DC 20536
Tel (202) 732-2427 *SIC* 9721 9311

■ **CITIZENSHIP & IMMIGRATION SERVICES US** p 311
20 Ma Ave Nw Rm 3000, Washington DC 20529
Tel (202) 272-1000 *SIC* 9721

■ **EMBASSY OF UNITED STATES OF AMERICA** p 490
2201 C St Nw, Washington DC 20520
Tel (202) 895-3500 *SIC* 9721

■ **PEACE CORPS** p 1125
1111 20th St Nw, Washington DC 20526
Tel (202) 692-2000 *SIC* 9721

■ **UNITED STATES DEPT OF STATE** p 1513
2201 C St Nw, Washington DC 20520
Tel (202) 632-9367 *SIC* 9721

DEPARTMENT OF ECONOMIC AND SOCIAL AFFAIRS p 430
Secretariat Bldg Unitedn, New York NY 10003
Tel (212) 963-1707 *SIC* 9721

EUROPEAN UNION DELEGATION TO UNITED NATION p 513
666 3rd Ave Fl 31, New York NY 10017
Tel (212) 401-0117 *SIC* 9721

UNITED NATIONS p 1510
405 E 42nd St Bsmt 1, New York NY 10017
Tel (212) 963-1234 *SIC* 9721

UNITED NATIONS DEVELOPMENT PROGRAMME p 1510
1 United Nations Plz Fl 3, New York NY 10017
Tel (212) 906-5000 *SIC* 9721

D-U-N-S 15-117-9652 IMP/EXP
■ 3M PURIFICATION INC
(*Suby of* 3M CO) ★
400 Research Pkwy, Meriden, CT 06450-7172
Tel (203) 237-5541 *Founded/Ownrshp* 2005
Sales 492.0MM^E *EMP* 2,200
SIC 3589 3569 Water purification equipment, household type; Filters; Filters, general line: industrial; Filters & strainers, pipeline
Ch Bd: Inge Thulin
**Ch Bd:* Mark G Kachur
**Pr:* Timothy B Carney
**CFO:* Frederick C Flynn Jr
VP: Andrew T Rensink
VP: David Schaefer
VP: Witold Witwicki
**Genl Mgr:* David Schaeffer
IT Man: Michael Brown
Software D: Dian Zheng
Opers Mgr: Raymond Ponden

D-U-N-S 06-773-8997 IMP
■ 3M TOUCH SYSTEMS INC
(*Suby of* 3M CO) ★
501 Griffin Brook Dr, Methuen, MA 01844-1870
Tel (978) 659-0053 *Founded/Ownrshp* 1983
Sales 120.3MM^E *EMP* 845
SIC 3577 Computer peripheral equipment
Pr: Ty Silberhorn
**Treas:* Scott Krohn
**VP:* Andrew Wong
**Dir Bus:* Terry Jones
Tech Mgr: Dick Driscoll
Ql Cn Mgr: Peter Naugler
Snr Mgr: Steve Martin
Board of Directors: Peter Brumme, Frank Manning, Edward J Stewart III

D-U-N-S 00-825-6356 IMP
■ 3M UNITEK CORP
(*Suby of* 3M CO) ★
2724 Peck Rd, Monrovia, CA 91016-5097
Tel (626) 445-7960 *Founded/Ownrshp* 1987
Sales 104.1MM^E *EMP* 480
SIC 3843 Orthodontic appliances; Dental hand instruments; Dental laboratory equipment
CEO: Mary Jo Abler
**VP:* Fred Palensky
Div Mgr: Richard Iverson
IT Man: Vincent Martinez
IT Man: James Pang
Mktg Dir: Barry Grant

D-U-N-S 79-177-7501
3MD INC
DENALI ADVNCED INTEGRATION DIV
17735 Ne 65th St Ste 130, Redmond, WA 98052-4924
Tel (425) 467-8000 *Founded/Ownrshp* 1992
Sales 238.1MM *EMP* 412^E
Accts Smith & Dekay Ps Bellevue Wa
SIC 5045 8742 Computers, peripherals & software; Business consultant
Pr: Mohamad Daher
**COO:* Chad Gardner
CFO: David Easley
**CFO:* David M Easley-CPA
**Treas:* Majdi Daher
VP: Bernardo Sicard
VP: Tracy Smith
Dir Bus: Al Panebianco
**CTO:* Michael Leeper
Dir IT: Jorge Legon
IT Man: John Madden

3PD
See XPO LAST MILE INC

D-U-N-S 00-910-4381 IMP/EXP
3V SIGMA USA INC
(*Suby of* 3V PARTECIPAZIONI INDUSTRIALI SPA)
888 Woodstock St, Georgetown, SC 29440-4789
Tel (843) 546-8556 *Founded/Ownrshp* 1978
Sales 111.5MM^E *EMP* 465
SIC 2869 2899 8731 Industrial organic chemicals; Chemical preparations; Biological research
Ex VP: Enrico Sigismondi
VP: Giorgio Ferraris
Brnch Mgr: John Centioni
Mktg Mgr: Sean Crews
Board of Directors: John Centioni, Paul Seccomandi, Enrico Sigismondi

3W WARREN FUELS
See WARREN FUEL CO

4

D-U-N-S 80-672-6261 EXP
4 EARTH FARMS INC
5555 E Olympic Blvd, Commerce, CA 90022-5129
Tel (323) 201-5800 *Founded/Ownrshp* 2001
Sales 209.0MM *EMP* 330^E
SIC 5148 Fresh fruits & vegetables
CEO: David Lake
**COO:* Robert Lake
**CFO:* Marc Serrio
VP: Jeff Thoreson
Dir IT: Ben Bowden

D-U-N-S 01-334-1420 IMP
4 OVER LLC (CA)
(*Suby of* FOUR CENTS HOLDINGS, INC.)
5900 San Fernando Rd D, Glendale, CA 91202-2773
Tel (818) 246-1170 *Founded/Ownrshp* 2001
Sales 173.3MM^E *EMP* 300^E
SIC 2759 7336 Commercial printing; Commercial art & graphic design
CEO: Zarik Megerdichian
**Pr:* Tina Hartounian
CFO: Larry Hariton
VP: Patrick Aristakian
Web Dev: Ryan West
Opers Supe: Vahe Safarian
Plnt Mgr: Rafi Majnonian

D-U-N-S 05-430-9000
4 RIVERS EQUIPMENT LLC
JOHN DEERE
1100 E Cheyenne Rd, Colorado Springs, CO 80905-2829
Tel (800) 364-3029 *Founded/Ownrshp* 1968, 1926
Sales 88.7MM^E *EMP* 300
SIC 5084

D-U-N-S 04-188-3971 IMP/EXP
■ 4 SURE.COM INC
TECH DEPOT
(*Suby of* OFFICE DEPOT INC) ★
55 Corporate Dr Ste 5, Trumbull, CT 06611-1377
Tel (203) 615-7000 *Founded/Ownrshp* 2001
Sales 100.1MM^E *EMP* 275
SIC 5045 5734 Computer software; Computer software & accessories
Pr: Stephen R Calkins
**Pr:* Bruce Martin
**CFO:* Jim Williams
**VP:* Karim Hadchiti
**VP:* Candy Murphy
IT Man: Charlie Huda

4 WHEEL PARTS PERFORMANCE CTRS
See TAP WORLDWIDE LLC

D-U-N-S 00-379-2041
4- COUNTY ELECTRIC POWER ASSOCIATION (MS)
5265 S Frontage Rd, Columbus, MS 39701-8562
Tel (662) 327-8900 *Founded/Ownrshp* 1938
Sales 118.7MM *EMP* 161
Accts Watkins Ward And Stafford Pl
SIC 4911 Distribution, electric power
CEO: Joe Cade
**CFO:* Marcus Stone
Dist Mgr: Cliff Wall

40 HOURS STAFFING
See 40 HRS INC

D-U-N-S 01-347-8835
40 HRS INC
40 HOURS STAFFING
1669 Flanigan Dr, San Jose, CA 95121-1682
Tel (408) 414-0158 *Founded/Ownrshp* 2006
Sales 31.7MM^E *EMP* 1,000
SIC 7361 Employment agencies
Pr: Bryan Phan

D-U-N-S 19-442-6011
4004 INC
12 Harbor Park Dr, Port Washington, NY 11050-4649
Tel (516) 829-4730 *Founded/Ownrshp* 1985
Sales 59.9MM^E *EMP* 1,000
SIC 5699 T-shirts, custom printed; Customized clothing & apparel
Ch Bd: Barry Prevor
**Pr:* Steven Shore
VP: AVI Sonpal

44 FINANCE DEPARTMENT
See COUNTY OF FORSYTH

D-U-N-S 36-228-4536
44 NEW ENGLAND MANAGEMENT CO
HHM
(*Suby of* HERSHA HOSPITALITY MANAGEMENT LP) ★
450 Friendship Rd, Harrisburg, PA 17111-1203
Tel (717) 412-5500 *Founded/Ownrshp* 2004
Sales 73.0MM^E *EMP* 1,600
SIC 7011 Hotels & motels
Pr: Naveen P Kakarla
**Pr:* Hasu Shah
**COO:* Michael Murray
**Ex VP:* Gregory Ade
**Ex VP:* Sal Shahriar
**Sr VP:* Dani Elhachem
**Sr VP:* Simon J Little
**VP:* Joann Weber
Genl Mgr: George Bottini
IT Man: Laurie Stone

D-U-N-S 07-984-3034
4701 NORTH MERIDIAN LLC
4218 Ne 22nd Ave Fl 2, Miami, FL 33137
Tel (305) 573-3900 *Founded/Ownrshp* 2012
Sales 550.0MM *EMP* 9^E
SIC 6531 Real estate managers

D-U-N-S 01-078-9605
488 PERFORMANCE GROUP INC (NY)
MADISON PERFORMANCE GROUP
18 E 41st St Fl 13, New York, NY 10017-6245
Tel (212) 758-4385 *Founded/Ownrshp* 1974
Sales 121.0MM *EMP* 140
Accts Baker Tilly Virchow Krause Ll
SIC 8742 Incentive or award program consultant
CEO: Werner Haase
**COO:* Alex Alaminois
**CFO:* James Edwards
Ex VP: Rick Evans
Sr VP: Chris Esposito
Sr VP: Mike Ryan
Sr VP: Kim Silberman
**VP:* Brian Thornsberry
Dir Bus: Craig Fuller
Dir Bus: John Tate
Dir Bus: Val Tate

D-U-N-S 07-659-5687
4E BRANDS NORTHAMERICA LLC
17806 W Interstate 10 # 30, San Antonio, TX 78257-8221
Tel (210) 819-7385 *Founded/Ownrshp* 2014
Sales 6.0MM *EMP* 1,000
SIC 2841 Soap & other detergents
Prin: Juan Carlos Gonzalez Olvera

D-U-N-S 00-609-8842 IMP/EXP
4FRONT ENGINEERED SOLUTIONS INC (WI)
4FRONT ENTREMATIC
(*Suby of* ENTREMATIC GROUP AB)
1612 Hutton Dr Ste 140, Carrollton, TX 75006-6642
Tel (972) 466-0707 *Founded/Ownrshp* 1953, 2012
Sales 275.8MM^E *EMP* 800
SIC 3537 Loading docks: portable, adjustable & hydraulic
Pr: Keith F Moore
**CFO:* Paul Venesky
**VP:* Al Thomson
IT Man: Amy Skoug
Opers Mgr: Allison Fitch
Plnt Mgr: Brian Barboza
Manager: Kim Hiter
Manager: John Swofford
Sls Mgr: Dan Linder

4FRONT ENTREMATIC
See 4FRONT ENGINEERED SOLUTIONS INC

D-U-N-S 82-982-3306
4FRONT HOLDINGS INC
(*Suby of* ASSA ABLOY AB)
1612 Hutton Dr Ste 140, Carrollton, TX 75006-6642
Tel (972) 466-0707 *Founded/Ownrshp* 2012
Sales 163.1MM *EMP* 650
Accts Bdo Usa Llp Dallas Tx
SIC 3537 3999 3448 Loading docks: portable, adjustable & hydraulic; Dock equipment & supplies, industrial; Prefabricated metal buildings
Pr: Keith F Moore
**CFO:* Paul R Venesky
**Treas:* Christopher Hughes
**Sr VP:* Stephen W Sprunger
**Sr VP:* Allan L Thomson
**VP:* Steven D Flear
**VP:* John A Hatherly
**VP:* Jon Kleinke

D-U-N-S 84-194-2852
4G WIRELESS INC
VERIZON WIRELESS
8871 Research Dr, Irvine, CA 92618-4236
Tel (949) 748-6100 *Founded/Ownrshp* 2007
Sales 450.0MM^E *EMP* 550^E
SIC 4812 Cellular telephone services
Pr: Mohammad Honarkar
Dist Mgr: Juan Collazo
Dist Mgr: James Hillman
Dist Mgr: Andrea Odom
Dist Mgr: Fernando Ramos
Dist Mgr: Matthew Scott
Store Mgr: Parisa Honarkar
CTO: Siavosh Talakar
Genl Couns: Ellie Sadeghi

D-U-N-S 12-207-1905
4IMPRINT INC
(*Suby of* 4 IMPRINT USA LIMITED)
101 Commerce St, Oshkosh, WI 54901-4864
Tel (920) 236-7272 *Founded/Ownrshp* 1995
Sales 479.2MM *EMP* 800^E
SIC 5199

4INKJETS.COM
See LD PRODUCTS INC

D-U-N-S 17-926-6288
4L TECHNOLOGIES INC
CLOVER GLOBAL
4200 Columbus St, Ottawa, IL 61350-9538
Tel (815) 431-8100 *Founded/Ownrshp* 1996
Sales 374.5MM^E *EMP* 1,280^E
SIC 3555 Printing trades machinery
Pr: Dan Ruhl
VP: Brian Hines

D-U-N-S 09-439-6223
4M BUILDING SOLUTIONS INC
MMMM
2827 Clark Ave, Saint Louis, MO 63103-2505
Tel (314) 535-2100 *Founded/Ownrshp* 1978
Sales 50.0MM *EMP* 2,800
SIC 7349 Janitorial service, contract basis; Window cleaning
Pr: Tim Murch
**COO:* Steve Crain
**CFO:* Judy Botz
Dir Bus: Kyle Brown
Dir Bus: Amy Olson
Rgnl Mgr: Greg Russell
Area Mgr: Layton Hartley
Area Mgr: Charlotte Romero
Area Mgr: Kimberly Stevenson
Brnch Mgr: Terry Miller
Dist Mgr: Lacey Brown

5

5 STAR RESORT
See SEA ISLAND CO

D-U-N-S 19-493-3768
50 X 20 HOLDING CO INC
SCHUMACHER HOMES
2715 Wise Ave Nw, Canton, OH 44708-1641
Tel (330) 478-4500 *Founded/Ownrshp* 1991
Sales 190.4MM^E *EMP* 277
SIC 1521 New construction, single-family houses
Pr: Paul T Schumacher
Pr: Larry Scheetz
**COO:* William Schumacher
CFO: Roger Hercl
CFO: Chad Kane
Genl Mgr: Ryan Gleaves
Genl Mgr: Brian Lambert
Genl Mgr: Tim Reese
Genl Mgr: Ryan Smith
Genl Mgr: Rich Smothers
Genl Mgr: Nick Wichman

D-U-N-S 13-582-9252 IMP/EXP
511 INC
5.11 TACTICAL SERIES
1360 Reynolds Ave Ste 101, Irvine, CA 92614-5535
Tel (949) 800-1511 *Founded/Ownrshp* 2003
Sales 84.7MM^E *EMP* 400^E
SIC 5699 2231 5139 2393 Uniforms & work clothing; Apparel & outerwear broadwoven fabrics; Boots; Canvas bags
CEO: Thomas Edward Davin
**Pr:* Dan Costa
**CFO:* Jeff Hamilton
CFO: Dave Unter
Ofcr: Bob Neapole
**VP:* Francisco Morales
VP: John Wicks
Creative D: Matt Frederick
CTO: Tim Terry
IT Man: Shawna Bailey
Opers Mgr: Ehsan Argand

5.11 TACTICAL SERIES
See 511 INC

555 EAST
See KINGS SEAFOOD CO LLC

D-U-N-S 09-806-1216
5LINX ENTERPRISES INC
GLOBALINX
1 S Clinton Ave Ste 800, Rochester, NY 14604-1796
Tel (585) 334-2600 *Founded/Ownrshp* 2002
Sales 112.0MM *EMP* 275^E
Accts Kasperski Owen & Dinan Cpas L
SIC 7389 Personal service agents, brokers & bureaus
VP: William Faucette
**CEO:* Craig Jerabeck
COO: David Shaffer
VP: Doris Anokye
**VP:* Mike Baron
VP: Marshall Fortson
**VP:* Jason Guck
VP: Tewan Lowe
VP: Daniel Lynem
**VP:* Jeb Tyler
Exec: Alexandra Benjamin
Exec: Jessica Boone
Exec: Kiara Cole
Exec: Frank Delgado
Exec: Oliver Green
Exec: Carol Hart-Alexander
Exec: Lagonia Hayes
Exec: Demond High
Exec: Chris Hildreth
Exec: Bobbi Keys
Exec: Terrell Lowery

6

D-U-N-S 95-838-8845
618 MAIN CLOTHING CORP
MADRAG 10 SPOT
5601 W Side Ave Ste 2, North Bergen, NJ 07047-6453
Tel (201) 319-1400 *Founded/Ownrshp* 1994
Sales 134.6MM^E *EMP* 900
SIC 5621 Women's clothing stores
Pr: Howard Hoffman
**VP:* Jason Hoffman
VP: Tony Sarno

D-U-N-S 96-353-0535
640 LAS VEGAS HEALTHCARE AND REHABIL
2832 S Maryland Pkwy, Las Vegas, NV 89109-1502
Tel (702) 735-5848 *Founded/Ownrshp* 2010
Sales 904.5MM *EMP* 17^E
SIC 8051 Skilled nursing care facilities

7

7 FOR ALL MANKIND
See SEVEN FOR ALL MANKIND LLC

7-ELEVEN
See PRIMA MARKETING LLC

7-ELEVEN
See SOUTHWEST CONVENIENCE STORES LLC

7-ELEVEN
See TFS NEWCO LLC

7-ELEVEN
See SEVEN-ELEVEN HAWAII INC

D-U-N-S 00-734-7602 IMP
7-ELEVEN INC
(*Suby of* SEVEN-ELEVEN JAPAN CO., LTD.)
3200 Hackberry Rd, Irving, TX 75063-0131
Tel (972) 828-0711 *Founded/Ownrshp* 1991
Sales 6.0MMM^E *EMP* 27,866
SIC 5411 6794 Convenience stores, chain; Franchises, selling or licensing
Pr: Joseph M Depinto
**COO:* Darren Rebelez
**COO:* Chris Tanco
**CFO:* Stanley Reynolds
CFO: Stanley W Reynolds
**Treas:* David Seltzer
Ex VP: Jesus H Delgado-Jenkins
**Ex VP:* Jesus Delgado Jenkins
Ex VP: Shizuma Noda
**Ex VP:* Bryan F Smith Jr
**Sr VP:* Rankin Gasaway
VP: Sean Duffy
VP: Sherri Durst
**VP:* Dave Fenton
VP: Steve Hall
VP: Daniel Hayes
VP: Steven Holland
VP: Brad Jenkins
VP: Sonja Lamb
VP: Gary Lockhart
VP: Bobby Schwerin

D-U-N-S 03-304-9487
7-ELEVEN LLC
2021 S Macarthur Blvd, Oklahoma City, OK 73128-1630
Tel (405) 682-5711 *Founded/Ownrshp* 1927
Sales 137.9MM^E *EMP* 900
SIC 5411 5541

700 CLUB
See CHRISTIAN BROADCASTING NETWORK INC

771 ROSE
See FLORAL SPECIALTIES INC

D-U-N-S 08-017-7952
7MOD2 LLC
6565 Wetherole St Apt 3j, Rego Park, NY 11374-4776
Tel (347) 581-3742 *Founded/Ownrshp* 2016
Sales 100.0MM *EMP* 2
SIC 8712 House designer

D-U-N-S 60-780-1214 IMP
80/20 INC
1701 S 400 E, Columbia City, IN 46725-8753
Tel (260) 248-8030 *Founded/Ownrshp* 1990
Sales 101.6MM[E] *EMP* 300
SIC 3354 Shapes, extruded aluminum
Pr: Don Wood
**VP:* Scott Brown
**VP:* David Wood
Dir IT: Dave Nelson
Tech Mgr: Kirby Young
Sls Mgr: Dan McLellan

D-U-N-S 11-996-8402
800-JR CIGAR INC
(*Suby of* ALTADIS SA)
301 State Route 10, Whippany, NJ 07981-2104
Tel (973) 884-9555 *Founded/Ownrshp* 2003
Sales 189.4MM[E] *EMP* 1,025
SIC 5194 5993 5961 Cigars; Tobacco stores & stands; Catalog & mail-order houses
Pr: Lew Rothman
Pt: Michael Keith
**CFO:* Michael E Colleton
**VP:* Lavonda M Rothman
**VP:* Jane Vargas

D-U-N-S 61-095-3614 EXP
84 LUMBER CO
1019 Route 519, Eighty Four, PA 15330-2813
Tel (724) 228-8820 *Founded/Ownrshp* 1995
Sales 2.1MMM[E] *EMP* 3,979
Accts Pricewaterhousecoopers Llp
SIC 2431 2439 5031 5211 Millwork; Structural wood members; Lumber, plywood & millwork; Lumber & other building materials
Pr: Maggie Hardy Magerko
Pt: Cheri Bomar
Pt: Joseph A Hardy
Pr: Mark Ingersoll
CEO: Joe Hardy
COO: Frank Cicero
CFO: Paul Lentz
CFO: Dan Wallac
VP: Billy Ball
VP: Phil Garuccio
VP: Ron Harbert
VP: Becky Mancuso
VP: Sid McAllister

D-U-N-S 17-774-2863
▲ 8X8 INC
2125 Onel Dr, San Jose, CA 95131-2032
Tel (408) 727-1885 *Founded/Ownrshp* 1987
Sales 209.3MM *EMP* 810[E]
Tkr Sym EGHT *Exch* NAS
SIC 4813 7372 Telephone communication, except radio; ; Prepackaged software
CEO: Vikram Verma
**Ch Bd:* Bryan Martin
CFO: Mary Ellen Genovese
Sr VP: Puneet Arora
Sr VP: Darren Hakeman
IT Man: Ryan Ritchie
Mktg Dir: Beth Carney
Sls Mgr: Mike Lally
Snr PM: Michael Yankey
Snr Mgr: Toussaint Celestin
Board of Directors: Guy L Hecker Jr, Vladimir Jacimovic, Ian Potter, Eric Salzman

D-U-N-S 83-290-6783
95TH IH ASSOCIATES LLC
EAST 95TH STREET APARTMENTS
238 E 95th St, New York, NY 10128-3848
Tel (212) 996-0646 *Founded/Ownrshp* 2009
Sales 25.3MM[E] *EMP* 1,828
SIC 6531 Real estate agents & managers

D-U-N-S 14-411-9468
99 BOSTON INC
99 RESTAURANT & PUB
(*Suby of* OCHARLEYS RESTAURANTS) ★
160 Olympia Ave, Woburn, MA 01801-2058
Tel (781) 933-8999 *Founded/Ownrshp* 2003
Sales 166.2MM[E] *EMP* 4,600
SIC 5812 5813 American restaurant; Cocktail lounge
Pr: Charlie Noyes
**Ex VP:* John Cussen
VP: Gregory Monahan
VP: Brad Schiff

99 CENT ONLY STORE
See NUMBER HOLDINGS INC

D-U-N-S 09-443-5237 IMP/EXP
99 CENTS ONLY STORES LLC (CA)
BARGAIN WHOLESALE
(*Suby of* 99 CENT ONLY STORE) ★
4000 Union Pacific Ave, Commerce, CA 90023-3202
Tel (323) 980-8145 *Founded/Ownrshp* 1982, 2012
Sales 2.0MMM *EMP* 15,000
SIC 5411 5331 5199 Grocery stores, chain; Variety stores; General merchandise, non-durable
CEO: Geoffrey Covert
**Ch Bd:* David Kaplan
Pr: Mike Matteri
**CFO:* Christopher A Laurence
**CFO:* Bradley Lukow
**CFO:* Felicia Thornton
CFO: Felicia D Thornton
**Chf Mktg O:* Michael Kvitko
**Ofcr:* Jack L Sinclair
Ex VP: James Ritter
Sr VP: Jeff Gold
**Sr VP:* Jim Parros
VP: Dan Abfalter
VP: Joseph Blanding
VP: Michael Botterman
VP: Alondra Cervantes
VP: Jose Gomez
VP: Jason Kidd
VP: Grant Kim
VP: Carlos Lopez
VP: Mario Medina
Board of Directors: Richard Anicetti, Norman Axelrod, Michael Fung, Andrew Giancamilli, Dennis Gies, Scott Nishi, Adam Stein

99 RANCH MARKET
See TAWA SUPERMARKET INC

99 RESTAURANT & PUB
See 99 BOSTON INC

A

D-U-N-S 04-849-1666
A & A MAINTENANCE ENTERPRISE INC
965 Midland Ave, Yonkers, NY 10704-1027
Tel (914) 969-0009 *Founded/Ownrshp* 1973
Sales 75.7MM[E] *EMP* 1,500
SIC 7349 1721 1542 4959 0782 Building maintenance services; Painting & paper hanging; Commercial & office buildings, renovation & repair; Snowplowing; Landscape contractors
Ch Bd: Armando Rodriquez Jr
Ex VP: Michael Dechristopher
VP: Ed Finkenstadt
VP: Anne Rossi
VP: Eric Wheeler
Opers Mgr: Angel Romero
Opers Mgr: John Tholl

D-U-N-S 05-053-9035
A & A MANUFACTURING CO INC (CA)
1675 Sampson Ave, Corona, CA 92879-1889
Tel (951) 371-8090 *Founded/Ownrshp* 1989
Sales 152.4MM *EMP* 3
Accts Roorda Piquet & Bessee Inc
SIC 3691 Storage batteries
Pr: Terry Agrelius
**CFO:* Steve Kay

D-U-N-S 02-118-0872
A & A STEPPING STONE MFG INC
10291 Ophir Rd, Newcastle, CA 95658-9504
Tel (530) 885-7481 *Founded/Ownrshp* 1974
Sales 13.5MM *EMP* 3,041
SIC 5211 3272 Concrete & cinder block; Precast terrazo or concrete products
Owner: Keith S Arellano
**VP:* Diane Arellano
Off Mgr: Kassie Jacinto

D-U-N-S 03-017-5350 IMP
■ A & B PROCESS SYSTEMS CORP
(*Suby of* JBT) ★
201 S Wisconsin Ave, Stratford, WI 54484-9678
Tel (715) 687-4332 *Founded/Ownrshp* 2015
Sales 224.7MM[E] *EMP* 440
SIC 3443 1799 8711 Industrial vessels, tanks & containers; Food service equipment installation; Mechanical engineering
CEO: Scott Doescher
Pr: Richard Angerhofer
**Pr:* Brian Gehrke
**Pr:* Glenn Linzmeier
**COO:* Troy Weik
**CFO:* Laura Strek
VP: Nancy Frodl
VP: Mark Schmidt
Genl Mgr: William Hilgemann
QA Dir: Travis Krall
Plnt Mgr: Scott Brandt

D-U-N-S 08-656-1024 IMP/EXP
A & B VALVE AND PIPING SYSTEMS LLC
3845 Cypress Creek Pkwy # 451, Houston, TX 77068-3551
Tel (281) 444-6996 *Founded/Ownrshp* 2005
Sales 99.0MM[E] *EMP* 45
SIC 5082

A & E DISTRIBUTION CENTER
See A & E STORES INC

D-U-N-S 07-103-5034 IMP
A & E STORES INC
A & E DISTRIBUTION CENTER
1000 Huyler St, Teterboro, NJ 07608-1142
Tel (201) 393-0600 *Founded/Ownrshp* 1986
Sales 160.8MM[E] *EMP* 1,000
Accts Cohnreznick
SIC 5621 8721 4226 7389 Ready-to-wear apparel, women's; Billing & bookkeeping service; Special warehousing & storage; Purchasing service
Ch Bd: Alan A Ades
**Ex VP:* Albert Erani
**Ex VP:* Dennis Erani
Sr VP: Murray Setton
VP: Bruce Kleiman
VP: Mark McNerney
Dist Mgr: Hyacinth Wilson
CIO: Bill Clayton
Opers Mgr: Luis Ruiz
VP Mktg: Jim Hamlin

D-U-N-S 15-523-1897 IMP
A & E TIRE INC
HARVEY'S TIRE EXCHANGE
3855 E 52nd Ave, Denver, CO 80216-2407
Tel (303) 308-6900 *Founded/Ownrshp* 1986
Sales 155.2MM[E] *EMP* 125
SIC 5014 7534 5531 Tires & tubes; Tire retreading & repair shops; Automotive & home supply stores
Pr: Patricia Elliott
**Sec:* Edward Elliot
**VP:* Del Tinscher
Store Mgr: Will Husted
IT Man: Roger Klapp
Site Mgr: Josh Hergert
Sls Mgr: Todd Holub

D-U-N-S 14-292-0458
A & G QUALITY BUILDERS INC
1413 Powhatan St, Alexandria, VA 22314-1343
Tel (703) 549-8682 *Founded/Ownrshp* 2003
Sales 150.0MM *EMP* 3
SIC 1522 Hotel/motel & multi-family home renovation & remodeling
Pr: Fernando Alvarez

A & I PRODUCTS
See ATI PRODUCTS INC

D-U-N-S 18-481-3350
A & K CONSTRUCTION INC
100 Calloway Ct, Paducah, KY 42001-9035
Tel (270) 441-7752 *Founded/Ownrshp* 1987
Sales 85.1MM *EMP* 100
Accts William Williams & Lentz Llp
SIC 1542 1541 Commercial & office building, new construction; Industrial buildings & warehouses
Pr: Ken Hunt
**Sec:* Beth Hunt
**Ex VP:* Mark White
**VP:* Ken Durbin
Snr PM: George Durbin

D-U-N-S 04-132-2256
A & K EARTH MOVERS INC
515 Windmill Dr, Fallon, NV 89406-5501
Tel (775) 825-1636 *Founded/Ownrshp* 1957
Sales 85.6MM[E] *EMP* 250
Accts Brown Fink Boyce & Astle Ll
SIC 1611 1542 Highway & street construction; Commercial & office building contractors
Pr: K Bart Hiatt
**Pr:* Bart Hiatt
**CFO:* Sharon Ream
**VP:* Michael A Hiatt
Genl Mgr: Kimberly Bell
Mtls Mgr: Lyle Kibbe

D-U-N-S 06-330-4166 IMP/EXP
A & K RAILROAD MATERIALS INC
1505 S Redwood Rd, Salt Lake City, UT 84104-5106
Tel (801) 974-5484 *Founded/Ownrshp* 2002
Sales 150.1MM *EMP* 500
Accts Schmidt Westergard & Company
SIC 5088 Railroad equipment & supplies
Pr: Rhonda Nicoloff
**CFO:* Jeff Galyean
**VP:* Doug Davis
**VP:* Phil Poce
**VP:* Rocky Smith

D-U-N-S 07-887-7280 IMP
A & M (2015) LLC
MANDEE
5901 W Side Ave Ste 500, North Bergen, NJ 07047-6451
Tel (201) 868-6220 *Founded/Ownrshp* 2013
Sales 172.8MM[E] *EMP* 1,500
SIC 5621 Ready-to-wear apparel, women's
Ch: Michael Gold

A & M BUSINESS INTERIOR SVCS
See OMNI WORKSPACE CO LLC

D-U-N-S 07-214-6702
A & M SPECIAL PURCHASING INC
OCEAN STATE JOBBERS
375 Commerce Park Rd, North Kingstown, RI 02852-8420
Tel (401) 295-2672 *Founded/Ownrshp* 1983
Sales 98.4MM[E] *EMP* 4,000
SIC 8721 Payroll accounting service
Pr: Marc Perlman
**CFO:* John Conforti
**VP:* Allan Perlman
Dir IT: Catherine Gilchrist
Dir IT: Patti Morley

D-U-N-S 00-325-2004 IMP/EXP
A & M SUPPLY CORP (VA)
ALLIED KITCHENS & BATH
6701 90th Ave N, Pinellas Park, FL 33782-4596
Tel (727) 541-6631 *Founded/Ownrshp* 1951
Sales 128.6MM[E] *EMP* 234
SIC 5031 Plywood; Lumber: rough, dressed & finished; Structural assemblies, prefabricated: wood; Building materials, interior
Pr: Raymond V Prozzillo II
**CEO:* Kenneth C Harris
Opers Mgr: Eric Duncan

A & P
See GREAT ATLANTIC & PACIFIC TEA CO INC

D-U-N-S 05-664-5351
A & R JANITORIAL SERVICE INC
10127 W Roosevelt Rd, Westchester, IL 60154-2643
Tel (708) 656-8300 *Founded/Ownrshp* 1967
Sales 3.0MM *EMP* 1,100
SIC 7349 Janitorial service, contract basis; Window cleaning
Pr: Deborah H Pintor
COO: Helen Pintor-Velasqu
**COO:* Helen Pintor-Velasquez
**Exec:* Kimberly A Pintor

D-U-N-S 17-480-0946
A & R SECURITY SERVICES INC
UNITED PROTECTION SERVICE
(*Suby of* UNIVERSAL PROTECTION SERVICE LP) ★
600 Holiday Plaza Dr # 500, Matteson, IL 60443-2239
Tel (708) 389-3830 *Founded/Ownrshp* 2012
Sales 26.6MM[E] *EMP* 1,100
SIC 7381 Security guard service
Pr: Chris Thornton Sr

D-U-N-S 06-958-6832
A & W RESTAURANTS INC (MI)
A&W RESTAURANT
(*Suby of* YORKSHIRE GLOBAL RESTAURANTS INC) ★
1648 Mcgrathiana Pkwy # 380, Lexington, KY 40511-1339
Tel (859) 219-0019 *Founded/Ownrshp* 1919, 1981
Sales 59.1MM[E] *EMP* 1,500
SIC 5812 6794 Drive-in restaurant; Franchises, selling or licensing
Pr: Kevin Bazner
Sr Cor Off: David Novak
**V Ch Bd:* Paul F Klapper

D-U-N-S 07-646-8735
■ A & W WATER SERVICE INC
(*Suby of* COMPLETE ENERGY SERVICES INC) ★
1900 S Sunset St Unit 1f, Longmont, CO 80501-6599
Tel (303) 659-6523 *Founded/Ownrshp* 1954
Sales 137.6MM[E] *EMP* 300
SIC 1389 Oil field services
Pr: Gary W Wright
**Co-Pr:* Donald G Wright
Sfty Mgr: Randy Ekx

D-U-N-S 01-099-1934
A 3 H FOODS LP
JACK IN THE BOX
13636 Breton Ridge St C, Houston, TX 77070-6077
Tel (832) 678-3590 *Founded/Ownrshp* 2007
Sales 92.5MM[E] *EMP* 1,998
SIC 5812 Fast-food restaurant, chain
Genl Pt: Arun Roy
Pt: Mohammed Ahmed
Pt: Mark Holmes
Pt: Ali Keshani

A A A AUTOMOBILE CLUB SO CAL
See AUTOMOBILE CLUB OF SOUTHERN CALIFORNIA

D-U-N-S 07-498-0749
A A A EAST CENTRAL
5900 Baum Blvd Ste 2, Pittsburgh, PA 15206-3854
Tel (412) 362-3300 *Founded/Ownrshp* 1903
Sales NA *EMP* 1,200
SIC 6411 Insurance agents, brokers & service
Ch Bd: Richard Hamilton
**Pr:* James E Lehman
**Pr:* James McGrath
**CFO:* Michael Pratt
**Ex VP:* James Lehman
VP: Allan Ruch
VP: Portia Ulinski
Dir IT: Laura Dilonardo

A A A TRAVEL AGENCY
See AAA AUTO CLUB SOUTH INC

A A C
See ADVANCED ACOUSTIC CONCEPTS LLC

D-U-N-S 02-689-0530 IMP
A A G STUCCHI NORTH AMERICA INC
3400 Peachtree Rd Ne # 945, Atlanta, GA 30326-1170
Tel (404) 806-5399 *Founded/Ownrshp* 2013
Sales 144.6MM[E] *EMP* 4,000
SIC 3678 Electronic connectors
CEO: Aristide R Stucchi

A A I
See RUSSELL BRANDS LLC

A A K
See AARHUSKARLSHAMN USA INC

A A VENDING SERVICE DIV
See LYONS SPECIALTY CO LLC

D-U-N-S 00-643-3924
A ACUITY MUTUAL INSURANCE CO
2800 S Taylor Dr, Sheboygan, WI 53081-8474
Tel (920) 458-9131 *Founded/Ownrshp* 1925
Sales NA *EMP* 1,100
SIC 6411 6331 Insurance agents, brokers & service; Automobile insurance
Pr: Benjamin M Salzmann
**Ch:* James A Feddersen
**Treas:* Wendy Schuler
Bd of Dir: Donald C Herzfeldt
Ex VP: Kenyon Murphy
Sr VP: Ira W Sangerl
VP: Karen Nocher
VP: Pat Quinn
VP: Richard A Waldhart
Creative D: Lionel Lima
Prgrm Mgr: Donovan Resh
Board of Directors: Lynn Admin

D-U-N-S 03-900-3504 IMP
A AND G INC
ALSTYLE APPAREL
(*Suby of* GILDAN ACTIVEWEAR INC)
1501 E Cerritos Ave, Anaheim, CA 92805-6400
Tel (714) 765-0400 *Founded/Ownrshp* 1980
Sales 214.5MM[E] *EMP* 1,023
SIC 2329 2253 Athletic (warmup, sweat & jogging) suits: men's & boys'; T-shirts & tops, knit
Pr: Keith S Walters
Genl Mgr: Cameron Adamson
Genl Mgr: Mucasser Siddiqi
VP Mfg: Kevin Potter

A B
See ADVANCED BIONICS LLC

A B B POWER TRANSMISSION
See ASEA BROWN BOVERI INC

D-U-N-S 80-600-2320
A B BOYD CO
BOYD CORPORATION
600 S Mcclure Rd, Modesto, CA 95357-0520
Tel (800) 554-0200 *Founded/Ownrshp* 2015
Sales 298.6MM[E] *EMP* 2,000[E]
SIC 3069 Molded rubber products
CEO: Mitchell Aiello
CFO: Kurt Wetzel